AMERICAN
MEN AND WOMEN
OF SCIENCE

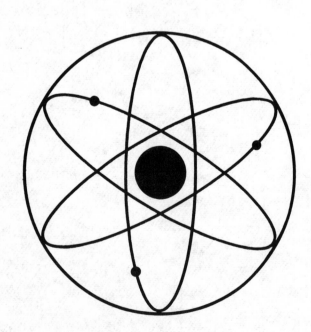

AMERICAN
MEN AND WOMEN
OF SCIENCE

Formerly American Men of Science

A biographical directory founded in 1906

Edited by the Jaques Cattell Press

12TH EDITION

THE PHYSICAL AND BIOLOGICAL SCIENCES

VOLUME 2, D-G

Jaques Cattell Press / R. R. Bowker Company   New York & London   1972

✸ CONTENTS

PREFACE ——————————————————————————————— vii

ABBREVIATIONS ——————————————————————————— ix

BIOGRAPHIES ——————————————————————————— 1289

ADDENDA —————————————————————————————— 2389

NECROLOGY ——————————————————————————— 2391

PREFACE

With this 12th edition, *American Men of Science* has been renamed *American Men and Women of Science*. The directory was first published in 1906 by Dr. J. McKeen Cattell. It was continued with increased coverage under the editorial leadership of Dr. Cattell's son, Jaques. In conjunction with the R. R. Bowker Company as publishers, the 10th and 11th editions were produced at the Jaques Cattell Press, which was established by Jaques Cattell prior to his death in 1961. The Jaques Cattell Press, as a unit of the R. R. Bowker Company, became part of the Xerox Education Group in 1967, and this edition carries the Cattell/Bowker imprint.

The policies established in previous editions have been followed in the 12th edition. Plans for the revision have been undertaken in consultation with Dr. John G. Truxal, Chairman of the Advisory Committee of *American Men and Women of Science*, member of the President's Science Advisory Committee, and Vice President for Academic Affairs, Polytechnic Institute of Brooklyn; Dr. William Bevan, Executive Officer of the American Association for the Advancement of Science; Dr. William C. Kelly, Director of the Office of Scientific Personnel, National Research Council; and Dr. Mina Rees, President, University Graduate Division, The City University of New York. These members served in an advisory capacity and are not responsible for the editorial content of the directory. The publishers and editors wish to thank them for their guidance.

Acknowledgment is gratefully extended by the editors to the individual scientists and to the universities, colleges, scientific societies, and industrial research laboratories of the United States and Canada for their assistance in the continuance of this great enterprise.

American Men and Women of Science will continue the pattern established for the two previous editions, with publication of the Physical and Biological Sciences Section first, to be followed by the Social and Behavioral Sciences. Biographies are arranged alphabetically within each section. To keep the biographical information as current as possible, questionnaires are mailed as work begins on each volume. An approximate four-month interval between volumes is scheduled, with an early 1973 completion date set for the Physical and Biological Sciences Section.

The A-C volume, published in November 1971, contained some 25,000 biographies. This volume presents the letters D–G and contains over 20,700. With the four remaining volumes (arranged H–K, L–O, P–Sr and St–Z), the six-volume set will comprise a total of approximately 150,000 entries.

The criteria for inclusion in *American Men and Women of Science* remain the same as in previous editions of *American Men of Science*:

1. Achievement, by reason of experience and training, of a stature in scientific work equivalent to that associated with the doctoral degree, coupled with presently continued activity in such work; or

2. Research activity of high quality in science as evidenced by publication in reputable scientific journals; or, for those whose work cannot be published because of governmental or industrial security, research activity of high quality in science as evidenced by the judgment of the individual's peers; or

3. Attainment of a position of substantial responsibility requiring scientific training and experience to the extent described for (1) and (2).

The editors have used their best efforts to include all material submitted within the scope of the established format, but no legal responsibility can be assumed for accidental omissions or errors. It is no longer practical to continue inclusion of biographees who have submitted no new information during the past ten years, nor those who did not return forms for this edition (unless confirmation of current activity was found). These exclusions are additional to the normal omissions of inactive emeriti and those in retirement or private practice. In no case will referrals to data in the previous edition be made. A separate necrology is shown in this volume in place of the alphabetical listing used heretofore.

Many valuable suggestions have been received during the compilation of this volume. These will be carefully considered in future planning. The existing invitation to make any criticisms or suggestions concerning the usefulness of this new edition is, again, extended to the readers. Please direct correspondence to The Editors, *American Men and Women of Science*, Jaques Cattell Press, Tempe, Arizona.

THE JAQUES CATTELL PRESS

Dorothy Hancock, *Managing Editor*

Fred Scott, *General Manager*

Malcolm C. Johnson, Jr., *Vice President and Editorial Director, Book Division R. R. Bowker Company*

MARCH 1972

AAAS—American Association for the Advancement of Science
abnorm—abnormal
abstr—abstract(s)
acad—academic, academy
acct—account, accountant, accounting
acoust—acoustic(s), acoustical
adj—adjunct, adjutant
adjust—adjustment
Adm—Admiral
admin—administration, administrative
adminr—administrator
adv—adviser, advisory
advan—advanced, advancement
advert—advertisement
aerodyn—aerodynamic(s)
aeronaut—aeronautic(s), aeronautical
aerophys—aerophysical, aerophysics
agr—agricultural, agriculture
agron—agronomic, agronomical, agronomy
agrost—agrostologic, agrostological, agrostology
AFB—Air Force Base
Ala—Alabama
allergol—allergological, allergology
Alta—Alberta
Am—America, American
anal—analysis, analytic, analytical
analog—analogue
anat—anatomic, anatomical, anatomy
anesthesiol—anesthesiology
angiol—angiology
Ann—Annal(s)
anthrop—anthropological, anthropology
anthropom—anthropometric, anthropometrical, anthropometry
antiq—antiquarian, antiquary, antiquities, antiquity
apicult—apicultural, apiculture
APO—Army Post Office
app—appoint, appointed
appl—applied
appln—application
Apr—April
apt—apartment(s)
aquacult—aquaculture
arbit—arbitration
Arch—Archives
archaeol—archaeological, archaeology
archit—architectural, architecture
Arg—Argentina, Argentine
Ariz—Arizona
Ark—Arkansas
artil—artillery
Asn—Association
assoc(s)—associate(s), associated
asst—assistant
astrodyn—astrodynamics
astron—astronomical, astronomy
astronaut—astronautical, astronautics
astronr—astronomer
astrophys—astrophysical, astrophysics
attend—attendant, attending
audiol—audiology
Aug—August
auth—author, authority
Ave—Avenue
avicult—avicultural, aviculture

b—born
bact—bacterial, bacteriologic, bacteriological, bacteriology
B.C—British Columbia
bd—board
behav—behavior, behavioral
Belg—Belgian, Belgium
bibliog—bibliographic, bibliographical, bibliography
biochem—biochemical, biochemistry
biol—biological, biology

biomet—biometric(s), biometrical, biometry
biophys—biophysical, biophysics
bldg—building
blvd—boulevard
bot—botanical, botany
br—branch
Brig—Brigadier
Brit—Britain, British
Bro(s)—Brother(s)
bryol—bryology
Bull—Bulletin
bur—bureau
bus—business
B.W.I—British West Indies

c—children, corps
Calif—California
Can—Canada, Canadian
cand—candidate
Capt—Captain
cardiol—cardiology
cardiovasc—cardiovascular
cartog—cartographic, cartographical, cartography
Cath—Catholic
C.Eng—Corps of Engineers
cent—central
cert—certificate, certified
chap—chapter
chem—chemical(s), chemistry
chemother—chemotherapy
chmn—chairman
citricult—citriculture
climat—climatological, climatology
clin(s)—clinic(s), clinical
co—companies, company, county
co-auth—co-author
co-ed—co-editor
col(s)—college(s), colonel
collab—collaboration, collaborative, collaborator
Colo—Colorado
Comdr—Commander
commun—communicable, communication(s)
comn(s)—commission(s)
comnr—commissioner
comp—comparative
compos—composition
comput—computation, computer(s), computing
comt(s)—committee(s)
conchol—conchology
conf—conference
cong—congress(es), congressional
Conn—Connecticut
conserv—conservancy, conservation, conservatory
consol—consolidated, consolidation
const—constitution, constitutional
construct—construction
consult—consultant, consulting
contrib—contributing, contributor
conv—convention
coop—cooperation, cooperative
coord—coordinating, coordination, coordinator
cor—corresponding
corp—corporate, corporation
coun—council, councilor
counsr—counselor
criminol—criminological, criminology
cryog—cryogenic(s)
crystallog—crystallographic, crystallographical, crystallography
ct—court
cult—cultural, culture
C.W.S—Chemical Warfare Service
cybernet—cybernetic(s)
cytol—cytological, cytology
C.Z—Canal Zone
Czech—Czechoslovakia

D.C—District of Columbia
Dec—December
Del—Delaware
del—delegate, delegation
demog—demographic, demography
demonstr—demonstrator
dendrol—dendrologic, dendrological, dendrology
dent—dental, dentistry
dep—deputy
dept—department
dermat—dermatologic, dermatological, dermatology
develop—development, developmental
diag—diagnosis, diagnostic
dipl—diploma, diplomate
dir(s)—director(s), directory
dist—district
distrib—distributed, distribution, distributors
div—division, divorced
DNA—deoxyribonucleic acid
document—documentation
Dom—Dominion
Dr—Doctor, Drive
Drs—Doctorandus

e—east
east—eastern
ecol—ecological, ecology
econ—economic(s), economical, economy
economet—econometric(s)
ed—edition, editor, editorial
educ—education, educational
elec—electric, electrical, electricity
electrochem—electrochemical, electrochemistry
electroencephalog—electroencephalographic, electroencephalography
electrophys—electrophysical, electrophysics
elem—elementary
embryol—embryologic, embryological, embryology
emer—emeritus
employ—employment
encycl—encyclopedia
endocrinol—endocrinologic, endocrinology
eng—engineering
Eng—England, English
engr(s)—engineer(s)
enol—enology
Ens—Ensign
entom—entomological, entomology
environ—environment(s), environmental
enzym—enzymology
epidemiol—epidemiologic, epidemiological, epidemiology
equip—equipment
espec—especially
estab—established, establishment
ethnog—ethnographic, ethnographical, ethnography
ethnol—ethnologic, ethnological, ethnology
Europ—European
eval—evaluation
evangel—evangelical
eve—evening
exam—examination, examiner(s)
except—exceptional
exec(s)—executive(s)
exhib(s)—exhibition(s)
exp—experiment, experimental
exped(s)—expedition(s)
explor—exploration(s), exploratory
expos—exposition
exten—extension

Feb—February
fed—federal
fedn—federation
fel(s)—fellow(s), fellowship(s)

fermentol—fermoltology
fertil—fertility, fertilization
Fla—Florida
floricult—floricultural, floriculture
for—foreign
found—foundation
FPO—Fleet Post Office
Fr—French
Ft—Fort

Ga—Georgia
gastroenterol—gastroenterology
gen—general
geneal—genealogical, genealogy
geod—geodesy, geodetic
geog—geographic, geographical, geography
geogr—geographer
geol—geologic, geological, geology
geom—geometric, geometrical, geometry
geophys—geophysical, geophysics
Ger—German, Germany
geriat—geriatric(s)
geront—gerontological, gerontology
glaciol—glaciology
gov—governing, governor(s)
govt—government, governmental
grad—graduate
Gt. Brit—Great Britain
guid—guidance
gym—gymnasium
gynec—gynecologic, gynecological, gynecology

helminth—helminthology
hemat—hematologic, hematological, hematology
herpet—herpetologic, herpetological, herpetology
hist—historical, history
histol—histological, histology
H.M—Her Majesty
hochsch—hochschule
homeop—homeopathic, homeopathy
hon—honorable, honorary
hort—horticultural, horticulture
hosp(s)—hospital(s)
hq—headquarters
HumRRO—Human Resources Research Office
husb—husbandry
hwy—highway
hydraul—hydraulic(s)
hydrodyn—dydrodynamic(s)
hydrol—hydrologic, hydrological, hydrology
hyg—hygiene, hygienic(s)

ichthyol—ichthyological, ichthyology
Ill—Illinois
illum—illuminating, illumination
immunol—immunologic, immunological, immunology
Imp—Imperial
improv—improvement
Inc—Incorporated
Ind—Indiana
indust(s)—industrial, industries, industry
info—information
inorg—inorganic
ins—insurance
inst(s)—institute(s), institution(s)
instnl—institutional
instr(s)—instruction, instructor(s)
int—international
intel—intelligence
introd—introduction
invert—invertebrate
invest(s)—investigation(s)
investr—investigator
irrig—irrigation
Ital—Italian

J—Journal
Jan—January
jour—journal
jr—junior
jurisp—jurisprudence

Kans—Kansas
Ky—Kentucky

La—Louisiana
lab(s)—laboratories, laboratory
lang—language(s)
laryngol—laryngology
lect—lecture
lectr—lecturer
legis—legislation, legislative, legislature
L.I—Long Island
lib—liberal
libr—library(ies)
librn—librarian
limnol—limnological, limnology
ling—linguistic(s)
lit—literary, literature
lithol—lithologic, lithological, lithology
L/Sgt—Lance Sergeant
Lt—Lieutenant
Ltd—Limited

m—married
mach—machine(s), machinery
mag—magazine
maj—major
malacol—malacology
mammal—mammalogy
Man—Manitoba
Mar—March
Mass—Massachusetts
mat—material(s)
mat. med—materia medica
math—mathematic(s), mathematical
Md—Maryland
mech—mechanic(s), mechanical
med—medical, medicinal, medicine
mem—member, memoirs, memorial
ment—mental, mentally
metab—metabolic, metabolism
metall—metallurgic, metallurgical, metallurgy
metallog—metallographic, metallography
metallogr—metallographer
metaphys—metaphysics
meteorol—meteorological, meteorology
metrol—metrological, metrology
metrop—metropolitan
Mex—Mexican, Mexico
mfg—manufacturing
mfr(s)—manufacture(s), manufacturer(s)
mgr—manager
mgt—management
Mich—Michigan
microbiol—microbiological, microbiology
micros—microscopic, microscopical, microscopy
mid—middle
mil—military
mineral—mineralogical, mineralogy
Minn—Minnesota
Miss—Mississippi
mkt—market, marketing
Mo—Missouri
mod—modern
monogr—monograph
Mont—Montana
morphol—morphological, morphology
M/Sgt—Master Sergeant
mt(s)—mount, mountain(s)
munic—municipal
mus—museum
musicol—musicological, musicology
mycol—mycologic, mycology

n—north
NASA—National Aeronautics & Space Administration
nat—national, naturalized
NATO—North Atlantic Treaty Organization
navig—navigation, navigational
N.B—New Brunswick
N.C—North Carolina
N.Dak—North Dakota
Nebr—Nebraska
nematol—nematology
neurol—neurological, neurology
neuropath—neuropathological, neuropathology
neuropsychiat—neuropsychiatric, neuropsychiatry
Nev—Nevada
New Eng—New England
Newf—Newfoundland
N.H—New Hampshire
N.J—New Jersey
N.Mex—New Mexico
nonres—nonresident
norm—normal
north—northern
northeast—northeastern
northwest—northwestern
Norweg—Norwegian
Nov—November
N.S—Nova Scotia
N.S.W—New South Wales
numis—numismatic
nutrit—nutrition, nutritional
N.Y—New York State
N.Y.C—New York City
N.Z—New Zealand

observ—observatory
obstet—obstetric(s)
occup—occupation, occupational
oceanog—oceanographic, oceanographical, oceanography
oceanogr—oceanographer
Oct—October
odontol—odontology
OEEC—Organization for European Economic Cooperation
off—office, officer, official
Okla—Oklahoma
olericult—olericulture
oncol—oncologic, oncology
Ont—Ontario
oper(s)—operation(s), operational, operative

ophthal—ophthalmologic, ophthalmological, ophthalmology
optom—optometric, optometrical, optometry
ord—ordnance
Ore—Oregon
org—organic
orgn—organization(s), organizational
Orient—Oriental
ornith—ornithological, ornithology
orthod—orthodontia, orthodontic(s)
orthop—orthopedic(s)
osteop—osteopathic, osteopathy
otol—otological, otology
otolaryngol—otolaryngologic, otolaryngology
otorhinol—otorhinologic, otorhinology

Pa—Pennsylvania
Pac—Pacific
paleobot—paleobotanical, paleobotany
paleont—paleontological, paleontology
Pan-Am—Pan-American
parasitol—parasitology
partic—participant, participating
path—pathologic, pathological, pathology
pedag—pedagogic(s), pedagogy
pediat—pediatric(s)
P.E.I—Prince Edward Islands
penol—penological, penology
periodont—periodontal, periodontic(s), periodontology
petrog—petrographic, petrographical, petrography
petrogr—petrographer
petrol—petroleum, petrologic, petrological, petrology
pharm—pharmacy
pharmaceut—pharmaceutic(s), pharmaceutical(s)
pharmacog—pharmacognosy
pharmacol—pharmacologic, pharmacological, pharmacology
Phila—Philadelphia
philol—philogical, philology
philos—philosophic, philosophical, philosophy
photog—photographic, photography
photogeog—photogeographic, photogeography
photogram—photogrammetry
photom—photometric, photometrical, photometry
phycol—phycology
physiog—physiographic, physiographical, physiography
physiol—physiological, physiology
pkwy—parkway
pl—place
P.O—Post Office
polit—political, politics
polytech—polytechnic
pomol—pomological, pomology
Pontif—Pontifical
pop—population
Port—Portugal, Portuguese
postgrad—postgraduate
P.R—Puerto Rico
prehist—prehistoric, prehistory
prep—preparation, preparative, preparatory
pres—president
Presby—Presbyterian
prev—prevention, preventive
prin—principal(s)
prob(s)—problem(s)
probtn—probation
proc—proceedings
proctol—proctologic, proctological, proctology
prod—product(s), production, productive
prof—professional, professor, professorial
prog(s)—program(s), programmed, programming
proj—project(s), projectional, projective
prom—promotion
protozool—protozoology
prov—province, provincial
psychiat—psychiatric, psychiatry
psychoanal—psychoanalysis, psychoanalytic, psychoanalytical
psychol—psychological, psychology
psychomet—psychometric(s)
psychophys—psychophysical, psychophysics
psychophysiol—psychophysiological, psychophysiology
psychosom—psychosomatic(s)
psychother—psychotherapeutic(s), psychotherapy
pub—public
publ—publication(s), publisher, publishing

qm—quartermaster
qual—qualitative, quality
quant—quantitative
quart—quarterly
Que—Quebec

radiol—radiological, radiology
R.A.F—Royal Air Force
R.A.F.V.R—Royal Air Force Volunteer Reserve
R.A.M.C—Royal Army Medical Corps
R.A.M.C.R—Royal Army Medical Corps Reserve
R.A.O.C—Royal Army Ordnance Corps
R.A.S.C—Royal Army Service Corps

R.A.S.C.R—Royal Army Service Corps Reserve
R.C.A.D.C—Royal Canadian Army Dental Corps
R.C.A.F—Royal Canadian Air Force
R.C.A.F.R—Royal Canadian Air Force Reserve
R.C.A.F.V.R—Royal Canadian Air Force Volunteer Reserve
R.C.A.M.C—Royal Canadian Army Medical Corps
R.C.A.M.C.R—Royal Canadian Army Medical Corps Reserve
R.C.A.O.C—Royal Canadian Army Ordnance Corps
R.C.A.S.C—Royal Canadian Army Service Corps
R.C.A.S.C.R—Royal Canadian Army Service Corps Reserve
R.C.E.M.E—Royal Canadian Electrical & Mechanical Engineers
R.C.N—Royal Canadian Navy
R.C.N.R—Royal Canadian Naval Reserve
R.C.N.V.R—Royal Canadian Naval Volunteer Reserve
rd—road
R.D—Rural Delivery
R.E—Royal Engineers
rec—record(s), recording
redevelop—redevelopment
ref—refining
refrig—refrigeration
registr—registrar, registration
rehab—rehabilitation
rel(s)—relation(s), relative
relig—religion, religious
R.E.M.E—Royal Electrical & Mechanical Engineers
rep—representative
repub—republic
res—research, reserve
ret—retired
rev—review, revised
rhet—rhetoric, rhetorical
R.I—Rhode Island
R.M—Royal Marines
R.N—Royal Navy
RNA—ribonucleic acid
R.N.R—Royal Naval Reserve
R.N.V.R—Royal Naval Volunteer Reserve
roentgenol—roentgenologic, roentgenological, roentgenology
R.R—Railroad, Rural Route
rwy—railway

s—south
sanit—sanitary, sanitation
Sask—Saskatchewan
S.C—South Carolina
Scand—Scandinavian
sch(s)—school(s)
scholar—scholarship
sci—science(s), scientific
S.Dak—South Dakota
SEATO—Southeast Asia Treaty Organization
sec—secondary
sect—section
secy—secretary
seismog—seismograph, seismographic, seismography
seismol—seismological, seismology
sem—seminar, seminary
Sept—September
serol—serologic, serological, serology

serv—service(s)
Sgt—Sergeant
silvicult—silvicultural, silviculture
soc(s)—social, societies, society
sociol—sociologic, sociological, sociology
south—southern
southeast—southeastern
southwest—southwestern
Span—Spanish
spec—special
spectrog—spectrograph, spectrographic, spectrography
spectrogr—spectrographer
spectrophotom—spectrophotometer, spectrophotometric, spectrophotometry
spectros—spectroscopic, spectroscopy
speleol—speleological, speleology
sr—senior
S/Sgt—Staff Sergeant
St—Saint, Street
sta(s)—station(s)
statist—statistical, statistics
Ste—Sainte
steril—sterility
stomatol—stomatology
stratig—stratigraphic, stratigraphy
struct—structural, structure(s)
stud—student, studentship
subcomt—subcommittee
subj—subject
Sub. Lt—Sub-Lieutenant
substa—substation
suppl—supplement, supplemental, supplementary
supt—superintendent
supv—supervising, supervision
supvr—supervisor
supvry—supervisory
surg—surgical, surgery
surv—survey, surveying
Swed—Swedish
Switz—Switzerland
syphil—syphilology
syst(s)—system(s), systematic(s), systematical

taxon—taxonomic, taxonomy
tech—technical, technique(s)
technol—technologic, technological, technology
tel—telegraph(y), telephone
Tenn—Tennessee
Terr—Terrace
Tex—Texas
theol—theological, theology
theoret—theoretical
ther—therapy
therapeut—therapeutic(s)
thermodyn—thermodynamic(s)
topog—topographic, topographical, topography
toxicol—toxicologic, toxicological, toxicology
trans—transactions
transl—translation(s), translator
treas—treasurer, treasury
trop—tropical
T/Sgt—Technical Sergeant
tuberc—tuberculosis
TV—television
twp—township

U.A.R—United Arab Republic
U.K—United Kingdom

UN—United Nations
unemploy—unemployment
UNESCO—United Nations Educational Scientific & Cultural Organization
UNICEF—United Nations International Childrens Fund
univ(s)—universities, university
UNRRA—United Nations Relief & Rehabilitation Administration
urol—urologic, urological, urology
U.S—United States
U.S.A—U.S. Army
U.S.A.A.F—U.S. Army Air Force
U.S.A.A.F.R—U.S. Army Air Force Reserve
U.S.A.F—U.S. Air Force
U.S.A.F.R—U.S. Air Force Reserve
U.S.A.R—U.S. Army Reserve
U.S.C.G—U.S. Coast Guard
U.S.C.G.R—U.S. Coast Guard Reserve
U.S.M.C—U.S. Marine Corps
U.S.M.C.R—U.S. Marine Corps Reserve
U.S.N—U.S. Navy
U.S.N.A.F—U.S. Naval Air Force
U.S.N.A.F.R—U.S. Naval Air Force Reserve
U.S.N.R—U.S. Naval Reserve
U.S.P.H.S—U.S. Public Health Service
U.S.P.H.S.R—U.S. Public Health Service Reserve
U.S.S.R—Union of Soviet Socialist Republics
U.S.W.M.C—U.S. Women's Marine Corps
U.S.W.M.C.R—U.S. Women's Marine Corps Reserve

Va—Virginia
veg—vegetable(s), vegetation
vent—ventilating, ventilation
vert—vertebrate
vet—veteran(s), veterinarian, veterinary
V.I—Virgin Islands
vinicult—viniculture
virol—virological, virology
vis—visiting
voc—vocational
vol(s)—voluntary, volunteer(s), volume(s)
v.pres—vice president
Vt—Vermont

w—west
W.A.C—Women's Army Corps
Wash—Washington
Wash, D.C—Washington, D.C.
W.A.V.E.S—Women accepted for Voluntary Emergency Service
west—western
WHO—World Health Organization
W.I—West Indies
wid—widow, widowed, widower
Wis—Wisconsin
W.R.C.N.S—Women's Royal Canadian Naval Service
W.R.N.S—Women's Royal Naval Service
W.Va—West Virginia
Wyo—Wyoming

YMCA—Young Men's Christian Association
YMHA—Young Men's Hebrew Association
YWCA—Young Women's Christian Association
YWHA—Young Women's Hebrew Association

zool—zoological, zoology

AMERICAN MEN AND WOMEN OF SCIENCE

D

DAAMS, HERMAN, b. Apeldoorn, Netherlands, May 8, 17; Can. citizen; m. 51; c. 1. PHYSICS. Engr, Delft, 49. Asst. x-ray diffraction, Delft, 49-52; patent exam. gen. physics, Patent Off, Hague, Holland, 52-54; sci. officer instrumentation, Delft, 54-57; RES. OFFICER FREQUENCY STANDARDS, PHYSICS DIV, NAT. RES. COUN. CAN, 57- Inst. Elec. & Electronics Eng; Can. Asn. Physicists; Netherlands Phys. Soc. X-ray diffraction, small angle scattering; instrumentation; atomic frequency standards. Address: Physics Division, National Research Council, Ottawa, Ont, Can.

DAANE, ADRIAN HILL, b. Stillwater, Okla, June 19, 19; m. 44; c. 3. PHYSICAL CHEMISTRY. B.S, Florida, 41; fel, Iowa State Col, 41-42, Ph.D. (chem), 50. Asst. phys. chem, Off. Sci. Res. & Develop. & Manhattan Proj, Iowa State, 42-43, group leader, 43-46, from assoc. chemist to sr. chemist, Atomic Energy Cmn. & asst. prof. to assoc. prof. CHEM, univ, 50-63; PROF. & HEAD DEPT, KANS. STATE UNIV, 63- Am. Chem. Soc; Am. Inst. Mech. Eng; Am. Vacuum Soc. High temperature chemistry; chemistry of rare earth metals; vapor pressures of metals; chemical education. Address: Dept. of Chemistry, Kansas State University, Manhattan, KS 66502.

DAANE, JOHN H, b. Holbrook, N.Y, July 6, 38; m. 59; c. 3. ANALYTICAL & PHYSICAL CHEMISTRY. B.S, Adelphi, 62; M.S, Union Col.(N.Y), 66. Res. asst. radiochem, Assoc. Univs, Inc, 58-62, chem. assoc, 62; res. training fel, res. lab, Gen. Elec. Co, 62-64, chemist, silicone prod. dept, 64-66; ASSOC. MEM. TECH. STAFF, BELL TEL. LABS, 66- Am. Sci. Affiliation; Am. Phys. Soc. Relationship between the structure and morphology of polymers and the resultant properties, especially in regard to ultimate properties. Address: Bell Telephone Labs, Room 1B208, Murray Hill, NJ 07974.

DAANE, ROBERT A, b. Oostburg, Wis, June 18, 21; m. 45; c. 1. ENGINEERING MECHANICS, MECHANICAL ENGINEERING. B.S.M.E, Wisconsin, 43, Ph.D.(eng. mech), 59; M.S, Purdue, 49. Engr, eng. div, Chrysler Corp, 43-46; instr. eng. mech, Purdue, 46-50; assoc. engr, Argonne Nat. Lab, 50-54; sr. engr, Nuclear Develop. Assoc, 54-55; res. engr, Beloit Corp, 55-59; assoc. prof. nuclear eng, Stanford, 59-61; area res. dir. heat transfer, BELOIT CORP, 61-67, dir. res, 67-69, V.PRES. RES, 69- Consult, Atomic Power Develop. Assocs, 58-62; Beloit Corp, 59-61. Am. Soc. Mech. Eng; Tech. Asn. Pulp & Paper Indust. Stress analysis; nuclear reactor dynamics and safety; heat transfer; numerical analysis and computer simulation of engineering problems; paper drying; industrial research management. Address: 150 W. Russell St, Townhouse 10, Rockton, IL 61072.

DAASCH, LESTER W(ILLIAM), b. Davenport, Iowa, May 17, 19; m. 45; c. 5. PHYSICAL CHEMISTRY. B.S, St. Ambrose Col, 41; M.S, Iowa State, 43. Asst. inorg. chem, Iowa State, 44-44; asst. to lab. dir, Naval Ord. Lab, 44-45, PHYS. CHEMIST, Naval Res. Lab, 45-61, CHEM. RES. & DEVELOP. LABS, EDGEWOOD ARSENAL, 61- Private consult. infrared & mass spectros. U.S.N.R, 44-45, Lt. Sci. Res. Soc. Am. Determination of structure of molecules by infrared and mass spectroscopy aided by gas chromatography and nuclear magnetic resonance; spectra in analytical chemistry. Address: Research Labs, Edgewood Arsenal, MD 21010.

DABBAH, ROBER, b. Alexandria, Egypt, Dec. 23, 37; U.S. citizen; m. 64; c. 1. MICROBIOLOGY, BIOCHEMISTRY. B.A, Univ. Minn, Minneapolis, 61, M.S, St. Paul, 65; Ph.D, Univ. Md, College Park, 70. Technician, Gen. Mills, Inc, Minn, 59-61; res. asst. dairy microbiol, Univ. Minnesota, 61-65; res. microbiologist, Agr. Res. Serv, U.S. Dept. Agr, 65-71; MGR. MICROBIOL, ROSS LABS, DIV. QUAL. ASSURANCE, ABBOTT LABS, 71- Am. Dairy Sci. Asn; Am. Soc. Microbiol; Int. Asn. Milk, Food & Environ. Sanit. Bacteriological quality control tests for milk and dairy products; heat resistance, heat injury and recovery of psychrophilic bacteria; inhibition of growth of Salmonella by citrus oils. Address: Ross Labs, 625 Cleveland Ave, Columbus, OH 43216.

DABBERDT, WALTER F, b. N.Y.C, Oct. 12, 42; m. 67; c. 2. METEOROLOGY. B.S, State Univ. N.Y, 64; M.S, Univ. Wis, 66, Ph.D.(meteorol), 69. Res. asst. meteorol, Univ. Wis, Madison, 64-69; Nat. Acad. Sci-Nat. Res. Coun. vis. scientist, U.S. Army Natick Labs, 69-70; RES. METEOROLOGIST, ATMOSPHERIC SCI. LAB, STANFORD RES. INST, 70- AAAS; Am. Meteorol. Soc. Momentum and heat transport in the planetary boundary layer; surface heat budget; urban diffusion modeling; optical propagation in the atmosphere. Address: Atmospheric Sciences Lab, Stanford Research Institute, 333 Ravenswood Ave, Menlo Park, CA 94025.

DABBS, D(ONALD) H(ENRY), b. Forestburg, Alta, Sept. 12, 21; m. 43; c. 3. HORTICULTURE. B.Sc, Alberta, 50, M.Sc, 52. Horticulturist, exp. farm, Can. Dept. Agr, 52-61; asst. prof. HORT, UNIV. SASK, 61-70, ASSOC. PROF, 70- R.C.A.F, 42-45, Flying Officer. Potato Asn. Am; Am. Soc. Hort. Sci; Can. Soc. Hort. Sci; Int. Soc. Hort. Sci; Agr. Inst. Can. Vegetable crops. Address: Dept. of Horticultural Science, University of Saskatchewan, Saskatoon, Sask, Can.

DABBS, JOHN W(ILSON) T(HOMAS), b. Nashville, Tenn, Dec. 11, 21; m. 45; c. 3. PHYSICS. B.S, Tennessee, 44, Ph.D.(physics), 55. Asst. physics, metall. lab, Chicago, 44-45; jr. physicist, applied physics lab, Hopkins, 45; PHYSICIST, OAK RIDGE NAT. LAB, 46- Ord. Dept, U.S.A, 45-46. Fel. Am. Phys. Soc. Cryogenics; nuclear physics; nuclear polarization; neutron time-of-flight studies; nuclear fission. Address: Oak Ridge National Lab, Box X, Oak Ridge, TN 37830.

DABICH, DANICA, b. Detroit, Mich, Aug. 6, 30. BIOCHEMISTRY. B.Sc, Michigan, 52; M.Sc, Ohio State, 55; fels. Nat. Insts. Health; Parke, Davis & Co; Am. Res. Corp. & Ph.D.(biochem), Illinois, 60. Anal. chemist, Phillips Petrol. Co, Okla, 52-53; asst. BIOCHEM, Edsel B. Ford Inst. Med. Res, Mich, 55-56; fel. Nat. Insts. Health, Freiburg, 60-61; res. assoc, COL. MED, WAYNE STATE UNIV, 61-63, instr, 63-65, asst. prof, 65-70, ASSOC. PROF, 70- AAAS; Am. Chem. Soc; N.Y. Acad. Sci; Soc. Exp. Biol. & Med. Enzymology; protein catabolism; biochemistry of development. Address: Dept. of Biochemistry, Wayne State University College of Medicine, 540 E. Canfield, Detroit, MI 48201.

DABNEY, JOHN BALDWIN, b. Framingham, Mass, Sept. 26, 34; m. 59; c. 3. METALLURGY. A.B, Bowdoin Col, 56; S.M, Mass. Inst. Tech, 58, Sc.D. (metall), 61. Metallurgist, Am. Brake Shoe Co, 61-68; PHYS. METALLURGIST, ABEX CORP, 68- Am. Soc. Metals; Am. Foundrymen's Soc. Physical metallurgy of ferrous materials; vacuum processing of iron and nickel base alloys; melting and casting of metals. Address: Metallurgical Research Center, Abex Corp, Ramapo Valley Rd, Mahwah, NJ 07430.

DABORA, ELI K, b. Baghdad, Iraq, Sept. 24, 28; U.S. citizen; m. 57; c. 4. GAS DYNAMICS. S.B, Mass. Inst. Tech, 51, S.M, 52, Ph.D.(mech. eng), Michigan, 63. Instr. mech. eng, Northeastern, 52-53; anal. engr, Power Generators Inc, 53-55; res. engr, sci. lab, Ford Motor Co, 55-56; res. assoc. heat transfer, Michigan, 57-61, assoc. res. engr. combustion, 61-64, res. engr. detonations, 64-68; ASSOC. PROF. AEROSPACE ENG, UNIV. CONN, 68- Consult, Feltman Res. Lab, Picatinny Arsenal, 70- Assoc. fel. Am. Inst. Aeronaut. & Astronaut; Combustion Inst. Combustion; heat transfer as related to the design of regenerative heat exchangers; detonation phenomena; standing detonation wave and detonation-boundary interactions; detonations in heterogeneous systems; two-phase phenomena. Address: Dept. of Aerospace Engineering, U-139, University of Connecticut, Storrs, CT 06268.

DACEY, G(EORGE) C(LEMENT), b. Chicago, Ill, Jan. 23, 21; m. 54; c. 3. SOLID STATE PHYSICS. B.S, Illinois, 42; fel, Calif. Inst. Tech, 46-50, Smith fel, 50-51, Ph.D.(physics), 51. Res. engr, Westinghouse Res. Lab, 42-45; mem. tech. staff & res. physicist, Bell Tel. Labs, Inc, 51-58, asst. dir. solid state electronic res, 58-60, dir, 60-61; v.pres. res, Sandia Corp, N.Mex, 61-63; exec. dir. tel. & power div, BELL TEL. LABS, INC, 63-68, v.pres. customer equip. develop, 68-70, V.PRES. TRANSMISSION SYSTS, 70- Elec. Eng. Asn. distinguished alumnus award, Univ. Ill, 71. Fel. Am. Phys. Soc; fel. Inst. Elec. & Electronics Eng. Semiconductors and transistors; semiconductor devices; microwave electronics. Address: Bell Telephone Labs, Inc, Holmdel, NJ 07733.

DACEY, J(OHN) R(OBERT), b. Manchester, Eng, Apr. 28, 14; Can. citizen; m. 40; c. 3. PHYSICAL CHEMISTRY. B.Sc, Dalhousie, 36, M.Sc, 38; Ph.D. (phys. chem), McGill, 40. Res. asst. Nat. Res. Coun. Can. 40; supt. Defense Res. Chem. Labs, 47-49; PROF. CHEM, ROYAL MIL. COL, 49-, PRIN, 67-, dean sci, 63-67. Mem, Order Brit. Empire. Can. Army, 40-47, Maj. Am. Chem. Soc; Chem. Inst. Can. Chemical warfare, smoke and flame warfare; surface chemistry, adsorption of gases on charcoal; chemical kinetics, photochemistry of fluorine compounds. Address: Dept. of Chemistry, Royal Military College, Kingston, Ont, Can.

DACHI, STEPHEN F, b. Budapest, Hungary, Apr. 21, 33; U.S. citizen; m. 56; c. 3. DENTISTRY. D.M.D, Univ. Ore, 56. Instr. oral surg, dent. sch, Univ. Ore, 58-59; asst. prof. oral diag. & med, col. dent, Univ. Ky, 61-63, assoc. prof, 63-67, chmn. dept. & dir. continuation educ, 61-67, chief dent. serv, Med. Ctr. Hosp, 62-67; dep. dir, PEACE CORPS, Colombia, 67-69, VENEZUELA, 69- Consult, U.S. Vet. Admin. Hosp, Lexington, Ky. Dipl. Am. Bd. Oral Path. AAAS; fel. Am. Acad. Oral Path; Am. Dent. Asn; Int.

Asn. Dent. Res. Experimental oral carcinogenesis; clinical studies on dental restorative materials and diagnostic tests. Address: Peace Corps, c/o American Embassy, Caracas, Venezuela, S.A.

DACHILLE, FRANK, b. N.Y.C, Sept. 15, 17; m. 42; c. 3. GEOCHEMISTRY, CHEMICAL ENGINEERING. B.Ch.E, City Col. New York, 39; Corning Glass Works Found. fel, Pa. State, 57-58, Ph.D.(geochem), 59. With res. & develop. resin lab, U.S. Indust. Chems, 39-41, plant construct. & chem. supv, 41-43, asst. plant mgr, Pensacola Div, 43-55; asst, PA. STATE UNIV, 55-59, res. assoc. geochem, 59-62, asst. prof. solid state technol, 62-63, GEOCHEM, 63-64, ASSOC. PROF, 64- Am. Chem. Soc; Geochem. Soc; Meteoritical Soc; Am. Ceramic Soc; Mineral Soc. Am. Application of x-ray methods to study of shock deformation of crystals; parameters and processes in formation of ancient and modern sediments. Address: 1429 Park Hills Ave. E, State College, PA 16801.

DACK, G(AIL) M(ONROE), b. Belvidere, Ill, Mar. 4, 01; m. 26; c. 2. MICROBIOLOGY. B.S, Illinois, 22; Ph.D.(bact), Chicago, 27, M.D. 33. Instr. hyg. & bact, UNIV. CHICAGO, 25-29, asst. prof, 29-37, assoc. prof. BACT, 37-46, prof, 46-66; EMER. PROF, 66-, dir. Food Res. Inst, 46-66. Part-time prof, Univ. Wis, Madison, 66-70. Mem. expert adv. panel environ. sanit, WHO, 54-59. Ricketts prize, 25; silver medallion award; merit, Nat. Restaurant Asn, 60. Dipl, Am. Bd. Microbiol, 61. With Res. & Develop. Bd; U.S.A; U.S. Pub. Health Serv; Nat. Res. Coun, 44. AAAS; Soc. Exp. Biol.& Med; Am. Pub. Health Asn; Am. Soc. Microbiol; Inst. Food Tech. (Babcock-Hart award, 56, Nicholas Appert award, 64). Botulism; ulcerative colitis; salmonella infection; staphylococcal food poisoning in general and intestinal bacteriology. Address: 494 Wing Park Blvd, Elgin, IL 60120.

DACK, SIMON, b. New York, N.Y, April,19, 08; m. 49; c. 2. MEDICINE. B.S, City Col, 28; M.D, N.Y. Med. Col, 32. Asst. & res. fel, cardiographic lab, MT. SINAI HOSP, 34-35, sr. clin. asst, cardiac clin, 35-41, adj. physician cardiol, 45-58, chief cardiac clinic, 49-55, CHIEF, PRENATAL CARDIAC CLINIC, 53-, ATTEND. PHYSICIAN CARDIOL, 70-; ASSOC. CLIN. PROF. MED, N.Y. MED. COL, 59-; ASSOC. PROF, MT. SINAI SCH. MED, 67-, CLIN. PROF, 70-, assoc. clin. prof, 66-67. Lectr, Columbia, 35-; asst. attend. physician, Flower Fifth Ave. Hosp, 55-59, assoc. attend. physician, 59-66, attend. physician, 66-; assoc. vis. physician, Metrop. Hosp, 55-61, vis. physician, 61-; assoc.attend.physician, Bird S. Coler Mem. Hosp, 55-; assoc. physician, Mt. Sinai Hosp, 58-70; asst. clin. prof, N.Y. Med. Col, 55-59. Ed. in chief, Am. Jour. Cardiol, 58- Mem. congenital cardiac group, Mt. Sinai Hosp, 45- Chief cardiovasc. sect, 3rd & 235th Gen. Hosp, 42-45, Med.C, 42-45, Maj. Am. Heart Asn; Am. Fedn. Clin. Res; fel. Am. Col. Physicians; fel. Am. Col. Chest Physicians; Am. Col. Cardiol.(pres, 56-57); fel. N.Y. Acad. Med; fel. N.Y. Acad. Sci; fel. Am. Med. Writers' Asn. Address: 1111 Park Ave, New York, NY 10028.

DACONS, JOSEPH C(ARL), b. Wilkesboro, N.C, May 22, 12; m. 43; c. 1. ORGANIC CHEMISTRY. B.S, Ohio State, 36, fel, 48-50, M.S, 48, Ph.D. (chem), 51. Assoc. prof. chem, Fisk, 50-53, acting chmn. dept, 51-53; prof. & chmn. dept, Agr. & Tech. Col. N.C, 53-55; RES. CHEMIST, U.S. NAVAL ORD. LAB, 56- U.S.M.C, 43-46. Am. Chem. Soc; Nat. Inst. Sci; Am. Inst. Chem. Isolation and study of the degradation products of cellulose; chromatographic resolution of complex mixtures of organic compounds; chemistry of high energy organic compounds; electronic spectra. Address: U.S. Naval Ordnance Lab, White Oak, Silver Spring, MD 20910.

Da COSTA, ESTHER (MRS. FREDERICK HOELZEL), b. Pittsburgh, Pa, Dec. 14, 03; m. 37. PHYSIOLOGY. B.S, Chicago, 24, M.S, 29, Ph.D.(physiol), 40. Tech. asst. physiol, Chicago, 33-41, asst, 41-44; instr, Milwaukee State Teachers Col, 44-46; physiologist & head animal res. div, U.S. Army Med. Nutrit. Lab, 46-54; mem. staff, CHICAGO STATE UNIV, 55-59, asst. prof. PHYSIOL, 59-64, assoc. prof, 64-69, PROF, 69- AAAS; Am. Physiol. Soc; Am. Inst. Nutrit. Physiology of dietary restriction and rehabilitation; calcium metabolism; etiology of gastrointestinal lesions. Address: Dept. of Physiology, Chicago State University, 6800 S. Stewart Ave, Chicago, IL 60621.

DA COSTA, WILLIAM A, b. Hamilton, Bermuda, June 21, 19; U.S. citizen; m. 52. BIOCHEMISTRY, ORGANIC CHEMISTRY. B.S, Wilberforce Univ, 42; M.S, Howard Univ, 47; Ph.D.(biochem), Georgetown Univ, 65. Instr. chem, HOWARD UNIV, 47-49, teaching asst. BIOCHEM, COL. MED, 49-54, instr, 55-65, asst. prof, 65-70, ASSOC. PROF, 70- AAAS; Am. Chem. Soc. Drug kinetics and metabolism; physicochemical properties of proteins. Address: Dept. of Biochemistry, Howard University College of Medicine, Washington, DC 20001.

DACQUISTO, M(ICHAEL) P(AUL), b. Mt. Vernon, N.Y, Sept. 9, 22; m. 53; c. 3. MEDICINE. M.D, Vermont, 49. Chief radiobiol. sect, Walter Reed Inst. Res, 56-59; dir. div. nuclear med, 59-62; chief med. div, U.S. Army Trop. Res. Med. Lab, P.R, 62-63, commanding officer & dir, 64-65, spec. asst. to dir, Walter Reed Army Inst. Res, 65-67; DIR. internal med, DOW CHEM. CO, 67-70, CLIN. RES, 70- Assoc. clin. prof, sch. med, Puerto Rico; clin. assoc. prof, sch. med, Ind. Univ. Dipl, Nat. Bd. Med. Exam. U.S.A, 42-46, Med.C, 50- AAAS; Radiation Res. Soc; Am. Col. Physicians; N.Y. Acad. Sci. Clinical pharmacology; therapeutic research; Radiobiology as applied to man; nuclear medicine; isotopes; reactors; nuclear weapons; tropical medicine; cytogenetics. Address: Dow Chemical Co, P.O. Box 10, Zionsville, IN 46077.

DACSO, MICHAEL M(IHALY), b. Hungary, June 25, 09; nat; m. 36; c. 1. MEDICINE. M.D, Royal Hungarian Univ, 34. Res. assoc, Munic. Res. Inst, Rheumatic Diseases, 34-40; intern & res, GOLDWATER MEM. HOSP, 41-44, assoc. vis. physician med, 49-52, DIR. DEPT. PHYS. MED. & REHAB, 49-; PROF. PHYS. MED. & REHAB, SCH. MED, N.Y. UNIV, 63-, assoc. prof, 54-63; DEAN INST. HEALTH SCI, HUNTER COL, 69- Dir. med. serv, Mary Manning Walsh Home, 51-53; attend. physician, univ. hosp, N.Y. Univ-Bellvue Med. Center, vis. physician, Bellevue Hosp, staff physician, inst. phys. med. & rehab. Consult, St. Barnabas Hosp, 55-; chronic disease br, bur. state serv, U.S. Pub. Health Serv, 57-; med. adv. comt, Soc. Security Admin, 61-; Manhattan State Hosp, N.Y, 64- Mem. planning comt, ed. sect, Nat. Conf. Aging, 50, chmn. comt. on int. rels, 58; nat. comt. aging, Nat.

Soc. Welfare Assembly, 53-, chmn. comt. rehab. older worker, 54, mem. adv. comt. archit. competition, 55; Nat. Adv. Comt. Chronic Disease & Health Aged, 57-; planning comt. health & med. care, White House Conf. Aging, 61, nat. comt. aging liaison comt. Dipl, Am. Bd. Phys. Med. & Rehab, 53. Am. Med. Asn; fel. Am. Col. Physicians; Am. Rheumatism Asn; Geront. Soc; sr. mem. Am. Fedn. Clin. Res; Am. Hosp. Asn; Am. Acad. Phys. Med. & Rehab.(v.pres, 64-). Clinical and physiological studies in geriatrics. Address: 108 E. 91st St, New York, NY 10028.

DA CUNHA, ANTONIO BRITO, b. São Paulo, Brazil, June 17, 25; m. 49; c. 2. POPULATION GENETICS, CYTOGENETICS. Ph.D, Univ. São Paulo, 48. Asst. BIOL, UNIV. SÃO PAULO, 45-48, privatdocent, 48-55, asst. prof, 55-60, ASSOC. PROF. 60-, HEAD DEPT. BIOL, 70-, acting head dept. 64-66, 68-70. Rockefeller Found. fels, 49, 61; vis. prof, Univ. Tex, Austin, 71. Soc. Study Evolution (v.pres, 62, 71); Am. Soc. Nat; Genetics Soc. Am; Brazilian Soc. Genetics; Brazilian Acad. Sci. Evolutionary processes; differentiation; chromosomal effects of pathogenic agents. Address: Dept. of Biology, Institute of Biosciences, University of São Paulo, Caixa Postal 8105, São Paulo, Brazil.

D'ADAMO, AMEDEO F(ILIBERTO), JR, b. Brooklyn, N,Y, Apr. 15, 29; m. 62; c. 1. BIOCHEMISTRY. B.Sc, Rutgers, 50, Off. Naval Res. fel. & Ph.D. (chem), 55. Res. assoc, Am. Cyanamid Co, 53-55; Columbia, 55-56; Ortho Res. Found, 56-58; asst. prof. biochem, Albert Einstein Col. Med, Yeshiva, 58-69; ASSOC. PROF. BIOL, YORK COL, CITY UNIV. N.Y, 69- Am. Inst. Chem. Life processes; mechanisms of enzymatic reactions; neurochemistry. Address: Dept. of Biology, York College, City University of New York, 158-11 Jewel Ave, Flushing, NY 11365.

D'ADAMO, ANTHONY, b. Newark, N.J, Apr. 22, 19; m. 48; c. 3. PHARMACEUTICAL CHEMISTRY. B.A, Rutgers, 48; M.A, Columbia, 50. Chemist, Montrose Chem. Co, 50-51; res. chemist, White Labs, 51-53; KNOLL PHARMACEUT. CO, 53-60, chief res. chemist, 60-68, DIR. ANAL. RES. DEPT, 68-, LIAISON OFF, NEW PROD, 70- U.S.A, 40-45. Acad. ·Pharmaceut. Sci; fel. Am. Inst. Chem; Am. Pharmaceut. Asn. Pharmaceutical liquid, parenteral and tablet dosage forms; product development in industrial pharmacy. Address: Knoll Pharmaceutical Co, Research Dept, 377 Crane St, Orange, NJ 07051.

DADDARIO, ALBERT SEBASTIANO, b. Hartford, Conn, Oct. 24, 25; c. 5. ENVIRONMENTAL SCIENCES. B.S, Univ. Conn, 51. Electronic scientist, underwater sound lab, U.S. Civil Serv. Comn, 51-53; chief engr, Ferroxcube Corp, 53-55; Aladdin Electronics, 55-59; commun. div, BENDIX CORP, 59-68, asst. dir. eng, 68-70, DIR. ENG, ENVIRON. SCI. DIV, 70- State dir, Air Force Mil. Affiliate Radio Syst, Md, 69-70. U.S.N, 43-46. Inst. Elec. & Electronics Eng; Am. Oceanic Orgn. Radiosondes and sensors for measurement of temperature, pressure and humidity; radar phased array techniques; adaptive memory systems; communications devices. Address: Engineering Dept, Environmental Science Division, Bendix Corp, 1400 Taylor Ave, Baltimore, MD 21204.

D'ADDIECO, A(LFRED) A(NTHONY), b. East Boston, Mass, Apr. 20, 23. ORGANIC CHEMISTRY. B.S, Tufts Col, 44; M.S, Mass. Inst. Tech, 46, Ph.D.(org. chem), 49. Tech. asst. wood chem, Inst. Paper Chem, 45; asst. org. chem, Mass. Inst. Tech, 46-49; res. chemist, ELECTROCHEM. DEPT, E.I. DU PONT DE NEMOURS & CO. INC, N.Y, 49-57, process res. supvr, 57-60, res. supvr, Del, 60-68, res. & sr. tech. supvr, Niagara Falls Lab, 68-70, SUPVR. PROD. MODIFICATION LAB, ELECTRONICS PROD. DIV, 71- Am. Chem. Soc. Cyclic polyolefins; nylon intermediates; heterocyclic compounds; carbohydrates; peroxygen compounds; chlorohydrocarbons; polymeric binders. Address: Product Modification Lab, Electronics Products Division, E.I. du Pont de Nemours & Co, Inc, Buffalo Ave. & Chemical Rd, Niagara Falls, NY 14302.

DADDOW, WILBUR T(ALBOT), b. Sherman Co, Nebr, Mar. 7, 06; m. 28; c. 2. CHEMISTRY. B.S, Hastings Col, 24; M.S, Iowa, 25, Ph.D.(org. chem), 28. Res. chemist, E.I. du Pont de Nemours & Co, N.J, 28-29, chem. supvr, 29-43, tech. specialist, Del, 43, chief supvr, N.J, 43-46, supt, 46-52, gen. supt, 52-71; RETIRED. With Atomic Energy Cmn, 43-46. Am. Chem. Soc. Organic chemistry; dyestuffs; intermediates. Address: 603 Rockwood Rd, Wilmington, DE 19802.

DADE, PHILIP EUGENE, b. Hutchinson, Kans, Feb. 2, 29; m. 56; c. 3. AGRONOMY. B.S, Kans. State Col, 51, M.S, 52; Ph.D.(forage crop prod), State Col. Wash, 59. RES. AGRONOMIST, Agr. Res. Serv, U.S. Dept. Agr, 57-67; O.M. SCOTT & SONS, 67- U.S.A, 53-55. Am. Soc. Agron; Crop Sci. Soc. Am. Pasture and forage crop management; forage seed production. Address: P.O. Box 327, Salem, OR 97308.

DADGAR, AHMAD, b. Tehran, Iran, Apr. 2, 34; m. 63; c. 2. PHYSICAL INORGANIC CHEMISTRY. B.S, Southwest Mo. State Col, 59; M.S, Ill. Inst. Tech, 61; Ph.D.(phys. chem), Fordham, 65. Anal. chemist, Nalco Chem. Co, Ill, 58-59; instr. phys. & inorg. chem, Manhattan Col, 63-65; asst. prof. Lowell Tech. Inst, 65-67; ASSOC. PROF. CHEM. & CHMN. DEPT, ARYA-MEHR UNIV. TECHNOL, 67- Am. Chem. Soc. Thermodynamic and kinetic studies of coordination compounds in aqueous and nonaqueous solvents; chemistry of the electrolytes in mixed solvent systems. Address: Dept. of Chemistry, Arya-Mehr University of Technology, Tehran, Iran.

DADURA, JAMES GERALD, b. Mt. Carmel, Pa, May 25, 33; m. 64. ORGANIC CHEMISTRY. B.S, St. Vincent Col, 55; Res. Corp. grant, Notre Dame, 56-58, Ph.D.(org. chem), 60. Assoc. chemist, TEXACO INC, 59-60, sr. chemist, 60-63, res. chemist, 63-66, group leader, 66-69, RES. TECHNOLOGIST, 69- Sci. Res. Soc. Am; Am. Chem. Soc. Grease, high temperature; synthetic lubricants; antioxidants; additives for diesel oils. Address: Texaco Research Center, P.O. Box 509, Beacon, NY 12508.

DAEHLER, MARK, b. Cedar Rapids, Iowa, Mar. 21, 34. PHYSICS. B.A, Coe Col, 55; Iowa, 55; M.A, Wisconsin, 57, Ph.D.(physics), 66. Fel, Los Alamos Sci. Lab, Univ. Calif, 66-68; staff physicist, Inst. Plasmaphysiks, Munich, Ger, 68-71; RES. PHYSICIST, U.S. NAVAL RES. LAB, 71- Optical

Soc. Am; Am. Phys. Soc. High resolution interferometric optical spectroscopy; solar and plasma spectroscopy; zodiacal light spectroscopy; infrared rocket astronomy. Address: U.S. Naval Research Lab, Washington, DC 20390.

DAEHLER, MAX, JR, b. Cedar Rapids, Iowa, Mar. 21, 34. PHYSICS. B.A, Coe Col, 55; M.A, Univ. Wis, 57, Ph.D, 62. Sr. engr. res, Autonetics Div, N.Am. Aviation, Inc, 62-68; SR. SCIENTIST, EXSAR CORP, 68- Electron spin resonance; star-tracking devices. Address: Exsar Corp, 3955 Birch St, Newport Beach, CA 92660.

DAEHNICK, WILFRIED A. W, b. Berlin, Germany, Dec. 30, 28; U.S. citizen; m. 60; c. 3. NUCLEAR PHYSICS. B.S, Munich Tech, 51; exchange fel, Washington (St. Louis), 51-52, univ. fel. & Ph.D.(physics), 58; Nat. fel, & M.A, Hamburg, 55. Res. assoc. NUCLEAR PHYSICS, Washington (St. Louis), 58-59; Princeton, 59-60, instr, 60-62; asst. prof, UNIV. PITTSBURGH, 62-65, assoc. prof, 65-69, PROF, 69- Fel. Am.Phys.Soc. Experimental and theoretical studies of nuclear structure and nuclear reactions induced by light and heavy ions; nuclear instrumentation; consulting. Address: Dept. of Physics, University of Pittsburgh, Pittsburgh, PA 15213.

DAELLENBACH, CHARLES BYRON, b. Minneapolis, Minn, Nov. 16, 39; m. 62; c. 3. PHYSICAL METALLURGY. B.S, Wisconsin, 62, Wis. Alumni Res. Found. fel, & M.S, 63. Extractive metallurgist, BUR. MINES, U.S. DEPT. INTERIOR, 63-64, res. extractive metallurgist, 64-66, RES. METALLURGIST, 66- Am. Inst. Mining, Metall. & Petrol. Eng. Extractive metallurgy and mineral beneficiation; physical and foundry metallurgy. Address: U.S. Bureau of Mines, Twin City Metallurgy Research Center, Minneapolis, MN 55111.

DAENIKER, HANS ULRICH, b. Zurich, Switz; Dec. 19, 24; m. 59; c. 3. ORGANIC CHEMISTRY. B.S, Swiss Fed. Inst. Tech, 49, Ph.D.(org. chem), 52. Fel, California, Los Angeles, 52-53; Harvard, 53-54; group leader pharmaceut. res, Ciba Ag, Switz, 55-65; res. assoc, Givaudan S.A, Switz, 65, v.pres. res, Givaudan Corp, N.J, 66-71, MANAGING DIR, GIVAUDAN AG, SWITZ, 71- Swiss Army, 44-56, 1st Lt. Am. Chem. Soc; fel. Am. Inst. Chem; Swiss Chem. Soc; Brit. Chem. Soc. Pharmaceutics; perfume and flavor chemistry. Address: Givaudan AG, 8600 Dubendorf, Switz.

DAESCHNER, CHARLES WILLIAM, JR, b. Houston, Tex, Dec. 24, 20; m. 48; c. 3. PEDIATRICS. B.A, Rice, Inst, 42; M.D, Texas, 45. Intern, Hermann Hosp, Houston, 45-46; jr. res. St. Louis Children's Hosp, 48-49, asst. res, 49-50; sr. res, Boston Children's Hosp, 50-51; assoc. prof. PEDIAT, med. col, Baylor, 51-60; PROF. & CHMN. DEPT. MED. BR, UNIV. TEX, 60- U.S.A.A.F, 46-48. Acad. Pediat; Soc. Pediat. Res. Metabolic and renal diseases in children. Address: Dept. of Pediatrics, University of Texas Medical Branch, Galveston, TX 77551.

DAESSLE, CLAUDE, b. France, Mar. 29, 29; Can. citizen; m. 64; c. 1. ORGANIC CHEMISTRY. Ch.E, Swiss Fed. Inst. Tech, 54, Dr.Sc.Phys, 57. Res. chemist, Monsanto Can. Ltd, 57-60; OWNER, ORG. MICROANAL, 60- General organic synthesis; especially natural products. Address: 5757 Decelles Ave, Montreal 251, Que, Can.

DAFERMOS, CONSTANTINE M, b. Athens, Greece, May 26, 41; m. 64. APPLIED MATHEMATICS. Dipl. civil eng, Athens Tech, 64; Ph.D.(mech), Johns Hopkins Univ, 67. Fel. THEORET. MECH, Johns Hopkins Univ, 67-68; asst. prof, Cornell Univ, 68-71; ASSOC. PROF, BROWN UNIV, 71- Stability theory in continuum mechanics. Address: Division of Applied Mathematics, Brown University, Providence, RI 02912.

DAGANI, MICHAEL JOHN, b. San Mateo, Calif, Aug. 29, 37; m. 63; c. 2. ORGANIC CHEMISTRY. B.S, San Jose State Col, 63; California, Berkeley, 63-64; Ph.D.(org. chem), Arizona, 67. Fel. org. chem, Wisconsin, 67-68; RES. CHEMIST, ETHYL CORP, 68- U.S.N, 55-58. Am. Chem. Soc. Studies of solvolysis mechanisms by isotope effects and by internal return phenomena. Address: Research and Development Dept, Ethyl Corp, P.O. Box 341, Baton Rouge, LA 70821.

DAGG, CHARLES P(ATRICK), b. Nebr, July 21, 23. EMBRYOLOGY. B.S, George Wash. Univ, 48; Ph.D.(zool), Univ. Calif, Los Angeles, 53. Asst. cancer, Univ. Calif, Los Angeles, 52-53; U.S. Pub. Health Serv. res. fel. embryol. & cancer, Sloan-Kettering Inst. 54-55, asst, 55-56; vis. asst. prof. biol, Brown Univ, 56-58; assoc. staff scientist, Jackson Lab, 58-59, staff scientist, 59-67; PROF. DENT, PROF. BIOL. & CHMN. DEPT, UNIV. ALA, BIRMINGHAM & PROF. BIOL, TUSCALOOSA, 67- U.S.A, 43-46. AAAS; Am. Soc. Zool; Am. Asn. Anat; Am. Genetic Asn; Am. Inst. Biol. Sci; Genetics Soc. Am; Soc. Develop. Biol; Soc. Study Reproduction. Embryology; genetics; teratology of mammals. Address: Dept. of Biology, University of Alabama in Birmingham, Birmingham, AL 35233.

DAGG, I(AN) R(ALPH), b. Winnipeg, Man, Mar. 20, 28; m. 57; c. 2. MICROWAVE PHYSICS. B.Sc, Manitoba, 49; M.S, Pa. State Col, 50; Ph.D.(physics), Toronto, 53. Lectr. physics, Toronto, 53-54; Nat. Res. Coun. Can. fel, Oxford, 54-55; asst. res. officer appl. physics, Nat. Res. Coun. Can, 55-59; assoc. prof. PHYSICS, UNIV. WATERLOO, 59-69, PROF, 69- Nat. Res. Coun. Can. res. grants, 60-65. Infrared and Raman spectroscopy; electric field induced and pressure induced absorption in infrared and microwave regions; acoustics, microphone standards and noise control. Address: Dept. of Physics, University of Waterloo, Waterloo, Ont, Can.

DAGGERHART, JAMES ALVIN, JR, b. Shelby, N.C, Dec. 6, 42; m. 63; c. 2. GAS DYNAMICS. B.S, N.C. State Univ, 64, Ph.D.(mech. eng), 69. Res. assoc. rarefied gas dynamisc, N.C. STATE UNIV, 66-69, ASST. PROF. AEROSPACE ENG, 69- NASA res. grant, 69-71. Am. Inst. Aeronaut. & Astronaut; Am. Vacuum Soc. Rarefied gas dynamics; cryoentrainment mechanism for vacuum pump application; high altitude simulation; performance of ionization type vacuum gauges in various environments. Address: 618 Birch Circle, Cary, NC 27511.

DAGGETT, ALBERT F(REDERICK), b. Concord, N.H, Oct. 23, 06; m. 31; c. 2. CHEMISTRY. B.S, New Hampshire, 28, M.S, 30; fel, Columbia, 33-34, Ph.D, 34. Instr. CHEM, New Hampshire, 28-31; asst. instr, Columbia, 31-33, res.

assoc, 34; instr, Hunter Col, 35; UNIV. N.H, 35-37, asst. prof, 37-41, assoc. prof, 41-46, PROF, 46-, dean grad. sch, 49-52, coordinator res, 49-52. Coordinator, Int. Co-op. Admin-Univ. New Hampshire tech. aid prog, Lima, 56-60, hon. prof, 58, vis. lectr, 64. Consult. Agency Int. Develop. to Peru, 62. Am. Chem. Soc. Analytical chemistry; rare earths; photochemistry. Address: Dept. of Chemistry, University of New Hampshire, Durham, NH 03824.

DAGGS, RAY G(ILBERT), b. McKees Rocks, Pa, June 26, 04; m. 29; c. 2. PHYSIOLOGY. B.S, Bucknell, 26, hon. D.Sc, 55; Ph.D.(physiol), Rochester, 30. Nat. Res. Coun. fel, Rochester, 27-29, asst. physiol, 29-30, instr, 30-33, asst. prof, 33-36; col. med, Vermont, 36-37, assoc. prof, 37-41, acting head dept, 41; dir. res, Army Med. Res. Lab, 46-56; EXEC. SECY-TREAS, AM. PHYSIOL. SOC, 56- U.S.A, 41-46, Col. AAAS; Am. Physiol. Soc.(ed, Physiologist, 58-, assoc. ed, Physiol. Rev, 58-). Physiological research; environmental physiology; physiology of nutrition; intermediary metabolism; scientific administration and education. Address: American Physiological Society, 9650 Rockville Pike, Bethesda, MD 20014.

DAGGY, RICHARD H(ENRY), b. St. Paul, Minn, Aug. 23, 14. ENTOMOLOGY, PUBLIC HEALTH. B.S, Minnesota, 34, M.S, 38, Ph.D.(entom), 41; M.P.H, Harvard, 52, Dr.P.H.(trop. pub. health), 58. Instr, high sch, Minn, 34; asst. Minnesota, 35-39; instr. biol, Bemidji State Col, 39-41; asst. entomologist, bur. entom. & plant quarantine, U.S. Dept. Agr, Fla, 42; assoc. entomologist, communicable disease center, U.S. Pub. Health Serv, 45; asst. prof. entom, Minnesota, 45-47; from med. entomologist to med. dir, Arabian Am. Oil Co, Saudi Arabia, 47-64; assoc. dean int. prog. & lectr. trop. pub. health, HARVARD, 64-71, ACTING DEAN, SCH. PUB. HEALTH, 71-; vis. lectr, 54-64. Hon. consult, U.S. Air Force, Europe, 57. U.S.N.R, 42-45, Lt. AAAS; Am. Entom. Soc; Am. Soc. Trop. Med. & Hyg; fel. Am. Pub. Health Asn; Royal Soc. Trop. Med. & Hyg. Biology and ecology of anophelines; malaria control; tropical public health. Address: School of Public Health, Harvard University, Boston, MA 02115.

DAGGY, TOM, b. Mooresville, Ind, July 16, 15; m. 39; c. 2. BIOLOGY. B.A, Earham Col, 37; M.S, Northwest. Univ, 39, Ph.D.(zool), 46. Asst. zool, Northwest Univ, 37-42; instr. BIOL, Maine Township Jr. Col, Ill, 39-42; Univ. Toledo, 42-43; tutor, Olivet Col, 43-47; assoc. prof, DAVIDSON COL, 47-55, PROF, 55- Biol. illustrator, 38-43. AAAS; Ecol. Soc. Am; Soc. Study Evolution; Soc. Syst. Zool. Ecology and taxonomy of insects; immature stages of Coleoptera. Address: Dept. of Biology, Davidson College, Davidson, NC 28036.

DAGIRMANJIAN, ROSE, b. Whitinsville, Mass, July 4, 30. PHARMACOLOGY. A.B, Clark, 52; M.S, Rochester, 54, Ph.D.(pharmacol), 60. Res. assoc. pharmacol, Rochester, 52-60; Riker Int. fel, Eng, 60-62; asst. prof. PHARMACOL, col. med, Ohio State, 63-69; ASSOC. PROF, SCH. MED, UNIV. LOUISVILLE, 69- AAAS; Am. Chem. Soc; Am. Soc. Pharmacol. & Exp. Therapeut; Soc. Toxicol; Soc. Exp. Biol. & Med; Soc. Neurosci. Pharmacology of tetrahydrocannabinols; effects of drugs and magnesium on the biogenic amines in the central nervous system; neuropharmacology of heavy metals. Address: Dept. of Pharmacology, University of Louisville Health Sciences Center, Louisville, KY 40201.

DAGLE, GERALD EUGENE, b. Seattle, Wash, July 12, 39; m. 61; c. 1. PATHOLOGY. D.V.M, Wash. State Univ, 63. Res. fel. path, Merck Inst, West Point, 65-69; PATHOLOGIST, COLO. STATE UNIV, 70- Vet.C, 63-65, Capt. Am. Vet. Med. Ans. Anatomical pathology; drug safety evaluation. Address: 2408 Purdue Rd, Fort Collins, CO 80521.

D'AGOSTINO, ANTHONY N, b. North Tonawanda, N.Y, Apr. 18, 32; m. 58; c. 4. PATHOLOGY, NEUROPATHOLOGY. B.A, Cornell Univ, 54; M.D, State Univ. N.Y. Buffalo, 58. Asst. prof. PATH, col. med, Univ. Utah, 63-67; ASSOC. PROF, UNIV. TEX.(SOUTHWEST) MED. SCH, DALLAS, 67- Int. Acad. Path; Am. Asn. Neuropath; Am. Asn. Clin. Path. Neuromuscular diseases. Address: Dept. of Pathology, University of Texas (Southwestern) Medical School, Dallas, TX 75235.

D'AGOSTINO, ANTHONY S, b. Italy, May 10, 31; U.S. citizen. BIOLOGY. B.A, N.Y. Univ, 57, M.S, 61, Ph.D.(biol), 65. Jr. chemist, dept. toxicol, Kings County Hosp, Brooklyn, N.Y, 57-58; res. asst. growth marine organisms, Haskins Labs, Inc, 59-64, assoc. researcher, 64-65; asst. prof. BIOL, ST. JOHN'S UNIV.(N.Y), 65-68, ASSOC. PROF, 68- Summer Nat. Sci. Found res. fel, Marine Biol. Labs, Woods Hole, 60; res. consult, Continental Brine Shrimp Holding Ltd, Sask, Can, 64; res. scientist, N.Y. Ocean Sci. Lab, 70. U.S.A, 52-53. AAAS; Am. Soc. Zool; Soc. Protozool; Am. Inst. Biol. Sci. Nutrition and physiology of marine and freshwater invertebrates. Address: Dept. of Biology, St. John's University, Jamaica, NY 11432.

D'AGOSTINO, MICHAEL D(OMINICK), b. New York, N.Y, Mar. 26, 33; m. 57; c. 3. NUCLEAR SCIENCE. B.Aero.Eng, N.Y. Univ, 54, M.Nuc.Eng, 67. Struct. engr, GRUMMAN AEROSPACE CORP, 54-55, res. scientist, 57-62, HEAD NUCLEAR & RADIATION EFFECTS GROUP, 62- Guest scientist, reactor div, Brookhaven Nat. Lab, 61-70; chmn, Grumman Isotopes Comt, 60-62; consult. partner, Radiation Technol. Assocs, N.Y, 66- U.S.A.F, 55-57, Res, 57-71, Capt. Inst. Elec. & Electronics Eng; Am. Nuclear Soc; Am. Inst. Aeronaut. & Astronaut. Neutron and proton activation cross sections; activation analysis; gamma ray spectra analysis; dosimetry; effects of radiation on materials. Address: Research Dept, Grumman Aerospace Corp, Bethpage, NY 11714.

D'AGOSTINO, RALPH B, b. Somerville, Mass, Aug. 16, 40; m. 65; c. 2. MATHEMATICAL & EXPERIMENTAL STATISTICS. A.B, Boston, 62, A.M, 64; Ph.D.(statist), Harvard, 68. Lectr. MATH, BOSTON UNIV, 64-68, asst. prof, 68-71, ASSOC. PROF, 71- Statist. consult, United Fruit Co, Mass; educ. div, Bolt, Beranek & Newman; Educ. Res. Corp, 68- Inst. Math. Statist; Am. Statist. Asn. Statistics. Address: Dept. of Mathematics, Boston University, 604 Commonwealth Ave, Boston, MA 02215.

DAGRADI, ANGELO E, b. New York, N.Y, Feb. 23, 17; m. 42; c. 1. INTERNAL MEDICINE, GASTROENTEROLOGY. A.B, N.Y. Univ, 36; M.D, L.I. Col. Med, 40. Asst. chief med. serv, VET. ADMIN. HOSP, Northport, N.Y,

48-51, ASST. CHIEF GASTROENTEROL, LONG BEACH, 51- Assoc. clin. prof, sch. med, California, Los Angeles, 51-, Irvine, 68- Consult, Harbor Gen. Hosp, Torrance, 51-; Orange County Hosp, 68- U.S.A, 42-46, Maj. First Prize Roerer Award, 69. Am. Col. Physicians; Am. Gastroenterol. Asn; Am. Soc. Gastrointestinal Endoscopy (treas); Am. Col. Gastroenterol. (secy-general); Am. Med. Asn. Diseases of the gastro-intestinal tract especially esophagus, stomach and liver. Address: Veterans Administration Hospital, 5901 E. Seventh St, Long Beach, CA 90801.

D'AGROSA, LOUIS S(ALVATORE), b. Brooklyn, N.Y, Oct. 23, 29; m. 54; c. 5. PHYSIOLOGY. B.S, City Col. New York, 52; univ. fel, St. Louis, 58-60, U.S. Pub. Health Serv. fel, 60-62, Ph.D.(physiol), 62. Pharmacol. res. asst, Nepera Chem. Co, N.Y, 54-56; sect. head, Grove Labs, Mo, 56-58; instr. PHYSIOL, ST. LOUIS UNIV, 62-65, asst. prof, 65-71, ASSOC. PROF, 71- Chem.C, U.S.A, 52-54. AAAS; Peripheral circulation in man and animal; temperature regulation; microcirculation. Address: Dept. of Physiology, St. Louis University, 1402 S. Grand Blvd, St. Louis, MO 63104.

D'AGUANNO, WILLIAM, b. Providence, R.I, Dec. 29, 23; m. 50; c. 3. PHYSIOLOGY, PHARMACOLOGY. B.S, Rhode Island, 49; M.S, Oklahoma, 50; Ph.D.(physiol), Fla. State, 55. Asst, Oklahoma, 50; Fla. State, 50-54; pharmacologist, FOOD & DRUG ADMIN, 56-70, DEP. DIR. DIV. NEUROPHARMACOL, OFF. NEW DRUGS, BUR. MED, 70- U.S.N, 43-46. AAAS; Soc. Toxicol. Pharmacodynamics; effect of drugs on heart; central nervous system; circulation; nerve; nerve muscle in vivo and in vitro; cellular physiology. Address: Division of Neuropharmacology, Office of New Drugs, Bureau of Medicine, U.S. Food & Drug Administration, Washington, DC 20204.

DAGUE, RICHARD R(AY), b. Little Sioux, Iowa, Feb. 20, 31; m. 52; c. 4. SANITARY ENGINEERING. B.S, Iowa State, 59, M.S, 60; Ph.D.(environ. health eng), Kansas, 67. Surv. party chief, Smith Eng. Co, Iowa, 53-55; design eng, B.H. Backlund & Assoc, Nebr, 60-61; instr. sanit. eng, Iowa State, 61-62; owner engr, Dague Eng. Co, Iowa, 62-64; asst. prof. SANIT. ENG, Kansas State, 66-67; UNIV. IOWA, 67-70, ASSOC. PROF, 70- U.S.N, 50-53; U.S.N. Civil Eng.C.R, Lt. Am. Soc. Civil Eng; Water Pollution Control Fedn; Am. Water Works Asn; Nat. Soc. Prof. Eng. Water quality control, especially chemical and biological water and wastewater treatment. Address: Dept. of Civil Engineering, College of Engineering, University of Iowa, Iowa City, IA 52240.

DAGUILLARD, FRITZ, b. Cayes, Haiti, June 1, 36; m; c. 1. IMMUNOLOGY, MEDICINE. M.D, Univ. Haiti, 61; U.S. Pub. Health Serv. fel, 64-69; M.P.H, Harvard, 65; Ph.D.(immunol), McGill Univ, 69. Resident med, Verettes Hosp, Haiti, 61-63; intern, med. ctr, Albert Einstein Col. Med, 63-64; res. fel. microbiol, Harvard, 66-67; immunol, Royal Victoria Hosp, McGill Univ. Clin, 67-69; ASST. PROF. MED, SCH. MED, LAVAL UNIV, 69- Res. grants, Quebec Med. Res. Coun, 69-71 & Med. Res. Coun. Can, 70- Can. Soc. Immunol; Can. Soc. Clin. Invest. Lymphocyte activation; cellular immunology; immune deficiency syndromes. Address: Immunobiology Lab, St-Sacrement Hospital, 1050 Chemin Ste-Foy, Quebec 6e, Que, Can.

DAHILL, ROBERT T, JR, b. Perth Amboy, N.J, Jan. 15, 37; m. 63; c. 1. ORGANIC CHEMISTRY. B.S, Tufts, 59; M.S, Worcester Polytech, 61; Ph.D. (org. chem), Stevens Inst. Tech, 64. GROUP LEADER, GIVAUDAN CORP, CLIFTON, 64- Am. Chem. Soc; Brit. Chem. Soc. Synthetic organic chemistry, especially compound of interest to flavor and fragrance industry. Address: 188 William St, Perth Amboy, NJ 08861.

DAHIYA, RAGHUNATH S, b. Halalpur, Punjab, India, Oct. 4, 31; m. 55; c. 2. FOOD MICROBIOLOGY. B.Sc, Govt. Agr. Col, Ludhiana, India, 51, M.Sc, 53; Ph.D.(food sci), N.C. State Col, 62. Agr. inspector, Punjab State Agr. Dept, India, 53-56; lectr. dairy sci. & dairy mgr, Govt. Agr. Col, Ludhiana, 56-58; res. assoc. food microbiol, N.C. State, 62-65, asst. prof, 65-71; CHIEF MICROBIOLOGIST, N.C. DEPT. AGR, 71- AAAS; Am. Soc. Microbiol; Am. Chem. Soc; Inst. Food Technol. Microbiological surveillance of foods, drugs and cosmetics for safety; development of faster and more accurate methods of identification of food born pathothegns. Address: Analytical Division, North Carolina Dept. of Agriculture, Raleigh, NC 27611.

DAHIYA, RAJBIR SINGH, b. Rattangarh, India, Dec. 3, 40; m. 66; c. 2. MATHEMATICS. B.Sc, Birla Sci. Col, Pilani, India, 60, M.Sc, 62; Ph.D. (math), Birla Inst. Sci. & Technol, 67. Asst. lectr. MATH, Birla Inst. Technol. & Sci, Pilani, India, 62-65, lectr, 65-68; ASST. PROF, IOWA STATE UNIV, 68- Am. Math. Soc. Special problems in integral transforms; operational calculus; special functions and use of these various transforms and special function for computation techniques in analysis. Address: Dept. of Mathematics, Iowa State University, Ames, IA 50010.

DAHL, ADRIAN H(ILMAN), b. Mott, N.Dak, Dec. 6, 19; m. 42; c. 2. BIOPHYSICS. B.A, St. Olaf Col, 41, Ph.D.(biophys), Rochester, 53. Jr. res. physicist, Eastman Kodak Co, N.Y, 41-43, Tenn. Eastman Corp, 43, sr. physicist, 43-46; physicist, Atomic Energy Cmn, 46-47: asst. chief radiation, instrument br, Washington Div. Prod, 47, chief, 47-49; chief instrumentation sect, atomic energy proj, sch. med, Rochester, 50-59; prin. scientist, Oak Ridge Inst. Nuclear Studies, 59-61; prof. phys. & radiation biol. & dir. radiol. health training prog, Colorado State, 61-69; chief astrogeophys, space sci. dept, Martin Marietta Corp, 69-71; CHIEF ENVIRON. BR, ATOMIC ENERGY COMN, 71- Fulbright lectr. health physics, Argentina, 59- Consult, radiation instrumentation, Armed Forces Spec. Weapons Proj, 48-52; Fed. Civil Defense, 56; Int. Atomic Energy Comn. expert radioisotope tech, Indonesia, 61. Assoc. Am. Phys. Soc; assoc. Am. Asn. Physics Teachers; Inst. Elec. & Electronics Eng; Health Phys. Soc. Nuclear radiation effects on photographic emulsions; industrial radiography; photographic dosimetry; circuit design of radiation detection; instruments and components; space physics; planetary geology and atmospheric science. Address: Health Science Lab, Atomic Energy Commission, P.O. Box 2108, Idaho Falls, ID 83401.

DAHL, ALTON, b. Clifton, Tex, Jan. 8, 37; m. 59. PHYSICAL CHEMISTRY. B.A, Tex. Lutheran Col, 59; M.S, Michigan, 61, Ph.D.(chem), 63. Instr. chem, Univ. Mich, 63-64; chemist, EXP. STA, E.I. DU PONT DE NEMOURS & CO, INC, 64-68, SR. RES. CHEMIST, 68- Am. Chem. Soc; Soc. Appl. Spectros; Sci. Res. Soc. Am. Infrared and Raman spectroscopy; polymerization; polymer development. Address: 2117 Meadow Lane, Wilmington, DE 19803.

DAHL, A(NTHONY) ORVILLE, b. Minneapolis, Minn, Apr. 18, 10. BOTANY. B.S, Minnesota, 32, M.S, 33, Ph.D.(bot), 38. Asst. bot, Minnesota, 32-38; instr. biol, Harvard, 38-41, faculty instr, 41-44, tutor, 38-44; assoc. prof. BOT, Minnesota, 44-47, prof, 48-67, chmn. dept, 47-57; PROF. & DIR, MORRIS ARBORETUM, UNIV. PA, 67- Res. assoc, Karolinska Inst, Sweden, 50-51, Denmarks Geol. Undersgelse, 57-58; res. investr, Pennsylvania, 64-66. Nat. Sci. Found. award, 57-64; Nat. Insts. Health award, 61-62; Nat. Aeronaut. & Space Admin. award, 63- Mem, Int. Comt. Palynol, 54-56. AAAS; N.Y. Acad. Sci; Am. Bot. Soc; Am. Soc. Nat; Int. Soc. Cell Biol; Int. Soc. Plant Taxon; Torrey Bot. Club. Cytology; pollen morphology; atmospheric pollen; cytotaxonomy; electron microscopy. Address: Morris Arboretum, University of Pennsylvania, 9414 Meadowbrook Ave, Chestnut Hill, Philadelphia, PA 19118.

DAHL, ARTHUR LYON, b. Palo Alto, Calif, Aug. 13, 42. PHYCOLOGY, MARINE ECOLOGY. A.B, Stanford Univ, 64; Nat. Defense Educ. Act Title IV fel, Univ. Calif, Santa Barbara, 64-67, Pub. Health Serv. fel, 67-68, Ph.D.(biol), 69; Nat. Sci. Found. grant, Univ. Wash, summer 65. Vis. res. assoc. bot, SMITHSONIAN INST, 69-70, ASSOC. CURATOR ALGAE, 70- AAAS; Bot. Soc. Am; Brit. Phycol. Soc; Ecol. Soc. Am; Int. Phycol. Soc; Marine Biol. Asn. U.K; Phycol. Soc. Am. Development, ultrastructure, and experimental ecology of benthic marine algae; tropical reef ecosystems and the algal communities of coral reefs. Address: Dept. of Botany, Smithsonian Institution, Washington, DC 20560.

DAHL, ARTHUR RICHARD, b. Des Moines, Iowa, Nov. 25, 30; m. 52; c. 4. GEOLOGY, CIVIL ENGINEERING. B.S, Iowa State Col, 54, M.S, 58; Ph.D. (geol, eng), Iowa State, 61. Assoc. civil eng, Iowa State, 57-61; geologist, Humble Oil & Ref. Co, 61-64; geol. engr, Esso Prod. Res. Co, 64-66; sr. geologist, HUMBLE OIL & REF. CO, 66-67, supv. geologist, 67-70, DIST. GEOLOGIST, 70- Off. Naval Res. grant, 58-60. Geol. Soc. Am; Am. Asn. Petrol. Geol; Am. Inst. Mining, Metall. & Petrol. Eng; Am. Geol. Inst. Geology and engineering of unconsolidated earth materials; exploration and exploitation of base metals and nuclear fuel. Address: Humble Oil & Refining Co, Minerals Dept, P.O. Box 120, Denver, CO 80201.

DAHL, BILLIE EUGENE, b. Cement, Okla, Oct. 24, 29; m. 53; c. 3. RANGE MANAGEMENT, ANIMAL HUSBANDRY. B.S, Okla. State, 51; M.S, Utah State, 53; Ph.D.(range mgt, soils), Idaho, 66. Range conservationist, Bur. Land Mgt, Wyo, 53, range mgr, 54-56; asst. range conservationist, agr. exp. sta, Colorado State Univ, 56-66, assoc. range conservationist, East. Colo. Range Sta, 66-67, assoc. prof. range econ. & ecol, Univ, 67; ASSOC. PROF. RANGE MGT, TEX. TECH UNIV, 67- Res. asst, range & forestry exp. sta, Univ. Idaho, 62-64. Soc. Range Mgt. Grazing management; systems of grazing; legume adaptation studies; range nutrition, improvement, ecology and economics. Address: Dept. of Range & Wildlife Management, Texas Tech University, Lubbock, TX 79409.

DAHL, DENNIS RAY, b. Colby, Kans, Feb. 20, 30; m. 52; c. 2. NEUROCHEMISTRY, NEUROBIOLOGY. A.B, Kansas, 56, U.S. Pub. Health Serv. fel, 56-57, M.D, 61, Ph.D.(biochem, physiol), 63. Nat. Inst. Neurol. Diseases & Blindness fel, 61-63; sci. officer, neuropsychiat. res. unit, Med. Res. Coun. Labs, Carshalton, Eng, 63-64; RES. ASSOC. NEUROBIOL, UNIV. KANS, 64- U.S.A, 52-54, Res, 54-56. Am. Soc. Cell Biol; Am. Physiol. Soc; Am. Soc. Neurochem; Am. Soc. Neurosci; Brit. Biochem. Soc; Int. Soc. Neurochem. Energy flow in the nervous system; chemistry and function of neurotubules. Address: Dept. of Physiology & Cell Biology, University of Kansas, Lawrence, KS 66044.

DAHL, ELMER V(ERNON), b. Colby, Kans, Apr. 17, 21; m. 44; c. 5. PATHOLOGY, EPIDEMIOLOGY. B.S, Southern California, 43, M.D, 52; M.S, Minnesota, 58. Intern, Walter Reed Army Hosp, U.S. Air Force, 52-53, fel. path, sch. med, Duke, 53-54, Mayo Found. fel, 54-59, chief path. br, U.S. Air Force Sch. Aerospace Med, 59-61, comdr. epidemiol. lab, Lackland Air Force Base, 61-68, epidemiol. flight, Manila, Philippines, 68-69; RES. ASSOC. PROF. PATH, MED. BR, UNIV. TEX, 69- Consult, U.S. Air Force Sch. Aerospace Med, 61-69, Surgeon Gen, 61-65, Aeromed. Res. Lab, Holloman Air Force Base, 64-69. Res. award, Mayo Alumni Asn, 58, U.S.A.F, 43-47, 52-69, Col. Am. Soc. Exp. Path; fel. Col. Am. Path; Int. Acad. Path; Soc. Trop. Med. & Hyg; Am. Med. Asn. Infectious diseases; experimental pathology. Address: 124 Tuna Ave, Galveston, TX 77550.

DAHL, GERD H, b. Gevelsberg, Germany, Sept. 3, 30; U.S. citizen; m. 57; c. 2. INORGANIC CHEMISTRY. B.S, Muskingum Col, 55; Indiana, 58-60; Ph.D.(chem), Iowa State, 60. Asst. prof. chem, North Dakota, 60-62; sr. res. chemist, PENNWALT CORP, 62-69, proj. leader, 69-70, GROUP LEADER, 70- Am. Chem. Soc. Synthesis and characterization of inorganic polymers; organometallics. Address: Pennwalt Corp, 300 First Ave, King of Prussia, PA 19406.

DAHL, HARRY M(ARTIN), b. Yonkers, N.Y, June 23, 26; m. 54; c. 3. GEOLOGY. A.B, Hunter Col, 50; A.M, Columbia, 51, Ph.D.(geol), 54. Geologist, U.S. Atomic Energy Cmn, Colo, 54-55, area geologist, 55-56, RES. GEOLOGIST, 56-57; RES. & TECH. DEPT, TEXACO, INC, 57-, PROJ. LEADER, 69- Chmn, co-ord. cmt, Am. Petrol. Inst. Res. Proj, 55, 64-66. U.S.A.A.F, 44-46. Mineral. Soc. Am; Geol. Soc. Am; Geochem. Soc; Clay Minerals Soc; Am. Asn. Petrol. Geol; Int. Asn. Sedimentol.(South. U.S. regional ed, Sedimentology, 63-68). Research and development of exploration techniques to aid in locating petroleum. Address: Research & Technical Dept, Texaco Inc, P.O. Box 425, Bellaire, TX 77401.

DAHL, HARVEY A, b. Waldheim, Sask, Can, Feb. 19, 26; U.S. citizen. PHYSICS. B.S, Stanford, 51, Ph.D.(physics), 63. Res. asst, high energy physics lab, Stanford, 56-62, res. assoc, 62-64; ASST. PROF. PHYSICS, NAVAL POSTGRAD. SCH, 64- Am. Phys. Soc; Am. Asn. Physics Teachers. High energy nuclear physics, especially electromagnetically induced disintegrations of nuclei; electron scattering at high energies. Address: Dept. of Physics, Naval Postgraduate School, Monterey, CA 93940.

DAHL, LAWRENCE F(REDERICK), b. Chicago, Ill, June 2, 29; m. 56; c. 3. PHYSICAL & INORGANIC CHEMISTRY. B.S, Louisville, 51; Ph.D.(phys. chem), Iowa State, 56. Atomic Energy Cmn. fel, Ames Lab, Iowa State, 57; instr. CHEM, UNIV. WIS, MADISON, 57-59, asst. prof, 59-63, assoc. prof, 63-64, PROF, 64- Alfred P. Sloan fel, 63-65; Guggenheim fel, 70-71. AAAS; Am. Crystallog. Asn; Am. Chem. Soc; Am. Phys. Soc; Brit. Chem. Soc; N.Y. Acad. Sci. Synthesis, structure and bonding of inorganic compounds, especially organometallic complexes and metal carbonyls; structural characterization of antibiotics and other biologically important compounds; x-ray crystallography and spectroscopy; molecular structure and valence. Address: Dept. of Chemistry, University of Wisconsin, Madison, WI 53706.

DAHL, LEWIS K(ITCHENER), b. Bawlf, Alta, Can, Dec. 11, 14; U.S. citizen; m. 49; c. 3. INTERNAL MEDICINE. B.Sc, Washington (Seattle), 35; M.D, Pennsylvania, 39. Intern, hosp, Pennsylvania, 39-41; asst. med, Harvard Med. Sch, 41-42, 46, 47; asst, Rockefeller Inst. & asst. physician, hosp, 48-52; head res. med. serv, MED. RES. CTR, BROOKHAVEN NAT. LAB, 52-68, CHIEF STAFF, HOSP, 68- Asst. res, Mass. Gen. Hosp, 41-42, res, 46, chief res, 47. Consult, Atomic Bomb Casualty Comn, Japan, 58, 62; Nutrit. Comn, Am. Heart Asn, 61-66; med. adv. bd, Coun. High Blood Pressure Res, 61- U.S.A, 42-45, Maj. Soc. Exp. Biol. & Med; Am. Inst. Nutrit; Am. Col. Physicians. Sodium metabolism in essential hypertension; epidemiology of hypertension and atherosclerosis; isotopes as tracers. Address: Medical Research Center, Brookhaven National Lab, Upton, NY 11973.

DAHL, NANCY ANN, b. Colby, Kans, July 18, 32; m. 52; c. 2. NEUROCHEMISTRY. A.B, Kansas, 56, U.S. Pub. Health Serv. fel, 60-62, Ph.D. (physiol), 62. Asst. instr. physiol, Kansas, 62-63; res. assoc, neuropsychiat. unit, Med. Res. Coun. Labs, Carshalton, Eng, 63-64; asst. prof. human develop, UNIV. KANS, 64-66, vis. asst. prof. physiol, 66-67, res. assoc. neurochem, 67-68, asst. prof. PHYSIOL, 68-70, ASSOC. PROF, 70- Am. Phyiol. Soc; Am. Soc. Cell Biol; Soc. Neurosci; Am. Soc. Neurochem; Brit. Biochem. Soc; Int. Soc. Neurochem. Neurobiology; energy flow in the nervous system. Address: Dept. of Physiology & Cell Biology, University of Kansas, Lawrence, KS 66044.

DAHL, NORMAN C(HRISTIAN), b. Seattle, Wash, May 21, 18; m. 43; c. 2. MECHANICAL ENGINEERING, APPLIED MECHANICS. B.S, Washington (Seattle), 41; Nat. Res. Coun. fel, Mass. Inst. Tech, 46-48, Sc.D.(mech. eng), 52; hon. Sc.D, Indian Inst. Technol, Kanpur, 68. Asst. engr, Nat. Res. Coun, 42-43; assoc. engr, Div. 2, Nat. Defense Res. Comt, 43-44; field serv. consult, Off. Sci. Res. & Develop, 44-45; asst. prof. mech. eng, Mass. Inst. Technol, 48-54, assoc. prof, 54-59, prof, 59-68; dep. rep. India, FORD FOUND, 68-71, PROG. ADV, 71- Fulbright lectr, Cambridge, 50-51; prog. leader, Kanpur Indo-Am. Prog, Indian Inst. Technol, 62-64. Am. Soc. Mech. Eng. Stress analysis; plates and shells; educational development. Address: Allendale, West Side Rd, Block Island, RI 02807.

DAHL, PER FRIDTJOF, b. Washington, D.C, Aug. 1, 32; m. 66; c. 2. NUCLEAR PHYSICS. B.S, Wisconsin, 56, M.S, 57, Ph.D.(nuclear physics), 60. Res. assoc. nuclear physics, Wisconsin, 60; Ford Found res. grant, inst. theoret. physics, Copenhagen, 60-62; proj. scientist, Air Force Weapons Lab, 62-63; asst. physicist, BROOKHAVEN NAT. LAB, 63-65, assoc. physicist, 65-71, PHYSICIST, 71- U.S.A, 49-52. AAAS; Am. Phys. Soc. Applied superconductivity; resonances with hydrogen molecular ions; low energy proton-proton scattering; charged particle spectroscopy; high energy accelerator design. Address: Accelerator Dept, Brookhaven National Lab, Upton, NY 11973.

DAHLBERG, ALBERT A, b. Chicago, Ill, Nov. 20, 18; m. 34; c. 3. DENTAL ANTHROPOLOGY. B.S. & D.D.S, Loyola Univ.(Ill), 32. Resident & instr. dent. surg, Univ. Chicago, 32-36; attend. dent. surgeon, Chicago Mem. Hosp, 37-53; RES. ASSOC. PHYS. ANTHROP, WALTER G. ZOLLER MEM. DENT. CLIN, UNIV. CHICAGO, 49-, PROF. & ACTING DIR. CLIN, 67- Res. assoc, Chicago Natural Hist. Mus. Practicing dentist, 36- Fel. AAAS; Am. Dent. Asn; Am. Asn. Phys. Anthrop; Am. Anthrop. Asn; fel. Am. Col. Dent. Genetics and morphology of the human dentition. Address: Walter G. Zoller Memorial Dental Clinic, University of Chicago, Chicago, IL 60637.

DAHLBERG, ALBERT EDWARD, b. Chicago, Ill, Sept. 19, 38; m. 63; c. 1. BIOCHEMISTRY. B.S, Haverford Col, 60; M.D, Univ. Chicago, 65, Ph.D, 68. Staff assoc. biochem, Nat. Cancer Inst, 67-70; AM. CANCER SOC. SR. FEL, DEPT. MOLECULAR BIOL, AARHUS UNIV, 70- U.S.P.H.S, 67-70, Lt. Comdr. Transferrin and red cell differentiation; polyribosome and ribonucleic acid metabolism. Address: Dept. of Molecular Biology, Aarhus University, Aarhus, Denmark.

DAHLBERG, DUANE A(RLEN), b. Parshall, N.Dak, July 15, 31; m. 57; c. 3. PHYSICS, ENVIRONMENTAL SCIENCES. B.S, Michigan Tech, 53, M.S, 54; B.D, Luther Theol. Sem, 60; Martin Luther Concordia Col. Nat. Sci. Found. Sci. fels. & Ph.D.(physics), Montana State, 67. Res. asst. neutron physics, Argonne Nat. Lab, 53-54; instr. PHYSICS, CONCORDIA COL.(MOORHEAD, MINN), 60-64, asst. prof, 67-68, ASSOC. PROF, 68- Transportation C, U.S.A, 55-57. Am. Asn. Physics Teachers; Optical Soc. Am; Inst. Environ. Sci. Neutron cross sections; optical excitation cross sections. Address: Dept. of Physics, Concordia College, Moorhead, MN 56560.

DAHLBERG, JAMES E(RIC), b. Chicago, Ill, May 30, 40; m. 63. BIOCHEMISTRY, MOLECULAR BIOLOGY. B.A, Haverford Col, 62; LaVerne Noyes fel, Univ. Chicago, 63-66, Ph.D.(biochem), 66. Res. assoc, Med. Res. Coun. Lab. Molecular Biol, Cambridge, Eng, 66-68; lab. biophys, Univ. Geneva, 68-69; ASST. PROF. PHYSIOL. CHEM, MED. SCH, UNIV. WIS, MADISON, 69- Fels, U.S. Air Force Off. Sci. Res, 66-67 & Am. Cancer Soc, 67-69. AAAS; Am. Soc. Biol. Chem. Structure and function of ribosomal and messenger RNA; nucleotide sequence of genetic punctuation. Address: Dept. of Physiological Chemistry, University of Wisconsin Medical School, 1215 Linden Dr, Madison, WI 53706.

DAHLBERG, MICHAEL D, b. Syracuse, N.Y, May 11, 40. ZOOLOGY. B.S, Cornell, 62; Ph.D.(zool), Tulane, 66. ASST. PROF. ZOOL, UNIV. GA, 66- Am. Soc. Ichthyol. & Herpet; Am. Fisheries Soc. Ichthyology; systematics and ecology of fish. Address: Marine Institute, University of Georgia, Sapelo Island, GA 31327.

DAHLBERG, MICHAEL LEE, b. Miami, Fla, Jan. 19, 39; m. 58; c. 2. FISHERIES, BIOMETRICS. B.S, Oregon State, 62, M.S, 63; Ph.D.(fisheries), Washington (Seattle), 68. Res. assoc. FISHERIES, fisheries res. inst, Washington (Seattle), 63-68; asst. prof, Va. Polytech, 68-70; FISHERIES RES. BIOLOGIST, NAT. MARINE FISHERIES SERV, 70- Consult, U.S. Bur. Sport Fisheries & Wildlife, 68-69; Sport Fishing Inst, Wash, D.C, 68-70. AAAS; Am. Inst. Fishery Res. Biol; Am. Fisheries Soc; Am. Statist. Asn; Asn. Comput. Mach. Population dynamics of freshwater and marine fish, including the application of digital computers to solving fishery research problems through data processing and systems simulation. Address: Auke Bay Research Center, National Marine Fisheries Service, Auke Bay, AK 99821.

DAHLBERG, RICHARD C(RAIG), b. Astoria, Ore, July 23, 29; m. 56; c. 3. PHYSICS. B.S, Oregon, 51; M.S, Michigan, 54; Ph.D, Rensselaer Polytech, 64. Prod. supvr, Hanford Works, Gen. Elec. Co, 51-53, mgr. reactor physics, Knolls Atomic Power Lab, 54-64, reactor physicist, gen. atomic div, Gen. Dynamics Co, 64-67, mgr. HT&R reactor physics, 67-69; MGR. NUCLEAR ANAL. & REACTOR PHYSICS DEPT, GULF GEN. ATOMIC DIV, GULF ENERGY & ENVIRON. SCI, GULF OIL CORP, 69- Am. Nuclear Soc. Reactor physics; nuclear engineering; reactor design. Address: 7733 Esterel Dr, La Jolla, CA 92037.

DAHLE, LELAND K(ENNETH), b. Marietta, Minn, June 19, 26; m. 58; c. 2. BIOCHEMISTRY, ORGANIC CHEMISTRY. B.A, St. Olaf Col, 50; M.S, Purdue, 53; Ph.D.(physiol. chem), Minnesota, 61. Instr. chem, Augsburg Col, 52-56; res. cereal chemist, flour mills, Peavey Co, 61-69; SR. RES. SCIENTIST, CAMPBELL SOUP CO, 69- U.S.A, 44-46. Am. Chem. Soc; Am. Asn. Cereal Chem. Lipid oxidation; autoxidation phenomena; thiobarbituric acid reaction assay; oxidative stability of carotenoid pigments; functional effects of flour protein sulfhydryl groups on dough rheology and behavior; functional properties of protein and starch in bread systems. Address: Campbell Soup Co, Campbell Place, Camden, NJ 08101.

DAHLEM, DAVID H, b. Los Angeles, Calif, Aug. 7, 35; m. 56; c. 3. GEOLOGY, COMPUTER SCIENCE. B.S, Mont. Sch. Mines, 57, M.S, 59; Ph.D. (geol), Michigan, 65. Jr. res. engr, metall. res. div, Anaconda Co, 59-61; res. scientist, mech. & process res, Allis-Chalmers Mfg. Co, 61-62; GEOLOGIST, BR. SURFACE PLANETARY EXPLOR, U.S. GEOL. SURV, 65- Geol. Soc. Am; Am. Inst. Mining, Metall. & Petrol. Eng; Mineral. Soc. Am; Asn. Comput. Mach. Structural mineralogy of silicates, sulfide mineral deposits and volcanics of the western United States; petrology of Colorado Front Range Precambrian; data storage and retrieval systems; mathematical geology. Address: 4921 E. Snowshoe Way, Flagstaff, AZ 86001.

DAHLEN, FRANCIS ANTHONY, JR, b. American Falls, Idaho, Dec. 5, 42; m. 67. GEOPHYSICS. B.S, Calif. Inst. Technol, 64; Nat. Sci. Found. fel, Univ. Calif, San Diego, 64-66 & 68-69, M.S, 67, Ph.D.(geophys), 69. Nat. Sci. Found. fel. geodesy & geophys, Cambridge, 70-71; ASST. PROF. GEOPHYS. & ALFRED P. SLOAN FOUND. FEL, PRINCETON, 71- Am. Geophys. Union. Theoretical seismology; free oscillations of the earth; rotation of the earth; seismic source mechanism. Address: Dept. of Geological & Geophysical Sciences, Princeton University, Princeton, NJ 08540.

DAHLEN, PAUL A(NDREW), b. Minneapolis, Minn, March 22, 13; m. 44; c. 2. CHEMICAL ENGINEERING. B.Ch.E, Minnesota, 36, M.S, 39. Shift supvr, Northwest Res. Found, 36-39; chem. engr, ammonia dept, E.I. DU PONT DE NEMOURS & CO, 39-41, explosives dept, N.J, & Ala, 41-43, tech. supvr, Manhattan proj, Del. & Wash, 43-46, chem. engr, plastics dept, N.J, 46-50, chief supvr. EXPLOSIVES DEPT, ATOMIC ENERGY DIV, SAVANNAH RIVER PLANT, 51-, asst. supt. reactor dept, 61-66, SUPT. REACTOR & HEAVY WATER DEPT, 66- Am. Chem. Soc. Nuclear reactor operation and safety; process development of synthetic resin. Address: E.I. du Pont de Nemours & Co, Savannah River Plant, Aiken, SC 29801.

DAHLEN, ROGER W, b. Iola, Wis, Sept. 7, 35; m. 62; c. 3. PHYSIOLOGY. B.A, Luther Col.(Iowa), 56; M.S, Iowa, 58, Ph.D.(physiol), 60. Instr. physiol, sch. med, Boston, 60-62; asst. prof, N.J. Col. Med. & Dent, 62-68; health scientist adminr, training grants & awards br, Nat. Heart Inst, NAT. INSTS. HEALTH, 68-71, CHIEF, RES, TRAINING & PUBL. DIV, NAT. LIBR. MED, 71- Cardiac electrophysiology; effects of hypothermia. Address: Extramural Programs, Research, Training & Publications Division, National Library of Medicine, National Institutes of Health, Bethesda, MD 20014.

DAHLEN, R(OLF) J(OHN), b. Wilmington, Del, Mar. 18, 37. MECHANICAL ENGINEERING. B.M.E, Delaware, 58; M.S.M.E, Purdue, 59, Ph.D.(mech. eng), 62. Res. engr, E.I. DU PONT DE NEMOURS & CO, 62-67, TECH. REP, PLASTICS DEPT, 67- AAAS. Heat and mass transfer; process development for plastics and plastic products. Address: Technical Services Lab, E.I. du Pont de Nemours & Co, Chestnut Run, Wilmington, DE 19898.

DAHLER, JOHN S, b. Wichita, Kans, May 7, 30; m. 54; PHYSICAL CHEMISTRY. B.S, Wichita, 51, Univ. Found. Indust. Res. fel. & M.S, 52; Alumni Res. Found. fel, Wisconsin, 52-54, General Motors fel, 54-55, Ph.D. (theoret. chem), 55. Nat. Sci. Found. fel, Univ. Amsterdam, 55-56; task scientist, Aeronaut. res. lab, Wright Air Develop Center, 56-58; asst. prof. chem. eng, UNIV. MINN, MINNEAPOLIS, 59-61, assoc. prof, 61-63, PROF. CHEM. ENG. & CHEM, 63- Sloan fel, 64-; Nat. Sci. Found. sr. fel, 65-66. U.S.A.F, 56-58, Res, 59-, 1st Lt. Am. Phys. Soc. Theoretical physical chemistry; equilibrium statistical mechanics; theory of fluid transport phenomena; molecular quantum mechanics. Address: Depts. of Chemical Engineering & Chemistry, University of Minnesota, Minneapolis, MN 55455.

DAHLGARD, MURIEL G(ENEVIEVE), b. West Haven, Conn, July 5, 20. ORGANIC CHEMISTRY. B.S, Connecticut, 46, M.S, 49; Ph.D.(org. chem), Kansas, 56. Asst, Connecticut, 46-48; asst. res. chemist, Nopco Chem. Co, N.J, 48-53; asst, Kansas, 53-56; asst. res. prof. cancer res. lab, Florida, 56-61; asst. prof. CHEM, RANDOLPH-MACON WOMAN'S COL,

61-64, ASSOC. PROF, 64- AAAS; Am. Chem. Soc. Aliphatic diamines; diaryl ethers; carbohydrates; carcinogenic derivatives of fluorene and biphenyl; antimetabolites. Address: Dept. of Chemistry, Randolph-Macon Woman's College, Lynchburg, VA 24504.

DAHLGREN, GEORGE, JR, b. Chicago, Ill, Apr. 12, 29; m. 51; c. 3. PHYSICAL CHEMISTRY. B.S, Ill. Wesleyan, 51; M.S, Wyoming, 56, fel. & Ph.D. (chem), 58. Res. assoc. CHEM, Cornell, 58-59; asst. prof. Alaska, 59-62, assoc. prof, 62-66, head dept. 64-66; PROF, UNIV. CINCINNATI, 66-, asst. head dept, 66-71. Am. Chem. Soc. Kinetics and thermodynamics. Address: Dept. of Chemistry, University of Cincinnati, Cincinnati, OH 45221.

DAHLGREN, ROBERT BERNARD, b. Walnut Grove, Minn, Jan. 27, 29; m. 51; c. 6. WILDLIFE MANAGEMENT, ZOOLOGY. B.S, S.Dak. State, 50; M.S, Utah State, 55. Small game biologist, S.Dak. Dept. of Game, Fish & Parks, 52-61, leader small game & furbearer res. proj, 61-65, asst. chief, game div, 65-67; ASST. LEADER, COOP. WILDLIFE RES. UNIT, BUR. SPORT FISHERIES & WILDLIFE, U.S. DEPT. INTERIOR, 67- Wildlife Soc. Population ecology and dynamics of wildlife populations; pesticide effects on game birds. Address: Cooperative Wildlife Research Unit, South Dakota State University, Brookings, SD 57006.

DAHLGREN, ROBERT R, b. Lincoln, Nebr, May 17, 35; m. 57; c. 2. VETERINARY PATHOLOGY. Colorado State, 57-59; D.V.M, Okla. State, 63, M.S, 66. Instr. path, Okla. State, 63-66; pathologist, Ralston Purina Co, 66-68; assoc. prof. path, Nebraska, 68-69; PATHOLOGIST, RALSTON PURINA CO, 69- Consult. comp. path, sch. med, Washington (St. Louis), 67- U.S.M.C, 54-57; U.S.A.R, 63- N.Y. Acad. Sci; Am. Vet. Med. Asn. Comparative neuropathology and immunology. Address: Ralston Purina Co, Checkerboard Square, St. Louis, MO 63199.

DAHLIN, D(AVID) C(ARL), b. Beresford, S.Dak, Sept. 3, 17; m. 41; c. 3. PATHOLOGY. B.S, South Dakota, 38; M.D, Chicago, 40; fellow, Minnesota, 45-48, M.S, 48. Intern & res. path, Ancker Hosp, St. Paul, 41, 42; CONSULT. SURG. PATH, MAYO CLIN, 48-; PROF. PATH, MAYO GRAD. SCH. MED, UNIV. MINN, 61-, asst. prof, 53-61. Med.C, U.S.A, 42-45. Am. Soc. Clin. Path; Am. Asn. Path. & Bact; Am. Med. Asn; Am. Cancer Soc. Bone tumors. Address: Dept. of Pathology, Mayo Graduate School of Medicine, University of Minnesota, Rochester, MN 55902.

DAHLIN, ERIK BJORN, b. Vadstena, Sweden, Apr. 15, 28; m. 52; c. 2. ELECTRICAL ENGINEERING. M.Sc, Royal Inst. Tech, Stockholm, 52; Ph.D.(elec. eng), Pennsylvania, 64. Res. engr, Royal Inst. Tech, Stockholm, 51-54; market mgr, Swedish Philips Co, 54-56; res. engr. & systs. anal. mgr, Honeywell Indust. Div, 56-64; adv. engr, Int. Bus. Mach. Corp, 64-68; V.PRES, MEASUREX CORP, 68- Inst. Elec. & Electronics Eng; Soc. Indust. & Appl. Math. Mathematical methods for dynamic control and economical optimization of industrial processes. Address: 330 Mathew St, Santa Clara, CA 95050.

DAHLKE, WALTER EMIL, b. Berlin, Germany, Aug. 24, 10; m. 40. PHYSICS, ELECTRICAL ENGINEERING. Dr. phil.(physics), Berlin, 36; Dr. habil.(physics), Jena, 39. Head microwave lab, German Aviation Res. Estab, 40-45; head appl. res. group & adv. develop, tube & semiconductor div. & inst. res, Telefunken AG, Germany, 49-65; PROF. ELEC. ENG, LEHIGH UNIV, 65-, Nat. Sci. Found. vis. prof, 64-65. Lectr, Heidelberg, 55-56; Stuttgart Tech, 56-59; Karlsruhe Tech, 60-65, hon. prof, 61. Fel. Inst. Elec. & Electronics Eng; German Phys. Soc; German Telecommun. Asn. Electronic devices; electrical noise. Address: Dept. of Electrical Engineering, Lehigh University, Bethlehem, PA 18015.

DAHLMAN, DOUGLAS LEE, b. Bertha, Minn, Sept. 29, 40; m. 60; c. 3. INSECT PHYSIOLOGY. B.S, St. Cloud State Col, 61; M.S, Iowa State, 63, Ph.D.(entom), 65. Res. assoc. ENTOM, Iowa State, 65; asst. prof, UNIV. KY, 65-71, ASSOC. PROF, 71- AAAS; Entom. Soc. Am. Insect behavioral responses to naturally occurring substances; insect-host relationships; biochemical and physiological aspects of insect pigments; growth, development and ageing. Address: Dept. of Entomology, University of Kentucky, Lexington, KY 40506.

DAHLQUIST, CARL A(LBIN), b. Grasston, Minn, Feb. 5, 14; m. 38; c. 4. CHEMICAL ENGINEERING. B.Ch.E, Minnesota, 34, 35, Minn. State Dept. Agr. fel, 36-37. Asst. bacteriologist, Am. Crystal Sugar Co, 37-43; chemist, MINN. MINING & MFG. CO, 43-51, res. assoc, 51-57, supvr. basic res, tape res. dept, 57-62, assoc. mgr, 62-66, SUPVR. POLYMER PLASTICS, 66- AAAS; fel. Am. Chem. Soc; Soc. Rheol; N.Y. Acad. Sci; Am. Soc. Test. & Mat. Adhesion; polymers; rheology. Address: Minnesota Mining & Mfg. Co, 2501 Hudson Rd, St. Paul, MN 55101.

DAHLQUIST, FREDERICK WILLIS, b. Chicago, Ill, June 15, 43; m. 63; c. 2. BIOPHYSICAL CHEMISTRY. B.A, Wabash Col, 64; Ph.D.(chem), Calif. Inst. Technol, 69. Fel. chem, Calif. Inst. Technol, 68-69; Miller fel. biochem, Univ. Calif, Berkeley, 69-71; ASST. PROF. CHEM, UNIV. ORE, 71- Nuclear magnetic resonance studies of biological systems; enzyme mechanisms; mechanism of chemotaxis in bacteria. Address: Dept. of Chemistry, University of Oregon, Eugene, OR 97403.

DAHLQUIST, WILBUR LYNN, b. DeQuincy, La, Sept. 2, 42; m. 61; c. 2. SOLID STATE PHYSICS. B.S, McNeese State Col, 63; NASA fel. & Ph.D. (physics), La. State, 67. Instr. PHYSICS, La. State, summer 64; asst. prof. McNEESE STATE UNIV, 67-69, ASSOC. PROF. & HEAD DEPT, 69- Am. Phys. Soc. Transport properties of electrons in metals at low temperatures utilizing resonance techniques. Address: Dept. of Physics, McNeese State University, Lake Charles, LA 70601.

DAHLSTEN, DONALD L, b. Clay Center, Nebr, Dec. 8, 33; m. 57; c. 2. FOREST ENTOMOLOGY. B.S, California, Davis, 56, M.S, Berkeley, 60, Ph.D.(entom), 63. Lab. technician forest entom, California, Berkeley, 59-62; asst. prof. zool, Calif. State Col. Los Angeles, 62-63; asst. entomologist, UNIV. CALIF, BERKELEY, 63-65, lectr. ENTOM, 65-68, asst. prof, 68-69; ASSOC. PROF, 69- AAAS; Am. Forestry Asn; Ecol. Soc. Am; Soc.

Am. Foresters; Entom. Soc. Am; Entom. Soc. Can. Biological control; population dynamics of forest insects, especially parasites and predators of bark beetles; neodiprion sawflies and the Douglas-fir tussock moth; evaluation of insectivorous birds in the forest and their role in natural control of forest pests. Address: Division of Biological Control, University of California, Berkeley, CA 94720.

DAHLSTROM, BERTIL PHILIP, JR, b. Elizabeth, N.J, Aug. 22, 31; m. 52; c. 3. PHYSICAL CHEMISTRY. B.S, Upsala Col, 53; M.S, Wisconsin, 55; M.B.A, Temple, 58. Tech. asst. chem, Wisconsin, 53-55; res. chemist, Rohm & Haas Co, 55-57, tech. asst. spec. prod, 57-60, staff asst, prod. control dept, 60-61, asst. mgr. spec. prod. dept, 61-63, mgr, 63-68; gen. mgr. indust. div, v.pres. & mem. bd. dirs, Sartomer Resins, Inc, 68-70; OWNER, DAHLSTROM ASSOCS, 70-; PRES, TREAS. & DIR, CHEM. INSTRUMENTS CORP, 71- Instr, Temple, 59-61. Am. Chem. Soc. High pressure reactions; stereospecific polymerization; physical properties of high polymers; sales management. Address: Dahlstrom Associates, P.O. Box 471, Woodbury, NJ 08096.

DAHLSTROM, DONALD A(LBERT), b. Minneapolis, Minn, Jan. 16, 20; m. 42; c. 5. CHEMICAL ENGINEERING. Macalester Col, 37-39; B.S, Minnesota, 42; Ph.D.(chem. eng), Northwestern, 49. Petrol. & chem. engr, Int. Petrol Co, Peru, 42-45; instr. chem. eng, Northwestern, 46-49, asst. prof, 49-51, assoc. prof, 51-56; dir. RES. & DEVELOP, Eimco Corp, 53-60, V.PRES. & DIR, 60-69, EIMCO ENVIROTECH, 69-; V.PRES. RES. & DEVELOP, PROCESS MACH. GROUP, ENVIROTECH CORP, 71- U.S.N, 45-46. Am. Inst. Chem. Eng.(v.pres, 63, pres, 64); Water Pollution Control Fedn; Am. Chem. Soc; Am. Inst. Mining, Metall. & Petrol. Eng.(Raymond award, 52); Filtration Soc; Can. Inst. Mining & Metall. Liquid cyclones; filtration; classification; flow of fluids; sedimentation; colloids; centrifugal forces in hydraulic fields; water; waste; sewage treatment. Address: 5340 Cottonwood Lane, Salt Lake City, UT 84117.

DAHLSTROM, R(OBERT) K(IRCHNER), b. Eau Claire, Wis, Apr. 4, 09; m. 42; c. 2. PHYSICS. B.S, Washington (Seattle), 30, Ph.D.(physics), 34. Assoc. prof. phys. sci, East. Wash. Col. Ed, 35-42; physicist, dept. terrestrial magnetism, Carnegie Inst. Wash, 42; APPL. PHYSICS LAB, JOHNS HOPKINS UNIV, 42-58, ASST. DIV. SUPVR, 58- Distinguished pub. serv. award, U.S. Navy, 61. Am. Phys. Soc. Weapon system evaluation; guided missile development; test instrumentation. Address: 1614 Sherwood Rd, Silver Spring, MD 20902.

DAHLSTROM, ROBERT V, b. Conrad, Mont, Mar. 1, 25; m. 52; c. 3. BIOCHEMISTRY. B.S, Idaho, 49, M.S, 51; Ph.D.(biochem), Cornell, 54. Biochemist biol. develop, Eli Lilly & Co, 54-57; sr. res. biochemist, RAHR MALTING CO, 57-62, V.PRES, Rahr Bio-Tech. Labs, 62-68, BIO-TECH. RESOURCES, 68- Am. Soc. Brewing Chem; Inst. Food Tech. Biochemical & bioengineering investigation of microbial processes, plant growth and food processing; new product development, waste disposal processes, natural product isolation and food formulations. Address: Bio-Technical Resources, Inc, Seventh & Marshall Sts, Manitowoc, WI 54220.

DAHM, ARNOLD J, b. Oskaloosa, Iowa, Sept. 12, 32; m. 68; c. 1. PHYSICS. B.A, Cent. Col.(Iowa), 58; M.S, Univ. Minn, Minneapolis, 60, Ph.D.(physics) 65. Fel. PHYSICS, Univ. Pa, 66-68; ASST. PROF, CASE WEST. RESERVE UNIV, 68- U.S.A, 53-55. Am. Phys. Soc. Liquid and solid helium and Josephson effects in superconductors. Address: Dept. of Physics, Case Western Reserve University, Cleveland, OH 44106.

DAHM, C(ORNELIUS) G(EORGE), b. St. Louis, Mo, Oct. 23, 08; m. 35; c. 3. SEISMOLOGY. A.B, St. Louis, 30, fel, 30-32, M.S, 32, Ph.D.(seismol), 34; Storrow fel, Nat. Res. Council, 32. Instr, St. Louis, 34-36; party chief, Root Petrol. Co, 36-38; Magnolia Petrol. Co, 38-53; CHIEF GEOPHYSICIST, HUNT OIL CO, 53- Am. Geophys. Union; Soc. Explor. Geophys. Seismology and seismic prospecting. Address: 11219 Shelterwood, Dallas, TX 75229.

DAHM, DONALD B, b. Fargo, N.Dak, Aug. 15, 38; m. 60; c. 3. PHYSICAL CHEMISTRY. B.S, N.Dak. State, 61; M.S, S.Dak. State, 61; Am. Chem. Soc. Petrol. Res. Fund fel, Ohio State, 62-64 & summer, 65, Ph.D.(phys. chem), 66. Asst. phys. chem, Ohio State, 61-62; sr. res. engr, Martin Co, 63; asst. phys. chem, Ohio State Univ, 64-66; res. chemist, res. ctr, Babcock & Wilcox Co, 66-68; res. specialist, Dayton Lab, Monsanto Res. Corp, 68-71; MEM. STAFF, SINRALCO LITHO PROD, 71- Am. Chem. Soc; The Chem. Soc. Chemical kinetics, fast reactions in gas and liquid phases and in shock tube; combustion kinetics, high temperature thermodynamics and mass spectrometer studies at high temperatures. Address: Sinralco Litho Products, P.O. Box 336, Vandalia, OH 45377.

DAHM, DONALD J, b. Mahaska Co, Iowa, Oct. 26, 41; m. 64; c. 2. X-RAY CRYSTALLOGRAPHY. B.A, Cent. Col.(Iowa), 63; Atomic Energy Comn. assistantship, Iowa State Univ, 63-68, Ph.D.(phys. chem), 68. SR. RES. CHEMIST, CENT. RES. DEPT, MONSANTO CO, 68- Am. Crystallog. Asn. Laboratory automation. Address: Central Research Dept, Monsanto Co, 800 N. Lindberg, St. Louis, MO 63166.

DAHM, DOUGLAS BARRETT, b. Buffalo, N.Y, Apr. 12, 28; m. 58; c. 3. SYSTEMS & ENVIRONMENTAL ENGINEERING. B.S, Northwest. Univ, 50; George Washington Univ, 58-62; M.S, State Univ. N.Y. Buffalo, 64. Exec. training engr, Caterpillar Tractor Co, 47-51; assoc. engr, CORNELL AERONAUT. LAB, INC, 56-58, res. engr, 58-62, prin. engr, 62-67, staff scientist, 67-70, DEPT. HEAD, ENVIRON. SYSTS, 70- U.S.A.F, 51-56, Lt; Distinguished Flying Cross; 3 Air Medals; Bronze Star Medal with V. Am. Inst. Aeronaut. & Astronaut; Marine Technol. Soc; Int. Asn. Pollution Control; Am. Ord. Asn; Int. Asn. Great Lakes Res. Multi-disciplinary programs to improve municipal and industrial waste systems; remote sensing of pollutants; environmental health; aircraft avionics systems, especially methods to improve the survivability of military aircraft. Address: Cornell Aeronautical Lab, Inc, Exploration Systems Dept, P.O. Box 235, Buffalo, NY 14221.

DAHM, KARL HEINZ, b. Duisburg, Ger, Jan. 20, 35; m. 68; c. 1. ORGANIC CHEMISTRY, MOLECULAR BIOLOGY. Freiburg, 55-58; Diplom-Chemiker, Göttingen, 61, Dr. rer. nat, 64. Sci. asst. org. chem. inst, Göttingen, 62-66; proj. assoc. zool, Wisconsin, Madison, 66-68; ASSOC. PROF. BIOL, TEX. A&M UNIV, 68-, CHEM, 71- Am. Chem. Soc; Soc. Ger. Chem. Chemistry of natural products; biochemistry of insect development; insect hormones and pheromones. Address: Institute of Life Science, Texas A&M University, College Station, TX 77843.

DAHM, PAUL A(DOLPH), b. Minneapolis, Minn, Nov. 15, 17; m. 41; c. 4. ENTOMOLOGY, BIOCHEMISTRY. A.B, Illinois, 40, M.A, 41, Ph.D.(entomol), 47. Asst. prof. ENTOM, Kans. State Col, 47-50, assoc. prof, 50-53, PROF, 53; IOWA STATE UNIV, 53- With Oak Ridge Inst. Nuclear Studies, 51. Charles F. Curtiss distinguished prof. agr, Iowa State Univ, 69. U.S.N, 43-46. AAAS; Entom. Soc. Am; Am. Asn. Biol. Chem; Am. Chem. Soc. Insect toxicology and biochemistry; medical and economic entomology; radiotracer methods in biology. Address: Dept. of Zoology & Entomology, Insectary Bldg, Iowa State University, Ames, IA 50010.

DAHMEN, JEROME J, b. Johnston, Wash, Nov. 22, 19; m. 47; c. 5. GENETICS, REPRODUCTIVE PHYSIOLOGY. B.S, Univ. Idaho, 47; M.S, Ore State Univ, 52, Ph.D.(genetics), 66. County agent, exten. serv, UNIV. IDAHO, 47-55, animal husbandman, 55-58, RES. PROF. ANIMAL SCI, CALDWELL BR. & SUPT. AGR. EXP. STA, 58- U.S.A, 43-46, Capt. Am. Soc. Animal Sci. Nutrition, steer feeding; breeding, sheep, wool and meat. Address: Route 8, Box 54, Caldwell, ID 83605.

DAHMER, LIONEL H(ERBERT), b. Milwaukee, Wis, July 29, 36; m. 59; c. 2. ANALYTICAL CHEMISTRY. B.S, Wisconsin, 59; M.S, Marquette, 62; Ph.D.(anal. chem), Iowa State, 66. Acting instr. chem, Wisconsin-Milwaukee, 60-62, sr. res. chemist, PPG INDUSTS, INC, BARBERTON, 66-68, RES. SUPVR. ANAL. CHEM, 68- Am. Chem. Soc. Inorganic column chromatographic separations. Address: 4480 W. Bath Rd, Akron, OH 44313.

DAHMS, ARTHUR STEPHEN, JR, b. Mankato, Minn, Sept. 12, 43; m. 66; c. 2. BIOCHEMISTRY. B.S, Col. St. Thomas, 65; Nat. Insts. Health fel, Mich. State, 67-69, Ph.D.(biochem), 69. Nat. Sci. Found. & Atomic Energy Comn. fels. CHEM, UNIV. CALIF, LOS ANGELES, 69-71, LECTR, 71- AAAS; Am. Chem. Soc. Carbohydrate chemistry; enzymology; oxidative phosphorylation; membrane transport; protein chemistry. Address: Dept. of Chemistry, University of California, Los Angeles, CA 90024.

DAHMS, HARALD, b. Bad Freienwalde, Germany, July 24, 34; m. 52. PHYSICAL CHEMISTRY, ELECTROCHEMISTRY. M.S, Halle, 58; Dr.rer.nat.(phys. chem), Dresden Tech, 60. Chief asst. phys. chem. & electrochem, Dresden Tech, 60-61; res. fel. electrochem, Pennsylvania, 61-63; sr. res. staff mem, Int. Bus. Mach. Corp, 63-69; CONSULT, DAHMS LABS, 69- Electrochem. Soc; Sci. Res. Soc. Am; Am. Chem. Soc. Structure of interfaces; electroplating; electrode kinetics; electroanalysis. Address: Dahms Labs, 22 Lakeview Rd, Ossining, N.Y. 10562.

DAHMS, R(EYNOLD) G(EORGE), b. Verden, Okla, Oct. 7, 12; wid, m. 62; c. 1. ECONOMIC ENTOMOLOGY. B.S, Okla. Agr. & Mech. Col, 33, M.S, 35; Ph.D.(entom), Kans. State Col, 42. Under sci. aide, div. cereal & forage insect invests, bur. entom. & plant quarantine, U.S. DEPT. AGR, Lawton, Okla, 35-41, asst. entomologist, 41-42, entomologist, Stillwater, 46-54, asst. head cereal & forage insects sect, ENTOM. RES. DIV, AGR. RES. SERV, 54-57, head, cereal insects sect, field crops insects & bee culture res. br, 57-60, CHIEF, GRAIN & FORAGE INSECTS RES. BR, 60- Asst, Okla. Exp. Sta, 35-42; asst. entomologist, Okla. Agr. & Mech. Col, 46-47, assoc. entomologist, 47-53, entomologist, 53-54. Sanit.C, U.S.A, 42-46. Am. Entom. Soc. Resistance of crop plants to insects; control of crop insects with insecticides. Address: Entomology Research Division, Plant Industry Station, Beltsville, MD 20705.

DAHMUS, MICHAEL E, b. Waterloo, Iowa, Feb. 20, 41; m. BIOCHEMISTRY. B.S, Iowa State Univ, 63; Ph.D.(biochem), Calif. Inst. Technol, 68. Fel, Calif. Inst. Technol, 68-69; ASST. PROF. BIOCHEM, UNIV. CALIF, DAVIS, 69- Biochemical aspects of gene regulation in higher organisms; mechanism of action of steroid hormones. Address: Dept. of Biochemistry & Biophysics, University of California, Davis, CA 95616

DAHNEKE, BARTON EUGENE, b. San Jose, Calif, Apr. 4, 39; m. 61; c. 4. THERMODYNAMICS. B.S, Brigham Young, 63; Nat. Defense Ed. Act fel, Minnesota, 63-66, M.S.M.E, 65, Ph.D.(mech. eng), 67. Res. fel. environ. health eng, Calif. Inst. Technol, 68-69; RES. SCIENTIST, INST. AEROBIOL, 5949 GRAFSCHAFT, GER, 69- Aerosol physics; aerodynamics of small particles; adhesion of particles; air pollution measurement; non-equilibrium thermodynamics and rate processes. Address: 1000 S. Seventh St, San Jose, CA 95112.

DAI, PETER K, b. Shanghai, China, Dec. 14, 34; m. 59; c. 2. CIVIL ENGINEERING. B.S, Cheng Kung Univ, Taiwan, 57; fel. & M.S, Illinois, 60, univ. & Gregory Indust. fels. & Ph.D.(civil eng), 63. Proj. engr, Chinese Navy Proj. Eng. Off, 57-59; res. assoc. civil eng, Illinois, 62-63; res. engr, metals & ceramics div, mat. lab, Wright-Patterson Air Force Base, 63-67; staff engr, adv. technol. dept, TRW SYSTS, 67-68, head eng. physics sect, 68-69, HEAD PROTECTIVE CONSTRUCTION SECT, APPL. TECHNOL. DIV, 69- Design engr, G. Shuirman & Assocs, summer, 59. Assoc. Am. Soc. Civil Eng. Structural mechanics; elastic and plastic behavior of composite beams; static and dynamic analyses of crack problem considering both elastic and plastic material properties. Address: 3903 W. 231st Pl, Torrance, CA 90505.

DAIBER, F(RANKLIN) C(ARL), b. Middletown, N.Y, Oct. 19, 19; m. 53; c. 2. ICHTHYOLOGY, ECOLOGY. A.B, Alfred, 41; M.S, Mich. State Col, 47; Ph.D.(ichthyol), Ohio State, 50. Lab. asst, Alfred, 40-41; asst, Mich. State Col, 41-42, 46-47; research asst, Ohio State, 47-49; asst. prof, Alfred, 49-52; BIOL. SCIS, UNIV. DEL, 52-59, assoc. prof, 59-68, PROF, 68- U.S.A.A.F, 42-46, Capt. Am. Soc. Ichthyol. & Herpet; Ecol. Soc. Am; Am. Fisheries Soc. Biology of fish; tide marsh ecology; elasmobranch studies. Address: 37 Kells Ave, Newark, DE 19711.

DAICOFF, GEORGE R(ONALD), b. Granite City, Ill, Nov. 10, 30; m. 53; c. 1. SURGERY. A.B, Ind. Univ, 53, M.D, 56. Extern, Sunnyside Sanitorium, Indianapolis, 54-56; intern, Univ. Chicago, 56-57, jr. asst. resident surg, 57-58, sr. asst. resident, 58-59, instr. & sr. resident, 61-62, chief resident gen. surg. & instr, 62, thoracic & cardiovasc. surg, 63; Schweppe Found. res. fel, 63-66; fel. cardiovasc. surg, Mayo Clin, 66; assoc. prof. THORACIC & CARDIOVASC. SURG, COL. MED, UNIV. FLA, 67-70, PROF, 70- Vis. colleague, Royal Postgrad. Med. Sch. London, 65. Am. Col. Surg; Am. Asn. Thoracic Surg; Am. Col. Cardiol; Int. Soc. Cardiol. Cardiovascular surgery. Address: 739 N.W. 23rd St, Gainesville, FL 32601.

DAIGER, G(EORGE) P(IERCE), b. Baltimore, Md, May 31, 09; m. 38; c. 2. ELECTRICAL ENGINEERING. B.S, Hopkins, 29, D.E, 32. Acoustical sect. head, The Hoover Co, 32-34, elec. sect. head, 34-39, staff engr, 39-40, dir. lab, 40-44, exec. engr, 44-50, chief engr, 50-51, V.PRES. ENG, 52-64, HOOVER WORLDWIDE CORP, 64- Am. Inst. Elec. Eng. Household appliances and refrigeration; administration of scientific activities; administration of personnel; mechanical engineering. Address: 2915 Woodcliff Rd. N.W, Canton, OH 44718.

DAIGGER, LOUIS A, b. Noel, Mo, May 17, 19; m. 45; c. 4. SOIL FERTILITY. B.Sc, Univ. Nebr, 42, M.Sc, 62. County exten. agent, UNIV. NEBR, 54-63, AREA EXTEN. SPECIALIST SOILS & ASSOC. PROF. AGRON, 63- U.S.A, 45. Am. Soc. Agron. Dryland fertility and wheat protein study. Address: Scotts Bluff Experiment Station, Mitchell, NE 69357.

DAIGH, JOHN D(AVID), b. Parsons, Kans, Jan. 14, 30; m. 51; c. 3. CIVIL ENGINEERING, MECHANICS. B.S, U.S. Mil. Acad, 51; M.S, Illinois, 57, Ph.D.(civil eng), 57. Instr. mech, U.S. Mil. Acad, 61-62, asst. prof, 62-64, assoc. prof, 64-71; INSTR. ENG, EASTFIELD COL, 71- C.Eng, U.S.A, 51-71, Lt. Col.(Ret). Am. Soc. Civil Eng; Nat. Soc. Prof. Eng; Soc. Am. Mil. Eng; N.Y. Acad. Sci; Am. Inst. Aeronaut. & Astronaut. Structural dynamics; civil and structural engineering; engineering mechanics; fluid mechanics. Address: Division of Science & Mathematics, Eastfield College, 3737 Motley Dr, Mesquite, TX 75149.

DAIGLE, DONALD J, b. St. Louis, Mo, Mar. 1, 39; m. 63; c. 1. CHEMISTRY. B.S, Tulane, 61, Ph.D, 65; M.S, Southern Mississippi, 63. RES. CHEMIST, SOUTH. REGIONAL RES. & DEVELOP. DIV, U.S. DEPT. AGR, 65- Nat. Guard, 61-67. Am. Chem. Soc; Am. Asn. Textile Chem. & Colorists; Sci. Res. Soc. Am. Phosphites, phosphonates and their respective acids; phosphines, diphosphines and their oxides; polymers containing phosphorus for use in textiles. Address: Southern Regional Research & Development Division, U.S. Dept. of Agriculture, P.O. Box 19687, New Orleans, LA 70119.

DAIGNAULT, LOUIS GILBERT, b. Greece, N.Y, May 31, 31; m. 53; c. 2. PHYSICAL & ANALYTICAL CHEMISTRY. B.S, Clarkson Tech, 53; Ph.D.(phys. chem), 57. Res. chemist, Texaco, Inc, 57-63; asst. prof. phys. chem, Rochester Inst. Technol, 63-71; SUPVR. RES. & DEVELOP, COMPUTERIZED POLLUTION ABATEMENT CORP, 71- U.S.A, 53-61, 1st Lt. Am. Chem. Soc; fel. Am. Inst. Chem. Kinetics and mechanisms of the thermal decomposition or isomerization of organic compounds; water pollution and control; metal waste recovery; ozone oxidation; chlorination; electrolysis; coagulation; surface active catalytic oxidation. Address: Computerized Pollution Abatement Corp, P.O. Box 25, Leicester, NY 14481.

DAIGNAULT, RONALD A, b. Woonsocket, R.I, Feb. 28, 39; m. 64; c. 2. ORGANIC CHEMISTRY. B.S, Providence Col, 59, M.S, 61; Ph.D.(org. chem), Notre Dame, 64. Sr. res. chemist, CIBA CORP, 64-69, PATENT AGENT, 69- Am. Chem. Soc. Lithium aluminum hydride and mixed hydride reductions of oximes, tetrahydropyranyl amines, ethers, thioethers and tetrahydrofuranyl ethers and thioethers; organic synthesis—aromatic and sulfur chemistry; steroid synthesis; patents. Address: CIBA Corp, 556 Morris Ave, Summit, NJ 07901.

DAIGNEAULT, AUBERT, b. Montreal, Que, Mar. 6, 32; m. 61; c. 1. MATHEMATICAL LOGIC. B.Sc, Montreal, 54, M.Sc, 56; Ph.D.(math), Princeton, 59. Lectr. MATH, Royal Mil. Col, Can, 58-59; asst. prof, Ottawa (Can), 59-60; Montreal, 60-63; vis. asst. prof, California, Berkeley, 63-64; assoc. prof, UNIV. MONTREAL, 64-70, PROF, 70- Nat. Res. Coun. Can. fel, 64-65. Am. Math. Soc; Math. Asn. Am; Asn. Symbolic Logic; Can. Math. Cong; Math. Soc. France. Algebraic logic. Address: Dept. of Mathematics, University of Montreal, P.O. Box 6128, Montreal 101, Que, Can.

DAIGNEAULT, ERNEST A(LBERT), b. Holyoke, Mass, Aug. 16, 28; m. 54; c. 4. PHARMACOLOGY. B.S, Hampden Col. Pharm, 52; M.S, Kansas City, 54; fel, Tennessee, 57, Ph.D.(pharmacol), 57. Asst. instr. pharm, Kansas City, 53-54; instr. PHARMACOL, Tennessee, 57-59, asst. prof, 59-60; LA. STATE UNIV, NEW ORLEANS, 60-62, assoc. prof, 62-69, PROF, 69- Summer res. participant, Oak Ridge Inst. Nuclear Studies, 58; Nat. Insts. Health spec. fel, 69-70. AAAS; Soc. Pharmacol. & Exp. Therapeut; Soc. Nuclear Med; Acoustical Soc. Am. Cardiovascular and autonomic nervous system; aspects of tachyphylaxis with sympathominetic amines; activation analysis; auditory pharmacology. Address: Dept. of Pharmacology, Louisiana State University Medical Center, 1542 Tulane Ave, New Orleans, LA 70112.

DAIL, CLARENCE W(ILDING), b. Germany, July 7, 07; U.S. citizen; m. 31; c. 2. PHYSICAL MEDICINE. A.B, Pacific Union Col, 30; M.D, Loma Linda, 35. From instr. to PROF. ORTHOP. SURG. & REHAB-PHYS. MED, SCH. MED, LOMA LINDA UNIV, 35- Mem. staff, hosps. Am. Med. Asn; Am. Cong. Rehab. Med; Am. Acad. Phys. Med. & Rehab; Am. Asn. Electromyog. & Electrodiag. Glossopharyngeal breathing; physiology of muscle breathing patterns and swallowing in muscle weakness. Address: Dept. of Physical Medicine & Rehabilitation, Loma Linda University School of Medicine, Loma Linda, CA 92354.

DAILEY, BENJAMIN P(ETER), b. San Marcos, Texas, Sept. 1, 19; m. 45; c. 3. CHEMISTRY. B.A, Southwest Texas State Teachers Col, 38; M.A, Texas, 40, Ph.D.(chem), 42. Res. assoc, Explosives Res. Lab, Pa, 42-45; fel, Harvard, 46-47; instr. CHEM, COLUMBIA UNIV, 47-49, asst. prof, 49-53, assoc. prof, 53-56, PROF, 56-, chmn. dept, 68-70. Nat. Sci. Found. sr.

fel, 63-64; Guggenheim fel, 71-72. With Off. Sci. Res. & Develop; U.S.N, 44. Am. Chem. Soc; fel. Am. Phys. Soc; fel. Am. Acad. Arts & Sci. Thermodynamic properties; molecular structure; microwave spectra; nuclear magnetic resonance. Address: Dept. of Chemistry, Columbia University, New York, NY 10027.

DAILEY, CHARLES E(LMER), III, b. Pittsburgh, Pa, Feb. 14, 26; m. 54; c. 3. CHEMICAL ENGINEERING. B.S, Carnegie Inst. Tech, 50, Standard Oil Co. Ind. fel, 51-52, M.S, 52, Shell Oil Co. fel, 52-53, Allied Chem. fel, 53-54, Ph.D.(chem. eng), 55. Chem. engr, org. chem. dept, plant tech. sect, Chambers Works, E.I. DU PONT DE NEMOURS & CO, 54-60, res. engr, Jackson Lab, 60-62, sr. res. engr, 62-64, GROUP SUPVR. ORG. CHEM. DEPT, CHAMBERS WORKS, 64- U.S.A, 44-46. Am. Inst. Chem. Eng; Am. Chem. Soc. Simultaneous heat, mass and momentum transfer; economic evaluation; long-range planning; market analyses; process simulation and hazards; physical properties; organic diisocyanates; organometallic compounds; fluorocarbons; air and water pollution abatement. Address: E.I. du Pont de Nemours & Co, Chambers Works, Deepwater, NJ 08023.

DAILEY, C(HARLES) L(EE), b. Reedley, Calif, Nov. 12, 17; m. 49; c. 6. AERONAUTICS. B.S, Calif. Inst. Tech, 41, M.S, 42, Ph.D, 54. With Douglas Aircraft Co, 42-45; chief aeronaut. res. eng. center, Southern California, 45-47; dir. aeronaut. dept, Wiancko Eng. Co, 57-60, CHIEF PLASMA PROPULSION PROJ, 60; TRW SYSTS, REDONDO BEACH, 60- Plasma propulsion; supersonic diffuser instability; airplane aerodynamics. Address: 953 Granvia Altamira, Palos Verdes Estates, CA 90274.

DAILEY, JOSEPH P(ATRICK), b. Penfield, Ill, Nov. 14, 22; m. 51; c. 5. ORGANIC CHEMISTRY. B.S, Illinois, 44; Ph.D.(chem), Notre Dame, 50. Chemist, Cent. Res. Labs, Gen. Aniline & Film Corp, 44-46; res. chemist, res. dept, Armour Labs, 49-53, head org. chem. dept, ARMOUR PHARMACEUT. CO, 53-59, DIR. res, 59-67, RES. & DEVELOP, 67- AAAS; Am. Heart Asn; Am. Chem. Soc; assoc. Royal Soc. Med. Pharmaceutical organic chemistry; chemotherapy; intravenous fat emulsions, quinolines; ethyleneimines; vinyl ethers; hypothalamic research; lipid metabolism; enzymes; hormones; blood components. Address: Armour Pharmaceutical Co, Box 511, Kankakee, IL 60901.

DAILEY, LOWELL ROBERTSON, b. Tucson, Ariz, Apr. 14, 11; m. 46; c. 3. CHEMISTRY. B.S, Montana, 32; M.S, Southern California, 35. Instr. chem, physics & math, sec. schs. & cols, Mont. & Calif, 32-42; dir. res. & develop, Cent. Intel. Agency, D.C, 50-52, tech. serv. lab, 52-53; v.pres. & gen. mgr, Chemold Co, Calif. 53-59; dep. asst. dir, intelligence & reconnaissance, Dept. Defense Res. & Eng, Off. Secy. of Defense, D.C, 59-64; HEAD SPEC. PROJS. DEPT, CORP. PLANNING, AEROSPACE CORP, 64- Engr, Univ. Southern California, 41-42. Nat. Guard, 27-30; U.S.N, 42-49, Res, 50-, Capt. Mathematics and geodesy; materials; data processing. Address: Aerospace Corp, P.O. Box 95085, Los Angeles, CA 90045.

DAILEY, ROBERT ENGLE, b. Martinsburg, W.Va, Oct. 3, 23; m. 49; c. 3. BIOCHEMISTRY, PHARMACOLOGY. B.S, George Washington, 48, M.S, 49. Pharmacologist, Smith Kline & French Labs, 49-51; biochemist, Vet. Admin. Center, W.Va, 51-66; RES. CHEMIST, FOOD & DRUG ADMIN, 66- Med. Serv.C, U.S.N.R, 43-46, Lt.(jg). AAAS. Steroid biochemistry; Metabolism of pesticides; nitrosamine formation from food additives. Address: Food & Drug Administration, Division of Toxicology, Food Toxicology Branch, Washington, DC 20204.

DAILY, JAMES W(ALLACE), b. Columbia, Mo, Mar. 19, 13; m. 38; c. 2. FLUID MECHANICS, HYDRAULIC ENGINEERING. A.B, Stanford, 35; M.S, Calif. Inst. Tech, 37, Ph.D.(mech. eng), 45. Test engr, Byron Jackson Co, Calif, 35; asst, Calif. Inst. Tech, 36-37, mgr. hydraul. mach. lab, 37-40, instr. mech. eng, 40-46, hydraul. eng, Off. Sci. Res. & Develop. Proj, 41-46; asst. prof. hydraul, Mass. Inst. Tech, 46-49, assoc. prof, 49-55, prof, hydrodynamics lab, 55-64; PROF. ENG. MECH. & CHMN. DEPT, UNIV. MICH, 64- Vis. prof, Delft Technol. Univ, 71; vis. scientist, E.D.F. Res. & Testing Ctr, Paris, 71. Naval Ord. Develop. award, 45. Am. Soc. Mech. Eng; Am. Soc. Civil Eng; Int. Asn. Hydraul. Res.(pres, 67-71); hon. mem. Japan Soc. Civil Eng. General fluid mechanics; hydraulic machinery; pumps and turbines; hydrodynamics of submerged bodies, cavitation; non-Newtonian fluid mechanics. Address: Dept. of Engineering Mechanics, 201 W. Engineering Bldg, University of Michigan, Ann Arbor, MI 48104.

DAILY, RAY K, b. Lithuania, Mar. 16, 91; nat; m; c. 1. OPHTHALMOLOGY. M.D, Univ. Tex, 13. PROF. CLIN. OPHTHAL, MED. COL, BAYLOR UNIV. Am. Acad. Ophthal. Otolaryngol.(past v.pres); fel. Am. Col. Surg; French Ophthal. Soc. Ocular surgery. Address: 1517 Medical Towers, Houston, TX 77025.

DAILY, WILLIAM A(LLEN), b. Indianapolis, Ind, Nov. 10, 12; m. 37. MICROBIOLOGY. B.S, Butler, 36; M.S, Northwestern, 38; fel, Cincinnati, 39-40. Lab. asst, Northwestern, 36-38; Cincinnati, 40-41; RES. MICROBIOLOGIST, ELI LILLY & CO, 41- Mem. staff, herbarium, Butler, 42- AAAS; Sci. Res. Soc. Am; Soc. Phycol. Am.(secy, 58, secy-treas, 59, pres, 63); Bot. Soc. Am; Int. Asn. Plant Taxon; Int. Phycol. Soc. Isolation and development of new antibiotics; preservation of microorganisms; taxonomy of the coccoid Myxophyceae; phytoplankton of Indiana. Address: 5884 Compton St, Indianapolis, IN 46220.

DAIN, JOEL A, b. New York, N.Y, Oct. 26, 31; m. 56; c. 3. BIOCHEMISTRY. B.S, Illinois, 53; Ph.D.(biochem), Cornell, 56. Res. fel, col. physicians & surgeons, Columbia, 56-57, res. fel. & assoc. biochem, 57-59; res. assoc. biochem. glycoproteins, Boston Dispensary & med. sch, Tufts, 59-62; asst. prof. BIOCHEM, UNIV. R.I, 62-66, ASSOC. PROF, 66- Nat. Insts. Health grant, 64-74. AAAS; Am. Chem. Soc; Am. Soc. Microbiol; Am. Soc. Biol. Chem; Am. Soc. Neurochem. Chemical embryogenesis of the nervous system and mechanisms of action of nervous tissue glycolipid synthetic enzymes. Address: Dept. of Biochemistry, University of Rhode Island, Kingston, RI 02881.

DAINES, ROBERT H(ENRY), b. Preston, Idaho, Apr. 14, 05; m. 31; c. 4. PLANT PATHOLOGY. B.S, Utah State Agr. Col, 29, M.S, 31; Ph.D.(plant path), Rutgers, 34. Asst. plant pathologist, N.J. Agr. Exp. Sta, 34-40; instr. PLANT PATH, RUTGERS UNIV, 37-39, assoc. prof, 40-47, PROF, 48- Assoc. plant pathologist, N.J. Agr. Exp. Sta, 40-47, res. specialist, 48- AAAS; Am. Phytopath. Soc. Influence of traffic volume on lead in the atmosphere, soils, and on plants; also relation of atmospheric lead near highways, on concentration of lead in human blood, and in blood and organs of rabbits. Address: Dept. of Plant Pathology, College of Agricultural & Environmental Sciences, Rutgers, The State University, New Brunswick, NJ 08903.

DAINTY, JACK, b. Mexborough, Eng, May 7, 19. PLANT PHYSIOLOGY. B.A, Cambridge, 40, M.A, 43; D.Sc.(plant biophys), Univ. Edinburgh, 58. Res. scientist, Cambridge, 40-46; Atomic Energy Can, 46-49; lectr. physics, Univ. Edinburgh, 49-52, sr. lectr. biophys, 52-58, reader, 58-63; PROF. biol, Univ. East Anglia, 63-69; BOT, Univ. Calif, Los Angeles, 69-71; UNIV. TORONTO, 71- Can. Soc. Plant Physiol; Am. Soc. Plant Physiol; Econ. Soc. Am; Brit. Ecol. Soc; Brit. Soc. Exp. Biol; Royal Soc. Edinburgh, Am. Ornith. Union. Transport of ions and water across the membranes of plant cells. Address: Dept. of Botany, University of Toronto, Toronto 181, Ont, Can.

DAIRIKI, SETSUO, b. Penryn, Calif, Feb. 11, 22; m. 45; c. 3. ELECTRICAL ENGINEERING. A.B, Stanford, 42; M.S, Nebraska, 45; M.S, Harvard, 47. Instr. physics, Nebraska, 43-45; engr, Lab. for Electronics, Inc, Mass, 48-51; Raytheon Mfg. Co, 51-53, sr. engr, 54-60; mem. staff commun, Lincoln Lab, Mass. Inst. Tech, 53-54; SR. RES. ENGR, STANFORD RES. INST, 60- Sci. Res. Soc. Am; Inst. Elec. & Electronics Eng. Electromagnetic theory and applications; communication theory and application. Address: Stanford Research Institute, Menlo Park, CA 94025.

DAIRMAN, WALLACE, b. Jersey City, N.J, Dec. 10, 38; m. 63; c. 2. PHARMACOLOGY, BIOCHEMISTRY. B.S, Rutgers Univ, 60; Nat. Insts. Health fel, Tufts Univ, 61-65, Ph.D.(pharmacol), 65. Res. scientist drug metab, Lederle Labs, 65-67, res. assoc. pharmacol. & toxicol, Nat. Insts. Health, 67-68; PHYSIOL. CHEM, ROCHE INST. MOLECULAR BIOL, 68-70, STAFF ASSOC, 71- Factors affecting the biosynthetic and catabolic enzymes of catecholamine synthesis; mechanism by which these enzymes interact to regulate and control catecholamine synthesis; development of fluorescent assay procedures for peptide and primary amines. Address: Roche Institute of Molecular Biology, Nutley, NJ 07110.

DAIS, CHARLES FRANKLIN, b. Fond du Lac, Wis, Dec. 20, 38; m. 60; c. 3. PHYSICAL & ORGANIC CHEMISTRY. B.S, Marquette Univ, 59, M.S, 61; U.S. Air Force fel. & Ph.D.(electron spin resonance), Tex. Tech. Col, 64; M.D, Univ. Tenn, 68. Analyst chem. res, Froedtert Malt Co, Wis, 59-61; INSTR. BIOCHEM, MED. UNITS, UNIV. TENN, 64-; RESIDENT PATH, BAPTIST MEM. HOSP, 68- Am. Chem. Soc; Am. Med. Asn. Organic synthesis; electron spin resonance; mechanism and structural elucidations; analytical chemistry; biochemical research on aromatic carcinogens. Address: 2116 Leyton Ave, Memphis, TN 38127.

DAIS, JACK LUDWIG, b. Detroit, Mich, May 2, 40. SOLID MECHANICS, APPLIED MATHEMATICS. B.S, Mich. State, 62, M.S, 63; Ph.D.(appl. math), Brown, 67. Summers, engr. in training, Tech. Center, Gen. Motors Corp, 61-62, mem. tech. staff, Bell Tel. Labs, 64-65 & mech. engr, Land Locomotion Div, U.S. Army Tank-Auto Command, 67; ASST. PROF. ENG. MECH, UNIV. MINN, MINNEAPOLIS, 67- Consult, Control Data Corp, 68- Applied mathematics; solid mechanics; plasticity; soil mechanics; foil bearings; urban transportation. Address: Institute of Technology, University of Minnesota, Minneapolis, MN 55455.

DAITCH, P(AUL) B(ERNARD), b. Boston, Mass, May 19, 25. NUCLEAR ENGINEERING & SCIENCE. B.S, Yale, 45; M.S, Brown, 47; Ph.D, Rochester, 52. Instr, Yale, 52-55; asst. prof, Nebraska, 55-56; sr. physicist, nuclear div, Combustion Eng, Inc, 56-60; PROF. NUCLEAR ENG. & SCI, RENSSELAER POLYTECH. INST, 60- Consult, Nuclear Div, Alco Prod. Inc, 61-62; Acad. Press, Inc, 63-64; Gen. Elec. Co, 64- Am. Phys. Soc; Am. Nuclear Soc. Low energy nuclear physics; analysis of nuclear reactors; transport theory; asymptotic and transient analysis of pulsed neutron systems. Address: Dept. of Nuclear Engineering & Science, Rensselaer Polytechnic Institute, Troy, NY 12181.

DAITZ, BERNARD DAVID, b. Brooklyn, N.Y, Jan. 21, 13; m. 40; c. 3. PHYSIOLOGY, PUBLIC HEALTH. A.B, Brooklyn Col, 36; M.S.P.H, Columbia, 38; Ph.D.(physiol), George Washington, 53. Consult, tuberc. rehabil, dept. med. & surg, Veterans Admin, 46-52; chief far east sect, med. intel. div, off. of surgeon gen, Dept. of Army, 52-56; consult, med. rehab, chronic disease div, U.S. Public Health Serv, DEPT. HEALTH, EDUC. & WELFARE, 56-68, SPEC. ASST. HEALTH MANPOWER COMMUN. HEALTH SERV, HEALTH SERV. & MENTAL HEALTH ADMIN, 68- Clin. asst. prof, sch. med, Georgetown Univ. Med.Serv.C, 42-45, Res, 45-70, Col. Fel. AAAS; Am. Cong. Rehab. Med; fel. Am. Pub. Health Asn. Medical rehabilitation; physiology of stress; etiology and ecology of disability. Address: 7822 Glenister Dr, Springfield, VA 22152.

DAJANI, ESAM ZAFER, b. Jaffa, Palestine, May 30, 40; m. 64; c. 2. PHARMACOLOGY, TOXICOLOGY. B.S, Missouri-Kansas City, 63; M.S, Auburn, 66; Ph.D.(pharmacol. & toxicol), Purdue, 68. SR. PHARMACOLOGIST, ROHM AND HAAS RES. LABS, 68- General and gastrointestinal pharmacology. Address: 7 Broadale Ct, Doylestown, PA 18901.

DAKE, EARL D(ANIEL), b. Wessington, S.Dak, Feb. 19, 02; m. 25; c. 2. CIVIL ENGINEERING. B.S, S.Dak. Sch. Mines, 24, C.E, 30; M.S, Iowa State Col, 27. Instr, S.DAK. SCH. MINES & TECHNOL, 24-27, asst. prof. CIVIL ENG, 27-30, PROF, 30, v.pres, 48-67. Supt. construct, S.Dak. State Engrs. Off; Firestone Rubber Co; archit. examiner, Fed. Housing Admin; chmn, cent. zone & dir, Nat. Coun. State Bds. Eng. Exam. Am. Soc. Civil Eng; Am. Soc. Eng. Educ; Am. Road Builders Asn. Wind resistance and super elevation of highways; reinforced concrete; concrete admixture. Address: Dept. of Civil Engineering, South Dakota School of Mines & Technology, Rapid City, SD 57701.

DAKIN, MATT E(ITEL), b. Skene, Miss, Dec. 11, 36; m. 57; c. 2. ENTOMOLOGY. B.S, Delta State Col, 58; M.S, Auburn, 60, Ph.D.(entom), 64.

Instr. biol, Univ. Southwest. La, 60-61, 63-64; asst. prof. zool, Auburn, 64; BIOL, UNIV. SOUTHWEST. LA, 64-68, ASSOC. PROF, 68- Entom. Soc. Am; Soc. Syst. Zool; Am. Entom. Soc. Taxonomy of the Orthoptera of the Southern United States. Address: Box 1435, University of Southwestern Louisiana, Lafayette, LA 70501.

DAKIN, THOMAS W(ENDELL), b. Minneapolis, Minn, May 5, 15; m. 42; c. 2. PHYSICAL CHEMISTRY. A.B, Minnesota, 35; M.S, Mich. State, 38; Christian fel, Harvard, 38-40, A.M, 39, Lehman fel, 40-41, Ph.D.(phys. chem), 41. Asst. phys. chem, Mich. State, 35-38; group leader, insulation dept, WESTINGHOUSE RES. LABS, 46-50, mgr. physics of insulation sect, 50-68, MGR. ELEC. PERFORMANCE INSULATION MAT, 68- Elec. insulation divisional ed, Electrochem. Technol. Chmn, Nat. Res. Coun. Conf. on Elec. Insulations, 57; U.S. rep. insulating mat, Int. Conf. Large Elec. Systs. Am. Chem. Soc; Am. Phys. Soc; fel. Inst. Elec. & Electronics Eng. Electrochemistry; viscosity of ionic solutions; dielectrics; microwave; high frequency measurements; high polymers; electrical insulation. Address: Westinghouse Research Labs, Beulah Rd, Churchill Borough, Pittsburgh, PA 15235.

DAKSHINAMURTI, KRISHNAMURTI, b. Vellore, India, May 20, 28; m. 61; c. 2. BIOCHEMISTRY. B.Sc, Madras, 46; M.Sc, Rajasthan, India, 52, Ph.D.(biochem), 57. Lectr. chem, Christian Med. Col, India, 52-56, sr. lectr. biochem, 56-58; res. assoc. animal nutrit, Illinois, 58-62; nutrit, Mass. Inst. Tech, 62-63; assoc. dir. res, St. Joseph Hosp, Lancaster, Pa, 63-65; ASSOC. PROF. BIOCHEM, UNIV. MANITOBA, 65- Am. Inst. Nutrit; Am. Diabetes Asn; Brit. Biochem. Soc; fel. Royal Inst. Chem; Am. Soc. Biol. Chem; Am. Soc. Neurochem. Metabolic functions of biotin and pyridoxine; development of the central nervous system; regulation of protein synthesis. Address: Dept. of Biochemistry, University of Manitoba, Winnipeg 3, Man, Can.

DAKSS, MARK LUDMER, b. N.Y.C, Mar. 1, 40. PHYSICAL OPTICS. B.E.E, Cooper Union, 60; Higgins fel, Columbia, 60-61, A.M, 62, univ. fels, 62-63, 64-65, Raytheon fel, 63-64, Ph.D.(physics), 66. Proj. engr, adv. electronics group, Eclipse-Pioneer Div, Bendix Corp, summer 60; res. asst, T.J. Watson Res. Lab, Int. Bus. Mach. Corp, N.Y, summer 61; radiation lab, Columbia, summer 62; res. staff mem, T.J. Watson Res. Lab, IBM Corp, 66-71; MEM. TECH. STAFF, GEN. TEL. & ELECTRONICS LABS, 71- Am. Phys. Soc; Inst. Elec. & Electronics Eng. Solid state physics and lasers; optical data processing; optical guided waves; acoustic surface waves; optical communications. Address: General Telephone & Electronics Labs, 208-20 Willets Point Blvd, Bayside, NY 11360.

DALAL, FRAM RUSTOM, b. Madras, India, Jan. 24, 35; m. 61; c. 1. CLINICAL CHEMISTRY, BIOCHEMISTRY. B.S, Univ. Bombay, 54 & 56, Ph.D. (biochem), 61. Coun. Sci. & Indust. Res. fel, Univ. Bombay, 60-61; chief technologist, D&P Prod. Ltd, India, 61-64; res. assoc. microbial biochem, sch. med, Univ. Pa, 64-67; assoc. prof. microbiol, dept. chem. technol, Univ. Bombay, 67-69; ASST. CHIEF BIOCHEM, DEPT. OF LABS, ALBERT EINSTEIN MED. CTR, 69- Am. Asn. Clin. Chem. Purine metabolism in salmonella; diagnostic applications of enzymes in blood and tissue; improvements in automation of enzyme assays. Address: Dept. of Laboratories, Albert Einstein Medical Center, York & Tabor Rds, Philadelphia, PA 19141.

D'ALARCAO, HUGO T, b. Lisbon, Portugal, Feb. 15, 37; m. 56; c. 3. ALGEBRA. B.A, Univ. Nebr, Lincoln, 59, M.A, 61; Ph.D.(math), Pa. State Univ, 66. Instr. MATH, Univ. Nebr, 61-62; Univ. Mass, 62-63; asst. prof, State Univ. N.Y. Stony Brook, 66-71; ASSOC. PROF, BRIDGEWATER STATE COL, 71- Vis. res. prof, Univ. Chile, fall 69. Am. Math. Soc; Math. Asn. Am. Algebraic theory of semigroups; universal algebra. Address: Dept. of Mathematics, Bridgewater State College, Bridgewater, MA 02324.

DALBEC, PAUL EUCLIDE, b. New Bedford, Mass, June 26, 35; m. 63; c. 1. SOLID STATE PHYSICS. Univ. fel, Univ. Notre Dame, 57-59, M.S, 59; univ. fel, Georgetown Univ, 61-64, NASA fel, 64-66, Ph.D.(physics), 66. Physicist, phys. sci. lab, Melpar, Inc, Va, 59-60; head thin films dept, appl. phys. lab, Gen. Instrument Corp, N,J, 60-61; asst. prof. PHYSICS, Am. Univ, 66-68; YOUNGSTOWN STATE UNIV, 68-71, ASSOC. PROF, 71- Am. Phys. Soc; Am. Asn. Physics Teachers; Am. Vacuum Soc; Inst. Fundamental Studies Asn. Photoelectric properties of solids in the vacuum ultraviolet; electronic properties of semiconductor and metallic thin films; vacuum ultraviolet spectroscopy; techniques for preparing thin films including epitaxial growth and sputtering. Address: Dept. of Physics and Astronomy, Youngstown State University, Youngstown, OH 44503.

DALBY, ARTHUR, b. Detroit, Mich, Mar. 13, 30; Brit. citizen; m. 52; c. 4. BIOCHEMICAL GENETICS. B.Sc, London, 50; Ph.D.(biochem), Leeds, 54. Fel. biochem, Prairie Regional Lab, Nat. Res. Coun. Can, 54-55; Surgeon Gen. Off. fel, Purdue, 55-59; lectr, Manchester Inst. Sci. & Tech, 59-64; res. assoc, PURDUE UNIV, 65-67, ASSOC. PROF. BIOCHEM. GENETICS, 67- Royal Inst. Chem; Brit. Biochem. Soc; Am. Soc. Plant Physiol. Microbial growth factors; biochemistry of inflammation; blood clot lysis; cell differentiation in algae; biochemical and genetic regulation of protein synthesis in maize. Address: Botany & Plant Pathology Dept, Purdue University, Lafayette, IN 47907.

DALBY, FREDERICK WILLIAM, b. Edmonton, Alta, May 5, 28; m. 52; c. 2. PHYSICS. B.Sc, Alberta, 50; M.A, British Columbia, 52; Ph.D.(physics), Ohio State, 55. Res. physicist, radiation physics lab, E.I. du Pont de Nemours & Co, 57-61; assoc. prof. PHYSICS, UNIV. B.C, 61-66, PROF, 66- Molecular spectroscopy, chemical physics. Address: Dept. of Physics, University of British Columbia, Vancouver 8, B.C, Can.

DALBY, GASTON, b. New Boston, Tex, Nov. 19, 07; m. 49. FOOD CHEMISTRY. B.A, Texas, 27; M.A, Princeton, 29. Food chemist, Nat. Biscuit Co, 29-32; Ward Banking Co, 32-48, dir. res, 48-61; CONSULT, MILLERS' NAT. FEDN, 61-; FOREIGN AGR. SERV, U.S. DEPT. AGR, 61- AAAS; Am. Asn. Cereal Chem; Am. Chem. Soc; Inst. Food Tech. Baking technology; food preservation. Address: Millers' National Federation, National Press Bldg, Washington, DC 20004.

DALBY, THOMAS GLENN, b. Minneapolis, Minn, Sept. 1, 26; m. 50; c. 3. ELECTRICAL ENGINEERING. B.S, Minnesota, 48, M.S, 51; Washington, 54. Res. engr, BOEING CO, 51-58, group engr. commun. & electromagnetic res. & develop, 58-62, sect. head command & control res. & develop, 62-64, tech. mgr. Voyager Spacecraft Systs, 65-66, Adv. Surface Missile Syst, 67-69, ENG. MGR, 69- Prog. chmn, Region Inst. Radio Eng, 62. U.S.N.R, 44-46. AAAS; Inst. Elec. & Electronics Eng. Antennas and microwave circuitry; communications. Address: Missiles & Information Systems, The Boeing Co, P.O. Box 3996, Seattle, WA 98124.

DALE, ALVIN C, b. Nashville, Tenn, Aug. 12, 19; m. 47; c. 4. AGRICULTURAL & CIVIL ENGINEERING. B.S, Tennessee, 41; M.S, Iowa State, 42, Ph.D.(agr. & civil eng), 50; cert, Chicago, 44. Jr. civil engr, U.S. Engrs. Off, Ill, 42-43, asst. civil engr, 46; instr. AGR. ENG, Iowa State, 46-47, asst. prof, 47-49; PURDUE, 49-52, assoc. prof, 52-56, PROF, 56- Award, Metal Bldg. Mfrs. Asn, 62. U.S.A.A.F, 43-46, Capt. Am. Soc. Agr. Eng; Am. Soc. Eng. Educ; Nat. Soc. Prof. Eng. Environmental control and structural areas of farm structures; farm waste handling and disposal. Address: Dept. of Agricultural Engineering, Purdue University, Lafayette, IN 47907.

DALE, BETTIE McSPEDDEN, b. Wichita Falls, Tex, July 7, 23; m; c. 3. NUCLEAR CHEMISTRY, MOLECULAR BIOLOGY. B.S, Baylor, 46; M.S, Ohio State, 51, Nat. Inst. Health fel, 52-54, Ph.D.(chem), 54. Asst. chemist, Am. Cyanamid & Chem. Corp, 44; Phillips Petrol. Co, 46-47; fel, Ohio State, 54-56, instr. CHEM, 56-57; Nat. Insts. Health fel, KANS. STATE UNIV, 64-66, res. assoc, 66-69, INSTR, 69- AAAS; Am. Chem. Soc. RNA control; bacteriophage. Address: 2120 College Heights, Manhattan, KS 66502.

DALE, CLARK H(ALL), b. Rochester, N.Y, June 6, 07; m. 31; c. 4. CHEMISTRY. B.S, Rochester, 29, M.S, 34, Ph.D.(org. chem), 36. Chemist, Vacuum Oil Co, N.J, 29-31; RES. CHEMIST, Todd Co, 31-32; Niacet Chem. Corp, 37-45; Durez Plastics & Chem, N.Y, 45-47; AM. OIL CO, STANDARD OIL CO.(IND), 47-70, STANDARD OIL RES. CTR, 70- Am. Chem. Soc. Technical information; documentation. Address: Standard Oil Research Center, Box 400, Naperville, IL 60540.

DALE, DOUGLAS KEITH, b. Ottawa, Ont, Oct. 10, 24; m. 51; c. 5. MATHEMATICAL STATISTICS. B.A, Queen's (Ont), 47, hons, 49; M.S, North Carolina, 58. Lectr. math, Queen's (Ont), 46-49; asst. to math. adv, Dominion Bur. Statist, 49-51, chief sampling & anal, 51-60; statist. div, Nat. Energy Bd, 60-62; assoc. prof. MATH, CARLETON UNIV.(ONT), 62-63, assoc. prof, 63-65, PROF, 65-, chmn. dept, 63-67, Lectr, Carleton (Can), 49-52, 53-60; consult, Can. Advertising Res. Found, 63-64; Bur. Broadcast Measurement, 63- Am. Statist. Soc; Math. Asn. Am; fel. Royal Statist. Soc; Can. Math. Cong. Sampling theory; distribution theory; probability theory. Address: Dept. of Mathematics, Carleton University, Ottawa 1, Ont, Can.

DALE, EDWARD E(VERETT), JR, b. Norman, Okla, Aug. 18, 20; m. 42; c. 2. BOTANY. B.A, Oklahoma, 42, M.S, 47; Indiana, 46-47; Ph.D, Nebraska, 51. Asst. bot, Indiana, 46-47; Nebraska, 47-50; asst. prof. biol, Baylor, 51-52; Texas Christian, 52-57; BOT, UNIV. ARK, FAYETTEVILLE, 57-61, assoc. prof, 61-68, PROF, 68- U.S.A, 42-46, Res, 46-55, Capt. Bot. Soc. Am; Ecol. Soc. Am; Am. Soc. Range Mgt. Grassland ecology; vegetation of Arkansas. Address: Dept. of Botany & Bacteriology, University of Arkansas, Fayetteville, AR 72701.

DALE, EDWIN, b. Louisville, Ky, Nov. 5, 33; m. 56; c. 3. ENDOCRINOLOGY. B.S, East. Ky. State Col, 54; M.S, Kentucky, 56; Ph.D.(zool), Iowa, 60. Res. assoc. endocrinol, Iowa, 60-61; trainee steroid biochem, Worcester Found. Exp. Biol, 61-62; instr. anat, col. med, Kentucky, 62-64, ASST. PROF. OBSTET. & GYNEC, 64-66, dept. zool, 66-68; SCH. MED, EMORY UNIV, 68- AAAS. Steroid biochemistry; distribution, metabolism and functions of steroids; metabolism of steroid hormones by neoplastic tissues; metabolism and effects of oral contraceptives, especially low dose and long acting progestational agents. Address: Dept. of Gynecology & Obstetrics, Emory University School of Medicine, 69 Butler St. S.E, Atlanta, GA 30303.

DALE, E(RNEST) BROCK, (JR), b. Jackson Co, Okla, Dec. 15, 18; m. 46; c. 3. PHYSICS. B.S, Oklahoma, 40, M.S, 44; Ph.D.(physics), Ohio State, 53. Engr. infrared anal, Phillips Petrol. Co, 44-47; res. assoc. infrared detecting systems, Ohio State, 49-50; proj. leader semiconductors, Battelle Mem. Inst, 52-57; assoc. prof. PHYSICS, KANS. STATE UNIV, 57-67, PROF, 67- Am. Phys. Soc. Channeling and Rutherford scattering; musical acoustics; solid state physics; thin films. Address: Dept. of Physics, Kansas State University, Manhattan, KS 66502.

DALE, F(REDERICK) H(AROLD), b. Redding, Calif, Nov. 6, 05; m. 28. WILDLIFE ECOLOGY. A.B, San Jose State Col, 28; M.A, California, 39; Ph.D.(zool), Maryland, 54. Mem. staff, wildlife mgt. res. & admin, State Dept. Conserv, Mich, 39-50; biologist, U.S. Fish & Wildlife Serv, 50-56, asst. dir, Patuxent Wildlife Res. Ctr, 56-59, staff specialist upland ecol, wildlife res. div, 59-64, dir. pesticides rev. staff, 64-67, chief div. pesticides registrn, Bur. Sport Fisheries & Wildlife, U.S. Dept. Interior, 67-70; RETIRED. Am. Wildlife Soc. rep, div. biol. & agr, Nat. Res. Coun, 56-62. Distinguished Serv. Award, U.S. Dept. Interior, 71. U.S.A, 43-45. AAAS; Wildlife Soc; Am. Soc. Mammal; Ecol. Soc. Am. Ecology of game animals. Address: 1901 Dayton Rd, Chico, CA 95926.

DALE, GLENN H(ILBURN), b. Mountain Park, Okla, Aug. 25, 23; m. 47; c. 3. CHEMICAL ENGINEERING. B.S, Oklahoma, 44. Chem. engr, PHILLIPS PETROL. CO, 44-47, group leader pilot plant, 47-49, process design engr, 50-51, pilot plant supvr, 52-57, sect. mgr. separations, 58-60, br. mgr. separations processes, 60-71, STAFF ENGR. PETROL. PROCESSES, 71- Am. Inst. Chem. Eng; Am. Chem. Soc. Equipment and process development in the separations field; distillation; adsorption; liquid-liquid extraction; crystallation; filtration; centrifugation. Address: 2900 Staats Dr, Bartlesville, OK 74003.

DALE, H(OMER) E(LDON), b. Minneapolis, Minn, June 11, 22; m. 47; c. 4. PHYSIOLOGY. D.V.M, Iowa State Col, 44, M.S, 49; Ph.D.(physiol), Univ.

Mo, 53. Instr. vet. physiol, Iowa State Col, 47-49; asst. prof, Agr. & Mech. Col. Tex, 49-50; instr. vet. sci, Univ. Wis, 50-51; vet. physiol, UNIV. MO-COLUMBIA, 51-53, assoc. prof, 53-56, PROF. VET. PHYSIOL. & PHARMACOL, 56- U.S.A, 43-46; U.S.A.F.R, 46-, Maj. AAAS; Am. Vet. Med. Asn; Am. Physiol. Soc. Environmental physiology, endocrinology; immunology. Address: Dept. of Veterinary Physiology, University of Missouri-Columbia, Columbia, MO 65201.

DALE, HUGH M(ONRO), b. Toronto, Ont, Nov. 24, 19; m. 45; c. 2. PLANT ECOLOGY. B.A, Toronto, 48, M.A, 50, Ph.D, 56; Ont. Col. Ed, 50, 51. Sr. chem. master, St. Andrew's Col, 50-52; lectr. BOT, Toronto, 53-56, asst. prof, 56-57; assoc. prof, UNIV. GUELPH (ONT), 57-68, PROF, 68- Res. fel, Univ. Calif, Davis, 66; mem. gov. bd, Biol. Coun. Can, 68-71. R.C.A.F, 41-46. Ecol. Soc. Am; Am. Inst. Biol. Sci; Can. Bot. Asn.(pres, 69-70); Humanities Asn. Can. Experimental ecology of weed species; developmental morphology of hydrophytes. Address: Dept. of Botany, University of Guelph, Guelph, Ont, Can.

DALE, JACK K(YLE), b. Manhattan, Kans, Apr. 6, 21; m. 47; c. 3. PHARMACEUTICAL CHEMISTRY. B.S, Florida, 43, M.S, 44, fel, 46-47, Ph.D. (pharmacy), 47. Asst. pharmacy & chem, Florida, 43-46; sr. scientist, Upjohn Co, 47-61, head vet. res. & develop. sect, 61-66; V.PRES. & TECH. DIR, KAPCO INC, 66- AAAS; sr. mem. Am. Chem. Soc; Am. Pharmaceut. Asn; Acad. Pharmaceut. Sci; Am. Mgt. Asn; Am. Inst. Mgt; N.Y. Acad. Sci; Royal Soc. Health. Zinc salt hydrolysis; isotonic, adjusted, buffered and preserved collyria; alkaloidal extraction; pharmacy of adrenal cortical hormones; penicillin, neomycin, erythromycin pharmacy; veterinary pharmacy; drug incompatibilities; antacids; drug stability. Address: Kapco Inc, 2220 Glendening St, Kalamazoo, MI 49001.

DALE, J(AMES) D(OUGLAS), b. Edmonton, Alta, Dec. 5, 39; m. 63; c. 1. MECHANICAL ENGINEERING, HEAT TRANSFER. B.S, Univ. Alta, 61, M.S, 63; Ph.D.(mech. eng), Univ. Wash, 69. Sessional lectr. mech. eng, Univ. Alta, 63-64; asst. res. off, Res. Coun. Alta, 64-65; ASST. PROF. MECH. ENG, UNIV. ALTA, 69- Can. Soc. Mech. Eng; assoc. mem. Am. Soc. Mech. Eng. Study of injection of steam into a gas turbine; natural convection heat transfer to non-Newtonian fluids; air pollution from combustion sources. Address: Dept. of Mechanical Engineering, University of Alberta, Edmonton 7, Alberta, Can.

DALE, J(AMES) L(OWELL), b. Olney, Ill, Dec. 1, 22; m. 46; c. 1. PLANT PATHOLOGY. B.S, East. Ill. State Col, 52; M.S, Illinois, 53, Ph.D.(plant path), 56. Asst. plant path, Illinois, 52-56; exten. plant pathologist, col. agr, UNIV. ARK, FAYETTEVILLE, 56-57, asst. prof. PLANT PATH, 57-60, assoc. prof, 60-65, PROF, 65- U.S.N.R, 43-46. Am. Phytopath. Soc; Am. Inst. Biol. Sci. Corn and pasture grass diseases; plant virus diseases. Address: Dept. of Plant Pathology, University of Arkansas, Fayetteville, AR 72701.

DALE, JAMES W(ILFRED), b. Toronto, Ont, July 12, 17; m. 41; c. 4. INORGANIC & ORGANIC CHEMISTRY. B.A, Toronto, 40; Ph.D.(inorg. chem), Cambridge, 55. Res. chemist, Ont. Res. Found, Can, 40-41; exp. sta, Dept. Nat. Defence, Alta, 41-42; Defence Res. Chem. Labs, Ottawa, 47-57; spec. proj. dept, Monsanto Chem. Co, Mass, 57-61, Monsanto Co, 61-68. Can. Army, 43-47, Capt. Am. Chem. Soc; Chem. Inst. Can. Fluorine chemistry, especially inorganic, organic, organometallic and electrochemical, as applied to chemical warfare, high temperature fluids, thermally stable polymers, high energy propellants and incendiaries. Address: Genevieve Lane, Green Harbor, MA 02041.

DALE, JOHN IRVIN, III, b. Knoxville, Tenn, May 14, 35; m. 62; c. 1. ORGANIC CHEMISTRY. B.S, Carson-Newman Col, 56; M.A, North Carolina, 59; Shell Found. fel, Virginia, 61-62, Ph.D.(org. chem), 63. Chemist, res. labs, TENN. EASTMAN CO, 62-65, SR. CHEMIST, 66-67, ORG. CHEM. DIV, 67- Am. Chem. Soc; Am. Asn. Textile Chem. & Colorists. Synthetic organic chemistry; heterocylic and aromatic compounds; textile dyes and intermediates. Address: 5300 Orebank Rd, Kingsport, TN 37664.

DALE, PETER P(AUL), b. Rochester, N.Y, Jan. 1, 13; m. 41; c. 4. OPERATIVE DENTISTRY, ORAL PATHOLOGY. A.B, Rochester, 37, Carnegie fel, 41-42, Nutrit. fel, 42-43, M.S, 48; D.M.D, Tufts Col, 40. Intern pedodont, Eastman Dent. Dispensary, 40-41; dent. toxicologist & pathologist, Manhattan Proj, 43-48; instr. & asst. dent. surg, Rochester, 48-60; prof. oper. dent. & chmn. dept, SCH. DENT. MED, TUFTS UNIV, 60-66, prof. dent. & dir. continuing educ, 66-69, sabbatical, 69-70, EMER. PROF. RESTORATIVE DENT, 70- Assoc, Rochester Gen. Hosp, 51-54; dent. consult, Hempohiliac Found, Rochester; Gen. Elec. Co, 60-62; Nat. Asn. Standard Med. Vocab, 62-; mem. nat. register sci. & tech. personnel, Nat. Sci. Found, 64; private practice. Mem. comt. sci. res. personnel, War Manpower Cmn, 44. U.S.A, 44-46, Capt. Am. Dent. Asn; fel. Am. Acad. Dent. Sci; Int. Asn. Dent. Res; fel. Int. Col. Dent. Dental education; oral pathology and clinical restorative dentistry. Address: 46 High St, Winchester, MA 01890.

DALE, WESLEY J(OHN), b. Milwaukee, Wis, Aug. 8, 21; m. 49; c. 1. ORGANIC CHEMISTRY. B.S, Illinois, 43; Nat. Res. Council fel, Minnesota, 46-49, Ph.D.(chem), 49. Asst, Minnesota, 43, res. chemist, Govt. Synthetic Rubber Res. Program, 43-46; asst. prof. chem, Univ. Mo-Columbia, 49-53, assoc. prof, 53-58, prof, 58-66, asst. to dean, col. arts & sci, 54-55, chmn. dept. chem, 61-64, PROF. ORG. CHEM. & DEAN SCH. GRAD. STUDIES, UNIV. MO-KANSAS CITY, 66-, UNIV. RES. ADMINR, 69-, ACTING PROVOST & DEAN FACULTIES, 71- Staff assoc, sci. facilities eval. group, div. instnl. prog, Nat. Sci. Found, 64, sr. staff assoc, sci. develop. eval. group, 64-66; chmn, Midwest Conf. Grad. Study & Res, 70-71. AAAS; Am. Chem. Soc. Chemistry and spectra of vinylaromatic systems; boronic acids; cyclopropanes; carbenes. Address: School of Graduate Studies, University of Missouri at Kansas City, Kansas City, MO 64110.

DALE, W(ILLIAM) ANDREW, b. Nashville, Tenn, Mar. 13, 20; m. 44; c. 4. SURGERY. A.B, Davidson Col, 41; M.D, Vanderbilt, 44. Intern surg, Strong Mem. Hosp, 44-45, asst. res, 45-46, 48-49, chief resident surgeon, 50; instr. surg, Rochester, 50-53, physiol, 53-54, surg. anat, 53-55, asst. prof. physiol, 54-57, surg, 54-58, dir. surg. exp. lab, 53-58, clin. asst. prof. surg, 58; PROF. CLIN. SURG, VANDERBILT UNIV, 58- Vol. fel, physiol, Rochester, 51-53; asst. prof. surg, Med. Col. Ala, 52. Asst. surgeon, Strong Mem. Hosp, 51-58; attend. surgeon, Genessee Hosp, 52-58; mem. attend. surg. staff, Vanderbilt Univ. Hosp, St. Thomas Hosp. & Mid-State Baptist Hosp. Dipl, Am. Bd. Surg; dipl, Am. Bd. Thoracic Surg. Med. Med.C, 46-48, Capt. Fel. Am. Col. Surg; Am. Med. Asn; Soc. Univ. Surg; Soc. Vascular Surg; Int. Cardiovasc. Soc. Address: 520 Mid-State Medical Center, Nashville, TN 37203.

DALE, WILLIAM E(DWARD), b. Atlanta, Ga, Aug. 31, 23; m. 46; c. 2. ANALYTICAL CHEMISTRY. B.S, Georgia, 51; North Carolina, 60. Res. chemist, U.S. Dept. Agr, 52-55; U.S. DEPT. HEALTH, EDUC. & WELFARE, 55-60, anal. chemist, CTR. DISEASE CONTROL, 60-67, RES. CHEMIST, 67- Anal. chemist, Oak Ridge Inst. Nuclear Studies, 66; mem. comt. on persistent pesticides, Nat. Acad. Sci-Nat. Res. Coun. U.S.A, 43-45. AAAS; Am. Chem. Soc. Fate or metabolism of pesticides in man and animal; toxicity and mode of action of pesticides. Address: Technical Development Lab, Center of Disease Control, U.S. Dept. of Health, Education & Welfare, P.O. Box 2167, Savannah, GA 31402.

DALE, WILLIAM FRANKLIN, b. Pittsburgh, Pa, Sept. 24, 42. THERMODYNAMICS, CHEMICAL ENGINEERING. B.S, Lehigh Univ, 64; M.A, Princeton, 66, Ph.D.(chem. eng), 70. ASST. PROF. CHEM. ENG, UNIV. S.C, 69- Consult. prod. liability actions, 69-; Nat. Sci. Found. res. grant, 71-72. Am. Chem. Soc; Am. Inst. Chem. Eng. Theory and calculation of transport properties of the liquid state; control and optimization of chemical processes; theory of homogeneous nucleation; statistical thermodynamics. Address: Dept. of Chemical Engineering, College of Engineering, University of South Carolina, Columbia, SC 29208.

DALE, WILLIAM I(SAAC), JR, b. Paris, Tenn, Dec. 1, 24; m. 47; c. 5. PHYSICS. B.S, Tennessee, 48; M.S, 51. Asst. prof. math. & physics, Carson-Newman Col, 49-50; head phys. test sect, HUNTSVILLE DIV, THIOKOL CHEM. CORP, 51-58, asst. proj. mgr, 58-62, proj. mgr, 62-64, prin. engr, 64-67, PROG. MGR, 67- Mem. Joint Army-Navy-Air Force panel, phys. properties solid propellants, 51-58, chmn, 56-58. U.S.A, 43-45. Assoc. fel. Inst. Aeronaut. & Astronaut. Development of solid propellant rocket motors. Address: 1803 Covewood Dr, Huntsville, AL 35801.

DALEHITE, THOMAS H, b. Memphis, Tenn, Sept. 14, 18; m. 42; c. 3. AERONAUTICAL ENGINEERING. B.S, Miss. State, 39. Gen. engr, Air Proving Ground Command, 51-58, tech. dir, 58-60, dir. plans & progs, Off. Secy. Air Force, Supreme Hq. Allied Powers Europe Tech. Ctr, Netherlands, 60-62, sci. adv. for. tech. Air Force Systs. Command, 62-63, dep. eng, Off. Secy. Air Force, 63-66, CHIEF SCIENTIST, Air Proving Ground Ctr, 66-68, ARMAMENT DEVELOP. & TEST CTR, 68- Consult. to U.S. Defense Rep, N.Atlantic Alliance, 60-62. Mem, Coun. Air Force Scientist, 62-63; group environ. panel, aeronaut. coord. bd, NASA-Dept. Defense, 63-66; tech. mgt. coun, Air Force Systs. Command, 66-; small arms adv. comt, Adv. Res. Projs. Agency, Dept. Defense, 68- Exceptional serv. decorations, Secy. Air Force, 62, 65 & 68. U.S.N, 41-45. Am. Ord. Asn; Inst. Aeronaut. & Astronaut. Non-nuclear munitions, guided missiles systems, and high performance aircraft exploratory, advanced and engineering development; global range instrumentation; electromagnetic warfare. Address: Armament Development & Test Center (CCN), Eglin Air Force Base, FL 32542.

D'ALELIO, G(AETANO) F(RANCIS), b. Charlestown, Mass, Dec. 26, 09; m. 32; c. 4. ORGANIC CHEMISTRY. A.B, Boston Col, 31; Ph.D.(org. chem), Hopkins, 35. Assoc. phys. chem, grad. sch, Boston Col, 35-36; dir. plastics res, plastics labs, Gen. Elec. Co, 41-43; v.pres. & dir. res, Pro-phy-lac-tic Brush Co, Mass, 43-46; mgr. high polymer res, Indust. Rayon Corp, 46-47; asst. dir. res, Koppers Co, Inc, 47-49, v.pres. & mgr. res, 49-54; head dept. CHEM, UNIV. NOTRE DAME, 55-60, RES. PROF, 60- Consult, referee bd, chem. br, Off. Prod. Res. & Develop, 42-44; Naval Bur. Ord, 44-45; Army Chem. Corps, 59-60; Scott Paper Co; Foster Grant Co; Xerox Corp. Mem. bd. dirs, BarDal Inc, Ill, 58-61; Dalmon Inc, Ohio, 59-; mem, adv. comt. mat, NASA, 61-63; labs. comt, Franklin Inst, 63-71; comt. radiation preservation of food, Nat. Acad. Sci, 65-; comt. vertically integrated prog. on polymers, U.S. Air Force, Wright Patterson Air Force Base, 66-; mem. Nat. Resources Coun. Wisdom Award of Honor & Wisdom Hall of Fame, 70; Knight of Mark Twain, 71. With Manhattan Proj; Naval Bur. Ord; Off. Sci. Res. & Develop; U.S.A.A.F, 44. AAAS; Am. Chem. Soc; fel. Am. Inst. Chem; Am. Inst. Chem. Eng; Am. Ord. Asn; Armed Forces Chem. Asn; Hist. Sci. Soc; Acad. Appl. Sci; fel. N.Y. Acad. Sci; Brit. Soc. Chem. Indust. Polymers and plastics; synthetic fibers; physical chemistry; resins; ion exchange resins; irradiation chemistry; high energy fuels; heat resistant and semiconductor polymers. Address: 2011 E. Cedar St, South Bend, IN 46617.

DALES, SAMUEL, b. Warsaw, Poland, Aug. 31, 27; Can. citizen; m. 52; c. 2. VIROLOGY, CELL BIOLOGY. B.A, British Columbia, 51, M.A, 53; Ph.D. (zool, biochem), Toronto, 57. Nat. Cancer Inst. Can. res. fel. cell biol, Toronto, 57-60; res. assoc. cytol. & cell biol, Rockefeller Inst, 60-61, asst. prof. virol. & cytol, 61-66; MEM, PUB. HEALTH RES. INST. CITY OF NEW YORK, 66-, RES. PROF. MICROBIOL, POST GRAD. MED. SCH, N.Y. UNIV, 70-, res. assoc. prof, 66-70. Harvey Soc; Am. Soc. Cell Biol; Electron Micros. Soc. Am. Cell virus interactions and the early events in the process of infection; cell fine structure and function; cell physiology. Address: Dept. of Cytobiology, Public Health Research Institute of the City of New York, Inc, 455 First Ave, New York, NY 10016.

D'ALESANDRO, PHILIP A(NTHONY), b. Bound Brook, N.J, Apr. 2, 27; m. 61. PARASITOLOGY, IMMUNOLOGY. B.Sc, Rutgers Univ, 52, M.Sc, 54; Logan fel, Univ. Chicago, 54-55, Ph.D.(microbiol), 58. Res. assoc. PARASITOL, Univ. Chicago, 58-59; guest investr, ROCKEFELLER UNIV, 59-61, asst. prof, 61-68, ASSOC. PROF, 68- U.S. Pub. Health Serv. res. fel, 59-61, U.S.A.A.F, 45-46, Sgt. Fel. AAAS; Am. Soc. Parasitol; Soc. Protozool. (asst. ed, J. Protozool, 64-65); Am. Soc. Trop. Med. & Hyg. Parasitic hemoflagellates; immunological, biochemical and nutritional aspects of the host-parasite relationship. Address: Dept. of Parasitology, Rockefeller University, New York, NY 10021.

D'ALESSANDRO B(ACIGALUPO), ANTONIO, b. Buenos Aires, Apr. 6, 26; m. 59; c. 2. PARASITOLOGY, TROPICAL MEDICINE. M.D, Buenos Aires, 51; WHO fel, Tulane, 56-57, M.P.H.&T.M, 57, Ph.D, 61. Asst. parasitiol, med. sch, Buenos Aires, 45-51, chief res, 52-55, asst. prof, 56-61, asst. prof. TROP. MED, TULANE UNIV, 61-63, ASSOC. PROF, 63-, univ. fel. trop. med. & pub. health, 57-61. Dazian Found. Med. res. fel, 57-59; liaison officer for Tulane Univ, Int. Center Med. Res. & Training, Cali, Columbia, 61-66, asst. dir, 66-; vis. prof, Univ. Valle, Colombia, 61- Am. Soc. Trop. Med. & Hyg; Royal Soc. Trop. Med. & Hyg; Am. Soc. Parasitol; Argentine Soc. Parasitol; Colombian Soc. Parasitol. & Trop. Med. Parasitology, especially American trypanosomiasis and echinococcosis. Address: Dept. of Tropical Medicine, School of Public Health & Tropical Medicine, Tulane University, 1430 Tulane Ave, New Orleans, LA 70112.

DALEY, DANIEL H, b. Elmira, N.Y, Mar. 9, 20; c. 4. THERMODYNAMICS, AERODYNAMICS. B.S, Purdue, 42; S.M.A.E, Mass. Inst. Tech, 46, 51-52; Ohio State, 47-51. U.S. AIR FORCE, 42-49, 51-, assoc. prof. & acting head mech. eng, U.S. Air Force Inst. Tech, 52-55, atomic test support group, Eniwetok, 55-56, 483rd Troop Carrier Wing, Japan, 56-58, chief aerodyn. sect, B-70 Proj. Off, Wright Patterson Air Force Base, 58-61; assoc. prof. aeronaut, U.S. Air Force Acad, 61-64, prof. & head dept, 64-65; head dept. mech. eng, Pakistan Air Force Col. Aeronaut. Eng, 65-67, PROF. AERONAUT. & HEAD DEPT, U.S. AIR FORCE ACAD, 67- U.S.A.F, 42-49, 51-, Col. Am. Inst. Aeronaut. & Astronaut; Japan Soc. Aeronaut. & Space Sci. Airplane performance; stability and control; thermodynamics; gas dynamics; aerospace propulsion. Address: U.S. Air Force Academy, CO 80840.

DALEY, HENRY O(WEN), JR, b. Quincy, Mass, June 18, 36; m. 61; c. 2. PHYSICAL CHEMISTRY. B.S, Mass. State Col. Bridgewater, 58; Nat. Sci. Found. fel, Boston Col, 60-63, Ph.D.(chem), 64. Res. chemist, Am. Cyanamid Co, 63-64; asst. prof. phys. chem, BRIDGEWATER STATE COL, 64-67, assoc. prof. CHEM, 67-71, PROF, 71- Am. Chem. Soc; Electrochem. Soc. Irreversible thermodynamics in electrochemistry; transport entropies and heat capacities of ions. Address: 115 Robinswood Rd, South Weymouth, MA 02190.

DALEY, JOHN L(INCOLN), b. Bridgeport, Conn, Feb. 12, 08. ELECTRICAL ENGINEERING. B.S, Yale, 29, M.S, 33, Ph.D.(elec. eng), 37. Test engr, Gen. Elec. Co, N.Y. & Mass, 29-31; instr. elec. eng, Yale, 31-40, asst. prof, 40-41; prof, U.S. Naval Acad, 46-68; RETIRED. U.S.N.R, 41-46, Comdr. Electronic circuits and applications; distribution of alternating current in a rectangular conductor. Address: Route 5, Box 54, Annapolis, MD 21401.

DALGARNO, ALEXANDER, b. London, Eng, Jan. 5, 28; m. 57; c. 4. THEORETICAL PHYSICS, ASTROPHYSICS. B.Sc, Univ. Col, London, 47, Ph.D. (physics), 51; hon. A.M, Harvard, 67. PROF. math, Queen's (Belfast), 51-67; ASTRON, HARVARD, 67-, CHMN. DEPT, 71-, acting dir. Harvard Col. Observ, 71-72. Mem, Smithsonian Astrophys. Observ, 67-; comt. atomic & molecular physics, Nat. Acad. Sci. Int. Acad. Quantum Molecular Sci. Prize, 67. Am. Geophys. Union; Am. Astron. Soc; fel. Am. Acad. Arts & Sci; fel. Brit. Inst. Physics & Phys. Soc. Theoretical atomic and molecular physics; planetary atmospheres; quantum chemistry; astrophysics. Address: Harvard College Observatory, Cambridge, MA 02138.

DALGLEISH, ARTHUR E, b. Wilmington, Calif, Aug. 14, 20; m. 43; c. 2. ANATOMY. B.A, La Sierra Col, 45; M.S, Loma Linda, 60; Ph.D.(anat), Stanford, 64. Instr. ANAT, LOMA LINDA UNIV, 64-65, ASST. PROF, 65- Development of the limbs of the mouse; development of the skeletal system. Address: Dept. of Anatomy, Loma Linda University, Loma Linda, CA 92354.

DALGLEISH, ROBERT CAMPBELL, b. Paisley, Scotland, Mar. 31, 40; U.S. citizen; m. 62; c. 2. SYSTEMATIC ENTOMOLOGY. B.S, San Diego State Col, 62; summer fels, Edmund Niles Huyck Preserve 64 & 65; Ph.D.(entom), Cornell Univ, 67. DIR. EDMUND NILES HUYCK PRESERVE, INC, 66-; ASST. PROF. BIOL, UNION COL.(N.Y), 69- Secy-treas, Orgn. of Inland Biol. Field Stas, 69-73. AAAS; Royal Entom. Soc. London; Entom. Soc. Can; Am. Entom. Soc; Ecol. Soc. Am; Am. Inst. Biol. Sci. Taxonomy and biology of biting lice. Address: Dept. of Biological Sciences, Union College, Schenectady, NY 12308.

DALIA, FRANK J, b. New Orleans, La, Nov. 10, 28; m. 51; c. 4. STRUCTURAL ENGINEERING. B.S, Tulane, 49, M.S, 52, Nat. Defense fel, 62, Ph.D.(econs), 64. Civil engr, F.C. Gandolfo & Assocs, 49-52; CONSULT. ENGR, 55-; PROF. CIVIL ENG, TULANE UNIV, 68-, assoc. prof, 60-68. U.S.N. Civil Eng.C, 52-55, Res, 55-70, Comdr.(Ret). Am. Soc. Civil Eng; Soc. Am. Mil. Eng; Am. Soc. Eng. Educ; Nat. Soc. Prof. Eng. Prestressed concrete; engineering economics. Address: Dept. of Civil Engineering, Tulane University, New Orleans, LA 70118.

DALIN, GEORGE A(BBE), b. Worcester, Mass, Oct. 7, 07; m. 39; c. 2. CHEMISTRY. B.S, Harvard, 28; Ph.D.(chem), Columbia, 35. Chief chemist, United Optical Co, 35-36; Plax Corp, 36-43; lab. dir, Stauffer Chem. Co, N.Y, 43-50; chief chem. div, Balco Res. Labs, 50-54, assoc. tech. dir, 54-56; asst. chief res. & develop, Yardney Elec, 56-64, chief electrochem. res, 64-65, dir. res, 65-66; asst. v.pres, Yardney Elec. Corp, 66-70; PATENT AGENT, BLUM, MOSCOVITZ, FRIEDMAN & KAPLAN, N.Y.C, 71- AAAS; Electrochem. Soc; Am. Chem. Soc; fel. Am. Inst. Chem. Chemical patent applications. Address: 821 Jersey Ave, Apt. 5A, Elizabeth, NJ 07202.

DALITSCH, WALTER W(ILLIAM), b. Chicago, Ill, Mar. 10, 98; m. 34; c. 1. SURGERY. D.D.S, Northwestern, 19; B.S, Chicago Collegiate Inst, 24; M.D, Chicago, 25. Asst. prof. med, Illinois, 24-46; ASSOC. PROF. oral surg, Northwestern, 50-55; OTOLARYNGOL, UNIV. ILL. COL. MED, 55- Dir, cleft palate inst, Northwestern, 50-54; attend. surgeon, Cook County Hosp. Dipl, Am. Bd. Oral Surg. U.S.N, 18-19, 42-48, Capt. Am. Med. Asn; Am. Dent. Asn; Am. Soc. Maxillo-Facial Surg; Am. Acad. Facial Plastic & Reconstruct. Surg. Cancer; maxillo-facial surgery. Address: 718 Mountain Rd, Lake Bluff, IL 60044.

DALKE, PAUL D(AVID), b. Ann Arbor, Mich, Sept. 12, 01; m. 27; c. 4. BIOLOGY. B.S.F, Michigan, 25, M.S.F, 28, fel, 31-33; Ph.D.(wildlife mgt), 34. Forester, Leila Arboretum, Mich, 26-27; scaler, Von Platen Fox Co, Iron Mt, 27-28; jr. instr. forest zool, sch. forestry & conserv, Michigan, 28-31; tech. foreman, U.S. Forest Serv, 33-34; dir. game mgt, State Bd. Fisheries & Game, Conn, 34-35; biologist & leader coop wildlife res. unit, Fish & Wildlife Serv, U.S. Dept. Interior, Conn, 35-37, Mo, 37-47, Idaho, 47-67; EMER. PROF. WILDLIFE MGT, UNIV. IDAHO, 67-, prof, 47-67. Meritorious serv. award, U.S. Dept. Interior, 67. Wildlife Soc.(treas, 46-49, v.pres, 52); Wilderness Soc. Forest and range wildlife; upland game bird research; big game research. Address: 642 N. Hayes St, Moscow, ID 83843.

DALKEY, N(ORMAN) C(ROLEE), b. Crowley, Colo, Nov. 22, 15; div; c. 3. MATHEMATICS. A.B, San Jose State Col, 37; Chicago; Ph.D.(philos), California, Los Angeles, 42. Instr. meteorol, California, Los Angeles, 41-42; physicist, radiation lab, California, 43-45; asst. dir. radio prods, Sherman H. Dryer, 45-48; MATHEMATICIAN, RAND CORP, 48- Chief planning anal. team, office of asst. opers. anal, Hqs. U.S. Air Force, 58-59. AAAS; Am. Acad. Polit. & Soc. Sci. Experiments in group judgment; decision theory. Address: Rand Corp, 1700 Main St, Santa Monica, CA 90401.

DALLA, RONALD H(AROLD), b. Silverton, Colo, Mar. 7, 42; m. 62; c. 2. MATHEMATICS, ALGEBRA. B.A, Ft. Lewis Col, 64; M.S, Univ. Wyo, 66, Ph.D.(math), 71. Instr. MATH, Colo. State Univ, 66-67; Univ. Wyo, 67-70; ASST. PROF, EAST. WASH. STATE COL, 70- Am. Math. Soc; Math. Asn. Am. Counting the number of solutions of matric equations over finite fields; finding a canonical form for orthogonal similarity of matrices over finite fields. Address: Dept. of Mathematics, Eastern Washington State College, Cheney, WA 99004.

DALLAIRE, LOUIS, b. Montreal, Que, Apr. 10, 35; m. 61; c. 4. MEDICINE, MEDICAL GENETICS. B.A, Univ. Montreal, 54; M.D, Laval Univ, 60; Mead Johnson fel, McGill Univ, 62-63, Ph.D.(genetics), 64. Mead Johnson scholar. pediat, Montreal Children's Hosp, 60-61, fel, McGill Univ. & Children's Hosp, 61-62; sci. dir. & dir. med. genetics lab, children's serv, Douglas Hosp, Montreal, 64-70; DIR. CLIN. MED. GENETICS, STE. JUSTINE HOSP, 70- Assoc. scientist, Royal Victoria Hosp, Montreal, 69, res. asst, med. genetics dept, 69; consult, med. genetics lab, Douglas Hosp, 70. Am. Soc. Human Genetics; Can. Pediat. Soc; Genetics Soc. Can; Can. Soc. Cell Biol. Role of chromosomal aberrations in familial multiple malformations; relationship between autoimmunity and chromosomal non-disjunction; effects of immunosuppressive drugs on human cells; study on the influence of maternal amino acid levels on the amino acid content of amniotic fluid; research on the mode of inheritance of multiple malformation syndromes. Address: Clinic of Medical Genetics, Ste. Justine Hospital, 3175 Chemin Ste. Catherine, Montreal 250, Que, Can.

DALLA LANA, I(VO) G(IOVANNI), b. Trail, B.C, July 5, 26; m. 56; c. 5. CHEMICAL ENGINEERING. B.A.Sc, British Columbia, 48; M.Sc, Alberta, 53; Ph.D.(chem. eng), Minnesota, 58. Develop. engr, Consol. Mining & Smelting Co, 48-51; instr. CHEM. ENG, UNIV. ALBERTA, 52-53, asst. prof, 58-60, assoc. prof, 60-68, PROF, 68- Summer indust. fel, Ohio Oil Co, 58. Am. Inst. Chem. Eng; fel. Chem. Inst. Can. Kinetics and heterogeneous catalysis; applications of IR spectroscopy; surface chemistry; chemical economics and design. Address: Dept. of Chemical & Petroleum Engineering, University of Alberta, Edmonton, Alberta, Can.

DALLAM, LAWRENCE N(ORWOOD), b. Kansas City, Mo, July 29, 29; m. 53; c. 3. CIVIL ENGINEERING. B.S, Univ. Mo, 54, M.S, 55; Ph.D, Okla. State Univ, 66. Asst. prof. CIVIL ENG, UNIV. MO-COLUMBIA, 57-66, ASSOC. PROF, 66- U.S.M.C, 46-48. Am. Soc. Civil Eng; Am. Concrete Inst; Int. Asn. Bridge & Struct. Eng. Ultimate strength concept in concrete; plastic theory of structural steel; bridge analysis and design; structural mechanics. Address: Dept. of Civil Engineering, University of Missouri-Columbia, Columbia, MO 65201.

DALLAM, RICHARD DUNCAN, b. Kansas City, Mo, Dec. 12, 25; m. 51; c. 2. BIOCHEMISTRY. A.B, Missouri, 48, M.A, 50, Ph.D.(biochem), 52. Res. assoc. BIOCHEM, Missouri, 52-53; instr, SCH. MED, UNIV. LOUISVILLE, 53-55, asst. prof, 55-58, assoc. prof, 58-70, PROF, 70- Estab. investr, Am. Heart Asn, 60-65. U.S.A.A.F, 43-46; Med.Serv.C.Res, 48-63, Capt. Am. Soc. Biol. Chem; Biophys. Soc. Oxidation phosphorylation; chemical fraction of mammalian spermatozoa and cellular particulates; cytochemistry of mitochondria; lipoproteins related to enzyme systems; vitamin K. Address: Dept. of Biochemistry, University of Louisville School of Medicine, Louisville, KY 40208.

DALLDORF, FREDERIC GILBERT, b. New York, N.Y, Mar. 12, 32; m. 56; c. 3. PATHOLOGY. B.A, Bowdoin Col, 54; M.D, Cornell, 58. Intern, PATH, New York Hosp, 58-59, resident, 59-60; N.C. Mem. Hosp, Chapel Hill, 60-63; projs. coord, path. div, U.S. Army Biol. Labs, Ft. Detrick, Md, 63-65; asst. prof. PATH, SCH. MED, UNIV. N.C, CHAPEL HILL, 65-69, ASSOC. PROF, 69- Nat. Insts. Health grant, 60-63; med. exam, Orange County, N.C, 65-; med. dir. blood bank, N.C. Mem. Hosp, 65-66, autopsy serv, 66- Cert. anat. & clin. path, Am. Bd. Path, 65. U.S.A, 63-65, Capt. AAAS; Am. Med. Asn; Am. Asn. Path. & Bact; Am. Soc. Exp. Path. Mechanisms of disease; natural history of rheumatic heart disease; endocrinologic aspects of arteriosclerotic vascular disease in man; mechanisms of shock and death in bacterial septicemias; capillary permeability and bacterial toxins; electron microscopy. Address: Dept. of Pathology, University of North Carolina, Chapel Hill, NC 27514.

DALLDORF, GILBERT, b. Davenport, Iowa, Mar. 12, 00; m. 26; c. 2. PATHOLOGY. B.S, Iowa, 21; M.D, N.Y. Univ, 24; hon. D.Sc, Bowdoin Col, 53; hon. Dr, Freiburg Univ, 57. Fel. path, Pathologisches Inst. Germany, 25-26; asst. pathologist, New York Hosp, 26-27, pathologist, 26-29; instr. path. anat, med. col, Cornell, 26-32; pathologist, Grasslands Hosp, N.Y, 29-45; dir. dept. labs. & res, Westchester Co, 43-45; div. labs. & res, State Dept. Health, N.Y, 45-57; res. dir, Nat. Found, 58; mem. WALKER LAB, SLOAN-KETTERING INST, 59-66, EMER. MEM, 66- Vis. prof, Buffalo, 48-55; prof. path. & bact, Albany Med. Col, 45-57; lectr. Harvard Sch. Pub. Health;

distinguished alumni lectr, N.Y. Univ, 66. Mem. comts. blood & infectious diseases, Nat. Res. Coun; comn. plasma fractionation, Protein Found; Sloan-Kettering Inst; trustee, Dudley Observ; chmn, Brown-Hazen Fund of Res. Corp; mem. comt, virus res, Nat. Found. for Infantile Paralysis. Fisher Memorial Award, Am. Chem. Soc, 55; N.Y. Univ. Col. Med. distinguished serv. award, 56. U.S.A, 18-19. Nat. Acad. Sci; Am. Med. Asn; Asn. Am. Physicians; Am. Pub. Health Asn.(Lasker Award, 59); Soc. Exp. Biol. & Med; Am. Soc. Exp. Path; N.Y. Acad. Med.(medal, 64); Am. Asn. Immunol. Experimental pathology of virus infections, especially tumor viruses and geographic pathology of tumors. Address: Oxford, MD 21654.

DALLEY, JOSEPH W(INTHROP), b. Aberdeen, Idaho, Aug. 12, 18; m. 43; c. 5. ENGINEERING MECHANICS, AERONAUTICAL ENGINEERING. B.S, Texas, 47, M.S, 51, Ph.D.(eng. mech), 59. Stress analyst, McDonnell Aircraft Corp, 47-48; instr. mech. eng, Texas, 48-49, eng. mech, 49-51, asst. prof. aeronaut. eng, 51-59; prof. & head dept, Wichita, 59-60; PROF. eng. mech, UNIV. TEX, ARLINGTON, 60-70, AEROSPACE & MECH. ENG, 70-, head dept. eng. mech, 60-70. Res. engr, defense res. lab, Texas, 48-59; consult, Boeing Aircraft Co, 59-60; LTV Vought Aeronaut, 60- U.S.A.F, 40-46, Lt. Col. Am. Inst. Aeronaut. & Astronaut; Am. Astronaut- Soc; Soc. Exp. Stress Anal; Am. Soc. Eng. Educ. Experimental mechanics; aircraft structures; structural dynamics; aeroelasticity. Address: Dept. of Aerospace & Mechanical Engineering, University of Texas at Arlington, Arlington, TX 76010.

D'ALLI, SEBASTIAN J(OHN), b. Messina, Italy, July 7, 21; U.S. citizen; m. 41; c. 3. AEROSPACE ENGINEERING. B.Ae.E, Polytech. Inst. Brooklyn, 50; M.S, Brevard Col, 61. Test engr, rocket propulsion, N.Am. Aviation, Inc, 51-52; field rep, Northrop Aeronaut. Inst, 52-54; supvr. interceptor missile launching, Boeing Co, 54-59; sect. chief re-entry vehicles, Avco-Res. & Adv. Develop. Div, 59-62; staff scientist, missile opers, Chrysler Corp, 63-68; prog-proj. rep, space div, N.Am. Rockwell Corp, 68-70; PROF. ENGR. SCIENTIST, 70- Summer tech. ed, Thiokol Corp, 52; v.pres. & consult, Tanner Thomson Corp, 59-63; instr. Brevard Eng. Col, 58-67; chmn. dept. space technol, 61-67. U.S.N, 39-45. Liquid propellant and variable thrust rocket propulsion systems; low emission combustion engineering and liquid cooled beryllium mirrors for reflecting high energy laser beams. Address: 2405 Ixora Ave, Sarasota, FL 33580.

DALLMAN, PETER R, b. Berlin, Ger, Nov. 19, 29; U.S. citizen; m. 59; c. 3. PEDIATRICS, HEMATOLOGY. B.A, Dartmouth, 51; Dartmouth Med. Sch, 50-52; M.D, Harvard Med. Sch, 54. Instr. PEDIAT, Stanford, 63-64, asst. prof, 64-68; SCH. MED, UNIV. CALIF, SAN FRANCISCO, 68-70, ASSOC. PROF, 70- Nat. Inst. Health award, 66-; res. biochem, Wenner-Gren. Inst, Stockholm, 67-68. Med.C, U.S.N, 55-57. AAAS; Am. Fedn. Clin. Res; Soc. Develop. Biol; Soc. Pediat. Res; Am. Acad. Pediat. Subcellular manifestations of nutritional deficiency. Address: Dept. of Pediatrics, School of Medicine, University of California, San Francisco, CA 94122.

DALLON, DALE SHERMAN, b. Boulder City, Nev, Aug. 28, 34; m. 57; c. 4. CHEMICAL ENGINEERING. B.S.Ch.E, Utah, 57, Nat. Defense Ed. Act fel, 62, NASA fel, 65, Ph.D.(fluid mech), 67; Colorado, 61-62. Asst. prof. naval sci, Colorado, 60-62; sr. res. chemist, RES. LABS, EASTMAN KODAK CO, 67-70, LAB. HEAD, 70- U.S.N, 57-62, Res, 62-, Lt. Comdr. Non-Newtonian fluid mechanics; diffusional operations; photographic science. Address: Eastman Kodak Co, Research Labs, B-59, Rochester, NY 14650.

DALLOS, PETER J(OHN), b. Budapest, Hungary, Nov. 26, 34; U.S. citizen; m. 61; c. 1. BIOMEDICAL ENGINEERING, BIOPHYSICS. B.S, Ill. Inst. Technol, 58; M.S, Northwest. Univ, 59, Ph.D.(elec. eng), 62. Asst. res. engr, Am. Mach. & Foundry Co, 59, consult. engr, mech. res. div, 59-60; asst. prof. audiol, NORTHWEST. UNIV, 62-65, assoc. prof, 65-69, PROF. AUDIOL. & ELEC. ENG, 69- Mem, comt. res. otolaryngol, Am. Acad. Ophthal. & Otolaryngol, 67-; comt. hearing, bioacoustics & biomech, Nat. Acad. Sci-Nat. Res. Coun, 67-; commun. disorders res. training comt, Nat. Inst. Neurol. Diseases & Stroke, 69-73. AAAS; fel. Acoustical Soc. Am; Biophys. Soc; Am. Speech & Hearing Asn; Inst. Elec. & Electronics Eng. Biophysics and physiology of hearing; physiological acoustics; theory of nonlinear systems, especially physiological control systems; acoustic instrumentation. Address: Auditory Research Lab, Speech Annex Bldg, Northwestern University, Evanston, IL 60201.

DALLY, EDGAR B, b. Akron, Ohio, Mar. 7, 31; m. 54; c. 4. HIGH ENERGY & NUCLEAR PHYSICS. B.A, Miami Univ, 53, M.A, 55; Ph.D.(high energy physics), Stanford Univ, 61. Res. assoc. high energy physics, Hansen Labs, Stanford Univ, 60-61; instr, physics inst, Univ. Zurich, 61-63; res. worker, inst. nuclear res, Univ. Strasbourg, 63-66; res. physicist, high energy physics, Hansen Labs, Stanford Univ, 66-68; staff mem, Stanford Linear Accelerator Ctr, 68-70; ASSOC. PROF. PHYSICS, NAVAL POSTGRAD. SCH, 70- Assoc. prof, Univ. Calif, Los Angeles, 70-71, partic. high energy physics exp. with Am. group, Russian accelerator, Serpukhov, 70-71. AAAS; Am. Phys. Soc. Nuclear and nucleon charge distributions; elementary particle physics. Address: Dept. of Physics, Naval Postgraduate School, Monterey, CA 93940.

DALLY, JAMES WILLIAM, b. Sardis, Ohio, Aug. 2, 29; m. 55; c. 1. ENGINEERING MECHANICS. B.S, Carnegie Inst. Tech, 51, M.S, 53; Ph.D. (mech), Ill. Inst. Tech, 58. Engr. in training, Mesta Mach. Co, 51-53; assoc. res. engr, Armour Res. Found, 53-55, res. eng, 55-57, sr. res. engr, 58; asst. prof. mech, Cornell Univ, 58-61; asst. dir. res, IIT Res. Inst, 61-64, prof. mech, Ill. Inst. Technol, 64-71; PROF. MECH. ENG. & HEAD DEPT, UNIV. MD, COLLEGE PARK, 71- Soc. Exp. Stress Anal.(pres, 71); Am. Soc. Mech. Eng; Am. Soc. Eng. Educ. Experimental stress analysis; photoelasticity; fatigue and fracture. Address: Dept. of Mechanical Engineering, University of Maryland, College Park, MD 20742.

DALLY, JESSE L(eROY), b. Fayette Co, Pa, Sept. 3, 23; m. 50; c. 2. GEOLOGY. B.S, West Virginia, 47; M.A, Columbia, 49, Ph.D.(geol), 56. Instr. geol, West Virginia, 49-56; chief paleontologist, Esso Standard, Inc, Turkey, 56-57, supvr. cent. lab, 57-58; staff geologist, Pan-Am. Petrol. Corp, Standard Oil Co.(Ind), 58-68; V.PRES, DESANA CORP, 68- Coop. geologist, W.Va. Geol. Surv, 53-56. U.S.A, 42-45. Geol. Soc. Am; Soc. Econ.

Paleont. & Mineral; Am. Asn. Petrol. Geol. Stratigraphy; sedimentology; paleontology; basin analysis. Address: 2508 Sinclair Ave, Midland, TX 79701.

DALLYN, STEWART L, b. Detroit, Mich, Sept. 7, 24; m. 50; c. 3. HORTICULTURE. B.S, Alberta, 47; M.S, Cornell, 49, Ph.D.(veg. crops), 50. Asst, Cornell, 47-50; assoc. prof. hort, Louisiana, 50-52; VEG. CROPS, L.I. VEG. RES. FARM, CORNELL UNIV, 52-70, PROF, 70- Am. Soc. Hort. Sci. Truck crops; plant physiology and nutrition; soil science. Address: College of Agriculture, Cornell University, Ithaca, NY 14850.

DALMAN, GARY, b. Grandville, Mich, Oct. 1, 36; m. 58; c. 3. ORGANIC CHEMISTRY. B.A, Hope Col, 58; Am. Chem. Soc. Petrol. Res. Fund fel, Okla. State, 59-62, Ph.D.(reactions of mercaptans), 63. Res. chemist, DOW CHEM. CO, 62-67, proj. leader, benzene res. lab, 67-69, group leader, ORG. CHEM. PROD. RES. DEPT, 69-70, RES. MGR, 70- Am. Chem. Soc. Chemistry of organic sulfur compounds, phenols and phenyl ether. Address: 1911 Laurel Lane, Midland, MI 48640.

DALMAN, G(ISLI) CONRAD, b. Winnipeg, Man, Apr. 7, 17; U.S. citizen; m. 41; c. 4. ELECTRICAL ENGINEERING. B.E.E, City Col. New York, 40; M.E.E, Polytech. Inst. Brooklyn, 47, D.E.E, 49. Lectr. elec. eng, City Col. New York, 52-54; adj. prof, Polytech. Inst. Brooklyn, 53-56; develop. engr. electronic tubes, R.C.A. Victor, 40-45; mem. tech. staff, Bell Tel. Labs, 45-57; sect. head microwave tubes, Sperry Gyroscope Co, 49-56; PROF. ELEC. ENG, CORNELL UNIV, 56- Consult, electronic tube div, Westinghouse Elec. Corp, 56-62; aeronaut. lab, Cornell, 56-57; consult. & founder, Cayuga Assoc. Inc. Cert. Distinction, Polytech Inst. Brooklyn, 57. AAAS; fel. Inst. Elec. & Electronics Eng; Am. Phys. Soc. Electron devices; solid state microwave devices; electrical noise problems; microwave subsystems; electrical engineering education. Address: Dept. of Electrical Engineering, Cornell University, Ithaca, NY 14850.

DALMASSO, AGUSTIN P(ASCUAL), b. Cordoba, Arg, Apr. 15, 33; m. 60; c. 3. MEDICINE, IMMUNOLOGY. M.D, Univ. Cordoba, 58, Dr.Med.S, 63. Instr. physiol, Univ. Cordoba, 58-60; res. fel. immunol, med. sch, Univ. Minn, 60-63; Scripps Clin. & Res. Found, 63-66; head sect. immunol, inst. med. res, Univ. Buenos Aires, 66-70; ASSOC. PROF. LAB. MED, MED. SCH, UNIV. MINN, MINNEAPOLIS, 70- Mem. staff, Vet. Admin. Hosp, Minneapolis, 70- Am. Asn. Immunol; Am. Med. Asn; Arg. Soc. Clin. Invest. Role of the thymus gland in immunology; chemistry and biology of the complement system and of cell membranes. Address: Dept. of Lab. Medicine, University of Minnesota Medical School, Minneapolis, MN 55455.

DALMAT, HERBERT T(HEODORE), b. N.Y.C, June.5, 19; m. 47; c. 2. MEDICAL ENTOMOLOGY. B.S, City Col. New York, 39; M.S, Iowa State, 41; Ph.D, George Washington, 57. Teacher, high sch, N.Y, 38-39; aide, exp. sta, Iowa State, 40-41; instr. med. entom. & parasitol, Cornell, 42-43; scientist, lab. trop. diseases, Nat. Insts. Health, 47-58, lab. trop. virol, 58-60, res. grants coordinator, Nat. Inst. Neurol. Diseases & Blindness, 60-62, asst. chief, Latin Am. Off, Rio De Janeiro, Brazil, 62-65, chief, res. & training grants br, div. air pollution, U.S. Pub. Health Serv, 65-67, off. res. grants, Nat. Ctr. Air Pollution Control, 67-68, spec. asst. to comnr, Nat. Air Pollution Control Admin, U.S. Dept. Health, Educ. & Welfare, 68; dep. chief, health & pop. div, Latin Am. Bur, U.S. DEPT. STATE, 69-71, POP. ADV, BUR. ASIA, AGENCY INT. DEVELOP, 71- Med. entomologist & chief, co-op. onchoceriasis proj, Pan-Am. sanit. Bur-U.S. Pub. Health Serv, Guatemala, Cent. Am, 47-52. Trustee, Thomas Say Found, 58-63. Sanit.C, U.S.A, 44-46, Capt. Entom. Soc. Am; Am. Soc. Parasitol; Am. Soc. Trop. Med. & Hyg; fel. Am. Pub. Health Asn; N.Y. Acad. Sci; Brazilian Entom. Soc. Anthropod transmission of parasitic and virus disease; virus tumors; onchocerciasis; international health and research, especially Latin America; research administration; population; family planning. Address: 3900 Watson Place N.W, Washington, DC 20016.

DALQUEST, WALTER W(OELBER), b. Seattle, Wash, Sept. 11, 17; m. 40; c. 1. VERTEBRATE ZOOLOGY. B.S, Washington (Seattle), 40, M.S, 41; Ph.D.(zool), Louisiana, 51. Res. assoc. mammals, Mus. Natural Hist, Kans, 45-49; fel. zool, Louisiana, 49-51, asst. biochem, 51-52; PROF. BIOL, MIDWEST. UNIV, 52-; AQUATIC BIOLOGIST, STATE GAME & FISH COMN, TEX, 53- Am. Soc. Mammal; Soc. Syst. Zool. Mammals and fishes. Address: Dept. of Biology, Midwestern University, Wichita Falls, TX 76308.

DALRYMPLE, DAVID LAWRENCE, b. Fredericktown, Ohio, Oct. 26, 40. ORGANIC CHEMISTRY. A.B, Col. Wooster, 62; Ph.D.(org. chem), Vermont, 66. Nat. Sci. Found. fel, Harvard, 66-67, res. fel, 67-68; ASST. PROF. CHEM, UNIV. DEL, 68- AAAS; Am. Chem. Soc; Brit. Chem. Soc. Physical-organic chemistry especially small-ring compounds, molecular rearrangements and orbital symmetry theory. Address: Dept. of Chemistry, University of Delaware, Newark, DE 19711.

DALRYMPLE, DESMOND G(RANT), b. Victoria, B.C, May 6, 38; m. 65; c. 1. APPLIED MECHANICS. B.Sc, Manitoba, 60; M.Sc, Saskatchewan, 62; Ph.D. (appl. mech), Manchester Col. Sci. & Tech, Eng, 67. Asst. res officer, Atomic Energy Can. Ltd, 62-64; Sir Charles Renold res. fe   -65; Nat. Res. Coun. Can. spec. res. fel, 65-66; MEM. STAFF, ATOM. ENERGY CAN. LTD, 67- Vibrations; fluid flow; theoretical and experimental stress analysis; explosive metal forming; sealing surface interaction; reactor decontamination. Address: Atomic Energy of Canada Ltd, Chalk River, Ont, Can.

DALRYMPLE, G(ARY) BRENT, b. Alhambra, Calif, May 9, 37; m. 59; c. 3. GEOLOGY. A.B, Occidental, 59; Nat. Sci. Found fels, California, Berkeley, 61-63, Ph.D.(geol), 63. GEOLOGIST, br. theoret. geophys, U.S. GEOL. SURV, 63-70, BR. ISOTOPE GEOL, 70- Coun, Am. Quaternary Asn; prin. investr, Apollo lunar samples. AAAS; Am. Geophys. Union; Geol. Soc. Am. Isotope geology; potassium-argon dating of young volcanic rocks; geochronology of secular variation and of reversals of the earth's magnetic field; thermoluminescence of geologic materials. Address: Branch of Isotope Geology, U. S. Geological Survey, 345 Middlefield Rd, Menlo Park, CA 94025.

DALRYMPLE, GLENN V(OGT), b. Little Rock, Ark, Dec. 28, 34; m. 55; c. 2. MEDICINE, RADIOBIOLOGY. B.S, Arkansas, 56, M.D, 58. Resident RADIOL, med. ctr, Arkansas, 59; asst, med. ctr, Colorado, 61-62, resident, 62, instr, 62-63; asst. prof, sch. med, UNIV. ARK, LITTLE ROCK, 65-68, assoc. prof, DEPTS. RADIOL, BIOMET, PHYSIOL. & BIOPHYS, MED. CTR, 68-71, PROF, 71-, HEAD DIV. NUCLEAR MED. & RADIATION BIOL, 69- Med.C, U.S.A.F, 63-65, Capt. Am. Col. Radiol; Soc. Nuclear Med; Radiation Res. Soc; Am. Statist. Asn; Am. Med. Asn; Biophys. Soc. Aspects of radiobiology dealing with the effects of radiation on mammalian cells in culture; mathematical biology and use of computing machinery in biomedical research; clinical radiology and nuclear medicine. Address: Division of Nuclear Medicine & Radiation Biology, University of Arkansas Medical Center, Little Rock, AR 72201.

DALRYMPLE, HENRY C(OY), b. Albany, N.Y, Jan. 16, 09; m. 42; c. 2. ELECTRICAL ENGINEERING, ACOUSTICS. B.S, Vermont, 30; M.S, Purdue, 38. Res. engr, West. Union Tel. Co, 30-33; field observer seismic surv, Nat. Geophys. Co, 38-39; res. engr, Guided Radio Corp, 40-42, chief engr, 42-46, v.pres. eng, 46-48; lab. supt. noise shock & vibration, eng. exp. sta, U.S. Dept. Navy, 48-57, dept. head appl. physics, 57-61, eng. dept, 61-62, res. coord. elec. marine eng. lab, 62-71; RETIRED. Inst. Elec. & Electronics Eng; Acoustical Soc. Am. Shipboard communications systems and equipment; machinery noise reduction; ship control systems and instrumentation. Address: 4 Sands Ave, Bay Ridge, Annapolis, MD 21403.

DALTER, RAYMOND S(TANLEY), b. Macedonia, Ohio, May 21, 15; m. 39; c. 3. CHEMISTRY. B.A, Ohio State, 39, M.S, 40. Spec. chemist, Carnegie-Ill. Steel Co, Ohio, 40-41; res. engr, Battelle Mem. Inst, 41-48; group leader, Commercial Solvents Corp, 48-53; asst. to assoc. dir, solid state physics div, res. & develop. labs, Franklin Inst, 53-58; staff specialist, Spencer Chem. Co, 58-61; ASST. LAB. DIR, CINCINNATI MILACRON CHEMICALS, INC, 61- Am. Chem. Soc; Soc. Plastics Eng; Am. Soc. Test. & Mat. Metallo-organics; polymerization; heterogeneous catalysis; process development. Address: Cincinnati Milacron Chemicals, Inc, Reading, OH 45215.

DALTON, A(LBERT) J(OSEPH), b. New London, Conn, Nov. 9, 05; m. 30; c. 3. BIOLOGY. B.S, Wesleyan, 27; fel, Harvard, 28-29, A.M, 29, Austin fel, 33-34, Ph.D.(embryol), 34. Asst. biol, Wesleyan, 26-28, tutor, City Col. New York, 29-32; asst. biol, Harvard, 32-33, instr. histol. & embryol, sch. med, Western Reserve, 34-38; lectr. anat, McGill, 38-41; res. fel, NAT. CANCER INST, 41-42, cytologist, 42-46, prin. cytologist, 46-64, chief lab. viral carcinogenesis, 64-67, chief viral biol. br, 67-70, COORD. ULTRASTRUCT. STUDIES, 70- Soc. Exp. Biol. & Med; Am. Asn. Anat; Am. Asn. Cancer Res; Am. Soc. Exp. Path; Electron Micros. Soc. Am. Virology; cytogenesis; cytopathology of neoplasio; chemical cytology; electron microscopy. Address: National Cancer Institute, Bethesda, MD 20014.

DALTON, CECILE K(APLAN), b. Chicago, Ill, Nov. 29, 36; m. 58; c. 2. ORGANIC CHEMISTRY. B.A, Northwestern, 58; Nat. Sci. Found. fel, California, Los Angeles, 58-59, Du Pont fel, 60-61, Ph.D.(org. chem), 62. Res. assoc. org. chem, Ohio State Univ, 63-65; Univ. Pa, 66-67; VIS. ASST. PROF. CHEM, TEMPLE UNIV, 67- Am. Chem. Soc. Synthesis and chemistry of novel aromatic systems; organic reaction mechanisms. Address: Dept. of Chemistry, Temple University, Philadelphia, PA 19122.

DALTON, CHARLES CHESTER, b. Powersburg, Ky, Feb. 19, 23; m. 52; c. 2. PHYSICS, MATHEMATICS. B.S, Kentucky, 49; M.A, Alabama, 57. Res. engr, Corning Glass Works, 49-50; physicist, Evans Signal Lab, 51-54; Air Force Armament Center, 54-55; supvry. physicist, Ord. Missile Labs, 55-56; supvry. engr, Army Ord. Missile Command, 56-59; physicist, Army Ballistic Missile Agency, 59-60; MARSHALL SPACE FLIGHT CENTER, NASA, 60-62, AEROSPACE ENGR, 62- Mem, Meteoroid Damage Working Group, Marshall Space Flight Center, 61-64, alternate mem, Meteoroid Tech. Adv. Working Group, NASA, 62-66, mem, ad hoc cmt. for prep. of monogr. on meteoroid environ, 66- U.S.N, 44-46. AAAS; Sci. Res. Soc. Am. Meteors and meteoroid technology; hypervelocity impact; solar activity; space environments; systems reliability; error propagation; operations research; infrared image conversion; remote sensing; inertial navigation. Address: 8012 Camille Dr. S.E, Huntsville, AL 35802.

DALTON, C(LARENCE) H(ENRY), b. Jackson, Mo, Jan. 17, 13; m. 53; c. 4. MATHEMATICS. B.S, Southeast Mo. State Col, 35; M.A, Univ. Mich, 40; summers, Univ. Colo, 58, Univ. Mo. & Univ. Southwest. La, 62, Univ. Ark, 65, Pa. State Univ, 69 & Univ. Ore, 71. Coach & head dept. MATH, high sch, 35-41; instr, Kemper Mil. Sch, 41-42; asst. prof, SOUTHEAST MO. STATE COL, 46-64, ASSOC. PROF, 64- U.S.A.F, 42-46, Res, 46-51, Capt. Math. Asn. Am. Computer programming; statistics; history and development of mathematics. Address: 2208 W. Cape Rock Dr, Cape Girardeau, MO 63701.

DALTON, COLIN, b. Hull, Eng, July 19, 36; m. 62; c. 2. BIOCHEMICAL PHARMACOLOGY. B.Sc, Univ. Hull, 60; fel, Kings Col, London, 60-62; Ph.D.(biochem. pharmacol), State Univ. N.Y. Buffalo, 65. Sr. biochemist, HOFFMANN-LA ROCHE INC, 65-70, RES. GROUP CHIEF BIOCHEM. PHARMACOL, 70- Fel. coun. on arteriosclerosis, Am. Heart Asn, 70. AAAS; Am. Soc. Pharmacol. & Exp. Therapeut; Am. Heart Asn. Mechanism of action of anti-hyperlipidemic drugs; effect of drugs on lipid metabolism and liver cell ultrastructure; factors controlling hormone sensitive lipase; automation of analytical biochemistry procedures. Address: Research Division, Hoffman-La Roche Inc, Nutley, NJ 07110.

DALTON, DAVID ROBERT, b. Chicago, Ill, Nov. 16, 36; m. 58. ORGANIC CHEMISTRY. B.A, Northwestern, 57; Ph.D.(org. chem), California, Los Angeles, 62. Res. chemist, Dayton Labs, Monsanto Res. Corp, 62-63; instr. chem. & fel, Ohio State, 64-65; asst. prof. CHEM, TEMPLE UNIV, 65-68, ASSOC. PROF, 68- Nat. Insts. Health fels, 62- Summers, prep. chemist, G.D. Searle & Co, 57, 58. AAAS; Am. Chem. Soc; Brit. Chem. Soc. Isolation, identification and synthesis of natural products. Address: 143 Gulph Hills Rd, Radnor, PA 19087.

DALTON, G(EORGE) RONALD, b. Detroit, Mich, Sept. 28, 32; m. 58; c. 3. NUCLEAR ENGINEERING. B.S, Michigan, 54, Ph.D.(nuclear eng), 60; Oak Ridge Sch. Reactor Tech, 54-55. Asst. prof. NUCLEAR ENG, UNIV. FLA, 60-63, assoc. prof, 63-68, PROF, 68-, acting chmn. dept. nuclear eng. sci, 68-69. Ford Found. eng. resident, atomic power div, Westinghouse Elec. Corp, 65-66. Am. Soc. Eng. Educ; Am. Nuclear Soc. Nuclear systems and numerical analysis; thermonuclear theory and plasmas; neutron transport theory; theory of radiation detection. Address: Dept. of Nuclear Engineering Science, University of Florida, Gainesville, FL 32601.

DALTON, HAROLD R, b. Jersey City, N.J, Jan. 25, 12; m. 59; c. 1. ORGANIC CHEMISTRY, ELECTRONICS. E.E, Polytech. Inst. Brooklyn, 38; Ph.D.(biol), Columbia, 40. PRES, DALTON RES. LABS, 30-; CONSULT, 70- Consult, Int. Tel. & Tel. Corp, 30-45; West. Union Tel. Co, 45-47; Plastic Film Corp, 45-61; Times Facsimile Corp. & Westrex Corp, 45-64; Pervel Corp, 45-48; Johnson & Johnson, 50-54; P.H. Glatfelter Co, 62-63; mem. bd. dir, Patent Equity Corp, 45-60. Am. Chem. Soc; Tech. Asn. Pulp & Paper Indust. Thin films; conductive and photoconductive compounds; transistor elements; lasers; solid state concepts. Address: 931 Rydal Rd, Jenkintown, PA 19046.

DALTON, HARRY P, b. Holyoke, Mass, Sept. 16, 29; m. 53; c. 8. MICROBIOLOGY, BIOCHEMISTRY. A.B, Am. Int. Col, 52; M.S, Massachusetts, 56, Ph.D.(microbiol, biochem), 62. Asst. prof. biochem, Hampden Col. Pharm, 59-62; chief microbiologist & teaching supvr, Holyoke Hosp, Mass, 56-62; Montefiore Hosp, 62-66; ASSOC. PROF CLIN. PATH, MED. COL. VA, 66- Res. grants, 63-71; asst. prof, Med. Col. Va. & dent. sch, Univ. Pittsburgh, 65-66. Med.Serv.C, U.S.A, 52-54. AAAS; Am. Soc. Microbiol; Am. Soc. Med. Technol; Am. Burn Soc; N.Y. Acad. Sci. Medical microbiology; mycoplasma; bacterial L-forms; diagnostics systems for rapid identification. Address: 9500 Tuxford Rd, Richmond, VA 23235.

DALTON, H(OWARD) CLARK, b. Brooklyn, N.Y, Aug. 7, 15; m. 48. EMBRYOLOGY, GENETICS. A.B, Wesleyan, 36, A.M, 37; Victor fel, Stanford, 39-40, Ph.D.(biol), 40. Instr. zool, Rochester, 40-41; biol, Brown, 46-47; asst. prof, Bates Col, 47-48; fel, genetics dept, Carnegie Inst, 48-50; asst. prof. BIOL, Wash. Sq. Col, N.Y. Univ, 50-54, assoc. prof, 54-61, prof. & chmn. dept. univ. col, 61-67; PROF, PA. STATE UNIV, 67- Med.C, 41-42, Sanit.C, 42-44, U.S.A.A.F, 44-45, Capt. Am. Soc. Zool; Soc. Develop. Biol; Am. Asn. Anat; Am. Soc. Nat; Int. Soc. Develop. Biol. Development of pigment patterns, genetic control of pigment development. Address: 316 Hubler Rd, State College, PA 16801.

DALTON, JACK L, b. Hominy, Okla, July 20, 31; m. 53; c. 3. BIOCHEMISTRY, ORGANIC CHEMISTRY. B.S, Chadron State Col, 53; M.S, Kans. State Univ, 58; Nat. Sci. Found. summer grants, Ft. Hays Kans. State Col, 62 & Ore. State Univ, 66. Instr. CHEM, Boise Jr. Col, 58-64; assoc. prof, BOISE STATE COL, 64-70, PROF. & CHMN. DEPT, 71-, acting chmn. dept, 68-70. U.S.A, 53-55. Plant waxes; isolation of natural products. Address: Dept. of Chemistry, Boise State College, 1907 Campus Dr, Boise, ID 83707.

DALTON, J(AMES) CHRISTOPHER, b. Corning, N.Y, Dec. 1, 43; m. 71. ORGANIC CHEMISTRY, PHOTOCHEMISTRY. B.S, Calif. Inst. Technol, 65; Nat. Insts. Health fel, Columbia Univ, 66-70, Ph.D.(chem), 70. ASST. PROF. CHEM, UNIV. ROCHESTER, 70- Am. Chem. Soc; The Chem. Soc. Organic photochemistry; fluorescence and phosphorescence properties of organic compounds. Address: Dept. of Chemistry, University of Rochester, Rochester, NY 14627.

DALTON, JOHN C(HARLES), b. Clintwood, Va, Apr. 11, 31; m. 64; c. 2. ZOOLOGY, PHYSIOLOGY. B.A, Virginia, 51; A.M, Harvard, 52, Ph.D.(biol), 55. Instr. biol, Buffalo, 57-58, asst. prof, 58-61, assoc. prof, 61-62; exec. secy, metab. study sect, div. res. grants, NAT. INSTS. HEALTH, 62-65, asst. chief for rev, res. grants rev. br, 65-70, CHIEF PROG. PLANNING STAFF, OFF. PROG, PLANNING & EVAL, BUR. HEALTH MANPOWER EDUC, 70- With U.S. Pub. Health Serv, 55-57. Am. Soc. Zool. Comparative physiology; neurophysiology. Address: Bureau of Health Manpower Education, National Institutes of Health, Bethesda, MD 20014.

DALTON, LONNIE GENE, b. Carter, Okla, July 20, 34; m. 60; c. 3. GENETICS, AGRONOMY. B.S, Okla. State, 56, M.S, 57; Nat. Cotton Coun. fel. & Ph.D.(genetics), N.C. State, 65. Asst. plant breeding, Okla. State, 57; genetics, N.C. State, 65; plant breeder, PIONEER SORGHUM CO, 65-67, DIR. RES, 67- U.S.M.C, 57-62, Capt. Am. Soc. Agron. Accumulation of knowledge, perfection of skills and development of material that leads to a major advance in commercial sorghum hybrids. Address: P.O. Box 788, Plainview, TX 79072.

DALTON, PATRICK D(ALY), b. Salt Lake City, Utah, Oct. 11, 22; m. 48; c. 3. ECOLOGY, BOTANY. B.S, Arizona State, 49; M.S, Utah State, 51; Nat. Sci. Found. fel, Arizona, 59-60, Ph.D.(plant ecol), 61. Range mgr, Soil Conserv. Serv, U.S. Dept. Agr, Utah, 51-52; Bur. Land Mgt, U.S. Dept. Interior, 52-53; instr, Liahona High Sch, Tonga, 53-55; asst. prof. agr, biol. & phys. sci, Church Col. Hawaii, 55-58; res. assoc. range res, Arizona, 58-61; asst. prof. range mgt, Nevada, Reno, 61-62; dir. range & forest res, UN Korean Upland Proj, 62-63; pres, Latter-day Saint Mission, Tonga, 63-66; PROF. BOTANY, CHURCH COL. HAWAII, 66- U.S.N, 42-45. AAAS; Am. Inst. Biol. Sci; Ecol. Soc. Am; Bot. Soc. Am; Am. Soc. Range Mt. Ecology of Southwestern ranges and Pacific Island. Address: Dept. of Biological Sciences, Church College of Hawaii, Box 46, Laie, Oahu, HI 96762.

DALTON, P(HILIP) B(ENJAMIN), b. New York, N.Y, July 21, 23; m. 44; c. 2. ORGANIC CHEMISTRY. B.A, Illinois, 44; M.S, Columbia, 47. Org. chemist, Sun Chem. Corp, 47-50; tech. engr, Colgate-Palmolive Co, 50-54; develop. engr, Commercial develop. dept, GAF CORP, 54-55, sales engr, acetylene chem. dept, 55-58, mgr, 58-61, mkt. mgr, 61-63, dir. commercial develop, 63-64, v.pres. develop, 64-67, photo & repro. div, 67, EXEC. V.PRES, 67- U.S.N, 43-46, Res, 46-, Lt. Am. Chem. Soc; Soc. Chem. Indust; Commercial Develop. Asn; Am. Inst. Chem. Reppe chemistry; reactions of acetylene and aldehydes under high pressure. Address: GAF Corp, 140 W. 51st St, New York, NY 10020.

DALTON, RICHARD L(EE), b. Wentzville, Mo, Aug. 24, 27; m. 46; c. 5. INORGANIC CHEMISTRY. A.B, Cent. Col.(Mo), 48; M.S, Illinois, 49, Ph.D.

(chem), 51. Res. chemist, indust. & biochem. dept, E.I DU PONT DE NEMOURS & CO, INC, 51-54, res. supvr, 54-65, develop. & serv. rep, 65-66, prod. mgr, 66-68, asst. sales mgr, 68-70, ASST. REGIONAL SALES MGR, 70- U.S.N.R, 45-46. Am. Chem. Soc; Sci. Res. Soc. Am. Inorganic complex compounds; inorganic colloids; analytical and agricultural chemistry. Address: Anvil Hills, R.D. 2, Kennett Square, PA 19348.

DALTON, ROBERT H(ENNAH), b. Christ Church, New Zealand, Oct. 21, 02; nat; m. 36; c. 3. CHEMISTRY. California, 21-22; B.S, Calif. Inst. Tech, 25, fel, 25-28, M.S, 26, Ph.D.(chem), 28. Ramsay fel, Oxford, 29-30; res. chemist, CORNING GLASS WORKS, 30-51, sr. res. assoc, 51-63, mgr. appl. chem. res, 64-66, assoc. dir. CHEM. RES, 66-68, CONSULT, 68- Wetherill medal, Franklin Inst, 53. Am. Chem. Soc.(Sullivan award); fel. Am. Inst. Chem; fel. Am. Ceramic Soc; Brit. Soc. Glass Technol; Franklin Inst. Qualitative analysis; rare elements; activation of molecules by electron impact; chain reactions in gases; glass composition; gases in glass; glass-metal seals; photosensitive glasses; solder glasses. Address: Research Lab, Corning Glass Works, Corning, NY 14830.

DALTON, WILLIAM OWEN, b. Mound City, Ill, Dec. 29, 35; m. 63; c. 1. PHYSICAL & COLLOID CHEMISTRY. B.S, Illinois, 61, Ph.D.(phys. chem), 66. Assoc. phys. chemist, Eli Lilly & Co, 61-62; sr. res. chemist, MONSANTO CO, Springfield, 66-67, RES. GROUP LEADER PHYS. & COLLOID CHEM, 67- Am. Chem. Soc. Interactions between charged colloidal particles; behavior of polymer blends and composites. Address: 12 Old Orchard Rd, Hampden, MA 01036.

DALUGE, SUSAN MARY, b. Lancaster, Pa, Apr. 8, 42; m. 63. ORGANIC & MEDICINAL CHEMISTRY. B.A, Macalester Col, 64; Nat. Sci. Found. fel, Univ. Minn, Minneapolis, 65-68, Ph.D.(org. chem), 69. RES. SPECIALIST MED. CHEM, UNIV. MINN, MINNEAPOLIS, 69- Am. Chem. Soc. Heterocyclic nitrogen compounds; nucleoside analogs inhibiting protein synthesis; nucleoside antibiotics. Address: Dept. of Medicinal Chemistry, University of Minnesota, Minneapolis, MN 55455.

DALVEN, RICHARD, b. Brooklyn, N.Y, Sept. 3, 31; m. 55. SOLID STATE PHYSICS. A.B, Columbia Univ, 53, A.M, 54; Union Carbide Corp. fel, Mass. Inst. Technol, 56-57, Ph.D.(chem. physics), 58. Mem. res. staff, Raytheon Corp, 58-62; RCA Labs, 62-71; VIS. RES. ASSOC. & LECTR, DEPT. PHYS, UNIV. CALIF, BERKELEY, 69-70, 71- Am. Phys. Soc. Optical and electrical properties of solids; semiconductors, especially with small energy gaps; low temperature studies; theoretical studies of the lead sulfide group of semiconductors. Address: Dept. of Physics, University of California, Berkeley, CA 94720.

DALY, B(ARTHOLOMEW) J(OSEPH), b. Brooklyn, N.Y, Jan. 3, 29; m. 59; c. 4. FLUID DYNAMICS. B.A, Wyoming, 50; M.A, Arizona State, 60. Seismologist, Petty Geophys. Eng. Co, 51-55; geophysicist, South. Geophys. Co, 55-57; party chief, Bible Geophys. Co, 57-59; STAFF MEM. NUMERICAL FLUID DYNAMICS, LOS ALAMOS SCI. LAB, UNIV. CALIF, 60- Numerical techniques for calculating compressible and incompressible fluid dynamics. Address: 533 Todd Loop, Los Alamos, NM 87544.

DALY, DANIEL F(RANCIS), JR, b. Brooklyn, N.Y, Sept. 19, 39. SOLID STATE PHYSICS. B.S, St. Bonaventure Univ, 61; Nat. Sci. Found. fel, Columbia Univ, 61-63, M.A, 63, Raytheon Corp. fel, 64-65, Ph.D.(physics), 66. Res. asst. SOLID STATE PHYSICS, Columbia Radiation Lab, Columbia Univ, 63-65; Purdue Univ, 65-66, res. assoc, 66-68; MEM. TECH. STAFF, BELL TEL. LABS, 68- Am. Phys. Soc; Am. Asn. Physics Teachers. Electron paramagnetic resonance; radiation damage in semiconductors; ion implantation; color centers in alkali halides. Address: Bell Telephone Labs, Whippany Rd, Whippany, NJ 07981.

DALY, DAVID D(eROUEN), b. St. Louis, Mo, Oct. 17, 19; m. 46; c. 4. NEUROLOGY. B.A, Stanford, 40; B.S, Minnesota, 42, B.M, 44, M.D, 45, Ph.D.(neurol), 51. Res. neurol, Minnesota, 45-46; fel. electroencephalog, Montreal Neurol. Inst, 46-47; asst. neurol, Minnesota, 47-48, instr, 48-49, asst. neurol. & electroencephalog, Mayo Clin, 49-51, asst. prof. neurol, Mayo Found, 56-59, assoc. prof, 59-61; chmn, div. neurol, Barrow Neurol. Inst, Ariz, 61-66; prof. NEUROLOGY, UNIV. TEX.(SOUTHWEST) MED. SCH, 66-70, SCOTTISH RITE PROF, 70- Consult, Mayo Clin, 51-61. Dipl, Am. Bd. Psychiat. & Neurol, 51. U.S.A.F, 53-55. Am. Neurol. Asn; fel. Am. Acad. Neurol; Am. Med. Asn; Soc. Clin. Neurol.(pres, 62); Pan-Am. Med. Asn; Am. Electroencephalog. Soc.(pres, 65-66). Electroencephalography; epilepsy; narcolepsy. Address: Dept. of Neurology, University of Texas (Southwestern) Medical School, Dallas, TX 75235.

DALY, DOUGLAS L(OWELL), b. Port Huron, Mich, Oct. 24, 18; m. 52. MATHEMATICS. A.B, Mich. State Normal Col, 41; M.A, Michigan, 45. Teacher, pub. sch, Mich, 41-45; asst. MATH, Indiana, 46; instr, Kentucky, 47-50; Maine, 51; Mo. Sch. Mines, 52-55; asst. prof, Ill. Wesleyan Univ, 56-67; head dept, 56-64; ASST. PROF, OHIO NORTH. UNIV, 67- AAAS; Math. Asn. Am. Analyses; complex variable. Address: 700 N. Main St, Ada, OH 45810.

DALY, F(REDERICK) T(HOMAS), S.J, b. Kansas City, Mo, Apr. 25, 13. MATHEMATICS. B.S, St. Louis, 35, M.S, 38. Instr. MATH, Creighton Prep. Sch, 38-41; lectr, St. Louis, 41-45; instr, Marquette, 49-50; asst. prof, Gonzaga, 52-53; HEAD DEPT, REGIS COL.(COLO), 53-, PROF, 66-, assoc. prof, 59-66. Am. Math. Soc; Math. Asn. Am. Number theory; nonlinear differential equations. Address: Dept. of Mathematics, Regis College, W. 50th & Lowell Blvd, Denver, CO 80221.

DALY, HOWELL V(ANN), b. Dallas, Tex, Oct. 30, 33; m. 53; c. 1. ENTOMOLOGY. B.S, Southern Methodist, 53; M.A, Kansas, 55, Nat. Sci. Found. fels, 55, 57, 58, univ. fel, 56, Ph.D.(entom), 60. Instr. zool, La. State Univ, 59-60; asst. prof. ENTOM, UNIV. CALIF, BERKELEY, 60-66, assoc. prof, 66-71, PROF, 71- Nat. Insts. Health res. grant, 62-67; Nat. Sci. Found. res. grant, 68-71. AAAS; Soc. Study Evolution; Soc. Syst. Zool; Am. Soc. Zool; Entom. Soc. Am. Systematic and evolutionary biology; biosystematics of Apoidea; comparative morphology of Hymenoptera. Address: Division of Entomology, University of California, Berkeley, CA 94720.

DALY, JAMES C(AFFREY), b. Hartford, Conn, June 10, 38; m. 62; c. 4. ELECTRICAL ENGINEERING. B.S, Connecticut, 60; M.E.E, Rensselaer Polytech, 62, Ph.D.(elec. eng), 67. Instr. elec. eng, Rensselaer Polytech, 62-66; mem. tech. staff, Bell Telephone Labs, 66-69; ASST. PROF. ELEC. ENG, UNIV. R.I, 69- Inst. Elec. & Electronics Eng. Optical beam waveguides; electromagnetic wave interactions with solid state plasmas. Address: 61 Central St, Narragansett, RI 02882.

DALY, JAMES WILLIAM, b. Chicago, Ill Jan. 5, 31; m. 53; c. 3. GYNECOLOGY, ONCOLOGY. Univ. Santa Clara, 48-51; M.D, Loyola Univ. Chicago, 55. Intern, St. Mary's Hosp, Gary, Ind, 56; mem. staff obstet. & gynec, U.S. Air Force Hosp, Lockbourne AFB, 57-59, chief prof. serv, 58-59; resident obstet. & gynec, U.S. Air Force Hosp, San Antonio, Tex, 59-62, chief gynec. serv. & training off. residency prog, 63-68; ASSOC. PROF. OBSTET. & GYNEC. & DIR. TUMOR DIV, UNIV. FLA, 68-, CHIEF GYNEC. SERV, 70-; DIR. TUMOR CLIN. & REGISTRY, SHAND'S TEACHING HOSP. & CLINS, 70- Fel. gynec. oncol, Univ. Tex. M.D. Anderson Hosp. & Tumor Inst, 62-63. Dipl, Am. Bd. Obstet. & Gynec, 66. U.S.A.F, 56-68, Maj. Am. Med. Asn; Am. Radium Soc; fel. Am. Col. Obstet. & Gynec; Soc. Gynec. Oncol; Am. Cancer Soc. Clinical research in cancer of the female genitalia. Address: Dept. of Obstetrics & Gynecology, University of Florida College of Medicine, Gainesville, FL 32601.

DALY, JOHN F, b. Jersey City, N.J, June 10, 12; m. 41; c. 1. OTOLARYNGOLOGY. A.B, Fordham, 33; M.D, L.I. Col. Med, 37. DIR. DEPT. OTOLARYNGOL, BELLEVUE HOSP, 47-, PROF. OTOLARYNGOL. & CHMN. DEPT, SCH. MED, N.Y. UNIV, 49-, DIR. OTOLARYNGOL. UNIV. HOSP, 49- Dir, Bellevue Hearing & Speech Center; consult. aural surgeon, N.Y. Eye & Ear Infirmary, 49-; consult, Hackensack Hosp, N.J, 53-; Vet. Admin. Hosp, Manhattan, N.Y, Bergen Pines County Hosp, N.J. & Holy Name Hosp, Teaneck, 54-; St. Albans Naval Hosp, N.Y. & Phelps Mem. Hosp. Asn, Tarrytown, 55-; Brookhaven Mem. Hosp. Asn, Patchogue, 56-; St. Joseph's Hosp, Stamford, Conn, 58-; Greenwich Hosp. Asn, Conn. & Nyack Hosp, N.Y, 59-; Elizabeth A. Horton Mem. Hosp, Middletown, 63-; Columbus Hosp, N.Y; Stamford Hosp, Conn; Speech Rehab. Inst, N.Y; Goldwater Mem. Hosp, N.Y. Mem, bd. dirs, Am. Bd. Otolaryngol; chmn. tech. adv. comt. hearing & speech, Dept. Health, New York; mem. proj. comt, Nat. Inst. Neurol. Diseases & Blindness, 64-70; chmn. sci. rev. comt, Deafness Res. Found, 64-70, mem, 70-; Am. Coun. Otolaryngol. U.S.A.A.F, 42-46. AAAS; fel. Am. Col. Surg; Am. Laryngol, Rhinol. & Otol. Soc; fel. Am. Laryngol. Asn; fel. Am. Acad. Ophthal. & Otolaryngol.(v.pres, 68-69); fel. Am. Otol. Soc; Soc. Univ. Otolaryngol.(v.pres, 63, pres, 66-67); Am. Cancer Soc; Am. Broncho-Esophagol. Asn; Am. Soc. Head & Neck Surg; Am. Col. Chest Physicians; Am. Med. Asn; James Ewing Soc; Pan-Am. Med. Asn. Audiology; otology; laryngology. Address: Postgraduate Medical School, New York University, 566 First Ave, New York, NY 10016.

DALY, JOHN FRANCIS, S.J, b. Kansas City, Mo, Dec. 27, 16. ALGEBRA. A.B, St. Louis, 40, M.S, 43. Teacher, private sch, 43-45; asst. prof. MATH, ST. LOUIS UNIV, 53-64, assoc. prof, 64-70, PROF, 70- Am. Math. Soc; Am. Soc. Eng. Educ; Math. Asn. Am. Modern abstract algebra; topology; algebraic topology; history of mathematics. Address: College of Arts & Sciences, St. Louis University, 221 N. Grand Ave, St. Louis, MO 63103.

DALY, JOHN J(OSEPH), JR, b. St. Paul, Minn, Aug. 7, 26; m. 50; c. 3. ORGANIC CHEMISTRY. B.S, Col. St. Thomas, 50; U.S. Navy fel, Wayne State, 50-51; U.S. Navy fel, Maryland, 51-52, Bakelite fel, 52-53, Du Pont fel, 53-54, Ph.D, 54. Res. chemist, E.I. DU PONT DE NEMOURS & CO, 54-61, develop. specialist, 62-68, tech. assoc, 68-69, MGR. TECH. & MKT. DEVELOP, 69- U.S.N, 44-46. Am. Chem. Soc. Organic intermediates; dyes; textile chemicals; synthetic lubricants and additives; fluorine chemistry and fluorocarbon development; pyrolysis of esters. Address: Organic Chemicals Dept, Freon Products Division, E.I. du Pont de Nemours & Co, Wilmington, DE 19898.

DALY, JOHN M(ATTHEW), b. Lexington, Ky, Aug. 1, 25; m. 53; c. 5. INORGANIC CHEMISTRY. B.S, Xavier (Ohio), 50, M.S, 51; Ph.D.(chem), Notre Dame, 58. Res. & develop, Kaiser-Frazer Corp, 51-52; chemist, E.I. du Pont de Nemours & Co, Charleston, Ind, 52-53; asst. prof. CHEM, BELLARMINE-URSULINE COL, 53-59, assoc. prof, 59-64, PROF, 64-, CHMN. DEPT, 59- U.S.N, 43-46. AAAS; Am. Chem. Soc. Stability of chelates compounds; effect of metal ions on organic reaction mechanisms; pk values or organic acids and bases; benzyne intermediates. Address: Dept. of Chemistry, Bellarmine-Ursuline College, Louisville, KY 40205.

DALY, JOHN WILLIAM, b. Portland, Ore, June 8, 33. ORGANIC CHEMISTRY, BIOCHEMISTRY. B.S, Ore. State Col, 54, Nat. Sci. Found. fel, 54-55, M.A, 56; Nichols & Whitaker fels, Stanford, 56-58, Ph.D.(org. chem), 58. RES. BIOCHEMIST, NAT. INST. ARTHRITIS & METAB. DISEASES, 60- U.S.P.H.S, 58-60, Sr. Asst. Scientist. Am. Chem. Soc. Natural products and structure elucidation; metabolic transformations of catecholamines and other neuroactive compounds. Address: Bldg. 4, National Institutes of Health, Bethesda, MD 20014.

DALY, JOSEPH F(RANCIS), b. Washington, D.C, Sept. 7, 11; m. 37; c. 2. MATHEMATICAL STATISTICS. A.B, Catholic Univ, 33, M.S, 34; Ph.D.(math), Princeton, 39. Instr. math, Princeton, 37-39; Catholic Univ, 39-42; STATISTICIAN, U.S. BUR. CENSUS, 46- U.S.N.R, 42-46. Am. Math. Soc; Math. Asn. Am; Int. Statist. Inst; fel. Am. Statist. Asn; fel. Inst. Math. Statist. Design of sample surveys statistical quality control; differential geometry; unbiased character of likelihood ratio tests for independence in normal systems; application of electronic computers to statistical data processing. Address: Bureau of Census, Dept. of Commerce, Washington, DC 20233.

DALY, J(OSEPH) M(ICHAEL), b. Hoboken, N.J, Apr. 9, 22; m. 51; c. 2. PLANT BIOCHEMISTRY & PHYSIOLOGY. B.S, R.I. State Col, 44; M.S, Minnesota, 47, Ph.D.(plant physiol), 52; Asst. plant path, Minnesota, 44-48, instr, 48-50, res. fel. bot, 50-51, MacMillan res. fel, 51-52; asst. prof. biol, Notre Dame, 52-55; UNIV. NEBR, LINCOLN, 55-57, assoc. prof. bot. & assoc. plant pathologist, exp. sta, 57-63, prof. bot. & biochem, UNIV, 63-66, C. PETRUS PETERSON PROF. BIOCHEM. & NUTRIT, 66- AAAS; Am.

Phytopath. Soc; Am. Soc. Plant Physiol. Biochemistry of disease resistance and microorganisms; biochemistry and physiology of plant diseases. Address: Dept. of Biochemistry & Nutrition, University of Nebraska, Lincoln, NE 68503.

DALY, KEVIN R(ICHARD), b. San Francisco, Calif, May 31, 31; m. 62; c. 1. GENETICS. B.S, California, Davis, 53; Ph.D.(genetics), Cornell, 58. Asst. genetics, Cornell, 54-56; res. fel, U.S. Pub. Health Serv, 58-60; asst. prof. BIOL, SAN FERNANDO VALLEY STATE COL, 60-64, ASSOC. PROF, 64- Soc. Study Evolution; Genetics Soc. Am. Quantitative genetics. Address: Dept. of Biology, San Fernando Valley State College, Northridge, CA 91324.

DALY, LAWRENCE H, b. Ft. Edward, N.Y, Sept. 12, 31; m. 61; c. 1. ANALYTICAL CHEMISTRY. B.A, State Univ. N.Y. Albany, 52, M.A, 53; Ph.D. (anal. chem), Rensselaer Polytech, 57. Asst. prof. CHEM, STATE UNIV. N.Y. ALBANY, 57-58, ASSOC. PROF, 58- Am. Chem. Soc; N.Y. Acad. Sci. Infrared and raman spectroscopy; vibrational assignments and absorption intensities; spectra of metal chelates. Address: Dept. of Chemistry, State University of New York at Albany, Albany, NY 12203.

DALY, MARIE MAYNARD, b. N.Y.C, Apr. 16, 21; m. 61. BIOCHEMISTRY. B.S, Queens Col.(N.Y), 42, fel, 42-43; M.S, N.Y. Univ, 43; Ph.D.(chem), Columbia, 47. Tutor, Queens Col.(N.Y), 43-44; instr, Howard, 47-48; Am. Cancer Soc. fel, Rockefeller Inst, 48-51, asst, 51-55; assoc, Columbia Univ. Res. Serv, Goldwater Mem. Hosp, 55-59; asst. prof. biochem, ALBERT EINSTEIN COL. MED, 60-71, ASSOC. PROF. BIOCHEM. & MED, 71-; CAREER SCIENTIST, HEALTH RES. COUN, CITY OF NEW YORK, 62- Fel. coun. arteriosclerosis, Am. Heart Asn. AAAS; Am. Chem. Soc; fel. N.Y. Acad. Sci; Am. Soc. Biol. Chem. Lipids; cardiovascular diseases. Address: Dept. of Biochemistry, Albert Einstein College of Medicine, Yeshiva University, Bronx, NY 10461.

DALY, P(ATRICK) J(OSEPH), b. Mullingar, Ireland, Feb. 2, 33; m. 62; c. 3. NUCLEAR CHEMISTRY. B.Sc, Nat. Univ. Ireland, 56, M.Sc, 59; D.Phil. (nuclear chem), Oxford, 63. Instr. CHEM, PURDUE, 63-64, asst. prof, 64-70, ASSOC. PROF, 70- Am. Phys. Soc. Nuclear reactions and spectroscopy. Address: Dept. of Chemistry, Purdue University, West Lafayette, IN 47907.

DALY, RICHARD F(ARRELL), b. Boston, Mass, Oct. 15, 26; m. 53; c. 3. PHYSICS. B.S, Bates Col, 48; M.A, Boston, 49; B.B.A, Northeastern, 55. Proj. engr. data processing, Anderson-Nichols & Co, 49-57; proj. mgr. electronic systs, Ramo-Wooldridge Corp, 57-58; chief prog. plans br, electronics res. directorate, Air Force Cambridge Res. Center, 58-59; sr. opers. res. scientist, RAYTHEON CO, 59-60, mgr. systs. requirements dept, 60-62, dir. adv. systs, equip. div, 62-67, prog. mgr, 67-69, DIR. GOVT. MKT, 69- U.S.N.R, 44-46, Ens. AAAS; Am. Phys. Soc; Opers. Res. Soc; Am. Engineering management; microwave optics; optical measuring devices; operations research and systems analysis; problems of research management. Address: Raytheon Co, 141 Spring St, Lexington, MA 02173.

DALY, ROBERT E, b. Cambridge, Mass, Mar. 1, 37; m. 66. MEDICINAL ANALYTICAL CHEMISTRY. B.S, Mass. Col. Pharm, 61, M.S, 63; Ph.D. (med. anal. chem), Purdue, 68. Scientist, WARNER-LAMBERT RES. INST, 67-71, SR. SCIENTIST, 71- Am. Chem. Soc; Am. Pharmaceut. Asn; Acad. Pharmaceut. Sci. Application of electroanalytic and/or spectroscopic methods to analysis of specific medicaments in complex pharmaceutical formulations. Address: 63 Ridge Rd, Dover, NJ 07801.

DALY, ROBERT WARD, Psychiat, Psychoanal, see 12th ed, Soc. & Behav. Vols.

DALY, WALTER J, b. Michigan,City, Ind, Jan. 12, 30; m. 53; c. 2. INTERNAL MEDICINE. A.B, Ind. Univ, 51, M.D, 55. Instr. physiol, IND. UNIV, 55, U.S. Pub. Health Serv. fel, MED, 60-62, instr, 62-63, asst. prof, 63-66, assoc. prof, 66-68, PROF, 68-, CHMN. DEPT, 70- Dipl. pulmonary disease, Am. Bd. Internal Med. Med.C, 57-59, Capt. Fel. Am. Col. Physicians; fel. Am. Col. Cardiol; Am. Soc. Clin. Invest; Am. Clin. & Climat. Asn. Pulmonary and cardiopulmonary physiology. Address: Dept. of Medicine, Indiana University Medical Center, 1100 W. Michigan St, Indianapolis, IN 46200.

DALY, WILLIAM F, b. New York, N.Y, Dec. 16, 28; m. 55; c. 5. MICROBIOLOGY. B.S, Georgetown, 50; Fordham, 53-54. Microbiologist, LEDERLE LABS, AM. CYANAMID CO, PEARL RIVER, N.Y, 54-61, supvr, 61-67, dept. head, 67-70, PROD. SUPT. CLIN. LAB. AIDS & DIAG, 70- Mem, Nat. Comt. Clin. Lab. Standards; Nat. Subcomt. Diag; Pharmaceut. Mfrs. Assocs. U.S.A, 51-53. Tissue Cult. Asn; Soc. Cyrobiol. Development of clinical laboratory aids and diagnostic agents; low temperature preservation of mammalian cells. Address: 87 Melville Rd, Hillsdale, NJ 07642.

DALY, WILLIAM H(OWARD), b. San Francisco, Calif, Jan. 22, 39; m. 60; c. 2. ORGANIC & POLYMER CHEMISTRY. B.Sc, Baldwin-Wallace Col, 60; Ph.D.(org. chem), Polytech. Inst. Brooklyn, 64. Fel. polymer synthesis, Mainz, 64-66; asst. prof. ORG. POLYMER CHEM, LA. STATE UNIV, 66-71, ASSOC. PROF, 71- Am. Chem. Soc; The Chem. Soc. Polyvinyl mercaptan synthesis and autoxidation; modification of polymers with sulfonyl isocyanates; purification of microbial proteins; reactivity of polymeric substrates. Address: Dept. of Chemistry, Louisiana State University, Baton Rouge, LA 70803.

DALZELL, ROBERT C(LINTON), b. Pittsburgh, Pa, Aug. 31, 19; m. 44; c. 3. MEDICAL MICROBIOLOGY, IMMUNOLOGY-SEROLOGY. B.S, Pittsburgh, 41; Hahnemann Med. Col, 41-42; M.S, Pa. State, 56, Ph.D.(microbiol), 57. Chief clin. lab, Army Hosp, Edgewood, Md, 45-48, sci. admin. biol. prod, biol. opers, U.S. Army, 57-58; chief biol. br, Chem. Corps Sch, 58-59, tech. adv, orientation course, Chem, Biol. & Radiol. Weapons, 59-62; asst. prof. microbiol, Morehead State Col, 62-63; asst. lab. mgr, Melpar, Inc, 63-64; res. scientist, Travelers Res. Ctr, Inc, 64-65; assoc. prof. BIOL, KY. WESLEYAN COL, 65-67, PROF, 67- Dipl, Am. Bd. Microbiol; Am. Acad. Microbiol. Chem.C, 42-62, Lt. Col. Am. Soc. Microbiol. Ultrasonic and sonic sound fields; serological studies of plant virus disease; life and medical sciences; immunology; serology. Address: Kentucky Wesleyan College, 3000 Frederica St, Owensboro, KY 42301.

DALZELL, WILLIAM HOWARD, b. Chatham, N.Y, Sept. 6, 36; m. 67; c. 2. CHEMICAL ENGINEERING. B.S, Mass. Inst. Technol, 58, S.M, 60, Sc.D, 65. Ford Found. res. fel, Mass. Inst. Technol, 65-67, asst. prof. chem. eng, 67-70; RES. GROUP LEADER, POLAROID CORP, 70- Vis. lectr. Imp. Col, Univ. London, 68-69. AAAS; Am. Chem. Soc; Am. Inst. Chem. Eng. Combustion; heat transfer; radiative heat transfer, light scattering; soot formation and burn out; photographic films. Address: 300 Old Ocean St, Marshfield, MA 02050.

DALZIEL, CHARLES F(RANCIS), b. San Francisco, Calif, June 6, 04; wid; m. 31, 69; c. 1. ELECTRICITY. B.S, California, 27, M.S, 34, E.E, 35. Testman & student engr, Gen. Elec. Co, 27-29; in charge syst. protection, San Diego Gas & Elec. Co, 29-32; instr, exten. dept, San Diego State Teachers Col, 32; assoc. ELEC. ENG. UNIV. CALIF, BERKELEY, 32-33, instr, 33-38, asst. prof, 38-42, assoc. prof, 42-48, prof, 48-67; EMER. PROF, 67-, supvr. eng. sci. mgt, war training prog, 41-44. Fulbright vis. prof, Galileo Ferraris Nat. Electrotech. Inst, Italy, 51-52. Cmnr, State Bd. Registration Civil & Prfnl. Engrs, Calif, 54, 56. Consult. engr, Kaiser Engrs. Div, Henry J. Kaiser Co; Los Alamos Sci. Lab, N.Mex; Lawrence Radiation Lab; Rucker Co; Atomic Energy Comn, Wash, D.C. Mem, cmt. occup. safety & health, Int. Labor Off, Geneva, 55-58. Del, Gen. Elec. Co. Profs. Conf, 53. Chief tech. aide, Nat. Defense Res. Cmn, Off. Sci. Res. & Develop, 44-45, sr. mem, rev. bd, U.S. Army Engrs, Far East Command, Gen. Hqs, expert witness, Japan, 51. Fel. Inst. Elec. & Electronics Eng.(prize, 51, 59, 60, 69, achievement award, 70); hon. mem. Am. Soc. Safety Eng. Electric shock; electrical safety; electrical hazards; power system stability and protection; causes of industrial short circuits, electrical fires and electrocutions. Address: Dept. of Electrical Engineering, College of Engineering, University of California, Berkeley, CA 94720.

DALZIEL, IAN W(ILLIAM) D(RUMMOND), b. Glasgow, Scotland, Nov. 26, 37; m. 60. STRUCTURAL GEOLOGY. B.Sc, Edinburgh, 59, Ph.D.(geol), 63. Asst. lectr. GEOL, Edinburgh, 59-63; vis. lectr, Wisconsin, 63-64, asst. prof, 64-66; ASSOC. PROF, COLUMBIA UNIV, 66-, MEM. STAFF, LAMONT-DOHERTY GEOL. OBSERV, 68- Co-leader exped. Somerset Island, Arctic Can, 64-65; consult, Que. Cartier Mining Co, 65-; leader expeds, S.Shetland Islands, S.Omchez Islands, Antarctic Peninsula & Tierra del Fuego, 69-; mem. deep sea drilling proj, Joint Oceanog. Insts. Deep Earth Sampling Antarctic Adv. Panel, 71- AAAS; fel. Geol. Soc. Am; fel. Geol. Soc. London; Am. Geophys. Union. Relations of deformation and metamorphism in orogenic belts; development of mountain belts; fault mechanics; stress history of folded rocks; reconstruction of Gondwanaland; development of island arc systems. Address: Lamont-Doherty Geological Observatory, Columbia University, Palisades, NY 10964.

DAM, CECIL F(REDERICK), b. Kalamazoo, Mich, June 30, 23; m. 50; c. 2. PHYSICS. B.A, Kalamazoo Col, 48; M.S, Cornell, 53; Ph.D.(physics), Ohio State, 56. Asst. prof. physics, math, Hamline, 57-58; PHYSICS, CORNELL COL, 58-60, assoc. prof, 60-62, PROF, 63- Resident res. assoc, Argonne Nat. Lab, 65-66. U.S.A.A.F, 43-46, Capt. Am. Asn. Physics Teachers; Am. Phys. Soc; Optical Soc. Am; Soc. Appl. Spectros; Am. Hist. Sci. Soc. X-ray total reflection studies of thin films; infrared studies of molecular spectra. Address: Dept. of Physics, Cornell College, Mt. Vernon, IA 52314.

DAM, RICHARD, b. Kalamazoo, Mich, Sept. 17, 29; m. 59; c. 1. BIOCHEMISTRY, NUTRITION. B.A, Kalamazoo Col, 51; M.S, Cornell, 56, Ph.D.(animal nutrit), 59. Asst. biochemist, UNIV. NEBR, LINCOLN, 58-60, ASST. PROF. BIOCHEM, 60- U.S.A, 52-54, Res, 54-60. AAAS; Am. Chem. Soc; Am. Inst. Nutrit; Am. Soc. Microbiol. Isolation and characterization proteins; protein complexes and interactions; nutritional utilization proteins. Address: Dept. of Biochemistry & Nutrition, University of Nebraska, Lincoln, NE 68503.

DAMADIAN, RAYMOND, b. New York, N.Y, Mar. 16, 36; m. 60; c. 2. BIOCHEMISTRY, BIOPHYSICS. B.S, Wisconsin, 56; M.D, Albert Einstein Col. Med, 60. Res. fel. BIOPHYSICS, Harvard, 63-65; sr. investr, U.S. Air Force Sch. Aerospace Med, 65-67; ASST. PROF, STATE UNIV. N.Y. DOWNSTATE MED. CTR, 67- Health Res. Coun. of City of New York res. grant, 67-69, career investr, 67-72. U.S.A.F, Capt. Am. Chem. Soc; Biophys. Soc; Am. Soc. Microbiol. Biophysical chemistry of alkali cation accumulation in living cells; physical chemistry of the submolecular structure of cells; nuclear magnetic resonance techniques for cancer detection. Address: Dept. of Medicine, State University of New York Downstate Medical Center at Brooklyn, 450 Clarkson Ave, Brooklyn, NY 11203.

DAMAN, ERNEST L, b. Hannover, Germany, Mar. 14, 23; U.S. citizen; m. 45; c. 3. MECHANICAL ENGINEERING. B.M.E, Polytech. Inst. Brooklyn, 43. Develop. engr, FOSTER WHEELER CORP, 46-49, proj. engr, 49-53, res. engr, 53-55, dept. dir. res, 55-59, DIR. RES, 59- Mem. exec. cmt, pressure vessel res. cmt, Welding Res. Coun, 63-; mem. Nat. Res. Coun. C.Eng, U.S.A, 44-46, Res, 46-52, 2nd Lt. Am. Soc. Mech. Eng; Am. Nuclear Soc; Soc. Naval Archit. & Marine Eng; Air Pollution Control Asn; N.Y. Acad. Sci. Heat transfer; fluid flow as applied to power generation equipment; metallurgy and structural analysis as applied to power generation. Address: 180 Lincoln Rd, Westfield, NJ 07090.

DAMANN, KENNETH E(UGENE), b. Castle Rock, Minn, Oct. 10, 15; m. 39; c. 4. BOTANY. B.S, Kent State, 38; M.S, Northwestern, 40, Ph.D.(bot), 43. Asst. bot, Northwestern, 38-43; sanit. engr, City Water Purification Div, Chicago, 43-44, biologist, 44-45, prin. filtration bacteriologist, 45-47; prof. bot, microbiol. & ecol, East. Ill. Univ, 47-66, head dept, 63-66; PROF. BIOL. SCI. & CHMN. DEPT, STATE UNIV. N.Y. COL. BROCKPORT, 66-, PROF. MICROBIOL, UNIV. IFE, NIGERIA, U.S. AGENCY INT. DEVELOP, 71- Consult, U.S. Pub. Health Serv, 49-55; mem, Ohio River Valley Sanit. Comn, 66- Am. Soc. Limnol. & Oceanog; Phycol. Soc. Am; Bot. Soc. Am; Am. Soc. Microbiol. Plankton periodicity; water purification and sanitation; analysis of plankton yields of Lake Michigan. Address: Dept. of Biological Sciences, State University of New York College at Brockport, Brockport, NY 14420.

DAMASK, ARTHUR C(ONSTANTINE), b. Woodstown, N.J, July 28, 24. PHYSICS. B.S, Muhlenberg Col, 49; M.S, Iowa State, 54, U.S. Secy. Army fel, 59-60, Dept. Army award, 61, Ph.D.(physics), 64. Physicist, Frankford Arsenal, 53-65; PROF. PHYSICS, QUEENS COL.(N.Y), 65- Guest scientist, Brookhaven Nat. Lab, 54-65, vis. scientist, 65-70; vis. prof, Am. Univ. Cairo, 70- U.S.A.A.F, 43-46. Fel. Am. Phys. Soc. Metals physics. radiation effects; defects in solids; organic crystals. Address: 29 Brewster Lane, Bellport, NY 11713.

DAMASKUS, CHARLES W(ILLIAM), b. Ill, Oct. 28, 24; m. 49; c. 3. BIOCHEMISTRY, ZOOLOGY. B.A, Valparaiso, 49. Res. chemist, Baxter Labs, 49-51; sr. scientist, Armour Pharmaceut. Co, 51-63; clin. res. scientist, Arnar Stone Labs, Am. Hosp. Supply Corp, 63-66; PRES, ALPAR LABS, INC, 66- U.S.C.G, 42-44; U.S.N, 44-47. Am. Chem. Soc; N.Y. Acad. Sci. Pharmaceutical new product clinical research; pharmaceutical development of layer lyophilized products. Address: Alpar Labs, Inc, P.O. Box 232, La Grange, IL 60525.

D'AMATO, HENRY E(DWARD), b. Shrewsbury, Mass, Oct. 3, 28; m. 53; c. 4. PHARMACOLOGY. A.B, Col. of Holy Cross, 49; M.A, Boston, 51, Ph.D. (physiol), 54. Instr. pharmacol, Tufts, 54-55, asst. prof, 55-59; pharmacologist, Astra Biol. Labs, 59-67, ASSOC. SCI. DIR, ASTRA PHARMACEUT. PROD, INC, 67- Lederle med. faculty award, 56-59. Experimental hypothermia; cardiovascular physiology and pharmacology; antispasmodic, antihistaminic and antiarrhythmic drugs; iron metabolism. Address: Astra Pharmaceutical Products, Inc, 7 Neponset St, Worcester, MA 01606.

D'AMATO, RICHARD JOHN, b. Springfield, Mass, Sept. 24, 40; m. 61; c. 2. PHYSICAL CHEMISTRY. B.A, Am. Int. Col, 62; M.S, Univ. Illinois, Champaign-Urbana, 65, Nat. Insts. Health fel, 68-70, Ph.D.(phys. chem), 71. Res. chemist polymer phys. chem, Monsanto Co, 65-67; SCI. SPECIALIST PHYS. CHEM, SCOTT GRAPHICS, INC, 70- Am. Chem. Soc. High temperature gas phase reaction kinetics; polymer physical chemistry with emphasis on relation between molecular structure and properties; physical chemical aspects of adhesion. Address: Sutphin Research Center, Scott Graphics, Inc, South Hadley, MA 01075.

DAMBERGER, HEINZ H(EINRICH), b. Komotau, Czech, Dec. 15, 33; m. 63; c. 3. GEOLOGY. Vordiplom, Mainz, 56; West Berlin, 56; Edinburgh, 56-57; dipl. geol, Clausthal Tech. Univ, 60, Dr.rer.nat.(geol), 66. Geologist, Saarbergwerke AG, W.Ger, 60-68; ASSOC. GEOLOGIST, ILL. STATE GEOL. SURV, 68- Lectr. geol. & mineral, Sch. Mining Eng, Saarbrücken, 61-68. Geol. Soc. Am; Am. Soc. Test. & Mat; Ger. Geol. Soc; Ger. Geol. Asn. Coal geology, including coal quality, coalification, coal mining geology and coal petrography; classification of coal; microstructure of coal. Address: Illinois State Geological Survey, Urbana, IL 61801.

DAMBORG, MARK J(OHANNES), b. Ft. Dodge, Iowa, Dec. 6, 39; m. 69. ELECTRICAL ENGINEERING. B.S, Iowa State Univ, 62; M.S.E, Univ. Mich, 63, Ph.D.(comput, info. & control eng), 69; Fulbright-Hayes fel, Technol. Univ. Delft, 66-67. Asst. res. engr, systs. eng. lab, Univ. Mich, 65-66, 67-69; ASST. PROF. ELEC. ENG, UNIV. WASH, 69-, Nat. Sci. Found. res. initiation grant, 71-72. AAAS; Inst. Elec. & Electronics Eng. Stability of nonlinear systems; large-scale system simulation and modeling of electrical energy generation and distribution systems. Address: Dept. of Electrical Engineering, University of Washington, Seattle, WA 98105.

D'AMBROSIO, NICHOLAS, b. Fraine, Italy, Mar. 8, 29; U.S. citizen; m. 57; c. 2. PHYSICAL SCIENCE, GEOLOGY. B.A, Montclair State Col, 53, M.A, 58; Sci. Manpower fel, Columbia, 59-60. Teacher, high sch, N.J, 55-58; ASSOC. PROF. ORG. CHEM, GEOL, PHYS. SCI. & ELEM. SCH. SCI, WILLIAM PATERSON COL. N.J, 58- Nat. Sci. Found. chem. summer inst, Montana State, 57. U.S.A, 53-55. Nat. Sci. Teachers Asn; Geol. Soc. Am; Am. Chem. Soc. Development and improvement of college physical science laboratory experiments to stimulate the nonscience students to learn, appreciate and apply the basic scientific ideas of their experiments to related problems. Address: Dept. of Physics & Earth Sciences, William Paterson College of New Jersey, Wayne, NJ 07470.

D'AMBROSIO, UBIRATAN, b. São Paulo, Brazil, Dec. 8, 32; m. 58; c. 2. MATHEMATICS. B.Sc, São Paulo, 54, Ph.D.(math), 63; Italian Govt. fel, Genoa, 61-62. Regente MATH, Faculty Philosophy, São Paulo, 60-64; res. assoc, Brown, 64-65; asst. prof, State Univ. N.Y. Buffalo, 65-66; assoc. prof, Rhode Island, 66-68; ASSOC. PROF. & DIR. GRAD. STUD, STATE UNIV. N.Y. BUFFALO, 68- Am. Math. Soc. study grant, summer seminar space math, Cornell, 63. Am. Math. Soc; Math. Union Italy; Math. Soc. France; London Math. Soc. Existence and regularity problems in the calculus of variations; stability and global properties of dynamical systems and systems with memory. Address: Dept. of Mathematics, State University of New York at Buffalo, Ridge Lea Campus, Amherst, NY 14226.

DAME, DAVID A(LLAN), b. Greenfield, Mass, Oct. 4, 31; m. 51; c. 2. ENTOMOLOGY. A.B, Dartmouth Col, 54; Ph.D.(entom), Massachusetts, 61. RES. ENTOMOLOGIST, INSECTS AFFECTING MAN & ANIMALS LAB, AGR. RES. SERV, U.S. DEPT. AGR, 61- Mem. expert comt. parasitic diseases, WHO; prof. entom, Univ. Fla. U.S.A, 54-56. AAAS; Entom. Soc. Am; Am. Mosquito Control Asn. Control of insects of medical importance involving insect behavior, ecology, chemosterilization, radiosterilization, juvenile hormones and insecticides. Address: Insects Affecting Man Research Lab, P.O. Box 1268, Gainesville, FL 32601.

DAMEROW, RICHARD A(ASEN), b. Thief River Falls, Minn, Sept. 4, 36; m. 57; c. 2. PHYSICS. B.S, Minnesota, 58, M.S, 60, Ph.D.(mass spectros), 63. Mem. staff, SANDIA CORP, 63-71, DIV. SUPVR, 71- AAAS; Am. Phys. Soc; Am. Asn. Physics Teachers. Mass spectroscopy, precision atomic masses; high magnetic fields; nuclear weapon effects. Address: 2924 Espanola N.E, Albuquerque, NM 87110.

DAMES, CHARLOTTE A, b. St. Louis, Mo, May 4, 16. PHYSICAL CHEMISTRY. B.A, Duchesne Col, 41; M.S, Catholic Univ, 49; Ph.D.(chem), Stanford, 54. Assoc. prof. CHEM, BARAT COL. SACRED HEART, 52-59, PROF, 59- Vis. prof, Digby Stuart Col, London, Eng, 69-70. AAAS; Am. Chem. Soc; Am. Asn. Physics Teachers; Am. Phys. Soc; Am. Math. Soc. Chemical kinetics; radiochemistry. Address: Dept. of Chemistry, Barat College of the Sacred Heart, Lake Forest, IL 60045.

DAMIAN, RAYMOND T, b. Philadelphia, Pa, Aug. 11, 34; m. 57; c. 3. PARASITOLOGY, IMMUNOLOGY. B.S, Akron, 56; M.S, Fla. State, 58, Nat. Sci. Found. fel, 59-60, U.S. Pub. Health Serv. fel, 60-62, Ph.D.(parasitol), 62. Res. assoc. parasitol, Fla. State Univ, 62-63; asst. prof. biol, Emory Univ, 63-67; immunologist, SOUTHWEST FOUND. RES. & EDUC, 67-69, ASSOC. FOUND. SCIENTIST, DEPT. IMMUNOL, 67- Med.Serv.C, 54-62, 2nd Lt. AAAS; Am. Soc. Parasitol; Am. Soc. Trop. Med. & Hyg. Immunological parasitology; schistosomiasis; immunology of nonhuman primates. Address: Dept. of Immunology, Southwest Foundation for Research & Education, P.O. Box 28147, San Antonio, TX 78228.

DAMIANO, VICTOR V, b. Philadelphia, Pa, Feb. 4, 25; m. 59. PHYSICAL METALLURGY. B.S, Pennsylvania, 50, M.S, 52, Ph.D.(metall. eng), 61. Res. asst. metall, Pennsylvania, 50-52; metallurgist, Phila. Naval Air Base, 52-53; sr. metallurgist, Burroughs Corp, 53-54, proj. leader magnetism, 54-56; sr. metallurgist, res. lab, Franklin Inst, Pa, 57-65, sr. staff metallurgist, 65-68, prin. scientist, 68-70; LAB. MGR, ALLOY SURFACES CO, 70- U.S.A, 43-45. Am. Inst. Mining, Metall. & Petrol. Eng; Sci. Res. Soc. Am. X-ray diffraction; electron microscopy; magnetism. Address: Alloy Surfaces Co, 100 S. Justison, Wilmington, DE 19899.

D'AMICO, JOHN J, b. Maynard, Ohio, Apr. 24, 15; m. 47; c. 1. ORGANIC CHEMISTRY. B.S, West Virginia, 38, M.S, 40; Navy fel, Texas, 48-50, Ph.D.(chem), 51. Tech. adv. chem. eng, ord. dept, U.S. War Dept, 40-44, materials engr, res. & develop, Qm. Corps, 44-45; pilot plant supvr. chem. eng, U.S. Bur. Mines, 45-47; teaching fel, Texas, 47-48; res. org. chemist, Monsanto Chem. Co, 51-65, scientist org. chem, RES. DEPT, MONSANTO CO, 65-66, adv. scientist, 66-70, SR. SCI. FEL, 70- Am. Chem. Soc; fel. Am. Inst. Chem. Organic chemistry of nitrogen and sulfur; accelerators and vulcanizing agents for rubber; herbicides and fungicides. Address: Research Dept, Monsanto Co, 260 Springside Dr, Akron, OH 44313.

DAMM, CHARLES CONRAD, b. New York, N.Y, Nov. 20, 24; m. 49; c. 2. PHYSICS. B.E.E, Rensselaer Polytech, 45; fel, Brookhaven Nat. Lab, 49-51; Ph.D.(physics), N.Y. Univ, 52. PHYSICIST, Picatinny Arsenal, N.J, 51-54; Brookhaven Nat. Lab, N.Y, 54-56; LAWRENCE LIVERMORE LAB, UNIV. CALIF, 56- U.S.N, 43-46, Lt.(jg), Am. Phys. Soc. Cosmic ray interactions; precision atomic mass measurements; plasma physics as related to controlled fusion research. Address: Lawrence Livermore Lab, University of California, Livermore, CA 94550.

DAMMAN, ANTONI W(ILLEM) H(ERMANUS), b. Utrecht, Netherlands, Apr. 21, 32; Can. citizen; m. 56; c. 2. PLANT ECOLOGY. B.Sc, Wageningen, 53, M.Sc, 56; fel, Lund, 56, univ. fel, Michigan, 62-64, Ph.D, 67. Res. officer, res. br, Newf. dist, Can. Dept. Forestry, 56-65, res. scientist & head tree biol. & land calssification sect, 65-67; ASSOC. PROF. PLANT ECOL, UNIV. CONN, 67- Univ. Conn. Res. Found. grant, 67-70; Nat. Sci. Found. grant, 69-71. Mem, Nat. Adv. Cmt. on Forest Land, Can, 64-67; subcmt. on conserv. of terrestrial ecosysts, Can. Int. Bot. Prog, 66-67. AAAS; Ecol. Soc. Am; Can. Bot. Asn; Can. Inst. Forestry; Can. Soc. Soil Sci; Int. Soc. Plant Geog. & Ecol; Int. Asn. Ecol. Vegetation survey and ecological land classification; soil vegetation relationships in boreal forests; effects of vegetation, especially, ericaceous dwarf shrubs on soil fertility; nutrition and growth of Sphagnum bogs. Address: Biological Sciences Group, Life Sciences Bldg, U-43, University of Connecticut, Storrs, CT 06268.

DAMMANN, ARTHUR ERLE, b. Lincoln, Nebr, Aug. 29, 20; m. 43; c. 3. ZOOLOGY. B.S, Ariz. State Univ, 52; M.S, Univ. Mich, 54, Ph.D.(zool), 61. Assoc. prof. zool, Ariz. State Univ, 55-69; dir. V.I. Ecol Res. Sta, St. John, 69-71; DIR. RES. & FED. GRANTS ADMIN, DEPT. CONSERV. & CULT. AFFAIRS, GOVT. V.I, 71- Asst. dir. poisonous animals res. lab, Ariz. State Univ, 55-61, dir. animal resource ctr, 61-64. U.S.A, 42-45. Am. Soc. Ichthyol. & Herpet. Biogeography and ecology. Address: Dept. of Conservation & Cultural Affairs, Government of the Virgin Islands, St. Thomas, VI 00801.

DAMMANN, JAMES E, b. Irving, Ill, Jan. 15, 34; m. 56; c. 2. COMMUNICATIONS. A.B, Illinois, 56; M.S, Michigan, 58, fel, 58, Ph.D.(commun. sci), 64. Assoc. engr, IBM CORP, N.Y, 59-61, mgr. adv. input-output technol, 61-65, asst. to dir. technol. & eng, 65-68, MACH. TECH. MGR, SDD LAB, BOULDER & ADJ. PROF. LING, UNIV. COLO, BOULDER, 68- Inst. Elec. & Electronics Eng; Acoustical Soc. Am; Ling. Soc. Am. Speech processing, especially speech recognition; general pattern recognition; linguistics; monolithic components; digital tape subsystems; dynamic data displays. Address: 460 College Ave, Boulder, CO 80302.

DAMMANN, J(OHN) FRANCIS, b. Chicago, Ill, Feb. 21, 17; m. 41; c. 4. SURGERY. A.B, Harvard, 41; M.D, Cincinnati, 43. Intern, Evanston Hosp, Ill, 44; researcher & chief resident, Children's Mem. Hosp, Chicago, 44-46, fel. pediat. cardiol, 48; sr. fel, Hopkins Hosp, 49-50; asst. prof. pediat, California, Los Angeles, 50-55; assoc. prof. surg. cardiol, univ. hosp, UNIV. VA, 55-60, surg. cardiol. & pediat, MED. CTR, 60-61, PROF, 61-68, PEDIAT. & BIOMED. ENG, 68-, NAT. INSTS. HEALTH CAREER RES. PROF, 62- Consult, Vet. Admin. Med.C, 46-47, Lt.(jg). AAAS; Am. Med. Asn; Am. Col. Cardiol; Am. Heart Asn; Soc. Pediat. Res. Critical care medicine; pediatric cardiology; postoperative care and monitoring. Address: University of Virginia Medical Center, Charlottesville, VA 22903.

DAMMIN, GUSTAVE J(OHN), b. New York, N.Y, Sept. 17, 11; m. 41; c. 3. MEDICINE, PATHOLOGY. A.B, Cornell, 34, M.D, 38; cert, Havana, 37; hon. M.A, Harvard, 53. Intern med, Hopkins Hosp, 39, asst. res, Peter Bent Brigham Hosp, 40; instr. path, col. physicians & surgeons, Columbia, 41; asst. prof. med. & path, sch. med, Washington (St. Louis), 46-48, assoc. prof, 48-50, prof. PATH. & chmn. dept, 51-52; prof, HARVARD MED. SCH.

53-62, FRIEDMAN PROF, 62-, PATHOLOGIST-IN-CHIEF, PETER BENT BRIGHAM HOSP, 52- Niles lectr, Cornell; Held lectr, Beth Israel Hosp, New York. Pathologist-in-chief, Barnes Hosp, St. Louis, Mo, 51-52. Consult, Surgeon Gen, U.S. Dept. Army, Far East, 56, 64, 66, Europe, 59, 63, 68, 70; Surgeon Gen, U.S. Pub. Health Serv; lab. consult, Off. Civil & Defense Mobilization, 50-60. Mem. cmn. enteric infections, Armed Forces Epidemiol. Bd, 51-, cmn. parasitic diseases, 54-, dir. cmn. parasitic diseases, 59-60, pres, bd, 60-; mem. trop. med. & parasitol. study sect, Nat. Insts. Health, 59-62, mem. cholera adv. comt, 65-; panel, Inst. Defense Anal, 61-62; sci. adv. bd, Armed Forces Inst. Path, 61-; subcomt. geog. path, Nat. Res. Coun, 62-; heart spec. proj. cmt, Nat. Heart Inst, 63-; chmn. Geneva expert cmt. enteric infections, WHO, 63-; mem. sci. adv. cmt, New England Regional Primate Res. Center; mem. bd. dirs, Gorgas Mem. Inst, 67-; mem, Leonard Wood Mem. Adv. Med. Bd, 69- Dipl, Nat. Bd. Med. Exam; dipl, Am. Bd. Path. Med.C.Res, 41-46, Col; Legion of Merit. Asn. Am. Physicians; Am. Asn. Path. & Bact; Am. Soc. Clin. Invest; Am. Soc. Exp. Path; Am. Soc. Trop. Med. & Hyg; N.Y. Acad. Sci; Asn. Mil. Surg. U.S; Infectious Diseases Soc. Am; Int. Acad. Path; hon. mem. Korean Med. Asn; hon. mem. Japanese-Am. Soc. Path; hon. mem. Asn. Mex. Path. Pathogenesis of diffuse vascular diseases; epidemiology of intestinal infections; kidney and other organ transplantation. Address: Dept. of Pathology, Harvard Medical School, Boston, MA 02115.

DAMON, ALBERT, b. Boston, Mass, July 7, 18; m. 52; c. 3. INTERNAL MEDICINE, PHYSICAL ANTHROPOLOGY. A.B, Harvard, 38; Henry fel, Oxford, 39; Soc. Sci. Res. Coun. fel. & Ph.D.(human develop), Chicago, 46; M.D, Harvard Med. Sch, 51. Asst. phys. anthrop, Harvard, 41, 50-51, 57-58; intern internal med, Mass. Gen. Hosp, Boston, 51; asst. physician & asst. res, Presby. Hosp, N.Y, 52-57; asst. prof. med. anthrop, sch. pub. health, HARVARD, 58-60, assoc. prof. epidemiol, 60-64, LECTR. ANTHROP. & EPIDEMIOL, 64-, SR. RES. ASSOC, PEABODY MUS, 68- U.S. Pub. Health Serv. fel, 52-54; Am. Heart Asn. fel, 56-57, estab. investr, 62-67; Guggenheim fel, 69-70. Consult, U.S. Air Force, 58-59; U.S. Pub. Health Serv, 62-; Vet. Admin, 63- U.S.A.F, 42-46, Res, 46-70, Lt. Col.(Ret). AAAS; Am. Asn. Phys. Anthrop; Am. Pub. Health Asn; Brit. Soc. Study Human Biol. Host factors in disease; constitutional medicine and anthropology; occupational anthropology; clinical medicine; human morphology and function; culture and disease; aging; human ecology. Address: Peabody Museum, Harvard University, Cambridge, MA 02138.

DAMON, D(WIGHT) H(ILLS), b. Northampton, Mass, Feb. 2, 31; m. 55; c. 2. PHYSICS. A.B, Amherst Col, 53; M.S, Purdue, 55, Ph.D.(physics), 61. Res. physicist, Westinghouse Res. Labs, 61-70; ASSOC. PROF. PHYSICS, UNIV. CONN, 70- Am. Phys. Soc. Solid state physics, principally in magnetic and transport properties, electrical and thermal conduction, and galvanomagnetic phenomena. Address: Dept. of Physics, University of Connecticut, U-46, Storrs, CT 06268.

DAMON, EDWARD GEORGE, b. Richland, N.Mex, Feb. 21, 27; m. 46; c. 3. PHYSIOLOGY, CYTOGENETICS. B.S, Eastern New Mexico, 50; M.S, Okla. State, 57; Ph.D.(biol. sci), New Mexico, 65. Teacher, high sch, N.Mex, 51-56; instr. res. cytogenetics, Okla. State, 57-58, res. assoc, 60-61; sci. instr, Jimma Agr. Tech. Sch. Ethiopia, 58-60; head sci. dept, high sch, N.Mex, 61-62; RES. BIOLOGIST, LOVELACE FOUND. MED. EDUC. & RES, 62- Med.C, US.A, 46. AAAS; Bot. Soc. Am. Blast biology; physiological effects of air blast; pulmonary physiology; cultivated sorghums of Ethiopia. Address: Lovelace Foundation for Medical Education & Research, 5200 Gibson Blvd. S.E, Albuquerque, NM 87108.

DAMON, EDWARD K(ENNAN), b. Concord, Mass, Jan. 3, 28; m. 50; c. 2. ELECTRICAL ENGINEERING. B.Sc, Bowdoin Col, 49; M.S, Ohio State Univ, 54. Res. assoc. elec. eng, ANTENNA LAB, OHIO STATE UNIV, 50-58, asst. supvr, 58-64, assoc. supvr, 64-67, TECHNICAL DIR, LASERS & OPTICAL PROPAGATION, 67-, ASSOC. PROF. ELEC. ENG, 71- Dir. & treas, Ladar Systs, Inc, 64-70; consult, Data Corp, 64-67; Custom Lasers Inc. & Battelle Mem. Inst, 70- Sr. mem. Inst. Elec. & Electronics Eng; Am. Phys. Soc; Optical Soc. Am. Electrical physics; microwave circuits and antennas; optical masers; nonlinear optical interactions. Address: 2193 Farleigh Rd, Columbus, OH 43221.

DAMON, GLENN H(ERBERT), b. Winnebago, Minn, Nov. 3, 01; m. 32; c. 3. PHYSICAL CHEMISTRY, CHEMICAL ENGINEERING. B.S, Wisconsin, 26, M.S, 27, Ph.D.(phys. chem), 32. Asst, Wisconsin, 26-27, 30-32; instr. chem, Mich. Col. Min. & Tech, 27-30, asst. prof, 32-40, assoc. prof, 40-43; admin. aide & sect. leader, Manhattan Proj, Columbia, 43-45; group leader, Manhattan Proj, Carbide & Carbon Chem. Corp, 45-46; chief jet propulsion br, U.S. Bur. Mines, 46-51, asst. chief, div. explosives tech, 51-60, staff res. coord. explosives, 60-71; RETIRED. Mem, comt. tanker hazards, U.S. Secy. Treas; comt. hazardous mat, Nat. Acad. Sci-U.S. Coast Guard; Fed. Fire Coun; comt. chem. & explosives, Nat. Fire Protection Asn; Interagency Fire Res. Comt. Distinguished Serv. award, U.S. Dept. Interior; tech. comt. serv serv. award, Nat. Fire Protection Asn. Fel. Am. Inst. Chem; Am. Chem. Soc; Am. Inst. Chem. Eng; assoc. fel. Am. Inst. Aeronaut. & Astronaut; Combustion Inst. Chemical engineering; combustion; jet propulsion fuels; explosives; atomic energy diffusion; corrosion; electrochemistry; photochemistry; utilization of industrial wastes. Address: 2445 N. Sycamore St, Arlington, VA 22207.

DAMON, P(AUL) E(DWARD), b. Brooklawn, N.J, Mar. 12, 21; m. 47; c. 2. GEOCHEMISTRY. B.S, Bucknell, 43; M.S, Missouri, 49; Ph.D, Columbia, 57. Asst. prof. physics, Arkansas, 49-54; res. assoc. geol. Lamont Geol. Observ, Columbia, 54-57; assoc. prof. GEOL. & GEOCHRONOLOGY, UNIV. ARIZ, 57-60, PROF, 61- Consult, Isotopes, Inc, 56-57. U.S.N.R, 43-46, Lt. AAAS; Geochem. Soc; Geol. Soc. Am; Am. Geophys. Union. Geology; environmental radioactivity; geologic history; geochemistry. Address: 2321 E. Hawthorne St, Tucson, AZ 85719.

DAMON, RICHARD ALAN, JR, b. Lowell, Mass, June 22, 21; m. 44; c. 1. BIOMETRICS, GENETICS. B.S, Massachusetts, 47; M.S, Minnesota, St. Paul, 49, Ph.D.(animal genetics), 51. Assoc. prof. genetics, La. State, 51-58; biometrician, agr. res. serv, U.S. Dept. Agr, 58-61; UNIV. MASS, AMHERST, 61-63, ASSOC. DIR. RES. BIOMET, AGR. EXP. STA, 63- U.S.A, 43-46, 1st Lt. Biomet Soc; Am. Soc. Animal Sci.(v.pres, 55). Animal genetics; design and analysis of experiments. Address: Room 300B, Stockbridge Hall, University of Massachusetts, Amherst, MA 01002.

DAMON, RICHARD W(INSLOW), b. Concord, Mass, May 14, 23; m. 46; c. 3. SOLID STATE PHYSICS. B.S, Harvard, 44, fel, 46-47, M.A, 47, fel, 49-50, Ph.D.(physics), 52. Asst. appl. physics, Harvard, 50-51; develop. engr, Raytheon Mfg. Co, 48-49; res. assoc. res. lab, Gen. Elec. Co, 51-60; dept. head microwave device develop, Microwave Assocs, 60-62; mem. staff, RES. CTR, SPERRY RAND CORP, 63, dept. head explor. studies, solid state sci, 64-67, assoc. mgr. solid state sci. lab, 67-70, DIR. APPL. PHYSICS LAB, 70- Vis. lectr, Harvard, 61-62; mem. adv. subcomt. electrophys, NASA, 66-71, chmn, 69-71, mem. adv. group electronic mat, 67-71, adv. comt. basic res, 69-71; lectr, Nat. Electronics Conf, 68; mem. adv. panel to electromagnetics div, Nat. Bur. Standards, Nat. Res. Coun, 69-, chmn, 71; nat. microwave lectr, Inst. Elec. & Electronics Eng-Microwave Theory & Tech, 69; lectr, Univ. Mich, summer 70-; mem. U.S. comn, Fr-Int. Sci. Radio Union, 70- U.S.N.R, 43-46, Res, 46-, Lt.(jg). AAAS; fel. Am. Phys. Soc; fel. Inst. Elec. & Electronics Eng. Microwave and optical properties of solids; magnetic resonance; microwave ultrasonics; quantum electronics; photoconductivity. Address: 1623 Main St, Concord, MA 01742.

DAMON, ROBERT A(RTHUR), b. Weston, Ore, July 21, 32; m. 57; c. 3. CHEMICAL ENGINEERING. B.S, Mont. State Col, 55, fel, 55-58, M.S, 59, Ph.D.(chem. eng), 61. Eng.aide, U.S. Bur. Reclamation, 52-53; asst. engr, Shell Oil Co, 54; asst. instr. math, 56-58; asst. prof. chem. eng, Arizona, 59-63; SR. RES. ENGR, CENT. RES. DIV, CROWN ZELLERBACH CORP, 63- Res. fel, 55-58. Am. Inst. Chem. Eng; Am. Chem. Soc. Exploratory and process research in pulp, paper and wood-chemicals; reaction kinetics; polymer fiber processes. Address: Central Research Division, Crown Zellerbach Corp, Camas, WA 98607.

DAMOUR, PAUL L(AWRENCE), b. Concord, N.H, Jan. 26, 37; m; c. 2. PHYSICAL CHEMISTRY. B.A, St. Anselm's Col, 58; Ph.D.(chem), Catholic Univ, 63. Instr. CHEM, ST. ANSELM'S COL, 62-65, asst. prof, 65-68, ASSOC. PROF, 68- Am. Chem. Soc. Photochemical reduction of coordinated complexes; electrokinetic properties of membrane electrodes. Address: Dept. of Chemistry, St. Anselm's College, Manchester, NH 03102.

DAMOUTH, DAVID E(ARL), b. Flint, Mich, Jan. 27, 37; m. 60; c. 2. PHYSICS. B.S.E.(eng. physics) & B.S.E.(eng. math), Michigan, 59, M.S, 60, Ph.D. (physics), 63. Teaching fel. physics, Univ. Mich, 59-61; res. scientist, XEROX CORP, N.Y, 63-67, sr. scientist, adv. eng. div, 67-68, mgr. recording processes area, info. systs. div, 68-71, MGR, PATTERN RECOG. BR, PALO ALTO RES. CTR, 71- Asn. Comput. Mach. Information recording technology; electronic circuits & systems; imaging systems; pattern recognition. Address: Palo Alto Research Center, Xerox Corp, 3180 Porter Dr, Palo Alto, CA 94304.

DAMPIER, FREDERICK WALTER, b. Winnipeg, Man, Oct. 1, 41. PHYSICAL CHEMISTRY. B.Sc, Manitoba, 62; M.S, Rensselaer Polytech, 64, Ph.D. (phys. chem), 68. Res. fel, Sea Water Conversion Lab, Univ. Calif, Berkeley, 68-70; SCIENTIST, RES. CTR, ESB INC, 70- Am. Chem. Soc; Chem. Inst. Can; Electrochem. Soc. Transport properties of molten salts, nonaqueous solutions and membranes; electrical conductance; batteries. Address: Research Center, ESB, Inc, 19 W. College Ave, Yardley, PA 19067.

DAMRAUER, ROBERT, b. Toledo, Ohio, June 30, 41; m. 65; c. 2. ORGANIC & ORGANOMETALLIC CHEMISTRY. Nat. Insts. Health fel, Mass. Inst. Technol, 64-68, Ph.D.(org. chem), 68. ASST. PROF. CHEM, UNIV. COLO, DENVER, 68- Nat. Sci. Found. fel, Harvard, 68-69. AAAS; Am. Chem. Soc. Organometallics of the main group; configurational stability of nitrogen; organometallic systems; organosilicon chemistry. Address: Dept. of Chemistry, University of Colorado, 1100 14th St, Denver, CO 80202.

DAMRON, BOBBY LEON, b. Ocala, Fla, Nov. 6, 41; m. 68. POULTRY NUTRITION. B.S.A, Florida, 63, M.S.A, 64, Ph.D.(animal sci), 68. Res. assoc. POULTRY NUTRIT, UNIV. FLA, 66-68, ASST. PROF, 68- Poultry Sci. Asn. Mineral interrelationships and requirements of chicks, broilers and laying hens; amino acid and energy requirements of laying hens; evaluation of various feed additives and nutrient sources. Address: Dept. of Poultry Science, University of Florida, Gainesville, FL 32601.

DAMRON, HARRY F(LETCHER), b. Hinton, W.Va, Sept. 15; m. 64; c. 3. PHYSICS, CHEMISTRY. B.A, Marshall Col, 40. Physicist, Ships Degaussing & Navig. equipment, U.S. Navy, 42-46, tech. officer res. projs, Harvard & Mass. Inst. Tech, 46-47; head navig. instrument design br, Bur. Ships, 47-56; coordinator navig. develop. & applied res, Off. Naval Res, 56-59, tech. adv. navig. & guidance, Office of the Chief of Naval Opers, 59-64, prog. planner & adminr, surveillance & navigation, OFF. OF THE CHIEF OF NAVAL DEVELOP, 64-66, head advan. concepts br, 66-67, spec. asst. tech. coord. explor. develop. div. & head surveillance, command & control br, 67-70, DEP. DIR. SURVEILLANCE, COMMAND & CONTROL & COMMUN. DIV, 70- All fields of science and engineering associated with surface-aerospace and undersea surveillance, command and control, communications, navigation, countermeasures and astronautics. Address: 7929 Wellington Rd, Alexandria, VA 22308.

DAMSCHRODER, R(UDOLPH) E(VERETT), b. Elmore, Ohio, Oct. 11, 10; m. 38; c. 2. CHEMISTRY. A.B, Hiram Col, 32; M.S, Syracuse, 34; Ph.D. (org. chem), Illinois, 37. Asst. chem, Syracuse, 32-34; Illinois, 34-37; res. chemist, EASTMAN KODAK CO, 37-47, asst. supt. emulsion res. div, 47-55, head div, 55-61, ASST. DIR. RES. LABS, 61- Am. Chem. Soc. Synthetic organic chemistry; photographic emulsions, gelatin and other proteins; derivatives of eight amino quinoline and of coumarone-2. Address: Research Labs, Eastman Kodak Co, 1669 Lake Ave, Rochester, NY 14650.

DAMSTEEGT, VERNON DALE, b. Waupun, Wis, Oct. 19, 36; m. 62; c. 2. PLANT PATHOLOGY. B.A, Cent. Col.(Iowa), 58; Ph.D.(plant path), Washington State, 62. Asst. plant. path, Washington State, 58-62; RES. PLANT PATHOLOGIST, crops div, U.S. Army Biol. Labs, 62-71; U.S. DEPT. AGR, 71- Am. Phytopath. Soc. Inheritance of resistance and pathogenecity; interaction of host and pathogen; epidemiology of virus diseases spread; modes of transmission and other general factors affecting disease severity. Address: Epiphytology Research Lab, Plant Science Research Division, Agricultural Research Service, U.S. Dept. of Agriculture, Frederick, MD 21701.

DAMUSIS, ADOLFAS, b. Toscica, Russia, June 16, 08; nat; m. 37; c. 4. CHEMISTRY. Chem. Eng, Univ. Vytautas the Great (Lithuania), 34; B.S. & M.S, Berlin-Charllot. Tech. Hochschule, Germany, 38, Ph.D.(chem), 40. Asst. chem. tech, Univ. Vytautas the Great (Lithuania), 34-39, assoc. prof tech. silicates, faculty eng, 40-43, dean, 42-43; consult, Lithuanian Dept. Bldg. Materials, 39-42; mem. staff, E. I. du Pont de Nemours & Co, 47-49, Sherwin-Williams Co, 49-57; RES. ASSOC, Wyandotte Chems. Corp, 57-71, BASF WYANDOTTE CORP, 71- Am. Chem. Soc; Soc. Rheol. Silicates; portland cements; adhesives; alumina-iron oxide ratio and shrinkage of portland cements; extender pigments; treatment of carbon blacks; silicate vehicles; amines as curing agents of epoxy-resins; urethane coatings and sealants; polymer research. Address: 25830 Forestview Dr, Southfield, MI 48075.

DANA, MALCOLM N(IVEN), b. Pomfret, Vt, Dec. 8, 22; m. 46; c. 2. HORTICULTURE. B.S, Vermont, 48; M.S, Iowa State Col, 49, Ph.D.(hort), 52. Asst. prof. HORT, UNIV. WIS, MADISON, 52-59, assoc. prof, 59-67, PROF, 67- U.S.A.A.F, 43-46. Am. Soc. Hort. Sci; Weed Sci. Soc. Am; Am. Pomol. Soc. Weed control in cranberries; cultural studies on strawberries. Address: Dept. of Horticulture, University of Wisconsin, Madison, WI 53711.

DANA, STEPHEN W(INCHESTER), b. Kelleys' Island, Ohio, Apr. 10, 20. GEOLOGY. A.B, Oberlin Col, 40; fel, Southern California, 40-42, M.S, 42, fel, Calif. Inst. Tech, 42-44, Ph.D.(geophysics), 44. Vis. lectr, Whittier Col, 41-42; computer, seismic surv. div, Shell Oil Co. Calif, 42, geophysicist, 45; technologist, exploitation eng. div, Shell Oil Co, Los Angeles, 44-45; assoc. prof. GEOL, UNIV. REDLANDS, 45-48, 49-53, PROF, 53- Geologist, U.S. Geol. Surv, 48-49, consult, 49-; res. geophysicist, United Geophys. Soc, Inc, 49-53; consult. geologist, S.Calif. Edison Co, 57- Fel. Geol. Soc. Am; Am. Geophys. Union; Soc. Explor. Geophys; Am. Asn. Petrol. Geol; Seismol. Soc. Am. Seismology; core analysis; petroleum engineering; sedimentation; refinement of field techniques of electrical, gravitational and magnetic prospecting; structural geology. Address: Dept. of Geology, University of Redlands, Redlands, CA 92373.

DANARD, MAURICE BEVERLEY, b. Flin Flon, Man, Nov. 21, 34; m. 59; c. 2. METEOROLOGY. B.A.Sc, British Columbia, 57; M.A, Toronto, 59; Ph.D. (meteorol), Chicago, 63. Weather forecaster & analyst, Can. Meteorol. Serv, 58-61, res. meteorologist, 61-66; Meteorol. Int. Inc, 66-67; ASSOC. PROF. METEOROL, U.S. Naval Postgrad. Sch, 67-68; UNIV. WATERLOO, 68- Can. Meteorol. Soc; Am. Meteorol. Soc; Royal Meteorol. Soc. Numerical methods of analysis and prediction of weather systems using electronic computers. Address: Dept. of Mechanical Engineering, University of Waterloo, Waterloo, Ont, Can.

DANBERG, JAMES E(DWARD), b. New Haven, Conn, Oct. 13, 27; m. 53; c. 5. AERONAUTICAL ENGINEERING. B.A.E, Catholic Univ, 49, M.A.E, 52, D.E, 64. Aeronaut. engr, field eval. div, U.S. Naval Ord. Lab, 51-55, aeronaut. res. engr, spec. problems br, aerophys. div, 55-56, hypersonics group, 56-60, chief, 60-62; prog. mgr, fluid physics br, res. div, off. adv. res. & tech, Hqs, NASA, 62-67; ASSOC. PROF. AERONAUT. ENG, UNIV. DEL, 67-, ASSOC. DEAN COL. ENG, 70- Lectr, George Washington, 60; mem. heat transfer panel, comt. aeroballistics, Bur. Naval Weapons, 61; exec. secy, res. adv. comt. fluid mech, NASA, 63-67. Am. Inst. Aeronaut. & Astronaut. Hypersonic aerodynamics; viscous flow and aerodynamic heating; heat transfer and skin friction characteristics of turbulent boundary layer including the effects of mass transfer at hypersonic speeds. Address: College of Engineering, University of Delaware, Newark, DE 19711.

DANBY, GORDON T(HOMPSON), b. Can, Nov. 8, 29; m. 62; c. 2. PHYSICS. B.Sc, Carleton (Can), 52; Ph.D.(physics), McGill, 56. MEM. STAFF, BROOKHAVEN NAT. LAB, UPTON, 57- Am. Phys. Soc. Accelerator development; apparatus for high energy physics, especially magnets and beam transport; experiments with neutrinos; magnetic levitation and applications to high speed vehicles. Address: P.O. Box 12, Wading River, NY 11792.

DANBY, JOHN MICHAEL ANTHONY, b. London, Eng, Aug. 5, 29; m. 58; c. 2. ASTRONOMY. B.A, Oxford, 50, M.A, 54; Ph.D.(astron), Manchester, 53. Asst. prof. astron, Minnesota, 57-61; Yale, 61-67; PROF. MATH. & PHYSICS, N.C. STATE UNIV, 67- Consult, Honeywell, Inc, 58-; Air Force Chart & Info. Ctr. Am. Astron. Soc; Int. Astron. Union; fel. Royal Astron. Soc. Celestial mechanics; stellar dynamics. Address: Dept. of Mathematics, North Carolina State University, Raleigh, NC 27607.

DANCE, ELDRED L(EROY), b. Blackfoot, Idaho, Dec. 22, 17; m. 46; c. 3. CHEMISTRY. B.S, California, 43. Res. & develop. chemist & chem. engr, DOW CHEM. CO, WALNUT CREEK, 43-63, sr. res. chem. engr, 63-66, ASSOC. SCIENTIST, 66- Am. Inst. Chem. Eng. Process evaluation and development including unit operations of reactor design; distillation; refrigeration; process control; heat and mass transfer; fluid mixing; production of plastics and polymers; hollow fiber technology. Address: 37 Hornet Ct, Danville, CA 94526.

DANCE, IAN GORDON, b. N.S.W, Australia, Sept. 8, 40; m. 68. INORGANIC CHEMISTRY. B.Sc, Sydney, 61, M.Sc, 63; Ph.D.(chem), Manchester, 66. Anal. Chemist, Dept. Mines, N.S.W, Australia, 61-63; lectr. chem, Manchester, 66; res. assoc, Wisconsin, 66-67; Mass. Inst. Tech, 67-68; ASST. PROF. CHEM, UNIV. WIS, MADISON, 68- Am. Chem. Soc; Brit. Chem. Soc. Transition metal complexes and their electronic structures; models for metalloenzymes. Address: Dept. of Chemistry, University of Wisconsin, Madison, WI 53706.

DANCHIK, RICHARD S, b. Pittsburgh, Pa, Mar. 21, 43. ANALYTICAL CHEMISTRY. B.S, Duquesne Univ, 65; assistantship, Wayne State Univ, 65-68, Ph.D.(anal. chem), 68. RES. SCIENTIST, ALCOA RES. LABS, ALUMINUM CO. AM, 68- Am. Chem. Soc; Sci. Res. Soc. Am. Indirect spectrophotometric and atomic absorption spectrometric methods of analysis; electroanalytical methods of analysis; investigation and application of selective ion electrodes; ultraviolet and visible absorption spectrometry; development of automated process control systems. Address: Alcoa Technical Center, P.O. Box 2970, Pittsburgh, PA 15230.

DANCIS, JOSEPH, b. New York, N.Y, Mar. 19, 16; m. 48; c. 2. MEDICINE, BIOCHEMISTRY. B.A, Columbia Col, 34; M.D, St. Louis, 38. Nat. Res. Found. res. fel, 51-53; Palmer sr. investr, 54-56; PROF. PEDIAT, COL. MED, N.Y. UNIV, 63- Markle scholar, 56-61; res. career investr, Nat. Insts. Health, 61- Borden Award, 71. U.S.A, 41-46. Am. Acad. Pediat; Soc. Pediat. Res; Am. Pediat. Soc; N.Y. Acad. Sci; Harvey Soc. Placental physiology; metabolic errors. Address: New York University Medical Center, 550 First Ave, New York, NY 10016.

DANCY, TERENCE E(RNEST), b. Coulsdon, Surrey, Eng, Mar. 5, 25; nat; m. 47; c. 2. METALLURGY. B.Sc, London, 45, Ph.D.(fuel tech) & Dipl, Imp. Col, 48. Sr. sci. officer, iron making div, Brit. Iron & Steel Res. Asn, 47-53; metall. liaison officer, Brit. Embassy, D.C, 53-54; prin. sci. officer commercial develop, Brit. Iron & Steel Res. Asn, 54-56; res. supvr, Jones & Laughlin Steel Corp, 56-61, asst. dir. res, 61-64, asst. to v.pres. eng. & plant, 64-66, mgr. process eng, 66-71; V.PRES. ENG. & DEVELOP, SIDBEC/DOSCO, 71- U.K. del, Orgn. European Econ. Co-op, France, 50-52, consult, European Productivity Agency, 54; U.K. rep, Comité Int. du Bas Fourneau, Belgium, 50-53. R.N, 44-45. Am. Soc. Metals; Am. Inst. Mining, Metall. & Petrol. Eng.(Hunt Award, 60); Asn. Iron & Steel Eng. (Kelly First Award, 64); Am. Iron & Steel Inst.(medal, 65); Brit. Iron & Steel Inst. Extractive metallurgy and steel processing research; blast furnace; steel refining and primary processing; engineering development. Address: Sidbec/Dosco, 507 Place D'Armes, Montreal 101, Que, Can.

DANDEKAR, BALKRISHNA S, b. Khed-Ratnagiri, India, Sept. 13, 33; m. 59; c. 2. GEOPHYSICS, AERONOMY. B.Sc, Univ. Poona, 53, Hons, 54, M.Sc, 55; Govt. of India scholar, Gujarat Univ, 55-58, Ph.D.(physics), 62. Lectr. physics, Khalsa Col, India, 55; jr. res. asst, Phys. Res. Lab, Ahmedabad, 58-61; prof. & head dept, Maharashtra Educ. Soc. Col, Poona, 61-62; res. physicist, Wentworth Inst, 62-65; sr. res. assoc. aeronomy, Northeast. Univ, 65-68; RES. PHYSICIST, AIR FORCE CAMBRIDGE RES. LAB, 68- Am. Geophys. Union. Optical emissions from the upper atmosphere; polar atmospheric processes. Address: Air Force Cambridge Research Lab, LKA, Hanscom Field, Bedford, MA 01730.

DANDLIKER, W(ALTER) B(EACH), b. Greensburg, Pa, Jan. 24, 18; m. 67; c. 3. BIOCHEMISTRY. B.S, Rollins Col, 40; Ph.D.(bio-org. chem), Calif. Inst. Tech, 45. Asst, Cutter Labs, Calif, 42-44; Calif. Inst. Tech, 44-45, fel. chem, 45-46; California, 46-47, instr, 47-48; Nat. Insts. Health fel, med. sch, Harvard, 48-50, res. assoc, 50-51; asst. prof. biochem, Washington (Seattle), 51-55, assoc. prof, 55-58; Miami (Fla), 58-59, prof, 59-63; HEAD BIOPHYS. CHEM. UNIT, SCRIPPS CLIN. & RES. FOUND, 63- Am. Chem. Soc; Am. Soc. Biol. Chem. Biophysical chemistry; immunochemistry; fluorescence polarization. Address: Dept. of Biochemistry, Scripps Clinic & Research Foundation, La Jolla, CA 92037.

D'ANDREA, CARL LOUIS, b. Brooklyn, N.Y, Aug. 10, 35; m. 64; c. 2. PHYSICAL CHEMISTRY. B.A, N.Y. Univ, 58, Ph.D, 66. Res. chemist, prod. div, E.I. du Pont de Nemours & Co, N.J, 64-66; PROJ. LEADER emulsion & polymer chem, INT. FLAVOR & FRAGRANCES, INC, 66-68, THERMAL ANAL, 69- Am. Chem. Soc; Brit. Chem. Soc. Emulsion and polymer chemistry; thermal analysis. Address: International Flavor & Fragrance, 1515 Highway 36, Union Beach, NJ 07735.

DANDY, JAMES WILLIAM TREVOR, b. Preston, Eng, July 18, 29; m. 59; c. 4. ZOOLOGY, PHYSIOLOGY. B.Sc, Natal, 53, M.Sc, 55; Ph.D.(zool), Toronto, 67. Lectr. ZOOL, Univ. Col. Fort Hare, 56-59; ASST. PROF, UNIV. MAN, 65- Nat. Res. Coun. Can. operating grant, 65-; Fisheries Res. Bd. Can. res. grant, 66- AAAS; Marine Biol. Asn. U.K; Brit. Soc. Exp. Biol; Can. Soc. Zool. Environmental physiology. Address: Dept. of Zoology, University of Manitoba, Winnipeg, Man. Can.

DANE, BENJAMIN; b. Boston, Mass, Nov. 22, 33; m. 57; c. 2. ANIMAL BEHAVIOR, PHYSIOLOGY. A.B, Harvard, 56; Ph.D.(zool), Cornell, 61. Asst. biol, Cornell, 59-60; res. assoc. physiol, med. ctr, N.Y. Univ, 61-62, instr, 62-63; acting asst. prof. animal behavior, Stanford, 63-66; asst. prof. BIOL, TUFTS UNIV, 66-69, ASSOC. PROF, 69- Consult, Santa Rita Tech, Inc, Calif, 64-66. AAAS; Am. Soc. Zool; Animal Behav. Soc; Cooper Ornith Soc; Am. Ornith Union; Wilson Ornith Soc. Address: Dept. of Biology, Tufts University, Medford, MA 02155.

DANE, CHARLES W(ARREN), b. Washington, D.C, Sept. 21, 34; m. 57; c. 2. ECOLOGY, AVIAN PHYSIOLOGY. B.S, Cornell, 56, M.S, 57; Res. Found. fel. & Webster fel, Purdue, Ph.D.(vert. ecol), 65. RES. BIOLOGIST AVIAN PHYSIOL, NORTH. PRAIRIE WILDLIFE RES. CTR, U.S. FISH & WILDLIFE SERV, 64- U.S.A.F, 58-60, Capt. Wildlife Soc; Am. Ornith. Union. Influence of environmental factors on waterfowl reproductive physiology. Address: Northern Prairie Wildlife Research Center, U.S. Fish & Wildlife Service, P.O. Box 1747, Jamestown, ND 58401.

DANEC, JOSEPH C(ARL), b. Columbus, Ohio, Apr. 30, 17; m. 42; c. 3. METALLURGY. B.Sc, Lafayette Col, 39. Res. engr, Battelle Mem. Inst, 39-41; res. lab, NORTON CO, 41-52, asst. to prod. engr, Norton Behr-Manning Overseas, Inc, 52-58, supvr. sales dept, 58-61, chief res. & develop, metal bond unit abrasive div, 61-66; staff engr, Diamond Prods, Norton Int, 66-68; plant mgr, STARLITE INDUSTS, INC, 68-69, V.PRES, 69- Am. Soc. Test. & Mat; Am. Soc. Metals. Electroplated metal-bonded diamond tools & wheels for glass ceramics & electronics industries; rotary, solid state carbide cutting and grinding tools for metal working. Address: Starlite Industries, Inc, 1111 Lancaster Ave, Rosemont, PA 19010.

DANEHY, JAMES P(HILIP), b. Ft. Wayne, Ind, Apr. 27, 12; m. 34; c. 3. ORGANIC CHEMISTRY. B.S, Notre Dame, 33, M.S, 34, Ph.D.(org. chem), 36. Res. chemist, Gen. Chem. Co, New York, 36-38; Harris-Seybold-Potter

Co, Cleveland, 38-42; group leader, Corn Prods. Ref. Co, Argo, Ill, 42-48; keratin group leader, Toni Co, 48-51; asst. prof. liberal educ, UNIV. NOTRE DAME, 51-55, ASSOC. PROF. CHEM, 55- Fulbright lectr, Univ. Col, Cork, 61-62. AAAS; Am. Chem. Soc. Chemistry of lithography; chemistry of vegetable proteins; zein; keratin; organic sulfur chemistry. Address: Dept. of Chemistry, University of Notre Dame, Notre Dame, IN 46617.

DANEK, JOHN JAMES, b. Cracow, Poland, July 23, 17; m. 54; c. 3. GENETICS, TROPICAL, PREVENTIVE & REHABILITATION MEDICINE. B.A, Cracow, 35; M.B, Ch.B. & M.D, Edinburgh, 45; M.P.H, Columbia, 51. Asst. human genetics, inst. animal genetics, Edinburgh, 42-46; res. assoc, col. physicians & surg, Columbia, 48-51; resident phys. med. & rehab, Vet. Admin. Hosp, Bronx, 59-61, staff physiatrist, Montrose, 61-63; dir. rehab. med, asst. health commissioner & consult. human genetics, Nassau County Health Dept, 63-67; LECTR, STATE UNIV. N.Y. DOWNSTATE MED. CTR, 62- Private practice; staff psychiatrist, L.I. Jewish Med. Ctr, 67-70. Med.C, Polish Army, 39-46, Lt. Fel. Am. Pub. Health Asn; Am. Soc. Human Genetics; Am. Cong. Rehab. Med; N.Y. Acad. Sci; Polish Inst. Sci; Royal Soc. Health. Biology, genetics, tropical medicine; preventive, industrial medicine; rehabilitation medicine. Address: 2767 80th Ave, New Hyde Park, NY 11040.

DANELLIS, JOAN VERNIKOS, b. Alexandria, Egypt, May 9, 34; wid; c. 2. PHARMACOLOGY, ENDOCRINOLOGY. B.Pharm, Alexandria, 55; Legg award, London, 58-60, Smith Kline & French fel, 59-60, Ph.D.(pharmacol), 60. Muelhaupt scholar, OHIO STATE UNIV, 60-61, ASST. PROF. PHARMACOL, COL. MED, 61-; RES. ASSOC, AMES RES. CENTER, NASA, 64- Endocrine Soc; Soc. Exp. Biol. & Med; Am. Physiol. Soc; Am. Soc. Pharmacol. & Exp. Therapeut; Int. Brain Res. Orgn. Endocrine pharmacology, particularly the use of drugs in the study of the mechanisms regulating pituitary adrenocorticotropic hormone secretion and the physiological response to stress. Address: Physiology Branch, Ames Research Center, National Aeronautical & Space Administration, Moffett Field, CA 94035.

DANEN, WAYNE C, b. Green Bay, Wis, Dec. 24, 41; m. 64; c. 2. ORGANIC CHEMISTRY. B.A, St. Norbert Col, 64; Nat. Insts. Health fel, Iowa State, 64-67, Ph.D.(org. chem), 67. ASST. PROF. ORG. CHEM, KANS. STATE UNIV, 67- Petrol. Res. Fund grant, 67-69, 71-73. AAAS; Am. Chem. Soc. Organic free radical chemistry; electron spin resonance studies of stable and transient free radicals. Address: Dept. of Chemistry, Kansas State University, Manhattan, KS 66502.

DANES, Z(DENKO) F(RANKENBERGER), b. Prague, Czech, Aug. 25, 20; nat; m. 45; c. 2. GEOPHYSICS. B.S, Charles Univ, Prague, 46, Ph.D. (math), 48, Ph.D.(physics), 49. Asst, State Geophys. Inst, Czech, 46-47; asst. prof, physics inst, Charles Univ, Prague, 48-50; geophys. interpreter, Gulf Res. & Develop. Co, Pa, 53-59; res. engr, Boeing Airplane Co, 59-62; PROF. PHYSICS, UNIV. PUGET SOUND, 62- Vis. prof, Minnesota, 62; consult, various oil & aerospace industs. Am. Geophys. Union; Soc. Explor. Geophys. Gravity; geomagnetism; radiation; constitution of earth; lunar physics; electromagnetic theory. Address: Dept. of Physics, University of Puget Sound, Tacoma WA 98416.

DANESE, ARTHUR E, b. Mt. Morris, N.Y, May 11, 22. MATHEMATICS. A.B, Rochester, 47, Ph.D, 56; A.M, Harvard, 49. Instr. math, Rochester, 48-54; asst. prof, Tennessee, 55; mathematician, Eastman Kodak Co, 55-58; asst. prof. MATH, Union (N.Y), 58-64; assoc. prof, State Univ. N.Y. Buffalo, 64-67; PROF, STATE UNIV. N.Y. COL. FREDONIA, 67- Sig.C, 44-45, 2nd Lt. Am. Math. Soc; Math. Asn. Am. Operational calculus; mathematical analysis; orthogonal polynomials; special functions; inequalities; classical analysis. Address: Dept. of Mathematics, State University of New York College at Fredonia, Fredonia, NY 14063.

DANESH, ANDRE, b. Broudjerd, Iran, Dec. 10, 33; m. 65; c. 1. INORGANIC & ANALYTICAL CHEMISTRY. B.S, Indiana State, 60; Ph.D.(chem), Montpellier, 62. Res. assoc. fel, Colorado, 62-64; res. adv. chem, Paris, 64-66; asst. prof, Univ. Mass, 66-67; pres, Mass. Chem. Lab, Inc, 67-70; PRES, CHEM-Z-CORP, 70- Animal nutrition; detergents; cancer; mercury and lead poisoning. Address: Chem-Z-Corp, 225 Crescent St, Waltham, MA 02154.

DANFORD, MERLIN D(ALE), b. Pleasant City, Ohio, Dec. 5, 26; m. 57; c. 3. PHYSICAL CHEMISTRY. B.S, Ohio, 50; Ph.D.(phys. chem), Purdue, 54. CHEMIST, OAK RIDGE NAT. LAB, 54- U.S.A, 45-46. Am. Chem. Soc; Sci. Res. Soc. Am. X-ray and neutron diffraction studies of structure in liquids; Raman and infrared spectroscopy. Address: 109 Colby Rd, Oak Ridge, TN 37830.

DANFORTH, D(AVID) N(EWTON), b. Evanston, Ill, Aug. 25, 12; m. 38; c. 1. PHYSIOLOGY. B.S, Northwestern, 34, M.S, 36, Ph.D.(physiol), 38, M.D, 39. Asst. physiol, med. sch, Northwestern, 35-38; intern, N.Y. Post-Grad. Med. Sch. & Hosp, Columbia, 38-39, asst. res. OBSTET. & GYNEC, Sloane Hosp. for Women, 39-41, res, 41-44; clin. asst, MED. SCH, NORTHWEST. UNIV, 46-47, asst. prof, 47-52, assoc. prof, 52-59, PROF, 59-, CHMN. DEPT, 65- Chief dept. obstet. & gynec, Evanston Hosp, 47-65; Chicago Wesley Mem. Hosp, 65-71. U.S.N.R, 44-46, Lt. AAAS; Am. Gynec. Soc; Am. Med. Asn; Am. Col. Obstet. & Gynec; Am. Col. Surg; Am. Fertil. Soc. (pres, 63); Soc. Exp. Biol. & Med. Anatomy and physiology of cervix; gynecological pathology. Address: Dept. of Obstetrics & Gynecology, Northwestern University Medical School, 303 E. Chicago Ave, Chicago, IL 60611.

DANFORTH, JOHN P(AUL), b. Massena, N.Y, Feb. 24, 24; m. 47; c. 4. ELECTRICAL ENGINEERING. B.E.E, Clarkson Tech, 47. Elec. designer, U.S. Atomic energy cmn. plants & labs, Giffels & Vallet, Inc, 48-50; elec. engr, Ford Motor Co, 50-52; sr. proj. engr, lab. design, GEN. MOTORS RES. LABS, 52-56, SR. RES. ENGR, isotope lab, 56-66, VEHICLE RES. DEPT, 66-, dir. Gen. Motors training prog, 57-59. U.S.A.A.F, 42-43. Application of computer techniques, physics and biomechanical tolerance to occupant protection aspects of motor vehicle design; research and development of occupant restraint systems; mathematical modeling of occupant dynamics and kinematics. Address: 11134 Charles Dr, Warren, MI 48093.

DANFORTH, JOSEPH D(AVIS), b. Danville, Ill, Mar. 7, 12; m. 40; c. 4. PHYSICAL CHEMISTRY. A.B, Wabash Col, 34; Ph.D.(phys. chem), Purdue, 38. Res. chemist, Universal Oil Prod. Co, 38-47; assoc. prof. CHEM, GRINNELL COL, 47-54, PROF, 54- AAAS; Am. Chem. Soc. Thermal analysis, catalysis; mechanisms and kinetics of solid state decompositions. Address: Dept. of Chemistry, Grinnell College, Grinnell, IA 50112.

DANFORTH, WILLIAM E(DGAR), b. Buffalo, N.Y, June 22, 05; m. 31; c. 2. PHYSICS. B.S, Union (N.Y), 27; M.A, Harvard, 29, Whiting fel, 29-31, Ph.D.(physics), 31. Asst, Gen. Elec. Co, 27-28; asst. to Prof. P.W. Bridgman, Harvard, 31-32; fel, BARTOL RES. FOUND, 32-46, ASST. DIR, SWARTHMORE, 46- Fel. Am. Phys. Soc. Dielectric phenomena; growth of single crystals; cosmic radiation; particle accelerators; physical electronics; surface physics. Address: 1530 Locust St, Philadelphia, PA 19102.

DANFORTH, WILLIAM (FRANK), b. Washington, D.C, Jan. 12, 28. CELL PHYSIOLOGY. A.B, Iowa, 48; A.M, Columbia, 49; Ph.D.(zool), California, Los Angeles, 53. Asst. prof. BIOL, ILL. INST. TECHNOL, 52-58, assoc. prof, 58-63, PROF, 63- AAAS; Am. Soc. Zool; Soc. Protozool. Physiology of protozoa and algae. Address: Dept. of Biology, Illinois Institute of Technology, Chicago, IL 60616.

DANFORTH, WILLIAM H, b. St. Louis, Mo, Apr. 10, 26; m. 50. MEDICINE. A.B, Princeton, 47; M.D, Harvard Med. Sch, 51. Intern, Barnes Hosp, St. Louis, 51-52, asst. res, 54-55, res, 56-57; asst. res, Children's Hosp, St. Louis, 55-56; instr. MED, SCH. MED, WASH. UNIV, 57-58, asst. prof, 58-65, assoc. prof, 65-67, PROF, 67-, CHANCELLOR, UNIV, 71-, fel. cardiol, 57-58, Nat. Insts. Health fel. biochem, 61-63, v.chancellor med. affairs & pres. sch. med. & assoc. hosps, 65-71. Physician, Vet. Admin. Hosp, St. Louis, 58-61; attend. physician, Barnes Hosp, 58- Muscle metabolism and biochemistry. Address: Washington University, Skinker & Forsyth Blvd, St. Louis, MO 63105.

DANG, (PETER) HUNG-CHEN, b. Kwangsi, China, Sept. 7, 18; U.S. citizen; m. 47; c. 4. PHARMACOLOGY, BIOCHEMISTRY. B.S, Nat. Cent. Univ, China, 44; M.S, Mont. State Col, 59; Ph.D.(pharmacol), Chicago, 64. Instr. chem, Pai Sha Col, China, 44-45; teacher, high sch, China, 45-46; res. assoc, Ord. Res. Inst, China, 46-56; asst. biochem, Vet. Res. Lab, Mont, 56-58; pharmacol, Chicago, 58-63; res. assoc, 64; animal nutrit. & disease, Cornell, 64-67; sr. res. chemist, FOOD & DRUG RES. LAB, 67-69, SR. PHARMACOLOGIST & SECT. HEAD, 69- AAAS; sr. mem. Am. Chem. Soc; N.Y. Acad. Sci. Enzymology, toxicity, physiological and pharmacological studies of jack bean urease; urea and ammonia metabolism; relation of nutrition and drugs to disease; studies on antiinflammatory agents, laxative and antispasmotic agents and parasympatholytic agents. Address: Food & Drug Research Labs, Inc, Maurice Ave. & 58th St, Maspeth, NY 11378.

DANGA, F(RITZ), b. St. Petrograd, Russia, Nov. 29, 08; nat; m. 45; c. 2. MICROBIOLOGY, LINGUISTICS. Latvia, 33; Royal Agr. Col. Sweden, 50-51. Analyst, State Chem. & Bact. Lab, Latvia, 40-42; res. asst, microbiol. inst, Royal Agr. Col. Sweden, 45-52; microbiologist, res. dept, Commercial Solvent Co, 52-56; biologist, Lederle Labs, Am. Cyanamid Co, 56-59; chief translator, sci. info. div, Norwich Pharmacal Co, 59-70; STAFF MEM, MED. DOCUMENTATION SECT, COL. PHYSICIANS PHILA, 70- Am. Soc. Microbiol; Soc. Indust. Microbiol; Am. Med. Writers' Asn. Antibiosis; antibiotic producing organisms; antibiotics; antimicrobial chemotherapeutics and linguistics. Address: 150 W. Evergreen Ave, Philadelphia, PA 19118.

DANGEL, HERBERT A(BRAHAM), b. Edon, Ohio, May 25, 97; m. 25; c. 2. MATHEMATICS. M.E, Univ. Cincinnati, 21, 23-30. Designer, Am. Roll. Mills Co, 17-18; Hooven-Owens-Rentschler Co, Ohio, 19-21; Am. Laundry Mach. Co, 21-22; instr. MATH, UNIV. CINCINNATI, 22-26, asst. prof, 27-42, assoc. prof, 43-50, prof, 50-70, dir. admissions, 57-70, EMER. PROF, 70- U.S.A, 17-19. Am. Soc. Eng. Educ. Solid mechanics. Address: Dept. of Mathematic, University of Cincinnati, Cincinnati, OH 45221.

D'ANGELO, HENRY, b. New York, N.Y, Dec. 20, 32; m. 62; c. 4. ELECTRICAL ENGINEERING. B.E.E, City Univ. New York, 55; M.S, Kansas State, 57; Nat. Sci. Found. fel, Wisconsin, 62-63, Ph.D.(elec. eng), 64. Instr, elec. eng, Kansas State, 55-57; engr. navig. systs, Sperry Gyroscope Co. div, Sperry-Rand Co, 57-60; asst. prof. ELEC. ENG, Denver, 60-62, 64-66, assoc. prof, 66-68, prof, 68-69; PROF. & HEAD DEPT, MICH. TECHNOL. UNIV, 69- Nat. Sci. Found. res. grant, 65-67; NASA res. grant, 66-67; vis. prof, dept. math, Morehouse Col, 68-69. Inst. Elec. & Electronics Eng; Am. Soc. Eng. Educ. Operations research; learning-adaptive control systems; linear and nonlinear time-varying systems; systems modeling. Address: Dept. of Electrical Engineering, Michigan Technological University, Houghton, MI 49931.

D'ANGELO, NICOLA, b. Ripatransone, Italy, Jan. 8, 31; U.S. citizen; m. 63. NUCLEAR PHYSICS. D.Sc, Rome, 53, specialization degree, 55; sch. nuclear sci. & eng, Argonne Nat. Lab, 55-56. Res. asst. physics, Rome, 53-54; Ist. Superior Sanità, 54-56; res. assoc, Argonne Nat. Lab, 56-59; res. physicist, Princeton, 59-66; leader plasma group, Danish Atomic Energy Comn, Risø, 66-68; head diag. group, EUROP. SPACE RES. INST, 68-70, DIR, 70- Am. Asn. Phys. Teachers; Am. Phys. Soc; Italian Phys. Soc. Cosmic rays; neutron, nuclear and plasma physics. Address: European Space Research Institute, Frascati, Rome, Italy.

D'ANGELO, SAVINO A(LBERT), b. Jersey City, N.J, July 19, 10; m. 43; c. 4. ENDOCRINOLOGY. A.B, N.Y. Univ, 36, fel, 37-40, M.S, 38, Ph.D.(biol), 40. Asst. instr, N.Y. Univ, 40-42, instr. 46-47, asst. prof, 47-49; JEFFERSON MED. COL, 49-51, assoc. prof, 51-58, PROF. HISTOL. & EMBRYOL, 58- Nat. Insts. Health career res. award, 62. Cressy-Morrison Award, 57. U.S.A.A.F, 42-46, Maj. Am. Soc. Zool; Am. Asn. Anat; Am. Physiol. Soc; Endocrine Soc; Am. Thyroid Asn; Soc. Exp. Biol. & Med; N.Y. Acad. Sci. Developmental physiology; hypoxia; maternal-fetal endocrine interrelations; bioassay; hypothalamus; neuroendocrine integration. Address: Dept. of Anatomy, Jefferson Medical College, Philadelphia, PA 19107.

DANGERFIELD, A(LMA) DEAN, b. Provo, Utah, Jan. 20, 24; m. 45; c. 5. ANALYTICAL CHEMISTRY. B.S, Brigham Young, 47. Rodman & Computer, Carter Oil Co, 47; supvr. fluorine lab, Columbia-Geneva Steel Div, U.S. Steel Corp, 47-65, assoc. res. chemist, appl. res. lab, div. 8, 65-67; methods develop. chemist, agr. & meteorol. sect, KENNECOTT COPPER CORP, 67-68, chief chemist, Arthur Concentrator Lab, 68, qual. control. engr, CONCENTRATORS, 68-70, PROCESS CONTROL SUPVR, 70- Eve. instr, Utah Trade & Tech. Inst; consult, Univ. Utah. U.S.N.R, 42-46, Res, 46-71, Comdr.(Ret). Sr. mem. Am. Chem. Soc. Analytical and instrumental research in the air pollution field. Address: Arthur Assay Lab, Kennecott Copper Corp, Magna, UT 84044.

D'ANGIO, GIULIO J, b. New York, N.Y, May 2, 22; m. 55; c. 2. RADIATION THERAPY. A.B, Columbia, 43; M.D, Harvard, 45. Intern, Children's Hosp, Boston, Mass, 45-46; fel. path, Babies Hosp, N.Y, 48; resident path, Vet. Admin. Hosp, West Roxbury, Mass, 48-49; radiol, Boston City Hosp, Mass, 49-53; asst, Harvard Med. Sch, 53-56, instr, 56-62, clin. assoc, 62-64; prof. radiol. & dir. div. radiation ther, Univ. Minnesota Hosps, 64-68; PROF. RADIOL, MED. COL, CORNELL UNIV, 68-; CHMN. DEPT. RADIATION THER, MEM. HOSP, 68- Asst, Boston City Hosp, 53-55, asst. physician, 55-64; asst, Children's Hosp, Boston, 56-59, assoc. radiologist, 59-62, radiotherapist, 63-64; res. assoc, Children's Cancer Res. Found, 56-59, radiotherapist, 59-64; asst. radiologist, Mass. Gen. Hosp, Boston, 61-62, consult, 62-64; assoc. res. radiologist, Donner Lab, California, Berkeley, 62-63, consult, Donner Lab. & Lawrence Radiation Lab, 64-; Hennepin County Gen. Hosp, 66-68; vis. radiation therapist, James Ewing Hosp, 68-; attend. radiation therapist, Mem. Hosp, 68-; attend. radiologist, N.Y. Hosp, 68-; div. chief, Sloan Kettering Inst. Cancer Res, 68- Chmn, Nat. Wilms' Tumor Study; radiation ther. comt, Children's Chemother. Study Group A; Soc. Chmn. Acad. Radiol. Depts. AAAS; Am. Med. Asn; Am. Asn. Cancer Res; Am. Col. Radiol; Am. Radium Soc; Am. Roentgen Ray Soc; Am. Soc. Therapeut. Radiol. Clinical radiotherapy; combined chemotherapy and radiotherapy; mechanisms of cancer growth; late radiation effects. Address: Dept. of Radiation Therapy, Memorial Hospital, 444 E. 68th St, New York, NY 10021.

DANGLE, RICHARD L, b. New Castle, Pa, July 24, 30; m. 56; c. 2. NUCLEAR PHYSICS. B.S, Westminster Col.(Pa), 58; M.S, Wisconsin, 60, Ph.D.(physics), 63. Fel. PHYSICS, Sao Paulo, 63-64; instr, Wisconsin, 64-65; asst. prof, UNIV. GA, 65-70, ASSOC. PROF, 70-, ASST. DEAN COL. ARTS & SCI, 68- U.S.A, 47-54. AAAS; Am. Phys. Soc. Low energy nuclear physics, primarily in charged particle spectroscopy. Address: Dean's Office, College of Arts & Sciences, University of Georgia, Athens, GA 30601.

DANHOF, IVAN EDWARD, b. Grand Haven, Mich, June 24, 28; m. 50; c. 4. PHYSIOLOGY. B.A. & M.A, N.Tex. State Col, 49; Ph.D.(physiol), Illinois, 53; M.D, Texas, 62. Teacher, pub. sch, 49-50; asst, Illinois, 50-53, instr. physiol, 53; res. assoc, SOUTHWEST. MED. SCH, UNIV. TEX, 53-54, instr. PHYSIOL, 54-56, asst. prof, 56-67, ASSOC. PROF, 67- Dir. med. educ, Methodist Hosp. Dallas, 69; Fulbright lectr, med. faculty, Nangrahar Univ, Afghanistan, 69-70. AAAS; assoc. mem. Soc. Exp. Biol. & Med; Am. Physiol. Soc. Motility and hormonal regulation of gastrointestinal tract; nutrition related to gastrointestinal function. Address: Southwestern Medical School, University of Texas, 5323 Harry Hines Blvd, Dallas, TX 75235.

DANIAN, MICHAEL S, b. Waukegan, Ill, Nov. 29, 31; m. 64. PHARMACY. B.S, Wisconsin, 53, M.B.A, 59, Ph.D, 64. Asst. pharm, Wisconsin, 60-61; asst. prof. PHARM. ADMIN, N.Dak. State, 62-63; asst. prof, Purdue, 64-66, COL. PHARM, UNIV. CINCINNATI, 66-68, ASSOC. PROF, 68- Med. Serv.C, 54-56, 1st Lt. Am. Asn. Cols. Pharm; Am. Pharmaceut. Asn. Pharmaceutical administration; economic, legal, and sociological aspects of pharmacy. Address: College of Pharmacy, University of Cincinnati, Cincinnati, OH 45221.

DANIEL, ALFRED C, b. Atlanta, Ga, Sept. 15, 32; m. 53; c. 4. SOLID STATE PHYSICS, ELECTRONIC ENGINEERING. B.S, Ga. Inst. Tech, 53, M.S, 57; Ph.D.(physics), Alabama, 64. Elec. engr, Air Force Armament Center, Eglin Air Force Base, Fla, 55-56; U.S. ARMY MISSILE COMMAND, REDSTONE ARSENAL, 57-60, physicist basic res. solid state physics, 60-68, RES. PHYSICIST, 68- Part-time asst. prof, Univ. Ala, Huntsville, 64-; mgr, Huntsville Div, Textile Rubber & Chem. Co, 70- U.S.A.F, 53-55, Lt. Am. Phys. Soc; Inst. Elec. & Electronics Eng. Magnetic resonance; spin-lattice relaxation; microwave techniques. Address: Physical Sciences Directorate, U.S. Army Missile Command, Redstone Arsenal, AL 35809.

DANIEL, ARTHUR FRANCIS, b. Birmingham, Ala, Sept. 27, 05; m. 33. CHEMISTRY, PHYSICS. B.S, North Carolina, 27, M.S, 28; Coffin fel, Chicago, 28-29; Stevens Inst, 40. Assoc. elec. eng, Harvard, 29-32; physicist, Gen. Chem. Co, N.Y, 33-35; chemist, Thomas A. Edison, Inc, N.J, 35-41; chem. engr, U.S. Army Sig. Res. & Develop. Lab, 41-46, dir. power sources div, 46-67, chief tech. staff, electronic components lab, U.S. Army Electronics Command, 67-71; CONSULT. POWER SOURCES, 71- Exceptional civilian award, U.S. Army, 47. Am. Chem. Soc; Electrochem. Soc; Am. Inst. Aeronaut. & Astronaut; Inst. Elec. & Electronics Eng. Energy sources and energy conversion techniques; electrochemical power sources; batteries, fuel cells; power conditioning; thermoelectrics, thermionics; thermo-photovoltaic and solar energy conversion. Address: 120 Hance Rd, Fair Haven, NJ 07701.

DANIEL, CHARLES D(WELLE), JR, b. San Antonio, Tex, Oct. 30, 25; m. 46; c. 2. NUCLEAR PHYSICS. B.S, U.S. Mil. Acad, 46; M.S, Tulane, 61, Ph.D. (nuclear physics), 68. U.S. ARMY, 46-, physicist, Defense Atomic Support Agency, 63-64, br. chief nuclear physics, 64-66, battalion comdr, 1st Infantry Div, South Vietnam, 66-67 stud, Indust. Col. Armed Forces, 67-68; div. chief, nuclear chem. biol. div, Off. Chief U.S. Army Res. & Develop. Dept. Army, 68-70, dir. missiles & space directorate, Off. Chief of Res. & Develop, 70-71, COMMANDING GEN, I CORPS ARTIL, KOREA, 71- Mem. ad hoc subcomt. shielding, Civil Defense Comt, Nat. Acad. Sci, 64-65. U.S.A, 46-, Brig. Gen; Silver Star Medal, 2 Legions of Merit, Distinguished Flying Cross, 5 Bronze Star Medals. Beta ray spectroscopy; solid state instrumentation for radiation detectors; nuclear weapons effects research to include radiation measurement; transient radiation effects on electronics; shielding against nuclear radiation. Address: 4904 Baltan Rd. N.W, Washington, DC 20016.

DANIEL, CHARLES PACK, b. Greenville, S.C, July 26, 25; m. 48; c. 2. BIOLOGY. B.S, Furman, 48; Maryland, 48-49; M.A, North Carolina, Chapel Hill, 55; M.S, Emory, 65. Teacher, pub. sch, Va, 49-52; instr. biol, High Point Col, 55-58; res. assoc. radiation ecol, Emory, 60-62; asst. prof. biol, Furman, 62-67; radiation ecol, Emory, 67; ASSOC. PROF. BIOL, GA. COL. MILLEDGEVILLE, 67- Med.C, U.S.A, 43-46. AAAS; Ecol. Soc. Am; Am. Inst. Biol. Sci. Effects of ionizing radiation on old-field succession; population changes; dominance related to environment; physiological changes in photoperiod and germination. Address: Dept. of Biology, Georgia College at Milledgeville, Milledgeville, GA 31061.

DANIEL, CHARLES WALLER, b. Annapolis, Md, June 16, 33; m. 61; c. 3. BIOLOGY. A.B, New Mexico, 54; M.S, Hawaii, 60; Ph.D.(zool), California, Berkeley, 65. Asst. prof. BIOL, COWELL COL, UNIV. CALIF, SANTA CRUZ, 65-70, ASSOC. PROF, 70- Normal and neoplastic biology of mammary tissues; differentiation in vitro; cellular aging. Address: Dept. of Biology, Cowell College, University of California, Santa Cruz, CA 95060.

DANIEL, DANIEL S, b. Basrah, Iraq, July 1, 34; m. 65; c. 3. PHYSICAL & ORGANIC CHEMISTRY. B.Sc, London, 55, Ph.D.(chem), 59. Res. chemist, Carnegie Inst. Tech, 60-63; sr. res. chemist, EASTMAN KODAK CO, 64-69, RES. ASSOC, RES. LAB, 69- Am. Chem. Soc; Brit. Chem. Soc. Electrochemical reductions of organic compounds; kinetics of organic reactions; syntheses of heterocyclic compounds; color and constitution. Address: Research Lab, Eastman Kodak Co, Rochester, NY 14650.

DANIEL, E(DWIN) E(MBREY), b. Chattanooga, Tenn, Sept. 23, 25; m. 48; c. 3. PHARMACOLOGY. B.A, Hopkins, 47, M.A, 49; Ph.D.(pharmacol), Utah, 52. Lab. instr. biol, anat. & physiol, Hopkins, 47-49; asst. PHARMACOL, Utah, 49-52; asst. prof, British Columbia, 52-60, assoc. prof, 60-61; PROF, UNIV. ALTA, 61-, head dept, 61-72. U.S.A, 44-46. AAAS; Am. Soc. Pharmacol. & Exp. Therapeut; Pharmacol. Soc. Can; Can. Physiol. Soc. Nature of control of activity of smooth and cardiac muscle, especially membrane phenomena and cations. Address: Dept. of Pharmacology, University of Alberta, Edmonton, Alta, Can.

DANIEL, ERIC D, b. London, Eng, June 6, 24; m. 53; c. 2. PHYSICS. M.A, Oxford, 45. Engr, P.O. Res. Sta, London, Eng, 45-46; res. dept, Brit. Broadcasting Corp, 46-56; physicist, Nat. Bur. Standards, D.C, 56-59; sr. staff physicist, Ampex Corp, Calif, 59-60, DIR. RES, Ampex Electronics Ltd, Eng, 60-61; MEMOREX CORP, 61- Sr. mem. Inst. Elec. & Electronics Eng. Magnetic recording in computer, instrumentation and audio fields, other recording and memory techniques; architectural and electroacoustics. Address: Memorex Corp, 1200 Memorex Dr, Santa Clara, CA 95052.

DANIEL, HARLEY A, b. Belgreen, Ala, Feb. 2, 04. AGRONOMY. B.S, Okla. Agr. & Mech. Col, 30, M.S, 32. Asst. agronomist, exp. sta, Okla. Agr. & Mech. Col, 30-34, 37-38; acting dir. & agronomist, exp. sta, Panhandle Agr. & Mech. Col, 34-37; agent & supt. Red Plains Conserv. Exp. Sta, in co-op. with soil conserv. serv, U.S. DEPT. AGR, 38-39, proj. supvr. soil & water conserv. res, 39-57, soil & water conserv. res. br, AGR. RES. SERV, Okla. Agr. & Mech. Col, 53-57, consult, off. adminstr, 57-60, STAFF SPECIALIST, for. res. & tech. prog. div, 60-66, INFO. DIV, 66-69, CROPS & SOILS, VISITORS SERV, 69- Am. Soc. Agron; Soil Sci. Soc. Am. Chemical composition of native grasses and other plants of Oklahoma; soil improvement crops; soil and water conservation; land use investigations. Address: Visitors Service, Agricultural Research Center, Information Division, Agricultural Research Service, Beltsville, MD 20705.

DANIEL, ISAAC M, b. Salonica, Greece, Oct. 7, 33; U.S. citizen. MECHANICS, STRESS ANALYSIS. B.S, Ill. Inst. Tech, 57, M.S, 59, Ph.D.(civil eng), 64. Asst. res. engr. STRESS ANAL, IIT RES. INST, 59-60, assoc. res. engr, 60-62, res. engr, 62-64, sr. res. engr, 64-66, MGR, 66- Lectr, Soc. Exp. Stress Anal. Am. Soc. Civil Eng.(award, Ill. sect, 57); Soc. Exp. Stress Anal.(best paper award, 70). Analysis of plates and shells; photoelasticity; moire analysis; wave propagation; viscoelasticity; experimental stress analysis; composite materials; brittle fracture; strain gages. Address: IIT Research Institute, 10 W. 35th St, Chicago, IL 60616.

DANIEL, J(ACK) LELAND, b. Spokane, Wash, Dec. 15, 24; m. 49; c. 3. PHYSICAL & ANALYTICAL CHEMISTRY. B.S, Washington (Seattle), 45, M.S, 48; California, Berkeley, 49-51; Ph.D.(anal. chem), Oregon State, 60. Applied res. chemist, Hanford Labs, Gen. Elec. Co, 48-49, sr. chemist, 51-57, specialist, tech. personnel placement, 57-59, sr. chemist, 59-60, sr. scientist, 60-64; RES. ASSOC. CERAMICS, ELECTRON. MICROS, PAC. NORTHWEST LABS, BATTELLE MEM. INST, 65- Specialist, U.S. team first U.S-Japan info. exchange meeting oxide & carbide fuels, Atomic Energy Cmn, 63; vis. chief res. scientist, Mitsubishi Atomic Power Indust, Tokyo, 65-66. U.S.N.R, 42-52, Lt.(jg). AAAS; N.Y. Acad. Sci; Am. Soc. Test. & Mat; Electron Micros. Soc. Am. Dynamic electron microscopy, especially of ceramics and high temperature materials; high temperature reactions and materials research; techniques of instrumental analysis, especially x-ray, quantitative metallography and emission spectroscopy; nuclear ceramic fuels. Address: Pacific Northwest Labs, Battelle Memorial Institute, P.O. Box 999, Richland, WA 99352.

DANIEL, JOHN H(AROLD), JR, b. Sutton-in-Ashfield, Eng, Jan. 1, 13; nat; m. 46; c. 4. CHEMISTRY. B.S, Alabama, 34; fel, Yale, 42, Ph.D.(org. chem), 44. Chemist, Nat. Aniline Co, N.Y, 34-35; anal. chemist, Am. Cyanamid Co, 36-41; lab. asst. chem, Yale, 41-43; teacher, prep. sch, Conn, 42-43; Am. Cyanamid Co, 43-46, group leader, tech. serv. div, 46-48, sr. chemist, 48-58, group leader, 58-65; tech. dir, Luxene, Inc, 65; asst. dir. res, Trojan Powder Co, 65-68, dir, 68-70; DIR. APPLN. RES, ALCOLAC, INC, 70- Am. Chem. Soc. Reinforced plastics; syntheses of guanidine derivatures for therapeutics; wet-strength resins for paper; organic and analytic chemistry; surface coating resins; stereospecific polymers; dental resins; surfactants and specialty monomers for uses in the cosmetics, textile, surface coatings, paper, water purification and plastics industries. Address: 484 Fair Oaks Dr, Severna Park, MD 21146.

DANIEL, JOHN H(ARRISON), b. Darlington, S.C, Sept. 6, 15; m. 42; c. 2. PHYSICS. B.S, The Citadel, 35; M.S, Kentucky, 37; fel, Mass. Inst. Tech,

37-40, Sc.D.(physics), 40. Asst, Kentucky, 35-37; res. fel, Nat. Cancer Inst, U.S. Pub. Health Serv, 40-41; asst. physicist, div. indust. hygiene, 41-42; res. physicist, Firestone Res. Lab, Ohio, 46-48; sr. physicist, lab. phys. biol, Nat. Insts. Health, 48-53; physicist, Evans Signal Lab, 53-56; ANALYST, INST. FOR DEFENSE ANAL, 56- Fel, ctr. advan. eng. stud, Mass. Inst. Technol, 69-70. U.S.A, 42-45, Ord.C.Res, Lt. Col. AAAS; Inst. Elec. & Electronics Eng; Am. Phys. Soc. Weapons systems evaluation; missile and air defense; electron theory and surface phenomena of metals; detection of nuclear radiation; electron microscopy; dielectric measurements. Address: 5502 Cromwell Dr, Washington, DC 20016.

DANIEL, JOHN NEWTON, b. Cruz Alta, Brazil, Mar. 15, 22; m. 46; c. 1. ELECTRICAL ENGINEERING. B.S, Texas, 42. Test engr, Westinghouse Elec. Co, Pa, 42-43; elec. inspector, Stone & Webster Eng. Co, 46-47; elec. engr, qual. eval. lab, U.S. Naval Mine Depot, 47-51, supvry. electronic engr, Naval Weapons Sta, 51-55, ord. engr, 55-56, dir, 56-59; res. engr, NASA, 59-69, ASST. BR. HEAD, LANGLEY RES. CTR, 69- U.S.N, 43-46, Lt. Nat. Soc. Prof. Eng; assoc. mem. Inst. Elec. & Electronics Eng. Instrumentation. Address: NASA Langley Research Center, Hampton Station, Hampton, VA 23365.

DANIEL, JOSEPH C(ARL), JR, b. Murphysboro, Ill, Aug. 21, 27; m. 51; c. 6. EMBRYOLOGY. B.S. St. Louis, 49; M.S, Michigan, 50; Ph.D, Colorado, 56. Lab. instr. biol, Denver, 50-51; from instr. to assoc. prof, Adams State Col, 52-60; sr. res. fel. biophys, med. ctr, Univ. Colo, Boulder, 60-62, asst. prof. biol, 62-65, assoc. prof, 65-66, Inst. Develop. Biol, 66-68, dept. molecular, cellular & develop. biol, 68-71; PROF. & HEAD DEPT. ZOOL. & ENTOM, UNIV. TENN, KNOXVILLE, 71- Guest lectr, Univ. Colo, 58; summer, Am. Physiol. Soc. fel, 58. U.S.N.R, 45-47. Fel. AAAS; Am. Soc. Zool; Am. Genetic Asn; Soc. Study Develop. Biol; Am. Soc. Cell Biol. Mammalian embryology and reproductive physiology. Address: 5505 Crestwood Dr, Knoxville, TN 37914.

DANIEL, KLAUS HERMANN, b. Zittau, Ger, June 2, 33; m. 67. STATISTICS. B.S, Cologne, 54; Found. of German People grant, Göttingen, 55-57, M.S, 57; German Acad. Exchange Serv. grant, California, Berkeley, 57-58, M.A, 59, Ph.D.(statist), 61. Vis. asst. prof. statist, Mich. State, 61-62; sci. asst, Münster, 63-64; asst. prof, UNIV. MD, 64-67, ASSOC. PROF. MATH, 67- Res. grants, German Res. Coun, 62, Nat. Sci. Found, 65 & 66. Am. Math. Soc; Inst. Math. Statist; Soc. Indust. & Appl. Math. Inventory control; queueing theory; dynamic and mathematical programming. Address: Dept. of Mathematics, University of Maryland, College Park, MD 20740.

DANIEL, LEONARD R(UPERT), b. Seattle, Wash, May 13, 26; m. 49; c. 2. CHEMICAL ENGINEERING. B.Ch.E, Ga. Inst. Tech, 46, Ph.D.(chem. eng), 52. Asst. prof. math, Ga. Inst. Tech, 46-52; prof. chem, Corpus Christi, 52-55, chmn. sci. & eng. div, 53-55; prof. chem, Howard Payne Col, 55-63, chmn. sci. & math. div, 58-63; prof. chem. & chmn. div. sci. & math, W.Ga. Col, 63-69; dean, CLAYTON JR. COL, 69-70, DIR. COMPUT. CTR, 70- Nat. Sci. Found. directorships, Howard Payne Col, high sch. teachers, summer insts, 59, 60, 61, 62, 63, in-serv. insts, 60-63, students, summer prog, 59, 60, W.Ga. Col, in-serv. insts. high sch. & elem. sch. teachers, 64-65, students, summer prog, 64. U.S.N, 44-46, Lt. AAAS; Asn. Comput. Mach. Science education. Address: Clayton Junion College, Morrow, GA 30260.

DANIEL, LOUISE J(ANE), b. Philadelphia, Pa, Oct. 28, 12. BIOCHEMISTRY. B.S, Pennsylvania, 35; M.S, Pa. State Col, 36; Ph.D.(nutrit), Cornell, 45. Prof. chem. & physics, Penn Hall Jr. Col, 36-42; res. assoc, CORNELL UNIV, 45-48, asst. prof. BIOCHEM, 48-51, assoc. prof, 51-58, PROF, 58- With U.S.N, 44. AAAS; Am. Inst. Nutrit; N.Y. Acad. Sci; Soc. Exp. Biol. & Med; Am. Chem. Soc; Am. Soc. Biol. Chem. Functions of folic acid and vitamin B$_{12}$ in intermediary metabolism; trace mineral interrelationships. Address: Section of Biochemistry & Molecular Biology, Cornell University, Ithaca, NY 14850.

DANIEL, O'DELL G, b. Paris, Ark, Aug. 15, 20; m. 44; c. 3. ANIMAL HUSBANDRY. B.S, Maryland, 49; M.S, Okla. State, 51, Ph.D.(animal husb), 57. Assoc. prof. animal husb, Panhandle Agr. & Mech. Col, 51-56, head div. agr, 57-58; PROF. & HEAD, EXTEN. ANIMAL SCI. DEPT, UNIV. GA, 58- U.S.A.F, 41-45, M/Sgt. Am. Soc. Animal Sci. Address: Extension Animal Science Dept, Agricultural Extension, University of Georgia, Athens, GA 30602.

DANIEL, PAUL MASON, b. Phila, Pa, July 12, 24; m. 48; c. 4. ZOOLOGY. B.S, Cincinnati, 49; M.S, Miami (Ohio), 54; fel, Ohio State, 63-64, Ph.D. (zool), 65. Asst. biol, West. Col, 49-50; prof. sci, Cuttington Col, Liberia, 50-54; teacher, pub. schs, Ohio, 54-59; instr. BIOL, MIAMI UNIV, 59-66, asst. prof, 66-70, ASSOC. PROF, 70- U.S.A, 42-45, S/Sgt. Am. Soc. Ichthyol. & Herpet; Nat. Asn. Biol. Teachers; Soc. Study Amphibians & Reptiles; Am. Inst. Biol. Sci. Ecology of benthic organisms; herpetology; biological science instruction in public schools. Address: Dept. of Zoology, Miami University, Oxford, OH 45056.

DANIEL, PHILIPPE E, b. St. Pere-en-Retz, France, Dec. 25, 26; m. 58; c. 5. VIROLOGY. Cert. physics, Rennes, 48, chem, 49; M.D, Paris, 51; cert. bact. & immunol, Pasteur Inst, 53. Fel. microbiol, Pasteur Inst, Paris, 52-54, asst, 54-61; ASSOC. PROF. VIROL, Laval, 61-70; FACULTY MED, UNIV. AMIENS, 70- Nat. Insts. Health fel, 59-61. French Army, 51-52. Tissue Cult. Asn; Can. Soc. Microbiol; Fr. Soc. Microbiol; N.Y. Acad. Sci. Persistent infection of cells in tissue cultures with para influenza type 3 virus KB cells carrier system; nucleic acid of paramyxovirus. Address: Faculty of Medicine, University of Amiens, Frederic Petit, 80 Amiens, France.

DANIEL, RICHARD A, b. N.Y.C, Apr. 26, 34; m. 61; c. 2. CHEMICAL ENGINEERING. B.A, Columbia Col, 54; B.S, Columbia, 55, M.S, 57, Ph.D.(chem. eng), 63. Res. engr. nylon develop, E.I. du Pont de Nemours & Co, Del, 60-63; process eng. & plastics, Celanese Res. Co, 63-65, group leader Celcon res, Celanese Plastics Co, N.J, 65-66, tech. mgr. resins, 66-69, lab. dir, 69-71, TECH. DIR, CELANESE CHEM. CO, N.Y.C, 71- Am. Inst. Chem. Eng; Am. Chem. Soc; Soc. Plastics Eng. Reaction and handling systems for synthetic polymers; spinning and texturing of fibers; thermoplastics pro-

cessing and finishing operations; new product process and application development; research administration. Address: 64 Greenhill Rd, Springfield, NJ 07081.

DANIEL, ROBERT EUGENE, b. Birmingham, Ala, Jan. 22, 38. ANALYTICAL & PHYSICAL CHEMISTRY. A.B, Samford, 60; M.S, Alabama, 63, fel. & Ph.D.(anal. chem), 66. Res. asst. chem, U.S. Army Missile Command, Redstone Arsenal, 64; asst. prof, Ala. Col, 65-66; Samford Univ, 66-71; ANAL. RES. CHEMIST, U.S. PIPE & FOUNDRY CO, 71- AAAS; Am. Chem. Soc. Structure and chemical characteristics of phenol complexes of tantalum, niobium, tungsten and molybdenum; kinetic aspects of the complexforming reaction. Address: U.S. Pipe & Foundry Co, 3300 First Ave. N, Birmingham, AL 35203.

DANIEL, ROBERT S(TRONGMAN), b. Pikeville, Ky, Jan. 2, 14; m. 40; c. 2. PSYCHOLOGY. A.B, DePauw, 36; A.M, Indiana, 38, Ph.D.(psychol), 41. Instr. PSYCHOL, Indiana, 40-42; act. asst. prof, UNIV. MO-COLUMBIA, 42-43, asst. prof, 45-47, assoc. prof, 47-54, PROF, 54-, chmn. dept, 55-61. Asst, Nat. Defense Res. Comt, 43-45. Consult, Air Force Personnel Training Res. Center, 51-57. AAAS; fel. Am. Psychol. Asn. Electrophysiological studies of behavior; perception. Address: Dept. of Psychology, University of Missouri-Columbia, Columbia, MO 65201.

DANIEL, ROLLIN A(UGUSTUS), JR, b. Union Point, Ga, June 14, 08; m; c. 2. SURGERY. B.A, Vanderbilt, 30, M.D, 33. Intern surg, univ. hosp, VANDERBILT UNIV, 33-34, asst. res, 35-37, res. surgeon, 37-38, asst. prof, SCH. MED, 41-47, assoc. prof, 47-51, PROF, 51-54, CLIN. SURG, 54-, CHIEF DEPT. SURG, ST. THOMAS HOSP, TENN, 70- Dipl. Am. Bd. Surg, 40; Am. Bd. Thoracic Surg, 48, mem. exam. bd, 60-, v.chmn, 64-, secytreas, 68- Am. Med. Asn; Am. Col. Surg; Soc. Univ. Surg; Am. Soc. Clin. Surg; Am. Asn. Thoracic Surg; Am. Surg. Asn. Address: St. Thomas Hospital, 2000 Hayes St, Nashville, TN 37203.

DANIEL, RONALD SCOTT, b. Spencer, Iowa, Oct. 10, 36; m. 57; c. 2. ELECTRON MICROSCOPY. B.A, San Jose State Col, 60, M.A, 63; Ph.D.(entom), Minnesota, Minneapolis, 68. Teacher, high sch, Calif, 61-64; res. asst. entom, Minnesota, 65-66, res. fel, 66-68; asst. prof. BIOL. SCI, CALIF. STATE POLYTECH. COL, KELLOGG-VOORHIS, 68-70, ASSOC. PROF, 70- AAAS; Am. Inst. Biol. Sci. Electron microscopy of blattids and their intracellular bacteroid symbiotes. Address: Dept. of Biological Sciences, California State Polytechnic College, Kellogg-Voorhis, 3801 W. Temple Ave, Pomona, CA 91766.

DANIEL, SALHA S, b. Basrah, Iraq, Nov. 3, 32. ANALYTICAL & INORGANIC CHEMISTRY. B.Sc, London, 54, Ph.D.(inorg. chem), 57. Fel. ion exchange anal, Battersea Col. Tech, Eng, 57-58; lectr, Shamash High Sch, Iraq, 59-60; RES. ASSOC. NEO-NATAL PHYSIOL, COL. PHYSICIANS & SURGEONS, COLUMBIA UNIV, 60- Acid base change in newborn infant; carbohydrate metabolism during asphyxia. Address: Dept. of Pediatric Research, Columbia Medical Center, 622 W. 168th St, New York, NY 10032.

DANIEL, THEODORE W(ILLIAM), b. San Francisco, Calif, Nov. 16, 07; m. 35, 47; c. 1. FOREST MANAGEMENT. B.S, California, 34, M.S, 36, Baker fel, 37, Ph.D.(plant physiol), 42. Tech. asst. forestry, California, 34-36; jr. forester, Calif. Forest & Range Exp. Sta, U.S. Forest Serv, 36-41; grazing specialist, exp. sta, State Col. Wash, 41-44; PROF. SILVICULT, FORESTRY, UTAH STATE UNIV, 44- Fulbright res. fel, Austria, 51-52; hon. senator, State Univ. Agr. & Forestry, Austria, 67. Fel. AAAS; Soc. Am. Foresters; Am. Soc. Plant Physiol; Am. Soc. Range Mgt; Ecol. Soc. Am. Silviculture; silvics; ecology; plant physiology; range management. Address: College of Natural Resources, Utah State University, Logan, UT 84321.

DANIEL, T(HOMAS) BRUCE, b. Kansas City, Mo, Sept. 7, 26; m. 54; c. 2. PHYSICS. B.S, Kansas, 50, M.S, 54, Ph.D.(physics), 59. Asst, radiation biophys. proj, Atomic Energy Cmn, Kansas, 51-53, instr. physics, 53-56; assoc. physicist, Midwest Res. Inst, 58-60, sr. physicist, 60-62; assoc. prof. PHYSICS, KANS. STATE COL. PITTSBURGH, 62-64, PROF, 64-, CHMN. DEPT, 62- U.S.A.A.F, 43-48. Solid state physics; friction of solids. Address: Dept. of Physics, Kansas State College of Pittsburg, Pittsburg, KS 66762.

DANIEL, VICTOR WAYNE, b. Baltimore, Md, July 21, 43. MATHEMATICS. B.S, Univ. N.C, Chapel Hill, 65; Ph.D.(math), Univ. Va, 70. ASST. PROF. MATH, UNIV. WYO, 70- Am. Math. Soc. Study of certain convolution and integral operators on Lebesque spaces of the half-line; determining their invariant subspaces and when they are Volterra, unicellular or similar to the integration operator. Address: Dept. of Mathematics, University of Wyoming, Laramie, WY 82070.

DANIEL, WILLIAM A, JR, b. Thomaston, Ga, May 13, 14. PEDIATRICS. B.S, Northwest. Univ, 36, M.D, 40. Intern, Charity Hosp, New Orleans, 39-40; resident PEDIAT, Children's Hosp, Dallas, 40-41; Children's Mem. Hosp, Chicago, 41-42; private practice, Ala, 42-66; PROF, SCH. MED, UNIV. ALA, 66-, DIR. ADOLESCENT UNIT, 66- Med. consult, State Bur. Child Welfare, 42-66; assoc. proj. dir, Children & Youth Proj. 622, 66-; mem, comt. on abortions, Univ. Ala; Univ. Ala, Birmingham Coun. Community Health Serv; med. bd, pediat. div, Proj. Hope; State Adv. Comt. Day Care; past chief-of-staff, St. Margaret's Hosp, Montgomery, Ala; mem. staff, Univ. Hosp. & Children's Hosp, Birmingham. Am. Med. Asn; Am. Acad. Pediat; Am. Acad. Cerebral Palsy; Soc. Adolescent Med. Address: Adolescent Unit, University of Alabama School of Medicine, Birmingham, AL 35233.

DANIEL, WILLIAM HUGH, b. Ark, Dec. 31, 19; m. 44; c. 2. AGRONOMY. B.A, Ouachita Col, 41; B.S.A, Arkansas, 46; M.S, Mich. State, 48, Ph.D. (agron, turf mgt), 50. PROF. TURF MGT, PURDUE UNIV, 50- Secy, Midwest Regional Turf Found, Purdue. U.S.A.A.F, 42-45, 2nd Lt. Fel. Am. Soc. Agron; Weed Sci. Soc. Am. Turfgrass management; soil science; crop ecology. Address: Dept. of Agronomy, Purdue University, Lafayette, IN 47907.

DANIEL, WILLIAM L, b. Wyandotte, Mich, Sept. 20, 42; m. 64. HUMAN & BIOCHEMICAL GENETICS. B.S, Mich. State, 64, Nat. Inst. Ment. Health fel, 65-67, Ph.D.(zool), 67. ASST. PROF. GENETICS, ILL. STATE UNIV, 67- AAAS; Am. Soc. Human Genetics. Biochemical and genetic factors in mental retardation, human development and cystic fibrosis, specifically genetic control of tissue proteins and enzymes. Address: Dept. of Biology, Illinois State University, Normal, IL 61761.

DANIELEY, (JAMES) EARL, b. Alamance Co, N.C, July 28, 24; m. 48; c. 3. ORGANIC CHEMISTRY. A.B, Elon Col, 46; M.A, North Carolina, 49, Ph.D. (org. chem), 54. Instr. chem, ELON COL, 46-47, asst. prof, 47-48, assoc. prof, 48-50, prof, 52-56, PRES, 57-, dean col, 53-56. Fel, Hopkins, 56-57; lectr. chem, North Carolina, 52. Summers, vis. prof, 53, 54, 56. Award, Elon Col, 58. Am. Chem. Soc. Cyclobutane compounds; porphyrins in petroleum. Address: Elon College, P.O. Box 245, Elon College, NC 27244.

DANIELL, HERMAN BURCH, b. Cadwell, Ga, May 25, 29; m. 57; c. 3. PHARMACOLOGY. B.S, Georgia, 51, M.S, 64; Nat. Insts. Health fel, Med. Col. S.C, 64-66, Ph.D.(pharmacol), 66. Instr. pharm, Georgia, 62-63; PHARMACOL, MED. COL. S.C, 66-67, assoc, 67-68, asst. prof, 68-70, ASSOC. PROF, 70- Med.Serv.C, 51-53, Capt. Am. Soc. Pharmacol. & Exp. Therapeut. Cardiovascular diseases. Address: Dept. of Pharmacology, Medical College of South Carolina, Charleston, SC 29401.

DANIELLI, JAMES F, b. Wembley, Eng, Nov. 13, 11; m. 37; c. 2. BIOLOGY. B.Sc, Univ. Col, London, 31, Ph.D.(chem), 33, D.Sc.(physiol), 38; Princeton, 33-35; Ph.D.(biochem), Cambridge, 42; hon. Sc.D, Ghent, 56. Physiologist, Marine Biol. Asn, 45-46; reader cell biol, Royal Cancer Hosp, Univ. London, 46-49, prof. & chmn. dept. zool, Kings Col, 49-62; prof. med. chem. & biochem. pharmacol. & chmn. dept, STATE UNIV. N.Y. BUFFALO, 62-65, DIR. CTR. THEORET. BIOL, 65-, provost, faculty natural sci. & math, 67-69. Ed, Int. Rev. Cytol, 50-; J. Theoret. Biol, 60-; Progress Surface & Membrane Sci, 62-; Coun. mem. & chmn. cmn, Int. Cell Res. Orgn, UNESCO, 62- Am. Soc. Cell Biol; fel, Royal Soc; Brit. Soc. Exp. Biol. (secy, 38); Brit. Biochem. Soc; Faraday Soc; Int. Soc. Cell Biol. (secy, 47). Cell biology; surface science; theoretical biology; physiology; chemotherapy. Address: Center for Theoretical Biology, State University of New York at Buffalo, 4248 Ridge Lea Rd, Amherst, NY 14226.

DANIELS, ALMA U(RIAH), b. Salt Lake City, Utah, Mar. 18, 39; m. 61; c. 3. MATERIALS SCIENCE & ENGINEERING. B.S, Utah, 61, Ph.D.(metall), 66. Oak Ridge Nat. Labs, res. asst. metall, Univ. Utah, 61-65; res. chemist, indust. & biochem. dept, exp. sta, E.I. du Pont de Nemours & Co, Inc, 65-69, sr. res. chemist, 69, develop. & serv. rep, 69-70; res. engr, Metcut Res. Assoc, Inc, Ohio, 70-71; SR. MAT. ENGR, ARTIFICIAL HEART TEST FACILITY, UNIV. UTAH, 71- Am. Soc. Metals. Biomaterials-properties, interaction with biosystem; refractory materials, properties, fabrication processes; cutting tool materials; metal removal processes. Address: 933 Newberry Rd, Salt Lake City, UT 84108.

DANIELS, BRIAN KENNETH, b. Leeds, Eng, July 4, 41; m. 64; c. 2. SOLID STATE PHYSICS. B.Sc, Birmingham, 61, Ph.D.(physics), 64. RES. PHYSICIST, CHEMSTRAND RES. CTR, INC, MONSANTO CO, 64- Structure and mechanical properties of ZNS single crystals; nylon 66 fibers; graphite fiber composites and steel tire cords. Address: Chemstrand Research Center, Inc, Monsanto Co, P.O. Box 731, Durham, NC 27702.

DANIELS, CRAIG EVAN, Exp. Psychol, see 12th ed, Soc. & Behav. Vols.

DANIELS, EDWARD G(EORGE), b. Lorain, Ohio, June 7, 32; m. 57; c. 3. BIOCHEMISTRY. A.B, DePauw, 54; Ph.D.(biochem), Univ. Ill, 58. RES. ASSOC. BIOCHEM, UPJOHN CO, 58- Am. Chem. Soc. Renal lipid chemistry; prostaglandin isolation and biosynthesis; peptide hormones. Address: Dept. of Experimental Chemistry, Upjohn Co, 301 Henrietta St, Kalamazoo, MI 49001.

DANIELS, EDWARD W(ILLIAM), b. Tracy, Minn, Jan. 19, 17; m. 43; c. 4. CELL BIOLOGY. B.A, Cornell, 41; M.S, Illinois, 47, univ. fel, 49-50, Ph.D.(zool, physiol), 50. Teacher, high sch, 41-43; from res. assoc. to mem. staff, toxicol. lab, Chicago, 50-51, U.S. Air Force Radiation lab, 51-53, asst. prof, 53-54; ASSOC. BIOLOGIST, DIV. BIOL. & MED. RES, ARGONNE NAT. LAB, 54- U.S.N, 43-46. AAAS; Soc. Protozool; Am. Soc. Zool; Nat. Soc. Med. Res; Radiation Res. Soc; Am. Soc. Cell Biol; Am. Asn. Cancer Res. Recovery of cells from radiation damage; transplantation tolerance; origin and fate of subcellular components studied with electron microscopy, micrurgy and ultracentrifugation. Address: Division of Biological & Medical Research, Argonne National Lab, 9700 S. Cass Ave, Argonne, IL 60439.

DANIELS, FARRINGTON, b. Minneapolis, Minn, Mar. 8, 89; m; c. 4. PHYSICAL CHEMISTRY. B.S, Minnesota, 10, M.S, 11; fel, Harvard, 11-12, Ph.D. (phys. chem), 14; hon. D.Sc, Rhode Island, 53, Minnesota, 59, Dakar, 60, Louisville, 64, Univ. Wis, Madison, 66. Asst. chem, Minnesota, 08-11; instr. & asst. prof. chem, Worcester Polytech, 14-18; electrochemist, fixed nitrogen res. lab, U.S. Dept. Agr, 19-20; asst. prof. CHEM, UNIV. WIS, MADISON, 20-24, assoc. prof, 24-28, prof, 28-59, chmn. dept, 52-59, EMER. PROF, 59-, Baker non-res. lectr, Cornell, 35. Assoc. ed, J. Chem. Physics, 35-37; J. Phys. Chem, 32-34. Assoc. dir. chem. div, metall. lab, Manhattan Dist, Chicago, 44-45, dir, 45-46, chmn. bd. gov, Argonne Nat. Lab, 46-48; off. investr, Nat. Defense Res. Comt, 42-44; Guggenheim Found. fel. Gibbs Medal; Priestly Medal; Norris Award. C.W.S, 18, Lt. Nat. Acad. Sci.(v.pres, 59-61); AAAS; Am. Chem. Soc.(assoc. ed, jour, 34-42, pres, 53); Geochem. Soc.(pres, 58); Am. Philos. Soc; Am. Acad. Arts & Sci; Solar Energy Soc.(pres, 64-65). Chemical kinetics, chiefly gas phase; photochemistry; photosynthesis; atomic power; thermoluminescence of crystals; nitrogen oxides and nitrogen fixation; utilization of solar energy. Address: Dept. of Chemistry, University of Wisconsin, Madison, WI 53706.

DANIELS, FARRINGTON, JR, b. Worcester, Mass, Sept. 29, 18; m. 51; c. 3. PHYSIOLOGY. B.A, Wisconsin, 40, M.A, 42; M.D, Harvard, 43, M.P.H, 52. Intern med, New York Hosp, 44; asst. resident & res. fel, New York Hosp. & med. sch, Cornell, 47-49; res. fel. nutrit, sch. pub. health, Harvard, 49-50; head physiol. unit, Qm. Climatic Res. Lab, Mass, 50-53; chief stress physiol. br, environ. protection div, Qm. Res. & Develop. Center, 53-55; asst. prof. dermat, med. sch, Oregon, 55-61; assoc. prof, Illinois, 61-62; assoc. prof. MED, MED. COL, CORNELL UNIV, 62-69, PROF, 69-, HEAD DERMAT. DIV, 62- Army rep. physiol. panel, cmt. med. sci, Res. & Develop. Bd, 51-53; mem. photobiol. comt, Nat. Acad. Sci. Med.C, 44-47, Capt. AAAS; Am. Dermat. Asn; Am. Acad. Dermat; Soc. Invest. Dermat; Human Factors Soc; N.Y. Acad. Med; N.Y. Acad. Sci; Am. Asn. Phys. Anthrop; Int. Soc. Biometeorol. Medicine; spinal cord concussion; environmental physiology; human adaptation to heat, cold and ultraviolet radiation; military load-carrying; effects of footwear and clothing on skin; effects of ultraviolet radiation and photosensitizing chemicals on skin; histochemistry of skin. Address: Dermatology Division, Cornell University Medical College, New York, NY 10021.

DANIELS, GERT L, b. Hamburg, Ger, Mar. 11, 14; m. 47; c. 3. ZOOLOGY, ANTHROPOLOGY. B.A, Texas, 39, M.A, 40; Loewey scholar, California, Berkeley, 40-42; Ed.D.(sci. ed), Columbia, 59. Instr. biol. & anthrop, West. Mont. Col, 48-49, asst. prof, 49-56, assoc. prof, 56-61; BIOL, MONTCLAIR STATE COL, 61-68, PROF, 68- Nat. Sci. Found. vis. scientist, 60-61, 64-, summers, mem. conf, 62, inst. 63, grant trop. biol, Costa Rica, 64; vis. prof, Univ. R.I, summers 67, 69, 70 & 71. U.S.A, 43-44. AAAS; Nat. Sci. Teachers Asn. Distribution of Paleolithic cultures in Europe; behavior development, ovulation and longevity in Coturnix japonica. Address: Dept. of Zoology, Montclair State College, Montclair, NJ 07043.

DANIELS, GILBERT S, b. Brooklyn, N.Y, June 19, 27; m. 49, 71; c. 3. BOTANY. A.B, Harvard, 48; M.A, California, Los Angeles, 67, Ph.D, 71. Proj. engr, Wright Air Develop. Center, U.S. Air Force, Dayton, Ohio, 49-53; dir. res. comput. eng, Panellit, Inc, Ill, 53-60; mgr. systs. design, Packard-Bell Comput. Corp, Calif, 60-61; dir. mkt, Sci. Data Systs, Inc, 61-63; nat. sales mgr, Wyle Labs, 63-64; asst. dir, HUNT BOT. LIBRARY, CARNEGIE-MELLON UNIV, 67-70, DIR, 70- U.S.N, 44-45; U.S.A.F, 50-53, 1st Lt. Address: Hunt Botanical Library, Carnegie-Mellon University, Pittsburgh, PA 15213.

DANIELS, J(AMES) M(AURICE), b. Leeds, Eng, Aug. 26, 24; m. 65; c. 2. PHYSICS. B.A, Jesus Col, Oxford, 45, M. A, 49, Nuffield fel, 51-52, D.Phil. (physics), 52. Asst. exp. officer, radar res. & develop. estab, Ministry Supply, 44-46; tech. officer physics, Imp. Chem. Industs, Ltd, 46-47; Imp. Chem. Industs. res. fel. low temperature physics, Clarendon lab, Oxford, 52-53; asst. prof. PHYSICS, British Columbia, 53-56, assoc. prof, 56-60, PROF, 60-61; UNIV. TORONTO, 61- Consult, Pa. State, 58; UNESCO expert exp. physics, Univ. Buenos Aires, 58-59; vis. prof, Balseiro Inst. Physics, Argentina, 60-61. Fel. Royal Soc. Can; Brit. Inst. Physics & Phys. Soc. (fel, Phys. Soc); Argentine Physics Asn; Can. Asn. Physicists. Adiabatic demagnetisation; spatial orientation of atomic nuclei; magnetic resonance and relaxation. Address: Dept. of Physics, University of Toronto, Toronto, Ont, Can.

DANIELS, JAMES T(HOMAS), b. N.Y.C, Nov. 23, 06; m. 45; c. 3. SURGERY. M.D, Georgetown, 36. Surg. intern & house surgeon, St. Vincent's Hosp, 36-38; res. neurol, N.Y. Neurol. Inst, Columbia-Presby. Med. Center, 38-39; res. fel, Montreal Neurol. Inst, McGill, 39-40; fel. neurosurg, Lahey Clin, 40-42; from assoc. prof. to clin. prof. neurosurg, N.Y. Univ. Med. Ctr, 51-70; DIR. RES. & CHIEF NEUROSURG, MISERICORDIA HOSP, 58- Asst. attend. neurosurgeon, St. Vincent's Hosp, 46-; Bellevue Hosp. & N.Y. Univ. Hosp, 51-, spec. lectr, grad. sch, St. John's, 48-; consult, neurosurgeon, Nyack Hosp, 49-; chief div. neurosurg, St. Clare's Hosp, 49-; St. Joseph's Hosp, 50-; attend. neurol. surgeon, Hosp. Holy Family, 50-; Manhattan Eye, Ear & Throat Hosp, 50-; consult, Hosps, 51- Dipl, Am. Bd. Neurol. Surg; Nat. Bd. Med. Exam. Liaison officer, sch. med, N.Y. Univ, Med.C, U.S.N.R, 42-, Capt. Fel. Am. Col. Surg; Am. Med. Asn; Cong. Neurol. Surg; Asn. Res. Nerv. & Ment. Disease; Asn. Mil. Surg. U.S; N.Y. Acad. Med. Impulse transmission spinal cord; stereotaxic surgery; hypophysectomy. Address: 415 W. 51st St, New York, NY 10019.

DANIELS, JESS D(ONALD), b. Sugar Land, Tex, Oct. 20, 34; m. 56; c. 3. FOREST GENETICS, FORESTRY. B.S, Montana State, 57; M.F, Idaho, 65, Ph.D.(forest genetics), 69. Forester, Forest Serv, U.S. Dept. Agr, 61-63, plant geneticist, Inst. Forest Genetics, summer 66; acting instr. forestry, col. forestry, wildlife & range sci, Idaho, 65-66; FOREST GENETICIST, FORESTRY RES. CENTER, WEYERHAEUSER CO, 68- U.S.N.R, 57-61, Lt. (jg). Soc. Am. Foresters; Am. Genetic Asn. Tree improvement, variation and inheritance of characteristics related to growth, yield and quality of wood; breeding for yield improvement; technology of seed production and orchard management. Address: Weyerhaeuser Forestry Research Center, P.O. Box 420, Centralia, WA 98531.

DANIELS, JOAN B(USH), b. Natick, Mass, Feb. 13, 09; m. 33; c. 1. VIROLOGY. B.S, Simmons Col, 30. Jr. state bacteriologist, Mass, 30-43, asst. bacteriologist, 43-57, sr. bacteriologist, 57-61, chief lab, 61-70; VIROLOGIST, CAPE COD HOSP, HYANNIS, 71- Lectr, Simmons Cpl, 55-64; asst. bact, Harvard Med. Sch, 58- AAAS; Am. Soc. Microbiol; Am. Asn. Immunol; N.Y. Acad. Sci. Ecology of equine encephalitis, particularly methods which can be applied in the laboratory to reveal latent infection; clinical virology, especially maternal rubella. Address: 26 Black Ball Hill Rd, Dennis, MA 02638.

DANIELS, JOHN HARTLEY, b. Regina, Sask, July 18, 31; m. 56; c. 2. STRUCTURAL ENGINEERING. B.Sc, Alberta, 55; M.S, Illinois, 59; Am. Iron & Steel Inst. fel, Lehigh, 66, Ph.D.(civil eng), 67. Resident engr, Dept. of Hwys, Alta, Can, 55-56, design engr, 56-58; chief struct. engr, Assoc. Eng. Serv, Ltd, 59-64; ASSOC. PROF. CIVIL ENG, LEHIGH UNIV, 67- Am. Soc. Civil Eng; Eng. Inst. Can; Am. Concrete Inst; Am. Soc. Eng. Educ. Plastic design and analysis of multi-story frames; plasticity; composite steel-concrete structures; optimization techniques. Address: Fritz Lab, Lehigh University, Bethlehem, PA 18015.

DANIELS, JOHN M(AYNARD), b. Binghamton, N.Y, Aug. 17, 35; m. 58; c. 3. PHYSICAL CHEMISTRY. B.S, Trinity Col, 57; Fulbright grant, Frankfurt, 57-58; Mass. Inst. Tech, 58-59; Ph.D.(chem), Brandeis, 65. Phys. chemist,

Nat. Bur. Standards, 64-66; ASST. PROF. CHEM, UNION COL.(N.Y), 66- Nat. Bur. Standards fel, 64- Am. Chem. Soc; Am. Asn. Physics Teachers. Electron paramagnetic resonance; molecular structure. Address: Dept. of Chemistry, Union College, Schenectady, NY 12308.

DANIELS, LESLIE B, b. Douglas, Wyo, Oct. 13, 01; m. 24; c. 2. ENTOMOLOGY. B.S, Colorado State, 27, M.S, 29; Ph.D.(entom), Minnesota, 54. Instr. ENTOM, COLO. STATE UNIV, 28-35, asst. prof, 35-43, assoc. prof, 43-52, head dept. & chief entomologist, 52-70, EMER. HEAD DEPT. & EMER. CHIEF ENTOMOLOGIST, 70- AAAS; Entom. Soc. Am. Applied entomology. Address: Dept. of Entomology, Colorado State University, Ft. Collins, CO 80521.

DANIELS, MALCOLM, b. Wingate, Eng, Jan. 27, 30; m. 64. PHYSICAL CHEMISTRY. B.Sc, Durham, 51, Ph.D.(chem), 55. Asst. radiation chem. & photochem, King's Col, Newcastle, 54-57; resident res. assoc, Argonne Nat. Lab, 59-60; lectr. chem, Univ. West Indies, 60-62; assoc. prof. radiation chem. & photochem, Puerto Rico, 62-65; head radiation prog, P.R. Nuclear Center, 62-65; ASSOC. PROF. DEPT. CHEM. & RADIATION CTR, ORE. STATE UNIV, 65- Radiation Res. Soc; The Chem. Soc; Faraday Soc. Radiation chemistry, photochemistry and spectroscopy; aqueous solutions of oxyanions; free radicals; transient species; radiation biophysics; transformations of nucleic acids and constituents. Address: Radiation Center, Oregon State University, Corvallis, OR 97331.

DANIELS, NORRIS E(UGENE), b. Lakin, Kans, Oct. 10, 18; m. 40; c. 1. ENTOMOLOGY. B.S, Kans. State Col. Agr, 51, M.S, 52. ASSOC. PROF, Southwest. Great Plains Res. Ctr, Tex. Agr. Exp. Sta, 52-71; TEX. AGR. EXP. STA, TEX. A&M UNIV, 71- U.S.A, 42-46. Am. Entom. Soc. Small grain and forage pest research. Address: Texas Agriculture Experiment Station, Texas A&M University, Bushland, TX 79012.

DANIELS, PETER J(OHN) L(OVELL), b. Stockport, Eng, June 7, 34. ORGANIC CHEMISTRY. B.Sc, Manchester, 56, M.Sc, 57; Ph.D.(chem), London, 60. Fel, Royal Inst. Tech, Sweden, 60-61; A.P. Sloane res. assoc, Hopkins, 61-62; RES. MEDICINAL CHEMIST, SCHERING CORP, 62- Am. Chem. Soc; Brit. Chem. Soc. Synthetic medicinals and natural products. Address: Dept. of Medicinal Chemistry, Schering Corp, 86 Orange St, Bloomfield, NJ 07003.

DANIELS, RALPH, b. N.Y.C, May 2, 21; m. 44; c. 3. ORGANIC CHEMISTRY. A.B, Brooklyn Col, 44; A.M, Harvard, 49, Ph.D, 50. Res. chemist, Givaudan-Delawanna Res. Inst, 44-46; fel, nonaromatic steroids, Wisconsin, 50-51; instr. CHEM, Purdue, 51-52; asst. prof, COL. PHARM, UNIV. ILL. MED. CTR, 52-58, assoc. prof, 58-62, PROF, 62-, ASST. DEAN, GRAD. COL, 70- Vis. scientist, Univ. London, 61-62. Am. Chem. Soc; The Chem. Soc. Synthesis of pharmacologically active compounds; natural products; heterocyclic chemistry; radiation protective compounds; reaction mechanisms; spectra of organic compounds. Address: University of Illinois at the Medical Center, P.O. Box 6998, Chicago, IL 60680.

DANIELS, RAYMOND BRYANT, b. Adair, Iowa, Feb. 15, 25; m. 45; c. 2. SOIL GENESIS, GEOMORPHOLOGY. B.S, Iowa State Col, 50, M.S, 55, Ph.D. (soil genesis), 57. Res. soil scientist, soil conserv. serv, U.S. Dept. Agr, N.C, 57-68; ASSOC. PROF. SOIL SCI, N.C. STATE UNIV, 68- Soil Sci. Soc. Am. Soil genesis and geomorphic interrelations. Address: Dept. of Soil Science, North Carolina State University, Raleigh, NC 27607.

DANIELS, RAYMOND D(eWITT), b. Cleveland, Ohio, Feb. 14, 28; m. 52; c. 1. PHYSICAL METALLURGY. B.S, Case, 50, M.S, 53, Ph.D.(phys. metall), 58. Physicist, Nat. Bur. Standards, 50-51; asst. physics, Case, 51-54; res. engr, Linde Co, 54-55; asst. & spec. lectr. metall, Case, 55-58; asst. prof. METALL. ENG, UNIV. OKLA, 58-61, assoc. prof, 61-64, PROF, 64-, INTERIM EXEC. DIR, RES. INST, 71-, chmn, sch. metall. eng, 62-63, dir. sch. chem. eng. & mat. sci, 63-65, 69-70, assoc. dean eng. for res. & grad. study, 65-68. Dupont res. grant, 58; Nat. Sci. Found. sci. faculty fel, Univ. Neuchâtel, 68-69. Consult, U.S. Air Force, 58-59; Autoclave Engrs, 59-62; Avco Corp, 63- U.S.A, 46-47. Am. Soc. Metals; Am. Inst. Mining, Metall. & Petrol. Eng; Am. Inst. Chem. Eng; Nat. Asn. Corrosion Eng; Am. Soc. Eng. Educ; Brit. Inst. Metals. Physical metallurgy; mechanical properties of metals; embrittlement phenomena; corrosion-fatigue. Address: Room 23, School of Chemical Engineering & Materials Science, University of Oklahoma, 202 W. Boyd, Norman, OK 73069.

DANIELS, REX O, JR, b. Spanish Fork, Utah, Nov. 15, 21; m. 44; c. 1. METALLURGICAL & CHEMICAL ENGINEERING. B.S, Utah, 49, Ph.D. (metall. eng), 52. Res. engr. chem. surfaces, Calif. Res. Corp, Standard Oil Co, Calif, 52-56, mkt. develop. rep. org. chem, Calif. Chem. Co, 56-62, prod. specialist alpha olefins, Chevron Chem. Co, 62-71; MGR. MKT. DEVELOP, PAC. SOAP CO, 71- U.S.A, 41-45, Maj. Am. Chem. Soc. Surface chemistry related to friction and lubrication of surfaces; organic processes; petrochemicals, products and processes in laboratories. Address: Pacific Soap Co, 301 W. Market St, San Diego, CA 92101.

DANIELS, ROBERT (SANFORD), b. Indianapolis, Ind, Aug. 12, 27; m. 50; c. 4. MEDICINE, PSYCHIATRY. S, Cincinnati, 48, M.D, 51. Asst. prof. psychiat, Univ. Chicago, 57-63, assoc. prof. & acting chmn. dept, 63-68, prof. psychiat. & soc. med, assoc. dean soc. & community med. & dir. ctr. health admin. studies, 68-71; PROF. PSYCHIAT. & DIR. DEPT, UNIV. CINCINNATI, 71- Consult, Cook Co. Hosp, 58-68; Ill. State Psychiat. Inst, 59-68; Thresholds, 63-67. U.S.A.A.F, 46-47; U.S.A.F, 51-54. Mileau research on inpatient psychiatric service; group psychotherapy; clinical psychiatric research, medical care organization and financing. Address: Dept. of Psychiatry, University of Cincinnati, Cincinnati, OH 45221.

DANIELS, T(ROY) C(OOK), b. Sheridan, Mo, Aug. 27, 99; m. 29; c. 2. PHARMACEUTICAL CHEMISTRY. B.S, Univ. Mich, 23, hon. D.Sc, 67; Ph.D.(chem), Ind. Univ, 29; hon. LL.D, Univ. Calif, 67. Instr. pharm. & chem, State Col. Wash, 23-24, asst. prof, 24-27; asst. org. chem, Ind. Univ, 28-29; asst. prof. pharm, SCH. PHARM, UNIV. CALIF, SAN FRANCISCO, 29-33, prof. PHARMACEUT. CHEM, 33-67, dean, 44-67, asst. dean, 37-44; EMER. PROF. & DEAN, 67- Mem, Am. Coun. Pharmaceut. Educ, 48-55; comt, Am. Pharmaceut. Asn. mission, Japan, U.S. Army, 49-50; revision comt, U.S. Pharmacopoeia, 50-60. Am. Chem. Soc; Am. Pharmaceut. Asn. (Found. Achievement award, 62); Am. Asn. Cols. Pharm.(pres, 52-53); fel. N.Y. Acad. Sci; hon. mem. Pharmaceut. Soc. Japan; Japanese Pharmaceut. Asn. Medicinal chemistry; physical properties in relation to bactericidal action; chemical structure and biological action. Address: School of Pharmacy, University of California, San Francisco, CA 94122.

DANIELS, WARREN S(IDNEY), b. Somerville, Mass, May 18, 12; m. 40; c. 3. CIVIL ENGINEERING. S.B, Mass. Inst. Tech, 33. Jr. engr, U.S. GEOL. SURV, 37-40, asst. engr, WATER RESOURCES DIV, 40-45, assoc. engr, 45-51, hydraul. engr, 51-56, asst. dist. engr, 56-63, asst. chief PLANNING SECT, 63-65, CHIEF, 65- Am. Geophys. Union. Water resources investigations; hydrology; hydraulics. Address: Water Resources Division, U.S. Geological Survey, 2223 GSA Bldg, Washington, DC 20242.

DANIELS, W(ILEY) E(DGAR), b. Reading, Pa, Oct. 23, 30; m. 60; c. 3. ORGANIC CHEMISTRY. B.S, Lebanon Valley Col, 54, M.S, Delaware, 56, fel, 54-58, Ph.D.(chem), 59. Res. chemist, cent. res. lab, Gen. Aniline & Film Corp, Easton, 58-70; SR. RES. CHEMIST, AIR PROD. & CHEM, INC, 70- Am. Chem. Soc. Organic synthesis and reaction mechanisms; polymer research. Address: 3760 Baldwin Dr, Easton, PA 18042.

DANIELS, WILLIAM B(URTON), b. Buffalo, N.Y, Dec. 21, 30; m. 58. PHYSICS. B.S, Buffalo, 52, M.S, Case, 55, Nat. Carbon Co. fel, 55-57, Ph.D, 57. Instr. physics, Case, 57-58, asst. prof, 58-59; res. scientist, res. labs, Nat. Carbon Co, 59-61; asst. prof. PHYSICS, PRINCETON, 61-62, assoc. prof, 63-67, PROF, 67- Consult, Bell Tel. Labs, 69-; res. collab, Brookhaven Nat. Lab. Am. Phys. Soc. Solid state and lattice dynamics at high pressure; solidified rare gases and molecular solids. Address: Dept. of Solid State Sciences, Princeton University, Princeton, NJ 08540.

DANIELS, WILLIAM F(OWLER), b. New Bern, N.C, Feb. 22, 20; m. 47; c. 3. BIOCHEMICAL ENGINEERING. B.S.Ch.E, La. State, 42; M.S, Florida, 50; Cincinnati, 52; Ph.D.(bact. physiol), Kentucky, 57. Consult. engr. & chemist bldg. mat, H.C. Nutting Co, 47-48; asst. indust. & eng. exp. sta, Florida, 49; res. bacteriologist water bact, environ. health ctr, U.S. Pub. Health Serv, 50-51; asst. bact, Kentucky, 52; res. chemist, hwy. res. lab, State Dept. Hwy, Ky, 53-55, head chem. sect, 56; prin. investr. biochem. eng, pilot plants div, Ft. Detrick, 56-58, process res. div, 58-61, process develop. div, 61-71; BIOLOGIST CONSULT, APPL. SCI. DIV, U.S. ADV. MAT. CONCEPTS AGENCY, ALEXANDRIA, VA, 71- Consult, 59- U.S.A, 42-47, Res, 47-, Col. Am. Soc. Microbiol; Am. Chem. Soc; Sci. Res. Soc. Am; fel. Am. Inst. Chem. Paper electrophoresis of carbohydrate compounds; constitution and characterization of asphalt; organic synthesis via microbial oxidation; sterile filtrations; submerged tissue and continuous bacterial fermentation. Address: 2119 Spout Spring Rd, Frederick, MD 21701.

DANIELS, WILLIAM R(ICHARD), b. Dayton, Iowa, Apr. 16, 31; m. 51; c. 4. RADIOCHEMISTRY. B.S, Iowa State, 53; M.A, Washington (St. Louis), 55; Ph.D.(radiochem), New Mexico, 65. STAFF MEM. RADIOCHEM, LOS ALAMOS SCI. LAB, 57- U.S.A.F, 53-57, Capt. Am. Chem. Soc; fel. Am. Inst. Chem. Short-lived fission products; nuclear spectroscopy; emanation techniques. Address: Los Alamos Scientific Lab, Box 1663, Los Alamos, NM 87544.

DANIELS, WILLIAM WARD, b. Norfolk, Va, Apr. 13, 26; m. 48; c. 6. PHYSICAL CHEMISTRY, SPECTROSCOPY. B.S, La. State, 49, M.S, 50, Ph.D. (phys. chem), 54. Res. chem, dacron res. lab, E.I. DU PONT DE NEMOURS & CO, INC, 53-58, res. supvr, 58-62, sr. supvr, Chattanooga Tech. Lab, 62-64, res. mgr, Carothers Res. Lab, 64-67, tech. supt, Seaford Tech. Lab, 67-69, LAB. DIR, DACRON RES. LAB, 69- U.S.A, 44-46. Am. Chem. Soc. Infrared and raman spectroscopy; fiber structure-property relationships. Address: 161 Whitehall Dr, Kinston, NC 28501.

DANIELSON, DAVID MURRAY, b. Aurora, Nebr, Feb. 24, 29; m. 53; c. 3. ANIMAL NUTRITION. B.S, Nebraska, 52, M.S, 58; Ph.D.(animal prod), Utah state, 64. ASSOC. PROF. ANIMAL NUTRIT, UNIV. NEBR, NORTH PLATTE, 58- U.S.A, 46-48. Am. Soc. Animal Sci. Carbohydrates for baby pig rations; limited feeding of growing-finishing swine rations; source and quantity of nitrogen and energy for swine gestation rations; automatic in rearing baby pigs; feeding corn, millet, wheat, grain sorghum alone or in combination to finishing swine. Address: North Platte Station, University of Nebraska, North Platte, NE 69101.

DANIELSON, DONALD ALFRED, b. Santa Maria, Calif, June 21, 42; m. 62; c. 2. APPLIED MATHEMATICS & MECHANICS. B.S, Mass. Inst. Technol, 64; M.A, Harvard, 65, fel & Ph.D.(appl. math), 68. ASST. PROF. APPL. MATH, UNIV. VA, 68- Development of equations for thin elastic shells and their application to problems such as the deformation of red blood cells. Address: Dept. of Applied Mathematics, University of Virginia, Charlottesville, VA 22904.

DANIELSON, GORDON C(HARLES), b. Dover, Idaho, Oct. 28, 12; m. 39; c. 4. PHYSICS. B.A, British Columbia, 33, M.A, 35; Ph.D.(physics), Purdue, 40. Research physicist, U.S. Rubber Co, Detroit, 40-41; asst. prof. physics, Idaho, 41-42; staff mem, radiation lab, Mass. Inst. Tech, 42-46; tech. staff mem, Bell Tel. Labs, 46-48; assoc. prof. PHYSICS, IOWA STATE UNIV, 48-53, prof, 53-64; DISTINGUISHED PROF. COL. SCI. & HUMANITIES, 64- Sr. physicist, Inst. Atomic Res, Guggenheim fel, Cambridge, 58-59; Am. Inst. Physics,vis. scientist, 60- Consult, Nat. Sci. Found, 63-66; univ. adv, Texas Instruments, Inc, 64-68. Chmn. comt. thermoelec. conversion, Off. Naval Res, 58; mem. metall. & solid state rev. comt, Argonne Nat. Lab, 60-63, chmn, 62-63; solid state sci. panel, Nat. Res. Coun, 63- With Off. Sci. Res. & Develop; Nat. Defense Res. Comt; U.S.A.A.F, 44. Fel. Am. Phys. Soc. Solid state physics; electrical conductivities and Hall coefficients of metals and semiconductors; thermal conductivity and thermal diffusivity of metals; diffusion coefficients and specific heats of metals; optical properties of counting diamonds; physical properties of sodium tungsten bronze; ferroelectric crystals; radar beacons; x-ray diffraction of liquids, Fourier analysis. Address: Dept. of Physics, Iowa State University, Ames, IA 50010.

DANIELSON, GORDON K(ENNETH), b. Burlington, Iowa, Dec. 5, 31; m. 61; c. 6. CARDIOVASCULAR SURGERY. B.A, Pennsylvania, 53, M.D, 56. Asst. instr. surg, Pennsylvania, 57-61, instr, sch. med, 61-62, assoc, 62-65, asst. prof, 65; assoc. prof, col. med, Kentucky, 65-67; ASST. PROF. SURG, MAYO GRAD. SCH. MED, UNIV. MINN, ROCHESTER, 67-, CONSULT. CARDIOVASCULAR SURG, MAYO CLIN, 67- Fel, Harrison Dept. Surg. Res, Pennsylvania, 57-62; phys. med. & rehab, 59-60; Am. Cancer Soc, 60-61, diagnosis & treatment of cancer, 61-62; Markle scholar, 62-67; vis. fel. to Dr. Clarence Crafoord, Stockholm, Sweden, 63-64; gen. & thoracic surgeon, hosp, Univ. Pennsylvania, 62-65, asst. chief surg. div. I, 62-65, asst. attending physician, dept. surg. & surg. specialities, Phila. Gen. Hosp, 64-65; attending physician Vet. Admin. Hosp, Phila, 64-65; assoc. surg. & chief cardiac surg, Univ. Hosp, Lexington, Ky, 66-67. Consult, Vet. Admin. Hosp, Lexington, Ky, 66-67; U.S. Pub. Health Serv. Hosp, 66-67; St. Mary's Hosp, Rochester, Minn, 67- Mem, cent. adv. comt, coun. cardiovasc. surg, Am. Heart Asn. Dipl, Am. Bd. Surg. & Am. Bd. Thoracic Surg, 63. AAAS; fel. Am. Col. Surg; Am. Fedn. Clin. Res; Am. Heart Asn; Am. Thoracic Soc; Am. Med. Asn; fel. Am. Col. Cardiol; fel. Am. Col. Chest Physicians; Soc. Thoracic Surg; Am. Soc. Artificial Internal Organs; Am. Asn. Thoracic Surg; Asn. Acad. Surg; Soc. Vascular Surg; Int. Cardiovasc. Soc. Cardiac physiology; cardiac and vascular surgery; cardiac transplantation; pacemaker function. Address: Surgical Section, Mayo Clinic, Rochester, MN 55901.

DANIELSON, JOHN T(ALMADGE), Exp. Psychol, see Suppl. I to 11th ed, Soc. & Behav. Vols.

DANIELSON, L(ORAN) L(EROY), b. Havelock, Nebr, July 2, 13; m. 33. PLANT PHYSIOLOGY. A.B, Iowa, 38, M.S, 40, Ph.D.(plant physiol), 41. Chemist & plant physiologist, Calif. Packing Corp, Ill, 41-44; asst. prof. bot, Mont. State Col, 45; research asst. & prof. hort, Iowa State Col, 45; PLANT PHYSIOLOGIST, Va. Truck Exp. Sta, 45-57; U.S. DEPT. AGR, AGR. RES. SERV, 57- Am. Chem. Soc; Am. Soc. Plant Physiol; Am. Soc. Hort. Sci; Weed Sci. Soc. Am. Nutrition of vegetable crops; chemical weed control; quality control of vegetable canning crops; photoperiodic response of plants. Address: Weed Investigation, Agricultural Research Service, U.S. Dept. of Agriculture, Beltsville, MD 20705.

DANIELSON, ROBERT E, b. Boy River, Minn, Dec. 14, 31; m. 57; c. 4. ASTROPHYSICS. B.S, Minnesota, 53, M.S, 55, Ph.D.(physics), 58. Res. assoc. & lectr. cosmic ray physics, Minnesota, 57-58; res. assoc. solar physics, PRINCETON, 58-62, asst. prof. ASTROPHYS. SCI, 62-65, assoc. prof, 65-68, PROF, 68- Am. Astron. Soc. Solar and planetary physics; high resolution astronomical photography. Address: Dept. of Astronomy, Princeton University, Princeton, NJ 08540.

DANIELSON, ROBERT E(LDON), b. Brush, Colo, Jan. 14, 22; m. 49; c. 2. SOIL PHYSICS. B.S, Colorado State, 48; M.S, Cornell, 49, Ph.D.(soil physics), Illinois, 55. Instr. soils, COLO. STATE UNIV, 49-52, asst. prof. SOIL PHYSICS, 55-58, assoc. prof, 58-64, PROF, 64- U.S.A.A.F, 42-45. Am. Soc. Agron; Soil Sci. Soc. Am. Soil physical properties; influence on the growth of plants; irrigation; soil aeration and structure. Address: Dept. of Agronomy, Colorado State University, Ft. Collins, CO 80521.

DANIELSON, WARREN E(VALD), b. Ft. Collins, Colo, Feb. 10, 23; m. 46; c. 2. PHYSICS. Fel, Calif. Inst. Tech, 52, Ph.D.(physics), 52. Mem. tech. staff, phys. electronics, BELL TEL. LABS, 52-57, head mil. res. dept, 57-60, dir, 60-66, EXEC. DIR, TRANSMISSION DIV, 66- U.S.A.A.F, 43-45, 1st Lt. Am. Phys. Soc. X-ray diffraction; defensive weapons systems; high frequency noise in electron streams; low noise microwave tubes; and parametric amplifiers; millimeter wave tuves; microwave systems; telecommunications transmission and maintenance systems. Address: Transmission Division, Bell Telephone Labs, Holmdel, NJ 07733.

DANIS, PETER G(ODFREY), b. Ottawa, Ont, Can, April 12, 09; nat; m. 31; c. 10. PEDIATRICS. B.S, St. Louis, 29, M.D, 31, fel, 32-34, M.S, 35. Asst. instr, pediat, SCH. MED, ST. LOUIS UNIV, 35-37, instr, 38-40, sr. instr, 41-47, assoc. prof, 48-50, PROF. CLIN. PEDIAT, 51- Chmn. dept. pediat, Univ. Hosps, St. Louis, 47-56; chief of staff, Cardinal Glennon Mem. Hosp. for Children, 56-58. Mem. Nat. Adv. Comt. United Cerebral Palsy Asn; pediatrician med. adv. bd. special ed, St. Louis county pub. schs. Am. Acad. Pediat; Am. Med. Asn; fel. Am. Acad. Cerebral Palsy; assoc. mem. Am. Acad. Neurol; Soc. Res. Child Develop. Neurology; cerebral palsy; convulsive disorders. Address: 2821 Ballas Rd, St. Louis, MO 63131.

DANISHEFSKY, ISIDORE, b. Poland, Apr. 3, 23; nat; m. 51; c. 2. ORGANIC & BIOLOGICAL CHEMISTRY. B.A, Yeshiva Univ, 44; M.Sc, N.Y. Univ, 47, Ph.D.(chem), 51. Asst. chem, Yeshiva,Univ, 44-46; res. chemist, Best Effect Chem. Co, 47; asst. chem, N.Y. Univ, 47-51; res. assoc, Polytech. Inst. Brooklyn, 51-52; res. chemist, Food Res. Labs, 52; res. assoc, Col. Physicians & Surgeons, Columbia, 52-56; ASST. PROF. BIOCHEM, N.Y. MED. COL, 56-60, assoc. prof, 60-64, PROF, 65- Fel. AAAS; Am. Chem. Soc; Am. Soc. Biol. Chem. Mucopolysaccharide structure and metabolism; polysaccharides; cancer research. Address: Dept. of Biochemistry, New York Medical College, Fifth Ave. at 106th St, New York, NY 10029.

DANK, MILTON, b. Phila, Pa, Sept. 12, 20; m. 54; c. 2. SOLID STATE PHYSICS, MATHEMATICS. B.A, Pennsylvania, 47, Ph.D.(physics), 53. Asst. instr. physics, Pennsylvania, 47-53; res. physicist, Owens-Ill. Glass Co, 53-56; Burroughs Corp, 56; consult. physicist, missile & space div, Gen. Elec. Co, 56-60, mgr. superpressure studies, space sci. lab, 60-68, consult. physicist laser effects, 68-71; CONSULT. SOLID STATE PHYSICS, NDA, INC, 71- U.S.A.A.F, 40-45, 1st Lt. Am. Phys. Soc; Am. Inst. Aeronaut. & Astronaut. Effect of dynamic high pressures on solids; shock wave phenomena in solids; equations of state of solids at megabar pressures; hypervelocity particle impact effects; laser effects on solids. Address: NDA, Inc, 1022 Serpentine, Wyncote, PA 19095.

DANKS, ARTHUR GORDON, b. Allamuchy, N.J, Dec. 10, 06; m; c. 4. VETERINARY MEDICINE. B.S, Pa. State Col, 29; D.V.M, Cornell Univ, 33. Asst. prof. vet. med, Kans. State Col, 34-36; instr. VET. SURG, Cornell Univ, 36-39, asst. prof, 40-41, assoc. prof, 42-44, prof, 45-48; Univ. Pa,

49-50; CORNELL UNIV, 50-70, head dept. & dir. large animal hosp, 50-62, dir, student admin, 62-70, EMER. PROF, 70- Ed, Cornell Veterinarian, 39-41. Am. Vet. Med. Asn. Surgical technique; anesthesia; chemotherapy. Address: 1620 Hanshaw Rd, Ithaca, NY 14850.

DANLY, DONALD E, b. Washington, D.C, June 14, 29; m. 53; c. 3. CHEMICAL ENGINEERING. B.Ch.E, Cornell, 52; Ph.D.(chem. eng), Florida, 58. Chem. engr, TEXTILES DIV, MONSANTO CO, 58-60, sr. chem. engr, 60-62, proj. leader CHEM. PROCESS DEVELOP, PILOT PLANT, 62-64, supvr, 64-65, SECT. HEAD, 65- U.S.A.F, 52-54, 1st Lt. Am. Inst. Chem. Eng; Am. Chem. Soc. Pilot plant studies on new and improved chemical processes for manufacture of intermediates used in production of synthetic fibers. Address: Textiles Division, Monsanto Co, Box 1507, Pensacola, FL 32502.

DANN, F(RANK) W(ARREN), b. Hamburg, Ger, Apr. 18, 11; nat; m. 37; c. 3. PHARMACEUTICAL CHEMISTRY. Hamburg, Ger, 33, Wuerzberg, 32-33; Ph.D.(chem), Genoa, 36. Chemist, Buffington, Inc, Mass, 40-44; Schering Corp, N.J, 44-48; Desitin Chem. Co, 48-63; CHEMIST IN CHARGE PROD, FINE CHEM. DIV, AM. HOECHST CORP, 63- Am. Chem. Soc;.Am. Inst. Chem; Am. Pharmaceut Asn. Pharmaceuticals; vitamins and hormones; fine chemicals. Address: 33 Nichols Lane, East Greenwich, RI 02818.

DANN, JOHN R(OBERT), b. Minneapolis, Minn, Sept. 6, 21; m. 43; c. 3. ORGANIC CHEMISTRY. B.A, South Dakota, 43; Ph.D.(chem), Colorado, 52. Chemist, State Chem. Lab, S.Dak, 41-43; EASTMAN KODAK CO, 43-44; group leader, 46-48, res. chemist, RES. LABS, 52-58, RES. ASSOC, 58- U.S.N.R, 44-46, Lt.(jg). Am. Chem. Soc. High polymers; Diels-Alder reaction; chemistry of gelatin; heterocyclic chemistry; theory of adhesion. Address: 182 Pinegrove Ave, Rochester, NY 14617.

DANNA, PETER ANTHONY, b. N.Y.C, June 23, 38; m. 60; c. 1. CHEMICAL ENGINEERING, ELECTROCHEMISTRY. B.Ch.E, Pratt Inst, 59, M.Ch.E, 62; Am. Electroplaters Soc. fel, Columbia, 64-66, Samuel Ruben fel, 66, D.Eng.Sc.(chem. eng), 67. Qual. control engr, steel & tubes div, Repub. Steel Corp, 59-60; res. engr, Engelhard Industs, 60-63; sr. res. engr, OLIN CORP, 66-71, MGR. PROCESS DEVELOP, 71- Electrochem. Soc.(ed, indust. electrolytics div, electrochem. tech. sect, jour, 69-); Am. Inst. Chem. Eng; Int. Electrochem. Soc. Electrochemical engineering in the areas of chlor-alkali production; hydrocarbon fuel cell systems; metal deposition mechanisms and kinetics. Address: Olin Corp, New Haven, CT 06504.

DANNENBERG, ARTHUR M(ILTON), JR, b. Phila, Pa, Oct. 17, 23; m. 48; c. 3. PATHOLOGY, IMMUNOLOGY. A.B, Swarthmore Col, 44; M.D, Harvard, 47; M.A, Pennsylvania, 51, Ph.D.(microbiol), 52. Intern, Albert Einstein Med. Center, 47-48; res. resident, Children's Hosp. of Phila, Pennsylvania, 48-49, Nat. Tuberc. Asn. fel. exp. path, Henry Phipps Inst, 50-52; Nat. Res. Coun. fel. biochem, Utah, 52-54; asst. prof. exp. path, Henry Phipps Inst, Pennsylvania, 56-64, microbiol, sch. med. & grad. sch. arts & sci, 58-64; ASSOC. PROF. RADIOL. SCI, SCH. HYG. & ASSOC. PROF. PATH, SCH. MED, JOHNS HOPKINS UNIV, 64- Dipl, Am. Bd. Microbiol; dipl, Nat. Bd. Med. Examiners. U.S.A, 43-46; U.S.N, 54-56, Lt. Comdr. Am. Soc. Exp. Path; Am. Asn. Immunol; Histochem. Soc; Soc. Exp. Biol. & Med; Am. Chem. Soc; Am. Thoracic Soc; Am. Soc. Microbiol. Reticuloendothelial Soc. Enzymes in pathogenesis of injury by allergic and infectious diseases and by radiation; tuberculosis; macrophages. Address: Dept. of Radiological Science, Johns Hopkins University School of Hygiene, 615 N. Wolfe St, Baltimore, MD 21205.

DANNENBERG, E(LI) M, b. Bridgeport, Conn, Oct. 10; 17; m. 44; c. 3. CHEMICAL ENGINEERING. S.B, Mass. Inst. Tech, 39, scholar, S.M, 40. Res. assoc, div. indust. cooperation, Mass. Inst. Tech, 40-43; res. chemist, labs, Am. Cyanamid Co, Conn, 43-44; Sprague Elec. Co, Mass, 44-45; mgr. rubber lab, Godfrey L. Cabot, Inc, 45-50, assoc. dir, res, 50-57, dir. res, CABOT CORP, 57-63, dir. res. & develop, 63-68, V.PRES. & SCI. DIR, PERFORMANCE CHEM. GROUP, 68- Am. Chem. Soc; Am. Inst. Chem; fel. Brit. Inst. Rubber Indust, N.Y. Acad. Sci. Rheology of clays; technology of carbon blacks; melamine and urea resins; surface chemistry of fine pigments; mechanism of rubber reinforcement; cross-linking and reinforcement of polyethylene. Address: 125 High St, Boston, MA 02176.

DANNENBERG, JOSEPH, b. N.Y.C. PHYSICAL ORGANIC & THEORETICAL CHEMISTRY. A.B, Columbia Col, 62; Nat. Sci. Found. fel, Calif. Inst. Technol, 62-63, Nat. Insts. Health fel, 63-66, Ph.D.(chem), 67. U.S. Pub. Health Serv. fel. theoret. chem, Centre du Mécanique Ondulatoire Appliquée, Paris, 66-67; res. assoc. phys. org. chem, Columbia Univ, 67-68; ASST. PROF. CHEM, HUNTER COL, 68- Am. Chem. Soc; Am. Phys. Soc; The Chem. Soc. Semiempirical theoretical energy surfaces for organic intermediates and transition states; structures of carbonium ions; internal energy transfer; intermediacy of vibrationally excited molecules in solution photochemistry; photochemistry of organometallic compounds. Address: Dept. of Chemistry, Hunter College, 695 Park Ave, New York, NY 10021.

DANNENBERG, KONRAD K, b. Weissenfels, Germany, Aug. 5, 12; U.S. citizen; m. 44; c. 1. MECHANICAL ENGINEERING. M.S, Hanover Tech, 38; Frankfurt, 39-40. Asst. combustion eng, Hanover Tech, 38-39; engr, VDO, Frankfurt, 39-40; rocket test sta, Peenemuende, 41-45; U.S. Army, Ft. Bliss, Tex, 45-50, develop. opers, Redstone Arsenal, Ala, 50-55, dir. Jupiter prog, Army Ballistic Missile Agency, 55-60, MARSHALL SPACE FLIGHT CENTER, NASA, 60-70, DEP. DIR, MISSIONS & PAYLOAD PLANNING PROG. DEVELOP, 70- Am. Inst. Aeronaut. & Astronaut; Am. Astronaut. Soc; Hermann Oberth Soc. Combustion engineering; rocket engine development; space vehicle design, test, check-out and launching; space station design and experiments. Address: Missions & Payload Planning Program Development, NASA-Marshall Space Flight Center, Huntsville, AL 35812.

DANNENBURG, WARREN N(ATHANIEL), b. Tulsa, Okla, Jan. 9, 26; m. 49; c. 3. BIOCHEMISTRY, NUTRITION. B.S, Va. Polytech, 48; fel, Agr. & Mech. Col, Tex, 53-57, M.S, 55, Ph.D.(biochem, nutrit), 57. Res. microbiologist, S.E. Massengill Co, 48-53; res. biochemist, R.J. Reynolds Tobacco Co, 57-60; res. asst. prof. biochem, Bowman Gray Sch. Med, 60-

65; RES. BIOCHEMISTRY, A.H. ROBINS CO, 65- Nat. Insts. Health career develop. award, 64-65. Am. Chem. Soc. Am. Inst. Nutrit; Soc. Exp. Biol. & Med. Unidentified growth factors; lipid metabolism. Address: Research Dept, A.H. Robins Co, 1211 Sherwood Ave, Richmond, VA 23220.

DANNER, DEAN JAY, b. Milwaukee, Wis, Sept. 26, 41; m. 68; c. 1. BIOCHEMISTRY. B.S, Lakeland Col, 63; M.S, North Dakota, 65, Nat. Insts. Health fel, 65-67, Ph.D.(biochem), 68. Res. fel. biochem, St. Jude Hosp, Univ. Tennessee, 67-70; ASST. PROF. CHEM, NORTHWEST. STATE UNIV, 70- AAAS; Am. Chem. Soc. Oxidative-phosphorylation; enzymology, purification and characterization of oxidative enzymes. Address: Dept. of Chemistry, Northwestern State University, Natchitoches, LA 71457.

DANNER, ELLIS, b. Astoria, Ill, Mar. 4, 07; m. 40; c. 1. HIGHWAY ENGINEERING, TRANSPORTATION. B.S, Illinois, 30, M.S, 49. Inspector & resident engr. hwy. construct, Ill. State Div. Hwys, 30-34, soils & res. engr, 34-40; asst. & assoc. prof. civil eng, UNIV. ILL, URBANA, 46-51, PROF. HWY. ENG. & DIR. ILL. COOP. HWY. RES. PROG, 51- Mem, Nat. Defense Exec. Reserve, 60-; Ill. Hwy. Study Comn, 64-; transportation systems planning group, Hwy. Res. Bd, Nat. Acad. Sci-Nat. Res. Coun, 71- Faculty travel award for summer hwy. transportation study in Europe, 63. C.Eng, 40-46, Lt. Col. Am. Soc. Test. & Mat. Highway engineering; materials and pavement behavior; urban unit and transportation systems. Address: 205 Engineering Hall, University of Illinois, Urbana, IL 61801.

DANNER, HORACE R, b. Pittsburgh, Pa, Aug. 13, 25; m. 50; c. 2. SOLID STATE PHYSICS. B.A, Oberlin Col, 49; M.S, Pa. State, 51, Ph.D.(physics), 54. Instr. physics, Pa. State, 53-54; vis. res. assoc, Brookhaven Nat. Lab, 54-57; vis. res. physicist, Center Study Nuclear Energy, Mol, Belgium, 57-60; assoc. physicist, Brookhaven Nat. Lab, 60-63; assoc. prof. PHYSICS, UNIV. MO-COLUMBIA, 63-69, PROF, 69- Nat. Sci. Found. grant, 65- Consult, Picatinny Arsenal & Army Mat. Res. Agency, Watertown Arsenal, Mass, 63-68. U.S.A, 44-46. Am. Phys. Soc; Am. Asn. Physics Teachers. Crystal structure determination utilizing neutron diffraction and the investigation of the motional dynamics of solids and liquids using the experimental techniques of neutron inelastic scattering. Address: Dept. of Physics, University of Missouri-Columbia, Columbia, MO 65201.

DANNER, RONALD PAUL, b. New Holland, Pa, Aug. 29, 39; m. 60; c. 2. CHEMICAL ENGINEERING. B.S, Lehigh, 61, M.S, 63, Ph.D.(chem. eng), 66. Sr. chemist, Eastman Kodak Labs, 65-67; ASST. PROF. CHEM. ENG, PA. STATE UNIV, 67- Am. Inst. Chem. Eng; Am. Chem. Soc; Am. Soc. Eng. Educ. Physical absorption of gas mixtures; adsorption of dyes from solution; bubble separation processes; physical properties of hydrocarbons; thermodynamics. Address: 169 Fairlawn Ave, State College, PA 16801.

DANNER, WILBERT R(OOSEVELT), b. Seattle, Wash, Feb. 28, 24. GEOLOGY. B.Sc, Washington (Seattle), 46, M.Sc, 49, Ph.D.(geol), 57. Asst, Washington (Seattle), 46-50; instr, Everett Jr. Col, 50; Col. of Wooster, 50-54; UNIV. B.C, 54-57, asst. prof. GEOL, 57-63, assoc. prof, 63-67, PROF, 67- Consult, Permanente Cement Co, 48; Northwest Portland Cement Co, 49-57; Riverside Cement Co, 56. Geol. Soc. Am; Soc. Econ. Paleont. & Mineral; Mineral Soc. Am; Am. Asn. Petrol. Geol; Mineral. Asn. Can; Nat. Asn. Geol. Teachers; Geol. Asn. Can. General geology; stratigraphy and regional geology; limestone. Address: Dept. of Geology, University of British Columbia, Vancouver 8, B.C, Can.

DANNER, W(ILLIAM) F(RED), b. Utica, N.Y, Feb. 5, 21; m. 44; c. 2. CHEMISTRY. A.B, Marietta Col, 43. Res. chemist, nitrogen div, Solvay Process Co, 43-48; chief chemist, Beaunit Fibers Div, Beaunit Corp, 64-66, tech. supt, Utica Plant, 66-71; STAFF CHEMIST, AM. VISCOSE DIV, FMC CORP, 71- Am. Chem. Soc; Am. Asn. Textile Chem. & Colorists; Am. Soc. Test. & Mat. Water treatment; analytical and cellulose chemistry; vicose rayon process. Address: 660 E. Walnut St, Lewiston, PA 17044.

D'ANNESSA, A(NTHONY) T(HOMAS), b. Youngstown, Ohio, July 10, 33; m. 57; c. 2. METALLURGY. B.W.E, Ohio State Univ, 58, M.Sc, 60. Res. engr, Columbus Div, N.Am. Aviation, Inc, 55-59; eng. exp. sta, Ohio State Univ, 59-61; sr. scientist, Lockheed-Palo Alto Lab. Div, LOCKHEED AIRCRAFT CORP, 61-65, RES. SCIENTIST, LOCKHEED-GA. RES. LAB. DIV, 65- Consult, 64-; tech. adv, consult. & mem. bd. dirs, Weldwire, Inc, Ga, 70- U.S.A, 52-54. Am. Soc. Metals; Am. Welding Soc.(award, 71). Welding engineering; effects of welding on heat-treat cracking of superalloys; fracture behavior of weldments; weld metal solidification mechanics; diffusion bonding of refractory and reactive metals; development of advanced nondestructive testing techniques. Address: 303 Ithica Dr. S.E, Marietta, GA 30060.

DANNHAUSER, WALTER, b. Munich, Ger, June 2, 30; nat; m. 53; c. 3. PHYSICAL CHEMISTRY. B.Sc, Rutgers, 51; Ph.D.(chem), Brown, 54. Res. chemist, E.I. du Pont de Nemours & Co, 54-56; proj. assoc. CHEM, Wisconsin, 56-57; asst. prof, Buffalo, 57-62; ASSOC. PROF, STATE UNIV, N.Y. BUFFALO, 62- AAAS; Am. Chem. Soc. Polymer physical chemistry; dielectrics. Address: Dept. of Chemistry, Acheson Hall, State University of New York at Buffalo, Buffalo, NY 14214.

DANNIS, MARK L(IBMAN), b. Los Angeles, Calif, Jan. 5, 17; m. 49; c. 4. PHYSICS. B.S, Armour Inst. Tech, 37; Ill. Inst. Tech, 37-39; M.S, Pennsylvania, 46. Jr. physicist, Gaertner Sci. Corp, Chicago, 37-39; instr. physics, Ill. Inst. Tech, 39; jr. physicist, Portland Cement Asn, Chicago, 39-41; asst. physicist & later assoc. physicist, U.S. Navy Dept, Baltimore, 42-44; assoc. physicist, ord. lab, Wash, D.C, 44-46; physicist, B.F. GOODRICH CO, 46-64, SR. RES. ASSOC, 64- AAAS; Am. Chem. Soc; Am. Phys. Soc. Sorption water on gels; rate process interpretation of adsorption and solution phenomena of high polymers; ionic conduction in non-aqueous media; sorption effects on mechanical properties; theory of rubbery behavior; glassy transitions and crystallization changes in polymers; time dependent mechanical properties including high speed tensile testing. Address: Research Center, B.F. Goodrich Co, Brecksville, OH 44141.

DANNLEY, RALPH LAWRENCE, b. Chicago, Ill, June 25, 14; m. 50; c. 3. CHEMISTRY. B.S, Denver, 36; Minnesota, 36-38; Ph.D.(org. chem), Chicago, 43. Res. chemist, Nat. Defense Res. Cmt, Chicago, 41-42, instr. chem, 42-43; dir. oil res, Devoe & Raynolds, Inc, 43-45; asst. prof. CHEM, CASE WEST. RESERVE UNIV, 45-57, assoc. prof, 57-64, PROF, 64- Am. Chem. Soc. Mechanism of polymerization; free radical chemistry; peroxides of elements other than carbon; heterocyclic phosphorus compounds; organic fluorine derivatives; aromatic arylsulfonoxylation. Address: Dept. of Chemistry, Case Western Reserve University, Cleveland, OH 44106.

DANOS, MICHAEL, b. Riga, Latvia, Jan. 10, 22; nat; m. 49; c. 2. NUCLEAR PHYSICS. M.S, Tech. Univ, Germany, 48; Ph.D.(physics), Heidelberg, 50. Jr. asst. weak current inst, Tech. Univ, Dresden, Germany, 44; asst. theoret. physics inst, Tech. Univ, Hanover, 48-49; Heidelberg, 49-50, physics inst, 51; res. assoc. radiation lab, Columbia, 52-54; PHYSICIST, NAT. BUR. STANDARDS, 54- Guggenheim fel, Heidelberg, 59-60, vis. prof, 59-60, 63; Maryland, 61; Freiburg & Saclay Nuclear Res. Ctr, France, 64. AAAS; Am. Phys. Soc; Fedn. Am. Sci. Theoretical nuclear physics; microwave physics. Address: National Bureau of Standards, Washington, DC 20234.

DANOWSKI, THADDEUS STANLEY, b. Wallington, N.J, Sept. 6, 14; m. 49; c. 1. MEDICINE. B.A, Yale, 36, M.D, 40. Asst. med, sch. med, Yale, 40-43, instr, 43-46, asst. prof, 46-47; PROF. MED, SCH. MED, UNIV. PITTSBURGH, 47-; CHIEF MED. & HEAD ENDOCRINE METAB. UNIT, MAGEE-WOMENS HOSP, 69- Guggenheim fel, 53. Intern, New Haven Hosp, 40-41; asst. res, 43-43; sr. staff physician, Presby, Children's & Women's Hosps, 47-; Elizabeth Steel Magee Hosp, 49-; Shadyside Hosp, 58-; consult, Vet. Admin. Hosp, 47-; spec. consult, Nat. Insts. Health, 57-61, 62- Achievement award, Polish Med. Alliance, 64; Banting Mem. Award, 64; Sword of Hope, Pa. div, Am. Cancer Soc, 66; Nat. Bronze Medal, Am. Cancer Soc, 68; Alfred Jurzykowski Award, 69. AAAS; Am. Soc. Clin. Invest; Am. Physiol. Soc; fel. Am. Col. Physicians; fel. Am. Med. Asn; Am. Diabetes Asn.(pres. elect, 64, pres, 65). Clinical investigation; fluid and electrolytes; diseases of the thyroid gland. Address: Dept. of Medicine, Magee-Womens Hospital, Pittsburgh, PA 15213.

DANSBY, DORIS, b. New Albany, Miss, Apr. 22, 18. BIOLOGY. B.A, Mississippi, 40; Cert. Med. Tech, Tennessee, 41. Med. technologist serol. & bact, Baptist Hosp. Lab, Tenn, 41-45; res. assoc. mycol. res, Lederle Labs. Div, Am. Cyanamid Co, N.Y, 45-54; pharmacologist hematol, MEAD JOHNSON RES. CTR, 54-63, SR. SCIENTIST, 63- Am. Soc. Microbiol; Am. Soc. Med. Technol; N.Y. Acad. Sci. Microbiology; antibiotics; mycology in relation to microorganisms producing antibiotics; hematologic aspects of the toxicology of potential therapeutic agents. Address: Mead Johnson Research Center, Evansville, IN 47721.

DANSER, JAMES W(EART), b. Long Branch, N.J, Oct. 15, 21; m. 46; c. 1. GEOLOGY. A.B, Colgate, 48; M.A, Missouri, 50. Eng. geologist clay deposits, prespecting dept, A.P. Green Fire Brick Co, 50-68, RAW MAT. MGR, A.P. GREEN REFRACTORIES CO, 68- Med.C, U.S.A, 42-46, Artil. C.R, 51-, 2nd Lt. Geol. Soc. Am. Refractory materials; geology of clay deposits. Address: 827 N. Calhoun, Mexico, MO 65265.

DANSEREAU, PIERRE, b. Montreal, Que, Can, Oct. 5, 11; m. 35. ECOLOGY. B.A, Montreal, 31; Centre des Recherches Agr. de Provence, 37-38; D.Sc. (plant taxon), Geneva, 39; hon. LL.D, Saskatchewan, 59; hon. D.Sc, New Brunswick, 59. Botanist, Montreal Bot. Garden, 39-40, asst. dir. tech. serv, 40-42; dir, Prov. Biogeog. Serv, 43-50; instr. bot, Montreal, 40-45; asst. prof, 45-50, asst. prof, Michigan, 50-52, assoc. prof, 52-55; chmn. dept. bot. & dean faculty sci, Montreal, 55-61; asst. dir. bot, New York Bot. Garden, 61-66, head dept. ecol, 61-68; PROF. ECOL, UNIV. MONTREAL, 68- Nat. Res. Coun. Can. grants, 40, 41, 44, 45-47, 48, 56-57, 59, 60; lectr, Macdonald Col, McGill, 42-44; Huyck Preserve grant, 44; Brazilian Res. Coun. & Nat. Geog. Coun. grant, 45, 46; vis. prof, Brazil, 46; Am. Philos. Soc. grant, 48; Nat. Sci. Found. grants, 54-55, 62-65; vis. prof, Paris, 58, New Zealand, 61, Puerto Rico, 63. Official Can. del, Pac. Sci. Cong, 49, del, 53, 61; Int. Bot. Cong, 54, 1st v.pres, 59; hon. counr, Adv. Coun. Sci. Res, Madrid, 60; hon. mem. Acad. Sci. Toulouse, 60. Mem. Baffin Land exped, 50. AAAS; Ecol. Soc. Am; Int. Soc. Plant Taxon; Am. Genetic Asn; fel. Am. Geog. Soc; Bot. Soc. Am; Soc. Study Evolution; Asn. Am. Geog; Torrey Bot. Club; fel. Royal Soc. Can; Can. Geog. Soc; Can. Inst. Forestry; Can. Soc. Natural Hist.(secy-gen, 40); French-Can. Asn. Adv. Sci.(secy-gen, 46, Parizean Medal, 65); Brit. Ecol. Soc; Bot. Soc. France; Italian Bot. Soc; Brazilian Geog. Soc; Int. Soc. Plant Geog. & Ecol; hon. mem. Royal Soc. N.Z. Taxonomy, cytology and evolution of Cistus, Potentilla, Viola and Acer; phytosociology of the St. Lawrence valley forests; comparative structure and dynamics of vegetation in tropical to arctic climates. Address: Faculty of Environmental Design, University of Montreal, P.O. Box 6128, Montreal, Que, Can.

DANSKIN, J(OHN) M(OFFATT), JR, b. Alhambra, Calif, Dec. 19, 23; m. 60; c. 3. MATHEMATICS. A.B, California, Los Angeles, 43; M.A, California, 48, Atomic Energy Cmn. fel, 48-49, Ph.D.(math), 49. Sci. analyst, opers. eval. group, U.S. Dept. Navy, 49-51, 53-55; res. mathematician, Rand Corp, 51-53; mem, Inst. Adv. Study, 55-58; asst. prof. math, Rutgers, 58-61; mem. staff, Inst. Naval Studies, Mass, 61-65; Ctr. Naval Anal, D.C, 65-68; PROF. MATH. & CHMN. DEPT, CLARK UNIV, 68- Consult, U.S. Air Force, 56-61; Jet Propulsion Lab. & RCA Corp, 60-61; mem. math. res. ctr, Univ. Wis, Madison, 67-68; U.S. Air Force grant, 70-; vis. prof, U.S. Naval Postgrad. Sch, Calif, 70- U.S.N.R, 43-46. Am. Math. Soc. Calculus of variations; topology; game theory; search theory; operations research. Address: Dept. of Mathematics, Clark University, Worchester, MA 01610.

DANSKY, LEONARD M(ARTIN), b. Bayonne, N.J, Aug. 16, 22; m. 53; c. 3. ANIMAL NUTRITION. B.S, Colo. Agr. & Mech. Col, 49; Ph.D.(nutrit), Cornell, 52. DIR. nutrit, D.A. Stickell & Sons, Inc, 52-55; RES, SAMUEL LIPMAN SONS, 55- U.S.N.R, 43-46. AAAS; Poultry Sci. Asn; Am. Chem. Soc; N.Y. Acad. Sci. Energy requirements of chickens. Address: Samuel Lipman Sons, P.O. Box 549, Augusta, ME 04430.

DANTI, AUGUST GABRIEL, b. New Eagle, Pa, Jan. 26, 23; m. 50; c. 1. PHARMACY, CHEMISTRY. B.S, Pittsburgh, 50, M.S, 52; Am. Found. Pharmaceut. Ed. fel, Ohio State, 54-55, Ph.D.(pharm), 55. Instr. PHARM, Pittsburgh, 52-53; asst. prof, Wayne State, 56-59; assoc. prof, SCH. PHARM,

NORTHEAST LA. UNIV, 59-64, PROF, 64-, head dept. allied health sci, 68-71. Serv. recog. award, Am. Heart Asn, 65, 67, 70; pres. award, Squibb & Sons, Inc, 69; McKesson-Robbins & Co, 69; A.H. Robins Bowl Hygeia, 70. U.S.A, 43-45, Sgt. AAAS; Am. Col. Apothecaries; Am. Asn. Col. Pharm.(serv. recog. award, 65, 66, 67); Acad. Pharmaceut. Sci; Am. Pharmaceut. Asn. The release of medicaments from various pharmaceutical dosage forms. Address: School of Pharmacy, College of Pharmacy & Allied Health Professions, Northeast Louisiana University, Monroe, LA 71201.

DANTIN, ELVIN J, SR, b. Golden Meadow, La, Jan. 13, 27; m. 47; c. 5. CIVIL ENGINEERING, WATER RESOURCES. B.S, La. State, 49, M.S, 52; Jones Mem. scholar. & Nat. Sci. Found. fel, Stanford, 58-60, Ph.D.(struct), 60. Instr. civil eng, LA. STATE UNIV, BATON ROUGE, 49-52, from asst. prof. to assoc. prof, 52-62, PROF. CIVIL ENG. & DIR. DIV. ENG. RES, 62-, DIR. LA. WATER RESOURCES RES. INST, 70- Consult, E.E. Evans, Consult. Engr, La, 54-58; Humble Oil & Ref. Co, Tex, 57; La. Dept. Pub. Works, 61. U.S.A, 44-47. Am. Soc. Civil Eng; Am. Soc. Eng. Educ; Am. Concrete Inst. Structural engineering; reinforced concrete; structures. Address: Division of Engineering Research, Louisiana State University, Baton Rouge, LA 70803.

D'ANTONIO, CARMINE R, b. Brooklyn, N.Y, Mar. 28, 31; m. 54; c. 6. PHYSICAL METALLURGY. B.M.E, Polytech. Inst. Brooklyn, 53, M.M.E, 56. Metallurgist, Curtiss-Wright Corp, 53-54; instr. METALL, POLYTECH. INST. BROOKLYN, 54-58, asst. prof, 58-63, assoc. prof, 63-68, PROF, 68- Nat. Sci. Found. res. grants, 63-71. Am. Soc. Metals; Am. Inst. Mining, Metall. & Petrol. Eng; N.Y. Acad. Sci. Mechanical behavior of thin metal films; solute-defect interactions in metals. Address: Dept. of Metallurgical Engineering, Polytechnic Institute of Brooklyn, 333 Jay St, Brooklyn, NY 11201.

D'ANTONIO, RENATO, b. Mamaroneck, N.Y, Nov. 18, 30; m. 55; c. 4. COMPUTER SCIENCE. B.S.E.E, Rhode Island, 56, IBM Corp. scholar, 63-65, Ph.D.(elec. eng), 65; M.S.E.E, Syracuse, 61. Staff engr, res. lab, fed. syst. div, IBM Corp, 56-61, commun. lab, 65-66, adv. engr, ctr. explor. studies, 66-68; PRES, INT. DATA SCI, INC, 68- U.S.N, 48-52. Inst. Elec. & Electronics Eng. Advanced digital communications systems; digital computer system design; information theory. Address: International Data Sciences, Inc, 100 Nashua St, Providence, RI 02904.

DANTZIG, GEORGE B(ERNARD), b. Portland, Ore, Nov. 8, 14; m. 36; c. 3. MATHEMATICAL STATISTICS. A.B, Maryland, 36; Horace Rackham scholar, Michigan, 36-37, M.A, 38; fel, California, 39-41, 46, Ph.D.(math), 46. Jr. statistician, U.S. Bur. Labor Statist, 37-39; statistician, Air Force, 41-45, chief mathematician, Air Force Hq. Comptroller, 45-52; res. mathematician, Rand Corp, 52-60; PROF. eng. sci. & chmn. oper. res. ctr, California, Berkeley, 60-66; OPER. RES. & COMP. SCI, STANFORD UNIV, 66- Mem. faculty, California, Los Angeles, 54-60. Nat. Acad. Sci; assoc. Am. Math. Soc; Inst. Math. Statist; fel. Economet. Soc; fel. Oper. Res. Soc; Soc. Indust. & Appl. Math; fel. Inst. Mgt. Sci.(pres, 66). Existence of similar regions in theory of mathematical statistics; mathematical theory of optimization in an interrelated system such as large scale enterprises; general theory of logistics. Address: Operations Research, Stanford University, Stanford, CA 94305.

DANTZLER, WILLIAM H(OYT), b. Mt. Holly, N.J, Aug. 25, 35; m. 59; c. 2. PHYSIOLOGY. A.B, Princeton, 57; M.D, Columbia Univ, 61; Ph.D.(zool), Duke Univ, 64. Intern med, hosp, Univ. Wash, 61-62; U.S. Pub. Health Serv. fel. zool, Duke Univ, 62-64; asst. prof. pharmacol, col. physicians & surgeons, Columbia Univ, 64-68; ASSOC. PROF. PHYSIOL, COL. MED, UNIV. ARIZ, 68- AAAS; Am. Soc. Zool; Am. Physiol. Soc. Comparative renal physiology; excretion of end products of nitrogen metabolism; control of excretion of ions and water in vertebrates. Address: Dept. of Physiology, College of Medicine, University of Arizona, Tucson, AZ 85724.

DANTZMAN, CHARLES L, b. St. John, Kans, Nov. 1, 17; m. 42; c. 2. SOIL CHEMISTRY. B.S, Univ. Ga, 53; M.A, Univ. Fla, 55, Ph.D.(soil chem), 60. ASST. SOILS CHEMIST, AGR. EXP. STA, UNIV. FLA, 59- U.S.A.F, 42-46. Am. Soc. Agron; Soil Sci. Soc. Am; Int. Soc. Soil Sci; Am. Inst. Chem. Soil fertility, genesis and morphology; botany; ecology; geology-geography; water quality; waste residue studies. Address: Agricultural Research Center, Ona, FL 33865.

DANZIG, MEYER H(ILLEL), b. Detroit, Mich, Aug. 6, 18; m. 41; c. 3. CHEMISTRY. B.S, Wayne, 39, M.S, 41; fel, Purdue, 41-44, Ph.D.(org. chem), 44. Asst. plastics, Case, 44-45; dir. res, chems. div, Glenn L. Martin Co, 46-50; head vinyl polymerization process develop, Naugatuck Chem. Div, U.S. Rubber Co, 50-55; plant mgr, Thompson Chem. Co, 55-60; chem. consult, 60-63; mem. staff, Pantasote Co, W.Va, 63-66; mgr. res. & develop, Cumberland Chem. Corp, N.J, 66-67, tech. dir, Airco Chem. & Plastics Div, 67-70; MGR. APPL. RES. & DEVELOP, AIR PROD. & CHEM, INC, 70- Mem. staff, Off. Sci. Res. & Develop, 44. Am. Chem. Soc. Polymerization; plastics. Address: Air Products & Chemicals, Inc, P.O. Box 4, Middlesex, NJ 08846.

DANZIG, MORRIS J(UDAH), b. Staten Island, N.Y, July 31, 25; m. 55; c. 2. ORGANIC & INORGANIC CHEMISTRY. B.S, Miami, 49, fel. & M.S, 51; E. Lilly & Res. Corp. fels, & Ph.D.(org. chem), Tulane, 53. Du Pont fel. org. chem, Minnesota, 53-54; supvry. chemist, North Regional Res. Lab, U.S. Dept. Agr, 54-56; from sr. org. chemist to head org. res, Lord Mfg. Co, 56-60; from sr. org. chemist to section leader, Am. Viscose Corp, 60-64; mgr. adv. develop. chem. & plastics, Gen. Tire & Rubber Co, 64-68; DIR. RES. & DEVELOP, Corn Prod. Corp, 68-70, CPC INT, 70- U.S.N, 43-46. Am. Chem. Soc. Nitrogen and sulfur organic systems heterocycles; organo metallics, carbohydrates, terpenes and other natural products; semiconductors; monomers and polymers; fatty acids; infrared and organic synthesis and mechanisms. Address: CPC International, Moffett Tech Center, Box 345, Argo, IL 60501.

DANZIGER, LAWRENCE, b. N.Y.C, July 17, 32; m. 60; c. 2. STATISTICS. B.A, City Col. New York, 53, M.A, 54; Ph.D.(indust. eng), N.Y. Univ, 71. Statistician, IBM CORP, 56-57, assoc. statistician, 57-58, staff statistician, 58-62, mgr. statist. anal, 62-68, mgr. appl. statist. res, 68-71, SR. STATISTICIAN, 71- Adj. prof, Union Col.(N.Y), 67- U.S.A, 54-56. Inst. Math. Statist; Am. Statist. Asn; Am. Soc. Qual. Control; Royal Statist. Soc. Applied statistics; statistical theory and application of extreme values to industrial reliability and quality control; statistical sampling plan theory and application. Address: 3 Spur Way, Poughkeepsie, NY 12603.

DAO, THOMAS L(ING) Y(UAN), b. Soochow, China, Apr. 27, 21; nat; m. 54; c. 4. MEDICINE. B.S, Soochow Univ, 40; M.S, St. Johns, China, 42, M.D, 45. Sr. fel. surg, Washington (St. Louis), 49-51; instr. sch. med, Chicago, 51-54, asst. prof, 54-57; SCH. MED, STATE UNIV. N.Y. BUFFALO, 57-66, RES. PROF. PHYSIOL, 66-, CHIEF DEPT. BREAST SURG, ROSWELL PARK MEM. INST, 57-; PROF. BIOL, NIAGARA UNIV, 67- AAAS; Am. Col. Surg; Endocrine Soc; Am. Asn. Cancer Res; N.Y. Acad. Sci; Soc. Exp. Biol. & Med; Soc. Univ. Surg; Am. Soc. Clin. Oncol. Physiology; endocrine physiology; endocrine aspect of neoplastic disease; chemical carcinogenesis; experimental pathology. Address: Roswell Park Memorial Institute, 666 Elm St, Buffalo, NY 14203.

DAO, TRONG TICH, m. 56; c. 3. COMPUTER ENGINEERING. B.S, Univ. Paris, 52; M.S, Nat. Sch. Advan. Telecommun, Paris, 55; M.S, Stanford Univ, 65. MEM. RES. STAFF, AMPEX CORP, REDWOOD CITY, 67- Inst. Elec. & Electronics Eng; Inst. Math. Statist. Digital memory systems; pattern recognition; applied probability theory to electrical engineering. Address: 22446 Linda Ann Ct, Cupertino, CA 95040.

DAOUD, ASSAAD S, b. Zebdani, Syria, Oct. 21, 23; U.S. citizen; m. 57; c. 3. PATHOLOGY. Damascus, 44-47; M.D, Paris, 51. Intern, St. Memmie Hosp, Chalons sur Marne, France, 50-51; path, Springfield Hosp, Mass, 52, res, 52-54; instr. path. & bact, ALBANY MED. COL, 54-56, asst. prof. PATH, 56-62, assoc. prof, 62-67, PROF, 67-; CHIEF LAB. SERV, VET. ADMIN. HOSP, 61- Mem, Coun. Arteriosclerosis & Coun. Epidemiol, Am. Heart Asn. Am. Med. Asn; Int. Acad. Path. Arteriosclerosis. Address: Laboratory Service, Veterans Administration Hospital, Albany, NY 12208.

DAOUD, GEORGES, b. Lattakiat, Syria, Mar. 27, 27; U.S. citizen; m. 54; c. 3. CARDIOLOGY. M.D, St. Joseph Univ, Beirut, 57. Asst. MED, COL. MED, UNIV. CINCINNATI, 61-67, CLIN. ASST. PROF, 67-, CLIN. ASSOC. PROF. PEDIAT, 67-; INSTR. & CLINICIAN, DEPT. INTERNAL MED. & DIR. CARDIAC LAB, GOOD SAMARITAN HOSP, 66- Am. Fedn. Clin. Res; assoc. fel. Am. Col. Chest Physicians; Am. Heart Asn.(fel. coun. clin. cardiol. & coun. thrombosis); fel. Am. Col. Cardiol; Int. Cardiovasc. Soc. Cardiac hemodynamics; phonocardiography; clinical cardiology. Address: Good Samaritan Hospital, 2328 Auburn Ave, Cincinnati, OH 45219.

D'AOUST, A(NDRE) L(UCIEN), b. Montreal, Que, Nov. 23, 40; m. 66; c. 2. PLANT PHYSIOLOGY & BIOCHEMISTRY. B.Sc, Univ. Montreal, 63, M.Sc, Queen's Univ.(Ont), 67, Ph.D.(plant physiol), 70. RES. SCIENTIST TREE BIOL, LAURENTIAN FOREST RES. CTR, LAND FOREST & WILDLIFE SERV, 69- Nat. Res. Coun. Can. fel, 70. AAAS; Am. Soc. Plant Physiol; Can. Soc. Plant Physiol; French-Can. Asn. Advan. Sci. Tree biology; tree physiology with special attention to genetic superiority. Address: Laurentian Forest Research Center, C.P. 3800, Ste-Foy 10, Que, Can.

D'AOUST, BRIAN GILBERT, b. Powell River, B.C, Mar. 7, 38; m. 59; c. 3. CELL PHYSIOLOGY, BIOCHEMISTRY. B.Sc, Queen's Univ.(Ont), 61; Earl J. Anthony Fund fel, Univ. Calif, San Diego, 61-67, Ph.D.(marine biol), 67. Nat. Res. Coun-Nat. Acad. Sci. res. fel. physiol, Naval Med. Res. Inst, Nat. Naval Med. Ctr, Md, 67-69; asst. res. physiologist, Univ. Calif. Naval Biol. Lab, Oakland, 70; INVESTR. HYPERBARIC RES. & DIVING PHYSIOL, VIRGINIA MASON RES. CTR, 70- Scientist, Seatransit Exped. & Bering Sea Exped, 68. AAAS; Am. Soc. Limnol. & Oceanog; Undersea Med. Soc; Aerospace Med. Asn. Catabolic processes in oxygen-adapted tissue and physiological studies of gas secretion in teleost swim bladder; natural, evolutionary and dynamic physiological adaptations to high gas and hydrostatic pressure; physiological adjustments to diving; hyperbaric physiology. Address: Virginia Mason Research Center, Division of Hyperbaric Research & Diving Physiology, 1000 Seneca St, Seattle, WA 98101.

DAOUST, DONALD ROGER, b. Worcester, Mass, Aug. 13, 35; m. 59; c. 3. MICROBIOLOGY. B.A, Connecticut, 57; M.S, Massachusetts, 59, Ph.D.(phage), 62. Sr. res. microbiologist, MERCK SHARP & DOHME RES. LABS, 62-70, RES. FEL, 70- AAAS; Am. Soc. Microbiol. Microbial production of natural substances. Address: Merck Sharp & Dohme Research Labs, Rahway, NJ 07065.

DAOUST, H(UBERT), b. Montreal, Que, Apr. 13, 28; m. 52; c. 4. PHYSICAL CHEMISTRY. B.Sc, Montreal, 50, M.Sc, 51, Ph.D.(chem), 54. Res. assoc, Baker Lab, Cornell, 53-54, asst. prof. CHEM, UNIV. MONTREAL, 54- Am. Chem. Soc; Chem. Inst. Can. Thermodynamics of high polymer solutions including polyelectrolytes and polypeptides; microcalorimetry; osmometry; viscosimetry; ultracentrifugation. Address: Dept. of Chemistry, University of Montreal, Montreal, Que, Can.

D'AOUST, MAURICE, b. Can, Dec. 26, 37. PLANT PHYSIOLOGY. B.Sc, Univ. Toronto, 61; Ph.D.(philos), Univ. Reading, 65. Res. off, Can. Dept. Agr, 65-66; ASST. PROF. BIOL, Univ. Sherbrooke, 66-67; UNIV. MONTREAL, 67- AAAS. Study of DNA and the RNA ribosomes of higher plant chloroplasts; study of DNA and RNA in relation to cold adaptation of higher plants. Address: Dept. of Biology, University of Montreal, P.O. Box 6128, Montreal 101, Que, Can.

DAOUST, ROGER, b. Valleyfield, Que, Oct. 13, 24; m. 50; c. 2. HISTOLOGY. B.Sc, Montreal, 47, M.Sc, 50; Ph.D.(anat), McGill, 53. Res. assoc, MONTREAL CANCER INST, NOTRE-DAME HOSP, 50-60, Nat. Cancer Inst. Can. res. scientist, 60-67, DIR. RES. LABS, 67-; PROF. ANAT, UNIV. MONTREAL, 67-, res. assoc. prof. med, 60-67. Damon Runyon Mem. Fund Cancer Res. fel, 52-55; Brit. Empire Cancer Campaign exchange fel, London, 55-56; Nat. Cancer Inst. Can. fel, Copenhagen, 56-57. AAAS; Histochem. Soc; Am. Asn. Cancer Res; N.Y. Acad. Sci. Cytology; histochemistry; nucleic acids metabolism in normal and neoplastic tissues. Address: Laboratoires de Recherche, Institut du Cancer de Montréal, 1560 Sherbrooke E, Montreal, Que, Can.

DAPPEN, GLEN MARSHALL, b. Guernsey, Iowa, Nov. 18, 35; m. 57; c. 3. ORGANIC CHEMISTRY. B.S, Wis. State Col, Superior, 57; Ph.D.(org. chem), Iowa State, 62. Res. chemist, EASTMAN KODAK CO, 61-64, sr. res. chemist, 64-69, RES. ASSOC, 70- Am. Chem. Soc. Organometallic chemistry; small ring organic compounds; synthetic organic, polymer and photographic chemistry. Address: Eastman Kodak Co, Research Lab, 343 State St, Rochester, NY 14650.

DAPPERT, GEORGE FREDERICK, b. New York, N.Y, Mar. 20, 22; m. 46; c. 3. CHEMICAL ENGINEERING; B.E, Yale, 43; M.Ch.E, Polytech. Inst. Brooklyn, 50. Shift supvr, Chas. Pfizer & Co, 46-48, supvr, 48-51, process engr, 51-56, proj. mgr, 56-60; gen. mgr, Isomet Corp, 60-61; mgr. process eng, dyestuff & chem. div, GAF CORP, N.Y, 61-65, dir. process eng, 65-66, plant mgr. photo plants, photo & reprod. div, 66-67, dir. mfg, photo opers, 68-69, GEN. MGR, INDUST. PHOTO DIV, 69- Consult, 61. U.S.N.R, 43-46, Lt. N.Y. Acad. Sci; fel. Am. Inst. Chem; Am. Inst. Chem. Eng. Science of mass production based upon chemistry, including process design, development, trouble shooting and new product introduction; management of all phases of production and development. Address: 57 Allwood Rd, Darien, CT 06820.

DAPPLES, EDWARD C(HARLES), b. Chicago, Ill, Dec. 13, 06; m. 31; c. 2. GEOLOGY. B.S, Northwestern, 28, M.S, 34; Townsend fel, Harvard, 34-35, M.A, 35; scholar, Wisconsin, 35-36, Ph.D.(geol), 38. Geologist, Zeigler Coal Co, 28; Truax-Traer Coal Co, 28-32, mine supt, 31-32; instr. GEOL. NORTHWEST. UNIV, 36-40, asst. prof, 41-42, assoc. prof, 42-51, PROF, 51- Asst. geologist, State Geol. Surv, Ill, 39; consult. geologist, Sinclair Oil Co, 45-50; Pure Oil Co, 51; sr. vis. scientist, Univ. Lausanne, 60-61; prof, Univ. Geneva, 70. AAAS; fel. Geol. Soc. Am; fel. Soc. Econ. Geol; Soc. Econ. Paleont. & Mineral.(pres, 70); Am. Inst. Min, Metall. & Petrol Eng; Am. Asn. Petrol. Geol; Am. Geophys. Union; Geochem. Soc; Int. Asn. Sedimentol. Petrography and deposition of sedimentary rocks. Address: Dept. of Geology, Northwestern University, Evanston, IL 60201.

D'APPOLONIA, BERT LUIGI, b. Capreol, Ont, Nov. 6, 39. CEREAL CHEMISTRY. B.A, Laurentian Univ, 62; M.S, N.Dak. State, 66, Ph.D.(cereal chem), 68. ASST. PROF. CEREAL CHEM, N.DAK. STATE UNIV, 68- AAAS; Am. Chem. Soc; Am. Asn. Cereal Chem; Inst. Food Technol. Detection of protein damage in wheat flour as caused by milling process; investigation of carbohydrates, including starch, pentosans and simple sugars of wheat products; continuous baking. Address: Dept. of Cereal Chemistry & Technology, North Dakota State University, Fargo, ND 58102.

D'APPOLONIA, ELIO, b. Coleman, Alta, Apr. 14, 18; m. 42; c. 5. CIVIL ENGINEERING. B.Sc, Alberta, 42, M.Sc, 46; Ph.D.(civil eng), Illinois, 48. Instr. CIVIL ENG, Alberta, 42-46; res. assoc, Illinois, 46-48; asst. prof, CARNEGIE-MELLON UNIV, 48-50, assoc. prof, 50-56, LECTR, 56-; PRES, E.D'APPOLONIA CONSULT. ENGRS, INC, 56- Consult, adv. comt. reactor safeguards, Atomic Energy Comn. & Oak Ridge Nat. Lab; mem. hwy. res. bd, Nat. Acad. Sci; partic, Int. Cong. Large Dams. Civilian with U.S.A, 44; struct. engr, Eng.C, U.S.A, 43-45. Am. Soc. Civil Eng.(Thomas.A. Middlebrooks Award, 69); Eng. Inst. Can.(O'Keefer Medal, 48); Am. Soc. Test. & Mat; Nat. Soc. Prof. Eng; Int. Asn. Bridge & Struct. Eng; Int. Soc. Rock Mech; Asn. Iron & Steel Eng; Am. Geophys. Union; Asn. Eng. Geol; Seismol. Soc. Am; Consult. Eng. Coun. Soil and rock mechanics; foundation and structural engineering; applied mechanics; permafrost; steel, petrochemical, power and mining industry consulting. Address: 1177 McCully Dr, Pittsburgh, PA 15235.

DAPSON, RICHARD W, b. Flushing, N.Y, Sept. 5, 41; m. 62; c. 2. ECOLOGY, VERTEBRATE MORPHOLOGY. B.S, Cornell, 63, Ph.D.(vert. zool), 66. Asst. prof. BIOL, UNIV. MICH, 66-69; ASSOC. PROF, 69- Atomic Energy Cmn. summer fel. & Res. Corp. grant, 69. N.Y. Acad. Sci; Am. Soc. Mammal; Am. Soc. Zool. Age determination; age structure in wild animal populations; morphological changes with age in amphibians and mammals; histochemistry of amphibian skin secretions. Address: Dept. of Biology, University of Michigan, Flint, MI 48503.

DARAVINGAS, GEORGE VASILIOS, b. Thessaloniki, Greece, Apr. 22, 34; m. 68. FOOD SCIENCE, BIOCHEMISTRY. B.S, Univ. Thessaloniki, 58; M.S, Ore. State Univ, 63, Ph.D.(food sci), 65. Qual. control chemist, Agr. Corp. Polygyrus, Greece, 57-58; med. serv. chemist, Geigy, Greece, 60-61; res. asst, Ore. Agr. Exp. Sta, 61-65; proj. leader FOOD RES. & DEVELOP, Hunt Wesson Foods, Div. of Norton Simon, 65-68; DEPT. MFR, GLIDDEN DURKEE, DIV. OF SCM CORP, 68- Instr, Euclides Univ. Prep. Inst, Greece, 60-61; lectr, Univ. Calif, Riverside & Irvine, 67-68. Am. Chem. Soc; Inst. Food Technol. Isolation and identification of anthocyanin pigments in raspberries, their kinetics of thermal and enzymatic degradation; tomato products processing and biochemistry; canned and frozen foods; seasonings technology. Address: 15555 Hilliard Rd, Lakewood, OH 44106.

DARBEE, LEONARD R(AY), b. Dunkirk, N.Y, Oct. 30, 27; m. 49; c. 4. PHYSICAL & INORGANIC CHEMISTRY. B.S, Allegheny Col, 46; M.A, Buffalo, 52, Ph.D.(chem), 56. Res. chemist, Becco Chem. Div, Food Mach. & Chem. Corp, 55-58, asst. mgr. & supvr, ACTIVE OXYGEN CHEM. SECT, 58-61, SECT. MGR, INORG. RES. & DEVELOP. DEPT, FMC CORP, 61- U.S.A, 46-48. Am. Chem. Soc. Homogeneous and heterogeneous catalysis; kinetics and mechanisms; chemistry of peroxides and active oxygen compounds; electrosynthesis; physical chemistry of explosions; crystallization and phase transformations; manufacture of inorganic chemicals. Address: 32 Allen Lane, Trenton, NJ 08638.

DARBY, CLARA RUTH, b. Otterbein, Ind, Sept. 30, 06. NUTRITION. B.S, Purdue, 28, M.S, 31, Ph.D.(nutrit), 36. Asst. dietitian, Baltimore City Hosp, 29-30; dietetics, med. center, Indiana, 34-38; asst. prof. foods & nutrit, Philippines, 39-41; 46-53; HOME ECON, SAN JOSE STATE COL, 53-56, assoc. prof, 56-59, PROF, 59- Lectr, California, Los Angeles, 45-46. Am. Home Econ. Asn; Am. Dietetic Asn; Philippine Asn. Nutrit. Effect of chlorophyll on calcium retention; utilization of calcium in leaf lettuce and American cheddar cheese. Address: Dept. of Home Economics, San Jose State College, San Jose, CA 95114.

DARBY, DAVID G, b. Oak Park, Ill, Sept. 10, 32; m. 57; c. 2. INVERTEBRATE PALEONTOLOGY. B.S, Univ. Mich, 59, Nat. Sci. Found. assistantship, univ. fel. & M.S, 61, Ph.D.(paleont), 64. Scientist, U.S. Antartic Res. Prog, 60-61; Nat. Sci. Found. Assoc. investr, 62-64; geologist, Mobil Oil Corp, Peru, 64-68; ASSOC. PROF. GEOL, UNIV. MINN, DULUTH, 68-, grad. sch. res. grant, 69-71. U.S.M.C, 51-52, Sgt. Fel. AAAS; Geol. Soc. Am; Soc. Econ. Paleont. & Mineral; Paleont. Soc. Ecology and taxonomy of recent and fossil Ostracoda; Precambrian algal remains. Address: Dept. of Geology, University of Minnesota, Duluth, MN 55812.

DARBY, E(DSEL) K(ENNETH), b. Montreal, Que, Can, April 23, 24; m. 47; c. 4. PHYSICS. M.S, Saskatchewan, 48; Ph.D.(physics), British Columbia, 52. GEOPHYSICIST, GULF RES. & DEVELOP. CO, 52- Soc. Explor. Geophys; Europ. Asn. Geophys. Geophysics. Address: Gulf Research & Development Company, P.O. Drawer 2038, Pittsburgh, PA 15230.

DARBY, ELEANOR M(URIEL) K(APP), b. Easton, Pa, Feb. 4, 05; m. 28. BIOCHEMISTRY. A.B, Columbia, 25, Gies fel, 41, Ph.D.(biochem), 42; M.Sc, Pennsylvania, 27. Asst. biol, Wash. Sq. Col, N.Y. Univ, 26-28; asst. entomologist, entom. lab, U.S. Dept. Agr, 28-31; technician, dept. med, col. physicians & surg, Columbia, 32-41, asst. dermat, 41-43, instr. chem, dept. nursing, 46-48, res. assoc, dept. orthop. surg, 46-48; exec. secy. cardiovasc. study sect, div. res. grants, NAT. INSTS. HEALTH, 48-58, head confs. & publ. sect, grants & training br, Nat. Heart Inst, 58-62, spec. projs. br, extramural progs, 62-69, EXEC. SECY. THERAPEUT. EVAL. BR, CLIN. APPLN. PROG, NAT. HEART & LUNG INST, 69- Asst, sch. nursing, N.Y. Hosp, 32-33; fel. coun. epidemiol, Am. Heart Asn. U.S.N.R, 43-45, Lt.(jg). Am. Heart Asn; Int. Soc. Cardiol. Salt balance in vertebrate blood; insect physiology, especially fruit flies; blood sedimentation; urinary porphyrins; salicylate metabolism; collagen behavior; spectroscopic analysis; immunochemistry; cardiovascular and cerebrovascular research; cooperative projects; research grant administration. Address: Route 2, Box 309, Mt. Airy, MD 21771.

DARBY, J(OHN) F(EASTER), b. Chester, S.C, Oct, 22, 16; m. 41; c. 2. PLANT PATHOLOGY. B.S.A, Univ. Fla, 48, M.S.A, 49; Ph.D.(plant path), Univ. Wis, 51. Asst. plant pathologist, Indian River Field Lab, UNIV. FLA, 51-54, assoc. plant pathologist, INST. FOOD & AGR. SCI, CENT. FLA. EXP. STA, 54-64, plant pathologist, 64-66, PROF. PLANT PATH. & DIR. AGR. RES. & EDUC. CTR, 66- U.S.A, 43-46, 1st Lt. Am. Phytopath. Soc. Diseases of vegetable crops. Address: Agricultural Research & Education Center, Central Florida Experiment Station, P.O. Box 909, Sanford, FL 32771.

DARBY, JOSEPH B(RANCH), JR, b. Petersburg, Va, Dec. 12, 25; m. 51; c. 4. PHYSICAL METALLURGY. B.S, Col. William & Mary, 48; B.S, Va. Polytech, 51; Union Carbide & Carbon fel, Illinois, 53-55, M.S, 55, Ph.D. (metall), 58. Chemist, Allied Dye & Chem. Corp, 48-49; metallurgist, Nat. Carbon Div, Union Carbide & Carbon Corp, 51-53; ASSOC. PHYS. METALLURGIST, ARGONNE NAT. LAB, 58-, GROUP LEADER, MAT. SCI. DIV, 66- Sci. res. coun. sr. fel, dept. phys. metall. & sci. of mat, Univ. Birmingham, 70-71. U.S.M.C, 44-46. Am. Soc. Metals; Am. Inst. Mining, Metall. & Petrol. Eng. Electronic structure of metals and alloys; alloy chemistry; thermodynamic properties of alloys; defects in solids. Address: Materials Science Division, Bldg. 212, Argonne National Lab, Argonne, IL 60439.

DARBY, J(OSEPH) R(AYMOND), b. Boonville, Mo, Aug. 6, 11; m. 46; c. 6. CHEMISTRY. B.S, St. Louis, 33. Anal. chemist, MONSANTO CO, 33, control chemist, 34-35, res. chemist, 35-46, group leader res. dept, 46-64, res. mgr, 64-68, MGR. PLASTICIZER RES, 68- AAAS; Am. Chem. Soc; Am. Soc. Test. & Mat; Soc. Plastics Eng. Plasticization; polymer modification; stabilization. Address: Monsanto Co, 1700 S. Second St, St. Louis, MO 63177.

DARBY, R(ALPH) L(EWIS), b. Youngstown, Ohio, Nov. 13, 18; m. 42; c. 2. INFORMATION SCIENCE, CHEMICAL ENGINEERING. B.Ch.E, Ohio State, 42; cert. meteorol, Chicago, 43. Res. engr. chem, Commonwealth Eng. Co, Ohio, 46-47; graphic arts res. div, BATTELLE MEM. INST, 47-51, prin. chem. engr, info. res. div, 52-63, group dir, dept. info. res. & econ, 63-65, div. chief, 65-70, CHIEF, PROJ. MGT, DEPT. SOCIAL & MGT. SCI, 70- U.S.A.F, 42-46, 52, Capt. Am. Chem. Soc; Am. Soc. Info. Sci; fel. Am. Inst. Chem. Scientific communication; design of information storage and retrieval systems; information center operations and management. Address: Battelle Memorial Institute, Dept. of Social & Management Sciences, 505 King Ave, Columbus, OH 43201.

DARBY, ROBERT A(LBERT), b. Birmingham, Ala, May 6, 30; m. 52; c. 4. ORGANIC CHEMISTRY. B.S, Birmingham-South. Col, 51; Nat. Insts. Health fel, Virginia, 52-53, M.S, 53, du Pont fel, 55-57, Ph.D.(chem), 57. Res. chemist, exp. sta, E.I. DU PONT DE NEMOURS & CO, 57-63, sr. res. chemist, Wash. Works, 63-66, sr. res. supvr, exp. sta, 66-69, res. mgr, polyolefins div, PLASTICS DEPT, 69-70, LAB. DIR, RES. & DEVELOP. DIV, 70- Chem.C, U.S.A, 53-55, res, 55-62. Am. Chem. Soc. Conjugation and unsaturation in 1, 2-diaroylcyclopropanes; fluorocarbon chemistry; fluorocarbon polymers synthesis and properties; nylon and acrylic polymer processes. Address: Research & Development Division, Plastics Dept, E.I. du Pont de Nemours & Co, Experimental Station, Wilmington, DE 19898.

DARBY, ROLLO E, b. Sebastopol, Calif, June 15, 18; m. 41; c. 1. ENTOMOLOGY, ZOOLOGY. A.B, California, Berkeley, 40, M.A, 47, Ph.D. (entom), Davis, 60. Teacher, pub. sch, Calif, 41-42; high sch, 47-52; instr. life sci, Am. River Jr. Col, 55-57; from asst. prof. to assoc. prof, SACRAMENTO STATE COL, 57-68, PROF, 68- U.S.N, 42-46, Lt. Entom. Soc. Am; Am. Soc. Mammal; Am. Soc. Zool; Cooper Ornith. Soc. Ecological investigations of midge larvae, family Chironomidae, order Diptera; food habits study of coyotes Canis latrans. Address: Dept. of Biological Sciences, Sacramento State College, 6000 Jay St, Sacramento, CA 95819.

DARBY, RONALD, b. La Veta, Colo, Sept. 12, 32; m. 61; c. 2. FLUID DYNAMICS, ELECTROCHEMISTRY. B.A. & B.S, Rice, 55, Nat. Sci. Found.

fel, 58-61, Ph.D.(chem. eng), 62. Nat. Sci. Found. fel. chem. eng, Cambridge, 61-62; sr. scientist electrochem, Ling-Temco-Vought Res. Ctr, 63-65; asst. prof. CHEM. ENG, TEX. A&M UNIV, 65-67, assoc. prof, 67-69, PROF, 69- U.S.N, 55-58, Res, 58-, Comdr. AAAS; Am. Inst. Chem. Eng; Electrochem. Soc; Soc. Rheol. Rheology; applied electrochemistry and corrosion; heat transfer; viscoelastic fluids; polymers; porous fuel cell electrodes; nucleate boiling; two phase fluid flow; non-Newtonian flow; process dynamics; rate processes. Address: Dept. of Chemical Engineering, Texas A&M University, College Station, TX 77843.

DARBY, THOMAS D(ILLARD), b. Columbia, S.C, Aug. 3, 25; m. 44; c. 3. PHARMACOLOGY. B.S, The Citadel, 52; M.S, Med. Col. S.C, 54; South Carolina Heart Asn. res. fel, 55-56, Ph.D.(pharmacol), 57. Res. asst. pharmacol, Med. Col. S.C, 52-54; asst. prof. chem, The Citadel, 54-55; assoc. pharmacol, Med. Col. S.C, 57-58, asst. prof, 58-60; sch. med, Tulane, 60-61, assoc. prof. med. & pharmacol, 61-62; pharmacol, med. center, W.Va, Univ, 62-65; sr. pharmacologist, Abbott Labs, Ill, 65-68; PROF. PHARMACOL. & CHMN. DEPT, SCH. MED, UNIV. LOUISVILLE, 68- Nat. Heart Inst. career develop. award, 62- U.S.A.F, 43-45, res, 45-52. Am. Soc. Pharmacol. & Exp. Therapeut; Soc. Exp. Biol. & Med. Cardiovascular pharmacodynamics and physiology; adrenergic autonomic pharmacology. Address: Dept. of Pharmacology, University of Louisville School of Medicine, Louisville, KY 40201.

DARBY, WILLIAM J(EFFERSON), b. Little Rock, Ark, Nov. 6, 13; m. 35; c. 3. BIOCHEMISTRY, NUTRITION. B.S, Arkansas, 36, M.D, 37; univ. fel, Michigan, 39-40, Rackham fel, 40-41, M.S, 41, Ph.D.(biochem), 42; hon. Sc.D, Univ. Mich, 66. Asst. physiol. chem, sch. med, Arkansas, 30-37, instr, 37-39; Nat. Res. Coun. fel. med. sci, col. physicians & surgeons, Columbia, 41-42; Rockefeller Found. spec. fel, sch. med, Vanderbilt, 42-43; asst. res. prof. pub. health nutrit, sch. pub. health, North Carolina, 43-44; dir. med. nutrit, State Bd. Health, N.C, 43-44; asst. prof. biochem. & med, SCH. MED, VANDERBILT UNIV, 44-46, assoc. prof. biochem, 46-48, PROF. BIOCHEM. & DIR. DIV. NUTRIT, 48-, HEAD DEPT. BIOCHEM, 49-, PROF. NUTRIT, 64-, PROF. MED. IN NUTRIT, 65- Instr, Duke, 43-44; mem. food & nutrit. bd, Nat. Res. Coun, 49-71, steering comt, 55-71; sci. adv. bd, Nat. Vitamin Found, 50-54, tech. adv. comt, Inst. Nutrit. Cent. Am. & Panama, 50-64; comt. food protection, Interdept. Comt. Nutrit. Nat. Develop, 50-71, chmn. 54-71, mem. comt. consults. & dir. surv, Philippines, Ethiopia, Ecuador, Lebanon, Jordan & Nigeria, 55-66; mem. joint exp. comt. nutrit, Food & Agr. Orgn, WHO, 54, 57, 61 & 66, chmn. 57 & 66, chmn. joint comt. food additives, 56, mem. protein adv. group, 56, 60; sci. adv. comt, Nutrit. Found, 58-65, 67-; mem. & chmn, adv. comt. nutrit. & metab, Off. Surgeon Gen, U.S. Army, 59-60; mem. adv. group, WHO-Food Agr. Orgn, UNICEF, 60-62; second citizens' comt, Food & Drug Admin, 61-62; sci. adv. comt, United Health Found, 62-, chmn, 65-; adv. comt. agr. sci, U.S. Dept. Agr, 63-, adv. bd, Corn Prod. Co, 64- Order Rodolfo Robles, 59; Star of Jordan, Hashemite, Kingdom Jordan, 63. Am. Soc. Biol. Chem; Am. Chem. Soc; Am. Soc. Clin. Invest; Am. Inst. Nutrit.(Mead-Johnson award, 47, pres, 58-59, Osborne-Mendel award, 62); Am. Med. Asn.(Goldberger Award, 64), Am. Pub. Health Asn; Soc. Exp. Biol. & Med; Asn. Am. Physicians; Am. Fedn. Clin. Res; fel. Am. Col. Physicians; Brit. Nutrit. Soc; hon. mem. Austrian Pub. Health Asn. Biochemistry of metabolism and nutrition; clinical nutrition; nutrition surveys and public health nutrition; nutritional anemias; vitamin B_{12}; folic acid; zinc metabolism. Address: Dept. of Biochemistry, Vanderbilt University School of Medicine, Nashville, TN 37203.

DARCEL, COLIN LE Q, b. St. Helier, Gt. Brit; Feb. 5, 25; m. 48; c. 2. VETERINARY VIROLOGY. M.R.C.V.S, Royal Vet. Col, London, 47, Animal Health Trust grant, London, 47-49, B.Sc, 48, Ph.D.(vet. sci), 52; B.A, Cambridge, 49, M.A, 54. Pathologist fowl tumors, Poultry Res. Sta, Eng, 49-52; Imp. Cancer Res. Fund, 52-55; VIROLOGIST FOWL TUMOR VIRUSES, ANIMAL DISEASES RES. INST, CAN. DEPT. AGR, 55- Path. Soc. Gt. Brit. & Ireland; Brit. Soc. Immunol; Brit. Soc. Gen. Microbiol. Biochemical aspects of pathogenesis of erythroblastosis virus, particularly changes that occur in serum lipoproteins and iron metabolism; infectious bovine rhinotracheitis and other cattle viruses. Address: Animal Diseases Research Institute, P.O. Box 640, Lethridge, Alta, Can.

D'ARCY, HAROLD MELVIN, b. Marlette, Mich, Feb. 16, 06; m. 29; c. 2. ORGANIC & PHYSICAL CHEMISTRY. A.B, Olivet Nazarene Col, 29; M.S, Mich. State, 31, fel, 46-47, Ph.D.(org. chem), 50. Instr. chem. & physics, East. Nazarene Col, 30-32, asst. prof, 32-37; assoc. prof, chem, John Fletcher Col, 37-41; prof. & head dept, Olivet Nazarene Col, 41-46; asst. prof. phys. sci. & physics, Mich. State, 47-54; assoc. prof. CHEM, Ferris State Col, 54-61; PROF, SOUTH. CONN. STATE COL, 61- Am. Chem. Soc. liaison, AAAS Conf. Guidelines Prep. Sec. Sch. Teachers Sci. & Math; Nat. Coun. Accreditation Teacher Educ; mem, Nat. Res. Scientists Goodwill People-to-People Del, Europe & U.S.S.R. Am. Chem. Soc. Reactions of various Grignard reagents with expoxides. Address: Dept. of Chemistry, Southern Connecticut State College, New Haven, CT 06515.

DARDAS, TERRY JAY, b. Bay City, Mich, June 10, 40; m. 63; c. 2. IMMUNOLOGY, INTERNAL MEDICINE. B.S, Cent. Mich. Univ, 62; M.S, Mich. State Univ, 64, Ph.D.(immunol), 67; M.D, Wayne State Univ, 71. Res. asst. IMMUNOL, MICH. STATE UNIV, 62-67, RES. ASSOC, 67- Resident int. med, Oakwood Hosp, Dearborn, Mich, 71-72; res. immunologist, Vet. Admin. Hosp, Allen Park, 71-72; grants, Mich. Tuberc. & Respiratory Disease Asn, Nat. Tuberc. & Respiratory Disease Asn. & U.S. Dept. Agr, Mich. State Univ. Kinetics of immunoglobulin formation; antigens of mycobacteria; cellular immunity. Address: Oakwood Hospital, Dearborn, MI 48124.

DARDEN, COLGATE W, III, b. Norfolk, Va, Nov. 6, 30; m. 52; c. 3. NUCLEAR PHYSICS. B.E.E, Virginia, 53, M.A, 54; Ph.D.(nuclear phys), Mass. Inst. Tech, 59. Physicist, Savannah River Lab, 58-62; v.pres, Columbia Eng, Inc, 62-64; ASSOC. PROF. PHYSICS, UNIV. S.C, 64- Am. Phys. Soc. Low energy nuclear physics; proton scattering and polarization; astrophysics. Address: Dept. of Physics, University of South Carolina, Columbia, SC 29208.

DARDEN, EDGAR B(ASCOMB), JR, b. Raleigh, N.C, Jan. 23, 20; m. 69. BIOPHYSICS. B.S, Col. William & Mary, 41; M.S, North Carolina, 50; Ph.D.(zool), Tennessee, 57. Instr. physics, Col. of William & Mary, 41-42; from jr. biologist to BIOLOGIST, OAK RIDGE NAT. LAB, 49- Sig.C, 42-46, Capt. Sci. Res. Soc. Am; Am. Phys. Soc; Radiation Res. Soc. Radiobiology; physiology; radiological physics. Address: Biology Division, Oak Ridge National Lab, P.O. Box Y, Oak Ridge, TN 37830.

DARDEN, GERALDINE C, b. Nansemond,Co, Va, July 22, 36. ALGEBRA. B.S, Hampton Inst, 57; Nat. Sci. Found. fel, Illinois, 59-60, M.S, 60; Nat. Sci. Found. fel, Syracuse, 64-65, M.S, 65, Int. Bus. Mach. grant, 65-67, Ph.D.(math), 67. Teacher, S.H. Clarke Jr. High Sch, Va, 57-59; instr. MATH, HAMPTON INST, 60-64, asst. prof, 64-68, ASSOC. PROF, 68- Lectr, Va. Acad. Sci, 67-; Nat. Urban League fel, Aluminum Co. Am, summer 68. Math. Asn. Am. Abelian group theory. Address: Dept. of Mathematics, Hampton Institute, P.O. Box 6038, Hampton, VA 23368.

DARDEN, SPERRY E(UGENE), b. Chicago, Ill, Aug. 16, 28; m. 54; c. 4. NUCLEAR PHYSICS. B.S, Iowa State Col, 50; M.S, Wisconsin, 51, Nat. Sci. Found. fel, 54-55, Ph.D.(physics), 55. Exchange asst, Basel, 55-56; instr. PHYSICS, Wisconsin, 56-57; from asst. prof. to assoc. prof, UNIV. NOTRE DAME, 57-65, PROF, 65- Sloan fel, 62-64; guest prof, Univ. Basel, 65-66. Am. Phys. Soc. Fast neutron interactions with atomic nuclei; polarization effects in nuclear reactions and scattering. Address: Dept. of Physics, University of Notre Dame, Notre Dame, IN 46556.

DARDEN, WILLIAM H, JR, b. Tuscaloosa, Ala, Apr. 25, 37; m. 59; c. 2. BIOLOGY, BOTANY. B.S, Alabama, 59, M.S, 61; univ. fel, Indiana, 61-63, Nat. Insts. Health fel, 63-65, Ph.D.(bot), 65. Asst. prof. BIOL, UNIV. ALA, TUSCALOOSA, 65-68, ASSOC. PROF, 68- Univ. Alabama res. grant, 65- AAAS; Phycol. Soc. Am. Cellular differentiation in algae with emphasis on the chemical control of sexual differentiation. Address: Dept. of Biology, Box 1927, University of Alabama, University, AL 35486.

D'ARDENNE, WALTER H, b. Jenkintown, Pa, Oct. 31, 32; m. 57; c. 3. NUCLEAR ENGINEERING. B.S, Pa. State Univ, 59; Ph.D.(nuclear eng), Mass. Inst. Technol, 64. Asst. prof. NUCLEAR ENG, PA. STATE UNIV, 64-69, ASSOC. PROF, 69- Am. Soc. Eng. Educ-Ford Found. residency, atomic power equip. dept, Gen. Elec. Co, 70-71. U.S.N, 55-57. Am. Nuclear Soc; Am. Soc. Mech. Eng; Am. Soc. Eng. Educ. Reactor design; nuclear design; thermal-hydraulic design; nuclear safety; system analysis; reactor physics. Address: Nuclear Engineering Dept, Pennsylvania State University, 231 Sackett Bldg, University Park, PA 16802.

DARDIRI, AHMED H(AMED), b. Cairo, Egypt, Mar. 10, 19; nat; m. 51. VIROLOGY. D.V.M, Cairo, 40, M.V.Sc, 46; M.Sc, Mich. State, 47, Ph.D.(bact), 50. Dir, poultry res. exp. sta, Cairo, 40-46; mem, Egyptian Ed. Mission to U.S.A, 46-50; sr. lectr, Cairo, 50-55; res. assoc. animal path, Rhode Island, 55-56, asst. prof, 56-59, assoc. prof, 59-61; prin. res. veterinarian, VET. RES. SCI. DIV, AGR. RES. SERV, U.S. DEPT. AGR, 61-66, LEADER DIAG. INVESTS, PLUM ISLAND ANIMAL DISEASE LAB, 66- Consult, Am. Tech. Aid to Egypt, Cairo, 51-55; adj. prof. animal path, Univ. R.I, 68- Am. Vet. Med. Asn; Am. Soc. Microbiol; Conf. Res. Workers Animal Diseases; N.Y. Acad. Sci; Am. Asn. Avian Path; Am. Pub. Health Asn; U.S. Livestock Sanit. Asn. Microbiology; genetics; veterinary science; poultry pathology and health. Address: Plum Island Animal Disease Lab, P.O. Box 848, U.S. Dept. of Agriculture, Greenport, NY 11944.

DARDIS, JOHN G, b. Kilkenney, Ireland, May 21, 28; U.S. citizen. ATOMIC & NUCLEAR PHYSICS. M.A. & Ph.D.(physics), Dublin, 55. Res. physicist, Radio Res. Sta, Slough, Eng, 55-57; asst. prof. nuclear physics, Kentucky, 57-62; res. physicist, U.S. Naval Radiol. Defense Lab, 62-64, phys. sci. administr, Calif, 64-67; PHYSICIST, PHYSICS BR, OFF. NAVAL RES, 67- Am. Phys. Soc; Am. Asn. Physics Teachers; Brit. Inst. Physics & Phys. Soc; Am. Nuclear Soc. Radio, cosmic ray, radiation transport, plasma, atomic and molecular physics. Address: Physics Branch, Office of Naval Research, Arlington, VA 22217.

DARDOUFAS, KIMON C, b. Athens, Greece, Apr. 25, 16; U.S. citizen; m. 59; c. 4. ORGANIC CHEMISTRY, CHEMICAL ENGINEERING. B.A, Nat. Univ. Athens, 35; B.S.Ch.E, Darmstadt Tech, 37; M.A, Dresden Tech, 39. Prod. supt, Tannerie-Ganferie Dardoufa S.A, 42-47, dir. & bd. mem, 47-50, proj. dir. new expansion, 50-54; mgr. indust. exports, Athens Off, Am. Merchandising Corp, 54-56; process engr, Gen. Aniline & Film Corp, 56-60, proj. leader polymer develop, 60-63; MGR. RES. & TESTING SERV, FIBERS DIV, ALLIED CHEM. CORP, 63- Greek Army, 40-41, Lt. Am. Inst. Chem. Eng; Am. Chem. Soc; fel. Am. Inst. Chem. Process development and economic evaluation in chemical industry; development of synthetic fibers; fiber lubrication. Address: Technical Dept, Fibers Division, Allied Chemical Corp, P.O. Box 31, Petersburg, VA 23804.

DARE, CHARLES ERNEST, b. Peoria, Ill, June 3, 38; m. 67; c. 1. INDUSTRIAL & CIVIL ENGINEERING. B.A, Iowa, 61, B.S, 62, M.S, 63, Ph.D.(indust. eng), 68. Instr. indust. eng, Iowa, 65-67, Nat. Sci. Found. trainee, CIVIL ENG, 67-68; ASST. PROF, Missouri-Rolla, 68-69; UNIV. COLO, BOULDER, 69- Mem. comt. on traffic control devices, Hwy. Res. Bd, Nat. Acad. Sci-Nat. Res. Coun, 69. Nat. Guard, 56-64, S/Sgt. Inst. Traffic Eng.(past pres. award, 69); Opers. Res. Soc. Am. Traffic and transportation engineering; operations research; computer simulation; highway safety; human factors research in industrial engineering. Address: Dept. of Civil Engineering, University of Colorado, Boulder, CO 80302.

DARENSBOURG, MARCETTA YORK, b. Artemus, Ky, May 4, 42; m. 67. INORGANIC & ORGANOMETALLIC CHEMISTRY. B.A, Union Col.(Ky), 63; Nat. Sci. Found. summer fel. & M.S, Illinois, Urbana, 65, Ph.D.(inorg. chem), 67. ASST. PROF. INORG. CHEM, Vassar Col, 67-69; State Univ. N.Y. Buffalo, 69-71; TULANE UNIV. LA, 71- Petrol. Res. Fund grant, 68-70, 71-73. Am. Chem. Soc. Structure and reaction of organolithium reagents; synthesis and bonding of transition metal-carbene complexes. Address: Dept. of Chemistry, Tulane University of Louisiana, New Orleans, LA 70118.

DAREWYCH, JURIJ W(ASYL'), b. Sukhoriche, Ukraine, Feb. 17, 39; Can. citizen; m. 62; c. 2. THEORETICAL & ATOMIC PHYSICS. B.Sc, Manitoba, 60,

M.Sc, 61; Ph.D.(theoret. physics), Alberta, 66. Lectr. math. physics, Manitoba, 61-62; fel. nuclear theory, Florida, 66-67; asst. prof. PHYSICS, YORK UNIV.(ONT), 67-71, ASSOC. PROF, 71- Am. Phys. Soc; Can. Asn. Physicists. Positron annihilation and scattering; statistical theory of many particle systems; collision theory; nonlinear classical field theory. Address: Dept. of Physics, York University, Downsview, Ont, Can.

DARIAN-SMITH, IAN, b. Adelaide, Australia, Mar. 31, 27; m. 57; c. 4. PHYSIOLOGY. M.B, B.S, Adelaide, 50, Nat. Health & Med. Res. Coun. fel, 52-55, M.D, 56. C.J. Martin fel. PHYSIOL, Nat. Inst. Med. Res, Mill Hill, London, 56-58; Nat. Health & Med. Res. Coun. Australia sr. res. fel, 58-60; assoc. prof, New South Wales, 61-66, prof, 66-68; ASSOC. PROF, SCH. MED, JOHNS HOPKINS UNIV, 69-, vis. lectr, 66. Brit. Physiol. Soc; Australian Physiol. Soc; Am. Physiol. Soc. Functional organization of somatic sensory system, especially the trigeminal system. Address: Dept. of Physiology, Johns Hopkins University School of Medicine, 725 N. Wolfe St, Baltimore, MD 21205.

DARK, HARRIS J(EREMIAH), b. Maury Co, Tenn, Feb. 8, 05; m. 32; c. 4. MATHEMATICS. B.A, Randolph-Macon Col, 34; M.A, Richmond, 40; Ph.D. (math), Peabody Col, 48. Prof. MATH, David Lipscomb Col, 42-57; PROF, MIDDLE TENN. STATE UNIV, 57-, head dept, 57-69. Math. Asn. Am. Analysis; statistics. Address: Dept. of Mathematics, Middle Tennessee State University, Murfreesboro, TN 37130.

DARKEN, LAWRENCE S(TAMPER), b. Brooklyn, N.Y, Sept. 18, 09; m. 39; c. 6. CHEMISTRY. A.B, Hamilton Col, 30; Loomis fel, Yale, 32-33, Ph.D. (phys. chem), 33. Fel, Yale, 33-34; res. chemist, H. Kohnstamm Co, N.Y, 34-35; phys. chemist, U.S. STEEL CORP, 35-54, asst. dir, FUNDAMENTAL RES. LAB, 54-57, assoc. dir, 57-62, DIR, 62- Adj. prof, Polytech. Inst. Brooklyn, 42-53. Francis J. Clamer Medal, Franklin Inst, 66; Gold Medal, Am. Soc. Metals, 71. AAAS; Nat. Acad. Sci; Am. Inst. Mining, Metall. & Petrol. Eng.(R.W. Hunt Award, 67); Am. Chem. Soc; fel. N.Y. Acad. Sci; Am. Inst. Chem; Royal Soc. Arts. Physical chemistry and thermodynamics of metals and metallic systems; diffusion in metals; solid state. Address: Research Center, U.S. Steel Corp, Monroeville, PA 15146.

DARKEN, MARJORIE A(LICE), b. Brooklyn, N.Y, July 15, 15. MICROBIOLOGY. B.S, St. Lawrence, 36; univ. scholar & Newcombe fel, Michigan, M.A, 37. Res. technician, hosp, Michigan, 37-39; asst, Neuropsychiat. Inst, Conn, 39-41, dir. labs, 41-43; res. microbiologist, Heyden Chem. Corp, N.J, 43-53; fine chem. div, AM. CYANAMID CO, 53-55, sr. tech. writer, 55-56, sr. res. scientist, LEDERLE LABS. DIV, 56-63, pharmacol. ed, 63-69, MED. ED, 69- Civilian with Off. Sci. Res. & Develop, 44. Fel. AAAS; Am. Soc. Microbiol; Am. Chem. Soc; Am. Med. Writers' Asn; Soc. Indust. Microbiol. Production of antibiotics, growth factors and steroids by microorganisms; microbial physiology and transformations; strain development. Address: 15 Rolling Ridge Rd, Montvale, NJ 07645.

DARKER, GRANT D(OOKS), b. Streetsville, Ont, Can, Dec. 23, 98; m. 38. BOTANY. B.A, Toronto, 22, M.A, 25; Ph.D, Harvard, 31. Asst. bot, Toronto, 22-28; Arnold Arboretum, Mass, 28-31, 32-33; res. assoc. mycol, Farlow Herbarium, Harvard, 33-40; asst. prof. bot, Henry Shaw Sch. Bot, Washington (St. Louis), 41-42; mycologist, Ben Venue Labs, Inc, 43-59; res. off, Can. Dept. Agr, 60-66, Dept. Fisheries & Forestry, 67-68; RETIRED. Sheldon traveling fel. from Harvard, Europe, 31-32; asst, Wash. Univ, 43. Mycol. Soc. Am; Torrey Bot. Club; Royal Can. Inst; Can. Phytopath. Soc. Taxonomy of fungi. Address: 1419 Chatelain Ave, Ottawa, Ont. K1Z 8A9, Can.

DARKO, LASZLO L, b. Monor, Hungary, Mar. 27, 35; U.S. citizen; m. 60; c. 2. ORGANIC CHEMISTRY. B.Sc, Hobart Col, 62; Ph.D.(med. chem), Univ. Iowa, 66. Sr. res. chemist, Ciba-Geigy Corp, N.Y, 66-71. Partic, exchange prog, Nat. Acad. Sci-Hungarian Acad. Sci, 71. U.S.A.R. Am. Chem. Soc. Medicinal chemistry—synthesis of new medicinal agents affecting the central nervous system; sedative-hypnotics; tranquilizers; anorectic agents. Address: 3368 Lorelei Dr, Yorktown Heights, NY 10598.

DARKOW, GRANT LYLE, b. Milwaukee, Wis, Jan. 7, 28; m. 54; c. 4. METEOROLOGY. B.Sc, Wisconsin, 49, M.Sc, 58, Ph.D.(meteorol), 64. Asst. prof. ATMOSPHERIC SCI, UNIV. MO-COLUMBIA, 61-65, assoc. prof, 65-69, PROF, 69- U.S.A.F, 50-56, 1st Lt. Am. Meteorol. Soc; Am. Geophys. Union. Infrared radiative transfer in the atmosphere; the dynamics of severe local storms. Address: Dept. of Atmospheric Science, University of Missouri-Columbia, 701 S. Hitt St, Columbia, MO 65201.

DARLAGE, LARRY JAMES, b. Brownstown, Ind, June 1, 45; m. 67. ORGANIC CHEMISTRY. B.A, Ind. Cent. Col, 67; Nat. Sci. Found. traineeship, Iowa State Univ, 68, Nat. Insts. Health fel, 68-71, Ph.D.(org. chem), 71. RES. ASSOC, REED LAB, UNIV. FLA, 71- Am. Chem. Soc. Comparison of the thermal, photochemical and mass spectral reactions of 1,2-benzisoxazolin-3-ones and some related five-membered heterocyclic compounds; isolation and characterization of sulfur-containing organic compounds in coal. Address: Reed Lab, University of Florida, Gainesville, FL 32601.

DARLAK, ROBERT (STANLEY), b. North Tonawanda, N.Y, Sept. 10, 37; m. 66; c. 3. ORGANIC CHEMISTRY. B.S, Mississipi, 60; Nat. Defense Ed. Act fel, West Virginia, 60-64, Du Pont fel. & Ph.D.(phys. org. chem), 64. Res. fel. org. chem. under Dr. Mel Newman, Ohio State, 64-66; SR. RES. CHEMIST, EASTMAN KODAK CO, 66- Am. Chem. Soc. Kinetics and synthesis in heterocyclic chemistry; synthesis in polycyclic aromatic compounds; polymer chemistry. Address: Eastman Kodak Co, Research Labs, 343 State St, Rochester, NY 14650.

DARLAND, RAYMOND W(INSTON), b. Codell, Kans, Mar. 22, 11; m. 33; c. 2. ECOLOGY. B.Sc, Ft. Hays Kans. State Col, 33, M.S, 36; Ph.D.(ecol), Nebraska, 47. Instr, high sch, Kans, 33-35, prin, 35-41; instr. plant ecol, Nebraska, 41-44, asst. prof. biol, 46-48; assoc. prof. bot, UNIV. MINN, DULUTH, 48-49, prof. biol. & head dept, 49-52, academic dean, 52-53, PROVOST, 53- U.S.N, 44-46, Lt. Ecol. Soc. Am. Degeneration of grassland; effects of grazing native grasslands; root and soil relationships. Address: University of Minnesota, Duluth, MN 55812.

DARLEY, ELLIS F(LECK), b. Monte Vista, Colo, Nov. 2, 15; m. 39; c. 3. PLANT PATHOLOGY. B.S, Colo. State, 38; Ph.D.(plant path), Minnesota, 45. Asst. forestry, Minnesota, 40-41; instr. bot. & plant path, Colo. State, 41-42; res. fel. & asst. plant path, Minnesota, 42-45; pathologist, Firestone Plantations Co, Liberia, W.Africa, 45-47; Off. For. Agr. Rel, Guatemala, 48-49; asst. plant pathologist, citrus exp. sta, UNIV. CALIF, RIVERSIDE, 49-55, assoc. plant pathologist, 55-61, PLANT PATHOLOGIST, AIR POLLUTION RES. CTR, 61- Guggenheim fel, Germany, 63-64. Air Pollution Control. Asn; Am. Phytopath. Soc. Diseases of Hevea rubber; diseases of palms, especially date; air pollution injury to plants. Address: Air Pollution Research Center, University of California, Riverside, CA 92502.

DARLEY, FREDERIC LOUDON, b. Caracas, Venezuela, Nov. 25, 18; U.S. citizen; m. 45; c. 3. SPEECH PATHOLOGY. A.B, N.Mex. State Teachers Col, 39; M.A, Iowa, 40, Ph.D.(speech path), 50. Instr. pub. speaking & Eng, Arkansas, 40-41; pub. speaking, California, Berkeley, 45-47; from instr. to assoc. prof. speech path. & audiol, Iowa, 47-61; consult. speech path, Mayo Clin, 61-69; PROF. SPEECH PATH, MAYO GRAD. SCH. MED, UNIV. MINN, 69- Mem, Acad. Aphasia, 62- U.S.A, 41-45, Res, 45-, Lt. Col. Fel. Am. Speech & Hearing Asn. Diagnosis and appraisal of communication disorders; organic disorders of speech and language. Address: Mayo Graduate School of Medicine, University of Minnesota, Rochester, MN 55901.

DARLEY, WARD, b. Denver, Colo, Oct. 30, 03; m. 30; c. 2. MEDICAL EDUCATION. A.B, Univ. Colo, 26, M.D, 29, LL.D, 58; D.Sc, Colo. Col, 54, Univ. Nebr, 56; hon. D.Sc, N.Y. Med. Col, 65, Univ. Ill, 65, Brown Univ, 66; LL.D, Loyola Univ. (Ill), 65, Northwest. Univ, 65, Univ. N.Mex, 66. Intern, med. center & med. sch, Colorado, 29-30, res. med, 30-31, asst. out-patient physician, 31-32, out-patient physician, 32, instr. med, 35, asst. prof, 41, assoc. prof, 44-46, prof, 46-56, dean, 45-48, dean col. med. & v.pres. univ, 49-53, pres, 53-56; exec. coun. Asn. Am. Med. Cols, 46-52, pres, 52-53, exec. dir, 57-64, consult. to the exec. dir, 64-68; VIS. PROF. MED. & PREV. MED, UNIV. COLO, DENVER, 65- Practicing physician, Denver, 31-44; exec. secy. Nat. Intern Matching Prog, 57-65, 67-68. Consult, adv. cmt, div. med. & pub. health, W.K. Kellogg Found, 48-53; Rockefeller Found, 52-55. Dipl, Nat. Bd. Med. Exam, 31; Am. Bd. Internal Med, 38. Mem. bd, trustees, Nat. Merit Scholar. Corp. Fel. Am. Col. Physicians; Asn. Am. Med. Cols.(pres, 52). Allergy; endocrinology; brucellosis; rheumatic fever; congenital heart disease; medical education. Address: 4200 E. Ninth Ave, Denver, CO 80220.

DARLEY, WILLIAM GEORGE, b. Galveston, Tex, May 7, 07; m. 33; c. 2. ELECTRICAL ENGINEERING. B.S, Tex. A&M Univ, 30, E.E, 37. Testman, Gen. Elec. Co, N.Y, 30-31, illum. engr, lamp dept, Ohio, 31-34, head indust. lighting activity, 34-36, head sch, lighting activity, 36-38, head lighting for seeing activity, 38-42, head gen. lighting sect, 42-45, dist. engr, Calif, 45-47; consult. engr, 53-60; ELEC. ENGR, Hq. U.S. Air Force Security Serv, Kelly AFB, 60-63; Hq. 4th U.S. Army, Ft. Sam Houston, Tex, 63-68; U.S. AIR FORCE SECURITY SERV, HQ. EUROP. SECURITY REGION, 69- Lectr, Univ. Tex, 48-67. Soc. Am. Mil. Eng. Lighting in textile; fluorescent lamps and air conditioning; chalk board visibility; design of luminaries for fluorescent lamps; lighting in drafting rooms; influence of white floors on illumination; effects of improved design on industrial reflectors. Address: U.S. Air Force Security Service, Headquarters European Security Region, Box 105, APO New York 09101.

DARLING, BYRON T(HORWELL), b. Napoleon, Ohio, Jan. 4, 12; m. 46. PHYSICS. B.S, Illinois, 33, M.S, 36; Wisconsin, 38-39; Ph.D.(physics), Michigan, 39. Instr. math, Mich. State Col, 39-41; res. physicist, U.S. Rubber Co, Detroit, 41-46; res. assoc, Wisconsin & Yale, 46-47; asst. prof. PHYSICS, Ohio State, 47-51, assoc. prof, 51-53; PROF, LAVAL UNIV, 55- With Off. Sci. Res. & Develop, 44. AAAS; Am. Asn. Physics Teachers; Am. Phys. Soc; N.Y. Acad. Sci; Can. Asn. Physicists; French-Can. Asn. Adv. Sci. Theory of rubber processing; molecular and nuclear theory; elementary particle theory. Address: Dept. of Physics, Faculty of Sciences, Laval University, Quebec 10, Can.

DARLING, CHARLES MILTON, b. Mineral Wells, Miss, Feb. 7, 34; m. 54; c. 3. PHARMACEUTICAL & MEDICINAL CHEMISTRY. B.S, Mississippi, 55, Am. Found. Pharmaceut. Ed. fel, 62-63, Nat. Insts. Health fel, 63-66, Ph.D.(pharmaceut. chem), 66. Mgr, Woods' Pharm, 55-62; sr. res. chemist, A.H. Robins Co, 66-69; ASSOC. PROF. PHARMACEUT. CHEM, AUBURN UNIV, 69- AAAS; Am. Asn. Cols. Pharm; Am. Chem. Soc; Am. Pharmaceut. Asn; Acad. Pharmaceut. Sci. Non-classical histamine antagonists; biodistribution. Address: School of Pharmacy, Auburn University, Auburn, AL 36830.

DARLING, DONALD A(LLAN), b. Los Angeles, Calif, May 4, 15; m. 39; c. 1. MATHEMATICS. A.B, California, Los Angeles, 40; Ph.D.(math), Calif. Inst. Technol, 47. Res. assoc, Cornell, 47-48; asst. prof. math, Rutgers, 48-49; Michigan, 49-52; Columbia, 52-53; Michigan, 53-55; assoc. prof, Chicago, 56-57; Michigan, 57-59, prof, 59-68; vis. prof. statist, UNIV. CALIF, Berkeley, 68-69, PROF. MATH, IRVINE, 69- Fel, Guggenheim Mem. Found, 58-59. Am. Math. Soc; fel. Inst. Math. Statist; Math. Asn. Am. Mathematical statistics; probability and applications; stochastic processes. Address: Dept. of Mathematics, University of California, Irvine, CA 92664.

DARLING, EUGENE MERRILL, JR, b. Cambridge, Mass, Jan. 13, 25. MATHEMATICS, METEOROLOGY. A.B, Harvard, 48; S.M, Mass. Inst. Tech, 53. Meteorologist, Pan Am. Grace Airways, Inc, 50-51; lectr. meteorol, New Mexico, 52; atmospheric physicist, Air Force Cambridge Res. Ctr, 52-62; aerospace technologist, NIMBUS Proj, Goddard Space Flight Ctr, NASA, 62-63, electronics res. task group, NASA Hqs, 64, Electronics Res. Ctr, NASA, 64-70; CHIEF, DATA TECHNOL. BR, TRANSPORTATION SYSTS. CTR, DEPT. OF TRANSPORTATION, 70- U.S.A.F, 43-46. Am. Meteorol. Soc; Pattern Recognition Soc. Lima, Peru terminal weather prediction research; analysis of meteorological support for United States Air Force aircraft and missiles; operational aspects of NIMBUS satellite cloud pictures; pattern recognition; imagery processing; management of programs in transportation systems modeling, simulation, image processing and communications. Address: Transportation Systems Center, Code TCD, Dept. of Transportation, 55 Broadway, Cambridge, MA 02142.

DARLING, GEORGE B(APST), b. Boston, Mass, Dec. 30, 05; m. 31. PUBLIC HEALTH. B.S, Mass. Inst. Tech, 27; Dr.P.H, Michigan, 31; hon. M.A, Yale, 47. Res. assoc, dept. health, Detroit, 27-32; assoc. exec. dir, assoc. secy. & treas, W.K. Kellogg Found, 32-34, exec. dir. & mem. finance comt, 34-37, mem. corp. & bd. trustees, assoc. dir. & comptroller, 37, mem. admin. comt, 38, pres, 40-43; exec. secy. comts. on mil. med, Nat. Res. Coun, 43-44, v.chmn. div. med. sci, 44-45, 47-48; exec. secy, Nat. Acad. & Nat. Res. Coun, 46; dir. med. affairs, YALE, 46-52, PROF. HUMAN ECOL, 52-, ON LEAVE FROM YALE AS DIR, NAT. RES. COUN. ATOMIC BOMB CASUALTY COMN, HIROSHIMA, JAPAN, 57- Dir, Grace-New Haven Community Hosp, Conn, 46-59; vis. prof, Hiroshima Schs, Med. & Nursing, Japan. With Nat. Defense Res. Comt; sci. observer, atomic bomb test, Joint Task Force 1, mem, Nat. Conf. Social Work. AAAS; fel. Am. Pub. Health Asn; Int. Acad. Polit. Sci; N.Y. Acad. Sci; Radiation Res. Soc. Japan; Japan Pub. Health Asn. Public health administration; epidemiology; statistics; medical administration; professional education. Address: Yale University, New Haven, CT 06520.

DARLING, H. VELPEAU, b. Wash, D.C, Aug. 19, 03; m. 26; c. 2. TRANSPORTATION ENGINEERING. B.S, George Washington, 33. Jr. engr. to spec. asst. for Miss. River Basin, Corps Eng, U.S. Army, 27-58; v.pres, Commonwealth Transportation Consult, Inc, 58-66, pres. & chmn. bd, 66-68; RETIRED. Consult. aquatic growth in Congo River, Belg. Embassy, 54; mem. surv. team, Mekong River, 56-57 & UN Int. team, 58, navig, Mekong, Ping, Nam, Chao & Phya Rivers, 57; mgt. study, dept. pub. works, State of R.I, 58-59; proj. mgr, UN team hydraul. develop, Taiwan, 61-63; proj. engr, comprehensive transportation study, Sierra Leone, 63-64; proj. dir, Cent. Am, 64-65; consult, navig. study, Mekong River, Laos & Thailand, 67-68; navig. study, N.C, 68; UN consult, 4th Navig. Cong. SEATO Nations, 68; mem, U.S. Comt. Large Dams. Fed. Am. Soc. Civil Eng; Soc. Am. Mil. Eng; Am. Geophys. Union. Natural resources and river basin development; hydraulic development projects; river and harbor planning; integrated transportation planning. Address: 6002 Talford Ct, Springfield, VA 22152.

DARLING, ROBERT C(ROLY), b. Syracuse, N.Y, March 17, 08; m. 38; c. 2. PHYSICAL MEDICINE & REHABILITATION. A.B, Harvard, 29, Sheldon traveling fel, 29-30, M.D, 34. Intern, Presby. Hosp, 35-37, asst. res. med, 37-38; res. physician, Robert B. Brigham Hosp, 37; res. physician, Goldwater Mem. Hosp. for Chronic Diseases, 38-40; from asst. to asst. prof. indust. physiol, fatigue lab, Harvard, 40-45; assoc. prof, med. COL. PHYSICIANS & SURG, COLUMBIA UNIV, 45-52; PROF. PHYS. MED. & REHAB. & CHMN. DEPT, 52- Tutor, Harvard, 40-43; consult. phys. med. & rehab, Vet. Admin. Hosp, Manhattan, 55-69; consult. & coord. teaching & educ, Blythedale Children's Hosp, Valhalla, N.Y, 67-; consult, Roosevelt Hosp, N.Y, 67-; sr. consult, N.Y. State Rehab. Hosp, West Haverstraw, 70- With Off. Sci. Res. & Develop; U.S.A, 44. Am. Physiol. Soc; Am. Soc. Clin. Invest. Physiology of pulmonary ventilation; respiratory physiology of the blood; methemoglobin and carbon monoxide hemoglobin; evaluation of physical fitness; high altitude; exercise physiology; physiology of sweat; temperature regulation. Address: Dept. of Rehabilitation Medicine, College of Physicians & Surgeons, Columbia University, 630 W. 168th St, New York, NY 10032.

DARLING, SAMUEL MILLS, b. Bradenton, Fla, Jan. 13, 17; m. 40; c. 4. CHEMISTRY. A.B, Carleton Col, 39; M.S, Western Reserve, 43, Ph.D. (chem), 47. Res. supvr, STANDARD OIL CO.(OHIO), 39-67, fuels res. supvr, 67-70, SUPVR. LUBRICANT RES, 70- AAAS; Am. Soc. Lubrication Eng; Am. Chem. Soc; Soc. Automotive Eng; fel. Am. Inst. Chem. Halide catalysis; catalytic cracking and reforming; performance of fuels and lubricants; nitrile chemicals and polymers. Address: Research Dept, Standard Oil Co.(Ohio), 4440 Warrensville Rd, Cleveland, OH 44128.

DARLING, STEPHEN D(EZIEL), b. Appleton, Wis, May 7, 31; m. 60; c. 2. ORGANIC CHEMISTRY. B.S, Wisconsin, 54; Nat. Sci. Found. fel, Columbia, 54-56, M.A, 57, Du Pont fel, 57-58, Nat. Insts. Health, 58-59, Ph.D. (org. synthesis), 59. Res. fel. ORG. CHEM, Columbia, 59-62; asst. prof, Univ. South. Calif, 62-68; South. Ill. Univ, 68-70; ASSOC. PROF. UNIV. AKRON, 70- Am. Chem. Soc; Brit. Chem. Soc. New synthetic methods; synthesis of terpenes; stereoselective metal reductions; marine natural products. Address: Dept. of Chemistry, University of Akron, Akron, OH 44304.

DARLING, S(TEPHEN) F(OSTER), b. De Smet, S.Dak, May 1, 01; m; c. 4. ORGANIC CHEMISTRY. B.S, Minnesota, 22, M.S, 24; Austin fel, Harvard, 24-26, A.M, 26, Ph.D, 28. Asst. instr, Minnesota, 22-24; instr, Harvard, 24-28; assoc. prof. CHEM, LAWRENCE UNIV, 29-38, PROF, 38-66, EMER. PROF, 66- Sheldon traveling fel. from Harvard, Vienna, 29; res. assoc, Inst. Paper Chem, 66-70, emer. res. assoc, 70- Am. Chem. Soc; fel. Am. Inst. Chem. Chemistry of nitrocyclopropanes. Address: 617 E. Alice St, Appleton, WI 54911.

DARLINGTON, J(AMES) M(cCOWN), b. New Bloomfield, Pa, Aug. 10, 08; m. 38; c. 1. ZOOLOGY. B.S, Franklin & Marshall Col, 30; M.A, Brown, 33, Ph.D.(cytol), 35. Instr. histol. & embryol, Brown, 32-33; zool, Scranton-Keystone Jr. Col, 35-37; Franklin & Marshall Col, 37-44; sr. bacteriologist, Wyeth, Inc, 44-47; asst. prof, R.I. State Col, 47-48; assoc. prof. ZOOL. & BACT, FRANKLIN & MARSHALL COL, 48-52, PROF, 52- AAAS; Am. Soc. Microbiol; Am. Pub. Health Asn. Cytology of moribund cells; blood substitute; pertussis toxin and antigenicity; polysaccharides of pneumococcus; immunity in Amphibia; mitochondrail reaction in degenerating cells; perfusion techniques; use of trypan blue in evaluation of cellular reactions to perfusion fluid. Address: Dept. of Biology, Franklin & Marshall College, Lancaster, PA 17603.

DARLINGTON, JULIAN T(RUEHEART), b. Barboursville, W.Va, Mar. 18, 18; m. 43; c. 2. INVERTEBRATE ZOOLOGY. M.A, Emory, 42; Ph.D.(biol), Florida, 53. Instr. BIOL, Emory, 46-49; asst. prof, Atlanta div, Georgia, 53-54, prof, Shorter Col, 54-59; Furman, 59-64; assoc. prof, SOUTHWESTERN AT MEMPHIS, 64-71, PROF, 71- U.S.A.A.F, 42-45. AAAS; Am. Micros. Soc. Taxonomy and distribution of Turbellaria. Address: Dept. of Biology, Southwestern at Memphis, Memphis, TN 38112.

DARLINGTON, P(HILIP) J(ACKSON), JR, b. Philadelphia, Pa, Nov. 14, 04; m. 42; c. 1. ENTOMOLOGY. A.B, Harvard, 26, M.S, 27, Ph.D.(entom), 31. Entomologist, Colombia Div, United Fruit Co, 28-29; asst. curator insects, MUS. COMP. ZOOL, HARVARD, 32-40, FALL CURATOR COLEOPTERA, 40-, ALEXANDER AGASSIZ PROF. ZOOL, UNIV, 62-, curator insects, mus, 52-64. Mem, Harvard exped, Australia, 31-32. Sanit.C, 42-45, Maj. Nat. Acad. Sci; Entom. Soc. Am; assoc. Am. Ornith. Union. Taxonomy and distribution of Coleoptera; zoogeography of the world; evolution. Address: Museum of Comparative Zoology, Harvard University, Cambridge, MA 02138.

DARLINGTON, ROBERT W(ELLS), b. Ironton, Ohio, Aug. 6, 24; m. 52; c. 1. VIROLOGY, ELECTRON MICROSCOPY. B.S, Kentucky, 56, M.S, 58; Ph.D. (virol), Mississippi, 62. Instr. & trainee MICROBIOL, sch. med, Mississippi, 62-63; asst. prof, COL. MED, UNIV. TENN, 63-67, ASSOC. PROF, 67-; RES. VIROLOGIST, ST. JUDE HOSP, 63- U.S.A, 43-45, 51-53, Sgt. Am. Asn. Exp. Path; Am. Soc. Microbiol; Electron Micros. Soc. Am. Virus-host cell relationships; viral tumorigenesis; ultra structure of virus infected cells; virus fine structure; purification and nucleic acid composition of viruses. Address: Dept. of Microbiology, St. Jude Hospital, Memphis, TN 38101.

DARLINGTON, SIDNEY, b. Pittsburgh, Pa, July 18, 06; m. 65; c. 2. MATHEMATICS. B.S.(physics), Harvard, 28; B.S.(elec. eng), Mass. Inst. Tech, 29; Ph.D.(physics), Columbia, 40. Mem. tech. staff, Bell Tel. Labs, Inc, 29-71; CONSULT, 71- Expert consult, office field serv, Office Sci. Res. & Develop. & tech. observer, U.S. Army, 44-45; with dept. elec. eng, Univ. N.H, 71- Civilian with U.S.A.A.F; U.S.N, 40-44. Fel. Inst. Elec. & Electronics Eng; assoc. fel. Am. Inst. Aeronaut. & Astronaut. Communication network theory; synthesis of networks which produce prescribed characteristics; smoothing and prediction of stochastic processes; guidance and control of missiles and space vehicles. Address: Dept. of Electrical Engineering, University of New Hampshire, Durham, NH 03824.

DARLINGTON, W(ALTER) A(LEXANDER), b. Montreal, Can, Oct. 28, 21; m. 48; c. 3. BIOCHEMISTRY. B.Sc, McGill, 49, Ph.D.(biochem), 52. Res. biochemist, MONSANTO CO, 52-58, scientist, 58-66, SR. SCI. FEL, 66- R.C.A.F, 42-45. AAAS; N.Y. Acad. Sci; Am. Chem. Soc. Absorption from the intestine; plant diseases; microbial synthesis; insecticides. Address: 9344 White Ave, St. Louis, MO 63144.

DARLINGTON, WILLIAM BRUCE, b. Wichita, Kans, July 21, 33; m. 57; c. 4. INORGANIC CHEMISTRY. A.B, Baker, 55; Ph.D.(chem), Kansas, 61. Chemist, Phillips Petrol. Co, 56-57; sr. res. chemist, Pittsburgh Plate Glass Co, 61-65, res. supvr. chem. div, 65-68, sr. supvr, PPG INDUSTS, 68-70, HEAD ELECTROCHEM. DEPT, 70- U.S.N, 56-57. Am. Chem. Soc; Electrochem. Soc. Nonaqueous solution and industrial electrochemistry; fused-salt chemistry; electrometallurgy; alkali metals; halogens. Address: PPG Industries, Box 4026, Corpus Christi, TX 78408.

DARMARA, FALIH NAZMI, b. Izmir, Turkey, Feb. 4, 11; nat; m. 39, 71; c. 3. METALLURGY. B.A, Izmir Col, 32; M.A, Harvard, 36, Ph.D.(phys. chem), 38; Mass. Inst. Tech, 38-39. Chief metallurgist, Utica Drop Forge & Tool Corp, 41-45; res. metallurgist, Nat. Adv. Cmt. Aeronaut, 45-47; res. lab, U.S. Steel Corp, Del, 47-49; dir. res, Utica Drop Forge & Tool Corp, 49-50, asst. to pres, 50-52, v.pres, 52-58, PRES, metals div, Kelsey-Hayes Co, 58-61; SPEC. METALS CORP, 61- Am. Soc. Metals; Am. Soc. Mech. Eng; Am. Iron & Steel Inst; Brit. Inst. Metals; Brit. Iron & Steel Inst. Properties of heat resisting alloys; recrystallization behavior of steels; high temperature alloys for gas turbine components and their fabrication; specific heats of gases at low temperatures; vacuum metallurgy. Address: Special Metals Corp, New Hartford, NY 13413.

DARMORY, FRANKLIN P, b. N.Y.C, June 6, 43; m. 66; c. 1. ORGANIC & POLYMER CHEMISTRY. B.S, Mass. Inst. Technol, 64; M.S, Columbia Univ, 65, Nat. Inst. Health fel, 65-68, Ph.D.(org. chem), 68; M.B.A, Iona Col, 70. Sr. res. chemist, Olin Corp, 68-69; CIBA-GEIGY CORP, 69-71, GROUP LEADER POLYMER CHEM, PLASTICS & ADDITIVES DIV, 71- Am. Chem. Soc; Sci. Res. Soc. Am. Indole alkaloid syntheses; amino acid syntheses; antioxidant and copper chelator syntheses; high temperature polymer synthesis, formulation and fabrication. Address: Plastics & Additives Division, Ciba-Geigy Corp, Ardsley, NY 10502.

DARNALL, DENNIS W, b. Glenwood Springs, Colo, Dec. 14, 41; m. 63; BIOCHEMISTRY. B.S, N.Mex. Inst. Min. & Tech, 63; Nat. Defense Ed. Act fel. & Ph.D.(chem), Tex. Tech. Col, 66. Nat. Insts. Health fel, Northwestern 66-68; ASST. PROF. CHEM, N.MEX. STATE UNIV, 68- Career develop. award, Nat. Insts. Health, 71-76. AAAS; N.Y. Acad. Sci; Am. Chem. Soc. Physical chemistry and chemical modification of proteins; metalloproteins and enzymes; protein subunit interactions. Address: Dept. of Chemistry, New Mexico State University, Las Cruces, NM 88001.

DARNELL, A(LFRED) J(EROME), b. Denton, Tex, Aug. 20, 24; m. 47; c. 1. PHYSICAL CHEMISTRY. B.A, San Diego State Col, 50; N.Am. Aviation fel, 63-64, Ph.D.(chem), California, Los Angeles, 64. SR. TECH. SPECIALIST, PHYS. CHEM. SECT, ATOMICS INT, 55-, PROJ. ENGR, 57- Consult. physics group, Hughes Res. Center. Cattrell res. award, 49. U.S.N.R, 42-46. AAAS; fel. Am. Inst. Chem; Am. Chem. Soc; Am. Phys. Soc. High temperature physical and inorganic chemistry; ultra high pressure physics and chemistry; low temperature physics; super conductivity; solid state chemistry and physics; metallurgy; electrochemistry; air pollution control; thermoelectric conversion. Address: 23030 Burbank Blvd, Woodland Hills, CA 91364.

DARNELL, FREDERICK J(EROME), b. Washington, D.C, May 24, 28; m. 52; c. 3. SOLID STATE PHYSICS. B.S, Yale, 50; M.S, Carnegie Inst. Tech, 51, Ph.D.(physics), 55. Res. physicist, CENT. RES. DEPT, E.I. DU PONT DE NEMOURS & CO, 55-62, res. supvr, 62-70, ASSOC. DIR. RES, 70- Inst. Elec. & Electronics Eng; Am. Phys. Soc; Sci. Res. Soc. Am. Semiconductors; electroluminescence; magnetism. Address: Experimental Station, E.I. du Pont de Nemours & Co, Wilmington, DE 19898.

DARNELL, JAMES E(DWIN), JR, b. Columbus, Miss, Sept. 9, 30. MEDICINE. B.A, Mississippi, 51; M.D, Washington (St. Louis), 55. Sr. asst. surgeon & virologist, Nat. Inst. Allergy & Infectious Diseases, 56-60; spec. fel, Pasteur Inst, Paris, 60-61; asst. prof. biol, Mass. Inst. Technol, 61-62, assoc. prof, 62-64; PROF. cell biol. & biochem, Albert Einstein Col. Med, 64-68; BIOL. SCI, COLUMBIA UNIV, 68- Virology; cellular biology. Address: Dept. of Biological Sciences, 908 Schermerhorn Hall, Columbia University, New York, NY 10027.

DARNELL, REZNEAT M(ILTON), (JR), b. Memphis, Tenn, Oct. 14, 24; m. 51; c. 1. ECOLOGY. B.S, Southwestern at Memphis, 46; fel. Rice, 46-48, M.A, 48; Ph.D.(zool), Minnesota, 53. Asst. zool, Minnesota, 48-52; instr, Tulane, 52-55; asst. prof. biol, Marquette, 55-60, assoc. prof, 60-66, prof, 66-69; vis. prof. oceanog. TEX. A&M UNIV, 68-69, PROF. OCEANOG. & BIOL, 69- Res. assoc, Milwaukee Pub. Mus, 60-; chmn, Wis. State Bd. Preservation Sci. Areas, 64-68; chmn, Wis. Sci. Areas Preservation Coun, 68-69. Fel. AAAS; Am. Soc. Ichthyol. & Herpet; Am. Soc. Limnol. & Oceanog; Ecol. Soc. Am; Soc. Study Evolution; Am. Fisheries Soc; Am. Soc. Zool; Int. Soc. Limnol. Ecology of streams, estuaries and oceans; subtropical aquatic ecology; community analysis; organic detritus; nitrogen and energy budgets; ecology and systematics of fishes. Address: Dept. of Oceanography, Texas A&M University, College Station, TX 77843.

DARNELL, W(ALTER) THOMAS, b. Harrisonburg, Va, Aug. 29, 31; m. 56; c. 3. CHEMICAL ENGINEERING. B.S, Va. Polytech, 53; Tau Beta Pi fel, Wisconsin, 53-54, M.S, 54; Gen. Foods Corp. fel, 54-55, Nat. Sci. Found. fel, 55-56, Ph.D.(chem. eng), 57. Engr. orlon res, textile fibers dept, Benger Lab, E.I. DU PONT DE NEMOURS & CO, Va, 53, res. engr, polychem. dept, exp. sta, 57-62, PLASTICS DEPT, WASHINGTON LAB, 62-65, sr. res. engr, 65-66, res. supvr. commercial resins div, 66-68, asst. div. supt, 68-69, chief chemist-color, 69, TECH. DIV. SUPT, 69- U.S.A.R, 53-61, 1st Lt. Soc. Plastics Eng; Am. Inst. Chem. Eng. Gas flow in spray drying; integrated process development for polymeric materials; drying processes; distillation processes; reactor design; fluid-solid systems; polymer compounding and finishing systems. Address: Plastics Dept, E.I. du Pont de Nemours & Co, Washington Works, Parkersburg, WV 26101.

DARNELL, W(ILLIAM) H(EADEN), b. Roanoke, Va, May 14, 25; m. 50; c. 1. CHEMICAL ENGINEERING. B.S, Va. Polytech, 50; M.S, Wisconsin, 51, Nat. Sci. Found. fel, 52-53, Ph.D.(chem. eng), 53. Asst, Wisconsin, 51-52; res. engr, process develop, polychem. dept, E.I. DU PONT DE NEMOURS & CO, 53-59, supvr. res. & develop. div, 59-60, tech. supt, nylon intermediates, 60-63, prod. develop. mgr, DEVELOP. DEPT, 63-64, prod. mgr, 64-69, RES. MGR, 69- U.S.A, 43-46; C.W.S.R, 48-53. Am. Inst. Chem. Eng. Atomization; process development; plastics manufacture. Address: Woodchuck Way, R.D. 2, Kennett Square, PA 19348.

DAROFF, MAXWELL A(BRAHAM), b. Philadelphia, Pa, Aug. 12, 14; m. 47; c. 2. ELECTRICAL ENGINEERING. B.S, Drexel Inst, 37; M.S, Pennsylvania, 54. Elec. engr, Veterans Admin, Philadelphia, Pa, 46-48; head power sect, U.S. Naval Air Develop. Center, 48-57, proj. engr, NAVAL AIR ENG. CTR, 57-68, HEAD SPEC. SUPPORT EQUIP. PROGS. BR, GROUND SUPPORT EQUIP. DEPT, 68- U.S.A.A.F, 41-45, Res, 45-, Lt. Col. Sr. mem. Inst. Elec. & Electronics Eng; sr. mem. Illum. Eng. Soc. Airfield lighting and marking; physical optics; visual landing devices or systems for shipboard use. Address: 7431 Ruskin Rd, Philadelphia, Pa. 19151.

DARON, GARMAN H(ARLOW), b. McPherson, Kans, Jan. 29, 04; m. 29, 43; c. 4. ANATOMY. B.S, McPherson Col, 24; California, 24-25; fel, Chicago, 30-32, Ph.D.(anat), 32. Instr. zool, Wyoming, 25-27, 28-29; asst. prof, Nebr. Wesleyan, 29-30; instr. ANAT, col. med, N.Y. Univ, 32-38; asst. prof, sch. med, Georgetown, 38-40, assoc. prof, 40-47; SCH. MED, UNIV. OKLA, 47-53, PROF, 53- Am. Asn. Anat. Vascularity of the uterus; vascular patterns in the brain; cerebellar nuclei. Address: School of Medicine, University of Oklahoma, Oklahoma City, OK 73104.

DARON, HARLOW H(OOVER), b. Chicago, Ill, Oct. 25, 30; m. 58; c. 2. BIOCHEMISTRY. B.S, Oklahoma, 56; Ph.D.(biochem), Illinois, 61. Nat. Sci. Found. res. fel. biol, Calif. Inst. Tech, 61-63; asst. prof. BIOCHEM, Tex. A&M Univ, 63-68; AUBURN UNIV, 68-70, ASSOC. PROF, 70- U.S.N, 51-54. AAAS. Mechanism of enzyme action. Address: Dept. of Animal Science, Auburn University, Auburn, AL 36830.

DaROOGE, MARGARET A, b. Detroit, Mich, May 5, 37. ORGANIC CHEMISTRY. B.A, Wayne State, 60, U.S. Pub. Health Serv. fel, 60-62, Ph.D.(org. chem), 62. Res. assoc. phys. org. chem, Wayne State, 62-63; synthetic org. chem, Detroit Inst. Cancer Res, 63-65; SR. RES. CHEMIST PHYS. ORG. CHEM, FORD MOTOR CO, 65- AAAS; Am. Chem. Soc. Conformational analysis; reaction mechanisms; organic free radicals. Address: Ford Motor Co, P.O. Box 2053, Dearborn, MI 48127.

DA ROSA, ALDO VIEIRA, b. Rio de Janeiro, Brazil, Nov. 15, 18; m. 45; c. 3. ELECTRICAL ENGINEERING, SPACE PHYSICS. B.S, Brazilian Aeronaut. Acad, 40; Engr, Stanford, 45, Ph.D.(ionospheric physics), 65. Head electronics res. div, Brazilian Fed. Aviation Admin, 45-51; assoc. prof. electronics, Tech. Inst. Aeronaut, Brazil, 51-54; dir. electronics & airplane develop. res. & develop. inst, Brazilian Air Ministry, 54-56 & 57-61; chmn, Brazilian Space Activities Cmn, 61-63; res. assoc. RADIOSCI, STANFORD UNIV, 65-69, SR. RES. ASSOC, 69- Lectr, Stanford, 66- Participant, Conf. Civil Aeronaut. Orgn, 46-50; chmn. Brazilian del, Geneva Conf. Int. Telecommun. Union, 51; Nat. Res. Coun, Brazil, 56-57; U.S. del, XVI Gen. Assembly, Union Radio Sci. Int, Ottawa, Oct. 69. Brazilian Army, 37; Brazilian Air Force, 41-66, Maj. Brigadier (Ret). AAAS; Inst. Elec. & Electronics Eng; Am. Geophys. Union; Int. Sci. Radio Union. Development of electronic equipment for air traffic control, helicopters, VTOL aircraft and pulse and ram jet engines; ionospheric physics; F-region dynamics; columnar electron content. Address: Radioscience Lab, Stanford University, Stanford, CA 94305.

DaROSA, EDMUND A, b. Viseu, Portugal, Oct. 16, 18; nat; m. 40; c. 3. AERONAUTICS. B.A, Col. Sem. São José, Portugal, 36; Lincoln Aeronaut. Inst, 37; Spartan Sch. Aeronaut, 38; B.S, Aeronaut. Univ, 42. Instr, Latin Am. dept, Spartan Sch. Aeronaut, 39-40; Lewis Sch. Aeronaut, 40-44, dir. aviation, Lewis Col, 48-64, assoc. prof, 54-64; ASSOC. PROF. AVIATION TECHNOL. & CHMN. DEPT, SOUTH. ILL. UNIV, 64- Aviation mech. exam, Civil Aeronaut. Admin, 53, aircraft inspector, 54. U.S.A.A.F, 44-46. Am. Inst. Aeronaut. & Astronaut. Transonic aerodynamics and jet powerplant. Address: Dept. of Aviation Technology VTI, Southern Illinois University, Carbondale, IL 62903.

DARR, J(ACK) E(DWIN), b. Shaffersville, Pa, Jan. 23, 21; m. 47; c. 8. ELECTRICAL ENGINEERING. B.S, Pa. State, 42, M.S, 48. Trainee, Bethlehem Steel Co, 42-43, asst. foreman power stas, 43-44; asst, eng. exp. sta, Pa. State, 46-48; asst. engr, WESTINGHOUSE ELEC. CORP, 48-50, assoc. engr, 50-51, eng. group leader, 51, sect. mgr, interceptor armament control systs, aerospace div, 51-59, dir. eng. electronic warfare proj, 59-60, mgr, astroelectronics lab, 60-61, airborne weapons control eng, 61-63, proj. serv, systs. opers, 63-65, dep. mgr, deep submergence systs, 65-67, mgr. planning & control, 67-68, MGR. OPERS. SERV, underseas div, 68-71, ORD. SYSTS. DEPT, AEROSPACE & ELECTRONICS SYSTS. DIV, 71- Summers, with Basalt Trap Rock Co, 39-41, asst. to supt, 46. U.S.N.R, 44-46. Inst. Elec. & Electronics Eng. Project management; military electronic systems. Address: Ordnance Systems Dept, Westinghouse Electric Corp, P.O. Box 1897, Baltimore, MD 21203.

DARR, WILLIAM C(HARLES), b. Fremont, Ohio, May 15, 29; m. 51; c. 6. PHYSICAL CHEMISTRY. B.S, Ohio, 51, M.S, 52. Chemist, Mound Lab, Monsanto Res. Corp, 52-54; res. chemist, MOBAY CHEM. CO, 54-59, proj. leader, 59-61, sr. res. chemist, 61-67, GROUP LEADER, 67- Am. Chem. Soc. Urethane chemistry and applications; physical and permanence properties of polymers; radiochemical techniques. Address: 1251 Satellite Circle, Pittsburgh, PA 15241.

DARRACH, MARVIN (DON), b. Vancouver, B.C, Nov. 18, 13; m. 41; c. 3. BIOCHEMISTRY. Lefevre scholar. & B.A, British Columbia, 35, Nicholson scholar. & M.A, 36; univ. open fels, Toronto, 37-38, Nat. Res. Coun. fels, 39-40, Ph.D.(biochem), 40. From mgr. antibiotic res. prod. & control, to dir. new prod. develop. & clin. res, Merck & Co, Can, 41-50; PROF. BIOCHEM, UNIV. B.C, 50-, asst. dean faculty med, 51-55. Mem. fel. cmt, Nat. Cancer Soc, 55-62; med. res. adv. cmt, Nat. Res. Coun. Can, 56-; mem. exec. cmt, Med. Res. Coun, 60-63, biochem. subcmt, 60-, chmn, 60-63; mem. expert cmt. prfnl. & tech. ed. for med. & auxiliary personnel, WHO, 60-65; adv. cmt, med. res, Dept. Vet. Affairs, 61-; adv. Med. Educ. Thailand, Can. Int. Develop. Agency, 70-; mem. med. adv. bd, B.C. Med. Res. Found, 70- Am. Cancer Soc; Am. Soc. Clin. Invest.(v.pres, 58-59); Can. Biochem. Soc.(v.pres, 59-60, pres, 60-61). Steroid metabolism; hormonal control of antibody production; cancer immunology; chemotherapy of tuberculosis. Address: Dept. of Biochemistry, University of British Columbia, Vancouver 8, B.C, Can.

DARRAGH, RICHARD T, b. Verdun, Que, Apr. 30, 31; m. 53; c. 5. FOOD SCIENCE, BIOCHEMISTRY. B.S, Montreal, 52; M.F.S, Cornell, 55, Ph.D. (biochem), 57. Asst. qual. controller, Birds Eye Co. Canada, 52; food technologist, Continental Can Co. Canada, 53; biochemist, PROCTER & GAMBLE CO, 57-63, sect. head food prod. develop, 63-68, assoc. dir, 68-71, DIR. INDUST. FOOD PROD. DEVELOP, 71- AAAS; N.Y. Acad. Sci. Food industry, especially research and development of retail and commercial food products; food biochemistry; consumer and market research. Address: 6071 Center Hill Rd, Cincinnati, OH 45224.

DARRAH, WILLIAM C(ULP), b. Reading, Pa, Jan. 12, 09; m. 34; c. 2. PALEOBOTANY. B.S, Pittsburgh, 31, Carnegie Mus. fel, 31-33. Asst. paleobot, Pittsburgh, 31-33; asst. bot. mus, Harvard, 34-35, instr. bot, 35-42, tutor & res. curator, 36-42; mat. eng, Raytheon Mfg. Co, Mass, 42-48, admin. asst. head magnetron res. & develop. labs, 48-51; private res, writing & lecturing, 51-57; PROF. BIOL, GETTYSBURG COL, 57- Cmn. Relief Belgium Ed. Found. grant, 35; Univ. Lille grant, 35. Civilian with U.S.A; U.S.A.A.F; U.S.N, 44. Bot. Soc. Am; Paleont. Soc; Soc. Hist. Technol; Brit. Palaeont. Asn; Int. Soc. Plant Taxon. Paleobotany of carbonacous sediments; upper Pennsylvanian stratigraphy; history of science in America. Address: R.D. 1, Spruce Hill, Gettysburg, PA 17325.

DARROW, FRANK W(ILLIAM), b. Syracuse, N.Y, Feb. 6, 40; m. 61; c. 2. PHYSICAL CHEMISTRY. B.A, Williams Col, 61; Ph.D.(chem), Pennsylvania, 65. Vis. asst. prof. CHEM. & Great Lakes Cols. Asn. teaching intern, Earlham Col, 65-66; asst. prof, ITHACA COL, 66-71, ASSOC. PROF, 71- AAAS; Am. Chem. Soc; Nat. Sci. Teachers Asn. Properties of electrolyte solutions and fused salt systems. Address: Dept. of Chemistry, Ithaca College, Ithaca, NY 14820.

DARROW, G(EORGE) M(cMILLAN), b. Springfield, Vt, Feb. 2, 89; m. 19; c. 6. HORTICULTURE. A.B, Middlebury Col, 10; A.M, Cornell, 11; Ph.D. (plant physiol), Hopkins, 27; hon. D.Sc, N.C. State, 63. Sci. asst, U.S. Dept. Agr, Wash, D.C, 11-, 57, prin. pomologist, Beltsville, Md, 46-57; RES. & WRITING, 57- Consult, U.S. Dept. Agr, 57- Distinguished serv. award, U.S. Dept. Agr, 54. Med.C, U.S.A, 18-19, Sgt. AAAS; fel. Am. Soc. Hort. Sci.(pres, 49); Am. Pomol. Soc.(Wilder Medal); Am. Genetic Asn; Am. Hort. Soc.(Liberty Hyde Bailey Award). Fruit breeding, chiefly berries; genetics and polyploidy of fruits; plant physiology of fruits; Hemerocallis and azalea breeding; bamboo propagation; strawberries. Address: Glenn Dale, MD 20769.

DARROW, KARL K(ELCHNER), b. Chicago, Ill, Nov. 26, 91; m. 43. PHYSICS. Paris & Berlin, 11-12; Ph.D, Chicago, 17. Physicist, West Elec. Co, 17-24; Bell Tel. Labs, 25-56; secy, AM. PHYS. SOC, 41-67, EMER. SECY, 67- Vis. prof, Columbia, Chicago, Stanford, Smith; Lowell lectr, 36. Compton award, 60. AAAS; Am. Acad. Arts & Sci; Am. Philos. Soc; Brit. Inst. Physics & Phys. Soc; French Phys. Soc; Int. Union Physics(v.pres, 47-51). Address: American Physical Society, 335 E. 45th St, New York, NY 10017.

DARROW, ROBERT A, b. Syracuse, N.Y, July 12, 31; m. 62; c. 3. BIOCHEMISTRY. A.B, Amherst Col, 52; Nat. Sci. Found. fel, Hopkins, 52-54, U.S. Pub. Health Serv. fel, 55-56, Ph.D.(biol), 57. Biochemist, chem. pharmacol. lab, Nat. Cancer Inst, Nat. Insts. Health, 57-59; fel, Jane Coffin Childs

Mem. Fund, Nat. Inst. Med. Res, London, 59-61; asst. biochemist, Mass. Gen. Hosp, 61-67; assoc. biol. chem, Harvard Med. Sch, 64-67; investr, CHARLES F. KETTERING LAB, 67-71, SECT. HEAD, 71- U.S. Pub. Health Serv. grant. AAAS; Am. Chem. Soc; Am. Soc. Biol. Chem. Intermediary metabolism; mechanism of enzyme action; control mechanisms and enzyme induction. Address: Charles F. Kettering Lab, Yellow Springs, OH 45387.

DARROW, ROBERT A(RTHUR), b. Saratoga Springs, N.Y, Dec. 15, 11; m. 36; c. 2. PLANT PHYSIOLOGY & ECOLOGY. B.S, N.Y. State Col. Forestry, 32; Idaho, 32-33; M.S, Arizona, 35; Ph.D.(bot), Chicago, 37. Instr. bot. & range ecol, Arizona, 36-39, asst. prof, 39-43, assoc. prof, 43-47, prof, 47-48; assoc. prof. range & forestry, Texas A&M, 48-50, prof, 50-59, acting head dept, 59-60, prof, 60-62; chief chem. br, crops div, U.S. ARMY BIOL. LABS, 62-67, chief plant physiol. div, 67-71, PRIN. INVESTR, VEGETATION CONTROL LAB, 71- Ed, plant ecol, Biol. Abstracts, 49-53; pres, South. Weed Conf, 60-61. Meritorious Civilian Serv. Award, 71. AAAS; Am. Bryol. & Lichenological Soc; Am. Soc. Range Mgt.(ed, J. Range Mgt, 54-56); Am. Soc. Plant Physiol; Ecol. Soc. Am; Weed Sci. Soc. Am. Range management; woody plant control; southwestern desert flora; herbicide and plant growth regulator physiology; lichen taxonomy. Address: Vegetation Control Lab, Dept. of the Army, Ft. Detrick, Frederick, MD 21701.

DARROW, THOMAS D, b. David City, Nebr, Apr. 26, 36; m. 56; c. 1. VERTEBRATE ZOOLOGY, HERPETOLOGY. B.S.Ed, Nebr. State Teachers Col, Wayne, 60; M.A, South Dakota, 61; Ph.D.(zool), Oregon State, 67. ASST. PROF. BIOL, LEWIS & CLARK COL, 66- Res. Corp. grant, 69- U.S.A, 54-56. Orientation and navigation mechanisms in urodels; breeding behavior of urodels. Address: Dept. of Biology, Lewis & Clark College, Portland, OR 97219.

DARSIE, RICHARD F(LOYD), JR, b. Scottdale, Pa, Jan. 28, 15; m. 42; c. 1. ENTOMOLOGY. A.B, Bethany Col.(W.Va), 37; M.S, Pittsburgh, 41; Ph.D.(entom), Cornell, 49. Asst. biol, Pittsburgh, 37-41; teacher, high sch, Del, 41; asst. entom, Cornell, 45-49; instr. biol, Franklin & Marshall Col, 49-50; asst. prof. entom, Delaware, 50-54, assoc. prof, 54-62; malaria specialist, U.S. Agency Int. Develop, 62-67; instr. entom, Malaria Eradication Training Ctr, Manila, Philippines, 67-71; CHIEF VECTORBORNE DISEASE TRAINING UNIT, LAB. DIV, CTR. DISEASE CONTROL, 71- Asst, Carnegie Mus, Pa, 38-40; scientist, U.S. Pub. Health Serv, 50-62, sr. scientist, 62-; entomologist, WHO, 60-61. U.S.A.F, 41-45, 1st Lt. Entom. Soc. Am; Am. Soc. Trop. Med. & Hyg; Am. Mosquito Control Asn; Royal Soc. Trop. Med. & Hyg; Indian Soc. Malaria & Communicable Diseases. Medical entomology; mosquito taxonomy and control. Address: Vectorborne Disease Training Unit, Center for Disease Control, Atlanta, GA 30333.

DARSOW, W(ILLIAM) F(RANK), b. Mankato, Minn, May 16, 20; m. 62; c. 2. MATHEMATICS. B.A, Minnesota, 42; Ph.D, Chicago, 53. Instr. MATH, Ill. Inst. Tech, 50-51; De Paul, 52-58, asst. prof, 58-60; ASSOC. PROF, ILL. INST. TECHNOL, 61- Am. Math. Soc; Math. Asn. Am. Abstract harmonic analysis; topological algebra. Address: 1109 Hohlfelder Rd, Glencoe, IL 60022.

DARST, PHILIP HIGH, b. Greensboro, N.C, June 8, 43; m. 68. ENTOMOLOGY. B.S, Wake Forest Univ, 66; M.S, Clemson Univ, 68; Ph.D.(entom), Purdue Univ, 71. ASST. PROF. BIOL, UNIV. MISS, 71- AAAS; Entom. Soc. Am; Am. Inst. Biol. Sci. Economic entomology; insect behavior. Address: Dept. of Biology, University of Mississippi, University, MS 38677.

DARST, RICHARD B, b. Chicago, Ill, Oct. 5, 34; m. 58; c. 4. MATHEMATICS. B.S, Ill. Inst. Tech, 57, M.S, 58, Nat. Sci. Found. fel, summer 59; Nat. Sci. Found. fel, La. State, 59-60 & summer, 60, Ph.D.(math), 60. Instr. MATH, Mass. Inst. Tech, 60-62; asst. prof, PURDUE UNIV, 62-64, assoc. prof, 64-70, PROF, 70- Math. Asn. Am; Am. Math. Soc. Measure and integration; functional analysis; probability and statistics. Address: Dept. of Mathematics, Purdue University, Lafayette, IN 47907.

DART, FRANCIS E(LIOT), b. Mt. Selinda, Africa, Nov. 20, 14; m. 42; c. 3. PHYSICS. A.B, Oberlin Col, 37; M.S, Notre Dame, 39; Ph.D.(physics), Cornell, 47. Asst. physics, Notre Dame, 37-39; exp. physicist, U.S. Rubber Co, Mich, 39-41, 42; asst. PHYSICS, Cornell, 41-45, instr, 45-46, res. assoc, 48-49; asst. prof, UNIV. ORE, 49-56, assoc. prof, 56-64, PROF, 64- AAAS; Am. Asn. Physics Teachers. Physical properties of rubber; electronics of solid state, photoconductivity; science and the developing nations. Address: Dept. of Physics, University of Oregon, Eugene, OR 97403.

DART, JACK CALHOON, b. Concord, Mich, Aug. 14, 12; m. 40; c. 4. CHEMICAL ENGINEERING. A.B, Albion Col, 34; B.S.E, Michigan, 35, M.S.E, 37. Res. assoc, faculty res, Michigan, 36; chem. engr, Universal Oil Prod. Co, 36-37; Pan-Am. Ref. Corp, Tex, 37-43; instr. chem. eng. exten, Agr. & Mech. Col, Tex, 41-42; supvr. pilot plant develop. group, Magnolia Petrol. Co, 43-44; La. Div, Esso Labs, Standard Oil Co.(N.J), 44-47; dir. develop, Houdry Process Corp, 47-52, mgr. res. & develop. div, 52-55, dir, v.pres. & gen. mgr. chem. div, 55-57, sales & serv. div, 57-62; OWNER, J.C. DART & ASSOCS, 62- Adj. prof. chem. eng, Cath. Univ. Am, 69- Fel. Am. Inst. Chem; Am. Inst. Chem. Eng; Am. Chem. Soc. Alkylation, isomerization and polymerization of light hydrocarbons; catalytic and thermal cracking of hydrocarbons; hydrocarbon synthesis; azeotropic distillation; hydrogenation; thermal and catalytic reforming; heat transfer, fluid flow, absorption and distillation; ammonia and methanol syntheses; phthalic anhydride. Address: J.C. Dart & Associates, 1518 K St. N.W, Washington, DC 20005.

DART, S(IDNEY) LEONARD, b. Cape Town, S.Africa, Aug. 24, 18; m. 42; c. 4. PHYSICS. A.B, Oberlin Col, 40; M.S, Notre Dame, 43, Ph.D.(physics), 46. Asst, Notre Dame, 40-43, instr. physics, 43-44, res. assoc, 44-46; sr. physicist, Am. Viscose Corp, 46-53; physicist, Dow Chem. Co, 53-54; PROF. PHYSICS, CLAREMONT MEN'S COL, 54- Consult, Dow Chem. Co, 56-59. With Office Sci. Res. & Develop, 44. AAAS; Am. Phys. Soc; Soc. Rheol; Soc. Social Responsibility Sci. Fundamental physical properties of high polymers including rubber, cork and textile fiber polymers; biophysics of muscle. Address: Dept. of Physics, Claremont Men's College, Claremont, CA 91717.

DARWENT, B(ASIL) de B(ASKERVILLE), b. Trinidad, B.W.I, May 20, 13; m. m. 38; c. 1. PHYSICAL CHEMISTRY. B.Sc, McGill, 41, Ph.D.(phys. chem), 43. Asst. res. chemist, Trinidad Leaseholds, Ltd, 36-40; res. assoc, McGill, 43-44; res. chemist, Nat. Res. Coun. Can, 44-52; mgr. dept. phys. chem, Olin Industs, Inc, 52-55; res. prof. CATH. UNIV. AM, 55-57, PROF. CHEM, 57- Am. Chem. Soc; Faraday Soc; Brit. Chem. Soc; Royal Soc. Can. Kinetics of elementary gas-phase reactions; photochemistry oxidation; reactions of excited species. Address: 1736 Q St. N.W, Washington, DC 20017.

DARWIN, JAMES T, JR, b. Decatur, Tex, Apr. 13, 33. MATHEMATICS. B.S, Univ. Tex, 54, M.A, 62, Ph.D.(math), 63. Asst. MATH, Univ. Tex, 58-63; asst. prof, Auburn Univ, 63-69; ASSOC. PROF, MEMPHIS STATE UNIV, 69- U.S.A.F, 54-58, 1st Lt. Am. Math. Soc; Math. Asn. Am. Representation of linear operators on linear spaces; kernels for linear transformations. Address: Dept. of Mathematics, Memphis State University, Memphis, TN 38111.

DARWISH, DAVID E(SMAEL), b. Ft. Simpson, N.W.T, Dec. 4, 31; m. 52; c. 4. PHYSICAL ORGANIC CHEMISTRY. B.S, Alberta, 53; Ph.D.(chem), California, Los Angeles, 57. Fel. CHEM, Harvard, 57-58; asst. prof, UNIV. ALTA, 58-63, assoc. prof, 63-71, PROF, 71- Am. Chem. Soc. Reaction mechanisms. Address: Dept. of Chemistry, University of Alberta, Edmonton, Alta, Can.

DARZYNKIEWICZ, ZBIGNIEW DZIERZYKRA J, b. Dzisna, Poland, May 12, 36; m. 66; c. 2. CELL BIOLOGY, CYTOCHEMISTRY. M.D, Med. Acad, Warsaw, 60, Polish Acad. Sci. fel. & Ph.D.(cell biol), 65. Physician, surgery ward, IVth City Hosp, Warsaw, 60-61; Polish Acad. Sci. res. fel. cell. biol. & histol, Med. Acad, Warsaw, 62-65; res. assoc. cytochem, molecular enzym. unit, State Univ. N.Y. Buffalo, 65-66; sr. res. asst. histol, Med. Acad, Warsaw, 66-68; res. assoc. cytol, inst. cell res, Med. Nobel Inst, Stockholm, 68-69; STAFF SCIENTIST, DEPT. CONNECTIVE TISSUE RES, BOSTON BIOMED. RES. INST, 69- Am. Cancer Soc. grant, 70-72. AAAS. Regulation of genome activity in mammalian cells. Address: Dept. of Connective Tissue Research, Boston Biomedical Research Institute, 20 Staniford St, Boston, MA 02114.

DAS, BADRI N(ARAYAN), b. Calcutta, India, Oct. 19, 27; U.S. citizen; m. 64; c. 2. PHYSICAL METALLURGY. B.E, Univ. Calcutta, 52; M.S, Univ. Ill, 58; Ph.D.(phys. metall), Ill. Inst. Technol, 64. Res. asst, Univ. Ill, 54-60; staff scientist, Tyco Lab, Inc, Mass, 64-67, sr. scientist, 67-70; staff metallurgist, mat. res. ctr, Allied Chem. Corp, N.J, 70; METALLURGIST, U.S. NAVAL RES. LAB, 70- Am. Crystallog. Asn; Am. Inst. Mining, Metall. & Petrol. Eng; N.Y. Acad. Sci. Metal physics; x-ray diffraction; material synthesis and characterization of semiconductor, ferroelectric, dieelectric, electro-optic and magnetic compounds and alloys; solidification and crystal growth of metallic compounds and alloys; superconductors. Address: Code 6350, U.S. Naval Research Lab, Washington, DC 20390.

DAS, GOPAL DWARKA, b. Shikarpur, India, Feb. 11, 33; m. 61; c. 2. NEUROEMBRYOLOGY, NEUROANATOMY. B.S, Mysore, 54; M.A, Poona, 57; fel, Mass. Inst. Tech, 62-65; Ph.D.(exp. psychol), Boston, 65. Lectr. exp. psychol, Gujarat Univ, India, 57-61; res. asst. neuroanat, Mass. Inst. Tech, 62-63, res. assoc, 63-65, lectr, 67-68; res. scientist, Max Planck Inst. Psychiat, 66-67; asst. prof. NEUROBIOL, PURDUE UNIV, 68-71, ASSOC. PROF, 71- Soc. Neurosci. Neuroembryogenesis and postnatal neurogenesis of the mammalian central nervous system. Address: Dept. of Biological Sciences, Purdue University, Lafayette, IN 47907.

DAS, MUKUNDA B, b. Khulna, E.Pakistan, Sept. 1, 31; m. 56; c. 2. ELECTRONICS. B.Sc, Dacca, 53, M.Sc, 55; Ph.D.(transistor electronics), London & dipl. Imp. Col, 60. Res. asst. physics, Dacca, 55-56; lectr. elec. eng, Imp. Col, London, 60-62; sr. res. officer appl. physics, E.Regional Lab, Coun. Sci. & Indust. Res, Pakistan, 62-64; from mem. sr. sci. staff to mem. prin. sci. staff semiconductors, Hirst Res. Centre, A.S.M. Ltd, Eng, 64-68; ASSOC. PROF. ELEC. ENG, PA. STATE UNIV, 68- Specialist lectureship, Chelsea Col. Sci. & Tech, London, 68. Consult, HRB-Singer, Inc, 69. Sr. mem. Inst. Elec. & Electronics Eng. Design and fabrication of semiconductor devices and integrated circuits; characterization and modeling and metal-oxide-silicon transistors and integrated circuits using bipolar and field effect devices. Address: Dept. of Electrical Engineering, Pennsylvania State University, University Park, PA 16802.

DAS, NABA KISHORE, b. Patna, India, Oct. 4, 34; m. 60; c. 1. MICROBIOLOGY. B.V.S, Bihar, 59; M.S, Missouri, Columbia, 63, Ph.D.(microbiol), 67. Vet. asst. surgeon, Govt. Bihar, India, 59-61; asst. microbiol, Missouri, Columbia, 63-67; SR. RES. MICROBIOLOGIST, Norwich Pharmacal Co, 67-69; RES. DIV, W.R. GRACE & CO, 69- AAAS; N.Y. Acad. Sci; Am. Soc. Microbiol; Indust. Vet. Asn. In vivo and in vitro staphylococcal bacteriophage activities in mastitis cows and in milk; host-parasite relationships and its pathogenesis in model gastrointestinal bacterial infections in laboratory animals, especially Shigella Flexner's infection. Address: Research Division, Washington Research Center, W.R. Grace & Co, Clarksville, MD 21029.

DAS, NIRMAL K(ANTI), b. Chittagong, E. Pakistan, Mar. 1, 28; U.S. citizen; m. 58; c. 2. CYTOLOGY, CYTOCHEMISTRY. B.Sc, Calcutta, 48, M.Sc, 50; Ph.D.(bot), Wisconsin, 57. Lectr. biol, Midnapore Col, 51-52; res. asst. cytochem, Carnegie Inst, 52-53; res. assoc. bot, Wisconsin, 56-58; asst. res. zoologist, UNIV. CALIF, BERKELEY, 58-65, ASSOC. RES. ZOOLOGIST, 65- AAAS; Bot. Soc. Am; Am. Soc. Cell Biol. Quantitative cytochemistry of nucleic acids and proteins; synergistic effects of indoleacetic acid and kinetin on DNA synthesis, mitosis and cytokinesis in tobacco pith tissue cultured in vitro; cytochemical studies on production of chromosomal abnormalities by ribonuclease. Address: Dept. of Zoology, University of California, Berkeley, CA 94720.

DAS, PHANINDRAMOHAN, b. Bholabo, E.Pakistan, Feb. 2, 26; m. 55; c. 3. ATMOSPHERIC PHYSICS, METEOROLOGY. B.Sc, Dacca, 47, M.Sc, 48; Ph.D.(meteorol), Chicago, 63. Res. asst. physics, Banaras Hindu Univ, 49-51; asst. meteorologist, India Meteorol. Dept, 51-55; asst. prof. appl. physics, Indian Inst. Tech, Kharagpur, 55-59 & 64-67; asst. & res. assoc. meteorol, Chicago, 59-64; asst. prof, Texas A&M, 67-68; res. physicist, Air Force Cambridge Res. Lab, 68-70; ASSOC. PROF. METEOROL, TEX. A&M UNIV, 70- Am. Meteorol. Soc; Royal Meteorol. Soc. Atmospheric physics, especially ionospheric physics; radar meteorology; cloud physics and dynamics. Address: 1005 Glade St, College Station, TX 77840.

DAS, SURYYA K, b. Calcutta, India, Feb. 14, 28; m. 61; c. 1. POLYMER & PHYSICAL CHEMISTRY. B.Sc, Calcutta, 49, M.Sc, 50, D.Phil.(chem), 60; fel, Reading, 56-58 & Syracuse, 58-60. Tech. off, Allied Resins & Chem. Ltd, 60-63; RES. ASSOC, NEW PROD. DIV, PPG INDUSTS, INC, SPRINGDALE, 63- Am. Chem. Soc. Thermodynamics of polymer solution; size and shape of long chain molecules; kinetics of chain transfer reaction in addition polymerization; synthesis of tailor-made polymers: kinetics of electron transfer reaction. Address: 110 Berg Dr, Dorseyville, Pittsburgh, PA 15238.

DAS, TARA PRASAD, b. India, July 7, 32; U.S. citizen; m. 58; c. 3. ATOMIC, MOLECULAR & SOLID STATE PHYSICS, B.S, Patna, 49; M.S, Calcutta, 51, Ph.D.(physics), 55. Lectr, theoret. physics, Saha Inst. Nuclear Physics, 53-55; res. assoc. chem, Cornell, 55-56; physics, California, Berkeley, 56-57; reader, Saha Inst. Nuclear Physics, 57-58; res. asst. prof, Illinois, 58-59; chem, Columbia, 59-60; sr. res. officer, Atomic Energy Estab, Govt. India, 60-61; assoc. prof. PHYSICS, California, Riverside, 61-65, PROF, 65-69; Univ. Utah, 69-71; STATE UNIV. N.Y. ALBANY, 71- Nat. Sci. Found. grants, 62- Fel. Am. Phys. Soc; Biophys. Soc. Electronic structures of atoms, simple molecules, and solid state, including theory of electron-nuclear hyperfine interactions; atomic and molecular scattering theory; electronic structure and properties of biologically imporant molecules. Address: Dept. of Physics, State University of New York Albany, Albany, NY 12203.

D'ASARO, L(UCIAN) A(RTHUR), b. Buffalo, N.Y, Jan. 20, 27; m. 53; c. 4. PHYSICS. B.S, Northwestern, 49, M.S, 50; Ph.D.(physics), Cornell, 55. Mem. tech. staff, SEMICONDUCTOR DEVICES, BELL TEL. LAB, 55-62, SUPVR, 62- Am. Phys. Soc; Inst. Elec. & Electronics Eng. Field emission from alloys and semiconductors; stepping transistors; diffusion and oxide masking in silicon; Esaki diodes; Schottky barrier diodes; gallium arsenide electroluminescence and lasers; avalanche multiplication photodiodes. Address: Bell Telephone Labs, Murray Hill, NJ 07974.

DASCH, CLEMENT E(UGENE), b. Steubenville, Ohio, Nov. 28, 25; m. 47; c. 4. ENTOMOLOGY, TAXONOMY. B.S, Cornell, 49, Ph.D.(entom), 53. Asst. prof. BIOL, MUSKINGUM COL, 53-56, assoc. prof, 56-61, PROF, 61-, CHMN. DEPT, 56-, COORD. SCI. DIV, 66- Nat. Sci. Found. res. grant, Michigan, 63-64. Summers, Am. Physiol. Soc. fel, Carolina Biol. Supply Co, 57, Am. Philos. Soc. res. grant, 64, Nat. Sci. Found. res. participant biochem. systs, Oregon State, 65. Mem. Nat. Sci. Found. Summer Insts, evolution, embryol. & genetics, Williams Col, 58, desert biol, Arizona State, 60, marine biol, Coos Bay Sta, Oregon, 62; systematics, Smithsonian Inst, 69. U.S.A, 64-65. AAAS; Soc. Syst. Zool. Systematics and ecology of parasitic wasps of the family Ichneumonidae. Address: Dept. of Biology, Muskingum College, New Concord, OH 43762.

DASCH, ERNEST JULIUS, b. Dallas, Tex, July 9, 32; m. 60. GEOCHEMISTRY. B.S, Sul Ross State Col, 56; M.A, Texas, Austin, 59; fel, Yale, 63-68, M.S, 67, Ph.D.(geochem), 69. Geologist, Magnolia Petrol. Co, 56; W.F. Guyton & Assoc, Tex, 59-61; Utah, summers 62 & 63; res. asst. GEOCHEM, Yale, 63-68; Fulbright vis. res. fel, Australian Nat. Univ, 68-70; ASST. PROF, ORE. STATE UNIV, 70- AAAS; Geol. Soc. Am; Am. Geophys. Union; Geochem. Soc. Strontium and lead geochemistry of selected igneous and sedimentary systems; petrology. Address: Dept. of Geology, Oregon State University, Corvallis, OR 97331.

DASCOMB, HARRY E(MERSON), b. Bath, N.Y, Aug. 12, 16; m. 39; c. 3. MEDICINE. A.B, Colgate, 38; fel, Rochester, 40-41, M.D, 43. Intern med, Rochester, 43; res. physician, Iola Sanatorium, 43-45; intern MED, Rochester, 45-46, Buswell fel, sch. med. & dent, 46-47; instr, SCH. MED, LA. STATE UNIV, NEW ORLEANS, 47-49, asst. prof, 49-55, assoc. prof, 55-59, PROF, 59- Dir. off. hosp. infections control, Charity Hosp. La, 68- Med.C, 53-54, Capt. Am. Med. Asn; Am. Fedn. Clin. Res; N.Y. Acad. Sci; fel. Am. Col. Physicians; Infectious Disease Soc. Am. Infectious disease. Address: School of Medicine, Louisiana State University, New Orleans, LA 70112.

DAS GUPTA, KAMALAKSHA, b. Calcutta, India, Feb. 1, 17; m. 47; c. 1. PHYSICS. M.Sc, Calcutta, 40; Ph.D.(physics), Liverpool, 52. Lectr. physics, Calcutta, 43-47, 52-56, reader, 59-61; sr. res. fel. PHYSICS, Calif. Inst. Technol, 61-66, consult. moon surveyor proj, jet propulsion lab, 63; PROF, TEX. TECH UNIV, 66- Am. Phys. Soc. Soft x-ray absorption and emission spectra of solids with crystals and ruled gratings up to about 700 Angstrom; x-ray diffraction of liquids, supercooled liquids, colloids and devitrification on processes; modified x-ray scattering. Address: Dept. of Physics, Texas Tech University, Lubbock, TX 79409.

DASGUPTA, SANJOY, b. Calcutta, India, June 18, 37; m. 63; c. 2. DEVELOPMENTAL BIOLOGY. B.Sc, Delhi, 56, M.S, 58; Ph.D.(biol), Tulane, 62. Res. assoc. cellular differentiation, Indiana, Bloomington, 62-63; sr. sci. officer, All-India Inst. Med. Sci, New Delhi, 64-67; ASSOC. PROF. BIOL, ST. LOUIS UNIV, 67- Am. Soc. Zool; Am. Inst. Biol. Sci. Address: Dept. of Biology, St. Louis University, 1402 S. Grand Ave, St. Louis, MO 63104.

DASGUPTA, SHARDA, b. India, Sept. 27, 24; Can. citizen; m. 51; c. 1. PHYSICAL & RADIATION CHEMISTRY. Ph.D.(phys. chem), Bombay, 47. Res. officer, phys. chem, Nat. Chem. Lab, India, 49-59; res. assoc. nuclear chem, McMaster, 59-60; res. & develop. scientist, ATOMIC ENERGY CAN, LTD, 60-68, HEAD NEW MAT. PROG, RES. DIV, 68- Coblentz Soc; Chem. Inst. Can; fel. Can. Asn. Appl. Spectros. Development of new products and materials using radiation induced reactions; infrared spectroscopy and other physicochemical investigation techniques; polymer and physical chemistry and electron spin resonance spectroscopy. Address: New Materials Program, Research Division, Commercial Products, Atomic Energy of Canada, Ltd, P.O. Box 6300, Ottawa, Ont. K2A 3W3, Can.

DAS GUPTA, TAPAS KUMAR, b. New Delhi, India, Feb. 22, 32; m. 66; c. 2. MEDICINE. M.B, B.S, Calcutta, 53; Ph.D, London, 67. Sr. lectr. anat, Guy's Hosp. Med. Sch, London, 65-67; clin. asst. attend. surgeon, gastric & mixed tumor serv, Mem. Hosp. Cancer & Allied Diseases, N.Y, 67-68; assoc. prof. surg. & head tumor clin, UNIV. ILL. COL. MED, 68-70, PROF. SURG, 70-, HEAD DIV. SURG. ONCOL, 68- Chief oncol. sect, Vet. Admin. West Side Hosp, Chicago; attend. physician, Cook County Hosp. AAAS; Am. Fedn. Clin. Res; James Ewing Soc; Reticuloendothelial Soc; N.Y. Acad. Sci; Am. Col. Surg; Am. Med. Asn; Am. Asn. Cancer Educ; Am. Asn. Cancer Res; Soc. Univ. Surg; Soc. Head & Neck Surg; Anat. Soc. Gt. Brit. & Ireland. Experimental oncology. Address: Division of Surgical Oncology, University of Illinois College of Medicine, 840 S. Wood St, Chicago, IL 60612.

DASH, BARRY H(AROLD), b. Bronx, N.Y, June 9, 31; m. 53; c. 3. PHARMACY. B.S, Columbia, 52, M.S, 54; Am. Found. Pharmaceut. Ed. fel, Florida, 54-56, Ph.D.(pharm), 56. Asst. prof. pharm, Columbia, 56-60; dir. prod. develop. res, WHITEHALL LABS, 60-70, ASST. V.PRES. PROD. DEVELOP, 70- Lectr, Columbia, 60- Summer, mem. staff res. & develop, Charles Pfizer & Co, Inc, 58. Consult, Indust. Pharmaceut, 57-60; Am. Prof. Pharmacist, 59-60. AAAS; Am. Pharmaceut. Asn; Soc. Cosmetic Chem. Product development; dosage design. Address: Division of American Home Products, Whitehall Labs, 685 Third Ave, New York, NY 10017.

DASH, BIBHU P(RASAD), b. Sambalpur, India, Sept. 11, 31; m. 59; c. 4. GEOPHYSICS. B.Sc, Ravenshaw Col, India, 49; M.Sc, Patna Univ, 52; Ph.D. (appl. geophys. & seismol), Univ. London & dipl, Imp. Col, 59. Lectr. physics, Univs. Bihar & Patna, 52-56; res. geophysicist, Nat. Inst. Oceanog. Res, Ger, 59-60; geophysicist, Prakla G.m.b.H, Hannover, 60-63; lectr. GEOPHYS, Imp. Col, Univ. London, 64-71; ASSOC. PROF, ROSENSTIEL SCH. MARINE & ATMOSPHERIC SCI, UNIV. MIAMI, 71- Vis. lectr, Univ. Birmingham, 65-66; consult, Place Oil Co, Can, 65-67; Trinidad Can. Oil Co, Eng, 65-67; Can. Indust. Gas, 65-67; UNESCO, 69; chief scientist, various int. geophys. marine expeds, 67-; vis. prof, inst. marine sci, Univ. Miami, 69-70; tech. adv. offshore mineral propecting, UN Econ. Comn. for Asia & Far East, 70- Fel. Brit. Inst. Physics; Soc. Explor. Geophys; Europ. Asn. Explor. Geophys; Am. Geophys. Union. Marine seismology; crustal studies of continental margins; seismic data processing; mineral exploration of off shore areas; development of geophysical instrument; global tectonics. Address: Rosenstiel School of Marine & Atmospheric Sciences, University of Miami, 10 Rickenbacker Causeway, Miami, FL 33149.

DASH, HARRIMAN H(ARVEY), b. New York, N.Y, May 26, 10; m. 42; c. 1. BIOCHEMISTRY, QUANTUM CHEMISTRY. B.S, City Col. New York, 33; cert, sch. med, Chicago, 44; M.S, Polytech. Inst. Brooklyn, 53. Res. chemist, Bellevue Hosp, New York, N.Y, 34-35, proj. chemist, univ. res. labs, Fordham, 35-38; Consumers Labs, 38-42; biochemist med. res, Nat. Jewish Hosp, Denver, Colo, 46-47; consult. chemist high polymers, 47-58; assoc. biochemist, med. lab, North Shore Hosp, Manhasset, N.Y, 58-62; CHIEF BIOCHEMIST, Nassau Hosp, Mineola, 62-66; Variety Children's Hosp, Miami, Fla, 66-68; RES. DIV, MIAMI HEART INST, 68- Med. Dept, 42-46, Capt. AAAS; Am. Chem. Soc. Clinical biochemistry and application of quantum theory of biochemistry. Address: 5315 S.W. 111th Ave. Miami, FL 33165.

DASH, J(AY) G(REGORY), b. Brooklyn, N.Y, June 28, 23; m. 45; c. 3. PHYSICS. B.S, City Col. New York, 44; A.M, Columbia, 49, Ph.D.(physics), 51. Mem. staff, Los Alamos Sci. Lab, 51-60; acting assoc. prof. PHYSICS, UNIV. WASH, 60-61, assoc. prof, 61-63, PROF, 63- Guggenheim fel, 57-58. Consult, Los Alamos Sci. Lab, 60-; Boeing Co, 61-64. U.S.N, 44-46. Fel. Am. Phys. Soc. Low temperature physics; solid state physics; liquid helium; magnetism; Mössbauer effect. Address: Dept. of Physics, University of Washington, Seattle, WA 98105.

DASH, JOHN, b. Hazleton, Pa, June 29, 33; m. 68; c. 3. PHYSICAL METALLURGY. B.S, Pa. State, 55, Ph.D.(metall), 66; M.S, Northwestern, 60. Res. metallurgist, Crucible Steel Co, 55-58; res. assoc. phase transformations, Res. Inst. Adv. Study, Martin Marietta Corp, Md, 60-63; asst. prof. PHYSICS, PORTLAND STATE UNIV, 66-71, ASSOC. PROF, 71- Electron Micros. Soc. Am; Am. Soc. Metals; Am. Inst. Mining, Metall. & Petrol. Eng. Solid state transformations in metals and alloys, including nucleation and growth reactions and martensitic transformations; electron microscopy and electron diffraction. Address: Dept. of Physics, Portland State University, Box 751, Portland, OR 97207.

DASHER, BENJAMIN J(OSEPH), b. Macon, Ga, Dec. 27, 12; m. 41; c. 6. ELECTRICAL ENGINEERING. B.S, Ga. Inst. Tech, 35, M.S, 45; Sc.D.(elec. eng), Mass. Inst. Tech, 52. Asst. prof. elec. eng, Ga. Inst. Tech, 40-46; commun. eng, Mass. Inst. Tech, 46-51; PROF. ELEC. ENG, GA. INST. TECHNOL, 51-, ASSOC. DEAN COL. ENG, 69-, dir. sch. elec. eng, 54-69. Fel. Inst. Elec. & Electronics Eng; Pattern Recognition Soc; Asn. Comput. Ling. Advanced network theory; acoustic phonetics; electronics. Address: College of Engineering, Georgia Institute of Technology, Atlanta, GA 30332.

DASHER, G(EORGE) F(RANKLIN), (JR), b. Russellville, Ky, Aug. 5, 22; m. 43; c. 4. PHYSICAL & SURFACE CHEMISTRY. B.A, Kalamazoo Col, 43; M.S, Michigan, 47, Univ. fel, 46-48, Atomic Energy Comn. fel, 48-49, Ph.D.(chem), 49. Chemist, Procter & Gamble Co, 49-61; asst. dir. res, CLAIROL INC, 61-65, dir. prod. develop, 65-67, V.PRES. RES. & DEVELOP, 67- Lectr, Xavier (Ohio), 60-61. U.S.M.C, 42-46, Res, 46-49. AAAS; Am. Chem. Soc; Faraday Soc; Am. Phys. Soc; Rheol. Soc; N.Y. Acad. Sci. Adsorption at phase boundaries; emulsion stability; surface activity in biological systems; mechanical properties of polymers; flow behavior of liquids; viscoelastic behavior of cosmetic materials. Address: Research Labs, Clairol Inc, 2 Blachley Rd, Stamford, CT 06902.

DASHER, J(OHN) O, b. Ky, June 11, 14; m. 38; c. 3. METALLURGICAL ENGINEERING. B.S, Alabama, 35. Asst. chem. engr, Bur. Mines, Md. & Ala, 37-42; chief res. dept, Tin Processing Corp, 42-46; exec. officer, Atomic Energy Cmn. Proj, Mass. Inst. Tech, 46-51; asst. chief metals group, Chem. Construct. Co, 51-55; res. supvr, Crucible Steel Co. Am, Pa, 55-63, proj. dir. procurement, 63-65; ENG. SPECIALIST, BECHTEL CORP, 65- Mem. adv. bd, Nat. Acad. Sci, 62. Am. Inst. Mining, Metall. & Petrol.

Eng; Asn. Iron & Steel Eng. Process metallurgy; mineral dressing; coal; nonmetallics; nonferrous and ferrous metals. Address: Bechtel Corp, 50 Beale, Box 3965, San Francisco, CA 94119.

DASHER, P(AUL) J(AMES), b. Pleasant Plains, Ill, June 4, 12; m. 35; c. 2. CHEMISTRY. B.S, Illinois, 34; A.M, Indiana, 35, Ph.D, 37. Res. chemist, B.F. Goodrich Co, 37-39, asst. dir. rubber res, 39-41, dir. develop. & eng, fuel cell div, 41-44, tech. supt, 44-45, consult. reclamation div, 45, dir. new process div, 45-46; PRES, Merit Chem. Co, 46-47; Summit Indust. Prod. Co, 46-59; DASHER RUBBER & CHEM. CO, FAIRPORT DEVELOP. CO, FAIRPORT TERMINAL CORP, 50-; V.PRES, LOWMANS, INC, 50-, dir, 43-50. Am. Chem. Soc. Electrolyte conductance in non-aqueous media; rubber research, emphasizing plant utilization of process; invention of new processes. Address: 1812 S.E. 14th St, Ft. Lauderdale, FL 33316.

DASINGER, BRUCE L, b. Dothan, Ala, May 29, 31; m. 56; c. 3. BACTERIOLOGY. B.S, Florida, 53; M.S, Wisconsin, 55, Ph.D.(bact), 60. Fel. microbiol, col. med, Florida, 60-62; RES. MICROBIOLOGIST, Jersey Prod. Res. Co, 62-64; Esso Prod. Res. Co, 65-69; CHARLES PFIZER & CO, 69- U.S.A.F, 55-57, 1st Lt. Am. Soc. Microbiol; Brit. Soc. Gen. Microbiol. Mechanisms of microbial pathogenicity; intermediary metabolism; microbial metabolism of hydrocarbons. Address: Building 126, Charles Pfizer & Co, Grotan, CT 06340.

DASKALAKIS, EMMANUEL G(EORGE), b. Detroit, Mich, Dec. 30, 24; m. 49; c. 3. BIOCHEMISTRY. B.S, Michigan, 49; Ph.D.(biochem), Washington (Seattle), 53. Jr. res. physiologist, California, 53-54, Damon Runyan Cancer Res. fel, 54-55; supvr. chromatog, G.D. Searle & Co, 55-67; asst. dir, ROSNER-HIXSON LABS, 67-69, EXEC. V.PRES. & DIR, 69- U.S.A.A.F, 43-46. Am. Chem. Soc. All phases of chromatography pertaining to organic and biochemistry. Address: Rosner-Hixson Labs, 7737 S. Chicago Ave, Chicago, IL 60619.

DASKAM, EDWARD, JR, b. Detroit, Mich, Mar. 1, 20; m. 48; c. 4. ELECTRICAL ENGINEERING, PHYSICS. B.S, Texas, 41; M.S, N.Y, Univ, 56. Engr, radar, Gen. Elec. Co, 42-44; radio commun, Gen. Tel. Serv. Corp, 46-49, dept. head, 49-51; engr, AIRBORNE INSTRUMENTS LAB, CUTLER-HAMMER, INC, DEER PARK, 51-52, sect. head, 52-58, prog. mgr, 58-62, DEPT. HEAD, 62- U.S.N.R, 44-46, Lt.(jg). AAAS; sr. mem. Inst. Elec. & Electronics Eng; Am. Phys. Soc. Electronic systems, including antennas, microwaves, solid state circuits and microminiaturization. Address: 909 Pear Rd, R.D. One, Huntington, NY 11743.

DASKIN, W(ALTER), b. Passaic, N.J, July 17, 26; m. 51; c. 2. MECHANICAL ENGINEERING. B.M.E, Cooper Union, 45; M.S.E, Michigan, 48; Hopkins, 48-54. Engr. vibration control, Jayburn Eng. Co, N.Y, 46-47; instr. mech. eng, Hopkins, 49-54; engr. fluid mech, Gen. Elec. Co, Ohio, 54-56, specialist heat transfer, 56; sr. scientist re-entry physics, Gen. Appl. Sci. Labs, N.Y, 56-58, proj. scientist, 58-60, sci. supvr, 60-64, asst. dir. res, 64-66; consult. appl. physics, GEN. ELEC. CO, 66-68, MGR, aeromech. & mat. lab. sect, 68-70, TECHNOL. ENG. SECT, 70- Res. asst, Johns Hopkins Univ, 50-54; adj. instr, Polytech. Inst. Brooklyn, 57. Consult, Carbide & Carbon Chem. Co, Tenn, 52-54 & Gen. Elec. Co, Ohio, 53-54. U.S.N, 45-46. AAAS; Am. Soc. Mech. Eng; assoc. fel, Am. Inst. Aeronaut. & Astronaut; Am. Phys. Soc. Heat transfer; fluid mechanics; system optimization techniques; management of research and development. Address: Re-entry & Environmental Systems Products Division, General Electric Co, P.O. Box 8555, Philadelphia, PA 19101.

DASLER, ADOLPH R(ICHARD), b. Conklin, Mich, Mar. 19, 33; m. 58; c. 3. PHYSIOLOGY. B.A. & M.A, Western Michigan, 60; Ph.D.(physiol), Mich. State, 66. Instr. med. tech. & physiol, Hackley Hosp, Clin. Labs, 55-60; res. asst. physiol, Mich. State, 61; MED. SERV. CORPS, U.S. NAVY, 61-, res. investr, NAVAL MED. RES. INST, BETHESDA, 62-63, head thermal stress sect, 63-64, HEAD HEAT STRESS FACILITY, 66-, HEAD THERMAL STRESS BR, BUR. MED. & SURG, 63-, DEP. HEAD ENVIRON. STRESS DIV. & MIL. OFF, ENVIRON. BIOSCI. DEPT, 70-, proj. officer shipboard toxicol. oper. protectional systs, 63-64. Officer-in-charge shelter habitability, Nat. Naval Med. Center & Bur. Med. & Surg, 62-64; U.S. Navy rep, med. adv. subcmt, thermal factors in environ, med. sci. div, Nat. Acad. Sci-Nat. Res. Coun, 63-65 & med. adv. cmt. environ. physiol, 66-; consult, Commandant U.S. Marine Corps, 66-; Naval Ships Eng. Ctr, 68-; U.S. Navy Environ. Health Ctr, 68-; career & prog. planning off, Navy Physiologist, 70- Hosp.C, U.S.N, 50-55. AAAS; Am. Soc. Heat, Refrig. & Air-Conditioning Eng; N.Y. Acad. Sci. Environmental physiology; temperature regulation; adaptation and tolerance to heat; etiology, prevention and treatment of heat illnesses. Address: 10005 Wildwood Court, Kensington, MD 20795.

DASLER, WALDEMAR, b. St. James, Minn, May 28, 10; m. 39; c. 3. BIOCHEMISTRY. B.S, Wisconsin, 32, M.S, 33, Ph.D.(biochem), 38. Chemist, B.S, Pearsall Co, Ill, 38-41; res. chemist, Nutrit. Res. Labs, 41-47, chief res. chemist, 47-48; asst. prof. BIOCHEM, CHICAGO MED. SCH, 48-54, assoc. prof, 54-59, PROF, 59- AAAS; Am. Chem. Soc; Am. Inst. Nutrit; Soc. Exp. Biol. & Med. Sterols; vitamin D; rickets; osteolathyrism; copper determination; experimental cataract. Address: Dept. of Biochemistry, Chicago Medical School, 220 W. Ogden Ave, Chicago, IL 60612.

DASMANN, RAYMOND F(REDRIC), b. San Francisco, Calif, May,27, 19; m. 44; c. 3. ECOLOGY. A.B, California, 48, M.A, 51, Nat. Sci. Found. fel, 52-54, Ph.D.(zool), 54. Asst. zool, California, 48-52; instr. biol, Duluth br, Minnesota, 53-54; prof. natural resources & chmn. dept, Humboldt State Col, 54-56; dir. int. progs, Conserv. Found, 66-70; SR. ECOLOGIST, INT. UNION CONSERV. NATURE, 70- Fulbright scholar, South Rhodesia, 59-60; lectr, Univ. Calif, 61-62. U.S.A, 41-45. Wildlife Soc; Ecol. Soc. Am; Am. Soc. Mammal; Asn. Trop. Biol; Brit. Fauna Preserv. Soc. Conservation of natural resources; human and wildlife ecology. Address: International Union for Conservation of Nature, 1110 Morges, Switz.

DASPIT, WOODSON B, b. Houma, La, Mar. 11, 26; m. 56; c. 4. PHYSICS. B.S, La. State, 49, M.S, 52. Physicist, U.S. Naval Ord. Test Sta, 49-51; Savannah River Lab, E.I. DU PONT DE NEMOURS CO, 52-55, process supvr, SAVANNAH RIVER PLANT, 55-62, sr. supvr, 62-69, ASST. CHIEF SUPVR, 69- U.S.M.C, 44-46. Am. Nuclear Soc. Reactor engineering; nuclear reactor instrumentation; zero power and production reactors. Address: 806 Oleander Dr. S.E, Aiken, SC 29801.

DAS SARMA, BASUDEB, b. India, Jan. 1, 23; m. 52; c. 2. CHEMISTRY. B.S, Calcutta, 44, M.S, 46, Palit fel. & Ph.D.(chem), 51. Lectr. chem, Calcutta, 50-53, 55-57; res. assoc. inorg. chem, Illinois, Urbana, 53-55; sr. chemist, Geol. Surv. India, 57-65; assoc. prof. CHEM, W.VA. STATE COL, 66-69, PROF, 69- Summer res. assoc, Illinois, Urbana, 67. Fel. Am. Inst. Chem; Am. Chem. Soc; Geochem. Soc. Stereo, structural and analytical aspects of coordination chemistry; analytical chemistry and geochemistry of minor and trace metals; solid state reactions in coordination complexes; inorganic pollutants in water. Address: Dept. of Chemistry, West Virginia State College, Institute, WV 25112.

DASSOW, JOHN A(LBERT), b. Spokane, Wash, June 30, 17; m. 36; c. 3. ANALYTICAL & FOOD CHEMISTRY. Nordigard Corp. fel, Washington (Seattle), 46-47, B.S, 49. Asst, fermentation res, Washington(Seattle), 37-40; fish anal, U.S. Fish & Wildlife Serv, 40, chemist fish anal. & preservation, 47-50, chief lab, Alaska, 50-55; eng. estimator prod. materials, Boeing Aircraft Co, Wash, 41; fishery technologist, Fisheries Exp. Cmn, Alaska, 41-45; plant chemist, Dawes Fisheries, 45-46; supvry. chemist fish anal. & preservation, U.S. BUR. COMMERCIAL FISHERIES, 55-70, RES. CHEMIST, NAT. MARINE FISHERIES SERV, 70- N.Y. Acad. Sci; AAAS; Inst. Food Technol. Chemical and physical methods of quality measurement; effects of freezing and cold storage on quality; preservation of chilled fish; control of oxidative rancidity; use of fishery resources for protein concentrates. Address: National Marine Fisheries Service, 2725 Montlake Blvd. E, Seattle, WA 98102.

DASTOLI, FRANK R, b. Cleveland, Ohio, Mar. 7, 36; m. 59; c. 2. BIOCHEMISTRY, ENZYMOLOGY. B.A, Syracuse, 58, M.S, 60; Ph.D.(zool), State Univ. N.Y, 64. Res. assoc. physiol. & biochem, Rutgers, 63-64; sr. biochemist, Boston Lab, Monsanto Res. Corp, 64-69; NAT. ACAD. SCI. ASSOC, U.S. ARMY NATICK LABS, 69- U.S. Pub. Health Serv. res. fel, 63-64. Enzymatic pathways of catabolism in invertebrates; mechanism of action of human adenosine triphosphatase ion activiated enzyme; denaturation of proteins-difference spectra; activity of enzymes in the crystalline state; area-taste receptor proteins. Address: PRL-Biochemistry, U.S. Army Natick Labs, Natick, MA 01760.

DATA, JOHN B(ATISTE), b. Novinger, Mo, Nov. 6, 08; m. 40; c. 2. PHARMACEUTICAL CHEMISTRY. B.S. & M.S, Michigan, 38, Sterns fel, 38-41, fel, 40, Ph.D.(pharmaceut. chem), 41. Asst, Michigan, 37-38; org. chemist, Lederle Labs. Div, Am. Cyanamid Co, N.Y, 41-45; org. res, Battelle Mem. Inst, 45-46; assoc. prof. pharmaceut. chem, Western Reserve, 46-47; Res. Found. fel, PURDUE UNIV, 47-48, ASSOC. PROF. PHARMACEUT, 48- Am. Chem. Soc; Am. Pharmaceut. Asn. Synthesis of organic compounds to study relationship to biological activity; development of labelled synthesis of organic compounds including drug to study their fate, localization and mechanism of action through radioactive methodology. Address: Purdue University School of Pharmacy & Pharmacal Science, West Lafayette, IN 47906.

DATARS, WILLIAM ROSS, b. Desboro, Ont, June 14, 32; Can. citizen; m. 59; c. 1. PHYSICS. B.Sc, McMaster, 55, M.Sc, 56; Ph.D.(physics), Wisconsin, 59. Sci. officer PHYSICS, Defence Res. Bd. Can, 59-62; asst. prof, McMASTER UNIV, 62-65, assoc. prof, 65-69, PROF, 69- E.W.R. Steacie res. fel, 68-70. Am. Phys. Soc; Can. Asn. Physicists. Electronic properties of solids; properties of semi-metals; electron spin resonance studies in solids. Address: Dept. of Physics, McMaster University, Hamilton, Ont, Can.

DATEO, GEORGE PHILIP, JR, b. Dedham, Mass, Aug. 29, 25; m. 55; c. 3. ORGANIC CHEMISTRY. A.B, Harvard, 49; Pennsylvania, 49-51; Ph.D. (chem), Rice, 61. Org. chemist, Phila. Qm. Depot, 52-57; RES. ORG. CHEMIST, PIONEERING RES. LAB, U.S. ARMY NATICK LABS, 61- U.S.A, 44-46. AAAS; Am. Chem. Soc; Sci. Res. Soc. Am. Volatile sulfur compounds from plant sources; mustard oil glucosides; isolation and characterization of insect sex attractants. Address: Pioneering Research Lab, U.S. Army Natick Labs, Natick, MA 01760.

DATERMAN, GARY EDWARD, b. Freeport, Ill, June 26, 39; m. 60; c. 3. FOREST ENTOMOLOGY, INSECT ECOLOGY. B.A, Univ. Calif, Davis, 62; M.S, Ore. State Univ, 64, Ph.D.(entom), 69. RES. SCIENTIST ENTOM, PAC. NORTHWEST FOREST & RANGE EXP. STA, U.S. FOREST SERV, 65-; ASST. PROF, ORE. STATE UNIV, 71- AAAS; Entom. Soc. Am; Entom. Soc. Can. Reproductive biology of European pine shoot moth, Rhyacionia buoliana; sex pheromone responses of Lepidoptera; barkbeetle flight patterns and pheromone responses; influence of physical environment on life processes. Address: Forestry Sciences Lab, Pacific Northwest Forest & Range Experiment Station, U.S. Forest Service, P.O. Box 887, Corvallis, OR 97330.

DATESH, JOHN N(ICHOLAS), b. Canton, Ohio, Feb. 5, 22; m. 46; c. 3. CHEMISTRY, CHEMICAL ENGINEERING. B.S, Carnegie Inst. Tech, 42, M.S, 46, fel, 47-49, D.Sc.(chem. eng), 50. Am. Chem. Soc; Am. Inst. Mining, Metall. & Petrol. Eng. Pressure drop and liquid hold up in packed columns; magnesium; mold coatings; fuel additives; adhesives; water treatment. Address: 714 Pinoak Rd, Pittsburgh, PA 15243.

DATSKO, JOSEPH, b. Pa, Feb. 4, 21; m. 46; c. 4. MECHANICAL ENGINEERING. B.S.M.E, Michigan, 43, M.S.E, 51. Prod. engr, Dynamic Tool Co, 43; chief engr. & plant mgr, Stevens Mfg. Co, 46-49, v.pres. & plant mgr, 52-53; instr. PROD. ENG, UNIV. MICH, 49-52, asst. prof, 53-56, assoc. prof, 56-63, PROF, 63- Consult, 52- U.S.N, 43-45. Am. Soc. Mech. Eng; Am. Soc. Metals; Am. Soc. Eng. Educ; Am. Foundrymens Soc. Correlation of microstructures, mechanical properties and fabricability. Address: Dept. of Mechanical Engineering, University of Michigan, Ann Arbor, MI 48104.

DATTA, DILIP KUMAR, b. Jorhat, India, Jan. 2, 39; m. 68. GEOMETRY. B.A, Gauhati Univ, India, 58; M.A, Delhi, 60, Ph.D.(math), 63. Lectr. math, Assam Eng. Col, 63; Brit. Govt. Commonwealth scholar, differential geom, 63-65; ASST. PROF. MATH, Calgary, 65-67; UNIV. R.I, 67- Am. Math. Soc; Math. Soc. Can. Differential geometry; linear connections; special Riemannian spaces; G-structures. Address: Dept. of Mathematics, University of Rhode Island, Kingston, RI 02881.

DATTA, PADMA R(AG), b. Jorhat, Assam, India, Feb. 27, 27; U.S. citizen; m. 52; c. 2. BIOCHEMISTRY, ECOLOGY. M.S, Massachusetts, 50; Ph.D. (agr. biochem), West Virginia, 56. Res. assoc. biochem, Fels Res. Inst, sch. med, Temple, 56-57; sr. res. fel. anal. & phys. chem, Am. Spice Trade Asn, east. regional lab, U.S. Dept. Agr, 57-61; res. chemist, Rohm and Haas Co, 61-63; res. biochemist, Food & Drug Admin, U.S. Dept. Health, Educ. & Welfare, 63-70; PHYS. SCI. ADV, OFF. PESTICIDES PROGS, ENVIRON. PROTECTION AGENCY, 71- AAAS; Am. Chem. Soc; N.Y. Acad. Sci. Advise on the research, monitoring and regulatory needs for pesticides and other toxic chemicals as they affect environmental ecosystems and human health. Address: 8514 Whittier Blvd, Bethesda, MD 20034.

DATTA, PRASANTA (KUMAR), b. Calcutta, India, Oct. 10, 29; m. 57; c. 2. BIOCHEMISTRY, CELL PHYSIOLOGY. B.Sc, Calcutta, 49, M.Sc, 51; Ph.D. (plant physiol), Washington (Seattle), 56. Lectr. bot, Ripon Col, Calcutta, 52-53; asst, Washington (Seattle), 53-54; teaching asst, 54-56, Playtex Park res. fel, 57-58; Nat. Res. Coun. Can. fel, 58-61; res. asst. prof. & res. assoc. molecular biol, Washington (St. Louis), 61-66; asst. prof. BIOL. CHEM, MED. SCH, UNIV. MICH, 66-68, ASSOC. PROF, 68- Res. fel, Bose Res. Inst, Calcutta, 52-53. AAAS; Am. Soc. Biol. Chem; Am. Soc. Microbiol. Enzymology; microbial physiology and biochemistry. Address: Dept. of Biological Chemistry, Medical School, University of Michigan, Ann Arbor, MI 48104.

DATTA, RANAJIT K, b. Sylhet, E.Pakistan, Feb. 1, 35. SOLID STATE & INORGANIC CHEMISTRY. B.Sc, Calcutta, 53; B.S. Hons, Indian Inst. Tech, Kharagpur, 56, M.Tech, 58; Ph.D.(geochem), Pa. State, 61. Res. asst. geochem, Pa. State, 58-61, res. assoc, 62; RES. CHEMIST, large lamp eng. sect, GEN. ELEC. CO, 62-64, LAMP DIV, 64- Part-time instr, Cuyahoga Community Col, 65. Am. Ceramic Soc. Crystal chemistry, especially phase equilibria and luminescence. Address: General Electric Co, Nela Park, East Cleveland, OH 44112.

DATTA, RANAJIT KUMAR, b. Munshiganj, E.Pakistan, Apr. 1, 33; m. 64. NEUROCHEMISTRY, BIOCHEMICAL PHARMACOLOGY. B.Sc, Calcutta, 56, M.Sc, 58, fel, 59-60, Ph.D.(biochem), 63. Asst. res. officer, Inst. Postgrad. Med. Ed. & Res, Calcutta, India, 60; lectr. chem, Jogamaya Devi Col, 61-63; asst. prof. biochem, Bengal Vet. Col, 63-64; sr. res. officer, U.S. Dept. Agr. Proj, Univ. Calcutta, 64-65; sr. res. scientist, N.Y. State Res. Inst. Neurochem. & Drug Addiction, 65-67; res. assoc. biochem, Col. Physicians & Surgeons, Columbia, 67-68; ASSOC. BIOPHYSICIST, BETH ISRAEL MED. CTR, 68- Hon. lectr, dept. agr, Calcutta, 64-65; assoc, dept. path, Mt. Sinai Sch. Med, 68-71, asst. prof, 71-; ed, Clinician, 70- Fel. Am. Inst. Chem; Am. Soc. Neurochem; Int. Soc. Neurochem; Brit. Biochem. Soc; Indian Brain Res. Asn.(joint-secy, 64-); Indian Soc. Biol. Chem. Metabolism of nucleic acids in brain tissue; biochemical properties of brain ribosomes; drug-induced changes in cerebral macromolecules; protein breakdown processes in the brain; methylation of nucleic acids in cancer; molecular pharmacology of narcotic drugs. Address: Division of Labs, Beth Israel Medical Center, New York, NY 10003.

DATTA, SAMIR KUMAR, b. Calcutta, India, June 14, 36; m. 66; c. 1. ELECTRICAL ENGINEERING. B.E.E, Jadavpur Univ, India, 58; fel, Manchester Univ, 62-66, M.S, 63, Ph.D.(control systs, electronics), 66. Electronic engr, Askania Werke, Ger, 58-60; Valvo, GmbH, 60-61; sr. develop, engr, speed variator dept, Gen. Elec. Co, 67-68; PROF. ELEC. ENG, CALIF. STATE POLYTECH. COL, SAN LUIS OBISPO, 68- Inst. Elec. & Electronics Eng. Power electronics; solid state energy conversion; electric motor controls. Address: Dept. of Electrical Engineering, California State Polytechnic College, San Luis Obispo, CA 93401.

DATTA, SURINDER P, b. Lahore, India, Apr. 29, 33; m. 63; c. 3. GENETICS, IMMUNOLOGY. B.Vet.Sci. Panjab, India, 55; M.S, Wisconsin, Madison, 59, Ph.D.(genetics, vet. sci), 63. Res. asst. immunogenetics, Indian Vet. Res. Inst, 55-57; Wisconsin, Madison, 58-63; res. assoc. immunol, Albert Einstein Col. Med, 63-64; lectr. path, med. col, Monash Univ, Australia, 64-67; assoc. scientist, Oak Ridge Assoc. Univs, 67-68; ASST. PROF. GENETICS, UNIV. WIS-PARKSIDE, 68- Res. participant, Atomic Energy Cmn. res. participation fel, med. div, Oak Ridge Assoc. Univs, 69. Am. Inst. Biol. Sci; Genetics Soc. Am. Immunogenetic analysis of blood groups in cattle, guinea pigs and marmosets; phytohemagglutinins; kidney transplantation in cattle; development of immune competence. Address: Division of Science, College of Science & Society, University of Wisconsin-Parkside, Kenosha, WI 53140.

D'ATTORRE, LEONARDO, b. La Plata, Argentina, Feb. 2, 20; nat; m. 49. PHYSICS. M.A, La Plata, 47, Ph.D, 52. Instr. fluid mech, La Plata, 48-52, assoc. prof. aerodyn, 52-56; sr. res. engr, Gen. Dynamics/Astronaut, 56-61; prof. fluid mech, La Plata, 61-62; staff scientist, space sci. lab, Gen. Dynamics/Convair, 62-69; MEM. PROF. STAFF, TRW SYSTS. GROUP, 69- Prof, Nat. Univ. of the South, Argentina, 54-56. Am. Math. Soc; Am. Inst. Aeronaut. & Astronaut. Fluid and classical mechanics; applied mathematics. Address: 1043 11th St, Santa Monica, CA 90403.

DATZ, SHELDON, b. New York, N.Y, July 21, 27; m. 48; c. 2. PHYSICAL CHEMISTRY, MOLECULAR PHYSICS. B.S, Columbia, 50, M.A, 51; Ph.D. (phys. chem), Tennessee, 60. Technician, substitute alloy mat. labs, div. war res, Columbia, 43-44, dept. physics, 46-50, asst. chem, 50-51; chemist, CHEM. DIV, OAK RIDGE NAT. LAB, 51-67, leader molecular beam group, 60-67, ASSOC. DIR, 67- Guest scientist, Lab. Mass Separation, Netherlands, 62-63. Consult, Gen. Atomic Div, Gen. Dynamics Corp, Calif, 60-62; Repub. Aviation Corp, L.I, 61-62. U.S.N, 45-46. AAAS; Am. Chem. Soc; Am. Phys. Soc; Sci. Res. Soc. Am. Molecular beam studies of chemically reactive collisions; molecular beam scattering from gases and surfaces; heavy ion-solid surface interactions; sputtering; high temperature chemistry. Address: Oak Ridge National Lab, P.O. Box X, Oak Ridge, TN 37830.

DAU, GARY JOHN, b. Lewiston, Idaho, Sept. 3, 38; m. 61; c. 2. NUCLEAR & MECHANICAL ENGINEERING. B.S, Idaho, 61; Ph.D.(nuclear eng), Arizona, 65. Sr. res. scientist, PAC. NORTHWEST LABS, BATTELLE MEM. INST, 64-66, MGR, res. & develop group, 66-68, nondestructive testing dept, 68-70, APPL. PHYSICS & INSTRUMENTATION DEPT; 70- Mem. ed. adv. comt, Nuclear Technol. J. AAAS; Am. Nuclear Soc; Am. Soc. Eng. Educ. Radiation effects on ceramic insulators; nondestructive testing; applied physics; instrumentation research; electromagnetics; lasers; holography; ultrasonic and thermal testing techniques. Address: Pacific Northwest Labs, Battelle Memorial Institute, P.O. Box 999, Richland, WA 99352.

DAUB, C(LARENCE) THEODORE, JR, b. Hagerstown, Md, Nov. 27, 36; m. 63. ASTROPHYSICS. B.A, Carleton Col, 58; Ph.D.(astron), Univ. Wis, 62. Instr. astron, Univ. Wis, 62; asst. prof. physics, Iowa State Univ, 62-67; ASTRON, SAN DIEGO STATE COL, 67-68, ASSOC. PROF, 68- Am. Astron. Soc. Physical processes in gaseous media. Address: Dept. of Astronomy, San Diego State College, San Diego, CA 92115.

DAUB, EDWARD E, b. Milwaukee, Wis, May 17, 24; m. 49; c. 5. HISTORY OF SCIENCE. B.S, Wisconsin, 45, M.S, 47, Ph.D.(hist. sci), 66; B.D, Union Theol. Sem.(N.Y), 50, S.T.M, 60. Assoc. prof. chem. eng, Doshisha, Japan, 57-62; asst. prof. hist. sci, Univ. Kans, 65-70, ASSOC. PROF, 70-71; HIST. TECHNOL, UNIV. WIS, MADISON, 71- Nat. Sci. Found. res. grant, 68-70; Danforth Found. Underwood fel, 71. U.S.N, 42-46, Ens. Soc. Hist. Technol; Hist. Sci. Soc. History of the second law of thermodynamics; relations between science and theology; history of technology. Address: College of Engineering, University of Wisconsin, Madison, WI 53706.

DAUB, GUIDO H(ERMAN), b. Milwaukee, Wis, Dec. 16, 20; m. 48; c. 3. ORGANIC CHEMISTRY. B.S, Wisconsin, 44, M.S, 47, Ph.D.(chem), 49. Chemist, Rohm & Haas Co, 44-45; asst. prof. CHEM, UNIV. N.MEX, 49-54, assoc. prof, 54-61, PROF, 61-, CHMN. DEPT, 70- Fel. AAAS; Am. Chem. Soc. Synthesis of polycyclic hydrocarbons, heterocyclics; Stobbe condensation; organic compounds as liquid scintillation solutes. Address: Dept. of Chemistry, University of New Mexico, Albuquerque, NM 87106.

DAUBEN, DWIGHT LEWIS, b. Ft. Smith, Ark, Feb. 28, 38; m. 63; c. 1. PETROLEUM ENGINEERING. B.S, Tex. Tech. Col, 61; M.S, Tulsa, 63; Ph.D. (eng. sci), Oklahoma, 66. Petrol. engr, Chevron Oil Co, Colo, 62-63; SR. RES. ENGR, PAN AM. PETROL. CORP. SUBSIDIARY, STANDARD OIL IND, 66- Am. Inst. Mining, Metall. & Petrol. Eng. Improved methods of recovering oil, particularly miscible processes and polymer flooding. Address: Pan American Petroleum Corp, Box 591, Tulsa, OK 74102.

DAUBEN, WILLIAM G(ARFIELD), b. Columbus, Ohio, 19; m. 47; c. 2. ORGANIC CHEMISTRY. B.A, Ohio State, 41; A.M, Harvard, 42, Ph.D. (chem), 44. Fel. Harvard, 44-45; instr. CHEM, UNIV. CALIF, BERKELEY, 45-47, asst. prof, 47-52, assoc. prof, 52-57, PROF, 57- Guggenheim Mem. Found. fels, 51 & 66; Nat. Sci. Found. fel, 58. Mem, med. chem. study sect, Nat. Insts. Health, 60-64; chem. panel, Nat. Sci. Found, 64-; bd. dir, Org. Synthesis, 69-; pres, Org. Reactions, Inc, 69-; ed-in-chief, Org. Reactions, 69-; mem. bd. ed, Organometallics in Chem. Synthesis, 70- Nat. Acad. Sci; Am. Chem. Soc.(award, 59); The Chem. Soc; Swiss Chem. Soc. Natural products; organic synthesis; synthetic hormones and drugs; stereochemistry. Address: Dept. of Chemistry, University of California, Berkeley, CA 94720.

DAUBENMIRE, REXFORD, b. Coldwater, Ohio, Dec. 12, 09; m. 38; c. 1. PLANT ECOLOGY. B.S, Butler, 30; M.S, Colorado, 32; Ph.D.(bot), Minnesota, 35. Acting asst. prof. BOT, Tennessee, 35-36; asst. prof, Idaho, 36-46, assoc. prof, WASH. STATE UNIV, 46-50, PROF, 50- Lectr, biol. sta, Minnesota, 37; asst. prof, sci. camp, Wyoming, 39. Ecol. Soc. Am. (pres, 67); Brit. Ecol. Soc. Forest classification for Northern Rockies; factors affecting seasonal growth in temperate and tropical trees; causes of forest distribution in Northern Rockies; ecology of grasslands in Columbia drainage; effect of temperature and drought on seedling survival; water requirement of desert plants; productivity of tropical savanna. Address: Dept. of Botany, Washington State University, Pullman, WA 99163.

DAUBENSPECK, BENJAMIN K, b. Allentown, Pa, Jan. 10, 17; m. 41; c. 6. CHEMICAL ENGINEERING. B.S, Lehigh, 37, fel, 39-41, M.S, 41. Res. engr, Dow Chem. Co, 37-39; sr. engr, REMINGTON ARMS CO, INC, 41-45, sr. res. engr, RES. & DEVELOP, 45-52, supvr, 52-62, MGR, 62- Fel. Am. Inst. Chem; Soc. Plastics Eng; Plastics processing; product development; propellants and explosives. Address: Remington Arms Co, Inc, Bridgeport, CT 06602.

DAUBERT, B(ERNARD) F(ORBES), b. Martins Ferry, Ohio, May 1, 05; m. 25; c. 2. CHEMISTRY. Ph.G, Pittsburgh, 25, B.S, 30, Ph.D.(biochem), 39. Asst. chem, sch. pharm, Pittsburgh, 25-30, instr, 30-32, asst. prof, 32-43, asst. res. prof. biochem, dept. chem, 43-45, assoc. res. prof, 45-46, res. prof, 46-51, res. adminstr, 47-51; asst. mgr. lab. sect, res. dept, Koppers Co, Inc, 51-54; assoc. dir. chem. res, res. center, GEN. FOODS CORP, 54-61, dir. NUTRIT, TECH. CTR, 61-70, CONSULT, 70- Swift & Co. fel, 43; assoc. ed, Food Res; mem. comt. on specifications, Food Chem. Codex & mem. indust. panel, food protection comt, Nat. Acad. Sci-Nat. Res. Coun, 66- Am. Chem. Soc; Am. Soc. Biol. Chem; Am. Oil Chemists' Soc; Inst. Food Technol. Synthesis of glycerides; molecular structure and configuration of glycerides; autoxidation: metabolism and x-ray and infrared analysis of fats and fatty acids; synthesis of organosilicon compounds; kinetics of hydrogenation and fatty acid distribution in fats; synthesis of phosphatides. Address: Technical Center, General Foods Corp, White Plains, NY 10625.

DAUBERT, THOMAS EDWARD, b. Pottsville, Pa, Oct. 14, 37; m. 67. c. 1. CHEMICAL ENGINEERING. B.S, Pa. State, 59, M.S, 61, Ph.D.(chem. eng), 64. Res. asst. CHEM. ENG, PA. STATE UNIV, 61, instr, 61-64, asst. prof, 65-68, ASSOC. PROF, 68- Year-in-indust. prof, E.I. du Pont de Nemours

& Co, 70-71. Am. Chem. Soc; Am. Inst. Chem. Eng; Am. Soc. Eng. Educ; Am. Inst. Chem. Rates and surface effects on free radical chain reactions; primarily oxidation; fluid-solid transport and heat transfer; applications of gas chromatography; thermodynamic and transport properties of hydrocarbons and oxygenated compounds. Address: 165 Chemical Engineering Bldg, Pennsylvania State University, University Park, PA 16802.

DAUBIN, SCOTT C, b. New London, Conn, Sept. 20, 22; m. 44; c. 5. ACOUSTICS, OCEAN ENGINEERING. B.S, U.S. Naval Acad, 44; U.S. Naval Postgrad. Sch, 50-51; M.A, Princeton, 53, Ph.D.(physics), 54. Proj. officer, undersea warfare br, Off. Naval Res, 54-56, tech. aide, 56-57, ship supt. Portsmouth Naval Shipyard, 57-58, asst. design supt, 58-61; head marine sci, AC Electronics Defense Res. Labs, Gen. Motors Corp, 61-67; CHMN. DEPT. OCEAN ENG, Woods Hole Oceanog. Inst, 67-71; UNIV. MIAMI, 71- Ed, U.S. Navy Jour. Underwater Acoustics, 54-56; mem. deep submergence systs. rev. group, Adv. Comt. Secy. Navy, 63. U.S.N, 44-61, Res, 63-71, Capt. Acoustical Soc. Am; Am. Asn. Physics Teachers; Am. Soc. Mech. Eng; Marine Tech. Soc. Underwater acoustics; instrumentation systems; signal processing; general underwater technology. Address: Dept. of Ocean Engineering, School of Marine & Atmospheric Science, University of Miami, 10 Rickenbacker Causeway, Miami, FL 33124.

DAUCHERT, EUGENE F(RANCIS), b. Appleton, Wis, Aug. 25, 23; m. 50; c. 3. CHEMICAL ENGINEERING. B.S. & M.S, Wisconsin, 51. Engr, E.I. DU PONT DE NEMOURS & CO, INC, 51-56, sr. engr, 56-69, SR. RES. ENGR, 69- U.S.A.A.F, 43-46, Res, 46-52, 1st Lt. Dacron polyester fiber development. Address: 1902 Hampton Rd, Kinston, NC 28501.

DAUDT, WILLIAM H(ERBERT), b. Washington, D.C, June 30, 16; m. 44; c. 5. CHEMISTRY. B.S, Haverford Col, 37; Ph.D.(org. chem), Harvard, 41. Asst, Nat. Defense Res. Cmt. proj, Harvard, 40-41; res. chemist, Corning Glass Works, N.Y, 41-49; DOW CORNING CORP, 49-55, res. supvr, 55-65, asst. dir. chem. res, 65-70, RES. ADMIN. ASST, 70- Am. Chem. Soc. Synthesis of organic polynuclear compounds; carcinogenic hydrocarbons; aromatic nitro compounds and silicones. Address: Dow Corning Corp, Midland, MI 48641.

DAUER, JERALD P(AUL), b. Toledo, Ohio, Mar. 2, 43; m. 67; c. 1. MATHEMATICS. B.A, Bowling Green State Univ, 65; M.A, Univ. Kans, 67, Nat. Sci. Found. traineeship, 69-70, Ph.D.(math), 70. ASST. PROF. MATH, UNIV. NEBR, LINCOLN, 70- Am. Math. Soc; Soc. Indust. & Appl. Math. Optimal control theory; contingency equations; ordinary differential equations. Address: Dept. of Mathematics, University of Nebraska, Lincoln, NE 68508.

DAUER, MAXWELL, b. Bayonne, N.J, Sept. 3, 13; m. 41; c. 2. RADIOLOGICAL PHYSICS. A.B, N.Y. Univ, 34, Sc.M, 37; LL.B, George Washington, 49; Ph.D.(pharmacol), Chicago, 51. Instr, N.Y. Univ, 35-39; instr. x-ray physics & radiation physicist, Walter Reed Army Center, 40-42, commandant, Army Sch. Roentgenol, 45; asst. med. dir, Manhattan Proj, 45-46; radiol. staff officer, Atomic Energy Cmn, 46-49; res. assoc. pharmacol, Chicago, 49-51; chief projs, res. & develop. div, Off. Surg. Gen, U.S. Army, 51-54, dept. of pharmacol, Walter Reed Army Inst. Res, 55, chief dept. biophysics, 406 med. gen. lab, Japan, 55-58, chief radiol. hyg. div, Army Environ. Health Lab, 58-61; assoc. prof. RADIOL. PHYSICS, SCH. MED, UNIV. MIAMI, 61-62, PROF, 62- Dipl, Am. Bd. Radiol; dipl, Am. Bd. Health Physics; dipl, Am. Bd. Indust. Hyg. U.S.A, 40-61, Lt. Col.(Ret). AAAS; Health Physics Soc; assoc. fel. Am. Col. Radiol; Am. Conf. Indust. Hygienists; Radiol. Soc. N.Am; Am. Nuclear Soc; Am. Pub. Health Asn; Radiation Res. Soc; Am. Asn. Physicists in Med. Radiological health physics; radiobiology; radioisotope applications; nuclear weapons effects. Address: Dept. of Radiology, University of Miami School of Medicine, Coral Gables, FL 33124.

DAUES, GREGORY W, JR, b. St. Louis, Mo, Oct. 1, 28; m. 52; c. 4. POLYMER & ANALYTICAL CHEMISTRY. B.S, St. Louis, 50; M.S, New Mexico, 52. Res. chemist, MONSANTO CO, 52-59, res. group leader, 59-67, MGR. RES, 67- Am. Chem. Soc; Soc. Plastics Eng. Plastics applications; spectroscopy. Address: Research Dept, Monsanto Co, P.O. Box 1311, Texas City, TX 77590.

DAUGHADAY, H(AMILTON), b. Chicago, Ill, Mar. 6, 18; m. 60; c. 1. AERONAUTICAL ENGINEERING, THEORETICAL PHYSICS. A.B, Harvard, 40, M.S, 41; Ph.D.(physics), State Univ. N.Y. Buffalo, 65. Stress & flutter anal, airplane div, Curtiss-Wright Corp, 41-44, head flutter & vibration group, 44-45; dynamic anal. helicopters & missiles, Bell Aircraft Corp, 45-50; prin. engr. aeroelasticity, CORNELL AERONAUT. LAB, 50-52, head helicopter sect, 52-57, tech. staff asst, appl. mech. dept, 57-70, PRIN. RES. ENGR, AEROSYSTS. RES. DEPT, 70- Am. Inst. Aeronaut. & Astronaut; Am. Helicopter Soc; Am. Phys. Soc. Aeroelasticity; stability and control; aerodynamics; variational treatment of thermal problems. Address: Aerosystems Research Dept, Cornell Aeronautical Lab, P.O. Box 235, Buffalo, NY 14221.

DAUGHADAY, W(ILLIAM) H(AMILTON), b. Chicago, Ill, Feb. 12, 18; m. 45; c. 2. MEDICINE. A.B, Harvard, 40, M.D, 43. Res. fel. med, SCH. MED, WASH. UNIV, 47-48, Nat. Insts. Health fel. biochem, 48-49, instr. med, 50, asst. prof. MED. & dir. metab. div, 51-57, assoc. prof, 57-63, PROF, 63- Consult, Barnes Hosp, 50- Ed, J. Lab. & Clin. Med, 61- Med.C, U.S.A, 44-46. Endocrine Soc; Am. Soc. Clin. Invest; Am. Fedn. Clin. Res; Asn. Am. Physicians. Adrenal cortical steroids; pituitary growth hormone; diabetes mellitus. Address: 1414 W. Adams, Kirkwood, MO 63122.

DAUGHERTY, DAVID M, b. Warren, Ohio, Mar. 29, 28; m. 48; c. 5. ENTOMOLOGY. B.Sc, Ohio State Univ, 52, M.Sc, 53; Ph.D.(entom), N.C. State Univ, 64. Res. fel. entom, Ohio State Univ, 52-53; agr. specialist, Ohio Dept. Agr, 53-56; registr. inspector econ. poisons, Univ. Ky, 56-59; res. entomologist, U.S. DEPT. AGR, 61-68, leader oilseed insects invests, 68-71, ASST. DIR, FAR EAST. REGIONAL RES. OFF, NEW DELHI, INDIA, 71- Res. assoc, Univ. Mo-Columbia, 61-64, asst. prof, 64-68, assoc. prof, 68-71; attache, agr. res, U.S. Embassy, New Delhi, 71- U.S.N, 46-48. Entom. Soc. Am; Ecol. Soc. Am. Biology, ecology and control of insects affecting cereals and forage crops; parasites, predators and diseases of insects and their utilization in insect control. Address: New Delhi/ARS, Dept. Of State, Washington, DC 20521.

DAUGHERTY, DON G(ENE), b. Mendon, Ill, Nov. 14, 35; m. 59; ELECTRICAL ENGINEERING. B.S, Wisconsin, 57, M.S, 58, Ph.D.(elec. eng), 64. Instr. ELEC. ENG, Univ. Wis, 59-61; asst. prof, UNIV. KANS, 63-67, ASSOC. PROF, 67- Sig.C, 58-59, Res, 59-, Lt. Inst. Elec. & Electronics Eng; Am. Soc. Eng. Educ. Theory and applications of semiconductor devices; methods of engineering education. Address: Dept. of Electrical Engineering, University of Kansas, Lawrence, KS 66044.

DAUGHERTY, FRANKLIN W, b. Alpine, Tex, June 20, 27; m. 45; c. 3. GEOLOGY, HYDROLOGY. B.S, Sul Ross State Col, 50; M.A, Univ. Tex, 49, Ph.D. (geol), 62. Mgr, Big Bend Mineral Explor. Co, 54-58; econ. geol. consult, 62-63; assoc. prof. geol, W.TEX. STATE UNIV, 63-71, PROF. GEOL. & COORD. EARTH SCI. RES, 71- Pres, Pinnacle Resources, Inc. Sig.C, 46-47, S/Sgt. AAAS; Geol. Soc. Am; Geochem. Soc. Economic geology; petrography of alkalic igneous rocks; hydrogeology. Address: Killgore Research Center, West Texas State University, Canyon, TX 79015.

DAUGHERTY, GUY WILSON, b. Richmond, Va, Sept. 25, 12; m. 40; c. 4. CLINICAL MEDICINE. B.S, Col. William & Mary, 37; M.D, Med. Col. Va, 37; M.D, Minnesota, 43. Practicing physician, W.Va, 38-40; fel. med, Mayo Found. Minnesota, 41-43; first asst, MAYO CLIN, 43-44, mem. sect. med, 47-62, ASSOC. CLIN. PROF, 62- Fel. coun. clin. cardiol, Am. Heart Asn, 70- Med.C, U.S.A, 44-47. Am. Med. Asn; fel. Am. Col. Physicians. Cardiovascular renal diseases. Address: Mayo Clinic, 200 First St. S.W, Rochester, MN 55901.

DAUGHERTY, J. DWIGHT, b. Baltimore, Md, Jan. 16, 00; m. 49. MATHEMATICS. A.B, Lebanon Valley Col, 22; A.M, Pennsylvania, 26; Ed.D, N.Y. Univ, 54. Teacher, high sch, Pa, 22-26, N.J, 26-36; head dept. MATH, 36-60; prof, KUTZTOWN STATE COL, 60-70, EMER. PROF, 70- Instr, Paterson State Col, 42-43; asst. prof, Fairleigh Dickinson, 55-60. U.S.A, 18. Am. Math Soc; Math. Asn. Am. Supervision of teaching secondary mathematics. Address: Dept. of Mathematics, Kutztown State College, Kutztown, PA 19530.

DAUGHERTY, KENNETH E, b. Pittsburgh, Pa, Dec. 27, 38; m. 61. ANALYTICAL CHEMISTRY. B.S, Carnegie Inst. Tech, 60; Du Pont summer fel, Washington (Seattle), 61, Shell Oil summer fel, 62, Nat. Sci. Found. summer fel, 63, Standard Oil Co, Calif, fel, 63-64, Ph.D.(anal. chem), 64; M.B.E, Claremont Grad Sch, 71. Res. chemist, Marbon Chem. Corp. Div, Borg-Warner Corp, W.Va, 60; instr. quant. anal, Washington (Seattle), 64; res. chemist, Rohm and Haas Chem. Co, Bristol, 64-66; sr. staff res. chemist, Am. Cement Corp, 66-71; ASSOC. PROF. CHEM, UNIV. PITTSBURGH, 71- Chem.C, 64-66, Capt. AAAS; Am. Chem. Soc; Am. Inst. Chem; Soc. Appl. Spectros; Sci. Res. Soc. Am; N.Y. Acad. Sci. Organic chelate chemistry; x-ray fluorescence and diffraction; thermogravimetry; spectroscopy; biodegradable surfactants; chemical warfare; cement, forensic and pollution chemistry; instrumental analysis. Address: Dept. of Chemistry, University of Pittsburgh, Pittsburgh, PA 15213.

DAUGHERTY, KENNETH I, b. Ky, Nov. 20, 35; m. 59; c. 1. GEODESY. B.S, Morehead State Col, 57; M.S, Ohio State Univ, 64. ASSOC. PROF. GEOD. & ASST. DIR. GEOPHYS, UNIV. HAWAII, 64- Am. Geophys. Union; Geol. Soc. Am. Gravimetry; external gravity field; dynamic geodesy; potential fields. Address: Hawaii Institute of Geophysics, 2525 Correa Rd, Honolulu, HI 96822.

DAUGHERTY, NED A(RTHUR), b. Ft. Wayne, Ind, Sept. 27, 34; m. 59; c. 2. INORGANIC CHEMISTRY. B.S, Purdue, 56; Ph.D.(chem), Mich. State, 61. Asst. prof. chem, Purdue, 61-63; Colorado State, 63-64; mem. staff, Los Alamos Sci. Lab, Univ. Calif, 64-66; asst. prof. INORG. CHEM, COLO. STATE UNIV, 66-67, ASSOC. PROF, 67- Am. Chem. Soc. Kinetics of oxidation-reduction reactions; coordination compounds; vanadium chemistry. Address: Dept. of Chemistry, Colorado State University, Ft. Collins, CO 80521.

DAUGHERTY, PATRICIA A, b. Mullens, W.Va, Oct. 24, 22. GENETICS, ZOOLOGY. A.B, Seton Hill Col, 44; M.A, Columbia, 46; Nat. Sci. Found. fel, Ohio State, 60-61, Ph.D.(genetics), 61. Instr. BIOL, Seton Hill Col, 46-48; West Virginia, 48-57; ASSOC. PROF, E.CAROLINA UNIV, 61- AAAS; Am. Genetic Asn. Genetics and immunology; genetics of laboratory mice and Peromyscus; Drosophila. Address: Box 2577, East Carolina University, Greenville, NC 27834.

DAUGHERTY, ROBERT M, JR, b. Kansas City, Mo, May 2, 34; m. 57; c. 3. PHYSIOLOGY, INTERNAL MEDICINE. B.A, Kansas, 56, M.D, 60; M.S, Oklahoma, 64, Ph.D.(physiol), 65. Resident, sch. med, Oklahoma, 61-63, clin. asst, 63-66, asst. prof. physiol, 65-66; assoc. prof. PHYSIOL. & MED, MICH. STATE UNIV, 66-71, PROF. & DIR, OFF. INTERDEPT. CURRICULUM, 71-, DIR. HYPERTENSION CLIN, 68- Nat. Insts. Health fel, 65-66, res. grant, 66- & prog. dir, undergrad. cardiovasc. training grant, 66-; Mich. Kidney Found. res. grant, 67-68; prin. investr. regional med. prog. grant physician ed. in hypertension, 68-; teaching scholar, Am. Heart Asn, 70. Am. Fedn. Clin. Res; Am. Heart Asn. Local regulation of blood flow; local and systemic effects on cardiovascular system of vasoactive agents, oxygen and carbon dioxide; hypertension. Address: Office of Interdepartmental Curriculum, College of Human Medicine, Michigan State University, East Lansing, MI 48823.

DAUGHTREY, ZOEL W, b. Sulphur Springs, Tex, June 30, 40; m. 65; c. 3. SOIL SCIENCE, PLANT PHYSIOLOGY. B.S, Tex. Tech Univ, 63; M.S, Okla. State Univ, 66; Ph.D.(soil sci), N.C. State Univ, 70. Instr. soil sci, Okla. State Univ, 64-66; agronomist, soil testing div, N.C. Dept. Agr, 66-70; ASSOC. PROF. AGR. & HEAD DEPT. AGR. SCI, NORTHWEST. STATE UNIV, 70- AAAS; Am. Soc. Agron; Soil Sci. Soc. Am; Crop Sci. Soc. Am. Reactions of phosphorus in organic soils of North Carolina; precipitation and nitrogen fertilizer interactions in winter wheat production in north central Oklahoma; nutrient requirements of alfalfa; effects of agricultural pollution in the Red River delta of Louisiana; environmental factors affecting the production of coastal Bermuda grass. Address: Dept. of Agricultural Sciences, Northwestern State University, Natchitoches, LA 71457.

DAUGHTRY, JAMES WILLIAM, b. Jan. 3, 33; U.S. citizen; m. 57; c. 2. PHYSICS. B.S, U.S. Mil. Acad, 54; M.S, N.C. State, 58, Atomic Energy Cmn. fel, 61-62, Ph.D.(physics), 65. Asst. physicist, ARGONNE NAT. LAB, 64-70, ASSOC. PHYSICIST, 70- U.S.A.F, 54-61, Capt. Am. Nuclear Soc. Experimental nuclear, neutron and nuclear reactor physics. Address: Argonne National Lab, Bldg. 316, 9700 S. Cass Ave, Argonne, IL 60439.

DAUL, GEORGE CECIL, b. Gretna, La, Oct. 27, 16; m. 40; c. 2. ORGANIC CHEMISTRY. A.B, Tulane, 37, A.M, 40. Teacher, high sch, La, 37-41; U.S. Weather Bur, 41-42; chief chemist & inspector trinitrotoluene, Longhorn Ord. Works, U.S. War Dept, Tex, 42-45; chemist, chem. properties sect, cotton fiber res. div, south. regional res. lab, bur. agr. & indust. chem, U.S. Dept. Agr, 45-54; res. lab, Courtaulds, Inc, 54-62; MGR, EAST. RES. DIV, ITT RAYONIER, INC, 62- Am. Chem. Soc; Am. Asn. Textile Chem. & Colorists; Fiber Soc. Chemical properties and derivatives of cellulose; cross linking of cellulosic fibers and fabrics; rayon spinning technology; cellulosic films; acetate fibers and plastics. Address: Eastern Research Division, ITT Rayonier, Inc, Whippany, NJ 07981.

DAUM, RICHARD J, b. Canton, Ohio, Dec. 30, 26; m. 64; ENTOMOLOGY, STATISTICS. B.Sc, Ohio State, 53, M.Sc, 54; Ph.D.(entom), Cornell, 60. Biometrician statist, U.S. Dept. Agr, 59-63; biochem. res. supvr, M & T Chems, Inc, 63-64; entomologist, U.S. DEPT. AGR, 64-69, AGRICULTURIST, PLANT PEST CONTROL, 69- U.S.N, 44-47 & 49-51, Diesel Engineman 2nd class. AAAS; Entom. Soc. Am; Biomet. Soc. New methods of control of the cotton boll weevil with use of insect control chemicals; statistical techniques applicable to dose-mortality data; measuring benefits and costs of plant protection programs. Address: U.S. Dept. of Agriculture, Federal Center Bldg, Hyattsville, MD 20782.

DAUM, SOL J(ACOB), b. New York, N.Y, Dec. 17, 33; m. 54; c. 2. ORGANIC CHEMISTRY. A.B, N.Y. Univ, 54; A.M, Brooklyn Col, 59; A.M, Columbia, 60, Nat. Insts. Health fel, 60-62, Ph.D.(chem), 62. Sr. technician, Sloan-Kettering Inst. Cancer Res, Mem. Hosp, New York, 56-59; asst. chem, Columbia, 60; assoc. res. chemist, STERLING WINTHROP RES. INST, 62-67, RES. CHEMIST, 67- AAAS; Am. Chem. Soc. Natural products; steroid and alkaloid chemistry. Address: Sterling Winthrop Research Institute, Dept. of Chemistry, Rensselaer, NY 12144.

DAUNS, JOHN, b. Riga, Latvia, June 11, 37; U.S. citizen. MATHEMATICS, ALGEBRA. B.S, Mass. Inst. Tech, 60; Wilson fel, Harvard, 61, Nat. Sci. Found. fels, 61-63, Ph.D.(math), 64. ASSOC. PROF. MATH, TULANE UNIV, 64- Am. Math. Soc. Rings and algebras. Address: Gibson Hall, Dept. of Mathematics, Tulane University, New Orleans, LA 70118.

DAUNT, JOHN GILBERT, b. Killiney, Ireland, June 30, 13; U.S. citizen. PHYSICS. B.A, Oxford, 35, Scott scholar, M.A. & Ph.D.(physics), 37. Demonstr. physics, Oxford, 37-39, lectr. & demonstr, 40-46, lectr, Exeter Col, Oxford, 40-46; asst. prof, Ohio State, 46-47, assoc. prof, 47-50, prof, 50-65; PROF. PHYSICS & ELEC. ENG. & DIR. CRYOGENICS CTR, STEVENS INST. TECHNOL, 65- Scott scholar, Oxford, 38; Guggenheim Mem. fels, Amsterdam, 53 & Harvard, 54, 58; vis. prof, São Paulo, 61; City Col. New York, 64; Columbia Univ, 65. Vis. scientist, Oak Ridge Nat. Lab, 49, consult, 50-53; vis. scientist & consult, Los Alamos Sci. Lab, California, 58-62. Adv. ed, Physics Condensed Matter & Physics Letters, 62-; ed. & founder, J. Low Temperature Physics, 69- Mem. adv. panel physics, Nat. Sci. Found, 60-63; pres. comn. low temperatures & mem. U.S. Nat. Comn, Int. Union Pure & Appl. Physics, 60-66. Sr. award, Oxford, 39; medal, Bruxelles, 55. Fel. Am. Phys. Soc; fel. Brit. Inst. Physics & Phys. Soc. (Duddell Medal, 56); Int. Inst. Refrig. Low temperature physics; superfluid helium; helium three; superconductivity; production of low temperatures; microwaves and microwave tubes; infrared detectors; noise theory. Address: Dept. of Physics & Cryogenics Center, Stevens Institute of Technology, Hoboken, NJ 07030.

DAUPHIN, JEWEL MADISON, b. Century, Fla, Aug. 11, 16; m. 41; c. 2. CHEMICAL ENGINEERING. B.S, Alabama, 39. Chemist, Atlas Powder Co, 40-41, supvr. TNT prod, 41-44, chem. engr, 44-52, plant engr, Atlas Point Plant, 52-57, mgr. indust. eng, 57-59, tech. supt, Marshall Plant, 59-61, asst. mgr. DARCO EXP. LAB, ATLAS CHEM. INDUSTS, INC, 61-62, MGR, 62- C.W.S, U.S.A, 39-40. Am. Inst. Chem. Eng. Activated carbon; development of new methods for process of current or new products. Address: Darco Experimental Lab, Atlas Chemical Industries, Inc, Marshall, TX 75670.

DAUPHINAIS, RAYMOND J(OSEPH), b. Chicago, Ill, May 30, 25. PHARMACY. B.S, Illinois, 48; J.D, Florida, 54; Food Law Inst. fel, N.Y, Univ, 55-56, LL.M.(trade regulation), 56. Lectr. pharm. law, Florida, 53-54, asst. prof, 54-55; lectr. pharmaceut. econ, Columbia, 55-56; asst. prof. pharmacy, Connecticut, 57-60; dir, legal div, Am. Pharmaceut. Asn, 60-64; PROF. PHARM, WAYNE STATE UNIV, 64-, asst. to dean, col. pharm, 64-68. Nat. Sci. Found. vis. scientist, 64-68; Am. Asn. Cols. Pharm. vis. lectr, 68- Food Law Inst. Award, 55-56. Am. Pharmaceut. Asn; Am. Asn. Cols. Pharm. Pharmaceutical economics; trade regulations; food & drug legislation; health-care administration; professional practice law in healing arts. Address: College of Pharmacy, Wayne State University, Detroit, MI 48202.

DAUPHINÉ, T(HONET) C(HARLES), b. North Battleford, Sask, Nov. 8, 13; U.S. citizen; m. 38; c. 4. CHEMICAL ENGINEERING. S.B, Mass. Inst. Tech, 35, Sc.D.(chem. eng), 39. Instr. chem. eng, Mass. Inst. Tech, 36-39; process engr, res. & develop. dept, Standard Oil Co. Calif, 39-43, supv. eng, Calif. Res. Corp, 43-46; east. mgr. prod. develop. dept, Oronite Chem. Co, 46-51; mgr. sales develop, Hooker Chem. Corp, N.Y, 51-57, mgr. prod. develop. plastics & polymers, 57-59, sr. develop. engr, corp. gen. develop, 59-62; v.pres. prod. & eng, Nease Chem. Co, 62-64; consult, 64-65; acting head, Chem. Process Corp, Conn, 65-66, V.PRES, 66-69; BADGER, INC, 69- Bldg. Res. Inst; Am. Chem. Soc; Am. Inst. Chem. Eng; Commercial Develop. Asn; Soc. Plastics Indust. Domestic and international venture analysis for chemicals and plastics; production sulfonated aromatics; pharmaceutical intermediates; fine chemicals; process development for various organic chemicals, including aromatic sulfonation and oxidation. Address: Badger, Inc, 363 Third St, Cambridge, MA 02142.

DAUPHINEE, JAMES A(RNOLD), b. New Westminster, B.C, Jan. 9, 03; m. 29; c. 1. CLINICAL MEDICINE. M.A, British Columbia, 23; fel, Toronto, 23-27, Ph.D.(biochem), 29, M.D, 30. Asst. chem, British Columbia, 22-23; Mickle fel, UNIV. TORONTO, 30-31, Brown Mem. fel, 33-34, jr. demonstr. med, 34-41, assoc, 45-47, prof. PATH. CHEM, 47-68, EMER. PROF, 68- Clin. asst, St. Bartholomew's Hosp, 30-31. Order of Brit. Empire, 46. R.C.A.M.C, 41-45, Lt. Col. Am. Soc. Clin. Invest; fel. Royal Col. Physicians Can; fel. Royal Soc. Can. Biochemistry; enzymes; diseases of the liver; electrolyte metabolism. Address: 214 Inglewood Dr, Toronto 7, Ont, Can.

DAUPHINEE, T(HOMAS) M(cCAUL), b. Vancouver, B.C, July 3, 16; m. 40; c. 3. PHYSICS. B.A, British Columbia, 43, M.A, 45, Nat. Res. Coun. Can. stud, 48, Nat. Res. Coun. Can. fel, 49, Ph.D, 50. Instr, dept. physics, Univ. B.C, 47-48; res. off. PHYSICS, NAT. RES. COUN. CAN, 45-67, sr. res. off, 67-70, PRIN. RES. OFF, 70- Am. Phys. Soc; Instrument Soc. Am; Can. Asn. Physicists. Thermometry; electrical measurements; instrumentation; thermal and electrical properties of matter; oceanographic measurements. Address: Division of Physics, National Research Council, Ottawa, Ont. K1A 0S1, Can.

D'AURIA, JOHN MICHAEL, b. New York, N.Y, Mar. 28, 39; m. 66; c. 2. NUCLEAR CHEMISTRY, RADIOCHEMISTRY. B.S, Rensselaer Polytech, 61; M.S, Yale, 62, Ph.D.(nuclear chem), 66. Res. asst. CHEM, Columbia, 66-68; ASST. PROF, SIMON FRASER UNIV, 68- Nat. Res. Coun. Can. grant, 68- Am. Phys. Soc. Nuclear spectroscopy of neutron excess and deficient isotopes; mechanisms of nuclear reactions. Address: Dept. of Chemistry, Simon Fraser University, Burnaby 2, B.C, Can.

DAUTENHAHN, DAVID (IMMANUEL), b. Valley Park, Mo, Jan. 4, 32; m. 53; c. 3. MATHEMATICS. B.S, Mo. Valley Col, 53; M.A, Vanderbilt, 54; California, Los Angeles, 60-61. Instr. MATH, St. John's Lutheran Col, 54-56; asst. prof, Missouri, Rolla, 56-65; ASSOC. PROF, MO. VALLEY COL, 65- Math. Asn. Am. Use of closed circuit and live television in teaching. Address: Dept. of Mathematics, Missouri Valley College, Marshall, MO 65340.

DAUTERMAN, W(ALTER) C(ARL), b. Closter, N.J, June 10, 32; m. 63; c. 2. INSECT TOXICOLOGY, BIOCHEMISTRY. B.S, Rutgers, 54, M.S, 57; Ph.D. (entom), Wisconsin, 59. Fulbright res. fel, Netherlands, 59-60; res. assoc, Cornell, 60-62; asst. prof. ENTOM, N.C. STATE UNIV, 62-64, ASSOC. PROF, 64- AAAS; Am. Chem. Soc; Entom. Soc. Am. Mode of action and the selectivity of organophosphorus insecticides. Address: 4623A Gardner Hall, North Carolina State University, Raleigh, NC 27607.

DAUWALDER, MARIANNE, b. Long Beach, Calif, Aug. 5, 35; m. 62; c. 5. BIOCHEMICAL CYTOLOGY. B.A, Occidental Col, 56; Nat. Insts. Health fel, California, Los Angeles & Texas, 59-63, Ph.D.(biol, cytol), Texas, 64. Res. asst, zool, California, Los Angeles, 59; RES. SCIENTIST ASSOC, CELL RES. INST, UNIV. TEX, AUSTIN, 63- Am. Soc. Cell Biol. Cellular differentiation; role of the nucleolus in embryonic development; differential activities of the Golgi apparatus in enzymatic and ultrastructural secretion in developing systems. Address: Cell Research Institute, University of Texas, Austin, TX 78712.

DAVANTZIS, JAMES C(ONSTANTINE), b. New York, N.Y, Dec. 27, 20; m. 46; c. 3. MECHANICAL ENGINEERING. B.S.M.E, Michigan, 44. Test engr, Manhattan Dist. Proj, Tenn, 44-45; mech. engr, plant oper. & maintenance, N.Y. Bd. Ed, 46-47; proj. engr, mat. div, Navy Bur. Ord, 48-56, sect. head, 56-60, value engr, eng. div, Bur. Naval Weapons, 60-62, prod. engr, off. of asst. chief prod. & qual. control, 62-71; GEN. ENGR, NAVAL ORD. SYSTS. COMMAND, ARLINGTON, VA, 71- U.S.N, 45-46. Am. Soc. Mech. Eng. Procurement and production of guided missile and weapon systems. Address: 11606 Gilsan St, Silver Spring, MD 20902.

DaVANZO, JOHN P(AUL), b. Seattle, Wash, Jan. 14, 27; m. 50; c. 5. BIOLOGY. B.Sc, Washington (Seattle), 49 & 51; M.Sc, New Mexico, 55, Ph.D, 57. Supvr. exp. surg. lab, sch. med, Washington (Seattle), 49-51; res. assoc. & N.J. Heart Asn. fel, Princeton, 57-59; with res. div, Upjohn Co, 59-62; head biochem. pharmacol, A.H. Robins Co, 62-68; DIR. PHARMACOL, ORTHO RES. FOUND, 68- Lectr, Med. Col, 62-, res. assoc, 64- Phi Sigma award, 56. U.S.A, 52-54. AAAS; Am. Asn. Pharmacol; Am. Physiol. Soc. Neurochemistry, especially the effects of drugs on the central nervous system. Address: 55 Manchester Dr, Basking Ridge, NJ 07920.

DAVAR, K(ERSI) S, b. Bombay, India, Oct. 3, 23; m. 50; c. 3. CIVIL ENGINEERING, HYDROLOGY. B.E, Univ. Poona, 46; M.I.E, Colo. State Univ, 57, Ph.D.(civil eng), 61. Asst. engr, Damodar Valley Corp, India, 50-55; asst. prof. hydrol. & fluid mech, Univ. N.B, 61-65; assoc. prof, Tex. Tech. Col, 65-66; assoc. prof. CIVIL ENG, UNIV. N.B, 66-68, PROF, 68- Mem, Can. Nat. Comt. for Int. Hydrol. Decade, 66-; adv. comt, Can. Ctr. Inland Waters, 69- Int. Asn. Hydraul. Res; Am. Soc. Civil Eng; Am. Water Resources Asn. Hydrology, watershed response, snow hydrology, soil moisture; water resources systems, optimization of multipurpose river systems; hydraulics, dispersive processes in streams and channels, resistance to flow in unsymmetrical channels. Address: Dept. of Civil Engineering, University of New Brunswick, Fredericton, N.B, Can.

DAVE, BHALCHANDRA A, b. Palanpur, India, Dec. 10, 31; U.S. citizen; m. 65; c. 2. MICROBIOLOGY, FOOD SCIENCE & TECHNOLOGY. B.Sc, St. Xavier's Col, India, 55, M.Sc, 58; M.S, Univ. Calif, Davis, 62, Ph.D.(microbiol), 68. Demonstr, St. Xavier's Col, India, 55-58; res. asst. food sci, Univ. Calif, Davis, 59-65, res. microbiologist, 66-70; RES. SCIENTIST, AGCHEM-DECCO DIV, PENNWALT CORP, MONROVIA, 70- Inst. Food Technol; Am. Soc. Microbiol. Food microbiology; pectic enzymes; storage of fresh fruits and vegetables; food industry sanitation. Address: 1629 S. Bradford Dr, Glendora, CA 91740.

DAVENPORT, ALAN GARNETT, b. Madras, India, Sept. 19, 32; Can. citizen; m. 57; c. 4. STRUCTURAL ENGINEERING, AERODYNAMICS. B.A, Cambridge, 54, M.A, 58; M.A.Sc, Univ. Toronto, 57; Ph.D.(eng), Bristol Univ, 61. Lectr. ENG, Univ. Toronto, 54-57, asst, Nat. Res. coun. Can, 57-58; Bristol Univ, 58-61; assoc. prof, UNIV. WEST. ONT, 61-66, PROF, 66- Consult. design, World Trade Ctr, N.Y.C, 64-65; mem, Am. Soc. Civil Eng-Int. Asn. Bridge & Struct. Eng. Joint Comt. on Tall Bldgs. R.C.N, 57-58. Am. Soc. Civil Eng.(Alfred Nobel Prize, 63); Eng. Inst. Can.(Duggan Prize, 62, Gzowski Medal, 63); Royal Meteorol. Soc; Int. Asn. Bridge & Struct. Eng. Meteorology. Address: Faculty of Engineering, University of Western Ontario, London, Ont, Can.

DAVENPORT, CALVIN ARMSTRONG, b. Gloucester, Va, Jan. 15, 28; m. 63. BACTERIOLOGY, IMMUNOLOGY. B.S, Va. State Col, 49; M.S, Mich. State, 50, Ph.D.(microbiol. & pub. health), 63; Nat. Univ. Mexico, 57. Bacteriologist, div. labs, State Dept. Health, Mich, 52-53, 55-57; ASSOC. PROF. MICROBIOL, Va. State Col, 63-69, head dept, 66-69; CALIF. STATE COL, FULLERTON, 69- U.S.A, 53-55. Am. Soc. Microbiol; Am. Pub. Health Asn; Am. Inst. Biol. Sci. Serology and immunology; sanitary bacteriology. Address: Dept. of Microbiology, California State College, Fullerton, 800 N. State College Blvd, Fullerton, CA 92631.

DAVENPORT, CHARLES H(ENRY), b. Revelstoke, B.C, Can, Apr. 2, 16; nat; m. 45; c. 2. CHEMICAL ENGINEERING. B.A.Sc, British Columbia, 38, Nicholson scholar, 39, M.A.Sc, 39; Ethyl Gas Corp. fel, Mass. Inst. Tech, 41-42, Sc.D.(chem. eng), 42, hon. grad, Alexander Hamilton Inst, 45. Instr. chem, British Columbia, 38-39; asst. chem. eng, Mass. Inst. Tech, 39-41; res. chemist & engr, Standard Oil Develop. Co, N.J, 42-44; chief engr. in charge res. & develop, plant food div, Swift & Co, Ind, 44-48; sr. group leader pilot plant opers, res. div, Lion Oil Co. Div, MONSANTO CO, 48-53, mgr. eng. & process develop, 53-55, asst. dir. res, 55-59, European tech. rep, 59-64, mgr. develop, inorg. div, 64-66, mgr. prod. coord, NUCLEAR OPERS, MONSANTO RES. CORP, 66-68, TECH. ASST. TO DIR, 69- LeFevre gold medal & scholar, Univ. B.C, 38. Am. Chem. Soc; Am. Inst. Chem. Eng. Recovery of manganese and nickel from low-grade ores; new and improved processes for manufacture of superphosphates, phosphoric acid and phosphate fertilizers; mineralogy; ammonia base wood pulping; petrochemicals; general pilot plant techniques and management. Address: 3461 Stonebridge Rd, Kettering, OH 45419.

DAVENPORT, DEMOREST, b. Utica, N.Y, Sept, 26, 11; m. 41; c. 2. ZOOLOGY, ENTOMOLOGY. A.B, Harvard, 33, Atkins fel, 36, Ph.D.(biol), 37; A.M, Colo. Col, 34. Asst. entom, Harvard, 36-37; instr. biol, Reed Col, 37-38, 38-40, asst. prof, 40-42; ZOOL, UNIV. CALIF, SANTA BARBARA, 46-52, assoc. prof, 52-58, PROF, 58-, CHMN. DEPT, 62- Bache Fund grant, Nat. Acad. Sci, 36; grants, Am. Acad. Arts & Sci, 49; Am. Philos. Soc, 50; Sigma Xi, 50; Guggenheim Found, 53; Off. Naval Res, 55-; Nat. Sci. Found, 66- U.S.A.A.F, 42-46, Capt. AAAS; Ecol. Soc. Am; Am. Soc. Limnol. & Oceanog; Am. Soc. Zool; Asn. Study Animal Behaviour. Insect taxonomy; pharmacology of invertebrate hearts; behavior in symbioses. Address: Dept. of Zoology, University of California, Santa Barbara, CA 93106.

DAVENPORT, DEREK A(LFRED), b. Leicester, Eng, Sept. 23, 27; m. 50. INORGANIC CHEMISTRY. B.Sc, London, 47, Ph.D, 50. Fel, Ohio State, 51-53; instr. CHEM, PURDUE UNIV, 53-54, from asst. prof. to PROF, 54- Am. Chem. Soc. Borderlands between organic and inorganic chemistry. Address: Dept. of Chemistry, Purdue University, Lafayette, IN 47907.

DAVENPORT, D(ONALD) E(MERSON), b. Yakima, Wash, Nov. 7, 20; m. 42; c. 2. PHYSICAL CHEMISTRY. B.S, Washington (Seattle), 42, fel, 42-44, M.S, 44; fel, Mass. Inst. Tech, 46-48, Ph.D.(phys. chem), 48. Res. scientist, Manhattan Proj, 44-46; physicist, Gen. Elec. Co, 48-55; Stanford Res. Inst, 55-64, dir. eng, link ord. div, Gen. Precision, Inc, 64-67, mgr. res. & develop, 67-68, dir. res. & develop. ord, Singer, 68-69, mgr. ord. prod. line, 69-70; V.PRES. & GEN. MGR. SUNNYVALE DIV, SPACE ORD. SYSTS. INC, 70- Civilian with Off. Sci. Res. & Develop, 44. Am. Chem. Soc; Am. Nuclear Soc. Gaseous diffusion through barriers; production and measurement of molecular beams; nuclear reactor physics; physics of high explosives and shock waves. Address: Sunnyvale Division, Space Ordnance Systems, Inc, 375 Santa Trinita Ave, Sunnyvale, CA 94086.

DAVENPORT, FRED M, b. Scranton, Pa, Nov. 30, 14; m. 41; c. 3. INTERNAL MEDICINE, EPIDEMIOLOGY. B.A, Columbia, 36, M.D, 40, Sc. Med.D, 45. Asst. instr. path, col. physicians & surgeons, Columbia, 46-47; Nat. Research Coun. fel, Rockefeller Inst, 47-49, res. assoc, sch. pub. health, UNIV. MICH, 49-51, asst. prof. EPIDEMIOL. & INTERNAL MED, SCH. PUB. HEALTH & UNIV. HOSP, 51-52, assoc. prof, 53-59, PROF, 59-, CHMN. DEPT. EPIDEMIOL, 69- Dir. Comn. Influenza, Armed Forces Epidemiol. Bd, Off. Surgeon Gen, 55-; mem. expert adv. panel virus diseases, WHO, 58-; chmn, U.S. viral diseases panel, U.S-Japan Coop. Med. Sci. Prog, Nat. Inst. Allergy & Infectious Diseases, Nat. Insts. Health, 69-; hon. mem, Robert Koch Inst, Berlin, Ger. Mem. Medal & Badge of Gamaleya, Inst. Epidemiol. & Microbiol, Acad. Med. Sci, U.S.S.R. Med.C, A.U.S, Capt, U.S.A, 42-46. Am. Acad. Microbiol; Am. Asn. Immunol; Am. Epidemiol. Soc. (v.pres, 71); fel. Am. Pub. Health Asn; Am. Soc. Clin. Invest; Asn. Am. Physicians; Asn. Teachers Prev. Med; Fedn. Soc. Exp. Biol; Harvey Soc; Am. Soc. Microbiol; Soc. Exp. Biol. & Med; Pan-Am. Med. Asn. Virus diseases of the respiratory tract. Address: 1006 School of Public Health, University of Michigan, Ann Arbor, MI 48104.

DAVENPORT, G(UY) RODMAN, b. Portland, Maine, May 29, 31; m. 56; c. 2. BIOCHEMISTRY. B.S, New Hampshire, 53, M.S, 55; Ph.D.(biochem), Wisconsin, 60. U.S. Pub. Health Serv. fel, Brussels, 60-61; res. instr. cancer res, Washington (St. Louis), 61-63; asst. prof. ANAT, SCH. MED, VANDERBILT UNIV, 63-69, ASSOC. PROF, 69- Chemical embryology; morphology; reproductive endocrinology; steroidogenesis; ovarian function. Address: Dept. of Anatomy, Vanderbilt University School of Medicine, Nashville, TN 37203.

DAVENPORT, HORACE W(ILLARD), b. Philadelphia, Pa, Oct. 20, 12; m. 45; c. 2. PHYSIOLOGY. B.S, Calif. Inst. Tech, 35, Ph.D.(biochem), 39; B.A, Oxford, 37, B.Sc, 38, D.Sc, 61. Lilly res. fel, SCH. MED, ROCHESTER, 39-40; Sterling res. fel, Yale, 40-41; instr. physiol, Pennsylvania, 41-43; Harvard Med. Sch, 43-45; PROF. PHYSIOL. & CHMN. DEPT, Utah, 45-46; UNIV. MICH, 46- Am. Physiol. Soc.(pres, 61-62). Damage and repair of gastric mucosa; metabolism of stomach; gastric secretion. Address: Dept. of Physiology, University of Michigan, Ann Arbor, MI 48104.

DAVENPORT, LEE L(OSEE), b. Schenectady, N.Y, Dec. 31, 15; m. 44; c. 2. PHYSICS. B.S, Union (N.Y), 37; M.S, Pittsburgh, 40, Ph.D.(physics), 46. Res. assoc. radar, Mass. Inst. Tech, 41-46; res. fel. construct. cyclotron, Harvard, 46-50; exec. v.pres, Perkin-Elmer Corp, 50-57; pres, Sylvania Corning Nuclear Corp, 57-60, v.pres. planning, Sylvania Elec. Prod, Inc, 60-62, PRES, GTE LABS, INC, 62-, DIR. GTE INT. SYSTS. CORP, 70- Asst. dir. electronics res. lab, Pittsburgh, 46. Mem. gen. adv. comt. atomic energy, N.Y. Off. Atomic Develop. With Off. Sci. Res. & Develop; Brit. Ministry Supply, 44; dir, Am. Nat. Standards Inst. AAAS; fel. Am. Phys. Soc; Sci. Res. Soc. Am; Inst. Elec. & Electronics Eng. Applied x-rays; x-ray diffraction; research spectroscopy; nuclear physics; microwave radar; particle accelerators; guided missile control system. Address: GTE Labs, Inc, 730 Third Ave, New York, NY 10017.

DAVENPORT, LESLIE B(RYAN), JR, b. Abingdon, Va, July 10, 28; m. 52; c. 3. VERTEBRATE ZOOLOGY, ECOLOGY. B.S, Col. Charleston, 47; M.S, Va. Polytech, 51; Ph.D.(zool), Georgia, 60. Teacher, Porter Mil. Acad, S.C, 47-49; PROF. BIOL. & HEAD DEPT, ARMSTRONG STATE COL, 59- Wormsloe Found. grant ecol. res, 64- U.S.A.F, 55-58, 1st Lt. AAAS; Ecol. Soc. Am; Am. Soc. Mammal; Am. Ornith. Union; Wildlife Soc. Dynamics and energy relationships of populations of mammals and birds. Address: Dept. of Biology, Armstrong State College, Savannah, GA 31406.

DAVENPORT, O. MALCOLM, b. Pittston, Pa, Feb. 13, 08; m. 35; c. 3. FORESTRY. B.S.F, Pa. State Col, 33; M.S, Purdue, 40. Instr. FORESTRY, Pa. State Col, 33-35; asst. prof, Purdue, 35-42; UNIV. KY, 47-53, assoc. prof, 53-56, PROF, 56-, in charge sect, 47-64, acting chmn. dept, 64-65. U.S.A.A.F, 42-47. Soc. Am. Foresters. Forest management and administration; logging and utilization; Christmas tree culture. Address: Dept. of Forestry, University of Kentucky, Lexington, KY 40506.

DAVENPORT, RICHARD, b. Battle Creek, Mich, Aug. 27, 30; m. 56. CYTOLOGY, CYTOCHEMISTRY. B.A, Mich. State, 53, B.S, 57; Ph.D.(biol), Hopkins, 60. Nat. Sci. Found. res. fel, Melbourne, 61-62; res. assoc, Hopkins, 63; asst. prof. CYTOL, UNIV. ILL, URBANA-CHAMPAIGN, 64-69, ASSOC. PROF, 69- Nat. Insts. Health res. grant, 64-67. U.S.A.F, 53-56, Lt. Cytoplasmic basic proteins in oocytes and early embryos. Address: Dept. of Zoology, University of Illinois, Urbana-Champaign, Urbana, IL 61801.

DAVENPORT, TOM FOREST, JR, b. Atlanta, Ga, Apr. 25, 30; m. 54; c. 3. ORGANIC CHEMISTRY. B.S, Ga. Inst. Tech, 51; Am. Oil Co. fel, Texas, 55-56, Ph.D.(chem), 57. Res. chemist, Am. Oil Co, Tex, 56-60; ETHYL CORP, 60-66, prod. rep, COMMERCIAL DEVELOP. DEPT, 66-67, Prod. mgr, 67-70, MKT. DEVELOP. ANALYST, 70- Summer, chemist, Monsanto Chem. Co, 55. Chem.C.R.Res, 51-, Maj. Am. Chem. Soc. Organometallics; hydrogenation; nitrogen compounds; synthesis. Address: Commercial Development Dept. Ethyl Corp, Baton Rouge, LA 70801.

DAVENPORT, WILBUR B(AYLEY) JR, b. Philadelphia, Pa, July 27, 20; m. 45; c. 2. ELECTRICAL COMMUNICATIONS. B.E.E, Ala. Polytech. Inst, 41; M.S, Mass. Inst. Tech, 43, Sc.D.(elec. eng), 50. Asst. elec. eng, MASS. INST. TECHNOL, 41-43, instr, radar sch, 43, elec. eng. dept, 46-49, asst. prof, 49-53, group leader, communication tech. group, Lincoln Lab, 51-55, assoc. div. head, communications & components div, 55-57, div. head, 57-58, info. processing div, 58-60, PROF. ELEC. ENG, 60-, ASSOC. HEAD ELEC. SCI. & ENG, 71-, asst. dir. lab, 63-65. Vis. asst. prof, California, 50. Guest, Int. Summer Sch. Info. Theory, Italy, 58. U.S.N.R, 43-51, Lt.(jg). Fel. AAAS; Math. Asn. Am; Soc. Indust. & Appl. Math; fel. Inst. Elec. & Electronics Eng. Statistical theory of communications; random processes in linear and non-linear systems. Address: 190 Garfield Rd, Concord, MA 01742.

DAVENPORT, WILLIAM H(ENRY), JR, b. Newark, N.J, Oct. 7, 21; m. 47; c. 2. CHEMISTRY. B.A, Wesleyan, 43. Asst, Manhattan Proj, Princeton, 43-46; jr. chemist, Clinton Labs, Oak Ridge, 46-47, assoc. chemist, 47-48; Oak Ridge Nat. Lab, 48-51; chemist, CHASE BRASS & COPPER CO, 51-61, chief chemist, RHENIUM DIV, 61-65, mgr. chem. opers, 65-70, DIR. CHEM. DEVELOP, 70- With Off. Sci. Res. & Develop, 44. Am. Chem. Soc; fel. Am. Inst. Chem. Inorganic analytical methods; electrochemistry and corrosion; chemical technology of rhenium. Address: 126 Locust Lane, Chagrin Falls, OH 44022.

DAVERN, CEDRIC I, b. Hobart, Tasmania, Nov. 13, 31; m. 63; c. 3. GENETICS, MOLECULAR BIOLOGY. B.S.Agr, Univ. Sydney, 53, M.S.Agr, 56; Ph.D.(biol), Calif. Inst. Technol, 59. Res. off. genetics, Commonwealth Sci. & Indust. Res. Orgn, Australia, 54-56, sr. res. off, 56-59; res. assoc. molecular biol, LAB. Quantitative Biol, Cold Spring Harbor, N.Y, 64-65, asst. dir, 65-67; assoc. prof. BIOL, UNIV. CALIF, SANTA CRUZ, 67-69, PROF, 69- Molecular mechanisms of DNA replication and its regulation. Address: Dept. of Natural Sciences, University of California, Santa Cruz, CA 95060.

DAVES, G(LENN) DOYLE, JR, b. Clayton, N.Mex, Feb. 12, 36; m. 59; c. 3. ORGANIC & BIO-ORGANIC CHEMISTRY. B.S, Ariz. State Univ, 59; Nat. Insts. Health fel, Mass. Inst. Technol, 62-64, Ph.D.(org. chem), 64. Res. chemist org.chem, Midwest Res. Inst, Mo, 59-61; res. assoc. bio-org. chem, Stanford Res. Inst, Calif, 64-67; asst. prof. BIO-ORG. & ORG. CHEM, ORE. GRAD. CTR, 67-70, ASSOC. PROF, 70- AAAS; Am. Chem. Soc. Isolation, structure elucidation and synthesis of natural products or other compounds having substantial biological importance; applications of nuclear magnetic resonance and mass spectrometry. Address: Oregon Graduate Center, Beaverton, OR 97005.

DAVES, MARVIN LEWIS, b. Lexington, Va, Jan. 26, 28; m. 52; c. 3. RADIOLOGY. B.A, Washington & Lee, 48; Denison scholar, Hopkins, 50-53, M.D, 53. Asst. radiologist, clin. center, Nat. Insts. Health, 57-59; asst.

prof. RADIOL. & acting head dept, med. center, Arkansas, 59-60; asst. prof, MED. CTR, UNIV. COLO, 60-62, acting chmn. dept, 61-62, PROF. & CHMN. DEPT, 62- U.S.A, 48-49. Fel. Am. Col. Radiol; Asn. Univ. Radiol; Radiol. Soc. N.Am. Cardiology; bone dysplasia. Address: Dept. of Radiology, University of Colorado Medical Center, 4200 E. Ninth Ave, Denver, CO 80220.

DAVEY, CHARLES B(INGHAM), b. Brooklyn, N.Y, Apr. 7, 28; m. 52; c. 3. SOIL MICROBIOLOGY. B.S, N.Y. State Col. Forestry, Syracuse, 50; M.S, Wisconsin, 52, Ph.D.(soils), 55. Soil scientist, Agr. Res. Serv, U.S. Dept. Agr, 57-62; assoc. prof. SOIL SCI, N.C. STATE UNIV, 62-65, PROF, 65-, HEAD DEPT. FORESTRY, 70- Chem.C, U.S.A, 55-57. Fel. AAAS; Fel. Am. Soc. Agron; Soil Sci. Soc. Am; Soc. Am. Foresters; Int. Soil Sci. Soc. Water structure and its relation to biological systems; microbial ecology in soil and rhizosphere; Mycorrhizae; tree nutrition. Address: Dept. of Forestry, North Carolina State University, Raleigh, NC 27607.

DAVEY, FREDERICK K(NOWLES), b. Columbus, Ohio, Aug. 4, 21; m. 48; c. 2. CERAMICS. B.S, Rutgers, 43, Ph.D.(ceramics), 52. Asst. res. specialist, Rutgers, 47-53; proj. engr, Friez Instrument Div, BENDIX CORP, 53-62, CHIEF ENGR, ENVIRON. SCI. DIV, 62- U.S.A.A.F, 43-47, Capt. Am. Ceramic Soc; Am. Meteorol. Soc. Semiconductors and thermistors; ceramic and metal combinations; meteorological instruments. Address: Environmental Science Division, Bendix Corp, 1400 Taylor Ave, Towson, MD 21204.

DAVEY, GERALD L(ELAND), b. Salt Lake City, Utah, Apr. 9, 30; m. 54; c. 4. APPLIED MATHEMATICS, SYSTEMS ANALYSIS. M.S, Stanford Univ, 54, Ph.D.(math), 59. Employee, Hughes Aircraft Co, Calif, 59-61; consult, Systs. Anal. Consult, 61; dir. bus. info. systs. div, Hughes Dynamics, Inc, 62-65; v. pres, Credit Data Corp, Calif. & N.Y, 65-68, pres, N.Y, 68-70, sr. v.pres, TRW Info. Serv, Inc, 70; PRES, MEDLAB COMPUT. SERV, INC, 70- Instr. math, exten. div, Univ. Calif, Los Angeles, 60-65; consult, TRW Info. Serv, Inc, 70- U.S.A.F, 57-59, 1st Lt. AAAS; Soc. Indust. & Appl. Math; Math. Asn. Am. Systems analysis in computer technology; computerized medical technology. Address: 2735 Sherwood Dr, Salt Lake City, UT 84108.

DAVEY, JOHN EDMUND, b. Buffalo, N.Y, July 15, 25; m. 50; c. 2. PHYSICS. B.S, Canisius Col, 49; M.S, Notre Dame, 51, Ph.D.(physics), 54. Res. Physicist, electron tubes br, U.S. NAVAL RES. LAB, 54-59, res. physicist, & Sect. head, solid state electronics br, 59-69, HEAD, SOLID STATE TECHNOL, BR, 69- U.S.A, 43-45. Am. Phys. Soc; Am. Vacuum Soc; sr. mem. Inst. Elec. & Electronics Eng. Thermionic, photoelectric, and Schottky emission from bulk metals, semiconductors and thin films; structural, electrical and optical properties of thin semiconducting and metal films; x-ray and electron diffraction; electron microscopy; high vacuum techniques. Address: Solid State Technology Branch, Naval Research Lab, Washington, DC 20390.

DAVEY, K(ENNETH) G(EORGE), b. Chatham, Ont, Apr. 20, 32; m. 59; c. 3. ENTOMOLOGY, PARASITOLOGY. B.Sc, Western Ontario, 54, M.S, 55; Ont. Res. Found. scholar & Ph.D.(zool), Cambridge, 58. Nat. Res. Coun. Can. fel, Toronto, 58-59; Drosier fel, entom, Gonville & Caius Col, Cambridge, 59-63; assoc. prof. parasitol, MACDONALD COL, McGILL UNIV, 63-64, DIR, INST. PARASITOL, 64-, PROF. PARASITOL, 67- Soc. Exp. Biol. & Med; Can. Soc. Zool; Entom. Soc. Can. Reproduction in arthropods; physiology of insect visceral muscles; neurosecretion in invertebrates; physiology of helminths. Address: Institute of Parasitology, Box 231, Macdonald College 800, Que, Can.

DAVEY, P(AUL) O(LIVER), b. West Monroe, La, Apr. 5, 31; m. 55. PHYSICS. B.S, La. Polytech, 51; M.S, Iowa State, 54; Oregon, 55-58; Ph.D.(physics), Nebraska, 64. Jr. physicist, Ames Lab, Atomic Energy Cmn, 54-55; asst. prof. math. & physics, Nevada, 58-61; ASSOC. PROF. PHYSICS, STATE UNIV. N.Y. COL. FREDONIA, 64- Am. Phys. Soc; Am. Inst. Physics; Am. Asn. Physics Teachers. Theoretical description of light nuclei; theory of the photodisintegration of light nuclei; theoretical physics. Address: Dept. of Physics, State University of New York College at Fredonia, Fredonia, NY 14063.

DAVEY, THOMAS RONALD ALBERT, b. Melbourne, Australia, Mar. 27, 25; m. 54; c. 3. METALLURGY. B.S, Univ. Melbourne, 47, B.Metall.Eng, 48, M.Metall.Eng, 54, D.Sc.A.(metall), 67. Res. off, Broken Hill Assoc. Smelters, Australia, 47-54; opers. engr, Norddeutsche Affinerie, Ger, 54-57; consult. Imperial Smelting Corp, Eng, 57-58; chief res. off, Broken Hill Assoc. Smelters, 59-60; consult, Imperial Smelting Corp, 60-63; sr. prin. res. scientist, Commonwealth Sci. & Indust. Res. Orgn, Australia, 63-69; PROF. METALL. ENG, COLO. SCH. MINES, 69-; PRES, METALL. ASSOCS. COLO, INC, 69- Consult. Inst. de Invest. Minero-Metall, Bolivia, 69-71; lead div, St. Joe Mineral Corp, 71; Nat. Lead Co, 71. Am. Inst. Mining, Metall. & Petrol. Eng.(gold medal, extractive metall. div, 55); Australasian Inst. Mining & Metall; Ger. Soc. Mining & Metall; Brit. Inst. Mining & Metall. New process development, process optimization, determination of phase diagrams and thermodynamic data, relevant to non-ferrous pyrometallurgy. Address: Dept. of Metallurgical Engineering, Colorado School of Mines, Golden, CO 80401.

DAVEY, TREVOR B(LAKELY), b. Winnipeg, Man, Can, Nov. 27, 31; U.S. citizen; m. 53; c. 3. MECHANICAL ENGINEERING. B.Sc, Manitoba, 53; M.E, McGill, 57. Engr, Can. Gen. Elec. Co, 53-55; sessional lectr, McGill, 55-57; develop. engr, Atomic Energy Can, 57; CHMN. DEPT. MECH. ENG, SACRAMENTO STATE COL, 57-, PROF, 67- Co-dir, bioeng. sect, cardiopulmonary dept, Sutter Hosps. Med. Res. Found, 63- Consult, Aerojet Gen. Corp, 57-64. Am. Soc. Mech. Eng; Am. Soc. Eng. Educ. Characteristics of fluid flow through prosthetic heart valves; design of heart assists. Address: Dept. of Mechanical Engineering, Sacramento State College, 6000 Jay St, Sacramento, CA 95819.

DAVEY, WINTHROP N(EWBURY), b. Jackson, Mich, May 19, 18; m. 59; c. 3. INTERNAL MEDICINE. A.B, Univ. Mich, 39, M.D, 42. From intern to res. & instr. internal med, hosp, Univ. Mich, 44-50, asst. prof, sch. med, 50-54, assoc. prof, 54-60, prof, 60-72, dir. med. tuberc. unit, hosp, 47-71; ASSOC. DIR. UNIV. AFFAIRS, TRAINING PROG, CTR. DISEASE CONTROL, U.S. PUB. HEALTH SERV, 71- Consult, tuberc. prog, Ctr. Disease Control, U.S. Pub. Health Serv, 60-71, mem. Nat. Adv. Tuberc. Control Comt, 61-68, Nat. Adv. Commun. Disease Coun, 68-69, Nat. Adv. Heart & Lung Coun, 70-71. AAAS; Am. Med. Asn; Am. Col. Chest Physicians; Am. Thoracic Soc.(pres-elect, 64-65, pres, 65-66); Am. Ornith. Union; Wilson Ornith. Soc. Tuberculosis; pulmonary disease. Address: Training Program, Center for Disease Control, Atlanta, GA 30333.

DAVIAULT, J. S. LIONEL, b. St. Jerome, Que, Feb. 26, 05; m. 54; c. 2. FOREST ZOOLOGY. B.Sc, Montreal, 24, D.Sc.(zool), 35; M.Sc, McGill, 27; dipl, Paris, 28. Officer in charge lab. forest entom, Can. Dept. Agr, Berthierville, 30-43, chief, bur. entom, dept. lands & forests, Que, 43-52, officer in charge forest entom. & path. lab, 52-65, dir. Que. Region, Dept. Forestry, 65-70; RETIRED. Prof, Laval, 43-70, emer. prof, 70- Mem. forest insects control bd, Dept. Resources & Develop, Can, 45-52. Fel. Royal Soc. Can; French-Can. Asn. Advan. Sci.(pres, 49). Ecology and control of forest insects. Address: 3180 Neilson, Ste-Foy 10, Que, Can.

DAVICH, T(HEODORE) B(ERT), b. McKeenlyville, W.Va, Jan. 3, 23; m. 45; c. 2. ECONOMIC ENTOMOLOGY. B.Sc, Ohio State, 48; M.S, Wisconsin, 50, Ph.D.(entom), 53. Asst. entom, Wisconsin, 50-53; assoc. entomologist, Va. Agr. Exp. Sta, 53-56; entomologist & head Tex. Cotton Insects Lab, ENTOM. RES. DIV, AGR. RES, SERV, 56-60, DIR, BOLL WEEVIL RES. LAB, 60- U.S.A.A.F, 44. Entom. Soc. Am. Insects affecting cotton. Address: Boll Weevil Research Lab, U.S. Dept. of Agriculture, Box 5367, State College, MS 39762.

DAVID, CARL W(OLFGANG), b. Hamburg, Germany, June 30, 37; U.S. citizen. PHYSICAL CHEMISTRY. B.S, Case, 58; M.S, Michigan, 60, Ph.D.(chem), 62. Res. fel. CHEM, Yale, 62-63; asst. prof, UNIV. CONN, 63-68, ASSOC. PROF, 68- Am. Chem. Soc. Statistical thermodynamics of liquids and liquid mixtures. Address: Dept. of Chemistry, University of Connecticut, Storrs, CT 06268.

DAVID, CHELLADURAI S, b. Coonoor, India, June 18, 36; U.S. citizen; m. 61; c. 2. IMMUNOGENETICS. B.S, Berea Col, 61; M.S, Kentucky, 62; Ph.D.(immunogenetics), Iowa State, 66. RES. ASSOC. IMMUNOGENETICS, Iowa State, 66-68; MED. SCH. UNIV. MICH, 68- AAAS; Genetics Soc. Am. Immunoglobulin allotypes in fowl; mouse histocompatibility system. Address: 3722 Medical Science II, University of Michigan, Ann Arbor, MI 48103.

DAVID, D(ONALD) J(OSEPH), b. St. Louis, Mo, June 25, 30; m. 52; c. 1. ANALYTICAL & INDUSTRIAL CHEMISTRY. B.S, St. Mary's Univ. (Tex), 52. Anal. chemist, Diamond Alkali Co, Tex, 54; chief spectrographer, Shilstone Testing Labs, 54-56, lab. dir, 56-58; methods develop. chemist, Callery Chem. Co, Okla, 58-59; res. anal. chemist, Mobay Chem. Co, 59-60, sr. res. anal. chemist, 60-61, group leader anal. res, 61-65, chief chemist, 65-66, group leader anal. res, 66-67; prog. mgr. gas chromatography, Tracor, Inc, 67, res. & develop. mgr. anal. instruments, 67-71; DIVISIONAL RES. & DEVELOP. MGR, COLUMBIA SCI. INSTRUMENTS, INC, 71- Lectr, Thermal Anal. Inst, 65. Mobay Chem. Co. res. award, 61. U.S.A, 52-54, 1st. Lt. Am. Chem. Soc; Instrument Soc. Am; Soc. Appl. Spectros. Thermal analysis; near-infrared spectroscopy; gas liquid chromatography; instrument design and development; polymer analysis and characterization; infrared spectroscopy; urethane analytical chemistry; emission spectroscopy. Address: 4021 Greenhill Pl, Austin, TX 78759.

DAVID, EDWARD E(MIL), JR, b. Wilmington, N.C, Jan. 25, 25; m. 50; c. 1. PHYSICS, ELECTRICAL ENGINEERING. B.E.E, Ga. Inst. Technol, 45; S.M. & Sc.D.(elec. eng), Mass. Inst. Technol, 50; hon. D.Eng, Stevens Inst. Technol, 71 & Polytech. Inst. Brooklyn, 71. Asst, electronics res. lab, Mass. Inst. Technol, 46-50; mem, Hartwell Proj, 50; mem. tech. staff, Bell Tel. Labs, 50-54, supvr, 54-56, engr. in charge acoustics res, 56-57, asst. dir. visual & acoustic res, 57-58, dir, 58-62, comput. & info. res, 62-65, exec. dir. commun. systs. res, 65-70; SCI. ADV. TO THE PRESIDENT & DIR. OFF. SCI. & TECHNOL, U.S. GOVT, 70- Adv, Nat. Sci. Found, 58-61; mem. bd. dirs, Comn. Eng. Educ, 62-70; consult, prosthetic & sensory aids serv, Vet. Admin, 63; Am. Found. Blind & NASA, 64-; prof, Stevens Inst. Technol, 66-; mem, Nat. Adv. Comt. on Educ. of Deaf, 66-69; Postmaster Gen. adv. comt, 67-68; v.pres. & mem. bd. dir, Summit Speech Sch, N.J, 68-70. Eta Kappa Nu Award, 54; Anak Award, 58. Nat. Acad. Sci; Nat. Acad. Eng; fel. AAAS; fel. Inst. Elec. & Electronics Eng; fel. Acoust. Soc. Am; fel. Audio Eng. Soc; Asn. Comput. Mach; Psychonomic Soc. Microwave techniques; acoustics; communication theory; human communication; psychophysics; computer usage and organization. Address: The White House, Washington, DC 20506.

DAVID, FLORENCE N, b. Hereford, U.K, Aug. 23, 09. STATISTICS, MATHEMATICS. B.Sc, London, 31, Ph.D.(statist), 38, D.Sc.(statist), 50. From lectr. to prof. statist, Univ. Col, London, 35-67; PROF. STATIST, UNIV. CALIF, Berkeley, 61-62, 64-65, RIVERSIDE, 67-, CHMN. DEPT, 68- Sr. statistician, Ministry of Home Security, U.K, 39-45. Consult, Pac. State Hosp, Pomona, 65-; forestry, U.S. Dept. Agr. Fel. Am. Statist. Soc; fel. Inst. Math. Statist; fel, Royal Statist. Soc; Int. Statist. Inst. Combinatorial and randomization methods; statistical applications. Address: Dept. of Statistics, University of California, Riverside, CA 92502.

DAVID, GARY SAMUEL, b. Aurora, Ill, Oct. 2, 42; m. 69. IMMUNOCHEMISTRY. B.S, Illinois, Urbana, 64, Ph.D.(microbiol), 68. U.S. Dept. Health, Educ. & Welfare fel. immunol, City of Hope Med. Ctr, 68-70; res. assoc, Salk Inst. Biol. Studies, 70-71; FEL. EXP. PATH, SCRIPPS CLIN. & RES. FOUND, 71- Am. Asn. Immunol. Immunogenetics; protein chemistry, cellular and developmental immunology. Address: Dept. of Experimental Pathology, Scripps Clinic & Research Foundation, 476 Prospect, La Jolla, CA 92037.

DAVID, G(EORGE) B(ERTHOLD), b. Rio de Janeiro, Brazil, Sept. 5, 30. BIOPHYSICS, NEUROBIOLOGY. B.Sc, Am. Univ, 52; D.Phil.(physiol), Oxford, 60. Scientist, Med. Res. Coun, Eng, 55-63; prof. histol. & neuroanat. & chmn. dept, Am. Univ. Beirut, 63-64; res. assoc. biol, Princeton, 64-66; res. assoc. & head biophys, electronics res. labs, Columbia Univ, 66-68; PROF. BIOL, UNIV. DENVER, 68- Vis. prof, Inst. Biophys, Brazilian Acad. Sci, 61 & 64; sci. consult, Am. Optical Corp, 66-; vis. scientist, State Univ. N.Y, Albany, 68; Nat. Ctr. Sci. Res, Paris, 71. Fel. Royal Micros. Soc; Tissue Cult. Asn; Soc. Exp. Biol. & Med; Soc. Gen. Physiol; Marine Biol. Asn. U.K. Biophysics of the functioning of nerve cells; physical microscopy, especially interferometry; ultraviolet and image enhancement theory; molecular biology of cell differentiation. Address: Dept. of Biological Sciences, University of Denver, Denver, CO 80210.

DAVID, H(ERBERT) A(RON), b. Ger, Dec. 19, 25; U.S. citizen; m. 50; c. 1. MATHEMATICAL STATISTICS. B.Sc, Univ. Sydney, 47; Ph.D.(statist), Univ. London, 53. Sr. lectr. STATIST, Univ. Melbourne, 55-57; PROF, Va. Polytech. Inst, 57-64; SCH. PUB. HEALTH, UNIV. N.C, 64- Biomet. Soc.(pres, east. N.Am. region, 63, ed, Biometrics, 67-); Am. Statist. Asn; fel. Inst. Math. Statist; Int. Statist. Inst. Order statistics; paired comparisons; inference; design of experiments. Address: Dept. of Biostatistics, University of North Carolina, Chapel Hill, NC 27514.

DAVID, ISRAEL A, b. Phila, Pa, Oct. 25, 25; m. 51; c. 2. ORGANIC CHEMISTRY. B.S, Pennsylvania, 48; Allied Chem. & Dye Corp. fel, Wisconsin, 53-54, Ph.D.(org. chem), 55. Sr. res. chemist, E.I. DU PONT DE NEMOURS & CO. INC, 54-64, RES. ASSOC, 65- U.S.A, 44-46. Am. Chem. Soc; Sci. Res. Soc. Am. Synthesis of organic compounds and polymers and the relationship between their molecular structures and properties; preparation and evaluation of synthetic fibres. Address: Textile Fibers Dept, Carothers Research Lab, E.I. du Pont de Nemours & Co, Wilmington, DE 19898.

DAVID, JEAN, b. Montreal, Que, Dec. 19, 21; m. 51; c. 3. BIOCHEMISTRY, FOOD TECHNOLOGY. L.S.A, Montreal, 40; Ph.D.(biochem), California, 49. Exten. specialist hort, Que. Dept. Agr, 41-44, food technologist, 49-63; asst. prof. HORT, MACDONALD COL, McGILL UNIV, 49-63, ASSOC. PROF, 63-, REGISTR, 69- Inst. Food Tech; Can. Inst. Food Tech. Food preservation; cold storage; canning and freezing; physiological and biochemical changes in fruits and vegetables after harvest and during storage. Address: Macdonald College, McGill University, Montreal, Que, Can.

DAVID, JOHN C, b. Chicago, Ill, Feb. 25, 26; m. 51; c. 3. ORGANIC CHEMISTRY. A.B, Princeton, 51; M.A. & Ph.D.(org. chem), Nebraska, 58. Chemist, Merck & Co, Inc, 51-53; SR. RES. CHEMIST PROD. DEVELOP, E.I. DU PONT DE NEMOURS & CO, INC, 58- U.S.N.R, 44-46. Am. Chem. Soc. Food technology; analytical methods; carcinogenically active heterocycles; product development, especially synthetic non-wovens. Address: 402 Seneca Rd, Richmond, VA 23226.

DAVID, JOHN R, b. Eng, Feb. 15, 30; U.S. citizen; m. 57; c. 2. INTERNAL MEDICINE, IMMUNOLOGY. B.A, Chicago, 51, B.S. & M.D, 55. Intern, Mass. Gen. Hosp, 55-57, asst. res, 55-57, res. med, 60-61; clin. assoc, Nat. Inst. Arthritis & Metab. Diseases, 57-59; trainee, Rheumatism Res. Unit, Eng, 59-60; fel, sch. med, N.Y. Univ, 61-64, asst. prof. MED, 64-66; HARVARD MED. SCH, 66-69, ASSOC. PROF, 69- U.S.P.H.S, 57-59, Surg. Am. Asn. Immunol; Am. Fedn. Clin. Res. Mechanisms of delayed hypersensitivity and cellular immunity; rheumatology. Address: Robert B. Brigham Hospital. Harvard Medical School, 125 Parker Hill Ave, Boston, MA 02120.

DAVID, LARRY GENE, b. Searcy, Ark, Apr. 11, 38; m. 64; c. 2. INDUSTRIAL ENGINEERING. B.S, Arkansas, 61, M.S, 62; Nat. Sci. Found. traineeship, Purdue, 65-67, Ph.D.(indust. eng), 68. Instr. physics lab, Arkansas, 58-60, comput. programming, 60-61; INDUST. ENG, Missouri-Columbia, 61-64; Purdue, 67-68; ASSOC. PROF, UNIV. MO-COLUMBIA, 68- Air Nat. Guard, 56-62, S/Sgt. Am. Inst. Indust. Eng. Manufacturing processes; electric discharge machining; regional blood inventory system; computerized instructional system for classroom supplement. Address: Dept. of Industrial Engineering, University of Missouri-Columbia, Columbia, MO 65201.

DAVID, LORE ROSE, b. Opladen, Germany, Oct. 23, 05; nat. BIOLOGY. Ph.D, Berlin, 31. Curator ichthyol, Belgian Congo Mus. Tervueren, Belgium, 34-37; res. assoc. geol. sci, Calif. Inst. Tech, 38-43; paleontologist, Richfield Oil Corp, Calif, 43-47; asst. prof. biol, Northwest. State Col.(La), 47-48; zool, Vermont, 48-50; prof. biol. & head dept, Wilberforce, 50-51; sci. analyst, Tech. Info. Serv, Atomic Energy Comn, 51-54; sci. documentalist, John Crerar Library, Ill, 54-60; asst. librn, U.S. Qm. Food & Container Inst, 60-62; sci. librn, Santa Clara County Libr, 62-71; RESEARCHER PALEOICHTHYOL, 71- Fel. Geol. Soc. Am; Soc. Vert. Paleont. Ichthyology; paleoichthyology; paleoecology; age determination, especially those based on petrified fish scales. Address: 486 Northlake Dr, San Jose, CA 95117.

DAVID, MORTON M(ORRIS), b. Denver, Colo, Apr. 22, 21; m. 51; c. 3. CHEMICAL ENGINEERING. B.S, Colorado, 42; Conn. State Water Comn. fel. & D.Eng, Yale, 50. Chem. engr. tech. serv, Standard Oil Co, Ind, 42-43; res. asst, metall. labs, Chicago, 43; res. assoc. solar energy utilization, eng. exp. sta, Colorado, 43-44, 46; asst. prof. CHEM. ENG, Utah, 49-52; from asst. to PROF, UNIV. WASH, 53- Fulbright lectr, Indian Inst. Sci, India, 52-53; Nat. Sch. Adv. Chem. Industs, France, 58-59; mem. staff, div. eng. & tech. res,UNESCO, France, 64-65; vis. prof, dept. civil & munic. eng, Univ. Col. London, 70-71. U.S.N, 44-46. Fel. AAAS; N.Y. Acad. Sci; Am. Inst. Chem. Eng; Soc. Eng. Educ. Heat transfer; mass transfer; ion exchange; design. Address: Dept. of Chemical Engineering, University of Washington, Seattle, WA 98105.

DAVID, NORMAN A(USTIN), b. San Francisco, Calif, Oct. 22, 02; m. 32; c. 2. PHARMACOLOGY. A.B, California, 25, Lilly fel, 30-32, M.D, 31. Asst, California, 30-32; asst. prof. & head dept. PHARMACOL, sch. med, West Virginia, 32-35; asst. prof, col. med, Cincinnati, 35-36, assoc. prof, 36-37; PROF. MED. SCH, UNIV. ORE, 37-, head dept, 37-69. Am. Soc. Pharmacol. & Exp. Therapeut; Am. Med. Asn; Soc. Exp. Biol. & Med. Chemotherapy of amebiasis; pharmacology of barbital drugs; chronic effects of opium drugs and synthetic analgesics. Address: Medical School, University of Oregon, Portland, OR 97201.

DAVID, PAUL R(EMBERT), b. Providence, R.I, Dec. 16, 07; m. 40; c. 2. ZOOLOGY. A.B, Col. of Charleston, 27; M.S, Pittsburgh, 30; Eidgenoessische Tech. Hochsch, Zurich, 36-37; Ph.D.(zool), Columbia, 37. Instr. biol, Col. of Charleston, 27-28; asst. genetics, Storrs exp. sta, Conn. State Col, 30-37; asst. prof. biol, Lafayette Col, 37-41; assoc. prof. med. genetics, Bowman Gray Sch. Med, Wake Forest Col, 41-47; ZOOL, UNIV. OKLA, 47-52, PROF, 52-, MED. GENETICS, MED. CTR, 69-, DIR, 58-, Inst. Human Studies, 49-53. Res. assoc, sch. hyg. & pub. health, Johns Hopkins Univ, 41-47. U.S.A, 43-46. AAAS; Genetics Soc. Am; Am. Soc. Human Genetics; Fedn. Am. Sci. Developmental, medicinal and human genetics; developmental genetics of poultry and mice. Address: Dept. of Medical Genetics, Medical Center, University of Oklahoma, Oklahoma City, OK 73105.

DAVID, PETER P, b. Szeged, Hungary, June 9, 32; m. 61; c. 3. GEOLOGY. Dipl, Univ. Szeged, 55; B.Sc, McGill Univ, 59, M.Sc, 61, Ph.D.(Pleistocene geol), 65. Prof, Leanygimnazium Hodmezövasarhely, Hungary, 55-56; lectr. GEOL, UNIV. MONTREAL, 64, asst. prof, 64-69, ASSOC. PROF, 69- AAAS; Geol. Soc. Am; Geol. Asn. Can; Arctic Inst. N.Am. Quaternary stratigraphy; eolien deposits. Address: Dept. of Geology, University of Montreal, P.O. Box 6128, Montreal 101, Que, Can.

DAVID, RICHARD FRANCIS, b. St. Louis, Mo, May 16, 38; m. 62; c. 4. SOLID STATE PHYSICS. B.S, St. Louis, 60; Westinghouse fel, Hopkins, 60-65, Ph.D.(solid state physics), 65. Sr. engr, Surface Div, Westinghouse Elec. Corp, 65-68; unit head microelectronics, DENVER DIV, MARTIN-MARIETTA CORP, 68-69, SECT. HEAD MICROELECTRONICS & PACKAGING, 69- Adj. asst. prof, elec. eng. dept, Denver, 68-; lectr, Martin-Marietta Indust. Sch, 69- Electron paramagnetic resonance; nuclear magnetic resonance; hybrid microelectronics, particularly thin film active elements and microwave microcircuits; operations research. Address: Microelectronics Lab, Martin-Marietta Corp, P.O. Box 179, Denver, CO 80201.

DAVIDOFF, ROBERT A(LAN), b. Brooklyn, N.Y, Oct. 5, 34; m. 67; c. 1. NEUROPHYSIOLOGY. B.S, N.Y. Univ, 55, M.D, 58. Instr. psychiat, sch. med, Ind. Univ, 65-66, asst. prof, 66-69, NEUROL, 68-69; ASSOC. PROF, SCH. MED, UNIV. MIAMI, 69-, PHARMACOL, 70- Res. assoc, Vet. Admin. Hosp, Indianapolis, Ind, 65-66, clin. investr, 66-69. Med.C, U.S.N.R, Lt. AAAS; Am. Acad. Neurol. Synaptic transmission. Address: Dept. of Neurology, School of Medicine, University of Miami, Miami, FL 33152.

DAVIDON, WILLIAM C(OOPER), b. Fla, Mar. 18, 27; m. 47, 63; c. 3. PHYSICS. B.S, Chicago, 47, M.S, 50, Ph.D.(physics), 54. Electronics engr, Mines Equip. Co, 43-44; dir. res, Nuclear Instrument & Chem. Corp, 48-56; assoc. physicist, Argonne Nat. Lab, 56-61; assoc. prof. PHYSICS, HAVERFORD COL, 61-69, PROF, 69- Fel, Chicago, 50-54, res. assoc, 54-56; Fulbright-Hays res. grant, physics, Aarhus Univ, 66- U.S.N.R, 45-46. Fedn. Am. Sci.(secy, 60-61); Soc. Social Responsibility Sci.(pres, 65-67); Am. Asn. Physics Teachers. Foundations of quantum mechanics; theory of elementary particles. Address: Dept. of Physics, Haverford College, Haverford, PA 19041.

DAVIDOVITS, PAUL, b. Moldava, Czech, Nov. 1, 35; Can. citizen; m. 57; c. 2. ATOMIC PHYSICS. B.S, Columbia, 60, M.S, 61, Ph.D.(appl. physics), 64. Staff engr, radiation lab, Columbia, 61-64, res. physicist & lectr, 64-65; asst. prof. ENG. & APPL. SCI, YALE, 65-70, ASSOC. PROF, 70- Consult, Varian Assocs, 64- Am. Phys. Soc. Quantum electronics; atomic time standards; physics of atomic collisions and recombinations; laser physics. Address: Dept. of Applied Science, Yale University, 1303A Yale Station, New Haven, CT 06520.

DAVIDOW, BERNARD, b. N.Y.C, Aug. 4, 19; m. 42; c. 3. TOXICOLOGY. B.S, Fordham, 42; M.S, Georgetown, 48, Ph.D, 50. Chief acute toxicity br, pharmacol. div, Food & Drug Admin, 46-56; dir. labs, New Drug Inst, 56-61; CHIEF FOOD & DRUG LAB, N.Y.C. DEPT. HEALTH, 61- Lectr, sch. pub. health, Columbia Univ. U.S.A, 42-45. AAAS; Soc. Toxicol; Am. Soc. Pharmacol. & Exp. Therapeut; Am. Pub. Health Asn; Am. Chem. Soc; N.Y. Acad. Sci. Toxicity and analysis of chemicals used in foods, drugs and cosmetics; detection of drugs subject to abuse in body fluids; detection of toxic metals in body fluids and food. Address: Food & Drug Lab, New York City Dept. of Health, 455 First Ave, New York, NY 10016.

DAVIDS, CARY NATHAN, b. Edmonton, Alta, Sept. 28, 40; m. 67. NUCLEAR PHYSICS, ASTROPHYSICS. B.Sc, Alberta, 61, Nat. Res. Coun. Can. bursary, 61-62, M.Sc, 62, Imp. Oil fel, 62-65; Ph.D.(nuclear physics), Calif. Inst. Tech, 67. Res. fel. PHYSICS, Calif. Inst. Tech, 67; res. assoc, Mich. State Univ, 67-69; ASST. PROF, CTR. NUCLEAR STUDIES, UNIV. TEX, AUSTIN, 69- Am. Phys. Soc. Experimental studies of stellar neutron sources; studies of light element production by proton spallation of carbon and other elements present in stellar atmospheres. Address: Dept. of Physics, Center for Nuclear Studies, University of Texas at Austin, Austin, TX 78712.

DAVIDS, NORMAN, b. New York, N.Y, Mar. 17, 18; m. 45; c. 3. MATHEMATICS. B.S, City Col, 37; M.S, N.Y. Univ, 38, Blumenthal fel, 38-40, Ph.D.(math), 40. Asst. math, N.Y. Univ, 40; tech. supvr, Math. Talbes Proj, New York, 40-41; instr. physics, Townsend Harris Sch, City Col, 41; physicist, Corps Engrs, U.S. War Dept, 42-43; mathematician, dept. terrestrial magnetism, Carnegie Institution, 43-45; instr. math, Hopkins, 45-47; assoc. prof. eng. res, ord. res. lab, PA. STATE UNIV, 47-50, PROF. ENG. MECHS, 53- Mem, Inst. Adv. Study, 42. Summer vis. instr, California, 46. Consult, Haller, Raymond & Brown Co; Nat. Insts. Health. Naval Ord. Develop. award. With Off. Sci. Res. & Develop; U.S.N; Bur. Standards. Am. Math. Soc; Am. Phys. Soc; Am. Soc. Eng. Educ; Am. Soc. Mech. Eng; Am. Acad. Mech. Elasticity; terrestrial magnetism; potential theory; general applied mathematics; wave theory and acoustics; ionosphere research; stress waves in solids; computer analysis methods in dynamics; biomechanics. Address: Pennsylvania State University, 230 Hammond Bldg, University Park, PA 16802.

DAVIDSOHN, I(SRAEL), b. Tarnopol, Austria, Apr. 20, 95; nat; m. 23; c. 2. PATHOLOGY. M.D, Vienna, 21; Berlin, 22-23; hon. D.Sc, Chicago Med. Sch, 64. Intern, Mt. Sinai Hosp, Phila, 23-24, chief res. physician, 24-25, res. pathologist, 25-26, pathologist & dir. labs, 26-30; from instr. to asst. prof. PATH, Rush Med. Col, 34-41; asst. prof. to assoc. prof, col. med, Illinois, 41-47; PROF, CHICAGO MED. COL, 47-, CHIEF, DIV. EXP. PATH, 70-, chmn. dept. path, 47-68. Fel, Res. Inst. Cutaneous Med, Phila, 26-30; dir. dept. path, Mt. Sinai Hosp, Chicago, 30-65, dept. exp. path, 65- Dipl, Am. Bd. Path. & Clin. Path. Parker award, Chicago Med. Sch, 56; City of Hope award, Chicago, 61. AAAS; fel. Am. Med. Asn; fel. Am. Col. Path; Am. Soc. Clin. Path.(pres, 51, ed. Jour, 41-45, assoc. ed, 46, gold medal, 43, Burdick award, 54); Am. Asn. Path. & Bact; Am. Soc. Exp. Path; Soc. Exp. Biol. & Med; Am. Asn. Immunol; fel. Am. Col. Physicians; Int. Soc. Hematol; Int. Acad. Path. Hematology; immunohematology and immunopathology. Address: Dept. of Experimental Pathology, Mt. Sinai Hospital Medical Center, 2755 W. 15th St, Chicago, IL 60608.

DAVIDSON, A(LEXANDER) G(RANT), b. Moncton, N.B, Sept. 23, 27; m. 53; c. 2. FOREST PATHOLOGY. B.Sc, New Brunswick, 48; M.A, Toronto, 51, Ph.D.(forest path), 55. Res. off, Forest Biol. Lab, New Brunswick, 48-58; head forest path. invests, Atlantic Provs. Res. Br, Can. Dept. Agr, 58-62; assoc. coord, FOREST INSECT & DISEASE SURV, CAN. FORESTRY SERV, 62-65, ASST. PROG. COORD, 65- Can. Phytopath. Soc; Can. Inst. Forestry. Forest disease survey. Address: Canadian Forestry Service, Canadian Dept. of Environment, Ottawa, Ont. K1A 0H3, Can.

DAVIDSON, ARNOLD B, b. Phila, Pa, June 5, 30; m. 52; c. 2. PSYCHOLOGY, BIOLOGY. B.A, Brooklyn Col, 51, M.A, 53; Ed.D.(psychol), Temple Univ, 64. High sch. teacher, N.Y.C. Bd. Educ, 51-53; jr. pharmacologist, SMITH KLINE & FRENCH LABS, 55-58, pharmacologist, 58-62, sr. pharmacologist, 63-68, SR. INVESTR, 68- Instr. psychol, Peirce Jr. Col, Pa, 66-69. Chem.C, U.S.A, 53-55. AAAS; Am. Psychol. Asn; Behav. Pharmacol. Soc. Interaction of drugs and behavior; psychophysiology. Address: 1754 Hillside Dr, Cherry Hill, NJ 08034.

DAVIDSON, ARTHUR CAMPBELL, b. Calgary, Alta, July 21, 14; m. APPLIED MECHANICS, STRUCTURAL ENGINEERING. B.S, Manitoba, 35, B.Sc, 36; M.A.Sc, Toronto, 49. Field engr, Dom. Bridge Co, Ltd, 37-38; demonstr. eng. drawing, Toronto, 38-40; inspector, Can. Inspection & Test. Co, 40-41; lectr. CIVIL ENG, UNIV. TORONTO, 46-53, asst. prof, 53-62, ASSOC. PROF, 62- Subway struct. designer, Toronto Transportation Cmn, 50-51, analyst, 60-62. Consult, Defense Construct. Ltd, 52-53; Cent. Mortgage & Housing Corp, 54-56; ed. booklets, Dept. Health, Ont, 63. R.C.E, 41-45. Eng. Inst. Can. Design of structures; application of analog computation to structural frames; electrical network analogues for structural frames; air-entraining mixes; concrete technology; nonmetallic mine construction and detection. Address: 106 Bideford St, Downsview, Ont, Can.

DAVIDSON, BETTY, b. Brooklyn, N.Y, Mar. 24, 33; m. 60; c. 2. BIOCHEMISTRY. B.S, Brooklyn Col, 53; M.S, Univ. Chicago, 61, U.S. Pub. Health Serv. fel, 60-64, Ph.D.(biochem), 64. Technician clin. biochem, Mt. Sinai Hosp, N.Y.C, 54-56; State Univ. N.Y. Downstate Med. Ctr, 56-58; med. sch, Northwest. Univ, 58-59; fel. biochem, Brandeis Univ, 65-70; RES. FEL, THYROID RES. UNIT, MASS. GEN. HOSP, 70- Am. Chem. Soc. Mechanism of enzyme action; protein structure and conformation. Address: 56 Beals St, Brookline, MA 02146.

DAVIDSON, BRUCE M, b. Ironwood, Mich, Mar. 16, 24; m. 49; c. 3. TRANSPORTATION ENGINEERING. B.S.E, Michigan, 49; M.S, Wisconsin, 51, Ph.D.(eng), 56. Instr. civil eng, Wisconsin, 49-51, 53-55; traffic engr, Wis, 55-56; asst. prof. civil eng, Univ. Wis, Madison, 56-60, assoc. prof, 60-64, prof, 64-66, asst. dean, 57-62, assoc. dean, 62-66; prof. & chmn. dept, Wash. State Univ, 66-71; ACAD. DEAN, U.S. NAVAL ACAD, 71- Consult, India prog, Agency Int. Develop, U.S. Dept. State, 69. U.S.A.F, 43-47, 51-53, Res, 53-, Col. Am. Soc. Civil Eng; Am. Soc. Eng. Educ; Am. Rwy. Eng. Asn. Optimization of traffic signal systems; driver response to geometric design of intersections; academic performance of engineering students. Address: U.S. Naval Academy, Annapolis, MD 21402.

DAVIDSON, CHARLES H(ENRY), b. Wash, D.C, Dec. 10, 20; m. 52; c. 2. COMPUTER SCIENCE. A.B, Am. Univ, 41; Ph.M, Univ. Wis, 43, Ph.D. (physics), 52. Instr. physics, Mary Wash. Col, 46-47; engr, Continental Elec. Co, 47-49; proj. assoc. elec. eng, UNIV. WIS, MADISON, 52-54, asst. prof, 54-58, assoc. prof, 58-66, PROF. ELEC. ENG. & COMPUT. SCI, 66-DIR, ENG. COMPUT. LAB, 61- Consult, AC Spark Plug Div, Gen. Motors Corp, 59-63; vis. prof, dept. comput. sci, Univ. Edinburgh, 68-69. Civilian Pub. Serv, 44-46. Asn. Comput. Mach; Am. Nat. Standards Inst; Inst. Elec. & Electronics Eng; Int. Asn. Cybernet. Computer education; artificial intelligence. Address: Dept. of Electrical Engineering, University of Wisconsin, Madison, WI 53706.

DAVIDSON, CHARLES MARTIN, b. Glasgow, Scotland, Oct. 1, 35; m. 62; c. 2. INORGANIC CHEMISTRY, CHEMICAL ENGINEERING. B.Sc, Glasgow, 57; Ph.D.(inorg. chem), St. Andrews, 64. Develop. engr, res. labs, Du Pont of Can, Ltd, 58-59, develop. chemist, Maitland Works Tech. Dept, Textile Fibers Div, 59-61; Nat. Res. Coun. Can. fel, 64-65; res. chemist, CENT. RES. LAB, CAN. INDUSTS. LTD, McMASTERVILLE, 65-70, RES. LEADER, 70- Chem. Inst. Can; Brit. Chem. Soc. Coordination chemistry; inorganic chemistry relevant to traditional heavy chemical industry; chemical economics. Address: 311 Lorncliff Crescent, Otterburn Heights, Que, Can.

DAVIDSON, CHARLES N(ELSON), b. Kankakee, Ill, Oct. 19, 37; m. 59; c. 3. NUCLEAR PHYSICS. B.S, The Citadel, 59; Nat. Sci. Found. fel, Fla. State, 61-62, Ph.D.(nuclear chem), 62. Chem. staff officer, radiol. div, U.S. ARMY COMBAT DEVELOP. COMMAND, 62-64, physicist, 64-66, effects div, INST. NUCLEAR STUDIES, 66-68, SCI. ADV, HQ, 68- Chem.C, 62-64, Res, 64-, Capt. Am. Chem. Soc; Am. Nuclear Soc. Nuclear weapons effects; nuclear defense; radiac instruments; fallout radiation; low energy nuclear physics. Address: 10116 Monaco Dr, El Paso, TX 79925.

DAVIDSON, CHARLES S(PRECHER), b. Berkeley, Calif, Dec. 7, 10. CLINICAL MEDICINE. A.B, California, 34; M.D. & C.M, McGill, 39; hon. M.A, Harvard, 53. Intern, San Francisco Hosp, 39-40, house officer med, 40-41; res. fel, HARVARD MED. SCH, 41-42, asst. MED, 42-45, instr, 45-47, Peabody fel, 47-48, assoc, 47-49, asst. prof, 49-51, asst. clin. prof, 51-52, assoc. prof, 53-69, PROF, 69- Asst. res. physician, Thorndike Mem. Lab, Boston City Hosp, 41-42, res. physician, 42-43, asst. physician, 43-48, assoc. physician, 48-63, assoc. dir, 63-, asst, hosp, 41-43, jr. vis. physician, 44-45, assoc. vis. physician, 56-63, vis. physician, 64-, res. dir. 2nd & 4th med. servs, 43-47, asst. dir, 47-48, assoc. dir, 48- Consult, Vet. Admin. Hosp, Boston, 52-; Lemuel Shattuck Hosp, 55-; nutrit. sect, Off. Int. Res, Nat. Insts. Health, Cambridge City Hosp; trustee, Age Ctr. New Eng, 65. With Off. Sci. Res. & Develop; U.S.A, 44. Am. Med. Asn; Am. Soc. Clin. Investr; Am. Fedn. Clin. Res; Am. Col. Physicians; Asn. Am. Physicians. Nutrition, metabolism and liver diseases in man. Address: 100 Memorial Dr, Cambridge, MA 02118.

DAVIDSON, DAVID E(DWARD), JR, b. Phila. Pa, Mar. 7, 35; m. 58; c. 2. VETERINARY MEDICINE, RADIATION BIOLOGY. V.M.D, Univ. Pa, 59; M.S, Univ. Rochester, 62; Ph.D, Georgetown Univ, 70. VET. CORPS, U.S. ARMY, 59-, vet. lab. off, dept. radiobiol, U.S. Army Med. Res. Lab, Ft. Knox, 59-61, VET. LAB. OFF, DIV. MED. CHEM, WALTER REED ARMY INST. RES, 62- Vet.C, U.S.A, Lt.Col, 59- Am. Vet. Med. Asn. Biological testing of pharmaceuticals in laboratory animals; pharmacology and toxicology of antiradiation, antimalarial and antischistosomal drugs. Address: 3933 Lantern Dr, Silver Spring, MD 20902.

DAVIDSON, DAVID F(RANCIS), b. N.Y.C, Aug. 9, 23; m. 53; c. 3. ECONOMIC GEOLOGY. B.A, Lehigh, 48. Geologist, U.S. Geol. Surv, 48-54, staff geologist, Spencer Chem. Co, Mo, 54-56; U.S. GEOL. SURV, 56-62, chief, off. exp. geol, br. geochem. census, 62-, geologist, br. for. geol, 68-69, dep. asst. chief geologist resources, 69-71, CHIEF BR. MID. EAST. & ASIAN GEOL, 71- U.S.A, 43-46. Geol. Soc. Am; Soc. Econ. Geol. Geology and geochemistry of selenium and tellurium; geology of ore deposits of sedimentary origin; automatic data processing of geologic data. Address: U.S. Geological Survey, Washington, DC 20242.

DAVIDSON, DAVID LYMAN, b. Providence, R.I, June 7, 10; m. 49. BIOLOGICAL CHEMISTRY. B.S, Brown, 33, M.S, 34, Ph.D.(biochem), 37. Sub-asst. biochem. & physiol, Brown, 34-35, asst. embryol, 35-37; instr. chem, Northeastern, 37-38; prof. biochem, Middlesex, 38-45, asst. to dean med. sch, 40-45; RES. CHEMIST, Esselen Res. Corp, Boston, 45-53; TECH. OPERS, INC, 53- Am. Chem. Soc. Sugar chemistry and metabolism; heat insulation; diabetic therapy and management; organic, food and photographic chemistry; photo-resist and thin film techniques. Address: Applied Sciences Dept, Technical Operations, Inc, South Ave, Burlington, MA 01803.

DAVIDSON, DAVID M, b. Lenoir, N.C, Oct. 6, 25; m. 51; c. 6. PHYSICAL & COLLOID CHEMISTRY. A.B, Emory, 46, M.S, 48; Ph.D.(chem), Ohio State, 51. Develop. chemist, nonwoven fabrics, Visking Corp, 51-56; supvr. coating develop, paperboard coatings, Gardner Bd. & Carton Co, 56, lab. develop, paperboard & cartons, 56-58; match develop, Diamond Nat. Corp, 59-60; supvr. explor. res, Standard Register Co, 60-61, asst. res. mgr, 61-66, res. mgr, 66-70; V.PRES. & ASST. TO PRES, MAZER CORP, 70- Sig.C, U.S.A, 44-46. Am. Soc. Test. & Mat; Am. Chem. Soc; Soc. Rheol; Tech. Asn. Pulp & Paper Indust. Fibers, adhesives, mix formulation and application of nonwoven fabrics; pigments, adhesives and chemistry of matches; composition and method of coating carbon papers, construction and properties of business forms; gas chromatography of waxes and oils. Address: 2518 Archwood Dr, Dayton, OH 45406.

DAVIDSON, DONALD H(OWARD), b. Suffern, N.Y, Nov. 16, 37; m. 60; c. 1. CHEMICAL ENGINEERING, APPLIED MATHEMATICS. B.Ch.E, Rensselaer Polytech, 59; M.Ch.E, N.Y. Univ, 62, Allied Chem. fel, 66, Ph.D.(chem. eng), 67. CHEM. ENGR, U.S. Rubber Co, N.J, 60-63; St. Regis Paper Co, N.Y, 63-66; Shell Develop. Co, 67-70; KENNECOTT COPPER CORP, 70- U.S.A, Capt. Am. Inst. Chem. Eng; Am. Chem. Soc. Fluid mechanics; heat transfer; applied mechanics. Address: Kennecott Copper Corp, 128 Spring St, Lexington, MA 02730.

DAVIDSON, DONALD M(INER), JR, b. Minneapolis, Minn, Oct. 21, 39; m. 66. GEOLOGY, GEOCHEMISTRY. B.A, Carleton Col, 61; M.A, Columbia Univ, 63, Ph.D.(geol), 65. Asst. prof. GEOL, UNIV. MINN, DULUTH, 65-69, ASSOC. PROF, 69- AAAS; Am. Mineral Soc; Soc. Econ. Geol; Geol. Soc. Am; Am. Inst. Mining, Metall. & Petrol. Eng. Geology of uranium deposits; computer analysis in geologic sciences. Address: Dept. of Geology, University of Minnesota, Duluth, MN 55812.

DAVIDSON, D(ONALD) W(EST), b. Moncton, N.B, June 25, 25; m. 54; c. 1. PHYSICAL CHEMISTRY. B.Sc, New Brunswick, 46, M.Sc, 47; Beaverbrook scholar. & dipl, Imp. Col, London, 48; Ph.D.(phys. chem), Brown, 51. Fel, NAT. RES. COUN. CAN, 51-53, asst. res. officer, 53-57, assoc. res. off, 57-61, SR. RES. OFF, 61- Am. Chem. Soc; Am. Phys. Soc; Chem. Inst. Can. Dielectric relaxation of liquids and solids; molecular structure and interactions in condensed phases; nuclear magnetic resonance. Address: Division of Chemistry, National Research Council, Ottawa, Ont. K1A 0R9, Can.

DAVIDSON, DONALD W(ILLIAM), b. Prairie Grove, Ark, June 8, 36; m. 69. ECOLOGY. B.A, Minnesota, 59; Ph.D.(plant ecol), Rutgers, 63. Asst. bot, Minnesota, 56-59; Rutgers, 59-63; asst. prof. BIOL, Alabama, 63-65; Wis. state Univ, 65-67, ASSOC. PROF, 67- Summers, asst, Quetics-Superior Wilderness Res. Center, 57, 58. AAAS; Ecol. Soc. Am. Forest ecology; botany; environment. Address: Dept. of Biology, Wisconsin State University, Superior, WI 54880.

DAVIDSON, DOUGLAS, b. North Shields, Eng, Mar. 22, 31. CYTOLOGY. B.Sc, Durham, 52; D.Phil.(cytol), Oxford, 55. Res. fel. cytol, Oxford, 55-58; vis. biologist, biol. div, Oak Ridge Nat. Lab, 58-61; lectr. bot, St. Andrews, 61-64; asst. prof. BIOL, Western Reserve, 64-66, assoc. prof, 66-69; PROF, McMASTER UNIV, 69- U.S. Atomic Energy Comn. grant, 66-68; Nat. Res. Coun. Can. grant, 69- Genetics Soc. Am; Bot. Soc. Am; Brit. Asn. Radiation Res. Root growth; chromosome aberrations; cell lineage studies in meristems; sensitivity to colchicine; chromosome coiling and its control. Address: Dept. of Biology, McMaster University, Hamilton, Ont, Can.

DAVIDSON, EDWARD S(TEINBERG), b. Boston, Mass, Dec. 27, 39; m. 64; c. 2. COMPUTER SCIENCE. B.A, Harvard Col, 61; M.S, Univ. Mich, Ann Arbor, 62; Ph.D.(elec. eng), Univ. Ill, Urbana, 68. Engr, Honeywell, Inc, 62-65; res. assoc. ELEC. ENG, Univ. Ill, summer 68; ASST. PROF, STANFORD UNIV, 68- Nat. Sci. Found. grant, NAND Network Design, 69-71. AAAS; Asn. Comput. Mach; Inst. Elec. & Electronics Eng. Pipeline computer architecture; computer system performance; logic design; design automation; technology assessment. Address: 1067 Cathcart Way, Stanford, CA 94305.

DAVIDSON, ERIC HARRIS, b. N.Y.C, Apr. 13, 37; m. 65. MOLECULAR & DEVELOPMENTAL BIOLOGY. B.A, Pennsylvania, 58; fel. & Ph.D.(cell biol), Rockefeller Inst, 63. Res. assoc. cell biol, Rockefeller Univ, 63-65, asst. prof. cell & develop. biol, 65-70; ASSOC. PROF. DEVELOP. BIOL, CALIF. INST. TECHNOL, 71- Genomic control over cell differention; genomic activity underlying early embryological development and oogenesis. Address: Dept. of Developmental Biology, California Institute of Technology, Pasadena, CA 91109.

DAVIDSON, ERNEST, b. Stuttgart, Ger, June 12, 21; U.S. citizen; m. 44; c. 1. MECHANICAL ENGINEERING. Southern California, 46-48; California, Los Angeles, 61-63. Design engr, Mitchell Camera Corp, 47-51; APPL. RES. LABS, INC, BAUSCH & LOMB, INC, 51-56, design eng. mgr, 56-61, prod. mgr, 61-63, eng. div. mgr, 63, V.PRES. ENG, 63- Lectr, Los Angeles City Col, 59-, mem. adv. comt, 64- U.S.A, 42-46, Sgt. Instrument Soc. Am; Optical Soc. Am; Am. Soc. Test. & Mat. Instrumentation for spectrochemical analysis. Address: Applied Research Labs, Inc, P.O. Box 129, Sunland, CA 91040.

DAVIDSON, ERNEST R(OY), b. West Terre Haute, Ind, Oct. 12, 36; m. 56; c. 4. PHYSICAL CHEMISTRY. B.S, Rose Polytech, 58; Nat. Sci. Found. fels, Indiana, 58-59, 60-61, Ph.D.(quantum chem), 61. Nat. Sci. Found. res. fel, theoret. chem. inst, Wisconsin, 61-62; asst. prof. CHEM, UNIV. WASH, 62-65, assoc. prof, 65-68, PROF, 68- Nat. Sci. Found. res. grant small molecules, 62-72. Laureate, Int. Acad. Molecular Quantum Sci, 71. Am. Chem. Soc; Am. Inst. Chem; Am. Phys. Soc. Theoretical physical chemistry; quantum mechanics of small molecules. Address: Dept. of Chemistry, University of Washington, Seattle, WA 98105.

DAVIDSON, EUGENE A(BRAHAM), b. N.Y.C, May 27, 30; m. 50; c. 4. BIOCHEMISTRY. B.S, California, Los Angeles, 50; Ph.D.(biochem), Columbia, 55. Res. assoc, Michigan, 55-56, instr. biochem, 57-58; asst. prof, Duke, 58-62, assoc. prof, 62-66, prof, 66-67; PROF. BIOL. CHEM. & CHMN. DEPT, MILTON S. HERSHEY MED. CTR, PA. STATE UNIV, 68- Consult, Nat. Cancer Inst, 60-62; Nat. Insts. Health, 63- Am. Chem. Soc; Am. Soc. Biol. Chem; Am. Rheumatism Asn; Brit. Biochem. Soc. Structural chemistry of connective tissue; metabolism of connective tissue mucopolysaccharides; hexosamine metabolism and chemistry. Address: Dept. of Biological Chemistry, Milton S. Hershey Medical Center, Pennsylvania State University, Hershey, PA 17033.

DAVIDSON, FLOYD FRANCIS, b. Ferris, Tex, Aug. 23, 06; m. 43. PHYSIOLOGY, PHYCOLOGY. B.A, Baylor, 32; M.A, 33; Ph.D.(biol), Texas, 41. Prin, high sch, 33-39; instr. BIOL, Texas, 39-41; PROF, Stephen F. Austin State Col, 41-42; BAYLOR UNIV, 46-, CHMN. DEPT, 67- Dahlgren Mem. fel, Mt. Desert Island Biol. Lab, 49; Nat. Insts. Health grant, 54- Med.-Admin.C, U.S.A.F, Capt. Parasitology; toxic properties of blue-green algae; parasites of fish; stinging mechanism of Megalopyge opercularis; tissue culture. Address: Dept. of Biology, Baylor University, Waco, TX 76703.

DAVIDSON, FREDERIC M, b. Glens Falls, N.Y, Feb. 11, 41; m. 68; c. 1. PHYSICS, QUANTUM OPTICS. B.Eng.Phys, Cornell Univ, 64; Ph.D.(physics), Univ. Rochester, 69. ASST. PROF. ELEC. ENG, Univ. Houston, 68-70; JOHNS HOPKINS UNIV, 70- AAAS; Am. Phys. Soc; Optical Soc. Am; Am. Soc. Eng. Educ. Statistical optics, particularly statistical properties of optical fields; coherence theory; quantum electronics. Address: Dept. of Electrical Engineering, Johns Hopkins University, Baltimore, MD 21218.

DAVIDSON, GILBERT, b. Omaha, Neb, June 10, 34; m. 58; c. 3. PHYSICS. S.B, Mass. Inst. Tech, 55, Ph.D.(physics), 59. Res. assoc. physics, Polytech. Sch, Paris, 59-60; sr. phys. scientist, AM. SCI. & ENG, INC, 60-64, sr. proj. dir. geophys, 64-67, V.PRES, educ. div, 67-69, geophys. div, 69-70, INSTRUMENT SYSTS. DIV, 70- Fulbright scholar, France, 59-60. AAAS; Am. Geophys. Union; Instrument Soc. Am; Am. Soc. Nondestructive Test; Am. Phys. Soc. High-energy physics; atomic physics; geophysics. Address: 23 Exmoor Rd, Newton Centre, MA 02159.

DAVIDSON, GRANT E(DWARD), b. Toronto, Ont, Oct. 13, 19; m. 46; c. 3. ELECTRICAL ENGINEERING. B.A.Sc, Toronto, 43. Asst. testing engr, ILLUM. LAB, RES. DIV, HYDRO ELEC. POWER COMN. ONT, 46-49, asst. res. engr, 49-52, res. engr, 52-57, illum. engr, 57-60, SR. ILLUM. ENGR, 60- Spec. lectr, dept. univ. exten, Toronto. Consult, Ont. Dept. Transport. Mem. Can. Nat. Comt, Int. Illum. Comn, 57-, Int. Electrotech. Comn, 59- Can. Army, 39-46, R.C.E.M.E, 46-, Res. Off. Fel. Am. Illum. Eng. Soc; Inter-Soc. Color Coun; fel. Illum. Eng. Soc. Gt. Brit. Radiation optics and illumination, especially photometry of light sources and luminaires. Address: 16 Glen Stewart Ave, Toronto, Ont, Can.

DAVIDSON, HAROLD, b. N.J, July 20, 19; m. 50; c. 3. LANDSCAPE HORTICULTURE. B.S, Univ. Calif, 49; M.S, Mich. State Univ, 53; Ph.D.(hort), 57. Coordinator nursery & landscape mgt, MICH. STATE UNIV, 50-57, asst. prof. ORNAMENTAL HORT. RES, 57-61, assoc. prof, 61-70, PROF, 70- Sig.C, 40-46, Res, 46-, Col. Am. Soc. Hort. Sci; Asn. Bot. Gardens & Arboretums; Am. Hort. Soc. Physiology of woody plants; photo-period; nutrition; propagation; weed control. Address: Dept. of Horticulture, Michigan State University, East Lansing, MI 48823.

DAVIDSON, H(AROLD), b. Brooklyn, N.Y, May 2, 21. CHEMICAL ENGINEERING. B.S, Columbia, 43, Ch.E, 48. Chem. engr, Kolker Chem. Works, 46-47; asst, Columbia, 48-49; chem. engr, Metal & Thermit Corp, 49-56; eng. statistician, Merck & Co, Inc, 57-60; CONTROL SYSTS. REP, IBM CORP, 60- U.S.A.A.F, 43-46, Capt. Am. Chem. Soc; Am. Inst. Chem. Eng; Am. Soc. Qual. Control; Inst. Mgt. Sci; Am. Statist. Asn; Inst. Math. Statist. Chemical engineering and applied mathematics; computer applications and computer control systems. Address: 330 W. 28th St, Apt. 20F, New York, NY 10001.

DAVIDSON, HAROLD F, b. New York, N.Y, Aug. 22, 19; m. 49; c. 4. ORGANIC CHEMISTRY. B.S, City Col. New York, 40; M.E.A, George Washington Univ, 61; M.S, Polytech. Inst. Brooklyn, 71. Clerk, bur. census, Dept. of Commerce, 40-41; sci. aide, U.S. Naval Gun Factory, 41-42; MAT. ENGR, res. & develop. div, bur. of ships, U.S. Dept. Navy, 42-44, mat. lab, N.Y. Naval Shipyard, 47-51, res. & develop. div, bur. naval weapons, 52-63; ARMY RES. OFF, D.C, 63- U.S.N, 44-45. Research planning; materials research and development in nonmetallics. Address: 9318 Convento Terr, Fairfax, VA 22030.

DAVIDSON, HAROLD MICHAEL, b. Boston, Mass, June 3, 24. BIOCHEMISTRY. A.B, Harvard, 44; M.A, Oregon, 49, Ph.D.(chem), 51. Chemist, Mass. Dept. Pub. Health, 46-47; fel. physiol. chem, Pennsylvania, 50-51; chemist cancer res, Overly Biochem. Res. Found, 51-52; res. assoc, sch. med, Tufts, 52-59; SCIENTIST-ADMINSTR. RES. GRANTS, NAT. INSTS. HEALTH, 61- Am. Cancer Soc. fel, 53-55; exec. secy, arthritis & metab. diseases prog-proj. cmt, div. res. grants, Nat. Insts. Health, 61- U.S.N.R, 44-46. AAAS; Am. Chem. Soc. Carbohydrate metabolism; enzymology; cancer; research grants review. Address: 6604 Hillandale Rd, Chevy Chase, MD 20015.

DAVIDSON, HAROLD O(SBORN), JR, b. Iron Mountain, Mich, Dec. 10, 18; m. 44; c. 2. ENGINEERING. B.M.E, Ga. Inst. Tech, 47, M.S, 48; Ph.D.(indust. eng), Ohio State, 51. Instr. indust. eng, Ga. Inst. Tech, 47-48; Ohio State, 48-51, asst. prof, 51-53; assoc. prof, Hopkins, 54-55; sr. scientist, U.S. Army Europe, Germany, 56-58; prof. indust. eng, Ga. Inst. Tech, 58-59; v.pres, Opers. Res, Inc, 59-64; pres, Davidson, Talbird & McLynn, Inc, 64-68; DIR, ARTHUR YOUNG & CO, 68- Mem. mkt. res. adv. comt, U.S. Dept. Agr, 64-70; sci. adv. group, U.S. Army Combat Develop. Command, 64-69. Consult, air traffic control, U.S.A.F, 51-53. Am. Inst. Indust. Eng.(ed, Monographs). Commercial operations research and management consulting. Address: 277 Park Ave, New York, NY 10017.

DAVIDSON, IVAN W(ILLIAM) F(REDERICK), b. Winnipeg, Man, July 31, 26; m. 50; c. 4. PHYSIOLOGY, PHARMACOLOGY. B.Sc, Manitoba, 54; fel, Toronto, 54-59, M.A, 56, Ph.D.(physiol), 59. Res. assoc, Univ. Toronto, 58-59; Union Carbide Chem. Co, 59-61; asst. prof. physiol. & pharmacol, BOWMAN GRAY SCH. MED, WAKE FOREST UNIV, 61-63, asst. prof. PHARMACOL, 63-66, assoc. prof, 66-70, PROF, 70-, ASSOC. PHYSIOL, 63- Mem. grad. faculty, Wake Forest Col, 62. Lederle Med. Faculty award, 64-67. AAAS; Am. Physiol. Soc; N.Y. Acad. Sci; Soc. Exp. Biol. & Med; Am. Inst. Biol. Sci. Endocrines; diabetes; mechanisms of hormone action, and control metabolism; drug metabolism. Address: Dept. of Pharmacology, Bowman Gray School of Medicine, Wake Forest University, Winston Salem, NC 27103.

DAVIDSON, JACK D(OUGAN), b. Newark, N.J, Jan. 31, 18; m. 46; c. 4. NUCLEAR MEDICINE. A.B, Princeton, 40; M.D, Columbia, 43. Intern med, Bellevue Hosp, 44, res, 47; res. fel. arteriosclerosis, Goldwater Mem. Hosp, 48-50; instr. med, 50-51; res. fel. cancer, Delafield Hosp, 51-57; asst. prof. med, col. physicians & surg, Columbia, 53-57; head biochem. sect, lab. chem. pharmacol, Nat. Cancer Inst, 57-66; chief, dept. nuclear med, clin. ctr, Nat. Insts. Health, 66-70; ASSOC. PROF, DIV. NUCLEAR MED, MED. CTR, DUKE UNIV, 70- Med.C, A.U.S, 44-46, Capt; U.S.P.H.S, 57-70, Med. dir. AAAS; Am. Soc. Pharmacol; N.Y. Acad. Sci; Soc. Nuclear Med. Nuclear medicine; radioisotopes; radiopharmaceuticals; nuclear instrumentation. Address: 3506 Westover Rd, Durham, NC 27707.

DAVIDSON, JAMES BLAINE, b. Oklahoma City, Okla, Nov. 10, 23; m. 48; c. 3. PHYSICS, ELECTRONICS. B.S, U.S. Naval Acad, 46; B.S, U.S. Naval Postgrad. Sch, 52; M.S, California, Los Angeles, 53. U.S. Navy, 46-67, anal. officer, Key West Test & Eval. Detachment, Oper. Test & Eval. Force, 55-57, asst. supt, submarine construct, Mare Island Naval Shipyard, 57-59, elec. officer, serv. squadron, 7th Fleet, 59-62, proj. officer, Off. Naval Res, 62-66, dir. undersea prog, 66-67; PROF. OCEAN ENG, FLA. ATLANTIC UNIV, 67- U.S.N, 46-67, Comdr. Am. Acoustical Soc. Long range, underwater acoustic propagation and submarine detection; submarine target classification; underwater acoustic television. Address: Dept. of Ocean Engineering, Florida Atlantic University, Boca Raton, FL 33432.

DAVIDSON, JAMES MELVIN, b. The Dalles, Ore, Apr. 16, 34; m. 57; c. 3. SOIL PHYSICS & CHEMISTRY. B.S, Ore. State Col, 56; M.S, 58; Ph.D.(soil physics), California, Davis, 65. Res. asst. SOIL PHYSICS, Oregon State, 56-58; lab. technician, California, Davis, 58-65; asst. prof, OKLA. STATE UNIV, 65-68, ASSOC. PROF, 68- Soil Sci. Soc. Am; Am. Soc. Agron; Am. Geophys. Union. Fluid and solute movement through various porous materials; soil management practices for soil and water conservation and good plant root environment. Address: Dept. of Agronomy, Oklahoma State University, Stillwater, OK 74074.

DAVIDSON, JIMMY LEE, b. Harrison, Ark, June 8, 42; m. 63; c. 1. SOLID STATE PHYSICS, MATERIAL SCIENCE. B.A, Hendrix Col, 62; M.S, Columbia, 65, Ph.D.(metall), 67. NASA fel, grad. sch, Columbia, 64-67; assoc. prin. engr, microelectronic div, Radiation, Inc, 67-70; SECT. HEAD ADVAN. TECHNOL, HARRIS SEMICONDUCTORS, 70- Am. Phys. Soc; Am. Soc. Metals. Point-defect dislocation interactions; solid state diffusion kinetics; semiconductor epitaxy; application of materials science to integrated circuit development and production. Address: Harris Semiconductors, P.O. Box 883, Melbourne, FL 32901.

DAVIDSON, JOHN A(NGUS), b. Elizabeth, N.J, July 26, 33; m. 57; c. 2. BIOLOGY. B.A, Columbia Union Col, 55; M.S, Maryland, 57, Ph.D.(entom), 60. Instr. BIOL, Columbia Union Col, 60-62, asst. prof, 62-65, assoc. prof, 65-66; asst. prof. DEPT. ENTOM, UNIV. MD, 66-71, ASSOC. PROF, 71- Prof. lectr, American Univ, 63- Entom. Soc. Am; Soc. Syst. Zool. Biosystematics of scale insects; biology and control of insect pests of ornamental plants; insect taxonomy and morphology. Address: Dept. of Entomology, University of Maryland, College Park, MD 20740.

DAVIDSON, JOHN EDWIN, b. Asheville, N.C, Oct. 27, 37; m. 58; c. 2. ANALYTICAL & INORGANIC CHEMISTRY. B.S. in Chem, Univ. Tenn, 60, M.S, 62, Ph.D.(chem), 65. ASSOC. PROF. CHEM, EAST. KY. UNIV, 65- Am. Chem, Soc. Solvent extraction of metal chelates; coordination chemistry. Address: Dept. of Chemistry, Eastern Kentucky University, Richmond, KY 40475.

DAVIDSON, J(OHN) F(RASER), b. Aberdeen, Scotland, Jan. 14, 11; U.S. citizen; m. 43; c. 8. PLANT TAXONOMY. B.A, British Columbia, 37, M.A, 40; Ph.D.(bot), California, 47. Instr. BOT, Univ. Calif, 47-48; asst. prof, UNIV. NEBR, LINCOLN, 48-55, from assoc. prof. to PROF, 55-, CURATOR HERBARIUM, 48- R.C.A.F, 44-45. Bot. Soc. Am. Evaluation of characters used in determining plant interrelationships. Address: 640 S. 40th St, Lincoln, NE 68510.

DAVIDSON, JOHN K(EAY), III, b. Mar. 30, 22, Lithonia, Ga; m; c. 4. INTERNAL MEDICINE, PHYSIOLOGY. B.S, Emory, 43, M.D, 45; Am. Diabetes Asn. res. fel, Toronto, 61-65, Ph.D.(physiol), 65. Intern surg, Grady Hosp, Atlanta, Ga, 45-46, asst. res. internal med, 48-49; chief res, Emory Univ. Hosp, 49-50; res, New Eng. Center Hosp, Boston, Mass, 50-51; private practice, Columbus, Ga, 51-60; asst. prof, Banting & Best Dept. Med. Res, Toronto, 64-66, asst. prof. physiol. & res. assoc. internal med, 65-66, assoc. prof. physiol. & clin. teacher internal med, 66-68, MED, SCH. MED, EMORY UNIV, PROF. & DIR. DIABETES UNIT, 68- Consult, Vet. Admin. Hosp, Tuskegee, Ala, 51-60; clin. asst, Toronto Gen. Hosp, 65-; dir. diabetes sect, Grady Mem. Hosp, 68- Dipl, Nat. Bd. Med. Exam, 51 & Am. Bd. Internal Med, 54. Starr medal, Toronto, 63. Med.C, U.S.A, 46-47, Capt. Am. Med. Asn; Am. Diabetes Asn; fel. Am. Col. Physicians; Am. Soc. Internal Med; Am. Physiol. Soc; Endocrine Soc; N.Y. Acad. Sci; Can. Physiol. Soc. Address: 1075 Lullwater Rd, N.E, Atlanta, Ga. 30307.

DAVIDSON, JOHN K(EITH), b. Fargo, N.Dak, Feb. 9, 25; m. 53; c. 4. CHEMICAL ENGINEERING. B.Ch.E, Cornell, 48; M.S, Union Col, 53. Chem. engr, Knolls Atomic Power Lab, Gen. Elec. Co, 48-54, unit supvr, 54-57; mgr. eng. anal. sect, gas cooled reactor, atomic energy div, Allis-Chalmers Mfg. Co, 57-60, thorium proj, 60-63, fuel & core components dept, 63-65, planning, 62-64; European nuclear consult, 65; PRES, NUCLEAR ASSOCS. INT. CORP, ROCKVILLE, 66- Coffin award, Gen. Elec. Co, 53. U.S.N.R, 43-46. Am. Inst. Chem. Eng; Am. Nuclear Soc. Solvent extraction; nuclear reactor engineering. Address: 200 Hermleigh Rd, Silver Spring, MD 20902.

DAVIDSON, JOHN P(IRNIE). PHYSICS. B.A, California, 48; A.M, Washington (St. Louis), 51, fel. & Ph.D, 52. Res. assoc. physics, Columbia, 52-53; asst. prof, Brazilian Ctr. Phys. Res, Rio de Janeiro, 53-55; res. scientist, Joint Estab. Nuclear Energy Res, Norway, 55-57; asst. prof. THEORET. PHYSICS, Rensselaer Polytech, 57-61, assoc. prof, 61-65, PROF, 65-66; UNIV. KANS, 66- Vis. scientist-in-residence, Naval Radiol. Defense Lab, 64-65. U.S.A, 43-46. Am. Phys. Soc; Norweg. Phys. Soc; Brit. Interplanetary Soc. Theoretical physics. Address: Dept. of Physics, University of Kansas, Lawrence, KS 66044.

DAVIDSON, JOSEPH KILLWORTH, b. Columbus, Ohio, Jan. 17, 38; m. 68. MECHANICAL ENGINEERING. B.M.E. & M.Sc, Ohio State, 60, Ph.D.(mech. eng), 65. Instr. MECH. ENG, OHIO STATE UNIV, 62-65, ASST. PROF, 65- Am. Soc. Mech. Eng. Kinematics and dynamics of machines; mechanical vibrations; machine design. Address: Dept. of Mechanical Engineering, Ohio State University, 206 W. 18th Ave, Columbus, OH 43210.

DAVIDSON, JULIAN M, b. Dublin, Eire, Apr. 15, 31; m. 60; c. 3. PHYSIOLOGY. M.S, Hebrew Univ, Israel, 56; Jesse T. Carr fel, California, Davis, 56-57, Ph.D.(physiol), Berkeley, 59. U.S. Pub. Health Serv. res. fels. anat, sch. med. California, Los Angeles, 59-60, psychol, Berkeley, 62-63; res. fel. neurol, Hadassah Univ. Hosp, Israel, 61-62; asst. prof. PHYSIOL, STANFORD UNIV, 63-69, ASSOC. PROF, 69- Co-ed, J. Hormones & Behav, 69-; mem. endocrinol. study sect, Nat. Insts. Health, 70-; Guggenheim vis. res. fel, dept. human anat, Oxford, 70-71. AAAS; Am. Physiol. Soc; Endocrine Soc; Animal Behav. Soc. Neuroendocrinology, especially regulation of adrenocorticotropic and gonadotropic hormone secretion; reproductive endocrinology, especially neural and endocrine determinants of reproductive behavior. Address: Dept. of Physiology, Stanford University, Stanford, CA 94305.

DAVIDSON, KEITH V(ERNON), b. Holdrege, Nebr, May 7, 23; m. 49; c. 2. METALLURGY. Met.E, Colo. Sch. Mines, 49, M.Sc, 50. Chemist, Am. Smelting & Ref. Co, 50-53; STAFF MEM. vacuum melting, LOS ALAMOS SCI. LAB, 53-60, POWDER METALL, 60- U.S.A.A.F, 43-45; C.Eng.Res, 49-53, 2nd Lt. Am. Soc. Metals. Preparation of high purity metals, alloys and metal carbides by vacuum melting, arc melting and powder metallurgy; carbide-graphite composite fabrication and physical properties; development and preparation of nuclear fuel materials. Address: 268 Chamisa, Los Alamos, NM 87544.

DAVIDSON, KENNETH LaVERN, b. Lake Mills, Iowa, May 13, 40; m. 60; c. 3. METEOROLOGY. B.S, Univ. Minn, Minneapolis, 62; N.Y. Univ, 62-63; M.S, Univ. Mich, 66, Nat. Sci. Found. trainee, 67-68, Ph.D.(meteorol), 70. Asst. res. meteorologist, Great Lakes Res. Div, Univ. Mich, 65-67, dept. meterol. & oceanog, 67-70; ASST. PROF. METEOROL, NAVAL POSTGRAD. SCH, 70- U.S.A.F, 62-65, 1st Lt. Am. Meteorol. Soc; Am. Geophys. Union. Properties of turbulent flow in the region adjacent to the earth surface responsible for exchange of heat, moisture and momentum between the atmosphere and boundary (ocean or land). Address: Dept. of Meteorology, Naval Postgraduate School, Monterey, CA 93940.

DAVIDSON, LEON, b. N.Y.C, Oct. 18, 22; m. 43; c. 3. COMPUTER SCIENCE. A.B, Columbia, 42, B.S, 43, Bridgham fel, 46-49, M.S, 47, Ph.D.(chem. eng), 51. Jr. scientist, s.a.m. labs, Columbia, 43-44; chem. engr, Thermal Diffusion Plant, Oak Ridge, 44-45, sr. tech. engr, Gaseous Diffusion Plant, 45-46; assoc. engr. Brookhaven Nat. Lab, 47; mem. staff, Los Alamos Sci. Lab, 49-52; opers. analyst, U.S. Atomic Energy Comn, 52-53; sr. engr, Nuclear Develop. Assocs, Inc, 53-58, mgr. Datatron Opers, 58-59; assoc. head prog. sect, lab, Gen. Precision, Inc, 59-60; sr. programmer, Teleregister Corp, 60-61, mgr. prog. sect, 61-62; adv. appl. develop, adv. systs. develop. div, Int. Bus. Mach. Corp, 62-63, metroprocessing proj, 63-68, tech. dir, Metroprocessing Assoc, 68, PRES, METROPROCESSING CORP. AM, 68- Asn. Comput. Mach. Alphanumeric computer input via pushbutton telephone dial; formation of bubbles at orifices; isotope separations; nuclear weapons and reactor design; economics of fissionable material productions; digital computer application and programming. Address: Metroprocessing Corp. of America, 64 Prospect St, White Plains, NY 10606.

DAVIDSON, LYNN BLAIR, b. Grosse Point Farms, Mich, Sept. 22, 40; m. 65. PETROLEUM & SYSTEMS ENGINEERING. B.S, Stanford, 62, M.S, 64, Ph.D.(petrol. eng), 66. Sr. reservoir engr, Mobil Oil Libya, Ltd, 66; res. engr, Chevron Res. Co, Standard Oil Calif, 66-70; OPERS. RES. ANALYST, GETTY OIL CO, 70- Soc. Petrol. Eng. Development of secondary recovery methods; methods of analysis and evaluation of large solid-fluid systems; optimal control of large, poorly-defined systems; investment analysis methods. Address: P.O. Box 155, Buena Park, CA 90620.

DAVIDSON, MAYER B, b. Baltimore, Md, Apr. 11, 35; m. 61; c. 2. ENDOCRINOLOGY, METABOLISM. A.B, Swarthmore Col, 57; M.D, Harvard, 61. Res. fel, dept. endocrinol. & metab, King County Hosp, Univ. Washington, 64-65; U.S. Pub. Health Serv. fel, Nat. Inst. Arthritis & Metab. Diseases, 65-66; res. internist, U.S. Army Inst. Environ. Med, 66-69; ASST. PROF. MED, SCH. MED, UNIV. CALIF, LOS ANGELES, 69- Med.C, U.S.A, 66-69, Maj. Am. Diabetes Asn.(1st prize, res. contest, 66); Endocrine Soc; Sci. Res. Soc. Am; Am. Fedn. Clin. Res. Diabetes; insulin antagonism; effect of chronic hypoxia on carbohydrate metabolism. Address: Dept. of Endocrinology & Metabolism, University of California School of Medicine, Los Angeles, CA 90024.

DAVIDSON, MELVIN G, b. Winnipeg, Man, Apr. 7, 38; U.S. citizen; m. 62; c. 2. NUCLEAR PHYSICS. A.B, Whitman Col, 60; Ph.D.(theoret. physics), Rennselaer Polytech. Inst, 64. Res. fel. theoret. physics, Australian Nat. Univ, 64-67; asst. prof. PHYSICS, WEST. WASH. STATE COL, 67-69, ASSOC. PROF, 69- Am. Phys. Soc; Am. Inst. Physics. Theoretical nuclear physics; nuclear collective model; elementary particle physics. Address: Dept. of Physics, Western Washington State College, Bellingham, WA 98225.

DAVIDSON, NORMAN (RALPH), b. Chicago, Ill, Apr. 5, 16; m. 42; c. 4. BIOPHYSICAL CHEMISTRY. B.S, Chicago, 37, Ph.D.(chem), 41; B.Sc, Oxford, 39. Res. assoc, Nat. Defense Res. Comt. proj, Southern California, 41; div. war res, Columbia, 42; Chicago, 42; instr. chem, Ill. Inst. Technol, 42; res. assoc, plutonium proj, Chicago, 43-45; res. physicist, Radio Corp. of Am, 45-46; instr. CHEM, CALIF. INST. TECHNOL, 46-49, asst. prof, 49-52, assoc. prof, 52-57, PROF, 57-, EXEC. OFF. CHEM, 67- Nat. Acad. Sci; Am. Chem. Soc.(G.N. Lewis Award, 54, Peter Debye Award, phys. chem, 71); Am. Soc. Biol. Chem; Biophys. Soc. Physical and chemical studies of nucleic acids. Address: Dept. of Chemistry, California Institute of Technology, 1201 E. California Blvd, Pasadena, CA 91109.

DAVIDSON, RALPH H(OWARD), b. Vandalia, Ohio, Jan. 19, 08; m. 36; c. 2. ENTOMOLOGY. B.S, Ohio State, 30, M.S, 31, Ph.D.(entom), 35. Asst. ENTOM, OHIO STATE UNIV, 30-35, instr, 35-36, asst. prof, 36-43, res. assoc, 43-46, assoc. prof, 46-58, PROF, 58- Summers, vis. prof, Univ. Wis, 49-50; North. Ariz. Univ, 69. With Off. Sci. Res. & Develop, 43-45. AAAS; Entom. Soc. Am. Leafhopper taxonomy; insect control, morphology, rearing and collecting. Address: Dept. of Entomology, Ohio State University, Columbus, OH 43210.

DAVIDSON, RICHARD LAURENCE, b. Cleveland, Ohio, Feb. 22, 41; m. 67. GENETICS. B.A, Case West. Reserve Univ, 63, Nat. Insts. Health fel. & Ph.D, 67. Air Force Off. Sci. res-Nat. Res. Coun. fel, Case West. Reserve Univ, 67-68; Nat. Ctr. Sci. Res, France, 68-69; Ctr. Molecular Genetics, Paris, 67-70; ASST. PROF. MICROBIOL. & MOLECULAR GENETICS, HARVARD MED. SCH, 70-, RES. ASSOC. CLIN. GENETICS, CHILDREN'S HOSP. MED. CTR, BOSTON, 70- AAAS; Tissue Cult. Asn. Genetic control of differentiation in mammalian cells. Address: Harvard Medical School, Children's Hospital Medical Center, 300 Longwood Ave, Boston, MA 02115.

DAVIDSON, R(ICHARD) S(HOOTS), b. Marion, Ohio, Apr. 30, 18; m. 42; c. 3. PLANT PATHOLOGY. B.S, Ohio State, 40, M.S, 42; Off. Sci. Res. & Develop. fel, Minnesota, 44-45, Ph.D.(plant path), 47. Asst. prof, Univ. R.I, 45-47; from asst. to assoc. prof, Ohio Agr. Exp. Sta, 47-51; prof, Ala. Polytech, 51-52; BATTELLE MEM. INST, 52-54, chief biosci. div, 54-65, DIR. BIOENVIRON. PROGS, 65- AAAS; Bot. Soc. Am; Am. Phytopath. Soc; Ecol. Soc. Am; Am. Soc. Plant Physiol; Am. Hist. Sci. Soc. Research administration of ecology and bioenvironmental research. Address: Battelle Memorial Institute, 505 King Ave, Columbus, OH 43201.

DAVIDSON, ROBERT A, b. Keokuk, Iowa, May 19, 27; m. 57; c. 2. BOTANY. A.B, Augustana Col, 51; M.S, Iowa, 52, Ph.D.(bot), 57. Asst. prof. BOT, Iowa, 59-60; vis. lectr, Wisconsin, 60-61; assoc. prof, CATH. UNIV. AM, 61-67, PROF, 67- Nat. Sci. Found. res. grant, 61-64, 65-, U.S. Merchant Marine, 45-47; U.S.A.F, 57-59; 1st Lt. AAAS; Bot. Soc. Am; Soc. Study Evolution; Am. Soc. Plant Taxon; Int. Asn. Plant Taxon. Systematics and evolution; cytotaxonomy; numerical taxonomy. Address: Dept. of Biology, Catholic University of America, Washington, DC 20017.

DAVIDSON, ROBERT L(EE), III, b. Nevada, Mo, May 10, 23; m. 50; c. 2. CHEMICAL ENGINEERING. B.S, Missouri-Columbia, 44, M.S, 47; Texas, Austin, 50-51. Process engr, Arabian Am. Oil Co, N.Y, 52-54; asst. ed, Petrol. Processing, McGraw-Hill, Inc, 54-55, assoc. ed, 55-57, sr. ed, Petrol. Week, 57-59; exec. assoc. W. Alec Jordan Assocs, N.Y, 59-63; account exec, G.M. Basford Co, N.Y, 63-64; chief ed, Petro/Chem. Engr, Tex, 64-66; sr. ed, CHEM. ENG, McGRAW-HILL, INC, 66-68, MANAGING ED, 68- C.Eng, A.U.S, 42-46, 1st Lt. AAAS; Am. Inst. Chem. Eng; Am. Chem. Soc; N.Y. Acad. Sci; Am. Petrol. Inst. Chemistry and related sciences; petroleum processing; technical editing; technical and scientific writing. Address: McGraw-Hill, Inc, Chemical Engineering, 330 W. 42nd St, New York, NY 10036.

DAVIDSON, ROBERT W, b. Buffalo, N.Y, Nov. 19, 21; m. 48; c. 1. WOOD PHYSICS. B.S, Montana State, 48; M.S, State Univ. N.Y. Col. Forestry, Syracuse, 56, Ph.D.(wood physics), 60. Salesman wood prod, Yaw-Kinney Co, Inc, 48-53; res. asst. STATE UNIV. N.Y. COL. FORESTRY, SYRACUSE UNIV, 57-59, instr. WOOD PHYSICS, 59-60, asst. prof, 60-63, assoc. prof, 63-69, PROF, 69-, asst. leader, org. mat. sci. prog, 69-71. Nat. Sci. Found. res. grants, 63-64 & 69-71; assoc. prof, col. forestry, Univ. Philippines, 64-65; Soc. Wood Sci. & Technol. & Nat. Sci. Found. vis. scientist, 67. U.S.A, 43-46, Capt. Soc. Rheol; Forest Prod. Res. Soc; Soc. Wood Sci. & Technol. Plasticizing wood with ammonia. Address: State University of New York College of Forestry at Syracuse University, Syracuse, NY 13210.

DAVIDSON, RONALD CROSBY, b. Norwich, Ont, July 3, 41; m. 63; c. 1. PLASMA PHYSICS. B.Sc, McMaster, 63; Ford Found. & Imp. Oil fels. & Ph.D.(plasma physics), Princeton, 66. Asst. res. physicist, California, Berkeley, 66-68; asst. prof. PHYSICS, UNIV. MD, COLLEGE PARK, 68-71, ASSOC. PROF, 71- Co-investr, Nat. Sci. Found. grant, 69-71; Alfred P. Sloan fel, 70-71. Consult, Naval Res. Lab, 69- Am. Phys. Soc. Plasma turbulence; nonlinear plasma theory; nonlinear wave-wave interactions; nonequilibrium statistical mechanics. Address: Dept. of Physics & Astronomy, University of Maryland, College Park, MD 20742.

DAVIDSON, RONALD G, b. Hamilton, Can, Oct. 24, 33; m. 57; c. 2. PEDIATRICS, MEDICAL GENETICS. M.D, Western Ontario, 57. Intern, Vancouver Gen. Hosp, B.C, 57-58, asst. resident pediat, 58-59; path, Childrens Hosp. Med. Center, Boston, 59-60; pediat, Boston City Hosp, 60-61; fel, hosp, Hopkins, 61-63; biochem. genetics, King's Col, London, 63-64; asst. res. prof. PEDIAT, STATE UNIV. N.Y. BUFFALO, 64-67, assoc. prof, 67-70, PROF. & ASSOC. CHMN. DEPT, 70-, DIR. DIV. HUMAN GENETICS, CHILDREN'S HOSP, 64- Assoc. chief pediat, Roswell Park Mem. Inst, 64-67. Am. Soc. Human Genetics; Soc. Pediat. Res. Human biochemical genetics; inherited enzyme variants and gene action in the X chromosome. Address: Children's Hospital, 219 Bryant St, Buffalo, N.Y. 14222.

DAVIDSON, ROSS W(ALLACE), b. Columbus, Kans, Aug. 12, 02; m. 30; c. 1. BOTANY. B.S, Ottawa (Kans), 27, hon. D.Sc, 68; M.S, Iowa, 28; George Washington, 29. Jr. mycologist, U.S. DEPT. AGR, 28-31, asst. mycologist, off. forest path, 31-37, assoc. mycologist, 37-44, pathologist, 44-51, forest pathologist, forest insect & disease lab, forest exp. sta, 51-57, forest disease lab, plant indust. sta, 57-61, res. pathologist, COL. FORESTRY, COLO. STATE UNIV, 61-68, RES. SPECIALIST, 68- Bot. Soc. Am; Am. Phytopath. Soc. Identification of forest fungi from cultural characteristics; fungus damage to wood and wood products. Address: 1205 Lory St, Ft. Collins, CO 80521.

DAVIDSON, S(AMUEL) JAMES, b. Chicago, Ill, Mar. 9, 37; m. 60; c. 2. BIOCHEMISTRY, CELL PHYSIOLOGY. A.B, Univ. Chicago, 56, B.S, 59, Nat. Insts. Health fel, 61, Ph.D.(biochem), 64. Res. assoc. biochem, Univ. Chicago, 64; Nat. Insts. Health fel, Brandeis Univ, 65-67; res. assoc, DEPT. PHYSIOL, SCH. MED, TUFTS UNIV, 67-68, instr, 68-70, ASST. PROF, 70- Dynamics of the vacuolar system. Address: Dept. of Physiology, Tufts University, 136 Harrison Ave, Boston, MA 02155.

DAVIDSON, STEVE E(DWIN), b. Dumas, Texas, July 2, 30; m. 53; c. 3. AGRONOMY. B.S, West Texas State Col, 51; M.S, Iowa State Col, 52; Ph.D. (agron), Agr. & Mech. Col. Texas, 56. Asst, Iowa State Col, 51-52; Agr. & Mech. Col. Texas, 52-56; soil scientist, soil conserv. serv, plant indust. sta, U.S. Dept. Agr, Md, 56-58; asst. prof. BIOL, EVANGEL COL, 58-64, PROF, 64- U.S.A.F, 53, Res, 59- Am. Soc. Agron; Soil Sci. Soc. Am. Soil physics; plant physiology. Address: Dept. of Biology, Evangel College, Springfield, MO 65802.

DAVIDSON, THEODORE, b. Chicago, Ill, Mar. 30, 39; m. 62; c. 1. MATERIALS SCIENCE, PHYSICAL CHEMISTRY. B.A, Cornell Univ, 60; M.S, Univ. Chicago, 62; Ph.D.(phys. chem), Rensselaer Polytech. Inst, 68. ASST. PROF. MAT. SCI. & CHEM. ENG, NORTHWEST. UNIV. (ILL), 67- Chem.C, U.S.A, 61, Res, 60-68, 1st Lt. AAAS; Am. Phys. Soc; Am. Chem. Soc; The Chem. Soc; Am. Soc. Metals; Int. Inst. Conserv Hist. & Artistic Works. Structure of crystalline and glassy polymers in relation to physical properties; physical chemistry of macromolecules; biomaterials; application of physical sciences to archeology. Address: Dept. of Materials Science, Northwestern University, Evanston, IL 60201.

DAVIDSON, THOMAS J, JR, b. Los Angeles, Calif, Dec. 1, 35; m. 61; c. 5. SOIL CHEMISTRY & FERTILITY. B.S, Calif. State Polytech. Col, 58; M.S, Ohio State, 61, Ph.D.(soil chem. & fertil), 63. Asst. prof. soil chem, Florida, 63-65; SR. AGRONOMIST, STANDARD FRUIT & STEAMSHIP CO, 65- Am. Soc. Agron; Soil Conserv. Soc. Am; Int. Soc. Soil Sci; Soil Sci. Soc. Am; Crop Sci. Soc. Am; Am. Inst. Biol. Sci. Clay mineralogy, phosphorus and potassium fixation studies using soil clays from Central America, soil acidity and related problems; soil fertility with shade tobacco; banana and other tropical fruit agronomics. Address: Honduras Division, Research Dept, Standard Fruit & Steamship Co, La Ceiba, Honduras, C.A.

DAVIDSON, T(HOMAS) R(ALPH), b. Alta, Mar. 9, 20; m. 49; c. 2. PLANT PATHOLOGY. B.Sc, Alberta, 43, M.Sc, 45. Assoc. plant pathologist virus diseases, RES. STA, CAN. DEPT. AGR, Alta, 44-54, St. Catharines, 54-67, RES. OFF, VINELAND-STA, 67- Am. Phytopath. Soc; Can. Phytopath. Soc; Agr. Inst. Can. Stone and pome fruit diseases. Address: Canada Dept. of Agriculture, Research Station, Box 185, Vineland-Station, Ont, Can.

DAVIDSON, WILLIAM DENNIS, b. Mohall, N.Dak, Oct. 15, 35; m. 70; c. 1. FOOD SCIENCE, MICROBIOLOGY. B.S, Minnesota, 59, M.S, 62, Ph.D.(animal sci), 66. Res. asst. animal sci, Minnesota, 60-66; asst. prof. food sci, Ore. State Univ, 66-70; MEM. RES. STAFF, FOOD RES. DIV, ARMOUR & CO, 70- U.S.N, 55-57. AAAS; Inst. Food Technol; N.Y. Acad. Sci; Am. Meat Sci. Asn. Food service research and product development. Address: Food Research Division, Armour & Co, 801 W. 22nd St, Oak Brook, IL 60521.

DAVIDSON, WILLIAM J(OHN), b. Janesville, Minn, May 19, 24; m. 46; c. 3. PHYSICAL CHEMISTRY. B.S, Hamline, 49; M.S, Connecticut, 55. Chemist, phys. chem. rocket fuels, U.S. Navy, 51; asst, Connecticut, 52-54; chemist, E.I. DU PONT DE NEMOURS & CO, 54-56, res. chemist, 56-63, sr. res. chemist, 63-66, tech. serv. rep, SPUNBONDED PROD, TEXTILE FIBERS DEPT, 66-69, TECH. SERV. SUPVR, 69- U.S.A, 42-46. Am. Chem. Soc. Physical chemistry of high polymers; and its application to textile fibers. Address: Textile Fibers Dept, Centre Rd. Bldg, E.I. du Pont de Nemours & Co, Wilmington, DE 19898.

DAVIE, EARL W, b. Tacoma, Wash, Oct. 25, 27; m. 52; c. 4. BIOCHEMISTRY. B.S, Washington (Seattle), 50, Ph.D.(biochem), 54. Nat. Found. Infantile Paralysis, fel, Mass. Gen. Hosp, 54-56; asst. prof. BIOCHEM, West. Reserve Univ, 56-62, assoc. prof, 62; SCH. MED, UNIV. WASH, 62-66, PROF, 66- Nat. Sci. Found. & Commonwealth Fund fel, inst. molecular biol, Univ. Geneva, 66-67; mem. Nat. Bd. Med. Exam, 71-75. U.S.N.R, 45-46. AAAS; Am. Chem. Soc; Am. Soc. Biol. Chem. Intermediary metabolism and enzymology. Address: Dept. of Biochemistry, School of Medicine, University of Washington, Seattle, WA 98195.

DAVIE, WILLIAM R(AYMOND), b. Aliquippa, Pa, Mar. 16, 24; m. 48. ORGANIC CHEMISTRY. B.S. Geneva Col, 47; M.S, Wisconsin, 49, Ph.D. (org. chem), 51. Sampler, J & L Steel Corp, 43-47; asst, Wisconsin, 47-50; asst, 50-51; asst. supvr, agr. res, Pittsburgh Coke & Chem. Co, 51-55; supvr, new prods. res, Chemagro Corp, 55-57; asst. supvr. Org. Res, Pittsburgh Coke & Chem. Co, 57-58, supvr, 59-64; GEN. ORG. RES, CHEM. DIV, U.S. STEEL CORP, 64-67, SR. RES. CHEMIST, APPL. RES. LAB, 67- Am. Chem. Soc. Organic research; agricultural chemical research; resins and protective coatings; phthalocyanine research; dibasic acids and their production. Address: 3100 Kane Rd, Aliquippa, PA 15001.

DAVIES, C(LARENCE) E(BENEZER), b. Utica, N.Y, March 15, 91; m. MECHANICAL ENGINEERING. M.E, Rensselaer Polytech, 14; hon. Dr.Eng, Clarkson Tech, 48; Dr.Eng, Drexel Inst, 50. Prod. engr, Remington Typewriter Co, 14-17, prod. supvr, 19-20; assoc. ed, Am. Soc. Mech. Eng, 20-21, asst. secy. & managing ed, 21-31, exec. secy, 31-34, secy, 34-57; exec. dir, United Eng. Center Proj, United Eng. Trustees, Inc, 57-61; dir, int. prog. Eng. Joint Coun, 62-67; CONSULT, AM. SOC. MECH. ENGRS, 67- U.S.A, 17-19, 41-45, Col. AAAS (v.pres); Am. Soc. Eng. Educ; hon. mem. Am. Soc. Mech. Eng; Am. Inst. Aeronaut. & Astronaut; Newcomen Soc. (pres, 39, 40); Brit. Inst. Mech. Eng; hon. mem. Eng. Inst. Can; Inst. Eng, Australia. Industrial management. Address: 345 E. 47th St, New York, NY 10017.

DAVIES, CLINTON KIRK, JR, b. Providence, R.I, Feb. 27, 33; m. 56; c. 1. FOOD CHEMISTRY. B.S, Rhode Island, 54; M.S, Purdue, 56, Ph.D.(food tech), 62. Chemist, State Control Labs, Purdue, 58-61; group leader, Fleischmann Labs, Standard Brands Inc, 61-62, proj. leader, 62-63, SUPVR. process develop. yeast fermentation, Standard Brands Inc, 63-64; confectionary lab, Beechnut Life Savers Inc, Portchester, 65-69; BIRDSEYE DIV, GEN. FOODS, 69- U.S.A, 57, Res, 57-, Capt. AAAS; Am. Chem. Soc; Inst. Food Technol; Am. Asn. Candy Technol. Food biochemistry; chemistry and technology of yeast fermentations, molasses, sugar and candy; bakery technology. Address: General Foods, Birdseye Division, 140 Spring St, Avon, NY 14414.

DAVIES, D. K, b. Ammanford, Wales, U.K, Sept. 5, 35; m. 62; c. 2. PHYSICS. B.Sc, Wales, 57, Ph.D.(physics), 61. Cent. Elec. Generating Bd. sr. res. fel. physics, Univ. Col. Swansea, Wales, 60-62; SR. PHYSICIST, RES. & DEVELOP. CENTER, WESTINGHOUSE ELEC. CORP, 62- Am. Phys. Soc; assoc. Brit. Inst. Physics & Phys. Soc. Spatial and temporal growth of ionization in gases; atomic collisional processes in gases; vacuum breakdown; analytical spectroscopy. Address: Research & Development Center, Westinghouse Electric Corp, Churchill Borough, Pittsburgh, PA 15235.

DAVIES, DAVID HUW, b. Tredegar, Eng, Oct. 29, 42; m. 66. PHYSICAL CHEMISTRY. B.Sc, Univ. Col, London, 64; Ph.D.(phys. chem), 67. SR. SCIENTIST, RES. & DEVELOP. CENTER, WESTINGHOUSE ELEC. CORP, 67- Am. Chem. Soc; Brit. Chem. Soc. Gas kinetics; mass spectrometry; mechanistic investigation of gas phase organic reactions; polymeric surface coatings; properties and applications of inorganic phosphors. Address: Research & Development Center, Westinghouse Electric Corp, Pittsburgh, PA 15235.

DAVIES, D(AVID) HYWEL, b. Swansea, Wales, Aug. 16, 24; m. 55; c. 1. CARDIOLOGY, INTERNAL MEDICINE. B.A. & M.A, Oxford, 49, B.M, B.Ch, 52, D.M, 66. Registr. internal med, St. Stephens Hosp, London, 55-57; resident cardiol, med. ctr, Univ. Colo, Denver, 57-58; registr, Nat. Heart Hosp, London, 58-60; asst. prof, Wayne State Univ, 60-62; sr. registr, Guy's Hosp, London, 62-67; ASSOC. PROF. MED, MED. CTR, UNIV. COLO, DENVER, 67-; CHIEF CARDIOL, VET. ADMIN. HOSP, 67- R.E, Brit. Army, 43-46, Lt. Brit. Cardiac Soc; fel. Royal Soc. Med; fel. Am. Col. Cardiol; fel. Am. Col. Chest Physicians; fel. Am. Col. Physicians. Lung function in congenital heart disease, including mechanisms of symptoms; arterial disease and its cause; design of an ultrasonic catheter for the cleaning of blocked arteries. Address: Veterans Administration Hospital, 1055 Clermont St, Denver, CO 80220.

DAVIES, DAVID K, b. Glamorgan, Wales, Oct. 10, 40; m. 64; c. 2. GEOLOGY. B.Sc, Wales, 62, Ph.D.(geol), 66; M.S, La. State, 64. Asst. prof. GEOL, Texas A&M, 66-68, assoc. prof, 68-70, asst. to dean, 66-70; ASSOC. PROF, UNIV. MO-COLUMBIA, 70- Summer vis. prof, glaciol. inst, Mich. State, 67. Geol. Soc. Am; Soc. Econ. Paleont. & Mineral; fel. Brit. Geol. Soc. Sedimentology of recent deltaic, marine, and glacio-fluvial deposits; palaeogeographic reconstruction; deep sea sediment and sedimentation; petrography of depositional environments; quantitative methods. Address: Dept. of Geology, University of Missouri-Columbia, Columbia, MO 65201.

DAVIES, DAVID R, b. Carmarthen, U.K, Feb. 22, 27; U.S. citizen; m. 51; c. 2. BIOPHYSICS, CRYSTALLOGRAPHY. B.A, Oxford, 49, D.Phil.(chem. crystallog), 52. A.A. Noyes fel. chem, Calif. Inst. Tech, 52-54; res. scientist, Albright & Wilson, Eng, 54-55; vis. scientist MOLECULAR BIOL, Nat. Inst. Ment. Health, 55-62, CHIEF SECT. MOLECULAR STRUCT, NAT. INST. ARTHRITIS & METAB. DISEASES, NAT. INSTS. HEALTH, 62- AAAS; Biophys. Soc; Am. Crystallog. Asn. Application of crystallographic techniques to the determination of structures of biological interest; nucleic acids and proteins; determination of precise crystal structures. Address: National Institutes of Health, Bldg. 2, Room 311, Bethesda, MD 20014.

DAVIES, DEAN F(LETCHER), b. Salem, Ohio, June 15, 17; m. 46; c. 4. MEDICINE. A.B, Wooster Col, 39; fels, Western Reserve, 30-43, M.S, 41, Ph.D. (biochem), 43, M.D, 45. Asst. path, sch. med, Columbia, 45-46; asst. surgeon, U.S. Pub. Health Serv, 46-47, sr. asst. surgeon, 47-48; instr. internal med, sch. med, Washington (St. Louis), 48-50, res. assoc, 50-52, asst. prof. biochem, 52-54; adminstr. res. lung cancer, Am. Cancer Soc, 55-60; assoc. prof. chronic disease, sch. hyg. & pub. health, Hopkins, 60-66; ASSOC. PROF. MED. & PROF. PREV. & COMMUNITY MED, MED. SCH, UNIV. TENN, 66- Res. assoc, sch. pub. health & admin. med, Columbia, 61- Intern, Presby. Hosp, N.Y, 45-46; asst. res, St. Luke's Hosp, St. Louis, 57. AAAS; Am. Physiol. Soc; Pub. Health Cancer Asn. Am; Soc. Cryobiol. Acid-base balance; kidney function; hypertension; amine metabolism; lung cancer; biochemical epidemiology. Address: 800 Madison Ave, Memphis, TN 38103.

DAVIES, DONALD H(ARRY), b. Ottawa, Ont, Can, Jan. 26, 38. PHYSICAL CHEMISTRY. B.Sc, Carleton (Can), 60; Ph.D.(chem), Bristol, 63. Nat. Res. Coun. Can. fel, 63-65; asst. prof. CHEM, Dalhousie, 65-69; ST. MARY'S UNIV, 69-71, ASSOC. PROF, 71- Sessional lectr, Carleton (Can), 65. Chem. Inst. Can; Brit. Chem. Soc; Faraday Soc. Surface chemistry and thermodynamics; polymer degradation. Address: Dept. of Chemistry, St. Mary's University, Halifax, N.S, Can.

DAVIES, DOUGLAS M(ACKENZIE), b. Toronto, Ont, May 11, 19; m. 48; c. 2. ENTOMOLOGY. B.A, Toronto, 42, Ont, Res. Found. bursary, Res. Coun. Ont. scholar, 47, Ph.D.(entom), 49. Res. fel, parasitol, Ont. Res. Found, 49-51; sessional lectr. ZOOL, McMASTER UNIV, 50-51, asst. prof, 51-57, assoc. prof, 57-63, PROF, 63- R.C.A.F, 42-45. Entom. Soc. Am; Am. Mosquito Control Asn; Entom. Soc. Can; fel. Royal Entom. Soc; Can. Soc. Zool. Ecology, physiology and systematics of simuliids, other blood sucking flies and muscids. Address: Dept. of Biology, McMaster University, Hamilton, Ont, Can.

DAVIES, EMLYN B, b. Minnedosa, Man, Feb. 23, 27; m. 62; c. 3. PHYSICS. B.Sc, Univ. Man, 48, M.S, Pa. State Univ, 51, Ph.D.(physics), 53. Sr. res. geophysicist, GULF RES. & DEVELOP. CO, 53-70, SECT. SUPVR, 70- U.S.A, 55-57. AAAS; Soc. Explor. Geophys; Acoust. Soc. Am; Am. Phys. Soc. Elastic wave propagation; information theory. Address: Box 2038, Pittsburgh, PA 15230.

DAVIES, E(VAN) T(OM), b. Pencader, U.K, Sept. 24, 04; m. 55; c. 1. GEOMETRY, PURE MATHEMATICS. B.Sc, Univ. Wales, 24, M.Sc, 26; D.Math, Univ. Rome, 27; Sorbonne & Col. France, 28-30; Ph.D.(math), Univ. London, 34, D.Sc.(math), 44. Fel, Univ. Wales, 28-30; asst. lectr. math, King's Col, London, 30-34, lectr, 34-46, reader, 46-47; prof, Univ. Southampton, 47-69, dep. v.chancellor, 54-57; PROF. MATH, Univ. Calgary, 69-71; UNIV. WATERLOO, 71- Nat. Res. Coun. of Italy vis. prof, summer 61; Brit. Coun. vis. prof, Japan, Philippines, Burma & India, 62. London Math. Soc; Edinburgh Math. Soc; Am. Math. Soc; Can. Math. Cong; Ital. Math. Union. Differential geometry, particularly in its points of contact with the calculus of variations. Address: Dept. of Applied Mathematics, University of Waterloo, Waterloo, Ont, Can.

DAVIES, FRANK T(HOMAS), b. Merthyr Tydfil, Wales, Aug. 12, 04; Can. citizen; m. 31; c. 2. TELECOMMUNICATIONS. B.Sc, Wales, 25; M.Sc, McGill, 28. Demonstrator physics, Saskatchewan, 25-26; McGill, 26-28; physicist, Byrd Antarctic exped, 28-30; assoc. physicist, dept. terrestrial magnetism, Carnegie Institution, 30-32, 34-36, in charge geophys. observ, Huancayo, Peru, 36-39; civilian with Intel. & Sci. Serv, Royal Can. Navy, 39-46; with Can. Defense Res. Bd, 47-59, chief supt, Defence Res. Telecommun. Estab, 59-69; RETIRED. Scientist, Can. Nat. Res. Coun, 41-42. In charge Can. Polar Year exped, Northwest Territories, 32-33. Fel. Arctic Inst. N.Am; Am. Geophys. Union; Can. Asn. Physicist; fel. Royal Soc. Can; sr. mem. Inst. Elec. & Electronics Eng. Rockets and satellites; geophysics; radio propagation; ionosphere; aurora; magnetic variations; condensation nuclei over Pacific and Atlantic Oceans. Address: 22 Clegg St, Ottawa, Ont, Can.

DAVIES, FRED REES, b. Brecon, Wales, July 14, 06; nat; m. 38; c. 3. PHYTOPATHOLOGY. B.Sc, Alberta, 30, Can. Res. Coun. fel, 30-32, M.Sc, 32, Ph.D.(plant path), Minnesota, 38. Exp. plot supvr, plant sci, Alberta, 28-30, plant disease crop surv, 30-32; weed inspector, Alberta Prov. Govt, 32-34; asst. plant path. & mycol, Minnesota, 34-36; Delaware, 36; indust. res. Rohm & Haas Co, 37-68; RETIRED. Am. Phytopath. Soc; Soc. Indust. Microbiol. Plant pathology; spray investigations; disease resistance; production, application and process control of enzymes. Address: Maple Beach, Bristol PA 19007.

DAVIES, GEORGE F(RANCIS), b. London, Eng, June 9, 15; U.S. citizen; m. m. 40; c. 1. CHEMICAL ENGINEERING. B.Sc, British Columbia, 38, M.Sc, 39; Standard Oil Co. Calif. fel, Ore. State Col, 39-41; Ph.D.(phys. chem), 41. From res. chemist to develop. engr, Can. Industs, Ltd, 41-50; PROCESS ENGR, Dom. Tar. & Chem. Co, 50-57, C.F. BRAUN & CO, 57- Shale oil; isomers of decahydronapthalene; thermochemistry of isomeric heptanes. Address: C.F. Braun & Co, Alhambra, CA 91801.

DAVIES, HAROLD WILLIAM, (JR), b. Norton, Kans, Aug. 2, 30; m. 56; c. 3. AQUATIC BIOLOGY, PHYCOLOGY. B.S, Kans. State Teachers Col, 56, M.S, 58; Ph.D.(bot), Mich. State, 66. Instr. biol, Kans. State Teachers Col, 57-58; instr. & ed. consult. BIOL. SCI, dept. sec. ed, New South Wales, 61-63; ASSOC. PROF. & SECT. CHMN, PURDUE UNIV, FT. WAYNE, 64- U.S.A.F, 48-52, S/Sgt. AAAS; Phycol. Soc. Am; Am. Micros. Soc; Am. Inst. Biol. Sci; Int. Phycol. Soc; Brit. Phycol. Soc. Ecology of the phytopsammon; freshwater algae morphology and ecology; limnology. Address: Dept. of Biological Sciences, Purdue University at Ft. Wayne, Ft. Wayne, IN 46805.

DAVIES, HELEN (JEAN) CONRAD, b. N.Y.C, Feb. 14, 25; m. 61; c. 2. BIOCHEMISTRY, MICROBIOLOGY. A.B, Brooklyn Col, 44; N.Y. Univ, 44-45; fel, Rochester, 48-49, M.S, 50; Johnson Found. fels, Pennsylvania, 49-51, 58-60, scholar, 56-58, Ph.D.(biochem), 60. Sci. worker biochem, Smith Kline & French Labs, Pa, 53-54; res. assoc, grad. sch. med, UNIV. PA, 54-56, Johnson Found. res. fel, 60-62, res. assoc. micorbiol, SCH. MED, 62-65, asst. prof, 65-71, community med, 70-71, ASSOC. PROF. PHYS. BIOCHEM, UNIV. PA, 71- Am. Chem. Soc; Am. Soc. Microbiol. Oxidative enzymes; cytochrome pigments; respiratory chain systems; steady-state growth of microorganisms; streptococci; recruitment and retention of minority group students in biomedical careers. Address: Dept. of Microbiology, University of Pennsylvania, Philadelphia, PA 19104.

DAVIES, J(ACK), b. Eng, Aug. 24, 19; m. 46; c. 2. ANATOMY, EMBRYOLOGY. Rockefeller scholar, Iowa, 41-43, M.D, 43; M.A, Cambridge, 46; M.D, Leeds, 47. Demonstr. ANAT, Leeds, 43-44; Cambridge, 44-49, fel. & lectr, 49-51; asst. prof, Iowa, 51-54, assoc. prof, 54-55; SCH. MED, Washington (St. Louis), 55-59, prof, 59-63; PROF. & CHMN. DEPT, VANDERBILT UNIV, 63- Markle scholar, 53. Consult, U.S. Pub. Health Serv, 58- AAAS; Am. Asn. Anat; Soc. Exp. Biol. & Med. Morphology and physiology of the placenta. Address: Dept. of Anatomy, Medical School, Vanderbilt University, Nashville, TN 37203.

DAVIES, JACK NEVILLE PHILLIPS, b. Devizes, Eng, July 2, 15; m. 44, 61; c. 3. EPIDEMIOLOGY. M.B,Ch.B, Bristol, 39, M.D, 48. Lectr. physiol. & demonstr. pharmacol, Bristol, 41-44; pathologist, Uganda Govt, 45-50; prof. path, med. sch, Makerere Univ. Col, Uganda, 50-61; reader morbid anat, postgrad. med. sch, London, 61-63; PROF. PATH, ALBANY MED. COL, 63- Commonwealth Fund. fel, Duke, 49-50; consult. pathologist, Uganda Govt, 50-61; mem. East African Med. Res. Coun, 52-61; cmt, Int. Soc. Geog. Path, 54-60; African Cancer Cmt, Int. Union Against Cancer, 55-62; Fox lectr, Bristol, 62; Musser lectr, Tulane, 64. Brit. Emergency Med. Serv, 40-44. Am. Asn. Path. & Bact; Path. Soc. Gt. Brit. & Ireland; Brit. Med. Asn. Morbid anatomy; geographic pathology, especially of cancer and cardiovascular disease. Address: Dept. of Pathology, Albany Medical College, Albany, NY 12208.

DAVIES, JAMES FREDERICK, b. Winnipeg, Man, Dec. 5, 24. ECONOMIC GEOLOGY, PETROLOGY. B.Sc, Manitoba, 46, M.Sc, 48; Ph.D.(geol), Toronto, 63. Lectr. geol, Manitoba, 47; geologist, Man. Dept. Mines & Natural Resources, 51-57, chief geologist, 57-67; PROF. GEOL, LAURENTIAN UNIV, 67- Hon. lectr, Manitoba, 57-; mem. Nat. Adv. Comt. Res. Geol. Sci-Can, 58-62. Fel. Geol. Asn. Can; fel. Mineral. Asn. Can; Can. Inst. Mining & Metall.(secy, geol. div, 61, Barlow Medal, 65). Regional mapping; compilation, analysis and interpretation of regional geology, tectonic features; geochemistry of Pre-Cambrian rocks, mineral deposits and wall-rocks; studies of Pre-Cambrian volcanic rocks; genesis of base metal sulphide deposits; fabrics of sulphides; deformation and remobilization of sulphide deposits. Address: Dept. of Geology, Laurentian University, Sudbury, Ont, Can.

DAVIES, JOHN A, b. Milwaukee, Wis, May 4, 31; m. 63; c. 2. PHYSICS. B.S, Maryland, 53, M.S, 54, Ph.D.(physics), 60. Res. asst. PHYSICS, Maryland, 53-60; vis. asst. prof, Cincinnati, 63; asst. prof, CLARK UNIV, 63-69, ASSOC. PROF, 69- U.S.A.F, 60-62, 1st Lt. Am. Phys. Soc. Lattice vibration theory. Address: Dept. of Physics, Clark University, Worcester, MA 01610.

DAVIES, JOHN ARTHUR, b. Prestatyn, N.Wales, Mar. 28, 27; Can. citizen; m. 50; c. 6. SOLID STATE SCIENCE, ATOMIC PHYSICS. B.A, Toronto, 47, M.A, 48, Ph.D.(phys. chem), 50. Asst. res. officer phys. chem, Chalk River Nuclear Labs, 50-54; Can. Ramsey fel. polymerization kinetics, Leeds, 54-56; assoc. & sr. res. off. NUCLEAR SCI, CHALK RIVER NUCLEAR LABS, 56-68, PRIN. RES. OFF, 68- Ammanuensis, physics inst, Aarhus Univ, 64-65; guest prof, 69-70; part time prof. physics & eng. physics, McMaster Univ, 70- T.D. Callinan award, 68. Am. Vacuum Soc; Royal Danish Acad. Sci. & Letters; Royal Soc. Can. Chem. Inst. Can.(Noranda award, 65). Ion transport and diffusion processes in solutions; polymerization kinetics; slowing down behaviour of energetic ions in solids; anodic oxidation of metals; channeling of energetic ion beams in crystals; ion implantation. Address: Chalk River Nuclear Labs, Station 15, Chalk River, Ont, Can.

DAVIES, K(ENNARD) MICHAEL, b. Los Angeles, Calif, May 26, 41; m. 71. PHYSICS. B.S, Loyola Univ. Los Angeles, 63; Danforth & Woodrow Wilson fels. & Ph.D.(physics), Univ. Notre Dame, 70. ASST. PROF. PHYSICS, CREIGHTON UNIV, 69- Am. Phys. Soc; Am. Asn. Physics Teachers. Equilibrium and non-equiligrium statistical physics; phase transitions and interphase surfaces. Address: Dept. of Physics, Creighton University, Omaha, NE 68131.

DAVIES, KENNETH, b. Wales, United Kingdom, Jan. 28, 28; m. 58; c. 3. PHYSICS. B.Sc, Wales, 49, Ph.D, 53. Sect. leader, Defence Res. Telecommunications Estab, Can, 52-55; asst. prof, Brown Univ, 56-58; GROUP LEADER, SPACE ENVIRON. LAB, NAT. OCEANIC & ATMOSPHERIC ADMIN, 58- Adj. prof, Univ. Colo, 64- AAAS; Am. Geophys. Union; Sci. Res. Soc. Am; Inst. Elec. & Electronics Eng. Upper atmosphere physics; radio propagation; teaching. Address: Environmental Research Lab, National Oceanic & Atmospheric Administration, Boulder, CO 80302.

DAVIES, K(ENNETH) THOMAS R(EED), b. Pittsburgh, Pa, Nov. 26, 34; m. 57; c. 3. NUCLEAR & THEORETICAL PHYSICS. B.S, Carnegie Inst. Tech, 57, Nat. Sci. Found. fel. & M.S, 59 & Ph.D.(physics), 62. Instr. physics, Carnegie Inst. Tech, 62; THEORET. PHYSICIST, OAK RIDGE NAT. LAB, 62- Am. Phys. Soc; Fedn. Am. Sci. Theoretical nuclear physics; S matrix theory; direct reactions scattering theory; polarization problems; Hartree-Fock and Brueckner-Hartree-Fock calculations of finite nuclei. Address: 110 W. Pawley Rd, Oak Ridge, TN 37830.

DAVIES, MERTON E(DWARD), b. St. Paul, Minn, Sept. 13, 17; m. 46; c. 3. MATHEMATICS. A.B, Stanford, 38. Instr. math, Nevada, 38-39; math. group leader, Douglas Aircraft Co, 40-48; MEM. SR. STAFF, RAND CORP, 48- Consult, Arms Control & Disarmament Agency, 65- Mem. U.S. Del, Surprise Attack Conf, Geneva, 58; mem, U.S. Observer Team, Antarctic, 67; TV exp. teams, Mariner 6 & 7, 69, Mariner 9, 71, Mariner Venus Mercury missions, 73. George W. Goddard Award, Soc. Photo-Optical Instrument. Eng, 66. AAAS; assoc. fel. Am. Inst. Aeronaut. & Astronaut; Am. Soc. Photogram. Spinning panoramic space camera; physics of aerial and space reconnaissance and observation; inspection for arms control; planetary geodesy. Address: 1414 San Remo Dr, Pacific Palisades, CA 90272.

DAVIES, MICHAEL DESMOND, b. Eng, Jan. 10, 40; m. 63; c. 1. PLANT PHYSIOLOGY. B.Sc, Univ. Wales, 63; M.S, Univ. Ill, 69, Ph.D.(biol), 71. Res. off. oil-palm physiol, Chemara Res. Sta. Layang-Layang, Johore, Malaysia, 63-67; FORD FOUND. RES. FEL. BIOL, FED. UNIV. VIÇOSA, 71- Am. Soc. Plant Physiol. Pollen germination and storage; enzyme regulation; effect of inhibitors and activators of enzyme activity and their role in plant growth and development. Address: Institute of Biology, School of Agriculture, Federal University of Viçosa, Minas Gerais, Brazil.

DAVIES, MICHAEL SHAPLAND, b. Cardiff, Wales, June 6, 39; m. 66; c. 1. ELECTRICAL ENGINEERING. M.A, Cambridge, 61; M.S, Illinois, 63, Ph.D.(elec. eng), 66. ASST. PROF. ELEC. ENG, UNIV. B.C, 66- Inst. Elec. & Electronics Eng; Simulation Coun. Stability of nonlinear control systems. Address: Dept. of Electrical Engineering, University of British Columbia, Vancouver 8, B.C, Can.

DAVIES, PETER JOHN, b. Sudbury, Eng, Mar. 7, 40; m. 67. PLANT PHYSIOLOGY. B.Sc, Reading, 62, Ph.D.(plant physiol), 66; M.S, California, Davis, 64. Instr. biol, Yale, 66-69; ASST. PROF. PLANT PHYSIOL, CORNELL UNIV, 69- AAAS; Am. Soc. Plant Physiol; Soc. Exp. Biol. & Med. Herbicide physiology; translocation and selectivity in plants; mode of action of plant hormones; interactions between plant hormones and plant nucleic acids; hormone transport; physiology of flowering and senescence. Address: Section of Genetics, Development & Physiology, Division of Biological Sciences, Cornell University, Ithaca, NY 14850.

DAVIES, P(HILIP) W(YNNE), b. Wauwatosa, Wis, March 18, 15; m. 43; c. 3. PHYSIOLOGY, BIOPHYSICS. B.S, Chicago, 36; Pennsylvania, 38-40, fel, 41-44, Ph.D.(biophys), 43; Cornell, 40-41. Mem. tech. staff, Bell. Tel. Labs, New York, 36-38; fel. biophys, Pennsylvania, 41-44, assoc, 44-49; asst. prof, JOHNS HOPKINS UNIV, 49-57, ASSOC. PROF. PHYSIOL, SCH. MED, 57- Am. Phys. Soc; Soc. Neurosci; Am. Physiol. Soc; Biophys. Soc. Thermistors; metabolism and function of nerve and central nervous system; oxygen cathode; membrane potential; intracellular perfusion. Address: Dept. of Physiology, Johns Hopkins School of Medicine, 725 N. Wolfe St, Baltimore, MD 21205.

DAVIES, RALPH K(AHRER), b. New Castle, Pa, Aug. 25, 17; m. 43; c. 1. INORGANIC CHEMISTRY. B.S, Westminster Col, 39; M.S, Western Reserve, 51. Res. chemist, H.J. Heinz Co, 40-41; teacher, pub. schs, 46-47; PROF. CHEM, BALDWIN-WALLACE COL, 47-, DIR, COOP. SCI. CTR, 68- Adv, Hawshaw Chem. Co, 51-52. U.S.A, 42-46. Am. Indust. Hyg. Asn; fel. Am. Inst. Chem. Geochemistry; crystals in minerals; electrophoresis and biological work; general chemistry; paper chromatography. Address: Dept. of Chemistry, Cooperative Science Center, Baldwin-Wallace College, Berea, OH 44017.

DAVIES, RICHARD E(DGAR), b. Schenectady, N.Y, Jan. 5, 15; m. 43; c. 1. ORGANIC CHEMISTRY, PLASTICS. B.S, Union Col, 35; Ph.D.(chem), Columbia, 41. Chemist, Catalin Corp. of Am, 42-46; Celanese Corp. of Am, 46-57; Air Reduction Inc, 57-65; ITT RAYONIER, INC, 65-71, ASST. RES. MGR, EAST. RES. DIV, 71- Am. Chem. Soc. Organic synthesis; hydrogenation; synthetic fibers; high polymers. Address: Eastern Research Division, ITT Rayonier Inc, Jefferson & Cedar Knolls Rd, Whippany, NJ 07981.

DAVIES, RICHARD GLYN, b. Congleton, Eng, Nov. 1, 34; m. 58; c. 3. PHYSICAL METALLURGY. B.Sc, Univ. Birmingham, 56, Ph.D.(phys. metall), 59. Prof. metall, inst. physics, Nat. Univ. Cuyo, Bariloche, 59-61; STAFF SCIENTIST, FORD MOTOR CO, 62- Brit. Inst. Metals; Am. Inst. Min, Metall. & Petrol. Eng. Stacking faults in copper base alloys; relationship of metallurgical structure to deformation behavior in ordered systems; nickel base precipitation hardened alloys and ferrous martensites; martensite morphology. Address: Metallurgy Dept, Scientific Research Staff, Ford Motor Co, P.O. Box 2053, Dearborn, MI 48121.

DAVIES, RICHARD O, b. Brantford, Ont, July 28, 31; m. 54; c. 3. MEDICINE, PHARMACOLOGY. B.Sc, Univ. Toronto, 54, res. fel, 54-58, M.A, 56, Ph.D. (pharmacol), 58, M.D, 62. Toxicologist, Attorney Gen. Lab, Ont, 54-56; res. fel. pharmacol, Univ. Toronto, 58-61; lectr. pharmacol, Univ. Man, 63-65; staff physician clin. invest, Deer Lodge Hosp, 64-65; asst. med. dir, AYERST LABS, LTD, 65-68, DIR. CLIN. PHARMACOL, N.Y.C. & MONTREAL, 68- Lectr, McGill Univ, 69. Pharmacol. Soc. Can. Clinical and laboratory pharmacology studies in cardiovascular problems including shock, hypertension and peripheral artery disease. Address: Ayerst Labs, P.O. Box 6115, Montreal 101, Que, Can.

DAVIES, RICHARD OELBAUM, b. N.Y.C, Oct. 8, 36; m. 65. PHYSIOLOGY. Brooklyn Col, 53-56; D.V.M, Cornell, 60; Ph.D.(physiol), 64. Scholar, Pa. Plan Develop. Scientists Med. Res, 60-64; assoc. PHYSIOL, SCH. VET. MED, UNIV. PA, 64-66, asst. prof, 66-69, ASSOC. PROF, 69- AAAS; Am. Vet. Med. Asn; Soc. Neurosci; Am. Soc. Vet. Physiol. & Pharmacol. Neurophysiology and respiratory control mechanisms. Address: Dept. of Animal Biology, School of Veterinary Medicine, University of Pennsylvania, 3800 Spruce St, Philadelphia, PA 19104.

DAVIES, ROBERT, b. Omaha, Nebr, May 5, 17; m. 56; c. 2. MATHEMATICS. Ph.D.(math), Wisconsin, 49. Mem. staff, radiation lab, Mass. Inst. Tech, 42-45; res. assoc, Rand Corp, 49-53; from engr, res. labs. to SPEC. ASST. PLANNING, GEN. MOTORS RES. LABS, 53- Fel. AAAS; Am. Math. Soc; Math. Asn. Am; Opers. Res. Soc. Am; Am. Soc. Mech. Eng; Soc. Eng. Sci. Applied mathematics. Address: 1601 Kirkway, Bloomfield Hills, MI 48013.

DAVIES, ROBERT DILLWYN, b. Bristol, Eng, Mar. 22, 39; m. 65; c. 2. PHYSICS. B.Sc, Wales, 62, Ph.D.(physics), 66. Fel. physics, Wales, 65-66, asst. lectr, 66-67; res. physicist, EXP. STA, E.I. DU PONT DE NEMOURS & CO, INC, 67-70, SR. RES. PHYSICIST, 70- Brit. Inst. Physics & Phys. Soc. Electrical breakdown in gases and vacuum; x-ray physics; surface physics. Address: 1117 N. Dolton Court, Darley Woods, Wilmington, DE 19810.

DAVIES, R(OBERT) E(RNEST), b. Lancashire, Eng, Aug. 17, 19; m. 61. BIOCHEMISTRY. B.S, Manchester, 41, M.S, 42, D.S, 52; Ph.D.(biochem), Sheffield, 49; M.A, Oxford, 56. Demonstr. chem, Manchester, 41; asst. lectr, Sheffield, 42-45, lectr. biochem, 48-54; mem. sci. staff, Med. Res. Coun, Sheffield & Oxford, 45-56; prof. biochem, UNIV. PA, 56-70, BENJAMIN FRANKLIN PROF. MOLECULAR BIOL, 70-, CHMN. DEPT. ANIMAL BIOL, SCH. VET. MED. & GRAD. GROUP MOLECULAR BIOL, 62- Guest prof, Heidelberg, 54; mem. faculty med, Oxford, 56-59. Home Guard, 40-44, Chem. Defense Res. Dept. U.K, 41-45, Nat. Fire Serv, 42-45. Am. Chem. Soc; Am. Soc. Biol. Chem; Am. Biophys. Soc; Am. Physiol. Soc; fel. Royal Soc; Brit. Biochem. Soc; Brit. Soc. Exp. Biol; The Chem. Soc. Mechanism of secretion of gastric acid; active transports of ions; energy source for contraction of muscle. Address: Labs. of Biochemistry, Dept. of Animal Biology, University of Pennsylvania School of Veterinary Medicine, Philadelphia, PA 19104.

DAVIES, RONALD EDGAR, b. Victoria, B.C, June 23, 32; m. 60; c. 6. BIOCHEMISTRY. B.S.A, Univ. B.C, 54, M.S.A, 56; Ph.D.(biochem, nutrit), Agr. & Mech. Col. Tex, 59. Asst. prof. poultry sci, Agr. & Mech. Col. Tex, 59-62; RES. ASST. PROF. BIOCHEM, MED. SCH, TEMPLE UNIV, 62-, ASSOC. PROF. DERMAT, 65-, asst. prof, 62-65. Biochemist, Skin & Cancer Hosp, 62- Biophys. Soc; Am. Inst. Nutrit; Am. Inst. Biol. Sci; N.Y. Acad. Sci. Cutaneous photobiology and photochemistry; chemical carcinogenesis; photocarcinogenesis; photochemistry of carcinogens. Address: Biochemistry Dept, Skin & Cancer Hospital, 3322 N. Broad St, Philadelphia, PA 19140.

DAVIES, RONALD W(ALLACE), b. London, Gt. Brit, Dec. 23, 40; m. 63; c. 2. ECOLOGY. B.Sc, Univ. Col. N.Wales, 62, Hons, 63, Ph.D.(ecol), 67; dipl. ed, Univ. Col. S.Wales, 64. Asst. lectr. zool, Univ. Col. N.Wales, 67-68; Can. Int. Biol. Programme fel. ecol, Inst. Fisheries, British Columbia, 68-69; ASST. PROF. ZOOL, UNIV. CALGARY, 69- AAAS; Am. Soc. Limnol. & Oceanog; Can. Soc. Zool; Ecol. Soc. Am; Brit. Ecol. Soc; Brit. Freshwater Biol. Asn. Population regulation of freshwater invertebrates. Address: Dept. of Biology, University of Calgary, Calgary 44, Alta, Can.

DAVIES, T(HOMAS) HARRISON, b. Baltimore, Md, Feb. 21, 12; m. 40; c. 3. BIOCHEMISTRY. A.B, Hopkins, 35, Ph.D.(biochem), 38. Asst. physiol. chem, Hopkins, 37-38; Nat. Res. fel, med, Calif. Inst. Technol, 38-40; res. chemist, Lederle Labs, 40-43; assoc. sect. chief chem. div, Clinton Labs, Tenn, 43-46; asst. prof. inst. for nuclear studies & dept. chem, Chicago, 46-49, assoc. prof, 50-52, acting dir, Inst. of Radio-Biol, 51-52; fel, Mellon Inst, 52-58, dir. res, 58-67, PROF. CHEM, CARNEGIE-MELLON UNIV, 67- Am. Chem. Soc; Am. Phys. Soc; Am. Ceramic Soc. Physical chemical equilibria in metallo-porphyrins; chemistry of hemoglobin and proteins; radio-chemical analysis; chemical effects in nuclear transmutations; glass physics and chemistry. Address: Dept. of Chemistry, Carnegie-Mellon Institute, 4400 Fifth Ave, Pittsburgh, PA 15213.

DAVIES, TUDOR T, b. Bridgend, U.K, Sept. 3, 38; m. 60; c. 3. PALEONTOLOGY, GEOCHEMISTRY. B.Sc, Wales, 60, Dept. Sci. & Indust. Res. fel. & Ph.D.(geol), 64. Geologist, Brit. Ceramic Res. Asn. Refractories, 63-64; Nat. Res. Coun. Can. fel. GEOL, Dalhousie, 64-66; asst. prof, UNIV. S.C, 66-69, ASSOC. PROF, 69- AAAS; Geol. Soc. Am; Soc. Econ. Paleont. & Mineral; Geochem. Soc; Brit. Paleont. Asn. Structure and chemistry of biologic skeletal precipitates; post mortem changes in skeletal material in the marine environment; geographic variation in growth rates density and diversity of invertebrate populations. Address: Dept. of Geology, University of South Carolina, Columbia, SC 29208.

DAVIES, WARREN L(EWIS), b. Scranton, Pa, Jan. 17, 20; m. 46; c. 2. MICROBIOLOGY. B.S, Pa. State Col, 46, M.S, 47; Ph.D.(microbiol), Wisconsin, 51. MICROBIOLOGY, STINE LAB, E.I. DU PONT DE NEMOURS & CO, 50- U.S.N, 42-46. Am. Soc. Microbiol. Viruses and bacteria. Address: P.O. Box 312, Newark, DE 19711.

DAVIESS, STEVEN N(ORMAN), Cedar Rapids, Iowa, Jan. 25, 18; m. 44; c. 2. GEOLOGY. B.A, California, Los Angeles, 40, Standard Oil Co. Calif. fel, 41-42, M.A, 42. Jr. geologist, U.S. Geol. Surv, 42-43, asst. geologist, 43-46; assoc. geologist, Cuban Gulf Oil Co, 46-48, Mozambique Gulf Oil Co, 48-53, staff geologist, Gulf N.Y. Prod. Div, 53-56, Gulf Eastern Co, 56-60, area mgr, Spanish Gulf Oil Co, 60-67; geologic adv, Nuclear fuels div, Gulf Oil Corp, 67-70; MGR. EXPLOR, GULF MINERAL RESOURCES CO, 70- Fel. Am. Petrol. Inst; fel. Geol. Soc. Am; fel. Am. Geog. Soc; Am. Asn. Petrol. Geol; Geol. Soc. S.Africa; fel. Geol. Soc. London. Petroleum Geology; economic geology. Address: Gulf Mineral Resources Co, 1780 S. Bellaire St, Denver, CO 80222.

DAVIGNON, JEAN, b. Montreal, Que, July 29, 35; m. 61; c. 2. MEDICINE. B.A, Univ. Paris, 53; M.D, Univ. Montreal, 58; M.Sc, McGill Univ, 60. Nat. Res. Coun. Can, med. res. fel, dept. clin. res, Hotel-Dieu Hosp, Montreal, 58-60, resident, 60-61; fel, internal med, Mayo Clin. & Mayo Found, Rochester, Minn, 61-62, res. asst, dept. physiol, 62-63; res. assoc. lipid metab, Rockefeller Univ. Hosp, 64-67; SR. INVESTR. & DIR. DEPT. LIPID METAB. & ATHEROSCLEROSIS RES, CLIN. RES. INST. MONTREAL, 67- Scholar, Ministry Educ, Que, 61-65; assoc. physician, Hotel-Dieu Hosp, 67-70, physician, 70-; asst. prof. dept. med, Univ. Montreal, 67-71, assoc. prof, 71-; asst. prof, dept. exp. med, McGill Univ, 70- Fel. coun. on arteriosclerosis, Am. Heart Asn, 68. Cert, Internal Med, Que, 63; fel, Royal Col. Physicians & Surgeons, Can, 63; Markle scholar acad. med, 67. Am. Fedn. Clin. Res; fel. Am. Col. Physicians; fel. Am. Col. Angiol; Am. Heart Asn; Harvey Soc; N.Y. Acad. Sci; Can. Soc. Clin. Invest; Can. Med. Asn; Asn. French Speaking Physicians Can. Peripheral vascular diseases; atherosclerosis; lipid and lipoprotein metabolism in hyperlipidemia. Address: Clinical Research Institute of Montreal, 110 Pine Ave. W, Montreal 130, Que, Can.

DAVILA, JULIO C, b. Mexico, Dec. 1, 21; U.S. citizen; m. 48; c. 4. CARDIAC SURGERY, CIRCULATION PHYSIOLOGY. A.B, Stanford, 45, M.D, 49. Instr. SURG, Pennsylvania, 58-61, asst. prof, 61-62; clin.

prof, Sch. med, Temple, 62-65, prof, 65-69; dir. cardiopulmonary inst, St. Joseph's Hosp, 69-71; CHIEF, DIV. THORACIC SURG, HENRY FORD HOSP, 71- Assoc. thoracic surgeon, Presby. Hosp, St. Christopher's Hosp. & Fitzgerald Mercy Hosp, 54-61; dir. cardiovasc. res, Presby. Hosp, 57-61, dir. res, 61-62; acting chief thoracic surg, Presby. Hosp. & St. Christopher's Hosp, 61-62; faculty assoc. & mem. seminar biomat, Columbia, 66-69; Consult, Valley Forge Army Hosp, 62-; Phila. Vet. Hosp, 64-69; Letterman Gen. Hosp, 69- Dipl, Am. Bd. Surg, 54; dipl, Am. Bd. Thoracic Surg, 56. Med.C, U.S.A, Capt. Fel. Am. Col. Surg; fel. Am. Col. Cardiol; fel. Am. Col. Chest Physicians; fel. Am. Col. Angiol; Am. Asn. Thoracic Surg; Soc. Thoracic Surg; Am. Thoracic Soc; Am. Heart Asn; Am. Med. Asn; Am. Soc. Test. & Mat. Cardiac surgery; circulation physiology research; biomaterials; prostheses for circulation especially artificial heart valves. Address: Division of Thoracic Surgery, Henry Ford Hospital, 2799 W. Grand Blvd, Detroit, MI 48202.

DAVINROY, THOMAS BERNARD, b. East St. Louis, Ill, Nov. 16, 32; m.·55; c. 3. CIVIL ENGINEERING, TRANSPORTATION ENGINEERING. B.S.E, Princeton, 54, M.S.E, 60; Rutgers, 60-61; Automotive Safety Found. fel, California, Berkeley, 61-63, D.Eng.(transportation eng), 66. Instr. mech. & graphics, Princeton, 59-61; asst. prof. CIVIL ENG, PA. STATE UNIV, 64-69, ASSOC. PROF, 69- Summers, soils engr, Moran, Proctor Mueser & Rutledge, N.Y, 58, eng. consult, Tanganyika proj, U.S. Peace Corp, 61, transportation engr, James C. Buckley Inc, N.Y, 63; consult, Gannett, Fleming, Corddry & Carpenter, Harrisburg, Pa, 68-69; Bruinette, Gruger, Stoffberg & Hugo, Pretoria, Repub. S.Africa, 70-71; head acad. support div, Pa. Transportation & Traffic Safety Ctr. U.S.M.C, 54-58, 1st Lt. Am. Soc. Civil Eng; Inst. Traffic Eng. Transportation planning; effects of weather and aircraft characteristics on airport design; air transport planning. Address: Dept. of Civil Engineering, 212 Sackett Bldg, Pennsylvania State University, University Park, PA 16802.

DAVIS, ABRAM, b. Cleveland, Ohio, Feb. 21, 26; m. 52; c. 4. SPECTROSCOPY, ANALYTICAL CHEMISTRY. A.B, Lake Forest Col, 50; M.S, Ill. Inst. Technol, 52. Res. chemist, CENT. RES, HOOKER CHEM. CORP, 51-58, group leader instrumental lab, 58-61, supvr, 61-69, supvr. anal, phys. & instrumental lab, 69-70, asst. sect. mgr, 70, SR. RES. ASSOC, 70- U.S.A, 44-46. AAAS; Soc. Appl. Spectros; Am. Chem. Soc; Coblentz Soc; Optical Soc. Am. Instrumental analysis of organic compounds; elucidation of structure and development of analytical methods of product control. Address: Hooker Chemical Corp, Central Research, P.O. Box 8, Niagara Falls, NY 14302.

DAVIS, ALBERT MARION, b. Provo, Utah, Nov. 9, 21; m. 46; c. 5. AGRONOMY. B.S, Brigham Young Univ, 43; M.S, Kans. State Univ, 48, Ph.D.(forage crop physiol), 54. Asst, Kans. State Univ, 47-48; instr, Univ. Ark, Fayetteville, 48-51, asst. prof, 53-57, assoc. prof. agron, 57-62, prof, 62-67; COLLAB. AGRON, U.S. DEPT. AGR, WEST. PLANT INTROD. STA, WASH. STATE UNIV, 67- Asst, Kans. State Univ, 51-53; asst. prof, Ala. Polytech. Inst, 53. U.S.A.A.F, 42-45. Am. Soc. Agron; Soc. Range Mgt. Range management; brush control; grass breeding and genetics; new crops. Address: Western Plant Introduction Station, Washington State University, Pullman, WA 99163.

DAVIS, A(LEXANDER) C(OCHRAN), b. Ottawa, Ont, Can, Oct. 6, 20; nat; m. 43; c. 2. ECONOMIC ENTOMOLOGY. B.S.A, Toronto, 42; Ph.D.(entom), Cornell, 50. Agr. scientist, div. entom, Can. Dept. Agr, Ottawa, 46; asst. ENTOM, Cornell, 47-50; asst. prof, N.Y. STATE AGR. EXP. STA, GENEVA, 50-54, ASSOC. PROF, 54- Can. Army, 42-46, 1st Lt. Entom. Soc. Am. Vegetable insect control. Address: 7 Cynthia Dr, Geneva, NY 14456.

DAVIS, ALFRED, JR, b. Johnson City, Tex, Feb. 10, 19; m. 41; c. 2. ENGINEERING. B.S, Texas, 41. Design engr, Westinghouse Elec. Co, Md, 41-45; res. engr, Defense Res. Lab, 46-62; proj. engr, TRACOR, INC, 62-67, SR. ENGR, PROD. ENG. DEPT, 67- Sr. mem. Inst. Elec. & Electronics Eng; Nat. Soc. Prof. Eng. Design of specialized microwave and data recording systems; production engineering of frequency standards and countermeasures systems. Address: Tracor Inc, 6500 Tracor Lane, Austin, TX 78721.

DAVIS, ALLEN SEYMOUR, b. Oklahoma City, Okla, July 25, 34; m. 55. MATHEMATICS. B.S, Oklahoma, 58, M.A, 60, Nat. Sci. Found. co-op. fel, 60-62, Ph.D.(math), 62. Asst. prof. MATH, UNIV. OKLA, 62-66, ASSOC. PROF, 66-, lectr, Nat. Sci. Found. Insts, 62-65. Clyde B. Thompson res. award, Sigma Xi, 62. Math. Asn. Am; Am. Math. Soc; Asn. Symbolic Logic. Mathematical logic and foundations; point-set topology. Address: Dept. of Mathematics, University of Oklahoma, Norman, OK 73069.

DAVIS, ALVIE D(OUGLAS), b. Ponce de Leon, Mo, Apr. 29, 45. THEORETICAL NUCLEAR PHYSICS. B.S, Wichita State Univ, 66; Nat. Defense Educ. Act fel. & M.S, Univ. Calif, Los Angeles, 68, Ph.D.(physics), 70. Teaching asst. physics, Univ. Calif, Los Angeles, 66-70, nuclear physics, 68-70; ASST. PROF. PHYSICS, EAST. ILL. UNIV, 70- Am. Asn. Physics Teachers. Nuclear shell structure; nuclear shape; holography. Address: Dept. of Physics, Eastern Illinois University, Charleston, IL 61920.

DAVIS, ALVIE LEE, b. Richardson, Tex, Jan. 22, 31; m. 61; c. 2. BIOCHEMISTRY. B.S, Abilene Christian Col, 55; Ph.D.(biochem), Univ. Tex, 60. Asst. prof. CHEM, ABILENE CHRISTIAN COL, 59-62, assoc. prof, 62-68, PROF, 68- Robert A. Welch Found. res. grant, 62- Am. Chem. Soc. Metabolic inhibitors; correlation of chemical structure and biological activity; nitrogen heterocycles; cyclic benzohydroxamic acids. Address: Dept. of Chemistry, Abilene Christian College, Abilene, TX 79601.

DAVIS, ALVIN H(ERBERT), b. Buffalo, N.Y, Jan. 26, 29; m. 56; c. 2. THEORETICAL PHYSICS. B.A, Buffalo, 49, M.A, 51; Sheffield Sci. fel, Yale, 51-52, Ph.D.(physics), 55. PHYSICIST, Livermore Radiation Lab, California, 55-57; Naval Res. Lab, 57-58; theoret. div, Goddard Space Flight Ctr, Md, 59-66; Environ. Res. Corp, Va, 66-69; LOS ALAMOS SCI. LAB, 69- AAAS; Am. Geophys. Union; Am. Phys. Soc; Am. Astron. Soc. Theoretical astrophysics; geophysics; astrophysics. Address: Los Alamos Scientific Lab, P.O. Box 1663, Los Alamos, NM 87544.

DAVIS, A(RTHUR) L(EE), b. New York, N.Y, Oct. 14, 17; m. 45; c. 2. ORGANIC & HIGH POLYMER CHEMISTRY. B.S, L.I. Univ, 39; Shellac Res. fel, Polytech. Inst. Brooklyn, 39-42, M.S, 42, Adv. Solvents & Chem. Co. fel, 42-43, Ph.D.(chem), 43. Instr. chem, Polytech. Inst. Brooklyn, 41-43; sr. polymer res. chemist, Firestone Tire & Rubber Co, 43-45; head resin res. div, U.S. Indust. Chem. Inc, 45-48; market develop. & tech. sales depts, Heyden Chem. Corp, 48-52; mgr. res. & develop, Irvington varnish & insulator div, Minn. Mining & Mfg. Co, 52-54; v.pres. & gen. mgr. electro tech. prod. div, Sun Chem. Co, 54-61; sales mgr, Geigy Chem. Corp, 61-64; dir. sales, Felton Chem. Co, 64-67; EXEC. V.PRES, KETCHUM LABS, INC, 67- Am. Chem. Soc; Tech. Asn. Pulp & Paper Indust; Commercial Chem. Develop. Asn; Am. Soc. Test. & Mat. Organic chemistry; high polymer chemistry; paint and varnish; pulp and paper; synthetic pharmaceuticals; rubber; x-ray diffraction; chemical market research; textiles. Address: 84 Cochrane Ave, Dobbs Ferry, NY 10522.

DAVIS, A(UDREY) K(ENNON), b. Chewalla, Tenn, Aug. 7, 20; m. 61; c. 3. PHYSIOLOGY. B.S, Memphis Col, 47; Ph.D.(physiol), Tennessee, 51. Res. assoc. chem, Tennessee, 46-49, instr. physiol, 51-52; biologist, U.S. Naval Radiological Defense Lab, 52-58, head biophys. br, 58-61, dir. exp. radiobiol. labs, div. radiol. health res. br, 61-67; physiologist, Colo. State Univ, 67-70; chief, epidemiol, Bur. Radiol. Health, 70-71; ASST. DIR, NAT. CTR. TOXICOL. RES, DEPT. HEALTH, EDUC. & WELFARE, 71- Lectr, George Washington Univ, 64; faculty affiliate, Colo. State Univ, 67-70. U.S.A, 44-46. AAAS; Health Physics Soc; Soc. Exp. Biol. & Med; Am. Physiol. Soc; Radiation Res. Soc. Radiation hematology; physiology of burns; fluid and ionic balance; radiation recovery; radiation epidemiology; carcinogenesis; teratology; chemical toxicology. Address: National Center Toxicological Research, Pine Bluff, AR 71601.

DAVIS, B(ENJAMIN) H(AROLD), b. Lafayette, Ind, Jan. 25, 05; m. 33; c. 2. PLANT PATHOLOGY. A.B, Wabash Col, 28; Ph.D.(plant path), Cornell, 34. Asst. plant path, Cornell, 28-29, instr, 29-34; sci, Va. State Teachers Col, Fredericksburg, 34-35; bot, Ohio State, 35-39; assoc. prof. PLANT PATH, RUTGERS UNIV, 39-51, prof, 51-71, chmn. dept. plant path, 56-63, dept. plant biol, 63-71, EMER. PROF, 71- Am. Phytopath. Soc; Mycol. Soc. Am. Diseases of vegetables. Address: 15 MacArthur St, High Bridge, NJ 08829.

DAVIS, BENJAMIN L(AWRENCE), b. Uzhorod, Czech, June 8, 12; U.S. citizen; m. 43; c. 3. CHEMISTRY, INDUSTRIAL ENGINEERING. B.S, George Washington, 37, M.A, 40, Ph.D.(biochem), Georgetown, 43. Jr. chemist, U.S. Dept. Agr, 38-41, asst. chemist, 41-45; sci. analyst, U.S. Dept. Commerce, 45-47; electronic scientist, Nat. Bur. Standards, 47-56; supvry. indust. engr, U.S. Dept. Army, 56-70; CONSULT, CATALYST RES. CORP, 70- Mem. adv. group electronic parts, Dept. Defense, 52-58; U.S. engr. mem. mutual weapons develop. team, NATO, 57-60; consult, Am. Ord. Asn, 57-70. Except. serv. award, U.S. Dept. Commerce, 54. Am. Chem. Soc; sr. mem. Inst. Elec. & Electronics Eng; Am. Ord. Asn. Development of printed circuit processes, materials, components and automated equipment for printed circuit production; production of ordnance fuzes; development, design and production of special purpose batteries for proximity fuzes. Address: 7811 13th St. N.W, Washington DC 20012.

DAVIS, BERNARD D(AVID), b. Franklin, Mass, Jan. 7, 16; m. 55; c. 3. BIOCHEMISTRY, MICROBIOLOGY. A.B, Harvard, 36, M.D, 40. Res. fel. & intern, Hopkins, 40-41; commissioned off, U.S. Pub. Health Serv, 42-54; prof. pharmacol. col. med, N.Y. Univ, 54-57; bact. & immunol, HARVARD MED. SCH, 57-68, ADELE LEHMAN PROF. BACT. PHYSIOL. & DIR. UNIT, 68- Vis. investr, col. physicians & surg, Columbia, 42-44; Pub. Health Res. Inst. N.Y, 44; Rockefeller Inst, 45-47; res. assoc, med. col, Cornell, 47-54. Nat. Acad. Sci; AAAS; Am. Soc. Microbiol; Soc. Gen. Physiol.(pres, 64-65); Am. Soc. Cell Biol; Am. Soc. Biol. Chem; Am. Acad. Arts & Sci. Microbial metabolism and genetics; chemotherapy. Address: Bacterial Physiology Unit, Harvard Medical School, Boston, MA 02115.

DAVIS, BERNARD ERIC, b. Milwaukee, Wis, Aug. 29, 37; m. 64; c. 2. METALLURGY, CHEMICAL ENGINEERING. B.S, Ore. State Univ, 60, univ. assistantship, 61-62, M.S, 65, U.S. Bur. Mines fel, 67-69, Ph.D.(metall. eng), 70. Process engr, org. chem. dept, E.I. du Pont de Nemours & Co, Inc, 60-61; res. metallurgist, Teledyne Wah Chang Albany Corp, Teledyne, Inc, 63-67; TECH. ADV. QUAL. CONTROL, NAVAL NUCLEAR FUEL DIV, BABCOCK & WILCOX CO, 70- U.S.A, 62-63, Res, 63-71, 1st Lt. Am. Inst. Min, Metall. & Petrol. Eng; Am. Soc. Metals; Am. Inst. Chem. Eng. Diffusion in metals; liquid extraction of metals. Address: 201 Collington Dr, Lynchburg, VA 24502.

DAVIS, BETTY S(CHUCK), b. Los Angeles, Calif, July 30, 21; m. 47; c. 2. ZOOLOGY. A.B, California, 44, Rosenberg fel, 47-48, U.S. Pub. Health Serv. fel, 49-50, Ph.D.(zool), 51. Asst. zool, California, 44-47; res. assoc, Southern California, 52; res. technician cardiac dept, Children's Hosp, Los Angeles, 52-53; independent res. worker, HASTINGS NATURAL HISTORY RESERVATION, 53-55, RES. FEL. ZOOL, 55-, ASST. RES. PARASITOLOGIST, 62- Soc. Protozool; Am. Soc. Parasitol; Wild Life Disease Asn. Blood protozoans, helminths and siphonapterans of wild birds and mammals; systematics, comparative morphology and life history studies; gonad cycles in birds; host-parasite ecology of wild rodents. Address: Hastings Natural History Reservation, Carmel Valley, CA 93924.

DAVIS, BILL, b. Spearman, Tex, Aug. 21, 31; m. 51; c. 4. ORGANIC CHEMISTRY. B.S, Panhandle Agr. & Mech. Col, 53; M.S, Okla. State, 56; Ph.D. (org. chem), 59. Asst. org. chem, Okla. State, 54-56, instr, 56-57, asst, 57-59; res. chemist, Convair Div, Gen. Dynamics Corp, 59-61; eng. specialist, Goodyear Aerospace Corp, 61-63; sr. res. chemist, Jefferson Chem. Co, 63-67; OWNER, TEX. URETHANES, 67- Organic research; synthesis of polymers; urethane foams and elastomers. Address: 6911 Ryan Dr, Austin, TX 78757.

DAVIS, BILL DAVID, b. Junction City, Kans, July 22, 37; m. 62; c. 2. DEVELOPMENTAL BIOLOGY. B.S, Kans. State Teachers Col, 59, M.S, 61; univ. fel, Purdue, 62-63, Nat. Insts. Health fel, 63-65, Ph.D.(biol), 65. Teacher, Manhattan Jr. High Sch, Kans, 60-62; asst. prof. BIOL. SCI,

DOUGLASS COL, RUTGERS UNIV, 65-69, ASSOC. PROF, 69- AAAS; Japanese Soc. Plant Physiol; Am. Soc. Plant Physiol; Bot. Soc. Am. Association of protein synthesis and the reorientation of the mitotic spindle in the early development of fern gametophytes, photomorphogenetic aspects of this control. Address: Dept. of Biological Sciences, Douglass College of Rutgers University, New Brunswick, NJ 08903.

DAVIS, BILLY J, b. Hobart, Okla, Oct. 27, 32; m. 53; c. 4. VERTEBRATE ZOOLOGY, ICHTHYOLOGY. B.S, Southwest. State Col.(Okla), 54, M.S, 57; Univ. N.Mex, 63; Univ. Okla, 64; Ph.D.(ichthyol), Okla. State Univ, 66. Teacher, pub. schs, Okla, 54-63; asst. prof. ZOOL, LA. TECH UNIV, 66-69, ASSOC. PROF, 69- Soc. Study Amphibians & Reptiles; Am. Soc. Ichthyol. & Herpet. Ecological and taxonomic studies of North American fresh-water fishes and herptiles, particularly the gross morphology of the cyprinid fish brain in relation to behavior; water pollution biology. Address: Dept. of Zoology, Louisiana Tech University, Ruston, LA 71270.

DAVIS, BRIANT LeROY, b. Brigham City, Utah, Nov. 18, 36; m. 57; c. 4. GEOLOGY, GEOPHYSICS. B.S, Brigham Young, 58, M.S, 59; Ph.D.(geol), California, Los Angeles, 64. Asst. res. geophysicist, Inst. Geophys. & Planetary Physics, California, Los Angeles, 61-62; asst. prof. geol. & geol. eng, S.DAK. SCH. MINES & TECHNOL, 63-66, ASSOC. PROF, 66-70, GEOPHYS, 70-, RES. GEOPHYSICIST, INST. ATMOSPHERIC SCI, 66- Summers, Jr. geologist, Union Pac. Oil Develop. Co, Wyo, 58, party chief geol. field mapping, Univ. Utah, 59, asst. res. geophysicist, Inst. Geophys. & Planetary Physics, 64. AAAS; Am. Meteorol. Soc; Am. Crystallog. Soc; Am. Geophys. Union. Petrofabric analysis by means of x-ray techniques; nucleation processes; cloud physics and weather modification; crystallography and x-ray diffraction. Address: Dept. of Meteorology, South Dakota School of Mines & Technology, Rapid City, SD 57701.

DAVIS, BRUCE W, b. Glendale, Calif, July 19, 37; m. 64; c. 2. PHYSICAL CHEMISTRY. B.S, Southern California, 60, Petrol. Res. Fund fel, 60-61, M.S, 62; Petrol. Res. Fund fel, California, Riverside, 61-64, Ph.D.(phys. chem), 64. Lab. technician, Kelite Corp, 57-58; teaching asst. chem, Southern California, 60; Army Res. Off, Durham assoc. critical phenomena, North Carolina, 64-66; ASST. PROF. CHEM, GA. INST. TECHNOL, 66- Petrol. Res. Fund grants, 68-71; Army Res. Off. Durham grants, 68-71. Am. Chem. Soc. Statistical mechanics and thermodynamics of the gas, liquid and adsorbed states; interactions of gases with solid substrates; critical phenomena. Address: School of Chemistry, Georgia Institute of Technology, Atlanta, GA 30332.

DAVIS, BRUCE W(ILSON), b. Owen Co, Ind, Dec. 22, 21; m. 48; c. 3. APPLIED MATHEMATICS. A.B, Indiana, 48; M.S, Purdue, 55. Teacher, high sch, Ind, 48-50; mathematician & math. consult, ord. plant, U.S. Navy, 50-55, asst. head math. div, avionics facility, 56-58; sr. res. engr, Allison Div, Gen. Motors Corp, Ind, 55-56, engr, head math. & comput. facility & chief adv. studies, Defense Systs. & Allison Div, 58-63; systs. anal supvr. & proj. dir, COLUMBUS LABS, BATTELLE MEM. INST, 63-70, MGR, SPACE SYSTS. PROG. OFF, 70- U.S.N, 42-45. Am. Inst. Aeronaut. & Astronaut; Am. Astronaut. Soc. Control systems; guidance; synthesis of electrical circuitry; operations research; systems analysis; space launch system analyses. Address: 683 Sternberger Place, Columbus, OH 43214.

DAVIS, BURNS, b. Fulton, Ky, Mar. 15, 31; m. 54; c. 2. POLYMER & ORGANIC CHEMISTRY. B.S, Murray State Col, 53, M.A, 59; Nat. Defense fel, Univ. Louisville, 59, Ph.D.(polymer chem), 62. Teacher, high sch, Ky, 56-58; res. chemist, TENN. EASTMAN CO, 62-65, sr. res. chemist, 65-71, RES. ASSOC, 71- U.S.A, 53-55. Am. Chem. Soc. Condensation and vinyl polymers. Address: 2019 Bruce St, Kingsport, TN 37664.

DAVIS, BURTRON H, b. Points, W.Va, Dec. 21, 34; m. 66; c. 2. PHYSICAL CHEMISTRY. B.S, W.Va. Univ, 58; M.S, St. Joseph's Col.(Pa), 62; Atomic Energy Comn. fel. & Ph.D.(chem), Univ. Fla, 65. Analyst, Atlantic Ref. Co, Pa, 59-62; res. assoc, Johns Hopkins Univ, 65-66; sr. res. chemist, Res. & Develop. Corp, Mobil Oil Corp, N.J, 66-70; ASST. PROF. CHEM, POTOMAC STATE COL, W.VA. UNIV, 70- U.S.A, 54-56, Res, 56-62. Am. Chem. Soc; Catalysis Soc. Heterogeneous catalysis; dehydrocyclization mechanism; radiotracer studies; dehydration mechanism. Address: 17 Arnold St, Keyser, WV 26726.

DAVIS, B(USTER) HALL, b. Williford, Ark, June 20, 22; m; c. 5. POULTRY NUTRITION. B.S.A, Arkansas, 50, M.S, 52; Ph.D, La. State, 59. Asst. prof, MARKET PROD. TECHNOL, LA. STATE UNIV, BATON ROUGE, 58-65; ASSOC. PROF, 65-, POULTRY SCI, 70- Consult, Owens-Ill. Glass Co, Ohio. U.S.A.A.F, 42-46. Fel. AAAS; Poultry Sci. Asn; Inst. Food Technol. Market products technology. Address: Route 1, Box 235, Zachary, LA 70791.

DAVIS, CARL F, b. Milo, Maine, May 12, 19; m. 45; c. 1. ELECTRICAL ENGINEERING, MATHEMATICS. B.A, Maine, 42; B.S, U.S. Air Force Inst. Technol, 55; M.S, Illinois, 56, Ph.D.(elec. eng), 60. U.S.AIR FORCE, 48-, commun. & electronics staff off, 48-60, assoc. prof. elec. eng, U.S. Air Force Acad, 60-68, CHIEF, ELECTRONICS DIV, AIR FORCE WEAPONS LAB, 68- Inst. Elec. & Electronics Eng; Am. Soc. Eng; Educ; N.Y. Acad. Sci. Nuclear radiation effects on weapon systems; transient radiation effects on electronics; electromagnetic pulse effects on systems; research and exploratory development of arming and fuzing systems for nuclear reentry vehicles. Address: 2254 Stockton Loop, Kirtland Air Force Base, NM 87118.

DAVIS, CARL LEE, b. Dunnville, Ky, Sept. 20, 24; m. 46; c. 5. NUTRITION, BIOCHEMISTRY. B.S, West. Ky. State Col, 52; M.S, Kentucky, 54; Ph.D. (dairy sci), Illinois, 59. Instr. dairy sci, West. Ky. State Col, 52-53; res. assoc, Kentucky, 53-54; UNIV. ILL, URBANA-CHAMPAIGN, 55-59, asst. prof, 60-69, PROF. NUTRIT, 69- U.S.N, 43-46. Am. Dairy Sci. Asn; Am. Inst. Nutrit. Nutrition of ruminant animals, epsecially as related to milk production. Address: 315 Animal Science Lab, University of Illinois at Urbana-Champaign, Urbana, IL 61801.

DAVIS, CARL O, b. Pine Bluff, Ark, June 21, 27; m. 51; c. 2. EDUCATIONAL MEASUREMENT, DENTISTRY. B.S, Univ. Ark, 50; Ark. A&M, 54-55; D.D.S, Univ. Tenn, 58; M.S, Univ. Iowa, 70, M.A. & Ph.D.(educ. psychol), 71. Private practice, Okla, 58-68; ASSOC. PROF. EDUC. RES. & DEVELOP. & DIR. EVAL, SCH. DENT, MED. COL. GA, 71- Partic, U.S. Pub. Health Serv. Pilot Prog. Model Dent. Teacher Training, 68-71. U.S.N, 45-46; U.S.A, 51-53, 1st Lt. Am. Dent. Asn; Am. Educ. Res. Asn; Int. Asn. Dent. Res. Quality of dentistry and dental education. Address: Medical College of Georgia School of Dentistry, AD 108, Augusta, GA 30902.

DAVIS, (HORACE) CHANDLER, b. Ithaca, N.Y, Aug. 12, 26; m. 48; c. 3. MATHEMATICS. B.S, Harvard, 45, M.A, 47, Ph.D.(math), 50. Teaching fel. math, Harvard, 47-48; instr, Michigan, 50-54; lectr, Columbia, 55-57; mem. Inst. for Adv. Study, 57-58; assoc. ed, 'Math. Reviews,' 58-62; assoc. prof. MATH, UNIV. TORONTO, 62-65, PROF, 65- U.S.N.R, 44-46, Ens. Soc. Indust. & Appl. Math; Am. Math. Soc; Can. Math. Cong. Linear spaces and operators. Address: Dept. of Mathematics, University of Toronto, Toronto 181, Ont, Can.

DAVIS, CHARLES (CARROLL), b. Azusa, Calif, Nov. 24, 11; m. 36; c. 2. LIMNOLOGY, INVERTEBRATE ZOOLOGY. A.B, Oberlin Col, 33; M.S, Washington (Seattle), 35, Ph.D.(zool), 40. Asst, Scripps Inst, California, 38-40; instr. sci, Nat. Training Sch, Mo, 40-42; biologist, State Dept. Res. & Ed, Md, 42-43; chemist, U.S. Navy Powder Factory, 43-44; instr. biol. chem, Jacksonville,Jr. Col, 44-47; asst. prof. zool, Miami (Fla), 47-48; BIOL, Western Reserve, 48-54, assoc. prof, 54-63, PROF, 63-68, MEM. UNIV, 68- Instr, San Diego Evening Jr. Col, 39. AAAS; Am. Soc. Limnol. & Oceanog; Ecol. Soc. Am; Int. Asn. Limnol. Crab fishery, marine and fresh-water plankton; pelagic copepoda of the Northeast Pacific Ocean; pollution; Lake Erie ecology; hatching mechanisms; invertebrates. Address: Dept. of Biology, Memorial University of Newfoundland, St. John's, Newf, Can.

DAVIS, CHARLES A, b. Beaumont, Tex, Dec. 15, 33; m. 56; c. 3. ANIMAL ECOLOGY. B.S, Tex. A&M Univ, 56, M.S, 58; Okla. Coop. Wildlife Res. Unit fel, Okla. State Univ, 60-63, Nat. Wildlife Fedn. fel, 61-63, Ph.D.(zool), 64. Asst. prof. biol, Ark. State Col, 63-66; Southwest. State Col.(Okla), 66; asst. prof. WILDLIFE SCI, N.MEX. STATE UNIV, 67-71, ASSOC. PROF, 71- Wildlife Soc; Wilson Ornith. Soc; Am. Ornith Union. Ecology of birds and mammals. Address: Dept. of Animal, Range & Wildlife Sciences, New Mexico State University, Box 3-1, Las Cruces, NM 88001.

DAVIS, CHARLES ALFRED, b. Marion, N.C, Mar. 6, 39; m. 62. APPLIED MATHEMATICS. B.S, N.C. State, 61, M.Ap.Math, 63, Ph.D.(appl. math), 68. Instr. MATH, N.C. State, 65-67; asst. prof, MEREDITH COL, 67-68, ASSOC. PROF, 68-, CHMN. DEPT, 67- Math. Asn. Am. Mathematics as applied to heat transfer with particular application of integral transforms. Address: Dept. of Mathematics, Meredith College, Raleigh, NC 27611.

DAVIS, CHARLES FREEMAN, JR, b. Chicago, Ill, Aug. 1, 25; m. 56; c. 3. PHYSICS. B.S, Northwestern, 48, M.S, 49; Ph.D.(physics), Mass. Inst. Tech, 54. Opers. analyst, opers. res. off, Hopkins, 54-56; staff mem. res. lab. electronics, Mass. Inst. Tech, 56-58; head microwave devices sect, device res. dept, Tex. Instruments, Inc, 58-60, br. mgr. microwave & photo sensors, diode dept, 60-63; eng. mgr. microwave diode dept, Sylvania Elec. Prod, Inc, Gen. Tel. & Electronics Corp, Mass, 63-67; prin. res. scientist, res. div, RAYTHEON CORP, 67-69, PRIN. ENGR, MISSILE SYSTS. DIV, 69- U.S.N.R, 44-46, Res, 46-, Comdr. Am. Chem. Soc; Opers. Res. Soc. Am; Am. Phys. Soc; Inst. Elec. & Electronics Eng. Microwave physics; masers; low temperature techniques; microwave and photosensitive semiconductor devices. Address: Missile Systems Division, Raytheon Corp, Hartwell Rd, Bedford, MA 01730.

DAVIS, CHARLES HARGIS, b. Tell City, Ind, Sept. 23, 38; m. 68. INFORMATION SCIENCE. B.S, Indiana, 60, A.M, 66, Ph.D.(info. sci), 69; German govt. fel, Munich, 60-61. Asst. ed. subj. index div, Chem. Abstracts Serv, 62-65; dir. systs. info. retrieval, Clearinghouse on Reading, Ed. Resources Info. Ctr, 68-69; asst. prof. grad. sch. library sci, Drexel Univ, 69-71; ASSOC. PROF. SCH. LIBRARY SCI, UNIV. MICH, 71- Vis. asst. prof, grad. library sch, Ind. Univ, 69. AAAS; Am. Soc. Info. Sci; Am. Chem. Soc; Am. Library Asn; Asn. Comput. Mach. Organic chemistry; chemical documentation; classification theory; computer programming for information processing; library automation. Address: School of Library Science, University of Michigan, Ann Arbor, MI 48104.

DAVIS, CHARLES HOMER, b. Glendale, Ariz, Feb. 13, 12; m. 37; c. 2. AGRONOMY. B.S, Arizona, 35; M.S, Iowa State Col, 36, Ph.D.(plant physiol. & crops), 39. Asst. agronomist, exp. sta, Arizona, 37-43; assoc. agronomist, guayule res. proj, bur. plant indust, U.S. Dept. Agr, 43-45; agronomist, bur. reclamation, U.S. Dept. Interior, 45-52; fieldman, Ariz. Fertilizer Inc, 52-62, agronomist, 62-69; CHIEF AGRONOMIST, FARM BUILDERS DIV, AM. BIOCULTURE INC, 69- Am. Soc. Agron; Am. Soc. Plant Physiol. Water and growth relations of plants; use of water by plants and by irrigation projects in relation to yields; chemical and cultural weed control. Address: 4415 N. 31st Dr, Phoenix, AZ 85017.

DAVIS, CHARLES M(ITCHELL), JR, b. Washington, D.C, July 2, 25; m; c. 4. PHYSICS. B.A, Cath. Univ. Am, 51, M.S, 54, Ph.D, 62. Gen. physicist, U.S. Naval Ord. Labs, 51-62; asst. prof. physics, Am. Univ, 62-66, assoc. prof, 66-70, prof, 70; SUPV. RES. PHYSICIST PHYS. ACOUST, NAVAL RES. LAB, 70- U.S.N, 42-46. Sci. Res. Soc. Am; Acoust. Soc. Am; Am. Phys. Soc. Thermodynamic properties of liquids and amorphous materials by acoustical techniques; theory of the liquid-state, associated and metallic liquids. Address: Acoustics Division, Naval Research Lab, Washington, DC 20390.

DAVIS, CHARLES PACKARD, b. Concord, Mass, May 24, 22; m. 46; c. 2. MECHANICAL ENGINEERING. B.S.M.E, Rensselaer Polytech, 48. Instr, Rensselaer Polytech, 48-53; develop. engr, Gen. Elec. Co, 51-58; prof. mech. eng, CALIF. STATE POLYTECH. COL, 58-61, HEAD AERONAUT. ENG. DEPT, 61- U.S.N.R, 42-46. Am. Soc. Eng. Educ. Shock vibration; mechanical design. Address: Dept. of Aeronautical Engineering, California State Polytechnic College, San Luis Obispo, CA 93401.

DAVIS, CHARLES STEWERT, b. Akron, Ohio, Apr. 22, 35; m. 57; c. 3. CLINICAL PHARMACOLOGY. B.S, W.Va. Univ, 57; M.S, Purdue Univ, 59, Am. Found. Pharmaceut. Educ. fel, 59-60, Ph.D.(med. chem), 61; M.D, State Univ. N.Y. Upstate Med. Ctr, 70. Fel. Univ. Va, 60-61; asst. prof. med. chem, Purdue Univ, 61-63; unit. leader, EATON LABS, NORWICH PHARMACAL CO, 63-71, ASST. DIR. CLIN. PHARMACOL, 71- Nat. Insts. Health Res. grant, 62. Am. Chem. Soc. Pathophysiology of endocrine diseases and the evaluation of drugs altering these conditions. Address: Eaton Labs, Norwich Pharmacal Co, Norwich, NY 13815.

DAVIS, CHESTER L, b. Charleston, W.Va, July 2, 23; m. 51; c. 4. COMPUTER SCIENCE, APPLIED MATHEMATICS. A.B, West. Mich. Univ, 47; A.M, Univ. Mich, 53; Nat. Sci. Found. fel, Mich. State Univ, 61-62, Ph.D. 65. Sr. tech. instr. math. & eng. mech, Gen. Motors Inst, 47-55; mathematician, Curtiss-Wright Res. Labs, 55-56; sr. math. programmer, data processing dept, Gen. Motors Res. Labs, 56-58; prof. math. & eng. mech. & chmn. dept, Tri-State Col, 58-61; assoc. prof. mech. eng, Univ. Toledo, 63-66, dir. comput. ctr, 64-66; PROF. MATH, WEST. KY. UNIV, 66-, DIR. INSTRUCTIONAL COMPUT. LAB, 70- Consult, Gen. Motors Res. Labs, 58-59. Am. Asn. Comput. Mach; Am. Soc. Eng. Educ; Am. Math. Soc. Address: Dept. of Mathematics, Western Kentucky University, Bowling Green, KY 42101.

DAVIS, CLARENCE D(ANIEL), b. Pittsford, N.Y, Nov. 20, 12; m. 39; c. 3. OBSTETRICS, GYNECOLOGY. S.B, Mass. Inst. Tech, 35; M.D, Hopkins, 39. Rotating intern, Robert Packer Hosp, Pa, 39-40; Genesee Hosp, N.Y, 40-41; intern obstet. & gynec, univ. hosp, Minnesota, 41-42; asst. res. endocrinol, dept. obstet. & gynec, hosp, Duke, 42, res, 42-43, instr, 43-46; clin. assoc. physiol. & clin. assoc. obstet. & gynec, med. sch, Washington (Seattle) & assoc, div. med. gynec, Mason Clin, 46-50; assoc, hosp, Duke, 50-52, asst. prof. obstet. & gynec, 52-54; prof. & chmn. dept, sch. med, Missouri, 54-57; assoc. prof. OBSTET. & GYNEC, SCH. MED, YALE, 57-64 PROF, 64- Dipl, Am. Bd. Obstet. & Gynec, 49. Fel. Am. Col. Obstet. & Gynec; Am. Asn. Obstet. & Gynec; Am. Med. Asn. Address: Dept. of Obstetrics, Yale University, New Haven, CT 06510.

DAVIS, C(LAUDE) MANNING, b. Memphis, Tenn, Dec. 6, 15; m. 43; c. 1. ANALYTICAL CHEMISTRY. B.A, Miss. Col, 38; M.S, Tulane, 40; Ph.D. (chem), Pittsburgh, 52. Asst, Tulane & Cornell, 38-40, 40-42; res. chemist, Fisher Sci. Co, 42-47; res. fel, Mellon Inst, 47-52; HEAD ANAL. SECT, RES. LAB, INT. NICKEL CO, BAYONNE, N.J, 52- Instr, Univ. Pittsburgh, 44. Am. Chem. Soc. Spectroscopy; spectrophotometry. Address: Bon Aire Park Apt, 11 Sussex Ct, Suffern, NY 10901.

DAVIS, CLYDE EDWARD, b. Glenns Ferry, Idaho, June 24, 37; m. 59; c. 1. INORGANIC CHEMISTRY. B.S, Col. Idaho, 59; M.S, Oregon State, 62; NASA fel, & Ph.D.(inorg. chem), Colorado State, 68. Teacher chem, Casper Col, 61-64; asst. prof, Calif. State Polytech. Col, 67-68; Nat. Insts. Health fel. for work with Dr. D. A. Buckinham & Dr. A.M. Sargeson, Res. Sch. Chem, Australian Nat. Univ, 68-69; ASST. PROF. CHEM, HUMBOLDT STATE COL, 69- Am. Chem. Soc. Kinetics and mechanisms of base hydrolysis of coordination compounds; reactions of coordinated ligands of biological interest; sequential analysis of polypeptides by cobalt complexes. Address: Dept. of Chemistry, Humboldt State College, Arcata, CA 95521.

DAVIS, CLYDE O(LIVER), b. Akron, Ohio, Jan. 9, 10; m. 34; c. 4. EXPLOSIVES. B.A, Hiram Col, 31; M.Sc, Ohio State, 33, Ph.D.(phys. chem), 34. Asst. chem, Ohio State, 31-34; res. chemist, east. lab, E.I. DU PONT DE NEMOURS & CO, INC, 34-38, sect. head, 38-43, tech. asst. & dir. res, Off. Sci. Res. & Develop. & U.S. Army contracts, 43-46, sect. head high explosives, 46-51, asst. dir, EAST. LAB, 51-59, DIR, 59- Tech. adv, cmt. hazards transport. ammonium nitrate, Nat. Res. Coun, 50- Cert, Off. Sci. Res. & Develop, 45; cert. appreciation, War Dept, 45. Mem, Picatinny Arsenal Sci. Adv. Cmt, C.Eng, 46, Joint War & Navy Depts, 47. AAAS; Am. Chem. Soc; Am. Ord. Asn; Armed Forces Chem. Asn. Ammonium nitrate explosives; shaped charges; properties of high explosives; calculation of thermodynamic properties of diatomic gases from spectroscopic data; chemical methods of separating hydrogen isotopes. Address: E.I. du Pont de Nemours & Co, Inc, Explosives Dept, Eastern Lab, Gibbstown, NJ 08027.

DAVIS, COURTLAND H(ARWELL), JR, b. Alexandria, Va. Feb. 14, 21; m. 42; c. 6. NEUROLOGY, SURGERY. B.A, George Washington, 41; M.D, Virginia, 44. Rotating intern, U.S. Marine Hosp, New Orleans, La, 44-45; asst. resident neurosurg, Virginia, 45-46; Nat. Insts. Health fel. neuropath, med. center, Duke, 48-49, neurol, 49-50, asst. resident NEUROSURG, 50-51, resident, 51-52; instr, BOWMAN GRAY SCH. MED, 52-55, asst. prof, 55-59, assoc. prof, 59-66, PROF, 66-; MEM. STAFF, N.C. BAPTIST HOSP, 52- Instr, Duke Hosp, 49-50; vis. prof, Kuala Lumpur, Malaysia & Vellore, Madras, South India, 66; vis. neurosurg, HOPE, Cartagena, Columbia, S.Am, 67, Jamaica, W.I, 71. Dipl, Am. Bd. Neurol. Surg. 54. U.S.A, 46-48, Capt. Fel. Am. Col. Surg; Am. Med. Asn; Cong. Neurol. Surg; Am. Asn. Neurol. Surg; Neurosurg. Soc. Am.(secy, 62-65, pres, 69); Am. Asn. Ment. Deficiency; Asn. Res. Nerv. & Ment. Disease; hon. mem. soc Brit. Neurol. Surg; Soc. Neurol. Surg; Am. Acad. Neurol. Surg. Applied research in neurology and neurosurgery. Address: Section of Neurosurgery, Bowman Gray School of Medicine, Winston-Salem, NC 27103.

DAVIS, CRAIG H, b. Pittsburgh, Pa, Mar. 31, 35; m. 57; c. 2. MOLECULAR BIOLOGY. B.S, Oregon State, 57; M.S, Washington (Seattle), 62, Ph.D.(biochem), 65; Calif. Inst. Tech, 67. ASST. PROF. BIOL, SAN DIEGO STATE COL, 67- U.S.N, 57-60, Lt.(jg). AAAS. Episomal nature of Crown-Gall induction. Address: Dept. of Biology, San Diego State College, San Diego, CA 92115.

DAVIS, D. WAYNE, b. Ponce de Leon, Mo, Nov. 7, 35; m. 65; c. 1. VERTEBRATE ZOOLOGY. B.S, Univ. Mo, 61; M.A, Univ. Sask, 63; Ph.D.(ecol), Univ. Ark, 69. Asst. prof. BIOL, SCH. OF OZARKS, 68-70, ASSOC. PROF, 70- U.S.A.F, 54-58, S/Sgt. Am. Soc. Mammal; Wildlife Soc. Rodent and avian ecology. Address: Dept. of Biology, School of the Ozarks, Point Lookout, MO 65726.

DAVIS, DAN LEE, b. Afton, Wyo, Jan. 7, 33; m. 59; c. 4. SOLID STATE PHYSICS. B.A, Brigham Young, 57; Nat. Defense Educ. Act fel, New Mexico State, 59-62, M.S, 61, Ph.D.(physics), 65. Resident student assoc. solid state physics, Argonne Nat. Lab, 62-65; PHYSICIST, LAWRENCE RADIATION LAB, UNIV. CALIF, LIVERMORE, 65- U.S.A, 57-59. Am. Asn. Physics Teachers. Beta-decay nuclear magnetic resonance. Address: University of California Lawrence Radiation Lab, L-34, P.O. Box 808, Livermore, CA 94550.

DAVIS, DANIEL LAYTEN, b. Waynesville, N.C, Apr. 25, 38; m. 60; c. 3. PLANT PHYSIOLOGY & GENETICS. B.S, Berea Col, 60; M.S, Mich. State, 62; Ph.D.(plant physiol), N.C. State, 67. ASST. PROF. physiol, Miss. State, 67; PHYSIOL. GENETICS, UNIV. KY, 67- Univ. Ky. Res. Found. tobacco & health res. & serv. contract, Agr. Res. Serv, U.S. Dept. Agr, 68-70. Am. Soc. Plant Physiol; Am. Soc. Agron; Crop Sci. Soc. Am. Physiological and genetic aspects of plant sterols including emphasis on the location of these compounds in plants, mode of inheritance and role of steroids in sex determination. Address: Dept. of Agronomy, University of Kentucky, Lexington, KY 40506.

DAVIS, DARRELL LAWRENCE, b. Corral, Idaho, Feb. 17, 27; m. 55; c. 4. PHYSIOLOGY. B.S, Ore. State Col, 49, M.A, 52; Nat. Sci. Found. fel, St. Louis, 53-54, Ph.D.(physiol), 56. Asst, Ore. State Col, 49-51; St. Louis, 51-53, 54-56; cardiovasc. trainee, MED. COL. GA, 56-57, asst. res. prof, 57-60, asst. prof. PHYSIOL, 60-64, ASSOC. PROF, 64- Am. Physiol. Soc. Cardiovascular; temperature regulation. Address: Dept. of Physiology, Medical College of Georgia, Augusta, GA 30902.

DAVIS, DARWIN D(ARRELL), b. Salem, Ill, Dec. 29, 29; m. 56; c. 4. ORGANIC CHEMISTRY. B.A, Southern Illinois, 51; Nat. Sci. Found. fel, Minnesota, 54-55, Ph.D.(chem), 55. Asst. chem, Minnesota, 51-54; res. chemist explor. & polymer, E.I. DU PONT DE NEMOURS & CO, 55-64, sr. res. chemist PLASTICS INTERMEDIATES RES. & PROCESS DEVELOP, 64-69, STAFF CHEMIST, 69- AAAS; Am. Chem. Soc. Synthetic organic chemistry; polymer chemistry; process development. Address: 105 Tampa Dr, Victoria, TX 77901.

DAVIS, DAVID, b. Poland, Dec. 20, 20; nat; m. 46; c. 2. PLANT PATHOLOGY. B.A, Cornell, 46; Ph.D, Illinois, 50. Plant pathologist, Conn. Agr. Exp. Sta, 50-55; res. lab, Merck Sharp & Dohme Div, 55-60; res. assoc, N.Y. Bot. Garden, 60-70; DIR. RES, PHYTA LABS, 70- U.S.A.A.F, 43-45. Am. Phytopath. Soc; Am. Inst. Biol. Sci. Evaluation of pesticides; biological control of plant disease. Address: Phyta Labs, Ghent, NY 12075.

DAVIS, DAVID A, b. Springfield, Tenn, Mar. 24, 18; m. 41; c. 2. MEDICINE. B.A, Vanderbilt, 38, M.D, 41. Instr. surg, Tulane, 47-49; assoc. prof. anesthesiol, Med. Col. Ga, 49-52; from prof. surg. in charge anesthesiol. to clin. prof. anesthesiol, sch. med, Univ. N.C, Chapel Hill, 52-71; PROF. ANESTHESIOL, MED. CTR, DUKE UNIV, 71- Pres, Monitor Instruments, 69- Med.C, U.S.A, 42-45. Am. Med. Asn; Am. Soc. Anesthesiol; Asn. Univ. Anesthetists. Muscle relaxants; circulatory effects of anesthetic agents; local anesthetic drugs. Address: Dept. of Anesthesiology, Duke University Medical Center, AA Box 3094, Durham, NC 27710.

DAVIS, DAVID E(DWARD), b. Chicago, Ill, July 18, 13; m. 42; c. 3. ZOOLOGY. A.B, Swarthmore Col, 35; A.M, Harvard, 36, Atkins traveling fel, 37-38, Ph.D.(zool), 39. Sheldon traveling fel. from Harvard, Arg, 39-40; asst, Chicago, 41; zoologist, Rockefeller Found, Brazil, 41-44; asst. sanitarian, U.S. Pub. Health Serv, 44-45; res. assoc, Hopkins, 45-48, asst. prof, 48-50, assoc. prof. comp. behav, 50-59, asst. dean, 57-59; prof. ZOOL, Pa. State, 59-67; PROF. & HEAD DEPT, N.C. STATE UNIV, 67- Am. Inst. Biol. Sci. (pres, 71); Ecol. Soc. Am; Am. Soc. Mammal; Am. Soc. Zool; Am. Ornith. Union; Cooper Ornith. Soc; Wilson Ornith. Soc; Wildlife Soc; Wildlife Disease Asn. Nesting habits of birds; endocrine basis of behavior; mammals and insects in relation to disease; management of vertebrate populations. Address: Dept. of Zoology, North Carolina State University, P.O. Box 5577, State College Station, Raleigh, NC 27607.

DAVIS, DAVID G, b. Dickinson, N.Dak, July 21, 35. PLANT PHYSIOLOGY, TISSUE CULTURE. B.S, N.Dak. State Univ, 60, M.S, 62; Nat. Sci. Found. summer fel, Wash. State Univ, 63, Ph.D.(bot), 65. Asst. bot, N.Dak. State Univ, 60-62; Wash. State Univ, 62-63, 63-65; Atomic Energy Comn. fel, Univ. Minn, 65-67; RES. PHYSIOLOGIST PLANT PHYSIOL, METAB. & RADIATION RES. LAB, AGR. RES. SERV, 67- U.S.A.F, 56-59. Am. Asn. Plant Physiol; Weed Sci. Soc. Am. Electron spin resonance signals from higher plants; plant surface-pesticide interactions; environmental development of plant cuticles; growth and development of tissues and organs in vitro as affected by pesticides and growth regulators. Address: Metabolism and Radiation Research Lab, Agricultural Research Service, State University Station, Fargo, ND 58102.

DAVIS, D(AVID) GALE, b. Leicester, N.C, July 21, 35; m. 57; c. 3. GENETICS. B.S, West. Carolina Col, 57; M.A, North Carolina, 60; fel, Georgia, 61-62, Ph.D.(zool), 63; fel, Oak Ridge Nat. Lab, 62-63. Asst. zool, North Carolina, 57-60; Georgia, 60-61; res. assoc, Oak Ridge Nat. Lab, 63-64; sr. lectr. zool, Monash Univ, Australia, 64-67; asst. prof, Univ. West. Ont, 67-68; Nat. Insts. Health spec. res. fel, lab. genetics, Univ. Wis, Madison, 68-69; ASSOC. PROF. BIOL, UNIV. ALA, TUSCALOOSA, 69- AAAS; Genetics Soc. Am. Chromosome mechanics; recombination; developmental genetics. Address: Dept. of Biology, University of Alabama, P.O. Box 1927, University, AL 35486.

DAVIS, DAVID ROBERT, b. Lakewood, Ohio, Aug. 22, 29; m. 53; c. 2. FOOD TECHNOLOGY, HORTICULTURE. B.Sc, Ohio State, 52, M.Sc, 57, Ph.D.(hort), 59. Asst. prof. hort, Ohio Agr. Exp. Sta, 59-62; sr. res. chemist, Colgate Palmolive Co, 62-66; sect. leader new prod. develop, Corn Prod. Co, 66-69; SR. FOOD SCIENTIST, DEVRO, INC, 69- Chem.C, U.S.A, 53-55. AAAS; Am. Inst. Food Technol; Am. Inst. Biol. Sci. Quality evaluation and processing of fruit and vegetable products; new product development; dehydrated food products. Address: Devro, Inc, Southside Ave, Somerville, NJ 08876.

DAVIS, DAVID S, b. N.Y.C, Mar. 24, 39; m. 61; c. 2. ORGANIC CHEMISTRY. B.A, Cornell, 59; U.S. Air Force fel, N.Y. Univ, 64-65, Ph.D.(org. chem), 69. Res. chemist, Witco Chem. Corp, 66-68; PROD. DEVELOP. ASSOC, HARCHEM DIV, WALLACE & TIERNAN, INC, 68- Am. Chem. Soc. Free radical substitution; organo-sulfur chemistry; fatty acid derivatives; amines; product development. Address: Harchem Division, Wallace & Tiernan, Inc, 110 E. Hanover Ave, Cedar Knolls, NJ 07927.

DAVIS, DAVID WARREN, b. Mankato, Minn, July 6, 30; m. 58. PLANT BREEDING, GENETICS. B.S, Hawaii, 51; M.S, Illinois, 56; Campbell Soup assistantship & Ph.D.(hort), Oregon State, 63. Res. asst. genetics, Illinois, 55-56; asst-in-training, exp. sta, Hawaiian Sugar Planter's Asn, 56-57, asst. geneticist, 58-61; agriculturist, Lihue Plantation Co, Hawaii, 57-58; res. horticulturist, veg. & ornamental crops res. br, Agr. Res. Serv, U.S. Dept. Agr, 63-65; assoc. prof. veg. crop breeding, INST. AGR, UNIV. MINN, ST. PAUL, 65-68, PROF. HORT, 69- U.S.A.F, 51-55. Fel. AAAS; Am. Soc. Hort. Sci. Genetic improvement of plant populations for adaptability to commercial needs in vegetable agriculture; disease resistance; raw product quality. Address: Dept. of Horticultural Science, University of Minnesota, St. Paul, MN 55101.

DAVIS, DELAND H(ODGMAN), b. Battle Creek, Mich, May 28, 06; m. 35; c. 2. ANALYTICAL CHEMISTRY, STATISTICAL ANALYSIS. B.S, Mich. State Univ, 29; M.S, Univ. Mich, 34. Trainee eng, Detroit City Gas Co, 29-30; res. chemist, Kellogg Co, 30-33; chemist, Post Div, Gen. Foods Corp, 37-41, 45-48, dir. qual. control, 48-57, chief chemist, 57-65, qual. engr, 65-71; RETIRED. U.S.A, 34-37; U.S.A.A.F, 41-45, Lt. Col. Fel. Am. Soc. Qual. Control(treas, 57); Am. Chem. Soc. Quality control. Address: 221 Summer St, Battle Creek, MI 49015.

DAVIS, DENNIS DUVAL, b. Cleveland, Ohio, Nov. 9, 41; m. 63; c. 3. ORGANIC & ORGANOMETALLIC CHEMISTRY. B.S, Case Inst. Tech, 63; Nat. Insts. Health fel, California, Berkeley, 64-66, Ph.D.(chem), 66. Asst. prof. CHEM, N.MEX. STATE UNIV, 66-71, ASSOC. PROF, 71- Am. Chem. Soc. Physical-organic chemistry; electrophilic aliphatic substitution reactions of organometallic compounds; free radical chemistry; chemistry of organo-transition metal compounds. Address: Dept. of Chemistry, New Mexico State University, Box 3C, Las Cruces, NM 88001.

DAVIS, DICK D, b. Hobart, Okla, Aug. 7, 33; m. 52; c. 5. AGRONOMY. B.S, Oklahoma, 60; Nat. Sci. Found. fel. & M.S, Okla. State, 63, Ph.D.(bot), 65. ASST. PROF. AGRON, N.MEX. STATE UNIV, 64- Am. Soc. Agron; Crop Sci. Soc. Am. Genetics of disease resistance and insect tolerance in cotton. Address: Dept. of Agronomy, New Mexico State University, Las Cruces, NM 88001.

DAVIS, DONALD A, b. St. Louis, Mo, Nov. 16, 25; m. 47; c. 2. PLASTICS ENGINEERING. A.B, Louisville, 47; M.S, Princeton, 62. Chemist, Int. Harvester, Ky, 47-50, prin. chemist, 50-53; engr, GEN. ELEC. CO, 53-58, tech. leader, 58-60, mgr. chem. eng, 60-64, plastics eng, 64-68, MGR. EQUIP DEVELOP. LAB, 68- U.S.N, 44-47, Ens. Plastics properties and processing; dynamic mechanical properties of plastics. Address: Major Appliance Labs, General Electric Co, Appliance Park, Bldg. 35, Room 406, Louisville, KY 40225.

DAVIS, DONALD ECHARD, b. Charleston, Ill, Jan. 12, 16; m. 40; c. 2. PLANT PHYSIOLOGY. B.Ed, East. Ill. State Col, 36, hon. D.Pd, 56; M.S, Ohio State Univ, 40, Nat. Res. Coun. fel, 45-46, Ph.D.(bot), 47. Inspector, Ravenna Ord. Plant, U.S. War Dept, 42-43; instr. bot, Ohio State Univ, 46-47; asst. prof, Auburn Univ, 48, assoc. prof. bot, univ. & assoc. botanist, exp. sta, 49-50; Atomic Energy Comn. agr. res. fel, Univ. Tenn, 51-52; assoc. prof. bot, AUBURN UNIV, 52-55, prof, 55-68, ALUMNI PROF. BOT. & MICROBIOL, 68-, BOTANIST, EXP. STA, 55-, assoc. botanist, 52-55. Vis. prof, Univ. Ill, 65; mem. comt. on persistent pesticide residues, Nat. Acad. Sci-Nat. Res. Coun, 68-69; mem. consult. comt. to rev. the use of 2,4,5-T, Nat. Acad. Sci, 70; mem, Nat. Adv. Panel Weed Res. U.S.A, 43-45. AAAS; Am. Soc. Plant Physiol; Weed Sci. Soc. Am; Am. Inst. Biol. Sci. Ecological plant physiology; aquatic pollution; physiology of herbicidal action; pesticide problems. Address: Dept. of Botany & Microbiology, Auburn University, Auburn, AL 36830.

DAVIS, D(ONALD) G, b. Stoneham, Mass, Aug. 23, 32; m. 54; c. 3. ANALYTICAL CHEMISTRY. B.A, Wesleyan, 54; Ph.D.(chem), Harvard, 57. Asst. prof. CHEM, Ga. Inst. Tech, 52-59; assoc. prof, LA. STATE UNIV, NEW ORLEANS, 59-63, PROF, 63-, chmn. dept. chem, 60-64, asst. dean acad. affairs, 64-65, dean grad. sch, 65-69. Sci. adv, Food & Drug Admin, 66-; res. assoc, Calif. Inst. Technol, 68. AAAS; Am. Chem. Soc; N.Y. Acad. Sci. Electroanalytical chemistry; biochemistry; coulometry; polarography; classical methods of inorganic analysis; electron transfer rates. Address: Dept. of Chemistry, Louisiana State University in New Orleans, Lake Front, New Orleans, LA 70122.

DAVIS, DONALD R(AY), b. Oklahoma City, Okla, Mar. 28, 34. ENTOMOLOGY. B.A, Kansas, 56; Ph.D.(entom), Cornell, 62. Assoc. curator LEPIDOPTERA, SMITHSONIAN INST, 61-64, CURATOR, 64- Am. Philos. Soc. summer grant, 63; Smithsonian Res. Found. grant, 66- Soc. Syst. Zool; Lepidop. Soc. Systematics, phylogeny and biology of the Microlepidoptera, particularly the superfamily Tineoidea and all members of the Monotrysia; biology of leaf mining Lepidoptera. Address: Dept. of Entomology, Smithsonian Institution, Washington, DC 20560.

DAVIS, DONALD ROBERT, b. La Jara, Colo, Mar. 19, 41. PHYSICAL CHEMISTRY. Calif. Inst. Tech, 59-62; univ. fel, California, Los Angeles, 62-63, Nat. Sci. Found. fel, 63-65, Ph.D.(chem), 66. Nat. Sci. Found. fel. phys. chem, Calif. Inst. Tech, 65-66, instr, 66-67; ASST. PROF. CHEM, UNIV. CALIF, IRVINE, 67- AAAS; Am. Phys. Soc; Am. Chem. Soc. Carboranes; radiation chemistry; gas kinetics; photochemistry; education. Address: Dept. of Chemistry, University of California, Irvine, CA 92664.

DAVIS, DONALD W(ALTER), b. San Francisco, Calif, May 30, 20; m. 43; c. 6. ENTOMOLOGY. B.S, California, 41, Ph.D, 50. Asst. entom, California, 46-50; res. entomologist, Calif. Spray-Chem. Corp, 50-54; assoc. prof. ENTOM, teaching & exp. sta, UTAH STATE UNIV, 54-67, PROF, DEPT. ZOOL, 67- U.S.A.F, 41-46, Res, 46-54, 1st Lt. Entom. Soc; Am. Biology and control of agricultural pests; spider mites of the genus Tetranychus; agricultural entomology. Address: Dept. of Zoology, Utah State University, Logan, UT 84321.

DAVIS, DORLAND J(ONES), b. Chicago, Ill, July 2, 11; m. 38; c. 2. MEDICINE. B.S, Illinois, 33; M.D, Hopkins, 37, Dr.P.H.(epidemiol), 39. COMMISSIONED MED. OFF, U.S. PUB. HEALTH SERV, 39-, chief, lab. infectious diseases, Nat. Microbiol. Inst, 54-56, assoc. dir, NAT. INST. ALLERGY & INFECTIOUS DISEASES, 56-64, DIR, 64- Mem. expert cmt. influenza, WHO, 52. Dipl, Am. Bd. Prev. Med. Fel. AAAS; fel. Am. Acad. Microbiol; fel. Am. Col. Prev. Med; Am. Soc. Microbiol; Am. Med. Asn; fel. Am. Pub. Health Asn; Infectious Diseases Soc. Am; Am. Asn. Immunol; Asn. Mil. Surg. U.S.(Stitt award, 55); Am. Epidemiol. Soc. Epidemiology of infectious diseases; influenza; psittacosis; bacterial conjunctivitis; infectious hepatitis; trypanosomiasis. Address: National Institutes of Health, Bethesda, MD 20014.

DAVIS, DUANE M, b. Indianapolis, Ind, July 10, 33; m. 57, 71; c. 2. AERONAUTICS. B.S, Purdue, 55, Ph.D.(aeronaut), 67; M.S, Pittsburgh, 57. Engr, Bettis Atomic Power Div, Westinghouse Elec. Co, 55-57; U.S. AIR FORCE, 57-, instr. AERONAUT, U.S. AIR FORCE ACAD, 66-67, asst. prof, 68-71, ASSOC. PROF, 71- U.S.A.F, 57-, Maj. Am. Inst. Aeronaut. & Astronaut. Optimization; weapons system selection and specification; optimal tactics for weapon system employment; automatic data acquisition; heat transfer. Address: Dept. of Aeronautics (DFAN), U.S. Air Force Academy, CO 80840.

DAVIS, EARLE ANDREW, JR, b. Aliquippa, Pa, June 1, 19; m. 43. NEUROPHYSIOLOGY. B.S, Grove City Col, 41; M.S, Pittsburgh, 43; Ph.D.(physiol. ecol), Illinois, 53. Asst. prof. biol, Elmhurst Col, 46-49, PROF, Buena Vista Col, 52-53; West Liberty State Col, 53-55; ANAT, UNIV. CALIF, IRVINE-CALIF. COL. MED, 55- Med.C, 43-46, Sgt. AAAS; Am. Soc. Zool; Am. Asn. Anat. Human gross and microanatomy; effects of metabolic rate on distribution of animals; sites of action of hallucinogenic drugs in cat brain. Address: Dept. of Anatomy, California College of Medicine, University of California, Irvine, CA 92664.

DAVIS, E(ARL) JAMES, b. St. Paul, Minn, July 22, 34; m. 64; c. 2. CHEMICAL ENGINEERING. B.S, Gonzaga, 56; Leeds & Northrup fel, Washington (Seattle), 57-60, Ph.D.(chem. eng), 60. Design engr, Union Carbide Chem. Co, W.Va, 56; res. engr, Boeing Airplane Co, Wash, 57; asst. prof. CHEM. ENG, Gonzaga, 60-65, ASSOC. PROF, 65-68; CLARKSON COL. TECHNOL, 68- Petrol. Res. Fund grants, 61-65; Nat. Sci. Found. res. grants, 63-64, 66-68 & 69-71, res. fel, Imp. Col, London, 64-65; Sigma Xi grant, 69; mem, inst. colloid & surface sci, Clarkson Col. Technol. AAAS; Am. Chem. Soc; Am. Inst. Chem. Eng; Am. Soc. Eng. Educ. Heat transfer and fluid mechanics aspects of two-phase flow; bubble and droplet phenomena; convective diffusion; aerosol physics. Address: Dept. of Chemical Engineering, Clarkson College of Technology, Potsdam, NY 13676.

DAVIS, EDWARD A(LEX), b. Houston, Tex, Jan. 2, 31; m. 52; c. 4. OPERATIONS RESEARCH. B.A. & Texaco fel, Rice, 55, M.A, 56, Atomic Energy Cmn. fel, 58-61, Ph.D.(nuclear physics), 61. Proj. officer, nuclear power off, U.S. Army Engr. Res. & Develop. Labs, 57-58; res. physicist, Texaco, Inc, 61-62; asst. prof. physics, Oklahoma City Univ, 62-64; SR. STAFF PHYSICIST OPERS. RES, JOHNS HOPKINS UNIV, 64-, MEM. FACULTY, EVE. SCH, 66- U.S.A, 56-58, 1st Lt. AAAS; Opers. Res. Soc. Am; Am. Asn. Physics Teachers; Math. Asn. Am; Inst. Mgt. Sci. Fast neutron physics; nuclear well-logging; tactical military operations analysis; command and control systems; transit systems analysis; applied mathematics; simulation; probabilistic models; design and analysis of instruction systems. Address: Applied Physics Lab, Johns Hopkins University, 8621 Georgia Ave, Silver Spring, MD 20910.

DAVIS, EDWARD ALLAN, b. San Francisco, Calif, Oct. 26, 17; m. 56; c. 3. MATHEMATICS. B.A, California, Berkeley, 40, M.A, 44, Ph.D.(math), 51. Teaching asst, assoc. & jr. instr. for Army Air Force in MATH, California, Berkeley, 40-47; instr, Nevada, 47-48, asst. prof, 48-55; UNIV. UTAH, 55-59, assoc. prof, 60-69, PROF, 69- Fund for Adv. Ed. res. fel, Stanford Univ. & Univ. Chicago, 53-54; summer vis. asst. prof, California, 57 & Oregon, 59; assoc. prog. dir. spec. proj. in sci. ed, Nat. Sci. Found, D.C, 61-62, consult, 62-67, prog. dir, student & coop. prog, 67-70, consult, 71- Am. Math. Soc; Math. Asn. Am. Mathematical economics; teaching training programs in mathematics. Address: Dept. of Mathematics, University of Utah, Salt Lake City, UT 84112.

DAVIS, E(DWARD) D(EWEY), b. Phila, Pa, Sept. 24, 33. MATHEMATICS. B.A, Pennsylvania, 55, M.A, 57; Ph.D.(math), Chicago, 61. Instr. MATH, Northwestern, 61-62; lectr. & res. assoc, Yale, 62-64; asst. prof, Purdue Univ, 64-67; STATE UNIV. N.Y. ALBANY, 67-68, ASSOC. PROF, 68- Am. Math. Soc. Commutative algebra, especially Northerian rings; algebraic geometry. Address: Division of Mathematical Sciences, State University of New York at Albany, 1400 Washington Ave, Albany, NY 12203.

DAVIS, EDWARD L(YON), b. Fall River, Mass, July 15, 29. BOTANY. B.A, Harvard, 51; M.S, Massachusetts, 53; Ph.D.(bot), Washington (St. Louis), 56. Instr. BOT, Massachusetts, 53; asst, Mo. Bot. Garden, 54-56; asst. prof, UNIV. MASS, AMHERST, 57-61, ASSOC. PROF, 61- Vis. lectr, Smith Col, 58-59. Bot. Soc. Am. Anatomy, systematics and evolution of higher plants; morphogenesis. Address: Dept. of Botany, Morrill Science Center, University of Massachusetts, Amherst, MA 01002.

DAVIS, EDWIN A(LDEN), b. New Haven, Conn, Dec. 28, 23; m. 51; c. 2. PLANT PHYSIOLOGY. B.S, Connecticut, 45; Ph.D.(plant physiol), Yale, 49. Res. fel. plant physiol, Carnegie Inst, Dept. Plant Biol, Stanford, Calif, 49-52; PLANT PHYSIOLOGIST agr. res, Dow Chem. Co, 53-57; agr. res. serv, U.S. DEPT. AGR, 58-63, FOREST SERV, 63- Bot. Soc. Am; Am. Soc. Plant Physiol; Weed Sci. Soc. Weed control; transpiration; photosynthesis; watershed management. Address: Forest Hydrology Lab, Arizona State University, Tempe, AZ 85281.

DAVIS, EDWIN GRIFFITH, b. Boise, Idaho, Sept. 1, 16; m. 50; c. 3. ORGANIC CHEMISTRY. A.B, Harvard, 38, A.M, 40, Ph.D.(org. chem), 42. Res. specialist chem, U.S. Air Force, 49-55; sect. chief atomic energy, U.S. Army, 55-62; ASST. SCI. ADV. GEN. SCI, TECH. APPLN. CTR, U.S. AIR FORCE, 62- U.S.A, 42-46, Lt. Col. Am. Chem. Soc; Am. Ornith. Union. Chemistry; atomic energy; geophysical sciences. Address: 1201 23rd St. S, Arlington, VA 22202.

DAVIS, EDWIN N(ATHAN), b. Corning, N.Y, Apr. 23, 09; m. 36; c. 8. MICROBIOLOGY. B.S, Cornell, 34, 38-40. Anal. & res. chemist, Pleasant Valley Wine Co, N.Y, 33-36; jr. chemist, bur. agr. chem, U.S. Dept. Agr, 36-39; asst. & instr. chem, N.Y. Exp. Sta, Geneva, 39-41; prod. supt, Mich. Wineries, Inc, 41-43; res. biochemist, Hiram Walker & Sons, Inc, 43-63; MICROBIOLOGIST, NORTH. REGIONAL RES. LAB, AGR. RES. SERV, U.S. DEPT. AGR, 63- AAAS; Am. Soc. Microbiol. Yeast fermentations, beverage and industrial alcohol; enzymatic starch hydrolysis; biosynthesis; microbial polymers; agripollution control. Address: Northern Regional Research Lab, U.S. Dept. of Agriculture, 1815 N. University, Peoria, IL 61604.

DAVIS, ELDON V(ERNON), b. Burwell, Nebr, Aug. 4, 23; m. 45; c. 1. VIROLOGY. B.S, Nebraska, 49, M.S, 51; Ph.D, Pennsylvania, 57. Jr. res. scientist, Upjohn Pharmaceut. Co, 50-52; scientist & head virus labs, 52-54; asst, Pennsylvania, 54-56, res. assoc, 56-57; asst. prof, univ. & fel, Wistar Inst, 57-58; virologist & head labs, U.S. Pub. Health Serv, 58-63; sr. virologist, Midwest Res. Inst, 63-64; from virologist to SR. RES. SCIENTIST, NORDEN LABS, INC, 64- U.S.A, 42-45. AAAS; N.Y. Acad. Sci; Tissue Culture Asn. Cell physiology, tissue culture; growth of mammalian cells in submerged culture; kinetics of viral growth; viral isolation and characterization; vaccines. Address: Norden Labs, Inc, 601 W. Cornhusker Hwy, Lincoln, NE 68501.

DAVIS, ELDRED JACK, b. Kelleyville, Okla, Oct. 14, 30; m. BIOCHEMISTRY. B.Sc, Abilene Christian Col, 56; M.Sc, Fla. State, 58; Can. Heart Asn. fel, McGill, 61-63, Ph.D.(biochem), 63. Res. biochemist, Lederle Labs, Am. Cyanamid Co, 58-61; U.S. Pub. Health Serv. fel, lab. biochem, Amsterdam, 63-65; asst. prof. BIOCHEM, SCH. MED, IND. UNIV, 65-69, ASSOC. PROF, 69- U.S.N, 50-54. AAAS; Am. Soc. Biol. Chem; Brit. Biochem. Soc. Metabolism of muscle; mitochondria and metabolic control; gluconeogenesis; anaplerotic pathways in mammalian systems. Address: Dept. of Biochemistry, Indiana University School of Medicine, Indianapolis, IN 46202.

DAVIS, ELIZABETH A(LLAWAY), b. N.Y.C, Jan. 5, 41; m. 68; c. 1. DEVELOPMENTAL BIOLOGY. B.A, Mt. Holyoke Col, 62; Nat. Insts. Health grant, Brandeis Univ, 63-68, Ph.D.(develop. biol), 69. Stud. with Dr. Lawrence Bogorad, biol. labs, Harvard, 68-69; ASST. PROF. BIOL, UNIV. MASS, BOSTON, 69- AAAS; Am. Soc. Plant Physiol; Soc. Protozool; Am. Soc. Zool. Physiology, genetics, multiplication and differentiation of intracellular organelles, particularly chloroplasts; regulatory roles and integration of organelles, particularly chloroplasts in the cell and the multicellular organism. Address: Dept. of Biology, University of Massachusetts, 100 Arlington St, Boston, MA 02116.

DAVIS, ELIZABETH YOUNG, b. Ft. Collins, Colo, Apr. 23, 20; m. 41; c. 3. NUTRITIONAL BIOCHEMISTRY, PHYSIOLOGY. B.S, Colorado State, 41; M.S, Auburn, 57, Ph.D.(nutrit. biochem), 64. Instr. foods & nutrit, Auburn, 57-60; assoc. prof. nutrit. res, Tuskegee Inst, 64-66; PROF. NUTRIT, AUBURN UNIV, 66-, RES. COORDINATOR HOME ECON, 69- AAAS; Am. Chem. Soc; Am. Dietetic Asn; Am. Pub. Health Asn; Inst. Food Tech. Lipid metabolism; biosynthesis of carnitine; incorporation of ethionine ethyl into phospholipids; ethylated ethanolamines in phospholipids; metabolism of N-alkyl amines; cholesterol; diethylstilbestrol; fatty acid relationships. Address: Dept. of Nutrition & Foods, School of Home Economics, Auburn University, Auburn, AL 36830.

DAVIS, ELMO W(ARREN), b. Idaho, Sept. 9, 20; m. 51; c. 4. GENETICS, HORTICULTURE. B.S, Univ. Idaho, 48; M.S, Univ. Calif, Davis, 49, Aggler Musser res. fel, 49-52, Ph.D.(genetics), 52. Assoc. prof. hort. & assoc. olericulturist, Kans. State Univ, 52-53; geneticist, U.S. Dept. Agr, 53-56, res. horticulturist, 57-66; DIR. AGR. RES. & DEVELOP, GILROY FOODS, INC, 66-, MEM. BD. DIRS, 70-, mem. jr. bd. exec, 67-69. U.S.A, 43-47, Res, 47-60. Am. Soc. Hort. Sci; Am. Genetics Asn. Genetics; seed production; breeding; horticulture characters of Allium species; hybrid onions. Address: Box 1088, Gilroy Foods, Inc, Gilroy, CA 95020.

DAVIS, ELWYN H, b. Leon, Iowa, Jan. 10, 42; m. 63; c. 1. MATHEMATICS. B.S.E, Univ. Mo-Columbia, 64, M.A, 66, Gregory fel, 68, Ph.D.(math), 69. ASST. PROF. MATH, KANS. STATE COL. PITTSBURG, 69- Nat. Sci. Found. grant, convexity conf, 71. Am. Math. Soc; Math. Asn. Am. Projective planes; nearfields and generalizations; construction of finite projective planes via coordinatizing systems; generalizations of projective planes and the coordinatizing systems. Address: Dept. of Mathematics, Kansas State College of Pittsburg, Pittsburg, KS 66762.

DAVIS, ERNST MICHAEL, b. Victoria, Tex, Oct. 12, 33; div; c. 1. AQUATIC BIOLOGY, SANITARY ENGINEERING. B.A, N.Tex. State Univ, 56, M.A, 62; Ph.D.(sanit. eng), Univ. Okla, 66. Nat. Sci. Found. grant, Univ. Tex, Austin, 66-67, Fed. grant sanit. eng, 66-68, Off. Water Resources Res. grant limnol. invests, 67-68, Fed. Water Pollution Control Admin. grant, 67-69, Tex. Water Qual. Bd. grant, 68, ASST. PROF. sanit. eng, 69-70; ENVIRON. HEALTH, UNIV. TEX. SCH. PUB. HEALTH, HOUSTON, 70- Tex. Water Develop. Bd. grant, Univ. Tex. Sch. Pub. Health, Houston, 70-72, NASA grant, 71-72; consult, Environ. Protection Agency, 70- Chem.C, U.S.A, 56-58, Res, 58-63, 1st Lt. AAAS; Am. Soc. Civil Eng; Water Pollution Control Fedn; Am. Water Works Asn; Int. Asn. Water Pollution Res; Am. Asn. Prof. Sanit. Eng. Natural systems engineering; water resources management; pollution abatement. Address: University of Texas School of Public Health, P.O. Box 20186, Astrodome Station, Houston, TX 77025.

DAVIS, FRANCIS J(OHN), b. Noonan, N.Dak, May 5, 15; m. 41; c. 3. PHYSICS. B.S, North Dakota, 36; Ph.D.(physics), Wisconsin, 40. Asst, North Dakota, 35-37; Wisconsin, 37-40; radio engr, U.S. Naval Res. Lab, 40-41; asst. physicist, Bur. Standards, 41-47; sr. physicist, OAK RIDGE NAT. LAB, 47-51, HEAD PHYSICIST, 51- With Off. Sci. Res. & Develop, 44. Am. Phys. Soc. Spectroscopy; electronics used in radio-activity; measurement and protection from radioactive radiations; gaseous electronics. Address: Oak Ridge National Lab, Oak Ridge, TN 37831.

DAVIS, FRANCIS K(AYE), JR, b. Scranton, Pa, May 4, 18; m. 41; c. 2. PHYSICAL METEOROLOGY. B.S, W.Chester State Col, 39; scholar, Mass. Inst. Tech, 43-44, M.S, 44; Ph.D, N.Y. Univ, 57. Asst, Mass. Inst. Tech, 43-44; PROF. PHYSICS, DREXEL UNIV, 46-, DEAN COL. SCI, 70- Staff meteorologist, WFIL-WFIL-TV, 47-; asst, Hopkins, 54- Meteorol. consult, 50-; C.W. Thornthwaite Assocs, 54-; Day & Zimmerman, 55-; City of Phila, 56-; Am. Mach. & Foundry Co, 57-; Radio Corp. Am, 58- U.S.A.A.F, 42-46, Capt. Am. Meteorol. Soc; Am. Phys. Soc; Am. Asn. Physics Teachers; Am. Geophys. Union. Storm damage; atmospheric pollution; physics of fog formation; upper atmosphere physics. Address: 103 Avonbrook Rd, Wallingford, PA 19086.

DAVIS, FRANK, b. New York, N.Y, Oct. 8, 17; m. 47; c. 3. BIOCHEMISTRY. B.A, Brooklyn Col, 40; M.S, Va. Polytech, 41; Mass. Inst. Tech, 43; Ph.D, Maryland, 48. Assoc. inspector powder & explosives, Radford Ord. Works, Va, 41-42; asst. poultry nutrit, exp. sta, Maryland, 47-48; bacteriologist microbiol, res. div, bur. agr. & indust. chem, U.S. Dept. Agr, 48-50; immunochemist, nat. naval med. center, Naval Med. Res. Inst, Md, 50-52; asst. chief assessment br, Ralph M. Parsons Co, 52-54; asst. dir. res. & develop, Block Drug Co, 54-57; tech. dir. Whitehall Labs. Div, Am. Home Prods, 57-66; v.pres. & tech. dir, J.B. Williams Co, 67-69; PRES, DAVIS LABS, INC, 69- U.S.A.A.F, 42-46. AAAS; Am. Soc. Microbiol; Am. Pharmaceut. Asn; Soc. Cosmetic Chem; Am. Chem. Soc. Vitamin deficiencies and respiratory quotient of rat; growth factors of the chick; bacterial nutrition and metabolism; bioorganic studies; enzymes; toxicology; detergents; fungicides; dentifrices; pharmaceuticals; aerosols. Address: Davis Labs, Inc, P.O. Box 747, Cherry Hill, NJ 08034.

DAVIS, FRANK F(RENCH), b. Pendleton, Ore, July 19, 20; m. 48; c. 2. BIOCHEMISTRY. B.S, Univ. Hawaii, 50; Ph.D.(biochem), Univ. Calif, 55. Jr. res. biochemist, Univ. Calif, 54-56, asst, 56-57; asst. prof. agr. biochem, RUTGERS UNIV, 57-59, assoc. prof, 59-64, PROF. BIOCHEM, 64- U.S.N, 44-46. AAAS; Am. Chem. Soc; Am. Soc. Biol. Chem. Physical and chemical studies on nucleic acids; enzymology. Address: Dept. of Biochemistry, Rutgers University, New Brunswick, NJ 08903.

DAVIS, FRANK R(OSCOE), b. Richmond, Va, Dec. 10, 03; m. 38; c. 2. ZOOLOGY. B.S, Va. Union, 27; M.S, Michigan, 32; Wisconsin, 40-46; Ph.D, St. Andrews, 58; Sc.D, London, 65. Instr. high sch, Va, 27-28, prin, 28-30; instr. math, Rust Col, 32-33; BIOL, Ft. Valley State Col, 34-42; PROF, PAINE COL, 44- Res. exten. fel, St. Andrews. AAAS; Nat. Asn. Biol. Teachers. Investigations in aphid control; phylogenetics of certain monocotyledons, primarily physiochemical reactions. Address: 1655 Douglas St, Augusta, GA 30901.

DAVIS, FRANKLIN A, b. Des Moines, Iowa, Apr. 1, 39; m. 67. ORGANIC CHEMISTRY. B.S, Wisconsin, 62; Ph.D.(org. chem), Syracuse, 66. Res. asst. ORG. CHEM, Syracuse, 63-66; Welch fel, Texas, 66-68; ASST. PROF, DREXEL UNIV, 68- Am. Chem. Soc. Organic boron compounds; synthesis and reactions of anti-aromatic and aromatic organoboron compounds; ^{11}B nuclear magnetic resonance chemical shifts as applied to structure and aromaticity; sulfenamides; thermal and photochemical rearrangement; synthesis of an aromatic sulfenamide. Address: Dept. of Chemistry, Drexel University, Philadelphia, PA 19104.

DAVIS, FRANKLIN O(TTO), b. Mt. Sterling, Ky, May 29, 09; m. 34; c. 4. ORGANIC CHEMISTRY. A.B, Centre Col, 30; Hopkins, 30-31, 32-34; Berlin, 31-32. Res. chemist, THIOKOL CORP, 34-47, asst. develop. mgr, 47-53, sr. res. chemist, 53-58, mgr. patent dept, 58-65, DIR. PATENTS, 65- AAAS; N.Y. Acad. Sci; Am. Chem. Soc; The Chem. Soc. Organic sulfur compounds; polysulfide polymers. Address: 11 Morningside Ave, Yardley, PA 19068.

DAVIS, FRED WEYMOUTH, b. Elizabeth City, N.C, Dec. 1, 04. INORGANIC & PHYSICAL CHEMISTRY. B.S, North Carolina, 27, M.S, 28; Oberlin Col, 31-32. Chemist, Am. Enka Corp, 29-31; instr. pub. sch, N.C, 33-36; consult. chemist, 36-39; chemist, U.S. Sugar Corp, Fla, 40-46; instr. chem, Miami (Fla), 47-49; pres, Chemurgics, Inc, 49-51; chemist, Am. Chlorophyll Co, 52-54; Permachem Corp, 55-56; nuclear fuels, Babcock & Wilcox Corp, 57-65; instr. phys. & chem, Bedford County Schs, 66-67; ASST. PROF. CHEM, LYNCHBURG COL, 67- Consult, Va. Res. Assocs, 65. AAAS; Am. Chem. Soc; Am. Nuclear Soc. Manufacture of nuclear fuels; radioactive wastes; inorganic colloids. Address: 1114 Dandridge Dr, Lynchburg, VA 24501.

DAVIS, FREDERIC W(HITLOCK), b. Somers, Conn, Nov. 13, 24; m. 51; c. 5. ZOOLOGY, WILDLIFE MANAGEMENT. B.S, Univ. Conn, 47; U.S. Bur. Sport Fisheries & Wildlife fel, Univ. Mass, Amherst, 62-64, M.S, 63, Ph.D. (zool), 68. Electronics engr, Naval Ord. Lab, Bur. Ord, U.S. Navy, Md, 47-50, fuze design engr, 50-54, supvry. electronics engr, Naval Ord. Lab, Calif, 54-59; instr. zool, Holyoke Community Col, 64-66, asst. prof, 66-67; BIOL, FITCHBURG STATE COL, 67-69, ASSOC. PROF, 69-, DIR, FIELD STA. & BIRD OBSERV, 68- U.S.N, 44-46, Res, 48-59, Ens. Am. Ornith. Union; Ecol. Soc. Am; Wilson Ornith. Soc; Brit. Trust Ornith. Ornithological investigations relating to pesticide effects, life history, breeding biology and ecological relations. Address: Dept. of Biology, Fitchburg State College, Fitchburg, MA 01420.

DAVIS, F(REDERICK) H(EUSTON), b. Vancouver, B.C, Can, Mar. 22, 21; m. 48; c. 3. PSYCHIATRY. M.D, Toronto, 43; McGill, 51; Col. Physicians & Surg, Canada, 52; New Orleans Psychoanal. Inst, 62. Demonstr. PSYCHIAT, McGill, 49-50; clin. teacher, Toronto, 50-53; asst. prof, sch. med, La. State, 54-57, assoc. prof, 57-61; CLIN. PROF, SOUTHWEST. MED. SCH, UNIV. TEX, DALLAS, 61- Dipl, Am. Bd. Psychiat, 56. R.C.A.M.C, 44-46, Capt. Fel. Am. Psychiat. Asn; Am. Psychoanal. Asn. Psychoanalysis; electromyography in relation to stress. Address: 5346 W. University Blvd, Dallas, TX 75209.

DAVIS, FREDERICK WILLIAM JESSOP, b. Waterford, Ireland, May 18, 33; Can. citizen; m. 53; c. 3. ENZYMOLOGY. B.S.A, Univ. Guelph, 65; fel, Univ. Man, 65, Ph.D.(microbiol), 70. Lectr, UNIV. MAN, 65-70, ASST. PROF. BIOL. & ADJ. PROF. MICROBIOL, 70- Mechanism of action and possible functions of alkaline phosphatases; enzymes of pentose metabolism; kinetics and regulatory mechanisms. Address: Biology Teaching Unit, University of Manitoba, Winnipeg 19, Man, Can.

DAVIS, GEORGE D(IAMENT), b. Ithaca, N.Y, May 7, 26; m. 50; c. 1. PHYS-IOLOGY. A.B, Princeton, 46; Ph.D.(physiol), Yale, 51. Instr. PHYSIOL, SCH. MED, LA. STATE UNIV, NEW ORLEANS, 51-53, asst. prof, 53-56, assoc. prof, 56-63, PROF, 63- Vis. prof, La. State-Agency Int. Develop. Contract, sch. med, Costa Rica, 61-63. AAAS; Am. Acad. Neurol; Am. Physiol. Soc; N.Y. Acad. Sci. Neurophysiology; biophysical instrumentation. Address: School of Medicine, Louisiana State University, 1542 Tulane Ave, New Orleans, LA 70112.

DAVIS, GEORGE H, b. Detroit, Mich, July 25, 21; m. 49; c. 2. GEOLOGY, HYDROLOGY. B.S, Illinois, 42; California, Los Angeles, 46-47. Asst. geol, State Geol. Surv, Ill, 42-46; geologist, U.S. GEOL. SURV, 48-68, RES. HYDROLOGIST, 68- First off, Inst. Atomic Energy Agency, Vienna, 66-68; ed, Water Resources Res, 69- U.S.A, 42-46. Geol. Soc. Am; Am. Geophys. Union. Geologic occurrence of ground water. Address: Water Resources Division, U.S. Geological Survey, Washington, DC 20242.

DAVIS, GEORGE H(ERBERT), b. Pittsburgh,Pa, Aug. 30, 42; m. 65; c. 2. STRUCTURAL & ECONOMIC GEOLOGY. B.A, Col. Wooster, 64; M.A, Univ. Tex. Austin, 66; NASA trainee, Nat. Sci. Found. fel. & Ph.D.(struct. & econ. geol), Univ. Mich, Ann Arbor, 71. Teaching asst, Univ. Tex, Austin, 66; ASST. PROF. GEOSCI, & DIR. SUMMER FIELD CAMP, UNIV. ARIZ, 70- Geol. Soc. Am. Origin and deformational history of strata-bound massive sulfide deposits; evaluation of fold mechanisms as functions of rock strength and temperature-pressure conditions; evolution of metamorphic foliations. Address: Dept. of Geosciences, University of Arizona, Tucson, AZ 85710.

DAVIS, GEORGE K(ELSO), b. Pittsburgh, Pa, July 2, 10; m. 36; c. 6. BIO-LOGICAL CHEMISTRY. B.S, Pa. State Univ, 32; Ph.D.(nutrit), Cornell, 37. Asst. animal nutrit, Cornell Univ, 34-37; asst. chem, Mich. State Univ, 37-42; PROF. NUTRIT, INST. FOOD & AGR. SCI, UNIV. FLA, 42-, DIR. DIV. SPONSORED RES, 70-, res. prof. & dir. nuclear sci, 60-65, dir. biol. sci, 65-70. Eli Lilly lectr; hon. prof, Univ. Chile; mem, Frasch Found. Awards Comt; Animal Nutrit. Comt; geochem. environ. comt, Nat. Res. Coun; sect. convenor, Spec. Comt. Int. Biol. Prog; mem, Int. Coun. Sci. Unions. Borden award. Fel. AAAS; Am. Chem. Soc.(Fla. Award); Am. Inst. Nutrit; Am.Soc. Biol. Chem; Am. Soc. Animal Sci; Am. Dairy Sci. Asn; Soc. Exp. Biol. & Med. Relation of nutrition to development of disease, trace substances, vitamins, mineral elements; use of radioactive tracers; metabolism of copper and cardiovascular disorders. Address: Division of Sponsored Research, 219 Graduate School & International Studies Bldg, University of Florida, Gainesville, FL 32601.

DAVIS, GEORGE MORGAN, b. Bridgeport, Conn, May 21, 38; m. 61; c. 2. MALACOLOGY. B.A, Marietta Col, 60; M.S, Michigan, 62, Ph.D.(zool), 65. Res. assoc. malacol, Univ. Mich, 61-65; chief malacol. sect, U.S. Army Med. Command, Japan, 65-70; ASSOC. CURATOR MOLLUSCA, ACAD. NAT-URAL SCI. PHILA, 70-; ASSOC. PROF, JEFFERSON MED. UNIV, 70- Adv, U.S. Educ. Comn, Japan, 66-67; consult, Agency Int. Develop, Mekong River Proj, 71; partic, U.S-Japan Coop. Med. Sci. Prog, 71. U.S. Govt. superior performance award, 68, 70. AAAS; Am. Inst. Biol. Sci; Am. Soc. Zool; Am. Malacol. Union; Japanese Soc. Parasitol; Korean Soc. Parasitol; Malacol. Soc. Japan; Ecol. Soc. Am; Ger. Malacol. Soc; Malacol. Soc. London; Europ. Malacol. Union. Systematic studies of freshwater, amphibious, brackish-water snails; medical malachology; morphological, immunochemical and biochemical studies of snails. Address: Dept. of Malacology, Academy of Natural Sciences of Philadelphia, 19th & Pkwy, Philadelphia, PA 19103.

DAVIS, GEORGE T(ANSEL), b. Vinita, Okla, Mar. 5, 13; m; c. 2. ANIMAL BEHAVIOR & GENETICS. B.S, Okla. Agr. & Mech. Col, 36, M.S, 43; Iowa State Col, 45; Ph.D, Wyoming, 53. Instr. poultry husb, Okla. State, 41-43; field agent poultry improv, Kentucky, 43-45; from asst. prof. to assoc. prof. poultry husb, Okla. State, 45-48; assoc. prof. animal prod, Wyoming, 48-57; prof. poultry indust. & head dept, MONT. STATE UNIV, 57-61, PROF. ANIMAL SCI. & GENETICS, 61- AAAS; Genetics Soc. Am; Poultry Sci. Asn. Address: Dept. of Animal & Range Sciences, Montana State University, Bozeman, MT 59715.

DAVIS, GEORGE THOMAS, b. High Point, N.C, Sept. 30, 32; m. 56; c. 5. ORGANIC CHEMISTRY. B.S, North Carolina, 54; M.S, Washington State, 57, Ph.D.(chem), Brown, 60. Res. assoc. chem, Pa. State, 59-60; SR. CHEMIST, Melpar, Inc, 60-61; Food & Drug Admin, 61-62; EDGEWOOD ARSENAL, 62- N.Y. Acad. Sci; Am. Chem. Soc. Solvent effects on kinetics and equilibria; ion-pairing effects on rates and equilibria; solution adsorption of pollutants; oxidation and elimination mechanisms; nucleophilic substitution reaction; organophosphorus and fluorine chemistry; chemistry of amines. Address: Defensive Research Dept, Research Lab, Edgewood Arsenal, MD 21010.

DAVIS, GEORGE THOMAS, b. Montour Falls, N.Y, Oct. 20, 33; m. 59; c. 5. PHYSICAL CHEMISTRY. B.Ch.E, Cornell, 56; Textile Res. Inst. fel, Princeton, 60-63, Ph.D.(chem), 63. Chem. engr, Esso Res. & Eng. Co, 56-60; acting asst. prof. chem, Virginia, 63-64; res. assoc. polymer physics, NAT. BUR. STANDARDS, 64-66, CHEMIST, 66- AAAS; Am. Chem. Soc. Secondary oil recovery; diffusion in solids; structure of polymers. Address: 8635 Hawkins Creamery Rd, Route 2, Gaithersburg, MD 20760.

DAVIS, GERALD GORDON, b. Owen Sound, Ont, July 7, 37; m. 59; c. 6. PHYSICAL & POLYMER CHEMISTRY. B.Sc, Queen's Univ.(Ont), 60, M.Sc, 61; D.Phil.(chem), Oxford, 63. Res. assoc, Cornell Univ, 63-64; asst. prof. chem, Queen's Univ.(Ont), 64-66; scientist, GLIDDEN CO. DIV, SCM(CAN) LTD, 66-68, TECH. DIR. POLYMER CHEM, 70- Am. Chem. Soc; Chem. Inst. Can. Physical chemistry of polymers and coatings. Address: Glidden Co. Division, SCM (Canada) Ltd, 351 Wallace Ave, Toronto 9, Ont, Can.

DAVIS, G(ERALD) T(ITUS), b. Kingsport, Tenn, Sept. 2, 32; m. 52; c. 2. ORGANIC CHEMISTRY. B.A, King Col, 54; Union Carbide Nuclear fel, Tennessee, 57-58, Ph.D.(chem), 58. ASSOC. MGR. PROD. ENG. MEAD PAPERS, MEAD CORP, 58- Printing and speciality coated papers. Address: 64 N. Fork Dr, Chillicothe, OH 45601.

DAVIS, GERALD WAYNE, b. Spartanburg, S.C, May 18, 40; m. 60; c. 1. OR-GANIC CHEMISTRY. B.S, Wofford Col, 62; Ph.D.(org. chem), North Carolina, Chapel Hill, 67. Fel, Polytech. Inst. Brooklyn, 66-67; res. & develop. chemist, FIBER INDUSTS, INC, 67-69, GROUP LEADER RES. & DEVELOP. ORG. CHEM, 69- Am. Chem. Soc. Peptide and polypeptide synthesis; biopolymer and poly-condensation studies; polymer chemistry. Address: Box 10038, Charlotte, NC 28201.

DAVIS, GLEN R, b. Topinabee, Mich, May 18, 17; m. 40; c. 2. CHEMICAL & PETROLEUM ENGINEERING. B.S, Michigan, 39; M.S, 40. Process engr, natural gas processing plants, Shell Oil Co, 40-45; res. assoc. hydrocarbon synthesis, chem. plant design, Pan Am. Petrol. Co, 46-58; staff engr, Sinclair Oil & Gas Co, 58-65, sulfur coord, 66-68; MGR. SULFUR OPERS, ATLANTIC RICHFIELD CO, 69- Sulfur land and exploration programs; Frasch sulfur plants design, construction, operation, sulfur transportation, distribution, sales. Address: Sulfur Operations, Atlantic Richfield Co, P.O. Box 1470, Midland, TX 79701.

DAVIS, GORDON R(ICHARD) F(UERST), b. Prince Albert, Sask, Apr. 5, 25; m. 49; c. 4. ZOOLOGY, INSECT PHYSIOLOGY. B.Sc, McGill, 48, M.Sc, 49; Carpenter fel, 50-51, Ph.D.(zool), 52. Tech. off, div. entom, biol. control lab, CAN. DEPT. AGR, Que, 48-49, agr. scientist, 49-52, insect nutrit, ENTOM. LAB, Saskatoon, 52-53, agr. res. off, 53-54, res. off, CAN. AGR. RES. STA, 54-65, RES. SCIENTIST, 65- Fel, lab. gen. zool, faculty sci, State Agron. Inst. Belg, 68-69. R.C.N.V.R, 44-45. Entom. Soc. Am; Nutrit. Soc. Can. Insect nutrition; enzymology. Address: Canada Agriculture Research Station, University Campus, Saskatoon, Sask, Can.

DAVIS, GRAHAM J(OHNSON), b. Trenton, N.C, Oct. 5, 25; m. 49; c. 1. PLANT PHYSIOLOGY. B.S, E.Carolina Col, 49; M.A, George Peabody Col, 50; Coker fel, North Carolina, 55-56, Ph.D.(bot), 56. Asst. prof. biol, Brenau Col, 50-53; Tennessee, 56-57; plant physiologist, crops res. div, U.S. Dept. Agr, 57-59; asst. prof. BIOL, E.CAROLINA UNIV, 59-60, assoc. prof, 60-63, PROF. & CHMN. DEPT, 63- U.S.C.G, 43-46. Am. Soc. Plant Physiol; Am. Soc. Limnol. & Oceanog. Photoperiodism and plant growth substances. Address: Dept. of Biology, East Carolina University, Greenville, NC 27843.

DAVIS, GREGORY A(RLEN), b. Portland, Ore, Jan. 29, 35; m. 58; c. 3. GEOLOGY. B.S, Stanford, 56, M.S, 57; Nat. Sci. Found. coop. fel, California, Berkeley, 59-61, Ph.D.(geol), 61. Asst. prof. GEOL, UNIV. SOUTH. CALIF, 61-65, ASSOC. PROF, 65- Vis. assoc. prof, Univ. Wash, 71. AAAS; Geol. Soc. Am; Am. Geophys. Union. Structural geology; geotectonics and nature of orogenesis; regional geology, North American Cordillera; geology of Klamath Mountains and Mojave Desert, California. Address: Dept. of Geological Sciences, University of Southern California, Los Angeles, CA 90007.

DAVIS, HALLOWELL, b. New York, N.Y, Aug. 21, 96; m. 23, 44; c. 3. PHYS-IOLOGY. A.B. & M.D, Harvard, 22; hon. Sc.D, Colby Col, 54, Northwestern, 62. Instr. physiol, Harvard, 23-25, instr. & tutor premed. sci, 25-27, chmn. bd. tutors, 26-27, secy. dept. med. sci, 26-46, instr. & tutor biol, 27-31, asst. prof. physiol, Harvard Med. Sch, 27-36, assoc. prof, 36-46, acting head dept, 42-43; res. prof. otolaryngol, SCH. MED, WASH. UNIV, 46-65, assoc. prof. PHYSIOL, 46-48, prof, 48-65, EMER. PROF, 65-; EMER. DIR. RES. & RES. ASSOC. CENT. INST. FOR DEAF, 65-, dir. res, 46-65. Vis. physiologist, Children's Hosp, Boston, 35-46; mem. div. med. sci, Nat. Res. Coun, 47-53, chmn. comt. hearing, 47-52; exec. secy, comt. hearing & bioacoustics, Armed Forces, Nat. Res. Coun, 53-59. Shambaugh prize, 53; Beltone Award, 66. With Off. Sci. Res. & Develop; Nat. Defense Res. Comt, 44-46. Nat. Acad. Sci; AAAS; Am. Acad. Arts & Sci; Am. Physiol. Soc. (treas, 41-48, pres, 58-59); fel. Acoustical Soc. Am.(pres, 53); assoc. Am. Neurol. Asn; Psychonomic Soc; assoc. Am. Otol. Soc; hon. mem. Am. Acad. Ophthal. & Otolaryngol; Asn. Res. Nervous & Ment. Diseases; Am. Psychosom. Soc; Am. Electroencephalog. Soc.(pres, 49); Biophys. Soc; Soc. Neurosci. Central nervous and auditory physiology; neurophysiology in audition; audiology; psychoacoustics; electroencephalography. Address: 7526 Cornell Ave, University City, MO 63130.

DAVIS, HAMILTON S(EYMOUR), b. Pittsburgh, Pa, Oct. 28, 20; m. 46; c. 4. MEDICINE. A.B, Colgate, 42; M.D, Western Reserve, 45. Consult. anesthesiologist, Vet. Admin. Hosp, Grand Junction, 50-52; asst. prof. anesthesiol, sch. med, Western Reserve, 52-54, assoc. prof, 54-61, prof, 61-66; PROF. ANESTHESIA & CHMN. DEPT, SCH. MED, UNIV. CALIF, DAVIS, 65-; DIR. DEPT. ANESTHESIA, SACRAMENTO MED. CTR, 66- Staff anesthesiologist, univ. hosps, 52-54, dir. anesthesia, Lakeside Hosp, 54- Temporary chmn. dept. anesthesia, St. Mary's Hosp, Colo, 51-52; attend. anesthesiologist, Cleveland City Hosp, Sunny Acres Hosp. & Highland View Hosp, 52- Med.C, 46-48, Capt. Dipl, Am. Bd. Anesthesiol, 53; Maroon Citation, Colgate Univ, 67. Am. Med. Asn; Am. Soc. Anesthesiol.(ed, Anesthesiology, 65-); Am. Col. Anesthesiol; Asn. Univ. Anesthetists; fel. Int. Anesthesia Res. Soc. Influence of anesthesia on hypovolemic shock; central nervous system effects of anesthetics. Address: Dept. of Anesthesia, University of California School of Medicine, Davis, CA 95616.

DAVIS, HARMER E(LMER), b. Rochester, N.Y, July 11, 05; m; c. 3. CIVIL & TRANSPORTATION ENGINEERING. B.S, California, 28, M.S, 30. Asst. CIVIL ENG, UNIV. CALIF, BERKELEY, 28-30, instr, 30-36, asst. prof, 36-39, assoc. prof, 39-48, PROF, 48-, chmn. dept, 54-59, DIR. INST. TRANS-PORTATION & TRAFFIC ENG, 48- Res. & develop. consultation work, 30-48. V.chmn, hwy. res. bd, Nat. Acad. Sci-Nat. Res. Coun, 58, chmn, 59, Crum award, 59, mem. div. eng. & indust. res, Nat. Res. Coun, 60-, exec. comt, 62-65. George S. Bartlett Award, hwy. res. bd, Nat. Acad. Sci-Nat. Res. Coun, 70. Nat. Acad. Eng; Am. Soc. Civil Eng.(James Laurie Prize, 67); Am. Soc. Test. & Mat; Am. Concrete Inst. Soil mechanics; portland cement concrete; bituminous materials; transportation engineering. Address: Institute of Transportation & Traffic Engineering, University of California, Berkeley, CA 94720.

DAVIS, HAROLD, b. South Bend, Ind, Mar. 13, 24; m. 61; c. 2. ELECTRICAL ENGINEERING. B.S, Univ. Calif, Berkeley, 49; M.S, Los Angeles, 50, Ph.D. (eng), 55. Instr. eng, California, Los Angeles, 54-55, asst. prof, 55-61; SR. SCI-

ENTIST, HUGHES AIRCRAFT CO, 61- Consult, 55- Am. Math. Soc; Soc. Indust. & Appl. Math; sr. mem. Inst. Elec. & Electronics Eng. Noise and random processes in communication and automatic control systems. Address: Hughes Aircraft Co, Canoga Park, CA 91304.

DAVIS, HAROLD L(ARUE), b. Phila, Pa, Nov. 18, 25; m. 57. NUCLEAR PHYSICS. B.S, Carnegie Inst. Tech, 49; Ph.D.(physics), Cornell, 54. Adj. asst. prof. atomic physics, Hartford Grad. Center, Rensselaer Polytech, 55-57; managing ed, Nucleonics, 57-69; ED, PHYSICS TODAY, AM. INST. PHYSICS, 69- Proj. engr, Pratt & Whitney Aircraft, 54-57. U.S.A, 43-46. Am. Nuclear Soc; Am. Phys. Soc. Reactor design and development; neutron cross sections; high energy physics and accelerators; particle detectors; scientific data processing. Address: American Institute of Physics, 335 E. 45th St, New York, NY 10017.

DAVIS, H(ARRY) F(LOYD), b. Colby, Kans, Oct. 2, 25; m. 61; c. 2. MATHEMATICS. Ph.D.(math), Mass. Inst. Tech, 54. Instr. MATH, Mass. Inst. Tech, 49-54; asst. prof, Miami (Ohio), 54-55; British Columbia, 55-58; assoc. prof, Royal Mil. Col, Can, 58-60; UNIV. WATERLOO, 60-66, PROF, 66- U.S.N, 44-46. Math. Asn. Am; Soc. Indust. & Appl. Math. Applied algebra. Address: Dept. of Mathematics, University of Waterloo, Waterloo, Ont, Can.

DAVIS, HARRY GLENWOOD, b. Dayton, Wash, June 25, 21; m. 48; c. 1. ENTOMOLOGY. B.A, East. Wash. State Col, 51; Ph.D.(entom), Washington State, 61. RES. ENTOMOLOGIST, ENTOM. RES. DIV, AGR. RES. SERV, U.S. DEPT. AGR, 61- U.S.A.A.F, 42-45, M/Sgt. Entom. Soc. Am; Am. Mosquito Control Asn. Insect attractants, especially for yellow jackets; chemosterilants and pathogens of the little house fly and other insects affecting man and animals. Address: U.S. Dept. of Agriculture, Entomology Research Division, 5544 Air Terminal Dr, Fresno, CA 93727.

DAVIS, HARRY I, b. N.Y.C, Dec. 2, 09; m. 31. PHYSICS, ELECTRONICS. B.S, City Col. New York, 31, E.E, 33; M.E.E, Polytech. Inst. Brooklyn, 48; Syracuse, 55-57. Proj. engr, Daniel Electronic Labs, 33-40; Sig.C, U.S. Army, 40-43, sect. chief radar & navig. aids, 43-45; lab. chief air navig. systs, Watson Lab, U.S. AIR FORCE, 45-50, tech. dir. Rome Air Develop. Center, Air Force Lab, 50-59, spec. asst. defense dir. res. & eng, Off. Secy. Defense, 60-61, dep. res, Off. Secy. Air Force, 61-65, dep. asst. secy. res. & develop, 65-69, DEP. UNDER SECY. AIR FORCE SYSTS. REV, 69- Lectr, Columbia Univ, 56; Univ. Calif, 67- Consult, Weapons Syst. Eval. Group, 55-56 & Rand Corp, 55; chmn. Multi-nat. group command & control for NATO, 62. Dept. Defense distinguished serv. award, 66; Air Force Asn. citation honor, 69; George W. Goddard award, Soc. Photo-Optical Instrumentation Eng, 69. Fel. Inst. Elec. & Electronics Eng.(Harry Diamond Mem. Prize, 68); Am. Phys. Soc; Am. Inst. Astronaut. & Aeronaut. Radar system design and development; navigation systems; communications; computer applications to command and control; information processing; reconnaissance systems; optical instruments; infrared. Address: SAFUSR, Headquarters of U.S. Air Force, The Pentagon, Room 4D873, Washington, DC 20330.

DAVIS, HARRY L, b. Marion, Ill, Mar. 8, 21; m. 49; c. 2. INTERNAL MEDICINE. B.Ed, Southern Illinois, 43, B.S, 46; M.D, Illinois, 50; M.S, Minnesota, Minneapolis, 55. Private practice, Monroe, Wis, 55-57; asst. chief pulmonary disease sect, col. med, Baylor & Jefferson Davis Hosp, Houston, Tex, 57-58; assoc. dir. cardiopulmonary lab, Baptist Mem. Hosp, Memphis, Tenn, 58-64; asst. prof. MED, col. med, UNIV. TENN, 61-65, assoc. prof, 66-70, clin. assoc. prof, MED. UNITS, 70-71, PROF, 71-, CHIEF PULMONARY DISEASE SECT, 71-, dir. pulmonary labs, 64-68. Consult, Baptist Mem. Hosp, Memphis, 58-; U.S. Naval Hosp, Millington, 62-69; dir. pulmonary lab, St. Joseph Hosp, 68- Dipl, pulmonary disease, Am. Bd. Internal Med. U.S.N.R, 42-50, Med.C.Res, 50-, Comdr. Fel. Am. Col. Chest Physicians; fel. Am. Col. Physicians; Am. Thoracic Soc. Pulmonary disease and clinical pulmonary physiology; pulmonary stretch receptors; diffuse obstructive pulmonary disease; pulmonary impairment in sickle cell disease. Address: Dept. of Medicine, University of Tennessee College of Medicine, 800 Madison Ave, Memphis, TN 38103.

DAVIS, HARRY WILLARD, b. Pelzer, S.C, Nov. 7, 15; m. 37; c. 3. ORGANIC CHEMISTRY. B.S, South Carolina, 37; M.S, Cincinnati, 39, Laws fel, 40-41, Ph.D.(org. chem), 41. Adj. prof. chem, UNIV. S.C, 41-44, assoc. prof, 44-49, prof. & head dept, 49-60, dean col. arts & sci, 60-66, v.pres. acad. affairs, 66-68, V.PRES. ADVAN. STUDIES & RES, 68- Prin. scientist, Oak Ridge Inst. Nuclear Studies, 59-60, mem. coun, 60-; mem. bd, Oak Ridge Assoc. Univs, 64-, pres, 70- Am. Chem. Soc. Organic halides; reaction mechanisms; carbon-14. Address: University of South Carolina, Columbia, SC 29208.

DAVIS, HARVEY SAMUEL, b. Columbus, Ohio, July 6, 36; m. 64; c. 2. MATHEMATICS. B.S, Eastern Illinois, 59; M.S, Miami (Fla), 61; Ph.D. (math), Illinois, 65. Asst. MATH, Miami (Fla), 59-61; Illinois, 61-65, instr, summer 65; asst. prof, MICH. STATE,UNIV, 65-69, ASSOC. PROF, 69- Am. Math. Soc. Point set topology; differential manifolds. Address: Dept. of Mathematics, Michigan State University, East Lansing, MI 48823.

DAVIS, HAWTHORNE ANTOINE, b. Richmond, Va, Oct. 4, 37; m. 62; c. 1. SOLID STATE PHYSICS. B.S, Col. William & Mary, 59; M.S, Virginia, 60, Ph.D.(physics), 62. Polymer physicist, E.I. DU PONT DE NEMOURS & CO, 62-69, SR. RES. PHYSICIST, 69- Am. Phys. Soc. Plastic deformation in sodium chloride single crystals; physical properties of crystalline polymers; structure and properties of amorphous and crystalline polymers. Address: Textile Fibers Dept, Fiber Surface Research Section, E.I. du Pont de Nemours & Co, Box 800, Kinston, NC 28501.

DAVIS, HENRY M(cRAY), b. Whitakers, N.C, Jan. 21, 28; m. 49; c. 2. ANALYTICAL & PHYSICAL CHEMISTRY. B.S, N.C. Col. Durham, 52; M.S, Howard Univ, 61. Anal. chemist, DIV. COLORS & COSMETICS TECHNOL, FOOD & DRUG ADMIN, WASH, D.C, 60-65, res. chemist, COSMETICS BR, 65-68, SUPVRY. CHEMIST, COSMETICS COMPOS. SECT, 68-, CHIEF SECT, 70- Asn. Off. Anal. Chem; Am. Chem. Soc; Soc. Cosmetic Chem. Methodology in cosmetic analysis, adsorption, ion-exchange and partition chromatographic techniques; infrared, ultraviolet and x-ray fluorescence spectroscopy; chrono-potentiometry of the iodide-iodine-triiodide system. Address: 14013 Cricket Lane, Silver Spring, MD 20904.

DAVIS, H(ENRY) M(AUZEE), b. Sherman, Tex, Oct. 25, 02. PHYSICAL CHEMISTRY. B.S, Oklahoma, 29, M.S, 30; Ph.D.(phys. chem), Minnesota, 34. Asst. chem, Oklahoma, 29-30; Minnesota, 30-34; in charge dept, Itasca Jr. Col, 34-36; asst. ceramics, PA. STATE, 36-37, res. assoc, 37-38, asst. prof, 38-41, assoc. prof, 41-42, asst. prof. METALL, 42-45, assoc. prof, 45-51, prof, 51-62, EMER. PROF, 62-; DIR. METALL. & CERAMICS DIV, U.S. ARMY RES. OFF-DURHAM, 62- Am. Ceramic Soc; Am. Chem. Soc; fel. Am. Soc. Metals; Am. Inst. Mining, Metall. & Petrol. Eng. Phase equilibria in metallic and refractory systems; physical chemistry of metallurgical systems; equilibria and kinetics of gas-metal reactions. Address: U.S. Army Research Office, Durham, Box CM, Duke Station-Durham, NC 27706.

DAVIS, HENRY WERNER, b. Cambridge, Mass, Aug. 31, 36; m. 62; c. 2. MATHEMATICS. B.A, Rice, 59; M.A, Colorado, 61, NASA fel, 63, Ph.D. (math), 65. Engr, Martin Co, 62-63; res. assoc. math, Spec. Res. Numerical Anal, Duke, 65-67; asst. prof, New Mex, 67-69; ASSOC. MATHEMATICIAN, BROOKHAVEN NAT. LAB, 69- Am. Math. Soc. Harmonic analysis. Address: Applied Mathematics Dept, Brookhaven National Lab, Upton, NY 11973.

DAVIS, HERBERT L, JR, b. Hendersonville, N.C, Aug. 18, 35; m. 57; c. 2. RADIATION BIOLOGY, CYTOGENETICS. B.S, Berry Col, 57; M.S, Emory, 61, Nat. Sci. Found. fel. & Ph.D.(radiation biol), 65. Instr. biol, West. Md. Col, 59-61; biol. & chem, Berry Col, 61-62; asst. prof. biol, Emory Univ, 65-70; CHMN. DIV. NATURAL SCI. & MATH, KENNESAW JR. COL, 70- McCandless Fund res. grant, 66-67. AAAS. Role of metabolic energy compounds on recovery from radiation damage; effects of inhibitors of desoxyribonucleic acid synthesis on recovery from radiation damage. Address: Division of Natural Science & Mathematics, Kennesaw Jr. College, Marietta, GA 30060.

DAVIS, HERBERT LEE, b. Wilmington, N.C, July 11, 42; m. 67; c. 1. AQUATIC ECOLOGY, WATER CHEMISTRY. B.A, Wilmington Col, N.C, 65; M.S, N.C. State Univ, 68, Ph.D.(marine sci), 72. CONSULT, AQUATIC ECOLOGIST, ENVIRON. ENG, INC, 71- AAAS; Ecol. Soc. Am; Am. Soc. Limnol. & Oceanog; Am. Chem. Soc. Relationship between community productivity, diversity and nutrient chemistry in natural waters, effects of natural and unnatural stresses on these relationships. Address: Environmental Engineering, Inc, 2324 S.W. 34th St, Gainesville, FL 32601.

DAVIS, HERBERT T(HADDEUS), III, b. Arcadia, Fla, June 12, 42; m. 64. STATISTICS, MATHEMATICS. B.S, Univ. Fla, 64, M.S, 66; Ph.D.(statist), Johns Hopkins Univ, 68. ASST. PROF. MATH. & STATIST, UNIV. N.MEX, 69- U.S.A, 68-70, Capt. Am. Statist. Asn; Inst. Math. Statist; Am. Math. Soc. Time series analysis. Address: Dept. of Mathematics, University of New Mexico, Albuquerque, NM 87106.

DAVIS, HORACE R(AYMOND), b. Clayton, Mo, Oct. 8, 22; m. 46; c. 4. ORGANIC CHEMISTRY. B.A, Illinois, 43; Ph.D.(chem), Minnesota, 49. Res. chemist, M.W. Kellogg Co, 49-51, res. supvr, 51-57; GROUP SUPVR, MINN. MINING & MFG. CO, 57- U.S.A, 44-46. AAAS; Am. Chem. Soc; fel. Am. Inst. Chem; Brit. Chem. Soc. Fluorocarbon chemistry; nucleophilic substitution; chemistry of high polymers. Address: 3035 Woodbridge St, St. Paul, MN 55113.

DAVIS, HOWARD FRED, b. Milwaukie, Ore, June 29, 31; m. 56; c. 3. PHYSICS. S.B, Mass, Inst. Tech, 53, S.M, 54; Ph.D.(physics), Rochester, 60. Mem. staff, adv. eng. prog, Gen. Elec. Co, 54-55; res. assoc, Pennsylvania, 59-61; asst. prof. PHYSICS, Washington (Seattle), 61-68; ASSOC. PROF, ORE. STATE UNIV, 68- Consult. syst. eng, Bonneville Power Admin, 69- Am. Phys. Soc; Inst. Elec. & Electronics Eng; Nat. Soc. Prof. Eng. High energy particle physics; instrumentation problems in particle physics experiments; electrical system engineering. Address: Dept. of Physics, Oregon State University, Corvallis, OR 97331.

DAVIS, H(OWARD) TED, b. Hendersonville, N.C, Aug. 2, 37; m. 60. PHYSICAL CHEMISTRY, CHEMICAL PHYSICS. B.S, Furman, 59; Nat. Sci. Found. fel. & Ph.D.(phys. chem), Chicago, 62. Nat. Sci. Found. fel, Brussels, 62-63; asst. prof. CHEM. ENG, MINNESOTA, MINNEAPOLIS, 63-66, assoc. prof, 66-69, PROF, 69- Sloan Found. fel, 67-69, Guggenheim fel, 69-70. Am. Phys. Soc; Am. Chem. Soc. Theoretical and experimental studies of transport processes in low-temperature liquids and fused salts; statistical mechanical studies of fluids, classical and quantum mechanical; electronic structure and radiation chemistry of hydrocarbon liquids and glasses. Address: Dept. of Chemical Engineering & Chemistry, University of Minnesota, Minneapolis, MN 55410.

DAVIS, HUBERT G(REENIDGE), b. Brooklyn, N.Y, July 8, 15; m. 45; c. 4. PHYSICAL CHEMISTRY. B.A, Columbia, 38, Ph.D.(chem), 41. Res. chemist, Westvaco Chlorine Prod. Co, Calif, 41-42; instr. chem, Trinity Col, 42-43; res. chemist, Manhattan Dist. proj, s.a.m. labs, Columbia, 42-45; chem. div, UNION CARBIDE CORP, 45-57, sr. res. scientist, 58-61, asst. dir. res. & develop, olefins div, 62-69, CORP. SR. RES. FEL, 69- Civilian with Off. Sci. Res. & Develop; U.S.A, 44. Pyrolysis, physical properties, chemistry of hydrocarbons; utilization of coal. Address: 228 Hayes Ave, Charleston, WV 25314.

DAVIS, IRVING, b. Bessarabia, Roumania, Sept. 22, 22; nat; m. 47; c. 1. MEDICAL MICROBIOLOGY. B.S, Wisconsin, 49; M.S, Pennsylvania, 54, Ph.D.(med. microbiol), 59. Chief lab, Health Dept, N.J, 49-50; clin. lab. chief, Air Force Hosp, Mitchel Air Force Base, 50-52, res. bacteriologist, Camp Detrick, 52, res. microbiologist & asst. chief, microbiol-cellular biol. br, U.S. Force Sch. Aviation Med, 54-59, res. microbiologist & chief astromicrobiol. br, 59-61, proj. officer, biosci. div, European Off. Aerospace Res, Brussels, Belgium, 61-64, asst. chief. biosci. dept, U.S. Air Force Sch. Aerospace Med, 64-65, biomed. sci. corps, 65-67, chief, biosci. br, 67-69; dir. health & med. res, Int. Paper Co, N.Y, 69-70; TECH. DIR,

BIOCHEM. PROCEDURES, 69- U.S.A.F, 42-45, Med.Serv.C, 50-69. Am. Soc. Microbiol; Aerospace Med. Asn; Sci. Res. Soc. Am; Am. Pub. Health Asn. Exobiology; aerospace medicine; public health. Address: Biochemical Procedures, 1350 Liberty Ave, Hillside, NJ 07207.

DAVIS, JACK, b. N.Y.C, May 21, 35; m. 59; c. 2. PHYSICS. B.S, Northeastern, 58, fels, 58-60, M.S, 60; dipl, Imp. Col. & Ph.D.(physics), London, 67. Res. assoc. physics, Maryland, 60-61; Northeastern, 61-63; staff scientist, Avco Corp, 63-67, sr. staff scientist, 67-68; sci. specialist theoret. physics, EG&G, INC, Mass, 68-70, DEPT. MGR, PHYS. SCI, 70- Res. assoc, Imp. Col, London, 65-67, fel, spectros. lab, 67. AAAS; Am. Phys. Soc. Plasma spectroscopy; quantum theory of scattering; pressure broadening, specifically the electron impact broadening of spectral lines; autoionization and dielectronic recombination; plasma-electromagnetic interactions; aeronomy and environmental sciences and laser propagation through the atmosphere. Address: EG&G, Inc, 933 Bradbury Dr, Albuquerque, NM 87106.

DAVIS, JACK H, b. Clinton, S.C, Nov. 22, 39; m. 62; c. 2. SOLID STATE PHYSICS. B.S, Clemson, 62, Ph.D.(physics), 66. Instr. PHYSICS, UNIV. ALA, HUNTSVILLE, 66, asst. prof, 66-69, ASSOC. PROF, 69- Am. Phys. Soc. Metal whiskers growth, strength and electrical properties. Address: Dept. of Physics, Research Institute, University of Alabama in Huntsville, P.O. Box 1247, Huntsville, AL 35807.

DAVIS, JAMES ALLEN, b. Toledo, Ohio, Jan. 18, 30; m. 58; c. 3. UNDERWATER ACOUSTICS, REACTOR PHYSICS. B.A, Toledo, 57; Westinghouse Elec. Corp. fel, Pittsburgh, 57-63, Ph.D.(physics), 64. Sr. scientist reactor physics, Bettis Atomic Power Lab, 57-67; ASST. SCIENTIST, WOODS HOLE OCEANOG. INST, 67- U.S.N, 48-53. Magnetization of thin films; solutions to transport equation in reactor physics; wave propagation using generalized WKB approximation in underwater acoustics problems. Address: Woods Hole Oceanographic Institution, Woods Hole, MA 02543.

DAVIS, JAMES AVERY, b. New Orleans, La, Aug. 13, 39. SYSTEMS ANALYSIS. A.B, Occidental Col, 61; M.A, Calif. State Col. Long Beach, 63; Nat. Sci. Found. fel. & Ph.D.(math), New Mexico, 67. Res. specialist, N.Am. Aviation, Inc, 62-67; res. assoc. probability & statist, Univ. Montreal, 67-68; STAFF MEM. APPL. MATH, SANDIA CORP, 68- Fel, Univ. Montreal, 67-68. Inst. Math. Statist; Am. Math. Soc. Probability theory; stochastic processes; convergence rates for sums of random variables. Address: Statistical Research Division 1723, Sandia Corp, Albuquerque, NM 87115.

DAVIS, JAMES E(RNEST), b. St. Thomas, Ont, Apr. 2, 92; nat; m. 22, 58; c. 2. MEDICINE. B.S, Chicago, 26, M.A, 28, Ph.D.(physiol, biochem), 32. Res. assoc, Lasker Found, dept. med, Chicago, 26-38; teacher pub. sch. system, Ill, 38-42; private med. investr, 37-42; chief chemist, Biochem. Res. Labs, 42-43; dir. biol. res, Huntsville Arsenal, 43-44; head physiol. dept, Wash. State Col, 44-46; head dept. physiol. & dir. cancer res, Los Angeles Col. Osteop. Physicians & Surgeons, 46-52; DIR. CANCER RES, BERNARD FOUND. MED. RES, 52- U.S.A, 42-44. AAAS; Am. Cancer Soc; N.Y. Acad. Sci. Cellular metabolism; endocrinology; cancer; mercury-indigo disulfonate. Address: 4547 N. Karlov Ave, Chicago, IL 60630.

DAVIS, JAMES E(UGENE), b. McComb, Miss, Sept. 12, 34; m. 65; c. 2. BIOCHEMISTRY. B.S, Miss. State, 56; Nat. Sci. Found. fel, Mass. Inst. Tech, 58, Ph.D.(phys. chem), 60. Nat. Sci. Found. fel. biophys, Calif. Inst. Tech, 60-61, Nat. Insts. Health fel, 61-63, inst. fel, 63-64; asst. prof. BIOCHEM, OAKLAND UNIV, 64-70, ASSOC. PROF, 70-, ASST. PROVOST, 69- Summer fel, Mass. Inst. Tech, 60. AAAS; Am. Chem. Soc; Biophys. Soc. Structure and replication of viruses; molecular genetics and biochemistry; physical chemistry of polymers. Address: Oakland University, Rochester, MI 48063.

DAVIS, JAMES H(OWELL), b. Matoaka, W.Va, Aug. 17, 24; m. 56; c. 2. ECONOMIC GEOLOGY. A.B, Duke, 50; Tennessee, 50-51; Wisconsin, 56-58, Ph.D, 60. Mine geologist, St. Joseph Lead Co, 51-56; asst. prof. geol, Texas, 59-61; mem. staff explor, N.J. Zinc Co, 61-62; econ. geol, regional resource develop, Tenn. Valley Auth, 62-67; CHIEF GEOLOGIST, MO. LEAD OPERATING CO, 67- Geol. Soc. Am; Soc. Econ. Geol; Geochem. Soc. U.S.A.A.F, 43-46. Mineral economics; regional development. Address: Missouri Lead Operating Co, P.O. Box 551, Salem, MO 65560.

DAVIS, JAMES K, b. Cleveland, Ohio, Sept. 4, 15; m. 47. CHEMISTRY. B.S, Michigan, 36. Bagley scholar. & M.S, 37, Ph.D.(chem), 40. Rackham fel, Michigan, 40-41; res. chemist, CORNING GLASS WORKS, 41-50, sr. res. assoc, 50-54, mgr. electronic prod. develop, 54-63, tech. anal, 63-66, STAFF RES. MGR, 66- Am. Chem. Soc; Am. Ceramic Soc; Inst. Elec. & Electronics Eng. Adsorption of liquid interfaces; semiconductors; glass resistors; surface coatings on glass; metallized glass attenuators; mercury-blackening-resistant glass; glass capacitors; ultrasonic delay lines; printed circuit boards. Address: Corning Glass Works, Houghton Park, Corning, NY 14830.

DAVIS, JAMES O(THELLO), b. Tahlequah, Okla, July 12, 16; m. 41; c. 2. PHYSIOLOGY. B.S, Northeast. Okla. State Col, 37; M.A, Missouri, 39, Ph.D.(zool), 42, B.S.(med), 43; M.D, Washington (St. Louis), 45. Asst. zool, Missouri, 37-42, anat, 42-43; intern, Barnes Hosp, St. Louis, 45-46; investr, Nat. Insts. Health, U.S. Pub. Health Serv. & Baltimore City Hosps, 47-49, lab. kidney & electrolyte metab, Nat. Heart Inst, 49-57, chief sect. exp. cardiovasc. disease, 57-66; PROF. PHYSIOL. & CHMN. DEPT, SCH. MED, UNIV. MO-COLUMBIA, 66- Fel, sch. med, Wash. Univ, 46; assoc. prof, sch. med, Temple Univ, 55-56; vis. assoc. prof, sch. med, Johns Hopkins Univ, 61-64; vis. prof, sch. med, Univ. Va, 64. Nat. Insts. Health extramural prog; v.chmn. coun. high blood pressure res, 70-72; mem. ed. bd, Am. Jour. Physiol, 61-63, 66-69; Endocrinol, 62-65; Circulation Res, 62-66. Am. Med. Asn. Golden Apple award, 68; Sigma Xi res. award, Univ. Mo, 71. Am. Physiol. Soc; Endocrine Soc; Am. Heart Asn; Soc. Exp. Biol. & Med. Cardiovascular, renal and endocrine physiology; physiology of congestive heart failure and hypertension. Address: Dept. of Physiology, M412 Medical Science Bldg, School of Medicine, University of Missouri, Columbia, MO 65201.

DAVIS, JAMES ROBERT, b. York, Nebr, Dec. 28, 29; m. 56; c. 3. PLANT PATHOLOGY. A.B, California, Riverside, 56, M.S, Davis, 61, Ph.D.(plant path), 67. Lab. technician I, California, Riverside, 56, lab. technician II, Davis, 56-68; ASST. RES. PROF. PLANT PATH, UNIV. IDAHO, 68- U.S.A, 50-52. Am. Phytopath. Soc. Studies in stone fruit pathology relating to canker diseases induced by low temperature, fungi and bacteria. Address: Branch Experiment Station, University of Idaho, Aberdeen, ID 83210.

DAVIS, JAMES ROYCE, b. Rison, Ark, Apr. 6, 38; m. 59; c. 2. MICROBIAL PHYSIOLOGY, CLINICAL MICROBIOLOGY. B.S, Tex. Col. Arts & Indust, 60; M.S, Univ. Houston, 62, Ph.D.(microbiol), 65. Lectr. MICROBIOL, Univ. Houston, 64-65; ASST. PROF, dent. br, Univ. Tex, 65-68; COL. MED, BAYLOR UNIV, 68-; DIR. MICROBIOL. SECT. CLIN. LAB, METHODIST HOSP, 68-; CHMN. COMBINED PROG. MED. TECHNOL, TEX. MED. CTR, 70- Am. Soc. Microbiol. Steroid metabolism by microorganisms; streptomycete taxonomy; chemical composition and microbial flora of saliva; rapid and automated techniques for diagnostic microbiology, Address: Dept. of Pathology, Methodist Hospital, 6516 Bertner, Houston, TX 77025.

DAVIS, J(AMES) WENDELL, b. Tulsa, Okla, Aug. 22, 27; m. 52; c. 4. BIOLOGICAL CHEMISTRY. B.S, Tulsa, 49, fel, 49-50; fel, Oregon State Col, 50-52, M.S, 52, Atomic Energy Cmn. fel, 52-54, Ph.D.(biochem), 54. Assoc. biochemist, biol. div, Oak Ridge Nat. Lab, 54-57; sr. instr. BIOCHEM, SCH. MED, ST. LOUIS UNIV, 57-59, asst. prof, 59-63, ASSOC. PROF, 63- Am. Chem. Soc; Endocrine Soc. Mechanism of hormone action; nucleotide metabolism. Address: Dept. of Biochemistry, St. Louis University School of Medicine, St. Louis, MO 63104.

DAVIS, JAMES W(ILTSE), b. St. Louis, Mo, June 24, 18; m. 43; c. 4. ORGANIC CHEMISTRY. A.B, Illinois, 39; Ph.D.(org. chem), Wisconsin, 42. Du Pont fel, Harvard, 42-43; res. chemist, HERCULES POWDER CO, 43-45, res. supvr, PMC RES. DIV, 45-55, MGR, 55- Am. Chem. Soc. Naval stores; paper chemicals; tall oil products; rubber chemicals. Address: Hercules Research Center, Wilmington, DE 19899.

DAVIS, JARED J(AMES), b. Custer, Wash, July 9, 20; m. 45; c. 3. LIMNOLOGY, RADIOECOLOGY. B.S, Washington (Seattle), 42; M.S, Wash. State, 48. Sr. scientist, aquatic biol. sect, Hanford Labs, Gen. Elec. Co, Wash, 48-57, mgr. radioecol. sect, 57-62; v.pres, Hazelton Nuclear Sci. Corp, Calif, 63; aquatic ecologist, environ. sci. br, div. biol. & med, U.S. Atomic Energy Comn, 64-65, 67-69; tech. asst, Off. Sci. & Technol, Exec. Off. President, 66; SCIENTIFIC DEPUTY, OFF. EFFECTS EVAL, NEV. OPERS. OFF, U.S. ATOMIC ENERGY COMN, 69- U.S.A, 43-46. AAAS; Am. Inst. Biol. Sci; Ecol. Soc. Am; Soc. Limnol. & Oceanog; Entom. Soc. Am; Polar Soc; Nat. Wildlife Fedn. Fate, effect, hazards & control of radioactive materials in ecological systems; ecology, environmental quality; limnology. Address: 4335 Woodcrest Rd, Las Vegas, NV 89109.

DAVIS, JAY C, b. Haskell, Tex, July 12, 42; m. 63; c. 2. NUCLEAR PHYSICS. B.A, Univ. Tex, Austin, 63, M.A, 64; Ph.D.(physics), Univ. Wis, Madison, 69. Teaching asst. physics, Univ. Tex, Austin, 63-64; Univ. Wis, Madison, 64-65, res. asst, 65-69, Atomic Energy Comn. fel, nuclear physics, 69-70, res. assoc, 70-71; PHYSICIST, LAWRENCE LIVERMORE LAB, 71- Fast neutron physics; accelerator technology. Address: L 313, Lawrence Livermore Lab, P.O. Box 808, Livermore, CA 94550.

DAVIS, JEFFERSON C(LARK), JR, b. Jacksonville, Fla, Mar. 20, 31; m. 54; c. 3. PHYSICAL CHEMISTRY. B.S, Univ. Ariz, 53, M.S, 54; Du Pont fel, Univ. Calif, 58-59, Ph.D.(chem), 59. Asst, Lawrence Radiation Lab, Univ. Calif, 56-59; instr. CHEM, Univ. Tex, 59-61, asst. prof, 61-65; ASSOC. PROF, UNIV. S.FLA, 65- Mem. adv. coun. col. chem, Int. Conf. Educ. in Chem. Chem.C, 54-56, 1st Lt. AAAS; Am. Chem. Soc; Am. Inst. Chem. Application of nuclear magnetic resonance spectroscopy to chemical problems; molecular association in solutions; chemical education. Address: Dept. of Chemistry, University of South Florida, Tampa, FL 33620.

DAVIS, JEFFREY ROBERT, b. Boise, Idaho, June 22, 35; m. 56; c. 3. MATHEMATICS. B.E.E, Rensselaer Polytech, 57, M.S, 59; Ph.D.(math), Washington (St. Louis), 63. Instr. MATH, California, Berkeley, 63-65; ASST. PROF, UNIV. N.MEX, 65- Am. Math. Soc. Toeplitz operators; Wiener-Hopf equations. Address: Dept. of Mathematics, University of New Mexico, Albuquerque, NM 87106.

DAVIS, JOE B(ILL), b. Forsyth Co, N.C, Dec. 2, 33; m. 58; c. 1. ANALYTICAL CHEMISTRY. B.S, West. Carolina Col, 60; Nat. Defense Ed. Act fel, Clemson, 61-64, M.S, 63, Ph.D.(anal. chem), 65. Lab. instr. CHEM, Fla. Presby. Col, 60-61; asst, Chemson, 62-65; asst. prof, WINTHROP COL, 65-70, ASSOC. PROF, 70- Summer Oak Ridge Inst. Nuclear Studies faculty res. partic, Savannah River Lab, E.I. du Pont de Nemours & Co, 66 & 71. U.S.A, 52-55, Sgt. Am. Chem. Soc; fel. Am. Inst. Chem; Am. Soc. Test. & Mat. Analytical instrument design and development; spectroscopy; electrochemistry; analysis of sulfate and sulfur compounds; analysis via buffer reactions. Address: Dept. of Chemistry, Winthrop College, Rock Hill, SC 29730.

DAVIS, JOHN, b. Woodmere, N.Y, Dec. 1, 16; m. 47. VERTEBRATE ZOOLOGY. B.A, Yale, 37; Ph.D.(zool), California, 50. Asst. zool, California, 47-48, assoc, 49, technician, Mus. Vert. Zool, 49-50; asst. prof. biol. & curator, Moore Lab. Zool, Occidental Col, 50-53; jr. res. zoologist, HASTINGS NATURAL HISTORY RESERVATION, 53-56, asst. res. zoologist, 56-62, ASSOC. RES. ZOOLOGIST & LECTR. ZOOL, 62- Guggenheim mem. fel, 59. Sanit.C, 43-46, 1st Lt. Am. Soc. Mammal; Am. Soc. Ichthyol. & Herpet; Soc. Study Evolution; Cooper Ornith. Soc.(secy, 53-65); fel. Ornith Union; Wilson Ornith. Soc. Avian systematics; life history studies; gonad cycles; lizard ecology and behavior. Address: Hastings Natural History Reservation, Star Route, Box 80, Carmel Valley, CA 93924.

DAVIS, JOHN A(LBERT), b. Pomona, Kans, Oct. 9, 03; m. 29; c. 1. ORGANIC CHEMISTRY. B.S, Ottawa (Kans), 27; Ottawa fel, Kansas, 27-28; M.S, 28, Ph.D.(org. chem), 35. Asst. prof. CHEM, south br, Idaho, 28-43; prof. & head dept, Ottawa, 43-57; WASHBURN UNIV, 57-67, EMER. PROF. & HEAD DEPT, 67- Am. Chem. Soc. Synthesis and proof of structure; thiazolidones. Address: 4712 W. 6th St, Apt. 663, Topeka, KS 66606.

DAVIS, JOHN ALBERT, JR, b. Pocatello, Idaho, Apr. 22, 36; m. 60; c. 2. CHEMICAL ENGINEERING. B.S, Kansas, 58; Nat. Sci. Found. fel. & M.S.E, Michigan, 59; Nat. Sci. Found. fel. & Ph.D.(chem. eng), Kansas, 63. Res. engr, MARATHON OIL CO, 63-64, adv. res. engr, 64-70, sr. res. engr, 70, MGR. PROD. SCI. DEPT, 70- Summers, develop. engr, E.I. du Pont de Nemours & Co, 58, 59. Am. Inst. Chem. Eng; Am. Chem. Soc; Soc. Petrol. Eng. Cryogenics; low temperature phase behavior and thermodynamics; secondary oil recovery processes. Address: Denver Research Center, Marathon Oil Co, P.O. Box 269, Littleton, CO 80122.

DAVIS, JOHN B, b. Rocky Point, N.C, Feb. 3, 26; m. 48; c. 4. MATHEMATICS. B.S, Wake Forest Col, 51; M.A, E.Carolina Col, 59; summers, Clemson Col, 60, Alabama, 61, La. State, 62 & Rutgers, 63. Assoc. prof. MATH, Wilmington Col.(N.C), 53-59; asst. prof, E.CAROLINA UNIV, 60-62, assoc. prof, 62-70, PROF. & DIR. INSTNL. RES, 70- Nat. Sci. Found. lectureship, 62-63. Math. Asn. Am. Address: Dept. of Mathematics, East Carolina University, Greenville, NC 27834.

DAVIS, JOHN BARNEY, b. Dallas, Tex, Dec. 13, 17; m. 42; c. 2. MICROBIOLOGY. B.S, N.Tex. Teachers Col, 38; Ph.D, Texas, 49. City bacteriologist, Dallas, 38-42; instr. bact, Texas, 46-48, Ciba Pharmaceut. Co. res. fel, 47-49; sr. res. technologist, FIELD RES. LAB, MOBIL RES. & DEVELOP. CORP, 49-57, RES. ASSOC, 57- U.S.N.R, 42-45. Am. Soc. Microbiol; Sci. Res. Soc. Am. Petroleum microbiology; microbial activities related to petroleum geochemistry and geology; microbial oxidation of hydrocarbons; microbial intracellular and extracellular products synthesized from hydrocarbons. Address: Field Research Lab, Mobil Research & Development Corp, Box 900, Dallas, TX 75221.

DAVIS, JOHN CLEMENTS, b. Neodesha, Kans, Oct. 21, 38; m. 61; c. 2. GEOLOGY. B.S, Kansas, 61; M.S, Wyoming, 63, Ph.D.(geol), 67. Asst. struct. mapping, U.S. Geol. Surv, summer, 61; summer geologist, Wyo. Geol. Surv, 62 & 64; Pan Am. Petrol. Corp, 63; instr. stratig, Idaho State, 64-66; res. assoc. sedimentary petrol, KANS. GEOL. SURV, 66-70, CHIEF GEOL. RES, 70-; ASSOC. PROF. CHEM. & PETROL. ENG, UNIV. KANS, 70- Vis. prof, Wichita State, 69; consult, Yacimentos Petroliferos Fiscales Bolivianos, Bolivia, 69; asst. ed, J. Math. Geol. Am. Asn. Petrol. Geol; Clay Minerals Soc; Pattern Recognition Soc; Int. Asn. Math. Geol; Mineral. Soc. Am; Soc. Econ. Paleont. & Mineral. Quantitative analysis of sedimentary rock parameters, especially by statistical means and by optical data processing; quantitative mineral analysis by x-ray diffraction. Address: State Geological Survey, University of Kansas, Lawrence, KS 66044.

DAVIS, JOHN DUNNING, b. Freeport, Maine, June 13, 29; m. 55; c. 2. INVERTEBRATE ZOOLOGY, MARINE ECOLOGY. A.B, Bowdoin Col, 52; M.Ed, Boston, 54; summers, Wesleyan, 58, Harvard, 60; M.S, New Hampshire, 61, Nat. Defense Ed. Act fel, 61-63, Ph.D.(zool), 63. Sci. teacher, high sch, N.H, 54-56, 57-60; teaching fel. biol, Bowdoin Col, 56-57; instr. zool, Smith Col, 63-65, asst. prof, 65-70; V.PRES, NORMANDEAU ASSOCS, INC, 70- Summer instr, Nat. Sci. Found. Inst. Bowdoin Col, 63, 64, 65; Nat. Sci. Found. grant, 64. AAAS; Am. Soc. Zool; Nat. Shellfisheries Asn; Ecol. Soc. Am. Systematics and biology of marine Pelecypod mollusks. Address: 26 Norfolk Ave, Northampton, MA 01060.

DAVIS, J(OHN) E(DWARD), JR, b. Welch, W.Va, Nov. 18, 22; m. 49; c. 1. ZOOLOGY. B.A, Virginia, 48, M.A, 50, Ph.D, 55. Instr. BIOL, Washington & Lee, 49-51, 54-56; asst, Virginia, 51-54; asst. prof, Wake Forest Col, 56-61, assoc. prof, 61-67, prof, 67-68; prof. & chmn. dept, MADISON COL, 68-71, ACTING PROVOST, 71- Med.C, U.S.A, 42-46. AAAS. Embryology. Address: Office of the Provost, Madison College, Harrisonburg, VA 22801.

DAVIS, JOHN E(MERSON), b. Detroit, Mich, Jan. 1, 07; m. 35; c. 1. PHARMACOLOGY. A.B, Oberlin Col, 30; M.S, Michigan, 31; Ph.D.(physiol), Chicago, 36. Instr. physiol, Med. Col. Va, 35-37; physiol. & pharmacol, Alabama, 37-38; asst. prof, Vermont, 38-42; assoc. prof. pharmacol. & physiol, med. sch. Arkansas, 42-45, acting head dept, 45, PROF. PHARMACOL, 45-51; UNIV. TEX, 51-, LECTR, MED. BR, 52- Guest lectr, U.S. Air Force Sch. Aviation Med, 48. Mem. pharmacol. & endocrinol. fel. review panel, Nat. Insts. Health, 60-64. AAAS; fel. Am. Col. Angiol; Am. Soc. Pharmacol. & Exp. Therapeut; Am. Physiol. Soc; Soc. Exp. Biol. & Med; Am. Pharmaceut. Asn; fel. Am. Col. Cardiol. Pharmacology of erythropoiesis; anemia and polycythemia; autonomic drugs; physiology of physical exercise. Address: 1413 Larkwood Dr, Austin, TX 78723.

DAVIS, J(OHN) F(REDERICK), b. Sandusky, Mich, Sept. 11, 08; m. 38; c. 2. SOIL SCIENCE. B.S, Mich. State Col, 33, M.S, 39, Ph.D.(soil science), 43. Asst, Agr. & Mech. Col, Tex, 33-34; soil science, Mich. State Col, 34-35, asst, 35-41, asst. prof, 41-43; assoc. prof. agron, Univ. Del, 43-44; asst. prof. veg. crops, Cornell Univ, 44-46; assoc. prof. SOIL SCI, MICH. STATE UNIV, 46-53, PROF, 53- Soil Sci. Soc. Am; Soil Conserv. Soc. Am; Am. Soc. Sugar Beet Technol. Soil fertility in organic soils; agricultural statistics; effect of some environmental factors on the set of pods of white pea beans. Address: Dept. of Crop & Soil Sciences, Michigan State University, East Lansing, MI 48823.

DAVIS, JOHN FREDERICK, b. Montreal, Que, Oct. 2, 17; m. 45; c. 2. BIOMEDICAL ENGINEERING, HOSPITAL ADMINISTRATION. B.S, McGill, 42, M.S, 49, M.D, 50. Res. engr, radio br, Nat. Res. Coun. Can, 42-45; res. assoc. psychiat, Allan Mem. Inst, McGill, 46-58, dir. electrophysiol. dept, 58-62; dir, Int. Inst. Med. Electronics & Biol. Eng, 62-69; int. dir, Med. Patents Inc, 69-70; DIR. TECHNOL. TRANSFER ASSOC, 70- Lectr, Carleton, 43-45; jr. intern, Royal Victoria Hosp, 50-51, consult, cent. tumor registry, 52-62, clin. fel, psychiat, 54-58, asst. psychiatrist, 58-62; consult, Montreal Neurol. Inst, 52-56. Asn. Comput. Mach; fel. Inst. Elec. & Electronics Eng; fel. Can. Soc. Electroencephalographers; Biophys. Soc; Soc. Psychophysiol. Res; Brit. Biol. Eng. Soc; French Nat. Asn. Med. Electronics; Royal Med. Soc. Electroencephalography; psychophysiology; physiological biophysics; medical electronics; instrumentation for data analysis as applied to research in psychiatry; organization and management; technology transfer. Address: 47 Boulevard de l'Hôpital, Paris 13, France.

DAVIS, JOHN H(ENRY), b. Cumberland Co, Va, July 16, 01; m. 31; c. 2. PLANT ECOLOGY. B.S. & A.M, Davidson Col, 24; fel, Chicago, 27-28, Ph.D.(bot, plant ecol), 29. Asst. prof. biol, Davidson Col, 23-24, assoc. prof, 25-30; prof, Presby. Col.(S.C), 30-35; Southwestern (Tenn), 35-41; asst, Fla. Geol. Surv, 41-46; prof. bot, UNIV. FLA, 46-70, EMER. PROF, 70- Vis. prof, Auckland Univ. Col, N.Z, 50; Mandalay, Burma, 58-60; Taiwan, Formosa, 64-65. Ecol. Soc. Am; Am. Bot. Soc. Vegetation of the Black Mountains, North Carolina and Florida; mangrove swamps and Everglades of Florida; peat deposits of Florida; forests of Burma. Address: 1729 N.W. Eighth Ave, Gainesville, FL 32601.

DAVIS, JOHN K, b. Webster, Mass, Nov. 30, 13; m. 40; c. 2. OPTICS, COMPUTER SCIENCE. A.B, Clark, 37. Asst, S. Slater & Sons, Inc, 31-35; teacher country day sch, Fla, 37-38; agent, Fla. Motor Lines, 38-39; res. dept, AM. OPTICAL CO, SOUTHBRIDGE, MASS, 39-49, head optics sect, appl. res. lab, 49-50, res. lab, 50-53, optical comput. & serv. sect, 53-58, ophthalmic lens sect, NEW PROD. DEVELOP. DEPT, 59-62, MGR. LENS TECHNOL. & DESIGN, 62- Master ophthalmic optics, Am. Bd. Opticianry. AAAS; Am. Acad. Optom; Optical Soc. Am; N.Y. Acad. Sci. Geometric optics; ophthalmic lenses; vision; optical instruments; automatic computing; quality control. Address: Prospect St, East Woodstock, CT 06244.

DAVIS, JOHN L(ITCHFIELD), b. Weymouth, Mass, Mar. 5, 32; m. 61; c. 2. SOLID STATE PHYSICS. A.B, Bowdoin Col, 53; Nat. Sci. Found. fel, Maryland, 55-56, Ph.D.(physics), 65. PHYSICIST, U.S. Naval Ord. Lab, 58-67; ANAL. SERV, INC, 67- U.S.A, 58, 2nd Lt. AAAS; Am. Phys. Soc; Oper. Res. Soc. Am; World Future Soc; Soc. Advan. Med. Syst. Microwave spectroscopy; physics of solid surfaces; systems analysis; operations research; health systems analysis. Address: Tactical Division, Analytic Services Inc, 5613 Leesburg Pike, Falls Church, VA 22041.

DAVIS, JOHN MARCELL, b. Kansas City, Mo, Oct. 11, 33; m. 60. PSYCHIATRY. A.B, Princeton, 56; M.D, Yale, 60. Intern, Mass. Gen. Hosp, 60-61; res. psychiat, Yale, 61-64; clin. assoc, Nat. Inst. Ment. Health, 64-66, specialist psychopharmacol, 66-69; chief unit clin. pharmacol, lab. clin. sci, Nat. Insts. Health, 69-70; ASSOC. PROF. PHARMACOL. & PROF. PSYCHIAT, VANDERBILT UNIV, 70-; DIR, CLIN. DIV, TENN. NEUROPSYCHIAT. INST, CENT. STATE HOSP, 70- Ed, Psychopharmacol. Bull, 66- U.S.P.H.S, 64-, Surg. Am. Psychiat. Asn; Am. Med. Asn; Am. Col. Neuropsychopharmacol; Psychiat. Res. Soc; Am. Col. Psychiat; N.Y. Acad. Sci. Biology of depression; psychopharmacology; biochemical factors in mania, depression and schizophrenia; catocholamines, scotonin and electrolite in mental disease; lithium treatment of mania sensory deprivation; medical anthropology; computer techniques in psychiatry. Address: Dept. of Pharmacology, Vanderbilt University, Nashville, TN 37203.

DAVIS, JOHN M(AXWELL), b. Mahomet, Ill, July 18, 19; m. 49; c. 3. CHEMISTRY, CHEMICAL ENGINEERING. B.Ed, Ill. State Nor. Univ, 41; fel, Purdue, 44-46, M.S, 45, Ph.D.(org. chem, chem. eng), 47. Lab. asst. org. chem, Purdue, 41-43; res. chemist, nylon res. sect, textile fibers dept, E.I. DU PONT DE NEMOURS & CO, 46-55, sr. res. chemist, CHATTANOOGA PLANT TECH. SECT, 55-64, ENG. ASSOC, 64- With Off. Sci. Res. & Develop, 44. Development of synthetic fibers; production of fluorine compounds; preparation of certain cyclic fluorocarbons and their derivatives. Address: Chattanooga Nylon Plant, E.I. du Pont de Nemours & Co, Chattanooga, TN 37401.

DAVIS, JOHN MILTON, b. Red Oak, Iowa, June 2, 18; m. 48; c. 2. CHEMISTRY. A.B, California, Berkeley, 40. Chemist, Victor Chem. Works, 41; engr, Lawrence Radiation Lab, California, 47-52; chief engr, Lermac, Inc, 52-53; Allied Eng. Co, 53-54; res. engr, Atomics Int. Div, N.Am. Aviation, Inc, 57-58, supvr. hot lab. opers, 58-63; tech. consult. to dir. hot lab. design, Nuclear Res. Estab, Juelich, W.Germany, 63-66; SECT. CHIEF HOT LAB. DESIGN, DONALD W. DOUGLAS LABS, 66- U.S.A.F, 42-47, Maj. Am. Nuclear Soc. Hot laboratory design and operational management; remotely-controlled equipment design. Address: 2922 S. Auburn Pl, Kennewick, WA 99336.

DAVIS, JOHN M(OULTON), b. Nottingham, U.K, Aug. 28, 38; U.S. citizen; m. 65. SOLAR PHYSICS, X-RAY ASTRONOMY. B.Sc, Univ. Leeds, 60, Ph.D.(physics), 64. Demonstr. physics, Univ. Leeds, 63-64; res. assoc. space physics, lab. nuclear sci, Mass. Inst. Technol, 64-67, ctr. space res, 67-70; SR. SCIENTIST, AM. SCI. & ENG, INC, CAMBRIDGE, 70- Am. Geophys. Union; Brit. Inst. Physics & Phys. Soc. Solar wind and the effects of its interaction with planetary bodies; x-ray imaging and Bragg spectroscopy of the sun and of galactic and extragalactic objects. Address: 10 Dane Rd, Lexington, MA 02173.

DAVIS, JOHN ROBERT, b. Mattoon, Ill, July 10, 29; m. 52; c. 3. PATHOLOGY. B.A, Iowa, 52, fel, 56-57, M.D, 59. Instr. path. & resident anat. path, col. med, Iowa, 60-63, assoc. PATH, 63-64, asst. prof, 64-67; ASSOC. PROF, COL. MED, UNIV. ARIZ, 67- Consult. pathologist, Vet. Admin. Hosp, Tucson, 68- U.S.A.F, 51-54, S/Sgt. AAAS; Am. Med. Asn; Col. Am. Path; Int. Acad. Path; Am. Soc. Cytol; Am. Asn. Path. & Bact. Experimental pathology and immunopathology of schistosomiasis, gynecopathology and miscellaneous infectious diseases; surgical pathology; cytopathology computer pattern analysis. Address: Dept. of Pathology, University of Arizona College of Medicine, Tucson, AZ 85721.

DAVIS, JOHN R(OWLAND), b. Minneapolis, Minn, Dec. 19, 27; m. 46; c. 4. AGRICULTURAL ENGINEERING. B.S, Minnesota, 49, M.S, 51; Ph.D.(agr. eng), Mich. State, 59. Hydraul. engr, U.S. Geol. Surv, 50-51; instr. agr. eng, Mich. State, 51-55; asst. prof, Purdue, 55-57; lectr. & specialist, California, Davis, 57-62; hydraul. engr, Stanford Res. Inst, 62-64; prof. agr. eng, Nebraska, 64-71, dean col. eng. & archit, 65-71; HEAD DEPT. AGR. ENG, ORE. STATE UNIV, 71- Consult, U.S. Dept. Agr, 60; Stanford Res. Inst, 64- U.S.N.R, 45-46. Am. Soc. Agr. Eng; Am. Soc. Civil Eng; Am. Soc. Eng. Educ; Nat. Soc. Prof. Eng. Hydrology; hydraulics, irrigation systems; methods of irrigation water application; irrigation feasibility; engineering education; teaching methods. Address: Dept. of Agricultural Engineering, Oregon State University, Corvallis, OR 97331.

DAVIS, JOHN STAIGE, IV, b. New York, N.Y, Oct. 28, 31; m. 56; c. 5. INTERNAL & PREVENTIVE MEDICINE. B.A, Yale, 53; M.D, Pennsylvania, 57. Instr. internal & prev. med, SCH. MED, VIRGINIA, 61-64, asst. prof, 64-67, ASSOC. PROF. INTERNAL MED. & HEAD DIV. RHEUMATOL, 67- Markle scholar acad. med, 64-69; sr. investr, Arthritis & Rheumatism Found, 64-69. AAAS; Am. Rheumatism Asn; Am. Fedn. Clin. Res; N.Y. Acad. Sci. Immune complexes in connective tissue diseases, especially the roles of rheumatoid factors, complement and cryoglobulins. Address: Dept. of Internal Medicine, University of Virginia School of Medicine, Charlottesville, VA 22901.

DAVIS, J(OHNNY) GORDON, b. Perry, Fla, Nov. 9, 33; m. 55; c. 3. INDUSTRIAL ENGINEERING. B.I.E, Florida, 60, M.S.E, 61; Ford fel, Ga. Inst. Technol, 62-64, Nat. Sci. Found. fel, summer 64, Ph.D.(indust. eng), 67. Teaching asst. eng. graphics, Florida, 60-61; instr. INDUST. ENG, GA. INST. TECHNOL, 61-62, asst. prof, 64-69, ASSOC. PROF, 69- U.S.A, 56-58. Am. Inst. Indust. Eng; Am. Soc. Eng. Educ. Project management systems design; network theory; transportation systems simulation. Address: School of Industrial & Systems Engineering, Georgia Institute of Technology, Atlanta, GA 30332.

DAVIS, JOHNNY H(ENRY), b. Crossville, Ala, May 3, 20; m. 41; c. 2. AGRONOMY. B.S, Ala. Polytech, 43; M.S, Purdue, 52, Ph.D.(plant breeding, genetics), 53. Asst. county agent, Ala. Agr. Exten. Serv, 43-50; jr. agronomist forage breeding, Purdue, 50-53; geneticist cotton genetics, Miss. Agr. Exp. Sta, 53-54; agronomist forage breeding, Tex. Res. Found, 54-56, assoc. head high plains sta, 57-58; asst. dir, High Plains Res. Found, 59-60; assoc. agronomist, LA. STATE UNIV, 60-68, PROF. AGRON, 68- Assigned to La. State Univ-U.S. Agency Int. Develop. Mission, Managna, Nicaragua, 71-72. U.S.N, 44-45. Am. Soc. Agron; Genetics Soc. Am. Plant breeding; crop production and management. Address: P.O. Box 1429, Crowley, LA 70526.

DAVIS, JOSEPH ANTHONY, b. New Albany, Ind, Sept. 30, 26; m. 53; c. 8. INORGANIC & SOLID STATE CHEMISTRY. B.S, Indiana, 51, M.A, 52, Ph.D. (inorg. & anal. chem), 55. Chemist anal. methods develop, Am. Oil Co, 55-56; mgr. solid state mat. develop, RCA Tube Div, 56-62; mat. res, ITT Indust. Labs, 62-66; asst. prof. CHEM, Ind. Univ, Ft. Wayne, 66-67; PURDUE UNIV, FT. WAYNE, 67-68, ASSOC. PROF, 68- U.S.A, 45-47. Am. Chem. Soc; Electrochem. Soc. Lanthanide compound chemistry; nonaqueous solvent chemistry; luminescence and solid state synthesis. Address: 1051 Rose Ave, New Haven, IN 46774.

DAVIS, JOSEPH B(ERRY), b. Piqua, Ohio, May 23, 13; m. 40; c. 2. RESEARCH ADMINISTRATION. B.S, Univ. Wis, 39; M.D, Rush Med. Col, Chicago, 41. Private practice, Calif, 46-54; dir. clin. res, Eaton Labs, 54-56; med. dir, Riker Labs, Inc, 56-57; asst. dir, Wash. Off, Am. Med. Asn, 57-58; MED. OFF. & DIR, DIV. CLIN. & MED. DEVICES, BUR. MED, FOOD & DRUG ADMIN, 59- Med.C, U.S.A.R, 41-57; U.S.A.F.R, 57-66, Lt. Col. (Ret). Am. Med. Asn; Aerospace Med. Asn; Am. Acad. Gen. Practice; Asn. Mil. Surg. U.S; Am. Col. Legal Med.(v.pres, 62, secy, 63-66); Biomed. Eng. Soc; Asn. Advan. Med. Instrumentation; N.Y. Acad. Sci. General practice; administration of medical clinical research programs; legal medicine; forensic science; aerospace medicine. Address: Bureau of Medicine, Food & Drug Administration, 5600 Fishers Lane, Rockville, MD 20852.

DAVIS, JOSEPH H(ARRISON), b. Flushing, N.Y, Apr. 16, 24; m. 52; c. 7. FORENSIC PATHOLOGY. M.D, L.I. Col. Med, 49. Intern surg, Univ. California Hosp, San Francisco, 49-50, asst. res. path, 50-51; asst. surgeon, U.S. Pub. Health Serv, 51-52, sr. asst. surgeon, U.S. Pub. Health Serv. Hosp, Seattle, Wash, 52-54, New Orleans, La, 54-55; instr. path, sch. med, La. State, 55-56; asst. med. exam, OFF. MED. EXAM, MIAMI, 56-57, MED. EXAM, 57-; PROF. LEGAL MED, SCH. MED, UNIV. MIAMI, 60- Consult. pathologist, Fed. Aviation Agency, 60- U.S.A, 43-46; U.S.P.H.S, 51-55, Surg. Am. Med. Asn; Am. Acad. Forensic Sci; Am. Soc. Clin. Path. Accident causation and prevention with emphasis on human factors involved. Address: Division of Legal Medicine, School of Medicine, University of Miami, Miami, FL 33136.

DAVIS, JOSEPH R(ICHARD), b. Chicago, Ill, May 13, 32; m. 58; c. 2. BIOCHEMICAL PHARMACOLOGY. B.S, Illinois, 56, M.D, 58, M.S, 59; Ph.D. (pharmacol), Baylor, 61. Instr. PHARMACOL, col. med, Baylor, 60-61; asst. prof, STRITCH SCH. MED, LOYOLA UNIV. CHICAGO, 61-64, assoc. prof, 64-69, PROF, 69- Am. Cancer Soc. fel, 58-61; Lederle Med. Faculty award, 62-65. Borden res. award, 58. Am. Asn. Cancer Res; Am. Soc. Pharmacol. & Exp. Therapeut. Biochemical approaches to cancer chemotherapy; protein synthesis of the normal and cryptorchid testis. Address: Dept. of Pharmacology, Stritch School of Medicine, Loyola University of Chicago, Maywood, IL 60153.

DAVIS, JOYCE S, b. Big Spring, Tex, Feb. 18, 24; m. 46; c. 4. MEDICINE, PATHOLOGY. B.S, Baylor, 45, M.D, 47. Asst. path, col. med, Washington (St. Louis), 47-48; res. physician, Methodist Hosp, Dallas, Tex, 49; instr. PATH, COL. MED, BAYLOR UNIV, 53-60, asst. prof, 60-67, ASSOC. PROF, 67- Attend. physician, Methodist Hosp, 65-69; Ben Taub Hosp, Houston, 65-; Vet. Admin. Hosp, Houston, 66- Diseases of kidney and liver. Address: Dept. of Pathology, Baylor University College of Medicine, 1200 Moursund Ave, Houston, TX 77025.

DAVIS, KENNETH ANDREW, b. Toronto, Ont, Mar. 19, 37. BIOCHEMISTRY. B.Sc, McGill Univ, 60; fel, Mass. Inst. Technol, 60-61; Prov. Ont. fel, Univ. Toronto, 64-66, Ph.D.(biochem), 66. Muscular Dystrophy Asn. Can. fel, BIOCHEM, Univ. Vienna, 66-68; FEL, SCRIPPS CLIN. & RES. FOUND, 68- San Diego County Heart Asn. advan. res. fel, 69-71, sr. investr, 71-72. Can. Biochem. Soc. Metal catalysis and mechanism of action of glyoxalase I; electron transport and oxidative phosphorylation in beef heart mitochondria; role of water structure in the organization of membranes and membrane components. Address: Dept. of Biochemistry, Scripps Clinic & Research Foundation, La Jolla, CA 92037.

DAVIS, KENNETH BRUCE, JR, b. Texarkana, Ark, Mar. 13, 40; m. 69. PHYSIOLOGY, VERTEBRATE ZOOLOGY. B.A, Univ. Ark, 63, M.S, 65; Ph.D.(physiol, vert. zool), La. State Univ, 70. Instr. gen. zool, La. State Univ, 68-69; ASST. PROF. BIOL, MEMPHIS STATE UNIV, 69- AAAS; Am. Inst. Biol. Sci; Am. Soc. Zool; Am. Ornith. Union. Role of diurnal rhythms of hormones in the regulation of daily and seasonal behavior of submammalian vertebrates, particularly birds; intra-extracellular electrolyte distribution and osmoregulation. Address: Dept. of Biology, Memphis State University, Memphis, TN 38111.

DAVIS, KENNETH E(DWARD), b. Chicago, Ill, Sept. 26, 14; m. 42; c. 3. PHYSICS. A.B, Kalamazoo Col, 37; M.A, Syracuse, 42; E.I. du Pont de Nemours & Co. fel, Rochester, 47-48, fel, 48, Ph.D.(physics), 48. Teacher high sch, Mich, 37-40; asst-Manhattan Dist. & instr. PHYSICS, Rochester, 43-46, grad. instr, 46-47; asst. prof, REED COL, 48-51, assoc. prof, 51-55, PROF, 55- Ford Found. fel, 52; Nat. Sci. Found. fel, 61-62; Fulbright-Hayes fel, 68. AAAS; Am. Phys. Soc; Am. Asn. Physics Teachers; Inst. Elec. & Electronics Eng; Brit. Inst. Physics & Phys. Soc. Electronics; spectroscopy; energy levels of nuclei; radiation dosage monitoring; angular distribution of inelastic scattering of protons by light nuclei; cosmic rays; solid state physics; luminescence. Address: Dept. of Physics, Reed College, Portland, OR 97202.

DAVIS, KENNETH JOSEPH, b. Spartanburg, S.C, Aug. 10, 37; m. 59; c. 4. MATHEMATICS. B.S, Wofford Col, 59; M.A, Tennessee, 62, Ph.D.(math), 63. Res. scientist, Marshall Space Flight Center, NASA, 63-65; ASSOC. PROF. MATH, Old Dom. Col, 65-66; E.CAROLINA UNIV, 66- U.S.A, 63-65, 1st Lt. Am. Math. Soc; Math. Asn. Am. Analytic number theory; control theory. Address: 1415 N. Overlook Dr, Greenville, NC 27834.

DAVIS, KENNETH P(ICKETT), b. Denver, Colo, Sept. 2, 06; m. 29; c. 4. FOREST MANAGEMENT. B.S.F, Montana, 28; M.F, Michigan, 32, Ph.D. (forest mgt), 40. Forest ranger, Absaroka Nat. Forest, 28-31; jr. instr, Michigan, 32; silviculturist, North. Rocky Mt. Forest & Range Exp. Sta, U.S. Forest Serv, 33-39, sr. silviculturist, Wash, D.C, 40-43, chief, div. forest management res, 44-45; dean, sch. forestry, Montana, 45-49; prof. forest mgt, sch. natural resources, Univ. Mich, 49-67, chmn. dept. forestry, 50-67, acting dean, sch. natural resources, 65-67; PROF. FOREST LAND USE, SCH. FORESTRY, YALE, 67- Pres, Mont. Conserv. Coun, 48-49; chmn. wood sect, Mich. Natural Resources Coun, 54-61; acting ed, Forest Sci, 57-58; consult. ed, McGraw-Hill Encycl. Sci. & Technol, 61-; mem, Nat. Comt. Advan. Forestry Educ, 62-63, chmn, 64-65; Fulbright lectr, Univ. Helsinki, 63. Univ. Helsinki Medal, 63. Fel. Soc. Am. Foresters(v.pres, 68-69, pres, 70-71). Silviculture; forest management; forest fire control and use; land use. Address: School of Forestry, Yale University, 205 Prospect St, New Haven, CT 06511.

DAVIS, KENT J, b. Cross Plains, Tex, Apr. 1, 25; m. 54; c. 1. VETERINARY MEDICINE, PATHOLOGY. B.S, Agr. & Mech. Col. Tex, 47, D.V.M, 53. Instr, Vet. Agr. Prog, 47-49; VET. PATHOLOGIST, bur. animal indust, agr. res. serv, U.S. Dept. Agr, 53-55; Food & Drug Admin, DEPT. HEALTH, EDUC. & WELFARE, 55-70, PESTICIDES OFF, ENVIRON. PROTECTION AGENCY, 70- U.S.A, 43-46, 1st Lt. Spontaneous and induced pathologic physiology, anatomy and histology in laboratory animals; pesticide toxicology and carcinogenicity. Address: 6311 Joyce Dr, Camp Springs, MD 20031.

DAVIS, LANCE A(LAN), b. Ridley,Park, Pa, Nov. 19, 39; m. 62; c. 3. MATERIALS SCIENCE, PHYSICS. B.S, Lafayette Col, 61; M.E, Yale, 63, Ph.D.(eng. & appl. sci), 66. Res. staff scientist, Yale, 66-68; RES. PHYSICIST, MAT. RES. CTR, ALLIED CHEM. CORP, 68- Am. Phys. Soc; Am. Soc. Metals; Am. Inst. Mining, Metall. & Petrol. Eng. Physical properties of materials at high pressure, particularly elastic, anelastic and plastic properties. Address: Materials Research Center, Allied Chemical Corporation, Box 3004, Morristown, NJ 07960.

DAVIS, LARRY A(LAN), b. Delano, Calif, June 1, 40; m. 60; c. 3. PLANT PHYSIOLOGY, AGRONOMY. B.A, La Verne Col, 62; M.S, Univ. Calif, Davis, 64, Nat. Defense Educ. Act fel, 66, Ph.D.(plant physiol), 68. Agronomist & asst. mgr, Alina Farms Corp, 64-65; agronomist & mgr, Calcot Pty, Ltd, Australia, 68-70; AGRONOMIST IN CHARGE & PRES, ALINA FARMS CORP, 70- Am. Soc. Plant Physiol; Am. Inst. Biol. Sci; Am. Soc. Agron; Crop Sci. Soc. Am; Bot. Soc. Am. Control of fruit growth and development in the cotton plant by means of plant hormones and the identification and measurement of these hormones by gas-liquid chromatography and other methods. Address: Alina Farms Corp, Route 1, Box 292, McFarland, CA 93250.

DAVIS, LARRY DEAN, b. Marathon, Iowa, June 23, 35; m. 58; c. 2. HUMAN PHYSIOLOGY. B.S, Univ. Dubuque, 57; Ph.D.(physiol), Univ. Wis, 61. U.S. Pub. Health Serv. fel, 61-63; instr. PHYSIOL, SCH. MED, UNIV. WIS, 63-64, asst. prof, 64-69, ASSOC. PROF, 69- Am. Physiol. Soc. Cardiac physiology, specifically cellular transmembrane potential changes involved in origin of arrhythmias and antiarrhythmic actions. Address: Dept. of Physiology, University of Wisconsin School of Medicine, Madison, WI 53705.

DAVIS, LARRY E, b. Wayne Co, Iowa, July 1, 36; m. 63. ANIMAL SCIENCE & NUTRITION. B.S, Iowa State, 58, M.S, 63; Colorado State, 64; Ph.D. (animal sci), Minnesota, 67. Instr, Corning Independent Schs, Iowa, 59-60; instr. animal sci, part-time, Iowa State, 60-63; assoc. prof. AGR, Northeast Mo. State Col, 67-71; ASSOC. PROF. & HEAD DEPT, MO. WEST. COL, 71- Mo. hon. state farmer, 71. AAAS; Am. Soc. Animal Sci. Ruminant nutrition; animal production and education. Address: Dept. of Agriculture, Missouri Western College, Saint Joseph, MO 64507.

DAVIS, LARRY W(ALLACE), b. Compton, Ill, May 10, 41; m. 61; c. 2. MATHEMATICS. B.A, N.Cent. Col.(Ill), 63; Gregory fel, Missouri-Columbia, 63, 65, NASA fel. & Ph.D.(math), 68. ASST. PROF. MATH, WIS. STATE UNIV, WHITEWATER, 68- Am. Math. Soc; Math. Asn. Am. Nonassociative algebra, especially characterizing nearly antiflexible division algebras. Address: Dept. of Mathematics, Wisconsin State University, Whitewater, WI 53190.

DAVIS, LARY VERNON, b. Tacoma, Wash, Nov. 9, 32; m. 60; c. 2. INVERTEBRATE ZOOLOGY, BIOLOGY. B.S, Puget Sound, 59, univ. & Rayonier fels. & M.S, 60; Nat. Sci. Found. fel, California, Berkeley, 62-65, Ph.D.

(zool), 65. Asst. prof. zool, Univ. Hawaii, 65-68; vis. asst. prof, Univ. Calif, Los Angeles, 68, Berkeley, 68-69; asst. prof. biol, Univ. Notre Dame, 69-70; STAFF BIOL, COMN. UNDERGRADUATE EDUC. BIOL. SCI, 70- Summers, vis. instr, Univ. Puget Sound, 61, Univ. Ore, 65. AAAS; Am. Soc. Zool. Developmental biology; chemical and/or physical control of growth and differentiation, especially during regeneration of various invertebrate organisms. Address: Commission of Undergraduate Education in the Biological Sciences, 3900 Wisconsin Ave. N.W, Washington, DC 20016.

DAVIS, L(AWRENCE) HARLAN, Agr. Econ, see Suppl. I to 11th ed, Soc. & Behav. Vols.

DAVIS, LAWRENCE W(ILLIAM), JR, b. Los Angeles, Calif, Oct. 21, 30; m. 66; c. 2. PHYSICS. B.A, Pomona Col, 52; M.S, Calif. Inst. Technol, 56; Ph.D.(physics), Stanford Univ, 61. Proj. engr. statist. mech, West. Develop. Labs, Philco Corp, 60-62, supvr, quantum electronics group, 62; sr. scientist, quantum electronics, Interphase Corp-West, 63-65; res. assoc, Stanford Electronics Labs, Stanford Univ, 65-66; lectr, dept. elec. eng, Univ. Calif, Berkeley, 66-68; asst. prof. PHYSICS, UNIV. IDAHO, 68-70, ASSOC. PROF, 70- U.S.A, 53-55. Am. Phys. Soc. Quantum electronics; optical spectroscopy. Address: Dept. of Physics, University of Idaho, Moscow, ID 83843.

DAVIS, LEODIS, b. Stamps, Ark, Sept. 25, 33; m. 62; c. 2. BIOCHEMISTRY. B.S, Univ. Kansas City, 56; M.S, Iowa State, 58, Ph.D.(biochem), 60. Res. asst. BIOCHEM, Iowa State, 60-61; asst. prof, Tennessee State, 61-63; col. med, Howard, 63-68; vis. prof. CHEM, UNIV. IOWA, 68-69, ASSOC. PROF, 69- Am. Chem. Soc. Mechanism of pyridoxal phosphate requiring enzymes. Address: Dept. of Chemistry, University of Iowa, Iowa City, IA 52240.

DAVIS, LEONARD REID, b. Douglas, Ga, Oct. 29, 10; m. 32. PARASITOLOGY. B.S, Union (Tenn), 31; M.S, Iowa State Col, 33, Ph.D.(entom, zool), 37. Teaching fel. biol, Iowa State Col, 31-32, asst. zool. & entom, 32-33, 35-36, instr, 36; assoc. prof. zool, Union (Tenn), 33-34, head dept. biol, 36-41; asst. protozool. res, bur. animal indust, U.S. DEPT. AGR, 41-44, protozoologist, REGIONAL PARASITE RES. LAB, 46-61, prin. res. parasitologist, 61-66, DIR, 66- Sanit.C, 44-46, Med.Serv.C. Res, 46-70, Lt. Col.(Ret). Assoc. Am. Soc. Parasitol; Soc. Protozool; Soc. Photog. Sci. & Eng. Bovine and ovine coccidiosis; general parasitology; photomicrography. Address: Regional Parasite Research Lab, U.S. Dept. of Agriculture, P.O. Drawer 952, Auburn, AL 36830.

DAVIS, LE ROY WELLINGTON, b. Cleveland, Ohio, May 29, 01; m. 26, 52; c. 2. METALLURGY, PHYSICS. B.S, Case Inst. Technol, 22, Met.E, 31. Metallurgist, forging plant, Aluminum Co. Am, 26-39, chief metallurgist, 39-43, asst. chief metallurgist, casting & forging div, 43-52; tech. supt. extrusions, Kaiser Aluminum & Chem. Corp, 52-54, forgings, 54-55; mgr, forgings, Harvey Aluminum, 55-58, chief res. metallurgist, res. & develop. div, 58-70; PRES, NEV. ENG. & TECHNOL. CORP, 71- Forging specialist, U.S. War Prod. Bd, 42-43; lectr, Univ. Wis. Extension, 67; Univ. Tenn, 68; Pa. State Univ, 68; Univ. Calif, Los Angeles, 68-70. Indust. Res. Mag. IR-100 Award, 68. Fel. Am. Soc. Metals; Am. Inst. Mining, Metall. & Petrol. Eng; Nat. Asn. Corrosion Eng; Am. Soc. Non Destructive Test; Am. Ord. Asn; Am. Ceramic Soc; Am. Soc. Test. & Mat; Am. Welding Soc. Development of methods of working light metals, particularly forging, extrusion and impact extrusion of aluminum, magnesium and titanium; plasma-spray deposition of metals, ceramics and cermets; metal-matrix composites, especially diffusion bonded boron-aluminum composites. Address: Nevada Engineering & Technology Corp, Suite 58, 21462 Pacific Coast Highway, Huntington Beach, CA 92646.

DAVIS, LEVERETT, JR, b. Elgin, Ill, March 3, 14; m. 43; c. 1. PHYSICS. B.S, Oregon State Col, 36; M.S, Calif. Inst. Tech, 38, Ph.D.(physics), 41, fel, Rockefeller Inst, 40-41. Instr. & res. staff mem. PHYSICS, CALIF. INST. TECHNOL, 41-46, asst. prof, 46-50, assoc. prof, 50-56, PROF, 56-, res. staff mem, 42-46, group supvr, 44-46. Nat. Sci. Found. sr. fel, Max-Planck Inst. Physics, Göttingen, 57-58; medal exceptional sci. achievement, NASA, 70. Civilian with Off. Sci. Res. & Develop, 44. Am. Phys. Soc; Am. Astron. Soc; Am. Geophys. Union; Int. Astron. Union. Interplanetary medium; cosmic rays; astrophysics; hydromagnetics; polarization of starlight. Address: Dept. of Physics, 412 Downs, California Institute of Technology, Pasadena, CA 91109.

DAVIS, LILY H(ERLINDA), b. Los Angeles, Calif, Dec. 7, 21; m. 49. PLANT PATHOLOGY. B.A, California, Los Angeles, 43, M.A, 45. Asst. bot. California, Los Angeles, 43-44, sr. lab. technician plant path, 45-49, prin. lab. technician, 49-61, lab. technician bot, 61-63; DIR, MYCOL. SUPPLIES, 63- Teacher, univ. exten, California, Los Angeles, 63-64. Consult, Soil & Plant Lab, Inc, 63- AAAS; Am. Phytopath. Soc; Mycol. Soc. AM. Brit. Mycol. Soc. Diseases of ornamental plants; seed-borne pathogens; morphology of fungi; fungus resistance tests. Address: Mycological Supplies, 2601 Westwood Blvd, Los Angeles, CA 90064.

DAVIS, LIONEL E(DWARD), b. Barking, U.K, Apr. 26, 35; m. 64; c. 3. ELECTRICAL ENGINEERING. B.Sc, Univ. Nottingham, 56; Ph.D.(elec. eng), Univ. London, 60. Res. engr, Mullard Res. Labs, U.K, 59-62, proj. leader microwave ferrite devices, 62-64; asst. prof. ELEC. ENG, RICE UNIV, 64-69, ASSOC. PROF, 69- Consult, Bendix Res. Labs, Mich, 67-70; vis. prof, Univ. Col, Univ. London, 70-71. AAAS; Brit. Inst. Elec. Eng; Inst. Elec. & Electronic Eng. Electromagnetic wave propagation in anistropic materials; liquid crystals and their applications; elastic wave propagation in solids and liquids. Address: Dept. of Electrical Engineering, Rice University, Houston, TX 77001.

DAVIS, L(LOYD) CRAIG, b. Council Bluffs, Iowa, May 29, 41; m. 63; c. 2. PHYSICS. B.S, Iowa State Univ, 63, Ph.D.(physics), 66; Nat. Sci. Found. fel, 63-65; M.S, Calif. Inst. Technol, 66. Res. assoc. physics, Iowa State Univ, 66-67; mem. tech. staff, micro-electronics lab, TRW Inc, Calif, summer 67; res. assoc. physics, Univ. Ill, Urbana 67-69; MEM. SCI. RES. STAFF, THEORET. SCI. DEPT, FORD MOTOR CO, 69- Nat. Sci. Found. fel, Univ. Ill, Urbana, 67-68. AAAS; Am. Phys. Soc. Magnetic levitation of high-speed ground vehicles; electron tunneling in solids; electron energy levels of solids in a magnetic field; sound velocity and lattice vibrations in semiconductors. Address: Dept. of Theoretical Sciences, Ford Motor Co, P.O. Box 2053, Dearborn, MI 48121.

DAVIS, LLOYD EDWARD, b. Akron, Ohio, Aug. 23, 29; m. 53; c. 2. PHARMACOLOGY. D.V.M, Ohio State Univ, 59; Ph.D.(pharmacol), Univ. Mo-Columbia, 63. Instr. vet. pharmacol, Univ. Mo-Columbia, 59-63, assoc. prof. PHARMACOL, sch. med, 63-69; PROF, OHIO STATE UNIV, 69- U.S.N, 50-53. AAAS; Am. Soc. Vet. Physiol. & Pharmacol; Am. Soc. Pharmacol. & Exp. Therapeut; Soc. Exp. Biol. & Med; Biophys. Soc; N.Y. Acad. Sci. Comparative pharmacology; drug metabolism and pharmacokinetics in domestic animals; clinical pharmacology. Address: College of Veterinary Medicine, Ohio State University, 1900 Coffey Rd, Columbus, OH 43210.

DAVIS, L(LOYD) WAYNE, b. Medicine Lodge, Kans, July 16, 29; m. 63; c. 3. PHYSICS, ELECTRICAL ENGINEERING. B.S, Univ. Kans, 52; M.S, Univ. N.Mex, 59. Staff mem, systs. anal. dept, Sandia Corp, 52-56, consult, 56-57; sr. res. physicist, DIKEWOOD CORP, 57-64, head, weapons effects div, 64-67, dep. tech. dir, 67-69, ASST. V.PRES, 69-, CORP. SECY, 70-, MEM. BD. DIRS, 71- Sr. mem. Inst. Elec. & Electronics Eng; Am. Phys. Soc. Nuclear weapons effects and phenomenology effects on personnel and complex military systems. Address: Dikewood Corp, 1009 Bradbury Dr, S.E, University Research Park, Albuquerque, NM 87106.

DAVIS, LOUIS E(LKIN), b. Brooklyn, N.Y, Sept. 10, 18; m. 44; c. 2. INDUSTRIAL ENGINEERING. B.S.M.E, Ga. Inst. Technol, 40; N.Y. Univ, 40-41; M.S, Univ. Iowa, 42; Columbia Univ, 44-46. Asst. prof. indust. eng, Ga. Inst. Technol, 42-43; supvr, Bell Aircraft Corp, Ga, 43-44; sr. indust. engr, West. Elec. Co, N.Y, 44-46; asst. chief indust. eng, Conmar Prods. Corp, N.J, 46-47; asst. prof, Univ. Calif, Berkeley, 47-53, assoc. prof, 53-60, PROF, 60-66, UNIV. CALIF, LOS ANGELES, 66-71, ORGN. SCI, 71-, chmn, grad. sch. bus. admin, 67-69, res. dir. bus. admin, 69-71, dir. ctr. orgn. stud, 71. Lucas prof, Univ. Birmingham, 62-63. Consult, Europ. Productivity Agency, France, 57-58; Maritime Transport Conf, Nat. Acad. Sci-Nat. Res. Coun, 58-62; range & exp. sta, U.S. Forest Serv, 62-; adv, Exec. Off. President, 62-64; comnr, Calif. State Comn. Manpower, Automation & Technol. & Manpower Adv. Comn, 63-67; res. fel, Tavistock Inst. Human Rels, London & Inst. Indust. Social Res, Norway, 66. Am. Inst. Indust. Eng; Human Factors Soc; Brit. Ergonomics Res. Soc; Brit. Inst. Indust. Psychol; Inst. Mgt. Sci. Human performance skills and measurement; job and organization design; socio-technical systems. Address: Graduate School of Management, University of California, Los Angeles, CA 90024.

DAVIS, LOYAL, b. Galesburg, Ill, Jan. 17, 96. SURGERY. Knox Col, 12-14, hon. Sc.D, 33; M.D, Northwestern, 18, M.S, 21, Ph.D, 23. Mem. res. staff, Cook County Hosp, 18-19; asst. to Dr. Allen B. Kanavel, 20-23; Nat. Res. Coun. fel, NORTHWEST. UNIV, 22-24, assoc. prof. SURG, MED. SCH, 25-32, PROF, 32-, dir. lab. surg. res, 25-32, chmn. div. surg, 32-64. Jr. assoc, Peter Bent Brigham Hosp, 23-24; attend. surgeon, Passavant Mem. Hosp, 28-; consult. surgeon, U.S. Vet. Admin, 25- Assoc. ed, Surg, Gynec. & Obstet, 27-33, asst. ed, 33-39, ed, 39- Med.C, 42-46, Col. Am. Surg. Asn.(past v.pres, pres, 57); Soc. Clin. Surg; Soc. Neurol. Surg.(pres, 46); Am. Neurol. Asn.(v.pres, 47); Am. Med. Asn. Neurologic surgery. Address: 55 E. Erie St, Chicago, IL 60611.

DAVIS, LUCKETT VANDERFORD, b. Smyrna, Tenn, Oct. 16, 32. INVERTEBRATE ZOOLOGY, MARINE ECOLOGY. B.S, Middle Tenn. State Col, 55; M.A, Duke, 58, Ph.D.(zool), 62. Instr. biol, Vanderbilt, 60-61; asst. prof, Southwestern Louisiana, 61-63; biol. sci, Univ. of the Pacific, 63-64; assoc. prof. BIOL, WINTHROP COL, 64-69, PROF, 69- Nat. Sci. Found. summer res. award, 62, 67. Ecol. Soc. Am; Am. Soc. Zool; Am. Soc. Limnol. & Oceanog. Ecology of salt marshes; ecology of intertidal invertebrates. Address: Dept. of Biology, Winthrop College, Rock Hill, SC 29730.

DAVIS, LUTHER, JR, b. Mineola, N.Y, July 12, 22; m. 51; c. 3. PHYSICS. B.S, Mass. Inst.Tech, 42, Ph.D.(physics), 49. Mem. staff, radiation lab, Mass. Inst. Tech, 42-45, res. assoc. physics, 45-49; mem. staff solid state physics, RES. DIV, RAYTHEON CO, 49-64, asst. mgr, 64-69, GEN. MGR, RES. DIV, 69- Consult. U.S. Air Force Sci. Adv. Bd, 58-59. Am. Phys. Soc; Inst. Elec. & Electronics Eng. Molecular beams; semiconductors; dielectrics; ferromagnetics. Address: Research Division, Raytheon Co, Waltham, MA 02154.

DAVIS, LYLE LELAND, b. Zearing, Iowa, Mar. 10, 04; m. 24; c. 4. FOOD TECHNOLOGY. B.S, Iowa State Col, 32, M.S, 33, Ph.D.(hort), 45; Minnesota, 38. Assoc. pathologist, bur. plant indust, U.S. Dept. Agr, Ind, 33; dir, subsistence gardens, Iowa Emergency Relief Admin, 33-34; asst. prof. hort, S.Dak. State Col, 34-38, assoc. prof. hort, Tennessee, 42-46; prof. Va. Polytech, 46-53; poultry & egg res, biol. sci. br, agr. mkt. serv, U.S. Dept. Agr, 53-57; consult, Mixon & Davis, 57-64; mem. staff, Cryovac Div, W.R. Grace & Co, 64-69; RETIRED. Packaging turkeys, chickens and ducks. Address: 117 Rollingreen Rd, Greenville, SC 29607.

DAVIS, MARGARET S. BRYAN, b. Boston, Mass, Oct. 23, 31; div. PALYNOLOGY, ECOLOGY. A.B, Radcliffe Col, 53; Fulbright fel, Copenhagen, 53-54; Nat. Sci. Found. fels, Harvard, 54-56, Am. Asn. Univ. Women fel, 56-57, Ph.D.(biol), 57. Nat. Sci. Found. res. fel. biol, Harvard, 57-58 & geol, Calif. Inst. Technol, 59-60; res. fel. zool, Yale, 60-61; res. assoc. bot, UNIV. MICH, 61-64, GREAT LAKES RES. DIV, 64-66, assoc. prof. zool. & assoc. res. paleoecologist, 66-70, PROF. ZOOL. & RES. PALEOECOLOGIST, 70- Nat. Sci. Found. grants, 61-; mem. U.S. comt. int. union quaternary res, Nat. Acad. Sci-Nat. Res. Coun, 66-; off. del, VIII Int. Union Quaternary Res. Cong, Paris, 69; mem. Panel for Nat. Sci. Found. Postdoctoral Fel. Prog, 71. Fel. AAAS; fel. Geol. Soc. Am; Ecol. Soc. Am; Am. Quaternary Asn.(secy, 69-70); Am. Soc. Limnol. & Oceanog; Int. Asn. Great Lakes Res; Int. Asn. Theoret. & Appl. Limnol. Paleoecology of the Quaternary Period, especially the late-glacial environment of northern United States; forest ecology and vegetation history; methodology of pollen analysis; sedimentation in lakes. Address: Dept. of Zoology, University of Michigan, Ann Arbor, MI 48104.

DAVIS, MARJORIE, b. Elkhart, Kans, Mar. 13, 36; m. 70; c. 1. DEVELOPMENTAL BIOLOGY, INVERTEBRATE ZOOLOGY. B.S, Panhandle State Col, 59; M.A, Univ. Kans, 62; Ph.D.(embryol), Kans. State Univ, 70. Instr. zool, Mankato State Col, 62-66; ASST. PROF. BIOL, MO. WEST. COL, 69- AAAS; Soc. Study Reproduction; Am. Asn. Anat; Am. Soc. Zool. Limnology, especially composition and distribution of zooplankton in various southwest Kansas ponds; differentation of mammalian limbs; DDT effects in some rodents. Address: Dept. of Biology, Missouri Western College, St. Joseph, MO 64507.

DAVIS, MARSHALL E(ARL), b. Richmond, Calif, Aug. 14, 31; m. 56; c. 2. PHYSICAL & NUCLEAR CHEMISTRY. B.S, W.Tex. State Col, 57; Ph.D. (phys. & nuclear chem), Purdue, 63. Res. staff mem, fission prod. characterization, Oak Ridge Nat. Lab, 62-65; sr. chemist, FUELS RES. SECT, TEXACO, INC, 65-70, RES. CHEMIST, 70- Sig.C, U.S.A, 53-55. N.Y. Acad. Sci; Am. Chem. Soc. Nuclear chemistry of the fission process; sorption of high temperature vapors by metal surfaces; fuel and fuel additive development; combustion; air pollution. Address: Texaco, Inc, P.O. Box 509, Beacon, NY 12508.

DAVIS, M(ARTIN) A(RNOLD), b. Montreal, Que, Apr. 24, 30; m. 56; c. 2. ORGANIC CHEMISTRY. B.Sc, McGill, 51; Ph.D.(org. chem), London, 55. Res. chemist, AYERST LABS, LTD, 55-64, head med. chem. group, 64-69, DIR. EXTERNAL PROJS, 69- Am. Chem. Soc; fel. Chem. Inst. Can; The Chem. Soc; Acad. Pharmaceut. Sci; Israel Chem. Soc. Medicinal chemistry; drugs affecting the central and autonomic systems; behavioral and spasmolytic agents, anticonvulsants, analgesics; cardiovascular drugs; newer techniques in syntheses; approaches to chemotherapy. Address: 4758 Meridian Ave, Montreal 29, Que, Can.

DAVIS, MARTIN (DAVID), b. N.Y.C, Mar. 8, 28; m. 51; c. 1. MATHEMATICAL LOGIC. B.S, City Col, 48; M.A, Princeton, 49, Ph.D.(math), 50. Res. instr. math, Illinois, 50-51, res. assoc, control syst. lab, 51-52; mem. sch. math, Inst. Adv. Study, 52-54; asst. prof. math, California, Davis, 54-55; Ohio State, 55-56; Rensselaer Polytech. Inst, 56-57; assoc. prof, grad. div, Hartford, 57-59; res. scientist, inst. math. sci, N.Y. Univ, 59-60; from assoc. prof. to PROF. MATH, Belfer Grad. Sch. Sci, Yeshiva, 60-65; COURANT INST, N.Y. UNIV, 65- Vis. prof, Belfer Grad. Sch. Sci, Yeshiva Univ, 70-71. Am. Math. Soc; Asn. Symbol. Logic; Asn. Comput. Mach. Recursive functions; Hilbert's tenth problem; theorem proving by computing machine. Address: Courant Institute, New York University, 251 Mercer St, New York, NY 10012.

DAVIS, M(ARVIN) L(ESTER), b. Brockton, Mass, Apr. 26, 16; m. 62. ORGANIC CHEMISTRY. B.A, Rochester, 37, M.S, 39. Chemist SYNTHETIC ORG. CHEM, EASTMAN KODAK CO, 39-54, supvr, 54-61, PATENT LIAISON, 62- Am. Chem. Soc. Organic synthesis relating to photography. Address: Eastman Kodak Co, Kodak Park, Bldg. 82, Rochester, NY 14650.

DAVIS, MERRITT McGREGOR, b. Ont, Feb. 16, 23; m. 47; c. 2. CIVIL ENGINEERING. B.Sc, Queen's (Ont), 45; M.Sc, Purdue, 49. Div. maintenance engr, Hwy. Dept, Ont, 49-51, res. engr, 51-55, design engr, 56; asst. prof. HWY. ENG, UNIV. TORONTO, 56-61, ASSOC. PROF, 61- Assoc. mem. Hwy. Res. Bd, Nat. Acad. Sci-Nat. Res. Coun. Can. Army, 45-46, Lt. Eng. Inst. Can. Frost action in soils; bituminous pavement mixes; traffic accident causes and crash injury performance. Address: 112 Three Valleys Dr, Don Mills, Ont, Can.

DAVIS, MERTON L(OUIS), b. Detroit, Mich, Nov. 27, 18; m. 62; c. 4. PHYSICAL CHEMISTRY. A.B, DePauw, 42; M.S, Michigan, 49, Ph.D.(chem), 51. Radiographer, Bohn Aluminum & Brass Co, 42; RES. CHEMIST, E.I. DU PONT DE NEMOURS & CO, 51- U.S.A, 42-46. AAAS; Am. Chem. Soc; Am. Inst. Chem. Thermodynamics; x-ray crystallography. Address: 1928 Forest Dr, Camden, SC 29020.

DAVIS, MICHAEL EDWARD, b. Jacksonville, Ill, May 17, 22; m. 47; c. 6. GEOLOGY. B.S, Kansas State, 50, M.S, 51. Instr. geol, Kansas State, 51-52; asst. prof, St. Joseph's Col.(Ind), 52-54; geologist, Knox-Bergman-Shearer, Colo, 54-57; ASSOC. PROF. GEOL, ST. JOSEPH'S COL.(IND), 57-, CHMN. DEPT, 61- Glacial geologist, Ind. Geol. Surv, 62-64; assoc. faculty mem, Ind. Univ. Northwest, summer 66; Nat. Sci. Found. Summer Inst, Millsaps Col, 68, Wayne State Univ, 70. U.S.A, 42-46, S/Sgt. Am. Asn. Petrol. Geol; Geol. Soc. Am; Nat. Asn. Geol. Teachers; Am. Inst. Prof. Geol. Use of photogeologic methods in interpretation of glacial features; photogeologic procedures as applied to geomorphic and structural phenomena; methods of preparation and study of Ostradoda of lower permian limestones. Address: Dept. of Geology, St. Joseph's College, Rensselaer, IN 47978.

DAVIS, MICHAEL I, b. London, Eng, July 17, 36; m. 70; c. 1. PHYSICAL CHEMISTRY. B.Sc, London, 58, Ph.D.(chem), 62. Instr. CHEM, UNIV. TEX, Austin, 61-64, asst. prof, 64-68, assoc. prof, EL PASO, 68-71, PROF, 71- Am. Chem. Soc; Am. Crystallog. Asn; Faraday Soc; The Chem. Soc. Molecular structure studies by gas phase electron diffraction. Address: Dept. of Chemistry, University of Texas at El Paso, El Paso, TX 79999.

DAVIS, MICHAEL M(OORE), b. Geneva, N.Y, Dec. 6, 38; m. 61; c. 4. RADIO ASTRONOMY. B.S, Yale, 60; Nat. Sci. Found. fel, Leiden, 60-66, Ph.D. (astron), 67. ASST. SCIENTIST, NAT. RADIO ASTRON. OBSERV, 67- Am. Astron. Soc. Extragalactic radio sources; the interstellar medium in our galaxy. Address: National Radio Astronomy Observatory, P.O. Box 2, Green Bank, WV 24944.

DAVIS, MILFORD H(ALL), b. Chicago, Ill, Aug. 20, 25; m. 62; c. 2. PHYSICS. B.S, Yale, 49; M.S, Calif. Inst. Tech, 50, Ph.D.(physics), 55. PHYSICIST, Rand Corp, 55-67; NAT. CTR. ATMOS. RES, 67- C.Eng, 43-46, T/Sgt. AAAS; Am. Phys. Soc. Cloud microphysics. Address: P.O. Box 3006, Boulder, CO 80303.

DAVIS, MILTON S, b. Boston, Mass, Sept. 26, 36; m. 60; c. 2. MEDICAL SOCIOLOGY. A.B, Boston Univ, 58; M.S, Purdue Univ, 61, Ph.D.(sociol), 62; S.M.Hyg, Harvard, 62. Russell Sage Found. residency, 61-62; res. assoc. sociol. in med, med. col, Cornell Univ, 62-67; ASSOC. PROF, DEPT. COMMUNITY MED. & PUB. HEALTH, SCH. MED, UNIV. SOUTH CALIF, 67- Nat. Insts. Health fel, 61-62; Nat. Inst. Ment. Health res. grant, 63-; lectr, Univ. Wis, 64; Hunter Col, 64- Am. Sociol. Asn; Am. Pub. Health Asn. Sociology of medicine; social-psychology research methods. Address: Dept. of Community Medicine & Public Health, University of Southern California School of Medicine, 2025 Zonal Ave, Los Angeles, CA 90033.

DAVIS, MILTON W(ICKERS), JR, b. Frederick, Md, Apr. 5, 23; m. 48; c. 2. CHEMICAL ENGINEERING. B.E, Hopkins, 43; M.S, California, Berkeley, 49, Ph.D.(chem. eng), 51. Asst. radiation lab, California, 47-50; res. eng, atomic energy. div, E.I. du Pont de Nemours & Co, 51-53, res. supvr, Savannah River Plant, 54-62; PROF. CHEM. ENG. UNIV. S.C, 62-, DIR. ENVIRON. RES. INST, 66- U.S.N.R, 43-46, Lt. Am. Chem. Soc; Am. Inst. Chem. Eng; Am. Soc. Eng. Educ; N.Y. Acad. Sci. Liquid extraction; ion exchange; nuclear chemistry and physics; chemical reaction kinetics. Address: 432 Berrie Rd, Aiken, SC 29801.

DAVIS, MONTE V, b. Cove, Ore, Apr. 29, 23; m. 47; c. 2. NUCLEAR PHYSICS. B.A, Linfield Col, 49; M.A, Oregon State, 51, Ph.D.(physics), 56. Sr. reactor physicist, Gen. Elec. Co, 51-57; group leader & proj. engr, Atomics Int. Div, N.Am. Aviation, Inc, 57-61; PROF. NUCLEAR ENG. & DIR. NUCLEAR REACTOR LAB, UNIV. ARIZ, 61- Consult, indust. & U.S. Govt, 61- U.S.A.A.F, 43-46. Am. Nuclear Soc; Am. Phys. Soc; Am. Inst. Aeronaut. & Astronaut. Reactor experiments to measure neutron resonance capture in different elements; effect of temperature and radiation fields on insulators, non-insulators and semiconductors; neutron interactions with moderators. Address: Dept. of Engineering, University of Arizona, Tucson, AZ 85721.

DAVIS, M(ORRIS) EDWARD, b. Cheyenne, Wyo, Oct. 27, 99; m. 27; c. 2. OBSTETRICS, GYNECOLOGY. B.S, Chicago, 20, M.D, Rush Med. Col, 22; Berlin & Vienna, 27-28. Intern, Los Angeles Gen. Hosp, Calif, 22-23; res. obstetrician, Chicago Lying-in Hosp, 25-27, adj. obstetrician, 28-29; instr. obstet. & gynec, med. sch, Northwestern, 29-30; asst. prof, sch. med, Chicago, 30-33; res. fel, Carnegie Inst. Embryol, Md, 33-34; assoc. prof. OBSTET. & GYNEC, SCH. MED, UNIV. CHICAGO, 34-42, prof, 42-47, Joseph Bolivar Delee prof, 47-66, chmn. dept, 54-66, EMER. JOSEPH BOLIVAR DELEE PROF. & CHMN. DEPT, 66- Chief serv, Chicago Lying-in Hosp, 54-; attend. gynecologist, Billings Mem. Hosp. Pres, Am. Asn. Maternal & Infant Health, 59-62, ed, Bul, 58-; assoc. ed, Geriatrics; ed, Mothers-to-be & Infant Care Mag, 63- Mem. perinatal res. comt, Nat. Inst. Neurol. Diseases & Blindness, 65-68; consult. & spec. asst. to med. dir, Am. Col. Obstet. & Gynec, 67-69. Fel. Am. Med. Asn.(gold medal, 35); Am. Gynec. Soc.(v.pres, 65); Soc. Exp. Biol. & Med; fel. Am. Col. Surg; Am. Fertil. Soc.(ed, Fertility & Sterility, 53-, Rubin Award, 60); Endocrine Soc; Am. Soc. Pharmacol. & Exp. Therapeut; Soc. Prof. Gynec. & Obstet; fel. Am. Col. Obstet. & Gynec; hon. fel. Obstet. & Gynec. Socs. Brazil, Cuba & Venezuela. Physiology of mammalian reproduction; steroid metabolism in normal pregnancy and its complications. Address: 5841 Maryland Ave, Chicago, IL 60637.

DAVIS, MORRIS S(CHUYLER), b. Brooklyn, N.Y, Dec. 14, 19; m. 45; c. 6. ASTRONOMY. B.A, Brooklyn Col, 46; M.A, Missouri, 47; Sheffield Sci. fel, Yale, 49-50, Ph.D.(astron), 50. Asst. instr. math, Missouri, 46-47; asst. astron, Yale, 47-49; instr. math. & astron, Kentucky, 50-51, asst. prof, 51-52, in charge Observ, 50-52; asst. prof. astron, North Carolina, 52-56, assoc. prof, 56; res. assoc. astron. & dir. comput. ctr, Yale, 56-66; pres. & dir, Triangle Univs. Comput. Ctr, Research Triangle Park, N.C, 66-70; MOREHEAD PROF. ASTRON, UNIV. N.C, CHAPEL HILL, 70- Tech. adv. & writer, Morehead Planetarium, 52-56; adj. prof, Univ. N.C, Chapel Hill, N.C. State Univ. & Duke Univ, 66-70. AAAS; Am. Astron. Soc; Asn. Comput. Mach; Int. Astron. Union. Computer science; celestial mechanics; numerical analysis; astrometry. Address: Dept. of Physics, University of North Carolina at Chapel Hill, Chapel Hill, NC 27514.

DAVIS, MORTON DAVID, b. Bronx, N.Y, May 31, 30; m. 63; c. 2. MATHEMATICS. A.B, Colorado, 52; M.A, California, Berkeley, 56, Ph.D.(math), 61. Mathematician, Int. Bus. Corp, 59-61; asst. prof. math, Rutgers Univ, 61-65; mem. faculty, CITY COL. NEW YORK, 65-70, ASSOC. PROF. MATH. & ASSOC. DEAN SUMMER SESSION, 70- Res. assoc. economet, Princeton, 61-63; consult, Mathematica, N.J, 62- U.S.N, 52-55; Lt.(jg). Game theory; infinite games of perfect information; n-person games; game theory models in disarmament. Address: 25 Brinkerhoff Ave, Teaneck, NJ 07666.

DAVIS, MOSS V(ERNON), b. Chattanooga, Tenn, Apr. 30, 20; m. 48; c. 2. PHYSICAL METALLURGY. B.S, The Citadel, 42; M.S, Florida, 48; Ph.D. (metall), Vanderbilt, 52. Asst. prof. chem, The Citadel, 46-49; develop. metallurgist, West. Elec. Co, Inc, N.C, 52-54; chief metallurgist, Anderson Elec. Corp, Ala, 55-59; STAFF ENGR, BENDIX CORP, 59- Am. conferee, Second World Metall. Cong, Chicago, 57. U.S.A, 42-46, 1st Lt. Am. Chem. Soc; Am. Soc. Metals; assoc. mem. Am. Inst. Mining, Metall. & Petrol. Eng. Light metals; foundry practice; dynamic properties of metals; mechanical testing at high energy rates; brass and bronze casting technology. Address: 201 Country Lane, Kansas City, MO 64114.

DAVIS, MYRTIS, b. Bessemer, Ala, Oct. 16, 18. MATHEMATICS. A.B, Birmingham-South. Col, 39; M.A, La. State, 48. Teacher pub. schs, Ala, 39-47; asst. prof. MATH, Southeast. La. Col, 48-49; instr, Miss. South. Col, 49-50; Nicholls State Col, 50-52, asst. prof, 52-54; assoc. prof, Wesleyan Col.(Ga), 54-61; GREENSBORO COL, 61-63, PROF, 63-, CHMN. DEPT. MATH. & SCI, 71- Am. Math. Asn; Math. Soc. Am. Address: Dept. of Mathematics, Greensboro College, Greensboro, NC 27402.

DAVIS, NEIL CLIFTON, b. Duston, Nebr, Apr. 5, 18; div; c. 1. BIOCHEMISTRY. B.Sc, Nebr. Wesleyan, 39; M.Sc, Nebraska, 41; Ph.D.(chem), Iowa State, 49. Nat. Cancer Inst. res. fel, Utah, 50-52; asst. res. prof. biochem, 52-58; assoc. prof. clin. med, sch. med, Pittsburgh, 58-60; res. pediat, UNIV. CINCINNATI, 60-71, biochem, MED. SCH, 62-71, PROF. RES. PEDIAT, 71- Fel, Children's Hosp. Res. Found, 60-; Fulbright summer fel, Univ. of the Repub, Uruguay, 64. U.S.A.A.F, 42-46, 2nd Lt. Am. Soc. Biol. Chem. Purification and study of enzymes; peptides synthesis; fractionation and study of plasma proteins; biochemical approach to teratology. Address: Children's Hospital Research Foundation, Cincinnati, OH 45229.

DAVIS, NEIL MONAS, b. Philadelphia, Pa, Apr. 17, 31; m. 59; c. 2. PHARMACY. B.S, Phila. Col. Pharm, 53, M.S, 55, Pharm.D, 70. Res. hosp. pharm, Jefferson Med. Col. Hosp, 53-55, asst. dir. pharm. 58-61, dir. pharm. serv, 61-65; instr. PHARM, Phila. Col. Pharm. & Jefferson Med. Col, 61-65; asst. prof, SCH. PHARM, TEMPLE UNIV, 65-69, ASSOC. PROF, 69-, DIR. PHARM. SERV, UNIV. HOSP, 65- Ed, Hosp. Pharm. U.S.A.F, 55-57, Capt. Am. Pharmaceut. Asn; Am. Soc. Hosp. Pharmacist. Hospital pharmacy administration and editing; hospital and clinical pharmacy education. Address: 9277 Darlington Rd, Philadelphia, PA 19115.

DAVIS, N(ORMAN) D(UANE), b. San Diego, Calif, May 7, 28; m. 52; c. 2. MICROBIOLOGY. B.Sc, Georgia, 53; M.Sc, Ohio State, 55, Ph.D, 57. Instr. BOT, Georgia, 57-58; asst. prof, AUBURN UNIV, 58-61, assoc. prof, 61-67, PROF, 67- U.S.M.C, 46-48; U.S.A.F, 50. AAAS; Am. Soc. Microbiol. Physiology and biochemistry of microbes; industrial and applied microbiology; mycotoxicology. Address: Dept. of Botany & Microbiology, Auburn University, Auburn, AL 36830.

DAVIS, NORMAN RODGER, b. Toronto, Ont, June 30, 43. BIOCHEMISTRY. B.Sc, Univ. Toronto, 66, Ph.D.(biochem), 70. Wellcome fel, Meat Res. Inst, Langford, Eng, 70-71; ASST. PROF. BIOCHEM, UNIV. ALTA, 71- Chemistry and structure of collagen crosslinks; mechanism of desmosine and isodesmosine crosslink formation in elastin. Address: Dept. of Oral Biology, Faculty of Dentistry, University of Alberta, Edmonton, Alta, Can.

DAVIS, NORMAN SEYMOUR, b. N.Y.C, Aug. 11, 29; m. 59; c. 3. MICROBIOLOGY, BIOCHEMISTRY. B.S, Oklahoma, 52, M.S, 53; Ph.D.(microbiol, biochem), Texas, 62. Bacteriologist, airborne pathogens study sect, Commun. Disease Ctr, U.S. Pub. Health Serv, Ga, 52; First U.S. Army Med. Lab, N.Y, 55; teaching asst. & res. scientist bact, Texas, 55-59; sr. bacteriologist, Mass. Inst. Tech, 59-60, sr. res. assoc. nutrit. & food sci, 60-63; dir. basic res, Wilmot Castle Co. N.Y, 63-67; sr. microbiologist, Philco-Ford Corp, Calif, 67-69; ASSOC. PROF. BIOL. SCI, SOUTH. ILL. UNIV, 69- Chem.C, 53-55, Res, 55-64, Maj. AAAS; Am. Soc. Microbiol; Soc. Indust. Microbiol; Geochem. Soc; Brit. Soc. Gen. Microbiol; Brit. Soc. Appl. Bact. Soil and water microbiology; biogeochemical transformations. Address: Dept. of Biological Sciences, Southern Illinois University, Edwardsville, IL 62025.

DAVIS, NORMAN T(HOMAS), b. DosCabezas, Ariz, Mar. 23, 27; m. 50; c. 4. ENTOMOLOGY. B.S, Ariz. State Univ, 49; M.S, Iowa State Col, 51; Ph.D, Univ. Wis, 54. Instr. ENTOM, UNIV. CONN, 54-59, asst. prof, 59-65, assoc. prof, 65-68, PROF, 68-, HEAD REGULATORY BIOL, 68- Hosp.C, U.S.N, 44-46. Am. Entom. Soc. Insect morphology; phylogeny; physiology. Address: Biological Sciences Group, University of Connecticut, Storrs, CT 06268.

DAVIS, OSCAR F, b. Oak Park, Ill, June 19, 28; m. 51; c. 4. PSYCHIATRY, PHARMACOLOGY. B.S, Roosevelt, 49; M.S, Loyola (Ill), 52, Ph.D.(pharmacol), 54, M.D, 58. Assoc. pharmacol, Stritch Sch. Med, Loyola (Ill), 53-58; intern, Michael Reese Hosp, 58-59; clin. instr. pschiat, col. med, Illinois, 60-62; clin. asst. prof. PSYCHIAT. & PHARMACOL, CHICAGO MED. SCH, 62-67, CLIN. ASSOC. PROF, 67-; DIR. CHILD & ADOLESCENT PSYCHIAT, MT. SINAI HOSP, 62-; ASST. PROF. PSYCHIAT, MED. SCH, NORTHWEST. UNIV, 70- Resident psychiat, Univ. Ill. Res. & Educ. Hosp, 59-62; Passavant Mem. Hosp; Children's Mem. Hosp; Evanston Hosp; fel, inst. juvenile res, Illinois, 61-63. Consult. pharmacologist, 52-63. Dipl, Am. Bd. Psychiat, 66. Am. Soc. Pharmacol. & Exp. Therapeut; Am. Psychiat. Asn; Am. Fedn. Clin. Res. Child, adolescent and adult psychiatry; infantile development and psychosomatic diseases in childhood. Address: 993 Forest Ave, Glencoe, IL 60022.

DAVIS, PAUL A, b. Lafayette, Ind, Dec. 10, 26; m. 53; c. 2. DAIRYING. B.S, Purdue, 50, fel, 51-53, M.S, 53. Foreman cottage cheese mfg, Borden Milk Co, 50-51; field bacteriologist, Pet Milk Co, Wis, 53-54, plant supvr, 54-58, chief dehydrated prod. sect, res. ctr, 58-60, asst. plant mgr, 60-62, plant mgr, 63-68, plant supt, Mich, 68-70, DIR. QUAL. CONTROL, GROCERY PROD. DIV, PET, INC, ST. LOUIS, MO, 70- U.S.A, 45-46. Dehydrated products in food industry, dairy products; pilot plant operation of new products. Address: 718 Charlotte Ave, Columbia, IL 62236.

DAVIS, PAUL A, b. Chicago, Ill, Aug. 31, 27; m. 54; c. 1. METEOROLOGY. B.S, Washington (Seattle), 50, M.S, 52; Ph.D.(meteorol), N.Y. Univ, 62. Res. meteorologist, Geophys. Res. Directorate, Air Force Cambridge Res. Labs, 52-56; asst. res. scientist meteorol, N.Y. Univ, 57-60; SR. RES. METEOROLOGIST, STANFORD RES. INST, 60- AAAS; Am. Geophys. Union; Am. Meteorol. Soc. Analysis of atmospheric heat balance and radiative transfer; interpretation of satellite radiation data; cloudiness; differential heating; energy transports; properties at lower boundary of atmosphere; lidar and radiometer applications. Address: Atmospheric Science Lab, L2094, Stanford Research Institute, Menlo Park, CA 94025.

DAVIS, PAUL COOPER, b. Glenville, W.Va, Mar. 14, 37; m. 60; c. 3. ELECTRICAL ENGINEERING. B.S.E.E, West Virginia, 59; M.S, Mass. Inst. Tech, 61; Ph.D.(elec. eng), Lehigh, 68. MEM. TECH. STAFF, READING BR, BELL TEL. LABS, 62- U.S.A, 60-62, 1st Lt. Inst. Elec. & Electronics Eng. Characterization of high speed switching transistors and diodes; design of linear and digital integrated circuits. Address: 3601 River Rd, Reading, PA 19605.

DAVIS, PAUL L(AWRENCE), b. Steubenville, Ohio, Sept. 6, 40; m. 69. MATHEMATICS. A.B. & M.S, W.Va. Univ, 62; Ph.D.(math), Carnegie-Mellon Univ, 69. Instr. MATH, W.Va. Univ, 62-64; ASST. PROF, LEHIGH UNIV, 69- Math. Asn. Am. Partial and functional differential equations. Address: Dept. of Mathematics, Lehigh University, Bethlehem, PA 18015.

DAVIS, P(AULS), b. Cesis, Latvia, Mar. 18, 21; nat; m. 50; c. 2. ORGANIC CHEMISTRY. Dipl. chem, Tübingen, 47, D.Sc.(org. chem), 49. Res. assoc. org. chem, Mass. Inst. Tech, 50-53; res. chemist, Burke Res. Co, 53-59; BASF WYANDOTTE CORP, 59-61, sr. res. chemist, 61-64, RES. ASSOC, 64- Am. Chem. Soc; Sci. Res. Soc. Am; Brit. Chem. Soc. Metalorganic compounds; synthetic fat-soluble vitamines; organic peroxides and ozonides; metalorganic polymerization catalysts; fire retardant polymers; organic halogenous compounds. Address: BASF Wyandotte Corp, Wyandotte, MI 48192.

DAVIS, PEYTON NELSON, b. Lodi, Calif, Apr. 4, 25; m. 47; c. 2. NUTRITION, BIOCHEMISTRY. B.Sc, Colo. State Univ, 48; M.Sc, Univ. Calif, Davis, 63, Ph.D.(nutrit), 66. Res. asst, exp. sta, Colo. State Univ, 48-52; lab. technician III, Univ. Calif, Davis, 52-66; sr. scientist, Vivonex Corp, 66-70; SR. NUTRITIONIST, DEPT. FOOD SCI, STANFORD RES. INST, 70- Poultry Sci. Asn; Inst. Food Technol; Animal Nutrit. Res. Coun. Feeding values of proteins; amino acid requirements; unidentified growth factors; vitamin requirements; pigmentation of shanks; mineral utilization and requirements; effects of chelating agents; chemically defined diets; carbohydrate affect upon atherosclerosis; purine utilization. Address: Dept. of Food Sciences, Stanford Research Institute, 333 Ravenswood, Menlo Park, CA 94025.

DAVIS, PHILIP, b. Lawrence, Mass, Jan. 2, 23; m. 44; c. 4. MATHEMATICS. Ph.D.(math), Harvard, 50. Mathematician, Nat. Bur. Standards, 51-58, chief numerical anal, 58-63; PROF. APPL. MATH, BROWN UNIV, 63- Guggenheim fel, 56-57. Am. Math. Soc. Numerical analysis; interpolation and approximation theory. Address: Dept. of Applied Mathematics, Brown University, Providence, RI 02912.

DAVIS, P(HILIP) C, b. Cornish, Ark, Apr. 18, 21; m. 44; c. 2. CHEMICAL ENGINEERING. S.B, Chicago, 43; B.S, Kansas, 48, M.S, 49, Ph.D.(chem. eng), 52. Process design engr, ETHYL CORP, 52, engr. process develop, 53-55, supvr, 55-59, sr. assoc, 59-64, head eng. & math. sci, 64-67, ASSOC. DIR. PROCESS DEVELOP, 67- U.S.A.A.F, 42-46, Capt. Am. Inst. Chem. Eng. Vapor-liquid phase equilibria; chemical processes; computer techniques. Address: Ethyl Corp, P.O. Box 341, Baton Rouge, LA 70821.

DAVIS, PHILIP K, b. Effingham, Ill, Aug. 29, 31; m. 55; c. 2. ENGINEERING MECHANICS. B.S, Texas, 58, M.S, 59; Ford Found. fel, Michigan, 60-63, M.S.E, & Ph.D.(eng. mech), 63. Res. engr, struct. mech. res. lab, Balcones Res. Center, Texas, 59; stress analyst, Boeing Airplane Co, Kans, 59-60; instr. eng. mech, Michigan, 63-64; asst. prof. fluid mech, SOUTH. ILL. UNIV, 64-65, prof. in charge, 65-67, assoc. prof, 67-71, PROF. FLUID MECH. & CHMN. DEPT. ENG. MECH. & MAT, 71- Lectr, Univ. Wichita, 59-60; res. engr, Univ. Mich, summer 63; Nat. Sci. Found. grant, 66-67; NASA grant, 68-70. U.S.A.F, 51-55. Am. Soc. Eng. Educ; Am. Soc. Mech. Eng; Int. Asn. Hydraul. Res. Motion of solid bodies in rotating viscous fluids; viscous and inviscid flows; liquid squeeze film motion. Address: Dept. of Engineering Mechanics & Materials, School of Engineering & Technology, Southern Illinois University, Carbondale, IL 62901.

DAVIS, RALPH A(NDERSON), b. Huntington, Ind, Aug. 14, 17; m. 40; c. 2. CHEMISTRY. A.B, Huntington Col, 39; M.A, Indiana, 42. Teacher, high sch, Ind, 39-41; asst. chem, Indiana, 41-42; res. chemist, DOW CHEM. CO, 42-63, SR. RES. CHEMIST, 63- Am. Chem. Soc. Organic and inorganic fluorides and other halides; catalysis; low temperature distillation; fluorine and high energy oxidizers. Address: 1160 Poseyville Rd, R.R. 7, Midland, MI 48640.

DAVIS, R(ALPH) L(ANIER), b. Ala, Sept. 10, 21; m. 43; c. 3. GENETICS, PLANT BREEDING. B.S, Ala. Polytech, 43; M.S, Purdue, 48, Ph.D.(genetics, breeding), 50. PROF. AGRON, SCH. AGR, PURDUE UNIV, 50-, ASSOC. DIR. DIV. SPONSORED PROGS, 66-, asst. dean, grad. sch, 65-71. Vis. prof, Oregon State, 59-60; N.C. State Col, 63; U.S.N, 43-46, Res, 46-, Comdr. Fel. AAAS; fel. Am. Soc. Agron; Crop Sci. Soc. Am(pres-elect & Acting pres, 62, pres, 63, ed, Crop Sci, 64-67). Address: Division of Sponsored Programs, Purdue Research Foundation, Purdue University, Lafayette, IN 47907.

DAVIS, RANDALL T, b. Winchester, Va, Jan. 9, 36; m. 59; c. 4. ENGINEERING MECHANICS. B.S, Va. Polytech, 60; Sloan Found. fel, Stanford, 60-61, M.S, 61, Nat. Sci. Found. fel, 61-62, Shell fel, 62-63, Ph.D.(eng. mech), 64. Asst. prof. eng. mech, Va. Polytech. Inst. & State Univ, 63-66, assoc. prof, 66-70, PROF, 70-71; PROF. AEROSPACE ENG. & APPL. MECH. & HEAD DEPT, UNIV. CINCINNATI, 71- Am. Soc. Mech. Eng; Am. Inst. Aeronaut. & Astronaut. Theoretical fluid mechanics, particularly laminar viscous flow; numerical methods applied to viscous flow problems. Address: Dept. of Aerospace Engineering & Applied Mechanics, University of Cincinnati, Cincinnati, OH 45221.

DAVIS, RAYMOND, JR, b. Washington, D.C, Oct. 14, 14; m. 48; c. 5. CHEMISTRY. B.S, Maryland, 37, M.S, 40; Ph.D.(phys. chem), Yale, 42. Res. chemist, Dow Chem. Co, Mich, 37-38; Atomic Energy Comn, Ohio, 46-48; SCIENTIST, BROOKHAVEN NAT. LAB, 48- U.S.A.A.F, U.S.A, 42-45. AAAS; Am. Geophys. Union; Geochem. Soc; Meteoritical Soc; Am. Phys. Soc. Nuclear chemistry; meteorites and cosmic rays; neutrino detection. Address: Brookhaven National Lab, Upton, L.I, NY 11973.

DAVIS, RAYMOND E, b. Hobbs, N.Mex, Nov. 7, 38; m. 60; c. 3. PHYSICAL CHEMISTRY. B.S, Kansas, 60; U.S. Pub. Health Serv. fel. & Ph.D.(phys. chem), Yale, 65. Cancer res. scientist, center crystallog. res, Roswell Park Mem. Inst, 64-65, sr. cancer res. scientist, 65-66; asst. prof. CHEM, UNIV. TEX, AUSTIN, 66-70, ASSOC. PROF, 70- Am. Crystallog. Asn; Am. Chem. Soc; The Chem. Soc. X-ray diffraction; molecular structure studies of organometallic and small ring organic compounds. Address: Dept. of Chemistry, University of Texas at Austin, Austin, TX 78712.

DAVIS, RAYMOND T(ILTON), JR, b. Easton, Md, Oct. 17, 18; m. 49; c. 4. CHEMISTRY. B.S, Va. Polytech, 40, M.S, 41; Ph.D.(chem. eng), Hopkins, 44. Petrol. Ref. fel, Mellon Inst, 43-46; instr. chem, Juniata Col, 46-47, asst. prof, 47-51, prof, 51-54; supv. technologist electrochem, appl. res. lab, U.S. STEEL CORP, 54-56, asst. div. chief, COATED METALL. PROD. DIV, APPL. RES. LAB, 56-60, DIV. CHIEF, 60- Am. Petrol. Inst. Proj. 42, Pa. State Univ, 51-54. Am. Chem. Soc; Electrochem. Soc. Adsorption of gases on solids; petroleum catalysis; high vacuum techniques; properties of liquid state; vapor pressures and optical properties of deuterohydrocarbons; surface treatment of steel, tinplate; electrochemistry. Address: Applied Research Lab, U.S. Steel Corp, Monroeville, PA 15146.

DAVIS, RAYMOND VINCENT, b. Chicago, Ill, Feb. 3, 27; m. 59; c. 3. BIOCHEMISTRY. B.S, Northwestern, 50; M.S, Wisconsin, 57; Ph.D.(biochem), Missouri, 65. Res. asst, Abbott Labs, 52-55, biochemist, 57-61; res. biochemist, Ames Res. Labs, Miles Labs, Inc, Ind, 64-70; SR. BIOCHEMIST, RES. DIV, HOFFMANN-LA ROCHE INC, 70- U.S.N, 45-46. Am. Chem. Soc. Effects of drugs in vitro on liver lipogenesis and carbohydrate metabolism and in vivo on brain nucleotides; in vivo synthesis of skin mucopolysaccharides and collagen and effects of drugs thereon. Address: Research Division, Hoffmann-La Roche Inc, Nutley, NJ 07110.

DAVIS, R(EES) B(ASIL), b. Glouster, Ohio, Apr. 28, 23; m. 47; c. 2. FOOD TECHNOLOGY, BIOCHEMISTRY. B.Sc, Ohio State, 49, M.Sc, 51, Ph.D.(food tech), 54. Marketing specialist, U.S. Dept. Agr, 49-50; asst, Ohio Agr. Exp. Sta, 50-53; instr, dept. hort, Ohio State, 53-55, asst. prof, agr. exten. serv, U.S. Dept. Agr, 54-55; res. food technologist pkg. mat, CONTINENTAL CAN CO, 55-64, sr. res. scientist, new prod. res, corporate res. & develop, 64-67, MGR. PROD. DEVELOP, RES, 67- Asst. prof, Ohio Agr. Exp. Sta, 54-55. U.S.A, 43-46. Inst. Food. Technol. Food technology of fruit, vegetable, meat, dairy and marine products; packaging materials and methods; primarily in metal containers; product and container factors affecting shelf life and performance. Address: Flexible Packaging Division, Continental Can Co, 1200 W. 76th St, Chicago, IL 60620.

DAVIS, RICHARD A, b. Chicago, Ill, June 15, 25; m. 60; c. 2. NEUROSURGERY. A.B, Princeton, 47; M.D, Northwestern, 51, fels, 52-58, M.S, 56. Asst. neurol, Nat. Hosp, London, 56-57; asst. prof. NEUROSURG, SCH. MED, UNIV. PA, 61-66, ASSOC. PROF, 66-, RES. ASSOC. PHYSIOL, 59- U.S. Pub. Health Serv. res. grant, 57-; Am. Cancer Soc. fel, 62-65. Staff surgeon, Hosp. Univ. Pennsylvania, 59- Med.C, U.S.N, 52-54, Lt. Am. Col. Surg; Am. Asn. Neurol. Surg. Central nervous system control of gastric secretion; clinical research in depth electrode recordings from brain. Address: Dept. of Neurosurgery, University Hospital, 3400 Spruce St, Philadelphia, PA 19104.

DAVIS, RICHARD ALBERT, JR, b. Joliet, Ill, Sept. 11, 37; m. 62; c. 2. GEOLOGY. B.S, Beloit Col, 59; M.A, Texas, 61; Ph.D.(geol), Illinois, Urbana, 64. Alumni Res. Found. fel, GEOL, Wisconsin, 64-65; asst. prof, WEST. MICH. UNIV, 65-69, ASSOC. PROF, 69- Soc. Econ. Paleont. & Mineral; Geol. Soc. Am; Am. Asn. Petrol. Geol; Int. Asn. Gt. Lakes Res; Int. Asn. Sedimentol. Physical stratigraphy and sedimentary petrography of Ordovician in Mississippi Valley; nearshore sedimentation and sedimentary structures of Lake Michigan; beach and nearshore processes. Address: Dept. of Geology, Western Michigan University, Kalamazoo, MI 49001.

DAVIS, RICHARD ARNOLD, b. Cedar Rapids, Iowa, Apr. 19, 42; m. GEOLOGY, PALEONTOLOGY. B.A, Cornell Col, 63; M.S, Univ. Iowa, 65, Nat. Sci. Found. fel, 65-67, Ph.D.(geol), 68. Asst. comput, Geophys. Serv, Inc, summer 63; asst. ocean bottom photog, Lamont Geol. Observ, Columbia Univ, summers 64 & 65; Nat. Sci. Found. fel. paleont, Univ. Col. Swansea, Wales, 68-69; ASST. PROF. GEOL. & CURATOR GEOL, UNIV. CINCINNATI, 69- Geol. Soc. Am; Paleont. Res. Inst; Paleont. Soc; Soc. Vert. Paleont. Lebensspuren; paleobiology of ammonoid cephalopods; biology and paleobiology of nautiloid cephalopods; conodonts. Address: Dept. of Geology, University of Cincinnati, Cincinnati, OH 45221.

DAVIS, RICHARD B, b. Moscow, Idaho, Oct. 9, 18; m. 40; c. 2. VERTEBRATE ECOLOGY, BIOMETRY. B.S.(chem) & B.S.(chem. eng), Tex. Col. Arts & Indust, 40; U.S. Naval Postgrad. Sch, 44; M.S, Agr. & Mech. Col, Tex, 51, Ph.D.(wildlife ecol), 52. Teacher, high schs, Tex, 40-41; aircraft engine mech, Army Air Force Tech. Training Command, Ill. & Miss, 41-43; game & range mgr, Copano Cattle Co. & O'Connor Estates, Tex, 52-56; res. assoc. bat ecol, Hopkins, 56-59; assoc. prof. wildlife ecol, Texas A&M, 59-64; res. biologist, entom. res. div, agr. res. serv, U.S. Dept. Agr, 64-67; PROF. & CAESAR KLEBERG CHAIR WILDLIFE ECOL, TEX. A&I UNIV, 67- Consult, Tex. Game & Fish Cmn, 59-64; assoc. mem, statist. inst, Texas A&M, 63-64. U.S.N.R, 43-46, Lt. Ecol. Soc. Am; Wildlife Soc; N.Y. Acad. Sci. Ecology of white-tailed deer, bob-white quail, Mexican free-tailed bats and screw-worm flies. Address: Dept. of Biology, Texas A&I University, Box 2176, Kingsville, TX 78363.

DAVIS, RICHARD BRADLEY, b. Iowa City, Iowa, Nov. 6, 26; m. 57; c. 3. MEDICAL SCIENCE, INTERNAL MEDICINE. B.S, Yale, 49; M.D, Iowa, 53; Am. Col. Physicians fel, Minnesota, Minneapolis, 58-59, Am. Cancer Soc. fel, 59-60, Ph.D.(internal med), 64. Instr. MED, Univ. Minn, Minneapolis, 59-64, asst. prof, 64-69; ASSOC. PROF, MED. SCH, UNIV. NEBR, 69- U.S. Pub. Health Serv. res. career develop. award, 61-69; vis. investr, Sir William Dunn Sch. Path, Oxford, 64-65. U.S.A, 45-46, T/Sgt. Am. Soc. Hemat; Am. Fedn. Clin. Res; Endocrine Soc; Soc. Exp. Biol. & Med; Am. Soc. Exp. Path; fel. Am. Col. Physicians; Am. Asn. Hist. Med; N.Y. Acad. Sci. Blood platelets and the effect of aggregating agents and bacterial endotoxin on blood platelets; vasoactive amines; carcinoid tumors. Address: University of Nebraska Hospitals, Omaha, NE 68105.

DAVIS, RICHARD C(ECIL), b. Lexington, N.C, Dec. 2, 20; m. 44; c. 2. TEXTILE CHEMISTRY. B.S, N.C. State Col, 48; M.A, Andrews Univ, 68. Instr. textile chem, N.C. State Col, 48-49, asst. prof, 49-53; salesman, indust. soap & chem. div, Armour & Co, 54-55, tech. serv. rep, 55-57; assoc. res. chemist, res. labs, WHIRLPOOL CORP, 57-59, res. chemist, 59-60, mgr. chem. div, 60-63, res. chemist, 63-64, MGR. res. serv, 64-68, TECHNOL. FORECASTING & ASSESSMENT, 68- U.S.A, 42-46, Sgt. Am. Inst. Chem; Am. Asn. Textile Chem. & Colorists; Sci. Res. Soc. Am. Surfactant and builders for detergent systems; physical and chemical interactions between fibers and surfactants; technology forecast applications. Address: 3346 Valley View Dr, St. Joseph, MI 49085.

DAVIS, R(ICHARD) F(RANCIS), b. Keene, N.H, Aug. 30, 24; m. 50; c. 2. ANIMAL NUTRITION. Ph.D.(animal nutrit), Cornell, 53. Acting asst. prof, animal nutrit, Cornell, 53-54; asst. prof. DAIRY HUSB, UNIV. MD, COLLEGE PARK, 54-56, assoc. prof, 56-58, PROF, 58-, HEAD DEPT, 56- U.S.A, 44-46. AAAS; Am. Soc. Animal Sci; Am. Dairy Sci. Asn; N.Y. Acad. Sci. Rumen physiology; energy evaluation of ruminant feeds; nutritive evaluation of forages. Address: Dept. of Dairy Science, University of Maryland, College Park, MD 20740.

DAVIS, RICHARD L(aVERNE), b. Minneapolis, Minn, May 20, 32; m. 64; c. 3. PATHOLOGY, NEUROPATHOLOGY. B.A, Minnesota, Minneapolis, 53, B.S. & M.D, 56. Intern med, Bellevue Hosp, New York, 56-57; res. path, Minnesota, Minneapolis, 57-60; Nat. Inst. Neurol. Diseases & Blindness training fel. neuropath, Armed Forces Inst. Path, 60-61, assoc. pathologist, 61-65; lab. serv, U.S. Naval Hosp, 65-69; ASSOC. PROF. PATH, MED. SCH, UNIV. SOUTH. CALIF. & CHIEF, CAJAL LAB. NEUROPATH, 69- Nat. Cancer Inst. training fel, Univ. Minn, Minneapolis, 58-60; clin. instr, sch. med, George Wash. Univ, 63-65. Consult, Wash. Hosp. Ctr, D.C, 61-65; Nat. Naval Med. Ctr, Md, 62-65; Long Beach Vet. Admin. Hosp, 70- U.S.N, 61-69, Res, 69-, Comdr. Am. Asn. Neuropath; Am. Soc. Exp. Path; Am. Asn. Path. & Bact; Am. Fedn. Clin. Res; Am. Acad. Neurol; Soc. Exp. Biol. & Med. Histochemistry; Schwartzman phenomenon; experimental tumors; radiation effects on central nervous system; brain tumors. Address: Cajal Laboratory of Neuropathology, University of Southern California-Los Angeles County Medical Center, 1200 N. State St, Los Angeles, CA 90033.

DAVIS, R(ICHARD) R(ICHARDSON), b. Ala, Dec. 7, 23; m. 45; c. 3. AGRONOMY. B.S, Auburn, 47; M.S, Purdue, 49, Ph.D, 50. Asst. AGRON, Purdue, 47-50; asst. prof, OHIO AGR. RES. & DEVELOP. CTR, 50-53, assoc. prof, 53-59, PROF, 59-, OHIO STATE UNIV, 62-, ASSOC. CHMN, 62-, ASST. DIR. CTR, 69- U.S.N.R, 43-46, Lt.(jg). AAAS; fel. Am. Soc. Agron; fel. Crop Sci. Soc. Am. Turfgrass management; weed control; pasture management. Address: Ohio Agricultural Research & Development Center, Wooster, OH 44691.

DAVIS, R(ICHARD) S(MITH), b. Winnipeg, Can, Mar. 1, 26; m. 52; c. 2. METALLURGY. B.A.Sc, Toronto, 51, M.A.Sc, 52, Russell fel, 52-54, Ph.D. (metall), 54. Special lectr. METALL, Toronto, 53-54; fel, div. eng. & appl. physics, Harvard, 54-55, lectr, 55-56, asst. prof, 56-59; staff mem, Arthur D. Little, Inc, 59-62, v.pres, 62-68; PROF. MAT. SCI. & DEAN, COL. TECHNOL, UNIV. N.H, 68- R.C.A.F, 43-44; Can. Army, 44-46. Am. Inst. Mining, Metall. & Petrol. Eng; Am. Soc. Metals; Am. Ceramic Soc. Mechanical properties of solids; imperfections in solids; oxidation of metals; crystallization of inorganics. Address: College of Technology, University of New Hampshire, Durham, NH 03824.

DAVIS, ROBERT, b. Delhi, N.Y, Feb. 22, 31; m. 56; c. 2. INSECT ECOLOGY. B.S, Georgia, 56, M.S, 61, Ph.D.(zool), 63; summers, Maryland, 57, 61, 62. Entomologist, Ga. State Dept. Entom, 56; med. entomologist, Third U.S. Army Med. Lab, 56-59; forest entomologist, Southeast. Forest Exp. Sta, U.S. Dept. Agr, 59-60, res. entomologist, south. grain insects res. lab, 63-65; asst. prof. entom, Univ. Ga, 65-69; DIR. STORED-PROD. INSECTS RES. & DEVELOP. LAB, AGR. RES. SERV, 69- Med.C, U.S.A, 52-54. Am. Entom. Soc. Acarology; taxonomy and ecology of eriophyidae; ecology of aphids attacking grains. Address: Stored Products Research & Development Lab, P.O. Box 5125, Savannah, GA 31403.

DAVIS, ROBERT A(RTHUR), b. Weehawken, N.J, June 15, 26; m. 47; c. 3; m. 62. SPACE SCIENCES, AERODYNAMICS. B.Ae.E, N.Y. Univ, 46, M.Ae.E, 48, D.Eng.Sci, 55. Asst. aeronaut, col. eng, N.Y. Univ, 46-47, instr, 47-50; sr. engr. & group leader aerodyn, Sparrow I Proj, Sperry Gyroscope Co, N.Y, 50-55; leader satellite opers, systs. opers. dept, Rand Corp, Calif, 55-62; GROUP DIR. STRATEGIC SYSTS, OFF. FOR DEVELOP. PLANNING, AEROSPACE CORP, 62- AAAS. Space and missiles research and development; flight test data analysis; operations research; satellite systems analysis; missile systems analysis. Address: Aerospace Corp, P.O. Box 95085, Los Angeles, CA 90045.

DAVIS, ROBERT BENJAMIN, b. Fall River, Mass, June 23, 26; m. 58; c. 2. MATHEMATICS. S.B, Mass. Inst. Technol, 46, S.M, 47, Ph.D.(math), 51. From asst. to instr. math, Mass. Inst. Technol, 46-51; asst. prof, Univ. N.H, 51-56; assoc. prof. math. & educ, SYRACUSE UNIV, 56-63, PROF. & DIR. MATH. EDUC, 63-, DIR, MADISON PROJ, 67- Dir. Madison Proj, Webster Col, Mo, 57-67, vis. prof. math, 64. Am. Math. Soc; Math. Asn. Am; Am. Phys. Soc; Am. Psychol. Asn; Am. Soc. Eng. Educ. Third order partial differential equations; mathematical physics; mathematics education. Address: Dept. of Mathematics Education, Syracuse University, 918 Irving Ave, Syracuse, NY 13210.

DAVIS, ROBERT B(ERNARD), b. Miami, Fla, Dec. 4, 35; m. 60; c. 4. ORGANIC & POLYMER CHEMISTRY. B.Ed, Miami (Fla), 57, B.S, 59, M.S, 61; Union Carbide Corp. fel, Mass. Inst. Tech, 64-65, Ph.D.(org. chem), 65. Res. chemist, textile fibers dept, pioneering res. div, E.I. du Pont de Nemours & Co, Del, 65-68; ASST. PROF. ORG. CHEM, NORTHEAST. UNIV, 68- Am. Chem. Soc. Aliphatic and aromatic nitroso compounds; carbene chemistry; organic synthesis; reactive polymers. Address: Dept. of Chemistry, Northeastern University, Boston, MA 02115.

DAVIS, ROBERT CLAY, b. Dallas, Tex, June 8, 41; m. 67; c. 1. PURE MATHEMATICS. B.A, South. Methodist Univ, 63; Nat. Sci. Found. fel, Tulane Univ, 63-67, Ph.D.(math), 67. ASST. PROF. MATH, SOUTH. METHODIST UNIV, 67- AAAS; Am. Math. Soc; Math. Asn. Am. Category theory; universal algebra. Address: Dept. of Mathematics, Southern Methodist University, Dallas, TX 75222.

DAVIS, ROBERT DABNEY, b. Kershaw, S.C, Apr. 13, 39. MATHEMATICS. B.S, N.C. State Univ, 61, M.S, 63; Ph.D.(math), Fla. State Univ, 69. Instr. MATH, Univ. Richmond, 63-65; ASST. PROF, UNIV. NEV, RENO, 69- Am. Math. Soc. Abstract algebra; ramification series of ramified v-rings. Address: Dept. of Mathematics, University of Nevada, Reno, NV 89507.

DAVIS, R(OBERT) E(ARL), b. Chicago, Ill, Oct. 25, 33; m. 55; c. 3. PHYSICAL ORGANIC CHEMISTRY. A.B, Indiana, 55; A.M, Harvard, 57, Ph.D. (chem), 58. Nat. Sci. Found. fel. CHEM, Mass. Inst. Tech, 58-59; asst. prof, PURDUE UNIV, 59-63, ASSOC. PROF, 63- Alfred P. Sloan fel, 62-66.

Am. Chem. Soc. Chemical kinetics; sulphur chemistry; electron spectroscopic chemical analysis spectroscopy. Address: Dept. of Chemistry, Purdue University, Lafayette, IN 47907.

DAVIS, R(OBERT) E(LLIOT), b. Chicago, Ill, Dec. 1, 22; m. 47; c. 4. SOLID STATE PHYSICS, ENGINEERING. B.S.E.E, Purdue, 44, fel, 46-49, M.S, 49. Res. physicist, Westinghouse Elec. Corp, 49-55, supvr. engr, solid state device develop. & appln, 55, sect. mgr, 55-58, dept. mgr, 58-60, mgr. semiconductor dept, Res. Labs, 60-62, adv. develop, semiconductor div, 62-65; V.PRES, ENGR. & MEM. BD. DIRS, PA. ELECTRONICS TECHNOL, INC, 65- Inst. Elec. & Electronics Eng; Am. Phys. Soc. Semiconductor physics; material preparation; electrical and optical measurements on materials and devices; device design and application. Address: Box 13, Murrysville, PA 15668.

DAVIS, ROBERT E(LLIOTT), b. Salt Lake City, Utah, Mar. 21, 30; m. 55; c. 3. INORGANIC CHEMISTRY. A.B, Utah, 51, Ph.D.(chem), 54. Res. anal. chemist, M.W. Kellogg Co, N.J, 54-57; res. proj. engr, Am. Potash & Chem. Corp, Calif, 57-60, head, new prod. sect, 60-63, process chem. sect, Trona Res. Lab, 63-67, mgr. heavy chem. res, 67-69; adminr. & res. consult, TECH. CTR, KERR-McGEE CORP, 69-70, MGR. CHEM. EXTRACTION SECT, 70- Am. Chem. Soc; Am. Inst. Mining, Metall. & Petrol. Eng. Coordination chemistry; solvent extraction; alkali metals, particularly cesium, rubidium and lithium; chemical process development; synthetic fuel from coal. Address: Kerr-McGee Corp, Technical Center, Kerr-McGee Bldg, Oklahoma City, OK 73102.

DAVIS, ROBERT F(OSTER), b. Greensboro, N.C, Apr. 12, 42; m. 69. CERAMICS. B.S, N.C. State Univ, 64; M.S, Pa. State Univ, 66; Ph.D.(ceramic eng), Univ. Calif, Berkeley, 70. Res. asst. mat. res, Lawrence Radiation Lab, 67-70; GLASS SCIENTIST, RES. CTR, CORNING GLASS WORKS, 70- Am. Ceramic Soc. Kinetics and mechanisms of solid state reactions in ceramic materials; nucleation and crystallization phenomena occuring in glass-ceramic materials and their fabrication as a useful product. Address: Glass-Ceramics Dept, Research Center, Corning Glass Works, Corning, NY 14830.

DAVIS, ROBERT F(OSTER), JR, b. Crowell, Tex, Apr. 24, 37. BOTANY, PLANT PHYSIOLOGY. B.A, North Texas State, 62, M.A, 64; Ph.D.(bot), Washington State, 68. Asst. bot, zool. & physiol. North Texas State, 60-64; Washington State, 64-66, res. asst. plant physiol, 66-68; Nat. Insts. Health, trainee, neurophysiol, col. physicians & surgeons, Columbia Univ, 68-69; ASST. PROF. BOT, RUTGERS UNIV, 69- AAAS; Am. Soc. Plant Physiol. Ion transport; electrophysiology; water relations; biophysics of flux processes. Address: Dept. of Botany, Rutgers, The State University, Newark, NJ 07102.

DAVIS, ROBERT H(ARRY), b. Wilkes Barre, Pa, July 16, 27; m. 54; c. 2. ENDOCRINOLOGY. B.S, Kings Col, 50; U.S. Pub. Health fel, Rutgers, 56-58, Ph.D.(endocrinol), 58. Med. technician, Wilkes Barre Gen. Hosp, 50-51; biologist, Warner-Chilcott Labs, 51-55; asst, zool, Rutgers, 55-56; sect. head, Wm. S. Merrell Co, 58-60; sr. physiologist, neuroendocrine res. unit, Willow Brook State Hosp, Staten Island, N.Y, 60-63; assoc. prof. endocrinol, Villanova Univ, 63-66; sr. reprod. teratologist, Merck Inst. Therapeut. Res, Pa, 66; chief reprod. endocrinol, Thomas M. Fitzgerald Mercy Hosp, Darby, Pa, 66-69; ASSOC. PROF. OBSTET. & GYNEC, PHYSIOL. & BIOPHYS, HAHNEMANN MED. COL, 69- U.S.N, 45-46. Am. Soc. Cytol; Soc. Exp. Biol. & Med; Endocrine Soc; Soc. Study Reproduction; Am. Asn. Lab. Animal Sci; Am. Physiol. Soc; N.Y. Acad. Sci. Nutrition and endocrines; anti-inflammation; physiology of reproduction; endocrinology of mental retardation and pineal gland; peritoneal fluid cytology; teratology. Address: Hahnemann Medical College, 230 N. Broad St, Philadelphia, PA 19102.

DAVIS, ROBERT H(OUSER), b. Long Island, N.Y, Mar. 20, 26; m. 56. NUCLEAR PHYSICS. B.S, Nebraska, 49; M.S, Wisconsin, 50, Ph.D.(physics), 55. Res. assoc. nuclear physics, Rice Inst, 55-57; asst. prof. PHYSICS, FLA. STATE UNIV, 57-61, assoc. prof, 61-64, PROF, 64- Am. Phys. Soc. Experimental nuclear physics; high vacuum technology; thin film physics. Address: Dept. of Physics, Florida State University, Tallahassee, FL 32306.

DAVIS, ROBERT I(RVING), b. Keene, N.H, July 1, 22; m. 49; c. 3. ECONOMIC GEOLOGY. B.S, New Hampshire, 47; M.S, Michigan, 49, Ph.D. (geol), 54. Geologist, Cia. Minera Sta. Maria De Oro, S.A, 49-50; Cia Minera De Penoles, 53-58; asst. prof. geol, St. Louis, 59-61; geologist, Am. Metal Climax, Inc, 61-68, PRES, AMAX EXPLOR. INC, 68- U.S.A, 43-46, 1st Lt. Geol. Soc. Am; Soc. Econ. Geol; Am. Inst. Mining, Metall. & Petrol. Eng. Geology; metalliferous ore deposits. Address: One Charcoal Lane, Westport, CT 06880.

DAVIS, ROBERT J(AMES), b. Omaha, Nebr, Oct. 26, 29; m. 53; c. 4. ASTROPHYSICS. A.B, Harvard, 51, A.M, 56, Ph.D.(astron), 60. ASTROPHYSICIST, SMITHSONIAN ASTROPHYS. OBSERV, CAMBRIDGE, 56- U.S.N.R, 51-59, Lt. Am. Astron. Soc; Int. Astron. Union. Space, television and stellar astronomy. Address: 307 Pleasant St, Belmont, MA 02178.

DAVIS, R(OBERT) J(AQUETTE), JR, b. Wilmington, Del, July 2, 27; m. 47; c. 4. SOIL MICROBIOLOGY. B.S, Univ. Del, 52, M.S, 53; Ph.D, Univ. Ill, 57. Asst. soil biol, Univ. Ill, 53-57; SOIL MICROBIOLOGIST, Agr. Res. Serv, U.S. Dept. Agr, 57-66, REGIONAL PULSE IMPROV. PROJ, U.S. DEPT. AGR-AGENCY INT. DEVELOP, NEW DELHI, 66- U.S.M.C, 45-49. Am. Soc. Agron; Soil Sci. Soc. Am; Am. Soc. Microbiol. Root nodule bacteria. Address: USAID/RPIP New Delhi, Dept. of State, Washington, DC 20521.

DAVIS, ROBERT KEPLER, b. Dayton, Ohio, Apr. 16, 15; m. 37; c. 2. ENDOCRINOLOGY. A.B, Kenyon Col, 37; M.A, Reed Col, 42; Ph.D.(physiol), Indiana, 48. Sect. chief biol. div, Mound Lab, Atomic Energy Cmn, 48-55; sect. chief air pollution, Taft Eng. Center, U.S. Pub. Health Serv, 55-56; asst. sect. chief physiol. br, Aero-Med. Lab, Wright-Patterson Air Force Base, 56-57; asst. prof. prev. med, col. med, Cincinnati, 57-63; sect. head endocrine res, Hess & Clark Div, Richardson-Merrell Inc, 63-68; COORD. TO DIR, ANIMAL HEALTH DIV, AYERST RES. LABS, DIV. AM. HOME PROD. CORP, 68-, HEAD TOXICOL. SECT, 70- Med.C, U.S.A, 43-46. AAAS; Am. Nuclear Soc; N.Y. Acad. Sci. Establishment of limits of radiation exposure and hazards; definition of toxicity of industrial pesticides; growth factors for domestic animals; reproductive control in domestic animals. Address: Animal Health Division, Ayerst Research Labs, Chazy, NY 12921.

DAVIS, ROBERT LANE, b. Henderson, Ky, Oct. 23, 36; m. 57; c. 3. ENGINEERING MECHANICS. B.S, Evansville Col, 58; M.S, Maryland, 62, Ford Found. fel, 63-64, Ph.D.(mech. eng), 65. Staff engr, Naval Ord. Lab, 58-60, mech. engr, 60-62; instr. mech. eng, Maryland, 62-63 & 64-65, asst, 63-64; asst. prof. ENG. MECH, UNIV. MO-ROLLA, 65-68, assoc. prof. 68-71, PROF, 71- Consult, Pressure Sci, Inc, 64- Am. Soc. Mech. Eng; Soc. Exp. Stress Anal; Am. Soc. Eng. Educ. Materials under extreme pressure; high-pressure fluid flow. Address: Edgar Star Route, Rolla, MO 65401.

DAVIS, ROBERT L(EO), b. New York, N.Y, Sept. 6, 17; m. 47; c. 3. BIOCHEMISTRY. B.S, Alabama, 38; Va. Polytech, 44; Lalor fel, Hopkins, 51-52, Sc.D, 53. Instr, Syracuse, 47-48; chief res. biochemist, Vet. Admin. Hosp, Md, 52-58, CHIEF, RES. LAB, VET. ADMIN. CTR, BAY PINES, 58- Res. assoc, Hopkins, 53-58; vis. assoc. prof, South Florida, 62-63, 64- Collum award, 51. U.S.A, 42-46. Am. Chem. Soc; Am. Asn. Clin. Chem; fel. Geront. Soc. Metabolism of vitamins; chemotherapy of tuberculosis; diseases of aging; trace elements; microbiology; radioisotopic studies of vitamins, minerals and biologicals; clinical chemistry; nutrition. Address: General Research Lab, Veterans Administration Center, Bay Pines, FL 33504.

DAVIS, ROBERT LLOYD, b. New York, N.Y, May 23, 19; m. 49; c. 1. MATHEMATICS. B.S, Chicago, 49, M.S, 51; Ph.D.(math), Michigan, 57. Res. asst. math. for soc. sci, Michigan, 51-54, instr. MATH, 54-56; asst. prof, Virginia, 56-59; Nat. Sci. Found. sci. faculty fel, Stanford, 59-60; asst. prof, UNIV. N.C, CHAPEL HILL, 60-61, assoc. prof, 61-70, PROF, 70- U.S.A, 41-46, 1st Lt. Am. Math. Soc; Math. Asn. Am. Lie rings; graph and relation theory; algebra and combinatorial theory; incidence algebras and other algebras. Address: Dept. of Mathematics, University of North Carolina, Chapel Hill, NC 27514.

DAVIS, ROBERT P(AUL), b. Malden, Mass, July 3, 26; m. 53; c. 2. BIOCHEMISTRY, MEDICINE. A.B, Harvard, 47, M.D, 51; A.M, 55; hon. A.M, Brown, 55. Asst. protein chem, univ. lab. phys. chem, Harvard Med. Sch, 48-51; med. house officer, Peter Bent Brigham Hosp, 51-52, asst. med, 52-55, sr. asst. res. physician, 55-56, chief res. physician, 56-57; asst. prof. med, sch. med, North Carolina, 57-59; Albert Einstein Col. Med, 59-66, assoc. prof, 66-67; career scientist, Health Res. Coun. City New York, 62-67; PROF. MED. SCI, BROWN UNIV. & PHYSICIAN-IN-CHIEF, MIRIAM HOSP, 67- Soc. of Fels. jr. fel. phys. chem. & kinetics, dept. chem, Harvard, 52-55, asst, 55-56, fel. med, 56-57; Willard O. Thompson Mem. Travel. Scholar, Am. Col. Physicians, 65; asst. vis. physician, Bronx Municipal Hosp. Ctr, 59-65, assoc. vis. physician, 66-67; trustee, Interhosp. Organ Bank, 69, treas, 70. Dipl. Am. Bd. Internal Med, 58. U.S.N.R, 44-46, M.C.R, 46-57, Lt.(jg). Fel. AAAS; Am. Col. Physicians; Harvey Soc; Biophys. Soc; Am. Soc. Cell Biol; Soc. Gen. Physiol; Am. Physiol. Soc; Am. Fedn. Clin. Res; Am. Soc. Artificial Internal Organs; Int. Soc. Nephrology; Am. Soc. Nephrology; N.Y. Acad. Sci; N.Y. Acad. Med. Enzyme kinetics; intermediary metabolism; renal physiology. Address: Division of Biological & Medical Sciences, Brown University, Providence, RI 02912.

DAVIS, ROBERT S(TEPHEN), b. Gary, Ind, Nov. 26, 30; m. 62. CHEMICAL ENGINEERING. B.S, Calif. Inst. Tech, 52, M.S, 53; French Petrol. Inst. fel, 53-54; Kimberly Clark Corp. fel, Mass. Inst. Tech, 54-55, Nat. Adv. Comt. Aeronaut. fel. & Sc.D.(chem. eng), 55. Proj. engr, Sci. Design Co, New York, 55-57, mgr. chem. eng, 57-58, dir. eng. develop, 58-62; asst. v.pres. & dir. develop, Halcon Int, Inc, 62-64; exec. v.pres, Chem. Systs, Inc, 64-66; pres, Realtime Systs, Inc, 66-68; Davis Comput. Systs, Inc, 68-71; PARTNER, INTERTECH GROUP, 71- Mem. adv. comt, dept. chem. eng, Princeton, 64-67. AAAS; Am. Inst. Chem. Eng; Am. Chem. Soc; Asn. Comput. Mach. Computer applications; process design, development and scale-up; operations research; economic evaluation; process control; reactor design; business administration; technology transfer; venture development; process licensing. Address: 200 E. 62nd St, New York, NY 10021.

DAVIS, ROBERT W(ILSON), b. Grinnell, Iowa, Oct. 20, 10; m. 38; c. 4. ANATOMY, PATHOLOGY. D.V.M, Colorado State, 35; M.S, 52. Jr. vet, U.S. Bur. Animal Indust, 35-36; asst. to deputy state vet, Mont, 35-37; asst. prof. anat. & med, COLO. STATE UNIV, 37-40, assoc. prof, ANAT, 41-42, prof, 46-70, CENTENNIAL PROF, 70-, head dept, 48-70. Harris T. Guard Distinguished Serv. Award, 60; Top Prof. award, 62. U.S.A, 43-45, Maj. AAAS; Am. Vet. Med. Asn; Am. Asn. Vet. Anat.(pres, 54); Wildlife Disease Asn; fel. N.Y. Acad. Sci; Am. Asn. Anat; Am. Soc. Zool; World Asn. Vet. Anat. Anatomy, physiology, and pathology dealing with domestic and big game animals; antler and bone growth in deer, emphasis connective and mineralized tissues. Address: Dept. of Anatomy, College of Veterinary Medicine & Biomedical Sciences, Colorado State University, Ft. Collins, CO 80521.

DAVIS, ROBIN EDEN PIERRE, b. Twickenham, Eng, Feb. 19, 34; m. 61; c. 3. PHYSICS. B.A, Oxford, 55, M.A, 59, D.Phil.(nuclear physics), 62. Res. assoc. Enrico Fermi Inst, Univ. Chicago, 62-64; Northwest. Univ, 64-66, asst. prof, 66-70; ASSOC. PROF. PHYSICS, UNIV. KANS, 70- Am. Phys. Soc. Experimental high energy physics. Address: Dept. of Physics & Astronomy, University of Kansas, Lawrence, KS 66044.

DAVIS, RODNEY J, b. Mt. Holly, Vt, Sept. 14, 25; m. 49; c. 4. PHYSICAL CHEMISTRY. B.S, New Hampshire, 48, M.S, 50; Ph.D.(anal. chem), Iowa State, 54. GROUP LEADER, OAK RIDGE NAT. LAB, 54- U.S.A, 44-46. AAAS; Sci. Res. Soc. Am. Physics and physical chemistry of aerosols; function of aerosol filters and scrubbers; function of adsorbers for noxious molecules. Address: Oak Ridge National Lab, P.O. Box X, Oak Ridge, TN 37830.

DAVIS, ROGER (EDWARD), b. Milwaukee, Wis, Aug. 7, 29; m. 58; c. 3. PHYSIOLOGY. B.Sc. & M.Sc, Michigan, 54; Ph.D.(zool), Wisconsin, 61. Res. assoc, dept. fisheries, 61-63, asst. res. zoologist, MENT. HEALTH RES. INST, 63-66, assoc. res. zoologist, 66-69, ASSOC. PROF. PSYCHOL, 69-, RES. PSYCHOBIOLOGIST, 70- U.S. Pub. Health Serv. training fel, 64- Nat. Inst. Ment. Health res. develop. award, 68. AAAS; Animal Behavior Soc. Animal behavior; biological clocks; learning memory physiology. Address: Dept. of Psychology, Mental Health Research Institute, University of Michigan, Ann Arbor, MI 48104.

DAVIS, RONALD STUART, b. Lethbridge, Alta, Aug. 3, 41. REACTOR & NUCLEAR PHYSICS. B.S, Univ. Alta, 63; Nat. Res. Coun. Can. scholar, Univ. B.C, 63, 64 & 67; M.S. & B.C, Hydro fel, 65, Ph.D.(physics), 68. Nat. Res. Coun. Can. fel, dept. theoret. physics, Oxford, 68-70; APPL. MATHEMATICIAN NUCLEAR REACTORS, CHALK RIVER NUCLEAR LAB, ATOMIC ENERGY CAN. LTD, 70- Can. Asn. Physicists. Complex energy and angular momenta in nuclear reactions; nuclear three-body problem, especially formalism; applications in particle physics; economics and control of nuclear power reactors. Address: Applied Mathematics Branch, Chalk River Nuclear Labs, Atomic Energy of Canada, Ltd, Chalk River, Ont, Can.

DAVIS, ROWLAND H(ALLOWELL), b. Boston, Mass, Dec. 8, 33; div. GENETICS. A.B, Harvard, 54, univ. fel, 54-55, U.S. Pub. Health Serv. fel, 56, Ph.D.(biol), 58. Resident tutor, Dunster House, Harvard, 55; Nat. Sci. Found. res. fel. biol, Calif. Inst. Tech, 58-60; asst. prof. BOT, UNIV. MICH, 60-63, assoc. prof, 63-67, PROF, 67- Res. grants, 67-71; mem. genetic biol. panel, Nat. Sci. Found, 67-70; assoc. ed, Genetics, 71- AAAS; Genetics Soc. Am; Am. Soc. Microbiol. Biochemical genetics; genetics of metabolic pathways of Neurospora crassa, with emphasis on pyrimidine and arginine synthesis; heterokaryosis in Neurospora crassa. Address: Dept. of Botany, University of Michigan, Ann Arbor, MI 48104.

DAVIS, RUSS E, b. San Francisco, Calif, Mar. 8, 41. PHYSICAL OCEANOGRAPHY. B.S, California, Berkeley, 63; Nat. Sci. Found. Coop. fel, Stanford, 64-67, Ph.D.(chem. eng), 67. Asst. res. geophysicist, Inst. Geophysics & Planetary Physics, UNIV. CALIF, SAN DIEGO, 67-68, ASST. PROF. PHYS. OCEANOG, SCRIPPS INST, 68- Fluid dynamics, including surface waves; motion in rotating and stratified fluids. Address: Scripps Institution of Oceanography, University of California, San Diego, P.O. Box 109, La Jolla, CA 92037.

DAVIS, RUSSELL E(DMUND), b. Leesburg, Ohio, Jan. 7, 03; m. 28; c. 3. BIOCHEMISTRY. B.S, Wilmington Col, 24; B.A, Ohio State, 25, Ph.D.(agr. chem), 28. Instr. chem, Wilmington Col, 28-29; res. chemist, Spreckels Sugar Corp, 29-31; asst. biochemist, bur. animal indust, U.S. Dept. Agr, 31-39, assoc. biochemist, 39-45, nutritionist, 45-55, biochemist animal husb. res, 55-63, asst. br. chief, 63-67; RETIRED. AAAS; Optical Soc. Am; Am. Chem. Soc; Am. Soc. Animal Sci. Metabolism of fats and proteins; fermentation of sugars by molds; oxidation of alcohols and aldehydes; spectrochemical analysis; effects of vitamins on reproduction. Address: 6304 Tecumseh Pl, Berwyn Heights, College Park, MD 20740.

DAVIS, RUSSELL P(RICE), b. Hanford, Calif, Aug. 24, 28; m. 51; c. 2. BIOLOGICAL SCIENCES. B.A, Redlands, 50; M.A, Long Beach State Col, 56; Ph.D.(zool), Arizona, 63. Teacher biol, Santa Ana Col, 56-59; asst. prof, South. Ore. Col, 63-64; ASSOC. PROF. BIOL, UNIV. ARIZ, 64- U.S.A.F, 51-55, S/Sgt. Wilderness Soc; Am. Soc. Mammal; Am. Soc. Ichthyol. & Herpet. Mammalogy; especially the natural history of bats. Address: Dept. of Biological Sciences, University of Arizona, Tucson, AZ 85721.

DAVIS, RUTH M(ARGARET), b. Sharpsville, Pa, Oct. 19, 28; m. 55. APPLIED MATHEMATICS. B.A, Am. Univ, 50; M.A, Univ. Md, 52, Ph.D. (math), 55. Mathematician, U.S. Bur. Standards, 50; res. assoc, inst. fluid dynamics & appl. math, Univ. Md, 52-55; mathematician, David Taylor Model Basin, 55-58, head opers. res. div, 57-61; staff asst, off. of spec. asst. intel. & reconnaissance, off. dir. defense res. & eng, U.S. Dept. Defense, 61-67; assoc. dir. res. & develop, Nat. Libr. Med, 67-68, dir, Lister Hill Nat. Ctr. Biomed. Commun, 68-70; DIR, CTR. COMPUT. SCI. & TECHNOL, NAT. BUR. STANDARDS, DEPT. COMMERCE, 70- Lectr, Univ. Md, 55-56; Am. Univ, 57-58; consult, Off. Naval Res, 57-58. AAAS; Am. Math. Soc; Math. Asn. Am; Opers. Res. Soc. Am; Asn. Comput. Ling. System design; information systems; artificial intelligence; computer systems organization. Address: National Bureau of Standards, Dept. of Commerce, Washington, DC 20234.

DAVIS, SAM H, JR, b. Houston, Tex, Dec. 19, 30; m; c. 2. CHEMICAL ENGINEERING, MATHEMATICS. B.A, Rice Univ, 52, B.S, 53; Sc.D, Mass. Inst. Technol, 57. Asst. prof. chem. eng, RICE UNIV, 57-62, assoc. prof, 62-69, PROF. CHEM. ENG. & MATH. SCI, 69- Consult, NASA Manned Spacecraft Ctr, 64-; Guggenheim fel, 64-65; dir. off. continuing studies, Rice Univ, 69- Am. Inst. Chem. Eng. Use of perturbation techniques in analysis of chemical reactors and adsorption systems; space oriented problems in atmosphere control; flame propagation models. Address: Dept. of Chemical Engineering, Rice University, Houston, TX 77001.

DAVIS, SANFORD, b. New York, N.Y, Sept. 29, 25; m. 47; c. 4. POLYMER CHEMISTRY. B.S, Polytech. Inst. Brooklyn, 44, M.S, 46; Southern California, 48-50. Res. assoc. polymer inst, Polytech. Inst. Brooklyn, 46-48; res. chemist, Gen. Cable Corp, 50-52; polyester resins, Marco Chem, Inc, 52-53, lab. mgr, Marco Div, Celanese Corp. Am, 53-54, sr. res. chemist, 54-56; sect. head URETHANE APPLN, BASF WYANDOTTE CORP, 56-59, res. supvr, 59-61, RES. MGR, 61- Am. Chem. Soc; Soc. Plastics Eng; Soc. Automotive Eng. Technology and development of polyurethane products and styrenated polyester resins. Address: Urethane Applications Research, BASF Wyandotte Corp, 3661 Biddle Ave, Wyandotte, MI 48192.

DAVIS, SARAH FREDERICKA, b. Pine Level, Ala, Feb. 28, 25; m. 56; c. 3. PEDIATRICS. A.B, Huntingdon Col, 45; M.D, Woman's Med. Col. Pa, 50. Intern, Jefferson-Hillman Hosp, Birmingham, Ala, 50-51, res. PEDIAT, 51-53; instr, SCH. MED, UNIV. ALA, BIRMINGHAM, 53-54, asst. prof, 54-56, assoc. prof, 56-59, PROF, 59- Dipl, Am. Bd. Pediat. Am. Acad. Pediat. Diseases of the chest and tuberculosis in children. Address: Dept. of Pediatrics, School of Medicine, University of Alabama in Birmingham, Birmingham, AL 35233.

DAVIS, SELBY B(RINKER), b. Washington, D.C, Dec. 26, 14; m. 48; c. 3. ORGANIC CHEMISTRY. B.S, George Washington, 37; A.M, Harvard, 41, fel, 41-42, Ph.D.(org. chem), 42. Res. chemist, Socony-Vacuum Oil Co, 37-39; res. fel, Harvard, 42-43; group leader, chemother. div, AM. CYANAMID CO, 43-56, HEAD MED. CHEM. DEPT, LEDERLE LABS, 56- With Nat. Defense Res. Comt, 42-43. AAAS; Am. Chem. Soc; N.Y. Acad. Sci; Brit. Chem. Soc. Stereochemistry; structure of natural products; chemotherapeutic agents. Address: Lederle Labs, American Cyanamid Co, Pearl River, NY 10965.

DAVIS, S(HERMAN) GILBERT, b. Detroit, Mich, Jan. 26, 20; m. 51; c. 2. CHEMISTRY, FOOD TECHNOLOGY. B.S, Univ. Mass, 41, fel, 41-42, M.S, 42, Ph.D.(food technol), 48, Kellogg Found. fel, 41. Asst. food technol, Univ. Mass, 42-43, teaching fel, 46-47, asst. res. prof, 47-48; v.pres, Davis & Bennett, Inc, 48-50, pres, 50-58; dir. res. & develop, Pyrotex Co, Inc, 58-60; dir. anal. lab, ASTRA PHARMACEUT. PROD, INC, 60-64, med. sales mgr, 64-68, DIR. SPEC. PROJ, 68- Sanit.C, 43-46, Capt. AAAS; fel. Am. Inst. Chem; Am. Chem. Soc; Inst. Food Technol; Soc. Plastics Eng; Asn. Mil. Surg. U.S. Microbiological assay methods; instrumental methods of analysis; protein composition and analysis; protective films and coatings; rubber and synthetic polymers; pharmaceutical and cosmetic formulations; pharmaceutical assay methods; innovative dosage delivery systems. Address: 1A Kensington Heights, Worcester, MA 01602.

DAVIS, SIDNEY, b. New York, N.Y, Apr. 20, 15; m. 43. BIOCHEMISTRY, RADIOCHEMISTRY. B.S, Polytech. Inst. Brooklyn, 37; M.S, N.Y. Univ, 41. Teaching fel. chem, N.Y. Univ, 38-40; anal. chem, penicillin div, Food & Drug Admin, 46-47; clin. chemist, Vet. Admin. Hosp, Oteen, N.C, 47-52; res. biochemist, med. res. labs, Vet. Admin. Hosps, Kansas City, Mo, 53-54 & chief res. biochemist, Indianapolis, Ind, 54-59; RES. ANAL. CHEMIST, pharmacol. div, bur. sci. res, FOOD & DRUG ADMIN, 59-70, DIV. FOOD TOXICOL, BUR. FOODS, 70- Mem. interlab. tech. adv. comt, U.S. Pub. Health Serv. & Food & Drug Admin, 63- Med.C, U.S.A, 41-45. Am. Chem. Soc. Analytical radiochemistry; clinical chemical methods in flame photometry. Address: Division of Food Toxicology, Bureau of Foods, Food & Drug Administration, Washington, DC 20204.

DAVIS, SPENCER H(ARWOOD), JR, b. Phila, Pa, Apr. 2, 16; m. 45. PLANT PATHOLOGY. B.S, Westminster Col.(Pa), 37; univ. scholar, Pennsylvania, 38-39, Harrison scholar, 39-40, Ph.D.(plant path), 44. Asst. instr, Pennsylvania, 42-43; res. assoc, Off. Sci. Res. & Develop, 43-45; asst. prof, Delaware, 46-48; assoc. prof, RUTGERS UNIV, 48-54, EXTENSION SPECIALIST, 54- Am. Phytopath. Soc. Diseases of ornamentals. Address: Dept. of Plant Pathology, Rutgers, The State University, New Brunswick, NJ 08903.

DAVIS, STANLEY D(AVID), b. San Francisco, Calif, Oct. 15, 40; m. 68. ZOOLOGY, BIOMEDICAL ENGINEERING. B.A, Univ. Calif, Berkeley, 63, Ph.D.(zool), Davis, 68; M.A, San Francisco State Col, 66. Nat. Insts. Health fel. BIOMED. ENG, col. med, Baylor Univ, 68-69; fel, CASE WEST. RESERVE UNIV, 69-70, RES. ASSOC, MICROELECTRONICS LAB. BIOMED. SCI, 70- AAAS; Am. Inst. Biol. Sci; Ecol. Soc. Am; Am. Soc. Mammal; Wildlife Diease Asn. Radio telemetry; mammalian ecology; mammalian physiology; hibernation; biological rhythms; ecology of parasites; protozoology; animal behavior; biomedical instrumentation; mammalian stress physiology; occupational physiology. Address: Engineering Design Center, Case Western Reserve University, Cleveland, OH 44106.

DAVIS, STANLEY G(ANNAWAY), b. Hancock Co, Ind, Aug. 18, 22. PHYSICAL CHEMISTRY. B.S, Purdue, 42; Shell Oil Co. fel, Atomic Energy Cmn. fel. & Ph.D.(chem), Chicago, 55. Jr. chemist & asst. radiation chem, metall. lab, Chicago, 43-44; jr. chemist anal. chem, Clinton Eng. Works, Tenn. Eastman Corp, 45-46; asst. res. chemist high temperature chem, inst. eng. res, California, 55-57; asst. prof. CHEM, RUTGERS UNIV, 57-63, ASSOC. PROF, COL. S.JERSEY, 63- Am. Phys. Soc. Chemical physics; high-temperature thermodynamics. Address: Dept. of Chemistry, College of South Jersey, Rutgers University, Camden, NJ 08102.

DAVIS, S(TANLEY) M(YRON), b. Norristown, Pa, Sept. 13, 20; m. 47; c. 3. PHYSICAL CHEMISTRY. B.S, Phila. Col. Pharmacy, 46; M.S, Hopkins, 49, Ph.D.(chem), 51. Supvr. identification & phys. measurements labs, Bound Brook Div, AM. CYANAMID CO, 51-56, group leader phys. chem. res, org. chems. div, 56-62, explor. res, 62-68, MGR. RES. SERV, 68- Am. Chem. Soc. High pressure studies; heterogeneous catalysis; electrochemistry. Address: 33 Stella Dr, Somerville, NJ 08876.

DAVIS, STANLEY N(ELSON), b. Rio de Janeiro, Brazil, Aug. 6, 24; U.S. citizen; m. 49; c. 6. GEOLOGY. B.S, Nevada, 49; M.S, Kansas, 51; Ph.D. (geol), Yale, 55. Instr. GEOL, Rochester, 53-54; asst. prof, Stanford, 54-61, assoc. prof, 61-65, PROF, 65-67; UNIV. MO-COLUMBIA, 67-, CHMN. DEPT, 70- Vis. prof, Chile, 60-61; Univ. Hawaii, 66. C.Eng, U.S.A, 43-46. AAAS; Geol. Soc. Am; Am. Water Resources Asn; Am. Geophys. Union; assoc. Soc. Econ. Paleont. & Mineral; Asn. Eng. Geol. Hydrogeology; engineering geology; late Cenozoic stratigraphy. Address: Dept. of Geology, University of Missouri-Columbia, Columbia, MO 65201.

DAVIS, STARKEY D, b. Atlanta, Tex, Jan. 29, 31; m. 57; c. 3. PEDIATRICS, IMMUNOLOGY. B.A, Baylor Univ, 53, M.D, 57. Rotating intern, Confederate Mem. Med. Ctr, Shreveport, La, 57-58; instr. prev. med, Emory Univ, 58-60; resident, PEDIAT, Baylor Univ, 60-62; asst, SCH. MED, UNIV. WASH, 62-64, instr, 64-65, asst. prof, 65-69, ASSOC. PROF, 69- Res. fel. pediat, Univ. Wash, 62-63, spec. res. fel, 62-65. U.S.P.H.S, 58-60, Sr. Asst. Surg. Am. Asn. Immunol; Am. Fedn. Clin. Res; Infectious Diseases Soc. Am; Soc. Pediat. Res. Address: Dept. of Pediatrics, University of Washington School of Medicine, Seattle, WA 98195.

DAVIS, STEPHEN H(OWARD), b. New York, N.Y, Sept. 7, 39; m. 66. MATHEMATICS, FLUID DYNAMICS. B.E.E, Rensselaer Polytech, 60, Nat. Defense Ed. Act fel, 61-63, M.S, 62, Ph.D.(math), 64. Teaching asst. math, Rensselaer Polytech, 60-61; mathematician, Rand Corp, 64-66; lectr. math, Imp. Col. London, 66-68; asst. prof. MECH, JOHNS HOPKINS UNIV, 68-70, ASSOC. PROF, 70- Lectr, California, Los Angeles, 65; exten, Southern California, 66. Asst, Nat. Sci. Found. summer seminar appl. math, Univ. Kansas, 62. Asst. ed, J. Fluid Mech, 69- Theory and applications of nonlinear hydrodynamic stability, particularly related to cellular convection; interfacial phenomena. Address: Dept. of Mechanics, Johns Hopkins University, Baltimore, MD 21218.

DAVIS, STEPHEN S(MITH), b. Philadelphia, Pa, Oct. 24, 10; m. 38; c. 1. MECHANICAL ENGINEERING. B.S.M.E, Howard, 36; M.S.M.E, Harvard, 47. PROF. MECH. ENG, HOWARD UNIV, 38-, dean, sch. eng. & archit, 64-70, head dept. mech. eng, 62-64. Asst. mech. engr, Nat. Bur. Standards, 43-46; consult. engr, Naval Ord. Lab, 53-62; v.chmn, bd. dirs, D.C. Redevelop. Land Agency, 68- AAAS; Am. Soc. Eng. Educ; Am. Soc. Mech. Eng; Nat. Soc. Prfnl. Eng. Engineering education. Address: 2847 University Terrace, N.W, Washington, DC 20016.

DAVIS, S(TUART) G(EORGE), b. Lethbridge, Alta, June 15, 17; m. 40; c. 1. PHYSICAL CHEMISTRY. B.Sc, Alberta, 39, Bd. Governors scholar, 39, M.Sc, 40; Nat. Res. Council Can. student, McGill, 40, Can. Industs, Ltd, fel, 41, Ph.D.(chem), 42. Lecturer CHEM, UNIV. ALBERTA, 42-43, asst. prof, 45-51, ASSOC. PROF, 51- Prize, Asn. Prfnl. Eng, 39; Stiernotte prize, 39. Am. Chem. Soc; Eng. Inst. Can; fel. Chem. Inst. Can. Adsorption; isotope effect in acid base catalysis. Address; Dept. of Chemistry, University of Alberta, Edmonton 7, Alta, Can.

DAVIS, SUMNER P, b. Burbank, Calif. PHYSICS. A.B, California, Los Angeles, 47; A.M, Illinois, 48; Ph.D.(physics), California, Berkeley, 52. Instr. PHYSICS, Mass. Inst. Tech, 52-55, res. staff mem, 55-59; lectr, UNIV. CALIF, BERKELEY, 59-60, asst. prof, 60-62, assoc. prof, 62-67, PROF, 67- NATO sr. fel. sci, 67-68. U.S.A.A.F, 43-46, 2nd Lt. Am. Phys. Soc; Optical Soc. Am. Optical spectroscopy; molecular spectra; atomic energy level analysis; hyperfine structure in atomic spectra. Address: Dept. of Physics, University of California, Berkeley, CA 94720.

DAVIS, TERRY C(HAFFIN), b. Pearisburg, Va, Apr. 12, 32; m. 59. FOREST PATHOLOGY. B.S, Va. Polytech, 59, M.S, 61; Ph.D.(plant path), W.Va. Univ, 65. ASST. PROF, forestry & forest path, AUBURN UNIV, 65-70, BOT. & PLANT PATH, 70- U.S.N, 51-55. Am. Phytopath. Soc; Mycol. Soc. Am. Microorganisms which cause tree diseases. Address: Dept. of Plant Pathology, Auburn University, Auburn, AL 36830.

DAVIS, THOMAS (ROBERT) (ALEXANDER), b. Rarotonga, Cook Islands, June 11, 17; U.S. citizen; m. 40; c. 3. MEDICINE, PHYSIOLOGY. M.A, Ch.B, Otago, N.Z, 45; scholar, Sydney, 49, D.T.M.&H, 50; fel, Harvard, 52-53, M.P.H, 54. Med. officer psychiat, Seacliffe Ment. Hosp, N.Z, 42-43; house surgeon, Auckland Pub. Hosp, 43-45; med. officer surg, Cook Islands Med. Serv, 45-49, chief med. officer surg. admin, 49-52; res. fel. physiol, sch. pub. health, Harvard, 53-54, res. assoc, 54-55; chief environ. med, Arctic Aero-Med. Lab, Alaska, 55-56; chief res. physician, U.S. Army Med. Res. Lab, Ky, 56-61, dir. environ. med, 57-61; dir. cold & altitude res, U.S. Army Res. Inst. Environ. Med, Mass, 61-63; SR. STAFF MEM. PHYSIOLOGIST, ARTHUR D. LITTLE, INC, 63- Lectr, Tufts, 60-61; med. monitor, Proj. Mercury, NASA, 60-63. Consult, Defense Res. Labs, Can, 64- N.Z. Armed Forces, 39-42. Am. Pub. Health Asn; Am. Soc. Trop. Med. & Hyg; fel. Royal Soc. Health; fel. Royal Soc. Trop. Med. & Hyg; Royal Soc. Med; Int. Soc. Biometeorol. Microbiology; environmental physiology; nutrition; sociology; space medicine; pulmonary physiology; clinical research and operant behavior; chemical pollution of fresh water and health; immunology; pharmacodynamics. Address: Arthur D. Little, Inc, 30 Memorial Dr, Acorn Park, Cambridge, MA 02142.

DAVIS, THOMAS ARTHUR, b. Columbia, S.C, Aug. 12, 39; m. 62; c. 1. CHEMICAL ENGINEERING. B.S, South Carolina, 61, NASA fel. & Ph.D. (eng. sci), 67. Jr. chem. engr, textile chem. pilot plant, Deering Milliken Res. Corp, 63-64; asst. chem. eng, South Carolina, 64-67; RES. CHEM. ENGR, SOUTH. RES. INST, 67- U.S.N, 61-63, Res, Lt. Am. Inst. Chem. Eng. Membrane processes research, particularly electrodialysis for desalination of brackish water, chemical processing and water pollution control; electro-regeneration of ion-exchange resins; development of artificial kidney devices. Address: Southern Research Institute, 2000 Ninth Ave. S, Birmingham, AL 35205.

DAVIS, THOMAS A(USTIN), b. Belgian Congo, May 31, 34; U.S. citizen; m. m. 59; c. 2. MATHEMATICS. A.B, Denison, 56; M.S, Michigan, 57; Ph.D. (math), Cambridge, 63. Asst. prof. math, DePAUW UNIV, 63-69, ASSOC. PROF. MATH, ASST. DEAN UNIV. & DIR. GRAD. STUDIES, 69- Am. Coun. Educ. acad. admin. intern, Princeton, 71-72. Math. Asn. Am. Banach algebras and Fourier analysis. Address: DePauw University, Greencastle, IN 46135.

DAVIS, THOMAS GENE, b. Galena, Mo, Dec. 26, 36; m. 61. ELECTRICAL ENGINEERING. B.A, California, Riverside, 58; Calif. Inst. Tech, 58-59; Rutgers, 59; M.S, Mass. Inst. Tech, 65, Ph.D.(elec. eng), 68. Physicist, U.S. Naval Ord. Lab, Corona, Calif, 60; res. engr, Autonetics Div, N.Am. Rockwell Corp, 60-63; ASST. PROF. ELEC. ENG, MASS. INST. TECHNOL, 68- Am. Phys. Soc. Ferroelectricity; lattice dynamics; Raman scattering in solids. Address: Dept. of Electrical Engineering, Massachusetts Institute of Technology, Cambridge, MA 02139.

DAVIS, THOMAS HAYDN, b. Phila, Pa, Sept. 4, 39; m. 61; c. 2. SOLID STATE & REACTOR PHYSICS. B.S, Lehigh Univ, 61; M.S, Carnegie-Mellon Univ, 66, Ph.D.(physics), 71. Assoc. scientist, Westinghouse Bettis Atomic Power Lab, Pa, 61-65 & summer 66; PHYSICIST, APPL. PHYSICS SECT, MAJOR APPLIANCE LABS, GEN. ELEC. CO, 71- Am. Phys. Soc. Electronic properties of alloys; liquid crystal research. Address: General Electric Co, Appliance Park 35-1101, Louisville, KY 40225.

DAVIS, T(HOMAS) NEIL, b. Greeley, Colo, Feb. 1, 32; m. 51; c. 3. GEOPHYSICS. B.S, Alaska, 55, Ph.D.(geophys), 61; M.S, Calif. Inst. Tech, 57. Assoc. prof. geophys, geophys. inst, Alaska, 61-64; aerospace technologist, Goddard Space Flight Ctr, NASA, 64-65; PROF. GEOPHYS. & DEP. DIR, GEOPHYS. INST, UNIV. ALASKA, 65- Nat. Acad. Sci-Nat. Res. Coun. resident res. assoc, Goddard Space Flight Ctr, 63-64. Am. Geophys. Union. Auroral morphology; geomagnetism; rocket-borne magnetometer study of ionosphere currents; seismology. Address: Geophysical Institute, University of Alaska, College, AK 99735.

DAVIS, THOMAS W(ILDERS), b. Nyack, N.Y, Aug. 1, 05; m. 42; c. 3. PHYSICAL CHEMISTRY. B.S, N.Y. Univ, 25, M.S, 26, fel, 27-28, Ph.D.(chem), 28; Columbia, 30. Res. chemist, Combustion Utilities Corp, N.J, 28-29; instr. CHEM, N.Y. UNIV, 29-39, asst. prof, 39-47, assoc. prof, 47-51, PROF, 51-, chmn. dept, 55-64. Instr, Rand Sch. Soc. Sci, 33; res. assoc, metall. lab, Chicago, 42; vis. prof. & mem. senate, Leeds, 64-65. Sr. chemist, Clinton Lab, Tenn, 46-47; res. chemist, Brookhaven Nat. Lab, 48, 50; U.S. Naval Ord. Test Sta, 52; Oak Ridge Nat. Lab, 54; Argonne Nat. Lab, 55, 56, res. assoc, 56. Am. Chem. Soc; fel. Am. Inst. Chem; Radiation Res. Soc; Fedn. Am. Sci. Reaction kinetics and mechanisms of reaction; photochemistry and radiation chemistry; thermodynamics; uses of radioactive tracers. Address: Dept. of Chemistry, New York University, Bronx, NY 10453.

DAVIS, V(ERNAM) TERRELL, b. Long Branch, N.J, July 14, 11; m. 36; c. 3. PSYCHIATRY. M.D, Washington (St. Louis), 36. Asst. surgeon drug addiction, hosp, U.S. Pub. Health Serv, Ft. Worth, Texas, 39-41, sr. asst. surgeon clin. psychiat, 41-43, exec. officer, 43-44, clin. dir, gen. hosp. admin, Staten Island, N.Y, 44-45, med. dir. psychiat. & neurol, 49-54, chief psychiat. & neurol, hosp, Ellis Island, 45-49; clin. assoc. prof. neuropsychiat, Wisconsin, 54-56, asst. dir, Psychiat. Inst, 54-56; PROF. PSYCHIAT, COL. MED. & DENT. N.J, NEWARK, 59-; MED. DIR, NAT. INST. MENT. HEALTH, 69- Chief med. off, Fed. Penitentiary, Lewisburg, Pa, 44; consult, U.S. Immigration Serv, 45-54; dir, Staten Island Ment. Health Clin, 53-54; asst. dir, div. ment. health, State Dept. Pub. Welfare, Wis, 54-56; clin. dir, Wis. Diag. Ctr, Madison, 54-63; dir. ment. health & hosps. N.J, 56-69; WHO fel, 62-; clin. prof, med. sch, Rutgers Univ, 68; ment. health prog. consult, region II, Nat. Inst. Ment. Health, N.Y.C. U.S.P.H.S, 41-49, Col. AAAS; fel. Am. Psychiat. Asn; Asn. Mil. Surg. U.S; Am. Med. Asn; Am. Pub. Health Asn; Nat. Asn. State Ment. Health Prog. Dirs.(pres, 63-65); fel. Am. Col. Psychiat. Psychotherapy; psychiatric training; relation of injury to psychiatric illness; relation of psychiatry to employment; psychoanalysis; mental health program administration; forensic psychiatry. Address: 99 Parkside Dr, Princeton, NJ 08540.

DAVIS, WALLACE, JR, b. Pawtucket, R.I, Dec. 17, 18; m. 42; c. 3. CHEMISTRY. Sc.B, Brown, 41; Eastman Kodak fel, Rochester, 41-42, Chem. Warfare fel, 45, Nat. Res. Coun. fel, 46-47, univ. fel, & Ph.D.(phys. chem), 47. With Off. Sci. Res. & Develop. Manhattan Proj, Columbia, 42-45; res. chemist, Kellex Corp, Tenn, 47; res. chemist, Oak Ridge Gaseous Diffusion Plant, UNION CARBIDE CORP, 47-58, GROUP LEADER, OAK RIDGE NAT. LAB, 58- Guest scientist, Atomic Energy Res. Estab, Harwell, Eng, 65-66. Fel. AAAS; fel. Am. Inst. Chem; Am. Chem. Soc. Photochemistry of gases; thermodynamic and phase properties of uranium-fluorine-fluorocarbon systems; isotope separation; gas-solid reaction kinetics; radiation chemistry; radiochemical reprocessing of nuclear fuels; thermodynamics of solvent extraction; foam separation. Address: Union Carbide Corp, Oak Ridge National Lab, Oak Ridge, TN 37830.

DAVIS, W(ALTER) S(TROTHER), b. Canton, Miss, Aug. 9, 05; m. 36; c. 1. AGRICULTURAL EDUCATION. B.S, Tenn. Agr. & Indust. State Col, 31; M.S, Cornell, 33, Ph.D, 41. Prof. agr. & dir. dept, TENN. STATE UNIV, 33-43, pres, 43-70, EMER. PRES, 70- State teacher trainer agr. ed, Tenn, 33-43; nat. exec. secy, New Farmers Am, 41-43; trustee, Meharry Med. Col, 51-; mem, Interim Metrop. Bd. Ed, 63. Address: Tennessee State University, Nashville, TN 37203.

DAVIS, WARD B, b. Fortville, Ind, Oct. 24, 93; m. 23; c. 3. BIOCHEMISTRY. A.B, Ind. State Norm. Sch, 18; Toulouse, 19; M.S, Chicago, 22, Ph.D.(plant physiol), 24. Asst. plant physiol, Chicago, 23-24; fel, biochem, Boyce Thompson Inst, 24-25; assoc. chemist, bur. agr. chem. & eng, U.S. Dept. Agr, 25-41, chemist, bur. agr. & indust. chem, 41-53, agr. res. serv, 53-58; ACAD. RES, WHITTIER COL, 58- U.S.A, 18-19. AAAS; Am. Soc. Plant Physiol; Am. Chem. Soc. Plant pigments; enzymes; volatile flavors. Address: 9106 E. Newby Ave, Rosemead, CA 91770.

DAVIS, WATSON M, b. Chelsea, Iowa, Oct. 5, 03; m. 27; c. 1. MATHEMATICS. A.B, Cornell Col.(Iowa), 26; M.S, Iowa, 28; Ph.D.(math), Chicago, 33. Asst. MATH, Iowa, 26-28; instr. Albion Col, 28-30; Ill. Inst. Tech, 31-35, asst. prof, 35-42; from asst. prof. to prof, CORNELL COL, 42-70, EMER. PROF, 70- Instr, U.S. Army Univ, Eng. Math. Asn. Am. Conjugete nets. Address: 517 Third Ave. S, Mt. Vernon, IA 52314.

DAVIS, WAYNE ALTON, b. Ft. Macleod, Alta, Nov. 16, 31; m. 59; c. 3. COMPUTER SCIENCE. B.S.E, George Washington Univ, 60; M.Sc, Univ. Ottawa, 63, Ph.D.(elec. eng), 67. Sci. off, Defence Res. Bd, Defence Res. Telecommun. Estab, 60-69; dept. commun, Commun. Res. Ctr, 69; ASSOC. PROF. COMPUT. SCI, UNIV. ALTA, 69- Lectr, Univ. Ottawa, 65-69; nat. leader, working panel S-3, subgroup S, Tech. Coop. Prog, 66-69; lectr, Carleton Univ, 67; mem. reactor safety adv. comt, Atomic Energy Control Bd, 67-69. Inst. Elec. & Electronics Eng; Asn. Comput. Mach; Can. Info. Processing Soc. Detection and diagnosis of errors in digital circuits; relationship between structure and behavior in digital circuits; detection and correction of errors in digital communications; digital pattern recognition in image processing. Address: Dept. of Computing Science, University of Alberta, Edmonton 7, Alta, Can.

DAVIS, WAYNE H(ARRY), b. Morgantown, W.Va, Dec. 31, 30; m. 58; c. 3. ZOOLOGY. A.B, West Virginia, 53; M.S, Illinois, 55, Ph.D.(zool), 57. Asst. zool, Illinois, 53-54, biol, 54-57; res. fel, Minnesota, 57-59; instr. biol, Middlebury Col, 59-62; asst. prof. ZOOL, UNIV. KY, 62-66, assoc. prof, 66-70, PROF, 70- Fel. AAAS; Am. Soc. Mammal. Life history of bats; taxonomy of mammals; plant evolution; insecticide toxicity to native mammals; human ecology. Address: Dept. of Zoology, University of Kentucky, Lexington, KY 40506.

DAVIS, W(ILBUR) MARVIN, b. Calumet City, Ill, Apr. 13, 31, m. 56; c. 2. PHARMACOLOGY. B.S, Purdue, 52, fel, 52-53, M.S, 53, fel, 53-55, Ph.D. (pharmacol), 55. Asst. prof. PHARMACOL, SCH. PHARM, Oklahoma, 55-59, assoc. prof, 59-63, prof, 63-64; assoc. prof, UNIV. MISS, 64-65, PROF, 65-, CHMN. DEPT, 68- Lalor Found. award, 58. AAAS; Am. Pharmaceut. Asn; Am. Soc. Zool; Am. Soc. Pharmacol. & Exp. Therapeut; Acad. Pharmaceut. Sci; Am. Ornith. Union; Animal Behavior Soc. Neuropsychopharmacology; circadian physiological and pharmacological rhythms; behavioral and CNS pharmacology; pharmacology of dependence-producing drugs. Address: Dept. of Pharmacology, University of Mississippi School of Pharmacy, University, MS 38677.

DAVIS, WILLARD E, b. Correctionville, Iowa, June 13, 05; m. 31; c. 1. GEOPHYSICS. B.S, Missouri-Rolla, 30. Engr, Ill. State Hwy. Cmn, 30-33; Mo. Geol. Surv, 33-43; geophysicist, U.S. Bur. Mines, 44-48; U.S. GEOL. SURV, 48-57, chief geophysicist, ground surv. sect, 57-60, GEOPHYSICIST, 60- Tech. advisor, water supply invests, ground water div, U.S. Agency Int. Develop, 63 & 66; mineral explor. prog, U.S. Geol. Surv, Saudi Arabia, 64-67. Soc. Explor. Geophys; Am. Geophys. Union. Application of geophysical techniques to geological and engineering problems; exploration for mineral deposits. Address: U.S. Geological Survey, 345 Middlefield Rd, Menlo Park, CA 94025.

DAVIS, W(ILLARD) KENNETH, b. Seattle, Wash, July 26, 18; m. 41; c. 3. CHEMICAL ENGINEERING. B.S, Mass. Inst. Tech, 40, M.S, 42. Asst. dir, Buffalo sta, sch. chem. eng. practice, Mass. Inst. Tech, 41-42; from res. engr. to sr. res. engr, Standard Oil Co. Calif. & Calif. Res. Corp, 42-47; sr. engr, Ford, Bacon & Davis, Inc, 47-49; assoc. prof. eng, California, Los Angeles, 49-53, prof, 53; asst. dir. reactor develop. div, U.S. Atomic Energy Comn, 54, dir, 54-58; V.PRES, BECHTEL CORP, 58-, V.PRES, BECHTEL OVERSEAS CORP, 71-, MGR. POWER & INDUST. DIV, 71-, mgr. sci. develop. dept, 58-67, int. power develop, 67-71. Lectr, exten. div, California, 47, Regents lectr, Los Angeles, 62. Chief develop. engr, Calif. Res. & Develop. Co, 50-52, mgr. res. div, 52-54. Mem. Interdepartmental Cmt. on Sci. Res. & Develop, 56-58. Mem. U.S. Nat. Cmt. World Power Conf, 55-; U.S. rep. UN Confs. on Peaceful Uses of Atomic Energy, 55, 58, 64; mem. comt. radioactive waste mgt, Nat. Acad. Sci, 68- Fleming award, 56. Chmn, Pac. Coast adv. cmt. mt. & winter warfare to Q.M.Gen, U.S. Army, 44-45. Nat. Acad. Eng; AAAS; Atomic Indust. Forum (v.pres, 62-64, pres, 64-66, hon. dir, 67-); Am. Chem. Soc; Am. Soc. Mech. Eng; Am. Soc. Eng. Educ; Am. Inst. Chem. Eng.(Prof. Progress award, 58, Robert E. Wilson award, 69); fel. Am. Nuclear Soc. Petroleum refining processes, especially catalytic reactors and processes; fluid mixing; combustion mechanisms and theory; mass transfer, especially with simultaneous heat transfer; development of nuclear chain reactors and associated processes and equipment; economics and evaluation of chemical, petroleum, and nuclear processes; administration and management of research and development. Address: Bechtel Corp, P.O. Box 3965, 50 Beale St, San Francisco, CA 94119.

DAVIS, WILLIAM ANTHONY, b. New York, N.Y, Apr. 8, 08; m. 47, 60. MEDICINE. Ph.D, Yale, 30; M.D, Harvard, 39; Rockefeller Found. fel, Hopkins, 40, M.P.H, 41. Staff mem, Rockefeller Found, 42-46; asst. prof. med. & asst. clin. prof. prev. med, col, med. N.Y. Univ, 46-53; mem. staff, dept. clin. res, Hoffman-La Roche, Inc, N.J, 54-58; med. dir, Wallace Labs, 58-64; CHIEF STAFF, VET. ADMIN. HOSP, Boston, Mass, 65-67, GRAND JUNCTION, COLO, 67- Medal, U.S. Typhus Cmn; hon. mem, Order of Brit. Empire. Med.C, 43-46, Maj. Fel. Am. Med. Asn; fel. Am. Col. Physicians. Hospital administration. Address: Veterans Administration Hospital, Grand Junction, CO 81501.

DAVIS, WILLIAM B, b. Rexburg, Idaho, Mar. 14, 02; m. 23; c. 2. WILDLIFE MANAGEMENT, CONSERVATION. A.B, Chico State Col, 33; M.S, California, 36, Ph.D.(vert. zool), 37. Prin. & teacher, elementary & high schs, Idaho, Wash. & Calif, 20-32; asst. zool, California, 34-37; prof. WILDLIFE MGT, TEX. A&M UNIV, 37-67, acting head dept, 37-47, head dept, 47-65, EMER. PROF, 67- Asst. leader, Tex. Co-op Wildlife Res. Unit, 38-52; curator, Tex. Co-op Wildlife Collection, 38-67; collab, fish & wildlife serv, U.S. Dept. Interior, 38-67. Mem. eval. comt. zool, Nat. Roster Sci. & Specialized Personnel, 40. Leader, wildlife expeds, Mex, 41-42, 49-53. Am. Soc. Mammal.(cor. secy, 38-40, ed, Jour. Mammal, 40-47, v.pres, 52, 54, pres, 55-58); Am. Ornith Union; Wildlife Soc; Cooper Ornith. Soc; Wilson Ornith. Soc. Ecology, differentiation and distribution of mammals in Idaho, Texas and Middle America; ecology and distribution of birds, reptiles and amphibians in the Southeast and Mexico. Address: Dept. of Wildlife & Fisheries Science, Box 154 FE, Texas A&M University, College Station, TX 77843.

DAVIS, WILLIAM BURSON, b. Clarendon, Tex, Feb. 20, 30; m. 50; c. 3. ENVIRONMENTAL ENGINEERING. B.S, Univ. Colo, Boulder, 52; S.M, Mass. Inst. Technol, 58, S.E, 59; Sc.D, Wash. Univ, 68. Engr, Freese, Nichols & Endress, Consult. Engrs, Tex, 52-55; res. asst. civil & sanit. eng, Mass. Inst. Technol, 55-57, sanit. eng, 57-58; consult, div. sanit. eng, Mass. State Health Dept, 58-59; sr. sanit. engr, Tex. State Health Dept, 59-62; Jefferson Chem. Co, Tex, 62-63; head dept. environ. eng, Tex. A&M Univ, 63-71; PRES, WILLIAM B. DAVIS & ASSOCS, 71- Pres, Consult. Res. Serv, Inc, Tex, 68-71. AAAS; Nat. Soc. Prof. Eng; Am. Soc. Civil Eng; Am. Water Resources Asn; Water Pollution Control Fedn; Am. Chem. Soc; Am. Soc. Eng. Educ. Pollution abatement and process control. Address: William B. Davis & Associates, P.O. Box 3596, Bryan, TX 77801.

DAVIS, WILLIAM C, b. Red Bluff, Calif, Feb. 12, 33; m. 56; c. 2. IMMUNOLOGY, ELECTRON MICROSCOPY. B.A, Chico State Col, 55; M.A. Stanford Univ, 59, Ph.D.(med. microbiol), 67. Fel, med. ctr, Univ. Calif, San Francisco, 66-68; ASST. PROF. VET. MICROBIOL. & IMMUNOL, COL. VET. MED, WASH. STATE UNIV, 68- U.S.A, 56-58. AAAS; Transplantation Soc; Am. Asn. Path. & Bact. Transplantation immunology; autoimmunity; host defense failure syndromes. Address: Dept. of Veterinary Microbiology, Washington State University, Pullman, WA 99163.

DAVIS, WILLIAM C(HESTER), b. Manchester, N.H, Dec. 22, 25; div; c. 4. PHYSICS. B.S, Tufts Col, 49; Ph.D.(physics), Hopkins, 54. Asst. PHYSICS, Hopkins, 51-54; MEM. STAFF, LOS ALAMOS SCI. LAB, 54- Vis. prof. physics, California, 57. U.S.N.R, 43-46. High explosives; shock and detonation waves; ultra-high-speed photography. Address: 2160 B 37th St, Los Alamos, NM 87544.

DAVIS, W(ILLIAM) CLAYTON, b. Phila, Pa, Jan. 26, 25; m. 53; c. 3. SURGERY. Yale, 42-43; M.D, Jefferson Med. Col, 47. Intern, Abington Mem. Hosp, Pa, 47-48; res. surg, South. Pac. Hosp, San Francisco, Calif, 48-49, 51-52; base surgeon, U.S. Naval Air Sta, Alaska, 49-50; battalion surgeon, 1st Marine Div, Korea, 50-51; res. surg, U.S. Naval Hosp, Bethesda, Md, 52-54, thoracic, 54-56, asst. chief surg, Bremerton, Wash, 56-57; thoracic surgeon assoc. chief surg, Man Mem. Hosp, W.Va, 57-61; asst. prof. SURG, sch. med, Pittsburgh, 61-66; assoc. prof, COL. MED, UNIV. NEBR, OMAHA, 66-68, PROF, 68-; CHIEF SURG. SERV, VET. ADMIN. HOSP, 66- Asst. chief surg. & dir. tumor bd, Vet. Admin. Hosp, Pittsburgh, 61-66. Instr. anat, sch. med, Georgetown, 54. Dipl, Am. Bd. Surg, 56; Am. Bd. Thoracic Surg, 58. Med.C, U.S.N, 47-57, Lt. Comdr. Fel. Am. Col. Surg; Am. Med. Asn; Am. Asn. Surg. of Trauma; Soc. Clin. Surg; Soc. Surg. Alimentary Tract. General and thoracic surgery; parenteral alimentation; pulmonary embolus; vascular surgery. Address: Surgical Service, Veterans Administration Hospital, 4101 Woolworth Ave, Omaha, NE 68105.

DAVIS, WILLIAM COURTNEY, b. North East, Pa, Feb. 8, 20; m. 44; c. 2. ELECTRICAL ENGINEERING. B.E.E, Ohio State, 43, M.Sc, 47. Instr. elec. eng, OHIO STATE UNIV, 46-47, assoc. prof. ELEC. ENG, 47-60, PROF, 60-, RES. ASSOC, RES. FOUND, 47- Res. specialist, N.Am. Aviation, Inc, 61- U.S.N.R, 44-46, Lt.(jg). Inst. Elec. & Electronics Eng. Radar systems; circuit systems. Address: Dept. of Electrical Engineering, Ohio State University, 2015 Neil Ave, Columbus, OH 43210.

DAVIS, WILLIAM D(ONALD), b. Miami, Fla, Aug. 6, 21; m. 45; c. 5. CHEMISTRY. B.S, Miami (Fla), 42; Ph.D.(phys. chem), Pittsburgh, 49. Asst. phys. chem, Office Naval Res. proj, Univ. Pittsburgh, 46-48; Manhattan proj, Rochester, 44-45; res. assoc. phys. sect, Knolls Atomic Power Lab, GEN. ELEC. CO, 49-59, PHYSICIST GEN. PHYSICS SECT, RES. LAB, 59- Adj. prof, Rensselaer Polytech. Inst, 67- AAAS; Am. Phys. Soc; Am. Vacuum Soc; Am. Soc. Mass Spectrometry. Combustion and reaction in solution calorimetry; gas discharges; vacuum physics; diffusion of gases in metals; mass spectroscopy. Address: Research Lab, General Electric Co, Schenectady, NY 12301.

DAVIS, WILLIAM D(UNCAN), JR, b. Brookhaven, Miss, Apr. 4, 18; m. 49; c. 3. MEDICINE, GASTROENTEROLOGY. B.S, Tulane, 39, M.D, 43. Intern, City Hosp, Cleveland, Ohio, 43, res, 44-45; instr. med, TULANE UNIV, 45-54, from asst. prof. to assoc. prof. CLIN. MED, 54-65, PROF, 65- Mem. staff dept. internal med, Ochsner Clin. & Found. Hosp, 45-, head sect. gastroenterol, 53- & dept. internal med, 68-, trustee & v.pres. Alton Ochsner Med. Found. Consult, dept. med, Charity Hosp. & Vet. Admin. Hosp, New Orleans; surgeon gen, Army Subcomt. Gastroenterol, 63-69. Dipl, Am. Bd. Internal Med, 50; Am. Bd. Gastroent, 54. Med.C, U.S.N.R, 54-56. Fel. Am. Col. Physicians; Am. Fedn. Clin. Res; Am. Gastroenterol. Asn; Am. Asn. Study Liver Disease. Hemochromatosis; liver disease; gastric secretion. Address: Ochsner Clinic, 1514 Jefferson Highway, New Orleans, LA 70121.

DAVIS, W(ILLIAM) E(DWARD), b. Stonington, Conn, Mar. 31, 15; m. 39; c. 3. CHEMISTRY. B.S, Syracuse, 35, M.S, 38, Ph.D.(cellulose chem), 41. Res. chemist, United Gas Improv. Co, Pa, 39-40; Solvay Process Co, N.Y, 40-42; Hercules Powder Co, Del, 42-69; MEM. STAFF, COMPUT. CTR, UNIV. DEL, 69- Am. Chem. Soc; Am. Math. Soc; Soc. Indust. & Appl. Math. Production and analysis of cellulose; method for preparation of high quality wood cellulose; preparation and properties of hydroxyethyl ethers of cellulose; applied mathematics. Address: Computing Center, University of Delaware, 560 DuPont Hall, Newark, DE 19711.

DAVIS, WILLIAM EDWIN, JR, b. Toledo, Ohio, Nov. 17, 36; m. 68. GEOLOGY, PALEONTOLOGY. B.A, Amherst Col, 59; M.A, Texas, 62; Ph.D. (paleont), Boston, 66. Instr. SCI, BOSTON UNIV, 65-66, asst. prof, 66-71, ASSOC. PROF, 71- Conodont fauna of the Tully limestone, New York State. Address: 127 East St, Foxboro, MA 02035.

DAVIS, WILLIAM E(LLSMORE), JR, b. Denver, Colo, June 22, 27; m. 54; c. 3. BIOCHEMISTRY. B.S, Stanford, 51, M.S, 53. Biochemist clin. res, Vet. Admin. Hosp, Oakland, Calif, 53-58; radiation biologist, U.S. Naval Radiol. Defense Lab, 58-69; res. biologist, Vet. Admin. Hosp, San Francisco, 69-71; CANCER BIOLOGIST, LIFE SCI. DIV, STANFORD RES. INST, 71- U.S. Naval Radiol. Defense Lab. Silver Medal Award for Sci. Achievement. AAAS; Am. Chem. Soc. Radiation Res. Soc; Soc. Exp. Biol. & Med. Radiation biology; tissue transplantation. Address: Life Sciences Division, Stanford Research Institute, Menlo Park, CA 94025.

DAVIS, WILLIAM F, JR, b. Lakeworth, Fla, Sept. 4, 30; m. 61; c. 2. PHYSIOLOGY. B.S, Florida, 57, M.S, 58; Ph.D.(physiol), Texas A&M, 61. Physiologist, Bur. Sports Fisheries & Wildlife, 60-61; res. assoc. animal sci, Cornell, 61-62; chief animal sci. br, Smithsonian Inst, 62-66; physiologist, DEPT. BEHAV. SCI, ARMED FORCES RADIOBIOL. RES. INST, 66-68, CHMN, 68- U.S.A, 52-53. Am. Soc. Animal Sci; Am. Inst. Biol. Sci; Radiation Res. Soc. Physiological effects of ionizing radiation. Address: Dept. of Behavioral Sciences, Armed Forces Radiobiology Research Institute, Bethesda, MD 20014.

DAVIS, WILLIAM H(ATCH), b. Holladay, Utah, Mar. 9, 25; m. 49; c. 5. PLANT BREEDING, GENETICS. B.S, Utah State, 53, M.S, 54; Ph.D.(plant breeding), N.C. State, 59. Res. instr, N.C. State, 55-59; plant breeder, Great West. Sugar Co, 59-63; DIR. SOYBEAN RES. & SR. RES. SCIENTIST, L. TEWELES SEED CO, 63- U.S.N, 43-46; U.S.A, 53, 2nd Lt. Am. Soc. Agron. Plant breeding, particularly statistical genetics of developing hybrid sugar beets; alfalfa and forage breeding; cytoplasmic male sterility in alfalfa; a source of male sterility in soybeans believed to be a cytoplasmic source. Address: Research Center, L. Teweles Seed Co, Route 1, Clinton, WI 53525.

DAVIS, W(ILLIAM) H(OWARD), b. Brockville, Ont, Can, Apr. 5, 22; m. 48; c. 2. PHYSICS. B.Sc, Queen's (Can), 45, M.Sc, 46; Ph.D.(physics), Brown, 48. Asst. prof. PHYSICS, Buffalo, 48-54; asst. prof. MARIETTA COL, 54-55, assoc. prof, 55-58, PROF, 58-, head dept, 58-70. Am. Phys. Soc; Am. Asn. Physics Teachers. Teaching; theory of atomic spectra. Address: Dept. of Physics, Marietta College, Marietta, OH 45750.

DAVIS, WILLIAM J, b. Portsmouth, Va, Feb. 7, 42; m. 64; c. 4. NEURO-BIOLOGY, NEUROPHYSIOLOGY. B.A, Univ. Calif, Berkeley, 64; U.S. Pub. Health Serv. fel, Univ. Ore, 64-67, Ph.D.(biol). 67. U.S. Pub. Health Serv. fel. neurobiol, Univ. Ore, 67-68; ASST. PROF; BIOL, UNIV. CALIF, SANTA CRUZ, 69- U.S. Pub. Health Serv. fel. neurobiol, Stanford Univ, 68-70 & res. grant, 70-73. AAAS; Soc. Neurosci; Soc. Exp. Biol. & Med. Functional and structural aspects of the neuronal control of locomotion; neuronal changes during learning and development; neuronal substrates of complex behavioral phenomena, habituation and discrimination; neurosciences; behavioral sciences. Address: Division of Natural Sciences-1, University of California, Santa Cruz, CA 95060.

DAVIS, W(ILLIAM) JACKSON, b. Warrenton, Va, Sept. 29, 30; m. 59. AQUATIC BIOLOGY. B.S, Va. Polytech, 53; Forestry, Fish & Game fel. & Ph.D. (zool), Kansas, 59. Asst, Kans. Biol. Surv, 53-57; Kansas, 58-59; asst. prof. biol, St. Cloud State Col, 59; Western Michigan, 59-63; assoc. marine scientist, VA. INST. MARINE SCI, 63-68, SR. SCIENTIST & HEAD DEPT. ICHTHYOL, 68- Wildlife Soc; Am. Fisheries Soc; Am. Soc. Limnol. & Oceanog. Fisheries science and management; limnology. Address: Dept. of Ichthyology, Virginia Institute of Marine Science, Gloucester Point, VA 23062.

DAVIS, WILLIAM JAMES, b. Wilmington, Del, Sept. 8, 40; m. 63; c. 4. PHYSIOLOGY, ENDOCRINOLOGY. A.B, Univ. Del, 62; M.S, Northwest. Univ, 65, Nat. Insts. Health fel, 67, Ph.D.(biol), 68. Tech. asst. rocket propellants, Thiokol Chem. Corp, 63; asst. biol, Northwest. Univ, 63-67, instr, summer 67; ASST. PROF. ZOOL, UNIV. TENN, KNOXVILLE, 68- Nat. Insts. Health biomed. support grant, 69. Am. Soc. Zool; Am. Inst. Biol. Sci. General, cellular and comparative physiology; cellular and comparative endocrinology; the biology of pigment cell effectors. Address: Dept. of Zoology, University of Tennessee, Knoxville, TN 37916.

DAVIS, W(ILLIAM) K(ING), b. Uvalde, Tex, Aug. 6, 21; m. 42; c. 2. VERTEBRATE ECOLOGY. B.S, Southwest Texas State Teachers Col, 47, M.A, 48. Instr. biol, Southwest Texas State Col, 48-51, asst. prof, 51-61; lectr. zool, Texas, 61-62; ASSOC. PROF. BIOL, SOUTHWEST TEX. STATE UNIV, 63- U.S.N.R, 42-45. Soc. Syst. Zool; Am. Soc. Ichthyol. & Herpet; Ecol. Soc. Am. Zoogeography; evolution and ecology of Texas neotenic salamanders, bufonids and introduced Mediterranean geckos. Address: Dept. of Biology, Southwest Texas State University, San Marcos, TX 78666.

DAVIS, W(ILLIAM) L(ANDON), b. Chatham, Va, Oct. 2, 23; m. 50; c. 3. CHEMICAL ENGINEERING. B.Ch.E, Virginia, 50; M.S, Ill. Inst. Tech, 58. Prod. overseer, Dan River Mills, Inc, Va, 50-51; res. chem. engr. chem. & radiol. labs, Army Chem. Center, Md, 51-52; sr. proj. engr. appl. res. south works, U.S. STEEL CORP, 52-58, from sr. technologist to SECT. SUPVR. RES. CTR, 58- Chem.C, 44-45, 1st Lt. Am. Inst. Chem. Eng; Am. Chem. Soc; Am. Asn. Cost Eng; Asn. Iron & Steel Eng. New methods for producing iron and steel; improving present methods; conducting technical and economic evaluations. Address: Applied Research Lab, U.S. Steel Corp, Monroeville, PA 15146.

DAVIS, WILLIAM O(SBORNE), b. Buffalo, N.Y, Nov. 11, 19; m. 41; c. 4. NUCLEAR PHYSICS. B.A, N.Y. Univ, 39, Ph.D.(physics), 50. Asst. physics, N.Y. Univ, 47, mem. staff, Los Alamos Sci. Lab, 50-52; v.chief. sci. res, hqs, Air Res. & Develop. Command, U.S. Air Force, 52-53, chief, 53-55, deputy comdr, off. sci. res, 55-57, asst. to dir. labs, Wright Air Develop. Center, 57-58; v.pres. res, Turbo Dynamics Corp, 58-59; dir. res, Huyck Corp, 59-66; phys. sci. adminr, & chief, plans & requirements div, Environ. Sci. Serv. Admin, U.S. DEPT. COMMERCE, 66-69, CHIEF, telecommun. & space div, 69-71, RES. APPL. DIV, NAT. OCEANIC & ATMOSPHERIC ADMIN, 71- Comdr, Order of Merit, Res. & Invention, France. U.S.A.F, 40-45, 47-58, Res, 58-, Col. Am. Phys. Soc; Am. Inst. Aeronaut & Astronaut; Am. Astron. Soc. Cosmic ray neutrons; high impulse mechanics; research management. Address: National Oceanic & Atmospheric Administration, U.S. Dept. of Commerce, 6010 Executive Blvd, Rockville, MD 20852.

DAVIS, WILLIAM P(OTTER), JR, b. Cleveland, Ohio, Aug. 27, 24; m. 47; c. 5. PHYSICS. A.B, Oberlin Col, 48; M.S. Michigan, 49, Ph.D.(physics), 54; hon. M.A, Dartmouth Col, 67. Instr. PHYSICS, Michigan, 54-55; DARTMOUTH COL, 55-57, asst. prof, 57-62, assoc. prof, 62-66, PROF, 66-, BUDGET OFF, 70-, assoc. provost, 67-70, acting dean, Thayer Sch. Eng, 69-70. Summer staff, Lincoln Lab, Mass. Inst. Technol, 57-58; assoc. prog. dir, stud. & curriculum improv. sect, pre-col. educ. in sci. div, Nat. Sci. Found, 65-66. U.S.N, 43-46, Res, 46-56, Lt.(jg). Cosmic rays; gas discharges; plasma physics. Address: 106 Parkhurst Hall, Dartmouth College, Hanover, NH 03755.

DAVIS, WILLIAM PRICE, III, b. Nyack, N.Y, Oct. 2, 39; m. 63; c. 1. BIOLOGICAL OCEANOGRAPHY, ICHTHYOLOGY. B.S, Cornell, 61; M.S, Miami, 64, Ph.D.(marine biol), 67. Fisheries biologist, Systs. Lab, U.S. Fish & Wildlife Serv, U.S. Nat. Mus, 68; prog. dir. vert. div, Aquatic Sci, Inc, 68-71; DIR. MEDITERRANEAN MARINE SORTING CTR, SMITHSONIAN INST, 71- U.S.A.R, 61-66; U.S.A, 66-68, Capt. Am. Soc. Ichthyol. & Herpet; Ecol. Soc. Am; Am. Fisheries Soc; Am. Soc. Zool; Marine Biol. Asn. U.K. Aquatic ecology in terms of interrelationship of vertebrates to specific habitats; morphology, behavior, reproductive and nutritional physiology of marine fishes and their ecological roles in the coral reef biotype. Address: Office of Environmental Science, Smithsonian Institution, Washington, DC 20560.

DAVIS, WILLIAM R, b. Los Angeles, Calif, Nov. 30, 23; m. 45; c. 4. CONTROL SYSTEMS, ELECTRONICS. B.S, Calif. Inst. Tech, 44, M.S, 47; Ph.D. (elec. eng), Stanford, 66. Res. engr, Hughes Aircraft Co, 47-51, Santa Barbara Pacific Mercury Res. Center, 51-52, group supvr, Detroit Controls Res. Div, 52-56; sr. staff scientist, LOCKHEED MISSILES & SPACE CO,

56-66, PROG. MGR. PRECISION ATTITUDE SYSTS, 66- Development of systems for precise determination and control of space vehicle attitude; optical sensors; gyros; airborne computers, particularly development of space precision attitude reference and pointing system. Address: 180 N. Castanya Way, Menlo Park, CA 94025.

DAVIS, WILLIAM R(ANDALL), b. St. Louis, Mo, July 7, 24; m. 53; c. 2. PHYSICS. B.S, Stanford, 49; Ph.D.(physics), Washington (Seattle), 53. Assoc. physicist, APPL. PHYSICS LAB, UNIV. WASH, 53, physicist, 53-55, sr. physicist, 55-65, ASST. DIR, 65- U.S.A, 42-46. AAAS; Am. Phys. Soc. Marine technology. Address: Applied Physics Lab, University of Washington, 1013 N.E. 40th, Seattle, WA 98105.

DAVIS, WILLIAM ROBERT, b. Oklahoma City, Okla, Aug. 22, 29; m. 70. PHYSICS. B.S, Oklahoma, 53, M.S, 54; Göttingen, 54-55; Dr. rer. nat, Hanover Tech, 56. Physicist, Trisophia Enterprises, Okla, 56-57; asst. prof. PHYSICS, N.C. STATE UNIV, 57-62, assoc. prof, 62-66, PROF, 66- Consult, Trisophia Enterprises, 57-59; Regulus Corp, Okla, 58-59; Lab. for Electronics, Inc, Calif, 62-63; Res. Triangle Inst, N.C, 64-; Guggenheim fel. theoret. physics, 70-71. AAAS; fel. Am. Phys. Soc; Am. Asn. Physics Teachers. Theoretical mechanics; electrodynamics; field theory; symmetry properties; the general theory of relativity. Address: P.O. Box 5383, North Carolina State University, Station, Raleigh, NC 27607.

DAVIS, WILLIAM S, b. Los Angeles, Calif, Sept. 16, 30; m. 60; c. 2. PLANT TAXONOMY & CYTOGENETICS. A.B, Whittier Col, 51, M.S, 59; Ph.D.(bot), California, Los Angeles, 64. Asst. prof. BIOL, UNIV. LOUISVILLE, 63-71, PROF, 71- U.S.N.R, 52-56, Lt. AAAS; Soc. Study Evolution; Am. Soc. Plant Taxon; Int. Asn. Plant Taxon; Bot. Soc. Am. Experimental taxonomy and cytotaxonomy of plants. Address: 2503 Kings Highway, Louisville, KY 40205.

DAVIS, WILLIAM SPENCER, b. Harrisonburg, Va, Sept. 23, 25; m. 60; c. 2. FISHERIES BIOLOGY. B.S, Va. Polytech. Inst, 50, M.S, 53. Fishery res. biologist, U.S. Bur. Commercial Fisheries, N.C, 54-59, Wash, 60-67; fishery biologist, br. resource mgt, bur. commercial fisheries, Dept. Interior, 67-70; BIOL. SCI. ADMINSTR, ENVIRON. PROTECTION AGENCY, 70-U.S.A.F, 43-45. Am. Fisheries Soc; Am. Inst. Fishery Res. Biol; Am. Soc. Ichthyol. & Herpet; Ecol. Soc. Am. Effect of human use of estuarine, oceanic and great lakes environments on communities of aquatic organisms; develop and evaluate means of abating and preventing pollution there. Address: Environmental Protection Agency, Washington, DC 20242.

DAVIS, WILLIAM THOMPSON, b. Champaign, Ill, Nov. 3, 31; m. 52; c. 2. VETERINARY MEDICINE. B.S, Illinois, 56, D.V.M, 58; M.B.A, Chicago, 67. Private practice, Wyo, 58-62; resident vet, Newhall Land & Farm Co, 62-63; farm vet, Abbott Labs, 63-64, mgr. res. farm, 64-65, int. liaison, 65-66, prod. mgr. int. animal health mkt, 66-67; asst. dir. animal health res, CIBA Corp, 67-69; DIR. ANIMAL HEALTH CLIN. RES, E.R. SQUIBB & SONS, INC, 69- Mem, Nat. Mastitis Coun. U.S.N, 51-53. Am. Vet. Med. Asn; Indust. Vet. Asn; N.Y. Acad. Sci. Animal health research including pharmaceuticals and biologicals, especially final developmental stages, product promotion, liaison with marketing, research organization and management. Address: Squibb Agricultural Research Center, Three Bridges, NJ 08887.

DAVIS, W(ILLIAM) W(INLAND), b. Parkersburg, W.Va, Apr. 3, 08; m. 34; c. 4. PHYSICAL CHEMISTRY. A.B, Wabash Col, 33; Ph.D.(phys. chem), Hopkins, 37. Res. chemist, ELI LILLY & CO, 37-45, head dept. phys. chem, 45-52, dir. phys. chem. res. div, 52-63, RES. ADV, 63- With Off. Sci. Res. & Develop. Am. Chem. Soc. Physical and surface chemistry of pure carcinogenic and related substances; physico-chemical factors in physiological processes; industrial physical, chemical and biological chemical research; design of optical, mechanical and electrical instruments; commercial processes and formula development. Address: 4124 N. Pennsylvania St, Indianapolis, IN 46205.

DAVISON, ALAN, b. West Ealing, Gt. Brit, Mar. 24, 36; m. 57; c. 3. INORGANIC CHEMISTRY. B.Sc, Wales, 59; Ph.D.(inorg. chem), London & dipl, Imp. Col, 62. Instr. CHEM, Harvard, 62-64; asst. prof, MASS. INST. TECHNOL, 64-67, ASSOC. PROF, 67- Brit. Chem. Soc; assoc. Royal Inst. Chem. Transition metal chemistry, especially, reactions on coordinated ligands; organometallic and metal carbonyls; electron transfer reactions on planar chelates. Address: Dept. of Chemistry, Massachusetts Institute of Technology, Room 6-331, Cambridge, MA 02139.

DAVISON, BEAUMONT, b. Atlanta, Ga, May 30, 29; m. 52; c. 2. ELECTRICAL ENGINEERING. B.E, Vanderbilt Univ, 50; M.E.E, Syracuse Univ, 52, Ph.D.(elec. eng), 56. Instr. & res. assoc, Syracuse Univ, 51-56; asst. prof. elec. eng, Case Inst. Technol, 56-59; exec. v.pres, Indust. Electronic Rubber Co, 59-67; chmn. dept. elec. eng, OHIO UNIV, 67-69, dean col. eng. & technol, 69-71, V.PRES. REGIONAL HIGHER EDUC, 71- Microwave devices; electronic circuit component development; rubber technology. Address: Cutler Hall, Ohio University, 134 S. Lamar Dr, Athens, OH 45701.

DAVISON, CLARKE, b. Washington, D.C, Nov. 8, 27; m. 53, 64; c. 2. PHARMACOLOGY. B.Sc, George Washington, 48, M.S, 49; Atomic Energy Cmn. fel, Harvard, 49-52, univ. fel, 52-53, Ph.D.(biochem), 54. Asst. pharmacol, George Washington, 47-49, asst. prof, 53-58, assoc. prof, 58-64, prof, 64-68; SECT. HEAD METAB. CHEM, STERLING WINTHROP RES. INST, 68-Consult, Vick Chem. Co. Am. Soc. Pharmacol. & Exp. Therapeut; Soc. Exp. Biol. & Med. Metabolism of sulfur compounds; drug metabolism. Address: Sterling Winthrop Research Institute, Rensselaer, NY 12144.

DAVISON, E(DWARD) J(OSEPH), b. Toronto, Ont, Can, Sept. 12, 38; m. 66; c. 2. ELECTRICAL ENGINEERING. B.A.Sc, Univ. Toronto, 60, M.A, 61, Athlone fel, 61-63, Ph.D.(control eng). 64. Asst. prof. ELEC. ENG, Univ. Toronto, 64-66; Univ. Calif, Berkeley, 66-68; ASSOC. PROF, UNIV. TORONTO, 68- Inst. Elec. & Electronics Eng. General area of high-order control systems, stability theory, computational methods, and biological modelling; large system optimization. Address: Dept. of Electrical Engineering, University of Toronto, Toronto, Ont, Can.

DAVISON, FREDERICK CORBET, b. Atlanta, Ga, Sept. 3, 29; m. 52; c. 2. VETERINARY PATHOLOGY & PHYSIOLOGY. Emory-at-Oxford, 46-48; Emory, 48; D.V.M, Georgia, 52; Ph.D.(path, biochem, physiol), Iowa State, 63. Private practice vet. med, Ga, 52-58; res. assoc, Iowa State, 58-59, asst. prof. physiol, 59-63; asst. dir, dept. sci. activities, Am. Vet. Med. Asn, 63-64; dean, sch. vet. med, Univ. Ga, 64-66; v.chancellor, Univ. Syst. Ga, 66-67; PRES, UNIV. GA, 67- Assoc, inst. atomic res, Iowa State, 58-63; proj. leader, U.S. Atomic Energy Cmn, 59-63. Mem. prof. ed. cmn, Inst. Lab. Animal Resources, Nat. Acad. Sci-Nat. Res. Coun, 63-; coun. biol. & therapeut. agents, Am. Vet. Med. Asn, 64- U.S.A.F.R, 59-63, Maj. Am. Soc. Vet. Physiol. & Pharmacol. Comparative toxicity of the lanthanide series of rare earths. Address: University of Georgia, Athens, GA 30601.

DAVISON, F(REDERICK) E(DWIN), b. Indianapolis, Ind, Jan. 9, 18; m. 42; c. 3. MECHANICAL ENGINEERING. B.S.M.E, Purdue, 40. Proj. engr, aircraft, Firestone Tire & Rubber Co, 40-42; airframe components, bur. aeronaut, U.S. NAVY DEPT, 46-49, head, mech. standards develop. sect, 49-52, mech. systems design sect, 52-54, actuating & flight controls sect, 54-56, asst. head, mech. equipment design br, 56-57, head, 57-63, tech. asst, airborne equip. div, bur. naval weapons, 63-66, EQUIP. & SUPPORT ADMINSTR, RES. & TECH. GROUP, NAVAL AIR SYSTS. COMMAND, 66- U.S.N.R, 42-46, Lt. Aircraft electrical, mechanical and fluid systems; flight controls; landing gear; inflight refueling; fire protection; environment control; emergency escape and life support systems; aerospace crew equipment. Address: 6636 Beacon Lane, Falls Church, VA 22043.

DAVISON, JOHN (AMERPOHL), b. Jamesville, Wis, June 24, 28; m. 50, 65; c. 2. GENERAL PHYSIOLOGY. B.S, Wisconsin, 50; Nat. Sci. Found. fel, Minnesota, 52-54, Ph.D, 55. Instr. ZOOL, Washington, 54-57; asst. prof, Fla. State, 57-60; La. State, 60-64; Rensselaer Polytech, 64-65, ASSOC. PROF, 65-67; UNIV. VT, 67- Am. Soc. Zool; Soc. Gen. Physiol. Body size and metabolism; cell form; developmental physiology of amphibia. Address: Dept. of Zoology, University of Vermont, Burlington, VT 05401.

DAVISON, JOHN A(LDEN), b. Olinda, Brazil, May 25, 17; U.S. citizen; m. 43; c. 2. PHYSICAL CHEMISTRY. B.S, Brown, 38; M.S, Pennsylvania, 39, Harrison fel, 39-41, du Pont fel, 41-42, Ph.D.(phys. chem), 42. Chemist, Sun Oil Co, 39-41; gen. labs, res. ctr, U.S. Rubber Co, 42-54, MGR. CHEM. ENG. RES, UNIROYAL, INC, 54-, RES. ASSOC, RES. CTR, 71-, chem. div, 65-71. Lectr, Univ. Conn, 65- Am. Inst. Chem. Eng; Am. Chem. Soc. Pilot plant development of plastics; synthetic rubber; organic chemicals; process development on synthetic rubber and plastics; development of instrumentation. Address: Apt. 4B, Swiss Village, Woodbury, CT 06798.

DAVISON, JOHN P(HILIP), b. Woodsville, N.H, Apr. 21, 17; m. 46; c. 5. BIOCHEMISTRY. S.B, Mass. Inst. Tech, 42; M.S, New Hampshire, 47; Ph.D, Michigan, 53. Asst. chem, New Hampshire, 46-47; teaching fel. biochem, Michigan, 47-51; asst. prof, North Dakota, 51-54; physiol. sci, Dartmouth Med. Sch, 54-58, CLIN. PATH, MED. SCH, UNIV. VA, 58-61, ASSOC. PROF, 61- U.S.A.A.F, 42-46. AAAS; Am. Chem. Soc; N.Y. Acad. Sci; Am. Asn. Clin. Chem. Clinical biochemistry; methods in clinical chemistry; bilirubin methodology and metabolism. Address: Dept. of Clinical Pathology, University of Virginia Medical School, Charlottesville, VA 22903.

DAVISON, J(OSEPH) W(ADE), b. Kansas City, Kans, Nov. 14, 21; m. 51; c. 2. CHEMICAL ENGINEERING. B.S, Kansas, 43. Jr. engr, process design br, RES. & DEVELOP, PHILLIPS PETROL. CO, 43-48, process engr, 48-52, sect. chief, 52-57, mgr, 57-64, DIR. optimization & eval, develop. div, 64-68, process develop, 66-69, RUBBER, CARBON BLACK & POLYOLEFINS RES. & DEVELOP, 69- U.S.N.R, 44-46. Am. Inst. Chem. Eng. Process development, design and optimization. Address: Phillips Petroleum Co, 160 Research Bldg. 1, Bartlesville, OK 74004.

DAVISON, KENNETH LEWIS, b. Hopkins, Mo, Dec. 27, 35; m. 57; c. 3. NUTRITION, PHYSIOLOGY. B.S, Missouri, 57; M.S, Iowa State, 59, Ph.D. (nutrit), 61. Res. assoc. nutrit, Cornell, 61-65; RES. PHYSIOLOGIST, METAB. & RADIATION RES. LAB, AGR. RES. SERV, U. S. DEPT. AGR, 65- Adj. asst. prof, N.Dak. State, 68- Am. Soc. Animal Sci; Am. Dairy Sci. Asn; Am. Inst. Nutrit. Accumulation of nitrate in plants and toxicity to animals; pesticide metabolism by animals. Address: Metabolism & Radiation Research Lab, Agricultural Research Service, U.S. Dept. of Agriculture, State University Station, Fargo, ND 58102.

DAVISON, LEE W(ALKER), b. Moscow, Idaho, Aug. 10, 37. APPLIED MECHANICS. B.S, Idaho, 59; M.S, N.Y. Univ, 61; Nat. Sci. Found. fel. & Ph.D.(appl. mech), Calif. Inst. Tech, 65. Mem. tech. staff, Bell Tel. Labs, 59-62; res. fel, Hopkins, 65-66; staff mem, SANDIA LABS, 66-68, SUPVR. SHOCK WAVE PHYSICS, RES. DIV, 68- Am. Soc. Mech. Eng; Am. Phys. Soc. Modern continuum mechanics, including nonlinear elastodynamics and liquid crystal theory; propagation of strong shock waves in solids. Address: 7900 Harwood Ave. N.E, Albquerque, NM 87110.

DAVISON, PERRY W(OODRUFF), b. Texas City, Tex, Sept. 17, 19, m. 43; c. 2. NUCLEAR PHYSICS. B.S, Amherst Col, 42; M.A, Rice, 43; Ph.D. (physics), Yale, 48. Radio engr, Naval Res. Lab, 43-44; res. physicist nuclear detector develop, RCA Labs, 48-53; sci. liaison, sci. & tech. unit, U.S. Navy, Ger, 53-56; supvr. nuclear reactor develop, atomic power dept, reactor eval. ctr, Westinghouse Elec. Corp, 56, mgr, 56-62; temporary adv. scientist nuclear reactor testing, Los Alamos Sci. Lab, 62-63; mgr. nuclear eng. for rocket vehicle appln. reactor test opers, Westinghouse Astronuclear Lab, 63-64, assoc. mgr, 64-65, dep. mgr. test systs. & opers, 65-69, mgr. technol. prog, 69-70, ADV. ENGR, WESTINGHOUSE ADVAN. REACTOR DIV, 70- Mem. fusion reactor study group, Princeton Plasma Physics Lab, 71- U.S.N.R, 44-45, Lt.(jg). AAAS; Am. Phys. Soc; Am. Nuclear Soc. Experimental nuclear and nuclear reactor physics; nuclear reactor testing and operations. Address: P.O. Box 519, Grindstone, PA 15442.

DAVISON, PETER F(ITZGERALD), b. London, Eng, Nov. 12, 27; m. 54; c. 2. PHYSICAL CHEMISTRY. B.Sc, London, 49; Ph.D.(chem), Inst. Cancer Res, London, 54. Chemist, Chester Beatty Res. Inst, Inst. Cancer Res, Eng, 51-56; Indust. Cellulose Res. Ltd, Can, 56-57; dept. biol, Mass. Inst. Tech, 57-69; DIR. DEPT. FINE STRUCTURE RES, BOSTON BIOMED. RES. INST, 69- Am. Chem. Soc; Am. Soc. Biol. Chem; Geront. Soc. R.A.F, 49-51, Res, 51- Physical chemistry of nucleoproteins; nucleic acids; proteins and synthetic polymers. Address: Dept. of Fine Structure Research, Boston Biomedical Research Institute, 20 Staniford St, Boston, MA 02114.

DAVISON, RAYMOND BERNARD, b. Rochester, N.Y, Oct. 3, 38; m. 60; c. 3. ORGANIC CHEMISTRY, PLASTICS. B.S, St. John Fisher Col, 61; Nat. Sci. Found. summer fel, Pittsburgh, 62, Nat. Insts. Health fel, 63-66, Ph.D.(organophosphorus chem), 66. Res. chemist, indust. chem. div, Allied Chem. Corp, N.Y, 66-67; sr. res. assoc, Schlegel Mfg. Corp, 68-70; RES. SCIENTIST, AM. STANDARD, INC, NEW BRUNSWICK, 70- Am. Chem. Soc. Organophosphorus chemistry; organic isocyanates and related compounds; thermoset polymer applications, particularly coatings and foams including those based on unsaturated polyester resins and epoxy resins; polymer identification and analysis. Address: 20 Gunpowder Dr, East Brunswick, NJ 08816.

DAVISON, RICHARD READ, b. Marlin, Tex, Apr. 3, 26; m. 51; c. 3. CHEMICAL ENGINEERING. B.S, Tex. Tech. Col, 49, M.S, Texas A&M, 58, Ph.D. (chem. eng), 62. Engr. gas indust, Lion Oil Co, 49-55; res. scientist, TEX. A&M UNIV, 55-61, instr. CHEM. ENG, 58-61, asst. prof, 61-65, assoc. prof, 65-68, PROF, 68- U.S.A, 44-46. Am. Chem. Soc; Am. Inst. Chem. Eng; Nat. Soc. Prof. Eng. Solvent extraction process for conversion of saline water and sewage effluent; extraction and desalination, including thermodynamics of solutions and solar energy utilization. Address: Dept. of Chemical Engineering, Texas A&M University, College Station, TX 77843.

DAVISON, ROBERT W(ILDER), b. Albany, N.Y, Dec. 30, 20; m. 49; c. 2. PHYSICAL CHEMISTRY. B.S, Union (N.Y), 42; fel, Mass. Inst. Tech, 47-48, Coffin fel, 48-50, Ph.D.(phys. chem), 50. Res. chemist, RES. CENTER, Hercules Powder Co, 50-66, HERCULES, INC, 66-67, SR. RES. CHEMIST, 67- U.S.N.R, 43-46, Lt.(jg). Am. Chem. Soc. Surface chemistry; colloidal systems; chemical additives for paper; physical properties of paper. Address: Hercules, Inc, Research Center, Wilmington, DE 19899.

DAVISON, SOL, b. Los Angeles, Calif, April 3, 22; m. 45; c. 2. PHYSICAL CHEMISTRY. B.A, Pomona Col, 47; Sinclair Oil Co. fel, Notre Dame, 47-51, Ph.D.(chem), 51. Atomic Energy Cmn. fel, Notre Dame, 51-52; res. assoc. radiobiol. & phys. chem. studies on foods, Mass. Inst. Tech, 52-56; CHEMIST, SHELL DEVELOP. CO, 56- U.S.A.F, 43-46. Am. Chem. Soc. Reaction kinetics and photochemistry; radiation chemistry and radiobiology; testing of polymers; physics and technology of elastomers. Address: Shell Development Co, 1400 53rd St, Emeryville, CA 94608.

DAVISON, SYDNEY GEORGE, b. Stockport, Eng, Sept. 6, 34; m. 59; c. 2. SURFACE PHYSICS. B.Sc, Manchester, 58, M.Sc, 62, Ph.D.(math), 64. Teacher, Salford Grammer Sch, 58-59; nuclear physicist, nuclear power div, G.E.C/Simon-Carvers, Eng, 59-60; demonstr. math, Manchester, 61-64; fel. physics, Waterloo, 64-65, asst. prof, 65-68, assoc. prof, 68-70, dir. quantum theory group, 68-70; PROF. PHYSICS, CLARKSON COL, 70- Am. Phys. Soc; fel. Brit. Inst. Physics & Phys. Soc; fel. N.Y. Acad. Sci; Can. Asn. Physicists. Solid state theory; quantum surface physics. Address: Dept. of Physics, Clarkson College, Potsdam, NY 13676.

DAVISON, T(HOMAS) M(ATTHEW) K(ERR), b. Scotland, Jan. 18, 39; Can. citizen; m. 64. MATHEMATICS. B.Sc, Sir George Williams, 60; M.A, Toronto, 62, Ph.D.(math), 65. Asst. prof. MATH, Waterloo, 64-66; NAT. RES. COUN. CAN. RES. FEL, Kings's Col, London, 66-68; asst. prof, McMASTER UNIV, 68-71, ASSOC. PROF, 71- Ed, Ont. Math. Gazette, 70- Am. Math. Soc; Can. Math. Cong. Algebra and number theory. Address: Dept. of Mathematics, McMaster University, Hamilton, Ont, Can.

DAVISON, TOLLIE B, b. Carthage, Tex, Nov. 6, 32. NUCLEAR PHYSICS. B.S, Texas, 55, M.A, 57; Ph.D.(physics), Washington (St. Louis), 68. Instr. PHYSICS, E.Tex. State, 59-61; asst. prof, STEPHEN F. AUSTIN STATE UNIV, 63-68, ASSOC. PROF, 68- Am. Asn. Physics Teachers. Theoretical nuclear physics; many body problems, especially liquid helium. Address: Box 3044, Stephen F. Austin Station, Dept. of Physics, Stephen F. Austin State University, Nacogdoches, TX 75961.

DAVISON, VERNE E(LBERT), b. Ashland, Kans, Jan. 10, 04; m. 23; c. 2. FISH & WILDLIFE BIOLOGY. Mgr. game refuge, State Game Dept, Okla, 21-35; soil, water, fisheries & wildlife biologist, southeast. states, Soil Conserv. Serv, U.S. Dept. Agr, 35-64, west. states, 64-69; RETIRED. Aquatic biologist, U.S. Dept. State, 52. Nash conserv. award, 53; Soil Conserv. Serv. award, 58; U.S. Dept. Agr. award, 59. Wildlife Soc; Soil Conserv. Soc. Am; Am. Ornith. Union; Nat. Audubon Soc. Wildlife developments with soil conservation districts for agricultural lands; life habits of lesser prairie chicken and bobwhite quail; classification of choice and fair foods that attract each individual species of all North American birds and game mammals; farm fishponds and fish farming; waterweed control and silt protection; soil and water conservation. Address: 245 Marla Ave, Jackson, MS 39204.

DAVISON, WALTER F(RANCIS), b. Chicago, Ill, Apr. 28, 26; div; c. 1. MATHEMATICS, PHYSICS. B.S, Calif. Inst. Technol, 51; Nat. Sci. Found. fel, Univ. Chicago, 52-53; du Pont fel, Univ. Va, 53-54, Ph.D.(math), 56. Instr. math, Univ. Mich, Ann Arbor, 56-60; sr. staff scientist, Collins Radio Co, Tex, 60-61; mem. tech. staff electronics, Space Gen. Corp, Calif, 61-62; branch head electrooptics, Tex. Instruments, 62; sr. scientist, Int. Tel. & Tel. Fed. Labs, Calif, 63-66; ASSOC. PROF. MATH, SAN FERNANDO VALLEY STATE COL, 66- Rackham faculty fel, Univ. Mich, Ann Arbor, 58; Nat. Sci. Found. Faculty fel, San Fernando Valley State Col, summer 68. U.S.N, 44-46. Am. Math. Soc. Closure operators; mosaic spaces; frechet equivalence; optical receivers; electrooptical demodulation; noise theory. Address: Dept. of Mathematics, San Fernando Valley State College, 18111 Nordhoff St, Northridge, CA 91324.

DAVISSON, CHARLOTTE M(EAKER), b. Phillipston, Mass, Oct. 7, 14; m. 47; c. 1. NUCLEAR PHYSICS. B.A, Wellesley Col, 36; M.A, Smith Col, 39; Ph.D.(nuclear physics), Mass. Inst. Tech, 48. Physicist, Eclipse-Pioneer

Div, Bendix Aviation Corp, 42-44; res. asst, Manhattan Proj, Columbia, 44-46; RES. PHYSICIST, radiation div, U.S. NAVAL RES. LAB, D.C, 54-67, nuclear physics div, 67-70, NUCLEAR SCI. DIV, 70- Fel. AAAS; Am. Phys. Soc; Am. Nuclear Soc. Interaction of gamma rays with matter; survey articles and Monte Carlo studies of sodium iodide detectors and gamma-ray albedos. Address: 4654 Cedar Ridge Dr, Oxon Hill, MD 20021.

DAVISSON, EDWIN O(RLANDO), b. Ind, Jan. 23, 23; m. 45; c. 3. PHYSICAL CHEMISTRY. A.B, Wabash Col, 48; Ph.D.(phys. chem), Illinois, 53. Asst, Illinois, 49-52; RES. CHEMIST PROTEINS, ELI LILLY & CO, INDIANAPOLIS, 52- U.S.A, 43-46. Am. Chem. Soc. Physical chemical properties of proteins and macromolecules; enzyme kinetics; mechanism of drug action. Address: 645 Williamsburg Ct, Greenwood, IN 46142.

DAVISSON, JAMES W(ILLANS), b. Pittsburgh, Pa, Oct. 23, 14; m. 47; c. 1. PHYSICS. A.B, Princeton, 38; Ph.D.(physics), Mass. Inst. Tech, 43. Asst, lab. insulation res, Mass. Inst. Tech, 39-43, res. assoc, 46-47; PHYSICIST, NAVAL RES. LAB, 47- U.S.A, 43-46. Fel. Am. Phys. Soc; Am. Crystallog. Asn. Orientation phenomena in crystals as shown by electrical breakdown and mechanical deformation. Address: Naval Research Lab, Code 6430, Washington, DC 20390.

DAVISSON, LEE DAVID, b. Evanston, Ill, June 16, 36; m. 57; c. 3. ELECTRICAL ENGINEERING. B.S.E, Princeton, 58; Ford Found. fel. & M.S.E, California, Los Angeles, 61, Ph.D.(eng), 64. Res. engr, Philco Corp, 60-62; mem. tech. staff ELEC. ENG, Hughes Aircraft Corp, 62-64; asst. prof, Princeton, 64-67, ASSOC. PROF, 67-70; UNIV. SOUTH. CALIF, 69- Consult, NASA, 65-70; Bell Tel. Labs, 68-69; sr. staff engr, Hughes Aircraft Co, 69- Princeton Eng. Soc. award, 65; outstanding young electrical engineering award, Eta Kappa Nu, 68. U.S.A, 58-60, 1st Lt. Inst. Elec. & Electronics Eng. Communication theory. Address: Dept. of Electrical Engineering, University of Southern California, Los Angeles, CA 90007.

DAVISSON, M. T, b. Grafton, W.Va, Dec. 23, 31; m. 55; c. 4. CIVIL ENGINEERING. B.C.E, Akron, 54; M.S, Illinois, 55, Ph.D.(civil eng), 60. Designer struct. eng, Clark, Dietz, Painter & Assocs, 55-56; instr. CIVIL ENG, UNIV. ILL, URBANA, 59-60, asst. prof, 60-63, assoc. prof, 63-71, PROF, 71- Indust. consult, 60- Summers, engr. munic. eng, E.J. McDonald, consult. engr, 54. Alfred A. Raymond Award, 59. Am. Soc. Civil Eng. (Collingwood Prize, 64); Am. Concrete Inst; Am. Rwy. Eng. Asn; Am. Soc. Test. & Mat; Nat. Soc. Prof. Eng. Deep foundations; soil dynamics; settlement of structures; waterfront structures; vibratory pile driving; protective construction. Address: 2217 Civil Engineering Bldg, University of Illinois, Urbana, IL 61801.

DAVITT, HARRY JAMES, JR, b. Philadelphia, Pa, Oct. 10, 39; m. 64; c. 2. CHEMICAL ENGINEERING. B.S, Pa. State, 61; Delaware, 62-64; M.S, Purdue, 66, Dow fel, 66-69, Procter & Gamble fel. & Ph.D.(chem. eng), 69. RES. ENGR, SUN OIL CO, 68- U.S.A.F, 61-64, 1st Lt. Fuel cells; extraction of bitumen from tar sands. Address: Sun Oil Co, Research & Engineering Division, P.O. Box 426, Marcus Hook, PA 19061.

DAVITT, RICHARD MICHAEL, b. Wilmington, Del, Mar. 13, 39; m. 66; c. 2. MATHEMATICS. B.S, Niagara, 63; M.S, Lehigh, 66, NASA fel, 65-67, Ph.D.(math), 69. Instr, St. Francis de Sales High Sch, Toledo, Ohio, 58-60; asst. MATH, Lehigh Univ, 64-65; instr, Lafayette Col, 67-69, ASST. PROF, 69-70; UNIV. LOUISVILLE, 70- Am. Math. Soc. Lattice-ordered groups; finite p-groups. Address: Dept. of Mathematics, University of Louisville, Louisville, KY 40208.

DAVY, LEE G(EORGE), b. Boulder, Colo, Nov. 16, 08; m. 31; c. 3. ORGANIC CHEMISTRY. A.B, Cornell, 31, Ph.D.(org. chem), 34. From res. chemist to asst. supt. hydroquinone div, TENN. EASTMAN CORP, 34-42, chem. control supt, Holston Ord. Works, 42-45, proj. leader, 45-46, asst. supt. hydroquinone div, 46-50, org. chem. div, 50-58, div. supt, 58-59, gen. supt. acid & org. chem. div, 59-60, dir. new prod. develop, 60-63, EXEC. V.PRES. DEVELOP, 63- With Off. Sci. Res. & Develop; U.S.A, 44. AAAS; fel. Am. Inst. Chem. Eng; fel. Am. Chem. Soc. Dipole association of nitro compounds; stereochemistry of trivalent nitrogen; abnormal reactions of benzyl magnesium chloride; synthetic chemicals; special explosives. Address: Tennessee Eastman Co, Kingsport, TN 37662.

DAVY, LEITA, b. Eldred, Pa. NUTRITION, MEDICAL SCIENCE. B.S, Wisconsin, 24, Ph.D.(med, nutrit), 33; M.S, Iowa, 25. Adj. prof. clin. path, sch. med, Texas, 25-28; asst. biochem, med. sch, Wisconsin, 28-30, res. assoc. radiol. med, 30-36; assoc. prof. anat, sch. med, Western Reserve, 36-37; field nutritionist, Ohio State Dept. Health, 37-40; prof. NUTRIT. & dept. head, Louisville, 40-44; prof. & dean, N.Dak. Agr. Col, 44-51; ASSOC. CLIN. PROF, WEST. RESERVE UNIV, 58-; MED. RES. NUTRITIONIST, HIGHLAND VIEW HOSP, 53- AAAS. Nutrition in chronic disease. Address: Marsol Towers, Suite 605, 6501 Marsol Rd, Mayfield Heights, OH 44124.

DAW, HAROLD A(LBERT), b. Granger, Utah, Oct. 25, 25; m. 53; c. 6. PHYSICS. B.S, Utah, 48, M.A, 52, Ph.D, 56. Chief lab. asst, elementary physics lab, Utah, 47-48, 50-52; res. physicist from Utah dept. astrophysics & phys. meteorol, Hopkins, 53-54; asst. prof. PHYSICS, NEW MEX. STATE UNIV, 54-58, assoc. prof, 59-61, PROF, 61-, ASSOC. DEAN ARTS & SCI, 71-, assoc. physicist, phys. sci. lab, 54-61, head dept. physics, 61-70, acting dean arts & sci, 70-71. Artil.C, U.S.A, 44-46. AAAS; Am. Phys. Soc; Optical Soc. Am; Am. Asn. Physics Teachers; Am. Inst. Physics. Optics; maser optics; instructional equipment; atmospheric physics. Address: Dept. of Physics, New Mexico State University, Las Cruces, NM 88001.

DAW, JOHN CHARLES, b. Tulsa, Okla, July 18, 31; c. 7. PHYSIOLOGY. B.A, Case West. Reserve Univ, 59, U.S. Pub. Health Serv. fel, 63-66, Ph.D. (physiol), 66. Res. assoc. physiol, Univ. Va, 66-67, U.S. Pub. Health Serv. fel, 67-68, instr, 68; asst. prof. lab. educ, Mt. Sinai Sch. Med, 68-69, assoc. dir. lab, 68-71, asst. prof. med. educ. & res. asst. prof. physiol, 69-71; ASST. PROF. PHYSIOL. & ASSOC. DIR. MED. SCI. TEACHING LABS, SCH. MED, UNIV. N.C, CHAPEL HILL, 71- U.S.A. 52-54. AAAS; Am. Chem. Soc; Am. Physiol. Soc. Glycogen metabolism; carbohydrate metabolism; cardiac metabolism; experimental shock; experimental burn; surgical research. Address: Medical Sciences Teaching Labs, School of Medicine, University of North Carolina, Chapel Hill, NC 27514.

DAW, NIGEL WARWICK, b. London, Eng, Dec. 12, 33; U.S. citizen; m. 63; c. 2. NEUROPHYSIOLOGY, PSYCHOPHYSICS. B.A, Cambridge, 56, M.A, 61; Nat. Insts. Health fel, Johns Hopkins Univ, 65-67, Ph.D.(biophys), 67. Assoc. scientist, Polaroid Corp, 58-63; fel. neurobiol, Harvard Med. Sch, 67-69; ASST. PROF. PHYSIOL. & OPHTHAL, MED. SCH, WASH UNIV, 69- Nat. Insts. Health fel, Harvard Med. Sch, 69-70, spec. fel, 70-71; consult. visual sci. study sect, div. res. grants, Nat. Insts. Health, 72- Brit. Army, 51-53, Res, 53-56. AAAS; Am. Physiol. Soc; Asn. Res. Vision & Ophthal. Neurophysiology and psychophysics of color vision; vision in goldfish, cat and monkey; effect of high intensities of light on vision; saturation of the visual system; development of vision. Address: Dept. of Physiology, Washington University Medical School, St. Louis, MO 63110.

DAWBER, THOMAS ROYLE, b. Duncan, B.C, Can, Jan. 18, 13; nat; m. 37; c. 2. INTERNAL MEDICINE, CARDIOLOGY. A.B, Haverford Col, 33; M.D, Harvard, 37, M.P.H, 58. Intern, U.S. Marine Hosps, Va, 37-38, med. res, 38-40, chief med, Mass, 41-42, asst, N.Y, 42, chief, Mass, 44-49, mem. staff diabetes res, Boston City Hosp, 49-50; chief heart disease epidemiol. study, U.S. Dept. Health, Educ. & Welfare, 50-66; ASSOC. PROF. MED, SCH. MED, BOSTON UNIV, 66-, prog. planning off, med. ctr, 66-68. Fel. coun. clin. cardiol, Am. Heart Asn, chmn, coun. epidemiol. U.S.C.G, 40, 42-44. Am. Col. Chest Physicians; Am. Col. Physicians; Am. Heart Asn. Epidemiology of coronary heart disease and hypertension; public health. Address: Dept. of Medicine, Boston University Medical Center, Boston, MA 02215.

DAWE, ALBERT R(OLKE), b. Milwaukee, Wis, June 1, 16; m. 42; c. 3. BIOLOGY. B.A, Yale, 38; M.A, Harvard, 51; Ph.D.(zool, physiol), Wisconsin, 53. Instr. zool, exten, div, Wisconsin, 46-50, asst. prof. physiol, med, sch, 53-56; biologist, OFF. OF NAVAL RES, CHICAGO, 56-58, CHIEF SCIENTIST, 58-, DEP. DIR, 67- Adj. prof, Stritch Sch. Med, Loyola (Ill), Chief biol. consult, World Book Encyclopedia. Mem, Comt. Hibernation Info. Exchange. U.S.N. 42-46, Lt. Am. Soc. Zool; Am. Physiol. Soc. Physiology of hibernation and torpor in mammals; information retrieval; research planning administration. Address: Office of Naval Research Branch Office, 536 S. Clark St, Chicago, IL 60605.

DAWE, CLYDE J(OHNSON), b. Easton, Pa, Jan. 20, 21; m. 47; c. 4. PATHOLOGY. A.B, Lafayette Col, 42; M.D, Hopkins, 45; Mayo Found. fel, Minnesota, 48-51, Ph.D, 56. Mem. staff, surg. path, Mayo Clinic, 51-54; MED. OFFICER LAB. PATH, NAT. CANCER INST, 55- Assoc. ed, J. Nat. Cancer Inst, 57-59. Dipl, Am. Bd. Path, 55. Med.C, U.S.N.R, 45-47, Lt. (jg). AAAS; Am. Asn. Cancer Res; Am. Soc. Exp. Path; Am. Asn. Path. & Bact; Int. Acad. Path; Tissue Cult. Asn.(ed, In Vitro, 65-68). Cancer; experimental carcinogenesis; neoplastic transformation in cell and organ culture; murine leukemias in cell culture; viral carcinogenesis; phylogeny and ontogeny as related to neoplasia. Address: National Cancer Institute, National Institutes of Health, Bethesda, MD 20014.

DAWE, HAROLD J(OSEPH), b. Deckerville, Mich, June 15, 12; m. 33; c. 4. CHEMISTRY. B.S, Cent. Mich. Col, Ed, 32; M.S, Michigan, 34, Ph.D.(chem), 40. Prod. develop engr, Acheson Colloids Co, 40-50, tech. dir, 50-56, res. dir, ACHESON INDUSTS. INC, 56-64, V.PRES. RES, 64- AAAS; Am. Chem. Soc; fel. Am. Inst. Chem; Am. Soc. Lubrication Eng; fel. Chem. Inst. Can. Colloid chemistry of dispersed solids; relation between the stability of suspensions and their interfacial free surface energies. Address: 5200 Lakeshore Rd, Port Huron, MI 48060.

DAWES, CLINTON JOHN, b. Minneapolis, Minn, Sept. 23, 35; m. 62; c. 3. CYTOLOGY, PHYCOLOGY. B.S, Minnesota, Minneapolis, 57; M.A, California, Los Angeles, 58, Nat. Sci. Found. fel, 59-61, Ph.D.(sci), 61. Teaching asst, bot. labs, California, Los Angeles, 57-59; Nat. Sci. Found. fel, 63-64; asst. prof. bot, UNIV. S.FLA, 64-70, ASSOC. PROF. BIOL, 70- Nat. Sci. Found. grants, 65-66, 69-71 & 70-72; Sea grant, 71-73. Summer asst. instr, Washington (Seattle), 59. U.S.A, 59-63, Capt. Bot. Soc. Am; Phycol. Soc. Am; Int. Phycol. Soc. Algal ultrastructure, especially in cell development and morphogenesis; cell wall fine structure and algal taxonomy; coenocytic ultrastructure of Caulerpa and ecological studies of local marine algae; ultrastructure techniques. Address: Dept. of Biology, University of South Florida, Tampa, FL 33620.

DAWES, DAVID HADDON, b. Cornwall, Ont, Aug. 14, 38; m. 62; c. 4. PHYSICAL CHEMISTRY, POLYMER SCIENCE. B.Sc, McGill, 59, Ph.D.(phys. chem), 62. Nat. Res. Coun. Can. fel. chem, 62-64; res. chemist, E.I. du Pont de Nemours & Co, 65-67, SR. RES. CHEMIST, DU PONT OF CAN, 67- Am. Chem. Soc; Chem. Inst. Can. Radiolysis of gases; product and process research and development. Address: P.O. Box 5000, Kingston, Ont, Can.

DAWES, J(AMES) W(ILKINSON), b. New Orleans, La, Aug. 21, 29; m. 64. INORGANIC & POLYMER CHEMISTRY. B.S, La. State, 51, M.S, 53; Ohio State, 54-56; Ph.D.(inorg. chem), Texas, 58. Chemist Polymer Chem, Exp. Sta, E.I. DU PONT DE NEMOURS & CO, Del, 58-63, SABINE RIVER WORKS, 63-67, STAFF SCIENTIST, FILM DEPT, 67- U.S.A.F, 53-55, 1st Lt. Am. Chem. Soc; Sci. Res. Soc. Am. Biologically active metal complexes; transition metal complexes of unusual oxidation states; photographic chemistry; ion-exchange systems; polymer intermediate synthesis; boron cage compounds; friction and mechanical wear of high temperature plastics; plastics extrusion technology. Address: Gunn Dr, Orange, TX 77630.

DAWES, JOHN LESLIE, b. Olney, Eng, Dec. 31, 42; m. 69. ORGANOMETALLIC & ORGANIC CHEMISTRY. B.S, Univ. Leicester, 64; Brit. Sci. Res. Coun. grant & Ph.D.(chem), 67. Nat. Sci. Found. Center of Excellence vis. asst. prof, La. State Univ, 67-69; CHEMIST, TEX. EASTMAN CO, 69- Am. Chem. Soc; Catalysis Soc. Inorganic chemistry; homogeneous and heterogeneous catalysis related to the preparation of organic compounds. Address: 115 Fredricks Cts, Route 5, Longview, TX 75601.

DAWES, R(OGER) CLARK, b. Kalkaska, Mich, Oct. 13, 08; m. 35; c. 2. PHYSICAL CHEMISTRY, CHEMICAL ENGINEERING. B.S, Mich. State Col, 31, M.S, 32, Ph.D.(phys. chem), 36; Chem.E, 41. Asst, Mich. State Col, 31-36; chief chemist, tin plate & electrochem. div, Pittsburgh Crucible Steel Co, 36-39; instr. chem. eng. & metall, Grove City Col, 39-40, asst. prof, 40-45; res. engr, Battelle Mem. Inst, 45-49; PROF. CHEM. ENG, GROVE CITY COL, 49-, CHMN. ENG. DEPT, 58- Am. Chem. Soc; Am. Soc. Metals. Measurement of chromium plate by recording interferometer; the electroplating of continuous steel strip; a universal laboratory amalgam lamp; the refractive index, molecular refraction and dispersion of phenol derivatives; electrochemistry; powder metallurgy; fluid flow; machinability. Address: Box 350, Grove City, PA 16127.

DAWES, WILLIAM REDIN, JR, b. Charlotte, N.C, Oct. 10, 40; m. 64; c. 1. HIGH ENERGY & SOLID STATE PHYSICS. B.S, North Carolina, 62; M.S, Arizona, 64, Ph.D.(physics), 68. Mem. tech. staff, BELL TEL. LABS, 68-70, SUPVR, SILICON DEVICE TECHNOL. GROUP, 70- Pion-proton elastic scattering at high energy; silicon device technology, especially field effect devices. Address: 1445 N. 39th St, Allentown, PA 18104.

DAWID, IGOR B(ERT), b. Czernowitz, Romania, Feb. 26, 35. BIOCHEMISTRY, DEVELOPMENTAL BIOLOGY. Ph.D.(chem), Univ. Vienna, 60. Lab. asst. chem, Univ. Vienna, 59-60; vis. lectr. BIOCHEM, Mass. Inst. Technol, 60-62; fel, CARNEGIE INST, 62-67, MEM. STAFF, DEPT. EMBRYOL, 67- Vis. mem, Max Planck Inst. Biol, Univ. Tübingen, 65-67; asst. prof. biol, Johns Hopkins Univ, 67-70, assoc. prof, 70- AAAS; Am. Soc. Biol. Chem; Soc. Develop. Biol; Am. Soc. Cell Biol; Int. Soc. Develop. Biol. Biochemistry of development; function of nucleic acids in development; physical chemistry of nucleic acids; biogenesis of mitochondria; cytoplasmic genetics. Address: Dept. of Embryology, Carnegie Institution of Washington, 115 W. University Pkwy, Baltimore, MD 21210.

DAWIRS, HARVEL N(ICK), b. Kutch, Colo, July 10, 20; m. 44; c. 3. ELECTRICAL ENGINEERING, MATHEMATICS. B.S, Colorado State, 42; M.Sc, Ohio State, 52, Ph.D.(elec. eng), 62. Student & jr. engr, Westinghouse Elec. Corp, Pa, 42-43, design engr, 43-46; sr. engr, airplane div, Curtiss-Wright Corp, Ohio, 47-48; res. assoc. & asst. supvr. microwave res, Ohio State Univ, 48-59, assoc. supvr, 60-62; staff consult. antisubmarine warfare res, U.S. Industs. Tech. Center, Fla, 60; PROF. ENG. SCI, FLA. STATE UNIV, 62- Consult, U.S. Industs. Tech. Center, 60-61; Molecular Res. Inc, 61; Kismet Eng. Co, 61-62; Recon, Inc, 62- Inst. Elec. & Electronics Eng. Microwave circuitry including filters, multiplexers, impedance measuring equipment and techniques, phase shifters, cold antennas, plasmas and antenna arrays. Address: School of Engineering Science, Florida State University, Tallahassee, FL 32306.

DAWKINS, GEORGE S(PANGLER), b. Hornell, N.Y, July 1, 31; m. 55; c. 3. INDUSTRIAL ENGINEERING, OPERATIONS RESEARCH. B.Sc, Princeton, 53; Ethyl Corp. fel, Illinois, 53-56, Ph.D.(chem. eng), 57. Res. technologist, Shell Chem. Co, 57-61; ASSOC. PROF. chem. eng, Rice, 61-64; INDUST. ENG, UNIV. HOUSTON, 64- Summers, Quaker Rubber Co, 51; Sun Oil Co, 52; Atlantic Ref. Co, 53; exp. sta, E.I. du Pont de Nemours & Co, 54; Shell Chem. Co, 55, 56. Inst. Mgt. Sci; Opers. Res. Soc. Am; Am. Statist. Asn; Am. Soc. Qual. Control. Applied statistics; computer applications; applied mathematics; industrial consulting. Address: Dept. of Industrial Engineering, University of Houston, Houston, TX 77004.

DAWKINS, WILLIAM PAUL, b. Houston, Tex, July 25, 34; m. 57; c. 2. CIVIL ENGINEERING. B.A. & B.S, Rice, 57, Ideal Cement Co. fel, 61-62, M.S, 62; Ph.D.(civil eng), Illinois, Urbana, 66. Sr. engr. Proj. Mohole, Brown & Root, Inc, Tex, 62-63; res. asst. CIVIL ENG, Illinois, Urbana, 63-65, res. assoc, 65-66; asst. prof, Texas, 66-69; ASSOC. PROF, OKLA. STATE UNIV, 69- U.S.N, 57-60, Lt.(jg). Am. Soc. Civil Eng. Application of computers to solutions of civil engineering problems, particularly to problems of structural analysis. Address: School of Civil Engineering, Oklahoma State University, Stillwater, OK 74074.

DAWN, FREDERIC S, b. Wusih, China, Nov. 24, 14; U.S. citizen; m. 34; c. 3. TEXTILE ENGINEERING, CHEMISTRY. B.Sc, Kwang Hwa Univ, 34; B.Sc, Nat. Inst. Technol, China, 36, D.Sc.(chem. & textile eng), 48; Lowell Tech. Inst, 38; M.Sc, Univ. N.C, 39; hon. D.Sc, China Inst. Agr. & Textile Technol, 38, China Acad, 67; Univ. Wis, 54-56. Chmn. textile eng, Nantung Univ, 39-42; China Inst. Agr. & Textile Technol, 42-43, v.pres, 46-48, pres, 48-50; chmn. textile eng, Shanghai Inst. Technol, 43-45; Shanghai Munic. Inst. Technol, 46-49; consult, textile & allied industs, Southeast Asia & S.Am, 51-54; lab. dir, Decar Plastics Corp, Wis, 56-60; sr. res. engr, non-metall. mat, Aeronaut. Systs. Div, Wright Patterson AFB, 60-62; aerospace engr, MAT. LAB, MANNED SPACECRAFT CTR, NASA, 62-64, chief of lab, 64-68, DIR, 68- Exec. positions, textile & mfg. orgn, China, 39-50; mem. adv. comts, Ministries Indust, Economic Affairs, Educ. & Agr. & Forestry, & mem, Bd. Prof. Certification Exam, Yuan, 46-49. Gemini achievement award, NASA, 66; Apollo achievement award, 69, superior achievement award, 69, invention award, 71. Am. Chem. Soc; Soc. Plastics Eng; Am. Soc. Mech. Eng; Soc. Aerospace Mat. & Process Eng; Nat. Soc. Prof. Eng; fel. Am. Inst. Chem; Am. Inst. Aeronaut. & Astronaut; N.Y. Acad. Sci; Am. Ord. Asn. Research and development of polymeric materials for aerospace applications and nonflammable materials for spacecraft, extravehicular activity space-suits, life support systems, astronaut equipment and commercial fire safety applications. Address: 1615 Richvale, Houston, TX 77058.

DAWSEY, LYNN H(UGH), b. McHenry, Miss, Dec. 14, 04; m. 30; c. 2. PHYSICAL CHEMISTRY. B.S, Ala. Polytech, 26; scholar, Hopkins, 28-29, Ph.D.(chem), 29. Asst, Ala. State Lab, 25-26; Hopkins, 26-27; prof. chem, Mt. St. Mary's Col, 29-30; asst. chemist, bur. chem. & soils, U.S. Dept. Agr, New Orleans, La, 30, bur. entom. & plant quarantine, 30-37, assoc. chemist, 37-39; chemist, Buffalo Electro-Chem. Co. 39-54; Pesticide Chem. Labs, U.S. Dept. Agr, 54-70; RETIRED. Consult, Mathieson Alkali Works, 33-35. AAAS; Am. Chem. Soc; Entom. Soc. Am. Photochemistry; electrochemistry; insecticides; peroxides. Address: 105 Lang Ave, Pass Christian, MS 39571.

DAWSON, CHANDLER R, b. Denver, Colo, Aug. 24, 30; m. 54; c. 3. OPHTHALMOLOGY. A.B, Princeton, 52; M.D, Yale, 56. U.S. Pub. Health Serv. epidemiologist, Commun. Disease Center, 57-60; res. OPHTHAL, SCH. MED, UNIV. CALIF, SAN FRANCISCO, 60-63, asst. clin. prof, 63-66, asst. res. prof, 66-69, ASSOC. PROF. IN RESIDENCE, 69- Fel, Middlesex Hosp. Med. Sch, London, Eng, 63-64. Consult, World Health Orgn, 65-66; Indian Health Serv, U.S. Pub. Health Serv, 65- Dir, World Health Orgn. Int. Ref. Ctr. for Trachoma, 70- U.S.P.H.S, 57-60. Am. Med. Asn.(Knapp award, 67, 69), Am. Soc. Microbiol; Am. Acad. Ophthal. & Otolaryngol; Asn. Res. Ophthal. Epidemiology of infectious eye diseases; pathogenesis of virus diseases of the eyes; electron microscopy of eye diseases. Address: Francis I. Proctor Foundation, University of California, San Francisco, CA 94122.

DAWSON, C(HARLES) E(RIC), b. Vancouver, B.C, Can. Dec. 6, 22; nat; m. 45; c. 2. MARINE BIOLOGY. B.Sc, Miami (Fla), 53. Fisheries technician, Miami (Fla), 48-49, oceanog. technician, 51; oyster biologist, State of Fla, 49-52, head div. oyster culture, 53-54; res. scientist III, Texas, 54-55, res. scientist IV, shrimp invest, 55, proj. dir, 55-56; biologist, Bears Bluff Labs. & ichthyologist, Charleston Mus, 57-58; marine biologist & curator, GULF COAST RES. LAB, 58-71, SR. ICHTHYOLOGIST & CURATOR, 71-; ASST. PROF. BIOL, UNIV. SOUTH. MISS, 71- Adj. assoc. prof, Miss. State Univ, 69- Fisheries consult, Arabian Am. Oil Co, Saudi Arabia, 57. Am. Fisheries Soc; Am. Soc. Ichthyol. & Herpet; Am. Inst. Fishery Res. Biol; Marine Biol. Asn. U.K; Soc. Syst. Zool. Ichthyology; marine fisheries research. Address: Gulf Coast Research Lab, Ocean Springs, MS 39564.

DAWSON, CHARLES H, b. Uniontown, Pa, Dec. 11, 16; m. 38; c. 2. ELECTRICAL ENGINEERING, MATHEMATICS. E.E, Cornell, 38; M.S, Rochester, 41; Ph.D.(elec. eng), Iowa State Col, 52. Instr. eng, Rochester, 38-42, 45, asst. prof, 46-49, assoc. prof, 49-57, prof, 57-58; prof. & head dept, Rhode Island, 58-59; sr. eng. specialist, Philco West. Develop. Labs, 59-62; sr. res. engr, RADIO SYSTS. LAB, STANFORD RES. INST, 62-67, STAFF SCIENTIST, 67- UNESCO assignment, specialist in telecommun, Univ. Brasilia, 67-68; prof, Univ. Prince Edward Island, 70-72. Sig.C, 42-45, Capt. Inst. Elec. & Electronics Eng. Information theory; space communication; error correction and detection coding; statistical detection theory; feedback control systems; digital computer systems. Address: Radio Systems Lab, L2086, Stanford Research Institute, Menlo Park, CA 94025.

DAWSON, C(HARLES) R(EGINALD), b. Peterboro, N.H, Apr. 9, 11; m; c. 3. ORGANIC CHEMISTRY. B.S, New Hampshire, 33, M.S, 35, hon. Sc.D, 53; univ. fel, Columbia, 37-38, Ph.D.(chem), 38. Instr. inorg. & anal. chem, New Hampshire, 33-35; statutory asst. org. chem, Columbia, 36-37, Cutting fel, Cambridge, 38-39, instr. ORG. CHEM, COLUMBIA UNIV, 39-42, asst. prof, 42-46, assoc. prof, 46-52, PROF, 52-, Medal Recognition, div. war res, 46. Consult, Am. Cyanamid Co; Irvington Varnish & Insulator Co; Union Carbide Res. Inst; Evans Res. & Develop. Corp; Basic Systs, Inc; Philip Morris Res. Ctr. Fel. AAAS; Am. Inst. Chem; Am. Chem. Soc; Am. Soc. Biol. Chem; fel. N.Y. Acad. Sci. Organic synthesis; natural products; alkenyl phenols of poison ivy and related plants; respiratory enzymes; copper-proteins. Address: 411 Havermeyer Hall, Dept. of Chemistry, Columbia University, New York, NY 10027.

DAWSON, DAVID FLEMING, b. Denton, Tex, Sept. 16, 26; m. 48; c. 6. MATHEMATICS. Ph.D.(math), Texas, 57. Asst. prof. MATH, Missouri, 57-59; N.TEX. STATE UNIV, 59-61, assoc. prof, 61-64, PROF, 64- U.S.N.R, 51-53, Res, 53-65. Am. Math. Soc. Analysis; continued fractions; complex variables. Address: 1015 Ector, Denton, TX 76201.

DAWSON, DAVID H, b. Brillion, Wis, Sept. 21, 19; m. 50; c. 4. FORESTRY, PLANT GENETICS. B.S, Mich. State, 48; Central Michigan, 56. Plant mat. specialist, agr. res. serv, U.S. Dept. Agr, 57-61, PLANT GENETICIST, Rocky Mt. Forest & Range Exp. Sta, U.S. FOREST SERV, 62-67, INST. FOREST GENETICS, 67- U.S.A, 41-46, Res, 46-, Maj. Ecol. Soc. Am; Soc. Am. Foresters, Selection and cultural trials of woody plants for maximum fiber yield. Address: Institute of Forest Genetics, Rhinelander, WI 54501.

DAWSON, DAVID W(ARFIELD), b. Scottdale, Pa, June 20, 28; m. 48; c. 3. MECHANICAL ENGINEERING. B.S, Pa. State, 50; Gen. Motors Corp. fel, 50-51, M.S.M.E, 55. Res. mech. engr, cent. res. lab, Borg-Warner Corp, 51-56; sr. res. engr, lab, Gen. Motors Corp, 56-69; chief eng. develop. br, div. motor vehicle res. & develop, Nat. Air Pollution Control Admin, U.S. Dept. Health, Educ. & Welfare, 69-70, chief advan. automotive power systs. br, 70-71, ASST. TO DIR, DIV. ADVAN. AUTOMOTIVE POWER SYSTS. DEVELOP, OFF. AIR PROG, ENVIRON. PROTECTION AGENCY, 71- Part-time instr, Wayne State Univ, 56-63. Soc. Automotive Eng; Air Pollution Control Asn. Automotive emissions research and low emission engine development. Address: Division of Advanced Automotive Power Systems Development, Environmental Protection Agency, 5 Research Dr, Ann Arbor, MI 48103.

DAWSON, DONALD ANDREW, b. Montreal, Que, June 4, 37; m. 64. MATHEMATICS. B.Sc, McGill, 58, M.Sc, 59; Ph.D.(math), Mass. Inst. Tech, 63. Sr. engr, commun. theory, Raytheon Corp, Mass, 62-63; asst. prof. MATH, McGill, 63-66; vis. asst. prof, Illinois, 66-67; PROF, CARLETON UNIV, 67- Am. Math. Soc; Soc. Gen. Syst. Res; Can. Math. Cong. Adaptive control systems; statistical mechanisms; stochastic processes; communications theory; functional analysis; probability theory. Address: Dept. of Mathematics, Carleton University, Ottawa, Can.

DAWSON, D(ONALD) E(MERSON), b. Detroit, Mich, Oct. 3, 25; m. 52; c. 1. ENGINEERING SCIENCE. B.S, Wayne State, 48; M.S, Pa. State, 56, Ph.D.(eng. mech), 58. Engr. commun, Mich. Bell Tel. Co, 48-50; physicist aerosol physics, Battelle Mem. Inst, 51-52; res. assoc, Pa. State, 52-53; res. engr. eng. sci, E.I. du Pont de Nemours & Co, 58-62; res. mgr, Armour Res. Found, 62-63; assoc. prof. eng. sci, MICH. TECHNOL. UNIV, 63-66, PROF. MATH. & MECH, 66- U.S.N, 43-45. AAAS; Am. Phys. Soc; Soc. Indust. & Appl. Math. Applied and engineering mathematics; dynamics; vibrations. Address: Royalwood Addition, U.S. Route 41, Houghton, MI 49931.

DAWSON, EARL B, b. Perry, Fla, Feb. 1, 30; m. 51; c. 4. BIOCHEMISTRY, NUTRITION. B.A, Kansas, 55; Bowman Gray Sch. Med, 55-56; M.A, Missouri, 60; Ph.D.(biochem & nutrit), Texas A&M, 63. Teacher, Salem Acad, N.C, 57-58; technician biochem, R.J. Reynolds Tobacco Co, 58; lab. instr. physiol, Missouri, 58-60; biochem, Texas A&M, 60-63; instr. BIOCHEM. & NUTRIT, MED. BR, UNIV. TEX, 63-66, ASST. PROF, 66- Biochemist consult, Inderdept. Cmt. Nutrit. Nat. Defense, Nat. Insts. Health, 65. Hosp.C, U.S.N, 51-52. AAAS; Am. Inst. Nutrit; Am. Soc. Clin. Nutrit; Am. Chem. Soc. Mammalian renal physiology; changes in oxidative enzyme activity associated with cataract formation; placental changes in enzyme activity associated with toxemia of pregnancy; clinical nutrition. Address: Dept. of Obstetrics & Gynecology, University of Texas Medical Branch, Galveston, TX 77550.

DAWSON, ELSIE H(ALSTROM), b. Reedley, Calif, Feb. 4, 13; m. 36; c. 1. FOOD & NUTRITION. A.B, 33, M.A, 35. Asst. foods & food anal, California, 33-35; instr. chem. & foods, Syracuse, 35-40; instr. exp. foods, Cornell, 40-41; food res. specialist, bur. human nutrit. & home econ, U.S. DEPT. AGR, 41-52, head food qual. & use sect, human nutrit. res. div, 52-56, chief food qual. lab, 56-65, head consumer use invests, 65-69, HEAD CONSUMER USE OF FOODS, CONSUMER & FOOD ECON. RES. DIV, AGR. RES. SERV, 69- Mem, Res. & Develop. Assocs. Superior serv. award, U.S. Dept. Agr, 51. Inst. Food Technol; Am. Home Econ. Asn; N.Y. Acad. Sci; Soc. Advan. Food Serv. Res. The chemical and physical characteristics of foods and the factors affecting food quality; suitability of agricultural commodities for use as food; home and institutional utilization of food; development of fundamental principles of food preparation and preservation. Address: Consumer & Food Economics Research Division, Agricultural Research Service, U.S. Dept. of Agriculture, Agricultural Research Center, Beltsville, MD 20705.

DAWSON, FRANK G(ATES), JR, b. Alliance, N.C, July 6, 25; m. 47; c. 3. NUCLEAR ENGINEERING. B.E.E, N.C. State Col, 50; Oak Ridge Sch. Reactor Tech, 55-56. Test engr, Gen. Elec. Co, 50-51, sr. tech. engr, aircraft nuclear propulsion dept, 51-55, prin. engr, 56-60, tech. specialist, Hanford Labs, 60, mgr. appl. physics, 60-63, reactor physics, 63-65; PAC. NORTHWEST LABS, BATTELLE MEM. INST, 65-68, mgr. physics & eng. div, 68-71, ASST. LAB. DIR, 71- Acting asst. prof, Univ. Cincinnati, 58-60; lectr, Univ. Calif, Los Angeles, 67-68. Mem. adv. comt. reactor physics, Atomic Energy Comn, 64-70; Europ-Am. Comt. Reactor Physics, 70-U.S. rep, panel on plutonium utilization, Int. Atomic Energy Agency, 68, chmn. panel on plutonium recycling in thermal power reactors, 71; U.S. del, UN Int. Conf. Peaceful Uses of Atomic Energy, 71. U.S.A.A.F, 43-46, 1st Lt. Reactor physics and design. Address: Pacific Northwest Labs, Battelle Memorial Institute, Richland, WA 99352.

DAWSON, GLADYS Q(UINTY), b. Trenton, N.J, Sept. 3, 24; m. 52. INORGANIC CHEMISTRY. B.S, Illinois, 46, Ph.D.(chem), 51. Prin. chemist, chem. res, Battelle Mem. Inst, 51-52; instr. chem, Pa. State, 52-58; patent liaison, E.I. du Pont de Nemours & Co, 58-63; teaching assoc, MICH. TECHNOL. UNIV, 63-67, asst. prof. CHEM, 67-71, ASSOC. PROF, 71- Am. Chem. Soc. Rare earth chemistry. Address: Royalewood Addition, Box 39, Houghton, MI 49931.

DAWSON, GLYN, b. New Mills, Eng, Mar. 24, 43; m. 66; c. 1. BIOCHEMISTRY. B.Sc, Univ. Bristol, 64, Sci. Res. Coun. grant & Ph.D.(biochem), 67. Fel, Univ. Pittsburgh, 67-68; res. assoc, Mich. State Univ, 68-69; ASST. PROF. PEDIAT. & BIOCHEM, UNIV. CHICAGO, 69- Biochem. Soc; Am. Soc. Neurochem. Glycosphingolipid glycoprotein and phospholipid metabolism in human cells especially cultured cells—fibroblasts, glial, neuroblastomas and other malignant cell lines; inborn errors of metabolism; carbohydrate structure; mass spectrometry. Address: Dept. of Pediatrics & Biochemistry, Joseph P. Kennedy, Jr. Mental Retardation Research Center, University of Chicago, Chicago, IL 60637.

DAWSON, HELEN L(UCERNE), b. Alton, Ill, Apr. 21, 04. ANATOMY. B.S, Shurtleff Col, 26; M.S, Washington (St. Louis), 29, Hannibal Pharmacal fel, 29-31, Johnson fel, 31-32, Ph.D.(anat), 32. Asst. anat, Washington (St. Louis), 32; res. assoc. anthrop, child welfare sta, Iowa, 32-35; Nat. Res. Coun. fel, Harvard, 35-36; instr. ANAT, COL. MED, UNIV. IOWA, 36-38, from assoc. to asst. prof, 38-53, assoc. prof, 53-68, prof, 68-69, EMER. PROF, 69- Mem. Harvard anthrop. exped, Ireland. Am. Asn. Anat; Am. Asn. Phys. Anthrop. Basic human anatomy; effect of specific light rays on growth of rats; hair growth and slope; growth of infants; histology; description of a cell found in the gall bladder of the cat; royal jelly. Address: 324 Woolf Ave, Iowa City, IA 52240.

DAWSON, HENK IWAN, b. Paramaribo, Surinam, Apr. 3, 40; m. 63; c. 2. METAL PHYSICS. B.S, Delft, 60, M.S, 62, Ph.D.(physics), 64. Res. assoc. metal physics, Delft, 64-65; mat. sci, Northwestern, 65-66; asst. prof. METALL. ENG, UNIV. WASH, 66-69, ASSOC. PROF, 69- Am. Phys. Soc; Am. Soc. Eng. Educ; Netherlands Phys. Soc. Defect properties in solids. Address: Dept. of Metallurgical Engineering, Roberts Hall, University of Washington, Seattle, WA 98105.

DAWSON, H(ENRY) DONALD, b. Haskins, Ohio, Jan. 7, 95; m. 16. PHYSICAL CHEMISTRY. B.S, Denison, 16; M.S, Ohio State, 30, Ph.D.(phys chem), 40. From works chemist, to cordite supt, Nobel Plant, 16-19; chief chemist, Beloeil Plant, Can. Explosives, Ltd, 20-21; supt. schs, Ohio, 22-28; asst. chem, Ohio State, 29-30; prof. & chmn. dept, Bethany Col.(W.Va), 30-43; from asst. tech. supt, Akron Plant, to tech. supt, Houston Plant, Goodyear Synthetic Corp, 44-46; prof. chem. & chmn. dept, East Tenn. State, 45-56; sect. head, anal. & design dept, Goodyear Atomic Corp, 56-63; prof. chem. & coord. undergrad. res, BETHANY COL.(W.VA), 63-70, EMER. DISTINGUISHED PROF. CHEM, 70- Consult, Hasche Eng. Corp. AAAS; Am. Chem. Soc. Thermal molecular cracking and reforming processes. Address: 14521 State Route 582, Bowling Green, OH 43402.

DAWSON, HORACE RAY, b. Wills Point, Tex, Mar. 29, 35; m. 56; c. 2. PHYSICS. B.A, North Texas State, 57, M.A, 61; Ph.D.(physics), Arkansas, 68. Instr. PHYSICS, East Texas State, 61-63; ASSOC. PROF, ANGELO STATE UNIV, 66- Am. Asn. Physics Teachers. Atomic collisions; radia-tive lifetimes of atoms; gamma ray spectroscopy. Address: Dept. of Physics, Angelo State University, San Angelo, TX 76901.

DAWSON, J. W, b. Toronto, Ont, Dec. 30, 28; m. 52; c. 4. INTERNAL MEDICINE, ENDOCRINOLOGY. M.D, Toronto, 53. ASSOC. DEAN, UNIV. CALGARY, 67-, PROF. MED, FACULTY MED, 68-, DIR. DIV. CONTINUING MED. EDUC, 71- Fel, Royal Col. Physicians Can, 58. Fel. Am. Col. Physicians; Can. Soc. Clin. Invest. Pituitary cytology; thyroidology; medical education. Address: Faculty of Medicine, University of Calgary, Calgary, Alta, Can.

DAWSON, JAMES CLIFFORD, b. Toronto, Ont, Apr. 19, 41; U.S. citizen; m. 71. SEDIMENTOLOGY, SEDIMENTARY PETROLOGY. B.A, Univ. Calif, Los Angeles, 65, M.S, 67; Wis. Alumni Res. Found. fel, Univ. Wis, Madison, 69-70, Ph.D.(geol), 70. ASST. PROF. GEOL, STATE UNIV. N.Y. COL. PLATTSBURGH, 70- Prin. investr, State Univ. N.Y. Res. Found. fel & grant-in-aid, 71. AAAS: jr. mem. Am. Asn. Petrol. Geol; Am. Geophys. Union; Geol. Soc. Am; Int. Asn. Sedimentol; Soc. Econ. Paleont. & Mineral. Carboniferous sedimentology of the Falkland Islands; upper Jurassic and lower Cretaceous sedimentology of the Colorado Plateau; chert petrography. Address: Dept. of Geology, State University of New York College at Plattsburgh, Plattsburgh, NY 12901.

DAWSON, JAMES PHILLIP, b. Drummond, Okla, Oct. 18, 32; m. 51; c. 2. PHYSICAL CHEMISTRY. B.S, Southwest. State Col.(Okla), 55; M.S, Okla. State, 59; fel, California, 61-62. Chemist, thermodyn. br, U.S. Bur. Mines, 55-57; res. asst. chem, Okla. State, 57-59; res. chemist, Sundstrand Turbo, Sundstrand Corp, 59-61; supvr. radiation physics sect, aerospace environ. facility, ARO, Inc, 62-66; chief eng. & opers. br, Lunar Receiving Lab, NASA Manned Spacecraft Ctr, 66-69; pres, Sci. Specialties Corp, 69-71; SPEC. ASST. TO GOV. OKLA, ADMINR. OFF. COMMUNITY AFFAIRS, 71- U.S.A, 50-52, Sgt. Am. Chem. Soc; Am. Inst. Aeronaut. & Astronaut. Design and development of environmental systems for basic research and measurement of physical properties; developed manipulator systems for processing lunar samples under 10^{-12} torr environments. Address: Governor's Office, State Capitol, Oklahoma City, OK 73105.

DAWSON, JAMES R(OBERTSON), JR, b. Birmingham, Ala, Jan. 19, 08. PATHOLOGY, BACTERIOLOGY. A.B, Vanderbilt, 28, M.D, 31. Asst. path, med. sch, Vanderbilt, 31-32, instr, 32-34; asst. Rockefeller Inst, 34-35; instr. bact, med. col, Cornell, 35-38; asst. prof. PATH, med. sch, Vanderbilt, 38-42, assoc. prof, 42-45, PROF, 45-49; med. col, Univ. Minn, Minneapolis, 49-69; MED. SCH, UNIV. MISS, 69- Human encephalitis; rabies. Address: Dept. of Pathology, University of Mississippi Medical School, Jackson, MS 39216.

DAWSON, J(EAN) H(OWARD), b. Stacy, Minn, Apr. 14, 33; m. 54; c. 5. AGRONOMY. B.S, Minnesota, 55; M.S, California, 57; Ph.D.(weed control), Oregon State, 61. Res. asst. agron, California, 55-57; RES. AGRONOMIST, U.S. DEPT. AGR, 57- Weed Sci. Soc. Am. Principles and practices of weed control in irrigated crops; annual weed control in sugarbeets; dodder control in alfalfa; herbicide mode of action and weed biology studies. Address: Irrigated Agriculture Research & Extension Center, U.S. Dept. of Agriculture, Prosser, WA 99350.

DAWSON, JOHN ALEXANDER, b. South Amboy, N.J, Mar. 13, 35; m. 66; c. 1. GEOPHYSICS. B.A, Rutgers, 56; M.Sc, Lehigh, 59; Ph.D.(geophys), Alaska, 65. Physicist, geomagnetism sect, Inst. Telecommun.Sci. & Aeronomy, Environ. Sci. Serv. Admin, 65-66; lectr. PHYSICS, AHMADU BELLO UNIV, NIGERIA, 67-70, SR. LECTR, 70- Am. Geophys. Union; Sci. Asn. Nigeria. Geomagnetic micropulsations. Address: School of Basic Studies, Ahmadu Bello University, Zaria, Nigeria.

DAWSON, JOHN E, b. Hamilton, Ohio, Oct. 19, 24; m. 69; c. 5. PHYSIOLOGY, ENDOCRINOLOGY. B.A, Univ. Cincinnati, 47, M.S, 56, Ph.D.(endocrinol), 62. Teacher, high sch. Ky, 47-53; Ohio, 53-55; asst. prof. gen. zool. & sci. educ, San Jose State Col. 58-64; gen. biol. & physiol, OHIO NORTH. UNIV, 64-67, ASSOC. PROF. PHYSIOL, 67- Res. fel, Univ. Wash. 68-69. AAAS. Effect of chronic administration of sodium tolbutamide on pregnant albino rats and their offspring; effect of luteinizing hormone on membrane permeability of frog oocytes. Address: 416 Willeke Ave, Ada, OH 45810.

DAWSON, JOHN FREDERICK, b. Springfield, Ohio, Jan. 4, 36; m. 58; c. 1. PHYSICS. B.S, Antioch Col, 58; Ph.D.(physics), Stanford, 63. Res. assoc. PHYSICS, McGill Univ, 62-64; asst. prof, Antioch Col, 64-65; vis. asst. prof, Oberlin Col, 65-66; res. assoc, Lowell Technol. Inst. Res. Found, 66-68; ASST. PROF, UNIV. N.H, 68- Am. Phys. Soc. Theoretical nuclear physics. Address: Dept. of Physics, University of New Hampshire, Durham, NH 03824.

DAWSON, JOHN MYRICK, b. Champaign, Ill, Sept. 30, 30; m. 57; c. 2. PLASMA PHYSICS. B.S, Maryland, 52, M.S, 54, Ph.D.(physics), 56. Res. physicist, proj. Matterhorn, PRINCETON UNIV, 56-62, PLASMA PHYSICS LAB, 62-64, assoc. head THEORET. GROUP, 64-66, HEAD, 66-, LECTR, 60- Consult, RCA Corp, 62-63; Boeing Co, 64; Fulbright fel, inst. plasma physics, Univ. Nagoya, 64-65; sci. adv, dir. Naval Res. Lab, 69- Am. Phys. Soc. Atomic and molecular physics; plasma physics. Address: Plasma Physics Lab, Princeton University, Princeton, NJ 08540.

DAWSON, JOHN W(ILLIAM), b. Great Falls, Mont, Nov. 8, 12; m. 44; c. 3. CHEMISTRY. B.S, Washington (Seattle), 34, Ph.D.(org. chem), 42. Explosives chemist, Nat. Defense Res. Cmt, Pa, 42-45; res. chemist, Rohm and Haas Co, 45-49, head org. chem. group, U.S. Army Res. Div, Redstone Arsenal, 49-51, chief, 51-53; dir. chem. div, Off. Ord. Res, 53-58, CHIEF SCIENTIST, 58-61; U.S. ARMY RES. OFF-DURHAM, 61- Explosives; insecticides; research supervision and administration; investigation of isoelectronic boron-nitrogen systems. Address: U.S. Army Research Office-Durham, Box CM, Duke Station, Durham, NC 27706.

DAWSON, L(AWRENCE) E, b. Mich, July 23, 16; m. 45; c. 1. FOOD SCIENCE. B.S, Mich. State Col, 42, M S, 46; Ph.D.(agr. mkt), Purdue, 49. Asst, Purdue, 46-49; PROF. FOOD SCI, MICH. STATE UNIV, 49- Res.

achievement award, Poultry & Egg Nat. Bd, 61. U.S.A.A.F, 44-45, 1st Lt. Poultry Sci. Asn; Inst. Food Technol; World Poultry Sci. Asn. Poultry and egg products technology, flavor, composition and preservation. Address: Dept. of Food Science & Human Nutrition, Michigan State University, East Lansing, MI 48823.

DAWSON, MARY (RUTH), b. Highland Park, Mich, Feb. 27, 31. VERTEBRATE PALEONTOLOGY. B.S, Mich. State, 52; Fulbright scholar, Edinburgh, 52-53; univ. fel, Kansas, 53-54, Nat. Sci. Found. fels, 54-56, Ph.D.(zool), 57. Instr. zool, Kansas, 56-57; Smith Col, 58-60, asst. prof, 60-61; asst. prog. dir, Nat. Sci. Found, 61-62; res. assoc, CARNEGIE MUS, 62-63, asst. curator, 63-65, assoc. curator, 65-70, acting curator, 70, CURATOR, 71- Am. Asn. Univ. Women fel, 57-58. Paleont. Soc; Geol. Soc. Am; Soc. Vert. Paleont. Paleontology of lagomorphs and rodents. Address: Section of Vertebrate Fossils, Carnegie Museum, 4400 Forbes Ave, Pittsburgh, PA 15213.

DAWSON, MURRAY DRAYTON, b. Christchurch, N.Z, Dec. 16, 25; U.S. citizen; m. 52; c. 6. SOILS, PLANT PHYSIOLOGY. B.Ag.Sc, New Zealand, 49, M.Ag.Sc, 51; M.S, Cornell, 52, Ph.D.(soils), 54. Res. scientist field husb, Can. Exp. Sta, Swift Current, Sask, 50-51; PROF. SOILS, ORE. STATE UNIV, 54- Consult. prof, Univ. Agr, Bangkok, 59-60. Am. Soc. Agron. Legume establishment growth and development on infertile acid soils, with special reference to sulfur nutrition and high levels of manganese. Address: Dept. of Soils, Oregon State University, Corvallis, OR 97331.

DAWSON, PETER HENRY, b. Derby, Eng, May 28, 37; m. 63; c. 2. PHYSICAL CHEMISTRY. B.Sc, London, 58, Dept. Sci. & Indust. grant, 58-61, Ph.D.(phys. chem), 61. Fel, Nat. Res. Coun. Can, 61-63; phys. chemist, res. lab, Gen. Elec. Co, N.Y, 63-69; RES. ASSOC, CTR. RES. ATOMS & MOLECULES, LAVAL UNIV, 69- Am. Phys. Soc; Am. Vacuum Soc; Am. Soc. Mass Spectrometry. Mass spectrometry and partial pressure analysis; development of quadrupole field instruments; vacuum techniques; chemical lasers and energy exchange processes; surface physics. Address: Center for Research on Atoms & Molecules, Laval University, Quebec 10, Que, Can.

DAWSON, PETER J, b. Wolverhampton, Eng, Feb. 17, 28. PATHOLOGY. B.A, Cambridge, 49, M.B, B.Ch, 52, M.A, 53, M.D, 60; dipl. clin. path, London, 55. House physician, Royal Berkshire Hosp, Reading, Eng, 52-53; house surgeon, Victoria Hosp. for Children, London, 53; demonstr. path, St. George's Hosp. Med. Sch, London, 53-54, registr. morbid anat, asst. lectr, postgrad. med. sch, 58-59, 59-60; vis. asst. prof. PATH, sch. med, California, San Francisco, 60-62; lectr, med. sch, Newcastle, 62-64; assoc. prof, MED. SCH, UNIV. ORE, 64-67, PROF, 67- Consult, Stanford Res. Inst, 64- Dipl, Am. Bd. Path, 68. Allingham Prize, St. George's Hosp. Med. Sch, London, 54. Am. Asn. Cancer Res; N.Y. Acad. Sci; Path. Soc. Gt. Brit. & Ireland; Royal Col. Path; Int. Acad. Path. Human and animal malignant lymphomas; virus-induced leukemias. Address: Dept. of Pathology, University of Oregon Medical School, 3181 S.W. Sam Jackson Park Rd, Portland, OR 97201.

DAWSON, PETER S(ANFORD), b. Phila, Pa, Apr. 16, 39; m. 59; c. 2. POPULATION BIOLOGY. B.S, Washington State, 60; Woodrow Wilson fel, California, Berkeley, 61-62, Kofoid fel, 62-63, Nat. Insts. Health fel, 63-64, Ph.D.(genetics), 64. Proj. asst, Univ. Wis, Madison, 65-66; asst. prof. ZOOL, Univ. Ill, Urbana, 66-69; ASSOC. PROF, ORE. STATE UNIV, 69- U.S.A, 64-66, Capt. AAAS; Genetics Soc. Am; Soc. Study Evolution; Am. Soc. Nat; Ecol. Soc. Am. Interspecific competition; population regulation and microevolution. Address: Dept. of Zoology, Oregon State University, Corvallis, OR 97331.

DAWSON, RAY F(IELDS), b. Muncie, Ind, Feb. 13, 11; m. 42. PLANT BIOCHEMISTRY. A.B, DePauw, 35; Hooker fel, Yale, 35-38, Ph.D.(plant physiol), 38. Nat. Res. Coun. fel, Columbia, 38-39; instr. BOT, DePauw, 39-40; asst. prof, Missouri, 40-42; Princeton, 42-45; Columbia, 45-46, assoc. prof, 46-52, prof, 52-59, Torrey prof, 59-66; PROF. PLANT BIOL. & DIR. INT. AGR. PROG, RUTGERS UNIV, 66- Guest investr, Exp. Plantations, Inc, Guatemala, 46; res. collab, Brookhaven Nat. Lab, 52-66; consult, tobacco & chem. industs, 52- Mem, DePauw Univ. Bot. Exped, Honduras, 36. 2nd annual award, Cigar Mfg. Asn. Am. & Cigar Inst, 52. Am. Chem. Soc; Am. Soc. Plant Physiol.(Hales Award, 44); Asn. Trop. Biol. Biosynthesis of plant constituents; isotopic tracers; general plant chemistry and biochemistry; natural products; development of new tropical crops for chemical and drug production. Address: Administration Bldg, College of Agriculture, Rutgers, The State University, P.O. Box 231, New Brunswick, NJ 08903.

DAWSON, REED, b. Lincoln, Nebr, Sept. 29, 18; m. 65; c. 4. MATHEMATICS. Ph.D.(math), Harvard, 53. Instr. math, Bowdoin Col, 48-49; mathematician, U.S. Dept. Defense, 49-60; Am. Systs. Inc, 60-62; dir. math. sci, Control Data Corp, 62-66; MacDonnell-Douglas Corp, 66-68; MATHEMATICIAN, DEPT. DEFENSE, 68- U.S.N.R, 42-46, Lt. Inst. Math. Statist; Am. Math. Soc; Soc. Indust. & Appl. Math. Mathematical statistics; operations analysis. Address: 305 Beaumont Rd, Silver Spring, MD 20904.

DAWSON, ROBERT LOUIS, b. Rochester, N.Y, Oct. 18, 36; m. 65. ORGANIC CHEMISTRY. B.S, Rochester, 58; Illinois, 58-59; Ph.D.(org. chem), Harvard, 62. RES. ORG. CHEMIST, E.I. DU PONT DE NEMOURS & CO, INC, 62- Am. Chem. Soc. Preparation of new synthetic elastomers and monomers. Address: 1220 Elderon Dr, Wilmington, DE 19808.

DAWSON, ROY C(ARLTON), b. Culpeper, Va, May 1, 07; m. 41; c. 2. MICROBIOLOGY, AGRICULTURE. B.S, Maryland, 37, M.S, 39; Ph.D.(soils), Nebraska, 47. Food inspector, Health Dept, Wash, D.C, 39-40; bacteriologist, U.S. Dept. Agr, Md, 41-50, consult. int. prog. off. of adminstr, Agr. Res. Serv, D.C, 51-55; tech. officer, N.Am. Regional Off, Food & Agr. Orgn, UN, 56-69; tech. info. off, Am. Type Culture Collection, 70-71; RETIRED. AAAS; Soil Sci. Soc. Am; Am. Soc. Microbiol. Soil conservation and microbiology; decomposition of crop residues by soil fungi; agricultural technical assistance; microbiology in developing countries. Address: 4019 Beechwood Rd, University Park, MD 20782.

DAWSON, THOMAS HENRY, b. Fredericksburg, Va, Oct. 13, 40; m. 69. MECHANICS. B.S, Va. Polytech. Inst, 63; Whitehead fel, Johns Hopkins Univ, 63-64 & 67-68, M.S, 65, NASA fel, 64-67, Ph.D.(mech), 68. ASST. PROF. CIVIL ENG, UNIV. VA, 68-, U.S. Navy res. grant, 69-70, Nat. Sci. Found. res. grant, 70-71. Mechanics of crystalline aggregate deformations; time effects in the elastic and plastic deformation of solids; fluid-structure interactions; waves in compressible fluids. Address: Dept. of Civil Engineering, School of Engineering & Applied Science, University of Virginia, Charlottesville, VA 22903.

DAWSON, THOMAS LARRY, b. Logan, W.Va, Nov. 7, 34; m. 57; c. 2. PHYSICAL & POLYMER CHEMISTRY. A.B, Berea Col, 56; M.S, Univ. Ky, 58, Eastman Kodak fel, 59, Ph.D.(phys. chem), 60. Chemist, Am. Viscose Corp, 56; CHEM. & PLASTICS DIVS, UNION CARBIDE CORP, 60-70, RES. SCIENTIST, 70- Am. Chem. Soc. Kinetics and mechanisms of reactions in solutions; reactions on polymers; polymer synthesis; kinetics of free radical polymerization. Address: 731 Churchill Dr, Charleston, WV 25314

DAWSON, VICTOR C(HARLES) D(OUGLAS), b. Chicago, Ill, Oct. 16, 26; m. 48; c. 4. MECHANICAL ENGINEERING. B.S, Mass. Inst. Tech, 48; M.S, Harvard, 51; M.E, Calif. Inst. Tech, 59; Ph.D, Maryland, 63. Res. engr, Carrier Corp, 48-50; F.C. Dawson Eng. Co, 50-51; U.S. NAVAL ORD. LAB, 51-61, chief GAS DYNAMICS DIV, 61-70, SUPVRY. RES. ENGR, 70- Lectr, Maryland, 63. Consult, 51. U.S.A.A.F, 45. Am. Soc. Mech. Eng; Soc. Exp. Stress Anal; Am. Inst. Aeronaut. & Astronaut. Gas dynamics; hydrodynamics; elastic and plastic stress waves in solids. Address: U.S. Navy, Code 322/Ordnance Lab, White Oak, Silver Spring, MD 20901.

DAWSON, WALLACE DOUGLAS, JR, b. Louisville, Ky, Mar. 15, 31; m. 57; c. 3. GENETICS, EVOLUTION. B.S, West. Ky. State Col, 54; M.S, Kentucky, 59; Ph.D.(genetics), Ohio State, 62. Asst. prof. BIOL, UNIV. S.C, 62-66, assoc. prof, 66-71, PROF, 71- U.S.A.F, 55-57, 1st Lt. AAAS; Am. Genetic Asn; Am. Soc. Mammal; Soc. Study Evolution; Genetics Soc. Am. Developmental genetics and evolution of rodents; speciation and endocrinology of Peromyscus. Address: Dept. of Biology, University of South Carolina, Columbia, SC 29208.

DAWSON, W(ILFRED) KENNETH, b. Que, Que, Oct. 6, 27; m. 54; c. 2. NUCLEAR PHYSICS. B.Sc.A, Laval, 51; Nat. Res. Council Can. bursary, Queen's (Can), 51, studentship 52, fel, 53, Ph.D.(physics), 55. Defense serv. sci. officer nuclear physics, Defense Res. Bd, Can, 55-59; from asst. prof. physics to assoc. prof, UNIV. ALTA, 59-70, PROF. NUCLEAR PHYS, 70- Am. Phys. Soc; Can. Asn. Physicists. Fast neutron time-of-flight spectroscopy; nuclear stripping reactions; photonuclear reactions. Address: Dept. of Physics, University of Alberta, Edmonton, Alta, Can.

DAWSON, WILLIAM R(YAN), b. Los Angeles, Calif, Aug. 24, 27; m. 50; c. 3. COMPARATIVE PHYSIOLOGY. Stanford; Ph.D.(zool), California, Los Angeles, 53; D.Sc.(eco-physiol), West. Australia, 71. Asst. zool, California, Los Angeles, 51-52; U.S. Pub. Health Serv. fel, 53; instr. ZOOL, UNIV. MICH, ANN ARBOR, 53-56, asst. prof, 56-59, assoc. prof, 59-62, PROF, 62- Guggenheim fel, 62-63; res. Australian-Am. Educ. Found, 69-70. U.S.N. 45-46, Ens. Ecol. Soc. Am; Am. Ornith. Union; Cooper Ornith. Soc; Am. Soc. Zool; Am. Physiol. Soc; Int. Soc. Biometeorol. Temperature regulation and water balance of birds and mammals; reptile physiology; avian paleontology. Address: Dept. of Zoology, University of Michigan, Ann Arbor, MI 48104.

DAWSON, WILLIAM WOODSON, b. Nashville, Tenn, May 21, 33; m. 55; c. 2. PHYSIOLOGICAL PSYCHOLOGY, BIOPHYSICS. B.A, Vanderbilt, 55; M.S, Fla. State, 57, Ph.D.(psychol), 61. Res. fel, biophys. trainee prog, Nat. Inst. Neurol. Diseases & Blindness, 60-61; asst. res. prof. psychol, Auburn, 63-64; Joseph P. Kennedy prof, George Peabody Col, 64-65; assoc. prof. ophthal, COL. MED, UNIV. FLA, 65-69, PROF. OPHTHAL. & PHYSIOL, 69-, MEM, CTR. NEUROBIOL. SCI, 66- Res. grants, assoc. investr, Nat. Inst. Neurol. Diseases & Blindness, 60-61, prin. investr, 66-; Army Med. Res. & Develop. Command, 63-64. Summer lectr, Nat. Sci. Found. Radiation Inst, Fla. State, 61. Consult, Donner Lab, Biophys. California, Berkeley, 61; Stanford Res. Inst, 62. Mem. vision comt, Nat. Acad. Sci-Nat. Res. Coun, 68-; dir, Ctr. Res. on Human Prostheses, 71- U.S.A, 61-63, Capt. Fel. AAAS; Radiation Res. Soc; Am. Psychol. Asn. Sense receptor electrophysiology and psychophysics, especially cutaneous quality, vision and receptor radiation biology. Address: Dept. of Ophthalmology, University of Florida, Gainesville, FL 32601.

DAY, ALBERT M, b. Humboldt, Nebr, Apr. 2, 97; m. 44; c. 3. BIOLOGY. B.S, Wyoming, 21. Asst, bur. biol. surv, U.S. Dept. Agr, 18-19, leader rodent control, 20-30, asst. chief div. predatory animal & rodent control, 30-35, chief div, 35-38, fed. aid in wildlife restoration, U.S. Fish & Wildlife Serv, 38-42, asst. dir, 42-46, adminstr, defense fisheries admin, 46-53, asst. to dir. serv, 53-55; dir. wildlife res, Arctic Inst. N.Am, 55-58; Oregon Fish Comn, 58-60; Pa. Fish Comn, 60-64; conserv. consult, 64-65; nat. resources specialist, U.S. Dept. Interior, 65-66; conserv. consult, U.S. Dept. Agr, 66-71; ENVIRON. CONSULT, 71- Mem, Int. Pac. Salmon Fisheries Comn, 47; spec. adv. comt, Secy. Interior, 56; adv, Int. N.Pac. Fisheries Comn; 58; U.S. sect, UN Conf. on Law of Sea; mem, Pac. Marine Fisheries Comn; spec. adv. comt, Pa. State Sanit. Bd, Water & Power Bd. Sig.C, U.S.A, 17-19. AAAS; Nat. Audubon Soc; Wildlife Soc; Am. Fisheries Soc; Am. Soc. Mammal; Am. Forestry Asn. North American waterfowl. Address: 1810 Pine St, Camp Hill, PA 17011.

DAY, ALLAN R(USSELL), b. Bluffton, Ohio, June 5, 99; m. 22; c. 1. CHEMISTRY. A.B, Bluffton Col, 21; M.S, Pennsylvania, 25, Ph.D.(chem), 27. Asst. prof. & later assoc. prof. CHEM, UNIV. PA, 30-51, prof, 51-70, EMER. PROF, 70- Am. Chem. Soc. Organic chemistry; organic medicinals; heterogeneous catalysis; mechanisms of organic reactions. Address: Dept. of Chemistry, University of Pennsylvania, Philadelphia, PA 19104.

DAY, A(RDEN) D(EXTER), b. Rutland, Vt, Mar. 16, 22; m. 45; c. 3. PLANT BREEDING. B.S, Cornell, 50; Ph.D, Mich. State, 54. Asst. prof. agron. & asst. agronomist, AGR. EXP. STA, UNIV. ARIZ, 54-56, assoc. prof. agron. & assoc. agronomist, 56-59, PROF. AGRON. & AGRONOMIST, 59- Am. Soc. Agron. Small grain breeding. Address: Dept. of Agronomy & Plant Genetics, University of Arizona, Tucson, AZ 85721.

DAY, ARNOLD, b. Blackpool, Eng, Apr. 10, 35; m. 66; c. 1. MINERAL ENGINEERING. B.S. & A.R.S.M, Royal Sch. Mines, Imp. Col, London, 58. Res. metallurgist, Ashanti Goldfields Corp, Ghana, W.Africa, 58-64; res. engr, White Pine Copper Co, Mich, 64-67; sr. minerals engr, AM. CYANAMID CO, 67-69, GROUP LEADER TECH. SERV, 69- R.A.F, 53-55. Am. Inst. Mining, Metall. & Petrol. Eng; Brit. Inst. Mining & Metall. Minerals beneficiation research and development especially flotation. Address: Central Research Division, American Cyanamid Co, 1937 W. Main St, Stamford, CT 06904.

DAY, BENJAMIN DOWNING, b. Nassawadox, Va, July 19, 36; m. 58; c. 2. THEORETICAL PHYSICS. B.A, Wesleyan, 58; Nat. Sci. Found. fel, Cornell, 58-62, Ph.D.(theoret. physics), 64. Asst. res. physicist, California, Los Angeles, 63-64, asst. prof. physics, 64-65; resident res. assoc, ARGONNE NAT. LAB, 65-67, asst. physicist, 67-69, ASSOC. PHYSICIST, 70- Guggenheim fel, 71. Am. Phys. Soc. Theoretical nuclear physics, especially the nuclear many-body problem. Address: Physics Division, Bldg. 203, Argonne National Lab, Argonne, IL 60439.

DAY, B(ILLY) N(EIL), b. Arthur, W.Va, Oct. 23, 30; m. 53; c. 5. ANIMAL HUSBANDRY. B.S, West Virginia, 52, M.S, 54; Ph.D.(animal husb), Iowa State Col, 58. Instr, ANIMAL HUSB, Iowa State Col, 57-58; asst. prof, UNIV. MO-COLUMBIA, 58-63, assoc. prof, 63-68, PROF, 68- U.S.A, 54-56. Am. Soc. Animal Sci; Brit. Soc. Study Fertil; Endocrine Soc; Soc. Study Reproduction. Physiology of reproduction in domestic animals. Address: 125 Mumford Hall, University of Missouri-Columbia, Columbia, MO 65201.

DAY, BOYSIE E(UGENE), b. Haile, La, Sept. 9, 17; m. 41; c. 3. PLANT PHYSIOLOGY. B.S, Univ. Ariz, 38, M.S, 40; Ph.D.(plant physiol), Univ. Calif, 50. Prof. plant physiol. & plant physiologist, UNIV. CALIF, RIVERSIDE, 50-66, PROF. HORT. SCI. & CHMN. DEPT, 66-, assoc. dir. citrus res. ctr. & agr. exp. sta, 68, dir, 68-71, ASSOC. DIR, AGR. EXP. STA, UNIV. CALIF, 71- Chmn. subcomt. weeds, Nat. Res. Coun. U.S.A, 40-46, Col. AAAS; Am. Soc. Plant Physiol; Bot. Soc. Am; Am. Soc. Hort. Sci; Weed Sci. Soc. Am. Chemical weed control; chemistry of herbicidal action. Address: Agricultural Experiment Station, University of California, University Hall, Berkeley, CA 94720.

DAY, BRUCE F(REDERICK), b. Clyde, N.Y, Jan. 12, 22; m. 48; c. 2. ORGANIC CHEMISTRY. Ph.D, California, Los Angeles, 49. Res. chemist, E.I. DU PONT DE NEMOURS & CO. INC, 49-52, res. supvr, 52-55, sr. res. supvr, 55-56, tech. investigator, 56-58, prod. specialist indust. & biochem. dept, 58-59, asst. sales mgr, tech. sales, 59-62, dir, sales tech. lab, 62-64, asst. dist. sales mgr, 65-66, Holotron Corp, 66-67, venture mgr, develop. dept, 67-69, MGR, PACKAGING SYSTS. & MKT. DEVELOP. DIV, FILM DEPT, 70- Civilian with Off. of Sci. Res. & Develop, 44-45. Synthetic organic chemistry; exploratory research in new polymer structures; polyolefins; fluorocarbons; thermosetting resins; developments in reinforced plastics; polyformaldehyde; nylon filaments and molding powders; polyimides; photo-copying; packaging films. Address: Film Dept, E.I. du Pont de Nemours & Co, Inc, Wilmington, DE 19898.

DAY, CECIL LEROY, b. Dexter, Mo, Oct. 4, 22; m. 48; c. 2. AGRICULTURAL ENGINEERING. B.S, Missouri, 45, M.S, 48; Ph.D.(eng), Iowa State, 57. Instr. AGR. ENG, UNIV. MO-COLUMBIA, 45-48, asst. prof, 48-54, assoc. prof, 54-62, PROF, 62-, CHMN. DEPT, 69- Am. Soc. Agr. Eng; Nat. Soc. Prfnl. Eng. Physical properties of forages; harvesting, handling, drying and storage of forages. Address: Dept. of Agricultural Engineering, University of Missouri-Columbia, Columbia, MO 65201.

DAY, DAVID ALLEN, b. Ann Arbor, Mich, Nov. 22, 24; m. 45; c. 5. ENGINEERING. B.C.E, Cornell, 45; M.S, Illinois, 51. Field supt, Raymond Concrete Pile Co, 46-47; tech. engr, Gen. Paving Co, Ill, 47-48; from instr. to assoc. prof. civil eng. & in-charge construct. option, Illinois, 48-58; prof. & chmn. dept, UNIV. DENVER, 58-60, dean col. eng, 60-68, PROF. CIVIL ENG, 68- Consult, State of Ill, 51-58; Bridge Off, Ill. Div. Hwys, 52-56. Mem. proj. adv. comt, Ill. Div. Hwys. & U.S. Bur. Pub. Rds, 54-58; Assoc. Gen. Contractors Am, 59-70. U.S.A, 42-43; U.S. Navy Res. Civil Eng.C, 43-46, Lt. Am. Soc. Civil Eng; Am. Soc. Eng. Educ; Nat. Soc. Prof. Eng. Construction engineering, structural design problems; economics and planning of construction operations; structural and construction materials. Address: College of Engineering, University of Denver, Denver, CO 80210.

DAY, D(ELBERT) E(DWIN), b. Avon, Ill, Aug. 16, 36; m. 56; c. 2. CERAMICS, MATERIALS SCIENCE. B.S, Mo. Sch. Mines, 58; Pittsburgh Plate Glass fels, Pa. State, 60, 61, M.S, 60, Ph.D.(ceramic tech), 61. Asst. prof. ceramic eng, Mo. Sch. Mines, 61-62; asst. prof, UNIV. MO-ROLLA, 64-65, assoc. prof, 65-67, PROF. CERAMIC ENG. & DIR. INDUST. RES. CTR, 67- U.S. Army Res. Off. grant, 64-71. C.Eng, 62-64, 1st Lt. Am. Ceramic Soc; Am. Soc. Test. & Mat; Am. Soc. Eng. Educ; Nat. Inst. Ceramic Eng; Brit. Soc. Glass Technol. Internal friction and anelasticity of vitreous materials; crystal structure and properties of crystalline materials in portland cement. Address: Box 357, Rolla, MO 65401.

DAY, DONALD LEE, b. Leedey, Okla, Aug. 14, 31; m. 54; c. 3. AGRICULTURAL ENGINEERING. B.S, Okla. State, 54, Ph.D.(agr. eng), 62; M.S, Missouri, 58. Instr. AGR. ENG, Tex. Tech. Col, 57-58; asst, Missouri, 58-59; Okla. State, 59-62; asst. prof, UNIV. ILL, URBANA, 62-67, assoc. prof, 67-71, PROF, 71- Nat. Center Urban & Indust. Health res. grant, 66-69. U.S.A.F, 54-57, 1st Lt. Am. Soc. Agr. Eng; Am. Soc. Eng. Educ. Crop drying; livestock housing and environmental factors; livestock waste disposal; air pollution in and around livestock buildings. Address: Dept. of Agricultural Engineering, University of Illinois, Urbana, IL 61801.

DAY, EDGAR A(LLAN), b. Romney, W.Va, Sept. 11, 28; m. 55; c. 5. FOOD SCIENCE. B.S, Maryland, 53; M.S, Pa. State, 55, Ph.D.(dairy sci), 57. Asst. prof. dairy sci, Maryland, 56-58; prof. food & dairy tech, Oregon State, 58-66; v.pres. flavor res, INT. FLAVORS & FRAGRANCES, INC, 66-67, v.pres. res. & develop, 67-71, V.PRES. & U.S. EXEC. V.PRES, 71- U.S.M.C, 46-48, 50-51. AAAS; Am. Chem. Soc.(Borden Award, 65); Am. Oil Chemists' Soc; Am. Dairy Sci. Asn; Inst. Food Tech.(award, 64); N.Y. Acad. Sci. Flavor chemistry of foods; chemical identification of natural and unnatural flavors; mechanism of flavor development; means for prevention of flavor deterioration in foods. Address: International Flavors & Fragrances, Inc, 1515 Highway 36, Union Beach, NJ 07735.

DAY, EDGAR WILLIAM, JR, b. New Albany, Ind, Sept. 7, 36; m. 59; c. 4. ANALYTICAL CHEMISTRY. B.S, Notre Dame, 58; Ph.D.(anal. chem), Iowa State, 63. SR. ANAL. CHEMIST, ELI LILLY & CO, 63- Am. Chem. Soc; Soc. Appl. Spectros; fel. Am. Inst. Chem. Infrared molecular spectroscopy; applied infrared spectometry; gas chromatography; general organic chemical analysis; pesticide formulation and residue analysis; radiochemistry; thin layer chromatography; organic mass spectrometry; computerization of analytical instrumentation. Address: 8718 Oriental Court, Indianapolis, IN 46219.

DAY, ELBERT J(ACKSON), b. Cullman, Ala, Mar. 11, 25; m. 48; c. 3. POULTRY NUTRITION. B.S, Ala. Polytech, 52, M.S, 53, Ph.D.(poultry nutrit), 56. Asst. animal nutritionist, Ala. Polytech, 55-56; asst. prof. POULTRY SCI, MISS. STATE UNIV, 56-57, assoc. prof, 58-59, PROF, 60-, nutritionalist, 56-59. U.S.A, 45-46. Poultry Sci. Asn. Effects of dietary modifications on pigmentation of broilers; proper dietary balance of protein and energy for poultry rations; improvement in performance of poultry rations with feed additives. Address: Dept. of Poultry Science, Mississippi State University, Box 5188, State College, MS 39762.

DAY, EMERSON, b. Hanover, N.H, May 2, 13; m. 37; c. 5. INTERNAL MEDICINE. A.B, Dartmouth Col, 34; M.D, Harvard, 38. Intern, med. serv, Presby. Hosp, New York, 38-40; Libman fel. med, Hopkins Hosp, 40-42; asst. res. med, N.Y. Hosp, 42; flight surg, intercontinent div, TransWorld Airline, Wash, D.C, 42-45, med. dir, int. div, New York, 45-47; asst. prof. pub. health & prev. med, med. col, Cornell, 47-50, assoc. prof, 50-54, prof. prev. med, Sloan-Kettering Div, 54-64, chief div. prev. med, Sloan-Kettering Inst, 54-64, head dept. prev. med, mem. ctr, 54-63; dir, Strang Clin, 63-69, pres. prev. med. inst, 66-69; V.PRES. & MED. DIR, MEDEQUIP CORP, 69- Dir, Kips Bay-Yorkville Cancer Detection Ctr, 47-50; Strang Cancer Prev. Clin, 50-63; attend. physician, Mem. Hosp, 50-63; assoc, Sloan-Kettering Inst, 52-54, mem, 54-64; advan. technol. comt, Ill. Regional Med. Prog. With Off. Sci. Res. & Develop; U.S.N, 47-50. Am. Med. Asn; Am. Asn. Cancer Res; Am. Cancer Soc.(bronze medal, 56); fel. Am. Col. Physicians; fel. Soc. Advan. Med. Systs; Harvey Soc; hon. fel. Int. Acad. Cytol; James Ewing Soc; fel. N.Y. Acad. Med; fel. N.Y. Acad. Sci.(pres, 65); Royal Soc. Med; Am. Soc. Cytol.(pres, 58). Preventive medicine; automated multiphase health testing; medical care systems; cancer detection and prevention; cardiology; aviation physiology; neurology; pain mechanisms. Address: 320 Pebblebrook Dr, Northbrook, IL 60062.

DAY, EMMETT E(LBERT), b. Paris, Texas, July 21, 15; m. 37; c. 2. MECHANICAL ENGINEERING. B.A, E. Texas State Teachers Col, 36; B.S, Mass. Inst. Tech, 45, M.S.(mech. eng), 47. Instr, pub. sch, Texas, 36-40; indust. specialist, War Prod. Bd, 40-42; instrument specialist, San Antonio Arsenal, 42-43; asst. instr. MECH. ENG, Mass. Inst. Tech, 44-46; instr, 46-47; asst. prof, UNIV. WASH, 47-50, assoc. prof, 60-65, PROF, 54- Gold Medal award, Pi Tau Sigma, 54. Soc. Exp. Stress Anal; Am. Soc. Mech. Eng.(v.pres, 62-66); Am. Soc. Eng. Educ.(ed, Mach. Design Bulletin, 54-57). Experimental stress analysis; materials of engineering. Address: 7520 57th Pl. N.E, Seattle, WA 98115.

DAY, EUGENE D(AVIS), b. Cobleskill, N.Y, June 24, 25; m. 46; c. 1. BIOCHEMISTRY. B.S, Union (N.Y), 49; M.S, Delaware, 50, Biochem. Res. Found. fel, 50-52, Ph.D.(biochem), 52. Res. assoc, Roscoe B. Jackson Mem. Lab, Maine, 52-54; sr. cancer res. biochemist, Roswell Park Mem. Inst, 54-58, assoc. cancer res. biochemist, 58-62, asst. res. prof. chem, Roswell Park Div, Sch. grad. studies, Buffalo, 57-62; assoc. prof. IMMUNOL, MED. CTR, DUKE UNIV, 62-65, PROF, 65- U.S.A, 43-46. Am. Asn. Cancer Res; Am. Asn. Immunol. Cancer immunology; immunochemistry; application of radio antibodies; subcellular fractionations; neuroimmunology. Address: Box 3045, Duke University Medical Center, Durham, NC 27710.

DAY, FRANK, JR, b. Bellaire, Ohio, March 12, 14; m. 36; c. 5. CHEMISTRY. A.B, Ohio State, 36; Ph.D.(chem), Pittsburgh, 41. Res. engr, Battelle Mem. Inst, 36-37; res. chemist, Corning Glass Works, 41-50, mgr. pilot plant & res. group, 50-55, chem. servs. dept, 55-58; mgr. melting res. dept, OWENS-CORNING FIBERGLAS CORP, 58, glass res. & tech, 59-69, dir. mfg. glass & control systs. technol, 69-70, DIR. ADVAN. DEVELOP, 70- Am. Chem. Soc; Brit. Soc. Glass Technol; Am. Ceramic Soc; Am. Inst. Chem. Eng. Metal corrosion; high temperature reactions in glass; development of optical glass melting; glass melting and forming developments. Address: 203 S. Cherry St, Granville, OH 43203.

DAY, GENE F, b. Stamford, Tex, June 17, 36; m. 59; c. 2. MATERIALS SCIENCE. A.B, California, Berkeley, 58, Nat. Sci. Found. fel, 58-59, M.S, 60, Ph.D, 64. SR. ENGR, cent. res. lab, VARIAN ASSOCS, 63-69, ELECTROPHOTOGRAPHICS UNIT, 69- AAAS; Am. Phys. Soc; Soc. Photog. Sci. & Eng. Optical and electronic properties of metals, semiconductors and insulators. Address: Electrophotographics Unit, Varian Assocs, 611 Hansen Way, Palo Alto, CA 94303.

DAY, GEORGE WESLEY, b. Hannaford, N.Dak, Sept. 24, 35; m. 59. MATHEMATICS. B.S, San Jose State Col, 56; M.A, Purdue, 58, Nat. Sci. Found. fel, 60-61, Ph.D.(math), 62. Instr. math, Purdue, 61-62; proj. engr, west. develop. labs, Philco Corp, 62-64; asst. prof. MATH, Dartmouth Col, 64-66; UNIV. WYO, 66-69, ASSOC. PROF, 69- Math. Asn. Am; Am. Math. Soc. Algebraic aspects of infinite Boolean algebras and other structures derived from the study of symbolic logic. Address: Dept. of Mathematics, University of Wyoming, Laramie, WY 82070.

DAY, GERALD I(RVING), b. Detroit, Mich, Dec. 10, 27; m. 57; c. 3. WILDLIFE MANAGEMENT. B.S, Arizona, 53, M.S, 63. Biologist, ARIZ. GAME & FISH DEPT, 53-60, RES. BIOLOGIST, 60- Mem, Desert Bighorn Coun. U.S.A, 46-48. Wildlife Soc. Capturing and marking techniques for deer, javelina, elk and desert bighorn sheep; factors influencing javelina populations; study of the effects of controlled hunting on a javelina population; determination of javelina herd integrity and size of home range. Address: 5971 E. 17th St, Tucson, AZ 85711.

DAY, HAROLD J, b. Milwaukee, Wis, May 22, 29; m. 53; c. 2. CIVIL ENGINEERING. B.S, Wisconsin, 52, M.S, 53, Ford Found. fel, 60-63, Ph.D. (civil eng), 63. Res. asst, hydraul. & sanit. lab, Wisconsin, 52-53, 62-63, instr. civil eng, 59-60; proj. engr, Scott Paper Co, 53-59; asst. prof. civil eng, Carnegie-Mellon Univ, 63-67, assoc. prof, 67-70; PROF. ENVIRON. CONTROL & CHMN. DEPT, UNIV. WIS, GREEN BAY, 70- . U.S.N, 46-48. Am. Geophys. Union; Am. Soc. Eng. Educ; Am. Soc. Civil Eng. Fluid mechanics; hydrology; water resources; hydraulics. Address: Dept. of Environmental Control, University of Wisconsin, Green Bay, WI 54305.

DAY, HAROLD R(ANSOM), b. Washington, Pa, Aug. 9, 27; m. 47; c. 2. PHYSICS, PHYSICAL ELECTRONICS. B.A, Washington & Jefferson Col, 47, M.A, 49; Ph.D.(physics), Missouri, 52. Instr, Washington & Jefferson Col, 47-49; Missouri, 49-52; assoc, res. lab, GEN. ELEC. CO, 52-63, mgr. thermoplastic recording proj, new bus. develop. oper, 64-67, MGR. LAMP ENG. RES, LIGHTING RES. LAB, 67- . Inst. Elec. & Electronics Eng; Soc. Motion Picture & TV Eng. Storage and camera tubes; thermoplastic recording. Address: Lighting Research Lab, General Electric Co, Nela Park, Cleveland, OH 44112.

DAY, HARRY G(ILBERT), b. Monroe Co, Iowa, Oct. 8, 06; m. 33, 69; c. 3. BIOLOGICAL CHEMISTRY. A.B, Cornell Col, 30, hon. Sc.D, 67; Sc.D. (biochem), Hopkins, 33. Nat. Res. fel, Hopkins, 33-34; Gen. Ed. Bd. fel, Yale, 34-36; assoc. BIOCHEM, sch. hygiene & pub. health, Hopkins, 36-40; asst. prof, IND. UNIV, BLOOMINGTON, 40-45, assoc. prof, 45-50, PROF, 50-, UNDERGRAD. ADV, 62-, ASSOC. DEAN RES. & ADVAN. STUDIES, 67-, chmn. dept. chem, 52-62. AAAS; Am. Chem. Soc; Am. Inst. Nutrit; Soc. Exp. Biol. & Med; Am. Soc. Biol. Chem. Boron, zinc and other trace inorganic elements in nutrition; fluorine and dental caries. Address: Dept. of Chemistry, Indiana University, Bloomington, IN 47401.

DAY, HARVEY JAMES, b. Souderton, Pa, Mar. 2, 29; m. 51; c. 3. INTERNAL MEDICINE, HEMATOLOGY. B.S, Villanova, 49; M.D, Hahnemann Med. Col, 53. Intern, Abington Mem. Hosp, Pa, 53-54, res. med, 54-56; Ohio State Univ. Hosp, 56-57, instr, 57-58; hemat, SCH. MED. TEMPLE UNIV, 58-60, assoc. MED, 61-63, assoc. prof, 63-64, PROF, 66-, DIR. HEMAT, 61- Consult, Abington Mem. Hosp, 59-; chief hemat, 65; Fulbright res. scholar, Univ. Oslo, 66-68; res. assoc, Inst. Thrombosis Res, Riks Hosp, Norway, 66-68. Dipl, Am. Bd. Internal Med. U.S.C.G, 44-46. Am. Med. Asn; Asn. Am. Med. Cols; Asn. Clin. Sci; assoc. Am. Col. Path; fel. Am. Col. Physicians; Am. Soc. Hemat; Am. Fedn. Clin. Res; Int. Soc. Hemat. Platelets in thrombosis; blood platelets. Address: Dept. of Medicine, Temple University School of Medicine, 3401 N. Broad St, Philadelphia, PA 19140.

DAY, H(ERMAN) O('NEAL), JR, b. Dallas, Tex, Dec. 4, 25; m. 52; c. 4. PHYSICAL CHEMISTRY. B.S, E.Tex. State Teachers Col, 45; fel, Texas, 45-50, A.M, 48, Ph.D.(phys. chem), 51. Asst, defense res. lab, Texas, 48-50; chemist, Oak Ridge Nat. Lab, 51-56; chemist, plant tech. sect, Chambers Works, org. chem. dept, E.I. DU PONT DE NEMOURS & CO, INC, 56-60, Jackson Lab, 60-63, process dept, CHAMBERS WORKS, ORG. CHEM. DEPT, 63-69, SR. PROCESS CHEMIST, 69-70, PETROL. CHEM. DIV. TECH. SECT, 70- Am. Chem. Soc. The pressure-volume-temperature relationships of gases and liquids; solution chemistry of the heavy elements; radiation corrosion in homogeneous nuclear reactors; manufacture of tetraalkyl lead. Address: Petroleum Chemicals Division Technical Section, Chambers Works, E.I. du Pont de Nemours & Co, Inc, Deepwater, NJ 08023.

DAY, J. H, b. Kingston, Ont, June 8, 31; m. 67; c. 1. INTERNAL MEDICINE. Hon. B.A, Queen's Univ.(Ont), 53; M.D, C.M, McGill Univ, 59. McLaughlin traveling fel, 66; lectr. MED, QUEEN'S UNIV.(ONT), 67-68, ASST. PROF, 68-, HEAD DIV. ALLERGY, 67-; KINGSTON GEN. HOSP, 67- Fel, Royal Col. Physicians & Surgeons of Can, 67. Royal Can. Armoured C, 52, Lt. Fel. Am. Acad. Allergy; fel. Can. Soc. Allergy & Clin. Immunol. Immunological paralysis; immunization against influenza; pathogenesis of asthma; waterfowl ecology. Address: Division of Allergy, Kingston General Hospital, Kingston, Ont, Can.

DAY, JACK CALVIN, b. Stamford, Tex, June 17, 36; m. 68. ORGANIC CHEMISTRY. A.B, California, Berkeley, 61; Ph.D.(org. chem), California, Los Angeles, 67. Res. assoc. CHEM, Columbia, 67-68; ASST. PROF, HUNTER COL, 68- Am. Chem. Soc. Physical organic chemistry; structure, mechanism and stereochemical studies in organo-sulfur chemistry; synthesis of optically active sulfur compounds. Address: Dept. of Chemistry, Hunter College, 695 Park Ave, New York, NY 10021.

DAY, JAMES M(EIKLE), b. Wickham, N.B, Oct. 20, 24; U.S. citizen; m. 51. INORGANIC & NUCLEAR CHEMISTRY, CHEMICAL ENGINEERING. B.S, New Hampshire, 45; M.S, Illinois, 52; Ph.D.(inorg. & nuclear chem), Arkansas, 54. Chem. engr, E.I. du Pont de Nemours & Co, N.Y, 45-46; chemist, Burgess Battery Co, Ill, 46-48; chem. engr, Anderson Phys. Lab, 48-51; res. assoc, Wisconsin, 53-54; radiation chemist, Phillips Petrol. Co, Okla, 54-56, nuclear chemist, Idaho, 56-58, reactor core physicist, 58-59; sr. res. chemist, Indust. Reactor Lab, N.J. for Am. Tobacco Co, Va, 59-62; mgr. chem. & physics res, WHIRLPOOL CORP, 62-70, STAFF CHEMIST, 70- AAAS; Am. Chem. Soc; Am. Nuclear Soc; Am. Oil Chemists' Soc; Am. Inst. Chem. Detergent chemistry; radiotracer techniques in soil measurement; chemical reactions and effects of radiation; hot atom chemistry. Address: Research Center, Whirlpool Corp, Monte Rd, Benton Harbor, MI 49022.

DAY, JAMES THOMAS, b. Elk City, Okla, Sept. 13, 32. MATHEMATICS. B.S, Oklahoma, 54; M.S, Okla. State, 56; Ph.D.(math), Wisconsin, 63. Programmer, Chance Vought Corp, 58-59; instr. math, Tulsa, 59-60; Off. Naval Res. fel. numerical anal, Swiss Fed. Inst. Tech, 63-64; asst. prof. MATH, Mich. State, 64-66; Univ. Wis-Milwaukee, 66-67; ASSOC. PROF, PA. STATE UNIV, 67- U.S.A, 55-57, 1st Lt. Am. Math. Soc. Numerical analysis; differential equations. Address: Dept. of Computer Science, 426 McAllister Bldg, Pennsylvania State University, University Park, PA 16802.

DAY, JESSE HAROLD, b. Bend, Ore, Oct. 27, 16; m. 38. PHYSICAL CHEMISTRY. B.A, Reed Col, 42; M.S, Case Sch. Appl. Sci, 45, Ph.D.(phys. chem), Case Inst. Technol, 48. Instr. CHEM, case Inst. Technol, 46-48; asst. prof. OHIO UNIV, 48-53, assoc. prof, 53-58, chmn. dept, 58-63, PROF, 63-, ASSOC. DEAN COL. ARTS & SCI, 69-, 67-68, acting dean 68-69, asst. dean, 66-67. Res. chemist, Rubber Reserve Bd, 44-45; Glenn L. Martin Co, 46-47; vis. prof, Univ. Idaho, 64. Civilian with Off. Sci. Res. & Develop. Fel. Am. Inst. Chem; Am. Chem Soc; Soc. Plastics Eng.(ed, jour, 45-58); fel. N.Y. Acad. Sci. Thermochromism; vinyl polymerization; chemistry of fulvenes. Address: College of Arts & Sciences, Ohio University, Athens, OH 45701.

DAY, JOE LEE (JACK), b. Cincinnati, Ohio, Feb. 15, 27. PSYCHOPHYSIOLOGY, PSYCHOLOGY. B.S, Houston, 59; San Antonio Jr, Col, 61. Res. asst. psychiat, col. med, Baylor, 58-61; res psychologist, U.S. Air Force Sch. Aerospace Med, 61-62; AEROSPACE TECHNOLOGIST, NASA MANNED SPACECRAFT CENTER, 62- Inst. Elec. & Electronics Eng; Soc. Psychophysiol. Res; Brit. Electrophysiol. Tech. Asn. Psychophysiological data collection. Address: Project Support Division, Bioinstrumentation Section, NASA Manned Spacecraft Center, Houston, TX 77058.

DAY, JOHN A(RTHUR), b. Salina, Kans, May 24, 13; m. 37; c. 5. ENVIRONMENTAL SCIENCES, METEOROLOGY. B.A, Colo. Col, 36; Cert. Boeing Sch. Aeronaut, 37; summers, Pa. State, 53, 57; M.S, Oregon State, 54, Ph.D. (physics), 57. Regional meteorologist, Pan Am. World Airways, 37-46; instr. PHYSICS, Oregon State, 46-56; vis. assoc. prof, Redlands, 56-58; PROF, LINFIELD COL, 58- Nat. Sci. Found. sci. faculty fel, Imp. Col, London, 62-63. U.S.N.R, 45-46, Res, 46-60, Lt. Am. Asn. Physics Teachers; Am. Meteorol. Soc. Nucleation studies; physics of precipitation; interrelationships between disciplines of science and religion; history of meteorological science. Address: Dept. of Physics, Linfield College, McMinnville, OR 97128.

DAY, JOHN T(ORNGREN), b. Los Angeles, Calif, Jan. 9, 24; m. 47; c. 2. ORGANIC CHEMISTRY. A.B, Minnesota, 47, Abbott fel, 50-51, Ph.D.(org. chem), 51. Asst. chem, Minnesota, 48-50; chemist, Merck & Co, Inc, 51-53, sr. chemist, 53-56, mgr. process develop, 56-64; DIR. RES. & DEVELOP, Grain Processing Corp, 64-69; ARAPAHOE CHEM. CO, DIV. SYNTEX CORP, 69- U.S.A.A.F, 42-46, Capt. N.Y. Acad. Sci; Am. Chem. Soc. Fermentation and organic chemicals process development. Address: 1503 Bradley Dr, Boulder, CO 80303.

DAY, LAWRENCE E(UGENE), b. Findlay, Ohio, Feb. 12, 33; m. 57; c. 3. MICROBIOLOGY, BIOCHEMISTRY. A.B, Miami (Ohio), 55; M.S, Mich. State, 60, Nat. Insts. Health fel, 60-62, Ph.D.(microbiol), 63. Res. microbiologist, med. res. lab, Chas. Pfizer & Co, Inc, Conn, 63-66; antibiotic develop, ELI LILLY & CO, 66-70, NEW FERMENTATION PROD. TEAM LEADER, 70- U.S.M.C, 55-58, Capt. Am. Soc. Microbiol. Antibiotic biosynthesis; fermentation technology; modes of action of antibiotics. Address: Dept. K418, Eli Lilly & Co, 1202 Kentucky Ave, Indianapolis, IN 46224.

DAY, LeROY E(DWARD), b. Doswell, Va, Jan. 2, 25; m. 47; c. 3. AERONAUTICAL ENGINEERING. B.Aero.Eng, Ga. Inst. Tech, 46; M.S, California, Los Angeles, 55; Sloan fel, Mass. Inst. Tech, 59-60, M.S, 60. Test engr. guided missile, U.S. Naval Missile Center, 48-51; head controls br. develop. & testing guid. systs, 51-56, head guid. div, 56-59, head inertial guid. div, develop. res. testing guid. systs. missiles, 59-60, dep. head, missile progs. dept, 60-62; chief, Proj. Gemini, NASA, 62-63, dir. Gemini Test Prog, MANNED SPACE FLIGHT, 63-66, dir. Apollo Test, 66-69, mgr. space shuttle task group, 69-71, DEP. DIR. SPACE SHUTTLE PROG, 71- Lectr, California, Los Angeles, 59. Consult, 59. U.S.N, 43-48, Res, 48-, Comdr. Sci. Res. Soc. Am. Automatic control and guidance of missiles and space vehicles; manned space flight. Address: 11709 Magruder Lane, Rockville, MD 20852.

DAY, L(EWIS) R(ODMAN), b. Harrowsmith, Ont, Apr. 23, 15; m. 43; c. 2. MARINE BIOLOGY. B.A, Queen's (Ont), 39; M.A, Western Ontario, 41. Zoologist, Atlantic Herring Invest. Cmt, 45-48; biologist, Fisheries Res. Bd, Can, 48-63, asst. dir, 55-63; EXEC. SECY, INT. CMN. NORTHWEST ATLANTIC FISHERIES, 63- Can. Army, 42-45, Lt. Fisheries biology. Address: International Commission for the Northwest Atlantic Fisheries, P.O. Box 638, Dartmouth, N.S, Can.

DAY, M. HANFORD, b. Sykesville, Md, Sept. 30, 29; m. 53; c. 2. AGRICULTURE, AGRONOMY. B.S, Maryland, 53, M.S, 55. Exten. seed specialist, UNIV. MD, 53-55, SUPV. MD. SEED INSPECTION SERV, 55, 57-, DIR, MD. SEED LAB, 57- U.S.A.F, 55-57, Res, 57-65, 1st Lt. Am. Soc. Agron; Asn. Off. Seed Anal. Seed technology; vigor testing; quick methods of varietal identification in seedling stages; seedling disease identification and control; new improved seed testing procedures; turf certification and turf law enforcement; seed certification and seed law enforcement; seed quality standards including quality control procedures. Address: Dept. of Agronomy, H.J. Patterson Hall, University of Maryland, College Park, MD 20742.

DAY, MAHLON M(ARSH), b. Rockford, Ill, Nov. 24, 13; m. 39, 52; c. 5. MATHEMATICS. B.S, Oregon State Col, 35; Sc.M, Brown, 38, Ph.D.(math), 39. Keene fel, Inst. Adv. Study, 39-40; instr. math, UNIV. ILL, URBANA, 40-43, assoc, 43-45, asst. prof. MATH, 45-47, assoc. prof, 47-49, PROF, 49-, head dept, 59-65. Res. assoc, Brown, 44-46; Nat. Sci. Found. sr. res. fel, 56-57. Fel. AAAS; Am. Math. Soc; Math. Asn. Am. Linear spaces; ordered systems; geometry of normed spaces; amenable semigroups. Address: Dept. of Mathematics, University of Illinois, Urbana, IL 61801.

DAY, MARION C(LYDE), JR, b. Malvern, Ark, Aug. 7, 27; m. 50; c. 3. INORGANIC & PHYSICAL CHEMISTRY. A.B, San Jose State Col, 50; Ph.D. (chem), Iowa State, 55. Asst. prof. INORG. CHEM, LA. STATE UNIV, 55-60, assoc. prof, 60-69, PROF, 69- U.S.N, 45-46. Am. Chem. Soc. Electrolytes in solvents of low dielectric constant; conductance of sodium aluminum alkyls in hexane, ether, benzene mixed solvent systems; ion solvent interactions. Address: Dept. of Inorganic Chemistry, Louisiana State University, Baton Rouge, LA 70803.

DAY, MAURICE J(EROME), b. Saginaw, Mich, Jan. 3, 13; m. 44; c. 4. PHYSICAL CHEMISTRY. B.S, Mich. State, 34, M.S, 35, Ph.D.(phys, chem), 37, hon. D.E, 64. Metallurgist, Carnegie-Ill. Steel Corp, 37-38; phys. chemist, res. lab, U.S. Steel Corp, 38-41; tech. trade rep, Carnegie-Ill. Steel Corp, 41-45, mgr. alloy bur, 45-47, metall. engr, 47-52; mgr. mat. & processes div, Armour Res. Found, Ill. Inst. Technol, 52-53, asst. dir, 53-54, dir. res, 54-55, v.pres. res, 55-58; tech, Crucible Steel Co. Am, 58-59, commercial, 59-63, sr. v.pres, 63-65; PRES, HAWLEY MFG. CO, 66-; CHMN, PRES. & DIR, ARGUS INC, 69- Chmn. bd, Packaging Found, Mich. State Univ, 63-; dir, Oxford Elec. Corp, 68 & Interphoto, Inc, 70- With U.S.A, 44. Mem. minerals & metals adv. bd, Nat. Res. Coun. Am. Inst. Mining, Metall. & Petrol. Eng; Soc. Automotive Eng; Am. Ord. Asn; Am. Soc. Metals; Am. Inst. Mgt; Am. Mgt. Asn; Brit. Inst. Metals. Metallurgy of steel products and methods of manufacture; development of alloy steels and ferroalloys. Address: 830 Larchmont Rd, Pittsburgh, PA 15243.

DAY, PAUL L(OUIS), b. Grants Pass, Ore, Dec. 26, 99; m. 22; c. 2. BIOCHEMISTRY. A.B, Willamette, 21; M.A, Columbia, 23, Ph.D.(biochem), 27; LL.D, Arkansas, 60. Instr. chem, Columbia Jr. Col, 21-22; prof, Montana-Wesleyan, 25-27; prof. biochem. & head dept, sch. med, Arkansas, 27-58, asst. dean grad. sch, 56-58; sci. dir, U.S. Food & Drug Admin, 59-62; SCI. ADMINSTR. EXTRAMURAL RES. & TRAINING, NAT. HEART & LUNG INST, 62- Mem. sci. adv. cmt, Nat. Vitamin Found, 53-55; mem. food & nutrit. bd, Nat. Res. Coun, 53-59, chmn, cmt. fats in human nutrit, 55-58, agr. bd, cmt. animal nutrit, 55-58; mem. sci. adv. cmt, Nutrit. Found, 60-62. U.S.A, 18. AAAS; Am. Chem. Soc; Am. Soc. Biol. Chem; Soc. Exp. Biol. & Med; Am. Soc. Animal Sci; Am. Med. Asn; Am. Inst. Nutrit.(v.pres, 51, pres, 52, Mead-Johnson award, 47). Ocular manifestations of riboflavin and tryptophan deficiency; xylose cataract; folic acid and nutritional cytopenia in the monkey; vitamin E deficiency in the monkey. Address: Extramural Research & Training, National Heart & Lung Institute, National Institutes of Health, Bethesda, MD 20014.

DAY, PAUL P(ALMER), b. Chicago, Ill, Dec. 16, 28; m; c. 2. PHYSICS. B.S, Ill. Inst. Tech, 51, M.S, 55. Assoc. physicist, CHEM. DIV, ARGONNE NAT. LAB, 51-68, GROUP LEADER COMPUT. SERV, 68- Am. Phys. Soc; Asn. Comput. Mach. Irradiation damage in solids; nuclear spectroscopy; nuclear level structure computations; design implementation of on-line multi experiment real time computer facility. Address: Division of Chemistry, Argonne National Lab, 9700 S. Cass, Argonne, IL 60439.

DAY, PAUL R(USSELL), b. Hollister, Calif, Sept. 6, 12; m. 41; c. 3. SOIL PHYSICS. A.B, Univ. Calif, 35, Ph.D.(soil physics), 41. Assoc. soils, Univ. Calif, Davis, 41, instr. soil physics & jr. soil physicist, UNIV. CALIF, BERKELEY, 41-45, asst. prof. & asst. soil physicist, 45-52, assoc. prof. & assoc. soil physicist, 52-58, PROF. SOIL SCI. & SOIL PHYSICIST, 58-, chmn. dept. soils & plant nutrit, 64-70. Fulbright sr. scholar, Cambridge, 62-63. U.S.A, 42-45. Fel. AAAS; Soil Sci. Soc. Am; fel. Am. Soc. Agron; Am. Geophys. Union. Thermodynamics of soil-moisture; soil structure; particle size analysis; water movement in soil; soil deformation. Address: Dept. of Soil Science, University of California, Berkeley, CA 94720.

DAY, P(ETER) R(ODNEY), b. Chingford, Eng, Dec. 27, 28; m. 51; c. 3. GENETICS. B.Sc, London, 50, Ph.D.(bot, genetics), 54. Sci. officer, John Innes Inst, Eng, 50-54, sr. sci. officer, 57-63; assoc. prof. bot. & plant path, Ohio State, 63-64; HEAD DEPT. GENETICS, CONN. AGR. EXP. STA, 64- Commonwealth Fund fel, Wisconsin, 54-56; lectr, Yale, 64-70; mem. comt. genetic vulnerability major crops, Nat. Acad. Sci, 71. AAAS; Bot. Soc. Am; Genetics Soc. Am; Am. Phytopath. Soc; Brit. Soc. Gen. Microbiol; Brit. Genetical Soc; Brit. Mycol. Soc.(secy, 62-63). Genetic systems in plant pathogenic and related fungi; genetic control of photosynthesis in crop plants. Address: Dept. of Genetics, Connecticut Agricultural Experiment Station, P. O. Box 1106, New Haven, CT 06504.

DAY, R(EUBEN) A(LEXANDER), JR, b. Atlanta, Ga, Feb. 3, 15; m. 43; c. 4. ANALYTICAL CHEMISTRY. A.B, Emory, 36, M.S, 37; Ph.D.(chem), Princeton, 40. Instr. CHEM, EMORY UNIV, 40-42, asst. prof, 42-46, assoc. prof, 46-56, PROF, 56-, chmn. dept, 57-68. Res. assoc, metall. lab, Chicago, 43; chemist, Clinton Labs, Oak Ridge, Tenn, 43-44; sr. chemist, Oak Ridge Nat. Lab, Tenn, 48. Am. Chem. Soc; Electrochem. Soc. Organic polarography; electrochemistry of organic compounds in micelles. Address: Dept. of Chemistry, Emory University, Atlanta, GA 30322.

DAY, RICHARD A(LLEN), b. Kellogg, Iowa, Apr. 4, 31; m. 56. BIOLOGICAL CHEMISTRY. B.S, Iowa State, 53; Am. Chicle Co. fel. & Ph.D.(chem), Mass. Inst. Tech, 58. Res. assoc. BIOCHEM, Mass. Inst. Tech, 57-59; asst. prof, UNIV. CINCINNATI, 59-63, assoc. prof, 63-68, PROF, 68- Nat. Insts. Health career develop. award, 68; Damon Runyon Soc. fel. AAAS; Am. Chem. Soc; Am. Soc. Microbiol. Protein structure; mass spectrometry of peptides; active site studies; chemical modification of proteins and nucleic acids; peptide synthesis; penicillinases. Address: Dept. of Chemistry, University of Cincinnati, Cincinnati, OH 45221.

DAY, RICHARD AUGUSTUS, b. Dayton, Kentucky, Sept. 19, 37; m. 62; c. 1. PHYSICS, ASTRONOMY. A.B, Villa Madonna Col, 57; Ph.D.(physics), Maryland, 65. Res. fel, Harvard Col. Observ, 65-67; ASST. PROF. PHYSICS, UNIV. OKLA, 67- Consult, Westinghouse Res. Lab, 66- Am. Phys. Soc. Stark broadening and pressure broadening of atomic spectral lines using shock tubes as light sources; laser induced plasmas; ultraviolet interferometry. Address: Dept. of Physics & Astronomy, University of Oklahoma, Norman, OK 73069.

DAY, RICHARD J(AMES), b. Atwater, Ohio, Mar. 4, 30; m. 61; c. 3. ORGANIC CHEMISTRY. A.B, Hiram Col, 52; M.S, Cornell, 55, Ph.D.(org. chem), 58. Res. chemist, INORG. RES. DEPT, MONSANTO CO, 57-61, SR. RES. CHEMIST, 61- Am. Chem. Soc. Synthesis of new nonionic surfactant intermediates such as alcohols and alkylphenols; small ring compounds and bicyclics derived from cyclopentadiene; relation of structure of surfactants to biodegradation. Address: Inorganic Research Dept, Monsanto Co, 800 N. Lindbergh Blvd, St. Louis, MO 63166.

DAY, RICHARD LAWRENCE, b. New York, N.Y, Mar. 28, 05; m. 36; c. 3. PEDIATRICS. S.B, Harvard, 27, M.D, 31. Intern, Hartford Hosp, Willard Parker Hosp. & Babies Hosp, 31-35; instr. pediat, Cornell, 39-42; asst. prof, Columbia, 42-48, assoc. prof, 48-53; prof, med. sch, State Univ. N.Y, New York, 53-60; prof. & chmn. dept, sch. med, Pittsburgh, 60-65; dir. med. dept, Planned Parenthood-World Population, 65-68; RETIRED. Prof, Mt. Sinai Sch. Med, City Univ. New York, 67-70; Physiologist, U.S.A, 42-45. Am. Pediat. Soc; Soc. Pediat. Res. Newborn infants. Address: Lakeview Terr, Westbrook, CT 06498.

DAY, ROBERT J(AMES), b. Newark, N.J, Feb. 2, 10; m. 34; c. 1. PHYSICAL CHEMISTRY, FUEL TECHNOLOGY. B.S, Union (N.Y), 33; Pittsburgh, 36-38; Consolidation fel, Pa. State, 47-49, Ph.D.(fuel tech), 49. Instr. petrol. prod, petrol. & natural gas eng. dept, Pa. State, 38-47; res. engr, Consolidation Coal Co, 49-52; res. dir. chem. process & fuel utilization, Phila. & Reading Corp, 52-56; chem. process develop. analyst, planning dept, Tex. Power & Light Co, 56-58; tech. dir. water & oil well conditioning, United Chem. Corp. N.Mex, 58-59; mgr. res. lab, J.M. Huber Corp, Tex, 60; chief chemist, Chem. Eng. Co, Inc, Tex, 60; staff engr, armament div, Universal Match Corp, 60-61; sr. engr-scientist, MISSILE & SPACE SYSTS. DIV. & AIRCRAFT DIV, McDONNELL DOUGLAS CORP, 61-70, CONSULT, 70- Mem. res. adv. cmt, Anthracite Inst. & anthracite res. adv. cmt, Pa. State, 52-56; Governor's Fuel Res. Adv. Cmt, 55. Am. Chem. Soc. Am. Inst. Mining, Metall. & Petrol. Eng; Am. Inst. Aeronaut. & Astronaut. Chemical process development; propellants development; propulsion systems design; reaction kinetics; hydrogenation; gasification; fuels processing and utilization; carbon and graphite properties and production; petroleum production; water conditioning; surfactants; sintering; calcining. Address: 3030 Merrill Dr, Apt. 26, Torrance, CA 90503.

DAY, ROBERT JAMES, b. Los Angeles, Calif, Feb. 7, 41. ANALYTICAL CHEMISTRY, ELECTROCHEMISTRY. B.A, California, Riverside, 62; Ph.D.(anal. chem), North Carolina, 66. Res. chemist, org. chem. dept, E.I. du Pont de Nemours & Co, 66-67; MEM. TECH. STAFF, TRW SYSTS. GROUP, 67- AAAS; Am. Chem. Soc. Magnetic resonance spectroscopy; electroanalytical chemistry; gas chromatography; electrobiochemistry; exobiology. Address: Mail Station R.1 2094, TRW Systems, One Space Park, Redondo Beach, CA 90278.

DAY, ROBERT WILLIAM, b. Worcester, Mass, Feb. 7, 24; m. 45; c. 2. THERMODYNAMICS. B.S, Massachusetts, 48; M.M.E, Rensselaer Polytech, 54. Instr. MECH. ENG, Rensselaer Polytech, 48-54; asst. prof, UNIV. MASS, AMHERST, 54-57, assoc. prof, 57-69, PROF, 69- Engr, Gen. Elec. Co, N.Y, 50-52; Mass, summers 55-59, consult, 57-64; engr, Boeing Airplane Co, 54; consult, Kollmorgan Optical Co, 57. West. Elec. Fund Award, 70. U.S.A, 44-46, Sgt. Am. Soc. Eng. Educ; Am. Soc. Mech. Eng. Application of thermodynamics and heat transfer to aircraft and space vehicles. Address: Dept. of Mechanical Engineering, University of Massachusetts, Amherst, MA 01002.

DAY, ROBERT WINSOR, b. Framingham, Mass, Oct. 22, 30; m. 57; c. 2. EPIDEMIOLOGY. Harvard, 49-51; M.D, Chicago, 56; M.P.H, California, Berkeley, 58, Ph.D.(epidemiol), 62. Trainee epidemiol, California, Berkeley, 57-60; res. specialist ment. retardation, Sonoma State Hosp, Calif, 60-62; asst. prof. prev. med, California, Los Angeles, 62-64; chief, hereditary defects unit, Calif. State Dept. Pub. Health, 64-65, Bur. Maternal & Child Health, 65-66, chief dep. dir, 66-67; assoc. prof. PREV. MED. & dir. div. health serv, UNIV. WASH, 68-69, PROF. & CHMN. DEPT, 70- Res. staff, Pac. State Hosp, Pomona Calif, 62-64; consult, Porterville State Hosp, 62-63; State Dept. Pub. Health, Berkeley, 63-64; lectr, sch. pub. health, Univ. Calif, Berkeley, 64-67; assoc. clin. prof, Univ. Calif, San Francisco, 66-67; vis. assoc. prof, Univ. Mich, 68. U.S.P.H.S, 56-57, Res, 66-, Asst. Surg. Am. Soc. Human Genetics; Am. Pub. Health Asn; Soc. Pediat. Res; Oper. Res. Soc. Am; Am. Epidemiol. Soc. Genetics and epidemiology; population; health services and medical care. Address: Dept. of Health Services, School of Public Health & Community Medicine, University of Washington, Seattle, WA 98195.

DAY, STACEY B(ISWAS), b. London, Eng, Dec. 31, 27; Can. citizen; m. 52; c. 2. MEDICINE, EXPERIMENTAL SURGERY. M.D, Royal Col. Surgeons, Ireland, 55; Ciba fel, McGill, 62-63, Ph.D.(exp. surg), 64; D.Sc, Univ. Cincinnati, 70. Res. fel. surg. & physiol, Minnesota, 56-60; clin. asst. med, St. George's Hosp, London, Eng, 60-61; demonstr. & prosector anat, McGill, 61-62, lectr. surg, 64-66; clin. investr, Hoechst Pharmaceut, Inc, Ohio, 66-68; regional med. dir. for New Eng, Hoffmann-La Roche Inc, N.J, 68-69; asst. prof. res. surg, col. med, Univ. Cincinnati, 69-71; ASST. PROF. PATH. & CONSERVATOR, BELL MUS. PATH, UNIV. MINN, MINNEAPOLIS, 71- Asst. prof, N.J. Col. Med, 68-69; assoc. dir. basic med. res, Shriners Hosp, Burns Inst, Cincinnati, Ohio, 69-71. Moynihan Prize & Medal. Brit. Army, 46-49. Fel. Zool. Soc. London; fel. Royal Micros. Soc; Asn. Surgeons Gt. Brit. & Ireland. Cardiovascular and renal surgery and physiology; history of medicine, cultural anthropology. Address: Bell Museum of Pathology, University of Minnesota School of Medicine, Minneapolis, MN 55455.

DAY, STEPHEN MARTIN, b. New York, N.Y, Dec. 17, 31; m. 53; c. 6. SOLID STATE PHYSICS. B.S, La. State, 57; M.A, Rice, 59, Ph.D.(physics), 61. Asst. prof. PHYSICS, UNIV. ARK, FAYETTEVILLE, 61-66, assoc. prof, 66-71, PROF, 71-, CHMN. DEPT, 69- U.S.A.F, 50-54. Am. Phys. Soc; Am. Asn. Physics Teachers. Low temperature properties of solids; magnetic resonance phenomena of solids. Address: Dept. of Physics, University of Arkansas, Fayetteville, AR 72701.

DAY, THOMAS B(RENNOCK), b. New York, N.Y, Mar. 7, 32; m. 53; c. 9. HIGH ENERGY PHYSICS. B.S, Notre Dame, 52; Ph.D.(physics), Cornell, 57. Res. assoc. PHYSICS, UNIV. MD, COLLEGE PARK, 57-58, asst. prof, 58-61, assoc. prof, 61-64, PROF, 64-, V.CHANCELLOR ACAD. PLANNING & POLICY, 70- Engr, Bendix Aviation Corp, 52-53; consult, U.S. Govt, 58- Am. Phys. Soc. Theoretical investigations in elementary particle physics and quantum mechanics; experimental work in high energy physics. Address: University of Maryland, College Park, MD 20740.

DAY, THOMAS G(ORDON), b. Milwaukee, Wis, Jan. 4, 09; m. 31; c. 4. CHEMISTRY. A.B, Carroll Col. (Wis), 30; M.S, Missouri, 32, Ph.D.(chem), 35. Asst, Mo. Sch. Mines, 30-35, instr. chem, 35-37, asst. prof. org. chem, 37-41, assoc. prof, 41-43; asst. prof, Missouri, 40-41, assoc. prof, 41-43; admin. aide to div. dir, Columbia div. war res, Manhattan Dist, 44-46; res. proj. leader, Carbide & Carbon Chem. Corp, 46-57; supvr. coal hydrogenation, Union Carbide Olefins Co, sub. UNION CARBIDE CORP, 57-58, asst. dir. res. & develop, corp, 58-66, MGR, tech. ctr, 66-67, CHEM. & PLASTICS DIV, 67- Am. Chem. Soc; Am. Inst. Chem. Eng. Analytical chemistry; electrolytical determination of small amounts of lead; organic chemistry; vapor phase hydrolysis; reaction of metals with acid halides; catalysis; coal; process development. Address: 2302 Winchester Rd, South Charleston, WV 25303.

DAY, WALTER R, JR, b. Fairfield, Ala, Aug. 12, 31; m. 58; c. 2. MICROWAVE ELECTRONICS. B.S.E.E, Auburn Univ, 53; M.S.E.E, Georgia Inst. Technol, 57. Sr. engr, Sperry Electronic Tube Div, 56-66; mem. tech. staff, plasma physics lab, Princeton, 66-67; SR. SCIENTIST, ELECTRON TUBE DIV, LITTON INDUSTS, INC, 67- U.S.N, 53-55, Lt. Inst. Elec. & Electronics Eng. Microwave electron devices including linear beam oscillators and amplifiers; electron beams and focusing systems; solid-state microwave devices and materials. Address: Litton Industries, Inc, Electron Tube Division, 960 Industrial Rd, San Carlos, CA 94070.

DAY, W(ILLIAM) FRANKLIN, b. Hindman, Ky, Aug. 7, 11; m. 47. ORGANIC CHEMISTRY. B.A, Duke, 34, M.A, 36. Teacher CHEM, PIKEVILLE COL, 42-62, assoc. prof, 62-64, PROF, 64- AAAS; Am. Chem. Soc. Address: Dept. of Chemistry, Pikeville College, Pikeville, KY 41501.

DAY, WILLIAM H, b. Wilmington, Del, Sept. 29, 34; m. 59; c. 1. ECONOMIC ENTOMOLOGY, INSECT ECOLOGY. B.S, Delaware, 55; Ph.D. (entom), Cornell, 65. Res. asst. entom, Cornell, 55-61; RES. ENTOMOLOGIST, PARASITE RES. LAB, AGR. RES. SERV, U.S. DEPT. AGR, 65- Med. Serv.C, 62-64, Res, 64-65, Capt. Entom. Soc. Am; Am. Entom. Soc.(pres, 71). Population dynamics of aphids; chemical control of potato and other vegetable insects; parasites and predators of insects; plant nutrition effects on insect populations; insect sampling and plot design. Address: Parasite Research Lab, Agricultural Research Service, U.S. Dept. of Agriculture, Box 150, Moorestown, NJ 08057.

DAY, WILLIAM W, b. Fargo, N.Dak, Jan. 10, 29; m. 49; c. 5. PHYSICS, SCIENCE EDUCATION. B.A, Wyoming, 56, M.S, 60, Nat. Sci. Found. fel, 57, 59, 60; Gen. Elec. fel, Syracuse, 58; Ed.D.(sci. ed), Nebraska, 64. Teacher, high sch, Wyo, 56-59; from instr. to asst. prof. sci. ed, Wyoming, 59-61; consult. math. & sci, Colo. State Dept. Ed, 62-63; dir. sci. ed, Ferris State Col, 63-68, dean, sch. educ, 68-70; DEAN SCH. PROF. STUDIES, STANISLAUS STATE COL, 70- Summer sr. lectr, NASA, 61; consult, State of Wyo, 60-61. U.S.A, 51-52, Capt. AAAS; Nat. Sci. Teachers Asn; Nat. Asn. Res. Sci. Teaching; Am. Asn. Physics Teachers. Chemistry. Address: School of Professional Studies, Stanislaus State College, Turlock, CA 95380.

DAY, W(INTERTON) U(NDERHILL), b. Alplaus, N.Y, Dec. 22, 16; m. 42; c. 2. CHEMISTRY. B.S, Union (N.Y), 38; Ph.D.(phys. chem), Wisconsin, 43. Chemist, KIMBERLY CLARK CORP, Wis, 42-44, tech. supt, N.Y, 44-48, WIS, 48-54, sanit. prods. res. lab, 54-67, SR. RES. SCIENTIST, 67- Chemical reaction kinetics; photochemical bromination of bromotrichloromethane. Address: Research & Engineering Center, Kimberly Clark Corp, Neenah, WI 54956.

DAYAN, JASON E(DWARD), b. Newburgh, N.Y, Aug. 6, 23; m. 52; c. 3. ORGANIC CHEMISTRY. B.S, Yale, 43, Ph.D.(org. chem), 49. Lab. instr, Yale, 46-47; process develop. chemist, Gen. Aniline & Film Corp, N.Y, 48-54, supvr. intermediate area, 54-56, azoic area, 56-59, chief chemist, intermediate area, N.J, 59-62; asst. to plant mgr, Geigy Chem. Corp, 62-71, ASST. TO V.PRES, PROD, PLASTICS & ADDITIVES DIV, CIBA-GEIGY CORP, 71- Mem. adv. comt. prof. educ, N.Y. State Educ. Dept, 58-59. U.S.N.R, 44-46. AAAS; Am. Chem. Soc. Drugs; drug and dye intermediates; brightening; brightening agents; specialty chemicals; textile auxiliaries; azoic dyes; pigments and plastics. Address: 21 Tanglewild Rd, Chappaqua, NY 10514.

DAYAN, VICTOR H, b. St. Petersburg, Fla, Apr. 26, 27; m. 59; c. 4. ANALYTICAL CHEMISTRY. B.S, Florida, 47, Ph.D.(biochem), 54. Chemist, Swift & Co, Fla, 47-48; asst, Florida, 51-54; res. chemist, Ethyl Corp, 56-61; acting chief chemist, U.S. Air Force Aerospace Fuels & Chem. Lab, Fla, 61-63; prin. scientist, ROCKETDYNE DIV, N.AM. ROCKWELL CORP, 63-70, MEM. TECH. STAFF, 70- C.Eng, U.S.A, 54-56. AAAS; Am. Chem. Soc. Halogen oxidizer analysis; propellant analysis; methods of analysis of organometallics; cryogenics analysis; polarography of amino acids; gas chromatography; microchemistry; leak detection; trace gas analysis. Address: 8427 Moorcroft Ave, Canoga Park, CA 91304.

DAYANANDA, MYSORE ANANTHAMURTHY, b. Mysore City, India, July 1, 34. MATERIALS SCIENCE, METALLURGICAL ENGINEERING. B.Sc.(hons), Mysore, 55; dipl, Indian Inst. Sci, Bangalore, 57; M.S, Purdue, 61; Ph.D.(metall. eng), 65. Sr. res. asst. metall, Indian Inst. Sci, Bangalore, 57-58; res. assoc. metall. eng, PURDUE UNIV, 65-66, asst. prof. MAT. SCI. & METALL. ENG, 66-70, ASSOC. PROF, 70- Am. Inst. Mining, Metall. & Petrol. Eng; Am. Soc. Metals; fel. Am. Inst. Chem; Electron Probe Anal. Soc. Am. Interactions of diffusing species in multicomponent metallurgical systems; application of electron microprobe and scanning electron microscope in science and engineering. Address: School of Materials Science & Metallurgical Engineering, Purdue University, Lafayette, IN 47907.

DAYBELL, MELVIN D(REW), b. Berkeley, Calif, May 8, 35; m. 59; c. 2. PHYSICS, LOW TEMPERATURE PHYSICS. B.S, New Mexico State, 56; Nat. Sci. Found. fel, Calif. Inst. Tech, 56-61, Ph.D.(physics), 62. Asst. prof. physics, New Mexico State, 61-65, ASSOC. PROF, 65-68; PHYSICS & ENG, UNIV. SOUTH. CALIF, 68- Vis. staff mem, Los Alamos Sci. Lab, 66-68. Am. Phys. Soc; Inst. Elec. & Electronics Eng. High energy physics; ultra low temperature physics; Kondo effect; optics. Address: Dept. of Physics, University of Southern California, Los Angeles, CA 90007.

DAYHOFF, E(DWARD) S(AMUEL), b. New York, June 26, 25; m. 48; c. 2. PHYSICS. A.B, Columbia, 46, M.A, 47, Ph.D.(physics), 52. Lab. asst, radiation lab, Columbia, 48-52; physicist, Bur. Standards, 52-55, NAVAL ORD LAB, 55-66, CHIEF, DIV. ELECTRONICS & ELECTROMAGNETICS, 66- Consult, U.S. Bur. Standards, 57-63. U.S.N.R, 44-46. Am. Phys. Soc; Optical Soc. Am. Free polarized electrons; spectrum of hydrogen atom; microwave optics; stellar image detection; magnetic resonance in solids; lasers. Address: Division of Electronics & Electromagnetics, Naval Ordnance Lab-White Oak, Silver Spring, MD 20910.

DAYHOFF, MARGARET O(AKLEY), b. Phila, Pa, Mar. 11, 25; m. 48; c. 2. PHYSICAL CHEMISTRY. B.A, N.Y. Univ, 45; M.A, Columbia, 46, Watson Lab. fel, 47-48; Ph.D.(chem), 48. Asst. phys. chem, Rockefeller Inst, 48-51; res. fel, Maryland, 57-59; SR. RES. SCIENTIST, NAT. BIOMED. RES. FOUND, 60-, HEAD DEPT. CHEM. BIOL, 62-; ASSOC. PROF. MED, SCH. MED, GEORGETOWN UNIV, 70- Ed, Atlas of Protein Sequence & Struct, 65- AAAS; Biophys. Soc.(secy, 71-); Am. Soc. Biol. Chem; Am. Chem. Soc; Asn. Comput. Mach; Coun. Biol. Ed; N.Y. Acad. Sci. Quantum chemistry; electrochemistry of solutions in centrifugal fields; precision densities of solutions; high-speed computer programs and strategy in protein and nucleic acid sequencing, thermodynamics, protein structure; evolution; genetics. Address: 1618 Tilton Dr, Silver Spring, MD 20902.

DAYKIN, PHILIP NORMAN, b. Vancouver, B.C, Sept. 11, 22; m. 52; c. 2. PHYSICS, MATHEMATICS. B.A, British Columbia, 47, M.A, 49, Ph.D. (physics), 52; Purdue, 49-50. Sr. sci. officer physics, res. labs, Gen. Elec. Co, Eng, 53-57; asst. res. physicist, B.C. Res. Coun, 57-59, assoc. res. physicist, 59-61, res. physicist, 61-70; PROF. MATH. & COMPUT. SCI. & COORD. UNIV. COMPUT. CTR, UNIV. LETHBRIDGE, 70- Nat. Res. Coun. Can. overseas fel. & Rutherford Mem. scholar, 52-53. R.C.A.F, 42-45. Asn. Comput. Mach. Theoretical and experimental general physics; physical environment of animals; sensory instrumentation of insects; applied mathematics; applications of computers; computer programming. Address: Dept. of Mathematical Sciences, University of Lethbridge, Lethbridge, Alta, Can.

DAYOT, VIVENCIO DALIPE, b. Dingle, Iloilo, P.I, Jan. 29, 05; m. 41; c. 3. ELECTRICAL ENGINEERING. B.S.E.E, Philippines, 27; M.S, Cornell, 42. Asst. engr, Manila Elec. Co, P.I, 31-36; instr. math. & eng, P.I. Mil. Acad, 36-40, head dept. eng, 40-41; asst. to mil. & tech. adv. to pres. of P.I, 44-46; from head academic group, P.I. Mil. Acad. to dean corps profs, Armed Forces of P.I, 46-57; prof. elec. eng, Wash. State Univ, 57-71; RETIRED. Chief signal officer, P.I. Army, 45-46. Mil. Merit medal, Armed Forces of Philippines, 55, Distinguished Serv. Star, 57. Inst. Elec. & Electronics Eng Electronics and communications engineering. Address: 10145 15th St, Seattle, WA 98168.

DAYTON, BENJAMIN B(ONNEY), b. Rochester, N.Y, Feb. 25, 14; m. 43; c. 2. PHYSICAL CHEMISTRY. B.S, Mass. Inst. Technol, 37; M.S, Univ. Rochester, 48. Teacher, high sch, N.Y, 38-40; res. physicist, Distillation Prod, Inc, 40-43, res. supvr, 43-53; dir. res, Consol. Vacuum Corp, 53, tech. dir, 54-62, chief physicist, 62-68; tech. dir, Bendix Vacuum Div, 68-69; chief scientist, BENDIX SCIENTIFIC INSTRUMENTS & EQUIP. DIV, 69-71, CONSULT, 71- U.S. ed, Vacuum, 59-; mem. Nat. Acad. Sci-Nat. Res. Coun. adv. panel 213, Nat. Bur. Standards, 65-69, adv. panel 232, 69-71; tech. dir, Int. Union Vacuum Sci. Tech. & Appln, 66-; chmn, adv. comn. to Am. Nat. Standards Inst, Int. Standards Orgn. Tech. Comn, 64-71; head, U.S. del. to Int. Standards Orgn, London, 65, Paris, 67, Berlin, 69. Am. Vacuum Soc.(pres, 61); Vacuum Soc. Japan; Am. Phys. Soc; Am. Chem. Soc; Instrument Soc. Am; Inst. Environ. Sci. High vacuum technology; atomic and molecular structure; particle physics. Address: Bendix Scientific Instruments & Equipment Division, 1775 Mt. Read Blvd, Rochester, NY 14603.

DAYTON, BRUCE R, b. Glen Cove, N.Y, Oct. 11, 37; m. 63; c. 1. PLANT ECOLOGY. B.S.F, State Univ. N.Y. Col. Forestry, Syracuse Univ, 59; M.A, Univ. N.C, Chapel Hill, 65, Ph.D.(bot), 68; Oak Ridge Assoc. Univs. fel, Savannah River Lab, S.C, 66-68. Asst. prof. BIOL, STATE UNIV. N.Y. COL, ONEONTA, 68-70, ASSOC. PROF, 70- Faculty res. fel, State Univ. N.Y. Res. Found, summers 69 & 70. U.S.A, 60-62. AAAS; Am. Inst. Biol. Sci; Ecol. Soc. Am. The influence of soils on plant distribution; primary productivity of terrestrial ecosystems; nutrient cycles in terrestrial ecosystems. Address: Dept. of Biology, State University of New York College at Oneonta, Oneonta, NY 13820.

DAYTON, DANIEL F(RANCIS), b. Hanover, N.H, June 26, 19; m. 42; c. 4. HORTICULTURE. B.Ed, N.H, Teachers Col, 42; B.S, New Hampshire, 49, M.S, 50; Ph.D.(hort), Illinois, 55. Instr. hort, New Hampshire, 49-50; instr. & first asst. PLANT BREEDING, UNIV. ILL, URBANA, 50-55, asst. prof, 55-59, assoc. prof, 59-66, PROF, 66- U.S.A.A.F, 42-46. Am. Soc. Hort. Sci. Breeding and genetics of deciduous fruit plants. Address: Dept. of Horticulture, University of Illinois. Urbana, IL 61801.

DAYTON, GLENN O(RVILLE). JR, b. Butte, Mont, June 15, 22; m. 46; c. 4. MEDICINE. Southern California, 40-43; M.D, George Washington, 46; M.Sc.Med, Pennsylvania, 53. Clin. assoc. SURG, SCH. MED, UNIV. CALIF, LOS ANGELES, 53-54, clin. instr, 54-56, clin. asst. prof, 56-58, asst. prof, 58-65, ASSOC. CLIN. PROF, 65- Attend. staff, Calif. Hosp, 52-; St. Vincent's Hosp, 54-; St. John's Hosp; consult, Better Vision Inst. Med.C, 46-48, Res, 56-58, Maj. Fel. Am. Col. Surg; Am. Acad. Ophthal. & Otolaryngol; Asn. Res. Vision & Ophthal; Am. Med. Asn; Pan-Am. Asn. Ophthal. Ophthalmic surgery and electrophysiology. Address: 10921 Wilshire Blvd, Los Angeles, CA 90024.

DAYTON, IRVING E(UGENE), b. Detroit, Mich, Jan. 31, 27; m. 52; c. 4. PHYSICS. B.A, Swarthmore Col, 48; Ph.D.(physics), Cornell, 52. Res. asst, Lab. of Nuclear Studies, Cornell, 48-52; instr. physics, Princeton, 52-54; group leader, exp. physics, atomic energy div, Babcock & Wilcox Co, 54-57; asst. prof. PHYSICS, Swarthmore Col, 57-61; PROF, MONT. STATE UNIV, 61-, V.PRES. ACAD. AFFAIRS, 66-, head dept. physics, 61-66. U.S. Agency Int. Develop-Nat. Sci. Found. consult, Madurai, India, 69; mem. gov. bd, Am. Inst. Physics. Am. Phys. Soc; Am. Asn. Physics Teachers(treas, 66-); Hist. Sci. Soc. Electronic and ionic impact phenomena; experimental nuclear and reactor physics. Address: Montana State University, Bozeman, MT 59715.

DAYTON, JAMES ANTHONY, JR, b. Chicago, Ill, Dec. 22, 37; m. 65. PLASMA PHYSICS. B.S, Ill. Inst. Tech, 59; M.S, Iowa, 60; Ph.D.(elec. eng), Illinois, 65. Res. electronics engr, Cornell Aeronaut. Lab, 65-67; AEROSPACE TECHNOLOGIST, LEWIS RES. CTR, NASA, 67- Adj. prof, Cleveland State Univ, 69- Inst. Elec. & Electronics Eng; Am. Phys. Soc; Nat. Soc. Prof. Eng. Acoustic wave propagation in plasmas; diagnostic techniques in hypersonic flow machines; gas discharge tubes; interaction of nuclear radiation with gases; thermionic conversion; power conditioning. Address: Lewis Research Center, NASA, 21000 Brookpark Rd, Mailstop 302-1, Cleveland, OH 44135.

DAYTON, P(ETER) G(USTAV), b. Szigishoava, Rumania, Mar. 9, 26; m. 53; c. 1. ORGANIC CHEMISTRY. B.S, Mass. Inst. Tech, 50; D.S, Paris, 53. Fel. med, col. med. N.Y. Univ, 54-64, res. scientist, 65-67; ASSOC. PROF. MED. & CHEM, EMORY UNIV, 67-, asst. prof. pharmacol, 67-71. Chemist, pharmacol. lab, Nat. Heart Inst, Md. U.S.N, 44-46. AAAS; Harvey Soc; Am. Soc. Pharmacol. & Exp. Therapeut; Am. Chem. Soc; Soc. Exp. Biol. & Med; N.Y. Acad. Sci; Chem. Soc. France. Chemical pharmacology; carbohydrate metabolism. Address: 151 Woodruff Memorial Bldg, Emory University, Atlanta, GA 30322.

DAYTON, RUSSELL WENDT, b. Albany, N.Y, Sept. 16, 10; m. 35; c. 2. ENGINEERING. Ch.E, Rensselaer Polytech, 31, fel, M.S, 32, Ph.D.(metall), 34. Res. engr, BATTELLE MEM. INST, 34-39, asst. supvr, 39-48, supvr, 48-53, asst. tech. dir, 53-64, asst. dir, 64-70, MEM. CORP. STAFF, 71- AAAS; Am. Nuclear Soc; Am. Soc. Metals; Am. Soc. Mech. Eng. Physical metallurgy; engineering design and heat transfer; nuclear engineering and metallurgy; bearings; friction and wear; theory and use of metallurgical polarizing microscope. Address: Battelle Memorial Institute, 505 King Ave, Columbus, OH 43201.

DAYTON, SEYMOUR, b. New York, N.Y, Jan. 15, 23; m. 49; c. 2. INTERNAL MEDICINE. A.B, Cornell, 42; M.D, State Univ. N.Y, 50. Intern med, Maimonides Hosp, 50-51; resident, Goldwater Mem. Hosp, 51-52, Life Ins. Med. Res. Fund fel, 52-54; res. med, Vet. Admin. Center, 54-55; SCH. MED, UNIV. CALIF, LOS ANGELES, 55-56, instr, 56-58, asst. clin. prof, 58-63, assoc. prof, 63-68, PROF. MED. & V.CHMN. SCH. MED, 68-; CHIEF MED. SERV, WADSWORTH VET. ADMIN. HOSP, 68-, clin. investr, 58-59, sect. chief, 59-68. Jr. consult, student health serv, Univ. Calif, Los Angeles, 56-58; mem. coun. arteriosclerosis & exec. bd, Am. Heart Asn. Med.C, U.S.A, 43-45. Am. Fedn. Clin. Res. Lipid metabolism and atherosclerosis; coronary heart disease. Address: Medical Service, Wadsworth Veterans Administration Hospital, Wilshire & Sawtelle Blvd, Los Angeles, CA 90073.

DAZA, CARLOS H(ERNAN), b. Cali, Colombia, Apr. 9, 31; m. 60; c. 3. NUTRITION, PUBLIC HEALTH ADMINISTRATION. M.D, Nat. Univ. Colombia, 54; M.S, Columbia Univ, 62, M.P.H, 63. Med. nutritionist, Nat. Inst. Nutrit, Colombia, 55; dep. dir, Secy. Pub. Health, Valle del Cauca, 56-57; adv. nutrit, nutrit. & health educ. prog, Interam. Coop. Pub. Health Serv, 58-60; dir. med. care dept, Secy. Pub. Health, Valle del Cauca, 63-65; MED. OFF. NUTRIT, PAN AM. HEALTH ORGN-WHO, 66- Am. Pub. Health Asn; Latin Am. Nutrit. Soc; Soc. Nutrit. Educ. Food sciences; epidemiology studies in nutrition; applied nutrition programs; operational research in the field of public health nutrition; teaching preventive medicine, public health and nutrition. Address: Pan American Health Organization-World Health Organization, Zona IV, Casilla 2117, Lima, Peru.

DAZZI, JOACHIM, b. Scanfs. Grisons, Switz, Aug. 22, 12; nat; m. 46; c. 3. ORGANIC CHEMISTRY. Chem.E, Eidge. Tech. Sch, Zurich, 37, Dr. Tech. Sci, 38. RES. CHEMIST, dye intermediates, J.R. Geigy, Switz, 38-40; org. syntheses, Rhone-Poulenc, France, 40-41; Monsanto Chem. Co, 41-58; J.R. GEIGY, INC, 58- Am. Chem. Soc. Styrene monomer; catalytic dehydrogenations; sulfochlorinations, plasticizers; addition reactions; fatty acid and rubber derivatives; new ethers as dielectrics; diglycidylethers of dihydroxypolychlorobiphenyls; new diimide synthesis; thermostable heterocyclic hydraulic fluids; lubricants and polycondensates; new iron chelates, stable in alkaline soils, to control iron chlorosis. Address: Exploratory Research, J.R. Geigy, Inc, Basle, Switzerland C H-4000.

D'AZZO, JOHN JOACHIM, b. New York, N.Y, Nov. 30, 19; m. 53; c. 1. ELECTRICAL ENGINEERING. B.E.E, City Col, 41; M.S, Ohio State, 50. Jr. engr. qual. control, West. Elec. Co, N.J, 41-42; proj. engr. res. & develop, Wright Air Develop. Center, WRIGHT-PATTERSON AIR FORCE BASE, 42-45, PROF. ELEC. ENG. & DEPUTY DEPT. HEAD, AIR FORCE INST. TECH, 47- Vis. assoc. prof, Dayton Campus, Ohio State, 64. U.S.A.A.F, 45-46, 2nd Lt. Am. Soc. Eng. Educ; Inst. Elec. & Electronics Eng. Feedback control systems; servomechanisms. Address: AFITENE, Dept. of Electrical Engineering, Air Force Institute of Technology, Wright Patterson Air Force Base, Dayton, OH 45433.

DE, NRIPENDRA N, b. West Bengal, India, Apr. 16, 02; wid. PHARMACOLOGY. M.B, Calcutta, 27. Res. worker PHARMACOL, sch. trop. med, Calcutta, 28-40; asst. prof, Indian Inst. Sci, Bangalore, 40-51; asst. dir, Cent. Drug Res. Inst, 51-62; ASST. PROF, SCH. PHARM, UNIV. MAN, 62- Am. Soc. Pharmacol. & Exp. Therapeut. Cardiovascular pharmacology; pharmacology of autonomic nervous system; endocrinology. Address: School of Pharmacy, University of Manitoba, Winnipeg, Man, Can.

DE, PARITOSH K, b. Calcutta, India, July 4, 30. PHYSICAL CHEMISTRY. B.Sc, Calcutta, 49, M.Sc, 52, scholar, 54-57, Ph.D.(chem), 58. Lectr. chem, Calcutta, 59; res. assoc, Iowa, 59-60; biochem, Duke, 60-61; sr. res. chemist, Jewish Hosp. Brooklyn, N.Y, 61-62; res. biochemist, Roosevelt Hosp, New York, 63; res. assoc. molecular biol, N.Y. Univ, 64; sr. chemist, Off. Chief Med. Exam, New York, 64-69; ASST. PROF. FORENSIC MED, POSTGRAD. MED. SCH, N.Y. UNIV, 69- Fulbright travel grant, 59-63. AAAS; Am. Chem. Soc; N.Y. Acad. Sci. Colloid chemistry; ion exchange; absorption; physical biochemistry of protein and nucleic acids; x-ray applied to biological chemistry and forensic toxicology; physical chemistry of collagen and bone formation. Address: Dept. of Forensic Medicine, New York University Post Graduate Medical School, 520 First Ave, New York, NY 10016.

DEA, FRANK J, b. Canton, China, Oct. 14, 38; m. 67; c. 1. PHARMACOKINETICS. Pharm.D.(biopharmaceut), Southern California, 66, Ph.D.(pharmacokinetics), 71. Res. assoc. ALLERGAN PHARMACEUT, 66-67, head dept. pharmaceut. res, 67-69, RES. CONSULT, 69-; RES. FEL, UNIV. SOUTH. CALIF, 69- Mem. rev. comt, Nat. Formulary XIII, 68-69. Lunsford Richardson pharm. award for grad. res, 67. Am. Pharmaceut. Asn. Automation of clinical chemistry procedures; application of nuclear magnetic resonance to biological systems. Address: Hoffman Medical Research Center, University of Southern California Medical School Campus, Los Angeles, CA 90033.

DeACETIS, WILLIAM, b. Joliet, Ill, June 1, 28; m. 63. ORGANIC CHEMISTRY. B.S, Illinois, 50; M.S, Wisconsin, 52, Ph.D.(chem), 54. Asst. alumni res. found, Wisconsin, 50-54; fel, California, Berkeley, 54-56; res. chemist high energy fuels, Olin Mathieson Chem. Co, 56-57; org. chem, Shell Develop. Co, Calif, 57-66, prod. develop. chemist, Shell Chem. Co, N.Y, 66-70; mem. staff, chem. econ. handbook, STANFORD RES. INST, 70-71, MGR. SURFACE-ACTIVE AGENTS SECT, 71- Am. Chem. Soc. Product and market development; market research; combustion; plastics; resins. Address: Surface-active Agents Section, Stanford Research Institute, Menlo Park, CA 94025.

DEACON, JAMES EVERETT, b. White, S.Dak, May 18, 34; m. 54; c. 2. VERTEBRATE ZOOLOGY. B.S, Midwestern, 56; Ph.D.(vert. zool, bot), 60. Asst, Kansas, 56-59, 60; asst. prof. zool, UNIV. NEV, LAS VEGAS, 60-64, asst. res. prof, desert res. inst, 64-65, assoc. prof. zool, 65-68, PROF. BIOL, 68- Nat. Sci. Found. res. grant, 64-65, summer inst, Va. Inst. Marine Sci, 60. Jewish War Vet. RISSECA. award, 64; wildlife conserv. award, Nat. Wildlife Fedn, 70. Am. Soc. Ichthyol. & Herpet; Am. Fisheries Soc; Ecol. Soc. Am. Fishes of Nevada; ecology of desert fish; ecology of desert mammals. Address: Dept. of Biology, University of Nevada, Las Vegas, NV 89109.

DEACON, WILBUR E(UGENE), b. Neligh, Nebr, Feb. 5, 07; m. 30; c. 2. MEDICAL MICROBIOLOGY. B.S, Nebraska, 31, M.S, 32; Ph.D.(bact), Oregon, 52. Asst. chief clin. invests, venereal disease res. lab, U.S. Pub. Health Serv, 52-54, microbiol. res, 56-61, asst. dir, 61-62, dep. dir, 62-64, dir, 64-66; RETIRED. Spec. consult, WHO, 62. Superior Service award, Dept. Health, Ed. & Welfare, 60; Kimble methodology res. award, 64. U.S.A, 42-47, Med.Serv.C, Res, 47-55, Maj. AAAS; Soc. Exp. Biol. & Med; Am. Soc. Microbiol; N.Y. Acad. Sci; Am. Pub. Health Asn. Isolation, identification and serologic behavior of Hemophilus ducreyi, Neisseria gonorrheae and related species; development of fluorescent treponemal antibody test for syphilis and fluorescent antibody identification of Treponema pallidum and Neisseria gonorrheae. Address: 1073 Clevemark Dr, Clarkston, GA 30021.

DEAL, ALBERT LEONARD, III, b. Hickory, N.C, Aug. 31, 37; m. 63. MATHEMATICAL ANALYSIS. B.S, North Carolina, 59, Woodrow Wilson fel, 60, M.A, 62, Ph.D.(differential equations), 65. Instr. MATH, VA. MIL. INST, 62-63, asst. prof, 63-65, assoc. prof, 65-71, PROF, 71- Summer mathematician, U.S. Army, Aberdeen Proving Ground, 59. AAAS; Soc. Indust. & Appl. Math; Math. Asn. Am; Am. Math Soc. Linear differential and difference boundary problems. Address: Dept. of Mathematics, Virginia Military Institute, Lexington, VA 24450.

DEAL, ANDREW S(TUART), b. Birch Tree, Mo, July 3, 18; m. 51; c. 4. ENTOMOLOGY. B.S, Univ. Calif, 50, M.S, 51; Ph.D, Ohio State Univ, 67. Farm adv. entom, AGR. EXTEN. SERV, UNIV. CALIF, RIVERSIDE, 52-56, EXTEN. ENTOMOLOGIST, 56- U.S.A.A.F, 43-45,S/Sgt. AAAS; Entom. Soc. Am. Insects and mites on vegetables; chemical and biological control of insects and mites on vegetables; field crops, citrus and ornamentals. Address: Agricultural Extension Service, University of California, Riverside, CA 92502.

DEAL, BRUCE E(LMER), b. Lincoln, Nebr, Sept. 20, 27; m. 50; c. 3. PHYSICAL CHEMISTRY. A.B, Nebr. Wesleyan, 50; M.S, Iowa State Col, 53, Ph.D. (chem), 55. Asst, Ames Lab, Atomic Energy Comn, 50-55; res. chemist, Kaiser Aluminum & Chem. Corp, 55-59; Rheem Semiconductor Corp, Calif, 59-63; Fairchild Semiconductor, 63-70, DEPT. DIR. RES. & DEVELOP. LAB, FAIRCHILD CAMERA & INST. CORP, 70- U.S.A, 46-47. AAAS; Int. Electrochem. Soc. Surface physics and chemistry of solids; electrochemistry; semiconductor materials and processing. Address: Fairchild Camera & Institute Corp, Research & Development Lab, 4001 Miranda Ave, Palo Alto, CA 94304.

DEAL, CARL H(OSEA), JR, b. Spartanburg, S.C, Dec. 26, 19; m. 44; c. 4. PHYSICAL CHEMISTRY. B.S, Duke, 41, Ph.D.(chem), 45. Asst. chem, Duke, 41-44; chemist, SHELL DEVELOP. CO, 44-55, SUPVR, 55- Exchange scientist, Koninklijkel Shell Laboratorium, Amsterdam, 62-63. With Off. Sci. Res. & Develop; U.S.N, 44. Am. Chem. Soc. Physical separations and separation processes; thermodynamics of solutions. Address: Shell Development Co, 4560 Horton St, Emeryville, CA 94608.

DEAL, D(ON) ROBERT, b. Dayton, Ohio, Sept. 26, 37; m. 62; c. 1. PLANT PATHOLOGY, BOTANY. B.A, Capital Univ, 60; M.A, Miami Univ, 65; fel, Cornell Univ, 68, Ph.D.(plant path), 69. Teacher, high schs, Ohio, 60-63; ASST. PROF. BIOL, GLENVILLE STATE COL, 69- Am. Inst. Biol. Sci; Am. Phytopath. Soc; Nat. Asn. Biol. Teachers. Specific replant disease of grape; morphogenesis and ecology of endophytic phycomycete mycorrhiza in perennial plants; pathogenesis of Diplodia pinea. Address: Dept. of Science, Glenville State College, Glenville, WV 26351.

DEAL, DWIGHT E(DWARD), b. Staten Island, N.Y, Apr. 18, 38, m. 65. GEOLOGY. B.S, Rensselaer Polytech. Inst, 59; M.S, Univ. Wyo, 63; Ph.D. (geol), Univ. N.Dak, 70. ASST. PROF. GEOL, SUL ROSS STATE UNIV, 67- Geologist, N.Dak. State Geol. Surv, summers 69 & 71. AAAS; Geol. Soc.

Am; Am. Asn. Petrol Geol; Am. Quaternary Asn; Nat. Speleol. Soc. Quaternary geology of southwestern New Mexico, central North Dakota and west Texas; glacial, fluvial and ground-water processes. Address: Dept. of Geology, Sul Ross State University, Alpine, TX 79830.

DEAL, ELWYN E(RNEST), b. Appling Co, Ga, Oct. 10, 36; m. 60; c. 3. AGRONOMY. B.S.A, Georgia, 58, M.S, 60; Ph.D.(turf mgt), Rutgers, 63. Asst. TURF MGT, Ga. Coastal Plain Exp. Sta, U.S. Dept. Agr, 58-60; Rutgers, 60-63; N.C. State, 63-64; asst. prof, UNIV. MD, COLLEGE PARK, 64-68, ASSOC. PROF, 68-, ASST. DIR. AGR. PROGS, COOP. EXT. SERV, 69- Am. Soc. Agron; Crop Sci. Soc. Am. Turfgrass management including species selection and adaptation; physiology, ecology, weed control, mowing, fertilization, irrigation and growth control of lawn, golf course and highway roadside turf. Address: Cooperative Extension Service, Symons Hall, University of Maryland, College Park, MD 20742.

DEAL, ERVIN R, U.S. citizen. MATHEMATICS. A.B, Nebr. Wesleyan Univ, 51; M.S, Kans. State Univ, 53; Ph.D.(math), Univ. Mich, 62. Asst. prof. MATH, COLO. STATE UNIV, 59-62, ASSOC. PROF, 62- AAAS; Math. Asn. Am; Am. Math. Soc. Functional analysis. Address: Dept. of Mathematics, Colorado State University, Ft. Collins, CO 80521.

DEAL, GLENN W, JR, b. Kannapolis, N.C, Apr. 3, 22; m. 41; c. 1. CHEMISTRY. A.B, Catawba Col, 48; M.S, Appalachian State Teachers Col, 56. Student chem. analyst, Tidewater Assoc. Oil Refinery, 46-46; chmn. dept. sci, Ro County High Sch, 46-60; ASSOC. PROF. CHEM, CATAWBA COL, 60- U.S.M.C, 43-45. Am. Chem. Soc. Education; analytical chemistry. Address: Dept. of Chemistry, Catawba College, Salisbury, NC 28144.

DEAL, RALPH MACGILL, b. Charlotte, N.C, May 29, 31; m. 53; c. 3. PHYSICAL CHEMISTRY. B.A, Oberlin Col, 53; Allied Chem. & Dye fel, Hopkins, Du Pont fel, & Ph.D.(chem), 58. Res. assoc, Monadnock Res. Inst, 58-59; Imp. Chem. Industs. fel, Keele, 59-61; Nat. Insts. Health trainee biophys. chem, Illinois, 61-62; asst. prof. CHEM, KALAMAZOO COL, 62-68, ASSOC. PROF, 68- Am. Chem. Soc; Am. Phys. Soc. Electron spin resonance; computer-assisted-learning. Address: Dept. of Chemistry, Kalamazoo College, Kalamazoo, MI 49001.

DEAL, SAMUEL J(OSEPH), b. Knoxville, Tenn, Mar. 9, 25; m. 56; c. 3. BACTERIOLOGY. B.S, Tennessee, 49, M.S, 50; Ph.D.(bact), Minnesota, 57. Res. bacteriologist, Walter Reed Army Inst. Res, 50-52; instr. BACT, Minnesota, 57-60, asst. prof, 60-61; W.VA. UNIV, 61-64, ASSOC. PROF, MED. CENTER, 64- U.S.A, 43-46. AAAS; Am. Soc. Microbiol. Bacterial physiology; nutrition and metabolism. Address: Dept. of Microbiology, West Virginia University Medical Center, Morgantown, WV 26506.

DEAL, WILLIAM C(ECIL), JR, b. Lake Providence, La, Mar. 21, 36; m. 57; c. 2. BIOCHEMISTRY. B.S, La. Col, 58; Ph.D.(phys. chem), Univ. Ill, Urbana, 62. Asst. prof. BIOCHEM, MICH. STATE UNIV, 62-66, assoc. prof, 66-71, PROF, 71- Summers, instr, Marine Biol. Labs, Woods Hole, Mass, 62, 63, lectr, sch. med, Univ. Wash, 65; Nat. Insts. Health grants, 63-70, 71-75, spec. res. fel, Univ. Munich, 69-70. U.S.A.R, 56-62. Am. Soc. Biol. Chem; Am. Chem. Soc. Physical biochemistry; subunit structure, control and reassembly of mammalian enzymes and multi-enzyme complexes, especially enzymes of glycolysis and fatty acid synthesis; ultra-centrifugation theory and techniques; computer applications. Address: Dept. of Biochemistry, Michigan State University, East Lansing, MI 48823.

DEAL, WILLIAM E, JR, b. Ft. Sam Houston, Tex, Sept. 24, 25; m. 49; c. 4. PHYSICS. B.S, Texas, 47, M.A, 49, Ph.D.(physics), 51. Mem. staff physics, LOS ALAMOS SCI. LAB, UNIV. CALIF, 50-60, group leader, 60-65, asst. div. leader, 65-70, ALTERNATE DIV. LEADER, 70- U.S.N.R, 44-46. Am. Phys. Soc. Near ultraviolet absorption spectra of polynuclear aromatics; shock hydrodynamics; explosives. Address: 159 Monte Rey Dr. S, Los Alamos, NM 87544.

de ALBA MARTINEZ, JORGE, b. Aguascalientes, Mex, Mar. 28, 20; m. 43; c. 4. REPRODUCTIVE PHYSIOLOGY, ANIMAL HUSBANDRY. B.S, Maryland, 41; M.S, Cornell, 42, Ph.D.(animal physiol), 44. Mgr, Hacienda Sierra Hermosa, Mex, 44-49; physiologist, Inter-Am. Inst. Agr. Sci, Costa Rica, 50-51, head dept. animal indust, 52-63; dean & founder col. agr, Univ. Sonora, Mex, 51-52; livestock adv, Bank of Mex, 63-67; FORD FOUND. FEL. ANIMAL SCI, CORNELL UNIV, 67- Guggenheim fel, 56-57; Kellogg authorship grant, 60-61. Mex. Asn. Animal Prod.(first pres, 64-66); Latin Am. Asn. Animal Prod.(first pres, 66-); Am. Soc. Animal Sci. Tropical animal production. Address: Juarez 48, Coyoacan, Mex. 21, D.F.

DE ALVAREZ, RUSSELL RAMON, b. New York, N.Y, June 21, 09; m. 43; c. 2. OBSTETRICS & GYNECOLOGY. B.S, Michigan, 31, M.D, 35, M.S, 40. Intern, Michigan, 35-36, asst. res. obstet. & gynec, 36-37, res, 37-38, sr. res, 38-39, instr, univ. hosp. & med. sch, 38-44; attend. gynecologist & asst. prof, univ. hosps, Oregon, 46-48; prof. OBSTET. & GYNEC. & first chmn, sch. med, Washington (Seattle), 48-64; PROF. & CHMN. DEPT, MED. CTR, TEMPLE UNIV, 64- Obstetrician & gynecologist-in-chief, univ. hosp, Washington (Seattle) & King County Hosp, 48-64. Consult, Michigan, 41-44; Vet. Admin. Hosp; Madigan Army Hosp; Nat. Insts. Health. Dipl. Am. Bd. Obstet. & Gynec, 41. Med.C, U.S.N, 43-45. Fel. Am. Col. Obstet. & Gynec.(award, 58); Am. Gynec. Soc; fel. Am. Col. Surg; Am. Soc. Clin. Res; Am. Med. Asn; Am. Asn. Obstet. & Gynec; Soc. Obstet. & Gynec. Can; Venezuelan Soc. Obstet. & Gynec. Gynecologist cancer; toxemias of pregnancy. Address: Dept. of Obstetrics & Gynecology, School of Medicine, Temple University Medical Center, Philadelphia, PA 19140.

DEALY, JAMES BOND, JR, b. Medford, Mass, Sept. 7, 20; m. 45; c. 6. RADIOLOGY. A.B, Yale, 42; M.D, Columbia, 45. Fel. med, Harvard, 50-52, RADIOL, 52, asst, 53-54, instr, 55, asst. clin. prof, 56-60, assoc. clin. prof, 60-66, acting head dept, 56-63, chmn. exec. comt, 60-63; PROF. RADIOL, TUFTS UNIV. & CHIEF DIAG. RADIOL, SERV, LEMUEL SHATTUCK HOSP, 67- Assoc. radiologist, Peter Bent Brigham Hosp, 53-55, acting radiologist-in-chief, 56, radiologist-in-chief, 57-66; consult, U.S. Vet. Admin, 56-; Brookline Health Dept, 56-; Mass. Ment. Health Ctr, 56-; Pondville Hosp, 60-; mem. comt. radiol, Nat. Acad. Sci-Nat. Res. Coun, 63-69; consult. staff, New Eng. Med. Ctr. Hosps, 68- Dipl, Am. Bd. Radiol, 52. Med.C.Res, 46-48, Capt. Radiol. Soc. N.Am; Asn. Univ. Radiol; Am. Col. Radiol; Am. Roentgen Ray Soc; Am. Radium Soc. Diagnostic and therapetic radiology; biological effects of ionizing irradiation. Address: Lemuel Shattuck Hospital, 170 Morton St, Boston, MA 02130.

DEAM, JAMES RICHARD, b. Springfield, Ohio, Jan. 9, 42; m. 66; c. 1. CHEMICAL ENGINEERING. B.S, Cincinnati, 64; Nat. Sci. Found. trainee, Okla. State, 64-66, M.S, 66, Phillips Petrol. Co. fel, 66-67, Natural Gas Processors Asn. grant, 67-68, Ph.D.(chem eng), 69. Coop. engr, Int. Harvester Co, 60-63; engr, Battelle Mem. Inst, summer 64; res. engr, Houston Res. Lab, Shell Oil Co, summer 66; SR. RES. ENGR, MGT. INFO. & SYSTS. DEPT, MONSANTO CO, 68- Am. Inst. Chem. Eng; Am. Chem. Soc. Chemical process simulation and mathematical modeling; distillation; absorption and extraction; physical property estimation and measurement; applied mathematics; digital computer control; surface tension; vapor-liquid equilibria; computerized inventory control. Address: Management Information & Systems Dept, Monsanto Co, 800 N. Lindbergh Blvd, St. Louis, MO 63166.

DEAMER, DAVID W(ILSON), JR, b. Santa Monica, Calif, Apr. 21, 39; m. 62; c. 1. BIOPHYSICS. B.S, Duke, 61; U.S. Pub. Health Serv. fel, Ohio State, 63-65, Ph.D.(biochem), 65. Trainee biophys, California, Berkeley, 65-66, U.S. Pub. Health Serv. fel, 66-67, asst. prof. ZOOL, UNIV. CALIF, DAVIS, 67-70, ASSOC. PROF, 70- Ionic interactions with membranes; membrane structure; lipid metabolism; degradation in biological systems. Address: Dept. of Zoology, University of California, Davis, CA 95616.

DEAN, ANTHONY MARION, b. Savannah, Ga, Aug. 26, 44; m. 66; c. 2. PHYSICAL CHEMISTRY. B.S, Spring Hill Col, 66; Nat. Sci. Found. fel, Harvard, 66-70, A.M, 67, Ph.D.(phys. chem), 70. ASST. PROF. PHYS. CHEM, UNIV. MO-COLUMBIA, 70- Am. Chem. Soc; Am. Phys. Soc. Gas phase kinetics; shock tube investigations of dissociation reactions; kinetics and mechanism of combustion reactions. Address: Dept. of Chemistry, University of Missouri-Columbia, Columbia, MO 65201.

DEAN, BENJAMIN T, b. Spickard, Mo, Sept. 22, 21; m. 48; c. 2. ANIMAL SCIENCE. B.S, Missouri, 47, M.S, 59, Ph.D.(animal husb), 61. Swine specialist, Hawaii, 61; livestock adv. exten, Agency Int. Develop, Santiago, Chile, 62-64; ASSOC. EXTEN. PROF. ANIMAL SCI, UNIV. KY, 64- U.S.M.C, 43-46, 50-52, 53-56, Res, 56-65, Lt. Col. Am. Soc. Animal Sci. Feeding and management of brood sows during gestation. Address: Dept. of Animal Science, University of Kentucky, Lexington, KY 40506.

DEAN, BURTON V(ICTOR), b. Chicago, Ill, June 3, 24; m. 58; c. 3. OPERATIONS RESEARCH. B.S, Northwestern, 47; M.S, Columbia, 48; fel, Illinois, 50-52, Ph.D.(math), 52. Instr. math, Columbia, 47-49; Hunter Col, 49-50; mathematician, Nat. Security Agency, 52-55; res. mathematician, Opers. Res, Inc, 55-57; assoc. prof. opers. res, CASE WEST. RESERVE UNIV, 57-65, PROF. orgn. sci, 65-67, OPER. RES. & CHMN. DEPT, 67-, chmn. opers. res. group, 65-67. Vis. prof, Israel Inst. Tech, 62-63. Indust. & govt. consult, 57- Sig.C, U.S.A, 42-45. Fel. AAAS (v.pres. sect. indust. sci); Inst. Mgt. Sci.(ed, 57-); Opers. Res. Soc. Am; Am. Math. Soc; Asn. Comput. Mach. Applications of operations research to industrial management; research budgeting and corporate growth; production and inventory control; corporate planning; mathematics of management systems. Address: Dept. of Operations Research, Case Western Reserve University, 10900 Euclid Ave, Cleveland, OH 44106.

DEAN, CHARLES E(ARLE), b. Pickens Co, S.C, May 23, 98; m. 27; c. 2. COMMUNICATION ENGINEERING. A.B, Harvard, 21; A.M, Columbia, 23; Ph.D.(physics), Hopkins, 27. Tech. asst, Bell Tel. Labs, 21-24; asst. physicist, Hopkins, 24-26; tech. writer, Am. Tel. & Tel. Co, 27-29; tech. writer & ed, Hazeltine Corp, 29-63; ED, ELECTRONICS & COMMUN. IN JAPAN, SCRIPTA PUBL. CORP, WASH, D.C, 63- U.S. Navy Cert. Commendation. Fel. Inst. Elec. & Electronics Eng.(v.pres, Inst. Elec. Eng, 61-62). Electronics engineering. Address: 115 Sherman Ave, Takoma Park, MD 20012.

DEAN, CHARLES E(DGAR), b. Monticello, Fla, Apr. 24, 29; m. 57; c. 1. PLANT BREEDING & GENETICS. B.S, Florida, 53, M.S, 57; Ph.D.(field crops), N.C. State, 59. Asst. agronomist, N.FLA. EXP. STA, 59-66, assoc. agronomist, 66-69, PROF. & AGRONOMIST, 69- U.S. Dept. Agr. res. grant, 64-68. Genetic Asn. Am; Am. Soc. Agron. Breeding and genetics of shade-grown cigar-wrapper tobacco. Address: North Florida Experimental Station, Quincy, FL 32351.

DEAN, C(HARLES) EDWIN, b. Redmesa, Colo, Mar. 3, 19; m. 43; c. 2. MATHEMATICAL STATISTICS, COMPUTER SCIENCE. B.S, Brigham Young, 48, M.S, 52. Instr, Brigham Young, 49-54; res. asst, Surv. Res. Ctr, Michigan, 55-58, head statist. serv. & data processing sect, Inst. Social Res, 58; dir. comput. res. ctr, Brigham Young Univ, 59-66; acad. assoc, systs. prog. div, Int. Bus. Mach. Corp, Calif, 66-67; ASSOC. PROF. COMPUT. SCI. & CHMN. DEPT, BRIGHAM YOUNG UNIV, 67- Consult. sampling techniques, Ford Motor Co, Mich, 58. U.S.A.A.F, 43-46, 1st Lt. Am. Statist Asn. Non-parametric statistical tests; digital computers; programming for computers. Address: 2145 N. 1220 East, Provo, UT 84601.

DEAN, CHRISTOPHER, b. Chicago, Ill, May 3, 20; m. 45; c. 3. PHYSICS. A.B, Harvard, 47, fel, 47-51, M.A, 49, Ph.D.(physics), 52. Res. physicist, proj. Lincoln, Mass. Inst. Tech, 52-53; asst. prof. PHYSICS, Pittsburgh, 53-58, assoc. prof, 58-60; sr. scientist, Allied Res. Assoc, Inc, 60-61, 62-63; Sperry Rand Res. Ctr, 61-62, assoc. prof, UNIV. N.MEX, 63-68, PROF, 68- Weather Serv, U.S.A.F, 41-45. Am. Phys. Soc; Am. Meteorol. Soc; Am. Crystallog. Asn. Radiofrequency spectroscopy; musical acoustics; satellite meteorology; high atmosphere. Address: Dept. of Physics & Astronomy, University of New Mexico, Albuquerque, NM 87106.

DEAN, DAVID, b. Paterson, N.J, Nov. 12, 26; m. 49; c. 3. BIOLOGICAL OCEANOGRAPHY, MARINE & AQUATIC ECOLOGY. A.B, Lehigh Univ,

49; Ph.D.(zool), Rutgers Univ, 57. Instr. biol, Norwich Univ, 49; zool, Univ. Conn, 57-61, asst. prof, 61-66; PROF. ZOOL. & DIR. DARLING CTR, UNIV. MAINE, 66-, PROF. OCEANOG. & ACTING CHMN. DEPT, 70- Co-investr, Maine Yankee Atomic Power Co. grants, 69-; prin. investr, Sea Grant Prog, 71- Chem.C, 51-53, 2nd Lt. AAAS; Am. Inst. Biol. Sci; Am. Soc. Zool; Am. Soc. Limnol. & Oceanog; Ecol. Soc. Am; Marine Biol. Asn. U.K. Definition of marine benthic communities and the interrelationships of their components; formation and larvae of benthic communities. Address: Ira C. Darling Center for Research, Teaching & Service, University of Maine, Walpole, ME 04573.

DEAN, DAVID CAMPBELL, b. Buffalo, N.Y, Apr. 19, 31; m. 56; c. 3. INTERNAL MEDICINE, CARDIOLOGY. B.A, Bowdoin Col, 52; M.D, Hopkins, 56. Res. fel. MED, Harvard, 60-61; clin. instr, STATE UNIV. N.Y. BUFFALO, 61-65, clin. assoc, 65-66, ASST. PROF, 66-; CHIEF CARDIOPULMONARY LAB, VET. ADMIN. HOSP, 62- Res. fel. cardiol, Mass. Gen. Hosp, Boston, 60-61; clin. asst, Buffalo Gen. Hosp, 61- Mem. coun. clin. cardiol, Am. Heart Asn. Dipl, Nat. Bd. Med. Exam, 57; Am. Bd. Internal Med, 66; Am. Bd. Cardiovasc. Disease, 67. Fel. Am. Col. Physicians; fel. Am. Col. Cardiol; Am. Fedn. Clin. Res; Am. Heart Asn; Am. Med. Asn. Electrophysiology of the heart and the electrical control of the heart. Address: 65 Huxley Dr, Snyder, NY 14226.

DEAN, DAVID W, b. Waukegan, Ill, July 20, 31. MATHEMATICS. A.B, Illinois, 53, M.S, 54, Ph.D, 58. Instr. MATH, Rochester, 58-59; Yale, 59-61; asst. prof, Duke, 61-64; OHIO STATE UNIV, 64-65, ASSOC. PROF, 65- Am. Math. Soc. Functional analysis. Address: Dept. of Mathematics, Ohio State University, Columbus, OH 43210.

DEAN, D(ONALD) E, b. Flushing, N.Y, June 3, 27; m. 51; c. 4. ANALYTICAL CHEMISTRY. B.A, Oberlin Col, 50; M.S, Stevens Inst. Technol, 57. Chemist, Am. Cyanamid Co, 50-52, anal. method develop, 52-54; mgr. control & anal. lab, Shulton, Inc, 54-65; mgr. anal. & qual. control, LEEMING/PACQUIN DIV, PFIZER INC, 65-69, MGR. COSMETIC & TOILETRIES RES, 69- U.S.N.R, 45-47, Res, 47-, Lt.(jg). Am. Chem. Soc. Organic analysis and characterization in pharmaceuticals, essential oils, toiletries materials and fine chemicals; instrumental analysis by infrared and ultraviolet absorption; vapor phase chromatography. Address: Leeming/Pacquin Division, Pfizer Inc, 100 Jefferson Rd, Parsippany, NJ 07054.

DEAN, DONALD L(EE), b. Litchfield, Ill, Nov. 25, 26; m. 49; c. 2. CIVIL ENGINEERING. B.S, Missouri, 49, M.S, 51; Riggs fel, Michigan, 53-54, Ph.D.(civil eng), 55. Instr. civil eng, Mo. Sch. Mines, 49-51, admin. asst. to dean, 52-53, asst. prof. civil eng, 54-55; assoc. prof, Kansas, 55-60; prof. & chmn. civil eng. & eng. mech, Delaware, 60-65, H. Fletcher Brown prof. CIVIL ENG, 62-65; PROF. & HEAD DEPT, N.C. STATE UNIV, 65- Prin. consult. engr, Dean & Assocs. U.S.N, 45-46. Am. Soc. Civil Eng; Am. Soc. Eng. Educ; Int. Asn. Shell Struct; Int. Asn. Bridge & Struct. Eng. Structural design and analysis; buckling; vibrations; latticed and ribbed shells; applied mathematics. Address: Dept. of Civil Engineering, North Carolina State University, Box 5993, Raleigh, NC 27607.

DEAN, DONALD S(TEWART), b. Lakewood, Ohio, Nov. 21, 16; m. 44; c. 3. BOTANY. B.S, Baldwin-Wallace Col, 38; M.S, Michigan, 49, fel. & Ph.D. (bot), 53. Teacher, pub. schs, Ohio, 38-42, 45-47; from instr. to assoc. prof. BIOL, BALDWIN-WALLACE COL, 47-58, PROF, 58-, CHMN. DEPT, 70- Nat. Sci. Found. faculty fel, 59-62; staff biologist, Comn. Undergrad. Educ. in Biol. Sci, 69-70. U.S.N.R, 42-46, Lt. AAAS; Bot. Soc. Am; Genetics Asn. Am. Genetics of grafted plants. Address: Dept. of Biology, Baldwin-Wallace College, Berea, OH 44017.

DEAN, EUGENE ALAN, b. Freeport, Tex, Nov. 30, 31; m. 56; c. 3. PHYSICS. B.S, Texas, El Paso, 58; M.S, New Mexico State, 64; Nat. Sci. Found. fel, Texas A&M, 65-67, Ph.D.(physics), 69. Physicist, Schellenger Res. Lab, 58-61, dir. spec. proj, 63-65; instr. PHYSICS, Texas, El Paso, 61-63; asst. prof, Texas Southern, 67-69; ASSOC. PROF, UNIV. TEX, EL PASO, 69- Asst. prof, Houston, 69. Consult, Globe Exploration Co, 65-68. U.S.A, 53-56, Sgt. Am. Asn. Physics Teachers. Atmospheric acoustics; plasma physics. Address: Dept. of Physics, University of Texas at El Paso, El Paso, TX 79999.

DEAN, F(LOYD) H(ENRY), b. Madoc, Ont, May 3, 34; m. 56; c. 6. ORGANIC CHEMISTRY, SPECTROSCOPY. B.S.A, Univ. Guelph, 57; McMaster Univ, 58-59; Can. Industs. Ltd. fel, Univ. West. Ont, 60, Ph.D.(org. fluorine chem), 64. Asst. control chemist, Naugatuck Chem, Ltd, Ont, 57-58; res. chemist, exp. sta, E.I. du Pont de Nemours & Co, Inc, 63-64; fel, Univ. Del, 65; res. chemist, Shawinigan Chem. Ltd, Que, 65-66; RES. SCIENTIST, ORG. CHEM. DEPT, ONT. RES. FOUND, 66- Spectroscopic methods; organic synthesis using modern and classical methods with product characterization largely by infrared and nuclear magnetic resonance spectroscopy; study of molecular conformation, mass spectrometry and reaction mechanisms. Address: Room 3092, Organic Chemistry Dept, Ontario Research Foundation, Sheridan Park, Ont, Can.

DEAN, FREDERICK C(HAMBERLAIN), b. Boston, Mass, May 22, 27; m. 50; c. 3. WILDLIFE MANAGEMENT. B.S, Maine, 50, M.S, 52; Ph.D, State Univ. N.Y, 57. Asst. prof. WILDLIFE MGT, UNIV. ALASKA, 54-57, assoc. prof, 57-66, PROF, 66-, ASST. LEADER, COOP, WILDLIFE RES. UNIT, 54-, ED, BIOL. PAPERS, 55-, head dept. wildlife mgt, 54- Fel. systs. anal. in ecol, dept. bot, Univ. Tenn, 68-69; Oak Ridge Nat. Lab, 68-69. Alaska sportsmens coun. water conserv. award, Nat. Wildlife Fedn, 65, conserv. educ. award, 71. U.S.N, 45-46. AAAS; Ecol. Soc. Am; Wildlife Soc; Am. Soc. Mammal; Arctic Inst. N.Am. Wildlife management, population ecology; grizzly bears, general ecology; subarctic and marsh ecology. Address: $1\frac{1}{2}$ Mile Ballaine Rd, Fairbanks, AK 99701.

DEAN, GEORGE RHOADES, b. Cleveland, Ohio, Sept. 8, 09; m. 37; c. 7. CHEMISTRY. A.B, Hiram Col, 32; Ph.D.(phys. chem), Pa. State Col, 37. Corn Products Ref. Co. res. fel, Miner Labs, Chicago, 37-40; res. chemist & group leader, Manhattan Dist. proj, Chicago, 43-44; res. chemist, Corn Prods. Ref. Co, 40-56; Miles Labs, Inc, 56-71; RETIRED. Am. Chem. Soc. Physical and sugar chemistry; crystallography and crystal structure; reaction kinetics and catalysis; radiochemistry; spectrum analysis; dextrose and starch syrups; solubility in grain boundaries of solid solutions. Address: 404 N. Buchanan St, Edwardsville, IL 62025.

DEAN, GORDON S(PENCER), b. Dedham, Mass, July 27, 30; m. 54; c. 3. PHARMACEUTICAL CHEMISTRY. B.S, Mass. Col. Pharm, 52, fel, 52-54, M.S, 54; Lilly Found. fel, Michigan, 54-55, Am. Found. Pharmaceut. Educ. fel, 54-57, M.S, 56, Ph.D.(pharmaceut. chem), 58. Instr, col. pharm, Michigan, 55-57; res. prog. adminstr, Smith, Kline & French Labs, 57-62, sales develop. group, 62-64; prod. mgr, spec. prod. dept, Rohm and Haas Co, Pa, 64-67, mgr. sales develop, 67-68, indust. chem. dept, 68-69; dir. mkt, OTT CHEM. CO, MUSKEGON, 69-70, V.PRES. MKT, 70- Mem. bd. dirs, Acme Resins, Ill, 71- Am. Chem. Soc. Antispasmodics; analgetics; Ivanov reaction; chemistry of thiazole; enzymes. Address: 580 Franklin St, North Muskegon, MI 49445.

DEAN, HAROLD DOUGLAS, b. Birmingham, Ala, Feb. 1, 28; m. 62; c. 1. BIOLOGY. B.S, Alabama, 50, M.S, 53, Ph.D.(biol), 59. Assoc. prof. BIOL, Abilene Christian Col, 53-57, head dept, 59-62; assoc. prof, PEPPERDINE COL, 62-70, PROF, 70- Summers, vis. lectr, Southern California, 62, 63. Nat. Asn. Biol. Teachers. Evolution; vertebrate zoology; endocrinology. Address: Dept. of Biology, Pepperdine College, Los Angeles, CA 90044.

DEAN, HARTZELL C(URTIS), b. Milan, Ind, Dec. 25, 08; m. 34; c. 3. SOILS. B.S, Iowa State, 31, fels, 31-35, M.S, 32, Ph.D.(soils), 35. Soil surveyor, Jackson Co, Iowa State & Bur. Chem. & Soils, 34; asst. soil surveyor & assoc. soil scientist, soil conserv. surv, E.Kans. Soil Conserv. Serv, U.S. DEPT. AGR, 35-39, proj. leader & soil scientist, Grand Neosho flood control surv, SOIL CONSERV. SERV, 39-41, soil conservationist, regional proj. plans, 41-47, flood control specialist & soil conservationist, flood control surv, 47-50, soil conservationist, comprehensive study Ark-White-Red basins, 50-55, STATE SOIL SCIENTIST, 55- Assoc. soil scientist, Soil Conserv. Serv, U.S. Dept. Agr, 37-39. Soil Sci. Soc. Am; Soil Conserv. Soc. Am. Soil and water conservation; watershed protection; soils and soil surveys. Address: 5305 Federal Bldg, Little Rock, AK 72201.

DEAN, H(ENRY) L(EE), b. Cumberland, Md, Mar. 13, 07. BOTANY. A.B, West Virginia, 29; M.S, Iowa, 30, Ph.D.(plant morphol), 36. Asst. BOT, West Virginia, 27-29; UNIV. IOWA, 30-36, instr, 37-39, assoc, 39-44, asst. prof, 44-49, ASSOC. PROF, 49- AAAS; Bot. Soc. Am; Nat. Asn. Biol. Teachers; Int. Soc. Plant Morphol. Host responses and host plants of Cuscuta; biological applications of ultraviolet light; floral variations and anatomy of Lychnis alba; microtechnique and histochemistry; photography. Address: Dept. of Botany, University, of Iowa, Iowa City, IA 52240.

DEAN, HERBERT A, b. Damon, Tex, Sept. 1, 18; m; c. 2. ENTOMOLOGY. B.S, Texas A&M, 40, M.S, 49; California, 52-53. Instr, TEX. AGR. EXP. STA, College Station, 46-49, asst. entomologist, 49-50, assoc. entomologist, 50-67, ASSOC. PROF, 67- U.S.N.R, 42-46, Lt.(jg). Entom. Soc. Am. Citrus mite control with selective miticides; biological control of citrus insects and mites; oil tolerance studies with citrus; citrus pest management through integrated control methods. Address: P.O. Box 942, Weslaco, TX 78596.

DEAN, JACK LEMUEL, b. Keota, Okla, Mar. 15, 25; m. 49; c. 2. PHYTOPATHOLOGY. B.S, Okla. State, 49, M.S, 52; Ph.D.(bot, phytopath), La. State, 65. PLANT PATHOLOGIST, Sugar Crops Field Sta, U.S. DEPT. AGR, Miss, 51-66, SUGARCANE FIELD STA, 66- U.S.N, 43-46. Am. Phytopath. Soc. Pathology of sugarcane and sugar sorghum. Address: 92 Dayton Rd, Lake Worth, FL 33460.

DEAN, JOHN A(URIE), b. Sault Ste. Marie, Mich, May 9, 21; m. 43; c. 5. ANALYTICAL CHEMISTRY. B.S, Univ. Mich, 42, fels, 42-44, 45-46, M.S, 44, Ph.D.(chem), 49. Chemist, Chrysler Corp, 44-45; lectr, Univ. Mich, 46-48; assoc. prof, Univ. Ala, 48-50; asst. prof, UNIV. TENN, KNOXVILLE, 50-53, assoc. prof, 53-58, PROF. CHEM, 58- Consult, nuclear div, Union Carbide Corp, 53-; Stewart Labs, Inc, 68- AAAS; Am. Chem. Soc; Soc. Appl. Spectros; Brit. Soc. Anal. Chem. Flame emission and atomic absorption spectrometry; chromatographic methods; solvent extraction; instrumental methods of analysis; colorimetric methods; polarography. Address: 1112 W. Nokomis Circle, Knoxville, TN 37919.

DEAN, JOHN E(LLIS), b. Lansing, Mich, Aug. 15, 08; m. 35. ELECTRICAL ENGINEERING. B.S, Mich. State, 30, E.E, 39; M.S, Iowa State, 46. Elec. engr, Detroit Edison Co, Mich, 30-42; instr. & asst. prof. ELEC. ENG, Iowa State, 42-47; assoc. prof, Vermont, 47-48; prof, Tex. Col. Arts & Indust, 48-52; PROF, COLO. STATE UNIV, 52-, head dept, 52-69. Am. Soc. Eng. Educ; Inst. Elec. & Electronics Eng; Nat. Soc. Prof. Eng. High voltage underground cables; communication systems; microwave transmission. Address: Dept. of Electrical Engineering, Colorado State University, Ft. Collins, CO 80521.

DEAN, JOHN G(ILBERT), b. Pawtuxet, R.I, Feb. 16, 11; m. 42; c. 3. CHEMISTRY. Ph.B, Brown, 31, M.S, 32; univ. fel, Columbia, 35-36, Ph.D.(chem), 36. Dir. res. div, Permutit Co, 36-40; teacher sci, Sarah Lawrence Col, 40-42; Int. Nickel Co. sr. fel, Mellon Inst, 42-45, in charge develop. & res. div, indust. chem. sect, 46-51; CHEM. CONSULT. & MGR, DEAN ASSOCS, 52- Dir. div. co-op. res, sch. eng, Columbia, 52-54; dir. res. & develop. div, Nickel Processing Corp. Div, Nat. Lead Co, 53-60. AAAS; Air Pollution Control Asn; Am. Chem. Soc; Am. Inst. Mining, Metall. & Petrol. Eng; Electrochem. Soc; Commercial Chem. Develop. Asn; Am. Inst. Chem. Management of chemical and metallurgical research; inorganic syntheses; ion exchange; catalysis; air & water pollution control; chemical economics; chemistry and chemical metallurgy of the metals, especially nickel, cobalt, copper, zinc, molybdenum, cadmium mercury and the precious metals. Address: Elmdale Rd, N. Scituate, RI 02857.

DEAN, JOHN MARK, b. Cedar Rapids, Iowa, Oct. 2, 36; m. 60; c. 3. AQUATIC ECOLOGY. B.A, Cornell Col, 58; M.S, Purdue, 60, David E. Ross fel. & Ph.D.(biol. sci), 62. Res. assoc, marine lab, Duke, 62-63; biol. scientist, Hanford Labs, Gen. Elec. Co, 63-64; Pac. Northwest Labs, Battelle Mem. Inst, 65-70; ASSOC. PROF. BIOL, BELLE W. BARUCH COASTAL RES. INST, UNIV. S.C, 70- Fel. AAAS; Ecol. Soc. Am; Am. Soc. Zool; Marine Biol. Asn. U.K. Physiological ecology of aquatic organisms; temperature acclimation in fish and Crustacea; water pollution. Address: Dept. of Biology, Belle W. Baruch Coastal Research Institute, University of South Carolina, Columbia, SC 29208.

DEAN, JOHN W(ILLIAM), b. New York, N.Y, Apr. 9, 31; m. 54; c. 2. ORGANIC CHEMISTRY. B.S, Rensselaer Polytech, 52, M.S, 55, Ph.D.(org. chem), 62. Asst. res. chemist, Sterling-Winthrop Res. Inst, 56-59, assoc. res. chemist, 59-66; RES. CHEMIST, SILICONE PROD. DEPT, GEN. ELEC. CO, 66- U.S.A, 54-56, Res, 57-59. AAAS; Am. Chem. Soc. Pharmaceutical and biological chemistry; steroidal endocrinological agents; cardiac and blood-lipid-modifying drugs; oligosaccharides derived from cellulose degradation; chromic acid oxidation mechanism; silicones, copolymers, organosilicon chemistry. Address: Bldg. 12-11, Silicone Products Dept, General Electric Co, Waterford, NY 12188.

DEAN, JOHN WYMAN, b. Cambridge, Mass, June 6, 29; m. 58. MECHANICAL ENGINEERING. B.S, La. State, 52; M.S, Colorado, 58. Test engr, Pratt & Whitney Aircraft Co, Inc, 54-56; engr, NAT. BUR. STANDARDS, 57-63, proj. leader cyrogenic instrumentation, 63-66, CRYOGENIC METROL, 66- Res. assoc, Rutherford High Energy Lab, Chilton Didcot, Eng, 71- U.S.A, 52-54. Sci. Res. Soc. Am; Instrument Soc. Am. The measurement of fundamental measurement coefficients and their application in pressure and temperature tranduction instruments for cryogenic instruments; heat transfer experiments and analysis; design of superconducting synchrotron cryogenic systems. Address: National Bureau of Standards, Boulder, CO 80302.

DEAN, KARL C(LYDE), b. American Fork, Utah, July 9, 17; m. 35; c. 5. METALLURGY, GEOGRAPHY. B.S, Univ. Utah, 57. Technologist metall, U.S. Bur. Mines, 41-45 & 48-51; metallurgist, Int. Coop. Admin, Mex, 51-53; SUPVRY. METALLURGIST, U.S. BUR. MINES, 53- Mem, desalting panel, U.S. Japan Coop. Develop. Natural Resources, 64- U.S.A, 45-48, Res, 48-65. AAAS. Extractive metallurgical research encompassing mineral beneficiation, hydrometallurgical and pyrometallurgical studies on various minerals; utilization and stabilization of solid mineral wastes. Address: U.S. Bureau of Mines, Salt Lake City Metallurgy Research Center, 1600 E. First S, Salt Lake City, UT 84112.

DEAN, LAURENCE B(ISHOP), JR, b. Alameda, Calif, Apr. 25, 24; m. 51; c. 5. PHYSICAL CHEMISTRY. B.S, California, 44; Ph.D.(chem), Ohio State, 49. Asst. chem, Manhattan proj, California, 44; chemist, Tenn. Eastman Corp, 44-46; res. assoc, Inst. Nuclear Studies, Chicago, 49-50; Res. Corp. fel. chem, Harvard, 50-51, instr, 51-53; oper. analyst, weapons systems evaluation group, off. of secy. defense, 53-56; staff mem. to dir. strategic warfare group, weapons systs. eval. div, Inst. Defense Anal, 56-64; proj. mgr, Lambda div, Defense Res. Corp, 64-65, v.pres, LAMBDA CORP, 66-68, PRES, 68- Oper. Res. Soc. Am. Nuclear chemistry; molecular structure; electron scattering; operations analysis; simulation; management information systems. Address: 7712 Curtis St, Chevy Chase, MD 20015.

DEAN, LESLIE L, b. Twin Falls, Idaho, Feb. 4, 19; m. 41; c. 7. PLANT PATHOLOGY & BREEDING. B.S, Idaho, 42, M.S, 47; Indust. fel, Purdue, 47-50, Ph.D.(hort), 51. Asst. plant pathologist, State Crop Pest Control. Comn, Idaho, 42-44, plant pathologist, 46-47; asst. plant pathologist, UNIV. IDAHO, 50-59, assoc. plant pathologist, 59-65, plant pathologist, 65-68, RES. PROF. PLANT PATH, 68- U.S.N.R, 44-46. Am. Phytopath. Soc; Am. Soc. Hort. Sci. Virus diseases of Phaseolus vulgaris; breeding disease-resistant varieties of Phaseolus vulgaris. Address: Bean Research Lab, P.O. Box 67, Twin Falls, ID 83301.

DEAN, LYMAN ARNOLD, b. Needham, Mass, Nov. 14, 07; m. 38; c. 3. SOILS. B.S, Hawaii, 31; M.S, Wisconsin, 32, Ph.D.(soil sci), 34. Nat. Res. fel, Rothamsted Exp. Sta, Eng, 35-36; asst. chem, agr. exp. sta, Hawaii, 36-38, assoc. chemist, 38-43, assoc. prof. soil chem, univ, 38-43; res. soil scientist, soil & water conserv. res. div, U.S. DEPT. AGR, 43-61, dir. U.S. Soils Lab, 61-68, DIR. COASTAL PLAINS SOIL AND WATER CONSERVATION RES. CTR, 68- Vis. prof, N.C. State Col, 54-55; soil sci. adv, Int. Co-op. Admin, India, 56-58. Soil Sci. Soc. Am; Am. Soc. Agron. Soil fertility; soil phosphates and the utilization of phosphates by plants; application of radioactive tracers to research with soils and fertilizers; nature of soil phosphates. Address: U.S. Dept. of Agriculture, Agricultural Research Service, P.O. Box 3039, Florence, SC 29501.

DEAN, MAURICE R, b. Galveston, Tex, July 25, 14; m. 42; c. 1. PETROLEUM ENGINEERING. B.S, Univ. Okla, 37. Apprentice engr, PHILLIPS PETROL. CO, 37-41, jr. engr, 41-46, sr. chem. engr, 46-52, group leader, 52-65, MGR. RESERVOIR EVAL. SECT, 65- Am. Inst. Mining, Metall. & Petrol. Eng; Soc. Petrol. Eng. Petroleum recovery processes. Address: Phillips Petroleum Co, RB No. 1, Bartlesville, OK 74004.

DEAN, MILTON LEE, b. Nampa, Idaho, July 9, 35; m. 57; c. 3. BIOLOGY, BOTANY. B.A, Northwest Nazarene Col, 56; M.S, Ore. State Col, 60; Ph.D. (syst. bot), Oregon State, 66. Teaching asst. gen. bot, Ore. State Col, 56-58; prof. biol, Northwest Nazarene Col, 58-60; teaching asst. & instr. gen. bot, Oregon State, 60-63; PROF. BIOL, NORTHWEST NAZARENE COL, 63- Am. Inst. Biol. Sci; Am. Soc. Plant Taxon. Plant taxonomy; biosystematic studies in the genus Aster, family Compositae. Address: Dept. of Biology, Northwest Nazarene College, Nampa, ID 83651.

DEAN, NATHAN W(ESLEY), b. Johnson City, Tenn, Dec. 10, 41; m. 63; c. 1. PHYSICS. B.S, North Carolina, 63, NASA fel, 64-65; Churchill scholar, Cambridge, 65-66, Nat. Sci. Found. fel, 66-68, Ph.D.(physics), 68. Vis. scientist, Europ. Orgn. Nuclear Res, Geneva, Switz, 67-68; instr. PHYSICS, Vanderbilt Univ, 68-69, ASST. PROF, 69-70; IOWA STATE UNIV, 70-; ASSOC. PHYSICIST, AMES LAB, ATOMIC ENERGY COMN, 70- Am. Phys. Soc. Theories of elementary particles and strong interactions. Address: Dept. of Physics, Iowa State University, Ames, IA 50010.

DEAN, PHILLIP NOLAN, b. Houston, Tex, Aug. 28, 34; m. 64; c. 1. PHYSICS, BIOPHYSICS. B.A, Rice, 56, M.A, 58. STAFF MEM, BIOMED. RES. BROUP, LOS ALAMOS SCI. LAB, 61- Mem. ad hoc comt. intercomparison human Cs-137 body burdens, div. biol. & med, U.S. Atomic Energy Comn, 63-66; sci. comt. 33, Nat. Coun. Radiation Protection & Measurements. U.S.A.F, 58-61, Res, 61-67, 1st Lt. Am. Pub. Health Asn; Health Physics Soc. Direct radiation measurements on reactors; health physics; radiation dosimetry; biological effects of radiation; whole body counting; application of computers to biomedical research. Address: 124 Bandelier Ave, Los Alamos, NM 87544.

DEAN, R(ALPH) W(ILLARD), b. Cleveland, Ohio, Mar. 20, 07; m. 40; c. 2. ENTOMOLOGY. B.Sc, Ohio State, 30, M.Sc, 32, Ph.D.(entom), 39. Asst. county agent, exten. serv, Ohio State, 30-31; tech. asst, N.Y. EXP. STA, GENEVA, 31-39, asst. & instr, 39-42, asst. prof. ENTOM, 42-47, assoc. prof, HUDSON VALLEY LAB, CORNELL UNIV, 47-51, prof, 51-70; EMER. PROF, 70- Vis. prof, col. agr, Philippines, 56-57. Entom. Soc. Am. Biology and control of fruit insect pests; internal anatomy of insects. Address: P.O. Box 57, Lawai, HI 96765.

DEAN, RICHARD A, b. Brooklyn, N.Y, Dec. 22, 35; m. 57; c. 3. MECHANICAL ENGINEERING. B.S, Ga. Inst. Tech, 57; M.S, Pittsburgh, 63, Ph.D, 70. Engr, Westinghouse Nuclear Energy Systs, Pittsburgh, 60-66, mgr. thermal-hydraul eng, 66-70; TECH. DIR. LWR FUEL DIV, GULF GEN. ATOMIC, 70- U.S.A, 57-59, 1st Lt. Am. Soc. Mech. Eng; Am. Nuclear Soc. Boiling heat transfer and two phase flow; nuclear reactor core design and development. Address: 6932 Paseo Laredo, La Jolla, CA 92037.

DEAN, RICHARD A(LBERT), b. Columbus, Ohio, Oct. 9, 24; m. 48; c. 1. MATHEMATICS. B.S, Calif. Inst. Tech, 45; B.A, Denison, 47; M.A, Ohio State, 48, Ph.D.(math), 53. Instr. physics, Middlebury Col, 47; Bateman fel. MATH, CALIF. INST. TECHNOL, 54-55, asst. prof, 55-59, assoc. prof, 59-66, PROF, 66- U.S.N, 43-46, Res, 52-54, Lt. Am. Math. Soc; Math. Asn. Am. Abstract algebra; partially ordered sets and lattices; groups; word problems. Address: 2186 Lambert Dr, Pasadena, CA 91107.

DEAN, RICHARD E(UGENE), b. Lincoln, Nebr, June 14, 20; m. 42; c. 4. CELLULAR PHYSIOLOGY, STATISTICAL ANALYSIS. B.S, Nebraska, 48, M.S, 50; fel, St. Louis, 50-53, Ph.D, 54. Asst, Nebraska, 48-50, asst. prof. biol, Col. St. Thomas, 53-55; Ripon Col, 55-56; Nat. Cancer Inst. fel, Nebraska, 56-58, instr. zool, 59-66; PRES, Haegen Assoc, Inc, 66-70; DEAN'S CUSTOM PENSIONS, INC, 70- Secy-treas, Haegen Assocs, Inc, 56-66. U.S.A.A.F, 42-45. AAAS; Am. Micros. Soc; Soc. Protozool. Cellular physiology, growth and respiration. Address: Dean's Custom Pensions, Inc, 11 W. Jefferson, Sullivan, IL 61951.

DEAN, RICHARD R(AYMOND), b. Pittsburgh, Pa, June 23, 40; m. 64; c. 1. PHARMACOLOGY. B.S, Duquesne Univ, 62; Nat. Insts. Health fel. & Ph.D. (pharmacol), Univ. Mich, 66. Res. investr. CARDIOVASC. PHARMACOL, G.D. SEARLE & CO, 66-71, sr. res. investr, 71-, GROUP LEADER, 71- Mem. coun. basic sci, Am. Heart Asn. Pharmacological and toxicological evaluation of drugs in the cardiovascular and autonomic nervous systems. Address: 914 Rosemary Terr, Deerfield, IL 600[illegible]5.

DEAN, ROBERT B(ERRIDGE), b. San Francisco, Calif, Feb. 20, 13; m. 39; c. 4. PHYSICAL CHEMISTRY, PHYSIOLOGY. A.B, California, 35; Copenhagen, 37-38; Ph.D.(exp. zool), Cambridge, 38. Asst. colloid sci, Cambridge, 38-39; physiol, Rochester, 39-49; jr. instr, Minnesota, 40-41; Bristol Meyers fel. & res. assoc. chem, Stanford, 41-44, biol, Off. Sci. Res. & Develop. Proj, 42; synthetic rubber proj, War Prod. Bd, 43-44; oil foam proj, Nat. Adv. Cmt. Aeronaut, 44; asst. prof. chem, Hawaii, 44-47; Oregon, 47-52; head anal. sect, Borden Chem. Co, 52-53, mgr. develop, 53-63; dir. lab. res, WATER QUAL. OFF, ENVIRON PROTECTION AGENCY, 64-67, CHIEF ULTIMATE DISPOSAL RES. ACTIVITIES, 67- With U.S.A. Am. Chem. Soc; Water Pollution Control. Fedn; Int. Asn. Water Pollution Res. Membranes and membrane phenomena, especially accumulation of electrolytes; diffusion; colloids; analytical methods; adhesives; water renovation; treatment and ultimate disposal of sludges and brines. Address: Water Quality Office, Environmental Protection Agency, 4676 Columbia Pkwy, Cincinnati, OH 45226.

DEAN, ROBERT CHARLES, JR, b. Atlanta, Ga, Apr. 13, 28; m. 51; c. 5. MECHANICAL ENGINEERING. S.B. & S.M, Mass. Inst. Tech, 49, Sc.D. (mech. eng), 54. Engr, Ultrasonic Corp, Mass, 49-51; asst. prof. mech. eng, Mass. Inst. Tech, 51-56; head adv. eng. dept, Ingersoll-Rand Co, N.J, 56-60; consult, Easton, Pa, 60; dir. res, Thermal Dynamics Corp, N.H, 60-61; PRES, CREARE INC, 61-; PROF. ENG, THAYER SCH. ENG, DARTMOUTH COL, 60- Indust. consult; mem. turbine & compressor subcomt, Nat. Adv. Comt. Aeronaut, 54-55; venture capital panel, Commerce Tech. Adv. Bd, Dept. of Commerce. Prod. Eng. Master Designer Award, 67. Am. Soc. Mech. Eng; Am. Inst. Aeronaut. & Astronaut. Research and engineering in fluid mechanics and machinery, plasma equipment, mining machinery and design. Address: Creare Inc, P.O. Box 71, Hanover, NH 03755.

DEAN, ROBERT G(EORGE), b. Laramie, Wyo, Nov. 1, 30; m. 54; c. 2. CIVIL ENGINEERING, OCEANOGRAPHY. B.S, California, Berkeley, 54; United Gas Co. fel, Agr. & Mech. Col. Tex, 54-55, M.S, 56; J.R. Freeman fel, Mass. Inst. Tech, 58-59, D.Sc.(hydrodyn), 59. Asst. prof. civil eng, Mass. Inst. Tech, 59-60; res. engr. coastal res, Calif. Res. Corp, Standard Oil Co, Calif, 60-63, sr. res. engr, 63-65; acting assoc. prof. oceanog, Univ. Wash, 65-66; PROF. COASTAL & OCEANOG. ENG. & CHMN. DEPT. & PROF. CIVIL ENG, UNIV. FLA, 66- AAAS; Am. Soc. Civil Eng; Am. Geophys. Union. Physical oceanography; nonlinear water wave mechanics; interaction of waves with structures; general coastal engineering problems; potential flow applications. Address: Dept. of Coastal Engineering, University of Florida, Gainesville, FL 32601.

DEAN, R(OBERT) R(EED), b. Bedford, Ind, Apr. 18, 14; m. 49; c. 2. CHEMISTRY. Indiana, 34-37; summer, Wisconsin, 36; Northwestern, 41. Chemist, Johns-Manville Prod. Corp, 38-40; U.S. Gypsum Res. Lab, 40-41; inspector, U.S. Army Ord, 41-42; chemist, Am. Cyanamid, 48-49; Diamond Alkali Co, 49-50; Va. Carolina Chem. Corp, 50-53; mgr. mkt. res, Westvaco Chlor-alkali div, FMC Corp, N.Y, 53-56, dir. mkt. res. & develop, res. labs, W.Va, 56-58, mgr. commercial develop, 58-59, mgr. inorg. chem. div, mkt. res. develop, 59-71; CONSULT. COMMERCIAL DEVELOP. & INDUST. MKT. RES, 71- U.S.N, 42-46, Res, 46-48, Lt. Comdr. Am. Chem. Soc; Am. Inst. Chem; Am. Inst. Aeronaut. & Astronaut; Chem. Mkt. Res. Asn; Commercial Chem. Develop. Asn. Introduction and commercial development of new chemicals; application of existing chemicals to new uses; evaluation of markets for all commercial chemicals. Address: 13 E. Second St, New Castle, DE 19720.

DEAN, ROBERT W(ATERS), b. West Chester, Pa, June 6, 29; m. 62; c. 5. FOOD CHEMISTRY, TECHNOLOGY. B.S, Bates Col, 51; M.S, Rutgers, 57, Bakelite Indust. Res. fel. & Gen. Foods fel, 58-59, Ph.D.(food chem, tech), 59. Chemist gelatin desserts, Standard Brands, Inc, 51-53; technologist, dessert prods. & beverages, Gen. Foods Corp, 53-55; res. chemist, Wilson & Co, 59-61; prod. develop. chemist, Glidden Co, 61-62; res. chemist, Peter Eckrich & Sons, 62-64; asst. tech. dir, F & F Labs, 64-67; chief chemist, Paradise Fruit Co, 67-70; CHEMIST, GROWERS PROC. SERV, INC, 71- Am. Chem. Soc; Am. Inst. Chem; Inst. Food Tech. Determination of pigments responsible for color of fresh meat. Address: Growers Processing Service, Inc, P.O. Box 338, Highland City, FL 33846.

DEAN, R(OBERT) Y(OST), b. Portland, Ore, Jan. 13, 21; m. 54; c. 2. MATHEMATICS. B.A, Willamette, 42; M.S, Calif. Inst. Tech, 42, Ph.D.(math), 52. Mem. staff, inst. math, Case, 46-48; sr. mathematician, Hanford Labs. Oper, Gen. Elec. Co, 52-63, MGR. math subsect, 64; math. sect, appl. math. dept, Pac. Northwest Labs, Battelle Mem. Inst, 64-68; PROF. & CHMN. DEPT. MATH, CENT. WASH. STATE COL, 68- Lectr, center grad. study, Washington, 52-; summer inst. secondary sch. teachers, Nat. Sci. Found, Idaho, 57, Alaska, 58, in-serv. inst. teachers math. southeast. Wash, 62-63. Math. Asn. Am; Am. Math. Soc; Soc. Indust. & Appl. Math. Applied mathematics. Address: Dept. of Mathematics, Central Washington State College, Ellensburg, WA 98926.

DEAN, RONALD S, b. Montreal, Que, Jan. 7, 36. GEOLOGY. B.S, McGill, 56, M.S, 58, Ph.D.(geol), 63. RES. SCIENTIST, MINERAL PROCESSING DIV, DEPT. ENERGY, MINES & RESOURCES, CAN, 61- Fel. Geol. Asn. Can; Clay Minerals Soc. Shale mineralogy. Address: 74 Fairmont Ave, Apt. 2, Ottawa, Ont. K1Y 1X5, Can.

DEAN, RUSSELL T(ATTERSHALL), b. Troy, Pa, Oct. 2, 12; m. 33; c. 1. ORGANIC CHEMISTRY. B.S, Lehigh, 33; Ph.D.(chem), Yale, 36. Res. chemist, Am. Cyanamid Co, 36-42; develop. chemist, Gen. Aniline & Film Corp, 42-44; res. chemist, Casein Co. Am, 44-45; develop. chemist, plastics div, Glenn L. Martin Co, Md, 45-46; mkt. develop, Shell Develop. Co, 46-47; res. chemist, Interchem. Corp, N.Y. 47-52, resin group leader, 52-54, dir. org. chem. dept, 54-59; res. supvr, Borden Chem. Co, 60-61; chief engr, Stackpole Carbon Co, 61-64; supvr. res. & develop, Great Lakes Chem. Corp, 65-69; SECT. HEAD, BETZ LABS, INC, 69- Am. Chem. Soc. Pharmaceuticals; synthetic resins; natural and synthetic rubber chemistry; market research and sales development. Address: 3302 St. Davids Rd, Newton Square, PA 19073.

DEAN, SHELDON WILLIAMS, JR, b. Flushing, N.Y, July 3, 35; m. 60; c. 3. CHEMICAL ENGINEERING, SURFACE CHEMISTRY. A.B, Middlebury Col, 58; Am. Oil fel. & S.B, Mass. Inst. Tech, 58, Nat. Sci. Found. fel, 60, Sc.D. (chem. eng), 62. Res. asst. chem. eng, Mass. Inst. Tech, 60-61; mem. sr. staff, res. lab, Int. Nickel Co, 61-64; eng. specialist metal finishing, METALS RES. LAB, OLIN CORP, 64-66, GROUP SUPVR. METAL FINISHING & BONDING, 66- Sea Horse Inst. award, 66; Hamden Jaycee DSA award, 70. AAAS; Electrochem. Soc; Am. Inst. Chem. Eng; Am. Chem. Soc; Sci. Res. Soc. Am; Nat. Asn. Corrosion Eng; Am. Soc. Test. & Mat; Am. Inst. Chem; Nat. Soc. Prfnl. Eng. Metal finishing; corrosion research, especially stress corrosion cracking of alloys containing nickel; electrochemical polarization measurements; contact angle hysteresis. Address: Metals Research Lab, Olin Corp, 91 Shelton Ave, New Haven, CT 06504.

DEAN, STEPHEN ODELL, b. Niagara Falls, N.Y, May 12, 36; m. 62; c. 3. PLASMA PHYSICS, NUCLEAR ENGINEERING. B.S, Boston Col, 60; U.S. Atomic Energy Comn. fel. & S.M, Mass. Inst. Technol, 62; Ph.D.(physics), Univ. Md, 71. Physicist, U.S. Atomic Energy Comn, 62-68; RES. PHYSICIST, PLASMA PHYSICS DIV, U.S. NAVAL RES. LAB, 68- Am. Phys. Soc. Collisionless shocks; thermonuclear research. Address: Plasma Physics Division, 7720, U.S. Naval Research Lab, Washington, DC 20390.

DEAN, THOMAS SCOTT, b. Sherman, Tex, July 6, 24; m. 45; c. 3. ARCHITECTURE, SOLID MECHANICS. B.S, North Texas State, 45, M.S, 47; Mass. Inst. Tech, 48-49; Southern Methodist, 55-59; Ph.D.(eng. mech), Texas, 63. Owner, Thomas Scott Dean, Architect & Engr. Dynamics Consult, Tex, 50-60; lectr. archit. eng, Texas, 60-64; CHMN. ARCHIT. SCI, OKLA. STATE UNIV, 64-, PROF. ARCHIT, 70- Lectr, Southern Methodist, 55-59; faculty fel, Latin Am. Studies Inst, 63; mem, Hot Weather Res. Inst, 63-64. Consult, Tex. Indust, Inc, 55-59; archit. eng. consult, Brackenridge Field Lab, 63-64. C.Eng, U.S.A, 42-43. Am. Inst. Archit; Nat. Soc. Prof. Eng; Am. Soc. Civil Eng; Am. Soc. Heat, Refrig. & Air Conditioning Eng; Am. Soc. Eng. Educ. Design criteria for research structures; variational methods for elastodynamic problems; innovative teaching methods; electrical analogs for problems in architecture; societal aspects of technology. Address: School of Architecture, Oklahoma State University, Stillwater, OK 74074.

DEAN, WAID H(AMPTON), b. Dallas, Tex, May 2, 29; m. 52; c. 2. PHYSIOLOGICAL PSYCHOLOGY. A.B, Kansas, 50; M.A, La. State, 55, Ph.D, 58. Instr. physiol, sch. med, La. State, 57-60; psychiat, Med. Col. of Georgia, 60-62, asst. prof, 62-69; AGENCY DIR, PASTORAL COUN. CENT. AUGUSTA, 69- U.S.A, 52-54. AAAS; Am. Psychol. Asn. Relationship between planned cerebral lesions and learned behavior in primates; personality variables; electroencephalography. Address: Suite 232 Bon Air Hotel, Augusta, GA 30904.

DEAN, WALTER A(LBERT), b. Bridgeport, Conn, Feb. 5, 05; m. 36; c. 1. METALLURGY. B.S, Cooper Union, 26; M.S, Rensselaer Polytech, 27, Ph.D.(metall), 29. Res. metallurgist, Aluminum Co. Am, 29-44, asst. plant mgr, 44-49, works chief metallurgist, 49-57, develop. metallurgist, Alcoa Res. Labs, New Kensington, 57-60, asst. dir. res, 60-70; RETIRED. Am. Inst. Mining, Metall. & Petrol. rep. adv. panel, Nat. Bur. Standards, 63-66. Am. Soc. Metals; Am. Inst. Mining, Metall. & Petrol. Eng.(past v.pres); Am. Ord. Asn.(Bronze medal & citation, 64); Brit. Inst. Metals. Properties of aluminum alloys; development of commercial aluminum alloys; improvement in processes for manufacturing aluminum alloy products. Address: 8600 Midnight Pass Rd, Sarasota, FL 33581.

DEAN, WALTER E, JR, b. Wilkes-Barre, Pa, July 12, 39; m. 61; c. 2. SEDIMENTOLOGY, LIMNOLOGY. A.B, Syracuse Univ, 61; M.S, Univ. N.Mex, 64, NASA fel, 64-67, Ph.D.(geol), 67. Res. asst. geol, Univ. N.Mex, 63-64; res. assoc. bot, Univ. Minn, 67-68; ASST. PROF. GEOL, SYRACUSE UNIV, 68- Geol. Soc. Am; Soc. Econ. Paleont. & Mineral; Am. Soc. Limnol. & Oceanog; Int. Asn. Gt. Lakes Res; Int. Asn. Theoret. & Appl. Limnol. Geochemistry of evaporite and carbonate deposits; geochemistry of lakes and lake sediments. Address: Dept. of Geology, Syracuse University, Syracuse, NY 13210.

DEAN, WALTER KEITH, b. Big Timber, Mont, Nov. 2, 17; m. 41; c. 4. INORGANIC CHEMISTRY. B.S, Wisconsin, 39; M.S, Missouri, Rolla, 41. Asst. chem, sch. mines & metall, Missouri, Rolla, 39-41; chemist, MALLINCKRODT CHEM. WORKS, 41-69, RES. SUPVR, SCI. PROD. DIV, 69- Lectr, univ. col, Washington (St. Louis), 53-62. Am. Chem. Soc. Chromatography chemicals; high-purity silicon; rhenium; analytical reagents; ultrapure organic solvents. Address: Science Products Division, Mallinckrodt Chemical Works, P.O. Box 5439, St. Louis, MO 63160.

DEAN, WALTER LEE, b. Lenoir City, Tenn, Dec. 13, 28; m. 53; c. 3. ORGANIC & INORGANIC CHEMISTRY. B.S, Maryville Col, 50; Res. Corp. fel, Tennessee, 51-52, M.S, 53, U.S. Dept. Agr. fel, 53-55, Ph.D.(org. chem), 56. RES. CHEMIST, BUCKEYE CELLULOSE CORP, 56- Am. Chem. Soc. Organic chemistry and synthesis; natural products; cellulose derivatives; graft polymer synthesis. Address: 5226 Quince Rd, Memphis, TN 38117.

DEAN, WARREN E(DGELL), b. Richwood, W.Va, Aug. 1, 32; m. 59; c. 3. PHYSICAL & INORGANIC CHEMISTRY. B.S, W.Va. Inst. Tech, 54; M.S, West Virginia, 57, DuPont fel, 57-58, Ph.D, 59. Instr. chem, West Virginia, 58-59; with Columbia-South. Chem. Corp, 59; SUPVR. PROCESS RES, CHEM. DIV, PPG INDUSTS, INC, 59- Am. Chem. Soc. Chelate compounds of alkanol-substituted ethylendiamines; process research; inorganic heavy chemicals. Address: PPG Industries, Inc, Chemical Division, New Martinsville, WV 26155.

DEAN, WILLARD W, b. Norton, Kans, July 4, 24; m. 58; c. 4. BACTERIOLOGY. B.S, Oklahoma, 53, M.S, 54; Ph.D.(bact), Arizona State, 66. Bacteriologist, St. Luke's Hosp, Phoenix, Ariz, 58-60; asst. dir. pub. health, Ariz. State Health Dept. Labs, 60-63; res. assoc. zool, Arizona, 63-66; ASST. PROF. bact, Univ. Ala, 66-69; BIOL. SCI, CALIF. STATE POLYTECH. COL, SAN LUIS OBISPO, 69- Res. grant, 67- Consult, Tuscaloosa Path. Labs, 67- U.S.N, 42-46, 48-52. Am. Soc. Microbiol. Virology; tissue culture; fluorescence microscopy. Address: Dept. of Biological Sciences, California State Polytechnic College, San Luis Obispo, San Luis Obispo, CA 93401.

DEAN, WILLIAM C(ORNER), b. Pittsburgh, Pa, Nov. 21, 26; m. 50; c. 2. ELECTRICAL ENGINEERING. B.S, Carnegie Inst. Tech, 49, M.S, 50, Ph.D, 52. Res. geophysicist, Gulf Res. & Develop. Co, 52-60; sr. eng. specialist, United Electrodynamics & Teledyne, Inc, 60-62, proj. eng, 62, chief res. sect, 62-66, mgr. seismic data lab, Teledyne, Inc, 66-70, MGR. SEISMIC ARRAY ANAL. CTR, TELEDYNE-GEOTECH, 70- U.S.N, 45-46. Inst. Elec. & Electronics Eng; Soc. Explor. Geophys. Circuit theory; information theory; data processing; analog and digital computers; potential fields; wave propagation. Address: Teledyne-Geotech, P.O. Box 334, Alexandria, VA 22313.

DEAN, WILLIAM GEORGE, Geog, Geomorphol, see Suppl. I to 11th ed, Soc. & Behav. Vols.

DEANE, CHARLES WILLIAM, b. Syracuse, N.Y, May 30, 10; m. 41; c. 4. CHEMICAL & ENVIRONMENTAL ENGINEERING. M.S, Univ. Rochester, 35; D.Sc.(chem. eng), N.Y. Univ, 44. Develop. engr, Alco Prod. Div, Am. Locomotive Co, 36-38; process engr, Standard Oil Develop. Co, N.J, 38-41; head chem. eng. dept, Colgate-Palmolive Co, 41-47; exec. engr. for. & domestic opers, E.R. Squibb & Sons, 47-49; eng. mgr. domestic plants, Lever Bros. Co, 49-52; coord. petrochem. plants, U.S. Indust. Chem, 52-55; CONSULT. ENGR, 55- Spec. lectr, Polytech. Inst. Brooklyn, 47-49. Fel. AAAS; Am. Soc. Mech. Eng; Am. Inst. Chem. Eng; Am. Soc. Eng. Educ. Organic chemical reactor technology; design methods—scale-up; diffusional processes, moisture control; solids blending and gas distribution—packed beds; pneumatic conveying, engineering economics; instrumentation; drying technology; incineration techniques; chemical feed systems; materials recovery; waste control; biological treatment. Address: 17 Sherbrooke Rd, Scarsdale, NY 10583.

DEANE, DARRELL D(WIGHT), b. Anacortes, Wash, Nov. 9, 15; m. 43; c. 3. DAIRY SCIENCE. B.S, Idaho, 38; M.Sc, Nebraska, 39; Ph.D.(bact), Pa. State, 42. Asst. prof. dairy husb, Nebraska, 46-51; dairy indust, Iowa State, 51-61; assoc. prof. DAIRY MFG, UNIV. WYO, 61-68, PROF, 68- With Off. Sci. Res. & Develop, Sanit.C, U.S.A, 42-46, Med.Serv.C.(Res), Lt. Col.(Ret). Am. Dairy Sci. Asn; Int. Asn. Milk, Food & Environ. Sanit. Production of penicillin from synthetic media; ripening of cheddar cheese; lactic streptococcus bacteriophages; microbial spoilage of cottage cheese; cheese packaging; direct acid manufacture of sour cream and cottage cheese. Address: Division of Animal Science, University of Wyoming, Laramie, WY 82070.

DEANE, GEORGE EDWARD, b. Brockton, Mass, May 9, 30; m. 54; c. 3. EXPERIMENTAL PSYCHOLOGY. A.B, Brown, 52; M.A, Connecticut, 54, Ph.D.(psychol), 59. Asst. PSYCHOL, Univ. Conn, 52-54, 56-58; asst. prof, Col. Wooster, 58-61; STATE UNIV. N.Y. BINGHAMTON, 61-65, assoc. prof, 65-69, PROF, 69-, CHMN. DEPT, 66- U.S.A, 55-56. AAAS; Am. Psychol. Asn. Autonomic conditioning; learning theory; sensory processes; comparative behavior. Address: Dept. of Psychology, State University of New York at Binghamton, Binghamton, NY 13901.

DEANE, NORMAN, b. Newark, N.J, Aug. 20, 21; m. 56; c. 2. INTERNAL MEDICINE, PHYSIOLOGY. B.A, Temple, 43, M.D, 46. Inter. physiol, col. med, N.Y. Univ, 49-51, instr. med, post grad. med. sch, 53-54, asst. prof. clin. med, 54-56, asst. prof. med, 56-61; lectr. physiol, col. med, 55-61, dir. clins, univ. hosp. & med. center, 56-60; ASSOC. PROF. MED. & ASSOC. ATTEND. PHYSICIAN, N.Y. MED. COL, FLOWER & FIFTH AVE. HOSPS, 61- Vis. investr, med. dept, Brookhaven Nat. Lab, 50-51; asst. vis. physician, fourth med. div, N.Y. Univ, 53-58, assoc. attend. physician, Univ. Hosp. & Med. Ctr, 58-61; Polachek fel. med. res, 56-61; assoc. attend. physician, Metropolitan Hosp, 61-70; vis. physician, 70-; attend. physician, Lenox Hill Hosp, 67- Mem. adv. coun, N.Y. State Kidney Disease Inst, 67-; renal dialysis comt, Health & Hosp. Planning Coun. South. N.Y, 67-; renal disease subcomt, New York Metrop. Regional Med. Prog, 68-; hypertension & renal disease comt, N.J. Regional Medicaid Prog, 68-; nephrology adv. comt, N.Y.C. Medicaid Prog, 68- Consult. physician, Englewood Hosp, 68-; Hackensack Hosp, 69-; Jersey City Med. Ctr, 70- Dipl, Am. Bd. Internal Med. Med.C, 51-53, Capt. Harvey Soc; Am. Physiol. Soc; Am. Fedn. Clin. Res; fel. Am. Col. Physicians; fel. Am. Col. Chest Physicians; Am. Soc. Artificial Internal Organs; N.Y. Acad. Med; Soc. Exp. Biol. & Med. Nephrology; integration of normal cardio-pulmonary, renal and liver function in man and alterations produced by disease; chemical composition and mechanisms of control of the internal environment of the body. Address: 112 E. 74th St, New York, NY 10021.

DEANIN, RUDOLPH D, b. Newark, N.J, June 7, 21; m. 46; c. 2. POLYMER CHEMISTRY. A.B, Cornell, 41; M.S, Illinois, 42, Ph.D.(org. chem), 44. Lab. asst. org. chem, Cornell, 40-41; jr. sci. aide, regional soybean indust. prod. res. lab, U.S. Dept. Agr, 41-42; asst. chem, Nat. Defense Res. Cmt. Proj, Illinois, 42, asst. instr, 42-43, asst. physics, 42-43; spec. res. asst, Off. Rubber Res, 43-47; res. chemist & proj. leader, Allied Chem. Corp, 47-60; dir. chem. res. & develop, DeBell & Richardson, Inc, Conn, 60-67; PROF. PLASTICS, LOWELL TECHNOL. INST, 67- Vis. lectr, Univ. Mass, 63-64; Brown Univ, 65-66; Northeast. Univ, 67-68. Am. Chem. Soc; Soc. Plastics Eng. Polymerization, compounding, properties, applications and economics of polymers and plastics. Address: Dept. of Plastics Technology, Lowell Technological Institute, Lowell, MA 01854.

DEANS, HARRY A, b. Dallas, Tex, June 17, 32; m. 56; c. 3. CHEMICAL ENGINEERING. B.A, Rice Inst, 53, B.S, 54, M.S, 56; Fulbright fel, Ger, 55-56; Ph.D.(chem. eng), Princeton, 60. Assoc. prof. CHEM. ENG, RICE UNIV, 59-70, PROF, 70- Fulbright lectr, Israel, 64; consult, Esso Prod. Res. Co. Am. Inst. Chem. Eng. Multiphase, multicomponent fluid flow in porous media; gas-liquid and gas-solid chromatography of chemically reactive systems; chemisorption; bubble-column chromatography; tracer methods in petroleum reservoir evaluation; continuous chromatographic separation technology. Address: Dept. of Chemical Engineering, Rice University, Houston, TX 77001.

DEANS, ROBERT J(ACK), b. Ft. Wayne, Ind, Dec. 4, 27; m. 50; c. 5. ANIMAL HUSBANDRY. B.Sc, Ohio State, 49; M.Sc, 50; Ph.D.(animal husb), Mich. State, 56. Instr. ANIMAL HUSB, Ohio State, 50-52; MICH. STATE UNIV, 52-56, asst. prof, 56-60, ASSOC. PROF, 60- Adv, Univ. Nigeria, 65. Am. Soc. Animal Sci; Am. Meat Sci. Asn. Effects of endocrine-like substances in meat-animal production; beef and lamb carcass investigations. Address: Dept. of Animal Husbandry, Michigan State University, East Lansing, MI 48823.

DEANS, SIDNEY A(LFRED) V(INDIN), b. Montreal, Que, Dec. 31, 18; m. 59; c. 1. ORGANIC CHEMISTRY. B.Sc, McGill, 39, Nat. Res. Coun. Can. bursary, 39, stud, 40, fel, 41, Ph.D, 42. Res. chemist, Can. Industs, Ltd, 42-46; develop. chemist, Ayerst, McKenna & Harrison Ltd, 47-56; assoc. dir. chem. develop, Union Carbide Can, Ltd, 56-62; TECH. DIR, PFIZER CO. LTD, 62- Am. Chem. Soc; Chem. Inst. Can. Synthesis of ethers; polymerization; penicillin; estrogenic sulfates; tetraethylthiuram disulfide; synthetic organic chemicals; petrochemicals; pharmaceuticals. Address: 361 Lethbridge Ave, Montreal 304, Que, Can.

DEAR, PAUL S(TANFORD), b. Norfolk, Va, Dec. 1, 05; m. 45; c. 2. CERAMIC ENGINEERING. B.S, Va. Polytech, 27, M.S, 32; N.Y. State Col. Ceramics, 35; M.S, Pa. State Col, 37. Instr. applied mech. & exp. eng, VA. POLYTECH. INST. & STATE UNIV, 28-29, CERAMIC ENG, 29-37, asst. prof, 37-47, assoc. prof, 47-51, prof. & head dept, 51-70; EMER. PROF, 70- Trustee, Va. Polytech. Res. Found, Inc. Fel. Am. Ceramic Soc; Nat. Inst. Ceramic Eng; Ceramic Ed. Coun.(past pres). Performance characteristics of reinforced brick masonry slabs; mortar bond characteristics of brick; petrographic methods in ceramics; elastico-viscous properties of several sodium metasilicate-silica glasses in the annealing range of temperatures; aplite, a new ceramic material; feldspars of Virginia; ceramic silica possibilities in Virginia. Address: Dept. of Ceramics, Virginia Polytechnic Institute & State University, Box 205, Blacksburg, VA 24060.

DEAR, R(OBERT) E(RNEST) A(RTHUR), b. Bristol, Eng, June 5, 33; m. 56; c. 3. ORGANIC CHEMISTRY. A.R.I.C, Bristol Col. Sci. & Tech, 56; Ph.D. (org. chem), Western Ontario, 63. Trainee chem, Imp. Smelting Corp, 50-56; res. chemist, Dow Chem. Can, 56-60; NATO fel, Cambridge, 63-64; SR. RES. CHEMIST, ALLIED CHEM. CORP, 64- Am. Chem. Soc; fel. Royal Inst. Chem, 68. Organic chemistry, particularly of fluorinated compounds; derivatives of polyfluoro-ketones. Address: Allied Chemical Corp, Corporate Chemical Research Lab, Box 405, Morristown, NJ 07960.

DEARBORN, CURTIS HOWARD, b. Weare, N.H, June 15, 12; m. 37; c. 5. HORTICULTURE. B.S, New Hampshire, 35; Ph.D.(veg), Cornell, 39. Veg. specialist, W. Atlee Burpee Co, Pa, 41-42; asst. prof, exp. sta, Cornell, 46-50; RES. HORTICULTURIST, AGR. RES. SERV, U.S. DEPT. AGR, Matanuska Exp. Sta, Univ. Alaska, 50-69, PLANT SCI. RES. DIV, 69- U.S.A, 42-46, Maj. AAAS; Am. Soc. Hort. Sci; Int. Soc. Hort. Sci; Am. Inst. Biol. Sci; Arctic Inst. N.Am; Potato Asn. Am. Continuous measurement of energy of the natural spectrum in 12 wave bands at 2 locations, Matanuska Experiment Station and Columbia, Missouri; evaluation of pea, potato and summer squash for freezing preservation. Address: Plant Science Research Division, Box AE, U.S. Dept. of Agriculture, Palmer, AK 99645.

DEARBORN, EARL H(AMILTON), b. Manhattan, Kans, June 10, 15; m. 43; c. 4. PHARMACOLOGY. A.B, Kansas, 38, M.A, 40; Ph.D.(pharmacol), Chicago, 42; Parke-Davis fel, Hopkins, 46-49, M.D, 49. Asst. physiol, Kansas, 37-38, asst. instr, 38-40; asst. pharmacol, Chicago, 40-43, instr, 43; Hopkins, 43-49, asst. prof, 49-52; prof. & chmn. dept, sch. med, Boston, 52-56; head dept. pharmacol. res, Lederle Labs, Am. Cyanamid Co, N.Y, 56-60, asst. dir. exp. therapeut. res. sect, 60-63, dir, 63-65, asst. dir. res, 65-69; dir. med. affairs, Dome Labs, MILES LABS, INC, 69-70, PRES. RES. DIV, 70- Lectr, sch. med, Boston Univ, 56-69; mem. drug res. bd, Nat. Acad. Sci-Nat. Res. Coun, 66-69, toxicol. info. prog. adv. comt, 68-71, chmn, 71-; chmn. toxicol. terminology comt, Nat. Libr. Med, 66-68; mem. clin. & preclin. pharmacol. adv. comt, Walter Reed Army Inst. Res. Am. Chem. Soc; Soc. Exp. Biol. & Med; Am. Soc. Pharmacol. & Exp. Therapeut; Soc. Toxicol; N.Y. Acad. Sci. Cardiovascular renal pharmacology and enzymology; chemotherapy of malaria; pharmacology of antibacterial agents; evaluation of drug safety. Address: Research Division, Miles Labs, Inc, 400 Morgan Lane, West Haven, CT 06516.

DEARBORN, JOHN H(OLMES), b. Bangor, Maine, Feb. 26, 33; m. 60; c. 2. MARINE ZOOLOGY & ECOLOGY. B.A, Univ. N.H, 55; M.S, Mich. State Univ, 57; Ph.D.(biol), Stanford Univ, 65. Asst, Stanford Univ, 58-64; ASSOC. MARINE ZOOL, MUS. COMP. ZOOL, HARVARD, 65-; ASSOC. PROF. ZOOL. & OCEANOG, UNIV. MAINE, 69-, asst. prof. zool, 66-69. Nat. Sci. Found. fel, 65-66; mem. higher invertebrates adv. comt, Smithsonian Oceanog. Ctr, 68- AAAS; Am. Soc. Limnol. & Oceanog; Ecol. Soc. Am; Am. Soc. Zool; Soc. Syst. Zool; Arctic Inst. N.Am; Nat. Audubon Soc; Marine Biol. Asn. U.K. Marine invertebrate zoology and ecology, especially Antarctic benthos; polar and deep sea echinoderms; marine mammals; oceanic birds. Address: Dept. of Zoology, University of Maine, Orono, ME 04473.

DEARBORN, ROLAND B(ALCH), b. Weare, N.H, Jan. 29, 06. HORTICULTURE. B.S, New Hampshire, 27, M.S, 30; fel, Cornell, 33-35, Ph.D.(olericult), 35. Mem. staff hort, exp. sta, New Hampshire, 29-32; fel. chem, N.Y. Agr. Exp. Sta, Geneva, 35-36; exec, seed dept, East. States Farmers Exchange, Mass, 36-42, seed prod. exec, 44-46, res. investr, 46-54, spec. invests, 54-58, head econ. res, 58-61; agr. economist, 61-66; admin. asst, N.H. STATE DEPT. HEALTH & WELFARE, 66-70, ASST. TO COMNR, 70- Training off. coop, Univ. Conn-U.S. Agency Int. Develop, Zambia, Africa, 65- U.S.A.A.F, 42-44, Capt. Fel. AAAS. Agricultural plant nutrition; biometry; quality investigation of miscellaneous farm supplies; agricultural economics. Address: R.F.D. 1, Weare, NH 03281.

DEARDEN, DOUGLAS MOREY, b. Echo, Utah, Aug. 25, 23; m. 48; c. 3. ZOOLOGY, GENETICS. B.A, Utah, 47, M.A, 49; California, Berkeley, 40-50; Ph.D.(sci. educ, zool), Minnesota, 59. Asst. biol. & genetics, Utah, 47-49; instr. BIOL, UNIV. MINN, MINNEAPOLIS, 50-51, assoc. prof, 52-69, PROF, 69- Summer, Tozer Found. field biol. scholar, 57. U.S.N, 42-46, Res, 51-52, Lt. AAAS; Nat. Asn. Res. Sci. Teaching. Drosophila and human genetics. Address: Dept. of Biology, General College, University of Minnesota, Minneapolis, MN 55455.

DEARDEN, LYLE C(ONWAY), b. Salt Lake City, Utah, Apr. 27, 22; m. 43; c. 3. ANATOMY. B.A, Utah, 47, M.A, 49, Ph.D.(vert. zool), 55. Asst. comp. anat, Utah, 47-49; asst. instr. comp. anat. & embryol, Kansas, 49-50; instr. zool, Massachusetts, 50-53; biol, St. Mary of Wasatch Col, 53-54; zool, Massachusetts, 54; biol, Utah, 53-54; zool, Massachusetts, 54-55; anat, med. sch, Southern California, 55-57, asst. prof, 57-59; assoc. prof, sch. med, George Washington, 59-63; with Nat. Sci. Found, 59-63, consult, 63-; prof. ANAT, Calif. Col. Med, 63-66, ASSOC. PROF, UNIV. CALIF-CALIF. COL. MED, 66- U.S.N.R, 42-45, Lt. Comdr. AAAS; Am. Soc. Mammal; Am. Asn. Anat. Gross anatomy; EM GI system. Address: Dept. of Anatomy, University of California Irvine, California College of Medicine, Irvine, CA 90031.

DEARDOFF, DONALD LEWIS, b. Crawsfordsville, Ind, June 12, 38; m. 59; c. 2. NUCLEAR PHYSICS. B.S, Manchester Col, 60; M.S, Purdue, 64, Ph.D.(physics), 68. Asst. prof. PHYSICS, BRIDGEWATER COL, 67-71, ASSOC. PROF, 71- Am. Asn. Physics Teachers. Critical phenomena; measurement of localized density of xenon near critical point using Beams densitometer. Address: Dept. of Physics, Bridgewater College, Bridgewater, VA 22812.

DEARDORFF, DWIGHT L(UVERNE), b. Yale, Iowa, Dec. 1, 07; m. 35; c. 2. PHARMACY, CHEMISTRY. B.S, Iowa, 30, scholar, 34-35, M.S, 35, Ph.D. (phys. chem), 38. Pharmacist, McDonald Drug Co, Iowa, 30-33; asst. chem, Iowa, 35-38; fel, corn, Corn Industs. Res. Found, 38-40; prof. chem. & head dept, Iowa Wesleyan Col, 40-42; indust. fel. fur tech, Mellon Inst, 42-47, fel, drug standards, U.S. Pharmacopeia, 47-48, sr. fel, 48-49; assoc. prof. pharmacy, UNIV. ILL, CHICAGO-CIRCLE, 49-51, PROF. MFG. PHARMACY, 51- Lectr, Duquesne, 46; Pittsburgh, 47-49. Mgt. consult, Alcon Labs, Inc, Texas, 56-58. AAAS; Am. Chem. Soc; Am. Pharmaceut. Asn; Am. Soc. Hosp. Pharmacists; Am. Soc. Qual. Control; Am. Col. Apothecaries. Streaming potentials of aqueous solutions; determination of moisture content of corn syrup; improvement of felting of fur; fur technology; iodine analysis; drug standardization; statistical quality control in pharmacy; influence of granulation size and surfactants on properties of compressed tablets; thin film tablet coating; cellulosic high polymers in ophthalmic vehicles; homogenization pressure and emulsion stability; production control; sterile filtration; determination of critical micelle concentration. Address: College of Pharmacy, University of Illinois at Chicago Circle, 833 S. Wood St, Chicago, IL 60680.

DEARING, L(E ROY) M(ATTHEW), b. Parma, Mich, Jan. 26, 08; m. 44; c. 2. CHEMISTRY. B.S, Antioch Col, 30, M.S, 33; fel, Ohio State, 32-35, Ph.D. (phys. chem), 35. Asst. chemist, Antioch Indust. Res. Inst, 30-32; asst. chem, Ohio State, 32-34; tech. supvr. Cine-Kodak Processing, Eastman Kodak Co, 35-42, color photog. processing res, 45; technicolor Motion Picture Corp, 46-47, dir. res, 48-56, tech. dir. consumer opers, 57-61; PRES, L.M. DEARING ASSOCS, INC, 62- U.S.N.R, 42-45, Comdr. AAAS; Am. Inst. Aeronaut. & Astronaut; Soc. Photog. Sci. & Eng; Am. Chem. Soc; Soc. Photo-Optical Instrument. Eng; Optical Soc. Am; assoc. Photog. Soc. Am; fel. Soc. Motion Picture & TV Eng. Sizes and shapes of organic molecules; color photography; photographic processes; photo-optical data recording; physics. Address: L.M. Dearing Associates, Inc, 12324 Ventura Blvd, Studio City, CA 91604.

DEARING, WILLIAM C(OCKRUM), b. Oakland City, Ind, Oct. 24, 06; m. 29; c. 2. CHEMISTRY. A.B, Oakland City Col, 26; A.M, Princeton, 27; Ph.D. (chem), Western Reserve, 35. Asst. chem, Princeton, 26-28; instr, Col. of Wooster, 29-37; res. chemist, Plaskon div, Libbey-Owens-Ford Glass Co, 37-45; assoc. dir. res, 45-47, dir. res, 47-49; electro-textile div, Behr-Manning Corp, 49-50; asst. mgr. lab. sect, Koppers Co, 50-51; sr. fel. Mellon Inst, 51-55, tech. dir, glaskyd dept, Am. Cyanamid Co, 55-65, res. assoc, 65-70; RETIRED. Soc. Plastics Eng; Am. Chem. Soc. Plastics; synthetic resins; adhesives; zirconium and its derivatives; electrochemistry. Address: 2127 Heatherwood Dr, Toledo, OH 43614.

DEARING, WILLIAM H(ILL), b. Memphis, Tenn, Dec. 3, 08; m. 36; c. 2. INTERNAL MEDICINE. A.B, Pennsylvania, 29, A.M. & M.D, 34; Mayo Found. fel, Minnesota, 36-39, Ph.D.(med), 41. Assoc. MED, Geisinger Mem. Hosp, 35-36; first asst, MAYO GRAD. SCH. MED, UNIV. MINN, 39-41, instr, 42-47, asst. prof, 47-53, assoc. prof, 53-62, PROF, 62-, HEAD A SECT. MED, 46-, consult, Mayo Clin, 41. Dipl, Am. Bd. Internal Med, 43. Am. Med. Asn; Am. Col. Physicians; Am. Fedn. Clin. Res; Am. Gastroenterol. Asn. Gastroenterology. Address: Rochester Towers, Apt. 1005, Rochester, MN 55901.

DEARMAN, HENRY HURSELL, b. Statesville, N.C, Aug. 28, 34; m. 61. PHYSICAL CHEMISTRY. B.S, North Carolina, 56; Nat. Sci. Found. fel, Calif. Inst. Tech, 56-59, Dow Chem. fel, 59-60, Ph.D.(chem), 60. Res. assoc. chem, Enrico Fermi Inst. Nuclear Studies, Chicago, 60-61; res. chemist, Chemstrand Res. Ctr, Inc, Monsanto Co, 61-62; asst. prof. CHEM, UNIV. N.C, CHAPEL HILL, 62-67, ASSOC. PROF, 67- Am. Chem. Soc; Am. Phys. Soc. Paramagnetic resonance spectra; electronic spectra of organic molecules and inorganic transition metal complexes. Address: Dept. of Chemistry, University of North Carolina at Chapel Hill, Chapel Hill, NC 27514.

DeARMON, IRA A(LEXANDER), JR, b. Charlotte, N.C, Sept. 18, 20; m. 50; c. 4. STATISTICS. B.S, Va. Polytech, 43, M.S, 48. Sanitarian, State Health Dept, Va, 47-50; chief statistician, biomath. div, Ft. Detrick, 54-60, res. analyst, Chem. Corps. Opers. Res. Group, Army Chem. Ctr, 60-64, OPERS. RES. ANALYST, OPERS. RES. GROUP, U.S. ARMY MUNITIONS COMMAND, EDGEWOOD ARSENAL, 64- Asst. prof. math, Harford Jr. Col, 66-; exec. dir, Pine Bluff Arsenal, Ark. U.S.A.R, 43-, Col. Opers. Res. Soc. Am; Biomet. Soc; Am. Ord. Asn. Operations research; systems analysis; design of experiment. Address: 219 Broadway, Bel Air, MD 21014.

DeARMOND, M. KEITH, b. Ft. Wayne, Ind, Dec. 10, 35. PHYSICAL & INORGANIC CHEMISTRY. B.A, DePauw, 58; Ph.D.(phys. chem), Arizona, 63. Res. assoc. magnetic resonance spectros, Illinois, 63-64; asst. prof. CHEM, N.C. STATE UNIV, 64-70, ASSOC. PROF, 70- Nat. Insts. Health trainee, 63-64. Am. Chem. Soc. Electronic structure and chemical bonding of transition metal complexes using low temperature spectroscopic techniques; investigation of luminescence of metal complexes to elucidate nonradiative energy transfer processes. Address: Dept. of Chemistry, North Carolina State University, P.O. Box 5247, Raleigh, NC 27607.

DEAS, THOMAS C, b. Augusta, Ga, Aug. 5, 21; m. 43; c. 2. ANESTHESIOLOGY. B.S, Georgia, 42; M.D, Ga. Sch. Med, 45. Intern, U.S. Naval Hosp, Parris Island, S.C, 45-46, med. officer, post med. detachment, 46-48; res. anesthesiol, Univ. Hosp, Augusta, Ga, 48-49; anesthesiologist, Navy Hosp. Ship Consolation, 49-51, Naval Hosp, Jacksonville, Fla, 51, res, Phila, Pa, 51-52, chief anesthesiol. serv, 56-63, anesthesiologist, Bainbridge, Md, 52-55; PROF. ANESTHESIOL, TEMPLE UNIV, 63- Consult, U.S. Naval Hosp, Phila, 63. Dipl, Am. Bd. Anesthesiol, 56. Fel. Am. Col. Anesthesiol; Am. Soc. Anesthesiol; Am. Med. Asn; Int. Anesthesia Res. Soc; Royal Soc. Med; Am. Nat. Standards Inst; Asn. Advan. Med. Instrumentation. Address: Dept. of Anesthesiology, Temple University Medical Center, 3401 N. Broad St, Philadelphia, PA 19140.

DEASON, HILARY J(OHN), b. Park City, Utah, May 21, 03; m. 44. ZOOLOGY. A.B, Michigan, 27, A.M, 28, Ph.D.(zool), 36. Asst, Bur. Fisheries, 27-30, asst. aquatic biologist, 30-40; assoc. aquatic biologist, U.S. Fish & Wildlife Serv, 40-43, sr. aquatic biologist, 43-46, asst. to dep. coordinator fisheries, 43-45, chief off. for. activities, 45-51; consult, Episcopal Diocese Wash, 53-55, dir. library prog, Am. Asn. Adv. Sci, 55-71; RETIRED. Tech. adv. to U.S. del, Int. Whaling Conf, London, 45, Wash, 46; Int. Fishery Conf, Mex, 48, Wash, 49, Madras, 51; Secy, Episcopal Diocese Wash, 56- Dep. U.S. comnr, Int. Whaling Cmn, 50-51; U.S. cmnr, Int. Cmn. Northwest Atlantic Fisheries, 50-51. Adv. to U.S. del, Indo-Fishery Coun, Singapore, 49. Fel. AAAS; Assoc. Am. Soc. Zool; Am. Fisheries Soc.(ed, Trans, 40-46); Am. Soc. Limnol. & Oceanog; Am. Library Asn; Nat. Sci. Teachers Asn. Systematic ichthyology; limnology; science education. Address: 3003 Van Ness St, N.W, Suite S-1105, Washington, DC 20008.

DEASON, JAMES R(ONALD), b. Benton, Ill, Feb. 4, 37; m. 56. ORGANIC CHEMISTRY. B.S, Illinois State, 58; M.A, Southern Illinois, 60; Ph.D.(org. chem), Minnesota, 64. SR. INVESTR, G.D. SEARLE & CO, 64- Am. Chem. Soc. Steroids; sulfur chemistry; stereochemistry. Address: G.D. Searle & Co, P.O. Box 5110, Chicago, IL 60680.

DEASON, TEMD R, b. York, Ala, Oct. 13, 31; m. 65; c. 2. BOTANY, PHYCOLOGY. B.S, Alabama, 54, M.S, 58; Ph.D.(bot), Univ. Tex, 60. Asst. prof. biol. sci, Delaware, 60-61; BIOL, UNIV. ALA, 61-63, assoc. prof, 63-69, PROF, 69- Co-prin. investr, U.S. Pub. Health Serv. grant, 63-64. U.S.A, 54-56, 1st Lt. Bot. Soc. Am; Am. Phycol. Soc; Int. Phycol. Soc. Morphology and taxonomy of soil algae; electron microscopy. Address: Dept. of Biology, University of Alabama, University, AL 35486.

DEASON, WALLACE R(AY), b. Hurst, Ill, Nov. 14, 25; m. 48; c. 3. PHYSICAL CHEMISTRY. B.S, South. Ill. Univ, 49; Ph.D.(phys. chem), Univ. Ill, 53. Res. chemist, Mound Lab, MONSANTO CO, Mo, 53, org. res. dept, 53-66, RES. SPECIALIST, RUBBER INSTRUMENT RES. LAB, 66- U.S.A, 43-46. AAAS; Am. Chem. Soc; Instrument Soc. Am. Colloids; general physical chemistry; instrumentation. Address: 2401 Woodpark Rd, Akron, OH 44313.

DEASY, CLARA L(OUISE), b. Cincinnati, Ohio, Dec. 10, 15. BIOCHEMISTRY, ORGANIC CHEMISTRY. A.B, Cincinnati, 37, M.S, 39, Ph.D.(chem), 40. Instr. chem, Nazareth Col, 40-42; Oberlin Col, 42-43; fel, bio-org. chem, Calif. Inst. Tech, 43-44; fel, org. chem, Illinois, 44-45; instr. bio-chem, sch. med, Temple, 45-47; fel, Calif. Inst. Tech, 47-48, sr. res. fel, 48-52; ASSOC. PROF. BASIC SCI, UNIV. CINCINNATI, 52-; SCI, COL. MT. ST. JOSEPH, 63- Managing ed, J. Am. Leather Chem. Asn, 69- Alsop award, Am. Leather Chem. Asn, 67. With U.S. Dept. Agr; U.S.N, 44. AAAS; Am. Chem. Soc. Synthetic organic chemistry; isolation and structure determination of natural products; protein chemistry; use of radioactive tracers in intermediary metabolism; chemistry of collagen. Address: Dept. of Chemistry, College of Mt. St. Joseph on the Ohio, Mt. St. Joseph, OH 45051.

DEATH, FRANK STUART, b. Winnipeg, Man, Can, Apr. 15, 32; m. 54; c. 5. METALLURGY. B.A.Sc, British Columbia, 55, M.A.Sc, 56. Engr, Tonawanda Labs, Linde Div, UNION CARBIDE CORP, 56-60, group leader melting & ref. process, 60-65, lab. div. head PHYS. CHEM. STEELMAKING, Newark Labs, 65-68, asst. mgr. mkt. develop, 68-70, MGR. AOD STEELMAKING, TARRYTOWN LABS, 70- Am. Inst. Mining, Metall. & Petrol. Eng. Metallurgical science; physical chemistry of steelmaking; thermochemical processes involving new techniques; metal-producing industry. Address: R.F.D. 1, Bucyrus Ave, Carmel, NY 10512.

DEATHERAGE, F(RED) E, b. Waverly, Ill, Dec. 30, 13; m. 42; c. 3. BIOCHEMISTRY. A.B, Ill. Col, 35; scholar from Ill. Col, Illinois, A.M, 36; fel, Iowa, 36-38, Ph.D.(biochem), 38; hon. D.Sc, Ill. Col, 60. Instr. biochem, Iowa, 38-40; Kroger fel. agr. chem, Ohio State, 40-42; in charge res. lab, food found, Kroger Co, Cincinnati, 42-46; asst. prof. agr. biochem, OHIO STATE UNIV, 46-48, assoc. prof, 48-51, PROF. BIOCHEM, 51-, ANIMAL SCI, OHIO AGR. RES. & DEVELOP. CTR, 51-, prof. agr. biochem. & chmn. dept, univ, 51-64. Mem, U.S. Agency Int. Develop-Ohio State Univ, São Paulo, 64-68; consult, food processing indust. AAAS; Am. Inst. Nutrit; Am. Chem. Soc; Am. Oil Chem. Soc; Am. Soc. Animal Sci; Inst. Food Technol; Am. Soc. Biol. Chem. Processing of meat; fundamental nature of quality in meat; antioxidation of fats; processing of foods; development of army rations; chemistry of coffee; hydrolysis of proteins; use of antibiotics in food preservation; mode of action of antibiotics. Address: Dept. of Biochemistry, Ohio State University, 484 W. 12th Ave, Columbus, OH 43210.

DeATLEY, LINDLEY S(HAFER), b. Kansas City, Mo, Aug. 2, 12; m. 37; c. 2. CHEMICAL ENGINEERING. B.S, Kansas, 33. Chemist, Thompson-Hayward Chem. Co, 34-36; chem. engr, Puritan Compressed Gas Corp, 36-38; chief chemist, THOMPSON-HAYWARD CHEM. CO, 38-42, lab. dir, 42-51, dir. res. & chem. eng, 51-53, v.pres. res. & develop, 53-69, SR. V.PRES. & DIR. RES. & DEVELOP, 69- AAAS; Am. Chem. Soc; Sci. Res. Soc. Am; Am. Inst. Chem. Eng; Entom. Soc. Am; Weed Sci. Soc. Am; Nat. Soc. Prof. Eng. Synthesis of chlorophenoxyacetic acid herbicides; low volatile esters of 2, 4-D and 2, 4, 5-T; synthesis of non-ionic emulsifiers for pesticides; chlorination of organic compounds; field testing and development of chemicals as pesticides. Address: 6601 Woodson Dr, Shawnee Mission, KS 66202.

DEATON, BOBBY C(HARLES), b. Pittsburg, Tex, Jan. 20, 36; m. 60; c. 2. PHYSICS. B.A, Baylor, 57, M.S, 59; Tex. Instruments fel, Texas, 60-61, Ph.D.(physics), 62. Sr. res. scientist, GEN. DYNAMICS/FT. WORTH, 61-66, STAFF SCIENTIST, 66- Res. Scientist, Texas, 63-64, adj. instr, Texas, Arlington, 66-67; adj. assoc. prof, Tex. Wesleyan Col, 67-, head dept. physics, 68- Am. Phys. Soc. Solid state physics involving Fermi surfaces of metals, superconductivity and study of materials at high pressures and temperatures. Address: Dept. of Physics, Texas Weselyan College, Ft. Worth, TX 76105.

DEATON, EDMUND IKE, b. Sulphur Springs, Tex, Aug. 18, 30; m. 54; c. 3. MATHEMATICS. B.A, Hardin-Simmons, 50; M.A, Texas, 56, Ph.D.(math), 60. Spec. instr. MATH, Texas, 56-60; assoc. prof, SAN DIEGO STATE COL, 60-69, PROF, 69- U.S.N, 50-54. Am. Math. Soc; Math. Asn. Am. Partial differential equations. Address: Dept. of Mathematics, San Diego State College, San Diego, CA 92115.

DEATON, JAMES WASHINGTON, b. Manning, Ark, June 29, 34; m. 56. POULTRY SCIENCE. B.S, Arkansas, 56; M.S, Texas A&M, 59, Ph.D.(poultry sci), 64. Poultry serviceman, Paymaster Feed Mills, Tex, 56-58; res. asst. poultry nutrit, Texas A&M, 58-59, poultry nutrit. & genetics, 61-63, res. assoc. poultry nutrit. & statist. eval. data, 63-64; poultry serviceman, DeKalb Agr. Asn, Inc, 59-61; Tex. Turkey Fedn. grant poultry disease, Tex. Agr. Exp. Sta, 64; res. poultry husbandman, s.cent. res. lab, U.S. DEPT. AGR, 64-68, DIR. S.CENT. POULTRY RES. LAB, AGR. RES. SERV, 68- Summer asst. hatchery mgr, R.E. Janes Turkey Hatchery, 58. AAAS; Poultry Sci. Asn; Am. Genetic Asn; World Poultry Sci. Asn. Poultry management and environmental research, including poultry nutrition, genetics and disease aspects and physiological relationships. Address: U.S. Dept. of Agriculture, Agricultural Research Service, P.O. Box 5367, State College, MS 39762.

DEATON, OLIVER WENDELL, b. London, Ky, May 30, 35; m. 63; c. 1. AGRICULTURE, GENETICS. B.S, Kentucky, 59, M.S, 60; Ph.D.(dairy genetics), Mich. State Univ, 64. Asst. prof. dairy, Univ. Ky, 63-69; ANIMAL PROD. OFF, FOOD & AGR. ORGN. UN, COSTA RICA, 69- U.S.A.F.R, 59-

Am. Dairy Sci. Asn; Am. Soc. Animal Sci. Dairy cattle and animal genetics; animal physiology and reproduction; applied statistics. Address: Food & Agriculture Organization of the United Nations, Interamerican Institute of Agricultural Sciences, Turrialba, Costa Rica.

DEAVEN, LARRY LEE, b. Hershey, Pa, Oct. 28, 40. CELL BIOLOGY. B.S, Pa. State Univ, 62, M.S, 64; Purdue Univ, 64-65; U.S. Pub. Health Serv. fel & Ph.D.(biomed. sci), Univ. Tex, 69. Instr. BIOL, Pa. State Univ, 64; fel, M.D. ANDERSON HOSP, UNIV. TEX, 65-69, NAT. CANCER INST. FEL, 69- AAAS; Am. Chem. Soc; Am. Soc. Cell Biol. Blood groups in fish; chromosome structure and physiology; DNA content and structure in mammalian metaphase chromosomes. Address: Dept. of Biology, M.D. Anderson Hospital, Houston, TX 77025.

DEAVER, BASCOM S(INE), JR, b. Macon, Ga, Aug. 16, 30; m. 51; c. 3. PHYSICS. B.S, Ga. Inst. Tech, 52; M.A, Washington (St. Louis), 54; Ph.D. (physics), Stanford, 62. Physicist, Air Force Spec. Weapons Command, 54-57; Stanford Res. Inst, 57-62; Nat. Sci. Found. fel, Stanford, 62-63, res. assoc. low temperature physics, 63-65; ASSOC. PROF. PHYSICS, UNIV. VA, 65- Physicist, Stanford Res. Inst, 63-65; Alfred P. Sloan fel, 66-68. U.S.A.F, 52-57, Res, 57-62, Capt. Am. Phys. Soc. Superconductivity; superconducting devices; low temperature physics. Address: Dept. of Physics, University of Virginia, Charlottesville, VA 22903.

DEAVER, FRANKLIN KENNEDY, b. Springdale, Ark, Jan. 10, 18; m. 45; c. 2. MECHANICAL ENGINEERING. B.S.Ch.E, Arkansas, 39, M.S.M.E, 60; Ph.D. (mech. eng), Minnesota, 69. Asst. mgr. construct, Pioneer Co, Ark, 39-49, mgr. construct, 49-55; asst. prof. MECH. ENG, UNIV. ARK, FAYETTEVILLE, 55-60, assoc. prof, 60-69, PROF. & HEAD DEPT, 69- U.S.N.R, 42-46, Lt. Am. Soc. Mech. Eng; Am. Soc. Eng. Educ; Nat. Soc. Prof. Eng. Heat transfer by natural convection. Address: Old Wire Rd. N, Route 9, Fayetteville, AR 72701.

DEAVERS, W(ILLIAM) P(URSER), JR, b. Alexandria, La, Sept. 13, 25; m. 46; c. 6. MECHANICAL ENGINEERING. B.S, Maryland, 51. Proj. engr. rocket & bomb fuzing, Naval Ord. Lab, White Oak, 51-54, sect. head, fuzes sect, Naval Ord. Test Sta, 54-55, head eng. br, fuzes & electromech. components, 55-58, res. & develop. undersea warfare, 58; dir. airborne weapon syst, TRW Space Tech. Labs, 58-65, asst. mgr, MINUTEMAN PROPULSION, TRW SYSTS, 65-69, MGR, 69- Mem, Joint Army, Navy, Air Force Fuze Comt, 55-57; tech. consult, mat. div, Bur. Ord. Rocket & Bomb Fuze Designs. Meritorious civilian serv. award, 54. U.S.N, 43-46, Res, 52-59, Lt.(jg). Am. Soc. Mech. Eng; Am. Ord. Asn. Ballistic missile systems; operations analysis; anti-submarine warfare weapons systems. Address: TRW Systems, Room 410, Bldg, 526, Norton Air Force Base, CA 92641.

DEB, SATYENDRA KUMAR, b. Sylhet, E. Pakistan, Mar. 1, 32; m. 56; c. 2. SOLID STATE PHYSICS. B.Sc, Dacca, 53, M.Sc, 55; Rhondda scholar, Cambridge, 56-59, Ph.D.(solid state physics), 59. Lectr. chem, Dacca, 55-56; res. fel, Nat. Res. Coun. Can, 60-62, asst. res. off, 62; res. chemist, CENT. RES. DIV, AM. CYANAMID CO, 62-66, RES. ASSOC, 66- Am. Phys. Soc; The Chem. Soc. Stability of solids to heat and light; physical properties of explosive materials; optical and electrical properties of solids; effect of ionizing radiation in solids; optical and electrical properties of thin films; electro-photography. Address: American Cyanamid Co, 1937 W. Main St, Stamford, CN 06904.

DE BACH, PAUL (HEVENER), b. Miles City, Mont, Dec. 28, 14; m. 40; c. 2. ENTOMOLOGY. B.S, Univ. Calif, 37, Ph.D.(entom), 40; Univ. Calif, Los Angeles, 41. Asst. zool, Univ. Calif, 37-38, entom, Citrus Exp. Sta, 38-41, res. assoc, 41-42; jr. entomologist, U.S. Pub. Health Serv, Calif, 42-43; entomologist, bur. entom. & plant quarantine, U.S. Dept. Agr, Miss, 43-45; asst. entomologist, UNIV. CALIF, RIVERSIDE, 45-51, assoc. entomologist, 51-57, ENTOMOLOGIST, 57-, PROF. BIOL. CONTROL, 61- Rockefeller fel. & consult, Brazil, 62; Fulbright res. fel, Greece, 62-63. Ed, sect. biol. control, Biol. Abstr, 59. Mem. task force biol. control, U.S. Nat. Comt. of Int. Biol. Prog, 67-69; panel mem, sect. environ. biol, Nat. Sci. Found, 67-68; int. coord, IBP World Proj. Biol. Control Scale Insects, 68-; assoc. dir, Int. Ctr. Biol. Control, Univ. Calif, Berkeley & Riverside, 70-; pres, Int. Orgn. Biol. Control, 71- AAAS; Entom. Soc. Am; Ecol. Soc. Am; Am. Inst. Biol. Sci; Int. Asn. Ecol; Japanese Soc. Pop. Ecol; Mex. Soc. Entom. Laboratory and field population studies of insect pests and their natural enemies, biological control; quantitative relations between parasite and host populations; biosystemics of scale insect parasites. Address: Division of Biological Control, University of California, Riverside, CA 92502.

DEBACKER, HILDA SPODHEIM, b. Bucharest, Rumania, July 17, 24; U.S. citizen; m. 48. ANATOMY, POLYMER CHEMISTRY. A.B, Cornell, 45; M.S, Polytech. Inst. Brooklyn, 49; fels, Med. Col. S.C, 55-62, M.S, 57, Ph.D. (anat), 67. Res. asst. chem, Calco Chem. Div, Am. Cyanamid Co, N.J, 45-46; lab. asst. polymer chem, Polytech. Inst. Brooklyn, 48; lit. searcher pharmaceut. chem, Warner Inst. Therapeut. Res, N.Y, 49-50: res. librn, Wallace & Tiernan Co, Inc, N.J, 50-52; teaching asst. ANAT, MED. UNIV. S.C, 53-55, instr, 62-67, assoc, 67-68, ASST. PROF, 68- AAAS; Am. Chem. Soc. Microscopic structure and function of living liver; microscopic observations of conjunctival circulation in health and disease in man; conjunctival circulation during cerebral ischemia and during electric shock therapy. Address: Dept. of Anatomy, Medical University of South Carolina, 80 Barre St, Charleston, SC 29401.

DeBAKEY, LOIS, b. Lake Charles, La. MEDICAL & SCIENTIFIC COMMUNICATIONS, LINGUISTICS. B.A, Tulane Univ, 44, M.A, 59, Ph.D.(Eng), 63. Med. ed, Tulane Univ, 44-58, instr. Eng, 60-63, asst. prof, 63, SCI. COMMUN, sch. med, 63-65, assoc. prof, 65-66, PROF, 66-68; BAYLOR COL. MED, 68- Prof, Tulane Univ, 68-70, lectr, 70- AAAS; fel. Am. Med. Writers' Asn.(co-ed, Bull, 60-62, distinguished serv. award, 70); Coun. Biol. Ed; Asn. Med. Cols; Nat. Asn. Sci. Writers; Int. Soc. Gen. Semantics. Medical and scientific writing; linguistics as a social science and essential part of physical and biological sciences; influence of science on literature. Address: 6535 Fannin St, Houston, TX 77025.

DeBAKEY, MICHAEL ELLIS, b. Lake Charles, La, Sept. 7, 08; m. 36; c. 4. SURGERY. B.S, Tulane Univ. La, 30, M.D, 32, M.S, 35, hon. LL.D, 65; hon. D.Sc, Univ. Lyon, 61, Free Univ. Brussels, 62, State Univ. Ghent & Nat. Univ. Athens, 64, Ft. Lauderdale Univ. & St. John's Univ.(N.Y), 70; hon. LL.D, Lafayette Col, 65; hon. Dr, Univ. Turin, 65, Univ. Ottawa, 70. Instr. SURG, Tulane Univ. La, 37-40, asst. prof, 40-46, assoc. prof, 46-48; PROF. & CHMN. DEPT, BAYLOR COL. MED, 48-, CHIEF EXEC. OFF, 68-, PRES, 69-, v.pres. med. affairs, univ, 68-69. Surgeon-in-chief, Ben Taub Gen. Hosp, Houston; sr. attend. surgeon, Methodist Hosp, Houston, dir. cardiovasc. res. ctr, 68-; mem. comt, Hoover Comn. Task Force & citizens comt, Hoover Report; nat. adv. health coun, Nat. Insts. Health, 61-65, nat. adv. gen. med. sci. coun, 65, nat. adv. coun. on regional med. progs, 65-; comt. on epidemiol. & vet. follow-up studies, Nat. Res. Coun; President's Comn. Heart Disease, Cancer & Stroke, 64; chmn. sci. adv. bd, Delta Regional Primate Res. Ctr, Tulane Univ. La, 65; hon. mem, Ital. Found. Cardiol, 69; consult. staff, dept. surg, Tex. Children's Hosp, Houston, 70-; patron's comt, Damon Runyon Mem. Fund for Cancer Res, 71. Matas Award, 54; Mod. Med. award, 57; Vishnevsky Medal, inst. surg, Acad. Med. Sci, U.S.S.R, 62; Grand Cross, Order of Leopold, Belg, 62; Lasker Award, 63; Orden Militar del SS, Salvador y Santa Brigida de Suecia Caballero Gran Oficial de Gracia Magistrad, 69; Organisation Mondiale de la Presse Diplomatique Prix Hammarskjoeld Academician de Nombre, 69; Accademia Internazionale di Pontzen di Lettere Scienze ed Arti Gran Collare Accademico d'Oro, 69; meritorious civilian serv. medal, Secy. Defense, 70; Gold Cup Award, 70. U.S.A.R, 42-46, Col; Legion of Merit, 45. Am. Med. Asn. (Hektoen Gold Medals, 54 & 70, distinguished serv. award, 59); Am. Asn. Thoracic Surg.(pres, 59); Am. Col. Surg; Am. Heart Asn; Am. Surg. Asn; Soc. Vascular Surg.(pres, 54); Int. Cardiovasc. Soc.(pres, 59); Int. Soc. Surg.(distinguished serv. award, 58, Leriche Award, 59); Asn. Advan. Med. Instrumentation. Cardiovascular and thoracic surgery; cardiovascular diseases, including aortic diseases; replacement of excised segments of arteries by homografts and plastic prostheses; venous thrombosis; aneurysms and occlusive diseases of arteries; peripheral vascular diseases and development of the artificial heart. Address: Baylor College of Medicine, 1200 Moursund Ave, Houston, TX 77025.

DE BALBIAN VERSTER, FLORIS, b. Netherlands, Aug. 17, 24; U.S. citizen; m. 49; c. 2. BIOCHEMISTRY, NEUROCHEMISTRY. B.S, Miami (Fla), 49, M.S, 51; Ph.D.(biochem), Tulane, 60. ASST. PROF. biochem, sch. med, Tulane, 61-64; PHARMACOL, SCH. MED, VANDERBILT UNIV, 65-, NEUROL, 69- Res. dir, Southeast. La. Hosp, 61-64; vis. scientist, Charity Hosp, New Orleans, 61-64. Am. Chem. Soc; Am. Soc. Cell Biol; Am. Col. Neuropsychopharmacol; Am. Inst. Chem; Int. Soc. Neurochem; Soc. Neurosci. Brain mechanisms of action; use of experimentally induced epilepsy in correlation of biochemical, physiological and pharmacological techniques; chemical basis of behavior. Address: Dept. of Pharmacology, School of Medicine, Vanderbilt University, Nashville, TN 37203.

DeBAR, ROGER B(RYANT), b. Eugene, Ore, Oct. 22, 34; m. 60. THEORETICAL PHYSICS. B.A, Reed Col, 56; M.S, Stanford, 57, Ph.D.(physics), 62. PHYSICIST, LAWRENCE RADIATION LAB, UNIV. CALIF, LIVERMORE, 61- Am. Phys. Soc. Numerical analysis; numerical solution of partial differential equations of physics, especially hydrodynamics; particle physics. Address: Lawrence Radiation Lab, University of California, Livermore, CA 94550.

DeBARBIERIS, IRVIN HENRY, b. New Orleans, La, Sept. 7, 22; m. 47; c. 3. PHYSICS, PHOTOGRAPHY. B.S, Loyola, 49; M.S, Tulane, 52. Res. assoc. physics & photog, Tulane, 50-56; physicist, KALVAR CORP, 56-59, dir. physics res, 59-70, V.PRES, CORP. & GEN. MGR, SDL EQUIP. DIV, 70- U.S.A.A.F, 43-45, 2nd Lt. Soc. Photog. Sci. & Eng; Soc. Photo-Optical Instrument Eng. Vesicular photography. Address: SDL Division, Kalvar Corp, 800 S. Jefferson Davis Pkwy, New Orleans, LA 70125.

DeBARDELEBEN, JOHN F, b. Houston, Tex, May 19, 37; c. 2. ORGANIC CHEMISTRY. B.S, Virginia, 60; fel, Texas A&M, 61-63, M.S, 63; Ph.D. (chem), Ga. Inst. Tech, 66. Chemist, Monsanto Chem. Co, 60-61; instr. chem, Ga. Inst. Tech, 63-65; RES. SCIENTIST & PROJ. LEADER, PHILIP MORRIS RES. CTR, 66- Am. Chem. Soc. Photochemical rearrangements; pyridine chemistry; sesquiterpenes; organophosphorus compounds; natural products. Address: Philip Morris, Inc, Box 26583, Richmond, VA 23261.

DeBAUN, JACK ROLLIE, b. Lewiston, Idaho, Sept. 14, 41; m. 65. BIOCHEMISTRY. B.S, Univ. Idaho, 63, M.S, 65; Ph.D.(exp. oncol), Univ. Wis, 69. Fel, dept. environ. toxicol, Univ. Calif, Davis, 69-70; RES. BIOCHEMIST, STAUFFER CHEM. CO, 70- Am. Chem. Soc. Investigation of the mechanism of action of carcinogenic aromatic amines; studies of the mode of action and metabolism of pesticides. Address: 125-6 Connemara Way, Sunnyvale, CA 94087.

DeBAUN, ROBERT M(ATTHEW), b. New York, N.Y, June 23, 24; m. 50; c. 4. CHEMISTRY, STATISTICS. B.S, Fordham, 47, M.S, 49, Ph.D.(chem), 51. Instr. org. chem, col. pharm, St. John's (N.Y), 50-51; assoc. scientist, Nat. Dairy Res. Labs, Inc, 51-54; proj. leader, cent. res. labs, Gen. Foods Corp, 54-55; statistician, AM. CYANAMID CO, 55, group leader, math. anal. group, Stamford labs, 56-58, ref. catalysts group, 58-61, mgr. tech. comput. corp. hq, 61-65, adv. plan, corp. data processing, 65, dir, 65-70, DIR. OPERS. ANAL, 70- U.S.A.A.F, 43-46. Am. Chem. Soc; Am. Statist. Asn. Industrial chemistry and research; applied statistics; management sciences. Address: 15 Lois Ct, Wayne, NJ 07470.

DEBBRECHT, FREDERICK J(OHN), b. Wichita, Kans, Feb. 19, 27; m. 55; c. 5. ANALYTICAL CHEMISTRY. B.S, Colorado, 50; M.S, Iowa State Col, 53, Ph.D.(anal. chem), 56. Asst, Iowa State Col, 50-56; res. chemist, anal. group, exp. sta, polychem. dept, E.I. du Pont de Nemours & Co, Del, 56-60; res. assoc, F & M Sci. Corp, 60-69; DIR. RES, ANAL. INSTRUMENT DEVELOP, INC, 69- U.S.A.A.F, 45-46. Am. Chem. Soc. Gas chromatography; organic analysis; environmental analysis. Address: Analytical Instrument Developments, Inc, 250 S. Franklin St, West Chester, PA 19380.

DEBEAU, DAVID E(DMUND), b. San Francisco, Calif, July 3, 16; m. 48; c. 1. PHYSICS, CHEMISTRY. B.S, California, 37, Ph.D.(physics), 44; A.M, Harvard, 38. Physicist phys. anal, Calif. Res. Corp, 44-46; opers. anal, U.S. Air Force, 47-52; opers. res. div, Battelle Mem. Inst, 52-59; asst. mgr. opers. res. group, N.AM. ROCKWELL CORP, LOS ANGELES, 59-63, dir. data processing dept, 63-65, CORP. DIR. MGT. TECHNOL, 65- AAAS; Am. Phys. Soc; Am. Chem. Soc; Opers. Res. Soc. Am. Operations research, military and industrial; physical properties of petrochemicals; contact electrification; electrical discharge in gases. Address: Apt. 3, 2012 Ruhland Ave, Redondo Beach, CA 90218.

DE BECZE, GEORGE I(MRE), b. Csikszereda, Hungary, Feb. 8, 03; nat; m. 38; c. 3. CHEMICAL ENGINEERING, INDUSTRIAL MICROBIOLOGY. B.A, Jozsef Nador Tech. Univ, Hungary, 25, M.A, 26, dipl. chem. eng, 27, Ph.D.(org. chem. technol. & food chem), 48; Royal Inst. Ampellology, 27; Inst. Appl. Bot, 31. Asst. prof. fermentation, Jozsef Nador Tech. Univ, Hungary, 23-27; chief engr, Krauss Moskovits R.T, 27-38; chem. adv, Schenley Distilleries, Inc, 38-45, assoc. dir. biochem. res, 45-47, mgr. distillery cent. control lab, 47-59, mgr. res. & distillery control, 59-69; physical scientist, Fed. Water Pollution Admin, U.S. Dept. Interior, 69-70; PROF. MICROBIOL, ST. THOMAS INST, 70- Vis. lectr, Inst. Divi Thomae, 47-70; mem, Distillers Feed Res. Coun, 48-, distinguished serv. citation, 69. Am. Chem. Soc; Am. Soc. Microbiol. Alcoholic beverages; industrial fermentation; yeasts; enzyme water pollution. Address: 210 Oakey Ave, Lawrenceburg, IN 47025.

DeBELL, ARTHUR GERALD, b. N.Y.C, June 10, 12; m. 42; c. 3. PHYSICS. Ch.E, Rensselaer Polytech. Inst, 35; N.Y. State Teacher Col, 38-40. Metall. chemist, Adirondack Steel Co, N.Y, 37-38; instr. physics, Siena Col, 38-41; PHYSICIST, U.S. Navy Yard, S.C, 42-44; Naval Ord. Test Sta, 44-52; White Develop. Corp, 52-55; Rocketdyne Div, N.Am. Aviation Inc, Canoga Park, 55-67, GROUP SCIENTIST, ELECTRO-OPTICAL LAB, AUTONETICS DIV, N.AM. ROCKWELL CORP, 67- Consult, Ballistic missile radiation anal. center, Michigan, 60- Optical Soc. Am. Design of optical, photographic and spectrographic instruments; infrared and rocket spectroscopy. Address: Autonetics Division, Dept. 447, North American Rockwell Corp, 3370 Miraloma Ave, Anaheim, CA 92803.

De BENEDETTI, SERGIO, b. Florence, Italy, Aug. 17, 12; nat; m. 44; c. 3. EXPERIMENTAL PHYSICS. Ph.D.(physics), Florence, 33. Asst. prof, Padua, 34-38; fel, Curie Lab, Paris, 34-35, 38-40; res. assoc, Bartol Res, Found, 40-43; assoc. prof. physics, Kenyon Col, 43-44; sr. physicist, Monsanto Co, Ohio, 44-45; prin. physicist, Clinton Labs, Oak Ridge Nat. Lab, 46-48; assoc. prof. PHYSICS, Washington (St. Louis), 48-49; PROF, CARNEGIE-MELLON UNIV, 49- Vis. prof, Rio de Janeiro, 52; Fulbright scholar, Turin, 56-57; summers, prof, Varenna Sch, 55; guest lectr, Brazilian Center Phys. Sci, 61; lectr, California, Berkeley, 63. Mem. exped. cosmic rays, Eritrea, E.Africa, 33. With U.S.A.A.F, 44. Fel. Am. Phys. Soc. Nuclear and high energy physics; cosmic rays; radioactivity; short-lived isomers; positrons; mesons; Mössbaur spectroscopy. Address: Dept. of Physics, Carnegie-Mellon University, Pittsburgh, PA 15213.

de BENNEVILLE, PETER L, b. Yokohama, Japan, Jan. 24, 15; U.S. citizen. CHEMISTRY. B.A, Pennsylvania, 35, Ph.D.(chem), 40. Res. chemist, Gen. Chem. Co, N.Y, 41-45; ROHM & HAAS CO, 45-63, RES. ASSOC, SPRING HOUSE, 63- AAAS; Am. Chem. Soc. Organic insecticides; cellulose modification; synthetic organic chemistry; surface active agents. Address: 2206 Rittenhouse Square, Philadelphia, PA 19103.

DEBER, CHARLES MICHAEL, b. Brooklyn, N.Y, Apr. 20, 42; m. 71. ORGANIC & BIOLOGICAL CHEMISTRY. B.S, Polytech. Inst. Brooklyn, 62; Nat. Insts. Health fel. & Ph.D.(org. chem), Mass. Inst. Technol, 67. Res. chemist, Argus Chem. Co, N.Y, 62; Am. Cyanamid Co, Conn, 64; Nat. Insts. Health res. fel. peptide synthesis & conformation, HARVARD MED. SCH, 67-69, ASSOC. BIOL. CHEM, 70- Merck, Sharp & Dohme res. fel. biophys, summer 70. Am. Chem. Soc. Transannular migrations in medium rings; conformations of polypeptides with nitroaromatic sidechains; synthesis and physical chemistry of glycine and proline linear and cyclic peptides as collagen models, particularly determination of conformation by nuclear magnetic resonance spectroscopy. Address: Dept. of Biological Chemistry, Harvard University Medical School, 25 Shattuck St, Boston, MA 02115.

de BETHUNE, ANDRE JACQUES, b. Schaerbeek-Brussels, Belgium, Aug. 20, 19; m. 49; c. 10. CHEMISTRY. B.S, St. Peter's Col, 39; Ph.D.(phys. chem), Columbia, 45. Res. chemist, Columbia, 42-45; Carbide & Carbon Chem. Corp, New York, 45; Nat. Res. fel, Mass. Inst. Tech, 45-47; asst. prof. PHYS. CHEM, BOSTON COL, 47-49, assoc. prof, 49-55, PROF, 55-, acting chmn. dept. chem, 65-67. Guggenheim fel, Yale, 60-61. Am. Chem. Soc; Am. Phys. Soc; Electrochem. Soc.(theoret. ed, Jour, 57-); Faraday Soc. Chemical kinetics; electrochemistry; catalysis; isotope separation; kinetic theory of gases; hydrogen overvoltage in salt and buffer solutions; oxygen reduction polarization; temperature effects on electrode potentials; statistics of child spacing. Address: Dept. of Chemistry, Boston College, Chestnut Hill, MA 02167.

DeBEY, HAROLD J(OHN), b. Cawker City, Kans, July 5, 23. BIOCHEMISTRY. A.B, Colo. State Col. Ed, 47; M.S, Wisconsin, 51; Ph.D.(biochem), Colorado, 57. Teacher, pub. sch, Colo, 47-50; instr. chem, Scottsbluff Jr. Col, 51-54; asst. prof, SAN JOSE STATE COL, 57-60, assoc. prof, 60-64, prof, 64-69, PROVOST, NEW COL, 69- Med.C, U.S.A, 43-46. AAAS; Am. Chem. Soc. Intermediary metabolism, particularly in metabolism of amino acids. Address: New College, San Jose State College, San Jose, CA 95114.

DeBIAS, DOMENIC A(NTHONY), b. Tresckow, Pa, Aug. 31, 25; m. 51; c. 5. PHYSIOLOGY. A.B, Temple, 49, A.M, 50; U.S. Pub. Health Serv. fel, Jefferson Med. Col, 51-54, Ph.D.(physiol), 56. Instr. & asst, biol, Temple, 49-50, physiol, sch. dent, 50-51, res. assoc. bact, 51; instr. PHYSIOL, sch. med, Pennsylvania, 55; sch. dent, Temple, 55; res. assoc, div. endocrine & cancer res, JEFFERSON MED. COL, 56-57, instr, 57-60, asst. prof, 60-64, assoc. prof, 64-69, PROF, 69- AAAS; Am. Physiol. Soc; Endocrine Soc; Am. Heart Asn. Mammalian physiology; physiology of the endocrine glands; endocrine regulation of cardiovascular and gastrointestinal functions; interrelationship of endocrine system and nervous system; environmental physiology. Address: Jefferson Medical College, Jefferson Hall, Room 408, 1025 Walnut St, Philadelphia, PA 19107.

DeBITETTO, D(OMINICK) J(OHN), b. Barre, Vt, Aug. 2, 23; m. 51; c. 3. EXPERIMENTAL PHYSICS. B.S.M.E, Oklahoma, 46; Ph.D.(physics), N.Y. Univ, 56. Anal. engr. power plant anal, Chance Vought Aircraft, United Aircraft Corp, 46-49; lab. asst. gas discharges, N.Y. Univ, 51-56, instr. eng. physics, 53-55; RES. ASSOC. MICROWAVE PHYSICS, PHILIPS LABS, INC, 56- U.S.N.R, 43-46, Res, 46-59, Lt.(jg). Am. Phys. Soc. Microwave physics; magnetic materials; gas discharges; mechanisms of electrical breakdown of gases. Address: 167 Washburn Rd, Briarcliff Manor, NY 10510.

DeBLOIS, RALPH W(ALTER), b. Benton Harbor, Mich, Jan. 11, 22; m. 59; c. 3. PHYSICS. B.S, Michigan, 43, M.S, 47; Ph.D.(physics), Rensselaer Polytech, 63. Asst, Manhattan Proj, Columbia, 43-46; fel, Michigan, 46-49; instr. physics, American Univ, Beirut, 50-53; res. lab, Gen. Elec. Co, 54-57, PHYSICIST, 57-66, GEN. ELEC. RES. & DEVELOP. CTR, 66- AAAS; Biophys. Soc; Am. Phys. Soc. Kinetics of magnetization; ferromagnetic domain structure; submicron particle analysis. Address: General Electric Research & Development Center, P.O. Box 8, Schenectady, NY 12301.

DEBNATH, LOKENATH, b. Dacca, India, Sept. 30, 35; m. 69; c. 1. APPLIED & PURE MATHEMATICS. B.S, Calcutta, 54, M.S, 56, Ph.D.(pure math), 64; dipl. & Ph.D.(appl. math), Imp. Col, London, 67. Lectr. math, Calcutta & Burdwan Univs, 57-65; res. fel. appl. math, Imp. Col, London, 65-67; sr. fel, Cambridge, 67-68; assoc. prof. MATH, E.CAROLINA UNIV, 68-69, PROF, 69- Math. Asn. Am; assoc. fel. Brit. Inst. Math. & Appln. Integral transforms with applications; complex analysis; generalized functions with applications; fluid dynamics; elasticity-wave motions; vibrations; elements of theory of elliptic and associated functions with applications; elements of general topology; magnetohydrodynamics; rotating and stratified flows; oceanography. Address: Dept. of Mathematics, East Carolina University, Greenville, NC 27834.

DEBNEY, GEORGE CHARLES, JR, b. Beaumont, Tex, Feb. 19, 39; m. 62; c. 1; div; m. 66; c. 2. MATHEMATICS, MATHEMATICAL PHYSICS. B.A, Rice, 61; fel, Texas, Austin, 64-65, Ph.D.(math), 67. Teaching asst. math, Texas, Austin, 62-63, res. asst. relativity theory, Relativity Center, 63-64 & 65-66; mem. tech. staff, TRW Systs. Group, 66-68; ASST. PROF. MATH, VA. POLYTECH. INST. & STATE UNIV, 68- Mathematician, Naval Res. Lab, Wash, D.C, summer 71. AAAS; Am. Math. Soc; Math. Asn. Am; Tensor Soc. Geometry and topology of Einstein-Lorentz manifolds; differential geometry; exact solutions of the field equations in general relativity theory. Address: Dept. of Mathematics, Virginia Polytechnic Institute & State University, Blacksburg, VA 24061.

DeBOER, ANDREW, b. Netherlands, Dec. 29, 41; U.S. citizen; m. 64. ORGANIC CHEMISTRY. B.S, Calvin Col, 64; Ph.D.(org. chem), Wayne State Univ, 67. Fel, Univ. Colo, 67-69; ASST. PROF. CHEM, UNIV. WYO, 69- AAAS; Am. Chem. Soc. Organic reaction mechanisms; addition reactions; bimolecular electrophilic substitution reactions. Address: Dept. of Chemistry, University of Wyoming, Laramie, WY 82070.

DeBOER, BENJAMIN, b. Grand Rapids, Mich, Sept. 13, 11; m. 39; c. 5. PHARMACOLOGY. A.B, Calvin Col, 33; M.A, Missouri, 39, Ph.D.(physiol), 42. Asst. zool, Missouri, 34-38, instr. pharmacol, sch. med, 41-43, asst. prof, 43-46; pharmacol, St. Louis, 46-49, assoc. prof, 49-51; PROF. PHYSIOL. & PHARMACOL, SCH. MED, UNIV. N.DAK, 51- Am. Physiol. Soc; Am. Soc. Pharmacol; Soc. Exp. Biol. & Med. Barbiturate hypnosis; narcotic analgesics. Address: University of North Dakota School of Medicine, Grand Forks, ND 58201.

DeBOER, CARL J(OHN), b. Westerbur, Netherlands, Oct. 12, 07; nat. VIROLOGY, IMMUNOLOGY. B.Sc, Illinois, 35, Ph.D.(bact. & immunol), 41; M.Sc, Rutgers, 37. Asst, Illinois, 41-42; asst. prof. dairy sci, Mass. State Col, 42-43; res. assoc, Lederle Labs, 43-48; asst. prof. infectious diseases, California, Los Angeles, 48-50; virologist, dept. pub. health, Los Angeles & U.S. Vet. Admin. Hosp, Van Nuys, 48-50; dir. virus res, Ciba Pharmaceut, Inc, 50-57; PRIN. VIROLOGIST, PLUM ISLAND ANIMAL DISEASE LAB, U.S. DEPT. AGR, 57- Am. Soc. Microbiol; Am. Asn. Immunol; N.Y. Acad. Sci. Viral and rickettsial research; tissue culture; chemotherapy of viral and rickettsial infections. Address: Plum Island Animal Disease Lab, U.S. Dept. of Agriculture, Greenport, NY 11944.

DEBOER, CHARLES D, b. Spirit Lake, Iowa, Apr. 10, 40; m. 67; c. 2. PHOTOCHEMISTRY. B.S, Iowa State, 62; Nat. Sci. Found. fel, Calif. Inst. Tech, 62-65, Ph.D.(chem), 66. Nat. Insts. Health fel, Columbia, 65-66; RES. ASSOC, EASTMAN KODAK CO, 66- Mechanisms of organic photochemistry. Address: Eastman Kodak Co. Research Labs, Rochester, NY 14650.

DeBOER, FRANK EDWARD, b. Grand Rapids, Mich, Feb. 15, 27; m. 56; c. 2. PHYSICAL CHEMISTRY. A.B, Calvin Col, 50; Ph.D.(chem), Northwestern, 54. Chemist, Standard Oil Co. Ind, 53-56; asst. chemist, Argonne Nat. Lab, 56-62; sr. metallurgist res. & Develop, Continental Can, 62-66; asst. prof. CHEM, N.PARK COL, 66-70, ASSOC. PROF, 70- U.S.N.R, 45-46, Lt.(jg). Electrochem. Soc. Magnetochemistry; catalysis; corrosion. Address: 1104 S. Mayfield Ave, Chicago, IL 60644.

DE BOER, J(AN), b. Djakarta, Indonesia, May 31, 32; m. 60; c. 4. SURGERY, PHYSIOLOGY. M.D, State Univ. Leiden, 60, Ph.D.(physiol), 64; Surg. Specialist, Univ. Amsterdam, 68. Lectr. physiol, State Univ. Leiden, 61-64; resident surg, Univ. Amsterdam, 64-68; asst. prof. physiol, UNIV. GUELPH, 68-70, ASSOC. PROF. BIOMED. SCI, 70- Netherlands Paracommando Regiment, 60-61, 1st Lt. Royal Dutch Med. Asn; Dutch Col. Surg; Netherlands Biophys. Soc; Am. Soc. Artificial Internal Organs; Europ. Dialysis & Transplant Asn. Experimental surgery; artificial organs; lung mechanics; drowning. Address: Dept. of Biomedical Sciences, University of Guelph, Guelph, Ont, Can.

DE BOER, JELLE, b. Gorredyk, Netherlands, Aug. 19, 23; U.S. citizen; m. 54. PHYSIOLOGY, RADIATION BIOLOGY. B.S, Agr. & Mech. Col, Tex, 54, M.S, 55, Ph.D.(physiol), 61; fel, Texas, 55-57. Radiobiologist, Air Force Spec. Weapon Center, 61-63, radiobiol. group, biophys. br, AIR FORCE WEAPONS LAB, 63-70, SR. SCI. ADV. & BIO-ANALYST, BIO-MED. GROUP, ANAL. DIV, 70- AAAS; N.Y. Acad. Sci. Radiation effects of whole and partial body, proton, neutron, x-ray and gamma irradiation. Address: 1716 Valencia N.E, Albuquerque, NM 87110.

DeBOER, JELLE, b. Zeist, Holland, Aug. 23, 34; m. 63; c. 3. GEOPHYSICS. Ph.D.(geol), Univ. Utrecht, 63. ASSOC. PROF. GEOL, WESLEYAN UNIV, 68- Geol. Soc. Am; Am. Geophys. Union. Geotectonics; use of paleomagnetism and rock magnetism for structural analyses. Address: Parmelee Rd, Haddam, CT 06438.

DE BOER, KATHARINE O(LIVE), b. Grant City, Mo, Feb. 23, 09; m. 39; c. 5. CYTOGENETICS, PHYSIOLOGY. B.A, Missouri, 31, M.A, 33, Ph.D.(zool), 38. Res. assoc. genetics, Missouri, 38-40, instr. zool, 43-46; PHYSIOL. & PYARMACOL, UNIV. N.DAK, 62-63, RES. ASSOC, 63- Plant genetics; cytology; mammalian physiology. Address: 312 Alpha Ave, Grand Forks, ND 58201.

DeBOER, KENNETH F, b. Verdi, Minn, Nov. 6, 38; m. 59; c. 5. BIOLOGY. B.A, Univ. Minn, Minneapolis, 61; M.A, Mankato State Col, 68; Nat. Insts. Health grant & Ph.D.(reproductive physiol), Iowa State Univ, 70. ASST. PROF. BIOL, WEST. STATE COL. COLO, 70- Am. Philos. Soc. res. grant, 71-73. U.S.N, Lt. Comdr. AAAS; Am. Inst. Biol. Sci. Organismal, cellular and molecular aspects of developmental biology, particularly amphibian metamorphosis and regeneration. Address: Dept. of Biology, Western State College of Colorado, Gunnison, CO 81230.

DE BOER, P(IETER) C(ORNELIS) TOBIAS, b. Leiden, Netherlands, May 21, 30; nat; m. 56; c. 3. PHYSICS, AEROSPACE ENGINEERING. Ing, Delft, 55; Ph.D.(physics), Maryland, 62. Res. asst. aerodyn. & hydrodyn, Delft, 54-55; res. assoc, inst. fluid dynamics & appl. math, Maryland, 57-62, res. asst. prof, 62-64; asst. prof. AEROSPACE ENG, GRAD. SCH. AEROSPACE ENG, CORNELL UNIV, 64-67, ASSOC. PROF, 67- Mem. tech. staff, Aerospace Corp, summers 63, 65, 67; consult, Conelec, Inc, 65-; NATO fel, 68; vis. prof, von Karman Inst. Fluid Dynamics, Belg, 68; Cornell Aeronaut. Lab, 68-69. Dutch Army, 55-57, 2nd Lt. Am. Phys. Soc; Am. Inst. Aeronaut. & Astronaut; Netherlands Royal Inst. Eng. Physics of fluids; ionized gases; relaxation phenomena; lasers; pollution by combustion processes. Address: Grumman Hall, Cornell University, Ithaca, NY 14080.

DeBOISBLANC, DESLONDE R(AYMOND), b. New Orleans, La, Sept. 15, 14; m. 40; c. 4. NUCLEAR ENGINEERING. B.S, La. State, 41; D.Sc, Idaho, 67. Physicist, res. & develop. dept, Phillips Petrol. Co, 41-51, chief instrument develop. sect, atomic energy div, 51-58, dir. reactor physics & eng, 58-64, instrument develop. br, 63-64, asst. mgr, div, 64-66; mgr, nuclear & chem. technol. div, Idaho Nuclear Corp, 66-69; CHIEF CONSULT. NUCLEAR ENGR. & MGR. RES. & DEVELOP, EBASCO SERVS, INC, 69- Mem. adv. cmt. reactor physics, Atomic Energy Cmn, 57; U.S. del, Geneva Conf, 58, 64; lectr, Utah, 64- AAAS; fel. Am. Nuclear Soc; Am. Soc. Eng. Educ. Detonation in internal combustion engines; instability in turbojet combustion chambers; seismograph detector development; nuclear physics instrumentation; nuclear reactor physics; design of high flux research and test reactors; breeder reactors. Address: Ebasco Services Inc, Research & Development Dept, Two Rector St, New York, NY 10006.

DeBOLT, HAROLD E(UGENE), b. Fredericktown, Ohio, June 9, 22; m. 46; c. 6. PHYSICS, ELECTRICAL ENGINEERING. B.S, Carnegie Inst. Tech, 47, M.S, 48, Sc.D.(elec. eng), 49. Sect. mgr, instrumentation & control, atomic power div, Westinghouse Elec. Corp, 49-50; br. chief, bur. ships, U.S. Dept. Navy, 50-55; mgr. nuclear instrumentation dept, Fairchild Camera & Instrument Corp, 55-60; SR. PROJ. SCIENTIST, res. & develop. div, AVCO CORP, 60-68, space systs. div, 68-69, APPL. TECHNOL. DIV, 69-71, SYSTS. DIV, 71- Sig.C, 43-46, S/Sgt. Inst. Elec. & Electronics Eng. Plasma phenomena; phenomena related to hypersonic reentry, specifically characteristics observable by radar and optical means; high strength, high modulus filaments research. Address: Avco Corp. Systems Division, 2 Industrial Park, Lowell, MA 01851.

DEBONO, MANUEL, b. Melliha, Malta, Sept. 3, 36; U.S. citizen; m. 60; c. 4. ORGANIC CHEMISTRY. B.S, Univ. San Francisco, 59; Ph.D.(chem), Univ. Ore, 63. RES. SCIENTIST, ELI LILLY & CO, 63- Am. Chem. Soc. Natural products; steroids; fertility control agents; photochemical syntheses. Address: Lilly Research Lab, Chemical Research Division, Indianapolis, IN 46206.

DEBONS, ALBERT F(RANK), b. Brooklyn, N.Y, Nov. 4, 29; m. 55; c. 3. PHYSIOLOGY. Scholar, Syracuse, 49-53, B.S, 53; M.S, George Washington, 55, Ph.D.(physiol), 58. Asst. MED. RES, George Washington, 53-58; res. assoc, Brookhaven Nat. Labs, 58-61; PRIN. SCIENTIST, VET. ADMIN. HOSP, Birmingham, Ala, 61-64, BROOKLYN, N.Y, 64- Nuclear medicine; endocrines as related to intermediary metabolism; mechanism of hormone action; obesity studies. Address: Radioisotope Service, Veterans Administration Hospital, Brooklyn, NY 11209.

DEBOO, PHILI B, b. Bombay, India, Dec. 5, 34; U.S. citizen; m. 60; c. 1. GEOLOGY, PALEONTOLOGY. B.Sc, Bombay, 53; M.S, La. State, 55, Ph.D. (geol), 63. Asst. prof. GEOL, Eastern New Mexico, 63-65; MEMPHIS STATE UNIV, 65-66, ASSOC. PROF, 66- Geol. Soc. Am. Mid-Tertiary biostratigraphy of the Central Gulf Coastal Plain. Address: Dept. of Geology, Memphis State University, Memphis, TN 38111.

DeBOO, ROBERT FORD, b. Quebec, Que, Aug. 31, 36; m. 60; c. 2. ECONOMIC & FOREST ENTOMOLOGY. B.Sc, Univ. N.B, 60; M.S, Univ. Maine, 62; Ph.D.(entom), Cornell Univ, 66. RES. SCIENTIST ENTOM, Forest Res. Lab, CAN. FORESTRY SERV, Man, 66-70, CHEM. CONTROL RES. INST, ONT, 70- Can. Army Militia, 51-56. Entom. Soc. Am; Entom. Soc. Can; Can. Inst. Forestry. Insect ecology, biology, and control. Address: Chemical Control Research Institute, Canadian Forestry Service, 25 Pickering Pl, Ottawa, Ont, Can.

DE BOOR, CARL (WILHELM) REINHOLD, b. Stolp, Ger, Dec. 3, 37; m. 60; c. 4. MATHEMATICS. Ph.D.(numerical anal), Michigan, 66. Assoc. sr. res. mathematician, Gen. Motors Res. Labs, 60-64; asst. prof. MATH. SCI, PURDUE UNIV, 66-68, ASSOC. PROF, 68- Am. Math. Soc. Numerical analysis; approximation theory. Address: Division of Mathematical Sciences, Purdue University, Lafayette, IN 47907.

DeBOSKEY, WENTZLE R, b. Wash, D.C, Sept. 25, 32; m. 52; c. 3. PHYSICS, METALLURGY. B.S, Va. Polytech, 55, M.S, 56. Instr. metall, Va. Polytech, 54-55; asst. engr, Bettis Atomic Power Lab, Westinghouse Elec. Corp, 55-60, engr, commercial atomic power div, 60-61; prin. engr, atomic power div, Babcock & Wilcox Co, Va, 61-63, res. div, 63-65; sr. metallurgist, Melpar, Inc, 65-66, sr. scientist, 66-67, supvr. mat. lab, metals & ceramics br, 67-68; staff metallurgist, systs. develop. div, IBM CORP, 68-69, MGR, DEPT, 314-1, 69- Am. Soc. Metals. Irradiation environmental testing; permeability of fluids through aerospace construction materials; fiber or whisker reinforcement of metallic and ceramic materials. Address: Box 6, Endicott, NY 13760.

DeBOW, LEE RICHARD, b. Oelwein, Iowa, Sept. 19, 40. ORGANIC CHEMISTRY. B.A, Northwestern, 62; Gilman fel, Hopkins, 62-67, M.A, 65, Ph.D. (org. chem), 67; fel, Univ. Chicago, 67-71, M.D, 71. FEL, GREATER BALTIMORE MED. CTR, 71- Am. Chem. Soc. General medicine; pyrrole chemistry; spectral analysis of hemoglobin model systems; peptide synthesis. Address: Apt. 11-C, 2850 N. Charles St, Baltimore, MD 21218.

DeBRA, DANIEL BROWN, b. New York, N.Y, June 1, 30; m. 54; c. 6. ENGINEERING MECHANICS. B.E, Yale, 52; S.M, Mass. Inst. Tech, 53; Ph.D. (eng. mech), 62. Proj. engr. boiler auxiliary equip, Thermix Corp, 53-54; supvr. dynamics & control anal, Lockheed Missiles & Space Co, 56-64; from res. engr. to ASSOC. PROF. GUID. CONTROL. & DIR. GUID. & CONTROL LAB, STANFORD UNIV, 64- Mem, mine adv. comt, Nat. Acad. Sci; res. & technol. adv. comt. space vehicles, NASA. U.S.A.F, 54-56, Res, 56-, Maj. Am. Inst. Aeronaut. & Astronaut; Am. Astronaut. Soc; Am. Astron. Soc; Inst. Elec. & Electronics Eng; Am. Soc. Mech. Eng; Soc. Automotive Eng; Brit. Interplanetary Soc. Guidance and attitude control of aerospace vehicles. Address: Dept. of Aeronautics & Astronautics, Stanford University, Stanford, CA 94022.

DE BRANGES, LOUIS, Math, see BRANGES, LOUIS DE

DE BREMAECKER, JEAN-CLAUDE, b. Antwerp, Belgium, Sept. 2, 23; m. 52; c. 2. GEOPHYSICS. Louvain, 48; M.Sc, La. State, 50; Ph.D.(geophys), California, 52. Res. scientist, geophysics, Inst. Sci. Res. Cent. Africa, 52-56, sr. scientist, 56-58; asst. prof. GEOPHYSICS, RICE UNIV, 59-60, assoc. prof, 60-65, PROF, 65- Boese fel, Columbia, 55-56; Harvard, 58-59. Belgian Army, 44-45. Mem, Nat. Belgium Cmt. of Geodesy & Geophys, 60-63. Seismol. Soc. Am; Soc. Explor. Geophys; Am. Geophys. Union; Int. Asn. Seismol. & Phys. Earth's Interior (secy. gen). Seismology; gravimetry; magnetism; tectonophysics. Address: 2506 Addison, Houston, TX 77025.

de BRETTEVILLE, ALEXANDER, JR, b. San Francisco, Calif. Mar. 20, 11; m. 39. PHYSICS. A.B, Stanford, 32, Lever Bros. fel, 40-41, Ph.D.(phys. chem), 42; M.S, California, 38. Jr. physicist, West. Sugar Ref, 34-36; elec. engr, Litton Eng. Lab, 39; sr. chemist, Lever Bros. Co, 41-43; Office Sci. Res. & Develop. proj, Mass. Inst. Tech, 43-45; PHYSICIST, U.S. ARMY SIG. CORPS, FT. MONMOUTH, 45- Am. Phys. Soc; Inst. Elec. & Electronics Eng; Fedn. Am. Sci. Ferroelectric dielectrics; thermodynamics of electric field induced phase transitions; application nuclear magnetic resonance to study ferroelectricity; application of ultrasonics to determination of elastic constants of crystals and attenuation in superconductors. Address: 224 Navesink Ave, Highlands, NJ 07732.

DeBROSSE, KENNETH LAWRENCE, b. Sidney, Ohio, Dec. 11, 23; m. 50; c. 3. PHYSICS. A.B, Miami (Ohio), 44, M.A, 50. Instr. chem, Miami (Ohio), 43; asst. chemist, Monsanto Chem. Co, 44, electronic engr, 46-48; exec. engr. & head radiation syst, INT. TEL. & TEL. LABS, 50-62, mgr. space & phys. sci. dept, 62-69, DIR. ENG, AEROSPACE/OPTICAL DIV, 69- Instr, Miami (Ohio), 50-51. With Atomic Energy Cmn, 46. U.S.N.R, 44-46. Assoc. Inst. Elec. & Electronics Eng. Electro-optical instrumentation; infrared optical devices; space instrumentation. Address: 6817 Lawnwood Dr, Ft. Wayne, IN 46803.

DeBRUIN, KENNETH E(DWARD), b. Oskaloosa, Iowa, May 29, 42; m. 69. ORGANIC CHEMISTRY. B.S, Iowa State Univ, 64; Nat. Sci. Found. fel, Univ. Calif, Berkeley, 64-66, Nat. Insts. Health fel, 66-67, Ph.D.(org. chem), 67. Nat. Insts. Health fel, Princeton, 67-69; ASST. PROF. CHEM, COLO. STATE UNIV, 69- Am. Chem. Soc; The Chem. Soc. Mechanisms of organic reactions; phosphorus stereochemistry; terpene biosynthesis. Address: Dept. of Chemistry, Colorado State University, Ft. Collins, CO 80521.

DeBRUNNER, LOUIS EARL, b. Cincinnati, Ohio, Dec. 9, 35; m. 58; c. 2. FOREST ECOLOGY. B.S, Cincinnati, 57; M.F, Yale, 59; D.For, Duke, 67. ASST. PROF. SILVICULT, AUBURN UNIV, 61- Soc. Am. Foresters. Regeneration of forest stands; forest recreation. Address: 1439 S. Gay St, Auburn, AL 36830.

DeBRUNNER, MARJORIE R, b. Auburn, Nebr, Feb. 21, 27. ORGANIC CHEMISTRY. B.Sc.Ed, Nebr. State Teachers Col.(Kearney), 48, M.S, 51; Avery fel, Nebraska, 51-53, Ph.D.(chem), 53. RES. CHEMIST, E.I. DU PONT DE NEMOURS & CO, 53- AAAS; Sci. Res. Soc. Am; Am. Chem. Soc. Synthetic hydrocarbon and fluorocarbon elastomers. Address: Elastomer Chemicals Dept, E.I. du Pont de Nemours & Co, Wilmington, DE 19898.

DEBRUNNER, PETER G(EORG), b. Sitterdorf, Switz, Mar. 11, 31; m. 55; c. 3. PHYSICS. Ph.D.(physics), Swiss Fed. Inst. Technol, 60. Res. assoc. PHYSICS, UNIV. ILL, URBANA, 60-63, res. asst. prof, 63-68, ASSOC. PROF, 68- Am. Phys. Soc. Angular correlation; Mossbauer experiments. Address: Dept. of Physics, University of Illinois, Urbana, IL 61801.

DeBRUNNER, RALPH E(DWARD), b. Cincinnati, Ohio, Oct. 11, 32; m. 56; c. 2. ORGANIC CHEMISTRY. B.S, Cincinnati, 54, Laws fel, 57-58, Procter & Gamble fel, 58-59, Ph.D.(org. chem), 60. Res. chemist, Chemstrand Corp, Ala, 54-55; spec. proj. dept, Monsanto Chem. Co, Mass, 60-61, sr. res. chemist, Dayton Lab, Monsanto Res. Corp, MONSANTO CO, 61-66, group leader, 66-68, SR. GROUP LEADER, CHEMSTRAND RES. CTR, N.C, 68- Am. Chem. Soc. Synthesis of thermally and oxidatively stable polymers, and preparation of high performance composites. Address: Chemstrand Research Center, P.O. Box 731, Durham, NC 27702.

DE BRUYN, P(ETER) P(AUL) H(ENRY), b. Amsterdam, Holland, July 28, 10; nat; m. 31; c. 2. HISTOLOGY. M.D, Amsterdam, 38. Asst, histol. lab, Amsterdam, 36-39, Stokvis-fonds fel, Chicago, 38; first asst, Inst. Prev. Med, Leyden, Holland, 39-40, chief bact. dept, 40-41; instr. ANAT, UNIV. CHICAGO, 41-44, asst. prof, 44-46, assoc. prof, 46-52, PROF, 52-, chmn, dept, 46-61. Med. off, Dutch Army, 39-40. With Atomic Energy Cmn, 46. AAAS; Am. Soc. Nat; Am. Asn. Anat; Am. Soc. Cell Biol; Radiation Res. Soc; Int. Soc. Cell Biol. Lipids of leucocytes; locomotion of leucocytes; histopathology of radiation effects; lymphatic tissue; vital straining of nuclei; fine structure of blood forming organs. Address: Dept. of Anatomy, University of Chicago, 1025 E. 57th St, Chicago, IL 60637.

De BRUYN, P(HILIP) L(OUIS), b. George, S.Africa, May 7, 21; nat; m. 53; c. 4. METALLURGY. M.Sc, Univ. Stellenbosch, 44; Sc.D.(metall), Mass. Inst. Technol, 52. Jr. lectr. geol, Univ. Stellenbosch, 42-44; asst. prof. METALL, MASS. INST. TECHNOL, 49-56, assoc. prof, 56-62, PROF, 62- Consult. metallurgist, Jones & Laughlin Steel Corp, 56-61; Calif. Res. Corp, 59-61; Whirlpool Corp, 60-; Int. Minerals & Chem. Corp, 63- Am. Chem. Soc; Am. Inst. Min, Metall. & Petrol. Eng. Surface chemistry and physics; flotation; chemical kinetics. Address: Dept. of Metallurgy, Massachusetts Institute of Technology, 77 Massachusetts Ave, Cambridge, MA 02139.

DEBS, ROBERT J(OSEPH), b. Chicago, Ill, Mar. 31, 19; m. 46; c. 2. MICROWAVE PHYSICS. Ph.D.(physics), Mass. Inst. Technol, 52. Jr. engr, Westinghouse Elec. Corp, 42-44; develop. engr, Raytheon Mfg. Co, 44-46; res. assoc. electronics & nuclear sci, Mass. Inst. Technol, 46-52; microwave lab, Stanford, 52-58; West Coast Labs, Gen. Tel. & Electronics Corp, 58-63; RES. SCIENTIST, AMES RES. CTR, NASA, 63- Inst. Elec. & Electronics Eng; Am. Phys. Soc. Low-intensity, low-temperature behavior of solar cells under charged-particle bombardment; superconducting magnetometry; low-level radioactivity counting. Address: NASA-Ames Research Center, Moffett Field, CA 94035.

DeBUSK, A(RON) GIB, b. Lubbock, Tex, Jan. 15, 27; m. 47; c. 6. GENETICS. B.S, Univ. Wash, 50; M.A, Univ. Tex, 52, Ph.D.(genetics), 54. Res. scientist, biochem. inst, Univ. Tex, 51-52, Genetics Found, 52-55; instr, DEPT. BIOL. SCI, Northwest. Univ, 55-57; asst. prof, FLA. STATE UNIV, 57-61, assoc. prof, 61-69, PROF, 69-, DIR. GENETICS TRAINING PROG, 62-, assoc. dir. inst. molecular biophys, 62-63, assoc. chmn. dept. biol. sci, 66-67. Vis. prof. Southwest. Univ, 54-55; mem. staff Brookhaven Nat. Lab, 56; vis. fel, Inst. Advan. Studies, Australian Nat. Univ, 68. U.S.A, 45-46. Am. Chem. Soc; Biophys. Soc; Am. Soc. Microbiol; Genetics Soc. Am; Am. Soc. Biol. Chem. Molecular and biochemical genetics; cellular transport, metabolic channeling, exoenzymes, mutational phenomena and protein synthesis in Neurospora. Address: Genetics Lab, Dept. of Biological Sciences, Florida State University, Tallahassee, FL 32306.

DEBUSKEY, MATTHEW, b. Baltimore, Md, Oct. 26, 07; m. 40; c. 1. PEDIATRICS. A.B, Hopkins, 28, M.D, 32. Asst. prof. PEDIAT, SCH. MED, JOHNS HOPKINS UNIV, 50-66, ASSOC. PROF, 66- Med.C, U.S.A, 42-46, Maj. Psychosomatic aspects of adolescence. Address: Dept. of Pediatrics, Johns Hopkins University School of Medicine, Baltimore, MD 21205.

DeBUTTS, EDWARD H(ERBERT), b. Front Royal, Va, Dec. 23, 22; m. 46; c. 3. CHEMISTRY. B.S. George Washington, 43; Ph.D.(phys. chem), Illinois, 48. Res. assoc, rocket sect. 8, div. 3, Nat. Res. Comt. proj, George Washington, 43-46; instr. chem, Harvard, 48-51, res. chemist, res. ctr, ALLEGANY BALLISTICS LAB, Hercules Powder Co, 51-62, supt. propellant res. dept, HERCULES INC, 62-67, mgr. res, 67-71, MGR. TECHNOL. MKT, 71- Am. Chem. Soc; Am. Inst. Aeronaut. & Astronaut. Polyelectrolytes; rheology; coordination catalysis; nitrogen chemistry; ballistics; propellants. Address: Allegany Ballistics Lab, Hercules Inc, P.O. Box 210, Cumberland, MD 21501.

DEBYE, PETER P(AUL) R(UPRECHT), b. Göttingen, Germany, Mar. 7, 16; U.S. citizen; m. 62; c. 3. PHYSICS. Ph.D.(physics), Cornell, 44. Physicist, Gen. Aniline & Film Corp, Pa, 44-46; Bell Tel. Labs, 46-52; Cornell Univ, 52-53; RAYTHEON CO, 53-59, MGR. RES. & DEVELOP, 59- Am. Phys. Soc; Optical Soc. Am. Photoconductors; infrared sensors; injection lasers; semiconductor properties; cryogenics; electron diffraction; spectroscopy; light scattering. Address: Infrared & Optical Research, Raytheon Co, Special Microwave Devices Operation, 130 2nd Ave, Waltham, MA 02154.

DeBYLE, NORBERT V, b. Green Bay, Wis, May 1, 31; m. 54; c. 2. FORESTRY, WATERSHED MANAGEMENT. B.S, Wisconsin, 53, M.S, 57; Ph.D. (forestry), Michigan 62. Conserv. aid wildlife mgt, Wis. State Dept. Conserv, 53-54; res. asst. forest & wildlife mgt, Univ. Wis, 56-57; lectr. forestry, Michigan, 58-59; res. forester, U.S. FOREST SERV, Nev, 61-64, RES. FORESTER & PROJ. LEADER, FORESTRY SCI. LAB, INTERMOUNTAIN FOREST & RANGE EXP. STA, 64- U.S.A, 54-56, Res, 56-67, 1st Lt. Fel. AAAS; Wildlife Soc; Soil Conserv. Soc. Am; Ecol. Soc. Am. Water yield and quality improvement from mountain watersheds; aspen autecology; plant nutrient cycling, forest soils; wildlife ecology. Address: Intermountain Forest & Range Experiment Station, U.S. Forest Service, 860 N. 12th East, Logan, UT 84321.

DEC, JOSEPH, b. Paterson, N.J, Jan. 12, 13; m. 44. ORGANIC CHEMISTRY. A.B, Indiana, 36; Ph.D.(org. chem), Illinois, 40. Org. res. chemist, Eastman Kodak Co, 40-43; tech. aide, Nat. Defense Res. Cmt. Wash, D.C, 43-46; res. sect. chief, JOHNS-MANVILLE, 46-55, res. dept. mgr, 56-60, assoc. dir. gen. res. & sci. serv, 61-63, RES. DIR. PACKINGS & FRICTION MAT. 64- Cert. of appreciation, U.S. Depts. War & Navy, 47. Am. Chem. Soc. (secy-treas, div. polymer chem, 53-56); Soc. Chem. Indust. Polymerization and structure of vinyl polymers; radiopaque compounds; adhesive tapes; reinforced plastics; packings, gaskets and friction materials; application of organic materials to asbestos-containing products and building materials. Address: Johns-Manville, Manville, NJ 08835.

DeCAMP, PAUL T(RUMBULL), b. Seoul, Korea, Feb. 26, 15; U.S. citizen; m. 45; c. 6. SURGERY. B.S, Wheaton Col, 35; M.D, Pennsylvania, 41. Asst. path, sch. med, Baylor, 42-44; surg, SCH. MED, UNIV. TULANE, 44-48, instr. & cancer coordinator, 48-50, asst. prof. surg, 50-59, ASSOC. PROF. CLIN. SURG, OCHSNER CLIN, 59- Med.C, 53-55, Maj. Am. Asn. Thoracic Surg; Am. Col. Surg; Soc. Vascular Surg; Soc. Univ. Surg; Int. Soc. Surg; Int. Cardiovasc. Soc. Venous thrombosis and embolism; venous pressure in post-phlebitic and related conditions; cancer of the lung; hypertension due to renal arterial stenosis; cerebrovascular insufficiency. Address: Dept. of Surgery, Ochsner Clinic, 1514 Jefferson Highway, New Orleans, LA 70121.

De CARLO, CHARLES R, b. Pittsburgh, Pa, May 7, 21; m. 46; c. 4. MATHEMATICS. B.E, Pittsburgh, 43, Ph.D.(math), 51. Lectr. math, Pittsburgh, 47-51; asst. dir, appl. sci. div, Int. Bus. Mach. Corp, 51-55, dir, 55-57, sales servs, 57-58, mkt. prog, 58, mgr. mkt. & serv, 58-59, asst. gen. mgr, data systs. div, 59-61, corp. dir, ed, 61-63, systs. res. & develop, 63-65, dir. automation res, 65-69; PRES, SARAH LAWRENCE COL, 69- Faculty mem, Am. Studies Inst, 68; trustee, Bank St. Col. Educ; Inst. of Man & Sci; consult, U.S. Off. Educ. U.S.N. 43-46. AAAS; Am. Acad. Arts & Sci; Soc. Indust. & Appl. Math; Instrument Soc. Am; Economet. Soc; Asn. Comput. Mach; Am. Math. Soc; Soc. Advan. Mgt; Indust. Math. Soc. Application of computers and automata to science and business. Address: Office of the President, Sarah Lawrence College, Bronxville, NY 10708.

DE CARLO, J(OHN) JR, b. Philadelphia, Pa, July 9, 18; m. 47; c. 3. RADIOLOGY. A.B, Temple, 40; M.D, Jefferson Med. Col, 44. DIR. dept. radiol, Baltimore City Hosps, 50-61; RADIOL, ST. JOSEPH'S HOSP, 62- Asst. prof, Maryland, 50-61; instr, Hopkins, 58-61. Dipl, Am. Bd. Radiol, 50. Med.C, U.S.N, 44-46. Am. Med. Asn; fel. Am. Col. Radiol; Radiol. Soc. N.Am. Diagnostic roentgenology. Address: 701 Seabrook Court, Baltimore, MD 21204.

DeCARO, THOMAS F, b. Brooklyn, N.Y, Mar. 10, 19; m. 50; c. 2. GENERAL & CELLULAR PHYSIOLOGY. B.S, Rutgers, 48; M.S, New Hampshire, 50; Ph.D, Pennyslvania, 63. Researcher, Smith, Kline & French Labs, 49-51; instr. BIOL, St. Michael's Col, 51-54; asst. prof, Villanova Univ, 54-65; ASSOC. PROF, PMC COLS, 66- Nat. Insts. Health fel, sch. med, Univ. Pa, 65-66. Med.C, & Vet.C, U.S.A, 41-45. AAAS; Am. Soc. Zool; Am. Soc. Cell Biol. Muscle physiology. Address: Dept. of Biology, PMC Colleges, Chester, PA 19013.

DeCARVALHO, SERGIO M, b. Lisbon, Portugal, 23; U.S. citizen; m. 48. IMMUNOLOGY, ONCOLOGY. B.A, B.S. & M.A, Univ. Lisbon, 41, M.D, 47, Ph.D.(med), 54. Res. fel, Rocha Cabral Inst. Sci. Res, Lisbon, 44; High Cult. Inst, Ministry Educ, Portugal, 46; intern, St. Antonio dos Capuchos Hosp, Lisbon, 48; asst. prof. histol. & embryol, sch. med, Univ. Lisbon, 48-52, assoc. prof, 52-54, resident path. & clin. pathologist, univ. hosp, 49-54; intern med, Doctors Hosp, Cleveland, Ohio, 54, resident, 55, hematologist, 55-65, assoc. dir. labs. & dir. res, 58-65, chmn. tumor bd, 62; dir. lab. immunobiol, med. res. dir. & v.pres. med. affairs, Biochem. Procedures, Inc, 65, consult. immunologist, 64; sr. res. physician, life sci. dept, N.Am. Aviation, Inc, 65-66, chief exp. med. sect, 66-70; DIR, BELMONT MED. CLIN, 70-; CHMN. BD. & DIR, AM. MED. CLINS, INC, 71- Vis. investr, Univ. Brazil, 51-52; Caroline Inst, Stockholm, Swed, 51-52; instr. path, West. Reserve Univ, 55; vis. prof, Wayne State Univ, 58; Ohio State Univ, 59; Univ. Minn, 60; Temple Univ, 60; lectr, Merck Inst, 59; Lederle Res. Labs, 59; Parke-Davis Labs, 59; Children's Hosp, Boston, 60; vis. prof, Univ. Tenn, 62; Howard Univ, 63; vis. lectr, Roussy Cancer Inst, France & Regina Elena Cancer Inst, Ital, 63; asst. prof, Univ. Calif-Calif. Col. Med, 65; vis. investr, Salk Inst, 66; vis. lectr, Univ. Vienna, 70. Jane Coffins Fund grant, 55; Bratenahl Found grants, 56-65; U.S. Army grant, 63. Hematologist, St. Antonio dos Capuchos Hosp, 52-54; consult, Bratenahl Found, 57; Sinai Hosp, Detroit, 63; consult. physician, Vatican, 63; staff physician, Vet. Admin. Hosp, Sepulveda, Calif, 65; staff physician & consult, Mid-Valley Hosp, Van Nuys, Calif, 66; staff physician, Mem. Hosp, Panorama City & Encino Hosp, Encino, Calif, 66; consult. & med. off, stud. health serv, San Fernando Valley State Col, 66; staff physician, San Pedro, Wilmington, Long Beach Community, Woodruff Gables, Bellwood Gen, Lakewood Gen, Pioneer, Artesia Community, Bellflower Community, Lincoln Community Hosps, 66; assoc, Bellflower Med. Group, 67, Bellflower Med. Arts, 68; vis. mem, Orange County Med. Ctr, 68; mem. health & safety comt, City of Cerritos, 68; partic, Int. Cancer Cong, Houston, 70; Int. Cong. Hemat, Munich, 70. Health Award, City of Cleveland. AAAS; Am. Soc. Hemat; Am. Med. Asn; Am. Asn. Cancer Res; Am. Soc. Cell Biol; N.Y. Acad. Sci; Am. Soc. Electron Micros; Tissue Cult. Asn; Am. Soc. Microbiol; Am. Soc. Nuclear Med; Am. Soc. Cytol; Am. Inst. Biol. Sci; Am. Fedn. Clin. Res; Asn. Clin. Sci; Int. Soc. Hemat; Europ. Soc. Hemat; Brazilian Soc. Hemat; Brazilian Biol. Soc; Brazilian Soc. Anat; Royal Soc. Med; Royal Micros. Soc; Int. Radiation Protection Asn. Molecular biology, pathology, cytology; biophysical methods in cytology; clinical immunology and immunopathology; clinical hematology; laboratorial hematology, cytological and biochemical; molecular biology of cancer. Address: Belmont Medical Clinic, 9837 E. Belmont St, Bellflower, CA 90706.

DeCASTRO, A(RTHUR), b. Newark, N.J, July 8, 11; m. 51; c. 1. ANALYTICAL CHEMISTRY. B.S, Newark Col. Eng, 31; Columbia Univ, 36-38. Chemist, Calco Chem. Co, 31-33; control chemist, NOPCO CHEM. CO, HARRISON, 33-36, anal. res. chemist, 36-38, chief chemist, anal. res. lab, 38-58, LAB. DIR. ANAL. RES. & PHYS. TESTING LABS, 58- Fel. Am. Inst. Chem; sr. mem. Am. Chem. Soc; Am. Soc. Test & Mat. Surfactants and processed chemicals used in detergent, textile, tanning, paper, paint and metal working. Address: 14 Midvale Dr, New Providence, NJ 07974.

DeCELLES, PAUL C, b. Kansas City, Mo, May 30, 34; m. 56; c. 4. PHYSICS. B.S, Rockhurst Col, 55; Ph.D.(physics), Hopkins, 60. Instr. PHYSICS,

Hopkins, 59-60; res. assoc, Brookhaven Nat. Lab, 60-62; mem, Inst. Adv. Study, 62-63; asst. prof, UNIV. NOTRE DAME, 63-64, ASSOC. PROF, 64- Sloan res. fel, 64-66. Am. Phys. Soc. Theoretical physics; quantum electrodynamics and elementary particle physics. Address: Dept. of Physics, University of Notre Dame, Notre Dame, IN 46556.

DE CHAMPLAIN, JACQUES, b. Quebec, Que, Mar. 13, 38; m. 61; c. 2. PHYSIOLOGY, PHARMACOLOGY. B.A, Montreal, 57, M.D, 62; Med. Res. Coun. Can. fel, McGill, 63-65, Ph.D.(invest. med), 65. Vis. res. assoc, Nat. Inst. Ment. Health, 65-67, Med. Res. Coun. Que. fel, 67-68; asst. prof. PHYSIOL, UNIV. MONTREAL, 68-71, ASSOC. PROF, 71- John & Mary Markle Found. scholar acad. med, 68; sr. investr, res. group on neurol. sci, Med. Res. Coun. Can, 69. AAAS; Am. Fedn. Clin. Res; Can. Physiol. Soc. Studies on the role of peripheral and central sympathetic nervous system in the regulation of normal blood pressure and in the pathogenesis of hypertensive diseases. Address: Dept. of Physiology, Faculty of Medicine, University of Montreal, P.O. Box 6128, Montreal, Que, Can.

DECHARY, J(OSEPH) M(ARTIN), b. Youngsville, La, Mar. 6, 22. ORGANIC CHEMISTRY. B.S, Louisiana, 43, M.S, 47, Coates fel, 51-52, Ph.D.(chem), 52. CHEMIST, SOUTH REGIONAL RES. LAB, U.S. DEPT. AGR, 48-50, 52- Chemist, sch. med, Tulane, 52-54. U.S.A, 44-46. Am. Chem. Soc; Sci. Res. Soc. Am; N.Y. Acad. Sci. Cottonseed; diazoketones; bromo-2-nitrobenzoic acids; reaction of quinones with ketones; biological antagonists; metabolic pathways in protozoa; spectrophotometry; gossypol chemistry; seed proteins; phytohemagglutinins; seed proteases and protease inhibitors; chemical modification of edestin. Address: 2820 General Pershing St, New Orleans, LA 70115.

DE CHAZAL, L(OUIS) E(DMOND) MARC, b. St. Denis, Réunion, Nov. 23, 21; m. 51; c. 2. CHEMICAL ENGINEERING. B.S, La. State, 49, M.S, 51; Ph.D.(chem. eng), Okla. State Univ, 53. Asst. prof. chem. eng, UNIV. MO-COLUMBIA, 53-57, assoc. prof, 57-63, CHEM. & NUCLEAR ENG, 63-66, PROF, 66- Res. assoc, Atomic Energy Res. Estab, Eng, 59-60 & 66-67; consult, Mo. Farmers Asn, Monsanto Co. & Esso Standard Oil. Royal Army, 39-46. AAAS; Am. Chem. Soc; Am. Soc. Eng. Educ; Am. Inst. Chem. Eng. Solvent extraction; heat transfer; thermodynamics; applications to nuclear energy; non-Newtonian fluid mechanics. Address: Dept. of Chemical Engineering, University of Missouri-Columbia, Columbia, MO 65201.

DeCICCO, BENEDICT T(HOMAS), b. Rahway, N.J, Feb. 7, 38; m. 60; c. 5. BACTERIOLOGY, BIOCHEMISTRY. A.B, Rutgers, 60, M.S, 62, Ph.D.(bact), 64. Asst. BACT, Rutgers, 60-62, sr. lab. technician, 62-63, res. asst, 63-64; asst. prof, CATHOLIC UNIV, 64-68, ASSOC. PROF, 68- Am. Soc. Microbiol. Genetics and metabolism of chemoautotrophs, especially hydrogen bacteria; limits of bacterial variability; tolerance to extreme environments. Address: Dept. of Biology, Catholic University of America, Washington, DC 20017.

DE CICCO, HENRY, b. Jersey City, N.J, May 17, 25; m. 54; c. 3. MATHEMATICS, OPERATIONS RESEARCH. A.B, N.Y. Univ, 50, M.S, 62. Analyst, Economet. Inst, Inc, 50-52; MATHEMATICIAN, DEPT. ARMY, 54- Mem, U.S. Army Math. Steering Comt, 60-; res. scientist & lectr. opers. res. N.Y. Univ, 63-64. U.S.A.A.F, 44-46, Sgt. Inst. Math. Statist; N.Y. Acad. Sci; Opers. Res. Soc. Am. Stochastic processes; differential equations; methodology of science; epistemology. Address: 78 Hillside Ave, Florham Park, NJ 07932.

De CICCO, JOHN, b. Brooklyn, N.Y, Apr. 5, 11; m. 41. MATHEMATICS. B.S, Brooklyn Col, 33; scholar, Columbia, 35-36, Ph.D.(math), 38. Instr. MATH, eve. session, Brooklyn Col, 33-40; asst, Long Island, 39-40; instr, Ill. Inst. Tech, 40-43, asst. prof, 43-46, assoc. prof, 47-49; prof. & chmn. dept, De Paul, 49-62; PROF, ILL. INST. TECHNOL, 62- Vis. assoc. prof, Columbia, 46-47. Award of Hon. Res, Brooklyn Col, 44. Am. Math. Soc; Math. Asn. Am; Tensor Soc; Math. Soc. Japan. Geometry of whirl series; rational functions and transformations of curves and surfaces in space; infinitesimal contact transformation of mechanics; polar theory of algebraic functions of n complex variables; potential theory in n dimensions; differential elements; Finsler spaces; Lie groups; partial differential equations of geometry and physics; conformal geometry and equilong geometry. Address: 7363 S. Coles Ave, Chicago, IL 60649.

De CICCO, PETER D(ONALD), b. Port Chester, N.Y, Sept. 15, 39. SOLID STATE PHYSICS. B.A, Amherst Col, 61; Ph.D.(physics), Mass. Inst. Technol, 65. Res. assoc. PHYSICS, MASS. INST. TECHNOL, 65-66, instr, 66, ASST. PROF, 66- Am. Phys. Soc. Energy band theory of solids; optical excitations in insulators; ferromagnetism; theory of atomic structure; self-consistent field calculations. Address: Dept. of Physics, Room 13-2138 Massachusetts Institute of Technology, Cambridge, MA 02139.

DECIOUS, DANIEL, b. Alturas, Calif, July 12, 38; m. 63. PHYSICAL CHEMISTRY. B.S, California, Berkeley, 60; Ph.D.(phys. chem), Washington (Seattle), 65. Res. assoc. theoret. chem, Hopkins, 65-67; ASST. PROF. CHEM, SACRAMENTO STATE COL, 67- Am. Phys. Soc. Theoretical determination of electronic properties of small molecules. Address: Dept. of Chemistry, Sacramento State College, Sacramento, CA 95819.

DECIUS, J(OHN) C(OURTNEY), b. San Francisco, Calif, Feb. 13, 20; m. 48; c. 3. PHYSICAL CHEMISTRY. A.B, Stanford, 41; Ph.D.(chem. physics), Harvard, 47. Res. assoc. & supvr. underwater explosives res. lab, Oceanog. Inst, Woods Hole, 44-47; res. assoc. CHEM, Brown, 47-49; asst. prof, ORE. STATE UNIV, 49-52, assoc. prof, 52-56, PROF, 56- Guggenheim fel, Fulbright res. scholar, Oxford, 55-56, Sloan Found. fel, 56-60; Nat. Sci. Found. fel, King's Col, London, 63-64. Fel. Am. Phys. Soc; Am. Chem. Soc. Molecular structure; vibrational spectra of solid state; energy transfer in gases. Address: Dept. of Chemistry, Oregon State University, Corvallis, OR 97330.

DECK, CHARLES F(RANCIS), b. Norfolk, Va, June 5, 30; m. 56; c. 2. INORGANIC & RADIO CHEMISTRY. B.S, St. Louis, 52; Ph.D.(chem), Washington (St. Louis), 56. Asst, Washington (St. Louis), 52-56; res. chemist, BASF WYANDOTTE CORP, 57-63, SR. RES. CHEMIST, 63- Am. Chem. Soc; Brit. Chem. Soc. Chemistry; kinetics and mechanism of chemical reactions. Address: 2805 Trenton Dr, Trenton, MI 48183.

DECK, H(AROLD) R, b. Chandler, Okla, Jan. 22, 38; m. 56; c. 2. ORGANIC CHEMISTRY. B.S, Southwest Mo. State Col, 59; Ph.D.(org. chem), Purdue Univ, 64. Chem. res, PHILLIPS PETROL. CO, 63-67, commercial develop. chem, 67-69, MGR. PROD. APPLNS. SECT, RES. & DEVELOP. DEPT, 69- Am. Chem. Soc. Organometallics; metal alkyls; transition metal complexes. Address: Research & Development Dept, Phillips Research Center, Bartlesville, OK 74004.

DECK, HOWARD JOSEPH, b. Cincinnati, Ohio, Sept. 25, 38; m. 60; c. 2. ELECTRICAL ENGINEERING. E.E, Cincinnati, 61, M.S, 63; NASA traineeship, Mich. State, 65-66, Ph.D.(elec. eng), 68. Instr. ELEC. ENG, Mich. State, 63-65, 67-68; ASST. PROF, OHIO UNIV, 68- Inst. Elec. & Electronics Eng; Am. Soc. Eng. Educ. Electromagnetic field theory; antenna and circuit theory; reduction of backscattered energy from receiving antennas; active receiving antennas. Address: 25 University Heights Dr, Athens, OH 45701.

DECK, J(AMES) DAVID, b. Atlanta, Ga, Nov. 6, 30; m. 55; c. 4. ANATOMY. B.S, Davidson Col, 51; Gen. Educ. Bd. scholar, Princeton, 51-52, M.A, 53, Ph.D.(biol), 54. Instr. ANAT, SCH. MED, UNIV. VA, 54-56, asst. prof, 56-62, ASSOC. PROF, 62- U.S. Pub. Health Serv. fel. anat, Harvard, 65-66. Soc. Develop. Biol; Am. Asn. Anat. Influence of nerves in amphibian regeneration; experimental production of regenerates in a non-regenerating system by implantations and microinfusions; histamine and antihistamines in regeneration; mammalian regeneration. Address: Dept. of Anatomy, School of Medicine, University of Virginia, Charlottesville, VA 22901.

DECK, JOSEPH CHARLES, b. Canton, Ohio, July 16, 36; m. 61; c. 4. PHYSICAL CHEMISTRY. B.S, Duquesne, 60; M.S, Illinois, 64, Ph.D.(phys. chem), 66. Chemist, Gulf Res. & Develop. Co, 60-62; asst. prof. CHEM, UNIV. LOUISVILLE, 66-70, ASSOC. PROF, 70- Am. Chem. Soc. Magnetic resonance; molecular structure; intermolecular and intramolecular interactions. Address: Dept. of Chemistry, University of Louisville, Louisville, KY 40208.

DECK, JOSEPH F(RANCIS), b. St. Louis, Mo, Mar. 19, 07; m. 36; c. 3. CHEMISTRY. A.B, St. Louis, 28, M.S, 30; Michigan, 29; fel, Kansas, 31-32, Ph.D.(chem), 32. Res. chemist, Stewart Inso Board Corp, St. Joseph, Mo, 32-35; quality supvr, U.S. Gypsum Co, 35; PROF. CHEM, UNIV. SANTA CLARA, 36- Anal. chemist, Richmond-Chase Co, 40- Am. Chem. Soc; Inst. Food Technol. Food analyses; synthetic organic chemistry; synthesis of heterocyclic ring compounds. Address: Dept. of Chemistry, University of Santa Clara, Santa Clara, CA 95053.

DECK, ROBERT THOMAS, b. Phila, Pa, Aug. 6, 35. THEORETICAL PHYSICS. B.A, La Salle Col, 56; Ph.D.(physics), Notre Dame, 61. Res. assoc. theoret. physics, Bartol Res. Found, Pa, 61-63; res. assoc. & instr, Michigan, 63-65; asst. prof. PHYSICS, UNIV. TOLEDO, 65-70, ASSOC. PROF, 70- Am. Phys. Soc. High and low energy theoretical nuclear physics; quantum electrodynamics; elementary particle theory. Address: Dept. of Physics, University of Toledo, Toledo, OH 43606.

DECK, RONALD J(OSEPH), b. New Orleans, La, May 16, 34. SOLID STATE PHYSICS. B.S, Loyola (La), 56; M.S, La. State, 58, Gottlieb fel, 58-59, Nat. Sci. Found. co-op. fel, 59-61, Ph.D.(physics), 61. Asst. prof. PHYSICS, La. State, 61-62; assoc. physicist, Oak Ridge Nat. Lab, 62-63; ASST. PROF, TULANE UNIV. LA, 63- Am. Inst. Physics. Galvanomagnetic and thermomagnetic effects in metals at low temperatures; behavior of superconducting alloys. Address: Dept. of Physics, Tulane University of Louisiana, New Orleans, LA 70118.

DECKER, A(LVIN) MORRIS, JR, b. Manocs, Colo, Oct. 12, 18; m. 43; c. 2. AGRONOMY. B.S, Colo. Agr. & Mech. Col, 49; M.S, Utah State Agr. Col, 51; Ph.D.(agron), Maryland, 53. Instr. AGRON, UNIV. MD, COLLEGE PARK, 52-53, asst. prof, 53-58, assoc. prof, 58-67, PROF, 67- Merit cert, Am. Forage & Grassland Coun, 69. U.S.A.A.F, 41-45. Fel. Am. Soc. Agron. Forage crop management and breeding. Address: Dept. of Agronomy, University of Maryland, College Park, MD 20742.

DECKER, CLARENCE F(ERDINAND), b. Taintor, Iowa, Nov. 9, 25; m. 48; c. 2. B.S, Western Michigan, 50; M.S, Mich. State, 52; Ph.D.(physiol), 54. Asst. physiol, Mich. State, 52-53, U.S. Pub. Health Serv. res. fel. biochem, 54-56; asst. scientist, div. biol. & med. res, Argonne Nat. Lab, 56-59, assoc. scientist, 59-61; chief biochemist, endocrinol. sect, Presby-St. Luke's Hosp, Chicago, 61-62; chief biochem. sect, radioisotope serv, Hines Vet. Admin. Hosp, Ill, 62-67; assoc. prof. BIOL. SCI, POINT PARK COL, 67, PROF. & CHMN. DEPT, 67- Consult. biochemist, dept. path, Presby-St. Luke's Hosp, 62-67. U.S.N.R, 43-46. Am. Chem. Soc; N.Y. Acad. Sci. Cardiovascular physiology; toxicity and metabolism of heavy metals; trace element metabolism; skeletal retention of radioactive isotopes of the alkaline earth; biosynthesis of collagen; neutron activation of trace elements in biological materials; ceruloplasmin and copper metabolism. Address: Dept. of Biological Sciences, Point Park College, 201 Wood St. & Blvd. of the Allies, Pittsburgh, PA 15222.

DECKER, DANIEL L(ORENZO), b. Provo, Utah, Sept. 22, 29; m. 54; c. 7. SOLID STATE PHYSICS. B.S, Brigham Young, 53, M.S, 55; Celanese Corp. Am. fel, Illinois, 56, Nat. Sci. Found. fel, 57, Ph.D.(physics), 58. Asst. math, Brigham Young, 52-53, physics, 53-55, appl. math, 55; PHYSICS, Illinois, 55-56; asst. prof, BRIGHAM YOUNG UNIV, 58-63, assoc. prof, 63-67, PROF, 67- Vis. staff mem, Los Alamos Sci. Lab, N.Mex, 64- Am. Phys. Soc; Am. Asn. Physics Teachers. High pressure physics; Mössbauer measurements; diffusion; superconductivity. Address: Dept. of Physics, Brigham Young University, Provo, UT 84601.

DECKER, DAVID G(ARRISON), b. Pittsford, N.Y, Sept. 14, 17; m. 41; c. 4. OBSTETRICS, GYNECOLOGY. A.B, Rochester, 39; M.D, Yale, 42; M.S, Minnesota, 51. Asst. biochem. & resident obstet, Mary Imogene Bassett Hosp, Cooperstown, N.Y, 46; fel, MAYO CLIN, 47-49, asst. OBSTET. &

GYNEC, 49, CONSULT, 50-, HEAD SECT. OBSTET. & GYNEC, 69-; PROF. OBSTET. & GYNEC. & CHMN. DEPT, MAYO GRAD. SCH. MED, UNIV. MINN, 69-, instr, 53-58, asst. prof, 58-65, assoc. prof, 65-69. Dipl, Am. Bd. Obstet. & Gynec. U.S.A, 43-46. Am. Asn. Obstet. & Gynec; Am. Fertil. Soc; Am. Col. Obstet. & Gynec. Infertility and pelvic malignancy. Address: Mayo Clinic, 200 First St. S.W, Rochester, MN 55901.

DECKER, DAVID RICHARD, b. Neptune, N.J, Aug. 11, 39; m. 66; c. 2. PHYSICAL ELECTRONICS, SOLID STATE PHYSICS. B.S, N.C. State Univ, 61; M.S, Lehigh Univ, 63, Ph.D.(elec. eng), 70. MEM. TECH. STAFF, BELL TEL. LABS, 61- AAAS; Inst. Elec. & Electronics Eng; Electrochem. Soc. Semiconductor electronics; microwave circuits and measurements; numerical mathematics; physical optics. Address: 105 Wyoming Ave, Wyomissing, PA 19610.

DECKER, FRED W(ILLIAM), b. Portland, Ore, July 5, 17; m. 42; c. 3. PHYSICS. B.S, Ore. State Col, 40, Ph.D.(physics), 52; M.S, N.Y. Univ, 43. Jr. meteorologist, U.S. Weather Bur, Calif, 40-41; instr. meteorol, N.Y. Univ, 41-44; instr. PHYSICS, Multnomah Col, 46; ORE. STATE UNIV, 46-52, asst. prof, 52-59, ASSOC. PROF, 59-; vis. for. res. assoc, Inst. Physics Atmosphere, Munich, 64-65; summer, Swiss Fed. Inst. Tech, 62. Consult, Adv. Cmt. Weather Control, 54-57; TV meteorologist, KOIN, Portland, Ore, 68; KOAC-KOAP, Portland & Corvallis, Ore, 68-70; consult, Fed. Water Pollution Control Agency, 68-69 ; U.S. Atomic Energy Comn, 69-70. U.S.A.A.F, 42-46, Res, 37-66, Lt.Col. Fel. AAAS; Am. Asn. Physics Teachers; Am. Geophys. Union; Int. Asn. Statist. in Phys. Sci; Am. Meteorol. Soc. Atmospheric ozone measurements; meteorological optics; short-period weather forecasting; weather modification evaluation; mesometeorology; weather radar. Address: Dept. of Atmospheric Sciences, Oregon State University, Corvallis, OR 97331.

DECKER, HENRY FLEMING, b. Camden, N.J, June 8, 30; m. 59. PLANT TAXONOMY. B.A, Rutgers Univ, 54, M.S, 58; M.S, Yale, 59, Ph.D.(bot), 62. Asst. prof. BOT, South. Conn. State Col, 60-62; OHIO WESLEYAN UNIV, 62-66, assoc. prof, 66-71, PROF, 71- Res. fel. plant breeding, Univ. Fla, 64-65. U.S.A, 53-56, 1st Lt. AAAS; Am. Genetic Asn; Bot. Soc. Am; Crop Sci. Soc. Am; Am. Soc. Plant Taxon; Int. Soc. Plant Taxon. Taxonomy, cytology and breeding of grasses. Address: Dept. of Botany, Ohio Wesleyan University, Delaware, OH 43015.

DECKER, HERBERT M(ORTIMER), b. New York, N.Y, Aug. 29, 18; m. 49; c. 1. SANITARY ENGINEERING. B.A, N.Y. Univ, 40; M.S, North Carolina, 43. Pub. health engr. & area supvr. malaria control, U.S. Pub. Health Serv, 42-43; sanit. engr, res. lab, Nat. Canners Asn, 46-47; consult. plant sanit, Insect Control & Res, 47-48; supvr. sanit. engr. personnel protection, chem. corps, U.S. Army Ft. Detrick, 48-56, br. chief, 56-71, DIV. CHIEF, BIOL. DEFENSE RES. LAB, 71- Med.Serv, U.S.A, 43-46, 1st Lt. Sci. Res. Soc. Am; fel. Am. Pub. Health Asn. Development and evaluation of air purification systems for removal of biological contaminants from the atmosphere; development and evaluation of equipment for collecting biological aerosols. Address: U.S. Army Biological Defense Research Lab, Edgewood Arsenal, MD 21010.

DECKER, JAMES D(AVIDSON), b. Butler, Pa, Feb. 22, 23; m. 46; c. 3. MECHANICAL ENGINEERING. B.S, Michigan, 47, M.S, 48. Instr. MECH. ENG, PA. STATE UNIV, 48-53, asst. prof, 53-55, ASSOC. PROF, 55- Consult, HRB-Singer, Inc, 63- U.S.A, 43-46. Am. Soc. Eng. Educ; Am. Soc. Mech. Eng; Am. Inst. Aeronaut. & Astronaut. Gas dynamics; heat transfer; combustion; gas turbines; rocket propulsion. Address: Dept. of Mechanical Engineering, Pennsylvania State University, University Park, PA 16802.

DECKER, JANE M, b. Cleveland, Ohio, June 22, 35; m. 59; c. 1. PLANT ANATOMY. A.B, Mt. Holyoke Col, 57; M.S, Yale, 58, Ph.D.(plant anat), 61. Instr. bot, Mass. State Col. Bridgewater, 60-61; taxonomist, Int. Plant Index, 61-62; instr. bot, South. Conn. State Col, 62; Ohio State, 62-64; asst. prof, Ohio Wesleyan Univ, 64-66; bot. & plant path, Ohio State Univ, 66-68; ASSOC. PROF. BOT, OHIO WESLEYAN UNIV, 68- Bot. Soc. Am; Int. Soc. Plant Morphol. Wood anatomy; plant morphology and phylogeny; plant morphogenesis and tissue culture. Address: Dept. of Botany & Bacteriology, Ohio Wesleyan University, Delaware, OH 43015.

DECKER, JESSE SMITH, b. Taylor, Ariz, Apr. 10, 08; m. 33; c. 7. INORGANIC CHEMISTRY. B.S, Brigham Young, 32; M.S, Iowa State Col, 39; Nat. Sci. Found. fel. & Ph.D.(inorg. chem), Univ. of the Pac, 64. Teacher, high sch, Ariz, 36-46; prof. CHEM, PHOENIX COL, 46-63, CHMN. DEPT, 63- Summers, vis. prof, Arizona State, 42, vis. lectr, 61-62, res. partic, Oak Ridge Inst. Nuclear Studies, Oak Ridge Nat. Lab, 55, res. & develop. chemist, Motorola Semiconductor Prod, Inc, 56-57; vis. prof, Brigham Young, 58-59. Fel. AAAS; Am. Chem. Soc; fel. Nat. Inst. Chem. Transition metal complexes of anthranilic acid and its derivatives. Address: Dept. of Chemistry, Phoenix College, 1202 W. Thomas Rd, Phoenix, AZ 85013.

DECKER, JOHN ALVIN, JR, b. Columbia, Mo, Oct. 25, 35; m. 57; c. 2. OPTICS, SPECTROSCOPY. B.Sc. & Aero. Eng, Mass. Inst. Technol, 58, Lockheed fel, 58-62; Ph.D.(plasma physics), Cambridge, 66. Eng. asst, eng. res. lab, N.Am. Aviation, Inc, Calif, 55-56; res. asst, naval supersonic lab, Mass. Inst. Technol, 57-58; res. staff mem. plasma physics, Sperry Rand Res. Ctr, Mass, 65-67; sr. scientist, Comstock & Wiscott, Inc, 67, dir. physics, space physics div, 67-71; PRES, SPECTRAL IMAGING, INC, 71- Summers, staff mem, aerodyn. res. group, Sandia Corp, N.Mex, 57, aerodyn. engr, aeroanal. group, Convair/Ft. Worth, Tex, 58; adj. prof, U.S. Air Force Inst. Technol, 63. U.S.A.F, 62-65, Capt. AAAS; Optical Soc. Am; sr. mem. Instrument Soc. Am; Soc. Appl. Spectros; Coblentz Soc; Am. Phys. Soc; Am. Inst. Aeronaut. & Astronaut. Multiplex infrared spectroscopy; Hadamard-transform spectrometry; infared gas and pollutant analysis; space and plasma physics, particularly quantum-devices and stability; aerodynamics. Address: Spectral Imaging, Inc, 572 Annursnac Hill Rd, Concord, MA 01742.

DECKER, JOHN D, b. Middletown, N.Y, July 10, 22; m. 45; c. 1. ANATOMY, EMBRYOLOGY. B.S, Florida, 50, M.S, 52; Ph.D.(anat), State Univ. N.Y. Upstate Med. Ctr, 65. Instr. biol, Hartwick Col, 52-53, asst. prof, 53-65; res. assoc, Wash. Univ, 65-67; asst. prof. ANAT, MED. CTR, UNIV. MO-COLUMBIA, 67-69, ASSOC. PROF, 69- U.S.N.R, 42-45. Neuroembryology and behavior. Address: Dept. of Anatomy, Medical Center, University of Missouri-Columbia, Columbia, MO 65201.

DECKER, JOHN L(AWS), b. Brooklyn, N.Y, June 27, 21; m. 54; c. 4. INTERNAL MEDICINE. B.A, Univ. Richmond, 42; M.D, Columbia Univ, 51. Instr. med, Columbia Univ, 54-55; clin. & res. fel, Mass. Gen. Hosp, 55-58; instr, Univ. Wash, 58-59, asst. prof, 59-62, assoc. prof, 62-65; CHIEF ARTHRITIS & RHEUMATISM BR, NAT. INST. ARTHRITIS & METAB. DISEASES, 65- U.S.N.R, 62-64. Am. Rheumatism Asn; Am. Fedn. Clin. Res. Clinical studies of rheumatoid arthritis and systemic lupus erythematosus. Address: Room 9N218, Bldg, 10, National Institutes of Health, Bethesda, MD 20014.

DECKER, JOHN P, b. Chicago, Ill, Aug. 16, 25; m. 51; c. 2. MOLECULAR PHYSICS, SPECTROSCOPY. B.S.E.E, Arkansas, 49, M.S, 53; Ph.D.(physics), Texas A&M, 64. Engr, Ark. Power & Light, 49-51; off. engr, F.E. Woodruff, 52-53; instr. PHYSICS, Ark. Agr. & Mech. Col, 53-56; Texas A&M, 56-61, asst. prof, 61-63; assoc. prof, Sam Houston State Col, 63-64, prof, 64-65; PROF. & HEAD DEPT, STEPHEN F. AUSTIN STATE COL, 65- U.S.A, 43-46. Am. Asn. Physics Teachers; Inst. Elec. & Electronics Eng. Investigations of the ultraviolet absorption spectra of sulfer dioxide with isotopic substitution and of selenium dioxide; development of gas lasers. Address: Dept. of Physics, Stephen F. Austin State College, Box 3044, SFA Station, Nacogdoches, TX 75961.

DECKER, JOHN P(ETER), b. Ione, Wash, Dec. 27, 15; m. 40; c. 3. APPLIED SYNECOLOGY. B.S, Idaho, 38; A.M, Duke, 40, Ph.D.(bot), 42; dipl, U.S. Air Force Sch. Aerospace Med, 42. Res. assoc, sch. forestry, Duke, 46; asst. prof. bot, Nebraska, 46-47; N.Y. State Col. Forestry, Syracuse, 47-54; chmn. audiovisual dept, Brooklyn Bot. Garden, 54-55; res. physiologist, U.S. Dept. Agr, 55-63; PROF. ENG, ARIZ. STATE UNIV, 63- U.S.A.A.F, 42-46. AAAS; Am. Soc. Plant Physiol; Int. Soc. Gen. Semantics. Photosynthesis; transpiration; ergometry; photorespiration synecology. Address: College of Engineering Science, Arizona State University, Tempe, AZ 85281.

DECKER, KENNETH H(AROLD), b. Kenosha, Wis, Aug. 19, 32; m. 57; c. 3. ANALYTICAL CHEMISTRY. B.S, Univ. Wis, 54, M.S, 59. Instr. gen. chem, Univ. Wis, 56-57; chemist anal. res, Morton Chem. Co, 59-68, res. assoc, 68-70, MGR. RES. SERV, MORTON INT. INC, 70- U.S.A, 54-56, Res, 56-64. Electroanalytical chemistry; polarography. Address: Morton-Norwich Products Inc, 1275 Lake Ave, Woodstock, IL 60098.

DECKER, L(OUIS) H, b. Monticello, N.Y, Nov. 23, 13; m. 38; c. 2. METALLURGY. Ch.E, Rensselaer Polytech, 35. Mem. methods dept, Rome Div, REVERE COPPER & BRASS, INC, 35-39, metall. chemist, res. dept, 39-43, chief chemist, ref. div, 43-45, supvr. chem. & metall. sect, res. dept, 45-64, asst. mgr. metall. dept, res. & develop. ctr, 64-67, RES. & DEVELOP. MGR, NEW BEDFORD DIV, 67- Am. Soc. Metals. Metallurgy of copper alloys. Address: New Bedford Division, Revere Copper & Brass, Inc, 24 N. Front St, New Bedford, MA 02741.

DECKER, LUCILE E(LLEN), b. Grand Rapids, Mich, Jan. 4, 27; m. 48; c. 2. BIOCHEMISTRY. B.S, Western Michigan, 48; M.S, Mich. State, 52, U.S. Pub. Health Serv. fel, 54-56, Ph.D.(biochem), 56. Chemist, Am. Cyanamid Co, Mich, 46-50; teaching asst. chem, Mich. State, 50-52, res. instr. foods & nutrit, 52-54; res. assoc. biochem, sch. med, Northwestern, 58-61; supv. biochemist, Hines Vet. Admin. Hosp, 61-67; asst. prof. biochem. & biophys, Stritch Sch. Med, Loyola Univ, Chicago, 63-67; assoc. prof. BIOL. SCI, POINT PARK COL, 67-71, PROF, 71- AAAS; Am. Chem. Soc. Enzymology; intermediary metabolism; transaminases and their coenzymes; trace metal metabolism and toxicity; substituted pyridine ring compounds. Address: Dept. of Biological Sciences, Point Park College, 201 Wood St, Pittsburgh, PA 15222.

DECKER, PAUL E(UGENE), b. Rolla, Mo, Sept. 12, 19; m. 61; c. 4. SANITARY ENGINEERING. B.S, Missouri, 42, M.S, 57. Dist. pub. health engr, Div. Health, Mo, 42-58, asst. chief water supply, 58-59; field engr, MO. WATER POLLUTION BD, 59-61, CHIEF DESIGN, CONSTRUCT. & OPERS, 61- Water Pollution Control Fedn. Address: Rural Route 5, 20 Rainbow Circle, Jefferson City, MO 65101.

DECKER, (GEORGE) PHARES, b. Holton, Kans, Aug. 1, 09; m. 37; c. 3. PLANT PATHOLOGY. B.S, Kans. State Col, 34; fel, Agr. & Mech. Col. Texas, 34-35, M.S, 35; Ph.D.(plant pathol), Cornell, 42. Asst, Kans. State Col, 33-34; Minnesota, 35-37; teaching asst, Cornell, 37-38, res. asst, 38-41, res. instr, 41-42; assoc. plant pathologist, UNIV. FLA, 42-46, plant pathologist, exp. sta, 46-55, prof. plant path. & head dept, 55-67, PROF. RES. & GRAD. TRAINING, 67- Am. Phytopath. Soc; Potato Asn. Am. Breeding for disease resistance in vegetable and winter legume forage and cover crops. Address: Dept. of Plant Pathology, University of Florida, Gainesville, FL 32601.

DECKER, Q(UINTIN) W(ILLIAM), b. Rochester, N.Y, Aug. 22, 30; m. 59; c. 2. ORGANIC & INDUSTRIAL CHEMISTRY. B.A, Buffalo, 53, M.A, 56, Allied Chem. & Dye fel, 56-57, Ph.D.(org. chem), 58. CHEMIST, Eastman Kodak Co, 54-55; CHEM. DIV, UNION CARBIDE CORP, SOUTH CHARLESTON, 57- Am. Chem. Soc; Am. Inst. Chem. Eng; Am. Soc. Qual. Control. Aliphatic silanes, organo-metallic sandwich compounds; aliphatic olefin, hydroxyl, carbonyl and amine reactions; hydrogenation and oxidation reactions and catalysts; dialdehyde tissue fixation. Address: 1006 Sand Hill Dr, St. Albans, WV 25177.

DECKER, R(AYMOND) F(RANK), b. Afton, N.Y, July 20, 30; m. 51; c. 4. METALLURGICAL ENGINEERING. B.S, Michigan, 52, M.S, 55, Ph.D. (metall. eng), 58. Asst. high temperature metall, eng. res. inst, Michigan, 54-58; res. metallurgist, alloy studies & develop, INT. NICKEL CO, INC, 58-59, sr. metallurgist, 59-60, sect. head nickel & stainless steels, 60-62, group leader nonferrous metals, 62-67, asst. to mgr, PAUL D. MERICA RES. LAB, 67-69, ASST. MGR, 69- Adj. prof, Polytech. Inst. Brooklyn, 62-66; N.Y. Univ, 68; mem. res. & technol. adv. panel mat. aircraft, NASA, 70-71. IR-100 Award, 64; Sesquicentennial Award, Univ. Mich, 67. Ord.

Dept, 52-54, Res, 54-60, 1st Lt. Fel. Am. Soc. Metals; fel. Am. Inst. Chem; Am. Inst. Mining, Metall. & Petrol. Eng; Sci. Res. Soc. Am; Am. Inst. Chem. Eng; Am. Soc. Test. & Mat. High temperature alloys and transformations; alloy, maraging and stainless steels; cast irons; nickel, copper, aluminum and magnetic alloys; extractive, powder and process metallurgy; welding; electrochemistry, corrosion, ceramics, paints, plastics. Address: Paul D. Merica Research Lab, International Nickel Co, Inc, Sterling Forest, Suffern, NY 10901.

DECKER, RICHARD H, b. Grand Rapids, Mich, Aug. 12, 34; m. 60; c. 3. BIOCHEMISTRY. A.B, Hope Col, 56; M.S, Univ. Ill, Urbana, 58; Ph.D.(biochem), Okla. State Univ, 60. Nat. Insts. Health fel. trytophan metab, sch. med, Univ. Wis, 60-62; res. assoc. & lectr. biochem, Mayo Grad. Sch. Med, Univ. Minn, 62-71; HEAD, SECT. INFECTIOUS DISEASES, ABBOTT LABS, 71- Nat. Insts. Health res. career develop. award, 66-71. U.S.N.R, 52-60. AAAS; Am. Chem. Soc; Soc. Invest. Dermat; Am. Soc. Exp. Path; Fedn. Am. Socs. Exp. Biol. Mechanism of cellular adhesion, acantholysis; phosphoproteins, protein kinase; control of epidermal metabolism; determination of steroids, antigens via radioimmunoassay, protein binding and enzyme competition. Address: Abbott Labs, North Chicago, IL 60064.

DECKER, RICHARD OVERTON, b. Wichita, Kans, Aug. 5, 21; m. 49; c. 2. ELECTRICAL ENGINEERING, DYNAMICS. B.S.E.E, St. Louis, 51; M.S.E.E, Pittsburgh, 54; fel, Mass. Inst. Tech, 56-57. Instr. elec. eng, Pittsburgh, 51-53; develop. engr, mat. eng. dept, Westinghouse Elec. Corp, 53-55, sr. engr, new prods. eng. labs, 55-56, fel. engr, 56-57, supvry. engr, 57-60, adv. engr. & sect. mgr, indust. systs. div, 60-63, adv. engr, systs. eng. studies, res. labs, 63-67; dir. eng, Crydom, Inc, 67-69; RES. MGR, CENT. RES. LAB, SINGER CO, 69- Del, Int. Fed. Automatic Control Conf, Moscow, 60. U.S.A.A.F, 42-45, 1st Lt. Sr. mem. Inst. Elec. & Electronics Eng; sr. mem. Instrument Soc. Am. Feedback and digital computer control systems; mathematical analysis of communication of control systems; computer simulation of complex systems; underwater communications; navigation. Address: Singer Co, Central Research Lab, 400 E. Main St, Denville, NJ 07834.

DECKER, ROBERT DEAN, b. Uniondale, Ind, July 7, 33; m. 57; c. 2. BOTANY. B.S, Purdue, 59, M.S, 61; Ph.D.(bot), N.C. State, 66. Lectr, bot, Butler, 61-62; asst. prof. BIOL. & BOT, UNIV. RICHMOND, 66-69, ASSOC. PROF, 69- U.S.A, 53-55. AAAS; Bot. Soc. Am. Plant morphogenesis. Address: Dept. of Biology, University of Richmond, Richmond, VA 23173.

DECKER, R(OBERT) W(AYNE), b. Williamsport, Pa, Mar. 11, 27; m. 50; c. 4. GEOPHYSICS. B.S, Mass. Inst. Tech, 49, M.S, 51; Sinclair fel, Colo. Sch. Mines, 51, D.Sc.(geol), 53. Asst. geologist, Bethelehm Steel Co, 49-50; geologist, New World Explor. Co, 52-54; asst. prof. geol, Illinois, 54; DARTMOUTH COL, 54-61, assoc. prof, 61-67, PROF. GEOPHYS, 67-, chmn. dept. geol, 63-65. Geophysicist, U.S. Geol. Surv, 57-, vis. scientist, nat. ctr. earthquake res, 69-70; assoc. prof, Inst. Technol. Bandung, Indonesia, 59-60; res. affiliate, Hawaii Inst. Geophys, Univ. Hawaii, 64-; Am. Philos. Soc-Nat. Sci. Found. grant, Iceland, 66-71; Nat. Sci. Found. grant, 68-71, mem. earth sci. grants rev. panel, 71-73. AAAS; fel. Geol. Soc. Am; fel. Am. Geophys. Union (v.pres, sect. volcanology, geochem. & petrol, 68-70); Seismol. Soc. Am. Physics of volcanoes; structural geology; applied geophysics. Address: Dept. of Earth Sciences, Dartmouth College, Hanover, NH 03755.

DECKER, ROLAN V(AN), b. Bartlesville, Okla, Nov. 4, 36; m. 61; c. 2. PHYSICAL BIOCHEMISTRY. B.S, Okla. State Univ, 58; Ph.D.(biochem), Purdue Univ, 65. Asst. prof. CHEM, SOUTHWEST. STATE COL.(OKLA), 65-70, ASSOC. PROF, 70- Am. Chem. Soc. Protein-ion and protein-small molecule interactions and their effects on protein conformation. Address: Rural Route 1, Weatherford, OK 73096.

DECKER, THOMAS ARNO, b. Hawley, Pa, July 13, 40; m. 61; c. 2. PSYCHOLOGY. B.A, Fla. State Univ, 62; M.S, Brown Univ, 64, Ph.D.(psychol), 66. Human factors analyst, Boeing Co, 66-68; ASST. PROF. neural sci, Univ. Tex. Grad. Sch. Biomed. Sci, Houston, 68-71; OPHTHAL, BAYLOR COL. MED, 71- NASA grant, Univ. Tex, 68-71, Baylor Col. Med, 71-; Max Krost Found. grant, Baylor Col. Med, 71- Pan Am. Asn. Ophthal; Optical Soc. Am; Asn. Res. Vision & Ophthal. Visual research; evaluation, integration and development of diagnostic vision testing systems for use in clinical ophthalmology and optometry; development of space borne vision testing systems. Address: Dept. of Ophthalmology, Baylor College of Medicine, 1200 Moursund Ave, Houston, TX 77025.

DECKER, THOMAS GARLAND, b. Ely, Nev, Aug. 25, 36; m. 59; c. 2. SURFACE CHEMISTRY, METALLURGY. B.S, Mass. Inst. Tech, 58, Ph.D. (metall), 64; M.S, Utah, 60. Res. asst. metall, Mass. Inst. Tech, 63-64; res. chemist, Union Carbide Corp, 64-67, chem. & plastics div, 67-70; GROUP MGR. CHEM. RES. & DEVELOP, GILLETTE CO, 70- Am. Chem. Soc. Contact angles, adsorption and foam stabilization; mineral beneficiation. Address: Chemical Research & Development, The Gillette Co, Gillette Park, South Boston, MA 02106.

DECKER, WALTER J(OHNS), b. Tannersville, N.Y, June 13, 33; m. 61; c. 2. BIOCHEMISTRY, TOXICOLOGY. B.A, State Univ. N.Y. Albany, 54, M.A, 55; Ph.D.(biochem), George Washington, 66. U.S. ARMY, 55-, res. asst, biochem, Walter Reed Army Inst. Res, 55-56, res. biochemist, 57-60 & 62-65, CHIEF indust. hyg. sect, 406th Med. Gen. Lab, Japan, 56-57, lab. sect, res. & develop. serv, William Beaumont Gen. Hosp, 65-71, CHEM, 5th U.S. ARMY AREA MED. LAB, FT. SAM HOUSTON, TEX, 71- Consult. to surgeon, White Sands Missile Range, 66-71; lectr, Univ. Tex, El Paso, 67-71. U.S.A, 55-, Lt. Col. Fel. AAAS; Am. Chem. Soc; Am. Fedn. Clin. Res; fel. Am. Inst. Chem; Am. Acad. Clin. Toxicol; Soc. Toxicol. Lipid biochemistry; nutrition; analytical and clinical toxicology; membrane biochemistry; radiobiology; industrial hygiene. Address: Fifth U.S. Army Area Medical Lab, Fort Sam Houston, TX 78234.

DECKER, WAYNE L(EROY), b. Madison County, Iowa, Jan. 24, 22; m. 43; c. 1. AGRICULTURAL CLIMATOLOGY. B.S, Cent. Col.(Iowa), 43; M.S, Iowa State Univ, 47, Ph.D.(soil physics & agr. climatol), 55. Meteorologist climatol, U.S. Weather Bur, 47-49; agr. climatologist, UNIV. MO, 49-67, CHMN. DEPT. ATMOSPHERIC SCI, 67- U.S.N.R, 43-46, Lt. AAAS; Am. Meteorol. Soc; Am. Geophys. Union; Soil Sci. Soc. Am; Am. Soc. Agron; Int. Soc. Biometeorol. Agricultural climatology and meteorology; soil physics; micrometeorology; synoptic meteorology. Address: Dept. of Atmospheric Science, University of Missouri, 701 Hitt St, Columbia, MO 65201.

DECKER, WINSTON M, b. Deckerville, Mich, Jan. 10, 23; m. 45; c. 2. VETERINARY MEDICINE. D.V.M, Mich. State, 46; Wayne State, 52-54. Private practice, 46-47; chief vet, Kalamazoo City County Health Dept, 47-49; pub. health vet, Mich. Dept. Health, 50-55, asst. to state health cmnr, 55-60; chief spec. projs. sect, milk & food br, div. environ eng. & food protection, Pub. Health Serv, 60-65, prog. planning officer, 65-66, asst. prog. officer, bur. state serv, 66-67, dir. Off. Res. & Develop, Bur. Disease Prev. & Environ. Control, 67-69; DIR. SCI. ACTIVITIES, AM. VET. MED. ASN, 69- U.S.A, 43-44, Res, 50-60, Capt; U.S.P.H.S, 60-, Commendation Medal, 64. Am. Vet. Med. Asn; Am. Pub. Health Asn. Relationships of environmental factors to cause, control or prevention of chronic and communicable disease and veterinary medicine's capability and productivity in meeting society's requirements upon it. Address: American Veterinary Medical Association, 600 S. Michigan Ave, Chicago, IL 60605.

DECKERS, JACQUES (MARIE), b. Antwerp, Belgium, Aug. 25, 27; Can. citizen; m. 58; c. 7. PHYSICAL CHEMISTRY. Candidat, Sci. Chim, Louvain, 49; Lic. Sci. Chim, Louvain, 51, fel, 55-56, D.Sc.(phys. chem), 56. Asst, Louvain, 56-58; res. assoc. chem. eng, Princeton, 58-61; assoc. prof. UNIV. TORONTO, 61-66, PROF, 66- Belgium Govt. travel award, 57. Belgium Army Res, 52- Am. Chem. Soc; Am. Phys. Soc; Chem. Inst. Can. Combustion; ions in flames; high energy particles in chemical reactions; molecular beams; electric discharges. Address: Dept. of Chemistry, University of Toronto, Toronto 181, Ont, Can.

DECKKER, B(ASIL) E(ARDLEY) L(EON), b. Ceylon, Sept. 25, 18; m. 53; c. 2. ENGINEERING. B.Sc, Birmingham, 49, M.Sc, 51, Birmingham, 49, Brit. Inst. Mech. Eng. James Clayton fel, 51-52, James Watt fel, 52-53, Ph.D. (mech. eng), 53. Lectr. ENG, Glasgow, 53-62; assoc. prof, UNIV. SASK, 62-66, PROF, 66- Mem. adv. comt. eng. res, Defense Res. Bd, Can; comt. combustion, Nat. Res. Coun. Can. R.N.V.R, Lt. Comdr. Fel. Brit. Inst. Mech. Eng; Brit. Inst. Marine Eng. Physics of fluids; steady and unsteady laminar combustion; supersonic diffusion flames. Address: Dept. of Mechanical Engineering, University of Saskatchewan, Saskatoon, Sask, Can.

DeCLARIS, N(ICHOLAS), b. Drama, Greece, Jan. 1, 31; m. 56. ELECTRICAL ENGINEERING, APPLIED MATHEMATICS. B.S, Agr. & Mech. Col, Tex; Sc.D, Mass. Inst. Tech. Res. engr, Calif. Res. Corp, 52; asst, electronic res. lab, Mass. Inst. Tech, 52-56; asst. prof. elec. eng. & appl. math, Cornell, 56-59, assoc. prof, 59-64, prof, 64-67; PROF. ELEC. ENG. & HEAD DEPT. & RES. PROF, INST. FLUID DYNAMICS & APPL. MATH, UNIV. MD, COLLEGE PARK, 67- Consult, Melpar, Inc, 54; Spencer-Kennedy Labs, 55-56; Gen. Elec. Co, 56-59; Int. Bus. Mach. Corp, 58-70. Jones achievement award, 52. Am. Soc. Eng. Educ; fel. Inst. Elec. & Electronics Eng.(assoc. ed, Transactions, 58); Sci. Res. Soc. Am; Am. Math. Soc. System theory and engineering; simulation; biomedical engineering. Address: Dept. of Electrical Engineering, College of Engineering, University of Maryland, College Park, MD 20740.

DE CLERCK, DONALD H(ERMAN), b. Rochester, N.Y, Mar. 6, 33; m. 61; c. 6. CHEMICAL ENGINEERING, COLLOID CHEMISTRY. B.S, Rochester, 54, M.S, 56, Ph.D.(chem. eng), 60. Res. assoc. ceramics, Pfaudler-Permutit, Inc, Rochester, 60-61, res. scientist, 61-63, Supvr. Phys. & Chem. Testing Res, 63-65, mgr. physico-chem. res. lab, Ritter Pfaudler, Inc, 65-70, MGR. CERAMIC SYSTS. RES, PFAUDLER CO, DIV. SYBRON INC, 70- Am. Inst. Chem. Eng; Am. Chem. Soc; Am. Ceramic Soc; Nat. Inst. Ceramic Eng. Electrokinetic and rheological properties of suspensions; nucleation and crystallization of glass and crystal composites; upgrading of analytical methods for evaluation of glasses and ceramics. Address: 2065 Rush Mendon Rd, Rush, NY 14543.

DeCOOK, KENNETH J(AMES), b. Hebron, Ind, June 7, 25; c. 4. GEOLOGY, HYDROLOGY. B.S, Univ. Ariz, 51, Ph.D.(water resources admin), 70; M.A, Texas, 57. Hydrologic asst, surface water br, U.S. Geol. Surv, Ariz. Dist, 50-51, geologist, ground water br, Ariz. & Tex. Dists, 51-58; res. assoc, inst. water utilization, Arizona, 58-59; consult. ground water hydrologist, Water Develop. Corp, 58-61; asst. dist. engr, San Carlos Irrig. & Drainage Dist, Ariz, 61-63; geologist & hydrologist, W.S. Gookin & Assocs, 63-65; res. assoc, WATER RESOURCES RES. CTR, UNIV. ARIZ, 65-70, ASSOC. HYDROLOGIST, 70- U.S.N.R, 42-51. Am. Inst. Prof. Geol; Am. Geophys. Union; Int. Asn. Math. Geol; Soc. Econ. Paleont. & Mineral. Arid zone hydrology; cretaceous stratigraphy; ground water geology and hydrology; water resources management; economic water allocation and transfer; legal institutions related to water resources. Address: 7009 Elbow Bay Dr, Tucson, AZ 85710.

DECORA, ANDREW W(AYNE), b. Rock Springs, Wyo, July 25, 28; m. 53; c. 2. PHYSICAL ORGANIC CHEMISTRY, SPECTROSCOPY. B.S, Wyoming, 50, M.S, 57, Ph.D.(kinetics), 62. Chemist, Laramie Petrol. Res. Center, U.S. Bur. Mines, 50-51, supvy. chemist, 53-59; asst. kinetics, Wyoming, 59-61; PROJ. LEADER, LARAMIE ENERGY RES. CTR, U.S. BUR. MINES, 61- U.S.A, 51-53. AAAS; Am. Chem. Soc; Soc. Appl. Spectros; Am. Soc. Test. & Mat; Am. Soc. Mass Spectrometry. Gas chromatography; kinetics and mechanisms of organic reactions; thermal and photochemical reactions of sulfur and nitrogen compounds; free radicals; mass, infrared, nuclear magnetic resonance, spectroscopy; shale oil and petroleum chemistry. Address: U.S. Bureau of Mines, Laramie Energy Research Center, Box 3395, University Station, Laramie, WY 82070.

DECOSSAS, KENNETH MILES, b. New Orleans, La, Aug. 14, 25. CHEMICAL ENGINEERING. B.E, Tulane, 44. Chem. Engr, SOUTH. MKT. & NUTRIT. RES. DIV, U.S. DEPT. AGR, 44-48, proj. leader & chem. engr, 48-54, unit supvr. indust. anal, 54-58, supvry. chem. engr, 58-61, INVESTS. HEAD ENG. COSTS & DESIGN, 61- U.S.A.R, 50-, Capt. Nat. Soc. Prof. Eng; Am. Inst. Chem. Eng; Am. Oil Chemists' Soc; Sci. Res. Soc. Am; Am. Asn. Cost Eng. Chemical engineering cost estimation, analysis, design and processing related to invention, development, and commercialization of new processes and products of agricultural utilization research. Address: 6529 General Diaz St, New Orleans, LA 70124.

DE COSSE, JEROME J, b. Valley City, N.Dak, Apr. 19, 28; m. 57; c. 5. MEDICINE. B.S, Col. St. Thomas, 48; M.D, Univ. Minn, 52; Ph.D.(anat), State Univ. N.Y. Upstate Med. Ctr, 69. Intern surg, Roosevelt Hosp, N.Y.C, 52-53, asst. resident, 53-55, asst. & chief resident, 58-60; sr. resident, Mem. Ctr, 60-62; asst, med. col, Cornell Univ, 62-63; asst. prof. & cancer coord, State Univ. N.Y. Upstate Med. Ctr, 63-66; assoc. prof. SURG, sch. med, Case West. Reserve Univ, 66-70, prof, 70-71; PROF. & CHMN. DEPT, MED. COL. WIS, 71- Fel. exp. med, Sloan Kettering Inst, 55-56; Markle scholar. acad. med, 64; consult, Nat. Insts. Health, 68- Boarden Award, 52. U.S.A, 56-58, Capt; Commendation Medal, 58. AAAS; Am. Asn. Cancer Res; Am. Col. Surg; Am. Fedn. Clin. Res; Am. Gastroenterol. Asn; Am. Soc. Cell. Biol; Am. Surg. Asn; Asn. Am. Med. Col; James Ewing Soc; Asn. Acad. Surg; Soc. Surg. Alimentary Tract; Soc. Head & Neck Surgeons; Soc. Univ. Surg. Cancer, cell biology and immunology; gastrointestinal physiology. Address: 1510 E. Goodrich Lane, Fox Point, WI 53217.

DeCOSTA, EDWIN J, b. Chicago, Ill; Mar. 25, 06; m. 35; c. 4. OBSTETRICS, GYNECOLOGY. B.S, Chicago, 26, M.D, 29. Mem. faculty, MED. SCH, NORTHWEST. UNIV, 46-52, PROF, DEPT. OBSTET. & GYNECOL, 52- Attend. obstetrician & gynecologist, Passavant Mem. Hosp, 52-; attend. gynecologist, Cook County Hosp, 58. Dipl, Am. Bd. Obstet. & Gynec. U.S.N, 40-46, Res, 46-, Capt. Am. Gynec. Soc; Am. Asn. Obstet. & Gynec; fel. Am. Col. Surg; fel. Am. Col. Obstet. & Gynec. Endocrinology. Address: 707 Fairbanks Court, Chicago, IL 60611.

DE COURCY, SAMUEL J(OSEPH), JR, b. Newport, R.I, June 13, 18; m. 44; c. 1. MEDICAL MICROBIOLOGY. B.Mus, Yale, 43; B.S, Rhode Island, 44; Haskell fel, Delaware, 48-51, M.S, 51; Pennsylvania, 60-61. Control.chemist, U.S. Naval Torpedo Sta, 44-46; fisheries biologist & chief collab, U.S. Fish & Wildlife Serv, 49; microbiologist, Biochem. Res. Found, Franklin Inst, 51-60; instr, Rutgers, 61-62; STAFF RES. MICROBIOLOGIST, VET. ADMIN. HOSP, PHILA, PA, 60- Mem. staff, Phila. Gen. Hosp, 64-; dir, Delmont Labs, Inc, 70- AAAS; Am. Soc. Microbiol; Am. Chem. Soc; N.Y. Acad. Sci; Reticuloendothelial Soc; Int. Soc. Quantum Biol. Ribosomal vaccines as protective antigens; staphage lysates as RES stimulators in the induction elicitation phenomenon as applied to blockage of oncogenesis. Address: U.S. Veterans Hospital, 39th & Woodland, Philadelphia, PA 19104.

DeCOURSEY, DONN G(ENE), b. Auburn, Ind, Oct. 21, 34; m. 57; c. 2. CIVIL ENGINEERING. B.S, Purdue, 57, M.S, 58; Ph.D.(civil eng), Ga. Inst. Technol, 70. Engr, Ind. Flood Control & Water Resources Comn, 58-61; res. hydraul. engr. SOUTH. PLAINS WATERSHED RES. CTR, AGR. RES. SERV, U.S. DEPT. AGR, 61-71, DIR. CTR, 71- Am. Soc. Civil Eng; Am. Soc. Agr. Eng; Am. Geophys. Union. Hydrologic and hydraulic engineering and research. Address: Southern Great Plains Watershed Research Center, P.O. Box 400, Chickasha, OK 73018.

De COURSEY, JOHN D(ONOVAN), b. Indianapolis, Ind, Apr. 1, 05; m. 31; c. 2. ENTOMOLOGY. A.B, La. State, 30; M.A, Illinois, 37, Ph.D.(entom), 41. Asst. entomologist, State Nat. Hist. Surv, Ill, 29-32; field aide to jr. entomologist truck crop insect invests, bur. entom. & plant quarantine, U.S Dept. Agr, 38-42; officer in charge malaria control unit, U.S. Dept. Navy, 42-45, insect pest control sect, bur. med. & surg, 46-50, head entom. dept, naval med. field res. lab, Camp Lejeune, N.C, 50-54, Naval Med. Res. Unit No. 3, 54-56, instr. Nat. Naval Med. Ctr, Naval Med. Sch. Med, 56-58; head, Vector Control Sect. bur. med. & Surg, 58-62; in charge, Mil. Entom. Info. Serv, 62-67, Navy rep, 67-70; RETIRED. U.S.N, 42-71, Capt.(Ret). Am. Mosquito Control Asn; Entom. Soc. Am. Medical entomology. Address: 6104 Greentree Rd, Bethesda, MD 20034.

DeCOURSEY, PATRICIA J, b. Madison, Wis, Dec. 28, 32; m. 54; c. 2. ZOOLOGY. B.A, Cornell, 54; Wis. Alumni Res. Found. fel, Wisconsin, 54-55, M.S, 55, Am. Asn. Univ. Women fel, 57, Nat. Sci. Found. fel, 58, Ph.D.(zool), 59. Proj. assoc. zool, Wisconsin, 59-60, hon. fel, 62; res. collab, Wash. State Univ, 63-67; lectr. BIOL, UNIV. S.C, 67-70, RES. ASSOC, BARUCH INST. COASTAL RES, 70- Sigma Xi res. grant-in-aid, 63. Am. Soc. Zool. Circadian rhythms in animals; general animal ecology and behavior. Address: Baruch Institute for Coastal Research, University of South Carolina, Columbia, SC 29209.

DeCOURSEY, R(USSELL) M(YLES), b. Indianapolis, Ind, Jan. 17, 00; m. 30; c. 2. ENTOMOLOGY, ZOOLOGY. A.B, dePauw Univ, 23; A.M, Univ. Ill, 25, Ph.D.(entom), 27. Asst. prof. entom, La. Univ, 27-29; ENTOM. & ZOOL, UNIV. CONN, 29-32, assoc. prof, 32-35, prof, 35-70, EMER. PROF, 70- Fel. AAAS; Am. Soc. Zool; Soc. Syst. Zool; Entom. Soc. Am. Bionomics of nymphs of Hemiptera; Pentatomidae. Address: Storrs Heights Rd, Storrs, CT 06268.

DeCOURSEY, W(ILLIAM) J(AMES), b. Rimbey, Alta, Sept. 14, 30; m. 57; c. 4. CHEMICAL ENGINEERING. B.Sc. & Athlone fel, Alberta, 51; dipl, Imp. Col, London & Ph.D, London, 55; Mass. Inst. Tech, 60-61. Process engr, Sherritt Gordon Mines, Ltd, Alta, 55-57, res. & develop. engr, 57-60; asst. prof. CHEM. ENG, UNIV. SASK, 61-64, assoc. prof, 64-71, PROF, 71- Can. Soc. Chem. Eng; Am. Inst. Chem. Eng; Chem. Inst. Can. Mass and heat transfer; fluid mechanics; process development. Address: Dept. of Chemistry & Chemical Engineering, University of Saskatchewan, Saskatoon, Sask, Can.

DEDDENS, JAMES ALBERT, b. Cincinnati, Ohio, Sept. 7, 43; m. 65; c. 1. MATHEMATICS. B.S, Univ. Cincinnati, 65; M.A, Ind. Univ, Bloomington, 67, Ph.D.(math), 69. ASST. PROF. MATH, Univ. Mich, Ann Arbor, 69-70; UNIV. KANS, 70- Nat. Sci. Found. grant, 69-71. Am. Math. Soc; Math. Asn. Am. Study of bounded linear operators on Hilbert space; functional analysis. Address: Dept. of Mathematics, University of Kansas, Lawrence, KS 66044.

DEDDENS, J(AMES) C(ARROLL), b. Louisville, Ky, March 25, 28; m. 53; c. 4. MECHANICAL & NUCLEAR ENGINEERING. B.M.E, Louisville, 52, fel, 52-53, M.M.E, 53; Oak Ridge Sch. Reactor Tech, 53-54. Nuclear engr, atomic energy div, BABCOCK & WILCOX CO, 53-54, nuclear engr. & group supvr, 54-58, proj. engr, Indian Point Reactor Proj, 58-62, proj. mgr, 62-64, asst. coord, utility mkt, 64-66, MGR. NUCLEAR SERV, NUCLEAR POWER GENERATION DEPT, POWER GENERATION DIV, 66- U.S. observer, Int. Conf. Peaceful Uses of Atomic Energy, Geneva, Switz, 64. Ord.C, U.S.A, 46-47. Am. Nuclear Soc; Am. Soc. Mech. Eng. Nuclear power plant design and operations; nuclear products marketing. Address: Babcock & Wilcox Co, P.O. Box 1260, Lynchburg, VA 24505.

DeDECKER, H(ENDRIK) K(AMIEL) J(OHANNES), b. Vorst, Belgium, Sept. 4, 15; nat; m. 40; c. 1. PHYSICAL CHEMISTRY. B.S, Amsterdam, 36; Ph.D. (chem), Utrecht, 41. Res. chemist, Nat. Sci. Orgn, Netherlands, 41-45; head corrosion res, Shell Petrol. Co, 45-47, sect. head crude distilling, 47-49, dir. res, Rubber Stichting, 49-55; mgr. polymer res. & develop. Tex-U.S. Chem. Co, 56-67; planning coord, Uniroyal Int, 67-71; MANAGING DIR, UNIROYAL PLASTICS EUROPE, 71- Polymer research and development; testing of materials; rubber technology; market development. Address: Uniroyal Plastics Europe, Humboldtstrasse 94, Frankfurt, Germany 6000.

DEDELL, THOMAS R(ICHARD), b. Utica, N.Y, July 2, 17; m. 44; c. 1. CHEMISTRY. B.S, Hamilton Col, 38; Loomis fel, Yale, Ph.D.(phys. chem), 41. Res. chemist, Imperial Paper & Color Co, N.Y, 41-43; instr. physics, Hamilton Col, 43-45; army specialized training program, N.Y. Univ, 45; DEVELOP. ENGR, EASTMAN KODAK CO, 45- Am. Chem. Soc. Electrochemistry; cells; development work on engineering problems involved in film making; ionization constant of propionic acid in dioxane-water mixtures. Address: Eastman Kodak Co, Kodak Park, Rochester, NY 14650.

DEDINAS, JONAS, b. Šakiai, Lithuania, Aug. 22, 29, U.S. citizen; m. 58; c. 1. PHYSICAL CHEMISTRY, CHEMICAL ENGINEERING. B.E, Johns Hopkins Univ, 54; M.Ch.E, Univ. Del, 58; Ph.D.(chem), Carnegie Inst. Technol, 65. Petrol. engr, Gulf Res. & Develop. Co, 56-62; sr. res. chemist, RES. LABS, EASTMAN KODAK CO, 65-70, RES, ASSOC. PHOTOCHEM, 71- Am. Chem. Soc. Petroleum refining and petrochemicals; radiation chemistry of tetramethylsilane; photochemistry of aromatic ketones; mass spectroscopy; reaction mechanisms; chemically induced dynamic nuclear polarization. Address: Eastman Kodak Co. Research Labs, 343 State St, Rochester, NY 14650.

DEDOLPH, RICHARD R, b. St. Paul, Minn, Dec. 13, 26; m. 61; c. 1. PLANT PHYSIOLOGY. B.S, Minnesota, 53, Dorr fel, 54; M.S, Maryland, 59, Ph.D. (hort), 59. Res. assoc. hort, Maryland, 58; asst. horticulturist, Hawaii, 58-60; Michigan, 60-63; res. assoc, Argonne Nat. Lab, 63-65, assoc. plant physiologist, 65-71; PLANT PHYSIOLOGIST, WEST. REGIONAL LAB, AGR. RES. SERV, U.S. DEPT. AGR, 71- Dow Chem. Co. award, 70. U.S.N, 44-46. AAAS; Am. Soc. Plant Physiol; Am. Soc. Hort. Sci; Bot. Soc. Am; Scandanavian Soc. Plant Physiol. Space biology; biophysics; biometrics. Address: U.S. Dept. of Agriculture, Agricultural Research Service, Western Regional Research Lab, Berkeley, CA 94710.

DeDOMINICIS, ALEX JOHN, b. New York, N.Y, May 13, 35; m. 70; c. 2. ORGANIC CHEMISTRY. B.S, N.Y. Univ, 56, Nat. Sci. Found. fels, 60-62, M.S, 61, Ph.D.(org. chem), 62. Res. chemist, TEXTILE FIBERS DEPT, E.I. DU PONT DE NEMOURS & CO, 62-68, RES. SUPVR, 68- Thiophene chemistry; fiber forming polymers. Address: 2638 Majestic Dr, Brandywood, Wilmington, DE 19810.

DEDRICK, DALLAS SMITH, b. Hobart, Okla, Oct. 6, 05; m. 32; c. 2. PHYSICAL & SURFACE CHEMISTRY. B.A, Oklahoma City Univ, 27; M.S, Iowa, 29, Ph.D.(phys. chem), 31. From instr. to assoc. prof. chem, N.Dak. State, 31-39; res. assoc. dairy chem, Iowa State, 39-41; asst. prof. chem, Oregon, 41-44; technologist phys. chem, res. div, Weyerhaeuser Co, 44-45, chief appl. physics, 46-52, patent liaison, 52-54, specialist phys. chem, 55-70; CONSULT, 70- Mem. nat. coun, YMCA, 58-61. Chem.C.Res, 30-40, 2nd Lt. Am. Chem. Soc; Forest Prod. Res. Soc. Surface tensions; adhesion; biomedical applications of interfacial tension depressants; wood-water relations; shrinking and swelling of wood substance. Address: 1515 22nd Ave, Longview, WA 98632.

DEDRICK, JOHN H, b. Milwaukee, Wis, July 10, 14; m. 59. METALLURGY. B.S, Wisconsin, 35; D.Sc.(metall), Mass. Inst. Tech, 48; Pa. State, 36-37. Asst. chief metallurgist, Reynolds Metals Co, 41-42; lab. mgr, S.K. Wellman Co, 42-45; asst. prof. metall, Cincinnati, 47-48; head adv. develop. sect, metall. lab, Sylvania Elec. Prods, 48-50; lab. mgr. parts div, REYNOLDS METALS CO, 50-56, tech. asst. to v.pres, 56-59, staff consult. metall. div, 59-65, dir. basic res, metall. res. div, 65-71, EXEC. ASST. TO EXEC. V.PRES. RES. & DEVELOP, 71- Am. Soc. Metals; Brit. Inst. Metals. Powder metallurgy; high temperature alloys; aluminum production and fabrication; surface treatments on aluminum and its alloys. Address: 7618 Cornwall Rd, Richmond, VA 23229.

DEDRICK, KENT GENTRY, b. Watsonville, Calif, Aug. 9, 23; m; c. 1. THEORETICAL PHYSICS. B.A, San Jose State Col, 46; M.S, Stanford, 49, Ph.D. (physics), 54. Res. asst. nuclear reactor tech, Michigan, 54-55; res. assoc. theoret. physics, W.W. Hansen Labs, Stanford, 56-59; staff mem, Stanford Linear Accelerator Center, 60-62; RES. PHYSICIST, STANFORD RES. INST, 62- U.S.N.R, 43-46, Lt.(jg). Am. Phys. Soc. Electromagnetic theory; nuclear theory; paramagnetic resonance; high energy physics; applied mathematics. Address: Stanford Research Institute, Menlo Park, CA 94025.

DEDRICK, ROBERT L(YLE), b. Madison, Wis, Jan. 12, 33; m. 55; c. 3. CHEMICAL ENGINEERING. B.E, Yale, 56; Gen. Elec. Co. fel, Univ. Mich, 56-57, M.S.E, 57; Nat. Sci. Found. sci. faculty fel, Univ. Md, 63-64, Ph.D. (chem. eng), 65. Asst. prof. mech. eng, George Wash. Univ, 59-62, eng. & appl. sci, 62-63, assoc. prof, 65-66; acting chief, CHEM. ENG. SECT, BIOMED. ENG. & INSTRUMENTATION BR, NAT. INSTS. HEALTH, 66-67, CHIEF, 67- Chem. engr, E.I. du Pont de Nemours & Co, summer 56; vis. scientist, Nat. Heart Inst, summer 65; lectr, Univ. Md. Annual award for sci. achievement in eng. sci, Wash. Acad. Sci. U.S.A.F, 57-59, 1st Lt. AAAS; Am. Soc. Eng. Educ; Am. Chem. Soc; Am. Inst. Chem. Eng; Am. Soc.

Artificial Internal Organs. Pharmacokinetics; cancer chemotherapy; thermodynamics and kinetics in living systems; biomaterials; artificial internal organs. Address: 1633 Warner Ave, McLean, VA 22101.

de DUVE, CHRISTIAN RENE, b. Thames-Ditton, Eng, Oct. 2, 17; m. 43; c. 4. BIOCHEMISTRY, CYTOLOGY. M.D, Louvain, 41, M.Sc, 46; hon. M.D, Turin, 69, Leiden, 70, Sherbrooke, 70. Lectr. BIOCHEM, LOUVAIN, 47-51, PROF, 51-; BIOCHEM. CYTOL, ROCKEFELLER UNIV, 62- Therese & Johan Anderson Stiftelse fel, Stockholm, 46-47; Rockefeller Found. fel, 47-48. Mem. faculty med, Santiago, Chile, 65; Pontifical Acad. Sci, 70. Prix Francqui, Belgium, 60; spec. award of merit, Gairdner Found, Can, 67; prix. quinquennal des science medicales, Belgian Govt, 67. Belgian Army, Lt. Am. Soc. Cell Biol; Am. Chem. Soc; Am. Soc. Biol. Chem; hon. mem. Brit. Biochem. Soc; Royal Acad. Med. Belgium(prix Pfizer, 57); corresponding mem. Royal Acad. Belgium; Belgian Biochem. Soc; French Soc. Biol. Chem; Int. Soc. Cell Biol. Carbohydrate metabolism; action of insulin and glucagon; tissue fractionation; intracellular distribution of enzymes; lysosomes; peroxisomes. Address: Dept. of Biochemical Cytology, Rockefeller University, York Ave. & 66th St, New York, NY 10021.

DEE, ARTHUR LAURENCE, b. San Francisco, Calif, May 17, 21; m. 46; c. 5. PATHOLOGY. B.A, Stanford, 43; M.D, Hopkins, 51. Pathologist & dir. path. lab, Antelope Valley Hosp, Lancaster, Calif, 56-59; pathologist, Hopkins Hosp, 59-62; Palo Alto Med. Clin, 62-65; PROF. PATH, CHMN. DEPT. & DIR. CYTOPATH, SCH. MED, UNIV. OKLA, 65- Consult, Edwards Air Force Base Hosp, Calif, 57-59; Vet. Admin. Hosp, Okla. City, 65- U.S.N.R, 42-46, Lt. Am. Soc. Cytol; Am. Med. Asn. Anatomic pathology; cytopathology. Address: Dept. of Pathology, University of Oklahoma School of Medicine, Oklahoma City, OK 73104.

DEEBEL, GEORGE FRANKLIN, b. Ringtown, Pa, Mar. 27, 11; m. 46; c. 1. ORGANIC CHEMISTRY. A.B, Maryville Col, 35; fel, Tennessee, 35-36, M.S, 36; Ph.D.(org. chem), North Carolina, 41. Instr. chem, Tennessee, 36-40; res. chemist, Monsanto Chem. Co, 41-49, group leader, 49-61, MONSANTO RES. CORP, 61-62, RES. SPECIALIST, 62- AAAS; Am. Chem. Soc. Phenol-formaldehyde reaction; sulfur chemistry; hydrocarbons; some derivatives of the isomeric nitro and aminobenzene sulfonic acids; new derivatives of butadiene and their uses; agricultural chemicals; functional fluids and lubricants; radiochemicals. Address: Monsanto Research Corp, Nicholas Rd, Dayton, OH 45407.

DEED, ELEANOR P(OLK), b. Texarkana, Tex, Aug. 11, 32; m. 56; c. 3. MEDICINE, RADIOLOGY. B.A, Henderson State Teachers Col, 52; M.D, Arkansas, 56. Intern, MED. CENTER, UNIV. ARK, LITTLE ROCK, 56-57, resident RADIOL, 57-60, instr, 60-62, asst. prof, 62-67, ASSOC. PROF, 67- Am. Col. Radiol; Radiol. Soc. N.Am. Address: Dept. of Radiology, Medical Center, University of Arkansas, 4301 W. Markham, Little Rock, AR 72201.

DEEDS, JOSEPH BIRD, b. Nashville, Tenn, June 1, 38; m. 60; c. 2. MATHEMATICS. B.S, Florida, 60; A.M, Michigan, 61, Ph.D.(math), 66. ASST. PROF. MATH, La. State Univ, 66-69; UNIV. N.C, 69- Am. Math. Soc. Functional analysis; operator theory. Address: Dept. of Mathematics, University of South Carolina, Columbia, SC 29208.

DEEDS, W(ILLIAM) EDWARD, b. Lorain, Ohio, Feb. 23, 20; m. 50; c. 4. PHYSICS. A.B, Denison, 41; fel, Calif. Inst. Tech, 42-43, M.S, 43; univ. scholar, Ohio State, 49-50, Texas Co. fel, 50-51, Ph.D.(physics), 51. Asst, Calif. Inst. Tech, 41-42, jr. physicist, 43-46; asst. prof. physics, Denison, 46-48; asst, Ohio State, 49, Texas Co. fels, 51-52; asst. prof. PHYSICS, UNIV. TENN, KNOXVILLE, 52-57, assoc. prof, 57-59, PROF, 59- Texas Co. fel, 51-52. Consult, Redstone Arsenal, 55-56; Chemstrand Corp, 56-; Oak Ridge Nat. Lab, 62- Am. Phys. Soc; Am. Asn. Physics Teachers. Theoretical physics; molecular spectroscopy; optics; acoustics. Address: Dept. of Physics, University of Tennessee, Knoxville, TN 37916.

DEEG, EMIL W(OLFGANG), b. Selb, Germany, Sept. 20, 26; m. 53; c. 4. CERAMICS, SOLID STATE PHYSICS. Diplom physics, Würzburg, 54, Dr. rer. nat.(phys. sci), 56; fel, Max Planck Inst. Silicates, 52-54. Res. asst. glass & ceramics, Max Planck Inst. Silicates, 54-59; mem. tech. staff ceramic eng, Bell Tel. Labs, Inc, Pa, 59-60; res. assoc. glass & ceramics, Jenaer Glaswerk Schott und Gen, Mainz, West Germany, 60, dir. res, 61-65; assoc. prof. physics & solid state sci, Am. Univ. Cairo, 65-67; MGR. CERAMIC RES, AM. OPTICAL CORP, SOUTHBRIDGE, 67- Mem. German Standards Cmt, 60-65; subcmts, B III & B VI, Int. Cmn. Glass, 64- German Army, 44-45. Am. Ceramic Soc; Optical Soc. Am; Ger. Phys. Soc; Ger. Soc. Glass Technol; N.Y. Acad. Sci. Glass structure; theory of ceramic manufacturing processes; physics of highly disordered solids; optical, laser and chalcogenide glasses; mechanical properties of glass and ceramics; theory of diffusion. Address: R.R. 2, Box 221, Woodstock, CT 06281.

DEEGAN, J(AMES) WAYNE, b. Peterson, Iowa, Aug. 3, 12; m. 36; c. 2. INDUSTRIAL & MANAGEMENT ENGINEERING. B.S, Iowa, 34, M.S, 35. Jr. design engr, John Deere Harvester Co, 35-36; staff asst. to chief indust. engr, Owens-Ill. Glass Co, 36-40; sr. indust. engr, Nat. Supply Co, 40-43; staff indust. engr, Armstrong Cork Co, 43-49; assoc. prof. indust. eng, UNIV. IOWA, 49-53, PROF. indust. eng. & chmn. mech. eng. dept, 53-62, indust. & mgt. eng. & chmn. dept, 62-71, INDUST. ENG, 71-, coord. placement, col. eng, 53-68, dir. mgt. course, 50-60. V.pres, Hall Eng. Co, 60-65; mem. design awards jury, Lincoln Arc Welding Found, 57, 61, 66, 70. Am. Soc. Mech. Eng; Am. Inst. Indust. Eng; Nat. Soc. Prfnl. Eng; Am. Soc. Eng. Educ. New techniques for and application of industrial engineering practice. Address: Dept. of Industrial & Management Engineering, 1202 Engineering Bldg, University of Iowa, Iowa City, IA 52240.

DEEGAN, R(OSS) A(LFRED), b. Montreal, Que, Aug. 19, 41; m. 66; c. 1. SOLID STATE PHYSICS. B.Sc, Loyola Col, Montreal, 61; B.Eng, McGill Univ, 63; Ph.D.(physics), McMaster Univ, 67. Nat. Res. Coun. Can. overseas fel, Cavendish Lab, Cambridge, 66-68; res. asst. prof. physics, Univ. Ill, Urbana, 68-71; RES. GEOPHYSICIST, GULF RES. & DEVELOP. CO, 71- Am. Phys. Soc; Can. Asn. Physicists. Solid state theory, especially band theory of transition metals. Address: Gulf Research & Development Co, P.O. Drawer 2038, Pittsburgh, PA 15230.

DEELEY, CHARLES W(ILLIAM), b. Waterbury, Conn, June 18, 31; m. 58; c. 8. PHYSICS. B.A, Wesleyan, 52; M.S, Pa. State, 54, Ph.D.(physics), 57. Asst. prof. physics, Pa. State Univ, 57-58; res. physicist, Armstrong Cork Co, 58-59; SR. RES. PHYSICIST, AM. CYANAMID CO, 59- Adj. assoc. prof, Univ. Bridgeport. Am. Asn. Physics Teachers; Soc. Plastic Eng. Mechanical properties of high polymers; rheology; polymer processing. Address: American Cyanamid Co, 1937 W. Main St, Stamford, CT 06904.

DEELY, JOHN JOSEPH, b. Cleveland, Ohio, Jan. 13, 33; m. 55; c. 5. MATHEMATICAL STATISTICS. B.E.E, Ga. Inst. Tech, 55; M.S, Purdue, 58, Ph.D. (math. statist), 65; summers, Florida, 60 & Okla. State, 62. Aeronaut. res. scientist, Nat. Adv. Cmt. Aeronaut, 55-56; asst. math, Purdue, 56-58, instr, Ft. Wayne exten, 58-60, res. asst, 60-61, instr, 61-65; mem. tech. res. staff, West. Elec-Bell Labs, Sandia Corp, 65-68; SR. LECTR, DEPT. MATH, UNIV. CANTERBURY, 68- Nat. Sci. Found. summer inst. award, 60 & 62. Consult, Naval Avionics Facility, Indianapolis, 63-64; naval contract, Purdue, summer 66. Am. Math. Soc; Inst. Math. Statist; Am. Statist. Asn. Applications of statistical decision theory to applied problems, especially multiple decision problems and empirical Bayes procedures. Address: Dept. of Mathematics, University of Canterbury, Christchurch, N.Z.

DEEM, WILLIAM BRADY, b. Parkersburg, W.Va, Mar. 23, 39; m. 63. CHEMICAL ENGINEERING. B.S, Lehigh, 61; Alumni Res. Found. fels, Wisconsin, 62-65, M.S, 62, Ph.D.(chem. eng), 65. Res. asst. chem. eng, Wisconsin, 61-65; engr, Esso Res. & Eng. Co, N.J, 65; chem. engr, Feltman Res. Labs, Picatinny Arsenal, Dover, 65-66, tech. opers. officer, Ammunition Eng. Directorate, 66-67; ENGR, ESSO RES. & ENG. CO, 67- Ord.C, U.S.A, 65-67, Capt. Am. Inst. Chem. Eng. Control of petroleum and petrochemical processes; mathematical modeling. Address: 131 Mine Brook Rd, Bernardsville, NJ 07924.

DEEMER, WALTER L(ORRAINE), b. Aquascalientes, Mex, Dec. 11, 09; m. 35; c. 2. STATISTICS. A.B, Lehigh, 35; Ed.D.(psychomet), Harvard, 42. Res. ed, Res. Corp, 38-42; chief biomet, Sch. Aviation Med, 46-47; OPERS. ANALYST, Hqs, U.S. Air Force, 49-65; U.S. ARMS CONTROL & DISARMAMENT AGENCY, 65- U.S.A.A.F, 42-46, Res, 46-; Legion of Merit. AAAS; Psychomet. Soc; Am. Math. Soc; Inst. Math. Statist; Opers. Res. Soc. Am.(Lanchester Prize, 57); Biomet. Soc; Am. Statist. Asn; Am. Psychol. Asn. Psychometrics; operations analysis. Address: 3624 Appleton St. N.W, Washington, DC 20008.

DEEMING, TERENCE JAMES, b. Birmingham, Eng, Apr. 25, 37. ASTRONOMY. B.Sc, Birmingham, 58; Ph.D.(astron), Cambridge, 61. Asst. observer, Cambridge, 61-62; vis. lectr, UNIV. TEX, AUSTIN, 62-64, asst. prof. ASTRON, 64-67, ASSOC. PROF, 67- Am. Astron. Soc; Royal Astron. Soc; Int. Astron. Union. Astronomical statistics; astrophysics. Address: Dept. of Astronomy, University of Texas, Austin, TX 78712.

DEEMS, R(OBERT) E(UGENE), b. Zanesville, Ohio, May 23, 27; m. 53; c. 2. PATHOLOGY. A.B. Marietta Col, 49; M.S, Ohio State, 51, Ph.D.(plant path), 56. PLANT PATHOLOGIST, Velsicol Corp, 51-52; AM. CYANAMID CO, 56- U.S.N, 45-46. Am. Phytopath. Soc. Plant disease control chemicals; agriculture attendent upon specialty. Address: 13 Lawnside Dr, Trenton, NJ 08638.

DEEN, HAROLD E(UGENE), b. Detroit, Mich, Aug. 7, 26; m. 48; c. 4. CHEMICAL ENGINEERING. B.S, Wayne, 48; M.S, Purdue, 51. Asst. foreman, Rinshed Mason Co, 48-50; engr, process res. div, Esso Res. & Eng. Co, 51-54, engr, Enjay Labs. Div, 54-58, group head, 58-61, sr. engr, 61-63, sect. head, 63-67, mkt. coord, 67-69, SR. ENG. ASSOC, ESSO RES. & ENG. CO, 69- U.S.A, 44-46. Am. Chem. Soc. Additives research for crank case motor oils; diesel lubricants; automatic transmission fluids. Address: 216 Oak Lane, Cranford, NJ 07016.

DEEN, ROBERT C(URBA), b. Henderson, Ky, May 26, 29; m. 52; c. 2. CIVIL ENGINEERING. B.S, Kentucky, 51, M.S, 58; Chicago, 51-52; Ph.D. (civil eng), Purdue, 64. Res. engr, Ky. Dept. Hwy, 55-58; sch. civil eng, Purdue, 58-60; sr. res. engr, KY. DEPT. HWY, 60-63, ASST. DIR, 63- Mem. Hwy. Res. Bd, Nat. Acad. Sci-Nat. Res. Coun. U.S.A.F, 51-55, Capt. Nat. Soc. Prof. Eng; Am. Soc; Civil Eng; Am. Soc. Test. & Mat. Soils and highway engineering. Address: Division of Research, Kentucky Dept. of Highways, 533 S. Limestone, Lexington, KY 40508.

DEENEY, ANNE O'CONNELL, b. Portland, Ore, Oct. 26, 26; m. 51. MICROBIOLOGY, BIOCHEMISTRY. B.S, Marylhurst Col, 48; M.S, Oregon State, 59, Ph.D.(microbiol), 63. Technologist, French Hosp, San Francisco, Calif, 49; Emanuel Hosp, Portland, Ore, 50-53; chief technologist, Good Samaritan Hosp, Corvallis, 54-61; ASST. PROF. BIOCHEM, ORE. STATE UNIV, 64- AAAS; Am. Chem. Soc; Am. Soc. Microbiol. Incidence, nutrition, biochemistry, and end-products of Micrococcus radiodurans; ribonucleic acid characterization of avian leukosis virus. Address: Dept. of Agricultural Chemistry, Oregon State University, Corvallis, OR 97331.

DEEP, IRA W(ASHINGTON), b. Dover, Tenn, July 26, 27; m. 52; c. 5. PLANT PATHOLOGY. B.A, Miami (Ohio), 50; M.S, Tennessee, 52; Ph.D.(plant path), Oregon State, 56. Instr. bot, Oregon State, 53-57, asst. prof. bot. & plant path, 57-62, assoc. prof, 62-68, asst. dean, grad. sch, 65-68; PROF. & CHMN. DEPT. PLANT PATH, OHIO STATE UNIV, 68- Staff biologist, Comn. Undergrad. Educ. Biol. Sci, Wash, D.C, 66-67. U.S.M.C.R, 45-46. AAAS; Am. Inst. Biol. Sci; Am. Phytopath. Soc. Plant diseases caused by bacteria. Address: Dept. of Plant Pathology, Ohio State University, 1735 Neil Ave, Columbus, OH 43210.

DEÉR, ANDRÁS, b. Budapest, Hungary, Jan. 5, 39; m. 62; c. 2. ORGANIC CHEMISTRY. Dipl, Swiss Fed. Inst. Tech, 61, Dr.sci.tech.(chem), 65. Res. fel. synthesis of polypeptide hormones, Syntex Res. Center, Calif, 65-66; sr. res. scientist, Squibb Inst. Med. Res, N.J, 66-67; TECH. DIR, MANN RES. LABS, 67- Am. Chem. Soc. Peptide chemistry; product development; management. Address: Mann Research Labs, 136 Liberty St, New York, NY 10006.

DEER, GEORGE WENDELL, b. Brookhaven, Miss, Nov. 2, 33; m; c. 2. MATHEMATICS & EDUCATION. B.S, Univ. South. Miss, 59, M.S, 61; Ed.D.(math. educ), Fla. State Univ. 69. Asst. prof. MATH, William Carey Col, 62-65; ASSOC. PROF, MISS. COL, 69- U.S.A.F, 54-57, Capt. Math. Asn. Am. Effects of teaching symbolic logic on students' ability to prove theorems in geometry. Address: Dept. of Mathematics, Mississippi College, Clinton, MS 39056.

DEERE, DON U(EL), b. Corning, Iowa, Mar. 17, 22; m. 44; c. 2. ENGINEERING GEOLOGY, CIVIL ENGINEERING. B.S, Iowa State Col, 43; M.S, Colorado, 49; Ph.D.(civil eng), Illinois, 55. Jr. mine engr, Phelps Dodge Corp, Ariz, 43-44; mine engr. explor. dept, Potash Co. of Am, N.Mex, 44-46; asst. prof. civil eng, Col. of A. & M, Univ. of Puerto Rico, 46-47, assoc. prof, 47-50, head of dept, 50-51; partner, Found. Eng. Co. of Puerto Rico, 51-55; assoc. prof. CIVIL ENG. & GEOL, UNIV. ILL, URBANA-CHAMPAIGN, 55-57, PROF, 57- Consult, found. eng. & eng. geol. Nat. Acad. Sci; AAAS; Geol. Soc. Am; Am. Geophys. Union; Am. Soc. Civil Eng. Stability of natural slopes; regional subsidence caused by withdrawal of groundwater, petroleum, or mined products. Address: Dept. of Civil Engineering & Geology, University of Illinois, Urbana-Champaign, Urbana, IL 61801.

DEERING, REGINALD A(TWELL), b. Brooks, Maine, Sept. 21, 32; m. 56; c. 4. BIOPHYSICS. B.S, Maine, 54; Nat. Sci. Found fel, Yale, 54-55, U.S. Pub. Health Serv. fel, 55-57, Ph.D.(biophysics), 58. Asst. prof. physics, Southern Illinois, 57-58; Fulbright res. grant, biophysics, Oslo, Norway, 58-59; res. assoc. BIOPHYSICS, Yale, 59-61; asst. prof, New Mexico Highlands, 61-63, assoc. prof, 63-64; PA. STATE UNIV, 64-69, PROF, 69- Mem. ed. bd, Biophys. Jour, 71. AAAS; Radiation Res. Soc; Biophys. Soc. Organization and function of living systems at the molecular level; radiation effects on single cell systems and their components. Address: Biophysics Dept, 606 Life Sciences Bldg, Pennsylvania State University, University Park, PA 16802.

DEERING, WILLIAM D(OUGLESS), b. Burleson, Tex, Dec. 18, 33; m. 54; c. 3. PHYSICS. B.A, Texas Christian, 56; Texas, 56-57; M.S, New Mexico State, 60, fel, 61-62, Ph.D.(physics), 63. Res. assoc. atmos. physics, Grad. Res. Center Southwest, 63-65; asst. prof. PHYSICS, N.TEX. STATE UNIV, 65-69, ASSOC. PROF, 69- Summers, nuclear engr, Gen. Dynamics/Ft. Worth, 56, physicist, New Mexico State, 59, Ling-Temco-Vought, Inc, 62. U.S.A, 57-59. Am. Phys. Soc. Statistical mechanics; plasma physics. Address: Dept. of Physics, North Texas State University, Denton, TX 76203.

DEES, BOWEN C(AUSEY), b. Batesville, Miss, July 20, 17; m. 37; c. 1. PHYSICS. A.B, Miss. Col, 37, hon. D.Sc, 63; Ph.D.(physics), N.Y. Univ, 42. Asst, N.Y. Univ, 37-42, instr. physics, 42-43; prof, Miss. Col, 43-44; staff mem, radar sch, Mass. Inst. Tech, 44-45; asst. prof. physics, Rensselaer Polytech, 45-47; physicist, sci. & tech. div, gen. hqs, Supreme Comdr. Allied Powers, Toyko, 47-50, div. chief, 50-51; prog. dir. fels, Nat. Sci. Found, 51-56, dep. asst, dir, sci. personnel & educ, 56-59, asst. dir, 59-63, assoc. dir, Planning, 63-66; v.pres, Univ. Ariz, 66-68, provost, acad. affairs, 68-70; PRES, FRANKLIN INST, 70- Mem. bd. trustees, Sci. Serv. Inc, Wash, D.C, 64-; consult, off. int. sci. activities, Nat. Sci. Found, 67-, mem. sci. info. coun, 70-; mem. bd. trustees, Argonne Univs. Asn, 69- Fel. Am. Phys. Soc; Am. Asn. Physics Teachers; Am. Soc. Eng. Educ. Electron scattering; design of special electronic timing equipment; scientific education; science policy studies. Address: Office of the President, Franklin Institute, Philadelphia, PA 19103.

DEES, SUSAN COONS, b. Hancock, Mich, May 26, 09; m. 35; c. 4. PEDIATRICS. A.B, Goucher Col, 30; M.D, Hopkins, 34; M.S, Minnesota, 38. House officer med. serv, Hopkins Hosp, 34-35, asst. dispensary physician, 38-39; asst. pediatrician, Duke Hosp, 39-48; asst. prof. pediat, SCH. MED, DUKE UNIV, 48-50, assoc. prof. PEDIAT. & ALLERGY, 50-58, PROF, 58- Asst. res, Strong Mem. Hosp, 35-36; intern, Baltimore City Hosp, 36-37. Fel. Am. Med. Asn; fel. Am. Col. Allergists; Am. Pediat. Soc; Am. Acad. Pediat; Am. Acad. Allergy. Allergy. Address: Dept. of Pediatrics, Medical Center, Duke University, Durham, NC 27710.

DEESE, DAWSON C(HARLES), b. Raleigh, N.C, Dec. 7, 32. BIOCHEMISTRY. B.S, Agr. & Tech. Col. N.C, 52; Carver Found. fel, Tuskegee Inst, 52-54, M.S, 54; Ph.D.(chem, biochem), Wisconsin, 61. Asst. gen. chem, Agr. & Tech. Col. N.C, 52; Tuskegee Inst, 53; biochem, Univ. Wis, Madison, 55-60, res. assoc. biochem. & vet. sci, 60-64, instr, 64-68, ASSOC. PROF. NUTRIT. SCI. & CHMN. DEPT, UNIV. WIS-GREEN BAY, 69- AAAS; Am. Chem. Soc; Am. Inst. Biol. Sci; N.Y. Acad. Sci. Digestive enzymes in the ruminant animal and ruminal metabolism of plant macromolecules; pectolytic enzymes in fungal disease and disease resistance of plants; auxin metabolism and plant growth substances; nutritional sciences. Address: College of Human Biology, University of Wisconsin-Green Bay, 120 S. University Circle Dr, Green Bay, WI 54305.

DEETER, CHARLES R(AYMOND), b. Norcatur, Kans, Dec. 30, 30; m. 57; c. 2. MATHEMATICS. B.S, Ft. Hays Kans. State Col, 52, M.S, 56; Ph.D.(discrete harmonic kernels), Kansas, 63. Asst. prof. MATH, TEX. CHRISTIAN UNIV, 60-65, assoc. prof, 65-70, PROF, 70- Summer, engr, Boeing Airplane Co, 57. U.S.A, 52-54, Res, 54-60, Sgt. AAAS; Math. Asn. Am; Am. Math. Soc; Soc. Indust. & Appl. Math. Finite difference methods for partial differential equations and analytic function theory. Address: Dept. of Mathematics, Texas Christian University, Ft. Worth, TX 76129.

DEETS, GARY L(EE), b. Sunbury, Pa, Feb. 28, 43; m. 61; c. 3. ORGANIC & POLYMER CHEMISTRY. B.S, Bloomsburgh State Col, 65; NASA fel, Univ. Pittsburgh, 67-69, Ph.D.(org. chem), 69. SR. RES. CHEMIST, MONSANTO CO, 69- Am. Chem. Soc. Mechanistic studies in pyridine N-oxide chemistry; fundamental and exploratory studies of the flame retardancy of styrene based polymeric systems. Address: 165 Woodland Rd, Springfield, MA 01129.

DEEVER, DAVID LIVINGSTONE, b. Dayton, Ohio, Aug. 31, 39; m. 61; c. 2. PURE MATHEMATICS. B.A. & B.S, Otterbein Col, 61; Ph.D.(math), Ohio State, 66. Asst. prof. MATH, Westmar Col, 66-71; ASSOC. PROF. & CHMN. DEPT, OTTERBEIN COL, 71- Nat. Guard, 57-65, S/Sgt. Math. Asn. Am; Am. Math. Soc. Set theory and transfinite arithmetic. Address: Dept. of Mathematics, Otterbein College, Westerville, OH 43081.

DEEVER, WILLIAM RAY, b. Parkersburg, W.Va, Sept. 30, 33; m. 64; c. 1. INORGANIC CHEMISTRY. B.S, Marietta Col, 61; Ph.D.(boron chem), Washington (Seattle), 68. SR. CHEMIST, RICHMOND RES. LABS, TEXACO, INC, 68- Lectr, eve. sch, Va. Commonwealth Univ, 68-69. U.S.A.F, 52-56, S/Sgt. Am. Chem. Soc. Preparation and characterization of boron hydride compounds; preparation and evaluation of complex compounds as homogenous catalysis. Address: Texaco Inc, Box 3407, Richmond, VA 23234.

DEEVEY, EDWARD S(MITH), JR, b. Albany, N.Y, Dec. 3, 14; m. 38; c. 3. BIOLOGY. B.A, Yale, 34, Ph.D.(zool), 38. Sterling fel. BIOL, Yale, 38-39; instr, Rice Inst, 39-43; res. assoc, Oceanog. Inst. Woods Hole, 43-46; asst. prof. biol, Yale, 46-51, assoc. prof, 51-57, prof, 57-68, dir. geochronomet. lab, 51-62; Killam res. prof, Dalhousie Univ, 68-71; GRAD. RES. PROF. FLA. STATE MUS, 71- Guggenheim fel, 53-54; Fulbright res. award, Denmark, 53-54; Nat. Sci. Found. sr. fel, New Zealand, 64-65. Ed, Radiocarbon, 58-71; mem, Bermuda Biol. Sta; prog. dir. environ. biol, Nat. Sci. Found, 67-68; mem. Fish Res. Bd. Can, 69-71; Can. Comn. Int. Biol. Prog, 69-71. Fel. AAAS; Am. Soc. Limnol. & Oceanog.(v.pres, 50); Ecol. Soc. Am.(ed. jour, 50-58; pres, 69-70); Am. Anthrop. Asn; Am. Soc. Nat; Soc. Am. Archaeol; fel. Geol. Soc. Am. Limnology; ecology; general and Pleistocene ecology. Address: Florida State Museum, Gainesville, FL 32601.

DEEVEY, GEORGIANA BAXTER, b. Pine Orchard, Conn, Feb. 24, 14; m. 38; c. 3. ZOOLOGY. A.B, Radcliffe Col, 34; Ph.D.(zool), Yale, 39. Technician, Oceanog. Inst. Woods Hole, 45-46; res. asst, Bingham Oceanog. Lab, Yale, 47-60, res. assoc, 60-67; Bermuda Biol. Sta, 67-71; res. assoc, inst. oceanog, Dalhousie, 68-71; ADJ. CURATOR, FLA. STATE MUS, 71- Marine Biol. Asn. U.K. Marine and freshwater zooplankton; invertebrate zoology and ecology. Address: Florida State Museum, Gainesville, FL 32601.

DEEX, OLIVER D, b. Cleveland, Ohio, July 13, 27; m. 52; c. 3. POLYMER & ORGANIC CHEMISTRY. B.S, Yale, 50; Ph.D.(org. chem), Harvard, 54. Chemist, CENT. RES. DEPT, MONSANTO CO, 53-59, GROUP LEADER, 59- U.S.A, 45-47. Am. Chem. Soc. Synthesis of vinyl polymers and copolymers. Address: 412 Oakley Dr, St. Louis, MO 63105.

DeFACIO, W(ILLIAM) BRIAN, b. Palestine, Tex, Dec. 14, 36; m. 64; c. 2. THEORETICAL HIGH ENERGY PHYSICS. B.S, Tex. A&M Univ, 63, fel. & M.S, 65, Ph.D.(physics), 67. Asst. prof. PHYSICS, UNIV. MO-COLUMBIA, 67-71, ASSOC. PROF, 71- U.S.A, 56-59. Am. Phys. Soc; Math. Asn. Am. Address: Dept. of Physics, University of Missouri-Columbia, Columbia, MO 65201.

DeFANTI, DAVID R, b. Wakefield, R.I, Nov. 12, 32; m. 58; c. 2. PHARMACOLOGY. A.B, Colgate, 55; M.S, Rhode Island, 57, Ph.D.(pharmacol), 62. ASST. PROF. PHARMACOL, UNIV. R.I, 61- Co-prin. investr, Nat. Insts. Health grant, 62-64; prin. investr, Rhode Island Heart Asn. grant, 64- Consult, R.I. State Labs, Sci. Criminal Invest, 63-70, asst. dir, 70-; dir. breath tests alcohol training, State of R.I, 70-; prin. investr, Law Enforcement Assistance Admin. grant, 70- U.S.A.R, 57-63. AAAS; Am. Heart Asn. Cardiovascular pharmacology; medico-legal toxicology. Address: College of Pharmacy, University of Rhode Island, Kingston, RI 02881.

DeFELICE, DOMENIC, b. Boston, Mass, Oct. 3, 14; m. 39; c. 3. FOOD TECHNOLOGY. B.S, Mass. State Col, 36, Mass, 38, Ph.D.(food technol), 40. Jr. chemist, bur. agr. chem. & eng, U.S. Dept. Agr, N.Y, 38-40; res. fel, Frosted Foods Sales Corp, New York, 40-42, field rep. prod. qual. control, 42-43; sect. head Birds Eye-Snider Labs. Div, Gen. Foods Corp, 43-50, staff technologist, res. & develop, 50-51, lab. dir, cent. labs, 51-53, res. mgr, assoc. prod. div, 53-59; assoc. dir, packaging & prod. develop, res. center, Gen. Foods Corp, 59-64, dir. sci. develop, Tech. Center, 64-68; V.PRES. RES. & DEVELOP, BEECH-NUT, INC, 68- Civilian with Qm.C, 44. Am. Chem. Soc; Inst. Food Tech; N.Y. Acad. Sci. Preservation of frozen and canned foods; effects of processing on carotenoid content of peaches. Address: Research & Development, Beech-Nut, Inc, 460 Park Ave, New York, NY 10022.

DeFELICE, EUGENE ANTHONY, b. Beacon, N.Y, Dec. 24, 27; m. 51; c. 2. INTERNAL MEDICINE. B.S, Columbia, 51; Ciba fel, Boston, 54-56, M.D, 56; Hahneman Med. Col, 62; Temple, 63; Rutgers, 65. Ciba fel. & lectr. pharmacol, sch. med, Boston, 56-57; assoc. prof. biol. sci, New Eng. Col. Pharm, 56-57, prof, 57-58; res. assoc. anesthesiol, Boston City Hosp, 57; intern, Newton-Wellesley Hosp, 57-58; private practice internal med, N.Miami, Fla, 58-61; asst. dir. clin. res, Warner-Lambert Res. Inst, N.J, 61-64; dir. clin. pharmacol, Bristol Labs, N.Y, 64-66; dir. clin. res, Norwich Hosp, Conn, 66-67; dir. clin. pharmacol, Sandoz Pharmaceut, 67-68, exec. dir. clin. res, 69, DIR. SCI. AFFAIRS & COMMERCIAL DEVELOP, SANDOZ-WANDER, INC, 70- Consult, Strasenburgh Labs, N.Y, 66-67. U.S.A, 46-47. AAAS; Am. Soc. Clin. Pharmacol. & Therapeut; Acad. Psychosom. Med; Am. Geriat. Soc; Am. Med. Asn; Am. Fedn. Clin. Res; N.Y. Acad. Sci. Pharmacology; Clinical pharmacology; clinical research; psychosomatic medicine; psychiatry. Address: 11 Corn Hill Dr, Morristown, NJ 07960.

DEFENDI, VITTORIO, b. Treviglio, Italy, Nov. 16, 28; m. 55; c. 3. PATHOLOGY. M.D, Univ. Pavia, Italy, 51. Instr. path. dept, Univ. Pavia, Italy, 51-52; Brit. coun. scholar, post-grad. med. sch, London, 52-53; Fulbright fel, med. sch, Vermont, 53-54; res. fel, Detroit Inst. Cancer Res, 54-56; pathologist virus sect, Lederle Labs, N.Y, 56-58; assoc. PATH, MED. SCH, UNIV. PA, 58-64, assoc. prof, 64-68, WISTAR PROF, 68-; MEM. STAFF, WISTAR INST, 64-, assoc. mem, 58-64. Leukemia Soc. scholar, 62-66; faculty res. award, Am. Cancer Soc, 68-72. Am. Soc. Cell Biol; Am. Soc. Exp. Path; Histochem. Soc; Am. Asn. Immunol; Am. Asn. Cancer Res. Viral oncology; tumor biology; mechanism of immunological defense; histochemistry. Address: The Wistar Institute, 36 & Spruce Sts, Philadelphia, PA 19104.

DeFEO, JOHN J(OSEPH), b. Southington, Conn, Mar. 14, 22; m. 55; c. 8. PHARMACOLOGY. B.S, Connecticut, 51; M.S, Purdue, 53, Ph.D.(pharmacol), 54. Instr, PHARMACOL, Pittsburgh, 54-55, asst. prof, 55-57; assoc. prof. COL. PHARM, UNIV. R.I, 57-64, PROF, 64- U.S.N.A.F, 43-46, Ens. AAAS; Am. Soc. Pharmacol; Soc. Toxicol; Am. Pharmaceut. Asn; N.Y. Acad. Sci. Cardio-vascular area. Address: Dept. of Pharmacology, College of Pharmacy, University of Rhode Island, Kingston, RI 02883.

DEFEO, RICHARD J(OSEPH), b. Kansas City, Mo, June 10, 32; m. 53; c. 2. ORGANIC CHEMISTRY. B.S, Missouri, 53, Lubrizol fel, 56-58, Ph.D.(org. chem), 58. Chemist, Shell Oil Co, 53; res. chemist, Esso Standard Oil Co, 58-61; Spencer Chem. Co, 61-63; Esso Standard Oil Co, 63-69; PROCESS SUPVR, ENJAY CHEM. CO, 69- U.S.A, 53-55. Am. Chem. Soc. Long range research on fuels and petrochemical processes. Address: Enjay Chemical Co, P.O. Box 241, Baton Rouge, LA 70821.

DE FEO, VINCENT J(OSEPH), b. New York, N.Y, Oct. 1, 25; m. 52; c. 2. ENDOCRINOLOGY, REPRODUCTIVE BIOLOGY. B.S, Juniata Col, 49; M.S, Rutgers, 51; fel, Ohio State, 52-54, Ph.D.(physiol), 54. Asst. zool, Rutgers, 50; physiol, Ohio State, 50-52, asst. prof, 54-55; Nat. Insts. Health fel. embryol, Carnegie Inst, Wash, D.C, 55-57; asst. prof. anat, col. med, Univ. Ill, 57-63; SCH. MED, Vanderbilt Univ, 63-64, assoc. prof. anat, obstet. & gynec, 64-66; ANAT. & REPRODUCTIVE BIOL, UNIV. HAWAII, 66-68, PROF, 68-, chmn. dept, 69. Mem. bd. dirs. nat. sex forum, Glide Found. U.S.A, 44-46. AAAS; Am. Asn. Anat; Endocrine Soc; Soc. Develop. Biol; Brit. Soc. Study Fertil; Soc. Study Reproduction. Anatomy and physiology of reproduction; ovum-uterine relationship; neuroendocrinology. Address: Dept. of Anatomy & Reproductive Biology, University of Hawaii School of Medicine, 1960 East-West Rd, Honolulu, HI 96822.

DEFFEYES, KENNETH S(TOVER), b. Oklahoma City, Okla, Dec. 26, 31; m. 62; c. 1. OCEANOGRAPHY. Geol.E, Colo. Sch. Mines, 53; M.S, Princeton, 56, Kennecott & Nat. Sci. Found. fels. & Ph.D.(geol), 59. Geologist, Shell Develop. Co, Tex, 58-63; asst. prof, Minnesota, 63-64; ASSOC. PROF. oceanog, Ore. State Univ, 65-67; GEOL. & GEOPHYS. SCIS, PRINCETON, 67- C.Eng, U.S.A, 53-55. Mineral. Soc. Am; Am. Asn. Petrol. Geol. Chemical oceanography; sedimentation. Address: Dept. of Geology, Princeton University, Princeton, NJ 08540.

de FIEBRE, CONRAD W(ILLIAM), b. Brooklyn, N.Y, Jan. 19, 24; m. 46; c. 6. MICROBIOLOGY, BIOCHEMISTRY. B.S, Rensselaer Polytech, 49; M.S, Wisconsin, 50, Ph.D.(bact), 52. Asst. bact, Wisconsin, 49-52; res. microbiologist, E.I. du Pont de Nemours & Co, Inc, 52-61; res. dir, Wilson Labs. Div, Wilson Pharmaceutical & Chem. Corp, 61-67, v.pres, res, 67-69; dir. RES. & DEVELOP, ROSS LABS. DIV, ABBOTT LABS, 69-71, V.PRES, 71- C.Eng, U.S.A, 43-46. Am. Soc. Microbiol; Am. Chem. Soc; fel. Am. Inst. Chem. Bacteriology; fermentation; enzymes; natural products; pharmaceutical development. Address: Research & Development, Ross Labs. Division, Abbott Labs, 625 Cleveland Ave, Columbus, OH 43216.

DeFIGIO, DANIEL A, b. Republic, Pa, June 4, 39; m. 66; c. 2. MYCOLOGY. B.S, California State Col.(Pa), 61; M.A, W.Va. Univ, 64; Ph.D.(mycol), Ill. State Univ, 70. Teacher, high sch, Pa, 61-64; instr. BIOL, Wash. & Jefferson Col, 64-66; teaching asst, Ill. State Univ, 66-70; ASSOC. PROF, EDINBORO STATE COL, 70- U.S.A, 57-65, Sgt. AAAS; Am. Inst. Biol. Sci; Bot. Soc. Am. Taxonomic analysis of the genus Hymenochaete. Address: Apt. 4-C, Box 768, Edinboro, PA 16412.

DE FIGUEIREDO, MARIO P, b. Goa, Port. India, Mar. 16, 35. FOOD SCIENCE & TECHNOLOGY. S.B, Mass. Inst. Tech, 55, S.M, 58, Gulbenkian Found. fel, 60-62, Ph.D.(food sci. & tech), 62. Mgr. anal. serv, qual. control & lab, Kitchens of Sara Lee, Ill, 62-67, qual. control. mgr, 67-71; V.PRES, RES. & DEVELOP, HOLLYWOOD BRANDS, 71- Am. Chem. Soc; Inst. Food Technol; Am. Asn. Cereal Chem; fel. Brit. Inst. Food Sci. & Technol; fel. Am. Pub. Health Asn; fel. Am. Inst. Chem; N.Y. Acad. Sci. Food research; flavor testing; microbiology; quality assurance. Address: Hollywood Brands, 836 S. Chestnut, Centralia, IL 62801.

DE FIGUEIREDO, RUI JOSÉ PACHECO, b. Pangim, Goa, India, Apr. 19, 29; m. 61; c. 4. APPLIED MATHEMATICS. S.B, Mass. Inst. Tech, 50, S.M, 52; Portuguese Overseas Res. Cmn. fel, Harvard, 55-58, Ph.D.(appl. math), 59. Develop. engr, Transistor Prod. Inc, Mass, 52-54; sci. adv, Portuguese Atomic Energy Cmn, 56-59; head appl. physics div, Lab. Nuclear Physics & Eng, Portugal, 59-62; assoc. prof. ELEC. ENG, Purdue, 62-64; vis. assoc. prof, Illinois, Urbana, 64-65; assoc. prof, RICE UNIV, 65-67, PROF, 67- Summer consult, Int. Atomic Energy Agency Vienna, 60; Portuguese Atomic Energy Comn. rep, group experts, Europ. Nuclear Energy Agency, 59-62. AAAS; Soc. Indust. & Appl. Math; Inst. Elec. & Electronics Eng. Control and communication systems; network, probability and approximation theories. Address: Dept. of Mathematical Sciences, Rice University, Houston, TX 77001.

DE FILIPPI, R(ICHARD) P(AUL), b. New York, N.Y, Mar. 26, 36; m. 58; c. 1. CHEMICAL ENGINEERING. A.B, Amherst Col, 57; Am. Cyanamid Co. fel, Mass. Inst. Tech, 58-59, S.M, 59, Union Carbide Corp. fel, 59-60, Sc.D. (chem. eng), 62. Org. chemist, Am. Cyanamid Co, 56, chem. engr, 57-58; Arthur D. Little Co, Inc, 59; res. engr. hydrogen processing petrol. ref, Calif. Res. Corp, 62-65; supvr. membrane separations sect, ABCOR, INC, 65-66, prog. mgr, 66-68, prog. dir, 68-70, V.PRES. & GEN. MGR. RES. & DEVELOP. DIV, 70- AAAS; Am. Inst. Chem. Eng; Am. Soc. Artificial Internal Organs; N.Y. Acad. Sci. Biomedical engineering; membrane technology; mass transfer; biomaterials. Address: Research & Development Division, Abcor, Inc, 345 Vassar St, Cambridge, MA 02139.

DEFOLIART, GENE R(AY), b. Stillwater, Okla. June 23, 25; m. 50; c. 3. MEDICAL & VETERINARY ENTOMOLOGY. B.S, Okla. State, 48; Ph.D. (entomol), Cornell, 51. Asst. prof. ENTOMOL, Wyoming, 51-56, assoc. prof, 56-59; RUSSELL LABS, UNIV. WIS, MADISON, 59-66, PROF, 66-, CHMN. DEPT, 68- U.S.N, 43-45. Entom. Soc. Am; Am. Mosquito Control Asn; Am. Soc. Trop. Med. & Hyg. Medical and veterinary entomology. Address: Dept. of Entomology, 237 Russell Labs, 1630 Linden Dr, University of Wisconsin, Madison, WI 53706.

DeFORD, DONALD D(ALE), b. Alton, Kans, Dec. 28, 18; m. 42; c. 2. ANALYTICAL CHEMISTRY. A.B, Kansas, 40, Ph.D.(chem), 48. Instr. CHEM, NORTHWESTERN UNIV, 48-50, asst. prof, 50-54, assoc. prof, 54-60, PROF, 60-, ASST. V.PRES. RES, 71-, chmn. dept. chem, 62-69, asst. to provost, 69-70, assoc. dean of faculties, 70-71. C.W.S, 41-46, U.S.A.R, 46-61, Col. AAAS; Instrument Soc. Am; Am. Chem. Soc. Analytical instrumentation; gas chromatography. Address: Dept. of Chemistry, Northwestern University, Evanston, IL 60201.

DeFORD, JOHN W, b. Lincoln, Nebr, Mar. 12, 36; m. 58; c. 3. SOLID STATE PHYSICS. B.A, Carleton Col, 57; M.S, Illinois, 59, Ph.D.(physics), 62. Asst. prof. PHYSICS, UNIV. UTAH, 62-67, ASSOC. PROF, 67- Am. Phys. Soc. Radiation damage in metals. Address: Dept. of Physics, University of Utah, Salt Lake City, UT 84112.

DeFORD, RONALD K(INNISON), b. San Diego, Calif, Jan. 22, 02; m. 37. GEOLOGY. E.M, Colo. Sch. Mines, 21, fel, 21-22, M.S, 22. From instr. to asst. prof. eng, 31-33; geologist, Midwest Ref. Co, Tex, 23-33; from geologist to chief geologist, Argo Oil Corp, 33-48; PROF. GEOL, UNIV. TEX, AUSTIN, 48-, DEPT. GRAD. ADV, 49- Instr, Colo. Sch. Mines, 22-24. Mem, Am. Cmn. Stratig. Nomenclature, 52-58, 64-, chmn, 54-56; Int. Comn. Stratig, 55-56; postdoctoral fel. cmt, div. earth sci, Nat. Res. Coun, 55-58. Mem. Int. Geol. Cong, USSR, 37, Algiers, 52, Mex, 56. AAAS; hon. mem. Am. Asn. Petrol. Geol; fel. Geol. Soc. Am; Am. Geophys. Union; Am. Inst. Mining, Metall. & Petrol. Eng; Geol. Soc. France. Surface and subsurface structure; stratigraphy; rock colors; petroleum geology; geology of Trans-Pecos Texas and northern Mexico. Address: University of Texas at Austin, Box 7609, Austin, TX 78712.

DEFORE, JESSE JACKSON, b. Macon, Ga, July 23, 26; m. 58; c. 3. PHYSICS. A.B, Mercer, 47; Cornell, 47-48; Emory, 51; Ga. Inst. Tech, 62-63; fel, Fla. State, 64-66, Ph.D, 66. Instr. chem. & physics, Mercer, 48-49; South. Tech. Inst, Ga. Inst. Tech, 49-50, asst. prof, 50-52, assoc. prof, 52-66, head dept, 50-66; dean, technol. & skills, Lake Mich. Col, 66-67; V.PRES, SEATTLE COMMUNITY COL, 67- Educ. consult, Assoc. Consult. Educ. Mem. Atomic Energy Cmn-Am. Soc. Eng. Ed. Inst. Tech. Inst. Instr, summer 58; participant, Am. Soc. Eng. Ed-Eng. Speaking Union Tech. Teachers Exchange, 61. U.S.A, 43-46. Am. Asn. Physics Teachers; Am. Soc. Eng. Educ. Engineering technology; educational administration. Address: Seattle Community College, 1718 Broadway, Seattle, WA 98122.

DEFOREST, ADAMADIA, b. Harrisburg, Pa, July 16, 33; m. 57. VIROLOGY. A.B, Hood Col, 55; M.S, Washington State, 57; Ph.D, Temple Univ, 68. Asst, Washington State, 55-57, sr. lab. technician, dept. vet. microbiol, 57-60; res. asst. & instr. MICROBIOL, SCH. MED, TEMPLE UNIV, 61-70, ASST. PROF, 70-, PEDIAT. VIROL, ST. CHRISTOPHER'S HOSP. FOR CHILDREN, 70-, instr, 67-70. Am. Soc. Microbiol; N.Y. Acad. Sci; Tissue Cult. Asn. Virus immunology and non-specific resistance to virus infections; inactivation of viruses by germicides. Address: Dept. of Pediatrics, St. Christophers' Hospital for Children, 2600 N. Lawrence St, Philadelphia, PA 19133.

DEFOREST, ELBERT M, b. Natoma, Kans, July 17, 17; m. 42; c. 2. PETROLEUM ENGINEERING. B.S, Univ. Tulsa, 40. Jr. petrol. engr, Gulf Oil Corp, 40-41; chemist, E.I. du Pont de Nemours & Co, 41-42, develop. process engr, 42-46; sr. process engr, Spencer Chem. Co, 46-47, mgr. process eng, 47-49; sr. proj. engr, Pan Am. Petrol. Corp, Standard Oil Co. Ind, 49-50, supt. chem. mfg, 50-52; mgr. new proj, Frontier Chem. Co. Div, VULCAN MAT. CO, 52-59, mgr. RES. & DEVELOP, 59-67, V.PRES, A&M DIV, OHIO, 67-, CHEM. DIV, KANS, 67-, METALLICS DIV, N.J, 67- AAAS; Am. Inst. Chem. Eng; Am. Chem. Soc; Am. Inst. Mining, Metall. & Petrol. Eng; Forest Prod. Res. Soc. Distillation technology and fluid mechanics; hydrocarbon chlorination technology; chemical plant design. Address: Research & Development, Chemicals Divisions, Vulcan Materials Co, Box 545, Wichita, KS 67201.

DE FOREST, PETER RUPERT, b. Los Angeles, Calif, Aug. 24, 41; m. 66. FORENSIC SCIENCE, CRIMINALISTICS. B.S, Univ. Calif, Berkeley, 64, fel, 67, D.Crim, 69. ASST. PROF. CRIMINALISTICS, JOHN JAY COL, CITY UNIV. NEW YORK, 69- Am. Acad. Forensic.Sci; Am. Soc. Test. & Mat. Instrumental methods for the chemical individualization of physical evidence. Address: Dept. of Criminalistics, John Jay College, City University of New York, 360 Park Ave. S, New York, NY 10010.

DE FOREST, RALPH E(DWIN), b. Detroit, Mich, Mar. 19, 19; m. 50; c. 4. MEDICINE. B.S, Wayne, 41, M.D, 43; M.S, Minnesota, 51. Fel. orthop. surg, Mayo Found, Minnesota, 44-46, phys. med. & rehab, 48-51; dir. dept. med. physics & rehab, AM. MED. ASN, 50-66, dir. postgrad. progs, 66-70, DIR. DEPT. MED. INSTRUMENTATION, 70- Instr, med. sch, Northwestern, 51. Secy. comt. rehab, Am. Med. Asn, 56, comt. nuclear med, 62-66, coun. sci. assembly, 66-70; chmn. President's Task Force on Physically Handicapped, 69-70. Med.C, 46-48, Capt. AAAS; Biophys. Soc; Am. Acad. Phys. Med. & Rehab; Am. Cong. Rehab. Med. Internal derangements of the knee; effects of physical agents on lymph flow; effects of ultrasound on bone. Address: 535 N. Dearborn, Chicago, IL 60610.

DE FRANCE, JOSEPH J, b. N.Y.C, Aug. 22, 09; m. 35; c. 2. ELECTRICITY, ELECTRONICS. B.S, City Col. New York, 30, E.E, 31; N.Y. Univ. 39-42. Lab. engr, City Col. New York, 31-39; instr, high school, N.Y, 39-43; prof. radio, electronics, Signal Corps Training Sch, 42-43; chief engr, int. div, Trans World Airline, 46-47; dept. head electronic tech, N.Y. COMMUNITY COL, 47-64, PROF. ELECTRONICS, 64- Consult, Cleveland Inst. Electronics, Ohio, 62-; mem. adv. bd, N.Y. Inst. Tech, 64- U.S.C.G, 43-46, Comdr, (ret). Am. Soc. Eng. Educ; Am. Tech. Educ. Asn; Inst. Elec. & Electronics Eng. Electronics communications; technical textbooks and pamphlets. Address: Dept. of Electronics, New York City Community College, 300 Pearl St, Brooklyn, NY 11201.

DeFRANCE, SMITH J, b. Battle Creek, Mich, Jan. 19, 96; m. 22. AERONAUTICAL ENGINEERING. B.S, Michigan, hon. D.Eng, 53; hon. LL.D, California, 52. Aeronaut. engr, aeronaut. lab, Nat. Adv. Cmt. Aeronaut, Langley Field, Va, 22-40; dir. Ames Aeronaut. Lab, Moffett Field, 40-58, Ames Res. Ctr, NASA, 58-65; AEROSPACE CONSULT, 65- Silver Star medal; medal for Merit; Nat. Civil Serv. League, Career Serv. award. U.S. Army, 17-19. U.S.A, 17-19, Maj. AAAS; fel. Am. Inst. Aeronaut. & Astronaut. Aerodynamics; astronautics; design of wind tunnels; flow over and loads in airships; transonic and supersonic flows; flight research. Address: 12220 Fairway Dr, Los Altos, CA 94022.

DeFRATE, LOUIS A, b. Jamestown, N.Dak, July 10, 17; m. 45; c. 2. MECHANICAL ENGINEERING. B.S, Mont. State Col, 41; M.S, Mass. Inst. Tech, 42, Sc.D.(mech. eng), 50. Engr, Nat. Adv. Cmt. Aeronaut, Moffett Field, Calif, 45-46; res. assoc, Mass. Inst. Tech, 46-50; engr, ENG. DEPT, E.I. DU PONT DE NEMOURS & CO, INC, 50-56, consult, 56-63, sr. consult, 63-71, PRIN. CONSULT, 71- U.S.N.R, 44-46, Lt.(jg). Am. Soc. Mech. Eng. Fluid flow; thermodynamics. Address: Engineering Dept, E.I. du Pont de Nemours & Co, Inc, Louviers Bldg, Wilmington, DE 19898.

de FREITAS, ANTHONY S, b. British Guiana, May 2, 30; Can. citizen; m. 57; c. 2. BIOCHEMISTRY, PHYSIOLOGY. B.Sc, McGill, 55, M.Sc, 57; Ph.D. (biochem), Minnesota, 62. Fel, BIOSCI, NAT. RES. COUN. CAN, 62-63, res. OFF, 63-67, ASSOC. RES. OFF, 67- AAAS; Am. Oil Chemists' Soc; Can. Biochem. Soc. Intermediary metabolism of lipids and carbohydrates as influenced by environmental factors. Address: Division of Biosciences, National Research Council, Ottawa, Ont, Can.

de FREMERY, DONALD, b. Oakland, Calif, Dec. 25, 27; m. 50; c. 2. BIOCHEMISTRY. A.B, California, 50, Ph.D.(biochem), 54. CHEMIST, med. center, California, 54-55; WEST. MKT. & NUTRIT. RES. DIV, AGR. RES. SERV, U.S. DEPT. AGR, 55- Res. award, Inst. Am. Poultry Industs, 65. U.S.A, 46-47. AAAS; Am. Chem. Soc; Inst. Food Tech. Isolation of food-grade protein from green leafy crops. Address: Western Marketing and Nutrition Research Division, Agricultural Research Service, U.S. Dept. of Agriculture, 800 Buchanan St, Albany, CA 94710.

DeFRIES, JOHN C(LARENCE), b. Delrey, Ill, Nov. 26, 34; m. 56; c. 2. GENETICS. B.S, Illinois, 56, M.S, 58, Ph.D.(genetics), 61. Asst. prof. genetics in dairy sci, Illinois, 61-63; U.S. Pub. Health Serv. res. fel. genetics, California, Berkeley, 63-64; asst. prof. genetics in dairy sci, Univ. Ill, Urbana, 64-66; assoc. prof. BEHAV. GENETICS, UNIV. COLO, BOULDER, 67-70, PROF, 70-, faculty fel, spring 71. Vis. lectr, NATO Adv. Studies Inst. Psychogenetics, Univ. Birmingham, 69; vis. prof, Univ. Hawaii, spring 71; ed, Behavior Genetics. Qm.C, 57; Chem.C.Res, 57-, 1st Lt. AAAS; Genetics Soc. Am; Am. Genetic Asn; Animal Behav. Soc. Behavioral genetics. Address: Institute for Behavioral Genetics, University of Colorado, Boulder, CO 80302.

DEGA, ROBERT LEWIS, b. Detroit, Mich, June 1, 18; m. 44; c. 2. MECHANICAL ENGINEERING. B.M.E, Gen. Motors Inst, Mich, 48. Res. engr, res. labs, GEN. MOTORS CORP, 41-52, sr. engr, electromotive div, 52-55, sr. res. engr, RES. LABS, 55-57, SUPVRY. RES. ENGR, 57- U.S.N, 42-46, Lt. Soc. Automotive Eng; Am. Soc. Test. & Mat; Am. Soc. Lubrication Eng. Static and dynamic sealing devices for fluids and gases; first U.S. application of hydrodynamic sealing principals to elastomeric shaft seals. Address: Mechanical Research Dept, General Motors Research Labs, 12 Mile & Mound Rds, Warren, MI 48090.

DEGANI, MEIR H(ERSHTENKORN), b. Warsaw, Poland, Jan. 4, 09; nat. 44; m. 48; c. 2. METEOROLOGY, PHYSICS. B.S, Mass. Inst. Tech, 32, M.S, 41, Sc.D.(phys. meteorol), 42; Haifa Inst. Tech, 37-39. Asst. meteorol, Mass. Inst. Tech, 41; instr. geophysics, Pa. State Col, 42, asst. prof, 42-43; chief instr. meteorol, Am. Export Airlines, Inc, 43-44; asst. prof. physics, STATE UNIV. N.Y. MARITIME COL, 46-47, CHMN. SCI. DEPT, 47- U.S.N, 44-45. AAAS; Am. Phys. Soc; Am. Meteorol. Soc; Am. Geophys. Union; Am. Asn. Physics Teachers. Long wave radiation emitted by atmosphere; atmospheric heat balance. Address: Dept. of Science, State University of New York, Maritime College, Ft. Schuyler, New York, NY 10465.

DeGARMO, E. PAUL, b. Lucerne, Mo, Jan. 29, 07; m. 34; c. 2. INDUSTRIAL ENGINEERING. B.S, Washington (Seattle), 30; M.S, Calif. Inst. Tech, 37. Indust. engr, Converse Co, Inc, Wash, 30-31; Firestone Tire & Rubber Co, Calif, 34-37; from instr. to PROF. INDUST. & MECH. ENG, COL. ENG, UNIV. CALIF, BERKELEY, 37- Am. Soc. Mech. Eng; Am. Inst. Indust. Eng; Am. Welding Soc.(Lincoln Gold Medal, 48); Am. Soc. Metals; Am. Soc. Eng. Educ; Nat. Soc. Prof. Eng. Manufacturing processes; engineering economy. Address: 299 Grizzly Peak Blvd, Berkeley, CA 94708.

DeGARMO, P(AUL) OLIVER, b. Wray, Colo, May 17, 16; m. 37; c. 4. ORGANIC CHEMISTRY. A.B, Nebr. Wesleyan, 38; M.A, Nebraska, 39, Ph.D. (chem), 41. Res. chemist, MONSANTO CO, 41-52, asst. dir. res, ORGAN. CHEM. DIV, 52-64, MGR. RES, 64- AAAS; Am. Chem. Soc. Organic synthesis; process development in laboratory, pilot plant and plant; food ingredients; microbiologically active chemicals; research management. Address: Monsanto Co, Organic Chemicals Division, 1700 S. Second St, St. Louis, MO 63177.

DeGEISO, R(ICHARD) C(HARLES), b. Newark, N.J, Oct. 19, 31; m. 53; c. 2. ANALYTICAL CHEMISTRY. B.S, Rutgers, 53; Ph.D.(chem), Mass. Inst. Tech, 57. Asst, Mass. Inst. Tech, 53-54, 54-57; res. chemist, E.I. DU PONT DE NEMOURS & CO, INC, 57-65, ANAL. SUPVR, 65- Am. Chem. Soc. General analytical chemistry; electrochemistry; chemical separations. Address: 777 Cherry Tree Rd, Apt. C-39, Chester, PA 19014.

DEGEN, VLADIMIR, b. Prague, Czech, Apr. 24, 31; Can. citizen; m. 61; c. 3. AERONOMY, ASTROPHYSICS. B.A, Toronto, 58, M.A, 60; Ph.D.(physics), Western Ontario, 66. Lectr. elem. physics, Ont. Agr. Col, 60-61; Royal Mil. Col, 61-63; Western Ontario, 63-64; fel, York (Ont), 66-67; NASA fel, lab. atmospheric & space physics, Univ. Colo, Boulder, 67-70; ASST. PROF. PHYSICS, UNIV. ALASKA, 70- Can. Asn. Physicists. Laboratory spectroscopy of aeronomically important molecules, particularly as applied to earth's night airglow emission. Address: Dept. of Physics, University of Alaska, College, AK 99701.

DEGENER, CURTIS DON, b. Markesan, Wis, Dec. 13, 30; m. 60; c. 1. FOOD TECHNOLOGY, BACTERIOLOGY. B.S, Wisconsin, 52, M.S, 58, Ph.D. (dairy & food sci), 60. Assoc, sterile milk concentrate res. proj, Univ. Wisconsin, 54-56, res. asst. dry milk, grad. sch, 56-60; mgr. prod. & process develop, gen. food prods, Kroger Co, 60-68; asst. dir. res. & develop, Universal Foods Corp, 68-71; OPERS. MGR, L.N. RENAULT, 71- U.S.A, 52-54, Res, 54-60, 1st Lt. Inst. Food Technol; Am. Dairy Sci. Asn. Development of fresh and sterile concentrated milk products; flavor stability of dry whole milk; administration in product and process development of general food products; research and product development in food and related products. Address: L.N. Renault, Norfolk Ave, Egg Harbor City, NJ 08215.

DEGENER, ISA IRMGARD, b. Berlin, Germany, Apr. 27, 24; m. 53. BOTANY. Freiburg, 44; Dr. rer. nat, Berlin, 49. Bot. asst, Bot. Mus, Berlin-Dahlem, Germany, 45-46, lectr. & lab. asst. to Drs. R. Pilger & H. Sleumer, 48-49, bot, 49-53; asst. pharmacog. to Drs. H. Sleumer & E. Werdermann, Free Univ. Berlin, 49-53; RES. & WRITING, 49- Nat. Sci. Found. res. grants for bot. explor. & pub. German Bot. Soc. Flora of Hawaiian Islands. Address: 68-617 Crozier Dr, Waialua, Oahu, HI 96791.

DEGENER, OTTO, b. East Orange, N.J, May 13, 99; m. 53. BOTANY. B.S, Mass. Col, 22; M.S, Hawaii, 23. D.Sc, Massachusetts, 52. Asst. bot, Mass. Col, 24-25; instr, Hawaii, 25-27; private res, 27-35; COLLAB. HAWAIIAN BOT, N.Y. BOT. GARDEN, 35- Naturalist, Hawaii Nat. Park, 29; Nat. Sci. Found. grants; consult, Fed. Aviation Agency; Civil Aeronaut. Admin. Botanist, Archbold Cheng-Ho sci. exped, Fiji, 40-41. Linne medal, Royal Swedish Acad. Sci. AAAS; Torrey Bot. Club. Taxonomy of Hawaiian vascular plants; flora of Hawaii; Degeneriaceae, a new family of flowering plants from Fiji Islands. Address: 68-617 Crozier Dr, Waialua, Oahu, HI 96791.

DEGENFORD, JAMES EDWARD, b. Bloomington, Ill, June 11, 38; m. 59; c. 6. ELECTRICAL ENGINEERING. B.S. & Sloan Found. fel, Illinois, 60, M.S. & Ford Found. fel, 61, Ph.D.(elec. eng), 64. Res. asst. elec. eng, Univ. Ill, Urbana-Champaign, 60-64, res. assoc, 64-65; sr. engr, appl. physics sect, WESTINGHOUSE ELEC. CORP, 65-69, FEL. ENGR, MICROWAVE PHYSICS GROUP, 69- Inst. Elec. & Electronics Eng. Investigation of transmission systems and detection techniques suitable for use at submillimeter wavelengths; microwave integrated circuits. Address: Westinghouse Electric Corp, Advanced Technology Lab, P.O. Box 1521, M.S. 3422, Baltimore, MD 21203.

DEGENHARDT, WILLIAM G(EORGE), b. Queens Co, N.Y, Apr. 16, 26; m. 58. VERTEBRATE ZOOLOGY. A.B, Syracuse, 50; fel, Northeastern, 51-53, M.S, 53; Ph.D.(zool), Texas A&M, 60. Asst, Agr. & Mech. Col, Texas, 53-54, instr. BIOL, 54-60; asst. prof, UNIV. N.MEX, 60-67, ASSOC. PROF, 67-67-; CURATOR REPTILES & AMPHIBIANS, MUS. SOUTHWEST. BIOL, 61- Collab, Nat. Park Serv, 55-59, 64-, ranger-naturalist, 60. U.S.N.R, 44-46. AAAS; Am. Soc. Ichthyol. & Herpet; Ecol. Soc. Am; Am. Soc. Mammal; Soc. Syst. Zool; Soc. Study Amphibians & Reptiles; Brit. Herpet. Soc; Soc. Study Evolution. Herpetology; vertebrate ecology. Address: Dept. of Biology, University of New Mexico, Albuquerque, NM 87106.

DE GENNARO, LOUIS D, b. N.Y.C, June 1, 24; m. 49; c. 5. ZOOLOGY. B.S, Fordham, 48; M.S, Boston Col, 50; Ph.D, Syracuse, 59. Asst, Boston Col, 48-49; instr. ZOOL, LE MOYNE COL, 49-53, asst. prof, 53-60, assoc. prof, 60-62, PROF, 62- U.S.A.A.F, 43-46. Am. Soc. Zool; Aerospace Med. Asn; Soc. Develop. Biol; N.Y. Acad. Sci. Experimental embryology; cellular physiology; tissue and organ culture. Address: Dept. of Biology, Le Moyne College, Syracuse, NY 13214.

DEGER, THOMAS EDWARD, b. Dayton, Ohio, Sept. 4, 11; m; c. 6. ORGANIC CHEMISTRY. B.S.Ch.E, Univ. Dayton, 33. Res. chemist, Sharples Solvents Corp, 33-42; group leader, Sharples Chems, Inc, 42-44, asst. res. dir, 44-52; admin. asst. dir, org. res, PENNSALT CHEMS. CORP, 52-55, asst. dir, 55-56, dir, 56-63, MGR. ADMIN, INFO. & SERV, 63- Am. Chem. Soc. Aliphatic organic synthesis, process development; amines; mercaptans; rubber chemicals. Address: 22 Whitpain Dr, Broad Axe Village, Ambler, PA 19002.

DEGERING, CHARLES, b. Seattle, Wash, Feb. 7, 19; m. 46; c. 1. DENTISTRY. B.A, Walla Walla Col, 42; D.D.S, Washington (Seattle), 50. Lab. asst. chem, Walla Walla Col, 39-41; instr. dent, Univ. Wash, 50-55, asst. prof, 55-63, assoc. prof, 63-70, consult, univ. hosp, 60-66; STAFF DENTIST, PORTERVILLE STATE HOSP, 70- U.S.N, 41-42. AAAS; Am. Dent. Asn; Am. Acad. Dent. Radiol; Int. Asn. Dent. Res. Clinical and radiographical evaluation of human alveolar bone morphology. Address: Porterville State Hospital, Porterville, CA 93257.

DEGGINGER, EDWARD R, b. Chicago, Ill, Oct. 12, 26; m. 49; c. 1. ORGANIC CHEMISTRY. B.S, Illinois, 49; M.S, Wisconsin, 51, Ph.D.(chem), 52. Res. supvr, Solvay Process Div, ALLIED CHEM. CORP, 52-67, from tech. assoc. to RES. GROUP LEADER, 67- U.S.N, 45-46. Am. Chem. Soc. Urethanes, pesticides and flame retardants. Address: Allied Chemical Corp, Bldg. M-2, Morristown, NJ 07960.

DEGHENGHI, R(OMANO), b. Rome, Italy, June 27, 30; m. 57; c. 2. ORGANIC & PHARMACEUTICAL CHEMISTRY. Milan, 48-51; Ph.D.(chem), Trieste, 53. Res. chemist, Purfina, Italy, 55; Recordati, 56-57; Western Ontario, 57-58; asst. prof. chem, Laval, 58-60; sr. res. chemist, AYERST LABS, 60-64, assoc. dir. chem. res, 64-69, V.PRES. & DIR. RES, 69- Am. Chem. Soc; Can. Inst. Chem. Address: Ayerst Labs, P.O. Box 6115, Montreal, Que, Can.

DeGIOVANNI-DONNELLY, ROSALIE F, b. Brooklyn, N.Y, Nov. 22, 26; m. 61; c. 2. MICROBIAL GENETICS, BIOCHEMISTRY. B.A, Brooklyn, 47, M.A, 53; Ph.D.(zool), Columbia, 61. Mem. staff, allergy lab, Univ. Hosp, Bellevue Med. Ctr, New York, 47-51; technician, sch. pub. health, Columbia, 52-54, asst. microbial genetics & biochem. of nucleic acids, col. physicians & surgeons, 54-62; sr. scientist, Bionetics Res. Labs, Inc, Va, 62-67; asst. prof. lectr. MICROBIOL, MED. CTR, GEORGE WASH. UNIV, 68-71, ASST. RES. PROF, 71-; RES. BIOLOGIST, GENETIC TOXICITY BR, BUR. SCI, FOOD & DRUG ADMIN, 68- Food & Drug Admin. award of merit. AAAS;

Am. Soc. Microbiol; N.Y. Acad. Sci. Microbial genetics; biochemistry of DNA; mechanisms of mutation. Address: Dept. of Microbiology, George Washington University Medical Center, 1339 H St, Washington, DC 20005.

De GIUSTI, DOMINIC L(AWRENCE), b. Treviso, Italy, March 31, 11, nat; m. 38; c. 3. PARASITOLOGY. B.S, St. Thomas Col. (Minn), 36; M.S, Michigan, 38; Ph.D.(zool), Wisconsin, 42; Army Med. Sch, 44. Instr. biol, Col. of St. Thomas, 36-38, asst. prof, 42-43, 46-47; teaching asst, biol. sta, Michigan, 40-41; asst. prof. prev. med, col. med, N.Y. Univ, 43-45; res. assoc. pharmacol, Minnesota, 47; asst. prof. biol, Catholic Univ, 47-49; assoc. prof, WAYNE STATE UNIV, 49-58, PROF. PARASITOL, LIB. ARTS COL. & PROF. PARASITOL. & MICROBIOL, COL. MED, 59-, CHMN. DEPT. BIOL, LAB. PARASITOL, 67- Markle Found. fel, Cent. Am; lectr, med. sch, Georgetown, 47-48; Fulbright fel, Stazione Zoologica, Naples, 52-53. Consult, Office Surgeon-Gen, 48-49; Office Sci. Res. & Develop; U.S. Pub. Health Serv, 48. Am. Soc. Parasitol; Am. Micros. Soc; Am. Zool. Soc; Am. Soc. Trop. Med. & Hyg; Soc. Protozool; N.Y. Acad. Sci. Life cycles of acanthocephala; histology and cytology of trematodes; biological studies on experimental schistosomiasis; blood protozoa of cold blooded vertebrates; life cycles of gregarines. Address: Lab. of Parasitology, Wayne State University, Detroit, MI 48202.

DE GOES, LOUIS L(ELANE), b. Honolulu, Hawaii, June 23, 16; m. 44; c. 3. ENGINEERING GEOLOGY. Geol.E, Colo. Sch. Mines, 41; M.S, Stanford, 50. Aerial navigator, U.S. Air Force, 41-44, chief navigator, Pac. Div, mil. air transport serv, 45-48, assoc. prof, U.S. Air Force Inst. Technol, 50-53, res. studies inst, Air Univ, 54-56, dir. terrestrial sci. lab, Air Force Cambridge Res. Labs, 57-61, dep. technol. & subsysts, foreign technol. div, Air Force Systs. Command, 62-66; EXEC. SECY, COMT. POLAR RES, NAT. ACAD. SCI, 67- Mem, Southeast Asia geog. exped, 55-56; panels earth physics, oceanog. & polar res, U.S. Dept. Defense, 57-61, arctic adv. comt, 70; proj. scientist, Fletcher's Ice Island res. prog, Int. Geophys. Year, 57-58. Sports Illustrated Silver Anniversary ALL-Am. award, 65. U.S.A.F, 41-67, Col; Accolade award, 61. Fel. Geol. Soc. Am; Am. Geophys. Union; Arctic Inst. N.Am; Glaciol. Soc. Site selection and construction in permafrost; polar geomorphology; applied glaciology; polar logistics. Address: 4727 38th St. N, Arlington, VA 22207.

DE GOES, PAULO, b. Rio de Janiero, Brazil, July 14, 13; m. 46; c. 4. MICROBIOLOGY, IMMUNOLOGY. M.D, Brazil, 36. Res. assoc. MICROBIOL, med. sch, UNIV. BRAZIL, 31-36, asst, 36-39; prof, nursery sch, 39-44, assoc. prof, MED. SCH, 44-54, PROF, 54-, PHARM. SCH, 46-, DIR. INST. MICROBIOL, 55- AAAS; Am. Acad. Microbiol; Am. Asn. Immunol; N.Y. Acad. Sci; Royal Soc. Trop. Med. & Hyg; French Soc. Microbiol; Argentine Acad. Med. Medical virology. Address: Av. Pasteur 250-Urca-Rio de Janeiro, G. B, Brazil.

DeGOWIN, ELMER L(OUIS), b. Cheboygan, Mich, Sept. 27, 01; m; c. 1. CLINICAL MEDICINE. A.B, Michigan, 23, M.D, 28. Instr. INTERNAL MED, Michigan, 30-32; UNIV. IOWA, 32-35, assoc, 35-40, res. assoc, 40-41, res. asst. prof, 41-45, assoc. prof, 45-50, prof, 50-68, EMER. PROF, 68- Mem. subcmt. blood substitutes, Nat. Res. Coun, 40-46, cmt. blood & blood derivatives, 48-50. Am. Med. Asn; Am. Soc. Clin. Invest; Soc. Exp. Biol. & Med. Am. Col. Physicians; Asn. Am. Physicians. Renal physiology; dynamics of circulation; blood transfusion; mechanism of hemolysis in disease; thyroid disease. Address: University Hospitals, University of Iowa, Iowa City, IA 52241.

DeGOWIN, RICHARD LOUIS, b. Iowa City, Iowa, May 14, 34; m. 57; c. 2. INTERNAL MEDICINE. Michigan, 52-55; M.D, Chicago, 59. Nat. Heart Inst. fel, 62-63; res. asst. internal med, Chicago, 63-64, res. assoc, 64-65, asst. prof, 65-68; ASSOC. PROF. INTERNAL MED, HOSP, UNIV. IOWA, 68-, RADIOBIOL, RADIATION RES. LAB, COL. MED, 68-; ATTENDING PHYSICIAN: VET. ADMIN. HOSP, 69- U.S. Pub. Health Serv. career develop. award, 68-69. Proj. supvr. hemat, Argonne Cancer Res. Hosp, 65-68. Med.C, U.S.A.R, 63-65, Capt. Soc. Exp. Biol. & Med; Am. Fedn. Clin. Res; Am. Soc. Hemat; Radiation Res. Soc. Am. Soc. Exp. Path. Hematology and radiobiology; hemopoietic stem cell kinetics; erythropoietin and erythropoiesis; postirradiation recovery of hemopoiesis; pathogenesis of leukemia; drug-induced hemolysis; malaria. Address: Dept. of Medicine, University of Iowa Hospitals, Iowa City, IA 52240.

DE GRAAF, ADRIAAN M, b. Naaldwijk, Netherlands, Aug. 4, 35; m. 64; c. 2. SOLID STATE PHYSICS. Ph.D.(physics), Swiss Fed. Inst. Technol, 62. Vis. prof. PHYSICS, Univ. São Paulo, 62-64; Ford Found. grant, 64-65 & vis. prof, Brazilian Centre Physics Res, 64-65; sr. res. scientist, sci. lab, Ford Motor Co, 65-68; ASSOC. PROF, WAYNE STATE UNIV, 68- Am. Phys. Soc. Theoretical solid state physics; electronic properties of metals and insulators. Address: Dept. of Physics, Wayne State University, Detroit, MI 48202.

DeGRAAF, DONALD E(ARL), b. Grand Rapids, Mich, June 17, 26; m. 48; c. 3. PHYSICS. Ph.D.(physics), Univ. Mich, 57. Instr. PHYSICS, UNIV. MICH, FLINT, 56-57, asst. prof, 57-61, assoc. prof, 61-67, PROF, 67- U.S.N, 53-55, Res, 55-, Lt. AAAS; Am. Sci. Affiliation; Am. Phys. Soc; Am. Asn. Physics Teachers. Physics education and curriculum design; helical physics; biophysics; molecular structure; infrared spectroscopy. Address: Dept. of Physics, University of Michigan-Flint, Flint, MI 48503.

DeGRAFF, ARTHUR C(HRISTIAN), b. Paterson, N.J, Dec. 3, 99; m. 26; c. 3. MEDICINE. B.S, N.Y. Univ, 20, M.D, 21. Instr. med, col. med, N.Y. Univ, 23-24; Crile fel. & lectr. physiol, Western Reserve, 24-25; instr, SCH. MED, N.Y. UNIV, 25-27, med, 27-30, asst. prof. THERAPEUT, 30-32, Samuel A. Brown prof, 32-70, PROF, 70- From intern to res. physician, Bellevue Hosp, 21-24, adj. asst. vis. physician, 27-30, asst. vis. physician, 30-32, assoc. vis. physician, 32-36, vis. physician, 36-, chmn. comt. drugs & formulary; res, Univ. Col, London, 32; sr. consult. cardiol, Bronx Vet. Hosp, 46-; atten. physician med. serv, univ. hosp, N.Y. Univ. Med. Center; dir. med, Jewish Mem. Hosp. Mem. revision comt, U.S. Pharmacopoeia, 40-, pres, U.S. Pharmacopoeial Conv, Inc, chmn. scope comt. Am. Med. Asn; Soc. Exp. Biol. & Med; fel. Am. Col. Physicians; Am. Therapeut. Soc. (v.pres, 48); Am. Soc. Pharmacol. & Exp. Therapeut; Am. Soc. Clin. Invest; Am. Heart Asn; Am. Physiol. Soc; Am. Psychosom. Soc; Biomet. Soc; Am. Fedn. Clin. Res; fel. N.Y. Acad. Med. Therapeutics; physiology of the heart and circulation; diseases of the heart. Address: Dept. of Therapeutics, New York University School of Medicine, 550 First Ave, New York, NY 10016.

DeGRAFF, BENJAMIN ANTHONY, b. Columbus, Ohio, Dec. 23, 38; m. 60; c. 2. CHEMICAL KINETICS. B.A, Ohio Wesleyan, 60; M.S, Ohio State, 63, Ph.D.(phys. chem), 65. Fel, Harvard, 65-67; ASST. PROF. PHYS. CHEM, UNIV. VA, 67- Am. Chem. Soc; Am. Phys. Soc; Faraday Soc. Kinetics of fast reactions; energy transfer processes; photochemistry. Address: Dept. of Chemistry, University of Virginia, Charlottesville, VA 22901.

DE GRANDPRE, JEAN LOUIS, b. Montreal, Que, Can, May 25, 29; m. 55; c. 3. SYSTEMS ANALYSIS. B.A, Montreal, 48, B.Sc, 52, M.Sc, 54. Engr, spec. weapons dept, Canadair Ltd, 54-55; coordinator systs, 55-57; Sparrow II simulation, missile div, Douglas Aircraft Co, Inc, 57-59; flight simulation, spec. weapons div, Canadair Ltd, 59-60; eng. systs. coordinator & chief programmer, Sperry Gyroscope Can, Ltd, 60-61; comput. & simulation coordinator, missile aero/thermodyn. sect, Douglas Aircraft Co, Inc, 61-62, asst. supvr. flight mech. & re-entry systs. anal, 62, sect. chief adv. prog. develop. & comput. coordination, missile & space systs. div, 63-64, br. mgr. methodology, 64-65; MEM. TECH. STAFF, GEN. RES. CORP, 65- Inst. Elec. & Electronics Eng; Am. Inst. Aeronaut. & Astronaut; Asn. Comput. Mach; Can. Asn. Physicists; Simulation Coun. Systems simulation and analysis; numerical analysis; programming; flight mechanics; operation analysis; counter-insurgency analysis; filtering. Address: General Research Corp, P.O. Box 3587, Santa Barbara, CA 93105.

DeGRASSE, ROBERT W(OODMAN), b. Yakima, Wash, July 4, 29; m. 52; c. 4. ELECTRONICS, DATA PROCESSING. B.S, Calif. Inst. Technol, 51; M.S, Stanford, 54, Ph.D.(elec. eng), 58. Res. engr. guided missile develop, jet propulsion lab, Calif. Inst. Technol, 51-53; asst, electronics res. lab, Stanford, 53-55, res. assoc. microwave tube res, 55-57; mem. tech. staff, Bell Tel. Labs, 57-60; dir. res. & develop, Microwave Electronics Corp, 60-64; v.pres, Quantum Sci. Corp, 64-69; V.PRES. & TECH. DIR, QUANTOR CORP, 69- Inst. Elec. & Electronics Eng. Microfilm and electronic data processing information systems; input-output theory data base for technology forecasting; satellite communications microwave masers, memories, solid state devices and tubes. Address: Quantor Corp, 19000 Homestead Rd, Cupertino, CA 95014.

DEGRAW, JOSEPH IRVING, JR, b. Wash, D.C, May 26, 33; m. 57; c. 2. ORGANIC CHEMISTRY. B.S, California, Berkeley, 56; Ph.D.(org. chem), Stanford, 61. ORG. CHEMIST, Merck & Co, N.J, 56-57; CANCER CHEMOTHER. & MED. CHEM, STANFORD RES. INST, 57- U.S.N.A.F.R, 50-60. Am. Chem. Soc. Urinary steroids; brain amino acids; terpenes of Simaruba glauca; folic acid antagonists; components of white snakeroot, indole alkylating agents; indole compounds; tryptamines, pyrimidines, pteridines, analgesics, histamine releasers and piperidines; synthesis of alkaloids; antileprotic drugs. Address: Stanford Research Institute, Menlo Park, CA 94025.

DeGRAY, RICHARD J(OHN), b. Harrisburg, Pa, March 30, 07; m; c. 1. PHYSICAL CHEMISTRY. Ch.E, Lehigh, 27, Ullmann fel. & M.S, 28; Ph.D. (chem), Columbia, 40. Instr. chem, Lehigh 28-35; asst. supvr, Socony-Vacuum Oil Co, 35-41; plant supt, McGean Chem. Co, 45-51; sr. res. assoc, Standard Oil Co, 51-65, supvr. fuels res, 65-70; RETIRED. Chem.C, 44-46, Lt. Col. AAAS; Am. Chem. Soc; Biomet. Soc; Am. Statist. Asn; fel. Am. Inst. Chem; sr. mem. Am. Soc. Qual. Control. Physical chemistry; statistical design of experiments; petroleum technology. Address: 934 Stuart Dr, South Euclid, OH 44121.

DE GRAY, RONALD WILLOUGHBY, b. Hartford, Conn, Feb. 10, 38. MATHEMATICS. B.A, Univ. Conn, 60, M.A, 62; Ph.D.(math), Syracuse Univ, 69. ASST. PROF. MATH, UTICA COL, 69- AAAS; Am. Math. Soc; Math. Asn. Am. Probability. Address: Dept. of Mathematics, Utica College, Utica, NY 13502.

DEGROAT, WILLIAM C(HESNEY), JR, b. Trenton, N.J, May 18, 38; m. 59; c. 2. PHARMACOLOGY. B.Sc, Phila. Col. Pharm, 60, Nat. Sci. Found. fel. & M.Sc, 62; Ph.D.(pharmacol), Pennsylvania, 65. Lab. instr, Phila. Col. Pharm, 60-62; U.S. Pub. Health Serv. fel. pharmacol, sch. med, Pennsylvania, 65-66; hon. fel. physiol, John Curtin Sch. Med. Res, Australian Nat. Univ, 66-68; ASST. PROF. PHARMACOL, SCH. MED, UNIV. PITTSBURGH, 68- Chemist, Vet. Admin. Hosp, Phila, Pa, 61-62; Nat. Sci. Found. fel, 66; Riker Int. pharmacol. fel, 66-67. AAAS; Am. Soc. Pharmacol. & Exp. Therapeut; Soc. Neurosci. Central autonomic mechanisms; nervous control of the urinary bladder and large bowel; physiology and pharmacology of transmission in peripheral autonomic ganglia. Address: Dept. of Pharmacology, School of Medicine, University of Pittsburgh, 1289 Scaife Hall, Pittsburgh, PA 15213.

DeGROFF, HAROLD M(ILLER), JR, b. Toledo, Ohio, May 10, 20; m. 47; c. 5. AERONAUTICAL ENGINEERING. B.Aero.Eng, Rensselaer Polytech, 46; M.S, Calif. Inst. Tech, 47, Aero Eng, 48, Ph.D.(aero. eng), 49. Engr, Fairchild Airplane Co, Oak Ridge, Tenn, 49-51; assoc. prof. aero. eng, Purdue, 51-54, prof. & acting head sch. aeronaut. eng, 54-55, head, 55-63; PRES, MIDWEST APPL. SCI. CORP, 63-, dir, 56-63. Consult, Globe Am. Co, 52-56; Allison Div. Gen. Motors Corp, 52-; Ross Gear & Tool Co, 53-; Chamberlain Corp, 53-55; Inst. Defense Anal, 66- U.S.N.R, 42-46. Aerodynamics; servomechanisms; aircraft stability and control. Address: Midwest Applied Science Corp, 1205 Kent Ave, West Lafayette, IN 47906.

DE GROOT, JACK, b. Bandoeng, Java, Apr. 24, 21; nat; m. 49; c. 3. ANATOMY, ENDOCRINOLOGY. B.M, Amsterdam, 47, Drs, 48, Ph.D.(neuroanat), 52. Instr. histol, Leiden, 49-51; res. assoc, Brain Res. Inst, Holland, 51-53; anat, California, Los Angeles, 55-56; asst. prof. gross anat. & neuroanat, Utrecht, 56-57; physiol, col. med, Baylor, 57-59; ANAT, UNIV. CALIF, SAN FRANCISCO, 59-62, assoc. prof, 62-69, PROF, 69- Res. fel, Netherlands Govt. Inst. Pure Sci. Res, 50-52; U.S. Pub. Health Serv. sr. res. fel, 59-64, career develop. award, 64. AAAS; Endocrine Soc; Am. Asn. Anat;

Am. Physiol. Soc; Soc. Exp. Biol. & Med. Anatomical and functional inter-relationships between endocrine system, hypothalamus and rhinencephalon. Address: Dept. of Anatomy, University of California San Francisco Medical Center, San Francisco, CA 94122.

DeGROOT, LESLIE JACOB, b. Ft. Edward, N.Y, Sept. 20, 28; m; c. 5. EN-DOCRINOLOGY. B.S, Union Col.(N.Y), 48; M.D, Columbia, 52. Intern & asst. res. med, Presby. Hosp. New York, 52-54; clin. fel, Nat. Cancer Inst, 54-55, pub. health physician, U.S. Oper. Mission, Afghanistan, 55-56; clin. & res. fel. med, Mass. Gen. Hosp, 56, resident, 57-58; asst, Harvard Med. Sch, 58-59, instr, 59-62, assoc, 62-66; assoc. prof. exp. med, Mass. Inst. Technol, 66-68, assoc. dir. dept. nutrit. & food sci, Clin. Res. Ctr, 66-68; PROF. ENDOCRINOL, THYROID STUDY UNIT, PRITZKER SCH. MED, UNIV. CHICAGO, 68- Clin. & res. fel. med, Mass. Gen. Hosp, 58-60, asst, 60-64, asst. physician, 64-66. Consult, Cambridge City Hosp, Mass. & U.S. Naval Hosp, Chelsea. Am. Thyroid Asn; Endocrine Soc; Am. Soc. Clin. Invest; Am. Fedn. Clin. Res. Address: Thyroid Study Unit, Pritzker School of Medicine, University of Chicago, 950 E. 59th St, Chicago, IL 60637.

DeGROOT, MORRIS H(ERMAN), b. Scranton, Pa, June 8, 31; m. 52; c. 2. MATHEMATICAL STATISTICS. B.S, Roosevelt, 52; M.S, Chicago, Ph.D. (statist), 58. Asst. prof. math, CARNEGIE-MELLON UNIV, 57-63, assoc. prof. math. & indust. admin, 63-66, PROF. MATH. STATIST. & HEAD DEPT, 66- Fel. Am. Inst. Math. Statist; Am. Math. Soc; fel. Am. Statist. Asn. Mathematical statistics and probability. Address: Dept. of Statistics, Carnegie-Mellon University, Pittsburgh, PA 15213.

DeGROOT, RODNEY C(HARLES), b. Racine, Wis, Dec. 24, 34; m. 54; c. 3. PLANT PATHOLOGY, MYCOLOGY. B.S, Wisconsin, 58, Alumni Res. Found. fel, 58-60, M.S, 60; Nat. Sci. Found. fels, State Univ. N.Y. Col. Forestry, 60-61, summer 62, Ph.D.(forest path), 63. Instr. bot, Syracuse, 62-63; sr. scientist bot, N.Y. State Mus. & Sci. Serv, 63-68; PRIN. PA-THOLOGIST, FOREST & WOOD PROD. DISEASE LAB, U.S. FORREST SERV, 68- U.S.A, 54-56. Mycol. Soc. Am; Am. Phytopath. Soc. Forest pathology; wood decay. Address: Forest & Wood Products Disease Lab, U.S. Forest Service, P.O. Box 2008, Evergreen Station, Gulfport, MS 39501.

DE GUZMAN, JOSE P, b. Lingayen, P.I, Feb. 10, 32; U.S. citizen; m. 50; c. 1. CHEMICAL ENGINEERING. B.S.Ch.E, Santo Tomas, 53; Fulbright scholar. & univ. fel, Purdue, 55-56, M.S.Ch.E, 58; M.B.A, Univ. Chicago, 67. Chem. engr, Nat. Power Corp, P.I, 53-55; asst. chem. eng, Purdue, 56-57; plant engr, Westinghouse Elec. Corp, Pa, 57-60; res. chem. engr, spunbonded prod. tech. div, E.I. du Pont de Nemours & Co, Tenn, 60-68; PROJ. MGR, VISTRON CORP, 68- Am. Inst. Chem. Eng; Am. Chem. Soc. Market research and development; economic and financial analysis; capital budgeting; management science; technological feasibility studies; market and financial planning; corporate long-range planning. Address: 3428 Rumson Rd, Forest Hills, Cleveland Heights, OH 44118.

DE HAAN, FRANK P, b. Paterson, N.J, Nov. 1, 34; m. 58; c. 4. PHYSICAL & INORGANIC CHEMISTRY. A.B, Calvin Col, 57; Nat. Sci. Found. fel, Purdue, 59-61, Ph.D.(chem), 61. Asst. prof. CHEM, OCCIDENTAL COL, 61-67, ASSOC. PROF, 67-, CHMN. DEPT, 70- Nat. Sci. Found. sci. faculty fel, 68-69. Am. Chem. Soc. Mechanisms of Friedel-Crafts and related reactions. Address: Dept. of Chemistry, Occidental College, Los Angeles, CA 90041.

DE HAAN, HENRY J(OHN), b. East St. Louis, Ill, Nov. 23, 20; m. 43. PHYS-IOLOGICAL PSYCHOLOGY. A.B, Washington (St. Louis), 42, A.M, 49; Ph.D. (psychol), Pittsburgh, 60. Chemist, Scullin Steel Co, 42-44, Mallinckrodt Chem. Co, 46-47; asst. psychol, Illinois, 51-54; Pittsburgh, 55-60, trainee physiol. psychol, Coatesville Vet. Admin. Hosp, 60-62; res. scientist, human resources res. off, George Washington, 62-64; RES. PSYCHOLOGIST, Armed Forces Radiobiol. Res. Inst, Nat. Naval Med. Ctr, 65-69; Dep. Chief of Staff Personnel, DEPT. ARMY, 69-70, BEHAV. & SYSTS. RES. LAB, 70- Mem. faculty, U.S. Dept. Agr. Grad. Sch, 67- U.S.N, 44-46. AAAS; Am. Psychol. Asn; Animal Behav. Soc; Int. Primatol. Soc; N.Y. Acad. Sci; Soc. Neurosci. Psychology; neuroscience, physiology. Address: 5403 Yorkshire St, Springfield, VA 22151.

DE HAAN, JAMES R(EGINALD), b. Kansas City, Mo, May 21, 21; m. 47; c. 2. PHYSICAL CHEMISTRY. B.S, Col. of William & Mary, 46; Ph.D.(phys. chem), Cornell, 49. Assoc. prof. chem. Texas West. Col, 49-56; lead engr, Beech Aircraft Corp, 56-60; res. specialist, Cryogenic Eng. Co, 60-68; RES. DIR, SHURTENDA STEAKS INC, 68- U.S.A, 43-46. Cryogenics; process engineering. Address: Shurtenda Steaks Inc, 2462 W. Second Ave, Denver, CO 80223.

DeHAAN, ROBERT L(AWRENCE), b. Chicago, Ill, Nov. 18, 30; m. 57; c. 2. BIOLOGY, EMBRYOLOGY. B.A, California, Los Angeles , 52, Ph.D.(zool), 56; M.A, California, Los Angeles, Amsterdam, 54. Jr. res. physiologist, California, Los Angeles, 54-56; RES. EMBRYOLOGIST, CARNEGIE INST, 56- Instr, Woods Hole Marine Biol. Lab, 62-64, 65; assoc. prof, dept. biol, Hopkins, 64-71, prof, 71-; Health, Educ. & Welfare-Nat. Insts. Health biol. study sect, 70- AAAS; Am. Soc. Cell Biol; Biophys. Soc; Soc. Develop. Biol; Tissue Cult. Asn. Formation of the heart; cell migration and morphogenetic movements; cell surface phenomena and intercellular adhesion; differentiation and physiology of cardiac pacemakers; heart cell culture. Address: Dept. of Embryology, Carnegie Institution of Washington, 115 W. University Pkwy, Baltimore, MD 21210.

DE HAAS, HERMAN, b. Northbridge, Mass, Jan. 6, 24; m. 51; c. 4. BIO-LOGICAL CHEMISTRY. B.S, Westminster Col.(Pa), 47; M.S, Michigan, 50, fel, 52-54, Ph.D.(biol. chem), 55. Asst, Michigan, 47-52, res. assoc. biochem, 54-55; asst. prof. chem, Westminster Col, 55-57, assoc. prof, 57-59; asst. prof. BIOCHEM, UNIV. MAINE, 59-63, assoc. prof, 63-71, PROF, 71- Summer instr, Pa. State Univ, 57. Am. Chem. Soc; Am. Sci. Affiliation. Protein nutrition; amino acids of marine gastropods; effects of stress on brain lipid metabolism. Address: Dept. of Biochemistry, 202 Hitchner Hall, University of Maine, Orono, ME 04473.

DE HALAS, D(ON) R(ICHARD), b. San Francisco, Calif, Mar. 16, 30; m. 56; c. 4. PHYSICAL CHEMISTRY. B.S, California, 52; M.S, Idaho, 55; Ph.D. (chem), Oregon State, 59. Asst, corrosion studies, Gen. Elec. Co, 52-58, graphite studies, 59-61, ceramics res, 62-64; ceramics res. & develop. sect, reactor & mat. tech. dept, Pac. Northwest Lab, Battelle Mem. Inst, 65-66, MGR. mat. dept, 66-67, chem. dept, 67-68, chem. & metall. div, 68-71; BUS. DEVELOP, JERSEY NUCLEAR CO, 71- AAAS; Am. Nuclear Soc. Radiation effects on corrosion; radiolytic decomposition of organic liquids; radiation damage to graphite; radiation induced gas-graphite reactions; ceramics; nuclear fuels. Address: Business Development, Jersey Nuclear Co, 777 106th N.E, Bellevue, WA 98004.

DeHART, ARNOLD O('DELL), b. Davy, W.Va, May 8, 26; m. 51; c. 3. ENGI-NEERING MECHANICS, HYDRAULICS. B.S.M.E, West Virginia, 50. Sr. res. engr, BEARING RES, GEN. MOTORS CO, 51-64, SUPVRY. RES. ENGR, 64- U.S.A.A.F, 44-45. Soc. Automotive Eng. General bearing; fluid film and rolling contact hydrodynamics; hydrostatics; tribology; system kine-matics. Address: Research Labs, GM Technical Center, General Motors Corp, Warren, MI 48090.

DeHART, ROBERT C(HARLES), b. Laramie, Wyo, Aug. 16, 17; m. 41; c. 2. STRUCTURAL ENGINEERING. B.S, Wyoming, 38; M.S, Ill. Inst. Tech, 40, Ph.D.(civil eng), 55. Design engr, Standard Oil Co, Ind, 40-46; assoc. prof. civil eng, Mont. State, 46-53; struct. analyst, Armed Forces Special Weap-ons Proj, 53-58; mgr, struct. mech, SOUTHWEST RES. INST, 58-59, DIR. STRUCT. RES. DEPT, 59- Lectr, George Washington, 55-58. N.Y. Acad. Sci; Am. Soc. Mech. Eng; Am. Soc. Civil Eng; Sci. Res. Soc. Am. Struc-tural dynamics; theoretical and applied mechanics; air, underwater and underground shock; underwater vehicles. Address: Southwest Research Institute, 8500 Culebra Rd, San Antonio, TX 78206.

DE HARVEN, ETIENNE, b. Brussels, Belgium, Mar. 5, 28; m. 53; c. 3. CYTOLOGY, ELECTRON MICROSCOPY. M.D, Brussels, 53. Asst, Univ. Libre, Brussels, 55-62 & in charge cytol, electron micros. lab, anat. inst, 58-62; asst. prof. cytol, SLOAN-KETTERING DIV, CORNELL UNIV, 62-69, PROF. BIOL, 69-; MEM. DIV. CYTOL, SLOAN-KETTERING INST. CAN-CER RES, 68-, assoc. mem, 64-68, assoc, 62-64. Fel, Inst. Cancer, France, 55-56; Belgian Am. Ed. Found. & Damon Runyon Res. fels, 56-57; vis. res. fel, Sloan-Kettering Inst. Cancer Res, 56-57, vis. assoc, sum-mers, 59, 61. Assoc, Nat. Fund Sci. Res, Belgium, 59-61; guest investr, Rockefeller Inst, 62. Belgian Army Med.C. Res, 53-55, Capt. Electron Micros. Soc. Am; N.Y. Acad. Sci; Int. Soc. Cell Biol. Electron microscope cytology; viruses associated with murine cancers. Address: Division of Cytology, Sloan-Kettering Institute for Cancer Research, 410 E. 68th St, New York, NY 10021.

de HEER, J(OSEPH), b. Eindhoven, Netherlands, Jan. 24, 22; nat. PHYSICAL CHEMISTRY. Chem. Eng, Delft Inst. Tech, 47; Ramsay Mem. fel, Leeds, Manchester Univ, & King's Col, London, 47-49; Ph.D.(physics, math), Am-sterdam, 50. Res. assoc. physics & astron, Ohio State, 50-52; asst. prof. CHEM, UNIV. COLO, BOULDER, 52-58, assoc. prof, 58-63, PROF, 63- Guggenheim fel, quantum chem. group, Uppsala Univ, Sweden, 59-60; Ful-bright res. scholar, Copenhagen, 63-64. Am. Chem. Soc; fel. Am. Phys. Soc. Quantum mechanics of molecules; valence theory. Address: Dept. of Chemistry, University of Colorado, Boulder, CO 80302.

DE HERTOGH, AUGUST A(LBERT), b. Chicago, Ill, Aug. 24, 35; m. 57; c. 3. PLANT PHYSIOLOGY. B.S, N.C. State Col, 57, M.S, 61; Ph.D.(plant phys-iol), Oregon State, 64. Asst. plant physiologist, Boyce Thompson Inst, 64-65; asst. prof. HORT, MICH. STATE UNIV, 65-69, ASSOC. PROF, 69- U.S.A, 57-59, 1st Lt. Am. Soc. Plant Physiol; Japanese Soc. Plant Physiol; Am. Soc. Hort. Sci. Biosynthesis of terpenes in bulbous crops; gibberelins in the development and flowering of bulbous crops; the influence of environ-mental factors on flowering of spring flowering bulbs. Address: Dept. of Horticulture, College of Agriculture, Michigan State University, East Lan-sing, MI 48823.

De HILSTER, CORNELIS CAREL, b. Amsterdam, Holland, Jan. 22, 13; nat; m. 34; c. 2. ORGANIC CHEMISTRY. Anal. chemist Sharples Chems, Inc, 35-42, res. chemist, 42-50, staff chemist, 50-58; applns. chemist, Pennsalt Chem. Prods. Applns, 58-63, develop. chemist, 63-70; RETIRED. Am. Chem. Soc. Organic chemicals as applied to natural and synthetic rubber; process development of rubber chemicals. Address: Box 250, Wyandotte, MI 48192.

DEHL, RONALD, b. Mattoon, Ill, Nov. 10, 32. PHYSICAL CHEMISTRY. A.B, Oberlin Col, 55; Ph.D.(chem), Michigan, 61. Res. assoc. chem, Columbia, 61-63; CHEMIST, NAT. BUR. STANDARDS, 63- Nuclear magnetic reso-nance spectroscopy; high resolution studies of polymers in solution; broad line and nuclear relaxation studies of crystalline and amorphous polymers; electron spin resonance of electrolytically generated free radicals. Ad-dress: Apt. F-78, 3895 Rodman St. N.W, Washington, DC 20016.

DEHLINGER, PETER, b. Berlin, Germany, Oct. 3, 17; nat; m. 41; c. 2. GEO-PHYSICS, OCEANOGRAPHY. B.S, Michigan, 40; M.S, Calif. Inst. Tech, 43, Ph.D.(geophysics), 50. Seismologist, Shell Oil Co, Inc, 43-48; geophys-icist, Battelle Mem. Inst, 50-53; assoc. prof. geophys, Tex. A&M Univ, 54-57, prof, 57-62; geophys. oceanog, Ore. State Univ, 62-68; PROF. GEOPHYS. & DIR. MARINE SCI. INST, UNIV. CONN, 68- Indust. consult, 57-; with U.S. Geol. Surv, 57-68; head geophys. prog, ocean sci. & technol. div, Off. Naval Res, Wash, D.C, 66-68. AAAS; fel. Geol. Soc. Am; Am. Geophys. Union; Am. Soc. Oceanog; Soc. Explor. Geophys. Gravity and seismic measurement at sea; tectonics of oceanic crustal and mantle structures. Address: Marine Sciences Institute, University of Connecticut, Groton, CT 06340.

DEHM, HENRY C(HRISTOPHER), b. Newark, N.J, Apr. 1, 21; m. 48, 67; c. 2. ORGANIC CHEMISTRY. B.S, Denver, 48, M.S, 49; Searle fel, Wisconsin, 52-54, Ph.D.(chem), 54. Asst. chem, Denver, 48-49; Wisconsin, 49-52; res. chemist, res. center, Hercules Powder Co, 54-61, tech. specialist, CHEM. PROPULSION DIV, 61-66, SR. TECH. SPECIALIST, HERCULES, INC, 66- Lectr, Brigham Young Univ, 63-; adj. prof. chem. eng, Univ. Utah, 67- U.S.A.A.F, 42-45. Am. Chem. Soc. Synthesis and stereochemistry of steroids; organic synthesis; halogenation; catalysis; metal complexes; polymers; ultrahigh energy compounds; adhesion; fundamental chemistry of solid propellants. Address: Hercules, Inc, Magna, UT 84044.

DEHM, RICHARD L(AVERN), b. Pontiac, Ill, Sept. 11, 27; m. 52; c. 3. ANALYTICAL CHEMISTRY. B.S, Ill. Wesleyan Univ, 50; M.S, Univ. Ill, 52, Ph.D.(chem), 54; M.B.A, Univ. Rochester, 69. Asst, Univ. Ill, 51-54; anal. chemist, EASTMAN KODAK CO, 54-60, tech. assoc, 60-65, asst. dir. indust. lab, 65-70, ASST. SUPT. PHOTOCHEM. DIV, 70- U.S.N.R, 45-46. Am. Chem. Soc; Soc. Appl. Spectros. Emission, x-ray and absorption spectroscopy; x-ray diffraction; concentration techniques; trace element analysis; microprobe; spark source mass spectroscopy. Address: 6 Bittersweet Rd, Fairport, NY 14450.

DEHMELT, HANS GEORG, b. Goerlitz, Germany, Sept. 9, 22. EXPERIMENTAL PHYSICS. Dr.Rer.Nat, Göttingen, 50. Res. assoc, Duke, 52-55; vis. asst. prof. PHYSICS, UNIV. WASH, 55-56, asst. prof, 56-57, assoc. prof, 57-61, PROF, 61- Res. fel, Göttingen, 50-52; lectr, Summer Sch. Theoret. Physics, Les Houches, France, 59. Consult, Varian Assocs, 56- AAAS; Am. Phys. Soc.(Davisson-Gerner Prize, 70). Nuclear quadrupole resonance; nuclear and electron paramagnetic resonance; optical detection of free atom orientation; spin exchange resonance; spectroscopy of stored ions. Address: Dept. of Physics, University of Washington, Seattle, WA 98105.

DEHN, FREDERICK C(HRIS), b. Millstadt, Ill, Nov. 24, 20; m. 46; c. 2. ORGANIC CHEMISTRY. B.S, St. Louis, 43, M.S, 48; Ph.D.(chem), Pa. State, 50. Chemist, Koppers Co, 43-46; asst. chief chemist, Columbia South. Chem. Co, 50-55, asst. to dir. res, 55-60; dept. head org. res, Pittsburgh Plate Glass Co, 60-65, asst. dir. res, 65-66, DIR. RES, NATRIUM TECH. CTR, PPG INDUSTS, INC, 66- Am. Chem. Soc. Heterogenous halogenation catalysis; organic chlorinations; synthesis and properties of aliphatic fluorine compounds; olefine oxidations; sulfur compounds. Address: Natrium Technical Center, PPG Industries, Inc, P.O. Box 191, New Martinsville, WV 26155.

DEHN, JOSEPH WILLIAM, JR, b. Brooklyn, N.Y, Feb. 18, 28; m. 53; c. 2. ORGANIC CHEMISTRY. B.A, Columbia Col, 49; M.S, Stevens Inst. Tech, 53; Ph.D.(org. chem), Polytech. Inst. Brooklyn, 64. Sr. org. chemist, cent. res. labs, Interchem. Corp, 49-64; group leader org. chem, Wallace & Tiernan, Inc, 65-67; sr. scientist, cent. res. labs, Shulton Inc, 68-70; SR. ORG. CHEMIST, NOPCO DIV, DIAMOND-SHAMROCK CHEM. CO, 71- AAAS; Am. Chem. Soc; Am. Inst. Chem; N.Y. Acad. Sci. Synthesis of dyes, pigments, organic intermediates and heterocyclic and organometallic compounds. Address: 52 Berkshire Rd, Great Neck, NY 11023.

DEHN, RUDOLPH A(LBERT), b. East Rutherford, N.J, Aug. 12, 19; m. 45; c. 3. ELECTRICAL ENGINEERING. B.S.E.E, Newark Col. Eng, 41. Develop. engr, GEN. ELEC. CO, 41-45, res. assoc, 45-60, consult. engr, 60-66, MGR. TUBE RES, MICROWAVE TUBE BUS. SECT, 66- With Off. Sci. Res. & Develop, 44. U.S.A. Inst. Elec. & Electronics Eng. New Methods of generating microwaves; design of attendant transmission networks; new microwave magnetrons; tetrodes; klystrons. Address: General Electric Co, 1 River Rd, Schenectady, NY 12305.

DEHNBOSTEL, NELLIE GWYNNE, b. Steubenville, Ohio, Jan. 16, 99; m. 26. PARASITOLOGY. M.A, Kent State Univ, 42. Assoc. prof. gen. sci, YOUNGSTOWN STATE UNIV, 41-64, supvr. nat. sci, 64-69, EMER. ASSOC. PROF. BIOL, 69- AAAS; Am. Chem. Soc; Am. Soc. Parasitol. Protozoology; regeneration. Address: 771 Willard N.E, Warren, OH 44483.

DEHNE, EDWARD J(AMES), b. Ft. Clark, N.Dak, June 28, 11; m. 32; c. 3. MEDICINE, PUBLIC HEALTH. B.S, North Dakota, 35; M.D, Oregon, 37; M.P.H, Hopkins, 41, D.P.H, 55. Indust. med. practice, Idaho, 38-39; dir, Coos County Health Dept, Ore, 39-41; asst. post surgeon, U.S. Army, Ft. McDowell, Calif, 41-43, civil affairs, Mil. Govt. Pub. Health, Eng, 43-44, civil affairs health off, Civil Affairs Ctr, Europ. Civil Affairs Div, Eng, 44, chief prev. med, Europ. Theater Opers, 44, surg, forward echelon, France, 44, exec. off, West. Europe, 44-45, chief prev. med, Off. Mil. Govt, Ger, 45-47, dir. off. occup. health, Edgewood Arsenal, Md, 48-50, hqs. Third U.S. Army, Ga, 50-51, Caribbean, C.Z, 51-55, comdr, U.S. Army Environ. Health Lab, 55-59, Second U.S. Army, 59-60, Brooke Army Med. Ctr, 60-63, dir. health & welfare, U.S. Civil Admin, Ryukyu Islands, 63-65, Fifth U.S. Army, 65-66; State of Nev. health off, 66-68; med. dir. W.Va. regional med. prog, med. ctr, Univ. W.Va, 68-69; dir. N.J. tuberc. serv, State of N.J. Dept. Health, 69-71; CHIEF MED. CONSULT, STATE OF NEV, 71- Consult, Off. Surgeon Gen, 57; mem. faculty Vietnam surv, sch. pub. health, Univ. Calif, Los Angeles, 68-69. Dipl, Am. Bd. Prev. Med, 49, occup. med, 55; Am. Bd. Indust. Hyg; mem, Order of Leopold, Belg. U.S.A, 41-46, Col.(Ret); Legion of Merit, 45. Fel. Am. Col. Physicians; fel. Am. Col. Prev. Med; fel. Am. Pub. Health Asn; fel. Am. Med. Asn; fel. Indust. Med. Asn; Am. Soc. Trop. Med. & Hyg; Am. Conf. Govt. Indust. Hygienists; Asn. Mil. Surg. U.S; fel. Royal Soc. Health; Asn. State & Territorial Health Off. Identifying, evaluating and minimizing important environmental health hazards in the Army; effects of environmental temperature upon susceptibility to toxic agents. Address: 308 N. Curry St, Carson City, NV 89701.

DEHNE, G(EORGE) CLARK, b. Pittsburgh, Pa, Oct. 2, 37; m. 58; c. 2. ANALYTICAL & INORGANIC CHEMISTRY. B.S, Allegheny Col, 59; M.S, Purdue, 61, Eli Lilly fel, 61-62, M.W. Kellogg summer fel, 62, Lubrizol fel, 62-63, Ph.D.(anal. chem), 63. Asst. prof. CHEM, CAPITAL UNIV, 63-67, ASSOC. PROF, 67-, CHMN. DEPT, 69- AAAS; Am. Chem. Soc; Am. Soc. Test. & Mat. Absorption spectroscopy; analytical instrumentation and spectrophotometry; heteropoly chemistry; computer applications in chemistry. Address: Dept. of Chemistry, Capital University, Columbus, OH 43209.

DEHNEL, PAUL A(UGUSTUS), b. Pomona, California, Dec. 31, 22; m. 43; c. 2. COMPARATIVE PHYSIOLOGY, MARINE INVERTEBRATE ZOOLOGY. B.A, San Diego State Col, 43; M.A, California, 48, Ph.D, California, Los Angeles, 54. Instr. zool, San Diego State Col, 48-50; assoc, California, Los Angeles, 53-55; asst. prof. MARINE INVERT, UNIV. B.C, 55-60, assoc. prof, 60-65, PROF, 65- U.S.M.C, 42-46, 1st Lt. Am. Physiol. Soc; Am. Soc. Zool. Electrolyte balance; water regulation; respiration marine invertebrates. Address: Dept. of Zoology, University of British Columbia, Vancouver 8, B.C, Can.

DEHNER, EUGENE W(ILLIAM), b. Burlington, Iowa, May 26, 14. BIOLOGY. B.Sc, St. Benedict's Col, 37; M.Sc, Cornell, 43, Ph.D.(zool), 46. Instr. BIOL, ST. BENEDICTS'S COL, 46-51, PROF, 51-, CHMN. DEPT, 53- Res. assoc, Clayton Found. Biochem. Inst, Univ. Tex, 66-67. AAAS; Wilson Ornith. Soc; Am. Soc. Zool. Functional anatomy of birds, especially the adaptation of bodily dimensions to the habits of these animals; wing dimensions of two doves of different flight habits; respiratory volume and specific gravity of diving and surface feeding ducks. Address: Dept. of Biology, St. Benedict's College, Second & Division Sts, Atchison, KS 66002.

DEHNER, THOMAS R, b. Richmond, Ind, Feb. 19, 40. INORGANIC CHEMISTRY, BIOCHEMISTRY. A.B, Earlham Col, 62; Ph.D.(chem), Notre Dame, 66. Instr. CHEM, Earlham Col, 66; Nat. Insts. Health fel, California, Berkeley, 66-68; ASST. PROF, STATE UNIV. N.Y. BINGHAMTON, 68- AAAS; Am. Chem. Soc. Coordination chemistry; chelating polymer; metal ion function in biological systems. Address: Dept. of Chemistry, State University of New York at Binghamton, Binghamton, N.Y. 13901.

DE HOFF, GEORGE R(OLAND), b. Baltimore, Md, Oct. 16, 23; m. 48; c. 3. CHEMICAL & PLASTICS ENGINEERING. B.E, Hopkins, 48, M.S, 50. Chem. engr, Nat. Plastics Prod. Co, 50-53; res. engr, PLASTICS DEPT, E.I. DU PONT DE NEMOURS & CO, 53-62, tech. rep, 62-67, CONSULT, 67- A.U.S, 43-46, Eng.C.Res, 48-, Lt. Col. Soc. Plastics Eng. Behavior of various thermoplastics in processing equipment, including relating the rheological properties of a resin to its processing characteristics. Address: Chestnut Run Labs, Plastics Dept, E.I. du Pont de Nemours & Co, Wilmington, DE 19898.

DEHOFF, PAUL HENRY, JR, b. York Twp, Pa, Mar. 12, 34; m. 56; c. 1. MECHANICAL ENGINEERING, SOLID MECHANICS. B.S, Pa. State, 56, M.S, 58; Ph.D.(solid mech), Purdue, 65. Mech. engr, York Div, Bendix Corp, 58-61; instr. aeronaut. & astronaut. eng. sci, Purdue, 61-65; res. engr, exp. sta, E.I. du Pont de Nemours & Co, Del, 65-66; asst. prof. MECH. ENG, BUCKNELL UNIV, 66-71, ASSOC. PROF. & COORD. GRAD. STUDIES, 71- Soc. Rheol; Am. Soc. Eng. Educ; Am. Soc. Mech. Eng. Solid deformations of polymeric material; creep and relaxation behavior under large strains; anisotropic behavior of polymers. Address: Dept. of Mechanical Engineering, Bucknell University, Lewisburg, PA 17837.

DeHOFF, ROBERT THOMAS, b. Sharon, Pa, Jan. 15, 34; m. 57; c. 2. METALLURGY. B.E, Youngstown State Univ, 55; M.S, Carnegie-Mellon Univ, 58, Alcoa fel. & Ph.D.(metall. eng), 59. Asst. prof. METALL. ENG, UNIV. FLA, 59-64, assoc. prof, 64-70, PROF, 70- Proj. engr, Carnegie-Mellon Univ, summer 57; consult, Hanford Labs, Gen. Elec. Co, Wash, 63-64; Sigma Xi faculty res. award, 64. Am. Inst. Mining, Metall. & Petrol. Eng; Int. Soc. Stereology (ed, Bull, 64-67); Am. Soc. Metals. Quantitative metallography; thermodynamic properties of surfaces; multicomponent diffusion. Address: Dept. of Metallurgy & Materials Engineering, University of Florida, Gainesville, FL 32601.

de HOFFMANN, FREDERIC, b. Vienna, Austria, July 8, 24; nat; m. 53. PHYSICS. B.S, Harvard, 45, Nat. Res. fel, 46-48, M.A, 47, Ph.D.(physics), 48. Staff mem, Los Alamos Sci. Lab, 44-46; consult, U.S. Atomic Energy Comn, 47-48; staff mem, Los Alamos Sci. Lab, 48-55; v.pres, Gen. Dynamics Corp, Calif, 55-67, gen. mgr, Gen. Atomic Div, 55-59, pres, 59-67; v.pres, Gulf Oil Corp, 67-69, pres, Gulf Gen. Atomic, 67-69; CHANCELLOR, SALK INST. BIOL. STUDIES, 70- Alternate asst. dir, Los Alamos Sci. Lab, 50-51; hon. prof, Univ. Vienna, 68. Great Commander Cross Medal & Cross for Sci. & Arts, Repub. of Austria. Fel. Am. Phys. Soc; fel. Am. Nuclear Soc. Fission process; theory of chain reactions, neutron diffusion; magnetohydrodynamic shocks; meson theory. Address, 9736 La Jolla Farms Rd, La Jolla, CA 92037.

DeHOLLANDER, W(ILLIAM) R(OGER), b. Grand Rapids, Mich, Nov. 15, 18; m. 47; c. 5. PHYSICAL CHEMISTRY. Eastman Kodak & du Pont fels, Washington(Seattle), Ph.D.(chem), 51. Sr. scientist, Hanford atomic prods. oper, GEN. ELEC. CO, 51-59, specialist, atomic prod. equip. dept, 59-67, MGR. PROCESS DEVELOP, NUCLEAR FUELS DEPT, 67- U.S.A, 41-46. Am. Chem. Soc; Electrochem. Soc. Gas chromatography; pyrophoricity; gas-solid reactions; kinetics; thermodynamics; reactor fuels and materials computer process control. Address: Nuclear Fuels Dept, General Electric Co, 175 Curtner, San Jose, CA 95125.

DEHORITY, BURK A(LLYN), b. Peoria, Ill, Sept. 3, 30; m. 53; c. 4. BIOCHEMISTRY, ANIMAL NUTRITION. B.A, Blackburn Col, 52; M.S, Maine, 54; Ph.D.(biochem), Ohio State, 57. Asst. prof. animal nutrit, Connecticut, 57-58; ANIMAL SCI, OHIO AGR. RES. & DEVELOP. CTR, 59-63, assoc. prof, 63-70, PROF, 70- Am. Soc. Microbiol; Am. Soc. Animal Sci; Am. Dairy Sci. Asn. Rumen microbiology. Address: Dept. of Animal Science, Ohio Agricultural Research & Development Center, Wooster, OH 44691.

DEIBEL, ROBERT H(OWARD), b. Chicago, Ill, Dec. 20, 24; m. 49; c. 4. BACTERIOLOGY. M.S, Chicago, 52, Ph.D, 62. Bacteriologist, Am. Meat Inst. Found, 52-64; assoc. prof. BACT, Cornell Univ, 64-66; assoc. prof, UNIV. WIS, MADISON, 66-69, PROF, 69- U.S.A, 43-46. Am. Soc. Microbiol; Can. Soc. Microbiol; Brit. Soc. Gen. Microbiol. Bacterial metabolism and taxonomy; food microbiology. Address: Dept. of Bacteriology, University of Wisconsin, Madison, WI 53706.

DEIBEL, RUDOLF, b. Berlin, Ger, Apr. 27, 24; U.S. citizen; m. 57; c. 3. PEDIATRICS, VIROLOGY. Cand. Med, Berlin, 50; Dr. Med, Freiburg, 53. Intern med, Wenckebach Krankenhaus, Berlin, Germany, 53-55; asst. path, inst. path, Univ. Freiburg, 55-56, res. asst. pediat. & virol, Children's Hosp, 56-58, 59-61; vis. scientist virol, N.Y. STATE DEPT. HEALTH, 58-59, assoc. med. virologist, 62-67, DIR. VIRUS LABS, 67- Asst. prof. pediat. & microbiol, Albany Med. Col, Union Univ.(N.Y), 65-69, assoc. prof, 69- Am. Asn. Immunol; Am. Soc. Trop. Med. & Hgy. Virus diseases in humans, especially respiratory infections in infants and children. Address: Division of Labs. & Research, New York State Dept. of Health, New Scotland Ave, Albany, NY 12201.

DEIBERT, MAX CURTIS, b. Lansing, Mich, May 19, 37; m. 61; c. 2. CHEMICAL ENGINEERING. B.Ch.E, Cornell, 60; Nat. Sci. Found. fel, Mass. Inst. Tech, 61-64, Sc.D.(chem. eng), 64. Asst. prof. chem. eng, Mass. Inst. Technol, 64-70; TECH. DIR. ANACON, INC, 70- Ford fel, 64-66; sr. res. chem. engr, Monsanto Res. Corp, Mass. 64-69; res. group leader, Ionics, Inc, Mass, 69-70. Am. Chem. Soc; Am. Inst. Chem. Eng; Electrochem. Soc. Process instrumentation; electrochemistry; surface chemistry; process control; materials properties; infrared technology; instrumentation science and technology. Address: Anacon, Inc, 30 Main St, Ashland, MA 01721.

DEICHMANN, ELISABETH, b. Copenhagen, Denmark, June 12, 96; nat. 32. ZOOLOGY. M.Sc, Copenhagen, 22; Ph.D.(zool), Radcliffe Col, 27. Asst. zool, Royal Agr. Col, Copenhagen, 21-23; Danish Rask Oersted Found for Res, Calif, 24; British Mus, 26, 53; asst, Bur. Fisheries, 27-28; Agassiz fel, MUS. COMP. ZOOL, HARVARD, 28-35, asst. curator MARINE INVERTEBRATES, 30-42, curator, 42-62, HON. ASSOC, 62- Hon. assoc, Smithsonian Inst, 65-; adj. prof, Univ. Miami, 66- AAAS; Am. Soc. Mammal; Soc. Syst. Zool; Am. Soc. Limnol. & Oceanog. Marine invertebrates; octocorals and echinoderms. Address: Museum of Comparative Zoology, Harvard University, Cambridge, MA 02138.

DEICHMANN, WILLIAM BERNHARD, b. Sept. 7, 02; nat; m. 28; c. 2. PHARMACOLOGY, TOXICOLOGY. A.B, Western Reserve, 32, M.S, 34; Cincinnati, 37-39, Ph.D.(toxicol), 39. Asst. biochem, Western Reserve, 28-34; jr. pharmacologist, Haskell Lab. Indust. Toxicol, 34-37; toxicologist, Kettering Lab, med. col, Cincinnati, 37-47; assoc. prof. PHARMACOL. & head div, Albany Med. Col, 47-50, prof, 50-53; prof. & chmn. dept, SCH. MED, UNIV. MIAMI, 53-69, EMER. PROF, 69-, DIR. RES. & TEACHING CTR. TOXICOL, 65- Ed. sect. toxicol. & indust. hyg, Biol. Abstracts, 46-50; Indust. Med. Workers, Arg. AAAS; Am. Indust. Hyg. Asn; Am. Soc. Pharmacol; fel. N.Y. Acad. Sci; Int. Col. Surg; fel. Am. Soc. Clin. Pharmacol. & Therapeut; Soc. Toxicol; Pan Am. Med. Asn; fel. Royal Soc. Med; cor. mem. Ger. Pharmacol. Soc. Pharmacodynamic action and toxicology of hydrazine, chloroprene, alkyl rhodanates, phenol, chlorophenols, glycerol, vanillin, cresols, methacrylates, 2-amino-thiazole, diphenyl, amino and nitrodiphenyls, kerosene glucuronic acid; DDT; organic phosphates; effects of air pollution, microwave radiation and pesticides in general. Address: Research & Teaching Center of Toxicology, University of Miami School of Medicine, P.O. Box 8216, Coral Gables, FL 33124.

DEIG, E. FRANK, b. Mt. Vernon, Ind, Dec. 11, 24; m. 63. VIROLOGY. A.B, California, Berkeley, 51; M.S, Utah, 58, Ph.D.(bact), 61. Technician bact. & virol, Cutter Labs, Calif, 51-55; res. worker, virol, Kaiser Found. Res. Inst. Exp. Biol, 61-62; ASST. RES. VIROLOGIST, NAVAL BIOMED. RES. LAB, UNIV. CALIF, 62- U.S.N, 42-45. Am. Soc. Microbiol. Biochemistry of virus infected cells in vitro; serology of virus-immune serum interactions in vitro; arbovirus characterization. Address: Naval Biomedical Research Lab, University of California, Naval Supply Center, Okland, CA 94614.

DEIGHTON, BRINTON S, JR, b. East Orange, N.J, Jan. 22, 34; m. 60; c. 2. CHEMICAL ENGINEERING. B.S, Cornell, 58; M.S, Calif. Inst. Tech, 59. Res. engr, PROCESS DESIGN, Calif. Res. Corp, 59-61, 62-64, group supvr, Chevron Res. Co, 64-66, STAFF ANALYST, COMPTROLLER'S DEPT, STANDARD OIL CO. CALIF, 66- Am. Inst. Chem. Eng. Design engineering. Address: 60 Lynwood Pl, Moraga, CA 94556.

DEIKE, GEORGE H(ERMAN), III, b. Pittsburgh, Pa, Mar. 10, 35. ENVIRONMENTAL SCIENCES. B.S, Pa. State Univ, 57, Ph.D.(geol), 67; M.A, Univ. Mo-Columbia, 61. Surveyor, Richard A. Marsico & Assoc, 69; ASST. PROF. geol, West. Ill. Univ, 69-71; EARTH SCI, DAVIS & ELKINS COL, 71- AAAS. Karst geomorphology; regional karst hydrology; structural control of karst; geometry of solution conduits; stream hydrology and chemistry; stream pollution. Address: Dept. of Earth Science, Davis & Elkins College, Elkins, WV 26241.

DEILY, FREDRIC H(ARRY), b. Evanston, Ill, June 9, 26; m. 47; c. 2. MECHANICAL ENGINEERING. B.S, Northwestern, 47, Ph.D.(mech. eng), 51. Asst, Nat. Defense Res. Coun-Off. Sci. Res. & Develop. Proj, Northwestern, 46-47, dept. mech. eng, 47-51; res. engr, Carter Oil Co, STANDARD OIL CO, N.J, 51-58, group head, Jersey Prod. Res. Co, 58-59, res. assoc, 60-63; eng. adv, Imp. Oil Ltd. Can, 59-60, drilling adv, Int. Petrol. Co, Peru, 63-64, RES. ASSOC, ESSO PROD. RES. CO, TEX, 64- Mem, drilling domain adv. comt, Am. Petrol. Inst, 60-63. Am. Soc. Mech. Eng; Am. Inst. Min, Metall. & Petrol. Eng. Oil well drilling research and engineering; rock behavior and failure; underground stress distribution; drilling fluid rheology and mechanics; drilling optimization. Address: 13410 Perthshire, Houston, TX 77024.

DEINDOERFER, FRED H, b. Chicago, Ill, Nov. 15, 29; m. 54; c. 2. BIOMEDICAL ENGINEERING, MICROBIOLOGY. B.S, Illinois, 51; M.S, Columbia, 54; Wilson S. Yerger fel, Pennsylvania, 58-59, Nat. Sci. Found. fel, 59-60, Ph.D.(chem. eng), 62. Microbiologist, Merck & Co, Inc, 51-56; sr. process chem. engr, E.R. Squibb & Sons Div, Olin-Mathieson Chem. Corp, 56-58; tech. dir, Indust. Biochem, Inc, 60-63; pres. res. equip. design & mfr, Fermentation Design, Inc, 63-64; dir. process res. & develop, Int. Minerals & Chem. Corp, 64-66, mgr. mkt. & int. Sales, 66-68; V.PRES. RES. & DEVELOP, McGAW LABS, DIV. AM. HOSP. SUPPLY CORP, 68- Medical device development; biochemical research; drug development; applied microbiology; process development. Address: Research & Development, McGaw Labs, Division of American Hospital Supply Corp, 1015 Grandview Ave, Glendale, CA 91201.

DEINES, PETER, b. Münden, Germany, Apr. 2, 36. GEOCHEMISTRY. M.Sc, Pa. State, 64, Ph.D.(geochem), 67. Res. asst. GEOCHEM, PA. STATE UNIV, 66-67, ASST. PROF, 67- Isotope geochemistry; variations in stable isotopes of carbon and oxygen. Address: 19 Mineral Science Bldg, Pennsylvania State University, University Park, PA 16802.

DEINET, A(DOLPH) J(OSEPH), b. Elberfeld, Germany, Oct. 29, 20; nat; m. 42; c. 2. ORGANIC CHEMISTRY. B.S, Virginia, 43, Ph.D.(chem), 46. Res. chemist, antimalarials, Off. Sci. Res. Develop, 44-46; SYNTHETIC ORG, HEYDEN DIV, TENNECO CHEM, INC, 46-70, RES. & DEVELOP. SUPVR, 70- General synthetic organic research and development. Address: 52 Valley Forge Dr, East Brunswick, NJ 08816.

DEINHARDT, FRIEDRICH, b. Germany, May 26, 26; m. 59. VIROLOGY. Goettingen, 45; Zurich; M.D, Hamburg, 51. Asst. path, Hamburg, 52-54; asst. prof. virol, dept. pub. health & prev. med, Pennsylvania & Children's Hosp. of Phila, 54-61; assoc. prof. MICROBIOL, RUSH MED. COL, 61-66, PROF, 66-; CHMN. DEPT, RUSH-PRESBY-ST. LUKE'S MED. CTR, 61- Dipl, Am. Bd. Microbiol. Am. Asn. Immunol; Tissue Cult. Asn; fel. Am. Acad. Microbiol; Am. Soc. Clin. Invest; Infectious Diseases Soc. Am. Immunology. Address: Dept. of Microbiology, Rush-Presbyterian-St. Luke's Medical Center, 1753 W. Congress Pkwy, Chicago, IL 60612.

DEININGER, ROBERT W(ADE), b. Monroe, Wis, Aug. 15, 27; m. 60; c. 2. GEOLOGY, PETROLOGY. B.S, Wisconsin, 50, M.S, 57; Welch Found. fel, Rice, 59-60, Ph.D.(geol), 64. Geologist, U.S. Army Engrs, Fla, 51-53, engr, 53-54; geologist, Tidewater Oil Co, 57-58; instr. GEOL, Connecticut, 60-62; Alabama, 62-64, asst. prof, 64-66; MEMPHIS STATE UNIV, 66-67, ASSOC. PROF, 67- Summers, geologist, Wis. Geol. Surv, 55, Laughlin Steel Corp, 56. U.S.N.R, 45-46. Geol. Soc. Am; Geochm. Soc. Relationships among tectonics, metamorphism and igneous activity. Address: Dept. of Geology, Memphis State University, Memphis, TN 38111.

DEININGER, ROLF A, b. Ulm, Germany, Feb. 13, 34; nat; m. 61; c. 2. CIVIL ENGINEERING, ENVIRONMENTAL HEALTH. Dipl. Ing, Stuttgart Tech, 58; M.S, Northwestern, 61, Ph.D.(civil eng), 65. Asst. prof. ENVIRON. HEALTH, SCH. PUB. HEALTH, UNIV. MICH, 63-68, ASSOC. PROF, 68- Consult, United Nations, WHO, U.S. Pub. Health Serv, U.S. Army Corps Eng. Am. Soc. Civil Eng; Am. Water Works Asn; Opers. Res. Soc. Am; Asn. Comput. Mach; Water Pollution Control Fedn. Investigation of pumped storage for flow augmentation; computer aided design of waste water collection and treatment systems; design of water distribution systems; optimal lake level control. Address: Dept. of Environmental Health, University of Michigan, Ann Arbor, MI 48104.

DEINKEN, HERMAN P(ORTER), b. Amistad, N.Mex, Apr. 9, 19; m. 46; c. 5. PHYSICS. B.S, Tex. Tech. Col, 42; B.S, Texas, 51, M.A, 52, fel, 54-55, Ph.D.(physics), 56. Res. scientist PHYSICS, Electro-Mech. Co, 53-54; ASST. GROUP LEADER & MEM. STAFF, LOS ALAMOS SCI. LAB, UNIV. CALIF, 56- U.S.A,F, 42-46, Res, 46-, Col. Am. Phys. Soc. Development of nuclear weapons and their components. Address: Los Alamos Scientific Lab, Los Alamos, NM 87544.

DEINZER, MAX LUDWIG, b. Weehauken, N.J, June 19, 37; m. 68; c. 1. ORGANIC CHEMISTRY. B.S, Rutgers Univ, 60; M.S, Univ. Ariz, 63; Ph.D. (org. chem), Univ. Ore, 69. RES. CHEMIST, E.I. du Pont de Nemours & Co, 69-71; ENVIRONMENTAL PROTECTION AGENCY, 71- U.S.A, 63-64, Capt. Am. Chem. Soc. Cage recombinations of free radical species. Address: Environmental Protection Agency, Cincinnati, OH 45246.

DEIRMENDJIAN, DIRAN, b. Adapazari, Turkey, Nov. 13, 17; nat; m. 49. METEOROLOGY. B.A, California, Los Angeles, 50, M.A, 52, fel, 53-55, Ph.D.(meteorol), 56. Asst. meteorol, California, Los Angeles, 51, jr. res. meteorologist, 51-56, lectr, 56-57; PHYS. SCIENTIST, SR. STAFF, RAND CORP, 56- Am. Astron. Soc; Am. Geophys. Union; Optical Soc. Am. Meteorological hydrodynamics; atmospheric physics and radiation; electromagnetic scattering; radiative transfer in planetary atmospheres. Address: Physical Sciences Dept, Rand Corp, 1700 Main St, Santa Monica, CA 90406.

DEIS, DANIEL WAYNE, b. Martinez, Calif, May 9, 43; m. 60; c. 3. SOLID STATE PHYSICS. B.S, Stanford, 64; NASA fel, Duke, 64-66, Ph.D.(physics), 68. Instr, physics, Duke, 67-68; SR. ENGR. CRYOGENICS, WESTINGHOUSE RES. & DEVELOP. CTR, 68- Inst. Elec. & Electronics Eng; Am. Phys. Soc. Cryogenics; superconductivity, semiconductors; ultrasonics; magnetism; production of very low temperatures. Address: Westinghouse Research Labs, Bldg. 401, Room 2X24, Beulah Rd, Pittsburgh, PA 15235.

DEISCHER, CLAUDE K(NAUSS), b. Emmaus, Pa, Oct. 14, 03; m. 29; c. 1. CHEMISTRY. B.S, Muhlenberg Col, 25; Lehigh Univ, 27; M.S, Univ. Pa, 28, Ph.D.(chem), 33. Teacher, pub. schs, 21-24, 25-27; instr. CHEM, UNIV. PA, 28-36, asst. prof, 36-53, assoc. prof, 53-71, asst. chmn. dept, 52-65; EMER. PROF, 71- Acting curator, E.F. Smith Mem. Libr, 55- Am. Inst. Chem; Am. Chem. Soc; Hist. Sci. Soc. Quantitative inorganic analysis; history and literature of chemistry; chemistry of rare elements. Address: 158 Idris Rd, Merion Station, PA 19066.

DEISHER, ROBERT WILLIAM, b. Bradford, Ill, Aug. 20, 20; m. 48; c. 3. MEDICINE, PEDIATRICS. A.B, Knox Col, 41; M.D, Washington (St. Louis), 44. Instr. PEDIAT, SCH. MED, UNIV. WASH, 49-51; asst. prof, 51-57, assoc. prof, 57-62, PROF, 62- Med.C, 46-48, Capt. Soc. Pediat. Res; Am. Acad. Pediat. Child growth and development; adolescence; school problems; delinquency; mental retardation. Address: Dept. of Pediatrics, University of Washington, Seattle, WA 98195.

DEISS, WILLIAM P(AUL), JR, b. Shelbyville, Ky, Feb. 1, 23; m. 48; c. 3. INTERNAL MEDICINE. B.S, Univ. Notre Dame, 42; M.D, Univ. Ill, 45. Intern, Univ. Wis, 45-46, resident internal med, 48-51, Arthritis & Rheumatism Found. res. fel, 51-54; asst. prof. med. & biochem, Duke Univ, 54-56, assoc. prof, 56-58; Ind. Univ, Indianapolis, 58-61, prof, 61-68; PROF. MED. & CHMN. DEPT, MED. BR, UNIV. TEX, 68- In charge med. serv, Durham Vet. Admin. Hosp, 56-58; consult, Nat. Insts. Health, 60-64, 68-72. Med.C, 46-48, Maj. Fel. Am. Col. Physicians; Am. Soc. Clin. Invest; Am. Fedn. Clin. Res.(secy-treas, 61-64); Asn. Am. Physicians; Am. Clin. & Climat. Asn; Endocrine Soc. Endocrinology and metabolism; bone and thyroid chemistry and physiology. Address: Dept. of Medicine, University of Texas Medical Branch, Galveston, TX 77550.

DEISSLER, ROBERT G(EORGE), b. Greenville, Pa, Aug. 1, 21; m. 50; c. 4. FLUID DYNAMICS, HEAT TRANSFER. B.S, Carnegie Inst. Tech, 43; M.S, Case Inst, Tech, 48. Engr. materials develop, Goodyear Aircraft Corp, Ohio, 43-44; AEROSPACE RES. SPEC. FLUID DYNAMICS & CHIEF FUNDAMENTAL HEAT TRANSFER BR, LEWIS RES. CTR, NASA, 47- NASA except. serv. award, 57. U.S.N.R, 44-45, Lt.(jg). AAAS; Am. Phys. Soc; Am. Inst. Aeronaut. & Astronaut; Am. Soc. Mech. Eng.(heat transfer div. mem. award, 64); Soc. Natural Philos. Fluid turbulence; turbulent heat transfer; thermal radiation; vortex flows; heat transfer in powders. Address: NASA Lewis Research Center, 21000 Brookpark Rd, Cleveland, OH 44135.

DEITCH, ARLINE D, b. N.Y.C, Mar. 12, 22; m. 42. CELL BIOLOGY, CYTOCHEMISTRY. B.A, Brooklyn Col, 44; M.A, Columbia, 46, Ph.D, 54. Asst. zool, Columbia, 44-48, lectr, 49-50, asst. surg, 53-55; U.S. Pub. Health Serv. fel, Nat. Inst. Neurol. Diseases & Blindness, Nat. Insts. Health, 55-56; res. assoc. surg, COLUMBIA UNIV, 56-58, microbiol, 58-62, ASST. PROF, 62-68, PATH, 68-, vis. fel, 55-56. Am. Soc. Cell Biol; Histochem. Soc. Cytochemical and cytological aspects of cellular differentiation. Address: Dept. of Pathology, Columbia University, 630 W. 168th St, New York, NY 10032.

DEITERMAN, LOUIS HENRY, JR, b. Temple, Tex, Dec. 14, 32; m. 56; c. 2. PHYSICS. B.S, Texas, Austin, 54, M.A, 57, univ. fel, 63, NASA fel, 64, Ph.D.(physics), 65. Nuclear engr, Gen. Dynamics Corp, 55-58; systs. engr, Bendix Systs. Div, 58-59; res. physicist, Tex. Instruments, Inc, 60-62; res. scientist, Defense Res. Lab, Texas, Austin, 62-63; proj. nuclear physicist, Gen. Dynamics Corp, 65; STAFF PHYSICIST, SCOTT & WHITE MEM. HOSP, 65- Consult, Vet. Admin. Hosp, Temple, Tex, 68- Am. Phys. Soc; Am. Asn. Physicists Med; Sci. Res. Soc. Am. Dosimetry of intense pulsed radiation fields; electroencephalograph effects due to auditory stimuli. Address: Dept. of Research, Scott & White Memorial Hospital, 2401 S. 31st St, Temple, TX 76501.

DEITERS, ROSE MARY, b. Cincinnati, Ohio, Apr. 28, 34. INORGANIC & PHYSICAL CHEMISTRY. B.A, Col. Mt. St. Joseph, 63; Nat. Sci. Found. fel, Univ. Cincinnati, 64-67, Ph.D.(chem), 67. Fel. CHEM, Univ. Mass, Amherst, 67-68; instr, COL. MT. ST. JOSEPH, 68-70, ASST. PROF, 70- Petrol. Res. Found-Am. Chem. Soc. res. grant, 69-71. Am. Chem. Soc; The Chem. Soc. Ion-molecule hydrogen bonds; spectroscopy and structure of pentacoordinated compounds; interaction of halide ions with carbon tetrahalides. Address: Dept. of Chemistry, College of Mt. St. Joseph-on-the-Ohio, St. Joseph, OH 45051.

DEITRICH, L(AWRENCE) WALTER, b. Pittsburgh, Pa, Oct. 17, 38; m. 64; c. 1. MECHANICAL & NUCLEAR ENGINEERING. B.M.E, Cornell, 61; M.S, Rensselaer Polytech, 63; Atomic Energy Cmn. fel, Stanford, 64-67, Ph.D. (mech. eng), 69. Engr, Knolls Atomic Power Lab, Gen. Elec. Co, 61-64; ASST. MECH. ENGR, ARGONNE NAT. LAB, 69- Am. Nuclear Soc; Am. Soc. Mech. Eng. Nuclear reactor safety and design; heat transfer; fluid mechanics; design and analysis of in-pile transient test of fuel elements. Address: Argonne National Lab, Reactor Analysis & Safety Division, Bldg. 208, 9700 S. Cass Ave, Argonne, IL 60439.

DEITRICH, RICHARD A(DAM), b. Monte Vista, Colo, Apr. 22, 31; m. 54; c. 3. PHARMACOLOGY, BIOCHEMISTRY. B.S, Colorado, 53, M.S, 54, Am. Found. Pharmaceut. Ed. fel, 56-59, Ph.D.(pharmacol), 59. Nat. Heart Inst. fel. physiol. chem, sch. med, Hopkins, 59-61, instr, 61-63; asst. prof. PHARMACOL, UNIV. COLO, DENVER, 63-69, ASSOC. PROF, 69- Lederle Faculty award med, 63-65; Nat. Inst. Neurol. Diseases & Blindness res. grant, 63-66, Nat. Inst. Gen. Med. Sci. res. career develop. award, 65-75, alcohol div, Nat. Inst. Ment. Health grants. U.S.A, 54-56. AAAS; Am. Chem. Soc; N.Y. Acad. Sci; fel. Am. Inst. Chem; Am. Soc. Pharmacol. & Exp. Therapeut; Am. Soc. Neurochem. Mechanism of enzyme action; biochemical basis of drug action; metabolic pathways for aldehydes. Address: Dept. of Pharmacology, University of Colorado School of Medicine, 4200 E. Ninth Ave, Denver, CO 80220.

DEITRICK, JOHN ENGLISH, b. Watsontown, Pa, April 13, 05; m. 36; c. 3. INTERNAL MEDICINE. B.S, Princeton, 29; M.D, Hopkins, 33. Asst. med, med. col, Cornell, 34-36, instr, 36-42, asst. prof. clin. med, 42-44, MED, 44-46, assoc. prof, 46-52; prof, Jefferson Med. Col, 52-57; PROF, MED. COL, CORNELL UNIV, 57-, EMER. DEAN, 69-, dean, 57-69. Vis. physician & dir. 2nd Cornell med. div, Bellevue Hosp, New York, 46-49, vis. physician, 57-; attending physician, N.Y. Hosp, 57-; dir, Assoc. Med. Schs. Greater New York. Am. Med. Asn; fel. Am. Col. Physicians; fel. N.Y. Acad. Med.(pres). Cardiovascular disease; mineral metabolism. Address: 69 Rockledge Rd, Bronxville, NY 10708.

DEITSCHMAN, GLENN H(OWARD), b. Westbrook, Minn, Jan. 26, 21; m. 49. FOREST MANAGEMENT. B.S, Minnesota, 47; M.F, Pa. State Col, 48. Asst. forest mgt, Pa. State Col, 47-48; RES. FORESTER, Cent. States Forest Exp. Sta, U.S. Forest Serv, 48-59, INTERMT. & RANGE EXP. STA, 59- U.S.A, 42-45. Soc. Am. Foresters. Ecology; silviculture. Address: Intermountain Forest & Range Experiment Station, P.O. Box 469, Moscow, ID 83843.

DEITZ, V(ICTOR) R(EUEL), b. Downingtown, Pa, Apr. 13, 09; m. 40; c. 4. PHYSICAL CHEMISTRY. Carnegie Inst. Tech, 26-27; Ph.D.(chem), Hopkins, 32. Asst, Hopkins, 32-33; Nat. Res. fel, Illinois, 33-35, spec. res. assoc, 36-37; with res. lab, Gen. Elec. Co, 37-38; res. assoc, U.S. Bur. Standards, U.S. Cane Sugar Res. Proj, 39-46, CHEMIST, 46-63; U.S. NAVAL RES. LAB, 63- Guggenheim fel, Imp. Col, London, 57-58. Am. Chem. Soc; Faraday Soc. Adsorption and adsorbents; molecular beams; sugar refining with bone char; carbon films and adsorbents. Address: Surface Chemistry Branch, U.S. Naval Research Lab, Washington, DC 20390.

DEITZ, WILLIAM H(ARRIS), b. Amsterdam, N.Y, June 14, 25; m. 46; c. 2. MICROBIOLOGY, BACTERIOLOGY. B.S, Hartwick Col, 49; M.S, Massachusetts, 51. Res. asst. bact, Sterling Winthrop Res. Inst, 52-62, res. assoc, 62-68, res. biologist, 68-70; DIR. ALUMNI AFFAIRS, HARTWICK COL, 70- U.S.N, 44-46, Res, 46-60, Lt.(jg). Am. Soc. Microbiol. Antibacterial agents; methods of bioassay; antibiotics; mode of action of nalidixic acid. Address: Hartwick College, Oneonta, NY 13820.

DEITZ, W(ILLIAM) ROBERT, b. Newton, Kans, July 6, 20; m. 42; c. 2. ANALYTICAL CHEMISTRY. B.S, Washburn Col, 45; M.S, Pittsburgh, 49. Asst. supvr. anal. lab, Pan Am. Ref. Co, 42-44; res. assoc, Mellon Inst, 44-47; instr. chem, Washington & Jefferson Col, 48-49; mgr. lab. servs, Neville Co, 49-52; chief chemist, Nat. Petrochems. Corp, 52-57, U.S. Indust. Chems, 57-68; V.PRES, INDUST. SOLVENTS GULF, INC, 68- AAAS; Am. Chem. Soc; Am. Inst. Chem. Petroleum chemistry; analytical chemistry. Address: 510 Branard, Apt. 8, Houston, TX 77006.

DEIWERT, GEORGE STEPHEN, b. Batesville, Ind, Dec. 8, 38; m. 64. MECHANICAL ENGINEERING, GAS DYNAMICS. B.S, Purdue, 62, M.S, 63, Ph.D.(mech. eng), 68; Stanford, 63-65. Res. scientist, Ames. Res. Center, NASA, 63-65; instr. mech. eng, Purdue, 65-66; RES. SCIENTIST, FLUID MECH, AMES RES. CTR, NASA, 67- Boundary layer studies; laminar and turbulent flows including effects of chemical reactions and mass addition. molecular flow simulation. Address: Ames Research Center, NASA, Moffett Field, CA 94035.

DEJAIFFE, ERNEST, b. Fernwood, Pa, Mar. 28, 12; m. 35; c. 1. CIVIL ENGINEERING. B.S, Pa. State, 33, M.S, 47; Juniata Col, 33-34. Teacher, Altoona Sch. Dist, Pa, 35-46, 47-52; instr. ENG, PA. STATE UNIV, 46-47, 52-58, asst. prof, 58-61, assoc. prof, 62-68, PROF, 68- Summers, proj. engr, City of Altoona, 51-59; design engr, Gwin Engrs, 64. English Speaking Union Award, 61. Am. Soc. Eng. Educ. Engineering education and technical institutes. Address: 214 21st Ave, Altoona, PA 16601.

DeJARLAIS, WILLIAM JAMES, b. Flint, Mich, Apr. 29, 32. ORGANIC CHEMISTRY. B.S, Michigan, 54; Ph.D.(org. chem), Illinois, 57. Assoc. chemist, NORTH. REGIONAL LAB, AGR. RES. SERV, U.S. DEPT. AGR, 57-59, RES. CHEMIST, 59- Organic synthesis; vinyl polymerization; reactions of fats, oils and their derivatives. Address: Northern Regional Lab, 1815 N. University St, Peoria, IL 61604.

DEJARNETTE, FRED ROARK, b. Rustburg, Va, Oct. 21, 33; m. 51; c. 2. AEROSPACE ENGINEERING. B.S, Ga. Inst. Tech, 57, M.S, 58; Ph.D.(aerospace eng), Va. Polytech, 65. Aerodyn. engr, Douglas Aircraft Co, Inc, 58-61; asst. prof. aerospace eng, Va. Polytech, 61-63; aerospace engr, Langley Res. Ctr, NASA, 63-65; assoc. prof. aerospace eng, Va. Polytech. Inst, 65-70; assoc. prof. MECH. & AEROSPACE ENG, N.C. STATE UNIV, 70-71, PROF, 71- Consult, Kaman Nuclear Corp, Colo, 65-66; Langley Res. Ctr, 66-; Brunswick Corp, Va, 66- U.S.A.R, 57-65, 1st Lt. Am. Astronaut. Soc; Soc. Eng. Sci; Am. Inst. Aeronaut. & Astronaut. Aerodynamics and high temperature gas dynamics. Address: Dept. of Mechanical & Aerospace Engineering, North Carolina State University, Raleigh, NC 27607.

DEJMAL, ROGER K(ENT), b. Hubbell, Nebr, Dec. 26, 40; m. 70. INSECT PHYSIOLOGY, BIOCHEMISTRY. B.A, Westmont Col, 63; M.S, Ore. State Univ, 67, Ph.D.(insect physiol), 69. Fel, environ. health sci. ctr, Ore. State Univ, summer 69; asst. prof. physiol, Sioux Falls Col, 69-70; VOL. FOOD BIOCHEM, INST. FISHERIES DEVELOP, PEACE CORPS, SANTIAGO, CHILE, 70- AAAS; Am. Sci. Affiliation. Protein synthesis and deposition during egg formation in insects; protein-lipid interaction in fish meat. Address: c/o Route 1, Box 68, Ontario, OR 97914.

DeJONG, DIEDERIK C(ORNELIS) D(IGNUS), b. Haarlem, Netherlands, Apr. 23, 31; Can. citizen; m. 56; c. 1. PLANT TAXONOMY. B.S.A, Univ. Guelph, 58, M.S.A, 60; Ph.D.(bot), Mich. State Univ, 64. Instr. bot, Miami Univ, 63-64, ASST. PROF, 64-66; McMicken Col.Arts & Sci, UNIV. CINCINNATI, 66-71, BIOL. & BOT, RAYMOND WALTERS GEN. & TECH. COL, 71- Am. Soc. Plant Taxon; Bot. Soc. Am. Address: Raymond Walters General & Technical College, Cincinnati, OH 45236.

DeJONG, DONALD WARREN, b. Doon, Iowa, Oct. 14, 30; m. 52; c. 5. PLANT CYTOCHEMISTRY. A.B, Calvin Col, 51; Michigan, 55; Nat. Sci. Found. summer fels, Yale, 60 & Occidental Col, 61; Nat. Defense Ed. Act fel, Georgia, 62-65, Ph.D.(bot), 65. Teacher, jr. high sch, 51-54, sr. high sch, Mich, 54-55; high sch, Guam, 55-57; instr. biol, Pac. Island Cent, Truk, 57-59; high sch, Mont, 59-61; Nat. Sci. Found. Inst. Sci. Teachers, 61-62; res. asst. histochem, Univ. Georgia, 63-64; res. biologist, plant enzyme pioneering res. lab, U.S. DEPT. AGR, 65-68, RES. CHEMIST, TOBACCO QUAL. INVESTS, PLANT SCI. RES. DIV, AGR. RES. SERV, 68-; ASSOC. PROF, N.C. STATE UNIV, 68- Nat. Sci. Found. summer res. participation for teachers, 62; Nat. Acad. Sci-Nat. Res. Coun. resident associateship, 65-67; Phi Sigma Soc. grad. res. award, 65. Am. Sci. Affiliation; Bot. Soc. Am; Am. Inst. Biol. Sci; Tissue Cult. Asn; Am. Soc. Plant Physiol; Phytochem. Soc. N.Am. Enzyme levels and isoenzyme patterns associated with physiological stages of growth in tobacco; biochemical properties of subcellular organelles during senescence of tobacco; postharvest alkaloid and phenolic metabolism in tobacco. Address: Tobacco Research Lab, U.S. Dept. of Agriculture, Oxford, NC 27565.

DE JONG, MARVIN LEE, b. Grand Rapids, Mich, Jan. 5, 39; m. 58; c. 2. RADIO ASTRONOMY. A.B, Hope Col, 60; M.S, Clarkson Tech, 62; Ph.D. (astron), Rensselaer Polytech, 65. Res. assoc. radio astron, Nat. Radio Astron, Observ, W.Va, 65-67; ASSOC. PROF. PHYSICS, COL. OF SCH. OF OZARKS, 67- Am. Astron. Soc. Extragalactic radio sources, particularly radio properties of normal galaxies. Address: Dept. of Mathematical Physics, College of the School of the Ozarks, Point Lookout, MO 65726.

DE JONG, REMY L(UCIEN) A(RNOUD), b. The Hague, Netherlands, Aug. 2, 33; U.S. citizen; m. 66; c. 2. HYDROLOGY, WATER RESOURCES. B.S, Hogere Tech. Sch, The Hague, 58; M.S, Univ. Pa, 60; Ph.D.(civil eng), Univ. Ariz, 69. Instr. math, Valley Forge Mil. Acad, 60-62; res. assoc. hydrol, Univ. Ariz, 64-68; asst. prof. civil eng, Univ. Tenn, Knoxville, 68-71; CONSULT. ENGR. WATER RESOURCES, 71- Consult. hydrologist, Rail N Ranch Corp, Ariz, 65-; prin. hydrologist, Soil Testing Serv. Inc, Ill, 71- Dutch Armed Forces, 53-55, 1st Lt. Am. Soc. Civil Eng; Nat. Soc. Prof. Eng; Int. Asn. Hydraul. Res; Am. Soc. Eng. Educ; Am. Geophys. Union;

Int. Asn. Sci. Hydrol. Effects of urbanization on runoff; stability of reinforced embankment dams; propagation of sudden releases and flood waves in open channels; application of systems engineering to water resources development. Address: Oracle Star Route, Box A-65, Tucson, AZ 85700.

deJONG, RUDOLPH H, b. Amsterdam, Netherlands, Aug. 10, 28; U.S. citizen; m. 56. MEDICINE, ANESTHESIOLOGY. B.S, Stanford, 51, M.D, 54. Asst. prof. anesthesia, med. center, California, San Francisco, 61-65; assoc. prof. ANESTHESIOL. & PHARMACOL, SCH. MED, UNIV. WASH, 65-70, PROF, 70-, res. career develop. award, 66- Consult, med. serv, Vet. Admin. & U.S. Navy, 61- Dipl, Am. Bd. Anesthesiol, 61. Med.C, 57-61, Capt. AAAS; Am. Med. Asn; Am. Soc. Anesthesiol. Physiology of central and peripheral nervous system. Address: Dept. of Anesthesiology RC-40, University of Washington School of Medicine, Seattle, WA 98105.

DeJONG, RUSSELL N(ELSON), b. Orange City, Iowa, Mar. 12, 07; m. 38; c. 3. NEUROLOGY. A.B, Michigan, 29, M.D, 32, M.S, 36. Instr. NEUROL, UNIV. MICH, 35-37, asst. prof, 37-41, assoc. prof, 41-50, PROF. & CHMN. DEPT, 50- Consult. & adviser, Selective Serv. Syst, Mich, 40-45; consult, Vet. Admin. Hosp, Ft. Custer, 46-, Ann Arbor, 53-; surgeon gen, Far East Command, U.S. Dept. Army, 49; Ypsilanti State Hosp, 51-; Fulbright fel, Nat. Hosp, London, 54-55. Pres, Am. Bd. Psychiat. & Neurol, 58. Ed. in chief, Neurol, 51- Am. Med. Asn; Am. Neurol. Asn.(pres, 64-65); Asn. Res. Nerv. & Ment. Disease; Am. Acad. Neurol; Int. League Against Epilepsy (pres, 54); Am. Psychiat. Asn. Clinical neurology and neurologic complications of systemic disease. Address: Dept. of Neurology, University Hospital, Ann Arbor, MI 48104.

DE JONG, SYBREN HENDRIK, b. East Kildonan, Man, Oct. 20, 08; m. 38; c. 4. GEODESY. B.Sc, Univ. Man, 31, M.Sc, 40; Nat. Res. Coun. Can. grant, Univ. B.C, 65; Ph.D, Ohio State Univ, 68. Eng. clerk, Topog. Surv. Can, 36-38, chief surv. party, 39-40; instr. civil eng, Toronto, 40-44, lectr. surv, 44-45; assoc. prof. CIVIL ENG, UNIV. B.C, 45-67, PROF, 67- Mem. subcomt. geod, assoc. comt. geod. & geophys, Nat. Res. Coun. Can; mem. adv. comt. surv, B.C. Inst. Technol. Am. Cong. Surv. & Mapping; Am. Soc. Civil Eng; Eng. Inst. Can; Can. Inst. Surv.(pres, 69). Electronic surveying measurements; crustal deformations of the earth. Address: Dept. of Civil Engineering, University of British Columbia, Vancouver 8, B.C, Can.

DeJONGH, DON C, b. Burnips, Mich, May 10, 37; m. 60; c. 3. ORGANIC CHEMISTRY. B.A, Hope Col, 59; Nat. Sci. Found. fel, Michigan, 60-62, Britton fel, 61, M.S, 61, Ph.D, 63. Res. assoc, Mass. Inst. Tech, 62-63; asst. prof. CHEM, WAYNE STATE UNIV, 63-66, assoc. prof, 66-71, PROF, 71- Vis. prof, dept. chem, Univ. Montreal, 71. Am. Chem. Soc; Am. Soc. Mass Spectrometry; The Chem. Soc. Application of mass spectrometry to structure problems in organic chemistry. Address: Dept. of Chemistry, Wayne State University, Detroit, MI 48202.

DEJU, RAUL A, b. Havana, Cuba, Mar. 14, 46; U.S. citizen; m. 68; c. 1. HYDROLOGY, GEOCHEMISTRY. B.S, N.Mex. Inst. Mining & Technol, 66, Ph.D.(geosci), 69. Res. asst. metall, State Bur. Mines & Mineral Resources, N.Mex. Inst. Mining & Technol, 62-65; NASA fel, inst. space physics, Columbia Univ, summer 65; res. asst. comput. sci, N.Mex. Inst. Mining & Technol, 66-69; vis. assoc. prof. hydraul, grad. sch. eng. & chmn. dept. geohydraul. & geochem, inst. geophys, Univ. Mex, 69-70; RES. GEOCHEMIST, GULF RES. & DEVELOP. CO, 70- Lectr, Univ. Pittsburgh, 70- Am. Inst. Mining, Metall. & Petrol. Eng. Groundwater hydrology; petroleum engineering; geology; water pollution; water management; flow through porous media. Address: Exploration Division, Gulf Research & Development Co, P.O. Drawer 2038, Pittsburgh, PA 15230.

DE JUREN, JAMES A(LRICH), b. Alameda, Calif, Dec. 14, 18; m. 46. PHYSICS. A.B, California, 40, Ph.D.(physics), 50. Asst. physics dept, California, 40-42, res. physicist calutron develop, radiation lab, 42-45; athodyds, appl. physics lab, Hopkins, 45-46; radiation lab, Univ. Calif, 46-50; neutron standards, Nat. Bur. Standards, 51-55; supvr. physics, Atomics Int, Calif, 61-67; Northrup Corp. Labs, 67-70; SELF-EMPLOYED, 70- Secy. nuclear sci. comt, Nat. Res. Coun, 51-; res. physicist, Bettis Atomic Power Div, Westinghouse Elec. Corp, 55-64. Am. Nuclear Soc. High energy neutron cross sections of nuclei; fission chambers; absolute calibration of neutron source; thermal flux; reactor parameter measurements; neutron transport and diffusion; pulsed measurements; dual space-time fast neutron spectrometer; nuclear pumped lasers; electron dosimetry; advanced radiation shield. Address: 12713 Kornblum, Hawthorne, CA 90250.

DEKABAN, ANATOLE S, b. Miedzna, Poland, June 22, 14; U.S. citizen; c. 2. NEUROLOGY. M.D, Warsaw, 44; M.Sc, McGill, 51, Ph.D.(neurol. sci), 54. Clin. instr. neurol, British Columbia, 52-55; CHIEF SECT. CHILD NEUROL, NAT. INST. NEUROL. DISEASES & STROKE, 55- Assoc. prof, med. sch, George Wash. Univ, 55- Am. Neurol. Asn; Am. Asn. Neuropath. Disorders affecting the nervous system in children; genetics; lipid metabolism. Address: Bldg. 10, National Institutes of Health, Bethesda, MD 20014.

DEKAZOS, ELIAS D(EMETRIOS), b. Merkovouni, Greece, Sept. 14, 20; U.S. citizen; m. 55; c. 2. PLANT PHYSIOLOGY. Dipl, Thessaloniki, 44; Agr. Bank Greece scholar, California, 52-54, M.S, 53, Ph.D.(plant physiol), 57. Prof. agr, Pedagogical Acad. Tripolis, Greece, 49-51; tech. adv, Agr. Bank, Greece, 45-54; res. assoc. & instr. bot, Chicago, 58-60; lectr. biochem, Loyola (Ill), 61-62; PLANT PHYSIOLOGIST, market qual. res. div, U.S. DEPT. AGR, Beltsville, 63-67, human nutrit. res. div, Agr. Res. Ctr, 67-70, RUSSELL AGR. RES. CTR, 70- Greek Army, 48-51. Am. Soc. Hort. Sci; Am. Soc. Plant Physiol; Inst. Food Technol. Anthocyanins; postharvest physiology of fruits and vegetables; objective methods of quality evaluation; color and texture; quality sorting; effects of agricultural practices and mechanical harvesting on the quality characteristics of foods. Address: Russell Agricultural Research Center, Agricultural Research Service, U.S. Dept. of Agriculture, P.O. Box 5677, Athens, GA 30604.

DEKIRMENJIAN, HAROUTUNE, b. Syria, Mar. 1, 36; U.S. citizen; m. 65. BIOCHEMISTRY. B.S, Am. Univ. Beirut, 58; Ph.D.(biochem), Univ. N.C, 65. Res. asst. biochem, Am. Univ. Beirut, 59-60; Univ. N.C, 60-65; res. scientist II, ILL. STATE PSYCHIAT. INST, 65-67, res. scientist III, 67-70, RES. SCIENTIST IV, 70- AAAS; Soc. Neurosci. B-glucuronidase activity in mammalian brain and human intracranial tumors; isolation, identification and chemical characterization of axons from whole brain; catecholamine metabolism of brain and their role in affective disorders. Address: 1601 W. Taylor St, Chicago, IL 60612.

DEKKER, ALBERT O(RNO), b. Chicago, Ill, Nov. 4, 13; m. 37; c. 2. PHYSICAL CHEMISTRY. B.S, Calif. Inst. Tech, 35, Ph.D.(phys. chem), 40; Inst. Int. Ed. Am-German exchange fel, Munich, 35-36. Assoc. prof. chem, Berea Col, 39-42; mem. dept, Calif, Inst. Tech, 42-46; prof, Berea Col, 46-48; MGR. ADVAN. PROPELLANTS & CHEM, AEROJET SOLID PROPULSION CO, 48- AAAS; Am. Chem. Soc; Am. Inst. Chem; Am. Inst. Aeronaut. & Astronaut. Kinetics of chemical reactions; chromatographic methods of chemical analysis; development and testing of solid propellants for rockets; solid propellant combustion. Address: Aerojet Solid Propulsion Co, P.O. Box 13400, Sacramento, CA 95813.

DEKKER, CHARLES ABRAM, b. Chicago, Ill, Apr. 9, 20; m. 47; c. 5. BIOCHEMISTRY. A.B, Calvin Col, 41; Ph.D.(biochem), Illinois, 47. Asst. biochem, Illinois, 41-43, teaching asst. chem, 43-44, teaching asst. biochem, 46-47; research asst, Yale, 47-49; fellow Am. Cancer Soc, Cambridge, 49-51; asst. prof. BIOCHEM, & asst, VIRUS LAB, UNIV. CALIF, BERKELEY, 51-56, assoc. prof. & assoc. res. biochemist, 56-62, PROF. & RES. BIOCHEMIST, 62- U.S.N, 44-46. Am. Chem. Soc; Am. Soc. Biol. Chem. Chemistry and enzymology of nucleic acids and their derivatives. Address: Dept. of Biochemistry, University of California, Berkeley, CA 94720.

DEKKER, DAVID B(LISS), b. Evanston, Ill, May 28, 19; m. 42; c. 2. MATHEMATICS. A.B, California, 41, Ph.D.(math), 48; M.S, Ill. Inst. Tech, 43. Asst. math, Ill. Inst. Tech, 41-43; mathematician, Lockheed Aircraft Corp, Calif, 43-44; Asst. MATH, California, 46-48; instr, UNIV. WASH, 48-51, asst. prof, 51-59, ASSOC. PROF, 59-, dir. comput. ctr, 56-66. U.S.N.R, 44-46, Lt.(jg). Am. Math. Soc. Foundations of geometry; metric differential geometry; hypergeodesic curvature and torsion; generalizations of hypergeodesics; numerical analysis. Address: Dept. of Mathematics, University of Washington, Seattle, WA 98105.

DEKKER, EUGENE E(ARL), b. Highland, Ind, July 23, 27; m. 58; c. 3. BIOCHEMISTRY. A.B, Calvin Col, 49; M.S, Univ. Ill, 51, Ph.D.(biochem), 54. Res. assoc. BIOCHEM, Univ. Ill, 54; instr, sch. med, Univ. Louisville, 54-56; life ins. med. res. fel. & instr, MED. SCH, UNIV. MICH, 56-58, asst. prof, 58-65, assoc. prof, 65-70, PROF, 70- Lederle med. faculty award, 58-61; Nat. Insts. Health res. fel, Univ. Calif, Berkeley, 65-66. U.S.N, 45-46, Res, 46-51. Am. Chem. Soc; Am. Soc. Biol. Chem; Am. Soc. Plant Physiol. Mechanism of action and comparative biochemistry of enzymes, especially aldolases; amino acid metabolism in animals, plants and bacteria; anaerobic fermentation of simple nitrogen compounds. Address: Dept. of Biochemistry, University of Michigan Medical School, Ann Arbor, MI 48104.

DEKKER, J(ACOB) C(HRISTOPH) E(DMOND), b. Hilversum, Netherlands, Sept. 6, 21; nat; m. 50. MATHEMATICS. Ph.D.(math), Syracuse, 50. Instr. MATH, Chicago, 51-52; Northwestern, 52-54, asst. prof, 54-55, vis. asst. prof, Chicago, 55-56; mem, Inst. Adv. Study, N.J, 56-58, assoc. prof, Kansas, 58-59; asst. prof, RUTGERS UNIV, 59-60, assoc. prof, 60-61, PROF, 61- Lectr, Nat. Univ. Mexico, 61; consult, Int. Bus. Machines Corp, 58, 60; mem, Inst. Advan. Study, 67-68. Math. Asn. Am; Am. Math. Soc; Asn. Symbolic Logic. Recursive functions; set theory. Address: 56 Jefferson Rd, Princeton, NJ 08540.

DEKLAU, BERNHARD, b. Tallinn, Estonia, Oct. 15, 30; U.S. citizen; m. 61; c. 3. FUEL TECHNOLOGY. B.A, Johns Hopkins Univ, 54, M.A, 55; Ph.D. (fuel technol), Pa. State Univ, 60. Sr. chemist, APPL. PHYSICS LAB, JOHNS HOPKINS UNIV, 60-, PROJ. SUPVR, 67-, asst. proj. supvr, 62-67. Am. Inst. Aeronaut. & Astronaut; Am. Chem. Soc. Physical chemistry; propulsion chemistry. Address: 9245 W. Stayman Dr, Ellicott City, MD 21043.

DEKLE, G(EORGE) W(ALLACE), b. Ocala, Fla, Nov. 4, 15; m. 42; c. 3. ENTOMOLOGY. B.S.A, Florida, 41. Grove inspector, DIV. PLANT INDUST, FLA. STATE DEPT. AGR. & CONSUMER SERV, 41-42, asst. entomologist, 46-53, entomologist, 53-71, TAXON. ENTOMOLOGIST, 71- U.S.A, 42-46, Capt. Entom. Soc. Am. Immature lepidoptera and coccoidea. Address: Division of Plant Industry, State Dept. of Agriculture & Consumer Services, Doyle Conner Bldg, P.O. Box 1269, Gainesville, FL 32601.

DE KLERK, JOHN, b. Dordrecht, S.Africa, Oct. 16, 17; m. 54; c. 2. PHYSICS. B.Sc, Cape Town, 42, M.Sc, 46; Ph.D.(physics), Imp. Col, London, 54. Mgr. electronics div, S.Machanick & Co, 46-48; sci. officer physics, S.African Bur. Standards, 48-50; res. assoc. appl. math, Brown, 55-56, asst. prof. physics, 56-59; MGR, PRAETERSONICS, WESTINGHOUSE RES. & DEVELOP. CTR, 60- S.African Sig.C, 43-45, Radar Officer. Inst. Elec. & Electronics Eng; Am. Phys. Soc; Am. Vacuum Soc. Measurement of elastic constants of single crystals between room and helium temperatures at high frequencies; phonon-phonon interactions in dielectric materials at microwave frequencies; surface elastic wave fundamental physics and device research. Address: Westinghouse Research & Development Center, Beulah Rd, Pittsburgh, PA 15235.

DeKLOET, S(IWO) R, b. Maarssen, Netherlands, Feb. 22, 33; m. 64; c. 2. BIOCHEMISTRY, MOLECULAR GENETICS. B.S, Utrecht, 53, M.S, 56, Ph.D.(biophys. chem), 61. Res. assoc. cell biol, Rockefeller Univ, 61-62; res. scientist, Philips Res. Labs, Eindhoven, Netherlands, 63-67, ASSOC. PROF. BIOL, FLA. STATE UNIV, 67- Med. Troops, Dutch Army, 56-58, Capt. Metabolism and properties of nucleic acids; genetics of fungi; metabolism of nucleotide analogues; mechanism of action of antibiotics. Address: Dept. of Biological Science, Florida State University, Tallahassee, FL 32306.

DEKORNFELD, THOMAS JOHN, b. Iregszemcse, Hungary, June 19, 24; U.S. citizen; m. 52; c. 4. ANESTHESIOLOGY. B.S, George Washington, 48, M.S. 49; M.D, Harvard Med. Sch, 53. Instr. anesthesiol, sch. med, Wisconsin,

56-57; asst. chief, Baltimore City Hosp, Md, 57-60, chief, 60-63; dir. clin. therapeut, Parke, Davis & Co, Mich, 63-64; assoc. prof. ANESTHESIOL, MED. SCH, UNIV. MICH, 64-68, PROF, 68- U.S.A, 46-47. Am. Med. Asn; Am. Soc. Anesthesiol; Am. Soc. Pharmacol. Clinical pharmacology; clinical and laboratory investigation of new narcotic and non-narcotic analgesics. Address: Dept. of Anesthesiology, University of Michigan Medical Center, Ann Arbor, MI 48104.

DE KORTE, AART, b. Rotterdam, Netherlands, Sept. 4, 34; U.S. citizen. PHYSICAL CHEMISTRY. B.A, N.Y. Univ, 58; M.S, Yale, 60, Nat. Insts. Health fel, 62-64, Ph.D.(chem), 65. Instr. CHEM, Queens Col.(N.Y), 64-66; asst. prof, FAIRLEIGH DICKINSON UNIV, 66-71, ASSOC. PROF, 71- Am. Chem. Soc; N.Y. Acad. Sci. Diffusion in liquid solutions; fluorescence in the condensed state. Address: Dept. of Chemistry, Fairleigh Dickinson University, Rutherford, NJ 07070.

DeKORTE, JOHN MARTIN, b. Grand Rapids, Mich, Sept. 20, 40; m. 63; c. 2. INORGANIC CHEMISTRY. B.A, Hope Col, 62; Ph.D.(inorg. chem), Purdue, 69. ASST. PROF. CHEM, NORTH. ARIZ. UNIV, 66- Summer res. chemist, Dow Chem. Co, 62. Am. Chem. Soc. Kinetics and mechanisms of oxidation-reduction reactions. Address: Dept. of Chemistry, Box 5698, Northern Arizona University, Flagstaff, AZ 86001.

DE KORVIN, ANDRE, b. Berlin, Ger, Dec. 13, 35; U.S. citizen; m. 67. MATHEMATICS. B.A, Univ. Calif, Los Angeles, 62, M.A, 63, Ph.D.(math), 67. Mathematician, IBM Corp, San Jose, Calif, 63-64, res. mathematician, sci. ctr, Los Angeles, 64-67; asst. prof. MATH, Carnegie-Mellon Univ, 67-69; IND. STATE UNIV, 69-71, ASSOC. PROF, 71-, vis. asst. prof, 68-69. AAAS; Am. Math. Soc; Math. Asn. Am. Functional analysis; algebra of operators; vector measures. Address: Dept. of Mathematics, Indiana State University, Terre Haute, IN 47809.

DE KOSTER, HEINZ A, b. Heidelberg, Ger, Apr. 11, 19; m. 42; c. 2. PHYSICS. M.S, Acad. Tech. Sci. & Arts, Rotterdam, Netherlands, 39; Ph.D.(appl. physics), Heidelberg, 45. Head lab. electronic res, Hasler A.G, Switz, 53-59; physicist, Allen-Bradley Co, Wis, 59-61; solid state-magnetics expert, 61-64; res. assoc. & head appl. physics lab, Gen. Time Corp, 64-68; exec. v.pres, Seggos Industs. Inc, 68-70; PRES, VIREX CORP, 70- AAAS; sr. mem. Inst. Elec. & Electronics Eng; Am. Phys. Soc; N.Y. Acad. Sci. Industrial physics; solid state; magnetics; thin films; gas discharges; displays; video recording systems; anti-world anti-time conceptions; electric field distribution in fluid and solid media; management sciences; scientific marketing. Address: 47 Caprice Dr, Stamford, CT 06902.

DE KRASINSKI, JOSEPH S, b. Mszana, Poland, June 15, 14; m. 47; c. 4. FLUID MECHANICS. B.Sc, London, 44, Ph.D.(aeronaut), 64. Res. scientist Royal Aircraft Estab, Farnborough, Eng, 44-46; head aerodyn. res, Argentine Aeronaut. Res. Inst, 47-67; ASSOC. PROF. FLUID MECH, UNIV. CALGARY, 66- Prof, Cordoba, 55-67. R.A.F, 40-47, Flight Lt; Distinguished Flying Cross. Am. Inst. Aeronaut. & Astronaut. Aerodynamics; gas dynamics; boundary layer theory; separated flows; atmospheric aerodynamics; compressible boundary layers; wind tunnelling; experimental techniques in wind tunnels; wind tunnel design. Address: Dept. of Mechanical Engineering, University of Calgary, Calgary 44, Alta, Can.

DELABARRE, EVERETT M(ERRILL), JR, b. Boston, Mass, Mar. 3, 18; m. 53; c. 4. MEDICINE. B.A, Columbia, 40, M.D, 43. Asst. path, Columbia, 44; clin. instr. med, Yale, 54-57; assoc. chief MED, Mem. Med. Center, Williamson, W.Va, 57-64; asst. chief, Vet. Admin. Hosp, 64-65; asst. prof. PHYS. MED. & REHAB, TUFTS UNIV, 65-70, ASSOC. PROF, 70- U.S.N, 44-46, 49-53, Capt. Am. Thoracic Soc; Asn. Mil. Surg. U.S; Asn. Am. Med. Cols. Chest disease and pulmonary physiology. Address: Rehabilitation Institute, 185 Harrison Ave, Boston, MA 02111.

de la CHAPELLE, CLARENCE E(WALD), b. New York, N.Y, Dec. 6, 97; m. 25; c. 2. MEDICINE. B.S, N.Y. Univ, 21, M.D, 22. Intern & house physician, Bellevue Hosp, 22224; instr. path, col. med, N.Y. UNIV, 24-26, med, 26-32, asst. prof, 32-38, acting chmn. dept, 37-38, prof. clin. med, 38-48, asst. dean, 42-45, assoc. dean, 45-63, POST-GRAD. MED. SCH, 48-, dir. post-grad. div, 45-48, PROF. MED, 45-, dir. regional hosp, div, N.Y. Univ-Bellevue Med. Center, 47-63; CONSULT, 63- Physician, sch. nursing, Bellevue Hosp, 25-45, asst. physician, out-patient dept. & from adj. asst. vis. physician to vis. physician, hosp, 25-; acting dir, 3rd med. div, 37-38; chief cardiac clinic, Lenox Hill Hosp, 33-48, assoc. vis. physician, 33-45, attend. cardiologist, 45-48, dir. med, 48-60, consult. med, 60-; consult. physician, St. Lukes Hosp, Newburgh, N.Y, 33-48; consult. cardiologist, Community Hosp, Glen Cove, 45-49, 58-, New Rochelle Hosp, 47-; Nassau Hosp, L.I, 51-56; North Shore Hosp, L.I, 57- Consult, Fitkin Mem. Hosp, N.J, 46-53; Flushing Hosp, L.I, 46-58; Vassar Bros. Hosp, 47-55; nat. consult, Surgeon Gen, U.S. Air Force, 58-64. Consult. & adv. prof. ed, U.S. War Dept, 42-44; mem, med. adv. panel, Fed. Aviation Agency, 65-68; consult. cardiovasc. diseases. Pres. Citation, N.Y. Univ, 63. AAAS; fel. Am. Med. Asn; fel. Am. Col. Physicians; fel. Am. Heart Asn; Am. Asn. Path. & Bact; fel. N.Y. Acad. Med; Int. Acad. Path. Cardiovascular pathology; correlation of clinical and pathological data in cardiovascular diseases; post-graduate and graduate medical education. Address: Dept. of Medicine, New York University Medical Center, 550 First Ave, New York, NY 10016.

DE LA CUESTA, HERNANDO, b. Pereira, Colombia, Dec. 7, 35; m. 57; c. 1. ELECTRICAL ENGINEERING, MATHEMATICS. B.S, Delaware, 51, Ph.D. (appl. sci), 62; M.A, Indiana, 60. Asst. dean eng, Univ. of the Andes, Colombia, 62; asst. prof. elec. eng, Vermont, 63-66; asst. prof. & head pre-eng. prog, Moorhead State Col, 66-68; ASST. PROF. ELEC. ENG, SACRAMENTO STATE COL, 68- Inst. Elec. & Electronics Eng; Am. Math. Soc; Am. Phys. Soc. Applied science; communication and information theory; heat transfer and nonlinear control theory. Address: Dept. of Electrical Engineering, Sacramento State College, Sacramento, CA 95819.

DeLACY, ALLAN C(LARK), b. Seattle, Wash, May 21, 12; m. 36; c. 3. FISHERIES. B.S, Washington (Seattle), 32, M.S, 33, Ph.D.(fisheries), 41. Sci. asst, Int. Fisheries Cmn, Seattle, 34-36; jr. aquatic biologist, U.S. Fish & Wildlife Serv, 36-43; fisheries biologist, State Fisheries Dept, Wash, 43-47; asst. prof, FISHERIES, UNIV. WASH, 47-51, assoc. prof, 51-58, PROF, 58- Am. Fisheries Soc; Am. Soc. Ichthyol. & Herpet; Am. Inst. Fisheries Res. Biol. Fish migration; early life histories of marine fishes. Address: College of Fisheries, University of Washington, Seattle, WA 98105.

DE LA FUENTE, ROLLO K, b. Mt. Province, Philippines, Oct. 6, 33; m. 61; c. 2. PLANT PHYSIOLOGY. B.S, Philippines, 55; Int. Coop. Admin. fel, Hawaii, 58-59, M.S, 59, Rockefeller Found. fel, 61-63, Ph.D.(bot), 64. Asst. instr. bot, Philippines, 55-58, instr, 59-61; res. asst, Hawaii, 63-64; res. fel. plant physiol, Purdue Univ, 64-69; ASST. PROF, KENT STATE UNIV, 69- Am. Soc. Plant Physiol. Plant hormone (auxin) transport; leaf abscission. Address: Dept. of Biological Science, Kent State University, Kent, OH 44242.

DELAGI, EDWARD F, b. New York, N.Y, Nov. 4, 11; m. 41; c. 2. MEDICINE. B.S, Fordham, 34; M.D, Hahnemann Med. Col.(Pa), 38. Assoc. prof. REHAB. MED, ALBERT EINSTEIN COL. MED, 59-64, PROF, 64- Asst. chief paraplegic sect, Vet. Admin. Hosp, Bronx, 51-53, chief ward sect, phys. med. & rehabil, 51-56, attend. physician, 56-; dir, Frances Schervier Hosp. & Home, Riverdale, 56-; vis. physician, Bronx Munic. Hosp. Center, 56-; adj. Jewish Hosp. Chronic Diseases, Brooklyn, 56-58; chief, St. Joseph's Hosp, Yonkers, 57-; Misericordia Hosp, Bronx, 58- U.S.A, 41-46, Lt. Col. AAAS; fel. Am. Med. Asn; fel. Am. Acad. Phys. Med. & Rehab; fel. Am. Cong. Rehab. Med; fel. Am. Col. Physicians. Physical medicine and rehabilitation; kinesiology; electromyography; electrodiagnostic methods. Address: Dept. of Rehabilitation Medicine, Albert Einstein College of Medicine, Eastchester Rd. & Morris Park Ave, New York, NY 10461.

de LAGUNA, WALLACE, b. Philadelphia, Pa, Apr. 20, 10; m. 33; c. 3. GEOLOGY. B.S, Haverford Col, 32; M.A, Harvard, 37, Ph.D.(geol), 38. Instr. geol, Queens Col, City Col, 38-47; GEOLOGIST, mil. geol. unit, U.S. Geol. Surv, 43-45, ground water br, 47-57; HEALTH PHYSICS DIV, OAK RIDGE NAT. LAB, 57- Geol. Soc. Am; Soc. Econ. Geol; Am. Geophys. Union. Ground water geology; radioactive waste disposal. Address: Oak Ridge National Lab, Oak Ridge, TN 37831.

DE LA HABA, G(ABRIEL) L(UIS), b. P.R, June 29, 26; m. 61. BIOLOGICAL CHEMISTRY. A.B, Hopkins, 46, Ph.D.(biol), 50. U.S. Pub. Health Serv. fel, N.Y. Univ, 51-52; Yale, 52-53, instr. biochem, 53-54, asst. prof, 54-55; sr. asst. scientist, U.S. Pub. Health Serv, 55-58; res. assoc, Hopkins, 58-59; ANAT, UNIV. PA, 59-68, ASSOC. PROF, SCH. MED, 68- Am. Soc. Biol. Chem. Metabolism of carbohydrates and proteins; biochemistry of development. Address: Dept. of Anatomy, University of Pennsylvania School of Medicine, Philadelphia, PA 19104.

DELAHAY, PAUL, b. Sas Van Gent, Netherlands, Apr. 6, 21; nat; m. 62. CHEMICAL PHYSICS. B.S, Brussels, 41, M.S, 45, Liege, 44; Ph.D.(chem), Oregon, 48. Instr. CHEM, Brussels, 45-46; res. assoc, Oregon, 48-49; asst. prof, La. State, 49-52; assoc. prof, 52-55, prof, 55-56, Boyd prof, 56-65; PROF, N.Y. UNIV, 65- Guggenheim fel, Cambridge, 55, N.Y. Univ, 71-72; Fulbright prof, Paris, 62-63. Univ. medal, Brussels, 63; Heyrovsky medal, Czech. Acad. Sci. AAAS; Am. Chem. Soc.(award in pure chem, 55, southwest award, 59); Electrochem. Soc.(Turner prize, 51, Palladium Medal Award, 67); Am. Phys. Soc. Photoelectron emission spectroscopy of solutions; electron scattering in gases; solvated electron. Address: Dept. of Chemistry, New York University, 4 Washington Pl, Room 410, New York, NY 10003.

DELAHAYES, JEAN, b. Rouen, France, June 9, 36; m. 57; c. 1. PHYSIOLOGY. Lic. ès Sci, Univ. Paris, 64, Dipl, 66, Dr. ès Sci.(physiol), 68. Teaching asst. PHYSIOL, Univ. Paris, 65-68; instr, OHIO STATE UNIV, 69-70, ASST. PROF, 70- French Armed Forces, 62-69, Sgt. Movements of ions across the cell membrane in heart during activity; problems of excitation cantiaction coupling; movements of Ca^{45} associated with heart activity. Address: Dept. of Physiology, Ohio State University, 370 W. Ninth Ave, Columbus, OH 43210.

DE LA HUERGA, J(ESÚS), b. Oviedo, Spain, Nov. 25, 15; U.S. citizen; m. 47; c. 5. MEDICINE, PATHOLOGY. M.D, Santo Domingo, 40; Ph.D.(path), Northwestern, 57. Dir. labs, Santo Domingo, 41-48; researcher, Hektoen Inst. Med. Res, 48-52; BIOCHEMIST, CHICAGO STATE TUBERC. SANITARIUM, 53- Asst. path, Northwestern, 60- Consult. biochem, Grant Hosp, Chicago, 53-64; Resurrection & St. Bernard's Hosps, 62-; S.Shore Hosp, 63-; W.Surburban Hosp, Oak Park, 60-64. Am. Soc. Exp. Path; Asn. Clin. Sci; Am. Asn. Study Liver Diseases. Biochemistry and clinical chemistry with emphasis on biochemistry in liver diseases. Address: 1414 Lincoln St, Evanston, IL 60201.

DE LAHUNTA, ALEXANDER, b. Concord, N.H, Dec. 3, 32; m. 55; c. 4. VETERINARY ANATOMY, NEUROLOGY. D.V.M, State Univ. N.Y. Vet. Col, 58; Ph.D.(vet. anat), Cornell, 64. Vet. practitioner, Cilley's Animal Hosp, N.H, 58-60; instr. VET. ANAT, STATE UNIV. N.Y. VET. COL, CORNELL UNIV, 60-63, asst. prof, 63-67, ASSOC. PROF, 67- Am. Vet. Med. Asn; Am. Asn. Vet. Anat; Am. Asn. Anat; Am. Asn. Vet. Neurol. Clinical neurology; neuropathology; neuroanatomy. Address: State University of New York Veterinary College, Cornell University, Ithaca, NY 14850.

DE LA IGLESIA, FELIX ALBERTO, b. Cordoba, Argentina, Nov. 27, 39; m. 64; c. 3. EXPERIMENTAL PATHOLOGY & TOXICOLOGY. B.Sc, Cordoba, 56, Argentine Armed Forces Inst. Tech. & Sci. Res. fel, 61, Argentine Nat. Acad. Med, fel, 62, M.D, 63. Instr. path, Cordoba, 59-62, res. asst. electron micros, 63-64; res. fel, Hosp. Sick Children, Toronto, 64-66, scientist, WARNER-LAMBERT RES. INST. CAN, 66-68, DIR. TOXICOL, 68- Med. Res. Coun. Can. res. fel; mem, Int. Study Group Res. in Cardiac Metab. Arg. Army, 53-56, Sub-Lt. AAAS; Histochem. Soc; Soc. Toxicol; fel. Royal Micros. Soc; Am. Soc. Exp. Path; Am. Inst. Biol. Sci; Am. Asn. Path. & Bact; Electron Micros. Soc. Am; N.Y. Acad. Sci; Int. Soc. Stereology; Can. Soc. Cell. Biol; Can. Asn. Res. Toxicol; Europ. Soc. Study Drug Toxicity; hon. mem. Dominican Repub. Med. Asn; hon. mem. Dominican Repub. Gastroenterol. Soc. Liver diseases; nutrition; adverse hepatic effects of therapeutic agents; toxicology; drug safety. Address: Warner-Lambert Research Institute of Canada, Sheridan Park Research Center, Mississauga, Ont, Can.

DeLAITSCH, DALE M, b. Colfax, Wis, Dec. 18, 22; m. 45; c. 2. ORGANIC CHEMISTRY. B.S, Univ. Chicago, 44; A.B, St. Olaf Col, 46; Ph.D.(chem), Univ. Minn, 50. Asst. prof. CHEM, UNIV. SOUTHWEST. LA, 50-52, assoc. prof, 52-63, PROF, 63- U.S.A.F, 43-46, 1st Lt. Am. Chem. Soc. Protection of hydroxyl and sulfhydryl groups. Address: Dept. of Chemistry, University of Southwestern Louisiana, Lafayette, LA 70501.

DE LA MARE, HAROLD E(LISON), b. Burley, Idaho, Aug. 5, 22; m. 52; c. 6. ORGANIC & POLYMER CHEMISTRY. B.S, Utah State, 44; Allied Chem. & Dye fel, 48-49, Ph.D.(org. chem), 51. Chemist, Eastman Kodak Co, N.Y, 44-46; asst. org. chem, Purdue, 46-48, 49-50, instr. chem, 50-51; RES. CHEMIST, SHELL DEVELOP. CO, 51- Am. Chem. Soc. Organic peroxide chemistry and oxidation reactions; free radical-metal ion interactions; coordination complex catalysis in elastomer synthesis; anionic polymerization. Address: Shell Development Co, 1400 53rd St, Emeryville, CA 94608.

DeLAMATER, EDWARD D(OANE), b. Plainfield, N.J, Jan. 24, 12; m. 43; c. 5. MICROBIOLOGY, ELECTRON MICROSCOPY. M.A, Hopkins, 37; Ph.D. (bact, dermat), Columbia, 41, M.D, 42. Asst. bot, Hopkins, 33-36; dermat, Columbia, 36-42, mycologist, Vanderbilt Clin, med. center, 36-42; fel. dermat. Mayo Found, Minnesota, 46-47, asst. prof. bact. & mycol, 47-48; mycologist, Mayo Clin, 46-48; assoc. res. prof. dermat, sch. med, Pennsylvania, 48-51, microbiol, 50-51, res. prof, 51-63, dermat, 51-63, dir. sect. cytol. & cytochem, 53-63, consult. to Pepper Lab. Hosp, 48-63; prof. & chmn. dept. microbiol, N.Y. Med. Col, 63-66; hosp. epidemiologist, New York City Dept. Health, 65-66; univ. prof. microbiol. & dean, col. sci, FLA. ATLANTIC UNIV, 66-68, DISTINGUISHED UNIV. PROF. SCI, 68- Guggenheim fel, 53; consult, Smith, Kline & French Lab, 48-51; Off. Surg. Gen, 48-63; Children's Hosp, Phila, 49-63; Skin & Cancer Hosp, 58-63. Med.C, U.S.A, 43-46. AAAS; Mycol. Soc. Am; Am. Col. Physicians; Bot. Soc. Am; Genetics Soc. Am; Am. Med. Asn; Torrey Bot. Club; Am. Soc. Trop. Med. & Hyg; Royal Soc. Med; fel. Royal Soc. Health. Cytology and cytochemistry of micro-organisms; medical mycology; life cycles of spirochetes. Address: College of Science, Florida Atlantic University, Boca Raton, FL 33432.

DeLaMATER, GEORGE (BEARSE), b. Oneonta, N.Y, Mar. 12, 22; m. 48; c. 2. ORGANIC CHEMISTRY. B.Ch.E, Cornell, 44; Nat. Res. Coun. fel, Harvard, 45-48, Ph.D.(phys. org. chem), 48. Res. chemist, nat. defense res. cmt, Cornell, 43-45; res. engr, Explosives Res. Lab, Pa, 45; res. chemist, Mallinckrodt Chem. Works, 48-53, assoc. dir. org. res, 53-56; dir. org. res, 56-60, dir. med. chem. res, 60-62, dir. res, indust. chem. div, 62-66; asst. dir. chem. res, Hondry Labs, AIR PROD. & CHEM, INC, 66-68, dir. chem. res, 68-70, TECH. DIR. INDUST. CHEM. DEPT, 70- Fel. AAAS; Am. Chem. Soc. Process development; research administration. Address: Air Products & Chemicals, Inc, Box 427, Marcus Hook, PA 19061.

de LAMIRANDE, G(ASTON), b. Montreal, Can, Dec. 22, 23; m. 50; c. 3. BIOLOGICAL CHEMISTRY. B.A, Montreal, 43, B.Sc, 46, Nat. Res. Coun. Can. student & fel, 47-48, 48-49, M.Sc, 47, Ph.D.(chem), 49. Lectr. org. chem, Montreal, 46-49; res. assoc. biochem, MONTREAL CANCER INST, NAT. CANCER INST, CAN, NOTRE DAME HOSP, 49-60, res. scientist, 60-67, ASSOC. DIR, 67-; RES. PROF. BIOL. CHEM, FACULTY MED, UNIV. MONTREAL, 67-, res. assoc. prof, 60-67. Damon Runyon Found. Cancer Res. fel, 52-55. AAAS; Am. Asn. Cancer Res; N.Y. Acad. Sci; Can. Physiol. Soc; Can. Biochem. Soc; Chem. Inst. Can. Chemistry and metabolism of nucleic acids and proteins; enzymology; cancer. Address: Montreal Cancer Institute, Notre Dame Hospital, Montreal, Que, Can.

DE LANCEY, GEORGE BYERS, b. Cresson, Pa, Oct. 19, 40; m. 63; c. 2. CHEMICAL ENGINEERING. B.S, Pittsburgh, 62, M.S, 65, NASA fel, 65-67, Ph.D.(chem. eng), 67. Res. eng, Jones & Laughlin Steel Corp, 63-65, consult, 65-66; res. assoc. math, Nat. Bur. Standards, 67-68; ASST. PROF. CHEM. ENG, STEVENS INST. TECHNOL, 68- Am. Inst. Chem. Eng. Interfacial mass transfer and heterogeneous catalysis. Address: Dept. of Chemistry & Chemical Engineering, Stevens Institute of Technology, Castle Point Station, Hoboken, NJ 07030.

De LANCIE, RICHARD, b. Berkeley, Calif, May 9, 15; m. 50; c. 3. OPERATIONS RESEARCH, MATHEMATICAL STATISTICS. A.B, California, Berkeley, 40. Geologist, Shell Oil Co, 41-42; asst. mgr. opers. res, econ. planning dept, Pac. Alaska Div, Pan Am. World Airways, 46-48; opers. analyst, West. Air Defense Force, 52-54; Broadview Res. Corp, 54-57, pres, URS SYSTS. CORP, 57-71, CHMN. & CHIEF EXEC. OFF, 71- Consult, Proj. Vista, 51-52; White House Task Force on Air Inspection, 55-56. U.S.N, 42-46, 51-52, Lt. Comdr. Economet. Soc; Opers. Res. Soc. Am; Inst. Math. Statist; Inst. Mgt. Sci. Operations research on commercial and military aircraft operations; design and analysis of experiments; application of photographic techniques to military intelligence. Address: URS Systems Corp, 155 Bovet Rd, San Mateo, CA 94402.

DELAND, ANDRE N, b. St. Johns, Que, Feb. 6, 26; m. 56; c. 1. GEOLOGY. B.A, Montreal, 51; M.Sc, McGill, 52; Ph.D.(geol), Yale, 55. Field geologist, Que. Dept. Mines, 55-65; ASST. PROF. GEOL, SIR GEORGE WILLIAMS UNIV, 65- Geol. Soc. Can; Can. Inst. Mining & Metall. Petrology; industrial minerals; field geology. Address: Dept. of Geology, Sir George Williams University, Montreal, Que, Can.

DeLAND, E(DWARD) C(HARLES), b. Lusk, Wyo, May 16, 22; m. 52. MATHEMATICS. B.S, S.Dak. Sch. Mines & Technol, 43; Ph.D.(math), Univ. Calif, Los Angeles, 56. Engr, Corning Glass Works, 43-46; asst. prof. physics, San Diego State Col, 46-48; dir. analog comput. facility, UNIV. CALIF, LOS ANGELES, 53-56, INSTR. ENG, 56-; MATHEMATICIAN, RAND CORP, 59-, dir. analog comput. facility, 56-59. Res. colloid sci, Cambridge, 65; Nat. Insts. Health Spec. Res. Resources Bd. fel, 67-68; consult, Nat. Ctr. Health Serv. Res. & Develop, 68- Math. Asn. Am; Asn. Comput. Mach; Int. Asn. Analog Comput. Computer design and applications; applied mathematics; pedagogy; biochemistry; psysiology; computer systems. Address: Rand Corp, 1700 Main St, Santa Monica, CA 90406.

DeLAND, FRANK H, b. Jackson, Mich, July 2, 21; m. 49; c. 4. NUCLEAR MEDICINE. B.S, Univ. Mich, Ann Arbor, 47; M.D, Univ. Louisville, 52; M.S, Univ. Minn, St. Paul, 56. Fel. path, Mayo Found, 53-56; instr, Ohio State Univ, 56-57; dir. lab. med, Lakeland, Fla, 57-67; Nat. Insts. Health fel, Johns Hopkins Univ, 66-67, assoc. prof. NUCLEAR MED, 67-70; PROF, UNIV. FLA, 70- Res. grants, U.S. Dept. Health Educ. & Welfare, 67-71 & Vet. Admin, 71- U.S.A.A.F, 42-46, Capt. Am. Soc. Clin. Path; Col. Am. Path; Int. Acad. Path; Soc. Nuclear Med. Application of radionuclides for in-vivo study and diagnosis of neoplastic, inflammatory and congenital disease; automation of microbiology by means of in-vitro radionuclide methodology. Address: Dept. of Radiology, University of Florida College of Medicine, Gainesville, FL 32601.

DELAND, RAYMOND J, b. Vila, New Hebrides, Aug. 16, 27; m. 56; c. 3. METEOROLOGY. B.S, Adelaide, 47; Ph.D.(meteorol), Pa. State, 59. Meteorologist, Australian Meteorol. Serv, 50-54; asst. prof. meteorol, Texas A&M, 57-59; meteorologist, Bendix Corp, 59; asst. prof. METEOROL, Wisconsin, 60-64; RES. ASSOC. PROF, N.Y. UNIV, 64- AAAS; Am. Meteorol. Soc; Royal Meteorol. Soc. Dynamic meteorology. Address: Dept. of Meteorology & Oceanography, New York University, Bronx, NY 10453.

DELANEY, C(HARLES) MacGREGOR, b. Ottawa, Can, July 16, 22; nat; div; c. 2. PHYSICAL CHEMISTRY. A.B, Detroit, 43; M.Sc, Syracuse, 47, Ph.D. (phys. chem), 52; Chicago; Wayne. Plastics engr, eng. div, Chrysler Corp, 44-45; asst. & asst. instr. chem, Syracuse, 45-52; res. chemist, Houston Research Lab, Shell Oil Co, 52-54; Gulf Found. fel, Mellon Inst, 54-56; lectr, Pittsburgh, 55, asst. prof, 56-58; assoc. prof. CHEM, WELLS COL, 58-63, PROF, 64- Fulbright lectr, Vidyodaya Univ, Ceylon, 64-65. Am. Chem. Soc. Vapor pressure of solutions by differential manometry; thermal cracking; catalysis; olefin polymerization; thermodynamics. Address: Dept. of Chemistry, Wells College, Aurora, NY 13026.

DELANEY, FRANK M(ICHAEL), b. Phila, Pa, May 8, 23; m. 53; c. 4. MATHEMATICS. B.S, Temple Univ, 52. Systs. analyst, UNIVAC DIV, SPERRY RAND CORP, 52-54, asst. dir, automatic programming, 54-58, asst. to mgr. commercial eng, 58-59, dir. appl. & mkt. res. div, prod. planning, 59-60, appln. & prog. res, 60-64, proj. mgr. vioso, 64-65, mgr. prod. prog, 65-69, dir. Phila. opers, systs. prog, 69-70, DIR. SOFTWARE DEVELOP. FOR SMALL & MEDIUM SCALE COMPUT, 70- U.S.A.A.F, 43-46. Asn. Comput. Mach. Programming; electronic computers; logical design; management; small and large scale computing devices; systems analyses of data processing and scientific applications. Address: Univac Division, Sperry Rand Corp, P.O. Box 500, Bluebell, PA 19422.

DELANEY, JOHN P, b. St. Paul, Minn, Oct. 1, 30; m. 60; c. 2. SURGERY, PHYSIOLOGY. B.S, Minnesota, 53, M.D, 55, Ph.D.(physiol), 63. Med. fel. SURG, UNIV. MINN, MINNEAPOLIS, 59-67, asst. prof, 67-69, ASSOC. PROF, 69- U.S. Pub. Health Serv. fel, 57-58, Capt. U.S.A, 57-58, Capt. Splanchnic blood flow; gastric freezing; cause of peptic ulcer. Address: Dept. of Surgery, University of Minnesota, Minneapolis, MN 55455.

DELANEY, PATRICK F(RANCIS), JR, b. Fall River, Mass, Mar. 11, 33; m. 54; c. 4. BIOCHEMISTRY. A.B, Providence Col, 54; A.M.T, Brown Univ, 61, Ph.D.(biol), 64. Teacher, high schs, Mass, 55-59, chmn. dept. math, 60-61; asst. biol, Brown Univ, 61-63, summer instr, 63; asst. prof. biochem. & physiol, Col. Holy Cross, 64-67, assoc. prof. BIOL, 67-69; PROF. & CHMN. DEPT, LINDENWOOD COLS, 69-, DEAN, LINDENWOOD COL. II, 71- Nat. Inst. Arthritis & Metab. Diseases res. grant, 64-70; summer fel, Brown Univ, 64. AAAS; N.Y. Acad. Sci. Renal metabolism; mitochondrial protein synthesis; hormonal regulation of metabolism. Address: Dept. of Biology, Lindenwood Colleges, St. Charles, MO 63301.

DELANEY, ROBERT, b. Pittsfield, Mass, May 20, 28; m. 53; c. 8. BIOCHEMISTRY. B.S, Boston Col, 52; Ph.D.(biochem), Albany Med. Col, 63. Res. scientist, div. labs. & res, N.Y. State Dept. Health, 60-63; Nat. Inst. Arthritis & Metab. Diseases fel, med. ctr, Duke, 63-66, res. assoc. BIOCHEM, 65-66; asst. prof, SCH. MED, UNIV. OKLA, 66-68, ASSOC. PROF, 68- U.S.A, 46-48, Sgt. Am. Asn. Immunol; Am. Soc. Biol. Chem. Protein structure in enzymology of ribonucleases and interrelations of antigen and antibody structure in determination of specificity. Address: Dept. of Biochemistry, University of Oklahoma School of Medicine, 801 N.E. 13th St, Oklahoma City, OK 73104.

DELANEY, ROBERT M(ICHAEL), b. Wood River, Ill, Nov. 13, 31. PHYSICS. B.S, St. Louis, 53, Ph.D.(physics), 58. Asst. prof. PHYSICS, ST. LOUIS UNIV, 56-65, assoc. prof, 65-68, PROF, 68- Am. Phys. Soc. Thermal neutron scattering; relativistic wave equations; high energy physics. Address: Dept. of Physics, St. Louis University, 221 N. Grand Blvd, St. Louis, MO 63103.

DeLANGE, ROBERT J, b. Richfield, Utah, Mar. 30, 37; m. 60; c. 5. BIOCHEMISTRY, PROTEIN CHEMISTRY. B.S, Brigham Young, 61; Nat. Insts. Health fel, Washington (Seattle), 62-65, Ph.D.(biochem), 65. Fel. BIOL. CHEM, SCH. MED, UNIV. CALIF, LOS ANGELES, 65-67, asst. prof, 67-71, ASSOC. PROF, 71- Am. Soc. Biol. Chem. Amino acid sequences of proteins as a means of studying structure-function relationships, including the role of naturally occurring derivatives of amino acids. Address: Dept. of Biological Chemistry, University of California School of Medicine, Los Angeles, CA 90024.

deLANGLADE, RONALD ALLAN, b. Indianapolis, Ind, May 20, 36; m. 62; c. 1. PLANT MORPHOLOGY. B.A, Wabash Col, 58; Mich. State, 58-59; M.S, Purdue, 61, Ph.D.(morphol), 64. Instr. BIOL, Wabash Col, 61-64; asst. prof, Eastern Kentucky, 64-65, assoc. prof, 65-67; asst. prof, WITTENBERG UNIV, 67-70, ASSOC. PROF, 70- Partic, Nat. Sci. Found. summer inst. radio-bot, 66. AAAS; Bot. Soc. Am. Plant succession in old-fields; leaf morphogenesis. Address: Dept. of Biology, Wittenberg University, Springfield, OH 45501.

DELANGRE, JOHN P(AUL), b. Clifton, N.J, Sept. 30, 21; m. 47; c. 2. ORGANIC CHEMISTRY. M.S, Louvain, 43, Sc.D.(org. chem), 44. Res. chemist, Union Chem. Co, Belgium, 44; res. group leader, Technicolor Motion

Picture Corp, 47-58; dir. res, Houston Fearless Corp, 58-59; mem. tech. staff, data systems proj. off, Ramo-Wooldridge, 59-61; mgr. space exp. dept, manned syst. div, Aerospace Corp, 59-69; SR. PROJ. ENGR, ADVAN. PROGS. DIV, LAND WARFARE SYSTS, HUGHES AIRCRAFT CO, 69- Sig.C, U.S.A, 46-47, Lt. Am. Chem. Soc; Soc. Motion Picture & TV Eng; Optical Soc. Am; Soc. Photo-Optical Instrument. Eng; Soc. Photog. Sci. & Eng. Preparative organic chemistry; structure of proteins; dyestuff research; motion picture color photography; polymer chemistry; imbibition dye transfer; photographic emulsions and processing; photographic equipment and systems engineering design studies for space inspection and reconnaissance systems; infrared systems; graphic arts; color lithography; light-sensitive systems; optical systems; night vision systems; management of research and engineering groups; technical sales and government contracts administration. Address: 210 N. Catalina St, Los Angeles, CA 90004.

DeLANNEY, LOUIS E(DGERTON), b. Omaha, Nebr, Feb. 2, 12; m. 41; c. 1. ZOOLOGY, BIOLOGY. B.A, California, Los Angeles, 35, M.A, 36; Rosenberg fel, Stanford, 39-40, Ph.D.(embryol), 40. Asst, California, Los Angeles, 35-36; Stanford, 36-39, instr. biol, 40-41; physiol, San Jose State Col, 41-45, asst. prof, 45-46; biol, Notre Dame, 46-49; assoc. prof. zool, Wabash Col, 49-57, prof, 57-66; PROF. BIOL. & CHMN. DEPT, ITHACA COL, 66- Ford faculty fel, 55-56; fel, Carnegie Inst, 57. U.S.A.A.F, 42-45. AAAS; Am. Soc. Naturalists; Am. Soc. Zool; Soc. Develop. Biol. Neoplasia in urodeles; amphibian embryology; role of ectoderm in determination of pigmentation; embryology of the spleen; biological specificity and development. Address: Dept. of Biology, Ithaca College, Ithaca, NY 14850.

DELANO, ERWIN, b. New York, N.Y, June 27, 26; m. 55. OPTICAL PHYSICS. B.S, Yale, 50; M.S, Rochester, 56, Ph.D.(optics), 66. Engr, Bausch & Lomb Optical Co, 51-53, sect. head optical design, 53-58, dept. head optical design & comput, Bausch & Lomb Inc, 58-63; asst. prof. PHYSICS, ST. JOHN FISHER COL, 63-66, assoc. prof, 66-69, PROF, 69-, CHMN. DEPT, 66- Intel.C, 45-47, Sgt. Optical Soc. Am. Geometrical optics, theory and practice of lens design; methods of synthesis for dielectric multilayer interference filters; theory of image evaluation. Address: Dept. of Physics, St. John Fisher College, 3690 East Ave, Rochester, NY 14618.

DeLANO, RALPH B(ENJAMIN), JR, b. Nov. 18, 19; m. 46; c. 2. ELECTRICAL ENGINEERING, MANAGEMENT SCIENCE. B.S, Mass. Inst. Tech, 41. Elec. & ultrasonic develop, Sperry Prods, Inc, 41-48; sr. engr, res. center, Int. Bus. Mach. Corp, 49-61, mgr. patent eng, components div, 61-69; fel, ctr. advan. eng, Mass. Inst. Technol, 69-70; SR. ENGR, COMPONENTS DIV, IBM CORP, HOPEWELL JUNCTION, 70- IBM Invention Award, 61. Inst. Elec. & Electronics Eng; Inst. Mgt. Sci. Cryogenic technology; digital computers; components; operations research; decision theory; information systems; patents. Address: Lane Gate Rd, Cold Spring, NY 10516.

DELANSKY, JAMES F, b. Philipsburg, Pa, July 27, 34; m. 59. ELECTRICAL ENGINEERING. B.S, Pa. State, 62; M.S, Cornell, 64, Ph.D.(elec. eng, math), 68. Technician, electronic tube div, Westinghouse Elec. Corp, 57, summers, 59-62 & 64; Remington Rand Corp, 58; ASST. PROF. ELEC. ENG, PA. STATE UNIV, 68- U.S.N, 53-57. Inst. Elec. & Electronics Eng. Circuit theory; synthesis of passive and active networks, including networks of several variables. Address: Dept. of Electrical Engineering, Pennsylvania State University, University Park, PA 16802.

DELANY, ANTHONY C(HARLES), b. Manchester, Eng, May 13, 40; m. 65; c. 2. COSMOCHEMISTRY, ATMOSPHERIC CHEMISTRY. B.Sc, Univ. Manchester, 62, M.Sc, 66; Ph.D.(cosmochem) Univ. Calif, San Diego, 70. SCIENTIST, cosmic dust, dept. physics & math, Liverpool Col. Technol, Eng, 65-66; ATMOSPHERIC AEROSOLS, NAT. CTR. ATMOSPHERIC RES, 70- High sensitivity, low level radiation counting of solar and galactic cosmic ray produced radionuclides in meteorites and lunar materials; cosmic dust influx rate; production and fate of atmospheric aerosols. Address: National Center for Atmospheric Research, P.O. Box 1470, Boulder, CO 80302.

DeLAP, JAMES H(ARVE), b. Carbondale, Ill, Feb. 6, 30; m. 59; c. 4. PHYSICAL CHEMISTRY. James B. Duke fel, Duke, 57-59, M.A, 59, Du Pont fel, 59-60, Ph.D.(chem), 60. Res. chemist, Chemstrand Res. Center, Monsanto Co, 60-62; asst. prof. CHEM, STETSON UNIV, 62-68, ASSOC. PROF, 68- Fulbright-Hays lectr, Tribhuvan Univ, Nepal, 70-71. U.S.A, 52-54. Am. Chem. Soc; Am. Phys. Soc. Photochemistry; electrochemistry. Address: Dept. of Chemistry, Stetson University, DeLand, FL 32720.

DE LA PAZ, ARMANDO, b. El Paso, Tex, Oct. 28, 33; m. 55; c. 4. CHEMICAL ENGINEERING. B.S, Tulane, 55, M.S, 56; Catholic Univ, 60-66. Asst. prof. chem. eng, Catholic Univ, 60-63; chief reactor eng. group, Army Nuclear Power Field Off, Ft. Belvoir, 63-65, chmn. reactor health & safety comt, DEPT. OF THE ARMY, 65-67, CHIEF FAST BURST REACTOR DIV, WHITE SANDS MISSILE RANGE, N.MEX, 67- Consult, NUS Corp, D.C, 60-62. U.S.N, 56-60, Lt. AAAS; Am. Nuclear Soc; Am. Soc. Eng. Educ; Am. Inst. Chem. Eng. Development of data and techniques for the evaluation of radioactivity release in nuclear reactor accidents. Address: 3110 Erica St, El Paso, TX 79925.

DELAPLANE, WILLIAM K(ERLIN), JR, b. Burlington, Ind, Sept. 1, 14; m. 40; c. 5. ENTOMOLOGY, PLANT PATHOLOGY. B.S, Purdue, 38; Iowa State, 39; M.A, Missouri, 41; Ph.D.(entom, plant path), Illinois, 58. Asst. entom, Illinois, 40-42; mgr-owner, Illini Pest Control, Inc, 42-63; prof. zool. & entom, Ohio State Univ, 64-66; mgr-owner, Illini Pest Control, Inc, 66-69; plant protection adv. to govt. Orissa, India, with Univ. Mo. U.S. Agency Internat. Develop. team, 69-71. Mem. wood-destroying organisms comt, Nat. Pest Control Asn, 47-49, rodent control comt, 50-52, chmn. sanit. comt. & mem. pub. rels. comt, 62-63, mem. sanit. comt, 63- U.S.N, 43-46, Lt.(jg). Entom. Soc. Am. General pest control; economic entomology. Address: R.R. 1, White Heath, IL 61884.

DeLAPP, DARWIN (FISKE), b. Woburn, Mass, Feb. 28, 20; m. 43; c. 2. ANALYTICAL CHEMISTRY. B.A, Amherst Col, 41. Anal. chemist, Procter & Gamble, 41-42; AM. CYANAMID CO, 42-47, asst. group leader, anal. lab, 47-56, group leader, anal. res, 56-57, fertilizer res, 57-61, sr. res. chemist, 61-66, group leader polymer appln, 66-71, PROJ. LEADER FIBRILLAR MAT, 71- Chemistry of primary plant nutrient manufacture; specialized polymer applications. Address: White Oak Shade Rd, New Canaan, CT 06840.

DE LAPP, WARREN W(ILLIAM), b. Cherokee, Kans, July 18, 12; m. 42; c. 2. CIVIL ENGINEERING. B.S, Kans. State Col, 35, M.Sc, Iowa, 40; Ph.D. (hydraul. eng), Minnesota, 47. State draftsman, Hwy. Dept, Kans, 35-36, rodman, 36-38; topog. draftsman, United Fruit Co, Guatemala, 38-39; instr. mech, Minnesota, 40-44, CIVIL ENG, 44-47; asst. prof. UNIV. COLO, BOULDER, 47-49, assoc. prof, 49-56, prof, 56-71, EMER. PROF, 71- Adv. univ. exchange prog, Int. Coop. Admin, Peshawar, 59-61. U.S.P.H.S.R, 57-, Sr. Sanit. Engr. Am. Soc. Civil Eng; Am. Soc. Eng. Educ. Hydraulics; high velocity flow in open channels. Address: Dept. of Civil Engineering, University of Colorado, Boulder, CO 80302.

DELAPPE, IRVING PIERCE, b. Boston, Mass, Oct. 28, 15; m. 42; c. 3. SCIENCE ADMINISTRATION. B.S, Harvard, 42, A.M, 46, fel, 46-48, Ph.D, 53. Asst. epidemiol, sch. pub. health, 48; asst. prof. bact. & pub. health, Mich. State Col, 48-54; adminstr, Am. Cyanamid Co, 54-60; exec. secy, microbiol. panel, NAT. INSTS. HEALTH, 60-62, asst. chief fel. & career awards, NAT. INST. ALLERGY & INFECTIOUS DISEASES, 62-65, CHIEF BIOCHEM. & PHYSIOL. BR, 65- Physiology of Histomonas meleagridis, Trichomonas gallinarum, Entamoeba histolytica studies. Address: 8907 Ridge Pl, Bethesda, MD 20034.

DeLaSALLE, LOUIS, F.S.C, b. Chicago, Ill, Dec. 8, 10. MATHEMATICS. A.B, De Paul, 31; Ph.D.(math), Catholic Univ, 36; summers, St. Louis Univ, 38, 39 & 53, Univ. Chicago, 41, Univ. Minn, 54. Instr. math, La Salle Norm. Col, 31-33; assoc. prof, St. Mary's Col.(Minn), 36-38, dean col, 38-51; prof. math, Christian Bros. Col, 51-53; St. Mary's Col.(Minn), 55-60, dean stud, 53-55; PROF. MATH, LEWIS COL, 65-, dean col, 60-65. Linear algebra; number theory. Address: Dept. of Mathematics, Lewis College, Lockport, IL 60441.

DE LA SIERRA, ANGELL O(RTIZ), b. Santurce, P.R, Feb. 28, 36; U.S. citizen; m. 60; c. 5. CELL BIOPHYSICS, CHEMISTRY. B.S, Univ. P.R, Rio Piedras, 54; M.S, City Univ. New York, 58; Jules Ochs Adler scholar, Cornell Univ, 60; Ph.D.(cell biophys), St. John's Univ.(N.Y), 63. Res. analyst biophys, Smithsonian Inst, 63-64; res. chemist, Armed Forces Radiobiol. Res. Inst, Dept. Defense, Md, 64-65; Nat. Insts. Health fel. biophys, col med, Georgetown Univ, 65-67; vis. prof, col. med, Univ. P.R, San Juan, 67, mem. faculty, 67-68; DIR. FACULTY NATURAL SCI, UNIV. P.R, CAYEY, 68- U.S.A.F.R, 63-, Capt. Biophys. Soc; Am. Chem. Soc; Radiation Res. Soc; N.Y. Acad. Sci. Chemistry of neoplastic transformation of normal cells; biophysical aspects of neoplasia; transformation of chemical energy to electrical energy in cellular systems; philosophy of science; educational philosophy. Address: Faculty of Natural Science, University of Puerto Rico, Cayey, PR 00633.

DE LA SOTA, ELIAS RAMON, b. Tucuman, Arg, Sept. 27, 32; m. 63; c. 1. BOTANY. Perito Agronomo, Nat. Univ. Tucuman, 51, M.S, 57, Ph.D.(bot), 59. Nat. Univ. Tucuman fel, Bot. Gardens, Rio de Janiero, 59-60; prof. & res. assoc. BOT, Nat. Univ. Tucuman, 60-62; res. assoc, LA PLATA NAT. UNIV, 62-64, assoc. prof, 64-68, PROF, 68-, RES. ASSOC, NAT. RES. COUN. ARG, 64- Nat. Res. Coun. grant, Bot. Gardens, Rio de Janeiro, 60; Guggenheim Mem. Found. fel, Michigan, 63-64; assoc. prof. bot, Orgn. Trop. Studies, Inc, Costa Rica, summer 67; Nat. Acad. Sci. sr. assoc, Smithsonian Inst, 68-69; mem. bot. exped. El Chocó, Columbia, Nat. Geog. Soc. & Smithsonian Res. Found, 71. N.Y. Acad. Sci; Bot. Soc. Arg; Arg. Paleont. Asn; Am. Fern Soc; Int. Asn. Plant Taxon. Fern flora of northwest Argentina and Juan Fernández Islands; morphology and taxonomy of Polypodiaceae, Grammitidaceae and Salviniaceae in the New World Tropics; epiphytic fern flora in the tropical Andes; Permian and Mesozoic pteridophytes of Patagonia. Address: Departamento de Botánica, Museo de La Plata, La Plata, Argentina.

DELATE, E(DWARD) J(OSEPH), b. Trenton, N.J, June 24, 26; m. 50; c. 11. APPLIED MATHEMATICS. B.S, N.J. State Teachers Col, 49; M.A, Columbia, 51; Ph.D.(math), Buffalo, 58. Teacher high sch, N.J, 49; statist. anal. group leader, E.I. DU PONT DE NEMOURS & CO, INC, 50-56, specialist data processing, film dept, 56-63, mgr. syst. eng, 63-67, CONSULT. MGT. SCI, treasurer's dept, 67-71, CENT. SYSTS. & SERV. DEPT, 71- U.S.A.A.F, 45-46. Am. Math. Soc. Data processing; systems engineering; forecasting. Address: 312 Hampton Rd, Wilmington, DE 19803.

DE LA TORRE, JACK C(ARLOS), b. Paris, France, Dec. 2, 37; U.S. citizen; m. 62. NEUROPHARMACOLOGY, NEUROSURGERY. B.S, Am. Univ, 61; S.M, Univ. Madrid, 63; Northwest. Univ, 63-65; Ph.D.(neuroanat), Univ. Geneva, 68. Res. asst. ophthal, Int. Eye Bank, Wash, D.C, 59-61; head microbiol, Armour & Co, Cent. Res. Lab, Ill, 64-65; clin. bacteriologist, Chicago Bd. Health, Ill, 65-66; summer trainee, psychiat. clin, Univ. Geneva, 68; instr. NEUROL. SURG, PRITZKER SCH. MED, UNIV. CHICAGO, 69-70, ASST. PROF, 70- Nat. Insts. Health res. grant, 70- AAAS; Asn. Res. Nerv. & Ment. Disease; Soc. Neurosci. Penetration of L-dopa through blood-brain barrier after peripheral dopa decarboxylase inhibition; brain serotonin and seizures; effects of psychotomimetics on brain amines; experimental head injury; basal ganglia disorders. Address: Division of Neurosurgery, Pritzker School of Medicine, 950 E. 59th St, Chicago, IL 60637.

de LAUBENFELS, DAVID J(OHN), b. Pasadena, Calif, Dec. 5, 25; m. 54; c. 4. GEOGRAPHY. A.B, Colgate, 49; fel, Illinois, 49-52, A.M, 50, Ph.D.(geog), 53. Asst. prof. geog. & geol, Georgia, 53-58; assoc. prof, 58-59; GEOG, SYRACUSE UNIV, 59-71, PROF, 71- Bowman fel, Johns Hopkins Univ, 55-56. U.S.A, 44-46, Sgt. Asn. Am. Geog; Am. Geog. Soc; Bot. Soc. Am; Ecol. Soc. Am; Nat. Coun. Geog. Educ; Am. Soc. Plant Taxon; Int. Soc. Plant Morphol. Vegetation geography; urban geography; morphology of conifers; climatology. Address: Dept. of Geography, Syracuse University, Syracuse, NY 13210.

DeLAUER, R(ICHARD) D(ANIEL), b. Oakland, Calif. Sept. 23, 18; m. 40; c. 1. AERONAUTICS. A.B, Stanford, 40; B.S, U.S. Naval Post-Grad. Sch, 49; Ph.D.(aeronaut), Calif. Inst. Tech, 53. Exp. eng. officer, Naval Aeronaut. Sch, N.J, 50-51; missile aerodyn. sect. head, Bur. Aeronaut, U.S. Navy, 53-54; mem, mil. staff, Los Alamos Sci. Lab, California, 54-57; warhead res. officer, Naval Air Spec. Weapon Facility, 57-58; dir. vehicle develop. lab, TRW INC, 58-60, titan weapon syst, 60-63, v.pres. & dir. systs. eng. & integration, 63-68, v.pres. & gen. mgr, 68-70, EXEC. V.PRES, 70- Instr, New Mexico, 55; California, 59; consult, Los Alamos Sci. Lab, California, 57- U.S.N, 43-58, Res, 58-, Comdr. Nat. Acad. Eng; AAAS; Am. Inst. Aeronaut. & Astronaut. Hypersonic aerodynamics; nuclear propulsion; space vehicle development. Address: 2222 Ave. of the Stars, Los Angeles, CA 90067.

DELAUP, PAUL S(IDNEY), b. New Orleans, La, Sept. 1, 02; m. 34. PHYSICS. B.E, Tulane, 23, M.S, 25; Ph.D.(physics), Chicago, 30. Instr. physics, Tulane, 23-25, 29-30; physics & astron, Chicago, 31-32; prof. physics, Univ. Southwest. La, 34-71, head dept, 34-67; RETIRED. Am. Asn. Physics Teachers; Am. Phys. Soc. Band spectra, vacuum tube circuits; Mössbauer effect. Address: Dept. of Physics, University of Southwestern Louisiana, Lafayette, LA 70501.

DeLAURENTIS, DOMINIC A, b. Chieti, Italy, Feb. 2, 25; U.S. citizen; m. 55; c. 4. SURGERY. B.S, St. Joseph's Col, 49; M.D, Temple, 53, D.Sc.(surg), 58. Instr. surg, med. sch, Temple, 58-62, assoc, 62-63, asst. prof, 63-66; SURGEON-IN-CHIEF, SPRINGFIELD HOSP, 66- Vascular consult, Episcopal & Skin & Cancer Hosps. & attend. consult, Vet. Admin. Hosp, Phila, 62- Dipl, Am. Bd. Surg, 59. Fel. Am. Col. Surg; Am. Med. Asn. Determination of left ventricular heart volume; lung transplantation; oxygen utilization during cardiopulmonary by-pass using five percent glucose in H_2O as a prime; aorto-renal flow patterns; factors influencing the patency of artificial venous grafts. Address: Springfield Hospital, 759 Chestnut St, Springfield, MA 01107.

DELAVAULT, ROBERT EDMUND, b. Edmonton, Alta, Dec. 3, 07; m; c. 2. GEOCHEMISTRY, METALLURGY. D.Sc.(phys. sci), Paris, 36, Lic. ès Sci, 28. Mem. res. staff, mineral. lab, Mus. Natural Hist, Paris, 41-43, lectr. geochem, 43-46; res. assoc. GEOL, UNIV. B.C, 47-64, ASSOC. PROF, 64- French Army, 39-40. Am. Chem. Soc; Geol. Soc. Am; Geochem. Soc. Chemistry of magnesium metallurgy; etch figures of crystals; trace metal analysis; biogeochemistry; geochemistry of ore deposits; applications of geochemistry to prospecting. Address: Dept. of Geology, University of British Columbia, Vancouver 8, B.C, Can.

DeLAY, PAUL D(ANIEL), b. Presho, S.Dak, Aug. 21, 08; m; c. 3. VETERINARY MEDICINE. S.Dak. State Col, 26-27; D.V.M, Iowa State, 34. Vet. pathologist, State Calif, 36-41; res. assoc. animal virus, California, 45-47; vet. pathologist, State Calif, 47-55; in charge foot & mouth disease res, European mission, U.S. DEPT. AGR, 55-57, in charge res. diagnostic invest, Plum Island Animal Disease Lab, 55-67, agr. adminstr, AGRI. RES. CTR, 67, DIR. VET. SCI. RES. DIV. & PARASITE RES. DIV, 67- Med.C, U.S.A, 41-45, Res, 45-, Maj. Am. Vet. Med. Asn; N.Y. Acad. Sci. Utilization and development of techniques for the diagnosis of infectious diseases. Address: Agricultural Research Center, Agricultural Research Service, U.S. Dept. of Agriculture, Beltsville, MD 20705.

DELBECQ, CHARLES J(ARCHOW), b. Toledo, Ohio, Aug. 19, 21; m. 47; c. 3. PHYSICAL CHEMISTRY. B.S, Toledo, 43; Ph.D.(chem), Illinois, 49. Assoc. chemist, ARGONNE NAT. LAB, 49-62, SR. CHEMIST, 62- U.S.A.A.F, 43-46, 1st Lt. Am. Phys. Soc. Study of imperfections in solids, especially the alkali halides. Address: SSS 200 A-173, Argonne National Lab, Argonne, IL 60439.

DEL BEL, ELSIO, b. Worthington, Ont, Can, Jan. 28, 20; U.S. citizen. ORGANIC CHEMISTRY. B.S, Clarkson Tech, 41; M.A, Columbia, 48; Ph.D. (fuel tech), Pa. State, 51. Metallurgist, Rochester Ord. Dist, War Dept, 41-42; chemist pharmaceut. prod, Ayerst Labs, 45-47; RES. ORG. CHEMIST, RES. DIV, CONSOL. COAL CO, 51- U.S.A.A.F, 42-45, Sgt. Am. Chem. Soc. Chemistry of phenolic compound, aryl mercaptans and coal chemicals. Address: 5697 Library Rd, Bethel Park, PA 15102.

DEL BENE, JANET ELAINE, b. Youngstown, Ohio, June 3, 39. QUANTUM CHEMISTRY. B.S, Youngstown State, 63, A.B, 65; Nat. Sci. Found. fel, Cincinnati, summer 66, Nat. Insts. Health fel, 66-68; Ph.D.(chem), 68. Fel, theoret. chem, inst, Wisconsin, 68-69; Nat. Insts. Health fel theoret. chem, Mellon Inst, 69-70; ASST. PROF. CHEM, YOUNGSTOWN STATE UNIV, 70- Am. Chem. Soc; Am. Phys. Soc. Theory of chemical bonding; ab-initio calculations on molecular ground and excited states; theory of the hydrogen bond. Address: Dept. of Chemistry, Youngstown State University, Youngstown, OH 44503.

DEL BIANCO, WALTER, b. Firenze, Italy, Feb. 28, 33; m. 67. NUCLEAR PHYSICS. Dr, Univ. Rome, 58; Ph.D, Univ. Pa, 61. Res. assoc, Univ. Pa, 61-62; res. physicist, nuclear physics div, Max Planck Inst. Chem, 62-65; asst. prof. PHYSICS, UNIV. MONTREAL, 65-67, ASSOC. PROF, 67- Am. Phys. Soc; Can. Asn. Physicist. Photonuclear reactions. Address: Dept. of Physics, University of Montreal, C.P. 6128, Montreal 101, Que, Can.

DELBRUCK, M(AX), b. Berlin, Germany, Sept. 4, 06; nat. 45; m. 41; c. 4. BIOLOGY. Tubingen & Berlin, 24, 25; Bonn & Berlin, 25, 26; fel, Bristol, 29-30; Ph.D.(physics), Göttingen, 30. Rockefeller Found. fel. physics, Copenhagen & Zurich, 31; asst, Kaiser Wilhelm Inst. für Chem, 32-37; Rockefeller Found. fel. biol, Calif. Inst. Tech, 37-39; instr. physics, Vanderbilt, 40-45, asst. prof, 45-46, assoc. prof, 46-47; PROF. BIOL, CALIF. INST. TECHNOL, 47- Recipient Nobel Prize Med, 69. Nat. Acad. Sci. Quantum theory of chemical bond; nuclear physics theory; mutations in Drosophila; bacterial viruses; sensory physiology. Address: Dept. of Biology, California Institute of Technology, Pasadena, CA 91109.

DELCAMP, R(OBERT) M(ITCHELL), b. Lexington, Ky, Apr. 18, 19; m. 40; c. 3. ORGANIC CHEMISTRY. A.B, Transylvania Col, 39; M.A, Cincinnati, 41, Ph.D.(chem), 54. Shift supvr, E.I. du Pont de Nemours & Co, 41-44; Tenn. Eastman Corp, 44-45; instr. ORG. CHEM, UNIV. CINCINNATI, 45-48, asst. prof, 48-53, assoc. prof, 53-58, PROF, 58-, ASSOC. DEAN COL. ENG, 67-, asst. dean, 62-67. Consult, Darling & Co, 47-48; Charles Straus & Assocs, 49-51; Tanner's Coun. Res. Lab, Cincinnati, 54-68. Am. Chem. Soc; Am. Soc. Eng. Educ. Preparation of novel vinyl monomers; preparation of low-condensation polymers as plasticizers; base-catalyzed condensation of aromatic aldehydes with compounds containing active hydrogen; enzymatic assay using epidermis as substrate; microbiological conversion of raw materials into useful organic chemicals; resin modification of leather. Address: College of Engineering, University of Cincinnati, Cincinnati, OH 45221.

Del CAMPO, A(NGELO) R(ALPH), b. Chicago, Ill, Dec. 24, 08; m. 35; c. 2. PHYSICS. B.S, U.S. Mil. Acad, 31; M.S, Mass. Inst. Tech, 48. Chief atomic energy appln. sect, ammunition develop. br. & res. & mat. br, Off. Chief Ord, 48-52; dir. ballistic res. labs, U.S. Army, Aberdeen Proving Ground, 53-56; mgr. Belgian Thermal Reactor Proj, Westinghouse Corp, 56-59, mgr, Carolinas-Va. Tube Reactor Proj, 58-64; MEM. STAFF, MITRE CORP, 64- Nuclear power plants; engineering management; heavy water moderated pressure tube power plant. Address: 6371 Burton Circle, Falls Church, VA 22041.

DEL CASTILLO, JOSE, b. Salamanca, Spain, Dec. 25, 20; U.S. citizen; m. 55; c. 2. NEUROPHYSIOLOGY. M.B, Salamanca, 45; M.D, Madrid, 47. Asst. prof. physiol, faculty med, Salamanca, 45-46; res. scholar, Middlesex Hosp, Med. Sch, London, 46-47; Sandoz res. fel, physiol. inst, Berne, 48-50; asst. lectr, Univ. Col, London, 50-52, biophys, 52-53, lectr, 53-56; vis. prof. physiol, State Univ. N.Y. Downstate Med. Center, 56-57; chief, sect. clin. neurophysiol, Nat. Inst. Neurol. Disease & Blindness, Md, 57-59; assoc. prof. PHARMACOL, SCH. MED, UNIV. PUERTO RICO, 59-60, PROF. & HEAD DEPT, 60-, DIR. LAB. NEUROBIOL, 67- Summer vis. scientist, Mass. Inst. Tech, 57; Nat. Inst. Neurol. Diseases & Blindness career res. professorship grant, 62. Am. Physiol. Soc; Int. Brain Res. Orgn; Brit. Physiol. Soc. Synaptic physiology and pharmacology; comparative neurophysiology. Address: Lab. of Neurobiology, School of Medicine, San Juan, PR 00905.

DEL CASTILLO, RAFAEL C(ARLOS), III, b. Brooklyn, N.Y, July 24, 19; m. 55; c. 4. ORGANIC CHEMISTRY, MATHEMATICS. B.S, Manhattan Col, 41. Chief control chemist, Triton Chem. Corp, 41-43; res. chemist, Stein, Hall & Co, Inc, 43-45; pres, Rafael Del Castillo & Co, Corp, 45-62; consult, 62-65; Balfour, Williamson, Inc, N.Y.C, 65-70, TRADER, BALFOUR, MacLAINE, INC, 70- Pres, S.Am. Develop. Servs, 50-; treas, Texas Empire Oil Co, Inc, 53-60. Consult, Refineria Chilena de Petroleos, Santiago; Indust. Processing Corp, Panama. Am. Chem. Soc; Am. Oil Chemists Soc; Asn. Consult. Chem. & Chem. Eng. Market studies and surveys; foreign administration; commercial development, management and technical problems in and for Latin American countries. Address: 129 S. Gillette Ave, Bayport, NY 11705.

DEL CERRO, MANUEL P(EREZ), b. Buenos Aires, Arg, Aug. 20, 31; m. 57; c. 2. ELECTRON MICROSCOPY. M.D, Univ. Buenos Aires, 58. Sr. instr. histol, sch. med, Univ. Buenos Aires, 58-61, assoc. prof, 61-64; res. assoc. neuroanat, CTR. BRAIN RES, STRONG MEM. HOSP, UNIV. ROCHESTER, 65-69, sr. res. assoc, 69-71, ASSOC. PROF. BRAIN RES. & NEUROL, 71- Lectr, Nat. Res. Coun, Arg, 62 & 63. AAAS; Am. Asn. Anat; Am. Asn. Neuropath; Am. Soc. Cell Biol; Electron Micros. Soc. Am. Brain research; microscopical, ultrastructural and biochemical study of neurogenesis; growth and regeneration of central nervous system; action of drugs on brain development; transplantation of nervous tissue and immune response to it. Address: Center for Brain Research, Strong Memorial Hospital, University of Rochester, Rochester, NY 14642.

DELCO, EXALTON ALFONSO, JR, b. Houston, Tex, Sept. 4, 29; m. 52; c. 4. VERTEBRATE ECOLOGY. A.B, Fisk, 49; M.S, Michigan, 50; Ph.D.(zool), Texas, 62. Instr. biol, Texas Southern, 50-54, assoc. instr, 54-57; res. asst. zool, Texas, 58-60; asst. prof. BIOL, HUSTON-TILLOTSON COL, 59-60, assoc. prof, 60-63, PROF, 63-, DEAN, 67- Co-investr, Nat. Sci. Found. grant, 58-62. U.S.A, 54-56. Fel. AAAS; Am. Fisheries Soc; Am. Soc. Ichthyol. & Herpet.(Stoye Prize, 60); Ecol. Soc. Am. Vertebrate speciation and ethology, especially isolating mechanisms in the vertebrate group. Address: Dept. of Biology, Huston-Tillotson College, Austin, TX 78702.

DEL DUCA, BETTY SPAHR, b. Warren, Ohio, Nov. 12, 30; div; c. 2. PHYSICAL CHEMISTRY. A.B, Mather Col, 52, M.S, Western Reserve, 54, Ph.D. (chem), 57. AEROSPACE SCIENTIST chem. kinetics, LEWIS RES. CTR, NASA, 57-62, ENERGY CONVERSION & ELECTROCHEM, CLEVELAND, 62- Electrochem. Soc. Trace element concentrations in biological material; heat transfer; chemistry of comets and upper atmosphere; electrochemistry-kinetics of electrode processes. Address: 2816 Tonawanda Dr, Rocky River, OH 44116.

DeLEEUW, J. H, b. Amsterdam, Netherlands, Jan. 4, 29; Can. citizen; m. 59; c. 3. AEROSPACE ENGINEERING. Dipl. eng, Delft, 53; M.S, Ga. Inst. Tech, 52; Ph.D.(aerophys), Toronto, 58. Res. engr. aerodyn, Nat. Aeronaut. Res. Inst, Netherlands, 52-53; asst. prof. AEROSPACE ENG, UNIV. TORONTO, 58-60, assoc. prof, 60-63, PROF, 63-, ASST. DIR. RES, 70- Am. Inst. Aeronaut. & Astronaut; Can. Aeronaut. & Space Inst. Rarefied plasma and gasdynamics; rocket sounding of upper atmosphere. Address: Institute for Aerospace Studies, University of Toronto, Toronto 181, Ont, Can.

DeLEEUW, KAREL, b. Chicago, Ill, Feb. 20, 30; m. 51; c. 3. MATHEMATICS. B.S, Chicago, 50, M.S, 51; Ph.D.(math), Princeton, 54. Instr. MATH, Dartmouth Col, 53-55; res. instr, Wisconsin, 55-57; from asst. prof. to assoc. prof, STANFORD UNIV, 57-66, PROF, 66- Mem, Inst. Adv. Study, 60-61; overseas fel, Churchill Col, Cambridge, 66-67. Am. Math. Soc. Harmonic and functional analysis. Address: Dept. of Mathematics, Stanford University, Stanford, CA 94305.

DeLEEUW, SAMUEL LEONARD, b. Grand Rapids, Mich, Aug. 2, 34; m. 56; c. 3. APPLIED MECHANICS, CIVIL ENGINEERING. B.S, Mich. State, 56, M.S, 58, U.S. Steel Found. fel, 58-60, Ph.D.(appl. mech), 61. Asst. prof,

CIVIL ENG, Yale, 60-65; PROF. & CHMN. DEPT, UNIV. MISS, 65- Int. Bus. Mach. Corp. res. assoc, Mass. Inst. Tech, 62-63. Summer consult, NASA, Marshall Space Flight Ctr, Ala, 65. Am. Soc. Civil Eng; Am. Soc. Eng. Educ; Am. Soc. Mech. Eng; Soc. Natural Philos. Bending and buckling of viscoelastic columns and plates with large deflections; finite element analysis, transportation. Address: Dept. of Civil Engineering, University of Mississippi, University, MS 38677.

DELENTE, JACQUES, b. Langannerie, France, Aug. 31, 39; m. 61; c. 2. BIOENGINEERING. Baccalaureate, Univ. Caen, 57, D.Eng, 66; Engr, Nat. Sch. Advan. Indust. Agr. & Nutrit, Paris, 62. Bioengr, Falstaff Brewing Corp, 62-64, sr. bioengr, 66-68; SR. ENGR, MONSANTO CO, 68- Vis. assoc. prof, Univ. Mo-St. Louis, 66- Monsanto Outstanding Res. Award, 70. Am. Chem. Soc; Am. Inst. Chem. Eng; Soc. Indust. Microbiol. Fermentor design; metabolic regulation; large scale enzyme production; genetic engineering; enzyme biochemistry. Address: 7300 Westmoreland, St. Louis, MO 63130.

DE LEON, CARLOS, b. Mexico City, Mex, Nov. 4, 38; m. 65; c. 1. PLANT PATHOLOGY. A.E, Nat. Sch. Agr, Mex, 60; M.Sc, Wisconsin, 65, Ph.D. (plant path), 66. Plant pathologist, Nat. Inst. Agr. Res, 61-62; prof. virol. & path, grad. sch, Chapingo, 65-66; PLANT PATHOLOGIST, INT. MAIZE & WHEAT IMPROV. CTR, 66- Lectr, grad. sch, Chapingo, 66. Mex. Phytopath. Soc.(secy, 66-68); Latin Am. Phytotech. Asn. Development of resistance to diseases in corn germ plasms; virology and micology. Address: International Maize & Wheat Improvement Center, Londres 40-ler Piso, Mexico 6, D.F.

DeLEON, MORRIS JACK, b. Seattle, Wash, June 21, 41; m. 69; c. 1. MATHEMATICS. B.A, Univ. Calif, Los Angeles, 63; M.S, Univ. Ill, 64; Ph.D. (math), Pa. State Univ, 68. ASST. PROF. MATH, FLA. ATLANTIC UNIV, 68- Am. Math. Soc; Australian Math. Soc; Math. Soc. France. Sequences; diophantine equations; algebraic number theory. Address: Dept. of Mathematics, Florida Atlantic University, Boca Raton, FL 33432.

DE LEON, ROGELIO PAMATMAT, b. Manila, Philippines, Feb. 5, 29; m. 54; c. 5. BIOLOGICAL & ANALYTICAL CHEMISTRY. B.S, Univ. Philippines, 54, fel, 56; Ph.D.(biochem), McGill Univ, 60. Res. fel, res. inst, McGill-Montreal Gen. Hosp, Can, 56-67; Nat. Cancer Inst. Can, 57-60; asst. prof. chem, Univ. Philippines, 60-61; chief biochemist, cancer inst, Philippine Gen. Hosp, 61-67; HEAD DEPT. ANAL. CHEM, anal. res, UNITED LABS. INC, 67-70, CENT. ANAL. LABS, 71- Int. Atomic Energy Agency fel, 64; mem, Nat. Res. Ctr, Philippines, 65-, res. grant, 65-68; lectr, Univ. Philippines, 65-67; Mapua Inst. Technol, 65- AAAS; Chem. Soc. Philippines; Am. Chem. Soc; Can. Biochem. Soc. Utilization of ethanol for biosynthesis in microbial cells; nucleic acid synthesis and metabolism in Ehrlich ascites carcinoma; isolation and characterization of subcellular ribonucleic and deoxyribonucleic acids; gas chromatographic separation and quantitation of pharmaceuticals. Address: Analytical Labs, United Labs Inc, United St, Mandaluyong, Rizal, D-713, Philippines.

DE LEONIBUS, PASQUALE S, b. Chester, Pa, Jan. 13, 26; m. 63; c. 1. OCEANOGRAPHY, METEOROLOGY. B.S, N.Y. Univ, 52, M.S, 55; Am. Univ, 54-60. CHIEF SCIENTIST, U.S. NAVAL OCEANOG. OFF, 54- Expert adv, Comn. Maritime Meteorol, 70- U.S.A, 44-46, Sgt. Am. Geophys. Union; Am. Meteorol. Soc. Air-sea interactions; ocean wave research; development of an air-sea boundary layer model from the point of view of ocean wave generation and wave forecasting. Address: Ocean Science Dept, U.S. Naval Oceanographic Office, Washington, DC 20390.

DELERAY, ARTHUR LOYD, b. Sonora, Calif, June 27, 36; m. 61; c. 2. CHEMICAL & NUCLEAR ENGINEERING. B.S.E, California, Berkeley, 59; M.S.E. & M.A, Princeton, 62, Ph.D.(chem. eng), 66. STAFF CHEM. ENGR, MB ASSOCS, 64- Fast neutron moderation; pyrotechnics; unique radar reflectors; miniature rocketry. Address: MB Associates, P.O. Box 196, San Ramon, CA 94583.

DeLEVIE, ROBERT, b. Amsterdam, Holland, July 21, 33; m. 60; c. 2. ELECTROCHEMISTRY. Drs, Univ. Amsterdam, 60, Ph.D, 63. Vis. asst. prof, La. State Univ, 63-65; asst. prof. CHEM. GEORGETOWN UNIV, 65-70, ASSOC. PROF, 70- U.S. ed, J. Electroanal. Chem, 70- Am. Chem. Soc; Royal Netherlands Chem. Soc. Mechanisms of electrode kinetics, especially electrocatalysis; double layer structure and its effects on electrode kinetics; photoelectrochemistry; membrane electrode kinetics; electrochemical instrumentation. Address: Dept. of Chemistry, Georgetown University, Washington, DC 20007.

DELEVORYAS, THEODORE, b. Chicopee Falls, Mass, July 22, 29; m. 56; c. 2. BOTANY. B.S, Massachusetts, 50; M.S, Illinois, 51, Ph.D, 54. Rockefeller fel, Nat. Res. Coun, Michigan, 54-55; asst. prof. bot, Mich. State, 55-56; instr, Yale, 56-58; asst. prof, 58-60; assoc. prof, Illinois, 60-62; BIOL, YALE, 62-68, PROF, 68-, CURATOR PALEOBOT, PEABODY MUS. NAT. HIST, 68-, assoc. curator, 62-68. AAAS; Int. Soc. Plant Morphol; Paleont. Soc; Brit. Paleont. Asn; Bot. Soc. Am; Torrey Bot. Club; Int. Asn. Plant Taxon. Morphology and evolution of fossil and living vascular plants. Address: Dept. of Biology, Yale University, New Haven, CT 06520.

DELFIN, ELISEO DAIS, b. San Andres, Manila, Philippines, Sept. 28, 25; m. 64. BIOLOGY, ENTOMOLOGY. B.S, Cent. Philippines Univ, 49, B.S.E, 51; Fulbright Stud. Exchange Prog. scholar, Univ. Colo, Boulder, 52-54, univ. fel, 52-56, M.A, 54; univ. fels, Ohio State Univ, 56-59, Ph.D.(entom), 60. Instr. biol, Cent. Philippines Univ, 49-52, asst. prof, 60-64, chmn. dept. life sci, 62-64; fel. acarology, Univ. Calif, Berkeley, 64-65; asst. prof. zool, San Jose State Col, 65-67; assoc. prof. BIOL, IND. CENT. COL, 67-71, PROF, 71-, CHMN. DEPT, 69- Consult, Philippine Bur. Plant Indust, Iloilo City Br, 60-64; summers, biol. lectr, Philippines Nat. Sci. Inst, 64, fels, inst. acarology, Ohio State Univ, 67 & inst. radiation biol, Univ. Calif, 69. AAAS; Am. Inst. Biol. Sci. Biology of mites and ticks of central Indiana; leafhoppers—Cicadellidae. Address: Dept. of Biology, Indiana Central College, 4001 Otterbein Ave, Indianapolis, IN 46227.

DELFINO, JOSEPH J, b. Port Chester, N.Y. WATER CHEMISTRY, CHEMICAL LIMNOLOGY. B.S, Col. Holy Cross, 63; M.S, Univ. Idaho, 65; Fed. Water Pollution Control Admin. fel. & Ph.D.(water chem), Univ. Wis, 68. U.S. AIR FORCE, 68-, instr. CHEM, U.S. AIR FORCE ACAD, 68-69, asst. prof, 69-71, ASSOC. PROF, 71- U.S.A.F, 68-, Capt. AAAS; Am. Chem. Soc; Am. Soc. Limnol. & Oceanog. Water chemistry of metal ions in environmental systems, including streams, lakes and waste effluents. Address: Dept. of Chemistry, U.S. Air Force Academy, CO 80840.

DELFLACHE, ANDRE P, b. Brussels, Belgium, 23; nat; m. 50; c. 4. CIVIL ENGINEERING. C.Eng. Mines, Brussels, 47, Sc.D.(soil mech), 64. Asst. prof. eng. geol, Brussels, 47-48; vis. prof. geol, La. State, 48-49; engr, explor. div, Petrofina, Brussels, 49-54; seismologist, United Geophys. Co, Calif, 54; European mgr. subsurface explor. in Europe & N.Africa, Independent Explor. Co, Tex, 54-58; PROF. CIVIL ENG, LAMAR UNIV, 58- Consult. soils eng. & foun, 58- Am. Soc. Civil Eng. Soil mechanics and foundations; exploration geophysics; ocean engineering; determination of engineering properties of soils and marine sediments by the use of seismic methods and underwater acoustics. Address: Dept. of Civil Engineering, Lamar University, Beaumont, TX 77704.

DEL FRANCO, GUY J, b. N.Y.C, Dec. 13, 34; m. 57; c. 2. POLYMER & ORGANIC CHEMISTRY. B.S, Brooklyn Col, 57, M.S, 63. Jr. chemist, INMONT CORP, 57-60, chemist, 60-62, res. chemist, 62-66, prin. scientist, 66-69, res. mgr, 69-70, RES. DIR, 71- U.S.A.R, 57-63. Am. Chem. Soc. Polymer synthesis and applications; synthesis of cross-linkable polymers, water soluble polymers and polyelectrolytes; organic and organometallic compounds; mechanism of cross-linking reactions and alkyl-tin hydride reactions. Address: Inmont Corp. Central Research Labs, 1255 Broad St, Clifton, NJ 07015.

DELFS, ELEANOR, b. Ohio, May 26, 08. OBSTETRICS. A.B, Hiram Col, 30; M.A, Oberlin Col, 31; M.D, Johns Hopkins Univ, 35. Instr. OBSTET, Johns Hopkins Univ, 40-45, asst. prof, 45-50, assoc. prof, 50-63; PROF, MED. COL. WIS, 63- Reproductive failure; trophoblastic tumors; x-ray pelvimetry. Address: Dept. of Gynecology & Obstetrics, Milwaukee County Hospital, Medical College of Wisconsin, 8700 W. Wisconsin Ave, Milwaukee, WI 53226.

DELGADO, JAIME N(ABOR), b. El Paso, Tex, July 28, 32; m. 54; c. 1. PHARMACEUTICAL & ORGANIC CHEMISTRY. B.S, Texas, 54, M.S, 55; S.E. Melendy fel, Minnesota, 57-59, Ph.D.(pharmaceut. chem), 60. Asst. PHARMACEUT. CHEM, Minnesota, 55-57; asst. prof, COL. PHARM, UNIV. TEX, AUSTIN, 59-63, ASSOC. PROF, 63- AAAS; Am. Pharmaceut. Asn; Am. Chem. Soc. Synthesis of organic medicinals and structure-activity studies; natural products; mechanisms of drug-receptor interactions; anticholinergics. Address: Dept. of Pharmaceutical Chemistry, University of Texas at Austin, Austin, TX 78712.

DELGADO, JOSE M(ANUEL) R(ODRIGUEZ), b. Ronda, Spain, Aug. 8, 15; NEUROPHYSIOLOGY. M.D, Madrid, 40, D.Sc, 42. Instr. physiol, sch. med, Madrid, 40-42, assoc. prof, 42-46; sr. fel, SCH. MED, YALE, 46-47, Brown fel, 50-52, instr, 52-53, asst. prof. PHYSIOL. & PSYCHIAT, 53-55, ASSOC. PROF, 55- Sr. fel, Spanish Nat. Res. Coun, Cajal Inst, Madrid, 43-45, assoc. prof, univ, 46; clin. & res. fel, Mass. Gen. Hosp, 51-52; Guggenheim fel, 63. Ramon y Cajal prize, Spanish Govt; Roel prize; Countess of Maudes prize. Am. Physiol. Soc; N.Y. Acad. Sci; fel. Am. Col. Neuropsychopharmacol. Brain physiology; physical analysis of mental activity; radio control of behavior. Address: School of Medicine, Yale University, 333 Cedar St, New Haven, CT 06511.

DELGASS, W. NICHOLAS, b. Jackson Heights, N.Y, Oct. 14, 42; m. 67; c. 1. CHEMICAL ENGINEERING. B.S, Univ. Mich, 64; Nat. Sci. Found. fel, Stanford Univ, 64-68, M.S, 66, Ph.D.(chem. eng), 69; Air Force Off. Sci. Res. fel, Univ. Calif. Berkeley, 68-69. Summers, Am. Cyanamid Co, 62, Dow Chem. Co, 63, Humble Oil Co, 64, N.Am. Aviation Sci. Ctr, 65 & 66; ASST. PROF. ENG. & APPL. SCI, YALE, 69- Grants, Am. Chem. Soc, 69-73; Chevron Res. Co, 69-72; Conn. Res. Comn, 70; Nat. Sci. Found, 70-72; consult, Am. Cyanamid Co, 70- Am. Inst. Chem. Eng; Am. Chem. Soc; Faraday Soc. Heterogeneous catalysis, especially application of Mössbauer and photoelectron spectroscopy to the study of catalysts and interactions of gases with catalytically active surfaces. Address: Dept. of Engineering & Applied Science, Yale University, New Haven, CT 06520.

DEL GRECO, FRANCESCO, b. Italy, Aug. 23, 23; nat; m. 56; c. 1. MEDICINE. M.D, Rome, Italy, 46. Res. fel. exp. med, Cleveland Clinic, 51-52, res. assoc, 52-54, asst. staff, 55-57; intern, PASSAVANT HOSP, 57-58, chief med. resident, 58-60, dir. metab. unit, 58-61, DIR. CLIN. RES. CTR, 61-, ATTEND. PHYSICIAN, 64-; assoc. prof, MED. SCH, NORTHWEST. UNIV, 64-67, PROF, 67- Danish govt. scholar, 51; Nat. Heart Inst. fel, Nat. Insts. Health, 52-53; voluntary asst, post-grad. med. sch, London, 54, hon. res. fel, St. Thomas' Hosp, 55; vis. attend. physician, Vet. Admin. Res. Hosp, Chicago, 60-; mem. coun. circulation, coun. arteriosclerosis & coun. kidney in cardiovasc. disease, Am. Heart Asn. AAAS; Am. Physiol. Soc; Soc. Exp. Biol. & Med; Am. Fedn. Clin. Res; Am. Soc. Clin. Pharmacol. & Therapeut; Am. Heart Asn; Am. Med. Asn; Am. Soc. Nephrology; N.Y. Acad. Sci; Int. Soc. Nephrology; Am. Soc. Artificial Internal Organs. Renal and cardiovascular physiology; metabolism of water and electrolytes. Address: Clinical Research Center, Passavant Memorial Hospital, Chicago, IL 60611.

DEL GROSSO, VINCENT A(LFRED), b. Newark, N.J, Aug. 9, 25; m. 51; c. 5. PHYSICS. B.S, Northeastern, 47; Ph.D, Cath. Univ. Am, 68. Phys. chemist, U.S. NAVAL RES. LAB, 48-52, PHYSICIST & HEAD ULTRASONICS SECT, 52- Res. assoc, Univ. Calif, Los Angeles, 70-71. U.S.N, 44-46. AAAS; sr. mem. Inst. Elec. & Electronics Eng; sr. mem. Am. Chem. Soc; Sci. Res. Soc. Am; fel. Acoustical Soc. Am. Physical acoustics; ultrasonics; underwater sound; physical chemistry; sonic and ultrasonic engineering. Address: 8610 Jefferson Rd, Oxon Hill, MD 20022.

DEL GUERCIO, LOUIS R(ICHARD) M(AURICE), b. N.Y.C, Jan. 15, 29; m. 57; c. 7. SURGERY, PHYSIOLOGY. B.S, Fordham, 49; M.D, Yale, 53. Am. Thoracic Soc. teaching & res. fel, 59-60; instr. surg. Albert Einstein Col.

Med, 60-61, asst. prof, 62-66, assoc. prof, 66-70, prof, 70-71, assoc. dir. clin. res. ctr, 63-67, dir, 67-71; PROF. SURG, N.J. COL. MED. & DENT. & DIR. SURG, ST. BARNABAS MED. CTR, 71- Assoc. attend, Bronx Munic. Hosp. Ctr, 60-65, attend, 65-71, pres. med. bd, 69; Health Res. Coun. New York res. grants, 64-66 & career scientist award, 66; res. grants, Am. Heart Asn, 65-68 & Nat. Insts. Health, 65-70; mem. tech. rev. comt. artificial heart test & eval. facilities, Nat. Insts. Health, 68, surg. study sect, div. res. grants, 70; comt. on shock, Nat. Acad. Sci-Nat. Res. Coun, 69-; consult, Mech. Technol, Inc. U.S.A.R, 46-51, 2nd Lt. Am. Surg. Asn; Am. Thoracic Soc; Am. Med. Asn; fel. Am. Col. Surg; Soc. Univ. Surg; N.Y. Acad. Sci. Cardiorespiratory physiology in clinical practice; thoracic surgery; surgery of biliary pancreatic system. Address: Saint Barnabas Medical Center, Old Short Hills Rd, Livingston, NJ 07039.

DELI, JOSEPH, b. Budapest, Hungary, July 30, 37; Can. citizen; m. 66. WEED SCIENCE, PLANT PHYSIOLOGY. B.S.A, Univ. Toronto, 64; Can. Res. Coun. scholar. & M.S, Univ. Guelph, 66; Can. Res. Coun. scholar. & Ph.D.(weed sci), Purdue Univ, 69. SR. RES. BIOCHEMIST, PPG INDUSTS, INC, 69- Am. Soc. Plant Physiol; Weed Sci. Soc. Am; Am. Soc. Hort. Sci. Weed and herbicidal physiology. Address: PPG Industries, Inc, P.O. Box 31, Barberton, OH 44203.

DELIA, THOMAS J, b. Brooklyn, N.Y, Nov. 19, 35; m. 64; c. 3. ORGANIC & MEDICINAL CHEMISTRY. B.S, Col. Holy Cross, 57; M.S, Va. Polytech. Inst, 59, Allied Chem. Corp. fel, 60-61, Ph.D.(org. chem), 62. Fel, Virginia, 61-62; res. assoc. bio-org. chem, Sloan-Kettering Inst. Cancer Res, 62-66; asst. prof. CHEM, CENT. MICH. UNIV, 66-69, ASSOC. PROF, 69- Nat. Acad. Sci. fel, Czech, 71-72. AAAS; Am. Chem. Soc; Int. Soc. Heterocyclic Chem. Synthesis of heterocyclic compounds as antimetabolites or carcinogens. Address: Dept. of Chemistry, Central Michigan University, Mt. Pleasant, MI 48858.

DeLIBAN, ROBERT, b. Chicago, Ill, Mar. 18, 18; m. 44; c. 2. ELECTRICAL ENGINEERING. B.S, California, 40. Plant engr, South Calif. Tel. Co, 40-41; radar engr, Sig. Corps, U.S. Army, 41-42; elec. design engr, radiation lab, California, 42-44, patent engr, 45-46, staff engr, antenna proj, 46-49, lectr. elec. eng. dept, 46-49; sr. engr, Aircraft Radiation Systs. Lab, Stanford Res. Inst, 49-53; DIR. ENG, BARRETT ELECTRONICS CORP, 53-, PRES, 64-, v.pres, 53-64. Eng. consult, eng. group, U.S. Army, 44-45. Civilian with U.S.N, 44. Inst. Elec. & Electronics Eng. Radio radiation systems; specialized electronic instrumentation; electronics; circuitry; industrial controls; automatic vehicle guidance systems. Address: Barrett Electronics Corp, 897 Commercial St, Palo Alto, CA 94025.

DELIHAS, NICHOLAS, b. New York, N.Y, Sept. 22, 32; m. 61; c. 3. BIOPHYSICS. B.S, Queens Col.(N.Y), 54; Nat. Insts. Health fel, Yale, 58-60, Ph.D.(biophys), 61. Jr. tech. specialist, biol. dept, Brookhaven Nat. Lab, 54-57; res. asst. biophys, Yale, 57-58; res. assoc, Sloan-Kettering Inst. Cancer Res, 60-62; assoc. scientist, MED. DEPT, BROOKHAVEN NAT. LAB, 62-68, SCIENTIST, 68-; ADJ. PROF. BIOL, SOUTHAMPTON COL, 70- Res. assoc, Sloan-Kettering Div, Cornell, 61-62; Nat. Insts. Health spec. fel, Ciba Res. Labs, Basel, Switz, 64-65. AAAS; Biophys. Soc; Am. Soc. Cell Biol; Am. Soc. Biol. Chem; Harvey Soc. Ribonucleic acid and ribosome structure and function. Address: Medical Dept, Brookhaven National Lab, Upton, NY 11973.

DELISLE, ALBERT L(ORENZO), b. Holyoke, Mass, Dec. 7, 10. BOTANY. B.S, Mass. State Col, 32; A.M, Harvard, 33, Atkins traveling fel. to Cuba, 36, Ph.D.(bot), 37. Asst, Harvard & Radcliffe Col, 33-37; Cabot res. fel, Harvard, 37-39; prof. biol, Suffolk, 39; asst. prof, Col. William & Mary, 39-42; exchange prof. bot, Nat. Univ. of Colombia, 46-47; assoc. prof. biol, Notre Dame, 47-56; life sci, SACRAMENTO STATE COL, 56-67, PROF. BIOL. SCI. & DIR. ARBORETUM, 67- Botanist, U.S. Dept. Interior, 57. Assoc. ed, Am. Midland Naturalist, 59- U.S.N, 43-46. AAAS; fel. Bot. Soc. Am; Mex. Acad. Sci. Cytogenetics; vegetative propagation of plants; auxins and plant morphogenesis; taxonomy; pollens in allergy. Address: Dept. of Biological Sciences, Sacramento State College, Sacramento, CA 95819.

DELISLE, CLAUDE, b. Quebec, Que, Nov. 15, 29; m. 58; c. 5. OPTICS, PHYSICS. B.A, Montreal, 51; B.Sc.A, Laval, 58, Ph.D.(optics), 63. Lectr. physics, Laval, 62-63; res. assoc. optics, Inst. Optics, N.Y, 63-65; asst. prof. PHYSICS, LAVAL UNIV, 65-69, ASSOC. PROF, 69- Nat. Res. Coun. Can. grants, 66- Consult, Centre Psychol. Res. Inc, Montreal, 69- Optical Soc. Am; Can. Asn. Physicists; French-Can. Asn. Adv. Sci. Repeated diffraction of (SinX)/X by a grating; pseudothermal sources; visibility of spectral density modulation of a light source after passing through an interferometer. Address: Dept. of Physics, Laval University, Quebec 10, Que, Can.

DE LISLE, DONALD G(ORDON), b. The Dalles, Ore, Mar. 31, 23; m. 49; c. 2. BOTANY. B.S, Oregon, 50, M.S, 51; Ph.D.(syst. bot), Iowa State, 62. Instr. biol, Willamette, 51-54; biologist, Ore. Pulp & Paper Co, 54-59; asst. bot, Iowa State, 59-62; asst. prof. BIOL, SIMPSON COL, 62-67, ASSOC. PROF. & CHMN. DEPT, 67- Sigma Xi res. grant-in-aid, 64; Nat. Sci. Found. res. grant, 66-71 & summer fel, 63-64. Hosp.C, U.S.N, 41-46. Bot. Soc. Am; Am. Soc. Plant Taxon; Int. Asn. Plant Taxon. Cytotaxonomy of the grass genus Cenchrus; cytotaxonomic studies of the grass genus Aristida of North America. Address: Dept. of Biology, Simpson College, Indianola, IA 50125.

DELIYANNIS, PLATON C(ONSTANTINE), b. Athens, Greece, Aug. 21, 31. MATHEMATICS. Dipl. eng, Nat. Tech. Univ. Athens, 54; M.S, Univ. Chicago, 55, Westinghouse fel, 60-61, Ph.D.(math), 63. Res. asst, Univ. Chicago, 55-56; instr. math, Ill. Inst. Technol, 61-63, asst. prof, 63-65; dir. Ctr. Advan. Studies, Greek Atomic Energy Comm, 66-69; ASST. PROF. MATH, ILL. INST. TECHNOL, 69- Greek Royal Navy, 57-59, Ens. Am. Math. Soc; Math. Asn. Am. Functional analysis and operator algebras; topological groups and representations; abstract quantum theory. Address: Dept. of Mathematics, Illinois Institute of Technology, 3300 S. Federal St, Chicago, IL 60616.

DELL, CURTIS G(EORGE), b. Buffalo, N.Y, Mar. 18, 24; m. 49; c. 4. ELECTRICAL ENGINEERING. B.S, Rutgers, 48; M.E.E, Cornell, 51. Engr, E.I. DU PONT DE NEMOURS & CO, 48-51, instrument engr, eng. dept, design div, 51-53, res. engr, eng. res. lab, applied physics sect, 53-58, res. proj. engr, 58-59, res. proj. supvr, 59-61, sr. res. engr, 61-64, sr. appln. engr, develop. dept, 64-67, eng. supvr, 67-69, RES. SUPVR, PHOTO PROD. DEPT, 69- Lectr, Delaware, 52-54. U.S.N, 44-46. Sci. Res. Soc. Am; Instrument Soc. Am; Inst. Elec. & Electronics Eng. Industrial research, development and marketing of laboratory and process analytical instruments. Address: Photo Products Dept, E.I. du Pont de Nemours & Co, Wilmington, DE 19898.

DELL, M(ANUEL) B(ENJAMIN), b. Chelsea, Mass, Apr. 12, 19. CHEMISTRY. B.S, Tufts Col, 40; M.S, Pa. State Col, 50, Ph.D.(fuel technol), 51. Res. chemist, bituminous prods, Barrett Div, Allied Chem. & Dye Corp, 47-48; res. investigator emulsions, Flintkote Co, 51-53; res. chemist, ALUMINUM CO. OF AM, 53-60, SCI. ASSOC, 60- U.S.A, 43-46. AAAS; Am. Inst. Mining, Metall. & Petrol. Eng; Am. Chem. Soc. Chemistry of coal tar, asphalt, coal; carbon electrodes; aluminum smelting; clay-stabilized emulsions. Address: 144 Woodshire Dr, Pittsburgh, PA 15215.

DELL, TOMMY RAY, b. New Orleans, La, May 21, 37; m. 57; c. 2. BIOMETRY. B.S, La. State Univ, 59; M.S, Univ. Ga, 64, Ph.D, 69. Res. forester, southlands exp. forest, Int. Paper Co, Ga, 60-61; CHIEF BIOMET. BR, SOUTH. FOREST EXP. STA, U.S. FOREST SERV, NEW ORLEANS, 63- U.S.A, 59-60, Res, 60-, Capt. Soc. Am. Foresters; Biomet. Soc. Design and analysis of studies on biological topics, particularly forest resources; research on biometrical procedures. Address: 353 Homestead Ave, Metairie, LA 70005.

DELLA-CORTE, JOSEPH P, b. N.Y.C, July 19, 03; m. 30; c. 1. INSTRUMENTATION. E.E, N.Y. Univ, 26, M.S, 43. Asst. to chief engr, Sonora Phono Co, Mich, 26-27; develop. res. engr, Conner-Crouse Corp, N.Y, 27-30; chief engr. & tech. adv. to pres, Walthal, 30-31; chief engr, Amplex Instrument Lab, 31-33; industrialist, 33-34; asst. to chief engr, Emerson Radio & TV Co, 34-35; chief engr, Radio Navig. Instrument Co, 35-36; engr. in charge, Fairchild Camera & Instrument Co, 36-45, chief engr, 45-51, dir. eng, 51-54; Anton Electronic Labs, 54-55; head dept, Sperry Gyroscope Co, 55-64, prog. control mgr, 64-69; prog. mgr. prod. support, Grumman Aircraft Eng. Corp, 69-71; RETIRED. With Nat. Bur. Standards, 44-46; Nat. Adv. Comt. Aeronaut; Off. Sci. Res. & Develop; U.S.A; U.S.A.A.F; U.S.N. Inst. Elec. & Electronics Eng; Am. Soc. Metals. Weapons system management; nuclear and electronic instruments; instrumentation for atomic submarines; ground and airborne communication and navigation equipment; automatic electronic test equipment; stellar inertial weapon system. Address: 33 Buckminster Lane, Manhasset, NY 11030.

de LLANO, CARLOS R(ODRIGO), b. Mex, Oct. 29, 29; m. 52; c. 3. ORGANIC CHEMISTRY. B.S, St. Mary's (Tex), 58; Ph.D.(chem), Texas, 68. Prod. mgr, Pan Am. Standard Brands, Inc, Mex, 51-55; plant supt, Du Pont, S.A, de C.V, 55-57; instr. chem, St. Mary's (Tex), 62-64, asst. prof, 64-67; res. chemist, Celanese Chem. Corp, 67-70; ASSOC. PROF. ORG. CHEM, UNIV. OF THE AMERICAS, 70- Am. Chem. Soc; The Chem. Soc. Theoretical organic chemistry; determination of molecular structure and photochemistry. Address: 114 Stanford Dr, San Antonio, TX 78212.

DELLA ROSA, R(OCCO) J(OHN), b. Naples, Italy, Jan. 13, 23; U.S. citizen; wid; c. 2. BIOCHEMISTRY, RADIATION BIOLOGY. A.B, Rochester, 48, M.S, 52, Ph.D.(radiation biol), 59. Res. assoc, Atomic Energy Cmn. Proj, Rochester, 48-60; assoc. res. radiobiologist, UNIV. CALIF, DAVIS, 60-70, SPECIALIST, LECTR, RADIATION BIOL, 70- Med.Serv.C, U.S.A, 44-46. Radiation Res. Soc; Health Phys. Soc. Biological effects of radiation, metabolism and toxicology of internal emitters; inhalation of alpha emitters; renal physiology of divalent cations; comparative toxicity of Sr^{90} and Ra^{226}; trace mineral metabolism. Address: Radiobiology Lab, University of California School of Veterinary Medicine, Davis, CA 95616.

DELLA TORRE, EDWARD, b. Milan, Italy, Mar. 31, 34; U.S. citizen; m. 56; c. 3. ELECTRICAL ENGINEERING, PHYSICS. B.E.E, Polytech. Inst. Brooklyn, 54; M.S, Princeton, 56; M.S, Rutgers, 61; D.Eng.Sc.(elec. eng), Columbia, 64. Assoc. prof. elec. eng, Rutgers, 56-67; mem. staff, Bell Tel. Labs, 67-68; assoc. prof. ELEC. ENG, McMASTER UNIV, 68-70, PROF. & ASSOC. CHMN. DEPT, 70- Inst. Elec. & Electronics Eng. Theoretical and experimental study of magnetic materials; electromagnetic theory; application of information and computer sciences. Address: Dept. of Electrical Engineering, McMaster University, Hamilton, Ont, Can.

DELLENBACK, ROBERT J(OSEPH), b. Los Angeles, Calif, June 3, 28; m. 58; c. 4. PHYSIOLOGY. B.A, California, Los Angeles, 50, M.A, 53, Ph.D. (zool, physiol), 55. Asst. zool & physiol, California, Los Angeles, 50-55; instr. physiol, col. physicians & surg, Columbia Univ, 56-60, asst. prof, 60-71. Eli Lilly fel. & Nat. Res. Coun. zool. inst, Univ. Wurzburg, Ger, 55-56. Am. Physiol. Soc; Soc. Exp. Biol. & Med; Harvey Soc. Hemorrhage; cardiac output; blood volume. Address: 370 Lydecker St, Englewood, NJ 07631.

DELLER, JOHN JOSEPH, JR, b. Pittsburgh, Pa, Nov. 3, 31; m. 53; c. 3. INTERNAL MEDICINE, ENDOCRINOLOGY. B.Sc, Pittsburgh, 53, M.D, 57. MED.C, U.S. ARMY, 56-, resident internal med, Walter Reed Gen. Hosp, D.C, 58-61, fel. endocrinol. & metab, California, San Francisco, 63-64, chief gen. med. serv, LETTERMAN GEN. HOSP, 64-68, dep. chief dept. med, 68-70, CHIEF DEPT. MED, 70-; ASST. CLIN. PROF, UNIV. CALIF, 67- Dipl, Am. Bd. Internal Med, 67. Med.C, U.S.A, 56-, Col. Fel. Am. Col. Physicians; Endocrine Soc. Endocrinology and metabolism. Address: 32 Bonnie Brae Dr, Marin Country Club Estates, Navato, CA 94947.

DELLEUR, JACQUES W(ILLIAM), b. Paris, France, Dec. 30, 24; nat; m. 57; c. 2. HYDRAULIC ENGINEERING. C.E. & Min.E, Nat. Univ. Colombia, S.Am, 48; M.S.Ce, Rensselaer Polytech, 50; D.Eng.Sc, Columbia, 55. Engr, R.J. Tipton & Assocs. Inc, 50-51; asst. civil eng. & eng. mech. dept, Columbia, 52-53, instr. civil eng, 53-55; asst. prof. HYDRAUL. ENG, SCH. CIVIL ENG, PURDUE UNIV, 55-57, assoc. prof, 57-63, PROF, 63-, ASSOC. DIR, WATER RESOURCES RES. CTR, 71-, head hydromech. & water resources area, 65, chmn. curriculum comt. & civil eng. lectr. comt, 58-59.

Summer res. engr, Stevens Inst. Technol, 55; U.S. Corp. Eng, 57; consult, res. staff, Gen. Motors Corp, 57-62; res. French Nat. Hydraulics Lab, France, 68-69. Del, Univs. Coun. Water Resources, 64- AAAS; Int. Asn. Sci. Hydraul. Hydrology of water resources, hydraulic engineering; turbulence; open channel hydraulics; theoretical and applied hydrodynamics. Address: School of Civil Engineering, Purdue University, Lafayette, IN 47907.

DELLINGER, THOMAS BAYNES, b. Crawfordsville, Ind, Jan. 31, 26; m. 49; c. 4. PETROLEUM ENGINEERING. B.S, Purdue Univ, 48; M.S, Univ. Tulsa, 62, Ph.D.(petrol. eng), 70. Engr, Creole Petrol. Corp, 48-59; res. engr, Jersey Prod. Res. Co 60-62; engr, Fenix & Scisson, Inc, 63-67; RES. ENGR, MOBIL RES. & DEVELOP. CORP, 70- U.S.A.A.F, 44-45. Address: 1010 Springwood Lane, Duncanville, TX 75116.

DELLMANN, H(ORST)-D(IETER), b. Berlin, Germany, June 6, 31; m. 55; c. 2. HISTOLOGY, NEUROANATOMY. D.V.M, Nat. Vet. Sch, Alfort, France, 54, M.S, 55; Ph.D.(anat, histol. & embryol), Munich, 61. Mem. staff. vet. med, Chemie Gruenenthal, Stolberg, Germany, 55-57; res. asst. ANAT, HISTOL, & EMBRYOL, vet. faculty, Munich, 57-61. privat-docent, 62-63, univ-docent, 64; vis. prof. & acting chmn. dept, faculty vet. med, Cairo, 63-64; assoc. prof, SCH. VET. MED, UNIV. MO-COLUMBIA, 64-65, PROF, 65- Fulbright travel grant, 64-65. Mem, Int. Cmn. Vet. Anat. Nomenclature, 59- Am. Asn. Anat; World Asn. Vet. Anat; European Asn. Vet. Anat; German Anat. Soc. Hypothalamus; neurosecretion; hypothalamo-hypophyseal system and male genital system; circumventricular organs; secretory activity of nerve cells in extrahypothalamic areas. Address: 125 Connaway Hall, University of Missouri, Columbia, MO 65201.

DELLOW, PETER GLYNN, b. Adelaide, South Australia, Oct. 24, 27; m. 70. PHYSIOLOGY. D.D.S, Univ. Adelaide, 50, M.D, 58. House dent. surgeon, Royal Adelaide Hosp, 50-52, resident med. off. gen. med, 57-58, registrar surg, 59-60; lectr. physiol, Univ. Adelaide, 61-64, oral biol, 65-66; ASSOC. PROF. PHYSIOL, UNIV. WEST. ONT, 66- Res. scholar, Bd. Anthrop. Res, Adelaide, 53-54; tutor, Univ. Adelaide, 59-60 & 61-66; teaching fel, Royal Australian Col. Surgeons, 60; hon. clin. asst, Royal Adelaide Hosp, 61-66. Fel. Australian Col. Dent. Surgeons; Int. Asn. Dent. Res; Can. Physiol. Soc. Oral biology; trigeminal sensory and motor mechanisms; controls of ingestion. Address: Dept. of Physiology, University of Western Ontario, London, Ont, Can.

DELLUVA, ADELAIDE M(ARIE), b. Bethlehem, Pa, Sept. 2, 20. BIOCHEMISTRY. B.S, Bucknell Univ, 39, M.S, 40; Ph.D.(physiol. chem), Univ. Pa, 46. Asst. instr. physiol. chem, UNIV. PA, 43-46, instr, sch. med, 46-54, asst. prof. BIOCHEM, 54-69, SCH. VET. MED, 69-71, ASSOC. PROF, 71- Organic synthesis of compounds with C-13 and C-14 for use in researches in physiological chemistry; various phases of metabolism using isotopes; carbon dioxide assimilation; adrenaline biosynthesis; lactate metabolism; alanine metabolism; gastric urease; anion transport in mitochondria; source of energy for muscle contractions. Address: Dept. of Animal Biology, University of Pennsylvania School of Veterinary Medicine, Philadelphia, PA 19104.

DELLWIG, LOUIS F(IELD), b. Washington, D.C, Feb. 13, 22; m. 48; c. 3. REGIONAL GEOLOGY, REMOTE SENSING. B.A, Lehigh, 43, M.S, 48; Ph.D. (geol), Michigan, 54. Instr, Michigan, 51-53; asst. prof. GEOL, UNIV. KANS, 53-57, assoc. prof, 57-63, PROF, 63- Fulbright res. fel, Göttingen, 63-64; summers, geologist, U.S. Geol. Surv, 48-52; Fulbright grant, Univ. Heidelberg, 71. Best paper award, J. Sedimentary Petrol, 54. U.S.A, 43-46, Lt. Am. Asn. Petrol. Geol; Geol. Soc. Am; Soc. Econ. Paleont. & Mineral. Field geology; evaporites; deformation by moving ice; use of radar in geologic mapping. Address: Dept. of Geology, University of Kansas, Lawrence, KS 66044.

DELMASTRO, JOSEPH RAYMOND, b. Joliet, Ill, Sept. 10, 40. ELECTRO-CHEMISTRY, ANALYTICAL CHEMISTRY. B.S, Northern Illinois, 62; Abbott Labs summer fel, Northwestern, 63, Nat. Sci. Found. summer fel, 64, Ph.D.(anal. chem), 67. RES. CHEMIST ELECTROCHEM, Idaho Nuclear Corp, 67-71; ALLIED CHEM. CORP, 71- Am. Chem. Soc. Theory of electroanalytical techniques; electrical double layer, radio frequency sputtering, thin film technology and porous metallic electrodes. Address: Allied Chemical Corp, CPP-624, Testing Station-Box 2204, Idaho Falls, ID 83401.

DELMER, DEBORAH J, b. Indianapolis, Ind, Dec. 7, 41; m. 65. PLANT PHYSIOLOGY, BIOCHEMISTRY. A.B, Ind. Univ, 63; Nat. Insts. Health fel, Univ. Calif, San Diego, 64-68, Ph.D.(biol), 68. Nat. Insts. Health fel. chem, Univ. Colo, 68-69; biol, UNIV. CALIF, SAN DIEGO, 69-70, ASST. RES. BIOLOGIST, 70- AAAS; Am. Soc. Microbiol; Am. Soc. Plant Physiol. Biosynthesis of tryptophon in higher plants; biochemistry of sucrose synthesis and metabolism in higher plants; enzymology. Address: Dept. of Biology, University of California, San Diego, P.O. Box 109, La Jolla, CA 92037.

DELMONTE, DAVID W(ILLIAM), b. Auburn, N.Y, May 29, 30; m. 58; c. 6. ORGANIC & POLYMER CHEMISTRY. B.S, Villanova, 52; fels, Notre Dame, Gen. Tire & Rubber Co, 54, Reilly Coal Tar & Chem. Co, 54-55, Shell Oil Co, 55-56 & Atomic Energy Cmn, 55-56, Ph.D.(org. chem), 57. Chemist, pioneering res. lab, textile fibers dept, E.I. du Pont de Nemours & Co, 52-53; asst, Notre Dame, 53-54; res. chemist, HERCULES, INC, 56-70, MKT. DEVELOP. REP, 70- Am. Chem. Soc. Condensation polymerization of esters and phosphorus compounds; isocyanate chemistry; polyurethane foam preparation and characterization; adhesives; polymer syntheses; printing inks. Address: Pine & Paper Chemicals Dept, Hercules, Inc, Wilmington, DE 19899.

DELMONTE, LILIAN, b. Hamburg, Ger, Mar. 19, 28; U.S. citizen. HEMATOLOGY. A.B, Mt. Holyoke Col, 50; M.Sc, N.Y. Univ, 52; French Govt. fels, 53-55; Dr. ès Sci.(hemat), Sorbonne, 57. Sr. chem. technician, dept. biophys, Sloan-Kettering Inst, 52-53; res. asst, lab. hemat. & blood groups, Inst. Pasteur, Paris, 53-55; lab. hemat, Hôpital de la Pitié, Paris, 55-57; hemat. lab. supvr, dept. pharmacol, Hoffmann-La Roche, 58-59; med. writer, Cyanamid Int, Am. Cyanamid Co, 59-62; U.S. Pub. Health Serv. spec. fel. ANAT, BAYLOR COL. MED, 62-64, instr, 64-65, ASST. PROF, 65- Int. Cancer Soc-Eleanor Roosevelt-Am. Cancer Soc. fel, Int. Union

Against Cancer, Geneva, Switz, 71-72; sr. vis. scientist, cancer res. unit, Walter & Eliza Hall Inst. Med. Res, Melbourne, Australia, 71-73; Nat. Cancer Inst. spec. fel, 72-73. Am. Asn. Cancer Res; Am. Soc. Hemat; Exp. Hemat. Soc. Hemopoietic self-regulatory mechanisms; leukemic cell regulation. Address: Dept. of Anatomy, Baylor College of Medicine, Houston, TX 77025.

DEL MORAL, ROGER, b. Detroit, Mich, Sept. 13, 43; m. 66. PLANT ECOLOGY. B.A, Univ. Calif, Santa Barbara, 65, Nat. Defense Educ. Act fel, 65-68, M.A, 66, Nat. Sci. Found. fel, summer 67, Ph.D.(biol), 68. ASST. PROF. BOT, UNIV. WASH, 68- Del, Int. Bot. Cong, 69; Nat. Sci. Found. grant, 70-; consult, King County Design Comn, 71- AAAS: Am. Inst. Biol. Sci; Ecol. Soc. Am. Allelopathy; evolution of plant chemicals; comparative physiological ecology; descriptive ecology. Address: Dept. of Botany, University of Washington, Seattle, WA 98195.

DELO, DAVID M(ARION), b. Mt. Marris, Ill, Dec. 20, 05; m; c. 3. GEOLOGY. A.B, Miami (Ohio), 26, hon. LL.D, 56, A.M, Kansas, 28; Austin fel, Harvard, 32-33, Ph.D.(geol), 35; hon.Sc.D, Hartwick Col, 54; L.H.D, Rollins Col, 69, Univ. S.Fla, 70. Asst. instr, Kansas, 26-28; geologist, South. Crude Oil Purchasing Co, 28-29; instr, Washington (St. Louis), 29-30; Northwestern, 30-32; asst. paleont. & stratig, Harvard, 33-34; instr. geol, Lawrence Col, 34-36, asst. prof, 36-37; Knox Col, 37-38, assoc. prof, 38-39, prof, 39-46, chmn. dept. geol. & geog, 37-46; chief, sci. manpower, Dept. Army, 46-49; exec. dir, Am. Geol. Inst. & exec. secy, div. geol. & geog, Nat. Res. Council, 49-52; pres, Wagner Lutheran Col, 52-58; UNIV. TAMPA, 58-71, CHANCELLOR, 71- Nat. res. grant, 36. Mem. cmt. geol. ed, Nat. Res. Council, 46, cmt. geol. personnel, 48. Instr, Civilian Pilot Training Program, 39-43; co-dir, Camp Norton Field Geol. Sch, 40-42; tech. aide, Office Sci. Res. & Develop, 44-45; chmn, Independent Col. & Univ. Fla, 66-68; pres, Fla. Independent Col. Found, 70-71. Consult, U.S.A.F, 51. Fel. Geol. Soc. Am.(Am. grants, 31-45); Asn. Geol. Teachers (pres, 52). Invertebrate paleontology; geomorphology; relation between history and geographic factors in the United States; mobilization and use of scientific manpower. Address: University of Tampa, Tampa, FL 33606.

DeLOACH, BERNARD C(OLLINS), JR, b. Birmingham, Ala, Feb. 19, 30; m. 51; c. 2. PHYSICS. B.S, Ala. Polytech, 51, M.S, 52, univ. fel, Ohio State, 55-56, Ph.D.(physics), 56. MEM. TECH. STAFF, BELL TEL. LABS, 56- Inst. Elec. & Electronics Eng. Solid state millimeter wave sources; semiconductor junction electroluminescence; solid state physics; microwave applications. Address: 134 Sagamore Dr, Murray Hill, NJ 07974.

DeLOACH, CULVER JACKSON, JR, b. Greensboro, N.C, July 25, 32; m. 57; c. 3. ENTOMOLOGY. B.S, Auburn, 54, M.S, 60; Ph.D.(entom), N.C. State, 64. Supply supvr. army engrs, U.S. Army in Korea & Japan, 57-58; asst. prof. entom, Univ. Hawaii in Japan, 64-65; RES. ENTOMOLOGIST, BIOL. CONTROL INSECTS LAB, U.S. DEPT. AGR, 65- U.S.A, 54-56, 1st Lt. Entom. Soc. Am. Biological control of insect pests of agricultural crops utilizing parasites, predators and pathogens. Address: P.O. Box A, Columbia, MO 65201.

De LOACH, WILL S(COTT), b. Dora, Ala, Dec. 22, 10. CHEMISTRY. B.S, Howard Col, 32, M.S, 34; Ph.D.(chem), Chicago, 39. Teacher, pub. sch, Ala, 34-35; asst. chem, Chicago, 36-39; instr, Norfolk div, Col. of William & Mary, 40; teacher, E.Carolina Teachers Col, 40-46, assoc. prof, 47-48; assoc. prof. to prof, Southwest, La. Inst, 46-47; Huntington Col, 48-50; Miss. State Col. for Women, 50-52, Ark. State Teachers Col, Conway, 52-56, head dept. phys. sci, 52-56; Florence State Col, 56-59; George Peabody Col, 59-63; PROF. CHEM, UNIV. N.C, WILMINGTON, 63- Chemist, Duke, 44; asst. sanitarian, Carter Labs, U.S. Pub. Health Serv, 45; with Off. Prod. Res. & Develop, 44. AAAS; Am. Chem. Soc; fel. Am. Inst. Chem. Chemical education. Address: Dept. of Chemistry, University of North Carolina at Wilmington, Wilmington, NC 28401.

DE LONG, CHESTER W(ALLACE), b. Seattle, Wash, Feb. 27, 25; m. 56; c. 3. BIOCHEMISTRY, PHYSIOLOGY. B.S, Washington (Seattle), 48; Ph.D. (chem), State Col. Wash, 56. Biochemist isotope metab, Hanford Atomic Power Labs, Gen. Elec. Co, Wash, 48-52; asst. chem, State Col. Wash, 54-55; biochemist, U.S. Govt, 56-68; CHIEF TRAINING GRANTS & CAREER DEVELOP. PROG, EDUC. SERV, DEPT. MED. & SURG, U.S. VET. ADMIN, 68- Vis. res. assoc, phys. biol. lab, Nat. Inst. Arthritis & Metab. Diseases, 62-63. U.S.N.R, 43-45, Lt.(jg). AAAS; Am. Chem. Soc. Intermediary metabolism; radioisotope toxicology and metabolism; chemistry of penicillin formation; electron paramagnetic resonance of biological materials; biochemistry of amino acids. Address: Education Service, 152-F, Dept. of Medicine & Surgery, U.S. Veterans Administration, 810 Vermont Ave. N.W, Washington, DC 20240.

DELONG, DONALD C(LIFFORD), b. Peoria, Ill, June 28, 30; m. 52; c. 3. BIOCHEMISTRY. B.S, Bradley, 52; M.S. & Ph.D.(biochem), Purdue, 58. Chemist, north. regional utilization lab, U.S. Dept. Agr, 52; biochemist, West. Fish Nutrit. Lab, 57; head nutrit. lab, A.E. Staley Mfg. Co, 58-62; group leader biochem. res, LILLY RES. LABS, 62-65, res. scientist BIOL. RES, 65-69, RES. ASSOC, 69- Med.C, U.S.A, 52-54. Biochemistry of virus; cell interactions and applications to virus chemotherapy. Address: Biological Research Division, Lilly Research Labs, Indianapolis, IN 46206.

DELONG, KARL T(HOMAS), b. Phila, Pa, July 18, 38; m. 63; c. 3. ECOLOGY. A.B, Oberlin Col, 60; Wilson fel, California, Berkeley, 60-61, univ. fel, 64-65, Ph.D.(ecol), 65. Asst. prof. BIOL, Ripon Col, 65-66; GRINNELL COL, 66-68, assoc. prof, 68-70, PROF, 70- Ecol. Soc. Am; Am. Soc. Mammal; Brit. Ecol. Soc. Population ecology of small mammals. Address: Dept. of Biology, Grinnell College, Grinnell, IA 50112.

DeLONG, MERRILL B, b. Ashland, Ky, Oct. 18, 23; m. 45; c. 2. OPTOMETRY. Hiram Col, 46-47; Ohio State, 47-48; B.S, North. Ill. Col. Optom, 48, O.D, 50. Optometrist, Walter Reed Army Med. Center, 53-54; optometrist & adminstr, Air Force Hosp, 54-65; consult. optometrist, 65-67; optometrist, U.S. PUB. HEALTH SERV, 67-68, planning consult. to dir, DIV. ALLIED HEALTH MANPOWER, 68-71, CHIEF ALLIED HEALTH PROFESSIONS BR, 71- Optom. consult, 5th Air Force & Pac. Air Force Surgeons,

58-61, 15th Air Force Surgeon, 64-65. U.S.A, 43-45, Res, 45-51; Med. Serv.C, U.S.A.F, 51-53, Res, 53-54, U.S.A.F, 54-65, Maj. Am. Optom. Asn. Visual optics; health manpower training and utilization; federal assistance to allied health manpower educational training programs. Address: 4304 Haverford Dr, Rockville, MD 20853.

DeLONG, ROBERT F(RANCIS), b. Seattle, Wash, June 17, 16; m. 41; c. 3. BACTERIOLOGY. B.A, Lawrence Col, 38; M.S, Wisconsin, 40. Lab. asst. bact, Inst. Paper Chem, 40-41; microbiologist, Nat. Aluminate Corp, 41-45; group leader, microbiol. packaging, paper prod. res, AM. CAN CO, 45-66, SUPVR. packaging sect, paper prod. res. & develop, 66-70, PROD. EVAL, LAB. SERV, PACKAGING TECH. SERV, 70- Am. Soc. Microbiol; Soc. Indust. Microbiol; Tech. Ans. Pulp & Paper Indust; Inst. Food Tech. Control growth of microorganisms in pulp and paper systems; retard spoiling of packaged foods; food packaging materials. Address: Packaging Technical Service, American Can Co, Neenah, WI 54596.

DE LONG, SHARON K(OEPCKE), b. Madison, Wis, Nov. 21, 36; m. 63; c. 3. MYCOLOGY. B.S, Wisconsin, 58; M.A, California, Berkeley, 60, Ph.D.(bot), 64. Res. assoc. bot, California, Berkeley, 63-64; ASST. PROF. life sci, Sacramento State Col, 64-65; BIOL, Ripon Col, 65-68, GRINNELL COL, 68- Bot. Soc. Am. Genetics and development of water molds. Address: Dept. of Biology, Grinnell College, Grinnell, IA 50112.

DeLOR, C(AMILLE) JOSEPH, b. Sandusky, Ohio, Jan. 24, 07; m. 32; c. 2. MEDICINE. A.B, Michigan, 28; M.Sc. & M.D, Ohio State, 34. Asst. path, Ohio State, 32-34; intern, St. Francis Hosp, 34-35, res. MED, Univ. Hosp, 36-37; asst, COL. MED, OHIO STATE UNIV, 37-38, instr, 38-41, asst. prof, 41-48, clin. assoc, 48-57, clin. prof. 57-62, PROF, 62-, dir. div. gastroenterol, 48-65. Dipl, Am. Bd. Internal Med, 47; Am. Bd. Gastroenterol, 60. Fel. Am. Col. Physicians; Am. Fedn. Clin. Res; Am. Gastroenterol. Asn; Am. Col. Gastroenterol. Diseases of the gastrointestinal tract. Address: Ohio State University College of Medicine, Columbus, OH 43221.

de LORENZO, A(NTHONY) J(OHN), b. Chicago, Ill, Apr. 24, 29; m. 50; c. 2. ANATOMY, CELL BIOLOGY. A.B, Wabash Col, 48; M.A, Hopkins, 50, M.D, 60; Ph.D, Washington (St. Louis), 56. Jr. instr, Hopkins, 48-50; chemist, Olin Industs, 51-52; teaching assoc, Indiana, 52-54; asst, Washington (St. Louis), 54-56, instr. anat, 57-58; asst. prof, otolaryngol. & anat. & dir. anat. res. lab, SCH. MED, JOHNS HOPKINS UNIV, 59-61, ASSOC. PROF. otolaryngol, DEPT. SURG. & ANAT, 61-70, LARYNGOL. & OTOL, 70- Nat. Inst. Neurol. Diseases & Blindness res. fel, 59-; mem. cmt. human communication & consult, U.S. Pub. Health Serv; mem. corp, Marine Biol. Lab, Woods Hole. U.S.N.R, 50-51, Lt.(jg). AAAS; Biophys. Soc; Am. Soc. Cell Biol; Am. Acad. Neurol; Am. Asn. Anat; Am. Acad. Ophthal. & Otolaryngol. Neuroanatomy; neurocytology; electron microscopy of nerve tissues; fine structure of sensory receptors; variation in synaptic fine structure. Address: Dept. of Anatomy, Johns Hopkins Hospital, Baltimore, MD 21205.

DE LORENZO, EUGENE JOSEPH, b. Niagara Falls, N.Y, Aug. 25, 30; m. 62. PHYSICAL CHEMISTRY. B.S, Niagara, 52; Ph.D.(phys. chem), N.Y. Univ, 64. Res. chemist, Olin Mathieson Chem. Corp, 52-56, group leader borane chem, 56-59; assoc. res. scientist, eng. res. div, grad. sch, N.Y. Univ, 59-61, res. asst. quantum chem, 61-64, asst. res. scientist, 64-65; sr. chemist, ITEK CORP, 65-71, MEM. SCI. STAFF, 71- Prog. consult. cosmic ray proj, N.Y. Univ, 64-66. Am. Chem. Soc. Theoretical determination of the electronic states and charge distributions in diatomic molecules; energy levels and energy transfer in solids. Address: Itek Corp, 10 Maguire Rd, Lexington, MA 02173.

DeLORENZO, WILLIAM F, b. Newark, N.J, Dec. 22, 19. BACTERIOLOGY, CHEMOTHERAPY. B.S, Illinois, 43, M.S, 47, Ph.D.(bact), 51. Asst. bact, Illinois, 46-50, fel, 50-52; med. bacteriologist, Chem. Corps, Camp Detrick, Md, 53-54; SR. BACTERIOLOGIST, HOFFMANN-LA ROCHE, INC, 54- AAAS; Am. Soc. Microbiol; Sci. Res. Soc. Am; N.Y. Acad. Sci. Address: Hoffmann-La Roche, Inc, Roche Park, Nutley, NJ 07110.

DELORIT, RICHARD JOHN, b. Door Co, Wis, May 22, 21; m. 42; c. 2. AGRONOMY, AGRICULTURAL EDUCATION. B.S, Wis. State, River Falls, 42; M.S, Wisconsin, 48, Ph.D.(agron), 59; Minnesota, 54. Teacher, high schs, Wis, 42-53; critic teacher voc. agr, Wis. State Univ. & River Falls High Sch, 53-55; asst. prof. agron, WIS. STATE UNIV, RIVER FALLS, 56-57, dean col. agr, 57-64, ACAD. V.PRES, 64- Weed Soc. Am; Am. Soc. Agron. Weed control; botany; ecology. Address: Dept. of Agronomy, Wisconsin State University, River Falls, WI 54022.

DELORME, JOACHIM, b. Boucherville, Que, Aug. 23, 09; m. 39; c. 2. CHEMISTRY, INDUSTRIAL PRODUCTION. B.A, Col. St-Marie, 31; L.Sc, Montreal, 34, M.Sc, 35, Ph.D.(chem), 37. PROF. INDUST. PROD. & HEAD DEPT, FACULTY BUS. ADMIN, UNIV. MONTREAL, 35-, GEN. CHEM, FACULTY MED, 52- Mem, Comt. Sugar Anal, Can, 38-52. David prize, 37. Fel. Chem. Inst. Can. Sugars in analytical field. Address: Dept. of Industrial Production, Faculty of Business Administration, University of Montreal, 5255 Decelles Ave, Montreal 250, Que, Can.

DE LOS REYES, B. WILLIAM, b. New Orleans, La, June 9, 24; m. 42; c. 2. ASTRONOMY, PHYSICS. B.S, U.S. Merchant Marine Acad, 44; M.S, Hofstra, 48; Dr.Ing, Berlin, 55; Ph.D.(phys. sci), N.Y. Univ, 62. Instr. astron, U.S. Merchant Marine Acad, 42-47; assoc. prof. PHYSICS, Madison Col. (Va), 56-58; asst. prof, Nassau Community Col, 58-60; assoc. prof, Longwood Col, 60-68; PROF, U.S. COMMERCE COL, 68- Nat. Sci. Found. fel, Cornell, 60-; Atomic Energy Comn. grant radio chem. & univ. grant, sch. eng, N.Y. Univ, 63- Consult. satellite navig, U.S. Navy, 63-64. U.S.N, 40-47, Lt. Comdr. AAAS; Royal Astron. Soc. Can. Thin films; growth and kinetics of monocrystals of aluminum; cyclic magnetic effect of sunspots. Address: 13136 Morning Spring Lane, Fairfax, VA 22030.

DELOUCHE, JAMES C(URTIS), b. La, Oct. 30, 30; m. 54; c. 3. BOTANY. B.S, Southwestern La. Inst, 51; M.S, Iowa State, 52, Ph.D.(econ. bot), 55. Asst. agronomist SEED TECH, MISS. STATE UNIV, 57-61, assoc. agronomist, 61-65, AGRONOMIST & PROF, 65-; STATE SEED ANALYST, MISS. DEPT. AGR, 58- Chem.C, U.S.A, 55-57. Am. Soc. Agron; Asn. Official Seed Anal. Economic botany; quality evaluation of seed; seed physiology; dissemination and germination of weed seeds. Address: Dept. of Agronomy, Mississippi State University, State College, MS 39762.

DELP, C(HARLES) J(OSEPH), b. St. Louis, Mo, May 9, 27; m. 49; c. 4. PLANT PATHOLOGY. B.S, Colorado State, 50; Ph.D.(plant path), California, 53. Res. asst, California, Davis, 50-53; sr. res. investr. plant path, E.I. DU PONT DE NEMOURS & CO, INC, 53-68, RES. SUPVR, 68- U.S.N.R, 45-46. Am. Phytopath. Soc. Diseases of grapes; environmental influence on grape powdery mildew; action of chemicals to control plant diseases. Address: Bldg. 268, Experimental Station, E.I. du Pont de Nemours & Co, Inc, Wilmington, DE 19898.

DELP, MAHLON (HENRY), b. Lenora, Kans, Nov. 26, 03; m. 24; c. 1. INTERNAL MEDICINE. B.S, Kansas, M.D, 34. Intern, MED. CENTER, UNIV. KANS, 34-35, res, 35-38, instr. internal med, 38-39, assoc. MED, 39-42, asst. prof, 42-48, assoc. prof, 48-50, PROF, 50-, assoc. dean, 57-70, chmn. dept, 60-70. Private practice internal med. U.S.A, 42-46, Col. Am. Col. Physicians; Am. Clin. & Climat. Asn; Asn. Am. Med. Cols. Therapeutic use of vitamin C; pharmacology of bismuth; neurological complications of diphtheria; iron metabolism and enzyme disturbances in liver disease. Address: Dept. of Medicine, School of Medicine, University of Kansas Medical Center, Kansas City, KS 66103.

DEL PESCO, THOMAS W(AYNE), b. Providence, R.I, July 26, 42; m. 65. PHYSICAL ORGANIC & ORGANOMETALLIC CHEMISTRY. B.S, California, Los Angeles, 60; Nat. Defense Ed. Act fel, California, Santa Barbara, 65-68, Ph.D.(org. chem), 68. RES. CHEMIST, E.I. DU PONT DE NEMOURS & CO, 68- Am. Chem. Soc. Reaction mechanisms of electrophilic and nucelophilic substitution reactions; homogeneous catalysis. Address: Dept. of Explosives, E.I. du Pont De Nemours & Co, Experimental Station, Wilmington, DE 19898.

DELPHIA, J(OHN) M(AURICE), b. Kans, Mar. 29, 25; m. 49; c. 5. VERTEBRATE MORPHOLOGY. B.S, St. Benedicts Col, 49; M.S, Kans. State Col, 50; Ph.D.(zool, anat), Nebraska, 59. Instr. zool, N.Dak. Agr. Col, 50-51, comp. anat, embryol. & histol, 52-54, asst. prof, 55; now asst. prof. ANAT, COL. MED, OHIO STATE UNIV, 64-70, ASSOC. PROF, 70- Nat. Insts. Health grants, 57, 58, 59. Med.C, U.S.N.R, 43-46. Am. Asn. Anat. Developmental and gross anatomy of avian lungs and airsacs; abnormalities in bovine endocrine glands. Address: Dept. of Anatomy, Ohio State University College of Medicine, Columbus, OH 43210.

DEL PICO, JOSEPH, b. Weymouth, Mass, May 13, 41; m. CHEMICAL ENGINEERING. B.S, Northeast. Univ, 66; S.M, Mass. Inst. Technol, 68; Ph.D, Tufts Univ, 71. RES. ENGR, Stone & Webster Eng. Corp, Mass, 66-68; ABCOR, INC, CAMBRIDGE, 68- U.S.A, 59-60. Am. Inst. Chem. Eng. Industrial and biomedical applications of membrane separations. Address: 202 Prospect St, Brockton, MA 02401.

DEL POZO, EFREN CARLOS, b. San Luis Potosi, Mex, Sept. 11, 07; m. 34; c. 1. PHYSIOLOGY. B.Sc, San Luis Potosi, 27; M.D, Nat. Univ. Mexico, 36. Instr. bot. & zool, San Luis Potosi, 28-30; prof. physiol, Nat. Sch. Biol. Sci, 38-40; secy. Pub. Ed. Mex. fel, 40; fel, physiol, Harvard Med. Sch, 40-53, Guggenheim fel, 41-43; prof, Nat. Sch. Med, NAT. UNIV. MEX, 43-50, v.pres, 53-61, MEM. RES. STAFF, INST. BIOMED. RES, 61- Res. work, physiol. inst, Cambridge; Nat. Inst. Med. Res, Eng; ward physician, Gen. Hosp, Mex, 38-40; dean, Nat. Sch. Biol. Sci, 43-44; head lab. physiol. & pharmacol, Inst. Pub. Health & Trop. Disease, 44-; with Mex. Pub. Health Serv; secy. gen, Univ. Union Latin Am, 61- AAAS; Am. Physiol. Soc; Soc. Exp. Biol. & Med; Mex. Acad. Med.(secy, 45, v.pres, 59, pres, 60); Mex. Gastroenterol. Asn; Mex. Soc. Psychiat. & Neurol. Neuromuscular transmission; accomodation in nerve; ganglionic transmission; uterine motility; pharmacology of digitalis and scorpion venom; ethnopharmacology; universities administration. Address: Instituto de Investigaciones Biomêdicas, Universidad Nacional Autônoma de Mexico, Mêxico 20, D.F.

DEL REGATO, JUAN A, b. Camaguey, Cuba, Mar. 1, 09; U.S. citizen; m. 39; c. 3. RADIOLOGY. M.D, Paris, 37; hon. D.Sc, Colo. Col, 67. Asst. roentgentherapist, Radium Inst. Paris, 36-37; asst. radiotherapist, Chicago Tumor Inst, 37-38; radiotherapist, Warwick Cancer Clin, Wash, D.C, 39-40; Nat. Cancer Inst, Baltimore, Md, 41-42; Ellis Fischel Cancer Hosp, 43-49; DIR, PENROSE CANCER HOSP, 49-; PROF. CLIN. RADIOL, UNIV. COLO, COLORADO SPRINGS, 49- Consult, Lackland Air Force Base Med. Center, Tex; Vet. Admin. Hosps; Fitzsimons Army Hosp, Denver, Colo. Mem. adv. comt, P.R. Nuclear Ctr; Nat. Adv. Cancer Coun; comt. genitourinary syst, Nat. Acad. Sci-Nat. Res. Coun; Nat. Adv. Cancer Coun. & Lung Cancer Task Force, 67- Laureat, French Acad. Med, 48; Order of Carlos Finlay, 55. Inter-Am. Col. Radiol.(gold medal; pres, 67-71); fel. Am. Col. Radiol. (gold medal); Am. Roentgen Ray Soc; Radiol. Soc. N.Am.(v.pres, 59-60, gold medal); Am. Radium Soc.(v.pres, 63-64, treas, 65, pres, 68-69); Radiation Res. Soc; Asn. Am. Med. Cols. Therapeutic radiology; radiotherapy of cancer of the maxillary sinuses; transvaginal roentgentherapy for cancer of the cervix; total body irradiation for chronic leukemia; radiotherapy of soft tissue sarcomas. Address: Penrose Cancer Hospital, 2215 N. Cascade Ave, Colorado Springs, CO 80907.

DEL RIO-E(STRADA), CARLOS, b. Mexico City, Mex, Feb. 28, 23; m. 64; c. 4. BIOCHEMISTRY. Q.B.P, Nat. Polytech. Inst, Mex, 48; Buenos Aires Convention fels, Cornell, 49-50, M.Sc, 50, Ph.D.(bact, biochem, org. chem), 53. Dir. control labs, Syntex, S.A, Mex, 52-55; prof. microbial biochem, Nat. Polytech. Inst, Mex, 55-56; res. assoc. appl. biochem, Mex. Inst. Tech. Invest, 56-57; PROF. BIOCHEM & MICROBIOL, NAT. UNIV. MEX, 57-, HEAD DEPT. MICROBIOL, FACULTY CHEM, 68- Organizer, Nat. Cong. Microbiol, Mex, 55-56. Fel. & res. assoc. biochem, sch. med, Duke, 65-66; specialist biol. sci, dept. sci. affairs, Orgn. Am. States, Wash, 68-70. Am. Soc. Microbiol.(pres, Mex. Br, 63-64); Mex. Biochem. Soc; Mex. Chem. Soc; Mex. Microbiol. Asn. Biochemistry of microorganisms; mode of action of antibiotics; competitive inhibition with vitamin analogs; microbial biosynthesis of nicotinic acid; comparative studies of microbial enzymes, especially phosphoglucomutase; microbial biochemistry; industrial microbiology. Address: P.O. Box 60-600, Mexico, D.F, Mex.

DEL ROSARIO, LETICIA, b. Yauco, P.R, June 4, 14. PHYSICS. B.S, Puerto Rico, 35; M.S, Chicago, 41, Ph.D.(physics), 48. From instr. to PROF. PHYSICS, UNIV. P.R, RIO PIEDRAS, 41-, DEAN STUDIES, 70-, chmn. dept, 49-54, phys. sci, 64-66. Consult, Dept. Ed, Govt. P.R, 51-60. Mem. orgn. cmt. for symp. P.R, Atomic Energy Cmn, 55-56. Nuclear physics; cosmic rays. Address: Dept. of Physics, University of Puerto Rico, P.O. Box 21488, UPR Station, Rio Piedras, PR 00931.

DELSEMME, A(RMAND) H(UBERT), b. Verviers, Belgium, Feb. 1, 18; m; c. 3. ASTROPHYSICS. B.A, Liége, 38, M.A. & M.Ed, 40, Ph.D.(physics), 51. Res. worker, res. labs, Belge de l' Azote Corp, Belgium, 46-51, head phys. res. lab, 51-53, mgr. & head res, 53-56; dir, Belgian Congo Astron. Observ. & sci. adv, Belgian Inst. Sci. Res. Cent. Africa, 56-61; head basic studies div, directorate sci. affairs, Orgn. Econ. Coop. & Develop, France, 61-66; PROF. ASTROPHYS, UNIV. TOLEDO, 66- Prof, Belgian State Univ, Elizabethville, Congo, 60; guest investr, C.R.B. adv. fel, Mt. Wilson & Palomar Observs, 60-61. Cor. mem, Belg. Nat. Comt. Astron, 58-64, assoc. mem, 64-68; chmn. int. govt. comn, Int. Ctr. Geothermal Res, 64-66; v.pres, comt. phys. study of comets, Int. Astron. Union, 70-73. Belg. Forces in U.K, 41-45. Am. Astron. Soc; Int. Astron. Union; Astron. Soc. France; Belg. Phys. Soc; assoc. Royal Belg. Acad. Overseas Sci. Molecular spectroscopy; thermodynamics; geophysics; volcanology; stellar astrophysics; cometary phenomena; air glow. Address: Dept. of Physics & Astronomy, University of Toledo, Toledo, OH 43606.

DEL TORO, VINCENT, b. N.Y.C, Sept. 17, 23; m. 65. ELECTRICAL ENGINEERING. B.E.E, City Col. New York, 46; M.E.E, Polytech. Inst. Brooklyn, 50. Tutor ELEC. ENG, CITY COL. NEW YORK, 46-50, instr, 50-54, asst. prof, 54-58, assoc. prof, 58-62, PROF, 63-, ASSOC. DEAN, SCH. ENG, 65-, asst. dean, 62-65. Summers, res. engr, Boeing Co, 55, design specialist, Gen. Dynamics/Convair, 56, sr. engr, 57 & N.Am, Aviation, Inc, 59. Consult. control systs, Gen. Dynamics/Convair, 57-59. Sr. mem. Inst. Elec. & Electronics Eng; Am. Soc. Eng. Educ. Self-adaptive control systems; feedback and nonlinear control systems; synchronous induction motors. Address: Dept. of Electrical Engineering, City College of New York, New York, NY 10031.

DE LUCA, CHESTER, b. Bristol, Pa, Sept, 7, 27; m. 54; c. 5. BIOCHEMISTRY. B.S, Georgetown, 52; Ph.D.(biochem), Hopkins, 56. Jr. instr. biol, Hopkins, 52-54, Nat. Cancer Inst, fel, 54-56; Am. Cancer Soc. fel, Rockefeller Inst, 56-59; instr. pediat, Hopkins, 59-62; sr. cancer res. scientist, Roswell Park Mem. Inst, 62-65; ASST. PROF. ORAL BIOL, SCH. DENT, STATE UNIV. N.Y. BUFFALO, 65- Res. assoc. pediat, Sinai Hosp, Baltimore, Md, 59-62. U.S.A, 46-47. AAAS; Am. Chem. Soc; Am. Soc. Cell Biol; Tissue Cult. Asn. Cell physiology; biochemical control mechanisms. Address: Dept. of Oral Biology, State University of New York at Buffalo, 4510 Main St, Buffalo, NY 14226.

DE LUCA, DONALD C(ARL), b. Amsterdam, N.Y, May 24, 36; m. 66; c. 2. ORGANIC CHEMISTRY, BIOCHEMISTRY. B.S, Rensselaer Polytech. Inst, 57; Ph.D.(org. chem), Univ. Minn, 63. Res. fel. BIOCHEM, SCH. MED, Johns Hopkins Univ, 64-66; ASST. PROF, UNIV. ARK, 66- U.S.A, 62-64, 1st Lt. AAAS; Am. Chem. Soc; The Chem. Soc. Photochemical oxidations; chemical and biological oxidative processes of nitrogen containing compounds; biochemistry of behavior. Address: Dept. of Biochemistry, University of Arkansas School of Medicine, 4301 W. Markham, Little Rock, AR 72205.

DeLUCA, HECTOR F(LOYD), b. Pueblo, Colo, Apr. 5, 30; m. 54; c. 4. BIOCHEMISTRY. B.A, Univ. Colo, 51; M.S, Univ. Wis, 53, Ph.D, 55. Res. asst. biochem, UNIV. WIS, MADISON, 51-55, proj. assoc, 55, fel, 56-57, instr, 57-59, asst. prof, 59-62, assoc. prof, 62-65, PROF. BIOCHEM. & HARRY STEENBOCK RES. PROF, 65-, CHMN. DEPT. BIOCHEM, 70- Vis. scientist, Strangeways Res. Labs, Eng, 60. Andre Lichtwitz Prize, 68; Mead Johnson Award, 68; Nicolas Andry Award, 71. Am. Chem. Soc; Am. Soc. Biol. Chem; Am. Inst. Nutrit. Mechanism of action and metabolism of vitamins and hormones, especially vitamin D. Address: Dept. of Biochemistry, University of Wisconsin, Madison, WI 53706.

DeLUCA, MARLENE, b. La Crosse, Wis, Nov. 10, 36; m. 59; 67; c. 1. BIOCHEMISTRY. B.S, Hamline Univ, 58; Ph.D.(biochem), Univ. Minn, 63. Fel. biol, McCollum-Pratt Inst, Johns Hopkins Univ, 62-65, ASST. PROF, univ, 65-70; BIOCHEM, SCHS. MED. & DENT, GEORGETOWN UNIV, 70- Am. Soc. Biol. Chem. Oxidative phosphorylation and enzyme mechanisms. Address: Dept. of Biochemistry, Schools of Medicine & Dentistry, Georgetown University, Washington, DC 20007.

DE LUCA, PATRICK PHILLIP, b. Scranton, Pa, Sept. 7, 35; m. 56; c. 6. PHARMACEUTICS. B.S, Temple, 57, Smith Kline & French fels, 59-62, M.S, 60, Ph.D.(pharm), 63. Jr. anal. chemist, Smith Kline & French Labs, 57-59; sr. res. pharmacist, Ciba Pharmaceut. Co, 63-66, plant mgr, Somerville opers, 66-69, Cormedics Corp, 69-70, dir. develop. & control, 70; ASSOC. PROF. PHARM, UNIV. KY, 70-, ASST. DEAN COL. PHARM, 71- Mem. U.S. Pharm. adv. panel; res. comt, Parenteral Drug Asn; indust. pharm. technol. screening comt, Acad. Pharmaceut. Sci-Int. Fedn. Pharm. Leo G. Penn Mem. Award, Temple Univ, 57; Lunsford-Richardson Pharm. award, 60, 62. Am. Pharmaceut. Asn; Acad. Pharmaceut. Sci. Pharmaceutical technology; kinetics and stabilization; lyophilization; sterile products. Address: College of Pharmacy, University of Kentucky, Lexington, KY 40506.

DeLUCA, ROBERT D(AVID), b. Passaic, N.J, Jan. 11, 41; m. 63; c. 3. METALLURGY, SOLID STATE PHYSICS; B.E, Stevens Inst. Technol, 62, M.S, 64, Ph.D.(metall), 66. SR. METALLURGIST, CORNING GLASS WORKS, 66- Am. Phys. Soc; Electrochem. Soc; Am. Inst. Min, Metall. & Petrol. Eng. Metal-glass reactions; high resistivity coatings on glass and glass-ceramics; electron multiplier materials; silicon deposition on glass; anodic banding of metals to glass; electron microscopy; strengthening mechanisms in metals; magnesium alloy technology; physical metallurgy. Address: Corning Glass Works, Research & Development Labs, Corning, NY 14830.

DE LUCIA, FRANK CHARLES, b. St. Paul, Minn, June 21, 43; m. 65. MOLECULAR PHYSICS, QUANTUM ELECTRONICS. B.S, Iowa Wesleyan Col, 64; Ph.D.(physics), Duke, 69. Instr. & res. assoc. PHYSICS, DUKE UNIV, 69-71, ASST. PROF, 71- AAAS; Am. Phys. Soc. Microwave spectroscopy; millimeter and submillimeter molecular beam masers. Address: Dept. of Physics, Duke University, Durham, NC 27706.

De LUCIA, JOHN J(OSEPH), b. New York, N.Y, Sept, 6, 15; m. 42; c. 1. ORGANIC CHEMISTRY. B.S, N.Y, Univ, 37; Rome, 37-39; M.S, Fordham, 42. Microanalyst, res. labs, Interchem. Corp, 41-43, org. chemist, 43-44, sr. chemist pigments & intermediates, 44-50, group leader, 50-57, color & chem. div, 57-67, mgr. pigment develop, 67, TECH. MGR. ORG. PIGMENTS RES. & DEVELOP, INMONT CORP, 67- Am. Chem. Soc. Synthesis of roboise; organic pigments and dyes; carbohydrates; textile products. Address: Inmont Corp, 150 Wagaraw Rd, Hawthorne, NJ 07506.

DeLUISI, JOHN J, b. Little Falls, N.Y, Oct. 4, 30; m. 59; c. 3. PHYSICS, METEOROLOGY. B.S, State Univ. N.Y. Albany, 57, M.S, 62; M.A.T. & Nat. Sci. Found. fel, Brown, 63; Ph.D.(meteorol), Fla. State, 67. Instr, high sch, N.Y, 59-61; SCIENTIST, NAT. CTR. ATMOSPHERIC RES, 67- U.S.N, 48-49, 51-53. Am. Meteorol. Soc. Ultraviolet radiative transfer in the atmosphere and atmospheric ozone. Address: 21 Porteus St, Little Falls, NY 13365.

DeLURY, DANIEL B(ERTRAND), b. Walker, Minn, Sept. 19, 07; Can. citizen; m. 41; c. 2. MATHEMATICS, STATISTICS. B.A, Toronto, 29, M.A, 30, Ph.D.(math), 36. Instr. math, Saskatchewan, 31-34; lectr, Toronto, 36-43, asst. prof, 43-45; assoc. prof. statist, Va. Polytech, 45-46, prof, 46-47, dir. dept. math. statist, Ont. Res. Found, 47-58; PROF. MATH, UNIV. TORONTO, 58-, chmn. dept, 58-68. Fel. AAAS; fel. Am. Statist. Asn; Am. Math. Soc; Inst. Math. Statist; Biomet. Soc; Int. Statist. Inst. Population dynamics; estimation of biological populations. Address: Dept. of Mathematics, University of Toronto, Toronto, 5, Ont, Can.

DELVAILLE, JOHN P(AUL), b. Riverside, Calif, Oct. 5, 31; m. 65. PHYSICS. B.A, California, Berkeley, 54; Ph.D.(exp. physics), Cornell, 62. Instr. & res. assoc. physics, Cornell, 62-63, acting asst. prof, 63-64, asst. prof, 64-70; RES. MEM, CTR. FOR SPACE RES, MASS. INST. TECHNOL, 70- AAAS; Am. Asn. Physics Teachers; Am. Phys. Soc. Cosmic rays; extensive air showers; gamma-ray and x-ray astronomy; atomic collisions; Address: Space Research Center, Room 37-507, Massachusetts Institute of Technology, Cambridge, MA 02139.

DEL VALLE, FRANK, b. Santa Rosa, Argentina, July 3, 33; m. 59; c. 2. INDUSTRIAL & FOOD CHEMISTRY. M.S, Buenos Aires, 57; Ph.D.(chem), 61. Lab. asst, Bull Dog S.A, Argentina, 58; lab. head, Trineo S.A, 58-63, RES. CHEMIST, Evans Res. & Develop. Corp, 63-64; A.E. STALEY MFG. CO, 64- Inst. Food Technol. Candy manufacture; canned foods processing; salad dressing. Address: A.E. Staley Manufacturing Co, 2200 E. Eldorado St, Decatur, IL 62521.

DEL VECCHIO, ALFRED, b. New York, N.Y, Mar. 20, 23; m. 44; c. 7. MECHANICAL ENGINEERING. B.M.E, N.Y. Univ, 44, M.M.E, 48. PROF. MECH. ENG, MANHATTAN COL, 59-, HEAD DEPT. MECH. ENG, 68- Nat. Soc. Prof. Eng; Am. Soc. Mech. Eng; Soc. Automotive Eng. Thermodynamics and research in vehicular emissions. Address: Dept. of Mechanical Engineering, Manhattan College, Manhattan College Pkwy, Riverdale, Bronx, NY 10471.

DEL VECCHIO, VITO GERARD, b. Dunmore, Pa, May 13, 39. BIOCHEMICAL GENETICS. B.S, Scranton, 61; M.S, St. John's (N.Y), 63; Ph.D.(biochem. genetics), Hahnemann Med. Col, 67. U.S. Pub. Health Serv. res. fel. microbiol, Univ. Geneva, 66-68; assoc. prof. BIOL, Stonehill Col, 68-69; ASST. PROF, UNIV. SCRANTON, 69- AAAS; Genetics Soc. Am; Am. Soc. Microbiol. Tyrosinase genetics; biochemistry and immunochemistry of Neurospora crassa morphogenesis; biochemical control of morphogenesis of Neurospora isozymes of Neurospora crassa. Address: Dept. of Biology, University of Scranton, Scranton, PA 18510.

DELVIGS, PETER, b. Riga, Latvia, June 28, 33; U.S. citizen; m. 65. ORGANIC & POLYMER CHEMISTRY. B.A, Western Reserve, 59; Minn. Mining & Mfg. Co. fel, Minnesota, Minneapolis, 61, Nat. Sci. Found. fel, 62, Ph.D. (org. chem), 63. Res. assoc. biochem, Cleveland Clin. Found, 63-67; AEROSPACE CHEMIST, NASA LEWIS RES. CTR, CLEVELAND, 67- U.S.A, 53-56. AAAS; Am. Chem. Soc. Synthesis, characterization and properties of new thermally stable polymers; development of fiber-reinforced resin composites. Address: 21290 Parkwood Ave, Fairview Park, OH 44126.

DELWICHE, C(ONSTANT) C(OLLIN), b. Wis, Nov. 26, 17; m. 43; c. 4. COMPARATIVE BIOCHEMISTRY. B.S, Wisconsin, 40; Ph.D, California, 49. PROF. SOIL SCI. & BIOCHEMIST, KEARNEY FOUND, UNIV. CALIF, DAVIS, 60-, CHMN. DEPT. SOILS & PLANT NUTRIT, 65- U.S.A, 42-46, Col. AAAS; Am. Soc. Plant Physiol; Arctic Inst. N.Am; Am. Soc. Biol. Chem; Am. Soc. Microbiol; Brit. Biochem. Soc. Inorganic nitrogen transformation; nitrogen fixation; inorganic energy metabolism; isotope distribution; mass spectrometry. Address: Kearney Foundation & Dept. of Soils & Plant Nutrition, University of California, Davis, CA 95616.

DELWICHE, EUGENE A(LBERT), b. Green Bay, Wis, Nov. 26, 17; m. 49; c. 4. BACTERIOLOGY. B.S, Wisconsin, 41; Ph.D, Cornell, 48. Asst. prof, BACT, CORNELL UNIV, 48-51, assoc. prof, 51-55, PROF, 55- Guggenheim fel, Karolinska Inst, Sweden, 64; summers, res. participant, Oak Ridge Nat. Labs, 51-53, consult, 51-59. U.S.A, 41-46, Chem.C.Res, 46-, Lt. Col. Am. Soc. Biol. Chem; Am. Acad. Microbiol; Am. Soc. Microbiol; Can. Soc. Microbiol. The physiology, biochemistry, nutrition and intermediary metabolism of bacteria and other microorganisms. Address: Stocking Hall, Cornell University, Ithaca, NY 14850.

DELZELL, DAVID E(DGAR), b. Toledo, Ohio, May 13, 15; m; c. 3. ZOOLOGY. Ph.D.(zool), Michigan, 57. Asst. prof. zool, McMaster, 50-55; instr, Michigan, 55-57; Wayne State, 57-59; assoc. prof, Col. William & Mary,

59; OLD DOMINION UNIV, 59-63, PROF. BIOL, 64- U.S.A, 42-45. Ecol. Soc. Am. Ecology of vertebrates. Address: Dept. of Biology, Old Dominion University, Norfolk, VA 23508.

DeMAGGIO, AUGUSTUS E(DWARD), b. Malden, Mass, Apr. 22, 32; m. 54; c. 3. BOTANY, PHYSIOLOGY. B.S, Mass. Col. Pharm, 54, fels, 54-56, M.S, 56; fel, Harvard, 56-59, A.M, 58, Ph.D, 60. Asst. prof. pharmacog, col. pharm, Rutgers, 59-62, assoc. prof, 62-64; asst. prof. BIOL. DARTMOUTH COL, 64-66, assoc. prof, 66-70, PROF, 70- Waksman Found. fel, France; univ. faculty fel, Rutgers & mem. staff, Nat. Ctr. Agr. Res, France, 62-63; res. fel, Harvard, 69-70. Fel. AAAS; Bot. Soc. Am; Am. Soc. Plant Physiol; Torrey Bot. Club; Am. Soc. Pharmacog; Am. Pharmaceut. Asn; Int. Soc. Plant Morphol. Experimental botany; morphogenesis; chloroplast biochemistry; plant chemistry. Address: Dept. of Biological Sciences, Dartmouth College, Hanover, NH 03755.

DEMAIN, ARNOLD L(ESTER), b. Brooklyn, N.Y, Apr. 26, 27; m. 52; c. 2. MICROBIOLOGY. B.S, Mich. State, 49; M.S, 50; Ph.D.(microbiol), California, 54. Asst. yeast physiol, California, 52-54; res. microbiologist, Merck, Sharp & Dohme Res. Labs, 54-64, head fermentol. res, 64-69; PROF. APPL. MICROBIOL, MASS. INST. TECHNOL, 69- Pharmacist, U.S.N, 45-47. Am. Soc. Microbiol; N.Y. Acad. Sci. Microbial nutrition; penicillin and cephalosporin biosynthesis; pectic enzymes; protein synthesis; nucleotide biosynthesis. Address: Dept. of Nutrition & Food Science, Room 56-123, Massachusetts Institute of Technology, Cambridge, MA 02139.

DE MAINE, PAUL ALEXANDER DESMOND, b. Koster, Transvaal, S.Africa, Oct. 11, 24; U.S. citizen; m. 55. COMPUTER SCIENCE. B.A, Witwatersrand, 48; Ph.D.(chem), British Columbia, 56. Res. spectros, Chicago, 54-55; math. & chem, Cambridge, 55-56; spectros, King's Col, London, 56; electrochem, Ottawa (Can), 57; assoc. prof. chem, State Univ. Col. Ed, Albany, 57, prof, 58-60; Mississippi, 60-63; vis. scientist, Illinois, 63-64; assoc. specialist, California, Santa Barbara, 64-65; Ctr. comput. sci. & technol, Nat. Bur. Standards, 65-67; assoc. prof. COMPUT. SCI, PA. STATE UNIV, 68-70, PROF, 70- Royal S.African Navy & Brit. Spec. Serv, 42-45. Am. Chem. Soc; Am. Soc. Info. Sci; Asn. Comput. Mach; The Chem. Soc. Computerized information storage and retrieval; data processing. Address: Dept. of Computer Science, McAllister Bldg, Pennsylvania State University, University Park, PA 16802.

de MALHERBE, MICHAEL CAESAR, b. Kamionka, Poland, Jan. 3, 19; m. ENGINEERING DESIGN. Dipl. Ing, Polish Univ. Col, London, 43; D.I.C. & Ph.D.(mech. eng), Imp. Col, London, 45. Asst. lectr. mech. eng, Polish Univ. Col, London, Eng, 44-45, lectr, 45-46; sr. lectr, Witwatersrand Tech. Col, 47-56; vis. prof, California, Berkeley, 56-57; v.prin, Witwatersrand Tech. Col, 57-59; sr. lectr, Imp. Col, London, 60-65; Prof. Transvaal Indust. chair, Witwatersrand, 65-67; PROF. MECH. ENG. & DIR. CENTER APPL. RES. & ENG. DESIGN, McMASTER UNIV, 67- Inst. Mech. Eng. Clayton grant, 59; vis. prof, California, Berkeley, 64; Nat. Sci. Found. sr. foreign scientist grant, Northwestern, 66. Exam, Dept. Ed, Arts & Sci, S.Africa, 52-; founder & dir, Prod. Inc. Ltd, S.Africa, 55-64; consult, Brit. Iron & Steel Res. Asn, 62-64; dir. fluid dynamics, firm consult, U.K, 63-66; consult, Anglo-Am. Corp. S.Africa, 65-; dir, Versatex Ltd, S.Africa, 67- Mem. planning cmt, State Serv. Act, State Ill, 66; chmn, Can. Inst. Metalworking, 67- R.A.F, 39-42. Fel. Brit. Inst. Mech. Eng; fel. Brit. Inst. Prod. Eng; Am. Soc. Mech. Eng; Can. Soc. Mech. Eng. Manufacturing processes; dissemination of scientific information to industry. Address: Centre for Applied Research & Engineering Design, McMaster University, Hamilton, Ont, Can.

DeMAN, J(OHN) M(ARIA), b. Rotterdam, Netherlands, Apr. 13, 25; Can. citizen; m. 54; c. 3. FOOD CHEMISTRY. Chem.Eng, Netherlands, 51; Ph.D. (dairy chem), Univ. Alta, 59. Res. chemist, Unilever Res. Labs, Holland, 49-54; res. asst, Univ. Alta, 54-59, asst. prof, 59-64, assoc. prof. dairy & food chem, 64-69; PROF. FOOD SCI. & CHMN. DEPT, UNIV. GUELPH, 69- Can. Inst. Food Technol.(past pres, ed-in-chief, Jour); Inst. Food Technol; Am. Oil Chemists Soc; Am. Dairy Sci. Asn; Brit. Soc. Rheol; Am. Asn. Cereal Chem. Food texture and rheology; instrumentation for food texture measurement; fat crystallization and polymorphism; triglyceride composition and structure; food contaminants; cereal and oilseed technology. Address: Dept. of Food Science, University of Guelph, Guelph, Ont, Can.

DEMANCHE, EDNA LOUISE, b. Marionville, Mo, Aug. 1, 15. SCIENCE EDUCATION, PLANT PHYSIOLOGY. B.S, Col. Mt. St. Vincent, 40; Nat. Sci. Found. fel, Notre Dame, 62-63, Schmidt scholar, 63-64, M.S, 64, Ph.D. (plant physiol), 69. Teacher, parochial schs, Hawaii, 40-59; sci. consult, 59-67; ADMIN. TECH. & PROF. ASST. EDUC. RES. & DEVELOP, UNIV. HAWAII, 67- Traveling team lectr, Hawaii, 65-66; Nat. Sci. Found. Summer Inst, teaching science teachers in Japan, 69. Consult. sci. fair projs, pub. & private schs, Hawaii, 59-68, part-time, Cath. schs, 67- AAAS; Nat. Asn. Biol. Teachers; Nat. Sci. Teachers Asn. Factors associated with changes in phyllotaxy; development of new laboratory-oriented procedures in ecology centered on local environmental phenomena and accompanying procedures for classroom implementation. Address: Maryknoll Sisters, 5415-A Kalanianaole Highway, Honolulu, HI 96821.

DeMAR, RICHARD, b. Cincinnati, Ohio, Mar. 27, 24; m. 51; c. 2. MATHEMATICAL ANALYSIS. B.S.Ed, Cincinnati, 48, M.Ed, 51; M.S, Wisconsin, 55, Ph.D.(math), 61. Instr. MATH, Miami (Ohio), 57-61, asst. prof, 61-63, assoc. prof, 63-65; Univ. Calif, Davis, 65-67; UNIV. CINCINNATI, 67-71, PROF, 71- Nat. Acad. Sci-Nat. Res. Coun. resident res. assoc, Nat. Bur. Standards, 62-63; summers, consult, aeronaut. res. lab, Wright-Patterson Air Force Base, 62 & res. analyst, aerospace res. lab, 64. U.S.A, 43-45. AAAS; Am. Math. Soc; Math. Asn. Am. Entire functions; existence and uniqueness of interpolating functions. Address: Dept. of Mathematics, University of Cincinnati, Cincinnati, OH 45221.

DeMAR, ROBERT E, b. Keene, N.H, Nov. 7, 31; m. 59. VERTEBRATE PALEONTOLOGY. A.B, Harvard, 53; George Washington, 54; M.S, Chicago, 60; Ph.D.(vert. paleont), 61. Geologist, U.S. Geol. Surv, 53-54; asst. GEOL, UNIV. ILL, CHICAGO CIRCLE, 56-58, instr, 58-61, asst. prof, 61-68, ASSOC. PROF, 68- Summer instr, Northwest. Univ, 58. AAAS; Soc. Study Evolution; Geol. Soc. Am; Soc. Vert. Paleont. Late Paleozoic vertebrates; jaw mechanics of synapsid reptiles. Address: Dept. of Geological Sciences, University of Illinois at Chicago Circle, P.O. Box 4348, Chicago, IL 60680.

DE MARCO, F(RANK) A(NTHONY), b. Italy, Feb. 14, 21; nat; m. 48; c. 11. CHEMICAL ENGINEERING. B.A.Sc, Toronto, 43, Int. Nickel scholar, M.A.Sc, 43, Nat. Res. Coun. fel, Ph.D.(chem. eng), 51. Instr, Toronto, 43-46; from asst. prof. to prof. chem. & head dept, Assumption Univ, UNIV. WINDSOR, 46-57, acting head eng. dept, 57-59, assoc. dean, arts & sci, 58, dean, faculty of appl. sci, 59-64, V.PRES, UNIV, 63-, PROF. CHEM. & CHEM. ENG, 70- Chmn. staff comt, Essex Col, Assumption, 56-59, prin, 59-63; chmn. bd. gov, St. Clair Col. Appl. Arts & Technol. Am. Soc. Eng. Educ; fel. Chem. Inst. Can; Eng. Inst. Can. Coordination compounds; electrorefining of copper; glueline studies; cyanine dye synthesis; solubilization of hydrocarbons. Address: R.R. No. 1, River Canard, Ont, Can.

DE MARCO, THOMAS JOSEPH, b. Farmingdale, N.Y, Feb. 12, 42; m. 66; c. 1. PHARMACOLOGY, PERIODONTOLOGY. B.S, Univ. Pittsburgh, 62, D.D.M, 65; cert. periodont. & Ph.D.(pharmacol), Boston Univ, 68. Nat. Inst. Dent. Res. fel, Boston Univ, 63-68; Asst. prof, PHARMACOL. & PERIODONT, DENT. SCH, CASE WEST. RESERVE UNIV, 68-70, ASSOC. PROF, 70-, ASST. PROF. PHARMACOL, MED. SCH, 69-, NURSING SCH, 71- Am. Chem. Soc; Am. Acad. Periodont; Am. Dent. Asn. Lymphatic drug absorption from the gastrointestinal tract and the sublingual area of the mouth. Address: Case Western Reserve University School of Dentistry, 2123 Abington Rd, Cleveland, OH 44106.

DeMARCUS, W(ENDELL) C(ARDEN), b. Anderson Co, Tenn, May 9, 24; m. 54; c. 2. PHYSICS. B.S, Kentucky, 47; M.S, Yale, 50, Ph.D.(physics), 51. Physicist, Carbide & Carbon Chems. Co, 51-52, sr. physicist, 52-56, prin. physicist, 56-57; assoc. prof. PHYSICS, UNIV. KY, 57-58, PROF, 58- Consult, Union Carbide Nuclear Co, 57- Am. Phys. Soc; Am. Astron. Soc; Int. Astron. Union; fel. Royal Astron. Soc. Astrophysics; solid state physics. Address: Dept. of Physics, University of Kentucky, Lexington, KY 40506.

DEMAREE, GALE E, b. Burwell, Nebr, Jan. 4, 31; m. 52. PHARMACOLOGY. B.Sc, Nebraska, 53, M.Sc, 55; M.P.H, North Carolina, 62; Ph.D.(pharmacol), Univ. Ala, 68. Investr. pharmacol, WALTER REED ARMY INST. RES, 62-68, RES. PHARMACOLOGIST, 68- U.S.A, 56-, Maj. Cardiovascular pharmacology; pharmacology of radiation chemoprophylatic agents. Address: Walter Reed Army Institute of Research, Washington, DC 20012.

DEMAREE, RICHARD S(POTTSWOOD), JR, b. Akron, Ohio, July 1, 42; m. 65. CYTOLOGY, PARASITOLOGY. B.S, Purdue Univ, 64; M.A, Ind. State Univ, 66; Nat. Insts. Health trainee, Colo. State Univ, 66-69, Ph.D.(zool), 69. HEAD ELECTRON MICROS. BR, PATH. DIV, U.S. ARMY MED. RES. & NUTRIT. LAB, FITZSIMONS GEN. HOSP, 69- Med.Serv.C, U.S.A.R, 69-, Capt. Electron Micros. Soc. Am; Am. Soc. Parasitol; Soc. Protozool. Parasite ultrastructure and morphogenesis; ultrastructural cytology and pathology; high altitude research. Address: Pathology Division, U.S. Army Medical Research & Nutrition Lab, Fitzsimons General Hospital, Denver, CO 80240.

DE MARGERIE, JEAN-MARIE, b. Prud'homme, Sask, Can, Dec. 11, 27; m. 55; c. 5. OPHTHALMOLOGY. B.A, Ottawa (Ont), 47; B.Ed, Laval, 49, M.D, 52; Rhodes scholar, Oxford, 52-55, D.Phil.(ophthal), 59. Asst. prof. OPHTHAL, Queen's (Ont), 60-66; PROF. & DIR. DEPT, UNIV. SHERBROOKE, 66- Head dept. ophthal, Hôtel-Dieu Hosp, Kingston, Ont, 64-66. Consult, Ont. Hosp, 60-66 & Armed Forces Hosp, Can, 64-66. Fel. Royal Col. Physicians & Surgeons, Can, 61. Can. Med. Asn; Can. Ophthal. Soc, fel. Am. Col. Surg; fel. Acad. Ophthalmol. & Otolaryngol; Asn. Res. Vision & Ophthalmol. Anatomy and pathology of ocular fundus; arterial hypertension; toxic retinopathies; ocular photography; fluorescein photography of the eye; diabetic retinopathies. Address: Dept. of Ophthalmology, University of Sherbrooke, Sherbrooke, Que, Can.

DeMARIA, ANTHONY JOHN, b. Italy, Oct. 30, 31; U.S. citizen; m. 53; c. 1. ENGINEERING PHYSICS. B.S.E.E, Connecticut, Ph.D, 65; M.S, Rensselaer Polytech, 60. Res. acoustic engr, Anderson Labs, Conn, 56-57; staff physicist phys. electronics, Hamilton Standard Div, UNITED AIRCRAFT CORP, 57-58, prin. scientist & group leader, res. labs, 58-70, CHIEF SCIENTIST, ELECTROMAGNETICS LABS, 70- Adj. prof, Rensselaer Polytech. Inst, 68-; mem. bd. dirs, Laser Indust. Asn; consult. lasers, Nat. Acad. Sci. Inst. Elec. & Electronics Eng; Am. Phys. Soc; Optical Soc. Am. Utilization of laser devices; interaction of elastic waves with coherent light radiation; generation, measurement and application of picosecond light pulses; gas laser research and applications. Address: Electromagnetics Labs, United Aircraft Research Labs, Silver Lane, East Hartford, CT 06108.

DE MARIA, F. JOHN, b. Sliema, Malta, Apr. 30, 28; Can. citizen; m. 58; c. 4. OBSTETRICS, GYNECOLOGY. M.D, Royal Univ. Malta, 52. House officer obstet. & gynec, postgrad. med. sch, London, 54-56; registr, Durham & Newcastle, 57-59; Ramsay res. fel, physiol, St. Andrew's 59-61; asst. prof. OBSTET. & GYNEC, British Columbia, 61-66; ASSOC. PROF, MED. SCH, UNIV. ORE, 66- Los Angeles County res. fel, 60-61; obstetrician & gynecologist, Vancouver Gen. Hosp, 61-66. Fel. Royal Col. Surg. Can, 63. Fel. Am. Col. Obstet. & Gynec; Royal Col. Obstet. & Gynec. Neuroendocrinology; placental enzymes and pre-eclampsia; temporal correlation between the hypothalamus and uterus; surgery of infertility. Address: Dept. of Obstetrics & Gynecology, University of Oregon Medical School, Portland, OR 97201.

DEMARIA, WILLIAM J(OHN) A(MSTERDAM), b. Westport, Conn, May 15, 23; m. 47; c. 3. PEDIATRICS. B.S, Connecticut, 44; M.D, Duke, 48. U.S. Pub. Health Serv. fel, DUKE UNIV, 48, training pediat, SCH. MED, 49-51, instr, 51-57, assoc. prof, 57-63, PROF. prev. med, 63-66, community health sci, 66-70, PEDIAT, 70-, ASST. DEAN CONTINUING EDUC, 67- Med. Sci. Award, 52. AAAS; Soc. Nuclear Med; Asn. Teachers Prev. Med; Soc. Pediat. Res. Vascular-renal disease and physiology. Address: Box 2991, Duke Hospital, Durham, NC 27706.

DeMARINIS, FRANK, b. Bari, Italy, Dec. 14, 12; nat; m. 37; c. 4. GENETICS. A.B, Western Reserve, 36, A.M, 37, Ph.D.(genetics), 40. Asst. biol, Western Reserve, 37-40; res. chemist, Petri Wine Lab, Calif, 40-41; res. chemist, S.K. Wellman Co, Ohio, 41-45; Aluminum Co. Am, 45-46; asst. prof. BIOL, Fenn Col, 46-50, prof. & chmn. dept, 50-65; PROF, CLEVELAND STATE UNIV, 65-, chmn. dept, 65-70. Consult, Off. Sci. Res. & Develop, 44; mem. Heredity Clin, Cleveland Metrop. Hosp, 57-58; mem. staff, atomic test series, Nev. Test Site, 57; dep. sci. attache, U.S. Embassy, Italy, 60-62; mem. vis. scientist prog, Ohio Acad. Sci-Nat. Sci. Found, 62-64; off-site radiol. surveillance, U.S. Pub. Health Serv-Atomic Energy Comn, Nev, 63, Dribble Proj, Miss, 64; mem. work group, Great Lakes Basin Comn, 68-; guest researcher genetics, Konan Univ, Japan; Inst. Genetics, Univ. Barcelona & vis. prof. genetics, inst. genetics, Univ. Rome, 70-71. U.S.P.H.S.R, 56-, sr. scientist. Fel. AAAS; Am. Chem. Soc; Soc. Develop. Biol; Genetics Soc. Am; Am. Soc. Human Genetics; N.Y. Acad. Sci. Genetics of Drosophila and man; genic action; role of amides in development of Drosophila. Address: 2611 Exeter Rd, Cleveland, OH 44118.

DEMARQUE, PIERRE, b. Fez, Morocco, July 18, 32; Can. citizen; m. 58; c. 2. ASTROPHYSICS. B.Sc, McGill, 55; M.A, Toronto, 57, F.S. Hogg fel, 57-58, C.A. Chant fel, 58-59, Ph.D.(astron), 60; hon. M.A, Yale, 68. Mem. staff appl. math, Canadair Ltd, Mont, 55-56; asst. prof. ASTRON, La. State, 59-60; Illinois, 60-62; Toronto, 62-64, assoc. prof, 64-66; Univ. Chicago, 66-67, prof, 67-68; PROF. ASTROPHYS. & CHMN. DEPT. ASTRON, YALE, 68- Mem. Can. Nat. Comt, Int. Astron. Union & nat. coun, Royal Astron. Soc. Can, 65- Am. Astron. Soc.(Warner prize, 67); Royal Astron. Soc. Can; Int. Astron Union. Stellar structure and evolution. Address: Yale University Observatory, Box 2023, Yale Station, New Haven, CT 06520.

DeMARR, RALPH ELGIN, b. Detroit, Mich, Jan. 17, 30. MATHEMATICS. B.S, Idaho, 52; M.A, Washington State, 54; Ph.D.(math), Illinois, 61. Mem. tech. staff MATH, Bell Tel. Labs, Inc, 54-56; Ford Found. study grant, Moscow State, 61-62; asst. prof, Univ. Wash, 62-68, ASSOC. PROF, UNIV. N.MEX, 68- Vis. lectr, Leningrad State Univ, 69; Tashkent State Univ, 70. Am. Math. Soc. Functional analysis; probability; statistics. Address: Dept. of Mathematics, University of New Mexico, Albuquerque, NM 87106.

DE MARS, CLARENCE JOHN, JR, b. Savannah, Ga, Dec. 28, 29; m. 58; c. 2. FOREST ENTOMOLOGY, INSECT ECOLOGY. B.S.F, Georgia, 53; Ph.D. (entom), California, Berkeley, 66. RES. ENTOMOLOGIST, U.S. FOREST SERV, 57- U.S.N, 53-56, Res, 56-69, Comdr. AAAS; Entom. Soc. Am; Ecol. Soc. Am; Entom. Soc. Can; Japanese Soc. Pop. Ecol. Population dynamics; forest insects; sampling problems and life table development for forest insects; computer simulation; ecological interrelationships of forest conditions. Address: 948 Arlington Blvd, El Cerrito, CA 94530.

DeMARS, ROBERT I(VAN), b. N.Y.C, Apr. 10, 28. MICROBIOLOGY. B.S, City Col, 49; Nat. Found. Infantile Paralysis fel. & Ph.D.(bact), Illinois, 53. Res. fel. biol, Calif. Inst. Technol, 53-54; instr. microbiol, med. sch, Washington (St. Louis), 54-56; microbiologist, Nat. Insts. Health, 56-59; asst. prof. MED. GENETICS, UNIV. WIS, MADISON, 59-66, assoc. prof, 66-69, PROF, 69- Intermediate stages in the multiplication of bacterial viruses; genetics of cultivated animal cells; differentiation in early embryos. Address: Dept. of Medical Genetics, University of Wisconsin, Madison, WI 53706.

DeMARTINI, JOHN, b. San Francisco, Calif, Oct. 11, 33; m. 55; c. 7. INVERTEBRATE ZOOLOGY. B.A, Humboldt State Col, 55, M.A, 60; U.S. Pub. Health Serv. fel, Oregon State, 61-63, Ph.D.(zool), 64. Instr, high sch, Calif, 56-59; zool, bot. & plant taxon, HUMBOLDT STATE COL, 59-61, asst. prof. ZOOL, 63-67, ASSOC. PROF, 67- Comparative and functional invertebrate morphology; marine ecology and invertebrate reproductive cycles. Address: Dept. of Biology, Humboldt State College, Arcata, CA 95521.

DeMARTINIS, FREDERICK DANIEL, b. Philadelphia, Pa, Dec. 10, 24; m. 66; c. 1. PHYSIOLOGY. B.A, Temple, 48, M.A, 50; U.S. Pub. Health Serv. fel, Jefferson Med. Col, 55-58, Ph.D.(physiol), 59. Asst. biol, Temple, 48-50, instr. PHYSIOL, sch. dent, 50-54; asst, Jefferson Med. Col, 57-58; instr, WOMAN'S MED. COL. PA, 58-61, assoc, 61-62, asst. prof, 62-68, ASSOC. PROF, 68- Lindbach Found. award distinguished teaching, 65. U.S.A, 44-46. AAAS; Am. Physiol. Soc; N.Y. Acad. Sci. Effect of thyroxine on metabolism; essential fats and metabolism; interrelationship of thyroxine and epinephrine; nutritional factors. Address: Dept. of Physiology, Woman's Medical College of Pennsylvania, 3300 Henry Ave, Philadelphia, PA 19129.

DeMASSA, THOMAS A, b. Detroit, Mich, Nov. 6, 37; m. 59; c. 3. ELECTRICAL ENGINEERING, SOLID STATE ELECTRONICS. B.S, Michigan, 60, M.S, 61 & 63, Nat. Defense Ed. Act fel. & Ph.D.(elec. eng), 66. Res. asst, Michigan, summers 59-64, res. assoc, 64-66; asst. prof. SOLID STATE ELECTRONICS, ARIZONA STATE, 66-68, ASSOC. PROF, 68- NASA faculty fel, Cleveland, summer 67. Consult, Udylite Corp, Mich, 66-68. Am. Soc. Eng. Educ; Inst. Elec. & Electronics Eng. Solid state devices. Address: Dept. of Engineering Sciences, Arizona State University, Tempe, AZ 85281.

DE MATTE, MICHAEL L, b. Bridgeport, Ohio, Nov. 3, 37; m. 62; c. 1. ORGANIC CHEMISTRY. B.S, Wheeling Col, 59; M.S, West Virginia, 61, Ph.D. (org. chem), 66. RES. CHEMIST, WESTVACO, INC, 66- Am. Chem. Soc. Polyaromatic synthesis; reaction mechanisms in heterocyclic N-oxides; chemistry of paper coatings. Address: 5056 W. Running Brook Rd, Columbia, MD 21043.

de MAURIAC, RICHARD ARTHUR, b. Phila, Pa, Sept. 17, 38. ORGANIC CHEMISTRY. B.S, Drexel Inst, 61; M.S, Yale, 63, Ph.D.(org. chem), 67. Lab. asst, Phila. Elec. Co, 57; res. asst, res. inst, Temple, 60; RES. CHEMIST, EASTMAN KODAK CO, 63- Summer eng. asst, E.I. du Pont de Nemours & Co, 58. Mem, Franklin Inst. Am. Chem. Soc. Novel heterocyclic compounds and their chemistry; structure and synthesis of cyanine dyes; synthetic organic photochemistry. Address: Research Labs, Eastman Kodak Co, 343 State St, Rochester, NY 14650.

DEMAYA, CHARLES B(ERTRAND), b. Para, Brazil, Sept. 12, 09; nat; wid; c. 2. CHEMICAL ENGINEERING. A.B, Columbia Univ, 33, B.S, 34, Ch.E, 35. Night supt, Wecoline Prod, 35; develop. engr, Trubek Corp, 36; Franklin Baker Div, Gen. Foods Corp, 37-41, tech. dir, 41-44, prod. supt, 44-47, lab. mgr, 47-54; OWNER, SUN TESTS UNLTD, 54-; PRES, FOOD PROD. CORP, 67- AAAS; Inst. Food Technol; Am. Oil Chem. Soc; Electrochem. Soc.(secy, 37); Am. Asn. Textile Chem. & Colorists. Applied foods research; exposure testing. Address: P.O. Box 3707, Sarasota, FL 33578.

DE MAYO, BENJAMIN, b. Atlanta, Ga, Aug. 4, 40; m. 71. PHYSICS. B.S, Emory, 62; M.S, Yale, 64; Ph.D.(physics), Ga. Inst. Tech, 69. Res. assoc. metal physics, Univ. Ill, Urbana-Champaign, 69-71; ASST. PROF. PHYSICS, W.GA. COL, 71- AAAS; Am. Phys. Soc. Metal and low temperature physics. Address: Dept. of Physics, West Georgia College, Carrollton, GA 30117.

de MAYO, PAUL, b. London, Eng, Aug. 8, 24; m. 49; c. 2. ORGANIC CHEMISTRY. B.Sc, London, 44, M.Sc, 52, Ph.D.(chem), 54; d. ès Sc, Univ. Paris, 70. Res. fel. CHEM, Univ. Col. Hosp, London, Eng, 50-52, Birkbeck Col, London, 52-53, asst. lectr, 54-55; lectr, Glasgow, 55-57; Imp. Col, London, 57-59; prof. UNIV. WEST. ONT, 59-61, SR. PROF, 61, DIR. PHOTOCHEM. UNIT, 69- Merck, Sharp & Dohme lect. award, 66. Am. Chem. Soc; Chem. Inst. Can; Royal Soc. Can; Brit. Chem. Soc. Address: Dept. of Chemistry, University of Western Ontario, London, Ont, Can.

DEMBER, ALEXIS B(ERTHOLD), b. Dresden, Germany, May 30, 12; nat; m. 44; c. 2. PHYSICS. Inst. Tech. Dresden, 30-31; Jena, 31-32; Göttingen, 32-33; Ph.D.(physics), German Univ, Prague, 35. Instr. & asst. physics, Istanbul Univ, 35-36; res. fel, Calif. Inst. Tech, 37-44; chief res. sect, Friez instrument div, Bendix Aviation Corp, Md, 44-47; radiation br, Eng. Res. & Develop. Labs, Va, 47-48; head photog. develop. br, U.S. Naval Ord. Test. Sta, 48-49, instrument develop. div, 49-56, asst. head test dept, 56-59; tech. consult. to dir. test. & eval, U.S. NAVAL MISSILE CTR, Pac. Missile Range, 59, dep. head, astronaut. dept, 59-60, HEAD, 60-69, ELECTRO-OPTICS DIV, LAB. DEPT, 69- Consult, spec. cmt. adequacy range facilities, Dept. Defense, 57-58. Mem. working group optical instrumentation, panel test range instrumentation, Res. & Develop. Bd, 48-51, chmn, 51-52; mem. inter-range instrumentation group, 56-58, v.chmn, 58-59; mem. starlight study group naval applications space tech, 62; sea bed study group adv. sea-based deterrent systs, 64. Am. Phys. Soc; Optical Soc. Am; Soc. Photo-Optical Instrument. Eng; Inst. Elec. & Electronics Eng; Sci. Res. Soc. Am. Visible and infrared optics; ballistic and meteorological instrumentation; low temperature crystal physics; semiconductors; military space systems. Address: 4275 Varsity St, Ventura, CA 93003.

DEMBINSKI, GEORGE W, b. Suwalki, Poland, July 24, 29; U.S. citizen; m. 51; c. 2. PHYSICAL ORGANIC CHEMISTRY, FUEL TECHNOLOGY. B.S. Warsaw Tech, 52, M.S, 54; Ph.D.(chem), Vienna Tech, 59. Mgr. tech. serv, B.P. Benzin und Petroleum A.G, Austria, 59-60; res. chemist, Sinclair Res, Inc, Ill, 60-62; res. fel. chem, Northwestern, 62-63, res. assoc, 63; res. chemist, Esso Res. & Eng. Co, 63-69; SCIENTIST, LINDE DIV. LAB, UNION CARBIDE CORP, 69- Adj. assoc. prof, N.Y. Univ, 67- Am. Chem. Soc. Catalysis; petrochemicals; hydrocarbons; mechanism of dehydrocyclization. Address: Linde Division Lab, Union Carbide Corp, Saw Mill River Rd, Tarrytown, NY 10591.

DEMBITZER, HERBERT, b. N.Y.C, June 18, 34; m. 61; c. 3. BIOLOGY. A.B, N.Y. Univ, 55, M.S, 58, Ph.D.(biol), 67. Res. asst. biol, N.Y. Univ, 58-62, asst. res. scientist, 62-63; electron microscopist, MONTEFIORE HOSP, 63-67, RES. ASSOC, 67- Soc. Protozool; Electron Micros. Soc. Am; N.Y. Acad. Sci. Fine structure and histochemistry of cellular development; fine structure and development of myelin. Address: Dept. of Pathology, Montefiore Hospital, 111 E. 210th St, Bronx, NY 10467.

DeMEDICIS, E. M. J. A, b. Etterbeek, Belgium, Dec. 17, 37; m. 62; c. 3. BIOCHEMISTRY, ORGANIC CHEMISTRY. Lic. in Sci, Univ. Louvain, 59, Ph.D.(org. chem), 62; fel, Nat. Inst. Sci. Res. Indust. & Agr, Belgium, 60-62. Asst. org. chem, lab. gen. & org. chem, Univ. Louvain, 63-67; part-time asst. lectr, dept. chem, faculty sci, UNIV. SHERBROOKE, 67-69, fel. BIOCHEM, FACULTY MED, 69-71, PROF, 71- Chem. Soc. Belgium; Can. Biochem. Soc; Chem. Inst. Can. Physical and kinetic properties of stilbenes and azomethines; purification of proelastase. Address: University Hospital Centre, University of Sherbrooke, Que, Can.

DeMEESTER, W(ILLIA)M A(LEXANDER), b. Paterson, N.J, June 6, 29; m. 54; c. 3. ORGANIC CHEMISTRY. A.B, Hope Col, 49; M.S, Vermont, 51; Ph.D, Illinois, 59. Asst. org. & inorg. chem, Vermont, 49-51; org. chem, Illinois, 56-59; assoc. prof. chem, Parsons Col, 59-60, prof. & chmn. dept, 60-65; prof. chem. & pres, Lea Col, 65-69; DIR. DEVELOP, HOPE COL, 69- Vis. scientist, Nat. Sci. Found-Iowa Acad; Danforth assoc. Am. Chem. Soc. Synthetic organic chemistry. Address: Hope College, Holland, MI 49423.

DeMEIO, JOSEPH L(OUIS), b. Hurley, Wis, Sept. 9, 17; m. 41; c. 1. MEDICAL MICROBIOLOGY. B.S, Marquette, 50, M.S, 53; Ph.D.(med. microbiol), Wisconsin, 58. Virologist, Naval Med. Res. Unit 4, 51-54, immunologist, 57-58; asst, Wisconsin, 54-57; asst. chief diag. reagents, communicable disease center, U.S. Pub. Health Serv, 58-59; VIROLOGIST, BIOL. LABS, NAT. DRUG CO, 59- U.S.A, 42-45. AAAS; N.Y. Acad. Sci; Am. Pub. Health Asn; Soc. Exp. Biol. & Med; Am. Asn. Immunol. Antigenic relationships among myxoviruses. Address: Biological Labs, National Drug Co, Swiftwater, PA 18370.

DeMEIO, R(OMANO) H(UMBERTO), b. Mendoza, Argentina, Aug. 9, 05; nat; m. 37; c. 1. BIOCHEMISTRY. Bachiller, Col. Nac. Mendoza, 22; prof, Inst. Nacional del Profesorado, 24-27; Ph.D.(chem), Buenos Aires, 28. Pharmacol. chemist, Rosario Med. Sch, Argentina, 29-33, prof. biochem, 30-42; res. assoc. dept. physiol. & pharmacol, Duke, 44-45; instr. indust. hygiene, Harvard, 45-47; res. assoc. exp. med, JEFFERSON MED. COL, 47-48, asst. prof. BIOCHEM, 48-50, assoc. prof, 50-63, PROF, 63- Rockefeller Found. fel, Harvard & Chicago, 33-35; vis. prof, sch. med, Univ. San Agustin, Peru;

Fulbright grant, div. sci. develop, Pan Am. Union. Pres, Argentine-N.Am. Cultural Soc, 43. AAAS; Am. Soc. Biol. Chem. Micromethods; biological oxidations; tissue respiration; tellurium; estradiol inactivation; biological synthesis of sulfuric acid esters; sulfate metabolism. Address: Jefferson Medical College, Philadelphia, PA 19107.

DE MELLO, W. CARLOS, b. Florianopolis, Brazil, Sept. 11, 31; m. 56; c. 4. PHYSIOLOGY. M.D, Rio de Janeiro, 55. Asst. prof. physiol, sch. med, Rio de Janeiro, 57-58, assoc. researcher physiol. & biophys, 58-66; assoc. prof. PHARMACOL, SCH. MED, UNIV. P.R, 66-70, PROF, 70- Guest fel. physiol, State Univ. N.Y, 58-59; vis. assoc. prof, sch. med, Puerto Rico, 63-64; Rockefeller Found. fel. physiol, Nat. Inst. Med. Res, Eng, 65-66; Nat. Heart Inst. res. grants, 65-71. Brazilian Army, 52. Am. Physiol. Soc; N.Y. Acad. Sci. Electrophysiology of the heart; ionic mechanisms of cardiac electrogenesis; excitatory and inhibitory processes in Ascaris; membrane biophysics and physiology. Address: School of Medicine, University of Puerto Rico, P.O. Box 4509, San Juan, PR 00905.

DE MEMBER, JOHN RAYMOND, b. Elmira, N.Y, Oct. 30, 42; m. 64; c. 2. ORGANIC CHEMISTRY. B.S, Niagara Univ, 64; NASA grant & Ph.D.(chem), George Wash. Univ, 68. Instr, Mt. Vernon Col, 64-68; Case West. Reserve Univ, 68-69, fel, 68-70; SCIENTIST CHEM, POLAROID CORP, 70- Am. Chem. Soc. Electronic energy transfer; carbonium ions; Raman and nuclear magnetic resonance spectroscopy; chemistry of photographic systems. Address: 730M-3 Research Labs, Polaroid Corp, Cambridge, MA 02139.

DE MENT, JACK (DONOVAN), b. Haughton, La, Sept. 14, 24; m. 52; c. 2. AGRONOMY. B.S, La. State, 49, M.S, 50; Ph.D, Ohio State, 54. Asst. agronomist, La. State, 49-52; dir. soil testing, Ohio State, 54-55; agronomist, Tenn. Valley Auth, 55-62; chief agronomist, Esso Res. & Eng, 62-64; DIR. RES, STANDARD FRUIT CO, 64- U.S.A, 44-46. Am. Soc. Agron. Research administration. Address: Standard Fruit Co, No. 2 Canal St, New Orleans, LA 70150.

DE MENT, JAMES A(LDERSON), b. Haughton, La, Dec. 22, 20; m. 41; c. 2. SOIL SCIENCE, GEOLOGY. B.S, La. State, 41; M.S, Cornell, 59, Ph.D. (soil sci), 62. SOIL SCIENTIST, SOIL CONSERV. SERV, 41- U.S.A.F, 42-46, 51-53, Lt. Col. Soil Sci. Soc. Am; Soil Conserv. Soc. Am. Soils and the interpretation of laboratory data; application and guidance for soil correlation and classification procedures. Address: Soil Conservation Service, P.O. Box 11222, Ft. Worth, TX 76110.

DEMENT, W(ILLIAM) C(HARLES), b. Wenatchee, Wash, July 29, 28; m. 56; c. 3. NEUROPHYSIOLOGY. B.S, Univ. Wash, 51; M.D, Univ. Chicago, 55, Ph.D.(physiol), 57. Intern, Mt. Sinai Hosp, 57-58, res. fel. PSYCHIAT, 58-63; assoc. prof, SCH. MED, STANFORD UNIV, 63-67, PROF, 67-, DIR. SLEEP LABS, DEPT. PSYCHIAT, 63-, DIR. SLEEP DISORDERS CLIN, 71- Chief ed. & founder, sleep rev. proj, Brain Info. Serv. Am. Psychiat. Asn. (Hofheimer Prize, 64); N.Y. Acad. Med.(Thomas W. Salmon Medal, 69); Asn. Psychophysiol. Study Sleep; Psychiat. Res. Soc; N.Y. Acad. Sci; Am. Psychosom. Soc; Am. Psychopath. Asn; Soc. Psychophysiol. Res; Soc. Neurosci. Physiology of dreaming and sleep; electroencephalography. Address: Dept. of Psychiatry, Stanford University School of Medicine, Stanford, CA 94305.

DEMEO, DANIEL AMADEO, b. Oakland, Calif, July 23, 42. PHYSICAL CHEMISTRY, SPECTROSCOPY. A.B, California, Berkeley, 63, Ph.D. (chem), Los Angeles, 69. CHEMIST, HUGHES AIRCRAFT CO, 69- AAAS; Soc. Appl. Spectros; Am. Phys. Soc. Microanalysis techniques; infrared analysis; vacuum ultraviolet and photoelectron spectroscopy; photoionization; fluorescence and phosphorescence. Address: Hughes Aircraft Co, Bldg. 6, M/S D134, Culver City, CA 90230.

DE MEO, EDGAR ANTHONY, b. Yonkers, N.Y, Jan. 14, 42; m. 68; c. 1. ELECTRICAL ENGINEERING, SOLID STATE PHYSICS. B.E.E, Rensselaer Polytech. Inst, 63; Charles L. Fortescue fel, Brown Univ, 63-64, Sc.M, 65, Gen. Tel. fel, 66-67, Ph.D.(elec. eng), 68. Mem. tech. staff, Bell Tel. Labs, summer 63; res. asst. ELEC. ENG, Brown Univ, 64-66; instr, U.S. Naval Acad, 67-69; ASST. PROF, BROWN UNIV, 69- U.S.N, 67-69, Lt. Inst. Elec. & Electronics Eng. Millimeter wave devices; anisotropic magnetic materials; magnetic resonance investigations; far infrared spectroscopy; Address: Division of Engineering, Brown University, Providence, RI 02912.

DEMERS, CHRISTIAN (ROLAND JOSEPH), b. Trois-Rivières, Que, Aug. 29, 27; m. 55; c. 3. PHYSICS. B.A, Seminaire de Trois-Rivières, 49; B.Sc, Montreal, 55. Trainee, meteorol. div, Dept. Transport, 55-56; prof. physics & math. & dir. dept. sci, Ctr. Acad. Study, 56-69; PROF. MECH, PHYSICS & MATH. & DEAN, UNIV. QUEBEC, TROIS-RIVIERS, 69-, mem. coun. admin. & comn. studies. N.Y. Acad. Sci; French-Can. Asn. Adv. Sci; Can. Asn. Physicists. Applied mathematics. Address: C.P. 500, University of Quebec, Trois-Rivières, Que, Can.

DEMERS, JEAN-MARIE, b. Quebec, Que, Dec. 6, 20; m. 47; c. 3. ANIMAL PHYSIOLOGY & NUTRITION. B.A, Laval, 41, Ph.D.(nutrit), 50; B.Sc.A, Montreal, 45; cert. biochem, Paris, 51; cert. physiol, Baylor, 62; hon. D.Sc, Bordeaux, 62. Asst. prof. biol, Oka Agr. Col, 46-51, assoc. prof, 51-52; asst. prof, UNIV. MONTREAL, 52-56, assoc. prof, 56-63, PROF. PHYSIOL, 63- Prov. Govt. Que, fel, 50-51; Nat. Insts. Health fel, 62; sr. res. fel, Nat. Res. Coun. Can, 64-65. AAAS; Nutrit. Soc. Can.(pres, 68-69); Brit. Nutrit. Soc; French Asn. Physiol.(secy. for Can, 61-); cor. mem. Toulouse Acad. Sci.(Fermat medal). Nutrition of ducklings, fats, amino acids, lipotropic factors and vitamins; electrophysiological studies on the cardiac muscle by voltage clamp technique. Address: Dept. of Biology, University of Montreal, C.P. 6128, Montreal 101, Que, Can.

DEMERS, LAURENCE MAURICE, b. Lawrence, Mass, May 9, 38; m. 62; c. 3. BIOCHEMISTRY, ENDOCRINOLOGY. A.B, Merrimack Col, 60; Ph.D. (biochem), State Univ. N.Y. Upstate Med. Ctr, 70. LALOR FOUND. FEL, LAB. HUMAN REPROD. & REPROD. BIOL, HARVARD MED. SCH, 70- Med.Serv.C, U.S.A, 61-65, 1st Lt. AAAS; Endocrine Soc. Biochemical endocrinology with particular emphasis on hormonal regulation of carbohydrate metabolism in reproductive tissue; physiology and metabo-

lism of the human endometrium under various endocrine states. Address: Lab. of Human Reproduction and Reproductive Biology, Harvard Medical School, Boston, MA 02115.

DEMERS, PIERRE (A.E), b. Deal, Eng, Nov. 8, 14. NUCLEAR PHYSICS. B.A, Montreal, 33, L.Sc, 35, M.Sc. & L.Sc, 36; Cornell; École Normale Supérieure, Agrégé de l'Université, France, 39; D.Sc, Paris, 50. Physicist, C.I.L. Res. & Develop. Lab, 40-43; Nat. Res. Council Can, 43-47; assoc. prof. NUCLEAR PHYSICS,DEPT. PHYSICS, FACULTY SCI, UNIV. MONTREAL, 47-50, PROF, 50- Pres, Soc. Phys. Math, Montreal, 49; mem. Coun. Arts Que; guest prof, Univ. Frankfurt/Main, 70-71. Am. Phys. Soc; Can. Asn. Physicists (treas, 50); fel. Royal Soc. Can; Ger. Soc. Photog. Scientific photography and ionography; theory of knowledge, noise and environment. Address: Faculty of Science, University of Montreal, Montreal 26, Que, Can.

DEMERS, PIERRE-PAUL, b. Quebec, Que, Sept. 14, 28; m. 63; c. 2. PEDIATRICS, CARDIOLOGY. B.A, Laval Univ, 48, M.D, 53. Assoc. prof. PEDIAT, UNIV. SHERBROOKE, 69-71, PROF. & HEAD DEPT, 71- Fel, Royal Col. Physicians of Can, 58. Address: Dept. of Pediatrics, Faculty of Medicine, University of Sherbrooke, Sherbrooke, Que, Can.

DEMERS, S(ERGE), b. Verdun, Que, June 17, 40; m. 68; c. 2. ASTRONOMY. B.Sc, Univ. Montreal, 61; M.A, Univ. Toronto, 63, Ph.D.(astron), 66. Astronr, U.S. Naval Observ, 67-68; resident astronr, Cerro Tololo Inter-Am. Observ, 68-69; ASST. PROF. ASTRON, LAURENTIAN UNIV, 69- Am. Astron. Soc. Variable stars; photoelectric photometry. Address: Institute of Astronomy, Laurentian University, Sudbury, Ont, Can.

DEMERSON, CHRISTOPHER, b. St. John, N.B, May 16, 42. ORGANIC & MEDICINAL CHEMISTRY. B.Sc, Univ. N.B, 64, Ph.D.(chem), 68. Fel, Univ. N.B, 68-69; RES. CHEMIST, AYERST LABS, 69- Am. Chem. Soc; Chem. Inst. Can. Synthesis of the alkaloid delphinine; development of synthetic methods; medicinal chemistry and the structure-activity relationship of drugs. Address: Ayerst Labs, P.O. Box 6115, Montreal, Que, Can.

DEMETRESCU, M, b. Bucharest, Romania, May 23, 29; m. 69; c. 1. NEURO-PHYSIOLOGY, MEDICAL ELECTRONICS. Dipl. electronics, Univ. Bucharest, 54; Prin. Investr. by Comt.(electrophysiol, neurophysiol), Romanian Acad. Sci, 57. Prin. investr. neurophysiol. & electroencephalog, Inst. Endocrinol, Romanian Acad. Sci, 58-66; scholar. & res. fel. neurophysiol, med. sch, Univ. Calif, Los Angeles, 66-67; ASST. RES. PHYSIOLOGIST, MED. SCH, UNIV. CALIF, IRVINE, 67- Del, Int. Cong. Electroencephalog. & Neurol, Austria, 65; Int. Cong. Electroencephalog, Calif, 69. Victor Babes Prize, Romanian Acad. Sci, 62. AAAS. Neurophysiology of active inhibition at thalamo-cortical level; cortical excitability and their control by diffuse subcortical mechanisms; clinical electroencephalography; electrophysiology of bladder stimulation in paraplegics; electronic-electrophysiologic research methods. Address: Dept. of Physiology, University of California Medical School, Irvine, CA 92664.

DEMETRIADES, ANTHONY, b. Athens, Greece, June 23, 30; U.S. citizen; m. 57; c. 3. AERODYNAMICS. A.B, Colgate, 51; M.S, Minnesota, 53; Ph.D.(aeronaut), Calif. Inst. Tech, 58. Res. fel, Calif. Inst. Tech, 58-60, sr. res. fel, 60-63; PRIN. RES. SCIENTIST, PHILCO CORP. DIV, FORD MOTOR CO, 63- Consult, MHD Res, Inc, 59-63. Am. Phys. Soc; Am. Inst. Aeronaut. & Astronaut. Experimental aerodynamics and plasma physics. Address: Fluid Mechanics Research Dept. L421, ATC 14, Aeronutronic Division, Philco Corp, Ford Rd, Newport Beach, CA 92663.

DEMETRIADES, STERGE T(HEODORE), b. Athens, Greece, June 30, 28; U.S. citizen; m. 56; c. 3. SCIENCE & TECHNOLOGY MANAGEMENT, PLASMA PHYSICS. A.B, Bowdoin Col, 50; M.S, Mass. Inst. Tech, 51; M.E, Calif. Inst. Tech, 58. Res. engr, Mass. Inst. Tech, 51-53; ord. engr, ballistic res. labs, U.S. Army Ord. Corps, 53-54; res. engr, Lear, Inc, 54-55; astronaut. dept, Aerojet-Gen. Corp, 58-59; Northrop Corp, 59-60, head space propulsion & power lab, 60-62, head plasma labs, 62-63; chief scientist, res. labs, Rocket Power Inc, 63-64; PRES. & DIR. RES, STD RES. CORP, 64-, PRES, STD INT. RES. & DEVELOP. CORP, 69- Consult, Aerojet-Gen. Corp, 55-62; Air Logistics Corp, 58-59; Hughes Tool Co, 59-60; Marquardt Corp, 60; McGraw-Hill, Inc, 61-; Jet Propulsion Lab, Calif. Inst. Tech, 62-63; adv. group aeronaut, res. & develop, NATO, summer 63; space sci. lab, Litton Industs, Inc, 63-64. Assoc. fel. Am. Inst. Aeronaut. & Astronaut.(sr. mem. Am. Rocket Soc). Electrostreaming birefringence; powered space flight; plasma accelerators and propulsive fluid accumulator engines; experimental magnetogasdynamics; measurement of plasma properties and energy conversion; magnetohydrodynamic power generation; scientific technology development; research and development program assessment and national science and technology planning. Address: STD Research Corp, Box 4127, Catalina Station, Pasadena, CA 91106.

DEMETRIOU, JAMES A, b. Santa Ana, Calif, Dec. 26, 23; m. 53; c. 4. CLINICAL CHEMISTRY, BIOCHEMISTRY. B.A, Southern California, 48, Ph.D.(biochem), 56. Fel. endocrinol, col. med, Utah, 57-58; asst. prof. biochem, sch. med, Southern California, 58-63; mem. sr. res. bioastronaut, Northrop Corp. Labs, 63-67; sr. res. scientist, BIO-SCI. LABS, 67-70, ASST. DIR. RES. DEPT, 70- AAAS; Am. Asn. Clin. Chem; fel Am. Inst. Chem; Am. Chem. Soc. Development of analytical methods for measurement of products in body fluids, application of these methods for detection of disease states, pathological processes or abnormal physiological states. Address: Bio-Science Labs, 7600 Tyrone Ave, Van Nuys, CA 91405.

DeMEYER, FRANK R, b. San Francisco, Calif, Nov. 7, 39; m. 67. MATHEMATICS. B.S, Seattle, 61; M.A, Oregon, 63, Ph.D.(math), 65. Asst. prof. MATH, Purdue, 65-68; COLO. STATE UNIV, 68-70, ASSOC. PROF, 70- Nat. Sci. Found. summer res. grants, 65 & 66. Math. Asn. Am. Mathematical economics; abstract algebra; decision problems in welfare economics. Address: Dept. of Mathematics, Colorado State University, Ft. Collins, CO 80521.

DE MIGNARD, VALENTIN A(LEXANDER), b. Kiotsk, Russia, Apr. 8, 20; U.S. citizen. ANATOMY, IMMUNOHEMATOLOGY. M.D, Charles Univ, Prague, 43; B.A, Los Angeles State Col, 58; M.S, Southern California, 64.

Private med. practice, Czech, 43-45, Germany, 48-49; dir. surg, UNRRA Hosp, Wilhelmstahl, Germany, 45-48; intern, Hollywood Presby. Hosp, Los Angeles, Calif, 49-50, res. surg, 51-53; med. dir, Arabian Exped, Am. Found. Study Man, 51; dir. blood bank, Hyland Labs, Baxter Labs, Inc, 53-60; RES. ASSOC. ANAT, UNIV. SOUTH. CALIF, 64- Admin. res, Hollywood Presby. Hosp, 52-53; consult, serum procurement & immunohemat, 60- Am. Soc. Microbiol; Reticuloendothelial Soc. Experimental surgery; blood groups and subgroups; reticuloendothelial system. Address: 1523 N. Winona Blvd, Los Angeles, CA 90027.

DEMING, JOHN MILEY, b. Prescott, Ariz, May 28, 25; m. 51; c. 5. AGRONOMY. B.S, Arizona, 48, M.S, 49; Ph.D.(agron), Purdue, 51. Agronomist, SOILS & FIELD RES, MONSANTO CO, 51-58, GROUP LEADER, 53-, BIOPHYS. GROUP LEADER, 58- U.S.N, 43-45. Biophysical investigation and formulation of commercial pesticides. Address: 1295 Woodcrest Lane, Hazelwood, MO 63042.

DEMING, P(HILIP) H(ARVEY), b. Urbana, Ill, Aug. 4, 17; m. 41; c. 3. PHYSICAL CHEMISTRY. B.A, Nebraska, 38; fel, Wisconsin, 42, Ph.D.(phys. chem), 43. Mem. staff, Wisconsin, 38-41, instr, 42-43; engr, Shell Develop. Co, 43-48, chemist, 48, sr. technologist, 49, admin. asst. to dir. res, 49-58, asst. head org. chem. dept, 59-61, head. gen. chem. dept, 61-69; CONSULT, EFFECTIVE METHODS, INC, 70- Consult, weapons systs. eval. group, U.S. Defense Dept, 55-56. Am. Chem. Soc. Chemical kinetics; thermodynamics; distillation; combustion; free radical processes; petrochemical technology; chemical economics; mathematics of resource use; information storage and retrieval; chemical research planning and evaluation; new product development. Address: Effective Methods, Inc, 54 Washburn St, Bridgeport, CT 06605.

DEMING, QUENTIN B(URRITT), b. N.Y.C, July 24, 19; m. 49; c. 2. MEDICINE. A.B, Dartmouth Col, 41; M.D, Columbia, 43. Intern MED, Presby. Hosp, 44, asst. resident, 47-48; res. fel, sch. med, Stanford, 48-50, instr, 50-52, asst. prof, 52-53; asst. prof, Columbia, 53-58, assoc. prof, 58-59; ALBERT EINSTEIN COL. MED, YESHIVA UNIV, 59-64, PROF, 64- Markle Found. scholar, 50-55; asst. vis. physician, Goldwater Mem. Hosp, Columbia, 53-; vis. physician, Bronx Munic. Hosp. Ctr, 59- Med.C, U.S.N, 44-46. Am. Soc. Clin. Invest; Harvey Soc; Am. Fedn. Clin. Res; Am. Heart Asn; N.Y. Acad. Sci. Hormonal aspects of edema formation; hypertension; atherosclerosis. Address: Dept. of Medicine, Albert Einstein College of Medicine, Yeshiva University, New York, NY 10461.

DEMING, ROBERT W, b. Wabasha, Minn, Apr. 5, 28; m. 60; c. 2. MATHEMATICS. B.S, Minnesota, 52, M.A, 60; Ph.D.(math), New Mexico State, 65. Instr. MATH, Minnesota, Duluth, 57-62; asst. prof, Idaho State, 65-67; ASSOC. PROF, STATE UNIV. N.Y. COL. OSWEGO, 67- U.S.N, 46-49. Math. Asn. Am; Am. Math. Soc. Applications of algebraic topology to the theory of uniform and uniform-like spaces. Address: Dept. of Mathematics, State University of New York College at Oswego, Oswego, NY 13126.

DEMING, W(ILLIAM) EDWARDS, b. Sioux City, Iowa, Oct. 14, 00; m. 32; c. 3. MATHEMATICAL STATISTICS. B.S, Wyoming, 21, hon. LL.D, 58; M.S, Colorado, 24; Ph.D.(physics), Yale, 28; London, 36. Instr. elec. eng, Wyoming, 21-22; physics, Colo. Sch. Mines, 22-23, asst. prof, 23-24; Colorado, 24-25; instr, Yale, 26-27; asst. physicist, bur. chem. & soils, U.S. Dept. Agr, 27-28, assoc. physicist, 28-36, physicist, 36-39; head mathematician & math.adv, U.S. Bur. Census, 39-46; prof. statist, N.Y. Univ, 46-48; STATIST. CONSULT, 48- Special lectr, Bur. Standards, 30-41; head dept. math. & statist, U.S. Dept. Agr. Grad. Sch, 33-53; statistician, Allied Mission to observe Greek Elections, 46; lectr, Univ. Kiel; Inst. Soc. Res, Frankfurt; Tech. Acad, Wuppertal-Elberfeld; Nürnberg Tech. Univ; Austrian Inst. Econ. Res, Vienna, 53. Adv. sampling, U.S. Bur. Budget, 45-53; consult, Secy. War, 40-50; India, 47, 51-52, 71; sampling tech, Supreme Command Allied Powers, Japan, 47-50; High Comnr. for Ger, 52-53; Ministry Econ, Mex, 54-55, Japan, 46, 50-52, 55, 60, 65, 68-; State Statist. Off. Turkey, 60-, Taiwan, 70, 71. AAAS; Math. Asn. Am; fel. Am. Statist. Asn.(v.pres, 41); fel. Inst. Math. Statist.(pres, 45); hon. mem. Am. Soc. Qual. Control; Biomet. Soc; Am. Soc. Human Genetics; hon. mem. Am. Soc. Test. & Mat; World Asn. Pub. Opinion Res; hon. fel. Royal Statist. Soc; Int. Statist. Inst; hon. mem. Union Japanese Sci. & Eng; hon. mem. Japanese Statist. Asn. Sampling in population research, administration, accounting, physical materials and depreciation; quality control; legal aspects of sampling. Address: 4924 Butterworth Pl, Washington, DC 20016.

DEMINT, ROBERT J(OSEPH), b. Shreveport, La, Aug. 10, 19; m. 38; c. 3. CHEMISTRY. B.S, Centenary Col, 40; M.S, Tulane, 54. Petrol. chemist, Ark. Fuel Oil Co, 39-41; inspector explosives & ord. mat, La. Ord. Plant, 41-43, admin. asst. transport, 46-48; chemist, south. regional res. lab, south utilization res. & develop. div, Agr. Res. Serv, U.S. Dept. Agr, 49-62; chemist, Colo. River Basin Proj. Lab, Water Pollution Control Admin, U.S. Dept. Health, Ed. & Welfare, 62-67; RES. CHEMIST, CROP PROTECTION RES. BR, PLANT SCI. RES. DIV, U.S. DEPT. AGR, 67- U.S.N.R, 43-46, 48-49, Res, 49-, Lt. Am. Chem. Soc; Sci. Res. Soc. Am; Weed Sci. Soc. Am. Analytical methods; radiation chemistry of cotton and polymers; radiochemistry of naturally occurring radionuclides; aquatic herbicide residues. Address: Crop Protection Research Branch, Plant Science Research Division, U.S. Dept. Agriculture, Denver Federal Center, Bldg. 56, Denver, CO 80225.

DEMIREL, T(URGUT), b. Bursa, Turkey, Mar. 2, 24; m. 50; c. 2. SOIL CHEMISTRY & ENGINEERING. M.Eng, Ankara, 49; M.Sc, Iowa State, 59, Ph.D.(soil eng), 62. Hwy. mat. engr, Gen. Directorate Turkish Hwys, 49-51, sr. res. engr, 51-56; asst. SOIL ENG, IOWA STATE, 57-58, res. assoc, 58-63, asst. prof, 63-65, assoc. prof, 65-70, PROF, 70- Assoc. mem, Hwy. Res. Bd, Nat. Acad. Sci-Nat. Res. Coun, 51. Ord.C, 56-57, 2nd Lt. AAAS; Clay Minerals Soc; Am. Soc. Test. & Mat. Load bearing capacity and physicochemical properties of soils; effects of chemical treatments on load bearing capactiy of soils; soil-water interaction. Address: Dept. of Civil Engineering, Iowa State University, Ames, IA 50010.

DEMIS, D(ERMOT) JOSEPH, b. N.Y.C, Apr. 19, 29. DERMATOLOGY, PHARMACOLOGY. B.S, Union (N.Y), 50; Ph.D.(pharmacol), Rochester, 53; M.D, Yale, 57. Chief, dept. dermat, Walter Reed Army Inst. Res, D.C, 60-64; assoc. prof. med. & dir. div. DERMAT, sch. med, Wash. Univ, 64-67; PROF, ALBANY MED. COL, 67- Consult, Barnes & Jewish Hosps, St. Louis, Mo. & Scott Air Force Base, Ill, 64- Mem. pharmacol. & exp. therapeut. study sect, Nat. Insts. Health, 60-; subcmt. dermat, U.S. Army Surgeon Gen. Adv. Cmt. Med, 63-64. Med.C, 57-64, Maj. Am. Soc. Pharmacol. & Exp. Therapeut; Am. Col. Physicians; Am. Therapeut. Soc; Am. Fedn. Clin. res; Microcirc. Conf. Investigative dermatology; role of vasoactive amines in pathophysiologic processes; physiologic control and pathologic alterations of microcirculation; mucopolysaccharide metabolism. Address: Dept. of Dermatology, Albany Medical College, 105 S. Lake Ave, Albany, NY 12208.

DEMITRAS, GREGORY CLAUDE, F.S.C, b. Pittsburgh, Pa, Dec. 21, 29. INORGANIC CHEMISTRY. A.B, La Salle Col, 52, M.A, 53; M.S, Pennsylvania, 58, Ph.D.(chem), 65. Teacher, La Salle Col. High Sch, 53-60; teacher & prefect of discipline, Trinity High Sch, Pa, 64-65; asst. prof. CHEM, LA SALLE COL, 65-70, ASSOC. PROF, 70- Am. Chem. Soc. Synthesis of inorganic fluorides. Address: Dept. of Chemistry, La Salle College, Philadelphia, PA 19144.

DEMKOVICH, PAUL A(NDREW), b. Zborova, Czech, Nov. 20, 22; nat; m. 47; c. 5. PETROLEUM, ANALYTICAL CHEMISTRY. B.S, Chicago, 47, M.S, 48. Group leader, res. & develop. dept, STANDARD OIL CO. IND, 47-65, SUPVR. ANAL. LAB, AM. OIL CO, WHITING, 65- U.S.N.R, 43-46, Lt. Comdr. Am. Chem. Soc. Petroleum analytical chemistry. Address: 7520 Magoun Ave, Hammond, IN 46324.

DEMMON, E(LWOOD) L(EONARD), b. Kendallville, Ind, Sept. 23, 92; m. 25; c. 3. FORESTRY. A.B, Michigan, 14, M.S.F, 16; hon. Sc.D, N.C. State Col, 55. Field asst, U.S. FOREST SERV, 14-15, forester & tech. adv, Goodyear Tire & Rubber Co, Sumatra, 16-23; silviculturist, south. forest exp. sta, 25-28, dir, 28-44, lake states forest exp. sta, 44-51, southeast. forest & range exp. sta, 51-56; forestry consult, U.S. Int. Co-op. Admin, Mutual Security Mission to China, 56-57; Asheville, 57-65; pres, ASHEVILLE-BILTMORE BOT. GARDENS, INC, 65-70, EMER. PRES, 71- Consult, South. Regional Ed. Bd, Ga, 58-59. Mem. special comt. on renewable natural resources, div. biol. & agr, Nat. Acad. Nat. Res. Council, 55-57. Exped, Firestone Tire & Rubber Co, Cent. Am. & Panama, 24; tech. leader, for. scientists vis. U.S. Agency Int. Develop, 59-67. Distinguished serv. award, U.S. Dept. Agr, 56. AAAS; Soc. Am. Foresters (v.pres, 52, pres, 54); Am. Forestry Asn. Forest management; forest fire; rubber culture. Address: 241 Old Toll Rd, Asheville, NC 28804.

DEMO, JOHN, b. North Adams, Mass, Oct. 20, 14; m. 37; c. 1. CHEMICAL ENGINEERING, CHEMISTRY. B.S, Mass. Inst. Tech, 35, M.S, 36. Develop. engr, Tidewater-Assoc. Oil Co, 36-39, asst. to v.pres, 39-41; asst. to pres, Barbasol Co, 45-46, v.pres. res. & prod, 47-49; res. chemist & engr, Avon Prod. Inc, 50-55, mgr. res. & develop, 56-66; PRES, C.B.X. ENTERPRISES, INC, 66- Ord.C, U.S.A, 41-45, Maj. Am. Chem. Soc; Soc. Cosmetic Chem. Development, production and marketing of packaged consumer products, including cosmetics, foods, pharmaceuticals, proprietaries and chemical specialties. Address: C.B.X. Enterprises, Inc, P.O. Box 235, Saddle River, NJ 07458.

DEMO, JOSEPH J(OHN), JR, b. North Adams, Mass, June 28, 32; m. 57; c. 3. PHYSICAL CHEMISTRY. B.S, Rochester, 54; Ph.D.(chem), Connecticut, 59. Asst. instr. chem, Connecticut, 57-59; chemist, E.I. DU PONT DE NEMOURS & CO. INC, 59-67, sr. res. phys. chemist, ENG. MAT. LAB, 67-69, SR. RES. SPECIALIST, 69- Summers, Eastman Kodak Co, 53, 54. Am. Soc. Metals; Nat. Asn. Corrosion Eng. Corrosion behavior of metals and alloys in aqueous and organic environments; ferritic stainless alloy development. Address: E.I. du Pont de Nemours & Co. Inc, Engineering Materials Lab, Experimental Station, Bldg. 304, Wilmington, DE 19898.

DEMOISE, CHARLES FRANCIS, b. Pittsburgh, Pa, Nov. 2, 31; m. 65; c. 1. BIOLOGY. A.B, St. Vincent Col, 54; M.S, Pittsburgh, 58, Ph.D.(biol), 67. Res. asst. biochem, grad. sch. pub. health, Pittsburgh, 62-64; fel, med. res. ctr, Brookhaven Nat. Lab, 67-69; res. instr, div. human genetics, dept. med. & psychiat, Emory Univ, 69-71; ASST. PROJ. OFF, CANCER RES. LAB, MICROBIOL. ASSOCS, 71- U.S.A, 54-56. Nuclear behavior of plant cell cultures; purification of radioactive phytohaemagglutinin and its localization in lymphocyte cultures; culturing of human cells in relation to disease and aging. Address: Cancer Research Lab, Microbiological Associates, 4733 Bethesda Ave, Bethesda, MD 20014.

DEMOND, JOAN, b. Los Angeles, Calif, Feb. 19, 27. MARINE BIOLOGY. B.A, California, Los Angeles, 48; fel, Mills Col, 48-49, M.A, 49; fel, Hawaii, 49-50. Fishery aide, Pac. Oceanic Fishery Invests, U.S. Fish & Wildlife Serv, 50-51; sci. asst, Inter-Am. Trop. Tuna Comn, 51-52; res. biologist, Scripps Inst, California, 53-54; syst. zoologist, div. mollusks, U.S. Nat. Mus, 54-55; res. assoc, UNIV. CALIF, LOS ANGELES, 55-65, MUS. SCIENTIST, DEPT. GEOL, 65-, INSTR, PHYS. SCI. EXTEN, 66-; CONSULT. UNIV. HAWAII & PAC. SCI. BD. PROJS, 55- Nat. Sci. Found. grant, 54-55. AAAS; Am. Malacol. Union. Ecology and systematics of recent Indo-Pacific reef-dwelling mollusks; zoogeographical distribution; phylogenetic and areal abundance of zooplankton of the central Pacific; taxonomy of mollusks of the Gulf of Mexico, west coast North America and Hawaiian Islands. Address: Dept. of Geology, University of California, Los Angeles, CA 90024.

DeMONEY, FRED WILLIAM, b. Oak Park, Ill, Nov. 25, 19; m. 44; c. 5. MECHANICAL ENGINEERING, METALLURGY. B.S, Ill. Inst. Tech, 41; M.S, Minnesota, 51, Ph.D.(mech. metall), 54. Design engr, Kimberly-Clark Corp, 41-44; asst, Ill. Inst. Tech, 44-45; engr, Parten Mach. Co, 45-47; prod. eng. supt, Maico Co, Inc, 47; instr. phys. metall, Minnesota, 47-51, res. assoc. mech. & metals, 51-54; res. metallurgist, magnesium dept, Dow Chem. Co, 54-55; res. engr, DMR, KAISER ALUMINUM & CHEM. CORP, 55-57, BR. HEAD MECH. METALL. & TECH. SUPVR. MECH. METALL, FABRICATION & APPLN. RES. DEPT, 66- Consult, Twin City Testing & Eng. Lab, 51-54; v.chmn, Cryogenic Eng. Conf, 66-69. Am. Soc. Metals; Am. Inst. Mining, Metall. & Petrol. Eng; Am. Soc. Mech. Eng. Engineering properties of aluminum for cryogenic service; fatigue; creep;

vibration; pressure vessel materials and applications; rolling and extrusion technology; formability; terminal ballistics; aluminum armor. Address: 1114 Innsbruck St, Livermore, CA 94550.

deMONSABERT, WINSTON R(USSEL), b. New Orleans, La, June 12, 15; m. 55; c. 1. CHEMISTRY, SCIENCE EDUCATION. B.S, Loyola, 37; A.M, Tulane, 45, Ph.D.(chem), 52. Prof, Warren Easton High Sch, 40-44; Behrman High Sch, 44-48; assoc. prof. chem, Loyola (La), 48-54, prof, 54-66; phys. scientist adminr, proj. off. & chief chemist, community studies div, pesticides prog, Nat. Commun. Disease Ctr, DEPT. HEALTH, EDUC. & WELFARE, Ga, 66-69, HEALTH SCIENTIST ADMINR. & DIR. CONTRACT LIAISON BR, NAT. CTR. HEALTH SERV. RES. & DEVELOP, 69- Assoc. prof, Tulane Univ, 57-58; res. chemist, Am. Cyanamid Co, summers 57 & 58. Fel. Am. Inst. Chem; Am. Chem. Soc. Health services research; chemical instrumentation, gas chromatography, spectrophotometry, and polarography; zirconium chemistry; complex-ion formation. Address: 604 Cobblestone Ct, Silver Spring, MD 20904.

DEMONT, ALBERT (MERTON), b. Worcester, Mass, Dec. 6, 07; m. 38; c. 2. ELECTRICAL ENGINEERING. B.S.E.E, Worcester Polytech, 31. Test engr, Navy Ord. Control, GEN. ELEC. CO, N.Y, 32-35, develop. engr, 35-38, proj. engr, 38-41, resident engr, 41-44, admin. asst. to mgr. eng, Navy Ord. & Army Guided Missiles, 44-51, mgr. eng, Naval Ord. Dept, Mass, 51-57, prog. develop, adv. tech. labs, 57-58, employee rels, 58-60, opers, 60-64, employee rels, 64-69, MGR. PROF. MANPOWER DEVELOP, CORP. RES. & DEVELOP, 69- Mem, N.Y. State Selective Serv. Adv. Comt, 60-71; trustee, Worcester Polytech. Inst, 64- Am. Ord. Asn; Am. Soc. Eng. Educ; Inst. Elec. & Electronics Eng. Professional personnel relations with colleges. Address: General Electric Co, Corporate Research & Development, P.O. Box 8, Schenectady, NY 12301.

deMOOY, CORNELIS JACOBUS, b. Rotterdam, Netherlands, July 1, 26; m. 53; c. 2. SOIL FERTILITY, PLANT NUTRITION. B.S, Wageningen, 51, M.S, 53; Ph.D.(soil fertil), Iowa State, 65. Assoc. soil surv. classification & genesis, Wageningen, 52-53; res. scientist, Commonwealth Sci. & Indust. Res. Orgn, 53-60; res. assoc. soil fertil, Iowa State, 60-65; ASST. PROF. soil sci, Utrecht, 65-67; SOIL FERTIL, IOWA STATE UNIV, 67- Consult, Sir Alexander Gibb & Partners, Cent. Africa, 66. Am. Soc. Agron; Netherlands Royal Soc. Agr. Sci. Soil classification and genesis; soil-plant relationships; nutritional requirements of crop plants; optimum fertilization; quantitative evaluation of soil properties and soil fertility factors in terms of land use potentialities. Address: 233 Agronomy Bldg, Iowa State University, Ames, IA 50010.

DEMOPOULOS, HARRY BYRON, b. N.Y.C, Feb. 14, 32; m. 55; c. 3. EXPERIMENTAL PATHOLOGY. M.D, State Univ. N.Y, 56. Intern, Kings County Hosp, Brooklyn, N.Y, 56-57; res. path, Bellevue Hosp, New York, 57-60, asst. pathologist, 60-61; asst. prof. PATH. & Nat. Cancer Inst. Res. career develop. award, sch. med, Univ. South. Calif, 63-66, ASSOC. PROF, 66-67; SCH. MED, N.Y, UNIV, 67- Nat. Insts. Health res. training grant, sch. med, N.Y. Univ, 57-61. U.S.P.H.S, 61-63, Sr. Asst. Surg. Am. Chem. Soc; Am. Soc. Exp. Path. Melanoma metabolism; vital respiratory role of tyrosinase in melanomas. Address: Dept. of Pathology, School of Medicine, New York University, 550 First Ave, New York, NY 10016.

DEMOREST, HOWARD L(ESTER), b. Tacoma, Wash, Oct. 21, 21; m. 44; c. 3. PHYSICS. B.S, Minnesota, 51. Asst. physics, Minnesota, 49-51, res. assoc, 51; physicist, med. physics, Vet. Admin. Hosp, 51-53; scientist, physics, instrumentation, Gen. Mills, Inc, 53-58, mgr. atmospherics & measurements, meteorol. & instrument, 58-63; res. physicist, Vet. Admin. Hosp, 63-66; PRES, MODERN CONTROLS INC, 66- Optical Soc. Am; Instrument Soc. Am; Am. Vacuum Soc. Mass spectrometry; radioactivity and meteorological instrumentation; stratospheric research involving methods of measuring atmospheric variables. Address: Modern Controls Inc, 3040 Snelling Ave. South, Minneapolis, MN 55406.

DeMORT, CAROLE LYLE, b. Independence, Mo, Apr. 1, 42. PHYCOLOGY, ECOLOGY. B.A, Park Col, 64; Univ. Ore, 64; M.S, Univ. Mo-Kansas City, 66; NASA trainee, Ore. State Univ, 66-69, Ph.D.(bot), 69. ASST. PROF. BIOL, ST. MARY'S COL. (IND), 69- Vis. researcher, sch. marine & atmospheric sci, div. fisheries, Univ. Miami, summer 70. AAAS; Am. Inst. Biol. Sci; Phycol. Soc. Am; Int. Phycol. Soc; Bot. Soc. Am; Torrey Bot. Club; Am. Soc. Limnol. & Oceanog. Relative nutritional value of phytoplankton species as food for shellfish and shrimp larvae; developmental morphology and biochemical analysis of estuarine phytoplankton species. Address: Dept. of Biology, St. Mary's College, Notre Dame, IN 46556.

DEMOS, CHRISTOPHER HARRY, b. Chatham, N.Y, Apr. 23, 25; m. 49; c. 2. MEDICINE. Union (N.Y), 42-43, M.D, Albany Med. Col, 47. Intern, Fordham Hosp, N.Y, 47-48; Univ. Hosp, 48-49, asst. resident, 49-50, fel. allergy, 50-51; resident med, Fordham Hosp, N.Y, 51-52; private practice med, 52-53; assoc. dir. dept. clin. pharmacol. & assoc. dir. prof. serv, Lederle Labs, Am. Cyanamid Co, 53-60; dir. clin. res, Syntex Labs, 60-61; med. dir, Squibb Inst. Med. Res, 61-68, clin. res. dir, N.J, 62-68; MED. DIR, BEECHAM INC, 68- Am. Med. Asn; Am. Rheumatism Asn; Am. Acad. Allergy; N.Y. Acad. Sci; Am. Col. Allergists; Am. Soc. Clin. Pharmacol. & Chemother. Clinical evaluation of new drugs in the field of endocrinology, corticosteroids and other anti inflammatory agents in therapeutics. Address: Beecham Inc, Industrial South, Clifton, NJ 07012.

DEMOS, M(ILTIADES) S(TAVROS), b. Constantinople, Turkey, Jan. 19, 02; nat; m. 31; c. 5. MATHEMATICS. B.S, Robert Col, Constantinople, 22; Ph.D.(math), Harvard, 26. Sheldon traveling fel. from Harvard, Munich, 26-27; instr, Harvard, 27-28; columbia, 28-31; asst. prof. MATH, New Hampshire, 31-43, 45-46; prof. & head dept, Pa. Mil. Col, 46-53; prof, Drexel Inst, 53-67; ASSOC. PROF, VILLANOVA UNIV, 67- U.S.A.F, 43-46, Capt. Math. Asn. Am. The characteristics of the linear quaternary group. Address: 234 E. Third St, Media, PA 19063.

DEMOS, PETER T(HEODORE), b. Toronto, Ont, Can; m. 41; c. 3. PHYSICS. B.Sc, Queen's (Ont), 41; Ph.D.(physics), Mass. Inst. Tech, 51. Instr. math, & physics, Queen's (Ont), 41-42; mem. ballistics res. staff, Nat. Res. Lab, Ont, 42-44; Can. Army Res. Estab, Que, 44-46; asst. PHYSICS, MASS. INST. TECHNOL, 46-51, mem. staff, LAB. NUCLEAR SCI, 51-52, lectr. & assoc. dir. lab, 52-61, PROF. & DIR. LAB, 61- AAAS; Am. Phys. Soc. Linear accelerator development; photonuclear studies. Address: Dept. of Physics, Massachusetts Institute of Technology, 77 Massachusetts Ave, Cambridge, MA 02139.

DeMOSS, JOHN A(LLEN), b. Indianapolis, Ind, Apr. 10, 30; m. 52; c. 2. MICROBIOLOGY. A.B, Indiana, 52; Ph.D.(microbiol), Western Reserve, 57. U.S. Pub. Health Serv. fel. microbiol, Yale, 57-59, asst. prof, 59-61; BIOL, UNIV. CALIF, SAN DIEGO, 61-64, assoc. prof, 64-69, PROF, 69- Am. Soc. Microbiol. Microbial physiology; genetics. Address: Dept. of Biology, University of California, San Diego, P.O. Box 109, La Jolla, CA 92037.

DeMOSS, RALPH D(EAN), b. Danville, Ill, Dec. 29, 22; m. 46; c. 4. BACTERIAL PHYSIOLOGY. A.B, Indiana, 48, Ph.D.(bact), 51. Atomic Energy Comn. fel, Brookhaven Nat. Labs, 51-52; asst. prof. biol, Hopkins, 52-56; assoc. prof. bact, UNIV. ILL, URBANA, 56-59, PROF. MICROBIOL, 59-HEAD DEPT, 71- Nat. Sci. Found. sr. fel, lab. genetic physiol, Nat. Ctr. Sci. Res, France, 62-63; ed, J. Bact, 65-70; chmn. microbiol. training comt, Nat. Inst. Gen. Med. Sci, 69-71. U.S.A, 42-46. AAAS; Am. Soc. Microbiol; Am. Soc. Biol. Chem; Brit. Soc. Gen. Microbiol. Structure and function of tryptophanase. Address: Dept. of Microbiology, University of Illinois, Urbana, IL 61801.

DEMOTT, B(OBBY) J(OE), b. Kans, Nov. 6, 24; m. 47; c. 5. DAIRY MANUFACTURING. B.S, Kans. State Col, 49; M.S, Idaho, 51; Ph.D.(dairy), Mich. State, 54. Instr, milk factory tests, Idaho, 49-51; asst. market milk, butter-making & cheese, Mich. State 51-54; asst. prof. DAIRY INDUST, Colorado State, 54-57; ASSOC. PROF, UNIV. TENN, KNOXVILLE, 57- U.S.N, 43-46. AAAS; Am. Dairy Sci. Asn. Homogenized milk; radioactive materials in milk. Address: 1617 Hollywood Dr, Knoxville, TN 37919.

DEMOTT, DONALD NORMAN, b. Wash, D.C, May 31, 32; m. 54; c. 3. ORGANIC CHEMISTRY. B.A, Sterling Col, 56; Dow grant, Kansas, 61-63, Ph.D.(chem), 63. RES. CHEMIST, Harris Res. Labs, Gillette Co, 58-60; Procter & Gamble Co, 63-66; DOW CHEM. CO, 66- U.S.A, 56-58. Am. Chem. Soc. Free radical halogenation of alkenes and alkanes with polyhaloalkanes; synthesis of surface active agents and the relation of structural changes with phase behavior in aqueous and perchlorethylene solutions. Address: Halogens Research Lab, 768 Bldg, Dow Chemical Co, Midland, MI 48640.

DeMOTT, HOWARD EPHRAIM, b. Bloomsburg, Pa, Oct. 24, 13; m. 40; c. 1. BOTANY. B.S, Bloomsburg State Col, 35; M.S, Bucknell, 40; Ph.D, Virginia, 65. Teacher, high schs, N.Y, 35-48; instr. BIOL, SUSQUEHANNA UNIV, 48-51, asst. prof, 51-58, assoc. prof, 58-65, PROF, 65- Bot. Soc. Am. Plant morphology and morphogenesis. Address: Dept. of Biology, Susquehanna University, Selinsgrove, PA 17870.

De MOTT, LAWRENCE LYNCH, b. Arlington, N.J, Jan. 16, 22; m. 49; c. 1. GEOLOGY, PALEONTOLOGY. B.A, Oberlin Col, 43; M.A, Chicago, 47; John Harvard fel, Harvard, 52-53, Danforth fel, 57-58, M.A, 53, Ph.D. (geol), 64. Instr. Eng, State Col. Wash, 47-51; GEOL, Oberlin Col, 54-62; KNOX COL.(ILL), 62-63, asst. prof, 65-66, ASSOC. PROF, 66- U.S.A.A.F, 43-45, Sgt. AAAS; Geol. Soc. Am; Paleont. Soc; Am. Asn. Geol. Teachers. Middle Ordovician trilobite faunas of North America. Address: Dept. of Geology, Knox College, Galesburg, IL 61401.

DE MOURA, JOHN M, b. Georgetown, Guyana, June 2, 35; Can. citizen. PLANT BIOCHEMISTRY & PHYSIOLOGY. B.S, Univ. B.C, 62; M.S, Univ. Idaho, 65, Ph.D.(agr. biochem), 69. Res. assoc. agr. chem, Wash. State Univ, 68-71. AAAS. Leaf proteolytic enzymes and inhibitors; senescence. Address: 521 E. First St, Moscow, ID 83843.

DeMOYER, ROBERT, b. Tamagua, Pa, Jan. 30, 07; m. 35; c. 1. CIVIL ENGINEERING. C.E. Lehigh Univ, 29; M.S, Swarthmore Col, 38. Construct. inspector, Reading R.R, 29-33; jr. draftsman, Pa. Dept. Hwys, 34; from asst. to prof. eng, Pa. Mil. Col, 35-42; asst. prof. civil eng, LAFAYETTE COL, 42-44, from asst. to assoc. prof. mech, 45-53, PROF. CIVIL ENG. & HEAD DEPT, 53- Ord. Dept, U.S.A, 44-45. Fel. Am. Soc. Civil Eng; Am. Soc. Eng. Educ; Am. Soc. Photogram; Am. Bd. Builders Asn; Am. Concrete Inst. Structure and applied mechanics. Address: Dept. of Civil Engineering, Lafayette College, Easton, PA 18042.

DEMPESEY, COLBY W(ILSON), b. Chicago, Ill, Mar. 12, 31; m. 52; c. 4. PHYSICS. B.A, Oberlin Col, 52; M.A, Rice Inst, 55, Shell Oil Co. fel, 56-57, Ph.D.(physics), 57. Instr. PHYSICS, AMHERST COL, 57-58, asst. prof, 58-63, assoc. prof, 63-67, PROF, 67- Am. Phys. Soc; Am. Asn. Physics Teachers. Low temperature physics. Address: Dept. of Physics, Amherst College, Amherst, MA 01002.

DEMPSEY, A(LVIN) H(UGH), b. Jackson, Ga, Feb. 17, 20; m. 48; c. 2. HORTICULTURE. B.S.A, Georgia, 42, M.S.A, 47; Ph.D.(hort), Ohio State, 53. Asst. horticulturist, GA. EXP. STA, 48-50, assoc. horticulturist, 50-56, HORTICULTURIST, 56- U.S.A, 43-46. Am. Soc. Hort. Sci. Genetics; cytogenetics; breeding of vegetables. Address: Georgia Experiment Station, University of Georgia, Experiment, GA 30212.

DEMPSEY, BARRY J, b. Galesburg, Ill, Mar. 17, 38; m. 63; c. 2. CIVIL ENGINEERING. B.S, Univ. Ill, Urbana, 60, M.S, 66, Ph.D.(civil eng), 69. Asst. resident engr. hwy. construct, State Ill. Hwy Dept, 60 & 63-64; res. asst. CIVIL ENG, UNIV. ILL, URBANA, 64-69, ASST. PROF, 69- Prin. investr, Ill. Div. Hwy, 68-; consult, N.Y. State Dept. Transportation, 70-71; mem, Hwy. Res. Bd, Nat. Acad. Sci-Nat. Res. Coun, 70-, A.W. Johnson Mem. Award, 70. C.Eng, U.S.A, 61-63, Res, 63-66, Capt. Am. Soc. Civil Eng; Soc. Am. Mil. Eng. Highway materials with major emphasis on the investigation of the influence climatic factors have on construction, design, behavior and performance of pavement systems. Address: 111 Talbot Lab, Dept. of Civil Engineering, University of Illinois, Urbana, IL 61801.

DEMPSEY, DANIEL F(RANCIS), b. Buffalo, N.Y, July 23, 29; m. 60; c. 3. PHYSICS. B.S, Canisius Col, 51; Ph.D.(physics), Notre Dame, 57. Asst. prof. PHYSICS, CANISIUS COL, 56-63, ASSOC. PROF, 63- Am. Phys. Soc.

Focusing trajectories for charged and neutral particles; general nuclear physics and particle accelerators. Address: 6641 Powers Rd, Orchard Park, NY 14127.

DEMPSEY, EDWARD, b. Glasgow, Scotland, Aug. 18, 30; m. 53; c. 3. THEORETICAL PHYSICS. B.S, St. Andrews, 52, Ph.D.(theoret. physics), 56. Sci. off. phys. metall. plutonium, Atomic Weapons Res. Estab, Eng, 55-57, sr. sci. off, 57-60; Nat. Res. Coun. Can. fel. theoret. chem, 58-59; staff mem. theoret. physics, Union Carbide Res. Inst, N.Y, 60-64; RES. ASSOC, MOBIL RES. & DEVELOP. CORP, 64- Fel. Brit. Phys. Soc. Statistical mechanics; metal physics; ionic crystal theory. Address: Mobil Research & Development Corp, Box 1025, Princeton, NJ 08540.

DEMPSEY, EDWARD W(HEELER), b. Buxton, Iowa, May 15, 11; m. 36; c. 3. ANATOMY, PHYSIOLOGY. A.B, Marietta Col, 32, hon. Sc.D, 54; Sc.M, Brown, 34, Ph.D.(biol), 37; hon. A.M, Harvard, 46. Nat. Res. Coun. fel, Harvard Med. Sch, 37-38; instr. physiol, 38-41, assoc. anat, 41-42, asst. prof, 42-46, assoc. prof, 46-50; prof. & head dept, Washington (St. Louis), 50-66, dean med, 58-64, spec. asst. to secy. Dept. Health Ed. & Welfare, 64-65; PROF. ANAT, COL. PHYSICIANS & SURGEONS, COLUMBIA UNIV, 66- Vis. prof, L.I. Col. Med, 43; sch. med, Stanford, 45; consult. Nat. Cancer Inst. Mem. Biol. Stain Cmn, 47. Am. Asn. Anat; Am. Physiol. Soc; Endocrine Soc; Soc. Exp. Biol. & Med; Am. Acad. Arts & Sci; N.Y. Acad. Sci. Endocrine control of behavior; neurophysiology of nerve and forebrain; histochemistry and electron microscopy of mammalian tissues; experimental production of estrus in the female guinea pig. Address: Dept. of Anatomy, College of Physicians & Surgeons, Columbia University, 630 W. 168th St, New York, NY 10032.

DEMPSEY, HUGH JAMES, b. Ottawa, Ont, Nov. 2, 29; U.S. citizen; m. 63; c. 1. INTERNAL MEDICINE, HEMATOLOGY. M.D, Ottawa (Ont), 53; B.Sc, Toronto, 55. Fel. hemat, Utah, 56-58; Ottawa (Ont), 58-60; Alabama, 60-62; instr. med, MED. CTR, UNIV. ALA, BIRMINGHAM, 62-63, asst. prof, 63-66, assoc. prof, 66-70, PROF. MED. & ASSOC. PROF. PATH, 70- Fel, Royal Col. Physicians Can, 60. AAAS; fel. Am. Col. Physicians; Can. Soc. Clin. Invest; Am. Soc. Hemat; Am. Heart Asn; Am. Inst. Nutrit; Fedn. Am. Socs. Exp. Biol; Am. Soc. Clin. Nutrit; Am. Fedn. Clin. Res; Can. Med. Asn. Clinical investigation of research problems in hematology and metabolic disease. Address: Dept. of Medicine, University of Alabama Medical College, 1919 Seventh Ave. S, Birmingham, AL 35233.

DEMPSEY, JOHN N(ICHOLAS), b. St. Paul, Minn, June 16, 23; m. 48; c. 3. PHYSICAL CHEMISTRY. B.S, Col. of St. Thomas, 48; DuPont fel, Iowa, 49-50, Atomic Energy Cmn. fel, 50-51, Ph.D.(phys. chem), 51. Asst, Iowa, 48-50; res. chemist, Ethyl Corp, 51-52; res. physicist, Minneapolis Honeywell Regulator Co, 52-56, res. sect. head, 56-60, asst. dir. res, 60-61, dir. res, HONEYWELL INC, 61-65, V.PRES, Corp. Res. Ctr, 65-67, SCI. & ENG, 67- U.S.N.R, 43-46, Lt.(jg). Am. Chem. Soc. X-ray crystal structures of coordination; complex compounds; intermetallic compounds and bond orders. Address: 2701 Fourth Ave. S, Minneapolis, MN 55408.

DEMPSEY, MARTIN E(WALD), b. Chicago, Ill, Mar. 28, 21; m. 45; c. 3. ELECTRICAL ENGINEERING. B.S, Purdue, 48, M.S, 49, Ph.D.(elec. eng), 55. Engr, voice commun. lab, Purdue, 48-49, chief engr, 50-55; tech. staff, Bell Tel. Labs, 49-50; dir. aid to hearing res, Zenith Radio Corp, 55-59; dir, psychoacoust. res, Beltone Res. Labs, 59-61; MGR, ADVAN. PHYS. DEVELOP, GTE AUTOMATIC ELEC. LABS, 61- Consult, dept. commun. disorders, Northwestern, 58-62. U.S.N.R, 42-45. Acoust. Soc. Am; Am. Vacuum Soc; Electrochem. Soc. Communication engineering; psychoacoustics; materials science. Address: 508 N. Pine St, Mt. Prospect, IL 60056.

DEMPSEY, MARY ELIZABETH, b. St. Paul, Minn, Sept. 23, 28. BIOCHEMISTRY. B.S, St. Catherine Col, 50; M.S, Wayne State, 52; Nat. Heart Inst. fel, Minnesota, 57-61, Ph.D.(enzym), 61. Res. biochemist, Minneapolis Vet. Admin. Hosp, 52-56; instr. clin. biochem, MED. COL, UNIV. MINN, MINNEAPOLIS, 56-58, res. fel. enzym, 58-61, instr. BIOCHEM, 61-65, asst. prof, 65-69, ASSOC. PROF, 69- Am. Heart Asn. res. fel, 61-63; res. grants, Am. Heart Asn, 62-63, Minn. Heart Asn, 61-64 & Nat. Heart Inst, 64-71, Muscular Dystrophy Asn. Am, Inc, 65-70. Am. Chem. Soc; Am. Soc. Biol. Chem; Soc. Exp. Biol. & Med. Enzymology; steroid and sterol biosynthesis; muscle contraction; oxygen-18 methodology; cholesterol biosynthesis. Address: Dept. of Biochemistry, Box 68, Mayo Bldg, University of Minnesota, Minneapolis, MN 55455.

DEMPSEY, WALTER B, b. San Francisco, Calif, Nov. 21, 34; m. 57; c. 4. BIOCHEMISTRY. B.S, San Francisco, 56; M.S, Michigan, 58, U.S. Pub. Serv. fel, 58-60, Ph.D.(biol. chem), 60. U.S. Pub. Health Serv. trainee & res. assoc. biol. chem, Michigan, 60; res. assoc. BIOCHEM, California, Berkeley, 60-62; instr, Florida, 62-63, asst. prof, 63-67, UNIV. TEX. (SOUTHWEST) MED. SCH. DALLAS, 67-68, ASSOC. PROF, 68-; RES. CHEMIST, VET. ADMIN. HOSP, DALLAS, 67- Nat. Sci. Found. fel, 60-62; U.S. Pub. Health Serv. res. grants, 63-68 & 69- Vet. Admin. distinguished res. award, 70. AAAS; Am. Soc. Microbiol; Am. Chem. Soc; Am. Soc. Biol. Chem. Mechanisms for metabolic control of coenzyme levels; pyridoxine chemistry and enzyme mechanisms; bacterial genetics. Address: Dept. of Biochemistry, University of Texas (Southwestern) Medical School at Dallas, Dallas, TX 75235.

DEMPSEY, WESLEY H(UGH), b. Waltham, Mass, Dec. 2, 26; m. 51; c. 2. GENETICS & PLANT BREEDING. B.S, Cornell, 49; M.S, California, 50, Germain Seed Co. fel, 50-51, Ph.D.(genetics), 54. Res. asst. genetics & plant breeding, California, 51-54; PROF. BIOL, CHICO STATE COL, 54- Nat. Sci. Found. sci. faculty fel, Wisconsin, 63-64; adj. prof. plant breeding, Pa. State Univ, 70-71. Summers, res. geneticist, veg. crops dept, California, Davis, 59- U.S.A, 45-46. Am. Soc. Hort. Sci. Tomato genetics, inheritance on consistency; red cotyledon in lettuce; pectic substances in tomatoes. Address: Dept. of Biology, Chico State College, Chico, CA 95927.

DEMPSEY, WILLIAM J, b. Melrose, Mass, Aug. 2, 12; m. 45; c. 9. GEOPHYSICS. B.S, Catholic Univ, 38, M.S, 40. Miner, Kerr Adison Gold Mines, 39-41, surveyor mining eng, 41-42; chief engr, Uchi Gold Mines, 42-43; proj. engr, U.S. Bur. Mines, 43-44; geophysicist, U.S. GEOL. SURV, 46-52, chief airborne surv. sect, 52-60, supv. geophysicist, 60-62, GEOL. SPECIALIST, U.S. AGENCY INT. DEVELOP, WASH, D.C, 62- Field asst, Nickel Offsets Mines, summer 38; mem. bd, Civil Serv. Exam, 49-62; lectr, Howard Univ, 55-62; instr, Univ. Md, 56-62; expert consult, UN Econ. Comn. Asia & Far East, Thailand & UN assignment, Uganda, 60. U.S.N.R, 44-46. Am. Geophys. Union; Soc. Explor. Geophys; Europ. Asn. Explor. Geophys. Airborne geophysical surveying, magnetic and radioactivity; design, plan and execute surveys; installation, modification, maintenance and repair of airborne magnetometers, radioactivity detectors and ancillary equipment. Address: 820 Rowen Rd, Silver Spring, MD 20910.

DEMPSKI, ROBERT E, b. Centermoreland, Pa, July 3, 34; m. 66; c. 2. PHARMACY, PHYSICAL CHEMISTRY. B.S, Phila. Col. Pharm, 56; fel, Wisconsin, 58-60, Ph.D.(pharm), 60. Instr. pharm, Wisconsin, 56-58; res. assoc, PHARM. RES, Merck & Co, Inc, 60-66, UNIT HEAD, MERCK SHARP & DOHME, WEST POINT, 66- Am. Pharmaceut. Asn. Design of new dosage forms for medicinals; study of new methods of dermatologic therapy. Address: 1629 Arran Way, Dresher, PA 19025.

DEMPSTER, ARTHUR P(ENTLAND), b. Toronto, Ont, Oct. 8, 29; m. 57; c. 3. STATISTICS. B.A, Toronto, 52, M.A, 53; Ph.D.(math. statist), Princeton, 56; hon. A.M, Harvard, 61. Lectr. math, Toronto, 56-57; mem. tech. staff, Bell Tel. Labs, 57-58; asst. prof. statist, HARVARD, 58-61, assoc. prof, 61-64, PROF. THEORET. STATIST, 64-, CHMN. DEPT. STATIST, 69- Am. Statist. Asn; Inst. Math. Statist; Biomet. Soc. Theoretical statistics. Address: Dept. of Statistics, Harvard University, 2 Divinity Ave, Cambridge, MA 02138.

DEMPSTER, C(ECIL) J(OHN), b. Winnipeg, Man, Feb. 21, 26; m. 49; c. 4. CEREAL CHEMISTRY. B.Sc, Manitoba, 48; Ph.D.(phys. chem), McGill, 51. CHEMIST, GRAIN RES. LAB, BD. GRAIN COMNR, 49- Am. Asn. Cereal Chem. Physicochemical and rheological aspects of cereal chemistry. Address: Grain Research Lab, Canadian Grain Commission, 190 Grain Exchange Bldg, Winnipeg 2, Man, Can.

DEMPSTER, EVERETT R(OSS), b. San Francisco, Calif, Mar. 17, 03; m. 27; c. 2. GENETICS. B.S, California, 28, Ph.D.(genetics), 41. Elec. engr, Magnavox Co, 27-33; asst. GENETICS, UNIV. CALIF, BERKELEY, 35-4 instr, 41-44, asst. prof, 44-50, assoc. prof, 50-55, prof, 55-70, EMER. PROF, 70-, chmn. dept, 64-71. Mem. staff, dept. exp. statist, N.C. State Col, 54; Oak Ridge Nat. Lab, 58; biol. br, Atomic Energy Comn, 67. With Off. Sci. Res. & Develop; Nat. Adv. Comt. Aeronaut, 44. AAAS; Genetics Soc. Am; Am. Soc. Human Genetics; Biomet. Soc; Am. Eugenics Soc. Genetic effects of radiations; population genetics; animal breeding. Address: Dept. of Genetics, University of California, Berkeley, CA 94720.

DEMPSTER, G(EORGE), b. Edinburgh, Scotland, June 28, 17; m. 42; c. 2. BACTERIOLOGY. M.B.Ch.B, Edinburgh, 40, B.Sc, 41, M.D, 52. Intern, Peel Hosp, Scotland, 40; asst, pub. health lab, Edinburgh, 41-42, lectr. bact, 42-46, 48-50; res. assoc, Connaught Med. Res. Lab, Toronto, 50-55; PROF. BACT, UNIV. SASK, 55-, HEAD DEPT, 56- Dir. bact, univ. hosp, Saskatoon, 55- R.A.M.C, 46-48. Can. Soc. Microbiol; Can. Neurol. Soc; Can. Med. Asn; Can. Pub. Health Asn. Virology; epidemic respiratory disease; influenza; atypical pneumonia and adenoviruses; neuro-tropic viruses, particularly Coxsackie viruses. Address: Dept. of Bacteriology, Medical College, University of Saskatchewan, Saskatoon, Sask, Can.

DEMPSTER, LAURAMAY TINSLEY, b. El Paso, Tex, May 11, 05; m. 27; c. 2. BOTANY, PLANT TAXONOMY. M.A, California, 27. Asst. bot, UNIV. CALIF, BERKELEY, 33-35, herbarium botanist, 51-61, res. geneticist bot, Nat. Sci. Found. grants, 59-69, RES. ASSOC, DEPT. BOT, 69- Am. Soc. Plant Taxon. Taxonomy of flowering plants of California; currently the genus Galium in western North America and Mexico. Address: Dept. of Botany, University of California, Berkeley, CA 94720.

DEMSKEY, SIDNEY, b. Brooklyn, N.Y, Oct. 4, 24; m. 49; c. 3. STATISTICS. B.A, Brooklyn Col, 48; M.B.A, City Col. New York, 53. Statistician, Dept. Health, N.Y, 48-50; sales analyst, Nestle-LeMur Co, 50-51; statistician & admin. asst, Schenley Industs, 51-59; statistician, Aerojet Gen. Corp, 59-60; SUPVRY. STATISTICIAN, REENTRY SYSTS. DEPT, GEN. ELEC. CO, 60- Lectr, eve. sch, City Col. New York; eve. session, Drexel Inst. Technol; Villanova Univ, 68-70. U.S.N.R, 43-46, Ens. Am. Statist. Asn; sr. mem. Am. Soc. Qual. Control. Business and industrial statistics; mathematics. Address: 128 Laurel Lane, Bromall, PA 19008.

DEMSKI, JAMES WILLARD, b. Sarver, Pa, Nov. 2, 32; m. 59; c. 2. PLANT PATHOLOGY. B.S, Clarion State Col, 58; Ph.D.(plant path), Pa. State, 66. ASST. PROF. PLANT VIRUS RES, UNIV. GEORGIA, 66- U.S.N, 51-55. Am. Phytopath. Soc. Isolation, separation and identification of viruses infecting cucurbits. Address: Dept. of Pathology, Georgia Experiment Station, Experiment, GA 30212.

DEMSKI, LEO S(TANLEY), b. Pittsburgh, Pa, Mar. 29, 43; m. 65. NEUROANATOMY, ANIMAL BEHAVIOR. A.B, Miami Univ, 65; Nat. Inst. Ment. Health fel. & Ph.D.(anat, neurobiol), Univ. Rochester, 69. Nat. Inst. Ment. Health fel, Am. Mus. Natural Hist, N.Y, 69-71; ASST. PROF. ANAT, SCH. MED, UNIV. N.MEX, 71- Animal Behav. Soc; Am. Soc. Zool; Am. Inst. Biol. Sci. Identification of neural systems controlling sound production and sexual, feeding and aggressive behavior in fishes using electrical stimulation of brain; neuroanatomy of fish telencephalon and hypothalamus. Address: Dept. of Anatomy, University of New Mexico, School of Medicine, Albuquerque, NM 87106.

DeMURLEY, JOHN E(DWARD) S(TIRLING), b. Albany, N.Y, Dec. 2, 26; m. 59; c. 3. ENVIRONMENTAL SCIENCES. B.A, Monmouth Col, 48; B.S, Univ. Md, 52; M.B.A, Univ. Richmond, 65. Bacteriologist, antibiotics div, U.S. Food & Drug Admin, Wash. D.C, 52-53; supvr. microbiol. assay lab, Heyden Chem. Co, 53-54; sr. supvr. process labs, Am. Cyanamid Co, N.J, 54-56, mgr. testing labs. dept, 56-59, field engr, 59-66, mkt. develop. engr, 66-68; prod. mgr. process, 68; mkt. mgr. reverse osmosis systs, Am. Standard, Inc, 69; corp. mgr. sales-mkt. ultrafiltration systs, Havens Int, 70; PROJ. LEADER ADVAN. WASTE TREATMENT METHODS, POLLUTION CONTROL VENTURE DEPT, ATLAS CHEM. INDUST, INC, 71- AAAS; Am. Inst. Chem. Eng; Tech. Asn. Pulp & Paper Indust; Am. Chem. Soc; Soc. Indust. Microbiol. Fermentation processes; process engineering; reverse osmosis; ultrafiltration; pollution control; desalinization of sea water; advanced wastewater treatment methods. Address: 16 Gerald Dr. River Plaza, Middletown, NJ 07701.

DeMUTH, GEORGE R(ICHARD), b. Sherwood, Ohio, Nov. 16, 25; m. 51; c. 4. PEDIATRICS. M.D, Cincinnati, 50. Instr. PEDIAT, MICHIGAN, 56-57, asst. prof, 57-63, assoc. prof, 63-65, PROF, 65-, ASSOC. DEAN, 68- Med.C, 54-56, Capt. AAAS; Soc. Pediat. Res; Asn. Am. Med. Cols. Address: University of Michigan Medical School, 1335 Catherine St, Ann Arbor, MI 48104.

DEMUTH, HOWARD B, b. Junction City, Kans, June 22, 28; m. 51; c. 4. ELECTRICAL ENGINEERING, COMPUTER SCIENCE. B.S, Colorado, 49; M.S, Stanford, 54, Ph.D.(elec. eng), 57. Staff mem. electronic comput, Los Alamos Sci. Lab, 49-53; res. asst. network synthesis, Stanford, 53-54; res. engr, Stanford Res. Inst, 54-56; proj. engr, Int. Bus. Mach. Res. Lab, 56-58; STAFF MEM. DIGITAL COMPUT. & CONTROL SYSTS. LOS ALAMOS SCI. LAB, 58- Part-time prof, New Mexico, 58-; vis. lectr, Colorado, 62-63, vis. prof, Univ. Hawaii, 68-69. Inst. Elec. & Electronics Eng. Digital data communication; digital control systems; information and communication theory. Address: 1350 45th St, Los Alamos, NM 87544.

DEMUTH, JOHN R(OBERT), b. St. Louis, Mo, Nov. 15, 24. ORGANIC CHEMISTRY. B.A, Washington (St. Louis), 49; M.S, Illinois, 52, Ph.D.(chem), 55. Asst, Washington (St. Louis), 49-50; Univ. Ill, 50-55; ASSOC. PROF. CHEM, UNIV. NEBR, LINCOLN, 55- U.S.A.A.F, 43-46. Am. Chem. Soc. Address: 210 Avery Lab, University of Nebraska, Lincoln, NE 68508.

DEMUTH, ORIN JACK, b. Seattle, Wash, Nov. 26, 26; m. 45; c. 2. FLUID DYNAMICS. B.S, Calif. Inst. Tech, 47; M.S, 48. Develop. engr, South. Calif. Coop. Wind Tunnel, Calif. Inst. Tech, 47-54; liquid engine div, AEROJET-GEN. CORP, Azusa, Calif, 54-57, sr. engr, systs. div, 57-59, MGR. AEROPHYS, SACRAMENTO, 59- U.S.A.A.F, 45, Res, 47-48, 2nd Lt. Am. Inst. Aeronaut. & Astronaut; Sci. Res. Soc. Am. Propulsion; transonic wind tunnel design; gasdynamic design of rocket nozzles; rocket motor heat transfer and propulsion analysis; missile stability and trajectory analysis; internal and external fluid dynamics including fluidic devices. Address: 9428 Shumway Dr, Orangevale, CA 95662.

DE MYER, WILLIAM ERL, b. South Charleston, W.Va, Aug. 7, 24; m. 52; c. 2. NEUROLOGY. B.S, Indiana, 52, M.D, 52. Intern, univ. hosp, Michigan, 52-53; resident neurol, med. ctr, IND. UNIV, 53-56, from instr. to PROF. NEUROL, SCH. MED. & DIR. NEUROANAT. LAB, 54- Mem. med. faculty training prog, Pennsylvania, 56-57; Nat. Insts. Health spec. fel, 62; consult, Marion County Gen. & Vet. Admin. Hosps, Indianapolis, 65- Dipl, Am. Bd. Psychiat. & Neurol, 58, cert. child neurol, 68. U.S.A, 43-46. Fel. Am. Acad. Neurol; Am. Neurol. Asn. Quantitative neuroanatomy; relation of congenital malformations of face and brain; developmental neuroanatomy and teratology. Address: Dept. of Neurology, Indiana University School of Medicine, 1100 W. Michigan St, Indianapolis, IN 46207.

DeNAPOLI, GERARD R, b. Boston, Mass, Aug. 5, 18; m. 43; c. 3. CHEMICAL ENGINEERING. B.S, Northeastern, 41, B.B.A, 50; cert, Mass. Inst. Tech, 44. Res. engr, Atlantic Res. Asn, 37-41, 42-43; asst. to gen. mgr, Aralac, Inc, 41-42; plant mgr, Nat. Atlantic Res. Corp, 46-48; tech. dir, Masury-Young Co, Mass, 48-57, gen. mgr. prod. res, 57-64, v.pres. mfg. & res, 64-65, opers, 65, exec. v.pres, 65-66, v.pres. mfg, Masury-Columbia Co, Ill, 66-67; PRES, ABORN CHEM. INDUSTS, INC, 67- Exec. v.pres, Culver Chem. Co, Ill, 66-67. U.S.N.R, 43-46, Lt.(jg). Am. Chem. Soc; Am. Soc. Test. & Mat. Chemical specialties, waxes, polishes, cleaners; emulsion and polymer chemistry. Address: Aborn Chemical Industries, Inc, 669 Elmwood Ave, Providence, RI 02907.

DeNAVARRE, MAISON G(ABRIEL), b. Poland, Mar. 27, 09; nat; m. 38; c. 2. COSMETICS. Ph.C, Wayne Univ, 29, B.S, 30, M.Sc, 62. Apprentice pharmacist, C.G. Meyer, Mich, 27-29, registered pharmacist, 29-30; Willis Pharmacy, 30-34; consult. chemist, 30-47; v.pres. charge mfg. & res, Cosmetic Labs, Inc, div. Beauty Counselors, Inc, 47-55, dir, 55-68; PRES. RES. & DEVELOP, VANDA BEAUTY COUNSR, REXALL DRUG & CHEM. CO, 68- Spec. instr, Wayne; v.pres. & dir, Helfrich Labs, Can, Ltd, 55; Beauty Counselors Can, Ltd. & Beauty Counselors London, Ltd, 61, Beauty Counsr. Int, 63. Consult, eng. bd, camouflage br, U.S. Army, 44. Tech. ed. & ed. dir, Am. Perfumer. Hon. mem, Ital. Comt. Esthetics & Cosmetics. Am. Chem. Soc; Am. Pharmaceut. Asn; hon. mem. Soc. Cosmetic Chem. (pres, 45, medal, 51, ed, jour, 46-61); Am. Oil Chemists' Soc; fel. Am. Inst. Chem; fel. N.Y. Acad. Sci; Span. Soc. Cosmetic Chem.(hon. pres, 71); Brit. Asn. Pub. Analysts; Ger. Cosmetic Chem. Soc; Fr. Soc. Cosmetics; Fr. Soc. Indust. Chem; Int. Fedn. Socs. Cosmetic Chem.(pres, 59); Mex. Soc. Cosmetic Chem.(hon. pres, 64); hon. mem. Australian, Brit, Danish & Swiss Socs. Cosmetic Chem; hon. mem. Ger. Soc. Aesthetic Med. Cosmetic emulsions; ultraviolet absorption; chemical anticorrosive agents; chemical heating mixture; production, control and analysis of cosmetics; cosmetic microbiology; preservatives. Address: Vanda Beauty Counselor, Rexall Drug & Chemical Co, P.O. Box 3433, Orlando, FL 32802.

DENAVIT, JACQUES, b. Paris, France, Oct. 1, 30; U.S. citizen; m. 54; c. 3. ENGINEERING. Baccalaureat, Univ. Paris, 49, cert, 51; M.S, Northwestern, 53, Ph.D, 56. Asst. prof. dept. mech. eng, NORTHWEST. UNIV, 58-60, assoc. prof. MECH. ENG. & ASTRONAUT. SCI, 60-65, PROF, 65- French Air Force, 56-57. Am. Soc. Mech. Eng; Am. Phys. Soc. Kinematic analysis and synthesis; plasma physics and kinetic theory. Address: 3205 Hartzell, Evanston, IL 60201.

DENBER, HERMAN C. B, b. N.Y.C, Oct. 9, 17; m. 44; c. 1. PSYCHIATRY, BIOCHEMICAL PHARMACOLOGY. B.A, N.Y. Univ, 38, M.S, 63, Ph.D.(biol), 67; B.M.S, Univ. Geneva, 41, fel, 42, M.D, 43. Assoc. res. scientist, MANHATTAN STATE HOSP, 54-55, DIR. PSYCHIAT. RES, 55-; PROF. PSYCHIAT, NEW YORK MED. COL, 66-, assoc. clin. prof, 60-66. Swiss-Am. Foun. res. fel, 52; instr. psychiat, col. physicians & surgeons, Columbia Univ, 56-60. Dipl, Am. Bd. Psychiat. & Neurol, 55; Chevalier de l'Ordre de la Sante, France, 60. Am. Med. Asn; Am. Psychiat. Asn; Asn. Res. Nerv. & Ment. Diseases; Soc. Biol. Psychiat; Am. Electroencephalog. Soc; N.Y. Acad. Med; Am. Soc. Pharmacol. & Exp. Therapeut; Am. Col. Neuropsychopharmacol; cor. mem. Fr. Soc. Psychol. Med; cor. mem. Turkish Col. Neuropsychopharmacol; cor. mem. Cong. Fr. Speaking Psychiat. & Neurol; hon. mem. Royal Belgian Soc. Ment. Med. Electroencephalography; clinical psychiatry; psychopharmacology; psychoanalysis; social psychiatry; molecular biology; neuropathology. Address: Dept. of Psychiatric Research, Manhattan State Hospital, New York, NY 10035.

DEN BESTEN, IVAN E(UGENE), b. Corsica, S.Dak, Jan. 11, 33; m. 60; c. 2. PHYSICAL CHEMISTRY. A.B, Calvin Col, 57; Ph.D.(chem), Northwestern, 61. Instr. CHEM, BOWLING GREEN STATE UNIV, 61-62, asst. prof, 62-66, assoc. prof, 66-70, PROF, 70- U.S.A, 53-55. AAAS; Am. Chem. Soc; N.Y. Acad. Sci. Catalysis by metals and metal oxides; photocatalysis and photochemistry; reactions in discharges; surface reactions. Address: 155 S. Prospect, Bowling Green, OH 43402.

DENBOW, CARL (HERBERT), b. Zanesville, Ohio, Dec. 13, 11; m. 39; c. 3. MATHEMATICS. B.S, Chicago, 32, M.S, 34, Ph.D.(math), 37. Instr. math, Ohio, 36-40, asst. prof, 40-43, assoc. prof, 43-46; math. & mech, U.S. Naval Postgrad. Sch, 46-50; PROF. MATH, OHIO UNIV, 50-, chmn. dept, 54-55 & 66-67. Ford faculty fel, Harvard, 55-56; coord, Int. Teacher Develop. Prog, 61, 62; chmn, Agency Int. Develop. Surv. Team, Cambodia, 62; dir. training prog, Peace Corps, Cameroon, 63, 64. U.S.N, 43-46, Lt. Am. Math. Soc; Math. Asn. Am. Applied mathematics; foundations of mathematics. Address: Dept. of Mathematics, Ohio University, Athens, OH 45701.

DENBY, L(YALL) G(ORDON), b. Regina, Sask, Oct. 4, 23. HORTICULTURE. B.S.A, British Columbia, 45; M.S.A, 50. Nursery sales & mgt, Hyland Barnes Nursery, 47-50; HEAD veg. crops. sect, exp. farm, CAN. DEPT. AGR, 50-59, VEG. & ORNAMENTALS, RES. STA, 59- Sadler Mem. gold medal, 45. Am. Soc. Hort. Sci; Can. Soc. Hort. Sci; Royal Hort. Soc. Vegetable cultural research and plant breeding; field tomatoes. Address: Research Station, Canada Dept. of Agriculture, Summerland, B.C, Can.

D'ENCARNACAO, PAUL S, b. Shanghai, China, Dec. 28, 29; U.S. citizen; m. 64; c. 2. PSYCHOPHARMACOLOGY, NEUROSCIENCES. B.A, Vanderbilt Univ, 63, U.S. Pub. Health Serv. fel, 63-67, Ph.D.(psychol, pharmacol), 68. ASST. PROF. PSYCHOL, Vanderbilt Univ, 67-68, MEMPHIS STATE UNIV, 68- U.S.A, 53-56. AAAS; Am. Psychol. Asn. Direct chemical stimulation of brain and relationship to behavior; localization site of action of psychotropic drugs in brain. Address: Dept. of Psychology, Memphis State University, Memphis, TN 38111.

DENCE, JOSEPH B, b. Toledo, Ohio, Dec. 16, 41. ORGANIC CHEMISTRY. B.A, Bowling Green State, 63; Ph.D.(org. chem), Calif. Inst. Tech, 69. ASST. PROF. CHEM, FLA. STATE UNIV, 68- AAAS; Am. Chem. Soc; Am. Inst. Chem; The Chem. Soc. Chemistry of sulfonium, iodonium and other families of onium salts; applications of molecular orbital theory to organic problems; nuclear magnetic resonance spectroscopy and its application to conformational analysis. Address: Dept. of Chemistry, Florida State University, Tallahassee, FL 32306.

DENCE, MICHAEL R(OBERT), b. Sydney, Australia, June 17, 31; m. 67; c. 2. GEOLOGY, METEORITICS. B.Sc, Sydney, 53; California, Berkeley, 55-56. Geologist, Falconbridge Nickel Mines Ltd, 53-54; res. asst. tectonics, geophys. lab, Toronto, 56-58; tech. officer, Dept. Mines & Tech. Surv, 59-61, RES. SCIENTIST, Dom. Observ, 62-70, DEPT. ENERGY, MINES & RESOURCES, 70- AAAS; Am. Geophys. Union; Meteoritical Soc; fel. Geol. Asn. Can; N.Y. Acad. Sci. Meteor crater studies; meteoritics; rock deformation; metamorphism; volcanology; tectonophysics; planetary sciences; lunar sample studies. Address: Gravity Division, Earth Physics Branch, Dept. of Energy, Mines & Resources, Ottawa, Ont. K1A 0E4, Can.

DENCH, EDWARD C(HARLES), b. Orange, N.J, June 12, 16; m; c. 3. ELECTRICAL ENGINEERING. B.S, Worcester Polytech, 39; M.S, Mass. Inst. Tech, 40. Mem. staff, lamp div, Westinghouse Elec. Co, 34-39; sr. physicist, Interchem. Corp, 40-44; consult. electronics & eng, Conn, 44-47; sect. head spec. tube develop, Raytheon Mfg. Co, Waltham, 47-59, mgr. crossed field tube lab, Burlington, 59-64, microwave heating applns, Spencer Lab, 64-67, mgr. eng. serv, microwave & power tube division, RAYTHEON CO, 67-70, STAFF CONSULT. RESIDENTIAL COMFORT SYSTS, NEW PROD. CTR, 70- Lectr, Connecticut, 44-46. Citation, Off. Sci. Res. & Develop, 45. Sr. mem. Inst. Elec. & Electronics Eng.(prize, Inst. Elec. Eng, 39). Gaseous discharge devices; electronic color correction; industrial electronics; electro-optical instruments; analogue computers; communication; electronic instruments; magnetrons; microwave amplifiers; backward wave oscillators; microwave heating applications. Address: New Products Center, Raytheon Co, Foundry Ave, Waltham, MA 02154.

DENDY, JOHN S(TILES), b. Walhalla, S.C, Sept. 29, 09; m. 36; c. 2. ZOOLOGY, LIMNOLOGY. B.S, Presby. Col, 30; M.A, North Carolina, 32; fel, Michigan, 40-42, Ph.D.(zool), 43. Prof. biol, Brevard Col, 34-38; asst, Michigan, 39-40; fisheries biologist & limnologist, Tenn. Valley Auth, 42-47; assoc. prof. ZOOL, AUBURN UNIV, 47-57, PROF, 57- Limnologist, food & agr. orgn, UN, 59-60. Ecol. Soc. Am.(treas, 57-59); Am. Fisheries Soc; Am. Soc. Limnol. & Oceanog; Am. Soc. Ichthyol. & Herpet. Invertebrate animals as food for fish; taxonomy of chironomidae, diptera; relation of stratification of water to distribution of fish. Address: Fisheries Bldg, Auburn University, Auburn, AL 36830.

DENEAU, GERALD A(NTOINE), b. Oxford, Mich, May 9, 28; m. 52; c. 3. PHARMACOLOGY. B.A, Western Ontario, 50, M.S, 52; Ph.D.(pharmacol), Michigan, 57. Instr. pharmacol, med. center, Michigan, 57-65; SR. PHARMACOLOGIST, SOUTH. RES. INST, 65- Am. Soc. Pharmacol. Physical dependence and tolerance development to addicting drugs; general pharmacology of all centrally-acting drugs. Address: Dept. of Pharmacology, Southern Research Institute, Birmingham, AL 35205.

DENEKAS, MILTON O(LIVER), b. Dempster, S.Dak, Apr. 20, 18; m. 49; c. 3. CHEMISTRY. B.A, Hope Col, 40; Western Reserve, 40-41; Ph.D.(chem), Michigan, 47. Jr. res. chemist, Upjohn Co, Mich, 45-47; instr. chem, Tulsa, 47-49, asst. prof, 49-57; RES. CHEMIST, ESSO PROD. RES. CO, 57- Am. Chem. Soc. Isoaromatization studies; drugs for amebiasis; amino acids and protein hydrolysates; synthesis of omega-omega diaminoalkanes; petroleum reservoir wetability studies; geochemistry; secondary petroleum recovery. Address: Esso Production Research Co, 3120 Buffalo Speedway, Houston, TX 77001.

DENELL, ROBIN E(RNEST), b. Peoria, Ill, Aug. 6, 42; m. 66; c. 1. GENETICS. B.A, Univ. Calif, Riverside, 65; Nat. Insts. Health trainee, Univ. Tex, Austin, 66-69, M.A, 68, Ph.D.(genetics), 69. Nat. Insts. Health trainee, Univ. Tex, Austin, 69-70; NAT. INSTS. HEALTH FEL. GENETICS, UNIV. CALIF, SAN DIEGO, 70- AAAS; Genetics Soc. Am. Genetic control of meiosis; process of fertilization in Drosophila and other organisms. Address: Dept. of Biology, University of California at San Diego, La Jolla, CA 92038.

DENENBERG, VICTOR H(UGO), b. Apr. 3, 25; m. 50; c. 4. PSYCHOBIOLOGY. B.A, Bucknell, 49; M.S, Purdue, 51, Ph.D.(psychol), 53. Res. assoc, human res. off. George Washington, 52-54; asst. prof. psychol, Purdue, 54-57, assoc. prof, 57-61, PROF, 61-69; PSYCHOBIOLOGY, UNIV. CONN, 69- Carnegie fel, Roscoe B. Jackson Mem. Lab, 55, vis. investr, 56-; Nat. Inst. Health spec. fel, Cambridge, 63-64. U.S.A, 43-45. AAAS; Am. Psychol. Asn. Experimental developmental psychology; ontogeny of behavior; animal behavior and early experience. Address: Dept. of Biobehavioral Sciences, U-154, University of Connecticut, Storrs, CT 06268.

DENES, PETER B, b. Budapest, Hungary, Nov. 9, 20. COMMUNICATION SCIENCES, ELECTRICAL ENGINEERING. B.Sc, Manchester, 41, M.Sc, 43; Ph.D.(eng), London, 60. Demonstr. elec. eng, Manchester, 41-44; res. engr, Welwyn Elec. Labs, 44-46; lectr. phonetics, Univ. Col, London, 46-61; mem. tech. staff, BELL TEL. LABS, INC, 61-67, HEAD SPEECH & COMMUN. RES. DEPT, 67- Vis. fel, Columbia, 53. Physicist, audiol. unit, Royal Nat. Throat, Nose & Ear Hosp, London, Eng, 52-61. Mem, med. & sci. comt, Nat. Inst. for Deaf, London, 47-61; subcomt. hearing aids & audiometers, Brit. Standards Inst, 52-61. Fel. Acoustical Soc. Am. Speech communication; automatic speech recognition; speech synthesis; hearing and deafness; hearing aids. Address: Bell Telephone Labs, Inc, Murray Hill, NJ 07974.

DE NEVERS, NOEL HOWARD, b. San Francisco, Calif, May 21, 32; m. 55; c. 3. CHEMICAL ENGINEERING. B.S, Stanford, 54; Fulbright fel, Karlsruhe Tech, 54-55; M.S, Michigan, 56, Ph.D.(chem. eng), 59. Res. engr, Calif. Res. Corp, Standard Oil Co. Calif, 58-63; PROF. CHEM. ENG, UNIV. UTAH, 63- Summers, atomic energy div, Phillips Petrol. Co, 64 & U.S. Army Harry Diamond Labs, 68; off. air progs, Environ. Protection Agency, 71-72. Am. Inst. Chem. Eng. Chromatographic transport in secondary recovery; general and multifluid flow; thermodynamics and thermodynamic properties; interaction of technology and society; teaching of technology to nontechnologists; air pollution control technology. Address: Dept. of Chemical Engineering, University of Utah, Salt Lake City, UT 84112.

DENGLER, C(ARL) E(UGENE), b. Passaic, N.J, Dec. 8, 23; m. 44; c. 4. CHEMICAL ENGINEERING. S.B. & S.M, Mass. Inst. Tech, 47, Sc.D.(chem. eng), 53. Res. engr, plastics dept, E.I. du Pont de Nemours & Co, 47-50, tech. investr. film dept. & supvervising econ. anal. for res. div, 52-54; res. supvr. process develop, Yerkes Res. Lab, 54-56, res. mgr, film dept, 56-62, tech. mgr. film res. & develop, 62-64, lab. dir, Yerkes Res. & Develop. Lab, N.Y, 64-68; lab. dir. explor. res, film dept, E.I. DU PONT DE NEMOURS & CO, INC, WILMINGTON, DEL, 68-69, prod. mgr. film dept, 70-71, PROD. MGR. POLYOLEFINS FILM DEPT, 71- U.S.A.A.F, 42-45, 1st Lt. Am. Chem. Soc; Am. Inst. Chem. Eng. Two-phase heat transfer; polymers; research administration. Address: R.D. 1, Kennett Square, PA 19348.

DENGLER, MADISON L, Exp. Psychol, see 12th ed, Soc. & Behav. Vols.

DENGO, GABRIEL, b. Heredia, Costa Rica, Mar. 9, 22; m. 50; c. 3. PETROLOGY, STRUCTURAL GEOLOGY. B.S, Univ. Costa Rica, 44; B.A, Wyoming, 45, M.A, 46; M.A, Princeton, 48, Procter fel, 48-49, Ph.D.(geol), 49. Res. assoc, Princeton, 50; geologist, Direccion de Geol, Ministerio de Minas e Hidrocarburos, Venezuela, 50-52; Union Oil Co. Calif, 53-62; consult, Orgn. Am. States, 62-64; dep. secy. gen, Permanent Secretariat Cent. Am. Econ. Integration Treaty, 64; mem. res. staff, CENT. AM. RES. INST. INDUST. TECHNOL, 65-70, ASSOC. DIR, 70- Geol. Soc. Am; Mineral. Soc. Am; Asn. Petrol. Geol; Ger. Geol. Asn; Soc. Econ. Geol; Mex. Geol. Soc; Costa Rican Geol. Asn. Economic geology; regional geology of Central America and Northern South America; tectonics. Address: Apartado 468, Guatamala City, Guatamala, Cent. Am.

DENHAM, JOSEPH M(ILTON), b. Port Jervis, N.Y, Jan. 21, 30; m. 51; c. 2. ORGANIC CHEMISTRY. B.S, Pa. State Univ, 51; M.S, Ohio Univ, 56, Ph.D.(chem), 59. Instr. math. & chem, Orange County Community Col, 51-52, 54; asst. prof. CHEM, HIRAM COL, 58-65, assoc. prof, 65-69, PROF, 69- Summers, res. chemist, Lubrizol Corp, 59; vis. asst. prof, Ohio Univ, 60; Nat. Sci. Found. res. partic, Univ. Fla, 63, vis. asst. prof, 64; res. fel, col. pharm, Ohio State Univ, 71-72. U.S.A, 52-54, Res, 54-58. Am. Chem. Soc. Organophosphorus compounds, synthesis of and applications as plant growth substances; heterocyclic; small ring compounds. Address: Dept. of Chemistry, Hiram College, Hiram, OH 44234.

DENHAM, RICHARD LANE, b. Louisville, Ky, Apr. 5, 13; m. 36, 70; c. 2. PETROLEUM & STRUCTURAL GEOLOGY. B.A, Wash. Univ, 33, M.S, 34; Univ. Okla, 34-35; Univ. Pittsburgh, 56; Univ. Tex, 66. Geologist, Mo. State Geol. Surv, 34; King-Wood Oil Co, Tex, 35; county supvr, Okla. State Geol. Surv, 35-36; paleontologist, W.Tex. Div, HUMBLE OIL & REF. CO, 36-39; geologist, 39-41, La. Div, 41-46, asst. div. geologist, Gulf Coast Div, 46-55, div. explor. mgr, 55-57, head unitization geologist, 57-66, sr. staff adv, SOUTHWEST. DIV, 66-68, sulfur proj. supvr, 68-71, SR. STAFF ADV, PETROL EXPLOR, 71- Fel. Geol. Soc. Am; Am. Asn. Petrol. Geol. Subsurface structure and stratigraphy of petroleum deposits of the Permian Basin of west Texas and southeastern New Mexico, the gulf coast of Louisiana and Texas and the bend arch and Ft. Worth Basin of north Texas; geology and chemistry of free sulfur deposits; petroleum exploration economics; igenous petrology; taxonomic affiliation of the conodonts. Address: P.O. Box 1600, Midland, TX 79701.

DENHARD, E(LBERT) E(DWIN), JR, b. Baltimore, Md, June 4, 20; m. 44; c. 3. MECHANICAL & METALLURGICAL ENGINEERING. B.S, Purdue, 41; M.S, Hopkins, 57. Inspector STAINLESS STEELS, ARMCO STEEL CORP, 41-43, jr. combustion engr, 43-48, res. engr, 48-57, SR. RES. ENGR, 57- Am. Soc. Test. & Mat; Nat. Asn. Corrosion Eng; Electrochem. Soc; Am. Soc. Metals. Corrosion research in stainless steels; alloy development; specifications, mechanical properties, patents and commercial development of stainless steels. Address: Research & Technology, P.O. Box 1697, Armco Steel Corp, Baltimore, MD 21203.

DENHARDT, DAVID TILTON, b. Sacramento, Calif, Feb. 25, 39; m. 61; c. 3. MOLECULAR BIOLOGY. B.A, Swarthmore Col, 60; Ph.D.(biophys, physics), Calif. Inst. Tech, 65. Instr. biol, Harvard, 64-66, asst. prof, 66-70; ASSOC. PROF. BIOCHEM, McGILL UNIV, 70- Am. Microbiol. Soc; Am. Soc. Biol. Chem; Can. Biochem. Soc. Mechanism of replication of bacteriophage ØX174; biochemistry of the replication, repair and synthesis of deoxyribonucleic acid; structure and evolution of the cell. Address: Dept. of Biochemistry, McIntyre Medical Bldg, McGill University, Montreal, Que, Can.

DEN HARTOG, J(ACOB) P(IETER), b. Ambarawa, Java, July 01; nat; m. 26; c. 2. ENGINEERING MECHANICS. E.E, Delft, 24; Ph.D.(math), Pittsburgh, 29; Göttingen, 30-31; hon. Dr.Eng, Carnegie Tech, 62; hon. Dr.Appl.Sc, Univ. Ghent, 65; hon. Dr.Tech.Sc, Univ. Delft, 66. Res. labs, Westinghouse Elec. & Mfg. Co, East Pittsburgh, 24-30, 31-32; asst. prof, Harvard, 32-36, assoc. prof. applied mech, 36-41; prof. MECH. ENG, MASS. INST. TECHNOL, 45-69, head dept, 54-58, EMER. PROF. & SR. LECTR, 69- Lectr, Univ. Pittsburgh, 28; Harvard, 31-32. U.S.N.R, 41-45, Capt. Nat. Acad. Sci; hon. mem. Am. Soc. Mech. Eng; fel. Am. Inst. Aeronaut. & Astronaut; Brit. Inst. Mech. Eng; hon. mem. Japan Soc. Mech. Eng. Dynamics and mechanical vibration; elasticity. Address: Dept. of Mechanical Engineering, Massachusetts Institute of Technology, Cambridge, MA 02139.

DENHOFF, ERIC, b. Brooklyn, N.Y, June 5, 13; m. 45; c. 3. MEDICINE. B.S, Vermont, 34, M.D, 38. Dir. clin. lab, EMMA PENDELTON BRADLEY HOME, 47-56, DIR. PHYSIOL. & BIOL. RES, 56-; MEM. INST. RES. HEALTH & SCI, BROWN UNIV, 58- Lectr, Rhode Island, 50-51, adj. prof; lectr, col. physicians & surgeons, Columbia, 52-58; med. sch, Syracuse, 52-57; postgrad. seminar, Connecticut, 52-53, 58; Ohio State, 55-56; United Cerebral Palsy Seminar, 56. Consult, Roger Williams Gen, Prov-Lying-In, Chapin & Bradley Hosps; Crippled Children & Adults of R.I, 47; med. dir, Meeting St. Sch. Children's Rehab, 47; chief pediat. & exec. comt, staff, Miriam Hosp, 54; physician, R.I. Hosp, 56. Nat. Inst. Neurol. Diseases & Blindness, Nat. Insts. Health, 55-59, mem. collaborative study of R.I. cerebral palsy proj, 56- Dipl, Nat. Bd. Med. Exam, 39; Am. Bd. Pediat, 46. Med.C, 41-46, Maj. Fel. Am. Acad. Cerebral Palsy.(pres, 63-64); fel. Am. Med. Asn; fel. Am. Acad. Pediat; assoc. Am. Acad. Neurol; assoc. mem. Am. Psychiat. Asn. Abnormal and normal child growth and development, particularly cerebral dysfunction. Address: Governor Medical Center, 293 Governor St, Providence, RI 02912.

DENHOLM, ALEC STUART, b. Glasgow, Scotland, Aug. 24, 29; U.S. citizen; m; c. 1. ELECTRICAL ENGINEERING, HIGH VOLTAGE TECHNOLOGY. B.Sc, Glasgow, 50, Caird scholar, 53-54, Ph.D.(elec. eng), 56. Assoc. res. off. elec. eng, Nat. Res. Coun. Can, 54-59; sr. engr, Ion Physics Corp, 59-63, dir. eng. & develop, 63-68, V.PRES, 68-69; ENERGY SCI. INC, 70- Am. Inst. Aeronaut. & Astronaut; Inst. Elec. & Electronics Eng; Brit. Inst. Elec. Eng. Electrical discharges in vacuum and gases; development of high voltage equipment. Address: South Great Rd, Lincoln, MA 01773.

DENIS, GUSTAVE, b. Weedon, Que, Sept. 7, 30; c. 3. NEPHROLOGY, METABOLISM. B.A, Univ. Ottawa, 52, M.D, 58. Asst. prof. PHYSIOL, UNIV. MONTREAL, 64-70, ASSOC. PROF, 70- Am. Fedn. Clin. Res; Can. Fedn. Biol. Soc; Int. Soc. Nephrology. Effect of morphine on calcium metabolism and diuresis; role of parathormone and calcitonine on glucose and protein utilization and the interrelationship of these dietary components with calcium and phosphorus metabolism. Address: Dept. of Physiology, University of Montreal, P.O. Box 6128, Montreal, Que, Can.

De NISCO, STANLEY GABRIEL, b. New York, N.Y, Sept. 24, 18; m. 41; c. 4. NUTRITION. B.A, Fordham, 40; M.A, N.Y. Univ, 46, Ph.D, 61. Chemist in charge qual. control, Sheffield Farms, Inc, 40-42; res. veg. oils, Best Foods, Inc, 42-44; asst. dir. appl. res, Standard Brands, Inc, 44-51; admin. asst. tech. serv, Chas. Pfizer & Co, Inc, 51-53; V.PRES. & MGR. SCI. DEPT, TED BATES & CO, INC, 53- AAAS; Am. Chem. Soc; Inst. Food Technol; N.Y. Acad. Sci. Nutrition; biochemistry; food chemistry; food technology. Address: 24 Monroe St, Pelham Manor, NY 10803.

DENISEN, E(RVIN) L(OREN), b. Austin, Minn, Nov. 10, 19; m. 43; c. 3. HORTICULTURE. B.S, Minnesota, 41; M.S, Iowa State, 47, Ph.D.(hort, plant physiol), 49. Voc. agr. instr, high sch, Minn, 41-42; instr. HORT, IOWA STATE UNIV, 46-49, asst. prof, 49-59, assoc. prof, 59-65, PROF, 65-, CHMN. DEPT, 67- Consult, U.S. Agency Int. Develop, Uruguay, 63; Proj. Unicorn, Inc. U.S.A.A.F, 42-46, Capt. Fel. AAAS; Weed Sci. Soc. Am; Am. Pomol. Soc; Am. Soc. Hort. Sci; Am. Soc. Plant Physiol; Int. Soc. Hort. Sci. Small fruit breeding; physiology of horticulture crops; chemical week control: air pollution; mechanical harvesting of strawberries. Address: 2137 Friley Rd, Ames, IA 50010.

DENISON, ADAM B(ENJAMIN), JR, b. Cleveland, Ohio, Nov. 18, 20. PHYSIOLOGY. B.S, Hamilton Col, 42; M.D, Western Reserve, 45. Instr. Physiol, Bowman Gray Sch. Med, Wake Forest Univ, 48-56, asst. prof, 56-66, assoc. prof, 66-71; RETIRED. V.pres, Carolina Med. Electronics, Inc. Med.C, U.S.A, 46-48. Am. Physiol. Soc. Circulation research and instrumentation. Address: 2034 Queen St, Winston-Salem, NC 27103.

DENISON, ARCHIBALD GEORGE, b. Walkerville, Ont, Sept. 2, 07; m. 46; c. 2. PEDIATRICS. M.D, Univ. West. Ont, 34; D.C.H, Univ. London, 38. Asst. prof. PEDIAT, UNIV. WEST. ONT, 47-71, ASSOC. CLIN. PROF, 71- Cert, Royal Col. Physicians Can. Med.C, Can. Army, 41-46, Lt.Col. Fel. Am. Acad. Pediat. Cerebral palsy. Address: Faculty of Medicine, University of Western Ontario, London, Ont, Can.

DENISON, ARTHUR B, b. Oakland, Calif, June 17, 36; m. 60; c. 3. PHYSICS. A.B, California, Berkeley, 59; Ph.D.(physics), Colorado, 63. Asst. prof. PHYSICS, UNIV. WYO, 63-67, ASSOC. PROF, 67- Vis. prof, Max Planck Inst. Med. Res, 67, 68, 69. Nuclear magnetic resonance, electron paramagnetic resonance and ultrasonic nuclear magnetic resonance in solids; nuclear magnetic resonance of paraffin hydrocarbons in liquid and solid state. Address: Dept. of Physics, University of Wyoming, Laramie, WY 82071.

DENISON, DEAN R, b. Spokane, Wash, June 25, 33; m. 63; c. 1. SURFACE PHYSICS. B.S, Washington State, 55, Ph.D.(physics), 63; M.S, California, Los Angeles, 57. Mem. tech. staff, Hughes Res. Labs, 63-64; RES. SCIENTIST, GRANVILLE-PHILLIPS CO, 64- Am. Vacuum Soc. Ultrahigh vacuum measurement; surface reaction probabilities; gaseous electronics. Address: Granville-Phillips Co, E. Araphne, Boulder, CO 80302.

DENISON, EILEEN, b. Mattoon, Ill, June 15, 27; ENDOCRINOLOGY, PHYSIOLOGY. A.B, Washington (St. Louis), 49; M.S, Purdue, 52, Ph.D.(endocrinol), 54. Am. Cancer Soc. fel, Okla. Found. Med. Res, 54-55; sect. chief physiol, U.S. Army Med. Res. Lab, 55-58; pres, Endocrine Consult. Labs, 58-69; ENDOCRINOLOGIST, INT. CLIN. LABS, 69- Res. assoc, sch. med, Univ. Ky, Louisville, 60-; res. consult, State Dept. Ment. Health, Ky, 64-; pres, Thoroughbred Res. Inc, 64- AAAS; Am. Soc. Zool; Am. Physiol. Soc; Am. Asn. Clin. Chem; Am. Soc. Biol. Chem. Adaptation of endocrine system to stress with emphasis on role of sex steroids; role of adrenal steroids in schizophrenia; endocrine system of thoroughbred horses and abnormalities resulting from racing. Address: International Clinical Labs, 250 E. Liberty, Louisville, KY 40202.

DENISON, F(RANK) W(ILLIS), JR, b. Temple, Tex, Jan. 5, 21; m. 48; c. 4. MICROBIOLOGY. Ph.D.(bact), Texas, 52. Sr. res. microbiologist, ABBOTT LABS, 52-55; group leader microbiol, 55-63, asst. mgr. microbiol. physiol, 63-64, MGR. MICROBIAL. CHEM, 64- Lectr, Lake Forest Col, 58-61. Med.C, 42-46, 1st Lt. Am. Chem. Soc. Antibiotics and submerged fermentations with special reference to pilot plant equipment; chemistry of microbial products and intermediary metabolism. Address: Abbott Labs, North Chicago, IL 60064.

DENISON, GEORGE H(AIGH), b. Oakland, Calif, Oct. 22, 10; m. 46; c. 4. CHEMISTRY. B.S, California, 32, Ph.D.(chem), 36. Res. chemist, Calif. Res. Corp, 32-44, div. supvr, 44-56, sr. res. scientist, 56-67, ASST. TO PRES, CHEVRON RES. CO, 67- Mem, Gordon Res. Conf. Coun, 69- Cert. of appreciation, Am. Petrol. Inst, 66. Am. Chem. Soc. Fundamentals on properties and behavior of petroleum products; organic selenium antioxidants; combinations of activators with organic sulfur antioxidants; organic sulfide antioxidants; metal phenates as lubricating oil additives; fuel additives; radiation resistant oils. Address: Chevron Research Co, 576 Standard Ave, Richmond, CA 94802.

DENISON, J(ACK) THOMAS, b. Gainesville, Fla, Mar. 8, 26; div; m. 63; c. 1. PHYSICAL CHEMISTRY. B.S, California, Los Angeles, 48, Atomic Energy Cmn. Res. fel, 50-51, Ph.D.(chem), 51. Res. chemist, PLASTICS DEPT, E.I. DU PONT DE NEMOURS & CO, 51-57, res. supvr, 57-62, sr. res. supvr, 62-70, RES. ASSOC, 70- U.S.N.R, 43-46, Res, 46-54, Lt. Am. Chem. Soc; Sci. Res. Soc. Am; Soc. Plastics Eng. Thermodynamics of electrolytes in non-aqueous media; high polymers; high temperature chemistry; digital computation; process research in low and high pressure polyethylene synthesis. Address: 2141 Yupon Rd, Orange, TX 77630.

DENISON, JOHN SCOTT, b. Waco, Tex, June 18, 18; m. 41; c. 2. ELECTRICAL ENGINEERING. B.S.E.E, New Mexico State, 48; M.S.E.E, Agr. & Mech. Col, Texas, 49. Instr. ELEC. ENG, TEX. A&M UNIV, 49-51, asst. prof, 51-54, assoc. prof, 54-67, PROF. & EXEC. DIR. ELEC. POWER INST, 67-, acting head dept, 66-67. Consult, 51- U.S.A.A.F, 42-45, 1st Lt. Inst. Elec. & Electronics Eng. Electrical transmission and distribution. Address: Dept. of Electrical Engineering, Texas A&M University, College Station, TX 77843.

DENISON, M. C(ARL), b. Sheboygan, Wis, Apr. 23, 04; m. 45; c. 2. ORGANIC CHEMISTRY. B.A, Wisconsin, 28, M.A, 29; fel, Purdue, 37-39, Ph.D.(org. chem), 40. Instr. chem, Mich. Col. Min. & Tech, 29-36; res. chemist, E.I. du Pont de Nemours & Co, 39-62; assoc. prof. CHEM, Danbury State Col, 62-66, PROF, WEST. CONN. STATE COL, 66- Am. Chem. Soc. Dye intermediates; tetraethyl lead; nylon; preparation of nitroparaffins from high molecular weight aliphatics; application of statistical methods to chemical research; thermodynamics; physical chemistry. Address: Dept. of Chemistry, Western Connecticut State College, White St, Danbury, CT 06810.

DENISON, M(ATHEW) RICHARD, b. Philadelphia, Pa, July 11, 27; m. 51; c. 3. MECHANICAL ENGINEERING. B.S, Pennsylvania, 50; M.S, Harvard, 51. With Philco Corp, 51-52; I-T-E Circuit Breaker Co, 52-53; N.Am. Aviation, Inc, 53-55; Lockheed Aircraft Corp, 55-56; mgr. aerochem, Aeronutronic Div, Ford Motor Co, 56-61; gas dynamics, Electro-Optical Systs, Inc, 61-65; PROJ. MGR, RES. & TECHNOL. OPER, TRW SYSTS, 65- U.S.N.R, 45-46. AAAS; Am. Inst. Aeronaut. & Astronaut. Fluid mechanics; plasma physics; thermodynamics; heat transfer. Address: 519 Linden Dr, Beverly Hills, CA 90210.

DENISON, ROBERT H(OWLAND), b. Somerville, Mass, Nov. 9, 11; m. 40; c. 2. VERTEBRATE PALEONTOLOGY. A.B, Harvard, 33; A.M, Columbia, 34, Ph.D.(vert. paleont), 38. Asst. curator mus, Dartmouth Col, 37-47, instr. zool, 38-43, asst. prof, 43-47; paleontologist, Univ. Calif. African exped, 47-48; curator fossil fishes, FIELD MUS. NATURAL HIST, 48-70, RES. ASSOC, 71- Guggenheim fel, Europe, 53-54; lectr, Univ. Chicago, 65- Morrison Prize, 37. AAAS; Soc. Vert. Paleont.(secy-treas, 59-60, pres, 62-63); Am. Soc. Zool; Geol. Soc. Am; Paleont. Soc. Fossil fishes. Address: Field Museum of Natural History, Chicago, IL 60605.

DENISON, RODGER ESPY, b. Ft. Worth, Tex, Nov. 11, 32; m. 57; c. 2. GEOLOGY. B.S, Oklahoma, 54, M.S, 58; Ph.D, Univ. Tex, 66. Geologist, Okla. Geol. Surv, 58-61; Crustal Studies Lab, Tex, 62-64; MOBIL OIL CORP, 64-68, SR. RES. GEOLOGIST, MOBIL RES. & DEVELOP. CORP,

FIELD RES. LAB, 68- U.S.A, 55-57, 1st Lt. Am. Asn. Petrol. Geol; Geol. Soc. Am. Petrology and geochronology of basement rocks in southern mid-continent and their influence on later geologic history. Address: Field Research Lab, Mobil Research & Development Corp, Box 900, Dallas, TX 75221.

DENISON, RUTH C(ORBET), b. Brooklyn, N.Y, Aug. 29, 10; m. 45. CHEMISTRY. A.B, Okla. Col. Women, 31; A.M, Oberlin Col, 32; Ph.D, Pa. State Col, 37. Asst. chem, Oberlin Col, 36-37, Hall res. instr, 37-39; res. biochemist, biochem. res. found, Franklin Inst, 39-43; res. chemist, Houdry Process Corp, 43-47; res. assoc, Delaware, 50-52; spec. instr. & res. chemist, Chattanooga, 54-61; lit. chemist, Vitro Chem. Co, 61-62; Barden Corp, 63; applns. chemist, Perkin-Elmer Corp, 64-66; asst. prof. CHEM, WEST. CONN. STATE COL, 66-70, ASSOC. PROF, 70- Am. Chem. Soc. Catalysis; physiological buffers; calorimetry. Address: Dept. of Chemistry, Western Connecticut State College, Danbury, CT 60810.

DENISON, WILLIAM C(LARK), b. Rochester, N.Y, June 1, 28; m. 48; c. 4. BOTANY. A.B, Oberlin Col, 50, A.M, 52; Ph.D.(mycol), Cornell, 56. Asst. prof. bot, Swarthmore Col, 55-58; vis. asst. prof, North Carolina, 58-59; asst. prof. biol, Swarthmore Col, 59-66; assoc. prof. BOT. & CURATOR MYCOL. HERBARIUM, ORE. STATE UNIV, 66- Bot. Soc. Am; Am. Soc. Plant Taxon; Int. Asn. Plant Taxon. Mycology, especially Pezizales, fungi of Central America; general botany; biology of Stellaria. Address: 1610 Highland Way, Corvallis, OR 97330.

DENK, RONALD H, b. Buffalo, N.Y, Sept. 17, 37. ORGANIC CHEMISTRY. B.S, Canisius Col, 59; Nat. Insts. Health fel, Villanova, 60-61, M.S, 61; Ph.D.(chem), Va. Polytech, 67. Chemist, TEXACO, INC, 66-67, SR. CHEMIST, 67- Asst. prof. chem, Genesee Community Col, 70- Sci. Res. Soc. Am; Am. Chem. Soc. Synthesis of potential anticarcinogenic agents; mechanism of the thermal decomposition of 1-bromo-2-(1-naphthyl) naphthyl carbinol and related diarylcarbinols; Ziegler-Natta copolymerization of alpha-olefins. Address: 11 Forest Ave, Oakfield, NY 14152.

DENKEWALTER, ROBERT G(EORGE), b. Chicago, Ill, March 3, 18; m. 43; c. 5. ORGANIC CHEMISTRY. B.S, Loyola (Ill), 39; Ph.D.(chem), Chicago, 43; hon. D.Sc, Loyola Univ, 69. Chemist, Nat. Defense Res. Comt. proj, Chicago, 40-43; res. chemist, MERCK, SHARP & DOHME RES. LABS, 43-50, mgr. nat. prod. develop, 50-52, dir. process develop, 52-54, process res. & develop, 54-56, exec. dir. develop. res, 56-58, V.PRES. phys. sci, 58-63, explor. res, 63-69, DEVELOP. RES, 69- AAAS; Am. Inst. Chem; Am. Chem. Soc; Asn. Res. Dirs; Soc. Chem. Indust. Peptides and biological macromolecules. Address: Merck Sharp & Dohme Research Labs, Rahway, NJ 07065.

DENKO, CHARLES W, b. Cleveland, Ohio, Aug. 12, 16; m. 50; c. 3. BIOCHEMISTRY. B.S, Geneva Col, 38; M.S, Pa. State Col, 39, Ph.D.(physiol. chem), 43; M.D, Hopkins, 51. Asst. physiol. chem, Pa. State, 40-43; instr. biochem, sch. med, West Virginia, 43; res. chemist, res. lab, S.M.A, Corp, Ohio, 44-45; prof. chem, Geneva Col, 48; intern, Illinois, 51-52; res, dept. med, Chicago, 52-53, fel, 53-55, res. assoc, 55-56; instr. internal med, med. sch, Michigan, 56-57, asst. prof, 57-59; med, Ohio State Univ, 59-66, with div. rheumatic diseases, Univ. Hosp, 59-66, res. assoc, res. ctr, 66-70; DIR. RES, FAIRVIEW GEN. HOSP, 68-; ASST. PROF. CLIN. MED, SCH. MED, CASE WEST. RESERVE UNIV, 70- Sr. investr, Arthritis & Rheumatism Found. Distinguished Serv. award, Geneva Col, 69. Dipl, Am. Bd. Nutrit, 52. Sanit.C, U.S.A, 45-46, Med.C.Res, 47- AAAS; Am. Chem. Soc; Am. Med. Asn; Am. Inst. Chem; Am. Rheumatism Asn; Am. Soc. Clin. Pharmacol. & Therapeut; N.Y. Acad. Sci. Synthesis and biochemical effects of organic gold compounds; nutritional biochemistry; metabolism of connective tissue; clinical work in rheumatology; experimental arthritis and clinical pharmacology. Address: Scott Research Lab, Fairview General Hospital, 18101 Lorain Ave, Cleveland, OH 44111.

DENKO, JOHN V, b. Ellwood City, Pa, July 22, 23; m. 47; c. 3. PATHOLOGY. B.S, Chicago, 46, M.D, 47. Intern, St. Luke's Hosp, Chicago, 47-48, resident path, 48-49; instr. col. med, Illinois, 50-52; clin. instr. path, Washington(Seattle), 52-54; PATHOLOGIST & DIR. LABS, NORTH WEST TEXAS HOSP, 54- Deputy chief path, U.S. Pub. Health Serv. Hosp, Seattle, 52-54. Consult, Veterans Admin. Hosp, Amarillo, 54-; Ed. med. bulletin, Panhandle Dist. Med. Soc, 58-; pres, Amarillo Found. Health & Sci. Educ, Inc, 67- Diplomate, Am. Bd. Path, 52. U.S.N.R, 43-45; U.S. Pub. Health Serv, 52-54, Lt. Comdr. Fel. Am. Soc. Clin. Path; fel. Col. Am. Path; Am. Med. Asn; Am. Med. Writers' Asn; Soc. Nuclear Med. Clinical pathology and surgical diagnostic pathology. Address: 2507 Harmony, Amarillo, TX 79106.

DENMAN, EUGENE D(ALE), b. Farmington, Mo, Mar. 15, 28; m. 52; c. 2. ELECTRICAL ENGINEERING, PHYSICS. B.S, Washington (St. Louis), 51; Atomic Energy Comn. fel, Vanderbilt, 52-53, M.S, 55; D.Sc, Virginia, 63. Engr. electronic equip, Magnavox Co, 51-52; engr, Sperry Gyroscope Co, 54-56; sr. engr, Midwest Res. Inst, 56-60; Sr. physicist, res. labs. eng. sci, Virginia, 60-63; asst. prof. ELEC. ENG, Vanderbilt, 63-69, PROF, UNIV. HOUSTON, 69- Sig.C, U.S.A, 46-48. Inst. Elec. & Electronics Eng. Electromagnetic propagation, microwave tubes; radiological systems; system engineering; numerical methods in engineering; mathematical modeling. Address: Cullen College of Engineering, University of Houston, Houston, TX 77004.

DENMAN, HARRY H(ARROUN), b. Riverside, N.J, Jan. 7, 25; m. 50; c. 4. THEORETICAL PHYSICS. B.S, Drexel Inst. Tech, 48; M.S, Cincinnati, 50, Hanna fel, 51-52, Ph.D.(theoret. physics), 52. Mem. res. staff, digital comput. lab, Mass. Inst. Tech, 52-54; asst. prof. PHYSICS, WAYNE STATE UNIV, 54-60, assoc. prof, 60-70, PROF, 71- Summers, mem, Midwestern Univ. Res. Asn, 56, 58, 60, res. physicist, Ford Sci. Lab, 61, Ames Lab, Atomic Energy Cmn, 63. Consult, Avco Corp, 56; Gen. Elec. Co, 59; Ford Motor Co, 66-; ed, J. Indust. Math. Soc, 66-69. Sig.C. & U.S.A.A.F, 43-45. Am. Phys. Soc. Applied mathematics; digital computers; group theory. Address: Dept. of Physics, Wayne State University, Detroit, MI 48202.

DENMAN, WAYNE L(EONARD), b. Corvallis, Oregon, Jan. 28, 03; m. 35; c. 2. SANITARY & WATER CHEMISTRY. B.S, Oregon State Col, 25; M.S, Iowa, 27, Ph.D.(chem), 29. Res. chemist, Dearborn Chem. Co, 29-41, chief chemist, 41, 45-50, directing chemist, 50-68; consult, 68- C.W.S, U.S.A, 41-45. Am. Chem. Soc; Am. Soc. Mech. Eng. Inhibitors of foaming in boiler water; corrosion inhibition and boiler sludge conditioning. Address: 710 Washington Blvd, Oak Park, IL 60302.

DENMARK, HAROLD A(NDERSON), b. Lamont, Fla, July 3, 21; m. 47; c. 2. TAXONOMIC ENTOMOLOGY. B.S.A, Florida, 52, M.S, 53. Interim instr, Florida, 53; entomologist, STATE PLANT BD, FLA. DEPT. AGR. & CONSUMER SERV, 54-55, acting chief entomologist, 56-58; CHIEF ENTOMOLOGIST, 58- U.S.N, 41-47. Entom. Soc. Am. Phytoseudae. Address: 10930 N.W. 12th Pl, Gainesville, FL 32601.

DENN, MORTON M(ACE), b. Passaic, N.J, July 7, 39; m. 62; c. 3. CHEMICAL ENGINEERING. B.S.E, Princeton, 61; Procter & Gamble & Nat. Sci. Found. fels. & Ph.D.(chem. eng), Univ. Minn, 64. Fel. chem. eng, UNIV. DEL, 64-65, asst. prof. chem. eng. & comput. sci, 65-68, assoc. prof. CHEM. ENG, 68-71, PROF, 71- Guggenheim fel, 71-72. Soc. Rheol; Am. Inst. Chem. Eng. Non-Newtonian fluid mechanics; optimal design and control; stability theory. Address: Dept. of Chemical Engineering, University of Delaware, Newark, DE 19711.

DENNEMEYER, RENE F(ELIX), b. Calif, Sept. 27, 21; m. 51; c. 3. MATHEMATICS. B.A, California, Los Angeles, 48, M.A, 49, Ph.D.(math), 56. Sr. scientist, Lockheed Aircraft Corp, 53-56; sr. res. engr, atomics int. div, N.Am. Aviation Corp, 56-57; assoc. prof. math, Long Beach State Col, 57-64, Aerospace Corp, 64-66; PROF. MATH, CALIF. STATE COL, SAN BERNARDINO, 66- U.S.A.A.F, 42-46, Capt. Am. Math. Soc; Math. Asn. Am; Soc. Indust. & Appl. Math. Differential equations; boundary value problems; calculus of variations. Address: Dept. of Mathematics, California State College, San Bernardino, CA 92407.

DENNEN, DAVID W, b. Clarks Summit, Pa, Mar. 20, 32; m. 54; c. 3. BIOCHEMISTRY, MICROBIOLOGY. B.S, Mass. Inst. Tech, 54; M.S, Indiana, 64, Nat. Inst. Gen. Med. Sci. fel, 65-66, Ph.D.(microbiol), 66. Assoc. phys. chemist, res. labs, ELI LILLY & CO, 54-56, phys. chemist, 59-64, sr. microbiologist anal. develop, Greenfield Labs, 66-67, ANTIBIOTIC DEVELOP. DIV, 67-69, mgr, 69-71, DIR, 71- Chem.C, U.S.A, 56-59; Nat. Guard, 59-, Lt. Col. Am. Chem. Soc; Am. Soc. Microbiol. Reaction kinetics; control mechanisms in cellular systems; enzyme regulation during morphogenesis; biosynthesis of antibiotics. Address: Eli Lilly & Co, 740 S. Alabama St, Indianapolis, IN 46206.

DENNEN, WILLIAM H(ENRY), b. Gloucester, Mass, Apr. 8, 20; m. 44; c. 3. GEOLOGY, GEOCHEMISTRY. S.B, Mass. Inst. Tech, 42, Ph.D.(geol), 49. Instr. GEOL, Mass. Inst. Tech, 49-51, asst. prof, 51-58, assoc. prof, 58-67; PROF. & CHMN. DEPT, UNIV. KY, 67-, ACTING DEAN GRAD. SCH. & COORD. RES, 70- U.S.M.C, 42-46, Lt. Col. Geol. Soc. Am; Geochem. Soc. Applications of spectrography to petrological problems. Address: Dept. of Geology, University of Kentucky, Lexington, KY 40506.

DENNETT, ROBERT K(INGSLEY), b. Honolulu, Hawaii, Oct. 18, 21; m. 47; c. 6. GENETICS. B.S, Cornell, 48; M.S, Hawaii, 50; Ph.D.(genetics), Pa. State, 52. Asst. olericulturist, Hawaii, 48-50; asst, Pa. State, 50-52; hybridizer, Bodger Seeds Ltd, 53-59; mgr, Alpha Seeds, 59-62; AGRONOMIST, Hunt Foods & Indust, Inc, 62-68; PLANT BREEDER, PETO SEED CO, INC, 68- U.S.A, 42-45. Am. Soc. Hort. Sci; Am. Genetic Asn; Am. Soc. Agron; Soil Sci. Soc. Am. Genetics and breeding in tomato, zinnia and petunia plants. Address: 801 Ojai Rd, Santa Paula, CA 93060.

DENNEY, DONALD B(EREND), b. Seattle, Wash, April 3, 27; m. 56. ORGANIC CHEMISTRY. B.S, Washington (Seattle), 49; Rosenberg fel, California, 51-52, Ph.D.(chem), 52. Asst, California, 49-51; res. chemist, E.I. du Pont de Nemours & Co, 52-53; fel. Hickrill Chem. Res. Found, 53-54; instr. CHEM, Yale, 54-55; asst. prof. RUTGERS UNIV, 55-58, assoc. prof, 58-62, PROF, 62- U.S. Coast Guard, 45-46. Am. Chem. Soc. Organic reaction mechanisms; organo phosphorus compounds. Address: School of Chemistry, Rutgers University, New Brunswick, NJ 08903.

DENNEY, DONALD D(UANE), b. Boone, Iowa, Nov. 30, 30; m; c. 3. PSYCHIATRY. B.A, Willamette, 53; M.S. & M.D, Oregon, 57. Resident PSYCHIAT, MED. SCH, UNIV. ORE, 59-62, instr, 62-63, asst. prof, 63-68, resident, internal med, 68-70, ASSOC. PROF, 70- U.S. Pub. Health Serv. career teachers' award, 62-64, career develop. award, 64-68. Am. Psychiat. Asn. Neurophysiology; psychiatric consultation in internal medicine. Address: Dept. of Psychiatry, University of Oregon Medical School, Portland, OR 97201.

DENNEY, DONALD J(OHN), b. Phila, Pa, Dec. 7, 20; m. 56; c. 3. PHYSICAL CHEMISTRY. B.S, Pennsylvania, 50, Nat. Sci. Found. fel, 52-54; Ph.D. (chem), Brown, 54. Res. chemist, E.I. du Pont de Nemours & Co, 54-55; res. assoc, Brown, 55-57; asst. prof. CHEM, HAMILTON COL, 57-61, assoc. prof, 61-68, PROF, 68- U.S.A, 43-46. Am. Chem. Soc; Am. Phys. Soc. Dielectric and flow properties of liquids. Address: Dept. of Chemistry, Hamilton College, Clinton, NY 13323.

DENNEY, JOSEPH M(YERS), b. Auburn, Wash, May 25, 27; m. 50; c. 3. PHYSICS, METALLURGY. B.S, Calif. Inst. Tech, 51, M.S, 52, Murray scholar. & Ph.D.(metall, physics), 54. Res. engr. solid state physics, Atomics Int, 52-54; res. assoc. phys. metall, Gen. Elec. Res. Lab, 55-57; res. fel, Calif. Inst. Tech, 57-59, dir. solid state physics lab, TRW Space Tech. Labs, 59-69; PRES, DIGITAL DEVELOP. CORP, SAN DIEGO, 69- Head radiation effects, Hughes Res. Labs, 58-59; consult, Nat. Acad. Sci, Wash, D.C, 70. Head radiation effects, Hughes Res. Labs, 58-59; consult, Nat. Acad. Sci, Wash, D.C, 70. U.S.N.R, 45-46. Assoc. fel. Am. Inst. Aeronaut. & Astronaut; sr. mem. Inst. Elec. & Electronics Eng; Sci. Res. Soc. Am. Radiation effects in solids; alloy theory; physics of semiconductors; space environment; satellite and spacecraft design and development; electronics. Address: 408 Via Almar, Palos Verdes Estates, CA 90274.

DENNEY, LOREN L, Sci. Educ, see 4th ed, Leaders in Education.

DENNING, DONALD G, b. Winton, Minn, Dec. 18, 10; m. 41; c. 1. ENTOMOLOGY. B.S, Macalester Col, hon. D.Sc, 53; M.S, Minnesota, 37, Ph.D. (entom), 41. Asst. entom, Minnesota, 33-38; jr. prfnl. asst, bur. entom, U.S. Dept. Agr, 39, sr. field asst, 39-42; asst. prof. entom, Wyoming, 46-50; ENTOMOLOGIST, Velsicol Corp, 50-56; CHEMAGRO CORP, 56- U.S.P.H.S, 42-46, Capt. Fel. Entom. Soc. Am. Taxonomy and biology of the Trichoptera; economic entomology and control methods; control of livestock insects; insects of public health importance; Hydropsychidae of Minnesota. Address: Chemagro Corp, 2828 Telegraph Ave, Berkeley, CA 94705.

DENNING, GEORGE SMITH, JR, b. Chicago, Ill, Dec. 4, 31; m. 55; c. 4. ORGANIC CHEMISTRY. B.S, Washington & Lee, 54; Ph.D.(org. chem), Cornell, 60. Res. assoc. biochem, med. col, Cornell, 60-61, instr, 61-62; RES. ASSOC. PEPTIDE CHEM, NORWICH PHARMACAL CO, 62- Scholar, Dept. Biol. Chem, Sch. Med, Univ. Calif, Los Angeles, 69-70. AAAS; Am. Chem. Soc; Brit. Chem. Soc. Chemistry of amino acids and peptides; organic synthesis; method development for drug analysis. Address: 158 N. Broad St, Norwich, NY 13815.

DENNING, JACK, b. San Francisco, Calif, Apr. 19, 23; m. 58; c. 1. BIOLOGY, ZOOLOGY. B.S, Washington (St. Louis), 51; M.S, Kans. State Teachers Col, 62; grant, Michigan, 63; Ill. Inst. Tech, 63; summer Hawaii, 64; Argonne Nat. Lab, 64. Teacher, pub. schs, Calif, 51-55; ed. specialist, U.S. Air Force, 55-57; teacher, pub. schs, Alaska, 57-60; asst. prof, BIOL, Mundelein Col, 63-68; PROF, CITY COLS. CHICAGO, Southeast Campus, 68-70, OLIVE-HARVEY COL, 70- Atomic Energy Comn-Nat. Sci. Found. summer grant, Argonne Nat. Lab, 65; Austrian Govt. grant, res, Waidhofen-Ybbs, Austria, summer 71. U.S.A.A.F, 42-46, M/Sgt. Am. Soc. Zool; Nat. Sci. Teachers Asn; Nat. Asn. Biol. Teachers. Radioisotopes and their effects on freshwater and marine invertebrates. Address: Dept. of Biology, Olive-Harvey College, Chicago City Colleges, 10001 S. Woodlawn, Chicago, IL 60628.

DENNING, PETER JAMES, b. N.Y.C, Jan. 6, 42; m. 64; c. 2. ELECTRICAL ENGINEERING, COMPUTER SCIENCE. B.E.E, Manhattan Col, 64; Nat. Sci. Found. fel, Mass. Inst. Tech, 64-66, M.S, 65, Nat. Sci. Found. traineeship, 66-67, Ph.D.(elec. eng), 68. ASST. PROF. ELEC. ENG. & COMPUTER SCI, PRINCETON, 68- Adv, off. comput. activities, Nat. Sci. Found. Asn. Comput. Mach.(best paper award, 70); N.Y. Acad. Sci; Inst. Elec. & Electronics Eng. Computer system design; organization, analysis, and modelling; dynamic allocation of computer resources. Address: Dept. of Electrical Engineering, Princeton University, Princeton, NJ 08540.

DENNIS, BERNARD K, b. New Holland, Ohio, July 7, 22; m. 51; c. 2. MATHEMATICS, PHYSICAL SCIENCE. B.S. & M.Ed, Cincinnati, 50. Teacher, St. Bernard High Sch, Ohio, 50-52; exec. asst, Fiberglass Contract & Supply Co, 52-53; specialist tech. commun, flight propulsion div, Gen. Elec. Co, 54-57, mgr. tech. info. ctr, 57-64; asst. dir. info. syst. res, BATTELLE MEM. INST, 64-65, assoc. dir. info. systs. eng, 65-67, assoc. chief, 67-70, DIR. INFO. SYSTS, WASH. D.C. OPERS, 70- U.S.A.A.F, 41-45, T/Sgt. AAAS; Spec. Libr. Asn; Am. Soc. Info. Sci. Technical information management; information center design, development and operation; information systems; automated information retrieval systems research, design development and operation. Address: Battelle Memorial Institute, 1755 Massachusetts Ave. N.W, Washington, DC 20036.

DENNIS, CLARENCE, b. St. Paul, Minn, June 16, 09; m. 39; c. 4. SURGERY, PHYSIOLOGY. B.S, Harvard, 31; M.D, Hopkins, 35; M.S, Minnesota, 38, Ph.D.(surg, physiol), 40. Instr. physiol, Minnesota, 38-39, from instr. to PROF. SURG, STATE UNIV. N.Y. DOWNSTATE MED. CTR, 40-, chmn. dept, 54- Dir. surg, univ. div, Kings County Hosp, 51-56, chief surg, 56-67, surgeon-in-chief, 67-; Univ. Hosp, 67- Mem. surg. study sect, Nat. Insts. Health, 62-66. Soc. Univ. Surg.(secy, 50-52); Am. Surg. Asn.(v.pres, 71-72); Soc. Clin. Surg; Soc. Exp. Biol. & Med; Am. Col. Surg; Am. Asn. Thoracic Surg; Soc. Vascular Surg.(pres, 65-66); Am. Asn. Surg. of Trauma; Int. Cardiovasc. Soc; Soc. Surg. Alimentary Tract; Am. Soc. Artificial Internal Organs (past pres); Int. Surg. Soc. Mechanical support in acute heart failure; gastrointestinal physiology. Address: Dept. of Surgery, State University of New York Downstate Medical Center, 450 Clarkson Ave, Brooklyn, NY 11203.

DENNIS, CLIFFORD J(OHN), b. Payette, Idaho, Aug. 11, 25; m. 46; c. 8. ENTOMOLOGY. B.S, Iowa State, 48, M.S, 49; Ph.D, Wisconsin, 51; B.A, E.Cent. State Col, 64. Instr. BIOL, Middle Tenn. State Col, 51-53; assoc. prof, E.Cent. State Col, 53-64; PROF, WIS. STATE UNIV-WHITEWATER, 64- U.S.N.R, 43-46, Res, 46-64, Lt. Soc. Syst. Zool; Am. Entom. Soc. Membracidae; social biology. Address: Dept. of Biology, Wisconsin State University-Whitewater, Whitewater, WI 53190.

DENNIS, DANIEL L, b. Chicago, Ill, Feb. 26, 32; m. 60; c. 3. SURGERY. B.S, Oregon, 56, M.S. & M.D, 58. Res. surg, MED. SCH, UNIV. ORE, 60-63, 64-65, instr. gen. surg, 65-67, asst. prof. surg, 67-69, ASSOC. PROF, 69-, PROG. DIR. GEN. CLIN. RES. CTR, 66- Clin. fel, Am. Cancer Soc, 63-64, adv. clin. fel, 65-68. Am. Col. Surg; Asn. Acad. Surg; N.Y. Acad. Sci. Cancer and cancer chemotherapy; metabolic and endocrine response to surgery; metabolic and hemodynamic responses to shock. Address: University of Oregon Medical School, 3181 S.W. Sam Jackson Park Rd, Portland, OR 97201.

DENNIS, DAVID THOMAS, b. Preston, Eng, Nov. 2, 36; m. 60; c. 2. PLANT BIOCHEMISTRY & PHYSIOLOGY. B.Sc, Univ. Leeds, 59, Ph.D.(biophys), 62. Fel, biosci. div, Nat. Res. Coun. Can, 62-63; fel. chem, Univ. Calif, Los Angeles, 63-65; scientist, Unilever Res. Inst, Colworth House, Eng, 65-68; ASSOC. PROF. PLANT PHYSIOL, QUEEN'S UNIV.(ONT), 68- Am. Chem. Soc; Can. Biochem. Soc; Can. Soc. Plant Physiol; Am. Soc. Plant Physiol; Am. Soc. Biol. Chem; Brit. Soc. Exp. Biol. Regulation of metabolism in plants; extraction, purification and kinetics of plant enzymes; mechanism of action and biosynthesis of plant hormones. Address: Dept. of Biology, Queen's University, Kingston, Ont, Can.

DENNIS, DON, b. Baltimore, Md, Feb. 22, 30; m. 49; c. 4. BIOCHEMISTRY. B.S, Maryland, 52; Nat. Insts. Health fel, Hopkins; Nat. Insts. Health fel. & Ph.D.(biochem), Brandeis, 59. Biologist pharmacol. Nat. Cancer Inst, 52-

55, Nat. Insts. Health fel. & biochemist org. chem, Harvard, 59-61; asst. prof. CHEM, UNIV. DEL, 61-70, ASSOC. PROF, 70- Enzymology; mechanism of enzyme action. Address: Dept. of Chemistry, University of Delaware, Newark, DE 19711.

DENNIS, EARL A(UBREY), b. Bloomdale, Ohio, June 9, 02; m. 28; c. 1. ZOOLOGY. A.B, Col. of Wooster, 25; Ph.D.(zool), Chicago, 34. Teacher, high sch, Ohio, 26-27; instr. biol, Tusculum Col, 27-28; Allegheny Col, 28-31; asst. zool, Chicago, 31-34; asst. prof. biol, Am. Univ, 35-39, assoc. prof, 39-42, prof, 42-46, dean col. arts & sci, 44-45; adv. sci. & tech, div. exchange persons, U.S. Dept. State, 46-47, head prof. & specialists br, div. int. exchange persons, 47-48, acting asst. chief div, 48, pub. affairs off. & attche, U.S. Embassy, N.Z, 49-51, chief, Brit. Commonwealth & N.Europ. Br, Int. Info. Admin, 51-53, pub. affairs off, U.S. Embassy, Denmark, 53-56; chief, study prog. div. int. ed, exchange serv, State Dept, 56-59; pub. affairs off, Am. Embassy, Sweden, 59-64; U.S. Info. Agency, 64-67; chief, fel. br, Inst. Int. Studies, U.S. Off. Educ, 67-69; RETIRED. Instr, U.S. Army Univ, France, 45-46; chmn. bd. dirs, U.S. Educ. Found, N.Z, 49-51; chmn, Denmark, 53-56. Experimental embryology and developmental physiology in birds and reptiles, particularly in relation to the sex hormones. Address: 4838 Butterworth Pl. N.W, Washington, DC 20016.

DENNIS, EDWARD A, b. Chicago, Ill, Aug. 10, 41; m. 69. BIOCHEMISTRY, PHYSICAL ORGANIC CHEMISTRY. B.A, Yale, 63; Nat. Insts. Health fel, Harvard, 63-67, M.A, 65, Ph.D.(chem), 68. Nat. Insts. Health res. fel, Harvard Med. Sch, 67-69; ASST. PROF. CHEM, UNIV. CALIF, SAN DIEGO, 70- Am. Chem. Soc. Detailed mechanism of enzyme catalysis; nuclear magnetic resonance studies of phospholipids and membrane structure; enzymes of phospholipid biosynthesis; phospholipid biosynthesis; mechanism of organo-phosphorus reactions and phosphate ester hydrolysis, pseudo-rotation. Address: Dept. of Chemistry, University of California, San Diego, La Jolla, CA 92037.

DENNIS, EDWARD WIMBERLY, b. Macon, Ga, July 31, 23; m. 48; c. 4. INTERNAL MEDICINE. B.S, Emory, 46, Life Ins. Res. Found. fel, 46-48, M.D, 49. Intern & res. internal med, Michigan, 49-52; jr. instr. med, COL. MED, BAYLOR UNIV, 53-54, from asst. prof. to assoc. prof, internal med, 54-67, PROF. MED, 67- Consult, Vet. Admin. Hosp; Texas Children's Hosp; dir. circulatory dynamics & electrocardiogram labs, Methodist Hosp; asst. attend. physician, Ben. Taub Hosp. Dipl, Am. Bd. Internal Med. Fel. Am. Heart Asn; fel. Am. Col. Cardiol; Am. Col. Physicians; Am. Fedn. Clin. Res. Cardiology; hypertension. Address: Methodist Hospital, 6516 Bertner Ave, Houston, TX 77025.

DENNIS, E(MERY) WESTERVELT, b. Oklahoma City, Okla, Dec. 19, 05; m. 31; c. 2. BACTERIOLOGY, PARASITOLOGY, CHEMOTHERAPY. A.B, Okla. City Univ, 27; A.M, California, 29, Ph.D.(protozool, bact), 31. Teaching fel, California, 27-30, assoc, California, Los Angeles, 30-31; adj. prof. bact, sch. med, Am. Univ. Beirut, 31-35, assoc. prof, 35-42, prof, 42-45, chmn. depts. bact. & parasitol, 31-46; assoc. dir. biol. res, STERLING-WINTHROP RES. INST, 46-50, DIR. BIOL. DIV, 50-71, CONSULT, 71- Rockefeller Found. fel, Harvard Med. Sch, 34-35; Medaille d'Honneur Merite Libanaise, 43. Consult, Brit. & French forces, 39-45. AAAS; Soc. Exp. Biol. & Med; Am. Soc. Trop. Med. & Hyg; Am. Soc. Microbiol; Am. Asn. Immunol; Am. Soc. Pharmacol; Brazilian Soc. Trop. Med; Royal Soc. Trop. Med. & Hyg. Piroplasmosis; life cycle of Babesia; bacterial toxins in blood dyscrasias; immunization against echinococcus; mechanism of invasion of streptococci; typhoid toxin and leukocidin; rickettsioses; malaria; tuberculosis; amebiasis; schistosomiasis. Address: 75 Willett St, Albany, NY 12210.

DENNIS, FOSTER L(EROY), b. West Milton, Pa, Jan. 1, 10; m. 38; c. 3. GEOMETRY. B.S, Ursinus Col, 31; M.S, Cornell, 32; Ph.D.(geometry), Illinois, 38. Teacher high sch, 33-34; instr. MATH, Ursinus Col, 34-35; asst, Illinois, 35-38; PROF, URSINUS COL, 38- Prof, exten. div, Pa. State, 41-43; State Dept. Pub. Instruction, Pa, 47-48; summers, res, Philco Corp, 55-58, consult, 58- Math. Asn. Am. Geometric properties of algebraic correspondences. Address: Dept. of Mathematics, Ursinus College, Collegeville, PA 19426.

DENNIS, FRANK G(EORGE), JR, b. Lyons, N.Y, Apr. 12, 32; m. 54. POMOLOGY, PLANT PHYSIOLOGY. B.S, Cornell, 55, Ph.D.(pomol), 61. Nat. Sci. Found. fel, 61-62; asst. prof. pomol, N.Y. State Agr. Exp. Sta, Cornell, 62-68; ASSOC. PROF, DEPT. HORT, MICH. STATE UNIV, 68- Am. Soc. Hort. Sci; Am. Soc. Plant Physiol. Fruit set and development; dormancy; flowering; plant growth substances; cold hardiness. Address: Dept. of Horticulture, Michigan State University, East Lansing, MI 48823.

DENNIS, JACK BONNELL, b. Elizabeth, N.J, Oct. 13, 31; m. 56; c. 1. COMPUTER SCIENCE. S.B. & S.M, Mass. Inst. Tech, 54, Sc.D.(elec. eng), 58. Asst. ELEC. ENG, MASS. INST. TECHNOL, 54-58, instr, 58-59, asst. prof, 59-65, assoc. prof, 65-69, PROF, 69- Inst. Elec. & Electronics Eng; Asn. Comput. Mach. Design and programming problems in general purpose multiprogrammed computation systems. Address: Dept. of Electrical Engineering, Massachusetts Institute of Technology, Cambridge, MA 02139.

DENNIS, JOE, b. Sherman, Texas, Dec. 5, 11; m. 35; c. 3. BIOLOGICAL CHEMISTRY. A.B, Austin Col, 33; A.M, Texas, 37, Ph.D.(biol. chem), 42; hon. D.Sc, Austin Col, 65. Tutor biol. chem, sch. med, Texas, 34-36, instr, 36-38; CHEM, TEX. TECH UNIV, 38-41, asst. prof, 41-45, assoc. prof, 45-47, PROF, 47-, head dept, 50-69. AAAS; Am. Chem. Soc; Am. Inst. Chem. Protein denaturation; blood potassium and calcium. Address: Dept. of Chemistry, Texas Tech University, Lubbock, TX 79409.

DENNIS, JOHN EMORY, JR, b. Coral Gables, Fla, Sept. 24, 39; m. 60; c. 7. MATHEMATICS. B.S, Miami (Fla), 62, M.S, 64; Nat. Sci. Found. summer fel, Utah, 65, NASA trainee, 65-66, Ph.D.(math), 66. Asst. prof. MATH, Univ. Utah, 66-68; COL. ENG, CORNELL UNIV, 68-69, ASSOC. PROF, 69- Am. Math. Soc; Soc. Indust. & Appl. Math. Numerical analysis. Address: Dept. of Computer Science, College of Engineering, Cornell University, Ithaca, NY 14850.

DENNIS, JOHN G(ORDON), b. Berlin, Germany, June 28, 20. GEOLOGY. B.S, London, 48; scholar, Neuchatel, 49-50; M.A, Columbia, 56, Ph.D.(geol), 57. Geologist, Mines Develop. Syndicate, Nigeria, 48-49; mining geologist, S.W. Africa Co, 50-52; consult, 52-53; asst. GEOL, Columbia, 53-56; asst. prof, Tex. Tech. Col, 56-62; from asst. prof. to ASSOC. PROF, CALIF. STATE COL. LONG BEACH, 62- Geologist, Vt. Geol. Surv, 54-59; Nat. Sci Found. grant, 62-65. British Army, 40-46. Geol. Soc. Am; Am. Geophys. Union; Am. Asn. Petrol. Geol; Geol. Asn. Can; Geol. Soc. London. Structural geology; structural control of ore deposits; tectonics. Address: Dept. of Geology, California State College, Long Beach, CA 90801.

DENNIS, KENT S(EDDENS), b. New Eagle, Pa, June 25, 28. PHYSICAL CHEMISTRY. B.S, Grove City Col, 50; M.S, Western Reserve, 53, Ph.D. (phys. chem), 54. Res. assoc, Western Reserve, 51-54; phys. chemist, DOW CHEM. CO, 54-62, proj. leader, 62-65, SR. RES. CHEMIST, 65- U.S.A, 54-56. Am. Chem. Soc; Sci. Res. Soc. Am; fel. Am. Inst. Chem. Polymer chemistry; anionic polymerization; polymer coatings and research; polymer characterization. Address: 5800 Highland Dr, Midland, MI 48640.

DENNIS, MARY, b. Toledo, Ohio, June 11, 26. INORGANIC CHEMISTRY. B.A, Madonna Col, 55; M.S. Creighton, 59; Ph.D.(chem), Notre Dame, 62. INSTR. CHEM, MADONNA COL, 62- Am. Chem. Soc. Coordination compounds. Address: Dept. of Chemistry, Madonna College, Livonia, MI 48150.

DENNIS, N(ORMAN) M(cLEOD), b. Ga, Dec. 13, 22; m. 54; c. 2. CHEMISTRY. B.S.A, Florida, 46, M.S.A, 48; Kans. State Col. Asst. pest control, Florida, 46-48; entomologist, bur. entomol. & plant quarantine, U.S. DEPT. AGR, 48-53, entomol. res. br, AGR. MKT. SERV, AGR. RES. SERV, 53-54, mkt. res. div, biol. sci. br, 54-64, MKT. QUAL. RES. DIV, 64-69, CHEMIST, STORED-PROD. INSECTS RES. & DEVELOP. LAB, 69- U.S.A, 43-45. AAAS; Am. Chem. Soc; Am. Entom. Soc. Gas chromatography; stored plant pests; pest control; biochemistry; radioactive tracers; insecticide residue analysis. Address: P.O. Box 5125, Savannah, GA 31403.

DENNIS, PATRICK P, b. Minneapolis, Minn, Nov. 19, 42; m. 69. GENETICS, MOLECULAR BIOLOGY. B.S, Wis. State, Eau Claire, 65; Ph.D.(genetics), Minnesota, 69. Res. fel, Roswell Park Mem. Inst, 69-71; RES. ASSOC, UNIV. TEX, DALLAS, 71- AAAS; Am. Soc. Microbiol. Regulation of ribonucleic acid synthesis; relationships between stable RNA synthesis, chromosome replication and the cell division cycle in Escherichia coli B/r; in vivo and in vitro activity of RNA polymerase. Address: University of Texas at Dallas, P.O. Box 30365, Dallas, TX 75230.

DENNIS, P(HILIP) E(LDON), b. Spring Glen, Utah, Jan. 17, 05; m. 42; c. 3. GEOLOGY. A.B, Brigham Young, 29, A.M, 31; Stanford, 31-35. Instr. geol, Brigham Young, 35-39; jr. geologist, ground water div, U.S. Geol. Surv, 39-42, asst. geologist, 42-46, geologist, 46-63, dist. geologist, 53-63, reports specialist, water resources div, 63-67; assoc. prof. geol, Angelo State Col, 67-68; CONSULT. HYDROGEOL, 68- Assoc. prof, Tex. Tech. Col, 46-53. Ground-water geologist, food & agr. orgn. of U.N, Mission to Iraq, 52-53, South. Rhodesia, 59, Afghanistan, 61; UNESCO hydrogeologist, Cent. Arid Zone Res. Inst, Jodhpur, India, 65. Ground water provinces of Southern Rhodesia; areal geology of Escalante Valley, Payant Valley, San Bernardino Mountains; ground water hydrology; geological history of Red River Valley of the North. Address: 2613 Yale Ave, San Angelo, TX 76901.

DENNIS, RICHARD, b. Boston, Mass, July 6, 20; m. 43; c. 5. CHEMICAL & SANITARY ENGINEERING. B.S, Northeastern, 43; M.S, Harvard, 47, fel, 49-53. Engr. INDUST. HYG, Employers Liability Ins. Corp, 46; Kennecott Copper Corp, 47-49; res. assoc, Harvard, 53-56, asst. prof, 56-64; prin. engr, aerosol physics dept, GCA Corp, 64-66; dir. res. aerosol sci, Cambridge Technol, Inc, 66-67; dept. mgr, TECHNOL. DIV, GCA CORP, 67-68, DIR. POLLUTION CONTROL LAB, 68- Assoc. prof, Harvard Sch. Pub. Health; lectr, U.S. Atomic Energy Comn, Iowa State, 52, Harvard, 57; U.S. Pub. Health Serv, Ohio, 57; Mass. Dept. Pub. Health, 58; Trudeau Sch. Tuberc, N.Y, 59; Northeast. Univ. U.S.N.R, 43-46, Lt.(jg). Am. Chem. Soc; Am. Indust. Hyg. Asn; Air Pollution Control Asn; Am. Ord. Asn. Military applications; industrial hygiene engineering; air pollution control, sampling techniques; design and evaluation of dust and fume collectors; aerosol technology and dessemination. Address: Technology Division, GCA Corp, Burlington Rd, Bedford, MA 01730.

DENNIS, ROBERT E, b. Adrian, Mich, Oct. 15, 20; m. 48; c. 3. AGRONOMY. B.S, Mich. State, 42, M.S, 53, Ph.D.(plant sci), 58. Teacher, pub. schs, Mich, 46-51; instr. agron, Mich. State, 51-59; PROF. AGRON. & EXTEN. AGRONOMIST, UNIV. ARIZ, 59- Consult, Bank Mex, 66; Oak Ridge Nat. Lab, Tenn, 67-71. U.S.A, 42-46, 1st Lt. Am. Soc. Agron; Am. Soc. Sugar Beet Technol; Weed Sci. Soc. Am. Production of agronomic plants in an irrigated desert environment. Address: Dept. of Agronomy & Plant Genetics, University of Arizona, Tucson, AZ 85721.

DENNIS, TOM ROSS, b. Macon, Ga, Jan. 17, 42; m. 69. ASTRONOMY. B.A, Univ. Mich, 63; Ph.D.(astrophys), Princeton, 70. ASST. PROF. ASTRON, MT. HOLYOKE COL, 70- Am. Astron. Soc. Observational work in optical astronomy; stellar radial velocities. Address: Williston Observatory, Mt. Holyoke College, South Hadley, MA 01075.

DENNIS, WARD B, b. Detroit Lakes, Minn, Aug. 28, 22; m. 48; c. 2. AERONAUTICAL ENGINEERING. B.S, Minnesota, 43; M.S, Michigan, 47; Hopkins. Develop. engr, Cornell Aeronaut. Lab, N.Y, 45-46; prof. aeronaut, U.S. Naval Postgrad. Sch, 47-50; opers. anal. engr, Rand Corp, 50-53; asst. chief weapons systs. anal, NORTHROP CORP, 53-58, corporate dir. develop. planning, 58-63, V.PRES, 63- Address: Northrop Corp, 1800 Century Park East, Century City, Los Angeles, CA 90067.

DENNIS, W(ARREN) B(REED), JR, b. Lynn, Mass, Mar. 4, 08; m. 31, 56; c. 3. ORGANIC CHEMISTRY. B.Chem, Cornell, 31. Res. chemist. cosmetics, Sales Affiliates, Inc, 31-37, 40-41; chief chemist, pharmaceuts, Amalgamated Drug & Cosmetic Co, Ltd, Australia, 37-38; Australian Cream Tartar Co, Ltd, 38-40; DIR, toiletries res. & develop, Shulton, Inc, 42-57;

PROD. DEVELOP. COSMETICS, COOPER LABS, INC, WAYNE, 58- Am. Chem. Soc; Soc. Cosmetic Chem.(pres, 62). Cosmetic research and product development. Address: 101 Thackeray Rd, Oakland, NJ 07436.

DENNIS, WARREN HOWARD, b. Louisville, Ky, Aug. 15, 25; m. 51; c. 5. PHYSIOLOGY, BIOPHYSICS. B.Ch.E, Louisville, 47, M.S, 55, Ph.D.(phys. chem, biophys), 59. Lectr. med. math, Louisville, 53-59, instr. community health, 59-61, asst. prof. PHYSIOL, 61-62, assoc. prof, 63-64; ASSOC. PROF. PHYSIOL, UNIV. WIS, MADISON, 64- Estab. investr, Am. Heart Asn, 61-66. AAAS; Am. Physiol. Soc; Biophys. Soc; Biomet. Soc. Electrophysiology of ion transporting systems with emphasis on gastric secretion; chemical biomedical engineering applications to mass transfer systems. Address: Dept. of Physiology, Service Memorial Institute, University of Wisconsin, Madison, WI 53706.

DENNIS, WILLIAM ERIC, b. Sunderland, U.K, Oct. 4, 26; m. 50; c. 2. METALLURGY, PHYSICAL CHEMISTRY. B.Sc, Durham, 49; Carnegie Inst. Tech, 49-50; Ph.D.(metall), Imp. Col, London, 53. Sr. sci. officer, Brit. Ministry Supply, 53-55; chief metallurgist, Atomic Energy Div, Gen. Elec. Co, 55-58; asst. gen. mgr, Redbourn Works, Richard Thomas & Baldwins, 58-60, dep. gen. mgr, 60-63, head develop. opers, head off, 63-66; asst. res. dir. PROCESS RES, JONES & LAUGHLIN STEEL CORP, 66-69, DIR. RES, 69- Inst. Min, Metall. & Petrol. Eng; fel. Brit. Inst. Metall; Brit. Iron & Steel Inst. Atomic energy; steel production and research management. Address: Jones & Laughlin Steel Corp, Graham Research Lab, 900 Agnew Rd, Pittsburgh, PA 15230

DENNISON, BYRON LEE, b. Clarksburg, W.Va, Dec. 8, 30; m. 54; c. 2. ELECTRICAL ENGINEERING. B.S.E.E, West Virginia, 53; M.S.E.E, Va. Polytech, 62; Nat. Sci. Found. summer fels, Worcester Polytech, 62-64, Ph.D.(elec. eng), 67. Sr. elec. engr, govt. & indust. div, Philco Corp, 53-58; assoc. prof. ELEC. ENG, Va. Polytech. Inst, 58-66; PROF, LOWELL TECHNOL. INST, 66-, HEAD DEPT, 68-, acting head dept, 67-68. Consult, Polysci. Corp, 62-63; mem, Simulation Coun, Inc, 64- Inst. Elec. & Electronics Eng; Am. Soc. Eng. Educ. The application of control system theory and simulation techniques to the study of biological systems, particularly to the study of the pupillary control system. Address: Dept. of Electrical Engineering, Lowell Technological Institute, Lowell, MA 01854.

DENNISON, CLIFFORD C, b. Riffle, W.Va, Mar. 26, 22; m. 42; c. 5. ZOOLOGY. B.A, Marshall Col, 52; Nat. Sci. Found. summer fel, Univ. N.C, 57; Nat. Sci. Found. summer fel, Marshall Univ, 59-61, M.A, 61; Nat. Defense Educ. Act fel, Univ. Fla, 62-64, Ed.D.(biol. curriculum & develop), 69; Nat. Sci. Found. summer fel, Univ. Mich, 65. Teacher biol, Lee Col.(Tenn), 55-61; ASSOC. PROF. LIFE & PHYS. SCI, Monroe Community Col, 64-65; LEE COL.(TENN), 65- U.S.A.A.F, 41-45, T/Sgt. AAAS; Am. Inst. Biol. Sci. Comparative evaluation of two approaches to teaching physical science materials to junior high school students. Address: Lee College, Cleveland, TN 37311.

DENNISON, DAVID M(ATHIAS), b. Oberlin, Ohio, Apr. 26, 00; m. 24; c. 2. PHYSICS. A.B, Swarthmore Col, 21, hon. D.Sc, 50; Ph.D.(physics), Michigan, 24. Int. Ed. Bd. fel, 24-26; instr, UNIV. MICH, 27-28, asst. prof, 28-30, assoc. prof, PHYSICS, 30-35, prof, 35-66, chmn. dept, 55-65, Harrison M.Randall univ. prof, 66-70, EMER. PROF, 70- Guggenheim fel, Calif. Inst. Tech, 40; Russel lectr, 52. Distinguished Faculty Achievement award, 63. With Off. Sci. Res. & Develop; U.S.N, 44. Nat. Acad. Sci; fel. Am. Phys. Soc. Molecular structure. Address: 2511 Hawthorn Rd, Ann Arbor, MI 48104.

DENNISON, DAVID S(EVERIN), b. Ann Arbor, Mich, Mar. 19, 32; m. 54; c. 2. BIOPHYSICS. B.A, Swarthmore Col, 54; Ph.D.(biophysics), Calif. Inst. Tech, 58. Asst, Calif. Inst. Tech, 54-58; instr. zool, DARTMOUTH COL, 58-60, asst. prof, 60-64, assoc. prof, 64-70, PROF, 70- Nat. Sci. Found. sci. faculty fel, 64; Nat. Insts. Health spec. res. fel, 69. Biophys. Soc. Photobiology; analysis of photoresponses of phycomyces sporangiophores. Address: Dept. of Biological Sciences, Dartmouth College, Hanover, NH 03755.

DENNISON, EDWIN W(ALTER), b. Ann Arbor, Mich, Mar. 22, 28; m. 50; c. 2. ASTRONOMY. B.A, Swarthmore Col, 49; Fulbright & Dutch Govt. fels, Utrecht, 49-50; Ph.D.(astron), Michigan, 54. Solar physicist, Sacramento Peak Observ, 54-63; MEM. STAFF & HEAD, ASTRO-ELECTRONICS LAB, HALE OBSERVS, 63- U.S.A.F, 56-59, 1st Lt. Am. Astron. Soc. Astronomical photometry; photographic and photoelectric data reduction; electronic image recorders; electronic observational instrumentation. Address: Astro-Electronics Lab, Hale Observatories, 1201 E. California Blvd, Pasadena, CA 91109.

DENNISON, JAMES EUGENE, b. Braxton Co, W.Va, July 28, 31; m. 57; c. 3. ANALYTICAL CHEMISTRY. B.A, Miami (Ohio), 54; M.S, Oregon State, 62, Ph.D.(anal. chem), 67. Teaching asst. chem. Oregon State, 54-56, 59-63, instr, 63-64; SR. RES. CHEMIST, WEST. ELEC. CO, 65- U.S.N, 56-59, Lt. AAAS. Gas chromatography; automatic process control; air and water pollution control; coulometric analysis; spectrophotometry; material characterization. Address: Western Electric Co, P.O. Box 900, Princeton, NJ 08540.

DENNISON, JOHN MANLEY, b. Keyser, W.Va, Apr. 13, 34; m. 57; c. 1. GEOLOGY. B.S, West Virginia, 54, M.S, 55, Ph.D.(geol), Wisconsin, 60. Asst. prof. GEOL, Illinois, 60-64, assoc. prof, 64-65; Tennessee, 65-67; PROF, UNIV. N.C, CHAPEL HILL, 67-, CHMN, DEPT, 69- Cooperating geologist, W.Va. Geol. Surv, 60- U.S.A, 55-57. Geol. Soc. Am; Am. Asn. Petrol. Geol; Paleont. Soc; Am. Statist. Asn. Appalachian structural geology and Devonian stratigraphy; Palinspastic maps; statistics in geology, especially sampling problems. Address: Dept. of Geology, University of North Carolina, Chapel Hill, NC 27514.

DENNISON, RAYMOND A(LEXANDER), b. Sedalia, Ind, July 12, 14; m. 42; c. 3. FOOD SCIENCE. A.B, Miami (Ohio), 36; M.S, Iowa, 40; Ph.D.(plant physiol), 42. Assoc. horticulturist, INST. FOOD & AGR. SCI, UNIV. FLA, 46-53, horticulturist, 53-56, head food technol. & nutrit. dept, 55-56, CHMN, FOOD SCI. DEPT, 66- U.S.N.R, 42-46. AAAS; Inst. Food Tech; Am. Soc. Plant Physiol; Am. Soc. Hort. Sci. Food chemistry; processing fruits and vegetables; food irradiation. Address: Institute of Food & Agricultural Sciences, University of Florida, Gainesville, FL 32603.

DENNISON, R(ICHARD) W(HEELER), b. Oswego, N.Y, July 16, 14; m. 40; c. 2. PHYSICS. B.S, Carnegie Inst. Tech, 36, fel, 37-41, M.S, 38, Sc.D. (physics), 41. Test engr, Gen. Elec. Co, 36-37; asst, Carnegie Inst. Tech, 37-41; asst. prof. physics, Swarthmore Col, 46; SR. RES. PHYSICIST, FIBERS DEPT, E.I. DU PONT DE NEMOURS & CO, 46- Lectr, Pa. Mil. Col. Patent liaison. Sig.C, U.S.A, 41-46, Lt. Col. Am. Phys. Soc. Dilatometry with copper-nickel alloys; process research in cellophane and other films; textile research. Address: Textile Fibers Dept, E.I. du Pont de Nemours & Co, Centre Rd, Wilmington, DE 19898.

DENNISTON, DONALD W(ILLIAM), JR, b. Sioux City, Iowa, Jan. 6, 21; m. 49; c. 4. PHYSICS. B.A, Hobart Col, 42; M.S, Lehigh, 48. Foreman prod, Am. Cyanamid Co, 42-43; physicist, U.S. Bur. Mines, 48-54; res. fel, Mellon Inst, 54-58; dept. head res, Pittsburgh Plate Glass Co, 58-66, asst. mgr, fiber glass res. & develop, 66-68, MGR. PROCESS & QUAL. CONTROL, FIBER GLASS DIV, PPG INDUSTS, INC, 68- U.S.A.A.F, 43-46, S/Sgt. Am. Phys. Soc; Combustion Inst; Am. Inst. Aeronaut. & Astronaut. Turbulent combustion of natural gas-air flames; formation of glass fibers, from theory to plant operation. Address: PPG Industries, Inc, Fiber Glass Division, 1 Gateway Center, Pittsburgh, PA 15222.

DENNISTON, ROLLIN H, II, b. Chicago, Ill, Dec. 16, 14; m. 41; c. 3. PHYSIOLOGY. B.A, Wisconsin, 36, M.A, 37; Ph.D.(zoophysiol), Chicago, 41. Instr. zool. & physiol, Arizona, 41-43; zool, physiol. & physics, Wyoming, 43-45, asst. prof. zoophysiol, 45-48, assoc. prof. Physiol, 48-53, Prof, 54-, dir. res. & develop, 65-70, CHIEF OF PARTY, AGENCY INT. DEVELOP-UNIV. WYO, KABUL, AFGANISTAN, 70- New York Zool. Soc. grants, 47-52; Ford Found. grant & fel. psychol, Yale, 52-53; Nat. Inst. Ment. Health grant, 53-60, sr. res. fel. neurophysiol, 60-61; Nat. Sci. Found-Nat. Res. Coun. conf. grant, 60-61. Dir. dept, Nat. Defense Ed. Act, 60-; res. consult, Jackson Lab, 63. U.S.A, 43-46. Am. Psychol. Asn; Am. Soc. Zool; Am. Physiol. Soc; Animal Behavior Soc; Psychonomic Soc. Endocrinology; behavior; reproduction neurophysiology. Address: Kabul (ID), U.S. Dept. of State, Washington, DC 20521.

DENNY, CHARLES S(TORROW), b. Brookline, Mass, Sept. 17, 11; m; c. 3. GEOLOGY. A.B, Harvard, 34, Ph.D.(geol), 38. Instr. geol, Dartmouth Col, 38-42; asst. prof, Wesleyan, 42-44; assoc. geologist, U.S. GEOL. SURV, 44-47, GEOLOGIST, 47- Fel. Geol. Soc. Am. Glacial geology; geomorphology. Address: U.S. Geological Survey, Bldg. 420, Agricultural Research Center, Beltsville, MD 20705.

DENNY, CLEVE B, b. Dallas, Texas, Oct, 12, 25; m. 51; c. 2. BACTERIOLOGY. B.A, Texas, 49. Jr. bacteriologist, WASH. RES. LAB, NAT. CANNERS ASN, 49-51, bacteriologist, 51-59, asst. chief bacteriologist, 59-65, HEAD, BACT. SECT, 65- Assoc. referee, bact, testing of canned foods, Asn. Off. Anal. Chem, 68- U.S.N, 44-46. Am. Soc. Microbiol; Inst. Food Tech. Antibiotic preservation of food; radiation sterilization of food; food poisoning; canned food spoilage organisms; heat inactivation of bacterial toxins. Address: National Canners Association, 1133 20th St. N.W, Washington, DC 20036.

DENNY, EDWARD C, b. De Soto, Mo, Feb. 1, 28; m. 50; c. 3. PHYSICS. B.A, Union Col.(Nebr), 50; M.S, Tennessee, 59. PHYSICIST, Nat. Bur. Standards, 51; Frankford Arsenal, 52-53; Union Carbide Nuclear Div, 54-61, Kemet Dept, Linde Co, 61-63, UNION CARBIDE NUCLEAR DIV, 63- U.S.A, 51-53. Electronics; instrumentation; semiconductor physics; electron microscopy; biomedical research; analog and digital instrument development. Address: 8113 Westmont Circle, Knoxville, TN 37919.

DENNY, FLOYD WOLFE JR, b. Hartsville, S.C, Oct. 22, 23; m. 46; c. 3. PEDIATRICS. B.S, Wofford Col, 44; M.D, Vanderbilt, 46. Asst. prof. pediat, Minnesota, 52-53; sch. Med, Vanderbilt, 53-55; prev. med. & pediat, sch. med, Western Reserve, 55-60, assoc. prof. prev. med. & asst. prof. PEDIAT, 60; PROF. & CHMN. DEPT, SCH. MED. UNIV. N.C, CHAPEL HILL, 60- Asst. to pres. Armed Forces Epidemiol. Bd, 55-57, mem, cmn. streptococcal diseases, 64-; dep. dir, 59-63; assoc. mem. cmn. acute respiratory diseases, 56-60, mem, 60, dep. dir, 63-; mem. cmt. prevention rheumatic fever & bact. endocarditis, Coun. Rheumatic Fever & Congenital Heart Disease, Am. Heart Asn, 59-61. Dipl, Am. Bd. Pediat. Streptococcal infections; rheumatic fever; viral infections. Address: Dept. of Pediatrics, School of Medicine, University of North Carolina, Chapel Hill, NC 27515.

DENNY, GEORGE H(UTCHESON), JR, b. Westfield, N.J, May 30, 28; m. 67; c. 1. ORGANIC CHEMISTRY. B.S, Washington & Lee, 50; M.A, Hopkins, 51, Du Pont fel, 53-54, Ph.D.(chem), 54. Jr. instr. chem, Hopkins, 51-53, res. chemist, nylon res. div, E.I. du Pont de Nemours & Co, 56-58; U.S. Pub. Health Serv. fel, CHEM, Wayne State, 58-59; asst. prof. Arlington State Col, 59-60; Va. Polytech, 60-63; assoc. prof, Peabody Col, 63-64; res. assoc, MERCK SHARP & DOHME RES. LABS, 64-65, SR. CHEMIST, 65- Summer, vis. assoc. prof, Vanderbilt, 64. Lind prize, Washington & Lee, 50. Med.C, U.S.A, 54-56. AAAS; Am. Chem. Soc. Chemistry of tetronic acids; enzyme assay; synthetic fibers; organic stereochemistry; medicinal chemistry. Address: 633 Shackamaxon Dr, Westfield, NJ 07090.

DENNY, J(OHN) P(ALMER), b. Pittsburgh, Pa, Mar. 7, 21; m. 45; c. 3. METALLURGY. E.Met, Colo. Sch. Mines, 42; fel, Utah, 47-50, M.S, 48, Ph.D, 50. Res. engr, Battelle Mem. Inst, 45-47; Phys. metallurgist, Gen. Elec. Co, N.Y, 50-59; sect. chief, Beryllium Corp, 59-69, MGR. BERYLLIUM DEVELOP, BERYLCO DIV, KAWECKI BERYLCO INDUSTS, INC, 69- U.S.A.A.F, 42-45, Capt. Am. Soc. Metals; Am. Inst. Mining, Metall. & Petrol. Eng. Physical metallurgy; alloy development; precipitation hardening; low melting alloys; high temperature materials. Address: Kawecki Berylco Industries, Inc, Berylco Division, P.O. Box 1462, Reading, PA 19607.

DENNY, WAYNE B(ELDING), b. Oberlin, Ohio, Feb. 4, 14; m. 39; c. 2. PHYSICS. A.B, Oberlin Col, 35; summers, Columbia, 36-39; Ph.D.(ed), Yale, 41; Case, 47-48. Instr, high sch, N.Y, 35-38; ed, Connecticut, 40-41; instr. PHYSICS, Emory, 41-43; vis. lectr, Oberlin Col, 43-46, asst. prof, 46-48; assoc. prof, GRINNELL COL, 48-55, PROF, 55- Fulbright prof, Robert Col, Istanbul, 58-59; Ahmednagar Col, India, 65-66; U.S. Agency Int. Develop. summer consult, N.Bengal, India, 65, Andhra Univ, 66, Gauhati Univ, 67, 68; vis. prof. physics, Silliman Univ, Philippines, 71-72. Am. Phys. Soc; Audio Eng. Soc; assoc. Inst. Elec. & Electronics Eng; Am. Asn. Physics Teachers. Electronics; acoustics. Address: Dept. of Physics, Grinnell College, Grinnell, IA 50112.

DENNY, WILLIAM F, b. Tryon, Okla, Aug. 15, 27; m. 49; c. 2. HEMATOLOGY, INTERNAL MEDICINE. B.S, Cent. State Col.(Okla), 49; M.D, Oklahoma, 53. Intern, George Washington Univ. Hosp, 53-54; resident med, sch. med, Oklahoma, 54-56, instr, 56, chief resident, 56-57; asst. prof. MED, sch. med, Univ. Ark, 61-67; ASSOC. PROF, COL. MED, UNIV. ARIZ, 67-; CHIEF MED. SERVS, VET. ADMIN. HOSP, 67- Clin. res. investr, consol. Vet. Admin. Hosp, Ark, 61-64, chief hemat. sect, med. serv, 64-67. Med.Serv.C, 54-61, Maj. AAAS; Am. Med. Asn; Am. Fedn. Clin. Res. Erythropoietin measurements in anemic and non-anemic individuals; non-immune hemolytic mechanisms. Address: Veterans Administration Hospital, Tucson, AZ 85713.

DENNY-BROWN, DEREK E(RNEST), b. Christchurch, N.Z, June 1, 01, nat. 51; m. 37; c. 4. MEDICINE. M.B. & Ch.B, Otago Univ, 24; Beit fellow, Oxford, 25-28, Ph.D.(physiol. nervous system), 28; hon. A.M, Harvard, 42; M.D, New Zealand, 46; hon. LL.D, Wayne State, 59, Glasgow, 71; hon. D.Sc, Univ. Otago, N.Z, 69. Demonstr. anat, Otago, N.Z, 24; lectr. neurol, Nat. Hosp, London, 31-39, res. med. off, 28-31; registrar in neurol, Guy's Hosp, 31-35; asst. physician, Nat. Hosp, 35-41; prof. neurol, Harvard, 41-46, James T. Putnam prof, 46-67; CHIEF, SECT. PHYSIOL. & ASSOC. DIR, NEW ENG. PRIMATE RES. CTR, 67- Rockefeller traveling fel, 36; neurologist, St. Bartholomew's Hosp, London, 35-41; dir, Harvard Neurol. Unit, Boston City Hosp, 41-67. Officer, Order of British Empire, 42. With Office Sci. Res. & Develop, 42-44. British Army, 39-46, Brigadier. Am. Neurol. Asn; Asn. Am. Physicians; Royal Soc. Med; fel. Royal Col. Physicians; Brit. Physiol. Soc. Applied physiology of nervous system; physiology of movement and concussion; neuropathology; histology of peripheral nerves. Address: New England Primate Research Center, Southborough, MA 01772.

DENO, NORMAN C, b. Chicago, Ill, Feb. 15, 21; m. 44; c. 2. PHYSICAL, ORGANIC CHEMISTRY. B.S, Illinois, 42; M.S, Michigan, 46, Ph.D.(chem), 48. Asst. CHEM, Michigan, 42-45; res. assoc, Ohio State, 48-50; PROF. PA. STATE UNIV, 50- Reaction mechanisms. Address: Dept. of Chemistry, Pennsylvania State University, University Park, PA 16801.

DENOON, C(LARENCE) E(NGLAND), JR, b. Richmond, Va, Feb. 25, 15; m. 42; c. 2. ORGANIC CHEMISTRY. B.S, Richmond, 34, M.S, 35; du Pont fel, Illinois, 37-38, Ph.D.(org. chem), 38. Asst, Illinois, 35-37; res. chemist, exp. sta, E.I. du Pont de Nemours & Co, 38-42; res. dir, Landers Corp, 42-45; mgr. spec. prod. dept, ROHM & HAAS CO, 45-58, asst. mgr. chem. & plastics div, 58-62, mgr. indust. chem. div, 62-65, mkt. mgr, 65-66, V.PRES, 66-71, CORP. VENTURES, 71- High polymers; corporate management. Address: Rohm and Haas Co, Independence Mall W, Philadelphia, PA 19105.

DeNOYER, JOHN M, b. Kalaw, Burma, May 19, 26; U.S. citizen; m. 51; c. 4. GEOPHYSICS. A.B, Chico State Col, 53; M.A, California, 55, Ph.D.(geophys), 58. Asst. seismol, California, 54-57; instr. geol, Michigan, 57-59, asst. prof, 59-64, assoc. prof, 64-65, acting head acoust. & seismics lab, 63-65; dep. dir. nuclear test detection off, advan. res. projs, agency, Dept. Defense, Wash, D.C, 65-67; asst. dir. res, U.S. Geol. Surv, Dept. Interior, 67-69; DIR. EARTH OBSERVATIONS PROG, NASA, 69- Mem. staff, Inst. Defense Anal, Wash, D.C, 62-63. Henry Russel Award, 64. U.S.A, 44-46, 50-51. AAAS; Geol. Soc. Am; Acoust. Soc. Am; Seismol. Soc. Am; Am. Geophys. Union. Wave propagation; signal processing; energy in seismic waves; strain energy in crustal deformation; crustal structure; remote sensing. Address: 4835 Drummond Ave, Chevy Chase, MD 20015.

DENSEN, PAUL M, b. N.Y.C, Aug. 1, 13; m. 39; c. 2. BIOSTATISTICS. B.A, Brooklyn Col, 34; D.Sc.(hyg), Hopkins, 39. Instr. in charge biostatist, dept. prev. med. & pub. health, sch. med, Vanderbilt, 39-41, asst. prof, 41-46, assoc. prof, 46; chief med. res. statist. div, U.S. Vet. Admin, 47-49, assoc. prof. biostatist, grad. sch. pub. health, Pittsburgh, 49-52, prof. biomet, 52-54; dir. res. & statist, Health Ins. Plan Greater New York, 54-59; dep. comnr. health, N.Y.C. Health Dept, 59-66, dep. health serv. adminr, 66-68; PROF. COMMUNITY HEALTH & DIR. CTR. COMMUNITY HEALTH & MED. CARE, SCH. PUB. HEALTH, HARVARD, 68- Lectr, grad. sch. pub. health, Univ. Pittsburgh. Fel. Am. Statist. Asn; fel. Am. Pub. Health Asn; Am. Epidemiol. Soc. Medical, hospital, public health and industrial health statistics. Address: Center for Community Health & Medical Care, Harvard University School of Public Health, 643 Huntington Ave, Boston, MA 02115.

DENSHAW, JOSEPH MOREAU, b. Trenton, N.J, Jan. 26, 29; m. 53; c. 5. ELECTRICAL ENGINEERING. B.S, Pennsylvania, 52, M.S, 63. Engr, Minneapolis Honeywell Regular Co, 52-56; missile & space div, GEN. ELEC. CO, 56-62, mgr, 62-64, develop. engr, 64-65, mgr. electro-optics, 65-70, PROD. DEVELOP. ENGR, REENTRY & ENVIRON. SYSTS. DIV, 70- U.S.N, 46-48. Inst. Elec. & Electronics Eng.(secy, 62-63, treas, 63-64, v.chmn, 64-65); Optical Soc. Am; Am. Inst. Physics. Synthesize and analyze information systems utilizing spacecraft vehicle, particularly development of new techniques in signal processing and information theory applications; controlled environment food production equipment; water treatment equipment; pollution avoidance and control equipment; medical communications; instrumentation engineering; utilization and disposal of waste products. Address: Re-Entry & Environmental Systems Division, General Electric Co, 3198 Chestnut St, Philadelphia, PA 19101.

DENSLOW, JOHN STEDMAN, b. Hartford, Conn, Dec. 19, 06; m. 34; c. 3. OSTEOPATHY. D.O, Kirksville Col, 29; hon. D.Sc, Chicago Col. Osteop, 41. Asst. dir, clin, Chicago Col, Osteop, 30-32, dir, 32-38; prof. & chmn. dept. osteop. tech, KIRKSVILLE COL. OSTEOP. & SURG, 38-65, dir. res. affairs, 45-65, V.PRES, 65- Private practice, Ill, 33-38; mem. Mo. State Bd. Health, 68-, chmn, 71; proj. rev. comt, Mo. Regional Med. Prog, 68-; Mo. Gov's Adv. Coun. Comprehensive Health Planning, 71- AAAS; Am. Osteop. Asn. Am. Asn. Osteop. Cols.(secy, 33-); Am. Physiol. Soc; N.Y. Acad. Sci. Reflex activity of the spinal cord; neuromuscular physiology; reflex and postural muscle contraction. Address: Kirksville College of Osteopathy & Surgery, Kirksville, MO 63501.

DENSON, COSTEL D, b. Aliquippa, Pa, June 14, 34; m. 55; c. 2. CHEMICAL ENGINEERING. B.S, Lehigh, 56; M.S, Rensselaer Polytech, 60; Phillips Petrol. fel, Utah, 61-62, Nat. Defense Ed. Act fel, 62-65, Ph.D.(chem. eng), 65. Eng. trainee, prod. depts, GEN. ELEC. CO, 56-60, develop. chemist, insulating mat. dept, 60-61, res. assoc. chem. eng. & fluid mech, res. & develop. ctr, 65-69, MGR. POLYMER RES, MAJOR APPLIANCE LABS, 69- Vis. assoc. prof. chem. eng, Lehigh Univ, 68-69. C.Eng, 56, Res, 56-63, Capt. Am. Inst. Chem. Eng; Soc. Rheol. Fluid mechanics, especially viscoelastic liquids; rheology. Address: General Electric Major Appliance Labs, Appliance Park, Louisville, KY 40225.

DENSON, J(UDSON) S(AMUEL), b. Dallas, Tex, Dec. 19, 18; m. 49; c. 2. MEDICINE, ANESTHESIOLOGY. A.B, Columbia, 40, M.D, 43. Intern, St. Luke's Hosp, New York, N.Y, 44; res, Bellevue Hosp, 47-49; asst. dir, ANESTHESIOL, LOS ANGELES COUNTY GEN. HOSP, 49-51, DIR, 51-; PROF. ANESTHESIOL, SCH. MED, UNIV. SOUTH. CALIF, 56-, CHMN. DEPT, 69-, assoc. clin. prof, 49-56. Assoc. clin. prof, sch. med, Loma Linda, 54-61, clin. prof, 61- Consult, Childrens Hosp. Med.C.Res, 44-46, Capt. AAAS; Am. Med. Asn; Am. Soc. Anesthesiol; Pan-Am. Med. Asn; Int. Anesthesia Res. Soc. Pharmacology of anesthetic drugs; physiology of circulation and respiration. Address: Dept. of Anesthesiology, University of Southern California School of Medicine, Los Angeles, CA 90033.

DENSTEDT, ORVILLE FREDERICK, b. Blyth, Ont, Mar. 2, 99; m. 38. BIOCHEMISTRY. B.Sc, Manitoba, 29; Ph.D.(biochem), McGill, 37. Asst, Pac. Fisheries Exp. Sta, 29-32; lectr. BIOCHEM, McGILL UNIV, 37-42, asst. prof, 42-46, assoc. prof, 46-61, prof, 61-65, Gilman Cheney prof, 65-67, EMER. PROF, 67- Mem, Fisheries Res. Bd. Can, 63-68. Am. Soc. Biol. Chem; N.Y. Acad. Sci; Am. Soc. Hemat; Can. Physiol. Soc.(past pres); Can. Inst. Food Tech.(pres, Can. Food Tech. Asn, 54); Can. Fedn. Biol. Socs; Can. Biochem. Soc.(pres, 59); Can. Nutrit. Soc; fel. Royal Soc. Can; Int. Hemat. Soc. Use of drying fish oils in protective coatings, especially in paints and varnishes; chemical constitution of fish oils; chemistry and physiology of hormones and lipids of anterior and posterior pituitary; melanophore hormone; urinary estrogens; blood preservation; enzymology oi red blood cells; liver function; iron, zinc and silicon metabolism; capillary fragility; biochemical action of insecticides; biochemistry of vascular disease and hemorrhagic shock. Address: Room 523, McIntyre Medical Sciences Bldg, McGill University, Montreal 110, Que, Can.

DENT, J(AMES) N(ORMAN), b. Martin, Tenn, May 10, 16; m. 45; c. 2. ZOOLOGY. A.B, Tennessee, 38; Ph.D.(zool), Hopkins, 41. Asst. anat, Hopkins, 38-41, zool, 41-42; asst. prof. biol, Marquette, 45-46; Pittsburgh, 46-49; assoc. prof. ZOOL, UNIV. VA, 49-58, PROF, 58- Guggenheim fel, St. Andrews, Scotland, 59-60. Consult, biol. div, Oak Ridge Nat. Lab, 55-70; U.S. Agency Int. Develop, Philippines, 63; U.S. Pub. Health Serv. spec. res. fel, Harvard, 69-70. Mem, Hopkins exped, Jamaica, B.W.I, 41. U.S.A.F, 42-45, Res, 45-, Lt. Col. AAAS; Am. Soc. Zool; Am. Asn. Anat; Radiation Res. Soc. Amphibian taxonomy, development and endocrinology; embryonic development of Plethodon cinereous as correlated with the differentiation of thyroid gland; developmental physiology; comparative endocrinology. Address: Dept. of Biology, Gilmer Hall, University of Virginia, Charlottesville, VA 22903.

DENT, SARA JAMISON, b. Lockhart, S.C, Feb. 5, 22. ANESTHESIOLOGY. M.D, South Carolina, 45. From asst. prof. to PROF. ANESTHESIOL, DUKE UNIV, 55- Staff anesthesiologist, Duke Univ. Hosp, 55-, attend, Vet. Admin. Hosp, 55- Am. Soc. Anesthesiol; Am. Med. Asn. General anesthesiology. Address: Dept. of Anesthesiology, Duke University, Box 3094, Durham, NC 27710.

DENT, THOMAS C(URTIS), b. Canton, Ohio, June 6, 28; m. 48; c. 2. BOTANY, PLANT TAXONOMY. B.A.Ed, Univ. Akron, 62; M.N.S, Univ. Okla, 64, Nat. Sci. Found. summer fels, 64-69, Ph.D.(plant taxon), 69. Teacher, Hoover High Sch, Ohio, 61-68; instr. BIOL, Kent State Univ, 68-69; ASSOC. PROF, GORDON COL, 69- Am. Inst. Biolog. Sci; Am. Soc. Plant Taxon; Nat. Asn. Biol. Teachers; Am. Forestry Asn. Relationships of two isolated groups of sugar maple in central Oklahoma to eastern and western species. Address: Dept. of Biology, Gordon College, 255 Grapevine Rd, Wenham, MA 01984.

DENTON, ARNOLD E(UGENE), b. Remington, Ind, March 18, 25; m. 50; c. 3. BIOCHEMISTRY. B.S, Purdue, 49; M.S, Wisconsin, 50, Ph.D, 53. Head, pet food res. div, res. lab, Swift & Co, 53-55, biochem. res. div, 55-58; dir. basic res, CAMPBELL SOUP CO, 58-66, v.pres. basic res, 66-70, V.PRES. TECH. ADMIN, 70- U.S.A.F, 43-46, Res, 46-55, 1st Lt. Am. Chem. Soc; Inst. Food Technol. Amino acid and vitamin assays; vitamin stability in foods and feeds; protein digestibility; by-product utilization; commercial applications of enzymes; meat tenderness; chemistry of flavors; nutritional value of foods. Address: Campbell Soup Co, Campbell Place, Camden, NJ 08101.

DENTON, J(AMES) FRED, b. Americus, Ga, May 26, 14; m. 39; c. 2. MEDICAL MICROBIOLOGY, ZOOLOGY. B.S, Georgia, 35, M.S, 38, M.D, 57; fel, Rice Inst, 38-41, Ph.D.(parasitol), 41. Instr. zool, Georgia, 36-38; prof. biol, Middle Ga. Col, 41-42; asst. prof. MED. MICROBIOL. & PUB. HEALTH, MED. COL, GA, 42-51, assoc. prof, 51-59, PROF, 59- Markle fel, sch. med, Tulane, 43, Honduras, 43, China Med. Bd. fel, med. sch, La. State, 55. Am. Soc. Trop. Med. & Hyg; Am. Soc. Parasitol; Am. Micros. Soc. Fungus and other infectious diseases. Address: Dept. of Cell & Molecular Biology, Medical College of Georgia, Augusta, GA 30902.

DENTON, J(ESSE) C(AMERON), b. Tarboro, N.C, Nov. 23, 23; m. 48; c. 2. MECHANICAL & AEROSPACE ENGINEERING. B.S, Swarthmore Col, 48; M.S, Calif. Inst. Tech, 49; cert, Pa. State, 56; cert, Int. Sch. Nuclear Sci. & Eng, 57; Nat. Sci. Found. fel, Texas A&M, 62-63, Ph.D.(mech. eng), 63. Mech. engr, turbojets, aeronaut. eng. lab, Phila. Navy Yard, 47-48; test. engr, Pratt Whitney Aircraft, 48; res. engr, hydrodyn. lab, Calif. Inst. Tech, 49-50; aeronaut. engr, stability & control, Ryan Aeronaut. Co, 50-51; thermodyn. engr. ramjets & heat transfer, Convair, Gen. Dynamics Corp, 51-53, sr. thermodyn. engr, aerothermodyn, 53-58, sect. head adv. weapon syst. anal, astronaut. div, 58; assoc. prof. mech. & aeronaut. eng, Southern Methodist, 58-60, prof, 60-68; staff assoc, NAT. SCI. FOUND, 68-71, PROG. MGR. & SPEC. ASST. TO ASST. DIR. RES. APPLNS, 71- Consult, Socony-Mobil Oil Corp, 59-68; Gen. Dynamics Corp, 61-62; Danforth teacher, 61-62; chmn, dept. mech/aerospace eng. & chief scientist for aerospace res, South. Methodist Univ, 65-68; prof. lectr, George Wash. Univ, 69- U.S.N, 43-46, Res, 46-48. AAAS; Am. Soc. Eng. Educ; Am. Soc. Mech. Eng; Combustion Inst; Am. Inst. Aeronaut. & Astronaut. Thermodynamics; heat transfer; gas dynamics; space flight mechanics; systems synthesis. Address: 6512 Machodoc Ct, Falls Church, VA 22043.

DENTON, J(OHN) J(OSEPH), b. Newkirk, Okla, Nov. 24, 15; m. 49; c. 3. ORGANIC CHEMISTRY. B.S, Okla. Agr. & Mech. Col, 37; Ph.D.(org. chem), Illinois, 41. Asst. chem, Illinois, 37-40, special asst, Office Sci. Res. & Develop, 40-41; res. chemist, calco chem. div, AM. CYANAMID CO, 41-45, group leader, pharmaceut. res, 45-50, sect. dir, 50-52, dir, Bound Brook, 52-54, tech. dir, fine chem, div, N.Y, 54-56, DIR. org. chem. res, LEDERLE LABS, 56-71, DIR, CARDIOVASC-RENAL RES, 71- AAAS; Am. Chem. Soc; N.Y. Acad. Sci. Brit. Chem. Soc. Medicinal chemistry. Address: Lederle Labs, American Cyanamid Co, Pearl River, NY 10965.

DENTON, RICHARD T, b. York, Pa, July 13, 32; m. 53; c. 10. ELECTRICAL ENGINEERING, SOLID STATE PHYSICS. B.S, Pa. State, 53, Nat. Sci. Found. fel. & M.S, 54; Nat. Electronics Conf. fel, Michigan, 58, Ph.D.(elec. eng), 60. Res. asst. computer circuits, Pa. State, 53-54; mem. tech. staff, Bell Tel. Labs, Inc, 54-56; res. assoc. solid state physics, res. inst, Michigan, 56-59; mem. tech. staff, BELL TEL. LABS, INC, 59-68; HEAD, SHORE TECHNOL. DEPT, 68- Am. Phys. Soc; Inst. Elec. & Electronics Eng. Digital signal processing; microwave properties of magnetic materials; microwave ultrasonic devices and study of ultrasonic properties of solids; optical processing. Address: Bell Telephone Labs, Inc, Whippany Rd, Whippany, NJ 07981.

DENTON, ROBERT ELDON, b. Caribou, Maine, Feb. 16, 21; m. 43; c. 3. FOREST ENTOMOLOGY. B.Sc, State Univ. N.Y. Col. Forestry, Syracuse, 48; M.F, Michigan, 50; Montana, 59 & 60. Entomologist, FOREST INSECTS, bur. entom. & plant quarantine, U.S. FOREST SERV, 50-54, RES. ENTOMOLOGIST, INTERMT. FOREST & RANGE EXP. STA, 54- U.S.A.A.F, 43-46, 1st Lt. Entom. Soc. Am. Biological control and ecology of forest insect defoliators, especially spruce budworm and larch casebearer. Address: Forestry Sciences Lab, P.O. Box 469, Moscow, ID 83843.

DENTON, TOM EUGENE, b. Montgomery, Ala, May 29, 37; m. 59; c. 2. BOTANY. B.A, Huntingdon Col, 59; M.S, Alabama, 63, Ph.D.(biol), 66. Asst. prof. BOT, SAMFORD UNIV, 65-69, ASSOC. PROF, 69- AAAS. Algal physiology and morphology. Address: 2224 Great Rock Rd, Birmingham, AL 35216.

DENTON, WILLIAM IRWIN, b. Paterson, N.J, July 5, 17; m. 41; c. 5. CHEMICAL ENGINEERING. B.S, Case, 38, M.S, 39. Res. engr, Am. Gas. Asn, 39-40; sr. chemist, Socony-Mobil Oil Co, 40-53; sect. chief, org. chem. res. dept. OLIN CORP, 53-59, DIR. PROCESS DEVELOP. 59- V.pres, Sprayed Reinforced Plastics Co, 59-60. Am. Chem. Soc; Am. Inst. Chem. Eng; Soc. Plastics Eng. New chemical processes; catalytic processes; petrochemicals; urethanes; alkoxylations; isocyanates. Address: Olin Corp, 275 Winchester Ave, New Haven, CT 06504.

DE NUCCIO, DAVID JOSEPH, b. Lawrence, Mass, May 29, 35; m. 60; c. 2. PHYSIOLOGY, ENDOCRINOLOGY. B.A, Merrimack Col, 59; fel, Boston Col, 60-61, M.S, 61; U.S. Pub. Health Serv. fel, 61-64 & 66-68; Ph.D.(med. sci), Univ. Tenn, Memphis, 69. Instr. HUMAN ANAT. & PHYSIOL, CENT. CONN. STATE COL, 64-66, ASST. PROF, 68- U.S. Pub. Health Serv. grant & res. assoc, med. units, Univ. Tenn, Memphis, summer, 70. AAAS. Neuroendocrine regulation of mammary gland secretion and milk ejection with emphasis on the measurement and biophysics of milk ejection; mammary compliance; nervous regulation of duct tone and gland capacity. Address: 25 Sequin St, Newington, CT 06111.

DENUES, A(RTHUR) R(USSELL) T(AYLOR), b. York, Pa, Aug. 16, 14; m. 42; c. 6. BIOCHEMICAL ENGINEERING, PHYSICAL BIOCHEMISTRY. B.E, Hopkins, 35, M.G.E, 37; fel, Maryland, 38-39, Ph.D.(chem. eng), 39; Pittsburgh, 39-42. Asst. gas eng, Hopkins, 35-37; co-op. investr, Chile Explor. Co, 37-38; chem. engr, U.S. Bur. Mines, 39-47; Am. Cancer Soc-Nat. Res. Coun. fel, Mass. Inst. Tech, 47-48; res. assoc, Detroit Inst. Cancer Res. & Wayne Univ, 48-50; asst, Sloan-Kettering Inst. Cancer Res, 50-53, assoc. & asst. to dir, 53-56, dep. dir, 56-60, mem, 56-62, acting dir, 59-60, v.pres, 60, chief electron micros. lab, div. path, 60-62; pres. & prog. dir. Cancirco, Inc, 62-69; PROF. & CHMN. DEPT. LIFE SCI. & ASSOC, OFF. RES, N.Y. INST. TECHNOL, 69- Lab. asst, U.S. Dept. Agr, 35-36; instr. Sloan-Kettering Div, Cornell, 52-54, asst. prof, 54-59, assoc. prof, 59-61, mem. grad. faculty, 58-61, dep. to dir. div, 53-61; instr, Norwalk Community Col, 63- Consult, Nat. Cancer Inst, 60-64; Biol. Eng. Res. Mgt. Consult. Opers, 63-; Yearbook of Cancer, 64- Mem. dissemination & field testing cmt, chem. biol. & radiol. warfare adv. coun, U.S. Army, Edgewood Arsenal, 58-59, 60- C.Eng, 42-46, Res, 35-59, Lt. Col; Legion of Merit, 45. Fel. AAAS; Am. Asn. Cancer Res; Am. Chem. Soc; Am. Pub. Health Asn; Am. Soc. Cell Biol; Electron Micros. Soc. Am; N.Y. Acad. Med; fel. N.Y. Acad. Sci; assoc. mem. Opers. Res. Soc. Am. Fuels and combustion; explosives and explosions; kinetics; munitions and weapons development; biophysics and biochemistry in carcinogenesis and invasion and metastasis of tumors; electron microscopy; fine structure of chromosomes; isolated chromosomes; graduate education and research management; viral etiology of human cancer; cancer chemotherapy research; worldwide cancer research cooperations. Address: Office of Research, New York Institute of Technology, Old Westbury, NY 11568.

DENYES, HELEN ARLISS, b. Kingston, Ont, Sept. 17, 22. ENVIRONMENTAL BIOLOGY. B.A, Queen's Univ.(Ont), 45; scholar, Univ. Mich, 45-46, M.S, 46, Ph.D.(ecol), 51; fels, Queen's Univ.(Ont), 46-49. Instr. physiol, Fla. State Univ, 49-51, asst. prof, 51-56; asst. prof. BIOL, Queen's Univ.(Ont), 56-63, ASSOC. PROF, 63-64; Mankato State Col, 66-67; SACRED HEART UNIV, 67- Ecol. adv, conserv. adv. comn, City of Bridgeport, Conn, 70- AAAS; Am. Inst. Biol. Sci; Am. Soc. Zool; Ecol. Soc. Am. Physiological-ecological adaptations in fish and mammals; lipid metabolism in cold exposed and hibernating mammals. Address: Dept. of Biology, Sacred Heart University, Park Ave, Bridgeport, CT 06604.

DENZEL, GEORGE EUGENE, b. Seattle, Wash, Nov. 1, 39; m. 58; c. 3. MATHEMATICS. B.S, Washington, 60, Nat. Sci. Found. fel, 63-65, M.S, 63, Ph.D.(math), 65. Res. instr. math, Dartmouth Col, 65-67; asst. prof. statist, Univ. Mo-Columbia, 67-71; ASSOC. PROF, MATH, YORK UNIV, 71- Am. Math Soc; Inst. Math. Statist. Markov processes and potential theory; Martingale theory; continuous parameter Markov chains. Address: Dept. of Mathematics, York University, 4700 Keele St, Downsview 463, Toronto, Ont, Can.

DEO, NARSINGH, b. Raniganj, India, Jan. 2, 36; m. 68; c. 1. ELECTRICAL ENGINEERING, COMPUTER SCIENCE. B.Sc, Patna, 56; dipl. elec. eng, Indian Inst. Sci, Bangalore, 59; Drake scholar, Calif, Inst. Tech, 59-60, M.S, 60; Ph.D.(elec. eng), Northwestern, 65. Assoc. electronic engr, electrodata Div, Burroughs Corp, 60-62 & summer 63, sr. elec. engr, 65-66; sr. res. engr, JET PROPULSION LAB, 66-69, MEM. TECH. STAFF, 69- Mem. eng. exten. faculty, Univ. Calif, Los Angeles, 65-; lectr, Calif. State Col. Los Angeles, 68- Electronic design consult, Center Behav. Ther, 67-; v.pres, Britt Electronics Corp, 68- Inst. Elec. & Electronics Eng; Am. Inst. Aeronaut. & Astronaut. Network topology and linear graphs; survivability of communication networks; self-diagnosable and self-repairable digital computers; redundancy techniques and ultra-reliable computers for spacecraft. Address: Jet Propulsion Lab, 4800 Oak Grove Dr, Pasadena, CA 91103.

DEOBALD, H(AROLD) J(OHN), b. Cleveland, Ohio, Oct. 6, 06; m. 31; c. 3. BIOCHEMISTRY. B.S, Ohio State, 28; M.S, Wisconsin, 31, Ph.D.(biochem), 35. Assoc. dir. biol. res, Allied Mills, Inc, 37-39, consult, Century Distilling Co, 39-40, head, pilot plant, Allied Mills, Inc, 40-54; tech. dir, Plains Co-op. Oil Mill, 54-57; HEAD RICE & SWEET POTATO INVESTS, SOUTH. REGIONAL RES. LAB, U.S. DEPT. AGR, 57- Consult, North. Utilization Res. & Develop. Div, Ill, 40-54. Am. Chem. Soc; Inst. Food Technol; Am. Inst. Chem. Sweet potato utilization, composition, biochemical reactions during curing, storage processing; rice utilization, composition, basic biochemical changes during aging, processing; oilseeds, extraction, processing and nutritional value of soy and cottonseed meals, protein isolation and biochemistry. Address: Southern Regional Research Lab, 1100 Robert E. Lee Blvd, New Orleans, LA 70119.

DEODHAR, SHARAD D(INKAR), b. Poona, India, Nov. 17, 29; U.S. citizen; m. 55; c. 3. PATHOLOGY, BIOCHEMISTRY. M.S, Pa. State, 52; fel, Western Reserve, 52-56: Ph.D, 56, M.D. Res. biochemist, Mt. Sinai Hosp, Cleveland, Ohio, 56-60; res. fel. path, Univ. Hosps. Cleveland, 60-64; pathologist, CLEVELAND CLIN. FOUND, 64-69, DIR. IMMUNOL, 69- Young Investigator's award, Am. Col. Cardiol, 63- Immunopathology; experimental hypertension. Address: Cleveland Clinic Foundation, 2020 E. 93rd St, Cleveland, OH 44106.

DeOME, K(ENNETH) B(ENTON), b. Kalkaska, Mich, July 22, 06; m. 40; c. 3. ONCOLOGY. A.B, Albion Col, 28; M.S, Mich. State Col, 34; Ph.D.(zool), California, 38. Instr. animal path, dept. vet. sci, UNIV. CALIF, BERKELEY, 38-43, asst. prof, 43-48, assoc. prof, 48-50, ZOOL, 50-54, PROF, 54-, DIR, CANCER RES. GENETICS LAB, 50-, jr. animal pathologist, exp. sta, 38-43, asst. animal pathologist, 44-47, assoc. animal pathologist, 47-50. AAAS; Am. Asn. Cancer Res. Tumor biology. Address: Cancer Research Genetics Lab, University of California, Berkeley, CA 94720.

DEONIER, DICK LEE, b. La Russell, Mo, June 27, 36; m. 65; c. 1. ENTOMOLOGY, ECOLOGY. B.S, Kans. State Col. Pittsburg, 59; Res. Found. fel, Iowa State, 59-60, M.S, 61, Turtox scholar, 61-62, Ph.D.(entom), 66. Med. entomologist, U.S. Army, SEATO Med. Res. Lab, Thailand, 65-66, instr. med. entom, Brooke Army Med. Center, Ft. Sam Houston, Tex, 66; ASST. PROF. ZOOL, MIAMI UNIV, 66- Mem, Rocky Mt. Biol. Lab. Corp. Med. Serv.C, 64-66, Capt. Entom. Soc. Am; Soc. Syst. Zool; Royal Entom. Soc. London. Systematics of Diptera; taxonomy and ecology of Ephydridae; insect ecology. Address: Dept. of Zoology, Miami University, Oxford, OH 45056.

DE PAGTER, JAMES KEITH, b. Kenosha, Wis, Aug. 22, 27; m. 61; c. 2. PHYSICS. B.S, Arkansas, 51; Ph.D.(physics), Washington (St. Louis), 58. Res. fel. Harvard, 58-65; assoc. prof. PHYSICS, SOUTHEAST. MASS. UNIV, 65-69, PROF, 69-, CHMN. DEPT, 71- U.S.A, 45-47. Am. Phys. Soc. High energy physics; elementary particles. Address: Dept. of Physics, Southeastern Massachusetts University, North Dartmouth, MA 02747.

de PAIVA, HENRY ALBERT RAWDON, b. Edmonton, Alta, Can, Feb. 29, 32; m. 64; c. 3. CIVIL ENGINEERING. B.S, Alberta, 55; M.Sc, Illinois, 60, Ph.D.(civil eng), 61. Res. bridge engr, Bridge Dept, Dept. Hwys, Alta, 55-57; asst. prof. CIVIL ENG, UNIV. CALGARY, 61-64, assoc. prof, 64-68, PROF, 68-, HEAD DEPT, 69-, asst. dean, 65-67, acting dean, 67-68. Am. Concrete Inst; Am. Soc. Civil Eng; Am. Soc. Eng. Educ; Eng. Inst. Can. Reinforced and prestressed concrete structures. Address: Dept. of Civil Engineering, University of Calgary, Calgary, Alta, Can.

DePALMA, ANTHONY F, b. Philadelphia, Pa, Oct. 12, 04; m. 34; c. 3. ORTHOPEDIC SURGERY. B.S, Univ. Md, 25; M.D, Jefferson Med. Col, 29. Prof. ORTHOP. SURG, JEFFERSON MED. COL, 50-70; EMER. PROF, 70-; PROF. & CHMN. DEPT, COL. MED. & DENT. N.J, 71- Dipl, Am. Bd. Orthop. Surg. U.S.N.R, 42-46. Fel. Am. Acad. Orthop. Surg; Am. Asn. Phys. Anthrop; Am. Col. Surg; Am. Med. Asn; Am. Geriat. Soc; Orthop. Res. Soc; Am. Med. Writers' Asn; N.Y. Acad. Sci; Int. Col. Surg; Int. Soc. Orthop. Surg. & Traumatol; World Med. Asn; Pan-Pac. Surg. Asn; Brazilian Acad. Med. Variational anatomy of the shoulder joint; degenerative changes of the musculocutaneous cuff. Address: Division of Orthopaedic Surgery, Martland Hospital, 65 Bergen St, Newark, NJ 07107.

DePALMA, JAMES JOHN, b. Rochester, N.Y, Oct. 30, 27; m. 52; c. 3. OPTICS, MATHEMATICS. B.S, Rochester, 55, M.S, 57. Sr. res. physicist, EASTMAN KODAK CO, 52-66, LAB. HEAD, PHYSICS DIV, RES. LABS, 66-, MEM. SR. STAFF, 67- Instr, Rochester Inst. Technol, 57- Jour. award, Soc. Motion Picture & Tele. Eng, 68. U.S.A, 46-48. Optical Soc. Am. (award, 62); Soc. Photog. Sci. & Eng. Optical and photographic physics, especially radiometry and photometry; psychophysics; optical filters. Address: Physics Division, Research Labs, Eastman Kodak Co, Lake Ave, Rochester, NY 14604.

DePALMA, PHILIP ANTHONY, b. Boston, Mass, Mar. 2, 30; m. 63; c. 1. MICROBIOLOGY. A.B, Boston, 60, A.M, 62, univ. fel, 62-64, Nat. Insts. Health fel, 64-65, Ph.D.(microbiol), 66. Instr. BIOL, BOSTON UNIV, 65-67, ASST. PROF, 67- AAAS; Am. Soc. Microbiol. Biochemistry of morphogenesis in fungi; biochemistry and electron microscopy of the cell wall of Candida albicans; relationship between virulence and morphology in the fungal pathogen, Candida albicans. Address: Dept. of Biology, Boston University, 2 Cummington St, Boston, MA 02215.

DEPALMA, RALPH G, b. N.Y.C, Oct. 29, 31; m. 55; c. 4. SURGERY. A.B, Columbia Univ, 53; M.D, N.Y. Univ, 56. Intern SURG, Columbia-Presbyterian Hosp, New York, 56-57; asst. resident, St. Lukes Hosp, 57-58 & 61-62; resident, Univ. Hosps. Cleveland, 62-64; instr, CASE WEST. RESERVE UNIV, 64-65, asst. prof, 65-69, assoc. prof, 69-71, PROF, 71-; ASSOC. SURGEON, UNIV. HOSPS. CLEVELAND, 70- Fel. Coun. Atherosclerosis, Am. Heart Asn, 70- U.S.A.F, 58-61, Capt. Am. Col. Surg; Soc. Univ. Surg; Am. Heart Asn; Europ. Soc. Exp. Surg. Vascular surgery, atherogenesis; lipid metabolism; cellular and subcellular changes in shock; electron microscopy. Address: University Hospitals of Cleveland, 2065 Adelbert Rd, Cleveland, OH 44106.

DE PANGHER, JOHN, b. Oakland, Calif, Apr. 6, 18; m. 45; c. 3. PHYSICS. A.B, California, 41, Ph.D.(physics), 53. Physicist, radiation lab, California, Berkeley, 42-45, 50-53; Naval Ord. Test. Sta, China Lake, Calif, 45-46; sr. physicist, Gen. Elec. Co, 53-62; staff scientist, Lockheed Missiles & Space Co, 62-70; SR. HEALTH PHYSICIST, STANFORD UNIV, 70- Civilian physicist, Manhattan Dist, 42-45. Am. Phys. Soc; Health Phys. Soc; Am. Nuclear Soc. Neutron dosimetry; radiological and radiation damage physics. Address: 809 Newell Rd, Palo Alto, CA 94303.

DEPATIE, DAVID A, b. St. Albans, Vt, Mar. 24, 34; m. 58; c. 2. PHYSICS. B.A, Vermont, 56, M.S, 58; Du Pont fel, Yale, 61-62, Ph.D.(physics), 64. Instr. PHYSICS, Vermont, 57-58; res. asst, Yale, 62-64; asst. prof, Amherst Col, 64-66; vis. staff mem, Los Alamos Sci. Lab, 66-67; ASST. PROF. PHYSICS, UNIV. VT, 67- Am. Phys. Soc. Low temperature physics; superfluid hydrodynamics; properties of rotating fluids. Address: Dept. of Physics, University of Vermont, Burlington, VT 05401.

DE PERCIN, FERNAND, b. New Brunswick, N.J, June 8, 21; m. 45; c. 4. PHYSICAL GEOGRAPHY, METEOROLOGY. B.Sc, Rutgers, 43; M.Sc, Calif. Inst. Tech, 47; Ph.D.(climat, geog), Harvard, 58. Instr. meteorol, Pa. State Col, 47-48; chief, qm. res. & develop. field off, Dept. of Army, 48-53, polar & mt. sect, environ. protection div, Qm. Res. & Develop. Command, 53-60, polar br, Army Res. Off, off. chief res. & develop, hqs, 60-61; assoc. prog. dir, phys. sci. facilities, Nat. Sci. Found, 61-63; chief spec. proj. br, ENVIRON. SCI. DIV, ARMY RES. OFF, OFF. CHIEF RES. & DEVELOP, HQS, 63-70, CHIEF, ATMOSPHERIC SCI. BR, 70- U.S.A.A.F, 43-46. Am. Meteorol. Soc; Am. Polar Soc. Sci. Res. Soc. Am; Asn. Am. Geog; Arctic Inst. N.Am; Royal Meteorol. Soc. Climatology; field investigations; physical environment of the arctic, subarctic and polar regions; climatology and microclimatology. Address: 5828 Wapakoneta Rd, Washington, DC 20016.

DEPEW, CREIGHTON A, b. Minneapolis, Minn, Mar. 30, 31; m. 52; c. 5. MECHANICAL ENGINEERING. B.S, California, Berkeley, 56, M.S, 57, Ph.D.(mech. eng), 60. Asst. prof, UNIV. WASH, 60-64, ASSOC. PROF, 64- U.S.N.R, 50-52. Heat transfer and fluid mechanics. Address: Dept. of Mechanical Engineering, University of Washington, Seattle, WA 98105.

dePEYSTER, FREDERIC A, b. Chicago, Ill, Nov. 8, 14; m. 48; c. 2. MEDICINE. B.A, Williams Col, 36; M.D, Chicago, 40. Asst. instr. SURG, Univ. Ill. Col. Med, 46-50, clin. instr, 50-54, clin. asst. prof, 54-59, clin. assoc. prof, 59-69, PROF, 69-71; RUSH MED. COL, 71- CLIN. PROF, COOK COUNTY GRAD. SCH. MED, 59- Asst. attend. surgeon, Presby. Hosp, 48-58, assoc. attend. surgeon, 58-62, attend. surgeon, Presby-St. Luke's Hosp, 62-; assoc. attend. surgeon, Cook Co. Hosp, 48-59, attend. surgeon, 59- Med.C, 43-46, Maj. Am. Med. Asn; Am. Col. Surg; Am. Asn. Cancer Res; Int. Soc. Surg. Surgery of the gastrointestinal tract; cancer of colon and rectum; behavior of experimental cancer in animals. Address: Dept. of Surgery, Rush Medical College, 1750 W. Harnson St, Chicago, IL 60612.

DePHILLIPS, HENRY ALFRED, JR, b. N.Y.C, Apr. 16, 37; m. 59; c. 3. PHYSICAL CHEMISTRY. B.S, Fordham, 59; Nat. Insts. Health fel, Northwestern, 60-63, Ph.D.(chem), 65. Asst. prof. CHEM, TRINITY COL.(CONN), 63-69, ASSOC. PROF, 69-, CHMN. DEPT, 71- Mem. corp, Marine Biol. Lab, Woods Hole. AAAS; Am. Chem. Soc; Soc. Appl. Spectros; N.Y. Acad. Sci. Physical biochemistry; spectrophotometric study of liquid water and effect of electrolytes on structure of aqueous solutions; structure-function relationships in respiratory proteins. Address: Dept. of Chemistry, Trinity College, Hartford, CT 06106.

de PIAN, L(OUIS), b. Athens, Greece, Nov. 22, 25; U.S. citizen; m. 55; c. 2. ELECTRICAL ENGINEERING. B.S, Nat. Tech. Univ, Greece, 49; M.S, Carnegie Inst. Tech, 50, Ph.D.(elec. eng), 52. Instr. elec. eng, Carnegie Inst. Tech, 52-53, asst. prof, 53-57; assoc. prof, George Washington Univ, 57-60, prof, 60-62, appl. sci, 62-69; DIR. ENG, WEINSCHEL ENG, 69- Consult, NASA, 63- Sr. mem. Inst. Elec. & Electronics Eng; Am. Soc. Eng. Educ; N.Y. Acad. Sci. Network theory; electronics and microelectronics; antennas and electromagnetic propagation; reliability; medical electronics. Address: Weinschel Engineering, Clopper Rd, Gaithersburg, MD 20760.

DePIERRE, VINCENT, b. N.Y.C, Aug. 29, 15; m. 42; c. 4. PHYSICAL METALLURGY. B.Ch.E, Cooper Union, 38. Jr. mat. engr. naval ord, U.S. Naval Gun Factory, D.C, 39-41, asst. mat. engr, 41-42, assoc. mat. engr, 42-45, metallurgist, 45-48, sr. metallurgist, 48-58, supvr. phys. metallurgist, 58-60; phys. metallurigst, AIR FORCE MAT. LAB. WRIGHT-PATTERSON AIR FORCE BASE, OHIO, 60-62, RES. PHYS. METALLURGIST, 62- Am. Soc. Metals; Am. Inst. Min, Metall. & Petrol. Eng. Development of melting, casting, mechanical working and heat treating processes for naval ordnance and air force weapons systems, coupling science with technology of mechanical working of high strength metals and alloys. Address: 6309 Rosebury Dr, Dayton, OH 45424.

DePIERRI, W(ILLIAM) G(OMAN), JR, b. Nashville, Tenn, Aug. 24, 30; m. 57; c. 3. ORGANIC CHEMISTRY. B.A, Vanderbilt, 52, M.A, 54; Ph.D.(chem), Illinois, 57. Asst, Illinois, 53-54, 55-57; RES. SPECIALIST, ESSO RES. & ENG. CO, LINDEN, 57- Summers, chemist, E.I. du Pont de Nemours & Co, Inc, 52-55; Old Hickory Chem. Co, 54. Am. Chem. Soc; Am. Inst. Chem. Eng; Soc. Plastics Eng. Polymer chemistry; elastomer technology; petroleum specialties; rubber extenders; scale inhibition. Address: 20 Mountain Ave, Warren, NJ 07060.

de PILLIS, JOHN, b. New York, N.Y, Dec. 21, 36; m. 60; c. 2. MATHEMATICS. M.E, Stevens Inst. Tech, 58; Nat. Sci. Found. fel, California, Berkeley, 58-59, M.A, 62, Ph.D.(math), 65. Asst. prof. MATH, San Francisco State Col, 62-65; UNIV. CALIF, RIVERSIDE, 65-69, ASSOC. PROF, 69-, CHMN. DEPT, 70- Vis. assoc. mathematician, Brookhaven Nat. Lab, 68-69. Am. Math. Soc; Math. Asn. Am. Functional analysis; operator algebras; convexity; iterative analysis. Address: Dept. of Mathematics, University of California, Riverside, CA 92502.

DePINTO, JOHN A, b. Youngstown, Ohio, Jan. 4, 37; m. 62; c. 3. MICROBIOLOGY, BIOCHEMISTRY. B.A, Youngstown, 58; Ph.D.(microbiol), Illinois, 65. Nat. Acad. Sci. Agr. Res. Serv. fel, microbiol. chem, North. Regional Res. Lab, U.S. Dept. Agr, Ill, 65-66; asst. prof. BIOL, BRADLEY UNIV, 66-69, ASSOC. PROF, 69- Am. Soc. Microbiol. Mechanism of action of microbial amylases. Address: Dept. of Biology, Bradley University, Peoria, IL 61606.

DEPOCAS, FLORENT, b. Montreal, Que, Jan. 1, 23; m. 52; c. 2. PHYSIOLOGY. B.Sc, Montreal, 46, Ph.D.(biochem), 51. Biochemist, Sacred Heart Hosp, Montreal, 51-52; asst. res. officer, DIV. BIOSCI, NAT. RES. COUN. CAN, 52-58, assoc. res. officer, 58-61, sr. res. officer, 61-69, ASST. DIR, 69- AAAS; Am. Physiol. Soc; Can. Physiol. Soc; Can. Biochem. Soc. Biochemistry and physiology of acclimation to cold in small mammals; glucose biokinetics. Address: Division of Biology, National Research Council, Montreal Rd, Ottawa, Ont. K1A 0R6, Can.

DePOE, CHARLES E(DWARD), b. Southampton, N.Y, Sept. 18, 27; m. 52. BOTANY. B.S.(ornamental hort) & B.S.(zool), N.C. State Col, 56, M.S, 58, Ph.D.(bot), 61. Tech. asst, Long Island Agr. & Tech. Inst, 53-54; asst. prof. BIOL, NORTHEAST LA. UNIV, 61-66, ASSOC. PROF, 66- Summer res. participant, Oak Ridge Nat. Lab, 64; chmn, La. Jr. Acad. Sci, 66- U.S.N, 45-46. AAAS; Bot. Soc. Am; Soc. Study Evolution; Ecol. Soc. Am; Am. Soc. Plant Taxon; Int. Soc. Plant Taxon. Distribution, ecology and productivity of aquatic macrophytes. Address: Dept. of Biology, Northeast Louisiana University, Monroe, LA 71201.

DEPOMMIER, PIERRE HENRI MAURICE, b. Montcy-St-Pierre, France, Dec. 15, 25; m. 56; c. 3. NUCLEAR PHYSICS. Lic. és Sci, Univ. Lille, 46; Lic. és Sci, Univ. Paris, 48; Ph.D.(physics), Univ. Grenoble, 61. Lectr, FACULTY SCI, Univ. Grenoble, 61-65, PROF, 65-69; UNIV. MONTREAL, 69-, DIR. LAB. NUCLEAR PHYSICS, 69- Am. Phys. Soc; Brit. Inst. Physics & Phys. Soc; French Phys. Soc. Nuclear reactions at low energy; nuclear spectroscopy. Address: Lab. of Nuclear Physics, University of Montreal, C.P. 6128, Montreal 101, Que, Can.

DEPP, WALLACE ANDREW, b. Summer Shade, Ky, Dec. 22, 14; m. 39; c. 1. ELECTRICAL ENGINEERING. B.S, Illinois, 36, M.S, 37. Mem. tech. staff, BELL TEL. LABS, 37-51, dept. head, electronic apparatus develop, 51-53, transmission systs. develop, 53-55, dir. spec. systs. develop, 55-61, dir. electronic PBX develop, 61-64, dir. electronic switching systs. lab, 64-68, EXEC. DIR, Holmdel switching div, 68-70, OPERATOR SERV. & SUBURBAN SWITCHING, 70- Fel. Inst. Elec. & Electronics Eng. Design of gas filled electron tubes; circuity; instrumentation; radar; data and voice transmission; electronic switching. Address: Bell Telephone Labs, Holmdel, NJ 07733.

DePREE, DAVID O(TTE), b. Amoy, China, Sept. 17, 18; m. 42; c. 2. ORGANIC CHEMISTRY. A.B, Hope Col, 40; fel, Massachusetts, 40-42, M.S, 42. Res. chemist dielectrics Gen. Elec. Co, 42-44; fuel additives, Ethyl Corp, 46-61; sr. chemist, Aerojet Gen. Corp, 61-67, ASSOC. SCIENTIST, 67-71, AEROJET SOLID PROPULSION CO, 71- U.S.N, 44-46. Am. Chem. Soc; Sci. Res. Soc. Am. Development of solid propellants for rocket motors; fundamental research on alkali metal organic compounds; development of new antioxidants for hydrocarbon fuels. Address: Aerojet Solid Propulsion Co, Dept. 4400, Bldg. 0525, P.O. Box 13400, Sacramento, CA 95813.

DePREE, JOHN DERYCK, b. Zeeland, Mich, Dec. 5, 33; m. 54; c. 4. MATHEMATICS. B.A, Hope Col, 55; M.S, Colorado, 58, Ph.D.(math), 62. Instr. appl. math, Colorado, 57-62; asst. prof. MATH, Oregon State, 62-65; assoc. prof, Va. Polytech, 65-68; PROF, N.MEX. STATE UNIV, 68- Am. Math. Soc; Math. Asn. Am. Theory of analytic functions; entire functions; integral equations. Address: Dept. of Mathematics, New Mexico State University, Las Cruces, NM 88001.

DePRIESTER, CORAL LEE, b. Jackson, Mich, Apr. 24, 22; m. 46; c. 2. CHEMICAL & PETROLEUM ENGINEERING. B.S, Michigan, 47, M.S, 48. Res. engr, Calif. Res. Corp, 48-58; chief engr, Richmond Explor. Co, Venezuela, 58-62; sr. eng. assoc, CHEVRON RES. CO, 62-68, SR. STAFF ENGR, 68- Eng.C, U.S.A, 43-46, Capt. AAAS; Am. Inst. Chem. Eng; Soc. Petrol. Eng. Light hydrocarbon vapor-liquid equilibrium; applied chemistry and physics for improving oil and gas well performance; analysis of oil, formation water and sedimentary rock to develop advanced practical technology. Address: Chevron Research Co, 200 Bush St, San Francisco, CA 94120.

DePRIMA, C(HARLES) R(AYMOND), b. Paterson, N.J, July 10, 18; m. 43, 51. MATHEMATICS. A.B, N.Y. Univ, 40, Ph.D.(math), 43. Instr. math, Wash. Sq. Col, N.Y. Univ, 41-43, lectr, grad. sch, 43-46, res. scientist, appl. math. panel, 42-46; asst. prof. appl. mech, CALIF. INST. TECHNOL, 46-51, assoc. prof, 51-54, PROF, 54-64, MATH, 64- Vis. prof, California, Los Angeles, 48-; N.Y. Univ, 63-64. Head math. br, Off. Naval Res, 51-52. Civilian with Off. Sci. Res. Develop; U.S.A.F, 44. Am. Math. Soc; Soc. Indust. & Appl. Math. Partial differential equations; mathematical theory of compressible gases and supersonic nozzle flows; water waves; functional analysis. Address: Dept. of Mathematics, California Institute of Technology, Pasadena, CA 91109.

DEPRIT, ANDRÉ A(LBERT) M(AURICE), b. St. Servais, Belgium, Apr. 10, 26; m. 59; c. 1. ASTRONOMY. M.A, Louvain, 48, M.Sc, 53, Ph.D.(math), 57. Lectr. celestial mech, Lovanium Univ, Congo, 57-58; Louvain, 58-62, prof, 62-64; mem. staff, Boeing Sci. Res. Labs, 64-71; PROF. ASTRON, UNIV. S.FLA, 71- NATO advan. res. fel, 63; vis. lectr, Univ. Wash, 65-67; vis. prof, Yale, 65-66; resident vis, Bell Telephone Labs, summer, 68; vis. prof, Univ. Liege, 70; Nat. Acad. Sci. sr. res. fel, 71. Agathon De Potter prize, Royal Acad. Sci, Belgium, 57; Adolphe Wattrems prize, 71. AAAS; fel. Am. Inst. Aeronaut. & Astronaut; Royal Astron. Soc; Am. Astron. Soc; Int. Astron. Union. Celestial and analytical mechanics; periodic orbits in the three body problem; axiomatic foundations of Hamiltonian formalisms; computer sciences. Address: Dept. of Mathematics, University of South Florida, Tampa, FL 33620.

DePROSPO, NICHOLAS D(OMINICK), b. N.Y.C, July 16, 23; m. 60; c. 1. ANATOMY. B.A, N.Y. Univ, 46, M.A, 47, Ph.D.(biol. ed), 57. From instr. to PROF. BIOL. & CHMN. DEPT, SETON HALL UNIV, 47-, ACTING DEAN COL. ARTS & SCI, 71- Summer, instr, Long Island Univ, 47. Med.Dept, U.S.A, 43-46. AAAS; Am. Soc. Zool; Am. Inst. Biol. Sci; Asn. Am. Med. Col. Interrelationships between the pineal gland and other endocrine glands; comparative vertebrate anatomy; comparative endocrinology and anatomy. Address: Dept. of Biology, Seton Hall University, South Orange, NJ 07079.

DEPUE, ROBERT H(EMPHILL), b. Pittsburgh, Pa, Aug. 15, 31; m. 56; c. 2. BIOCHEMISTRY, MICROBIOLOGY. B.S, Carnegie Inst. Tech, 53; Nat. Sci. Found. fel, Hahnemann Med. Col, 60, Ph.D.(microbiol), 63. Res. asst. biochem, Illinois, 53-54; fel. biophysics, Mellon Inst, 62-65, U.S. PUB. HEALTH SERV. OFF, NAT. CANCER INST, 65- U.S.A, 54-58, Res, 58-, Capt. AAAS. Enzymology; molecular biology; biophysics of muscle proteins; electron microscopy; viral oncology. Address: National Cancer Institute, Room 11A11, Bldg. 31, Bethesda, MD 20014.

DE PUY, CHARLES H(ERBERT), b. Detroit, Mich, Sept. 10, 27; m. 49; c. 4. ORGANOMETALLIC CHEMISTRY. B.S, California, Berkeley, 48; A.M, Columbia, 52; Ph.D.(chem), Yale, 53. Res. fel, California, Los Angeles, 53-54; asst. prof. CHEM, Iowa State, 54-60, assoc. prof, 60-63, PROF, 63-64; UNIV. COLO, BOULDER, 64-, chmn. dept, 66-68. Nat. Insts. Health fel, Univ. Basel, 69-70; vis. prof, Univ. Ill, 54; Univ. Calif, Berkeley, 60; consult, A.E. Staley Co; Marathon Oil Co. Med.C, U.S.A, 46-47. Am. Chem. Soc; Brit. Chem. Soc. Organic reaction mechanisms and stereochemistry; Address: Dept. of Chemistry, University of Colorado, Boulder, CO 80302.

DePUY, GLENN WILLIAM, b. Denver, Colo; c. 3. MATERIALS SCIENCE. Geol.E, Colo. Sch. Mines, 52; M.S, Univ. Colo, Boulder, 60. Geologist, U.S. BUR. RECLAMATION, 55-67, PHYS. SCIENTIST, 67- C.Eng, U.S.A, 52-54, 1st Lt. Fel. Geol. Soc. Am; Asn. Eng. Geol. Polymer science; concrete technology; concrete-polymer materials; materials testing; geology; engineering petrography; rock properties. Address: 1685 S. Monaco St, Denver, CO 80222.

DE RAFOLS, WIFREDO, b. Barcelona, Spain, Oct. 23, 15; U.S. citizen; m. 42; c. 2. BIOCHEMISTRY, AGRONOMY. Ph.D.(agron, eng), Madrid, 47. Asst. biochem, Nat. Inst. Agr, Res, Spain, 48-50, assoc. res. indust. utilization agr. prod, 52-55, dept. head, 55-61; fel, J.E. Seagram's Co, Ky, 50-51; Calif. Inst. Tech, 51-52; RES. BIOCHEMIST, UNIV. CALIF, DAVIS, 61- Scholar, Nat. Coun. Sci. Res, Spain, 47-49; assoc. prof, Madrid, 59-61; consult, developing countries. Nat. award, Dept. Agr. Spain, 55. C.Eng, 36-40, Lt. Am. Chem. Soc. Plant biochemistry and physiology; ecology; chemical engineering; fermentations; food technology; nutrition; mineral deficiencies in experimental animals; relations between food and behavior. Address: 427 Anza Ave, Davis, CA 95616.

DERANLEAU, DAVID A, b. Seattle, Wash, Apr. 9, 34. BIOPHYSICAL CHEMISTRY. B.A, San Francisco State Col, 56; M.S, Stanford Univ, 58; Ph.D. (biochem), Univ. Wash, 63. Nat. Insts. Health fel. biochem, Univ. Wash, 63-65; Swiss Fed. Inst. Technol, 65-67, Ciba res. fel, 67-68; ASST. PROF. BIOCHEM, UNIV. WASH, 69- Vis. scientist, Am. Univ. Beirut, spring 67. Multiple equilibria; theory of binding measurements; polarized fluorescence; charge transfer; energy transfer in biological systems; solution conformation of biomolecules. Address: Dept. of Biochemistry, University of Washington, Seattle, WA 98105.

DERBENWICK, FRANK, b. Concord, Calif, Feb. 18, 09; m. 42; c. 4. CHEMICAL ENGINEERING. B.A, Stanford, 32, M.A, 33, Ph.D.(phys. chem), 37. Construct. supvr, county govt, Hilo, Hawaii, 33-34; technologist petrol, Shell Oil Co, Calif, 37-43, supvr. petrochem, Shell Chem. Co, Tex, 43-44; sr. chem. engr, Am. Cyanamid Co, 44-45; eng. res. mgr, Gerber Prod. Co, 46-47; process engr, Calif. Res. Corp, 47-48; sr. chem. engr, Am. Cyanamid Co, 49-50, proj. engr, 50-51, group leader, 51-52, asst. dir. chem. eng. dept, 52-55, tech. dir. chemicals, 55-56, consult. synthetic fibers, 56-57, asst. to dir. polymer res, 58-59; independent consult, 60-62; asst. prof. CHEM. ENG, MANHATTAN COL, 62-64, assoc. prof, 64-68, PROF, 68-, DIR. MASTER'S DEGREE PROG, 67- Consult, Badger Mfg. Co; Sohio Chem. Co; Carwin Co; M.W. Kellog.Co, 63-; Pfizer, Inc, 70- Am. Chem. Soc; Am. Inst. Chem. Eng; Am. Soc. Eng. Educ. Process design, reaction kinetics and environmental engineering. Address: 36 Bramble Lane, Riverside, CT 06878.

DERBY, ALBERT, b. Antwerp, Belg, Nov. 12, 39; U.S. citizen; m. 62; c. 2. DEVELOPMENTAL BIOLOGY, ENDOCRINOLOGY. B.S, City Col. New York, 61; M.S, N.Y. Univ, 64; Ph.D.(biol), City Univ. New York, 69. Teacher gen. sci, N.Y.C. Bd. Educ, 62-64; Nat. Insts. Health training grant develop. biol, Yale, 68-70; ASST. PROF. BIOL, UNIV. Mo-ST. LOUIS, 70- Partic, Conf. Hormones Develop, Eng, 68; First Conf. Amphibian Metamorphosis, Fla. State Univ, 69. AAAS; Am. Soc. Zool; Soc. Develop. Biol. Developmental study, both in vivo and in vito, of the biochemistry and endocrinology of amphibian metamorphosis. Address: Dept. of Biology, University of Missouri-St. Louis, 8001 Natural Bridge Rd, St. Louis, MO 63121.

DERBY, PALMER, b. Washington, D.C, May 23, 20; m. 41; c. 2. ELECTRICAL ENGINEERING. Va. Polytech; Mass. Inst. Tech. Proj. engr. magnetron develop. lab, RAYTHEON CO, 42-52, head develop. eng. sect, 52-54, mgr. microwave power tube div, 54-59, asst. mgr. Spencer Lab, 59-60, mkt. mgr, MICROWAVE & POWER TUBE DIV, 61-62, ASST. GEN. MGR, 62-, V.PRES, 67- Microwave electron tubes. Address: Raytheon Co, Microwave & Power Tube Division, 190 Willow St, Waltham, MA 02154.

DERBY, RICHARD, b. Cluj, Rumania, July 7, 36; U.S. citizen; m. 58; c. 3. ORGANIC CHEMISTRY. B.S, City Col. New York, 58; Ph.D.(org. chem), Purdue, 63. SR. CHEMIST, ROHM & HAAS CO, 63- Am. Chem. Soc. Organic synthesis and mechanisms; polymer stabilization; adhesion and adhesives. Address: 3529 Oriole Dr, Huntington Valley, PA 19006.

DERBY, STANLEY K(INGDON), b. Bangor, Mich, Sept. 12, 20; m. 43; c. 3. PHYSICS. B.S, Chicago, 44; M.S, Michigan, 48, fel, 50-54, Ph.D, 57. From asst. prof. to PROF. PHYSICS, WEST. MICH. 55- U.S.A.F, 42-46, Res, 46-, Col. AAAS; Am. Asn. Physics Teachers. Faraday effects; analysis of biological material by ultraviolet emission spectroscopy. Address: Dept. of Physics, Western Michigan University, Kalamazoo, MI 49001.

DERBYSHIRE, WILLIAM D(AVIS), b. Paterson, N.J, June 26, 24; m. 47; c. 2. PHYSICS. M.E, Stevens Inst. Tech, 45; M.S, Purdue, 51, Ph.D.(physics), 58. Engr, Gen. Elec. Co, 45-47; instr. PHYSICS, Stevens Inst. Tech, 47-48; asst, Purdue, 48-56; asst. prof, COLO. STATE UNIV, 56-61, ASSOC. PROF, 61- Am. Phys. Soc. Ferromagnetism; statistical physics. Address: Dept. of Physics, Colorado State University, Ft. Collins, CO 80521.

DERDERIAN, GEORGE, b. Rochester, N.Y, Nov. 19, 22; m. 53; c. 4. OPTICS. B.S, Queens Col.(N.Y), 47; N.Y. State scholar, N.Y. Univ, 49-51, M.S, 51. Instr. physics, Pratt Inst, 47-50; physicist, U.S. Signal Corps, 50-55; sr. engr. dynamics, Repub. Aviation Corp, 55-56, prin. engr. optics, 56-58, res. specialist infrared eng. optics, 58-59; sr. res. engr, optics, Fairchild Camera & Instrument Corp, 59-60; res. engr. infrared-optics, Sperry Gyroscope Co, 60-64; RES. PHYSICIST, U.S. NAVAL TRAINING DEVICE CTR, 64-, HEAD PHYS. SCI. LAB, FLA, 68- Eve. instr, Hofstra, 56-58, asst. prof, 58-67; lectr, Rollins Col. U.S.A, 43-46; Bronze Star Medal. Fel. AAAS; Optical Soc. Am; Am. Asn. Physics Teachers; Soc. Photog. Sci. & Eng; Brit. Interplanetary Soc. Star detection using polarization techniques; laser beam deflector; application of the laser to optical systems. Address: 921 Gillis Ct, Maitland, FL 32751.

DeREMER, RUSSELL JAY, b. Bell, Calif, May 2, 40; m. 62; c. 2. PHYSICS. A.B, Occidental Col, 61; M.S, Indiana, 63, Ph.D.(high energy physics), 66. Asst. prof. PHYSICS, CALIF. STATE COL, SAN BERNARDINO, 66-69, ASSOC. PROF, 69-, ASSOC. DEAN ACTIVITIES & HOUSING, 68- Am. Phys. Soc; Am. Asn. Physics Teachers. High energy physics. Address: Dept. of Physics, California State College at San Bernardino, 5500 State College Pkwy, San Bernardino, CA 92407.

DE RENZO, E(DWARD) C(LARENCE), b. Passaic, N.J, Sept. 29, 25; m. 50; c. 4. BIOLOGICAL CHEMISTRY. B.S, Fordham, 45, M.S, 47, Ph.D.(biochem), 50. Instr. chem, Fordham, 45-50; res. chemist, LEDERLE LABS. DIV, AM. CYANAMID CO, 51-54, GROUP LEADER & SR. RES. BIOCHEMIST, 54- Am. Soc. Biol. Chem. Activation of plasminogen; streptokinase; fibrinolysis; metabolism. Address: Metabolic Chemotherapy Dept, Lederle Labs, American Cyanamid Co, Pearl River, NY 10965.

DERENZO, STEPHEN E(DWARD), b. Chicago, Ill, Dec. 31, 41; m. 66; c. 2. PARTICLE PHYSICS. B.S, Univ. Chicago, 63, M.S, 65, Assoc. Midwest Univs. fel, 65-66, Shell Found. fel, 67-68, Ph.D.(physics), 69. Technician, Univ. Chicago, 59-64, res. asst, Enrico Fermi Inst, 64-68; PHYSICIST, LAWRENCE BERKELEY LAB, UNIV. CALIF, 68- Lectr, Univ. Calif, Berkeley, 69-70; consult, Nat. Sci. Found. computer facilities grant to Lawrence Hall of Sci, Univ. Calif, Berkeley, 70- Am. Phys. Soc. Muon decay; particle detector development; strong interaction resonances; computers in education; infrared astronomy. Address: Group A, Lawrence Berkeley Lab, University of California, Berkeley, CA 94720.

DE REPENTIGNY, JACQUES, b. Montreal, Que, May 15, 20; m. 46; c. 1. BACTERIOLOGY, IMMUNOLOGY. B.Sc, Univ. Montreal, 44, M.Sc, 45, Ph.D.(org. chem), 48. Res. asst. microbiol, Inst. Microbiol. & Hyg, UNIV. MONTREAL, 47-52, res. assoc, 54-64, assoc. prof. bact. & immunol, FACULTY MED, 64-66, PROF. MICROBIOL. & IMMUNOL, 66-, CONSULT, INST. MICROBIOL. & HYG, 64-, univ. fel. biochem, Univ. Paris, 52-53 & immunol, Nat. Inst. Med. Res, London, Eng, 53-54. Am. Soc. Microbiol; Chem. Inst. Can; Can. Biochem. Soc; Can. Pub. Health Asn; Can. Soc. Microbiol. (pres, 71, award, 69); Can. Soc. Immunol; Brit. Soc. Gen. Microbiol; Brit. Biochem. Soc; Int. Asn. Microbiol. Socs. Purification of antigens and antibodies; antigenic structure of microorganisms; immunofluorescence and fluorescence microscopy; nucleic acids and virulence in bacteria; metabolism and pathogenicity in pyogenic bacteria. Address: Dept. of Microbiology & Immunology, Faculty of Medicine, University of Montreal, P.O. Box 6128, Montreal 101, Que, Can.

DERESIEWICZ, HERBERT, b. Czechoslovakia, Nov. 5, 25; nat; m. 55; c. 3. THEORETICAL & APPLIED MECHANICS. B.M.E, City Col. New York, 46; M.S, Columbia, 48, univ. fel, 49-50, Ph.D.(mech), 52. Res. engr, sr. staff, appl. physics lab, Hopkins, 50-51; res. assoc, civil eng, COLUMBIA UNIV, 51-53, asst. prof, 53-55, MECH. ENG, 55-57, assoc. prof, 57-62, PROF, 62- Fulbright sr. res. scholar, Italy, 60-61; Fulbright lectr, Israel, 66-67. U.S.A, 46-47. AAAS; Am. Soc. Mech. Eng; Seismol. Soc. Am; N.Y. Acad. Sci. Theory of elasticity; vibrations of crystals; thermoelasticity; elastic contact theory; mechanics of granular media; wave propagation in porous media. Address: 336 Broad Ave, Englewood, NJ 07631.

DERFER, JOHN M(ENTZER), b. Navarre, Ohio, Aug. 9, 20; m. 44. ORGANIC CHEMISTRY. A.B, Col. Wooster, 42; fel, Ohio State, 46, Ph.D.(org. chem), 46. Asst, Ohio State, 42-45, res. assoc. & ed. res. proj, Am. Petrol. Inst, 45, air res. & develop. command proj. 572, res. assoc, Univ. Res. Found, 47-55, assoc. dir. petrol. inst. res. proj, 55-59; mgr. res. labs, Glidden Co, 59-61, dir. res, org. chem. div, 61-66, MGR. EXPLOR. RES, ORG. CHEM. GROUP, GLIDDEN-DURKEE DIV, SCM CORP, 66- Dwight P. Joyce Award, SCM Corp, 67. Am. Chem. Soc; Am. Oil Chemists' Soc; N.Y. Acad. Sci. Synthesis of low molecular weight hydrocarbons; synthesis and infrared spectra of cyclic hydrocarbons; synthesis of carcinols and bromides and oxidation of hydrocarbons; knocking characteristics of hydrocarbons; pre-flame reactions of fuels; terpene chemistry; rosin; fatty acids; naval stores; essential oils; flavor and perfume chemicals. Address: Organic Chemicals Group, Glidden-Durkee Division, SCM Corp, Box 389, Jacksonville, FL 32201.

DERGARABEDIAN, PAUL, b. Racine, Wis, Jan. 19, 22; m. 47; c. 4. MECHANICAL ENGINEERING, PHYSICS. B.S, Wisconsin, 48, M.S, 49; Shell fel. & Ph.D.(mech. eng, physics), Calif. Inst. Tech, 52. Acting head hydrodyn. br, U.S. Naval Ord. Test. Sta, 52-55; from mgr. syst. design & anal. dept. to STAFF MGR, TRW SYSTS, REDONDO BEACH, 55- Vis. prof, Calif. Inst. Technol, 71-72. U.S.A.A.F, 43-46. Am. Astron. Soc.(pres, 69-71). Mechanism of cavitation; water-entry impact; rotational non-viscous flow; missile systems design and analysis; powered-flight mechanics; space technology; meteorology and theoretical analysis of tornadoes and hurricanes. Address: 29322 Stadia Hill Lane, Palos Verdes Peninsula, CA 90274.

DERGE, G(ERHARD JULIUS), b. Lincoln, Nebr, Feb. 11, 09; m. 37; c. 2. METALLURGY. A.B, Amherst Col, 30; Ph.D.(phys. chem), Princeton, 34. Metallurgist, metals res. lab, CARNEGIE-MELLON UNIV, 34-39, asst. prof. & later assoc. prof. METALL, 39-49, prof, 49-51, Jones & Laughlin prof, 51-64, PROF, 64- Am. Chem. Soc; Am. Inst. Mining, Metall. & Petrol. Eng.(ed, Metall. Trans, 58-); fel. Am. Soc. Metals; Brit. Iron & Steel Inst; fel. Metall. Soc. The palladium-hydrogen system; crystallography of metallic transformations and reactions; factors controlling grain size in steel; properties of tin and its alloys; ferrous metallurgy; kinetics and mechanisms of slag-metal reactions; analysis and control of gases in steel; slag constitution. Address: Dept. of Metallurgy & Materials Science, Carnegie-Mellon University, Schenley Park, Pittsburgh, PA 15213.

DE RIDDER, CHRISTA-MARIA, b. Germany, Apr. 15, 31; U.S. citizen. APPLIED MATHEMATICS. B.S, Louisville, 53; B.A, Oxford, 56, M.A, 60. STAFF MEM, LINCOLN LAB, MASS. INST. TECHNOL, 57- Electromagnetic scattering problems; analysis of reentry radar data. Address: Lincoln Lab, Massachusetts Institute of Technology, Lexington, MA 02173.

DERIEG, MICHAEL E, b. Jan. 24, 35; U.S. citizen; m. 62; c. 3. ORGANIC CHEMISTRY. B.S, Nebraska, 56, M.S, 58, Ph.D.(org. chem), 60; Fordham, 63-66. Asst. org. chem, Nebraska, 55-59; res. chemist, Celanese Corp, 60-61; appointee, Mass. Inst. Technol, 61-62; sr. chemist, HOFFMANN-LA ROCHE INC, 62-71, TECH. COORD, DIV. ANIMAL HEALTH, 71- Am. Chem. Soc; Brit. Chem. Soc; fel. Am. Inst. Chem; N.Y. Acad. Sci. Naphthenic acids; exocyclic olefins; macrocyclic and pyrimidine nucleoside antibiotics; reaction mechanisms; heterocyclic chemistry, especially benzodiazepines, benzodiazocines, flavones, and quinazolines. Address: Hoffmann-La Roche, Inc, Nutley, NJ 07110.

DeRISI, MARY C(HRISTINE), b. Schenectady, N.Y, Sept. 14, 05; m. 38. DENTISTRY. D.D.S, Pennsylvania, 27. From instr. to assoc. prof. prosthetic dent, SCH. DENT, GEORGETOWN UNIV, 28-66, PROF. PROSTHODONTICS, 66- Fel. Am. Col. Dent; Am. Dent. Asn; Asn. Am. Women Dentists (secytreas, 54, pres-elect, 55, pres, 56). Prosthetic dentistry. Address: Dept. of Prosthodontics, Georgetown University School of Dentistry, Washington, DC 20007.

DERMAN, CYRUS, b. Phila, Pa, July 16, 25; m. 61; c. 2. MATHEMATICAL STATISTICS. A.B, Pennsylvania, 48, A.M, 49; Ph.D.(math. statist), Columbia, 54. Instr. math, Syracuse, 54; PROF. indust. eng, COLUMBIA UNIV, 55-68, OPERS RES, 68- Vis. prof, Israel Inst. Technol, 61-62; Stanford Univ, 65-66. U.S.N.R, 43-46, Ens. AAAS; fel. Inst. Math. Statist; fel. Am. Statist. Asn. Probability theory; mathematical statistics; operations research. Address: 312 S.W. Mudd Bldg, Columbia University, New York, NY 10027.

DER MARDEROSIAN, ARA H(AROLD), b. Somerville, Mass, Jan. 6, 35; m. 61; c. 1. PHARMACOGNOSY. B.S, Mass. Col. Pharm, 56, fel, 56-58, M.S, 58, indust. grant, 58-59; U.S. Pub. Health Serv. grant, Rhode Island, 62-64, Ph.D.(pharmaceut. sci), 64. Asst. pharmaceut. chem. & pharmacog, Rhode Island, 59-62; asst. prof. pharm, PHILA. COL. PHARM, & 64-68, ASSOC. PROF. PHARMACOG, 68- Nat. Guard, 57-62. Am. Chem. Soc; Am. Soc. Pharmacog; Am. Pharmaceut. Asn. Psychotomimetic botanicals; medicinal plants; poisonous plants; hallucinogenic morning glories; use of dimethyl sulfoxide in drug plant extraction and pharmacological and chemical testing of potentially toxic household plants; marine pharmacognosy; chemistry and botany of drugs of abuse. Address: Dept. of Pharmacy, Philadelphia College of Pharmacy & Science, 43rd & Kingsessing Ave, Philadelphia, PA 19104.

der MATEOSIAN, EDWARD, b. N.Y.C, Aug. 6, 14; m. 47; c. 2. NUCLEAR PHYSICS. B.A, Columbia, 35, M.A, 41. Res. chemist, Barrett Co, 38-41; asst. physics, Indiana, 41-42; PHYSICIST, geiger Mueller tube res, U.S. Naval Res. Lab, 42-46; NUCLEAR PHYSICS, isomeric states, Argonne Nat. Lab, 47-49; BROOKHAVEN NAT. LAB, 49- Fel. Am. Phys. Soc. Radioactive decay; nuclear energy levels; techniques in scintillation spectrometry; heavy ion reactions. Address: Brookhaven National Lab, Upton, NY 11973.

DERMATIS, STEVEN N, b. Astakos, Greece, Nov. 30, 29; U.S. citizen; m. 64; c. 2. ELECTRICAL ENGINEERING. B.Sc, Mass. Inst. Tech, 53, M.Sc, 55. Res. engr, Reliance Elec. & Eng. Co, 55; engr, Westinghouse Elec. Corp, 55-60, sr. engr, 60-63; sr. res. staff, mat. ctr, Mass. Inst. Tech, 63-66; res. assoc. semiconductor thin films, Northeast. Univ, 66-69; ENG. MGR, ALPHA INDUSTS. CO, NEWTON UPPER FALLS, 69- Sr. mem. Inst. Elec. & Electronics Eng; Electrochem. Soc. Servomechanisms and electronic materials; analysis and design of control systems; study and development of crystal growth. Address: 26 Mystic Valley Pkwy, Winchester, MA 01890.

DERMEN, HAIG, b. Constantinople, Turkey, Oct. 22, 95; U.S. citizen; m. 27; c. 3. BOTANY. B.S, Conn. State Col, 25; M.S, Maine, 27; M.S, Harvard, 31, Ph.D.(cytol), 33. Instr. bot. & genetics, Maine, 25-29; asst. cytol, Arnold Arboretum, Harvard, 29-37; asst. cytologist, bur. plant indust, U.S. Dept. Agr, 37-43, bur. plant indust, soils & agr. eng, 43-44, assoc. cytologist, 44-48, cytologist, 48-53, hort. crops res. br, AGR. RES. SERV, 53-56, sr. cytologist, 56-63, res. cytologist, 63-65, COLLAB, PLANT INDUST. STA, CROPS RES. DIV, 65- AAAS; fel. Bot. Soc. Am; fel. Genetics Soc. Am; fel. Am. Genetic Asn; fel. Am. Soc. Hort. Sci; fel. Am. Soc. Nat. Colchicine polyploidy of fruit and floricultural plants; cytohistology; study of periclinal chimeras. Address: Plant Industry Station, Crops Research Division, Agricultural Research Service, Beltsville, MD 20705.

DERMER, O(TIS) C(LIFFORD), b. Hoytville, Ohio, Nov. 11, 09; m. 35; c. 3. ORGANIC CHEMISTRY. B.S, Bowling Green State, 30, hon. D.Sc, 60; fel, Ohio State, 33-34, Ph.D.(chem), 34. Instr. CHEM, OKLA. STATE UNIV, 34-36, asst. prof, 36-38, assoc. prof, 38-47, PROF, 47-, head dept, 49-71. Am. Chem. Soc; Brit. Chem. Soc. Chemicals from petroleum and natural gas; organic nomenclature; chemical literature. Address: Dept. of Chemistry, Oklahoma State University, Stillwater, OK 74074.

DERMIT, GEORGE, b. Istanbul, Turkey, Feb. 9, 25; U.S. citizen; m. 50; c. 2. SOLID STATE PHYSICS, ELECTRONICS. B.S, Robert Col, Istanbul, 47; M.S, Cornell, 49; Ohio State, 49-52; Ph.D.(physics), Polytech. Inst. Brooklyn, 61. Engr. electronics, Sylvania Elec. Prod, Inc, 52-54; sr. engr, Link Aviation, Inc, 54-56; chief scientist semiconductors, Gen. Transistor Corp, 56-59; sect. head, Gen. Tel. & Electronics Lab, Inc, 59-63; OWNER, G. DERMIT ELECTRONICS, 63- Am. Phys. Soc; Inst. Elec. & Electronics Eng. Crystal gorwth; materials purification; semiconductor devices; metals and alloys. Address: G. Dermit Electronics, 198-31 27th Ave, Flushing, NY 11358.

DERMODY, WILLIAM J(OSEPH), b. New York, N.Y, Aug. 8, 15; m. 41, 57; c. 3. ORGANIC CHEMISTRY. B.A, Alfred, 39. Lab. asst. & res. chemist, Am. Hard Rubber Co, 40-46; asst. chief chem, Jos. Stokes Rubber Co, 46; from asst. chief chem. to supvry. chem. engr, Stokes Molded Prods. Div, ELEC. STORAGE BATTERY CO, 46-57, group leader org. CHEM, RES. CTR, 57-63, proj. leader, appl. theory, 63-67, SR. SCIENTIST, POLYMERIC MAT, 67- Am. Chem. Soc; Am. Soc. Test. & Mat; Soc. Plastic Eng. Chemistry of hard rubber; vulcanization and degradation mechanisms; polymer structure; cross linking; electrochemistry; adhesives. Address: Wilfred Ave, Titusville, NJ 08560.

DERN, RAYMOND JAMES, b. Rochester, N.Y, July 5, 18; m. 48; c. 5. INTERNAL MEDICINE. B.A, Rochester, 40, fel, 40-42, Ph.D.(physiol), 46, M.D, 47. Intern, clinics, Chicago, 47-48; asst. resident surg, Rochester, 48-49; U.S. Pub. Health Serv. fel, MED, clinics, Chicago, 49-50, from asst. resident to resident, 50-52, instr, 52, asst, 52-54, asst. prof. STRITCH SCH. MED, LOYOLA UNIV. CHICAGO, 54-57, assoc. prof, 57-61, PROF, 61- Res. assoc, Hektoen Inst, 57-; attend. physician, Cook County Hosp, 58-Med.C, 52-54, Capt. Am. Soc. Hemat; Soc. Nuclear Med; Am. Fedn. Clin. Res; fel. Int. Soc. Hemat. Hematology; iron metabolism; hereditary enzymopathies. Address: Hektoen Institute for Medical Research, 627 S. Wood St, Chicago, IL 60612.

DE ROBERTIS, EDUARDO DIEGO PATRICIO, b. Buenos Aires, Arg, Dec. 11, 13; m. 38; c. 2. HISTOPHYSIOLOGY, CYTOLOGY. M.D, Buenos Aires, 39; hon. Dr, Loyola Univ, 69, Univ. Madrid, 71. Instr, inst. gen. anat. & embryol. & chief practical works in histol. & embryol, Univ. Buenos Aires, 33-37, 39, chief sect. cytol. & histophysiol, 41-46; Arg. Nat. Acad. Med. traveling fel, Chicago, 39-40; Rockefeller traveling fel, Chicago & Hopkins, 40-41; res. assoc, Mass. Inst. Tech, 46-49, Guggenheim fel, 46-47, U.S. Pub. Health Serv. fel, 48-49; head dept. cell ultrastruct, Inst. Res. Biol. Sci, 49-56; PROF. HISTOL. & EMBRYOL. & DIR. INST. GEN. ANAT, UNIV. BUENOS AIRES, 57- Practitioner, Clin. Hosp. Buenos Aires, 36-38; Rockefeller grant, Lab. Biophys, Rio de Janeiro, 44; Walker-Ames prof, Washington (Seattle), 53. Prize, Mitre Inst, 37; gold medal, Buenos Aires, 38; Arg. nat. prize, 37, 40; Van. Meter prize award, Asn. Study Goiter, 47; prize, Arg. Found. Against Polio, 49; prize, Shell Found, 69. Assoc. Am. Asn. Anat; assoc. Electron Micros. Soc. Am; Histochem. Soc; Soc. Exp. Biol. & Med; Am. Soc. Cell Biol; hon. mem. Am. Col. Physicians; Arg. Nat. Acad. Sci; Arg. Biol. Soc; assoc. Arg. Anat. Asn. Histophysiology of liver, thyroid and parathyroid; microdissection of thyroid follicles; ultrastructure of nervous tissue; electron microscopy. Address: Institute of General Anatomy & Embryology, Faculty of Medicine, University of Buenos Aires, Argentina.

DeROCCO, ANDREW G(ABRIEL), b. Westerly, R.I, July 31, 29; div; c. 1. CHEMICAL PHYSICS. B.S, Purdue, 51; fel, Michigan, 51-53, M.S, 53, Rackham Arthritis res. found. fel, 54, DuPont fels, 54-55, Ph.D.(chem), 56. Instr. chem, Michigan, 53-56, Nat. Acad. Sci. fel. physics, 56-57, instr. CHEM, 57-60, asst. prof, 60-62; INST. MOLECULAR PHYSICS, UNIV. MD, COLLEGE PARK, 63-64, assoc. prof, 64-69, PROF, 69-; MEM. STAFF PHYS. SCI. LAB, DIV. COMPUT. RES. & TECHNOL, NAT. INSTS. HEALTH, 69- Mem. staff, Colorado, 62-63. AAAS; Am. Phys. Soc. Statistical physics, especially the theory of fluids, liquid crystals, ensemble methods in biophysics, anesthesia, muscle, biorhythms. Address: Institute for Molecular Physics, University of Maryland, College Park, MD 20742.

DEROME, J(ACQUES) F(LORIAN), b. Montreal, Que, Apr. 20, 41; m. 67. DYNAMIC METEOROLOGY. B.S, McGill Univ, 63, M.S, 64; Tecumseh Prod. Co. fel, Univ. Mich, 64-65, Rackham fel, 65-67, Ph.D.(meteorol), 68. Res. fel. meteorol, Mass. Inst. Technol, 68-69; RES. SCIENTIST, DYNAMIC PREDICTION RES. UNIT, ATMOSPHERIC ENVIRON. SERV, DEPT. ENVIRON, 69- Lectr, McGill Univ, 71. Mem. Can. Meteorol. Soc; Prof. mem. Am. Meteorol. Soc; fel. Royal Meteorol. Soc. Numerical weather prediction; effects of energy sources and sinks in numerical models of the atmosphere; structure and stability of lage-scale waves in the atmosphere. Address: c/o Central Analysis Office, Dept. of the Environment, Box 158, Montreal AMF, Montreal International Airport, Dorval, Que, Can.

DEROME, JEAN-ROBERT, b. Montreal, Que, Feb. 10, 37; m. 61; c. 2. THEORETICAL PHYSICS. B.Eng, McGill Univ, 59; M.Sc, Univ. Alta, 62; Nat. Res. Coun. Can. stud, Univs. Alta. & Toronto, 63-64; Int. Nickel Co. fel, Univ. Toronto, 64-65, Ph.D.(math), 65. Res. engr, Dom. Eng. Works Ltd, Que, 59-61; Nat. Res. Coun. Can. res. fel, Lab. Theoret. Physics & High Energies, Orsay, France, 65-67; asst. prof. PHYSICS, UNIV. MONTREAL, 67-71, ASSOC. PROF, 71- Am. Phys. Soc; Am. Math. Soc; Can. Asn. Physicists. Racah algebra; symmetry principles in physics. Address: Dept. of Physics, University of Montreal, C.P. 6128, Montreal 101, Que, Can.

DEROMEDI, FRANK D(ENIS), b. Arma, Kans, Jan. 10, 16; m. 44; c. 3. BACTERIOLOGY. B.S, Washington, 41; M.B.A, California, 59. Bact. deck hand biol. sta, Washington, 41, lab. technician health ctr, 41; res. virologist, CUTTER LABS, 42-44, mgr. penicillin plant, 44-46, supt. biol. prod, 46-55, PROD. SUPT, 55-67, PLANT MGR, 67- Inst. Mgt. Sci. Scientific management of technical people and processes. Address: Cutter Labs, 1800 Crutchfield St, Chattanooga, TN 37406.

De ROO, H(ENDRIK) C(HRISTIAAN), b. The Hague, Holland, May 7, 13; U.S. citizen; m. 39; c. 2. SOILS, AGRONOMY. Ph.D.(soil sci), Agr. Univ. Col, Wageningen, Holland, 53. Soil scientist, govt. inst. soil res, Gen. Agr. Exp. Sta, Bogor, Java, 39-47; Soil.Surv. Inst. Netherlands, Wageningen, 47-52; AGRONOMIST, VALLEY LAB, CONN. EXP. STA, 52- Soil surveyor, dept. agron, N.Y. State Col. Agr, Cornell, 52. Dutch E.Indes Army, 42-45. Am. Soc. Agron; Soil Sci. Soc. Am; Int. Soc. Soil Sci; Am. Soc. Hort. Sci. Soil management and fertility. Address: Valley Lab, Connecticut Agricultural Experiment Station, P.O. Box 248, Windsor, CT 06095.

DE ROOS, JAMES BARRY, b. Denver, Colo, Oct. 2, 40; m. 64. INORGANIC CHEMISTRY. B.S, Calvin Col, 62; Ph.D.(inorg. chem), Wayne State, 66. ASST. PROF. CHEM, WASH. UNIV, 66- Am. Chem. Soc. Kinetic studies of exchange reactions in organometallic systems; nuclear magnetic resonance spectra in neumatic liquid crystals. Address: Dept. of Chemistry, Lauderman Hall, Washington University, St. Louis, MO 63130.

deROOS, ROGER McLEAN, b. Fresno, Calif, Aug. 11, 30; m. 55; c. 3. ZOOLOGY. B.A, California, Berkeley, 55, U.S. Pub. Health Serv. fel, 60-61, Ph.D.(zool), 61; M.S, Utah State Univ, 58. Asst. prof. zool, UNIV. MO-COLUMBIA, 61-65, assoc. prof, 65-70, PROF. BIOL. SCI, 70-, assoc. dir. div, 71. U.S.A, 51-53, Sgt. AAAS; Am. Soc. Zool; Soc. Exp. Biol. & Med. Comparative endocrinology; adrenal cortex functions and control; reproductive physiology. Address: Division of Biological Sciences, 24 Lefevere Hall, University of Missouri-Columbia, Columbia, MO 65201.

DeROSE, ANTHONY F(RANCIS), b. Chicago, Ill, June 7, 20; m. 52; c. 6. BIOCHEMISTRY. B.S, Illinois, 41, fel, 41-43, M.S, 43. Asst. pharmacog. & pharmacol, col. pharmacy, Illinois, 41-43; res. biochemist, res. div, ABBOTT LABS, 46-60, supvr. res. serv, 60-64, mgr. dept. sci. bldg. serv, sci. div, 64-66, res. pharmaceut. chemist, new prod. div, 66-70, CHIEF PHARMACIST & MGR. RES. & DEVELOP. PILOT PLANT OPERS, HOSP. PROD. DIV, 70- U.S.A.F, 42-45, Res, 45-, Col; Distinguished Flying Cross. AAAS; Am. Chem. Soc. Chemical constitution; pharmacognosy and pharmacology of medical plants; isolation and chemistry of substances of biochemical origin; antibiotic and vitamin research; pharmaceuticals. Address: Research & Development, Hospital Products Division, Abbott Labs, AP4, North Chicago, IL 60064.

DeROSIER, DAVID J, b. Milwaukee, Wis, Feb. 22, 39; m. 62; c. 2. BIOPHYSICS, MOLECULAR BIOLOGY. B.S, Chicago, 61, U.S. Pub. Health Serv. fel, 62, Nat. Sci. Found, fel, 63-65, Ph.D.(biophys), 65. Visitor, Lab. Molecular Biol, Cambridge, 65-69; ASST. PROF. CHEM, UNIV. TEX, AUSTIN, 69- Air Force Off. Sci. Res. fel, 65-66; Am. Cancer Soc. fel, 66-67; Nat. Sci. Found. fel, 67-68. Determination and interpretation of the three-dimensional structure of complexes of biological macromolecules, especially multi-enzyme complexes. Address: Dept. of Chemistry, University of Texas, Austin, TX 78712.

deROSSET, ARMAND JOHN, b. N.Y.C, Jan. 10, 15; m. 39; c. 5. CHEMISTRY. B.S, Lafayette Col, 36; Alumni Res. fel. & Ph.D.(chem), Univ. Wis, 39. Jr. chemist, State Hwy. Comn. Wis, 36-39; res. chemist, UNIVERSAL OIL PRODS. CO, 39-64, ASST. DIR. RES, CORP. RES. CTR, 64- U.S.A.A.F, 42-46, Chem.C.R, 46- Am. Chem. Soc; Newcomen Soc. Process and catalyst research in the petroleum refining and petrochemical field of hydrotreating and separation via adsorbents; fundamental studies of catalyst surface chemistry, fuel cells and gas diffusion. Address: Corporate Research Center, Universal Oil Products Co, 10 UOP Plaza, Des Plaines, IL 60016.

de ROTH, GERARDUS C(ABBLE), b. Bloomfield, N.J, May 14, 20; m. 42; c. 2. ZOOLOGY. B.S, Maine, 42, M.S, 49; Ph.D.(zool), Michigan, 53. Inst. fisheries, Michigan, 52-54; res. zoologist, California, 54; lectr, Nevada, 55-56; PROF. ECOL, DEFIANCE COL, 56-, chmn. sci. div, 59-66. Res. assoc, Ohio State, 58-; mem. exec. coun. & bd. adv, Ohio Biol. Surv, 70- U.S.A.A.F, 43-46. Am. Soc. Ichthyol. & Herpet; Wildlife Soc; Ecol. Soc. Am; Am. Fisheries Soc. Ecology and physiology of fishes; age and growth, populations, distribution, respiratory and circulatory metabolism; biostatistics; terrestrial ecology and biological photography. Address: Dept. of Natural Systems, Defiance College, Defiance, OH 43512.

DEROW, MATTHEW A(RNOLD), b. New York, N.Y, Apr. 29, 09; m. 41; c. 2. MICROBIOLOGY. B.S, City Col. New York, 29; A.M, Columbia, 30; M.D, Boston, 34, Ph.D.(med. sci, biochem), 41; Dipl, Army Med. Sch, 43. Teaching fel. biochem, SCH. MED, BOSTON, 35-37, instr. bact. & immunol, 36-56, ASST. PROF. MICROBIOL, 57-, China Med. Bd. fel. trop. med, 56. Chemist & bacteriologist, Natick, Mass, 35-53; vis. physician, allergy clin, Mass. Mem. Hosp, 36-43; path. consult, Norfolk County Hosp, 42- AAAS; Am. Soc. Microbiol; fel. Am. Med. Asn; N.Y. Acad. Sci. Vitamin assays; blood groups; immunochemistry; allergy; chemotherapeutic agents and antibiotics; bacterial toxins and enyzmes; medical parasitology. Address: Dept. of Microbiology, Boston University School of Medicine, 80 E. Concord St, Boston, MA 02118.

DERR, PAUL F(RANKLIN), b. Nuremberg, Pa, Feb. 24, 16; m. 58; c. 1. PHYSICAL CHEMISTRY. B.S, Duke, 38, A.M, 39, fel, 40-41, Ph.D.(phys. chem), 41. Asst, Duke, 38-40; res. chemist cellulose acetate, E.I. du Pont de Nemours & Co, 41-43, chief chemist, heavy water plant, Ala. Ord. Works, 43-45; res. chemist, Westvaco div, FMC CORP, 45-47, proj. chemist, 48-51, group supvr, 52-56, res. lab. dir, 57-58, tech. coordinator, rocket fuel program, 58-59, tech. asst. to dir, inorg. res. & develop. dept, 59-63, mgr. planning & eval, RES. & DEVELOP. DEPT, 63-67, ASST. DIR, 67- AAAS; Am. Chem. Soc; Electrochem. Soc; Am. Inst. Aeronaut. & Astronaut; Am. Inst. Chem; fel. Chem. Mkt. Res. Asn. Electromotive force cells; metal-amine complex ions; cellulose acetate products; heavy water production; halogens, alkalis, halogenated organic and inorganic compounds; hydrazine compounds; inorganic phosphates and peroxygen compounds. Address: Research & Development Dept, FMC Corp, P.O. Box 8, Princeton, NJ 08540.

DERR, VERNON E(LLSWORTH), b. Baltimore, Md, Nov. 22, 21; m. 43; c. 4. PHYSICS. A.B, St. Johns Col, 48; Ph.D, Hopkins, 59. Asst. appl. physics lab, Hopkins, 50, res. assoc, radiation lab, 51-59; prin. res. scientist, Martin Co, 59-67, RES. SCIENTIST, WAVE PROPAGATION LAB, ENVIRON. RES. LABS, NAT. OCEANIC & ATMOSPHERIC AGENCY, 67- Adj. prof, Rollins Col, 59-67; adj. prof, Univ. Colo, 71- Sig.C, U.S.A, 42-46. Am. Phys. Soc; Inst. Elec. & Electronics Eng; Sci. Res. Soc. Am; Am. Geophys. Union. Microwave, infrared and optical spectroscopy; remote sensing of atmospheric parameters; statistical decision theory; statistical mechanics; laser development. Address: R45.3, Wave Propagation Lab, Environmental Science Service Administration Research Labs, National Oceanic & Atmospheric Agency, Boulder, CO 80302.

DERR, WILLIAM FREDERICK, b. Reading, Pa, June 27, 39; m. 61; c. 2. BOTANY, PLANT ANATOMY. B.S, Lebanon Valley Col, 60; M.S, Wisconsin, 62, Ph.D.(bot), 64. Asst. bot, Wisconsin, 60-64; asst. prof. BIOL, CHICO STATE COL, 64-69, ASSOC. PROF, 69- Nat. Sci. Found. res. grant, 65-67. AAAS; Bot. Soc. Am. Seasonal development of cambium, ontogeny, and structure of phloem; histochemical studies of differentiating cells. Address: Dept. of Biology, Chico State College, Chico, CA 95926.

DERRICK, FINNIS RAY, b. Ballentine, S.C, May 1, 11; m. 37; c. 2. ZOOLOGY. B.S, South Carolina, 34, M.S, 37, Ph.D.(zool), 55. Teacher, pub. sch, S.C, 38-41; instr. BIOL, Augusta Jr. Col, 41-46; PROF. & HEAD DEPT, APPLACHIAN STATE UNIV, 46- Aquatic biology; conservation. Address: Dept. of Biology, Appalachian State University, Boone, NC 28608.

DERRICK, G(RACE) ETHEL, b. Guthrie, Okla, April 14, 06. EMBRYOLOGY. A.B, Phillips, 25; A.M, Oklahoma, 27, Ph.D.(zool), 35. Teacher, pub. schs, Ariz, 27-30; instr. biol, Phillips, 30-32; zool, Oklahoma, 33-35; assoc. prof. BIOL, CENT. STATE UNIV.(OKLA), 35-51, PROF, 51- AAAS; Am. Soc. Zool; Am. Inst. Biol. Sci; Nat. Asn. Biol. Embryology of the insect eye; mitotic index of chick embryos. Address: Dept. of Biology, Central State University, Edmond, OK 73034.

DERRICK, JOHN RAFTER, b. Clayton, Ga, Jan. 17, 22; m. 51; c. 6. SURGERY. B.S, Clemson Col, 43; M.D, Tulane, 46. Instr. chest & cardiovasc. surg, sch. med, Emory, 56-57; assoc. prof. thoracic surg. & acting chief div. thoracic & cardiovasc. surg, MED. BR, UNIV. TEX, 57-67, PROF. THORACIC SURG. & CHIEF DIV. THORACIC & CARDIOVASC. SURG, 67- U.S.A.F, 47-49. Am. Asn. Thoracic Surg; Am. Col. Angiol; Am. Col. Cardiol; Am. Col. Surg; Am. Fedn. Clin. Res; Am. Heart Asn; Am. Med. Asn; Soc. Univ. Surg; Soc. Vascular Surg; Int. Cardiovasc. Soc. Cardiovascular and thoracic surgery. Address: Division of Thoracic & Cardiovascular Surgery, University of Texas Medical Branch, Galveston, TX 77550.

DERRICK, MALCOLM, b. Hull, Eng, Feb. 15, 33; m. 57; c. 1. PHYSICS. B.Sc, Birmingham, 54, Ph.D.(physics), 59; M.A, Oxford, 61. Instr. physics, Carnegie Inst. Tech, 57-60; sr. res. officer nuclear physics, Oxford, 60-63; asst. physicist, ARGONNE NAT. LAB, 63-64, assoc. physicst, 64-67, SR. PHYSICIST, 67- Am. Phys. Soc. Elementary particle interactions and decays using bubble chambers; construction and development of techniques for high energy physics experiments, particularly bubble chambers and separated beams. Address: Argonne National Lab, 9700 S. Cass Ave, Argonne, IL 60439.

DERRICK, WILLIAM RICHARD, b. Oklahoma,City, Okla, May 18, 38; m. 60; c. 3. MATHEMATICS. B.S, Okla. State, 58, M.S, 60; Nat. Sci. Found. fel, Indiana, 65, Ph.D.(math), 66. Physicist, Naval Electronics Lab, summer 59; programmer, Int. Bus. Mach. Corp, 60-61; ASST. PROF. MATH, UNIV. UTAH, 66- Vis. assoc. prof, Ariz. State Univ. Qm.C, U.S.A, 60, Res, 60-67, Capt. Am. Math. Soc. Complex analysis, particularly quasiconformal mappings in space. Address: Dept. of Mathematics, University of Utah, Salt Lake City, UT 84112.

DERRICK, W(ILLIA)M S(HELDON), b. Millville, Pa, Mar. 5, 16; m. 42; c. 2. ANESTHESIOLOGY. A.B, George Washington, 40, M.D, 42. Head anesthesiol. sect, Peter Bent Brigham Hosp, 48-54; HEAD ANESTHESIOL. SECT, M.D. ANDERSON HOSP. & TUMOR INST, UNIV. TEX, 54-, PROF. ANESTHESIOL, 54- Assoc. anesthesia, med. sch, Harvard, 48-54. Sr. consult, Vet. Admin. Hosp, Rutland Heights, Mass, 50-54, West. Roxbury, 53-54; consult, Murphy Army Hosp, 50-54; Cancer Yearbook, 56-; St. Joseph's Hosp, 55-; St. Luke's Episcopal Hosp, 56- Alumni achievement award, George Wash. Univ, 57. Med,C, 43-46, Maj. Am. Soc. Anesthsiol; Am. Heart Asn; Am. Med. Asn; N.Y. Acad. Sci; Int. Anesthesia Res. Soc. Respiratory physiology. Address: M.D. Anderson Hospital, G-415, Houston, TX 77025.

DERRICKSON, CHARLES M, b. Simpson, Ky, Apr. 26, 27; m. 49; c. 3. ANIMAL SCIENCE. B.S, Kentucky, 51, M.S, 56; Ph.D.(animal sci), Mich. State, 65. Asst. county agent exten, Kentucky, 52-57, supt, Robinson Agr. Exp. Substa, 57-65; assoc. prof. ANIMAL SCI, MOREHEAD STATE UNIV, 65-68, PROF. & HEAD DEPT. AGR, 68- U.S.N, 45-46. Am. Soc. Animal Sci. Basic and applied research in field of animal nutrition. Address: 405 Edgewood Dr, Morehead, KY 40351.

D'ERRICO, MICHAEL J(OSEPH), b. N.Y.C, July 11, 33; m. 64; c. 3. PHYSICAL ORGANIC CHEMISTRY. B.A, Cornell Univ, 54; M.A, Columbia Univ, 55, David W. & Ellen A. Ferguson fel, 57-58, Ph.D.(chem), 60. Res. chemist petrochem, AM. CYANAMID CO, 58-62, proj. leader, paper chem, 62-65, SR. RES. CHEMIST OIL PROD. CHEM, 65- Am. Chem. Soc; Soc. Petrol. Eng. Research in the product and process of petrochemicals; dielectric polymer; rosin size and paper sizing mechanisms of paper chemicals; development of chemicals for oil well drilling, production, stimulation and completions. Address: American Cyanamid Co, 1937 W. Main St, Stamford, CT 60904.

DERRY, DUNCAN R(AMSAY), b. Eng, June 27, 06; Can. citizen; m. 35; c. 2. GEOLOGY. B.A, Cambridge, 27; M.A, Toronto, 28, Ph.D.(geol), 31. Lectr. geol, Toronto, 31-35; geologist, Ventures, Ltd & associated co, 35-47, chief geologist, 47-54; v.pres. explor. Rio Tinto Mining Co. Can, 54-60; consult. geologist. & pres, Duncan R. Derry, Ltd, 60-69; PARTNER, DERRY, MICHENER & BOOTH, 69- R.C.A.F, 40-45, Squadron Leader. Fel. Geol. Soc. Am; Am. Soc. Econ. Geol; fel. Geol. Asn. Can; Can. Inst. Mining. & Metall; fel. Brit. Geol. Soc. Mining geology; pegmatites; ore deposits. Address: 401 Bay St, Suite 2302, Toronto, Ont, Can.

DERRYBERRY, (CARLEY) MAYHEW, b. Columbia, Tenn, Dec. 25, 02; m. 30. PUBLIC HEALTH. A.B, Tennessee, 25; A.M, Columbia, 27; Ph.D.(health, phys. ed), N.Y. Univ, 33. Assoc. dir. res, Am. Child Health Asn, 26-33; assoc. dir. field studies, Pub. Health Asn, New York, 33-34; secy. to sanit. supt, City Health Dept, New York, 34-36; sr. pub. health statistician, U.S. Pub. Health Serv, D.C, 36-42, chief off. health ed, 42-49, div. pub. health ed, 49-63, health ed. adv, Agency Int. Develop, India, 63-67; prof. in residence, sch. pub. health, Univ. Calif, Berkeley, 67-71; RETIRED. Res. asst, N.Y. Univ, 32-36; Nyswander lectr, 57. Prentiss Nat. award, 50; U.S. Pub. Health Serv. meritorious award, 63. Fel. Am. Pub. Health Asn; Am. Asn. Health, Phys. Ed. & Recreation; Soc. Psychol. Study Social Issues. Health protection for the preschool child; statistical methods; measurement of health attitude; effectiveness of public health effort; methods of health education; public opinion polling; school health; family planning. Address: 1401 Walnut St, Berkeley, CA 94709.

DERRYBERRY, O(SCAR) MERTON, b. Columbia, Tenn, June 12, 10; m. 35; c. 3. OCCUPATIONAL MEDICINE, PUBLIC HEALTH. A.B. & M.D, Tennessee, 34; M.P.H, Hopkins, 40. Rotating intern, John Gaston Hosp, Tenn, 35-36; field med. staff, TENN. VALLEY AUTHORITY, 36-48, asst. dir. health, 48-51, dir. health, 51-69, MGR. HEALTH & ENVIRON. SCI, 69- Lectr. prev. med, Tennessee, 54-69. Consult. prev. & indust. med, Baroness Erlanger Hosp. & Mem. Hosp, 52-; temporary consult, WHO, 60, 65, 67. Diplomate, Am. Bd. Prev. Med. & Pub. Health, 50; Am. Bd. Occupational Med, 56. Fel. Am. Med. Asn; fel. Am. Col. Prev. Med; fel. Am. Acad. Occupational Med; fel. Am. Pub. Health Asn. Industrialization and medicine; employee health and safety; environmental hygiene; mass screening techniques; malaria control; fluorides and worker health. Address: Tennessee Valley Authority, 715 Edney Bldg, Chattanooga, TN 37401.

DERSCH, FRITZ, b. Kassel, Germany, March 6, 04; nat; m. 33; c. 4. ORGANIC CHEMISTRY. Ph.D.(chem), Marburg, Germany, 28. Asst. steric chem, Univ. Marburg, Germany, 28-29; alkali, org. compounds, Heidelberg, 29-31; hemocyanine, Harvard, 31-32; ergosterol, Univ. Goettingen, Germany, 33; chemist, Agfa-Wolfen, 33-34; head lab, Agfa-Ansco, N.Y, 34-45; dept. mgr. film emulsion dept, Ansco, 45-52, group leader & res. specialist, res. dept, 52-65, tech. assoc. develop. & res, 65-69; INDEPENDENT CONSULT, 69- Am. Chem. Soc; Royal Photog. Soc. Gt. Brit; Soc. Photog. Sci. & Eng. Photographic emulsion; chemical sensitizers; antifoggants; stabilizers; accelerators; solarization; hypersensitizing; photographic gelatins. Address: Four Edgewood Rd, Binghamton, NY 13903.

DERSCHEID, LYLE A(UGUST), b. S.Dak, Dec. 14, 16; m; c. 3. AGRONOMY. B.S, S.Dak. State, 43, M.S, 48; Ph.D.(crop prod. & plant physiol), Iowa State, 51. Asst. S.DAK. STATE UNIV, 46-47, asst. agronomist WEED CONTROL RES, 47-51, assoc. agronomist, 51-58, assoc. prof, 57-58, PROF, 58-, EXTEN. AGRONOMIST, 60-, agronomist, 58-60. U.S.A, 43-46, 1st Lt. Am. Soc. Agron; Am. Soc. Plant Physiol; Weed Sci. Soc. Am. Weed control; pasture improvement and management; crop production. Address: Plant Science Dept, South Dakota State University, Brookings, SD 57006.

DERSHEM, HERBERT L, b. Troy, Ohio, Mar. 26, 43; m. 68; c. 1. COMPUTER SCIENCE, MATHEMATICS. B.S, Univ. Dayton, 65; Nat. Defense Educ. Act fel, Purdue Univ, 65, M.S, 67, Honeywell Corp, fel, 68, Ph.D. (comput. sci), 69. ASST. PROF. MATH, HOPE COL, 69- Res. Corp. res. grant, 70. Asn. Comput. Mach; Am. Math. Soc. The numerical solution of ordinary differential equations; finite difference treatment of singularities in boundary value problems; Monte Carlo methods in numerical analysis. Address: Dept. of Mathematics, Hope College, Holland, MI 49423.

DeRUDDER, RONALD DEAN, b. Sioux Falls, S.Dak, Sept. 6, 32; m. 54; c. 2. GEOLOGY. B.S, Indiana, 58, Arketex Ceramic Corp. fel. & M.A, 60, Nat. Sci. Found. fels. & Ph.D.(geol), 62. Res. geologist, Bellaire Res. Labs, Texaco Inc, Tex, 62-64; asst. prof. geol, Va. Polytech, 64-65; res. geologist, BELLAIRE RES. LABS, TEXACO INC, 65-67, SUPVR. GEOL. RES, 67- U.S.A.F, 52-56. AAAS; Geol. Soc. Am; Mineral Soc. Am; Clay Minerals Soc; Int. Asn. Sedimentol. Mineralogy-petrology of Northeastern Adirondack Mountains; petroleum geology; mineralogy; petrology; geochemistry; sedimentology. Address: Bellaire Research Labs, Texaco Inc, P.O. Box 425, Bellaire, TX 77401.

DERUSSO, PAUL M(ADDEN), b. Albany, N.Y, Sept. 9, 31; m. 53; c. 3. ELECTRICAL ENGINEERING. B.E.E, Rensselaer Polytech, 53, M.E.E, 55; E.E, Mass. Inst. Tech, 58, Sc.D.(elec. eng), 59. Asst. prof. ELEC. ENG, RENSSELAER POLYTECH. INST, 59-61, assoc. prof, 61-64, PROF, 64-, CHMN. SYSTS. ENG. DIV, 67- Summers, test engr, Gen. Elec. Co, 52, elec. engr, 54, systs. engr, 59, 62; consult, Gen. Elec. Co, 60-; Du Pont Year-In-Indust. prof, 66-67; field reader, off. educ, U.S. Dept. Health, Educ. & Welfare, 70- Sig.C, U.S.A, 60, Res, 60- Inst. Elec. & Electronics Eng. Systems engineering, especially automatic control systems. Address: Systems Engineering Division, Rensselaer Polytechnic Institute School of Engineering, Troy, NY 12181.

DERZKO, NICHOLAS ANTHONY, b. Kapuskasing, Ont, Jan. 19, 40; m. 66. MATHEMATICS, PHYSICS. B.S, Toronto, 62; Ph.D.(math, physics), Calif. Inst. Tech, 65. Asst. prof. MATH, UNIV. TORONTO, 65-70, ASSOC. PROF, 70- Soc. Indust. & Appl. Math; Am. Math. Soc; Can. Math. Cong. Matrix theory; mathematical scattering theory; Monte Carlo methods. Address: Dept. of Mathematics, University of Toronto, Toronto 5, Ont, Can.

De Sa, RICHARD J(OHN), b. New York, N.Y, Aug. 4, 38; m. 59; c. 3. BIOCHEMISTRY, MICROBIOLOGY. B.S, St. Bonaventure, 59; U.S. Pub. Health Serv. fel, Illinois, 62-64, Ph.D.(biochem), 64. Trainee BIOCHEM, Johnson Res. Found, Pennsylvania, 64-65; Cornell Univ, 65-68; ASST. PROF, UNIV. GA, 68- Bioluminescence of marine organisms; enzyme kinetics; particularly flavin enzymes; instrumental design and construction. Address: Dept. of Biochemistry, University of Georgia, Athens, GA 30601.

DESAI, BIPIN RATILAL, b. Hansot, India, Oct. 5, 35; m. 61. HIGH ENERGY & NUCLEAR PHYSICS. B.Sc, Bombay, 54; M.S, Illinois, 57; Ph.D.(physics), California, Berkeley, 61. Physicist, Lawrence Radiation Lab, California, 61; res. assoc. physics, Indiana, 61-63; Wisconsin, 63-64; asst. res. physicist, California, Los Angeles, 64-65, asst. prof. PHYSICS, UNIV. CALIF, RIVERSIDE, 65-67, assoc. prof, 67-71, PROF, 71- Am. Phys. Soc. Regge poles; dispersion relations; s-matrix theory. Address: Dept. of Physics, University of California, Riverside, CA 90024.

DESAI, INDRAJIT DAYALJI, b. Nairobi, Kenya, Jan. 7, 32; Can. citizen. NUTRITION, BIOCHEMISTRY. B.Sc, Gujarat Univ, India, 54, Indian Coun. Agr. res. fel, 56-58, M.Sc, 58; Fulbright fel, Univ. Calif, Davis, 58-61, Ph.D. (nutrit), 63. Instr. dairy sci, Gujarat Univ, India, 54-55; res. assoc. nutrit, Cornell Univ, 63-64; biochem, UNIV. B.C, 65-67, asst. prof. HUMAN NUTRIT, 67-70, ASSOC. PROF, 70-, CHMN. DIV, 71- Gilmore Award, Univ; Calif, Davis, 63. Am. Inst. Nutrit; Can. Biochem. Soc; Nutrit. Soc. Can. Indian Dairy Sci. Asn. Dietary regulation of lysosomal enzymes; nutritional role of vitamin E; lipid peroxidation; ceroids and biology of aging; biochemical assessment of nutritional status; biochemical and nutritional studies of planktonic algae, selenium, antioxidants. Address: Division of Human Nutrition, University of British Columbia, Vancouver 8, B.C, Can.

DESAI, KANTILAL PANACHAND, b. Mota-Samadhiala, India, Feb. 7, 29; m. 60; c. 3. GEOPHYSICS. B.S, Univ. Bombay, 52; fel, Colo. Sch. Mines, 55-57, Gp.E, 56, M.S, 57; Ph.D.(petrol. eng), Univ. Tulsa, 68. Trainee well logging, Seismograph Serv. Corp, 58, log analyst, Birdwell Div, 58-61, area engr, 61-62; geophysicist, res. ctr, Sinclair Oil Co, 62-67, sr. res. geophysicist, 67-69, SR. RES. ENGR, Atlantic Richfield Co, 69; FIELD RES. LAB, MOBIL OIL CORP, 69- Soc. Prof. Well Logg Analysts; Am. Inst. Mining, Metall. & Petrol. Eng. Design and development of laboratory measuring system which precisely and sequentially measures both the longitudinal and shear velocities of a rock sample under triaxial pressure. Address: 6006 Hunters View, Dallas, TX 75232.

DESAI, PRATEEN V, b. Baroda, India, Aug. 14, 36. MECHANICAL ENGINEERING. B.Eng, Baroda, 59; Ohio State, 61; M.S, Va. Polytech, 63; Ph.D. (mech. eng), Tulane, 67. Asst. engr, Nat. Mach. Mfrs, India, 59-61; asst. prof. MECH. ENG, GA. INST. TECHNOL, 66-71, ASSOC. PROF, 71- Design engr, Avondale Shipyards, summer 64; consult, Lockheed-Ga. Co, 68-; vis. prof, Univ. Carabobo, Venezuela, fall 71. Am. Soc. Eng. Educ. Thermal sciences; turbulent boundary layers; fluid vibrations; fluidics; biomechanics; whiplash studies. Address: School of Mechanical Engineering, Georgia Institute of Technology, Atlanta, GA 30332.

DESAI, RAJENDRA G, b. Junagadh, India, Nov. 7, 23; U.S. citizen; m. 55; c. 4. HEMATOLOGY. M.B, B.S, Bombay, 49; Ph.D.(physiol), Boston, 55. Indian Coun. Med. Res. fel. hemat, 49-52; res. fel, New England Center Hosp, Boston, 52-55; hematologist, Nat. Med. Col, India, 56-57; res. assoc. hemat, sch. med, Stanford, 57-62; asst. prof. med, sch. med, Boston Univ. & Univ. Hosp, 62-65; CHIEF HEMAT, ORANGE COUNTY GEN. HOSP, 65- Fulbright scholar, 52-55; Damon Runyon fel, 53-55; Anna Fuller Fund travel award, Far East, 60. Am. Fedn. Clin. Res; fel. Am. Col. Angiol; Microcirculatory Soc; fel. Int. Soc. Hemat. Microcirculation; transplantation immunity; kinetics of cell transfer across placenta; clinical and therapeutic aspects of various blood disorders. Address: Suite 201, Park Lido Professional Bldg, 351 Hospital Rd, Newport Beach, CA 92660.

DESAI, RAMAN LALBHAI, b. Vedcha, India, Oct. 26, 27; m. 60; c. 2. PHYSICAL CHEMISTRY. B.Sc, Bombay, 48, M.Sc, 51, scholar, 51-53, Ph.D. (phys. chem), 53; scholar, McGill, 59-60, fel, 60-61, Ph.D.(phys. chem), 62. Jr. res. asst. chem, Cent. Salt Res. Inst, Bhavnagar, India, 53-55, sr. sci. asst, 58; sr. chemist, N.M. Precious Metal Ref, Bombay, 55-58; chemist, Forest Prod. Lab, Ont, 61-62; pool officer, dept. chem. tech, Bombay, 62-64; RES. SCIENTIST, CHEM, FOREST PROD; LAB, 64- Am. Chem. Soc; fel. Brit. Chem. Soc; assoc. Royal Inst. Chem. Colloid and surface chemistry; solubility studies; light scattering in gel systems; photochemical degradation of cellulosic materials; adhesion and performance of paints and coatings. Address: 18 Redenda Crescent, Ottawa 5, Ont, Can. K2G ON6

DESAI, RASHMI C, b. Amod, India, Nov. 12, 38; m. 63; c. 1. PHYSICS. B.Sc, Univ. Bombay, 57; fel, Cornell Univ, 64-65, Ph.D.(appl. physics), 66. Trainee physics, Atomic Energy Estab. Trombay, Bombay, India, 57-58, sci. off. theoret. physics, 58-62; res. assoc. statist. physics, Mass. Inst. Technol, 66-68; asst. prof. PHYSICS, UNIV. TORONTO, 68-71, ASSOC. PROF, 71- Am. Phys. Soc; Am. Asn. Physics Teachers; Can. Asn. Physicists. Nonequilibrium and equilibrium statistical mechanics; molecular transport phenomena in liquids and gases; inelastic neutron and light scattering; kinetic theory of molecular gases and Boltzmann equation. Address: Dept. of Physics, University of Toronto, St. George Campus, Toronto 181, Ont, Can.

de SALEGUI, MIRIAM, b. N.Y.C, Aug. 23, 25; m. 52. BIOCHEMISTRY. B.S, Queens Col.(N.Y), 46; M.S, Wisconsin, 54, Ph.D.(biochem), 57. Prof. biochem, Nat. Polytech. Inst, Mex, 57-59; Inst. Cancer Res. fel, Col. Physicians & Surgeons, Columbia, 59-60; instr. & res. assoc. biochem, N.Y. Med. Col, 61-63, asst. prof, 63-69; ASSOC. PROF. PHYSIOL, MT. SINAI SCH.

MED, 69- Am. Chem. Soc. Hyaluronidases; hyaluronic acid; structure and function of epithelial mucins; connective tissue. Address: Dept. of Physiology, Mt. Sinai School of Medicine, 10 E. 102nd St, New York, NY 10029.

DE SALVA, S(ALVATORE) J(OSEPH), b. New York, N.Y, Jan. 14, 24; m. 48; c. 8. NEUROLOGY, PHARMACOLOGY. B.S, Marquette, 47, fel, 47-49, M.S, 49; Ph.D, Loyola, 57. Asst. anat, Marquette, 47-49; asst. neuroanat, sch. med, Illinois, 50-51, instr, 51-52; asst. prof. anat. & physiol, Chicago Col. Optom, 51-53; pharmacologist, Armour Lab, 53-59; head pharmacol. sect, biol. res. lab, COLGATE-PALMOLIVE CO, 59-66, SR. RES. ASSOC, 66- Biochemist, Milwaukee County Gen. Hosp, 50-51; lectr. pharmacol, Stritch Sch. Med, Loyola, 57- U.S.N, 41-46. AAAS; Soc. Exp. Biol. & Med; N.Y. Acad. Sci; Soc. Pharmacol. & Exp. Therapeut; Inst. Elec. & Electronics Eng. Forebrain of primate; cytoarchitectonic of cerebral cortex in man, primate and squirrel; anti-convulsion and brain excitability; brain excitability and endocrine; interdependencies; pulmonary pharmacology; analgesimetry; dental pharmacology; experimental dermatology. Address: Research & Development Dept, Colgate-Palmolive Co, 909 River Rd, Piscataway, NJ 08854.

DeSANCTIS, ARMAND N(EAL), b. Pa, Feb. 5, 23; m. 46; c. 2. BIOLOGY. B.S, Pa. State Teachers Col, 49; M.S, Jefferson Med. Col, 51; M.D, N.Y. Med. Col, 63. Asst, Houdry Process Corp, 45-47; instr, high sch, N.J, 50-51; res. assoc. biol. develop, Sharp & Dohme Div, Merck & Co, Inc, 51-59; virol, Smith Kline & French Labs, 59-63; DIR. MICROBIOL. RES, NAT. DRUG CO, 63- Nat. Insts. Health fel, Costa Rica, 62. U.S.A, 42-45. AAAS; N.Y. Acad. Sci. Biological development; blood plasma fractionation; plasma substitutes; trichinella antigen; mass spectrometric analysis; virus vaccines; chemotherapy and immunology. Address: National Drug Co, Haines & McCallum St, Philadelphia, PA 19144.

DE SANDO, RICHARD JOHN, b. Haverhill, Mass, Apr. 18, 32; m. 65. PHYSICAL & INORGANIC CHEMISTRY. B.S, Massachusetts, 54, M.S, Purdue, 57; Ph.D.(phys. & inorg. chem), Cincinnati, 61. Sr. res. chemist, MONSANTO RES. CORP, 61-69, GROUP LEADER, 69- Am. Chem. Soc; Am. Crystallog. Asn. X-ray diffraction studies of liquids and solutions, and metals and alloys. Address: 112 Logic Circle, Centerville, OH 45459.

DeSANTO, ROBERT S(PILKA), b. New Rochelle, N.Y, Sept. 21, 40; m. 64; c. 2. MARINE ZOOLOGY, CYTOLOGY. B.S, Tufts, 62; Boese fel, Columbia, 66, pres. fel. & Ph.D, 67. Lectr. ZOOL, Columbia, 62-64; ASST. PROF, CONN. COL, 68-, DIR. SUMMER MARINE SCI. PROG, 69- Soc. Sigma Xi res. grant, 68-69; West. Elec. Col. Gift Prog. equip. grant, 68-70; consult, Conn. Res. Comn, Conn. Seaport Surv, 70; mem. bd. dirs, Thames Sci. Ctr; exec. dir, Biomarine Assocs; contrib. & consult. ed, Animal Encyclop, Grolier Enterprises, Inc; mem, Univ. Res. Inst. Conn, Inc. U.S.N, 68. AAAS; Am. Soc. Zool. Ecology, physiology and cytology of invertebrates; curricula design and education. Address: 8 Sylvan Glen, East Lyme, CT 06333.

DE SAPIO, RODOLFO VITTORIO, b. New York, N.Y, Aug. 16, 36. MATHEMATICS. City Col. New York, 55-57; Michigan, 57-59; M.S, Chicago, 61, Ph.D.(math), 64. Instr. MATH, Stanford, 64-66; asst. prof, California, Los Angeles, 66-69; ASSOC. PROF, Belfer Grad. Sch. Sci, Yeshiva Univ, 69-71; UNIV. CALIF, LOS ANGELES, 71- Mem, Inst. Advan. Study, 68-69; Nat. Sci. Found. grant, 70-72. Am. Math. Soc; Math. Asn. Am. Topology and geometry of manifolds; algebraic topology, including homotopy theory and homology theory as applied to classification problems in differential topology. Address: Dept. of Mathematics, University of California, Los Angeles, CA 90024.

De SAUSSURE, GERARD, b. Geneva, Switz, Nov. 22, 24; U.S. citizen; m. 55; c. 2. NUCLEAR PHYSICS. Dipl, Swiss Fed. Inst. Tech, 49; Ph.D.(physics), Mass. Inst. Tech, 54. Res. asst. physics, Mass. Inst. Tech, 52-54; PHYSICIST, NEUTRON PHYSICS DIV, OAK RIDGE NAT. LAB, 55- Am. Phys. Soc; Am. Nuclear Soc; Ital. Phys. Soc. Measurement of neutron transport parameters by the pulsed neutron source technique; measurement of neutron cross sections, especially of fissionable isotopes, by the time of flight technique. Address: 209 Louisiana Ave, Oak Ridge, TN 38103.

DeSAUSSURE, RICHARD L(AURENS), JR, b. Macon, Ga, Dec. 29, 17; m. 48; c. 2. NEUROSURGERY. A.B, Univ. Va, 39, M.D, 42. Intern, Univ. Va. Hosp, 42-43, resident, neurol. surg, 46-49; neuropath. & neurophysiol, Cincinnati Gen. Hosp, 47-48; asst. chief neurosurg, Kennedy Vet. Admin. Hosp, 49-50; chief, 50; asst. prof. NEUROSURG, MED. SCH, UNIV. TENN, MEMPHIS, 50-65, clin. assoc. prof, 65-70, CLIN. PROF, 70- Private practice, 50-; mem. exec. comt, Baptist Mem. Hosp, 62, 65-67. Dipl, Am. Bd. Neurol. Surg, 51. Med.C, A.U.S, 43-46, Maj. Am. Med. Asn; Cong. Neurol. Surg.(pres, 61-62); Am. Col. Surg; Harvey Cushing Soc; Am. Acad. Neurol. Surg; Soc. Neurol. Surg. Concussion experiments. Address: Dept. of Neurosurgery, University of Tennessee Medical School, Memphis, TN 38103.

DE SAUSSURE, VALERIA A(RTEL), b. Cleveland, Ohio, Oct. 20, 21; m. 64. PHYSICAL CHEMISTRY, IMMUNOCHEMISTRY. A.B, Western Reserve, 43; Nat. Lubricating Grease Inst. fel, Southern California, 53-55, M.S, 59, Ph.D. (phys. chem), 65. Asst. res. chemist, chem. & phys. res. div, Standard Oil Co, Ohio, 43-46, leader, patent & info. group, 46-53; res. chemist, Chevron Res. Corp, 55-63; assoc. res. specialist phys. chem. sea water, Scripps Inst. Oceanog, 64-66, res. assoc, IMMUNOCHEM, SCRIPPS CLINIC & RES. FOUND, 66-69, ASSOC, 69- Am. Chem. Soc; N.Y. Acad. Sci; fel. Am. Inst. Chem. Immunochemistry; solute-solvent interactions; biophysical chemistry techniques; organic coatings; petroleum products; tumor immunology. Address: Dept. of Biochemistry, Scripps Clinic & Research Foundation, 476 Prospect St, La Jolla, CA 92037.

DESBOROUGH, GEORGE A, b. Panama, Ill, Jan. 15, 37; m. 66. GEOLOGY, MINERALOGY. B.A, Southern Illinois, 59, M.A, 60; Union Carbide fel, Wisconsin, 63-64, Ph.D.(geol), 66. Res. assoc. geol, Univ. Wisconsin, Madison, 64-66, fel, 66; GEOLOGIST, br. astrogeol, U.S. GEOL. SURV, 66-67, BR. HEAVY METALS, 67- Summers, asst. geologist, Ill. State Geol. Surv, 61 & 62; consult, Ray-O-Vac Res. & Develop, 62; U.S. Forest Serv. Regional Off, 64; assoc. prof, dept. geol, Colo. State Univ, 70; Mineral Soc. Am. rep, Int. Comn. Ore Micros, 71-73. Fel. Mineral. Soc. Am; Meteoritical Soc; fel. Geol. Soc. Am; Electron Probe Anal. Soc. Am; Am. Inst. Mining, Metall. & Petrol. Eng; Soc. Econ. Geol; Mineral. Soc. Gt. Brit. & Ireland. Mineralogy and origin of ore deposits. Address: Branch of Heavy Metals, U.S. Geological Survey, Bldg. 25, Federal Center, Denver, CO 80225.

DESCARRIES, LAURENT, b. Montreal, Que, Jan. 27, 39; m. 62; c. 1. NEUROBIOLOGY, NEUROANATOMY. B.A, Univ. Paris, 56; M.D, Univ. Montreal, 61. Intern med, Maisonneuve Hosp, Montreal, 60-61; resident, Notre-Dame Hosp, 61-62; Maisonneuve Hosp, 62-63; fel. neurol. & neuropath, Mass. Gen. Hosp, Boston, 63-67; neurobiol, dept. biol, Commissariat Atomic Energy, Ctr. Nuclear Studies, Saclay, France, 67-69; ASST. PROF. PHYSIOL, FACULTY MED, UNIV. MONTREAL, 69-, mem, Ctr. Res. Sci. Neurol, 70- Clin. & res. fel. neurol, med. sch, Harvard, 63-64, res. fel. neuropath, 64-65, exp. neuropath, 65-67; Med. Res. Coun. Can. fel, 63-67, centennial fel, 67-69, scholar, 69- Cert. neurol, Col. Physicians & Surgeons Prov. Que, 66; fel, Royal Col. Physicians & Surgeons Can, 66. Can. Neurol. Soc; French Soc. Electron Micros; Can. Asn. Anat; Am. Asn. Anat; Soc. Neurosci. Ultrastructure of nervous tissue; synaptic transmission; metabolism of neurotransmitters; high resolution radioautography; dynamics of the neuron; central nor-adrenergic systems; constituents, effects of drugs, physiological role, experimental pathology; medical education. Address: Center for Research in the Neurological Sciences, University of Montreal, BP 6128, Montreal 101, Que, Can.

DESCHERE, ALLEN R(ICHARD), b. New York, N.Y, Sept. 1, 17; m. 45; c. 4. MECHANICAL ENGINEERING. B.S.M.E, Worcester Polytech, 38; M.S, Lehigh, 40. Instr, Lehigh, 38-40; indust. engr. & supvr, E.I. du Pont de Nemours & Co, Inc, 40-43; asst. prof. mech. eng, Colorado, 46-49, assoc. prof, 49-51; head rocket develop. sect, ROHM AND HAAS CO, 51-54, dir. res, Redstone Div, 54-56, gen. mgr, 56-63, asst. dir. res, RES. DIV, SPRINGHOUSE, 63-70, DIR. INFO. SERV, 70- Consult, Gates Rubber Co, 51. Ord. Dept, 43-46, Capt. Am. Soc. Mech. Eng. Fluid flow; thermodynamics; administration. Address: 2966 Grisdale Rd, Roslyn, PA 19001.

DE SCHMERTZING, HANNIBAL, b. Budapest, Hungary, Aug. 21, 16; U.S. citizen; m. 59; c. 1. ANALYTICAL CHEMISTRY. M.S, Pazmany Univ, Budapest, 38, Ph.D.(anal. chem), 43. Asst. anal. chem, Eötvös Lóránd, Budapest, 40-43; chief chemist, testing lab, Middle Slovakian Ironworks, 47-48; interpreter translations, Counter Intel. Corps, 48-49; chemist res, Austrian Nitrogen Work, 49-50; bookkeeping, construct, Cie. Africaine Emballage et Conditionement, 50-51; chief chem. sect, Porter Urquhardt Skidmore Owings & Merrill Assocs, 51-53; head cent. lab, Mediterranean Div, U.S. Army Corps Engrs, Morocco, 53-56; res. chemist, Allied Chem. Co, 56-59; sr. scientist, Melpar Inc, 60-68; GODDARD SPACE FLIGHT CTR, NASA, 68- Hungarian Mil. Serv, 43-45, Lt. Am. Chem. Soc; Am. Soc. Test. & Mat; Am. Inst. Aeronaut. & Astronaut. Titrimetry; gravimetry; colorimetry; qualitative and quantitative micro analysis; thin layer chromatography; x-ray diffraction and fluorescence analysis. Address: 1025 Towlston Rd, McLean, VA 22101.

DESCHNER, ELEANOR E(LIZABETH), b. Jersey City, N.J, Oct. 18, 28; m. 57; c. 2. RADIOBIOLOGY, CYTOLOGY. B.A, Notre Dame Col, Staten Island, 49; M.S, Fordham, 51, Ph.D.(biol), 54. Asst, Fordham, 51-52; jr. tech. specialist, Brookhaven Nat. Lab, 52, Atomic Energy Cmn. fel, 52-54, res. collab, 54; U.S. Pub. Health Serv. fel, Nat. Cancer Inst. & British Empire Cancer Campaign, Res. Unit in Radiobiol, Mt. Vernon Hosp, Eng, 54-57; RES. ASSOC. Columbia, 58-59; MED. COL, CORNELL UNIV, 60-, ASST. PROF. RADIOL, 63-, ASST. PROF. RADIOBIOL. MED, 68- AAAS; Radiation Res. Soc; Am. Soc. Cell Biol; Genetics Soc. Am; Royal Soc. Med. Tissue culture; autoradiographic studies of the gastrointestinal tract; cytological effects of thermal neutron and x-irradiation on meiotic plant cells; factors effecting the radiosensitivity of ascites tumors. Address: 2776 Kennedy Blvd, Jersey City, NJ 07306.

DeSELM, H(ENRY) R(AWIE), b. Columbus, Ohio, Nov. 1, 24; m. 48; c. 2. PLANT ECOLOGY. Ph.D.(bot), Ohio State, 53. Asst. bot, Ohio State, 50-53, asst. instr, 54; instr. biol, Middle Tenn. State Col, 54-56; instr. & res. assoc. BOT, UNIV. TENN, KNOXVILLE, 56-60, asst. prof, 60-65, ASSOC. PROF, 65- U.S.M.C, 44-46, 1st Lt. Fel. AAAS; Ecol. Soc. Am; Bot. Soc. Am. Natural vegetation distribution; production; mineral and fission product cycling; calciphiles; ecological races; remote sensing of environment. Address: Dept. of Botany & Graduate Program in Ecology, University of Tennessee, 408 Tenth St, Knoxville, TN 37916.

DE SELMS, ROY CHARLES, b. San Pedro, Calif, Dec. 17, 32; m. 59; c. 2. ORGANIC CHEMISTRY. B.S, Washington (Seattle), 54; fel, Dartmouth Col, 54-55; Ph.D.(chem), Stanford, 59. Res. chemist, res. labs, Eastman Kodak Co, N.Y, 59-62; fel. alkaloid biosynthesis, California, Berkeley, 62-63; res. chemist, Ortho Div, Chevron Chem. Co, 63-66; sr. res. chemist, EASTMAN KODAK CO, 66-70, RES. ASSOC, 70- Instr, Univ. Calif, Berkeley, 64; assoc. instr, Univ. Rochester Exten, 67- Am. Chem. Soc. Organic chemistry of heterocyclics, carbenes, alicyclics, pesticides and photoreproduction. Address: Eastman Kodak Research Labs, B82 Kodak Park, Rochester, NY 14650.

DESER, STANLEY, b. Poland, Mar. 19, 31; nat; m. 56; c. 3. THEORETICAL PHYSICS. B.S, Brooklyn Col, 49; M.A, Harvard, 50, Atomic Energy Cmn. fel, 51-52, Nat. Sci. Found. fel, 52-53; Ph.D.(physics), 53. Mem. & Jewett fel, inst. adv. study, Princeton, 53-55; Nat. Sci. Found. fel, Inst. Theoret. Physics, Denmark, 55-57; lectr. PHYSICS, Harvard, 57-58; assoc. prof, BRANDEIS UNIV, 58-65, PROF, 65- Res. assoc, radiation lab, California, 54; Fulbright & Guggenheim fels 66-67; vis. prof, Univ. Sorbonne, 66-67, 71-72; Fulbright prof, Univ. of the Repub, Uruguay, 70. Am. Phys. Soc. Elementary particle physics; field theory; relativity. Address: Dept. of Physics, Brandeis University, Waltham, MA 02154.

de SERRES, FREDERICK J(OSEPH), b. Dobbs Ferry, N.Y, Sept. 24, 29; m. 54; c. 5. MICROBIAL GENETICS. B.S, Tufts, 51; Pub. Health Serv. fel, Yale, 52-54, M.S, 53, Wadsworth fel, 54-55, Ph.D.(bot), 55. Res.

assoc. BIOL. DIV, OAK RIDGE NAT. LAB, 55-57, SR. STAFF BIOLOGIST, 57-, COORD. ENVIRON. MUTAGENESIS PROG, 69-; LECTR, UNIV. TENN-OAK RIDGE GRAD. SCH. BIOMED. SCI, 71- Consult, genetics study sect, div. res. grants, Nat. Insts. Health, 67; biosci. exp. surv, NASA, 68; joint Food & Agr. Orgn, Int. Atomic Energy Agency WHO, expert comt. irradiated food, 69. Mem. panel non-psychiat. hazards of drugs & abuse, Nat. Inst. Ment. Health, Dept. Health Educ. & Welfare, 69; comt. RBE of neutrons, Int. Comn. Radiol. Protection task group, 69-70; comt. assessment nitrate accumulation in environ, agr. bd, div. biol. & agr, Nat. Res. Coun, 70-71, rep, Genetics Soc. Am. on div. biol. & agr, 70-73; chmn, Neurospora Info. Conf, 61, local comt, 66; consult, DDT adv. comt, Environ. Protection Agency, 71. AAAS; Bot. Soc. Am; Genetics Soc. Am; Radiation Res. Soc; Soc. Gen. Physiol; Environ. Mutagen Soc.(ed-in-chief, Newsletter); N.Y. Acad. Sci. Microbial genetics; radiation; chemical and environmental mutagenesis; space biology; mutagenicity of carcinogens. Address: Biology Division, Oak Ridge National Lab, P.O. Box Y, Oak Ridge, TN 37830.

DE SESA, MICHAEL A(NTHONY), b. Boston, Mass, Feb. 21, 27; m. 53; c. 2. ANALYTICAL CHEMISTRY. B.S, Boston Col, 49; Ph.D.(anal. chem), Mass. Inst. Tech, 53. Res. chemist, raw mat. develop. lab, Atomic Energy Cmn, 53-54, anal. group leader, 54-58, chem. group leader, 58-59, dept. head inorg. process develop, feed mat. prod. center, 59-62, asst. tech. dir. uranium chem. & metall, 62-63, assoc. tech. dir, 64; asst. sect. chief mech, chem. & thermal properties, res. & adv. develop. div, Avco Corp, 64-67; HEAD ANAL. & PHYS. RES. DEPT, CENT. RES. LAB, NL INDUSTS, INC, 67- U.S.N, 45-46. Am. Chem. Soc; Soc. Appl. Spectros. Instrumental methods of analysis; uranium hydrometallurgy; production of uranium compounds and metal; properties of ablative plastics; development of inorganic chemical products. Address: 33 Haddon Park, Fair Haven, NJ 07701.

DESFORGES, JANE F(AY), b. Melrose, Mass, Dec. 18, 21; m. 48; c. 2. MEDICINE. B.A, Wellesley Col, 42; M.D, Tufts, 45. Intern path, Mt. Auburn Hosp, 45-46; med, Boston City Hosp, 46-47; resident, 48-50, res. fel. hematol, 50-52; Nat. Insts. Health res. fel. hemat, Salt Lake City Hosp, 47-48; asst. prof. MED, SCH. MED, TUFTS UNIV, 52-62, ASSOC. PROF, 62-, ASSOC. DIR. TUFTS UNIV. HEMAT. LABS, BOSTON CITY HOSP, 56-, LABS, 57-, ASSOC. DIR. I & III MED. SERV, 68-, asst. dir, 52-68, physician in charge immunohemat. lab, hosp, 52-68, acting dir. clin. labs, 67-69. Assoc. ed, N.E. J. Med, 60- Am. Fed. Clin. Res; Am. Soc. Hemat; Int. Soc. Hemat; Am. Soc. Exp. Path. Hematology. Address: Tufts University Hematology Lab, Boston City Hospital, 818 Harrison Ave, Boston, MA 02118.

DeSHAW, JAMES RICHARD, b. Monticello, Iowa, June 19, 42; m. 65; c. 1. BIOLOGY, ENVIRONMENTAL SCIENCES. B.S, Loras Col, 65; M.S, Tex. A&M Univ, 67, Ph.D.(biol), 70. ASST. PROF. BIOL, SAM HOUSTON STATE UNIV, 70- AAAS; Am. Soc. Indust. Microbiol; Am. Soc. Microbiol. Recycling industrial organic waste materials and biological effects of heavy metals in aquatic systems. Address: Dept. of Biology, Sam Houston State University, Huntsville, TX 77340.

DE SHAZER, LARRY GRANT, b. Wash, D.C, Nov. 3, 34; m. 60; c. 2. PHYSICS. B.S, Maryland, 56; Gilman fel, Hopkins, 57-61, Ph.D.(physics), 63. Physicist, aerospace group, Hughes Aircraft Co, 63-66; asst. prof. PHYSICS, ELEC. ENG. & MAT. SCI, UNIV. SOUTH. CALIF, 66-70, ASSOC. PROF, 70- AAAS; Am. Phys. Soc; Optical Soc. Am. Solid-state lasers; spectrocopy of rare-earth ions and organic dyes; nonlinear absorption spectroscopy; open optical resonators; propagation of high-power optical beams; physics of dielectric thin films. Address: Dept. of Physics, University of Southern California, Los Angeles, CA 90007.

DeSHAZO, MARY LYNN DAVISON, b. Carthage, Tex, Aug. 14, 29; m. 64. BIOCHEMISTRY. B.S, E.Tex. Baptist Col, 49; Arkansas, 56; M.Ed, Houston, 57; Sam Houston State Col, 58-60, 63; Nat. Insts. Health fel, Baylor, 61-62; Nat. Sci. Found. fel. & Ph.D.(biochem), Tex. A&M Univ, 68. Secy, First Baptist Church, Groves, Tex, 49-51; teacher, pub. schs, 51-57; asst. prof. CHEM, SAM HOUSTON STATE UNIV, 57-67, ASSOC. PROF, 68- Am. Chem. Soc. Proteolytic enzymes of Aeromonas proteolytica. Address: Dept. of Chemistry, Sam Houston State University, Huntsville, TX 77340.

DESHMANE, SHARAD S, b. Poona, India, July 19, 35; m. 60; c. 2. ORGANIC CHEMISTRY. B.Sc, Univ. Bombay, 57, Ph.D.(org. chem), 66. Sr. sci. asst. ORG. CHEM, Nat. Chem. Lab, Poona, India, 58-68; RES. ASSOC, DEPT. MED, UNIV. HOSPS. CLEVELAND, 68- Chemistry of natural products; solvolytic rearrangements of steroids. Address: Dept. of Medicine, University Hospitals of Cleveland, Cleveland, OH 44106.

DESHMUKH, ASHOK R(AJESHWAR), b. Achalpur, India, Feb. 24, 40; m. 69. PLASMA & SPACE PHYSICS. B.S, Univ. Nagpur, 59, M.S, 61; Stevens Inst. Technol, 64, Ph.D.(physics), 68. Sci. off. nuclear physics, Indian Atomic Energy Comn, 61-63; res. asst. plasma physics, Stevens Inst. Technol, 64-68; res. coord, space physics, AERO GEO ASTRO, DIV. AIKEN INDUST, 68-69, HEAD SPACE PHYSICS, 69- AAAS; Am. Phys. Soc; Am. Geophys. Union; Am. Inst. Aeronaut. & Astronaut. Plasma-field interactions; plasma accelerators; plasma diagnostics; solar wind and terrestrial field interaction; magnetospheric, plasmaspheric, ionospheric, and aeronomic studies using satellite borne ion spectrometers. Address: 14321 Sturtevant Rd, Silver Spring, MD 20904.

DESHOTELS, WARREN J(ULIUS), b. New Orleans, La, Jan. 3, 26; m. 51; c. 11. PHYSICS. B.S, Tulane, 45, M.S, 47; fel. & Ph.D.(physics), St. Louis, 53. Dir. physics, Xavier (La), 48-53; chief instrumentation engr, Jackson & Church Co, Mich, 53-55; sr. physicist, Clevite Res. Center, Ohio, 55-64; ASSOC. PROF. PHYSICS, MARQUETTE UNIV, 64-, CHMN. DEPT, 65- AAAS; Am. Phys. Soc; Am. Asn. Physics Teachers. Solid state and electron physics. Address: Dept. of Physics, Marquette University, Milwaukee, WI 53233.

DESHPANDE, K(RISHNANATH) B(HASKAR), b. India, Nov. 1, 21; m. 50; c. 2. PHYSICAL & INORGANIC CHEMISTRY. B.S, Bombay, 43, M.S, 46, Ph.D. (phys. chem), 51. Instr. chem, Bombay, 43-46, lectr. inorg. & phys. chem, 47-57; curators grant, Missouri, 57, Am. Petrol. Inst. fel, 57-60; res. assoc. phys. chem, North Carolina, 60-65; PROF. CHEM, FISK UNIV, 61-, dir. Nat. Sci. Found. acad. year inst, 69-71. Chadraseniya Kayastha Prabhu scholar, 57-60; Fulbright travel grant, U.S. State Dept, 57-60; Am. Petrol. Inst. fel, Oak Ridge Inst. Nuclear Studies, 60; res. chemist, U.S. Atomic Energy Comn, 60-65; dir, U.S. Off. Educ-Inst. Advan. Studies in Phys. Sci, 70-; consult, Univ. Tenn-Atomic Energy Comn. Agr. Res. Lab, Tenn. Am. Chem. Soc; Clay Minerals Soc; Indian Chem. Soc. Colloid chemistry of systems containing soaps and organic solvents; electrochemistry of clay-electrolyte systems; surface chemistry; ion exchange in inorganic exchangers using radioisotopes; ion exchange thermodynamics. Address: Dept. of Chemistry, Fisk University, Nashville, TN 37203.

DESHPANDE, NARAYAN V(AMAN), b. Bhadwan, India, May 4, 38; m. 66; c. 1. MECHANICAL ENGINEERING, APPLIED MATHEMATICS. B.Eng, Univ. Poona, 61; M.S, Univ. Rochester, 64, Ph.D.(fluid mech), 66. Eng. asst, Tata Thermal Power Co, India, 61-62; res. assoc. fluid instabilities, Culham Lab, U.K. Atomic Energy Auth, 66-67; ASST. PROF. MECH. & AEROSPACE SCI, UNIV. ROCHESTER, 67- Ctr. Naval Anal. res. grant, 68-70. Fluid mechanics and magnetohydrodynamics; the stability of magnetohydrodynamic boundary layer type flows and the two-stream instability; study of a boundary layer over a moving surface. Address: Dept. of Mechanical & Aerospace Sciences, University of Rochester, Rochester, NY 14627.

DESHPANDE, NILENDRA GANESH, b. Karachi, Pakistan, Apr. 18, 38; m. 60; c. 2. ELEMENTARY PARTICLE PHYSICS. B.Sc, Madras, 59, M.A, 60, M.Sc, 61; Ph.D.(physics), Pennsylvania, 65. Res. fel. theoret. physics, Imp. Col, London, 65-66; mem, Inst. Math. Sci, Madras, India, 66; res. assoc. PHYSICS, NORTHWEST. UNIV, 66-67, ASST. PROF, 67- Am. Phys. Soc. Distinction between elementary particles and bound states; relation between field theory and bootstraps; spontaneous breakdown of symmetry; chiral symmetry breaking and sum rules; high energy behavior of field theory. Address: Dept. of Physics, Northwestern University, Evanston, IL 60201.

DESHPANDE, SHIVAJIRAO M, b. Dec. 20, 36; Indian citizen; m. SOLID STATE PHYSICS, ELECTRICAL ENGINEERING. B.Sc, Osmania Univ, India, 56, M.Sc, 58; M.Tech, Indian Inst. Technol, Bombay, 60; Ph.D.(physics), Univ. Vt, 71. Sci. off. electro-vacuum & thin films, Bhaba Atomic Res. Ctr, India, 60-66; ENGR. SEMICONDUCTOR PHYSICS, COGAR CORP, 69- Design and development of electrooptical systems; changes in the electrical conductivity of discontinuous molybdenum films upon exposure to oxygen; development of $Al + Al_2O_3$ alloy metallurgy for enhanced electromigration resistance in monolithic circuits. Address: Information Systems Division, Cogar Corp, Cosby Manor Rd, Schuyler, NY 13502.

DESHPANDE, SHREEKANT N, b. Belgaum, India, June 25, 29. FOOD & RADIATION CHEMISTRY. B.Sc, Col. Agr, Dharwar, India, 50; M.S, Purdue, 62, Ph.D.(food tech), 65. Supt. agr, Dept. Agr, Hyderabad, India, 50-54; govt. nominee canning tech, Cent. Food Tech. Res. Inst, Mysore, 54-55; agr. officer, Govt. Hyderabad & Bombay, 55-56; instr. hort, Col. Agr, Poona, 57-59; asst. food tech, Purdue, 59-64; asst. prof. isotope tech. & food sci, Tuskegee Inst, 64-66; asst. prof. CHEM. (ad honorum), UNIV. P.R, MAYAGUEZ, 66-69, ASSOC. PROF, 69-, SCIENTIST, P.R. NUCLEAR CTR, 69-, assoc. scientist, 66-69. Summer res. participant, U.S. Atomic Energy Cmn. grant, P.R. Nuclear Center, 65; lectr. scientist & consult, Atoms for Peace mission & exhibit, U.S. Atomic Energy Cmn, Costa Rica, Nicaragua, Guatemala, 66; res, Max Planck Inst. Biochem, W.Germany, 69; sci. consult, Cent. Am. Res. Inst. Indust, Guatemala, summers, 69, 70, 71. Am. Chem. Soc; Inst. Food Tech; Soc. Indust. Microbiol. Biochemistry of radiation; comparative study of the effects of thermal processing and ionizing radiation on natural polymers, essential amino acids, and enzymes in plant products; effect of ionizing radiation on simulated enzyme systems. Address: Puerto Rico Nuclear Center, University of Puerto Rico, College Station, Mayaguez, PR 00708.

DESIDERATO, ROBERT, JR, b. New York, N.Y, Aug. 21, 39; m. 68; c. 1. PHYSICAL CHEMISTRY. A.B, Columbia, 61; Ph.D.(chem), Rice, 66. Res. assoc. crystallog, Pittsburgh, 65-66; ASST. PROF. CHEM, N.TEX. STATE UNIV, 66- Am. Chem. Soc; Am. Crystallog. Asn. X-ray structure and analysis of biologically important compounds and transition metal complexes; computer programming. Address: Dept. of Chemistry, North Texas State University, North Texas Station, Denton, TX 76203.

DESIDERIO, DOMINIC MORSE, JR, b. McKees Rocks, Pa, Jan. 11, 41; m. 65; c. 2. ANALYTICAL CHEMISTRY. B.A, Pittsburgh, 61; S.M, Mass. Inst. Tech, 64, Ph.D.(anal, chem), 65. Control chemist, Pittsburgh Coke & Chem. Co, 59-61; res. chemist, Pittsburgh, 61; res. asst, Mass. Inst. Tech, 61-65; res. chemist, Stamford Res. Labs, Am. Cyanamid Co, 66-67; asst. prof. CHEM, INST. LIPID RES, BAYLOR COL. MED, 67-71, ASSOC. PROF, 71-, ASSOC. PROF. BIOCHEM, DEPT. BIOCHEM, 71- Fel. Intrasci. Res. Found. AAAS; Am. Inst. Chem; Am. Chem. Soc; Am. Soc. Mass Spectrometry. The application of mass spectrometry to the structural elucidation of organic and biological compounds; computer techniques in mass spectrometry. Address: Institute for Lipid Research, Baylor College of Medicine, Texas Medical Center, Houston, TX 77025.

DeSIENO, ROBERT P, b. Scranton, Pa, Sept. 1, 33; m. 62; c. 2. PHYSICAL CHEMISTRY. B.S, Union Col.(N.Y), 55, M.S, 62; Ph.D.(chem), California, Davis, 66. Chemist, Gen. Elec. Co, 57-62; res. asst, Univ. California, 62-65; sr. chemist, Rohm and Haas Corp. Res. Labs, 65-68; ASST. PROF. CHEM, WESTMINSTER COL.(PA), 68- U.S.A.F, 55-57, Res, 57-68, 1st Lt. AAAS; Am. Chem. Soc. Science and literature; spectroscopic properties of electrically exploded wires; conductance in solution. Address: Dept. of Chemistry, Westminster College, New Wilmington, PA 16142.

DESILETS, BRIAN H, b. Leominster, Mass, Oct. 7, 27; m. 70; c. 1. PHYSICS. B.A, Marist Col, 50; M.S, St. John's (N.Y), 54; M.S, N.Y. Univ, 58; Ph.D.(physics), Catholic Univ, 64. Teacher, Bishop Dubois High Sch, 50-54; instr. math. & physics, Marist Col, 54-56, asst. prof. physics, 56-60; lectr. elec. eng, Catholic Univ, 63-64; asst. prof. PHYSICS, MARIST COL, 65-66, assoc. prof, 66-70, PROF, 70- Res. assoc, Catholic Univ, 62-64. Consult, x-ray labs, Int. Bus. Mach. Corp, N.Y, 57-60. Am. Asn. Physics Teachers. Solid state physics; x-ray studies; microwave attenuation; photoconductivity. Address: Dept. of Physics, Marist College, Poughkeepsie, NY 12601.

DeSILVA, ALAN W, b. Los Angeles, Calif, Feb. 8, 32; m. 59; c. 3. PLASMA PHYSICS. B.S, California, Los Angeles, 54, Ph.D.(physics), Berkeley, 61. Res. physicist, Lawrence Radiation Lab, California, Berkeley, 61-62; Nat. Sci. Fel. plasma spectros, Culham Lab, United Kingdom Atomic Energy Authority, 62-63, res. assoc, 63-64; asst. prof. PHYSICS, UNIV. MD, 64-68, ASSOC. PROF, 68- Sig.C, U.S.A, 54-56. Am. Phys. Soc; Inst. Elec. & Electronics Eng. Plasma physics, including hydromagnetic wave phenomena and radiations from plasmas; interactions of electromagnetic radiation with plasmas; collision free shockwaves and turbulence in plasmas. Address: Dept. of Physics & Astronomy, University of Maryland, College Park, MD 20742.

DeSILVA, CARL NEVIN, b. British Guiana, Aug. 6, 23; U.S. citizen; m. 54; c. 6. ENGINEERING MECHANICS. B.S, Columbia, 49, M.S, 50; Ph.D.(mech), Michigan, 55. Res. asst, Michigan, 52-55, res. assoc, 55-57; unit chief mech. res, Boeing Airplane Co, 57-60; assoc. prof. aeronaut. & eng. mech, Minnesota, 60-64, prof, 64-66; PROF. ENG. MECH. & CHMN. DEPT. MECH. ENG. SCI, WAYNE STATE UNIV, 66- Consult, Boeing Airplane Co, 60-62; Honeywell Corp, 62-63; Gen. Mills, Inc, 63-64; Geophysics Corp, Am, 65-66. U.S.N, 44-46. Am. Math. Soc; Am. Soc. Mech. Eng; Soc. Natural Philos. Solutions of problems in the classical theory of elastic shells; development of nonlinear theories of elastic shells and of non-Newtonian fluids; constitutive equations of viscoelastic materials with memory; analysis of fluid suspensions as applied to blood flow. Address: Dept. of Mechanical Engineering Sciences, Wayne State University, Detroit, MI 48202.

DE SILVA, JOHN ARTHUR F, b. Colombo, Ceylon, Sept. 23, 33; U.S. citizen; m. 59; c. 1. ANALYTICAL CHEMISTRY. B.Sc, Ceylon, 56; M.S, Rutgers, 58, Ph.D.(soil chem), 61. Res. chemist, agr. div, Am. Cyanamid Co, N.J, 61-63; sr. res. chemist, dept. clin. pharmacol, HOFFMANN-LA ROCHE INC, 63-70, RES. GROUP CHIEF BIOANAL. METHOD DEVELOP, DEPT. BIOCHEM. & DRUG METAB, 70- AAAS; Am. Chem. Soc; fel. Am. Inst. Chem; N.Y. Acad. Sci. Residue methods for drugs and metabolites in biological fluids; analytical toxicology; drug metabolism; chromatography, especially gas-liquid chromatography, liquid-liquid chromatography and thin layer chromatography; luminescence, especially fluorescence and phosphorescence; spectrophotometry, especially ultraviolet and infrared; electrochemical analysis; polarography; radiochemical isotope tracer techniques. Address: Dept. of Biochemistry & Drug Metabolism, Hoffmann-La Roche Inc, Kingsland St, Nutley, NJ 07110.

DESIO, P(ETER) J(OHN), b. Boston, Mass, June 29, 38. ORGANIC & ORGANOMETALLIC CHEMISTRY. B.S, Boston Col, 60; Ph.D.(org. chem), New Hampshire, 65. Asst. gen. & org. chem, New Hampshire, 60-63, teaching fel. org. chem, 63-64; res. assoc. mat. div, Mass. Inst. Tech, 64-66; ASSOC. PROF. ORG. CHEM, UNIV. NEW HAVEN, 66- Am. Coun. on Ed; Am. Chem. Soc; Am. Inst. Chem; N.Y. Acad. Sci; Brit. Chem. Soc. Structure, particularly ring-chain tautomerism in acids and alcohols; organocadmium reactions as well as other organometallics. Address: Dept. of Chemistry, University of New Haven, 300 Orange Ave, West Haven, CT 06516.

DESJARDINS, CLAUDE, b. Fall River, Mass, June 13, 38; m. 62; c. 3. ANIMAL PHYSIOLOGY. B.S, Rhode Island, 60; M.S, Michigan State, 64, Ph.D.(animal physiol), 67. Instr. reproductive physiol, Michigan State, 60-67; assoc. staff scientist, Jackson Lab, Maine, 67-68; asst. prof. PHYSIOL, OKLA. STATE UNIV, 68-70, ASSOC. PROF, 70- Am. Soc. Zool; Am. Asn. Anat; Soc. Study Reproduction; Brit. Soc. Study Fertil; Am. Physiol. Soc; Soc. Exp. & Biol. Med. Endocrinology; influence of environmental factors on hypothalamo-hypophyseal-gonadal interrelationships; testis function and male sex behavior. Address: Dept. of Physiological Sciences, Oklahoma State University, Stillwater, OK 74074.

DESJARDINS, PAUL R(OY), b. Cheyenne, Wyo, Aug. 7, 19; m. 47; c. 3. PLANT PATHOLOGY. B.S, Colo. State Univ, 42; Ph.D.(plant path), Univ. Calif, Berkeley, 52. Res. asst, UNIV. CALIF, Berkeley, 47-50, jr. plant pathologist, RIVERSIDE, 52-53, asst. plant pathologist, 53-59, assoc. prof. PLANT PATH, 61-70, PROF, 70- Res. assoc, Nat. Acad. Sci-Nat. Res. Coun, 64-65. U.S.A, 42-46; Chem.C, 51-52. AAAS; Am. Phytopath. Soc; Electron Micros. Soc. Am; Torrey Bot. Club. Seed transmission; electron microscopy, purification and serological studies of plant viruses; cytological studies of virus infected tissues; virus structure and morphology; virus nucleic acid and disease of citrus, avocado and other plants. Address: 4168 Quail Rd, Riverside, CA 92507.

DESJARDINS, RAOUL, b. Montreal, Que, Oct. 8, 33; m. 61; c. 2. PHARMACOLOGY, BIOCHEMISTRY. B.S, Col. Andre-Grasset, 53; M.D, Montreal, 58; M.S, Baylor, 64, Ph.D.(pharmacol), 66. Med. dir, Candiac Med. Clin, 59-62; asst. prof. pharmacol, Baylor, 66; asst. dir. CLIN. RES, ORTHO RES. FOUND, 66-67, assoc. dir, 67-68, DIR, 68- AAAS; Am. Col. Clin. Pharmacol. & Chemother; Am. Therapeut. Soc; Am. Fedn. Clin. Res; Geront. Soc; N.Y. Acad. Sci. Human reproduction; molecular biology; anti tumor agents; sex steroids; anesthesia; biology of ageing; contraception. Address: Ortho Research Foundation, Raritan, NJ 08869.

DESKIN, WILLIAM A(RNA), b. Mo, Aug. 16, 24; m. 49; c. 3. INORGANIC CHEMISTRY. B.S. & A.B, Northeast Mo. State Teacher Col, 48; M.A, Missouri, 50; Ph.D.(chem), Iowa, 57. Phys. chemist, Chem. Labs, U.S. Army Chem. Center, Md, 50-51; prof. chem. & physics, Upper Iowa, 52-54; asst. prof. CHEM, CORNELL COL, 56-59, assoc. prof, 59-63, PROF, 63-, chmn. dept, 61-70. Resident res. assoc, Argonne Nat. Lab, 63-64. U.S.A, 43-46, 51-52, 1st Lt. Am. Chem. Soc. Coordination compounds of transition metals with sulfur containing ligands; interhalogen compounds. Address: Dept. of Chemistry, Cornell College, Mt. Vernon, IA 52314.

DESKINS, W(ILBUR) EUGENE, b. Morgantown, W.Va, Feb. 20, 27; m. 53; c. 1. MATHEMATICS. B.S, Kentucky, 49; M.S, Wisconsin, 50, Ph.D.(math), 53. Instr. MATH, Wisconsin, 53; Ohio State, 53-55, asst. prof, 55-56; Mich. State Univ, 56-59, assoc. prof, 59-62, prof, 62-71; PROF. & CHMN. DEPT, UNIV. PITTSBURGH, 71- Staff assoc, comprehensive sch. math. prog, Cent. Midwest. Regional Educ. Lab, 69- U.S.A, 44-47, Res, 47-50. Am. Math. Soc; Math. Asn. Am. Algebra. Address: Dept. of Mathematics, University of Pittsburgh, Pittsburgh, PA 15213.

DESLATTES, RICHARD D, JR, b. New Orleans, La, Sept. 21, 31; m. 56; c. 5. RADIOLOGY, PHYSICS. B.S, Loyola (La), 52; Ph.D.(physics), Hopkins, 59. Instr, Loyola (La), 54-55; res. assoc. physics, Fla. State, 56-58; Cornell, 58-62; physicist solid state physics, NAT. BUR. STANDARDS, 62-68, CHIEF QUANTUM METROL. SECT, OPTICAL PHYSICS DIV, 68- Consult, Air Force Cambridge Res. Center, 60-62. AAAS; Am. Phys. Soc. X-ray spectroscopy of solids; atomic spectroscopy of high excited systems; x-ray diffraction microscopy. Address: Optical Physics Division, National Bureau of Standards, Washington, DC 20234.

DESLOGE, E(DWARD) A(UGUSTINE), b. St. Louis, Mo, Aug. 31, 26; m. 58. PHYSICS. B.S, Notre Dame, 47; M.S, St. Louis, 55, Ph.D.(physics), 57. Instr. PHYSICS, Yale, 58-59; asst. prof, FLA. STATE UNIV, 59-65, assoc. prof, 65-69, PROF, 69- U.S.N.R, 44-46, Ens. Am. Phys. Soc. Thermal and statistical physics. Address: Dept. of Physics, Florida State University, Tallahassee, FL 32306.

DESLONGCHAMPS, PIERRE, b. St. Lin, Que, May 8, 38; m. 60; c. 2. ORGANIC CHEMISTRY. B.Sc, Montreal, 59; Ph.D.(org. chem), New Brunswick, 64. Asst. prof. CHEM, Univ. Montreal, 65-67; adj. prof, UNIV. SHERBROOKE, 67, ASSOC. PROF, 67- Res. fel. chem, Harvard, 64-65; A.P. Sloan fel, 70-72; E.W.R. Steacie mem. fel, 71-72. Chem. Inst. Can. Synthesis in organic natural products. Address: Dept. of Chemistry, University of Sherbrooke, Sherbrooke, Que, Can.

DES MARAIS, ANDRE, b. Pierreville, Que, Apr. 23, 19; m. 44; c. 4. PHYSIOLOGY. B.A, Montreal, 40, B.Sc, 43; travelling fel, Nat. Res. Coun, 45; summer prov. fel, California, 47; Ph.D.(physiol), Laval, 48. Instr. gen. physiol, Montreal, 44; mammalian physiol, Laval, 45-50, asst. prof, 50-55, assoc. prof, 55-58; prof. biol, Univ. Ottawa, 58-69, chmn. dept. & secy. faculty, 64-69; PRIN. SCI. ADV, PRIVY COUN. OFF, 69- Rockefeller fel, Harvard, 50-51. AAAS; Am. Physiol. Soc; N.Y. Acad. Sci; fel. Royal Soc. Can; Can. Physiol. Soc. Mammalian endocrinology; physiology of cold adaptation, adrenal and thyroid. Address: Privy Council Office, 171 E. Block, Ottawa, Ont, Can.

DesMARTEAU, DARRYL D, b. Garden City, Kans, May 25, 40; m. 62; c. 3. INORGANIC & FLUORINE CHEMISTRY. B.S, Wash. State Univ, 63, Ph.D.(chem), Univ. Wash, 66. ASST. PROF. CHEM, Univ. Wash, 66-67; Northeast. Univ, 67-71; KANS. STATE UNIV, 71- U.S.M.C.R, 60-66. Am. Chem. Soc. Synthesis and properties of nonmetal fluorine compounds, especially compounds of phosphorus, sulfur and strong oxidizers such as peroxides, fluoroxides and xenon compounds. Address: Dept. of Chemistry, Kansas State University, Manhattan, KS 66502.

DESMOND, ALTON H(AROLD), b. Springfield, Vt, Aug. 3, 22; m. 45; c. 1. BIOLOGY. B.S, Hartwick Col, 49; Sc.M, Brown, 51, Eli Lilly fel, 52-53, Ph.D.(biol), 54. Asst. prof. ZOOL, GEORGE WASH. UNIV, 53-59, assoc. prof, 59-63, PROF, 63-, CHMN. DEPT, 69- U.S.C.G, 42-46. AAAS; Am. Soc. Zool; Am. Soc. Cell Biol; Am. Micros. Soc; Am. Acad. Forensic Sci. Histophysiology and histopathology of the liver and endocrines; histophysiologic and toxicologic effects of food, drug and cosmetic dyes; forensic science. Address: 4907 Erie St, Annandale, VA 22003.

DESMOND, MURDINA MACFARQUHAR, b. Isle of Lewis, Scotland, Nov. 14, 16; nat; m. 48; c. 2. PEDIATRICS. B.A, Smith Col, 38; M.D, Temple, 42. Fel. PEDIAT, George Washington Sch, Med, 47-58; instr, COL. MED, BAYLOR UNIV, 48-52, asst. prof, 52-57, assoc. prof, 57-64, PROF, 64- U.S.N.R, 44-46, Lt. Soc. Pediat. Res; Am. Pediat. Soc; Am. Acad. Ment. Deficiency. Neonatology; transition of infant from intrauterine to extrauterine life; relation newborn area to later development. Address: Dept. of Pediatrics, Baylor University College of Medicine, Houston, TX 77025.

DESNOYERS, J(ACQUES) E(DOUARD), b. Ottawa, Ont, Jan. 28, 35; m. 64; c. 2. PHYSICAL CHEMISTRY. B.Sc, Ottawa (Can), 58, Nat. Res. Coun. Can. scholar, 58-61, Ph.D.(phys. chem), 61. NATO & Ramsay fels, Battersea Col. Tech. & Manchester Univ, Eng, 61-62; lectr. PHYS. CHEM, UNIV. SHERBROOKE, 62-63, asst. prof, 63-67, assoc. prof, 67-71, PROF, 71- Am. Chem. Soc; Electrochem. Soc; Chem. Inst. Can. Theoretical and experimental studies of thermodynamic properties of aqueous solutions in relation with solute-solvent and solute-solute interactions; microcalorimetry. Address: Dept. of Chemistry, University of Sherbrooke, Sherbrooke, Que, Can.

DE SOBRINO, R(ICARDO), b. Cádiz, Spain, Mar. 22, 21; U.S. citizen; m. 57; c. 3. SYSTEMS ENGINEERING, COMMUNICATIONS. E.E, Span. Navy Postgrad. Sch, 47; M.E.E, Polytech. Inst. Brooklyn, 51; D.Eng.Sci.(info. theory), Columbia Univ, 53. Res. engr, Naval Bur, Madrid, 53-57; engr, Nat. Inst. Indust, 57-59; mem. staff commun. acoust, RCA Labs, N.J, 59-62; STAFF SCIENTIST ENG. SYSTS, STANFORD RES. INST, 62- Prof, Span. Navy Postgrad. Schs, 53-58. Span. Navy, 45-58, Lt. Comdr. Sr. mem. Inst. Elec. & Electronics Eng. Engineering systems; nuclear power; speech recognition; communication acoustics; operations research; oceanography. Address: 3440 Janice Way, Palo Alto, CA 94303.

DESOER, CHARLES A(UGUSTE), b. Brussels, Belgium, Jan. 11, 26; nat; m. 51; c. 3. ELECTRICAL ENGINEERING. Dipl, Liege, Belgium, 49; Sc.D, Mass. Inst. Tech, 53. Mem. tech. staff, Bell Tel. Labs, Inc, 53-58; assoc. prof. ELEC. ENG, UNIV. CALIF, BERKELEY, 58-62, PROF, 62- Guggenheim fel, 70-71. Belg. Army, 44-45. Fel. Inst. Elec. & Electronics Eng; Am. Math. Soc; Soc. Indust. & Appl. Math; Math. Asn. Am. System theory; control and circuits. Address: Dept. of Electrical Engineering & Computer Science, University of California, Berkeley, CA 94720.

DeSOMBRE, EUGENE ROBERT, b. Sheboygan, Wis, May 6, 38; m. 60; c. 2. BIOCHEMISTRY, ENDOCRINOLOGY. B.S, Univ. Chicago, 60, M.S, 61, Ph.D.(org. chem), 63. Res. assoc, BEN MAY LAB. CANCER RES, UNIV.

CHICAGO, 63-65, instr, 65-67, ASST. PROF, 67- U.S.A.R, 55-63. AAAS; Am. Chem. Soc. Organophosphorous chemistry; steroid mechanism of action; estrogen endocrinology; hormone dependent cancer. Address: Ben May Lab. for Cancer Research, Univ. Chicago, 950 E. 59th St, Chicago, IL 60637.

DE SOUSA, ARTHUR, b. Lisbon, Portugal, Aug. 26, 09; m. 63. INORGANIC & PHYSICAL CHEMISTRY. M.D, Lausanne, 32, D.Sc.(chem), 39; Ph.D. (philosophy), Fribourg, 39. Prof. chem, Lisbon, 40-60; Mt. Allison, 61-66; res. chemist, Kawecki Berylco Indust, Inc, 67-71. Consult, Fabrica Ceramica Sacavem, Portugal, 40-60, Companhia Mineira Do Lobito, Angola, 42-60, dir. gen. of mines & geol. surv, Portugal, 44-60 & Martin Correia Co. for tin, 41-60. The Chem. Soc; fel. Chem. Inst. Can; Am. Chem. Soc; Inst. Food Technol; Microchem. Soc; fel. Am. Inst. Chem; Am. Acad. Arts & Sci. Analytical chemistry; extraction of metals; complex formation; kinetics; methods of analysis. Address: Buchert Rd, R.D. 1, Boyertown, PA 19512.

DESOWITZ, ROBERT, b. New York, N.Y, Jan. 2, 26; m. 54; c. 2. PARASITOLOGY, IMMUNOLOGY. B.A, Buffalo, 48; Fulbright scholar & Ph.D.(parasitol), London, 51, D.Sc,(parasitol), 60. Prin. sci. officer, colonial med. res. serv, W.African Inst. Trypanosomiasis Res, 51-60; prof. parasitol. & head dept, Singapore, 60-65; chief dept. parasitol, SEATO Med. Res. Lab, Bangkok, Thailand, 65-68; PROF. TROP. MED. & PUB. HEALTH, LEAHI HOSP, SCH. MED, UNIV. HAWAII, 68- Mem, expert cmt. parasitic diseases, WHO, 64- Am. Soc. Parasitol; fel. Royal Soc. Trop. Med. Hyg. Host-parasite relationships, especially malaria, trypanosomiasis and filariasis; immunologic response to malaria, trypanosomiasis and filariasis. Address: Leahi Hospital, School of Medicine, University of Hawaii, 3675 Kilauea Ave, Honolulu, HI 96816.

DESPAIN, ALVIN M(ARDEN), b. Salt Lake City, Utah, July 2, 38; m. 57; c. 2. ELECTRICAL ENGINEERING, PHYSICS. B.S, Utah, 60, M.S, 64, Ph.D. (elec. eng), 66. Engr. trainee elec. eng, South. Calif, Edison Co, 57; res. asst. elec. eng. & physics, Utah, 57-60, res. engr, 60-66, asst. res. prof. ELEC. ENG. & PHYSICS, 66-67; asst. prof, UTAH STATE UNIV, 66-69, ASSOC. PROF, 69-, ASST. DIR. ELECTRODYN. LABS, 67- Inst. Elec. & Electronics Eng; Am. Asn. Physics Teachers; Am. Soc. Eng. Educ. Aeronomy; Fourier spectrometry and interferometry; electrooptics and holography; communication-information theory; data communications and computer design. Address: Dept. of Electrical Engineering, Utah State University, Logan, UT 84321.

DESPAIN, LEWIS G(AIL), b. Salt Lake City, Utah, Feb. 7, 28; m. 56; c. 4. SPACE PHYSICS. B.S, Utah, 55, M.S, 57, Ph.D.(physics), 62. Sr. scientist, space sci. div, Jet Propulsion Lab, Calif. Inst. Tech, 61-64, group supvr, 64-66, assoc. proj. scientist, 66-67; SUPVR, SPACE PHYSICS GROUP, BOEING SCI. RES. LABS, BOEING CO, SEATTLE, 67- U.S.A.F, 46-48, Capt. Am. Asn. Physics Teachers. Direction of specialized group which conducts theoretical and experimental research in space physics. Address: 2715 S.W. 322nd St, Federal Way, WA 98002.

DESPOINTES, RENE H, b. Can, Sept. 17, 25. ENDOCRINOLOGY. B.Sc, Caen, 44; M.D, Paris, 50, lic.es sc, 55; Ph.D.(invest. med), McGill, 62. Res. fel. endocrinol, Harvard & Peter Bent Brigham Hosp, Boston, Mass, 55-57, asst. med, 56-57; res. asst. endocrinol, McGill & Childrens Hosp, Montreal, 58-62; asst. prof. path, Dalhousie & Victoria Gen. Hosp, 63-65; asst. dir. steroid res. lab, Dept. Pub. Health, N.S, 63-65; ASSOC. PROF. BIOCHEM. & DIR. STEROID RES. LAB, LAVAL UNIV, 65-; CHMN. DEPT. BIOCHEM, HOSP. CTR, SHERBROOKE UNIV, 67- Ciba res. fel, 60-61; hon. lectr. biochem, 64; Can. Heart Found. & Med. Res. Coun. Can. grants, 64-66. Endocrine Soc; Can. Soc. Clin. Invest; Can. Fedn. Biol. Soc; Can. Soc. Clin. Chem; Royal Soc. Med. Steroid biochemistry; studies on the mechanism of secretion of antidiuretic, adrenocorticotrophic and aldosterone hormones; sex steroides; renin. Address: Dept. of Biochemistry, University Hospital Center, Sherbrooke University, Sherbrooke, Que, Can.

DESPOMMIER, DICKSON, b. New Orleans, La, June 5, 40; m. 63; c. 1. PARASITOLOGY, IMMUNOLOGY. B.S, Fairleigh Dickinson, 62; M.S, Columbia, 64; Ph.D.(microbiol), Notre Dame, 67. Asst. parasitol, sch. pub. health & admin. med, Columbia, 62-63; biol, Notre Dame, 64-65; U.S. Pub. Health Serv. guest investr. PARASITOL, Rockefeller, 67-70; ASST. PROF. SCH. PUB. HEALTH, COLUMBIA UNIV, 70- AAAS; Am. Soc. Parasitol. Effects of the immune state in the biology of nematode parasites in mammalian hosts; molting and morphogenesis of nematodes in culture. Address: Dept. of Tropical Medicine, School of Public Health, College of Physicians & Surgeons, Columbia University, 630 W. 168th St, New York, NY 10032.

DESPOPOULOS, AGAMEMNON, b. N.Y.C, Aug. 12, 24; m. 50; c. 4. PHYSIOLOGY. M.B. & B.S, Minnesota, 47, M.D, 48. Fel, Rockefeller Inst, 48-49; Phila. Gen. Hosp, 49-50; Nat. Insts. Health trainee, U.S. Pub. Health Serv. Hosp, 50-51, sr. asst. surgeon, 51-53; instr. internal med, med. sch, Tulane, 53-54; sr. asst. surgeon, Nat. Heart Inst, Nat. Insts. Health, 54-55, surgeon, 56-57; asst. prof. PHARMACOL, Louisville, 57-64, assoc. prof, SCH. MED, UNIV. N.MEX, 64-71, PROF, 71- Established investr, Am. Heart Asn, 59. U.S.A, 43-44. Harvey Soc; Am. Physiol. Soc. Renal physiology; enzyme systems as related to renal transport mechanisms; hormonal effects on renal transport systems; active transport in kidney, liver, brain and eye. Address: Dept. of Physiology, University of New Mexico School of Medicine, Albuquerque, NM 87106.

DESPRES, THOMAS A, b. Grand Rapids, Mich, Nov. 13, 32; m. 59; c. 2. MECHANICAL & METALLURGICAL ENGINEERING. B.S.I.E, Michigan, 56, M.S.M.E, 59, Ph.D.(mech. eng), 64. Test & eval. missile components, Redstone Arsenal, 57-58; teaching fel. mech. & metall. eng, UNIV. MICH-DEARBORN, 58-63, asst. prof. MECH. ENG, 63-66, ASSOC. PROF, 66- Summers, test & eval. engr, Explorer IV & V, Army Ballistic Missile Agency, 58, missile div, Chrysler Corp, 59, res. engr. turbines, Ford Motor Corp, 60; consult. Ord.C, U.S.A, 56-58. Metallurgical and solid state research in fatigue of metals; mechanical properties of metals and application of electron microscopy to metallurgical and mechanical properties study. Address: 135 Ft. Dearborn Rd, Dearborn, MI 48124.

DES PREZ, ROGER MOISTER, b. Chicago, Ill, Mar. 14, 27; m. 65; c. 7. INTERNAL MEDICINE, INFECTIOUS DISEASES. A.B, Dartmouth Col, 51; M.D. Columbia, 54. Intern, asst. med. resident & chest med. resident, N.Y. Hosp, 54-57; physician, Ft. Defiance Tuberc. Sanatorium, 57-59; instr. med, med. col, Cornell, 57-62; asst. prof. MED, med. col, Cornell, 62-63; assoc. prof, SCH. MED, VANDERBILT UNIV, 63-68, PROF, 68- Teaching fel, Am. Trudeau Soc, 56-57, Edward Livingston Trudeau fel, 59-63; physician outpatients, N.Y. Hosp, 59-63; chief med. serv, Vet. Admin. Hosp, Tenn, 63- Dipl, Am. Bd. Internal Med, 62. U.S.A.F, 45-47. Am. Fedn. Clin. Res; Am. Soc. Clin. Invest; Soc. Exp. Biol. & Med; Asn. Am. Physicians. Patterns of tissue injury; immunologic injury to rabbit platelets. Address: Veterans Administration Hospital, Nashville, TN 37203.

DESROSIER, NORMAN W(ILFRED), b. Athol, Mass, Dec. 6, 21; m. 46; c. 4. FOOD TECHNOLOGY. B.S, Massachusetts, 47, fel, 46-48, M.S, 48, Ph.D. (food tech), 49. Asst. prof. food tech, Massachusetts, 48-49; Purdue, 49-51, assoc. prof, 51-54, prof, 54-62; dir. res. & develop, Beech-Nut Life Savers, Inc, N.Y, 63, v.pres, 63-65; CORP. DIR. RES, RES. CTR, NABISCO, INC, 65- Dep. sci. dir. radiation res, U.S. Army Qm. Food & Container Inst, 57-58; consult, Food & Agr. Agency, OEEC, Paris, 58, Food & Agr. Agency & Europ. Nuclear Energy Agency, 60; U.S. Air Force Aerospace Med. Labs, Dayton, Ohio, 62. U.S.A, 42-45, Sgt. AAAS; Asn. Res. Dirs; Inst. Food Technol; Am. Chem. Soc. Industrial research and development management; food science and technology; human nutrition and biochemistry; radiation research and effects; technology of food preservation. Address: Research Center, Nabisco, Inc, 2111 Route 208, Fair Lawn, NJ 07410.

DESROSIERS, J(OSEPH) A(DELARD) JACQUES, b. Matane, Que, Jan. 30, 31; m. 56; c. 2. OBSTETRICS & GYNECOLOGY, PHYSIOLOGY. B.A, Laval Univ, 53, M.D, 58; med. lic, Med. Col. Can, 58; specialist cert, Prov. Que, 63. Asst. prof. OBSTET. & GYNEC, UNIV. MONTREAL, 64-70, AGGREGATE PROF, 70- Private practice, Maisonneuve Hosp, Montreal, Que, 64-, lectr, nurses sch; sr. consult, Inst. Cardiol, Montreal, Que, 65-; lectr, Inst. Marguerite Youville, Montreal. Fel, Royal Col. Physicians & Surg. Can, 63. Sr. mem. Am. Fertil. Soc; Can. Med. Asn; Can. Soc. Fr. Speaking Obstet. & Gynec; Fedn. Socs. Fr. Speaking Gynec. & Obstet; Can. Fertil. Soc. Family planning; effective therapy, physio-pathology, anatomy and histology of the underdeveloped uterus in young women. Address: Dept. of Obstetrics & Gynecology, University of Montreal, Montreal 250, Que, Can.

DESROSIERS, RUSSELL, b. Saylesville, R.I, May 22, 16; m. 54; c. 4. PLANT PATHOLOGY. B.S, Rhode Island, 38, M.S, 40; M.A, Harvard, 49, Ph.D. (biol), 54. Asst, United Fruit Co, Honduras, 41-42; asst. plant pathologist, Everglades Exp. Sta, Fla, 45-46; plant pathologist, estacion exp. trop, S.C.I.A, Ecuador, 49-58, Adv. Trop. Crops, U.S. Opers. Mission, Costa Rica, 58-68; AGR. RES. ADV, AGENCY INT. DEVELOP, RIO DE JANEIRO, 68-70, GUAYAQUIL, ECUADOR, 70- Med. Dept, U.S.A.A.F, 42-45. Am. Phytopath. Soc. Diseases of cacao and bananas. Address: Guayaquil, Dept. of State, Washington, DC 20521.

DESS, HOWARD M(ELVIN), b. Chicago, Ill, Dec. 23, 29; m. 51; c. 3. INORGANIC CHEMISTRY. B.S, Indiana, 51; M.S, Michigan, 53, Ph.D.(chem), 55. Res. chemist, Electrometall. Co, 55-56; Pennsalt Chem. Corp, 56-58; Union Carbide Corp, 58-63, group leader crystal prod. res, Speedway Lab, Linde Div, 63, res. & develop. supvr, crystal prod. dept, electronics div, 63-68, group mgr, 68; asst. tech. dir, Nat. Lead Co, 68, dir. res, Hightstown cent. res. lab, 68-70, MGR, COMMERCIAL CRYSTALS DEPT, TITANIUM PIGMENT DIV, NL INDUSTS, INC, 70- Am. Chem. Soc. Inorganic fluorine chemistry; extractive metallurgy; crystal growth. Address: 316 Goldfinch Dr, Somerville, NJ 08876.

DESSAU, R. M, b. Amsterdam, Holland, Aug. 25, 38; U.S. citizen; m. 63; c. 1. ORGANIC CHEMISTRY. B.A, Columbia, 60, M.A, 61, Ph.D.(chem), 65. RES. CHEMIST, CENT. RES. DIV. LAB, MOBIL OIL CORP, 65- Am. Chem. Soc. Organic reaction mechanisms; cycloaddition reactions; free radical reactions. Address: Central Research Division Lab, Mobil Oil Corp, Princeton, NJ 08540.

DESSAUER, GERHARD, b. Aschaffenburg, Ger, Sept. 19, 10, nat. 43; m. 46; c. 4. NUCLEAR PHYSICS. M.Sc, Frankfurt, 35; M.A, California, 39; Ph.D. (physics), Rochester, 41. Res. assoc. physics, Rochester, 41-43, assoc. biophys, Manhattan Dist. proj, 43-46, instr. physics, 43-45, asst. prof, 45-46; res. assoc. exp. physics, Knolls Atomic Power Lab, Gen. Elec. Co, 46-51; E.I. DU PONT DE NEMOURS & CO, 51-54, DIR. PHYSICS SECT, SAVANNAH RIVER LAB, 54- Mem, adv. comt. reactor physics, Atomic Energy Comn. Am. Phys. Soc; fel. Am. Nuclear Soc. Reactor and nuclear physics. Address: Savannah River Lab, E.I. du Pont de Nemours & Co, Aiken, SC 29801.

DESSAUER, H(ERBERT) C(LAY), b. New Orleans, La, Dec. 30, 21; m. 50; c. 3. BIOCHEMISTRY. Ph.D.(biochem), La. State Univ, 52. Teaching fel. BIOCHEM, SCH. MED, LA. STATE UNIV, 49-50, asst, 50-51, instr, 51-53, asst. prof, 53-57, assoc. prof, 57-63; PROF, 63- Consult, Vet. Admin. Hosp, New Orleans, La, 62-; mem, panel for advan. sci. educ, Nat. Sci. Found, 65-67. U.S.A.A.F, 43-46. AAAS; Am. Physiol. Soc; Am. Soc. Ichthyol. & Herpet; Soc. Exp. Biol. & Med; Soc. Syst. Zool. Biochemistry of the lizard Anolis carolinensis; comparative biochemistry; blood proteins; protein taxonomy. Address: 7100 Dorian St, New Orleans, LA 70126.

DESSAUER, JOHN H(ANS), b. Aschaffenburg, Ger, May 13, 05; nat; m. 36; c. 3. CHEMISTRY, CHEMICAL ENGINEERING. B.S, Munich Tech, 26; Master, Aachen Tech, 27; D.Ing.Sc, 29; hon. L.H.D, Le Moyne Col, 63. Res. chemist, Ansco, N.Y, 29-35; res. chemist & dir, Haloid Co, 35-51, v.pres. in charge res. & prod. develop. & dir, 46-58, exec. v.pres. res. & eng, XEROX CORP, 59-66, v.chmn. bd. & exec. v.pres. res. & advan. eng, 66-70, DIR, 59-, dir, Rank Xerox Ltd, 59-70. Trustee, Fordham Univ. & Rochester Mus. & Sci. Ctr; mem, N.Y. State Adv. Coun. Advan. Indust. Res. & Develop; bd. overseers, chem. vis. comt, Harvard Col; vis. comt. chem. eng, Mass. Inst. Technol; eng. adv. comt, mech. & aerospace sci. dept, Univ. Rochester. Coun. Nat. Acad. Eng; fel. N.Y. Acad. Sci; fel. Am. Inst.

Chem; Am. Chem. Soc; Am. Phys. Soc. Photo research; organic chemistry; xerography. Address: P.O. Box 373, 57 Monroe Ave, Pittsford, NY 14534.

DESSAUER, ROLF, b. Nürnberg, Ger, Nov. 3, 26; nat; m. 68; c. 2. ORGANIC CHEMISTRY. B.S, Chicago, 48, M.S, 49; Ph.D.(chem), Wisconsin, 52. Res. chemist, ORG. CHEM. DEPT, E.I. DU PONT DE NEMOURS & CO, INC, 52-62, sr. res. chemist, 62-68, RES. ASSOC, 69- U.S.A, 44-46. Am. Chem. Soc; Nat. Microfilm Asn; Am. Soc. Photog. Sci. & Eng. Steroids; dyes; photochemistry; photochromism; imaging systems; liquid crystals; chemical marketing. Address: 100 Kirk Rd, Greenville, DE 19807.

DESSEL, NORMAN F, b. Ida Grove, Iowa, July 9, 32; m. 55; c. 3. PHYSICS, PHYSICAL SCIENCE. B.A, Iowa, 57, M.A, 58, Ph.D.(physics, sci. ed), 61. Asst. prof. physics, SAN DIEGO STATE COL, 61-64, assoc. prof, 64-68, PROF. PHYSICS & PHYS. SCI, 68-, CHMN. DEPT. PHYS. SCI, 69- Consult, U.S. Naval Electronics Lab, 62- U.S.A.F, 53-55; Air Nat. Guard, 55-61, Capt. AAAS; Optical Soc. Am; Am. Asn. Physics Teachers. Coherent optical information processing and holography in laser communications and physics education. Address: Dept. of Physics & Physical Science, San Diego State College, San Diego, CA 92115.

DESSER, SHERWIN S, b. Winnipeg, Man, Sept. 2, 37; m. 63; c. 1. ZOOLOGY, PARASITOLOGY. B.Sc, Manitoba, 59, M.Sc, 63; Ph.D.(protozool), Toronto, 67. Res. fel, PARASITOL, Toronto, 67; Hebrew Univ, Israel, 67-68; asst. prof, UNIV. TORONTO, 68-71, ASSOC. PROF, 71- Am. Soc. Parasitol; Soc. Protozool; Royal Soc. Trop. Med. & Hyg. Protozoology; Haemosporidia. Address: Dept. of Parasitology, School of Hygiene, University of Toronto, Toronto 5, Ont, Can.

DESSLER, ALEXANDER J(ACK), b. San Francisco, Calif, Oct. 21, 28; m. 52; c. 4. SPACE SCIENCE. B.S, Calif. Inst. Tech, 52; Ph.D.(physics), Duke, 56. Res. assoc, Duke, 55-56; sr. scientist SPACE SCI, Lockheed Missiles & Space Co, 56-57, group leader, 57-59, sect. head, 59-62; prof, Southwest Center for Advan. Studies, 62-63; PROF, RICE UNIV, 63-, chmn. dept, 63-69. Mem, U.S. nat. comt, Int. Sci. Radio Union, 60-63, 67-70; co-ed, J. Geophys. Res, 65-69; sci. adv, Nat. Aeronaut. & Space Coun, 69-70; co-ed, Rev. Geophys. & Space Physics, 70- U.S.N, 46-48. AAAS; fel. Am. Geophys. Union (James B. Macelwane Award, 63); Am. Astron. Soc; Int. Sci. Radio Union. Low temperature physics; geomagnetism; theory of geomagnetic storms; plasma physics; hydromagnetism; interplanetary physics. Address: Dept. of Space Science, Rice University, Houston, TX 77001.

DESSOUKY, DESSOUKY AHMAD, b. Mitgamr, U.A.R, Jan. 18, 32; m. 69; c. 1. ANATOMY, ELECTRON MICROSCOPY. M.D, Ain Shams Univ, Cairo, 56, M.S, 60; Ph.D.(anat), Tulane Univ. La, 64. Instr. ANAT, sch. med, Ain Shams Univ, Cairo, 57-61; GEORGETOWN UNIV, 64-66, ASST. PROF, 66-67, 70-, resident obstet. & gynec, 67-70. AAAS; Am. Asn. Anat; Am. Col. Obstet. & Gynec; Am. Fertil, Soc. Fine structure of corpus luteum, uterine wall and uterine blood vessels in normal and abnormal pregnancy; electron microscopy of female reproductive system. Address; Dept. of Obstetrics & Gynecology, Georgetown University Hospital, 3800 Resevoir Rd. N.W, Washington, DC 20007.

DESSUREAUX, LIONEL, b. Ste-Genevieve de Batiscan, Que, June 28, 17; m. 44; c. 5. AGRONOMY, GENETICS. B.A, St. Joseph Col, 40; B.Sc.A, Laval, 44; M.S, Wisconsin, 45, Ph.D.(agron, genetics), 47. Asst. agron, Wisconsin, 44-47; plant breeder, Dom. Exp. Farm, Que, 47-65; OTTAWA RES. STA, CENT. EXP. FARM, 65-66, GENETICIST, 66- Agr. Inst. Can; Can. Soc. Agron. Breeding methods in legumes; combining ability in legumes; biometrical genetics of tetraploids. Address: Ottawa Research Station, Central Experimental Farm, Ottawa, Ont, Can.

DESSY, RAYMOND E(DWIN), b. Reynoldsville, Pa, Sept. 3, 31. PHYSICAL ORGANIC CHEMISTRY. B.S, Pittsburgh, 53, Nat. Sci. Found. fel, 53-55, Ph.D, 56. Fel. & instr, Ohio State Univ, 56-57; asst. prof. CHEM, Univ. Cincinnati, 57-61, assoc. prof, 61-66; PROF, VA. POLYTECH. INST. & STATE UNIV, 66- Sloan fel, 62-64; Nat. Sci. Found. sr. fel, 63-64. Am. Chem. Soc; Am. Pharmaceut. Asn. Kinetics, mechanics and electrochemistry of organometallic compounds; computer controlled experiments; interfacing and software development. Address: Dept. of Chemistry, Virginia Polytechnic Institute & State University, Blacksburg, VA 24061.

de STEVENS, GEORGE, b. Tarrytown, N.Y, Aug. 21, 24; m. 50. ORGANIC CHEMISTRY. B.S, Fordham, 49, M.S, 50, Ph.D, 53. Instr. chem, Fordham, 52-53; lectr. org. chem, Marymount Col.(N.Y), 52; res. chemist, Remington Rand Corp, 53-55; sr. res. scientist, CIBA Pharmaceut. Co, 55-61, dir. med. chem. res, 62-66, dir. chem. res, chem. res. dept, CIBA Pharmaceut. Prod. Inc, 66-67, v.pres. res, CIBA Pharmaceut. Co, 67-70, EXEC. V.PRES. & DIR. RES, CIBA-GEIGY PHARMACEUT. RES. LABS, 70- U.S.A, 42-46. Am. Chem. Soc; fel. N.Y. Acad. Sci. Cyanine dyes as therapeutics; diuretics; analgesics; tranquilizers; chemistry of heterocyclics; spectral properties or organic compounds. Address: CIBA-Geigy Pharmaceuticals Division, 556 Morris Ave, Summit, NJ 07901.

DESU, MANAVALA MAHAMUNULU, b. Ongole, India, Nov. 11, 31; m. 58; c. 2. STATISTICS. B.A, Andhra, India, 50; M.A, Madras, 53; Ph.D.(statist), Minnesota, 66. Lectr. math, S.S.N. Col, Narasaraopet, India, 53-55; math. & statist, S.V. Univ. Tirupati, India, 59-62; math. statist, STATE UNIV. N.Y. BUFFALO, 65-66, asst. prof. STATIST, 66-69; ASSOC. PROF, 69- Inst. Math. Statist; Am. Statist. Asn; Royal Statist. Soc. Inference; ranking and selection problems. Address: Dept. of Statistics, State University of New York at Buffalo, Ridge Lea Campus, Amherst, NY 14226.

DeSUA, FRANK C(RISPIN), b. Monessen, Pa, Oct. 26, 21; m. 45; c. 1. MATHEMATICS. B.S, Pittsburgh, 44, Ph.D.(math), 56. Instr. math, Pittsburgh, 44-54, asst. prof, 56-57; asst. prof, Ohio, 54-56; mem. tech. staff, Bell Tel. Labs, 57-58; assoc. prof. MATH, Col. William & Mary, 58-60; prof. & chmn. dept, Simmons Col, 60-70; PROF, SWEET BRIAR COL, 70-, CHMN. DEPT, 70- Am. Math. Soc; Math. Asn. Am. Foundations of mathematics; symbolic logic; meta-mathematics; point-set topology. Address: Dept. of Mathematics, Sweet Briar College, Sweet Briar, VA 24595.

DeSUTO-NAGY, G(YULA) I(LON), b. Cegled, Hungary, Aug. 19, 10, nat. 46; m. 39. PATHOLOGY, BIOCHEMISTRY. M.D, Budapest, 35, M.S, 38; Ph.D. (org. chem), Yale, 46. Asst. path, Budapest, 30-33, asst. exp. path, 35-36, instr, 36-37, asst. prof, 37-39; exchange fel. chem. grad. sch, YALE, 39-40, Coxe fel. physiol. chem, 40-41, instr. res. path, 41-43, Nat. Tuberc. Asn. fel. chem, 43-47, asst. prof. res. path, 47-52, clin. instr, 52-58, ASST. CLIN. PROF. PATH, 58- Asst. chief pathologist, Vet. Admin. Hosp, West Haven. Dipl, Am. Bd. Path. With Off. Sci. Res. & Develop, 44. AAAS; Am. Med. Asn; Am. Asn. Path. & Bact; Am. Chem. Soc; Col. Am. Path; N.Y. Acad. Sci. Chemistry and pathology of cardiovascular, renal diseases and tuberculosis; blood coagulation; chemical composition of tubercle bacilli; steroid hormones; pyrimidine chemistry; chemotherapy; lipids; clinical pathology. Address: Veterans Administration Hospital, West Haven, CT 06516.

DESY, DONALD H(ERBERT), b. Pittsburgh, Pa, June 30, 20; m. 63. PHYSICAL METALLURGY. B.S, Univ. Ky, 42; M.Met.E, Rensselaer Polytech. Inst, 48; D.Eng.Sc, Columbia Univ, 57. Metallurgist, Crucible Steel Co. Am, N.J, 42; exp. sta, E.I. du Pont de Nemours & Co, Del, 48-50; res. assoc. metall, Columbia Univ, 53-56; res. investr, Fulmer Res. Inst, Buckinghamshire, Eng, 56-58; sr. metallurgist, Stanford Res. Inst, Calif, 58-60; sr. engr, Varian Assocs, 60-63; Signetics Corp, 64; SUPVRY. METALLURGIST, ROLLA METALL. RES. CTR, BUR. MINES, U.S. DEPT. INTERIOR, 65- U.S.A.A.F, 42-46, 1st Lt. Metall. Soc; Am. Soc. Metals. Mechanical properties of metals; dispersion strengthening of metals. Address: U.S. Dept. of the Interior, Bureau of Mines, Rolla Metallurgy Research Center, P.O. Box 280, Rolla, MO 65401.

de SYLVA, DONALD P(ERRIN), b. Rochester, N.Y, July 20, 28; m. 50; c. 2. ICHTHYOLOGY. B.S, Cornell, 52, Denison fel, 57-58, Ph.D.(vert. zool), 58; scholar. & M.S, Miami (Fla), 53; scholar, California, Los Angeles, 53-54. Asst. fish collection, Cornell, 51-52, asst. oceanog, 52; zool, Miami (Fla), 52-53; asst. biomet. & statist, California, 53-54; res. instr. oceanog, Miami (Fla), 54, fisheries, 54-56; asst. vert. zool, Cornell, 56-57; asst. prof. biol. sci, Delaware, 58-61; asst. prof. MARINE SCI, UNIV. MIAMI, 61-66, ASSOC. PROF, 66- Consult, Dr. Edward C. Raney, Cornell, 57. Summers, aquatic biologist, N.Y. State Conserv. Dept, 51; res. aide, Miami (Fla), 53. Scientist in charge, Pac. Billfish Exped, Lou Marron & Univ. Miami, Chile, 56. U.S.A, 46-48. AAAS; Am. Fisheries Soc; Am. Soc. Zool; Am. Soc. Ichthyol. & Herpet; Am. Soc. Limnol. & Oceanog; Am. Inst. Fisheries Res. Biol. Marine ecology; fisheries biology; life history, ecology and systematics of marine fishes, particularly barracudas, tunas and marlins; relationship of fishes to oceanographic conditions; poisonous fishes; estuarine ecology. Address: School of Marine and Atmospheric Science, University of Miami, Miami, FL 33149.

DESZYCK, E(DWARD) J(OHN), b. Central Falls, R.I, Aug. 26, 10; m. 48; c. 3. BIOCHEMISTRY. B.S, Rhode Island, 33, M.S, 42; Ph.D.(biochem), Purdue, 50. Asst. chemist, R.I. Agr. Exp. Sta, 33-36, assoc. chemist, 36-43; asst. chemist, Texas Agr. Exp. Sta, 46; biochem. dept, Purdue, 46-49, research asst, 49-50; assoc. horticulturist biochem, Citrus Exp. Sta, 50-60; sr. res. scientist, PHILIP MORRIS RES. & DEVELOP, 61-62; ASSOC. PRIN. SCIENTIST, 63- U.S.N, 43-46, Lt. Am. Chem. Soc; Am. Soc. Hort. Sci. Biochemistry of natural products; citrus maturity and quality; tobacco, tobacco aroma and smoke flavor composition of, development of tobacco flavors. Address: Philip Morris Inc, McComas Research Center, P.O. Box 30, Richmond, VA 23206.

de TAKACSY, NICHOLAS BENEDICT, b. Budapest, Hungary, Feb. 24, 39; Can. citizen; m. 62; c. 1. NUCLEAR PHYSICS. B.Sc, Loyola Col.(Can), 59; M.Sc, Montreal, 63; Ph.D.(nuclear theory), McGill, 66. Lectr. physics, Loyola Col.(Can.), 61-63; res. fel. NUCLEAR THEORY, Calif. Inst. Tech, 66-67; ASST. PROF, Loyola Col.(Que), 67-68; McGILL UNIV, 68- Res. fel, McGill Univ, 67-68. Nuclear shell model calculations. Address: Dept. of Physics, McGill University, Montreal, Que, Can.

DeTAR, DeLOS F(LETCHER), b. Kansas City, Mo, Jan. 18, 20; m. 43; c. 4. ORGANIC CHEMISTRY. B.S, Illinois, 41; M.S, Pennsylvania, 43, Ph.D.(org. chem), 44. Res. chemist, pioneering res. sect, rayon dept, tech. div, E.I. du Pont de Nemours & Co, 44-46; fel, Illinois, 46; instr. CHEM, Cornell, 46-50, asst. prof, 50-53; assoc. prof, South Carolina, 53-56, PROF, 56-60; FLA. STATE UNIV, 60-, CHMN. DEPT, 70- Nat. Sci. Found. sr. fel, Harvard, 56-57; vis. prof, California, Berkeley, 60. Am. Chem. Soc; fel. Chem. Soc. Gt. Britain. Mechanisms of organic reactions; peptides and enzyme models; computer techniques. Address: Dept. of Chemistry, Florida State University, Tallahassee, FL 32306.

DETAR, REED L, b. Oil City, Pa, May 14, 32; m. 59; c. 4. PHYSIOLOGY. A.B, Susquehanna, 54; Pennsylvania, 54-55; M.S, Hahnemann Med. Col, 59; Ph.D.(physiol), Michigan, 68. Assoc. scientist, Warner-Lambert Res. Inst, 59-63; instr. PHYSIOL, Univ. Michigan, fall 67 & 68; ASST. PROF, DARTMOUTH MED. SCH, 69- Assoc. mem. Am. Physiol. Soc. Control of vascular smooth muscle contractility; metabolism. Address: Dept. of Physiology, Dartmouth Medical School, Hanover, NH 03755.

DETENBECK, ROBERT W(ARREN), b. Buffalo, N.Y, Feb. 11, 33; m. 54; c. 2. PHYSICS. B.S, Rochester, 54; Nat. Sci. Found. fel, Princeton, 54-56, Gen. Elec. fel, 56-58, Ph.D.(nuclear physics), 62. Instr. PHYSICS, Princeton, 58-59; asst. prof, Maryland, 59-67; assoc. prof, UNIV. VT, 67-70, PROF, 70- Summer physicist, U.S. Naval Ord. Lab. 63. AAAS; Am. Phys. Soc; Am. Asn. Physics Teachers. Quantum optics; instrumentation. Address: Dept. of Physics, University of Vermont, Burlington, VT 05401.

DETERLING, RALPH A(LDEN), JR, b. Williamsport, Pa, Apr. 29, 17; m. 47; c. 4. SURGERY. B.A, Stanford, 38, M.D, 42; M.S, Minnesota, 46, Ph.D. (surg), 47. Asst. prof. surg, col. physicians & surg, Columbia, 48-50, assoc. prof, 50-53, clin. surg, 53-59, dir. surg. res. labs, 53-59; PROF. SURG. & CHMN. DEPT, SCH. MED, TUFTS UNIV, 59- Asst. attend. surgeon, Presby. Hosp, 48-50, assoc. attend. surgeon, 50-59; vis. surgeon, Francis Delafield Hosp, 53-59; dir. first surg. serv, Boston City Hosp, 59-; surgeon-in-chief, Tufts-New England Med. Ctr. Hosps, 59- Consult. surg, Manhattan Veterans Admin. Hosp. & Paterson Gen. Hosp; U.S. Naval Hosp, 52-59; Boston Vet. Admin. Hosp, 60-; St. Elizabeth's Hosp, Brighton, 61-;

Mt. Auburn Hosp, Cambridge, 62-; chief surg. consult, Lemuel Shattuck Hosp, Boston, 59- Malmö Surg. Found. award, 63; outstanding achievement award, Minnesota, 64. Cert, Am. Bd. Surg, 49; Bd. Thoracic Surg, 54. AAAS; Int. Cardiovasc. Soc.(secy-gen, 63); Int. Soc. Surg; Am. Med. Asn; Am. Acad. Arts & Sci; Am. Col. Surg; Am. Thoracic Soc; Soc. Vascular Surg; Am. Heart Asn; Am. Asn. Thoracic Surg; Soc. Univ. Surg; Am. Col. Chest Physicians; Colombian Col. Surg; Colombian Cardiol. Soc; Cuban Surg. Soc; Soc. Angiol. Argentina. Blood vessel replacement; cardiovascular surgical technics; application of hypothermia to cardiac surgery; extracorporeal circulation for cardiac surgery; surgical applications of laser; organ homotransplantation. Address: Dept. of Surgery, Tufts University School of Medicine, Medford, MA 02155.

DE TERRA, NOEL, b. New York, N.Y, Dec. 31, 33; m. 62. ZOOLOGY. B.A, Barnard Col, Columbia, 55; U.S. Pub. Health Serv-Nat. Cancer Inst. fel, 55-59; Ph.D.(zool), California, Berkeley, 59. U.S. Pub. Health Serv-Nat. Cancer Inst. fel, 59-61; res. assoc. biochem. genetics, Rockefeller Inst, 61-62; asst. res. zoologist, California, Los Angeles, 62-63, asst. res. biophysicist, lab. nuclear med. & radiation biol, sch. med, 63-67; ASST. MEM, INST. CANCER RES, 67- Soc. Protozool; Am. Soc. Cell Biol. Protozoan physiology and morphogenesis; cell and developmental biology; nucleo-cytoplasmic interactions. Address: Institute for Cancer Research, 7701 Burholme Ave, Philadelphia, PA 19111.

DETERS, JOHN F(REDERICK), b. Willow Lake, S.Dak, Nov. 27, 15; m. 41; c. 3. INORGANIC CHEMISTRY. B.S, Iowa, 39; M.S, Chicago, 45; Ph.D.(chem), Notre Dame, 64. Res. chemist, Standard Oil Co. Ind, 39-52; asst. supt, F.K. Ketler Co, 52-57; asst. prof. CHEM, VALPARAISO UNIV, 57-65, assoc. prof, 65-70; PROF, 70- Am. Chem. Soc. Address: Dept. of Chemistry, Valparaiso University, Valparaiso, IN 46383.

DETERS, MERRILL EDGAR, b. Goodhue, Minn, Sept. 30, 05; m. 35; c. 3. FORESTRY. B.S, Minnesota, 28, Doerr fel, 29-30, M.S, 31, Ph.D.(silvicul. & ecol), 40. Asst. div. forestry, Minnesota, 29-30, instr, 30-34; assoc. forester, soil conserv. serv, U.S. Dept. Agr, 34-36; asst. prof. FORESTRY, Mich. State Col, 36-40; prof, UNIV. IDAHO, 40-71, EMER. PROF, 71- Soc. Am. Foresters; Am. Soc. Plant Physiol; Ecol. Soc. Am. Silviculture; forest management; forest genetics. Address: College of Forestry, University of Idaho, Moscow, ID 83843.

DETERT, DAVID G, b. Billings, Mont, Mar. 15, 38; m. 60; c. 3. ELECTRICAL ENGINEERING. S.B, Mass. Inst. Tech, 60; M.S, Illinois, 62, Ph.D.(elec. eng), 65. Res. asst. elec. eng, radiolocation res. lab, Illinois, Urbana, 60-65; sr. scientist, res. & develop. div, AVCO CORP, 65-67, staff scientist, space systs. div, 67-68, SECT. CHIEF GEOPHYS. SECT, SYSTS. DIV, 68- Am. Geophys. Union; Am. Meteorol. Soc. Ionospheric physics; high frequency radio wave propagation; high frequency radar systems. Address: Systems Division, Avco Corp, 201 Lowell St, Wilmington, MA 01887.

DETERT, FRANCIS LAWRENCE, b. San Diego, Calif, Apr. 13, 23. ORGANIC CHEMISTRY. B.S, Santa Clara, 44; M.S, Stanford, 48, Ph.D.(org. chem), 50. Res, Hickrill Chem. Res. Found, 50-52; res. chemist, Calif. Res. Corp, 52-60; PROD. TECH. SPECIALIST, CHEVRON CHEM. CO, SAN FRANCISCO, 60- U.S.N.R, 44-46, Lt.(jg). Am. Chem. Soc. Diazonium coupling of furans; chemistry of cycloheptatrienone; synthetic detergents; chemical process development; gas odorants, xylenes and polybutenes; chemical market research and economics. Address: 6127 Outlook Ave, Oakland, CA 94605.

DETHIER, BERNARD E(MILE), b. Boston, Mass, June 5, 26; m. 52; c. 4. METEOROLOGY. B.S, Calif. Inst. Tech, 46, M.S, 47; Ph.D.(geog), Hopkins, 58. Dir. Climat. div, Patterson Weather Serv, 47-48; asst. prof. math, Nazareth Col, 48-51, assoc. prof, 51-52; asst. prof. agr. climatol, CORNELL UNIV, 58-61, assoc. prof, 62-69, PROF. METEOROL, 69- U.S.N, 52-54, Res, 54-, Lt. Am. Meteorol. Soc; Asn. Am. Geog. Precipitation patterns and probabilities; atmospheric influence on ecosystems and satellite sensing; air pollution problems in the northeastern United States; cloud climatology utilizing data from satellites. Address: Division of Meteorology, Cornell University, Ithaca, NY 14850.

DETHIER, V(INCENT) G(ASTON), b. Boston, Mass, Feb. 20, 15; m. 60; c. 2. INSECT PHYSIOLOGY. A.B, Harvard, 36, A.M, 37, Ph.D.(entom), 39; fel, Clark, 37; hon.Sc.D, Providence Col, 64, Ohio State Univ, 70. Entomologist, G.W. Pierce Lab, N.H, 37-38; asst, Cruft Physics Lab, Harvard, 39; instr. biol, John Carroll, 39-41, asst. prof, 41; res. physiologist, Army Chem. Corps, 46; prof. zool & entom, Ohio State, 47; assoc. prof. biol, Hopkins, 48-52, prof, 52-58; zool. & psychol, Pennsylvania, 58-67, assoc, Inst. Neurol. Sci, Sch. Med, 58-67; CLASS 1877 PROF. BIOL, PRINCETON, 67- Res. fel, Atkins Inst, Cuba, 39-40; Belgian-Am. Ed. Found, Belgian Congo, 52; Fulbright sr. scholar, London Sch. Hyg. & Trop. Med, 54-55; Guggenheim fel, Wageningen, 64-65. U.S.A.F, 42-45, Res, 45-, Lt. Col. Nat. Acad. Sci; AAAS; Am. Entom. Soc; Am. Soc. Zool; Am. Physiol. Soc; Am. Acad. Arts & Sci; hon. fel. Royal Entom. Soc. Chemoreception in insects; chemistry of food plant choice by larvae; life histories of Lepidoptera; insect physiology. Address: Dept. of Biology, Princeton University, Princeton, NJ 08540.

DETHLEFSEN, LYLE A, b. Oakes, N.Dak, Feb. 27, 34; m. 57; c. 2. MOLECULAR BIOLOGY, ONCOLOGY. B.S, Colorado State, 60, D.V.M, 62; U.S. Pub. Health Serv. grant, Pennsylvania, 62-66, Ph.D.(molecular biol), 66. Lectr. radiation biol, St. Joseph's Col.(Pa), 65; ASST. PROF. RADIOLOGY, SCH. VET. MED, UNIV. PA, 66-, RADIOLOGICAL SCI, SCH. MED, 68- U.S. Pub. Health Serv. res. career develop. award, 69- U.S.A, 53-55. AAAS; Radiation Res. Soc; Am. Soc. Cell Biol; Am. Asn. Cancer Res. Cell biology; tumor growth; tumor cell kinetics; radiobiology. Address: Dept. of Radiology, University of Pennsylvania, School of Medicine & Veterinary Medicine, 3400 Spruce St, Philadelphia, PA 19104.

DETHLEFSEN, ROLF, b. Niebuell, Ger, Aug. 30, 34; U.S. citizen; m; c. 3. PLASMA PHYSICS, ELECTRICAL ENGINEERING. Dipl. Ing, Brunswick Tech. Univ, 61; M.S, Mass. Inst. Technol, 62, Sc.D.(physics of fluids), 65. Staff scientist. space sci. lab, Convair Div, Gen. Dynamics Corp, Calif, 65-68; DIR. ELEC. POWER TECHNOL, ADVAN. TECHNOL. CTR, ALLIS CHALMERS MFG. CO, MILWAUKEE, 68- Am. Inst. Aeronaut. & Astronaut; Inst. Elec. & Electronics Eng; Asn. Ger. Eng. Electric arcs. Address: 13705 Old Oak Lane, New Berlin, WI 53151.

DETIG, ROBERT HENRY, b. Pittsburgh, Pa, Oct. 6, 35. APPLIED PHYSICS, ELECTRICAL ENGINEERING. B.S, Carnegie Inst. Tech, 57, M.S, 58, Ph.D.(elec. eng), 62. Staff engr, satellite commun. agency, U.S. Army, 62-63; asst. prof. elec. eng, Carnegie Inst. Tech, 63-65; scientist, res. div, Xerox Corp, 65-68; MGR. ELECTRONICS RES. BR, OLIVETTI CORP. AM, 68- Sig.C, 61-63, Res, 63-, 1st Lt. Inst. Elec. & Electronics Eng. Reprographics; non-impact printing; information display; chemical and surface physics. Address: 1 De Berg Dr, Old Tappan, NJ 07675.

DETLEF, JOHN FRANK, b. Cleveland, Ohio, May 7, 27. MATHEMATICS, ASTRONAUTICS. B.A, Baldwin-Wallace Col, 48; M.A, Columbia, 50; Stanford, 57-61. Mathematician, Ballistic Res. Labs, 52-56; res. engr. & sr. scientist, Lockheed Missiles & Space Co, Calif, 57-61; res. engr, Jet Propulsion Labs, Calif. Inst. Tech, 61-62; sr. engr, Sylvania Elec. Prod, Inc, 62-64; ASSOC. PROF. MATH, State Univ. N.Y. Col. Fredonia, 64-66; UNIV. MINN, MORRIS, 66-, CHMN. MATH. DIV. & CO-CHMN. SCI. DIV, 67- C.H. Smith scholar, Harvard, 48; lectr, Delaware, 56-57; Foothill Col, 60-61. Summer consult, Cape Kennedy, 62. Am. Astronaut. Soc; Brit. Interplanetary Soc. Mathematical research; astrodynamics; fluid dynamics; thermodynamics. Address: Dept. of Mathematics, University of Minnesota, Morris, MN 56267.

DE TOMMASO, GABRIEL L(OUIS), b. Providence, R.I, Aug. 19, 34; m. 56; c. 4. ORGANIC & POLYMER CHEMISTRY. B.S, Rhode Island, 56; Ph.D.(org. chem), Illinois, 60. Org. polymer chemist, Air Reduction Co, Inc, 59-62; SR. CHEMIST, ROHM & HAAS CO, INC, SPRING HOUSE, 62- Am. Chem. Soc. Organic synthesis; solution, suspension and emulsion polymerization of vinyl monomers; films; plastics; polymer structure. Address: 249 Laurel Lane, Lansdale, PA 19446.

DETORO, FREDERIC E(DWARD), b. Providence, R.I, Nov. 29, 32; m. 54; c. 4. ORGANIC & POLYMER CHEMISTRY. Sc.B, Brown, 54; Allied Chem. & Dye Corp. fel, Duke, 56-57, Ph.D.(chem), 58. Asst, Duke, 54-55; Off. Naval Res, 55-56; res. scientist, AM. CYANAMID CO, 57-61, group leader chem. develop, 61-64, mgr. chem. & fiber develop, FIBERS DIV, 64-66, prod. mgr, 66-68, mgr. fiber res, 68-69, MGR. APPAREL & INDUST. PRODS, 69- Am. Chem. Soc. Polymer and fiber research and development. Address: Fibers Division, American Cyanamid Co, Wayne, NJ 07470.

de TOROK, DENES G(ABOR), b. Sopron, Hungary, May 27, 31; U.S. citizen; m. 59; c. 3. BIOLOGY. B.Sc, Eötvös Lóránd, Budapest, 53, M.Sc, 54, Ph.D.(biol), 56; M.A, Harvard, 61. Head cytol. lab, plant breeding inst, Hungarian Nat. Acad. Sci, 55-56; asst. prof. plant biochem, Budapest Tech, 56-57; res. asst, Mich. State, 57-58; res. assoc, Roscoe B. Jackson Mem. Lab. Biomed. Res, Maine, 58-59; officer of instr. & res. fel, Harvard, 59-62; asst. prof. bot, PA. STATE UNIV, 62-68, PROF. BIOL. SCI, 68- Consult, Am. Polymer & Chem. Co, 62; prin. investr, Soc. Sigma Xi & Sci. Res. Soc. Am. res. grants, 63-64; dir. res. proj, Nat. Sci. Found. Instnl. grant, 63-64; prin. investr, Am. Cancer Soc. res. grant, 63-65; chmn. photosynthesis study group & consult, comn. undergrad. educ. biol. sci, Nat. Sci. Found, 65-; vis. prof, Carnegie-Mellon Univ, 68-; Commonwealth of Pa. med. res. scientist, Mayview State Hosp, Bridgeville, 68-; prin. investr, Scaife Found. res. grants, 69-71; res. dir. biochem. & genetic studies on alcoholism, M. Hamilton & C. Hagan Found. grants, 69-71. AAAS; Am. Inst. Biol. Sci; Int. Asn. Plant Tissue Cult; Am. Soc. Plant Physiol; Bot. Soc. Am; Tissue Cult. Asn; N.Y. Acad. Sci; Scandinavian Soc. Plant Physiol. Etiology of plant tumors; using cell and tissue cultures for the study of differences between normal and tumor chromosome numbers; nutritional requirements and base ratios; biochemistry and genetics of alcoholism; chromosomal and enzymatic studies on alcoholics. Address: Dept. of Biology, Pennsylvania State University, University Dr, McKeesport, PA 15132.

DETRA, RALPH W(ILLIAM), b. Thompsontown, Pa, Mar. 23, 25; m. 47; c. 2. AERONAUTICAL ENGINEERING. B.S, Cornell, 46, M.Aero.E, 51; Nat. Res. Coun. fel, Swiss Fed. Inst. Tech, 51-52, Dr.Sc.Tech, 53. Flight test proj. engr, U.S. Naval Air Test Center, Md, 46-49; instr. mech, eng. Cornell, Corp, 53-55; prin. res. scientist, Avco-Everett Res. Lab, 55-59, v.pres. missile prog, Avco Res. & Adv. Develop. Div, AVCO CORP, 59-65, v.pres. & asst. gen. mgr. missile systs, 65-66, V.PRES. & GEN. MGR. AVCO SYSTS. DIV, 66- U.S.N, 43-47, Ens. Am. Inst. Aeronaut. & Astronaut; Am. Astronaut. Soc. Hypervelocity flight; high temperature gasdynamics. Address: Avco Systems Division, Avco Corp, 201 Lowell St, Wilmington, MA 01887.

DeTRAY, DONALD E(RVIN), b. Napoleon, Ohio, Nov. 9, 17; m. 40; c. 2. VETERINARY MEDICINE. D.V.M, Ohio State, 40. Private practice, 40-47; veterinarian, Mex-U.S. Cmn. Eradication Foot & Mouth Disease, 47-48; res. veterinarian, U.S. Dept. Agr, 49-51, E.Africa, 51-61, asst. to dir, animal disease & parasite res. div, Agr. Res. Serv, Md, 61-63, asst. dir, 63-64, assoc. dir, 64-66; REGIONAL LIVESTOCK ADV, U.S. AGENCY INT. DEVELOP, Lagos, Nigeria, 66-68, Nairobi, Kenya, 68-70, ETHIOPIA, 70- Am. Field Serv. Ambulance Corps, 41-42. AAAS; Am. Vet. Med. Asn; U.S. Livestock Sanit. Asn; Conf. Res. Workers Animal Diseases; Asn. Advan. Agr. Sci. Africa; Kenya Vet. Asn. Bovine and porcine brucellosis; rinderpest of cattle and African swine fever; research administration in animal diseases and parasites. Address: U.S. Agency for International Development, Ethiopia, APO New York 09319.

DETRE, THOMAS PAUL, b. Budapest, Hungary, May 17, 24; m. 56; c. 2. PSYCHIATRY. B.A, Gymnasium of Piarist Fathers, 42; jr. fel, Clin. Nerv. & Ment. Diseases, Italy, 47-50; M.D, Rome, 52. Consult. psychologist, Salvator Mundi Int. Hosp, Rome, Italy, 51-53; chief resident PSYCHIAT, SCH. MED, YALE, 57-58, instr, 57-59, asst. prof, 59-62, assoc. prof, 62-70, PROF, 70-; PSYCHIATRIST-IN-CHIEF, YALE-NEW HAVEN HOSP, 68-, dir. psychiat. inpatient serv, 60-68. Consult, Fairfield Hosp, Newton, Conn, 58-61; Vet. Admin. Hosp, West Haven, 61-; Norwich Hosp, 62-; Nat. Inst. Ment. Health grant, 64-65. Dipl. psychiat, Am. Bd. Psychiat. & Neurol, 59. AAAS; fel. Am. Psychiat. Asn; N.Y. Acad. Med; Pan-Am. Med. Asn. Clinical research in psychopharmacology; hospital psychiatry. Address: Dept. of Psychiatry, School of Medicine, Yale University, 333 Cedar St, New Haven, CT 06510.

deTREVILLE, ROBERT T. P, b. Beaufort, S.C, Feb. 19, 25; m. 53; c. 5. PREVENTIVE MEDICINE, INDUSTRIAL HYGIENE. B.S, The Citadel, 48; M.D, Med. Col. S.C, 48; Sc.D.(indust. med), Cincinnati, 56. Intern, St. Francis Xavier Infirmary, Charleston, S.C, 47-48; Roper Hosp, 48-49; private practice, 49-51; vis. lectr, med. ctr, Univ. Calif, Los Angeles, 60-61; asst. prof. indust. health, col. med, Univ. Cincinnati, 61-63; PRES, INDUST. HEALTH FOUND, INC, 63- U.S. Air Force liaison mem. comt. toxicol, Nat. Res. Coun, 56-60, subcomt. atmospheric & indust. hyg, 57-60; physician, Ethyl Corp, 61-62, asst. med. dir, 62-63; adj. prof, grad. sch. pub. health, Pittsburgh, 63-; managing dir. indust. hyg. found, Mellon Inst, 63-68, adv. fel, 69-; consult. staff, West. Pa. Hosp, Pittsburgh, 64- Dipl, Am. Bd. Prev. Med, 57. Med.C, 51-61, Maj. AAAS; Am. Med. Asn; Aerospace Med. Asn; Asn. Mil. Surg. U.S; fel. Indust. Med. Asn; Am. Indust. Hyg. Asn; fel. Am. Acad. Occup. Med; fel. Am. Col. Physicians; Am. Pub. Health Asn; Am. Col. Prev. Med. Environmental and occupational health research and education. Address: Industrial Health Foundation, 5231 Centre Ave, Pittsburgh, PA 15232.

DETRICK, JOHN K(ENT), b. Denver, Colo, Mar. 10, 20; m. 47; c. 1. CHEMICAL ENGINEERING. B.S, Denver, 41; M.S, Cincinnati, 43. Res. engr. east. lab, res. & develop. div, EXPLOSIVES DEPT, E.I. DU PONT DE NEMOURS & CO, INC, 42-47, Burnside Lab, 47-49, supvr. east. lab, 49-53, tech. asst. res. & develop. staff, Del, 53-57, supt, Repauno Develop. Lab, 57-67, EAST. LAB, 67-68, spec. asst. dept. engr. sect, 68-70, RES. ASSOC, 70- Am. Chem. Soc. Process development in polymer intermediates; new mining and metal winning ventures. Address: Explosives Dept, E.I. du Pont de Nemours & Co, Inc, Eastern Lab, Gibbstown, NJ 08027.

DETRICK, R(OBERT) SHERMAN, b. Denver, Colo, Feb. 3, 18; m. 41; c. 4. CHEMISTRY. B.S, Denver, 39; M.Ch.E, Rensselaer Polytech, 40. Jr. fel, Mellon Inst, 40-43, fel, 43-47, sr. fel, 47-51; mgr. tar prod. res, RES. DEPT, KOPPERS CO, INC, 51-54, asst. mgr. lab. res, 54-56, mgr, 56-57, asst. mgr. tech. planning, 57-58, mgr. applns. eval. res, 58-66, develop, assoc. opers, 66-67, systs. develop, 67-71, MGR. ENVIRON. HEALTH & SAFETY, 71- Am. Chem. Soc; Soc. Plastics Eng. Reinforced plastics and environmental control. Address: Koppers Co, Inc, Research Dept, 440 College Park Dr, Monroeville, PA 15146.

DETRIO, JOHN A, b. Miami, Fla, June 13, 37; m. 63; c. 3. SOLID STATE PHYSICS. B.S, Spring Hill Col, 59; M.S, Alabama, 61; Fairleigh Dickinson Univ, 64-65; Stevens Inst. Tech, 65-66. Res. asst, Alabama, 59-61; physicist, Army Rocket & Guided Missile Agency, Ala, 61; Army Munition Command, Picatinny Arsenal, 61-66; RES. PHYSICIST, UNIV. DAYTON, 66- U.S.A, 61-63, Res, 63-69, 1st Lt. Am. Phys. Soc. Electroluminescence; solid state lasers; optical properties of solids; photoconductivity; atomic spectra; electrical properties of solids; infrared, ultra violet and visible spectroscopy and photometry. Address: Dept. of Physics, University of Dayton, Dayton, OH 45409.

DETROY, ROBERT WILLIAM, b. Jasper, Ind, Aug. 20, 41; m. 64; c. 2. BIOCHEMISTRY, MICROBIOLOGY. B.S, Indiana State, 62; M.S, Wisconsin, 65, Ph.D.(bact. biochem), 67. RES. CHEMIST, NORTH. REGIONAL RES. LAB, U.S. DEPT. AGR, 67- Am. Soc. Microbiol. Fungal metabolism and synthesis of secondary metabolites. Address: Northern Regional Research Lab, U.S. Dept. of Agriculture, 1815 N. University St, Peoria, IL 61604.

DETTBARN, WOLF DIETRICH, b. Berlin, Germany, Jan. 30, 28; U.S. citizen; m. 60; c. 2. NEUROCHEMISTRY, NEUROPHARMACOLOGY. Dr.med, Göttingen, 53. Intern, med. sch, Göttingen, 54; res. assoc, Ciba, Switzerland, 54-55; physiol. inst. med. sch, Saarlandes, 55-58; NEUROCHEM, Col. Physicians & Surgeons, Columbia Univ, 58-61, asst. prof, 61-67, assoc. prof, 67-68; PROF, SCH. MED, VANDERBILT UNIV, 68- Mem. Marine Biol. Lab. Corp, Woods Hole, 63. AAAS; Am. Physiol. Soc; Soc. Gen. Physiol; Am. Soc; Neurochem. Harvey Soc; Int. Soc. Toxinol. Neurophysiology; neurochemistry; neuropharmacology; peripheral nerve; ion flux; membrane permeability. Address: Dept. of Pharmacology, Medical School, Vanderbilt University, Nashville, TN 37203.

DETTELBACH, HAROLD R(UDOLPH), b. Chicago, Ill, Aug. 7, 22; m. 49; c. 2. PHYSIOLOGY, PHARMACOLOGY. B.S, Roosevelt, 48; Dr. Phil. Nat. (zoophysiol), Berne, 52. Sr. investr, G.D. Searle & Co, 52-57; asst. dir. explor. develop, Smith Kline & French Labs, 57-59; dir. res, Jensen-Salsbery Labs, 59-64; mgr. mkt. opers, Lloyd Bros, Inc, 64-68; DIR. SCI. MKT. OPERS, HOECHST PHARMACEUT. CO, 68- U.S.A, 42-45. AAAS; Soc. Exp. Biol. & Med; Am. Soc. Zool; Am. Soc. Vet. Physiol. & Pharmacol; Am. Fedn. Clin. Res; N.Y. Acad. Sci; Swiss Zool. Soc. Renal physiology; cardiovascular-renal pharmacology; water and electrolyte physiology; pituitary secretions; regeneration; comparative physiology; drug development. Address: Hoechst Pharmaceutical Co, 1385 Tennessee Ave, Cincinnati, OH 45229.

DETTINGER, DAVID, b. Little Falls, N.Y, June 1, 19; m. 52; c. 2. RADIO ENGINEERING. B.S, St. Lawrence, 41; Mass. Inst. Tech, 41-42. Engr, Hazeltine Electronics Corp, 42-45; Teleregister Corp, 45-47; v.pres. & chief engr, Wheeler Labs, 47-61; HEAD, COMMUN. DEPT, MITRE CORP, 61- Sr. mem. Inst. Elec. & Electronics Eng. Communications engineering; microwaves; antennas; communication systems. Address: Three Penn Rd, Winchester, MA 01890.

DETTMAN, JOHN W(ARREN), b. Oswego, N.Y, July 14, 26; m. 50; c. 3. MATHEMATICS. A.B, Oberlin Col, 50; M.S, Carnegie Inst. Tech, 52, Ph.D. (math), 54. Instr. math, Carnegie Inst. Tech, 53-54; mem. tech. staff, Bell Tel. Labs, 54-56; asst. prof. MATH, Case, 56-62, assoc. prof, 62-64; PROF, OAKLAND UNIV, 64- Nat. Sci. Found. faculty fel, 62-63; sr. res. fel, Univ. Glasgow, 70-71. U.S.N, 44-46. Soc. Indust. & Appl. Math; Am. Math. Soc; Math. Asn. Am. Differential equations; functional analysis. Address: Dept. of Mathematics, Oakland University, Rochester, MI 48063.

DETTMERS, ALMUT E(DEL), b. Oldenburg, Germany, Oct. 29, 15. ANIMAL BREEDING. Dipl, Posen, 43; M.S, Minnesota, 55, Ph.D.(animal breeding), 62. Res. asst, animal husb, Minnesota, St. Paul, 53-62, res. fel, 63, assoc. scientist, 64-66, scientist, 66-69; SR. LECTR. ANIMAL BREEDING & RES. IN PIG, BEEF, GOAT & DAIRY BREEDING, UNIV. IBADAN, 70- Fel. AAAS; Am. Soc. Animal Sci; Am. Genetic Asn. Research in poultry and large animals; swine and sheep; development of a miniature pig for research purposes. Address: Dept. of Animal Science, University Ibadan, Ibadan, Nigeria.

DETTRE, ROBERT H(AROLD), b. Philadelphia, Pa, Aug. 20, 28; m. 57; c. 2. PHYSICAL CHEMISTRY. B.S, Lafayette Col, 52; M.A, Hopkins, 54, Ph.D.(phys. chem), 57. Res. chemist, E.I. DU PONT DE NEMOURS & CO, INC, 57-65, sr. res. chemist, 65-70, RES. ASSOC, 70- U.S.A, 46-48. AAAS; Am. Chem. Soc. Thermodynamics of solutions; calorimetry; surface chemistry. Address: 509 Brentwood Dr, Wilmington, DE 19803.

DETTWILER, H(ERMAN) A(NDREW), b. Monroe, Wis, Mar. 1, 10; m. 40; c. 5. BACTERIOLOGY. B.S, Wisconsin, 35; M.S, Ohio State, 37, Ph.D. (bact), 39. Asst, Christ Hosp. Inst. Med. Res, Cincinnati, 39-40; bacteriologist, ELI LILLY & CO, 40-46, asst. dir. biol. prod. div, 46-52, dir, 52-64, biol. prod, develop. & control div, 64-69, RES. ADV, GREENFIELD LABS, 69- AAAS; Am. Soc. Microbiol; Am. Soc. Trop. Med. & Hyg; Am. Asn. Immunol. Chemotherapy of the pneumococcus; viruses and rickettsiae; development and production of typhus, poliomyelitis and influenza vaccines and biological products. Address: Eli Lilly & Co, Greenfield Labs, Box 708, Greenfield, IN 46140.

DETTY, WENDELL EUGENE, b. Bemidji, Minn, June 30, 22; m. 45; c. 4. ORGANIC CHEMISTRY. B.A, Am. Univ, 44, 46-47; M.S, Georgetown, 49; Off. Naval Res. fel, 49-50; univ. res. inst. fel, Oklahoma, 52-53; Ph.D. (chem), 53. Asst. chem. lab, Am. Univ, 41-42; Bur. Standards & Am. Petrol. Inst, Wash, D.C, 42-44; biochemist, nat. cancer inst, U.S. Pub. Health Serv, 47-50; res. chemist, South. Dyestuff Corp, 53-59; prof. CHEM, Belmont Abbey Col, 54-59; PROF. & CHMN. DEPT, CATAWBA COL, 59- M.D, U.S.A, 44-46. AAAS; Am. Chem. Soc. Chromatographic analysis of podophyllin; preparation of new compounds for use in chemotherapy of cancer; amperometric titrations of flavonoid pigments with metal salts; synthesis of vat, sulfur and acetate dyestuffs and intermediates. Address: Dept. of Chemistry, Catawba College, Salisbury, NC 28144.

DE TURK, ELDER P(ATTISON), b. Reading, Pa, Dec. 13, 11; m. 40; c. 3. PHYSICS. B.S, Texas, 39, M.A, 42. Asst. proj. engr, Sperry Gyroscope Co, 42-44; instr. physics, Texas, 44-46, staff mem, war res. lab, 44-46; physicist, armament test, Naval Air Test Center, 46-47, head, assessment & ground test, 47-52, chief proj. engr, 52-57, consult. chief of bur. aeronaut, 56-57; assoc. mgr. syst. test dept, Thor Prog. Off. & Commun. satellite prog. off. Space Tech. Labs, Inc, Calif, 57-60; mgr. syst. test & test dir. prog, AEROSPACE CORP, 60-62, head test opers. dept, 62-69, MGR. DEFENSE SUPPORT PROG. OPERS, 69- Superior accomplishment award, U.S. Navy, 55. Civilian with Off. Sci. Res. & Develop; U.S.N.A.F, 44. Am. Phys. Soc; Am. Asn. Physics Teachers. Satellite flight test planning and operations. Address: Operations & Systems Analysis Office, Satellite Systems Division, Aerospace Corp, 2350 El Segundo Blvd, El Segundo, CA 90245.

DETWEILER, D(AVID) K(ENNETH), b. Phila, Pa, Oct. 23, 19; m; c. 6. PHYSIOLOGY, PHARMACOLOGY. V.M.D, Pennsylvania, 42, M.S, 49; hon. D.Sc, Ohio State Univ, 66; hon. D.M.V, Vienna, 68, Torino, 69. Asst. instr. physiol. & pharmacol, SCH. VET. MED, UNIV. PA, 42, instr, 43-45, assoc, 45-47, asst. prof, 47-51, assoc. prof. physiol, 51-62, prof. & head lab. physiol. & pharmacol, 62-68, PROF. & HEAD LAB, PHYSIOL, 68-, HEAD GRAD. GROUP COMP. MED. SCI, 71-, DIR. COMP. CARDIOVASC. STUDIES UNIT, 60-, grad. sch. med. chmn. dept. vet. med. sci, 56-70, assoc. prof, grad. sch. arts & sci. & grad. sch. med, 56-62. Guggenheim fel, Zurich, 55-56; guest prof, Munich, 63, Berlin, 68. Consult, WHO, 58 Food & Drug Admin, 70- Mem, expert panel vet. ed, Food & Agr. Orgn, 63-; physiol. training grant comt, Nat. Inst. Gen. Med. Sci, 67-70; coun. basic sci, Am. Heart Asn. U.S.P.H.S.R, 60- Fel. AAAS; Am. Physiol. Soc; Am. Pub. Health Asn; Am. Vet. Med. Asn.(Gaines award & medal); Am. Geront. Soc; N.Y. Acad. Sci. Comparative cardiology; electrocardiography; cardiovascular physiology. Address: School of Veterinary Medicine, University of Pennsylvania, 3800 Spruce St, Philadelphia, PA 19104.

DETWEILER, W(ILLIAM) KENNETH, b. Quakertown, Pa, Jan. 27, 23; m. 44; c. 2. ORGANIC CHEMISTRY. B.S, Ursinus Col, 47; M.S, Lehigh, 49, Ph.D. (chem), 51. Group leader org. chem. res, Union Carbide & Carbon Chems. Corp, 51-55; sect. head, new uses & new areas res, ESSO RES. & ENG. CO, STANDARD OIL CO.(N.J), 55-66, asst. dir. lubricants & petrol. specialties, 66-67, COORD. hq. mkt, 67-68, PROD. QUAL. RES, 68- U.S.N.R, 43-45, Lt. Am. Chem. Soc; Soc. Automotive Eng; Am. Inst. Chem. Eng. Synthesis and characterization of heterocyclic nitrogen derivatives, acyl aldehydes, polyglycol ethers, alcohols and phosphate esters; study of the effect of structure upon plasticizing action; synthetic lubricants; diesel fuels and diesel lubricants; recruiting; industrial lubricants and greases; new uses and new areas research; petroleum research management. Address: 205 Sylvania Pl, Westfield, NJ 07090.

DETWILER, D(ANIEL) P(AUL), b. Woodbury, Pa, Feb. 16, 27; m. 49; c. 3. SOLID STATE PHYSICS. A.B, Swarthmore Col, 49; M.S, Yale, 50, Ph.D. (physics), 52. Res. physicist, lab, Franklin Inst, 52-54; asst. prof. PHYSICS, State Univ. N.Y. Col.Ceramics, Alfred, 54-58, assoc. prof, 58-59, assoc. prof. & chmn. dept, 59-60; prof, Wilkes Col, 60-66, chmn. dept, 61-66, chmn. div. natural sci. & math. & dir, res. & grad. ctr, 63-66; physics specialist, Nat. Sci. Found-India Liaison Off, New Delhi, 66-69; staff physicist, Comn. Col. Physics, 69-70; PROF. & CHMN. DEPT, CALIF. STATE COL, BAKERSFIELD, 70- AAAS; Am. Asn. Physics Teachers; Am. Phys. Soc. Low temperature physics; semiconductivity; dielectrics; internal friction. Address: Dept. of Physics, California State College, Bakersfield, CA 93309.

DETWILER, THOMAS C, b. Hannibal, Mo, Dec. 28, 33; m. 62; c. 2. BIOCHEMISTRY. B.S, Illinois, 57, Ph.D.(nutrit), 60. Res. assoc, Oak Ridge Nat. Lab, 60-61; Phila. Gen. Hosp, Pa, 61-63; McCollum-Pratt Inst, Hopkins, 63-65; instr. BIOCHEM, STATE UNIV. N.Y. DOWNSTATE MED. CTR, 65-66, ASST. PROF, 66- U.S.A, 53-55. Regulation of metabolism; metabolism of platelets. Address: Dept. of Biochemistry, State University of New York Downstate Medical Center, 450 Clarkson Ave, Brooklyn, NY 11203.

DETWYLER, ROBERT, b. Middletown, N.Y, Apr. 16, 29; m. 51; c. 2. ZOOLOGY. B.S, State Univ. N.Y. Col. New Paltz, 54; M.S, New Hampshire, 59, Ph.D.(zool), 63. Instr, campus elem. sch, N.Y. State Teachers Col, New Paltz, 54-55; teacher, pub. sch, 55-57; instr, New Hampshire, 62-63; asst. prof. BIOL, Nasson Col, 63-65; NORWICH UNIV, 65-67, ASSOC. PROF, 67-, CHMN. DEPT, 68- AAAS; Am. Fisheries Soc; Am. Soc. Ichthyol. & Herpet. Intertidal ecology; fish embryology; biology of the sea snail, Liparis atlanticus. Address: Dept. of Biology, Norwich University, Northfield, VT 05663.

DETWYLER, THOMAS R(OBERT), b. Jackson, Mich, Aug. 10, 38; m. 60; c. 1. GEOGRAPHY. B.S, Michigan, 60; Fulbright fel, Otago, N.Z, 61-62; Nat. Defense Ed. Act fel, Hopkins, 63-65, Beaumont fel, 65-66, Ph.D.(phys. geog), 66. Asst. prof. GEOG, UNIV. MICH, ANN ARBOR, 66-71, ASSOC. PROF, 71- Summer res. asst, Univ. Mich, 62; U.S. Geol. Surv, 63; coinvestr, high mt. environ. proj, Arctic Inst. N.Am, 67-68; mem. phys. geog. panel, Comn. Col. Geog, 69-70. AAAS; Am. Geog. Soc; Geol. Soc. Am; Arctic Inst. N.Am. Plant geography; man's impact on environment; relations between vegetation and geomorphic processes; plant dispersal; mountain environments; development of vegetation concepts; landscape perception and aesthetics. Address: Dept. of Geography, University of Michigan, Ann Arbor, MI 48104.

DEUBEN, ROGER R, b. Detroit, Mich, Sept. 9, 38; m. 66; c. 1. PHARMACOLOGY, PHYSIOLOGY. B.S, Mich. State Univ, 60, Nat. Insts. Health assistantship & M.S, 64; Nat. Insts. Health traineeship & Ph.D.(pharmacol), Univ. Pittsburgh, 69. Physiologist, Mich. State Univ, 61-63; instr. physiol, SCH. DENT. MED, UNIV. PITTSBURGH, 65-66, ASST. PROF. PHARMACOL, 69- AAAS; Int. Asn. Dent. Res. Studies on the central effects of angiotensin II and its possible role in the etiology of hypertension; regulation of anterior pituitary hormone secretion; role of prostaglandins in the above fields. Address: Dept. of Pharmacology & Physiology, University of Pittsburgh School of Dental Medicine, Pittsburgh, PA 15213.

DEUBER, CARL G(EORGE), b. St. Louis, Mo, Dec. 19, 98; m. 22; c. 1. PLANT PHYSIOLOGY. B.S, Missouri, 21, Ph.D.(plant physiol), 25; M.S, Washington (St. Louis), 22; Polytech. Inst. Brooklyn, 44. Instr. biol, Clemson Col, 22-23; plant physiol, Yale, 25-29, asst. prof, 29-42; chemist, Stauffer Chem. Co, 42-48; asst. dir, Centro Res. Labs, 48-50; DIR, DEUBER LABS, 50- Res. fel, Harvard, 40-41. U.S.A, 18. AAAS; Bot. Soc. Am; Am. Soc. Plant Physiol; Am. Chem. Soc; Nat. Asn. Corrosion Eng; N.Y. Acad. Sci. Plant physiology; chlorophyll development; chemical toxins; stimulating agents; mineral nutrition; fermentation of citric acid; fungicide formulation and testing; insecticides; preservatives; plant hormones; textile fungicides; bacterial corrosion. Address: 531 Ashford Ave, Ardsley, NY 10502.

DEUBERT, KARL HEINZ, b. Weissensee, Germany, Feb. 1, 29; nat; m. 50. ENVIRONMENTAL BIOLOGY. M.S, Halle, 53, Ph.D.(agr. zool), 55. Asst. agr. zool, Halle, 53-60; sr. asst. phytopath, Cent. Biol. Inst, Berlin, Germany, 60-61; prof. biol, Nat. Univ. Honduras, 62-65; res. assoc. phytopath, CRANBERRY EXP. STA, UNIV. MASS, 65-67, ASST. PROF, RESIDUE ANAL, 67- AAAS; Soc. Am. Nematol; Am. Inst. Biol. Sci; Soc. European Nematol. Pesticide residues in soil, water and tissues; compounds interfering with identification of pollutants. Address: Cranberry Experiment Station, University of Massachusetts, East Wareham, MA 02538.

DEUBLER, EARL E(DWARD), JR, b. Sayre, Pa, May 19, 27; m. 51; c. 4. VERTEBRATE ZOOLOGY, ICHTHYOLOGY. B.S, Moravian Col, 50; Ph.D. (vert. zool), Cornell, 55. Asst, Cornell, 50-55; fisheries res. biol, U.S. Fish & Wildlife Serv, 55-56; asst. prof. zool, inst. fisheries res, North Carolina, 56-57, assoc. prof, 57-61; biol, Hartwick Col, 61-62; fisheries biol, Massachusetts, 62-63; zool, Inst. Fisheries Res, Univ. N.C, 63-67; BIOL, HARTWICK COL, 67-69, PROF, 69-, CHMN. DEPT, 71-, acting chmn. dept, 70-71. U.S.N.R, 45-46. Am. Soc. Ichthyol. & Herpet; Am. Soc. Zool. Systematic ichthyology; ecology; life histories of marine and brackish water fishes. Address: Dept. of Biology, Hartwick College, Oneonta, NY 13820.

DEUBLER, M(ARY) JOSEPHINE, b. Philadelphia, Pa, May 4, 17. VETERINARY MEDICINE. V.M.D, Pennsylvania, 38, M.S, 41, Ph.D.(path), 44. Asst. instr. vet. path, sch. vet. med, Pennsylvania, 40-44; res. assoc. parasitol, Jefferson Med. Col, 44-46; instr. bact, SCH. VET. MED, UNIV. PA, 41-51, ASST. PROF. VET. PATH, 51- Am. Vet. Med. Asn; Women's Vet. Med. Asn; N.Y. Acad. Virus, feline enteritis; anatomy and histology of the horse's eye; veterinary hematology and clinical bacteriology; mycology. Address: 2811 Hopkinson House, Washington Square S, Philadelphia, PA 19106.

DEUBNER, RUSSELL L(EIGH), b. Jamestown, Ohio, Aug. 10, 19; m. 44; c. 2. METALLURGY. B.Met.E, Ohio State, 42. Asst. metall, Ohio State, 40-42; res. engr. & asst. to supvr. res. div, graphic arts, Battelle Mem. Inst, 45-50, mgr, Battelle Develop. Corp, 50-58, admin. dept. econ, Battelle Mem. Inst, 57-58; gen. mgr, chrome plating div, Gen. Develop. Corp, 58-61; Ohio Semiconductors, Inc, 61-62; chmn. & treas, SCI. COLUMBUS, INC, DIV. ESTERLINE CORP, 62-69, PRES, 69- U.S.N.R, 44-45. Am. Soc. Metals. Metallurgy of case hardening chromium alloys; improvements in photo-engraving processes; development of xerography; printing; electroplating; patent and invention management; diversification studies and new product development; semiconductor product sales and production; Hall effect and thermoelectric devices and systems; corporate financing. Address: 2420 Donna Dr, Columbus, OH 43220.

DEUFEL, ROBERT, b. Chicago, Ill, Mar. 22, 28; m. 52; c. 5. BACTERIOLOGY. B.S, Elmhurst Col, 50; M.S, Illinois, 51, Ph.D.(bact), 57. Supvr. microbiol. assay develop, Eli Lilly & Co, 58-59, head dept. microbiol. testing & assay develop, 59-63, mgr. microbiol. assay develop, 63; assoc. prof. BIOL, Ind. Cen. Col, 63-64, PROF. & CHMN. DEPT, 64-69; CENTE-

NARY COL, 69- Chem.C, U.S.A, 51-53. AAAS; Am. Soc. Microbiol. Micro-biological assay methods for vitamins and antibiotics; mechanisms of antibiotic activity; cellular nutrition and physiology; biosynthesis of microbial pigments; aspects of microbial ecology. Address: Dept. of Biology, Centenary College, Shreveport, LA 71104.

DEUL, MAURICE, b. Tel Aviv, Palestine, May 12, 21; nat; m. 45; c. 2. MINERALOGY. B.S, Union Col, 42; M.S.(mineral), Colorado, 47. Instr. geol, Union Col, 47-48; geologist, mineral & petrog, U.S. Geol. Surv, 48-57; Bituminous Coal Res, Inc, 57-60; res. & develop. div, Consolidation Coal Co, 60-63; res. geologist, PITTSBURGH MINING & SAFETY RES. CTR, U.S. BUR. MINES, 63-67, supvry. geologist & res. mgr. environ. control sci, 67-71, RES. COORD. PROJ. COAL MINING GEOL, 71- U.S.A, 42-45. Mineral. Soc. Am; Geol. Soc. Am; Soc. Econ. Geol. Geochemistry of coal; removal of mineral matter from coal; geologic relations of bacteria; gases in coal; mining geology. Address: Pittsburgh Mining & Safety Research Center, U.S. Bureau of Mines, Forbes St, Pittsburgh, PA 15213.

DEURBROUCK, ALBERT WILLIAM, b. Kansas City, Mo, Jan. 2, 32; m. 61; c. 2. MINING ENGINEERING, MINERAL DRESSING. B.S, Idaho, 57. Mining engr, U.S. BUR. MINES, 57-61, supvry. mining methods res. engr, 61-64, SUPVRY. MINING ENGR, 64- U.S.A, 51-52. Soc. Mining Eng; Am. Mining Cong. Research on flotation characteristics of American coals; pyritic sulfur reduction potential of conventional and non-conventional coal washing devices; liquid-solid separation. Address: U.S. Bureau of Mines, 4800 Forbes Ave, Pittsburgh, PA 15213.

DEUSCHLE, FREDERICK M(ARION), b. Williamson, W.Va, Nov. 17, 04; m. 30; c. 1. ANATOMY, ORTHODONTICS. D.D.S, Cincinnati, 27. Clin. instr. anat, UNIV. CINCINNATI, 49-50, asst. prof. appl. anat, 50-59, assoc. prof. ANAT, 59-69, PROF, 69- Fel. AAAS; Am. Dent. Asn; Am. Asn. Anat; Am. Asn. Orthod; Int. Asn. Dent. Res; Int. Soc. Cranio-Facial Biol; Teratology Soc. Dento-facial growth; congenital malformations induced by dietary deficiencies and teratogenic agents. Address: University of Cincinnati College of Medicine, Room 127, Cincinnati, OH 42019.

DEUSCHLE, KURT W, b. Kongen, Germany, Mar. 14, 23; nat; m. 46; c. 3. MEDICINE. B.S, Kent State, 45; M.D, Michigan, 48. Intern med, Colo. Med. Center, 48-49; asst. res. internal med, Syracuse Med. Center, 49-50; res, col. med, State Univ. N.Y. Upstate Med. Center, 50-51, instr, 51-52, 54-55, dir. tumor clin. & cancer coordinator, 54-55; chief tuberc, Ft. Defiance Indian Hosp, U.S. Pub. Health Serv, 52-54; asst. prof. pub. health & prev. med. & dir. Navajo-Cornell Field Health Proj, med. col, Cornell, 55-60; prof. COMMUNITY MED. & chmn. dept, med. col, Kentucky, 60-68, prof, MT. SINAI SCH. MED, 68-69, LAVANBURG PROF, 69-, CHMN. DEPT, 68- Dipl, Am. Bd. Internal Med; Nat. Bd. Med. Exam. U.S.A, 43-46. Am. Med. Asn; Am. Pub. Health Asn; Am. Thoracic Soc; Asn. Teachers Prev. Med; Int. Epidemiol. Asn. Clinical investigations of antituberculous chemotherapeutic agents; cross-cultural medical research in areas of low economic development. Address: Dept. of Community Medicine, Mt. Sinai School of Medicine, 100th St. & Fifth Ave, New York, NY 10029.

DEUSER, WERNER GEORG, b. Duesseldorf, Germany, Oct. 31, 35; m. 59; c. 2. GEOCHEMISTRY. Vordiplom, Bonn, 57; M.S, Pa. State, 61, Ph.D. (geochem), 63. Consult. geochemist, Nuclide Corp, 61-63; res. scientist, Geol. Surv. W.Germany, 63-64; res. geochemist, Nuclide Corp, 64-66; res. assoc, GEOCHEM, WOODS HOLE OCEANOGRAPHIC INST, 66-67, ASSOC. SCIENTIST, 67- AAAS; Geochem. Soc. Mass spectrometry applied to geological problems; isotope geology; radioactive age determinations; stable isotope geochemistry, chemical and geological oceanography. Address: Dept. of Chemistry, Woods Hole Oceanographic Institution, Woods Hole, MA 02543.

D'EUSTACHIO, ANTHONY JOHN, b. Riverside, N.J, Dec. 7, 33; m. 55; c. 2. MICROBIOLOGY, BIOCHEMISTRY. B.S, Juniata Col, 54; M.S, Pennsylvania, 57, Ph.D.(microbiol), 60. Lab. asst. microbiol, Univ. Pa, 56-57; asst. instr, 58-59; res. assoc, 59-60; res. biochemist, cent. res. dept, E.I. du Pont de Nemours & Co, Inc, 60-65, proj. leader, development dept, 65-69; dir. microbiol. res. div, Hyland Div, Travenol Labs, Inc, 69-70; PRES, CENTAUR CHEM. CO, 70- U.S.A, 57, Res, 57-64, Capt. AAAS; Am. Soc. Microbiol; Am. Chem. Soc; Am. Inst. Chem; N.Y. Acad. Sci. Biological nitrogen fixation; energy metabolism; bacterial spores; immunochemistry; proteins. Address: Centaur Chemical Co, 4 W. Kenosia Ave, Danbury, CT 06810.

D'EUSTACHIO, D(OMINIC), b. Pittsburgh, Pa, Feb. 19, 04; m. 45; c. 2. PHYSICS. B.S, Columbia, 26; Ph.D.(physics), N.Y. Univ, 36. Res. assoc, Columbia, 27-28; asst. & instr. physics, N.Y. Univ, 29-35; instr, Polytech. Inst. Brooklyn, 36-42; chief crystal res. sect, Ft. Monmouth, N.J, 42-44; res. dir, Bliley Mfg. Co, 44-47; head physics res, Pittsburgh-Corning Corp, 47-60, res. dir, res. & eng. ctr, 60-65, v.pres, res, 65-69; PROF. MAT. SCI, UNIV. P.R, MAYAGUEZ, 69- AAAS; Acoustical Soc. Am; Am. Phys. Soc. Hyperfine structure; surface properties of crystalline solids; high vacuum techniques; physical properties of glass; thermal conductivity at low temperatures; acoustics; portland cement and related materials. Address: General Engineering Dept, University of Puerto Rico, Mayaguez, PR 00708.

DEUSTER, RALPH W(ILLIAM), b. Paterson, N.J, June 28, 20; m. 46; c. 3. MECHANICAL ENGINEERING, NUCLEAR PHYSICS. B.S.M.E, Purdue, 42; M.S, Princeton, 50; Cert. Bus. Mgt, Univ. Pittsburgh, 67. Proj. mgr, Armour Res. Found, Ill, 54-55; with Babcock & Wilcox Co, 55-70; V.PRES. & GEN. MGR, REACTOR FUELS DIV, NUCLEAR FUEL SERV, INC, 70- U.S.A, 43-54, Res, 54-70, Lt. Col. Am. Nuclear Soc; Am. Soc. Mech. Eng. Economics of nuclear reactor fuels; beta spectroscopy. Address: Reactor Fuels Division, Nuclear Fuel Services, Inc, 6000 Executive Blvd, Rockville, MD 20852.

DEUTCH, B(ERNHARD) I(RWIN), b. New York, N.Y, Sept. 29, 29; m. 63; c. 2. PHYSICS. N.Y. State scholar. & B.A, Cornell, 51, univ. scholar. & M.S, 53; Tyndale fel, Pennsylvania, 53-54, Harrison fel, 54-58, Ph.D. (physics), 59. Asst. biophys, Cornell, 51-53; nuclear physics, Pennsylvania, 54-58; physicist, Bartol Res. Found, 58-62; amanuensis physics, Aarhus, 62-64; physicist, Nobel Inst. Physics, 64-65; lectr. PHYSICS, UNIV. AARHUS, 65-70, DEPT. LEADER, 70- Vis, Orsay, Brookhaven Nat. Lab, 67; Niels Bohr Inst, 69; chmn, Int. Hyperfine Conf, Aarhus, 71. AAAS; Am. Phys. Soc. Low energy physics; nuclear physics; hyperfine interactions. Address: Institute of Physics, University of Aarhus, Aarhus, Denmark.

DEUTCH, JOHN MARK, b. Brussels, Belgium, July 27, 38; U.S. citizen; m. 63; c. 2. PHYSICAL CHEMISTRY, STATISTICAL MECHANICS. B.A, Amherst Col, 61; B.S, Mass. Inst. Tech, 61, Ph.D.(phys. chem), 66. Systs. analyst, Off. Secy. Defense, 61-65; Nat. Acad. Sci-Nat. Res. Coun. fel, Nat. Bur. Standards, 65-66; asst. prof. CHEM, Princeton, 66-70; ASSOC. PROF, MASS. INST. TECHNOL, 70- Consult, bur. budget, Exec. Off. President, 66- Am. Phys. Soc. Nuclear magnetic relaxation theory; liquids; transport processes; light scattering. Address: Dept. of Chemistry, Massachusetts Institute of Technology, Cambridge, MA 02139.

DEUTCH, MICHAEL JOSEPH, b. Smolensk, W. Russia, Aug. 26, 07; nat; m. 34; c. 3. CHEMICAL & ELECTRICAL ENGINEERING. C.E, M.E, E.E, Ghent, 28-29; Ph.D.(econ), Brussels, 30. Chief engr. & mgr. develop, Sofina, Ltd, 30-40; prin. consult. eng. staff warfare anal, U.S. Govt, 41; chief scheduling & construct. br, War Prod. Bd, 41, tech. asst. to chmn, 41-44; head planning & statist, Off. War Mobilization, 44-46; CONSULT. ENGR, 46- Consult, Dept. of State, 50, 66-; Gen. Staff, U.S. Army, 51; Secy-Gen, Pan Am. Union, 60-63; Agency Int. Develop, 65. Mem. U.S. Surv. Mission to P.I, 50; Presidential Inaugural Cmt, 61, 65; U.S. Govt. Trade Mission to Mex, 63, Roumania & Poland, 65; Coun. For. Rels. Soc. Am. Mil. Eng; Inst. Elec. & Electronics Eng; Am. Soc. Mech. Eng; Am. Ord. Asn. Research and development; fertilizers, sulphur and potash mining; food processing; petrochemicals; synthetic fibers; venture analysis; cybernetics; plastics, packaging and water treatment. Address: 1025 Connecticut Ave. N.W, Suite 409, Washington, DC 20036.

DEUTSCH, A(LBERT) S(IMON), b. New York, N.Y, Dec. 16, 29. ORGANIC CHEMISTRY. B.S, City Col. New York, 51; fel, Ill. Inst. Tech, 55-56, Ph.D. (chem), 56. Asst, Sloan Kettering Inst. Cancer Res, 51-53; res. chemist, org. chem. dept, E.I. du Pont de Nemours & Co, 56-63; res. specialist, photo & reprod. div, Gen. Aniline & Film Corp, 64-71; MEM. STAFF, RES. LAB, POLYCHROME CORP, 71- Am. Chem. Soc. Dye, heterocyclic and steroid chemistry; application of dyes and chemicals to paper and textiles; photo-imaging systems based on photo-coloration; electrophotography and photo-electropolymerization. Address: Research Lab, Polychrome Corp, 2 Ashton Ave, Yonkers, NY 10702.

DEUTSCH, DANIEL H(AROLD), b. New York, N.Y, Aug. 29, 22; m. 46; c. 2. ORGANIC & NUCLEAR CHEMISTRY. B.S, Calif. Inst. Tech, 48, Ph.D. (chem), 51. Fel. cyclobutane chem, Calif. Inst. Technol, 51; PRES, CALIF. FOUND. BIOCHEM. RES, 51-, DIR, 53-; CALBIOCHEM, 58-, CONSULT, 70-; PRES. & DIR, BASIC DEVELOP. CORP, LOS ANGELES, 71- V.pres, Calbiochem, 58-70. Sig.C, U.S.A, 43-46. Am. Chem. Soc; Am. Nuclear Soc. Commercial production of research biochemicals; medicinal chemistry; separation science; discursive and disquisitional analysis in chemistry. Address: 1355 Cresthaven Dr, Pasadena, CA 91105.

DEUTSCH, DENNIS L(ESLIE), b. Budapest, Hungary, May 21, 21; nat; m. 49; c. 1. ORGANIC CHEMISTRY. C.E, Swiss Fed. Inst. Tech, 44, Dr.Tech.Sc. (org. chem), 46. Chemist, dyestuff & chem. div, Gen. Aniline & Film Corp, 47-57; consult, Rhein-Chemie A.G, Switz, 57-59; PROD. mgr, tech. appln. prod. dept, CIBA CORP, 59-67, Ciba Pty, Ltd, Australia, 67-68, MGR. PROJ. PLANNING, P&A DIV. CIBA-GEIGY CORP, 68- Am. Chem. Soc. Intermediates; dyestuffs; surfactants; textile auxiliary products; optical brighteners; resins; agricultural chemicals. Address: 118 Fairacres Dr, Toms River, NJ 08753.

DEUTSCH, EDWARD ALLEN, b. N.Y.C, July 13, 42; m. 63; c. 1. INORGANIC CHEMISTRY. B.S, Univ. Rochester, 63; U.S. Pub. Health Serv. fel, Stanford Univ, 65-67, Ph.D.(inorg. chem), 67. U.S. Pub. Health Serv. fel, Univ. Calif, San Diego, 67-68; ASST. PROF. INORG. CHEM, UNIV. CHICAGO, 68- AAAS; Am. Chem. Soc. Kinetics and mechanisms of homogeneous reactions; catalytic processes; electron transfer reactions; chemistry of vitamin B_{12}; inorganic models for biochemical systems. Address: Dept. of Chemistry, University of Chicago, Chicago, IL 60637.

DEUTSCH, EMMANUEL, b. Cambridge, Mass, Mar. 4, 09; m. 49; c. 2. MEDICINE. Intern, Boston City Hosp, 36-37, res, 37-38; asst. MED, MED. SCH, TUFTS UNIV, 38-43, instr, 45-60, ASST. CLIN. PROF, 60-, instr. clin. med, dent. sch, 38-41. Instr. grads, Harvard Med. Sch, 39-42, med, 68-; staff physician med. dept, Mass. Inst. Tech; fel, surg. res. lab, Boston City Hosp, 37-43; lectr, med. sch, Boston Univ, 69- Outpatient physician; asst. physician & chief gastroenterol. dept, Boston Dispensary; prin. investr, Nat. Inst. Health grant, 60-63; gastroscopist, Boston Dispensary & Pratt Diag. Hosp; Mass. Gen. Hosp, 37, 46; internist, Boston Induction Sta, 41-43; med. consult, Marlborough Hosp; Vet. Admin. Hosp, N.H; regional Vet. Admin. Off, Mass; Soldiers' Home Hosp; Quincy City Hosp; Cambridge City Hosp; jr. vis. physician, Carney Hosp. Panelist, World Cong. Gastroenterol, Germany. Med.C, 43-45, Maj. Fel. Am. Col. Physicians; Am. Med. Asn; Am. Gastroenterol. Asn. Gastric secretion of bound glucose in gastrointestinal pathology; a new technique of gastric analysis, diseases of the gastrointestinal tract; diseases of the liver; total and ester cholesterol determination; phospholipids and total lipids determination; hippuric acid excretion; urinary urobilinogen excretion; fractional bromsulphthalein excretion; prothrombin levels in the blood; contributions of gastroscopy to the diagnosis of benign and malignant lesions of the stomach. Address: 469 Beacon St, Boston, MA 02115.

DEUTSCH, ERNST R(OBERT), b. Frankfurt, Germany, May 13, 24; Can. citizen; m. 49; c. 2. GEOPHYSICS. B.A, Toronto, 46, M.A, 49; Ph.D.(geophys), London & dipl, Imp. Col, 54. Seismic explor, Texaco Explor. Co, Alta, 49-51; res. asst, physics dept, Imp. Col, London, 54-57; res. engr. hydrodyn, Imp. Oil Ltd, Alta, 57-63; assoc. prof. GEOPHYS, MEM. UNIV. NEWF, 63-68, PROF, 68- Vis. lectr, Western Ontario, 57; mem. assoc. comt. geod. & geophys, Nat. Res. Coun. Can, 64-70. Soc. Explor. Geophys; Can. Asn. Physicists; Am. Geophys. Union; Soc. Geomagnetism & Geoelec. Japan. Magnetic properties of rocks at high temperatures; palaeomagnetism and application to hypotheses of polar wandering and continental drift; miscible displacement of liquids in porous media. Address: Dept. of Physics, Memorial University of Newfoundland, St. John's, Newf, Can.

DEUTSCH, GEORGE C, b. Budapest, Hungary, Apr. 19, 20; U.S. citizen; m. 42; c. 3. MATERIALS SCIENCE, METALLURGY. B.S, Case West. Reserve Univ, 42. Metallurgist, Copperweld Steel Co, 42-44; res. metallurgist, Lewis Res. Ctr, NASA, 46-60, asst. dir. res. mat. sci. & eng, OFF. ADVAN. RES. & TECHNOL, 60-70, DIR. MAT. & STRUCT. DIV, 70- Mem, Nat. Mat. Adv. Bd, 62-65; coord. comt. mat. res. & technol, Fed. Coun. Sci. & Technol, 63-69; chmn. interagency comt. mat, Nat. Acad. Sci, 70-71. NASA exceptional serv. medal, 67. U.S.N, 44-46, Lt.(jg). Fel. Am. Soc. Metals; Am. Inst. Mining, Metall. & Petrol. Eng. High temperature nickel and cobalt base alloys; powder metallurgy; refractory metals; cermets. Address: Office of Advanced Research & Technology, NASA Headquarters, 600 Independence Ave. S.W, Washington, DC 20546.

DEUTSCH, H(AROLD) F(RANCIS), b. Sturgeon Bay, Wis, Sept. 2, 18; m. 42; c. 2. CHEMISTRY. Ph.B, Wisconsin, 40, Ph.D.(physiol. chem), 44. Asst. cancer res, McArdle Lab, UNIV. WIS, MADISON, 40-41, teaching asst. PHYSIOL. CHEM, 42-44, res. assoc, SCH. MED, 44-45, asst. prof, 45-46, assoc. prof, 47-56, PROF, 56- Rockefeller Found. fel. nat. scis, Stockholm, 50-51; vis. prof, Brazil, 50; São Paulo, 54; Univ. Hokkaido, 71. Vis. scientist, Rockefeller Found, 60; Max-Planck Inst. Biochem, Munich, 60, 64. With Off. Sci. Res. & Develop, 44. Am. Chem. Soc; Am. Soc. Biol. Chem. Separation and characterization of plasma, erythrocyte and tissue protein; immunochemistry. Address: Dept. of Physiological Chemistry, School of Medicine, University of Wisconsin, Madison, WI 53706.

DEUTSCH, HOWARD, b. Los Angeles, Calif, Apr. 23, 40; m. 64; c. 2. ORGANIC & PAPER CHEMISTRY. B.S, Ga. Inst. Tech, 62, Nat. Insts. Health-U.S. Pub. Health Serv. grant, 63-66, Ph.D.(org. chem), 67. RES. SCIENTIST, UNION CAMP CORP, 66- Am. Chem. Soc; Tech. Asn. Pulp & Paper Indust; Brit. Chem. Soc. Nuclear magnetic resonance spectroscopy; structure of antibiotics; bleaching chemistry. Address: Union Camp Corp, Box 412, Princeton, NJ 08540.

DEUTSCH, JOHN L(UDWIG), b. New York, N.Y, May 5, 38; m. 61. PHYSICAL CHEMISTRY, SPECTROSCOPY. B.S, Tulane, 59; Rhodes scholar, Oxford, 59-63, D.Phil.(ultraviolet spectros), 63. Nat. Sci. Found. fel. & tutor CHEM, Oxford, 63-64; vis. asst. prof. Pomona Col, 64-66; ASSOC. PROF, STATE UNIV. N.Y. COL. GENESEO, 66- AAAS; Am. Chem. Soc; Brit. Chem. Soc. Electronic Spectra of simple molecules and nuclear magnetic resonance spectroscopy. Address: Dept. of Chemistry, State University of New York College at Geneseo, Geneseo, NY 14454.

DEUTSCH, MARSHALL E(MANUEL), b. N.Y.C, Aug. 17, 21; m. 47; c. 3. CLINICAL CHEMISTRY. B.S, City Col. New York, 41; Ph.D.(physiol. sci), N.Y. Univ, 51. Asst. & assoc. biochem, N.Y. Univ-Bellevue Med. Ctr, 47-51; jr. assoc, Henry Ford Hosp, 51-53; head chem. microbiol, Warner-Chilcott Res. Labs, 53-55, sr. scientist biochem, 55-58; dir. prod. develop, G.W. Carnrick Co, 58-59, res. & develop, 59-60; dir. life sci. res, Becton, Dickinson & Co, 60-66; tech. dir, NEN Pharmaceut, 66-68; consult, Farbwerke Hoechst AG, 68, tech. dir, Picker-Hoechst, Inc, 69-70; V.PRES. & TECH. DIR, MEAD DIAG, INC, 70- U.S.A.A.F, 42-45, 1st Lt. Fel. AAAS; Soc. Nuclear Med; Am. Asn. Clin. Chem; Sci. Res. Soc. Am; N.Y. Acad. Sci; Am. Chem. Soc; Fedn. Am. Sci; Int. Soc. Gen. Semantics. Thyroid and antithyroid drugs; effects of viricides; chemical kinetics; diagnostic reagents; pharmaceutical products. Address: 41 Concord Rd, Sudbury, MA 01776.

DEUTSCH, MARTIN, b. Vienna, Austria, Jan. 29, 17; nat; m. 39; c. 2. PHYSICS. B.S, Mass. Inst. Tech, 37, fel, 39-41, Ph.D.(physics), 41. Instr, physics, Mass. Inst. Tech, 41-45; scientist, California, Los Alamos, 44-46; asst. prof. PHYSICS, MASS. INST. TECHNOL, 45-49, assoc. prof, 49-53, PROF, 53- Civilian with Off. Sci. Res. & Develop; U.S.N, 44. Nat. Acad. Sci; AAAS; fel. Am. Phys. Soc. Study of radioactive radiations; study of the fission process; nuclear spectroscopy; elementary particle physics. Address: Dept. of Physics, Massachusetts Institute of Technology, Cambridge, MA 02138.

DEUTSCH, MIKE JOHN, b. Denver, Colo, Apr. 4, 20; m. 42; c. 5. BIOCHEMISTRY. B.S, Denver, 42. Biochemist, FOOD & DRUG ADMIN, 57-61, SUPVRY. BIOCHEMIST, 61- U.S.A.A.F, 43-45. Asn. Off. Agr. Chemists. Vitamin methodology. Address: Division of Nutrition, Food & Drug Administration, 200 C St, S.W, Washington, DC 20204.

DEUTSCH, MORRIS, b. Bethelem, Pa, Feb. 2, 25; m. 69; c. 3. HYDROLOGY. A.B, Syracuse, 49; M.S, Mich. State, 60. Geologist, U.S. GEOL. SURV, 50-57, dist. geologist, ground water br, Mich, 57-62, res. geologist, 63-68, CHIEF, OFF. REMOTE SENSING, WATER RESOURCES DIV, 69- Hydrol. coord, earth resources observ. syst. prog, U.S. Dept. Interior. U.S.A, 43-45. AAAS; Geol. Soc. Am. Hydrology; quality; contamination of ground-water resources; remote sensing of hydrologic phenomena. Address: Water Resources Division, Rm. 210, U.S. Geological Survey, 801 19th St. N.W, Washington, DC 20242.

DEUTSCH, M(URRAY) L(EWIS), b. Boston, Mass, July 30, 18; m. 41; c. 2. PHYSICS. B.A. & M.S, Michigan, 39. Physicist, Air Materiel Command, Aircraft Lab, 41-46; asst. supvr, res. sect, res. & develop. lab, Socony Mobil Oil Co, Inc, 47-59, supvr. appl. math, res. dept, 59-64, MGR, catalysis & math. res. sect, 64-70, PRINCETON COMPUT. & MATH. SERV. CTR, MOBIL OIL CORP, 70- Am. Phys. Soc; Asn. Comput. Mach; Soc. Indust. & Appl. Math. Partial differential equations; numerical analysis; digital computation; operations research; systems using digital computers. Address: Princeton Computer & Mathematical Services Center, Mobil Oil Corp, P.O. Box 1025, Princeton, NJ 08540.

DEUTSCH, ROBERT W(ILLIAM), b. Far Rockaway, N.Y, Mar. 21, 24; m. 49; c. 2. NUCLEAR ENGINEERING. B.S, Mass. Inst. Tech, 48; Ph.D.(physics), California, 53. Physicist high energy nuclear physics, radiation lab, California, 50-53; res. assoc. theoret. nuclear physics, Knolls Atomic Power Lab, 53-57; chief physicist, Gen. Nuclear Eng. Corp, 57-62; consult. physics, Martin Co, 62-64; PROF. & CHMN. DEPT. NUCLEAR SCI. & ENG, CATHOLIC UNIV, 64- Pres, Gen. Physics Corp, 66- U.S.A, 43-46. AAAS; Am. Nuclear Soc; Am. Phys. Soc; Am. Inst. Aeronaut. & Astronaut; N.Y. Acad. Sci. Reactor physics; fission physics; nuclear power plant training programs. Address: 8502 Arborwood Rd, Baltimore, MD 21208.

DEUTSCH, S(ID), b. New York, N.Y, Sept. 19, 18; m. 41; c. 3. ELECTRICAL ENGINEERING. B.E.E, Cooper Union, 41; M.E.E, Polytech. Inst. Brooklyn, 47, D.E.E, 55. Technician elec. motor, Rite-Way Fur Machine Co, 35-40; designer electro-mech. equipment, Otis Elevator Co, 40-41; Allied Process Engrs, 41-43; instr. physics, Hunter Col, 43-44; TV, Madison Inst, 46-50; engr. electronics, Polytech. Res. & Develop. Co, 50-54; instr, commun, POLYTECH. INST. BROOKLYN, 51-56, PROF. ELEC. ENG, 56-, proj. engr. electronics, microwave res. inst, 54-60. Instr, City Col. New York, 55-57. Designer, Fairchild Camera & Instrument Co, 43-44; consult, Polytech. Res. & Develop. Co, 57; Budd Electronics Co, 58-60; Rockefeller Inst, 61-64. U.S.N, 44-46. Inst. Elec. & Electronics Eng. Communications and electronics; information and network theory; biomedical electronics. Address: 205 W. 89th St, New York, NY 10024.

DEUTSCH, STANLEY, b. Yonkers, N.Y, Oct. 28, 21; m. 48; c. 3. ENGINEERING & INDUSTRIAL PSYCHOLOGY. B.A, Brooklyn Col, 48; M.S, Purdue, 51, Ph.D.(indust. psychol), 57. Asst. statistician, Brooklyn Col. Test. & Advisement Unit, 48; res. psychologist, U.S. Navy Electronics Lab, 48-57; head human factors support, Denver Div, Martin Co, 57-58; head personnel subsyst. eval, Air Force Ballistic Missiles Div, 58; head life sci. space systs, Douglas Aircraft Co, 58-61, head human factors tech. staff, 61-62; chmn. sci. staff. & v.pres. res. & develop, Consad Corp, 62; chief systs. res, NASA, 62-64, chief man-systs. integration, 64-70, ASSOC. DIR. LIFE SCI, 70- Mem. comt. hearing, acoustics & biomech, Nat. Acad. Sci-Nat. Res. Coun, 63-, alternate mem. exec. coun, comt. on vision, 63-69; exec. secy, res. & adv. comt. biotechnol. & human res, NASA, 63-68, mem. life sci. working group space sci. res. & technol, Aeronaut. & Astronaut. Coord. Bd, 64-, v.chmn. extravehicular activities comt, 67, chmn, panel space med. & human factors, 69-71, teleoperator/robot develop. task team, 70, bioeng. panel, 71. U.S.A, 42-46. Fel. AAAS; Fel. Human Factors Soc.(secy-treas, 68-69); sr. mem. Am. Astronaut. Soc. Space, aeronautical and electronic sciences, especially engineering psychology, industrial psychology and human factors; systems engineering and analysis; human augmentation; bio-instrumentation; habitability; human oriented systems; telefactors and remote control systems. Address: Bioengineering Division, Code MME, Headquarters, NASA, Washington, DC 20546.

DEUTSCH, STANLEY, b. Brooklyn, N.Y, Apr. 4, 30; m. 54; c. 2. ANESTHESIOLOGY, PHARMACOLOGY. B.A, N.Y. Univ, 50; M.A, Boston, 51, Parke-Davis fel, 52-53, fel, 53-56, Ph.D.(physiol), 55, fel, 56-57, M.D, 57. Rotating intern, grad. hosp, Pennsylvania, 57-58, instr. anesthesiol, 58-61, assoc, 63-64, asst. prof, 64-65; assoc. in anaesthesia, Harvard Med. Sch, 65-68, asst. prof, 68-69; assoc. surg, Peter Bent Brigham Hosp, 68-69; prof. ANESTHESIOL, Univ. Chicago & chmn. dept, Michael Reese Hosp, 69-71; PROF. & CHMN. DEPT, SCH. MED, UNIV. OKLA, 71- Consult, Vet. Admin. Hosp, Phila, Pa, 60-61, 63-; mem. sect. anesthesia, Nat. Acad. Sci-Nat. Res. Coun, 70- Dipl, Am. Bd. Anesthesiol. Med.C, 61-63, Capt. AAAS; N.Y. Acad. Sci; Am. Soc. Anesthesiol; Asn. Univ. Anesthetists. Cardiovascular and renal effects of anesthesia and surgery; pharmacology of anesthetics and drugs used in association with anesthesia; cardiovascular and renal physiology. Address: 800 N.E. 13th St, Oklahoma City, OK 73104.

DEUTSCH, THOMAS, b. Vienna, Austria, Apr. 24, 32; nat. LASERS. B.Eng. Phys, Cornell, 55; Nat. Sci. Found. fel, 55-56; A.M, Harvard, 56, Union Carbide Co. fel, 56-57, Standard Oil of Calif. fel, 57-59, Ph.D.(appl. physics), 61. From sr. res. scientist to PRIN. RES. SCIENTIST, RES. DIV, RAYTHEON CO, 60- Am. Phys. Soc; Inst. Elec. & Electronics Eng. Gas lasers; chemical lasers; optical properties of materials. Address: Research Division, Raytheon Co, 28 Seyon St, Waltham, MA 02154.

DEUTSCHE, CRAIG W(ILLIAM), b. Minneapolis, Minn, July 23, 39; m. 65. PHYSICAL CHEMISTRY. B.S, Yale, 60; A.M, Harvard, 62; Ph.D.(phys. chem), Minnesota, 64. Nat. Inst. Health fel, CHEM, Minnesota, 64-66; ASST. PROF, UNIV. CALIF, LOS ANGELES, 66- Am. Phys. Soc. Theoretical chemistry; optical properties of molecules; surface electronic structure of semiconductors. Address: Dept. of Chemistry, University of California, Los Angeles, CA 90024.

DEUTSCHER, MURRAY P(AUL), b. New York, N.Y, Sept. 1, 41; m. 66. BIOCHEMISTRY. B.S, City Col. New York, 62; Nat. Insts. Health fel. & Ph.D. (biochem), Albert Einstein Col. Med, 66. Am. Cancer Soc. fel. BIOCHEM, sch. med, Stanford, 66-68; ASST. PROF, HEALTH CTR, UNIV. CONN, 68- Vis. scientist. Weizmann Inst, 68-69. AAAS; Am. Chem. Soc; Am. Soc. Biol. Chem. Enzymology of protein biosynthesis; biochemistry of sporulation; enzymology of deoxyribonucleic acid replication. Address: Dept. of Biochemistry, University of Connecticut Health Center, Farmington, CT 06032.

DEUTSCHMAN, ARCHIE JOHN, JR, b. Chicago, Ill, Nov. 21, 17; m. 46; c. 5. CHEMISTRY. B.S, Illinois, 39; M.S, Lawrence Col, 41, Ph.D.(chem), 43. Special asst, Illinois, 44-45; chief chemist, Graham, Crawley & Assocs, Chicago, 45-46; sr. res. chemist, Phillips Petrol. Co, Okla, 46-47; dir. chem. res, Spencer Chem. Co, 47-57; PROF. AGR. BIOCHEM, UNIV. ARIZ, 57- With War Prod. Bd, 44. U.S.A.A.F, 42-46. Am. Chem. Soc. Organic chemistry; high pressure reactions; vapor phase and solution; furfural polymer control; butadiene chemistry; polymerizations; electrical conductivity of paper; hydrothermal crystal growth; copper recovery. Address: Dept. of Agricultural Biochemistry, University of Arizona, Tucson, AZ 85721.

DEV, VASU, b. Lahore, Panjab, Mar. 18, 33; m. 63; c. 2. ORGANIC & MEDICINAL CHEMISTRY. B.Sc, Panjab, 51, Hons 53, M.Sc, 54; Ph.D. (chem), California, Davis, 62. Chemist, Drug Res. Lab, India, 55-56; Govt.

Med. Col, India, 56-59; res. assoc. org. chem, Chicago, 63-64; asst. prof. med. chem, Tennessee, 64-65; phys. sci. dept, CALIF. STATE POLYTECH. COL, 65-68, ASSOC. PROF. CHEM, 68-, CHMN. DEPT. 70- Res. assoc. org. chem, California, Davis, fall 62. Am. Chem. Soc; Brit. Chem. Soc; Reaction mechanisms, natural products and organic synthesis; synthesis and study of products prossessed with pharmacodynamic properties. Address: Dept. of Chemistry, California State Polytechnic College, Pomona, CA 91768.

DEVALL, W(ILBUR) B(OSTWICK), b. Phelps, N.Y, Mar. 17, 15; m. 38; c. 1. FORESTRY. B.S, Syracuse, 37; M.S, Florida, 41. Field asst, Northeast. Forest Exp. Sta, Cooperstown, N.Y, 37; teaching fel, Florida, 37-41, instr, 41-43, asst. prof, 43; assoc. forester, U.S. Forest Serv, Fla, 43-45, South. Forest Exp. Sta, 45-46; ASSOC. PROF. FORESTRY, AUBURN UNIV, 46-, HEAD DEPT, 51- Mem. bd, State Bd. Registr. Foresters, Ala; Forest Farmers Asn; mem. & past chmn, Ala. Forestry Coun. With U.S. Census Bur. Soc. Am. Foresters. Forest ecology of Florida and Alabama; taxonomy of Pinus caribaea in Florida; visual aids for teaching dendrology. Address: Dept. of Forestry, Auburn University, Auburn, AL 36830.

DEVANEY, DENNIS M(ICHAEL), b. Los Angeles, Calif, Aug. 9, 38; m. 61; c. 2. INVERTEBRATE ZOOLOGY. A.B, Occidental Col, 60; M.A, California, Los Angeles, 62; Ph.D.(zool), Hawaii, 67. Lectr. zool, Hawaii, 65-66; INVERT. ZOOLOGIST, BERNICE P. BISHOP MUS, 66- Nat. Res. Coun. vis. res. assoc, div. invert. zool, Smithsonian Inst, 68- AAAS. Marine ecology, especially epifaunal communities in reef associated habitats; commensalism as it exists between echinoderms as hosts and their associates; systematics and zoogeography of chilophiurid Ophiuroidea. Address: Bernice P. Bishop Museum, P.O. Box 6037, Honolulu, HI 96818.

DEVANEY, JOSEPH J(AMES), b. Boston, Mass, April 29, 24; m. 54; c. 1. THEORETICAL PHYSICS. S.B, Mass. Inst. Tech, 47, Atomic Energy Cmn. fel, 48-50, Ph.D.(theoret. physics), 50; Texas Tech. Col; U.S. Coast Guard Acad. MEM. STAFF, THEORET. DIV, LOS ALAMOS SCI. LAB, 50-; PROF. PHYSICS, UNIV. N,MEX, 59-, math, 56-59. Mem. Gov. Policy Bd. Air & Water Pollution, 70. U.S.A, 42-44; U.S. C.G, 44-45. Am. Phys. Soc. Theoretical nuclear physics. Address: T-Do, Box 1663, Los Alamos, NM 87544.

DEVANEY, RICHARD G(EORGE), b. Sharpsburg, Pa, May 21, 23; m. 46; c. 2. ELECTRICAL ENGINEERING. B.S.E.E, Pa. State, 43. Tech. supvr. magnetic separation, Manhattan Proj, Clinton Eng. Works, Tenn, 43-45; proj. engr. elec, TENN. EASTMAN CO, 45-46, res. engr. electronics & physics, 46-56, sr. res. engr. dielectrics, 56-66, sr. res. engr. & lab. supvr, 66-68, NEW PRODS. ANALYST, 68- Mem, conf. elec. insulation, Nat. Res. Coun-Nat. Acad. Sci; exec. comt, Int. Wire & Cable Symp. Nat. Soc. Prfnl. Eng; Inst. Elec. & Electronics Eng; Am. Chem. Soc. Dielectric properties of new insulating materials; design and development of new scientific instruments; solid state infrared detectors; semi-permeable membranes. Address: Research Labs, B-150B, Tennessee Eastman Co, P.O. Box 511, Kingsport, TN 37662.

DE VAUCOULEURS, GERARD HENRI, b. Paris, France, Apr. 25, 18; m. ASTRONOMY. B.Sc, Paris, 36; Lic. es sc, Paris, 39, D. Univ, 49; D.Sc, Australian Nat. Univ, 57. Res. fel, Inst. Astrophys, Nat. Center Sci. Res, France, 45-50; Australian Nat. Univ, 51-54; observer, Yale-Columbia South. Sta, Australia, 54-57; astronomer, Lowell Observ, Ariz, 57-58; res. assoc, Harvard Col. Observ, 58-60; assoc. prof. ASTRON, UNIV. TEX, AUSTIN, 60-65, PROF, 65- Am. Astron. Soc; Royal Astron. Soc; Soc. Astron. France; French Phys. Soc; Int. Astron. Union. Stellar photometry; planetary physics; extragalactic research. Address: Dept. of Astronomy, Physics Bldg. 426, University of Texas at Austin, Austin, TX 78712.

DeVAULT, DON (CHARLES), b. Battle Creek, Mich, Dec. 10, 15; m. 48; c. 2. PHYSICAL CHEMISTRY. B.S, Calif. Inst. Tech, 37; Ph.D.(chem), California, 40. Asst, California, 37-40; jr. res. assoc. chem, Stanford, 40-42; assoc. investr, Nat. Defense Res. Cmt. Proj, 42; instr, inst. nuclear studies, Chicago, 46-48; assoc. prof. chem. & physics, Col. Pacific, 49-58; engr, Bionic Instruments, Inc, Pa, 59-63; Johnson Found. fel. BIOPHYS, MED. SCH. UNIV. PA, 63-64, assoc, 64-67, ASST. PROF, JOHNSON FOUND, 67- Conscientious objectr, 43-46. Biophys. Soc. Artificial radioactivity; inorganic chemistry; electronic guidance devices for the blind; laser flash photo-reactions in biological systems; energy transduction in biological electron transport; non-violence. Address: Dept. of Biophysics, Johnson Foundation, Medical School University of Pennsylvania, Philadelphia, PA 19104.

DEVAULT, GUILLAUME P(IERRE), b. Livingston, Mont, Oct. 7, 32; m. 55; c. 2. PHYSICS. B.S, Montana State Col, 54; M.S, Lehigh, 56, Ph.D.(physics), 59. Staff mem. PHYSICS, Sandia Corp, 59-61; Los Alamos Sci. Lab, 61-62, 63-68; res. assoc, Lehigh, 62-63; ASSOC. PROF, MONT. COL. MINERAL SCI. & TECHNOL, 68- Am. Phys. Soc. Elastic wave propagation; nonequilibrium statistical mechanics. Address: Dept. of Physics, Montana College of Mineral Science & Technology, Butte, MT 59701.

DeVAY, JAMES E(DSON), b. Minneapolis, Minn, Nov. 23, 21; m. 47; c. 6. PLANT PATHOLOGY. B.S, Minnesota, 49, fel, 51-53, Ph.D.(plant path), 53. Agent, U.S. Dept. Agr, Minnesota, 49, asst. PLANT PATH, 49-52, instr, 53-54, asst. prof, 54-57, assoc. prof, 57; asst. prof, UNIV. CALIF, DAVIS, 57-59, assoc. prof, 59-65, PROF, 65- U.S.N, 42-46. Fel. AAAS; Am. Phytopath. Soc; Mycol. Soc. Am. Physiology and biochemistry of host-parasite relationships. Address: Dept. of Plant Pathology, University of California, Davis, CA 95616.

de VEBER, LEVERETT L, b. Toronto, Ont, Jan. 27, 29; m. 54; c. 6. HEMATOLOGY, IMMUNOLOGY. M.D, Univ. Toronto, 53. Jr. intern, St. Michael's Hosp, Toronto, 53-54; sr. intern med, Shaughnessey Hosp, Univ. B.C, 54-55; sr. house off. pediat, Univ. Manchester, 57-58; registr, Univ. Liverpool, 58; jr. asst. resident, N.Y. Univ, 59-60; asst. resident pediat. & path, Univ. Toronto, 60-61; Mead-Johnson fel. immunohemat, Univ. Man, 61-62; lectr. PEDIAT. & PATH. CHEM, UNIV. WEST. ONT, 62-65, asst. prof, 65-68, ASSOC. PROF, 68-, DIR. Rh RES. LAB, 64-; DIR. IMMUNO-

HEMAT. DIV, Rh SERV. & BLOOD BANK, VICTORIA HOSP, LONDON, 62- Can. Life Ins. Co. fel, 62-64; West. Can. Rh Prev. Prog. investr, 64-; Nat. Health & Welfare res. investr, 64-68, chief investr, 68- Fel, Royal Col. Physicians & Surgeons Can, 61. R.C.N.R, 48-60, Surg-Lt. Can. Soc. Immunol.(treas, 68-); Can. Fedn. Biol. Sci. Prevention of Rh sensitization with Rh immune globulin; detection of early Rh sensitization with serological and lymphocyte culture techniques; detection of Rh antigen on amniotic cells with fluorescent antibody technique. Address: Dept. of Pediatrics, University of Western Ontario, London 72, Ont, Can.

DeVELIS, JOHN BERNARD, b. Cranston, R.I, Jan. 24, 35. THEORETICAL PHYSICS. A.B, Boston, 57, A.M, 59, Ph.D.(physics), 64. Instr. PHYSICS, Emmanuel Col, 59-62; res. asst, Boston, 62-63; asst. prof, MERRIMACK COL, 64-65, assoc. prof, 65-68, PROF, 68- Fel, Univ. Pa. & vis. prof. Towne Sch, 66; lectr, Univ. Calif. Los Angeles, summers, 66-71; summer, physicist optics, Tech. Opers, Inc, 64, consult, 64-67; v.pres, Optronics Int. Inc, 69-70; co-chmn. second Soc. Photog. Instrument. Eng. Seminar Holography, 71. Statistical optics and quantum theory of radiation. Address: Dept. of Physics, Merrimack College, North Andover, MA 01845.

DEVENS, W(ILLIAM) GEORGE, b. Ft. Eustis, Va, Mar. 2, 26; m. 48; c. 8. ENGINEERING & EDUCATION. B.S, U.S. Mil. Acad, 46; M.S, Univ. Ill, Urbana-Champaign, 53; U.S. Army Command & Gen. Staff Col, 60-61. Dep. commandant cadets, Norwich Univ, 66-67; asst. prof. eng. & assoc. dir, VA. POLYTECH. INST. & STATE UNIV, 67-69, ASSOC. PROF. ENG. & DIR. DIV. ENG. FUNDAMENTALS, 69- C.Eng, U.S.A, 46-66, Lt. Col.(Ret). Soc. Am. Mil. Eng; Am. Soc. Eng. Educ; Nat. Soc. Prof. Eng. Educational technology. Address: Division of Engineering Fundamentals, Randolph Hall, Virginia Polytechnic Institute & State University, Blacksburg, VA 24061.

DeVENUTO, FRANK, b. Giovinazzo, Italy, July 28, 28; nat; m. 57; c. 3. ORGANIC & BIOLOGICAL CHEMISTRY. B.S, Matteo Spinelli Col, Italy, 46; Ph.D.(org. & biol. chem), Rome, 51. Asst. org. res, Rome, 48-51; sr. chemist oil res, Gaslini Oil Co, 51-52; antibiotic res, Leo-Penicillin Co, 52; consult, chemist abrasive res, Ace Abrasive Labs, N.Y, 52-53; CHIEF SECT, STEROID HORMONES RES, U.S. ARMY MED. RES. LAB, 55- Asst. prof, Louisville, 60- U.S.A, 53-55. AAAS; Soc. Exp. Biol. & Med; N.Y. Acad. Sci; Am. Soc. Biol. Chem. Metabolism and mechanism of action of steroid hormones; carbohydrate metabolism; steroid and protein methodology. Address: Biochemistry Division, U.S. Army Medical Research Lab, Ft. Knox, KY 40121.

DE VENUTO, GIOVANNI, b. Giovinazzo, Bari, Italy, Jan. 5, 37; U.S. citizen; m. 65. ORGANIC & POLYMER CHEMISTRY. Bari, 55-58; Ph.D.(chem), Rome, 60. Res. chemist, SNAM Res. Center, Milan, Italy, 61-62, sr. res. chemist, 62; res. fel. polymer kinetics, Louisville, 62-65; RES. CHEMIST, E.I. DU PONT DE NEMOURS & CO, 65- AAAS; Am. Chem. Soc; Sci. Res. Soc. Am. Synthesis of monomers from isopropenyl acetylene; kinetics of copolymerization of styrene and pure divinylbenzene; polyolefins reinforcement. Address: Plastics Dept, Experiment Station, E.I. du Pont de Nemours & Co, Wilmington, DE 19898.

DEVENY, C(HARLES) A(LBERT), JR, b. Corsicana, Tex, Mar. 2, 24; m. 64; c. 1. MECHANICAL ENGINEERING. B.S, Texas, 48. Staff engr, HUMBLE OIL & REF. CO, 48-65, operating supvr, 65-70, MECH. SUPVR, MAINTENANCE & CONSTRUCT. DIV, 70- U.S.A.A.F, 43-46. Am. Soc. Mech. Eng. Engineering and design of oil refinery equipment and processes. Address: 2108 N. Fisher Courts, Pasadena, TX 77502.

DEVER, DAVID F(RANCIS), b. Quebec, Que, Can, Oct. 9, 31; m. 57; c. 4. PHYSICAL CHEMISTRY. B.S, Spring Hill Col, 53; M.S, Fla. State, 55; U.S. Pub. Health Serv. fel, Ohio State, 57-59, Ph.D.(phys. chem), 59. Off. Naval Res. fel. thermodyn, Ohio State, 60-61, univ. fel, molecular spectros, 62-63; asst. prof. chem, Miami, 61-62; res. photochemist, U.S. Bur. Mines, 63-64; proj. leader air pollution res, 64-66; chmn. dept. chem, Col. Petrol. & Minerals, Dhahran, Saudi Arabia, 66-69; CHMN. DIV. NATURAL SCI. & MATH, MACON JR. COL, 69- M.D. Marshall award, 53. AAAS; Am. Chem. Soc. Solution thermodynamics; photo-chemistry; gas kinetics; high temperature thermodynamics; automotive air pollution. Address: 556 Pierce Dr. W, Macon, GA 31204.

DEVER, DONALD A(NDREW), b. Sudbury, Ont, Sept. 18, 26; m. 47; c. 2. ENTOMOLOGY. B.S.A, Ont. Agr. Col, 49; M.Sc, Wisconsin, 50, Ph.D. (entom. plant path), 53. Tech. asst, dom. parasite lab, Can. Sci. Serv, Ont, 45-48, proj. leader, 49; asst, Wisconsin, 49-53, asst. prof, 53-56; dist. res. entomologist, res. & develop, Calif. Spray-Chem. Corp, 56-62; tech. dir, Niagara Brand Chem. Div, FMC Mach. & Chem. Ltd, 62-69, MGR. INT. DEVELOP, NIAGARA CHEM. DIV, FMC CORP, N.Y, 69-; SECY-GEN, CAN. GRAINS COUN, 69- Dir, Manitoba Res. Coun. R.C.A.F, 43-45. Entom. Soc. Am; Can. Entom. Soc; Can. Agr. Chem. Asn.(pres, 67-68). Administration; maximize export and domestic sales of Canadian grain through market analysis and development. Address: Canadian Grains Council, 200-177 Lombard Ave, Winnipeg 2, Man, Can.

DEVER, JOHN E, JR, b. Camden, N.J, Sept. 24, 32; m. 52; c. 2. PLANT PHYSIOLOGY, BIOCHEMISTRY. B.A, Rutgers, 60; M.S, Oregon State, 62; Ph.D.(plant physiol, biochem), Mich. State, 67. Lectr. biol, Flint Col, Michigan, 67; ASST. PROF. BOT, FT. LEWIS COL, 67- Nat. Sci. Found. res. fel, Univ. Tex, Austin, summer 70. U.S.A.F, 52-56, S/Sgt. Am. Soc. Plant Physiol; Am. Inst. Biol. Sci; Scand. Soc. Plant Physiol. Cell wall structure and metabolism; exocellular enzymes in root cell walls. Address: Dept. of Biology, Ft. Lewis College, Durango, CO 81301.

DEVERALL, LaMAR I(VAN), b. Taylorsville, Utah, Nov. 9, 24; m. 63. APPLIED MATHEMATICS & MECHANICS. B.S, Utah, 46, M.S, 48, Ph.D. (math), 54. Instr. math, Utah, 48-53; MATHEMATICIAN, Dugway Proving Ground, 53-56; Phillips Petrol. Co, 56-57; radiation lab, California, 57-62; UNITED TECHNOL. CTR, UNITED AIRCRAFT CORP, 62- Theory of elasticity; viscoelastic analysis of solid rocket motor grains; numerical methods for engineering analysis; random vibration analysis. Address: United Technology Center, United Aircraft Corp, P.O. Box 358, Sunnyvale, CA 94086.

DEVEREAUX, R(ICHARD) G(AYLE), b. Stockton, Calif, Jan. 17, 28; m. 53; c. 5. INTERNAL MEDICINE. A.B, California, 51, M.D, 54. Res, Long Beach Vet. Admin. Hosp, 55-56; clin. instr, MED. SCH, UNIV. CALIF, Los Angeles, 56-57, clin. fel. gastroenterol, 57-58, res. fel, 58-64, ASST. CLIN. PROF. MED, SAN FRANCISCO, 64- Private practice, 59- Res, Long Beach Vet. Admin. Hosp, 56-57; Fort Miley Vet. Admin. Hosp, 58-59; chief, gastrointestinal clin, Mary's Help Hosp, San Francisco; consult, San Quentin Prison, 59-64; dist. med. consult, Calif. State Dept. Vocational Rehab, 65- U.S.C.G, 46-47. Am. Soc. Internal Med; Am. Med. Asn; fel. Am. Col. Physicians; Royal Soc. Med. Gastroenterology. Address: 384 Post St, San Francisco, CA 94108.

DEVEREUX, OWEN FRANCIS, b. Lexington, Mass, Aug. 23, 37; m. 57, 69; c. 4. CORROSION, METALLURGY. S.B, Mass. Inst. Tech, 59, S.M, 60, Ph.D.(metall), 62. Res. chemist, Chevron Res. Corp, 62-64; Corning Glass Works, 64-66; Chevron Res. Corp, 66-68; ASSOC. PROF. METALL, INST. MAT. SCI, UNIV. CONN, 68- Metall. Soc; Electrochem. Soc. Thermodynamics; transport phenomena; oxidation corrosion; environmental effects on mechanical behavior. Address: Dept. of Metallurgy, Institute of Materials Science, University of Connecticut, Storrs, CT 06268.

DEVEREUX, ROBERT FRANCIS, b. Winchester, Mass, Nov. 9, 26; m. 59; c. 3. OCEANOGRAPHY, METEOROLOGY. Boston Univ, 46-49. Prog. mgr, Ocean Data Systs, Convair Div, Gen. Dynamics Corp, 60-71; SPEC. ASST. HEAD, OFF. FOR INT. DECADE OF OCEAN EXPLOR, NAT. SCI. FOUND, 71- U.S.N.R, 44-46. Am. Geophys. Union; Am. Meteorol. Soc; Am. Soc. Limnol. & Oceanog; Instrument Soc. Am; Marine Technol. Soc. Acquisition of environmental data from the sea. Address: Office for International Decade of Ocean Exploration, National Science Foundation, 1800 G. St. N.W, Washington, DC 20550.

DEVERMAN, JERONE NELSON, b. Pekin, Ill, July 4, 38; m. 60; c. 2. MATHEMATICAL STATISTICS. B.S, Purdue, 60, M.S, 62, Ph.D.(math. statist), 69. Vis. lectr. math, New Mexico, 67-68; mem. tech. staff, explor. systs. res, Sandia Labs, Calif, 68-69; supvr. opers. & systs. anal, Braddock, Dunn & McDonald, Inc, 69-70; MEM. TECH. STAFF, QUAL. ASSURANCE ADVAN. PLANNING, SANDIA LABS, N.MEX, 70- U.S.A, 66-68, Capt. Inst. Math. Statist; Am. Statist. Asn. Mathematical and probabilistic modeling pursuant to weapons systems analysis; numerical analysis, computing and simulation. Address: Organization 7425, Sandia Labs, P.O. Box 5800, Albuquerque, NM 87115.

de VILLAFRANCA, GEORGE W(ARREN), b. Meriden, Conn, Nov. 21, 23; m. 47, 65; c. 3. ZOOLOGY. B.S, Yale, 48, Ph.D.(zool), 53. Lab. asst. ZOOL, Yale, 48-51; instr, SMITH COL, 51-54, asst. prof, 54-59, assoc. prof, 59-63, PROF, 63-, CHMN. DEPT, 68-, asst. to pres, 61-66. Lalor fel, Marine Biol. Lab, Woods Hole, 53, 56, clerk corp, 64-66, mem. corp; Am. Cancer Soc. fel, Inst. Muscle Res, 54-55. U.S.A.A.F, 43-46. Biophys. Soc; Am. Soc. Zool; Am. Soc. Gen. Physiol. Comparative and developmental muscle biochemistry and molecular biology. Address: Dept. of Biological Sciences, Smith College, Northampton, MA 01060.

DeVILLEZ, EDWARD JOSEPH, b. Covington, Ky, Apr. 12, 39; m. 59; c. 4. COMPARATIVE PHYSIOLOGY. B.S, Xavier (Ohio), 59; M.S, Miami (Fla), 61; Ph.D.(physiol), Illinois, Urbana, 64. Res. assoc. comp. digestive enzym. & Nat. Sci. Found. fel, Friday Harbor Labs, Univ. Washington, 64-65; asst. prof. ZOOL, MIAMI UNIV, 65-69, ASSOC. PROF, 70- Nat. Insts. Health res. grant, 66-70. AAAS; Am. Soc. Zool; Am. Physiol. Soc. Isolation and characterization of proteolytic digestive enzymes in invertebrates. Address: Dept. of Zoology, Miami University, Oxford, OH 45056.

DEVIN, CHARLES, JR, b. New York, N.Y, Mar. 29, 24. ACOUSTICS, HYDRODYNAMICS. B.S, George Washington, 53, M.S, 57; Maryland, 58-60; David Taylor Model Basin scholar, Catholic Univ, 64, Ph.D.(appl. physics), 70. Meteorol. aide, U.S. Weather Bur, 46-47; weather observer, 47-52, jr. physicist, phys. res. div, 52-54; asst. proj. mgr, SHIP ACOUSTICS DEPT, NAVAL SHIP RES. & DEVELOP. CTR, 54-57, proj. mgr, 57-60, sr. proj. mgr, 60-61, SUPVY. PHYSICIST, HYDRODYNAMIC NOISE SECT, 61- Lectr, eve. session, George Washington, 63-64. Superior accomplishment award, 64, 65. U.S.A.A.F, 42-45, Sgt. AAAS; Acoustical Soc. Am; Am. Asn. Physics Teachers; Am. Meteorol. Soc. Sonar, signal processing, sound propagation, bubble noise, turbulent boundary layer noise, noise radiated by marine propellers. Address: Code 1935, Naval Ship Research & Development Center, Ship Acoustics Dept, Washington, DC 20034.

DEVINATZ, ALLEN, b. Chicago, Ill, July 22, 22; m. 52, 56; c. 2. MATHEMATICS. B.S, Ill. Inst. Tech, 44; A.M, Harvard, 47, Pierce scholar, 49, Ph.D.(math), 50. Instr. math, Ill. Inst. Tech, 50-52; Nat. Sci. Found. fel, Inst. Adv. Study, 52-53, mem, 53-54; asst. prof. MATH, Connecticut, 54-55; Washington (St. Louis), 55-57, assoc. prof, 57-60; Nat. Sci. Found. sr. fel, 60-61; PROF, Wash. Univ, 61-67; NORTHWEST. UNIV, 67- U.S.N.R, 45, Ens. Am. Math. Soc. Analysis. Address: Dept. of Mathematics, Northwestern University, Evanston, IL 60201.

DEVINE, JAMES F(RANCIS), b. Westernport, Md, May 19, 34; m. 58; c. 3. GEOPHYSICS, GEOLOGY. B.S, West Virginia, 57. Oceanogr, U.S. Coast & Geod. Surv, 58, geophysicist, 58-61; res. geophysicist, U.S. Bur. Mines, 61-67; GEOPHYSICIST, ENVIRON. RES. LAB, NAT. OCEANIC & ATMOSPHERIC ADMIN, 67- U.S.A, 57-58, Res, 58-, Maj. Seismol. Soc. Am; Soc. Mining Eng; N.Y. Acad. Sci. Seismic instrumentation; vibrations from blasting; effect of charge weight, presplitting, geologic structure and composition on seismic signals; structural response to seismic signals; seismicity of U.S; relationship of seismicity to geologic and tectonic structure; evaluation of seismic adequacy of proposed nuclear power plant sites. Address: National Oceanic & Atmospheric Administration, Washington Science Center, Rockville, MD 20852.

DEVINE, JOHN EDWARD, b. Du Bois, Pa, Feb. 14, 23; m. 53; c. 5. MECHANICAL ENGINEERING. B.S, Carnegie Inst. Tech, 48. Res. engr, Al-Res. Labs, ALUMINUM CO. AM, 48-60, construct. proj. engr, Alcoa Bldg, 60-65, head bldg. serv. dept, ALCOA TECH. CTR, 65-67, ENG. ADV, 67- U.S.A.A.F, 43-45, 1st Lt. Am. Soc. Mech. Eng. Research in quenching of metals; design of laboratory buildings, systems and equipment. Address: Alcoa Technical Center, Aluminum Co. of America, P.O. Box 2970, Pittsburgh, PA 15230.

DEVINE, LEONARD F(RANCIS), b. Phlox, Wis, Oct. 6, 24; m. 58. BACTERIOLOGY. B.S. & M.S, Wisconsin, 54. MED. SERV.C, U.S. NAVY, 54-, res. immunol, Biol. Warfare Labs, Md, 54-56, instr, Army Chem. Corps Sch, Ala, 56-59, res, Univ. Calif, 59-65, res. NAVAL MED. RES. UNIT 4, 65-67, CHIEF BACT. DIV, U.S. NAVAL HOSP, 67- U.S.N, 42-46, 50-52, 54-, Comdr. AAAS; N.Y. Acad. Sci; Asn. Mil. Surg. U.S; Am. Soc. Microbiol. Immunology; aerobiology; virology; epidemiology; meningococci; antibiotics. Address: Naval Medicine Research Unit 4, U.S. Naval Hospital, Great Lakes, IL 60088.

DEVINE, MARJORIE M, b. East Machias, Maine, May 19, 34. NUTRITION. B.S, Maine, 56, M.S, 62; Gen. Foods fel, Cornell, 65-66, U.S. Pub. Health Serv. fel, 66, Ph.D.(nutrit), 67. Teacher, high sch, Conn, 56-58; high sch, Maine, 58-62; instr. food sci, Maine, 62-64; ASST. PROF. HUMAN NUTRIT. & FOOD, CORNELL UNIV, 67- Ascorbic acid metabolism. Address: Dept. of Food Nutrition, Cornell University, Ithaca, NY 14850.

DEVINE, ROBERT T, b. San Francisco, Calif, Dec. 29, 40. THEORETICAL PHYSICS. B.S, San Francisco, 62; St. Louis, 62-63; M.A, California, Davis, 65, Ph.D.(physics), 68. Physicist, U.S. Naval Radiol. Defense Lab, 63-69; Armed Forces Radiobiol. Res. Inst, 69-71; HEAD MED. PHYSICS DEPT, U.S. NAVAL MED. RES. UNIT 2, REPUB. OF CHINA, 71- Med.Serv.C, U.S.N, 71-, Res, 69-71, Lt. Seismol. Soc. Am; Am. Nuclear Soc; Soc. Nuclear Med. Medical physics; immunology; radiobiological dosimetry. Address: 2631-38th Ave, San Francisco, CA 94116.

DEVINE, THOMAS EDWARD, b. N.Y. GENETICS, BOTANY. B.S, Fordham Univ, 59; M.S, Pa. State Univ, 63; Ph.D.(plant breeding), Iowa State Univ, 67. Asst. prof. plant breeding, Cornell Univ, 67-69; RES. GENETICIST, PLANT SCI. DIV, AGR. RES. SERV, U.S. DEPT. AGR, 69- AAAS; Am. Inst. Biol. Sci; Am. Soc. Agron. Interspecific hybridization; induced allopolyploidization; analysis of chromosome pairing relationships; selection and development of disease and insect resistant plant populations. Address: Alfalfa Investigations, Plant Industry Station, U.S. Dept. of Agriculture, Beltsville, MD 20705.

DEVINEY, MARVIN LEE, JR, b. Kingsville, Tex, Dec. 5, 29; m. 58; c. 2. PHYSICAL CHEMISTRY. B.S, Southwest Tex. State Col, 49; fel, Texas, 50-52, M.A, 52, Humble Oil Co. fel, 53-54, Ph.D.(phys. chem), 56. Develop. chemist, plant lab, Celanese Corp. Am, Tex, 56-58; res. chemist, indust. chem. res. lab, Shell Chem. Co, 58-66; sr. scientist, United Carbon Co, 66-68; mgr. phys. & anal. res, Ashland Chem. Co. Div, ASHLAND OIL, INC, 68-70, MGR. PHYS. CHEM. RES. SECT, RES. & DEVELOP. DIV, 70- Mem. sci. adv. comt, Am. Petrol. Inst. Res. Proj, 60. Nat. Guard, 49-65; U.S.A.R, 65-, Lt. Col. AAAS; Am. Chem. Soc.(best paper awards, rubber div, 67, 70); Am. Ord. Asn; fel. Am. Inst. Chem; N.Y. Acad. Sci. Surface chemistry; rubber technology; industrial petrochemicals; physical separation methods; homogeneous and heterogeneous catalysis; thermodynamic electrochemistry; liquid and gas chromatography; defense against chemical, biological and radiological agents; physico-chemical measurements; pressure-volume-temperature relations; radiochemical methods; quality improvement; vapor liquid equilibria. Address: Research & Development Division, Ashland Oil, Inc, P.O. Box 2219, Columbus, OH 43216.

DEVINS, DELBERT W(AYNE), b. Warwick, Okla, Sept. 6, 34; m. 66. NUCLEAR PHYSICS. B.S, Fresno State Col, 58; M.S, Southern California, 62, Ph.D.(physics), 64. Vis. asst. prof. PHYSICS, Southern California, 64-65; asst. prof, IND. UNIV, BLOOMINGTON, 65-69, ASSOC. PROF, 69- Sr. sci. off, Rutherford High Energy Lab, Eng, 65-66. U.S.N.R. Res, 53-61. AAAS; Am. Phys. Soc; Am. Asn. Physics Teachers. Medium energy nuclear reactions; optical model; neutron polarization. Address: Dept. of Physics, Indiana University, Bloomington, IN 47401.

DEVINY, EDWARD JOHN, b. Owatonna, Minn, July 14, 39; m. 61; c. 3. ORGANIC CHEMISTRY, PHOTOCHEMISTRY. B.S, Hamline, 61; Ph.D.(org. chem), California, Berkeley, 65. RES. SPECIALIST, MINN. MINING & MFG. CO, 65- Am. Chem. Soc. Synthetic and mechanistic organic chemistry; organic photochemistry; cleavage reactions of organic ring systems; non-conventional imaging processes. Address: 2814 Merrill St, St. Paul, MN 55113.

DeVITA, VINCENT T, JR, b. Bronx, N.Y, Mar. 7, 35; m. 57; c. 2. INTERNAL MEDICINE, PHARMACOLOGY. B.S, Col. William & Mary, 57; M.D, George Washington, 61. Intern med, med. center, Michigan, 61-62; res, Gen. Hosp, med. serv, George Washington, 62-63; clin. assoc, lab. chem. pharmacol, Nat. Cancer Inst, 63-65; res. med, Yale New Haven Med. Center, 65-66; sr. investr, MED. BR, NAT. CANCER INST, 66-68, CHIEF SOLID TUMOR SERV, 68- Assoc. prof, sch. med, George Washington Univ. Consult, Wash. Vet. Admin. Hosp, 67- Assoc. ed, Jour. Nat. Cancer Inst, 68-; sci. ed, Cancer Therapy Reports, 70- Dipl, Am. Bd. Internal Med, 68. U.S.P.H.S, 63-68, Lt. Comdr. Am. Asn. Cancer Res; Am. Soc. Hemat; Am. Fedn. Clin. Res; Am. Soc. Clin. Oncol; fel. Am. Col. Physicians. Pharmacology of anti tumor agents in relation to tumor cell kinetics; chemotherapy of the lymphomas. Address: Medicine Branch, Bldg. 10, 12N228, National Cancer Institute, Bethesda, MD 20014.

DeVITO, CARL LOUIS, b. New York, N.Y, Oct. 21, 37; m. 65; c. 1. MATHEMATICS. B.S, City Col. New York, 59; Ph.D.(math), Northwestern, 67. Instr. MATH, DePaul, 65-67; ASST. PROF, UNIV. ARIZ, 67- Invited speaker Liège Colloquium, Belgium, 70. Am. Math. Soc. Theory of locally convex, topological vector spaces, particularly the completions of these spaces for various topologies and the relations among these completions, and study of the weakly compact subsets of these spaces; applications of functional analysis to the theory of functions of a real variable. Address: Dept. of Mathematics, University of Arizona, Tucson, AZ 85721.

DeVITO, JUNE LOGAN, b. Alta, Jan. 12, 28; m. 53; c. 4. NEUROANATOMY, NEUROPHYSIOLOGY. B.A, Univ. B.C, 47, M.A, 49; fels, Univ. Wash, 49-53, Ph.D.(physiol), 54. Asst. embryol. & physiol, Univ. B.C, 47-49; res. assoc. physiol. & biophys, SCH. MED, UNIV. WASH, 54-55, acting instr, 55-58, res. instr, 58-60, instr, 60-63, res. instr. neurosurg, 63-65, RES. ASST. PROF. NEUROL. SURG, 65-, RES. STAFF MEM, REGIONAL PRIMATE RES. CTR, 71- U.S. Pub. Health Serv. fel, 61-62. AAAS; Am. Asn. Anat; Soc. Neurosci. Central pathways subserving weight discrimination; effects of sensory stimulation on activity; supplementary motor area projections; corticothalamic connections of sensory cortices; septo-hippocampal pathways. Address: Regional Primate Research Center, University of Washington, Seattle, WA 98105.

DEVLIN, H(ENRY) B(LESSING), b. Detroit, Mich, June 21, 14; m. 41; c. 2. BIOCHEMISTRY. B.S, Wayne, 37, M.S, 39; Lever Brothers fel, Iowa, 39-42; Ph.D.(biochem), 42. SR. RES. IMMUNOLOGIST, PARKE, DAVIS & CO, 42. Antigens and antibodies. Address: 1133 Kensington Rd, Grosse Point Park, MI 48230.

DEVLIN, J(OSEPH) PAUL, b. Hale, Colo, Jan. 11, 35; m. 57; c. 3. PHYSICAL CHEMISTRY. B.S, Regis Col.(Colo), 56; Ph.D.(phys. chem), Kansas State, 60. Res. assoc. spectros, Minnesota, 60-61; asst. prof. PHYS. CHEM, OKLA. STATE UNIV, 61-66, assoc. prof, 66-70, PROF, 70- Atomic Energy Comn. grant, 66-67. Am. Chem. Soc. Vibrational spectra and structures of molten salts; disordered crystals, matrix isolated high temperature species, and solid state charge transfer complexes. Address: Dept. of Chemistry, Oklahoma State University, Stillwater, OK 74074.

DEVLIN, LEO JOHN, b. San Francisco, Calif, Feb. 9, 08; m. 36; c. 4. AERONAUTICAL ENGINEERING. B.A, Stanford, 30, Aeronaut. Eng, 32. Engr, Northrop Div, DOUGLAS AIRCRAFT CO, INC, 33-58, chief engr, El Segundo Div, 58-61, V.PRES. & TECH. DIR. eng. & prod. develop, Aircraft Div, 61-65, AIRCRAFT GROUP, LONG BEACH, 65- Fel. Am. Inst. Aeronaut. & Astronaut. Aero engineering. Address: 1322 San Pablo Dr, Lake San Marcos, CA 92069.

DEVLIN, RICHARD GERALD, JR, b. Philadelphia, Pa, Aug. 4, 42; m. 65; c. 1. ZOOLOGY, IMMUNOLOGY. B.A, LaSalle Col, 64; M.S, Villanova, 66; Ph.D. (immunol), Maryland, 69. Asst. biol, Villanova, 64-66; zool, Maryland, 66-69; Nat. Insts. Health fel. biol, Pennsylvania, 69-71; SR. SCIENTIST. BIOCHEM, MEAD JOHNSON CO, 71- AAAS. Developmental, transplantation and radiation biology; cell physiology; cellular immunology. Address: Biochemistry Research Dept, Mead Johnson Co, Evansville, IN 47721.

DEVLIN, ROBERT M(ARTIN), b. U.S. citizen; Oct. 13, 31; m; c. 3. PLANT PHYSIOLOGY, BIOCHEMISTRY. B.S, State Univ. N.Y. Albany, 59; M.A, Dartmouth Col, 61; Ph.D.(biol), Maryland, 63. Asst. prof. PLANT PHYSIOL, N.Dak. State Univ, 63-65; ASSOC. PROF, AGR. EXP. STA, LAB. EXP. BIOL, UNIV. MASS, 65- U.S.A, 53-54. Plant hormone effects, herbicide metabolism and nature of seed dormancy. Address: Dept. of Plant Physiology, Lab. of Experimental Biology, Agricultural Experiment Station, University of Massachusetts, Cranberry Station, East Wareham, MA 02538.

DEVLIN, SHAUN S, b. Detroit, Mich, June 24, 37; m. 57; c. 3. SOLID STATE PHYSICS. B.S, Chicago, 57; M.S, Case, 61, Ph.D.(physics), 64. Physicist, semiconductor res, electronic res. div, Clevite Corp, 57-64; mem. tech. staff, Bell Tel. Labs, Inc, 64-67; PHYSICIST, FORD SCI. LAB, 67- Am. Phys. Soc. Electrical and optical properties of semiconductors and the properties of their defects; computerized control systems. Address: Ford Scientific Lab, P.O. Box 2053, Dearborn, MI 48121.

DEVLIN, THOMAS J(OSEPH), JR, b. Jenkintown, Pa, Aug. 23, 35; m. 62; c. 2. PHYSICS. B.A, La Salle Col, 57; M.A, California, Berkeley, 59, Ph.D.(physics), 61. Res. assoc. PHYSICS, Lawrence Radiation Lab, California, Berkeley, 61-62; instr, Princeton, 62-65, asst. prof, 65-67, res. assoc. Princeton-Pa. Accelerator, 62-67; ASSOC. PROF, RUTGERS UNIV, 67- Vis. scientist, C.E.R.N, Geneva, 70-71. Am. Phys. Soc. Elementary particles; experimental high energy physics of strong interactions of mesons and nucleons. Address: Dept. of Physics, Rutgers, The State University, New Brunswick, NJ 08903.

DEVLIN, THOMAS M(cKEOWN), b. Philadelphia, Pa, June 29, 29; m. 53; c. 2. BIOCHEMISTRY. B.A, Pennsylvania, 53; Nat. Sci. Found. fel, Hopkins, 54-55, U.S. Pub. Health Serv. fel, 55-57, Ph.D.(physiol. chem), 57. Asst. org. chem, Sharples Corp, Pa, 47-49; asst. biophysics, Johnson Found, Pennsylvania, 49-53; res. assoc. enzyme chem, Merck Inst, 57-61, sect. head, biol. cancer res, 61-66, dir. enzymol, 66-67; PROF. & CHMN. DEPT. BIOL. CHEM, HAHNEMANN MED. COL. & HOSP, 67- Vis. res. scientist, Brussels, 64-65. AAAS; Am. Soc. Biol. Chemists; Am. Asn. Cancer Res; Biochem. Soc; Am. Soc. Cell Biol; Am. Chem. Soc; N.Y. Acad. Sci. Enzyme chemistry; oxidative phosphorylation and electron transport; mitochondrial physiology and biogenesis; biochemical control mechanisms; intermediary metabolism of malignant tissues; cancer chemotherapy; spectrophotometric techniques. Address: Dept. of Biological Chemistry, Hahnemann Medical College, 235 N. 15th St, Philadelphia, PA 19102.

DeVOE, ARTHUR GERARD, b. Seattle, Wash, Mar. 24, 09; m. 39; c. 3. OPHTHALMOLOGY. A.B, Yale, 31; M.D, Cornell, 35; D.M.Sc, Columbia, 40. Assoc. OPHTHAL, col. physicians & surgeons, Columbia, 40-50; prof, post-grad. med. sch, N.Y. Univ-Bellevue Med. Ctr, & dir. eye serv, Bellevue & Univ. Hosps, 50-59; prof, COL. PHYSICIANS & SURGEONS, COLUMBIA UNIV, 59-70, EDWARD SHARKNESS PROF, 70-, CHMN. DEPT, 59- Dir. inst. ophthal, Presby. Hosp, 59- Med.C, 42-46, Maj. Am. Med. Asn; Am. Ophthal. Soc; Am. Acad. Ophthal. & Otolaryngol; Am. Col. Surg; Asn. Res. Vision & Ophthal; Ophthal. Soc. Diseases of the eye. Address: Dept. of Ophthalmology, College of Physicians & Surgeons, Columbia University, 635 W. 165th St, New York, NY 10032.

De VOE, CHARLES F(REEMAN), b. Freeport, Ill, Apr. 5, 09; m. 34; c. 2. PHYSICS. Ph.B, Wisconsin, 30, Ph.M, 32, Ph.D.(physics), 36. Physicist, Corning Glass Works, 36-47, mgr, pilot plants, 48-53, dir. mfg. staffs, 54-56, ceramic res, 57-63, mgr, staff res. optical dept, 64-71; RETIRED. AAAS; fel. Am. Chem. Soc; Am. Ceramic Soc; Am. Phys. Soc; Brit. Soc.

Glass Technol; Optical Soc. Am. Glass melting; ceramics; refractories; optical materials and application. Address: 3 Overbrook Dr, Painted Post, NY 14870.

DeVOE, HOWARD J(OSSELYN), b. White Plains, N.Y, Dec. 10, 32; m. 63; c. 3. PHYSICAL CHEMISTRY. A.B, Oberlin Col, 55; Ph.D.(chem), Harvard, 60. Univ. fel, California, Berkeley, 60-61; res. chemist, phys. chem. sect, Nat. Inst. Ment. Health, 61-68, ASSOC. PROF. CHEM, UNIV. MD, COLLEGE PARK, 68- AAAS; Am. Chem. Soc. Molecular interactions in nucleic acids; dye aggregation; hydrophobic interactions; theory of optical properties of molecular aggregates and biopolymers. Address: Dept. of Chemistry, University of Maryland, College Park, MD 20742.

DeVOE, IRVING W(OODROW), b. Brewer, Maine, Oct. 4, 36; m. 60; c. 4. MICROBIOLOGY, ELECTRON MICROSCOPY. B.S, Aurora Col, 64; Nat. Insts. Health fel, Univ. Ore, 64-68, Ph.D.(microbiol), 68. Fel, Macdonald Col, McGill Univ, 68-69; ASST. PROF. MICROBIOL, Aurora Col, 69-70; MACDONALD COL, McGILL UNIV, 70- Res. assoc, Argonne Nat. Lab, 69-70; consult, shoreline surv, Fisheries Res. Bd. Can, 71. U.S.A.R, 54-57; U.S.N, 57-61. AAAS; Am. Soc. Microbiol; Can. Soc. Microbiol. Bacterial physiology; role of inorganic ions in metabolism of marine bacteria; carrier mediated transport; membrane-cell wall interactions during phagocytosis; water quality. Address: Dept. of Microbiology, Macdonald College, Que, Can.

DEVOE, JAMES R(OLLO), b. Sterling, Ill, Sept. 27, 28; m. 56; c. 3. RADIOCHEMISTRY. B.S, Illinois, 50; M.S, Minnesota, 52; Ph.D.(chem), Michigan, 59. Consult, subcmt. radiochem, Nat. Acad. Sci-Nat. Res. Coun, 60-61; phys. chemist, anal. & inorg. chem. div, NAT. BUR. STANDARDS, 61-63, CHIEF radiochem. sect, anal. chem. div, 63-66, activation anal. sect. & radiochem. anal. sect, 66-69, TECH. SUPPORT GROUP & RADIOCHEM. ANAL. SECT, 69- Mem. subcmt. low background counting, Nat. Acad. Sci-Nat. Res. Coun, 63-69; working cmt. lunar probe, NASA, 64-65. Nat. Bur. Standards distinguished serv. award, 64. U.S.N.R, 52-56, Lt. Am. Chem. Soc. Radioisotope techniques in analysis; Mossbauer effect; hot atom chemistry; activation analysis; low level radiation detection; analytical radiochemistry; laboratory automation with digital computers. Address: 17708 Parkridge Dr, Gaithersburg, MD 20760.

DEVOE, ROBERT, b. White Plains, N.Y, Oct. 7, 34; m. 60; c. 2. PHYSIOLOGY, BIOPHYSICS. A.B, Oberlin Col, 56; Ph.D.(biophys), Rockefeller Inst, 61. Instr. PHYSIOL, SCH. MED, JOHNS HOPKINS UNIV, 61-64, asst. prof, 64-69, ASSOC. PROF, 69- Dir. Year I prog, off. dean, 70- AAAS; Am. Physiol. Soc; Biophys. Soc. Visual receptor excitation; electrophysiology of vision; flicker and arthropod vision. Address: School of Medicine, Johns Hopkins University, 725 N. Wolfe St, Baltimore, MD 21205.

DE VOL, LENTZ C(LINE), b. Equity, Ohio, Sept. 27, 11; m. 44; c. 4. PHYSICS. A.B, Marietta Col, 35; Laws fel, Cincinnati, 36, M.S, 39. Instr. math. & physics, Valparaiso, 46-49, asst. prof, 49-56; assoc. prof. & head dept, Iowa Wesleyan Col, 56-61; ASSOC. PROF, PHYSICS, SWEET BRIAR COL, 61- U.S.A, 42-46. Am. Asn. Physics Teachers. Teaching of physics. Address: Dept. of Physics, Sweet Briar College, Sweet Briar, VA 24595.

DE VOLPI, ALEXANDER, b. New York, N.Y, Feb. 28, 31; m. 55; c. 4. NUCLEAR PHYSICS. B.A, Washington & Lee, 53; M.S, Va. Polytech, 58, Ph.D.(physics), 67; Int. Inst. Nuclear Sci. & Eng, Argonne Nat. Lab, 58-60. PHYSICIST, ARGONNE NAT. LAB, 60- U.S.N.R, 53-56, Res, 56-, Lt. Comdr. AAAS; Am. Phys. Soc. Nuclear parameters of use in nuclear reactor physics design, especially fission parameters; development of a fast neutron hodoscope used in nuclear reactor safety research; environmental aspects of nuclear power; relationships between science and society. Address: Reactor Analysis & Safety Division, D208, Argonne National Lab, Argonne, IL 60439.

DEVONS, SAMUEL, b. Bangor, N.Wales, U.K, Sept. 30, 14; m. 38; c. 4. PHYSICS. B.A, Cambridge, 35, M.A, 39, Ph.D.(physics), 39; hon. M.Sc, Manchester, 59. Sci. officer, Air Ministry, ministry supply, 39-45; fel. & dir. studies, Cambridge, 46-49; prof. physics, Imp. Col, London, 50-55; Langworthy prof. & dir. phys. labs, Manchester, 55-60; PROF. PHYSICS, COLUMBIA UNIV, 60-, chmn. dept, 63-67. Lectr, Cambridge, 46-49; UNESCO tech. aide, mission to Argentina, 57; vis. prof, Columbia, 59-60; Royal Soc. vis. prof, Andhra Univ, India, 67-68; dir, Barnard-Columbia Hist. Physics Lab, vis. prof, Barnard Col, 69- With RAF, 44-45. Am. Phys. Soc; fel Royal Soc; fel. Brit. Inst. Physics & Phys. Soc.(v.pres, 53-55, Rutherford medal & prize, 70). Radar; nuclear and elementary particle physics; history of physics. Address: Dept. of Physics, Columbia University, New York, NY 10027.

DEVONSHIRE, LEONARD N(ORTON), b. Wichita Falls, Tex, Oct. 26, 24; m. 52. INORGANIC & ANALYTICAL CHEMISTRY. B.S, Oklahoma, 49, M.S, 51, Ph.D.(chem), 54. Asst. prof. CHEM, Alabama, 54-58; assoc. prof, UNIV. TULSA, 58-66, PROF, 66-, acting head dept, 58-66. Res.partic, Oak Ridge Inst. Nuclear Studies, summer 55. U.S.A, 43-46. Am. Chem. Soc. Chemistry of fluorophosphates and reactions in nonaqueous media. Address: 1266 E. 28th St, Tulsa, OK 74114.

DEVOR, ARTHUR W(ILLIAM), b. El Paso Co, Colo, Apr. 13, 11; m. 38; c. 2. BIOCHEMISTRY. B.S, McPherson Col, 35; M.S, Kans. State Col, 37; Ph.D.(biochem), Southern California, 47. Asst, Kans. State Col, 36-41; instr. chem, Erie Ctr, Univ. Pittsburgh, 41-43; Adelphi Col, 43-45; asst. biochem, Southern California, 45-46; assoc. South Dakota, 47; prof. chem. & head dept, N.Dak. State Teachers Col, Minot, 47-48; asst. prof. biochem, S.Dak. State Col, 48-50, assoc. prof, 50-51; asst. prof. PHYSIOL. CHEM. COL. MED, OHIO STATE UNIV, 52-57, assoc. prof, 57-71, PROF, 71- AAAS; Am. Chem. Soc. Oxidation of monosaccharides; dehydration of bile acids; blood proteins; chemical education; sulfonated alpha-naphthol as carbohydrate test; dialysis; lyophilization; cerebrosides; sulfonated resorcinol as carbohydrate test; studies on nondialyzable materials in human urine. Address: Ohio State University College of Medicine, 1645 Neil Ave, Columbus, OH 43210.

DEVORE, ARCHIE L(EE), b. Mulberry Grove, Ill, July 3, 42; m. 68; c. 1. REPRODUCTIVE PHYSIOLOGY. B.S, Univ. Ill, Urbana, 65, Ph.D.(dairy sci), Univ. Ill, Urbana-Champaign, 70; Allied Chem. Found. fel, Purdue Univ, 66-68, M.S, 67. ASST. PROF. AGR, EAST. KY. UNIV, 70- Am. Soc. Animal Sci; Am. Dairy Sci. Asn. Physiological control mechanisms responsible for the onset of labor and parturition in mammals; factors influencing length of gestation in mammals; physiology of lactation. Address: Dept. of Agriculture, Eastern Kentucky University, Richmond, KY 40475.

DeVORE, GEORGE W(ARREN), b. Laramie, Wyo, Apr. 29, 24; m. 52; c. 2. GEOLOGY. B.A, Wyoming, 46; Ph.D.(geol), Chicago, 52. Instr. GEOL, Chicago, 50-54, asst. prof, 54-60; assoc. prof, FLA. STATE UNIV, 60-64, PROF. & CHMN. DEPT, 64- Geologist, U.S. Geol. Surv, 48-60. U.S.A.A.F, 42-45. Mineral. Soc. Am; Am. Clay Minerals Soc. Geochemistry and petrology; the distribution of elements in minerals and minerals in rocks. Address: Dept. of Geology, Florida State University, Tallahassee, FL 32306.

de VOS, ANTOON, b. Laren, Netherlands, July 13, 17; nat. Can; m. 48; c. 3. VERTEBRATE ZOOLOGY. Dipl, Trop. Agr. Col, Holland, 38; Chicago Nat. Hist. Mus. fel, Wisconsin, 46, M.Sc, 47, Ph.D.(zool), 51. Tech. asst. zool. mus, Indonesia, 39-43; asst. zool, Wisconsin, 46, 51; biologist, Ont. Dept. Lands & Forests, 47-55; assoc. prof. wildlife mgt. Ont. Agr. Col, 55-64; wildlife ecologist, Food & Agr. Orgn, UN, 64; prof. vert. ecol, Univ. Waterloo, 64-67, dir. planning & resources inst, 66-67; head wildlife res. div, E.African Agr. & Forestry Res. Orgn. & wildlife off, FOOD & AGR. ORGN, UN, 67-68, regional wildlife & nat. parks off. for Africa, 68-70, CHIEF WILDLIFE SECT, FOREST RESOURCES DIV, 70- Am. Soc. Mammal; Wildlife Soc; Am. Ornith. Union; Ecol. Soc. Am; Soil Conserv. Soc. Am; Can. Soc. Wildlife & Fisheries Biol. Ecology; behavior and management of the higher vertebrates; biogeography; resources development. Address: Wildlife Section, Forest Resources Division, Food & Agriculture Organization, United Nations, Via Delle Terme di Caracalla, Rome, Italy.

DEVOY, ROBERT J, b. Brooklyn, N.Y, Dec. 26, 28; m. 61; c. 4. ELECTRICAL ENGINEERING. B.E.E, Polytech. Inst. Brooklyn, 51; Pittsburgh, 52-55. Control engr, BETTIS ATOMIC POWER LAB, WESTINGHOUSE ELEC. CORP, 51-56, supvr. control eng, 56-62, mgr. control eng. & plant anal, 62-66, PWR Proj. Plant Eng, 66-70, SGA prog. mgr, 70-71, DEPT. MGR, OPERATING PLANTS, POWER PLANT ENG, 71- Sr. mem. Instrument Soc. Am; Inst. Elec. & Electronics Eng. Control, instrumentation and analysis for large atomic power plants of the pressurized water type. Address: Operating Plants, Power Plant Engineering, Bettis Atomic Power Lab, P.O. Box 79, West Mifflin, PA 15230.

DE VRIES, DALE BYRON, b. Zillah, Wash, Apr. 21, 36; m. 59; c. 2. PHYSICAL CHEMISTRY, PHYSICS. A.B, Calvin Col, 58; Ph.D.(phys. chem), Iowa State, 64. Mem. tech. staff microelectronics, TEX. INSTRUMENTS, INC, 64-70, SECT. HEAD PROCESS TECHNOL, 70- AAAS; Am. Chem. Soc; Electrochem. Soc. Radiochemistry, especially radiation chemistry and hot atom chemistry; solid state diffusion and photoresist as related to integrated circuit fabrication; ion implantation techniques for semiconductors. Address: Texas Instruments, Inc, P.O. Box 5012, Dallas, TX 75222.

DEVRIES, DAVID J, b. Grand Rapids, Mich, Sept. 22, 42; m. 65. MATHEMATICS. A.B, Calvin Col, 65; Nat. Defense Ed. Act fel, Pa. State, 65-69, M.A, 66, Ph.D.(math), 69. Asst. prof. math, Hobart & William Smith Cols, 69-71; ASST. PROF. & CHMN. DEPT. MATH. & PHYSICS, MARS HILL COL, 71- Am. Math. Soc; Math. Asn. Am. General prime number theory; algebraic number theory. Address: Dept. of Mathematics, Mars Hill College, Mars Hill, NC 28754.

DeVRIES, DONALD M, b. Royal Oak, Mich, Nov. 27, 23; m. 45; c. 2. PHYSICAL & ANALYTICAL CHEMISTRY. B.A, Walla Walla Col, 50; M.S, Idaho, 52. Phys. chemist, Shell Chem. Co, 52-58, anal. chemist, 58-64, supvr. anal. serv, 64-66, lab. mgr, N.J, 66-68, RES. SUPVR. RESIDUE CHEM, SHELL DEVELOP. CO, 68- U.S.A.A.F, 43-45, Sgt. Am. Chem. Soc; assoc. referee, Asn. Off. Anal. Chem. Crystal growth rates and habit modification in $(NH_4)_2SO_4$ and $(NH_4)_2HPO_4$; analytical methodology in pesticide residues in environmental samples; cross contamination in pesticide formulations; pesticide chemistry including metabolism. Address: Biological Research Center, Shell Development Co, P.O. Box 4248, Modesto, CA 95352.

DeVRIES, FREDERICK WILLIAM, b. New York, N.Y, Feb. 5, 30; m. 59; c. 3. CHEMICAL ENGINEERING. A.B, Columbia, 49, B.S, 50, M.S, 51. From jr. engr. to prod. asst, E.I. DU PONT DE NEMOURS & CO, INC, 51-53, process supvr, 53-55, sr. supvr. & engr, 56-61, supvr, 61-64, semiworks supvr, 64-66, eng. supvr, 66-71, PROD. SPECIALIST, 71- Am. Chem. Soc; Am. Inst. Chem. Eng. Tetrahydrofuran, methyl and methylene chloride; chemical reactions under extremes of temperature and pressure; polymerization reactions; process design and economic evaluation polyvinyl alcohol. Address: Electrochemicals Dept, Chestnut Run Lab, E.I. du Pont de Nemours & Co, Inc, Wilmington, DE 19898.

DE VRIES, JOHN E(DWARD), b. Fenton, Ill, Oct, 4, 19; m. 46; c. 2. CHEMISTRY. A.B, Hope Col, 41; fel, Illinois, 42-44, Ph.D.(chem), 44. Asst, chem, Illinois, 41-42; res. chemist, Manhattan proj, Standard Oil Co, Ind, 44-46; asst. prof. chem, Kans. State, 46-48, assoc. prof, 48-51, head gen. anal. res. sect, Naval Ord. Test Sta, 51-55; sr. chemist & mgr. anal. serv, Stanford Res. Inst, 55-64; PROF. CHEM, CALIF. STATE COL. HAYWARD, 64- Lectr, California, Berkeley, summer, 64, 66; Stanford, 68. AAAS; Am. Chem. Soc. Organic analytical reagents; spectroscopy in chemical analysis; spectrophotometry; analytical applications of phenanthrolinium and related compounds; analysis of rocket propellants; nitrogen compounds; polarography; analysis of atmosphere; pesticide residue analysis; gas chromatography. Address: 886 Garland Dr, Palo Alto, CA 94303.

DeVRIES, K. LAWRENCE, b. Ogden, Utah, Oct. 27, 33; m. 58; c. 2. MECHANICAL & MATERIALS ENGINEERING, PHYSICS. B.S, Utah, 59, Ph.D.(physics), 62. Design engr. hydraulics, Convair Aircraft, Tex, 57; asst. prof. MECH. ENG, UNIV. UTAH, 60-65, assoc. prof, 65-68, PROF, 68-, CHMN. DEPT, 70- Consult, 60- AAAS; Am. Soc. Mech. Eng; Am. Phys.

Soc; Soc. Exp. Stress Anal. Mechanical properties of solids; rock mechanics; polymer science; dental & medical engineering. Address: Dept. of Mechanical Engineering, University of Utah, Salt Lake City, UT 84112.

DE VRIES, RICHARD N, b. Cortland, Nebr, May 24, 32; m. 58; c. 2. ENVIRONMENTAL ENGINEERING, WATER RESOURCES. B.S, Univ. Nebr, 58, M.S, 63; Nat. Defense Educ. Act fel, Utah State Univ, 66-67, Ph.D.(water resources eng), 69. Draftsman, Lincoln Tel. & Tel. Co, 54; storage engr, North. Natural Gas Co, Nebr, 58-60; dist. engr. & mgr, Sanit. Dist. 1, Lancaster County, 60-62; asst. prof. CIVIL ENG, Univ. Nebr, Lincoln, 63-66, 68-69; ASSOC. PROF, OKLA. STATE UNIV, 69- Co-investr, res. grants, 64-66; prin. investr. res. grants, Univ. Nebr, 68-69; Okla State Univ, 69-70 & Okla. Water Resources Res. Inst, 70-71. U.S.A, 51-54, Sgt. Am. Soc. Civil Eng; Nat. Soc. Prof. Eng; Am. Geophys. Union; Am. Water Resources Asn; Am. Soc. Eng. Educ. Bioenvironmental and water resources engineering; hydrology; hydraulics; urban planning. Address: Dept. of Bioenvironmental Engineering, School of Civil Engineering, Oklahoma State University, Stillwater, OK 74074.

DeVRIES, R(OBERT) C(HARLES), b. Evansport, Ohio, Oct. 10, 22; m. 43; c. 3. MINERALOGY. B.A, DePauw, 48; Ph.D.(mineral), Pa. State, 53. Asst. mineral, Pa. State, 50-53, res. assoc, 53-54; mem. tech. staff, metall. & ceramic div, res. lab, Gen. Elec. Co, 54-61; assoc. prof. ceramics, Rensselaer Polytech, 61-65; MEM. TECH. STAFF, METALL. & CERAMIC DIV, RES. LAB, GEN. ELEC. CO, 65- U.S.A.A.F, 43. Fel. Mineral. Soc. Am; fel. Am. Ceramic Soc; Am. Chem. Soc; Am. Geochem. Soc. Phase equilibria studies at high temperatures and pressures and crystal-chemical relationships in silicate, titanate and fluoride systems of geologic and ceramic interest; crystal growth; microstructure; property relationships in ceramics. Address: General Electric Research & Development Center, The Knolls, Schenectady, NY 12301.

DEVRIES, RONALD CLIFFORD, b. Chicago, Ill, Dec. 4, 36; m. 63; c. 3. ELECTRICAL ENGINEERING, COMPUTER SCIENCE. B.S, Northwestern, 59; M.S, Arizona, 62, Ph.D.(elec. eng), 68. Coop. student, Wells-Gardner & Co, 56-58; jr. engr, data-stor div, Cook Elec. Co, 59-60; asst, Arizona, 61-64; ASST. PROF. ELEC. ENG, San Diego State Col, 64-66; UNIV. N.MEX, 67- NASA-Am. Soc. Eng. Ed. fel, NASA Electronic Res. Center, Mass, summer 68. Inst. Elec. & Electronics Eng. Logic design; minimization, computer organization and arithmetic; iterative circuits and cellular arrays; decomposition. Address: Dept. of Electrical Engineering & Computer Science, University of New Mexico, Albuquerque, NM 87106.

DeVRIES, T(HOMAS), b. Smilde, Netherlands, July 15, 01; nat; m. 31, 39; c. 2. ANALYTICAL CHEMISTRY. A.B, Hope Col, 23; M.S, Illinois, 24, Ph.D.(chem), 26. Instr. chem, Purdue Univ, 26-27, asst. prof, 27-34, assoc. prof, 34-40, prof, 40-69; RETIRED. Mem. staff, Counseling Off, Sch. Sci, Purdue Univ; sect. leader, Manhattan Proj, Columbia Univ, 43-44. Assoc. Optical Soc. Am; Am. Chem. Soc. Electrode potentials; heat capacity of vapors; chemical spectroscopy; physico-chemical methods of analysis; polarography in nonaqueous solvents and fused salts. Address: 112 Meridian St, W. Lafayette, IN 47906.

DeVRIES, VERN GORDON, b. Zillah, Wash, Oct. 13, m. 60; c. 4. ORGANIC CHEMISTRY. A.B, Calvin Col, 60; Kettering Found. fel, Ohio State, 62-63, Union Carbide Corp. fel, 64-65, Ph.D.(org. chem), 65. Asst. org. chem, Ohio State, 60-61; RES. CHEMIST, LEDERLE LABS, AM. CYANAMID CO, 65- Am. Chem. Soc. Alkylation of α and β-unsaturated ketones with polymethylene dibromides. Address: 425 Farview St, Ridgewood, NJ 07450.

DE VRIEZE, JERRY D, b. Austin, Minn, May 11, 42; m. 69. ORGANIC CHEMISTRY. B.A, Augsburg Col, 64; Ph.D.(org. chem), Mich. State Univ, 68. RES. CHEMIST, DOW CHEM. CO, 69- Am. Chem. Soc; Sci. Res. Soc. Am. Cellulose chemistry, especially reactions of cellulose to produce useful products. Address: Dow Chemical Co, 1604 Bldg, Midland, MI 48640.

DEW, JESS (EDWARD), b. Okemah, Okla, July 18, 20; m. 44; c. 3. CHEMICAL ENGINEERING. B.S, Oklahoma, 43; S.M, Mass. Inst. Tech, 48. Asst. chem. engr, Humble Oil & Ref. Co, 43-47; chem. engr, Stanolind Oil & Gas Co, 48-52; sr. engr, Chem. Co. Div, Deere & Co, 52-53, asst. chief engr, 53-56, chief engr, 56-61, v.pres, 61-63, prod. supt, Planter Works Div, 63-64, gen. supt, 64-65; Helena Plant mgr, Ark-La. Gas Co, 65-67; v.pres. fertilizer opers, Ark-La. Chem. Corp, 67-69; PROJ. MGR, CHEM. CONSTRUCT. CORP, 69- Am. Inst. Chem. Eng. Process and general engineering; petrochemicals; ammonia; urea; phosphatic fertilizers. Address: Chemical Construction Corp, 320 Park Ave, New York, NY 10022.

DEW, JOHN N(ORMAN), b. Okemah, Okla, Feb. 27, 22; m. 53; c. 5. CHEMICAL ENGINEERING. B.S, Oklahoma, 43; M.S.E, Michigan, 49, Mich. Gas Asn. fel, 49-53, Ph.D.(chem. eng), 53. Res. engr, res. & develop. div, N.Mex. Sch. Mines, 43-47; prod. res, CONTINENTAL OIL CO, 53-54, sr. res. engr, 54-55, res. group leader, 55-57, supvr. res. engr, 57-61, supv. res. scientist, 61-66, asst. dir. prod. res. div, 66-67, asst. mgr. prod. res. div, RES. & DEVELOP. DEPT, 67-68, MGR. PROJ. DEVELOP, 68- Asst, Oklahoma, 47-48. Off. Sci. Res. & Develop, 43-47. Am. Soc. Petrol. Eng; Am. Inst. Chem. Eng. Reaction kinetics; technological forecasting research planning and coordination project evaluations; recovery of petroleum. Address: 800 Dalewood Ave, Ponca City, OK 74601.

DEW, WILLIAM CALLAND, b. Belle Valley, Ohio, Dec. 30, 16; m. 42; c. 2. DENTISTRY. D.D.S, Ohio State, 41. Intern prosthodontics, COL. DENT, OHIO STATE UNIV, 41-42, instr, 42-44, asst. prof, 44-48, assoc. prof, 48-60, PROF. DENT, 60-, asst. dean col, 64-70, ASSOC. DEAN COL, 70- Mem, Callahan Mem. Comn. Am. Dent. Asn; Am. Col. Dent. Fixed and removable prosthodontics; operative dentistry; dental materials. Address: College of Dentistry, Ohio State University, 305 W. 12th Ave, Columbus, OH 43210.

DE WAARD, DIRK, b. Hilversum, Netherlands, Feb. 5, 19; m. 50. GEOLOGY. Drs, Utrecht, 43, Sc.D.(geol), 47. Sci. assoc. GEOL, Utrecht, 47-52; prof. ordinarius, Indonesia, Bandung, 52-58; vis. lectr, California, Berkeley, 58-59; assoc. prof, SYRACUSE UNIV, 59-64, PROF, 64- Privat-docent, Utrecht, 49-52; Nat. Sci. Found. res. grants, 60-66; Guggenheim fel, 64-65. Fel. AAAS; fel. Geol. Soc. Am; fel. Mineral. Soc. Am; Am. Geophys. Union; Royal Netherlands Geol. & Mining Soc; cor. mem. Royal Netherland Acad. Sci; Geol. Soc. Finland; Norweg. Geol. Soc; German Geol. Asn. Structural and metamorphic petrology. Address: Dept. of Geology, 314 Lyman Hall, Syracuse University, Syracuse, NY 13210.

DE WALD, CHARLES G(RIFFITH), b. Baltimore, Md, July 13, 37; m. 68. OPERATIONS RESEARCH, APPLIED MATHEMATICS. B.E.S, Johns Hopkins Univ, 60, Ph.D.(elec. eng. & opers. res), 68. ASST. PROF. INDUST. ENG, STATE UNIV. N.Y. BUFFALO, 68- Network analysis and optimization; mathematical programming. Address: Dept. of Industrial Engineering, Faculty of Engineering & Applied Science, State University of New York at Buffalo, Buffalo, NY 14214.

DeWALD, (ARTHUR) EUGENE, b. Emlenton, Pa, Apr. 24, 24; m. 47; c. 4. ORGANIC CHEMISTRY. B.S, Allegheny Col, 47; Ph.D.(chem), Minnesota, 54. Chemist, SMITH KLINE & FRENCH LABS, 47-49, 54-62, dept. mgr, QUAL. CONTROL, 62-67, dir, 67-70, V.PRES, 70- Mem. Nat. Formulary Bd, 70-75. Am. Chem. Soc; Am. Pharmaceut. Asn. U.S.A, 44-46. Steric effect of methylene groups. Address: 1448 Jericho Rd, Abington, PA 19001.

DeWALD, HORACE A(LBERT), b. Emlenton, Pa, Oct. 25, 22; m. 55; c. 6. ORGANIC CHEMISTRY. B.S, Allegheny Col, 44; Eastman Kodak fel, Illinois, 49-50, Ph.D.(chem), 50. Chemist org. synthesis, Eastman Kodak Co, 44-46; res. chemist synthetic detergents, Gen. Aniline & Film Corp, 50-52; Parke Davis & Co. fel. med. chem, Mellon Inst, 52-57; res. chemist, PARKE DAVIS & CO, 57-66, SR. RES. CHEMIST, 66- Sig.C, U.S.A, 46-47. Am. Chem. Soc. Addition of Grignard reagents to olefinic hydrocarbons; synthesis of new detergents; preparation of potential chemotherapeutic agents. Address: Research Dept, Parke Davis & Co, Ann Arbor, MI 48104.

DEWALD, ROBERT REINHOLD, b. Twining, Mich, Aug. 31, 35; m. 63; c. 1. PHYSICAL CHEMISTRY. B.S, Central Michigan, 58; Ph.D.(chem), Mich. State, 63. Asst. prof. CHEM, TUFTS UNIV, 65-70, ASSOC. PROF, 70- U.S.A, 63-65, 1st Lt. Am. Chem. Soc. Kinetics of fast reactions in solution; properties of metal nonaqueous solutions; kinetics of microbial systems. Address: Dept. of Chemistry, Tufts University, Medford, MA 02155.

DE WALL, GORDON, b. Muskegon, Mich, Feb. 6, 41; m. 63; c. 2. ORGANIC CHEMISTRY. B.S, Calvin Col, 62; M.S, Michigan, 64, Allied Chem. Co, Petrol. Res. Found. & Am. Cyanamid fels, 64-67, Ph.D.(chem), 67. Res. chemist, BURDICK & JACKSON LABS, INC, 67-70, RES. MGR, 70- Am. Chem. Soc. Synthesis of organic compounds, especially nitrogen heterocycles, hydrazines, diamines and tetramines. Address: 1752 Kregel Ave, Muskegon, MI 49442.

DeWALL, RICHARD A, b. Appleton, Minn, Dec. 16, 26; c. 3. THORACIC & CARDIOVASCULAR SURGERY. B.A, Minnesota, 49, B.S, 50, M.B, 52, M.D, 53, M.S, 61. Instr. SURG, Minnesota, 59-62, asst. prof, 62; prof. & chmn. dept, Chicago Med. Sch. & Mt. Sinai Hosp, 62-66; CHIEF SURG, COX HEART INST, 66-; COORD. SURG. RESIDENCY, KETTERING HOSP, 66- Estab. investr, Am. Heart Asn, 60-65. U.S.N, 45; U.S.P.U.H.S, 52-53. Am. Med. Asn; Am. Col. Surg; Soc. Univ. Surg; Am. Asn. Thoracic Surg; Am. Col. Chest Physicians. Open heart surgery. Address: Dept. of Surgery, Cox Heart Institute, 3525 Southern Blvd, Kettering, OH 45429.

DeWALLE, DAVID RUSSELL, b. St. Louis, Mo, June 18, 42; m. 65; c. 3. HYDROLOGY, METEOROLOGY. B.S, Univ. Mo-Columbia, 64, M.S, 66; Ph.D.(watershed mgt), Colo. State Univ, 69. ASST. PROF. FOREST HYDROL, PA. STATE UNIV, 69- Am. Geophys. Union; Soc. Am. Foresters; Am. Meteorol. Soc. Water and energy cycling in natural systems with applications to forest runoff, forest evaporation and thermal pollution of rivers. Address: Institute for Research on Land & Water Resources, Research Bldg. A, Pennsylvania State University, University Park, PA 16802.

DeWALT, CURTIS W, b. Homestead, Pa, Sept. 17, 17; m. 44; c. 4. ORGANIC CHEMISTRY. B.A, Ohio Wesleyan, 40; M.Sc, Ohio State, 42, Ph.D.(org. chem), 48. Staff mem, coal res. lab, Carnegie Inst. Tech, 48-51; fel, Mellon Inst, 51-58; sr. fel, 58-62; MEM. STAFF RES, PA. INDUST. CHEM. CORP, 62- U.S.N.R, 42-45. Am. Chem. Soc. Antibiotic structures; coal chemicals; resins and related products. Address: Pennsylvania Industrial Chemical Corp, 120 N. State St, Clairton, PA 15025.

DeWAMES, ROGER, b. Menin, Belgium, Dec. 9, 31; U.S. citizen; m. 56; c. 3. PHYSICS. B.S, St. Mary's (Tex), 56, B.A, 56; M.A, Texas Christian, 58; Ph.D.(physics), Texas A&M, 61. MEM. TECH. STAFF THEORET. PHYSICS, SCIENCE CTR, N.AM. AVIATION, INC, 61- Fel. Am. Phys. Soc; Sci. Res. Soc. Am. Solid state physics, molecular spectroscopy. Address: Science Center, North American Aviation, Inc, 1049 Camino Dos Rios, Thousand Oaks, CA 91360.

DEWAN, EDMOND M, b. Forest Hills, N.Y, Feb. 17, 31; m. 59; c. 2. THEORETICAL PHYSICS, APPLIED MATHEMATICS. B.S, Duke, 53; Ph.D.(theoret. physics), Yale, 57. Physicist, microwave physics lab, Air Force Cambridge Res. Labs, 59-63; adj. asst. prof. biol, Brandeis, 63; THEORET. PHYSICIST, DATA SCI. LAB, U.S. AIR FORCE CAMBRIDGE RES. LABS, 64- Res. asst, Yale, 53-57; res. assoc, Brandeis, 61-63; consult. psychiat. res, Mass. Gen. Hosp, Boston, Mass, 63-64, res. assoc, 64; Harvard Med. Sch, 64. Aerospace Educ. Found. 1st Prize, Nat. Air Force Symposium Sci, 63. U.S.A.F, 57-59, Capt. AAAS; Am. Phys. Soc; Inst. Elec. & Electronics Eng; Soc. Indust. & Appl. Math; Sci. Res. Soc. Am; Am. Epilipsy Soc; Asn. Psychophysiol. Study Sleep; Am. Soc. Cybernet.(v.pres, 68-). Plasma physics; special relativity; mathematics of nonlinear oscillations and applications to physical and biological oscillations; theory of sleep and rapid eye movement state; electroencephalographic analysis; control of human ovulation cycles by photic stimulation. Address: Data Science Lab, (BRS), U.S. Air Force Cambridge Research Labs, L.G. Hanscom Field, Bedford, MA 01730.

DEWAR, JAMES P, b. Troy, N.Y, May 28, 13; m. 41; c. 2. PATHOLOGY. B.Sc, McGill, 36, M.D. & C.M, 39. Asst. dir. path. anat. & clin. path, Bender Hygenic Lab, 47-48; fel, PATH, Mem. Center Cancer & Allied

Disease, 48-49; assoc. prof, SCH. MED, UNIV. OKLA, 50-57, prof, 57-68, CLIN. PROF, 68-, dir. labs, UNIV. HOSP, 50-57, DIR. SURG. PATH, 57-, CHMN. DEPT, BAPTIST MEM. HOSP, 63- U.S.A, 41-46, Lt. Col. Col. Am. Path. Address: Dept. of Pathology, Baptist Memorial Hospital, 5800 N.W. Grand Blvd, Oklahoma City, OK 73112.

DEWAR, MICHAEL J(AMES) S(TEUART), b. Ahmednagar, India, 18; Brit. citizen; m. 44; c. 2. CHEMISTRY. B.A, Oxford, 40, Ph.D.(chem), 42, M.A, 43. Imp. Chem. Industs. res. grant, Oxford, 42-45 & fel, 45; phys. chemist, Courtaulds Ltd, 45-51; prof. CHEM. & head dept, Queen Mary Col, London, 51-59; prof, Chicago, 59-63; ROBERT A. WELCH PROF, UNIV. TEX, AUSTIN, 63- Reilly lectr, Notre Dame, 51; Tilden lectr, Brit. Chem. Soc, 54; vis. prof, Yale, 57; Falk Plant lectr, Columbia & Daines Mem. lectr, Kansas, 63; Glidden Co. lectr, West. Reserve & William Pyle Philips vis, Haverford, 64; Arthur D. Little vis. prof, Mass. Inst. Technol. & Marrhan vis. lectr, Newcastle-upon-Tyne, England, 66; Glidden Co. lectr, Kent State, 67; Grehm lectr, Eidg. Technische Hochschule, Zurich, 68; Barton lectr, Univ. Okla, 69; Kahlbaum lectr, Univ. Basel & Benjamin Rush lectr, Univ. Pa, 71; Venable lectr, Univ. N.C, Chapel Hill, 71. Consult, Monsanto Chem. Ltd, Eng, 54-59, Monsanto Co, U.S, 59- Am. Chem. Soc.(Howe award, 62); fel. Am. Acad. Arts & Sci; Brit. Chem. Soc.(hon. secy, 57-59); fel. Royal Soc. Interpretation of structure and chemical reactivity in terms of fundamental physical theory; organic, inorganic, physical and theoretical chemistry. Address: Dept. of Chemistry, University of Texas at Austin, Austin, TX 78712.

DEWAR, NORMAN E(LLISON), b. Rochester, N.Y, Nov. 14, 30; m. 55; c. 3. MICROBIOLOGY, BIOCHEMISTRY. B.S, Syracuse, 52, Atomic Energy Cmn. res. fel, 52-55; M.S, Purdue, 55, Nat. Insts. Health fel, 55-58, Ph.D. (microbiol, biochem), 59. Head div. microbiol, Vestal Labs, Inc, 59-62, dir. res, VESTAL DIV, W.R. GRACE & CO, 62-69, V.PRES. RES, 69- Chmn, disinfectant & sanitizers div, Chem. Specialists Mfrs. Asn, 71. AAAS; Am. Chem. Soc; Am. Soc. Microbiol; Am. Pub. Health Asn; Am. Asn. Contamination Control; N.Y. Acad. Sci. Physiology and biochemistry of microorganisms; chemoautotrophic carbon dioxide assimilation; development of environmental biocidal agents; environmental microbiology. Address: 7145 Westmoreland Dr, St. Louis, MO 63130.

DEWAR, WILLIAM J(AMES), b. Pembroke, Ont, Can, Mar. 27, 12; nat; m. 46; c. 1. CHEMISTRY, PLASTICS. N.Y. Univ, 32, 35; Plastics Inst. Calif, 40-41. Chemist, Petrol. Chem. Co, 30-32; sales engr, Socony Vacuum Oil Co, 35-40; asst. tech. dir, Plastics Inst, 40-48, tech. dir, 48-52; chief chemist, Flexfirm Prods, 52-54; chief engr, Standard Plastics, 54-56; tech. dir, FURANE PLASTICS, INC, 56-68, MEM. EXEC. STAFF, 68- Fel, Adhesive & Sealant Coun, v.pres, 70-71. West. Plastics Man of Year award, 61. Fel. Am. Chem. Soc; fel. Soc. Plastics Indust; fel. Soc. Plastics Eng. Chemical resistant plastics; design of hydraulic mechanisms; molding and laminating compounds; coated fabrics; mold design; epoxy resins; adhesives. Address: 8511 Keokuk Ave, Canoga Park, CA 91306.

DEWART, GILBERT, b. New York, N.Y, Jan. 14, 32. GEOPHYSICS. B.S, Mass. Inst. Tech, 53, M.S, 54; Ph.D.(geol), Ohio State Univ, 68. Seismologist, U.S.-Int. Geophys. Year Antarctic Exped, Arctic Inst. N.Am, Calif. Inst. Tech, 56-58, res. engr, seismol. lab, 58-59, exchange scientist with Soviet Antarctic Exped, 59-61, res. engr, seismol. lab, 61-63; prin. investr. SEISMOL. GRAVIMETRY, INST. POLAR STUDIES, OHIO STATE UNIV, 64, 65, 66, 67, 68, 69, 70, RES. ASSOC, 69-, adj. asst. prof. geol, 69-71. Summer field geophysicist, U.S. Geol. Surv, 62. Antarctic serv. cert, U.S. Nat. Cmt, Int. Geophys. Year, 56-58. U.S.A, 54-56, Res, 56-62. AAAS; Soc. Explor. Geophys; Seismol. Soc. Am; Am. Geophys. Union. Seismic study of earth's crust; seismic effects of underground nuclear explosions; seismic properties of glacier ice. Address: Institute of Polar Studies, 125 S. Oval Dr, Columbus, OH 43210.

DEWEER, PAUL JOSEPH, b. Avelgem, Belg, July 15, 38; m. 65; c. 3. BIOPHYSICS, PHYSIOLOGY. B.S, Cath. Univ. Louvain, 59, M.D, 63, M.S, 64; hon. fel. Belg-Am. Educ. Prog, Univ. Md, Baltimore, 65-66, fel, 65-69, Ph.D.(biophys), 69. Res. assoc. endocrinol, med. sch, Cath. Univ. Louvain, 63-65; instr. BIOPHYS, SCH. MED, UNIV. MD, BALTIMORE, 69-70, ASST. PROF, 70- Nat. Insts. Health res. career develop. award, 70- Biophys. Soc; Am. Physiol. Soc. Active transport of ions through epithelia and cell membranes; effect of hormones and metabolism. Address: Dept. of Biophysics, University of Maryland, 600 W. Redwood St, Baltimore, MD 21201.

DEWEES, ANDREW A(ARON), b. Herrin, Ill, Feb. 17, 39; m. 63; c. 3. POPULATION GENETICS. B.A, Southern Illinois, 61, M.A, 63; Nat. Insts. Health fel. & Ph.D.(genetics), Purdue, 68. Asst. prof. BIOL, SAM HOUSTON STATE UNIV, 67-71, ASSOC. PROF, 71- AAAS; Genetics Soc. Am; Biomet. Soc. Insect population genetics; role of crossing over between linked genes in evolution. Address: Dept. of Biology, Sam Houston State University, Huntsville, TX 77340.

DeWEESE, DAVID D, b. Columbus, Ohio, Mar. 16, 13; m. 38; c. 2. OTOLARYNGOLOGY, SURGERY. A.B, Michigan, 34, M.D, 38. Res. & instr. OTOLARYNGOL, med. sch, Michigan, 42-44; chmn. dept, Portland Clin, 44-62; PROF. & CHMN. DEPT, MED. SCH, UNIV. ORE, 62- Mem, bd. regents, Marylhurst Col; res. training cmt. communicative disorders, Nat. Insts. Health, 63-67; adv. coun, Nat. Inst. Neurol. Diseases & Stroke, 68-69. Dipl, Am. Bd. Otolaryngol, 43, asst. exam, 57-59, mem. bd. dir, 60- Am. Med. Asn; Am. Acad. Ophthal. & Otolaryngol.(award, 59); Am. Otol. Soc; Am. Laryngol, Rhinol. & Otol. Soc; Am. Laryngol. Asn; Am. Broncho-Esophagol. Asn. Deafness and hearing loss; vertigo and dizziness; diseases of ear, throat and nose. Address: Dept. of Otolaryngology, Medical School, University of Oregon, 3181 S.W. Sam Jackson Park Rd, Portland, OR 97201.

DeWEESE, JAMES A, b. Kent, Ohio, Apr. 5, 25; m. 50, 62; c. 6. SURGERY. Harvard, 42-43; Kent State, 43-44; M.D, Rochester, 49. Instr. SURG, MED. CTR, UNIV. ROCHESTER, 55-58, asst. prof, 58-63, assoc. prof, 63-69, PROF, 69-, SURGEON, 68-, dir. surg. res, 58-62. Asst. surgeon, Strong Mem. Hosp, 56-58, assoc. surgeon, 58-; consult, Rochester Gen. Hosp, 59-; Batavia & Bath Vet. Hosps, 63- U.S.A.R, 52-54, 1st Lt. Am. Med. Asn; Am. Col. Angiol; Soc. Vascular Surg; Soc. Univ. Surg; Int. Cardiovasc. Soc; fel. Am. Col. Surg; Am. Surg. Asn; Am. Asn. Thoracic Surg. Cardiovascular diseases; hypothermia in cardiac surgery; venous thrombosis, phlebography, arterial reconstructions and venous reconstructions. Address: Dept. of Surgery, School of Medicine & Dentistry, University of Rochester, Rochester, NY 14620.

DeWEESE, MARION S(PENCER), b. Corydon, Ind, Aug. 17, 15; m. 41; c. 3. SURGERY. A.B, Kent State, 35; M.D, Michigan, 39, M.S, 48. Instr. surg, Michigan, 48-50, asst. prof, 50-51; private practice, Calif, 51-53; assoc. prof. SURG, Michigan, 53-64, PROF. & CHMN. DEPT, MED. CTR, SCH. MED, UNIV. MO, COLUMBIA, 64- Chief surg. serv, Ann Arbor Vet. Admin. Hosp, 53-56; consult, 56-64. Mem, Am. Bd. Surg. Med.C, 41-45, Res, 39-52, Lt. Col. Am. Med. Asn; Am. Surg. Asn; fel. Am. Col. Surg. Vascular disease; diseases of aorta and peripheral arteries; thromboembolism; thermal injury and wound healing. Address: Dept. of Surgery, Med.Ctr, School of Medicine, University of Missouri, Columbia, MO 65201.

DEWEIN, LOUIS F, b. Ashtabula, Ohio, Feb. 4, 41. PHYSIOLOGY. B.S, Ohio State Univ, 62, M.S, 64, Ph.D.(physiol), 70. Instr. BIOL, CAPITAL UNIV, 68-69, ASST. PROF, 69- AAAS. Factors influencing the development of hepatic dehydrogenase activity in the perinatal rat. Address: Dept. of Biology, Capital University, 2199 E. Main St, Columbus, OH 43201.

DEWELL, E(DGAR) H(ARRISON), b. Bellevue, Nebr, Jan. 30, 23; m. 44; c. 4. PHYSICAL CHEMISTRY. B.S, Iowa State, 48, M.S, 51. Jr. res. assoc. chem, Ames Lab, Atomic Energy Comn, 51-54, res. assoc, 54-55; radiochemist, Babcock & Wilcox Co, 55-56, sect. chief chem, 56-59; assoc. chemist, Argonne Nat. Lab, 60-63; MGR. CHEM. LAB, LYNCHBURG RES. CTR, BABCOCK & WILCOX CO, 63- U.S.A.A.F, 42-47, 1st Lt. Am. Nuclear Soc; Am. Chem. Soc. Nuclear chemistry; nuclear fuel processing; reactor technology. Address: Babcock & Wilcox Co, Lynchburg Research Center, P.O. Box 1260, Lynchburg, VA 24505.

DeWET, JAN M. J, b. Vredefort, S.Africa, July 4, 27; m. 50; c. 2. GENETICS. B.Sc, Pretoria, 49; Ph.D.(genetics), California, Berkeley, 52. Instr. microbiol, Pretoria, 48-49; prfnl. officer, div. hort, Dept. Agr, S.Africa, 52-54, sr. prfnl. officer, div, bot, 54-59; asst. prof. exp. taxon, Okla. State, 60-62, assoc. prof, 62-67; PROF. CYTOGENETICS, UNIV. ILL, URBANA, 67- Nat. Res. Coun. Can. fel, 59-60; Nat. Sci. Found. res. grants, 60- S.African Cadet Corps, 40-43, 1st Lt. Bot. Soc. Am; Am. Soc. Plant Taxon; Torrey Bot. Club; Int. Asn. Plant Taxon; Asn. Taxon. Study Trop. African Flora. Experimental taxonomy of the Gramineae; experimental control of reproduction; genetics of apomixis; chromosome pairing. Address: Dept. of Agronomy, University of Illinois, Urbana, IL 61801.

DeWET, PIETER D, b. Caledon, S.Africa, Nov. 3, 27; m. 53; c. 3. NEUROSCIENCE. Dipl, Agr, Col. Agr, Grootfontein, S.Africa, 49; D.V.M. & Imp. Chem. Indust. award, Univ. Pretoria, 53, Int. Ford Found. award, 63; Nat. Insts. Health fel, Univ. Minn, 64, Ph.D.(neuroanat), 66. State vet, div. vet. serv, Dept. Agr, S.Africa, 54-55; private practice, 55-61; asst. prof. vet. histol. & anat, col. vet. med, Univ. Pretoria, 62-63; res. asst. neuroanat, col. vet. med, Univ. Minn, 63-66; ASSOC. PROF. vet histol. & anat, Univ. Pretoria, 67-69; NEUROL. SCI, COL. VET. MED, OHIO STATE UNIV, 69- Nat. Insts. Health grant, 69-70; Ohio State Univ. Col. Vet. Med. rep, multimedium prog. tech. conf, Purdue Univ. World Asn. Vet. Anat; Med. & Vet. Asn. Anat. S.Africa; S.Africa Vet. Med. Asn; Neurol. Soc. S.Africa. Comparative basic neurology. Address: Dept. of Veterinary Anatomy, Ohio State University, 190 N. Oval Dr, Columbus, OH 43210.

DE WETTE, FREDERIK WILLEM, b. Bussum, Netherlands, June 29, 24; m. 52; c. 3. SOLID STATE PHYSICS. Drs, Utrecht, 50, Dr.(theoret. physics) 59. Res. assoc, Utrecht, 50-52, asst. prof, 55-60; vis. lectr. physics, Brown, 52-53; res. assoc. chem, Maryland, 53-55; res. asst. prof. physics, Illinois, 60-62; res. physicist, Netherlands Reactor Center, 62-63; resident res. assoc, solid state sci. div, Argonne Nat. Lab, 63-65; PROF. PHYSICS, UNIV. TEX, AUSTIN, 65-, CHMN. DEPT, 69- Consult, Argonne Nat. Lab, 65- Fel. Am. Phys. Soc; Europ. Phys. Soc. Molecular physics; relaxation phenomena in molecular collisions; polarization effects in ionic crystals; lattice dynamics, anharmonic and surface properties of crystals. Address: Dept. of Physics, University of Texas at Austin, Austin, TX 78712.

DEWEY, BRADLEY, JR, b. Pittsburgh, Pa, Apr. 10, 16; m. 40; c. 5. CHEMICAL ENGINEERING. B.S, Harvard, 37; Sc.D.(chem. eng), Mass. Inst. Tech, 41. Indust. res, Dewey & Almy Chem. Co, 40-43, dir. develop. dept, 45-50, v.pres, 50-56; pres, Cryovac Div, W.R. Grace & Co, 56-64, sr. v.pres. chem. group, 64-70; PRES, THERMAL DYNAMICS CO, 70- C.W.S, 43-45, Capt. Am. Chem. Soc; Am. Inst. Chem. Eng; Soc. Chem. Indust; Am. Inst. Chem. Creaming of latex; colloid chemistry. Address: 43 Occom Ridge, Hanover, NH 03755.

DEWEY, C(LARENCE) FORBES, JR, b. Pueblo, Colo, Mar. 27, 35; m. 63. FLUID MECHANICS, PLASMA PHYSICS. B.E. & univ. scholar, Yale, 56; M.S. & Douglas scholar, Stanford, 57; Nat. Sci. Foun. fel. & Ph.D.(aeronaut), Calif. Inst. Tech, 63. Mem. tech. staff aerodyn, Aeronutronic Div, Philco Corp, 57-59; Nat. Sci. Found. fel. aeronaut, Calif. Inst. Tech, 59-63; asst. prof. aerospace sci, Colorado, 63-68, ASSOC. PROF. MECH. ENG, MASS. INST. TECHNOL, 68- Consult, Rand Corp, 60-; lectr, Univ. Calif, Los Angeles, 64; consult, Swissident, Inc, 64-65; adv. group aerospace res. & develop, NATO, 66-67; Eng. & Develop. Co. Colo, 66-68; Xenon Corp, 69-; Sausum Clin, 70; and others. Am. Phys. Soc; Am. Inst. Aeronaut. & Astronaut. Gas physics; ionization and collision phenomena; applied laser technology using wavelength-tunable lasers; fluid mechanics in biomedical engineering, including noninvasive diagnostic techniques. Address: Dept. of Mechanical Engineering, Room 3-258, Massachusetts Institute of Technology, Cambridge, MA 02139.

DEWEY, DONALD H(ENRY), b. Geneva, N.Y, April 25, 18; m. 47; c. 2. HORTICULTURE. B.S, Cornell, 39; Ph.D.(veg. crops), 50. Jr. olericulturist, Cheyenne hort. field sta, U.S. Dept. Agr, 39-45, horticulturist, Fresno lab, 45-51; PROF. HORT, MICH. STATE UNIV, 51- Orgn. European Econ. Coop.

Sr. Vis. fel, Ditton Lab, Eng, 60. U.S.A.A.F, 41-45. Am. Soc. Hort. Sci; Inst. Food Tech; Am. Soc. Heating, Refrig. & Air-Conditioning Eng; Int. Soc. Hort. Sci. Harvesting; handling and storage of fruits and vegetables; controlled atmosphere storage of fruit; physiology of maturation, ripening and senescence. Address: Dept. of Horticulture, Michigan State University, East Lansing, MI 48823.

DEWEY, DOUGLAS R, b. Brigham City, Utah, Oct. 23, 29; m. 49; c. 3. CYTOGENETICS, PLANT BREEDING. B.S, Utah State, 51, M.S, 54; Ph.D. (plant genetics), Minnesota, 56. Res. agronomist, U.S. DEPT. AGR, 56-62, RES. GENETICIST, 62- Qm.C, 51-53, 1st Lt. Am. Soc. Agron; Bot. Soc. Am; Crop Sci. Soc. Am. Genetics, cytology, interspecific and intergeneric hybridization of species of the Triticeae tribe of grasses. Address: Crops Research Lab, Utah State University, Logan, UT 84321.

DEWEY, EDWARD R(USSELL), b. Elmira, N.Y, May 2, 95; m. 22; 35; c. 2. STATISTICS. S.B, Harvard, 20. Instr, California, 27-29, Southern California, 27-29; chief current statist, U.S. Census Bur, 29-30, indust. mkt, 29-31, hotel census, 30-31; asst. to dir, Bur. For. & Domestic Commerce, 31-33, chief econ. analyst, 31-33; asst. dir. inst. appl. econ, Nat. Indust. Conf. Bd, 36; indust. consult, 37-39; dir, FOUND. FOR STUDY OF CYCLES, 40-69, PRES, 69-; ADJ. RES. PROF, UNIV. PITTSBURGH, 64- Adminr, Int. Comt. Res. & Study of Factors of the Environ, 70- AAAS; fel. World Acad. Art & Sci; N.Y. Acad. Sci; Soc. Biol. Rhythm; Int. Soc. Biometeorol. Analysis of non-harmonic periodic functions. Address: Foundation for the Study of Cycles, 124 S. Highland Ave, Pittsburgh, PA 15206.

DEWEY, FRED McALPIN, b. Akron, Ohio, Sept. 9, 39; m. 59; c. 5. ORGANIC CHEMISTRY. B.S, Colorado State, 61; Nat. Sci. Found. fel. & Ph.D. (chem), Colorado, 65. Res. chemist, Hooker Chem. Corp, summer 65; Harry Diamond Labs, D.C, 65-67; Air Force Rocket Propulsion Lab, Calif, 67-68; ASST. PROF. CHEM, METROP. STATE COL, 68- U.S.A, 65-67, Capt. Am. Chem. Soc. Synthesis; stereochemistry. Address: 2179 S. Field Way, Denver, CO 80227.

DEWEY, J(AMES) E(DWIN), b. Geneva, N.Y, Jan. 15, 17; m. 43; c. 1. ENTOMOLOGY. B.S, Cornell, 40, Ph.D.(entom), 44; M.S, Tennessee, 41. Instr. exten. entom, N.Y. STATE COL. AGR, CORNELL UNIV, 44-45, asst. prof, 45-47, assoc. prof. INSECT TOXICOL, 47-54, PROF, 54-, PROG. LEADER, CHEM-PESTICIDES PROG, 64- Entom. Soc. Am; Am. Chem. Soc. Insect toxicology; insect resistance to insecticides; synergism; bioassay; insecticide formulation; fruit insect control. Address: Dept. of Entomology, State University of New York College of Agriculture, Cornell University, Ithaca, NY 14850.

DEWEY, JANE M(ARY), b. Chicago, Ill, July 11, 00. PHYSICS. A.B, Columbia, 22; Ph.D.(phys. chem), Mass. Inst. Tech, 25. Asst. phys. chem, Mass. Inst. Tech, 24-25; int. fel. from Barnard Col, Univ. Inst. for Theoret. Physics, Copenhagen, 25-27; Nat. Res. Found. fel, Princeton, 27-29; res. fel, Rochester, 29-31; assoc. physics, Bryn Mawr Col, 31-33, assoc. prof, 33-36; lectr, Hunter Col, 40-42; physicist, gen. labs, U.S. Rubber Co, 42-47; ballistic res. lab, Aberdeen Proving Ground, Md, 47-70; RETIRED. Am. Phys. Soc. Stark effect; recombination spectra; atomic theory; dielectrics; theory of elasticity; blast; detonation. Address: 219 Elizabeth St, Key West, FL 33040.

DEWEY, JOHN FREDERICK, b. London, Eng, May 22, 37; m. 61; c. 2. STRUCTURAL GEOLOGY. B.Sc, Univ. London, 58, dipl, Imp. Col. & Ph.D (struc. geol), 60; M.A, Cambridge, 64. Asst. lectr. GEOL, Univ. Manchester, 60-62, lectr, 62-64; Cambridge, 64-70; PROF, STATE UNIV. N.Y. ALBANY, 70- Res. assoc, Lamont-Doherty Geol. Observ, 67-; commonwealth fel, Memorial Univ, 70; comt. mem, Int. Geodynamics Proj, 71- Daniel Pidgeon Fund award, Geol. Soc. London, 64 & Murchison Fund award, 71. Fel. Geol. Soc. London; fel. Geol. Asn. Can; Am. Geophys. Union. Stratigraphic-structural evolution of the Appalachian-Caledonian orogen and the Alpine orogen of Europe; significance of plate tectonics for the evolution of continental margins and orogenic belts. Address: Dept. of Geological Sciences, State University of New York at Albany, Albany, NY 12203.

DEWEY, J(OHN) L(YONS), b. Savannah, Ga, Sept. 24, 19; m. 46; c. 1. CHEMICAL ENGINEERING. B.S, Ga. Inst. Tech, 42; Illinois. Chem. engr. res. dept, Tenn. Copper Co, 42-46; Texas Gulf Sulfur asst, Illinois, 47-48, asst. prof. chem. eng, Cincinnati, 48-49; sr. chem. engr, Battelle Mem. Inst, 50-53; sect. head, res. dept, Maxwell House Coffee Div, Gen. Foods Co, 53-54; reduction res. lab, REYNOLDS METALS CO, 54-68, ENG. DIR, ALUMINA RES. DIV, 68- Am. Inst. Chem. Eng; Am. Chem. Soc; Am. Ceramic Soc; Electrochem. Soc. Application of chemical engineering to extractive metallurgy; iodide titanium; thermal and electrolytic aluminum; sulphate salts; mass transfer at high temperatures and reduced pressures; digital control systems. Address: Alumina Research Division, Reynolds Metals Co, Bauxite, AR 72011.

DEWEY, JOHN M(ARKS), b. Portsmouth, Eng, Mar. 23; 30; m. 51; c. 2. PHYSICS, FLUID MECHANICS. B.Sc, London, 50, Ph.D.(physics), 64. Sci. master physics, De La Salle Col, Channel Islands, 50-53, head sci. dept, 53-56; scientist, planning & reporting sect, Suffield Exp. Sta, Can, 56-58, physics sect, 58-63, leader aerophys. group, 63-64, head aerophys. & shock tube sect, 64-65; asst. prof. PHYSICS, UNIV. VICTORIA (B.C), 65-66, ASSOC. PROF, 66- Am. Phys. Soc; fel. Inst. Physics; assoc. Can. Asn. Physicists. Physics of blast waves; effects of blast waves; shock tube flows; measurement techniques in high speed fluid flows; tidal flows. Address: Dept. of Physics, University of Victoria, Victoria, B.C, Can.

DEWEY, L(OVELL) J(UNIOR), b. Kalamazoo, Mich, Feb. 17, 27; m. 60; c. 2. BIOCHEMISTRY. B.A, Kalamazoo Col, 50; Ph.D.(biochem), Mich. State, 54. Instr. BIOCHEM, Mich. State, 54-55; jr. res. assoc, AM. TOBACCO CO, 55-64, RES. ASSOC, 64- Res. assoc, Med. Col. Va, 55-67. U.S.N.R, 45-46. AAAS; Am. Chem. Soc. Plant metabolism; nicotine biogenesis and metabolism in tobacco plants; identification and metabolism of minor pyridine alkaloids. Address: P.O. Box 799, Hopewell, VA 23860.

DEWEY, MAYNARD M(ERLE), b. Hickory Corners, Mich, June 26, 32; m. 55; c. 2. ANATOMY. A.B, Kalamazoo Col, 54; M.S, Michigan, 56, U.S. Pub. Health Serv. fel, 56-57, Ph.D, 58; Nat. Res. Council fel, Karolinska Inst, Sweden, 57-58. Asst, A.M. Todd Co, Mich, 51-54; instr. ANAT, Michigan, 58-60, asst. prof, 60-64, assoc. prof, 64-66; PROF. & CHMN. DEPT, Med. Col. Pa, 66-71; HEALTH SCI. CTR, STATE UNIV. N.Y. STONY BROOK, 71- AAAS; Histochem. Soc; Soc. Gen. Physiol; Am. Physiol. Soc; Biophys. Soc; Am. Asn. Anat. Electron microscopy; cytochemistry; membrane structure; intercellular communication; muscle. Address: Dept. of Anatomical Sciences, Health Sciences Center, State University of New York at Stony Brook, Stony Brook, NY 11790.

DEWEY, PHILLIP H(OLMES), b. Hopkinsville, Ky, June 17, 09; m. 33; c. 2. PHYSICAL CHEMISTRY. B.S, Union (N.Y), 31; M.S, Cornell, 32. Staff mem, Coal Res. Labs, 32-36; indust. fel, Mellon Inst, 36-41; proj. engr, West. Elec. Co, 41-45; sr. chemist, R-B-H Dispersions Div, Interchem Corp, 45-48, group leader, cent. res. labs, 48-55, admin. asst, 55-58, asst. dept. dir. applns. res, 58-59, admin. asst, 59-68, ASST. TO TECH. V.PRES, INMONT CORP, 68- Am. Chem. Soc. Thermodynamics of carbon; pH of strong alkalies; forming of plate glass; dispersion of pigments. Address: Inmont Corp, 1255 Broad St, Clifton, NJ 07015.

DEWEY, RAY SCHELL, b. Keokuk, Iowa, Dec. 24, 32. ORGANIC CHEMISTRY. B.S, Ill. Inst. Technol, 55; Ph.D.(chem), Harvard, 60. Univ. fel, Univ. Wis, 59-61; sr. chemist, MERCK & CO, 61-68, RES. FEL, 68- AAAS; Am. Chem. Soc; The Chem. Soc. Aromatic ketones; peptide synthesis; diazoketones; diimide and phosphate esters. Address: Research & Development, Merck & Co, Rahway, NJ 07065.

DEWEY, VIRGINIA C(AROLINE), b. Forest Hills, Mass, Dec. 18, 13; m. 43; c. 1. BIOLOGY, BIOCHEMISTRY. B.S, Simmons Col, 34; Michigan, 38; A.M, Vassar Col, 39; Edwards fel, Brown, 41, Ph.D.(protozool), 42. Lab. technician, Harvard Med. Sch, 34-37; asst. physiol, Vassar Col, 37-39; protozool, Marine Biol. Lab, 39-41; res. & anal. chemist. Lever Bros, Co, 42-44; RES. ASSOC, AMHERST COL, 46- Abbott fel, Brown, 44. Am. Soc. Biol. Chem. Nervous control of circulation; vitamins; growth factors of protozoa; nutrition and metabolism of Tetrahymena pyriformis and other ciliates; chemotherapy of cancer. Address: Biological Lab, Amherst College, Amherst, MA 01002.

DEWEY, WADE G, b. Los Angeles, Calif, Aug. 10, 27; m. 51; c. 4. PLANT BREEDING, GENETICS. B.S, Utah State, 53; Nat. Sci. Found. fel, Cornell, 55-56, Ph.D.(plant breeding), 56. Asst. prof. agron, Utah State, 56-58; geneticist, U.S. Dept. Agr, 58-59; asst. prof. AGRON, UTAH STATE UNIV, 59-61, assoc. prof, 61-66, PROF, 66- U.S.A, 45-47. Am. Soc. Agron. Plant breeding and genetics of the cereal crops, particularly winter wheat. Address: Dept. of Plant Science, Utah State University, Logan, UT 84321.

DEWEY, W(ILLIAM) CORNET, b. Omaha, Nebr, Nov. 4, 29; m. 51; c. 4. RADIATION BIOLOGY. B.S, Washington (Seattle), 51; Ph.D.(radiation biol), Rochester, 58. Asst. radiation biol, Rochester, 54-58; asst. physicist, Anderson Hosp. & Tumor Inst, 58-61, assoc. physicist, 61-65; PROF. RADIATION BIOL, COLO. STATE UNIV, 65- U.S.N, 51-54, Res, 54- Physiology; biological effects of radiation; utilization of radioisotopes in biological problems. Address: Dept. of Radiation Biology, Colorado State University, Ft. Collins, CO 80521.

DEWEY, WILLIAM LEO, b. Albany, N.Y, Oct. 21, 34; m. 60; c. 5. PHARMACOLOGY, BIOCHEMISTRY. B.S, St. Bernardine of Siena Col, 57; M.S, Col. St. Rose, 64; Ph.D.(pharmacol), Connecticut, 66. Asst. res. biologist, Sterling-Winthrop Res. Inst, 59-64; asst, PHARMACOL, sch. pharm, Univ. Conn, 64-66; fel, sch. med, UNIV. N.C, CHAPEL HILL, 66-68, instr, 68-70, ASST. PROF, SCHS. MED. & PHARM, 70- U.S.A, 57-59. AAAS; Am. Soc. Pharmacol. & Exp. Therapeut; Am. Pharmaceut. Asn; Am. Chem. Soc. Agents that affect the central nervous system, especially anorexigenics, analgesics, stimulants and tranquilizers. Address: 5304 Newhall Rd, Durham, NC 27707.

DEWHIRST, KENNETH CARL, b. Fresno, Calif, May 26, 32; m. 57. ORGANIC CHEMISTRY. B.S, California, Berkeley, 54, Nat. Sci. Found. fel, Los Angeles, 56-58, Ph.D.(org. chem), 58; Nat. Sci. Found. fel, Basel, 58-59; Munich, 63-64. Chemist, SHELL DEVELOP. CO, 59-64, SUPVR. ORGANOMETALLIC CHEM, 64- Am. Chem. Soc. Organometallic coordination chemistry; synthesis and properties of organic molecules of unusual geometry; synthesis and catalytic reaction of organometallic complexes. Address: Shell Development Co, 1400 53rd St, Emeryville, CA 94608.

DEWHIRST, LEONARD W(ESLEY), b. Marquette, Kans, Sept. 28, 24; m. 46; c. 3. ZOOLOGY. B.S, Kans. State Col, 49, M.S, 50; Ph.D.(parasitol), 57. Res. asst. parasitol, Kans. State Col, 49-52, instr. zool, 52-57; asst. prof. & asst. animal pathologist, UNIV. ARIZ, 57-60, assoc. prof, 60-63, PROF. ANIMAL PATH. & ANIMAL PATHOLOGIST, AGR. EXP. STA, 63- U.S.N.R, 43-45, Lt.(jg). Am. Soc. Parasitol; Am. Micros. Soc. Agricultural parasitology; biology, treatment, and control of parasites of domestic animals. Address: Dept. of Animal Pathology, University of Arizona, Tucson, AZ 85721.

DEWHURST, H(AROLD) A(INSLIE), b. Ottawa, Can, June 18, 24; m. 48; c. 4. PHYSICAL CHEMISTRY. B.S, McGill, 46, Ph.D.(phys. chem), 50. Res. chemist radiation chem, Can. Atomic Energy Proj, 47-50; res. fel, Edinburgh, 50-52; res. assoc. phys. chem, Notre Dame, 52-54; res. lab, Gen. Elec. Co, 54-60, liaison scientist chem, 60-61, personnel & admin, metall. & ceramics res, 62-64, mgr. structures & reactions studies, 64-65, mgr. gen. chem. lab, res. & develop. ctr, 65-68, mat. sci. & eng, 68; MGR. RES. GROUP, OWENS-CORNING FIBERGLAS CORP, 68- Am. Chem. Soc; Faraday Soc. Kinetics of reactions; radiation chemistry of water and aqueous solutions; photochemistry of aqueous solutions; radiation chemistry of nonaqueous solutions; electric discharge chemistry. Address: Research Group, Owens-Corning Fiberglas Corp, Technical Center, Granville, OH 43023.

DE WIEST, ROGER J. M, b. Lebbeke, Belgium, Feb. 6, 25; U.S. citizen; m. 52; c. 4. HYDROLOGY. Elec. engr, Univ. Ghent, 49, dipl. struct. eng, 54; M.Sc, Calif. Inst. Technol, 55; Ph.D.(civil eng), Stanford Univ, 59; B.Sc.Med, Free Univ. Brussels, 70. Engr, Dept. Labor, Belgium, 50-54; hydraul.

engr, SOFINA, Brussels, 56-57; asst. prof. CIVIL & GEOL. ENG, PRINCETON, 59-61, assoc. prof, 61-65, PROF, 65-, CHMN. WATER RESOURCES PROG, 70- Freeman fel, Am. Soc. Civil Eng, 63-64; consult, Bowling Green State, 64-65; Delaware, 65-66; Del. Basin Cmn, N.J, 64-; NATO vis. prof, Univ. Iceland, 71-72. Am. Soc. Civil Eng; Am. Geophys. Union. Geohydrology; flow through porous media; hydrogeology. Address: E-326 Engineering Quadrangle, Princeton University, Princeton, NJ 08540.

DEWILDE, ANDRIES C, b. Batavia, Java, Indonesia, Dec. 19, 04; m. 30; c. 5. MECHANICAL & NUCLEAR ENGINEERING. M.S.M.E, Delft, 28, M.S.M.E, 31; M.E, Michigan, 54. Asst. inspector ships, Java-China-Japan Line, Holland, 30-31; designer diesel engines, Werkspoor, Holland, 31-32; test engr, Stork Bros, Holland, 32-36; chief engr. & oper. mgr, Surinaamsche Bauxite Cy. div, Aluminum Co. Am, 36-44; diesel specialist, ExCell-O Corp, Mich, 44-46; res. engr, Detroit Edison Co, 46-54; sr. proj. engr, power develop. div, Gen. Motors Corp, 54-62; eve. instr, Detroit Inst. Tech, 44-62; prof. mech. eng, Univ. Detroit, 62-70; CONSULT. ENGR, 70- Ed, Univ. Detroit Translation Ctr. Royal Dutch Corps Engrs. Res, 28-49, Capt. Am. Soc. Mech. Eng; Am. Soc. Eng. Educ; Soc. Automotive Eng; Am. Nuclear Soc. Address: 274 Desert Breeze Dr, California City, CA 93505.

DEWING, STEPHEN BRONSON, b. Princeton, N.J, Dec. 18, 20; m. 43; c. 1. RADIOLOGY. A.B, Princeton, 42; M.D, Columbia Univ, 45. Dir. radiol, Hunterdon Med. Ctr, Flemington, N.J, 53-65; assoc. prof. radiol, W.Va. Univ, 65-69; DIR. RADIOL, STEPHENS MEM. HOSP, NORWAY, MAINE, 69-; NORTH. CUMBERLAND MEM. HOSP, BRIDGTON, 69- Assoc. clin. prof, N.Y. Univ, 53-65. Dipl. Am. Bd. Radiol, 53. Med.C, 46-48, Capt. AAAS; Am. Col. Radiol; Am. Med. Asn; Radiol. Soc. N.Am. Clinical radiology. Address: R.F.D. 2, Harrison, ME 04040.

DeWIRE, JOHN W(ILLIAM), b. Milton, Pa, June 12, 16; m. 43; c. 2. NUCLEAR PHYSICS. B.S, Ursinus Col, 38; Ph.D.(physics), Ohio State, 42. Assoc. scientist, Nat. Defense Res. Cmt, Princeton, 42-43; Los Alamos Sci. Lab, N.Mex, 43-46; res. assoc. PHYSICS, CORNELL UNIV, 46-47, asst. prof, 47-51, assoc. prof, 51-58, PROF, 58-, ASSOC. DIR. LAB. NUCLEAR STUDIES, 68- Nat. Sci. Found. sr. fel, Frascati, Italy, 60-61; Fulbright scholar. & vis. prof, Univ. Bonn, 68. AAAS; Am. Phys. Soc. High energy electron and meson physics; accelerators. Address: Lab. of Nuclear Studies, Cornell University, Ithaca, NY 14850.

DE WIT, M(ICHIEL), b. Amsterdam, Netherlands, June 6, 33; U.S. citizen; m. 57; c. 5. PHYSICS. B.S, Ohio Univ, 54; Sterling fel, Yale, 57-58, Ph.D. (physics), 60. MEM. TECH. STAFF, TEX. INSTRUMENTS INC, 59- Am. Phys. Soc; Optical Soc. Am. Theoretical and experimental studies of defects in solids via electron paramagnetic resonance, photo and thermo luminescence, Zeeman and Raman spectroscopy; development of solid state lasers and nonlinear optical devices. Address: Physics Research Lab, Texas Instruments Inc, P.O. Box 5936, M.S. 134, Dallas, TX 75222.

deWIT, ROLAND, b. Amsterdam, Netherlands, Feb. 28, 30; U.S. citizen; m. 54; c. 2. SOLID STATE PHYSICS. B.S, Ohio, 53; univ. fel, Illinois, 53-55, M.S, 55, Gulf Oil Co. fel, 57-58, Ph.D.(physics), 59. Asst, Illinois, 53-59, res. assoc, 59; asst. res physicist, California, Berkeley, 59-60; PHYSICIST, NAT. BUR. STANDARDS, 60- Summer, tester, Frigidaire Div, General Motors Corp, Ohio, 53. Am. Phys. Soc; Electron Micros. Soc. Am; Metall. Soc; Am. Soc. Metals; Am. Soc. Mech. Eng; Int. Soc. Stereology. Theory of dislocations and other defects in crystals. Address: Metallurgy Division, National Bureau of Standards, Washington, DC 20234.

DeWITT, BERNARD JAMES, b. Oak Harbor, Wash, Jan. 29, 17; m. 42; c. 2. CHEMISTRY. A.B, Hope Col, 37; D.Sc.(phys. chem), Carnegie Inst. Tech, 41. Res. chemist, Pittsburgh Plate Glass Co, 40-51; sr. supvr. anal. & phys. chem, Columbia-South Chem. Corp, 51-59, mgr, 59-64; ASST. DIR. RES, PPG INDUSTS, 64- Am. Chem. Soc. Thermodynamics of bimetallic systems; specific heat determinations at low temperatures; titanium pigments; polymerization of alkyl compounds; chlorination aliphatic organics; purification of titanium tetrachloride; silica pigments; physical testing of rubber products; analysis of chlorinated hydrocarbons and particle size analysis. Address: PPG Industries, Barberton, OH 44203.

DeWITT, BRYCE SELIGMAN, b. Dinuba, Calif, Jan. 8, 23; m. 51; c. 4. THEORETICAL PHYSICS. B.S, Harvard, 43, M.A, 47, Ph.D.(physics), 50. Mem, Inst. adv. study, N.J, 49-50; Fulbright fel, Tata Inst. Fundamental Res, India, 51-52; sr. physicist, radiation lab, California, 52-55; res. prof. PHYSICS, UNIV. N.C, CHAPEL HILL, 56-59, prof, 60-64, AGNEW HUNTER BAHNSON, JR. PROF, 64-, DIR. RES, INST. FIELD PHYSICS, 56- Mem, Inst. Advan. Study, 54, 64; Fulbright lectr, France, 56; consult, Gen. Atomic Div, Gen. Dynamics Corp, 59; mem, Int. Comt. Relativity & Gravitation, 59-; Nat. Sci. Found. sr. fel, 64; Fulbright lectr, Japan, 64-65. U.S.N, 44-45. Fel. Am. Phys. Soc. Scattering and perturbation theory; non-abelian gauge field theory; topology; theory of gravitation; space physics. Address: Dept. of Physics, University of North Carolina at Chapel Hill, Chapel Hill, NC 27515.

DeWITT, CALVIN B(OYD), b. Grand Rapids, Mich, Nov. 7, 35; m. 59; c. 2. BIOLOGY, PHYSIOLOGY. B.A, Calvin Col, 57; M.A, Michigan, 58, Nat. Sci. Found. fel, 60-63, Ph.D.(zool), 63. Asst. biol, Calvin Col, 58-59; asst. prof. BIOL, UNIV. MICH, DEARBORN, 63-66, assoc. prof, 66-69, PROF, 69-, chmn. sect. natural sci, 68-70. Summer lectr, Univ. Mich, 63; hon. fel. zool, Univ. Wis, 70-71. AAAS; N.Y. Acad. Sci; Int. Soc. Biometeorol. Ecological physiology; behavioral control of the internal environment; physiology of desert reptiles; thermal energy exchange between organisms and environment; body temperature regulation. Address: Dept. of Experimental Biology, University of Michigan, Dearborn Campus, 4901 Evergreen Rd, Dearborn, MI 48128.

DeWITT, CECIL M(ORETTE), b. Paris, France, Dec. 21, 22; m. 51; c. 4. THEORETICAL PHYSICS. Lic. ès sc, Caen, 43; dipl, Paris, 44, Ph.D.(theoret. physics), 47. Mem, Inst. Adv. Studies, Ireland, 46-47; Univ. Inst. Theoret. Physics, Denmark, 47-48; Inst. Adv. Study, Princeton, 48-50; teacher res, Inst. Henri Poincaré, France, 50-51; res. assoc. & lectr, California, 52-55; vis. res. prof, Univ. N.C, Chapel Hill, 56-67, dir. inst. field

physics, 58-66, LECTR. physics, 67-71; ASTRON, UNIV. TEX, AUSTIN, 71- Dir. & founder, summer sch. theoret. physics, Les Houches, France, 51- Summer, vis. prof, Brazilian Center Physics Res, Rio de Janeiro, 49. Theory of field; elementary particles; gravitation. Address: Dept. of Astronomy, University of Texas at Austin, Austin, TX 78712.

DeWITT, C(HARLES) W(AYNE), JR, b. Akron, Ohio, Oct. 16, 21; m. 46; c. 3. IMMUNOLOGY, BACTERIOLOGY. B.S, Morris Harvey Col, 49; M.S, Ohio State, 51, State Tuberc. Asn. fel, 51-52, Ph.D.(bact), 52. Res. scientist bact, Upjohn Co, 52-55, res. assoc. infectious diseases, 55-61; asst. prof, depts. microbiol. & surg, sch. med, Tulane, 61-62, assoc. prof. surg, 62-66, PROF, 66-68; PATH. & SURG, MED. CTR, UNIV. UTAH, 68- U.S.M.C, 42-45. AAAS; Am. Soc. Microbiol; N.Y. Acad. Sci; Am. Asn. Immunol; Transplantation Soc. Bacterial infection and host resistance tissue transplantation immunity. Address: Dept. of Pathology, University of Utah Medical Center, Salt Lake City, UT 84112.

DeWITT, DAVID P, b. Bethlehem, Pa, Mar. 2, 34; m. 57; c. 3. THERMODYNAMICS. B.S, Duke, 55; S.M, Mass. Inst. Tech, 57; Ph.D.(mech. eng), Purdue, 63. Instr. thermodyn, col. eng, Duke, 57-59; physicist, Nat. Bur. Standards, 63-64; ASSOC. PROF. MECH. ENG. & DEP. DIR. THERMOPHYS. PROPERTIES RES. CTR, PURDUE UNIV, 65- Guest worker, Nat. Phys-Tech. Inst, Bur. Standards, Brunswick, Ger, 70-71. Thermophysical properties of matter, especially thermal radiation properties of materials, experimental procedures and techniques. Address: Thermophysical Properties Research Center, Purdue University, Lafayette, IN 47906.

DeWITT, EARL G(EORGE), b. Holland, Mich, Dec. 19, 20; m. 45; c. 2. ORGANIC CHEMISTRY. A.B, Hope Col, 43; M.S, Ohio State, 47, Ph.D.(chem), 49. Asst, Ohio State. 47-49; Los Alamos Sci. Lab, California, 46; res. assoc, Clinton Lab, 44-46; res. chemist, ETHYL CORP, 49-52, asst. res. supvr, combustion res, 52, res. supvr. fuel & oil additives, 52-58, supt. bus. res. planning, 58-63, dir. develop. & planning, plastics, 63-68, gen. mgr. PVC films div, 68-70, MGR. COMMERCIAL DEVELOP, PLASTICS DIV, 70- Am. Chem. Soc; Commercial Chem. Develop. Asn. Plastics and polymers. Address: Ethyl Corp, 451 Florida, Baton Rouge, LA 70801.

DeWITT, ELMER J(OHN), b. Grand Junction, Mich, Aug. 6, 24; m. 50; c. 4. ORGANIC CHEMISTRY. B.S, Maine, 50; M.S, New Hampshire, 53; fel. & Ph.D.(org. chem), Emory, 55. Technologist ORG. CHEM, B.F. GOODRICH CO, 55-57, jr. technologist, 57-58, sr. technologist, 58-64, SR. RES. CHEMIST, 64- U.S.N, 42-45, 50-52. Am. Chem. Soc. Polymer derivatives; organic oxidations; organic boron chemistry; diels-alder reaction; emulsion polymerizations and plastics. Address: Research Center, B.F. Goodrich Co, 9921 Brecksville, OH 44041.

DE WITT, H(OBSON) D(EWEY), b. New Bern, N.C, July 12, 23; m. 48; c. 3. ORGANIC CHEMISTRY. B.A, Erskine Col, 44; Ph.D.(chem), Vanderbilt, 51. Chemist, E. I. du Pont de Nemours & Co, 44; res. chemist, Southland Paper Mills, 50-52; The Chemstrand Corp, 52-56; PROF. CHEM. & CHMN. DEPT, WESTMINSTER COL, 56- U.S.N, 45-46. Am. Chem. Soc; Sci. Res. Soc. Am; fel. Am. Inst. Chem. Synthesis of amino acid derivatives; chemistry of hydrazine; monomers; polymers of textile interest; resolution of optically active compounds. Address: Dept. of Chemistry, Westminster College, New Wilmington, PA 16142.

DE WITT, HUGH E(DGAR), b. Memphis, Tenn, May 27, 30; m. 56; c. 3. THEORETICAL PHYSICS. B.S, Stanford, 51; Fulbright fel, Heidelberg, 55-56; Ph.D, Cornell Univ, 57. THEORET. PHYSICIST, RADIATION LAB, UNIV. CALIF, LIVERMORE, 57- Am. Phys. Soc. Quantum statistical mechanics; plasma physics; astrophysics; theoretical nuclear physics. Address: Radiation Lab, Box 808, University of California, Livermore, CA 94551.

DE WITT, HUGH HAMILTON, b. San Jose, Calif, Dec. 28, 33; m. 56; c. 3. ICHTHYOLOGY, MARINE BIOLOGY. B.A, Stanford Univ, 55, M.A, 60, Ph.D.(biol), 66. Res. assoc. biol. sci, Hancock Found, Univ. South. Calif, 62-67; ASST. PROF. marine biol, Univ. S.Fla, 67-69; ZOOL, IRA C. DARLING CTR. RES, TEACHING & SERV, UNIV. MAINE, WALPOLE, 69-, OCEANOG, 70- Am. Soc. Ichthyol. & Herpet; Am. Inst. Fishery Res. Biol; Am. Fisheries Soc. Freshwater fishes of southeastern Asia; polar marine fishes. Address: Ira C. Darling Center for Research, Teaching & Service, University of Maine, Walpole, ME 04573.

De WITT, JOHN W(ILLIAM), JR, b. Pawhuska, Okla, Dec. 16, 22; m. 47; c. 1. FISHERIES BIOLOGY, AQUATIC ECOLOGY. Ph.D, Oregon State, 63. Fishery biologist, U.S. Fish & Wildlife Serv, 48-49; PROF. FISHERIES, HUMBOLDT STATE COL, 49- Dir. fisheries training & overseas support progs, Peace Corps, Chile, 66-69; fishery biologist, Lake Nasser Develop. Ctr, Food & Agr. Orgn. U.N, U.A.R, 69-71. C.Eng, 43-46, 1st Lt. Am. Fisheries Soc; Water Pollution Control Fedn; Am. Soc. Ichthyol. & Herpet; Am. Soc. Limnol. & Oceanog. Address: Dept. of Fisheries, Humboldt State College, Arcata, CA 95521.

DE WITT, ROBERT M(ERKLE), b. Wolcott, N.Y, May 31, 15. ZOOLOGY. B.S, Michigan, 40, M.S, 41, Ph.D, 53. Teacher, high schs, N.Y, 41-46; asst. prof. BIOL, Sampson Col, 46-49; teaching asst, Michigan, 49-50, teaching fel, 50-52, instr, 52-54, Lloyd fel, 53-54; asst. prof, UNIV. FLA, 54-59, ASSOC. PROF, 59-, acting chmn. dept, 69-71. AAAS; Am. Malacol. Union; Am. Micros. Soc; Ecol. Soc; Am; Am. Soc. Zool. Morphological and physiological factors of adaptation in amphibious snails; reproduction, ecology, population biology and systematics of fresh-water mollusks. Address: Dept. of Zoology, University of Florida, Gainesville, FL 32601.

DeWITT, RONALD N, b. New York, N.Y, Aug. 4, 36; m. 63; c. 2. GEOPHYSICS, ATMOSPHERIC PHYSICS. B.S, Michigan,Tech, 58; M.S, Alaska, 61, Ph.D.(geophys), 65; Colorado, 60-62. Res. asst. physics, Alaska, 58-60, asst. prof, 62-66; res. assoc, Chicago, 66-67; staff physicist, ITT ELECTRO-PHYSICS LABS, INC, 67-70, HEAD THEORET. SECT, RES. DEPT, 70- Mem. Cmn. 3, Int. Sci. Radio Union, 69- Am. Geophys. Union. Geomagnetic and auroral phenomena; effect of upper atmospheric phenomena on information content of radio signals propagated via the ionosphere. Address: ITT Electro-Physics Labs, Inc, 3355 52nd Ave, Hyattsville, MD 20781.

DE WITT, WARREN P(EYTON), b. Savannah, Ga, Oct. 10, 18; m. 46; c. 2. MATHEMATICS. B.S, South Carolina, 49; Maryland. Mathematician, U.S. NAVAL RES. LAB, 48-56, head, instrumentation & calculators sect, 56-61, analog. comput. sect, 61-68, CONSULT, RES. COMPUT. CTR, 69- Assoc. math, George Washington, 57-64, asst. prof. lectr, 64- U.S.A, 40-46, Res, 46-51, 1st Lt. Int. Asn. Cybernet. Theory of ordinary differential equations; linear operators; functional analysis; logic. Address: Research Computation Center, U.S. Naval Research Lab, Washington, DC 20390.

DEWITT, WILLIAM, b. Washington, D.C, Nov. 28, 39. MICROBIOLOGY, BIOCHEMISTRY. B.A, Williams Col, 61; M.A, Princeton, 63, U.S. Pub. Health Serv. fel, 64-66, Ph.D.(biol), 66. Res. assoc. biochem, Mass. Inst. Technol, 66-67; ASST. PROF. BIOL, WILLIAMS COL, 67- Genetic control of colicin synthesis in enteric bacteria; synthesis of hemoglobin and other specific proteins during amphibian development. Address: Dept. of Biology, Williams College, Williamstown, MA 01267.

DeWITT, WILLIAM B(RADLEY), b. Birmingham, Ala, June 3, 21; m. 49. PARASITOLOGY. A.B, Howard Col, 48; M.A, George Washington, 51, Ph.D. (zool), 56. Scientist, parasitic diseases lab, NAT. INSTS. HEALTH, U.S. Pub. Health Serv, 49-65, assoc. dir. lab. resources, DIV. RES. SERV, 65-69, DIR, 69- U.S.N, 42-46. Am. Soc. Parasitol; Am. Soc. Trop. Med. & Hyg.(ed, News); N.Y. Acad. Sci. Helminthology; schistosomiasis; effects of nutrition on host-parasite relationship. Address: Division of Research Services, National Institutes of Health, Bethesda, MD 20014.

DeWITTE, A(DRIANN) J(AN), b. Bergen op Zoom, Netherlands, Jan. 16, 24; nat; m. 48; c. 3. GEOLOGY, GEOPHYSICS. Drs, Leiden, 48. Geologist, Standard Vacuum Oil Co, Indonesia, 48-49; Continental Oil Co, Tex, 50-53, res. engr, Okla, 53-55; res. geophysicist, head well logging unit, Gulf Res. & Develop. Co, 55-61; PROF. PETROL. ENG. UNIV. ILL, URBANA, 61- Summers, vis. scientist, Oceanog. Inst, Woods Hole, 62-65. Free Dutch Army, 44-45. Geophysics; oceanography. Address: Dept. of Metallurgy & Mining, University of Illinois, Urbana, IL 61801.

DE WOLF, DAVID ALTER, b. Dordrecht, Netherlands, July 23, 34. THEORETICAL PHYSICS. B.Sc, Univ. Amsterdam, 55, Drs, 59; Dr. Tech, Univ. Eindhoven, 68. Res. physicist, Nuclear Defense Lab, Edgewood Arsenal, Md, 62; MEM. TECH. STAFF, DAVID SARNOFF RES. CTR, RCA CORP, 62- Mem. comn. 2, U.S. Nat. Comt, Int. Sci. Radio Union. Inst. Elec. & Electronics Eng; Optical Soc. Am; Netherlands Phys. Soc. Quantum statistical N-body problem; electromagnetic wave propagation in plasma. Address: David Sarnoff Research Center, RCA Corp, Princeton, NJ 08540.

DeWOLF, GORDON P(ARKER), JR, b. Lowell, Mass, Aug. 17, 27; m. 55. TAXONOMIC BOTANY. B.Sc, Massachusetts, 50; M.Sc, Tulane, 52; Fulbright grant, Malaya, 52-53, M.Sc, 54; Ph.D, Cambridge, 59. Asst. bot, Tulane, 50-52; Bailey Hortorium, Cornell, 53-54, res. assoc, 54-56; sr. sci. off, Royal Bot. Gardens, Eng, 59-61; assoc. prof. bot, Ga. South. Col, 61-64, prof. 64-67, acting head dept. biol, 66-67; hort. taxonomist, ARNOLD ARBORETUM, HARVARD, 67-70, HORTICULTURIST, 70- Am. Hort. Soc; Am. Soc. Plant. Taxon; Int. Asn. Plant Taxon. Ficus of Africa and America; taxonomy of cultivated plants. Address: 102 Wellesley St, Weston, MA 02193.

De WOLF, ROBERT A(BEL), b. Orange, Mass, Oct. 20. 05; m. 29; c. 3. ZOOLOGY. B.S, Norwich, 27, M.S, 30; Brown, 27-28. Instr. ZOOL, Norwich, 28-30; UNIV. R.I, 30-42, assoc. prof, 42-57, PROF, 57- AAAS. Vertebrate anatomy. Address: Dept. of Zoology, University of Rhode Island, Kingston, RI 02881.

DeWOLFE, BARBARA B(LANCHARD) O(AKESON), b. San Francisco, Calif, May 14, 12; m. 50, 60. VERTEBRATE ZOOLOGY. A.B, California, 33, fel, 35-36, Ph.D.(zool), 38. Asst. zool, California, 33-35, 36-37, instr. zool, col. agr. & jr. zoologist, exp. sta, 42-43; Palmer fel, Wellesley Col, 38-39; instr, jr. col, Calif, 39-42; ZOOL, Smith Col, 43-45; lectr, UNIV. CALIF, SANTA BARBARA, 46, asst. prof, 46-51, assoc. prof, 51-57, PROF, 57- Cooper Ornith. Soc; Am. Ornith Union; Ecol. Soc. Am. Environment, annual cycle and migration in white-crowned sparrows; vertebrate cycles and microclimates. Address: Dept. of Biological Sciences, University of California, Santa Barbara, CA 93106.

DEWOLFE, ROBERT H(ILL), b. Goldwaite, Texas, Oct. 8, 27; m. 60. ORGANIC CHEMISTRY. B.S, Texas, 50, M.A, 51, Ph.D.(chem), 53. Res. chemist, UNIV. CALIF, Los Angeles, 53-55, instr, SANTA BARBARA, 55-57, asst. prof. CHEM, 57-63, assoc. prof, 63-71, PROF, 71- U.S.A, 46-47. AAAS; Am. Chem. Soc; Brit. Chem. Soc. Kinetics and mechanisms of reactions of organic compounds at the carboxyl level of oxidation. Address: Dept. of Chemistry, University of California, Santa Barbara, CA 93106.

DEWS, EDMUND, b. Medford, Ore, Oct. 1, 21; m. 53, 59; c. 4. ATMOSPHERIC PHYSICS, SYSTEMS ANALYSIS. B.A, Stanford, 43; dipl, Washington (Seattle), 44; M.A, California, Los Angeles, 47; Rhodes scholar, Oxford, 47-50, B.A, 51, M.A, 54, dipl, Air War Col, 70. Chief air weather serv. upper air forecast sect, Oper. Crossroads, Kwajalein-Bikini, 46; instr. math. & physics, South. Ore. Col, 46; res. meteorologist, Air Force Cambridge Res. Ctr, 55-56, br. chief & aeronaut. res. adminstr. geophys, 57-58; v.pres. & managing ed, Pergamon Press, Inc, 59-60; MEM. ECON. DEPT, RAND CORP, 60-, asst. head, 64-66. Mem, Secy. of Air Force's Spec. Study Group on Air Power in Southeast Asia, 67-68. U.S.A.F, 43-46, Res, 47-70, Lt. Col. Am. Meteorol. Soc; Am. Geophys. Union; Royal Meteorol. Soc. Hurricane meteorology, dynamics of vertical motions, political economy of research and development; research and development organization and decision making; history of science; information storage and retrieval; military systems analysis; tactical air warfare. Address: Rand Corp, 1700 Main St, Santa Monica, CA 90406.

DEWS, PETER B(OOTH), b. Ossett, Eng, Sept. 11, 22; nat; m. 49; c. 4. PSYCHIATRY. M.B, Ch.B, Leeds, 44; Ph.D.(physiol), Minnesota, 52. Lectr. pharmacol, Leeds, 46-47; Wellcome res. fel, Wellcome Res. Lab, 48-49; from fel. to 1st asst. physiol. & res. assoc. biomet, Mayo Found, Minnesota, 50-51, 52; from instr. to assoc. prof. pharmacol, HARVARD MED. SCH, 53-62, STANLEY COBB PROF. PSYCHIAT. & PSYCHOBIOL, 62- Am. Soc. Pharmacol; Am. Physiol. Soc. Pharmacology of the central nervous system; psychobiology. Address: 181 Upland Rd, Newton, MA 02160.

DE WYS, EGBERT CHRISTIAAN, b. Soerabaja, Netherlands E. Indies, Apr. 9, 24; U.S. citizen; m. 49; c. 4. CRYSTALLOGRAPHY. B.A, Miami (Ohio), 50, M.A, 51; Bownocker scholar, & Ph.D.(mineral), Ohio State, 55. Asst, Miami (Ohio), 50-51; geologist, Creole Petrol. Corp, 51-53; scientist, Owens-Corning Fiberglas Corp, 55-57; mgr. crystal chem. dept, Ferro Corp, 57-59; staff physicist, fed. systs. div, Int. Bus. Mach. Corp, 59-60; adv. physicist, 60-63, sr. physicist, & mgr. process control dept, gen. prod. div, 63-64; dir. internal market develop, Bunker Ramo Corp, 64-65; supvr. ceramic physics, Int. Pipe & Ceramics Corp, 65-66; sr. scientist, Jet Propulsion Lab, Calif. Inst. Technol, 66-69; assoc. prof. mat. sci, Univ. Denver, 69-70; PROF. GEOCHEM, TEX. TECH UNIV, 70- Asst. prof, San Jose State Col, 62-63. Fel. Mineral. Soc. Am; Am. Ceramic Soc; Am. Geochem. Soc; fel. Royal Micros. Soc. Thermochemical crystallography; atomic structure of grain boundaries; solid state reaction kinetics; planetological research on Mars and the Moon. Address: Dept. of Geosciences, Texas Tech University, Lubbock, TX 79409.

DEXTER, A(RTHUR) H(ARLAN), b. Amsterdam, N.Y, Apr. 21, 23; m. 45; c. 5. PHYSICS. B.S, Rensselaer Polytech, 50, M.S, 51. Physicist, Argonne Nat. Lab, E.I. DU PONT DE NEMOURS & CO. INC, 51-53, SAVANNAH RIVER LAB, 53-54, res. supvr, 54-63, SR. PHYSICIST, 63- U.S.A.A.F, 42-44, Res, 46-53, Capt. Am. Phys. Soc; Am. Nuclear Soc. Radioisotopes; reactor and in-line instrumentation; nondestructive testing of fuel elements; pile, nuclear and applied physics; materials science; interaction of gases and metals. Address: 325 Homestead Lane, Aiken, SC 29801.

DEXTER, D(AVID) L(AWRENCE), b. Ashland, Wis, July 2, 24; m. 48; c. 5. PHYSICS. B.S, Michigan State; M.S, Wisconsin, 48, Ph.D.(physics), 51. Asst, Wisconsin, 48-50; res. assoc, Illinois, 51-52; UNIV. ROCHESTER, 52-53, asst. prof, 53-56, assoc. prof, 56-58, PROF. PHYSICS, 58- Consult, Naval Res. Lab, 52-; vis. Fulbright prof, Univ. Alexandria, 60-61; Univ. Genoa, 62-63; vis. prof, Univ. Rome, 69-70. U.S.A.A.F, 43-46. Fel. Am. Phys. Soc. X-rays; theory of solids. Address: Dept. of Physics, University of Rochester, Rochester, NY 14627.

DEXTER, DEBORAH MARY, b. Oakland, Calif, Sept. 28, 38. MARINE ZOOLOGY & ECOLOGY. B.A, Stanford, 60, M.A, 62; Nat. Sci. Found. fel, North Carolina, Chapel Hill, 64-66, Nat. Insts. Health fel, 66-67, Ph.D. (zool), 67. Asst. prof. ZOOL, SAN DIEGO STATE COL, 67-70, ASSOC. PROF, 70- Am. Soc. Limnol. & Oceanog; ecol. Soc. Am. Marine invertebrate zoology and ecology; population ecology of benthic invertebrates; sandy beach ecology. Address: Dept. of Zoology, San Diego State College, San Diego, CA 92115.

DEXTER, F(RANKLIN) D(UNBAR), b. Omaha, Nebr, Jan. 21, 18; m. 48; c. 3. ENGINEERING PHYSICS. B.S, Maine, 41. Physicist, UNION CARBIDE PLASTICS CO, 46-51, group leader, 51-53, asst. div. head, 53-56, asst. dir. develop, 56-60, assoc. dir. develop, 60-62, prod. mgr, 62-66, OPERS. MGR, 66-; MKT. AREA MGR, UNION CARBIDE CORP, 66- U.S.A, 41-46. AAAS; Am. Chem. Soc; Soc. Rheol.(v.pres, 51-55, pres, 55-57); Am. Phys. Soc; N.Y. Acad. Sci. Rheological properties of thermoplastics; polyvinyl chloride resin production and use. Address: 783 Watchung Rd, Bound Brook, NJ 08805.

DEXTER, MORRIS W, b. New York, N.Y, June 21, 09; m. 38; c. 4. MEDICINE. B.S, City Col, 31; M.A, Columbia, 32; fel, 33-37, Ph.D, 37; M.D, Cincinnati, 42. Instr. col. med, Cincinnati, 45-53, fel, dept. cardiol, 48-49; chief cardiol. sect. BAY PINES VET. ADMIN. CTR, FLA, 55-59, ASST. CHIEF. MED. SERV, 57- Dipl, Am. Bd. Internal Med, 50. U.S. Pub. Health Serv. Res, 44-46. Fel. Am. Col. Physicians; fel. Am. Col. Cardiol. Internal medicine and cardiology. Address: 409 Bayview Dr, Route 13, Clearwater, FL 33516.

DEXTER, RALPH W(ARREN), b. Gloucester, Mass, Apr. 7, 12; m. 38; c. 2. ECOLOGY. B.S, Mass. State Col, 34; Ph.D.(ecol), Illinois, 38. Asst. zool, Illinois, 34-37; instr. BIOL, KENT STATE UNIV, 37-40, asst. prof, 40-45, assoc. prof, 45-48, PROF, 48- Res. contract, U.S. Atomic Energy Cmn, 56-62. AAAS; Ecol. Soc. Am; Soc. Syst. Zool; Am. Malacol. Univ.(v.pres, 64-65, pres, 65-66); Am. Ornith. Union; Wilson Ornith. Soc; Am. Nature Study Soc; Hist. Sci. Soc; Marine Biol. Asn. India. Ecology of marine communities, Crustacea, Mollusca and Anostracan Phyllopods; life history of chimney swift; history of American naturalists; studies of bird-banding. Address: 1228 Fairview Dr, Kent, OH 44240.

DEXTER, RICHARD J(OHN), b. Kankakee, Ill, Aug. 26, 38; m. 57; c. 3. PHYSICS. B.S, Aurora Col, 61; M.S, North. Ill. Univ, 63; Ph.D.(physics), Va. Polytech. Inst, 70. Instr. physics, Millikin Univ, 63-65, chmn. dept, 65-66; MEM. TECH. STAFF SOLID STATE PHYSICS, SEMICONDUCTOR RES. & DEVELOP. LAB, TEX. INSTRUMENTS, INC, 69- Am. Asn. Physics Teachers. Ion implantation and effects of radiation damage in semiconductors, dielectrics, and thin films; theoretical studies in neutron transport theory. Address: Semiconductor Research & Development Lab, Texas Instruments Inc, Box 5012, Mail Station 72, Dallas, TX 75080.

DEXTER, RICHARD N(EWMAN), b. Port Huron, Mich, Sept. 2, 33; m. 61; c. 2. INTERNAL MEDICINE. A.B, Harvard, 55; M.D, Cornell Univ, 59. Intern, internal med, hosps, Univ. Minn, 59-60, resident, 60-62; res. assoc, Nat. Insts. Health, Bethesda, 62-64; resident, Peter Bent Brigham Hosp, Boston, 64-65; fel. endocrinol. & instr. med, sch. med, Vanderbilt Univ, 65-67; asst. prof. MED, SCH. MED, IND. UNIV, 67-70, ASSOC. PROF, 70- Dipl, Am. Bd. Internal Med. U.S.P.H.S, 62-64, Sr. Asst. Surg. Endocrine

Soc; fel. Am. Col. Physicians; Am. Fedn. Clin. Res. Endocrinology; metabolism. Address: Dept. of Medicine, Indiana University Medical Center, 1100 W. Michigan St, Indianapolis, IN 46202.

DEXTER, RICHARD N(ORMAN), b. Ashland, Wis, Nov. 22, 27; m. 58; c. 4. PHYSICS. B.S, Mich. State, 49; M.S, Wisconsin, 51, Ph.D.(physics), 55. Staff microwave res, Lincoln lab, Mass. Inst. Tech, 52-55, solid state physics, 53-55; asst. prof. PHYSICS, UNIV. WIS, MADISON, 55-58, assoc. prof, 58-61, PROF, 61- Alfred P. Sloan Found. fel, 55-59. U.S.N.R, 45-46. AAAS; fel. Am. Phys. Soc. Experimental solid state physics; energy band structure determinations; optical properties in vacuum ultraviolet. Address: Dept. of Physics, Sterling Hall, University of Wisconsin, Madison, WI 53706.

DEXTER, S(TEPHEN) T(ORREY), b. New London, Wis, Oct. 28, 97; m. 22; c. 4. AGRONOMY, CHEMISTRY. B.S.A, Wisconsin, 19, M.S, 25, fel, 29-31, Ph.D.(agr. biochem), 31. Teacher, high sch, Minn, 19-20; prof. chem. & physics, Northland Col, 21-30; Nat. Res. fel. biol, 31-33; head dept. science, Minn. State Teachers Col, Bemidji, 33-34; asst. prof. farm crops, Mich. State & res. assoc, Agr. Exp. Sta, 34-40, assoc. prof. & res. assoc, 40-48, prof, 48-68; RETIRED. Instr, U.S. Army Univ, England, France, 45-46. U.S.M.C, 18-19. AAAS; Am. Chem. Soc; Am. Soc. Plant Physiol; Am. Soc. Agron. Plant chemistry and physiology; determination of hardiness of plants by the electrical conductivity method; physiology of weeds; forage crop production, storage and utilization; moisture control and testing in crops; physiology; sugarbeet physiology and chemical analyses. Address: 727 Linden St, East Lansing, MI 48823.

DEXTER, T(HEODORE) H(ENRY), b. Preston, Cuba, June 1, 23; U.S. citizen; m. 52; c. 3. INORGANIC CHEMISTRY. B.S, Tulane, 44, M.S, 47; Ph.D.(chem), Illinois, 50. Asst. chem, Tulane, 43-44, 46-47; chemist, E.I. du Pont de Nemours & Co, 44-45; Gen. Aniline asst, Illinois, 47-49; chief inorg. res. sect, chem. div, Olin Mathieson Chem. Corp, 49-60; SUPVR, INORG. RES, HOOKER CHEM. CORP, 60- U.S.N.R, 45-46. Am. Chem. Soc; Electrochem. Soc. Inorganic specialty and heavy chemicals; applications to detergents, pulp, paper textiles, leather; fused salts; coordination compounds; chemistry of non-metallic elements, especially nitgrogen, phosphorus, oxygen, sulfur, fluorine and chlorine. Address: 850 Hillside Dr, Lewiston, NY 14092.

DEXTER, WARREN L(ORIS), b. Oakland, Calif, Nov. 3, 20; m. 47; c. 1. ELECTRICAL ENGINEERING. B.S, Polytech. Col. Eng, Calif, 41. Elec. engr, Westinghouse Elec. Co, Calif, 41-43; SUPV. ENGR, LAWRENCE RADIATION LAB, UNIV. CALIF, 43-, GROUP DIR. & TECH. CONSULT, PROJ. PATENT GROUP, 50-, designer H.V. equip, 45-50, coordinator eng, 88 & 90 inch cyclotron, hilac heavy ion accelerator & omnitron heavy ion synchrotron, 55-56. Consult, Yale, 57-58; Southern California, 58-60; Stanford, 58-64; Argonne Nat. Lab; Colorado; Naval Res. Radiol. Lab; Maryland; Texas A&M. Citation, Secy. War. With Off. Sci. Res. & Develop, 44. Sr. mem. Inst. Elec. & Electronics Eng. Design of electronic equipment; circuitry for particle accelerators. Address: 55 Orchard Rd, Orinda, CA 94563.

DEYE, J(AMES) A(LAN), b. Covington, Ky, June 1, 44; m. 68; c. 2. NUCLEAR & HEALTH PHYSICS. B.A, Thomas More Col, 65; Atomic Energy Comn. fel, Vanderbilt Univ, 65-68, M.S, 69, Ph.D.(nuclear physics), 70; Oak Ridge Assoc. Univs. fel, Oak Ridge Nat. Lab, 68-70. ASST. PROF. PHYSICS, UNIV. DAYTON, 70- Am. Phys. Soc; Health Physics Soc. Nuclear spectroscopy via direct elastic and inelastic proton scattering; conversion electron-gamma ray angular correlation; applied problems in health and radiological physics. Address: Dept. of Physics, University of Dayton, Dayton, OH 45409.

DEYOE, CHARLES W, b. Two Buttes, Colo, Mar. 12, 33; m. 56; c. 5. BIOCHEMISTRY, NUTRITION. B.S, Kansas State, 55; M.S, Texas A&M, 57, Nat. Insts. Health fel, 58-59, fel, 59-60, Ph.D.(biochem), 59. Asst. prof. biochem. & poultry nitrit, Texas A&M, 60-62; FEED TECHNOL, KANS. STATE UNIV, 62-63, assoc. prof, 63-68, PROF, 68- Am. Soc. Animal Sci; Poultry Sci. Asn; Am. Chem. Soc; Am. Asn. Cereal Chem; World Poultry Sci. Asn; Inst. Food Technol. Nutrition of farm animals and biochemistry related to animal processes; feed technology and chemical relationships between foodstuffs and nutritive values. Address: Dept. of Grain Science & Industry, Kansas State University, Manhattan, KS 66504.

DE YOUNG, DAVID S(PENCER), b. Colorado Springs, Colo, Nov. 29, 40. THEORETICAL ASTROPHYSICS. B.A, Univ. Colo, 62; Woodrow Wilson fel, 62-63; Nat. Sci. Found. fel, 63-64; NASA trainee, 65-67; Ph.D.(physics), Cornell Univ, 67. Res. Scientist, Los Alamos Sci. Lab, 67-69; ASST. SCIENTIST, NAT. RADIO ASTRON. OBSERV, 69- Consult, Los Alamos Sci. Lab, 70- AAAS; Am. Astron. Soc; Am. Phys. Soc; Am. Geophys. Union. Origin and evolution of extended extragalactic radio sources; physics of galactic nuclei and quasi-stellar objects; evolution of dense stellar systems; solar flares and interplanetary disturbances. Address: National Radio Astronomy Observatory, Edgemont Rd, Charlottesville, VA 22901.

DeYOUNG, EDWIN L(AWSON), b. Milwaukee, Wis, Jan. 14, 29; m. 56; ORGANIC CHEMISTRY. B.S, Louisville, 52, Nat. Sci. Found. fel, 52-53, M.S, 53; Minn. Mining & Mfg. Co. fel, Illinois, 53-56, Ph.D.(org. chem), 56. Res. chemist, Reynolds Metals Co, Ky, 52-53; Minn. Mining & Mfg. Co, 54; Shell Develop. Co, Colo, 55; Whiting Res. Labs, Standard Oil Co. Ind, 56-60; R B & P Chem. Co, Wis, 60-62; Universal Oil Prod. Co, Des Plaines, 62-68; PROF. CHEM. & CHMN. DEPT. PHYS. SCI, CHICAGO CITY COL, LOOP BR, 68- U.S.A, 46-49. Am. Inst. Chem; Am. Chem. Soc. Metal organic compounds; synthesis and reactions; pi-complexes and metal aromatic compounds. Address: Dept. of Physical Science, Chicago City College, Loop Branch, 64 E. Lake St, Chicago, IL 60601.

DeYOUNG, JACOB J, b. Grand Rapids, Mich, May 14, 26; m. 57; c. 4. ORGANIC CHEMISTRY. A.B, Hope Col, 50; M.S, Wayne State, 52, fel, 53-56, Ethyl Corp. fel, 56-57, Ph.D, 58. Chemist, Merck Chem. Co, 52-53; from asst. prof. to ASSOC. PROF. CHEM, ALMA COL, 57- Nat. Sci. Found. Summer Inst, 59. U.S.A, 45-46. Am. Chem. Soc. Organic synthesis; isolation and synthesis of natural products from plants. Address: Dept. of Chemistry, Alma College, Alma, MI 48801.

DE YOUNG, MARVIN, b. Grand Rapids, Mich, Nov. 23, 26; m. 48; c. 7. PHYSICS, PHYSICAL CHEMISTRY. A.B, Calvin Col, 48; M.A, South Dakota, 61; Ph.D.(chem), Univ. of the Pacific, 65. Teacher, high sch, 48-58; instr. chem, DORDT COL, 58-61, asst. prof, 61-65, assoc. prof. chem. & physics, 65-70, PROF. PHYSICS, 70- Am. Phys. Soc; Am. Asn. physics Teachers; Nat. Sci. Teachers Asn; Am. Geophys. Union; Am. Meteorol. Soc. Electronic engineering; agricultural meteorology. Address: Dept. of Physics, Dordt College, Sioux Center, IA 51250.

DeYOUNG, WILLARD G, b. Chicago, Ill, June 20, 08; m. 35; c. 2. INTERNAL MEDICINE. B.S, Wheaton Col.(Ill), 30; M.D, sch. med, Univ. Chicago, 36. Chief med, stud. health serv. & res. assoc. med, sch. med, Univ. Chicago, 61-67; co-dir. med. educ, ILL. CENT. HOSP. ASN, 67, DIR. MED. EDUC, 67-, DIR. OUTPATIENT SERV, 70-, coord. outpatient serv, 67-70. Guest exam, Am. Bd. Internal Med, 50; asst. to chief med. off. & attend. physidian, Univ. Ill. Div, Cook County Hosp, 69- Dipl, Am. Bd. Internal Med, 47. Am. Col. Health Asn; Am. Med. Asn. Vitamin deficiency and parasitic infections; diagnosis of amoebiasis; steroids in the treatment of infectious mononucleosis; early diagnosis of atherosclerosis. Address: Illinois Central Hospital Association, 5800 Stony Island Ave, Chicago, IL 60637.

DEYRUP, A(LDEN) JOHNSON), b. Chicago, Ill, Nov. 30, 09; m. PHYSICAL CHEMISTRY. A.B, Columbia, 28, A.M, 29, Ph.D.(phys. chem), 32. Nat. Res. fel, Wisconsin, 32-34; Wisconsin Alumni Res. Found. fel, 34-35; res. chemist, E.I. du Pont de Nemours & Co, 35-70; RETIRED. Am. Chem. Soc. Very acid solutions; reaction kinetics; catalysis of acetal reaction; adiabatic calorimetry; ceramic product and pigment development; high temperature inorganic chemistry. Address: 6 Penn Dr, West Chester, PA 19380.

DEYRUP, JAMES ALDEN, b. Englewood, N.J, Oct. 13, 36; m. 61; c. 1. ORGANIC CHEMISTRY. B.A, Swarthmore Col, 57; Ph.D.(org. chem), Illinois, 61. Nat. Sci. Found. fel, Univ. Zurich, 61-62; instr. CHEM, Harvard, 62-65; asst. prof, UNIV. FLA, 65-69, ASSOC. PROF, 69-, ASST. DEAN PREPROF; EDUC, COL. MED. & DENT, 71- Chemistry of small ring compounds including heterocyclics; natural products. Address: Dept. of Chemistry, University of Florida, Gainesville, FL 32601.

DEYRUP-OLSEN, INGRITH J(OHNSON), b. Nyack, N.Y, Dec. 22, 19; m. 62. ZOOLOGY. A.B, Columbia, 40, Ph.D.(physiol), 44. Instr. physiol, col. physicians & surg, Columbia, 42-47, lectr. ZOOL, Barnard Col, 47, asst. prof, 47-52, assoc. prof, 52-59, prof, 59-64; res. prof, UNIV. WASH, 64-69, PROF, 69- Guggenheim fel, 53-54; Fulbright fel. Denmark, 53-54. AAAS; Soc. Gen. Physiol; Am. Soc. Zool; Am. Physiol. Soc; N.Y. Acad. Sci. Physiology; circulation; kidney; circulatory changes following subcutaneous injection of histamine in dogs; water and electrolyte exchange of tissue slices. Address: Dept. of Zoology, University of Washington, Seattle, WA 98105.

DEYSACH, LAWRENCE GEORGE, b. Milwaukee, Wis, July 9, 36; m. 66. MATHEMATICAL BIOLOGY. B.S, Marquette, 57, Danforth fels, 57-59; univ. fel, Harvard, 62-63, A.M, 63, Danforth fel, 63-66; Danforth fel, Chicago, 66-69. Lectr. math. biol, Chicago, 67-69; MEDICAL STATISTICIAN, G.D. SEARLE & CO, SKOKIE, 69- AAAS; Biophys. Soc. Topological dynamics; mathematical ecology and biophysics; general systems theory; experimental design of clinical trials; pharmacokinetics; stochastic processes. Address: 944 Wesley, Evanston, IL 60202.

de ZAFRA, ROBERT L(EE), b. White Plains, N.Y, Feb. 15, 32; m. PHYSICS. A.B, Princeton, 54; Ph.D.(physics), Maryland, 58. Res. asst. PHYSICS, Princeton, 55; Maryland, 57-58; instr, Univ. Pa, 58-61; asst. prof, STATE UNIV. N.Y. STONY BROOK, 61-64, ASSOC. PROF, 64- Nat. Res. Coun. sr. fel, NASA, 70-71. Am. Phys. Soc; Am. Asn. Physics Teachers. Atomic and molecular physics; quantum electronics. Address: Dept. of Physics, State University of New York at Stony Brook, Stony Brook, NY 11790.

DE ZEEUW, CARL H(ENRI), b. East Lansing, Mich, Dec. 6, 12; m. 39; c. 5. WOOD TECHNOLOGY, MECHANICS. B.A, Mich. State Col, 34, B.S, 37; M.S, State Univ, N.Y. Col. Forestry, Syracuse, 39, Ph.D.(wood anat), 49. Instr. wood tech, N.Y. State Col. Forestry, 47-49, asst. prof, 49-55; assoc. prof. STATE UNIV. N.Y. COL. FORESTRY, SYRACUSE UNIV, 55-61, PROF. WOOD PROD. ENG, 61- Consult. col. forestry, Univ. Philippines, State Univ. N.Y. & U.S. Int. Coop. Admin, 59-61; Food & Agr. Orgn, Philippines, 66, Venezuela, 68, Arg, 71. U.S.A.A.F, 41-46, Lt. Col. Forest Prod. Res. Soc; Am. Soc. Test. & Mat; Int. Asn. Wood Anat. Interrelationship of gross wood anatomy, ultra structure and composition of the woody cell wall and the physical properties of wood. Address: Dept. of Wood Products Engineering, State University of New York College of Forestry at Syracuse University, Syracuse, NY 13210.

deZEEUW, DONALD J(OHN), b. East Lansing, Mich, July 6, 11; m. 50; c. 1. PLANT PATHOLOGY. B.S, Mich. State Col, 33; M.S, Minnesota, 41, Ph.D, 49. Agent, U.S. Dept. Agr, 34-38; res. asst. plant path, Minnesota, 38-41, 46-48; biologist, Butler County Mushroom Farms, Inc, Pa, 41-43; asst. res. prof. VEG. PATH, MICH. STATE UNIV, 48-55, assoc. res. prof, 55-62, RES. PROF, 62- Med.C, U.S.A, 43-45. Am. Phytopath. Soc. Vegetable seed treatment; diseases of Cucurbits; breeding for resistance to vegetable diseases; plant virus diseases. Address: Dept. of Plant Pathology, Michigan State University, East Lansing, MI 48823.

DE ZEEUW, JOHN ROBERT, b. Brooklyn, N.Y, Apr. 6, 28; m. 50; c. 2. BIOCHEMISTRY. B.S, Cornell, 49, Ph.D.(biochem), 54. Chemist, Chas. Pfizer & Co, Inc, 49-50; asst, Cornell, 50-53; biochemist, PFIZER, INC, 54-64, mgr. microbiol. res, 64-67, ASST. DIR. BIOCHEM. RES, 67- Genetics Soc. Am; Am. Soc. Microbiol. Microbial genetics. Address: Montauk Ave, Stonington, CT 06378.

DEZENBERG, GEORGE JOHN, b. Tientsin, China, Jan. 12, 35; U.S. citizen; m. 60; c. 4. ELECTRICAL ENGINEERING. B.E.E, Auburn, 60; M.S, Arkansas, 62; Ph.D.(elec. eng), Ga. Inst. Tech, 66. RES. ELECTRONIC ENGR, PHYS. SCI. LAB, U.S. ARMY MISSILE COMMAND, 65- Ord.C, U.S.A, 65-67, Capt. Inst. Elec. & Electronic Eng; Optical Soc. Am. Carbon dioxide laser research, including Q-switching, mode locking, multipath, and mode control techniques. Address: 910 San Ramon Ave, Huntsville, AL 35802.

DE ZOETEN, GUSTAAF A, b. Tjepoe, Indonesia, July 5, 34; m. 61; c. 2. PLANT PATHOLOGY & VIROLOGY. M.Sc, Wageningen, 60; Ph.D.(plant path), California, Davis, 65. Tech. asst. plant physiol, West. Prov. Res. Sta, S.Africa, 57-58; lab. technician plant path, California, Davis, 62, 64-65, asst. res. plant pathologist, Berkeley, 65-67; asst. prof. PLANT PATH, UNIV. WIS, MADISON, 67-70, ASSOC. PROF, 70- Royal Dutch Navy, Lt.(jg). Am. Phytopath. Soc; Dutch Phytopath. Soc; Royal Soc. Agr. Sci. Netherlands. Physiology and cytology of virus host relationships; electron microscopy. Address: Dept. of Plant Pathology, University of Wisconsin, Madison, WI 53706

D'HAENENS, I(RNEE) J, b. Mishawaka, Ind, Feb. 3, 34; m. 55; c. 4. SOLID STATE PHYSICS, PHYSICAL ELECTRONICS. B.S, Notre Dame, 56, Hughes fel. & Ph.D.(physics), 66; M.A, Southern California, 58. SECT. HEAD QUANTUM ELECTRONICS & SR. STAFF PHYSICIST, HUGHES RES. LABS, 56- Am. Phys. Soc. Laser and maser physics; surface barrier analysis through study of periodic Schottky deviations in thermionic emission. Address: Hughes Research Labs, 3011 Malibu Canyon Rd, Malibu, CA 90265.

DHALIWAL, AMRIK S, b. Punjab, India, Nov. 17, 34; m. 62; c. 2. HORTICULTURE, VIROLOGY. B.Sc, Punjab, India, 55; M.Sc, Utah State, 59, Ph.D. (hort), 62. Res. assoc. plant virol, Utah State Univ, 62-65, ASST. PROF. bot, 65-66; BIOL, LOYOLA UNIV. CHICAGO, 66- AAAS. Cytogenetics and plant breeding of field and horticultural crops; post harvest physiology, pathology and biochemistry of fruits and vegetables; biochemistry and in vitro synthesis of plant viruses. Address: Dept. of Biology, Loyola University of Chicago, 6525 N. Sheridan Rd, Chicago, IL 60626.

DHALIWAL, RANJIT S, b. Bilaspur, India, June 21, 30; m. 58; c. 1. APPLIED MATHEMATICS. B.A, Punjab, India, 51, M.A, 55; fel, Indian Inst. Tech, Kharagpur, 58-60, Ph.D.(appl. math), 60. Lectr. MATH, Guru Nanak Col. Dabwali, Punjab, India, 55-56, Guru Nanak Eng. Col, Ludhiana, 56-61; Indian Inst. Tech, New Delhi, 61-63, asst. prof, 63-66; assoc. prof, UNIV. CALGARY, 66-71, PROF, 71- Visitor, Imp. Col, Univ. London, 64-65; vis. prof, City Univ. London, 71-72; sr. res. assoc, Glasgow Univ, 71-72. Am. Acad. Mech; Am. Math. Soc; Soc. Indust. & Appl. Math; Can. Math. Cong; Indian Math. Soc; Indian Soc. Theoret. & Appl. Mech. Theory of plates; elastodynamics; viscoelasticity; thermoelasticity. Address: Dept. of Mathematics, University of Calgary, Calgary, Alta, Can.

DHALLA, NARANJAN SINGH, b. Punjab, India, Oct. 10, 36. PHYSIOLOGY, PHARMACOLOGY. M.S, Univ. Pa, 63; Ph.D.(pharmacol), Univ. Pittsburgh, 65; F.I.C, Inst. Chem, India. Res. assoc. biochem, sch. med, St. Louis Univ, 66, ASST. PROF. pharmacol, 66-68; PHYSIOL, FACULTY MED, UNIV. MAN, 68- Mem, Int. Study Group Res. Cardiac Metab. Am. Soc. Pharmacol. & Exp. Therapeut; Am. Physiol. Soc; Can. Physiol. Soc; Pharmacol. Soc. Can; fel. Inst. Chem. India. Pathophysiology of heart, muscle contraction, membrane transport and autonomic nervous system. Address: Dept. of Physiology, Faculty of Medicine, University of Manitoba, Winnipeg 3, Man, Can.

DHAMI, KEWAL SINGH, b. Punjab, India, Jan. 10, 33; Can. citizen; m. 59; c. 1. ORGANIC & POLYMER CHEMISTRY. B.Sc, Panjab Univ, India, 54, M.Sc, 55; Welsch Found. fel, Univ. Tex, summer 60; Petrol. Res. Fund fel. & Ph.D.(org. chem), Univ. West. Ont, 64. U.S. Air Force assoc. chem, Ohio State Univ, 64-65; SR. RES. CHEMIST, res & develop. div, Polymer Corp. Ltd, Ont, 65-69; ITT WIRE & CABLE DIV, INT. TEL. & TEL. CORP, 69- Am. Chem. Soc; fel. The Chem. Soc. C^{13} nuclear magnetic resonance studies of organic compounds; preparation and properties of new polymers; mechanical and physical properties of polymers; degradation of polymeric compounds; synthesis of new sulfur compounds. Address: Research & Development Division, ITT Wire & Cable, International Telephone & Telegraph Corp, Clinton, MA 01510.

DHANAK, AMRITLAL M(AGANLAL), b. Bhavnagar, India, July 13, 25; nat; m. 54; c. 3. MECHANICAL ENGINEERING. M.S, California, 51, Ph.D. (mech. eng), 56. Res. engr, California, 52-56; proj. engr, Gen. Elec. Co, 56-58; assoc. prof, Rensselaer Polytech, 58-61; PROF. MECH. ENG, MICH. STATE UNIV, 61- Sr. staff scientist & consult, Avco Mfg. Corp, 59-62. AAAS; N.Y. Acad. Sci; Am. Soc. Eng. Educ; Am. Soc. Mech. Eng. Heat transfer; thermodynamics and fluid dynamics with specializations in nuclear and missile fields. Address: Dept. of Mechanical Engineering, Michigan State University, East Lansing, MI 48823.

DHARIWAL, ANAND P. S, b. India, Dec. 21, 35. PHYSIOLOGY, NEUROENDOCRINOLOGY. B.S. & M.S, Agra, 54; fel, Univ. Ill, 55, Ph.D.(agr. chem), 58. Fel. biochem, sch. med, Georgetown, 59-60; res. assoc. med. & biochem, sch. med, Western Reserve, 60-61; instr. med. res. & biochem, col. med, Baylor, 61-63; assoc. physiol, sch. med, Pennsylvania, 63-65; asst. prof, Southwest. Med. Col, Univ. Tex, 65-70; MEM. STAFF, KERN GEN. HOSP, 70- Res. scientist, Vet. Admin. Hosp, 61-63; consult, Wilson Labs, Chicago, Ill, 62; Sci. Glassblowing Co, 66; Stanford, 66- Endocrine Soc; N.Y. Acad. Sci. Chemistry of dentine protein; development of method for determination of fixed ammonia; purification and isolation of gastric hormones; physiology and biochemistry of hypothalamic factors which influence pituitary secretion. Address: Kern General Hospital, 1830 Flower St, Bakersfield, CA 93305.

D'HEEDENE, ROBERT NORMAN, b. Hempstead, N.Y, Dec. 5, 34; m. 61; c. 4. MATHEMATICS. B.Eng.Phys, Cornell, 57; A.M, Harvard, 58, Ph.D.(appl. math), 60. Mathematician, appl. res. lab, Sylvania Elec. Prod, Inc, Mass, 60; Nat. Sci. Found. fel, 60-61; instr. math, Polytech. Inst. Brooklyn, 61-62, asst. prof, 62-68; RES. SCIENTIST, GRUMMAN AEROSPACE CORP, 68- Mem. adjunct staff, Adelphi Univ. Am. Math. Soc; Soc. Ind. & Appl. Math. Applied mathematics; differential equations; decision theory; special functions; numerical analysis. Address: 30 Bryce Ave, Glen Cove, NY 11542.

DHINDSA, K. S, b. India, Jan. 24, 32; Can. citizen; m. 60. CELL BIOLOGY, PSYCHOBIOLOGY. B.Sc, Panjab Univ, India, 51, Hons, 53, scholar, 53-54, M.Sc, 54; Univ. Calif, Los Angeles, 62-63; Ph.D.(zool), Univ. Helsinki, 70. Demonstr. zool, Panjab Univ, 53-56, lectr, Col. Faridkot, 55-61, sr. lectr. biol, Dairy Sci. Col, 61-62; asst. zool, Univ. Calif, Los Angeles, 62-63; biol, Inst. Biol. Res, Culver City, Calif, 63-65; ASST. PROF. zool, Panjab Agr. Univ. India, 65-66; BIOL, LOYOLA COL. MONTREAL, 67-, res. grant, 69. Nat. Res. Coun. Can. res. grants, 69 & 71-72. AAAS; fel. Royal Micros. Soc, 65; Am. Soc. Zool; Can. Soc. Cell Biol. The effect of psychotherapeutic drugs on brain and endocrine metabolism; RNA synthesis in brain and other tissues in mammals using histochemical and radiographic methods. Address: Dept. of Biology, Loyola College of Montreal, Montreal 262, Que, Can.

DHINGRA, YOG R, b. Leiah, Pakistan, Aug. 31, 33; Can. citizen; m. 65; c. 1. ORGANIC CHEMISTRY. B.Sc, D.A.V. Col, Dehra Dun, 53; M.Sc, Lucknow, 57; Ph.D.(chem), Purdue, 62. Preservation asst, chem. labs, Dept. Archaeol, Govt. India, 54-55; res. asst. biochem, Christian Med. Col. & Hosp, India, 58; RES. CHEMIST, St. Clair River Works, du Pont Can. Ltd, 62-68; ORG. CHEM. PROD. RES, DOW CHEM. CO, 68- Am. Chem. Soc; sr. mem. Chem. Inst. Can. Organo fluorine compounds. Address: Organic Chemicals Production Research, 1710 Bldg, Dow Chemical Co, Midland, MI 48640.

DHYSE, F(REDERICK) G(EORGE), b. Hinkley, Utah, June 23, 18; m. 50; c. 2. BIOCHEMISTRY. B.A, California, 41. Chemist control & prod. res, Cutter Labs, Calif, 41-46; vitamins in canned foods, Gerber Prods. Co, 46-47; biochemist endocrinol. sect, Nat. Cancer Inst, NAT. INSTS. HEALTH, 48-50, res. analyst document. sect, 50-63, biochemist cancer studies, 53-66, SCI. INFO. OFF, NAT. INST. CHILD HEALTH & HUMAN DEVELOP, 66- AAAS; Am. Chem. Soc. Vitamin function; biotin; hormonal activity; antivitamins, antimetabolites in cancer; machine and punch-card applications to problems of scientific literature. Address: National Institutes of Health, Bethesda, MD 20014.

DIAB, IHSAN M, b. Jaffa, Palestine, Aug. 26, 33; U.S. citizen; m. 61; c. 2. PHARMACOLOGY, BIOCHEMISTRY. B.S, Roosevelt Univ, 60; U.A.R. fel, Cairo Univ, 60-62; U.S. Pub. Health Serv. fel. & Ph.D.(pharmacol), Univ. Ill, Chicago, 68. Instr. med. technol, Chicago Sch. Med. Technicians, 55-60; asst. instr. biochem, med. sch, 60-63; Cairo Univ, pharmacol, Univ. Ill. Med. Sch, 63-67; ASSOC. PROF. & RES. ASSOC, UNIV. CHICAGO, 68- Med.C, U.S.A, 53-55. AAAS; Am. Chem. Soc. Pharmacological action, localization and distribution of lysergic acid diethylamide as well as other hallucinogenic drugs; action of various drugs on body hormones and neurohumors. Address: Dept. of Pharmacology, University of Chicago, Chicago, IL 60637.

DIAB, KHALED M, b. Acre, Israel, May 20, 27; m. 57; c. 1. ELECTRICAL ENGINEERING, MATHEMATICS. B.S, Iowa, 56, M.S, 57, Ph.D.(elec. eng), 59; M.B.A, State Univ. N.Y. Buffalo, 63. Teacher, Govt. Palestine, 46-48; Govt. Syria, 48-53; engr, Westinghouse Elec. Corp, 57-58, sr. engr, 57-61; eng. specialist, Sylvania Elec. Prods, Inc, Gen. Tel. & Electronics Corp, 61-62, sr. eng. specialist, 62-63, res. dept. mgr. elec. eng, 63-64, sr. scientist, 64-67; from mgr. info. sci. res. to DIR. ADVAN. PROGS. & PLANNING COMMUN. & ELECTRONICS, MARTIN-MARIETTA CO, 67- Adv, State Univ. N.Y. Buffalo, 59, lectr, 61; summer asst. engr, Westinghouse Elec. Corp, 56. Sr. mem. Inst. Elec. & Electronics Eng; Am. Mgt. Asn. Anti-jam secure and advanced communication; feedback theory and control; utilization of computers in advanced control and communication systems. Address: 3013 Cullen Lake Shore Dr, Orlando, FL 32809.

DIACHUN, STEPHEN, b. Phenix, R.I, Aug. 20, 12; m. 38; c. 2. PLANT PATHOLOGY. B.S, R.I. State Col, 34; M.S, Illinois, 35, Ph.D.(plant path), 38. Asst. bot, Illinois, 34-37; PLANT PATH, EXP. STA, UNIV. KY, 37-46, asst. prof, 47-51, assoc. prof, 51-53, PROF, 53-, PLANT PATHOLOGIST, 50-, assoc. plant pathologist, 46-50. AAAS; Am. Phytopath. Soc; Bot. Soc. Am. Relation of environment to bacterial and fungus leaf spots of tobacco; growth of bacteria on roots; distribution of tobacco mosaic virus in plants; inoculation methods with streak virus of tobacco; virus diseases of forage legumes. Address: Dept. of Plant Pathology, University of Kentucky, Lexington, KY 40506.

DIACUMAKOS, ELAINE G, b. Chester, Pa, Aug. 11, 30; m. 58. CELL BIOLOGY. B.S, Univ. Md, 51; M.S, N.Y. Univ, 55, Ph.D.(biol), 58. Lab. instr, microsurg, N.Y. Univ, 56-58, res. assoc, 58-66; Sloan-Kettering Inst. Cancer Res, 58-60, assoc, 60-71, sect. head, 64-69; res. assoc, Sloan-Kettering Div, Grad. Sch. Med. Sci, Cornell Univ, 59-63, instr, 63-71; SR. RES. ASSOC, ROCKEFELLER UNIV, 71- Guest investr, Rockefeller Inst, 62-64; U.S. Pub. Health Serv. spec. fel, 63-64. N.Y. Acad. Sci. Cancerigenesis; somatic cell and biochemical genetics; congenital malformations; microsurgery; automation. Address: Dept. of Biochemical Genetics, Rockefeller University, New York, NY 10021.

DIAL, NORMAN A(RNOLD), b. Kell, Ill, June 17, 26; m. 58; c. 4. ZOOLOGY. A.B, Ill. Col, 49; M.S, Illinois, 52, Ph.D.(zool), 60. ASSOC. PROF. ZOOL, IND. STATE UNIV, 60- Med.C, U.S.A, 52-54. Causal factors in cellular differentiation during embryonic development. Address: Dept. of Life Sciences, Indiana State University, Terre Haute, IN 47802.

DIAL, ROY E(VERETT), b. East St. Louis, Ill, Nov. 18, 17; m. 42; c. 4. INORGANIC CHEMISTRY. B.S, Illinois, 41, Ph.D.(inorg. chem), 48. Chem. engr, Gen. Chem. Co, Ill, 41; res. chemist, Gen. Aniline & Film Corp, 48-51, sr. res. chemist, Aluminum res. lab, Aluminum Co. Am, 52-57; supvr. engr, CARBORUNDUM CO, 57-60, asst. to dir. res. & develop, 60-62, mgr. tech. br, REFRACTORIES & ELECTRONICS DIV, 62-64, mkt. mgr, 64-68, mgr. sales eng, 68-70, WEST. REGIONAL SALES MGR, 70- Sig.C, 41-46, U.S.A.R, 46-, Col. Am. Chem. Soc; Am. Ceramics Soc; Am. Inst. Chem. Eng. Bayer process of producing aluminum oxides and hydrated oxides;

refractory nitrides; corrosion of ceramics; binders for abrasives; fundamentals of grinding; infrared spectroscopy; semiconductors; ceramic fibers; super refractory products. Address: Refractories & Electronics Division, Carborundum Co, P.O. Box 367, Niagara Falls, NY 14302.

DIAL, WILLIAM R(ICHARD), b. Washington Court House, Ohio, Aug. 30, 14; m. 36; c. 1. ORGANIC CHEMISTRY. A.B, Ohio Wesleyan, 36; fel, Illinois, 36-39, Ph.D.(org. chem), 39. Org. chemist, Columbia Chem. Div, Pittsburgh Plate Glass Co, 39-52; Columbia-South. Chem. Corp, 52-59, mgr. appl. org. res, CHEM. DIV, Pittsburgh Plate Glass Co, 59-64, ASST. DIR. RES, 64-69, PPG INDUSTS, INC, 69- Am. Chem. Soc; Soc. Plastic Eng; Soc. Plastic Indust. Synthetic resins and plastics; plasticizers; casting synthetic resins; structure of gossypol; chlorinated hydrocarbons; polymerization catalysts; reinforcing rubber and paper fillers; phosgene derivatives. Address: 438 Roslyn Ave, Akron, OH 44320.

DIALAMEH, GHOLAM H(OSSEIN), b. Tehran, Iran, July 06, 28. BIOCHEMISTRY. B.S, Tehran Col, Iran, 47; Ph.D.(pharm), Univ. Tehran, 52; Pasteur Inst, 52-54. Dir. pub. health lab, Ministry Health, Iran, 54-55; incharge med. biochem. lab. & food control, Univ. Tehran & Pasteur Inst, 55-56; res. asst. biochem, Purdue, 56-57; Am. Cancer Soc. res. fel, BIOCHEM, Pittsburgh, 57-59, res. assoc, grad. sch. pub. health, 59-65; ASST. PROF, SCH. MED, ST. LOUIS UNIV, 65- AAAS; Am. Chem. Soc; Brit. Biochem. Soc. Address: Dept. of Biochemistry, St. Louis University School of Medicine, St. Louis, MO 63103.

DIAMANTIS, WILLIAM, b. New York, N.Y, May 27, 23; m. 50; c. 2. BIOLOGICAL SCIENCES. B.S, Fordham, 44, M.S, 55, Ph.D.(biol), 59. Asst. instr. physiol. & pharmacol, col. pharm, Fordham, 44-45, instr. pharmacog, 45-58, asst. prof. pharmacog, microbiol. & physiol, 58-60; SR. PHARMACOLOGIST, WALLACE LABS. DIV, CARTER-WALLACE, INC, 60- AAAS; N.Y. Acad. Sci. Autonomic pharmacology; gastrointestinal pharmacology; inflammation; antipyresis; chemical mediators in anaphylaxis; pharmacology of natural products. Address: Pharmacology, Wallace Labs. Division, Carter-Wallace, Inc, Cranbury, NJ 08512.

DIAMOND, AINSLEY HERBERT, b. San Francisco, Calif, May 27, 09. MATHEMATICS. A.B, California, Berkeley, 30, M.A, 31, Ph.D.(math), 33. Am. Field Serv. fel, Paris, 33-34; instr. math. & physics, Col. St. Scholastica, 34-35; math, exten. div, California, 35-37, lectr, Los Angeles, 37-38; prof. & head dept, Okla. Agr. & Mech. Col, 38-42, 46-51; prof, Kansas, 51-52; head math. br, off. ord. res, U.S. Army, N.C, 52-53; PROF. MATH, Stevens Inst. Tech, 53-59; Webb Inst, 59-60; STEVENS INST. TECHNOL, 60- Dir. prog, Nat. Sci. Found. grant, 63- U.S.A.A.F, 42-46, Capt. Am. Math. Soc. Mathematical logic. Address: Dept. of Mathematics, Stevens Institute of Technology, Hoboken, NJ 07030.

DIAMOND, BEN ELKAN, b. New York, N.Y, Aug. 22, 11; m. 41; c. 3. BACTERIOLOGY. B.S, Kansas State, 38; M.A, South Dakota, 39. Asst, State Health Lab, 38-39, sr. bacteriologist, 40-45; asst. dir, DIV. LABS, S.DAK. STATE DEPT. HEALTH, 45-46, DIR, 46- Chmn, Conf. State & Prov. Pub. Health Lab. Dirs, 59. Fel. AAAS; Am. Soc. Microbiol; fel. Am. Pub. Health Asn; Am. Soc. Prfnl. Biol. Public health bacteriology and serology; diagnostic antigens; laboratory methodology. Address: Division of Labs, South Dakota State Dept. of Health, Pierre, SD 57501.

DIAMOND, DAVID J(OSEPH), b. New York, N.Y, Dec. 31, 40; m. 62; c. 3. REACTOR PHYSICS, NUCLEAR ENGINEERING. B.E.P, Cornell, 62; M.S, Arizona, 64; Atomic Energy Cmn. fel, Mass. Inst. Tech, 67-68, Ph.D.(nuclear eng), 68. Nuclear engr, Westinghouse Astronuclear Lab, 63-64; res. asst. reactor physics, BROOKHAVEN NAT. LAB, 65, NUCLEAR ENGR, 68- Am. Nuclear Soc. Transport theory; reactor safety. Address: Brookhaven National Lab, Upton, NY 11973.

DIAMOND, EARL L(OUIS), b. Tiffin, Ohio, Nov. 8, 28; m. 60; c. 1. STATISTICS. A.B, Miami (Fla), 50; M.A, North Carolina, 52, Ph.D.(math. statist), 58. Asst. math. statist, North Carolina, 52-54, biostatist, 56-57, asst. prof, 57-59; sr. asst. sanitarian, communicable disease center, U.S. Pub. Health Serv, 54-56; asst. prof. BIOSTATIST. & EPIDEMIOL, SCH. HYG. & PUB. HEALTH, JOHNS HOPKINS UNIV, 59-64, assoc. prof, 64-69, PROF, 69- U.S.P.H.S, 54-56. AAAS; Am. Statist. Asn; Biomet. Soc; Inst. Math. Statist; Am. Pub. Health Asn. Biostatistics; epidemiology. Address: School of Hygiene & Public Health, Johns Hopkins University, 615 N. Wolfe St, Baltimore, MD 21205.

DIAMOND, HAROLD GEORGE, b. Wurtsboro, N.Y, Feb. 15, 40; m. 63; c. 2. MATHEMATICS. A.B, Cornell, 61; univ. & Woodrow Wilson fels, Stanford, 61-62, Nat. Sci. Found. fel, 63-65, Ph.D.(math), 65. Nat. Sci. Found. fel, Swiss Fed. Inst. Tech, 65-66; Inst. Adv. Study, 66-67; asst. prof. MATH, UNIV. ILL, URBANA, 67-69, ASSOC. PROF, 69- Am. Math. Soc. Analytic number theory; mathematical analysis; asymptotic distribution of multiplicative arithmetical functions; application of Banach algebras and harmonic analysis in number theory. Address: Dept. of Mathematics, 374 Altgeld Hall, University of Illinois, Urbana, IL 61801.

DIAMOND, HERBERT, b. Chicago, Ill, July 28, 25; m. 48; c. 1. NUCLEAR CHEMISTRY. Ph.B, Chicago, 47, B.S, 48. Asst. chemist NUCLEAR CHEM, ARGONNE NAT. LAB, 49-58, ASSOC. CHEMIST, 58- U.S.A, 43-46. Am. Chem. Soc; Am. Phys. Soc. Production and characterization of new nuclides; nuclear half-lives; cross sections; decay schemes; nuclear aspects of cosmic and geochemical problems; separations chemistry. Address: Argonne National Lab, Bldg. 200, M167, Argonne, IL 60439.

DIAMOND, HOWARD, b. Detroit, Mich, Aug. 11, 28; m. 51; c. 4. PHYSICAL ELECTRONICS. B.S, Michigan, 52, M.S, 54, Ph.D.(physics & elec. eng), 60. Res. assoc, eng. res. inst, UNIV. MICH, 57-59, instr. ELEC. ENG, 58-59, asst. prof, 59-63, ASSOC. PROF, 63- Nat. Sci. Found. grant, 62-63. Consult, Lear Siegler Inc, Mich, 60-62, Electrovoice Corp, 63-; pres, Transidyne-Gen. Corp, 67- Mem. conf. elec. insulation, Nat. Acad. Sci. AAAS; Am. Phys. Soc. Semiconductor and dielectric theory; theory of ferroelectricity and piezoelectricity. Address: Dept. of Electrical Engineering, University of Michigan, Ann Arbor, MI 48104.

DIAMOND, IRVING T(HOMAS), b. Chicago, Ill, Sept. 17, 22; m. 57; c. 3. PSYCHOLOGY. Ph.D.(psychol), Chicago, 52. Instr. & exam. nat. sci, Chicago, 49-52, asst. prof, 52-54, PSYCHOL, 54-58; assoc. prof, DUKE UNIV, 58-64, PROF, 64- Consult, Vet. Admin. U.S.A, 43-46. AAAS; Am. Psychol. Asn; Am. Physiol. Soc; Fedn. Am. Socs. Exp. Biol. Brain functions; physiological psychology. Address: Dept. of Psychology, Duke University, Durham, NC 27706.

DIAMOND, ISRAEL, b. Flint, Mich, Aug. 1, 14; m. 42; c. 1. PATHOLOGY. B.Sc, City Col. New York, 34; L.R.C.P. & L.R.C.S, Edinburgh, 39. Fel. embryol, Boston, 46-48; instr. path, Harvard, 48-52; assoc. prof. sch. med, Louisville, 52-60; dir. labs, Lutheran Med. Ctr, 60-68; clin. assoc. prof. path, N.Y. Med. Col, 64-68; PROF. PATH, BROWN UNIV, 68-; DIR. LABS, ROGER WILLIAMS GEN. HOSP, 68- Clin. assoc. prof, State Univ. N.Y. Downstate Med. Center, 60-64. Assoc. pathologist, Children's Med. Center, Mass, 48-52; dir. labs, Children's Hosp, Ky, 52-60, tumor clin, 55-60; consult, Muscatatuck Children's Inst, 54-55; Kosair Crippled Children's Hosp, 53-60; Vet. Admin. Hosp, Ky, 54-60; Ireland Army Hosp, 55-60; Nat. Inst. Neurol. Disease & Blindness, 63, 64. U.S.A, 42-46, Maj. Fel. Am. Soc. Clin. Path; fel. Col. Am. Path. Pediatric pathology; morphology of malnutrition; tissue transplantation. Address: Roger Williams General Hospital, 825 Chalkstone Ave, Providence, RI 02908.

DIAMOND, IVAN, b. Brooklyn, N.Y, May 7, 35; m. 62; c. 2. NEUROANATOMY. A.B, Chicago, 56, B.S, 57, M.D, 61, Ph.D.(neuroanat), 67. Intern med, New Eng. Ctr. Hosp, Boston, Mass, 61-62; res. neurol, Chicago, 62-65, instr. sch. med, 65-67; asst. Beth Israel Hosp, Boston, 67-69; ASST. PROF. NEUROL. & PEDIAT, MED. CTR, UNIV. CALIF, SAN FRANCISCO, 68- U.S. Pub. Health Serv. res. fel. neurol, Chicago, 64-65, spec. res. fel. biol. chem, Harvard Med. Sch, 67-69, career develop. award, 69. Joseph A. Capps Prize, Inst. Med. Chicago, 66. AAAS; Am. Acad. Neurol; Am. Fedn. Clin. Res. Bilirubin metabolism and neurotoxicity; biochemistry of synaptic function; pre-synaptic permeability and the accumulation of acetylcholine. Address: Dept. of Neurology & Pediatrics, Medical Center, University of California, San Francisco, CA 94122.

DIAMOND, J. PHILIP MORRIS, b. Passaic, N.J, Oct. 29, 30; m. 53; c. 4. SYSTEMS & MECHANICAL ENGINEERING. B.M.E, N.Y. Univ, 51; M.S.M.E, Buffalo, 54; Ph.D.(mech. eng), Purdue, 58. Rocket res. engr, Bell Aircraft Corp, N.Y, 51-53; res. asst, jet propulsion ctr, Purdue, 53-58; mem. staff, Convair Div, Gen. Dynamics Corp, Tex, 58-61; mgr. vehicle systs, AEROSPACE CORP, LOS ANGELES, 61-66, group dir. advan. orbital systs, 66-68, GEN. MGR, OFF. DEVELOP. PLANNING, 68- Instr. aero. eng, South. Methodist Univ, 60-61; adj. prof, Tex. Christian Univ, 60-61; ed-evaluator, McGraw-Hill Book Co, Inc, 60-63; consult, adv. group aerospace res. & develop, NATO, 63. Am. Inst. Aeronaut. & Astronaut. Rocket and space propulsion and space power systems; spacecraft, satellite, space and missile systems development; space and missile systems engineering. Address: 2044 Via Visalia, Palos Verdes Estates, CA 90274.

DIAMOND, JACK, b. Winnipeg, Man, Apr. 30, 38. PHARMACOLOGY. B.Sc, Alberta, 59, M.Sc, 62; Ph.D.(pharmacol), Michigan, 65. Res. assoc. PHARMACOL, med. sch, Michigan, 65-66; Brown, 66-67, instr, 67-68; ASST. PROF, MED. SCH, NORTHWEST. UNIV, 68- N.Y. Acad. Sci. Pharmacology of uterine smooth muscle, utilizing biochemical and electrophysiological techniques. Address: Dept. of Pharmacology, Northwestern University Medical School, Chicago, IL 60611.

DIAMOND, J(ACOB) J(OSEPH), b. New York, N.Y, July 25, 17; m. 44; c. 2. PHYSICAL CHEMISTRY. B.A, Brooklyn Col, 37. Chemist, NAT. BUR. STANDARDS, 40-70, PROG. MGR. PROTECTIVE EQUIP, 70- Assoc, George Washington, 47-48. Assoc. mem, cmn. high temperatures & refractories, Int. Union Pure & Appl. Chem, 59-67. Ed, Bibliog. High Temperature Chem. & Physics of Mat. in Condensed State, 57-70. Student medal, Am. Inst. Chem, 37. Fel. AAAS; Am. Chem. Soc; Am. Ceramic Soc. Standards for law enforcement equipment; protective equipment; body armor; performance standards and testing; instrumental methods of chemical analysis; analysis of silicates; optical glass; flame photometry; image-furnace research; vaporization of refractory materials; high temperature chemistry. Address: Law Enforcement Standards Lab, National Bureau of Standards, Washington, DC 20234.

DIAMOND, JARED MASON, b. Boston, Mass, Sept. 10, 37. BIOLOGY. B.A, Harvard, 58; D.Phil.(physiol), Cambridge, 61. Fel. biochem, Max-Planck Inst. Biochem, 61; fel. physiol, Trinity Col, Cambridge, 61-65; jr. fel. biophys, Soc. of Fels, Harvard, 62-65, assoc, sch. med, 65-66; assoc. prof. PHYSIOL, MED. CTR, UNIV. CALIF, LOS ANGELES, 66-70, PROF, 70- Lederle award, 68-71. Am. Physiol. Soc. Physiology and biophysics; biological membranes; biological transport processes; ecology and evolutionary biology; New Guinea birds. Address: Dept. of Physiology, University of California Medical Center, Los Angeles, CA 90024.

DIAMOND, JULIUS, b. Philadelphia, Pa, Apr. 12, 25; m. 53; c. 3. MEDICINAL CHEMISTRY. B.S, Pennsylvania, 45; M.A, Temple, 53, Ph.D.(chem), 55. Org. res. chemist, Wyeth Labs, 50-56; dir. labs, G.F. Harvey Co, N.Y, 56-57; proj. leader, Wallace Labs, N.J, 57-59; tech. dir, Lincoln Labs, Ill, 59-62; group leader, WILLIAM H. RORER, INC, 62-67, mgr. org. chem. dept, 67-69, asst. dir. RES, 69-71, ASSOC. DIR, 71- Lectr, Pa. State Univ, 64-65. Am. Chem. Soc; fel. Am. Inst. Chem; Acad. Pharmaceut. Sci. Pharmaceuticals; medicinal chemistry; organic synthesis; metabolic chemistry; gastrointestinal drugs; antiinflammatory drugs; antihypertensives; synthetic analgesics; narcotic antagonists. Address: 120 Red Rambler Dr, Lafayette Hill, PA 19444.

DIAMOND, LOUIS, b. Baltimore, Md, July 13, 40; m. 67; c. 2. PHARMACOLOGY. B.Sc, Univ. Md, 61, M.Sc, 64, Ph.D.(pharmacol), 67. Asst. prof. PHARMACOL, UNIV. KY, 67-71, ASSOC. PROF, 71- Nat. Heart Inst. fel, 68; Nat. Sci. Found. grant, 68-70. AAAS; N.Y. Acad. Sci. Pulmonary pharmacology. Address: Dept. of Pharmacology, Albert B. Chandler Medical Center, University of Kentucky, Lexington, KY 40506.

DIAMOND, LOUIS H(AROLD), b. St. Louis, Mo, July 16, 29; m. 55; c. 3. INORGANIC CHEMISTRY. B.A, Southern Illinois, 51; Olin Industs. fel, Illinois, 52, Ph.D.(chem), 54. Asst, Illinois, 52-54; res. chemist, FMC CORP, 54-58, supvr, 58-61, mgr, 62-63, prod. res, 64-67, asst. dir. RES, INORG. CHEM. DIV, 67-68, DIR, 68- Chem.C, U.S.A, 55-57. Am. Chem. Soc. Chemistry of hydrazine and derivatives; nitrogen chemistry; liquid propellants; inorganic phosphates; chlorinated hydrocarbons. Address: FMC Corp, P.O. Box 8, Princeton, NJ 08540.

DIAMOND, LOUIS K(LEIN), b. New York, N.Y, May 11, 02; m. 29; c. 2. MEDICINE, PEDIATRICS. A.B, Harvard, 23, M.D, 27. Res. fel. pediat, Harvard Med. Sch, 27-28, asst. pediat. & path, 30-32, PEDIAT, 32-33, instr, 33-35, assoc, 35-41, asst. prof, 41-49, assoc. prof, 49-64, prof, 64-68; MED. SCH, SAN FRANCISCO MED. CTR, UNIV. CALIF, 68-70, RESIDENT PROF, 70- Mem. res. staff, Children's Hosp, 28-30, asst. physician, 31, assoc. physician, 32-33, assoc. vis. physician, 34-38, sr. physician, 38-45, assoc. physician-in-chief, 46-; med. dir. nat. blood prog, Am. Nat. Red Cross, 48-50; mem. hemat. study sect, Nat. Insts. Health, 49-53, human embryo & develop. study sect, 54-59, 64-68; subcmt. blood & related problems, Nat. Res. Coun. Carlos J. Findlay Gold Medal, Cuba, 51; merit award, Netherlands Red Cross, 59; Karl Landsteiner Award, 62; Theodore Roosevelt Award, 64; George R. Minot Award, 65. Am. Acad. Pediat. (Mead-Johnson Award, 46); Soc. Pediat. Res; Am. Pediat. Soc; Am. Soc. Clin. Invest; Am. Med. Asn; Am. Acad. Arts & Sci. Children's diseases, especially diseases of the blood. Address: Dept. of Pediatrics, University of California Medical School, San Francisco Medical Center, San Francisco, CA 94122.

DIAMOND, LOUIS S(TANLEY), b. Phila, Pa, Feb. 6, 20; m. 39; c. 3. ZOOLOGY. A.B, Pennsylvania, 40; M.S, Michigan, 41; U.S. Pub. Health Serv. fel, Minnesota, 47-49, Ph.D, 58. Wildlife res. biologist, Patuxent Res. Refuge, U.S. Fish & Wildlife Serv, 51-53; vet. parasitologist, animal disease & parasite res. br, agr. res. serv, U.S. Dept. Agr, 53-58; MED. PARASITOLOGIST, LAB. PARASITIC DISEASES, NAT. INST. ALLERGY & INFECTIOUS DISEASES, NAT. INSTS. HEALTH, U.S. DEPT. HEALTH, EDUC. & WELFARE, 59- Sanit.C, 43-46; Med.Serv.C.Res, 46-, Maj. Am. Soc. Parasitol; Am. Micros. Soc; Soc. Protozool; Am. Soc. Trop. Med. & Hyg; Soc. Cryobiol.(secy). Morphology, taxonomy and axenic culture of parasitic sarcodina and mastigophora; stain technology. Address: Room 211, Bldg. 5, Lab. Parasitic Diseases, National Institute of Allergy & Infectious Diseases, National Institutes of Health, Bethesda, MD 20014.

DIAMOND, MARIAN C, b. Glendale, Calif, Nov. 11, 26; m. 50; c. 4. NEUROBIOLOGY. A.B, California, Berkeley, 48, M.A, 49, Ph.D.(anat), 53; summer, Oslo, 48. Res. asst. neurobiol, Harvard Col, 52-53; res. asst. & instr, Cornell, 54-58; lectr. anat, sch. med, UNIV. CALIF, San Francisco, 59-67, res. assoc. psychol, BERKELEY, 61-65, asst. prof. ANAT, 65-68, ASSOC. PROF, 68-, ASSOC. DEAN COL. LETTERS & SCI, 70-, asst. dean, 68-70. Res. grants, Nat. Sci. Found, 61-62, 66-71 & 71-74 & Nat. Insts. Health, 66-69. Fel. AAAS; Soc. Neurosci; Int. Soc. Psychoneuroendocrinol; Am. Asn. Anat; N.Y. Acad. Sci. Environmentally induced anatomical and chemical brain changes; pituitary hormones and brain development. Address: College of Letters & Science, University of California, Berkeley, CA 94704.

DIAMOND, MARTIN J, b. N.Y.C, June 10, 20; m. 64. ORGANIC CHEMISTRY. B.A, Wisconsin, 41; Ph.D.(org. chem), Stanford, 53. Res. chemist, Chem. Process Co, 51-52; sr. res. chemist, Calif. Spray Chem. Co, 53-58; RES. CHEMIST, WEST. REGIONAL RES. LAB, AGR. RES. SERV, U.S. DEPT. AGR, 59- U.S.A.A.F, 41-46. Am. Chem. Soc; The Chem. Soc. Synthetic organic chemistry; stereochemistry; pesticides; fatty acids; graft polymers; textile finishes. Address: 6131 Hillegrass Ave, Oakland, CA 94618.

DIAMOND, MILTON, b. N.Y.C, Mar. 6, 34; m. 55; c. 4. REPRODUCTIVE PHYSIOLOGY, SEXOLOGY. B.S, City Col. New York, 55; Nat. Res. Coun. fel, Univ. Kans, 59-62, Ph.D.(anat), 63. Instr. micros. anat. & neuro-anat, sch. med, Louisville, 62-63, asst. prof, 63-67; assoc. prof. ANAT, SCH. MED, UNIV. HAWAII, 67-71, PROF, 71- Res. grants, 63-; vis. scientist, Ky. Acad. Sci, 64-65; Lederle Med. Faculty Award, 68-71. C.Eng, 55-58, 1st Lt. AAAS; Am. Soc. Zool; Animal Behav. Soc; Soc. Study Reproduction; Am. Asn. Anat; Soc. Sci. Study Sex; Brit. Soc. Study Fertil. Endocrine and neural parameters of sexual behavior and reproduction; normal development of reproductive and sexual patterns and methods of alteration; abortion; contraception; sexual behavior and practices. Address: Dept. of Anatomy, University of Hawaii School of Medicine, Honolulu, HI 96822.

DIAMOND, MURRAY ALLEN, b. Philadelphia, Pa, Mar. 2, 10; m. 36; c. 2. PSYCHIATRY. B.S, Tulane, 33, M.D, 36; M.P.H, Hopkins, 47. Staff physician, hosp, U.S. Pub. Health Serv, Ky, 37-39, Ft. Worth, Tex, 40-42, clin. dir, 42-44, chief psychiat. serv, La. 44-46, regional ment. health consult, N.Y, 47-49, clin. Ky, 49-54, asst. chief div. hosps, bur. med. serv, D.C, 54-55, dept. chief personnel & consult, Off. Surgeon Gen, 55-58, med. officer in charge hosp, Ky, 58-62, asst. surg. gen. personnel, D.C, 62-66; EXEC. DIR, TOURO INFIRMARY, 66- U.S.P.H.S, 37-66, Asst. Surgeon Gen. Personnel. AAAS; fel. Am. Psychiat. Asn; fel. Am. Med. Asn; Am. Hosp. Asn; Am. Pub. Health Asn. Hospital and personnel administration. Address: Touro Infirmary, 1401 Foucher St, New Orleans, LA 70115.

DIAMOND, NORMAN, b. Brooklyn, N.Y, Aug. 2, 14; m. 41; c. 4. INTERNAL MEDICINE. Fordham; M.D, Bonn Univ, Germany, 38. ASSOC. CLIN. PROF. MED, N.Y. MED. COL, 59-; INSTR. PHYSIOL, 59-; ATTEND. PHYSICIAN, FLOWER & FIFTH AVE. HOSPS, 62-, assoc. attend, 59-62. Attend. physician, Manhattan Gen. Hosp. 51; Bird S. Coler Hosp, 55; Metropolitan Hosp, 55; assoc. attend. physician, Jewish Mem. Hosp, 55. Chief consult, City of Hope Med. Center, Calif, 53; consult, Am. Med. Center, Colo, 50. Dipl. Am. Bd. Internal Med, 50- Med.C, 44-46, Maj. AAAS; N.Y. Acad. Sci; fel. Am. Col. Chest Physicians; Am. Thoracic Soc. Chest diseases; pulmonary physiology. Address: New York Medical College, Flower & Fifth Ave. Hospitals, New York, NY 10023.

DIAMOND, RAY BYFORD, b. Louisa, Ky, Jan. 10, 33; m. 57; c. 2. SOIL SCIENCE. B.S, Ohio State, 54; M.S.A, Florida, 61, Ph.D.(soils), 63. Agriculturist FERTILIZER USAGE, TENN. VALLEY AUTH, 63-64, AGRONOMIST, 64- Mem. agron. comt, Nat. Fertilizer Solutions Asn, 70- U.S.N, 54-59, Lt. Am. Soc. Agron; Soil Sci. Soc. Am. Evaluation of agronomic properties of new fertilizer products under a variety of soil, climatic and cropping conditions. Address: Tennessee Valley Authority, NFDC, F-201, Muscle Shoals, AL 35660.

DIAMOND, R(ICHARD) M(ARTIN), b. Los Angeles, Calif, Jan. 7, 24; m. 50; c. 4. NUCLEAR CHEMISTRY. B.S, California, Los Angeles, 47; Ph.D. (nuclear chem), California, 51. Instr. chem, Harvard, 51-54; asst. prof, Cornell, 54-58; MEM. STAFF, LAWRENCE BERKELEY LAB, UNIV. CALIF, 58- Guggenheim fel, Denmark, 66-67. U.S.A, 43-46. Am. Chem. Soc; Am. Phys. Soc. Nuclear spectroscopy; coulomb excitation; ion exchange resin and solvent extraction mechanisms; solution chemistry. Address: Lawrence Berkeley Lab, University of California, Berkeley, CA 94720.

DIAMOND, SIDNEY, b. N.Y.C, Nov. 10, 29; m. 53; c. 2. ENGINEERING MATERIALS. B.S, Syracuse, 50; M.F, Duke, 51; Ph.D.(soil chem), Purdue, 63. Asst, U.S. Army Eng. Res. & Develop. Labs, 51-53; hwy. res. engr, U.S. Bur. Pub. Roads, 53-62; asst, Purdue, 62-63; res. chemist, U.S. Bur. Pub. Roads, 64-65; assoc. prof. ENG. MAT, PURDUE UNIV, 65-70, PROF, 70- Mem, Hwy. Res. Bd, Nat. Acad. Sci-Nat. Res. Coun. AAAS; Am. Chem. Soc; Clay Minerals Soc; Am. Ceramic Soc; Am. Soc. Test. & Mat. Cement hydration and microstructure and physical chemistry of hydration products; soil physical chemistry; clay mineralogy; soil stabilization; microstructure and pore structure of civil engineering materials and relations to engineering behavior. Address: School of Civil Engineering, Purdue University, Lafayette, IN 47907.

DIAMOND, WILLIAM J(OHN), b. Philadelphia, Pa, Jan. 23, 19; m. 55; c. 2. PHYSICAL CHEMISTRY. B.A, La Salle Col, 41; Evansville Col, 46-48; Oak Ridge Inst. Nuclear Studies, 55; Mass. Inst. Technol, 55; M.S, Univ. Ky, 71. Anal chemist, refrig. div, Int. Harvester Co, 45-51, mat. engr, 51-54; res. chemist, Whirlpool Corp, 54-55, supvr, radio chem. res, 55-57; sr. chem. engr, Brunswick-Balke Collender Co, 58-62; ADV. STATISTICIAN, IBM CORP, 62- C.Eng, 41-46, Res, 46-52, Capt. Am. Soc. Qual. Control. Ion-exchange; radio chemistry; detergency; infrared analysis; reinforced plastics; statistical design and analysis of experiments; physical chemistry of dilute solutions; insulation. Address: 287 Farmington Rd, Lexington, KY 40502.

DIAMONDSTONE, THOMAS I(RA), b. New York, N.Y, Apr. 29, 35; m. 58; c. 4. BIOCHEMISTRY. B.A, Chicago, 54, B.S, 57; Ph.D.(biochem), Rutgers, 63. Res. investr. chem, Pennsylvania, 62-64; ASST. PROF. BIOCHEM, Ohio State, 64-69; JEFFERSON MED. COL, 69- AAAS; Am. Chem. Soc. Enzyme kinetics; mechanism of enzyme action. Address: Dept. of Biochemistry, Jefferson Medical College, 1020 Locust St, Philadelphia, PA 19107.

DIANA, GUY DOMINIC, b. New Haven, Conn, July 21, 35; m. 60; c. 2. ORGANIC CHEMISTRY. B.S, Yale, 57; Ph.D.(org. chem), Rice, 61. Assoc. res. chemist, STERLING-WINTHROP RES. INST, 61-67, res. chemist, 67-70, SR. RES. CHEMIST, 70-, GROUP LEADER, 67- Am. Chem. Soc. Synthesis of compounds with potential pharmacological activity. Address: Sterling-Winthrop Research Institute, Rensselaer, NY 12144.

DIANA, JOHN N, b. Lake Placid, N.Y, Dec. 19, 30; m. 54, 66; c. 3. PHYSIOLOGY. B.A, Norwich, 52; Ph.D.(physiol), Louisville, 65. Biochemist, Inst. Med. Res, Louisville, Ky, 54-56; physiologist, U.S. Army Med. Res. Lab, Ft. Knox, Ky, 56-58; res. asst. cardiovasc. physiol, sch. med, Louisville, 58-61, res. assoc, 62-65; fel, sch. med, Oklahoma, 65-66; asst. prof, col. human med, Mich. State, 66-68; ASSOC. PROF. PHYSIOL. & BIOPHYS, COL. MED, UNIV. IOWA, 68- Am. Heart Inst. fel, 65-67. U.S.A, 52-53, 61-62, Res, 54-61, 62-71, Maj. AAAS; Am. Fedn. Clin. Res; Am. Physiol. Soc; Microcirc. Soc. Cardiovascular research, especially venomotor activity, transcapillary fluid movement and capillary permeability in skin and skeletal muscle during infusion of vasoactive agents; effects of vasoactive agents on hypertension, hypotension and shock. Address: Dept. of Physiology & Biophysics, College of Medicine, University of Iowa, Iowa City, IA 52240.

DIANA, LEONARD M, b. Columbia, Pa, Jan. 26, 23; m. 50; c. 3. PHYSICS. B.S, Ga. Inst. Tech, 48; Ph.D.(physics), Pittsburgh, 53. Asst, Pittsburgh, 48-50, instr, 49-52, res. assoc, 51-53; proj. physicist res. & develop. Standard Oil Co, 53-59; physicist, Am. Tobacco Co, 59-62; assoc. prof. PHYSICS, Univ. Richmond, 62-65; UNIV. TEX, ARLINGTON, 65-71, PROF, 71- Va. State chmn, Vis. Scientists Prog. Physics, high schs, 63-65; specialist, U.S. Agency Int. Develop, India, 66. U.S.A, 43-46. AAAS; Am. Phys. Soc; Am. Asn. Physics Teachers; Optical Soc. Am; N.Y. Acad. Sci. Experimental nuclear physics; theoretical physics; computing; instrumentation. Address: Dept. of Physics, University of Texas, Arlington, TX 76010.

D'IANNI, JAMES D(ONATO), b. Akron, Ohio, Mar. 11, 14; m. 40; c. 1. CHEMISTRY. B.S, Akron, 34; Procter & Gamble Co. fel, Wisconsin, 37-38, Ph.D.(org. chem), 38. Asst. chem, Wisconsin, 34-37; res. chemist, GOODYEAR TIRE & RUBBER CO, 38-51, asst. to v.pres. res. & develop, 52-61, chem. prod. liaison, 61-63, assoc. dir. res, 63-65, from asst. dir. to DIR. RES, 65- Instr. Akron, 41-46; chief polymer res. br, off. rubber reserve, Reconstruct. Finance Corp, 46-47. Chmn, Gordon Res. Conf. Elastomers, 52. Am. Chem. Soc; Am. Inst. Chem; Am. Inst. Chem. Eng. Catalytic hydrogenation of hydroxyamides and lignin; synthesis of polymerizable monomers; synthetic rubber; vinyl resin; chemical derivatives of rubbers. Address: Goodyear Tire & Rubber Co, 142 Goodyear Blvd, Akron, OH 44316.

DIAPER, ERNEST WILLIAM J, b. Southampton, Eng, Nov. 16, 26; m. 50; c. 2. CIVIL & SANITARY ENGINEERING. B.S, London, 46 & 49, M.S, 63. Asst. engr, Southampton Munic. Waterworks, Eng, 49-53; asst. chief civil eng, Glenfield & Kennedy, Ltd, 53-66, v.pres, Glenfield & Kennedy, Inc, King of Prussia, 66-68; MGR. MUNIC. WATER & WASTE TREATMENT, COCHRANE DIV, CRANE CO, 68- Lectr, Univ. London, 53-66. R.E. Brit. Army, 46-48, Lt. Am. Soc. Civil Eng; Am. Water Works Asn; Brit. Inst. Civil Eng; Brit. Inst. Water Eng; Brit. Inst. Water Pollution Control. Water and waste water treatment. Address: 327 Greene Rd, Berwyn, PA 19312.

DIASSI, PATRICK A(NDREW), b. Morristown, N.J, July 1, 26; m. 52. ORGANIC CHEMISTRY. B.Sc, St. Peter's Col, (N.J), 46; M.Sc, Rutgers, 50, DuPont fel, 50-51, Ph.D.(chem), 51. Asst, Rutgers, 47-50; res. assoc, SQUIBB INST. MED. RES, 51-63, res. supvr, 63-66, sr. res. assoc, 66-68, asst. dir. dept. org. chem, 68-71, DIR. DEPT. CHEM. PROCESS DEVELOP, 71- U.S.A, 44-46. AAAS; Am. Chem. Soc; The Chem. Soc. Chemistry of natural products. Address: Squibb Institute for Medical Research, New Brunswick, NJ 08901.

DIAZ, J(OAQUIN) BASILIO, b. Arecibo, P.R, Apr. 15, 20; m. 44; c. 2. MATHEMATICS. A.B, Texas, 40; Ph.D.(appl. math), Brown, 45. Asst, nat. adv. cmt. aeronaut, Brown, 43-44, res. assoc, Pratt & Whitney Co. & Watertown Arsenal contracts, 44-46; asst. prof. math, Carnegie Inst. Tech, 46-47; asst. prof, Brown, 47-50; assoc. prof, Univ. Md, 51-56, prof, 56-66; prof. math. & chmn. dept, Univ. Calif, Riverside, 66-67; ALBERT EINSTEIN PROF. SCI, RENSSELAER POLYTECH. INST, 67- Consult, U.S. Naval Ord. Lab, Md, 55-; vis. prof, Mass. Inst. Technol, 56-57; Am. Math. Soc. Hydrodynamics; elasticity; partial differential equations; class of partial differential equations of even order; quadratic functionals. Address: Rensselaer Polytechnic Institute, Troy, NY 12181.

DIAZ, JUSTO A, b. Veguitas, Cuba, Oct. 30, 36; m. 61; c. 1. PHYSICS. B.S, Ottawa (Kans), 53; Ph.D.(physics), California, Berkeley, 62. ASST. PROF. PHYSICS, OTTAWA UNIV, 62-65, ASSOC. PROF, 65- Summers, resident res. assoc, Argonne Nat. Lab, 63, res. assoc, Illinois, 64. Mu-meson interactions and atomic systems; neutron penetration through cavity; neutron transport modeling relationships; x-ray diffraction. Address: Dept. of Physics, Ottawa University, Ottawa, KS 66067.

DIAZ, RAFAEL, b. Santurce, P.R, Sept. 26, 27; m. 52. PHYSICAL CHEMISTRY. B.S.(chem. eng) & B.S.(metall), Univ. P.R, 48; M.S, Univ. Minn, 52. Instr. chem, Univ. P.R, 49-50; chemist, res. & develop, Minneapolis-Honeywell Regulator Co, 52-55; mgr. chem. & metall. labs, semiconductor div, Westinghouse Elec. Corp, 56-64, mkt. mgr, 65-69; mgr. new. prod, Kennametal, Inc, 64-65; MGR. NEW PROD. PLANNING, N.AM. ROCKWELL CORP, 69- Am. Chem. Soc; Electrochem. Soc; Am. Electroplaters Soc. (award of honor, 61); Am. Mgt. Asn. Technical management; commercialization of new products. Address: North American Rockwell Corp, Fifth Ave & Wood St, Pittsburgh, PA 15222.

DiBARI, GEORGE ANGELO, b. Brooklyn, N.Y, Feb. 8, 34; m. 56; c. 3. CHEMISTRY, METALLURGY. B.S, Brooklyn Col, 55; M.S, Polytech. Inst. Brooklyn, 63; Ph.D.(metall), Pa. State Univ, 70. CHEMIST, Curtiss-Wright Corp, 55-57; Int. Nickel Co, 57-67; ord. res. lab, Pa. State Univ, 67-71; INT. NICKEL CO, 71- Electrochem. Soc; Am. Electroplaters Soc; Nat. Asn. Corrosion Eng. Research and development in electrochemistry, corrosion, metallurgy; electrochemistry of accelerated corrosion testing; anodic behavior of metals; development of sulfur-depolarized electronickel; use of electrochemical methods in corrosion; corrosion protection of equipment in marine environments. Address: 1 New York Plaza, New York, NY 10004.

DI BARTOLO, BALDASSARE, b. Trapani, Italy, Jan. 5, 26; m. 68; c. 1. SOLID STATE PHYSICS, MICROWAVE ENGINEERING. D.Sc.(indust. eng), Palermo, 50; dipl, Inst. Telecommun, Rome, 51; scholar, Nat. Res. Coun. Italy, 52, dipl. radar tech, 53; Ph.D.(physics), Mass. Inst. Tech, 64. Design engr, Microlambda, Italy, 53-56; microwave engr, Studio Tecnico di Consulenza Elettronica, 56-57; vis. fel. physics, Mass. Inst. Tech, 57-58; res. staff mem, lab. insulation res, Mass. Inst. Tech, 58-63; sr. scientist & dir. spectros. lab, Mithras Div, Sanders Assocs. Inc, 64-68; ASSOC. PROF. PHYSICS, BOSTON COL, 68- Lectr, cybernetics study center, Naval Inst, Naples, 54-56; mem. for. student summer proj, res. lab. electronics, Mass. Inst. Tech, 56; microwave engr, Sindel, Italy, summer 59. AAAS; Am. Phys. Soc; Ital. Phys. Soc; N.Y. Acad. Sci; Am. Chem. Soc; Europ. Phys. Soc. Solid state spectroscopy; maser and laser theory; theory of atomic and crystal spectra; information theory; microwave technique; flash photolysis. Address: Dept. of Physics, Boston College, Chestnut Hill, MA 02167.

DIBBERN, JOHN C(OOPER), b. Los Angeles, Calif, May 30, 19; m. 47; c. 1. PLANT ECOLOGY. B.S, Arizona, 40; Ph.D.(bot), Chicago, 47. Jr. range exam, Soil Conserv. Serv, 41-42; asst. prof. bot, Arizona, 47-48; range ecologist, Southwest. Forest & Range Exp. Sta, 48-49; asst. prof. animal husb, Arizona, 49-50; range conservationist, BUR. INDIAN AFFAIRS, Papago, 50-54, land opers. off, Ft. Apache, 54-55, prog. off, cent. off, 55-56, asst. to asst. chmn. resources, 56-57, supt, Colo. River Agency, 57-63, asst. area dir. econ. develop, Gallup Area Off, 63-66, DIR. MO. RIVER BASIN INVESTS, 66- U.S.A, 42-46. Am. Soc. Range Mgt. Range Management. Address: 1930 Northridge Circle, Billings, MT 59102.

DIBBLE, HAROLD L(EWIS), b. Deposit, N.Y, July 13, 22; m. 43; c. 2. THEORETICAL MECHANICS. B.M.E, Cornell, 49, fel, 49-50, M.M.E, 50, Ph.D. (mech), 55. Sr. res. engr, Autonetics Div, N.Am. Aviation, Inc, 50-52, guid. anal. specialist, 55-58; asst. prof, Cornell, 52-55; sr. engr. qual. anal, missile test proj, Radio Corp. Am, Patrick AFB Fla, 58-62; group leader, AUTONETICS DIV, N.Am. Aviation, Inc, 62-63, sr. scientist, 63-64, mgr. systs. eng, 64-70, SCI. ADV, N.AM. ROCKWELL CORP, 70- Res. consult, Proj. Lincoln, Mass. Inst. Tech, 53-54; dean, Brevard Eng. Col, 58-62. U.S.A.A.F, 42-45. Inst. Elec. & Electronics Eng; Soc. Indust. & Appl. Math; Am. Inst. Aeronaut. & Astronaut. Inertial guidance; systems analysis; data reduction and analysis; servomechanisms and control systems; engineering education; space navigation; applied mathematics. Address: Autonetics Division, North American Rockwell Corp, 3370 Miraloma Ave, Anaheim, CA 92803.

DIBBLE, MARJORIE VEIT, b. Brooklyn, N.Y, Jan. 11, 28; m. 54; c. 2. NUTRITION, FOOD SCIENCE. B.S, Hunter Col, 49; M.S, Univ. Tenn, Knoxville, 50; Columbia Univ, 57-58. Instr. foods & nutrit, Syracuse Univ, 51-57; foods, teachers col, Columbia Univ, 57-58; asst. prof. foods & nutrit, SYRACUSE UNIV, 58-67, ASSOC. PROF. NUTRIT. & FOOD SCI, 67-, CHMN. DEPT, 66-, NUTRIT. SUPVR, CHILDREN'S CTR, 70- Am. Dietetic Asn; fel. Am. Pub. Health Asn; Inst. Food Technol. Nutritional status surveys of adolescents and older age adults; relationship of nutrition to growth and development. Address: Dept. of Nutrition & Food Science, Syracuse University, Syracuse, NY 13210.

DIBBLE, WILLIAM E, b. Schenectady, N.Y, Dec. 25, 30. PHYSICS. B.S, Calif. Inst. Technol, 54, Ph.D.(physics), 60. From asst. prof. to PROF. PHYSICS, BRIGHAM YOUNG UNIV, 61- AAAS; Am. Phys. Soc. Small-angle x-ray scattering. Address: Dept. of Physics, Brigham Young University, Provo, UT 84601.

DIBELER, VERNON H(AMILTON), b. Elizabeth, N.J, July 20, 18; m. 43; c. 3. CHEMICAL PHYSICS. B.S, Duke, 39, M.A, 40; Nat. Inst. Health fel, Columbia, 47-48, Ph.D.(chem), 50. Asst. chemist, Duke, 39-41; asst. phys. chemist, NAT. BUR. STANDARDS, 42-45, PHYS. CHEMIST, 45- Meritorious serv. award, 52; Dept. of Commerce gold medal award, 69. AAAS; Am. Chem. Soc; Am. Phys. Soc; Am. Inst. Chem. Separation and use of isotopes in chemical research; mass spectrometry, theory and analytical application; bond dissociation energies and dissociation of isotopically-substituted molecules by electron and photon impact. Address: Physical Chemistry Division, National Bureau of Standards, Washington, DC 20234.

DIBELIUS, NORMAN RICHARD, b. Richmond Hill, N.Y, Dec. 24, 22; m. 46; c. 2. MECHANICAL ENGINEERING. B.M.E, Polytech. Inst. Brooklyn, 53; M.S.M.E, Rensselaer Polytech, 60. Engr, gas turbine dept, GEN. ELEC. CO, 53-55, gen. eng. lab, 55-59, proj. engr, adv. tech. labs, 59-65, proj. engr, res. & develop. ctr, 65-69, MGR. COMBUSTION & CONTROL DEVELOP, GAS TURBINE DEVELOP. ENG, 69- U.S.A, 43-46, Sgt. Am. Soc. Mech. Eng. Development of combustion systems and controls for gas turbines and incinerators to burn various fuels with minimum atmospheric pollution. Address: Gas Turbine Operations, General Electric Co, Bldg. 53-331, 1 River Rd, Schenectady, NY 12345.

DiBELLA, EUGENE P(ETER), b. New York, N.Y, June 19, 28; m. 50; c. 4. ORGANIC CHEMISTRY. B.S, Fordham, 48, M.S, 50, Ph.D.(chem), 53. Asst. chem, Fordham, 49-53; res. chemist, Heyden Chem. Corp, 53-66, supvr. res, Heyden Chem. Div, TENNECO CHEM, INC, 66-70, GROUP LEADER ORG. SYNTHESIS, INTERMEDIATES DIV, 70- Instr, Fairleigh Dickinson Univ, 53- Am. Chem. Soc. Synthetic organic chemistry. Address: 168 Chestnut St, Rochelle Park, NJ 07662.

DiBENEDETTO, ANTHONY T, b. New York, N.Y, Oct. 27, 33; m. 55; c. 4. CHEMICAL ENGINEERING, MATERIALS SCIENCE. B.Ch.E, City Col. New York, 55; M.S, Wisconsin, 56, Ph.D.(chem. eng), 60. Chem. engr, Bakelite Co, Union Carbide Corp, 54-55; instr. chem. eng, Wisconsin, 56-60, asst. prof. 60-64, assoc. prof, 64-66; Wash. Univ, 66-68, prof. CHEM. ENG. & dir. mat. res. lab, 68-71; PROF. & HEAD DEPT, UNIV. CONN, 71- Am. Inst. Chem. Eng. Physical properties of organic high polymers; polymerization process; ion exchange polymers. Address: Dept. of Chemical Engineering, University of Connecticut, Storrs, CT 06268.

DiBERARDINO, MARIE ANTOINETTE, b. Philadelphia, Pa, May 2, 26. EMBRYOLOGY, CYTOLOGY. B.S, Chestnut Hill Col, 48; Nat. Cancer Inst. fel, Pennsylvania, 58-60, Ph.D.(zool), 62. Res. assoc. embryol, Inst. Cancer Res, 60-64, asst. mem, 64-67; assoc. prof. ANAT, MED. COL. PA, 67-71, PROF, 71- Am. Soc. Zool; Soc. Develop. Biol. Nucleo-cytoplasmic interactions in cell differentiation and cancer, investigation by methods of experimental embryology, cytology, and cell physiology. Address: Dept. of Anatomy, Medical College of Pennsylvania, 3300 Henry Ave, Philadelphia, PA 19129.

DIBLE, WILLIAM T(ROTTER), JR, b. Oakmont, Pa, Sept. 7, 25; m. 48; c. 4. CHEMISTRY. B.S, Pa. State Col, 49; Ph.D, Univ. Wis, 52. Asst, Univ. Wis, 49-52; prod. planning mgr, Int. Minerals & Chem. Corp, 52-64, dir. mkt, 64; PRES, TERRA CHEM. INT. INC, 64- Boron determination in plants and soils; response of alfalfa to and its distribution in the plant. Address: 2430 W. Solway, Sioux City, IA 51104.

DIBOLL, ALFRED, b. San Diego, Calif, Aug. 30, 30; m. 67; c. 2. DEVELOPMENTAL & PLANT ANATOMY. B.S, San Diego State Col, 56; M.A, Claremont Grad. Sch, 59; Ph.D.(bot), Texas, 64. Sr. lab. technician, UNIV. CALIF, Riverside, 51-53, asst. prof. bot, Los Angeles, 63-68; HEAD FACULTY BIOL, MACON JR. COL, 68- U.S.A, 53-56. Bot. Soc. Am. Comparative and developmental plant anatomy; electron microscopy; histochemistry. Address: Faculty of Biology, Macon Junior College, Macon, GA 31206.

DiCAPUA, RICHARD ANTHONY, b. Brooklyn, N.Y, May 5, 36; m. 60; c. 5. IMMUNOLOGY, IMMUNOCHEMISTRY. B.S, Rutgers, 58, M.S, 63, Ph.D. (immunol), 64. Serologist, Ortho Pharmaceut. Corp, N.J, 59-62 & immunologist, Ortho Res. Found, 60-62; fel. IMMUNOL, sch. vet. med, California, Davis, 64-66; ASSOC. PROF, DEPT. ANIMAL DISEASES & SCH. PHARM, UNIV. CONN, 66- Vis. investr, Bur. Commercial Fisheries, summer, 66. U.S.A, 59-60. AAAS; Am. Soc. Microbiol; Reticuloendothelial Soc; Am. Chem. Soc. Mechanisms of cellular immunity; physico-chemical properties of antigen-antibody reactions; application of immunological techniques for the assay of marine species; Herpes induced neoplasias. Address: Dept. of Animal Disease, School of Pharmacy, University of Connecticut, Storrs, CT 06268.

DiCARLO, ERNEST N(ICHOLAS), b. Phila, Pa, Jan. 27, 36; m. 59; c. 3. PHYSICAL CHEMISTRY. B.S, St. Joseph's Col.(Pa), 58, Esso Found. fel, Princeton, 59, Nat. Sci. Found. fel, 60, Ph.D.(chem), 62. Asst. CHEM, Princeton, 58-59, res. asst, 60-62; res. chemist, Gulf Res. & Develop. Co, 62-63; asst. prof. ST. JOSEPH'S COL.(PA), 63-66, assoc. prof, 66-70, PROF, 70- Am. Chem. Soc. Dipole moments; microwave absorption of liquids; nuclear magnetic resonance; electron spin resonance. Address: Dept. of Chemistry, St. Joseph's College, 54th & City Line Ave, Philadelphia, PA 19131.

Di CARLO, FREDERICK J(OSEPH), b. New York, N.Y, Nov. 24, 18; m. 43; c. 3. CHEMISTRY. B.S, Fordham, 39, M.S, 41; Ph.D.(org. chem), N.Y. Univ, 45. Asst. chem, N.Y. Univ, 41-44; res. assoc. Squibb Inst. Med. Res, 44-45; res. chemist, Fleischmann Labs, Standards Brands, Inc, 45-46, dept. head, 47-53, head biochem. div, 53-60; sr. res. assoc, WARNER-LAMBERT RES. INST, 60-70, DIR, DEPT. DRUG METAB, 70- Adj. assoc. prof, Col. St. Elizabeth, 68-; ed-in-chief, Drug Metab. Rev. With Off. Sci. Res. & Develop, 44. AAAS; Am. Chem. Soc; Am. Soc. Biol. Chem; Soc. Exp. Biol. & Med; Reticuloendothelial Soc.(secy-treas, 65-67, pres, 69); Am. Soc. Pharmacol. & Exp. Therapeut; Int. Soc. Biochem. Pharmacol. Nitrogen heterocycles; penicillin; nucleic acids; amylases; fermentation; yeast derivatives; coffee, tea and whiskey flavors; metabolism of drugs, purines and pyrimidines; host defense mechanisms. Address: Dept. of Drug Metabolism, Warner-Lambert Research Institute, Morris Plains, NJ 07950.

DiCARLO, JAMES A(NTHONY), b. Buffalo, N.Y, Jan. 15, 38; m. 66; c. 4. PHYSICS. B.S, Canisius Col, 59; Nat. Sci. Found. fel, Pittsburgh, 60-63, Ph.D.(physics), 65. Res. assoc. solid state physics, Brookhaven Nat. Lab, 65-67; SOLID STATE PHYSICIST, LEWIS RES. CTR, NASA, 67- Am. Phys. Soc. Crystal imperfections and their interactions in metals; radiation effects in solids. Address: Lewis Research Center, National Aeronautics & Space Administration, Cleveland, OH 44135.

DICE, H(ENRY) K(IMMELL), b. Somerset, Pa, May 31, 08; m. 34; c. 2. CHEMICAL ENGINEERING. B.Ch.E, Pittsburgh, 32. Inspector, Youngstown Sheet & Tube Co, 32-34; chem. engr, Celanese Corp, of Am, 34-40, pilot plant supt, 40-44, prod. supt, 44-47, mgr. res. & develop, 47-59, v.pres. & tech. dir, Celanese Chem. Co, 59-61, subdir. gen, Quimica Gen, S.A, 61-63; consult, 63-; engr, TEX. HWY. DEPT, 67-68, SR. RESIDENT ENGR, 68- AAAS; Am. Chem. Soc; Nat. Soc. Prof. Eng; Am. Inst. Chem. Eng. Synthesis of petrochemicals and derivatives; research and development management. Address: 10215 Briar Dr, Houston, TX 77042.

DICE, JOHN R(AYMOND), b. Ann Arbor, Mich, Jan. 11, 21; m. 44; c. 4. MEDICINAL CHEMISTRY. B.S, Michigan, 41, fel, 41-44, M.S, 42, Abbott Labs. fel, 43-44, univ. fel, 45-46, Ph.D.(chem), 46. Shift foreman, Manhattan proj, Tenn. Eastman Co, 44-45; asst. prof. chem, Texas, 46-51; res. chemist, PARKE, DAVIS & CO, 51-57, sr. res. chemist, 57-61, lab. dir, 61-62; group dir, 63-69, ASST. DIR. CHEM. RES, 70- Am. Chem. Soc; N.Y. Acad. Sci. Chemistry of phenanthrenes; chemotherapy of virus diseases and cancer; chemistry of peptides and protein; drugs affecting the central nervous system. Address: Chemical Research, Parke, Davis & Co, Ann Arbor, MI 48106.

DICE, STANLEY FROST, b. Pittsburgh, Pa, July 26, 21. MATHEMATICS. A.B, Oberlin Col, 42; M.Litt, Pittsburgh, 51, Ph.D.(math), 58. Instr. math. & physics, West Liberty State Col, 51-52; MATH, Detroit, 52-55; Bucknell, 55-59, asst. prof, 59-62; Carleton Col, 62-66; ASSOC. PROF, WITTENBERG UNIV, 66- U.S.A.A.F, 42-45, 2nd Lt. Am. Math. Soc; Math. Asn. Am. Summability of divergent series. Address: Dept. of Mathematics, Wittenberg University, Springfield, OH 45501.

DICELLO, JOHN FRANCIS, JR, b. Bradford, Pa, Dec. 18, 38; m. 62; c. 2. RADIOLOGICAL & NUCLEAR PHYSICS. B.S, St. Bonaventure, 60; M.S, Pittsburgh, 62; Atomic Energy Cmn. fel, Texas A&M, 63-67, Ph.D.(physics), 68; fel, Los Alamos Sci. Lab, 65-67. Instr. physics, St. Bonaventure 62-63; res. scientist, COLUMBIA UNIV, 67-69, RES. ASSOC. RADIOL. PHYSICS, 69- N.Y. Acad. Sci; Radiation Res. Soc; Am. Phys. Soc. Microdosimetry; radiological physics; nuclear structure. Address: Radiological Research Lab, College of Physicians & Surgeons, Columbia University, New York, NY 10032.

diCENZO, COLIN D, b. Hamilton, Ont, July 26, 23; m. 50; c. 6. ELECTRICAL ENGINEERING. B.Sc. & Brydone-Jack scholar, New Brunswick, 52, Athlone fel, 52-54, M.Sc, 57; dipl. elec. eng, Imp. Col, London, 53. Lectr. elec. eng, Royal Mil. Col.(Ont), 54-57; dep. head sonar group, Royal Can. Naval Hq, Ottawa, 57-60, head underwater fire control, 60-62; assoc. prof. elec. eng, McMASTER UNIV, 65-68, DIR. UNDERGRAD. STUD, FACULTY ENG, 68- Nat. Res. Coun. res. grants, 66-70. R.C.N, 41-66, Res, 66-, Comdr. Can. Elec. Asn; sr. mem. Inst. Elec. & Electronics Eng; Am. Soc. Eng. Educ. Underwater acoustic systems; fire-control systems; application and design of permanent magnet devices; management systems. Address: 28 Millen Ave, Hamilton, Ont, Can.

DI CENZO, ROBERT J, b. Boston, Mass, Mar. 30, 30; m. 51. PHARMACEUTICAL CHEMISTRY. B.S, Northeastern, 53; M.S, Connecticut, 57, Penick Mem. fel, 57-59, Ph.D.(pharmaceut. chem), 60. Asst. prof. drug anal, Ferris State Col, 59-62; assoc. res. anal. chemist, Sterling-Winthrop Res. Inst, 62-64; SR. ANALYST, UNIV. CONN, 64- U.S.A, 47-49, Sgt. Am. Pharmaceut. Asn. Gas chromatography; terpenoids; medicinal chemistry; pharmaceutical analytical methods development; quality control; stability testing; atomic refractions; lipids analysis. Address: R.R. 2, Timer Dr, Storrs, CT 06268.

DICHTER, MICHAEL, b. Jan. 15, 12; U.S. citizen; m. 39; c. 1. PETROLEUM & POLYMER CHEMISTRY. Ph.D, Polish Acad. Sci, 33; M.Sc, Lvov Polytech. Inst, 36. Sr. eng, Petrol. Refineries, Poland, 36-41; USSR, 41-44; dir. petrochem. prod, Trzebinia, Poland, 45-48; dir. planning, Ministry For. Trade, Warsaw, 48-55, dep. for. trade secy, 55-56; DIR. RES, Cent. Lab. Petrol. Prod, 57-62; Inst. Petrol. Technol, Cracow-Warsaw, 63-69; POLYMER RES. CORP, 69- Pres, State Comn. Petrol Prods, Warsaw, Poland, 65-69. Polish Govt. Golden Award of Merit, 47; Order of Polonia Restituta, 2nd class, 54, 1st class, 64. New high quality lubricants and fuels for modern engines and machines; corrosion and water pollution prevention in petroleum refineries; Groft polymerization; polymer modification of solving problems, specifically surface modification, adhesion, nonflammable textiles and improved additives for petroleum products. Address: Polymer Research Corp, 2186 Mill Ave, Brooklyn, NY 11234.

DiCIANNI, NICHOLAS M, b. Fall River, Mass, Feb. 22, 39; m. 63. COMPUTER SCIENCE, SYSTEMS PROGRAMMING. B.S, Providence Col, 60; Ph.D.(chem), Notre Dame, 65. Asst. prof. comput. sci, Notre Dame, 65-68; Staff consult. to v.pres. systs. programming, UNIVAC DIV, SPERRY RAND CORP, 68-70, DIR. APPLNS. SOFTWARE, 70- U.S.A.R, 56-63, Sgt. Asn. Comput. Mach. Design of computer operating systems; programming language processors; industry oriented computer applications. Address: Univac Division, Sperry Rand Corp, P.O. Box 500, Blue Bell, PA 19422.

DICK, B(ERTRAM) G(ALE), b. Portland, Ore, June 12, 26; m. 56; c. 3. PHYSICS. B.A, Reed Col, 50; M.A, Oxford, 57; Ph.D.(physics), Cornell Univ, 58. Res. assoc. PHYSICS, Univ. Ill, 57-59; asst. prof, UNIV. UTAH, 59-62, assoc. prof, 62-65, PROF, 65-, acting chmn. dept, 64-65, chmn, 65-67. Consult, Minn. Mining & Mfg. Co, 60-67; vis. prof, Munich Tech. Univ, 67-68. U.S.N, 44-46. Am. Phys. Soc. Solid state physics; ionic crystals; phonons and phonon-defect interactions; paraelectric defects; color centers. Address: Dept. of Physics, University of Utah, Salt Lake City, UT 84112.

DICK, CHARLES E(DWARD), b. Fort Wayne, Ind, Apr. 24, 37; m. 58; c. 2. NUCLEAR PHYSICS. B.S, St. Procopius Col, 58; U.S. Rubber Co. fel, Notre Dame, 62, Ph.D.(physics), 63. PHYSICIST, NAT. BUR. STANDARDS, 62- Am. Phys. Soc. Low energy electron scattering; bremstrahlung production; low energy electro-magnetic interactions; x-ray analysis; applications of x-rays. Address: Applied Radiation Division, National Bureau of Standards, Washington, DC 20234.

DICK, C(LARENCE) R(INEHEART), b. Galveston, Tex, Feb. 15, 31; m. 51; c. 3. ORGANIC CHEMISTRY. B.S, N.Texas State, 52, M.S, 54; Ph.D, Kansas State, 57. CHEMIST, DOW CHEM. U.S.A, FREEPORT, 57- Am. Chem. Soc. Chemistry of quinoid type compounds; allylic and Fries rearrangements; small ring compounds. Address: 105 Ligustrum, Lake Jackson, TX 77566.

DICK, DONALD E(DWARD), b. Little Rock, Ark, Apr. 23, 42; m. 63. BIOMEDICAL & ELECTRICAL ENGINEERING. B.S, Calif. Inst. Technol, 64; M.S, Univ. Wis, Madison, 65, Nat. Insts. Health fel, 66-68, Ph.D.(elec. eng), 68. Res. asst. elec. eng, Univ. Wis, Madison, 64-66, fel, summer 68; ASST. PROF. ELEC. ENG, UNIV. COLO, BOULDER, 68-, PHYS. MED. & REHAB, MED. CTR, DENVER, 68- Nat. Insts. Health grant biomed. sci, 69-70. AAAS; Inst. Elec. & Electronics Eng; Am. Soc. Eng. Educ. Biomedical simulation and computer-aided patient monitoring in cardiovascular intensive care units; systems analysis of the delivery of health care; minicomputers and process control. Address: Dept. of Electrical Engineering, University of Colorado, Boulder, CO 80302.

DICK, ELLIOT C(OLTER), b. Miami, Fla, June 30, 26; m. 50; c. 2; m. 67; c. 1. MICROBIOLOGY. B.A, Minnesota, 50, M.S, 53, Ph.D, 55. Asst. prof, Kansas, 55-59; med, Tulane, 59-61; UNIV. WIS, MADISON, 61-63, ASSOC. PROF. PREV. MED, 64- Consult, Kans. State Bd. Health, 55-59; Watkins fel, Univ. Kans, 59; U.S. Pub. Health Serv. career res. develop. awards, 64-; vis. prof, Delta Regional Primate Ctr, Tulane Univ, 67. Dipl, Am. Bd. Microbiol, 68. U.S.A, 44-46. AAAS; Am. Soc. Microbiol; Soc. Exp. Biol. & Med; N.Y. Acad. Sci. Growth stimulation by antibiotics; rapid diagnostic methods in respiratory microbiology; epidemiology of respiratory infections. Address: Dept. of Preventive Medicine, University of Wisconsin Medical School, Madison, WI 83706.

DICK, GEORGE W, b. Toronto, Ont, Can, June 12, 31; m. 53; c. 3. ELECTRICAL ENGINEERING. B.A.Sc, Toronto, 53, M.A.Sc, 57, Ph.D.(eng), 60. Mem. staff elec. res. & develop, apparatus engr. lab, Can. Gen. Elec. Co, 53-55; commun. res, BELL TEL. LABS, 59-65, MEM. TECH. STAFF, 68- Assoc. prof. elec. eng, Univ. Toronto, 65-68. Assoc. Inst. Elec. & Electronics Eng. Communication principles; display communications techniques including gas plasma display panels, light emitting diodes and associated data transmission electronics. Address: Bell Telephone Labs, Holmdel, NJ 07733.

DICK, HENRY MARVIN, b. Duchess, Alta, June 1, 31; m. 57; c. 3. ORAL PATHOLOGY. D.D.S, Alberta, 57; fel, Manitoba, 66-67, Nat. Res. Coun. Can. fel, 67-68, M.Sc, 68. Dentist, gen. practice, 57-66; ASSOC. PROF. ORAL PATH, UNIV. ALTA, 68- Immunopathology of periodontal disease. Address: Faculty of Dentistry, University of Alberta, Edmonton, Alta, Can.

DICK, JAMES GARDINER, b. Perth, Scotland, Oct. 22, 20; Can. citizen; m. 56; c. 2. ANALYTICAL CHEMISTRY, ELECTROCHEMISTRY. B.Sc, Sir George Williams Univ, 47. Chief chemist, Can. Bronze Co, Ltd, 41-47, chief chemist & metallurgist, 47-54, dist. mgr. prod, res. & sales, Montreal Bronze Ltd, 54-58, mgr. mfg. prod, control & res, Can. Bronze Co, Ltd, 58-63; asst. prof. chem. & mat. sci, SIR GEORGE WILLIAMS UNIV, 63-67, assoc. prof. CHEM, 67-71, V.CHMN, 71- Mgr, Roast Labs Registered, 41-47; lectr, Sir George Williams Univ, 47-63; pres, Technitrol Ltd, 63-68, consult, 68-; Can. Metal Co, Ltd, Metals & Alloys Co, Ltd. & Ingot Metal Co, Ltd, 68- Am. Foundrymen's Soc; Am. Soc. Metals; Chem. Inst. Can; Spectros. Soc. Can; Brit. Inst. Metals; Can. Standards Asn. X-ray spectrochemical analysis; electrochemical kinetics; polarography. Address: Dept. of Chemistry, Sir George Williams University, 1435 Drummond St, Montreal, Que, Can.

DICK, JAMES L, b. Harrisburg, Pa, July 8, 21; m. 43; c. 1. NUCLEAR CHEMISTRY. B.S, Indiana State Col.(Pa), 42; M.S, Pittsburgh, 48; Ph.D.(nuclear chem), Ohio State, 53. Instr, high sch, Pa, 42-43; meteorologist, U.S. Weather Bur, 46; res. chemist, Solvay Process Co, 48; instr. radiation & chem. warfare, U.S. Air Force, 48-50, res. chemist, 54-59, chief res. planning, off. aerospace res, 59-62, res. dir, Defense Atomic Support Agency, 62-63, chief weapons effects br, weapons lab, 63-65, v.comdr, Air Force Cambridge Res. Labs, 65-67, dir, Air Force Avionics Lab, 67-69; ALBUQUERQUE DIV. GEN. MGR, EDGERTON, GREMESHAUSEN & GRIER, 69- U.S.A.F, 43-46, 48-69, Col. Sci. Res. Soc. Am; Health Physics Soc. Nuclear radiation effects on personnel including fallout and plutonium; planning of research programs in the physical sciences; geophysics and electronics. Address: Edgerton, Gremeshausen & Grier, 933 Bradbury Dr. S.E, Albuquerque, NM 87106.

DICK, JOHN M(ITCHELL), b. Indiana, Pa, Mar. 14, 32; m. 60; c. 3. MEDICINE, PHYSICS. B.S, Pa. State Univ, 54, M.S, 59; M.D, Jefferson Med. Col, 63. Dir. space med, Douglas Space Ctr, 64-66; consult. & chief space med, Ritchie Assoc, Inc, 66-67; PRES, DAND R. MED. MGT. SERV, 67-; HEALTH PHYS. SURV. LABS, INC, 67-; JOHN M. DICK, M.D. & ASSOC.

MED. GROUP, INC, 67- U.S.N, 54-58, Res, 58-63, Med.C, 63-64, Res, 64-, Lt. Aerospace medicine; ballistocardiography; physiology; medical electronics; nuclear medicine; biophysics; basic physics; bone densitometry. Address: 5360 Burlingame Ave, Buena Park, CA 90620.

DICK, JOHN N, b. N.Y.C, May 16, 03; m. 37; c. 2. INDUSTRIAL ENGINEERING, MATERIALS SCIENCE. Armed Forces Staff Col, 47; Wisconsin, 48; Indust. Col. Armed Forces, 49. From phys. dir. to asst. supt, YMCA, 19-25; chief indust. rels. & personnel, Procter & Gamble Co, 25-32; rep. Mayor LaGuardia, eng. studies, For. Trade Zones, 32-39; chief mfg. methods, Wright-Patterson Air Force Base & dep. dir. indust. resources, Pentagon, U.S. Air Force, 45-58; dist. mgr. res, develop. & sales, Allegheny Ludlum Steel Corp, 58-68; PRES, J. NICHOLAS DICK ASSOCS, 68- Rep. stockpile comt, U.S. Air Force, 49-53, consult, ad hoc comt. requirements, 63-64, mem. ad hoc tool adv. comt, 64-65; initiator & panel mem. aerospace appln. requirements comt, Mat. Adv. Bd, Nat. Acad. Sci, 58-65. U.S.A.F, 40-58, Col.(Ret). AAAS; N.Y. Acad. Sci; Am. Soc. Metals; Inst. Mgt. Materials engineering; increasing the production of titanium; foreign trade zones; manufacturing methods; research development; the nickel titanium alloy, Nitinol. Address: 5922 Overlea Rd, Washington, DC 20016.

DICK, KENNETH ANDERSON, b. Vancouver, B.C, July 30, 37; m. 59; c. 2. PHYSICS. B.Sc, British Columbia, 60, M.Sc, 63, Ph.D.(physics), 66. Res. assoc. physics, Hopkins, 66-69, assoc. res. scientist, 69; ASST. PHYSICIST, PLANETARY SCI. DIV, KITT PEAK NAT. OBSERV, 69- AAAS; Optical Soc. Am; Am. Geophys. Union; Can. Asn. Physicists. Atomic spectroscopy; auroral and airglow spectroscopy. Address: Planetary Sciences Division, Kitt Peak National Observatory, 950 N. Cherry Ave, Tucson, AZ 85717.

DICK, RICHARD IRWIN, b. Sanborn, Iowa, July 18, 35; m. 58; c. 4. SANITARY ENGINEERING. B.S, Iowa State, 57; M.S, Iowa, 58; U.S. Pub. Health Serv. fel, Illinois, Urbana, 63-65, Ph.D.(sanit. eng), 65. Sanit. engr, Clark, Daily, Dietz & Assocs, Consult. Engrs, 60-62; instr. SANIT. ENG, UNIV. ILL, URBANA-CHAMPAIGN, 62-63, asst. prof, 65-68, assoc. prof, 68-70, PROF, 70- U.S.P.H.S, 58-60, Sr. Asst. Sanit. Engr. Am. Water Works Asn; Am. Soc. Civil Eng; Water Pollution Control Fedn; Am. Asn. Prof. Sanit. Eng; Brit. Inst. Water Pollution Control; Int. Asn. Water Pollution Res. Unit operations and processes used in water and waste water treatment; treatment and disposal of sludges. Address: 3230 Civil Engineering Bldg, University of Illinois, Urbana-Champaign, Urbana, IL 61801.

DICK, RONALD STEWART, b. Queens, N.Y, Jan. 14, 34; m. 58; c. 2. MATHEMATICAL STATISTICS, MATHEMATICS. B.S, Queens Col, 55; fel, Columbia, 55-56, M.A, 57, Ph.D.(math. statist), 68. Math. statistician, U.S. Census Bur, Wash, D.C, 56-57; lectr. math, Queens Col.(N.Y), 57-62; sr. mem. tech. staff, I.T.T. Defense Commun, N.J, 60-68; asst. prof. math, C.W. Post. Col, Long Island, 63-68; ASSOC. PROF. MGT, GEORGE WASH. UNIV, 68- Asst, Columbia Univ, 56-57; engr, Sperry Gyroscope Co, N.Y, 57-59; reliability engr, Am. Bosch Arma, 59-60; vis. lectr, Stevens Inst, 63. Opers. Res. Soc. Am; Inst. Math. Statist; Am. Statist. Asn. Queueing theory with balking; reliability of repairable complex systems. Address: 1412 Chilton Dr, Silver Spring, MD 20904.

DICK, T(HOMAS) M(ILNE), b. New Stevenston, Scotland, Dec. 11, 31; Can. citizen; m. 56; c. 4. HYDRAULICS. B.Sc, Glasgow Univ, 53; A.R.T.C, Univ. Strathclyde, 54; M.Sc, Queen's Univ.(Ont), 60, Ph.D.(hydraul), 69. Engr, City Port Arthur, Ont, 53-55; design engr, C.D. Howe Co. Ltd, 55-58; res. asst. hydraul, Queen's Univ.(Ont), 58-60; engr, Dept. Pub. Works, 60-61; Dept. Transport, 61-64; res. off, Nat. Res. Coun. Can, 64-69; HEAD HYDRAUL, Dept. Energy, Mines & Resources, 69-70, DEPT. ENVIRON, 70- Lectr, Queen's Univ.(Ont), 66-67. Am. Geophys. Union; Int. Asn. Hydraul. Res; Int. Asn. Great Lakes Res. Coastal engineering; transportation; river hydraulics; ice in rivers; sediment transport. Address: Dept. of the Environment, Canada Centre for Inland Waters, 867 Lakeshore Rd, Box 5050, Burlington, Ont. Can.

DICK, WALTER J(OHN), Statist, see 12th ed, Soc. & Behav. Vols.

DICK, WILLIAM EDWIN, JR, b. Waynesboro, Va, Oct. 31, 36; m. 58; c. 2. CHEMISTRY. B.S, N.C. State, 58; M.S, Purdue, 62, Ph.D, 66. CHEMIST, NORTH. UTILIZATION RES. LAB, U.S. DEPT. AGR, 65- U.S.A.R, 58-67, Capt. Am. Chem. Soc. Synthesis and characterization of potentially valuable mono- and disaccharide derivatives. Address: Northern Utilization Research Lab, 1815 N. University Ave, Peoria, IL 61604.

DICKASON, ALAN FREDERICK, b. Lynn, Mass, July 23, 36; m. 54; c. 4. ORGANIC CHEMISTRY. B.S, Univ. N.H, 59; Ph.D.(chem), Univ. Va, 69. RES. CHEMIST, SUN OIL CO, 69- Catalysis Soc; Am. Chem. Soc. Liquid phase oxidation of organic compounds; heterogeneous gas phase catalytic oxidation; synthesis of nitrogen heterocycles for polymers. Address: Research & Development, Sun Oil Co, Marcus Hook, PA 19061.

DICKASON, ELVIS A(RNIE), b. Ore, Oct. 9, 19; m. 46; c. 2. ENTOMOLOGY. B.S, Oregon State, 47, M.S, 49; Ph.D.(entom), Mich. State, 59. Instr. ENTOM, Oregon State, 49-51, asst. prof, 51-61, assoc. prof, 61-70; PROF. & CHMN. DEPT, UNIV. NEBR, LINCOLN, 70- Grant-in-aid entom, IRI Res. Inst, Salvador, Brazil, 66-67. U.S.N.R, 41-45. Entom. Soc. Am. Applied entomology; insect ecology. Address: Dept. of Entomology, University of Nebraska, Lincoln, NE 68503.

DICKASON, WILLIAM CHARLES, b. Kansas City, Kans, Sept. 30, 43; m. 68; c. 1. CHEMISTRY. A.B, Rockhurst Col, 65; Allied Chem. fel, Purdue Univ, 68, Ph.D.(chem), 70. Nat. Sci. Found. fel. chem, Purdue Univ, 70; RES. CHEMIST, TENN. EASTMAN CO, 70- Am. Chem. Soc. Polymers; polymer intermediates; organic chemistry. Address: Tennessee Eastman Co, Bldg. 150, Kingsport, TN 37660.

DICKE, F(ERDINAND) F(REDERICK), b. New Bremen, Ohio, Aug. 25, 99; m. 29; c. 3. ENTOMOLOGY. B.S, Ohio State, 27; George Washington, 38-42. Field asst, bur. entom. & plant quarantine, U.S. Dept. Agr, Mich, 27-28, jr. entomologist, 28-29, asst. entomologist, Va, 29-33, Arlington Farm, 33-42, Beltsville Res. Ctr, 42, assoc. entomologist, Ohio, 42-50, entomologist, entom. res. div, Agr. Res. Serv, 50-63; ASSOC. PROF. ENTOM, IOWA STATE UNIV, 57-; ENTOMOLOGIST, PIONEER HI-BRED INT. INC, 63- U.S. Dept. Agr. Superior Serv. Award, 56. AAAS; Entom. Soc. Am. Cereal and forage crop insects; plant resistance to insects; entomogenous fungi. Address: 1430 Harding Ave, Ames, IA 50010.

DICKE, ROBERT H(ENRY), b. St. Louis, Mo, May 6, 16; m. 42; c. 3. PARTICLE PHYSICS. A.B, Princeton, 39; Ph.D.(physics), Univ. Rochester, 41. Staff mem. radiation lab, Mass. Inst. Technol, 41-46; asst. prof. PHYSICS, PRINCETON, 46-47, assoc. prof, 47-55, prof, 55-57, CYRUS FOGG BRACKETT PROF, 57-, chmn. dept, 68-70. Vis. prof, Harvard, 54-55; mem. adv. panel physics, Nat. Sci. Found, 59-61, chmn. adv. comt. radio astron, 67-69; chmn. adv. comt. atomic physics, Nat. Bur. Standards, 61-63; mem. comt. physics, NASA, 63-70, chmn, 63-66, mem. lunar ranging exp. team, 66-; chmn. physics panel, adv. to Comt. Int. Exchange of Persons, Fulbright Fels, 64-66; mem, Nat. Sci. Bd, 70- Nat. Medal Sci, 71. Nat. Acad. Sci; AAAS; fel. Am. Acad. Arts & Sci.(Rumford Premium Award, 67); fel. Am. Phys. Soc; fel. Am. Geophys. Union; Am. Asn. Physics Teachers; Am. Astron. Soc. Gravitation; relativity; astrophysics; solar physics; cosmology. Address: Joseph Henry Labs, Dept. of Physics, Jadwin Hall, Princeton University, Princeton, NJ 08540.

DICKE, ROBERT J(EROME), b. Sheboygan Falls, Wis, June 16, 12; m. 40; c. 4. ENTOMOLOGY. Univ. Wis, 40, Ph.D.(econ. entom), 43. Asst. UNIV. WIS, MADISON, 40-43, asst. prof. ENTOM, 46-49, assoc. prof, 49-52, PROF, 52-, chmn. dept, 59-68. U.S.N, 43-46. Fel. AAAS; Entom. Soc. Am. Insects affecting man and domestic animals, stored food products; morphology. Address: Dept. of Entomology, University of Wisconsin, Madison, WI 53706.

DICKEL, DANIEL F(REDERICK), b. Phila, Pa, Jan. 9, 20; m. 47; c. 2. ORGANIC CHEMISTRY. B.S, Phila. Col. Pharm, 42; Ph.D.(chem), Pittsburgh, 51. Chemist, U.S. Dept. Agr, 42-44; SR. CHEMIST, CIBA-GEIGY LTD, SUMMIT, 52- Am. Swiss Found. fel. Med.C, U.S.A, 44-46. Am. Chem. Soc; Swiss Chem. Soc. Chemistry of natural products with chief emphasis on the isolation of compounds with useful medical applications. Address: 32 Wilson Dr, Berkeley Heights, NJ 07922.

DICKEL, JOHN RUSH, b. New York, N.Y, Mar. 29, 39; m. 61; c. 2. ASTRONOMY. B.S, Yale, 60; Ph.D.(astron), Michigan, 64. Res. asst. ASTRON, Nat. Radio Astron. Observ, summer 60; Michigan, 60-64; asst. prof, UNIV. ILL, URBANA, 64-68, ASSOC. PROF, 68- Am. Astron. Soc; Int. Sci. Radio Union. Radio astronomical studies of the planets; supernova remnants. Address: Dept. of Astronomy, University of Illinois, Urbana, IL 61801.

DICKENS, CHARLES H(ENDERSON), b. Thomasville, N.C, Nov. 22, 34; m. 65; c. 2. MATHEMATICS & EDUCATION. B.S, Duke Univ, 57, Woodrow Wilson fel, 63, James B. Duke fel, 63 & 64, M.Ed, 64, D.Educ.(math. educ), 66. Res. technician, Nat. Security Agency, 57-58 & 60-62; teacher, high sch, N.C, 62-63; instr. educ, Wake Forest Col, 65-66, asst. prof. math & educ, 66-67; planning specialist, planning & eval. unit, off. assoc. dir. educ, NAT. SCI. FOUND, 67-69, ASSOC. PROG. DIR, STUD-ORIGINATED STUDIES PROG, DIV. UNDERGRAD. EDUC. SCI, 69- Consult, pub. schs, High Point, Yadkin County & Surry County, N.C, 65-67; Am. Political Sci. Asn. & U.S. Civil. Serv. Comn. Cong. fel, 71-72. U.S.A, 58-59, Res, 60-61, 1st. Lt. AAAS; Am. Educ. Res. Asn. In-service education in mathematics for elementary school teachers; evaluation of federal programs in science and mathematics education. Address: Student-Originated Studies Program, National Science Foundation, Washington, DC 20550.

DICKENS, JOHN E(RNEST), b. Sheffield, Eng, Aug. 20, 29; m. 56; c. 2. PHYSICAL CHEMISTRY. B.A, Oxford, 51, M.A. & D.Phil, 54. Tech. officer, Imp. Chem. Industs, Scotland, 54-55, 56-57; res. fel, Northwest. Univ, 55-56; RES. SUPVR, PHOTO PRODS. DEPT, E.I. DU PONT DE NEMOURS & CO, INC, 58- Complexions; propellants; magnetic recording; photopolymers. Address: 18 Boulderbrook Dr, Wilmington, DE 19803.

DICKENS, JUSTIN KIRK, b. Syracuse, N.Y, Nov. 2, 31; m. 57; c. 4. NUCLEAR PHYSICS. A.B, Southern California, 55, Ph.D.(physics), 62; M.S, Chicago, 56. PHYSICIST, LOW ENERGY NUCLEAR PHYSICS, OAK RIDGE NAT. LAB, 62- U.S.A, 50-52, S/Sgt. AAAS; Am. Phys. Soc. Nuclear reaction mechanisms, experimental and theoretical. Address: Oak Ridge National Lab, Oak Ridge, TN 37830.

DICKENS, LAWRENCE EDWARD, b. North Kingstown, R.I, Dec. 8, 32; m. 52; c. 7. ELECTRICAL & ELECTRONIC ENGINEERING. B.S.E.E, Hopkins, 60, M.S.E.E, 62, D.Eng, 64. Field engr, radio div, Bendix Corp, 53-56, asst. proj. engr, 56-58, proj. engr, 58-60; res. staff asst. electronic design, radiation lab, Hopkins, 60-62, res. assoc. microwave semiconductors, 62-64, res. scientist, 64-65; Adv. Tech. Corp, 65-69; ADV. ENGR, WESTINGHOUSE ELEC. CORP, 69- Consult, radio div, Bendix Corp, 60-63; Appl. Microwave Elec. Corp, 61; Am. Electronics Labs, Inc, 63; res. div, Electronic Commun, Inc, 63-64; Pinkerton Electro-Security Co, 65-66. U.S.A, 50-53. Inst. Elec. & Electronics Eng. Development of low noise communications systems and components; microwave and millimeter wave semiconductor components and their applications. Address: Advanced Technology Labs, Westinghouse Electric Corp, Box 1521, MS-3422, Baltimore, MD 21203.

DICKENS, LESTER EMERT, b. Palisade, Colo, Nov. 18, 19; m. 45. PLANT PATHOLOGY. B.S, Colorado State, 50, M.S, 53; Ph.D, Cornell, 57. Asst. prof. bot. & plant path. & asst. plant pathologist, COLO. STATE UNIV, 57-63, exten. plant pathologist, 63-70, EXTEN. PROF. PLANT PATH, 70- Partic, workshop plant path, tech. task force comt, Great Plains Agr. Coun, 69- U.S.A.A.F, 42-45. AAAS; Am. Phytopath. Soc. Extension plant pathology. Address: College of Natural Sciences, Colorado State University, Ft. Collins, CO 80521.

DICKENS, S(AMUEL) P(EIRSON), b. Enfield, N.C, Oct. 28, 22; m. 45; c. 5. CHEMICAL ENGINEERING. B.Ch.E, N.C. State Col, 43. Res. chem. engr, Texaco res. & develop. lab, Texas Co, 43-56, asst. supvr. fuels res. dept,

56, supvr. proj. evaluation res, Texaco Res. Center, 57-60, dir. fuels process commercialization, 60-61, dir. fuels & chem. res, Port Arthur Res. Ctr, 61-66, mgr. admin. serv, res. & tech. dept, TEXACO, INC, 66-67, mgr. commercial develop, 67-69, coord. strategic plant dept, 69-70, COORD. SUPPLY & DISTRIB; DEPT, 70- Am. Chem. Soc; Am. Inst. Chem. Eng; Am. Asn. Cost. Eng. Economic evaluation; engineering design of research projects; fuels process development; research administration. Address: Texaco, Inc, 135 E. 42nd St, New York, NY 10007.

DICKENS, WILLIAM ALLEN, b. Milwaukee, Wis, Apr. 25, 32; m. 59; c. 3. CHEMICAL ENGINEERING. A.B, Williams Col, 54; S.M, Mass. Inst. Tech, 56. Chem. engr, RES. & DEVELOP. DIV, KIMBERLY-CLARK CORP, 56-60, supt, chem. eng. lab, 60-63, pioneering res. lab, 63-64, chem. eng. lab, 64-67, develop. engr, 67-68, MGR. NONWOVEN LAB, 68- Transport phenomena; heat and mass transfer drying. Address: Research & Engineering, Kimberly-Clark Corp, Neenah, WI 54956.

DICKENSON, DONALD D(WIGHT), b. Paris, Ill, Jan. 15, 25; m. 46; c. 4. PLANT GENETICS & PATHOLOGY. B.S, Illinois, 49, M.S, 50; Ph.D.(grass breeding), Minnesota, 57. Plant breeder, HOLLY SUGAR CORP, 53-62, asst. dir. agr. res, 62-66, DIR. AGR. RES, 66- U.S.A, 43-45. Am. Soc. Agron; Am. Soc. Sugar Beet Technol; Am. Phytopath. Soc; Am. Genetics Asn; Crop Sci. Soc. Am; Soil Sci. Soc. Am. Administration of variety improvement program for breeding new hybrid varieties of sugar beets with improved yield, sugar, processability and disease resistance; assessment of agronomic problems with appropriate action—all areas. Address: Holly Sugar Corp, P.O. Box 1052, Colorado Springs, CO 80901.

DICKER, DANIEL, b. Brooklyn, N.Y, Dec. 30, 29; m. 51; c. 2. ENGINEERING, APPLIED MATHEMATICS. B.C.E, City Col. New York, 51; M.C.E, N.Y. Univ, 55; Quincy Ward Boese fel, Columbia, 58, Eng.Sc.D.(appl. mech), 61. Engr, Bogert-Childs, 51-52, 54-55; proj. engr, Praeger-Kavanagh, 55-58; res. asst. eng, Columbia, 59-60, instr, 60-61, asst. prof, 61-62; STATE UNIV. N.Y. STONY BROOK, 62-64, assoc. prof, 64-68, PROF, APPL. MATH, 68-, asst. dean grad. sch, 65-69, exec. off, col. eng, 70-71. Nat. Sci. Found. grant, 63-; NATO fel, Imp. Col, Univ. London, 69-70. U.S.A, 52-54, Res, 54-61, 2nd Lt. AAAS; Am. Soc. Civil Eng.(Norman Medal, 67); Soc. Indust. & Appl. Math; Am. Geophys. Union. Hydrodynamics; approximate solutions of boundary value problems; heat conduction; structural dynamics; transient flow in porous media; boundary layer theory. Address: Dept. of Applied Mathematics, State University of New York at Stony Brook, Stony Brook, NY 11790.

DICKER, PAUL EDWARD, b. Philadelphia, Pa, June 17, 25; m. 53; c. 4. ELECTRICAL ENGINEERING. B.Sc, Swarthmore Col, 45; M.Sc, Ohio State, 48. Asst. math, Ohio State, 46-47, instr. elec. eng, 47-48; Princeton, 48-51; res. assoc, eng. res. inst, Michigan, 51-54; asst. prof. elec. eng, Vanderbilt, 54-58, assoc. prof, 58-59; instr. elec. eng, Tenn. State Univ, 59-64; chief engr, ALADDIN ELECTRONICS, 59-65, asst. gen. mgr, 65-67, MGR. OPERS. & DIR. PROD. DEVELOP, 67- Work on N.J. Turnpike; plant engr, Kaiser-Frazer Corp, 52- Consult, Avco Mfg. Co; Miniature Electronic Components; Essex Electronics. U.S.N.R, 44-46, Lt.(jg). Sr. mem. Inst. Elec. & Electronics Eng. Electronics; magnetic components. Address: 6110 Elizabethan Dr, Nashville, TN 37205.

DICKER, STANLEY, b. Brooklyn, N.Y, July 30, 27; m. 49; c. 2. THERMODYNAMICS, FLUID DYNAMICS. B.M.E, Polytech. Inst. Brooklyn, 49; M.M.E, N.Y. Univ, 54; Eng.Sc.D.(mech. eng), Columbia, 61. Proj. engr, S.J. O'Brien Co, 49-50; Voorhees, Walker, Foley & Smith, 50-54; air conditioning power plants, Westinghouse Elec. Int. Co, 54-57; res. engr, heat & mass flow anal. lab, Columbia, 57-61; proj. engr, minuteman heat transfer, Space Tech. Labs, Inc, Thompson Ramo-Wooldridge, Inc, 61-62; thermodyn. specialist, Repub. Aviation Corp, 62-64; assoc. prof. mech. eng, Hofstra, 64-69; INDEPENDENT CONSULT. ENGR, 69- Lectr, State Univ. N.Y. Stony Brook, 63. Consult, Cent. Gen. Hosp, Plainview, N.Y, 63-; Doctors Hosp, Freeport & Smithtown Gen. Hosp, 64- U.S.A, 46-47. Am. Inst. Aeronaut. & Astronaut; Am. Soc. Heat, Refrig. & Air-Conditioning Eng. Medical engineering; thermodynamics and fluid dynamics relating to biological systems; simulation of convective heat transfer with continous media analogs. Address: 507 Fifth Ave, New York, NY 10017.

DICKERHOFE, THOMAS EDWARD, b. Canton, Ohio, June 3, 41; m. 66; c. 2. ORGANIC & PHARMACEUTICAL CHEMISTRY, POLYMER SCIENCE. B.Sc, Illinois, Chicago, 63, Ph.D.(chem), 66. Asst. pharmaceut. chem, Illinois, Chicago, 63-66; RES. CHEMIST, E.I. DU PONT DE NEMOURS & CO, 66- Am. Chem. Soc. Heterocyclic chemistry; high temperature polymers; emulsion polymerization; dielectric films; product and process development of industrial and packaging films. Address: Research & Development Lab, E.I. du Pont de Nemours & Co, Circleville, OH 43113.

DICKERHOOF, DEAN W, b. Akron, Ohio, Nov. 9, 35; m. 58; c. 2. INORGANIC CHEMISTRY. B.S, Akron, 57; M.S. & Ph.D.(inorg. chem), Illinois, 61. Asst. prof. CHEM, COLO. SCH. MINES, 61-66, ASSOC. PROF, 66- Chem.C, U.S.A.R, 57-65, Capt. Am. Chem. Soc; The Chem. Soc. Preparation of organometallic compounds in which a simple organic group is bonded to a transition metal; use of physical measurements to investigate the structure and chemical bonding in such compounds. Address: Dept. of Chemistry, Colorado School of Mines, Golden, CO 80401.

DICKERMAN, C(HARLES) E(DWARD), b. Carbondale, Ill, Mar. 9, 32; m. 54; c. 4. NUCLEAR PHYSICS. B.A, Southern Illinois, 51, M.A, 52; dipl, Imp. Col, London, 53; Ph.D.(physics), Iowa, 57. ASSOC. PHYSICIST, ARGONNE NAT. LAB, 57- Am. Phys. Soc; Am. Nuclear Soc. Low energy nuclear physics; nuclear safety of fast reactors. Address: Reactor Analysis and Safety Division, Argonne National Lab, 9700 S. Cass Ave, Argonne, IL 60439.

DICKERMAN, E(LDIE) E(UGENE), b. Oswego, Kans, Jan. 22, 03; m. 27; c. 2. BIOLOGY. A.B, Grand Island Col, 26; M.S, Northwestern, 31, Ph.D. (zool), 36; Ohio State, 35. Teacher, high sch, Nebr, 26-29; asst. zool, Northwestern, 29-31, instr, 31-36; asst. prof. biol, Bowling Green State Univ, 36-43, assoc. prof, 43-48, prof, 48-69; RETIRED. AAAS; Am. Soc. Parasitol; Am. Micros. Soc. Trematode life history; life history studies on the trematode family Azygiidae. Address: Las Cruces, NM 88001.

DICKERMAN, HERBERT W, b. New York, N.Y, Aug. 3, 28; m. 63; c. 3. BIOCHEMISTRY, INTERNAL MEDICINE. M.D, State Univ. N.Y, 52; Ph.D.(biol), Hopkins, 60. Instr. med, sch. med, Hopkins, 60-63; investr. clin. biochem, Nat. Heart Inst, 63-66; ASSOC. PROF. MED, SCH. MED, JOHNS HOPKINS UNIV, 66- Estab. investr, Am. Heart Asn, 60-66; Nat. Insts. Health res. career develop. award, 66- U.S.N.R, 54-56, Lt. Am. Soc. Biol. Chem. Folate and vitamin B_{12} metabolism, biochemical control mechanisms; ribonucleic acid metabolism; hematopoesis. Address: Dept. of Medicine, Johns Hopkins Hospital, Baltimore, MD 21205.

DICKERMAN, J(OHN) M(ELVILLE), b. Spencer, Mass, Oct. 26, 22; m. 45; c. 4. MICROBIOLOGY. B.S, Massachusetts, 44; M.S, Michigan, 47, Ph.D. (bact), 49. Asst. res. prof. bact, Massachusetts, 49-51; asst. prof. bact, Colo. Agr. & Mech. Col, 51-54; DIR. LABS. & RES, EAST. N.C. SANATORIUM, 54- Adj. prof. biol. sci, Atlantic Christian Col, 54- Registered, Nat. Registry Microbiol. Am. Acad. Microbiol; Am. Soc. Microbiol. Studies on the mechanism of the resistance-lowering action of hog gastric mucin; ozone as an agent for the purification of rural water supplies; decomposition of wood cellulose and beet pulp by microorganisms; antibiotic in cabbage; diagnostic antigen for vibrio fetus; evaluation of C-reactive protein determinations of the serum of tuberculosis patients; simplification of the rapid method of susceptibility testing c̄ adaptation to a wider spectrum of anti-tuberculosis drugs. Address: 1804 W. Nash St, Wilson, NC 27893.

DICKERMAN, M(URLYN) B, b. Hamden, Conn, July 29, 12; m. 39. FORESTRY. B.S, Connecticut, 34; M.S.F, California, 36. Forest economist, Northeast. Forest Exp. Sta, 37-40; Lake States Forest Exp. Sta, 41-44; Allied Control Cmn, Italy, 45-46; chief div. forest econs, North. Rocky Mt. Forest & Range Exp. Sta, 46-51; dir. forest res, Lake States Forest Exp. Sta, 51-64; staff asst, prog. develop. & eval, U.S. DEPT. AGR, 65-66, ASSOC. DEP. CHIEF RES, U.S. FOREST SERV, 66- Consult. forester, UNRRA, 46. Soc. Am. Foresters; Soil Conserv. Soc. Am; Forest Prod. Res. Soc; Am. Forestry Asn. Research program development and administration. Address: 3900 Gresham Pl, Alexandria, VA 22305.

DICKERMAN, RICHARD CURTIS, b. Chicago, Ill, Jan. 31, 34; m. 60; c. 2. GENETICS, ZOOLOGY. B.A, Col. Wooster, 56; Ph.D.(genetics), Texas, 62. Asst, Genetics Found, Texas, 61-62; asst. prof. biol, Kans. State Teachers Col, 62-65; resident res. assoc, div. biol. & med. res, Argonne Nat. Lab, 65-67; asst. prof. BIOL, CLEVELAND STATE UNIV, 67-69, ASSOC. PROF, 69- Med.C, U.S.A, 57-59. AAAS; Genetics Soc. Am; Nat. Asn. Biol. Teachers. Genetic studies of x-irradiated Drosophilia oocytes; genetic studies of irradiated Drosophilia populations; radiation and chemical induced mutations in Drosophilia. Address: Dept. of Biology, Cleveland State University, Cleveland, OH 44115.

DICKERMAN, S(TUART) CARLTON, b. Worcester, Mass, July 15, 18; m. 46; c. 1. ORGANIC CHEMISTRY. B.S, Worcester Polytech. Inst, 40; fel, N.Y. Univ, 45-46, Ph.D.(org. chem), 47. Asst, N.Y. Univ, 40-42, instr, 42-44; chemist, Squibb Inst. Med. Res, 44; Columbia, 44-45; instr, N.Y. UNIV, 46-47, asst. prof. ORG. CHEM, 47-57, assoc. prof, 57-66, PROF, 66-, CHMN. DEPT. CHEM, 70- With Office Sci. Res. & Develop, 44. AAAS; Am. Chem. Soc; The Chem. Soc. Free radicals; structure and mechanism; synthesis. Address: Dept. of Chemistry, New York University, New York, NY 10453.

DICKERSON, C(HARLESWORTH) L(EE), b. Fredericksburg, Va, Dec. 14, 27; m. 59; c. 2. ORGANIC CHEMISTRY. B.S, Col. William & Mary, 49; M.S, Virginia, 51, Ph.D.(org. chem), 54. Res. chemist, Am. Enka Corp, 54-55; sr. chemist appl. res, S.C. JOHNSON & SON, INC, 57-65, prod. res, 65-67, tech. librn-info. specialist, 67, SR. RES. CHEMIST & INFO. SPECIALIST, 67- U.S.A, 55-57. AAAS; Am. Chem. Soc; Am. Soc. Info. Sci; Spec. Libr. Asn; Nat. Microfilm Asn; Brit. Inst. Info. Sci. Action of Grignard reagents on 2, 3-unsaturated-1, r-diketones and related furans; high polymer compositions and properties; synthesis of insecticides. Address: 1525 Howe St, Racine, WI 53403.

DICKERSON, CHESTER T, JR, b. Lewes, Del, Apr. 26, 39; m. 60; c. 2. WEED SCIENCE, OLERICULTURE. B.S, Delaware, 62, M.S, 64; Ph.D. (weed sci), Cornell, 68. SUPVR. WEED SCI, MONSANTO CO, 68- Weed Sci. Soc. Am. Herbicide research and development. Address: 1006 Bryant St, Sagamore Hills, Allentown, PA 18104.

DICKERSON, DORSEY GLENN, b. Indianapolis, Ind, Mar. 1, 41; m. 61; c. 2. ORGANIC & PHYSICAL CHEMISTRY. B.S, Purdue Univ, 63; Nat. Sci. Found. fels, Univ. Wash, summers 65 & 66, Standard Oil fel, 66-67, Ph.D. (chem), 67. SR. RES. CHEMIST, PHOTOG. RES. DIV, EASTMAN KODAK CO, 67- Am. Chem. Soc. Kinetics and thermodynamics of aldehyde hydration; mechanisms of catalysis by bovine erythrocyte carbonic anhydrase and inhibition of same; enzyme isolation and purification; mechanisms and kinetics of novel photographic processes. Address: Research Labs, Eastman Kodak Co, Kodak Park, Rochester, NY 14650.

DICKERSON, G(ORDON) E(DWIN), b. La Grande, Ore, Jan. 30, 12; m. 33; c. 4. ANIMAL BREEDING. B.S, Mich. State, 33; scholar, Wisconsin, 33-34, M.S, 34, Ph.D.(animal genetics), 37. Asst. genetics, Wisconsin, 34-35, instr. genetics & dairy records, 35-39, genetics & dairy husb, 39-41; assoc. geneticist, regional swine breeding lab, bur. animal indust, U.S. Dept. Agr, 41-47; prof. animal husb, Missouri, 47-52; geneticist, Kimber Farms, 52-65; res. br, Can. Dept. Agr, 65-67; PROF. ANIMAL SCI, UNIV. NEBR, LINCOLN & GENETICIST, U.S. MEAT ANIMAL RES. CTR, AGR. RES. SERV, U.S. DEPT. AGR, 67- AAAS; fel. Am. Soc. Animal Sci.(breeding-genetics award, 70); Genetics Soc. Am; Am. Genetic Asn; Am. Dairy Sci. Asn; Biomet. Soc; Poultry Sci. Asn; Soc. Study Evolution. Animal genetics; experimental design; effectiveness of selection and breeding systems in swine, dairy and beef cattle, poultry, mice. Address: 225 Baker Hall, University of Nebraska, Lincoln, NE 68503.

DICKERSON, JAMES PERRY, b. Bunn, N.C, May 8, 39; m. 70. ORGANIC CHEMISTRY. B.S, Univ. N.C, Chapel Hill, 62; Ph.D.(org. chem), Wayne State Univ, 66. SR. RES. CHEMIST, Ash Stevens Inc, 66-68; R.J. REYNOLDS INDUSTS, INC, 68- Am. Chem. Soc. Carbohydrates; organic synthesis; natural products; amino sugars; tobacco science. Address: Research Dept, R.J. Reynolds Industries, Inc, Winston-Salem, NC 27102.

DICKERSON, L(OREN) L(ESTER), JR, b. Fitzgerald, Ga, May 11, 18; m. 53; c. 3. AEROSPACE ENGINEERING. B.S, Emory, 39; Sc.D.(chem. eng), Mass. Inst. Tech, 42. Res. chem. engr, Arthur D. Little, Inc, 42-44; res. assoc. metall, Mass. Inst. Tech, 44-45; res. supvr. process metall, Reynolds Metals Co, 45-46, proj. engr. process develop, 46-48; private consult. & mfg. printing & embroidering methods, 48-53; dir. reduction res, Reynolds Metals Co, 53-57, assoc. dir. & leader fundamental res. dept, 57-60; consult. & prin. sci. investr, Army Missile Command, 60-70; AEROSPACE ENGR. & COORD. NUCLEAR EFFECTS STUDIES, SAFEGUARD SYST. COMMAND, DEPT. DEFENSE, 70- Fel. AAAS; Am. Inst. Mining, Metall. & Petrol. Eng; Am. Chem. Soc; Electrochem. Soc; Faraday Soc; Int. Soc. Gen. Semantics. Electrical and control engineering; electronics; instrumentation; chemical, metallurgical and nuclear engineering. Address: 411 Echols Ave. S.E, Huntsville, AL 35801.

DICKERSON, MALON H(OWARD), b. Omaha, Nebr, Mar. 3, 12; m. 55; c. 2. CHEMISTRY, PHYSICS. Asst. org. chemist, exp. sta, E.I. du Pont de Nemours & Co, Del, 36-42, dir. photog. sect, eng. dept, 42-45; res. chemist, color res. dept, Ansco Div, Gen. Aniline & Film Corp, N.Y, 45-51; chem. physicist & dir. photog. tech, physics dept, Southwest Res. Inst, Tex, 51-54; dir. photog. res, Southwest Prod, Inc, 54-55; res. chemist & consult, aerial reconnaissance lab, Wright-Patterson Air Force Base, Ohio, 55-56; res. chemist, anal. sect, Humko Co, Tenn, 56-57; sr. res. assoc, Horizons, Inc, 57-58; sr. res. chemist & consult, Picker X-Ray Corp, 58-64; v.pres. & tech. dir, Redox Corp, 64-65, pres. & tech. dir, 65-66; res. chemist & consult, Perolin Co, 66-68; State Mfg. Co, 68-69; investment analyst, Pa. Securities Co, 69-70; ACCOUNT SERV. EXEC, GAC PROPERTIES, INC, 70- Lectr, San Antonio Col, 52. Consult, Wright Air Develop. Center, Ohio, 51-56; Apeco, Mansfield Industs. & Argus, Inc, Ill; Franklin Inst, Pa; Picker X-Ray Corp, 56-64. Off. Sci. Res. & Develop. award, 44. AAAS; Am. Chem. Soc; Photog. Soc. Am; Am. Soc. Oil Chemists; Royal Photog. Soc. Organic synthesis; photographic technology; colloidal chemistry; rapid processing of photo materials; photo sensitization of aluminum plates; synthesis of antibiotics; silver recovery from photo film materials; area-source mounting method for radioactive isotopes; metal brighteners. Address: Gac Properties, Inc, 7880 Biscayne Blvd, Miami, FL 33138.

DICKERSON, OTTIE J, b. Mulberry, Ark, Sept. 4, 33; m. 55; c. 2. NEMATOLOGY, PLANT PATHOLOGY. B.S, Univ. Ark, 55, M.S, 56; Ph.D.(plant path), Univ. Wis, 61. Asst. prof. NEMATOL, KANS. STATE UNIV, 61-66, ASSOC. PROF, 66- U.S.A, 56-58. Am. Phytopath. Soc; Soc. Nematol. Biology and control of plant parasitic nematodes. Address: Dept. of Plant Pathology, Dickens Hall, Kansas State University, Manhattan, KS 66502.

DICKERSON, RICHARD E(ARL), b. Casey, Ill, Oct. 8, 31; m. 56; c. 5. PHYSICAL CHEMISTRY. Westinghouse scholar. & B.S, Carnegie Inst. Tech, 53; Nat. Sci. Found. fel, Dow Chem. fel. & Ph.D.(phys. chem), Minnesota, 57. Nat. Sci. Found. fel, Leeds, 57-58; Cavendish lab, Cambridge, 58-59; asst. prof. phys. chem, Illinois, 59-63; assoc. prof. CHEM, CALIF. INST. TECHNOL, 63-68, PROF, 68- AAAS; Am. Inst. Physics; Am. Soc. Biol. Chem; Am. Crystallog. Asn. X-ray crystallography and molecular structure of proteins; evolution at the molecular level; molecular biology. Address: Gates & Crellin Labs, California Institute of Technology, Pasadena, CA 91109.

DICKERSON, RICHARD T, JR, b. Cincinnati, Ohio, Feb. 11, 23; m. 51; c. 4. ORGANIC CHEMISTRY. Ch.E, Cincinnati, 49; Ph.D, Rensselaer Polytech, 56. Polymer chemist, DOW CHEM. CO, 54-71, RES. CHEMIST, 71- U.S.A.A.F, 43-46. Am. Chem. Soc. Kinetics and mechanism of some reactions of aromatic sulfinic acid esters; development of plastic products; organic chemistry of bromine, sulfur and phosphorus; hydrocarbon chemistry; oxidation; polymerization. Address: 4111 Arlington St, Midland, MI 48640.

DICKERSON, ROBERT H(ARVEY), b. Yuma, Ariz, Aug. 15, 37; m. 65; c. 1. PHYSICS. B.S, Arizona, 59, Nat. Defense Ed. Act fel, 59-62, M.S, 63, Ph.D.(physics), 64. Res. assoc. PHYSICS, Illinois, Urbana, 64-66; ASST. PROF, Calif. State Col. Hayward, 66-70; CALIF. STATE POLYTECH. COL, SAN LUIS OBISPO, 70- AAAS; Am. Phys. Soc; Am. Asn. Phys. Teachers. High pressure physics; metal physics; diffusion. Address: Dept. of Physics, California State Polytechnic College, San Luis Obispo, CA 93401.

DICKERSON, R(ONALD) F(RANK), b. Middletown, N.Y, Jan. 27, 22; m. 44; c. 2. METALLURGICAL ENGINEERING. B.S, Va. Polytech, 47, M.S, 49. Prin. metallurgist reactor mat, Battelle Mem. Inst, 48-53, asst. div. chief, 53-56, div. chief, 56-62, asst. mgr. metall. & physics dept, 62-64, staff mgr, Pac. Northwest Lab, 64-68, asst. dir. BMI Int, 68-70, MGR. SPEC. PROJS, BATTELLE DEVELOP. CORP, 70- U.S.A, 42-44, Res, 46-53, Capt. Am. Soc. Metals; Electrochem. Soc; Am. Nuclear Soc; Am. Foundrymen's Soc. Fuel alloy development for reactor cores, melting and casting or uranium, zirconium, thorium, niobium, molybdenum and other rare metals; metallography of these materials and irradiation damage. Address: Battelle Development Corp, 505 King Ave, Columbus, OH 43201.

DICKERSON, RUSSELL B, b. Sussex, N.J, June 21, 04; m. 27; c. 4. AGRICULTURAL EDUCATION. B.S, Pa. State, 27, Ph.D.(admin. ed), 43; M.S, Rutgers, 33. Teacher, high sch, Pa, 27-28; N.J, 28-37; supvr. voc. agr, Sussex County Voc. Sch, 37-38; instr. agr. ed, Pa. State, 38-41; asst. prof, 41-43, assoc. prof, 43-47; proprietor, Orchard Crest Farms, N.J, 47-49; assoc. dean COL. AGR, PA. STATE UNIV, 49-70, EMER. ASSOC. DEAN, 70-, EMER. PROF. AGR. EDUC, 70-, coord. int. agr. develop, 65-70. Vis. prof, Cornell-Los Banos-contract, col. agr, Univ. Philippines, 56-58; adv. agr. educ. & admin. & chief of party, U.S. Agency Int. Develop, AUD-Pa. State Univ. contract, 68-70. Chmn, Nat. Cmt. for Series Work Conf. for Dirs. Resident Instr. in Up-Grading the Admin. Agr. Instr, 58-64; fellowship officer, Agr. Develop. Coun. Inc, N.Y, 64-65. Nat. 4-H Alumni Recognition Award, Olin Mathieson Chem. Corp, 56-57. Food production training for farmers; evaluation of college of agriculture administration and instruction; improvement of instruction in Philippine agricultural enterprises; education of American and foreign students for international agricultural development. Address: 540 E. Prospect Ave, State College, PA 16801.

DICKERSON, STEPHEN L(ANG), b. Rockford, Ill, Jan. 6, 40; m. 62; c. 2. MECHANICAL ENGINEERING. B.S, Ill. Inst. Tech, 62; Sloan fel. & M.S, California, Berkeley, 63; Whitney & Nat. Sci. Found. fels. & Sc.D.(eng), Mass. Inst. Tech, 65. Asst. prof. MECH. ENG, GA. INST. TECHNOL, 65-70, ASSOC. PROF, 70- NASA summer faculty fel, 66. Am. Soc. Mech. Eng; Inst. Elec. & Electronics Eng. Automatic control systems; fluid power; complex engineering systems design. Address: School of Mechanical Engineering, Georgia Institute of Technology, Atlanta, GA 30332.

DICKERT, HERMAN A(LONZO), b. Newberry, S.C, Jan. 16, 03; m. 27; c. 2. INDUSTRIAL CHEMISTRY. A.B, Newberry Col, 23, Sc.D, 55; M.A, North Carolina, 25. Res. chemist, food & nutrit. lab, State Dept. Agr, N.C, 24-25; cellulose & rayon, E.I. du Pont de Nemours & Co, 25-31, supvry. work, rayon div, 34-45; dir, A. French Textile Sch, Ga. Inst. Technol, 45-58, prof. textile eng, 58-70; RETIRED. Fulbright lectr, tech. sch. indust. eng, Barcelona, 63-64; consult. & lectr, Israel Inst. Tech, 64; pres, Nat. Coun. Textile Sch. Deans, 52. Food and nutrition studies; motion picture film base; synthetic and natural fibers including manufacturing processes for synthetics, fabricating, dyeing, finishing and application to plastic laminates. Address: 1059 Citadel Dr. N.E, Atlanta, GA 30324.

DICKES, ROBERT, b. N.Y.C, Apr. 15, 12; m. 38; c. 2. PSYCHIATRY. B.S, City Col. N.Y, 33; M.S, Emory Univ, 34, M.D, 38. Commonwealth fel. med, 41-42; asst. prof. PSYCHIAT, STATE UNIV. N.Y. DOWNSTATE MED. CTR, 49-54, assoc. prof, 54-63, PROF, 63-, ACTING CHMN. DEPT, & TRAINING & SUPV. ANALYST, PSYCHOANAL. INST, 70-, PSYCHIATRIST-IN-CHIEF, UNIV. HOSP, 70- Dir, Kings County Hosp, 66-, psychiatrist-in-chief, 70- Consult, Vet. Admin, 46-51; bur. hearings & appeals, Dept. Health, Educ. & Welfare, 64- Med.C, 42-46, Maj. Fel. Am. Col. Physicians; fel. Am. Psychiat. Asn; Am. Fedn. Clin. Res; Am. Psychosom. Asn; Am. Psychoanal. Asn. Psychoanalysis; human depth psychology; organic aspects of psychoses and the effects of drugs; cardiovascular and renal system. Address: Kings County Hospital, 606 Winthrop St, Brooklyn, NY 11203.

DICKEY, DANA H, b. Easton, Maine, May 16, 30; m. 58; c. 3. SOLID STATE PHYSICS. B.S, Maine, 52; Ph.D.(physics), Mass. Inst. Tech, 57. MEM. STAFF, LINCOLN LAB, MASS. INST. TECHNOL, 57- Am. Phys. Soc. Development of far infrared techniques and infrared sensor systems. Address: Tower Rd, South Lincoln, MA 01773.

DICKEY, D(AVID) F(ARIS), b. Muskogee, Okla, Feb. 3, 17; m. 44; c. 4. METALLURGY. Okla. Agr. & Mech. Col. Prin. inspector engr. mat, U.S. Dept. Navy, 41-45; mgr. qual. control, Reynolds Metals Co, 45-49; Firth Sterling, Inc, 49-51, asst. to v.pres. res. & develop, 51-53, mgr, 53-58, dir, 58-59; PRES, D.F. DICKEY, INC, 59- Sr. mem. Am. Soc. Qual. Control; Am. Soc. Test. & Mat. Methods of manufacturing sponge iron; powder metallurgy with particular reference to sintered carbides; electro spark machining of hard metals. Address: 642 Orange St, Macon, GA 31201.

DICKEY, D(AYTON) D(ELBERT), b. Des Moines, Iowa, June 1, 27; m. 54; c. 3. GEOLOGY. B.S, Iowa State, 50. GEOLOGIST, Fed. Power Comn, 50; mineral deposits & eng. br, U.S. GEOL. SURV, 52-61, SPEC. PROJ. BR, 61- Engr, res. & develop. lab, U.S. Army, 50-52. AAAS; Geol. Soc. Am; Asn. Eng. Geol; Am. Geophys. Union; Seismol. Soc. Am. Stress and strain of earth associated with faulting and underground nuclear explosions. Address: 1680 S. Iris Way, Denver, CO 80226.

DICKEY, E(DWARD) T(HOMPSON), b. Oxford, Pa, Nov. 16, 96; m. 44; c. 2. ELECTRONICS. B.S, City Col, 18. Engr, radio res, Radio Corp. Am, 18-24, sample testing & equip. develop, T & T Dept. 24-29, field res. radio competitive anal, 29-40, admin. asst. radio ed. work on res. projs, 41-61; pub. acquisition, library, plasma physics lab, PRINCETON, 62-66, FILM SCANNER, JADWIN HALL, 68- Sr. mem, Inst. Elec. & Electronics Eng. Development of radio test equipment; hi-speed transoceanic reception equipment; radio receiver circuit development; Poulsen arc research. Address: 104 Jefferson Rd, Princeton, NJ 08540.

DICKEY, FRANK H(OST), b. N.Y.C, Feb. 20, 18; m. 41. ORGANIC CHEMISTRY. B.S, Calif. Inst. Technol, 41, Ph.D.(chem), 49. Res. chemist, Shell Develop. Co, 41-46; Noyes fel, 49-50; Guggenheim fel, 50-51; instr. chem, California, 51-53; RES. CONSULT, CONTINENTAL OIL CO, 53- AAAS; Am. Chem. Soc. Chemistry of organic peroxides; specific adsorption; chemical induction of mutation; evolution. Address: 5501 Ocean Blvd, Long Beach, CA 90803.

DICKEY, FRANK R(AMSEY), JR, b. San Antonio, Tex, Apr. 10, 18; m. 44; c. 3. ELECTRICAL ENGINEERING. B.S, Texas, 39; M.S, Harvard, 46, Ph.D.(appl. physics), 51. Engr, Gen. Elec. Co, 50-53; mem. res. staff, Melpar, Inc, 53-54; CONSULT. ENGR, HEAVY MIL. ELECTRONICS DEPT, GEN. ELEC. CO, 54- U.S.A.A.F, 41-45, Maj. Fel. Inst. Elec. & Electronics Eng. Radar and communications systems. Address: 112 Cornwall Dr, Dewitt, NY 13214.

DICKEY, FREDERICK PIUS, b. Zanesville, Ohio, Sept. 1, 16; m. 42; c. 3. PHYSICS. B.S, Muskingum Col, 38; M.S, Ohio State, 39, Ph.D.(physics), 46. Instr. PHYSICS, OHIO STATE UNIV, 46-47, asst. prof, 47-54, assoc. prof, 54-60, PROF, 60- U.S.N.R, 41-45, Lt. Comdr. Am. Phys. Soc. Infrared; microwaves; lasers. Address: Dept. of Physics, Ohio State University, Columbus, OH 43210.

DICKEY, GEORGE LAVERNE, b. Enid, Okla, Sept. 23, 39; m. 58; c. 1. INDUSTRIAL & HUMAN FACTORS ENGINEERING. B.S.I.E, Kansas State, 61, M.S, 63; Ph.D.(mech. eng), Nebraska, 69. Indust. engr, Collins Radio Co, 62-63; head dept. indust. eng, Wichita State, 63-64; instr. Kansas State, 64-

67; ASSOC. PROF. mech. eng, UNIV. NEBR, LINCOLN, 67-69, INDUST. & MGT. SYSTS. ENG, 70- Engr, Coleman Co, Inc, summer 64. Consult. assoc, Richard Muther & Assocs, 66-68. Am. Soc. Mech. Eng; Am. Soc. Eng. Educ; Human Factors Soc; Am. Inst. Indust. Eng. Engineering management; management decision theory; work measurement; learning theory; communications of work methods; biomechanics; engineering psychology; industrial training; production control; inventory control; facilities planning. Address: Dept. of Industrial & Management Systems Engineering, University of Nebraska-Lincoln, Lincoln, NE 68508.

DICKEY, HOWARD CHESTER, b. Durand, Mich, June 26, 13; m. 39; c. 4. DAIRY HUSBANDRY. B.S, Mich. State, 34; M.S, West Virginia, 36; Ph.D. (dairy husb), Iowa, 39. Asst. dairy husb, West Virginia, 34-36; Iowa State, 36-39; asst. prof. animal husb, Colorado State, 39-42, assoc. prof, 42-45; dairy husb, Vermont, 45-47; PROF. & HEAD DEPT. animal indust, UNIV. MAINE, 47-57, ANIMAL SCI, 57- Animal nutrit. consult, Jackson Lab. Am. Dairy Sci. Asn; Am. Genetic Soc; Am. Soc. Animal Sci. Dairy cattle nutrition and inheritance; animal nutrition; relationship between the curd tension in milk and its rate and percentage of digestibility. Address: Rogers Hall, Dept. of Animal & Veterinary Sciences, University of Maine, Orono, ME 04473.

DICKEY, JOHN SLOAN, JR, b. Wash, D.C, Jan. 24, 41; m. 63; c. 1. PETROLOGY. A.B, Dartmouth Col, 63; Fulbright scholar, Univ. Otago, N.Z, 64, M.Sc, 66; NASA fel, Princeton, 65, Kennecott fel, 68, Ph.D.(geol), 69. Field geologist, Brit. Newf. Explor. Co. Ltd, 63-64; res. assoc. lunar geol, Smithsonian Astrophys. Obser, 69-70; RES. FEL. PETROL, GEOPHYS. LAB, CARNEGIE INST, 70- Nat. Sci. Found. res. grant, 70-72. Geochem. Soc; Mineral Soc. Am; Am. Geophys. Union. Petrology of mafic and ultramafic igneous rocks; lunar petrology; experimental petrology of chromium-bearing silicate systems; comparative petrology of terrestrial planets. Address: Geophysical Lab, Carnegie Institution of Washington, Washington, DC 20008.

DICKEY, JOHN W(AKEMAN), b. Marshall, Mich, Aug. 8, 08; m. 38; c. 2. CHEMICAL & METALLURGICAL ENGINEERING. M.S. Michigan, 32, B.S.E, 31. Dir. eng. paint labs, Nash-Kelvinator Corp, 35-41; ord. engr, Detroit ord. dist, War Dept, 42-43; develop. engr, eclipse mach. div, Bendix Aviation Corp, 43-46; staff engr, Curtiss-Wright Corp, 56-58, gen. mgr, res. div, 58-61; res. dir. & consult, Develop. Consult, Inc, Ohio, 61-71; FACILITIES COORD, UNIV. VA, 71- Consult, Ellerman Assocs, N.Y, 64- Am. Ord. Asn. Nuclear systems and related projects; advanced propulsion systems; metallurgy; chemistry; new products, processes and production techniques. Address: The Old Rectory, Stanardsville, VA 22973.

DICKEY, JOSEPH FREEMAN, b. Orange County, N.C, Apr. 1, 34; m. 59; c. 2. REPRODUCTIVE PHYSIOLOGY, ELECTRON MICROSCOPY. B.S, N.C. State Col, 56, M.S, 62; Ph.D.(dairy sci), Pa. State, 65. Asst. prof. DAIRY SCI, CLEMSON UNIV, 65-69, ASSOC. PROF, 69- U.S.A, 56-59, 1st Lt. Am. Dairy Sci. Asn; Am. Soc. Animal Sci; Soc. Study Reproduction. Physiology and endocrinology of reproduction in mammals; histochemistry and electron microscopy of reproductive tissues. Address: Dept. of Dairy Science, Clemson University, Clemson, SC 29631.

DICKEY, PARKE A(THERTON), b. Chicago, Ill, Mar. 3, 09; m. 35; c. 4. PETROLEUM GEOLOGY. Ph.D.(geol), Hopkins, 32. Jr. sci. aide, U.S. Bur. Mines, 28; geologist, Pittsburgh Coal Co, Pa, 29; petrographer, Lago Petrol. Corp, Venezuela, 30-31; geologist, Trop. Oil Co, Colombia, 32-38; geologist in charge oil & gas, Pa. State Geol. Surv, 38-42; chief geologist, Forest Oil Corp, 42-44; prod. engr, Quaker State Oil Ref. Co, 44-46; head geol. res, Carter Oil Co, 46-56, asst. chief res, 56-58; geologist, Creole Petrol. Corp, Venezuela, 58-60; mgr, geol. div, Jersey Prod. Res. Co, 60-61; PROF. GEOL. & HEAD DEPT. EARTH SCI, UNIV. TULSA, 61- Am. Inst. Min, Metall. & Petrol. Eng; Am. Asn. Petrol. Geol; fel. Geol. Soc. Am; Am. Geophys. Union. Petroleum geology including exploration, production and research. Address: Dept. of Earth Science, University of Tulsa, Tulsa, OK 74104.

DICKEY, PAUL S(MITH), b. Monticello, Ind, Sept. 21, 03; m. 37; c. 4. MECHANICAL ENGINEERING. B.S, Purdue, 25, M.E, 35, hon. D.E, 53. Mech. engr, Bailey Meter Co, 25-32, res. engr, 32-38, dir. res, 38-44, chief engr, 44-47, v.pres, 47-55, pres, 55-69; RETIRED. Am. Soc. Mech. Eng; Soc. Naval Archit. & Marine Eng; Am. Soc. Naval Eng; Instrument Soc. Am; Sci. Apparatus Makers Asn.(pres, 63-64). Instruments and automatic controls for industrial processes. Address: 16224 Brewster Rd, East Cleveland, OH 44112.

DICKEY, RICHARD PALMER, b. Napoleon, Ohio, Feb. 10, 35; m. 57; c. 4. OBSTETRICS, GYNECOLOGY. B.A, Ohio State Univ, 56, M.M.Sc, 65, Ph.D, 70; M.D, West. Reserve Univ, 60. Res. assoc. OBSTET. & GYNEC, OHIO STATE UNIV, 65-70, ASST. PROF, 70-, INSTR. PHARMACOL, DIR. DIV. REPROD. ENDOCRINOL. & DIR. FAMILY PLANNING, 71- Nat. Insts. Health trainee gynec. endocrinol, 63-66. U.S.A, 66-68, Capt. Dipl, Am. Bd. Obstet. & Gynec, 67. AAAS; Am. Med. Asn; Am. Col. Obstet. & Gynec. Reproductive endocrinology; infertility; population control and family planning; mechanisms of actions of steroids in contraception; neuropharmacology of gonadotropic secretion; perinatalogy; high risk obstetrics. Address: Dept. of Obstetrics & Gynecology, Ohio State University Hospital, Columbus, OH 43210.

DICKEY, ROBERT S(HAFT), b. Riverside, Calif, Jan. 18, 21; m. 46; c. 3. PLANT PATHOLOGY. B.S, California, 48, Ph.D.(plant path), 54. Asst. PLANT PATH, California, 48-51; asst. prof, CORNELL UNIV, 52-55, assoc. prof, 55-69, PROF, 69- U.S.A, 42-46. AAAS; Am. Inst. Biol. Sci; Am. Soc. Microbiol; Am. Phytopath. Soc. Bacterial diseases of plants; phytopathogenic bacteria. Address: Dept. of Plant Pathology, Cornell University, Ithaca, NY 14850.

DICKEY, RONALD WAYNE, b. Compton, Calif, Mar. 12, 38; m. 65. APPLIED MATHEMATICS. A.B, California, Los Angeles, 59; M.S, N.Y. Univ, 62, Ph.D.(math), 65. Vis. mem. MATH, Courant Inst, N.Y. Univ, 65-67; asst. prof, UNIV. WIS, MADISON, 67-69, ASSOC. PROF, 69- Sci. Res. Coun. sr. vis. fel, Univ. Newcastle, 71-72. Am. Math. Soc; Soc. Indust. & Appl. Math. Nonlinear differential and integral equations and their relations to problems in elasticity. Address: Dept. of Mathematics, University of Wisconsin, Madison, WI 53706.

DICKHAUS, DONALD WILLIAM, b. St. Louis, Mo, Apr. 9, 25; m. 60; c. 2. INTERNAL MEDICINE, CARDIOLOGY. A.B, Missouri, 50, B.S, 54; M.D, Tulane, 56. Intern med, St. Louis City Hosp, Mo, 56-57, asst. resident, 57-59; Twenty-Thirty Int. fel. cardiol, California, San Francisco, 59-61; chief cardiol, Denver Vet. Admin. Hosp, 61-66; ASSOC. PROF. MED, UNIV. MO-COLUMBIA, 66- U.S.A.F, 43-46, 50-52, 1st Lt. Arteriosclerotic heart disease. Address: Dept. of Medicine, University of Missouri-Columbia, Columbia, MO 65201.

DICKIE, HELEN AIRD, b. North Freedom, Wis, Feb. 19, 13. MEDICINE. B.A, Univ. Wis, 35, M.D, 37. Instr. MED, SCH. MED, UNIV. WIS, MADISON, 42, asst. prof, 43-45, assoc. prof, 45-54, PROF, 54- Am. Med. Asn; fel. Am. Col. Physicians; Am. Thoracic Soc; Am. Fedn. Clin. Res. Bacillus Calmette-Guèrin vaccination for prevention of tuberculosis; pulmonary resection in tuberculosis; sarcoidosis and diffuse interstitial disease. Address: Dept. of Medicine, School of Medicine, University of Wisconsin, 1300 University Ave, Madison, WI 53711.

DICKIE, JOHN P(ETER), b. Waseca, Minn, Apr. 4, 34; m. 56; c. 3. BIOCHEMISTRY, ORGANIC CHEMISTRY. B.A, Minnesota, 56; M.S, Wisconsin, 58, Ph.D.(biochem), 60. Wis. Alumni Res. Found. fel. CHEM, Wisconsin, 60-61; res. fel, Mellon Inst, 61-68; GROUP MGR, RES. DEPT, KOPPERS CO, INC, 68- Am. Chem. Soc. Antimycins; chemistry and origin of natural bitumens; antibiotic structure; mechanism of antibiotic action. Address: Research Dept, Koppers Co, Inc, 440 College Park Dr, Monroeville, PA 15146.

DICKIE, L(LOYD) M(ERLIN), b. Canning, N.S, March 6, 26; m. 52; c. 3. MARINE BIOLOGY. B.Sc, Acadia, 46; M.Sc, Yale, 48; Ph.D.(zool), Toronto, 53. Asst. biol, Acadia, 43-46; Yale, 46-48; demonstr, Toronto, 48-51; asst. scientist biol, biol. sta, St. Andrews, FISHERIES RES. BD. CAN, 51-53, in charge clam & scallop invest, 53-57, assoc. scientist in charge population dynamics studies, groundfish invest, 57-65, DIR, MARINE ECOLOGY LAB, 65-; ASSOC. PROF. BIOL. & OCEANOG, DALHOUSIE UNIV, 65- Marine ecology; population dynamics of molluscan shellfish and marine demersal species; fisheries biology. Address: Marine Ecology Lab, Bedford Institute, Fisheries Research Board of Canada, Dartmouth, N.S, Can.

DICKIE, RAY ALEXANDER, b. Minot, N.Dak, Jan. 19, 40; m. 65; c. 2. POLYMER & PHYSICAL CHEMISTRY. B.S, Univ. N.Dak, 61; Ph.D.(phys. chem), Univ. Wis, Madison, 65. Res. fel, Glasgow Univ, 66; chemist, Stanford Res. Inst, 67-68; RES. SCIENTIST, FORD MOTOR CO, 68- AAAS; Am. Chem. Soc; Soc. Rheol. Viscoelastic and other mechanical properties of polymers and polymer blends; viscoelastic properties and large deformation behavior of cross-linked rubbers; emulsion polymerization. Address: Scientific Research Staff, Ford Motor Co, Box 2053, Dearborn, MI 48121.

DICKIESON, A(LTON) C(ONANT), b. New York, N.Y, Aug. 16, 05; m. 51; c. 2. ELECTRICAL ENGINEERING. Polytech. Inst. Brooklyn, 22-29. Mem. tech. staff, Bell Tel. Labs, Inc, 23-29; eng. staff, Fox-Case Corp, 29-30; supvr, Bell Tel. Labs, Inc, 30-45, dept. head, 46-51, dir. transmission systs. develop, 51-61, exec. dir. transmission div, 61-66, v.pres, transmission develop, 66-70; CONSULT, 70- U.S. Naval Ord. award, 45; Gen. Vandenberg Award, Arnold Air Soc, 62; H.H. Arnold Award, Air Force Asn, 62. Fel. Inst. Elec. & Electronics Eng; Nat. Acad. Eng; assoc. fel. Am. Inst. Aeronaut. & Astronaut. Radio and transmission systems; long distance communications systems; Telstar experimental communications satellite. Address: Box 1243, Sedona, AZ 86336.

DICKINSON, ALICE B, b. N.Y.C, Apr. 11, 21; m. 44; c. 2. MATHEMATICS. A.B, Michigan, 41, univ. fel, 45-48, Am. Asn. Univ. Women fel, 49-50, Ph.D.(math), 52; M.A, Columbia, 47. Asst. proj. engr, Sperry Gyroscope Co, 42-44; mem. staff, radiation lab, Mass. Inst. Tech, 44-45; instr, Pa. State, 50-56; assoc. prof. MATH, SMITH COL, 59-70, PROF, 70- Lectr, Univ. Baroda, 68. Founders award, Hampshire Col, 70. Math. Asn. Am. Topology. Address: 218 E. Pleasant St, Amherst, MA 01002.

DICKINSON, CLIFFORD L(EE), JR, b. Freeport, Ill, Nov. 11, 30; m. 52; c. 3. ORGANIC CHEMISTRY. B.S, Illinois, 52; Du Pont fel, Rochester, 54-55, Ph.D.(chem), 56. Lab. instr. org. chem, Rochester, 52-54; res. chemist, E.I. DU PONT DE NEMOURS & CO, 56-70, RES. SUPVR, 70- Am. Chem. Soc. Cyanocarbon chemistry; heterocyclic compounds; medicinal chemistry. Address: 2403 Brickton Rd, Wilmington, DE 19803.

DICKINSON, DALE FLINT, b. Galveston, Tex, Oct. 11, 33; m. 63; c. 2. PHYSICS. B.S, Texas, 55; Ph.D.(physics), California, 65. RES. ASSOC, radio astron. lab, Univ. California, 66-67; SMITHSONIAN ASTROPHYS. OBSERV. & HARVARD COL. OBSERV, 67- U.S.N, 55-57. Am. Astron. Soc. Spectral line radio astronomy; OH molecule radiation in emission and absorption; maser models for OH emission; atomic hydrogen; galactic structure studies. Address: Harvard College Observatory, 60 Garden St, Cambridge, MA 02138.

DICKINSON, DAVID (JAMES), b. Denver, Colo, Sept. 16, 20; m. 44; c. 2. MATHEMATICS. B.A, Denver, 42; A.M, Columbia, 47; fel, Michigan, 46-48, univ. scholar, 48-49, Ph.D.(math), 54. Mem. staff radiation lab, Mass. Inst. Tech, 42-45; lectr, Columbia, 45-46; instr. MATH, Pa. State, 50-58; ASSOC. PROF, UNIV. MASS, AMHERST, 58- Am. Math. Soc. Classical analysis; special functions; orthogonal polynomials; theoretical linguistics. Address: Graves Rd, Ashfield, MA 01330.

DICKINSON, DAVID B(UDD), b. New York, N.Y, Jan. 10, 36; m. 61. PLANT PHYSIOLOGY. B.S, New Hampshire, 57; Ph.D.(hort), Illinois, 62. Instr. PLANT PHYSIOL, UNIV. ILL, URBANA, 61-64, asst. prof, 64-68, ASSOC. PROF, 68- U.S.A.R, 53-61, Sgt. AAAS; Am. Chem. Soc; Am. Soc. Plant Physiol; Am. Soc. Hort. Sci. Metabolic transformations in germinating pollen and mechanisms regulating germination; post-harvest physiology of fruits, particularly respiratory metabolism and biochemical basis of ripening. Address: Dept. of Horticulture, University of Illinois, Urbana, IL 61801.

DICKINSON, DAVID F(RANKLIN), b. Coffeyville, Kans, Jan. 28, 14; m. 50; c. 1. CHEMICAL ENGINEERING. A.B, Kans. State Teachers Col, 34, M.S, 36; fel, Illinois, 36-37; fel, Iowa State Col, 37-38, Ph.D.(chem. eng), 41. Res. chemist, Maytag Co, 41-43; Benson Process Eng. Co, N.Y, 43; jr. chem. engr, Mathieson Alkali Works, N.Y, 43-46; chem. engr, Armour Res. Found, Ill, 46-47; asst. prof. chem. eng. Mich. State Col, 47-50; chmn. dept. chem. eng, Indiana Tech. Col, 50-54; mem. staff, chem. eng. dept, Tulsa, 54-56; prof, New Mexico, 56-57; resident res. assoc, Argonne Nat. Lab, 57-58; PROF. NUCLEAR ENG. & CHMN. DEPT, UNIV. NEV, RENO, 58- Am. Chem. Soc; Am. Soc. Metals; Am. Inst. Chem. Eng; Am. Nuclear Soc. Drying; coal tar; mechanism of drying of ideal porous materials. Address: Dept. of Nuclear Engineering, University of Nevada, Reno, NV 89507.

DICKINSON, DEAN RICHARD, b. Highland Park, Ill, May 21, 28. CHEMICAL ENGINEERING. B.Ch.E, Cornell, 51; M.S, Wisconsin, 54, Ph.D.(chem. eng), 58. SR. CHEM. ENGR, Hanford Labs, Gen. Elec. Co, 58-64; PAC. NORTHWEST LAB, BATTELLE MEM. INST, 65- U.S.A.F, 51-53, 1st Lt. Am. Inst. Chem. Eng; Am. Chem. Soc; Am. Nuclear Soc. Coolant systems of nuclear reactors; corrosion and heat transfer. Address: Pacific Northwest Lab, Battelle Memorial Institute, 112 Lee Blvd, Richland, WA 99352.

DICKINSON, DEANNE, b. N.Y.C, Sept. 29, 41; m. 64. APPLIED MATHEMATICS. B.S, Mass. Inst. Technol, 63, Nat. Sci. Found. fel, & Ph.D.(math), 66. Asst. prof. math, Univ. Mass, Boston, 66-68; RES. PHYSICIST, ROCKY FLATS PLANT, DOW CHEM. CO, 68- Am. Math. Soc. Numerical analysis; differential equations. Address: Rocky Flats Plant, Dow Chemical Co, Box 888, Golden, CO 80401.

DICKINSON, EDWIN JOHN, b. Carlisle, Eng, Oct. 15, 33; m. 59; c. 5. FLUID MECHANICS. B.A, Cambridge, 55, M.A, 58; Ph.D.(fluid mech), Laval Univ, 65. Engr. servomechanisms, A.V. Roe, Manchester, 56-58; res. asst. aeronaut, Laval Univ, 59-61; teaching asst. fluid mech, 61-63; res. asst. boundary layers, Univ. Poitiers, 63-64; asst. prof. APPL. MATH, LAVAL UNIV, 64-67, ASSOC. PROF, 67- Defense Res. Bd. Can. res. grant, 65. Assoc. fel. Royal Aeronaut. Soc; Can. Aeronaut. & Space Inst. Experimental determination of turbulent skin friction, particularly the development of floating element skin friction balances for this purpose. Address: Dept. of Mechanical Engineering, Faculty of Science, Laval University, Quebec 10, Que, Can.

DICKINSON, E(RNEST) M(ILTON), b. Boston, Ohio, May 12, 05; m. 27; c. 2. VETERINARY MEDICINE. D.V.M, Ohio State, 27; M.S, Oregon State, 35. Asst. poultry pathologist & asst. prof. vet. med, Oregon State, 27-36; jr. veterinarian, California, 36-38; assoc. prof. vet. med. & assoc. veterinarian, ORE. STATE UNIV, 38-41, PROF. VET. MED. & VETERINARIAN, 41-, HEAD DEPT, 55- AAAS; Am. Vet. Med. Asn; Am. Asn. Avian Path. Poultry diseases; coccidiosis; erysipelas infection in turkeys; salmonellosis in chickens and turkeys; ornithosis. Address: Dept. of Veterinary Medicine, Oregon State University, Corvallis, OR 97331.

DICKINSON, FRANK N, b. Boston, Mass, July 25, 30; m. 57; c. 3. GENETICS, STATISTICS. B.S, Massachusetts, 53; M.S, Illinois, 58, Ph.D.(dairy sci), 61. Dairy husbandman, agr. res. serv, U.S. Dept. Agr, Univ. Ill, 57-61; anal. statistician, biomet. serv, Md, 61-65; asst. prof. animal sci, Univ. Mass, 65-68; INVEST. LEADER, DAIRY HERD IMPROV. INVESTS, 69- U.S.A, 53-55, Res, 55-61, Lt. Am. Soc. Animal Sci; Am. Dairy Sci. Asn; Biomet. Soc. Biological statistics; improvement of production in dairy cattle. Address: Dairy Herd Improvement Investigations, Bldg. 263, Agricultural Research Center, Beltsville, MD 20705.

DICKINSON, FRED E(UGENE), b. Beltrami Co, Minn, Dec. 29, 12; m. 38; c. 3. WOOD TECHNOLOGY. B.S, Minnesota, 38; M.S, Mich. State, 41; California, Los Angeles, 42; Ph.D.(forest prods. econ), Yale, 51. Forestry foreman & dir. civilian conserv. corps enrollees, U.S. Forest Serv, 38-39; asst. wood utilization lab, Mich. State, 39-41; dir. dept. forestry, Lassen Jr. Col, Calif, 41-42; technologist, forest prods. lab, U.S. Forest Serv, 42-45, packaging technician, U.S. War Dept, France, 45; asst. prof. lumbering, Yale, 45-51, assoc. prof, 51-52; wood utilization & chmn. dept. wood tech, Michigan, 52-55; PROF. FORESTRY & DIR. FOREST PROD. LAB, UNIV. CALIF, BERKELEY, 55- Mem. adv. comt. prevention deterioration, Nat. Res. Coun, 54-57; U.S. del, Food & Agr. Orgn, Conf. Wood Technol, 63; comt. forestry res, agr. bd, Nat. Res. Coun-Nat. Acad. Sci, 64-; chmn prof. group terminology, div. 5, Int. Union Forest Res. Orgns, 66- Heinrich Christian Burckhardt Medal, Univ. Göttingen, 70. AAAS; fel. Soc. Am. Foresters; Forest Prod. Res. Soc.(pres, 63-64); fel. Int. Acad. Wood Sci.(pres, 69-); Soc. Wood Sci. & Technol; Forest Hist. Soc. Physical processing of wood. Address: Forest Products Lab, University of California, Berkeley, CA 94804.

DICKINSON, HILLMAN, b. Independence, Mo, Feb. 9, 26; m. 49; c. 2. PHYSICS. B.S, U.S. Mil. Acad, 49; M.A, Columbia, 56; Ph.D.(physics), Stevens Inst. Tech, 61. U.S. ARMY, 45-, instr. chem, U.S. Mil. Acad, 56-57, asst. prof. physics, 57-60, instr. math, Maryland, 61-62, prog. mgr, Adv. Res. Proj. Agency, 62-63, br. chief, 63-66, asst. dep. dir. & div. chief, Defense Commun. Planning Group, 68-70, DEP. DIR, DEFENSE SPEC. PROJ. GROUP, 70- U.S.N, 43-45; U.S.A, 45-, Col. Am. Phys. Soc; Am. Asn. Physics Teachers. Plasma physics, instabilities; upper atmospheric and space physics; nuclear effects; optics; geophysics; electronic and communication systems. Address: Defense Special Projects Group, Bldg. 56, Naval Observatory, 34th & Massachusetts, Washington, DC 20305.

DICKINSON, JAMES M(ILLARD), b. Waterloo, Iowa, July 31, 23; m. 47; c. 3. PHYSICAL METALLURGY. B.S, Iowa State Col, 49, Ph.D.(phys. chem. & metall), 53. Jr. chemist, PHYS. METALL. RES, Atomic Energy Cmn, Ames Lab, Iowa State Col, 46-53; METALLURGIST & MEM. STAFF, LOS ALAMOS SCI. LAB, UNIV. CALIF, 53- U.S.M.C, 42-45. Am. Soc. Metals. General physical metallurgy of the less common metals; very high temperature metallurgy; phase diagrams, metal reduction, casting and fabrication; graphite fabrication, properties and structure; powder metallurgy. Address: 354 El Viento, Los Alamos, NM 87544.

DICKINSON, J(OHN) G, b. Glens Falls, N.Y, Oct. 1, 32; m. 56; c. 3. INORGANIC CHEMISTRY. B.A, Colgate, 54; M.S, Connecticut, 57, Ph.D.(inorg. chem), 60. Res. chemist, electrochem. dept, E.I. DU PONT DE NEMOURS & CO, 60-62, PIGMENTS DEPT, 62-69, RES. SUPVR, 69- AAAS; Am. Chem. Soc. Preparative inorganic chemistry; x-ray crystallography. Address: E.I. du Pont de Nemours & Co, Experimental Station, Wilmington, DE 19898.

DICKINSON, JOHN OTIS, b. Champaign, Ill, Aug. 29, 24; m. 47; c. 3. VETERINARY PHARMACOLOGY. B.S, Illinois, 48 & 61, D.V.M, 63, M.S, 65, Ph.D.(vet. med. sci), 68. Instr. vet. physiol. & pharmacol, Illinois, 63-64, Nat. Inst. Arthritis & Metab. Diseases fel, 64-66; ASST. PROF. VET. PHYSIOL. & PHARMACOL, WASH. STATE UNIV, 66- U.S.N, 43-46, Ens. Am. Soc. Vet. Physiol. & Pharmacol; Soc. Study Reproduction. Oral histamine metabolism in ruminants; plasma corticosteroid levels in swine; effect of chlorinated hydrocarbon pretreatment on toxicity of carbamate insecticides; mechanism of allium poisoning; cacodylic acid and monosodium acid methane arsonate toxicity in cattle. Address: Dept. of Veterinary Physiology & Pharmacology, Washington State University, Pullman, WA 99163.

DICKINSON, J(OSHUA) C(LIFTON), JR, b. Tampa, Fla, Apr. 28, 16; m. 36; c. 3. ORNITHOLOGY. B.S, Florida, 40, fel. & M.S, 46, Ph.D, 50; Cornell, 37; Du Pont fel, Virginia, 40. Asst. biol, UNIV. FLA, 40-42, instr. biol. & geol, 46-50, asst. prof. BIOL, 50-55, ASSOC. PROF, 55-, DIR. & CURATOR ORNITH, FLA. STATE MUS, 61-, curator biol. sci, 53-59, acting dir, 59-61. Mus. comp. zool. res. fel. & Gen. Ed. Bd. fel, Harvard, 51-52; vis. investr, Woods Hole Oceanog. Inst, 52. Mem. Univ. Florida exped, Honduras, 46; Fla. State Mus. exped, Baffin Island, 55, Bahama Islands, 58, 59, 60, 61, 66, 67, Sombrero Island, 64, Navassa Island, 67; mem, Conf. Dir. Syst. Collections; adv. coun, Nat. Endowment for Arts, 70. U.S.C.G, 42-45, Comdr. AAAS; Am. Soc. Naturalists; Am. Soc. Zool; Am. Ornith. Union; Wilson Ornith. Soc; Am. Asn. Mus.(secy, 70-); Asn. Sci. Mus. Dir.(v.pres, 67-69). Taxonomy and zoogeography; general ecology. Address: Florida State Museum, University of Florida, Gainesville, FL 32601.

DICKINSON, KENDELL A, b. Walker, Minn, Jan. 25, 31; m. 57; c. 3. GEOLOGY. B.A, Minnesota, M.S, 59, Tozer Found. fel. & Ph.D.(geol), 62. Instr. geol, Oberlin Col, 61-62; GEOLOGIST, U.S. GEOL. SURV, 62- U.S.A, 54-56. Soc. Econ. Paleont. & Mineral; Geol. Soc. Am; Am. Asn. Petrol. Geol. Fresh water ostracoda; Upper Jurassic stratigraphy of the Gulf Coast; clay mineralogy; sedimentary petrology; deep sea sediments and uranium geology of South Texas. Address: U.S. Geological Survey, Bldg. 25, Federal Center, Denver, CO 80225.

DICKINSON, L(EONARD) CHARLES, b. Glasgow, Ky, Dec. 12, 41; m. 66; c. 1. PHYSICAL CHEMISTRY. A.B, Bellarmine Col.(Ky), 63; Ph.D.(phys. chem), Univ. Wis, Madison, 69. Sci. res. fel, Univ. Leicester, 69-70; ASST. PROF. CHEM, UNIV. MASS, AMHERST, 70- Am. Phys. Soc; Am. Chem. Soc. Magnetic relaxation in gases and solutions; structure of active sites in hematin enzymes. Address: Dept. of Chemistry, University of Massachusetts, Amherst, MA 01002.

DICKINSON, LIONEL A, b. Northenden, Eng, Feb. 24, 24; m; c. 3. PHYSICAL & ORGANIC CHEMISTRY. M.A, Oxford, 49. Head cordite rocket motors, rocket propulsion dept, Ministry of Supply, U.K, 49-55; chief rocket engine develop, Defense Res. Bd. Can, 55-62; assoc. dir. propulsion sci, Stanford Res. Inst, 62-65, dir. polymer & propulsion sci, 65-67; dir. advan. technol, Naval Ord. Sta, 67-70, TECH. DIR, NAVAL EXPLOSIVE ORD. DISPOSAL FACILITY, 70- Mem. working group solid propellant combustion, Dept. Defense, 64-; U.S. observer, NATO-Adv. Group Aeronaut. Res. Develop, 65. R.E, 43-47, Lt. Am. Inst. Chem. Eng; fel. The Chem. Soc; fel. Royal Inst. Chem. Rocket engine propellants, combustion, materials and design; industrial polymers, combustion instability; pyrotechnics of liquid propellants, ordnance. Address: Naval Explosive Ordnance Disposal Facility, Code D, Indian Head, MD 20640.

DICKINSON, MARTHA, b. Glasgow, Ky, Dec. 26, 39. ELEMENTARY PARTICLE PHYSICS. B.S, Kentucky, 61; M.S, Wisconsin, 63; Ph.D.(physics), Colorado, 69. Visitor high energy physics, European Orgn. Nuclear Res, 64; lectr. physics, STATE UNIV. N.Y. ALBANY, 69, RES. ASSOC. HIGH ENERGY PHYSICS, 69- Am. Phys. Soc. Bubble chamber analysis of elementary particles. Address: Dept. of Physics, State University of New York, 1400 Washington Ave, Albany, NY 12203.

DICKINSON, PETER CHARLES, b. London, Eng, Sept. 30, 39; m. 65; c. 1. STATISTICS. B.S, Univ. London, 65; M.S, Rutgers Univ, 67, Ph.D.(statist), 69. Engr, res. & develop. labs, E.M.I. Ltd, Eng, 58-64; teaching asst. STATIST, Rutgers Univ, 65-69; ASST. PROF, UNIV. SOUTHWEST. LA, 69- Biomet. Soc; Inst. Math. Statist; Am. Statist. Asn; Am. Soc. Qual. Control. Non-parametric statistics; experimental design; order statistics. Address: Dept. of Mathematics, University of Southwestern Louisiana, Lafayette, LA 70501.

DICKINSON, ROBERT G(ERALD), b. El Paso, Tex, Dec. 19, 30; m. 66. GEOLOGY. B.S, Univ. Tex, El Paso, 52; M.S, Univ. Ariz, 60, Ph.D.(geol), 66. Sampler, New Park Mining Co, Utah, 52-54; asst. stope geologist, Anaconda Co, Calif, 56-57; geologist, U.S. GEOL. SURV, 61-68, DIST. GEOLOGIST, BR. MINERAL CLASSIFICATION, CONSERV. DIV, 68- Fel. Geol. Soc. Am. Cretaceous and Pleistocene stratigraphy; coal geology. Address: U.S. Geological Survey, Conservation Division, Branch of Mineral Classification, Box 3521, Federal Bldg, Denver, CO 80202.

DICKINSON, ROBERT W, b. Pasadena, Calif, Oct. 6, 20; m. 42; c. 2. NUCLEAR ENGINEERING. B.A, California, 41; M.S, U.S. Naval Postgrad. Sch, 48; S.M, Mass. Inst. Tech, 53. Head components sect, naval reactors, Atomic Energy Cmn, 54-56; asst. to gen. mgr, Gen. Atomic Div, Gen. Dynamics Corp, 56; chief proj. engr, S.G.R. Prog, Atomics Int. Div, N.Am. Aviation, Inc, 56-60, dir, eng. & develop, 60-63; opers. mgr. & res. dir, SNAP-8 Div, Aerojet-Gen. Corp. Div, Gen. Tire & Rubber Co, 63-64; dir, liquid metal eng. ctr, N.Am. Rockwell Corp, 66-71; MGR. MARITIME REACTORS, BABCOCK & WILCOX, NAVAL PROVING GROUND, 71- Mem. sodium components working group, Atomic Energy Comn, 57-62. U.S.N,

41-56, Capt; Silver Star Medal. Am. Soc. Metals; Am. Nuclear Soc; Am. Soc. Test. & Mat. Liquid metals and fast reactor technology; reactor system components and metallurgy. Address: 117 Oakwood Pl, Lynchburg, VA 24505.

DICKINSON, STANLEY KEY, JR, b. Clarksburg, W.Va, Feb. 16, 31; m. 63; c. 1. GEOLOGY, PHYSICAL CHEMISTRY. B.S, W.Va. Univ, 53, M.S, 55; Ph.D.(geol), Harvard, 68. Res. develop. off, magnetics sect, AIR FORCE CAMBRIDGE RES. CTR, 54-56, res. geologist, summers, 57-59, RES. PHYS. SCIENTIST, SOLID STATE SCI. LAB, 62- U.S.A.F, 54-56, Res, 56-70, Capt. AAAS; Geochem. Soc; Mineral Soc. Am. Inorganic equilibria and phase relationships; high pressure chemistry; mineral synthesis and stability relations; general inorganic geochemistry; crystallography, earth mantle geophysics; x-ray diffraction analysis; stratigraphy; paleontology; historical geology. Address: Solid State Sciences Lab, Air Force Cambridge Research Lab, Air Force Systems Command, Hanscom Field, Bedford, MA 01730.

DICKINSON, WADE, b. Hickory Township, Pa, Oct. 29, 26; m. 52; c. 3. NUCLEAR PHYSICS, BIOPHYSICS. B.S, West Point, 49; Oak Ridge Sch. Reactor Technol, 50-51; Ohio State, 51-52. Proj. officer aircraft nuclear propulsion, Wright Air Develop. Center, 51-53, nuclear physicist, Rand Corp, 53-54; PRIN. ENGR. & CONSULT, BECHTEL CORP, 54-; PRES. & CHIEF EXEC, W.W. DICKINSON CORP, 62-; PRES. & CHIEF EXEC, AGROPHYSICS, INC, 68- Consult, Rand Corp, 54-56; tech. consult, 85th Cong. Joint Comt. Atomic Energy, 57-58. U.S.A.F, 49-54, Capt. Am. Phys. Soc; Am. Nuclear Soc; Am. Soc. Mech. Eng. Estrus control/ovulation induction in animals by devices; human contraceptive devices; ultra-sonic measurement of heart performance; high speed, precision seed planters; non-destructive tests of seed vigor and genotype; nuclear engineering and physics. Address: 360 Pine St, San Francisco, CA 94104.

DICKINSON, WILLIAM B(ORDEN), b. Norfolk, Va, Jan. 20, 26. ORGANIC CHEMISTRY. A.B, Emory Univ, 46, M.S, 47; Du Pont fel, Univ. Wis, 49-50, Ph.D, 50. Res. assoc, STERLING-WINTHROP RES. INST, 50-57, assoc. mem-res. chemist, 57-65, SR. RES. CHEMIST, 65-; group leader, 58. Am. Chem. Soc. Ester condensations; hindered ketones; steroids; heterocyclic compounds; synthetic therapeutic agents; organic nomenclature. Address: Sterling-Winthrop Research Institute, Rensselaer, NY 12144.

DICKINSON, W(ILLIAM) C(LARENCE), b. St. Joseph, Mo, Mar. 15, 22; m. 47; c. 2. PHYSICS. A.B, California, 45; fel, Mass. Inst. Tech, 46-47, Ph.D.(physics), 50. Asst. physics, Mass. Inst. Tech, 48-50; mem. staff, physics div, Los Alamos Sci. Lab, 50-54; prof. physics & head dept, Indonesia, 54-57; MEM. STAFF, neutronics div, LAWRENCE RADIATION LAB, UNIV. CALIF, LIVERMORE, 57-61, TEST DIV, 61- Lectr, Univ. N.Mex, 53-54. U.S.N.R, 43-46, Ens. Am. Phys. Soc; Am. Asn. Physics Teachers. Nuclear magnetic resonance; nuclear reactions; neutron physics; nuclear radiation detectors. Address: 54 Panoramic Way, Berkeley, CA 94704.

DICKINSON, W(ILLIAM) JOSEPH, b. Pasadena, Calif, June 17, 40; m. 63; c. 2. DEVELOPMENTAL GENETICS. B.A, Univ. Calif, Berkeley, 63; Nat. Sci. Found. fel, Johns Hopkins Univ, 65-69, Ph.D.(biol), 69. Sci. investr, cellular radiobiol. br, U.S. Navy Radiol. Defense Lab, Calif, 63-65; ASST. PROF. BIOL, Reed Col, 69-72; UNIV. UTAH, June 72- Vis. scientist, dept. zool, Univ. B.C, 71. U.S.N, 63-65, Lt. AAAS; Am. Inst. Biol. Sci; Genetics Soc. Am; Soc. Develop. Biol. Genetics of aldehyde oxidase and related enzymes in Drosophila; genetic regulation of differential enzyme synthesis. Address: Dept. of Biology, University of Utah, Salt Lake City, UT 84112.

DICKINSON, WILLIAM R(ICHARD), b. Tenn, Oct. 26, 31; m. 53, 70; c. 2. GEOLOGY. B.S, Stanford, 52, M.S, 56, Nat. Sci. Found. fel, 56-57, Ph.D (geol), 58. Asst. prof. GEOL, STANFORD UNIV, 58-63, assoc. prof, 63-68, PROF, 68- Guggenheim fel, 65. AAAS; Geol. Soc. Am; Soc. Econ. Paleont. & Mineral; Int. Asn. Sedimentol; Am. Geophys. Union; Nat. Asn. Geol. Teachers. Petrology; structural geology; sedimentology; plate tectonics; environmental geology. Address: Dept. of Geology, Stanford University, Stanford, CA 94305

DICKINSON, WILLIAM TREVOR, b. Toronto, Ont, Aug. 30, 39; m. 63; c. 2. HYDROLOGY. B.S.A, Univ. Toronto, 61, Int. Nickel Co. scholar. & B.A.Sc, 62, M.S.A, 64; Nat. Res. Coun. scholar, Colo. State Univ, 65, Ph.D.(hydrol; hydraul), 67. Lectr. eng, UNIV. GUELPH, 63-64, asst. prof. HYDROL, 67-70, ASSOC. PROF, 70- Characterization of hydrological variables; development of watershed response concepts. Address: School of Engineering, University of Guelph, Guelph, Ont, Can.

DICKISON, H(ARRY) LEO, b. Ashland, Ky, Sept. 3, 12; m. 35; c. 2. PHARMACOLOGY. A.B, Vanderbilt, 35, M.S, 36, Ph.D.(org. chem), 39; Michigan, 39. Asst. pharmacol, med. sch, Vanderbilt, 39-41, res. assoc, 41-45, asst. prof, 45-47; dir. pharmacol. res, BRISTOL LABS, 47-58, asst. dir. res, 51-58, dir. labs, 58-66, dir. res. U.S, 66-68, GEN. MGR. VET. PROD, 68- Lectr, State Univ. N.Y. Syracuse, 49- With Off. Sci. Res. & Develop, 44. Am. Soc. Pharmacol. & Exp. Therapeut; Am. Fedn. Clin. Res; Am. Chem. Soc; Soc. Toxicol. Hypnotics; anesthetics; analgetics; metabolic fate of drugs; antibiotics; antihistaminics; terpenoid amines; isomeric thujyl amines. Address: Bristol Labs, P.O. Box 657, Syracuse, NY 13201.

DICKISON, WALTER L(EE), b. Montrose, Mo, Oct. 19, 13; m. 39; c. 2. PHARMACY, CHEMISTRY. B.S.Ed, Cent. Mo. State Col, 41; B.S, Colorado, 49, M.S, 56, Ph.D.(pharm), 57. Instr. pharm, Colorado, 49-51, 55-57; pharmacist, Stanton Drug Co, 51-55; assoc. prof. PHARM, SCH. PHARM, SOUTHWEST. STATE COL.(OKLA), 57-59, PROF, 59-, DEAN SCH, 65- U.S.C.G.R, 42-46, Lt. Am. Pharmaceut. Asn. Am. Asn. Cols. Pharm. Antibiotic drugs; preservatives; prescription practices; pharmacy education. Address: School of Pharmacy, Southwestern State College, Weatherford, OK 73096.

DICKISON, WILLIAM CAMPBELL, b. Jamaica, N.Y, Mar. 12, 41; m. 63; c. 1. PLANT MORPHOLOGY & ANATOMY. B.S.Ed, Western Illinois, 62; A.M, Indiana, 64, Ph.D.(bot), 66. ASST. PROF. BOT, Va. Polytech. Inst. &

State Univ, 66-69; UNIV. N.C, CHAPEL HILL, 69- Bot. Soc. Am; Int. Soc. Plant Morphol; Int. Soc. Plant Taxon. Morphology and phylogeny of vascular plants; comparative morphology and relationships of the Dilleniaceae and allies. Address: Dept. of Botany, University of North Carolina, Chapel Hill, NC 27514.

DICKLER, DONALD J(OSEPH), b. Brooklyn, N.Y, May 9, 21; m. 43; c. 3. MEDICINE. B.A, N.Y. Univ, 42, M.D, 45. Res. anesthesia, Halloran Vet. Admin. Hosp, 48-49; Jewish Hosp, Brooklyn, N.Y, 49-50, asst. & adj. attend. anesthesiologist, 50-57; dir. dept. anesthesia, JEWISH HOSP. ST. LOUIS, 57-64, ATTEND. ANESTHESIOLOGIST, 64-; ASST. CLIN. PROF. SURG, SCH. MED, WASH. UNIV, 57- Private practice. From asst. to assoc. attend. anesthesiologist, Queens Gen. Hosp, 55-57; attend. anesthesiologist, Brooklyn Vet. Admin. Hosp, 54-57; clin. instr, State Univ. N.Y, 54-57. Dipl, Am. Bd. Anesthesiol, 53. Med.C, U.S.A, 46-48. Am. Med. Asn; Am. Soc. Anesthesiol; Am. Col. Anesthesiol. Anesthesiology. Address: Dept. of Anesthesia, Jewish Hospital of St. Louis, 216 S. Kings Hwy, St. Louis, MO 63110.

DICKMAN, ALBERT, b. Lake Placid, N.Y, Nov. 3, 03; m. 28; c. 1. BIOLOGY. A.B, Hopkins, 24; M.S, Pennsylvania, 31, Ph.D.(bact), 33. Teacher, pub. schs, Md, 24-25; asst. to curator, Commercial Mus, Pa, 25-26; teacher biol, pub. schs, 28-41; DIR. DICKMAN LABS, 33- Mem. adv. cmt. lab. procedures, Pa. Dept. Health; nat. adv. serol. coun, U.S. Pub. Health Serv; Conf. State & Prov. Pub. Health Dirs. Dipl, Am. Bd. Microbiol. Fel. Am. Pub. Health Asn; Am. Asn. Clin. Chem; Am. Chem. Soc; Am. Soc. Microbiol. Medical laboratory science; serology; general clinical laboratory field. Address: Dickman Labs, 1415 W. Erie Ave, Philadelphia, PA 19140.

DICKMAN, JOHN THEODORE, b. Hamilton, Ohio, Oct. 27, 27; m. 56; c. 2. BIOCHEMISTRY. B.S, Ohio State, 50, M.S, 57, Nat. Heart Inst. fel, 59-60, Ph.D.(physiol. chem), 60. Instr, high sch, Ohio, 50-53; asst. ed, biochem. sect, CHEM. ABSTRACTS SERV, 60-63, asst. dept. head, biochem. edit. dept, 63-64, dept. head, 64-65, asst. managing ed, abstract issues, 65-69, mgr. editing, 69-71, ASST. MANAGING ED. PUBLICATIONS, 71- Teaching assoc, Ohio State Univ, 65-71. U.S.A, 53-55. AAAS; Am. Chem. Soc. Science education; toxicology; lipid chemistry; chemical documentation. Address: Chemical Abstracts Service, Ohio State University, Columbus, OH 43210.

DICKMAN, MICHAEL, b. Pittsburgh, Pa, June 30, 40; m. 62; c. 1. LIMNOLOGY, ECOLOGY. B.A, Univ. Calif, Santa Barbara, 62; M.Sc, Univ. Ore, 65; Fisheries Res. Bd. Can. fel, Univ. B.C, 68, Ph.D.(zool), 69. Thord-Grey Am. Scand. Found. fel, Univ. Uppsala, 69-70; ASST. PROF. BIOL, UNIV. OTTAWA, 70- Consult, Environ. Control Consult. & Comput. Devices Can, 70- Can. Soc. Zool; Int. Asn. Theoret. & Appl. Limnol; Can. Soc. Wildlife & Fishery Biol. Studies of factors affecting the composition, diversity and primary productivity of periphyton and plankton communities in order to illucidate the general principles governing community organization. Address: Dept. of Biology, University of Ottawa, Ottawa, Ont. K1N 6N5, Can.

DICKMAN, RAYMOND F, JR, b. Cincinnati, Ohio, July 8, 37; m. 63. MATHEMATICS, TOPOLOGY. B.S, Univ. Miami, 61, M.S, 63; Francis I. Dupont fel, Univ. Va, 64, Nat. Sci. Found. fel, 65-66, Ph.D.(math), 66. Asst. prof. MATH, Univ. Miami, 66-70, ASSOC. PROF, 70-71; VA. POLYTECH. INST. & STATE UNIV, 71- Am. Math. Soc. Mappings; extensions of spaces and mappings; compactifications; unicoherence. Address: Dept. of Mathematics, Virginia Polytechnic Institute & State University, Blacksburg, VA 24061.

DICKMAN, SHERMAN R(USSELL), b. Buffalo, N.Y, Jan. 15, 15; m. 41; c. 3. BIOCHEMISTRY. B.S, Pa. State Col, 36; M.S, Illinois, 37, Ph.D.(soil chem), 40. First asst. soil serv. anal, Illinois, 40-41, special asst. chem, 41-45; asst. chem, Argonne Nat. Lab, Chicago, 45-46; res. assoc. med. biochem, col. physicians & surgeons, Columbia, 46-47; asst. prof. BIOCHEM, SCH. MED, UNIV. UTAH, 47-52, assoc. prof, 52-67, PROF, 67- AAAS; Am. Chem. Soc; Am. Soc. Biol. Chem; Brit. Biochem. Soc. Nucleic acid metabolism protein biosynthesis. Address: University of Utah School of Medicine, 3C112 Medical Center, Salt Lake City, UT 84112.

DICKMANN, DONALD I(RVIN), b. Milwaukee, Wis, Sept. 6, 41; m. 61; c. 1. FOREST PHYSIOLOGY. B.S, Univ. Wash, 64; Ph.D.(forestry bot), Univ. Wis, 69. Plant physiologist, n.cent. forest exp. sta, U.S. Forest Serv, Wis, 69-70; ASST. PROF. biol, W.Ga. Col, 70-71; FORESTRY, IOWA STATE UNIV, 71- AAAS; Am. Soc. Plant Physiol. Reproductive physiology of pine; photosynthesis and phloem translocation in developing leaves; protein metabolism and the onset of photosynthesis in developing leaves; intensive culture of forest trees. Address: Dept. of Forestry, Iowa State University, Ames, IA 50010.

DICKS, JOHN B(ARBER), JR, b. Natchez, Miss, Mar. 10, 26; m. 52; c. 4. PHYSICS. B.S, Univ. of the South, 48; Ph.D.(physics), Vanderbilt Univ, 55. Assoc. prof. PHYSICS, Tenn. Polytech. Inst, 53; asst. prof, Univ. of the South, 54-58, assoc. prof, 59-63; PROF, SPACE INST, UNIV. TENN, 63-, lectr, 60-63. Pres, J.B. Dicks & Assocs, 67-; chmn. steering comt, Symp. Eng. Aspects Magnetohydrodynamics. Am. Phys. Soc; assoc. fel. Am. Inst. Aeronaut. & Astronaut; Am. Soc. Mech. Eng. Plasma physics; magnetohydrodynamics; opencycle magnetohydrodynamic power generation. Address: P.O. Box 216, Sewanee, TN 37375.

DICKS, R(OBERT) S(TANLEY), b. Barnwell, S.C, Dec. 23, 17; m. 45; c. 2. CHEMICAL ENGINEERING. B.S, North Carolina, 38; M.S, Va. Polytech. Inst, 39; Ph.D.(chem. eng), Pennsylvania, 44. Lab. asst, Va. Polytech. Inst, 38-39; asst. instr. chem. eng, Pennsylvania, 39-43, instr, 43-44; technologist, Shell Oil Co, 44-46, res. engr. & group leader in charge pilot plant work, 46-53; mgr. process eng. dept, textile div, CELANESE CORP. AM, 53-58, dir. mfg. develop, 58-63, tech. mgr, BAY CITY PLANT, CELANESE CHEM. CO, 63-65, tech. plant mgr, 65, PLANT MGR, 65- Am. Inst. Chem. Eng. Processing and refining of petroleum; hydrolysis of peanut hulls; extractive distillation of hydrocarbon mixtures in a packed column; processing and production of synthetic fibers. Address: Celanese Chemical Co, P.O. Box 509, Bay City, TX 77414.

DICKSON, A(RTHUR) D(AVID), b. Londonderry, Northern Ireland, Mar. 2, 25; m. 52; c. 2. EMBRYOLOGY, ENDOCRINOLOGY. B.A.O. & M.B, B.Ch, Queen's(Belfast), 49, M.D, 54; M.A, Cambridge, 55. Demonstr. ANAT, Queen's(Belfast), 50-51, asst. lectr, 51-54; univ. demonstr, Cambridge, 54-56; lectr, Aberdeen, 56-63; assoc. prof, Dalhousie Univ, 63-66; Univ. West. Ont, 66-67, prof, 67-68; PROF. & HEAD DEPT, UNIV. CALGARY, 68-, ASST. DEAN MED. EDUC, 70-, mem. med. res. coun, 68-71. Res. grants, Dept. Sci. & Indust. Res, U.K, 59-60, Pop. Coun, 63-68, Can. Med. Res. Coun, 65- Am. Asn. Anat; Can. Asn. Anat.(v.pres, 69-71, pres, 71-); Soc. Study Reproduction; Anat. Soc. Gt. Brit. & Ireland; Brit. Soc. Endocrinol. Ovo-implantation and placentation. Address: Division of Morphological Science, University of Calgary, Calgary 44, Alta, Can.

DICKSON, ARTHUR DONALD, b. Lowellville, Ohio, Apr. 26, 27; m. 52; c. 6. PHYSICAL CHEMISTRY, PHYSICS. B.Sc, Carnegie Inst. Technol, 50; Ph.D. (phys. chem), Minnesota, 55. Naval Ord. Pub. fel, Minnesota, 54-55; SR. RES. CHEMIST, electrochem. dept, E.I. du Pont de Nemours & Co, 55-57; MINN. MINING & MFG. CO, 57- U.S.N, 45-46. Am. Vacuum Soc. Infrared spectroscopy; absorption spectra of propellant flames; high pressure gas absorption spectra; colorimetry of fluorescent pigments; thermographic reaction kinetics; catalytic pyrolysis of carbon fabrics; vacuum deposition of photoconductive films; glow discharge polymerization of dielectric films. Address: 2301 Hudson Rd, St. Paul, MN 55119.

DICKSON, DAVID ROSS, b. Chicago, Ill, Oct. 22, 31; m. 54; c. 3. SPEECH PATHOLOGY. B.A, Grinnell Col, 53; M.A, Northwestern, 54, Ph.D.(speech path), 61. Assoc. prof. speech path, sch. speech, Northwest. Univ, 58-68, lectr. cleft palate, dent. sch, 65-68; ASSOC. PROF. SPEECH & ANAT, UNIV. PITTSBURGH, 68- Med.C, U.S.A, 54-56. Am. Speech & Hearing Asn. Speech science; cleft palate. Address: 320 Salk Hall, University of Pittsburgh, Pittsburgh, PA 15213.

DICKSON, DON R(OBERT), b. Devil's Slide, Utah, May 19, 25; m. 53; c. 7. METEOROLOGY. B.S, Utah, 50, M.S, 53. Lectr. meteorol, New Mexico, 51-52; physicist, U.S. Geol. Surv, 53-55; asst. prof. METEOROL, Okla. State, 55-57; UNIV. UTAH, 57-65, ASSOC. PROF, 65-, CHMN. DEPT, 67-, acting head dept, 63-67, U.S.A.F, 43-45. Am. Meteorol. Soc; Am. Geophys. Union; Royal Meteorol. Soc. Physical meteorology; microclimatology; meteorological instruments; atmospheric pollution; severe storm damage. Address: Dept. of Meteorology, University of Utah, Salt Lake City, UT 84112.

DICKSON, DONALD WARD, b. Dickson, Tenn, Dec. 9, 38; m. 62; c. 2. NEMATOLOGY, PLANT PATHOLOGY. B.S, Austin Peay State, 63; M.S, Okla. State Univ, 65; Ph.D.(plant path), N.C. State Univ, 68. Plant pathologist, UNIV. FLA, 68-70, NEMATOLOGIST, 70- Soc. Nematol; Am. Phytopath. Soc. Nematode control; biology of root-knot nematodes and comparative biochemistry of nematodes. Address: Dept. of Entomology & Nematology, University of Florida, Gainesville, FL 32601.

DICKSON, D(OUGLAS) G(RASSEL), b. Montclair, N.J, Nov. 11, 24; m. 52; c. 2. MATHEMATICS. B.A, Wesleyan, 47; A.M, Harvard, 49; Nat. Sci. Found. fel, Columbia, 57-58, Ph.D.(math), 58. Instr. MATH, Dartmouth Col, 48-49; lectr, Hunter Col, 49-51; Columbia, 51-52, instr, 52-57; asst. prof, UNIV. MICH, 58-64, ASSOC. PROF, 64- U.S.A.A.F, 43-46. Am. Math. Soc. Complex analysis. Address: Dept. of Mathematics, University of Michigan, Ann Arbor, MI 48104.

DICKSON, FRANK W(ILSON), b. Oplin, Tex, Nov. 29, 22; m. 45; c. 4. GEOLOGY. B.A, California, Los Angeles, 50, B.S, 53. Res. geologist, California, Los Angeles, 52-55; Shell Develop. Co, Tex, 55-56; asst. prof. GEOL, Univ. Calif, Riverside, 56-61, assoc. prof, 61-69; PROF, STANFORD UNIV, 69- Shell Oil fel, 53-54; Fulbright res. scholar, 62-63; Guggenheim fel, 62-63. U.S.A.A.F, 42-45. Geol. Soc. Am; Geochem. Soc; Nat. Asn. Geol. Teachers; Soc. Econ. Geol. Field and laboratory genesis of ore deposits; equilibria in systems of metal sulfides and water, as functions of temperature and pressure; field and theoretical studies on the origin of coarse grained plutonic rocks. Address: 960 Mears Ct, Stanford, CA 94305.

DICKSON, JAMES F, JR, Psychol, see Suppl. I to 11th ed, Soc. & Behav. Vols.

DICKSON, JAMES FRANCIS, III, b. Boston, Mass, May 4, 24; m. 58; c. 3. MEDICINE, ELECTRICAL ENGINEERING. A.B, Dartmouth Col, 44; M.D, Harvard Med. Sch, 47; M.S, Drexel Inst, 61. Res. assoc, Mass. Inst. Technol, 62-65; DIR. ENG. IN BIOL. & MED, NAT. INST. GEN. MED. SCI, 65- Nat. Insts. Health spec. fel. eng, Mass. Inst. Technol, 61-65; assoc. prof, sch. med, Boston Univ, 63-65. Sr. consult, President's Comn. Technol, Automation & Econ. Progress, 65; President's Adv. Coun. Mgt. Improv, 71. Dipl, Am. Bd. Surg, 56. Med.C, 52-54, 1st Lt. Nat. Acad. Sci; Inst. Med; Biomed. Eng. Soc; Am. Phys. Soc; Inst. Elec. & Electronics Eng; Asn. Comput. Mach; Instrument Soc. Am. Surgery; systems engineering; digital computation. Address: National Institutes of Health, Bethesda, MD 20014.

DICKSON, JAMES G(ILLESPIE), JR, b. Newport News, Va, Dec. 3, 25; m. 48; c. 1. MEDICINE, PHYSIOLOGY. B.S, U.S. Naval Acad, 46; M.D, Univ. Pa, 60. Intern, Univ. hosp, UNIV. PA, 60-61, resident anesthesia, 61-62, instr. PHARMACOL, SCH. MED, 62-63, assoc, 64-67, ASST. PROF, 67- U.S. Pub. Health serv. training grant, 61-64; consult. diving physiol, Smithsonian Inst, 63-64; Pa. Plan scholar. med. res, 64-69. U.S.N, 43-55, Lt. Mechanisms of respiratory control; physiological effects of altered environmental pressures; diving physiology; pharmacology and toxicology of oxygen, carbon dioxide and inert gases. Address: 820 Merion Square Rd, Gladwyne, PA 19035.

DICKSON, KENNETH L(YNN), b. Jacksboro, Tex, Nov. 20, 43; m. 66; c. 2. AQUATIC BIOLOGY, ENVIRONMENTAL SCIENCES. B.S, N.Tex. State Univ, 66, M.S, 68; Ph.D.(zool), Va. Polytech. Inst. & State Univ, 71. ASST. PROF. ZOOL. & ASST. DIR. CTR. ENVIRON. STUDIES, VA. POLYTECH. INST. & STATE UNIV, 70- Consult, Nat. Acad. Sci, 71- Water Pollution Control Fedn. Limnology of reservoirs and rivers; microbiotic cycles in reservoirs; development of biological pollution monitoring systems; effects of pollution on aquatic organisms; biological diversity indices of community structure; effects of carbon, nitrogen and phosphorus on aquatic communities. Address: Dept. of Biology, Virginia Polytechnic Institute & State University, Blacksburg, VA 24061.

DICKSON, LEROY DAVID, b. New Brighton, Pa, June 26, 34; m. 54; c. 4. ELECTRICAL ENGINEERING. B.E.S, Hopkins, 60, M.S.E, 62, Ph.D.(elec. eng), 68. Res. assoc. optical data processing, Barton Lab, Hopkins, 61-68; mem. tech. staff laser atmospheric transmission, Bell Tel. Labs, N.J, 68; STAFF ENGR, COMPUTER APPLN. LASER TECHNOL, IBM CORP, 68- Ord.C, U.S.A, 54-57. Optical Soc. Am. Optical data processing; holography; laser technology; applications of laser and laser systems to information processing. Address: 2006 Arlen Dr, Rochester, MN 55901.

DICKSON, M(ICHAEL) H(UGH), b. England, Apr. 2, 32; nat. Can; m. 58; c. 3. PLANT BREEDING. B.S, McGill, 55; M.S, Mich. State Univ, 56, Ph.D.(veg. breeding), 58. Asst. prof. HORT, Guelph, 58-64; N.Y. STATE AGR. EXP. STA, GENEVA-CORNELL, 64-69, ASSOC. PROF, 69- Am. Soc. Hort. Sci; Am. Soc. Agron. Breeding and genetics of snap beans, with special emphasis on disease resistance and plant efficiency; breeding cabbage and broccoli, especially production of hybrids by use of male sterility. Address: Dept. of Vegetable Crops, New York State Experimental Station, Geneva, NY 14456.

DICKSON, PAUL W(ESLEY), JR, b. Sharon, Pa, Sept. 14, 31; m. 52; c. 3. PHYSICS. B.S. & M.S, Arizona, 54; Ph.D.(physics), N.C. State, 62. Jr. engr. metall. res, Hanford Labs, Gen. Elec. Co, 54-55; sr. scientist, ASTRONUCLEAR LAB, WESTINGHOUSE ELEC. CORP, 63-64, fel. engr, 64-66, MGR. nuclear weapons, 66, weapons systs, 66-69, ADVAN. PROJS, 69- U.S.A.F, 55-63, Capt. Am. Nuclear Soc; Am. Inst. Mining, Metall. & Petrol. Eng. Isotope power sources; weapon system and nuclear isotope analysis; nuclear reactor physics, analysis and design; space trajectory analysis. Address: 3300 Appel Rd, Bethel Park, PA 15102.

DICKSON, PHILIP F, b. Huron, S.Dak, Aug. 5, 36; m. 56; c. 3. CHEMICAL ENGINEERING. B.S, S.Dak. Sch. Mines & Tech, 58; Ph.D.(chem. eng), Minnesota, 62. Res. engr, Esso Res. & Eng. Co, 58-59; Humble Prod. Res. Div, Humble Oil & Ref. Co, 62-63; assoc. prof. CHEM. ENG, COLO. SCH. MINES, 63-70, PROF, 70- Summer prod, Denver Div, Martin Co, 63. Chem.C, 59, 2nd Lt. Am. Inst. Chem. Eng; Am. Soc. Eng. Educ; Asn. Asphalt Paving Technol. Mass and heat transfer; chemical reactor analysis; heat transferred during asphalt paving operations. Address: Dept. of Chemical & Petroleum Refining, Colorado School of Mines, Golden, CO 80401.

DICKSON, RICHARD E(UGENE), b. Carbondale, Ill, Sept. 13, 32; m. 56; c. 2. FORESTRY, PLANT PHYSIOLOGY. B.S, Southern Illinois, 60, M.S, 62; Ph.D.(plant physiol), California, Berkeley, 68. Res. asst, California, Berkeley, 62-68; RES. PLANT PHYSIOLOGIST, N.Cent. Forest Exp. Sta, U.S. FOREST SERV, 68-70, INST. FOREST GENETICS, 70- U.S.M.C, 51-54. AAAS; Am. Soc. Agron; Ecol. Soc. Am; Soil Sci. Soc. Am; Am. Soc. Plant Physiol. Water relations studies on ecology of bottomland hardwoods; water and oxygen relationships of swamp trees and herbaceous plants; water relations studies on walnut; translocation of organic compounds; physiology of wood formation. Address: Institute of Forest Genetics, Star Route 2, Rhinelander, WI 54501.

DICKSON, ROBERT C(LARK), b. St. Marys, Ont, Sept. 24, 08; m. 39; c. 3. INTERNAL MEDICINE. M.D, Toronto, 34. Jr. demonstrator MED, Toronto, 45-47, sr. demonstrator, 47-48, assoc, 48-50, asst. prof, 50-52, assoc. prof, 52-55; PROF. & HEAD DEPT, DALHOUSIE UNIV, 56- Consult physician, Sunnybrook Hosp, Dept. Veterans Affairs, 46, Camp Hill Hosp, 56; Royal Can. Navy, 56; Halifax Childrens Hosp, 56; head dept. med, Victoria Gen. Hosp, 56-69, sr. consult. physician, 69- Fel, Royal Col. Physicians & Surgeons Can, pres, 70-72. Med.C, Royal Can. Army, 39-45, Lt. Col; Order Brit. Empire, 45. Am. Gastroenterol. Asn; fel. Am. Col. Physicians (regent, 68-); Can. Med. Asn; Can. Cardiovasc. Soc; Can. Asn. Gastroenterol.(pres, 63). Medicine; gastroenterology; infection; metabolism. Address: Dept. of Medicine, Dalhousie University, Halifax, N.S, Can.

DICKSON, R(OBERT) C(OWDEN), b. Redlands, Calif, Dec. 22, 04; m. 29; c. 3. ENTOMOLOGY. A.B, Redlands, 29; M.S, California, 38, Ph.D.(entom), 47. Jr. plant quarantine inspector, bur. entom. & plant quarantine, U.S. Dept. Agr, 29-32; lab. asst, Citrus Exp. Sta, Univ. Calif, Riverside, 38-41, assoc, 41-47, asst. entomologist, 47-53, assoc. entomologist, 53-59, entomologist, 59-62, prof. entom, 62-72; RETIRED. Entom. Soc. Am; Am. Phytopath. Soc. Photoperiodism and diapause in insects; insect transmission of plant viruses; taxonomy of aphids; vector populations and behavior. Address: 3456 Sunnyside, Riverside, CA 92506.

DICKSON, SAMUEL ADRIAN, JR, b. Ft. Lewis, Wash, Feb. 18, 37. PHYSICS. B.S, Alabama, 59; Ph.D.(physics), Duke, 64. Asst. prof. PHYSICS, Davidson Col, 64-65; West. Carolina Col, 65-66; lectr, UNIV. N.C, ASHEVILLE, 66-67, ASST. PROF, 67- Am. Phys. Soc; Am. Asn. Physics Teachers. Low temperature and solid state physics. Address: Dept. of Physics, University of North Carolina at Asheville, Asheville, NC 28801.

DICKSON, SPENCER E, b. Topeka, Kans, Dec. 17, 38; div; c. 3. MATHEMATICS. B.A, Kansas, 60; M.S, New Mexico State, 61, Nat. Defense Ed. Act fel, 60-63, Ph.D.(math), 63. Asst. prof. MATH, Univ. Nebr, 63-66, assoc. prof, 66-67; on leave from Nebr, Off. Naval Res. res. assoc, Univ. Ore, 66-67; assoc. prof, Univ. South. Calif, 67-68; IOWA STATE UNIV, 68-71, PROF, 71- Vis. prof, Univ. Newcastle, summer, 70. Am. Math. Soc; Math. Asn. Am. Homological algebra with applications to ring theory and theory of modules. Address: Dept. of Mathematics, Iowa State University, Ames, IA 50010.

DICKSON, STANLEY, b. N.Y.C, Sept. 3, 27; m. 50; c. 3. SPEECH PATHOLOGY, AUDIOLOGY. B.A, Brooklyn Col, 50, M.A, 54; Ed.D, Buffalo, 61. Speech clinician, N.Y.C. Bd. Educ, 50-51; Rochester Bd. Educ, 51-52; exec. dir, Rochester Hearing & Speech Ctr, 52-56; assoc. prof. SPEECH PATH. & AUDIOL, STATE UNIV. N.Y. COL. BUFFALO, 56-60, PROF, 60- Speech clinician, Cerebral Palsy Ctr. Rochester, 51-52; coord. workshop audiol,

State Univ. N.Y. Col. Geneseo, 54; lectr, Rochester & Nazareth Col, 54-56; consult, Edith Hartwell Clin, LeRoy, N.Y, 54-56; Children's Rehab. Ctr, Buffalo, N.Y, 63-64, audiol. consult, 68-71. U.S.C.G, 55-56. Am. Speech & Hearing Asn. Developmental speech and hearing disorders and factors related to its inception and remediation. Address: Dept. of Communication Disorders, State University of New York College at Buffalo, 1300 Elmwood Ave, Buffalo, NY 14222.

DICKSON, WILLIAM M(ORRIS), b. Denver, Colo, Oct. 22, 24; m. 46; c. 2. VETERINARY PHYSIOLOGY. D.V.M, Colo. Agr. & Mech. Col, 49; M.S, State Col. Wash, 53; Ph.D, Minnesota, 61. Instr. VET. PHYSIOL. & PHARMACOL, State Col. Wash, 49-53, asst. prof, 53-55; instr, Minnesota, 55-57; asst. prof, WASH. STATE UNIV, 57-61, assoc. prof, 61-66, PROF, 66-Endocrinol. consult, Hanford Biol. Lab, 62-63. U.S.A, 43-44; U.S.N, 44-46. Am. Vet. Med. Asn; Am. Physiol. Soc; Soc. Exp. Biol. & Med; Soc. Study Reproduction. Veterinary endocrinology; reproductive physiology. Address: 308 Sunset Dr, Pullman, WA 99163.

DICKSTEIN, JACK, b. Phila, Pa, Dec. 14, 25; m. 50; c. 3. POLYMER CHEMISTRY. B.S, Pa. State, 46; M.A, Temple, 51; Off. Naval Res. fel, Rutgers, 56-58, Ph.D.(polymer chem), 58. Res. chemist, Lederle Labs, Am. Cyanamid Co, 46-48; asst, Temple, 49-51; chemist, parenteral formulations, E.R. Squibb & Sons Div, Olin Mathieson Chem. Corp, 51-56; prof. org. chem. Alma White Col, 57-58; group leader adhesives, BORDEN CHEM. CO, 58-60, develop. mgr. monomer polymer labs, 60-61, thermoplastics div, 61-67, DIR. RES, 67- Mem, Smithsonian Inst. AAAS; Am. Chem. Soc; Franklin Inst; Soc. Plastic Eng; Tech. Asn. Pulp & Paper Indust. High polymers; emulsions; medicinals; adhesives; physical chemistry. Address: 318 Keats Rd, Huntingdon Valley, PA 19006.

DiCOSTANZO, CHARLES J(AMES), b. Fabyan, Conn, June 2, 25; m. 47; c. 3. FISHERY RESEARCH BIOLOGY. B.S, Massachusetts, 53; M.S, Iowa State Col, 54, Ph.D, 56. Fishery res. biologist, Bur. of Commercial Fisheries, U.S. Fish & Wildlife Serv, 56-70; DEP. LAB. DIR, NAT. MARINE FISHERIES SERV, U.S. DEPT. COMMERCE, 70- U.S.M.C, 43-45. Am. Fisheries Soc. Biometrics. Address: P.O. Box 352, Auke Bay, AK 99821.

DI CUOLLO, C. JOHN, b. Scotch Plains, N.J, Jan. 1, 35. BIOCHEMISTRY, MICROBIOLOGY. B.S, Va. Polytech. Inst, 56; Ph.D.(biochem), Rutgers Univ, 60. Sr. res. biochemist, Colgate Palmolive Co, 60-63; SMITH KLINE & FRENCH LABS, 63-67, asst. dir. microbiol, 67-71, MGR. BIOANAL. SECT, ANIMAL HEALTH PROD. DIV, 71- AAAS; Am. Soc. Microbiol; Am. Chem. Soc. Applications of radioisotopes to biological problems; metabolic fate of drugs; development of automation in the field of microbiology. Address: 353 Colonial Ave, Collegeville, PA 19426.

DIDCHENKO, R(OSTISLAV), b. Poland, Dec. 24, 21; nat; m. 53. INORGANIC CHEMISTRY. Vor-Diplom, Inst. Tech, Munich, 50; fel, Harvard, 52, Natvar fel, 53, Ph.D.(chem), 54. GROUP LEADER inorg. & phys. chem, Nat. Carbon Res. Labs, UNION CARBIDE CORP, 54-57, PARMA TECH. CENTER, 57-65, CARBON PROD, 65- Meyer Jr. award, Am. Ceramic Soc. Am. Chem. Soc. Carbon technology; high temperature materials; composite materials; surface chemistry; management. Address: Parma Technical Center, Union Carbide Corp, P.O. Box 6116, Cleveland, OH 44101.

DIDDLE, ALBERT W, b. Hamilton, Mo, July 1, 09; m. 42; c. 2. OBSTETRICS, GYNECOLOGY. A.B, Missouri, 30, M.A, 33; M.D, Yale, 36. Asst. anat, Missouri, 31-33; Yale, 33-36; instr. OBSTET. & GYNEC, Iowa, 39-40, assoc, 40-42; assoc. prof, southwest. med. sch, Texas, 45-48; regional consult, Vet. Admin, Ga, 48-55; clin. prof, UNIV. TENN, KNOXVILLE, 56-68, PROF, 68-, CHMN. DEPT, 56- Consult, Vet. Admin, Tex, 46-48; Oak Ridge Hosp, 49- Med.C, 42-46, Lt. Comdr. Am. Asn. Obstet. & Gynec; fel. Am. Col. Obstet. & Gynec; Continental Gynec. Soc. Anatomy; endocrinology; oncology. Address: Memorial Research Center & Hospital, University of Tennessee, Knoxville, TN 37916.

DI DIO, LIBERATO JOHN ALPHONSE, b. São Paulo, Brazil, May 7, 20; m. 60; c. 4. ANATOMY, ELECTRON MICROSCOPY. B.S, São Paulo, 39, M.D, 45, D.Sc.(anat), 49, Ph.D.(anat), 52. Instr. physiol, faculty med, São Paulo, 42-43, anat, 43-45, asst. prof, 46-51, assoc. prof, 52-53; prof. topog. anat. & head dept, Cath. Univ. Minas Gerais, 53-54; prof. ANAT. & chmn. dept, med. sch, Minas Gerais, 54-63; prof, med. sch, Northwestern, 63-67; PROF. & CHMN. DEPT, MED. COL. OHIO, 67- Intern, hosp. med. sch, São Paulo, 44-45; vis. prof, Messina, 55; sch. med, Brazil, 57; Parma, 58; Rockefeller Found. fel, sch. med, Washington (Seattle); guest investr, Rockefeller Inst. Med. Res, N.Y. & sch. med, Harvard, 60-61. Mem, Order Med. Merit Presidency Brazilian Repub; Int. Anat. Nomenclature Cmt; Nat. Coun. Sci. Res, Brazil, 56-60; co-chmn. 41st session, Int. Anat. Meeting, N.Y, 60; Brazilian del, Int. Cong. Electron Micros, Phila, 62; treas, Brazilian Asn. Schs. Med, 62-64, secy, 64-66. Medal Sci. Merit, Govt. State Minas Gerais; Star Solidarity Italy & Medal Cultural Merit, 62, Presidency Repub. Italy; William H. Rorer Award, 70. Fel. AAAS; Am. Asn. Anat; Asn. Am. Med. Cols; Electron Micros. Soc; Am. Soc. Cell Biol; N.Y. Acad. Sci; Pan Am. Asn. Anat.(pres); Int. Col. Surg; Anat. Soc. Gt. Brit. & Ireland; Brazilian Soc. Anat.(1st secy); Brazilian Soc. Adv. Sci; Brazilian Col. Anat; French Asn. Anat; French Nat. Soc. Gastroenterol; Italian Soc. Anat; German Anat. Soc; Japanese Anat. Asn; Chilean Asn. Anat. & Path. Gross anatomy; surgical anatomy; coronary circulation; electron microscopy of the prostate; pineal body and heart musculature. Address: Dept. of Anatomy, Medical College of Ohio, P.O. Box 6190, Toledo, OH 43614.

DIDISHEIM, PAUL, b. Paris, France, June 3, 27; U.S. citizen; m. 52; c. 3. HEMATOLOGY, CARDIOVASCULAR DISEASES. B.A, Princeton, 50; Borden Award & M.D, Hopkins, 54. Life Ins. Med. Res. Fund fel, Sch. Med, Pittsburgh, 55-57; Nat. Heart Inst. spec. res. fel, Nat. Blood Transfusion Center, Paris, France, 57-58; instr. med, col. med, Univ. Utah, 58-63, asst. prof, 63-65; exp. path, MAYO GRAD. SCH. MED, UNIV. MINN, 66-70, ASSOC. PROF. CLIN. PATH, 70-, MEM. STAFF, DEPT. LAB. MED, MAYO CLIN, 71-, DIR, THROMBOSIS RES. LAB, 65-, mem. staff, sect. clin. path, 65-70. Chief coagulation lab. & assoc. physician, Salt Lake County Gen. Hosp, 58-65; coagulation subdiv, div. hemat, dept. med, col. med, Univ. Utah, 58-65; attend, Salt Lake City Vet. Admin. Hosp, Utah, 59-65; mem. med. adv. coun, Nat. Hemophilia Found, 65-, subcomt. res. policy, 70-; ad hoc comt. standardization human antihemophiliac factor assay, Nat. Acad. Sci-Nat. Res. Coun, 63; comt. plasma fractionation & coagulation res, Am. Nat. Red Cross, 67-, mem. adv. bd, coun. on circulation, Am. Heart Asn, 68-, exec. comt, coun. thrombosis, 71- Am. Fedn. Clin. Res; Am. Physiol. Soc; Am. Soc. Hemat; Int. Soc. Hemat; Soc. Exp. Biol. & Med; Int. Soc. Biorheol; Europ. Microcirculation Soc; Int. Soc. Thrombosis & Haemostasis; Microcirculatory Soc. Blood coagulation; hemostasis; thrombosis; hemorrhagic diseases. Address: Dept. of Lab. Medicine, Mayo Clinic, Rochester, MN 55901.

DiDOMENICO, M(AURO), JR, b. N.Y.C, Jan. 12, 37; m. 64; c. 2. SOLID STATE PHYSICS. B.S, Stanford, 58, M.S, 59, Ph.D.(elec. eng), 63. MEM. TECH. STAFF, BELL TEL. LABS, 62-, supvr, 66, dept. head, 70. Am. Phys. Soc; Inst. Elec. & Electronics Eng. Quantum electronics; lasers; nonlinear optical phenomena; ferroelectricity; luminescence in semiconductors; optical communications. Address: Bell Telephone Labs, 600 Mountain Ave, Murray Hill, NJ 07974.

DIDRIKSEN, JANICE E, b. London, Eng, Mar. 12, 35; U.S. citizen; m. 69. PLANT BIOCHEMISTRY, BOTANY. B.Sc. & cert, London, 56; M.A, Columbia, 58. Technician microbiol, Haskins Lab, N.Y, 57-58; asst. photosynthesis, Carnegie Inst. Div. Plant Biol, 58-61; PLANT BIOCHEMIST, Stanford Res. Inst, 61-69; AGR. RES. CTR, STAUFFER CHEM. CO, 69- Plant and microbial metabolism and nutrition; photosynthesis; structure and function of the chloroplast-pigment complex as related to Hill reaction activity. Address: Stauffer Chemical Co, Agricultural Research Centre, P.O. Box 760, Mountain View, CA 94040.

DIDWANIA, HANUMAN P(RASAD), b. Bhagalpur, India, Mar. 13, 35. PHYSICAL CHEMISTRY. B.Sc, Bihar, 55; M.S, Inst. Paper Chem, 65, Ph.D.(chem), 68. Shift-in-charge pulp & paper mfg, Orient Paper Mills Ltd, India, 55-61; tech. supt, Sirpur Paper Mills Ltd, 61-63; Inst. Int. Educ. develop. fel, 65-66; RES. SCIENTIST, UNION CAMP CORP, 68- AAAS; Am. Chem. Soc; Tech. Asn. Pulp & Paper Indust; assoc. Am. Inst. Chem. Eng; Indian Inst. Eng. Pulping, bleaching, soda recovery; physics and chemistry of papermaking; chemical modification of cellulose; effect of hydroxyethylation of fibers on strength properties of paper; paper product development. Address: Union Camp Corp, Princeton, NJ 08540.

DIEBALL, DONALD EDWARD, b. Chicago, Ill, May 25, 30. ELECTROCHEMISTRY, ANALYTICAL & INORGANIC CHEMISTRY. B.S, Northwest. Univ, 52; Ph.D.(chem), Ind. Univ, 57. Supvr. anal. res. & develop, Visking Div, Union Carbide Corp, 56-63; RES. CHEMIST, INT. MINERALS & CHEM. CORP, LIBERTYVILLE, 63- Electroanalytical chemistry. Address: 3347 W. Belle Plaine Ave, Chicago, IL 60618.

DIEBEL, CLARENCE E, b. Palouse, Wash, Dec. 29, 02; m; c. 2. INORGANIC CHEMISTRY. B.A, Univ. Ore, 29, M.A, 38, D.E.D, 59; fel, Carnegie Inst. Technol, 52. Head dept, pub. sch, Ore, 29-53; assoc. prof. SCI, SOUTH. ORE. COL, 53-58, prof, 58-69, EMER. PROF, 69- Consult, Ore. State Dept. Educ, 33-; asst. prof, Drake Univ, summers 48-50; Miami Univ, 52-53; Univ. Ore, 56-58, assoc. prof, 59-, dir. Nat. Sci. Found. traveling demonstration lect. prog, 59- AAAS; Am. Chem. Soc; Nat. Sci. Teachers Asn. Science teaching and curriculum. Address: Dept. of Science, Southern Oregon College, Ashland, OR 97520.

DIEBEL, R(OBERT) NORMAN, b. Chico, Calif, May 15, 27; m. 51; c. 3. PHYSICAL CHEMISTRY, RADIOCHEMISTRY. B.S, Oregon, 50, M.S, 54; Ohio State, 53-59. Chemist radiol. sci, Hanford Labs, Gen. Elec. Co, 60-65; SR. SCIENTIST, PAC. NORTHWEST LABS, BATTELLE MEM. INST, 65- U.S.N, 44-46. AAAS; Am. Chem. Soc. Electron magnetic resonance studies of free radicals produced by irradiation of water solutions; neutron activation analysis of tissues and nuclear chemical analytical techniques. Address: 1925 Everest, Richland, WA 99352.

DIEBERT, CURTIS E(DWARD), b. Fresno, Calif, Aug. 19, 39; m. 61; c. 2. ORGANIC CHEMISTRY. B.S, Fresno State Col, 61; Ph.D.(org. chem), Univ. Calif, Los Angeles, 66. SR. RES. CHEMIST, RES. LABS, TENN. EASTMAN CO, 66- Am. Chem. Soc; The Chem. Soc. Organic reaction mechanisms; organophosphorus and heterocyclic chemistry. Address: 312 Castaway Dr, Kingsport, TN 37663.

DIEBNER, ROBERT LESTER, b. Shreveport, La, June 8, 42; m. 67. PHYSICAL & INORGANIC CHEMISTRY. B.S, La. State, Baton Rouge, 64; M.S, Illinois, Urbana, 66, Ph.D.(chem), 69. Res. chemist, optical spectros. br, U.S. Army Missile Command, Redstone Arsenal, Ala, 69-70; SR. RES. CHEMIST, DOW CHEM. CO, FREEPORT, 70- Ord.C, U.S.A, 68-71, Capt. Am. Chem. Soc. Flash heating and kinetic spectroscopy; high temperature chemistry; chemical lasers; organic synthesis and coordination chemistry. Address: Apt. 4, 130 Oyster Creek Dr, Lake Jackson, TX 77566.

DIEBOLD, JAMES L(OUIS), b. Chicago, Ill, July 14, 34. PHARMACEUTICAL CHEMISTRY. B.S, Loyola (Ill), 57; M.S, Wisconsin, 59; Ph.D.(pharmaceut. chem), Kansas, 64. SR. RES. CHEMIST, WYETH LABS, INC, 64- Am. Chem. Soc. Synthetic organic chemistry related to chemical mechanisms; drug synthesis. Address: Wyeth Labs, Inc, P.O. Box 8299, Philadelphia, PA 19101.

DIECK, HAROLD ANDREW, b. New Orleans, La, May 28, 42. ORGANIC CHEMISTRY. B.S, Tulane, 63; Ph.D.(org. chem), Texas, Austin, 68. RES. CHEMIST, UNIROYAL RES. CTR, WAYNE, 68- AAAS; Am. Chem. Soc. Chemistry of cyclobutadiene iron tricarboxyl complexes; synthetic organic chemistry, especially applications of radiation and organosulfur chemistry. Address: 311 Redwood Ave, B24, Paterson, NJ 07522.

DIECKAMP, HERMAN MAIER, b. Jacksonville, Ill, June 19, 28; m. 55; c. 2. ENGINEERING PHYSICS. B.S, Illinois, 50. Res. engr, systs. nuclear auxiliary power reactors, ATOMICS INT. DIV, N.AM. ROCKWELL, 50-58, proj. engr, 58-60, group leader, 60-61, sect. chief, systs. nuclear auxiliary power 10A, 61-62, dept. dir. space systs, 62-66, v.pres. NUCLEAR ENG, 66-70, PRES, 70- Guest lectr, California, Los Angeles, 61-65; George

Washington, 63. Consult, Adv. Group Aeronaut. Res. & Develop, Belgium, 64. Am. Inst. Aeronaut. & Astronaut. Nuclear energy for space and central station power. Address: Atomics International Division, North American Rockwell, 8900 DeSoto Ave, Canoga Park, CA 91304.

DIECKE, F(RIEDRICH) P(AUL) J(ULIUS), b. June 27, 27; m. 55; c. 2. PHYSIOLOGY. Göttingen; Dr.rer.nat, Würzburg, 53. Jr. res. zoologist, California, Los Angeles, 53-55; asst. comp. physiol, Würzburg, 55-56; instr, Tennessee, 56-57, asst. prof, 57-59; guest investr, Rockefeller Inst, 59; assoc. prof. physiol, sch. med, George Washington, 59-63; PROF. PHYSIOL. & BIOPHYS, COL. MED, UNIV. IOWA, 63- Ger. Army, 44-45. AAAS; Biophys. Soc; Fedn. Am. Socs. Exp. Biol; Am. Physiol. Soc. Neurophysiology; bioelectric phenomena of nerve; ion exchange in nerve and muscle; sensory physiology. Address: Dept. of Physiology & Biophysics, University of Iowa College of Medicine, Iowa City, IA 52240.

DIECKERT, JULIUS W(ALTERS), b. Houston, Tex, June 15, 25; m. 50; c. 4. BIOCHEMISTRY. B.S, Agr. & Mech. Col, Tex, 49, M.S, 51, Ph.D.(biochem), 55. Biochemist, res. found, Agr. & Mech. Col, Tex, 53-55; res. chemist south. utilization res. br, U.S. Dept. Agr, 55-60; ASSOC. PROF. BIOCHEM. & NUTRIT, TEX. A&M UNIV, 60- Asst. prof, med. sch, Tulane, 59. U.S. Dept. Agr. award, 58. U.S.A, 43-45. Am. Chem. Soc; Sci. Res. Soc. Am; Am. Soc. Plant Physiol. Chemistry of natural products, isolation and identification of lipides, saponins, and proteins; glass paper chromatography, theory and application of natural products; plant cytochemistry, histochemical and cytochemical organization of seeds. Address: Dept. of Biochemistry & Biophysics, Texas A&M University, College Station, TX 77843.

DIEDERICH, F(RANKLIN) W(OLFGANG), b. Dusseldorf, Ger, Apr. 4, 22; U.S. citizen; m. 49; c. 3. SYSTEMS ENGINEERING, MANAGEMENT. B.M.E, Cooper Union, 43, M.E, 51; M.Aero.E, N.Y. Univ, 44; Ph.D.(aeronaut, math), Calif. Inst. Technol, 54. Instr. aeronaut. eng, N.Y. Univ, 43-44; power plant analyst, Repub. Aviation, 45; res. scientist, Langley Lab, Nat. Adv. Comt. Aeronaut, 45-57; mgr. aerodyn, radioplane div, Northrop Corp, 57-59; chief engr, v.pres. eng, res. & advan. develop. div, Avco Corp, 59-65, v.pres. advan. projs, missiles, space & electronics group, 66-68; MGR. ADVAN. SYSTS. RES, UNITED AIRCRAFT CORP, 68- Gano Dunn Medal. Systems analysis and engineering; transportation systems; pollution control; industrial dynamics; urban dynamics. Address: United Aircraft Research Labs, United Aircraft Corp, 400 Main St, East Hartford, CT 06108.

DIEDRICH, DONALD F(RANK), b. Passaic, N.J, May 17, 32; m. 58; c. 1. BIOCHEMISTRY. B.S, Illinois, 54; M.S, Wisconsin, 56, Ph.D.(biochem), 59. Res. fel. physiol, col. med, Cincinnati, 59; res. instr, col. med. & dent, Rochester, 59-63; asst. prof. PHARMACOL, COL. MED. & DENT, UNIV. KY, 63-66, ASSOC. PROF, 66- Fulbright award, 71; vis. scientist, Max Planck Inst. Biophys, 71. AAAS; Am. Chem. Soc; N.Y. Acad. Sci. General cellular biology; transport of metabolites across cell membranes; carbohydrate chemistry; drug-receptor interrelationships. Address: Dept. of Pharmacology, University of Kentucky College of Medicine & Dentistry, Lexington, KY 40506.

DIEDRICH, JAMES L(OREN), b. St. Paul, Minn, Jan. 13, 25; m. 50; c. 6. ORGANIC CHEMISTRY. B.Chem, Minnesota, 45; A.M, Indiana, 47, Ohio Oil Co. fel, 46-49, Ph.D.(chem), 49. Res. assoc, Northwestern, 49-50; instr. chem, Loyola (Ill), 50-51; res. chemist, A.B. Dick Co, 51-52; Minn. Mining & Mfg. Co, 52-58; serv. engr, Northwest Orient Airlines, Inc, 58-60; proj. leader, Borden Chem. Co, Mass, 60-67; SR. RES. ASSOC. POLYMERS, H.B. FULLER CO, 67- Am. Chem. Soc. Emulsion polymerization; thiophenes; graphic arts. Address: 2181 Princeton Ave, St. Paul, MN 55105.

DiEDWARDO, ANTHONY ALEXANDER, b. Boonton, N.J, June 9, 29; m. 55; c. 2. NEMATOLOGY, ENTOMOLOGY. B.S, Rutgers, 57, M.S, 59, Ph.D. (nematol), 60. Asst. prof. NEMATOL, Florida, 60-64; STAFF SPECIALIST, AGR. CHEM. DIV, CIBA-GEIGY LTD, ARDSLEY, 64- U.S.A.F, 51-53, Sgt. Am. Inst. Biol. Sci; Am. Soc. Nematol. Host parasite relationships of nematodes affecting plants; nematicides. Address: 12 Duane Ave, New City, NY 10956.

DIEFENDERFER, ALFRED JAMES, b. Sharon, Pa, June 22, 30; m. 51; c. 2. ELECTROCHEMISTRY, INSTRUMENTATION. B.S, Pittsburgh, 57; Ph.D. (anal. chem), Mass. Inst. Tech, 61. ASSOC. PROF. CHEM, LEHIGH UNIV, 64- U.S.A, 51-54, Sgt. AAAS; Am. Chem. Soc. Organic electrode mechanisms; correlation of structure with electrochemical activity; atomic absorption spectrometry; instrumentation electronics. Address: Dept. of Chemistry, Lehigh University, Bethlehem, PA 18015.

DIEFENDORF, ADELBERT, b. Newark, N.J, May 19, 91; m. 13; c. 2. CIVIL ENGINEERING. B.S, Ohio Northern, 11, C.E, 14; Illinois, 21-24; Iowa State Col, 32-33. With Am. Bridge Co, 11-14; engr. of structures, Guggenheim Co, N.Y, 14-16; chief engr, Krajewski-Pesant Corp, Cuba, 16-17; plant maintenance engr, Semet Solvay Co, N.Y, 17-20; chief engr, Lackawanna Bridge Co, 20-21; instr, col. eng, Illinois, 21-24; asst. prof. civil eng, S.Dak. Sch. Mines, 24-27; prof. & head dept, New Mexico, 27-30; prof. Pittsburgh, 30-39; prof. & head dept, Utah, 39-56; dean sch. eng, Univ. of the Pacific, 57-62; CONSULT. ENGR, ORANGEBURG MFG. CO, INC. DIV, FLINTKOTE CO, 62- Consult. engr, Republics of Mex, 40, Cuba, 47 & Guatemala, 52; Costa Rica, 55, 59, Mex, 56; mem, State Bd. Standards; mem. cmt. transportation & econ, Hwy. Res. Bd, Nat. Acad. Sci-Nat. Res. Coun; mem. Nat. Res. Coun. Am. Soc. Civil Eng; Am. Road Builders Asn; Soc. Am. Mil. Eng; Am. Soc. Eng. Educ. Address: 176 Glacier Circle, Vacaville, CA 95688.

DIEFENDORF, RUSSELL JUDD, b. Mount Vernon, N.Y, Aug. 28, 31; m. 52; c. 4. PHYSICAL CHEMISTRY, MATERIALS SCIENCE. B.S, Rochester, 53; Ph.D.(phys. chem), Toronto, 58. Scientist graphite, missile & ord. dept, Gen. Elec. Co, 58-59, vapor deposition, res. lab, 60-65; assoc. prof. MAT. SCI, RENSSELAER POLYTECH; INST, 65-71, PROF, 71- Am. Chem. Soc; Am. Ceramic Soc; Am. Soc. Metals. Mechanical properties; structure to properties; graphite; pyrolytic materials; boron and carbon fibers; composites; high temperature materials; electrochemical power sources; gas phase kinetics. Address: Dept. of Materials Engineering, Rensselaer Polytechnic Institute, Troy, NY 12181.

DIEHL, ANTONI MILLS, b. Minneapolis, Minn, Nov. 5, 24; m. 48; c. 4. PEDIATRICS, CARDIOLOGY. B.S, Minnesota, 46, M.B, 47; M.D, 48. Intern, Michigan, 47-48; res. pediat, univ. hosp, Minnesota, 48-50, fel. pediat. cardiol, 50-51; instr, SCH. MED, UNIV. KANS, 53-55, asst. prof. PEDIAT, 55-58, assoc. prof, 58-67, PROF, 67- Med. Dir, Children's Cardiac Center, 53-64. Dipl, Am. Bd. Pediat, Sub-Bd. Cardiol, 53- Med.C.Res, 51-53, Lt. Am. Heart Asn; fel. Am. Acad. Pediat; fel. Am. Col. Cardiol; fel. Am. Col. Chest Physicians; Am. Med. Asn. Pedatric cardiology; rheumatic fever. Address: Dept. of Pediatrics, School of Medicine, University of Kansas Medical Center, Kansas City, KS 66103.

DIEHL, FRED A, b. Staunton, Va, Aug. 15, 36; m. 58; c. 4. DEVELOPMENTAL BIOLOGY. B.A, Bridgewater Col, 60; Virginia, 60-61; Ph.D.(biol), Western Reserve, 65. Nat. Insts. Health fel. BIOL, Brussels, 64-65; res. fel, Virginia, 65-66; instr, Western Reserve, 66-67; ASST. PROF, UNIV. VA, 67- Summer researcher, Woods Hole Marine Biol. Labs. Am. Soc. Zool; Soc. Develop. Biol. Studies of form genesis and regulation in coelenterates; specific pathways of cellular differentiation, cellular migration and controlling mechanisms of morphogenesis examined in Hydra, Cordylophora and various other hydroids. Address: Dept. of Biology, University of Virginia, Charlottesville, VA 22903.

DIEHL, HAROLD S(HEELY), b. Nittany, Pa, Aug. 4, 91; m. 21; c. 2. PUBLIC HEALTH, MEDICAL ADMINISTRATION. A.B, Gettysburg Col, 12, hon. Sc.D, 35; Syracuse, 14; M.D, Minnesota, 18, A.M, 21. Teacher & asst. prin, high sch, N.Y, 12-14; instr. chem, Augsburg Sem, 14-16; asst. bact. & path, Minnesota, 16-18, pathologist & electrocardiologist, univ. hosp. & instr. path, univ, 21, dir. students health serv, 21-35, from asst. prof. to prof. prev. med. & pub. health & chief dept, 22-35, dean med. sci, 35-58, sr. v.pres. res. & med. affairs & dept. exec. v.pres, AM. CANCER SOC, 58-68, CONSULT. RES. & MED. AFFAIRS, 68- Chmn. health serv. sect, Nat. Conf. Col. Hyg, N.Y, 31; mem. health coun, Boys Clubs Am; dir. health studies, Am. Youth Comn; mem. nat. adv. health coun, U.S. Pub. Health Serv, 39-43, consult, 60-70, mem. cancer control adv. comt, 62-68; mem. directing bd. & chmn. comt. allocation med. personnel, U.S. Procurement & Assignment Serv. physicians Dentist & Veterinarians, 41-45; mem. adv. coun. health servs, Am. Red Cross, 45-48; coun. nat. defense, Am. Med. Asn, 46-57, chmn, 54-57; mem. U.S. del. to World Health Assembly, 54, 55 & 58; v.chmn. health resources adv. comt, Off. Defense Mobilization & Nat. Adv. Comt, Selective Serv, 50-57; v.chmn, Nat. Interagency Coun. Smoking & Health, 64-68; mem, Nat. Food & Drug.Adv. Coun, 65-68. Dipl, Am. Bd. Prev. Med; Pologna Restituta Medal, Polish Sejm, 22; hon. consult, Secy-Gen. Navy, 54-58. Med.C, U.S.A, 17-19; Am. Red Cross Comn, Poland, 19-20, Chief north div. AAAS; fel. Am. Pub. Health Asn; fel. Am. Med. Asn; Am. Col. Health Asn.(pres, 27-29); hon. fel. Am. Col. Chest Physicians. Preventive medicine; blood pressure and albuminuria in young adults; student health; treatment and prevention of acute respiratory infections; anthropometry physique and health in relation to unemployment; medical education; cancer; cigarette smoking. Address: 11 Riverside Dr, New York, NY 10023.

DIEHL, HARVEY (CLARENCE), b. Detroit, Mich, Nov. 2, 10; m. 36; c. 6. ANALYTICAL CHEMISTRY. B.S, Michigan, 32, Ph.D.(chem), 36. Instr. ANAL. CHEM, Cornell, 36-37; Purdue, 37-39; asst. prof, IOWA STATE UNIV, 39-42, assoc. prof, 42-47, PROF, 47-, DISTINGUISHED PROF. SCI. & HUMANITITES, 65- Wilkinson teaching award, Iowa State, 65. With Off. Sci. & Develop, 44. Anachem Award, Asn. Analytical Chemists, Detroit, Mich, 66. AAAS; Am. Chem. Soc.(Fisher award, 56, gold medal, 61). Coordination and chelate ring compounds; electro analysis; tridentate compounds of cobalt; chemical structure of vitamin B_{12}; organic reagents for iron, copper, calcium, magnesium, cobalt and beryllium; perchlorate chemistry. Address: Dept. of Chemistry, Iowa State University, Ames, IA 50010.

DIEHL, JOHN EDWIN, b. Sunbury, Pa, Feb. 7, 29; m. 53; c. 4. BIOCHEMISTRY. A.B, Susquehanna, 52; M.S, Pa. State, 54, Ph.D.(biochem), 60. Sr. res. biochemist, Va. Inst. Sci. Res, 59-64; asst. prof. CHEM, Dickinson Col, 64-65; SHEPHERD COL, 65-68, ASSOC. PROF, 68- Gen. chmn, Tobacco Chemists' Res. Conf, Va, 62. Chem.C, U.S.A, 54-56. AAAS; Am. Chem. Soc; N.Y. Acad. Sci. Enzymes; sheep erythrocyte sphingolipides and tobacco leaf proteins; histone chemistry and neurochemistry. Address: Dept. of Chemistry, Shepherd College, Shepardstown, WV 25443.

DIEHL, RICHARD C, b. Flushing, N.Y, Dec. 30, 42; m. 65; c. 1. PHYSICAL & NUCLEAR CHEMISTRY. A.B, Adelphi Univ, 65; Ph.D.(phys. chem), Univ. Pittsburgh, 70. Chem. res. technician, Univ. Pittsburgh, summer 65, asst. phys. chem, 65-67, low energy nuclear physics res, 67-69; RES. CHEMIST, Mobil Res. & Develop. Corp, 69-70; U.S. BUR. MINES, DEPT. OF INTERIOR, 70-, chemist, 66-67. Am. Chem. Soc; Am. Phys. Soc; Catalysis Soc. One nucleon transfer reactions; low energy nuclear spectroscopy; internal conversion electron spectroscopy; diesel and residual fuel development; air pollution; catalytic reduction and decomposition of NO; trace metals emissions; coal combustion. Address: U.S. Bureau of Mines, Pittsburgh, PA 15213.

DIEHL, ROBERT E(UGENE), b. Phila, Pa, May 27, 34; m. 60; c. 1. ORGANIC CHEMISTRY. B.S, St. Joseph's Col, 56; M.S, Delaware, 58, Ph.D. (org. chem), 61. RES. CHEMIST, AM. CYANAMID CO, 60- Am. Chem. Soc. Chlorination studies on thioethers; olefin epoxidation; mechanism of reactions; synthesis of new heterocycles as potential herbicides. Address: American Cyanamid Co, P.O. Box 400, Princeton, NJ 08540.

DIEHL, STANLEY G(REGG), b. Kansas City, Mo, Sept. 22, 19; m. 44; c. 1. BOTANY. B.S, Cent. Col. Mo, 49; M.S, Okla. Agr. & Mech. Col, 53; Ph.D. (bot), Oklahoma State, 57. Instr. biol, Cameron State Agr. Col, 49-54; asst, Oklahoma State, 54-56; PROF. BOT, SOUTHEAST MO. STATE COL, 56- U.S.A, 41-46, Maj. Am. Inst. Biol. Sci; Bot. Soc. Am; Am. Bryol. & Lichenological Soc. Cytology and histogenesis; microtechniques. Address: 1448 Price Dr, Cape Girardeau, MO 63701.

DIEHL, WILLIAM PAUL, b. Reading, Pa, Mar. 3, 33; m. 55; c. 3. MICROBIAL GENETICS. B.S, Arizona, 55; San Diego State Col, 62-64; Ph.D. (genetics of phage lambda), California, Los Angeles, 68. ASSOC. PROF. BIOL, SAN DIEGO STATE COL, 68- Nat. Sci. Found. grant, 70-72. Genetics Soc. Am. Genetic study of the virulent mutant of lambda, the mutations involved, their location and function. Address: Dept. of Biology, San Diego State College, San Diego, CA 92115.

DIEHN, BODO, b. Hamburg, Germany, June 22, 34. BIOPHYSICAL CHEMISTRY, RADIOCHEMISTRY. B.S, Hamburg, 60; fel, Brookhaven Nat. Lab, 62-64; Ph.D.(phys. chem), Kansas, 64. Res. assoc. biochem, Arizona, 64-66; asst. prof. CHEM, UNIV. TOLEDO, 66-69, ASSOC. PROF, 69- Adj. assoc. prof, Med. Col. Ohio Toledo, 70- Am. Chem. Soc; Biophys. Soc. Radio-atom and hot-atom chemistry; photosynthesis and phototaxis; origin of life; membrane phenomena. Address: Dept. of Chemistry, University of Toledo, Toledo, Toledo, OH 43606.

DIEKE, SALLY H(ARRISON), b. Belvoir, Va, Feb. 7, 13; m. 38. ASTRONOMY. Ph.D.(chem), Hopkins, 38. Asst. chem, Hopkins, 42-43, psychobiol, 43-47, instr, 47-53; vis. lectr, astron, Goucher Col, 50-59, adj. prof, 59-69; RES. FEL. ASTRON, JOHNS HOPKINS UNIV, 66- Hist. Sci. Soc; Am. Astron. Soc. General astronomy; variable stars; biological effects of thiourea derivatives; hair growth and color in rats; history of astronomy, especially 19th century and early 20th century astronomers. Address: History of Science Dept, Johns Hopkins University, Baltimore, MD 21218.

DIEKENBERGER, ELIZABETH BENTINCK, b. West Hartlepool, Eng, June 30, 15; U.S. citizen; m. 41; c. 6. HORTICULTURE. M.S, Agr. Univ. Minais Gerais, 38; Agr. Univ. Pernambuco, 38-40. Res. asst. hort, Brooklyn Bot. Garden, 45-50, res. assoc, 50-56; mem. res. staff, Jackson Perkins Co, 60-64; CONSULT. HORT. & ENVIRON. PLANNING, 65- Am. Soc. Hort. Sci; Am. Hort. Soc. Effects of sequestrene chelate on growth and disease resistance in semitropical plants of the saline soil areas; soil chemistry; development of plant growth without soil; effects of pollution on plants. Address: 8554 E. MacKenzie Dr, Scottsdale, AZ 85251.

DIEKHANS, HERBERT HENRY, b. West Palm Beach, Fla, Mar. 4, 25; m. 55; c. 2. MATHEMATICS. B.S, Alabama, 50, M.A, 51; Nat. Sci. Found. fel, Illinois, Urbana, 62-63, Ph.D.(math), 64. Instr. MATH, Ohio, 55-60; Illinois, Urbana, 64; assoc. prof, IND. STATE UNIV, TERRE HAUTE, 64-70, PROF, 70- U.S.N, 43-47. Am. Math. Soc; Math. Asn. Am. Mathematical analysis. Address: Dept. of Mathematics, Indiana State University, Terre Haute, IN 47809.

DIEKMAN, ROBERT, b. Elgin, Ill, Apr. 29, 22; m. 47; c. 2. CHEMICAL ENGINEERING. B.S, Northwestern, 44, M.S, 48. Chem. engr, process div, res. dept, Standard Oil Co. Ind, 47-51, group leader, 51-61, head engr, process eng. div, eng. dept, AM. OIL CO, 61-66, supvr. long-range planning, mfg. dept, 66-68, SUPT. TECH. SERV, WHITING REFINERY, 68- U.S.N.R, 44-46, Lt.(jg). Am. Inst. Chem. Eng; Am. Chem. Soc. Address: American Oil Co, Box 710, Whiting, IN 46394.

DIEKMANN, JURGEN, b. Ludwigshafen, Germany, Dec. 21, 34; U.S. citizen; m. 60; c. 3. ORGANIC & PHYSICAL CHEMISTRY. B.A, Kalamazoo Col, 56; Ph.D.(org. chem), Illinois, 60. Mem. staff chem, cent. res. dept, E.I. DU PONT DE NEMOURS & CO, INC, 59-64, tech. rep, FILM DEPT, Del, 64-66, res. supvr, Yerkes Lab, N.Y, 66-68, RES. MGR, CIRCLEVILLE LAB, OHIO, 68- Am. Chem. Soc. Cyano carbons; carbenes; photochemistry; chemiluminescence; films; electrical insulation materials. Address: Film Dept, Circleville Lab, E.I. du Pont de Nemours & Co, Inc, Circleville, OH 43113.

DIEM, HUGH E(GBERT), b. Arendtsville, Pa, Mar. 31, 22; m. 48; c. 2. POLYMER CHEMISTRY. A.B, Ohio Wesleyan, 47; M.A, Ohio State, 49. Asst. chem, Ohio State, 47-49; res. chemist, Colgate-Palmolive-Peet Co, 50-51; develop. engr, B.F. Goodrich Chem. Co, 51-54, res. chemist, B.F. GOODRICH CO, 57-58, proj. leader, 59-61, sect. leader olefin rubbers, 61, RES. ASSOC, 63- U.S.M.C, 42-43; U.S.N, 43-46, Res, 46-, Ens. AAAS; Am. Chem. Soc. Polymer chemistry; polymerization mechanisms; relation of polymer properties to physical structure; polymer reactions; infrared spectroscopy. Address: Research Center, B.F. Goodrich Co, Brecksville, OH 44141.

DIEM, JOHN E(DWIN), b. Bridgeport, Conn, Dec. 7, 37; m. 63; c. 2. MATHEMATICS. B.A, Pa. State, 61, M.A, 62; Ph.D.(math), Purdue, 65. ASSOC. PROF. MATH, TULANE UNIV, 65- Math. Asn. Am. Probability-stochastic processes; mathematical genetics; partially-ordered algebraic structures. Address: Dept. of Mathematics, Tulane University, New Orleans, LA 70118.

DIEM, KENNETH LEE, b. Milwaukee, Wis, Apr. 17, 24; m. 50; c. 2. ZOOLOGY. B.S, Lawrence Col, 48; M.S, Utah State, 52, Sigma Xi grant-in-aid, 55, 57, Nat. Wildlife Fedn. fel, 56, Nat. Res. Coun. grant, 57, Ph.D.(wildlife mgt), 58. Game technician, N.Kaibab Deer Herd, Ariz. Game & Fish Comn, 51-54; asst. prof. ZOOL. & GAME MGT, UNIV. WYO, 57-62, assoc. prof, 62-65, PROF, 65- Nat. Res. Coun. grant, Wyoming, 58; N.Y. Zool. Soc. grant, 61-63; U.S. Nat. Park Serv. grant, 63. U.S.N.R, 41-46, Lt.(jg). Fel. AAAS; Am. Ornith. Union; Wildlife Soc; Am. Soc. Mammal; Ecol. Soc. Am; Cooper Ornith. Soc; Am. Inst. Biol. Sci. Animal ecology; particularly dynamics of wildlife populations; big game and avian populations. Address: 22 Corthell Rd, Laramie, WY 82070.

DIEMER, E(DWARD) DEVLIN, b. Pittsburgh, Pa, Nov. 4, 33; m. 56; c. 4. METEOROLOGY. B.S, St. Louis, 55, M.Pr.Gph, 60, Ph.D.(meteorol, math), 65; Weather Bur. scholar, Mass. Inst. Technol, 64-65. Forecaster, U.S. Weather Bur, Mo, 59-64, asst. regional meteorologist, Utah, 65-66, chief sci. serv. div, ALASKAN REGION, NAT. WEATHER SERV, NAT. OCEANIC & ATMOSPHERIC ADMIN, 66-71, METEOROLOGIST-IN-CHARGE, WEATHER SERV. FORECAST OFF, 71- Lectr, Univ. Alaska, 66- U.S.A.F, 55-59, Capt. AAAS; Am. Meteorol. Soc. Weather forecasting; synoptic meteorology; energy transformations; numerical weather prediction. Address: 5326 Wandering Dr, Anchorage, AK 99502.

DIEMER, F(ERDINAND) P(ETER), b. N.Y.C, Oct. 16, 20; m. 52; c. 8. ELECTRICAL ENGINEERING. B.S.E.E, Cooper Union, 48; M.S.E.E, N.Y, Univ, 50; Polytech. Inst. Brooklyn, 51-54; California, Los Angeles, 54-55. Commun. engr, Telephonics Corp, 41-44; group leader instruments & electronics, Celanese Corp, N.J, 46-49; asst. mgr. res. lab. & staff adv. to v.pres, Fleischman Labs, Standard Brands, Inc, 49-51; sr. develop. engr, control inst. div, Burroughs Corp, 51-52; proj. coord. & sr. res. engr, Am. Bosch Arma Corp, 52-54; mgr. appl. physics, G.M. Giannini & Co, Inc, 54-57, tech. dir, Giannini Res. Lab, Calif, 56-57; dir. eng. & tech. consult, Cal-Tronics Corp, 57-58; proj. mgr. & sr. staff engr, Hughes Aircraft Co, 58-60; v.pres. & dir. eng, Daystrom, Inc, 60-61; asst. dir. advan. prog. & dir. eng, Martin-Marietta Corp, 61-66; exec. engr, TRW Systs, Inc, Wash, D.C, 66-67, mgr. command & control, 67-71; PHYS. SCI. ADMINR. OCEAN SCI, OFF, NAVAL RES, ARLINGTON, VA, 71- Consult, indust. eng. dept, Columbia Univ, 50-61; lectr, Univ. South. Calif, 56-; consult, electrodata div, Burroughs Corp, 57; lectr, Univ. Calif, Los Angeles, 57-; lectr, Am. Univ. Sig.C, U.S.A, 44-46. Inst. Elec. & Electronics Eng; Am. Inst. Aeronaut. & Astronaut; Asn. Comput. Mach; Indust. Math. Soc; Soc. Indust. & Appl. Math; Am. Ord. Asn; Solar Energy Soc. Information and control systems; data processing computer technology; program management; technical consultation. Address: 5307 Springlake Way, Baltimore, MD 21212.

DIEN, C(HI)-K(ANG), b. China, Sept. 18, 24; nat; m. 52; c. 3. ORGANIC CHEMISTRY. B.S, Nat. Fuh Tan Univ, 47; Ph.D.(chem), Texas, 53. Res. chemist, China Textile Industs. Inc, 47-49; fel, Virginia, 53-56; res. chemist, Nat. Aniline Div, ALLIED CHEM. CORP, 56-68, SR. SCIENTIST, SPECIALTY CHEM. DIV, 68- Am. Chem. Soc. Conjugated systems; furan derivatives; heterocyclic compounds; anthraquinone and azo dyestuffs; organic pigment and intermediates. Address: 365 Getzville Rd, Buffalo, NY 14226.

DIENA, BENITO B, b. Rhodes, Greece, Apr. 17, 26; Can. citizen; m. 50; c. 3. BACTERIOLOGY, VETERINARY MEDICINE. D.V.M, Parma, 50; M.Sc, McGill, 54, Ph.D.(bact), 56. BACTERIOLOGIST, LAB. HYG, CAN, 56-, HEAD RES. DIV, 66- Dipl, Am. Bd. Microbiol, 64. Can. Soc. Microbiol; Can. Soc. Immunol. Medical bacteriology; immunology. Address: Lab. of Hygiene, Tunneys Pasture, Ottawa, Ont, Can.

DIENER, ROBERT G, b. Brookville, Pa, Apr. 12, 38; m. 61. AGRICULTURAL ENGINEERING. B.S, Pa. State, 60, M.S, 63; Ph.D.(agr. eng), Mich. State, 66. Tech. & develop. engr, Int. Harvester Co, Ill, 60-61; asst, Pa. State, 61-62; Mich. State, 63-65; asst. prof. AGR. ENG, Mich. State Univ, 65-68; W.VA. UNIV, 68-71, ASSOC. PROF, 71- Agr. engr, U.S. Dept. Agr, 65-68. Am. Soc. Agr. Eng; Soc. Rheol. Mechanical viscoelastic behavior of engineering; agricultural materials; mechanization of harvest of fruits and vegetables. Address: Dept. of Agricultural Engineering, West Virginia University, Morgantown, WV 26506.

DIENER, ROBERT MAX, b. Zurich, Switz, Jan. 15, 31; U.S. citizen; m. 54; c. 4. TOXICOLOGY, PATHOLOGY. B.S, Cornell, 53; D.V.M, Mich. State, 60, M.S, 61. Instr. clin. vet. med, Mich. State, 60-61; sr. vet, CIBA PHARMACEUT. CO, 61-63, asst. dir. toxicol, 63-69, DIR. TOXICOL. & PATH, 69- Med.C, U.S.A, 53-55. Dipl, Am. Col. Vet. Path. Am. Vet. Med. Asn; Am. Asn. Lab. Animal Sci; Am. Col. Vet. Toxicol; Soc. Toxicol; Int. Acad. Path; Europ. Soc. Study Drug Toxicity. Animal toxicology, pathology and teratology. Address: CIBA Pharmaceutical Co, 556 Morris Ave, Summit, NJ 07901.

DIENER, T(HEODOR) O(TTO), b. Zurich, Switz, Feb. 28, 21; nat; m. 50, 68; c. 3. PLANT VIROLOGY. Dr.sc.nat.(plant path), Swiss Fed. Inst. Tech, 48. Asst, Swiss Fed. Inst. Tech, 46-48; plant pathologist, Swiss Fed. Exp. Sta. Wine, Fruit & Hort, Waedenswil, 49; asst. plant pathologist, R.I. State Col, 50; Wash. State, 50-55, assoc. plant pathologist, 55-59; RES. PLANT PATHOLOGIST, PLANT VIROL. LAB, U.S. DEPT. AGR, 59- Assoc. ed, Virology, 64-67, ed, 68-; regents' lectr, Univ. Calif, 70; mem. ed. comt, Annual Rev. Phytopath, 70- Campbell Award, Am. Inst. Biol. Sci, 68; superior serv. award, U.S. Dept. Agr, 69. AAAS; Am. Phytopath Soc. Plant viruses and virus diseases; physiology of virus diseases; discovery and characterization of novel class of pathogens. Address: Plant Virology Lab, Plant Industry Station, U.S. Dept. of Agriculture, Beltsville, MD 20705.

DIENER, URBAN L(OWELL), b. Lima, Ohio, May 26, 21; m. 56. PLANT PATHOLOGY. A.B, Miami(Ohio), 43; A.M, Harvard, 45; Columbia, 45-46; Ph.D.(plant path), N.C. State, 53. Indust. mycologist, Sindar Corp, 45-47; asst. plant pathologist, S.C. Agr. Exp. Sta, 47-48; AUBURN UNIV, 52-57, assoc. prof. PLANT PATH, 57-63, PROF, 63- Fel. AAAS; Phytopath. Soc; Am. Soc. Microbiol. Mycotoxicology; mycotoxins; fungus ecology; toxin production by fungi. Address: Dept. of Botany & Microbiology, Auburn University, Auburn, AL 36830.

DIENES, G(EORGE) J(ULIAN), b. Budapest, Hungary, Apr. 28, 18; nat; m. 40; c. 1. CHEMISTRY. B.S, Carnegie Inst. Tech, 40, M.S, 42, D.Sc.(phys. chem), 47; M.A, Columbia, 46. Instr. chem, Washington & Jefferson Col, 40-41; asst, Carnegie Inst. Tech, 41-43; res. chemist, Ridbo Labs, N.J, 43-44; group leader, physics div, Bakelite Corp, 44-49; res. specialist, N.Am. Aviation, 49-51; SR. PHYSICIST, BROOKHAVEN NAT. LAB, UPTON, 51- AAAS; Am. Chem. Soc; Soc. Rheol.(secy-treas, 49-53); fel. Am. Phys. Soc. Theory of diffusion in crystals; infrared spectra of resins; flow and mechanical properties of high polymers; action of plasticizers; diffusion of dyes; molecular weight distributions; solid state physics; imperfections in crystals; radiation effects in solids. Address: P.O. Box 435, Stony Brook, NY 11790.

DIENES, JOHN K, b. Boston, Mass, Sept. 21, 28; m. 57; c. 2. MECHANICAL ENGINEERING, MATHEMATICS. B.A, Pomona Col, 50; M.S, Calif. Inst. Tech, 58, Ph.D.(mech. eng), 61. Engr, N.Am. Aviation, Inc, 50-55; Minneapolis-Honeywell Regulator Co, 56-57; specialist, Convair Div, Gen. Dynamics Corp, 61-62, STAFF MEM. SPEC. PROJ, Gen. Atomic Div, 62-68; SYSTS, SCI. & SOFTWARE, 68- Vibrations of nonlinear systems; random processes; hypervelocity impact; continuum mechanics; hydrodynamics; computing. Address: 8855 Robin Hood Lane, La Jolla, CA 92037.

DIENHART, CHARLOTTE MARIE, b. Sioux Falls, S.Dak, Aug. 14, 23. ANATOMY. B.S, St. Catherine Col, 45; M.S, Iowa, 47; Minnesota, 56-58, Nat. Sci. Found. summer fel, 56; Ph.D.(anat), Mich. State, 60; Emory, 62-64. Res. asst. nutrit, Minnesota, 47-48; instr. anat, St. Catherine Col, 48-56; asst. physiol, Minnesota, 57-58; ANAT, Mich. State, 58-60; instr, EMORY UNIV, 60-67, ASST. PROF, 67- U.S.N. Research Res, 52-, Lt.

Comdr. N.Y. Acad. Sci. Human anatomy; nervous system; histochemistry of motor neurons. Address: Dept. of Anatomy, Emory University, Atlanta, GA 30322.

DIERCKS, FRED H(ERMAN), b. Greenville, Tex, Aug. 1, 20; m. 42; c. 4. MICROBIOLOGY, VIROLOGY. B.A, East Texas State Teachers Col, 41; fel, Texas, 41; M.S, Maryland, 51; M.P.H, Pittsburgh, 57, D.Sc.(microbiol), 59. Virologist Naval Med. Res. Inst, 46-48; med. serv. corps, U.S. Army, 48-67, mem. staff, Walter Reed Army Med. Center, 48-64, hq, U.S. Army Med. Res. & Develop. Command, Off. Surgeon Gen, D.C, 64-67; ASSOC. PROF. BIOL, MARS HILL COL, 67- Dipl, Am. Bd. Microbiol, 64. U.S.N.R, 42-45. AAAS; Am. Soc. Microbiol; fel. Am. Pub. Health Asn; N.Y. Acad. Sci. Epidemiology; public health; immunology; diagnostic laboratory procedures for viral and rickettsial infections; tropical medicine, including scrub typhus, typhoid fever, arthropod-borne viruses. Address: Dept. of Biology, Mars Hill College, Mars Hill, NC 28754.

DIERCKS, FREDERICK O(TTO), b. Rainy River, Ont, Sept. 8, 12; U.S. citizen; m. 37; c. 2. PHOTOGRAMMETRY, CARTOGRAPHY. B.S, U.S. Mil. Acad, 37; M.S, Mass. Inst. Tech, 39; M.S, Syracuse, 50. Corps Eng, U.S. Army, 37-67, engr. photogram. res, Wright Field, Ohio, 37-38, co. comdr, photomapping, Ft. Belvoir, Va, 39-41, topog. eng, Ft. Jackson, S.C, 41-42, officer-in-charge hydrographic surv, Nicaragua Canal Surv, 42, batallion comdr, eng. aviation batallion, Geiger Field, Wash, 42-44, topog. eng. batallion, France & Germany, 44-45, officer-in-charge topog. eng. res, Ft. Knox, Ky, 45-47, batallion comdr. geod. surv, Philippines, 47-48, officer-in-charge eng. intel. & mapping, Gen. Hq, Far East Command, Tokyo, 48-49, topog. eng. ed, Ft. Belvoir, 50-52, eng. intel. mapping, Hq, U.S. Army Europe, Heidelberg, 53-56, commanding officer, Map Serv, D.C, 57-61, asst. dir. mapping, charting & geod, Defense Intel. Agency, 61-63, dep. engr, eng. sect, Korea, 63-64, dir, Coastal Eng. Res. Center, 64-67; ASSOC. DIR. AERONAUT. CHARTING & CARTOG, NAT. OCEAN SURV, 67- Lectr, Catholic Univ, 50-51; mem, nat. atlas cmt. & adv. cmt. on cartog, Nat. Acad. Sci, 57-61; U.S. mem, cmn. cartog, Pan-Am. Inst. Geog. & Hist, Orgn. Am. States, 61-67, alternate U.S. mem, dir. coun. & v.chmn, U.S. Nat. Sect, 70- Grand Cross, Order of King George II, Greece, 59; Comdr, Most Exalted Order of White Elephant, Thailand, 68. C.Eng, U.S.A, 37-67, Col; Legion of Merit, 67. Am. Soc. Civil Eng; Soc. Am. Mil. Eng; Am. Soc. Photogram.(pres, 70-71, Luis Struck Award, 69); Am. Cong. Surv. & Mapping. Geodetic and topographic surveying and mapping instruments and methods; photogrammetric plotting equipment and techniques; wave theory, shore processes, tides, inlet and estuary dynamics; coastal works design and construction techniques; aeronautical chart design and production; cartographic methods and equipment. Address: Office of Cartography, National Ocean Survey, Washington Science Center, 6001 Executive Blvd, Rockville, MD 20852.

DIERDORFF, LEE H(ENRY), JR, b. Moline, Ill, Apr. 29, 22; m. 54; c. 2. CHEMICAL ENGINEERING. B.S, Northwestern, 43. Asst. chem. engr, plant design, Tenn. Eastman Corp, 43-45; proj. engr, process develop, Becco Chem. Div, FMC CORP, 48-52, proj. leader, 52-53, chem. engr, 53-54, supvr, liaison eng. chem. econ, inorg. res. & develop. dept, 54-61, res. engr, CENT. RES, 61-67, SR. RES. ENGR, 67- C.Eng, 45-46. Am. Inst. Chem. Eng; Am. Asn. Cost Eng; Combustion Inst. Hydrogen peroxide properties and processes; supercooling; crystallization; correlation and estimation of physical properties; engineering economics; process development. Address: Central Research Dept, FMC Corp, P.O. Box Eight, Princeton, NJ 08540.

DIERENFELDT, KARL E(MIL), b. Eureka, S.Dak, Mar. 17, 40. PHYSICAL & NUCLEAR CHEMISTRY. B.S, S.Dak. State, 62; Ph.D.(phys. chem), California, Davis, 66. ASST. PROF. CHEM, CONCORDIA COL.(MOORHEAD, MINN), 66- Am. Chem. Soc. Production of light fragments in high energy nuclear reactions; free radicals in solid organic glasses. Address: Dept. of Chemistry, Concordia College, Moorhead, MN 56560.

DIERKS, CHRISTA, b. Switz, July 28, 30; U.S. citizen; m. 59; c. 2. BIOCHEMISTRY. Dipl. chem, Univ. Lausanne, 54; D.Phil.(biochem), Oxford, 57. Res. asst. biochem, Oxford, 57; Iowa, 57-58, res. assoc. surg, col. med, 58-60; chief chemist, Iowa Lutheran Hosp, Des Moines, 60-61, res. assoc. internal med, Hopkins Hosp, Baltimore, Md, 63-65; lab scientist, Rosewood State Hosp, 65-71; RES. SCIENTIST, FRIEDRICH MIESCHER-INST, SWITZ, 71- Instr. sch. med, Univ. Md, 65-67, asst. prof, 67-71. Am. Soc. Cell Biol. Enzymology; control mechanism. Address: Friedrich Miescher-Institute, Basle, Switz.

DIERKS, RICHARD ERNEST, b. Flandreau, S.Dak, Mar. 11, 34; m. 56; c. 3. VIROLOGY, VETERINARY MEDICINE. B.S, Minnesota, 57, D.V.M, 59, M.P.H. & Ph.D.(microbiol), 64. Field vet, Minn. State Livestock Sanit. Bd, 59; Nat. Insts. Health fel, Minnesota, 59-64; vet. officer in charge rickettsial diseases lab, spec. projs. unit, lab. br. commun. disease center, U.S. Pub. Health Serv, Ga, 64-66, chief rabies invests. lab. vet. pub. health sect, epidemiol. br, 66-68; ASSOC. PROF. VET. MED, VET. MED. RES. INST, IOWA STATE UNIV, 68- Nat. Inst. Allergy & Infectious Diseases grant, 68-71; Air Force Off. Sci. res. grant, 69-71; Nat. Insts. Health res. career develop. award, 69-74; Agr. Res. Serv, U.S. Dept. Agr. grant, 70-72. U.S.M.C.R, 55-59; U.S.P.H.S, 64-, Lt. Comdr. Am. Vet. Med. Asn; Am. Pub. Health Asn; Am. Asn. Avian Path; Am. Soc. Microbiol; Soc. Exp. Biol. & Med; Am. Soc. Trop. Med. & Hyg. Characterization of avian mycoplasma; rickettsial diseases; leprosy; oncogenic viruses; rabies; rhabdoviruses; bovine respiratory viruses. Address: Veterinary Medical Research Institute, College of Veterinary Medicine, Iowa State University, Ames, IA 50010.

DIERMANN, JOACHIM, b. Leipzig, Ger, Apr. 7, 32; U.S. citizen. ELECTRONIC ENGINEERING. Dipl. Ing, Aachen Tech. Univ, 56. Design engr, Atlas Werke A.G, Ger, 56-60; Raytheon Co, Mass, 60-61, sect. head marine radar, Calif, 61-64; sr. engr, RS Electronics Corp, Calif, 64-66; mem. res. staff, AMPEX CORP, 66-69, MGR. ELECTRON BEAM RECORDING SECT, 69- Electron and laser beam technology; recording technology. Address: 3440 Kenneth Dr, Palo Alto, CA 94303.

DIERMEIER, HAROLD F(REDERICK), b. Stratford, Wis, Sept. 12, 17; m. 46; c. 4. PHYSIOLOGY. B.S, River Falls State Col, 41; M.A, Syracuse, 48, Ph.D.(zool), 50. Instr. pharmacol, State Univ. N.Y, 50-53, asst. prof, Upstate Med. Center, 53-58; PHARMACOLOGIST, LEDERLE LABS, 58- Qm.C, 42-46, Capt. AAAS; Am. Soc. Pharmacol. & Exp. Therapeut; Soc. Toxicol. Relationship of nucleic acids to protein synthesis and growth; toxicology; pharmacology. Address: Lederle Labs, Pearl River, NY 10965.

DIEROLF, JACK, b. Rock Island, Ill, Sept. 14, 25; m. 46; c. 2. PHYSICAL CHEMISTRY. B.A, Augustana Col.(Ill), 53. Res. chemist, Rock Island Arsenal, Ord. Dept, U.S. Army, 52-56; U.S. Naval Ord. Test Sta, 56-59, gen. engr, 59-63, res. chemist, 63-70, COMPUT. PROGRAMMER, NAVAL WEAPONS CTR, 70- U.S.A, 43-46, 51. Am. Ord. Asn. Packaging materials; rocket propulsion; solid, liquid and hybrid rocket propellants; explosives. Address: Management Data Processing, Code 1783, Naval Weapons Center, China Lake, CA 93555.

DIERSCHKE, DONALD JOE, b. Rowena, Tex, Nov. 30, 34; m. 56; c. 2. ANIMAL PHYSIOLOGY. B.S. & Danforth Found. fel, Texas A&M, 56; Danforth Found. fel, Montana State, 56-57, M.S, 57; Ralston Purina fel, California, Davis, 61-62, U.S. Pub. Health Serv. & Danforth Found. fels, 63-64, Ph.D.(reprod. endocrinol), 65. Assoc. prof. biol, Oklahoma City Univ, 65-69; U.S. Pub. Health Serv. spec. res. fel. PHYSIOL, SCH. MED, UNIV. PITTSBURGH, 69-71, RES. ASST. PROF, 71- Nat. Insts. Health res. grant, 67-69; Eli Lilly res. grant, 68-69. U.S.A.F, 57-60, Res, 60-, Capt. Am. Soc. Animal Sci; Soc. Study Reproduction; Am. Physiol. Soc; Endocrine Soc. Endocrine control mechanisms in reproduction of mammals. Address: Dept. of Physiology, University of Pittsburgh School of Medicine, Pittsburgh, PA 15213.

DIESCH, STANLEY L, b. Blooming Prairie, Minn, May 16, 25; m. 56; c. 2. VETERINARY PUBLIC HEALTH, VETERINARY MICROBIOLOGY. B.S, Minnesota, St. Paul, 51, D.V.M, 56, M.P.H, Minneapolis, 63. Teacher, veterans agr. training, Belle Plaine Schs, Minn, 51-52; private practice, 57-62; U.S. Pub. Health Serv. traineeship, 62-63; asst. prof. prev. med. & environ. health, col. med, Iowa, 63-66; VET. MICROBIOL. & PUB. HEALTH, COL. VET. MED, UNIV. MINN, 66-70, ASSOC. PROF, 70-, EPIDEMIOL, SCH. PUB. HEALTH, 70- U.S. Pub. Health Serv. res. grant, 68- Consult, Meat Hyg. Training Center, Chicago, Ill, 67-68; adv. in vet. pub. health to Venezuela, Pan-Am. Health Orgn, 68. Chmn. epidemiol. sect, Leptospirosis Res. Conf, 66-67. Am. Vet. Med. Asn; Am. Pub. Health Asn; Conf. Pub. Health Vets; Asn. Teachers Vet. Pub. Health & Prev. Med. Epidemiology of leptospirosis in animals and man; zoonotic diseases. Address: Dept. of Veterinary Microbiology & Public Health, University of Minnesota College of Veterinary Medicine, St. Paul, MN 55101.

DIESEM, CHARLES D, b. Galion, Ohio, July 5, 21; m. 45; c. 3. VETERINARY ANATOMY. D.V.M, Ohio State, 43, M.Sc, 49, Ph.D.(anat), 56. Instr, VET. ANAT, OHIO STATE UNIV, 47-56, asst. prof, 56-59, assoc. prof, 59-61, PROF, 61- Vet.C, U.S.A, 44-47, Res, 47-69, Lt. Col. AAAS; Am. Asn. Anat; Am. Vet. Med. Asn; Conf. Res. Workers Animal Diseases. Gross anatomy and histology; ophthomology and hematology. Address: 1872 Berkshire Rd, Columbus, OH 43221.

DIESEN, CARL EDWIN, b. Cloquet, Minn, Aug. 21, 21; m. 49; c. 2. MATHEMATICS. B.A, Minnesota, Minneapolis, 42, M.A, 49; Wisconsin, 49-51. mgr. electronic data processing, Bell Aircraft Corp, 51-60; eng. systs, Hughes Aircraft Co, 60-61; electronic data processing, Gen. Dynamics/Astronaut, 61-64; digital comput, Telecomput. Serv, Inc, 64-66; data processing & comput, Ling-Temco-Vought, Inc, 66-67; CHIEF COMPUT. CTR. DIV, U.S. GEOL. SURV, 67- Sig.C, 42-46, 1st Lt. Asn. Comput. Mach; Math. Asn. Am; Data Processing Mgt. Asn. Numerical analysis for digital computation and for business information systems design and data processing. Address: 8617 Red Coat Lane, Rockville, MD 20854.

DIESEN, RONALD W, b. Highland, Ill, Oct. 16, 31; m. 51; c. 2. PHYSICAL CHEMISTRY. B.A, Southern Illinois, 53; Ph.D.(phys. chem), Washington (Seattle), 58. Res. chemist, DOW CHEM. CO, 58-64, SR. RES. CHEMIST, 64- Am. Chem. Soc; Sci. Res. Soc. Am. High temperature kinetics; shock tube applications; free radical and combustion reactions; mass spectrometry; laser photochemistry; photochemical recoil spectroscopy. Address: Chemical Physics Research Lab, Dow Chemical Co, 1603 Bldg, Midland, MI 48640.

DIESENDRUCK, LEO, b. Budweis, Czech, July 1, 20; nat; m. 42; c. 4. PHYSICS. B.A, Cincinnati, 41; Ph.D.(physics), Hopkins, 50. Jr. instr. physics, Hopkins, 41-43; physicist theoret. aerodynam, Nat. Adv. Cmt. Aeronaut, 44-46; assoc. prof. PHYSICS, Rhode Island, 49-59, PROF, 59-63; QUEENS COL.(N.Y), 63- U.S.A.A.F.R, 44-46. Am. Phys. Soc. Aerodynamics of perfect fluids; theory of nuclear reactions; upper air measurements of solar radiation; normal mode theory of sound transmission; relativistic electrodynamics and Cherenkov effect. Address: Dept. of Physics, Queens College, Flushing, NY 11367.

DIESTEL, JOSEPH, b. Westbury, N.Y, Jan. 27, 43; m. 64; c. 2. MATHEMATICS. B.S, Dayton, 64; Ph.D.(math), Catholic Univ, 68. Res. scientist, Tech. Opers. Res, Inc, Wash, D.C, 67-68; sr. scientist, Consultec, Inc, 68; asst. prof. MATH, W.GA. COL, 68-70, ASSOC. PROF, 70- Opers. res. consult, Consultec, Inc, Md, 68-; eng. consult, Southwire Int, Inc, Ga, 69- Am. Math. Soc; Math. Asn. Am. Functional analysis; measure and integration; topological algebra; general topology; operations research. Address: Dept. of Mathematics, West Georgia College, Carrollton, GA 30117.

DIESTLER, DENNIS JON, b. Ames, Iowa, Oct. 23, 41. THEORETICAL CHEMISTRY. B.S, Harvey Mudd Col, 64; Nat. Sci. Found. fel. & Ph.D. (chem), Calif. Inst. Tech, 68. ASST. PROF. CHEM, Missouri, St. Louis, 67-69; PURDUE UNIV, 69- AAAS; Am. Chem. Soc; Am. Phys. Soc. Energy transfer in molecular collisions. Address: Dept. of Chemistry, Purdue University, Lafayette, IN 47907.

DIETEMANN, ALLAN B, b. Kiowa, Colo, Apr. 15, 12; m. 43; c. 1. CHEMISTRY. B.S, Denver, 35. Jr. engr. mech. time fuzes, off. chief ord, U.S. Dept. of Army, Wash, D.C, 42-43; ord. engr. mech. rocket & projectile fuzes, bur. ord, Dept. of Navy, 47-50; explosive components, guided missile destructors, U.S. NAVAL ORD. LAB, 50-53, dep. div. chief mechanism & serv. div, fuze dept, 53-56, ammunition div, fuzes & explosive components, 56-57, consult, explosive devices, 57-60, long range planning, 60-66, CHIEF CHEM. ENG. DIV, CHEM. DEPT, 66- Ord. Dept, U.S.N, 43-47, Lt. Comdr. Fuzes; explosive train mechanisms; explosive components; propellants. Address: 407 Kerwin Rd, Silver Spring, MD 20901.

DIETER, CLARENCE DEWEY, b. Pittsburgh, Pa, July 19, 98; m. 29, 68. MICROSCOPIC ANATOMY. B.S, Univ. Pittsburgh, 22, Ph.D.(biol), 34; fel, Washington & Jefferson Col, 22-24, M.S, 24, hon. D.Sc, 67; summers, Univ. Chicago, 24, 29. Asst, Univ. Pittsburgh, 20-22; instr, WASHINGTON & JEFFERSON COL, 24-27, asst. prof. BIOL, 27-35, prof. & head dept, 35-66, EMER. PROF, 66-; COORD. BASIC SCI, WASHINGTON HOSP, 66- Instr, sch. med, Univ. Pittsburgh, 42-43, spec. lectr, 43. Rush Medals. Am. Cancer Soc. Nervous system of triturus viridescens. Address: 655 Murdock St, Washington, PA 15301.

DIETER, GEORGE E(LLWOOD), JR, b. Phila, Pa, Dec. 5, 28; m. 52; c. 2. PHYSICAL METALLURGY. B.S, Drexel Inst, 50; D.Sc.(metall), Carnegie Inst. Tech, 53. Res. coordinator, ballistics res. lab, Aberdeen Proving Ground, 53-55; res. engr, eng. res. lab, E.I. du Pont de Nemours & Co, 55-58, res. supvr, 58-62; PROF. METALL. ENG. & HEAD DEPT, DREXEL UNIV, 62-, DEAN COL. ENG, 69- Mem, mat. adv. bd, Metalworking Processes & Equip. Cmt. Ord. Dept, 53-55, 1st Lt. Am. Soc. Metals; Am. Inst. Mining, Metall. & Petrol. Eng. Mechanical metallurgy; fatigue of metals; fracture; materials processing. Address: College of Engineering, Drexel University, Philadelphia, PA 19104.

DIETER, MICHAEL PHILLIP, b. Joplin, Mo, Jan. 1, 38; m. 62; c. 3. PHYSIOLOGY, ENDOCRINOLOGY. B.S, Notre Dame, 60; M.A, Missouri, 65, Nat. Sci. Found. traineeship, 67, Ph.D.(zool), 68. Asst. zool, Missouri, 62-67; staff fel. physiol, Nat. Insts. Health, 67-69, sr. staff fel, 69-71; PHYSIOLOGIST, BUR. SPORTS FISHERIES & WILDLIFE, U.S. DEPT. INTERIOR, 71- U.S.A, 60-61, Res, 61-66. AAAS; Am. Soc. Zool; Soc. Exp. Biol. & Med. Lymphatic tissue growth and metabolism; vitamin C-hormone relationships; biochemical study of exercise and cold physiology; pesticides; environmental pollutants. Address: Patuxent Wildlife Research Center, Bureau of Sports Fisheries & Wildlife, Laurel, MD 20810.

DIETER, NANNIELOU H(EPBURN), b. Springfield, Ill, June 10, 26; m. 55; c. 2. ASTRONOMY. A.B, Goucher Col, 48; M.A, Radcliffe Col, 57, Ph.D.(astron), 58. ASTRONOMER, U.S. Naval Res. Lab, 51-55, U.S. Air Force Cambridge Res. Ctr, 58-65; RADIO ASTRON. LAB, UNIV. CALIF, BERKELEY, 65- Nat. Sci. Found. fel. Am. Astron. Soc. Radio astronomy. Address: Radio Astronomy Lab, 652 Campbell Hall, University of California, Berkeley, CA 94720.

DIETERICH, ROBERT A(RTHUR), b. Salinas, Calif, Mar. 22, 39; m. 67; c. 2. LABORATORY ANIMAL MEDICINE. B.S, Univ. Calif, Davis, 61, D.V.M, 63. Private practice, Calif, 63-67; VET. & ASSOC. ZOOPHYSIOLOGIST, INST. ARCTIC BIOL, UNIV. ALASKA, 67- Am. Vet. Med. Asn; Wildlife Disease Asn; Am. Asn. Lab. Animal Sci; Am. Soc. Lab. Animal Practitioners. Wild animal medicine; developing and characterizing wild rodents; various pathological lesions found in arctic mammals; animal facility management; data processing programs for animal colony records. Address: Institute of Arctic Biology, University of Alaska, College, AK 99701.

DIETERT, SCOTT EDWARD, b. Bartlesville, Okla, Oct. 12, 36; m. 61; c. 2. ANATOMY, PATHOLOGY. B.A, Rice, 58; M.D, Washington (St. Louis), 62. Intern med, med. sch, Minnesota, 62-63; fel. ophthal, sch. med, Washington (St. Louis), 63-64; lab. assoc, Nat. Cancer Inst, 64-66; ASST. PROF. ANAT, SCH. MED, UNIV. N.MEX, 66-, SR. RESIDENT PATH, 70- Nat. Inst. Child Health & Human Develop. res. grant, 67-69. U.S.P.H.S, 64-66, Sr. Asst. Surg. Am. Asn. Anat; Am. Soc. Cell Biol; jr. mem. Am. Soc. Clin. Path; jr. mem. Col. Am. Path. Functional cytology of the male reproductive system and mammalian kidney; cytology-histology. Address: Dept. of Anatomy, University of New Mexico, Albuquerque, NM 87106.

DIETHORN, WARD SAMUEL, b. Waukegan, Ill, Sept. 8, 27; m. 53; c. 2. NUCLEAR ENGINEERING, CHEMISTRY. B.S, Lake Forest Col, 50; M.S, Carnegie Inst. Tech, 53, Ph.D.(chem), 56. Asst. div. chief, radio-isotope & radiation div, Battelle Mem. Inst, 56-60; asst. prof. NUCLEAR ENG, PA. STATE UNIV, 60-61, assoc. prof, 61-64, PROF, 64- AAAS; Am. Chem. Soc. Am. Nuclear Soc. Radiation damage; nuclear reactor materials; radioisotope technology. Address: Dept. of Nuclear Engineering, 231 Sackett Bldg, Pennsylvania State University, University Park, PA 16802.

DIETLEIN, LAWRENCE FREDERICK, b. New Iberia, La, Feb. 9, 28; m. 61; c. 3. MICROSCOPIC ANATOMY, INTERNAL MEDICINE. B.S, La. State, 48; Atomic Energy Cmn. fel, Harvard, 48-51, M.A, 49, M.D, 55. Intern med, Harvard Med. Serv, Boston City Hosp, 55-56, asst. res, 56-57; res. fel. & instr, sch. med, Tulane, 57-59; from res. to chief med. res,U.S. Pub. Health Serv. Hosp, New York, 59-61, chief outpatient serv, New Orleans, La, 61-62; chief space med. br, MANNED SPACECRAFT CTR, NASA, 62-65, asst. div, chief, crew systs. div, 65-66, chief biomed. res. off, 66-68, ASST. DIR. RES, MED. RES. & OPERS DIRECTORATE, 68- Mem. cmt. hearing & bioacoust, Nat. Res. Coun, 62- NASA Commendation Award, 71. U.S.P.H.S, 57-, Med. Dir. Am. Med. Asn; Aerospace Med. Asn. Human physiology, particularly cardiovascular, as affected by the space environment; histology and histochemistry of endocrines and their target organs. Address: Medical Research & Operations Directorate, Mail Code: DA, NASA Manned Spacecraft Center, TX 77058.

DIETMEYER, DONALD L, b. Wausau, Wis, Nov. 20, 32; m. 57; c. 4. ELECTRICAL ENGINEERING. B.S, Wisconsin, 54, M.S, 55, Ph.D.(elec. eng), 59. Asst. prof. ELEC. ENG, UNIV. WIS, MADISON, 58-63, assoc. prof, 63-67, PROF, 67- Sr. assoc. engr, Int. Bus. Mach. Corp, 63-64, consult, 64-; summers, mem. tech. staff, Bell Tel. Labs, 59, 61. Sig.C, 57, Res, 57-, Capt. Inst. Elec. & Electronics Eng; Asn. Comput. Mach. Digital computer use and design; switching theory. Address: Dept. of Electrical Engineering, University of Wisconsin, Madison, WI 53706.

DIETRICH, FRANK S, b. San Francisco, Calif, Aug. 19, 38; m. 69. NUCLEAR PHYSICS. B.A, Haverford Col, 59; Ph.D.(physics), Calif. Inst. Technol, 64. Asst. prof. physics, Stanford Univ, 64-70; PHYSICIST, LAWRENCE LIVERMORE LAB, 70- Alfred P. Sloan res. fel, 65-67; visitor, Niels Bohr Inst, Copenhagen, Denmark, 67-68. Am. Phys. Soc. Nuclear structure physics; experimental studies of nuclear structure; neutron and gamma spectroscopy. Address: Lawrence Livermore Lab, P.O. Box 808, Livermore, CA 94550.

DIETRICH, HEINZ J(URGEN), b. Breslau, Ger, Feb. 10, 25; nat; m. 49; c. 4. ORGANIC CHEMISTRY. B.S, Heidelberg, 49, M.S, 51, Ph.D.(chem), 53. Res. chemist, polymers, Monsanto Chem. Co, 55-60; sr. res. assoc, Olin Mathieson Chem. Corp, Conn, 60-69; mem. staff, tech. ctr, Owens-Ill, Inc, Ohio, 69-71; DEPT. MGR, TEROSON-WERKE GMBH, W.R. GRACE & CO, 72- Am. Chem. Soc; Sci. Res. Soc. Am. High polymer chemistry; catalysis; metalorganic synthesis; liquid crystals; monomer synthesis; adhesives. Address: Teroson-Werke GmbH, P.O. Box 1720, 69 Heidelberg 1, West Germany.

DIETRICH, JOHN P, b. Monroe Co, Ohio, Nov. 30, 18; m. 43; c. 2. PHYSIOLOGY, ZOOLOGY. B.S, Ohio State, 49, M.S, 51; Ph.D.(physiol), Mich. State, 61. Asst. prof. dairy, Maryland, 51-56; asst, Mich. State, 56-61; asst. prof. BIOL, ROCHESTER INST. TECHNOL, 61-63, assoc. prof, 63-64, PROF. & HEAD DEPT, 70-, staff chmn, 64-70. Sig.C, U.S.A, 41-46. AAAS; Am. Soc. Med. Technol; Am. Dairy Sci. Asn; Nat. Sci. Teachers Asn. Effects of stimulatory and inhibitory drugs on the behaviour of animals; aggressive behavior of animals through training. Address: Dept. of Biology, Rochester Institute of Technology, Rochester, NY 14608.

DIETRICH, JOSEPH J(ACOB), b. Bismarck, N.Dak, Oct. 31, 32; m. 59. ORGANIC CHEMISTRY. Sr. res. chemist, Columbia-South. Corp, 57-59; res. chemist, Spencer Chem. Co, 60, sr. staff mem, 61-63; sr. res. engr, Diamond Alkali Co, 64-66, group leader, T.R. EVANS RES. CTR, 66-69, MGR. org. prod. & processes, 69-70, ORG. PROD. & POLYMERS, DIAMOND SHAMROCK CORP, 70- Am. Chem. Soc. Heterocyclic compounds; organometallic compounds; condensation polymers; high pressure polymerization; polymer development. Address: T.R. Evans Research Center, Diamond Shamrock Corp, P.O. Box 348, Painesville, OH 44077.

DIETRICH, J(OSEPH) R(OBERT), b. Miles City, Mont, Aug. 25, 14; m. 43; c. 3. PHYSICS. B.S, Col. of William & Mary, 35; M.S, Virginia, 37, Coffin fel, 37-39, Ph.D.(physics, 39. Head ignition res. sect, Lewis Lab, Nat. Adv. Cmt. Aeronaut, 43-45, rockets sect, 45-46; eng. anal. power pile div, Oak Ridge Nat. Lab, 47-48; naval reactor physics sect, Argonne Nat. Lab, 49-53, assoc. dir, reactor eng. div, 54-56; v.pres. & dir. physics dept, Gen. Nuclear Eng. Corp, 56-64; CHIEF SCIENTIST, NUCLEAR POWER DEPT, COMBUSTION ENG, INC, 64- Ed, Power Reactor Tech, 57-64. Fel. Am. Nuclear Soc. Design and development of nuclear reactors; reactor physics. Address: Nuclear Power Dept, Combustion Engineering, Inc, 1000 Prospect Hill Rd, Windsor, CT 06095.

DIETRICH, L(AROY) S(EIBERT), b. Gettysburg, Pa, Feb. 17, 26; m. 48; c. 3. BIOCHEMISTRY. B.S, Wagner Col, 48; M.S, Wisconsin, 50, Ph.D.(biochem) 52. Asst. BIOCHEM, Wisconsin, 48-52; Columbia, 52-53, res. assoc, 53-56, asst. prof, 56-58; assoc. prof, SCH. MED. UNIV. MIAMI, 58-65, PROF, 65- U.S. Pub. Health Serv. sr. res. fel, 58-62, career develop. award, 62-68. U.S.A, 43-46. AAAS; N.Y. Acad. Sci; Am. Soc. Cell Biol; Am. Soc. Biol. Chem; Am. Asn. Cancer Res; Am. Chem. Soc; Soc. Exp. Biol. & Med; Harvey Soc. Enzymology; intermediary metabolism related to vitamin B-complex metabolism and energy-producing reactions; mechanism of action of vitamin antagonists; cancer chemotherapy. Address: Dept. of Biochemistry, Medical Research Bldg, University of Miami, 1600 N.W. Tenth Ave, Miami, FL 33136.

DIETRICH, MARTIN W(ALTER), b. Chicago, Ill, Feb. 2, 35; m. 60; c. 3. PHYSICAL CHEMISTRY. B.A, Northwestern, 57; Ph.D.(chem), Washington (St. Louis), 62. Res. chemist, MONSANTO CO, 61-67, GROUP LEADER, 67- Am. Chem. Soc; Sci. Res. Soc. Am. Nuclear magnetic resonance spectroscopy; mass spectrometry; environmental science. Address: Monsanto Co, 1700 S. Second St, St. Louis, MO 63177.

DIETRICH, RICHARD V(INCENT), b. La Fargeville, N.Y, Feb. 7, 24; m. 46; c. 3. PETROLOGY. A.B, Colgate, 47; M.S, Yale, 50, Ph.D.(geol), 51. Geologist, State Geol. Surv, Iowa, 47; asst. prof. geol, Va. Polytech, 51-52, assoc. prof, 52-56, prof, 56-69, assoc. mineral technologist, 52-56, assoc. dean col. arts & sci, 66-69; PROF. GEOL. & DEAN ARTS & SCI, CENT. MICH. UNIV, 69- Fulbright vis. scholar, Mineral-Geol. Mus, Univ. Oslo, Norway, 58-59. U.S.A.F, 43-46. Fel. Geol. Soc. Am; Soc. Econ. Geol; fel. Mineral Soc. Am; Geol. Soc. Finland; Norweg. Geol. Soc. Petrology of northwestern Adirondacks; geology of Blue Ridge Mountains; petrology of Migmatites and banded gneises; dolomite-chert petrogenesis; feldspar geothermometry; Zr under high T-P conditions. Address: Anspach Hall, Central Michigan University, Mt. Pleasant, MI 48858.

DIETRICH, VERNE E(UGENE), b. Bremen, Ind, Feb. 11, 19; m. 40; c. 3. MATHEMATICS, PHYSICS. B.Sc, Purdue, 40, fel, 47-50, Ph.D.(math), 51; fel, Notre Dame, 46-47, M.Sc, 47. Actuarial clerk, Metrop. Life Ins. Co, 40-43; asst. automotive res, Studebaker Corp, 43-44; instr. & prof. math, Ala. Polytech. Inst, 50-53; PROF. PHYSICS & HEAD DEPT, N.CENT. COL. (ILL), 53- U.S.N.R, 44-46. Am. Math. Soc; Math. Asn. Am; Am. Asn. Physics Teachers. Non-desarguesian geometry. Address: Dept. of Physics, North Central College, Naperville, IL 60540.

DIETRICK, HARRY J(OSEPH), b. Cleveland, Ohio, Aug. 15, 22; m. 43; c. 2. PHYSICAL CHEMISTRY. B.S, Western Reserve, 48, M.S, 50, Ph.D.(chem), 51. Anal. chemist, Cosma Labs. Co, 40-43, 46-49; asst. phys. chem, Western Reserve, 49-51, res. assoc, 51-53, tech. man, B.F. GOODRICH CO, 53-55, sr. tech. man, 55-59, sect. leader, 59-63, MGR. aerospace & indust. prod. res, 63-64, TIRE RES, 65- C.W.S, 43-46, Chem.C.Res, 46-53, Capt. Fel. AAAS; Am. Chem. Soc; Acoust. Soc. Am; fel. Am. Inst. Chem. Electrode potentials; primary batteries; ultrasonics; physical chemistry of high polymers; space materials; tires. Address: 7354 Brookside Pkwy, Cleveland, OH 44130.

DIETSCHY, JOHN MAURICE, b. Alton, Ill, Sept. 23, 32; m. 59; c. 4. INTERNAL MEDICINE, GASTROENTEROLOGY. A.B, Wash. Univ, 54, M.D, 58. U.S. Pub. Health Serv. trainee gastroenterol, sch. med, Boston Univ, 61-63, asst. med, 62-63; fel. metab, SOUTHWEST. MED. SCH, UNIV. TEX, DALLAS, 63-65, asst. prof. internal med, 65-69, assoc. prof, 69-71, PROF. MED, 71- Markle Scholar acad. med, 66-71; consult. diabetes & metab. training grants comt, Nat. Insts. Health, 70. AAAS; Am. Fedn. Clin. Res; Am. Gastroenterol. Asn; Am. Soc. Clin. Invest; Gastroenterol. Res. Group. Mechanisms of control of cholesterol metabolism in liver and intestine; mechanisms of intestinal absorption of bile acids. Address: Dept. of Internal Medicine, University of Texas Southwestern Medical School at Dallas, 5323 Harry Hines Blvd, Dallas, TX 75235.

DIETTERT, R(EUBEN) A(RTHUR), b. North Judson, Ind, Sept. 22, 01; m. 26; c. 3. BOTANY. A.B, DePauw, 25; M.S, Mich. State, 27; Ph.D.(bot), Iowa, 37. Asst. BOT, Mich. State, 25-27; asst. prof, Idaho, 27-35; asst, Iowa, 36-37; instr, UNIV. MONT, 37-38, asst. prof, 38-41, assoc. prof, 41-48, PROF, 48-, chmn. dept, 56-66. Bot. Soc. Am; Nat. Sci. Teachers Asn. Mycology; phycology; morphology; anatomy. Address: Dept. of Botany, University of Montana, Missoula, MT 59801.

DIETZ, ALBERT (GEORGE HENRY), b. Lorain, Ohio, Mar. 7, 08; m. 36; c. 2. ENGINEERING. A.B, Miami (Ohio), 30; B.S, Mass. Inst. Tech, 32, Sc.D. (eng), 41. Designer & job foreman, Peter Dietz, Lorain, Ohio, 32-33; mill foreman, Nat. Tube Co, 33-34; asst, MASS. INST. TECHNOL, 34-36, instr, 36-41, asst. prof. struct. eng, dept. bldg. eng. & construct, 41-45, assoc. prof. struct. design, 45-51, prof. struct. eng, 51-53, PROF. BLDG. ENG. & CONSTRUCT, DEPT. CIVIL ENG. & DEPT. ARCHIT, 53- Sr. consult. engr, forest prod. lab, U.S. Dept. Agr, 42. Mem, Eng. Ed. Mission, Japan, 51; bldg. res. adv. bd, Nat. Acad. Sci-Nat. Res. Coun. Derham Int. award, Plastics Inst. Australia, 62. With Off. Sci. Res. & Develop, 44. New Eng. Award, Eng. Socs. New Eng, 69. Fel. AAAS; fel. Am. Soc. Civil Eng; Am. Soc. Mech. Eng; fel. & hon. mem. Am. Soc. Test. & Mat.(Templin Award); Am. Soc. Eng. Educ; Forest Prod. Res. Soc; Soc. Plastics Eng.(int. award plastics sci. & eng, 71); Soc. Plastics Indust; fel. Am. Acad. Arts & Sci. Distribution around timber connectors; spacing of timber connectors; fatigue of plywood and wood adhesives; properties of compregnated wood; high frequency curing of wood-resin combinations; deterioration of adhesives; fundamental mechanical properties of plastics; solar energy for house heating; industrialized building. Address: Room E21-213, Massachusetts Institute of Technology, Cambridge, MA 02139.

DIETZ, ALBERT, b. Mt. Lookout, W.Va, Feb. 10, 13; m. 39; c. 6. ORGANIC CHEMISTRY. A.B, Marshall Col, 35; assoc. fel, Ohio State, 45-46, fel, 46-48, Ph.D.(chem), 48. Teacher, high sch, 35-39; chemist anal, Electro Metall. Co, 40-42; res, Standard Ultramarine Co, 42-45, asst. gen. mgr, Standard Ultramarine & Color Co, 52-55; sr. develop. chemist, pigments div, Am. Cyanamid Co, 55-56, group leader process develop. titanium pigments, 56-57, dir. develop, 57-58, asst. dir. tech. serv, 58-61, dir, 61-62; sr. res. assoc, chem. div, PITTSBURGH PLATE GLASS CO, 62-64, SR. RES. SUPVR, 64-68, TiO_2 PROCESS RES, 68- Am. Chem. Soc. Pigments; chlorine and chlorine chemicals. Address: R.D. 2, Box 151A, Wadsworth, OH 44281.

DIETZ, ALBERT A(RNOLD CLARENCE), b. Port Huron, Mich, Aug. 15, 10; m. 37; c. 2. BIOCHEMISTRY. B.S, Toledo, 32, M.S, 33; Heidelberg, 34; Michigan, 35; fel, Purdue, 39-41, Ph.D.(org. chem), 41. Biochemist, Enza-Vita Labs, Ohio, 33-39; Off. Sci. Res. & Develop-Nat. Defense Res. Cmt. fel, Purdue, 41-42; mem. staff, U.S. Rubber Co, 42-43; BIOCHEMIST, Inst. Med. Res, Toledo Hosp, Ohio, 43-59; Armour & Co, 59-60; VET. ADMIN. HOSP, 60-; ASSOC. PROF. BIOCHEM. & BIOPHYS, STRITCH SCH. MED, LOYOLA UNIV. CHICAGO, 69- Asst. prof, Chicago Med. Sch, 62-69. Fel. AAAS; Am. Chem. Soc.(treas, 45); Am. Asn. Clin. Chem; N.Y. Acad. Sci. Electrophoresis; enzymology; proteins. Address: Research Service, Veterans Administration Hospital, Box 54, Hines, IL 60141.

DIETZ, ALBERT J, JR, b. Baltimore, Md, Mar. 9, 41; m. 64; c. 1. CLINICAL PHARMACOLOGY, BIOCHEMISTRY. B.S, Loyola Col.(Md), 63; fel, Maryland, 63-65, Ph.D.(pharmacol), 66. Res. assoc. pharmacol, sch. med, Maryland, 65-66; head metab. res. lab. & radiation safety officer, Hunting-ton Res. Center, Inc. Div, Becton Dickinson Co, 66-67; ASST. PROF. PHARMACOL, SCH. DENT, UNIV. MD, BALTIMORE COUNTY, 67- Grants, U.S. Pub. Health Serv, 68 & 69-70, Dr. Frederick F. Drew Fund, 68 & Nat. Inst. Ment. Health, 69-70. AAAS; Am. Chem. Soc; Int. Soc. Biochem. Pharmacol. Effects of drugs on brain amine metabolism; drug interactions and metabolism. Address: University of Maryland School of Dentistry, 618 W. Lombard St, Baltimore, MD 21201.

DIETZ, ALFRED, b. Aschaffenburg, Germany, Apr. 26, 30; U.S. citizen. ENTOMOLOGY, APICULTURE. B.S, Kansas, 61; M.S, Minnesota, 64, Ph.D. (entom), 66. Res. asst. apicult, Minnesota, 61-66; asst. prof. entom, Maryland, 66-68; prof. biol. sci, Clark Col, 68-69; ASSOC. PROF. ENTOM, UNIV. GA, 69- U.S.A, 55-58, S/Sgt. AAAS; Entom.Soc.Am; fel. Royal Entom. Soc. London; Bee Res. Asn. Nutritional requirements, caste determination; hatching mechanisms; developmental biology of honey bees; scanning electron microscopic studies of honey bee structures; bee products and the bee louse; mineral constituents of honey bees. Address: Dept. of Entomology, University of Georgia, Athens, GA 30601.

DIETZ, DAVID (HENRY), b. Cleveland, Ohio, Oct. 6, 97; m. 18; c. 3. GENERAL SCIENCE. A.B, Western Reserve, 19, Litt.D, 48; Case, 32; hon. LL.D, Bowling Green State Univ, 54. ED. STAFF, CLEVELAND PRESS, 15-; SCI. ED, SCRIPPS-HOWARD NEWSPAPERS, 21-; SCI. COMMENTATOR, NAT. BROADCASTING CO, 45- Lectr, West. Reserve Univ, 27-45. Consult, Surgeon Gen, U.S. Army, 44-47. Mem, cmt. publicity, div. med. sci, Nat. Res. Coun, 39-46. Pulitzer Prize in journalism, 37; Goodrich Award, 40; Westinghouse Distinguished Sci. Writers Award, 46; Lasker Award, Am. Pub. Health Asn, 54; Grady Award, Am. Chem. Soc, 61. U.S.A, 17-19. AAAS; Nat. Asn. Sci. Writers (pres); Am. Astron. Soc; fel. Am. Geog. Soc; fel. Royal Astron. Soc; French Astron. Soc. Scientific journalism; history of science; popularization of sciences and medicine; history of atomic energy. Address: Scripps-Howard Newspaper, Cleveland Press Bldg, Cleveland, OH 44114.

DIETZ, EARL D, b. Avon, Ohio, Jan. 22, 28; m. 50; c. 1. CERAMICS, MINERALOGY. B.S. & M.S, Ohio State, 59, Ph.D.(ceramic eng), 65. Proj. engr, CORP. RES. DEPT, OWENS-ILL. INC, 59-62, res. scientist, TECH. CTR, 62-66, dir. glass & ceramic res, 66-70, DIR. CORP. RES. LABS, 70- Mem. comt. A & exec. comt, Int. Comn. Glass. Intel.C, U.S.A, 52-54. Am. Ceramic Soc; Nat. Inst. Ceramic Eng; Sci. Res. Soc. Am; Brit. Soc. Glass Technol; Am. Geophys. Union. Glass; glass-ceramics; chemistry; physics; life sciences; polymers and polymer properties; glass and glass-ceramic properties; engineering including theoretical and applied; electronic materials nucleation and crystallization of inorganic oxides. Address: Technical Center, Owens-Illinois, Inc, P.O. Box 1035, Toledo, OH 43651.

DIETZ, FRANK T(OBIAS), b. Bridgeport, Conn, Aug. 13, 20; m. 45; c. 2. PHYSICS, ACOUSTICS. B.S, Bates Col, 42; M.A, Wesleyan, 46; Ph.D.(physics), Pa. State, 51. Asst. physics, Wesleyan, 42-44; mem. staff, radiation lab, Mass. Inst. Tech, 45; asst, Wesleyan, 45-47; instr. physics, Pa. State, 47-49, asst, 49-51; res. assoc, Woods Hole Oceanog. Inst, 51-54; asst.prof. marine physics & res. assoc. phys. oceanog, Narragansett Marine Lab, UNIV. R.I, 54-56, asst. prof. PHYSICS, 56-58, assoc. prof, 58-64, PROF, 64- Vis. assoc. prof, inst. marine sci, Miami (Fla), 63-64. U.S.N.R, 44-45. Am. Asn. Physics Teachers; Acoust. Soc. Am; Am. Geophys. Union. Underwater acoustics. Address: Dept. of Physics, University of Rhode Island, Kingston, RI 02881.

DIETZ, GEORGE ROBERT, b. Schofield Barracks, Hawaii, Jan. 15, 31; m. 52; c. 4. NUCLEAR SCIENCE. B.S, U.S. Mil. Acad, 52; M.S, Ga. Inst. Tech, 62. Proj. officer, Atomic Energy Cmn. food irradiation prog, U.S. Army Radiation Lab, Mass, 60-64; chief facilities eng. sect, div. isotopes develop, Atomic Energy Cmn, 64-69; asst. v.pres. opers, RADIATION MACH. CORP, 69-70, MGR. RADIATION SERV, NUCLEAR DIV, RADIATION INT, INC, 70- Qm.C, 52-64, Maj. Am. Nuclear Soc. Preservation of foods by ionizing energy and related processing facilities; all aspects of radioisotope applications to commercial radiation facilities and processing. Address: Fox Chase Rd, Chester, NJ 07930.

DIETZ, JAMES R(EGINALD), b. Lookout, W.Va, Nov. 15, 29; m. 58; c. 3. CHEMICAL ENGINEERING. B.S, West Virginia, 52, M.S, 54, Ph.D.(chem. eng), 56. Asst. metallurgist, Great Lakes Steel Corp, 56-58, res. engr, 58-59; NAT. STEEL CORP, 59-60, supvr. blast furnace & coke oven res, 60-61, assoc. dir. process metall, 62-63, asst. dir, res. & develop. dept, 63-69, DIR. RES, 69- Asn. Iron & Steel Eng; Am. Inst. Mining, Metall. & Petrol. Eng; Am. Soc. Metals. Coal carbonization; process metallurgy. Address: Research Center, National Steel Corp, Weirton, WV 26062.

DIETZ, JOHN W, b. Rainelle, W.Va, Dec. 17, 34; m. 62; c. 3. CHEMICAL & METALLURGICAL ENGINEERING. B.S, West Virginia 56; Standard Oil Found. fel, Cornell, 57-58, Procter & Gamble fel, 58-59, Ph.D.(chem. eng), 60. Res. chem. engr, EXP. STA, E.I. DU PONT DE NEMOURS & CO, INC, 60-68, RES. SUPVR, 68- Am. Chem. Soc. Colloidal chemistry; unsteady-state fluid flow. Address: E.I. du Pont de Nemours & Co, Inc, Bldg. 324, Experimental Station, Wilmington, DE 19898.

DIETZ, L(EONARD) A(LLAN), b. Manistee, Mich, Nov. 18, 22; m. 50; c. 3. PHYSICS. B.S, Michigan, 49, M.S, 50. Develop. engr. mass spectrometry, gen. eng. lab, GEN. ELEC. CO, 50-55, physicist, KNOLLS ATOMIC POWER LAB, 55-66, MGR. MASS SPECTROMETER RES. & DEVELOP, 66- U.S.A.A.F, 43-46, 1st Lt. Am. Phys. Soc; Am. Soc. Mass Spectros. Mass spectrometry of solids; ion optics; electron multipliers and pulse counting; ion microprobe. Address: 1124 Mohegan Rd, Schenectady, NY 12309.

DIETZ, PAUL LUTHER, JR, b. Pittsburgh, Pa, Mar. 31, 30. PHYSICAL CHEMISTRY. B.S, Pittsburgh, 51, Ph.D.(phys. chem), 55. Sr. res. chemist, Pittsburgh Plate Glass Co, 55-60, res. assoc, 60-62, supvr. phys. chem. res, 62-68, sr. supvr, 68-69, SR. RES. ASSOC, PPG INDUSTRIES, INC, 69- Am. Chem. Soc. Kinetics of nucleation and crystal growth; linear crystallization velocities of sodium acetate in supersaturated solutions. Address: Research Lab, PPG Industries Inc, P.O. Box 31, Barberton, OH 44203.

DIETZ, RICHARD D(ARBY), b. Rahway, N.J, Sept. 28, 37. SOLAR PHYSICS. B.S, Calif. Inst. Tech, 59; Ph.D.(astrogeophys), Colorado, 65. Asst. astronomer, Univ. Hawaii, 65-69; ASST. PROF. ASTRON, UNIV. NORTH. COLO, 69- AAAS; Am. Phys. Soc; Am. Astron. Soc; Am. Asn. Physics Teachers. Theoretical studies in radiative transfer and atomic physics and their application to problems of the solar atmosphere. Address: Dept. of Earth Sciences, University of Northern Colorado, Greeley, CO 80631.

DIETZ, ROBERT A(USTIN), b. N.Y.C, Feb. 14, 22; m. 60; c. 4. CYTOTAXONOMY, ECOLOGY. Ph.D.(bot, zool), Washington (St. Louis), 52. Instr. bot, Tennessee, 52-54; assoc. prof. biol, TROY STATE UNIV, 54-70, PROF. BOT, 70- Bache fel, Nat. Acad Sci, 57. U.S.A.A.F, 42-45, 2nd Lt. AAAS; N.Y. Acad. Sci. Variation in southeastern liliaceous genera; orchid genetics; historical ecology; coastal plain historical ecology; Central American orchid speciation. Address: Dept. of Biology, Troy State University, Troy, AL 36081.

DIETZ, ROBERT E, b. Joplin, Mo, May 8, 31; m. 56; c. 2. SOLID STATE PHYSICS. B.S, Tex. Tech. Col, 56; Abbott Labs. fel, Northwestern, 56, Ph.D.(phys. chem), 60. MEM. TECH. STAFF, CRYSTAL PHYSICS DEPT, BELL TEL. LABS, 59- U.S.A, 51-54, Sgt. Am. Phys. Soc. Effect of chemisorbed gases on the magnetic properties of small ferromagnetic particles; optical spectroscopy of crystals, including semiconductors and insulators; magneto-optic effects; solid state lasers; spectroscopic studies of magnetically ordered crystals. Address: Crystal Physics Dept, Bell Telephone Labs, Murray Hill, NJ 07974.

DIETZ, ROBERT SINCLAIR, b. Westfield, N.J, Sept. 14, 14; m. 55; c. 2. GEOLOGY, OCEANOGRAPHY. B.S, Illinois, 37, M.S, 39, Ph.D.(geol), 41. Asst, Ill. State Geol. Surv, 35-37; Scripps Inst, California, 37-39; OCEANOGR, Navy Electronics Lab, 46-52, 54-58; U.S. Coast & Geod. Surv, 58-65; inst. oceanog, Environ. Sci. Serv. Admin, Md, 65-67, FLA, 67-70, ATLANTIC OCEANOG. & METEOROL. LABS, NAT. OCEANIC & ATMOSPHERIC ADMIN, 70- Fulbright scholar, Tokyo, 52-53; lectr, Scripps Inst, California. Mem. London Br, Off. Naval Res, 54-58. U.S.A.A.F, 41-46, Lt. Col. Geol. Soc. Am;

Am. Geophys. Union (Bucher Medal, 71); Meteoritical Soc; Geol. Soc. London, Mineral. Soc. Am; Geochem. Soc. Marine geology and oceanography; underwater sound; sediments and structure of sea floor; submarine processes; nature of continental shelves and slopes; bathyscaph and deep submersibles; selenography and meteoritics; astroblemes; plate tectonics; sea floor spreading; continental drift. Address: Atlantic Oceanographic & Meteorological Labs, National Oceanic & Atmospheric Administration, 901 S. Miami Ave, Miami, FL 33130.

DIETZ, R(UDOLPH) J(OHN), b. New Brunswick, N.J, Feb. 26, 33; m. 55. INORGANIC CHEMISTRY. B.S, Mass. Inst. Tech, 54, Nat. Sci. Found. fel, 54-55, Visking fel, 56-57, Ph.D.(chem), 58. Chemist, New Brunswick Lab, U.S. Atomic Energy Cmn, 53, Savannah River Proj, 55; STAFF MEM, Mass. Inst. Tech, 54-58; LOS ALAMOS SCI. LAB, UNIV. CALIF, 58- Nuclear fuel processing; liquid-liquid extraction; reactor and high temperature technology; physical properties of non-metallic materials; nuclear engineering; radioactive waste disposal. Address: 1261 Second St, Los Alamos, NM 87544.

DIETZ, SHERL M, b. Ames, Iowa, Nov. 29, 27; m. 51; c. 2. PLANT PATHOLOGY. B.S, Oregon State, 50; Ph.D.(plant path), Washington State, 63. Agr. res. aide plant path, U.S. DEPT. AGR, 54-57, res. plant pathologist, 57-66, COORDINATOR PLANT INTROD, 66- Am. Phytopath. Soc; Soc. Econ. Bot. Stem smut of grasses; screening plants for disease resistance; coordination of use of introduced plant germ plasm in twelve western states. Address: Regional Plant Introduction Station, Room 59, Johnson Hall, Washington State University, Pullman, WA 99163.

DIETZ, THOMAS H(OWARD), b. Tacoma, Wash, Jan. 22, 40; m. 62; c. 1. PHYSIOLOGY. B.S, Wash. State Univ, 63, M.S, 65; Nat. Insts. Health fel. & Ph.D.(physiol), Ore. State Univ, 69. Instr. zool, Ore. State Univ, 68-69; Nat. Insts. Health fel. biophys, Cardiovascular Res. Inst, Univ. Calif, San Francisco, 69-71; ASST. PROF. ZOOL. & PHYSIOL, LA. STATE UNIV, BATON ROUGE, 71- AAAS; Am. Soc. Zool; Soc. Study Amphibians & Reptiles. Osmotic and ionic regulation in animals; mechanism of ion transport; control of ion and water balance. Address: Dept. of Zoology & Physiology, Louisiana State University at Baton Rouge, Baton Rouge, LA 70803.

DIETZ, THOMAS J(ULIUS), b. Oswego, N.Y, Oct. 4, 08; m. 35; c. 1. PHYSICS. B.S, Union (N.Y), 32, M.S, 34. Special asst. physics, Union (N.Y), 34-35; physicist, res. lab, Gen. Elec. Co, 35-36; res. biophysicist, biochem. res. found, Franklin Inst, 36-40, asst. dir, 40-42; in charge phys. testing subsect, east. regional res. lab, Bur. Agr. & Indust. Chem, U.S. Dept. Agr, 42-47, sect. head, 47-50; in charge phys. testing, Del. Res. & Develop. Corp, 50-52, tech. dir, 52-65; DIR. RES, J.E. RHOADS & SONS, INC, 65- Am. Chem. Soc. Rubber and plastics technology; coatings; adhesives. Address: J.E. Rhoads & Sons, Inc, 2100 W. Eleventh St, Wilmington, DE 19899.

DIETZLER, A(NDREW) J(OSEPH), b. Wis, Feb. 13, 05; m. 30; c. 6. ORGANIC CHEMISTRY. B.S, Wisconsin, 28; M.S, Purdue, 30. Chemist org. chem. res, Dow Chem. Co, 30-46, group leader, 46-66, res. scientist, 66-70; RETIRED. Am. Chem. Soc; Sci. Res. Soc. Am. Phenods; phenol derivatives; catalysis. Address: 306 St. Nicholas, Midland, MI 48640.

DIETZMAN, BURTON D, b. La Farge, Wis, Sept. 22, 07; m. 35; c. 3. ANALYTICAL CHEMISTRY. B.S, Greenville Col, 34; M.A, Indiana, 40. Instr. sci, Wessington Springs Col, 34-41; assoc. prof. chem, Greenville Col, 41-43; chemist in charge anal. labs, Permutet Co, N.Y, 43-46; assoc. prof. CHEM, SEATTLE PAC. COL, 46-49, PROF, 49- Nat. Sci. Found. grant, summer inst, Oregon State, 59. Am. Chem. Soc. Effects of solutions on the potential of glass electrodes; water purification. Address: Dept. of Chemistry, Seattle Pacific College, Seattle, WA 98119.

DiFAZIO, LOUIS T, b. Brooklyn, N.Y, Jan. 22, 38; m. 61; c. 2. PHARMACEUTICAL CHEMISTRY, PHARMACY. B.S, Rutgers Univ, 59; Ph.D.(pharmaceut. chem), Univ. R.I, 64. Res. scientist, Colgate-Palmolive Co, 64-65; E.R. SQUIBB & SONS, INC, 66-67, SECT. HEAD, gen. pharm, 67-71, PREFORMULATION STUDIES, 71- Am. Chem. Soc; Am. Pharmaceut. Asn; Soc. Cosmetic Chem. Synthesis of potential psychotherapeutic agents; factors effecting bioavailability of drugs; physical-chemical studies of pharmaceutical agents and products; preservation of cosmetical and pharmaceutical products. Address: E.R. Squibb & Sons, Inc, 5 Georges Rd, New Brunswick, NJ 08903.

DI FERRANTE, NICOLA MARIO, b. Fontana Liri, Italy, Jan. 26, 25; U.S. citizen; m. 56; c. 4. MEDICINE, BIOCHEMISTRY. M.D, Rome, 42; Fulbright traveling fel, 52; univ. fel, Rochester, 52-53, Arthritis & Rheumatism Found. fel, 57-61, Ph.D.(biochem), 61. Asst. med, Inst. Med. Path, Rome, 50-52; biochem, Rockefeller Inst. & Hosp, 53-56; assoc. scientist, Brookhaven Nat. Lab, 56-57; asst. prof. physiol, Cincinnati, 61-63, assoc. prof, 63-64; assoc. biochem, Retina Found, 64-65; ASSOC. PROF. BIOCHEM. DEPTS. BIOCHEM. & MED. & DIV. ORTHOP. SURG, TEX. MED. CTR, BAYLOR COL. MED, 65- Asst, United Hosps, Rome, Italy, 50-51; res. assoc, 1st Superior Sanitá, Italy, 51-52; Helen Hay Whitney Found. res. fel, 60-63; sci. collab, Brookhaven Nat. Lab, N.Y, 63-; estab. investr, Am. Heart Asn, 63-; consult, Vet. Admin. Hosp, Houston, Tex, 71- Connective tissue, glycoproteins and glycosaminoglycans; metabolism, immunochemistry of components of ground substance; labeling of glycosaminoglycans with isotopes. Address: Dept. of Biochemistry, Texas Medical Center, Baylor College of Medicine, Houston, TX 77025.

DIFFORD, WINTHROP CECIL, b. East Liverpool, Ohio, Nov. 12, 21; m. 44; c. 3. GEOLOGY. B.S, Mt. Union Col, 43; fel. & M.S, West Virginia, 47; fel. & Ph.D.(geol), Syracuse, 54. Asst. geol, Ohio State, 42-43; instr, West Virginia, 47-48; asst. area geologist, U.S. Bur. Reclamation, Nebr, 48-49, area geologist, Colo, 50-51; from asst. prof. geol. to assoc. prof, Dickinson Col, 54-58, prof, 61-66; assoc. prof. geol, asst. dean & dir. grad. studies, col. arts & sci, Univ. Bridgeport, 66-68; PROF. GEOG, DEAN GRAD. COL. & DIR. SUMMER SESSION, WIS. STATE UNIV, STEVENS POINT, 68- Am. Geol. Inst. vis. scientist, 63-65; intern. acad. admin, Ellis L. Phillips Found, 65-66; summer, Link Found. grant. & dir, inst. oceanology, 64. Consult, Soc. Visual Ed. U.S.N.R, 43-46, 51-52, Comdr. (Ret). Geol. Soc. Am; Marine Tech. Soc. Oceanography; engineering geology. Address: Room 240 Main, Wisconsin State University, Stevens Point, WI 54481.

DI FRANCO, ROLAND B, b. N.Y.C, July 26, 36; m. 65; c. 2. MATHEMATICS, ALGEBRA. B.S, Fordham Univ, 58; M.S, Rutgers Univ, 60; Ph.D.(math), Ind. Univ, 65. ASST. PROF. MATH, Fordham Univ, 65-66; SWARTHMORE COL, 66- Nat. Sci. Found. sci. faculty fel, Univ. Calif, Berkeley, 69-70; Danforth assoc, 70- Am. Math. Soc; Math. Asn. Am; Asn. Symbolic Logic. Extending a norm residue symbol to inseparable extensions; logic. Address: Dept. of Mathematics, Swarthmore College, Swarthmore, PA 19081.

DI GANGI, FRANK E(DWARD), b. West Rutland, Vt, Sept. 29, 17; m. 46; c. 2. CHEMISTRY. B.Sc, Rutgers, 40; M.Sc, Western Reserve, 42; Ph.D.(Pharmaceut. chem), Minnesota, 48. Ass. prof. PHARMACEUT. CHEM, UNIV. MINN, MINNEAPOLIS, 48-51, assoc. prof, 51-57, PROF, 57-, ASST. DEAN, 69- Lederle fel. U.S.N, 42-45. Fel. Am. Pharmaceut. Asn; fel. Am. Chem. Soc. Synthesis of organic medicinals and phytochemistry. Address: College of Pharmacy, University of Minnesota, Minneapolis, MN 55455.

DIGBY, JAMES F(OSTER), SYSTEMS ANALYSIS, INTERNATIONAL AFFAIRS. B.S, La. Polytech, 41; Hicks fel. & M.A, Stanford, 42. Res. engr, Watson Labs, U.S. Air Force, 45-49; Rand Corp, 49, head opers. dept, 55-59, spec. asst. to head eng. div, 59-60; assoc. mem. res. coun, 61-62, prog. mgr, int. security affairs, 63-65; asst. to pres, NATO Force Planning, 65-66; PROG. MGR. INT. STUDIES, NATO, 66- Consult. & comt. mem, Presidents Sci. Adv. Comt; Federal Aviation Agency; Dept. Defense; mem, Presidents task force on air traffic control, 61. Consult. & comt. mem, Dept. Defense. U.S.A, 42-45, Radar Officer. Inst. Elec. & Electronics Eng; Oper. Res. Soc. Am. Evaluation of defense weapon systems; military strategy. Address: 20773 Big Rock Dr, Malibu, CA 90265.

DIGBY, PETER SAKI BASSETT, b. London, Eng, Jan. 15, 21; m. 47; c. 4. MARINE BIOLOGY, PHYSIOLOGY. B.A, Cambridge, 43, M.A, 47; D.Sc, London, 67. Res. asst. agr. entom, agr. adv. serv, Cambridge, 42-46; res. marine biol, Marine Lab, Plymouth & Exped. to Spitsbergen, 46-48; entom, Oxford, 48-50, 51-52; in field res. grant, Marine Plankton Exped. to Greenland, 50-51; lectr. biol, St. Thomas's Hosp. Med. Sch, 52-64, sr. lectr, 64-67; PROF. ZOOL, McGILL UNIV, 67- Res. grants, Develop. Comn, 46-48; Agr. Res. Coun, 48-50, Browne Fund, 50-51, Percy Sladen Mem. Fund, 56. AAAS; Marine Biol. Asn. U.K; Royal Geog. Soc; Royal Entom. Soc. London; Royal Meteorol. Soc; Brit. Ecol. Soc; Soc. Exp. Biol. & Med; Brit. Physiol. Soc; Zool. Soc. London; Glaciol. Soc; Challenger Soc; Arctic Inst. N.Am; Am. Physiol. Soc; Can. Physiol. Soc; Biophys. Soc. Marine biology, ecology and physiology; plankton; geographical aspects of biology, especially in arctic; physiological mechanisms, especially pressure sensitivity; calcification in shell, bone and teeth and its apparent electrochemical basis; organic semiconductors; physiology and ecology of insects and marine organisms. Address: Dept. of Biology, McGill University, Montreal, Que, Can.

DI GEORGE, ANGELO M(ARIO), b. Phila, Pa, Apr. 15, 21; m. 51; c. 3. ENDOCRINOLOGY, PEDIATRICS. A.B, Temple Univ, M.D, 46, M.S, 52. Intern, univ. hosp, Temple Univ, 47; pediat. resident, univ. hosp, Temple Univ. & St. Christopher's Hosp. for Children, 49-52; instr. PEDIAT, SCH. MED, TEMPLE UNIV, 52-57, assoc, 57-58, asst. prof, 58-61, assoc. prof, 61-67, PROF, 67-; CHIEF ENDOCRINE & METAB. SERV, ST. CHRISTOPHER'S HOSP. FOR CHILDREN, 61-, DIR. CLIN. RES. CTR, 63-, asst. attend. pediatrician & endocrinologist, 52-56, assoc. attend. pediatrician & endocrinologist, 56-61. Nat. Inst. Arthritis & Metab. Diseases fel, Jefferson Med. Col, 52-54; asst. chief pediat, Phila. Gen. Hosp, 56-66; consult. & lectr, U.S. Naval Hosp, Phila, 67- Dipl, Am. Bd. Pediat. U.S.A, 47-49, Capt. AAAS; Am. Pediat. Soc; Am. Soc. Human Genetics; Soc. Pediat. Res; Am. Acad. Pediat; Endocrine Soc; Am. Diabetes Asn; Am. Fedn. Clin. Res; N.Y. Acad. Sci; French Soc. Pediat. Endocrinologic, metabolic and genetic disorders of growth and development. Address: St. Christopher's Hospital for Children, 2600 N. Lawrence St, Philadelphia, PA 19133.

DIGGINS, MAUREEN R(ITA), b. Omaha, Nebr, July 17, 42. ANIMAL ECOLOGY & BEHAVIOR. B.A, Mt. Marty Col, 66; M.S, Northwest. Univ, 68, Arthur J. Schmitt Found. fels, 68-71, Ph.D.(biol. sci), 71. Instr, St. Agnes Sch, 62-65; BIOL, MT. MARTY COL, 67-71, ASST. PROF, 71- AAAS; Ecol. Soc. Am. Biological rhythms research—activity rhythms of crayfish and their relations to geomagnetic activity; eutrophication of prairie lakes; benthic life of South Dakota rivers; pollution from cattle feedlot runoff into rivers and streams of southeastern South Dakota, special emphasis on fecal and total coliforms. Address: Dept. of Biology, Mt. Marty College, Yankton, SD 57078.

DIGGS, DONALD R(OGER), b. Richmond, Va, June 28, 24; m. 47; c. 4. MECHANICAL ENGINEERING. B.S, Northwestern, 44, M.S, 47, Ph.D. (mech. eng), 53. Res. engr, Nat. Adv. Cmt. Aeronaut, 44-46; instr. mech. eng, Northwestern, 47-50; mech. engr, combustion res. group, petrol. lab, E.I. DU PONT DE NEMOURS & CO, INC, 50-53, supvr, engine test group, 53-56, tech. asst, 56-58, supvr, combustion res. group, 58-59, head combustion div, 59-61, tech. asst, PETROL. CHEM. DIV, 61-64, asst. tech. mgr, 64-70, TECH. DIR, 70- Soc. Automotive Eng. Internal combustion engines; combustion; fuel and lubricant additives. Address: Petroleum Chemicals Division, E.I. du Pont de Nemours & Co, Inc, Wilmington, DE 19898.

DIGGS, LEMUEL WHITLEY, b. Hampton, Va, Jan. 8, 00; m. 30; c. 4. MEDICINE. A.B, Randolph-Macon Col, 21, A.M, 22; M.D, Hopkins, 26. Intern & asst. res. med, Rochester & Strong Mem. Hosp, 26-28, instr, med, 28-29; asst. prof. path, col. med, Tennessee, 29-36, med, 36-38, assoc. prof, 38-45; clin. pathologist, Cleveland Clin. Found, 45-47; prof. MED, COL. MED, UNIV. TENN, 47-63, Goodman prof, 63-69, EMER. PROF, 69-, chmn. dept, 64-69. Markle fel, Guatemala, 43; clin. pathologist, John Gaston Hosp, Memphis, 47-; consult, Tenn. Valley Authority, 42-45; Armed Forces Inst. Path, 51- Fel. Am. Med. Asn; Am. Soc. Clin. Path.(Ward Burdick award, 64); Int. Soc. Hematol. Sickle cell anemia; hemorrhagic diseases; blood cell morphology. Address: 7340 Raleigh-La Grange Rd, Cordova, TN 38018.

DIGHE, SHRIKANT VISHWANATH, b. Murud, India, Nov. 29, 33; m. 64; c. 2. ORGANIC CHEMISTRY. B.Sc, Bombay, 55, M.Sc, 57; Petroleum Res. Fund fel, Cincinnati, 59-62, Laws fel, 64-65, Ph.D.(org. chem), 65. Res. asst. med. drugs, Haffkine Inst, India, 57-58; RES. CHEMIST, W.R. GRACE & CO, 65- AAAS; Am. Chem. Soc; N.Y. Acad Sci. Organometallic chemistry; chemistry of metal carbonyls, sulfur compounds and polymer synthesis; coordination chemistry. Address: W.R. Grace & Co, Washington Research Center, Clarksville, MD 21029.

DI GIACOMO, ARMAND, b. N.Y, Jan. 26, 29; m. 54; c. 4. PHYSICAL CHEMISTRY. B.S, Long Island, 50; M.A, Princeton, 52, Ph.D.(chem), 53. SR. RES. CHEMIST, E.I. DU PONT DE NEMOURS & CO. INC, 53- Dielectric studies; polymer chemistry; elastomers; coatings. Address: 1140 Webster Farm, Wilmington, DE 19803.

DI GIORGIO, JOHN, b. Somerville, Mass, Jan. 14, 25; m. 57; c. 3. CLINICAL CHEMISTRY. B.S, Northeast. Univ, 50; M.A, Univ. Buffalo, 56, Ph.D.(biochem), 58. Anal. chemist, Mass. Inst. Technol, 48-50; sr. technician nutrit. biochem, sch. pub. health, Harvard, 51-53; teaching asst. biochem, sch. med, Univ. Buffalo, 53-57; asst. biochemist, Wash. State Inst. Technol, 57-58; res. asst. biochem, Children's Cancer Res. Found, Boston, Mass, 58-59; res. assoc. nutrit. biochem, sch. pub. health, Harvard, 59-62; biochem, sch. med, Boston Univ, 62-64; sr. res. fel. clin. chem, sch. med, Univ. Wash, 64-66; asst. chief prod. sect, spec. prod. div, Bio-Sci. Labs, 66; dept. head, tech. serv. & develop. labs, Dow Chem. Co, Ind, 66-69; SR. RES. SCIENTIST, BIO-SCI LABS, 69- U.S.A, 43-46. Am. Asn. Clin. Chem; Am. Chem. Soc; Am. Inst. Chem; Asn. Clin. Sci; Can. Soc. Clin. Chem. Nutritional biochemistry. Address: Dept. of Research, Bio-Science Labs, 7600 Tyrone Ave, Van Nuys, CA 91405.

DiGIORGIO, JOSEPH B(RUN), b. San Francisco, Calif. Aug. 4, 32; m. 57; c. 6. PHYSICAL ORGANIC CHEMISTRY. B.E, Hopkins, 54, Chem. Found. fel, 55, Am. Cyanamid fel, 56, Du Pont fel. M.A, 57, Union Carbide fel, 58, Nat. Sci. Found. summer fel, 59, Ph.D, 60. Res. assoc. org. chem, Hopkins, 59, Nat. Insts. Health fel, 60-61; Nat. Insts. Health fel, vis. scientist & Nat. Res. Coun. Can. fel, Nat. Res. Coun. Can, Ottawa, 61-63; res. assoc, Johns Hopkins Univ, 63-64; asst. prof. CHEM, SACRAMENTO STATE COL, 64-67, assoc. prof, 67-70, PROF, 70- AAAS; Am. Chem. Soc; Brit. Chem. Soc. Steroids and natural products; relationship between reactivity and geometry; conformational analysis; infrared and Raman spectroscopy of complex organic compounds. Address: Dept. of Chemistry, Sacramento State College, 6000 J St, Sacramento, Calif. 95819.

DiGIOVANNA, CHARLES V, b. Brooklyn, N.Y, Aug. 11, 39; m. 66. ORGANIC CHEMISTRY. B.S, St. John's (N.Y), 61; Ph.D.(org. chem), Notre Dame, 65. Fel. org. chem, Notre Dame, 64-65; SR. CHEMIST, REILLY TAR & CHEM. CO, 65- Am. Chem. Soc. Synthetic chemistry of amino and other nitrogen containing compounds, particularly pyridines and derivatives; fixed bed catalyzed reactions including oxidation, hydrogenation, alkylation, hydration; physiological activity of new compounds. Address: Reilly Tar & Chemical Co, 11 S. Meridian St, Merchants Bank Bldg, Indianapolis, IN 46204.

DI GIROLAMO, RUDOLPH GERARD, b. Brooklyn, N.Y, Jan. 26, 34; m. 64; c. 1. MARINE BIOLOGY, MICROBIOLOGY. B.S, Mt. St. Mary's Col.(Md), 55; Pfizer res. fel, St. John's Univ.(N.Y), 55-56; Univ. Rome, 57-64; U.S. Pub. Health Serv. fel, Univ. Wash, 65-69, Ph.D, 69. Res. assoc. microbiol, St. John's Univ.(N.Y), 55-56; microbiol. & virol, Univ. Wash, 64-69, res. assoc. prof. sanit. eng, 69; ASST. PROF. BIOL. & CHMN. DEPT, COL. NOTRE DAME (CALIF), 70- Chmn. comt. environ. sci, Col. Notre Dame (Calif), 70- AAAS; Am. Soc. Microbiol; Nat. Shellfisheries Asn. Uptake and survival of viruses in shellfish and Crustacea; survival of gastroenteric bacteria in shellfish; microbial quality of the aquatic environment. Address: Dept. of Biology, College of Notre Dame, Belmont, CA 94002.

DIGMAN, ROBERT V, b. Wendel, W.Va, Jan. 9, 30; m. 53; c. 4. ORGANIC CHEMISTRY. B.S, Alderson-Broaddus Col, 51; M.S, Maine, 53; Nat. Sci. Found. fel, Pa. State, 62-63, Ph.D.(chem), 63. Instr. chem, Alderson-Broaddus Col, 54-56; res. asst. petrol. chem, Pa. State, 56-59; asst. prof. chem, Marshall, 59-64, assoc. prof, 64-65; PROF. CHARLES McCLUNG SWITZER CHAIR CHEM. & CHMN. DEPT. NATURAL SCI, ALDERSON-BROADDUS COL, 65- Supvr, Petrol. Res. Fund summer grant, 64. Am. Chem. Soc. Vapor-phase oxidation of hydrocarbons; reactions of epoxides. Address: Division of Natural Sciences, Alderson-Broaddus College, Philippi, WV 26417.

DIGNAM, M(ICHAEL) J(OHN), b. Toronto, Ont, May 25, 31; m. 53; c. 5. PHYSICAL CHEMISTRY. B.A, Toronto, 53, Nat. Res. Coun. Can. stud, 54-55, fel, 55-56, Ph.D.(phys. chem), 56. Demonstr. chem, Toronto, 53-54; res. chemist, Aluminium Labs, Ltd, 56-58; lectr. CHEM, UNIV. TORONTO, 58-59, asst. prof, 59-62, assoc. prof, 62-66, PROF, 66- Electrochem. Soc; Faraday Soc; Chem. Inst. Can. Surface chemistry; anodic oxidation and tarnishing reactions; ellipsometric and conventional spectroscopy of adsorbed species. Address: Dept. of Chemistry, University of Toronto, Toronto, Ont, Can.

DIGNAM, WILLIAM J(OSEPH), b. Manchester, N.H, Aug. 11, 20; m. 47; c. 4. OBSTETRICS, GYNECOLOGY. A.B, Dartmouth Col, 41; M.D, Harvard, 43. Intern, Boston City Hosp, 44; resident obstet. & gynecol, Kansas, 46-48; endocrinol, Duke, 48; instr, OBSTET. & GYNEC, Univ. Calif, San Francisco, 51-53; asst. prof, SCH. MED, UNIV. CALIF, LOS ANGELES, 53-59, assoc. prof, 59-66, PROF, CTR. HEALTH SCI, 66- U.S.N, 45-46, Lt. Am. Med. Asn; Am. Fedn. Clin. Res; Endocrine Soc; Am. Gynec. Soc. Gynecologic endocrinology. Address: School of Medicine, University of California Center for Health Sciences, Los Angeles, CA 90024.

DI GREGORIO, GUERINO JOHN, b. Phila, Pa, May 11, 40; m. 63. PHARMACOLOGY. B.S, Pa. State, 62; Ph.D.(pharmacol), Hahnemann Med. Col, 66. Instr. PHARMACOL, HAHNEMANN MED. COL, 66-68, asst. prof, 68-70, ASSOC. PROF, 70- Am. Chem. Soc. Isolation of biologically active compounds from plants; structure activity relationships of autonomic nervous system; synthesis of quinoline compounds; drug analysis and toxicology. Address: Dept. of Pharmacology, Hahnemann Medical College, 235 N. 15th St, Philadelphia, PA 19102.

Di ILIO, CHARLES CARMEN, b. Phila, Pa, May 10, 12; m. 37; c. 3. MECHANICAL ENGINEERING. B.S, Pa. State, 34, M.S, 35. Machine designer, Yale & Towne Mfg. Co, 35-37; instr. MECH. ENG, Rensselaer Polytech, 37-41; asst. prof. to PROF, PA. STATE UNIV, 41-, MEM. GRAD. SCH. FACULTY, 49-, excellence in teaching citation, 60. Exam. mech. eng, Pa. State Registr. Bd. Prof. Engrs, 58-62; consult, Consumers Res. Inc, 50-56; Curtis Wright Corp; Fairchild Stratos Corp. Am. Soc. Mech. Eng; Am. Soc. Eng. Educ. Heat power; thermodynamics; refrigeration; air conditioning; internal combustion engines; rocket motors; fluid mechanics; heat transfer. Address: Dept. of Mechanical Engineering, 209 Mechanical Engineering Bldg, Pennsylvania State University, University Park, PA 16802.

DIKE, PAUL A(LEXANDER), b. Mt. Vernon, Iowa, Nov. 26, 12; m. 45; c. 3. GEOLOGY. B.A, Johns Hopkins Univ, 37, univ. fel, 37-38; M.A, Bryn Mawr Col, 50; Rutgers Univ, 54-65. Instr. geol, Univ. Pa, 46-53; master, parochial sch, Pa, 53-54; foreman phys. testing lab, E.L. Conwell & Co, Pa, 54-55; asst. prof. geol. & dir. dept, Temple Univ, 55-62; asst. prof. sci, GLASSBORO STATE COL, 62-70, ASSOC. PROF. GEOL, 70-, CHMN. DEPT. PHYS. SCI, 71- Lectr, Drexel Inst. Technol, 48-62; tutor, Bryn Mawr Col, 50-55; consult, E.L. Conwell & Co, 55-; Ambric Testing & Eng. Assocs, Inc, 56-; Rowle & Henderson, 57-; Asphalt Technol, 62-; lectr, Gloucester County Col, 68-70. U.S.N.R, 41-45, Lt. Field studies with magnetometer, earth resistivity and seismology locating mineral deposits; geology of Central Delaware County, Pennsylvania; Coastal Plains materials. Address: Dept. of Physical Science, Glassboro State College, Glassboro, NJ 08028.

DIKE, SHELDON H(OLLAND), b. Atlantic City, N.J, Oct. 23, 16; div; c. 5. ELECTRICAL ENGINEERING, FINANCE. B.S, New Mexico, 41, 42-43; Ph.D.(elec. eng), Hopkins, 51. Asst. physicist, dept. terrestrial magnetism, Carnegie Institution, Wash, D.C, 41-42; radio engr, New Mexico, 42-43; res. assoc. electronics, Michigan, 43-44; scientist, California, Los Alamos, N.Mex, 44-45; res. engr, Glenn L. Martin Co, Baltimore, 46-47; res. physicist, Hopkins, 47-51; supvr. systs. anal. div, Sandia Corp, 51-56; pres, Dikewood Corp, 56-69, chmn. bd, 69-70; PRES, EDDE SECURITIES CORP, 67- Consult, Nat. Defense Res. Comt, Naval Ord. Develop. award, 45. Fel. Inst. Elec. & Electronics Eng; fel. Am. Phys. Soc. Systems analysis; operations research; computerized analysis of the stock market and investment strategies. Address: Edde Securities Corp, 1420 Carlisle Blvd. N.E, Albuquerque, NM 87110.

Di LAVORE, PHILIP, III, b. Lawrence, Mass, Apr. 24, 31; m. 53; c. 4. PHYSICS. A.B, Dakota Wesleyan, 54; M.S, Michigan, 61, Ph.D.(physics), 67. Teacher, high schs, S.Dak, 53-54 & Mich, 56-58; lectr. physics, Univ. Mich, 62 & 64; asst. prof, Univ. Md, 65-71, assoc. chmn. dept. physics & astron, 69-71; ASSOC. PROF. PHYSICS, IND. STATE UNIV, 71- Staff physicist, Comn. Col. Physics, 67-69. U.S.A, 54-56, Sgt. Am. Asn. Physics Teachers; Am. Phys. Soc. Level-crossing spectroscopy; optical pumping; quantum electronics; nuclear physics. Address: Dept. of Physics, Indiana State University, Terre Haute, IN 47809.

DILCHER, DAVID L, b. Cedar Falls, Iowa, July 10, 36; m. 61. BOTANY, GEOLOGY. B.S, Minnesota, 58, M.S, 60; Illinois, 60-62; Culman fel, Yale, 63-64, Ph.D.(biol), 64. Instr. biol, Yale, 65-67; asst. prof. BOT, IND. UNIV, BLOOMINGTON, 67-70, ASSOC. PROF, 70- Sigma Xi grants-in-aid, 61, 62 & 66; Nat. Sci. Found. fel, 64-65, res. grants, 66-68, 69, 70-71 & 71-73; mem, Int. Asn. Paleobot, Int. Union Biol. Sci. AAAS; Bot. Soc. Am; Am. Inst. Biol. Sci. Tertiary floras of southeastern United States; study of assemblage of fossil plants found in Eocene deposits in Tennessee, Mississippi, Alabama and Kentucky. Address: Dept. of Botany, Indiana University, Bloomington, IN 47401.

DILENGE, DOMENICO, b. Grassano, Italy, June 11, 25; m. 69. RADIOLOGY. B.A, Univ. Bari, 43; M.D, Univ. Naples, 49, Med. Specialist, 53; Docente, Univ. Pisa, 64; M.M.Sc, Univ. Paris, 64. Asst. neuroradiol, St. Anne Hosp, Paris, 53-60; Pitié Hosp, 60-66; prof. angioneuroradiol, Univ. Nantes, 66-68; assoc. prof. RADIOL, Wash. Univ, 68; PROF. & CHMN. DEPT, UNIV. SHERBROOKE, 68- Int. Brain Res. Orgn. Coord, Int. Round Table Cerebral Circulation, Paris, 67. Italian Army Med. Corps, 1st Lt. Laureat French Acad. Med; hon. mem. French Neurol. Soc; hon. mem. Soc. Neurol. & Electroencephalog, Luxembourg; sr. mem. Am. Soc. Neuroradiol; Am. Col. Radiol; Can. Asn. Radiol. Cerebral circulation; angiography of cerebral and spinal circulation; clinical neuroradiology; ophthalmic angiography; gas myelography. Address: Dept. of Radiology, University of Sherbrooke, Sherbrooke, Que, Can.

DiLEONARDO, D. J, b. Pittsburgh, Pa, May 6, 35; m. 65. NUCLEAR PHYSICS. B.S, Carnegie Inst. Technol, 56; Westinghouse fel, Pittsburgh, 57-63, M.S, 59, Ph.D.(mech. eng), 63. Jr. engr. thermal & hydraul. anal, BETTIS ATOMIC POWER LAB, WESTINGHOUSE ELEC. CORP, 56-57, assoc. engr, 57-61, engr, 61-63, SR. ENGR, 63-64, NUCLEAR REACTOR DESIGN, 64- Am. Soc. Mech. Eng. Heat transfer; fluid flow; reactor design. Address: Bettis Atomic Power Lab, Westinghouse Electric Corp, Box 79, West Mifflin, PA 15122.

DiLEONE, GILBERT R(OBERT), b. Providence, R.I, Oct. 30, 35; m. 65; c. 2. IMMUNOLOGY. A.B, Boston, 58; M.S, Rhode Island, 60, Ph.D.(biol. sci), 64. Res. assoc. immunol, Brown, 64-66; ASSOC. BIOL, DEPT. CANCER RES, R.I. HOSP, PROVIDENCE, 66- AAAS; Am. Soc. Microbiol; Tissue Cult. Asn; Reticuloendothelial Soc. Nature of recognition of antigens and synthesis of antibodies; cellular immunology; nature of antigen sensitive memory cells; tumor immunology. Address: 24 Old Lyme Dr, Warwick, RI 02886.

DILGEN, ST. FRANCIS, b. Brooklyn, N.Y, Feb. 27, 24. ORGANIC CHEMISTRY. B.S, St. John's (N.Y), 53; M.S, Fordham, 55, Ph.D.(chem), 59. Asst,

Fordham, 53-57; lectr. CHEM, ST. JOSEPH'S COL.(N.Y), 57-58, instr, 58-59, asst. prof, 59-62, assoc. prof, 62-70, PROF. & CHMN. DEPT, 70- Am. Chem. Soc; N.Y. Acad. Sci. Reactions of α, β-epoxy ketones and related compounds with organometallic compounds and ring opening reagents. Address: Dept. of Chemistry, St. Joseph's College, Brooklyn, NY 11205.

DILGER, WILLIAM C, b. White Plains, N.Y, Apr. 20, 23; m. 49; c. 5. VERTEBRATE ZOOLOGY. B.S, Cornell Univ, 49, M.S, 51, Ph.D.(vert. zool), 55. Curator birds, Cornell Univ, 49-55; asst. prof. biol, St. Lawrence Univ, 55-56; asst. prof. ornith, CORNELL UNIV, 56-60, assoc. prof. biol. & asst. dir. res. lab. ornith, 60-64, LECTR. PSYCHOL. & ASSOC. PROF. ETHOLOGY, 64- U.S.A, 42-46, Sgt. Fel. Am. Ornith. Union; Cooper Ornith. Soc; Wilson Ornith. Soc; Soc. Syst. Zool; Ecol. Soc. Am; Animal Behav. Soc. (v.chmn, 61, chmn, 62); Brit. Avicult. Soc; Am. Soc. Zool. Vertebrate ethology; birds and fish. Address: College of Arts & Sciences, Cornell University, Ithaca, NY 14850.

DILGREN, RICHARD EVARTS, b. Oberlin, Ohio, Nov. 3, 33. PHYSICAL ORGANIC CHEMISTRY. B.A, Wittenberg, 55; Ph.D.(org. chem), Wisconsin, 59. Res. chemist, explor. & prod. res. div, Shell Develop. Co, 59-69, MGR. QUAL. CONTROL LAB, SHELL CHEM. CO, 69- Am. Chem. Soc. Mechanisms of allylic rearrangements; well stimulation; characterization of petroleum acids; kinetics of interfacial reactions. Address: Shell Chemical Co, P.O. Box 2633, Deer Park, TX 77536.

DiLIDDO, BART A(NTHONY), b. Cleveland, Ohio, Mar. 5, 31; m. 55. CHEMICAL ENGINEERING. B.S, Fenn Col, 54; Sinclair fel. & M.S, Ill. Inst. Tech, 56; Union Carbide fel. & Ph.D.(chem. eng), Case, 60. Mem. staff, res. ctr, B.F. GOODRICH CO, 56-67, proj. mgr, Avon Lake Develop. Ctr, 67-70, PROCESS MGR, 70- Assoc. mem. Am. Inst. Chem. Eng. New chemical processes. Address: 3235 Lancelot Dr, Orange, TX 77630.

DiLIELLO, LEO R(ALPH), b. Baltimore, Md, Jan. 17, 32; m. 54; c. 3. MICROBIOLOGY. B.S, Maryland, 54, M.S, 56, Ph.D, 58. Res. asst, Maryland, 54-58; assoc. prof. MICROBIOL, STATE UNIV. N.Y. AGR. & TECH. COL. FARMINGDALE, 58-68, PROF, 68- Am. Soc. Microbiol; Am. Inst. Food Technol. Veterinary medicine; oral bacteria; dairy and food microbiology; medical microbiology. Address: Dept. of Biological Sciences, State University of New York Agricultural & Technical College at Farmingdale, Farmingdale, NY 11735.

DILKS, ELEANOR, b. Richmond, Ind, Jan. 29, 21. ZOOLOGY. A.B, Earlham Col, 42; M.S, Wisconsin, 44, Ph.D.(zool), 48. Instr. biol, Earlham Col, 42-43; asst. zool, Wisconsin, 43-45; instr, Drury Col, 45-47; Buffalo, 47-50, asst. prof, 50-52; assoc. prof. biol, ILL. STATE UNIV, 52-61, PROF. ZOOL, 61- Nat. Sci. Found. faculty fel, 57-58, participant, conf. marine biol. & tropical ecol, P.R, 64. AAAS; Am. Soc. Zool; Marine Biol. Asn. U.K. Serology; precipitin formation; embryology; endocrinology; invertebrate zoology; electron microscopy. Address: Dept. of Biological Sciences, Illinois State University, Normal, IL 61761.

DILL, ALOYS J(OHN), b. Jersey City, N.J, Jan. 8, 40; m. 62; c. 1. ELECTROCHEMISTRY. A.B, Hunter Col, 62; M.A, City Col. New York, 64; Ph.D.(chem), City Univ. New York, 68. RES. CHEMIST, PAUL D. MERICA RES. LAB, INT. NICKEL CO, INC, 67- Am. Chem. Soc; Electrochem. Soc; Am. Electroplaters Soc. Electrodeposition of metals. Address: International Nickel Co. Inc, Sterling Forest, Suffern, NY 10901.

DILL, CHARLES W(ILLIAM), b. Greenville, S.C, June 1, 32; m. 54; c. 3. FOOD SCIENCE, ORGANIC CHEMISTRY. B.S, Berea Col, 54; M.S, N.C. State Col, 57, Ph.D.(food sci), 62. Instr. food chem, N.C. State Col, 59-62; asst. prof. dairy sci, Nebraska, 62-66; ASSOC. PROF. ANIMAL SCI, TEX. A&M UNIV, 66- AAAS; Inst. Food Tech; Am. Dairy Sci. Asn. Thermal denaturation and degradation of proteins; instrumentation and control in systems for heating fluid products; flavor stability of fats and oils. Address: Dept. of Animal Science, Texas A&M University, College Station, TX 77843.

DILL, DALE ROBERT, b. Towanda, Kans, Jan. 10, 34; m. 55; c. 3. ORGANIC & PHARMACEUTICAL CHEMISTRY. B.S, Kansas, 55, Ph.D.(pharmacuet. chem) 58. Res. assoc. pharmaceut. chem, Kansas, 58-59; sr. res. chemist, MONSANTO CO, 59-63, res. specialist, 63-67, GROUP LEADER, 67- Nat. Insts. Health grant, 58-59. Am. Chem. Soc; N.Y. Acad. Sci; Tech. Asn. Pulp & Paper Indust. Anti-hypertensive drugs; plasticizers; paper chemicals; cancer drugs. Address: Monsanto Co, 800 N. Lindbergh Blvd, St. Louis, MO 63166.

DILL, DAVID B(RUCE), b. Eskridge, Kans, Apr. 22, 91; m. 45; c. 2. PHYSIOLOGY. B.S, Occidental Col, 13, hon. D.Sc, 59; M.A, Stanford, 14, fel, 23-25, Ph.D.(biochem), 25. Teacher, high sch, 14-18; asst. chemist, bur. chem, U.S. Dept. Agr, 18-22, assoc. chemist, 22-25; Nat. Res. Coun. fel. chem, Harvard, 25-27, asst. prof. biochem, 27-36, assoc. prof. indust. physiol, 36-38, prof, 38-47, dir. res. Fatigue Lab, 27-47; sci. dir. chem. corps. Med. Labs, Army Chem. Center, Md. 47-61; res. scholar, Indiana, 61-66; RES. PROF, LAB. ENVIRON. PATHOPHYSIOL, DESERT RES. INST. UNIV. NEV, 66- Vis. lectr, Harvard, 50-61. Leader physiol. exploratory expeds, Andes, C.Z. & Colo. Desert. Legion of Merit. With Off. Sci. Res. & Develop, 44. U.S.A.A.F, 41-43, Qm.C, 43-46, Col. AAAS; Am. Chem. Soc; Am. Soc. Biol. Chem; Am. Physiol. Soc.(treas, 46-50, pres, 50); Aerospace Med. Asn; Am. Acad. Arts & Sci; hon. fel. Am. Col. Cardiol; Am. Col. Sports Med.(pres, 60-61). Physico-chemical properties of blood; physiology of exercise; environmental physiology; physiology of aging. Address: Laboratory of Environmental Pathophysiology, Desert Research Institute, University of Nevada System, Boulder City, NV 89005.

DILL, ELLIS HAROLD, b. Pittsburgh Co, Okla, Dec. 31, 32; m. 53; c. 2. CIVIL ENGINEERING. Ph.D.(civil eng), California, 57. PROF. AERONAUT. & ASTRONAUT, UNIV. WASH, 56- Am. Inst. Aeronaut. & Astronaut; Soc. Eng. Sci; Am. Soc. Civil Eng. Applied mechanics. Address: Dept. of Aeronautics & Astronautics, University of Washington, Seattle, WA 98105.

DILL, FREDERICK H(AYES), JR, b. Sewickley, Pa, Mar. 1, 32. ELECTRICAL ENGINEERING, PHYSICS. B.S, Carnegie Inst. Tech, 54, M.S, 56, Ph.D.(elec. eng), 58. MEM. RES. STAFF, THOMAS J. WATSON RES. CTR, IBM Corp, 58- Mackay vis. lectr, Univ. Calif, Berkeley, 68-69. Sig.C, 58-59, 1st Lt. Semiconductor junction phenomena and devices. Address: Thomas J. Watson Research Center, IBM Corp, P.O. Box 218, Yorktown Heights, NY 10598.

DILL, JOHN C, b. Vancouver, B.C, Nov. 20, 39; m. 62; c. 2. COMPUTER SCIENCE, BIOENGINEERING. B.A.Sc, Univ. B.C, 62; M.S, N.C. State Univ, 64; Nat. Insts. Health fel, Calif. Inst. Technol, 65-70, Ph.D.(info. sci), 70. COMPUT. SCIENTIST, RES. LABS, GEN. MOTORS TECH. CTR, 70- Asn. Comput. Mach; Inst. Elec. & Electronics Eng; Eng. Inst. Can. Computer graphics; computer applications in physiology and medicine. Address: Computer Technology Dept, General Motors Research Labs, 12 Mile & Mound Rds, Warren, MI 48090.

DILL, NORMAN H(UDSON), b. Wilmington, Del, Apr. 6, 38. BOTANY, PLANT ECOLOGY. B.A, Delaware, 60; Woodrow Wilson fel, Rutgers, 60-61, M.S, 62, Ph.D.(plant ecol), 64. PROF. biol, DEL. STATE COL, 64-66, BIOL. & NATURAL RESOURCES, 66- Consult, U.S. Agency Int. Develop-Nat. Sci. Found. Sci. Educ. Improv. Prog. for India, 68 & 69; mem. bd. experts, Rachel Carson Trust for Living Environ. AAAS; Ecol. Soc. Am; Am. Inst. Biol. Sci; Am. Nature Study Soc; Nat. Asn. Biol. Teachers. Forest productivity; vegetation management; plant geography; use of wild shrubs in songbird management; effects of periodic cicada on forest ecosystems. Address: Dept. of Biology & Natural Resources, Delaware State College, Dover, DE 19901.

DILL, ROBERT FLOYD, b. Denver, Colo, May 25, 27; m. 45; c. 4. MARINE GEOLOGY. B.S, Univ. South. Calif, 50, M.S, 52; Ph.D, Univ. Calif, San Diego, 64. Oceanogr, U.S. Navy Electronics Lab, 51-68, MARINE GEOLOGIST, NAVAL UNDERSEA RES. & DEVELOP. CTR, 68- Consult-owner, Gen. Oceanog, Inc, 53-; mem. faculty, San Diego State Col, 68-; investr, inst. oceanog. res, Univ. Baja Calif. Dipl, Mex. Comt. Eng. for Ocean Resources, 70. U.S.N, 45-47. Fel. Geol. Soc. Am; Am. Asn. Petrol. Geol. (Leverson Award, 69); Soc. Econ. Paleont. & Mineral. Marine sedimentation, erosion and sediment distribution patterns in present and ancient seas; mass physical properties of sediments, Pleistocene sea level fluctuations, carbonate reefs, submarine canyons, scientific application of scuba and submersibles. Address: 610 Tarento Dr, San Diego, CA 92106.

DILL, RUSSELL E(UGENE), b. Rising Star, Tex, July 27, 32; m. 54; c. 3. PHYSIOLOGY, NEUROANATOMY. B.A, N.Tex. State Col, 53, M.S, 57; Ph.D. (physiol), Illinois, 60. Fel. ANAT, med. br, Texas, 60-61, instr, 61-65; asst. prof, COL. DENT, BAYLOR UNIV, 65-70, ASSOC. PROF, 70- U.S.A, 54-56. AAAS; Am. Asn. Anat; Soc. Neurosci. Experimental neurology; extrapyramidal motor systems; central nervous system pharmacology. Address: Dept. of Microscopic Anatomy, Baylor University College of Dentistry, Dallas, TX 75226.

DILLARD, C(LYDE) R(UFFIN), b. Norfolk, Va, Apr. 17, 20. INORGANIC CHEMISTRY. B.S, Va. Union, 40; Rosenwald fel, Chicago, 47-48, M.S, 48, Ph.D, 49. Res. chemist, Manhattan proj, Chicago, 43-45, asst. CHEM, 45-48; prof, Tenn. Agr. & Ind. State, 48-53; Morgan State Col, 53-59; assoc. prof, BROOKLYN COL, 59-69, PROF, 69-, ASSOC. DEAN FACULTIES, 70- Fulbright res. scholar, Osaka Univ, 65-66. AAAS; Am. Chem. Soc; N.Y. Acad. Sci; Soc. Appl. Spectros.(asst. ed, Appl. Spectros, 63-). Chemistry of volatile hydrides; organotin compounds; infrared spectroscopy; radiochemistry and isotopic tracer techniques. Address: Dept. of Chemistry, Brooklyn College, Brooklyn, NY 11210.

DILLARD, DAVID H(UGH), b. Spokane, Wash, May 14, 23; m. 48; c. 7. SURGERY. A.B, Whitman Col, 46; M.D, Hopkins, 50. Intern, Univ. Hosp, Hopkins, 51; instr. SURG, SCH. MED, UNIV. WASH, 55-57, assoc. prof, 57-69, PROF, 69-, resident, 58. Med.C, 55-57, Lt. Esophageal and cardiovascular research; general and thoracic surgery. Address: Dept. of Surgery, University of Washington School of Medicine, Seattle, WA 98105.

DILLARD, EMMETT U(RCEY), b. Sylva, N.C, Aug. 12, 17; m. 40; c. 4. ANIMAL GENETICS. B.S.A, Berea Col, 40; Georgia, 40; M.S, N.C. State Col, 48; Ph.D.(animal husb), Missouri, 53. Asst. county supvr, farm security admin, U.S. Dept. Agr, 40-43, county supvr, 43-44, instr. ANIMAL HUSB, bur. animal indust, N.C. STATE UNIV, 47-49, asst. prof, 49-60, ASSOC. PROF, 60- Livestock res. adv, North Carolina Agr. Res. Mission to Peru, 58-60 & 67-68. U.S.N, 44-46. Am. Soc. Animal Sci. Livestock, improvement through breeding and management. Address: Dept. of Animal Science, North Carolina State University, Raleigh, NC 27607.

DILLARD, GARY EUGENE, b. Ridgway, Ill, Apr. 26, 38; m. 59; c. 2. PHYCOLOGY, AQUATIC ECOLOGY. B.A, Southern Illinois, 60, M.S, 62; Ph.D.(bot), N.C. State, 66. Asst. taxon, Southern Illinois, 59-60, bot, 60-62; phycol, N.C. State, 62-65; asst. prof. bot. Clemson, 65-68; ASSOC. PROF. BIOL, WEST. KY. UNIV, 68- Phycol. Soc. Am; Am. Micros. Soc; Int. Phycol. Soc. Taxonomy and ecology of freshwater algae, especially stream benthos. Address: Dept. of Biology, Western Kentucky University, Bowling Green, KY 42102.

DILLARD, JOE G, b. Chillicothe, Mo, Feb. 24, 37; m. 60; c. 3. ZOOLOGY. B.S, Missouri, 63, M.A, 65. FISHERY BIOLOGIST, MO. DEPT. CONSERV, 65- Am. Fisheries Soc. General fishery biology. Address: Missouri Dept. of Conservation, P.O. Box 180, Jefferson City, MO 65101.

DILLARD, JOHN GAMMONS, b. Kermit, Tex, Nov. 1, 38; m. 63; c. 2. INORGANIC & PHYSICAL CHEMISTRY. B.A, Austin Col, 61; Okla. State, 61-63; NASA fel, Kansas State. 63-66, Ph.D.(chem), 66. Asst. CHEM, Okla. State, 61-63; Kansas State, 63-66; fel, Rice, 66-67; asst. prof, VA. POLYTECH. INST. & STATE UNIV, 67-70, ASSOC. PROF, 70- Am. Chem. Soc; Am. Soc. Mass Spectrometry. Mass Spectrometry; coordination compounds. Address: 201 Craig Dr, Blacksburg, VA 24060.

DILLARD, MORRIS, JR, b. York, Ala, Apr. 27, 27. METABOLISM, INTERNAL MEDICINE. A.B, Birmingham-South. Col, 49; Ph.D.(anat), Emory, 54,

M.D, 59. Fels, Yale, 61-62, 63-64, instr. med, SCH. MED, YALE, 63-64, asst. prof, 64-69, ASSOC. PROF. CLIN. MED, 69- Chem.C, U.S.A, 54-56. Address: Dept. of Clinical Medicine, Yale School of Medicine, 333 Cedar St, New Haven, CT 06520.

DILLARD, ROBERT DELANE, b. New Albany, Ind, Jan. 3, 35; m. 57; c. 3. PHYSICAL & BIOLOGICAL SCIENCES. B.S, Indiana, 57, M.S, 59. CHEMIST, RES. DIV, Armour & Co, 59-60; ELI LILLY & CO, 60- Am. Chem. Soc. Synthetic organic chemistry; research in cancer chemotherapy. Address: Research Labs, Eli Lilly & Co, Indianapolis, IN 46206.

DILLARD, WALTER LAWRENCE, b. Chicago, Ill, Nov. 9, 35; m. 65; c. 2. CELL BIOLOGY. B.S, Oklahoma, 61, Nat. Defense Ed. Act fel, 61-64, Nat. Sci. Found. fel, 64-65, Ph.D.(zool), 66. Fel. cell biol, Max Planck Inst. Cell Biol, 66-69; ASST. PROF. ZOOL, OKLAHOMA, 69- U.S.A, 57-60. AAAS; Am. Inst. Biol. Sci. Influence of RNA synthesis in nuclear control of morphogenesis in Acetabularia. Address: Dept. of Zoology, University of Oklahoma, Norman, OK 73069.

DILLARSTONE, ALAN, b. Seaham, Eng, Mar. 12, 38; m. 62. COLLOID & INORGANIC CHEMISTRY. B.Sc, Sheffield, 59, Ph.D.(colloid chem), 62. Sr. res. chemist, RES. & DEVELOP. CTR, COLGATE-PALMOLIVE CO, 62-66, sect. head explor. prod, 66-68, SECT. HEAD ANAL. CHEM, 68- Am. Chem. Soc. Interaction of polar compounds with soaps and detergents; fluoridation and fluorides in toothpastes. Address: Colgate-Palmolive Co, Research & Development Center, 909 River Rd, Piscataway, NJ 08854.

DILLAWAY, ROBERT BEACHAM, b. Washington, D.C, Nov. 10, 24; m. 47; 71; c. 6. PHYSICS, MECHANICAL ENGINEERING. B.S.(math) & B.S.(mech. eng), Michigan, 45; M.S, Illinois, 51, Ph.D.(mech), 53. Develop. engr, Carrier Corp, 45-46; Eng. Res. Assocs, Inc, 47-48; instr. mech. eng, Illinois, 48-53; sr. res. engr, Rocketdyne Div, N.Am. Aviation, Inc, 53-54, res. specialist, 54-56, supvr. basic studies, 56-67, group leader basic studies & nuclear propulsion, 57-58, mgr. nucleonics subdiv, space power res. & develop, 58-64, corp. dir. res. & tech. mkt. planning, 64-68; dep. dir. & dep. for systs. anal, Off. Prog. Appraisal Secy. Navy Staff, 68-69; DEP. FOR LABS, LAB. & RES. MGT, U.S. ARMY MAT. COMMAND, 69- Exten lectr, Univ. Calif, 53-; indust. consult, Proj. Rover, Los Alamos Sci. Lab, 54-55; astronaut. comt. del, Int. Aeronaut. Fedn, 60-64; chmn, Intersoc. Comt. on Transportation, 71-73. Am. Soc. Mech. Eng; Am. Inst. Aeronaut. & Astronaut; Soc. Exp. Stress Anal; Brit. Interplanetary Soc. Fluid mechanics; heat transfer and thermodynamics; nuclear reactors for propulsion; transient fluid flow and boundary layer behavior; high speed temperature measurement. Address: U.S. Army Materials Command, Bldg. T-7, Room 2748, Washington, DC 20315.

DILLE, JAMES M(ADISON), b. Omaha, Nebr, June 9, 07; m. 35; c. 3. PHARMACOLOGY. B.S, Nebraska, 30, M.S, 33; Ph.D.(pharmacol), Georgetown, 35; M.D, Illinois, 46. Instr. physiol, Nebraska, 32-34; teaching fel. PHARMACOL, sch. med, Georgetown, 33-34, instr, 35-36; assoc. prof, UNIV. WASH, 36-40, prof, 40-43, PROF. & CHMN. DEPT, 46- Am. Soc. Pharmacol. & Exp. Therapeut; Soc. Exp. Biol. & Med; Am. Pharmaceut. Asn. Psychopharmacology. Address: Dept. of Pharmacology, School of Medicine, University of Washington, Seattle, WA 98105.

DILLE, J(OHN) ROBERT, b. Waynesburg, Pa, Sept. 2, 31; m. 55; c. 2. AEROSPACE MEDICINE. B.S, Waynesburg Col, 52; M.D, Pittsburgh, 56; M.I.H, Harvard, 60. Resident aerospace med, U.S. Air Force Sch. Aviation Med, Harvard, FED. AVIATION ADMIN, 59-62, prog. adv. officer, Civil Aeromed. Res. Inst, 63-65, regional flight surgeon, West. Region, Los Angeles, 65, CHIEF, CIVIL AEROMED. INST, 65- Assoc. prof, sch. med, Oklahoma, 62- Dipl, Am. Bd. Prev. Med. & cert. aerospace med, 64. U.S.A.F, chief aviation med. serv, hosp, Loring Air Force Base, Maine, 57-59, Capt. Aerospace Med. Asn; Am. Med. Asn; fel. Am. Col. Prev. Med. Aircraft accident investigation; pulmonary physiology; toxicity of drugs and pesticides; penetrating eye injuries. Address: Civil Aeromedical Institute, Federal Aviation Administration, P.O. Box 25082, Oklahoma City, OK 73125.

DILLE, KENNETH LEROY, b. Caldwell, Idaho, May 9, 25; m. 52; c. 4. ORGANIC & PETROLEUM CHEMISTRY. B.A, Col. Idaho, 50; M.A, Ore. State Col, 52, fels, 50-54, Ph.D.(org. phys. chem), 54. Asst. org. chem, Ore. State Col, 50-52; res. chemist, TEXACO, INC, BEACON, 54-62, group leader chem. res, 62-64, fuels res, 64-68, ASST. SUPVR. FUELS RES. SECT, 68- Texaco proj. leader with U.S. Govt, 60-62. U.S.A, 43-46, T/Sgt. Am. Chem. Soc; Sci. Res. Soc. Am. Synthesis and development of additives for improving motor and aviation gasolines, diesel and jet fuels and antifreezes; product development of petrochemicals. Address: 86 Remsen Ave, Wappingers Falls, NY 12590.

DILLE, ROGER, M(cCORMICK), b. Caldwell, Idaho, Apr. 19, 23; m. 55; c. 1. CHEMISTRY. B.S, Col. Idaho, 44. Chemist, Texaco Ref, 44-51, Montebello Lab, TEXACO, INC, 51-58, res. chemist, 58-63, sr. res. chemist, 63-70, SUPVR. ANAL. & TESTING, RICHMOND RES. LAB, 70- Am. Chem. Soc. Petrochemicals; synthetic fuels; partial oxidation. Address: 4731 Bonnie Brae Rd, Richmond, VA 23234.

DILLEMUTH, FREDERICK J(OSEPH), S. J, b. New York, N.Y, Apr. 15, 23. PHYSICAL CHEMISTRY. B.S, Spring Hill Col, 48; M.S, Boston Col, 51; S.T.L, Woodstock Col. Md, 55; Ph.D, Fordham Univ, 60. Instr. gen. chem, St. Peters Col, 48-49; Fordham Univ, 60; fel. CHEM, Columbia Univ, 59-60; asst. prof, FORDHAM UNIV, 62-68, ASSOC. PROF, 68-, chmn. dept, 68-71. Am. Chem. Soc. Hydrocarbon oxidation; kinetics of gas phase reactions. Address: Dept. of Chemistry, Fordham University, Bronx, NY 10458.

DILLER, EROLD R(AY), b. New Stark, Ohio, May 4, 22; m. 43; c. 2. BIOCHEMISTRY, PHARMACOLOGY. B.A, Bowling Green State, 49; M.S, Indiana, 51. Res. assoc. biochem, Indiana, 49-51; sr. scientist, LILLY RES. LABS, 51-66, res. scientist, 66-71, RES. ASSOC, 71- Med.C, 42-46, Sgt. Sci. Res. Soc. Am; Soc. Exp. Biol. & Med. Intermediary metabolism and metabolic control mechanisms; lipid and sterol metabolism and metabolic control mechanisms; lipid and sterol metabolism; biochemical pharmacology; absorption. Address: Lilly Research Labs, P.O. Box 618, Indianapolis, IN 46206.

DILLER, IRENE COREY, b. North Woodstock, N.H, May 19, 00; m. 38. CYTOLOGY. A.B, George Washington, 25; A.M, Pennsylvania, 31, Ph.D.(zool), 33. Res. info. serv, Nat. Res. Coun, 22-25; res. asst, dept. zool, Pennsylvania, 25-33, res. assoc, 33-42, secy. to dir. dept, 25-33; res. biologist, Lankenau Hosp, Res. Inst, Phila, 42-46; assoc. mem, INST. CANCER RES, 46-56, sr. mem, 56-65, EMER. SR. MEM, 65- Fel, Keio Univ, Japan, 33-34; mem. corp, Marine Biol. Lab. Secy. & interpreter, anthropoid exped, Cuba, 24; interpreter, Int. Cong. Zool, Uruguay, 30. AAAS; Am. Soc. Zool; Am. Asn. Cancer Res; Soc. Develop. Biol; N.Y. Acad. Sci. Cytology of Orthoptera; chromosomes of insects; cytology of tumors. Address: Institute for Cancer Research, 7701 Burholm Ave, Fox Chase, Philadelphia, PA 19111.

DILLER, O(LIVER) D(ANIEL), b. Columbus Grove, Ohio, Jan. 16, 05; m. 34; c. 2. FOREST ECOLOGY. B.A, Bluffton Col, 30; M.Sc, Ohio State, 32, Ph.D.(bot), 34. Asst. bot, Ohio State, 30-34; technician, U.S. Forest Serv, 34, asst. conservationist, 35-37; asst. forester, OHIO AGR. RES. & DEVELOP. CTR, 37-38, assoc. forester, 38-70, prof. FORESTRY & chmn. dept, 50-70, EMER. PROF, 70- Asst. prof. forestry, Ohio State Univ, 43-46, assoc. prof, 46-52; forester, Ohio Forestry Asn, 58-52; curator, Secrest Arboretum, 66-70. Soc. Am. Foresters. Limiting factors in the natural regeneration of oak-hickory woodlands following excessive grazing. Address: 1368 E. Wayne Ave, Wooster, OH 44691.

DILLER, VIOLET M(ARION), b. Cincinnati, Ohio, Feb. 7, 14. BIOPHYSICS. B.A, Cincinnati, 34, B.E, 35, Lederle fel, 44-47, M.S, 45, Ph.D.(physics), 47; Ohio State, 43; Columbia, 45. Instr. physics, UNIV. CINCINNATI, 43-44, asst. prof. BIOPHYS, GRAD. SCH, 47-51, ASSOC. PROF, 51- With U.S.A.F, 42. Fel. AAAS; Int. Phycol. Soc; Am. Asn. Physics Teachers; Phycol. Soc. Am; Bot. Soc. Am; Am. Soc. Plant Physiol; Biophys. Soc. Production of mutants in microorganisms by physical methods; metabolism of nonfilamentous algae; metabolism of liverworts. Address: Dept. of Physics, University of Cincinnati, Cincinnati, OH 45221.

DILLER, WILLIAM F(REY), JR, b. Lancaster, Pa, July 26, 02; m. 38. ZOOLOGY. A.B, Franklin & Marshall Col, 23; Ph.D, Pennsylvania, 28. Instr. zool, Pennsylvania, 23-25, 27-30; Franklin & Marshall Col, 25-27; Sterling fel, Yale, 30-31; instr. ZOOL, Dartmouth Col, 31-36, asst. prof, 36-39; UNIV. PA, 39-48, assoc. prof, 48-59, PROF, 59- AAAS; Am. Soc. Nat; Am. Soc. Zool; Soc. Protozool; Am. Soc. Parasitol; Micros. Soc. Am. Protozoology; nuclear behavior and life history of ciliated Protozoa. Address: Dept. of Biology, University of Pennsylvania, Philadelphia, PA 19104.

DILLERY, DEAN G(EORGE), b. Fremont, Ohio, Nov. 18, 28; m. 51; c. 4. ZOOLOGY. B.S, Ohio State Univ, 52, M.S, 55, Ph.D.(ornith), 61; N.C. State Univ, 55-56. Instr. zool, Ohio Wesleyan Univ, 59-60; ASSOC. PROF. BIOL, ALBION COL, 60- Entom. Soc. Am. Biology and taxonomy of aphids; population biology and behavior of amphipods. Address: Dept. of Biology, Albion College, Albion, MI 49224.

DILLEY, DAVID R(OSS), b. South Haven, Mich, Mar. 10, 34; m. 56; c. 3. PLANT BIOCHEMISTRY, HORTICULTURE. B.S, Mich. State Col, 55; M.S, Mich. State, 57; Ph.D.(bot), N.C. State Col, 60. Technician HORT, MICH. STATE UNIV, 56-57, asst. prof, 60-64, assoc. prof, 64-67, PROF, 67- Chmn. Gordon Res. conf. Post Harvest Physiol, 72. Consult, United Fruit Co; Cent. Am. Res. Inst. Indust. AAAS; Am. Soc. Plant Physiol; Am. Soc. Hort. Sci.(Dow Chem. award). Physiology and biochemistry of fruits during growth, maturation and senescence; handling, transportation and storage of perishable commodities. Address: Dept. of Horticulture, Michigan State University, East Lansing, MI 48823.

DILLEY, JAMES PAUL, b. Athens, Ohio, Feb. 19, 34. THEORETICAL PHYSICS. A.B, Ohio, 55, M.S, 56; Ph.D.(physics), Syracuse, 64. Asst. prof. PHYSICS, OHIO UNIV, 63-67, ASSOC. PROF, 67- Nat. Sci. Found. summer fel, theoret. physics inst, Colorado, 64; res. fel, theoret. physics inst, Univ. Alta, 68-69. U.S.A.F, 56-59, Capt. AAAS; Am. Phys. Soc. Neutron diffusion; measurements in nuclear emulsions; strong interactions and S-matrix theory. Address: Dept. of Physics, Ohio University, Athens, OH 45701.

DILLEY, JAMES V, b. Tillamook, Ore, Feb. 15, 28; m. 68; c. 2. TOXICOLOGY, PHARMACOLOGY. B.S, Portland, 59; Ph.D.(pharmacol), Chicago, 64. Biol. scientist, Pac. Northwest Labs, Battelle Mem. Inst, 64-67, sr. scientist, 67-71; SCIENTIST, BROWN & ROOT-NORTHROP, MANNED SPACECRAFT CTR, 71- U.S.A, 46-49, Res, 50-53, S/Sgt. AAAS; Am. Pub. Health Asn. Chemical protection against radiation exposure; drug metabolism and detoxification; fate and removal of inhaled particulates; inhalation toxicology; carcinogenesis; immunology of inhalation carcinogenesis; pulmonary pharmacology. Address: Toxicology Lab, Manned Spacecraft Ctr, Brown & Root-Northrop, P.O. Box 34416, Houston, TX 77034.

DILLEY, RICHARD ALAN, b. South Haven, Mich, Jan. 12, 36; m. 60; c. 4. BIOCHEMISTRY, PLANT PHYSIOLOGY. B.S, Mich. State, 58, M.S, 59; Ph.D.(biochem, plant physiol), Purdue, 63. Nat. Insts. Health, C.F. Kettering Res. lab, 63-64; vis. asst. prof. biophys, Rochester, 65; staff scientist, C.F. Kettering Res. Lab, 66-68, investr, 69-71; ASSOC. PROF. BIOL. SCI, PURDUE UNIV, 71- AAAS; Am. Soc. Plant Physiol; Biophys. Soc; Am. Soc. Cell Biol; Am. Inst. Biol. Sci; Am. Soc. Biol. Chem. Membrane biochemistry in energy transducing systems; ion and electron transport; photophosphorylation and membrane structure in the photosynthetic apparatus; quinones of plants. Address: Dept. of Biological Sciences, Purdue University, Lafayette, IN 47907.

DILLEY, WILLIAM G, b. Van Nuys, Calif, Sept. 21, 42; m. 65; c. 1. CELL BIOLOGY, ONCOLOGY. A.B, Univ. Calif, Berkeley, 65, Nat. Insts. Health trainee, 65-70, M.A, 67, Ph.D.(endocrinol), 70. ASST. PROF. ANAT, COL. PHYSICIANS & SURGEONS, COLUMBIA UNIV, 70- AAAS. Mammary gland endocrinology and tumorigenesis; ovarian tumorigenesis. Address: Dept. of Anatomy, Columbia University, 630 W. 168th St, New York, NY 10032.

DILLING, E(LMER) D(ONALD), b. Grandview, Wash, Nov. 19, 13; m. 39; c. 2. PHYSICAL METALLURGY. B.A, Washington State, 37. Jr. res. engr,

Washington State Col, 37-40; U.S. Bur. Mines, Wash, 40-42, res. engr, magnesium pilot plant, Mich, 42-44, proj. engr, Ore, 44-47, zirconin prod, 47-52, chief rare metals br, 52-55; supvr. develop. eng, TITANIUM METALS CORP. AM, Nev, 55-66, CHIEF DEVELOP. ENGR, 66- Am. Inst. Mining, Metall. & Petrol. Eng; Am. Soc. Metals; Sci. Res. Soc. Am. Recovery metallurgy processes for magnesium, zirconium and titanium metals; physical metallurgical processes for hot and cold fabrication of zirconium and titanium. Address: Titanium Metals Corp. of America, P.O. Box 309, Toronto, OH 43964.

DILLING, ROGER LEON, b. Bluffton, Ind, June 16, 39; m. 62. THEORETICAL PHYSICS. B.A, Manchester Col, 61; Nat. Sci. Found. fels, Michigan State, 61-66, M.S, 63, Ph.D.(physics), 66. Instr. physics, Michigan State, 66; Nat. Ctr. Sci. Res. attaché res. physics, Faculty Sci. Paris, 68; ASST. PROF. PHYSICS, FORDHAM UNIV, 68- Nat. Sci. Found. fel, 67-68. AAAS; Am. Phys. Soc; Am. Asn. Physics Teachers; French Phys. Soc. Interpretation and analysis of infrared and microwave spectra of symmetric-top molecules; application of computer techniques to the study of molecular vibration-rotation Hamiltonians. Address: Dept. of Physics, Fordham University, Bronx, NY 10458.

DILLING, WENDELL LEE, b. Bluffton, Ind, June 16, 36; m. 58; c. 1. ORGANIC CHEMISTRY. B.A, Manchester Col, 58; Nat. Sci. Found. fel, Purdue Univ, 59-62, Ph.D.(org. chem), 62. Org. res. chemist, DOW CHEM. CO, 62-68, SR. RES. CHEMIST, 68- Am. Chem. Soc; Sci. Res. Soc. Am; The Chem. Soc. Organic photochemistry; benzyne chemistry; carbonium ion and pentacyclodecane chemistry; reaction mechanisms; spectroscopy. Address: 1810 Norwood Dr, Midland, MI 48640.

DILLINGER, JOSEPH R(OLLEN), b. Carbondale, Ill, May 20, 16; m. 42; c. 3. PHYSICS. B.Ed, South. Ill, 38; Ph.D.(physics), Wisconsin, 47. Staff mem, radiation lab, Mass. Inst. Tech, 41-46; instr. PHYSICS, UNIV. WIS, MADISON, 47-48, asst. prof, 48-55, assoc. prof, 55-60, PROF, 60- Am. Phys. Soc; Am. Asn. Physics Teachers.(treas, 62-66). Photoelectric and thermionic emission; development of power pulse generators; gas discharge tubes; low temperature physics. Address: Dept. of Physics, University of Wisconsin, Madison, WI 53706.

DILLINGHAM, ELWOOD O(LIVER), b. Daytona Beach, Fla, Apr. 30, 26; m. 50; c. 3. CELL BIOLOGY, BIOCHEMISTRY. A.B, DePauw, 49, M.A, 51; fel, Purdue, 51-53, Ph.D.(bot, mycol), 55. Asst. bot, Purdue, 53-54; microbiol, Inst. Paper Chem, 54-57, res. assoc, 57-63, chief biochem. group, biol. sect, 63-70; RES. ASSOC. PROF. PHARMACEUT, MOLECULAR & QUANTUM BIOL, UNIV. TENN, MEMPHIS, 70- Head cellular toxicol. sect, Mat. Sci. Toxicol. Labs. U.S.A, 44-46, 1st Lt. Soc. Indust. Microbiol; Am. Soc. Microbiol; Inst. Food Technol. Selective toxicity; microbiological degradation and biosynthesis of cellulose and lignin; tissue culture and biochemical genetics; quantitative structure-activity relationships in drug design; toxicological properties of biomaterials. Address: Dept. of Biology, University of Tennessee, Memphis, TN 38103.

DILLMAN, L(OWELL) THOMAS, b. Huntington, Ind, Aug. 31, 31; m. 54; c. 4. NUCLEAR PHYSICS. B.A, Manchester Col, 53; M.S, Illinois, 55, Gen. Elec. Indust. fel, 57-58, Ph.D.(physics), 58. Asst, Illinois, 53-57; asst. prof. PHYSICS, OHIO WESLEYAN UNIV, 58-62, assoc. prof, 62-68, PROF, 68- Summers, asst, Los Alamos Sci. Lab, 58 & res. partic, Oak Ridge Nat. Lab, 67-69, consult, health physics div, 67- Am. Phys. Soc; Am. Asn. Physics Teachers; Health Physics Soc. Health physics internal dosimetry. Address: Dept. of Physics, Ohio Wesleyan University, Delaware, OH 43015.

DILLMAN, RICHARD CARL, b. Ft. Dodge, Iowa, Sept. 4, 31; m. 64; c. 2. VETERINARY MEDICINE, PATHOLOGY. B.S, Iowa State Univ, 59, D.V.M, 61; Nat. Defense Educ. Act fel, Kans. State Univ, 62-64, M.S, 64, Ph.D. (path), 68. Instr. VET. PATH, Kans. State Univ, 64-68; asst. prof, IOWA STATE UNIV, 68-70, ASSOC. PROF, 70- U.S.N, 51-55. Clinical pathology; serum proteins; bovine respiratory diseases; reproductive disorders of domestic livestock. Address: Veterinary Diagnostic Lab, Iowa State University, Ames, IA 50010.

DILLON, DONALD J, b. New York, N.Y, Apr. 26, 26; m. 55; c. 4. PSYCHOLOGY. B.S, Yale, 49; M.A, Fordham, 52, fel, 53-54, Ph.D.(psychol), 55. Asst. psychol, Fordham, 52-54; res. scientist, N.Y. STATE PSYCHIATRIC INST, 54-56, SR. RES. SCIENTIST, 56-; ASST. PROF. MED. PSYCHOL, COL. PHYSICIANS & SURGEONS, COLUMBIA UNIV, 69-, instr. psychiat, 58-67, res. assoc, 67-69. Summer asst, Fordham Univ, 53; adj. asst. prof, Manhattan Col, 63-67, adj. assoc. prof, 67- U.S.N, 44-46. AAAS; Optical Soc. Am; Am. Psychol. Asn; N.Y. Acad. Sci. Vision; psychophysics; psychophysiology; experimental psychopathology. Address: Dept. of Research Psychology, New York State Psychiatric Institute, 722 W. 168th St, New York, NY 10032.

DILLON, HUGH C, JR, b. Auburn, Ala, July 4, 30. MEDICINE. B.S, Ala. Polytech. Inst, 51; M.D, Med. Col. Ala, 55. Intern pediat, Univ. Hosp, Birmingham, 55-56, resident, 56-57; fel, Univ. Minn. Hosp, 57-58; private practice, Ala, 60-61; Nat. Found. fel, dept. pediat, Univ. Minn, 61-63; asst. prof. PEDIAT, SCH. MED, UNIV. ALA, 63-66, assoc. prof, 66-69, PROF, 69-, ASSOC. PROF. MICROBIOL, PUB. HEALTH & EPIDEMIOL, 70-, DIR. DIV. INFECTIOUS DISEASES, UNIV. HOSP. & CHILDREN'S HOSP, 66-, asst. prof. epidemiol, sch. med, 66-70, asst. prof. pub. health & epidemiol, 66-70. Co-chmn. comt, infections, Univ. Hosp, Univ. Ala, 63-68, chmn, 68-69, mem, 69-, dir. pediat. out-patient clin, Children's Hosp, 64-65, dir. sr. teaching prog, sch. med, 64-67, dir. pediat. postgrad. prog, 64-67, consult. clin. microbiol. sect, 66-, mem. comt. admissions, 69-, consult. dent. caries study, sch. dent, 67-, coursemaster, integrative concepts sect, basic med. sci. curriculum, schs. med. & dent, 70- Mem. comt. prophylaxis streptococcal infections, Armed Forces Epidemiol. Bd, 66-, assoc. mem. comn. streptococcal & staphylococcal diseases, 68-69, full mem, 69-; mem. comt. rheumatic fever, Am. Heart Asn, 69- Am. Acad. Pediat; Am. Fedn. Clin. Res; Soc. Pediat. Res; Am. Soc. Microbiol; Infectious Disease Soc. Am; N.Y. Acad. Sci. Address: Dept. of Pediatrics, University of Alabama School of Medicine, Birmingham, AL 35299.

DILLON, JOHN A(NDREW), JR, b. Pawtucket, R.I, Sept. 24, 23; m. 53; c. 2. PHYSICS. B.Sc, Fordham, 47, M.Sc, Brown, 49, fel, 52-53, Ph.D.(physics), 54. Asst, Brown, 48-49; instr. physics, Fairfield, 49-51; Providence Col, 51-52; res. physicist, Air Force Cambridge Res. Ctr, 53-54; asst. prof. physics, Brown Univ, 54-60, asst. to dean col, 58-60, assoc. prof, 60-63, prof. & exec. off. dept, 63-66; PROF. PHYSICS & DEAN GRAD. SCH, UNIV. LOUISVILLE, 66- Vis. prof, R.I. Col, 60-61; Cambridge, 63. U.S.A.A.F, 43-46. Fel. Am. Phys. Soc; Am. Asn. Physics Teachers; sr. mem. Am. Vacuum Soc. Surface physics and chemistry; thin films. Address: Graduate School, University of Louisville, Louisville, KY 40208.

DILLON, JOHN B(ARTLEY), b. San Benito, Tex, Oct. 11, 11; m. ANESTHESIOLOGY. B.S, Mt. St. Mary's Col.(Md), 36; M.S, St. Louis, 40, M.D, 43. Chief anesthesia, Letterman Gen. Hosp, 45; dept. anesthesia, Los Angeles County Gen. Hosp, 46-50; assoc. clin. prof. surg, Southern California, 46-51; anesthesia, Col. Med. Evangelists, 46-53; prof. surg. & chief div. anesthesia, SCH. MED, UNIV. CALIF, LOS ANGELES, 53-71, PROF. ANESTHESIOL. & ACTING CHMN. DEPT, 71-, ASST. DEAN PROF. SOCIAL RELATIONSHIPS, 66- Consult. anesthesiologist, hosps. Med.C, U.S.A, 43-46. Am. Med. Asn; Am. Soc. Anesthesiol; Asn. Anesthetists Gt. Brit. & North. Ireland. Circulation; respiration. Address: Dept. of Anesthesiology, University of California School of Medicine, Los Angeles, CA 90024.

DILLON, J(OHN) H(ENRY), b. Ripon, Wis, July 10, 05; m. 35, 63; c. 2. CHEMICAL PHYSICS. A.B, Ripon Col, 27; Ph.D.(physics), Wisconsin, 31; hon. Sc.D, Ripon Col, 50; hon. M.Sc, Lowell Textile Inst, 51; hon. D.Sc, Southeast. Mass. Univ, 71. Asst. physics, Wisconsin, 27-31; physicist, Firestone Tire & Rubber Co, 31-37, head physics res. div, 37-44, asst. dir. res, 44-46; dir. res, Textile Found. & Textile Res. Inst, 46-51, dir, Textile Res. Inst, 51-59, pres, 59-70; CONSULT. PHYSICIST & LECTR, 70- Vis. lectr, Princeton, 46-51, prof, 52-; Edward R. Schwarz mem. lectr, Am. Soc. Mech. Eng, 69; Gosset mem. lectr, N.C. State Univ, 71; v.pres, Nat. Coun. Textile Educ, 57-58, pres, 58-59; hon. fel. Textile Res. Inst, 71; chmn, Gordon Res. Conf. Textiles, 49; physicists group, Nat. Acad. Sci-Nat. Res. Coun. adv. comt, Nat. Bur. Standards, 61-64; trustee, Phila. Col. Textiles & Sci; Ripon Col; Smith mem. medal, Am. Soc. Test. & Mat, 55. Am. Chem. Soc; fel. Am. Phys. Soc; Soc. Rheol.(v.pres, 39-41, 53-57); hon. mem. Am. Fiber Soc.(v.pres, 60-61, pres, 61-62); Am. Asn. Textile Technol; Am. Asn. Textile Chem. & Colorists; hon. mem. & fel. Textile Inst. Eng; Brit. Soc. Chem. Indust. Chemistry and physics of high polymers, rubbers and fibers; rubber and textile products; applied radioactivity; spark breakdown; photoelectric properties of zinc single crystals. Address: Bayshore Estates, Bayview Court, Rt. Two, Seneca, SC 29678.

DILLON, J(OSEPH) F(RANCIS), JR, b. Flushing, N.Y, May 25, 24; m. 46; c. 2. PHYSICS. A.B, Virginia, 44, A.M, 48, U.S. Rubber fel, 48-49, Ph.D. (physics), 49. Physicist, Naval Ord. Lab, 48; Brit. Agr. Res. Coun. Lab, U.S. Dept. of Agr, 49-52; MEM. TECH. STAFF, BELL TEL. LABS, 52- Vis. scientist, inst. solid state physics, Univ. Tokyo, 66-67; Guggenheim fel, 66-67. U.S.N.R, 44-46. Am. Phys. Soc. Ultracentrifuge; physical properties of viruses; electron microscope; ferromagnetism; ferroelectrics; ferrites; crystal growth; ferrimagnetic resonance; ferrimagnetic garnets; optical properties of solids; magnetic domains. Address: Room 1 D-328, Bell Telephone Labs, Murray Hill, NJ 07974.

DILLON, LAWRENCE S(AMUEL), b. Reading, Pa, Apr. 6, 10; m. 32; c. 1. EVOLUTION. B.S, Pittsburgh, 33; M.S, Agr. & Mech. Col. Texas, 50, Ph.D. (entomol), 54. Chemist, Glidden Co, 34-37; curator entomol, Reading Pub. Mus, 37-48; instr. BIOL, TEX. A&M UNIV, 48-50, asst. prof, 50-55, assoc. prof, 55-61, PROF, 61- Nat. Sci. Found. sci. faculty fel, Queensland, Australia, 59-60. Fel. AAAS; N.Y. Acad. Sci; Ecol. Soc. Am; Soc. Study Evolution; Acad. Zool; Soc. Syst. Zool; Am. Soc. Zool. Evolution and phylogeny of living things; pleistocene paleoecology and bioclimatology; systematic zoology; speciation; evolution of mammalian brain; neuroanatomy. Address: Rockwood Park Estates, Route 4, Box 306, Bryan, TX 77801.

DILLON, MARCUS LUNSFORD, JR, b. Charleston, W.Va, Feb. 7, 24; m. 47; c. 8. SURGERY. B.S. & M.D, Duke Univ, 48. Intern surg, univ. hosp, Duke Univ, 47-49, jr. asst. res, 49-50, sr. asst. res, 53-55, resident SURG, 55-56, instr, 53-56, asst. prof, 56-59, ASSOC. PROF, 59-71; UNIV. KY, 71- Asst. chief surg. serv, Vet. Admin. Hosp, Durham, 56-71, chief thoracic surg, 64-71; asst. chief surg. serv. & chief thoracic & cardiovasc. surg, Vet. Admin. Hosp, Lexington, 71- Med.C, U.S.A, 50-52. Am. Col. Surg; Am. Asn. Thoracic Surg; Soc. Thoracic Surg; Am. Med. Asn. Hypothermia; extracorporeal circulation and coagulation; cardiovascular disease and hypothermia; infections; cancer. Address: Veterans Administration Hospital, Lexington, KY 40507.

DILLON, MICHAEL A, b. May 7, 36; U.S. citizen. CHEMISTRY. B.S, Canisius Col, 60; Ph.D.(chem), Notre Dame, 65. Res. assoc. chem, Notre Dame, 65-66; FEL. CHEM. PHYSICS, CARNEGIE-MELLON UNIV, 66- Am. Chem. Soc; Am. Phys. Soc. Radiation chemistry; collision phenomena. Address: Mellon Institute of Science, Carnegie-Mellon University, 4400 Fifth Ave, Pittsburgh, PA 15213.

DILLON, OLAN W(ILLIAM), JR, b. Arlington, Tex, Aug. 7, 17; m. 44; c. 1. WILDLIFE MANAGEMENT. B.S, Agr. & Mech. Col, Texas, 44. Work unit conservationist, SOIL CONSERV. SERV, U.S. DEPT. AGR, 48-54, biologist, 54-64, REGIONAL BIOLOGIST, SOUTH. DIV, 64- Wildlife Soc; Soil Conserv. Soc. Am; Am. Soc. Mammal; Am. Soc. Range Mgt; Am. Fisheries Soc. Habitat management of wild game as part of a complete conservation program on a farm or ranch. Address: Soil Conservation Service, Regional Technical Service Center, P.O. Box 11222, Ft. Worth, TX 76110.

DILLON, OSCAR WENDELL, JR, b. Franklin, Pa, May 27, 28; m. 60; c. 4. ENGINEERING MECHANICS. Aero.Eng, Cincinnati, 51; M.S, Columbia, 55, Guggenheim fel, 59. Aeronaut. engr, Cornell Aeronaut. Lab, 53-54; asst. prof. mech, Hopkins, 58-63; lectr. aerospace eng, Princeton, 63-65; assoc. prof. ENG. MECH, UNIV. KY, 65-67, PROF. & CHMN. DEPT, 67- Univ. Ky. Res. Found. res. award, 68. U.S.A.F, 51-53, 1st Lt. Soc. Natural Philos; Am. Soc. Eng. Educ.(res. award, 67); Am. Soc. Mech. Eng. Theoretical and experimental mechanics of solids, especially in the inelastic range. Address: Dept. of Engineering Mechanics, University of Kentucky, Lexington, KY 40506.

DILLON, RAYMOND D(ONALD), b. Superior, Wis, Apr. 19, 25; m. 50; c. 3. ZOOLOGY. B.S, Wisconsin State, Superior, 49; M.S, Syracuse, 51; Ph.D. (zool. & vet. sci), Wisconsin, 54. Asst. prof. biol, Nebr. State Teachers Col, 54-60; Ball State Teachers Col, 60-62; zool. & physiol, Nebraska, 62-65; PROF. ZOOL, UNIV. S.DAK, 65-, chmn. dept, 65-69. Partic, Nat. Sci. Found. U.S. Arctic Res. Prog, 67-69, Arctic Biome Prog, Naval Arctic Res. Lab, Alaska, 71-72. U.S.A.F, 43-45, Res, 59-, Maj. AAAS; Soc. Protozool; Nat. Asn. Biol. Teachers; Am. Inst. Biol. Sci; Am. Micros. Soc; Phycol. Soc. Am. Protozoology. Address: Dept. of Biology, University of South Dakota, Vermillion, SD 57069.

DILLON, ROBERT L(EE), b. Portland, Ore, Apr. 8, 20; m. 47; c. 3. PHYSICAL CHEMISTRY. A.B, Reed Col; M.S, Northwestern, 47, Ph.D.(chem), 51. Instr. chem, Idaho State Col, 47-48; from chemist to sr. scientist, Hanford Labs, Gen. Elec. Co, 51-59, mgr. chem. metall, 59-64; mgr. corrosion & coolant chem, PAC. NORTHWEST LABS, BATTELLE MEM. INST, 65-68, mgr. sodium chem. subdept, 68-70, mgr. corrosion res. & eng, 70-71; MGR. CHEM. METALL, 71- U.S.A.A.F, 42-45. Am. Chem. Soc; Am. Nuclear Soc. Water, gas, and liquid metal coolant chemistry; corrosion. Address: Fuels & Materials Dept, Battelle-Northwest, P.O. Box 999, Richland, WA 99352.

DILLON, ROBERT MORTON, b. Seattle, Wash, Oct. 27, 23; m. 43; c. 3. BUILDING RESEARCH. B.Arch, Washington (Seattle), 49; M.A.Arch, Florida, 52. Asst. prof. archit, Clemson Col, 49-50; instr, Florida, 50-52, asst. prof, 52-55; staff architect, BLDG. RES. ADV. BD, NAT. RES. COUN-NAT. ACAD. SCI, 55-57, proj. dir, 57-58, EXEC. DIR, 58- Exec. secy, U.S. Nat. Cmt. for Int. Coun. Bldg. Res, Studies & Documentation, Nat. Res. Coun, Nat. Acad. Sci-Nat. Acad. Eng, 62- Lectr, Catholic Univ, 57-63; guest lectr, U.S. Air Force Inst. Tech, 64-65. Designer-draftsman, S.C, 49-50 & architect, Fla, 52-55. Consult, Ed. Facilities Labs, Inc, N.Y, 58- Ed. reports & pub, Bldg. Res. Adv. Bd, 58- Adv. bd. dirs, Washington Center Metrop. Studies, 58-60; mem. sub-panel housing, White House Panel Civilian Tech, 61-62; adv. cmt. on low income housing demonstration prog, Dept. Housing & Urban Develop, 64-66; chmn. Am. Inst. Architects adv. cmt, Voc. Rehab. Admin, Dept. Health, Ed. & Welfare, 67-68; mem, ERIC-CEF Adv. Coun, Univ. Wisconsin, 67-69. U.S.N, 42-45. Corp. mem. Am. Inst. Archit; Am. Welding Soc. Housing building and city planning. Address: Bldg. Research Advisory Board, National Research Council National Academy of Sciences-National Academy of Engineering, 2101 Constitution Ave, Washington, DC 20418.

DILLON, ROBERT T(ROUTMAN), b. Pasadena, Calif, Feb. 2, 04; m. 30; c. 4. ORGANIC CHEMISTRY, BIOCHEMISTRY. B.S, Calif. Inst. Tech, 25, M.S, 27, fel, 28-29, Ph.D.(org. chem), 29. Asst, Calif. Inst. Tech, 25-26; Petrol. Inst, 26-28; Rockefeller Inst, 29-31, hosp, 31-37; G.D. Searle & Co, 37-41, head anal. div, 41-69; RES. CONSULT, PFANSTIEHL LABS, INC. & G.D. SEARLE & CO, 69- Mem. bd. dirs, Pfanstiehl Labs, Inc, 60- Am. Chem. Soc; Am. Soc. Biol. Chem; Soc. Appl. Spectros; Coblentz Soc. Normal butenes; synthesis and identification; reaction rates; Raman spectra; intestinal nucleotidases; gas and electrolyte equilbria in blood; bile and bile acids; analytical chemistry; enzymes; sugar chemistry; spectroscopy. Address: G.D. Searle & Co, Box 5110, Chicago, IL 60680.

DILLON, ROY D(EAN), b. Peoria, Ill, Dec. 10, 29; m. 53; c. 3. AGRICULTURE. B.S, Illinois, 52, Ed.M, 58, Ed.D, 65. Teacher, high schs, Ill, 52-53, 54-61; asst. dir. safety, Ill. Agr. Asn, 61-62; assoc. prof. agr, Morehead State Univ, 64-67; UNIV. NEBR, LINCOLN, 67-70, PROF. AGR. & SEC. EDUC, 70- U.S.A.F, 53-54, 1st Lt. Knowledges and abilities required in agriculture by workers in off-farm agricultural occupations. Address: 302 Agriculture Hall, University of Nebraska, Lincoln, NE 68506.

DILLON, THOMAS EDWARD, b. Girard, Ohio, Aug. 26, 13; m. 43; c. 2. ORGANIC CHEMISTRY. B.S, Notre Dame, 37, M.S, 40, Ph.D.(org. chem), 42. Res. chemist, E.I. DU PONT DE NEMOURS & CO, INC, 42-43, plant supvr, 43-50, sr. supvr, 50-69, SR. CHEMIST, CHAMBER WORKS, 69- Am. Chem. Soc; Am. Soc. Qual. Control; Am. Asn. Textile Chem. & Colorists. Wetting agents; detergents; water repellants; rubber and petroleum chemicals; camphor. Address: P.O. Box 278, Bear, DE 19701.

DILLON, WILLIAM PATRICK, b. Fall River, Mass, Dec. 13, 36; m. 61; c. 3. GEOLOGICAL OCEANOGRAPHY. B.S, Bates Col, 58; M.S, Rensselaer Polytech. Inst, 61; Nat. Insts. Health trainee, Univ. R.I, 64-66, Ph.D.(geol. oceanog), 69. Res. assoc. marine geol, Narragansett Marine Lab, Univ. R.I, 61-64, instr. oceanog, grad. sch. oceanog, 68-69; asst. prof. geol, San Jose State Col, 69-71; GEOLOGIST MARINE GEOL, U.S. GEOL. SURVEY, 71- Consult, Mystic Oceanog. Co, Conn, 68-69; Chevron Overseas Petrol. Inc, Calif, summer 70. Geol. Soc. Am; Am. Geophys. Union. Structure and development of continental margins; coastal evolution. Address: Office of Marine Geology, U.S. Geological Survey, 345 Middlefield Rd, Menlo Park, CA 94025.

DILLS, CHARLES E, b. La Moure, N.Dak, Apr. 20, 22; m. 61; c. 1. PHYSICAL & ORGANIC CHEMISTRY. B.S, N.Dak. State, 49; M.S, George Washington, 51; Ph.D.(chem), Harvard, 56. Res. assoc. org. chem, Columbia, 54-56; res. chemist, Nat. Res. Corp, Mass, 56-58; instr. chem, Northwest Mo. State Col, 58-59, asst. prof, 59-60; asst. ed. res, Chem. & Eng. News, 60-61; prof. sci, Deep Springs Col, 61-63; asst. prof. CHEM, CALIF. STATE POLYTECH. COL. SAN LUIS OBISPO, 63-67, ASSOC. PROF, 67- U.S.A.F, 42-45, Res, 47-, Maj. Mechanisms of organic reactions. Address: Dept. of Chemistry, California State Polytechnic College, San Luis Obispo, CA 93402.

DILLS, WILLIAM L(EONARD), b. Newton, Kans, July 9, 11; m. 41; c. 3. CHEMISTRY. A.B, Columbia Univ, 37, Ph.D.(chem), 42. RES. CHEMIST, PIGMENTS DEPT, E.I. DU PONT DE NEMOURS & CO, 41- Address: 2 Penarth Dr, Wilmington, DE 19803.

DiLORENZO, JAMES V, b. New York, N.Y, Feb. 27, 41; m. 63; c. 2. PHYSICAL & INORGANIC CHEMISTRY. B.S, Hofstra, 62, M.S, State Univ. N.Y. Stony Brook, 62, Ph.D.(chem), 67. Fel. chem, Yale, 67-68; MEM. TECH. STAFF, BELL TEL. LABS, 68- Electrochem. Soc; Am. Chem. Soc. Epitaxial growth of compound semiconductors; growth of gallium arsenide as epitaxial structures for microwave device applications. Address: Bell Telephone Labs, Murray Hill, NJ 07971.

DI LORENZO, JOSEPH JOHN, b. Brooklyn, N.Y, Aug. 7, 14; c. 3. BACTERIOLOGY. B.S, Iowa, 36, M.S, 37; Ph.D, Georgetown, 50. Bacteriologist, U.S. Army Engrs, 41-42; U.S. Pub. Health Serv, 42-43; bacteriologist, FOOD & DRUG ADMIN, Fed. Security Agency, 46-53, specialist antibiotic mfr, 53-70, HEALTH SCIENTIST ADMINR, OFF. INT. AFFAIRS, 70- Sanit.C, U.S.A, 43-46. Am. Soc. Microbiol; Am. Pub. Health Asn. Antibiotics; microbiology; parasitology; clinical and epidemiological use of typhoid bacteriophage. Address: Office of International Affairs, Food & Drug Administration, 5600 Fishers Lane, Rockville, MD 20852.

DI LORETO, ALDO G(ENE), b. Rochester, N.Y, Nov. 14, 27; m. 57; c. 2. ELECTRICAL ENGINEERING, PHYSICS. B.S, Calif. Inst. Tech, 56, M.S, 57, Ph.D.(elec. eng, physics), 62. Teaching asst. elec. eng, Calif. Inst. Tech, 58-60; supvr, U.S. Naval Ord. Test Sta, 62-70, HEAD MODELING & ANAL. DIV, NAVAL UNDERSEA RES. & DEVELOP. CTR, 70- Lectr, Southern California, 63- U.S.M.C, 45-48, 50-51, S/Sgt. Noise sources in solid state devices; low frequency holography; development of sonar simulation models. Address: Naval Undersea Research & Development Center, 3202 E. Foothill Blvd, Pasadena, CA 91107.

DIL PARE, ARMAND LEON, b. New York, N.Y, Aug. 12, 32; m. 52; c. 1. MACHINE DESIGN, AUTOMATIC CONTROL SYSTEMS. B.M.E, City Col. New York, 53; M.S.M.E, Columbia, 57, Ph.D.(kinematics mechanisms), 65. Instr. mech. eng, City Col. New York, 53; struct. engr, Repub. Aviation Corp, 53-56; mem. tech. staff, Bell Tel. Labs, N.Y, 56-62; div. engr, Lundy Electronics & Systs. Inc, 62-65; asst. prof. mech. eng, Columbia Univ, 65-70; ASSOC. DIR. RES. & DEVELOP, DEFENSE SYSTS. DIV, LUNDY ELECTRONICS & SYSTS, INC, 70-, consult, 65-70. Am. Soc. Mech. Eng; Am. Soc. Eng. Educ. Kinematic analysis and synthesis of mechanisms; dynamics of machinery; electronic warfare and countermeasures. Address: Defense Systems Division, Lundy Electronics & Systems, Inc, Glen Head, NY 11545.

DILS, RAY R, b. Seattle, Wash, July 19, 35; m. 57; c. 2. METALLURGY, SOLID STATE PHYSICS. B.S, Stanford, 57, M.S, 59, Ph.D.(mat. sci), 65. Sr. res. assoc. mat. sci, ADV. MAT. RES. & DEVELOP. LAB, PRATT & WHITNEY AIRCRAFT DIV, UNITED AIRCRAFT CORP, 62-67, GROUP LEADER PHYSICS GROUP, 67- U.S.A.R, 58. Electron probe microanalysis; oxidation behavior of materials in dynamic fluids and related surface physics. Address: Advanced Material Research & Development Lab, Pratt & Whitney Aircraft, Middletown, CT 06458.

DILS, ROBERT E(ARL), b. Ohio, July 6, 19; m. 42; c. 3. FORESTRY. B.S.F, Colo. Agr. & Mech. Col, 46, M.F, 47; Ph.D.(soil sci), Mich. State Col, 52. Res. asst. forestry, Colo. Agr. Exp. Sta, 46-47; timber mgt. asst, Helena Nat. Forest, Mont, 57; instr. forestry, Mich. State Col, 47-49, asst. prof, 49-54, assoc. prof, 54-55; Univ. Mich, 55-58; PROF. WATERSHED MGT, COLO. STATE UNIV, 58-, DEAN COL. FORESTRY & NATURAL RESOURCES, 69-, leader watershed mgt. unit, 58-65, assoc. dean col. forestry & natural resources, 65-69. Cooperator, Coweeta Hydrol. Lab, Ga, 52-56; collab, Mich. Hydrol. Res. Proj, 53-55; Lake States Forest Exp. Sta, U.S. Forest Serv, 53-58, Rocky Mt. Forest & Range Exp. Sta, 59-; consult, U.S. State Dept, Taiwan, summer 63; Fulbright res. scholar, N.Z, 64-65; consult, Food & Agr. Orgn, UN, Arg. U.S.A.A.F, 42-46. Fel. Soc. Am. Foresters (assoc. ed, J. Forestry); Am. Geophys. Union; fel. Soil Conserv. Soc. Am; Am. Soc. Agron; Soil Sci. Soc. Am. Forest soils, ecology and influences; watershed management. Address: College of Forestry & Natural Resources, Colorado State University, Ft. Collins, CO 80521.

DILS, ROBERT JAMES, b. Dayton, Ohio, Oct. 2, 19; m. 47; c. 4. PHYSICAL SCIENCE. B.S, Eastern Kentucky, 43; M.A, Marshall, 60; Ohio State, 62-64. Teacher, high sch, Ky, 48-51; instr. chem, Ashland Jr. Col, 51-57; chmn. dept. sci, Paul G. Blazer High Sch, 57-62; coord. sci, sec. sch, Ashland, Ky, 62-63; asst. prof. MARSHALL UNIV, 64-67, ASSOC. PROF. PHYS. SCI, 67- U.S.A.A.F, 43-46, Res, 46-50, T/Sgt. AAAS; Am. Asn. Higher Educ. Science education and curriculum development in college and secondary schools. Address: Dept. of Physical Sciences, Marshall University, Huntington, WV 25701.

DILTS, JOSEPH A(LSTYNE), b. Sommerville, N.J, Sept. 12, 42. INORGANIC CHEMISTRY. B.A, Ohio Wesleyan Univ, 64; Ph.D.(chem), Northwest. Univ, 69. Fel, Ga. Inst. Technol, 68-70; ASST. PROF. CHEM, UNIV. N.C, GREENSBORO, 70- Am. Chem. Soc; The Chem. Soc; N.Am. Thermal Anal. Soc. Organometallic and hydride chemistry of the main group elements; application of thermal analysis techniques to organometallic chemistry. Address: Dept. of Chemistry, University of North Carolina at Greensboro, Greensboro, NC 27412.

DILTS, R(OBERT) V(OORHEES), b. Plainfield, N.J, June 18, 29. ANALYTICAL CHEMISTRY. A.B, Wesleyan, 51; M.A, Princeton, 53, Ph.D.(chem), 54. Instr. CHEM, Williams Col, 54-57, asst. prof, 57-60; VANDERBILT UNIV, 60-68, ASSOC. PROF, 68-, dir. undergrad. prog. chem, 67-69. Vis. assoc. prof, Univ. Kans, 69-70. Am. Chem. Soc. Coulometric titrations; atomic absorption spectroscopy; complexometric titrations. Address: Dept. of Chemistry, Vanderbilt University, Nashville, TN 37203.

DI LUZIO, NICHOLAS R(OBERT), b. Hazelton, Pa, May 4, 26; m. 48; c. 3. PHYSIOLOGY. B.S, Scranton, 50; U.S. Pub. Health Serv. fel, Tennessee, 52-54, Ph.D.(physiol), 54. Instr, med. units, Tennessee, 55-57, asst. prof, 57-59, assoc. prof, 59-62, prof. physiol. & biophys, 62-68, chmn. dept, 65-68; PROF. & CHMN. DEPT. PHYSIOL, SCH. MED, TULANE UNIV, 68- Summers, res. participant, Oak Ridge Nat. Lab, 56, U.S. Naval Radiol. Defense Lab, 58; Lederle med. faculty award, 58-61; mem. Tenn. Adv. Comt. Atomic Energy, 58-68; sci. adv. comt, Nat. Coun. Alcoholism, 63-68; consult, Riker Lab, 61-70; Uniroyal, 68-70. U.S.A.A.F, 44-46. AAAS; Am. Physiol. Soc; Soc. Exp. Biol. & Med; Radiation Res. Soc; Reticuloendothelial Soc.(res. award, 64, ed, Advan. Exp. Med. & Biol, Jour); Am. Heart Asn. Metabolism of lipids and radioactive colloids; hepatic cell function, liver injury; physio-pathology of reticuloendothelial system. Address: Dept. of Physiology, Tulane University School of Medicine, 1430 Tulane Ave, New Orleans, LA 70112.

DILWORTH, BENJAMIN CONROY, b. Monroe, La, Sept. 29, 31; m. 55; c. 3. POULTRY NUTRITION, BIOCHEMISTRY. B.S, Miss. State, 59, M.S, 62, Ph.D.(poultry nutrit), 66. Res. asst. POULTRY NUTRIT, MISS. STATE UNIV, 59-66, ASST. PROF. POULTRY SCI, 66- U.S.N, 50-54. Poultry Sci. Asn; World Poultry Sci. Asn. Calcium, phosphorus and vitamin D_3 interrelationships and requirements of poultry; protein quality of feedstuffs; unidentified factors and nutritional factors affecting the incidence of blood spots in eggs. Address: Dept. of Poultry Science, Mississippi State University, P.O. Box 5188, State College, MS 39762.

DILWORTH, HAROLD C, b. Jasper, Ala, Mar. 27, 28; m. 53; c. 3. SPECTROSCOPY, INORGANIC CHEMISTRY. B.S, Alabama, 52. Chemist, Stockham Valves & Fittings, Inc, 52-55; Chicago Bridge & Iron Co, 55-62; Nat. Bur. Standards, 62-65; spectrochemist, ARMCO STEEL CORP, 65-70, SUPV. RES. SPECTROCHEMIST, 70- Soc. Appl. Spectros; Am. Soc. Test. & Mat. Optical emission and x-ray fluorescence analysis of metals. Address: Research & Technology, Armco Steel Corp, 703 Curtis St, Middletown, OH 45042.

DILWORTH, JOHN RICHARD, b. Dubuque, Iowa, May 21, 14; m. 37; c. 3. FORESTRY. B.S, Iowa State Col, 37, M.S, 38; Ph.D, Washington, 56. Instr. forestry, Louisiana, 38-46; asst. prof, ORE. STATE UNIV, 46-51, assoc. prof, 51-55, PROF. FOREST MGT. & HEAD DEPT, 55- U.S.A, 42-45, Maj. Soc. Am. Foresters; Am. Soc. Photogram. Silviculture; aerial photo mensuration; log scaling and timber cruising. Address: School of Forestry, Oregon State University, Corvallis, OR 97331.

DILWORTH, ROBERT HAMILTON, III, b. Bryson City, N.C, Aug. 6, 30; m. 53; c. 4. ELECTRONIC ENGINEERING. B.S, Tennessee, 52. Chief engr, Spec. Instruments Lab, Inc, Tenn, 54-55; instrument engr, Oak Ridge Inst. Nuclear Studies, 55-56, develop. engr, Oak Ridge Nat. Lab, 56-62, chief electronics engr, ORTEC, INC, 62-66, prod. mgr. electronics, 66-68, MGR. LIFE SCI. PROD, 68- U.S.A.F, 52-54, 1st Lt. Sci. Res. Soc. Am; Inst. Elec. & Electronics Eng. Analysis and management of new technological ventures; modular nuclear instrumentation for physics research; engineering and product line management. Address: ORTEC, Inc, 100 Midland Rd, P.O. Box C, Oak Ridge, TN 37830.

DILWORTH, ROBERT P(ALMER), b. Hemet, Calif, Dec. 2, 14; m. 40; c. 2. MATHEMATICS. B.S, Calif. Inst. Tech, 36, fel, 36-39, Ph.D.(math), 39. Sterling res. fel, Yale, 39-40, instr. MATH, 40-43; asst. prof, CALIF. INST. TECHNOL, 43-45, assoc. prof, 45-51, PROF, 51- With U.S.A.A.F, 44. Am. Math. Soc; Math. Asn. Am. Lattice theory; mathematical statistics; structure and arithmetical theory of noncommutative residuated lattices. Address: Dept. of Mathematics, California Institute of Technology, Pasadena, CA 91107.

DiMAGGIO, ANTHONY, III, b. New Orleans, La, Aug. 17, 35; m. 60; c. 2. BIOCHEMISTRY. B.S, Loyola (La), 56; Ph.D.(biochem), La. State, 61. Asst. prof. CHEM, LOYOLA (LA), 61-64, ASSOC. PROF, 64-, CHMN. DEPT, 67-, chmn. grad. coun, 68-70. Dir. res, strontium fallout in tooth study, 64-66, co-prin. investr, 66-68; consult, Photo-Dek, Inc, 64-66. AAAS; Am. Chem. Soc; Am. Soc. Ichthyol. & Herpet. Comparative biochemistry of reptiles, especially the lizard, Anolis carolinensis, particularly its endocrinology and metabolism. Address: Dept. of Chemistry, Loyola University, New Orleans, LA 70118.

DiMAGGIO, FRANK L, b. N.Y.C, Sept. 2, 29; m. 63; c. 2. APPLIED MECHANICS. B.S, Columbia Univ, 50, M.S, 51, Ph.D.(eng. mech), 54. Instr. CIVIL ENG. & ENG. MECH, COLUMBIA UNIV, 50-54, PROF, 56- Consult, Paul Weidlinger, Consult Engr, N.Y, 56-; Nat. Sci. Found. sr. fel, 62-63. U.S.A, 54-56. Am. Soc. Civil Eng. Dynamic response of structures and interaction with fluids; material models for soils. Address: Dept. of Civil Engineering, School of Engineering & Applied Science, Columbia University, New York, NY 10027.

DI MARCO, G(ABRIEL) ROBERT, b. Camden, N.J, July 31, 27; m. 49; c. 5. FOOD SCIENCE. B.S, Rutgers, 54, Ph.D.(plant path), 59. Asst. plant path, RUTGERS UNIV, 54-57, exten. assoc. FOOD SCI, 57-59, asst. prof, 59-62, assoc. prof, 62-65, PROF, 65-, CHMN. DEPT, 63- Am. Phytopath. Soc; Inst. Food Tech. Maintaining quality and the objective measurement of quality of harvested fruits and vegetables; food additives; post-harvest pathology; food packaging; processed meat products; food science. Address: Dept. of Food Science, Rutgers, The State University, New Brunswick, NJ 08903.

DI MARI, SAMUEL JOSEPH, b. Omaha, Nebr, May 17, 38. BIO-ORGANIC CHEMISTRY. B.Sc, Creighton, 60, M.Sc, 62; Nat. Insts. Health fel, California, Berkeley, 63-66, Ph.D.(bio-org. chem), 67. Am. Cancer Soc. res. fel. BIOCHEM, Univ. Calif, Berkeley, 68-71; ASST. PROF, SCH. MED, VANDERBILT UNIV, 71- AAAS; Am. Chem. Soc. Biosynthesis of natural products; enzyme reaction mechanisms; neurochemistry. Address: Dept. of Biochemistry, Vanderbilt University, Nashville, TN 37203.

DIMARZIO, EDMUND ARMAND, b. Philadelphia, Pa, Mar. 23, 32; m. 56; c. 3. PHYSICS. B.S, St. Joseph's Col.(Pa), 55; M.S, Univ. Pa, 60; Ph.D, Cath. Univ. Am, 67. Physicist, Am. Viscose Co, 56-62; mem. tech. staff theoret. chem, Bell Tel. Labs, 62-63; PHYSICIST, NAT. BUR. STANDARDS, 63- High polymer physics prize, 67; Stratton Award, 71. Fel. Am. Phys. Soc. Helixcoil transition in biological macromolecules; glass transition in polymers; liquid crystal phase transitions; surface polymers; kinetics of crystallization. Address: Polymer Physics Section, National Bureau of Standards, Washington, DC 20034.

DIMASCIO, ALBERTO, b. Philadelphia, Pa, Feb. 8, 28; m. 49; c. 5. PSYCHOLOGY. A.B, Harvard, 51; M.A, Boston, 53. Res. psychologist, Atomic Energy Proj, sch. med, Boston, 51-53; res. assoc, dept. psychiat, Harvard Med. Sch, 53-57; exp. stress & caries proj, Boston, 58-61, pharmaco-therapeut. res. proj, 57-61, Dutch Stipple Proj, 59-61; prin. investr, psychopharmacol. res. lab, Mass. Ment. Health Ctr & Dept. Psychiat, Harvard Med. Sch, 59-68; DIR. PSYCHOPHARMACOL. RES, STATE OF MASS, 68- Consult, Boston Psychopathic & Metrop. State Hosp. & Boston Vet. Admin. Hosp, 59-61; assoc. prof. psychiat, sch. med, Tufts Univ, 69- Am. Col. Neuropsychopharmacol; Am. Psychol. Asn; Soc. Biol. Psychiat; Int. Col. Neuropsychopharmacol; World Psychiat. Asn. Psychopharmacology and psychophysiology; experimental psychopathology; research design and statistics. Address: Boston State Hospital, 591 Morton St, Boston, MA 02124.

DiMASI, GABRIEL JOSEPH, b. Harrison, N.J, July 11, 36; m. 62; c. 3. ELECTROCHEMISTRY, CHEMICAL ENGINEERING. B.S.Ch.E, Newark Col. Eng, 58, M.S, 63; U.S. Army Electronics Command fel, Univ. Pa, 65. Chem. engr. primary batteries, U.S. ARMY ELECTRONICS COMMAND LABS, 58-60, fuel cells, 60-63, magnesium batteries, 63-65, res. engr, 66-67, GROUP LEADER ELECTRODE KINETICS, 67-, CHMN. DEPT. CHEM, EDUC. & TRAINING, 66- Spec. awards, U.S. Army Electronics Command, 68, 69, 70. Electrochem. Soc; Am. Inst. Chem. Eng; Am. Inst. Chem. Kinetics of hydrocarbon oxidation and reduction on platinum electrodes and other noble metals; on-line computer data collection and reduction; anodic dissolution of magnesium electrodes in various halide electrolytes and in magnesium perchlorate, magnesium sulfate, and sodium perchlorate; metal-air batteries. Address: 24 Pal Dr, Wayside, Ocean, NJ 07712.

DIMEFF, JOHN, b. Detroit, Mich, July 2, 21; m. 44; c. 2. PHYSICS. B.S, Harvard, 42. Radio engr, Naval Res. Lab, 43-44, 45-46; physicist, AMES RES. CTR, NASA, 46, aeronaut. res. scientist, 46-53, chief, wind tunnel instrument br, 56-59, asst. chief, INSTRUMENTATION DIV, 59-67, chief, 67-71, ASST. DIR. INSTRUMENTATION RES, 71- Sensors; instrumentation; electronics; data processing. Address: Instrumentation Division, Ames Research Center, NASA, Moffett Field, CA 94035.

DIMENT, JOHN ARTHUR, b. Sydney, Australia, Aug. 10, 43; m. 70. BIO-ORGANIC CHEMISTRY, IMMUNOLOGY. B.Sc, Univ. Sydney, 64, M.Sc, 66, Ph.D.(chem), 69. Eleanor Sophie Wood travelling fel. biochem. from Univ. Sydney, Univ. London, 69-70; RES. ASSOC. IMMUNO-CHEM, UNIV. MANITOBA, 70-, Can. Med. Res. Coun. fel, 70-72. Can. Soc. Immunol; Am. Chem. Soc; Royal Australian Chem. Inst. The nature of cellular receptors and antigens and their chemistry; peptide and natural product synthesis and biosynthesis. Address: Dept. of Immunology, University of Manitoba, 795 McDermot Ave, Winnipeg 3, Man, Can.

DIMENT, WILLIAM H(ORACE), b. Oswego, N.Y, Oct. 15, 27; m. 58; c. 3. GEOPHYSICS. A.B, Williams Col, 49; A.M, Harvard, 51, Ph.D.(geophys), 54. Explor. geophysicist, Calif. Co, 53-56; geophysicist, U.S. Geol. Surv, 56-60, chief, br. theoret. geophys, 60-62, res. geophysicist, 62-65; PROF. GEOL, UNIV. ROCHESTER, 65. Nat. Sci. Found. sr. fel, Yale, 64-65. U.S.N.R, 45-46. AAAS; Geol. Soc. Am; Seismol. Soc. Am; Am. Geophys. Union; Soc. Explor. Geophys. Terrestrial heat flow; seismology; gravity; limnology. Address: Dept. of Geological Sciences, University of Rochester, Rochester, NY 14627.

DIMICK, PAUL SLAYTON, b. Burlington, Vt, Sept. 15, 35; m. 58; c. 3. FOOD CHEMISTRY. B.S, Vermont, 58, M.S, 60; Ph.D.(dairy sci), Pa. State, 64. Asst. dairy sci, Vermont, 58-60; PA. STATE UNIV, 61-63, res. asst, 63-64, res. assoc, 64-66, asst. prof. FOOD SCI, 66-70, ASSOC. PROF, 70- U.S.A, 60-61, Res, 61-69, Capt. Am. Dairy Sci. Asn; Inst. Food Technol. Ruminant lipid metabolism, especially milk fat synthesis; flavor research, especially lipid precursors. Address: 116 Borland Lab, Pennsylvania State University, University Park, PA 16802.

DI MILO, ANTHONY J, b. Philadelphia, Pa, May 6, 24; m. 48, 70; c. 2. CHEMISTRY. A.B, Temple, 48; fel, Indiana, 48-49; Ph.D.(org. chem), Mass. Inst. Tech, 53. Res. chemist, Atlantic Ref. Co, 53-58; chemist, AEROJET SOLID PROPULSION CO, 58-60, sr. chemist, 60-66, CHEM. SUPVR, 66- Adj. prof, Drexel Inst, 55-58. U.S.A, 43-46. Am. Chem. Soc; Sci. Res. Soc. Am. Reaction kinetics; petrochemicals; chemistry of solids rocket propellants; chemistry of isocyanates, epoxides and aziridines. Address: Aerojet Solid Propulsion Co, P.O. Box 13400, Sacramento, CA 95813.

DIMITMAN, JEROME E(UGENE), b. N.Y.C, Sept. 24, 20; m. 44; c. 3. PLANT PATHOLOGY. B.S, Univ. Calif, 43, M.S, 49, Ph.D, 58. Assoc. plant pathologist, State Dept. Agr, Calif, 47-49; PROF. BIOL. & CHMN. DEPT. BIOL. SCI, CALIF. STATE POLYTECH. COL, POMONA, 49- U.S.N, 43-46, U.S.N.R, 46-70, Comdr. Am. Phytopath. Soc; Bot. Soc. Am. Citrus diseases, viruses; Phytophthora physiology; subtropical plants; crop diseases. Address: Dept. of Biological Sciences, California State Polytechnic College, Pomona, CA 91766.

DIMITRIADES, BASIL, b. Thessaloniki, Greece, Nov. 9, 29; U.S. citizen. PHYSICAL CHEMISTRY. Dipl. chem. eng, Athens Tech, 54; M.S, Miami (Fla), 59, Ph.D.(phys. chem), 62. Res. chemist, U.S. BUR. MINES, 62-64, proj. leader AIR POLLUTION RES, 64-69, ASST. PROJ. COORD, 69- Chmn. exhaust sampling & anal. group, Coord. Res. Coun-Air Pollution Res. Adv. Comt, 70- Greek Royal Navy, 54-57, Ens. Am. Chem. Soc; Air Pollution Control Asn. Reaction mechanisms in rocket propellant combustion systems; air pollution systems associated with automotive engine exhaust gases; atmospheric reactions mechanisms. Address: 2301 Silver Lake Rd, Bartlesville, OK 74003.

DIMITROFF, EDWARD, b. Nancy, France, Feb. 27, 27; U.S. citizen; m. 51; c. 2. ORGANIC & PHYSICAL CHEMISTRY. B.S, Denver, 56; M.S, St. Mary's (Tex), 65. Res. chemist, U.S. Naval Ord. Test Sta, 56-59; assoc. res. chemist, SOUTHWEST RES. INST, 59-60, sr. res. chemist, 60-66, staff scientist, 66-69, MGR. PETROL. TECHNOL, 70- Am. Chem. Soc; fel. Am. Inst. Chem. Eng; Soc. Automotive Eng. Liquid rocket propellants and combustion phenomena; mechanisms of dispersancy in oil media; engine sludge, varnish, rust formation and induction system deposition; thermodynamics and kinetics of combustion and precombustion; liquid fuels crystallization. Address: 4838 Rollingfield Dr, San Antonio, TX 78228.

DIMITROFF, GEORGE ERNEST, b. N.Y.C, July 22, 38; m. 61; c. 2. MATHEMATICS, ALGEBRA. B.A, Reed Col, 60; M.A, Oregon, 62, Ph.D.(math), 64. ASST. PROF. MATH, KNOX COL.(ILL), 64- Am. Math. Soc; Math. Asn. Am. Partially ordered topological spaces. Address: Dept. of Mathematics, Knox College, Galesburg, IL 61401.

DIMITROV, JOHANNA, b. Aussig, Czech, Jan. 9, 32; m. 68; c. 1. ORGANIC CHEMISTRY. Dipl. chem, Univ. Mainz, 58; Dr. rer. nat.(chem), Munich Tech. Univ, 65. Mkt. res. chemist, Battelle Inst, Ger, 58-62; patent chemist, Consortium Electrochemie, 66-69; LIT. CHEMIST, LEDERLE LABS. DIV, AM. CYANAMID CO, 69- Kinetic studies on enzymes; kinetic studies on tritium exchange reactions with hydrocarbons in gas atmosphere in electric discharge. Address: Lederle Labs. Division, American Cyanamid Co, Pearl River, NY 10965.

DIMLER, ROBERT J(ULIUS), b. Pekin, Ill, Sept. 28, 14; m. 41; c. 3. ORGANIC CHEMISTRY. B.S, Bradley, 36; Alumnae Res. Found. scholar & fel, Wisconsin, 36-38, M.S, 38, Ph.D.(org. chem), 40. Asst. biochem, Wisconsin, 38-40; biochem. & carbohydrate chem, 40-41; chemist, starch & dextrose sect, NORTH. MARKETING & NUTRIT. RES. DIV, U.S. DEPT. AGR, 41-48, in charge starch struct. group, 48-55, head chem. reactions & struct. invests, 55-60, chief cereal properties lab, 60-64, DIR. DIV, 64- Instr, Bradley, 47- Am. Chem. Soc; Am. Asn. Cereal Chem. Structure of starch and dextran; reactions of dextrose; qualitative and quantitative determination of sugars; cereal grain proteins; other chemical constituents of cereal grains; utilization of cereal grains, soybeans, flaxseed and other plants, seeds and fibers. Address: Northern Marketing & Nutrition Research Division, U.S. Dept. of Agriculture, Peoria, IL 61604.

DIMMEL, DONALD R, b. Waseca Co, Minn, May 26, 40; m. 60; c. 2. ORGANIC CHEMISTRY. B.S, Minnesota, Minneapolis, 62; Nat. Insts. Health fel, Purdue, 64-66, Ph.D.(org. chem), 66. Nat. Insts. Health fel. photochem, Cornell, 66-67; ASST. PROF. ORG. CHEM, MARQUETTE UNIV, 67- Am. Chem. Soc. Organic photochemistry; chemistry of strained polycyclic compounds; molecular rearrangements; mass spectrometry. Address: Dept. of Chemistry, Marquette University, Milwaukee, WI 53233.

DIMMICK, HENRY M, b. Canton, Ohio, Sept. 27, 22; m. 58; c. 2. ELECTRONICS. B.S, Pa. State, 48. Res. physicist, Preston Labs, Pa, 48-51, chief engr. instrument develop, 51-52; prod. engr, Brockway Glass Co, 52-53; owner, Dimmick Assocs, Pa, 53-61; V.PRES. ENG. & DEVELOP. INSTRUMENT DESIGN, AM. GLASS RES, INC, 61- U.S.A.F, 42-45, Sgt. Soc. Motion Picture & TV Eng; Audio Eng. Soc. Fracture of brittle materials; electronic, mechanical and optical instrument systems for research or industrial process control. Address: American Glass Research, Inc, P.O. Box 149, Butler, PA 16001.

DIMMICK, JOHN F(REDERICK), b. Thomson, Ill, Aug. 7, 21; m. 46; c. 2. PHYSIOLOGY, BIOLOGY. B.S, Western Illinois, 48, M.S, 49; Ph.D.(mammalian physiol), Illinois, 60. Teaching asst. biol, Western Illinois, 48-49; teacher, high schs, Ill, 49-59; res. asst. physiol, Illinois, 59-60, U.S. Dept. Agr. fel, 60-61; TEACHER & RES. ANIMAL PHYSIOL. & GEN. BIOL, WAKE FOREST UNIV, 61- Vis. lectr, N.C. Acad. Sci, 63-; dir. training center, high sch. teacher's inserv. training proj, Nat. Sci. Found-N.C. Acad. Sci, 64-68. U.S.A , 42-45. AAAS; Nat. Sci. Teachers Asn; Nat. Asn. Biol. Teachers. Digestion and utilization of legume protein by mammals. Address: Dept. of Biology, Wake Forest University, P.O. Box 7325, Reynolda Station, Winston-Salem, NC 27109.

DIMMICK, RALPH W, b. Chicago, Ill, Nov. 18, 34; m. 54; c. 2. ANIMAL ECOLOGY, WILDLIFE MANAGEMENT. B.A, Southern Illinois, 57, M.A, 61; Ph.D.(zool), Wyoming, 64. Asst. prof. animal ecol, Tenn. Tech. Univ, 64-66; FORESTRY, UNIV. TENN, KNOXVILLE, 66-71, ASSOC. PROF, 71- U.S.A, 57-59. Wildlife Soc. Ecology and management of waterfowl resources. Address: Dept. of Forestry, University of Tennessee, Knoxville, TN 37916.

DIMMICK, ROBERT L(EWELLYN), b. Parkersburg, W.Va, Jan. 4, 20; m. 42; c. 1. MICROBIOLOGY. A.B, Marietta Col, 47; M.S, Purdue, 49, Ph.D, 53. Asst, Purdue, 47-52; asst. res. bacteriologist, aerobiol, Naval Biol. Labs, Univ. Calif, Berkeley, 53-59, assoc. res. bacteriologist, 59-65, res. bacteriologist, 65-68; prof. biol. & dir. ctr. advan. med. technol, San Francisco State Col, 68-71, RES. BACTERIOLOGIST, NAVAL BIOMED. RES. LABS, 71- U.S.A.A.F, 41-46, 1st Lt. AAAS; Am. Chem. Soc; Am. Soc. Microbiol; fel. Am. Acad. Microbiol. Survival and free radicals in bacteria. Address: 124 Denslowe Dr, San Francisco, CA 94132.

DIMMIG, DANIEL ASHTON, b. Lansdale, Pa, Mar. 5, 24; m. 51; c. 2. ORGANIC CHEMISTRY. B.S, Muhlenberg Col, 45; M.S, Pennsylvania, 48; Ph.D.(org. chem), Pittsburgh, 63. Res. chemist, nitrogen div, Allied Chem. Corp, 48-55; U.S. Steel jr. fel. utilization of coal tar chem, Mellon Inst, 55-63; sr. res. chemist, Pennsalt Chem. Corp, 63-67, PROJ. LEADER, PENNWALT CORP, 67- Am. Chem. Soc. Monomer and polymer synthesis; polymer evaluation. Address: Research & Development Dept, Pennwalt Corp, 900 First Ave, King of Prussia, PA 19406.

DIMMOCK, JOHN O, b. Garden City, N.Y, Nov. 24, 36; m. 58; c. 3. PHYSICS. B.S, Yale, 58, Ph.D.(physics), 62. Res. scientist solid state physics, Raytheon Co, 62-63; mem. staff, LINCOLN LAB, MASS. INST. TECHNOL, 63-66, LEADER APPL. PHYSICS GROUP, 66- Am. Phys. Soc; Inst. Elec. & Electronics Eng. Theoretical and experimental solid state physics; magnetism and semiconductors. Address: Lincoln Lab, Massachusetts Institute of Technology, Lexington, MA 02173.

DIMMOCK, JONATHAN R(ICHARD), b. Southampton, Eng, July 6, 37; m. 68. PHARMACEUTICAL CHEMISTRY. B.Pharm, Univ. London, 59, assistantship, 60-63, Ph.D.(pharmaceut. chem), 63. Org. res. chemist, Chesterford Park Res. Sta, Saffron Waldon, Eng, 63-67; asst. prof. PHARMACEUT. CHEM, UNIV. SASK, 67-69, ASSOC. PROF, 69- Res. grants, Can. Found. for Advan. Pharm, 68, Nat. Res. Coun. Fund, 68-70 & Smith Kline & French Labs, Pa, 71. Pharmaceut. Soc. Gt. Brit; The Chem. Soc; assoc. Royal Inst. Chem. Synthesis and stereochemistry of novel compounds screened against cancers; relationship between flexibility and rigidity in biologically active molecules; antimicrobial agents; analgesics; pesticides. Address: Dept. of Pharmaceutical Chemistry, University of Saskatchewan, Saskatoon, Sask, Can.

DIMOCK, ARTHUR WATSON, b. Middleboro, Mass, June 20, 08; m; c. 4. PLANT PATHOLOGY. B.S, California, 33, M.S, 34, Ph.D.(plant path), 36. Asst, dept. plant path, California, 32-35; asst. pathologist, div. forest path, bur. plant indust, U.S. Dept. Agr, 35-38; asst. prof. PLANT PATH, CORNELL UNIV, 38-43, assoc. prof, 43-47, PROF, 47- AAAS; Am. Inst. Biol. Sci; Am. Phytopath. Soc.(treas, 58-64, v.pres, 66-67, pres-elect, 67-68, pres, 68-69). Diseases of ornamental plants; environmental factors and disease development. Address: Dept. of Plant Pathology, Cornell University, Ithaca, NY 14850.

DIMOCK, DIRCK L, b. Braintree, Mass, June 23, 30; m. 52; c. 3. PHYSICS. B.S, Antioch Col, 52; Ph.D.(physics), Hopkins, 57. Mem. res. staff, Plasma Physics Lab, Princeton, 57-62; vis. scientist, Max Planck Inst. Physics & Astrophys, 62-63; ASSOC. HEAD, EXP. DIV, PLASMA PHYSICS LAB, PRINCETON, 63-, lectr. astrophys. Sci, 63-66. Consult, Princeton Appl. Res. Corp, 64-65. AAAS; Am. Phys. Soc. Plasma physics; spectroscopic and optical plasma diagnostics, and atomic structure. Address: Plasma Physics Lab, P.O. Box 451, Princeton University, Princeton, NJ 08540.

DIMOCK, RONALD V(ILROY), JR, b. Melrose, Mass, Apr. 11, 43; m. 66; c. 2. INVERTEBRATE ZOOLOGY, PHYSIOLOGICAL ECOLOGY. B.A, Univ. N.H, 65; M.S, Fla. State Univ, 67; Ph.D.(invert. zool), Univ. Calif, Santa Barbara, 70. ASST. PROF. BIOL, WAKE FOREST UNIV, 70- AAAS; Am. Soc. Zool; Marine Biol. Asn. U.K. Invertebrate chemical communication; physiological ecology of marine invertebrates; chemosensory basis of host recognition by the symbiotic polychaete Arctonoe pulchra. Address: Dept. of Biology, Wake Forest University, Winston-Salem, NC 27109.

DIMOND, ALBERT E(UGENE), b. Spokane, Wash, May 11, 14; m. 56; c. 1. PLANT PATHOLOGY. A.B, Wisconsin, 36, A.M, 37, Ph.D.(bot), 39. Res. fel, crop protection inst, exp. sta, Connecticut, 40-42; asst. prof. bot, Nebraska, 42-45, physics, 43-44, asst. agr. chemist & plant pathologist, agr. exp. sta, 44-45; assoc. plant pathologist, CONN. AGR. EXP. STA, 46-50, PLANT PATHOLOGIST, 50-, CHIEF, DEPT. PLANT PATH. & BOT, 50-, V.DIR, 72-, asst. chief, 49-50, Johnson distinguished scientist, 69. Lectr, sch. forestry, Yale, 48-; vis. lectr, Am. Inst. Biol. Sci, 62-65, mem. comt. pub. probs, 52, finance comt, 71-; vis. lectr, Inst. Nac. Tech. Agropecuaria, Arg, 62, 64. Assoc, Johnson Res. Found, Univ. Pa, 44-45; consult, Nat. Sci. Found, 61-65; coop. state res. serv, U.S. Dept. Agr, 63-64; mem. subcomt. plant pathogens, Nat. Acad. Sci-Nat. Res. Coun, 63-; & mem. exec. comt. & nat. comt. & chmn. finance comt, Int. Bot. Cong, 65-69. Fel. AAAS; fel. Am. Phytopath. Soc.(treas, 50-52, v.pres, 62, pres-elect, 63, pres, 64); Bot. Soc. Am; Am. Soc. Plant Physiol; Indian Photopath. Soc. Physiology of fungi; physiology of pathogenism; biological effects of ionizion radiation; mode of action of fungicides; chemotherapy of plant diseases; vascular wilt diseases of plants. Address: Dept. of Plant Pathology & Botany, Connecticut Agricultural Experiment Station, Box 1106, New Haven, CT 06504.

DIMOND, E(DMUNDS) GREY, b. St. Louis, Mo, Dec. 8, 18; m. 44; c. 3. CARDIOLOGY. B.S, Indiana, 42, M.D, 44. Lectr, Sch. Aviation Med, Randolph Field, 49; dir. cardiovasc, lab, med. ctr, Kansas, 50-60, prof. med. & chmn. dept, sch. med, 53-60; dir. Inst. Cardiopulmonary Diseases, Scripps Clin. & Res. Found, 60-68; DISTINGUISHED PROF. MED, UNIV. MO-KANSAS CITY, 68-, PROVOST HEALTH SCI, 70- Med. consult, U.S. Bur. Labor, 55-60; Fulbright prof, Netherlands, 56; vis. prof, Nat. Heart Inst, London, 59; State Dept. Am. Specialists Abroad Prog, Phillipines, Taiwan, 61; Columbia Chile, 63; Czech, Ceylon, Indonesia & Vietnam, 64; res. assoc, Univ. Calif, San Diego, 64-67, prof. med-in-residence, 67-68; spec. consult. med. educ. to Under Secy. Health, Dept. Health, Educ. & Welfare, 68-69. Med.C, 45-47, Capt. Am. Col. Physicians; Am. Col. Cardiol.(pres, 61). Cardiovascular physiology. Address: 5650 Ward Pkwy, Kansas City, MO 64113.

DIMOND, HAROLD L(LOYD), b. Paterson, N.J, May 1, 22; m. 49; c. 2. ORGANIC CHEMISTRY. A.B, N.Y. Univ, 48; M.S, Carnegie Inst. Tech, 52, Ph.D.(chem), 53. Asst. chem, Carnegie Inst. Tech, 48-50; res. chemist, Pittsburgh Coke & Chem. Co, 53-56; Gulf Res. & Develop. Co, 56-66; res. chemist, Hilton-Davis Chem. Co, Sterling Drug, Inc, 66, SR. RES. CHEMIST, 66-69; DRACKETT CO, BRISTOL-MYER CO, 69- U.S.N.A.F, 42-46. Am. Chem. Soc. Preparation of 3-pyrrolidones; industrial work on preparation of derivatives of coal tar chemicals; alkylation; petrochemicals; detergents; oxidation; general synthetic work; process development; product evaluation; new product and process development. Address: Research & Development Dept, Drackett Co, Bristol-Myer Co, 5020 Spring Grove Ave, Cincinnati, OH 45232.

DIMOND, JOHN B(ARNET), b. Providence, R.I, July 20, 29; m. 55; c. 2. ENTOMOLOGY, ECOLOGY. B.S, Univ. R.I, 51, M.S, 53; Ph.D.(entom), Ohio State Univ, 57. Sr. entomologist, Maine State Forest Serv, 56-59; asst. prof. ENTOM, UNIV. MAINE, 59-63, assoc. prof, 63-66, PROF, 66- AAAS; Entom. Soc. Am; Entom. Soc. Can. Medical insects; insect nutrition; forest insects; insect ecology; populations. Address: 313 Deering Hall, University of Maine, Orono, ME 04473.

DIMOND, MARIE THERESE, S.N.D, b. Valdez, Alaska, Nov. 13, 16. ZOOLOGY. A.B, Trinity Col.(D.C), 38; M.S, Catholic Univ, 52, Ph.D.(biol), 54. Instr. German, TRINITY COL. D.C, 38-39, BIOL, 48-53, asst. prof, 53-57, assoc. prof, 57-60, PROF, 60- Teacher, high schs, Md. & Pa, 39-48; summers, U.S. Pub. Health Serv. res. fel. turtle heart, Pennsylvania, 56, Nat. Sci. Found. sci. faculty fel. marine biol, marine lab, Duke, 59, Plymouth Lab, 60, Hopkins Marine Sta, 61; res. assoc, Univ. B.C, 70. AAAS; assoc. Am. Physiol. Soc; Am. Soc. Zool; Nat. Asn. Biol. Teachers; Am. Inst. Biol. Sci. Embryology; endocrinology; reptiles; fish. Address: Dept. of Biology, Trinity College, Washington, DC 20017.

DIMOPOULLOS, GEORGE T(AKIS), b. Flushing, N.Y, Nov. 24, 23; m. 45; c. 1. MICROBIOLOGY. B.S, Pa. State, 49, M.S, 50; fel. & Ph.D.(bact), Mich.

State, 52. Lab. asst. bact, Pa. State, 47-48, asst, 49; virol, Mich. State, 50-52; res. assoc, Wisconsin, 52-53; virologist, animal disease & parasite res. div, agr. res. serv, U.S. Dept. Agr, 53-57; PROF. VET. SCI, LA. STATE UNIV, 57- Spec. fel, Nat. Insts. Health, 64-65. Dipl, Am. Bd. Med. Microbiol; res. award of merit, Gamma Sigma Delta, 66. U.S.A, 43-46. Fel. AAAS; fel. Am. Acad. Microbiol; Am. Soc. Microbiol; Conf. Res. Workers Animal Diseases; Soc. Exp. Biol. & Med. Tissue culture; immunological and biophysical investigation of antiviral sera and animal viruses; inactivation of viruses; foot-and-mouth disease; infectious anemias; anaplasmosis; malaria; pathological biochemistry; experimental pathology; lipid chemistry; biosynthesis of fatty acids in blood; parasites; immunochemistry; autoimmunity. Address: Dept. of Veterinary Science, Louisiana State University, Baton Rouge, LA 70803.

DIMPFL, L(UDWIG) H(ANS), b. Regensburg, Ger, Mar. 12, 20; nat; m. 42; c. 4. CHEMISTRY. B.S, California, 40. Res. chemist, Calif. Ink Co, 40-42; Calif. Res. Corp, 42-50, sr. res. chemist, 50-57, group supvr, 57-60; sect. head, develop. lab, Iranian Oil Ref. Co, Iran, 60-62; group supvr. paving & indust. asphalts, Calif. Res. Corp, 63-68; SR. RES. ASSOC, CHEVRON RES. CO, 68- Am. Chem. Soc. Petroleum fuels, especially nonengine applications; combustion theory; storage stability; gum formation; incompatibility; additives; solvents and solubility theory; asphalt technology; application of petroleum products in developing nations for roads, housing and agriculture. Address: Chevron Research Co, 576 Standard Ave, Richmond, CA 94802.

DIMROTH, ERICH, b. Wurzburg, Ger, Apr. 14, 34. GEOLOGY. Univ. Wurzburg, 53-54; Dipl. Geol, Univ. Munich, 58, Dr.rer.nat.(geol), 60. Res. assoc. geol, McGill Univ, 61-63; GEOLOGIST, PROV. QUE. DEPT. NATURAL RESOURCES, 63- AAAS; Ger. Geol. Asn; Geol. Asn. Can; Geol. Soc. Am. Tectonic and Paleotectonic evolution of Precambrian geosynclines in Quebec; sedimentology of Precambrian cherty iron formation. Address: Dept. of Natural Resources, Quebec, Que, Can.

DIMSDALE, BERNARD, b. Sioux City, Iowa, Aug. 3, 12; m; c. 2. MATHEMATICS. B.Ch, Minnesota, 33, A.M, 35, Ph.D.(math), 40. Instr, Idaho, 38-42; assoc. instr, U.S. War Dept, 42-43; instr. math, Purdue, 46; mathematician, Ballistic Res. Lab, Aberdeen Proving Ground, 47-51; Raytheon Mfg. Co, Waltham, Mass, 51-56; sr. mathematician, IBM CORP, 56-69, MGR, 69- U.S.A, 43-46. Am. Math. Soc; Asn. Comput. Mach. Approximation theory; numerical analysis; optimization techniques. Address: 315 Palisades Ave, Santa Monica, CA 90401.

DINA, STEPHEN J(AMES), b. Bronx, N.Y, May 2, 43; m. 65. BOTANY, PLANT ECOLOGY. B.S, Mt. Union Col, 65; M.S, Ohio State Univ, 67; Ph.D.(biol), Univ. Utah, 70. ASST. PROF. BIOL, ST. LOUIS UNIV, 70- AAAS; Ecol. Soc. Am; Brit. Ecol. Soc; Am. Inst. Biol. Sci; Am. Soc. Plant Physiol. Implications of vascular plant distribution patterns expressed through understanding of the differential effects of the environment on plant physiology; water relations; organic energy balance; environmental stress conditions. Address: Dept. of Biology, St. Louis University, 1504 S. Grand Ave, St. Louis, MO 63104.

DINAN, FRANK J, b. Buffalo, N.Y, Dec. 3, 33; m. 54; c. 2. ORGANIC & ANALYTICAL CHEMISTRY. B.A, State Univ. N.Y. Buffalo, 59, Allied Chem. Corp. fel, 62-63, Ph.D.(chem), 64. Jr. chemist anal. chem, Carborundum Metals Co, 53-59; chemist, Hooker Chem. Corp, 59-61; res. chemist org. chem, E.I. du Pont de Nemours & Co, 63-64; res. assoc. anal. chem, Cornell, 64-66; asst. prof, CHEM, CANISIUS COL, 66-70, ASSOC. PROF. & CHMN. DEPT, 70- Am. Chem. Soc. Heterocyclic chemistry and instrumental methods of analysis and structure determination. Address: Dept. of Chemistry, Canisius College, Buffalo, NY 14208.

DINBERGS, KORNELIUS, b. Riga, Latvia, June 5, 25; nat; m. 58. ORGANIC CHEMISTRY. Mag.Pharm, Ukrainian Tech. Inst, Germany, 49; M.A, Baylor, 51; Viol Mem. fel. & Ph.D.(org. chem), Purdue, 56. Tech. man, B.F GOODRICH CO, 56-57, sr. tech. man, 57-61, SR. RES. CHEMIST, 61- Am. Chem. Soc. Solution polymerizations; polyurethanes; absorbers. Address: Research Center, B.F. Goodrich Co, Brecksville, OH 44141.

DINDAL, DANIEL L(EE), b. Findlay, Ohio, Sept. 17, 36; m. 58; c. 3. ECOLOGY. B.S.(wildlife mgt.) & B.S.(sci. ed), Ohio State, 58, M.A, 61, Ph.D. (ecol), 67. Teacher high sch, Ohio, 58-63; teaching asst. zool. & ecol, Ohio State, 63-64, U.S. Fish & Wildlife Serv. res. assoc, 64-66; asst. prof. TERRESTRIAL INVERTEBRATE ECOL, STATE UNIV. N.Y. COL. FORRESTRY, SYRACUSE UNIV, 67-71, ASSOC. PROF, 71- Acarology Inst. traineeship adv. acarine taxon, Ohio State, 68, 70; Atomic Energy Comn. res. grant, 68-70. Ecol. Soc. Am; Soil Sci. Soc. Am. Ecology of soil invertebrates in natural and manipulated terrestrial microcommunities; effects of dichloro-diphenyltrichloroethane on invertebrate microcommunities and species diversity; succession and interspecific relationships of invertebrates in bird nests, carrion and soil litter. Address: State University of New York College of Forestry, Syracuse, NY 13210.

DINEEN, CLARENCE F(RANCIS), b. DeGraff, Minn, Apr. 1, 16; m. 43; c. 4. ZOOLOGY, ECOLOGY. B.E, Minn. State Teachers Col, 39; M.S, Minnesota, 48, Ph.D, 50. Asst. prof. BIOL, Notre Dame, 50-56; CHMN. DEPT, ST. MARY'S COL.(IND), 56- U.S.A.A.F, 41-46, Capt. AAAS; Ecol. Soc. Am; Am. Soc. Zool. Osteology of fishes; aquatic ecology. Address: 505 N. Greenlawn, South Bend, IN 46617.

DINEEN, EUGENE JOSEPH, b. Niagara Falls, N.Y, Nov. 12, 20. ORGANIC & ANALYTICAL CHEMISTRY. B.S, Niagara, 42; M.S, Notre Dame, 46; Ph.D.(chem), Ohio State, 51. Prod. chemist, Lake Ont. Ord. Works, Chem. Construct. Corp, N.Y, 42-43; res. asst, S.A.M. Labs, Columbia, 43-44; res. chemist, Hooker Chem. Co, N.Y, 51-53; O-Cel-O Div, Gen. Mills Inc, 53-54; chief chemist, Banite Co, 55-56; res. chemist, Nat. Aniline Div, Allied Chem. Co, 56-57; pres. & res. dir, Swevco Inc, 57-59; ASSOC. PROF. CHEM, W.Va. State Col, 59-63; NIAGARA UNIV, 63- U.S.A, 44-46. AAAS; Am. Chem. Soc; Optical Soc. Am; fel. Am. Inst. Chem. Urethane foams and coatings; electroorganic and mechanisms of organic reactions; instrumental methods of chemical analysis. Address: Dept. of Chemistry, Niagara University, NY 14109.

DINEGAR, ROBERT H(UDSON), b. N.Y.C, Dec. 18, 21; m. 42; c. 3. PHYSICAL CHEMISTRY. A.B, Cornell Univ, 42; A.M, Columbia, Univ, 48, Ph.D. (phys. chem), 51. Asst. chem, Columbia Univ, 46-50; RES. PHYS. CHEMIST, LOS ALAMOS SCI. LAB, UNIV. CALIF, 50- Lectr, Los Alamos residence ctr, Univ. N.Mex, 70- U.S.N.R, 42-, Comdr. Am. Chem. Soc; fel. Am. Inst. Chem; prof. mem. Am. Meteorol. Soc; N.Y. Acad. Sci. Kinetics of phase changes and explosions; physics and chemistry of explosives; properties and reactivity of small particles. Address: 2317 46th St, Los Alamos, NM 87544.

DINERSTEIN, ROBERT A(LVIN), b. N.Y.C, Jan. 4, 19; m. 41; c. 3. CHEMISTRY. B.S, City Col. New York, 39; M.S, Pa. State Univ, 40. Chemist, AM. OIL CO, 46-52, group leader, 52-55, sect. leader, 55-62, mgr. info. & commun, Ind, 62-68, MGR. COMPENSATION & ORGN, 68- Harvey Washington Wiley lectr, Purdue Univ, 57; orgn. planning consult, Standard Oil Co. (Ind), 66- Ord. Dept, U.S.A, 44-46. AAAS; Am. Chem. Soc. Hydrocarbon reactions, properties, separation and analysis; distillation; chromatography; information science; documentation. Address: American Oil Co, 910 S. Michigan Ave, Chicago, IL 60680.

DINES, ALLEN I, b. Pittsburgh, Pa, Dec. 16, 29; m. 53; c. 2. PHARMACEUTICAL & MEDICINAL CHEMISTRY. B.S, Pittsburgh, 51; M.S, Ohio State, 53, Am. Found. Pharmaceut. Ed. fels, 53, 55-58, Ph.D.(pharmaceut. chem), 58. Assoc. dir. prod. develop, Flint Labs, Baxter Labs, Inc, Ill, 58-60; group leader pharmaceut. res. & develop, Miles Prod. Div, Miles Labs, Inc, Ind, 60-64; lab. dir, Warren-Teed Pharmaceut. Inc, Rohm and Haas Co, 64-69; dir. res, Strong Cobb Arner, Inc, 69-70; DIR. RES. & DEVELOP, MILAN PHARMACEUT, INC, 71- Am. Chem. Soc; Am. Pharmaceut. Asn; Acad. Pharmaceut. Sci. Pharmaceutical research and development. Address: Milan Pharmaceuticals, Inc, P.O. Box 4293, Morgantown, WV 26505.

DINESS, ARTHUR M(ICHAEL), b. N.Y.C, Apr. 21, 38; m. 63; c. 2. MATERIALS SCIENCE. B.A, N.Y. Univ, 58; M.S, Pa. State Univ, 60, Ph.D.(solid state sci), 66. Asst. chem, Pa. State Univ, 58-60, mat. res. lab, 60-64; res. specialist mat. res, appl. res. lab, Philco Corp, 64-65, supvr, solid state mat. sect, 65-66; CHEMIST, METALL. PROG, OFF. NAVAL RES, 66- Res. scientist, Ford Sci. Lab, Pa, 66. Am. Ceramic Soc. Ceramics and glasses; solid state chemistry; materials research and engineering. Address: Metallurgy Program, Office of Naval Research, Arlington, VA 22217.

DINGA, G(USTAV) P(AUL), b. Haugen, Wis, Oct. 6, 22; m. 48; c. 4. INORGANIC CHEMISTRY. B.A, St. Olaf Col, 47, Dearborn Chem. Co. fel, 47-48; fel. & M.S, Louisville, 49; Concordia Col.(Moorhead, Minn). grant, Wyoming, 58-59, Ph.D.(inorg. chem), 62. Asst, Kentucky, 49-50; instr. CHEM, Ill. Wesleyan, 50-51; St. Cloud Teachers Col, 51-53; asst. prof, CONCORDIA COL.(MOORHEAD, MINN), 53-58, assoc. prof, 58-64, PROF, 64-, CHMN. DEPT, 69- Summer, asst, Minnesota, 54, 55; physics & chem. inst, Wyoming, 57, univ, 56, 57; researcher, Utah, 60; nuclear sci. inst, Washington State, 62; resident res. assoc, Argonne Nat. Lab, 63; vis. prof, Augustana Col.(S.Dak), 64; faculty res. appointee, Pac. Northwest Labs, Battelle Mem. Inst, 68-69; partic, instrumental methods inst, Rensselaer Polytech. Inst, summer 70; mem. grad. faculty, N.Dak. State Univ, 71. U.S.A.A.F, 43-46. Am. Chem. Soc; fel. Am. Inst. Chem. Qualitative and quantitative chemistry; synthesis and identification of organic foam inhibiting compounds and p-tolylmethyl ether; determination of physical constants for non-aqueous solvents at very low temperature; zirconium compounds and complexes. Address: Dept. of Chemistry, Concordia College, Moorhead, MN 56560.

DINGEE, DAVID A(ARON), b. Detroit, Mich, Jan. 30, 29; m. 50; c. 5. PLASMA & NUCLEAR PHYSICS, LASERS. B.S, Mich. State Univ, 49, M.S, 51; Ph.D.(physics), Ohio State Univ, 71. Proj. engr. hydrodynamics, Stevens Inst. Tech, 51-54; div. chief appl. nuclear physics, BATTELLE MEM. INST, 54-69, assoc. mgr. physics dept, 69-70, CHIEF PLASMA PHYSICS DIV, 70- U.S.C.G, 46-47. Am. Nuclear Soc; Am. Phys. Soc. Nuclear reactor physics and experimentation; mathematical physics; energy conversion physics and engineering. Address: Plasma Physics Division, Battelle Memorial Institute, 505 King Ave, Columbus, OH 43201.

DINGELL, JAMES V, b. Detroit, Mich, Oct. 10, 31; m. 59; c. 2. PHARMACOLOGY, CHEMISTRY. B.S, Georgetown, 54, M.S, 57, Ph.D.(chem), 62. Chemist, lab. chem. pharmacol, Nat. Heart Inst, 55-62; instr. PHARMACOL, SCH. MED, VANDERBILT UNIV, 62-65, asst. prof, 65-69, ASSOC. PROF, 69- Ord.C.Res, 54-60; U.S.P.H.S.R, 60-62. Am. Chem. Soc. Drug metabolism, distribution in tissues, assay and mechanism of action, especially in area of psychotherapeutic agents. Address: Dept. of Pharmacology, Vanderbilt University School of Medicine, Nashville, TN 37203.

DINGER, HAROLD E(UGENE), b. Barberton, Ohio, May 7, 05; m. 29; c. 2. PHYSICAL SCIENCE. Akron, 30-31; Maryland, 47-51; U.S. Dept. Agr. Grad. Sch, 47-51. Chief instr, McKim Tech. Inst, 29-38; transmitter engr, Ohio Broadcasting Co, 39-40; electronic scientist, U.S. Naval Res. Lab, 40-71; WRITER & CONSULT, 71- Consult, ionospheric physics panel, Int. Geophys. Year. Mem, U.S. Nat. Cmn, Int. Sci. Radio Union, chmn, cmn. IV, 51-53; U.S. del, Sydney, 52, Boulder, 57, Tokyo, 63; mem. exec. cmn. & U.S. del, int. radio consult. cmt, Int. Telecommun. Union, London, 53, Warsaw, 56, Geneva, 58, Los Angeles, 59; U.S. del, Int. Electrotech. Cmn, Lucerne, 47, U.S. Navy Meritorious Civilian Serv. award, 45. U.S.N.R, 29-33. Fel. AAAS; fel. Inst. Elec. & Electronics Eng; Sci. Res. Soc. Am. Radio wave propagation; electro-magnetic compatibility; frequency management. Address: 2106 Keating St. S.E, Washington, DC 20031.

DINGER, J(ACOB) E(RNST), b. Kahoka, Mo, April 23, 14; m. 42; c. 3. PHYSICS. B.S, N.E. Mo. State Teachers Col, 37; M.S, Iowa State Col, 39, Ph.D. (physics), 41. Res. physicist, NAVAL RES. LAB, 41-50, HEAD ATMOSPHERIC PHYSICS BR, 50- Am. Phys. Soc; Instrument Soc. Am; Am. Meteorol. Soc; Sci. Res. Soc. Am; Am. Geophys. Union. Atmospheric electricity; meteorological instruments; atmospheric physics; cloud physics. Address: 3704 Andover Pl, Suitland, MD 20023.

DINGLE, A(LBERT) NELSON, b. Bismarck, N.Dak, May 22, 16; m. 41; c. 2. METEOROLOGY. B.S, Minnesota, 39; M.S, Iowa State Col, 40; S.M, Mass.

Inst. Tech, 45, Sc.D.(meteorol), 47. Asst. physics, dept. agr. eng, Minnesota, 40-41; asst. prof, Hampton Inst, 41-42; res. assoc. meteorol, Mass. Inst. Tech, 43-47; asst. prof. physics & meteorol, Ohio State, 47-54; assoc. res. meteorologist, eng. res. inst, UNIV. MICH, 54-56, assoc. prof. METEOROL, 56-64, PROF, 64- Res. assoc, mapping & charting res. lab, Ohio State Res. Found, 50-54. AAAS; Am. Meteorol. Soc; Am. Geophys. Union. Rain clensing of the atmosphere; drop-size distributions in rain; study of convective storms by use of tracer indium; air and precipitation chemistry; waste disposal capacity of the atmosphere. Address: Dept. of Meteorology & Oceanography, University of Michigan, 4072 E. Engineering Bldg, Ann Arbor, MI 48104.

DINGLE, ALLAN DOUGLAS, b. Hamilton, Ont, May 3, 36; m. 62. DEVELOPMENTAL BIOLOGY. B.Sc, McMaster, 58; M.Sc, Illinois, 60; Ph.D.(biol), Brandeis,64. Nat. Insts. Health trainee develop. biol, 64-65; ASST. PROF. BIOL, McMASTER UNIV, 65- AAAS; Am. Soc. Cell Biol; Soc. Develop. Biol; Can. Soc. Cell Biol. Development of flagella and their basal bodies during cell differentiation; pigment cell differentiation and development of pigment patterns in fish. Address: Dept. of Biology, McMaster University, Hamilton, Ont, Can.

DINGLE, ARTHUR D(URWIN), b. Wawota, Sask, Aug. 6, 26; m. 55; c. 2. MATHEMATICS, STATISTICS. B.Sc, Manitoba, 49, 52-53. Tech. officer, electronics dept, Defense Res. Bd, 50-52; res. physicist, DUNLOP RES. CENTER, 53-58, MGR. PHYS. RES. DEPT, 58- Royal Can. Army, 45-46. Am. Soc. Test. & Mat; Soc. Rheol; Am. Chem. Soc; Can. Asn. Physicists. Static and dynamic properties of elastomers and textiles; rheology of viscoelastic materials; statistical analysis; tensor analysis; thermoelectrical effects. Address: Physics Research Dept, Dunlop Research Center, Sheridan Park, Ont, Can.

DINGLE, GEORGE W(ILLIAM), b. Newcastle, Ind, Dec. 30, 03; m. 24. CHEMISTRY. A.B. & M.A, Indiana, 31, Ph.D.(phys. chem), 35. Asst. instr. chem, Indiana, 31-34; asst. document exam, Fed. Bur. Invest, 35-36, assoc. document exam, 37-38; prin. document exam, 38-43, lectr. forensic sci, 37-69, spec. agent, 38-69, consult. document specialist, res. & sci. chief & asst. admin. chief document sect, Fed. Bur. Invest. Lab, 43-69; RETIRED. Fed. Bur. Invest. cert. hon. serv, meritorious awards. Am. Chem. Soc; fel. Am. Acad. Forensic Sci. Gas phase catalysis in organic synthesis; catalytic activity of mixed silver catalysts and of copper on silica gel in reduction of nitrobenzene. Address: R.F.D. 1, Riley's Lock Rd, Poolesville, MD 20837.

DINGLE, JOHN H(OLMES), b. Cooperstown, N.Dak, Nov. 24, 08; m. 46; c. 2. PREVENTIVE MEDICINE. Ph.C, B.S, Washington(Seattle), 30, M.S, 31; Sc.D.(immunol), Hopkins, 33; Cabot fel, Harvard, 36-39, M.D, 39. Asst, McDermott Found, Washington(Seattle), 29-31; asst. bacteriologist, State Dept. Health, Md, 33; bacteriologist, Upjohn Co, 33-35; house off. med, Infants & Children's Hosp, Boston, 39-40; asst. med, bact. & immunol, Harvard Med. Sch, 40-41, Peabody fel. med. & instr. bact. & immunol, 40-42, instr. med, 41-42, assoc, 42-46; PROF. PREV. MED, SCH. MED, CASE WEST. RESERVE UNIV, 46-, MED, 65-, assoc. prof, 46-65. Asst, Boston City Hosp, 40-46, asst. physician, 41-46; assoc. physician, univ. hosps, Cleveland, 46-68, physician, 68- Dir. comn. acute respiratory diseases, Armed Forces Epidemiol, Bd, 42-55, mem. bd, 51-67, pres, 55-57, assoc. mem. comn, 55-; mem. bd. consult. med. & pub. health, Rockefeller Found, 52-55. Lasker Award, 59; Bristol Award in infectious diseases, 68. U.S.A, 44-46, Legion of Merit. Nat. Acad. Sci; AAAS; Am. Epidemiol. Soc.(pres, 58); Am. Asn. Immunol. (v.pres, 56, pres, 57); Asn. Am. Physicians; Am. Med. Asn; Am. Soc. Clin. Invest; Soc. Exp. Biol. & Med; Am. Soc. Microbiol; Am. Clin. & Climat. Asn; Am. Fedn. Clin. Res; Asn. Teachers Prev. Med; Am. Acad. Arts & Sci. Immunology; infectious diseases. Address: Case Western Reserve University School of Medicine, Cleveland, OH 44106.

DINGLE, JOHN R(EGINALD), b. Halifax, N.S, July 24, 20. PHYSICAL CHEMISTRY. B.Sc, Dalhousie, 41, M.Sc, 42; A.M, Harvard, 47; Ph.D.(chem), Toronto, 49. Assoc. scientist, HALIFAX LAB, FISHERIES RES. BD, CAN, 49-59, RES. SCIENTIST, 59- R.C.N.V.R, 42-45. Chem. Inst. Can. Chemical kinetics; proteins of fish muscle. Address: 1020 Bellevue Ave, Halifax, N.S, Can.

DINGLE, RAYMOND, b. Perth, Australia, Sept. 5, 35; m. 58; c. 3. SOLID STATE & CHEMICAL PHYSICS. B.Sc, Univ. West. Australia, 55, hons, 57, Ph.D.(chem), 65. Sr. demonstr. phys. chem, Univ. West. Australia, 59-62; fel. chem, Univ. Col, London, 62-63; amanuensis phys. chem, Copenhagen Univ, 63-66, lektor solid state chem, 64-66; MEM. TECH. STAFF SOLID STATE PHYSICS, BELL TEL. LABS, 66- Electronic properties of solids; spectroscopic techniques such as absorption, emission, reflectivity. Address: Bell Telephone Labs, Murray Hill, NJ 07974.

DINGLE, R(ICHARD) D(OUGLAS) HUGH, b. Penang, Malaya, Nov. 4, 36; U.S. citizen; m. 59; c. 3. ANIMAL BEHAVIOR, ECOLOGY. B.A, Cornell, 58; M.Sc, Michigan, 59, Nat. Sci. Found. fel, 60-61, Ph.D.(zool), 62. Instr. ZOOL, Michigan, 61-62; Nat. Sci. Found. fel, Cambridge, 62-63; Nat. Inst. Ment. Health training fel, Michigan, 63-64; Asst. Prof. ZOOL, UNIV. IOWA, 64-67, ASSOC. PROF, 67- Nat. Insts. Health fel, Univ. Nairobi, 69-70. AAAS; Am. Soc. Zool; Brit. Soc. Exp. Biol; Am. Soc. Naturalists; Entom. Soc. Am; Ecol. Soc. Am. Insect and crustacean behavior and populations; insect migration. Address: Dept. of Zoology, University of Iowa, Iowa City, IA 52240.

DINGLE, RICHARD W(ILLIAM), b. Bismarck, N.Dak. Jan. 5, 18; m. 47; c. 2. FORESTRY, SILVICULTURE. B.S, Minnesota, 41; M.F, Yale, 47, Ph.D. (forestry), 53. Instr. FORESTRY, dept. forestry, Missouri, 48-53; asst. prof, WASH. STATE UNIV, 53-60, assoc. prof, 60-69, PROF, 69- U.S.N.R, 43-46, Lt.(jg). AAAS; Am. Forestry Asn; Soc. Am. Foresters. Artificial regeneration and grafting of ponderosa pine in eastern Washington; vegetative regeneration of conifers; windbreak establishment and culture in Columbia Basin and Eastern Washington drylands; Christmas tree production and culture; forest ecology; forest tree physiology; forest genetics; silviculture. Address: Dept. of Forestry, Washington State University, Pullman, WA 99163.

DINGLE, THOMAS WALTER, b. Burnaby, B.C, Aug. 6, 36; m. 63. THEORETICAL CHEMISTRY. B.Sc, Alberta, 58, Prov. Alta. Govt. fel, 60-61, Ph.D.(phys. chem), 65. Ramsay Mem. fel. CHEM, Math. Inst, Oxford, 64-66; fel, Ottawa, 66-67; ASST. PROF, UNIV. VICTORIA, 67- Molecular orbital calculations. Address: Dept. of Chemistry, University of Victoria, P.O. Box 1700, Victoria, B.C, Can.

DINGLEDY, DAVID PETER, b. Youngstown, Ohio, Mar. 11, 19; m. 44; c. 8. PHYSICAL CHEMISTRY, PHOTOCHEMISTRY. B.S, John Carroll, 40; M.S, Marquette, 42; Ph.D.(phys. chem), Ohio State, 62. Res. chemist, Owens-Corning Fiberglas, 43-53; res. assoc. cryogenics, res. found, Ohio State, 53-55; teacher, high schs, Ohio, 55-57; instr. CHEM, Ohio Wesleyan, 57-59; ASSOC. PROF, STATE UNIV. N.Y. COL. FREDONIA, 62- State Univ. N.Y. Res. Found. grants in aid, 63-, res. assoc. & grant, atmospheric sci. res. ctr, summers 63-64, faculty res. fels, 70 & 71; vis. assoc. prof, mat. res. lab, Pa. State Univ, 68-69. Am. Chem. Soc. Physical chemistry of glass; photochemical processes in and structure of inorganic glasses; inorganic glasses as radiation detectors. Address: Dept. of Chemistry, State University of New York College at Fredonia, Fredonia, NY 14063.

DINGLEY, EDWARD NELSON, JR, b. Kalamazoo, Mich, July 18, 02; m. 28; c. 2. ELECTRONICS. B.S, George Washington, 36. Technician, res. lab, Radio Corp. Am, N.Y, 25-26; asst. radio inspector, Navy Yard, Wash, D.C, 26-28; radio engr, Navy Bur. Eng, 28-29; Mackay Radio & Tel. Co, 29-30; Radiotron Co. Div, Radio Corp. Am, 30-32; U.S. Naval Res. Lab, 32-34; bur. ships, U.S. Dept. Navy, 34-42; supvry. electronic scientist, Nat. Security Agency, 46-57, spec. asst. to chief, off. res. & develop, 52-54, chief commun. engr, 54-57; prin. eng. scientist, Electronic Commun. Inc, 57-63; CONSULT. ENGR, 63- Distinguished Civilian Serv. award, U.S. Dept. Defense, 56. U.S.N.R, 42-46, Capt. Fel. Inst. Elec. & Electronics Eng; Nat. Soc. Prof. Eng. Telecommunication equipment and systems engineering. Address: 11165 Fourth St. E, Treasure Island, St. Petersburg, FL 33706.

DINGMAN, C(HARLES) WESLEY II, b. Springfield, Mass, June 2, 32; m. 54; c. 3. CELL BIOLOGY, BIOCHEMISTRY. A.B, Dartmouth, 54; M.D, Rochester, 59. Res. assoc. neurochem, dept. psychiat, sch. med. & dent, Rochester, 57-58; biochem, Nat. Inst. Neurol. Diseases & Blindness, 60-64; RES. MED. OFF, NAT. CANCER INST, 64- U.S. Pub. Health Serv, 60-64, Surg. AAAS; Biophys. Soc; Am. Soc. Biol. Chem. Biochemical studies of nucleic acid synthesis and metabolism; effect of carcinogens on nucleic acid structure and metabolism; DNA repair mechanisms. Address: 10113 Bevern Lane, Potomac, MD 20854.

DINGMAN, JOSEPH F(RANCIS), b. New York, N.Y, Aug. 20, 21; m. 45; c. 5. ENDOCRINOLOGY, INTERNAL MEDICINE. M.D, Buffalo, 50. Res. fel. med, Harvard Sch. Med, 51-54, asst, 55-56, instr, 56; asst. prof. sch. med, Tulane, 56-59, assoc. prof, 59-61; dir. med. res, Lahey Clin. Found, 61-67; SR. ASSOC. MED, PETER BENT BRIGHAM HOSP, 65-, DIR. MED. LIPID LAB, 67- Lectr, Harvard Med. Sch, 61- Med. house officer, Peter Bent Brigham Hosp, 50-51, sr. asst. res. physician, 54-55; jr. assoc, 56, assoc. staff, 61-67; vis. physician, Charity Hosp, La, 56-61. Med. Admin. Corp, U.S.A, 42-46. AAAS; Endocrine Soc; Am. Fedn. Clin. Res. Basic and clinical research endocrinology; metabolism diseases; neuroendocrinology; neurohypophysis. Address: Peter Bent Brigham Hosp, 721 Huntington Ave, Boston, MA 02115.

DINGMAN, REED (OTHELBERT), b. Rockwood, Mich, Nov. 4, 06; m. 32; c. 3. PLASTIC SURGERY. B.A, Univ. Mich, 28, D.D.S, 31, M.S, 32, M.D. 36. Maxillofacial & plastic surgeon, Geisinger Mem. Hosp, 37-39; asst. prof. oral surg, MED. SCH, UNIV. MICH, 40-44, assoc. prof, 44-66, PROF. SURG. & HEAD SECT. PLASTIC SURG, DEPT. SURG, 66-, asst. prof. surg, 53-64, assoc. prof, 64-66. Consult, Vet. Admin. Hosp, Ann Arbor; chief dept. plastic surg, St. Joseph Mercy Hosp, Ann Arbor. Am. Col. Surg; Am. Col. Dent; Am. Asn. Plastic Surg; Am. Soc. Plastic & Reconstruct. Surg; Am. Soc. Maxillofacial Surg; Am. Cleft Palate Asn; Am. Surg. Asn; Asn. Surg. Trauma. Facial trauma and reconstruction; cleft palate and facial deformities. Address: 221 N. Ingalls St, Ann Arbor, MI 48104.

DINGMAN, ROSS E(VAN), b. Covina, Calif, June 8, 28; m. 49; c. 3. VERTEBRATE BIOLOGY. B.S, Calif. State Col. Long Beach, 63; NASA fel, Arizona, 64, M.S. & Ph.D.(zool), 66. Draftsman, Moffatt & Nichol, Engrs, 57-62; asst. prof. biol, COL. MEN, UNIV. SAN DIEGO, 66-71, ASSOC. PROF, 71-, chmn. dept, 68-69. Am. Soc. Mammal; Soc. Syst. Zool; Soc. Vert. Paleont. Mammalian systematics, taxonomy, distribution and evolution; ecological physiology of the higher vertebrates. Address: Dept. of Biology, University of San Diego College for Men, San Diego, CA 92110.

DINHOFER, ALVIN D(AVID), b. Bronx, N.Y, June 30, 32; m. 60; c. 3. SOLID STATE PHYSICS. B.S, Brooklyn Col, 54; Columbia, 54; N.Y. Univ, 56-58; Ph.D.(physics), Maryland, 63. Mem. tech. staff theoret. physics, physics res. lab, Tex. Instruments, Inc, 63-68; TRW Systs, Inc, Wash. Opers, D.C, 66-68; ASST. PROF. PHYSICS, STATE UNIV. N.Y. COL. PLATTSBURGH, 68- U.S.A, 54-56. Application of the Mössbauer effect to lattice dynamics; acoustoelectric effects in semiconductors. Address: Dept. of Physics, State University of New York College at Plattsburgh, Plattsburgh, NY 12901.

DINIUS, DAVID A(LLEN), b. Warsaw, Ind, July 23, 42; m. 64; c. 3. ANIMAL NUTRITION. B.S, Purdue Univ, 64, univ. fel, 64-65, M.S, 65; univ. fel, Univ. Wis, Madison, 66-67; Nat. Sci. Found. fel, Pa. State Univ, 68-69, Ph.D.(animal sci), 69. RES. ANIMAL HUSBANDMAN, U.S. DEPT. AGR, 69- Am. Soc. Animal Sci; Am. Dairy Sci. Asn. Ruminant nutrition; regulation of food intake; utilization of cellulosic materials. Address: Animal Science Research Division, Bldg. 200, U.S. Dept. of Agriculture, Beltsville, MD 20705.

DINIUS, JAMES H(ENRY), b. Huntington, Ind, Nov. 3, 17; m. 41; c. 2. CHEMICAL ENGINEERING. B.S.Ch.E, Purdue, 39; Iowa, 39-40. Jr. chemist, Phillips Petrol. Co, Okla, 40; asst. occupational analyst, U.S. Civil Serv. Cmn, Wash, D.C, 40-41; asst. chem. engr, Chem. Warfare Serv, U.S. Army, Md, 41-43; res. assoc, Mass. Inst. Tech, 43-45; supt. paper & news print lab, KIMBERLY-CLARK CORP, 45-66, mgr. paper & specialties, res. & eng, 66-70, MGR. ADVAN. DEVELOP, CORP. RES. & ENG, 70- With Off.

Sci. Res. & Develop, 44. Tech. Asn. Pulp & Paper Indust; Am. Chem. Soc. Book paper manufacture; paper coating development; gas mask filters. Address: Research & Engineering Center, Kimberly-Clark Corp, Neenah, WI 54956.

DINKEL, C(HRISTIAN) A(LFRED), b. Springfield, S.Dak, June 18, 22; m. 46; c. 2. ANIMAL BREEDING, GENETICS. B.S, Iowa State, 48, Ph.D.(animal breeding, genetics), 53; M.S, S.Dak. State, 49. Instr. gen. animal husb, Iowa State, 49-50; PROF. ANIMAL BREEDING, S.DAK. STATE UNIV, 51- U.S.A.A.F, 42-45, 2nd Lt. Am. Soc. Animal Sci. Beef cattle breeding and genetics; experimental design. Address: Dept. of Animal Science, South Dakota State University, University Station, Brookings, SD 57006.

DINKINES, FLORA, b. McLoud, Okla, April 6, 10. MATHEMATICS. B.S, Fla. State Col. for Women, 29; fel, Texas, 37-38; A.M, Michigan, 40; Ph.D. (math), Chicago, 51. Teacher high sch, Fla, 29-42; instr. to adj. prof, South Carolina, 42-45; lectr, Univ. Col, 46-49; instr. to asst. prof. MATH, UNIV. ILL, CHICAGO CIRCLE, 50-59, assoc. prof, 59-64, PROF, 64- Asst, Univ. Chicago, 46-47. Am. Math. Soc; Math. Asn. Am. Group theory. Address: Dept. of Mathematics, University of Illinois at Chicago Circle, Box 4348, Chicago, IL 60680.

DINKLAGE, KENNETH T(AYLOR), Clin. Psychol, see 12th ed, Soc. & Behav. Vols.

DINMAN, BERTRAM DAVID, b. Phila, Pa, Aug. 9, 25; m. 50; c. 4. OCCUPATIONAL & ENVIRONMENTAL MEDICINE. Temple Univ, 46-47, M.D, 51; fel, Univ. Cincinnati, 54-57, Sc.D.(occup. med), 57. Asst. prof. prev. med, col. med, Ohio State Univ, 57-59, assoc. prof, 59-64, PROF, 64-65; INDUST. HEALTH, UNIV. MICH, 65-, DIR. INST. ENVIRON. & INDUST. HEALTH, 70- Mem. comn. environ. hyg, Armed Forces Epidemiol. Bd, 65-; comt. toxicol, Nat. Res. Coun, 65, comt. biol. effects of atmospheric pollutants, 69, comt. acceptable concentrations of toxic dusts & gases, 70. Dipl, Am. Bd. Prev. Med, 60. Fel. Am. Acad. Occup. Med; fel. Am. Col. Prev. Med; Soc. Toxicol. Cellular toxicology; enzymatic response to chemical injury; environmental toxicology. Address: Institute of Environmental & Industrial Health, School of Public Health, University of Michigan, Ann Arbor, MI 48104.

DINNEEN, GERALD P(AUL), b. Elmhurst, N.Y, Oct. 23, 24; m. 47; c. 3. MATHEMATICS. B.S, Queens Col, 47; M.S, Wisconsin, 48, Ph.D.(math), 52. Teaching asst. math, Wisconsin, 47-51; sr. develop. engr, Goodyear Aircraft Corp, Ohio, 51-53; staff mem, LINCOLN LAB, MASS. INST. TECHNOL, 53-58, sect. leader, data processing group, 58, asst. leader, 58-60, leader, 60, assoc. head info. processing div, 60-63, commun. div, 63-64, head, 64-66, asst. dir, 66-68, assoc. dir, 68-70, DIR, 70-, PROF. ELEC. ENG, 71- Consult, Air Force Sci. Adv. Bd, 59-60, mem. electronics panel, 60-65, chmn. info. processing panel, 63-65; mem, Defense Intell. Agency Sci. Adv. Cmt, 65-66, v.chmn, 66-; mem. command control commun. task force, Defense Sci. Bd. Panels, 66-67, ballistic missile defense panel, 66-67. Decoration exceptional civilian serv, U.S. Air Force, 66. U.S.A.A.F, 42-46, Res, 46-53, 1st Lt. Am. Math. Soc. Matrix Algebra; probability theory; logical design of digital computers; military systems design; satellite communications. Address: 216 Garfield Rd, Concord, MA 01742.

DINNEEN, GERALD U(EL), b. Denver, Colo, May 6, 13; m. 38; c. 2. CHEMISTRY. B.S, Denver, 34. Chemist, Richards Labs, Colo, 34-38; soil conserv. serv, U.S. Dept. Agr, N.Mex, 38-42; U.S. Customs Serv, Calif, 42-44; chemist in charge, lab. invests, U.S. Maritime Cmn, 44-45; res. chemist & supvr, LARAMIE ENERGY RES. CTR, U.S. BUR. MINES, 45-64, RES. DIR, 64- AAAS; Am. Inst. Chem. Eng; Am. Chem. Soc; Geochem. Soc. Composition and reactions of shale oil and petroleum; chemistry of hydrocarbons and organic nitrogen, sulfur and oxygen compounds; origin of petroleum and oil shale; recovery and processing of shale oil. Address: Laramie Energy Research Center, U.S. Bureau of Mines, P.O. Box 3395, University Station, Laramie, WY 82070.

DINNING, JAMES S(MITH), b. Franklin, Ky, Sept. 28, 22; m. 44; c. 4. BIOCHEMISTRY. B.S, Kentucky, 46; M.S, Okla. State, 47, Ph.D, 48. Asst. prof, med. sch, Arkansas, 48-52, assoc. prof. biochem, 53-58, prof. & head dept, 59-63; MEM. STAFF, ROCKEFELLER FOUND, 63- Asst. prof, Pittsburgh, 52-53; spec. consult, U.S. Pub. Health Serv; assoc. ed, Nutrit. Rev. Lederle Med. Faculty Award, 55. U.S.A, 42-46. Soc. Exp. Biol. & Med; Am. Chem. Soc; Am. Soc. Biol. Chem; Am. Inst. Nutrit.(assoc.ed, J. Nutrit, Mead-Johnson Award, 64). Metabolic effects of vitamin deficiencies; blood cell formation. Address: Rockefeller Foundation, General Post Office Box 2453, Bangkok, Thailand.

DINOS, NICHOLAS, b. Tamaqua, Pa, Jan. 15, 34; m. 55; c. 3. CHEMICAL ENGINEERING. B.S, Pa. State Univ, 55; U.S. Steel fel, Lehigh Univ, 65, NASA fel. & M.S, 66, Ph.D.(chem. eng), 67. Chem. engr, E.I. du Pont de Nemours & Co, Ind, 55-57, res. engr. nuclear eng, Savannah River Lab, S.C, 57-62, reactor engr. nuclear safety, 62-64; teaching asst. chem. eng, Lehigh Univ, 64-65; ceramics engr, Bethlehem Steel Corp, Pa, 65; ASSOC. PROF. CHEM. ENG, OHIO UNIV, 66- AAAS; Am. Chem. Soc; Am. Inst. Chem. Eng. Applications of chemical engineering to biology and vice versa; transport phenomena, mathematics. Address: Dept. of Chemical Engineering, Ohio University, Athens, OH 45701.

DINOWITZ, MARSHALL, b. Baltimore, Md, Sept. 1, 39; m. 69; c. 2. MICROBIOLOGY. B.S, Univ. Md, College Park, 60; Nat. Cancer Inst. trainee & M.Sc, Johns Hopkins Univ, 64, Nat. Cancer Inst. trainee & Sc.D, 67. Nat. Cancer Inst. fel, inst. molecular virol, St. Louis Univ, 67-69; ASST. PROF. MICROBIOL, COL. MED, UNIV. ARIZ, 69- Nat. Cancer Inst. res. grant, 71- AAAS; Am. Soc. Microbiol. Effects of oncogenic virus infections on host macromolecular synthesis; responses of cells to adenovirus infections; virus induced tumors; tumor regression, recurrence and immunity. Address: Dept. of Microbiology, University of Arizona Medical Center, Tucson, AZ 85724.

DINSMORE, BRUCE H(EASLEY), b. Indiana, Pa, Sept. 18, 15; m. 39; c. 3. ECOLOGY, AQUATIC BIOLOGY. B.S, Indiana Univ. Pa, 37; M.A, Columbia Univ, 41; M.S, Univ. Pittsburgh, 54, Ph.D.(ecol), 58. Teacher, pub. schs, Pa. & N.Y, 37-47; from asst. prof. to PROF. BIOL. & CHMN. DEPT. BIOL. SCI, CLARION STATE COL, 47- U.S.N.R, 41-45, Lt. Comdr. Ecol. Soc. Am; Am. Inst. Biol. Sci. Ecological studies of plant and animal communities of strip mine ponds in Pennsylvania; ecology of streams receiving acid mine drainage. Address: 203 South St, Clarion, PA 16214.

DINSMORE, HOWARD L(IVINGSTONE), b. Patton, Pa, May 27, 21; m. 42; c. 7. PHYSICAL CHEMISTRY. A.B, Hopkins, 42; Nat. Res. fel, Minnesota, 46-49, Ph.D.(phys. chem), 49. Chemist, U.S. Naval Res. Lab, 42-46; res. assoc. phys. chem, Brown, 49-50; chemist, Smith Kline & French Labs, 50-51; Commercial Solvents Corp, 51-54; M.W. Kellogg Co, 54-56; PROF. CHEM, Bethel Col, 56-66; FLA. SOUTH. COL, 66- Am. Chem. Soc. Infrared and mass spectroscopy applied to chemical analysis. Address: 730 S. Mississippi Ave, Lakeland, FL 33801.

DINSMORE, JAMES J(AY), b. Owatonna, Minn, Feb. 25, 42; m. 64; c. 3. ORNITHOLOGY. B.S, Iowa State Univ, 64; M.S, Univ. Wis, 67; Ph.D.(zool), Univ. Fla, 70. ASST. PROF. zool, Univ. Fla, 70-71; NATURAL SCI, UNIV. TAMPA, 71- Am. Ornith. Union; Cooper Ornith. Soc; Wilson Ornith. Soc. Avian biology of island populations; ethology of colonial seabirds; foraging behavior of birds. Address: Dept. of Natural Science, University of Tampa, Tampa, FL 33606.

DINSMORE, R(AY) P(UTNAM), b. Tewksbury, Mass, Apr. 24, 93; m. 19; c. 2. CHEMICAL ENGINEERING. B.S, Mass. Inst. Tech, 14; hon.D.Eng, Case, 40. Mem. tech. staff, Goodyear Tire & Rubber Co, 14-16, asst. chemist, Can, 16-19, chief chemist, Calif, 19-21, chief chemist & res. dir, Ohio, 21-32, asst. to factory mgr, 32-39, asst. develop. mgr, 39-40, develop. mgr, 40-43, v.pres. res. & develop, 43-61, dir, 60-64; ENG. MGT. CONSULT, 61- Trustee, Midwest Res. Inst, 46-61; mem, Mass. Inst. Technol. Corp, 54-59; trustee, Kent State Univ, 59-66. Organizer synthetic rubber res, Off. Rubber Dir, Wash, D.C, 42-43. AAAS; Am. Chem. Soc.(Goodyear Medal, 55); Soc. Automotive Eng; Am. Inst. Chem. Eng.(Founders Award, 64); hon. mem. Am. Inst. Chem.(pres, 55-56, chmn. bd, 57); Soc. Indust. Chem.(pres, Am. Sect, 58-60); Brit. Inst. Rubber Indust.(Colwyn Gold Medal, 48). Design and compounding of tires; development of flexible and fiber-forming plastics. Address: 9 Overwood Rd, Akron, OH 44313.

DINTZIS, HOWARD M(ARVIN), b. Chicago, Ill, May 28, 27; m. 51; c. 3. BIOPHYSICS. B.S, California, Los Angeles, 48; fel, Harvard, 52-53, Ph.D. (med. sci), 53; D.Sc, Lawrence, 64. Lilly res. fel, Harvard, 52-53; Nat. Sci. Found. fel, Yale, 53-54; fel, Cambridge, 54-56; asst. prof. chem, Calif. Inst. Tech, 56-58; sr. res. assoc. biol, Mass. Inst. Tech, 58-61; PROF. BIOPHYS. & DIR. DEPT, SCH. MED, JOHNS HOPKINS UNIV, 61- U.S.N.R, 45-46. Am. Chem. Soc. Structure and biosynthesis of proteins and nucleic acids. Address: 4413 Norwood Rd, Baltimore, MD 21218.

DINUS, RONALD JOHN, b. Ford City, Pa, Feb. 19, 40; m. 64. FOREST GENETICS. B.S, Pa. State, 61; M.S, Washington (Seattle), 63; Hill Family Found. fel, Oregon State, 64-65, Ph.D.(forest genetics), 67. RES. PLANT GENETICIST, INST. FOREST GENETICS, SOUTH. FOREST EXP. STA, FOREST SERV, U.S. DEPT. AGR, 68- Am. Inst. Biol. Sci; Soc. Am. Foresters. Characterization of intraspecific variation in photoperiodic responses of Douglas-fir populations from several geographic areas; selection, progenytesting and breeding of slash and loblolly pines resistant to fusiform rust. Address: Institute of Forest Genetics, P.O. Box 2008, Evergreen Station, Gulfport, MS 39501.

DINUSSON, WILLIAM E(RLING), b. Svold, N.Dak, Apr. 28, 20; m. 44; c. 2. AGRICULTURE. B.S, Okla. Agr. & Mech. Col, 41; Ph.D.(animal nutrit), Purdue, 49. Asst, Texas A&M, 41-42; Purdue, 46-48; asst. prof. ANIMAL HUSB, EXP. STA, S.Dak. State Col, 48-49; assoc. prof, N.DAK. STATE UNIV, 49-56, PROF, 56-, faculty lectr. award, 66. Fulbright res. scholar, Iceland, 60-61; mem. subcomt. sheep, Nat. Res. Coun. U.S.N.R, 42-45, Lt.(sg). Fel. AAAS; Am. Soc. Animal Sci. Nutrition of farm animals; nutritional investigations with laboratory animals. Address: Dept. of Animal Science, North Dakota State University, Fargo, ND 58102.

DINWIDDIE, J(AMES) A(LVIN), b. Tyler, Tex, Oct. 25, 12; m. 36; c. 2. CHEMICAL ENGINEERING. A.B. & A.M, Texas, 35, Ph.D.(chem. eng), 41. Instr. chem. & chem. eng, Texas, 34-38; asst. supt, water purification plant, Austin, Tex, 38-39; res. chemist, ESSO RES. & ENG. CO, 39-42, asst. sect. head, 42-45, sr. res. chemist, 45-53, res. specialist, 53-59, sect. head, 59-66, res. assoc, 66-69, SR. RES. ASSOC, 69- Am. Chem. Soc. Nitrogen bases from kerosenes and coal tar; deviations from Raoult's law; lube oil processing; catalyst development; exploratory petroleum processing. Address: Esso Research & Engineering Co, P.O. Box 4255, Baytown, TX 77520.

DINWIDDIE, JOSEPH GRAY, JR, b. Penns Grove, N.J, Oct. 7, 22; m. 45; c. 4. ORGANIC CHEMISTRY. B.S, Randolph-Macon Col, 42; Ph.D.(chem), Univ. Va, 49. Asst. prof. chem, Clemson Univ, 48-51, assoc. prof, 51-60, prof, 60-68; ACAD. DEAN, AUGUSTA COL, 68- U.S.N.R, 44-46, Comdr. Fel. AAAS; Am. Chem. Soc. Synthetic medicinals; stereochemistry; molecrearrangements. Address: 3606 St. Croix Ct, Augusta, GA 30904.

DION, ANDRE R. b. Quebec, Que, May 3, 26; m. 59; c. 3. PHYSICS. B.Sc.A, Laval, 49, M.Sc, 50, D.Sc.(physics), 53. Defense res. sci. officer, Defense Res. Bd, Can, 53-60; MEM. STAFF, LINCOLN LAB, MASS. INST. TECHNOL, 60- Inst. Elec. & Electronics Eng. Electromagnetic waves; microwaves; antennas; propagation. Address: 600 Hayward Mill Rd, Concord, MA 01742.

DION, ARNOLD SILVA, b. Laconia, N.H, June 26, 39; m. 61; c. 3. BIOCHEMISTRY. B.S, Univ. N.H, 64, M.S, 66, U.S. Pub. Health Serv. fels, 66-69, Ph.D.(biochem), 69. Nat. Insts. Health fel, Univ. Pa, 68-70, res. assoc. BIOCHEM, 70-71; ASSOC, INST. MED. RES, 71- AAAS. Correlations between polyamine and nucleic acid synthesis during development in Drosophila melanogaster and in bacteriophage infected cells; biochemical characterization of oncornaviruses, including RNA-dependent DNA polymerase. Address: Institute for Medical Research, Copewood St, Camden, NJ 08103.

DION, H(ENRY) G(EORGE), b. Saskatoon, Sask, Oct. 18, 15; m. 43; c. 3. SOILS. B.S.A, Saskatchewan, 39; Ph.D.(soils), Wisconsin, 42. Instr. soils, Saskatchewan, 42; soil chemist, Rothamsted Exp. Sta, England, 43-45; Macaulay Inst. Soil Res, Scotland, 45-46; assoc. prof. soils, Saskatchewan, 46-51; soils specialist, Food & Agr. Orgn, Rome, Italy, 51-54; PROF. SOIL CHEM, MACDONALD COL, McGILL UNIV, 54-, dean faculty agr, 55-71. Fel. Agr. Inst. Can. Clay minerals in soils; phosphorus fertilizers. Address: Faculty of Agriculture, Macdonald College, McGill University, Ste. Anne de Bellevue, Que, Can.

DION, HENRY W(ILLIAM), b. Worcester, Mass, Apr. 28, 21; m. 46. ORGANIC CHEMISTRY. B.S. & M.S, Col. of the Holy Cross, 43, fel, 44; fel, Clark, 45-48, Ph.D.(org. chem), 48. RES. CHEMIST, R.P. Scherer Corp, 48-50; PARKE, DAVIS & CO, 50- Am. Chem. Soc. Nitro compounds; isolation of vitamins, hormones and antibiotics. Address: 11910 E. Outer Dr, Detroit, MI 48224.

DIONNE, GERALD F(RANCIS), b. Montreal, Que, Feb. 5, 35; m. 63; c. 1. PHYSICS, ENGINEERING. B.Sc, Loyola Col.(Can), 56; B.Eng, McGill, 58, Nat. Res. Coun. Can. studentship, 61-64, Ph.D.(physics), 64; M.S, Carnegie Inst. Tech, 59. Engr. I, Bell Tel. Co. Can, 58-59; jr. engr, Int. Bus. Mach. Corp, N.Y, 59-60; sr. engr, gen. tel. & electronics semiconductor div, Sylvania Elec. Prod, Inc, Mass, 60-61; res. asst. physics, Eaton Electronics Res. Lab, McGill, 63-64; res. assoc, advan. mat. res. & develop. lab, Pratt & Whitney Aircraft Div, United Aircraft Corp, 64-66, sr. res. assoc, 66-67; STAFF MEM, LINCOLN LAB, MASS. INST. TECHNOL, 67- Asst, Carnegie Inst. Technol, 58-59. Am. Phys. Soc; sr. mem. Inst. Elec. & Electronics Eng. Semiconductor device development; paramagnetic resonance and spin-lattice relaxation in solids; electron emission; surface ionization; ferrite materials; ferrimagnetism; magnetic anisotropy; magnetostriction. Address: 182 High St, Winchester, MA 01890.

DIONNE, JEAN-CLAUDE, b. Luceville, Que, Jan. 3, 35; m. 66; c. 1. GEOLOGY, GEOGRAPHY. B.A, Moncton, 57; M.A, Montreal, 61; Ph.D.(geog), Paris, 64. RES. OFFICER GEOMORPHOL, Bur. Amenagement l'Est Que, Mont-Joli, 64-66; DEPT. FORESTRY & RURAL DEVELOP. CAN, 66- Prof. coastal morphol. & photo-interpretation, Laval, 66-67. Consult, Urban Planning Off. Que, 66-68. Can. Army, 54-56, Lt. AAAS; Asn. Am. Geog; Geol. Asn. Can; Arctic Inst. N.Am; Soc. Econ. Paleont. & Mineral; Am. Soc. Photogram; French-Can. Asn. Adv. Sci; Can. Asn. Geog. Geomorphology; physical geography; quaternary geology; sedimentology; coastal and marine geology; oceanography; photo-interpretation. Address: Laboratoire de Recherches Forestieres, C.P. 3800, Sainte-Foy, Que. 10, Can.

D'IORIO, ANTOINE, b. Montreal, Que, Apr. 22, 25; m. 50; c. 7. BIOCHEMISTRY. B.Sc, Montreal, 46, Ph.D.(biochem), 49. Lectr. physiol, Montreal, 49-51, asst. prof, 52-56; fel. enzymol, Wisconsin, 51-52; pharmacol, Oxford, 56-57; assoc. prof. physiol, Montreal, 57-61; PROF. BIOCHEM, UNIV. OTTAWA, 61-, DEAN SCI, 69-, head dept. biochem, 61-69. Am. Chem. Soc; N.Y. Acad. Sci; Am. Asn. Biol. Chem; Soc. Exp. Biol. & Med; Can. Physiol. Soc.(treas, 58-61); Can. Fedn. Biol. Soc.(hon. treas, 62-66); Brit. Biochem. Soc. Physiology and biochemistry of catecholamines. Address: Faculty of Pure & Applied Science, University of Ottawa, Ottawa, Ont. K1N 6N5, Can.

DIOSY, ANDREW, b. Szarvas, Hungary, Mar. 27, 24; Can. citizen; m. 55; c. 2. INTERNAL MEDICINE. M.D, Szeged, 50; M.Sc, Manitoba, 59. Asst. prof. physiol, Szeged, 50-52; res. fel, Aviation Hosp, Budapest, Hungary, 52-56; res. asst, Univ. Manitoba, 57-59; jr. intern med, Winnipeg Gen. Hosp, Man, 59-60; sr. intern, Deer Lodge Hosp, 60-61; res. fel. endocrinol, St. Michael's Hosp, Toronto, Ont, 61-62, resident med, 62-63; res. assoc. pharmacol, Univ. Toronto, 63-65; dir. clin. res, WARNER-LAMBERT RES. INST. CAN. LTD, 65-70, MED. DIR, WARNER-LAMBERT CAN. LTD, 70- Fel, Royal Col. Physicians & Surgeons Can, 63. E.L. Drewry Mem. Award, 59. Can. Med. Asn; Can. Soc. Study Fertil; Can. Asn. Res. Toxicol; N.Y. Acad. Sci. Clinical pharmacology; new drug research. Address: Warner-Lambert Canada Ltd, 2200 Eglinton Ave. E, Scarborough, Ont, Can.

DiPALMA, JOSEPH R(UPERT), b. N.Y.C, Mar. 21, 16; m. 48; c. 5. PHARMACOLOGY. B.S, Columbia, 36; fel, L.I. Col. Med, 38, M.D, 41. Instr. physiol. & pharmacol, L.I. Col. Med, 41-42, asst. med, 44-48; assoc. physiol. & pharmacol, 46-48, asst. prof. med, 48-50; PROF. PHARMACOL, HAHNEMANN MED. COL, 50-, DEAN, 67-, head dept. pharmacol, 50-67. Fel, Harvard Med. Sch, 46; consult. malaria, Surgeon Gen, 67-69. Am. Physiol. Soc; Am. Soc. Clin. Invest; Harvey Soc; Am. Med. Asn; Am. Soc. Pharmacol. & Exp. Therapeut; Am. Soc. Clin. Pharmacol. & Chemother. Heart muscle; antifibrillatory drugs; chemical warfare agents; anthocyanins. Address: 235 N. 15th St, Philadelphia, PA 19102.

DI PAOLA, ROBERT ARNOLD, b. New York, N.Y, Nov. 28, 33. MATHEMATICS. B.S, Fordham, 56, M.A, 59; Ph.D.(math), Yeshiva, 64. Prof. math, California, Los Angeles, 64-66; MATHEMATICIAN, RAND CORP, 66- Consult, Rand Corp, 65-66; Systs. Develop. Corp, summer, 63. Am. Math. Soc; Asn. Symbolic Logic; Asn. Comput. Mach. Recursive function theory; theory of formal undecidability; applications to computation. Address: Rand Corp, 1700 Main St, Santa Monica, CA 90406.

DiPAOLO, JOSEPH A(MEDO), b. Bridgeport, Conn, June 13, 24; m. 52; c. 2. GENETICS. A.B, Wesleyan, 48; M.S, Western Reserve, 49; Ph.D. (genetics), Northwestern, 51. Asst. instr. genetics & biol, Northwestern, 49-51; dept. biol, Loyola, 51-53; clin. & exp. path, med. sch, Northwestern, 53-55; sr. cancer res. scientist, Roswell Park Mem. Inst, N.Y, 55-63; asst. res. prof. biol, grad. sch, State Univ. N.Y. Buffalo, 55-63; HEAD CYTOGENETICS & CYTOL. SECT, BIOL. BR, NAT. CANCER INST, 63-; ASSOC. PROFESSIONAL FEL. LECTR. ANAT, GEORGE WASHINGTON UNIV, 65- U.S.N, 43-46. AAAS; Am. Asn. Cancer Res; Am. Soc. Human Genetics; Am. Soc. Exp. Path; Genetics Soc. Am; fel. N.Y. Acad. Sci; Tissue Cult. Asn. Experimental cancer research; cell biology. Address: 6605 Melody Lane, Bethesda, MD 20034.

DiPASQUALE, GENE, b. N.Y.C, July 17, 32; m. 62; c. 1. BIOLOGY, PHYSIOLOGY. B.S, Iona Col, 54; M.S, L.I. Univ, 60; Ph.D, N.Y. Univ, 70. From asst. scientist to SR. RES. ASSOC. & HEAD SECT. ANTI-INFLAMMATORY & ANTIFERTILITY STUDIES, WARNER-LAMBERT RES. INST, 57- Med.C, U.S.A, 54-56. AAAS; N.Y. Acad. Sci; Am. Physiol. Soc. Connective tissue metabolism in relation to inflammation, wound healing and atherosclerosis, especially effects of drugs in these areas; study of drugs and their relation to pregnancy and general endocrine interrelations; search for compounds which possess anti-fertility and anti-inflammatory properties. Address: Physiology Dept, Warner-Lambert Research Institute, Morris Plains, NJ 07950.

DIPERT, ARNOLD WILLIAM, b. Grovertown, Ind, Dec. 22, 32; m. 57; c. 2. ELECTRICAL ENGINEERING. B.S, Illinois, 58, M.S, 60, univ. fel, summer, 60, Collins Radio Co. fel, 60-62, Ph.D.(elec. eng), 65. Asst. gen. eng, UNIV. ILL, URBANA, 53-54, ELEC. ENG, 58-60, instr, 60-65, ASST. PROF, 65- U.S.A, 55-57. Inst. Elec. & Electronics Eng. Nonlinear systems; physical electronics; analog and digital computation. Address: Dept. of Electrical Engineering, University of Illinois at Urbana, Urbana, IL 61801.

DI PIETRO, DAVID LOUIS, b. Philadelphia, Pa, Jan. 16, 32; m. 61; c. 3. BIOCHEMISTRY. B.A, Temple, 55, M.A, 57, Ph.D.(biochem), 61. Res. fel. med, Harvard Med. Sch, 61-62; res. assoc. BIOCHEM, div. res, Lankenau Hosp, Phila, 62-63; res. instr, sch. med, & res. investr, Fels Res. Inst, Temple Univ, 63-66, res. asst. prof, 66-68; ASST. PROF, SCH. MED, VANDERBILT UNIV, 68- Am. Chem. Soc; Brit. Biochem. Soc. Enzymes of carbohydrate metabolism in liver and placenta; metabolism of estrogens in pregnancy. Address: Dept. of Obstetrics & Gynecology, School of Medicine, Vanderbilt University, Nashville, TN 37203.

DiPIETRO, JOSEPH, b. Messina, Italy, Apr. 21, 32; U.S. citizen; m. 62; c. 3. ORGANIC & POLYMER CHEMISTRY. B.S, Brooklyn Col, 55; M.S, Maryland, 58; Ph.D.(org. chem), Pennsylvania, 61. Chemist, res. labs, Interchem. Corp, N.Y, 56; res. chemist, res. labs, Rohm & Haas Co, Pa, 58-59; chemist, Du Pont Labs, 60; instr. org. chem, Pennsylvania, 61; NATO fel. polymer chem, Milan Polytech, 61-62; res. chemist polymer chem, res. labs, Celanese Corp. Am, 62-67; dir. RES. & DEVELOP, MICH. CHEM. CORP, 67-69, V.PRES, 69- Am. Chem. Soc. off. rep, Milan, Italy, 61-62. Am. Chem. Soc. Synthetic organic chemistry; pyrolysis of ethers and esters; carbene chemistry; anionic and cationic polymerizations; stereospecific polymerization of α-olefins, diolefins, acrylates; free radicals in solution. Address: 217 Westview Dr, Alma, MI 48801.

DI PIPPO, ASCANIO G, b. Providence, R.I, Jan. 21, 32; m. 61; c. 4. ORGANIC & CLINICAL CHEMISTRY. B.S, Univ. R.I, 54, M.S, 58, Ph.D.(chem), 61. Sr. res. chemist, labs, Olin Mathieson Chem. Corp, 61; Nat. Labs. Res. & Testing, 61-62; asst. prof. ORG. CHEM, SALVE REGINA COL, 62-65, assoc. prof, 65-69, PROF, 69- Nat. Sci. Found. acad. year grant & summer fel. col. teachers, Univ. Colo, 64; consult, Newport Hosp, R.I, 64- Cert, Nat. Registry Clin. Chem. Med.C, U.S.A, 54-56. Am. Chem. Soc. Organic mechanisms; organoboron compounds; effects of radiation on organic compounds. Address: Dept. of Chemistry, Salve Regina College, Newport, RI 02840.

DiPIPPO, RONALD, b. Providence, R.I, June 2, 40; m. 62; c. 3. MECHANICAL ENGINEERING, THERMODYNAMICS. Sc.B, Brown, 62, Sc.M, 64, Ph.D.(eng), 66. Fel, Brown, 66; mech. engr, res. dept, U.S. Naval Underwater Weapons Res. & Eng. Sta, 66-67; ASSOC. PROF. MECH. ENG, SOUTHEAST. MASS. UNIV, 67- Mem. adv. comt, Mass. Bd. Higher Educ, 70- Am. Soc. Eng. Educ. Measurement and correlation of transport properties of gases; propulsion systems. Address: Dept. of Mechanical Engineering, Southeastern Massachusetts University, North Dartmouth, MA 02747.

DIPPEL, WILLIAM A(LAN), b. Jersey City, N.J, June 12, 26; m. 52; c. 5. ANALYTICAL CHEMISTRY. A.B, Princeton, 50, McCay fel, 53-54, Ph.D. (chem), 54. Res. chemist, RES. DIV, EXPLOSIVES DEPT, E.I. DU PONT DE NEMOURS & CO, 54-59, anal. supvr, 59-62, ANAL. SUPT, 62- U.S.N.R, 44-46. Am. Chem. Soc; Am. Inst. Chem. Analytical research and development; instrumental methods of analysis; flame photometry; absorption spectroscopy; gas chromatography; wet methods. Address: 1102 Crestover Rd, Graylyn Crest, Wilmington, DE 19803.

DIPPELL, RUTH V(IRGINIA), b. Hungtington, Ind, June 25, 20. CYTOLOGY, GENETICS. Fel, Ind. Univ, Bloomington, 48, Ph.D.(zool), 49. Asst, IND. UNIV, BLOOMINGTON, 42-45, res. assoc. ZOOL, 45-67, ASSOC. PROF, 67-, fel, 50. Adj. prof, Ind. State Univ, 66-67. AAAS; Am. Soc. Zool; Soc. Protozool.(v.pres, 65-66); Am. Soc. Cell Biol; Int. Soc. Cell Biol. Cytology and genetics of unicellular organisms. Address: Dept. of Zoology, Indiana University, Jordan Hall 218, Bloomington, IN 47401.

DIPPOLD, WALTER JOHN, b. Perryville, Mo, Oct. 21, 26; m. 53; c. 4. ELECTRICAL ENGINEERING, SOLID STATE PHYSICS. B.S.E.E, Milwaukee Sch. Eng, 57; Marquette, 58-59; Ventura Col, 64-65. Asst. prof. elec. eng, Milwaukee Sch. Eng, 57-58, acting chmn. dept. phys. sci, 58-60; sr. res. & develop. engr, astroelectronics lab, Westinghouse Elec. Corp, 61-66; sr. engr, OPTRONICS DIV, BENDIX CORP, 66-69, CHIEF ENGR, MICRO-CHANNEL PLATES & TUBES, 69- Atomic Energy Comn. lectr, Pa. State Univ, 59; Nat. Sci. Found. lectr, prog. modern concepts physics, Milwaukee Sch. Eng, 59-60. U.S.A.A.F, 44-46; U.S.N, 48-52. Am. Asn. Physics Teachers. Image tube development; electron physics; special materials. Address: Optronics Division, Bendix Corp, 1975 Green Rd, Ann Arbor, MI 48107.

DIPPREY, DUANE F(LOYD), b. Minneapolis, Minn, Dec. 22, 29; m. 52; c. 2. MECHANICAL ENGINEERING. B.S, Minnesota, 51, M.S.M.E, 53; Ph.D. (mech. eng, physics), Calif. Inst. Tech, 61. Develop. engr, JET PROPULSION LABS, CALIF. INST. TECHNOL, 53-56, sr. develop. engr, 56-60, eng. group supvr, 60-62, asst. sect. mgr. LIQUID ROCKETS, 62-64, SECT. MGR. LIQUID PROPULSION, 64- Lectr, Southern California, 63-65. Inst. Aeronaut. & Astronaut. Heat transfer from roughened surfaces to flowing fluids; propulsion systems analysis. Address: Liquid Propulsion Section, Jet Propulsion Lab, 4800 Oak Grove Dr, Pasadena, CA 91103.

DI PRIMA, RICHARD CLYDE, b. Terre Haute, Ind, Aug. 9, 27; m. 54; c. 2. APPLIED MATHEMATICS. B.S, Carnegie Inst. Tech, 50, M.S, 51, Ph.D. (math), 53. Res. assoc, Mass. Inst. Tech, 53-54; res. fel, Harvard, 54-56; physicist, Hughes Aircraft Co, Calif, 56-57; asst. prof. MATH, RENSSELAER POLYTECH. INST, 57-59, assoc. prof, 59-62, PROF, 62-, ASSOC. DEAN GRAD. SCH, 68-, chmn. faculty coun, 69-70. Fulbright lectr, Weizmann Inst, Israel. Consult, Mech. Tech, Inc, N.Y. U.S.A, 42-48. Am. Math. Soc; Math. Asn. Am; Soc. Indust. & Appl. Math; Am. Acad. Mech; Am. Soc. Mech. Eng; Soc. Natural Philos. Hydrodynamics stability; fluid mechanics; singular perturbation theory; lubrication. Address: Dept. of Mathematics, Rensselaer Polytechnic Institute, Troy, NY 12181.

DIRECTOR, STEPHEN WILLIAM, b. Brooklyn, N.Y, June 28, 43; m. 65; c. 1. ELECTRICAL ENGINEERING. B.S, State Univ. N.Y, Stony Brook, 65; M.S, California, Berkeley, 67, Ph.D.(elec. eng), 68. Asst. prof. ELEC. ENG, UNIV. FLA, 68-71, ASSOC. PROF, 71- Consult, Radiation, Inc. Inst. Elec. & Electronics Eng. Automated network design; network theory; system theory. Address: Dept. of Electrical Engineering, University of Florida, Gainesville, FL 32601.

DIRENDE, JOSEPH S(ICILIANO), b. Vasto, Italy, Sept. 23, 40; nat; m. 43; c. 5. ENGINEERING. B.S.M.E, Newark Col. Eng, 42; M.Eng, Yale, 44, D.Eng, 49. Instr, Yale, 42-44, 46-51; sect. head, res. div, Curtiss-Wright Corp, 51-53; assoc. prof, Delaware, 53-55; prin. engr, Nuclear Develop. Corp. Am, 55-58; dir. res. & sci. dir, Army Transportation Res. Command, 58-62; tech. dir, aeronaut. turbine lab, Naval Air Turbine Test Sta, 62-66; ASSOC. TECH. DIR, U.S. NAVY AIR & SURFACE WEAPONS DEVELOP, U.S. NAVAL ORD. LAB, 66- Am. Soc. Mech. Eng; Am. Inst. Aeronaut. & Astronaut. Aeronautical, nuclear, transportation and propulsion engineering. Address: 14509 Notley Rd, Silver Spring, MD 20904.

DIRKS, B(RINTON) MARLO, b. Newton, Kans, July 20, 20; m. 44; c. 2. AGRICULTURAL BIOCHEMISTRY. B.S. & M.S, Kans. State Col, 48; fel, Minnesota, 48-52, Ph.D.(agr. biochem), 53. Chemist, Moundridge Milling Co, 38-40; chief operator, Tenn. Eastman Corp, 45-46; head, biochem. res. sect, Pillsbury Mills, Inc, 52-56; group leader, FOOD PROD. DIV, PROCTER & GAMBLE CO, 56-60, head flavor develop. sect, 60-68, HEAD FLOUR TECHNOL. SECT, 68- U.S.A.A.F, 43, C.Eng, 44-46. Am. Chem. Soc; Am. Asn. Cereal Chem; Inst. Food Technol. Enzymes of cereal grains, fungi and related materials; biochemistry of prepared baking mixes and other food products; flavor chemistry and application. Address: 8862 Woodview Dr, Cincinnati, OH 45231.

DIRKS, J(OHN) HERBERT, b. Winnipeg, Man, Aug. 20, 33; m. 61; c. 4. PHYSIOLOGY, NEPHROLOGY. B.Sc. & M.D, Univ. Manitoba, 57. Med. Res. Coun. fels, McGill Univ, 60-61; Nat. Insts Health, 62-64, vis. scientist, 64-65; asst. prof. med, ROYAL VICTORIA HOSP, 65-68, ASSOC. PROF. MED. & ASSOC. PHYSICIAN, 68-, ASSOC. PROF, PHYSIOL, McGILL UNIV, 70-, DIR. RENAL & ELECTROLYTE DIV, UNIV. CLIN, 65-, asst. prof. physiol, 68-69. Grants, Med. Res. Coun, 65-, Nat. Inst. Health, 66-68, Life Ins. Med. Res. Fund, 67-, Banting Res. Found. & Can. Cystic Fibrosis Found, 70-71, Can. Arthritis & Rheumatism Soc. & Hoechst Pharmaceut. Co, 70-, Que. Med. Res. Coun, 71- Fel. Royal Col. Physicians & Surgeons Can, 63. Am. Heart Asn; Am. Fedn. Clin. Res; Am. Physiol. Soc; Am. Soc. Clin. Invest; Am. Soc. Nephrology; Can. Physiol Soc; Can. Soc. Clin. Invest; Can. Soc. Nephrology; Int. Soc. Nephrology. Renal physiology, using, primarily, micropuncture research; sodium, potassium and water reabsorption by proximal and distal tubules in different physiological conditions; effects of diuretics on Na and K transport; clearance and micropuncture studies of magnesium transport in the renal tubule; ATPase and acidification; microencapsulated charcoal hemodialysis; micropuncture project on uric acid. Address: Renal & Electrolyte Division, Royal Victoria Hospital, 687 Pine Ave. W, Montreal 112, Que, Can.

DIRKS, RICHARD A(LLEN), b. Belmond, Iowa, Nov. 11, 37; m. 65; c. 2. DYNAMIC & SYNOPTIC METEOROLOGY. B.S, Wheaton Col.(Ill), 59; M.A, Drake Univ, 62; M.S.T, Cornell Univ, 65; Ph.D.(atmospheric sci), Colo. State Univ, 70. Jr. meteorologist, Colo. State Univ, 68-69; ASST. PROF. ATMOSPHERIC RESOURCES, UNIV. WYO, 69- U.S.A, 60, Capt. AAAS; Am. Meteorol. Soc; Am. Sci. Affiliation. Observation and modeling of small scale airflow including such areas as convective circulations, thunderstorms, mountain airflow, urban circulations and boundary layer flow; airflow studies employing meteorological satellites. Address: Dept. of Atmospheric Resources, University of Wyoming, Laramie, WY 82070.

DIRKS-EDMUNDS, JANE CLAIRE, b. Baxter Co, Ark, June 9, 12; m. 44. BIOECOLOGY. A.B, Linfield Col, 37; Ph.D.(zool), Illinois, 41. Asst. zool, Illinois, 37-41; instr. BIOL, LINFIELD COL, 41-44, asst. prof, 46-48, assoc. prof, 48-60, PROF, 60- Prof. & head dept, Whitworth Col, 44-45. Ecol. Soc. Am; Am. Inst. Biol. Sci; Nat. Audubon Soc; Defenders of Wildlife. Comparison of biotic communities; Douglas fir-hemlock community succession; desert ecology. Address: Dept. of Biology, Linfield College, McMinnville, OR 97128.

DIRKSE, T(HEDFORD) P(RESTON), b. Holland, Mich, Jan. 5, 15; m. 42; c. 4. CHEMISTRY. A.B, Calvin Col, 36; A.M, Indiana, 37, Ph.D.(gen. & phys. chem), 39. Instr. chem, Iowa State Col, 39-41; asst. prof, Hamline, 41-42; chemist, U.S. Naval Res. Lab, Wash, 42-46; asst. prof. CHEM, Hamline, 46-47; assoc. prof, CALVIN COL, 47-51, PROF, 51- Am. Chem. Soc; Electrochem. Soc; Faraday Soc. Electroplating from nonaqueous media; electrical conductance of solutions; alkaline batteries; conductance of salts in monoethanolamine. Address: Dept. of Chemistry, Calvin College, Grand Rapids, MI 49506.

DIRKSEN, A(LVIN) J(OSEPH), Inorg. Chem, Int. Bus, see 12th ed, Soc. & Behav. Vols.

DIRKSEN, THOMAS REED, b. Pekin, Ill, Nov. 5, 31; m. 55; c. 6. DENTISTRY, BIOCHEMISTRY. B.S, Bradley, 53; D.D.S, Illinois, 57; Nat. Insts. Health fel, Eastman Dent. Center, 58-60, cert. pedodontics, 60; San Antonio Col, 60-62; M.S, Rochester, 61, Nat. Insts. Health fel, 62-67, Ph.D.(biochem), 68. Assoc. prof. ORAL BIOL, SCH. DENT, MED. COL. GA, 67-71, PROF, 71-, ASSOC. PROF. CELL & MOLECULAR BIOL, SCH. MED, 71-, assoc. prof. biochem, 67-71. Nat. Inst. Arthritis & Metab. Diseases study grant, 68- Mem, Am. Asn. Dent. Schs, 67- Dent.C, U.S.A.F, 60-62, Capt. AAAS; Am. Dent. Asn; Int. Asn. Dent. Res; N.Y. Acad. Sci. Lipid synthesis by bone and bone cell cultures; lipid constituents of calcified structures; pH of carious cavities. Address: Dept. of Oral Biology, School of Dentistry, Medical College of Georgia, Augusta, GA 30902.

DIRSTINE, PHILIP H(UGH), b. Pullman, Wash, Mar. 11, 15; m. 46; c. 5. ORGANIC CHEMISTRY, BIOCHEMISTRY. B.S, Gonzaga, 36; M.S, Washington (Seattle), 38; Ph.D.(org. chem), Stanford, 42. Res. & develop. engr, Dow Chem. Co, 41-44; res. assoc, California, Los Angeles, 45; instr, Santa Clara, 46; res. chemist, Food Mach. & Chem. Corp, 46-49; dir. clin. biochem. lab. & staff mem. intern & res. training prog. & lab. tech. sch, U.S. Naval Hosp, Oakland, 49-53; chem, biol. & radiol. specialist, U.S. Army Chem. Corps, Ft. McClellan, Ala, 53-56; sr. res. chemist, Gustin-Bacon Mfg. Co, Mo, 56-59; hosp. biochemist, Mercy Hosp, Bakersfield, Calif, 60; head clin. chem. lab, Huntington Mem. Hosp, Pasadena, 61-62; consult, asst. res. dir, South. Calif. Cancer Ctr, Los Angeles, 62-63; HEAD BIOCHEMIST, ALPHA CLIN. LABS, VAN NUYS, 63- Dow Chem. Co. fel, 45. Dipl, Am. Bd. Clin. Chem. Am. Chem. Soc; fel. Am. Asn. Clin. Chem. Product and process development. Address: 20758 Dumont St, Woodland Hills, CA 91364.

D'ISA, FRANK ANGELO, b. Youngstown, Ohio, Mar. 30, 21; m. 50; c. 1. MECHANICAL ENGINEERING. B.S, Youngstown, 43; M.S, Carnegie Inst. Tech, 47; Ph.D.(mech. eng), Pittsburgh, 60. Asst. prof. MECH. ENG, YOUNGSTOWN STATE UNIV, 47-56, assoc. prof, 56-60, PROF, 60-, CHMN. DEPT, 56- Watson Found. distinguished prof. award, 63. U.S.A, 43-46. Am. Soc. Mech. Eng; Nat. Soc. Prof. Eng; Am. Soc. Eng. Educ; Sci. Res. Soc. Am. Strength of materials, elasticity, plasticity, creep, impact, fatigue; engineering mechanics, dynamics of machinery, vibrations. Address: Dept. of Mechanical Engineering, Youngstown State University, 410 Wick Ave, Youngstown, OH 44503.

DI SABATO, GIOVANNI, b. Venice, Italy, Mar. 2, 29; m. 63. BIOCHEMISTRY. M.D, Univ. Padua, 54. Res. fel. BIOCHEM, Univ. Milan, 54-58; Brandeis Univ, 59-61, sr. res. assoc, 61-63; Am. Cancer Soc. scholar, Carlsberg Lab, Copenhagen, Denmark, 63-65; res. asst. prof, Brandeis Univ, 65-66; asst. prof, VANDERBILT UNIV, 66-68, ASSOC. PROF, 68- AAAS; Am. Soc. Biol. Chem. Mechanism of action of enzymes; pyridine nucleotide coenzymes; biological oxidation-reductions. Address: Dept. of Molecular Biology, Vanderbilt University, Nashville, TN 37203.

DiSALVO, JOSEPH, b. Hammonton, N.J, Aug. 7, 38; m. 59; c. 2. ANALYTICAL CHEMISTRY. B.S, Indiana, 60, Du Pont & Nat. Insts. Health fels, & Ph.D.(chem), 65. Instr. chem. & asst. dir. aerospace res. appln. ctr, IND. UNIV, 65-67, ASST. PROF. CHEM. & DIR. AEROSPACE RES. APPLN. CTR, 67- Consult, Ind. Instrument & Chem. Corp, 62- Am. Chem. Soc. Electroanalytical chemistry; polarography, coulometry, chronopotentiometry, especially development and refinement of associated instrumentation. Address: Aerospace Research Applications Center, Indiana University, Bloomington, IN 47405.

DI SALVO, NICHOLAS A(RMAND), b. New York, N.Y, Nov. 2, 20; m. 45; c. 2. ORTHODONTICS, PHYSIOLOGY. B.S, City Col, 42; D.D.S, Columbia, 45, Ph.D.(physiol), 52. Dental intern, Mem. Hosp, 45; dent. fel. physiol, col. physicians & surgeons, COLUMBIA UNIV, 47-50, U.S. Pub. Health Serv. fel, inst. dent. res, 50-52, asst. prof, 52-57, assoc. prof. & dir. div. orthodont, SCH. DENT. & ORAL SURG, 57-58, PROF. & DIR. DIV. ORTHODONT, 58- Dent.C, 45-47, Lt. Am. Dent. Asn; Harvey Soc; fel. N.Y. Acad. Sci; Am. Asn. Orthodont; Am. Physiol. Soc; Int. Asn. Dent. Res; Int. Soc. Cranio-Facial Biol.(pres). Posture and movement of jaws; growth and development of jaws and teeth. Address: Dept. of Orthodontics, Columbia University School of Dental & Oral Surgery, 630 W. 168th St, New York, NY 10032.

DiSALVO, WALTER A, b. Harrison, N.J, Dec. 23, 20; m; c. 2. CHEMICAL ENGINEERING. B.S, Newark Col. Eng, 47, M.S, 51. Technician, Nopco Chem. Co, 39-47, head pilot lab, 47-53; sr. res. engr, COLGATE-PALMOLIVE CO, 53-64, sect. head, 64-66, res. coordinator, 66-70, SR. RES. ASSOC, 70- Am. Chem. Soc. Process development of pharmaceuticals such as vitamins and hormones; product and process development of detergents, paper and plastics. Address: Colgate-Palmolive Co, 105 Hudson St, Jersey City, NJ 07302.

di SANT'AGNESE, PAUL E(MILIO) A(RTOM), b. Rome, Italy, Apr. 23, 14; nat; m. 43; c. 2. PEDIATRICS. M.D, Univ. Rome, 38; Sc.D.(med), Columbia Univ, 48; hon. Dr.Med, Univ. Giessen, 62. Intern, N.Y. Post-Grad. Hosp, 40-41, asst. resident, 42-43, chief resident, 43-44; intern, Willard-Parker Hosp, 41-42; instr. pediat, col. physicians & surgeons, Columbia Univ, 44-46, assoc, 46-51, asst. prof. & head, cystic fibrosis & celiac prog, 51-59; CLIN. PROF. PEDIAT, MED. SCH, GEORGETOWN UNIV, 60-; CHIEF, PEDIAT. METAB. BR, NAT. INSTS. HEALTH, 60- Asst. pediat, Presby. Hosp, New York, N.Y, 44-46, asst. attend. pediatrician, 48-59; chief, pediat. div, Vanderbilt Clin, 44-53; lectr. pediat, Johns Hopkins Univ, 60-63; dir. cystic fibrosis care res. & teaching ctr, Children's Hosp, D.C, 60-67, mem. acad. staff & consult, 60-; from v.chmn. to chmn. & trustee, gen. med. & sci. adv. coun, Nat. Cystic Fibrosis Res. Found, 62-67, mem. exec. comt. & chmn. res. comt, 67-; trustee & mem. exec. comt, Int. Cystic Fibrosis Asn, 65-, chmn. sci. med. adv. coun, 65-69. Dipl, Am. Bd. Pediat. Am. Pediat. Soc; Soc. Pediat. Res; Am. Acad. Pediat; Am. Med. Asn; Am. Inst. Nutrit; Am. Pub. Health Asn; Am. Thoracic Asn; Harvey Soc; N.Y. Acad. Med; N.Y. Acad. Sci. Cystic fibrosis; pediatric gastroenterology; glycogen storage disease; immunology in children. Address: National Institutes of Health, Bldg. 10, Room 8N250, Bethesda, MD 20014.

DISCH, RAYMOND L, b. Lynbrook, N.Y, June 10, 32. PHYSICAL CHEMISTRY. A.B, Colgate, 54; Nat. Insts. Health fel, Harvard, 55-58, A.M, 56, Ph.D.(phys. chem), 59. Nat. Insts. Health fel. phys. chem, Oxford & Nat. Phys. Lab, Eng, 59-63; asst. prof. CHEM, Columbia, 63-68; ASSOC. PROF, QUEENS COL.(N.Y), 68- Optical Soc. Am. Experimental physical chemistry; electric, magnetic and optical properties of fluids; molecular physics. Address: Dept. of Chemistry, Queens College, Flushing, NY 11367.

DISCHER, CLARENCE A(UGUST), b. Oshkosh, Wis, July 22, 12; m. 41. PHYSICAL & INORGANIC CHEMISTRY. Ed.B, Oshkosh Teachers Col, 35; M.A, Indiana, 45, Ph.D.(chem), 47. Teacher, sch, Wis, 36-37; lab. asst. chem, Oshkosh Teachers Col, 38-39, instr, 43, preflight sch, U.S.A.F, 43-

44; powder inspector, Kankakee Ord. Works, U.S. War Dept, 42; chemist, Interlake Pulp & Paper, Wis, 42-43; asst. CHEM, Indiana, 44-47; asst. prof. COL. PHARMACY, RUTGERS UNIV, 47-51, assoc. prof, 51-55, PROF, 55- Am. Chem. Soc. Theoretical electrochemistry; instrumental methods of analysis; photodecomposition; drug metabolite inter-reactions; inorganic pharmaceutical chemistry. Address: Dept. of Pharmaceutical Chemistry, Rutgers, The State University, New Brunswick, NJ 08903.

DISHAL, MILTON, b. Phila, Pa, Mar. 20, 18; m. 42; c. 2. RADIO ENGINEERING. B.S, Temple, 39, fel, 39-41; M.A, 41; Columbia, 41-42. Sr. scientist & head subsysts. tech. group, ITT FED. LABS, 41-69, SR. SCIENTIST & HEAD RECEIVERS & CIRCUITS LAB, AVIONICS DEPT, 69- Fel. AAAS; fel. Inst. Elec. & Electronics Eng. Ultra high frequency radio receivers and direction finder indicators; scanning receivers and indicators; receivers from 14 kc to 1500 Mc for D.F. radar and communications; electronic phase meters. Address: Receivers & Circuits Lab, Avionics Dept, ITT Federal Labs, 500 Washington Ave, Nutley, NJ 07110.

DISHART, K(ENNETH) T(HOMAS), b. Pittsburgh, Pa, July 31, 31. ORGANIC CHEMISTRY. B.Sc, Pittsburgh, 53, Ph.D.(chem), 58. Res. chemist, PETROL. LAB, E.I. DU PONT DE NEMOURS & CO, INC, 58-68, supvr. fuels performance group, 68-70, HEAD CHEM. DIV, 70- Am. Chem. Soc. Organic synthesis; fluorine chemistry; petroleum chemicals; automotive emissions. Address: Petroleum Lab, E.I. du Pont de Nemours & Co, Inc, Wilmington, DE 19898.

DISHBURGER, HENRY J(OSEPH), b. Texas City, Tex, Nov. 4, 26; m. 51; c. 3. BIOCHEMISTRY, ORGANIC CHEMISTRY. B.S, Stephen F. Austin State Col, 50; M.S, Okla. State, 53. Trainee, Hanford Atomic Prod. Oper, Gen. Elec. Co, 52-53, jr. scientist radio-biochem, 53-54, biol. scientist II, 54-55, biol. scientist I, 55-56; chemist, org. res. dept, DOW CHEM. CO, 56-57, res. chemist, 57-59, SR. RES. CHEMIST, 59-64, BIOCHEM, BIOPROD. RES. LAB, 64- U.S.N, 43-46. Radiation Res. Soc; Am. Chem. Soc; Asn. Off. Anal. Chem. Biochemistry, metabolism of pesticides; radioactive tracers; relative biological effect of ionizing radiation on living cells; organic synthesis. Address: Dow Chemical Co, P.O. Box 188, Lake Jackson, TX 77566.

DISKO, MICHAEL DAVID, b. Summit, N.J, Dec. 14, 36; m. 61; c. 3. HYDRAULICS, HYDROLOGY. B.S, Newark Col. Eng, 59, M.S, 62; Stevens Inst. Tech, 62-64; Nat. Sci. Found. fel, N.Y. Univ, 65-66, Ph.D.(water resources), 67. Instr. civil eng, Newark Col. Eng, 59-64, asst. prof, 64-67; Drexel Univ, 67-69; proj. mgr, Quirk, Lawler & Matusky Engrs, N.Y, 69; CONSULT. ENGR, 69- AAAS; Am. Soc. Civil Eng; Am. Geophys. Union; Am. Water Resources Asn; Nat. Soc. Prof. Eng; Water Pollution Control Fedn. Dispersion of pollutants in estuaries; surface and groundwater hydrology; sanitary engineering; water resources; solid wastes; sanitary engineering. Address: 2014 Morrison Ave, Union, NJ 07083.

DISMAN, MURRAY, b. Brooklyn, N.Y, Aug. 18, 31; m. 53; c. 2. ELECTRONICS. B.E.E, N.Y. Univ, 53; M.Sc, Stanford, 55, Ph.D.(elec. eng), 59. Div. mgr. microwave tubes, Eitel-McCullough, Inc, 59-65; v.pres. advan. technol. div, QUANTUM SCI. CORP, 65-71, PRES, 71- Inst. Elec. & Electronics Eng. Microwave tubes and circuits; masers microwave heating; consulting in various technological areas. Address: Quantum Science Corp, 851 Welch Rd, Palo Alto, CA 94304.

DISMANT, JOHN H, b. Glenwood Springs, Colo, Aug. 12, 12; m. 46. METALLURGY. E.M, Colo. Sch. Mines, 39; M.S, Utah, 51, Ph.D.(geol, metall), 55. Exp. mining engr, oil shale demonstration mine, U.S. Bur. Mines, Colo, 45-46; safety & fire control engr, N.J. Zinc Co, Colo, 46-47; asst. prof. extraction metall, N.Mex. Inst. Min. & Tech, 47-49, assoc. res. engr, 49-50; indust. res. div, Washington State, 53-55; private consult, Colo. & S.Dak, 55-57; prin. res. engr, res. lab, Int. Mineral & Chem. Corp. Fla, 57-58; assoc. prof. extraction metall, Tex. West. Col, 58-59; prof. mining eng, North Dakota, 59-61; sr. res. engr, Southwest Res. Inst, Tex, 61-62; assoc. prof. geol. & chmn. dept, Sul Ross State Col, 62-67; PROF. GEOL. & EARTH SCI, ODESSA COL, 67- Summer grant, Univ. N.Dak, 60; consult, La Domincia, Dow Chem. Co, La Linda, Mex, summer 67; Wolfe Ridge Mining Corp, 68; U.S. Air Force Mat. Command, Okla. C.Eng, 41-46, Res, 46-, 1st Lt. Nat. Asn. Geol. Teachers; Soc. Mining Eng. Phosphate exploration and beneficiation, especially by electrostatics; alumina from clay; iron and cobalt reduction in electric arc furnaces; new theory of friction and boundary lubrication; flotation of oxidized zinc ores; lightweight basic ceramics. Address: 2513 Spur, Odessa, TX 79720.

DISMAS REHFUSS, MARY, C.S.J, Org. Chem, see REHFUSS, MARY, C.S.J.

DISMORE, PADEN F(ASOLD), b. Chicago, Ill, June 25, 22; m. 53; c. 3. ORGANIC CHEMISTRY. B.S, Illinois, 43; Maryland, 43-44; Ph.D.(org. chem), Indiana, 48. Chemist, Textile Found, Wash, D.C, 44; Harris Res. Labs, 45; RES. CHEMIST, Mound Lab, Monsanto Chem. Co, Ohio, 48-50; nylon div, textiles dept, E.I. DU PONT DE NEMOURS & CO, 50-66, JACKSON LAB, 66- Am. Chem. Soc; Am. Phys. Soc. Organic synthesis; water repellant clothing; atomic energy; by-products of catalytic hydrogenation of aromatic aldehydes; high polymers. Address: Jackson Lab, E.I. du Pont de Nemours & Co, P.O. Box 525, Wilmington, DE 19899.

DISMUKES, EDWARD B(ROCK), b. Georgiana, Ala, Oct. 9, 27; m. 54; c. 2. PHYSICAL CHEMISTRY. B.S, Birmingham-South. Col, 49; M.S, Univ. Wis, 51, Ph.D.(chem), 53. Asst. phys. chem, Univ. Wis, 49-52; chemist, phys. div, SOUTH. RES. INST, 53-58, sr. chemist, 58-59, HEAD PHYS. CHEM. SECT, 59-66, 71-, chem. defense sect, 66-71. Lectr, Birmingham-South. Col, 55-60. U.S.A, 46-47. Am. Chem. Soc. Analysis of pollutants in air and water; properties of molten silicates; properties of aqueous complexion systems; electrochemistry; colloid chemistry; infrared spectrophotometry. Address: Southern Research Institute, 2000 Ninth Ave. S, Birmingham, AL 35205.

DISMUKES, JOHN P(ICKETT), b. Greenville, S.C, Nov. 16, 33. INORGANIC CHEMISTRY. B.S, Ala. Polytech, 55; Nat. Sci. Found. fel, Univ. Ill, 56-57, Minn. Mining & Mfg. Co. fel, 57-58, univ. fel, 58-59, Ph.D.(chem), 59. MEM. TECH. STAFF INORG. CHEM, DAVID SARNOFF RES. CTR, RCA CORP, 59- Nat. Sci. Found. fel, 59-60. Am. Chem. Soc. High temperature inorganic and coordination chemistry; rare earth chemistry and materials for thermoelectric power generation; hydrothermal synthesis of Cr O_2; vapor phase etching and growth of Si; vapor phase growth of (III-V)-(II-VI) alloys and of rare earth mononitrides. Address: David Sarnoff Research Center, RCA Corp, Princeton, NJ 08540.

DISNEY, RALPH L(YNDE), b. Baltimore, Md, Feb. 27, 28; m. 55; c. 3. INDUSTRIAL ENGINEERING. B.E, Hopkins, 52, scholar & M.S.E, 55, D.Eng.(indust. eng), 64. Engr, Indust. Diecraft, Inc, 53-55; res. analyst, Opers. Res. Off, 55-56; asst. prof. eng, Lamar State Col. Tech, 56-59; assoc. prof, Buffalo, 59-63; vis. assoc. prof, UNIV. MICH, 63-64, assoc. prof, 64-68, PROF. INDUST. ENG, 68-, vis. lectr, 62-63. Orgn. Am. States vis. prof, Inst. Aeronaut. Technol, Brazil, 70-71; del, NATO Conf. on Opers. Res. Educ. AAAS; Am. Inst. Indust. Eng; Soc. Indust. & Appl. Math; Am. Math. Asn; Inst. Math Statist; Inst. Mgt. Sci.(div. ed). Stochastic networks and processes; operations research. Address: 910 Kuebler Dr, Ann Arbor, MI 48103.

DISNEY, RALPH WILLARD, b. Kansas City, Mo, Mar. 13, 23; m. 44; c. 4. GEOLOGY. B.S, Oklahoma, 48, M.S, 50, Ph.D.(geol), 60. Instr. geol, Oklahoma, 49-54, asst. prof, 54-55; staff geologist, Sinclair Oil & Gas Co, 60-65, res. assoc, 65-67; independent consult. geologist, 67-69; V.PRES. & MGR. EXPLOR, WEST. DIVERSIFIED INDUSTS, INC, 69- Found. award, Oklahoma, 54. U.S.A.A.F, 43-46. Am. Asn. Petrol. Geol. Petroleum exploration. Address: Western Diversified Industries, Inc, 406 Beacon Bldg, Tulsa, OK 74103.

DISNEY, V(IRGIL) H(AWTHORNE), b. Moberly, Mo, Nov. 28, 13; m. 42; c. 3. ELECTRICAL ENGINEERING. B.S, Missouri, 36. Test engr, Gen. Elec. Co, 36-37; elec. engr, Am. Can. Co, 37-42; instr. radio & calculus, Ill. Inst. Tech, 42-43; proj. engr, C.E. Conn, Ltd, 43-46; Sperry Gyro Co, 47-48; asst. sect. head res, Curtiss-Wright Co, 46-47, 48-49; supvr. electronics, Armour Res. Found, 48-51, asst. mgr. elec. eng. dept, 51-54, mgr, 54-60, dir. electronics div, 60-62, v.pres, IIT Res. Inst, 62-70; DIR. RES, BANK ADMIN. INST, PARK RIDGE, 70- Inst. Elec. & Electronics Eng. Electronics instrumentation; servomechanism; regulators; missile systems. Address: 40 S. Stough St, Hinsdale, IL 60521.

DISTAD, PAUL A(NDREW), b. S.Dak, Feb. 20, 27; m. 54; c. 1. BACTERIOLOGY. B.A, South Dakota, 50, M.A, 52. Res. bacteriologist, Gen. Biochem, Inc, 52-56; chief chemist, Gerson-Stewart Corp, 56-60, tech. dir, 60-64; PRES, SCOT LABS, INC, 64- U.S.N, 45-46. Am. Chem. Soc. Emulsion polymerization; wax and resin emulsions; germicidal agents. Address: 67 Morningside Dr, Chagrin Falls, OH 44022.

DISTEFANO, G(EORGE) PAUL, b. Baton Rouge, La, Apr. 8, 38; m. 60; c. 3. CHEMICAL ENGINEERING, MATHEMATICS. B.S, La. State, 60; M.S, Florida, 62, Ph.D.(chem. eng, math), 64. Engr. aid, La. State Dept. Hwy, 57, summer 58; asst, Florida, 63; sr. mathematician, Monsanto Co, 64-66; sr. engr, comput. applns. res. dept, Electronic Assocs, Inc, 66-69; ASST. V.PRES, COMPUTER COMPLEX, INC, 69- Summers, mem. staff, Solvay Process Div, Allied Chem. Co, 59 & 60. Am. Inst. Chem. Eng. Systems engineering; applied mathematics. Address: Computer Complex, Inc, Computer Center, 6400 Southwest Freeway, Houston, TX 77036.

DI STEFANO, HENRY S(AVERIO), b. Palermo, Italy, Jan. 1, 20, U.S. citizen; m. 51; c. 2. ANATOMY. B.A, Brooklyn Col, 41; M.A, Columbia, 46, Ph.D.(zool), 48. Instr. ANAT, COL. MED, Syracuse, 48-51, STATE UNIV. N.Y. UPSTATE MED. CTR, 51-53, asst. prof, 53-58, assoc. prof, 58-65, PROF, 65- U.S.N.R, 43-45, Lt.(jg). Histochem. Soc; Am. Asn. Anat; Am. Soc. Cell Biol; Electron Micros. Soc. Am. Cytochemistry and electron microscopy; viral induced avian and murine leukemias. Address: Dept. of Anatomy, State University of New York Upstate Medical Center, Syracuse, NY 13210.

DISTEFANO, JOSEPH JOHN, III, b. Brooklyn, N.Y, Apr. 30, 38. BIOENGINEERING, CONTROL SYSTEMS. B.E.E, City Col. New York, 61; M.S, Univ. Calif, Los Angeles, 64, Ph.D.(control systs, biocybernet), 66. Res. engr, Autonetics Div, N.Am. Aviation, Inc, 61-63; ASST. PROF. ENG. SYSTS. & MED, UNIV. CALIF, LOS ANGELES, 66- NATO fel. clin. med, radiol. lab, Univ. Rome, 67-68. Consult, Photo-Sonics, Inc, Calif, 66-67; Cooper-Levine Assocs, 69- Inst. Elec. & Electronics Eng; Simulation Coun; N.Y. Acad. Sci; Int. Soc. Psychoneuroendocrinol. Feedback control systems theory and applications; computer applications and simulation; bioengineering systems; biocybernetics; modeling of biological regulatory systems and biochemical phenomena, especially in neuroendocrinology. Address: Dept. of Engineering Systems, University of California, Los Angeles, CA 90024.

DiSTEFANO, THOMAS HERMAN, b. Phila, Pa, Dec. 21, 42. SOLID STATE PHYSICS. B.S, Lehigh Univ, 64; Nat. Sci. Found. fel, Stanford Univ, 64-66, M.S, 65, Ph.D.(appl. physics), 70. STAFF MEM, Stanford Linear Accelerator Ctr, Stanford Univ, 69-70; T.J. WATSON RES. CTR, IBM CORP, 70- Consult, Synvar Assocs, 69-70. AAAS; Am. Phys. Soc. Photoemission spectroscopy and electronic bands in insulating materials; hot electron scattering by photoinjection; internal photoemission and interfaces. Address: Dept. of Physical Science, Research Center, IBM Corp, P.O. Box 218, Yorktown Heights, NY 10598.

DiSTEFANO, VICTOR, b. Rochester, N.Y, Mar. 17, 24; m. 47; c. 5. PHARMACOLOGY. A.B, Univ. Rochester, 49, Ph.D.(pharmacol), 53. Instr. PHARMACOL, sch. med, Marquette Univ, 53-54; SCH. MED, UNIV. ROCHESTER, 54-57, asst. prof, 57-63, ASSOC. PROF, 63-, TOXICOL. & RADIATION BIOL, 70- U.S.A, 42-46. Am. Soc. Pharmacol. Autonomics; antiradiation; central nervous system. Address: 1055 Quaker Rd, Scottsville, NY 14546.

DISTLER, RAYMOND JEWEL, b. Paducah, Ky, July 3, 30; m. 51; c. 4. ELECTRICAL ENGINEERING. B.S.E.E, Kentucky, 51, M.S.E.E, 60, Ph.D. (math, elec. eng), 64. Mem. tech. staff, Bell Tel. Labs, N.J, 51-58; instr. ELEC. ENG, UNIV. KY, 58-64, asst. prof, 64-66, ASSOC. PROF, 66- Inst. Elec. & Electronics Eng; Am. Math. Soc. Design and development of magnetic amplifiers; control systems and information theory. Address: Dept. of Electrical Engineering, University of Kentucky, Lexington, KY 40506.

DiTARANTO, ROCCO A, b. Phila, Pa, Aug. 12, 26; m. 56; c. 4. ENGINEERING MECHANICS. B.S, Drexel Inst, 47; M.S, Pennsylvania, 50, Ph.D.(eng. mech), 61. Jr. engr, Philco Corp, 48-50; sr. engr, Vertol Helicopter Co, 50-53; anal. engr, aviation gas turbine div, Westinghouse Elec. Co, 53-55, shock & vibration consult, RCA Defense Electronics Prod, 55-59; assoc. prof. mech. eng, Drexel Inst, 59-62; PROF. ENG, PMC COLS, 62- Eng. consult, U.S. Navy Marine Eng. Lab, 61-; vis. prof, inst. sound & vibration, Univ. Southampton, 69-70. Am. Soc. Mech. Eng; Am. Soc. Eng. Educ; Am. Inst. Aeronaut. & Astronaut; Acoust. Soc. Am; Sci. Res. Soc. Am. Shock and vibrations; vibration damping; dynamics of structures and shells; mechanics of laminated structures. Address: Dept. of Engineering, PMC Colleges, Chester, PA 19013.

DITMAN, JOHN G(ORDON), b. Kenton, Ohio, Jan, 20, 09; m. 32; c. 1. PHYSICAL CHEMISTRY. A.B, Wooster Col, 31; Ph.D.(phys. chem), N.Y. Univ, 35. Asst, N.Y. Univ, 31-35; asst. chemist, Standard Oil Develop. Co, 35-37; head lub. oil group, petrol. tech. serv. lab, Esso Standard Oil Co, 37-48; LAB. & PILOT PLANT COORD, PROCESS PLANTS DIV, FOSTER WHEELER CORP, 48- Instr, Polytech. Inst. Brooklyn, 53-54. Am. Chem. Soc. Rates of thermal decomposition; refining of heavy petroleum oils. Address: Apt. 9-D, 35 Manor Dr, Newark, NJ 07106.

DI TORO, MICHAEL JOHN, b. Campobasso, Italy, June 24, 10; nat; m. 41; c. 4. ELECTRICAL ENGINEERING, ACOUSTICS. E.E, Polytech. Inst. Brooklyn, 31, M.E.E, 33, D.E.E, 46. Res. engr, T.A. Edison Co, 34-41; sr. elec. engr, Hazeltine Electronics Corp, 41-46; asst. dir. microwave res. inst, Polytech. Inst. Brooklyn, 46-47; div. head, Fed. Tel. Labs, 47-52; asst. tech. dir, DuMont Labs, 52-53; head electronics, Fairchild Guided Missile Div, 53-55; dir. eng, electronics div, Harris Intertype Corp, 55-61; v.pres. res, CARDION ELECTRONICS, INC, 61-69, V.PRES. SCI, 69- Adj. prof, grad. sch, Polytech. Inst. Brooklyn. Fel. Inst. Elec. & Electronics Eng; fel. Acoustical Soc. Am. Electro-acoustics, piezoelectric and electromagnetic transducers, tracing distortion analysis, speech compression; speech noise suppression and secrecy systems; phase distortion and transmission dispersion analysis, phase-correct lumped and distributed delay lines; various instrumentation such as digital real-time spectrum analyzers, microwave calorimeters; telemetering and adaptive communications systems. Address: Cardion Electronics, Inc, Long Island Expressway, Woodbury, NY 11797.

D'ITRI, FRANK M, b. Flint, Mich, Apr. 25, 33; m. 55; c. 4. ANALYTICAL & WATER CHEMISTRY. B.S, Mich. State Univ, 55, Nat. Insts. Health summer fel, 64-67, M.S. & Ph.D.(anal. chem), 66. Technologist, Dow Chem. Co, 60-62; asst. anal. chem, MICH. STATE UNIV, 62-68, ASST. PROF. WATER CHEM, INST. WATER RES, 68- Nat. Insts. Health fel, 67-68; prin. investr, Off. Water Resources Res, U.S. Dept. Interior, 69-; adv, environ. mercury pollution, Mich. House Rep, 70-; mem. Critical Pollution Mat. Comt, Mich. Water Resources Comn, 71-; adv, revision water qual. criteria publ, Nat. Acad. Sci, 71- U.S.A.F, 56-60, Capt. Am. Chem. Soc. Analytical aspects of water and sediment chemistry with special interest on the transformation and translocation of mercury. Address: Room 334, Natural Resources Bldg, Michigan State University, East Lansing, MI 48823.

DITTER, JEROME F(RANCIS), b. Minneapolis, Minn, June 6, 23; m. 45; c. 2. PHYSICAL CHEMISTRY. B.S, St. Mary's Col.(Minn), 48; M.S, Cath. Univ. Am, 51, Naval Res. Lab. fel, 51-52, Ph.D.(phys. chem), 52. Chemist, Standard Oil Co, Ind, 52-54; group leader, Olin Mathieson Corp, Calif, 54-59; sr. staff mem, Nat. Eng. Sci. Co, 59-63; sr. chemist, Dynamic Sci. Corp, 63-65; sr. scientist, res. & educ. ctr, Space-Gen. Corp, 65-70; RES. MGR, V.PRES. & MEM. BD. DIRS, CHEM. SYSTS, INC, 70- U.S.N, 43-46. AAAS; Am. Chem. Soc. Nucleation and crystallization processes; high vacuum techniques; infrared and mass spectra studies; borane and carborane chemistry, especially applications for ultimate high temperature polymers; high strength materials, primarily refractory filaments. Address: Chemical Systems, Inc, 1852 McGaw Ave, Santa Ana, CA 92705.

DITTERT, LEWIS WILLIAM, b. Phila, Pa, Jan. 22, 34; m. 57; c. 2. PHARMACY. B.S, Temple, 56; M.S, Wisconsin, 60, Ph.D.(pharm), 61. Pharmacist, Smith Kline & French Labs, summers 56 & 57, sr. res. pharmacist, 61-67; asst. prof. PHARM, COL. PHARM, UNIV. KY, 67-69, ASSOC. PROF, 69- AAAS; Am. Pharmaceut. Asn; Am. Chem. Soc. Physical pharmacy; biopharmaceutics. Address: College of Pharmacy, University of Kentucky, Lexington, KY 40506.

DITTFACH, JOHN HARLAND, b. St. Paul, Minn, Apr. 17, 18; m. 44; c. 5. MECHANICAL ENGINEERING. B.S.M.E, Minnesota, 47, M.S.M.E, 48. Instr. MECH. ENG, Minnesota, 47-48; from asst. prof. to PROF, UNIV. MASS, AMHERST, 48- U.S.A, 42-45. Experimental testing techniques; energy conversion. Address: Dept. of Mechanical Engineering, University of Massachusetts, Amherst, MA 01002.

DITTMAN, FRANK W(ILLARD), b. Pittsburgh, Pa, July 22, 18; m. 46; c. 4. CHEMICAL ENGINEERING. B.S, Pittsburgh, 40; M.Ch.E, Cornell, 43, Ph.D.(chem. eng), 45. Asst. chem. eng, Cornell, 40-44, instr. math, 43-44; process engr, Koppers Co, Inc, 46-52; Rust Process Design Co, 52-55, chief chem. process consult, 55-58; res. technologist, appl. res. lab, U.S. Steel Corp, Pa, 58-62; PROF. CHEM. ENG, RUTGERS UNIV, 62- Instr, Carnegie Inst. Tech, 47-50. Res. engr, Rubber Reserve Co, 43-44. U.S.N.R, 44-46. Am. Inst. Chem. Eng; Nat. Soc. Prof. Eng. Mass, heat and momentum transfer, including filtration; thermodynamics and kinetics—theory and experiment under widely varying conditions; design, construction and economics of chemical plants—organic, inorganic and metallurgical; metals processing; waste treatment and river aeration to combat pollution. Address: Dept. of Chemical Engineering, Rutgers, The State University, New Brunswick, NJ 08903.

DITTMAN, RICHARD HENRY, b. Sacramento, Calif, July 5, 37; m. 62; c. 2. PHYSICS. B.S, Santa Clara, 59; Atomic Energy Cmn. fel, Notre Dame, 64-65, Ph.D.(physics), 65. Guest scientist, Fritz-Haber-Inst, W.Berlin, 65-66; asst. prof. PHYSICS, UNIV. WIS-MILWAUKEE, 66-71, ASSOC. PROF, 71- Am. Asn. Physics Teachers. Field electron emission microscopy; flash filament spectrometry; classical gravitation experiments. Address: Dept. of Physics, University of Wisconsin-Milwaukee, Milwaukee, WI 53201.

DITTMAR, BRUCE I, b. Wilmington, Del, Oct. 20, 34; m. 60. ORGANIC CHEMISTRY. B.S, Bucknell Univ, 56; M.S, Univ. Wis, 58; Ph.D.(org. chem), Univ. Pa, 61. From chemist to SR. RES. CHEMIST, E.I. DU PONT DE NEMOURS & CO, INC, 61- Am. Chem. Soc. Synthesis of heterocyclic compounds; information storage and retrieval. Address: 302 Plymouth Rd, Fairfax, Wilmington, DE 19803.

DITTMER, DONALD C(HARLES), b. Quincy, Ill, Oct. 17, 27. ORGANIC CHEMISTRY. B.S, Illinois, 50; Atomic Energy Comn. fel, Mass. Inst. Technol, 51, Nat. Sci. Found. fel, 52, Ph.D.(org. chem), 53. Fel. CHEM, Harvard, 53-54; instr, Pennsylvania, 54-56, asst. prof, 56-61; E.I. du Pont de Nemours & Co. fel, 61-62; assoc. prof, SYRACUSE UNIV, 62-66, PROF, 66- U.S.A, 46-47. Am. Chem. Soc; The Chem. Soc. Model enzyme systems; small-ring heterocyclic chemistry; organic reaction mechanisms. Address: Dept. of Chemistry, Syracuse University, Syracuse, NY 13210.

DITTMER, HOWARD J(AMES), b. Pekin, Ill, Jan. 29, 10; m. 41; c. 1. BOTANY, MORPHOLOGY. A.B, New Mexico, 33, A.M, 34; Ph.D.(plant morphol), Iowa, 38. Prof. sci, Chicago Teachers Col, 38-43; assoc. prof. BIOL, UNIV. N.MEX, 43-52, PROF, 52-, ASSOC. DEAN COL. ARTS & SCI, 70-, asst. dean, 56-70. AAAS (past pres, Southwest. & Rocky Mt. Div); Bot. Soc. Am; Ecol. Soc. Am. Investigation of subterranean plant parts; quantitative study of roots and root hairs and their relation to physics of soil; flora of New Mexico; lawn problems of the southwest; phylogeny and form in the plant kingdom. Address: College of Arts & Science, University of New Mexico, Albuquerque, NM 87106.

DITTMER, JOHN C(HARLES), b. El Reno, Okla, Mar. 27, 28. BIOCHEMISTRY. B.S, Oklahoma, 54; Eli Lilly fel, Washington (Seattle), 57-58, Ph.D. (biochem), 58. Asst. BIOCHEM, Washington (Seattle), 54-58; U.S. Pub. Health Serv. res. fel, Agr. Res. Coun. Inst. Animal Physiol, Cambridge, Eng, 58-60; asst. prof. Southern California, 60-61; Kentucky, 62-65, assoc. prof, 65; St. Louis Univ, 65-68, PROF, 68-71; MEM. UNIV, 71- Am. Soc. Biol. Chem; Am. Chem. Soc; Am. Oil Chemists' Soc; Brit. Biochem. Soc. Lipids; chemical structure and metabolism. Address: Faculty of Medicine, Memorial University of Newfoundland, St. John's, Newf, Can.

DITTMER, JOHN EDWARD, b. Colesburg, Iowa, May 10, 39; m. 62; c. 2. DEVELOPMENTAL BIOLOGY. B.S, Arizona State, 62; M.A.T, Brown, 66, Nat. Insts. Health trainee, 66-69, Ph.D.(develop. biol), 70. Instr, high sch, Kans, 62-65; lab. instr. biol, Brown, 66-69; res. asst. ANAT, SCH. MED, BOSTON UNIV, 69, ASST. PROF, 69- AAAS; Am. Soc. Zool. Development; regeneration; compensatory renal hypertrophy. Address: Dept. of Anatomy, School of Medicine, Boston University, 80 E. Concord, Boston, MA 02118.

DITTMER, KARL, b. Hebron, N.Dak, Jan. 18, 14; m. 49; c. 3. CHEMISTRY. B.A, Jamestown Col, 37; M.A, Colorado, 39; Ph.D.(biochem), Cornell, 44. Fel. antibiotins and penicillin assay methods, biochem. dept, med. col, Cornell, 44-45; asst. prof. chem, Colorado, 45-47, assoc. prof, 47-49; prof. & head dept, Fla. State, 49-58; head, div. grants & fels. prog. adminstr. petrol. res. fund, Am. Chem. Soc, 58-64; v.pres. acad. affairs, Fla. State Univ, 64-66; DEAN COL. SCI, PORTLAND STATE UNIV, 66- With Off. Sci. Res. & Develop; Off. Naval Res, 44. AAAS; Am. Chem. Soc; Am. Soc. Biol. Chem. Structural basis for antimetabolites; antivitamins; antibiotins; antiamino acids synthesis and properties; amino acid metabolism of rats and bacteria; biosynthesis of vitamins and amino acids; synthesis of nucleosides and derivatives; microbiological study of structural specificity of biotin. Address: College of Science, Portland State University, Portland, OR 97207.

DITTNER, PETER FRED, b. Vienna, Austria, Mar. 24, 37; U.S. citizen, m. 58; c. 2. ATOMIC PHYSICS. B.S, N.Y. Univ, 58, Ph.D.(physics), 65; Nat. Sci. Found. fel, Mass. Inst. Tech, 58-59. RES. ASSOC. CHEM, OAK RIDGE NAT. LAB, 65- Am. Phys. Soc. Address: Chemistry Division, Oak Ridge National Lab, P.O. Box X, Oak Ridge, TN 37830.

DiTULLIO, V, b. Montreal, Que, Jan. 21, 38; m. 64; c. 2. ORGANIC CHEMISTRY, ENZYMOLOGY. B.Sc, McGill Univ, 59, Ph.D.(chem), 64. Fel. chem, Univ. Ottawa (Ont), 64-65; Nat. Res. Coun. Can. fel, Swiss Fed. Inst. Technol, 65-66; fel. biochem, Univ. Ottawa (Ont), 66-71; SR. RES. DIR. CHEM, BRISTOL LABS, 71- Am. Chem Soc; Can. Biochem. Soc. Photochemistry; steroid chemistry. Address: Bristol Labs, 100 Industrial Ave, Candiac, Que, Can.

DIUGUID, LINCOLN ISAIAH, b. Lynchburg, Va, Feb. 6, 17; m. 52; c. 4. ORGANIC CHEMISTRY. B.S, W.Va. State Col, 38; M.S, Cornell, 39, Ph.D.(org. chem), 45. Head chem. dept, Ark. State Col, 39-43; anal. chemist, Pine Bluff Arsenal, Chem. Warfare Serv, U.S. Army, 42-43; Merrill res. fel, Cornell, 43-45, Off. Sci. Res. & Develop. res. fel, 45-46, res. assoc, 46-47, B.F. Goodrich rubber res. fel, 47; RES. DIR, DU-GOOD CHEM. LAB, 47-; PROF. CHEM, HARRIS TEACHERS COL, 54-, CHMN. DEPT. PHYS. SCI, 70- Cancer res, Jewish Hosp. St. Louis, 59-; mem, Leukemia Res. Proj, 61-63; v.pres, Leukemia Guild, Mo. & Ill, 64- Am. Chem. Soc; fel. Am. Inst. Chem; Asn. Consult. Chemists & Chem. Eng. New method synthesis of primary aliphatic alcohols, large carbon ring compounds and benzothiazole derivatives; new micromethods for organic quantitative analyses; industrial development. Address: 1215 S. Jefferson Ave, St. Louis, MO 63104.

DIVADEENAM, MUNDRATHI, b. Pulukurthy, India, June 21, 35; m. 64; c. 1. PHYSICS, NUCLEAR PHYSICS. B.Sc, Osmania, India, 54, M.Sc, 56; associateship, Saha Inst. Nuclear Physics, 59, Atomic Energy Comn. fel, 59-60; Ph.D.(nuclear physics), Duke, 67. Lectr. physics, Osmania, India, 56-57; jr. sci. asst. physics, Int. Geophys. Year sponsored, 57-58; res. asst. nuclear physics, Duke, 60-66, res. assoc, 67-69; ASST. PROF. PHYSICS, Prairie View Agr. & Mech. Col, 69-70; N.C. CENT. UNIV. & DUKE UNIV, 70- Am. Phys. Soc. Average and high resolution neutron total cross sections; strength functions; optical model; doorway states; intermediate structure; analog states; nuclear structure. Address: Dept. of Physics, Triangle Universities Nuclear Lab, Duke University, Durham, NC 27706.

DIVELBISS, JAMES E(DWARD), b. Pueblo, Colo, Oct. 12, 33; m. 54; c. 4. ZOOLOGY, GENETICS. B.A, Westmar Col, 55; M.S, Iowa, 59, Nat. Sci. Found. fel, 59-61, Ph.D.(zool, genetics), 61. Asst. prof. BIOL, WESTMAR COL, 61-63, assoc. prof, 63-71, PROF, 71- Res. partic, Nat. Sci. Found. summer insts, Ore. State Univ, 66, Univ. Ill, 67, Hopkins Marine Sta, 70; Nat. Sci. Found. sr. faculty fel, 71-72. Am. Inst. Biol. Sci; Am. Soc. Human Genetics; Genetics Soc. Am; Am. Genetic Asn. Fine structure of gene in Drosophila; pteridine of Drosophila. Address: Dept. of Biology, Westmar College, Le Mars, IA 51031.

DIVELEY, WILLIAM R(USSELL), b. Royal Center, Ind, June 13, 21; m. 49; c. 1. ORGANIC CHEMISTRY. B.S, Manchester Col, 43; M.S, Purdue, 50, Ph.D.(chem), 52. Res. chemist, HERCULES, INC, 52-63, sr. res. chemist, 63-71, RES. SCIENTIST, 71- U.S.N.R, 42-46. Am. Chem. Soc. Synthetic organic chemistry; agricultural chemicals-pesticides; organophosphorous chemistry. Address: 3713 Valleybrook Rd, Oakwood Halls, Wilmington, DE 19808.

DIVEN, B(ENJAMIN) C(LINTON), b. Chico, Calif, Jan. 5, 19; m. 51; c. 3. NUCLEAR PHYSICS. A.B, California, 41; M.S, Illinois, 48, Ph.D.(physics), 50. MEM. STAFF, LOS ALAMOS SCI. LAB, UNIV. CALIF, 43-45, 50- Fel. Am. Phys. Soc. Experimental nuclear physics. Address: Box 1663, Los Alamos, NM 87544.

DIVEN, R(ICHARD) H, b. Caldwell, Idaho, Mar. 10, 33; m. 55; c. 2. BIOCHEMISTRY. B.S, Oregon State, 55; M.S, Washington State, 57; Ph.D.(biochem), Arizona, 59. Asst. pathologist animal path, Arizona, 60-63; res. biochemist animal health & nutrit, sci. div, Abbott Labs, 63-67; V.PRES, E.S. ERWIN & ASSOCS, 67- Infectious diseases; toxicology; ruminant physiology. Address: E.S. Erwin & Associates, 4018 W. 51st Ave, Amarillo, TX 79109.

DIVEN, WARREN F(IELD), b. St. Louis, Mo, Oct. 10, 31; m. 54; c. 3. BIOCHEMISTRY. B.A, Hastings Col, 52; M.S, Nebraska, 60, Du Pont, Monsanto & Dow fels. & Ph.D.(chem), 62. Nat. Insts. Health fel, Wisconsin, 62-64; asst. prof. biochem, SCH. MED, UNIV. PITTSBURGH, 64-71, ASSOC. PROF. PATH. & BIOCHEM, 71- U.S.A.F, 52-58, Capt. Am. Chem. Soc; Am. Asn. Biol. Chem; Am. Asn. Clin. Chem; N.Y. Acad. Sci. Clinical biochemistry; enzyme defects in inborn errors of metabolism; enzymology; molecular mechanisms of metabolic control. Address: Dept. of Biochemistry, Unisity of Pittsburgh School of Medicine, Pittsburgh, PA 15213.

DIVETT, ROBERT THOMAS, b. Salt Lake City, Utah, Nov. 4, 25; m. 53; c. 6. INFORMATION SCIENCE, HISTORY OF MEDICINE. B.S, Brigham Young Univ, 53; M.A, George Peabody Col, 55; Emory Univ, 56; Ed.D.(educ. admin. & media), Univ. Utah, 68. Teacher-librn, jr. high sch, Idaho, 53-54; first asst, med. libr, Vanderbilt Univ, 54-56; asst. prof. libr. sci. & med. librn, Univ. Utah, 56-62; ASSOC. PROF. MED. BIBLIOG. & MED. SCI. LIBRN, UNIV. N.MEX, 63-; DIR. HEALTH SCI. INFO. & COMMUN. CTR, 68- Nat. Libr. Med. res. grant, 65-69; consult, Okla. Med. Ctr, 66; Mayo Clin, 68. Vis. assoc. prof, Univ. Wash, 69; contrib, Third Int. Cong. Med. Librarianship, Amsterdam, 69. U.S.M.C, 44-47, Sgt. Med. Libr. Asn.(Murray Gottlieb Prize, 59 & 62); Spec. Libr. Asn; Am. Soc. Info. Sci. Computer file structures for on-line storage and retrieval of literature citations and other biomedical data and information; history of medicine on the American frontier, particularly in the mountain West; patterns of acquisition and use of biomedical information by medical practitioners in small New Mexico communities. Address: Library of the Medical Sciences, University of New Mexico, Albuquerque, NM 87106.

DIVILBISS, JAMES LEROY, b. Parsons, Kans, Jan. 17, 30. ELECTRICAL ENGINEERING. B.S, Kansas State, 52; M.S, Illinois, 55, Ph.D.(elec. eng), 62. Res. assoc. elec. eng, co-ord. sci. lab, Illinois, 55-63; mem. tech. staff elec. eng, Bell Tel. Labs, Inc, 63-65; sr. res. engr, dept. comput. sci, UNIV. ILL, URBANA-CHAMPAIGN, 65-70, ASSOC. PROF, GRAD. SCH. LIBR. SCI. & SR. RES. ENGR, COORD. SCI. LAB, 70- U.S.A, 52-54. Inst. Elec. & Electronics Eng. Logical design of computers; pattern recognition; magnetic logic; memory design; computer music; information retrieval; library automation. Address: 1912 Robert Dr, Champaign, IL 61820.

DiVINCENZO, GEORGE D, b. Rochester, N.Y, Sept. 18, 41; m. 62; c. 2. BIOCHEMISTRY. B.S, St. John Fisher Col, 63; N.Y. State Dept. Health fel, State Univ, N.Y. Buffalo, 66, Ph.D.(biochem), 69. BIOCHEMIST, LAB. INDUST. MED, EASTMAN KODAK CO, 68- AAAS; Am. Chem. Soc. Phospholipid metabolism in nerve tissue; metabolic fate of volatile compounds; biological monitoring of solvent exposures; clinical chemistry; immunology with specific reference to delayed hypersensitivity. Address: Lab. of Industrial Medicine, Bldg. 320, Eastman Kodak Co, Kodak Park, Rochester, NY 14650.

DIVINE, JAMES R(OBERT), b. Stockton, Calif, Mar. 11, 39. CHEMICAL ENGINEERING. B.S, California, Berkeley, 61; Nat. Defense Ed. Act fel, Oregon State, 61-64, Ph.D.(chem. eng), 65. Chem. engr. food processing, Western Regional Res. Labs, U.S. Dept. Agr, 61; SR. RES. ENGR. CORROSION, PAC. NORTHWEST. LABS, JOINT CTR. GRAD. STUD, 65- Nat. Asn. Corrosion Eng; Am. Inst. Chem. Eng; Am. Chem. Soc; Electrochem. Soc. Corrosion and transport of corrosion products through coolant systems. Address: P.O. Box 999, Battelle-Northwest, Richland, WA 99352.

DIVINSKY, NATHAN J(OSEPH), b. Winnipeg, Man, Oct. 29, 25; m. 47; c. 3. MATHEMATICS. B.Sc, Univ. Manitoba, 46; M.Sc, Univ. Chicago, 47, scholar, 47-48, Ph.D.(math), 50. Res. assoc. MATH, Cowles Comn, Chicago, 49-50; asst. prof, Ripon Col, 50-51; Univ. Manitoba, 51-57, assoc. prof, 57-59; UNIV. B.C, 59-64, PROF, 64-, ASST. DEAN SCI, 69- Royal Soc. Can. scholar, 57-58; Can. Coun. fel. vis. prof, Queen Mary Col, London, 65-66. Am. Math. Soc; Math. Asn. Am; Can. Math. Cong; London Math. Soc. Power-associative algebras; theory of rings; radicals. Address: Dept. of Mathematics, University of British Columbia, Vancouver, B.C, Can.

DIVIS, ROY R(ICHARD), b. Berwyn, Ill, July 23, 28; m. 51; c. 4. POLYMER CHEMISTRY. B.G.Ed, Morton Jr. Col, 48; B.S, St. Mary's Col.(Minn), 50; fel. & M.S, Detroit, 53. Chemist L.R. Kerns Co, 52-53; Amphenol-Borg Electronics, 53-55, head plastics & elastomers res, 59-60; chief chemist, Alkalon Corp, 55-59; mgr. res, plastic container div, Continental Can Co, 60-66; DIR. APPLN. DEVELOP, FOSTER GRANT CO, 66- Am. Chem. Soc; Soc. Plastics Eng. Polymer properties and resins fabrication technology. Address: Foster Grant Co, 289 Main St, Leominster, MA 01453.

DIWAN, JOYCE JOHNSON, b. Brooklyn, N.Y, Dec. 25, 40; m. 70. CELL BIOLOGY. A.B, Mt. Holyoke Col, 62; U.S. Pub. Health Serv. fel. & Ph.D. (physiol), Univ. Ill, Chicago, 67. Johnson Res. Found. fel, Univ. Pa, 66-69; ASST. PROF. BIOL, RENSSELAER POLYTECH. INST, 69- Nat. Sci. Found. res. grant, 70-72. AAAS; Am. Soc. Cell Biol; Biophys. Soc. Physiology of intra-cellular membranes, particularly mechanisms of solute transport and related metabolic processes in isolated mitochondria; permeability and light scattering properties of microsomal fractions. Address: Dept. of Biology, Rensseler Polytechnic Institute, Troy, NY 12181.

DIX, ALAN WILLARD, b. Framingham, Mass, Aug. 31, 41; m. 64; c. 2. MATERIALS SCIENCE, METALLURGY. B.S, Rensselaer Polytech. Inst, 63, Ph.D.(mat), 71. Res. assoc. MAT, RENSSELAER POLYTECH. INST, 67-68, instr, 68-71, ASST. PROF, 71- Am. Welding Soc; Am. Soc. Metals. Welding metallurgy; solidification mechanics; physical metallurgy of high temperature alloys. Address: Materials Division, Rensselaer Polytechnic Institute, Troy, NY 12181.

DIX, C(HARLES) HEWITT, b. Los Angeles, Calif, Mar. 27, 05; m. 70. GEOPHYSICS. B.S, Calif. Inst. Tech, 27; A.M, Rice Inst, 28, fel, 28-29, Ph.D.(math), 31. Instr. math, Rice Inst, 29-34; res. geophysicist, Humble Oil & Ref. Co, 34-37; geophysicist, Socony-Vacuum Oil Co, 39-41; chief seismologist & v.pres, United Geophys. Co, 41-47; assoc. prof. GEOPHYS, CALIF. INST. TECHNOL, 48-54, PROF, 54- Civilian consult, U.S. Navy, 44; consult, 48-; French Inst. Petrol, Paris, 52; Fulbright fel, Univ. Tokyo, 63-64. AAAS; Am. Phys. Soc; Seismol. Soc. Am; hon. life mem. Soc. Explor. Geophys. Am. Geophys. Union. Potential theory; theory of elastic wave propagation. Address: Geology Division, California Institute of Technology, Pasadena, CA 91109.

DIX, JAMES S(EWARD), b. Colton, Calif, Jan. 6, 32; m. 54; c. 2. ORGANIC CHEMISTRY. B.S, Iowa, 54; Ph.D.(org. chem), Illinois, 57. Res. chemist, Phillips Petrol. Co, 57-66, mgr. fiber additives sect, res. & develop. dept, 66-70, PROJ. MGR, PHILLIPS FIBERS CORP, 70- AAAS; Am. Chem. Soc; Am. Asn. Textile Chem. & Colorists. Organic nitrogen chemicals. Address: Phillips Fibers Corp, P.O. Box 66, Greenville, SC 29602.

DIX, ROBERT KNIGHT, b. Gallatin, Mo, June 10, 17; m. 41; c. 4. CHEMICAL ENGINEERING. B.S, Iowa State Col, 39; Little fel, Mass. Inst. Tech, Sc.D.(chem. eng), 43. Process engr, Esso Standard Div, Humble Oil & Ref. Co, 43-46, group supvr, 46-47, organizer & coord. tech. orientation, 47, asst. head chem, tech. serv. dept, 48, head, 48-54, supt. lubricants & wax dept, 54-57, asst. gen. mgr, Baton Rouge Refinery, 57-59, v.pres, Enjay Chem. Co, 59-65, pres, 65-70; SR. V.PRES. & DIR, ESSO CHEM. CO. INC, 70- Mem. faculty consultor comt, Manhattan Col, 69- With Nat. Defense Res. Comt, 55. AAAS; Am. Chem. Soc. Kassner and Du Motay systems for oxygen absorption and desorption. Address: Esso Chemical Co. Inc, 60 W. 49th St, New York, NY 10020.

DIX, ROLLIN CUMMING, b. New York, N.Y, Feb. 8, 36; m. 60. MECHANICAL ENGINEERING. B.S, Purdue, 57, M.S, 58, Ph.D,(mech. eng), 63. Sr. engr, Bendix Mishawaka Div, 62-64; asst. prof. MECH. ENG, ILL. INST. TECHNOL, 64-68, ASSOC. PROF, 68- Fulbright lectr, Univ. of the Republic, Uruguay, summer 70- Ord.C, 60-61, 2nd Lt. Am. Soc. Elec. Eng; Asn. Comput. Mach; Am. Soc. Eng. Educ; Am. Soc. Mech. Eng. Heat transfer, numerical computation and design optimization. Address: Dept. of Mechanical Engineering, Illinois Institute of Technology, 3300 S. Federal St, Chicago, IL 60616.

DIXIT, BALWANT N, b. Kerawade, INDIA, JAN. 7, 33; m. 69; c. 1. PHARMACOLOGY. B.S, Poona, 54, Hons, 55, M.S, 56; fel, Baroda, 59-60, M.S, 62; Int. Union Physiol. Sci. Riker Int. fel, Pittsburgh, 62-63, Ph.D.(pharmacol), 65. Res. asst. PHARMACOL, Indian Coun. Med. Res, med. col, Baroda, 56-59, sr. res. fel, coun. sci. & indust. res, 60-62; res. asst, UNIV. PITTSBURGH, 63-65, asst. prof, 65-68, ASSOC. PROF. & ASST. CHMN. DEPT, SCH. PHARM, 68- AAAS; assoc. Am. Pharmaceut. Asn; Acad. Pharmaceut. Sci; Am. Soc. Pharmacol. & Exp. Therapeut; N.Y. Acad. Sci. Autonomic and biochemical pharmacology; neuroendocrinology; drug interactions; analytical biochemistry. Address: Dept. of Pharmacology, University of Pittsburgh School of Pharmacy, 809 Salk Hall, Pittsburgh, PA 15213.

DIXON, ANDREW D(ERART), b. Belfast, North. Ireland, Oct. 27, 25; m. 48; c. 3. ANATOMY. B.D.S, Queen's (Belfast), 49, M.D.S, 53, Nuffield Found. fel, 53-54, B.Sc, 54, D.Sc, 65; Ph.D.(anat), Manchester, 58. Demonstr. dent. prosthetics, Queen's (Belfast), 48-49; lectr. anat, Manchester, 54-62, sr. lectr, 62-63; vis. assoc. prof, Iowa, 59-61; PROF. ORAL BIOL. & ANAT, SCH. MED, UNIV. N.C, 63-, ASST. DEAN & COORD. DENT. RES, 66-, DIR. DENT. RES. CTR, 67-, ASSOC. DEAN RES, SCH. DENT, 69- Fulbright travel award, 59-61; Commonwealth Fund traveling fel, 61; external exam. dent. anat, Queen's (Belfast), 61-63. AAAS; Am. Soc. Cell Biol; Am. Asn. Anat; Electron Micros. Soc. Am; Anat. Soc. Gt. Brit. & Ireland; Brit. Dent. Asn; Int. Asn. Dent. Res; Int. Soc. Craniofacial Biol. Development and growth of the jaws; innervation of oral tissues; electron microscopy of nerve tissue. Address: Dental Research Center, University of North Carolina, Chapel Hill, NC 27514.

DIXON, ARTHUR EDWARD, b. Woodstock, N.B, Can, Nov. 16, 38; m. 63; c. 3. PHYSICS. B.Sc, Mt. Allison, 60; M.Sc, Dalhousie, 62; Ont. Grad. fel, McMaster, 63-66, Ph.D.(solid state physics), 66. ASST. PROF. PHYSICS, UNIV. WATERLOO, 66- R.C.A.F, 57-60, Flying Officer. Am. Phys. Soc. Fermi surface of metals using magnetoresistance; cyclotron resonance; de Haas van Alphen effect. Address: Dept. of Physics, University of Waterloo, Waterloo, Ont, Can.

DIXON, C(ARL) E(UGENE), b. Lewiston, Idaho, Dec. 25, 20; m. 46; c. 2. SOLID STATE PHYSICS. B.S, State Col. Wash, 42, M.S, 48; D.Sc.(physics), Carnegie Inst. Tech, 51. Instr. physics, Wash. State Col, 42-44; res. engr, atomic energy res. dept, N.Am. Aviation, Inc, 51-55, supvr, 55-58, group leader solid state & metall, Atomics Int. Div, 58-63; TECH. SPECIALIST, AEROJET NUCLEAR SYSTS. CO, SACRAMENTO, 63- U.S.N.R, 44-46, Lt. (jg). Am. Phys. Soc; Am. Nuclear Soc; Am. Soc. Metals. Radiation effects and mechanical properties of solids; physical metallurgy. Address: 959 Mammoth Way, El Dorado Hills, CA 95630.

DIXON, CARL F(RANKLIN), b. La Junta, Colo, Sept. 14, 26; m. 60; c. 3. PARASITOLOGY, ZOOLOGY. B.A, Colorado, 50; Ph.D.(parasitol), Kansas State, 60. Vet. parasitologist, U.S. Dept. Agr, 60-64; asst. prof. PARASITOL, AUBURN UNIV, 64-70, ASSOC. PROF, 70- Med.C, U.S.A, 44-46. Am. Soc. Parasitol. Interrelationship of helminth parasites and nutrition as a cause of disease in domestic animals. Address: Dept. of Zoology-Entomology, Auburn University, Auburn, AL 36830.

DIXON, DAVID ALLEN, b. Waukegan, Ill, Sept. 19, 40; m. 64; c. 2. STRUCTURAL MECHANICS, MARINE ENGINEERING. B.S, Northwestern, 63, M.S, 64, Ph.D.(struct. mech), 66. SR. RES. ENGR, RES. CENTER, AMOCO PROD. CO, 66- Am. Soc. Civil Eng. Design of marine structures for offshore petroleum production. Address: Research Center, Amoco Production Co, P.O. Box 591, Tulsa, OK 74102.

DIXON, DWIGHT R, b. Fairfield, Idaho, June 16, 19; m. 49; c. 6. PHYSICS. B.Sc, Utah State, 42; Ph.D.(nuclear physics), California, Berkeley, 55. Mem. staff electronics, radiation lab, Mass. Inst. Tech, 42; proj. engr, Sperry Gyroscope Co, N.Y, 42-46; physicist, radiation lab, California, Berkeley, 48-55; sr. engr. nuclear eng, Schlumberger Well Surv. Corp, Tex, 55-57; missile eng, Utah eng. lab, Sperry Gyroscope Co, 57-58, eng. sect. head, 58-59; asst. prof. PHYSICS, BRIGHAM YOUNG UNIV, 59-62, assoc. prof, 62-66, PROF, 66- Am. Asn. Physics Teachers. Nuclear structure physics; musical acoustics. Address: 596 E. 2875 North, Provo, UT 84601.

DIXON, FRANK J(AMES), b. St. Paul, Minn, Mar. 9, 20; m. 46; c. 3. PATHOLOGY. B.S, Univ. Minn, 41, M.B, 43, M.D, 44. Intern, U.S. Naval Hosp, Ill, 43-44; res. fel. path, Harvard, 46-48; instr, Washington Univ, 48-50, asst. prof, 50-51; prof. & chmn. dept, med. sch, Univ. Pittsburgh, 51-60; CHMN. DEPT. EXP. PATH, SCRIPPS CLIN. & RES. FOUND, 61-, CHMN. DEPT. BIOMED. RES, 70- Adj. prof, Univ. Calif, San Diego, 61- Mem, expert adv. panel immunol, WHO; sci. adv. comt, Helen Hay Whitney Found; Dernham Fel. Comt, Am. Cancer Soc; comt. res, Nat. Found; sci. adv. bd, Nat. Kidney Found; adv. comt. fundamental res, Multiple Sclerosis Soc. Mem, bd. sci. consult, Sloan-Kettering Inst. Cancer Res; comt. tissue transplantation, Nat. Res. Coun; adv. comt. biol, Oak Ridge Nat. Lab; res. & educ. career develop. comt, Vet. Admin. Theobald Smith Award, 52; Parke-Davis Award, 57; Award Distinguished Achievement, Modern Med, 61; Martin E. Rehfuss Award, 66; Von Pirquet Medal, Annual Forum Allergy, 67; Bunim Gold Medal, Am. Rheumatism Asn, 68; Mayo Soley Award, West. Soc. Clin. Res, 69; Gairdner Found. Int. Award, 69. U.S.N.R, 43-46. Nat. Acad. Sci; AAAS; N.Y. Acad. Sci; Am. Soc. Exp. Path.(pres, 66); Soc. Exp. Biol. & Med; Am. Soc. Clin. Invest; Am. Acad. Allergy; Am. Asn. Path. & Bact; Am. Asn. Immunol.(pres, 71); Am. Asn. Cancer Res; Int. Acad. Path. Immunopathology. Address: Dept. of Experimental Pathology, Scripps Clinic & Research Foundation, 476 Prospect St, La Jolla, CA 92037.

DIXON, FRANKLIN PAINTER, b. Corpus Christi, Tex, Jan. 25, 27; m. 51; c. 1. PHYSICS, MATHEMATICS. B.S, Texas, 54; Agr. & Mech. Col, Tex, 44-45; M.S, Calif. Inst. Technol, 57, Ph.D.(physics, math), 60. Asst, Los Alamos Sci. Lab, 54; Synchrotron Lab, Calif. Inst. Technol, 54-59; supvr. flight exp, Aeronutronic Div, Ford Motor Co-Philco Corp, Calif, 59-61, supvr. reconnaissance systs, 61-62, prin. scientist, 62, adv. prog. mgr, 62-63, mgr. adv. space systs, 63-64, mgr. reconnaissance & intel. prog, 64; dir. manned planetary mission studies, hq, NASA, Wash, D.C, 64-67, dir. manned lunar mission studies, 65, dir. manned spacecraft, adv. manned missions prog, 67-68; mgr. mil. electronics & space, corp. hq, ITT Europe, Inc, 68-71; V.PRES. SYSTS. PROD. MGT, FRIDEN DIV, SINGER CO, SAN LEANDRO, 71- U.S.A.F, 44-52, 1st Lt. Am. Phys. Soc; Am. Geophys. Union; Am. Inst. Aeronaut. & Astronaut; cor. mem. Int. Acad. Astronaut. Science and technology for space research; space physics; advanced study of manned planetary exploration missions; high energy photoproduction of particles; high energy physics; information systems; data processing; communications systems. Address: 714 Widgeon St, Foster City, CA 94404.

DIXON, GEORGE SUMTER, JR, b. Asheville, N.C, Mar. 28, 38; m. 66; c. 1. SOLID STATE PHYSICS, MAGNETISM. B.S, Univ. Ga, 60, M.S, 63, Ph.D.(physics), 67. Asst. prof. physics, Tenn. Technol. Univ, 67-68; Atomic Energy Comn. fel, solid state div, Oak Ridge Nat. Lab, 68-70; ASST. PROF. PHYSICS, OKLA. STATE UNIV, 70- Am. Phys. Soc. Phase transitions. Address: Dept. of Physics, Oklahoma State University, Stillwater, OK 74074.

DIXON, GLEN J(ACKSON), b. Van Buren, Ark, Aug. 15, 28; m. 49; c. 3. BIOCHEMISTRY. B.S, Arkansas, 50, M.S, 53, Ph.D.(biochem), 57. Asst. bact, Arkansas, 51-53, instr. bot. & bact, 53-54, asst. biochem, 54-57; HEAD VIRUS SECT, SOUTH. RES. INST, 57- Lectr, Birmingham-South. Col, 58- AAAS; Am. Soc. Microbiol; N.Y. Acad. Sci. Chemotherapy of cancer and virus diseases; drug susceptibility and resistance of normal and malignant cells in tissue culture; radiation biology; radiation modifying drugs; survival and persistence of viruses on cotton and woolen fabrics. Address: Southern Research Institute, 2000 Ninth Ave. S, Birmingham, AL 35205.

DIXON, GORDON H, b. Durban, S.Africa, Mar. 25, 30; Can. citizen; m. 54; c. 4. BIOCHEMISTRY. B.A, Cambridge, 51; Ph.D.(biochem), Toronto, 56. Assoc. BIOCHEM, Washington (Seattle), 55-56, asst. prof, 56-58; med. res. coun. mem, Oxford, 58-59; res. assoc, Toronto, 59-60, asst. prof, 60-62, assoc. prof, 62-63; UNIV. B.C, 63-66, PROF, 66- Vis. scientist, Med. Res. Coun. Lab. Molecular Biol, Cambridge, 70-71. Steacie Prize, 66. Am. Soc. Biol. Chem; Brit. Biochem. Soc; Can. Biochem. Soc.(Ayerst Award, 66); Royal Soc. Can. Biochemistry of differentiation; structure and function of chromosomal proteins; protamines and histones; biochemistry of spermatogenesis; sequence analysis of messenger RNA; protein evolution. Address: Dept. of Biochemistry, University of British Columbia, Vancouver 8, B.C, Can.

DIXON, HARRY S(TERLING), b. Woodland, Calif, Nov. 30, 10; m. 37; c. 4. ELECTRICAL ENGINEERING. B.A, Stanford, 31, E.E, 36; Ph.D, Purdue, 52. Asst. engr, Reclamation Dist. No. 108, Calif, 34-37; instr. elec. eng, Purdue, 37-42; elec. test engr, Douglas Aircraft Co, Calif, 42-44; elec. design engr, N.Am. Aviation, Inc, 44-45; prof. elec. eng. & chmn. dept, N.Dak. Agr. Col, 45-51; lectr, Univ. Calif, Berkeley, 51-52, 56-57; prof. & chmn. dept, Newark Col. Eng, 52-56; CONSULT. ENGR, 57- UNESCO int. expert, Lagos, 64-65. AAAS; Inst. Elec. & Electronics Eng; Nat. Soc. Prof. Eng; Am. Soc. Eng. Educ; Illum. Eng. Soc; Am. Ord. Asn; Am. Arbit. Asn. Engineering education; aircraft electrical design; illumination design; electrical power transmission; electrical control; gaseous electrical phenomena; safety; fires and explosions, causes. Address: 950 Creston Rd, Berkeley, CA 94708.

DIXON, H(ELEN) ROBERTA, b. Belvidere, Ill, Aug. 13, 27. GEOLOGY. B.A, Carleton Col, 49; M.A, Univ. Calif, 56; Ph.D.(geol), Harvard, 69. GEOLOGIST, U.S. GEOL SURV, 55- Am. Geol. Soc; Mineral. Soc. Am. Igneous and metamorphic petrology; metamorphics of eastern Connecticut. Address: U.S. Geological Survey, Denver Federal Center, Bldg. 25, Denver, CO 80225.

DIXON, H(ENRY) MARSHALL, III, b. New York, N.Y, June 4, 29. PHYSICS. B.A, Virginia, 50, M.S, 52, du Pont fel, 53-54, Ph.D.(physics), 54. Asst. prof. physics, Tulane, 54-55; physicist, White Sands Signal Agency, 55-57; asst. prof. PHYSICS, N.Mex. Col, 56-57; BUTLER UNIV, 57-58, assoc. prof, 58-65, PROF, 65- U.S.A, 55-57. AAAS; Am. Phys. Soc; Am. Asn. Physics Teachers. Chemical Physics. Address: Dept. of Physics, Butler University, Box 44, Indianapolis, IN 46208.

DIXON, JACK R(ICHARD), b. Michigan, Oct. 29, 25; m. 50; c. 3. PHYSICS. B.S, Western Reserve, 48, M.S.(physics), 50; Ph.D, Maryland, 56. Asst. physics, Western Reserve, 48-50; physicist, chem. & radiation lab, U.S. Army Chem. Corps, 50-52; RES. ASST. physics, Maryland, 52-55; U.S. NAVAL ORD. LAB, 55- Assoc. prof, Maryland, 63- U.S.A.A.F, 44-45. Am. Phys. Soc. Theoretical chemical weapons analysis; study of decay rates of metastable noble atoms; experimental solid state physics. Address: U.S. Naval Ordnance Lab, Silver Spring, MD 20910.

DIXON, J(AMES) K(ENNETH), b. Baltimore, Md, Mar. 20, 06; m. 30; c. 3. PHYSICAL CHEMISTRY. B.S, Hopkins, 26; Ph.D.(chem), Yale, 29. Nat. Res. Coun. fel, Princeton & Berlin, 29-31; Sterling Chem. Lab, Yale, 31-33; res. chemist, Calco Chem. Co, Am. Cyanamid Co, N.J, 33-41, group leader, Conn, 41-53, asst. to dir, 53-55, mgr. ref. & mining chems, 55-57, dir. res. serv. dept, 57, indust. chem. res. dept, 57-65; sr. res. assoc, Columbia, 65; asst. prof. CHEM, UNIV. CONN, 65-70, ASSOC. PROF, 70- Civilian with Manhattan Proj, 44-46. Am. Chem. Soc; Am. Inst. Chem. Water pollution and conservation; catalysis; colloids; high polymers; catalytic cracking; styrene derivatives; emulsifying agents; dyeing assistants; paper chemicals. Address: Dept. of Chemistry, University of Connecticut, Torrington, CT 06790.

DIXON, JAMES RAY, b. Houston, Tex, Aug. 1, 28; m. 53; c. 5. HERPETOLOGY, ZOOLOGY. B.S, Howard Payne Col, 50; M.S, Texas A&M, 57, Ph.D.(zool), 61. Curator reptiles, Ross Allen Reptile Inst, 54-55; asst. prof. vet. med, Texas A&M, 56-61; wildlife mgt, New Mexico State, 61-65; curator herpet, life sci. div, Los Angeles County Mus, 65-67; ASSOC. PROF. WILDLIFE SCI, TEX. A&M UNIV, 67- Nat. Sci. Found. grant, 64-66; consult, N.Mex. State Dept. Game & Fish, 64-65. Sigma Xi res. award, 60. U.S.N.R, 47-50, U.S.M.C, 50-53, S/Sgt. Am. Soc. Ichthyol. & Herpet; Zool. Soc. London; Soc. Study Amphibians & Reptiles. Zoogeography, systematics, and ecology of lizards of the family Gekkonidae; systematics of reptiles and amphibians of southwestern United States, Mexico and South America, especially Peru; ecology of fish in impounded waters; general natural history of vertebrates. Address: Dept. of Wildlife Science, Texas A&M University, College Station, TX 77843.

DIXON, JAMES WILLIAM, JR, b. Wingate, Tex, July 12, 13; m. 38. GEOLOGY, GEOGRAPHY. A.B, Baylor, 34, M.A, 35; Ph.D.(geol), Wisconsin, 55. Teacher, pub. schs, Tex, 35-42; instr. navig, U.S. Navy Flying Training Prog, BAYLOR UNIV, 42-45, PROF. GEOL. & CHMN. DEPT, 45- Nat. Asn. Geol. Teachers; Paleont. Soc. Cretaceous stratigraphy and paleontology; stratigraphy and structural geology of Rocky Mountains. Address: Dept. of Geology, Baylor University, Waco, TX 76703.

DIXON, JOE B(ORIS), b. Clinton, Ky, Nov. 15, 30; m. 52; c. 2. SOIL SCIENCE. B.S, Kentucky, 52, M.S, 56; Ph.D.(soil sci), Wisconsin, 58. Nat. Sci. Found. fel. soil sci, 58-59; assoc. prof, Auburn Univ, 59-68; PROF. SOIL MINERAL, TEX. A&M UNIV, 68- U.S.A, 53-55, Sgt. AAAS; Am. Soc. Agron; Soil Sci. Soc. Am; Mineral. Soc. Am; Int. Soil Sci. Soc. Clay mineralogy of soils; soil genesis and classification; weathering of minerals in soils and rocks; surface properties of clays. Address: Dept. of Soil and Crop Sciences, Texas A&M University, College Station, TX 77843.

DIXON, J(OE) M(AURICE), b. Dustin, Okla, Nov. 6, 17; m. 43; c. 2. VETERINARY SCIENCE. B.S, Okla. State, 48, D.V.M, 52, M.S, 58. Private practice, 52-55; assoc. prof. VET. SCI, LA. STATE UNIV, 55-68, PROF, 68- U.S.A, 41-45. Poultry Sci. Asn; Am. Vet. Med. Asn. Avian diseases; poultry pathology. Address: Dept. of Veterinary Science, University College, Louisiana State University, Baton Rouge, LA 70803.

DIXON, JOHN A(LDOUS), b. Provo, Utah, July 16, 23; m. 44; c. 3. SURGERY, PHYSIOLOGY. B.S, Univ. Utah, 44, M.D, 47. EXEC. V.PRES, UNIV. UTAH & PROF. SURG, COL. MED, 70- Dipl, Am. Bd. Surg, 54. U.S.N.R, 43-46; U.S.A.F, 51-53, Capt, chief surg, Johnson Air Force Hosp, Honshu, Japan & surg. consult, Far East Air Force, 52-53. Fel. Am. Col. Surg; Am. Gastroenterol. Asn; Soc. Surg. Alimentary Tract; Pan-Am. Med. Asn. Gastrointestinal surgery and diseases; motility of intestine; absorption and secretion. Address: University of Utah, 210 Park Bldg, Salt Lake City, UT 84112.

DIXON, JOHN C(HARLES), b. Chicago, Ill, July 21, 31; m. 63; c. 2. ENTOMOLOGY, ZOOLOGY. B.S, Beloit Col, 53; M.S, Wisconsin, 55, Ph.D.(entom, zool), 61. Entomologist, S.E. Forest Exp. Sta, Forest Serv, U.S. Dept. Agr, 59-64; asst. prof. BIOL, Chicago State Col, 64-68; WIS. STATE UNIV, EAU CLAIRE, 68-70, ASSOC. PROF, 70- AAAS; Entom. Soc. Am. Ecological studies of defoliating insects; population studies and ecology of pine bark beetles. Address: Dept. of Biology, Wisconsin State University, Eau Claire, WI 54701.

DIXON, JOHN D(OUGLAS), b. Buffalo, Minn, July 29, 24; m. 49; c. 4. ELECTRICAL ENGINEERING. B.E.E, Minnesota, 49; M.S, Missouri, 52; Wisconsin. Instr. ELEC. ENG, Missouri, 49-52, asst. prof, 52-53; UNIV. N.DAK, 53-56, assoc. prof, 56-63, PROF, 63- Am. Soc. Eng. Educ; Inst. Elec. & Electronics Eng. Control systems; computers. Address: Dept. of Electrical Engineering, University of North Dakota, Grand Forks, ND 58201.

DIXON, JOHN DOUGLAS, b. Ewell, Eng, Jan. 18, 37; m. 61; c. 3. PURE MATHEMATICS. B,S, Melbourne, 57, M.A, 59; Ph.D.(math), McGill, 61. Instr. MATH, Calif. Inst. Tech, 61-64; sr. lectr, New South Wales, 64-67, assoc. prof, 68; CARLETON UNIV.(ONT), 68-71, PROF, 71- London Math. Soc; Am. Math. Soc; Math. Asn. Am; Math. Soc. Can; Australian Math. Soc. Algebra and number theory; theory of linear groups and representation theory. Address: Dept. of Mathematics, Carleton University, Ottawa, Ont. K1S 5B6, Can.

DIXON, JOHN E(LVIN), b. Roseburg, Ore, Mar. 23, 27; m. 48; c. 2. AGRICULTURAL ENGINEERING. B.S.(agr. eng) & B.S. (agr), Ore. State Univ, 51; Colo. State Univ, 51-54; M.S, Univ. Idaho, 57. Instr. agr. eng, Colo. State Univ, 51-54; Univ. Idaho, 54-57, asst. prof, 57-64, assoc. prof, 64-67; agr. eng. adv, Kans. State Univ. at Hyderabad, India, 67-69; ASSOC. PROF. AGR. ENG, UNIV. IDAHO, 69-, DIR. PROF. ADV. SERV. CTR, 69- Fallout shelter analyst instr, Off. Civil Defense, 70- U.S.N.R, 45-46. Am. Soc. Agr. Eng; Am. Soc. Eng. Educ; Nat. Soc. Prof. Eng. Farm structures with emphasis on environmental control; poultry housing; crop storage. Address: Dept. of Agricultural Engineering, University of Idaho, Moscow, ID 83843.

DIXON, JOHN F(RANCIS) C(LEMOW), b. Ottawa, Ont, Mar. 1, 19; m. 46; c. 4. ORGANIC CHEMISTRY. B.Sc, McGill, 42, Nat. Res. Coun. fels. & Ph.D. (chem), 47. Res. chemist high polymers, Ont. Res. Found, 42-44; high polymers & explosives, Cent. Res. Lab, CAN. INDUSTS. LTD, 47-53, group leader explosives, 53-56, asst, explosives div, 56-58, res. mgr, 58-60, tech. mgr, CHEM. DIV, 61-65, gen. sales mgr, 65-69, EDUC. RELS. MGR, 69- Lectr, Sir George Williams Col, 46. Chem. Inst. Can. Cellulose chemistry; vinyl polymerization; protective coatings; chemistry of chlorine and derivatives; bleaching of wood pulps; manufacture of heavy chemicals. Address: Canadian Industries Ltd, P.O. Box 10, Montreal 101, Que, Can.

DIXON, J(OHN) M(ICHAEL) S(IDDONS), b. Derby, Eng, Aug. 22, 28; m. 52; c. 2. BACTERIOLOGY. M.B,B.Ch, Wales, 50, M.D, 60; dipl. bact, London, 57. Dir, Pub. Health Lab, Ipswich, Eng, 59-66; chief BACT, Wellesley Hosp, Toronto, Ont, 66-67; PROF, UNIV. ALTA, 67- Prov. bacteriologist, Alta, 67-; dir, Prov. Lab. Pub. Health, Edmonton & Calgary, 67-; consult. bacteriologist, Univ. Alberta Hosp, Edmonton, 67- Fel, Royal Col. Physicians & Surgeons. Can, 69. R.A.M.C, 52-54, Capt. Can. Asn. Med. Microbiol.(pres, 70-); Am. Soc. Microbiol; Am. Pub. Health Asn; Can. Soc. Microbiol; Can. Pub. Health Asn; Col. Path. Eng; Brit. Soc. Gen. Microbiol. Bacteria of the intestine; epidemiology of salmonella infections. Address: Provincial Lab. of Public Health, University of Alberta, Edmonton 7, Alta, Can.

DIXON, JOHN R, b. Akron, Ohio, Oct. 19, 30; m. 51; c. 1. MECHANICAL ENGINEERING. B.S, Mass. Inst. Tech, 52, M.S, 53; Ph.D.(mech. eng), Carnegie Inst. Tech, 60. Engr, Jarl Extrusions, Inc, N.Y, 55-57; proj. engr, Joseph Kaye & Co, Mass, 57-58; asst. prof. mech. eng, Carnegie Inst. Tech, 60-61; assoc. prof, Purdue, 61-65; eng, Swarthmore Col, 65-66; PROF. MECH. & AEROSPACE ENG, UNIV. MASS, AMHERST, 66-, head dept, 66-71. U.S.A, 53-55. AAAS; Am. Soc. Mech. Eng; Am. Soc. Eng. Educ. Address: Dept. of Mechanical & Aerospace Engineering, University of Massachusetts, Amherst, MA 01002.

DIXON, J(ONATHAN) S(TANTON), b. Rochester, N.H, Sept. 23, 19; c. 3. BIOCHEMISTRY. B.S, New Hampshire, 42; M.S, Haverford Col, 43; Ph.D. (org. chem), Washington (St. Louis), 53. Res. chemist, Manhattan Proj, Chicago, 43-45; Atomic Energy Comn, Los Alamos, N.Mex, 45-46; RES. BIOCHEMIST HORMONES, UNIV. CALIF, BERKELEY, 53- Am. Chem. Soc. Radio chemistry; structural studies of nucleic acids; protein-peptide chemistry. Address: 2326 Russell St, Berkeley, CA 54720.

DIXON, JOSEPH A(RDIFF), b. Phila, Pa, Nov. 4, 19; m. 42; c. 2. CHEMISTRY. B.S, Pa. State, 42, M.S, 45, Ph.D.(org. chem), 47. Asst. chemist, east. regional res. lab, bur. agr. & indust. chem, U.S. Dept. Agr, 42-44; instr. chem, Pa. State, 47-51; chemist, Calif. Res. Corp, 51-52; assoc. prof. CHEM, Lafayette Col, 52-55; PA. STATE UNIV, 55-60, PROF, 60-, HEAD DEPT, 71- Am. Chem. Soc. Correlation of properties with molecular structures; synthesis and properties of hydrocarbons; organo-lithium chemistry. Address: Dept. of Chemistry, Pennsylvania State University, University Park, PA 16802.

DIXON, KEITH L(EE), b. El Centro, Calif, Jan. 20, 21; m. 49; c. 1. ZOOLOGY. A.B, San Diego State Col, 43; M.A, California, 48, Ph.D.(zool), 53. Mus. technician, mus. vert. zool, California, 47-52, asst. zool, 47-49; Off. Naval Res. Artic Res. Lab, Alaska, 52; asst. prof. wildlife mgt, Agr. & Mech. Col. Tex, 52-57, assoc. prof, 57-58; asst. res. zoologist, Hastings Natural Hist. Reservation, 58-59; asst. prof. ZOOL, Utah State, 59-61, assoc. prof, 61-67, PROF, 67- Leader Mex. expeds, Agr. & Mech. Col. Tex, 53-54; mem. field expeds, Calif, Mont, Ariz. & Tex. U.S.N.R, 43-46. AAAS; Am. Soc. Mammal; fel. Am. Ornith. Union; Cooper Ornith. Soc. (asst. ed, 49-52); Wilson Ornith. Soc.(ed. bul, 55-58); Ecol. Soc. AM; Animal Behav. Soc. Ecology, social behavior and distribution of birds and mammals. Address: Dept. of Zoology, Utah State University, Logan, UT 84321.

DIXON, KEITH R, b. Portsmouth, Eng, Dec. 4, 40; m. 66. INORGANIC CHEMISTRY. B.A, Cambridge, 63; Ph.D.(fluorine chem), Strathclyde, 66. Fel. INORG. CHEM, Western Ontario, 66-68; ASST. PROF, UNIV. VICTORIA, 68- Chem. Inst. Can; Brit. Chem. Soc. Chemistry of complex fluorides; organometallic chemistry of the precious metals. Address: Dept. of Chemistry, University of Victoria, Victoria, B.C, Can.

DIXON, LINDA K(AY), b. Brownsville, Pa, Aug. 20, 40. BEHAVIORAL GENETICS. B.S, California State Col.(Pa), 62; M.S, California, Berkeley, 64; Inst. Int. Educ. fel, Würzburg, 65-66; Ph.D.(behav. genetics), Illinois, Urbana, 67. Res. assoc, inst.behav.genetics, UNIV. COLO, Boulder, 68, ASST. PROF. GENETICS, DENVER, 69- Behav. genetics training grant, Inst. Behav. Genetics, Boulder, Colo, 68-69. AAAS; Genetics Soc. Am; Am. Inst. Biol. Sci; Am. Genetic Asn. Developmental genetics of mouse behavior; possible relationships between chromosomal aberrations and behavioral abnormalities in humans. Address: Dept. of Biology, University of Colorado, 1100 14th St, Denver, CO 80202.

DIXON, LOUIS H, b. Belcher, La, Sept. 2, 12; m. 63; c. 1. GEOLOGY. B.A, Centenary Col, 35; M.A, Texas, 41; California, Berkeley, 41-42, Los Angeles, 58-59; Ph.D.(geol), La. State, 63. Asst. geol, Bur. Econ. Geol, Tex, 37-41, 46-47; petrol. geologist, Brazil. Govt, 47-50; Standard Oil Co, 51-58; res. geologist, La. Geol. Surv, 61-63; econ. geologist, Ga. Dept. Mines, Mining & Geol, 64-65, chief geologist, 65; ECON. GEOLOGIST, LA. GEOL. SURV, 65- U.S.N.R, 42-46, Lt. Am. Asn. Petrol. Geol; Geol. Soc. Am. Stratigraphy; economic geology. Address: Louisiana Geological Survey, Box G, University Station, Baton Rouge, LA 70803.

DIXON, L(YLE) J(UNIOR), b. Osborne, Kans, Feb. 28, 24; m. 42; c. 3. MATHEMATICS. B.S, Okla. State, 48, fel, 48-49, M.S, 50; Ph.D, Kansas, 63. Instr. math, Okla. State, 47-48; Southwest. State Col, 49-50; asst. instr, Kansas, 50-51; asst. prof, Ark. State Col, 51-53, supvr. sci. & math. areas, gen. ed, 53-57, registr, 57-58, dir. res, 58-59, assoc. prof. MATH, 59-63; KANS. STATE UNIV, 63-67, PROF, 67- U.S.N.R, 43-45. Math. Asn. Am. Algebra; matrix theory; mathematics education. Address: Dept. of Mathematics, Kansas State University, Manhattan, KS 66502.

DIXON, MARK A(DRIAN), b. Ft. Lauderdale, Fla, June 18, 31; m. 56; c. 4. PHYSICAL GEOLOGY, PETROLOGY. B.S, Florida, 52; M.S, La. State, 54, Ph.D.(phys. geol), 63. RES. TECHNOLOGIST GEOL, FIELD RES. LAB, SOCONY MOBIL OIL CO, INC, 63- U.S.N, 54-59. Am. Asn. Petrol. Geol. Sedimentary petrology; speleology; fish otoliths. Address: Mobil Oil Corp, P.O. Box 900, Dallas, TX 75221.

DIXON, MARVIN PORTER, b. Kansas City, Mo, Nov. 10, 38; m. 61; c. 3. PHYSICAL & PHYSICAL ORGANIC CHEMISTRY. B.A, William Jewell Col, 60; M.S, Univ. Ill, Urbana, 63, E.I. du Pont de Nemours & Co, Sloan Found. & U.S. Army Res. Off. fels. & Ph.D, 65. Asst. prof. CHEM, WILLIAM JEWELL COL, 65-66, ASSOC. PROF, 66- Summers, res. asst, Midwest Res. Inst, 61, assoc. prof, Nat. Sci. Found. Summer Inst. for Mo. Jr. High Sch. Teachers, 68; Kans. City Regional Coun. Higher Educ. faculty develop. grant. Am. Chem. Soc. Ambident ion chemistry; kinetics; reaction mechanisms; organometallic chemistry. Address: Dept. of Chemistry, William Jewell College, Liberty, MO 64068.

DIXON, PEGGY A, b. Cleveland, Ohio, June 9, 28; m. 50; c. 3. PHYSICS. A.B, Western Reserve, 50; M.S, Maryland, 54, Ph.D.(physics), 59. Physicist munitions res, Chem. Corps, U.S. Army, 50-52; asst. PHYSICS, Maryland, 52-58, res. assoc, 58-61; asst. prof, MONTGOMERY COL, 59-67, assoc. prof, 67-70, PROF, 70- Nat. Sci. Found. res. fel, 62; Chmn. panel on physics in two-year col, Comn. Col. Physics, 68-69; vis. prof, Univ. Md, 70-71. AAAS; Am. Asn. Physics Teachers. Solid state theory; ferromagnetism; lattice vibration theory. Address: Dept. of Physics, Montgomery College, Takoma Park, MD 20902.

DIXON, PETER S(TANLEY), b. Redcar, Eng, Nov. 29, 28; m. 55; c. 3. BOTANY. B.Sc, Manchester, 49, M.Sc, 50, Ph.D.(bot), 52. Asst. lectr. bot, Liverpool, 54-56, lectr, 56-64, sr. lectr, 64-65; assoc. prof, Washington (Seattle), 65-67; PROF. BIOL. SCI, UNIV. CALIF, IRVINE, 67-, CHMN. DEPT. POP. & ENVIRON. BIOL, DIR. UNIV. ARBORETUM & DIR. MUS. SYST. BIOL, 69- Brit. Army, 52-54, Lt. Developmental morphology, ecology and taxonomy of algae, particularly Rhodophyta. Address: Dept. of Population & Environmental Biology, University of California, Irvine, CA 92664.

DIXON, RICHARD W(AYNE), b. Hubbard, Ore, Sept. 25, 36; m. 70. SOLID STATE PHYSICS. A.B, Harvard, 58, Nat. Sci. Found. fels, 59-62, M.A, 60, Ph.D.(appl. physics), 64. Res. fel, APPL. PHYSICS, Harvard, 64-65; staff mem, BELL TEL. LABS, INC, 65-68, SUPVR, 68- AAAS; Am. Phys. Soc; Inst. Elec. & Electronics Eng. Research and development of acoustooptic and electroluminescent materials and devices. Address: Bell Telephone Labs, Inc, Murray Hill, NJ 07974.

DIXON, ROBERT LOUIS, b. Sacramento, Calif, Feb. 9, 36; m. 58; c. 3. PHARMACOLOGY, BIOCHEMISTRY. B.S, Idaho State Univ, 58; M.S, Univ. Iowa, 61, Ph.D.(pharmacol), 63. Sr. investr, Nat. Cancer Inst, 63-65; asst. prof. pharmacol, sch. med, Univ. Wash, 65-69, assoc. prof, 69; CHIEF LAB. TOXICOL, CHEMOTHER, NAT. CANCER INST, 69- Med.Serv.C, 59, Res, 59-66, Lt. AAAS; Am. Asn. Cancer Res; Soc. Exp. Biol. & Med; Am. Soc. Pharmacol. & Exp. Therapeut; Soc. Toxicol; N.Y. Acad. Sci. Preclinical toxicology; biochemical pharmacology; developmental and reproductive pharmacology. Address: Bldg. 37, Room 5B18, National Cancer Institute, Bethesda, MD 20014.

DIXON, ROBERT MORTON, b. Leon, Kans, May 30, 29; m. 56; c. 2. SOILS, PLANT PHYSIOLOGY. B.S, Kansas State, 59, M.S, 60; Ph.D, Wisconsin, 66. Instr. soils, Kansas State, 59-60; soil scientist, soil & water conserv. res. div, U.S. Dept. Agr, 60-66, north. plains soil & water res. ctr, Mont, 66-67; irrig. specialist, Ford Found, 67-68; RES. SOIL SCIENTIST & FIELD STA. LEADER, SOIL & WATER CONSERV. RES. DIV, U.S. DEPT. AGR, UNIV. NEV, 68- U.S.A, 54-56. Am. Soc. Agron; Soil Sci. Soc. Am; Crop Sci. Soc. Am; Soil Conserv. Soc. Am. Water infiltration into soils; drainage and tillage of soils; management of crop residues; surface runoff and erosion from soils. Address: University of Nevada, Box 8858, Reno, NV 89507.

DIXON, S(TUART) E(DWARD), b. Minto, N.B, Oct. 11, 22; nat; m. 55; c. 3. ENTOMOLOGY. B.A, McMaster, 47; M.S.A, Toronto, 51; Ph.D.(entom), Cornell, 55. Lectr. entom, UNIV. GUELPH, 47-55, asst. prof, 55-60, ASSOC. PROF. ZOOL, 60- Can. Soc. Zool; Can. Physiol. Soc. Growth, development and physiology of insects; insect morphology. Address: Dept. of Zoology, University of Guelph, Guelph, Ont, Can.

DIXON, THELMA H(UDSON) DUNNEBACKE, b. Nashville, Tenn, Dec. 23, 25; m. 54; c. 3. EMBRYOLOGY, ZOOLOGY. A.B, Washington (St. Louis), 47, M.A, 49, Ph.D, 54. Instr, dept. zool, Smith Col, 49-50; U.S. Pub. Health Serv. fel, VIRUS LAB, UNIV. CALIF, BERKELEY, 55-57, jr. res. biologist, 57-58, ASST. RES. BIOLOGIST, 58- Biological, cytological and electron microscopical aspects of virus growth and multiplication in tissue cultured cells; polio, coxsackie and Reo viruses in human and animal cells. Address: 2326 Russell St, Berkeley, CA 94705.

DIXON, THOMAS F(RANCIS), b. Nashville, Tenn, Mar. 15, 16; m. 43; c. 4. AERONAUTICAL ENGINEERING. B.S, Vanderbilt, 38; B.S, Michigan, 39, M.S, 40; M.S, Calif. Inst. Tech, 45; Kent Col. Law, 46-48. Develop. engr, Am. Maize Prods. Co, Ind, 40-41; Westinghouse Elec. Co, Pa, 41-42; extrusion off, Naval Powder Factory, U.S. Navy, Md, 42-43, div. head solid propellant rocket res. & develop. dept, Bur. Ord, D.C, 43-44, liaison off, Calif. Tech. Liaison, 44-45, div. head propellant rocket progress, Bur. Ord, 45; group leader propulsion & dir, eng. propulsion center, 46-55, chief engr, Rocketdyne Div, 55-59, dir. eng, 59-60, v.pres. res. & eng, 60; dep. assoc. adminstr, Nat. Aeronaut. & Space Admin, 61-63; v.pres. mkt. planning, N.Am. Aviation, Inc, 63-67; chmn. bd, AIRTRONICS, INC, 67-69, PRES, 69- Goddard Mem. award, 57; Lewis W. Hill transportation award, 60. Fel. Am. Inst. Aeronaut. & Astronaut; Soc. Automotive Eng; Aerospace Indust. Asn. Am. Liquid and solid propellant rocket engines. Address: Airtronics, Inc, Dulles International Airport, Washington, DC 20041.

DIXON, THOMAS PATRICK, b. San Antonio, Tex, Feb. 21, 22; m. 44; c. 3. ELECTRONIC ENGINEERING, OPTICAL PHYSICS. B.S.E.E, Southern California, 50; California, Los Angeles, 52-60. Supvr. elec. res. & develop. labs, Technicolor Motion Picture Corp, 50-57; group supvr, electronic systs, Radioplane Co, 57-59; sr. mem. tech. staff, ITT Aerospace, INT. TEL. & TEL. CORP, 59-63, exec. engr, 63-66, dep. dir. ELECTROOPTICAL SYSTS, ITT AEROSPACE/OPTICAL DIV, 66-67, DIR, 67- U.S.A.A.F, 43-46. Inst. Elec. & Electronics Eng; Soc. Photo-Optical Instrument. Eng. Electro-optical systems for guidance and navigation of space vehicles; laser communication, ranging and tracking, color picture analysis and synthesis; optical surveillance and low-light-level imaging systems. Address: ITT Aerospace/Optical Division, International Telephone & Telegraph Corp, 15151 Bledsoe St, San Fernando, CA 91342.

DIXON, WALLACE C(LARK), JR, b. Winston-Salem, N.C, Dec. 18, 22; m. 46; c. 2. PHYSIOLOGY. A.B, East. Nazarene Col, 46; A.M, Boston, 47, Ph.D. (biol), 56. Instr. BIOL, East. Nazarene Col, 48-50, asst. prof, 50-54; col. basic studies & grad. sch, Boston Univ, 56-59, assoc. prof, 59-65, prof, 65-68; PROF. & CHMN. NATURAL SCI. DEPT, CENT. UNIV. COL, EAST. KY. UNIV, 68- Am. Soc. Zool. Cellular physiology; endocrinology; science in general education. Address: Dept. of Natural Science, Central University College, Eastern Kentucky University, Richmond, KY 40475.

DIXON, WILFRID JOSEPH, b. Portland, Oregon, Dec. 13, 15; m. 38; c. 2. MATHEMATICAL STATISTICS. B.A, Oregon State Col, 38; Alumni Res. Found. scholar, Wisconsin, 38-39, M.A, 39; Ph.D.(math. statist), Princeton, 44. Asst, Princeton, 39-41, Nat. Defense Res. Cmt. Proj, 41-42, res. assoc. & consult, joint target group, Air Corps & Air Serv, intel. & opers. analyst, 20th Air Force, 44-45; instr. math, Oklahoma, 42-43, asst. prof, 43-44, assoc. prof, 45-46; Oregon, 46-52, PROF, 52-55; biostatist, UNIV. CALIF, LOS ANGELES, 55-67, BIOMATH, 67- Consult, Office Naval Res; Rand Corp; Vet. Admin; State Dept. Ment. Hyg, Calif; Nat. Insts. Health. Am. Math. Soc; Am. Statist. Asn; Inst. Math. Statist.(assoc. ed, Annals Math. Statist, 55-58); Biomet. Soc.(assoc. ed, Biomet, 52-66). Mathematical theory of serial correlation; sensitivity experiments; inefficient statistics; computers in medical research. Address: Dept. of Biomathematics, School of Medicine, University of California Center for the Health Sciences, Los Angeles, CA 90024.

DIXON, WILLIAM BRANDT, b. Saxton, Pa, Nov. 24, 29; m. 54; c. 3. ORGANIC & INORGANIC CHEMISTRY. B.S, Juniata Col, 51. Metall. observer, U.S. Steel Co, 51-52; pharmaceut. chemist, Zemmer Co, 54-56; res. asst. propellant chem, Allegany Ballistics Lab, Hercules Inc, 56-58, res. chemist, 58-60, sect. supvr. instrumental anal, 60-63, tech. editing & specifications, 63-67, proj. engr, 67-70, SR. RES. CHEMIST, 70-71; PA. ELEC. CO, 71- U.S.Army, 52-53. Wet and instrumental analytical methods development; solid propellant process development; development of composite materials for aerospace applications and water purification systems. Address: Hampton Court Apartments, Apt. 201, 2170 Lazor St, Indiana, PA 15701.

DIXON, WILLIAM B(RIGHTMAN), b. Fall River, Mass, Dec. 18, 35; m. 57; c. 2. PHYSICAL CHEMISTRY. B.S, Wheaton Col.(Ill), 57; Nat. Sci. Found. fel, Harvard, 57-60, A.M, 59, Ph.D.(phys. chem), 61; Fulbright scholar, Copenhagen, 60-61. Nat. Sci. Found. fel, Nat. Res. Coun, Ottawa, 61-62, Nat. Res. Coun. Can. fel, 62-63; asst. prof. CHEM, Wheaton Col.(Ill), 63-67, assoc. prof, 67-68; STATE UNIV. N.Y. COL. ONEONTA, 68-69, PROF, 69- AAAS; Am. Chem. Soc; Am. Phys. Soc. Molecular Spectroscopy. Address: Dept. of Chemistry, State University of New York College at Oneonta, Oneonta, NY 13820.

DIXON, WILLIAM R(OSSANDER), b. Scott, Sask, Can, July 3, 25. PHYSICS. B.A, Saskatchewan, 45, M.A, 47; Ph.D.(physics), Queen's (Can), 55. RES. OFF, NAT. RES. COUN, CAN, 50- Can. Asn. Physicists. Nuclear physics. Address: X-rays & Nuclear Radiations, National Research Council, Ottawa, Ont, Can.

DIXSON, H(ENRY) PHILIP, b. Des Moines, Iowa, Aug. 18, 13; m. 39; c. 3. CHEMISTRY. B.Sc, Iowa State Col, 35; Ph.D.(paper & pulp chem), Lawrence Col, 39. Tech. dir, FOX RIVER PAPER CORP, 39-50, v.pres. mfg, 50-59, pres. mfg, 59-69, V.PRES, 69- Assoc. Tech. Asn. Pulp & Paper Indust. Pulp and paper technology; relation between sheet strength and fiber surface conditions. Address: Fox River Paper Corp, 401 S. Appleton St, Appleton, WI 54911.

DI ZIO, STEVEN F(RANK), b. Newark, N.J, Dec. 15, 38; m. 58; c. 1. CHEMICAL ENGINEERING. B.S, Oregon State, 61; Texaco fel, Rensselaer Polytech, 61-62, Procter & Gamble fel, 62-63, Lummus Co. fel, 63-64, Ph.D.(chem. eng), 64. Asst. prof. chem. eng, Rensselaer Polytech. Inst, 64-68, assoc. prof, 68-69, chmn. dept. biomed. eng, 67-69; V.PRES, AERO VAC CORP, 69- Adj. assoc. prof, Rensselaer Polytech. Inst, 69- AAAS; Am. Inst. Chem. Eng; Am. Chem. Soc; Am. Soc. Eng. Educ; Soc. Cryobiol. Application of engineering principles to medicine; development of a coherent academic program to train bioengineers. Address: Aero Vac Corp, P.O. Box 448, Troy, NY 12181.

DJERASSI, CARL, b. Vienna, Austria, Oct. 29, 23; nat; m. 43; c. 2. ORGANIC CHEMISTRY. A.B, Kenyon Col, 42, hon. D.Sc, 58; Ph.D.(org. chem), Univ. Wis, 45; hon. D.Sc, Nat. Univ. Mex, 53, Fed. Univ. Rio de Janeiro, 69. Res. chemist, Ciba Pharmaceut. Prods, Inc, 42-43, 45-49; assoc. dir. chem. res, Syntex, S.A, Mexico City, 49-52, v.pres, 57-60, MEM. BD. DIRS, SYNTEX CORP, 60-, PRES, SYNTEX RES. DIV, 68-; PROF. CHEM, STANFORD UNIV, 59- Assoc. prof, Wayne State Univ, 52-54, prof, 54-59; chmn. bd, Zoecon Corp, 69- Intrasci. Res. Found. Award, 70; Freedman Patent Award, Am. Inst. Chem, 71. Nat. Acad. Sci.(mem. bd. sci. & technol. develop); Am. Chem. Soc.(pure chem. award, 58, Baekeland Medal, 59, Fritzsche Medal, 60); hon. fel. Brit. Chem. Soc.(centenary lectr, 64); Am. Acad. Arts & Sci; hon. fel. Acad. Pharmaceut. Sci; Brazilian Acad. Sci; Mex. Acad. Sci. Res; Leopoldine Ger. Acad. Researchers Natural Sci. Chemistry of steroids; structure of alkaloids; antibiotics and terpenoids; synthesis of drugs, particularly antihistamines, oral contraceptives, anti-inflammatory agents; optical rotatory dispersion studies, organic mass spectrometry; magnetic circular dichroism of organic compounds. Address: Dept. of Chemistry, Stanford University, Stanford, CA 94305.

DJERASSI, ISAAC, b. Bulgaria, July 27, 21; nat; m. 54; c. 2. HEMATOLOGY. M.D, Hebrew Med. Sch, Israel, 51. Res. pediat, Hadassah Hosp, Israel, 53-54; assoc. path, Children's Med. Center, Children's Cancer Res. Found, 55-60; assoc. dir. clin. labs. & dir. blood bank & donor ctr, Children's Hosp. Phila, 60-69; DIR. DONOR CTR. & RES. HEMAT, MERCY CATH. MED. CTR, 69- Res. assoc, Harvard Med. Sch, 57-60; asst. prof. pediat, sch. med, Univ. Pa, 60-69; consult, Children's Cancer Res. Found, Boston, Mass, 61- Mem, acute leukemia task force, Nat. Cancer Inst, Nat. Insts. Health. Prize, Cong. Hemat, 56. Soc. Pediat. Res; Am. Asn. Cancer Res; Am. Soc. Exp. Path. Pediatric hematology and hemostasis. Address: Mercy Catholic Medical Center, Philadelphia, PA 19143.

DJINIS, WILLIAM, b. Poughkeepsie, N.Y, Jan. 9, 22; m. 48; c. 3. PHYSICS. B.S, U.S. Air Force Tech. Sch, 43; B.S, Rensselaer Polytech, 48, M.S, 50; N.Y. Univ, 50-52; N.Y. State scholar, 52-56; Pratt Inst, 55-57. Instr. elec. eng, Rensselaer Polytech, 48-49, physics, 49; group leader eng. physics, Vitro Corp. Am, 51-54; engr, Am. Bosch Arma Corp, 54-55; sr. proj. engr, Reeves Instrument Corp, 55-58; dept. head physics res, Gen. Bronze Electronics Corp, 58-59; chief engr, Electro Sonic Labs, Inc, 59-60; proj. engr. electronics, Grumman Aircraft Eng. Corp, 60-62, lunar module, 62-63, sect. chief electronics systs, 63-64, asst. to pres, 64-67, prog. mgr. Shedlight Prog, 67; sci. adv. res. & develop, air staff, U.S. Air Force, 67-69; DIR. MIL, SPACE, GRUMMAN AEROSPACE CORP, BETHPAGE, 69- Participant, Dr. Theodore von Karman's Adv. Physics Summer Seminar, 59; Adv. Group Aeronaut. Res. & Develop; NATO Conf, London, 64. Bd. dirs. & v.pres, Gen. Securities Corp, 58-62; bd. dirs, Dynatran Electronics Corp, 58-65 & Cyclomatics Corp, 60-63. U.S.A.F, 42-46, Res, 46-, Col. Assoc. fel. Am. Inst. Aeronaut. & Astronaut; sr. mem. Inst. Elec. & Electronics Eng; Sci. Res. Soc. Am. Electromagnetic wave refraction by nuclear bomb fireball; thermal energy transfers to perform analog computational functions; cadmium sulfide detector development; advanced missile guidance and control systems. Address: 25 Woodlea Rd, Muttontown, NY 11791.

DJORDJEVIC, BOZIDAR, b. Belgrade, Yugoslavia, Jan. 5, 29; m. 55; c. 1. RADIOBIOLOGY, BIOPHYSICS. Ing. Agr, Univ. Belgrade, 52; Ph.D.(microbiol), Rutgers Univ, 60. Res. asst. radiobiol, biol lab, Inst. Nuclear Sci, Belgrade, 53-56; genetics, Carnegie Inst, N.Y, 56-57; res. assoc. RADIOBIOL, biol. lab, Inst. Nuclear Sci, Belgrade, 60-64; dept. genetics, Inst. Biol. Res, Belgrade, 64-66; DIV. BIOPHYS, SLOAN-KETTERING INST. CANCER RES, N.Y.C, 66-69, ASSOC, 69- Res. fel. radiol, sch. med, Wash. Univ, 64-66; asst. prof, Sloan-Kettering Div, grad. sch. med. sci. med. sch, Cornell Univ, 70- Europ. Soc. Radiation Biol; Radiation Res. Soc. Radiation sensitization by pyrimidine analogs; radiosensitivity of synchronized mammalian cells in culture; repair of radiation damage; effect of metabolic inhibitors on radiation response; radiation response of chronically hypoxic cells. Address: Sloan-Kettering Institute for Cancer Research, 425 E. 68th St, New York, NY 10021.

DJORDJEVIC, MILAN S, b. Belgrade, Yugoslavia, Aug. 22, 13; m. 38. MECHANICAL ENGINEERING. B.S, Belgrade, 36; Ph.D.(mech. eng), Munich, 39. Asst. prof. MECH. ENG, Belgrade, 46-50, assoc. prof, 50-60, PROF, 60-64; Duke, 64-66; UNIV. ALA, TUSCALOOSA, 66- Chmn. motor inst, Serbian Acad. Sci, 48-58; consult, State of Ala. Bd. Planning & Indust. Develop, 68. Am. Soc. Mech. Eng. Internal combustion engines; therodynamics and heat transfer. Address: Dept. of Mechanical Engineering, University of Alabama in Tuscaloosa, P.O. Box 6307, University, AL 35486.

DJURIĆ, DUŠAN, b. Novi Sad, Yugoslavia, Jan. 17, 30; m. 55; c. 2. METEOROLOGY. Dipl, Belgrade, 53, Dr.Sc.(meteorol), 60; Int. Meteorol. Inst, Stockholm, 55-57. Asst. meteorol, col. sci. Belgrade, 54-60, docent, 60-65; vis. scientist, Nat. Center Atmospheric Res, Colo, 65-66; asst. prof. METEOROL, TEX. A&M UNIV, 66-68, ASSOC. PROF, 68- Docent, dept. meteorol, Darmstadt Tech, 62-63. Am. Meteorol. Soc; Meteorol. Soc. Serbia. Numerical weather forecasting. Address: Dept. of Meteorology, Texas A&M University, College Station, TX 77843.

DLAB, VLASTIMIL, b. Bzí, Czech, Aug. 5, 32; m. 59; c. 2. PURE MATHEMATICS. RNDr, Charles Univ, Prague, 56, C.Sc, 59, D.Sc.(algebra), 66; Ph.D.(algebra), Khartoum, 62. Sr. lectr. MATH, Charles Univ, Prague, 57-59, reader, 64-65; sr. lectr, Khartoum 59-64; sr. res. fel, Inst. Adv. Studies, Australian Nat. Univ, 65-68; PROF, CARLETON UNIV, 68-, CHMN. DEPT, 71- Am. Math. Soc; Math. Asn. Am; Can. Math. Cong; London Math. Soc. Theory of groups; theory of rings and modules; general algebra. Address: Dept. of Mathematics, Carleton University, Ottawa, Ont. K1S 5B6, Can.

DMOCHOWSKI, LEON (LUDOMIR), b. Tarnopol, Poland, July 1, 09; m. 50; c. 1. BACTERIOLOGY, PATHOLOGY. M.B. & Ch.B, Lwow, 33, M.D, Warsaw, 37; fel, Potocki Found. Invests. Cancer, 36-38; travelling fel, Potocki Found, Imp. Cancer Res. Fund, London, 38-39; Ph.D, Leeds, 49. House physician & surgeon, univ. clinics, Lwow, 34-35; asst, dept. bact. & exp. med, State Inst. Hyg, Warsaw, 35-38; res. worker, Imp. Cancer Res. Fund, London, 39-46; Milligan asst, dept. exp. path. & cancer res, sch. med, Leeds, 46-49, lectr. exp. path, 49-50, reader in cancer res, 50-54; vis. assoc. prof. microbiol, col. physicians & dent. br, Univ. Tex, 54-55; consult, UNIV. TEX. M.D. ANDERSON HOSP. & TUMOR INST, 54-55, PROF. EXP. PATH, POSTGRAD. SCH. MED, UNIV, 55-, VIROL, DIV. CONTINUING EDUC, GRAD. SCH. BIOMED. SCI, 65-, PROF. VIROL. & HEAD DEPT, HOSP. & INST, 66-, chief virol. & electron micros, 55-65, acting head dept. virol, 65-66. Adv, UN Relief & Rehab. Admin, 39-45; clin. prof, Baylor Univ, 55-; distinguished lectr, Med. Col. Ga, 66; mem. nat. med. & sci. adv. comt, Leukemia Soc, 66-70, nat. bd. trustees, 66-; hon. mem, Latin Am. Cong. Cancer, 67- Dipl. virol. & pub. health, Am. Bd. Med. Microbiol, 64. Brit. Soc. Gen. Microbiol; Electron Micros. Soc. Am; Am. Asn. Cancer Res; Soc. Exp. Biol. & Med; fel. Geront. Soc; Am. Soc. Microbiol; fel. Am. Acad. Microbiol; Am. Med. Writers' Asn; Am. Asn. Med. Cols; fel. N.Y. Acad. Sci; Path. Soc. Gt. Brit. & Ireland; fel. Royal Soc. Med; Brit. Med. Asn; Royal Soc. Trop. Med. & Hyg; for. cor. mem. Italian Cancer Soc; hon. mem. Chilean Soc. Cancerology. Serological specificity of experimental animal tumors; serological analysis of filterable tumor agents in fowls and mammals; estrogens and lymphoid tumors in mice; biological ultracentrifugation and electron microscope studies of the mammary tumor inducing agent in mice; freeze-drying of tumor tissues; virology and electron microscopy. Address: Dept. of Virology, University of Texas M.D. Anderson Hospital & Tumor Institute, 6723 Bertner Dr, Houston, TX 77025.

DMYTRYSZYN, MYRON, b. St. Louis, Mo, Dec. 26, 24; m. 47; c. 2. CHEMICAL ENGINEERING. B.S, Washington (St. Louis), 47, M.S, 49, Dc.S, 57. Res. chem. engr, MONSANTO CO, 47-57, proj. leader, econ. & eng. eval. group, 57-58, group leader, 58-60, eng. specialist, 60-64, proj. mgr. eng. develop, 64-65, eng. mgr, cost & eval. eng, CENT. ENG. DEPT, 65-68, mgr. eng, 68-69, dir. eng. sci, 69-70, DIR. DESIGN & CONSTRUCT, 70- Am. Inst. Chem. Eng; Am. Asn. Cost Eng. Process development. Address: Central Engineering Dept, Monsanto Co, 800 N. Lindbergh Blvd, St. Louis, MO 63166.

DOAK, G(EORGE) O(SMORE), b. Prince Albert, Sask, Can, Dec. 25, 07; nat; m. 33; c. 2. PHARMACEUTICAL CHEMISTRY. B.A.(chem), 29, B.A. (pharm), Saskatchewan, 30; A.M, Wisconsin, 32, Ph.D.(chem), 34. Asst, Wisconsin, 32-33; asst. chemist, N.Dak. Regulatory Dept, Bismarck, 34-36; res. chemist, George A. Breon Co, 36-38; chemist, U.S. Pub. Health Serv, 38-51, asst. dir. V.D. exp. lab, 51-57, assoc. dir, 57-61; PROF. CHEM, N.C. STATE UNIV, 61- Instr. med, Hopkins Hosp, 38-46; res. assoc, Hopkins, 46-48; assoc. prof, sch. pub. health, North Carolina, 48-61. Am. Chem. Soc; The Chem. Soc; Ger. Chem. Soc. Synthesis of organometallic compounds, particularly those of arsenic, antimony and bismuth; preparation of organo-phosphorus compounds; biochemistry of treponemata; stereochemistry of trigonal bipyramids. Address: Dept. of Chemistry, North Carolina State University, Raleigh, NC 27607.

DOAK, KENNETH W(ORLEY), b. Gallatin, Mo, Jan. 27, 16; m. 45; c. 3. POLYMER CHEMISTRY. A.B, Cent. Col.(Mo), 38; Warner fel, Hopkins, 38-42, Ph.D.(phys. org. chem), 42. Res. chemist, U.S. Rubber Co, 42-55; res. assoc, res. center, Koppers Co. Inc, 55557, mgr. plastics res, 58-60; asst. dir. Polymer res, Rexall Chem. Co, Paramus, 60-65, dir. cent. res, 65-70; MGR. PLASTICS RES, RES. CTR, KOPPERS CO, INC, 71- Co-ed, Crystalline Olefin Polymers. Am. Chem. Soc; Acad. Appl. Sci; fel. Am. Inst. Chem. Theory of polymerization; free radical reactions; polymer properties; vulcanization and compounding; polyethylene, polypropylene and polystyrene development. Address: Research Center, Koppers Co, Inc, 440 College Park Dr, Monroeville, PA 15146.

DoAMARAL, JEFFERSON RIBEIRO, b. Timbauba, Brazil, May 17, 17; m. 50; c. 3. ANALYTICAL & ORGANIC CHEMISTRY. B.S, Mil. Inst. Eng, Brazil, 49; Brazilian Coun. Res-Brazilian Army fel, 54-56; M.S, Stanford Univ, 56; Ph.D. (anal. org. chem), Univ. Brazil, 62. Asst. prof. org. chem, Mil. Inst. Eng, Brazil, 50-51, assoc. prof, 51-61; sr. engr, Urea Plant, Nitrobrasil S.A, Brazil, 61-64; res. assoc. org. chem, Stanford Univ, 64-66; protein chem, sch. pharm, Univ. Calif, San Francisco, 66; med. chem, Mt. Zion Hosp, San Francisco, Calif, 66-69; consult. chem. & chem. eng, I.J. Wilk & Assocs, Calif, 69-70; RES. ASSOC. ANAL. ORG. CHEM, SCH. MED, STANFORD UNIV, 70- Brazilian Army, 39-61, Col. Am. Inst. Chem. Eng; Am. Chem. Soc; Asn. Psychophysiol. Study Sleep; N.Y. Acad. Sci. Radio isotopes; mechanism of reactions; analytical chemistry; spot tests; amino sugar chemistry; protein chemistry, particularly synthesis of polypeptides; meddicinal chemistry, particularly antimalarials and anticancer compounds; analytical chemistry, particularly brain metabolism; gas-liquid chromatography. Address: 2150 Prospect St, Menlo Park, CA 94025.

DOAN, ARTHUR SUMNER, JR, b. Fort Wayne, Ind, July 29, 33; m. 60; c. 3. PHYSICAL CHEMISTRY & METALLURGY. A.B, Wabash Col, 55; M.S, Iowa State, 58; Boettcher fel, Colo. Sch. Mines, 61-62, D.Sc, 63. Chemist, Ames Lab, Atomic Energy Cmn, 55-59; physicist, U.S. Army Biol. Res. Lab, Md, 59-61; physicist refractory mat, Lewis Res. Ctr, NASA, 62-68, METALLURGIST, GODDARD SPACE FLIGHT CTR, 68- Chem.C, 58-60, Res, 60-62, Sgt. AAAS; Am. Chem. Soc; Meteoritical Soc; Am. Soc. Mass Spectrometry. Lunar rock and metals analysis; meteorite materials analysis; computer data reduction for mass spectrometry and electron microprobe. Address: NASA, Goddard Space Flight Center, Code 644, Greenbelt Rd, Greenbelt, MD 20771.

DOAN, DAVID B(ENTLEY), b. State College, Pa, Jan. 9, 26; m. 54; c. 4. GEOLOGY, MINERALOGY. B.S, Pa. State, 48, M.S, 49. Asst. mineral, Pa. State, 48-49, instr. geol, 49; geologist, U.S. Geol. Surv, 49-62; opers. analyst, Res. Anal. Corp, 62-68; TREAS, EARTH SCI. GROUP, INC, WASH, D.C, 68- Consult. geologist, 62-; consult, Chief of Engr, U.S. Army, North. Que. Explorers Ltd, Res. Anal. Corp, S.Hopkins Coal Co. Inc, Earth Sci. Pakistan, Ltd, Wall Corp, U.S. Coast Guard, Bobcat Properties, Inc. & Coulon Oil Co; mem, Tech. Comt. Mil. Geol; pres, Phebe Doan of Wash, Inc. U.S.N.R, 43-46, Lt.(jg). AAAS; Geol. Soc. Am; Am. Inst. Prof. Geol; Am. Geophys. Union; Am. Soc. Photogram; Soc. Am. Mil. Eng. Sedimentary petrology; areal geology; terrain analysis; methodologies in model construction; heuristics in military science; engineering geology; mineral exploration; geology of Pacific Basin and Southeast Asia. Address: 5635 Bent Branch Rd, Bethesda, MD 20016.

DOAN, DONALD J(AY), b. Francis, Okla, Mar. 11, 10; m. 37. METALLURGY. B.S, Washington (Seattle), 31; U.S. Bur. Mines fel, Arizona, 31-32, M.S, 32; U.S. Bur. Mines fel, Mo. Sch. Mines, 32-35, Ph.D.(metal), 35. RES. METALLURGIST, EAGLE-PICHER CO, 35-42, 46- C.W.S, 42-45, Maj. Am. Chem. Soc; Faraday Soc. Metallurgy of lead and zinc; batteries. Address: 216 N. Byers Ave, Joplin, MO 64801.

DOAN, RICHARD L(LOYD), b. Lapel, Ind, Sept. 7, 98; m. 26; c. 2. PHYSICS. A.B, Indiana, 22, A.M, 23; Ph.D.(physics), Chicago, 26. Instr, Indiana, 22-23; Reed Col, 23-24; Nat. Res. fel, Chicago, 26; res. engr, West. Elec. Co, 26-33; physicist, Chicago, 33-36; sect. chief in charge geophys. res. & assoc. dir. res, Phillips Petrol. Co, 36-42; chief admin. officer, metall. lab, Chicago, 42-43; dir. res, Clinton Lab, Oak Ridge, 43-45; asst. dir. res, Phillips Petrol. Co, 45-50, dir, 50-52, mgr, atomic energy div, 51-63; dir. reactor licensing, U.S. Atomic Energy Comn, 64-68, asst. dir. regulation spec. projs, 68-70; RETIRED. Mem. atomic safety & licensing bd. panel, U.S. Atomic Energy Comn. Fel. AAAS; fel. Am. Phys. Soc; fel. Am. Nuclear Soc; Am. Chem. Soc. Refraction and reflection of x-rays; cosmic rays; magnetic materials; petroleum exploration and production. Address: 5769 E. 14th St, Tucson, AZ 85711.

DOANE, BENJAMIN KNOWLES, b. Phila, Pa, May 9, 28; Can. citizen; m. 61; c. 2. PSYCHIATRY, PHYSIOLOGY. A.B, Princeton, 50; M.A, Dalhousie, 52, M.D, 62; Ph.D.(psychol), McGill, 55. Res. off. psychol, Defense Res. Bd. Can, 51-53; res. assoc, Montreal Neurol. Inst, McGill, 55-57; McLaughlin fel, Maudsley Hosp, London, Eng, 64-65; Med. Res.Coun. fel, Univ. Montreal, 65-66; asst. prof. PSYCHIAT, DALHOUSIE UNIV, 66-69, ASSOC. PROF, 69-, LECTR. PHYSIOL, 66- Fel, Royal Col. Physicians & Surgeons, Can, 67. Can. Psychiat. Asn; Can. Med. Asn. Physiological psychology; behavioral physiology. Address: Dept. of Psychiatry, Faculty of Medicine, Dalhousie University, Halifax, N.S, Can.

DOANE, C(HARLES) C(HESLEY), b. Bradford, Ont, July 19, 25; U.S. citizen; m. 53. ENTOMOLOGY. B.S, Ont. Agr. Col, 49; M.S, Wisconsin, 51, Ph.D, 53. Mem. staff, prod. develop. dept, Shell Chem. Corp, 53-56; asst. entomologist, CONN. AGR. EXP. STA, 56-60, ASSOC. ENTOMOLOGIST, 60- Mem, Int. Orgn. Biol. Control Noxious Animals & Plants. Soc. Invert. Path; Entom. Soc. Am; Entom. Soc. Can. Forest insect problems; biological and ecological studies directed toward control of particular pests. Address: Connecticut Agricultural Experiment Station, P.O. Box 1106, New Haven, CT 06504.

DOANE, ELLIOTT P, b. Ill, July 11, 29; m; c. 4. CHEMICAL ENGINEERING. A.B, Harvard, 51; Visking Corp. fel, Illinois, 52-54, M.S, 53, Ph.D. (chem. eng), 55. Chem. engr, Hooker Chem. Co, N.Y, 54-57, supvr. pilot plant, 57-60; res. engr, Tex. Butadiene & Chem. Co, 61, dir. res. lab, 62; res. engr, Phillips Petrol. Co, 63-66, mgr. hydrocarbon processes br, 66-69; MGR. PROCESS DEVELOP. DEPT, WEST. RES. CTR, STAUFFER CHEM. CO, 69- Am. Chem. Soc; Am. Inst. Chem. Eng. High pressure studies; kinetics; absorption; catalysis. Address: Western Research Center, Stauffer Chemical Co, 1200 S. 47th St, Richmond, CA 94804.

DOANE, F(RANCES) W, b. Halifax, N.S, Aug. 30, 28. MICROBIOLOGY, ELECTRON MICROSCOPY. B.Sc, Dalhousie Univ, 50; M.A, Univ. Toronto, 62. Res. asst. virol, UNIV. TORONTO, 53-57, Hosp. Sick Children, 57-58, fel, SCH. HYG, 58-62, lectr, 62-65, asst. prof, 65-69, ASSOC. PROF, 69-, HEAD ELECTRON MICROS. UNIT, 62- AAAS; Am. Soc. Microbiol; Can. Soc. Microbiol; Electron Micros. Soc. Am; Royal Micros. Soc. Research and development of rapid methods of virus diagnosis, notably by electron microscopy; investigation of the structure, cytopathology and morphogenesis of reoviruses, herpesviruses, arboviruses and myxoviruses. Address: Dept. of Microbiology, University of Toronto School of Hygiene, Toronto, 181, Ont, Can.

DOANE, JOSEPH WILLIAM, b. Bayard, Nebr, Apr. 26, 35; m. 58; c. 2. PHYSICS. B.S, Missouri, 58, M.S, 62, O.M. Stewart fel. & Ph.D.(physics), 65. Asst. prof. PHYSICS, KENT STATE UNIV, 65-69, ASSOC. PROF, 69- Faculty summer res. fel, 66, faculty res. time grant, 66-67. U.S.A, 58-60, 1st Lt. Am. Phys. Soc; Am. Asn. Physics Teachers. Nuclear magnetic resonance studies in the solid and liquid crystal states. Address: Dept. of Physics, Kent State University, Kent, OH 44240.

DOANE, MARSHALL GORDON, b. Syracuse, N.Y, June 11, 37. BIOPHYSICS. B.S, Rochester, 59, M.S, 61; Nat. Inst. Gen. Med. Sci. fel, Maryland, 63-67, Ph.D.(biophys), 67. Res. asst. phys. optics, Rochester, 59-61; optical physicist, Aerojet-Gen. Corp, 61; physicist, Bausch & Lomb, Inc, 61-62; res. fel. CORNEAL RES, RETINA FOUND, 67-69, res. assoc, 69-71, ASSOC. SCIENTIST, 71- Oxidative metabolism of single nerve cells; pyridine nucleotide fluorescence in nerve cells; corneal physiology and metabolism; active transport and dehydration mechanisms in the cornea; corneal prostheses; bioinstrumentation; optics; biomedical engineering. Address: Retina Foundation, Dept. of Cornea Research, 20 Staniford St, Boston, MA 02114.

DOANE, TED H, b. Fairview, Okla, May 12, 30; m. 54; c. 1. ANIMAL BREEDING. B.S, Okla. State Univ, 52; M.S, Kans. State Univ, 53, Ph.D. (animal breeding), 60. Exten. county agent, UNIV. NEBR, LINCOLN, 55-56, exten. livestock specialist, 56-58, 60-64, ASSOC. PROF. ANIMAL SCI, AGR. EXTEN, 62- Prof. agr. exten. admin, Univ. Nebr-Ataturk Univ. contract, Turkey, 64-66. Vet.C, U.S.A, 53-55. Am. Soc. Animal Sci. Animal production and management. Address: Dept. of Animal Science, University of Nebraska, Lincoln, NE 68503.

DOANE, WILLIAM M, b. Covington, Ind, Sept. 26, 30; m. 52; c. 4. ORGANIC CHEMISTRY. B.S, Purdue Univ, 52, M.S, 60, Ph.D.(biochem), 62. Teacher, sec. sch, Ind, 54-55; res. chemist, NORTH. MKT. & NUTRIT. RES. LAB, U.S. DEPT. AGR, 62-70, LEADER NONSTARCH PROD. INVESTS, 70- Instr. chem, Bradley Univ, 64- U.S.A, 52-54. Am. Chem. Soc. Reaction mechanisms in carbohydrate chemistry; sulfur derivatives of carbohydrates; synthesis and characterization of starch derivatives; starch graft copolymers. Address: Northern Marketing & Nutrition Division, U.S. Dept. of Agriculture, Peoria, IL 61604.

DOANE, WINIFRED W(ALSH), b. New York, N.Y, Jan. 7, 29; m. 53; c. 1. GENETICS. B.A, Hunter Col, 50; M.S, Wisconsin, 52; Nat. Sci. Found. fel, Yale, 58-60, Ph.D.(zool), 60. Asst. zool, Wisconsin, 50-51, Alumnae Found. res. asst, 51-53; asst. prof. biol, Millsaps Col, 54-55; lab. asst. genetics, YALE, 56-58, Nat. Insts. Health res. trainee, 60-62, RES. ASSOC. DEVELOP. GENETICS, 62-, LECTR, 65- AAAS; Genetics Soc. Am; Am. Soc. Zool; Am. Soc. Nat; Am. Soc. Cell Biol; Soc. Develop. Biol. Analysis of lethal and female-sterility mutants, endocrine control of reproduction in relation to lipid and carbohydrate metabolism, and genetic control of enzymes in developmental and physiological genetics of Drosophila. Address: Dept. of Biology, Yale University, New Haven, CT 06520.

DOBAN, ROBERT CHARLES, b. Kenosha, Wis, Feb. 25, 24; m. 47; c. 1. ORGANIC CHEMISTRY. B.S, Yale, 49; Ph.D.(chem), Wisconsin, 52. Res. chemist, plastics dept, E.I. DU PONT DE NEMOURS & CO, INC, 52-57, res. supvr, 57-60, sr. supvr, 60-63, prod. mgr, 63-64, lab. mgr, exp. sta. lab, 64-66, res. mgr, commercial resins div, 66-68, lab. dir, plastics dept, 68-70, MGR, AUTOMATIC CLIN. ANAL, 70- U.S.N.R, 43-46, Lt.(jg). AAAS; Am. Chem. Soc; Soc. Plastics Indust; The Chem. Soc. Synthesis, physics and chemistry of high polymers; research management. Address: Photo Products Dept, Instrument Products Division, E.I. du Pont de Nemours & Co, Inc, Wilmington, DE 19898.

DOBAY, DONALD G(ENE), b. Cleveland, Ohio, Sept. 12, 24; m. 45, 66; c. 3. POLYMER CHEMISTRY. A.B, Oberlin Col, 44; Rackham fel, Michigan, 44-45, M.S, 45, Allied Chem. & Dye fels, 45-47, univ. fel, 47-48, Ph.D.(colloid chem), 48. Res. chemist, Linde Air Prod, 48-51; sr. res. chemist, B.F. Goodrich Res. Ctr, Ohio, 51-60, tech. coord, B.F. GOODRICH SPONGE PROD, CONN, 60-62, MGR. POLYMER DEVELOP, 62- Am. Chem. Soc; N.Y. Acad. Sci; Am. Inst. Chem; Soc. Plastics Eng. Polymerization; polymer characterization and degradation; latex agglomeration; synthetic rubber production; plasticization; chromatography; process engineering; foam and sponge manufacture; thermal and acoustic insulation; cryogenic properties; flammability. Address: 11 University Pl, New Haven, CT 06511.

DOBBELSTEIN, THOMAS NORMAN, b. Wyandotte, Mich, Oct. 14, 40; m. 60; c. 3. ANALYTICAL CHEMISTRY. B.S, Eastern Michigan, 64; M.S, Iowa State, 66, Ph.D.(anal. chem), 67. Instr. CHEM, Iowa State, summer 67; ASST. PROF, YOUNGSTOWN STATE UNIV, 67- Am. Chem. Soc. Ion-responsive membranes. Address: Dept. of Chemistry, Youngstown State University, 410 Wick Ave, Youngstown, OH 44503.

DOBBEN, GLEN D, b. Fremont, Mich, Sept. 25, 28; m. 54; c. 5. MEDICINE. B.S, Calvin Col, 50; M.D, Marquette, 53. Intern med, Blodgett Mem. Hosp, Grand Rapids, Mich, 53-54; res. radiol, Henry Ford Hosp, Detroit, Mich, 54-55, 57-59; instr, Chicago, 59-61; res. fel. neuro-radiol, Lund, 61-62; asst. prof. RADIOL, UNIV. CHICAGO, 62-66, ASSOC. PROF, 66-; DIR. DIV. RADIOL, COOK COUNTY HOSP, 69- U.S.A.F, 55-57, Capt. Asn. Univ. Radiol; Asn. Am. Med. Cols. Diagnostic radiological sciences as applied to neuroradiology. Address: P.O. Box Two, South Holland, IL 60473.

DOBBIE, JAMES M(cQUEEN), b. Pittston, Pa, Mar. 1, 13; m. 40; c. 3. MATHEMATICS. B.S, Bucknell, 33, fel, 33-34, M.S, 34; fel, Illinois, 34-38, Ph.D, 38. Asst. math, Illinois, 34-38; instr, Case, 38-40; Northwestern, 40-43, assoc. prof, 46-47; with opers. eval. group, div. sponsored res, Mass. Inst. Tech, 47-62, dep. dir. group, 57-60; mem. res. staff, ARTHUR D. LITTLE, INC, 62, SR. ANALYST, 62- With Off. Sci. Res. & Develop, 43-46. Am. Math. Soc; Opers. Res. Soc. Am. Mathematical analysis; Lambert series; analytic number theory; operations research. Address: Arthur D. Little, Inc, 15 Acorn Park, Cambridge, MA 02140.

DOBBINS, B(ILLY) D(OUGLAS), b. Lufkin, Texas, Mar. 5, 22; m. 43. ELECTRONICS. A.S, John Tarleton Agr. Col, 41; B.S, Southern Methodist, 48, Maryland. Prin. prof. staff & group supvr. guid. system develop, APPL. PHYSICS LAB, JOHNS HOPKINS UNIV, 48-66, ASST. DIV. SUPVR. MISSILE SYSTS. DIV, 66- Chmn. advan. tech. objectives working group fleet defense, Dir. Navy Labs. Sig.C, 42-43; U.S.A.A.F, 43-46, Res, 46-54, Capt. Inst. Elec. & Electronics Eng. Electronic systems; guidance and control of missiles. Address: 117 Piping Rock Dr, Silver Spring, MD 20904.

DOBBINS, JAMES T(ALMAGE), JR, b. Chapel Hill, N.C, June 13, 26; m. 51; c. 2. ANALYTICAL CHEMISTRY. B.S, North Carolina, 47, Ph.D.(anal. chem), 58. Chief indust. hyg. sect, dept. chem, 406th Med. Gen. Lab, U.S. Army, 54-56, head dept. chem, 56; res. chemist, R.J. REYNOLDS INDUSTS, 58-66, HEAD METHODS DEVELOP. SECT, 66-, ANAL. INSTRUMENTATION SECT, 67- U.S.A, 53-56, Res, 56- Maj. AAAS; N.Y. Acad. Sci; Am. Chem. Soc. Atomic absorption spectroscopy; analytical chemistry of tobacco and tobacco products. Address: Analytical Division, Research Dept, R.J. Reynolds Industries, Winston-Salem, NC 27102.

DOBBINS, JOHN P(OTTER), b. Tientsin, China, July 4, 14; U.S. citizen; m. 55; c. 4. PHYSICAL CHEMISTRY. A.B, California, Berkeley, 35; M.S, Saxon Inst. Tech, Dresden, 38; Ph.D.(photophysics), Swiss Fed. Inst. Tech, 63. Chemist, Best Foods Co, Inc, Calif, 35-36, W.P. Fuller & Co, 38-40; chem. engr, N.Am. Aviation, Inc, 40-44, res. supvr. heat transfer, 45-51, res. consult. info processing, 51-54; tech. dir. photodocumentation, Records Serv. Corp, 54-57; consult. engr, self-employed, Switz. & Conn, 57-65; sr. staff scientist, Hycon Mfg. Co, McDonnell-Douglas Corp, Calif, 66-68; CONSULT. ENGR, 68- Instr. eng. exten. div, California, Los Angeles, 50, lectr. systs. & procedures, Spec. Libraries Assoc. Conf, 52; v.pres, Prof. Consult, Inc, 59-61. Consult, Contraves, A.G, Switz, 59-60, Apollo Lunar Orbiter Prog, 65 & Gen. Cinetics, Ltd, Calif, 68. AAAS; Am. Chem. Soc; Am. Soc. Info. Sci; Int. Soc. Gen. Semantics; Soc. Photog. Sci. & Eng. Thermodynamics; reaction kinetics; metals; corrosion; plastics; heat transfer; radiometry; emittance, color and vision; instrumentation; information management and documentation; cameras and sensors; photoemulsions; light scattering; statistics; automation; computerized anti-counterfeiting; semantics; oceanography. Address: 615 Allen Ave, San Marino, CA 91108.

DOBBINS, RICHARD ANDREW, b. Burlington, Mass, July 15, 25; m. 53; c. 2. FLUID DYNAMICS, AEROSPACE & MECHANICAL ENGINEERING. S.B, Harvard, 48; M.S, Northeastern, 58; Ph.D, Princeton, 61. Res. engr. rocket power plants, Arthur D. Little, Inc, 50-53; sr. engr. heat transfer, Sylvania Elec. Prod. Inc, 53-57; asst. prof. ENG, BROWN UNIV, 60-64, ASSOC. PROF, 64- Consult, Lockheed Electronics Co, 58; Curtiss-Wright, 58-59; Hercules Powder Co, 62; Aeroneutronic Div, Ford Motor Co, 63-64; assoc. ed, Combustion Sci. & Technol. U.S.N.R, 43-46, Ens. AAAS; Am. Inst. Aeronaut. & Astronaut; Combustion Inst; Am. Phys. Soc. Aerospace propulsion; aerosol science and technology; high temperature effects in fluid dynamics; heat transfer; atmospheric fluid mechanics. Address: Dept. of Engineering, Brown University, Providence, RI 02912.

DOBBINS, ROBERT J(OSEPH), b. Buffalo, N.Y, Aug. 16, 40; m. 64; c. 2. PHYSICAL & INORGANIC CHEMISTRY. B.S, Fordham, 62; Atomic Energy Cmn. fel. & Ph.D.(phys. chem), State Univ. N.Y. Buffalo, 66. RES. CHEMIST, INDUST. CHEM. DIV, AM. CYANAMID CO, 66- Am. Chem. Soc; Am. Tech. Asn. Pulp & Paper Indust. Cellulose-water-electrolyte interactions; adsorption from aqueous solutions; chemistry of pulping and bleaching processes; mechanisms of inorganic reactions; coordination chemistry. Address: Industrial Chemicals Division, American Cyanamid Co, 1937 W. Main St, Stamford, CT 06904.

DOBBINS, THOMAS E(DWARD), b. Frankfort, N.Y, Oct. 10, 13; m. 45; c. 3. CHEMICAL ENGINEERING, PAPER TECHNOLOGY. B.S, Syracuse, 39. Chemist, paper mfr, Hamersley Mfg. Co, 39-41; container tech. serv. dept, AM. CAN CO, 41-50, supvr, tech. serv. dept, 50-64, SR. RES. ASSOC, PAPER PRODS. RES, 64- Am. Chem. Soc; Am. Tech. Asn. Pulp & Paper Indust. Technology of pulp and paper, plastics, adhesives, and petroleum waxes; packaging engineering; materials testing, specifications, and quality control; new products development. Address: American Can Co, 333 N. Commercial Ave, Neenah, WI 54956.

DOBBINS, WILLIAM E(ARL), b. Woburn, Mass, Mar. 1, 13; m. 52; c. 3. HYDRAULIC & SANITARY ENGINEERING. B.S, Mass. Inst. Tech, 34, M.S, 35, Sc.D.(sanit. eng), 41. Asst. civil & sanit. eng, Mass. Inst. Tech, 35-36, 39-40; instr. civil eng, Robert Col, Istanbul, 36-39; engr, Charles T. Main, Inc, Boston, 40-41; Stone & Webster Eng. Corp, 41; Corps Engr, 42-43; Fay, Spofford & Thorndike, Boston, 46-50; assoc. prof. sanit. eng, col. eng, N.Y. Univ, 50-57, prof, 57-61, civil eng, 61-68; PARTNER, TEETOR-DOBBINS CONSULT. ENGR, 66-; PRES, AQUA SCI, INC, 70- Dipl, Inter-Soc. Bd. Environ. Eng. U.S.N, 43-46, Lt.(jg). AAAS; fel. Am. Soc. Civil Eng.(Hering Medal, 59, 65); N.Y. Acad. Sci; Am. Water Works Asn; Am. Geophys. Union; Water Pollution Control Fedn; Am. Acad. Environ. Eng. Hydraulics; hydrology; water resources. Address: 10 Three Pond Rd, Smithtown, NY 11787.

DOBBS, FRANK W, b. Chicago, Ill, Sept. 8, 32; m. 58; c. 3. PHYSICAL CHEMISTRY. B.A, Chicago, 53, M.S, 55; Ethyl Corp. fel, Mass. Inst. Tech, 57-58, Ph.D.(phys. chem), 61. Asst. prof. CHEM, NORTHEAST. ILL. UNIV, 59-63, assoc. prof, 63-67, PROF, 67-, CHMN. DEPT, 71- AAAS; Am. Chem. Soc. Nuclear magnetic resonance. Address: 2728 Noyes, Evanston, IL 60201.

DOBBS, H(ARRY) DONALD, b. Atlanta, Ga, Nov. 23, 32; m. 53; c. 3. BIOLOGY. A.B, Emory, 53, M.S, 54, Ph.D.(biol), 67. Res. asst. parasitol, Emory, 54-55; asst. prof. BIOL, WOFFORD COL, 55-57, assoc. prof, 57-70, PROF, 70- Am. Soc. Zool; Am. Inst. Biol. Sci. Parasitology, especially trichiniasis in mice; anatomical and physiological adaptations of invertebrates. Address: Dept. of Biology, Wofford College, Spartanburg, SC 29301.

DOBBS, JOHN MacGREGOR, b. Hankow, China, June 30, 36; U.S. citizen; div; c. 1. PHYSICS. B.S, Pennsylvania, 59, M.S, 61, Ph.D.(physics), 67. ASST. PROF. PHYSICS, WASH. UNIV, 66- Am. Phys. Soc. Elementary particles, weak interactions of strange particles, development of improved counter-spark chamber techniques. Address: Dept. of Physics, Washington University, St. Louis, MO 63130.

DOBELL, JOSEPH P(ORTER), b. Corvallis, Ore, July 28, 15; m. 47; c. 4. GEOLOGY. B.S, Oregon State Col, 48, M.S, 49; univ. fel, Washington (Seattle), 49-51, Ph.D, 55. Instr. geol, Mich. Tech, 52-54, asst. prof, 54-57, assoc. prof, 57-65, prof, 65-68; CHMN. DEPT. SCI. & DIR. FIELD STA, CENT. WYO. COL, 68- Summers, geologist, U.S. Bur. Reclamation, 49; U.S. Geol. Surv, 51, 54-55; Am. Zinc Co, 52; Geol. Surv. Can, 56; Am. Metals Climax, 57; inst. minerals res, Michigan Tech, 65. Geol. Soc. Am; Am. Inst. Min, Metall. & Petrol. Eng; Am. Inst. Prof. Geol. Mineralogy; petrology; economic geology; geomorphology. Address: Dept. of Science, Central Wyoming College, Riverton, WY 82501.

DOBERENZ, ALEXANDER R, b. Newark, N.J, Aug. 17, 36; m. 58; c. 2. BIOCHEMISTRY, NUTRITION. B.S, Tusculum Col, 58; M.S, Arizona, 60, Ph.D. (biochem), 63. Res. assoc. biophys, Arizona, 63-69; vis. assoc. prof. nutrit, Hawaii, 69; assoc. prof. nutrit, UNIV. WIS-GREEN BAY, 69-71, PROF, NUTRIT. SCI, 71-, ASST. DEAN COL. HUMAN BIOL, 69- Nat. Inst. Dent. Res. fel, 63-66 & res. career develop. award, 66-69. Soc. Exp. Biol. & Med; Am. Chem. Soc; Am. Inst. Nutrit; fel. Am. Inst. Chem; Int. Asn. Dent. Res. Calcified tissue; mineral metabolism. Address: College of Human Biology, University of Wisconsin-Green Bay, Green Bay, WI 54305.

DOBERNECK, RAYMOND C, b. Milwaukee, Wis, June 17, 32; m. 57; c. 5. SURGERY. B.S, Marquette Univ, 53, M.D, 56; Ph.D.(surg), Univ. Minn, Minneapolis, 65. Asst. prof. SURG, sch. med, Creighton Univ, 65-68, assoc. prof, 68-70; PROF. & V.CHMN. DEPT, SCH. MED, UNIV. N.MEX, 70- John

& Mary R. Markle Found. scholar. acad. med, 66. Med.C, U.S.A, 61-63, Capt. Am. Col. Surg; Soc. Univ. Surg; Asn. Acad. Surg; Am. Gastroenterol. Asn; Soc. Head & Neck Surg. Head and neck tumors; hepatic hemosiderosis in surgical states; deglutition after oral and pharyngeal resection for cancer. Address: Dept. of Surgery, University of New Mexico School of Medicine, Albuquerque, NM 87106.

DOBES, WILLIAM LAMAR, b. Shiner, Tex, Apr. 21, 12; m. 39; c. 2. DERMATOLOGY. A.B, Emory, 31, M.D, 37. Asst. prof. CLIN. DERMAT, MED. SCH, EMORY UNIV, 45-60, assoc. prof, 60-71, PROF, 71- Pan-Am. Med. Asn; Am. Med. Asn; Am. Geriat. Soc; Int. Soc. Trop. Dermat; Latin-Am. Dermat. Soc; fel. Am. Acad. Dermat; Am. Dermat. Asn. Mycology and therapy of skin diseases. Address: 478 Peachtree St, Atlanta, GA 30308.

DOBINSON, FRANK, b. Bolton, Eng, Oct. 4, 31; nat; m. 60; c. 2. ORGANIC & POLYMER CHEMISTRY. B.S, Birmingham, 53, Ph.D.(chem), 56. Res. fel. ozone org. chem, dept. mining, Birmingham, 56-59; fel. chem, Texas, 59-61; res. chemist, MONSANTO CO, 61-69, GROUP LEADER, TEXTILES DIV, 69- Am. Chem. Soc; fel. Am. Inst. Chem. Reactions of ozone with organic compounds; new organic polymers with special properties. Address: 802 Poinciana Dr, Gulf Breeze, FL 32561.

DOBKIN, ALLEN BENJAMIN, b. Toronto, Ont, June 25, 23; m. 47; c. 2. ANESTHESIA. B.A, Toronto, 45, M.D, 49. U.S. Pub. Health Serv. fel, Minnesota, 51-52; clin. instr. ANESTHESIA, 52-53; Nat. Res. Coun. Can. fel, McGill, 53-54; sr. instr. & res. assoc, sch. med, Western Reserve, 54-55; asst. prof, col. med, Saskatchewan, 55-57, assoc. prof, 57-60; PROF. & CHMN. DEPT, STATE UNIV. N.Y. UPSTATE MED. CTR, 60-; DIR. ANESTHESIOL, UNIV. HOSP, VET. ADMIN. HOSP, SYRACUSE, SYRACUSE MEM. HOSP, 60- Vis. consult, St. Joseph's Hosp, Syracuse & City Hosp, 61-; Psychiat. Hosp, Syracuse, 63-; specialist, Royal Col. Physicians & Surgeons, Can, 55; dipl, Am. Bd. Anesthesiol, 56. R.C.A.M.C.R, 53-, Capt. Am. Med. Asn; Am. Soc. Pharmacol. & Exp. Therapeut; Am. Soc. Anesthesiol; fel. Am. Col. Anesthesiol; N.Y. Acad. Sci; Can. Med. Asn; Can. Fedn. Biol. Soc; Can. Anesthetists Soc; Int. Anesthesia Res. Soc; fel. Soc. Anesthetists Gt. Brit. & Ireland; hon. mem. Scandinavian Soc. Anesthesiol. Pharmacology; screening and testing new drugs; equipment; anesthesia; physiology; resuscitation and techniques. Address: Dept. of Anesthesiology, State University of New York, Upstate Medical Center, Syracuse, NY 13210.

DOBKIN, SHELDON, b. N.Y.C, Nov. 12, 33; m. 59; c. 3. BIOLOGICAL OCEANOGRAPHY, INVERTEBRATE ZOOLOGY. B.S, City Col. New York, 57; M.S, Miami (Fla), 60, Ph.D.(marine biol), 65. Asst. to curator marine invert, marine lab, Miami (Fla), 58, res. aide, 58-61, res. instr, 61-63, instr. marine biol, 63-64; asst. prof. ZOOL, FLA. ATLANTIC UNIV, 64-70, ASSOC. PROF, 70- U.S.A, 54-56. AAAS; Am. Soc. Zool; Soc. Syst. Zool. Larval development of decapod crustaceans, particularly the caridean and penaeidean shrimps; taxonomy of caridean shrimps; larval development of marine invertebrates. Address: Dept. of Biological Sciences, Florida Atlantic University, Boca Raton, FL 33432.

DOBO, EMERICK J(OSEPH), b. Szeged, Hungary, Oct. 23, 19; U.S. citizen; m. 50; c. 3. CHEMICAL ENGINEERING. B.S, Michigan, 42; M.S, Washington (Seattle), 48; Ph.D.(chem. eng), Texas, 54; Duke, 62-65. Develop. chem. engr, Crown Zellerbach Corp, Wash, 48-51; sr. develop. chem. engr, Chemstrand Corp, Ala, 54-57, group leader chem. eng, 57-62; group leader explor. eng, CHEMSTRAND RES. CTR, MONSANTO CO, 62-70, supvr, 70, ENG. FEL, 70- Chem.C, 43-46, 1st Lt. Am. Inst. Chem. Eng; Am. Chem. Soc. Engineering and chemistry related to high polymers and fibers. Address: 315 E. Cornwall Rd, Cary, NC 27511.

DOBRATZ, CARROLL J, b. Park Rapids, Minn, Oct. 13, 15; m. 42; c. 4. CHEMICAL ENGINEERING. B.Ch.E, Minnesota, 38; Ph.D.(chem. eng), Cincinnati, 43. Instr. chem. eng, Cincinnati, 41-43; sr. res. chemist, Shell Oil Co, Tex, 43-46; RES. & DEVELOP. ENGR, DOW CHEM. CO, PITTSBURG, 46- Am. Chem. Soc; Am. Inst. Chem. Eng. Heat and mass transfer; applied kinetics; thermodynamics. Address: 156 Estates Dr, Danville, CA 94526.

DOBRIN, MILTON B(URNETT), b. Vancouver, B.C, Can, Apr. 7, 15; m. 44, 48; c. 5. GEOPHYSICS. B.S, Mass. Inst. Tech, 36; scholar, Columbia, 36-37; Ph.D.(geophys), 50; M.S, Pittsburgh, 41. Asst. physics, Columbia, 37; asst. geophysicist, Gulf Res. & Develop. Co, 37-40, geophysicist, 40-42; physicist, Naval Ord. Lab, 42-49; sr. res. technologist, field res. labs, Magnolia Petrol. Co, 49-55; sr. interpretation geophysicist, Triad Oil Co, Can, 56-61; chief geophysicist, United Geophys. Corp, 61-69, v.pres, 67-69; W.S. Farish vis. prof. geophys, Univ. Tex, Austin, 69; PROF. GEOL, UNIV. HOUSTON, 69- Britton scholar, Columbia, 47-48, lectr, 48-49. Mem. atomic bomb test, Bikini, 46; Arctic Res. Lab, 48. AAAS; Soc. Explor. Geophys.(ed, 53-55, first v.pres, 61-62, pres, 69-70); Geol. Soc. Am; Am. Asn. Petrol. Geol; Seismol. Soc. Am; Am. Geophys. Union; European Asn. Explor. Geophys. Seismic prospecting; experimental geology; underwater acoustics; noise production by marine life; seismic exploration of atolls; seismic surface waves; seismic data processing; use of laser light for optical filtering of geophysical data. Address: Dept. of Geology, University of Houston, Houston, TX 77004.

DOBRIN, PHILIP B(OONE), b. Passaic, N.J, Dec. 21, 34; m. 61; c. 3. MEDICAL & CARDIOVASCULAR PHYSIOLOGY. B.A, N.Y. Univ, 58; M.A, Conn. Col, 62; Nat. Insts. Health fel. & Ph.D.(physiol), Loyola Univ. Chicago, 68. Res. asst. psychopharmacol, Chas. Pfizer Res. Labs, 59-63; ASST. PROF. MED. PHYSIOL, STRITCH SCH. MED, LOYOLA UNIV. CHICAGO, 68- Consult, Nat. Insts. Health, 68- Am. Physiol. Soc. Biomechanics of the arterial wall; physiology of vascular smooth muscle; physiology of the circulation. Address: Dept. of Physiology, Stritch School of Medicine, Loyola University of Chicago Medical Center, 2160 S.First Ave, Maywood, IL 60153.

DOBROGOSZ, WALTER JEROME, b. Erie, Pa, Sept. 3, 33; m. 53; c. 4. MICROBIOLOGY, BIOCHEMISTRY. B.S, Pa. State, 55, M.S, 57, Ph.D.(bact, biochem), 60. Nat. Insts. Health fel. MICROBIOL, Illinois, 60-62; asst. prof, N.C. STATE UNIV, 62-65, assoc. prof, 65-71, PROF, 71- Nat. Insts. Health career develop. award, 63-, res. grant, 64-; Nat. Sci. Found. res. grant, 64-; Atomic Energy Comn. res. grant, 68- Am. Soc. Microbiol. Metabolic regulatory mechanisms in bacteria and higher organisms including studies on regulation of carbohydrate metabolism and nucleic acid and enzyme synthesis formation and the role of cyclic AMP in these processes. Address: Dept. of Microbiology, North Carolina State University, Raleigh, NC 27607.

DOBROTT, ROBERT D, b. Guymon, Okla, Sept. 28, 32; m. 62; c. 2. CRYSTALLOGRAPHY, PHYSICAL CHEMISTRY. B.S. & M.S, Wichita, 59; Ph.D. (phys. chem), Harvard, 64. Anal. chemist, Cessna Aircraft, Kans, 54-59; MEM. TECH. STAFF, TEX. INSTRUMENTS INC, 64- Am. Chem. Soc; Am. Crystallog. Asn. X-ray and electron diffraction and microscopy; electron probe microanalysis. Address: Central Research Labs, Texas Instruments Inc, P.O. Box 5936, Dallas, TX 75222.

DOBROV, W(ADIM) (IVAN), b. Masur, Russia, July 14, 26; nat; m. 56; c. 4. SOLID STATE PHYSICS. Göttingen, 50; Ph.D.(physics), California, 56. Asst. nuclear moments, California, 54-56, res. scientist, SOLID STATE PHYSICS, LOCKHEED RES. LAB, 56-65, staff scientist, 65-66, SR. STAFF SCIENTIST, 66- Am. Phys. Soc; Inst. Elec. & Electronics Eng. Nuclear moments; paramagnetic resonance; ferroelectricity; microwave ultrasonics; lasers and infrared technology. Address: Lockheed Research Lab, Palo Alto, CA 94304.

DOBROVOLNY, CHARLES GEORGE, b. Budapest, Hungary, July 19, 02; nat; m. 32; c. 1. VIROLOGY, PUBLIC HEALTH. A.B, Montana, 28; M.S, Kans. State Col, 33; Ph.D.(parasitol, zool), Michigan, 38. Teacher, high sch, Idaho, 28-29; instr. zool, Kans. State Col, 29-35; Michigan, 35-40; asst. prof, New Hampshire, 40-45, assoc. prof, 45-48, chmn. div. biol. sci, 47-48; parasitologist, div. trop. diseases, Nat. Insts. Health, U.S. PUB. HEALTH SERV, 48-51, consult. schistosomiasis control, WHO, Brazil, 51-57, yellow fever & trop. virus invest, Guatemala, 57-59, trop. virus studies, Panama, 59-60, malaria studies, Malaya & Atlanta, Ga, 61-64, int. demonstration proj. for communicable disease control, Tex, 65-66, pesticide studies, 66-67, proj. off. pesticides prog, 67-68, PROJ. OFF, Food & Drug Admin, 68-70, ENVIRON. PROTECTION AGENCY, 70- U.S.P.H.S, 46-66, Capt. AAAS; Am. Soc. Parasitol; Am. Micros. Soc; Am. Soc. Trop. Med. & Hyg. General and experimental parasitology; malarian chemotherapy; schistosomiasis; tropical virology; pesticides; virology parasitology. Address: Division of Pesticides Community Studies, Environmental Protection Agency, 4770 Bufford Hwy, Chamblee, GA 30341.

DOBROVOLNY, ERNEST, b. Delmont, S.Dak, Aug. 27, 12; m. 40; c. 4. GEOLOGY. B.S, Kans. State Col, 35; M.S, Michigan, 40. Chem. analyst, E.I. du Pont de Nemours & Co, 35-37; asst. geol, Michigan, 38-40; asst. geologist, State Hwy. Cmn. Kans, 40-42; regional geologist, 43-44; asst. hwy. engr, Pub. Rds. Admin, Alaska, 42-43; geologist, U.S. GEOL. SURV, Ariz, 44, N.Mex, 45-46, Mont, 46-48, Colo, 48-54, asst. chief eng. geol. br, 49-54, geologist, in charge munic. geol. & eng, La Paz, Bolivia, 54-55, res. geologist, Nev. Test Site, 56-59, consult. eng. geol. earthquake studies, Chilean Geol. Surv, 60, geologist, mapping proj, Ky, 60-61, RES. GEOLOGIST, SCI. & ENG. TASK FORCE, FED. RECONSTRUCT. & DEVELOP. PLANNING CMN. ALASKA, 64- Mem, comt. Alaska Earthquake, Nat. Acad. Sci, chmn. comt. eng. geol, Hwy. Res. Bd, 63- Geol. Soc. Am; Asn. Eng. Geol. Stratigraphy; military geology; civil engineering; mapping geology. Address: U.S. Geological Survey, Federal Center, Denver, CO 80225.

DOBROVOLNY, JERRY S(TANLEY), b. Chicago, Ill, Nov. 2, 22; m. 47; c. 2. CIVIL ENGINEERING. B.S, Illinois, 43, M.S, 47. From instr. to assoc. prof. GEN. ENG, UNIV. ILL, URBANA, 45-59, PROF. & HEAD DEPT, 59- Summers, spec. asst, Ill. State Geol. Surv, 45-47, 49-52; civil engr, Ill. State Hwy. Dept, 48-53-54; consult, 55-59; mem, State of Ill. Adv. Coun. Voc. Educ, 69-72; Nat. Adv. Coun. Voc. Educ, 70-72; exam, comn. insts. higher educ, N.Cent. Asn. Cols. & Sec. Schs. C.Eng, 42-44, Sgt. Fel. AAAS; Am. Soc. Civil Eng; Am. Soc. Eng. Educ.(Arthur L. Williston Award); Hist. Sci. Soc; Am. Asn. Petrol. Geol; Soc. Hist. Technol; Am. Tech. Educ. Asn; Nat. Soc. Prof. Eng. Engineering geology and technology; soil mechanics. Address: 1104 S. Prospect, Champaign, IL 61820.

DOBROVSKY, TODOR MANOLOFF, b. Bulgaria, Oct. 24, 04; nat; m. 41. ENTOMOLOGY. B.S, Wisconsin, 31, M.S, 41; Ph.D, Cornell, 49. Dist. entomologist, La. Dept. Agr. & Immigration, 42-47; exten. entomologist, N.Carolina State Col. Agr, 49-52; asst. entomologist, Fla. Agr. Exp. Sta, 52-55; plant protection specialist grain storage, Food & Agr. Orgn, UN, 56-68; PROF. BIOL. & HEAD DEPT. & CHMN. SCI. DIV, FLAGLER COL, 68- Insect pests of stored grains and vegetables; insect morphology and histology. Address: Science Division, Flagler College, St. Augustine, FL 32084.

DOBROWOLSKI, J(ERZY) ADAM, b. Katowice, Poland, May 9, 31; Can. citizen; m. 59; c. 3. PHYSICAL OPTICS. B.Sc, London, 53, M.Sc, & dipl, Imp. Col, 54, Ph.D, 55. Nat. Res. Coun. Can. fel, 55-56; asst. res. officer, DIV. PHYSICS, NAT. RES. COUN. CAN, 56-60, assoc. res. off, 60-71, SR. RES. OFF, 71- Optical Soc. Am. Design and fabrication of optical thin film systems; optical filters. Address: Division of Physics, National Research Council, Ottawa, Ont, K1A 0S1, Can.

DOBRY, ALAN (MORA), b. Chicago, Ill, Mar. 19, 27; m. 50; c. 2. PHYSICAL CHEMISTRY. Ph.B. & S.B, Chicago, 45, S.M, 48, Ph.D.(chem), 50; M.Litt, Pittsburgh, 56. Fel. calorimetry peptide reactions, Yale, 51; res. engr. PHYS. CHEM. LUBRICATION, Westinghouse Elec. Co, 52-56; SR. RES. SCIENTIST, AM. OIL CO, 56- Am. Chem. Soc; Fedn. Am. Sci; Brit. Chem. Soc. Emulsions; particle size distributions; adsorption from solutions; physical chemistry of lubrication, antioxidants; high-temperature polymers; radiochemistry. Address: Research & Development Dept, American Oil Co, Whiting, IN 46394.

DOBRY, REUVEN, b. Bialistok, Poland, Apr. 13, 30; nat; m. 60; c. 2. CHEMICAL ENGINEERING. B.Ch.E, Syracuse, 54; M.S, Illinois, 55; Ph.D.(chem. eng), Cornell, 58. Res. chem. engr, Bioferm Corp, 58-63; sr. chem. engr, Battelle Mem. Inst, 63-67; sr. proj. leader, Standard Brands Inc, 67-69; ENG. RES. GROUP LEADER, BEECHNUT INC, 69- Am. Chem. Soc; Am.

Inst. Chem. Eng. Special techniques for isolation and purification of biochemicals; engineering research and process/product development, related to foods and beverages. Address: Beechnut Inc, North Main St, Port Chester, NY 10573.

DOBSON, ALAN, b. London, Eng, Dec. 20, 28; m. 54; c. 4. PHYSIOLOGY. B.A, Cambridge, 52, M.A, 70; Ph.D.(physiol), Aberdeen, 56. From sci. officer to prin. sci. officer, dept. physiol, Rowett Res. Inst, Scotland, 52-64; assoc. prof. physiol, STATE UNIV. N.Y. VET. COL, CORNELL UNIV, 64-70, PROF. VET. PHYSIOL, 70-, vis. prof, 61-62. Wellcome fel, sch. vet, Cambridge, 70-71. R.A.F, 47-49. Am. Physiol. Soc; Brit. Physiol. Soc; Brit. Biochem. Soc. Physiology of the ruminant digestive tract; homeostasis in the ruminant; control of absorption. Address: Dept. of Physiology, State University of New York Veterinary College, Cornell University, Ithaca, NY 14850.

DOBSON, ANN LILLIAN (MRS. CATLETT), b. Mineola, N.Y, Jan. 26, 36; m. 68. MICROBIOLOGY. B.S, Va. Polytech, 58; Fla. State, 59; M.S, West Virginia, 62, Ph.D.(microbiol), 64. Teacher, pub. schs, Mont, 59-60; technician microbiol, West Virginia, 62-63; supply instr, Wyoming, 64-65, asst. prof, 65-66; microbiologist, Kitchawan Res. Lab, Brooklyn Bot. Garden, 66-69; ASSOC. PROF. MICROBIOL, EL PASO COL, 69- Am. Soc. Microbiol; Mycol. Soc. Am. Biological degradation of some hydrocarbons in soils; investigations into factors affecting decomposition in sanitary landfills; effect of air pollution on microorganisms. Address: Dept. of Microbiology, El Paso College, 5 W. Las Vegas, Colorado Springs, CO 80901.

DOBSON, DAVID A, b. Oakland, Calif, Mar. 28, 37; m. 57. NUCLEAR & ATOMIC PHYSICS. B.S, California, Berkeley, 59, Ph.D.(physics), 64. Physicist, Lawrence Radiation Lab, Livermore, 64-69; ASST. PROF. PHYSICS, BELOIT COL, 69- AAAS; Am. Phys. Soc. Investigation of weak interactions by a study of asymmetries and angular correlations in beta decay of polarized nuclei. Address: Dept. of Physics, Beloit College, Beloit, WI 53511.

DOBSON, DONALD C, b. Central, Idaho, Sept. 18, 26; m. 49; c. 9. NUTRITION, BIOCHEMISTRY. B.S, Utah State Univ, 54; M.S, Cornell Univ, 55; Ph.D.(nutrit, biochem), Utah State Univ, 61. Res. asst. biochem, Univ. Utah, 55-57; nutrit. biochem, UTAH STATE UNIV, 57-60, asst. prof. turkey res, 60-70, ASSOC. PROF. ANIMAL SCI, 70- U.S.A, 45-47, T/Sgt. Poultry Sci. Asn. Poultry nutrition and management, especially turkeys. Address: Dept. of Animal Science, Utah State University, Ephraim, UT 84627.

DOBSON, ERNEST L, b. Peking, China, Apr. 25, 14; U.S. citizen; m. 39; c. 2. PHYSIOLOGY, BIOPHYSICS. B.S, California, 37, M.A, 46, Ph.D. (biophys), 50. Instr, high sch, 39-45; Napa Jr. Col, 45-46; PHYSIOLOGIST, LAWRENCE BERKELEY LAB, UNIV. CALIF, BERKELEY, 46-, LECTR. PHYSIOL, UNIV. AAAS; Am. Physiol. Soc; Soc. Exp. Biol. & Med; Reticuloendothelial Soc.(v.pres, 63-64). Circulatory physiology; body fluids; homeostatic mechanisms; biological effects of radiation; reticulo-endothelial system. Address: Donner Lab, Lawrence Berkeley Lab, University of California, Berkeley, CA 94720.

DOBSON, GERARD R(AMSDEN), b. East Rockaway, N.Y, May 4, 33; m. 62; c. 3. INORGANIC CHEMISTRY. B.S, Fla. South. Col, 55; M.Ed, Temple, 58; Ph.D.(chem), Fla. State, 64. Teacher, high sch, Pa, 55-58; asst. prof. inorg. chem, Georgia, 63-67; ASSOC. PROF. CHEM, Univ. S.Dak, 67-69; N.TEX. STATE UNIV, 69- U.S.A.R, 53-61. Am. Chem. Soc; The Chem. Soc. Organotransition metal chemistry; kinetics and mechanism of reactions of metal carbonyls and derivatives; physical methods of molecular structure determination. Address: Dept. of Chemistry, North Texas State University, Denton, TX 76203.

DOBSON, HAROLD L(AWRENCE), b. Liberty Co, Tex, May 10, 21; m. 45; c. 3. BIOCHEMISTRY, INTERNAL MEDICINE. B.S, Baylor, 43, M.D, 46, M.S, 56. Intern, Salt Lake County Hosp, Utah, 46-47; instr. biochem, COL. MED, BAYLOR UNIV, 47-48, U.S. Pub. Health Serv. fel. biochem. & internal med, 48-50, instr. internal med, 53-55, asst. prof, 55-62, assoc. prof, 62-70, CLIN. ASSOC. PROF, 71-; DIR. OUT PATIENTS SERV, HERMANN HOSP, 71- Res: Vet. Admin. Hosp, Houston, 50-51; fel, coun. on atherosclerosis, Am. Heart Asn. U.S.N.R, 43-45; Med.C, 51-53, Capt. AAAS; Am. Med. Asn; Am. Col. Cardiol; Am. Soc. Pharmacol. & Exp. Therapeut; Am. Soc. Nephrol; Am. Diabetes Asn. Metabolic disease; diabetes. Address: Hermann Hospital, 1203 Ross Sterling Ave, Houston, TX 77025.

DOBSON, PETER N, JR, b. Baltimore, Md, Sept. 15, 36; m. 57; c. 3. THEORETICAL & HIGH ENERGY PHYSICS. B.S, Mass. Inst. Tech, 58; Nat. Sci. Found. fel, Maryland, 60-64, Ph.D.(physics), 65. Physicist, Raytheon Corp, 58-59; Westinghouse Elec. Corp, 59-60; asst. prof. PHYSICS, UNIV. HAWAII, 65-70, ASSOC. PROF. & ASSOC. PHYSICIST, 70- Am. Phys. Soc. The theory of elmentary particles and their interactions at high energy. Address: Dept. of Physics & Astronomy, University of Hawaii, Honolulu, HI 96822.

DOBSON, R(ICHARD) C(ECIL), b. Florence, Mont, Dec. 29, 19; m. 45; c. 3. ECONOMIC ENTOMOLOGY. B.S, Wisconsin, 46, M.S, 47; Ph.D, Oregon State Col, 53. Res. asst, entom, Wisconsin, 45-47; instr. biol, N.Mex. State, 48-50, entomologist, fruit insects div, U.S. Dept. Agr, 50-51; asst. entom, Oregon State Col, 51-53; exten. serv, N.Mex. State, 53-54; state entomologist, plant quarantine serv, 54-55, res. entomologist, dept. bot. & entom, 55-58; PROF. ENTOM, PURDUE UNIV, 58- Mem, forest pest action, cmt. Ariz. & N.Mex, 53-58. U.S.A.A.F, 41-45, S/Sgt. AAAS; Entom. Soc. Am. Livestock insect research. Address: Dept. of Entomology, Entomology Hall, Purdue University, Lafayette, IN 47907.

DOBSON, RICHARD LAWRENCE, b. Boston, Mass, Apr. 12, 28; m. 50; c. 3. DERMATOLOGY. M.D, Chicago, 53. Instr. DERMAT, North Carolina, 57-58, asst. prof, 58-61; assoc. prof, MED. SCH, UNIV. ORE, 61-64, PROF, 64- Nat. Insts. Health res. fel, 56-57; attend. physician, Univ. sch, Oregon Hosps, 61-; consult, Vet. Admin. Hosp, Portland, 61-; scientist, Ore. Regional Primate Ctr, 63-68; mem. gen. med. study sect, Nat. Insts. Health, 65-69, chmn, 70-; vis. prof, Univ. Nijmegen, Netherlands, 69-70. Asst. chief ed, Arch. Dermat, 64-69, mem. ed. bd, 69- Dipl, Am. Bd. Dermat, 59. U.S.N, 46-47. AAAS; Am. Physiol. Soc; Histochem. Soc; Am. Asn. Cancer Res; Am. Acad. Dermat; Am. Col. Clin. Pharmacol. & Chemother; Soc. Invest. Dermat; Am. Col. Physicians; Am. Dermat. Asn. Cutaneous carcinogenesis; physiology of eccrine sweat gland. Address: Dept. of Dermatology, Medical School, University of Oregon, Portland, OR 97201.

DOBSON, WILLIAM J(ACKSON), b. Sherman, Tex, Aug. 8, 15; m. 44; c. 1. ZOOLOGY. B.A, Austin Col, 39; Ph.D.(zool), Texas, 46. Instr. zool, Texas, 39-46; asst. prof, Miss. State Col, 46; California, Los Angeles, 47; BIOL, TEX. A&M UNIV, 47-50, assoc. prof, 50-55, PROF, 55- Fel, Kerchoff Marine Labs, Calif. Inst. Technol, 47. AAAS; Am. Soc. Zool; Am. Soc. Cell Biol. Chromosomal chemistry; cytology; mammalian anatomy; ultrastructure of cells. Address: Dept. of Biology, Texas A&M University, College Station, TX 77843.

DOBY, RAYMOND, b. N.Y.C, Oct. 9, 23; m. 49; c. 2. CONTINUUM & FLUID MECHANICS. B.M.E, N.Y. Univ, 47, M.S, 51; Ph.D.(eng. mech), Pennsylvania, 62. Sr. engr, steam div, Westinghouse Elec. Corp, 53-62; sr. staff scientist, Avco Corp, 62-63; adv. engr, astronuclear labs, Westinghouse Elec. Corp, 63-66; ASSOC. PROF. ENG, SWARTHMORE COL, 66- Adj. asst. prof, eve. col, Drexel Inst, 56-62. U.S.A.A.F, 43-46, 1st Lt. AAAS; Am. Soc. Mech. Eng; Soc. Indust. & Appl. Math. Gas dynamics; boundary layer analysis; heat and mass transfer; biomechanics; interaction of science and society. Address: Dept. of Engineering, Swarthmore College, Swarthmore, PA 19081.

DOBY, TIBOR, b. Budapest, Hungary, Aug. 23, 14; U.S. citizen; m. 48. RADIOLOGY, NUCLEAR MEDICINE. M.D, Univ. Budapest, 38. Resident int. med, med. sch. hosp, Univ. Budapest, 38-44, asst. prof, 44-48, radiol, 48-50; assoc. radiologist, Trade Union & Rwy Employees Hosp, Budapest, 50-56; resident, St. Raphael's Hosp, New Haven, Conn, 57-59; instr, med. sch, Yale, 59-60; assoc. radiologist, MERCY HOSP, 60-65, DIR. RADIOL. DEPT, 65- Dipl, Am. Bd. Radiol, 62. Am. Col. Radiol; Radiol. Soc. N.Am; Soc. Nuclear Med. Circulatory shock; hemodynamics; history of medicine. Address: Dept. of Radiology, Mercy Hospital, 144 State St, Portland, ME 04101.

DOBYNS, BROWN M, b. Jacksonville, Ill, May 14, 13; m. 40; c. 3. SURGERY. B.A, Ill. Col, 35; M.D, Hopkins, 39; Mayo Found. fel, Minnesota, 40-43, M.S, 44, Ph.D, 46. Intern SURG, Johns Hopkins Hosp, 39-40; resident, Kahler Hosp, Mayo Clin, 43-45; Mayo Clin, 45-46, asst. to surg. staff, 46; res. fel. surg, med. sch, Harvard, 46-48, asst. prof. surg, 48-51; asst. chief SURG. SERV, CLEVELAND METROP. GEN. HOSP, 51-66, ASSOC. CHIEF, 67-, PROF, SCH. MED, CASE WEST. RESERVE UNIV, 58-, assoc. prof, 51-58. Asst, Mass. Gen. Hosp, 46-51; asst. surgeon, Univ. Hosps, Cleveland, Ohio, 51-; courtesy staff, St. Luke's Hosp, Cleveland, 51- Dipl, Am. Bd. Surg. AAAS; Am. Surg. Asn; Soc. Univ. Surg; Am. Col. Surg; Am. Soc. Clin. Invest; Int. Soc. Surg; Am. Thyroid Asn.(Van Meter prize, 46, merit award, 54, pres, 56-57); Endocrine Soc. General surgery; thyroid physiology. Address: Cleveland Metropolitan General Hospital, 3395 Scranton Rd, Cleveland, OH 44109.

DOBYNS, LEONA DANETTE, b. Shelby, Mont, Jan. 28, 30. PHYSICAL CHEMISTRY. B.S, Col. Great Falls, 58; Ph.D.(phys. chem), Univ. Notre Dame, 64. Asst. prof. CHEM, SEATTLE UNIV, 64-69, ASSOC. PROF, 69- Res. grant, Univ. Notre Dame, 68. Am. Chem. Soc; Am. Phys. Soc. Microwave spectroscopy and molecular structure. Address: Dept. of Chemistry, Seattle University, Seattle, WA 98122.

DOBYNS, ROY A, b. Bristol, Va, Jan. 31, 31; m. 55; c. 2. MATHEMATICS. B.A, Carson-Newman Col, 53; M.A, Vanderbilt, 54; Ph.D.(math), George Peabody Col, 63. Asst. prof. MATH, La. Col, 56-58; McNeese State Col, 58-61, assoc. prof, 62-64, prof, 64-68; PROF. & CHMN. DEPT, GEORGETOWN COL, 68- Mem. conf. linear algebra & numerical anal, Univ. Miami, 63. U.S.A, 54-56, Res, 56-63. Math. Asn. Am. Modern algebra; mathematical statistics. Address: Dept. of Mathematics, Georgetown College, Georgetown, KY 40324.

DOBYNS, SAMUEL WITTEN, b. Norton, Va, Mar. 7, 20; m. 45; c. 3. CIVIL ENGINEERING. B.S, Va. Mil. Inst, 41; M.S, Lehigh, 49; Nat. Sci. Found. fels, American Univ, 60 & Houston, 63. Sr. instrumentman construct, E.I. du Pont de Nemours & Co, 46; instr. CIVIL ENG, VA. MIL. INST, 46-50, asst. prof, 50-54, assoc. prof, 54-60, PROF, 60-, DIR. EVE. PROG, 67- Summer apprentice, Carnegie Ill. Steel Corp, 41; dir, Robert A. Marr Sch. Surv. & Comput. Clin, 50-72; partner, Dobyns & Morgan Consult. Engrs, 52-64; NASA faculty fel, Manned Spacecraft Ctr, Univ. Houston, Tex. A&M Univ, 67; Off. Civil Defense fel, W.Va. Univ, 69; consult, Thompson & Litton, 70- U.S.A, 41-42; U.S.A.F, 42-45, Res, 45-69, Lt. Col.(Ret). Adult Educ. Asn. U.S; Am. Soc. Civil Eng; Am. Soc. Photogram; Am. Cong. Surv. & Mapping; Am. Soc. Eng. Educ. Bridge design; structural analysis; computer programming and applications; project management; photogrammetry; solid waste; surveying; nuclear defense. Address: Dept. of Civil Engineering, Virginia Military Institute, Lexington, VA 24450.

DOBZHANSKY, THEODOSIUS, b. Nemirov, Russia, Jan. 25, 00; nat; m; c. 1. ZOOLOGY, BIOLOGY. Dipl, Univ. Kiev, 21; Int. Educ. Bd. fel, Rockefeller Found, 27-29; hon. D.Sc, Univ. São Paulo, 43, Col. Wooster, 45, Univ. Münster, 58, Univ. Montreal, 58, Univ. Chicago, 59, Univ. Sydney, 60, Oxford, 64, Columbia Univ, 64, Col. Agr, Louvain, Belg, 65, Clarkson Col. Technol, 65, Kalamazoo Col, 66; Univ. Mich, 66, Syracuse Univ, 67, Univ. Padua, Italy, 68, Univ. Calif, 68, Northwest. Univ, 68, Wittenberg Univ, 70, St. Mary Col, 71. Asst. prof. genetics, Calif. Inst. Technol, 29-36, prof, 36-40; ZOOL, COLUMBIA UNIV, 40-62, ADJ. PROF, 62-; EMER. PROF, ROCKEFELLER UNIV, 70-, prof, 62-70. Adj. prof, Univ. Calif, Davis, 71- Anisfield-Wolf Award, 63; Piere Lecomte du Nouy Award, 63; Nat. Medal of Sci, 64. Nat. Acad. Sci.(Elliott Medal, 46, Kimber Award, 58); Genetics Soc. Am.(pres, 41); Am. Soc. Naturalists (past pres); Soc. Study Evolution (past pres); Am. Soc. Zool.(past pres); Am. Philos. Soc; Royal Swedish Acad. Sci; Royal Danish Acad. Sci; Brazilian Acad. Sci; Leopold Carol Ger. Acad. Res. Natural Sci.(Darwin Medal, 59); Nat. Acad. Lincei. Genetics of Drosophilia; population genetics; biological evolution. Address: Dept. of Genetics, University of California, Davis, CA 95616.

DOCHINGER, LEON S(TANLEY), b. Woodbridge, N.J, Aug. 30, 24; m. 53; c. 2. PLANT PATHOLOGY. B.S, Rutgers, 50, Shade Tree fel, 52-56, Ph.D.(plant path), 56; M.S, Cornell, 52. Asst, Cornell, 50-52; plant pathologist, U.S. FOREST SERV, 56-70, PROJ. LEADER, 70- U.S.A, 43-46. Soc. Am. Foresters; Am. Phytopath. Soc. Relationship of air pollution to hardwood forests of the northeastern United States. Address: Forest Disease & Insect Lab, P.O. Box 365, Delaware, OH 43015.

DOCK, DONALD STONE, b. N.Y.C, Aug. 8, 27. INTERNAL MEDICINE. A.B, Princeton, 50; M.D, Johns Hopkins Univ, 54. Resident internal med, Yale, 55-57; Univ. Miami, 57-58; res. fel. MED, Harvard, 58-60; asst. clin. prof, YALE, 63-70, ASSOC. CLIN. PROF, 70- Dipl. cardiovasc. disease, Am. Bd. Internal Med, 65. Chief med, Hosp. of St. Raphael, New Haven, Conn, 63- Sig.C, U.S.A, 46-47. Cardiology. Address: 1450 Chapel St, New Haven, CT 06511.

DOCK, W(ILLIAM), b. Ann Arbor, Mich, Nov. 1, 98; m. 24; c. 2. MEDICINE. B.S, Washington (St. Louis), 20; M.D, Rush, Chicago, 23. Res. med, sch. med, Stanford, 24-25, instr, 25-26; asst. prof, 26-29, assoc. prof, 29-36; prof. path, 36-41; med. col, Cornell, 41-44; L.I. Col. Med, 44-50; State Univ. N.Y. Downstate Med. Center, 50-63; chief med. serv, VET. ADMIN. HOSP, Brooklyn, 64-69, CONSULT, N.Y.C, 69- Shattuck lectr, 47; consult, Army Inst. Path. Med.C, 42-43, Maj; Croix de Guerre, 17. AAAS; Asn. Am. Physicians; Am. Soc. Clin. Invest.(pres, 41); master Am. Col. Physicians; Harvey Soc; Soc. Exp. Biol; Am. Col. Cardiol; Am. Heart Asn; Pan-Am. Med. Asn; N.Y. Acad. Sci. Internal medicine. Address: 145 E. 16th St, New York, NY 10003.

DOCKEN, ADRIAN (MERWIN), b. Holt, Minn, Nov. 17, 13; m. 41; c. 4. CHEMISTRY. B.A, Luther Col, 37; Ph.D.(org. chem), Univ. Wis, 41. Asst, Univ. Wis, 37-41; res. assoc, Northwest. Univ, 41-42; PROF. CHEM, LUTHER COL, 42-, head dept, 42-70. Faculty fel, Fund Advan. Educ, Yale, 54-55; Nat. Sci. Found. faculty fel, Imp. Col, Univ. London, 61-62; Am. Chem. Soc. Petrol. Fund faculty award, Stanford Univ, 67-68. AAAS; Am. Chem. Soc; The Chem. Soc. Organic synthesis; philosophy and history of science. Address: Dept. of Chemistry, Luther College, Decorah, IA 52101.

DOCKENDORF, WILLIAM G(EORGE), b. N.Y.C, Feb. 24, 18; m. 46. BIOCHEMISTRY. B.A, N.Y. Univ, 46. Anal. chemist, U.S. Testing Corp, 46-47; biochemist, Nopco Chem. Co, Inc, 48-57, head vitamin assay lab, 57-60; GROUP LEADER, FLEISCHMANN LABS, STANDARD BRANDS, INC, 60- Chem.C, U.S.A, 42-45. Am. Chem. Soc; N.Y. Acad. Sci; Inst. Food Tech. Food research and development; analytical biochemistry; vitamins; nutrition; cereal chemistry. Address: 1 Apple Tree Dr, Stamford, CT 06906.

DOCKERTY, MALCOLM BIRT, b. Cardigan, P.E.I, Can, Sept. 19, 09; nat; m. 37; c. 1. PATHOLOGY. Hon. dipl, Prince Wales Col, 28; M.D. & C.M, Dalhousie Univ, 34; hon. D.Sc, Prince Wales Univ, 67. Fel. path, MAYO GRAD. SCH. MED, UNIV. MINN, 34-37, first asst. surg. path, 37, instr, 37-42, asst. prof. PATH, 42-45, assoc. prog, 45-52, PROF, 52-, CHMN. SURG. PATH, 69-; CHIEF DEPT. SURG. PATH, MAYO CLIN, 58-, head sect, 45-58. Civilian consult, Armed Forces Inst. Path, 52-55. Am. Med. Asn; Am. Soc. Clin. Path; Am. Asn. Path. & Bact. Surgical pathology; solid ovarian tumors. Address: Dept. of Surgical Pathology, Mayo Clinic, Rochester, MN 55901.

DOCKERTY, STUART M(ILLS), b. Cardigan, P.E.I, Can, Feb. 20, 11; nat; m. 37; c. 2. PHYSICS. B.A, Dalhousie, 31, M.A, 33; Ph.D.(physics), Toronto, 36. Physicist, fiber prods. div, Corning Glass Works, N.Y, 36-38; Owens-Corning Fiberglas Corp, Ohio, 38-40; mech. develop. dept, CORNING GLASS WORKS, R.I, 40-44, mech. res. dept, N.Y, 44-61, SR. ENG. ASSOC. IN PROCESS RES, 61- Nat. Res. Coun. Can. scholar. Viscous flow; heat transfer; mechanics; theory of glass working; manufacture of glass fibers; glass tubing. Address: Corning Glass Works, Corning, NY 14830.

DOCKERY, JOHN T, b. Cleveland, Ohio, May 2, 36; m. 61; c. 3. PHYSICS, SYSTEMS ANALYSIS. B.S, John Carroll, 58; Atomic Energy Cmn. fel, Rice, 58-59; Woodrow Wilson fel, 58-59; M.S, Fla. State Univ, 62, Ph.D. (physics), 65. Physicist, U.S. Naval Weapons Lab, Va, 60-61; engr, Boeing Aerospace, Wash, 63-64; res. physicist, Bendix Aerospace Systs, Mich, 65-66; sr. scientist, res. inst, Ill. Inst. Tech, 66-68; OPERS. RES. ANALYST, WEAPONS-SYSTS. ANAL, OFF. CHIEF OF STAFF, U.S. ARMY, 68- Rep, Army Math. Steering Cmt, 68- Am. Phys. Soc; Am. Geophys. Union; Am. Inst. Aeronaut. & Astronaut. Computational, nuclear and particle physics; surfaces of terrestrial planets; simulation of large systems in engineering analysis. Address: 2507 Pegasus Lane, Reston, VA 22070.

DOCKSTADER, WILMER B(ELDON), b. St. Ansgar, Iowa, Sept. 23, 18; m. 41; c. 3. MICROBIOLOGY. B.S, Iowa State Col, 41; Hormel fel, Minnesota, 48-49, M.S, 49; Ph.D.(bact), State Col. Wash, 52. Jr. scientist, fats & oils, Hormel Inst, 45-47; hosp. prod. res. & develop, Bauer & Black, 52-55; develop. chemist, Froedtert Malt Corp, 55-56; fermentologist, Clinton Corn Processing Co, 56-62; supvry. microbiologist & chief bact. unit, sanit. sect, environ. serv. br, div. res. serv, Nat. Insts. Health, 62-68; FOOD & DRUG OFF, GRAS REV. BR, FOOD & DRUG ADMIN, 68- U.S.A, 41-46. Am. Soc. Microbiol; Inst. Food Technol; Am. Inst. Chem; Am. Inst. Biol. Sci. Environmental sanitation and sanitary microbiology; bacteriological and biochemical; poultry products and nutrition; hospital product research and development; fermentation research; Salmonella methodology research. Address: GRAS Review Branch (BF-335), Food & Drug Administration, 200 C St. S.W, Washington, DC 20204.

DOCKUM, NORMAN LESLIE, b. Peabody, Mass, June 12, 15; m. 41; c. 2. HISTOLOGY. B.S, Purdue Univ, 39; M.A, Univ. Minn, 42. Biol. scientist, Hanford Labs, Gen. Elec. Co, Wash, 58-63; res. instr. HISTOL, col. med, Univ. Utah, 63-68; ASSOC. PROF, SCH. DENT, UNIV. NEBR, 68- U.S.A, 41-46, Capt. Electron Micros. Soc. Am; N.Y. Acad. Sci. Optical and electron microscopy of mineralized tissues of interest in dentistry. Address: Dept. of Anatomy, University of Nebraska School of Dentistry, Lincoln, NE 68503.

DOCTOR, B(HUPENDRA) P(ANNALAL), b. Surat, India, May 1, 30; nat; m; c. 2. BIOCHEMISTRY, NUTRITION. B.Sc, Univ. Bombay, 52; M.S, Agr. & Mech. Col. Tex, 55; fel, Univ. Md, 56-58, Ph.D.(biochem), 59. Asst. biochem, Agr. & Mech. Col. Tex, 53-55; chem, Univ. Tex, 55-56; fel. biochem, Cornell Univ, 59-60; res. biochemist, WALTER REED ARMY INST. RES, 61-70, CHIEF DEPT. BIOL. CHEM, 70- Res. assoc, Chas. Pfizer & Co, Inc, summer 55; Secy. U.S. Army res. & study fel, 67-68. Tech. achievement award, res. & develop. command, U.S. Army. AAAS; Am. Chem. Soc; Am. Soc. Biol. Chem. Biological value of proteins; mechanism of protein synthesis; methods of determination of biologically important compounds; metabolism of naturally occurring amines; nucleic acids metabolism; chemistry and structure of nucleic acids; biochemical genetics; isolation of RNA genes; x-ray crystallography of nucleic acids; protein nucleic acid interaction. Address: Division of Biochemistry, Walter Reed Army Institute of Research, Washington, DC 20012.

DOCTOR, NORMAN J(OSEPH), b. Brooklyn, N.Y, Oct. 5, 29; m. 56; c. 3. PHYSICS. B.S, Purdue Univ, 51. Physicist, Nat. Bur. Standards, 51-53; Diamond Ord. Fuze Labs, 53-56, res. & develop. supvr, 56-63, HARRY DIAMOND LABS, ARMY MATERIEL COMMAND, 63-69, chief electron devices br, 69-70, CHIEF ELECTRONIC TIMING BR, 70- Meritorious civilian serv. award, U.S. Dept. Army, 59; Arthur S. Flemming Award, 62. Inst. Elec. & Electronics Eng. Dielectric and magnetic measurements; printed circuit technology; microelectronics; thin films; ammunition electronics; electronic timing. Address: 3814 Littleton St, Wheaton, MD 20906.

DOCTOR, V(ASANT) M(ANILAL), b. Surat, India, Mar. 19, 26; m. 53; c. 3. BIOCHEMISTRY. B.Sc, Royal Inst. Sci, India, 46 & 48; M.S, Wisconsin, 51; Ph.D, Agr. & Mech. Col, Tex, 53. Fel. biochem, Tex. Agr. Exp. Sta, 53-54; Hite fel, exp. med, M.D. Anderson Hosp. & Tumor Inst, Texas, 54-55, asst. biochemist, 55-57, assoc. biochemist, 57-62, U.S. Pub. Health Serv. res. career develop. award, dent. br, 59-62; chief biochemist, Hindustan Antibiotics, Ltd, 62-65; assoc. prof. CHEM, Univ. Houston, 65-68; PROF, PRAIRIE VIEW AGR. & MECH. COL, 68- Am. Soc. Biol. Chem; Soc. Exp. Biol. & Med. Model enzyme systems; active site of nucleases; blood clotting mechanisms; cancer chemotherapy. Address: Dept. of Chemistry, Prairie View Agricultural & Mechanical College, Prairie View, TX 77445.

DOCZI, JOHN, b. Budapest, Hungary, Jan. 3, 11; nat; m. 41; c. 1. PHARMACEUTICAL CHEMISTRY. M.Pharm. Chem, Royal Hungarian Peter Pazmany Univ, 32. Develop. & mfg. pharmaceuts, cosmetics, dietetic food, opium alkaloids & parenteral ampuled prods, 32-45; asst, Warner Inst. Therapeut. Res, 45-48; sr. scientist BIOCHEM, Warner-Chilcott Lab, 48-57, SR. RES. ASSOC, 57-64, WARNER-LAMBERT RES. INST, 64- AAAS; Am. Chem. Soc; fel. Am. Inst. Chem. Natural and synthetic drugs and medicine. Address: 19 Gallagher Rd, Morristown, NJ 07960.

DODD, ARTHUR V, b. Philadelphia, Pa, Jan. 9, 24; m. 49; c. 2. GEOGRAPHY, METEOROLOGY. B.S, Pa. State, 49, M.S, 50; Ph.D.(geog), Boston, 64. Meteorologist, environ. protection sect, Off. Qm. Gen, Va, 50-53, climatologist, Qm. Res. & Develop. Center, Mass, 53-57, meteorologist, Qm. Res. & Eng. Center, 57-61; earth sci. div. U.S. Army Natick Labs, 61-68; U.S. ARMY RES. OFF, 68-70, DIR, DIV. ENVIRON. SCI, 70- U.S.A.F, 42-46, Res, 47-56, 1st Lt. AAAS; Sci. Res. Soc. Am; Am. Geophys. Union; Am. Meteorol. Soc; Am. Geog. Soc. Applied military climatology and geography; microclimatology, climatology at extremes. Address: 2101 N. Lake Shore Dr, Chapel Hill, NC 27514.

DODD, CHARLES G(ARDNER), b. St. Louis, Mo, Jan. 26, 15; m. 43; c. 4. PHYSICAL CHEMISTRY. B.S, Rice Inst, 40; M.S, Michigan, 45, Ph.D.(phys. chem), 48. Chem. engr, Freeport Sulphur Co, La, 40-41; asst. chem, Am. Petrol. Inst. Proj, Michigan, 42, res. investr. war res. proj, Off. Emergency Mgt. & Cmt. Med. Res, 43-44, teaching fel. chem, 44-45, instr, 45-47; asst. prof. ceramics, Pa. State Col, 47-48; sr. phys. chemist, petrol. exp. sta, U.S. Bur. Mines, 48-52; res. assoc. develop. & res. dept, Continental Oil Co, 52-55; assoc. prof. chem, Lehigh, 55-56; Halliburton prof. petrol. eng, Oklahoma, 56-62; chief advan. mat. res, Owens-Ill, Inc, 62-68; ASSOC. PRIN. SCIENTIST, PHILIP MORRIS, INC, 68- Fel. AAAS; fel. Am. Inst. Chem; Am. Mineral. Soc; Clay Minerals Soc; Electron Probe Anal. Soc. Am; Am. Vacuum Soc; Am. Chem. Soc; Am. Crystallog. Soc; Am. Geochem. Soc; Am. Ceramic Soc; N.Y. Acad. Sci; Mineral. Soc. Gt. Brit. & Ireland. Surface chemistry and physics; colloid science; x-ray physics; materials science; x-ray spectroscopy; electron microprobe technology; clay mineralogy and geochemistry; thin films. Address: 509 West Drive Circle, Richmond, VA 23229.

DODD, C(HARLES) M(ITCHENER), b. New Philadelphia, Ohio, Aug. 13, 95; m. 21; c. 2. B.Cer.E, Ohio State, 27, Cer.E, 33. Construct. engr, Eljer Co, Pa, 20; ceramic engr, Canton Brick Co, Ohio, 26; asst. ceramic engr, Robinson Clay Prod. Co, 27; asst. prof. ceramics, Mo. Sch. Mines, 27-28, assoc. prof, 28-32, acting head dept. ceramic eng, 32-35; prof. & head dept, 35-39; PROF, IOWA STATE, 39-, head dept, 39-61, acting eng. personnel officer, 42-45. Dir, Mo. Clay Testing & Res. Labs, 32-39. C.Eng, U.S.A, 17-19. Fel. Am. Ceramic Soc; Nat. Inst. Ceramic Eng.(secy, 38, v.pres, 45, pres, 46, Walker award, 63); Am. Soc. Eng. Ed; Ceramic Ed. Coun. (secy, 42, v.pres, 43, pres, 44). Dry pressing of refractories; ceramic kiln design. Address: 2009 Cessna St, Ames, IA 50010.

DODD, CURTIS WILSON, b. Fulton, Mo, Nov. 4, 39; m. 63; c. 1. ELECTRICAL ENGINEERING. B.S, Missouri, Rolla, 63, M.S, 64; Ph.D.(control theory), Arizona State, 68. Faculty assoc. elec. eng, Arizona State, 64-66; ASST. PROF. ELEC. SCI, SOUTH. ILL. UNIV, CARBONDALE, 67- U.S.A.F, 57-58, 61-62. Optimal control of distributed parameter systems. Address: School of Technology, Southern Illinois University, Carbondale, IL 62901.

DODD, EDWARD E(LLIOTT), b. Rochester, N.Y, June 27, 22; m. 46; c. 2; m. 64. PHYSICS. B.S, Rochester, 43; Ph.D.(physics), California, 52. Physicist, Nat. Bur. Standards, 52-53; Naval Ord. Lab, 53-54; Motorola, Inc, 54-63; res. specialist, Lockheed Missiles & Space Co, Calif, 63-66, STAFF ENGR, LOCKHEED ELECTRONICS CO, 66- Sig.C, 43-46, 1st Lt.

Am. Phys. Soc; Audio Eng. Soc. Weapons systems; inertial sensors; computer programming; satellite mission analysis; government information systems; spacecraft telecommunications. Address: 1723 Gunwale Rd, Houston, TX 77058.

DODD, EVERETT E, b. Whittier, Calif, Jan. 24, 30; m. 58; c. 2. PROTOZOOLOGY, CYTOLOGY. A.B, California, Davis, 55, M.A, 57, Ph.D.(zool), 61. Asst. zool, California, Davis, 56-59, assoc, 59-60, Santa Barbara, 60-61; instr. BIOL, ST. MARY'S COL. CALIF, 61-62, asst. prof, 62-70, ASSOC. PROF, 70- U.S.A, 50-52, Sgt. AAAS; Am. Soc. Zool; Am. Soc. Protozool. Biochemical cytology; cytochemical and cytological investigations of ciliate protozoa. Address: Dept. of Biology, St. Mary's College of California, St. Mary's College, CA 94575.

DODD, J(ACK) GORDON, (JR), b, Spokane, Wash, June 19, 26; m. 51; c. 2. ATOMIC & MOLECULAR PHYSICS. B.S, Ill. Inst. Tech, 51; M.S, Arkansas, 57, Ph.D, 65. Res. technician physics, Argonne Nat. Lab, 51-53; teacher, pub. sch, 53-55, prin, 56-57; asst. PHYSICS, Arkansas, 55-56; asst. prof. & dir. Govt. Contract, Drury Col, 57-60; assoc. prof. & chmn. dept, Ark. Polytech. Col, 62-67, assoc. prof, Univ. Tenn, Knoxville, 67-71; CHARLES A. DANA PROF, COLGATE UNIV, 71- Summer, prin. investr, Arkansas, 57. Consult, 56-57; Roosevelt, 60-63; McCrone Assocs, 61-; staff consult, Rockwell Mfg. Co, 63-64; consult, Honeywell, Inc, 64- U.S.N.R, 44-46. Am. Asn. Physics Teachers. Photodecomposition; optical interactions in solids, liquids and gases; theoretical kinetics; chain reactions in explosives; pure quadrupole resonance; Mössbauer effect. Address: Dept. of Physics, Colgate University, Hamilton, NY 13346.

DODD, JAMES ROBERT, b. Bloomington, Ind, Mar. 11, 34; m. 56; c. 2. GEOLOGY. A.B, Indiana, 56, A.M, 57; Nat. Sci. Found. fel, 56-60; Ph.D. (geobiol), Calif. Inst. Tech, 61. Ford Found. fel. oceanog, Calif. Inst. Tech, 61; geologist res. labs, Texaco Inc, Tex, 61-63; asst. prof. GEOL, Case West. Reserve Univ, 63-66; ASSOC. PROF, IND. UNIV, BLOOMINGTON, 66- U.S.N.R, 52-64. AAAS; Geol. Soc. Am; Soc. Econ. Paleont. & Mineral. Quantitative paleoecology and biogeochemistry; carbonate petrology; paleoecology and biogeochemistry. Address: Dept. of Geology, Indiana University, Bloomington, IN 47401.

DODD, J(IMMIE) D(ALE), b. Esbon, Kans, Aug. 6, 31; m. 54; c. 4. PLANT ECOLOGY, SOILS. A.B, Ft. Hays Kans. State Col, 56, M.S, 57; Ph.D.(plant ecol, soils), Saskatchewan, 60. Asst. prof. forestry, Ariz. State Col, 60-61; bot, N.Dak. State, 61-63; RANGE & FORESTRY, TEX. A&M UNIV, 63-66, assoc. prof, 66-70, PROF, 70- Nat. Sci. Found. summer grant, radiation ecol. inst, Oak Ridge Nat. Lab, 64; secy, range sci. educ. coun, Southwest. Naturalist. U.S.N, 51-54. Ecol. Soc. Am; Bot. Soc; Am; Am. Soc. Range Mgt. Soil-plant relationships in native vegetation; effects of prescribed fire on native vegetation; use of radionuclides in the study of ecological systems; native vegetation manipulation to increase production. Address: Dept. of Range Science, Texas A&M University, College Station, TX 77843.

DODD, JOHN D(URRANCE), b. Tarrytown, N.Y, March 15, 17; m. 40; c. 3. BOTANY. B.S, Syracuse, 38; M.S, Vermont, 40; Ph.D.(bot), Columbia, 47. Teaching asst. & asst. bot, Vermont, 38-41; morphol. lab, Columbia, 41-43, 46-47; instr. BOT, Wisconsin, 47-49; asst. prof, DEPT. BOT. & PLANT PATH, IOWA STATE UNIV, 49-53, assoc. prof, 53-60, PROF, 60- U.S.N, 43-46. Bot. Soc. Am. Interspecific grafts in Viola; cell shape; plant morphology; freshwater algae; diatoms; aquatic plant biology. Address: Dept. of Botany & Plant Pathology, Iowa State University, Ames, IA 50010.

DODD, M(ATTHEW) C(HARLES), b. Circleville, Ohio, Mar. 24, 10; m. 33; c. 3. BACTERIOLOGY. A.B, Ohio State, 33; Ph.D.(bact), Michigan, 41. Asst. pharmacologist, Parke, Davis & Co, Mich, 33-37; asst. instr. bact, med. sch, Michigan, 37-41; chief, dept. bact. & pharmacol, Eaton Labs, N.Y, 41-46; asst. prof. BACT, OHIO STATE UNIV, 46-49, assoc. prof, 49-54, PROF, 54-, chmn. dept, microbiol, 67-70. AAAS; Am. Soc. Microbiol; Am. Asn. Immunol; Soc. Exp. Biol. & Med; Am. Fedn. Clin. Res; Tissue Culture Asn. Nitrofuran chemotherapy; immunology of hemolytic anemia; autoimmunity; antibodies to nucleic acids; inhibitors of Rh antibody; immunology of cancer. Address: Dept. of Microbiology, Ohio State University, 484 W. 12th Ave, Columbus, OH 43210.

DODD, RICHARD ARTHUR, b. Eng, Feb. 11, 22; m. 47; c. 3. METALLURGY. B.S, London, 44, M.S, 47; fel, Birmingham, 47-50, Ph.D.(metall), 50. Res. metallurgist, Rolls Royce Ltd, Eng, 44-47; sr. lectr, Witwatersrand, S.Africa, 50-54; res. metallurgist, Dept. Mines, Ottawa, 54-56; asst. prof. METALL. ENG, Pennsylvania, 56; PROF, UNIV. WIS, MADISON, 56- Am. Inst. Mining, Metall. & Petrol. Eng; Am. Soc. Metals; Brit. Iron & Steel Inst; Brit. Inst. Metals; fel. Royal Inst. Chem. General physical metallurgy. Address: Dept. of Mining & Metals, College of Engineering, Engineering Research Bldg, University of Wisconsin, Madison, WI 53706.

DODD, ROBERT B(RUCE), b. Fairbury, Nebr, Apr. 12, 21; m. 49; c. 3. ANESTHESIOLOGY. Chicago, 39-41; Nebraska, 41-42, M.D, 45. Dir, dept. anesthesia, Columbia Hosp, 48-50; asst. res, Mass. Gen. Hosp, 50, asst. anesthetist, 51; assoc. anesthesiologist, Parkland Hosp, 51-53; clin. instr. ANESTHESIOL, Southwest Med. Sch, Texas, 51-52, clin. assoc. prof, 52-53; prof. & head dept, sch. med, Maryland, 53-56; Mallinckrodt prof. & head div, sch. med, Washington (St. Louis), 56-69; CLIN. PROF, SCH. MED, SOUTH. ILL. UNIV, CARBONDALE, 69- Anesthesiologist-in-chief, Barnes Hosp, St. Louis, Mo, 56-68; consult, U.S. Pub. Health Serv. Hosp, Baltimore, Md, 55-56; Vet. Admin. Hosp, St. Louis, Mo, 56-69; Phillips Hosp, 58-69; City Hosps. St. Louis, 58-69. Dipl. Am. Bd. Anesthesiol. Med.C, 46-48, Capt. Am. Soc. Anesthesiol; Am. Med. Asn; fel. Am. Col. Anesthesiol. Effects of anesthesia on man. Address: 2178 Huntleigh Rd, Springfield, IL 62704.

DODD, ROBERT TAYLOR, b. Bronx, N.Y, July 11, 36; m. 58; c. 3. MINERALOGY, PETROLOGY. A.B, Cornell, 58; M.A, Princeton, 60, Ph.D. (geol), 62. Spec. scientist, Air Force Cambridge Res. Labs, 62-65, gen. phys. scientist, 65; asst. prof. MINERAL, STATE UNIV. N.Y. STONY BROOK, 65-69, ASSOC. PROF, 69- U.S.A.F, 62-65, 1st Lt. AAAS; Geol. Soc. Am; Mineral. Soc. Am; Am. Geochem. Soc; Am. Geophys, Union; Meteoritical Soc. Igneous and metamorphic petrology; petrology and mineralogy of meteorites; lunar surface history. Address: Dept. of Earth & Space Sciences, State University of New York at Stony Brook, Stony Brook, NY 11790.

DODDS, ALVIN F(RANKLIN), b. Starkville, Miss, Jan. 20, 19; m. 43; c. 3. BIOCHEMISTRY, PHARMACEUTICAL CHEMISTRY. B.S, Miss. State Col, 40; M.S, Northwestern, 42, Ph.D.(biochem), 43; B.S, Med. Col. S.C, 49. Asst. biochem, dental sch, Northwestern, 40-43; res. chemist, Pan Am. Ref. Corp, Texas, 43-45; asst. prof. PHARMACEUT. CHEM, Loyola (La), 45-47; assoc. prof. MED, UNIV. S.C, 47-52, PROF, 52- Am. Chem. Soc; Am. Pharmaceut. Asn. Synthesis of local anesthetics; toxicity of synthetic vitamin K; metabolism of mouth bacteria; medicinal chemistry. Address: Dept. of Pharmaceutical Chemistry, Medical University of South Carolina, 80 Barre St, Charleston, SC 29401.

DODDS, DONALD GILBERT, b. North Rose, N.Y, Oct. 4, 25; m. 45; c. 2. WILDLIFE BIOLOGY, ECOLOGY. B.Sc, Cornell, 53, M.Sc, 55, Ph.D.(wildlife mgt), 60. Asst, Cornell, 53-55, 58-60; wildlife biologist, Dept. Mines & Resources, Newf, 55-58; big game biologist, Dept. Lands & Forests, N.S, 60-63, asst. dir. wildlife conserv, 63-64, acting dir, 64-65; assoc. prof, WILDLIFE BIOL, ACADIA UNIV, 64-70, PROF, 70-, ASSOC. PROF. BIOL, 70-, vis. prof, 61-64. Summer assoc, wildlife biol, Cornell, 60; summer Can. Nat. Sportsmens Show grant, 60; Food & Agr. Orgn. ecologist, Zambia, 66-67; resource consult, East. Can. 67-71. Wildlife Soc; Can. Soc. Wildlife & Fishery Biol; Am. Inst. Biol. Sci; Population ecology study of snowshoe hare; general ecological and management studies of white-tailed deer, moose, weasel, fox, Hungarian partridge, beaver and lynx; forest-wildlife interrelationships and population ecology; resource and environmental planning studies. Address: Dept. of Biology, Acadia University, Wolfville, N.S, Can.

DODDS, WAYNE S(AMUEL), b. Iowa, March 29, 18; m. 49; c. 3. CHEMICAL ENGINEERING. B.S, Iowa State, 41; Ph.D, Northwestern, 53. Supvr. res. dept, Merck & Co, 41-42, design engr, 45-49; exec. dir. chem. eng. lab, Northwestern, 49-54; asst. lab. dir, res. center, Gen. Foods Corp, 54-56, lab. dir, 56-62; v.pres, TRONCHEMICS RES, INC, 62-63, PRES, 63- Patent agent, U.S. Patent Off. U.S.A.A.F, 42-45, Capt. Am. Chem. Soc; Am. Inst. Chem. Eng; Inst. Food Tech; Am. Mgt. Asn; Am. Inst. Mgt; Am. Ord. Asn; N.Y. Acad. Sci; Am. Inst. Chem. Mass and heat transfer; thermodynamics; gas absorption; food engineering; air purification; drying. Address: P.O. Box 6073, Burbank, CA 91505.

DODDS, WELLESLEY JAMISON, b. Faulkton, S.Dak, Oct. 18, 15; m. 37; c. 4. ELECTRICAL ENGINEERING. B.S, S.Dak. State Col, 38; Slosson scholar, Kansas, 40-41, M.S, 41; Illinois, 41-42. Asst. physics, S.Dak. State Col, 38-39; Kansas, 39-40; Illinois, 41-42; power tube design engr, Victor Div, Radio Corp. Am, Pa, 42-44, res. engr, labs. div, N.J, 45-54, mgr. microwave adv. develop, tube div, 54-55; mgr. traveling wave tube develop, Varian Assocs, 55-59; v.pres. eng, Bomac Labs, Inc, 59-63; mgr. microwave solid state eng, RCA CORP, 63-66, mem. staff, electronic components & devices, 66-70, MEM. TECH. PLANNING STAFF, ELECTRONIC COMPONENTS, 70- Consult, U.S. Dept. Defense, 55-; Nat. Acad. Sci, 63. With Off. Sci. Res. & Develop, 44. AAAS; Inst. Elec. & Electronics Eng. Invention and research in microwave radio; electrets; biophysics of nerve. Address: RCA Corp, Electronic Components, 415 S. Fifth St, Harrison, NJ 07029.

DODERER, GEORGE C(HARLES), b. Monticello, N.Y, Aug. 3, 28; m. 58; c. 4. CHEMISTRY, PHYSICS. B.S, Union (N.Y), 50. Asst, physics prog, Gen. Elec. Co, N.Y, 50-51, spectroscopist metals, Mass, 51-52, researcher vacuum insulation, Pa, 52-54, instrumental analyst, Ky, 54-55; guest worker polymers, Nat. Bur. Standards, 56-57; instrumental chem. analyst, GEN. ELEC. CO, 58-68, mgr. anal. chem, 68-71, MGR. CHEM. DIV, 71- U.S.A, 56-57. Soc. Appl. Spectros; Am. Chem. Soc. Instrumental chemical analysis; chemistry of hermetic refrigerating systems; flat panel vacuum thermal insulation; vacuum technology; chemistry of laundering and dishwashing. Address: General Electric Co, Appliance Park 35-1101, Louisville, KY 40225.

DODES, IRVING ALLEN, b. N.Y.C, Apr. 11, 15; m. 41; c. 2. NUMERICAL ANALYSIS. B.S, City Col, 34; A.M, Columbia, 37; Ph.D.(admin. & supvr. tech. ed), 45. Phys. chemist, Harry Koster Labs, 34-37; LaMar Labs, 38; Agron. Res. Inst, 39; asst. chief chemist, City Chem. Corp, 39-41; teacher in training, high sch, N.Y, 41-42; teacher, high sch, N.Y, 42-52; lectr. math, Hunter Col, 52-54; asst. prof, Queens Col.(N.Y), 54-56; instr, Polytech. Inst. Brooklyn, 57-64; mem. staff, Columbia, 63-65; PROF. MATH, KINGSBOROUGH COMMUNITY COL, 65-, chmn. dept. math. & sci, 65-67, dean faculty, 67-69. Lectr, N.Y. Univ, 45-55; instr, Cooper Union, 49-52; chmn, math. dept, high schs, N.Y, 52; coordinator math, New York, 59-60; Nat. Sci. Found. fel. Consult, Int. Bus. Mach, 57-65. Math. Asn. Am. Computer programming; statistical analysis of educational problems; application of numerical analysis to computers. Address: 100-10 67th Rd, Forest Hills, NY 11375.

DODGE, ALICE HRIBAL, b. Fullerton, Calif; c. 2. ANATOMY, CELL BIOLOGY. A.B, Univ. Calif, Berkeley, 48, M.A, 51; Nat. Insts. Health fel, Stanford Univ, 68-69, Ph.D.(anat), 69. Res. asst. ANAT, SCH. MED, STANFORD UNIV, 60-68, RES. ASSOC, 70-; ASST. PROF, CALIF. COL. PODIATRIC MED, 70-, instr, 69-70. Nat. Cancer Inst. grant, 71-74. AAAS; Am. Soc. Cell. Biol; Histochem. Soc. Subcellular localization of enzymes; electron microscopic and electrophoretic study of androgen-estrogen induced hamster tumors; electron microscopic study of plantar warts. Address: 2038 Maryland St, Redwood City, CA 94061.

DODGE, AUSTIN A(NDERSON), b. Waukesha Co, Wis, Aug. 27, 06; m. 38. PHARMACY. Ph.C, Valparaiso, 28; B.S, Wisconsin, 38, Fritzsche Bros. fel, 38-41, Ph.D.(pharmaceut. chem), 41. Instr. pharm, Phila. Col. Pharm, 41-42, asst. prof, 42-45, assoc. prof, 45-48; PROF. pharmaceut. chem, SCH. PHARM, UNIV. MISS, 48-60, PHARMACOG, 60-, ASSOC. DEAN, 63- AAAS; Am. Med. Writers Asn; Am. Soc. Pharmacog; Am. Inst. Hist. Pharm; Am. Chem. Soc; Am. Pharmaceut. Asn; Entom. Soc. Am. Plant chemistry;

volatile oils; derivatives of isophorone; applications of the aerosol wetting agents in pharmaceutical formulations for creams and lotions. Address: University of Mississippi School of Pharmacy, University, MS 38677.

DODGE, BARNETT F(RED), b. Akron, Ohio, Nov. 29, 95; m. 18; c. 2. CHEMICAL ENGINEERING. B.S, Mass. Inst. Tech, 17; Sc.D.(chem. eng), Harvard, 25; hon. M.A, Yale, 35; hon. D.Sc, Worcester Polytech, 56; hon. Dr, Toulouse, 61. Chem. engr, E.I. du Pont de Nemours & Co, 17-20; Lewis Recovery Corp, 20-22; lectr. chem. eng, Harvard & Worcester Polytech, 21-25; asst. prof, YALE, 25-30, assoc. prof, 30-35, prof, 35-64, acting chmn. dept, 30-31, chmn, 31-64, chmn. cmt. study eng. ed. & dean sch. eng, 60-61, EMER. PROF. CHEM. ENG, 64-; CONSULT. WATER POLLUTION PROBLEMS & DESALINATION SEA WATER, 64- Lectr, N.Y. Univ, 43-44; U.S. Dept. State lectr, Barcelona, 54; lectr, Venezuela, 57, hon. prof, 61; Fulbright lectr, Toulouse, 51, Univ. Lille & Cath. Univ. Lille, 58; Reilly lectr, Notre Dame, 63; vis. prof, Buenos Aires, 65-66; first Sigma Xi lectr, Latin Am. & Fulbright vis. prof, Univ. Republic, Uruguay, 66; vis. prof, Univ. New S. Wales, 67; Yugoslavia, 69; Pahlavi Univ, Iran, 70. Chem. engr, fixed nitrogen res. lab, U.S. Dept. Agr, 25; spec. investr, Nat. Defense Res. Cmt. Contracts, 41-43, assoc. dir. cent. eng. lab, div. 11, Phila, Pa, 43-44; tech. dir, Ferjcleve Corp, Tenn, 44-45, tech. eng. consult, 45-46; consult, off. saline water, U.S. Dept. Interior, 54- Mem. adv. screening cmt. basic res, Army Res. Off, 61- Am. ed, Chem. Eng. Sci, 53-60. AAAS; Am. Chem. Soc; Am. Inst. Chem. Eng.(Walker award, 50, v.pres, 54, pres, 55, Founders award, 62, Lewis award, 630; Am. Soc. Eng. Educ; fel. Am. Acad. Arts & Sci. Thermodynamic properties at high pressure; chemical equilibria; rate of absorption and heat transfer; catalytic gas reactions; treatment of saline water and industrial waste water. Address: 108 Middle Rd, Hamden, CT 06517.

DODGE, CARROLL W(ILLIAM), b. Danby, Vt, Jan. 20, 95; m. 25; c. 2. BOTANY. A.B, Middlebury Col, 15, A.M, 16; fel, Washington (St. Louis), 15-18, Ph.D. (bot), 18; hon. Dr, Guatemala, 42; Chile, 50. Instr. BOT, Brown, 19-20; asst. prof, 20-21; instr, Harvard, 21-24, asst. prof. & curator, Farlow Library & Herbarium, 24-31; prof, SHAW SCH. BOT, WASH. UNIV, 31-63, EMER. PROF, 63-; PROF, UNIV. VT, 63- Asst. prof, California, 21; fel, Inst. Res. Trop. Am, 25; Guggenheim fel, Costa Rica, 29-30, Europe, 30-31; mycologist, Mo. Bot. Garden, 31-63; U.S. Exchange prof, Guatemala, 40-42; La. State, 49; Chile, 50; Brazil, 59-60. Harvard bot. exped, Gaspe Peninsula, 23; Washington (St. Louis) bot. exped, Panama, 34-35, Costa Rica, 36. V.pres, sect. mycol, Int. Cong. Microbiol, 50. Med. Dept, U.S.A, 18-19, Sgt. AAAS; Bot. Soc. Am; Am. Micros. Soc.(pres, 38); Am. Phytopath. Soc; Mycol. Soc. Am; Torrey Bot. Club; N.Y. Acad. Sci; Brit. Mycol. Soc; fel. Indian Phytopath. Soc. Mycology; Hymenogastraceae; Plectascales; fungi pathogenic to man; lichenology; flora of tropical America, Africa and Antarctica. Address: Dept. of Botany, University of Vermont, Burlington, VT 05401.

DODGE, CHARLES F(REMONT), b. Dallas, Texas, May 28, 24; m. 50; c. 2. GEOLOGY. B.S, Southern Methodist, 49, M.S, 52; summer inst, Illinois, 58; Ph.D, Univ. N.Mex, 67. Valuation engr, T.Y. Pickette, 47-48; instr. geol, Arlington Col, 48-50; geologist, Concho Petrol. Co, 50-52; Intex Oil Co, 52-53; district geologist, Am. Trading & Prod. Corp, 53-57; assoc. prof. GEOL, UNIV. TEX, ARLINGTON, 57-67, PROF, 67- Nat. Sci. Found. sci. faculty fel, 65-66. Consult, McCord & Assocs. & Lewis Eng, 59; Core Labs, 58; Atlantic Ref. Co, 59-61; Sun Oil Co, 66-67; Coastal Plains Oil, 68; Tex. Steel, 69; Sonatrach (Algeria), 69-70; res. proj. 91A, Am. Petrol. Inst, 66-70. U.S.A.A.F, 43-46; C.Eng. Res, 46-, Capt. Am. Asn. Petrol. Geol; Soc. Econ. Paleont. & Mineral. Reservoir geology; x-ray mineralogy; clastic sedimentology. Address: 1301 Briarwood, Arlington, TX 76013.

DODGE, DONALD W(ILLIAM), b. Worcester, Mass, Aug. 29, 28; m. 50; c. 2. CHEMICAL ENGINEERING. B.S, Worcester Polytech, 50, M.S, 52; Ph.D. (chem. eng), Delaware, 58. Chem. engr, Arthur D. Little, Inc, 52-53; res. engr, E.I. DU PONT DE NEMOURS & CO, INC, 57-60, staff engr, 60-62, supvr. res, 62-63, mgr, 63-66, tech. supt, 66-67, mfg. supt, 67-68, PROD. MGR, FILM DEPT, 68- C.Eng, U.S.A, 53-55. Am. Inst. Chem. Eng. Plastics processing and technology; fluid mechanics; rheology. Address: E.I. du Pont de Nemours & Co, Inc, Film Dept, Wilmington, DE 19898.

DODGE, E(LDON) R(AYMOND), b. Eland, Wis, June 17, 10; m. 39; c. 3. CIVIL ENGINEERING. B.S, Wisconsin, 32, M.S, 35, Ph.D.(civil eng), 42. Engr, Wis. Hwy. Comn, 32-33; asst, Wisconsin, 33-35; instr. civil eng, Case, 35-37; Wisconsin, 37-43; div. engr, Fairbanks, Morse & Co, 43-46; PROF. CIVIL ENG. & ENG. MECH, MONT. STATE UNIV, 46- Fel. Am. Soc. Civil Eng; Am. Soc. Eng. Educ. Hydraulics; hydrology. Address: Montana State University, Bozeman, MT 59715.

DODGE, FRANKLIN C. W, b. Oakland, Calif, Sept. 18, 34; m. 53. GEOLOGY. B.A, California, Berkeley, 59; M.S, Stanford, 60, Rodger fel, 61-62, Ph.D. (geol), 63. GEOLOGIST, U.S. GEOL. SURV, 63- U.S.N, 52-55. Geol. Soc. Am; Mineral. Soc. Am; Mineral. Asn. Can; Norweg. Geol. Soc. Geochemical and mineralogical study of the Sierra Nevada batholith, California. Address: U.S. Geological Survey, 345 Middlefield Rd, Menlo Park, CA 94025.

DODGE, FRANKLIN TIFFANY, b. Uniontown, Pa, Nov. 11, 36; m. 68; c. 1. MECHANICAL ENGINEERING. B.S, Tennessee, 60; M.S, Carnegie Inst. Tech, 61, Nat. Sci. Found. fel. & Ph.D.(mech. eng), 63. Coop. engr, Pittsburgh DesMoines Steel Co, 56-59; res. asst. fluid mech, Carnegie Inst. Tech, 60-61; sr. res. engr, dept. mech. sci, Southwest Res. Inst, 63-70, group leader, fluid mech. & eng. anal, 70-71; ASST. PROF. MECH. & AEROSPACE ENG, UNIV. TENN, KNOXVILLE, 71- Am. Inst. Aeronaut. & Astronaut; Am. Soc. Mech. Eng. Hydrodynamics and thermodynamics; fuel sloshing; ablation; hydrodynamic lubrication; hydroelasticity. Address: Dept. of Mechanical & Aerospace Engineering, University of Tennessee, Knoxville, TN 37916.

DODGE, FREDERICK ARTHUR, JR, b. Medford, Mass, Aug. 17, 33; m. 71. BIOPHYSICS. A.B, Pennsylvania, 55; Ph.D.(biophys), Rockefeller Inst, 63. Res. assoc. BIOPHYS, ROCKEFELLER UNIV, 63-64, affiliate, 64-69, ADJ. ASSOC. PROF, 70-; STAFF MEM. APPL. MATH, THOMAS J. WATSON RES. CTR, IBM CORP, 64- Biophys. Soc; Am. Soc. Neurosci. Ionic permeability mechanisms underlying excitation of the nerve membrane; emperical mathematical models of neurons and their interaction. Address: Thomas J. Watson Research Center, IBM Corp, P.O. Box 218, Yorktown Heights, NY 10598.

DODGE, HAROLD F(RENCH), b. Lowell, Mass, Jan. 23, 93; m. 22; c. 3. ELECTRICAL ENGINEERING. S.B, Mass. Inst. Technol, 16; A.M, Columbia, 22. Instr. elec. eng; Mass. Inst. Tech, 16-17; develop. engineer, West. Elec. Co, 17-25; qual. results engr, Bell Tel. Labs, 25-58; prof. appl. math. statist, Rutgers Univ, 58-70; CONSULT, 58- Consult. to Secy. War, U.S. Dept. War, 42-44; Sandia Corp, 58-67; NASA, 61-62. Mem. & chmn, Borough Planning Bd, 31-48. AAAS; fel. hon. mem. Am. Soc. Qual. Control (Shewhart medal, 49); fel. hon. mem. Am. Soc. Test. & Mat.(Award of Merit, 50); fel. Am. Statist. Asn.(Samuel S. Wilks Mem. Medal, 71); fel. Inst. Math. Statist. Sampling inspection; quality assurance and quality control techniques. Address: 96 Briarcliff Rd, Mountain Lakes, NJ 07046.

DODGE, HAROLD T, b. Seattle, Wash, May 20, 24; m. 51; c. 2. INTERNAL MEDICINE, CARDIOLOGY. Washington (Seattle), 42-44; M.D, Harvard, 48. Intern med, Peter Bent Brigham Hosp, Mass, 48-49; resident, King County Hosp, Wash, 49-50; res. fel. & asst, sch. med, Washington (Seattle), 50-51; clin. investr, Nat. Heart Inst, Md. 51-52; fel. cardiol, Emory, 52-53; instr. MED, sch. med, Georgetown, 53-56; asst. prof, sch. med, Duke Univ, 56-57; Univ. Wash, 57-64, assoc. prof, 64-65, prof, 65-66; prof. & dir. cardiovasc. div, med. ctr, Univ. Ala, 66-69; PROF. & DIR. CARDIOVASC. RES. & TRAINING CTR, SCH. MED, UNIV. WASH, 69-, CO-DIR. DIV. CARDIOL, 71- Clin. investr, Nat. Heart Inst, Md, 53-56; chief cardiol, Durham Vet. Admin. Hosp, 56-57, Seattle Vet. Admin. Hosp, 57-66. U.S.P.H.S, 51-56. Am. Fedn. Clin. Res; Am. Soc. Clin. Invest; Asn. Univ. Cardiol; Asn. Am. Physicians. Cardiovascular research; physiological aspects of heart disease; electrocardiography; drug research. Address: Dept. of Medicine, School of Medicine, University of Washington, Seattle, WA 98105.

DODGE, HOMER L(EVI), b. Ogdensburg, N.Y, Oct. 21, 87; m. 17; c. 2. PHYSICS. A.B, Colgate, 10, hon. Sc.D, 32; M.S, Iowa, 12, Ph.D.(physics), 14; Columbia, 13; hon. Sc.D, Vermont, 45, LL.D, Middlebury Col, 45. Mem. physics staff, Iowa, 10-19; prof. Oklahoma, 19-44, head dept, 19-42, dir. sch. eng. physics, 24-44, dean grad. sch, 26-44, organizer & dir. univ. res. inst, 41-44; dir. off. sci. personnel, Nat. Res. Coun, 42-44; pres, Norwich, 44-50; dir, Cabot Prog. in Aviation, 50-53; chmn, Cabot Fund Admin. Comt, 49-59; LECTR, CONSULT, 59- Topog. staff, U.S. Geol. Surv, 05-14; field dir. surv, col. teaching, Asn. Univ. Prof, 32-33. Ed. res. in physics, Sch. Sci. & Math, 16-24. Comt. on spec. training, War Dept, 19; nat. adv. comt, Eng. Sci. & Mgt. Defense Training, 41-45; acad. adv. bd, U.S. Merchant Marine Acad, 47-52. Consult, War Manpower Comn; Navy Dept; U.S. Army, 44-46. Mem. Eng. Ed. Mission, Japan, 50; pioneer study of Soviet ed, 55. AAAS; fel. Am. Phys. Soc; Am. Soc. Eng. Educ; Am. Asn. Physics Teachers (pres. 30-32, Oersted medal, 44); Newcomen Soc. Elasticity; electric measurements and instruments. Address: Cremona Farm, Mechanicsville, MD 20659.

DODGE, H(ORACE) J(ACKSON), b. Colo, June 13, 10; m. 42; c. 3. PREVENTIVE MEDICINE, PUBLIC HEALTH. M.D, Colorado, 42; M.P.H, Michigan, 45. Intern, Colo. Gen. Hosp, Denver, 42-43, res. physician, 43-44; health officer in training, Michigan, 44-45; dir, Kootenai Co. Health Unit, Coeur d'Alene, Idaho, 45-47; asst. prof. prev. med. & pub. health, sch. med, Colorado, 47-49, assoc. prof, 49-53, PROF, 53-57; EPIDEMIOL, SCH. PUB. HEALTH, UNIV. MICH, 57- Med.C, 54-56, Maj. Am. Pub. Health Asn; Am. Epidemiol. Soc. Epidemiology. Address: School of Public Health, University of Michigan, Ann Arbor, MI 48104.

DODGE, JAMES STANLEY, b. Washington, D.C, June 22, 39; m. 61; c. 2. POLYMER CHEMISTRY, RHEOLOGY. B.S, Case Inst. Tech, 61, M.S, 66, Nat. Sci. Found. fel. & Ph.D.(macromolecular sci), Case Western Reserve, 69. Res. engr, TRW, Inc, 61-63; SR. RES. CHEMIST, SHERWIN-WILLIAMS CO, 69- Am. Chem. Soc; Soc. Rheol. Physical properties of polymers; rheology of polymers and colloids; physical chemistry. Address: Sherwin-Williams Co, 10909 Cottage Grove Ave, Chicago, IL 60628.

DODGE, JOHN WESLEY, b. Worcester, Mass, June 10, 33; m. 59; c. 3. FOOD TECHNOLOGY. B.S, New Hampshire, 56; M.S, Purdue, 58, Ph.D. (food tech), 59. Asst. food tech, Purdue, 56-59; mem. res. staff, poultry prods, Nichols Inc, 59-64; fel. Cornell, 64-65; DIR. res, egg mkt. div, AGWAY, INC, 65-67, develop. & qual. control, mkt. div, 67-69, POULTRY MGT, 69- Mem. exec. comt. res. coun, Int. Poultry Industs; chmn. tech. adv. comt, Poultry & Egg Nat. Bd; dir, Gromark, Inc. U.S.A.R, 56-64, 1st Lt. Poultry Sci. Asn; Inst. Food Tech. Meat and egg quality; animal products technology; production, processing; marketing. Address: N. Lake Rd, Cazenovia, NY 13035.

DODGE, PHILIP ROGERS, b. Beverly, Mass, Mar. 16, 23; m. 47; c. 3. PEDIATRICS. M.D, Rochester, 48. Instr. neurol, Harvard Med. Sch, 55-58, assoc, 58-61, asst. prof, 62-67; PROF. PEDIAT. & NEUROL. & HEAD EDWARD MALLINCKRODT DEPT. PEDIAT, SCH. MED, WASH. UNIV, 67- Investr, J.P. Kennedy, Jr. Lab. Study Ment. Retardation, 63-67; hon. prof, Puerto Rico, 67- Pediatric neurologist, Boston Lying-In Hosp, 61-67; neurologist & pediatrician, Mass. Gen. Hosp, 63-67; med. dir, St. Louis Children's Hosp, 67-; assoc. neurologist, Barnes & Allied Hosps, 67- Consult, Fernald State Sch. Retarded Children, 63-67. Mem, Surgeon Gen. comt. epilepsy, U.S. Pub. Health Serv, 66-70, child develop. & ment. retardation rev. comt, 66-70, gen. clin. res. ctrs. comt, 71- Med.C, U.S.A, 50-56, Maj. Am. Acad. Neurol; Am. Neurol. Asn; Soc. Pediat. Res; Am. Pediat. Soc. Pediatric neurology; clinical and laboratory investigations of neurologic disorders of childhood, especially infectious, nutritional and metabolic diseases. Address: Dept. of Pediatrics, 500 S. Kingshighway, St. Louis, MO 63110.

DODGE, RICHARD P(ATRICK), b. Wichita, Kans, Mar. 17, 32. PHYSICAL CHEMISTRY. B.S, Wichita, 54; Ph.D, California, 58. Asst. chem, California, 54-55, assoc, 55-56, asst. Lawrence Radiation Lab, 56-58; res. chemist, Union Carbide Res. Inst, 58-64; asst. prof. CHEM, UNIV. OF THE PACIFIC, 64-69, ASSOC. PROF, 69- Consult, Lawrence Radiation Lab,

Univ. Calif, 64- AAAS; Am. Crystallog. Soc. X-ray diffraction; molecular structure. Address: Dept. of Chemistry, University of the Pacific, Stockton, CA 95204.

DODGE, STEPHEN WEBSTER, JR, b. Brooklyn, N.Y, June 8, 01; m. 25; c. 2. ORGANIC CHEMISTRY. B.Chem, Cornell, 24. Anal. chemist, Lehn & Fink, Inc, N.J, 24-28, res. chemist, 28-29; radio engr. develop, Westinghouse Lamp Co, 29-30; radio engr. adv. develop, Radio Corp. Am. Mfg. Co, 30-38, qual. control engr, Victor Div, Radio Corp. Am, 38-39, transmitting tube engr, 39-43, res. engr, labs, 43-64; res. engr, Shady Harbor Assocs, 64-71; RETIRED. With Off. Sci. Res. & Develop; U.S.A; U.S.N, 44. AAAS; Inst. Elec. & Electronics Eng; Am. Chem. Soc. Electronics; oceanography. Address: Shady Harbor Associates, R.D. One, Box 424, Westerly, RI 02891.

DODGE, WARREN FRANCIS, b. Scottdale, Pa, May 5, 28; m. 49; c. 2. PEDIATRICS, PREVENTATIVE MEDICINE & COMMUNITY HEALTH. B.S, Tennessee, 53, M.D, 55. Intern, Jefferson Davis Hosp, 55-56; res. pediat, col. med, Baylor, 56-58, fel. renal diseases of childhood, 58-60; asst. prof. PEDIAT, MED. BR, UNIV. TEX, 60-66, ASSOC. PROF, 66- Jessie Jones fel, 58. U.S.A, 45; U.S.A.F, 45-48, Sgt. AAAS; Soc. Pediat. Res; Am. Fedn. Clin. Res; Am. Soc. Nephrology; Am. Soc. Pediat; Am. Pub. Health Asn; Am. Med. Asn. Renal diseases of children, especially the natural course of these diseases and their relation to chronic renal insufficiency in later life; epidemiology of renal disease and hypertension; delivery of health care. Address: Dept. of Pediatrics, University of Texas Medical Branch, School of Medicine, Galveston, TX 77550.

DODGE, WILLIAM G, b. Wells River, Vt, Aug. 31, 07; U.S. citizen; m. 32; c. 4. CHEMISTRY, CHEMICAL ENGINEERING. B.A, Dartmouth Col, 29; M.S, Mass. Inst. Tech, 31. Instr, Mass. Inst. Tech, 31-32; tech. adv, N.Y. Daily News, 32-39; prod. mgr, Phila. Ledger, 39-40; mgr. tech. servs, Int. Paper Sales Co, Ind, 40-60; pres, Int. Cellulose Res. Ltd, 60-66; from gen. mgr. to DIR, CORP. RES. CTR, INT. PAPER CO, 66- Am. Tech. Asn. Pulp & Paper Indust; Can. Pulp & Paper Asn; fel. Chem. Inst. Can. Newsprint, Kraft paper and board; dissolving pulps. Address: Corporate Research Center, International Paper Co, Box 797, Tuxedo Park, NY 10987.

DODGE, WILLIAM R, b. Oregon City, Ore, Mar. 21. 29; m. 55. PHYSICS. B.S, Stanford, 56, Ph.D.(physics), 62. PHOTONUCLEAR PHYSICIST, NAT. BUR. STANDARDS, WASH, D.C, 61- Mem. panel semiconductor radiation detectors, Nat. Acad. Sci, 63-; adj. prof, Am. Univ, 66- Am. Phys. Soc. Electron and photon induced nuclear disintegration reactions; semiconductor radiation detectors; linear accelerator physics. Address: 8200 Raymond Lane, Potomac, MD 20854.

DODGEN, CHARLES LEE, b. Goodnight, Tex, Dec. 20, 25; m. 53. TOXICOLOGY. B.A, Texas Christian, 50; Ph.D.(biochem), Vanderbilt, 55. Asst. BIOCHEM, Vanderbilt, 50-54; instr. col. med, State Univ. N.Y, Brooklyn, 55-57, asst. prof, 57-58; ASSOC. PROF, SCH. MED, UNIV. MISS, 58- U.S.N.R, 44-46. AAAS; Am. Chem. Soc; N.Y. Acad. Sci. Comparative biochemistry; intermediary metabolism; bile pigments. Address: Dept. of Biochemistry, University Medical Center, University of Mississippi, Jackson, MS 39216.

DODGEN, DURWARD F, b. Winnsboro, Tex, Apr. 10, 31; m. 54; c. 2. CHEMISTRY. B.S, North Texas State, 52; M.S, Mississippi, 57; Kentucky, 56-57. Res. chemist, Phillips Petrol. Co, 52-55; anal. chemist, Am. Pharmaceut. Asn. Lab, 57-59; med. serv. rep, Chas. Pfizer & Co, Inc, 59-60; pub. coordinator, Warren-Teed Pharmaceut. Div, Rohm and Haas Co, 60-61; asst. dir, Food Chem. Codex, Nat. Acad. Sci-Nat. Res. Coun, 61-65, assoc. dir, 65-66; asst. dir. nat. formulary & asst. dir. sci. div, Am. Pharmaceut. Asn, 66-69, assoc. ed, J. Pharm. Sci, 67-69; DIR. FOOD CHEM. CODEX & STAFF OFF. FOOD PROTECTION COMT, DIV. BIOL. & AGR, NAT. ACAD. SCI-NAT. RES. COUN, 69- Observer joint expert comt. food additives, Food & Agr. Org, WHO, 64, 65, 67, 70 & 71-; Nat. Formulary Bd, 66-; U.S. Adopted Names Coun, 67-69; adv. panel pharmaceut. ingredients, U.S. Pharmacopeia, 70-; assoc. mem, Food Additives & Contaminants Comn, Int. Union Pure & Appl. Chem, 71- Am. Pharmaceut. Asn; Am. Chem. Soc. Specifications for food additives; pharmaceutical analysis; standards for food additives and drugs. Address: National Academy of Sciences-National Research Council, 2101 Constitution Ave. N.W, Washington, DC 20418.

DODGEN, HAROLD W(ARREN), b. Blue Eye, Mo, Aug. 31, 21; m. 45; c. 3. PHYSICAL CHEMISTRY. B.S, California, 43, Ph.D.(phys. chem), 46. Asst, Manhattan Dist. Proj, California, 43-46; Inst. Nuclear Studies fel, Chicago, 46-48; asst. prof. CHEM, WASH. STATE UNIV, 48-52, assoc. prof, 52-59, PROF, 59-, CHMN. CHEM. PHYSICS PROG, 68-, dir. nuclear reactor proj, 55-59. With Off. Sci. Res. & Develop, 44. Am. Chem. Soc; Am. Nuclear Soc; Am. Phys. Soc. Theory of ammonium chloride phase transition; complex ions of iron and thorium with fluoride; neutron scattering; radioactive exchange; quenching of fluorescence; application of radioisotopes in physical chemistry; spectrochemical analysis; nuclear magnetic and quadrupole resonance. Address: Dept. of Chemistry, Chemical Physics Program, Washington State University, Pullman, WA 99163.

DODINGTON, SVEN HENRY MARRIOTT, b. Vancouver, B.C, Can, May 22, 12; nat; m. 40; c. 3. ELECTRICAL ENGINEERING. A.B, Stanford, 34. From jr. engr. to head elec. dept, Scophony Ltd, London, 35-41; dept. head, Int. Tel. & Tel. Fed. Labs, INT. TEL. & TEL. CORP, 41-50, div. head, 51-54, lab. dir, 54-58, v.pres, 58-69, ASST. TECH. DIR, 69- Assoc. fel. Am. Inst. Aeronaut. & Astronaut; fel. Inst. Elec. & Electronics Eng; Am. Inst. Navig; Am. Ord. Asn. Navigation; countermeasures; television; microelectronics. Address: International Telephone & Telegraph Corp, 320 Park Ave, New York, NY 10022.

DODSON, B. C, b. Magnolia, Ark, Dec. 6, 24; m. 46; c. 3. INORGANIC CHEMISTRY, SCIENCE EDUCATION. B.S.E, Ark. State Teachers Col, 48; M.S, Arkansas, 58; Ed.S, Kans. State Teachers Col, 61; Nat. Sci. Found. fel, Okla. State Univ, 60-61; Ed.D, Univ. Okla, 69. Teacher, high schs, Ark, 48-54; Tex, 54-55; Ark, 55-56, teacher & sci. coord, 56-60; asst. prof. chem, SOUTH. STATE COL, 60-70, PROF CHEM. & SCI. EDUC. & CHMN. DIV. SCI. & MATH, 70-, acting head dept. chem, 66-69. Nat. Sci. Found. sci. faculty fel, 65-66. U.S.A.A.F, 43. Am. Chem. Soc. Analysis of the objectives, materials and methods used in the introductory college chemistry course in selected colleges and universities. Address: Division of Science & Mathematics, P.O. Box 1397, Southern State College, Magnolia, AR 71753.

DODSON, CALAWAY H, b. Selma, Calif, Dec. 17, 28; m. 60; c. 2. BOTANY. B.A, Fresno State Col, 54; M.A, Claremont Cols, 56, Ph.D.(bot), 59. Dir, bot. inst, Guayaquil, 59-60; taxonomist & curator living plants, Mo. Bot. Garden, 60-64; asst. prof. BOT, UNIV. MIAMI, 64-66, assoc. prof, 66-70, PROF, 70-, CURATOR HERBARIUM, 64- Nat. Sci. Found. res. grants, 61-71; Fulbright lectr, Peru, 64. U.S.A, 46-49, 50-51, Sgt. AAAS; Soc. Study Evolution; Am. Soc. Plant Taxon; Ecol. Soc. Am. Study of evolution of characteristics and taxonomic relationships among tropical American orchidaceae; adaptations to specialized pollinators which act as barriers to hybridization between species; biologically active chemicals in pollinator attraction. Address: Dept. of Biology, University of Miami, Coral Gables, FL 33124.

DODSON, CHARLES L(EON), JR, b. Knoxville, Tenn, Mar. 15, 35; m. 58; c. 1. PHYSICAL CHEMISTRY. B.S, Emory & Henry Col, 57; M.S, Tennessee, 62, Ph.D.(chem), 63. Asst. prof. CHEM, UNIV. ALA, HUNTSVILLE, 66-67, ASSOC. PROF, 67-, dept. head, 68-70. European Off, U.S. Off. Aerospace Agency grant, Univ. Birmingham, 63-64; Nat. Res. Coun. fel, Can, 64-66. AAAS; Am. Chem. Soc; Am. Phys. Soc. Infrared, microwave and electron spin resonance spectroscopy. Address: Dept. of Chemistry, University of Alabama in Huntsville, Huntsville, AL 35807.

DODSON, CHESTER L(EE), b. Eastland, Tenn, Dec. 18, 21; m. 47; c. 2. GEOLOGY, HYDROLOGY. B.S, West Virginia, 50, M.S, 53. Geologist, U.S. Geol. Surv, 52-63; ASST. PROF. HYDROL. & DIR. WATER RES. INST, W.VA. UNIV, 63- U.S.A.A.F, 42-46. AAAS; Geol. Soc. Am; Am. Geophys. Union; Am. Water Resources Asn. Groundwater geology; geology of mineral deposits; water resources. Address: Water Research Institute, West Virginia University, Morgantown, WV 26506.

DODSON, EDWARD O, b. Fargo, N.Dak, April 26, 16; m. 40; c. 6. ZOOLOGY. B.A, Carleton Col, 39; Ph.D.(zool), California, 47. Asst. zool, California, 39-46; instr, Dominican Col, 46-47; BIOL, Notre Dame, 47-49, asst. prof, 49-52, assoc. prof, 52-57; UNIV. OTTAWA, 57-59, PROF, 59- Lectr, California, Los Angeles, 45; vis. prof, Montreal, 62; vis. res. prof, Roswell Park Mem. Inst, 64-65. AAAS; Genetics Soc. Am; Soc. Study Evolution; Genetics Soc. Can. Chromosomes of vertebrates; evolution; mutation; tissue culture. Address: Dept. of Biology, University of Ottawa, Ottawa, Ont, K1N 6N5, Can.

DODSON, HELEN W(ALTER), (MRS. EDMOND L. PRINCE), b. Baltimore, Md, Dec. 31, 05; m. 56. ASTRONOMY. A.B, Goucher Col, 27, hon.D.Sc, 52; A.M, Michigan, 32, Ph.D.(astron), 34. Asst. statistician, State Dept. Ed, Md, 27-31; instr. astron, Wellesley Col, 33-37, asst. prof, 37-45; assoc. prof. astron. & math, Goucher Col, 45-50; astron, McMATH-HULBERT OBSERV, UNIV. MICH, 49-57, PROF. ASTRON. & ASSOC. DIR. OBSERV, 57- Staff mem. radiation lab, Mass. Inst. Tech, 43-45. AAAS; fel. Am. Astron. Soc; Am. Geophys. Union; Astron. Soc. France. Solar physics, especially solar prominences and flares; solar radio astronomy; solar terrestrial relationships. Address: McMath-Hulbert Observatory, University of Michigan, 895 N. Lake Angelus Rd, Pontiac, MI 48055.

DODSON, MARION LESTER, JR, b. Jacksboro, Tex, Oct. 17, 42; m. 66; c. 1. MOLECULAR BIOLOGY. B.A, Texas, Austin, 65, Ph.D.(molecular biol), Texas, Houston, 70. Asst. prof. molecular biol, grad. sch. biomed. sci, Univ. Tex, Houston, 69-70; Nat. Insts. Health fel, Yale, 70-71; ASST. PROF. BIOL, UNIV. LOUISVILLE, 71- AAAS. Mechanism of action of ribonucleic acid polymerase; mechanism of transcription control in virus-infected and in differentiating cells. Address: Dept. of Biology, University of Louisville, Louisville, KY 40208.

DODSON, NORMAN E(LMER), b. Gregory, Ky, Oct. 18, 09; m. 36; c. 1. MATHEMATICS. A.B, Berea Col, 33; A.M, Alabama, 47. Teacher, high sch, Ky, 33-34, 35-37; Fla, 37-39; headmaster & teacher math, Jefferson Mil. Col, 38-42; assoc. prof, Newberry Col, 42-45; asst. Alabama, 45-46, asst. prof. statist, 46-47; assoc. prof. MATH, Lenoir-Rhyne Col, 47-57; asst. prof, WITTENBERG UNIV, 57-67, ASSOC. PROF, 67- Math. Asn. Am. Algebra and new trends in mathematical education. Address: 1218 N. Lowry, Springfield, OH 45504.

DODSON, R(AYMOND) M(ONROE), b. West Hazleton, Pa, July 8, 20; m. 43; c. 4. ORGANIC CHEMISTRY. B.S, Franklin & Marshall Col, 42; nat. res. fel, Northwestern, 46-47, Ph.D.(org. chem), 47. Asst. prof. org. chem, Minnesota, 47-51; chemist, G.D. Searle & Co, 51-55, asst. to dir. chem. res, 55-60, PROF. CHEM, UNIV. MINN, MINNEAPOLIS, 60- With Off. Sci. Res. & Develop, 44-46; Nat. Bur. Standards, 42. Mem. endocrinol. study sect, Nat. Insts. Health, 62-66. AAAS; fel. Am. Chem. Soc; N.Y. Acad. Sci; Brit. Chem. Soc. Heterocyclic compounds; organic sulfur-containing compounds; steroids; stereochemistry of cholesterol and its derivatives; fermentation of steroids. Address: Dept. of Chemistry, University of Minnesota, Minneapolis, MN 55455.

DODSON, RICHARD W(OLFORD), b. Kirksville, Mo, Jan. 15, 15; m. 37; c. 2. PHYSICAL CHEMISTRY. B.S, Calif. Inst. Tech, 36; Ph.D.(chem), Hopkins, 39. Am. Can Co. fel, Johns Hopkins Univ, 36-40; Nat. Res. fel, Calif. Inst. Tech, 40, mem. staff, Nat. Defense Res. Comt. proj, Calif. Inst. Tech. & Northwestern, 40-43; group leader & later asst. div. leader, Los Alamos Lab, N.Mex, 43-45; asst. prof. CHEM, Calif. Inst. Technol, 46-47; assoc. prof, COLUMBIA UNIV, 47-53, PROF, 53-; SR. CHEMIST, BROOKHAVEN NAT. LAB, 48-, chmn. dept. chem, 47-68. Secy. gen. adv. comt, Atomic Energy Comn, 51-56. AAAS; Am. Phys. Soc; Am. Chem. Soc. Reaction kinetics; radiochemistry. Address: Dept. of Chemistry, Brookhaven National Lab, Upton, NY 11973.

DODSON, RONALD FRANKLIN, b. Paris, Tex, Feb. 14, 42; m. 65. ELECTRON MICROSCOPY, CYTOLOGY. B.A, East Texas State, 64, M.A, 65;

Ph.D.(biol. electron micros), Texas A&M, 69. Asst. instr. biol, East Texas State, 64-65; instr. & res. fel. electron micros. center, Texas A&M, 65-69; res. assoc. anat, Med. Sch, Univ. Tex, San Antonio, 69-70, ASST. PROF. NEUROL, BAYLOR UNIV, COL. MED, 70- AAAS; Am. Chem. Soc; Inst. Biol. Sci; Electron Micros. Soc. Am. Irradiation damage of central nervous system ultrastructure; ultrastructural and functional relationships between various organelles within the central nervous system. Address: Dept. of Neurology, Baylor College of Medicine, Texas Medical Center, Houston, TX 77025.

DODSON, V(ANCE) H(AYDEN), JR, b. Oklahoma City, Okla, June 12, 22; m. 53. INORGANIC CHEMISTRY. B.Ch.E, Toledo, 44, M.S, 47; Ph.D. (chem), Purdue, 52. Mat. engr, Curtiss-Wright Corp, 44-45; instr. chem, Toledo, 45-48, asst. prof, 50-53, assoc. prof, 53-57; asst. instr, Purdue, 48-50; res. chemist, Elec. Autolite Co, Ohio, 57-58, res. mgr, battery div, 58-61; res. mgr. construct. specialties, DEWEY & ALMY CHEM. CO, CAMBRIDGE, 61-63, DIR. RES, CONSTRUCT. MAT. DIV, 63- Am. Chem. Soc; Am. Ceramic Soc; Am. Concrete Inst; Am. Soc. Test & Mat. Silicates; elastomers; organic coatings; lead alloys; electrochemical sources of energy. Address: 40 Oak Hill Rd, Needham, MA 02192.

DODSON, VERNON N, b. Benton Harbor, Mich, Feb. 19, 23; m. 55; c. 5. TOXICOLOGY, BIOCHEMISTRY. Mich. State Col, 41-43, 46; Oregon, 43-44; M.D, Marquette, 51; Michigan, 51-52, B.S, 52. Asst. pathologist, sch. med, Hopkins, 52-53; instr. internal med, Michigan, 57-60, asst. prof. internal & indust. med. & toxicol, 60-65, assoc. prof, 65-71, res. assoc. nuclear med, 59-60, indust. health, 60-71; PROF. MED. & ENVIRON. MED, MED. COL. WIS, 71- Lectr, inst. social work, Univ. Mich, 57-58, sch. dent, 57-59, sch. nursing, 58-60, dept. postgrad. med, 59-71; med. dir. Delco Electronics Div, Gen. Motors Corp, Wis. U.S.A, 42-45. Am. Med. Asn; Am. Fedn. Clin. Res; Brit. Biochem. Soc; fel. Am. Col. Physicians; fel. Am. Col. Prev. Med; Am. Acad. Occup. Med. Auto-immunity; immunotoxicology; clinical medicine; thyroid metabolism and diseases; electrophoresis; rheumatology. Address: Dept. of Environmental Medicine, Allen Bradley Medical Science Lab, Medical College of Wisconsin, 8700 W. Wisconsin Ave, Milwaukee, WI 53226.

DODSWORTH, BARBARA M, b. West Warwick, R.I, Aug. 15, 33. PHYSICS. B.S, Rhode Island, 54; Ph.D.(physics), California, Berkeley, 63. Res. asst. PHYSICS, California, Berkeley, 59-63, fel, 63-64; instr, N.Y. Univ, 64-67; res. fel, lab. spectros. hertzian waves, faculty sci, Paris, 67-69; res. assoc, Univ. N.Hamp, 69-70; ASST. PROF. PHYSICS, WELLESLEY COL, 70- Marie Curie fel, 67-68. Am. Phys. Soc. High resolution optical spectroscopy; atomic beams; measurement of spins, hyperfine structure separations and magnetic moments of radioactive isotopes. Address: Dept. of Physics, Wellesley College, Wellesley, MA 02181.

DOE, BRUCE, b. St. Paul, Minn, Apr. 24, 31; m. 58. GEOLOGY. B.S. & B.Geol.E, Minnesota, 54; M.S, Mo. Sch. Mines, 56; Pan Am. Petrol. fel, Calif. Inst. Technol, 56-57, Kennecott Copper Co. fel, 57-59, Ph.D.(geol), 60. Fel. isotope chem, geophys. lab, Carnegie Inst, 60-61; GEOLOGIST ISOTOPE CHEM. & GEOL, U.S. GEOL. SURV, D.C, 61-63, Colo, 63-68, Switzerland, 68-69, D.C, 69-71, COLO, 71- Vis. investr, geophys. lab, Carnegie Inst, 61-62; Japan-U.S. Sci. Coop. Prog, 65; acad. guest, Swiss Fed. Inst. Technol, Zurich, 68-69; staff scientist, lunar sample prog, NASA, 69-71, mem. lunar sample anal. planning team, Houston, 70-71. Outstanding performance award, U.S. Geol. Surv, 68. AAAS; fel. Geol. Soc. Am; Mineral. Soc. Am; Geochem. Soc; Am. Geophys. Union; Soc. Econ. Geol. Trace element and isotope geochemistry; radiogenic tracer analysis; volcanology; ore genesis; lunar petrology. Address: Isotope Geology Branch, U.S. Geological Survey, Denver, CO 80225.

DOE, LEARMONT ANSTICE EARLSTON, b. Paget, Bermuda, Mar. 7, 16; Can. citizen; m. 44; c. 4. OCEANOGRAPHY, METEOROLOGY. B.A, Toronto, 38, M.A, 49; univ. fel, N.Y. Univ, 53-54, Ford Found. fel, 60-61, Ph.D.(oceanog, meteorol), 63. Asst. scientist phys. oceanog, Fisheries Res. Bd. Can, 49-52; oceanogr, Creole Petrol. Corp, Venezuela, 55-60; fel, Woods Hole Oceanog. Inst, 60-61; oceanogr, Bedford Inst. Oceanog, 61-68; sr. sci. adv, CAN. DEPT. ENERGY, MINES & RESOURCES, 68-70, DEPARTMENTAL PLANNING OFF, 70- R.C.N, 42-45, Lt. Am. Geophys. Union; Am. Soc. Limnol. & Oceanog; Can. Asn. Physicists. General physical oceanography; limnology of Lake Maracaibo; air-sea interaction and energy exchanges. Address: Dept. of Energy, Mines & Resources, 588 Booth St, Ottawa, Ont. K1A 0E4, Can.

DOE, RICHARD P, b. Minneapolis, Minn, July 21, 26; m. 50; c. 2. ENDOCRINOLOGY, INTERNAL MEDICINE. B.S, Minnesota, 49, M.B, 51, M.D, 52, Ph.D, 66. Chief chemist, MINNEAPOLIS VET. ADMIN. HOSP, 55-60, CHIEF METAB. & ENDOCRINE SECT, 60-; PROF. MED. & HEAD ENDOCRINE SECT, MED. SCH, UNIV. MINN, 69-, instr. med, 51-66, assoc. prof, 66-69. U.S.N, 44-46. Endocrine Soc; Am. Fedn. Clin. Res. Circadian variation in plasma and urinary 17OH-CS in normals and Cushing's syndrome; method for measurement of 11DO-CS after SU4885 test; isolation; characterization and measurement of transcortin. Address: Mayo Memorial Hospital, University of Minnesota, Box 57, Minneapolis, MN 55455.

DOEBBLER, GERALD F(RANCIS), b. San Antonio, Tex, June 27, 32; m. 57; c. 7. BIOCHEMISTRY. B.S, Univ. Tex, 53, M.A, 54, Rosalie B. Hite fel, 55-57, Ph.D.(chem), 57. Scientist Biochem. Inst. Tex, 53-55; res. chemist, Linde Co. div, UNION CARBIDE CORP, 57-60, sr. res. chemist, 60-68, Ocean Systs, Inc, 68-69, RES. ASSOC, 69-71, CORP. RES. DEPT, 71- Fel. AAAS; Am. Chem. Soc; Am. Soc. Microbiol; Biophys. Soc; Soc. Cryobiol; Undersea Med. Soc. Biochemistry, biophysics, physiology of inert gases and decompression sickness; cryobiology; blood and cell preservation; analytical biochemistry; enzymology; low temperature spectroscopy; sulfur metabolism; biochemical individuality; ecological and aquatic biochemistry. Address: Corporate Research Dept, Technical Center, Union Carbide Corp, Saw Mill River Rd, Tarrytown, NY 10591.

DOEBEL, KARL J, b. Frankfurt, Germany, Feb. 21, 23; m. 55; c. 3. ORGANIC & MEDICINAL CHEMISTRY. Ph.D.(chem), Basle, 47. Swiss Nat. Fund res. fel, Basel, 47-48, Cambridge, 48-49; sr. res. chemist, F. Hoffmann-La Roche & Co, Switz, 49-59, 60, N.J, 59-60; Geigy Chem. Corp, 61-62, res. supvr, 62-65, assoc. dir. med. chem, 65-71, DIR. ORG. CHEM, CIBA-GEIGY LTD, 67- Am. Chem. Soc; N.Y. Acad. Sci; Swiss Chem. Soc. Synthesis of novel organic compounds; extraction of natural products from plants; structural elucidation of natural products; synthesis of biologically active natural products; synthesis of medicinal agents; development of drugs. Address: Ciba-Geigy Ltd, Saw Mill River Rd, Ardsley, NY 10502.

DOEDE, CLINTON M(ILFORD), b. Bonfield, Ill, Oct. 17, 10; m. 35; c. 4. CHEMISTRY. B.S, Chicago, 31, fel, 32-34, Ph.D.(phys. chem), 34. Res. chemist, Firestone Tire & Rubber Co, Ohio, 34-37, head phys. chem. res. div, 37-39; v.pres. & gen. mgr, Conn. Hard Rubber Co, 39-55; PRES, QUANTUM, INC, 48-; JOCLIN MFG. CO, 55-; CHMN. BD, WINDSOR NUCLEAR, INC, 67- Lectr, Yale, 48-50. Fel. AAAS; Am. Chem. Soc; Am. Phys. Soc; fel. Am. Inst. Chem; Faraday Soc; Nat. Security Indust. Asn. Physical chemistry of rubbers, especially silicones; photochemistry; applications of radiant energies. Address: 26 Underhill Rd, Hamden, CT 06517.

DOEDE, DOROTHY R(UTH), b. Chicago, Ill, Feb. 16, 10; m. 35; c. 4. BACTERIOLOGY. B.S, Chicago, 31; Ph.D, Yale, 44. Biochemist, Nelson Morris Inst, 32-35; West. Reserve, 35-37; TREAS. & BACTERIOLOGIST, QUANTUM, INC, 48- AAAS; Am. Soc. Microbiol. Biochemistry; industrial bacteriology; radiation biology; biological growth factors. Address: 26 Underhill Rd, Hamden, CT 06517.

DOEDE, JOHN HENRY, b. Chicago, Ill, Sept. 29, 37; m. 60; c. 2. PHYSICS, PHYSICAL CHEMISTRY. A.B, Harvard, 59; M.S, Chicago, 62, Ph.D.(chem), 63. Res. assoc. high energy physics, Argonne Nat. Lab, 63-64, asst. physicist, 64-66; mgr. prog, EMR Comput. Div, Electro-Mech. Res, Inc, 66-67; pres, Data Int. Inc, Minn, 67-70; V.PRES, HEIZER CORP, 70- Am. Geophys. Union; Am. Phys. Soc. Weak interaction particle physics; laser development and applications; computer applications and data reduction. Address: Heizer Corp, 20 N. Wacker Dr, Chicago, IL 60606.

DOEDEN, GERALD E(NNEN), b. Onarga, Ill, Oct. 16, 18; m. 42; c. 1. ANALYTICAL CHEMISTRY. B.S, Cent. Norm. Col.(Ind), 40; M.A, Indiana, 50, Nat. Sci. Found. fel, 60-61, Ph.D.(anal. chem), 65. Teacher, high schs, Ind, 40-41, 46-56 & Ariz, 45-46; analyst, E.I. du Pont de Nemours & Co, Ind, 41-43; asst. prof. CHEM, BALL STATE UNIV, 56-65, assoc. prof, 65-70, PROF, 70- AAAS; fel. Am. Inst. Chem; Am. Chem. Soc; Soc. Appl. Spectros. Coulometric analysis; gas chromatography; spectrophotometry. Address: Dept. of Chemistry, Ball State University, Muncie, IN 47306.

DOEDENS, ROBERT JOHN, b. Milwaukee, Wis, Dec. 15, 37; m. 61; c. 2. PHYSICAL & INORGANIC CHEMISTRY. B.S, Wisconsin-Milwaukee, 61, Nat. Sci. Found. fel, Wisconsin-Madison, 61-64, Ph.D.(chem), 65. Res. asst. & instr. CHEM, Northwestern, 65-66; ASST. PROF. UNIV. CALIF, IRVINE, 66- Am. Chem. Soc; Am. Crystallog. Asn; Brit. Chem. Soc. X-ray crystallography; crystal and molecular structures of coordination compounds and organometallic derivatives of the transition elements. Address: Dept. of Chemistry, University of California, Irvine, CA 92664.

DOEG, KENNETH A(LBERT), b. Weehawken, N.J, Aug. 5, 31; m. 57; c. 2. BIOCHEMISTRY. A.B, N.J. State Teachers Col, 52; Nat. Sci. Found. fel, Rutgers, 56-57, Ph.D.(zool), 57. Smith, Kline & French fel, Rutgers, 57-58; fel, enzyme inst, Wisconsin, 58-61; asst. prof. clin. sci, sch. med, Pittsburgh, 61-64; asst. prof. zool, UNIV. CONN, 64-69, ASSOC. PROF. BIOL, 69- AAAS; Am. Chem. Soc; Soc. Study Reproduction; Endocrine Soc; fel. Am. Inst. Chem; Am. Soc. Zool. Mechanisms of hormone action; mitochondrial enzymology. Address: Section of Biochemistry & Biophysics, Box U-125, University of Connecticut, Storrs, CT 06268.

DOEGE, THEODORE CHARLES, b. Lincoln, Nebr, Dec. 11, 28; m. 57; c. 2. PREVENTIVE MEDICINE, EPIDEMIOLOGY. A.B, Oberlin Col, 50; M.D, Rochester, 58; M.S, Washington (Seattle), 65. Intern med, Salt Lake County Gen. Hosp, Utah, 58-59; asst. res. pediat, Univ. Hosps, Seattle, Wash, 61-63; chief res. pediat, King County Hosp, 63; instr. & fel. PREV. MED, sch. med, Univ. Wash, 63-65, asst. prof, 65-67; ASSOC. PROF, UNIV. ILL. COL. MED, 67- Fel, trop. med, La. State Univ, 66; vis. assoc. prof, Chiengmai Univ, 67-70. Dipl, Am. Bd. Prev. Med. Med.C, U.S.A, 50-52; U.S.P.H.S, 59-61, Sr. Asst. Surg. Fel. Am. Pub. Health Asn; Am. Col. Prev. Med. International and community health; health care problems; acute, chronic infectious diseases; prevention of illness, infections, accidents; environmental health; health economics and nutrition; pediatric problems; congenital malformations and genetics. Address: Dept. of Preventive Medicine & Community Health, University of Illinois College of Medicine, P.O. Box 6998, Chicago, IL 60680.

DOEHLER, ROBERT W(ILLIAM), b. Mt. Olive, Ill, Aug. 7, 29; m. 54; c. 2. MINERALOGY. B.S, Illinois, 51, M.S, 53, Ill. Clay Prods. fel, 55-57, Ph.D.(geol), 57. Res. geologist, Jersey Prod. Res. Co, 57-60; dir. chem. res, Am. Colloid Co, 60-69; ASSOC. PROF. GEOL, NORTHEAST. ILL. STATE UNIV, 69- U.S.A, 53-55. Production and industrial applications of non-metallic minerals. Address: Dept. of Geology, Northeastern Illinois State University, Chicago, IL 60625.

DOEHRING, DONALD O, b. Milwaukee, Wis, Sept. 8, 35; m. 58; c. 2. GEOMORPHOLOGY, SEDIMENTOLOGY. A.B, Univ. Calif, Berkeley, 62; M.A, Claremont Grad. Sch. & Univ. Ctr, 65; NASA fel, Univ. Wyo, 66-67, Ph.D. (geol), 68. Instr. GEOL, Univ. Wyo, 67-68; vis. asst. prof, Pomona Col, 68-69; Wash. & Lee Univ, 69-70; fel, State Univ. N.Y. Binghamton, 70-71; ASST. PROF, UNIV. MASS, AMHERST, 71- AAAS; Geol. Soc. Am; Nat. Asn. Geol. Teachers. Arid region geomorphology, quantitative modeling and analysis of landforms, slope process studies, environmental geomorphology and hydrology in karst terrains; sedimentological studies of depositional environments and primary sedimentary structures. Address: Dept. of Geology, University of Massachusetts, Amherst, MA 01002.

DOELL, RICHARD RAYMAN, b. Oakland, Calif, June 28, 23; m. 50; c. 2. GEOPHYSICS. A.B, California, 52, Ph.D.(geophysics), 55. Lectr. geophysics, Toronto, 55-56; asst. prof, Mass. Inst. Technol, 56-59; GEOPHYSICIST,

U.S. GEOL. SURV, 59- Vetlesen prize, 71. U.S.A, 43-45. Nat. Acad. Sci; Am. Geophys. Union; Geol. Soc. Am; fel. Royal Astron. Soc. General geophysics, especially the earth's magnetic field; remnant magnetism in rocks. Address: U.S. Geological Survey, 345 Middlefield Rd, Menlo Park, CA 94025.

DOELL, RUTH G(ERTRUDE), b. Vancouver, B.C, Can, Mar. 24, 26; nat; m. 50; c. 2. BIOLOGY. A.B, California, 52, Ph.D.(comp. biochem), 56. Instr. physiol, med. sch, Tufts, 56-59; res. assoc. biochem, sch. med, Stanford, 59-60, pediat, 60-65, MED. MICROBIOL, 65-67; lectr, SAN FRANCISCO STATE COL, 67-69, ASSOC. PROF, 69- Viral and chemical carcinogenesis; immunology. Address: Dept. of Biology, San Francisco State College, 1600 Holloway, San Francisco, CA 94132.

DOELLING, HELLMUT HANS, b. N.Y.C, July 25, 30; m. 60; c. 7. GEOLOGY. B.S, Utah, 56, Ph.D.(geol), 64. Geologist, Utah Geol. & Mining Surv, 64; asst. prof. geol, Midwestern, 64-66; ECON. GEOLOGIST, UTAH GEOL. & MINERAL. SURV, 66- U.S.A, 51-53, Res, 53-56. AAAS. Economic geology, especially coal, uranium, clay deposits, copper, mercury and bituminous sands. Address: 103 Utah Geological Survey Bldg, University of Utah, Salt Lake City, UT 84112.

DOELP, LOUIS C(ONRAD), JR, b. Philadelphia, Pa, Jan. 8, 28; m. 50; c. 2. CHEMICAL ENGINEERING. B.S, Pennsylvania, 50. Plant engr, Am. Foam Rubber Corp, 50-51; chem. engr. develop, HOUDRY PROCESS & CHEM. CORP. DIV, AIR PROD. & CHEM, INC, 51-55, proj. dir. process develop, 55-61, sect. head, 61-69, DIR. RES. & DEVELOP, CATALYSTS & PROCESSES, 69- Am. Chem. Soc. Process development, catalysis, kinetics. Address: Houdry Process & Chemical Corp, Box 427, Marcus Hook, PA 19061.

DOEMEL, WILLIAM NAYLOR, b. Pittsburgh, Pa. MICROBIOLOGY, MICROBIAL ECOLOGY. B.S, Heidelberg Col, 66; Nat. Insts. Health grant & Ph.D.(microbiol), Ind. Univ, 70. ASST. PROF. BIOL, WABASH COL, 70- Partic, Inst. Surtsey & Iceland, environ. ctr, Boston Col, summer 70; res. fel, Thomas D. Brock Lab. Thermal Biol, summer 70. AAAS; Am. Soc. Microbiol; Am. Soc. Limnol. & Oceanog. Physiological ecology of microorganisms existing in extreme environments including thermal effluents, acid effluents and polluted streams. Address: Dept. of Biology, Wabash College, Crawfordsville, IN 47933.

DOEMLING, DONALD B(ERNARD), b. Chicago, Ill, Nov. 20, 30; m. 59; c. 2. PHYSIOLOGY. B.S, St. Benedict's Col, 52; M.S, Illinois, 54, Ph.D.(physiol), 58. Asst. physiol, Illinois, 52-57; instr. physiol. & pharmacol, dent. sch, Northwestern, 57-59, asst. prof, 59-60; instr. Jefferson Med. Col, 61-62, asst. prof, 62-68, assoc. prof, 68; PROF. PHYSIOL. & CHMN. DEPT, SCH. DENT, LOYOLA UNIV, ILL, 68- AAAS; Am. Physiol. Soc. Lymph flow and composition; intestinal absorption, secretion and motility. Address: Dept. of Physiology, School of Dentistry, Loyola University, 2160 S. First Ave, Maywood, IL 60153.

DOEPKER, RICHARD DuMONT, b. Findlay, Ohio, Jan. 22, 33; m. 59; c. 3. PHYSICAL CHEMISTRY. B.S, Xavier (Ohio), 55, M.S, 57; M.S, Carnegie Inst. Tech, 60, Ph.D.(chem), 61. Nat. Acad. Sci-Nat. Res. Coun. res. assoc. photoradiation chem, Nat. Bur. Standards, 63-65; ASST. PROF. CHEM, UNIV. MIAMI, 65- U.S.A, 61-63, Res, 55-61, 63-64, Capt. AAAS; Am. Chem. Soc. Photoradiation chemistry; reaction of hot radicals; modes of decomposition of highly excited molecules produced through vacuum ultraviolet photolysis and electron impact; photo-ionization; H-atom reactions; Lyman absorption technique. Address: Dept. of Chemistry, University of Miami, Coral Gables, FL 33124.

DOERFLER, LEO G, b. New York, N.Y, June 25, 19; m. 43; c. 4. AUDIOLOGY. A.B, N.Y. Univ, 39; Cent. Inst. Deaf scholar, Washington (St. Louis), 40-41, M.S, 41; Bunch fel, Northwestern, 46-47, Ph.D.(audiol), 48. Instr. & psychologist, Iowa State Sch. Deaf, 41-43; instr. AUDIOL, Northwestern, 47-48; PROF, SCH. MED, UNIV. PITTSBURGH, 48-, DIR. DEPT. AUDIOL, EYE & EAR HOSP, 48- Pres, Am. Bd. Exam. Speech Path. & Audiol, 60-62, chmn. prof. serv. bd, 60-64; consult, Vet. Admin; Nat. Insts. Health; U.S. Off. Educ; U.S. Pub. Health Serv; Social & Rehab. Serv, Dept. Health, Educ. & Welfare. Med.C, 43-46, 1st Lt. Fel. AAAS; fel. Am. Speech & Hearing Asn.(pres, 67); Am. Psychol. Asn; Acoust. Soc. Am; Am. Indust. Hyg. Asn. Psychophysics of audition; diagnosis and rehabilitation of auditory disability; differential diagnosis of communicative disorders in children and adults; development of special measures of auditory function. Address: Dept. of Audiology, Eye & Ear Hospital, 230 Lothrop St, Pittsburgh, PA 15213.

DOERFLER, WALTER, b. Weissenburg, W.Germany, Aug. 11, 33; m. 60; c. 1. BIOCHEMISTRY, VIROLOGY. M.D, Munich, 59. Res. fel, Max Planck Inst. Biochem, 61-63; dept. biochem, sch. med, Stanford, 63-66; asst. prof. virol, Rockefeller Univ, 66-69, assoc. prof, 69-72; PROF. GENETICS, UNIV. COLOGNE, 72- Am. Soc. Biol. Chem; Am. Soc. Microbiol; Am. Inst. Chem. Structure and function of nucleic acids; biochemistry of virus infected cells; mechanism of interaction between viral and host genomes. Address: Institute for Genetics, University of Cologne, 121 Weyertal, 5 Köln, West Germany.

DOERING, CHARLES HENRY, b. Munich, W.Ger, Jan. 7, 35; U.S. citizen; m. 61; c. 4. BIOCHEMISTRY, ENDOCRINOLOGY. B.Sc, San Francisco, 56; M.Sc, Munich, 59; Stanford, 58-59; Ph.D.(biochem), California, San Francisco, 64. Asst. biochem, Univ. Calif, San Francisco, 59-63; res. fel, Harvard Sch. Med, 63-67; RES. ASSOC. PSYCHIAT. MED. CTR, STANFORD UNIV, 67- AAAS; Am. Chem. Soc. Biosynthesis of steroid hormones and its control; influence of steroid hormones on behavior; correlation between androgens and aggressiveness. Address: Dept. of Psychiatry, Stanford University Medical Center, Stanford, CA 94305.

DOERING, EUGENE J(OHNSON), b. Plankinton, S.Dak, Aug. 28, 28; m. 54; c. 2. AGRICULTURAL ENGINEERING. B.S, S.Dak. State, 51, M.S, 58. Engr, Boeing Airplane Co, Kans, 52; agr. engr, soil conserv. serv, U.S. DEPT. AGR, 54-56, AGR. ENGR, AGR. RES. SERV, Calif, 58-65, N.DAK, 65- U.S.A, 46-47, 52-54, Sgt. Am. Soc. Agr. Eng. Salinity in agriculture; reclamation, irrigation, drainage and flow of water in saturated and unsaturated soil. Address: Agricultural Research Service, U.S. Dept. of Agriculture, P.O. Box 459, Mandan, ND 58554.

DOERING, JOHN P, b. Jackson, Miss, Aug. 20, 37; m. 58; c. 4. CHEMICAL PHYSICS. B.A, Hopkins, 58; Woodrow Wilson fel, California, Berkeley, 58-59, Nat. Sci. Found. fel, 59-60, Dow fel, 60-61, Ph.D.(chem), 61. Staff mem, chem. physics, Los Alamos Sci. Lab, California, 61-64; asst. prof. CHEM, JOHNS HOPKINS UNIV, 64-68, assoc. prof, 68-70, PROF, 70- Am. Phys. Soc. Electronic and ionic collision phenomena in gases; low energy electron and positive ion spectroscopy; atmospheric collision phenomena in the aurora and airglow. Address: Dept. of Chemistry, Johns Hopkins University, Baltimore, MD 21218.

DOERING, WILLIAM V(ON) E(GGERS), b. Ft. Worth, Texas, June 22, 17; m. 47; 69; c. 3. ORGANIC CHEMISTRY. B.S, Harvard, 38, Ph.D.(org. chem), 43. Res. chemist Nat. Defense Res. Comt. proj, Harvard, 41-42; Polaroid Corp, Mass, 43; instr. org. chem, Columbia, 43-45, asst. prof, 45-48, assoc. prof, 48-52; prof, Yale, 52-67, dir. div. sci, 62-65; prof. ORG. CHEM, HARVARD, 67, MALLINCKRODT PROF, 68- Dir. res, Hickrill Chem. Res. Found, N.Y, 47-59; consult, Upjohn Co, 56-; Procter & Gamble Co, 58-; co-chmn, Coun. Livable World, 62- Scott Award, 45; Hoffman Medal, Ger. Chem. Soc, 62. Nat. Acad. Sci; Am. Chem. Soc.(pure chem. award, 53, synthetic chem. award, 63). Carbenes; thermal reorganizations; small rings; bullvalene; fluxional molecules; stable carbonium ions; conjugative interactions; mechanisms of hydrogenation, displacement, asymmetric reduction and Cope rearrangement; synthesis of quinine, nonbenzenoid aromatics, tropylium ion and tropolone. Address: Dept. of Chemistry, Harvard University, 12 Oxford St, Cambridge, MA 02138.

DOERMANN, A(UGUST) H(ENRY), b. Blue Island, Ill, Dec. 7, 18; m. 47; c. 2. BIOLOGY. A.B, Wabash Col, 40; M.A, Illinois, 41; Ph.D.(biol), Stanford, 46. Fel. bacteriophage res, Vanderbilt, 45-47, vis. instr. biol, 46; fel, Carnegie Inst. Genetics Res. Unit, 47-49; biologist, Oak Ridge Nat. Lab, 49-53; assoc. prof. biol, Rochester, 53-56, PROF, 56-58; Vanderbilt, 58-64; GENETICS, UNIV. WASH, 64- Vis. res. fel, Calif. Inst. Tech, 49; vis. prof, Cologne, 57-58; sci. assoc, Basel Inst. Immunol, 70-71. AAAS; Am. Soc. Nat; Genetics Soc. Am. Microbiological and biochemical genetics; gene structure, replication and recombination; radiation genetics of bacteriophage. Address: Dept. of Genetics, University of Washington, Seattle, WA 98105.

DOERNER, ROBERT C(ARL), b. St. Cloud, Minn, Sept. 26, 26; m. 54; c. 5. PHYSICS. B.S, St. John's (Minn), 49; M.S, St. Louis, 52, Ph.D.(physics), 55. Fel. nuclear physics, ARGONNE NAT. LAB, 55-56, ASSOC. PHYSICIST, 56- Vis. assoc. prof, Cornell, 62. U.S.N, 44-46, Res, 46-54. Am. Nuclear Soc. Experimental reactor and experimental fast reactor physics; neutron slowing down; thermal reactor spectra; resonance integrals; Beta and Gamma ray spectroscopy; nuclear rocket reactors. Address: Argonne National Lab, 9700 S. Cass Ave, Argonne, IL 60440.

DOERNER, WILLIAM A(LLEN), b. Pullman, Wash, Feb. 24, 20; m. 50; c. 5. CHEMICAL ENGINEERING. B.S, Ore. State Col, 42; M.S.E, Michigan, 47, M.S, 49, Sc.D.(chem. eng), 52. Res. engr. develop. dept, EXP. STA, E.I. DU PONT DE NEMOURS & CO, INC, 51-66, develop. supvr, photo prod. dept, 66-69, GROUP LEADER, CENT. RES. DEPT, 69- U.S.N.R, 42-46, Res, 46-57, Lt. AAAS; Am. Chem. Soc; Am. Inst. Chem. Eng. Powder metallurgy; thermodynamics of power fluids and magnetic materials. Address: 19 Baynard Blvd, Wilmington, DE 19803.

DOERR, HANS O, Psychophysiol, see Suppl. I to 11th ed, Soc. & Behav. Vols.

DOERR, MARVIN LeROY, b. Oklahoma City, Okla, Oct. 16, 39; m. 63; c. 2. ORGANIC CHEMISTRY. A.B, Washington (St. Louis), 61; Ph.D.(org. chem), Ga. Inst. Tech, 67. Chemist, A.E. Staley Mfg. Co, 61-62; technician, Anheuser-Busch, Inc, 63; Du Pont grad. teaching asst. award, 66-67; PROCESS ENGR, FIBER INDUSTS, INC, 67- Am. Chem. Soc. Synthesis of pharmaceuticals; synthesis of polymers for coatings and fiber applications; process development for commercial polymer manufacture and fiber spinning. Address: P.O. Box 10038, Charlotte, NC 28201.

DOERR, ROBERT GEORGE, b. Winona, Minn, Jan. 26, 41; m. 70. ORGANIC & ANALYTICAL CHEMISTRY. B.A, St. Mary's Col.(Minn), 63; Ph.D.(chem), Pa. State, 67. Fel, Pa. State, 67; prof. chem, Luther Col.(Iowa), 67-68; CHEMIST, WATKINS PROD. INC, 68- Am. Chem. Soc. Organic diradicals, particularly trimethylenemethane. Address: Watkins Products Inc, Winona, MN 55987.

DOERR, THEODORE C, b. Galveston, Tex, Nov. 17, 36; m. 60; c. 2. PETROLEUM ENGINEERING. B.S, Univ. Tex, 64, M.S, 66, Ph.D.(petrol. eng), 71. Res. assoc, Tex. Petrol. Res. Comn, 63-70; RES. ENGR, TENNECO OIL CO, 70- Am. Inst. Mining, Metall. & Petrol. Eng. Reservoir engineering; recovery processes; two-phase flow; fluid mechanics. Address: 5443 Stillbrooke Dr, Houston, TX 77035.

DOERSAM, CHARLES H(ENRY), JR, b. New York, N.Y, Nov. 1, 21; m. 53; c. 3. ENGINEERING. Scholar, B.S, Columbia, 42, M.S, 44. Prod. engr, Pratt & Whitney Aircraft, 41; mem. tech. staff, Bell Tel. Labs, 42-44, sr. proj. engr, Off. of Naval Res, 46-53; Sperry Gyroscope Co, 53-56; sr. res. engr, Fairchild Camera & Instrument, 56-57; head eng. sect, microwave electronics div, Sperry Gyroscope Co, 57-58, proj. engr, countermeasures div, 58-59; asst. chief engr. & dir. new prod. planning, Potter Instrument Co, 59-61; dir. mkt. & chief engr, Instruments for Indust, 61-64; vis. prof. elec. & mech. eng, Polytech. Inst. Brooklyn, 64-69; PRES, COM COMP INC, 69- Consult, PRD Electronics div, Harris-Intertype Corp; Soroban Eng; Ins. Bus. Mach. Corp; West. Elec. Co. U.S.N, 44-46, Lt. (jg). Inst. Elec. & Electronics Eng. Digital techniques applied to automatic control and information handling. Address: Com Comp Inc, 1324 Motor Pkwy, Hauppauge, NY 11787.

DOERSCH, RONALD ERNEST, b. Cleveland, Wis, Sept. 13, 35; m. 57; c. 4. AGRONOMY. B.S, Wisconsin, 58, M.S, 61, Ph.D.(soils), 63. Asst. prof. WEED CONTROL, UNIV. WIS, MADISON, 62-66, ASSOC. PROF, 66-, EXTEN. SPECIALIST, U.S. DEPT. AGR, 62- Weed Sci. Soc. Am; Am. Soc. Agron; Soil Sci. Soc. Am. Weed control in field crops; the influence of soil properties upon soil-applied herbicides and their responses in terms of total crop management. Address: Dept. of Agronomy, University of Wisconsin, Madison, WI 53706.

DOERSCHUK, ALBERT P(ETER), b. Kansas City, Mo, Dec. 13, 23; m. 49; c. 4. ORGANIC CHEMISTRY, ECONOMICS. B.S, Pittsburgh, 43, Ph.D. (chem), 49; M.B.A, New York, 59. Instr. chem, Columbia, 48-51; group leader biochem, chem. process improv. dept, Lederle Labs, Am. Cyanamid Co, 51-54, head, 54-57, tech. asst. to plant mgr, 57, asst. to dir. res, 57-58, mgr. pharmaceut. prod. develop. sect, 58-60, tech. dir. fine chem. dept, 60-64, sr. mgt. analyst, commercial develop. div, 64-66; staff asst. to dir. planning, Lederle Labs. Div, 66-69; asst. dir. DIVERSIFICATION, G.D. SEARLE & CO, 69-71, ASSOC. DIR, 71- U.S.A, 44-46. AAAS; Am. Chem. Soc; Am. Pharmaceut. Asn; N.Y. Acad. Sci. Chemistry, radiochemistry, chemical physics; drugs; natural products; instrumentation; economics; acquisitions; management. Address: Dept. of Diversification, G.D. Searle & Co, P.O. Box 5110, Chicago, IL 60680.

DOETSCH, RAYMOND N(ICHOLAS), b. Chicago, Ill, Dec. 5, 20; m. 48; c. 3. BACTERIOLOGY. B.S, Illinois, 42; A.M, Indiana, 43; Ph.D.(bact), Maryland, 48. Asst. bactr, Indiana, 42-43; bacteriologist, Nat. Dairy Res. Lab, Baltimore, 43-45; asst. BACT, UNIV. MD, COLLEGE PARK, 45-46, instr, 46-48, asst. prof, 48-54, assoc. prof, 54-60, PROF, 60- Guggenheim fel, Rowett Inst, Aberdeen, 56; vis. lectr, inst. hist. med, Johns Hopkins Univ, 63. U.S.A, 42. AAAS; Am. Soc. Microbiol; N.Y. Acad. Sci; Am. Soc. Cell Biol; Am. Acad. Microbiol; Am. Asn. Hist. Med; Brit. Soc. Gen. Microbiol; Can. Soc. Microbiol. Bacterial cytology; general microbiology; history of science. Address: Dept. of Microbiology, University of Maryland, College Park, MD 20742.

DOFF, S(IMON) D(AVID), b. Russia, Oct. 12, 11; nat; m. 43; c. 3. MEDICINE, PUBLIC HEALTH. B.S, Pittsburgh, 32; M.D, L.I. Col. Med, 39; M.P.H, Columbia, 51. Clin. instr. med, sch. med, Yale, 43-48; asst. dir. bur. tuberc. control, Fla. State Bd. Health, 49-51, dir. div. heart disease control, 51-58, dir. bur. maternal & child health, 58-60, bur. spec. health serv, 60-65; CHMN. DEPT. COMMUNITY MED. & OUTPATIENT SERVS, UNIV. HOSP. JACKSONVILLE, 65- Fel, WHO, 63. Epidemiologist, New Haven Health Dept, 43-48; consult, heart disease control prog, U.S. Pub. Health Serv, 56-59. Dipl, Am. Bd. Prev. Med. Am. Thoracic Soc; fel. Am. Col. Cardiol; fel. Am. Col. Chest Physicians; Am. Soc. Internal Med. Epidemiology chronic disease; preventive medicine. Address: University Hospital, Jacksonville, FL 32203.

DOFT, FLOYD S(HELTON), b. Griswold, Iowa, May 19, 00; m. 35; c. 1. BIOCHEMISTRY, NUTRITION. A.B, Simpson Col, 21, hon. D.Sc, 52; Ph.D. (org. chem), Yale, 26. Traveling fel. from Yale, Carlsberg Lab, Copenhagen, Denmark, 26-27; asst. physiol, Harvard, 27-29; Lilly fel, Yale, 29-31; instr. exp. path. & biochem, Univ. Rochester, 31-37; biochemist, Nat. Insts. Health, 37-53, dir. Nat. Inst. Arthritis & Metab. Diseases, 53-62; CONSULT, 62- Asst. ed, Nutrit. Rev, 44-47; mem. sci. adv. comt, Nutrit. Found, 56-62; Nat. Vitamin Found, 57; vis. prof, Albert Einstein Col. Med, 62-66. Dipl, Am. Bd. Nutrit. U.S.A, 18; U.S.P.H.S, 45-62; Distinguished Serv. Medal. Fel. AAAS; Am. Inst. Chem; Am. Rheumatism Asn; Am. Chem. Soc; Am. Inst. Nutrit.(assoc. ed, J. Nutrit, 51-55, pres, 60-61); Am. Soc. Biol. Chem; Am. Soc. Hemat; Soc. Exp. Biol. & Med; Int. Soc. Hemat. Germ-free animals; vitamins; proteins and amino acids; liver cirrhosis and experimental dietary liver necrosis; experimental blood dycrasias. Address: 6416 Garnett Dr, Chevy Chase, MD 20015.

DOGGER, JAMES R(USSELL), b. Milwaukee, Wis, July 31, 23; m. 46; c. 3. ENTOMOLOGY. B.S, Wisconsin, 47, M.S, 48, Ph.D.(entom), 50. Instr. econ. entom, Wisconsin, 48-49; asst. prof. entom, Okla. Agr. & Mech. Col, 50-52; N.C. State Col, 52-57, assoc. prof, 57-58; prof. entom. & chmn. dept, N.Dak. State Univ, 58-69; state entomologist, N.Dak, 58-69; Fulbright prof, Univ. Nat. Trujillo, Peru, 67-68; ASST. CHIEF STORED PRODS, MKT. QUAL. RES. DIV, AGR. RES. SERV, U.S. DEPT. AGR, 69- U.S.A, 43-45. Entom. Soc. Am. Insects affecting stored products, forage and related crops; immature insects; taxonomic, Coleoptera, Elateridae, Carabidae. Address: Stored Product Insects Research Branch, Market Quality Research Division, Agricultural Research Service, U.S. Dept. Agriculture, Hyattsville, MD 20782.

DOGGETT, VIRGINIA C, b. Denton, Tex, July 13, 25; m. 60. ANATOMY, PHYSIOLOGY. B.A. & B.S, N.Texas State Col, 46, M.S, 49; fel. Illinois, 50-52, Ph.D.(physiol), 52. Asst. biol, N.Texas State Col, 43-46, instr, 46-48; asst. physiol, Illinois, 48-50; asst. prof, Southwest. Med. Sch, Texas, 52-53; fel. Med. Sch, Western Reserve, 53-54, U.S. Pub. Health Serv. fel, 54-56; asst. prof. ANAT, UNIV. TEX.(SOUTHWEST) MED. SCH, 56-70, ADJ. ASST. PROF, 70- AAAS; Am. Asn. Anat; N.Y. Acad. Sci. Reproductive endocrinology; blood androgens. Address: Dept. of Anatomy, University of Texas (Southwestern) Medical School, Dallas, TX 75235.

DOGGETT, WESLEY OSBORNE, b. Brown Summit, N.C, Jan. 24, 31; m. 53; c. 8. PLASMA PHYSICS. B.S, N.C. State Col, 52, B.S, 53; Nat. Sci. Found. Fel, California, Berkeley, 52-54, M.A, 54, Ph.D.(physics), 56. Res. assoc. physics, radiation lab, Univ. California, 54-56; tech. proj. co-ord, Airforce Nuclear Eng. Test Reactor, Wright Air Develop. Ctr, 56-58; asst. prof. PHYSICS, N.C. STATE UNIV, 58-60, assoc. prof, 60-62, PROF, 62-, asst. dean, sch. phys. sci. & appl. math, 64-68. Summer guest lectr, Inst. Fundamental Shielding Probs, Kansas State, 62. Consult, Repub. Aviation Corp, 56-59; Res. Triangle Inst, 62-; NASA, Langley Field, 63; Off. Civil Defense, 63- Mem. Am. Inst. Physics, 56-; dir, Troxler Electronics, Inc, 62- U.S.A.F.R, 56-58, Capt. AAAS; Am. Phys. Soc; Am. Soc. Eng. Educ; Am. Nuclear Soc; Am. Asn. Physics Teachers. Nuclear reactor physics; development and analysis of statistical methods for investigating half-lives of daughter radioactivities that are in secular equilibrium with parent activities; theoretical analysis of gammaray penetration in matter; relativistic electron beam studies. Address: School of Physical Sciences & Applied Mathematics, North Carolina State University, Raleigh, NC 27607.

DOGON, LEON I, b. Krugersdorp, S.Africa, Apr. 13, 30; m. 61; c. 1. DENTISTRY, ORAL BACTERIOLOGY. L.D.S, Royal Col. Surgeons, 57; D.M.D. & cert, Harvard, 63. Res. fel. dent. med, HARVARD, 60-63, res. assoc, 63-64, ASSOC. OPER. DENT, 64-, CHMN. DEPT, SCH. DENT. MED, 69- MEM. STAFF DENT. MED, FORSYTH DENT. CTR, 63- Harvard fel, 61-63. AAAS; Am. Soc. Microbiol; Int. Asn. Dent. Res. Oral Biology; antibacterial agents in human saliva; physiology of salivary secretion. Address: Forsyth Dental Center, 140 Fenway, Boston, MA 02115.

DOHANY, JULIUS E(UGENE), b. Banatski Karlovac, Yugoslavia, May 28, 26; nat; m. 51; c. 2. POLYMER CHEMISTRY. M.Ch.E, Budapest Tech, 50; Sc.D, Swiss Fed. Inst. Tech, 63. Supvr. plant, Coal Chem. Co, Hungary, 51-53, mgr, 53-56; supvr. pilot plant, Viscose Co, Switz, 56-58, res. lab, 58-59; res. chemist, Cryovac Div, W.R. Grace & Co, 63-64; sr. res. chemist, Pennsalt Chem. Corp, 64-66, proj. leader, 66-67, GROUP LEADER, PENNWALT CORP, 67- Am. Chem. Soc; Soc. Plastics Eng. Synthesis and characterization of polymers; vicose fiber process; synthetic fibers; textile chemistry; tar distillation; coal carbonization; gas desulfurization; fluorine containing polymers, coatings, film, polymer rheology. Address: 480 Howellville Rd, Berwyn, PA 19312.

DOHENY, EDWARD JOHN LAWRENCE, b. N.Y.C, Nov. 1, 35; m. 62; c. 1. GEOLOGY. B.S, City Col. New York, 62; M.A, Indiana, 64, Ph.D.(geol), 67. ASST. PROF. CIVIL ENG, DREXEL UNIV, 67- U.S.N, 54-56, Res, 53-54, 56-61. AAAS; Am. Geophys. Union; Soc. Econ. Paleont. & Mineral; Am. Geol. Inst. Petrology of carbonate and evaporite rocks; clay mineralogy; clay-water interaction; adsorbed water. Address: Dept. of Soil, Water & Urban Engineering, Drexel University, Philadelphia, PA 19104.

DOHERTY, DAVID G(EORGE), b. Brooklyn, N.Y, July 22, 15; m. 46; c. 5. BIOCHEMISTRY. B.S, Polytech. Inst. Brooklyn, 35, M.S, 40; Nat. Insts. Health jr. fel, Wisconsin, 46-48, Ph.D.(biochem), 48. Technician, Rockefeller Inst, 35-41; asst, Wisconsin, 41-42; asst. chemist, east. regional res. lab, bur. agr. & indust. chem, U.S. Dept. Agr, 42-44, assoc. chemist, 46; SR. BIOCHEMIST, BIOL. DIV, OAK RIDGE NAT. LAB, 48-; DIR. TOXICOL. INFO. QUERY & RESPONSE CTR, NAT. LIBR. MED, 71- Instr. evening classes, Oak Ridge div, Tennessee, 49- U.S.N, 44-46, Lt. AAAS; Am. Chem. Soc; Am. Soc. Biol. Chem; Radiation Res. Soc; Am. Inst. Chem; N.Y. Acad. Sci. Proteolytic enzymes; amino acid, protein analysis and methods; methods of peptide synthesis; carbohydrate anticoagulants; protein plastics; nucleic acids; chemical protection against radiation damage; inhalation cocarcinogenesis. Address: Biology Division, Oak Ridge National Lab, Oak Ridge, TN 37830.

DOHERTY, GEORGE OLIVER PLUNKETT, b. Derry, Ireland, Oct. 26, 36; m. 61; c. 3. ORGANIC CHEMISTRY. B.Sc, Univ. Col. Dublin, 57 & 59, Ph.D (chem), 62. Res. asst. org. chem, sch. pharm, London, 62-65, lectr, 65-66; SR. ORG. CHEMIST, LILLY RES. LABS, 66- Structure determination of bacterial metabolities; synthesis of pharmacologically active agents. Address: Lilly Research Labs, Eli Lilly & Co, Indianapolis, IN 46206.

DOHERTY, JAMES EDWARD, III, b. Newport, Ark, Nov. 22, 23; m. 48; c. 2. INTERNAL MEDICINE, CARDIOLOGY. B.S, Univ. Ark, 44, M.D, 46. Intern, Columbus City Hosp, Ga, 46-47; res. MED, SCH. MED, UNIV. ARK, 49-52, from instr. to assoc. prof, 52-68, PROF, 68-; DIR. DIV. CARDIOL, UNIV. ARK. MED. CTR-VET. ADMIN. HOSPS, 69- Chief cardiol, Little Rock Vet. Admin. Hosp, 57-69. Dipl, Am. Bd. Internal Med, 55, Am. Bd. Cardiovasc. Disease, 59. Med.C, 47-49, Capt. Am. Fedn. Clin. Res; Soc. Nuclear Med; Am. Col. Physicians; Am. Col. Cardiol. Cardiovascular disease, primarily the metabolism of radioactive digoxin and cholesterol. Address: 48 Wingate Dr, Little Rock, AR 72205.

DOHERTY, L(OWELL) R(ALPH), b. San Diego, Calif, Mar. 12, 30. ASTRONOMY. B.A, California, Los Angeles, 52; fel, Michigan, 53-54, M.S, 54, Nat. Sci. Found. fel, 54-56, Ph.D.(astron), 62. Lectr. ASTRON. & res. fel, Harvard, 57-63; asst. prof, UNIV. WIS, MADISON, 63-69, ASSOC. PROF, 69- Am. Astron. Soc. Solar physics; stellar spectroscopy. Address: Dept. of Astronomy, Sterling Hall, University of Wisconsin, Madison, WI 53706.

DOHERTY, PATRICK D, S.J, b. Los Angeles, Calif, Mar. 18, 24. NUCLEAR PHYSICS. B.S, U.S. Mil. Acad, 46; Univ. South. Calif, 46-47; B.S, Calif. Inst. Technol, 49; M.A, St. Louis Univ, 59, Ph.D.(physics), 62; M.A, Univ. Santa Clara, 66. ASST. PROF. PHYSICS, LOYOLA UNIV. LOS ANGELES, 67- U.S.A, 43-46. Am. Phys. Soc. Medium energy nuclear reactions; the few nucleon problem. Address: Dept. of Physics, Loyola University of Los Angeles, 7101 W. 80th St, Los Angeles, CA 90045.

DOHERTY, PAUL EDWARD, b. Cambridge, Mass, June 24, 36; m. 62. PHYSICAL METALLURGY. A.B, Harvard, 58, A.M, 60, Ph.D.(metall), 61. Res. asst, Harvard, summer 58; metallurgist, ARTHUR D. LITTLE, INC, 59-61, STAFF ASSOC, CAMBRIDGE, 61- Am. Inst. Mining, Metall. & Petrol. Eng. Interaction of vacancies with defects in crystals; origin of defects during solidification of metals; development and application of new technique for studying oxidation of metals; kinetic studies in ternary alloys; development of new technique for preparing thin sections of ceramics from bulk for direct observation by transmission electron microscopy. Address: 4 Fairbanks Rd, Lexington, MA 02173.

DOHERTY, W(ILFRED) T(HOMAS), b. Houston, Tex, Mar. 23, 98; m. 31, c. 2; m. 67; c. 2. CHEMICAL ENGINEERING. B.S, Agr. & Mech. Col. Tex, 43; hon. D.Sc, Tex. Tech. Col, 63. Mem. staff process lab. & res, Humble Oil & Ref. Co, 22-27, in charge chem. eng, prod. dept, 27-32, petrol. engr, Gulf Coast Div, 32-34, engr. in charge petrol. eng. dept, 34-36, div. supt, 36-38; gen. supt, R.A. Welch Interests, 39-48; pres. & dir, Mound Co, 48-63; FOUND. CONSULT, 63- V.pres. & dir, Fidelity Oil & Royalty Co, 48-55; dir, Agr. & Mech. Col. Texas Syst, 53-59, pres. bd. dir, 55-59, councilor, res. found, 58-; trustee, Robert A. Welch Found, 53-70, sr. trustee & pres, 70- Citation of Serv, Am. Petrol. Inst, 51. U.S.N, 17-18. AAAS; Am.

Chem. Soc; Am. Asn. Petrol. Geol; Am. Inst. Mining, Metall. & Petrol. Eng. fel. Am. Inst. Chem. Chemical and petroleum engineering; basic research in chemistry. Address: 2010 Bank of the Southwest Bldg, Houston, TX 77002.

DOHERTY, WILLIAM H(UMPHREY), b. Cambridge, Mass, Aug. 21, 07; m. 39; c. 2. ELECTRONICS, COMMUNICATIONS. S.B, Harvard, 27, S.M, 28; hon. Sc.D, Catholic Univ, 50. Res. assoc, Nat. Bur. Standards, 28-29; mem. tech. staff radio equip. develop, Bell Tel. Labs, Inc, N.J, 29-48, dir, electronic & TV res, 49-55, asst. v.pres, admin, Am. Tel. & Tel. Co, N.Y, 55-57, mgr. govt. mil. contracting, West. Elec. Co, Inc, 58-60, patent license mgr, 60-61; asst. to pres. sci. & tech. rels, Bell Tel. Labs, Inc, 61-70; RETIRED. Naval Ord. Develop. award, 45. Fel. Inst. Elec. & Electronics Eng.(Morris Liebmann Mem. Prize, Inst. Radio Eng, 37). Electronics and electrical communications, especially telephony, television and physical sciences related thereto. Address: Belted Kingfisher Rd, Hilton Head Island, SC 29928.

DOHLMAN, CLAES-HENRIK, b. Uppsala, Sweden, Sept. 11, 22; m. 48; c. 6. OPHTHALMOLOGY. Lic. Med, Lund, 50, Med.Dr, 57. Res. fel. ophthal, Retina Found, 53-54; asst. surgeon, univ. eye clin, Univ. Lund, 55-57; fel, MASS. EYE & EAR INFIRMARY, 58-63, DIR. CORNEA SERV, 64-, ASSOC. PROF. OPHTHAL, 69-; DIR. DEPT. CORNEA RES, RETINA FOUND, 67-, res. assoc, 58-62. Asst. prof, univ. eye clin, Univ. Lund, 57; asst. surgeon, Mass. Eye & Ear Infirmary, 66-69. Swedish Navy, 48. Diseases of the cornea of the eye. Address: Retina Foundation, 20 Staniford St, Boston, MA 02114.

DOHNANYI, JULIUS S, b. Budapest, Hungary, Aug. 29, 31; U.S. citizen; m. 60; c. 1. THEORETICAL PHYSICS. Ga. Inst. Tech, 51-52; M.S, Fla. State, 55; Ph.D.(physics), Ohio State, 60. Mem. staff, Sandia Corp, 60-63; MEM, TECH. STAFF, BELLCOMM, INC, 63- Summer asst, Westinghouse Elec. Corp, 56, N.Am. Aviation, Inc, 57, Bell Tel. Labs, 58. Am. Phys. Soc; Am. Geophys. Union. Physics of interplanetary debris; nuclear magnetic resonance; superconductivity; statistical models of the nucleus. Address: Bellcomm, Inc, 1100 17th St. N.W, Washington, DC 20036.

DOHNER, LUKE D, b. Jan. 1, 26; U.S. citizen; m. 52; c. 3. PLANT SCIENCE, ENTOMOLOGY. B.S. in Agr, Florida, 52, M.S, in Agr, 53. Mgt. trainee, W.R. Grace & Co, 53-55; mem. res. staff, Ortho Div, Chevron Chem. Co, 55 & 64-65, salesman, 55-58, sales mgr, 58-64; salesman, ELI LILLY & CO, 66, MEM. RES. STAFF. PLANT SCI, 66- U.S.N, 43-46. Entom. Soc. Am. Agricultural economic research; industrial agricultural research; chemical pesticides, entomology, plant pathology and plant physiology. Address: 1975 Richard Lane, West Palm Beach, FL 33406.

DOHOO, ROY McGREGOR, b. Essex, Eng, Sept. 3, 19; Can. citizen; m. 49; c. 2. COMMUNICATIONS. B.A, Cambridge, 41, M.A, 44. Exp. officer radar, Air Ministry, U.K, 47-48; sci. officer electronic fuzing, Armament Design Estab, 48-52; defence res. telecommun. estab, Defence Res. Bd. Can, 52-55, sect. leader radar systs, 55-57; res. engr, Rand Corp, Calif, 57-59; sci. officer, Defence Res. Bd. Can, 59-62, sect. leader microwave propagation, Defence Res. Telecommun. Estab, 62-67, supt, commun. lab, 67-69; DIR. NAT. COMMUN. LAB, COMMUN. RES. CTR, DEPT. COMMUN, 69- R.A.O.C. & R.E.M.E, 41-47, Maj. Sr. mem. Inst. Elec. & Electronics Eng; fel. Brit. Inst. Elec. Eng. Telecommunications; radar systems; electronic fuzing; microwave propagation. Address: 2092 Woodcrest Rd, Ottawa, Ont, K1H 6H8, Can.

DOHRENWEND, CLAYTON O(LIVER), b. New Britain, Conn, May 20, 09; m. 32; c. 2. ENGINEERING MECHANICS. C.E, Rensselaer Polytech, 31, M.C.E, 35, M.S, 37; Ph.D.(mech), Michigan, 40. Instr. civil eng. & eng. mech, Rensselaer Polytech, 31-37; Armour Inst. Tech, 37-39, mem. staff, stress anal, Armour Res. Found, 37-39; asst. prof. civil eng. mech, Connecticut, 39-41; res. engr, eng. mech, Armour Res. Found, 41-42, chmn. div. mech. res, 41-45; head dept. mech, Ill. Inst. Tech, 45-46; res. consult. to pres, Midwest Res. Inst, 46-47, asst. dir. res, 47-49; prof. mech. & chmn. dept, RENSSELAER POLYTECH. INST, 49-52, dean grad. sch, 52, acting dean, sch. sci, 54, dean, 58, V.PRES. & PROVOST, 59- Organized Hartford Grad. Ctr, Rensselaer Polytech. Inst, 55. Am. Soc. Civil Eng; fel. Am. Soc. Mech. Eng; Soc. Exp. Stress Anal.(pres, 47); Am. Soc. Eng. Educ. Stress analysis. Address: Vice President & Provost, Rensselaer Polytechnic Institute, Troy, NY 12181.

DOI, KUNIO, b. Tokyo, Japan, Sept. 28, 39; m. 62; c. 2. MEDICAL PHYSICS, OPTICS. B.Sc, Waseda Univ. Japan, 62, D.Sc, 69. Chief radiography res, Kyokko Res. Labs. Dai Nippon Toryo Co, Ltd, Japan, 62-69; ASST. PROF. RADIOL, UNIV. CHICAGO, 69- Instr, faculty med, Tohoku Univ, Japan, 66-69. Am. Asn. Physicists in Med; Optical Soc. Am; Soc. Nondestructive Test; Japanese Appl. Physics Soc.(award, 68); Physical Soc. Japan; Japanese Radiol. Soc. Image quality of radiologic imaging systems; solid state inorganic luminescent materials. Address: Dept. of Radiology, University of Chicago, 950 E. 59th St, Chicago, IL 60637.

DOI, ROY H(IROSHI), b. Sacramento, Calif, Mar. 26, 33; m. 58; c. 2. MICROBIOLOGY. A.B, California, Berkeley, 53, A.B, 57; M.S, Wisconsin, 58, Ph.D.(bact), 60. U.S. Pub. Health Serv. fel, 60-63; asst. prof. BACT. & BOT, Syracuse, 63-65; UNIV. CALIF, DAVIS, 65-66, assoc. prof, 66-69, PROF, 69- Vis. prof, dept. genetics & cell. biol, Nat. Polytech. Inst, Mexico City, Mex, 70; Nat. Sci. Found. sr. fel, 71-72; mem, microbiol. training comt, Nat. Inst. Gen. Med. Sci, 68-71. U.S.A, 53-55. Am. Soc. Microbiol; Am. Soc. Biol. Chem. Interrelationship between proteins and nucleic acids during morphogenesis and phage infection. Address: Dept. of Biochemistry & Biophysics, University of California, Davis, CA 95616.

DOIDGE, JEROME G, b. Iowa, Feb. 15, 34. ELECTRICAL ENGINEERING. B.S, Iowa State Univ, 60, M.S, 61, Ph.D, 63. Res. asst, Iowa State Univ, 60-63; sr. res. engr, AUTONETICS DIV, N.Am. Aviation, Inc, 63-64, RES. SPECIALIST, N.AM. ROCKWELL CORP, 64- Optical Soc. Am; Am. Nuclear Soc. Thin film and electro-optic devices. Address: Autonetics Division, North American Rockwell Corp, 3370 Miraloma Ave, Anaheim, CA 92803.

DOIG, RONALD, b. Montreal, Que, Feb. 14, 39. GEOLOGY, GEOPHYSICS. B.Sc, McGill, 60, M.Sc, 61, Ph.D.(geol), 64. Mem. staff gamma-ray spectrometry, geophys. div, Geol. Surv. Can, 62-64; lectr. isotope geol, geophys, McGILL UNIV, 64-66, asst. prof. GEOL. SCI, 66-70, ASSOC. PROF, 70- Am. Geophys. Union; Geol. Asn. Can. Isotope geology; geochronology; stable isotopes; terrestrial heat flow; gamma-ray spectrometry. Address: Dept. of Geological Sciences, McGill University, Montreal, Que, Can.

DOIGAN, PAUL, b. Greenfield, Mass, June 8, 19; m. 53; c. 3. PHYSICAL CHEMISTRY. B.S, Connecticut, 41; B.S, N.Y. Univ, 43, Ph.D.(chem), 50; M.S, Massachusetts, 46. Res. assoc. chem, atomic res. inst, Iowa State Col, 46; instr. chem, Massachusetts, 46-47; Univ. Conn, 50-51; res. chemist, GEN. ELEC. CO, 51-55, prof. personnel, 55-58, consult. engr. & mgr. personnel placement & facility planning, 59-60, mgr. eng. admin, missile & space vehicle dept, 60-62, spacecraft dept, 62-64, consult. specialist, 65-66, proj. mgr. col. placement coun, 66-67, MGR. DOCTORAL & INT. RECRUITING, 67- Mem. conf. elec. insulation, Nat. Res. Coun. U.S.A.F, 43-46, Res, 46-, Maj. AAAS; Am. Chem. Soc; Electrochem. Soc; Inst. Elec. & Electronics Eng; Am. Soc. Qual. Control; Sci. Res. Soc. Am; Am. Soc. Eng. Educ. Engineering administration; space vehicles; manned space laboratory. Address: 2275 Sweetbrier Rd, Schenectady, NY 12309.

DOISY, E(DWARD) A(DELBERT), b. Hume, Ill, Nov. 13, 93; m. 18; c. 4. PHYSIOLOGY, BIOCHEMISTRY. A.B, Illinois, 14, M.S, 16, Ph.D.(biochem), Harvard, 20; hon. Sc.D, Washington (St. Louis), 40, Yale, 40, Chicago, 41, Central Col, 42, Illinois, 60, Gustavus Adolphus Col, 63; hon. Dr.Paris, 45; hon. LL.D, St. Louis, 55. Asst. BIOCHEM, Harvard Med. Sch, 15-17; instr, sch. med, Washington (St. Louis), 19-20, assoc, 20-22, assoc. prof, 22-23; prof. SCH. MED, ST. LOUIS UNIV, 23-, distinguished serv. prof, 51-65, dir. dept, 24-65, EMER. PROF. & EMER. DIR. EDWARD A. DOISY DEPT. BIOCHEM, 65- Numerous hon. lectureships, 31-46. Mem. cmt. standardization sex hormones, League of Nations, 32-35; cmt. biol. & med, Atomic Energy Cmn. Gold medal, St. Louis Med. Soc, 35; Conne medal, 35; Gibbs medal, 41; award, Am. Pharmaceut. Mfg. Asn, 42; co-winner Nobel prize, 43; Squibb award, 44; Fleur de Lis, St. Louis. Univ, 51; Illini Achievement award, Univ. Illinois, 58. With Nat. Adv. Cancer Coun, 41-43, 48-51. Sanit.C, 17-19, 2nd Lt. Nat. Acad. Sci; AAAS; Am. Soc. Bio. Chem.(v.pres, 41, pres, 43-45); Am. Chem. Soc; Endocrine Soc.(pres, 49); Am. Asn. Cancer Res; Soc. Exp. Biol. & Med.(v.pres, 47-49, pres, 49-51); Am. Philos. Soc; Am. Acad. Arts & Sci; Pontifical Acad. Metabolism; insulin; blood buffers; isolation and chemical characterization of theelin, theelol and dihydro-theelin; ovarian hormones and estrogenic substances; gonadotropic and thyrotropic principles; vitamin K; antibiotics; bile acids; metabolism of steroids. Address: Edward A. Doisy Dept. of Biochemistry, St. Louis University School of Medicine, 1402 S. Grand Blvd, St. Louis, MO 63104.

DOISY, E(DWARD) A(DELBERT), JR, b. St. Louis, Mo, Mar. 15, 20; m. 42; c. 4. BIOCHEMISTRY. B.S, Illinois, 41; M.D, Harvard, 44. Intern med, Mass. Gen. Hosp, 44-45; instr. int. med, SCH. MED, ST. LOUIS UNIV, 47-51, asst. prof, 51-55, assoc. prof, 55-59, PROF. BIOCHEM, 59-, ASSOC. PROF. INT. MED, 68- Med.C, U.S.A, 45-47. AAAS; Am. Chem. Soc; Am. Oil Chemists' Soc; Soc. Exp. Biol. & Med; Am. Soc. Biol. Chem. Nutrition; solubilities of some estrogens; metabolism of inositol and lindane; metabolism of radioactive sex and adrenal hormones and bile acids; nutritional influences on bile; vitamin K, human requirement and environmental concentration. Address: Dept. of Biochemistry, St. Louis University School of Medicine, St. Louis, MO 63104.

DOISY, R(ICHARD) J(OSEPH), b. St. Louis, Mo, Jan. 30, 26; m. 50; c. 2. BIOCHEMISTRY. B.S, Missouri, 46; M.S, Nebraska, 51; Ph.D.(biochem), Syracuse, 54. Asst. chem, Nebraska, 48-51; res. fel. biochem, State Univ. N.Y, 51-54; Am. Cancer Soc. fel, enzyme inst, Wisconsin, 54-56; instr. BIOCHEM, STATE UNIV. N.Y, UPSTATE MED. CTR, 56-60, asst. prof, 60-65, ASSOC. PROF, 65- Am. Soc. Biol. Chem; Am. Inst. Nutrit. Insulin assay; adipose tissue metabolism; glucose tolerance; chromium; diabetes; nutrition. Address: 601 Waldorf Parkway, Syracuse, NY 13224.

DOKU, H(RISTO) CHRIS, b. Istanbul, Turkey, Apr. 17, 28; U.S. citizen; m. 58; c. 1. ORAL SURGERY. D.D.S, Istanbul, 51; D.M.D, Tufts, 58, M.D.S, 60. Instr. ORAL SURG, SCH. DENT. MED, TUFTS UNIV, 58-59, asst. prof, 59-63, assoc. prof, 63-67, PROF, 67-, CHMN. DEPT, 65- U.S. Pub. Health Serv. trainee, 58-60 & prin. investr, 60- Hatton award, Chicago, 60. Am. Dent. Asn; Am. Soc. Oral Surg; Int. Asn. Dent. Res. Blood clotting factors; thromboplastic activity and its relation to saliva; wound healing; age and dentition. Address: Dept. of Oral Surgery, School of Dental Medicine, Tufts University, 136 Harrison Ave, Boston, MA 02111.

DOLAK, LESTER A(RTHUR), b. Joliet, Ill, Mar. 25, 42; m. 64; c. 3. ORGANIC CHEMISTRY. B.A, Hopkins, 63, Ph.D.(chem), 66. RES. ASSOC, Stanford, 66-67; ORG. CHEM, UPJOHN CO, 67- Am. Chem. Soc. Nitrogen chemistry; olefinic cyclizations; antibiotics; synthesis. Address: Upjohn Co, Unit 7254, 301 Henrietta St, Kalamazoo, MI 49003.

DOLAN, DESMOND DANIEL, b. South Nelson, N.B, Nov. 19, 16; nat; m. 49; c. 3. PLANT PATHOLOGY. B.Sc, McGill, 37, M.Sc, 39; Ph.D.(plant breeding), Cornell, 46. Veg. pathologist, Dom. Pathol. Lab, 38-41; asst, Catholic Univ, 41-42; plant breeding & veg. crops, Cornell, 42-46; assoc. res. prof. hort, Rhode Island, 46-53; COORD. & HORTICULTURIST-IN-CHARGE, PLANT INTRODUCTION, N.Y. STATE AGR. EXP. STA, PLANT SCI. RES. DIV, U.S. DEPT. AGR, 53- Assoc. prof, Cornell Univ, 55- Am. Soc. Hort. Sci; Am. Phytopath. Soc; Am. Soc. Agron. Fungus causing stem-streak on melons; breeding Iroquois muskmelon, Rhode Island Red watermelon and Rhode Island Early and Summer Sunrise tomatoes; plant germ plasm for the Northeast. Address: Plant Introduction, Sturtevant Hall, Room 201, New York State Agriculture Experiment Station, Geneva, NY 14456.

DOLAN, JAMES MICHAEL, b. N.Y.C, Feb. 27, 37. ZOOLOGY. B.S, Mt. St. Mary's Col, 59; Long Island, 59-60; Thyssen fel, Kiel, 60-63, Ph.D. (zool), 63. From assoc. curator birds to CURATOR, SAN DIEGO ZOOL. GARDEN, 63-; SAN DIEGO WILD ANIMAL PARK, 69- German Soc. Mammal. Taxonomy and conservation of artiodactyls, perisodactyls and small felines. Address: P.O. Box 551, San Diego, CA 92112.

DOLAN, JOSEPH FRANCIS, b. Rochester, N.Y, Sept. 17, 39; m. 71. ASTRONOMY, ASTROPHYSICS. B.S, St. Bonaventure, 61; univ. fel, Harvard, 61-62, Nat. Sci. Found. fel, 62-63, 64-65, A.M, 63, Ph.D.(astrophys), 66. Physicist, Smithsonian Astrophys. Observ, 65-66; sr. scientist, Jet Propulsion Lab, Calif. Inst. Tech, 66-68; ASST. PROF. ASTRON, CASE WESTERN RESERVE UNIV, 68- AAAS; Am. Astron. Soc. X-ray and gamma ray astronomy; astronomical polarization. Address: Warner & Swasey Observatory, Taylor & Brunswick Rds, East Cleveland, OH 44112.

DOLAN, KENNETH WILLIAM, b. Yakima, Wash, July 23, 40; m. 63; c. 3. NUCLEAR PHYSICS. B.S, Washington (Seattle), 62; Nat. Defense Ed. Act fel, Oregon, 63-66, M.S, 64, Ph.D.(nuclear physics), 68. Tech. staff mem. nuclear physics, Naval Radiation Defense Lab, Calif, summer 63 & 64; res. asst, Oregon, 66-68; TECH. STAFF MEM. PHYSICS, SANDIA LABS, 68- Am. Phys. Soc. Experimental low energy nuclear physics. Address: 4048 Pomona Way, Livermore, CA 94550.

DOLAN, THOMAS, b. Philadelphia, Pa, Apr. 16, 23; m. 42; c. 3. ENVIRONMENTAL SCIENCES. B.S, Cornell, 48; Pennsylvania, 48-54. Sci. asst. limnol, Acad. Nat. Sci. Phila, 48-54; pres, Consult. Biologists, Inc, 54-63; exec. dir, Wissahickon Valley Watershed Asn, 63-70; PRES. & EXEC. DIR, ENVIRON. PLANNING & INFO. CTR. PA, 70- With Am. Field Serv, 43-44; v.chmn, Citizen's Adv. Coun, Pa. Dept. of Environ. Resources. Am. Fisheries Soc; Wildlife Soc; Entom. Soc. Am; Am. Inst. Biol. Sci. Dissemination and coordination of environmental efforts in Pennsylvania; investigation of environmental issues and problems with statewide or major regional impact; review and evaluation of environmental projects in Pennsylvania. Address: 721 Glengarry Rd, Philadelphia, PA 19118.

DOLAN, THOMAS J(AMES), b. Chicago, Ill, Dec. 29, 06; m. 29; c. 2. MECHANICAL ENGINEERING. B.S, Illinois, 29, M.S, 32. Asst. & instr. THEORET. & APPL. MECH, UNIV. ILL, URBANA-CHAMPAIGN, 29-37, asst. prof, 37-41, assoc. prof, 41-42, RES. PROF, 45-, HEAD DEPT. ENG. MECHS, 52- Eng. consult. & bd. dirs, Packer Eng. Am. ed, Appl. Mat. Res, 62- Mem, Nat. Res. Develop. Bd, 48; eng. adv. bd, Nat. Sci. Found, 52-57; Nat. Res. Coun, 55- Ord. Dept, 42-45, Capt. Am. Soc. Mech. Eng. (v.pres, 58-60); Am. Soc. Test. & Mat.(Dudley medal, 52, Templin award, 54); Soc. Exp. Stress Anal.(pres, 51); Am. Soc. Eng. Educ. Fatigue of metals; photoelastic stress analysis; properties of metals; mechanical vibrations; metallurgy; failure analysis; product liability. Address: Talbot Lab, University of Illinois, Urbana-Champaign, Urbana, IL 61801.

DOLAN, WILLIAM M, b. Grand Junction, Colo, Sept. 29, 29; m. 52; c. 4. GEOPHYSICS. B.Sc. & M.Sc, Utah, 56. Res. assoc. geophys, Utah, 57-58; geophysicist, Newmont Explor, Ltd, Conn, 58-67, CHIEF GEOPHYSICIST, Newmont Mining Corp. Can, Ltd, 67-70; AMAX EXPLO. INC, 70- Consult. geophysicist, Cyprus Mines Corp, 63-65. U.S.N.A.F, 48-52. Soc. Explor. Geophys; Can. Inst. Mining & Metall. Radio wave scattering in mountainous terrain; regional gravity and seismic crustal studies in Utah; electromagnetic prospecting scheme. Address: 677 Meadow Wood Rd, Clarkson, Ont, Can.

DOLAN, WINTHROP W(IGGIN), b. Agawam, Mass, Mar. 13, 09; m. 33; c. 3. MATHEMATICS. A.B, Denison, 30; Ohio State, 30-31; A.M, Harvard, 37; Ph.D.(math), Oklahoma, 47. Dean jr. col. & instr. math, Bacone Jr. Col, 31-42; asst, Oklahoma, 42-43; asst. prof. MATH, Denison, 43-45; instr, Oklahoma, 45-47, asst. prof, 47-48; PROF. & HEAD DEPT, LINFIELD COL, 48-, V.PRES, 68-, acting pres, 68. Asst. to dir, Linfield Res. Inst, 56-59. Math. Asn. Am. Metric differential geometry of reciprocal rectilinear congruences; educational administration; field emission theory. Address: Linfield College, McMinnville, OR 97128.

DOLANSKY, LADISLAV, b. Vienna, Austria, May 6, 19; nat; m. 46; c. 2. PHYSICS. Ing, Czech High Tech. Learning, Prague, 46; M.S, Mass. Inst. Tech, 49, E.E, 52; Ph.D.(applied physics), Harvard, 59. Asst. elec. lab, Czech High Tech. Learning, 45-47; elec. communications, Mass. Inst. Tech, 47-52, asst. prof. RES. ELEC. COMMUNICATIONS, NORTHEAST. UNIV, 52-55, assoc. prof, 55-63, PROF, 63- Instr. fundamental elec, Sig. Corps, Czech, 45-47; Nat. Sci. Found. fel, Case Inst. Technol, 60-; Fulbright scholar, Royal Inst. Technol, Stockholm, 66-67. Consult, Harvard, 59; Radio Corp. Am, 60; Sylvania Elec. Prod, Inc. div, Gen. Tel. & Electronics Corp, 60-62. Opers. Res. Soc. Am; Soc. Gen. Systs. Res; Acoustical Soc. Am; Inst. Elec. & Electronics Eng. Weather radar; electrical communications; pulse code modulation; speech analysis; noise and random processes; systems analyses; acoustics. Address: Room 308 DA, Northeastern University, 360 Huntington Ave, Boston, MA 02115.

DOLAR-MANTUANI, LUDMILA, b. Celje, Yugoslavia, July 5, 06; nat. Can; m. 30; c. 1. GEOLOGY. Dipl. Ph, Ljubljana, Yugoslavia, 29, Ph.D.(petrol), 35. Private docent & lectr. applied petrol, Univ. Ljubljana, Yugoslavia, 36-40, lectr. & asst. prof. crystallog, mineral & petrol, 40-45; Lady Davis Found. fel, British Columbia, 49-50, lectr. petrol, 50-51; petrographer res. div, Ont. Hydroelec. Power Comn, 52-71; CONSULT, 71- Mem. hwy. res. bd, Nat. Acad. Sci-Nat. Res. Coun. Am. Concrete Inst; fel. Mineral. Soc. Am; Geochem. Soc; Mineral Asn. Can; Am. Soc. Test. & Mat. Igneous rocks, particularly feldspar group; universal stage methods; petrography of building materials and concrete. Address: Postal St. W, P.O. Box 184, Toronto 15, Ont, Can.

DOLBEAR, GEOFFREY E(MERSON), b. Richmond, Calif, June 1, 41; m. 61; c. 2. INORGANIC CHEMISTRY. B.S, Univ. Calif, Berkeley, 62; Nat. Sci. Found. fel, Stanford;Univ, summer 63, Allied Chem. Corp. fel, 64-65, Ph.D. (inorg. chem), 66. Chemist asst, U.S. Naval Radiol. Defense Lab, San Francisco, Calif, summers 61 & 62; RES. CHEMIST, film res. lab, E.I. du Pont de Nemours & Co, Inc, Del, 65-68; cracking catalyst res. dept, DAVISON DIV, W.R. GRACE & CO, CLARKSVILLE, 68-70, AUTOMOTIVE EXHAUST EMISSIONS CONTROL RES. DEPT, 70- Am. Chem. Soc. Mechanisms of inorganic reactions in solution; preparation and evaluation of heterogeneous catalysts. Address: 5217 Lightning View Rd, Columbia, MD 21043.

DOLBEARE, FRANK ARNOLD, b. Barry, Ill, Mar. 11, 33; m. 57. BIOCHEMISTRY. B.A, Louisville, 57, Ph.D.(biochem), 61. Lab. analyst, Spencer Chem. Co, 51-53; mem. staff, lab, Indiana Arsenal, 53; lab. technician, Colgate-Palmolive Co, 54-56; Clayton & Lambert Mfg. Co, 56-57; res. fel, biochem, Brandeis, 61-62; asst. prof. chem, Ky. South. Col, 62-65; fel. biochem, Brandeis Univ, 65-66; asst. prof. neurol. & biochem, Northwest. Univ. & mem. res. staff, Vet. Admin. Hosp, 66-68; SR. SCIENTIST, ELI LILLY & CO, 68- Am. Chem. Soc. Ribonucleic and amino acid incorporation; structure of protein; structure of desoxyribonucleic acid, denaturation and renaturation. Address: Eli Lilly & Co, Indianapolis, IN 46206.

DOLBIER, WILLIAM READ, JR, b. Elizabeth, N.J, Aug. 17, 39; m. 61; c. 3. ORGANIC CHEMISTRY. B.S, Stetson, 61; Proctor & Gamble fel, Cornell, 63-64, Ph.D.(org. chem), 65. Fel. ORG. CHEM, Yale, 65-66; ASSOC. PROF, UNIV. FLA, 66- A.P. Sloan fel, 70-72. Am. Chem. Soc. Thermal rearrangement of small ring hydrocarbons; kinetic and deuterium isotope effect studies of nomechanism reactions; carbene chemistry; reactive organometallic intermediates. Address: Dept. of Chemistry, University of Florida, Gainesville, FL 32601.

DOLBY, LLOYD J(AY), b. Elgin, Ill, Oct. 5, 35; m. 56; c. 2. ORGANIC CHEMISTRY. B.S, Illinois, 56; Dow fel, California, Berkeley, 58-59, Ph.D. (chem), 59. Nat. Sci. Found. fel. CHEM, Wisconsin, 59-60; asst. prof, UNIV. ORE, 60-64, assoc. prof, 64-69, PROF, 69- Alfred P. Sloan res. fel, 65-67. Am. Chem. Soc. Synthesis of natural products; reaction mechanisms. Address: Dept. of Chemistry, University of Oregon, Eugene, OR 97403.

DOLCE, THOMAS JOSEPH, b. Silver Creek, N.Y, Dec. 29, 32; m. 68; c. 2. POLYMER & ORGANIC CHEMISTRY. B.S, Rochester, 54; Ph.D.(chem), Buffalo, 58. Chemist, Celanese Corp, 58-64, develop. engr, CELANESE PLASTICS CO, 64-65, group leader appl. develop. plastics, N.Y, 65-69, MGR, CHEM. RES. & PROD. DEVELOP. POLYESTER FILM, 70- Am. Chem. Soc. Polymerization; polymer stabilization; plastics and plastic film technology. Address: Celanese Plastics Co, Box 828, Greer, SC 29651.

DOLCH, JOHN P(ARKER), b. Champaign, Ill, Oct. 22, 20; m. 47; c. 2. COMPUTER SCIENCE. B.S, Illinois, 46, M.M, North Texas State, 48; M.A, Iowa, 51, Ph.D.(audiol), 53. Instr. music, North Texas State, 47-48; res. assoc. audiol, Iowa, 52-54; psychologist psycho-acoustics, Radio Corp. Am, N.J, 54-55; engr. electronics, testing progs, UNIV. IOWA, 55-58, dir. COMPUT. CTR, 58-64, HEAD RES, 64-, ASSOC. PROF. EDUC. & PROF. COMPUT. SCI, 69- Consult, Radio Corp. Am, N.J, 55-56. Sig.C, U.S.A, 43-46. Asn. Comput. Mach. Computer teaching methods; man-computer interaction; heuristic programming research; psychoacoustics. Address: Computer Center, University of Iowa, Iowa City, IA 52240.

DOLCH, W(ILLIAM) L(EE), b. Kansas City, Mo, July 11, 25; m. 48; c. 2. PHYSICAL CHEMISTRY. B.S.Ch.E, Purdue, 47, M.S, 49, Ph.D.(chem), 56. Asst. hwy. eng, JOINT HWY. RES. PROJ, PURDUE UNIV, 47-56, res. assoc. & asst. prof, 56-60, assoc. prof, 60-65, PROF. ENG. MAT, 65- Mem, Hwy. Res. Bd, Nat. Acad. Sci-Nat. Res. Coun. U.S.N, 44-46. Am. Soc. Test. & Mat.(Dudley medal, 66); Am. Concrete INST.(Wasson medal, 68). Physico-chemical properties of engineering materials; concrete and concrete aggregates; surface chemistry. Address: Dept. of Civil Engineering, Purdue University, Lafayette, IN 47907.

DOLCIANI, MARY PATRICIA, b. N.Y.C, Mar. 3, 23. ALGEBRA. B.A, Hunter Col, 44; Erastus Brooks fel, Cornell, 44-45, M.A, 45, Olmstead fel, 45-47, Ph.D.(algebra), 47. Instr. MATH, Hunter Col, 45; Sigma Delta Epsilon fel, Inst. Adv. Study, 47-48; instr, Vassar Col, 48-50, asst. prof, 50-55; from asst. prof. to PROF, HUNTER COL, 55-, CHMN. DEPT, 69- Fund Adv. of Ed. faculty fel, Univ. Col, London; summer dir, Hunter Col. Math. Inst. for High Sch. Teachers, 58. Am. Math. Soc; Math. Asn. Am; Can. Math. Cong; London Math. Soc. Quadratic forms; analytic number theory. Address: Dept. of Mathematics, Hunter College, New York, NY 10021.

DOLE, H(OLLIS) M(ATHEWS), b. Paonia, Colo, Sept. 4, 14; m. 43; c. 2. GEOLOGY. B.S, Oregon State Col, 40, M.S, 42; Ph.D.(geol), Utah, 54. Mining engr, U.S. Bur. Mines, 42-43; geologist, U.S. Geol. Surv, 46; state geologist & dir, state dept, geol. & mineral indust, Ore, 46-69; ASST. SECY, MINERAL RESOURCES, U.S. DEPT. INTERIOR, 69- U.S.N.R, 43-45, Lt. Am. Asn. Petrol. Geol; Am. Inst. Mining, Metall. & Petrol. Eng. Ultrabasics; economic geology. Address: U.S. Dept. of the Interior, Washington, DC 20240.

DOLE, JIM, b. Phoenix, Ariz, May 28, 35; m. 57; c. 3. VERTEBRATE ECOLOGY. B.A, Arizona State, 57; M.S, Michigan, 59, Nat. Sci. Found. fel, 60-62, Ph.D,(zool), 63. Instr. zool, Michigan, 62-63; asst. prof. BIOL, SAN FERNANDO VALLEY STATE COL, 63-67, assoc. prof, 67-70, PROF, 70- AAAS; Ecol. Soc. Am; Am. Soc. Ichthyol. & Herpet. Vertebrate ecology and behavior; population ecology. Address: Dept. of Biology, San Fernando Valley State College, Northridge, CA 91326.

DOLE, MALCOLM, b. Melrose, Mass, March 4, 03; m. 28; c. 2. PHYSICAL CHEMISTRY. A.B, Harvard, 24, A.M, 26, Ph.D.(chem), 28; Leipzig, 29. Asst. Rockefeller Inst, 28-30; instr. phys. chem, NORTHWEST. UNIV, 30-35, asst. prof, 35-38, assoc. prof, 38-45, prof. CHEM, 45-69, MAT. SCI, 64-69, chmn. mat. res. ctr, 64-68, EMER. PROF, 69-; ROBERT A. WELCH PROF, BAYLOR UNIV, 69- Hon. faculty mem, Chile, 51; San Marcos, Peru, 55. Mem. bd. trustees, Gordon Res. Conf, 58-61; chmn. chem. rev. cmt, Argonne Nat. Lab, 57-63; mem. adv. panel, off. inst. prog. Nat. Sci. Found, 62-65. With Off. Sci. Res. & Develop; Atomic Energy Cmn, 44. Army-Navy Cert. Appreciation, 47. AAAS; Am. Chem. Soc.(assoc. ed, 'Chem. Rev'); Electrochem. Soc.(v.pres, 40); Am. Phys. Soc; cor. mem. Peruvian Chem. Soc. Viscosity and transference numbers of strong electrolytes; glass electrode; oxygen isotopes; physical and radiation chemistry of high polymers. Address: Dept. of Chemistry, Baylor University, Waco, TX 76703.

DOLE, STEPHEN H(ERBERT), b. West Orange, N.J, June 26, 16; m. 41; c. 1. CHEMISTRY. B.S, Lafayette Col, 37; U.S. Naval Acad, 44-45. Student engr.

anal. chem, Standard Oil Develop. Co, 37-40, res. engr. petrol. processing 45-53; ed. trade mag, MacNair-Dorland Co, 40-42; res. engr. missile tech, RAND CORP, 54-59, GROUP LEADER HUMAN ENG, 59- Secy, Working Group Extraterrestrial Resources, 62-63, mem. steering cmt, 63- U.S.N.R, 42-45, Lt. Am. Chem. Soc; Am. Inst. Aeronaut. & Astronaut; Am. Astronaut. Soc. Life support systems; oxygen recovery; human ecology as related to space flight; general properties of planetary bodies; origin of planetary systems. Address: Rand Corp, 1700 Main St, Santa Monica, CA 90406.

DOLE, VINCENT P(AUL), b. Chicago, Ill, May 8, 13; m. 42; c. 3. MEDICINE. A.B, Stanford, 34; Wisconsin, 34-36; M.D, Harvard, 39. Intern, Mass. Gen. Hosp, Boston, 40-41; asst. resident, Rockefeller Inst, 41-46; fel, Harvard Med. Sch, 46-47; assoc, ROCKEFELLER UNIV, 47-51, from physician to SR. PHYSICIAN & MEM, 51-, PROF. MED, 59- Co-ed, J. Exp. Med, 56-65. U.S.N.R, 42-46. AAAS; Am. Soc. Clin. Invest; Soc. Exp. Biol. & Med; Asn. Am. Physicians; Am. Physiol. Soc; Biophys. Soc. Cardiovascular and metabolic research. Address: Rockefeller University, 66th St. & York Ave, New York, NY 10021.

DOLEN, R(ICHARD), b. N.Y.C, Jan. 20, 36. THEORETICAL PHYSICS, ELEMENTARY PARTICLE PHYSICS. B.Engr.Phys, Cornell Univ, 57; Gen. Elec. Co. fel, Calif. Inst. Technol, 57-60, univ. fel, 61, Ph.D.(theoret. physics), 66; Fulbright fel, Univ. Tokyo, 65. Teaching asst. theoret. physics, Calif. Inst. Technol, 63-64; fel, Univ. Calif, Los Angeles, 67-68, acting asst. prof, 68-69; asst. prof, Calif. State Col, Los Angeles, spring 70; sr. res. fel, Calif. Inst. Technol, 70-71; PHYSICIST, RES. & DEVELOP. ASSOCS, 71- Am. Phys. Soc. Many body theory; quantum field theoretic treatment of regge poles; application of finite energy sum rules to pion nucleon scattering; plasma physics. Address: Research & Development Associates, P.O. Box 3580, Santa Monica, CA 90403.

DOLEZAL, VACLAV J, b. Ceska Trebova, Czech, May 21, 27; m. 63; c. 3. APPLIED MATHEMATICS. Ing, Tech. Univ. Prague, 49; C.Sc.(appl. math), Czech. Acad. Sci, 56, Dr.Sc.(appl. math), 66. Res. assoc. math, math. inst, Czech. Acad. Sci, 51-56, mathematician, 56-65; vis. prof. appl. math, eng. col, State Univ. N.Y. Stony Brook, 65-66; mathematician, math. inst, Czech. Acad. Sci, 66-68; PROF. APPL. MATH, STATE UNIV. N.Y. STONY BROOK, 68- Theory of control; analysis and synthesis of electrical networks; linear dynamical systems; distribution theory; stability of nonlinear control systems. Address: Dept. of Applied Mathematics & Statistics, State University of New York at Stony Brook, Stony Brook, NY 11790.

DOLEZALEK, HANS, b. Berlin, Ger, May 14, 12; U.S. citizen; m. 51; c. 3. ATMOSPHERIC SCIENCES, ELECTROMETRY. Univ. Munich, 46-50; Univ. Tübingen, 50-53; Diplom, Aachen Tech. Univ, 56. Chief int. relations, Dept. For. Acad, Charlottenburg, Ger, 36-41; physicist, Aeronautic Commun. Res. Inst, Oberpfaffenhofen, 44-45; scientist with Dr. H. Israël, Aachen, 50-57; asst. head, Meteorol. Observ, 57-61; group leader atmospheric physics, space systs. div, Avco Corp, 61-66; consult, Boston Col, 66-67; ATMOSPHERIC SCIENTIST, OFF. NAVAL RES, 67- Chmn. subcomt. I, Int. Comn. Atmospheric Elec, Int. Asn. Meterol. & Atmospheric Physics, 63-, secy, comn, 64-; mem. U.S. del, Gen. assemblies, Int. Union Geod. & Geophys, Berkeley, 63, Lucerne, 67, Moscow, 71; secy, Int. Union Geod. & Geophys. & Int. Coun. Sci. Unions, 64-; mem. working group atmospheric elec, comn. atmospheric sci, World Meteorol. Orgn, 68-, U.S. del, session V, 70. Ger. Air Force, 41-45, Lt. AAAS; Am. Meteorol. Soc; Am. Geophys. Union. Theoretical and experimental research on basic problems of atmospheric electricity, consulting and guidance for research projects and initiation of coordinated efforts in atmospheric electricity on national and international scale. Address: 1812 Drury Lane, Alexandria, VA 22307.

DOLFINI, J(OSEPH) E, b. Middletown, N.Y, July 11, 36; m. 62. ORGANIC CHEMISTRY. B.S, Michigan, 57, M.S, 61, Ph.D.(chem), 62. Nat. Insts. Health fel. org. chem, Columbia, 61-63; asst. prof. chem, Purdue, 63-65; RES. SUPVR, SQUIBB INST, 65- Am. Chem. Soc; Brit. Chem. Soc. Synthetic organic chemistry; heterocyclic and carbocyclic synthesis; new reaction mechanisms; natural products synthesis. Address: Section of Organic Chemistry, Squibb Institute, New Brunswick, NJ 08903.

DOLGE, KENDALL L(UCAS), b. Worcester, Mass, July 22, 24; m. 48; c. 2. ANIMAL NUTRITION. B.A, Connecticut, 49, M.S, 51; Ph.D.(animal nutrit), Cornell, 55. Res. technician, Connecticut, 50-52, instr. animal nutrit, 52-56; res. dept, Wirthmore Feeds, Inc, Mass, 56-59; tech. prod. serviceman, Corn Prod. Sales Co, N.Y, 60-61; ANIMAL NUTRITIONIST, Co-op. G.L.F, Exchange, Inc, 61-64; AGWAY, INC, BUFFALO, 64- U.S.A, 43-46. Am. Dairy Sci. Asn; Am. Soc. Animal Sci; N.Y. Acad. Sci. Nutrition of the young dairy calf, especially vitamin A metabolism. Address: 275 Hillside Dr, Orchard Park, NY 14127.

DOLGOFF, ABRAHAM, b. New Brunswick, N.J, Aug. 10, 33; m. 56; GEOLOGY, ENGINEERING GEOLOGY. B.S, City Col, New York, 53; Polytech. Inst. Brooklyn, 55-56; M.S, N.Y. Univ, 58; univ. fel, Rice, 58-59, Nat. Sci. Found. fel, 59-60, Ph.D.(geol), 60. Jr. civil engr, bd. water supply, City New York, 53-55, asst. civil engr, dept. pub. works, 55-58; res. geologist, Rice, 60-61; Bellaire Labs, Texaco, Inc, 61-66; SPECIALIST, eng. geol. of dams, Gerard Eng. Inc, 66-71; ENG. GEOL. OF DAMS & TUNNELS, HARZA ENG. CO, 71- Lectr, Hunter Col, 70- Geol. Soc. Am; Am. Asn. Petrol Geol; Asn. Eng. Geol. Regional geology of southeastern New York; volcanic rocks of the Great Basin; Gulf Coast structural geology; sedimentary petrology of Gulf Coast Jurassic rocks; engineering geology of dams, tunnels, roads and public works. Address: 7800 N. Nordica Ave, Niles, IL 60648.

DOLIAN, FRANK E(UGENE), b. Coalmont, Ind, Aug. 16, 09; m. 38; c. 3. CHEMISTRY. A.B, Indiana, 30, A.M, 31, Ph.D.(phys. chem), 33. Asst. instr. chem, Indiana, 30-33; res. staff, COMMERCIAL SOLVENTS CORP, 33-39, market develop. staff, 39-42; tech. serv. staff, 46-48, asst. mgr. tech. serv. div, 48-51, mgr. mkt. develop. dept, 51-60, tech. staff sales div, 60-63, acting sales mgr, animal nutrit. dept, 63-64, MGR. TECH. STAFF, sales div, 64-66, MKT. DIV, 66- Chem.C, 42-46, Maj. Am. Chem. Soc; Commercial Develop. Asn.(pres, 57-58); Inst. Food Technol. Properties of nonaqueous solutions; development of antifreezes; absorbents for gas mask canisters. Address: Marketing Division, Commercial Solvents Corp, 245 Park Ave, New York, NY 10017.

DOLID, JACOB, b. Russia, Sept. 30, 97; nat; m. 25; c. 1. ORGANIC CHEMISTRY. Ph.B, Yale, 19; M.Sc, McGill, 21, Ph.D.(chem), 23. Res. chemist, Raybestos Div, 28-33; tech. dir. & consult, Flertex Neuilly, France, 33-37; DIR, BRIDGEPORT TESTING LAB, 37- Am. Chem. Soc; Am. Soc. Metals; Am. Oil Chem. Soc; Soc. Nondestructive Test; fel. Am. Inst. Chem. Friction materials; elastomers; carrotting of fur; testing of materials. Address: 3900 Park Ave, Bridgeport, CT 06604.

DOLIN, M(ORTON) I(RWIN), b. Brooklyn, N.Y, Dec. 24, 20. BIOCHEMISTRY. B.S, City Col. New York, 42; M.S, Kentucky, 44; U.S. Pub. Health Serv. fel, Indiana, 49, Ph.D.(bact), 50. Res. fel, Illinois, 50-52; BIOCHEMIST, OAK RIDGE NAT. LAB, 52- Guggenheim fel, 59-60. U.S.A, 44-46. Am. Soc. Microbiol; Am. Soc. Biol. Chem. Electron transport reactions; pyridine nucleotides; flavoproteins. Address: Oak Ridge National Lab, Oak Ridge, TN 37830.

DOLIN, RICHARD, b. Brooklyn, N.Y, May 16, 21; m. 45; c. 3. ELECTRICAL ENGINEERING. B.S, N.Y. Univ, 47, M.S, 50; Columbia, 51-53. Instr. elec. eng, N.Y. Univ, 47-51; engr-in-charge commun. & control systs, res. labs, Sylvania Elec. Prod, N.Y, 51-56; prin. engr. reconnaissance & electronic systs, Bulova Res. & Develop. Labs, 56-58; sr. res. engr, Fairchild Camera & Instrument Co, 58-59; consult, Airborne Instruments Lab. Div, Cutler-Hammer Inc, 59-61; assoc. prof. ENG. SCI, HOFSTRA UNIV, 61-70, PROF, 70-, chmn. dept, 68-70. Summers, consult, Telemet Corp. Div, Giannini Sci. Corp, N.Y, 62, sr. res. engr, space & info. systs. div, N.Am. Aviation, Inc, Calif, 64, mem. tech. staff, Aerospace Corp, 65; Grumman Corp, N.Y, 66 & 67; NASA summer faculty res. fel, Electronics Res. Ctr, Mass, 68. Sr. mem. Inst. Elec. & Electronics Eng; Am. Soc. Eng. Educ. Analysis and design of communications and reconnaissance systems. Address: Dept. of Engineering Science, Hofstra University, 1000 Fulton Ave, Hempstead, NY 11710.

DOLIN, STANLEY A, b. N.Y.C, Sept. 4, 26; m. 53; c. 2. OPTICS, SPECTROSCOPY. B.Sc, Brown, 50; N.Y. Univ, 52-53. Physicist, Ansco Corp, 50-52; Barnes Eng. Co, 53-55; proj. engr, optical instrumentation, Perkin-Elmer Corp, 55-59; chief engr, control instrument div, Warner & Swasey Co, 59-70; ENG. & DEVELOP. MGR, OCLI INSTRUMENTS, S.NORWALK, 70- Consult, McBeth Corp, N.Y, 52-54; Color Res. Corp, 52-55; Stewart Otto Co, Conn, 52-56; Aro Inc, Tenn, 64-65. U.S.N.R, 44-46. Fel. Optical Soc. Am. Geometric optics; spectroscopic transient analysis; photographic color sensitometry; emission; molecular spectroscopy; optical instrumentation. Address: 107 Briar Brae Rd, Stamford, CT 06903.

DOLKART, RALPH ELSON, b. Moline, Ill, Feb. 1, 13; m. 40; c. 6. INTERNAL MEDICINE. B.S, Northwest. Univ, 34, M.S, 35, M.D, 38. Rotating intern, St. Luke's Hosp, Chicago, Ill, 39; med. house off, Peter Bent Brigham Hosp, Boston, Mass, 39-40; Ward fel, med, NORTHWEST. UNIV, 41, dir. med. clin, 42-46, asst. prof. MED, 47-56, assoc. prof, 56-64, PROF, 64- Attend. physicians, St. Luke's Hosp, 41-51; Passavant Mem. Hosp, 51-, pres, med. staff, 69-71; dir, Chicago Health Res. Found, 66-71; pres. bd. dir, Comprehensive Health Planning Inc. Metropolitan Chicago, 69-71. U.S.P.H.S.R, 58-71, Sr. Surgeon. Am. Med. Asn; Am. Col. Physicians; Am. Fedn. Clin. Res; Am. Heart Asn; Am. Diabetes Asn. Metabolic effects of stereotactic induced hypothalamic lesions. Address: Passavant Hospital, 303 E. Superior St, Chicago, IL 60611.

DOLL, CHARLES G(EORGE), b. Providence, R.I, Aug. 22, 98; m. 40; c. 2. GEOLOGY. Ph.B, Brown, 24, A.M, 26; A.M, Harvard, 31; Ph.D, Columbia, 51. Asst. GEOL, Brown, 24-26; instr, UNIV. VT, 27-32, asst. prof, 32-50, assoc. prof, 50, prof, 51-69, chmn. dept, 46-69; EMER. PROF, 69-; acting state geologist, Vt, 35, 39, state geologist, 47-69; RETIRED. Curator geol. collections, Fleming Mus. Chmn. Edward Hitchcock Centennial, 61. U.S.N, 17-19. Fel. Geol. Soc. Am; Am. Geophys. Union; Seismol. Soc. Am. Structural and stratigraphic geology and geologic mapping in Vermont. Address: 1 Mansfield Ave, Essex Junction, VT 05452.

DOLL, EDWARD B, b. San Diego, Calif, Sept. 24, 12; m. 40, 64; c. 2. ELECTRICAL ENGINEERING, PHYSICS. B.S, Calif. Inst. Tech, 34, Tau Beta Pi fel, 34-35, M.S, 35, Ph.D.(elec. eng), 38. Jr. engr, Bur. Power & Light, Los Angeles, 35-36; asst. prof. elec. eng, Kentucky, 38-40, assoc. prof, 40-41; engr, Naval Ord. Lab, Wash, D.C, 41-42; chief physicist, U.S. Navy Yard, Pearl Harbor, 42-43; engr. & physicist, Manhattan Proj, Los Alamos, N.Mex, 43-46; chief engr, N.Am. Phillips Co, 46-49; chmn. physics dept, Stanford Res. Inst, 49-55; v.pres. eng. div, Space Tech. Labs, Thompson-Ramo-Wooldridge, Inc, 55-59, v.pres, TRW SYSTS. GROUP, 59-69, sr. v.pres, 69-71, V.PRES. & ASST. GEN. MGR, 71- Inst. Elec. & Electronics Eng. Applied physics and electrical engineering; instrumentation, television and electronics; weapon development and weapon effects and systems analysis. Address: TRW Systems Group, 1 Space Park, Redondo Beach, CA 90278.

DOLL, EUGENE C(ARTER), b. Ft. Benton, Mont, Feb. 15, 21; m. 47; c. 3. SOIL FERTILITY. B.S, Mont. State Col, 49, M.S, 51; fel, Wisconsin, 51-53, Ph.D.(soils), 53. Asst, Mont. State Col, 50-51; asst. agronomist, soil fertil, Kentucky, 53-56, assoc. agronomist, 56-60, assoc. prof. soils, 58-60; MICH. STATE UNIV, 60-65, PROF. SOIL SCI, 65- Regional maize adv, Int. Atomic Energy Agency, 66; regional dir. N.C. State Univ. proj. for U.S. Agency Int. Develop. Ecuador & Panama, 70-71. U.S.A, 42-45. Am. Soc. Agron; Soil Sci. Soc. Am. Potassium nutrition of sugar beets; feeding power of plants for the phosphorus of rock phosphate; general soil fertility, especially nitrogen, phosphorus and potash requirements of general farm crops. Address: Dept. of Crop & Soil Sciences, Michigan State University, East Lansing, MI 48823.

DOLL, JAMES PHILIP, b. Perham, Minn, Feb. 10, 19. MEDICAL BACTERIOLOGY. A.B, Notre Dame, 42; D.C, Col. of Holy Cross, 46; Ph.D.(bact), California, 54. Mem. res. staff, Lobund Inst, Notre Dame, 54-64; assoc. prof. biol, Univ. Portland, 64-68; ASST. PROF. MICROBIOL, LOBUND

LABS, UNIV. NOTRE DAME, 68- Am. Soc. Microbiol. Medical aspects of gnotobiotic research. Address: Lobund Labs, University of Notre Dame, Notre Dame, IN 46556.

DOLLAHITE, J(AMES) W(ALTON), b. Center Point, Tex, May 1, 11; m. 34; c. 2. VETERINARY MEDICINE. D.V.M, Agr. & Mech. Col, Texas, 33, M.S, 61. Private practice, 33-34, 39-42, 46-52; jr. veterinarian disease control, bur. animal indust, U.S. Dept. Agr, 34-36, path. div, 36-39; supt. animal disease invest. lab, Texas Agr. Exp. Sta, 52-61; mem. res. staff, COL. VET. MED, TEX. A&M UNIV, 61-64, assoc. prof. vet. path, 64-65, PROF, 65-67, PHYSIOL. & PHARMACOL, 67-68, TOXICOL, 68- Dipl. Am. Bd. Vet. Toxicol. U.S.A, 42-46; U.S.A.F.R, 46-, Lt. Col. AAAS; Am. Vet. Med. Asn; Am. Col. Vet. Toxicol.(pres, 69-71); Soc. Toxicol; Am. Acad. Clin. Toxicol. Animal diseases; toxic plants. Address: Dept. of Veterinary Physiology & Pharmacology, Texas A&M University, College Station, TX 77843.

DOLLAHON, JAMES CLIFFORD, b. Roswell, N.Mex, Sept. 27,30; m. 54. ORGANIC CHEMISTRY. B.S, New Mexico State, 52; M.S, Florida, 56, Ph.D. (animal husb), 58. Asst, Florida, 55-58; asst. prof. animal husb, Miss. State, 58-60; PROF. ANIMAL SCI, WIS. STATE UNIV, RIVER FALLS, 60-, DEAN, COL. AGR, 64- U.S.A.F, 52-54, Res, 54- Am. Soc. Animal Sci; Am. Genetic Asn. Population; physiological and statistical genetics; differential and integral calculus. Address: Office of the Dean, College of Agriculture, Wisconsin State University, River Falls, WI 54022.

DOLLAR, ALEXANDER M, b. Vancouver, Can, Apr. 7, 21; U.S. citizen; m. 44; c. 1. ANIMAL NUTRITION, FOOD BIOCHEMISTRY. B.S, California, Berkeley, 48, M.S, 49; Southern California, 53-55, univ. fel, 55; Ph.D.(nutrit. & biochem), Reading, 58. Asst. prof. food sci, col. fisheries, Washington (Seattle), 59-62, assoc. prof, 62-67; SUPVR, HAWAII DEVELOP. IRRADIATOR, HAWAII DEPT. AGR, 67- U.S.N, 43-46, Lt. AAAS; Am. Chem. Soc; Inst. Food Tech; Brit. Biochem. Soc; Brit. Nutrit. Soc. Address: 700 Richards St, No. 1504, Honolulu, HI 96813.

DOLLARD, JOHN D, b. New Haven, Conn, Jan. 19, 37. PHYSICS, MATHEMATICS. B.A, Yale, 58; Nat. Sci. Found. fel, Princeton, 58-62, M.A, 60, Ph.D.(physics), 63. Res. assoc. physics, Princeton, 63-65; asst. prof. math, Univ. Rochester, 65-68; vis. asst. prof. math. & physics, Yale, 68-69; ASSOC. PROF. MATH, UNIV. TEX, AUSTIN, 69- Am. Phys. Soc. Quantum mechanical scattering theory; relativistic quantum field theory. Address: Dept. of Mathematics, University of Texas at Austin, Austin, TX 78712.

DOLLE, WALTER CHARLES, b. New Braunfels, Tex, Dec. 29, 16; m. 39; c. 3. ELECTRONICS ENGINEERING. B.S, U.S. Mil. Acad, 39; M.S, Michigan, 49. Staff Engr, Page Commun. Eng, Inc, 60-62; sr. res. engr, SOUTHWEST RES. INST, 63-67, MGR. ELECTROMAGNETIC COMPATIBILITY SECT, 67- Sig.C, U.S.A, 39-60, Col. Sr. mem. Inst. Elec. & Electronics Eng. Circuit theory and analysis; electromagnetic energy radiation and propagation. Address: Dept. of Electronic Systems Research, Southwest Research Institute, P.O. Box 28510, San Antonio, TX 78284.

DOLLEAR, FRANK G(ILBERT), b. Chicago, Ill, July 5, 13; m. 43. CHEMISTRY. A.B, Ill. Col, 33; M.S, Northwestern, 36. Chemist, Regional Soybean indust. prod. lab, U.S. DEPT. AGR, 37-39, SOUTH. REGIONAL RES. LAB, bur. agr. chem. & eng, 39-42, bur. agr. & indust. chem, 42-52, asst. head oilseed sect, 52-58, HEAD special properties invests, 58-59, indust. oils invests, 59-64, PEANUT PROD. INVESTS, 64- AAAS; Am. Chem. Soc; Am. Oil Chem. Soc. Chemistry of fats, oils and oilseeds; composition and utilization of cottonseed, peanut and tung oils and meals; polymers; fire retardant paints; new oilseed crops; peanut flavor and aroma; mycotoxins. Address: Southern Regional Research Lab, 1100 Robert E. Lee Blvd, New Orleans, LA 70179.

DOLLING, GERALD, b. Dunstable, Eng, Nov. 21, 35; m. 59; c. 3. SOLID STATE PHYSICS. B.A, Cambridge, 57, Ph.D.(physics), 61. RES. OFF. PHYSICS, ATOMIC ENERGY CAN. LTD, 61- Am. Phys. Soc; Can. Asn. Physicists. Lattice and magnetic dynamics; neutron scattering from condensed systems; Ferroelectricity. Address: Neutron Physics Branch, Chalk River Nuclear Labs, Chalk River, Ont, Can.

DOLLINGER, E(LWOOD) J(OHNSON), b. Lynchburg, Ohio, Apr. 20, 20; m. 52; c. 2. CYTOGENETICS, PLANT BREEDING. B.Sc, Ohio State, 44; M.Sc, Pa. State, 47; Ph.D.(cytogenetics, bot), Columbia, 53. Agent, U.S. Reg. Pasture Res. Lab, 44-47; asst, Columbia, 47-48; Illinois, 49-50; res. assoc, Carnegie Institution, 50-51; Brookhaven Nat. Lab, 51-53; U.S. Pub. Health Fel, Nat. Cancer Inst, 53-55; PROF. CYTOGENETICS, OHIO AGR. RES. & DEVELOP. CTR, 55- Genetics Soc. Am; Am. Genetic Asn; Am. Soc. Agron. Cytogenetics of maize; radiation induced mutation of maize; corn breeding. Address: Dept. of Agronomy, Ohio Agricultural Research & Development Center, Wooster, OH 44691.

DOLLINGER, MICHAEL BARRY, b. New York, N.Y, Apr. 29, 43. MATHEMATICS. A.B, Rochester, 63; Int. Bus. Mach. fel, Illinois, Urbana, 64-65, M.S, 65, univ. fel, 65-66, Nat. Sci. Found. fel, 66-67, Ph.D.(math), 68. ASST. PROF. MATH, LA. STATE UNIV, BATON ROUGE, 68- Res. assoc, Univ. Calif, Berkeley, 71-72. Am. Math. Soc; Math. Asn. Am. Operator theory; functional analysis. Address: Dept. of Mathematics, Louisiana State University, Baton Rouge, La. 70803.

DOLLIVER, CLAIRE VINCENT, b. Wash, D.C, Oct. 25, 23; c. 3. GEOMORPHOLOGY, GEOLOGY. B.S, Towson State Col, 60; Nat. Sci. Found. fel, Univ. Fla, 63-64, M.S, 65; Ph.D.(geol), Pa. State Univ, 68. Asst. prof. geol, Ind. State Univ, 68-70; ASSOC. PROF. GEOMORPHOL. & CHMN. DEPT. GEOG, RADFORD COL, 70- Geologist, Am. Archaeol. Mission, Mus. Natural Hist, Afghanistan, 70- AAAS; Geol. Soc. Am; Am. Asn. Petrol. Geol; Soc. Econ. Paleont. & Mineral. Arid region processes; quaternary stratigraphy and fluvial processes; Pleistocene geology. Address: Dept. of Geography, Radford College, Radford, VA 24141.

DOLLOFF, NORMAN, b. Oldtown, Maine, May 12, 07; m. 40; c. 1. GEOLOGY, GEOCHEMISTRY. B.S, Mass. Inst. Tech, 30; M.A, Columbia, 36; Ph.D.(metall), Stanford, 50. Teacher, sec. schs, Maine, 31-35; Cranbrook Sch, Mich, 37-43; instr. chem. & geol, SAN JOSE STATE COL, 46-48, asst. prof. GEOL, 48-56, assoc. prof, 56-60, PROF, 60-, chmn. dept, 65-69. U.S.N.R, 43-46, Lt. Comdr. AAAS; Nat. Asn. Geol. Teachers; Am. Geochem. Soc. Electrolytic reactions of ore minerals; entropy between natural and social sciences. Address: Dept. of Geology, San Jose State College, 125 S. Seventh St, San Jose, CA 95114.

DOLLWET, HELMAR H(ERMANN) A(DOLF), b. Merzig, Ger, Jan. 20, 29; U.S. citizen; m. 57; c. 4. PLANT PHYSIOLOGY & BIOCHEMISTRY. B.S, Univ. Mich, 58; Nat. Defense Educ. Act fel. & M.S, Univ. Calif, Riverside, 67, Nat. Insts. Health fel. & Ph.D.(plant sci. & physiol), 69. ASST. PROF. BIOL, UNIV. AKRON, 70- Mechanism of formation of ethylene, a plant hormone; site of action and mode of action of ethylene. Address: Dept. of Biology, University of Akron, Akron, OH 44304.

DOLMAGE, VICTOR, b. Souris, Man. GEOLOGY. B.A, Manitoba, 12; Ph.D, Mass. Inst. Tech, 17. Austin fel, Mass. Inst. Tech, 16-17; asst. geologist, Geol. Surv. Can, 17-20, assoc. geologist, 20-25, geologist, 25-29, in charge B.C. br, 23-29; CONSULT. GEOL. ENGR, 29- Fel. Geol. Soc. Am; fel. Royal Soc. Can; Can. Inst. Min. & Metall. (Barlow medal, 45); Eng. Inst. Can. (Leonard medal, 59). Geology and mineral deposits of British Columbia; engineering geology of various projects in Canada. Address: 314 Marine Bldg, Vancouver, B.C, Can.

DOLMAN, CLAUDE E(RNEST), b. Porthleven, Cornwall, England, May 23, 06; m. 31, 55; c. 6. BACTERIOLOGY. M.B. & B.S, London, 30, D.P.H, 31, Ph.D.(bact), 35. House surgeon, St. Mary's Hosp, 29; clin. asst, Royal Chest Hosp. & Hosp. Sick Children, London, 30; res. scholar, St. Mary's Hosp. Inst. Path. & Res, 31; clin. assoc. & res. asst, CONNAUGHT LABS, TORONTO, 31-33, res. & clin. assoc, 33-35, demonstr, hyg. & prev. med, 33-35, RES. MEM, 35-; EMER. PROF. MICROBIOL, UNIV. B.C, 71-, assoc. prof. bact. & prev. med. & acting head dept, 35-36, prof. & head dept, 36-51, prof. bact. & immunol. & head dept, 51-65, res. prof. microbiol, 65-71; acting head dept. nursing & health, 35-43, prof. & head dept, 43-51. Dir. div. labs, Dept. Health, B.C, 35-56; hon. consult. bacteriologist, Vancouver Gen. Hosp, 36- Fel. Royal Col. Physicians, London; fel. Royal Col. Physicians & Surgeons. Can. Fel. Am. Pub. Health Asn; Am. Asn. Immunol; Can. Soc. Microbiol; Can. Pub. Health Asn; fel. Royal Soc. Can. (pres, 69-70); Am. Soc. Microbiol. Staphylococcus toxins; botulinum toxins; brucellosis; cholera; salmonellosis; bacterial food poisoning; history of bacteriology. Address: 1611 Cedar Crescent, Vancouver 9, B.C, Can.

DOLNICK, ETHEL H(ELEN), b. Cincinnati, Ohio, Nov. 9, 13. ZOOLOGY. B.S, George Washington, 43, M.A, 47, Ph.D.(anat), 55. RES. BIOLOGIST, fish & wildlife serv, U.S. Dept. Interior, 43-46; bur. animal indust. U.S. DEPT. AGR, AGR. RES. CTR, 46-53, animal husb. res. div, AGR. RES. SERV, 53-70, ANIMAL SCI. RES. DIV, 70- Am. Soc. Zool; Soc. Exp. Biol. & Med; Am. Asn. Anat. Influence of diet, hormones, environment on biology of skin of wool and fur-bearing animals; study of natural and/or induced fiber shedding; development of chemical shearing of sheep. Address: Sheep & Fur Animal Research Branch, Animal Science Research Division, Agricultural Research Service, U.S. Dept. of Agriculture, Beltsville, MD 20705.

DOLOWITZ, DAVID A(UGUSTAS), b. N.Y.C, Nov. 13; m. 45; c. 5. OTOLARYNGOLOGY. A.B, Hopkins, 33, fel, 39-43; M.D, Yale, 37; M.A, Utah, 51. Asst. otol, Hopkins, 39-40, otolaryngol, 40-42, instr, 42-43, UNIV. UTAH, 43-46, asst. clin. prof, 46-49, assoc. clin. prof, 49-62, assoc. prof. SURG, 62-69, CLIN. PROF. & ADJ. PROF. SPEECH PATH. & AUDIOL, 69-, chmn. div. otolaryngol, 49-69. Nat. Insts. Health res. fel, Lund, 60-61. U.S.A, 43-46, Capt. Am. Med. Asn; Am. Acad. Ophthal. & Otolaryngol; fel. Am. Col. Surg; Am. Laryngol, Rhinol. & Otol. Soc; Am. Otol. Soc; Am. Soc. Ophthal. & Otolaryngol. Allergy. Basic otolaryngology; labrynthine studies heredity factors in otolaryngology; effect of inflammation on connective tissue. Address: Dept. of Surgery, College of Medicine, University of Utah, Salt Lake City, UT 84112.

DOLOWY, WILLIAM C, b. Chicago Heights, Ill, Jan. 13, 27; m. 55; c. 2. VETERINARY MEDICINE, MOLECULAR BIOLOGY. B.S, Illinois, 48 & 51, M.S, 49, D.V.M, 53. Adminstr, med. res. lab, Illinois, 54-67; PROF. EXP. ANIMAL MED. & CHMN. DEPT, UNIV. WASH, 67- Consult. vet, Presby-St. Luke's Hosp, Chicago, Ill, 54-67; Mt. Sinai Med. Res. Found, 55-67; Vet. Admin. Hosp, West Side, Chicago, 60-67; Hines, 62-67, Seattle, Wash, 68-; Vet. Admin. Res. Hosp, Chicago & Lutheran Gen. Hosp, Park Ridge, 66-67. Sr. mem, center for zoonoses res, Illinois, Urbana, 66-67; mem, health res. facilities sci. rev. cmt, div. res. facilities & resources, Nat. Insts. Health, 68- U.S.N, 45-46. Am. Asn. Cancer Res; Soc. Exp. Biol. & Med; Am. Vet. Med. Asn. Amino acid requirements of malignant cells, exploitable by enzymes such as L-asparaginase; diseases of experimental animals. Address: Dept. of Experimental Animal Medicine, School of Medicine, University of Washington, Seattle, WA 98105.

DOLPH, CHARLES L(AURIE), b. Ann Arbor, Mich, Aug. 27, 18; m. 44; c. 2. MATHEMATICS. B.A, Michigan, 39; Brown, 41; M.A, Princeton, 41, Ph.D. (math), 44. Asst, Nat. Defense Res. Cmt, Princeton, 41-42, instr. math, 42; theoret. physicist, Naval Res. Lab, Wash, D.C, 43-45; mem. tech. staff, math. group, Bell Tel. Labs, 45-46; asst. prof. MATH, UNIV. MICH, 46-54, assoc. prof, 54-59, PROF, 59-, math. res, eng. res. inst, 46-64, head theoret. & comput. div, Willow Run Res. Center, 52-64. Guggenheim fel, 57; vis. res. prof, Army Math. Res. Center, Wisconsin, 65. Consult, Ramo-Wooldridge, 54-57; Bendix Aviation Corp, 59- Mem. Nat. Acad. Sci-Nat. Res. Coun. adv. comt. math. to Off. Naval Res, 64-66. Thompson prize, Inst. Elec. & Electronics Engrs. U.S.N, 44-45. Am. Math. Soc. Nonlinear integral equations; antenna theory; theory of compressible flow; stochastic processes; vibration theory; anomalous propagation theory; transform theory. Address: Dept. of Mathematics, University of Michigan, Ann Arbor, MI 48104.

DOLPHIN, DAVID HENRY, b. London, Eng, Jan. 15, 40; m. 63; c. 3. ORGANIC CHEMISTRY. B.Sc, Nottingham, 62, Ph.D.(chem), 65. Res. fel. CHEM, HARVARD, 65-66, instr, 66-69, asst. prof, 69-71, ASSOC. PROF, 71- Am. Chem. Soc; Brit. Chem. Soc; Royal Inst. Chem. Structure, synthesis, chemistry and biochemistry of porphyrins, vitamin B_{12}, and related macrocycles. Address: Dept. of Chemistry, Harvard University, 12 Oxford St, Cambridge, MA 02138.

DOLPHIN, JOHN M(ICHAEL), b. Mahanoy City, Pa, Nov. 21, 23; m. 50; c. 3. PATHOLOGY. Villanova; M.D, Hahnemann Med. Col.(Pa), 47. Res. PATH, Hahnemann Med. Col. & Hosp.(Pa), 49-50, 52-54; Pa. Hosp, 54-55; asst. prof, HAHNEMANN MED. COL, 56-63, ASSOC. PROF, 63- U.S.N.R, 43-46, 50-52, Res, 52-54. Am. Med. Asn; Col. Am. Path. Pathology of tumors; hypertensive vascular lesions. Address: Hahnemann Medical College of Philadelphia, 235 N. 15th St, Philadelphia, PA 19102.

DOLPHIN, LAMBERT TYLER, JR, b. Shoshone, Idaho, May 24, 32. PHYSICS. A.B, San Diego State Col, 54; Stanford, 54-56. Asst. mgr, Radio physics lab, Stanford Res. Inst, 56-68; CONSULT. & LECTR, 68- AAAS; Acoustical Soc. Am; Inst. Elec. & Electronics Eng; Am. Inst. Aeronaut. & Astronaut; Sci. Res. Soc. Am; Am. Geophys. Union. Physics of upper atmosphere and ionosphere; space physics; radio propagation. Address: 945 Old Trace Rd, Palo Alto, CA 94306.

DOLPHIN, ROBERT EARL, b. Worcester, Mass, Oct. 4, 29; m. 47; c. 2. ENTOMOLOGY. B.A, San Jose State Col, 58; Ph.D.(entom), Purdue, 66. Lab. technician, aluminum prod. res. dept, Kaiser Chem. & Aluminum Co, 56-58; mgr. entom, Mosquito Abatement Dist, Calif, 58-61; instr. agr. entom, agr. exp. sta, Purdue, 61-65; res. entomologist, ENTOM, RES. DIV, AGR. RES. SERV, U.S. DEPT. OF AGR, 65-70, SUPVR. RES. ENTOMOLOGIST & INVEST. LEADER, 70- U.S.M.C, 46-49, 50-51, 52-55, 1st Lt. AAAS; Entom. Soc. Am. Biological control and ecology of deciduous fruit insects with attention to life histories. Address: Entomology Research Division, U.S. Dept. of Agriculture, P.O. Box 944, Vincennes, IN 47591.

DOLYAK, FRANK, b. Stratford, Conn, Nov. 13, 27; m. 51; c. 3. PHYSIOLOGY. B.A, Connecticut, 50; Ph.D.(zool), Kansas, 55. Asst. instr. zool, Kansas, 51-54; instr. physiol, Connecticut, 54-59, asst. prof, 59-65, assoc. prof, 65; assoc. prof. BIOL. & chmn. dept, Augusta Col, 65-66; PROF. & CHMN. DEPT, R.I. COL, 66- U.S.N.R, 45-46, 56, Lt. AAAS; N.Y. Acad. Sci. Serology; radiation biology; immunogenetics. Address: Dept. of Biology, Rhode Island College, Providence, RI 02908.

DOMAGALA, ROBERT F, b. Chicago, Ill, Jan. 23, 29; m. 51; c. 3. PHYSICAL METALLURGY. B.S, Ill. Inst. Tech, 50, M.S, 54. Mgr. metall. serv, IIT Res. Inst, 50-66; ASSOC. PROF. METALL, UNIV. ILL, CHICAGO CIRCLE, 66- Am. Soc. Metals. Determination of binary and more complex phase diagrams; high temperature properties of metals. Address: Dept. of Materials Engineering, University of Illinois at Chicago Circle, Chicago, IL 60680.

DOMALSKI, E(UGENE) S(TANLEY), b. Buffalo, N.Y, Sept. 13, 31. PHYSICAL CHEMISTRY. B.A, Buffalo, 53, Allied Chem. Corp. Nat. Aniline fel, 57-58, Ph.D.(chem), 59. Asst. chem, Buffalo, 53-59; PHYS. CHEMIST, THERMOCHEM. SECT, IMR, NAT. BUR. STANDARDS, 59- Summer, chemist, metals res. lab, Union Carbide Corp, 57. Am. Chem. Soc; Faraday Soc. Fluorine combustion calorimetry; evaluation of combustion data on organic compounds. Address: A157 Chemistry Bldg, National Bureau of Standards, Washington, DC 20234.

DOMAN, ELVIRA (MRS. JOHN H. HOLDER), b. N.Y.C. BIOCHEMISTRY, ENZYMOLOGY. B.A, Hunter Col, 55; M.S, N.Y. Univ, 59; fel, Columbia Univ, 59-60, M.A, 60; U.S. Pub. Health Serv. fel, Rutgers Univ, 62-64, univ. fel. & Ph.D.(physiol, biochem), 65. Jr. technician, N.Y. Univ. Hosp, 55-56; sr. technician, cancer chemother, Sloan Kettering Inst. Cancer Res, 56-57; endocrinol, col. physicians & surgeons, Columbia Univ, 57, res. asst, 58; phys. chem, Sloan Kettering Inst. Cancer Res, 60-61; Pop. Coun. fel. endocrinol, Rockefeller Univ, 65-66, res. assoc, 66-68; LECTR, DEPT. BIOL. SCI, DOUGLASS COL, RUTGERS UNIV, 70- AAAS; Am. Chem. Soc; N.Y. Acad. Sci. Cancer chemotherapy; steroidogenesis and the physical chemistry of the nucleic acids; isolation and characterization of enzymes in respiratory chain of beef heart, of enzymes in rat liver related to endocrinology, and of enzymes involved in the growth of yeast cells. Address: Dept. of Biological Sciences, Douglass College, Rutgers, The State University, New Brunswick, NJ 08903.

DOMAN, MICHAEL JOHN, b. Medina, N.Y, Oct. 3, 38; m. 61; c. 2. PHYSICS. B.A, California, Santa Barbara, 60; M.S, San Diego State Col, 63; fel, State Univ. N.Y. Buffalo, 67-68, Ph.D.(physics), 68. Summers, physicist, Naval Electronics Lab, Calif, 62, U.S. Naval Radiol. Defense Lab, 63 & Titanium Alloy Div, Nat. Lead Co, N.Y, 64 & 65; res. assoc. biophys, chem. physics & liquid state, State Univ. N.Y. Buffalo, 66-67; ASST. PROF. PHYSICS, MONT. COL. MINERAL SCI. & TECH, 68- NASA summer faculty fel, Stanford Univ. & Ames Res. Center, NASA, 69- AAAS; Am. Phys. Soc. Nucleation and condensation phenomena in aqueous solutions; cosmic ray physics. Address: Montana College of Mineral Science & Technology, Butte, MT 59701.

DOMANSKI, GEORGE, b. Hansk, Poland, May 15, 16; U.S. citizen; m. 42; c. 3. ORGANIC CHEMISTRY. Ph.D.(indust. chem), Milan, 46. Chief chemist, Moder Paints, Ltd, Eng, 47-48; chemist, Lewis Berger, Ltd, 48-52, supvr. org. coatings, 52-55; Sherwin-Williams Co, 55-60; SECT. HEAD WATER REDUCIBLE ORG. COATINGS, GLIDDEN-DURKEE DIV, SCM CORP, 60- Polish Armed Forces under British Command, World War II, 2nd Lt. Am. Chem. Soc. Development of coatings suitable for application by electrochemical deposition process. Address: 4354 W. 140th St, Cleveland, OH 44135.

DOMANSKI, THADDEUS J(OHN), b. Jersey City, N.J, June 14, 11; m. 34; c. 1. BIOCHEMISTRY, TOXICOLOGY. B.S, N.Y. Univ, 32, M.S, 36, Ph.D.(col. sci. teaching), 49. Sr. chemist, path. dept, Med. Center, Jersey City, N.J, 35-43; biochemist, lab. serv, 8th Gen. Hosp, U.S. Air Force, 44-45, chief, bur. labs, Dept. Pub. Health & Welfare, Hqs, Korea, 46-47, biochemist, Sch. Aviation Med, 50, chief lab, 50-54, chief lab. servs. & acting chief, dept. path, 54-57, rep. Off. Air Force Surgeon Gen, U.S. Army Biol. Labs, Ft. Detrick, Md, 57-58, chief, epidemiol. lab, Aerospace Med. Center, Tex, 58-61, chief, toxicol. br, Armed Forces Inst. Path, 61-66, assoc. chief clin. biores. lab. sci. Biomed. Sci. Corps, 65-66; scientist adminstr. pharmacol. & toxicol, res. grants br, Nat. Inst. Gen. Med. Sci, 66-68; CHIEF AWARD REV. & TECH. ADMIN. BR. & PROG. DIR. CARCINOGENESIS, NAT. CANCER INST, 68- U.S.A.F, 43-66, Col. Aerospace Med. Asn; assoc. Soc. Clin. Path; fel. Am. Acad. Forensic Sci. Investigation of fatal aircraft accidents, based on postmortem toxicologic analyses of victim's body fluids and tissues; human physiologic response to in-flight operations as related to experience and analogous factors. Address: National Cancer Institute, Room 850, Westwood Bldg, 5333 Westbard Ave, Bethesda, MD 20014.

DOMASH, L(IONEL), b. New York, N.Y, Feb. 14, 26; m. 48; c. 2. PHYSICAL CHEMISTRY. A.B, N.Y. Univ, 48; M.S, Purdue, 50, Atomic Energy Cmn. fel, 50-52, Ph.D.(chem), 52. Res. chemist, Westvaco Chem. Co, 52-53; Gulf Res. & Develop. Co, Pa, 53-59, group leader, 59-61; chemist, ESSO RES. & ENG. CO, 61-71, SR. RES. ENGR, 71- U.S.A, 44-46. Am. Chem. Soc; Am. Inst. Chem. Eng. Catalysis; petroleum chemistry; thermodynamics; phase equilibria; cryogenics. Address: Esso Research & Engineering Co, P.O. Box 101, Florham Park, NJ 07932.

DOMASK, W(ILLIAM) G(ERHARD), b. Port Arthur, Tex, Mar. 11, 20; m. 48; c. 6. CHEMICAL ENGINEERING. B.S, Tex. A&M Univ, 42, M.S, 48; Ph.D. (chem. eng), Texas, 53. Res. chemist, Jefferson Chem. Co, 45-46; sr. chem. engr, HUMBLE OIL & REF. CO, 52-60, mgr. S.W. region sales eng, 60-65, TECH. ADV, HQ. MKT, 66- C.W.S, U.S.A, 42-45, U.S.A.R, 45-53. AAAS; Soc. Automotive Eng; Am. Chem. Soc; Sci. Res. Soc. Am; Am. Inst. Chem. Eng.(publ. award, 52). Synthesis of chlorinated hydrocarbons; process engineering research; chemicals, plastics and petroleum products development; products research coordination. Address: 11603 Starwood Dr, Houston, TX 77024.

DOMBA, ELEMER, b. Szeged, Hungary, Dec. 11, 14; U.S. citizen; m. 48. ORGANIC & COLLOID CHEMISTRY. M.S, Pazmany Peter Univ, Hungary, 36, Ph.D.(chem), 39. Asst. prof. org-phys. chem, Pazmany Peter Univ, Hungary, 37-39; head biochem. res, Gedeon Richter Pharmaceut. Co, 39-42; Chinoin Pharmaceut. Co, 42-45; owner, Colloid Lab, 45-50; head res. org. & polymer chem, Asn. Technochem, 51-56; res. chemist, G.D. Searle & Co, 57-58; Finnegan Res. Center, 58-59; sr. res. chemist, Armour Chem. Co, 59-60; group leader surface chem, NALCO CHEM. CO, 60-67, SR. RES. SCIENTIST, 67- Rockefeller fel, 56. Tech. consult, Budapest Commercial Bank, 42-44. Prize, Hungarian Nat. Inst. Fermentation, 54. Hungarian Royal Air Force, 44, Lt. Am. Chem. Soc; Sci. Res. Soc. Am; N.Y. Acad. Sci. Surface chemistry; inorganic polymers; organic synthesis. Address: Nalco Chemical Co, 6216 W. 66th Pl, Chicago, IL 60638.

d'OMBRAIN, GEORGE LEE, b. Walton, Eng, July 7, 14; m. 35; c. 3. COMPUTER SCIENCE. B.Eng, London, 31, Ph.D.(elec. eng), 34, dipl, Imp. Col, 32. Res. asst. elec. eng, Imp. Col, London, 31-34, asst. lectr, 34-35, lectr, 38-48; tech. mgr, Kingsway Elec, Eng, 35-38; chmn. dept. ELEC. ENG, Alexandria, 48; Battersea Col, London, 48-59; PROF, McGILL UNIV, 59- Consult, Eng, U.S. & Can, 49-; mem. assoc. comt. automatic control, Nat. Res. Coun. Can; new learning media comt, Asn. Univ. & Col. Can. Sr. mem. Inst. Elec. & Electronics Eng; Brit. Inst. Elec. Eng; assoc. City & Guilds London Inst. Automatic process control engineering; optimal control and industrial instrumentation; digital computation; computer aided education. Address: Faculty of Engineering, McGill University, Montreal 101, Que, Can.

DOMBRO, ROY S, b. Brooklyn, N.Y, Oct. 21, 33; m. 67; c. 1. BIOCHEMISTRY. B.S, Brooklyn Col, 54; M.S, Wisconsin, 56, Ph.D.(biochem), 58. Res. assoc. biochem, Rockefeller Inst, 58-64; mem. staff, Inst. Muscle Disease, 64-65; assoc, dept. surg, Albert Einstein Col. Med, 65-67, asst. prof. biochem, surg, 67-70; RES. SCIENTIST SURG, MED. SCH, UNIV. MIAMI, 70- Res. Chemist, Vet. Admin. Hosp, Miami. AAAS; Am. Chem. Soc. Design and synthesis of antimetabolities; neurochemistry; amino acid metabolism; vasoactive amines and peptides. Address: 11205 N. Kendall Dr, Miami, FL 33156.

DOMBROW, BERNARD ALBERT, b. New York, N.Y, July 5, 08; m. 36; c. 2. ORGANIC CHEMISTRY. B.S, City Col, 29; M.A, Columbia, 39, Ph.D.(phys. chem), 44. Anal. chemist, Nat. Oil Prods. Co, 29-32, res. chemist, NOPCO DIV, DIAMOND SHAMROCK CORP, 32-52, lab. dir. plastics div, 52-62, SR. RES. ASSOC, 62- AAAS; N.Y. Acad. Sci; Am. Chem. Soc; Soc. Plastics Eng; Soc. Plastics Indust. Synthesis of fatty oil derivatives; wetting agents; plasticizers; emulsifiers; general organic synthesis; oil soluble vitamin extraction and uses; ultracentrifugal and viscometric studies of amylose acetates; foam plastics; polyurethanes. Address: 536 Martense Ave, Teaneck, NJ 07666.

DOMBROWSKI, GEORGE E(DWARD), b. Bayonne, N.J, Feb. 22, 27; m. 54; c. 5. ELECTRONICS. B.E.E, Cooper Union, 49; fel, Michigan, 49-50, M.S.E, 50, Ph.D.(elec. eng), 57. Jr. engr, Raytheon Mfg. Co, 50-51; proj. engr, Sperry Gyroscope Co, 51-52; res. assoc, Michigan, 52-57; sr. engr, Raytheon Co, 57-61; assoc. prof. ELEC. ENG, UNIV. CONN, 61-71, PROF, 71- U.S.N, 45-46. Microwave electronics, energy transmission and conversion; microwave electron tubes, high power levels with crossed electric and magnetic fields; magnetrons and amplitrons; plasma electronics; computer simulation. Address: Dept. of Electrical Engineering, University of Connecticut, Storrs, CT 06268.

DOMBROWSKI, HENRY S(TEPHEN), b. Bayonne, N.J, Sept. 27, 25; m. 51; c. 3. CHEMICAL ENGINEERING. B.Ch.E, Cooper Union, 47; M.S.Ch.E, Michigan, 48, fel, 48-52, Ph.D.(chem. eng), 52. Res. engr, E.I. DU PONT DE NEMOURS & CO, 52-59, RES. SUPVR, 59- U.S.N.R, 44-46. Am. Chem. Soc. Fluid flow through porous media; process development; reactive metals; silicon; oxides for magnetic tape. Address: Photo Products Dept, E.I. du Pont de Nemours & Co, Newport, DE 19804.

DOMENICALI, CHARLES A(NGELO), b. Albuquerque, N.Mex, Dec. 27, 17; m. 44; c. 3. SOLID STATE PHYSICS. B.S, New Mexico, 39; Ph.D.(physics), Mass. Inst. Tech, 49. Physicist ballistics, New Mexico, 42; radar, U.S. Naval Res. Lab, 42-45; electron. rocket sights, Calif. Inst. Tech, 45; res. assoc. physicist magnetism, Mass. Inst. Tech, 47-49; assoc. prof. physics & chmn. dept, Alfred, 49-52; res. physicist, solid state physics, Franklin Inst, 52-55; res. physicist & head solid state physics sect, Honeywell Res. Center, 55-57, sr. staff physicist, 57-61; Arizona State, 61-63; res. physicist, Union Carbide Res. Inst, N.Y, 63-64; PROF. PHYSICS, TEMPLE UNIV, 65-, chmn. dept, 65-68. Vis. lectr. elec. eng, Univ. Minn, 59- Am.

Phys. Soc. Solid state physics; irreversible thermodynamics; magnetism; thermoelectricity. Address: Dept. of Physics, Temple University, Philadelphia, PA 19122.

DOMER, FLOYD R(AY), b. Cedar Rapids, Iowa, July 12, 31; m. 65. PHARMACOLOGY. B.S, Iowa, 54, M.S, 56; Ph.D.(pharmacol), Tulane, 59. Asst. pharm, Iowa, 54-55; pharmacol, 55-56; Tulane, 56-59; fel, Life Ins. Med. Res. Fund, Nat. Inst. Med. Res, Eng, 59-60; U.S. Air Force res. contract, Istituto Superiore Sanità, Italy, 60-61; asst. prof. PHARMACOL, col. med, Cincinnati, 61-62; TULANE UNIV, 63-65, ASSOC. PROF, 65- Consult, Pan-Am. Sanit. Bur. Regional Off, Argentina, WHO, 71; hon. res. fel, Univ. Col, Univ. London, 71-72. AAAS; Soc. Exp. Biol. & Med; Am. Soc. Pharmacol. & Exp. Therapeut. Transport systems, ways of affecting them, particularly the blood-brain barrier. Address: Dept. of Pharmacology, Tulane University, 1430 Tulane Ave, New Orleans, LA 70112.

DOMERMUTH, CHARLES HENRY, JR, b. St. Louis, Mo, Nov. 16, 28; m. 52; c. 3. MICROBIOLOGY. B.S, Elmhurst Col, 51; M.S, Kentucky, 55; Ph.D. (microbiol), Va. Polytech. Inst, 62. Assoc. prof. VET. SCI, VA. POLYTECH. INST. & STATE UNIV, 54-70, PROF, 70- Res. microbiologist, Statens Serum Inst, Denmark, 62-63; E.African Vet. Res. Orgn, Kenya, 64-66; U.S. Dept. Agr, 64- Am. Soc. Microbiol. Electron microscopy of infected tissue; studies of Mycoplasmataceae and diseases caused by them. Address: Dept. of Veterinary Science, Virginia Polytechnic Institute & State University, Blacksburg, VA 24061.

DOMESHEK, S(OL), b. New York, N.Y, Dec. 6, 20; m. 42; c. 2. MECHANICAL ENGINEERING. B.S, City Col. New York, 41; B.M.E, N.Y. Univ, 56. Jr. engr, U.S. Geol. Surv, 42-44; proj. engr, U.S. Naval Training Device Ctr, 46-51, sr. proj. engr, 51-57, head visual systs. br, 57-61, staff eng. consult, 61-64, head phys. sci. lab, 64-66; DIR. INSTRUMENTATION, AVIONICS LAB, U.S. ARMY ELECTRONICS COMMAND, FT. MONMOUTH, 66- U.S.N.R, 44-46. Nat. Soc. Prof. Eng; Optical Soc. Am; Am. Soc. Photogram. Optics; photogrammetry; opto-electrical instrumentation as applied to training. Address: 24 Springfield Ave, Cranford, NJ 07016.

DOMHOLDT, LOWELL CURTIS, b. Tyler, Minn, Mar. 17, 34; m. 55; c. 4. MECHANICAL ENGINEERING. B.S, Minnesota, 55, Westinghouse Corp. fel, 55-56, M.S, 57; univ. fel, Case, 58-60, Ph.D.(fluid mech), 63; Ohio State, 56-58, Nat. Sci. Found. summer fel, 60. Instr. MECH. ENG, Ohio State, 58; Case West. Reserve Univ, 60-63, asst. prof, 63-67, assoc. prof, 67; ASSOC. PROF, CLEVELAND STATE UNIV, 67- Summers, mech. engr, Ethyl Corp, 55; res. engr, Tapco Div, Thompson-Ramo-Wooldridge Corp, 59; Nat. Sci. Found. consult, India Prog, 70. U.S.A.F, 56-57, Capt. Soc. Automotive Eng.(Ralph R. Teetor award, 67); Am. Soc. Mech. Eng; Am. Soc. Eng. Educ; Instrument Soc. Am. Address: Dept. of Mechanical Engineering, Cleveland State Univ, Cleveland, OH 44115.

DOMIER, KENNETH WALTER, b. Norquay, Sask, Aug. 30, 33; m. 56; c. 2. AGRICULTURAL ENGINEERING. B.Sc, Saskatchewan, 55, M.Sc, 57. Fuels & lubricants engr, Federated Coops. Ltd, 55-58; asst. prof. AGR. ENG, Univ. Man, 58-69; PROF. & CHMN. DEPT, UNIV. ALTA, 69- Am. Soc. Agr. Eng; Can. Soc. Agr. Eng. Fuels; lubricants; tractors; machinery. Address: Dept. of Agricultural Engineering, University of Alberta, Edmonton, Alta, Can.

DOMINGO, W(AYNE) E(LWIN), b. Weeping Water, Nebr, June 30, 16; m. 37; c. 4. PLANT BREEDING. B.S, Nebraska, 38, fel, Utah State Col, 38-40, M.S, 40; fel, Illinois, 40-42, Ph.D.(plant breeding), 42. Assoc, Illinois, 42-43; assoc. plant breeder, bur. plant indust, soils & agr. eng, U.S. Dept. Agr, 43-45, agronomist, 45-46; DIR. OILSEEDS PROD. DIV, BAKER CASTOR OIL CO, 46- Am. Soc. Agron; Soc. Econ. Bot. Hybridization of forage grasses; genetics of soybean; breeding condiment, insecticide and drying oil plants; domestic and foreign production of oilseeds. Address: 10002 County View Rd, La Mesa, CA 92041.

DOMINGOS, HENRY, b. Massena, N.Y, Sept. 17, 34; m. 58; c. 2. SOLID STATE ELECTRONICS. B.E.E, Clarkson Tech, 56; M.S.E.E, Southern California, 58; Ph.D.(elec. eng), Washington (Seattle), 63. Mem. tech. staff electronics, Hughes Aircraft Co, 56-58; asst. prof. ELEC. ENG, Nevada, 58-60; acting instr, Washington (Seattle), 60-63; ASSOC. PROF, CLARKSON COL. TECHNOL, 63- Am. Phys. Soc; Inst. Elec. & Electronics Eng; Am. Soc. Eng. Educ. Semiconductor devices and integrated circuits. Address: Rt. 1, Potsdam, NY 13676.

DOMINGUE, GERALD JAMES, b. Lafayette, La, Mar. 2, 37; m. 58; c. 5. BACTERIOLOGY, IMMUNOLOGY. B.S, Southwestern Louisiana, 59; U.S. Pub. Health Serv. trainee, Tulane, 60-64, Ph.D.(med. microbiol, immunol), 64. Teaching asst. bact, Southwestern Louisiana, 59-60; asst. res. instr. pediat, sch. med, State Univ. N.Y. Buffalo, 64-66; instr. microbiol, sch. med, St. Louis, 66-67; asst. prof. SURG. & MICROBIOL-IMMUNOL, SCH. MED, TULANE UNIV, 67-70, ASSOC. PROF, 70- U.S. Pub. Health Serv. fel, Children's Hosp, Buffalo, 64-66; dir. microbiol, Snodgras Lab. Path. & Bact, St. Louis City Hosp, 66-67; lectr, sch. dent, Washington (St. Louis), 66-67; consult. bacteriologist, South. Baptist Hosp, New Orleans, 68-; consult. res. scientist, Vet. Admin. Hosp, New Orleans, 69- Nat. Guard & U.S.A.R, 55-63. AAAS; N.Y. Acad. Sci; Soc. Exp. Biol. & Med; Am. Soc. Microbiol. Significance of L-phase microorganisms in chronic infections; biological studies on the common enterobacterial antigen; immune response in urinary tract infections; systematic approaches for identifying medically important bacteria. Address: Section of Urology, Tulane University School of Medicine, 1430 Tulane Ave, New Orleans, LA 70112.

DOMINGUEZ, OSCAR V, b. Mexico City, D.F, Dec. 19, 25; m. 54; c. 3. BIOCHEMISTRY, ENDOCRINOLOGY. B.Biol.Sc, Nat. Polytech. Inst, Mex, 44, Q.B.(Ph.D), 50. Teacher, Franco-English Sch, Mex, 44-49; lab. asst. physiol. & pharmacol, superior sch. ed, Nat. Polytech. Inst, Mex, 45-48, asst. prof, 49-52, assoc. prof. biochem, 53-55; res. assoc. biochem, Utah, 56-57, res. instr. endocrinol, 57-60; asst. prof. biochem, McGill, 61-62; vis. prof, Hosp. Nutrit, Mexico City, 62-63; sr. res. scientist, Am. Med. Ctr. Denver, 63-66; dir. res. & educ. biochem, NAT. MED. CTR, MEXICO CITY, 66-69, HEAD DIV. BIOCHEM, DEPT. SCI. RES, 70- Res. biochemist, Ingram Labs, 50-52; res. div, Syntex Labs, Mex, 52-53, chief dept. hormone anal,

53-56; prin. investr, Am. Cancer Soc. res. grant, 56-60; U.S. Pub. Health Serv. res. grant, 63-66; Ford Found. grant, 69-72. Consult, Mex. Inst. Cardiol, 53-58; Univ. Utah, 60-65. Mex. Army, 42-43, Lt. Endocrine Soc; Royal Soc. Med; Mex. Soc. Biol. Chem; Mex. Asn. Study Pharmaceut. & Therapeut; Mex. Chem. Soc; Mex. Soc. Nutrit. & Endocrinol. Biosynthesis of steroid hormones in normal endocrine glands and tumors; steroid biochemistry; isolation, purfication, identification and biosynthesis of steroid hormones by paper chromatography. Address: Dept. of Scientific Research, National Medical Center, Apartado Postal 73-032, Mexico 73, D.F.

DOMINIANNI, SAMUEL JAMES, b. New York, N.Y, Sept. 21, 37; m. 68. ORGANIC CHEMISTRY. B.S, Queens Col.(N.Y.), 58; M.S, Massachusetts, 60; Petrol. Res. Fund fel, North Carolina, 62-64, Ph.D.(org. chem), 64. Res. assoc. fel. chem, Iowa State, 64-66; SR. ORG. CHEMIST, ELI LILLY & CO, 66- AAAS; Am. Chem. Soc; The Chem. Soc. Heterocyclic synthesis; organic photochemistry. Address: Research Labs, Eli Lilly & Co, Indianapolis, IN 46206.

DOMINO, E(DWARD) F(ELIX), b. Chicago, Ill, Nov. 20, 24; m. 48; c. 5. PHARMACOLOGY. B.S, Univ. Ill, 48, M.D. & M.S, 51. Rotating intern, Presby. Hosp, Chicago, 52; instr. PHARMACOL, Univ. Ill, 52-53; UNIV. MICH, 53-54, asst. prof, 54-58, assoc. prof, 58-62, PROF, 62-, DIR. NEURO-PSYCHOPHARMACOL. RES. PROG, UNIV. MICH. & LAFAYETTE CLIN, DETROIT, 66- Vis. prof. pharmacol, Wayne State Univ, 65- Sigma Xi Prize, 51; award, Mich. Soc. Neurol. & Psychiat, 55; first prize, Am. Soc. Anesthesiol, 63; Nikolai Pavlovich Kravkov Mem. Medal, Acad. Bd. Inst. Pharmacol. & Chemother, Acad. Med. Sci, U.S.S.R, 68. U.S.N.R, 43-46. AAAS; Am. Soc. Pharmacol; N.Y. Acad. Sci; Soc. Exp. Biol. & Med; Soc. Psychophysiol. Res; fel. Am. Col. Neuropsychopharmacol; Am. Col. Clin. Pharmacol. & Chemother; assoc. mem. Am. Electroencephalog. Soc; Am. Med. Asn; Soc. Biol. Psychol. Neuropharmacology and psychopharmacology as a means of understanding brain function in animals and in man; central neural transmitters, especially cholingeric substances and interaction of various psychoactive drugs with neural transmitters; biology of mental disease, particularly schizophrenia. Address: Dept. of Pharmacology, University of Michigan, Ann Arbor, MI 48104.

DOMINY, BERYL W, b. Davison, Mich, Apr. 2, 41. ORGANIC CHEMISTRY. B.S, Mich. State, 63; Inst. Cancer fel, Michigan, 66-67, Ph.D.(chem), 67. ORG. CHEMIST, CHAS. PFIZER & CO, 67- Am. Chem. Soc. Heterocyclic chemistry. Address: Chas. Pfizer & Co, Groton, CT 06340.

DOMKE, CHARLES J, b. Chicago, Ill, Nov. 4, 14; m. 45; c. 1. CHEMISTRY, PHILOSOPHY. B.S, Loyola (Ill), 41; Purdue, 62-64. Res. chemist, Burgess Battery Co, 41; asst. chemist, Standard Oil Co.(Ind), 41-46, chemist, 46-48, asst. proj. automotive engr, 49-56, proj. automotive engr, 56-65; sr. proj. automotive engr, Am. Oil Co, 66-67; procedures & standards coord, DEPT. HEALTH, EDUC. & WELFARE, 67-69, CHIEF SURVEILLANCE BR, ENVIRON. PROTECTION AGENCY, 69- Leader, anal. & report writing panel, Coord. Res. Coun, 60, vapor lock prog, 64-65, expression for fuel volatility panel, 64- Soc. Automotive Eng. Design and use of motor fuels under extreme environmental conditions, and/or in high compression engines; development of engine to run without crankcase lubrication; use of ammonia and hydrazine as fuels for spark ignition and compression ignition engines; automation and automatic data logging. Address: 41181 Crestwood Dr, Plymouth, MI 48170.

DOMM, L(INCOLN) V(ALENTINE), b. Near Ayton, Ont, Oct. 22, 96, nat. 31; m. 25; c. 1. ANATOMY, ZOOLOGY. A.B, N.Cent. Col, 21; fel, Chicago, 22-23, Ph.D.(zool), 26. Asst. biol, N.Cent. Col, 20-21; zool, Chicago, 23-28, research assoc, 28-38, research assoc. & asst. prof, 38-46, assoc. prof, 46-47, ANAT, 47-52; PROF. & CHMN. DEPT, STRITCH SCH. MED, LOYOLA UNIV. CHICAGO, 52- Prof, Y.M.C.A. Col, Chicago, 28-, chmn. dept, 34-40; guest, inst. animal genetics, Edinburgh & inst. animal nutrit, col. agr, Cambridge, 35; vis. prof. Edinburgh, 54, 64; Col. of France, Paris, 55. Del, World's Poultry Cong, Edinburgh, 54; Int. Anat. Cong, Paris, 55; Int. Zool. Cong, London, 58; Int. Cong. Comp. Endocrinol, Osio, Japan, 61; Int. Cong. Endocrinol, London, Eng. S.A.T.C, 17. AAAS (v.pres, 50-51); Am. Soc. Nat; Am. Soc. Zool.(secy, 39-48, v.pres, 49-50); Am. Asn. Anat; Endocrine Soc; Soc. Exp. Biol. & Med, Genetics Soc. Am; Wilson Ornith. Soc. Sexuality in birds; effects of sinistral and bilateral ovariectomy; phenomena of sex-inversion and intersexuality; hypo and hyperthyroidism; modifications of plumage pattern through hormones and other agents; pituitary gonadal interrelationships; sexual precocity; effects of early hormone treatment on embryonic and post-embryonic development; factors controlling erythrocyte concentration; changes in avian bone; hormones and tooth development; internal secretions. Address: Stritch School of Medicine, Loyola University, Chicago, IL 60612.

DOMMERT, ARTHUR ROLAND, b. Crowley, La, Apr. 3, 37; m. 63; c. 4. VETERINARY MICROBIOLOGY, BIOCHEMISTRY. B.S, Texas A&M, 60, D.V.M, 61; M.S, La. State, 63, Ph.D.(microbiol, biochem), 66. Nat. Insts. Health fel. microbiol. & biochem, La. State, 61-66; assoc. prof. vet. microbiol, Univ. Mo-Columbia, 66-71; PROF. VET. MICROBIOL. & PARASITOL. & HEAD DEPT, LA. STATE UNIV, BATON ROUGE, 71- Dipl. Am. Col. Vet. Microbiol, 69. AAAS; Am. Vet. Med. Asn; Am. Soc. Microbiol; fel. Am. Inst. Chem; Conf. Res. Workers Animal Diseases. Biochemical and biophysical changes in animal tissues during infections with pathogenic organisms; pathogenesis and immune responses associated with infectious anemias; isolation and identification of obligate anaerobic bacteria, gastrointestinal microflora and pathogenesis of anaplasmosis. Address: Dept. of Veterinary Microbiology & Parasitology, School of Veterinary Medicine, Louisiana State University, Baton Rouge, LA 70803.

DOMROESE, KENNETH A(RTHUR), b. Vincennes, Ind, May 23, 33; m. 57; c. 3. INVERTEBRATE PHYSIOLOGY. B.S, Concoradia Teachers Col. (Ill), 55; M.S, DePaul, 62; Nat. Sci. Found. fel, Northwestern, 60-61, Ph.D. (biol. sci), 63. Asst. prof, BIOL. SCI, CONCORDIA TEACHERS COL.(ILL), 61-64, ASSOC. PROF, 64- AAAS; Am. Soc. Zool. Lipid metabolism in insect flight muscle and invertebrate endocrinology. Address: Dept. of Biology, Concordia Teachers College, River Forest, IL 60305.

DOMSKY, IRVING I(SAAC), b. Racine, Wis, Feb. 3, 30; m. 64; c. 3. ANALYTICAL ORGANIC CHEMISTRY. B.S, Wisconsin, 51, Ph.D.(anal. org. chem), 59. Anal. chemist, Qm. Food & Container Inst, Ill, 54; res. asst. chem, Yale, 58-60; res. assoc, div. oncol, Chicago Med. Sch, 60-64; anal. chemist, Abbott Labs, 64-67; SR. ANAL. CHEMIST, ARMOUR DIAL, INC, 67- Chem.C, U.S.A, 51-53. AAAS; Am. Chem. Soc; Am. Oil Chem. Soc. Gas chromatography; new analytical methods. Address: 7404 N. Talman Ave, Chicago, IL 60645.

DON, CONWAY J, b. Newcastle, U.K, Dec. 1, 22; m. 49; c. 5. RADIOLOGY. M.B, B.S, Univ. Col, London, 46; dipl. radiol, Royal Col. Physicians, Eng, 53 & Can, 58. House physician, Univ. Col, London, 46; house physician & house surgeon, Addenbrooke Hosp, Cambridge, Eng, 47; resident med. officer, Univ. Col, London, 48-49, med. registrar, 50-51, registrar, x-ray dept, 51-54, sr. registrar, 55-56, teaching fel, Harvard Col, 56-57; DIR. X-RAY DEPT, OTTAWA GEN. HOSP, 57-; PROF. & HEAD DEPT. RADIOL, UNIV. OTTAWA, 57- Clin. fel, Mass. Gen. Hosp, Boston, 56-57; Ont. Heart Found. grants, 61-63. Can. Asn. Radiol. Coronary arteriography; renal arterial disease in hypertension. Address: Dept. of Radiology, University of Ottawa, Ottawa, Ont, Can.

DONABEDIAN, AVEDIS, b. Beirut, Lebanon, Jan. 7, 19; nat; m. 45; c. 3. PUBLIC HEALTH. B.A, American Univ, Beirut, 40, M.D, 44; M.P.H, Harvard, 55. Physician & acting supt, Eng. Mission Hosp, Jerusalem, 45-47; asst. dermat. & venerology; American Univ, Beirut, 48-54, instr. physiol, 48-50, univ. physician, 49-51, dir, univ. health serv, 51-54; res. assoc. med. care, sch. pub. health, Harvard, 55-57; asst. prof. prev. med, N.Y. Med. Col, 57-60, assoc. prof, 60-61; PUB. HEALTH ECON, SCH. PUB. HEALTH, UNIV. MICH, 61-64, PROF, 64- Vis. lectr, sch. pub. health, Harvard, 57-58. Med. assoc, med. care eval. studies, United Community Serv, Boston, 55-57. Nat. Acad. Sci. Inst. Med; fel. Am. Pub. Health Asn; Asn. Teachers Prev. Med. Medical care organization. Address: School of Public Health, University of Michigan, Ann Arbor, MI 48104.

DONACHIE, MATTHEW J(OHN), JR, b. Orange, N.J, Oct. 23, 32; m. 55; c. 4. PHYSICAL METALLURGY. B.Met.E, Rensselaer Polytech, 54; Armco Found. fel, Mass. Inst. Tech, 54-58, S.M, 55, Met.E, 57, Sc.D.(x-ray & lattice strains), 58. Metallurgist, Adv. Metals.Res. Corp, 58; res. scientist, res. labs, United Aircraft Corp, 58-59; group leader high temperature metall, Gen. Dynamics/Electric Boat, 59-61; supvr. phys. metall, Chase Brass & Copper Co, 61-63; gen. supvr. metall. eng, PRATT & WHITNEY AIRCRAFT DIV, UNITED AIRCRAFT CORP, 63-67, develop. metallurgist, 67-69, PROJ. MAT. ENGR, 69- Adj. asst. prof, Rensselaer Polytech. Inst, 58-65, adj. assoc. prof, 65-68, adj. prof, 68- Am. Inst. Mining, Metall. & Petrol. Eng; Brit. Inst. Metals; Brit. Inst. Metall; Brit. Iron & Steel Inst. Metallurgy of high temperature alloys; x-ray metallurgy; mechanical behavior of metals; environmental effects in metals; electron microscopy. Address: Pratt & Whitney Aircraft, Main St, East Hartford, CT 06108.

DONAGHY, JAMES JOSEPH, b. Cumberland, Ky, Mar. 13, 35; m. 60. PHYSICS. B.S, Florida, 59; Woodrow Wilson fel, North Carolina, 59, Ph.D.(physics), 65. Opers. analyst, North Carolina, 64-65; asst. prof. physics, Va. Mil. Inst, 65-66; opers. analyst, U.S. Govt, 66-67; ASST. PROF. PHYSICS, WASHINGTON & LEE UNIV, 67-, vis. prof, 66. Am. Phys. Soc; Am. Asn. Physics Teachers. Positron annihilation in solids; Fermi surface in metals. Address: Dept. of Physics, Washington & Lee University, Lexington, VA 24450.

DONAGHY, R(AYMOND) M(ADIFORD) PEARDON, b. Eastman, Que, Can, Aug. 18, 10; nat; m. 41; c. 4. NEUROSURGERY. B.S, Vermont, 33, M.D, 36. Intern. neurol, Montreal Gen. Hosp, Can, 36-37, asst. res. internal med, 37-38; res. gen. surg, Children's Mem. Hosp, 38-39; asst. res. neurosurg, Mass. Gen. Hosp, 39-40; res. psychiat, McLean Hosp, 40-41; fel. neurosurg, Lahey Clin, 41-42; from assoc. prof. to PROF. NEUROSURG, COL. MED, UNIV. VT, 46- Dalton scholar, Mass. Gen. Hosp, 42, res, 42-43. Med.C, 43-46. Fel. Am. Col. Surg. Brain abscess; spastic element in cerebral thrombosis; neurovascular surgery. Address: Medical Center Hospital, University of Vermont, Burlington, VT 05401.

DONAHOE, F(RANK) J, b. Ashland, Pa, Mar. 12, 22; m. 43; c. 2. PHYSICS. B.A, La Salle Col, 43; Ph.D.(physics), Pennsylvania, 54. Instr. math. & phys. chem, La Salle Col, 48-49; asst, Pennsylvania, 49-51; res. physicist, Franklin Inst, 51-64; assoc. prof. PHYSICS, WILKES COL, 64-68, PROF, 68- U.S.A, 43-45. AAAS; Inst. Elec. & Electronics Eng; Am. Phys. Soc; Am. Asn. Physics Teachers. Low temperature physics of metals; order-disorder in ferromagnetic alloys; solid state physics; thermoelectricity; cosmogony. Address: Dept. of Physics, Wilkes College, Wilkes Barre, PA 18703.

DONAHOE, HUGH B(URKMAN), b. Kansas City, Mo, Jan. 6, 22. MEDICINAL CHEMISTRY. B.S, Rockhurst Col, 43; M.S, Kansas, 47, fel, 47-49, Ph.D. (chem), 50. Asst. chem, Rockhurst Col, 41-43, lectr. physics, 73rd Col. Training Detachment, 43-44; asst. instr. CHEM, Kansas, 44-46; instr, ST. LOUIS UNIV, 49-50, asst. prof, 51-57, assoc. prof, 57-61, PROF, 62-, CHMN. SPACE SCI. RES. & DEVELOP. COMT, 65-, ASSOC. CHMN. DEPT. CHEM, 71-, acting dir. dept, 50-51, exec. secy, 50-52. AAAS; Am. Chem. Soc; fel. Am. Inst. Chem. Structure-activity relationships of medicinal agents; synthesis of curariform compounds; synthetic organic chemistry. Address: St. Louis University, P.O. Box 8089, Pierre Laclede Sta, St. Louis, MO 63156.

DONAHOO, PAT, b. Van Buren, Ark, July 22, 28; m. 65; c. 2. ANALYTICAL CHEMISTRY. B.S, Hendrix Col, 50; M.S, Okla. State, 52, Ph.D.(chem), 55. Chemist, Tex. Co, 52-53; res. chemist, Lion Oil Co. Div, Monsanto Co, 55-56, inorg. chem. div, 56-60; Griffiths Labs, Inc, 60-62, chief chemist, 62-66, tech. mkt. mgr, 66-71; DIR. GROC. PROD. DEL, ANDERSON CLAYTON FOODS, 71- Am. Chem. Soc; Inst. Food Tech; Soc. Adv. Food Serv. Res. Seasonings for food products; soy proteins; hydrolyzed plant proteins; oil based grocery products; spices. Address: Anderson Clayton Foods, 3333 N. Central Expressway, Richardson, TX 75080.

DONAHUE, D(ANIEL) JOSEPH, b. Joliet, Ill, May 11, 26; m. 49; c. 3. PHYSICAL CHEMISTRY. B.S, Michigan, 47, M.S, 48, Ph.D.(phys. chem), 51. Engr. & eng. leader, RCA CORP, 51-58, mgr. semiconductor advan. develop, 58-62, chief engr, indust. semiconductors dept, 62-65, mgr. dept, 65-67, solid state oper, 67-69, SOLID STATE, 69-70, DIV. V.PRES, EUROPE, 70- Surface physics; color kinescopes; solid state materials; processes and devices, power, signal, microwave and integrated circuits; engineering; manufacturing; marketing; distribution; sales; P&L; international. Address: RCA Ltd, Lincoln Way, Windmill Rd, Sunbury-on-Thames, Middlesex, England.

DONAHUE, DOUGLAS J(AMES), b. Wichita, Kans, Oct. 26, 24; m. 48; c. 5. NUCLEAR PHYSICS. B.S, Oregon, 47, M.S, 48; Ph.D, Wisconsin, 52. Physicist, Hanford Labs, Gen. Elec. Co, 52-57; asst. prof. PHYSICS, Pa. State, 57-61, assoc. prof, 61-63; UNIV. ARIZ, 63-64, PROF, 64- U.S.N.R, 43-46. Am. Phys. Soc. Low energy nuclear physics; reactor physics. Address: Dept. of Physics, University of Arizona, Tucson, AZ 85721.

DONAHUE, FRANCIS M(ARTIN), b. Phila, Pa, May 8, 34; m. 60; c. 4. ELECTROCHEMICAL ENGINEERING. B.A, La Salle Col, 56; Ph.D.(eng), California, Los Angeles, 65. Res. chemist, Tasty Baking Co, 56-59; group leader corrosion res, Betz Labs, Inc, 59-61; electrochemist, Stanford Res. Inst, 61-63; res. engr, California, Los Angeles, 63-65; asst. prof. CHEM. ENG, UNIV. MICH, 65-69, ASSOC. PROF, 69- U.S.A, 57, Res, 56-57, 58-64, 1st Lt. Electrochem. Soc; Nat. Asn. Corrosion Eng; Am. Inst. Chem. Eng; Am. Electroplaters Soc. Corrosion and corrosion inhibition; electrochemical energy conversion; electrocatalysis; electrosynthesis; electrodeposition. Address: 300 Montgomery Ave, Ann Arbor, MI 48103.

DONAHUE, HAYDEN HACKNEY, b. El Reno, Okla, Dec. 4, 12; m. 47; c. 3 PSYCHIATRY. B.S, Kansas, 39, M.D, 41. Intern, univ. hosps, Georgia, 41-42, instr. med. & psychiat, sch. med, 42; lectr. hosp. admin. & psychiat, residency prog. & asst. mgr, Vet. Admin. Hosp, North Little Rock, Ark, 46-49; dir. ed. & res, Ark. State Hosp, 49-51; asst. med. dir, Tex. State Bd. Hosps. & Spec. Schs, 51-53; dir. ment. health, State of Okla, 53-59; asst. supt, Ark. State Hosp, 59-61; SUPT. CENT. STATE GRIFFIN MEM. HOSP, 61-; DIR, DEPT. MENT. HEALTH, STATE OF OKLA, 70-, asst. dir, 66-70. Assoc. prof. psychiat, sch. med, Arkansas, 49-51, 60-61; consult. asst. prof. neurol. & psychiat, Oklahoma, 54-58, assoc. prof. psychiat, 58-67, clin. prof, 67- Lectr. legal med, sch. law, Texas, 52; homicide inst, Univs. Oklahoma & Texas, 53-; instr, Okla. State, 58-59; lectr, Oklahoma, 64- Consult, Ark. State Dept. Health, 49-51; chief consult, Okla. State Penitentiary, 63-; consult, Okla. State Crime Bur, 63-; Base Hosp, Tinker Field, 64- Adv, Okla. Cmt, President's Cmt. Employ. Handicapped, 57-59 & 61-71, v.chmn. Okla. Cmt, White House Conf. Children & Youth, 59; mem. Okla. Gov. Cmn, White House Conf. Aging, 59-60, Ark. Gov. Comn, 60-61, nat. adv. comt, 59-61, chmn. sect. ment. health & aging, 60-61; nat. prog. comt, Coun. Soc. Work Ed, 59; mem. state, county & local adv. comts. & couns. ment. health. Mem. bd. dirs, Pan Am. Training Exchange Prog. Psychiat, 61-63, treas, 63; Am. Psychiat. Asn-Pan Am. Exchange rep, Latin Am. Seminar Ment. Health, WHO, Buenos Aires, 63; secy. sect. psychopharmacol, Am. Mex. Joint Ment. Health Conf, Mexico City, 64; co-chmn. sect. private & pub. ment. hosps, Nat. Conf. Ment. Illness & Health, Chicago, 64. Med.C, U.S.A.A.F, 43-46. Fel. AAAS; Am. Med. Asn; fel. Am. Psychiat. Asn. (treas, 68-); fel. Am. Asn. Ment. Deficiency; fel. Am. Geriat. Soc; fel. Am. Col. Psychiat. (regent, 65, treas, 66-71); Med. Correctional Asn; Acad. Relig. & Ment. Health; Nat. Rehab. Asn. War neurosis; tuberculosis; narcosynthesis; problems of the aged; psychological selection and training of professional, technical and ancillary hospital personnel; hospital operations and management problems; use of special drugs in treatment of mental patients and rehabilitative therapies in care and treatment of institutionalized patients. Address: P.O. Box 151, 107 State Dr, Norman, OK 73069.

DONAHUE, JACK D(AVID), b. Chicago, Ill, Nov. 21, 38; m. 65; c. 2. GEOLOGY. B.A, Illinois, Urbana, 60; Nat. Sci. Found. fel, Columbia, 60-62, J.F. Kemp fel, 64-65, Ph.D.(geol), 67. Lectr. GEOL, Queens Col. (N.Y), 64-67, ASST. PROF, 67-70; UNIV. PITTSBURGH, 70- Participant, field surv. Azores Islands, Gulbenkian Found, Portugal, 67; geol. consult, Econ. Develop. Admin, P.R, 68. AAAS; Geol. Soc. Am; Soc. Econ. Paleont. & Mineral; Paleont. Soc. Paleozoic sedimentary depositional environments; evolution and environments of Paleozoic marine benthic communities. Address: Dept. of Earth & Planetary Sciences, University of Pittsburgh, Pittsburgh, PA 15213.

DONAHUE, JAMES KENNETH, b. New Haven, Conn, Dec. 16, 05; m. 36; c. 2. PHYSIOLOGY. B.A, Iowa, 30; Ph.D.(endocrinol), Princeton, 33; hon. LL.D, Hamilton Col, 69. Asst, Princeton, 33-35; prof. biol, Col. Charleston, 35-48; prof. zool. & chmn. dept, Utica Col, 48-63, pres, 63-70; VIS. PROF. BIOL, HAMILTON COL, 71- Consult, State Dept. Sea & Shore Fisheries, Maine. U.S.C.G.R, 44-45. AAAS; Soc. Exp. Biol. & Med; Am. Soc. Zool; N.Y. Acad. Sci. Estrogens in marine invertebrates; physiology of ecdysis in American lobster; physiology of extremity veins. Address: 30 Marvin St, Clinton, NY 13223.

DONAHUE, JOSEPH E, b. Milwaukee, Wis, Oct. 2, 23; m. 61; c. 2. ORGANIC CHEMISTRY. B.S, Agr. & Mech. Col, Tex, 48. Chemist, E.I. DU PONT DE NEMOURS & CO, Tenn, 48-51, anal. chem, Ga, 51-53, area supvr. radiation chem, 53-56, process supvr, N.Y, 56-61, RES. CHEMIST TEXTILE FIBERS, Va, 61-62, TEXTILE RES. LAB, 62- Med.C, 43-46, 48-51, 2nd Lt. Analytical chemistry. Address: Chestnut Run, Textile Research Lab, E.I. du Pont de Nemours & Co, Wilmington, DE 19898.

DONAHUE, RAYMOND JOSEPH, b. Chicago, Ill, Oct. 3, 41; m. 64; c. 2. METALLURGY. B.S, Ill. Inst. Tech, 63, Ph.D.(metall. eng), 66. Instr. metall. eng, Ill. Inst. Tech, 65-66; ASST. PROF. METALL, UNIV. CONN, 66- Am. Soc. Metals; Am. Inst. Mining, Metall. & Petrol. Eng. X-ray diffraction and electron microscopy techniques for solving physical and mechanical metallurgy problems; alloy theory. Address: Dept. of Metallurgy, School of Engineering, University of Connecticut, Storrs, CT 06268.

DONAHUE, ROY L(UTHER), b. Ringgold, Texas, Nov. 3, 08; m; c. 3. SOIL SCIENCE. B.S, Mich. State, 32; Ph.D, Cornell, 39. Instr. soils, Mich. State, 34-35; assoc. prof. forest soils & head dept. forestry, Miss State, 35-37; asst. forestry, Cornell, 37-39; assoc. prof. agron, Texas A&M, 39-52, exten. agronomist, 45-52; agronomist & chmn. dept. agron, New Hampshire, 52-

56; prof. agron, Kansas State Univ-U.S. Agency Int. Develop, India, 56-61, consult. soils & fertilizer, Ford Found, 61-66; PROF. SOIL SCI, MICH. STATE UNIV, 66- Sr. Forester, Rubber Develop. Corp, Brazil, 43; state supvr. farm unit demonstration work, Tenn. Valley Authority & Tex. A&M Univ, spec. fertilizer surv. of Greece for Koppers Co, 55; vis. prof. soil sci, Univ. Ryukyus, Okinawa, 66-67; agronomist, Mich. State Univ-U.S. Agency Int. Develop, African Mechanization Study, Inst. Agr. Res, Ethiopia, 67-69. Soil Sci. Soc. Am; Am. Soc. Agron; sr. mem. Soc. Am. Foresters; Soil Conserv. Soc. Am; Asn. Advan. Agr. Sci. Africa; Indian Soc. Soil Sci; Indian Soc. Agron; Soil Conserv. Soc. India; Int. Soc. Soil Sci. Forest soils of University of Michigan biological tract; land use and forest soils in northern Michigan; tree growth as related to soil morphology in central Adirondack Mountains of New York; influence of forest fires on soil fertility. Address: 133 Kenberry Dr, East Lansing, MI 48823.

DONAHUE, SHEILA, b. Northolt, England, Nov. 1, 16; U.S. citizen. PATHOLOGY, NEUROPATHOLOGY. M.R.C.S. & L.R.C.P, 43; M.R.C.Path, 63. House physician, Elizabeth Garret Anderson Hosp, England, 43; house surgeon, Royal Surrey County Hosp, 44; fel. path, col. med, N.Y. Univ, 47-48, asst, 48-51, instr, 53-55; fel. neuropath, Bellevue Hosp, N.Y, 55-56; Col. Physicians & Surgeons, Columbia Univ, 56-58; spec. trainee, sect. neurocytol, Nat. Inst. Neurol. Diseases & Stroke, 58; assoc. neuropath, Col. Physicians & Surgeons, Columbia Univ, 58-60, asst. prof, 60-63; path, sch. med, Ind. Univ, 63-66, assoc. prof, 66-70; ASSOC. RES. SCIENTIST, N.Y. STATE INST. BASIC RES. MENT. RETARDATION, 70- Resident, Bellevue Hosp, N.Y, 48-50, asst. pathologist, 50-51, 53-55. Dipl, Am. Bd. Path, 57. R.A.M.C, 44-47, Capt. Path. Soc. Gt. Brit. & Ireland; fel. Col. Am. Path; assoc. Am. Acad. Neurol; Electron Micros. Soc. Am; Am. Asn. Path. & Bact; Am. Asn. Neuropath. Structure and function of the nervous system in the normal and diseased states including the morphology as it appears in the electron microscope. Address: New York State Institute for Basic Research in Mental Retardation, 1050 Forest Hill Rd, Staten Island, NY 10314.

DONAHUE, THOMAS M(ICHAEL), b. Healdton, Okla, May 23, 21. PHYSICS. A.B, Rockhurst Col, 42; Nat. Res. fel, Hopkins, 46-47, Ph.D.(physics), Hopkins, 48. Asst. math, Rockhurst Col, 41-42; jr. instr. PHYSICS, Hopkins, 42-43, instr, 42-44, 47-49, asst. prof, 49-50; from assoc. prof. to PROF, UNIV. PITTSBURGH, 50- U.S.A, 44-46. Am. Phys. Soc; Am. Asn. Physics Teachers. Aurora; airglow; cosmic rays; electrical discharges in gases. Address: Dept. of Physics, University of Pittsburgh, Pittsburgh, PA 15213.

DONAHUE, WILLIAM E, b. Lower Peach Tree, Ala, June 3, 19; m. 54. ORGANIC CHEMISTRY. A.B, Bradley, 47; M.S, Washington State, 51; Ph.D. (org. chem), Lehigh, 55. Prof. & chmn. dept. CHEM, Ind. Inst. Tech, 55-59; assoc. prof, Southwestern Louisiana, 59-61; State Univ. N.Y. Col. Oneonta, 61-63; assoc. prof, PURDUE UNIV, FT. WAYNE, 63-65, PROF, 65-, sect. chmn, 63-68, asst. dean acad. affairs, 67-71. Sabbatical, Univ. Provence, 71-72. Nat. Sci. Found. res. participant summer progs, Kansas, 62, Boston, 63, 64, exten. grant, 64-66. Am. Chem. Soc. Synthesis of purine-like heterocycles; keto-enol tautormerism of β-aromatic pyruvate esters. Address: Purdue University at Fort Wayne, 2101 Coliseum Blvd. E, Ft. Wayne, IN 46805.

DONAHUE, WILLIAM H, C.S.C, b. Phila, Pa, Aug. 22, 22. PLANT ECOLOGY. A.B, Univ. Notre Dame, 45; Ph.D.(bot), Cath. Univ. Am, 54. Assoc. prof. BIOL, KING'S COL.(PA), 53-66, PROF, 66- Ecol. Soc. Am; Am. Asn. Biol. Teachers. Plant ecology. Address: Dept. of Biology, King's College, Wilkes Barre, PA 18702.

DONAL, JOHN S(COTT), JR, b. Philadelphia, Pa, June 19, 05; m. 36; c. 1. ENGINEERING. A.B, Swarthmore Col, 26; M.S, Michigan, 27, Ph.D.(physics), 30. Instr. physics, Michigan, 26-30; Johnson Found. fel. & res. assoc. pharmacol, Pennsylvania, 30-32, fel. pharmacol, 32-36; res. engr, res. & develop. lab, radiotron div, Radio Corp. Am. Mfg. Co, 36-42, RCA Labs, 42-59, administr. staff of v.pres, 59-70; RETIRED. Inst. Elec. & Electronics Eng. Cardiac output in man; blood-gas micro-method; abnormal shot-effect; television light valves; magnetrons and magnetron modulation. Address: 264 Snowden Lane, Princeton, NJ 08540.

DONALD, DOUGLAS D(UNN), b. New York, N.Y, June 12, 22; m. 46; c. 2. ECONOMIC GEOLOGY. B.S, Princeton, 43; M.S, Columbia, 48. Asst. explor. geologist, Mingus Mt. Mining Co, 47-49; geologist & develop. engr, Annville Stone Co, 49-51; chief mining engr, Bertha Mineral Div, N.J. Zinc Co, 51-56; consult. mining & geol, Behre Dolbear & Co, 56-64; mineral economist, SCUDDER STEVENS & CLARK, 64-70, V.PRES. RES, 70- U.S.N.R, 44-46, Res, 46-54, Lt.(jg). Geol. Soc. Am; Soc. Econ. Geol. Mineral economics. Address: Scudder Stevens & Clark, 345 Park Ave, New York, NY 10022.

DONALD, ELIZABETH ANN, b. Edmonton, Alta, Can, Feb. 14, 26. NUTRITION. B.Sc, Alberta, 49; M.S, Washington State, 55; Ph.D.(nutrit), Cornell, 62. Dietitian, Alberta, 50-51; acting jr. home economist, Washington State, 55-59; asst. prof. FOODS & NUTRIT, Cornell Univ, 62-66, ASSOC. PROF, 66-69; UNIV. ALTA, 69- AAAS; N.Y. Acad. Sci; Am. Inst. Nutrit; Can. Nutrit. Soc; Am. Dietetic Asn; Am. Home Econ. Asn. Foods; nutritional status; vitamin B_6; vitamin B_6 requirement of young women using anovulatory steroids. Address: School of Household Economics, University of Alberta, Edmonton, Alta, Can.

DONALD, H(AROLD) JACK, b. Lethbridge, Alta, Aug. 30, 23; m; c. 3. FUEL TECHNOLOGY. B.Sc, Alberta, 46; fel, Pa. State, 53-54, Ph.D.(fuel tech), 55. Tech. supvr, Consol. Mining & Smelting Co. Can, Ltd, 46-48; asst, Pa. State, 49-53; fel, Mellon Inst. Indust. Res, 54-56; chem. engr, DOW CHEM. CO, 56-70, ASSOC. SCIENTIST, 70- Soc. Plastics Eng; Am. Chem. Soc; Am. Soc. Metals; Sci. Res. Soc. Am. Utilization of the properties of plastic; properties of coal and its benification and utilization. Address: 1306 Wallen St, Midland, MI 48640.

DONALD, WILLIAM DAVID, b. Donalds, S.C, Apr. 27, 24; m. 48; c. 4. MEDICINE. A.B, Erskine Col, 45; M.D, Vanderbilt, 47. Instr. PEDIAT, sch. med, Vanderbilt, 50-51; asst. prof, sch. med, Alabama, 53-56, ASSOC. PROF, 56-59; Med. Col. Ga, 59-60; SCH. MED, VANDERBILT UNIV, 60- U.S.A.F, 51-53, Capt. AAAS; Am. Acad. Pediat; Am. Fedn. Clin. Res. Infectious diseases in children. Address: Dept. of Pediatrics, Vanderbilt University, Nashville, TN 37203.

DONALDSON, ALAN C, b. Northampton, Mass, Oct. 23, 29; m. 57; c. 4. GEOLOGY. B.A, Amherst Col, 51; M.S, Massachusetts, 53; Calif. Co, fel, & Ph.D.(geol), Pa. State, 59. Asst. prof. GEOL, W.VA. UNIV, 57-62, assoc. prof, 62-69, PROF, 69- Soc. Econ. Paleont. & Mineral; Am. Asn. Petrol. Geol. Modern sediments and their depositional environments, sedimentary rocks, stratigraphy and sedimentation. Address: Dept. of Geology, West Virginia University, Morgantown, WV 26506.

DONALDSON, ALAN W(ESTON), b. Alliance, Ohio, June 3, 16; m. 41; c. 3. BIOLOGY. B.S, Mt. Union Col, 37; Michigan, 37-38; Sc.D.(parasitol), Hopkins, 43. Instr. biol. & German, Mt. Union Col, 37-39; field biologist, State Dept. Health, Ga, 40-41; asst. parasitol, Hopkins, 41-43, chief helminth. unit, parasitol. sect, communicable disease center, U.S. Pub. Health Serv, Ga, 46-53, asst. chief lab. br, 53-55, spec. asst, develop. & eval, exec. off, 55-56, asst. chief, 56-60, dep. chief, 60-64, assoc. chief opers, bur. state serv, community health, D.C, 64-67, assoc. dir, bur. disease prev. & environ. control, 67-68, assoc. administr, health serv. & mental health admin, 68-70; ASSOC. DEAN, SCH. PUB. HEALTH, UNIV. ILL. MED. CTR, 71- Assoc. med. sch, Emory, 47-52. Mem, Conf. State & Prov. Pub. Health Lab. Dirs. Sanit.C, 43-46, Capt; U.S.P.H.S, 53-70, Asst. Surg. Gen; Meritorious Serv. Medal, 68. Am. Soc. Trop. Med. & Hyg; Sci. Res. Soc. Am. Laboratory diagnostic procedures; helminthology; research and public health administration. Address: School of Public Health, University of Illinois at the Medical Center, Box 6998, Chicago, IL 60680.

DONALDSON, COLEMAN DUPONT, b. Phila, Pa, Sept. 22, 22; m. 45; c. 5. AERONAUTICAL ENGINEERING. B.Aero.E, Rensselaer Polytech, 43; M.A, Princeton, 54, Ph.D.(aeronaut. eng), 57. Mem. staff, Nat. Adv. Cmt. Aeronaut, 43-44, head aerophys. sect, 46-52; aeronaut. engr, Bell Aircraft Corp, 46; PRES. & SR. CONSULT, AERONAUT. RES. ASSOCS. OF PRINCETON, INC, 54- Consult, Martin-Marietta Corp, 55-; Gen. Elec. Co, 56-; Gen. Precision Equip. Corp, 57-67; Thompson Ramo Wooldridge Inc, 58-61; Grumman Aerospace Corp, 64-; mem. res. & adv. subcomt. fluid mech, NASA; vehicle response group, Defense Atomic Support Agency; indust. prof. adv. comt, Pa. State Univ, Robert H. Goddard vis. lectr, Princeton, 70-71, mem. adv. coun. U.S.A.A.F, 45-46. Am. Phys. Soc; Acad. Appl. Sci; Am. Inst. Navig; N.Y. Acad. Sci; assoc. fel. Am. Inst. Aeronaut. & Astronaut. Fluid and gas dynamics; viscous and other transport phenomena; turbulence and turbulent transport phenomena; chemical aspects of high temperature gas flows. Address: Aeronautical Research Associates of Princeton, Inc, 50 Washington Rd, Princeton, NJ 08540.

DONALDSON, DAVID M(ILLER), b. Ogden, Utah, Oct. 2, 24; m. 47; c. 4. BACTERIOLOGY, IMMUNOLOGY. B.S, Univ. Utah, 50, M.S, 52, Ph.D. (bact), 54. Lab. fel, Univ. Utah, 50-52, asst, 52-54, res. instr, 54-55; PROF. bact, BRIGHAM YOUNG UNIV, 55-68, MICROBIOL, 68- U.S.A, 43-46. Address: Dept. of Microbiology, Brigham Young University, Provo, UT 84601.

DONALDSON, DONALD JAY, b. Toledo, Ohio, Feb. 15, 40; m. 60. HUMAN ANATOMY, DEVELOPMENTAL BIOLOGY. B.Ed, Toledo, 62; Ph.D.(anat), Tulane, 68. Instr. histol. & embryol, MED. UNITS, UNIV. TENN, 68-70, ASST. PROF, ANAT, 70- Control of growth and differentiation-regeneration of appendages in Amphibia. Address: Dept. of Anatomy, University of Tennessee Medical Units, Memphis, TN 38103.

DONALDSON, E(DWARD) E(NSLOW), b. Wenatchee, Wash, Mar. 7, 23; m. 46; c. 1. PHYSICS. B.S, Washington State, 48, Ph.D, 53. Physicist radiological physics, Hanford Labs, Gen. Elec. Co, 53-57; asst. prof. PHYSICS, WASH. STATE UNIV, 57-64, assoc. prof. & acting chmn. dept, 64-67, PROF. & CHMN. DEPT, 67- Vis. prof, Univ. Liverpool, 68. U.S.A, 43-45. AAAS; Am. Asn. Physics Teachers; sr. mem. Am. Vacuum Soc; Am. Phys. Soc. Physics and chemistry of surfaces. Address: Dept. of Physics, Washington State University, Sloan Hall, Pullman, WA 99163.

DONALDSON, EDWARD MOSSOP, b. Whitehaven, Eng, June 25, 39; Can. citizen; m. 64. ENDOCRINOLOGY, ZOOLOGY. B.Sc, Sheffield, 61; B.C. Sugar Ref. Co. studentship, British Columbia, 62-63, Nat. Res. Coun. Can. studentship, 63-64, Ph.D.(zool), 64. U.S. Pub. Health Serv. fel. steroid biochem, Minnesota, Minneapolis, 64-65; SCIENTIST, W.VANCOUVER LAB, FISHERIES RES. BD. CAN, 65- Vis. res. scientist, Oceanic Inst, Hawaii, 69; res. assoc, British Columbia, 69- Consult. zool, California, Berkeley, 68; mem. orgn. comt, Int. Symp. Comp. Endocrinol, 69- Can. Soc. Zool; Can. Biochem. Soc; Am. Soc. Zool. Purification of gonadotropin, corticotropin and prolactin from salmon pituitary glands and investigation of their functions in fish and other vertebrates; changes in steroid secretion rates during sexual maturation in salmon. Address: Fisheries Research Board of Canada, 4160 Marine Dr, West Vancouver, B.C, Can.

DONALDSON, ERLE C, b. Tela, Honduras, Dec. 30, 26; m. 54; c. 5. SURFACE, PETROLEUM & ENVIRONMENTAL CHEMISTRY, ENGINEERING. B.S, The Citadel, 53; M.S, South Carolina, 55; B.S, Houston, 61. Anal. chemist, Signal Oil & Gas Co, 55-59, chem. engr, 59-61; PROJ. LEADER, U.S. BUR. MINES, 61- Am. Chem. Soc; Soc. Petrol. Eng. Surface chemistry of oil production; effect on oil production of additives in floodwater and the role played by natural surfactants in oil; subsurface disposal of liquid industrial wastes; petroleum production and environmental pollution abatement. Address: Research Center, U.S. Bureau of Mines, P.O. Box 1398, Bartlesville, OK 74003.

DONALDSON, FRANK T(HOMAS), b. Helena, Mont, July 13, 06; m. 34; c. 5. CHEMISTRY. B.Sc, Mont. State Col, 30; Ph.D.(biochem), Minnesota, 37. Asst. chem, exp. sta, Mont. State Col, 30-31, asst. prof, 34-39; asst. biochem, Minnesota, 31-34; res. chemist, Firestone Tire & Rubber Co, 39-43; Avoset Co, 43-46, mgr, Gustine Creamery Div, 46-50; res. chemist, Firestone Tire & Rubber Co, 52-53, chief chem. res. & develop, Foamex Div, Firestone Rubber & Latex Prod. Co, 53-71; RETIRED. Am. Chem. Soc.

Movement of minerals in wheat plant during growth; causes of variation in properties of hevea latex; colloidal properties of foamed hevea and synthetic latex; technology of polyurethane foam. Address: 3 Hailes Hill Rd, Swansea, MA 02777.

DONALDSON, JAMES A, b. Madison, Fla, Apr. 17, 41. MATHEMATICS. A.B, Lincoln (Pa), 61; M.S, Illinois, 63, Ph.D.(math), 65. Asst. prof. MATH, Howard Univ, 65-66; Univ. Ill, Chicago-Circle, 66-70; ASSOC. PROF, UNIV. N.MEX, 70- Math. Asn. Am; Am. Math. Soc. Differential and integral equations. Address: Dept. of Mathematics, University of New Mexico, Albuquerque, NM 87106.

DONALDSON, JAMES A(DRIAN), b. St. Cloud, Minn, Jan. 22, 30; m. 50; c. 5. OTOLOGY. B.A, Minnesota, 50, B.S, 52, M.D, 54, M.S, 61; Nat. Insts. Health fel, Southern California, 60-61. Instr. otolaryngol, Southern California, 60-61; asst. prof. otolaryngol. & maxillofacial surg, col. med, Iowa, 61-63, assoc. prof, 63-65; PROF. OTOLARYNGOL, & HEAD DEPT, SCH. MED, UNIV. WASH, 65- U.S.P.H.S.R, 55-57, Sr. Asst. Surg. Am. Acad. Ophthalmol. & Otolaryngol; fel. Am. Laryngol, Rhinol. & Otol. Soc; fel. Am. Col. Surg; Soc. Univ. Otolaryngol; Am. Med. Asn. Surgical anatomy of the temporal bone. Address: Dept. of Otolaryngology, University Hospital, University of Washington, Seattle, WA 98105.

DONALDSON, JAMES BOWIE, b. Clydebank, Scotland, Apr. 11, 16; U.S. citizen; m. 45; c. 6. MEDICINE. M.D, Temple, 44, Asst. prof. med, Hahnemann Med. Col, 52-56, assoc. prof, 56-59, acting chmn. dept, 58-59; prof. clin. med, TEMPLE UNIV, 59-66, PROF. MED, 66-, ASSOC. DEAN SCH. MED, 67- Dir, Div. B, Phila, Gen. Hosp, 59-66; chief staff, Temple Univ. Hosp, 67- Med.C, U.S.N, 46-47, Lt.(jg). Am. Med. Asn; fel. Am. Col. Physicians; fel. Am. Col. Cardiol; Am. Soc. Internal Med; dipl. mem, Pan-Am. Med. Asn. Address: School of Medicine, Temple University, 3401 N. Broad St, Philadelphia, PA 19140.

DONALDSON, JOHN ALLAN, b. Chatham, Ont, Oct. 15, 33; m. 57; c. 2. GEOLOGY. B.Sc, Queen's (Ont), 56; Ph.D.(geol), Hopkins, 60. Geologist, Geol. Surv. Can, 59-65, res. scientist, 65-68; ASSOC. PROF. GEOL, CARLETON UNIV.(ONT), 68- Soc. Econ. Paleont. & Mineral; Geol. Asn. Can; Int. Asn. Sedimentol. Dispersal patterns in sedimentary rocks; Precambrian sedimentation; primitive life. Address: Dept. of Geology, Carleton University, Rideau River Campus, Ottawa 1, Ont, Can.

DONALDSON, JOHN R(ILEY), b. Dallas, Tex, Nov. 24, 25; m. 51; c. 4. PHYSICS. B.S, Rice Inst, 45, M.A, 47; M.S, Yale, Ph.D.(physics), 51. Nuclear physicist, Calif. Res. & Develop. Co, 50-53; assoc. prof. PHYSICS, Arizona, 53-54; FRESNO STATE COL, 56-67, PROF, 67- U.S.A, 54-56. AAAS; Am. Asn. Physics Teachers; Am. Phys. Soc. General and nuclear physics. Address: Dept. of Physics, Fresno State College, Fresno, CA 93710.

DONALDSON, JOHN RUSSELL, b. Helena, Mont, Jan. 14, 29; m. 51; c. 3. LIMNOLOGY, FISHERIES BIOLOGY. B.S, Washington (Seattle), 51, M.S, 54, Ph.D.(limnol), 66; Fulbright fel, Oslo, 51-52. Aquatic chemist, Wash. Dept. Game, 54-63; asst. prof. LIMNOL, ORE. STATE UNIV, 66-70, ASSOC. PROF, 71- Am. Fisheries Soc; Am. Soc. Limnol. & Oceanog. Limnological research involving biological production, especially artificial enrichment of lakes and ponds. Address: Dept. of Fisheries & Wildlife, Oregon State University, Corvallis, OR 97331.

DONALDSON, LAUREN R(USSELL), b. Tracy, Minn, May 13, 03; m. 27; c. 2. BIOLOGY. A.B, Intermountain Union Col, 26; M.S, Washington (Seattle), 31, Ph.D.(fisheries), 39; hon. D.Sc, Rocky Mountain Col, 58; hon. D.Sc, Hamline Univ, 65. Prin. & teacher, high sch, Mont, 26-30; from asst. to PROF. FISHERIES, UNIV. WASH, 32-, dir. lab. radiation biol, 58-66, appl. fisheries lab, 43-57. Lectr, Oslo, 52-; Helsinki, 59. Biologist, State Dept. Fisheries, Wash, 42-43; chief div. radiobiol, radiol. safety sect, Oper. Crossroads, Bikini, 46, div. radiobiol, Bikini Sci. Resurv, 47-48, Bikini-Eniwetok Resurv, 49; biologist, Oper. Ivy, 52; dir. radiobiol. studies, Pac. Weapons Testing Prog, 54- Consult, fish & wildlife serv, U.S. Dept. Interior, 35-40; Gen. Elec. Co, 47-; Gen. Mills, Inc. Rep, Atomic Energy Cmn, Japan, 54. AAAS; Am. Fisheries Soc.(v.pres, 39); Am. Soc. Ichthyol. & Herpet; Wildlife Soc; Radiation Res. Soc; Am. Soc. Limnol. & Oceanog. Fisheries management; fresh water biology; radiobiology; genetics of salmonoid fishes; nutrition of the chinook salmon, particularly histological changes. Address: College of Fisheries, University of Washington, Seattle, WA 98105.

DONALDSON, MALCOLM M, b. New York, N.Y, Nov. 7, 31; m. 51; c. 3. ORGANIC CHEMISTRY. B.A, Middlebury Col, 53; M.A, Princeton, 57, Ph.D.(chem), 60. Chemist, Stauffer Chem. Co, 58-61; Am. Cyanamid Co, 61-68; gen. partner, Mason B. Starring & Co, 68-70; PRES, SPECTRUM SPORTS, INC, 71- Am. Chem. Soc. Organic chemistry; organo-metallic chemistry; plastic film and film coating. Address: Rt, 7, Brookfield, CT 06804.

DONALDSON, MERLE RICHARD, b. Silverdale, Kans, Apr. 7, 20; m. 43; c. 2. ELECTRICAL ENGINEERING. B.E.E, Ga. Inst. Tech, 46, M.S, 47, Ph.D.(elec. eng), 59. Instr. elec. eng, Ga. Inst. Tech, 46-50, asst. prof, 50-51; engr, Oak Ridge Nat. Lab, 51-55, sr. engr. in charge res. & develop. cyclotrons, 55-57; proj. engr, basic study projs, Norden-Ketay Corp, 57; res. engr, Electronic Commun, Inc, 57-58, sr. staff engr, adv. tech. group, 58-60, prin. eng. scientist, 60, mgr, adv. develop. sect, 60-61, dir, adv. develop. lab, 61-63; acad. supvr, off-campus grad. ctr. & assoc. prof. ELEC. ENG, Univ. Fla, 62-64; PROF. & CHMN. DEPT, UNIV. S.FLA, 64- Consult, Univ. Colo, 57; Am. Lava Corp, 59; Capital Radio Eng. Inst, 60-; Sperry Microwave Electronics Co, 63-70. U.S.N, 40-46, Res, 46-60, Lt. AAAS; Inst. Elec. & Electronics Eng.(ed, Newsletter, 58-59, Transactions, 59-60). Microwave theory and techniques. Address: Dept. of Electrical Engineering, College of Engineering, University of South Florida, Tampa, FL 33620.

DONALDSON, PAUL, b. Ephrata, Wash, July 4, 16; m. 40; c. 2. MICROBIOLOGY. B.S, Washington (Seattle), 39; M.S, Wisconsin, 45, Ph.D, 47. Bacteriologist, virus res, Cutter Labs, 40-42; instr. med. bact, Wisconsin, 42-47; asst. prof, Tulane, 47-51; MICROBIOL, Southwest. Med. Sch, Univ. Tex, 51-67; ASSOC. PROF. & HEAD DEPT, NORTHWEST. STATE UNIV, 67- Am. Soc. Microbiol. Agglutination with adsorbed antigens; immunocytochemical studies of Miyagawanella; nutrition and constituents of Hemophilus pertussis; phagocytosis. Address: Dept. of Microbiology, Northwestern State University, Natchitoches, LA 71457.

DONALDSON, RAYMOND E(DWIN), b. Atlanta, Ga, April 4, 20; m. 46; c. 2. ORGANIC CHEMISTRY. B.S, Berry Col, 42; M.S, Emory, 47, Ph.D.(chem), 49. Instr. chem, Emory, 47-48; CHEMIST, TENN. EASTMAN CO, 50- C.W.S, U.S.A, 42-45. Am. Chem. Soc. Synthesis and parachors of organic compounds. Address: 2112 Montrose Ave, Kingsport, TN 37664.

DONALDSON, ROBERT E(DWARD), b. Indianapolis, Ind, Sept. 2, 22; m. 44; c. 3. CHEMICAL ENGINEERING. B.S, Purdue, 43. Pilotplant operator, process develop. sect, Gulf Res. & Develop. Co, 43-44, supvr. pilot plant opers, 44-47, proj. leader, 47-53, group leader, 53-57, asst. sect. head, 57-61, sect. head, 61-65, staff engr, Pa, 65-68, supv. engr. process, Pac. Gulf Oil, Ltd, Japan, 68-70; PROCESS DESIGN ENGR, KOREA LUBRICANTS CO. LTD, 70- Am. Chem. Soc; Am. Inst. Chem. Eng. Petroleum refining; process development work; catalytic cracking; hydrogenation; lubricating oil processing; catalyst development and evaluation. Address: Korea Lubricants Co. Ltd, I.P.O. Box 2808, Seoul, Korea.

DONALDSON, R(OBERT) E(VANS), b. Bakersfield, Calif, Sept. 3, 21; m. 48, 71; c. 3. NUCLEAR PHYSICS. Ph.D.(nuclear physics), Univ. Calif, 56. Sr. thermodyn. engr, Convair, 56-57; PHYSICIST, LAWRENCE RADIATION LAB, UNIV. CALIF, 57- U.S. Merchant Marine, 38-45. Am. Phys. Soc. Low energy nuclear physics; neutron optics. Address: Lawrence Radiation Lab, University of California, P.O. Box 808, Livermore, CA 94551.

DONALDSON, ROBERT M, JR, b. Hubbardston, Mass, Aug. 1, 27; m. 50; c. 2. INTERNAL MEDICINE, GASTROENTEROLOGY. B.S, Yale, 49; M.D, Boston, 52. U.S. Pub. Health Serv. fel, Harvard Med. Sch, 57-59; asst. prof. MED, sch. med, Boston, 59-64; assoc. prof, Wisconsin, 64-67; SCH. MED, BOSTON UNIV, 67-70, PROF, 70- Chmn. gastroenterol. res. eval. comt, Vet. Admin, 68-71; chmn. gastroenterol. & nutrit. training comt, Nat. Insts. Health, 69- U.S.N.R, 53-55. Am. Gastroenterol. Asn.(ed. jour, 70-); Am. Soc. Clin. Invest. Gastric; secretion; intestinal absorption; gastrointestinal bacteriology. Address: University Hospital, 750 Harrison Ave, Boston, MA 02118.

DONALDSON, ROBERT R(YMAL), b. Hornell, N.Y, Feb. 27, 17; m. 42; c. 3. SCIENCE EDUCATION, PHYSICS. B.A, Syracuse, 40, M.A, 43; Ph.D.(sci. ed), Cornell, 55. Teacher, pub. sch, 40-43, 46-51, 54-55; PROF. PHYSICS, COL. ARTS & SCI, STATE UNIV. N.Y. COL. PLATTSBURGH, 55- Ed. consult, spec. proj, Ford Found, Ankara, Turkey, 64-65; summer, consult, phys. sci. study cmt, Mass. Inst. Tech, 57. U.S.A.F, 43-46, 51-53, Res, 53-, Lt. Col. AAAS; Am. Asn. Physics Teachers; Nat. Sci. Teachers Asn. Introductory courses in physics and physical science; meteorology; astronomy; science education. Address: Dept. of Physics, College of Arts & Science, State University of New York College at Plattsburgh, Plattsburgh, NY 12901.

DONALDSON, VIRGINIA HENRIETTA, b. Glen Cove, N.Y, Oct. 3, 24. MEDICINE. A.B, Vermont, 47, M.D, 51. Intern, Strong Mem. Hosp, Rochester, N.Y, 51-53, asst. res. pediat, Strong Mem. & Genessee Hosps, 53-54; Buffalo Children's Hosp, 54-55; res. fel. pediat, sch. med, Western Reserve, 55-57, res. fel. med, 57-62, instr, 62-63, sr. instr, 63-67; mem. res. staff, St. Vincent Charity Hosp, 63-67, estab. investr, Am. Heart Asn, 64-67; assoc. prof. med, COL. MED, UNIV. CINCINNATI, 67-71, PROF. PEDIAT. & MED, 71- Asst. attend. pediat. & asst. dir. out patient dept, Babies' & Children's Hosp, Cleveland, Ohio, 56-57; assoc, res. div, Cleveland Clin, 57-62, asst. mem. staff, 62-63; dir. hemat, Cincinnati Shrine Burn Inst, 67-70. AAAS; Am. Fedn. Clin. Res; Am. Soc. Hemat; Am. Soc. Clin. Invest. Studies of hydrolytic enzymes of human blood as related to blood coagulation; fibrinolysis; action of first component of complement and relation of fibrinolytic mechanisms to complement action. Address: Dept. of Medicine, University of Cincinnati College of Medicine, Cincinnati, OH 45221.

DONALDSON, (LESLIE) WAYNE, b. Portsmouth, Ohio, Dec. 7, 10; m. 43; c. 2. BIOCHEMISTRY. A.B, Ohio State, 33. Chemist, Williams Mfg. Co, Ohio, 34-36; pharmaceut, Warren-Teed Prod. Co, 36-41; fine chem, Swann Chem. Co, Ala, 41-43; biochemist. pharmaceut, PARKE, DAVIS & CO, 43-63, MGR. ED. SERV, 63- Drug Info. Asn. Biological extractions; endocrinology; pituitary; clear writing; clinical research reports of new drugs for physicians and regulatory agencies. Address: Parke, Davis & Co, Ann Arbor, MI 48106.

DONALDSON, WILLIAM E(MMERT), b. Baltimore, Md, Dec. 19, 31; m. 55; c. 5. POULTRY NUTRITION. B.S, Maryland, 53, M.S, 55, Ph.D.(poultry nutrit), 57. Asst. POULTRY NUTRIT, Maryland, 53-57; asst. prof, Rhode Island, 57-62; N.C. STATE UNIV, 62-64, assoc. prof, 64-68, PROF, 68- AAAS; Am. Inst. Nutrit; Poultry Sci. Asn. Fat metabolism, especially fatty acid biosynthesis and interconversion. Address: Dept. of Poultry Science, North Carolina State University, Raleigh, NC 27607.

DONALDSON, WILLIAM T(WITTY), b. Statesboro, Ga, June 26, 27; m. 48; c. 2. ANALYTICAL CHEMISTRY. B.S, Georgia, 48. Chemist, Ethyl Corp, 48-51; res. supvr, E.I. du Pont de Nemours & Co, 51-63, lab. supvr, 63-66; supvry. chemist, FED. WATER POLLUTION CONTROL ADMIN, 66-69, CHIEF, CONTAMINANTS CHARACTERIZATION RES. PROG, SOUTHEAST WATER LAB, 69- U.S.N.R, 45. Am. Chem. Soc. Applied analytical chemistry. Address: 186 Spruce Valley Rd, Athens, GA 30601.

DONALDSON, W(ILLIS) LYLE, b. Cleburne, Tex, May 1, 15; m. 38; c. 4. ELECTRICAL ENGINEERING. B.S, Tex. Tech Univ, 38, distinguished engr, 69. Distribution engr, Tex. Elec. Serv. Co, 38-42, distribution supvr, 45-46; asst. prof. elec. eng, Lehigh, 46-51, assoc. prof, 53-54; sr. res. engr, SOUTHWEST RES. INST, 54-55, mgr. communications res, 55-59, dir, elec. & electronics dept, 59-63, V.PRES, 63- U.S.N, 42-53, Capt. Sci. Res. Soc. Am; Soc. Nondestructive Test; Inst. Elec. & Electronics Eng; Nat. Soc. Prof. Eng.

Communication systems and techniques; radio direction finding; nondestructive testing; bioengineering; social and management sciences. Address: Southwest Research Institute, P.O. Drawer 28510, San Antonio, TX 78284.

DONART, GARY B, b. Howard, Kans, Sept. 6, 40; m. 61; c. 3. RANGE MANAGEMENT, PLANT PHYSIOLOGY. B.S, Ft. Hays Kans. State Col, 62, M.S, 63; Ph.D.(range sci), Utah State, 68. ASST. PROF. range mgt, Humboldt State Col, 65-68; RANGE SCI, TEX. A&M UNIV, 68- Consult, nat. parks, 65-66. Am. Soc. Range Mgt; Am. Soc. Agron; Crop Sci. Soc. Am; Ecol. Soc. Am. Ecology and management of range lands; poison plant problems; livestock management; forage plant physiology; soil-plant relations. Address: Dept. of Range Science, Texas A&M University, College Station, TX 77843.

DONARUMA, L(ORRAINE) GUY, b. Utica, N.Y, Sept. 6, 28; m. 50; c. 3. ORGANIC CHEMISTRY. B.S, St. Lawrence, 49; Ph.D.(org. chem), Carnegie Inst. Tech, 53. Sr. chemist, explosives dept, east. lab, E.I. du Pont de Nemours & Co, Inc, 53-55, res. chemist, 55-57, sr. res. chemist, 57-60, res. assoc. & supvr, 60-62; asst. prof. CHEM, CLARKSON COL. TECHNOL, 62-64, assoc. prof. & exec. off. dept, 65-67, PROF, 67-, ASSOC. DEAN GRAD. SCH, 68- Am. Chem. Soc; N.Y. Acad. Sci; The Chem. Soc. Medicinal chemistry; halogenation of alpha, beta-unsaturated ketones; pyrolysis of alpha-phenyl-cinnamic acid; reduction of nitroparaffins; preparation of oximes, amides and lactams; preparation and reaction of nitroso paraffins; polymer chemistry; chelate chemistry. Address: 22 Grove St, Potsdam, NY 13676.

DONAT, FRANK J, b. Cleveland, Ohio, June 13, 32; m. 57; c. 3. CHEMISTRY, PHYSICS. B.I.Ch, Case, 54. Dow fel, 55-56, M.S, 56, Ph.D.(org. chem), 59. Res. chemist plastics, B.F. GOODRICH CO, 59-61, sr. res. chemist rubber & plastics, 61-66, sect. leader, 66-69, MGR. CHEM. RES, 69- Am. Chem. Soc. Physical chemistry. Address: 5099 Coldbrook Dr, Mantua, OH 44255.

DONATH, E(RNEST) E, b. Sternberg, Austria-Hungary, Nov. 4, 02; nat; m. 27; c. 2. PHYSICAL CHEMISTRY. Dip. Ing, Tech. Univ. Breslau, 24, Dr.Ing, 26. Chemist, group leader & chief chemist for res, high pressure dept, Badische Anilin & Soda-Fabrik Plant, I.G. Farbenindustrie, Ludwigshafen, 26-46; sci. adv, synthetic liquid fuels sta, Bur. Mines, Mo, 47-49; mgr. fuels res, tech. planning & contract res. sect, Koppers Co, Inc, 49-64; RES. CONSULT, 64- Am. Gas Asn; Am. Inst. Chem. Eng; Am. Chem. Soc; Inst. Min, Metall. & Petrol. Eng. Synthetic liquid fuels; high pressure reactions; coal carbonization and gasification; hydrocarbon conversion. Address: P.O. Box 1068, Christiansted, VI 00820.

DONATH, FRED A(RTHUR), b. St. Cloud, Minn, July 11, 31; m. 52; c. 2. GEOLOGY, GEOPHYSICS. B.A, Minnesota, 54; Univ. fel, Stanford, 54-56, M.S, 56, Ph.D.(geol), 58. Asst. prof. GEOL, San Jose State Col, 56-57; Columbia Univ, 58-62, assoc. prof, 62-66, prof, 66-67; PROF. & HEAD DEPT, UNIV. ILL, URBANA-CHAMPAIGN, 67- Vis. lectr, Am. Geol. Inst, 65-; lectr, continuing educ. prog, Am. Asn. Petrol. Geol, 65-; ed, Annual Rev. Earth & Planetary Sci, 71- Semicentennial medallion, Rice Univ, 62. Fel. AAAS; fel. Geol. Soc. Am.(acting ed, 64); Am. Geophys. Union; Am. Asn. Petrol. Geol; fel. Geol. Soc. London. Structural geology; experimental rock deformation; mechanics of earth deformation; Basin-Range structure, Oregon. Address: 249 Natural History Bldg, Dept. of Geology, University of Illinois, Urbana-Champaign, Urbana, IL 61801.

DONATH, WILM E(RNST), b. Mannheim, Germany, July 13, 32; nat. PHYSICAL CHEMISTRY. B.S, Carnegie Inst. Tech, 54; Ph.D.(chem), California, 58. Res. assoc. electrochem, Brooklyn Polytech. Inst, 58-59; RES. SCIENTIST, THOMAS J. WATSON RES. CTR, IBM CORP, 59- Summer, res. fel, Lawrence Radiation Lab, Univ. Calif, 58. Am. Inst. Chem. Design automation; theoretical chemistry. Address: IBM Corp, Thomas J. Watson Research Center, P.O. Box 218, Yorktown Heights, NY 10598.

DONATI, EDWARD JOSEPH, b. Wilkes-Barre, Pa, Sept. 9, 24; m. 48. ANATOMY. B.A, King's Col.(Pa), 51; Ph.D.(anat), Maryland, 64. Technician, Med. labs, U.S. Army Chem. Center, 52-56, biologist-histologist, 56-60; sect. chief. microanat-cytol, directorate med. res, Edgewood Arsenal, 60-67, acting chief path. br, med. res. labs, 67-68; ASST. PROF. ANAT, SCH. MED, UNIV. MD, BALTIMORE COUNTY, 68- U.S.A, 45-46. Electron Micros. Soc. Am. Ultrastructural effects of radiation and anti-mitotic drugs; labelling antibody with uranium; use of uranium-labelled antibody for localization and staining of antigens for electron microscopy. Address: Dept. of Anatomy, School of Medicine, University of Maryland, Baltimore County, 29 S. Greene St, Baltimore, MD 21201.

DONATI, ROBERT M, b. Richmond Heights, Mo, Feb. 28, 34. INTERNAL & NUCLEAR MEDICINE. B.S, St. Louis, 55, M.D, 59. Intern, St. Louis City Hosp, 59-60; asst. res, John Cochran Hosp, St. Louis, 60-62; fel. nuclear med, MED. SCH, ST. LOUIS UNIV, 62-63, instr, 63-65, asst. prof, 65-68; ASSOC. PROF. & DIR. SECT. NUCLEAR MED, 68- Staff physician, St. Louis Univ. & John Cochran Hosp, 63- Consult, Walter Reed Army Inst. Res, 68- Med.C, U.S.A.R, 66-68, Capt. Am. Med. Asn; Am. Fedn. Clin. Res; Soc. Exp. Biol. & Med; Soc. Nuclear Med; N.Y. Acad. Sci; Am. Soc. Hemat; fel. Int. Soc. Hemat. Humoral control of cellular proliferation in a variety of systems including the red blood cell, the gastrointestinal epithelial cell and the fibroblast. Address: St. Louis University School of Medicine, John Cochran Hospital, 915 N. Grand, St. Louis, MO 63106.

DONAWICK, WILLIAM JOSEPH, b. Troy, N.Y, Aug. 18, 40; m. 61; c. 2. TRANSPLANTATION BIOLOGY, VETERINARY SURGERY. D.V.M, Cornell, 63. Instr. vet. clin. med. & surg, UNIV. PA, 64-66, U.S. Pub. Health Serv. res. fel. transplantation biol, 66-69, ASST. PROF. SURG, 69- Delaware Heart Asn. res. grant, 69-71; Nat. Insts. Health, 69-72. Veterinary clinical surgical investigation. Address: University of Pennsylvania School of Veterinary Medicine, New Bolton Center, Kennett Square, PA 19348.

DONCHIN, EMANUEL, b. Tel Aviv, Israel, Apr. 3, 35; m. 55; c. 3. PHYSIOLOGICAL PSYCHOLOGY. B.A, Hebrew Univ, Israel, 61; M.A, California, Los Angeles, 63, Ph.D.(psychol), 64. Res. asst. psychol, California, Los Angeles, 61-64, res. assoc, 64-65; neurol, sch. med, Stanford, 65-67; neurobiol, Ames Res. Ctr, NASA, 66-69; ASSOC. PROF. PSYCHOL, UNIV. ILL, URBANA-CHAMPAIGN, 69- Am. Electroencephalog. Soc; Psychonomic Soc; Soc. Psychophysiol. Res; N.Y. Acad. Sci. Physiological mechanisms of attention and perception; computer analysis of brain waves. Address: Dept. of Psychology, University of Illinois, Champaign, IL 61820.

DONDERO, NORMAN C(ARL), b. Somerville, Mass, May 22; 18; m. 52; c. 1. MICROBIOLOGY. B.S, Massachusetts, 41; M.S, Connecticut, 43; Ph.D.(bact), Cornell, 52. Instr. animal diseases, Connecticut, 46-48; res. assoc. bact, Cornell, 51-53, asst. prof, 53-54; assoc, inst. microbiol, Rutgers Univ, 54-56, asst. prof. sanit, 56-59, assoc. prof, 59-63, prof. environ sci, 63-66, chmn. microbiol. sect, 63-65; PROF. APPL. MICROBIOL, CORNELL UNIV, 66- U.S.A, 43-46. Am. Soc. Mircobiol; Brit. Soc. Appl. Bact; Brit. Soc. Gen. Microbiol; Am. Soc. Limnol. & Oceanog; Water Pollution Control Fedn; Int. Asn. Theoret. & Appl. Limnol; Int. Asn. Gt. Lakes Res. Aquatic microbiology; water pollution. Address: Dept. of Food Science, Cornell University, Ithaca, NY 14850.

DONDERSHINE, FRANK H(ASKIN), b. Newark, N.J, Dec. 29, 31; m. 58. BIOLOGY. A.B, Seton Hall, 55. Asst. hematologist, Martland Med. Ctr, N.J, 51-54; MICROBIOLOGIST, Warner-Lambert Res. Inst, 57-62; ETHICON, INC, 62- U.S.A, 55-57. AAAS; Am. Soc. Microbiol; Soc. Indust. Microbiol. Antimicrobial product evaluations; general antimetabolite and clinical evaluations; antiseptics, disinfectants and sterilizers development; ultrasonics; aerosols; antibiotics; dental research. Address: 5 Catalina Dr, Somerville, NJ 08876.

DONDES, SEYMOUR, b. N.Y.C, Apr. 3, 18; m. 45; c. 3. PHYSICAL CHEMISTRY. B.A, Brooklyn Col, 39; M.S, Rensselaer Polytech. Inst, 50, Ph.D.(chem), 54. Res. scientist radiation chem, RENSSELAER POLYTECH. INST, 52-70, ASSOC. PROF. CHEM, 70- U.S.A, 39-52, Res, 52-, Col. AAAS; Am. Chem. Soc. Radiation chemistry; photochemistry; kinetics of gas reactions; nuclear reactor technology. Address: Dept. of Chemistry, Rensselaer Polytechnic Institute, Troy, NY 12181.

DONE, ALAN K(IMBALL), b. Salt Lake City, Utah, Sept. 23, 26; m. 47; c. 4. PEDIATRICS, TOXICOLOGY. B.A, Utah, 49, M.D, 52. From intern to assoc. pediatrician, Salt Lake County Gen. Hosp, 53-58; from res. instr. to res. asst. prof. PEDIAT, col. med, Utah, 56-58; asst. prof, Stanford, 58-60; assoc. res. prof, COL. MED, UNIV. UTAH, 60-68, PROF, 68-, ADJ. PROF. PHARMACOL, 69-, PROF. CLIN. PHARMACOL. & TOXICOL, COL. PHARMACY, 70- Am. Heart Asn. fel, 54-57. U.S.N, 43-46. AAAS; Am. Pediat. Soc; Soc. Pediat. Res; fel. Am. Acad. Pediat; Soc. Exp. Biol. & Med; Asn. Am. Med. Cols; N.Y. Acad. Sci; Am. Pharmaceut. Asn. Developmental pharmacology. Address: Dept. of Pediatrics, University of Utah, Salt Lake City, UT 84112.

DONEEN, LLOYD DAVID, b. Oakesdale, Wash, Sept. 22, 05; m. 33; c. 4. IRRIGATION. B.S, State Col. Wash, 28, fel, 28-32, M.S, 30, Ph.D.(soils), 33. Jr. irrig. agronomist, COL. AGR, UNIV. CALIF, DAVIS, 32-40, asst. irrig. agronomist, 40-46, assoc. irrig. agronomist, 46-53, PROF. WATER SCI. & IRRIG. & IRRIGATIONIST, EXP. STA, 53- Irrigation of field and truck crops; quality of irrigation water; soil technology; nitrogen in relation to composition growth and yield of wheat. Address: Dept. of Irrigation, University of California, Davis, CA 95616.

DONEFER, EUGENE, b. Brooklyn, N.Y, Jan. 2, 33; m. 53; c. 3. ANIMAL NUTRITION. B.S, Cornell Univ, 55, M.S, 57; Ph.D.(nutrit), McGill Univ, 61. Asst. prof. ANIMAL SCI, MACDONALD COL, McGILL UNIV, 61-67, ASSOC. PROF, 67- Mem. subcomt. rabbit nutrit, Nat. Acad. Sci-Nat. Res. Coun, 60-; Nat. Sci. Found. fel, Swiss Fed. Inst. Technol, 62-63; mem. bd. dirs, Am. Forage & Grassland Coun; Can. Comt. Animal Nutrit; consult, Beef Prod. Proj. Caribbean, Barbados. Am. Soc. Animal Sci; Am. Dairy Sci. Asn; Am. Inst. Nutrit; Nutrit. Soc. Can. Ruminant nutrition; nutritive evaluation of forages; improving low-quality forages; utilization of sugar cane as feed; rabbit nutrition. Address: Dept. of Animal Science, Macdonald College, Que, Can.

DONEGAN, JOSEPH W(ILLARD), b. New Brunswick, N.J, Sept. 22, 08. CHEMISTRY. B.S, Rutgers, 29. Res. chemist, Barber Asphalt Corp, N.J, 29-34, asst. chief chemist, 34-41; supvr. bituminous res, Barrett Div, Allied Chem. & Dye Corp, 41-59, asst. to dir. res. & develop. dept, 59-62, mgr. tech. serv, 62-66, dir, 66-67; sr. res. scientist, Jim Walter Res. Corp, 67-71; RETIRED. Am. Chem. Soc; fel. Am. Inst. Chem; Am. Soc. Test. & Mat. Plastic building materials and thermal insulations; ceramic roofing granules; asphalt technology and applications; coal tar technology; refining and applications; production of asphalt emulsions; bituminous chemistry; activated carbon. Address: 5253 Dover St. N.E, St. Petersburg, FL 33703.

DONELSON, JOHN G(ARHART), b. Huntingdon, Pa, July 21, 11; m. 38; c. 2. CHEMISTRY. B.S, Juniata Col, 33; Ph.D.(phys. chem), Yale, 37. Asst. instr, Juniata Col, 33-34; from chemist to DIR. APPL. RES, U.S. STEEL CORP, 37- Am. Chem. Soc; Am. Soc. Metals; Electrochem. Soc. Surface chemistry of metals; gas-metal reactions; electrochemistry of corrosion; protective films for metals. Address: Applied Research Lab, United States Steel Corp, Monroeville, PA 15146.

DONELY, PHILIP, b. Boston, Mass, Jan. 7, 09; m. 33. AERONAUTICAL ENGINEERING. B.S, Mass. Inst. Technol, 31. Jr. flight engr, nat. adv. comt. aeronaut, NASA, 31-49, assoc. div. chief, dynamic loads, 49-58, chief flight mech. & tech. div, 58-70, CHIEF ENG, OFF. OF DIR, 70- Mem. subcomt. meteorol. problems, Nat. Adv. Comt. Aeronaut, 45-49, aircraft loads, 49-58, comt. on loads, NASA, 59; Adv. Am. Del, Int. Civil Aviation Orgn, 53-57. Laura Tabor Barbour Air Safety Award, 64; Exceptional Serv. Medal, NASA, 68. Assoc. fel. Am. Inst. Aeronaut. & Astronaut. Loads research pertaining to aircraft; effects of atmospheric turbulence on aircraft; flight research techniques. Address: Mail Stop 102A, Langley Research Center, NASA, Hampton, VA 23365.

DONERMEYER, DONALD D, b. Stevens Point, Wis, Aug. 28, 34; m. 60; c. 8. PHYSICAL CHEMISTRY. B.S, Wisconsin, 56, Ph.D.(phys. chem), 61. CHEMIST, Shawinigan Resins Corp, 61-65, MONSANTO CO, 65- Am. Chem. Soc. Antigen-antibody reactions; relationship between structure and properties of polymers; synthesis of novel polymers; warp sizing mechanisms; textile finishing. Address: Research Dept, Monsanto Co, P.O. Box 2130, Springfield, MA 01101.

DONEY, DEVON LYLE, b. Franklin, Idaho, Mar. 31, 34; m. 58; c. 5. PLANT GENETICS. B.S, Utah State, 60, M.S, 61; Ph.D.(plant breeding, genetics), Cornell, 65. Tomato breeder, Libby, McNeil & Libby, 64-65; RES. GENETICIST PLANT SCI. RES. DIV, U.S. DEPT. AGR, 65- U.S.A, 57-58, Res, 58-63, Sgt. 1/C. Crop Sci. Soc. Am; Am. Soc. Sugarbeet Technol. Physiological genetics of sugarbeet with special emphasis on isozymes and mitochondrial complementation. Address: Crops Research Lab, Utah State University, Logan, UT 84321.

DONG, RICHARD GENE, b. Sacramento, Calif, Mar. 16, 35. MECHANICAL ENGINEERING, MECHANICS. B.S, California, Berkeley, 57, M.S, 59, Ph.D. (civil eng), 64. Develop. engr, Aerojet-Gen. Corp, Calif, 59-61; ENGR, LAWRENCE RADIATION LAB, UNIV. CALIF, 63- Am. Soc. Mech. Eng. Mechanical behavior, including failure behavior of materials from the theoretical and experimental points of view; thermodynamics as applied to materials behavior. Address: 38 Hornet Ct, Danville, CA 94526.

DONG, STANLEY B, b. Canton, China, Apr. 2, 36; U.S. citizen; m. 64; c. 3. STRUCTURAL MECHANICS. B.S, California, Berkeley, 57, M.S, 58, Ph.D. (struct. mech), 62. Sr. res. engr, Aerojet-Gen. Corp, 62-65; asst. prof. ENG, UNIV. CALIF, LOS ANGELES, 65-69, ASSOC. PROF, 69- Am. Soc. Civil Eng. Structural laminates. Address: School of Engineering & Applied Science, University of California, Los Angeles, CA 90024.

DONHOWE, JOHN M, b. Story City, Iowa, Jan. 30, 26; m. 49; c. 6. NUCLEAR PHYSICS. B.A, St. Olaf Col, 49; California, Berkeley, 49-51; B.D, Luther Theol. Sem, 54; Nat. Sci. Found. fel, Wisconsin, 62-64, Ph.D.(physics), 66. Instr. physics, St. Olaf Col, 61-62; asst. prof. NUCLEAR ENG, UNIV. WIS, MADISON, 66-70, ASSOC. PROF, 70- U.S.A.A.F, 44-46, 2nd Lt. Am. Phys. Soc. High voltage accelerator design; high voltage electron microscope instrumentation. Address: Dept. of Nuclear Engineering, University of Wisconsin, Madison, WI 53706.

DONIA, ROBERT A(LAN), b. Zeeland, Mich, Nov. 16, 17; m. 42; c. 3. ORGANIC CHEMISTRY. A.B, Hope Col, 39; Ph.D.(org. chem), Pittsburgh, 43. Res. chemist, Firestone Tire & Rubber Co, 43-46; from asst. prof. to assoc. prof. chem, Michigan Tech, 46-49; mgr. FINE CHEM. PROD, UPJOHN CO, 49-66, asst. dir, 66-70, DIR, 70- Am. Chem. Soc. Pharmaceuticals. Address: Fine Chemical Production, Upjohn Co, Kalamazoo, MI 49001.

DONIACH, SEBASTIAN, b. Paris, France, Jan. 25, 34; m. 55; c. 4. THEORETICAL PHYSICS. B.A, Cambridge, 54; Ph.D.(theoret. physics), Liverpool, 58. Imp. Chem. Industs. fel. theoret. physics, Liverpool, 58-60; lectr. physics, Queen Mary Col, London, 60-64, Imp. Col, 64-66, reader, 67-69; PROF. APPL. PHYSICS, STANFORD UNIV, 69- Vis. scientist, European Orgn. for Nuclear Res, Geneva, 63; res. assoc, dept. physics, Harvard, 67-68. Consult, Atomic Energy Res. Estab, Harwell, Eng, 66-69; Bell Tel. Res. Labs, 67, 70, 71; dept. physics, California, San Diego, 68; Argonne Nat. Lab, Atomic Energy Comn, 70- Brit. Inst. Physics & Phys. Soc; Am. Phys. Soc. Methods of quantum field theory applied to many body problems in solids and quantum liquids. Address: Dept. of Applied Physics, Stanford University, Stanford, CA 94305.

DONIKIAN, MARC R(OUPEN), b. Harar, Ethiopia, July 2, 14; U.S. citizen; m. 39; c. 2. PHARMACEUTICAL CHEMISTRY, CLINICAL PATHOLOGY. Ph.G, American Univ, Beirut, 37, Ph.C, 38, Cert. pub. anal, 43, M.D, 52. Instr. pharmaceut. chem, sch. pharm, American Univ, Beirut, 38-43, instr. chem. & asst. prof. bot, sch. arts & sci, 42-43; owner & dir, Clin. Lab. & Mfg. Pharm, 44-59; res. biologist, STERLING-WINTHROP RES. INST, RENSSELAER, 59-68, SR. RES. BIOLOGIST & DIR. CLIN. PATH. LABS, 68- Consult. forensic med, Lebanese Govt, 56-57. AAAS; N.Y. Acad. Sci; assoc. mem. Am. Soc. Clin. Path. Clinical pathological study of safety of new drugs. Address: 251 S. Manning Blvd, Albany, NY 12208.

DONIN, MILTON NORMAN, b. Allentown, Pa, July 25, 21; m. 46; c. 3. ORGANIC CHEMISTRY. B.S, Muhlenberg Col, 42; M.S, Pittsburgh, 44, Ph.D. (chem), 48. Res. assoc, Allegany Ballistics Lab, 44-45; SQUIBB INST. MED. RES, 48-53, head tech. data dept, 53-55, assoc. mgr. prod. planning, 56-58, assoc. dir. clin. res, 58-66, DIR. CLIN. SERV, 66- Am. Chem. Soc. Research administration; new drug investigation. Address: Squibb Institute for Medical Research, New Brunswick, NJ 08903.

DONINGER, JOSEPH EUGENE, b. Chicago, Ill, Aug. 18, 39; m. 61; c. 3. CHEMICAL ENGINEERING, INORGANIC CHEMISTRY. B.S, Illinois, 61; M.S, Northwestern, 62, Ph.D.(chem. eng), 65. Res. engr, GROWTH SCI. CTR, INT. MINERALS & CHEM. CORP, 64-69, CHEM. ENG. SPECIALIST, 69- Summers, lab. chemist, E.I. du Pont de Nemours & Co, 60; process engr, Chicago Bridge & Iron Co, Ill, 61-63. Am. Inst. Chem. Eng. Process control and optimization; cryogenics; pollution control; production of periclase for use in basic refractories; application of new technologies to chemical processing, particularly high temperature reactions. Address: International Minerals & Chemicals Corp, Growth Sciences Center, Libertyville, IL 60048.

DONISCH, VALENTINA, b. Novocherkassk, Russia, Nov. 29, 19; Can. citizen; m. 45. BIOCHEMISTRY. M.D, Bonn, 47; Nat. Cancer Inst. Can. fel, Western Ontario, 61-65, Ph.D.(biochem), 65. Physician, Extrapulmonal Tuberc. Sanatorium, 47-52; Lutheran Mission Hosp, Eket, Nigeria, 52-54; govt. hosps, Accra & Kumasi, Ghana, 55-59; Victoria Hosp, London, Ont, 59-61; fel, 65-66; instr. BIOCHEM, MED. SCH, UNIV. WEST. ONT, 66-67, lectr, 67-68, ASST. PROF, 68- Extrapulmonal tuberculosis; phospholipids and cancer. Address: Dept. of Biochemistry, Medical School, University of Western Ontario, London, Ont, Can.

DONIVAN, FRANK F(ORBES), JR, b. Inglewood, Calif, Oct. 19, 43; m. 66; c. 1. ASTRONOMY. B.A, Univ. Calif, Los Angeles, 66; Ph.D.(astron), Univ. Fla, 70. ASST. PROF. PHYS. SCI. & ASTRON, UNIV. FLA, 70- Am. Astron. Soc. Radio astronomy; radio investigation of clusters of galaxies; quasars. Address: Dept. of Physics & Astronomy, University of Florida, Gainesville, FL 32601.

DONKER, J(OHN) D, b. New Brunswick, N.J, Mar. 2, 20; m. 48; c. 1. ANIMAL SCIENCE. B.S, Univ. Calif, 48; Ph.D.(reproductive physiol), Univ. Minn, 52. Dir. dairy cattle nutrit. lab, Univ. Ga, 54-56; assoc. prof. DAIRY HUSB, UNIV. MINN, MINNEAPOLIS, 56-65, PROF, 65- Fel, Am. Inst. Indian Studies, 64. Am. Dairy Sci. Asn; Am. Soc. Animal Sci. Nutrition of dairy cows; evaluation of energy contents of forages and/or rations; lactational physiology. Address: 1868 Draper, St. Paul, MN 55113.

DONLAN, CHARLES J, b. Lawrence, Mass, July 15, 16; m. 42; c. 2. AERONAUTICAL ENGINEERING. S.B, Mass. Inst. Tech, 38. Aeronaut. res. scientist & engr, Langley Aeronaut. Lab, Nat. Adv. Comt. Aeronaut, 38-51, tech. asst. to assoc. dir, 51-58, assoc. dir. Proj. Mercury, NASA, 58-61, Langley Res. Ctr, 61-67, dep. dir, 67-68, DEP. ASSOC. ADMINR. MANNED SPACE FLIGHT TECHNOL, HQ, WASH, D.C, 68- Am. Inst. Aeronaut. & Astronaut. Aeronautical and space research, especially in field of stability and control. Address: 1113 E. Collingwood Rd, Alexandria, VA 22308.

DONLEY, DAVID EDWARD, b. Morgantown, W.Va, Nov. 7, 28; m. 52; c. 3. ENTOMOLOGY, ZOOLOGY. B.S, Waynesburg Col, 50; M.S, West Virginia, 51; Ph.D.(entom), Ohio State, 59. Prev. med. specialist, U.S. Air Force, 52-55; RES. ENTOMOLOGIST, U.S. FORESTRY SERV, 56-, RES. PROJ. LEADER FOREST INSECT ECOL, 62- Entom. Soc. Am; Ecol. Soc. Am. Ecology of forest and forest plantation insects. Address: 287 W. Heffner St, Delaware, OH 43015.

DONLEY, HUGH L(ANCELOT), b. Seneca Falls, N.Y, Aug. 9, 07; m. 35; c. 1. PHYSICS. B.S, Hobart Col, 30; M.S, Brown, 32, fel, 34, Ph.D.(physics), 35. Asst. physics, Brown, 30-33; res. engr, Radio Corp. Am. Mfg. Co, Inc, 35-42, MEM. TECH. STAFF, COMMUN. RES. LAB, RCA CORP, 42- Inst. Elec. & Electronics Eng; Acoust. Soc. Am. Properties of and applications for ferroelectric and ferromagnetic ceramics; communication systems including underwater sound. Address: RCA Corp, Communications Research Lab, Princeton, NJ 08540.

DONLEY, MICHAEL WILLIAM, b. Cleveland, Ohio, Jan. 4, 42; m. 64. GEOGRAPHY, GEOMORPHOLOGY. B.A, Kent State Univ, 64, M.A, 66; Ph.D. (geog), Univ. Ore, 71. Cartographer, Guatemala Nat. Atlas Proj, 68-69; ASST. PROF. GEOG, San Fernando Valley State Col, 70-71; UNIV. ORE, 71- Consult, Environ. Dynamics Inc, 71- Asn. Am. Geog; Am. Soc. Photogram. Thematic cartography; terrain representation; resource inventory and remote sensing; environmental geomorphology. Address: Dept. of Geography, University of Oregon, Eugene, OR 97403.

DONN, BERTRAM (DAVID), b. Brooklyn, N.Y, May 25, 19. ASTRONOMY. A.B, Brooklyn Col, 40; Ph.D.(astron), Harvard, 53. Physicist, Elec. Test. Labs, 40-41; asst. physicist, Sig. Corps Labs, 41-43; res. assoc, radiation lab, Columbia, 43-46; from instr. to assoc. prof, physics & astron, Wayne State Univ, 50-59; HEAD ASTROCHEM. BR, GODDARD SPACE FLIGHT CTR, NASA, 59- Res. assoc, Inst. Nuclear Studies, Chicago, 54-56. AAAS; Am. Phys. Soc; Am. Astron. Soc; Am. Geophys. Union; Int. Astron. Union. Interstellar matter; comets; cosmic chemistry. Address: NASA, Goddard Space Center, Code 691, Greenbelt, MD 20771.

DONN, WILLIAM L, b. Brooklyn, N.Y, Mar. 2, 18; m. 60; c. 2. GEOLOGY, GEOPHYSICS. B.A, Brooklyn Col, 39; M.A, Columbia, 46, Ph.D.(geol, geophysics), 51. Geologist, Del. Aqueduct Proj, 41; U.S. Engr, 42; res. consult, Oceanog. Inst, Woods Hole, 46-47; instr. GEOL, Brooklyn Col, 46-53, asst. prof, 54-57, assoc. prof, 58-60, PROF, 61-63; CITY COL. NEW YORK, 63-; SR. RES. SCIENTIST, LAMONT-DOHERTY GEOL. OBSERV, COLUMBIA UNIV, 51- Chief scientist, microseism eval. study, Off. Naval Res, 49-52; dir. tornado warning proj, Res. Corp, 55-56; storm surge proj, Eng. Found, 55-57; dir. & chief scientist U.S. Atlantic Island Observs. Prog, Int. Geophys. Year, 58-59; Int. Geophys. Coop, 59-60; dir. atmospheric microwaves proj, Nat. Sci. Found, 59-72; co-dir. climate change proj, U.S. Steel Found, 59-65; Nat. Sci. Found. sr. fel, 59-60; prin. investr, atmospheric infrasound proj, Army Res. Off, 68-72; arctic climate change proj, Nat. Sci. Found, 69; wave propagation neutral atmosphere & ionosphere, U.S. Army Electronics Command, 69-72. Distinguished nat. lectr, Am. Asn. Petrol. Geologists & Soc. Explor. Geophysicists, 60. U.S.C.G.R, 42; U.S.N.R, 42-46, Lt. Fel. AAAS; Am. Meteorol. Soc; fel. Geol. Soc. Am; Seismol. Soc. Am; Am. Geophys. Union; N.Y. Acad. Sci; Int. Union Geodesy & Geophys. Geological and geophysical education; physical oceanography; microseisms; ocean waves and wave forecasting; sea level change; climate change and Ice ages; gravity and acoustic wave propagation in the atmosphere; pregeologic earth history. Address: Dept. of Geology, City College of New York, New York, NY 10031.

DONNALLEY, JAMES R, JR, b. Camden, N.J, June 6, 18; m. 46; c. 3. CHEMICAL ENGINEERING. B.S, Pa. State, 39; Ph.D.(chem. eng), Cornell, 44. Res. assoc. silicones, res. lab, GEN. ELEC. CO, 43-46, group leader silicone process develop, chem. div, 46-48, mgr. waterford plant, 48-52, mfg. silicone prod. dept, 52-60, GEN. MGR. insulating mat. dept, 60-66, SEMICONDUCTOR PRODS. DEPT, 66- Am. Chem. Soc; Am. Inst. Chem. Eng. Silicates for adsorption and catalyses; process research on freeze-preservation of food; chemical process research on chlorosilanes and silicones; chemical research high temperature polymers. Address: 1 Cove Lane, Fayetteville, NY 13066.

DONNALLY, BAILEY LEWIS, b. Deatsville, Ala, June 22, 30; m. 55; c. 3. ATOMIC PHYSICS. B.S, Auburn, 51, M.S, 52; Ph.D.(physics), Minnesota, 61. Instr. PHYSICS, Col. St. Thomas, 56-61; asst. prof, LAKE FOREST COL, 61-63, assoc. prof, 63-66, PROF, 66-, CHMN. DEPT, 71- Vis. prof, Auburn Univ, summer, 61; vis. fel, Yale, 66-67; mem. comn. col. physics, Am. Asn. Univ. Prof. AAAS; fel. Am. Phys. Soc; Am. Asn. Physics Teachers (pres). Mass spectrometry; polarized proton sources; nuclear scattering with polarized protons; atomic collision processes; development of experiments for advanced undergraduate laboratories. Address: Dept. of Physics, Lake Forest College, Lake Forest, IL 60045.

DONNAN, ALVAN, b. Washington, Pa, Dec. 26, 14; m. 42; c. 2. ORGANIC CHEMISTRY. A.B, Washington & Jefferson Col, 36; Ph.D.(org. chem), Wisconsin, 40. Res. chemist, E.I. DU PONT DE NEMOURS & CO. INC, 40-48, PATENT LIAISON CHEMIST, 48- Am. Chem. Soc. Dyes; water repellants; anti-static agents; textile softeners and lubricants; leather, paper and petroleum chemicals; fluorocarbons; explosives; polymer intermediates; films. Address: R.D. 2, Box 296, Hockessin, DE 19707.

DONNAN, WILLIAM W, b. Keystone, Iowa, June 15, 11; m. 35; c. 3. CIVIL ENGINEERING. B.S, Iowa State, 34, C.E, 46. Jr. engr, soil conserv. serv, U.S. Dept. Agr, 34-39, assoc. engr, Calif, 39-41, res. engr, 41-53, sr. res. engr. Agr. Res. Serv, 53-57, res. invest. leader, 57-61, br. chief S.W. Br, soil & water conserv. res, 61-71; CONSULT. ENGR, 71- Grant, West. Europe, 58. Mem. soil & water conserv. cultural exchange group, U.S.S.R, 58; tech. activities cmt, Int. Cmn. Irrig. & Drainage, 60-65; consult, Indus Basin W. Pakistan, 60; Khusistan Basin, Iran, 66; Upper Ferat Basin, Turkey, 69; Tisza River Basin, Hungary, 71. Fel. Am. Soc. Civil Eng.(R.J. Tipton medal, 71); Am. Soc. Agr. Eng.(Hancock Drainage Eng. Award, 66). Drainage of irrigated land including the spacing and depth of drains and criteria for the design of drainage systems. Address: 3521 Yorkshire Rd, Pasadena, CA 91107.

DONNAY, GABRIELLE (HAMBURGER), b. Landeshut, Ger, Mar. 21, 20; nat; m. 49; c. 2. CRYSTALLOGRAPHY. B.A, California, Los Angeles, 41; Owens-Illinois, fel, Mass. Inst. Tech, 46-48, Ph.D.(crystallog), 48. Res. chemist, Mass. Gen. Hosp, 44-45; div. indust. co-op staff mem, Mass. Inst. Tech, 45-46, Little fel, 48-49; fel, Hopkins, 49-50; fel, Geophys. Lab, Carnegie Inst, 50-52; physicist, U.S. Geol. Surv, 52-54; crystallographer, geophys. lab, Carnegie Inst, 55-70; PROF. CRYSTALLOG, McGILL UNIV, 70- Guest scientist, Sorbonne, 58-59. Am. Crystallog. Asn; Mineral. Soc. Am; Geochem. Soc; Fr. Soc. Mineral. & Crystallog; Mineral. Asn. Can. Structural interpretation of solid solutions; crystal structure and chemistry. Address: Dept. of Geological Sciences, McGill University, Montreal 110, Que, Can.

DONNAY, J(OSEPH) D(ESIRE) H(UBERT), b. Grandville, Belgium, June 6, 02; nat. 39; m. 31, 49; c. 4. CRYSTALLOGRAPHY, MINERALOGY. E.M, Liège, 25; Cmn. Relief Belgium Ed. Found. Fel, 25-26, 27-28; Ph.D.(geol), Stanford, 29. Engr. & geologist, Syndicat des Petroles au Maroc, French Morocco, 29-30; teaching fel, mineral & res. assoc. geol, Stanford, 30-31; assoc. mineral, Hopkins, 31-39; prof. CRYSTALLOG. & MINERAL, Laval, 39-45; JOHNS HOPKINS UNIV, 45-71, EMER. PROF, 71- Res. chemist, Hercules Powder Co, 42-45; prof, Liège, 46-47; Fulbright lectr, Sorbonne, Paris, 58-59; guest prof, Univ. Marburg, 66; lectr, Univ. Montreal, 70-71. U.S. del, Int. Union Crystallog. Cong, U.S.A, 48, Sweden, 51, France, 54, Can, 57, U.S.S.R, 66. Fel. Geol. Soc. Am.(v.pres, 54); fel. Mineral Soc. Am. (v.pres, 49, 52, pres, 53, Roebling Medal, 71); Am. Crystallog. Asn.(secy-treas, Crystallog. Soc. Am, 44, secy, 45-46, v.pres, 46, 48, 55, pres, 49, 56); Geochem. Soc; fel. Mineral. Soc. Gt. Brit. & Ireland; French Mineral Soc.(v.pres, 49); Italian Mineral Soc; Geol. Soc. Belgium (v.pres, 46-47); Asn. Belgian Eng; cor. mem. Liège Royal Soc. Sci; Norweg. Geol. Soc. Crystallography, especially crystal optics and relationships between crystal morphology and structure. Address: 320 Cote Saint-Antoine Rd, Montreal 217, Que, Can.

DONNELL, CONARD K, b. Philadelphia, Pa, July 25, 17; m. 43; c. 2; m. 53. ORGANIC CHEMISTRY. A.B, Temple, 39, M.A, 41. Asst. chem, Temple, 39-41; res. chemist, SUN OIL CO, 41-53, GROUP LEADER catalytic cracking, 53-59, APPL. PHYSICS SECT, 59- Am. Chem. Soc. Adsorption; distillation columns; alkylation of hydrocarbons; catalytic hydrogenation; process analysis instrumentation. Address: Sun Oil Co, Applied Physics Lab, Newton Square, PA 19073.

DONNELL, GEORGE N(INO), b. Shanghai, China, Dec. 21, 19; U.S. citizen; m. 42; c. 3. PEDIATRICS. A.B, Pomona Col, 40; M.D, Washington (St. Louis), 44. Asst. PEDIAT, sch. med, Washington (St. Louis), 45-46; instr, UNIV. SOUTH. CALIF, 50-52, asst. prof, 52-56, assoc. prof, 56-61, PROF, 61- Mem. & consult, Nat. Kidney Disease Found, chmn. sci. adv. coun, Southern Calif. Chapter, 58-59. Dipl, Am. Bd. Pediat, 50. Med.C, 46-48, 52, Capt. AAAS; Am. Acad. Pediat; Soc. Pediat. Res; Am. Pediat. Soc; Soc. Nuclear Med; Am. Soc. Human Genetics; Am. Diabetes Asn; Am. Med. Asn; N.Y. Acad. Sci; fel. Royal Soc. Med. Hypoglycemia; glycogen storage disease; patients with defective resistance to infection; patients with hemolytic uremic syndrome; evaluation of the usefulness of renal biopsy in the diagnosis of patients with various forms of renal disease; long term study of effects of steroids on nephrosis. Address: Children's Hospital of Los Angeles, 4650 Sunset Blvd, Los Angeles, CA 90054.

DONNELL, H(ENRY) DENNY, JR, b. Vandalia, Ill, June 21, 35; m. 58; c. 3. EPIDEMIOLOGY. A.B, Greenville Col, 57; M.D, Wash. Univ, 60; M.P.H, Univ. Calif, Berkeley, 65. Intern, Butterworth Hosp, Grand Rapids, Mich, 60-61, asst. resident surg, 61-62; asst. chief prev. med. div, Ft. Leonard Wood, Mo, 62-63, chief, 63-64; resident epidemiol, Calif. State Dept. Health, Berkeley, 65-66; asst. prof, DEPT. COMMUN. HEALTH & MED. PRACTICE, SCH. MED, UNIV. MO-COLUMBIA, 66-71, CLIN. ASST. PROF, 71-; DIR. BUR. COMMUN. DISEASE CONTROL, DIV. OF HEALTH OF MO, 71- Chief prog. methodology unit, Mo. Regional Med. Prog, 69-71, consult, 71-; dir. grad. stud. community health, Univ. Mo-Columbia, 69-70. Dipl, Am. Bd. Prev. Med, 70. Med.C, U.S.A, 62-64, Capt. AAAS; Am. Pub. Health Asn; Asn. Teachers Prev. Med; Royal Soc. Health. Studies of distribution of disease, especially heart, cancer, stroke and infectious diseases; distribution of health manpower in relationship to distribution of population and various influencing variables. Address: 1403 St. Christopher, Columbia, MO 65201.

DONNELLAN, J(AMES) EDWARD, JR, b. Cleveland, Ohio, May 27, 32; m. 54; c. 2. BIOPHYSICS. B.S, Yale, 54, Ph.D.(biophys), 58. Asst. biophys, Yale, 54-57, instr. radiol, sch. med, 57-60; BIOPHYSICIST, bact. lab, pioneering res. div, U.S. Army Natick Labs, Mass, 60-63; BIOL. DIV, OAK RIDGE NAT. LAB, 63- AAAS; Biophys. Soc; Radiation Res. Soc. Radiation effects on biological systems; physiology of bacterial spore germination and post-germinative development; radiation dosimetry. Address: Biology Division, Oak Ridge National Lab, Oak Ridge, TN 37830.

DONNELLY, A(ARON) V(AN), b. Bonaparte, Iowa, June 2, 16. ELECTRICAL ENGINEERING. B.S, Iowa, 39, M.S. 40, Ph.D.(elec. eng), 47; Roberts fel, Columbia, 40-41, M.A, 41. Asst, Iowa, 39-40; inspection engr, Day & Zimmermann, 41-42; instr. eng. sci. & mgt. war training, Iowa, 42-43, instr. elec. eng, 43-44; res. engr, Stromberg-Carlson Co, N.Y, 44-45; Collins Radio Co, Iowa, 45-47; asst. prof. elec. eng, Iowa, 47-55; tech. consult, Pac. Missile Range, 55-62; assoc. prof. elec. eng, ARIZ. STATE UNIV, 62-67, PROF. ENG, 67- Inst. Elec. & Electronics Eng; Sci. Res. Soc. Am. Microwave and electronic systems; electrical networks. Address: College of Engineering Sciences, Arizona State University, Tempe, AZ 85281.

DONNELLY, E(DWARD) D(ANIEL), b. Birmingham, Ala, Dec. 5, 19; m. 47; c. 3. PLANT BREEDING. B.S, Auburn, 46, M.S, 48; Ph.D.(plant breeding), Cornell, 51. Res. asst. & instr. forage crops, AUBURN UNIV, 48, assoc. plant breeder, 51-58, PROF, 58- Res. asst, Cornell, 51. U.S.A, 42-45. Fel. Am. Soc. Agron. Forage crops breeding; improving for disease and insect resistance; increased palatability and nutritive value; earlier development and larger seeded; reseeding winter annual legumes. Address: Dept. of Agronomy & Soils, Auburn University, Auburn, AL 36830.

DONNELLY, GRACE MARIE, b. Providence, R.I, Apr. 5, 29. CYTOLOGY. B.S, Rhode Island, 52; M.S, Brown, 56; Ph.D.(cytol), Connecticut, 62. Res. librarian, citrus exp. sta, Univ. Florida, 52-54; biol. fel, Brookhaven Nat. Lab, 62-64; res. assoc. biol, City of Hope Med. Ctr, 64-67; instr. CELL BIOL, MED. SCH, UNIV. KY, 67-70, ASST. PROF, 70- AAAS; Genetics Soc. Am; Am. Soc. Cell Biol; Am. Genetic Asn; Radiation Res. Soc. Cytology of the domestic fowl; radiosensitivity of amphibians; chromosome cytology; cellular requirements for ribonucleic acid synthesis; effect of environmental agents on cells. Address: Dept. of Cell Biology, University of Kentucky Medical School, Lexington, KY 40506.

DONNELLY, JOHN, b. Liverpool, Eng, June 9, 14; nat; m. 49; c. 3. PSYCHIATRY. M.B, Ch.B, Liverpool, 38; D.P.M, London, 48. Sr. registrar, Cane Hill Hosp, Eng, 48-49; chief serv. psychiat, INST. LIVING, 49-52, clin. dir, 52-56, med. dir, 56-65, PSYCHIATRIST-IN-CHIEF, 65-; LECTR. PSYCHIAT, MED. SCH, YALE, 68-, asst. clin. prof, 52-64, assoc. clin. prof, 64-68. Fel. Am. Psychiat. Asn; Asn. Res. Nerv. & Ment. Diseases; Am. Med. Asn; fel. Am. Col. Physicians; fel. Royal Soc. Med; Royal Medico-Psychol. Asn. Psychodynamic and biophysical correlates; forensic aspects of the practice of psychiatry. Address: Institute of Living, 200 Retreat Ave, Hartford, CT 06106.

DONNELLY, JOHN J(AMES), JR, b. Phila, Pa, Sept. 28, 19; m. 45; c. 1. PHYSICS, BALLISTICS. Drexel Inst; B.S, Temple, 49; California, Los Angeles, 61; Michigan, 61; Mass. Inst. Tech, 64. Physicist, gas mechanics sect, physics lab, FRANKFORD ARSENAL, 47-53, chief, 53-58, ballistics br, PITMAN DUNN LAB, 58-61, DEP. CHIEF OBJECTIVES ANAL, 61- Tech. dir, Technalysis, Inc, 46-55; consult, govt. agencies. Ord. Dept, 42-45, Sgt. Am. Phys. Soc; Opers. Res. Soc. Am; Sci. Res. Soc. Am; Am. Ord. Asn. Weapon systems; optics; photographic measurements; long range technological planning; research management. Address: Pitman Dunn Lab, Frankford Arsenal, Bridge & Tacony St, Philadelphia, PA 19147.

DONNELLY, JOHN KINDELAN, b. Terre Haute, Ind, July 16, 43; m. 65. CHEMICAL ENGINEERING. B.Sc, Alberta, 65, Ph.D.(chem. eng), 68. Asst. prof. CHEM. ENG, UNIV. CALGARY, 68-70, ASSOC. PROF, 70- Am. Inst. Chem. Eng; Can. Soc. Chem. Eng. System engineering; process control; applied mathematics; heat transfer with phase charge; capsule flow in pipe lines. Address: Dept. of Chemical Engineering, University of Calgary, Calgary 44, Alta, Can.

DONNELLY, JOSEPH L(AWRENCE), b. Newport, Ky, July 5, 94. MEDICINE. A.B, Cincinnati, 17, A.M, 19, Ph.D.(org. chem), 21, B.M, 27, M.D, 28. Asst. chem, lab, Cincinnati, 16-18, instr, 20-22, asst. col. med, 23-27, asst. & instr. physiol, 32-41; intern & houseman, Cincinnati Gen. Hosp, 27-29, fel, 28; CHIEF LAB, VET. ADMIN. HOSP, Ky, 46-53, Cincinnati, Ohio, 53-59, FT. THOMAS, KY, 59- Asst. prof. clin. path, col. med, Cincinnati, 53- Nat. Res. Coun. fel, Princeton, 22-23; practicing physician, 29-32. Med.C, U.S.A, 42-46. Fel. Am. Med. Asn; Am. Asn. Clin. Chem; fel. Am. Soc. Clin. Path; fel. Colloid Soc. Ger. Organic chemistry; colloid chemistry of proteins; diabetes mellitus. Address: 1620 N. Ft. Thomas Ave, Ft. Thomas, KY 41075.

DONNELLY, JOSEPH P(ETER), b. Brooklyn, N.Y, May 10, 39; m. 68; c. 1. ELECTRICAL ENGINEERING, SEMICONDUCTOR PHYSICS. B.E.E, Manhattan Col, 61; Nat. Sci. Found. fel, Carnegie Inst. Tech, 61-65, M.S, 62, Ph.D.(elec. eng), 66. NATO fel, Imp. Col, London, 65-66; STAFF MEM. APPL. PHYSICS, LINCOLN LAB, MASS. INST. TECHNOL, 67- Inst. Elec. & Electronics Eng. Semiconductor heterojunctions; infrared detectors; ion implantation into compound semiconductors; light emitting diodes. Address: Lincoln Lab, Massachusetts Institute of Technology, P.O. Box 73, Lexington, MA 02173.

DONNELLY, KENNETH GERALD, Audiol, see 12th ed, Soc. & Behav. Vols.

DONNELLY, R(USSELL) J(AMES), b. Hamilton, Ont, Apr. 16, 30; m. 56; c. 1. PHYSICS. B.Sc, McMaster Univ, 51, M.Sc, 52; M.S, Yale, 53, Ph.D.(physics), 56. Instr, dept. physics & James Franck Inst, Univ. Chicago, 56-57, asst. prof, 57-61, assoc. prof, 61-65, prof, 65-66; PROF. PHYSICS CHMN. DEPT, UNIV. ORE, 66- Alfred F. Sloan res. fel, 59-63; consult, Gen. Motors Res. Labs, 58-68; Nat. Sci. Found, 68-; mem. adv. panel physics, 69-71, chmn, 71-72. Gov. Northwest Sci. Award, Ore. Mus. Sci. & Indust. AAAS; fel. Am. Phys. Soc; Am. Asn. Physics Teachers; Am. Astron. Soc. Experimental and theoretical low temperature physics, especially superfluidity; fluid dynamics; hydrodynamic stability; astrophysics; air pollution. Address: Dept. of Physics, University of Oregon, Eugene, OR 97403.

DONNELLY, THOMAS H(ENRY), b. Endicott, N.Y, Apr. 20, 28; m. 55; c. 4. PHYSICAL CHEMISTRY. B.S, Rensselaer Polytech, 50; Ph.D, Cornell, 55. PHYS. CHEMIST, RES. & DEVELOP. CTR, SWIFT & CO, OAK BROOK, 55- Am. Chem. Soc. Physical chemistry of proteins and polymers. Address: 4633 Grand Ave, Western Springs, IL 60558.

DONNELLY, THOMAS W(ALLACE), b. Detroit, Mich, Dec. 23, 32; m. 56; c. 1. GEOLOGY. B.A, Cornell Univ, 54; M.S, Calif. Inst. Technol, 56; Ph.D.(geol), Princeton, 59. Asst. prof. GEOL, Rice Univ, 59-64, assoc. prof, 64-66; STATE UNIV. N.Y. BINGHAMTON, 66-69, PROF, 69- Res. assoc, Fla. State Collection Arthropods, 66- Geol. Soc. Am. Petrology and structural geology of island arcs; mineralogy and petrology of volcanic rocks; geology of West Indies and Central America. Address: Dept. of Geology, State University of New York at Binghamton, Binghamton, NY 13901.

DONNER, HENRY F(REDERICK), b. Wilson, N.Y, Sept. 1, 02; m. 27. GEOLOGY. B.S, Michigan, 25, M.S, 27, Sc.D.(geol), 36. Testing dept, Gen. Elec. Co, 25-26; astronomer, Lamont-Hussey Observ, Michigan; Bloemfontein, S.Africa, 27-33; instr. geol, Western Reserve, 36-38, asst. prof, 38-43, assoc. prof. geol. & acting head dept, 43-45, assoc. prof. geol. & astron. & acting head dept. geol-geog. & dept. astron, 45-46, prof. geol. & astron. & head dept. geol-geog. & dept. astron, 46-61, prof. GEOL, 61-68, EMER. PROF, CASE WEST. RESERVE UNIV, 68- Am. Geophys. Union; Am. Astron. Soc; Am. Asn. Petrol. Geol; fel. Geol. Soc. Am. Geologic field mapping and interpretation in northwestern Colorado; structural geology; photogeology; binary stars. Address: 3094 E. Overlook Rd, Cleveland Heights, OH 44118.

DONNER, MARTIN W, b. Leipzig, Germany, Sept. 5, 20; U.S. citizen; m. 51; c. 3. MEDICINE, RADIOLOGY. M.D, Leipzig, 45. Intern, univ. hosp, Leipzig, 45-46, res. med, 46-50; radiol, Radiol. Center, Cologne, Germany, 50-54; Mt. Park Hosp, St. Peters, Fla, 54-57; fel, univ. hosp, JOHNS HOPKINS UNIV, 57-58, instr, SCH. MED. & HOSP, 58-60, asst. prof, 60-63, assoc. prof, 63-66, PROF. RADIOL. & RADIOLOGIC SCI. & CHIEF DIV. DIAG. ROENTGENOL, 66- Mem. ed. staff, Am. J. Med. Sci, 62-68. Vis. investr, Carnegie Inst, 62-; prof, Free Univ. Berlin, summer 64; consult, Good Samaritan Hosp; Rosewood State Hosp; Vet. Admin. Hosp, Baltimore. AAAS; Am. Med. Asn; fel. Am. Col. Radiol; Asn. Univ. Radiol; Ger. Radiol. Soc; Ger. Soc. Internal Med. Hematology; metabolitic joint diseases; radiotherapy and blood coagulation; cineradiography of intestinal motility; roentgen diagnosis of gastrointestinal diseases and abdominal calcifications; radioangiography of placental circulation; radiography of diabetic complications and diseases involving the hands; Roentgen tomography. Address: Johns Hopkins Hospital, Baltimore, MD 21205.

DONNER, W(ALTER), b. Pasadena, Calif, May 10, 25; m. 43; c. 2. PHYSICS, ELECTRONICS. Pasadena City Col; California, Los Angeles Res. technician, electronic engr. & proj. engr, BECKMAN INSTRUMENTS, INC, 46-53, chief engr, mass spectrom. res. 53-59, proj. mgr, 59-62, mgr. space eng, dept, 62-65, TECH. MGR, ADV. TECHNOL. OPER, 65- U.S.A, 43-45. Inst. Elec. & Electronics Eng. Instrument Soc. Am; Soc. Appl. Spectros; Am. Inst. Aeronaut. & Astronaut. Mass spectrometry; infrared spectrophotometry; electronic research. Address: Beckman Instruments, Inc, Advanced Technology Operation, 2500 Harbor Blvd, Fullerton, CA 92634.

DONNERSTAG, PHILIP, b. Brooklyn, N.Y, May 27, 17; m. 54; c. 2. GEOLOGY. B.S, City Col, 47. Field geophysicist, U.S. Bur. Mines, Md, 44-45; geologist, N.Y. State Sci. Serv, 47-50; proj. geologist, explor. br, raw materials div, Atomic Energy Cmn, 51; geologist, res. div. Texas Co, 52-54; chief geologist, Climax Uranium Co. Unit, Am. Metal Climax, Inc, 55-66; MGR. DENVER EXPLOR. OFF, DENISON MINES, LTD, 66- Am. Inst. Mining, Metall. & Petrol. Eng; Soc. Econ. Geol. Economic geology. Address: 670 Cody Court, Denver, CO 80215.

DONOGHUE, JOHN T, b. Holyoke, Mass, July 23, 35; m. 63; c. 2. INORGANIC CHEMISTRY. B.S, Massachusetts, Amherst, 58, Commonwealth fel. & M.S, 60; Nat. Sci. Found. & univ. fels. & Ph.D.(chem), Illinois, Urbana, 63. Res. chemist, E.I. du Pont de Nemours & Co, 63-65, lab. supvr, 65-66; res. chemist, Union Carbide Corp, 66-67; asst. prof. chem, Univ. Ark, 67-69; res. chemist, E.I. du Pont de Nemours & Co, 69-71; LAB. MGR, NEW BEDFORD PLANT, POLAROID CORP, 71- Petrol. Res. Fund grant, 67-69. Am. Chem. Soc; The Chem. Soc. Synthesis and characterization of coordination compounds exhibiting unusual coordination geometries. Address: New Bedford Plant, Polaroid Corp, New Bedford Industrial Park, New Bedford, MA 02741.

DONOGHUE, TIMOTHY R, b. Milton, Mass, May 3, 36; m. 64; c. 2. NUCLEAR PHYSICS. B.S, Boston Col, 57; Ph.D.(physics), Notre Dame, 63. Instr. Physics, Notre Dame, 62-63; fel, OHIO STATE UNIV, 63-64, asst. prof, 64-68, ASSOC. PROF, 68- Vis. staff scientist, Los Alamos Sci. Labs, 71. Am. Phys. Soc. Neutron and charged particle cross section; polarized beam investigations of nuclear reaction mechanisms and nuclear level structure; sources of polarized neutrons. Address: Dept. of Physics, Ohio State University, Columbus, OH 43210.

DONOGHUE, WILLIAM F, JR, b. Rochester, N.Y, Sept. 7, 21. MATHEMATICS. A.B, Rochester, 47, M.Sc, 48; Ph.D.(math), Wisconsin, 51. Assoc. mathematician, appl. physics lab, Hopkins, 51-52; asst. prof. math, Kansas, 52-57; assoc. prof, 57-62; temporary mem, Courant Inst. Math. Sci, N.Y. Univ, 63-64; vis. prof. MATH, Mich. State Univ, 64-66; PROF, UNIV. CALIF, IRVINE, 66- Guggenheim fel, 58-59. U.S.A, 42-46. Linear topological spaces; Eigenvalue problems. Address: Dept. of Mathematics, University of California, Irvine, CA 92664.

DONOHO, CLIVE W(ELLINGTON), JR, b. Nashville, Tenn, Jan. 16, 30; m. 55; c. 4. HORTICULTURE, PLANT PHYSIOLOGY. B.S, Kentucky, 52; M.S, N.C. State, 58; Ph.D.(hort), Mich. State, 60. Asst. prof. res. hort, Ohio Agr. Res. & Develop. Ctr, 60-64, assoc. prof, 64-66, prof, 66-67; PROF. HORT. SCI. & HEAD DEPT, N.C. STATE UNIV, 67- Nat. Sci. Found. travel grant, Int. Hort. Cong, Brussels, 62- U.S.A.F, 52-56, S/Sgt. Am. Soc. Hort. Sci; Int. Soc. Hort. Sci. Fruit physiology; natural auxins; absorption, translocation and metabolism of synthetic growth regulators; influence of pesticide chemicals on fruit physiology; water relations in fruit crops. Address: Dept. of Horticultural Science, North Carolina State University, Raleigh, NC 27607.

DONOHO, PAUL LEIGHTON, b. Ft. Worth, Tex, Sept. 7, 31; m. 54; c. 3. PHYSICS. B.A, Rice, 52; Ph.D.(physics), Calif. Inst. Tech, 58. Mem. tech. staff, Bell Tel. Labs, 57-59; asst. prof. PHYSICS, RICE UNIV, 59-63, assoc. prof, 63-69, PROF, 69- Am. Phys. Soc; Am. Asn. Physics Teachers. Magnetic resonance; magnetic thin films. Address: Dept. of Physics, Rice University, Houston, TX 77001.

DONOHOE, HEBER CLARK, b. Hampton, Iowa, Feb. 15, 05; m. 31. ENTOMOLOGY, ECOLOGY. B.S, Mont. State Col, 27; M.S, Wash. State Univ, 28; Ph.D.(entom), Univ. Minn, 38. Asst, Illinois, 28-29; instr, sch. agr, Minnesota, 29-31; entomologist, dried fruit insect invests, bur. entom. & plant quarantine, U.S. Dept. Agr, Calif, 31-38, entomologist in charge Japanese beetle treatment tests, div. control invests, N.J, 38-43; res. dir, Wm. Peterman, Inc, 43-48; farm & livestock consult, 48-50; chmn. dept. biol. sci, Trenton Jr. Col, 50-67, acad. dean, 55-59; chmn. dept. biol, MERCER COUNTY COMMUNITY COL, 67-70, dept. biol. chem, 70-71, COORD. ORNAMENTAL HORT. TECHNOL, 71- Address: Dept. of Biology, Mercer County Community College, 101 W. State St, Trenton, NJ 08608.

DONOHOO, H(ORRIE) V(AN) W(ALDO), b. Tucumcari, N.Mex, June 7, 14; m. 33; c. 2. GEOPHYSICS. Drake, 31-34; Colo. Sch. Mines, 36-39, 45-46; Columbia, 47. Computer, Stanolind Oil & Gas Co, Okla, 39-40; Phillips Petrol. Co, 40-41; instr. mech, Cornell, 41-43; geophys, Colo. Sch. Mines, 46-47; asst. prof, Utah, 47-51; geophys. engr, Columbia-Geneva Div, U.S. Steel Corp, 53-57; mgr. mining explor. & chief geophysicist, TEX. GULF SULPHUR CO, 57-66, gen. mgr, potash div, 66, V.PRES, 67-70, AGR. DIV, 70- Res. engr, Columbia Univ, 47, consult. New Park Mining Co, Utah, 48. Distinguished Achievement Medal, Colo. sch. mines. U.S.N.R, 43-46, 51-52, Lt. Comdr. Am. Inst. Min, Metall. & Petrol. Eng; Am. Asn. Petrol. Geol; Soc. Explor. Geophysics; Am. Soc. Econ. Geol; European Soc. Explor. Geophys; Mining & Metall. Soc. Am; Newcomen Soc. N.Am. Mining exploration and geophysics of the Western Hemisphere. Address: 5309 Parkwood Dr, Raleigh, NC 27609.

DONOHOO, JOHN T, S.M, b. St. Louis, Mo, Feb. 26, 19. ZOOLOGY, CELL PHYSIOLOGY. M.S, Marquette, 52; Atomic Energy Cmn. fel, Notre Dame, 54-56, Ph.D.(biol), 56. Instr. chem, physics & aeronaut, Chaminade Col, (Mo), 40-44; instr. sci. & athletic dir, Don Bosco High Sch, Wis, 44-50; instr. chem, ST. MARY'S UNIV, SAN ANTONIO, 50-52, PROF. BIOL. & CHMN. DEPT, 56- Res. participant, Oak Ridge Nat. Labs, summer 63. AAAS; Nat. Asn. Biol. Teachers; Am. Soc. Microbiol. Radiation effects on bacterial viruses and inorganic chemical protectors. Address: Dept. of Biology, St. Mary's University of San Antonio, 2700 Cincinnati Ave, San Antonio, TX 78228.

DONOHUE, DAVID ARTHUR TIMOTHY, b. Montreal, Que, Apr. 11, 37; U.S. citizen; m. 61; c. 1. PETROLEUM. B.S, Oklahoma, 59; Pan Am. Petrol. fel, Pa. State, 59, Gulf Oil fel, 60-61, Ph.D.(petrol. eng), 63; J.D, Boston Col, 71. Prod. engr, Imp. Oil Ltd, Can, 58, res. engr, 63-64; asst. prof. petrol. & natural gas eng, Pa. State Univ, 64-68, assoc. prof, 68-69; PRES, HUMAN RESOURCES DEVELOP. CO, 69- Chmn, Pa-N.Y. Chap, Petrol. Inst, 67-68. Am. Inst. Mining, Metall. & Petrol. Eng; Soc. Petrol. Eng. (Cedric K. Ferguson Medal, 68); Am. Inst. Chem. Eng; Am. Soc. Eng. Educ. Experimental and theoretical research dealing with developing new methods and improving old methods of producing crude oil from underground formations. Address: 100 Goddard Ave, Brookline, MA 02146.

DONOHUE, JERRY, b. Sheboygan, Wis, June 12, 20; m. 45; c. 2. CRYSTALLOGRAPHY. A.B, Dartmouth Col, 41, M.A, 43; fel, Calif. Inst. Tech, 43, Ph.D.(chem), 47. Instr. chem, Dartmouth Col, 41-43, Nat. Res. Coun. fel, 46-47, asst, 43-47, res. fel, 47-52, Guggenheim fel, 52-53; asst. prof. CHEM, Univ. South. Calif, 53-54, assoc. prof, 54-58, PROF, 58-66; UNIV. PA, 66- Nat. Sci. Found. fel, 59-60. With Off. Sci. Res. & Develop; U.S.N, 44. AAAS; Am. Crystallog. Asn. X-ray crystal structures; structures of compounds of biological interest; hydrogen bonds; structures of the elements. Address: Dept. of Chemistry, University of Pennsylvania, Philadelphia, PA 19104.

DONOHUE, JOHN J, b. Totowa, N.J, Feb. 17, 19; m. 45; c. 3. GEOLOGY. B.A, Maine, 44, M.Sc, 49; fel, Rutgers, 49-51, Ph.D.(geol. sci), 51. Field geologist, State Geol. Surv. Maine, 47-49; proj. dir. & consult, Off. Naval Res, 51-54; sr. res. & explor. geologist, Arabian Am. Oil Co, 51-61; dir. & consult, Geo-Tek Assocs, 60-64; PROF. PHYS. SCI, BENNETT COL.(N.Y), 64, CHMN. SCI-MATH. DEPT, 67- Asst, Maine, 48-49; sr. res. marine geologist, head sect. & assoc. prof, marine lab, Rhode Island, 51-59; res. & tech. consult, 54- U.S.A.R, 43- Geol. Soc. Am; Am. Asn. Petrol. Geol; Am. Geophys. Union. Physico-chemico, engineering and glacial geology; mineralogy; sedimentology; marine geodynamics; astrogeophysics. Address: Dept. of Science-Mathematics, Bennett College, Millbrook, NY 12545.

DONOHUE, PAUL CHRISTOPHER, b. Brooklyn, N.Y, June 28, 38; m. 66; c. 2. SOLID STATE & INORGANIC CHEMISTRY. B.S, St. John's (N.Y), 60; M.S, Connecticut, 63, Ph.D.(inorg. chem), 65. RES. CHEMIST, CENT. RES. DEPT, E.I. DU PONT DE NEMOURS & CO, 65- AAAS. Synthesis of new solid state ternary oxides and structural studies by x-ray crystallography; synthesis of new solid state sulfides and phosphides, crystal growth and x-ray crystallography. Address: Central Research Dept, E.I. du Pont de Nemours & Co, Inc, Wilmington, DE 19898.

DONOHUE, ROBERT J, b. Chicago, Ill, Jan. 31, 34; m. 57; c. 4. SPECTROSCOPY, PHYSICAL OPTICS. B.S, DePaul, 55, M.S, 57; Wayne State, 57-62. Res. asst. physics, DePaul, 54-56; res. physicist, GEN. MOTORS RES. LABS, 56-61, SR. RES. PHYSICIST, 61- U.S.A, 57. Optical Soc. Am. Plasma spectroscopy; nuclear physics; geometrical and physical optics; illumination and lighting systems. Address: General Motors Research Labs, 12 Mile & Mound Rds, Warren, MI 48092.

DONOHUE, ROBERT T, b. Boston, Mass, Nov. 10, 24; m. 49; c. 4. PHYSICS, ENGINEERING SCIENCE. B.S, Harvard, 48; M.S, Mass. Inst. Tech, 53. Instr. physics, Worcester Polytech, 48-49; asst. instrument res, Mass. Inst. Tech, 49-55, lectr. aeronaut. instrumentation, 52-54; vis. asst. prof. eng, California, Los Angeles, 55-56; mgr. weapon systs, Radio Corp. Am,

56-60; mem. tech. staff space systs. & ballistic missile defense, Inst. Defense Anal, 60-61; DIR. SYSTS. RES, GCA CORP, 61- U.S.N.R, 43-46. Theory of missile guidance and control; systems research on advanced weapons; geophysics of upper atmosphere; infrared and visible and ultraviolet instruments; applied research in metrology, photometry, spectroscopy and lasers. Address: GCA Corp, Burlington Rd, Bedford, MA 01730.

DONOHUE, WILLIAM B, b. Vancouver, B.C, Jan. 20, 29; m. 54; c. 2. PATHOLOGY, SURGERY. D.D.S, McGill, 53; W.K. Kellogg fel, Illinois, 54-56; M.Sc, Montreal, 61. Asst. prof. PATH, UNIV. MONTREAL, 59-64, assoc. prof, 64-70, PROF, 70- Nat. Res. Coun. Can. grants, 59-60, 61-62. Am. Acad. Oral Path; Int. Asn. Dent. Res. Growth and radiation; metabolic variations in oral mucosa. Address: Dept. of Oral Pathology, Faculty of Dental Surgery, University of Montreal, Montreal, Que, Can.

DONOHUE, WILLIAM L(ESLIE), b. Niagara Falls, Ont, Aug. 8, 06; m. 40; c. 3. PATHOLOGY. B.A, Toronto, 29, M.D, 32, M.A, 36. Intern, Hamilton Gen. Hosp, Ont, 32-33; res. path, Hosp. Sick Children, 33-34; fel. path, Toronto, 34-36, col. physicians & surgeons, Columbia, 36-37; mem. staff, Nat. Hosp. Nerv. Diseases, London, Eng, 37-38; asst. pathologist, HOSP. SICK CHILDREN, 38-47, CHIEF PATH, 47-; PROF. PATH, UNIV. TORONTO, 65- Fel, Royal Col. Physicians & Surgeons, Can, 62. R.C.A.F, 41-45, Wing Comdr. Am. Asn. Path. & Bact; Am. Soc. Pediatric pathology. Address: Hospital for Sick Children, 555 University Ave, Toronto 101, Ont. Can.

DONOIAN, HAIG C(ADMUS), b. Ramallah, Palestine, Apr. 8, 30; U.S. citizen; m. 57; c. 2. PHYSICAL & COLLOID CHEMISTRY. B.S, Lowell Tech. Inst, 52; scholar, Clark, 52-54, M.A, 54, fel, 54-57, Ph.D.(chem), 58. RES. CHEMIST, Am. Cyanamid Co, 57-63; Cabot Corp, Mass, 63-67; ORG. CHEM. DIV, AM. CYANAMID CO, 67- Am. Chem. Soc; Optical Soc. Am. Diffusion of substances in solution; colloidal chemistry and optical properties of carbon black. Address: Organic Chemicals Division, American Cyanamid Co, Bound Brook, NJ 08805.

DONOSO, JULIAN, b. Sucre, Bolivia, Aug. 12, 24; U.S. citizen; m. 58; c. 1. SOIL SCIENCE. M.S, Cornell, 55, Ph.D.(soil sci), 58. Asst. eng, Nat. Sch. Agr, Mex, 51; asst, Cornell, 55-58; soil chemist, United Fruit Co, 58-60; head CHEM. DEPT, WOODARD RES. CORP, 61-70, DIR, 70- AAAS; Soil Sci. Soc. Am; Am. Chem. Soc. Pesticide analysis; clinical chemistry; chemistry and fertility of soils. Address: Chemistry Dept, Woodard Research Corp, 12310 Pinecrest Rd, Herndon, VA 22070.

DONOVAN, ALLEN F(RANCIS), b. Onondaga, N.Y, Apr. 22, 14; m. 40; c. 1; m. 53; c. 2. AERONAUTICAL ENGINEERING. B.S.E, & M.S, Michigan, 36, hon. D.Eng, 64. Stress analyst, Curtiss Aeroplane & Motor Co, N.Y, 36-38; sr. stress analyst, Glenn L. Martin Co, Md, 38-39; asst. chief struct, Stinson Aircraft Div, Aviation Mfg. Corp, Mich, 39-40; chief struct, Nashville Div, Vultee Aircraft Corp, 40-41; asst. chief exp. design engr, airplane div, Curtiss Wright Corp, N.Y, 41-42, asst. head struct. dept, res. lab, 42-44, head, 44-46; head aero mech. dept, Cornell Aero Lab, Cornell Univ, 46-55; dir. aero res. & develop. staff, Space Tech. Labs, Inc, 55-58, v.pres, 58-60; SR. V.PRES, TECH, AEROSPACE CORP, 60- Consult, President's Sci. Adv. Cmt, 59- Mem, U.S. Air Force Sci. Adv. Bd, 48-57, 59-68, chmn. propulsion panel, 59-60, 63-68; U.S. del, Geneva Conf. Suspension of Nuclear Test, 59. U.S. Air Force Assoc. Sci. Award, 61, Medal for Exceptional Civilian Serv, 68. Nat. Acad. Eng; fel. Am. Inst. Aeronaut. & Astronaut. Space and ballistic missile system design and development. Address: 4033 via Marina, Apt. G-323, Marina del Rey, CA 90291.

DONOVAN, EDWARD FRANCIS, b. Columbus, Ohio, Nov. 20, 18; m. 43; c. 5. VETERINARY MEDICINE. D.V.M, Ohio State, 49. Private practice, Ohio, 49-52; assoc. dir. clin. res, Am. Cyanamid Co, 52-56; asst. prof. VET. MED, OHIO STATE UNIV, 56-59, assoc. prof, 59-62, PROF, COL. VET. MED. & GRAD. SCH, 62-, LECTR. OPHTHAL, COL. MED, 65- Morris Animal Found. res. dir, 62-; mem. cmt. prof. ed, inst. lab. animal resources, Nat. Acad. Sci, 66- U.S.A.F, 60-65, 1st Lt. Am. Vet. Med. Asn. Veterinary opthalmology; retinal diseases; animal endocrinology. Address: Dept. of Veterinary Medicine, Ohio State University, 2578 Kenny Rd, Columbus, OH 43210.

DONOVAN, E(DWARD) T(HOMAS), b. Chicago, Ill, Apr. 23, 99; m. 23; c. 4. MECHANICAL ENGINEERING. B.S, Wisconsin, 21. Instr. mech. eng, Purdue, 21-24; asst. engr, C.M. & St.P. Ry, 24-26; asst. prof, New Hampshire, 26-42; field rep. eng, sci. & mgt. war training, U.S. Off. Ed, 42-43, prin. specialist eng. ed, 43-46; assoc. prof. MECH. ENG, UNIV. N.H, 46-49, prof, 49-68, chmn. dept, 49-64, acting dean col. technol, 55-59, EMER. PROF, 68- Am. Soc. Mech. Eng; Am. Soc. Eng. Educ. Thermodynamics; heat power. Address: Dept. of Mechanical Engineering, University of New Hampshire, Durham, NH 03824.

DONOVAN, GERALD A(LTON), b. Hartford, Conn, Feb. 10, 25; m. 48; c. 3. POULTRY NUTRITION, BIOCHEMISTRY. B.S, Connecticut, 50, M.S, 52; Ph.D.(poultry nutrit, biochem), Iowa State, 55. Asst. poultry res, Connecticut, 51-52; res. assoc, Iowa State, 52-55; in charge poultry nutrit. res, agr. res. dept, Charles Pfizer & Co, Inc, 55-60; assoc. prof. poultry sci, UNIV. VT, 60-66, PROF. ANIMAL SCI, 66-, ASSOC. DIR. COL. AGR. & HOME ECON, 67-, ACTING DEAN, COL. AGR. & HOME ECON, 70-, assoc. dir, agr. exp. sta, 66-67. Asst. chemist, milk chem. lab, State of Conn, summers 49, 50. U.S.N, 43-46. Poultry Sci. Asn; Animal Nutrit. Res. Coun; Am. Inst. Nutrit. Vitamins, particularly vitamin A; antibiotics; hormones; chemotherapeutic agents. Address: College of Agriculture & Home Economics, University of Vermont, Burlington, VT 05401.

DONOVAN, GERARD ANTHONY, Microbiol, Biochem, see O'DONOVAN, GERARD ANTHONY.

DONOVAN, JAMES, b. Vancouver, Wash, Oct. 26, 06; m. 31; c. 2. CHEMICAL ENGINEERING. B.S, Mass. Inst. Tech, 28. Instr. chem. eng, Mass. Inst. Tech, 28-29; chem. engr, Hird & Connor, Inc, 29-32; Acme Indust. Equip. Co, 32-34; CHIEF ENGR. & EXEC, Artisan Metal Prods, Inc, 34-61, ARTISAN INDUST. INC, 61- Exec, Jet-Vac Corp; Kontro Co, Inc; Anyl-Ray Corp. Am. Inst. Chem. Eng; Am. Chem. Soc; Am. Welding Soc; Inst. Food Technol. Chemical engineering process; evaporation, distillation and reaction costs. Address: Artisan Industries Inc, 73 Pond St, Waltham, MA 02154.

DONOVAN, JOHN C(HARLES), b. Scranton, Pa, Nov. 15, 19; m. 47; c. 2. MEDICINE. B.S, Notre Dame, 41; M.D, Rochester, 45. Fel. path, med. sch, Rochester, 43-44; intern surg, Yale, 45-46; fel. psychiat, UNIV. ROCHESTER, 48-49, asst. res. OBSTET. & GYNEC, 46-48, chief res, 49-50, instr, 50-54, asst. prof, 54-60, assoc. prof, 60-66, PROF, 66- Mem, Am. Bd. Obstet. & Gynec. Dipl, Nat. Bd. Med. Exam. AAAS; Am. Med. Asn; fel. N.Y. Acad. Sci; Am. Psychosom. Soc; Am. Col. Obstet. & Gynec. Blood volume alterations in pregnancy and etiologic factors; psychosomatic aspects of obstetrics and gynecology; medical education. Address: Strong Memorial Hospital, University of Rochester Medical Center, Rochester, NY 14620.

DONOVAN, JOHN E(DWARD), b. Haverhill, Mass, June 29, 04; m. 33; c. 1. PHYSICAL CHEMISTRY. B.S, New Hampshire, 26; fel, N.Y. Univ, 26-30, M.Sc, 27, Ph.D.(chem), 30. Asst. res. chemist, Am. Potash & Chem. Corp, 30-32; prof. chem, St. Benedict's Col, 32-34; instr, Bergen Jr. Col, N.J, 34-35; from tech. examiner to asst. examiner in charge phys. sci, Civil Serv. Comn, 35-46; personnel off, Bur. Standards, 46-47, personnel adminr, 47-48; asst. to dir, NEW BRUNSWICK LAB, ATOMIC ENERGY COMN, 48-53, CHIEF ADMIN. BR, 53- Prof, Mt. St. Scholastica's Col, 33-34. AAAS; Am. Inst. Chem; Am. Chem. Soc; Am. Soc. Pub. Admin. Separation and solubilities of rare earths; phase rule applications to inorganic salt systems; analytical chemistry. Address: Atomic Energy Commission, Box 150, New Brunswick, NJ 08903.

DONOVAN, JOHN FRANCIS, b. St. John, N.B, Nov. 11, 35; m. 63; c. 2. ECONOMIC GEOLOGY, EARTH SCIENCES. B.Sc, St. Francis Xavier Univ, 57; M.S, Univ. Iowa, 59; Ph.D.(geol), Cornell Univ, 63. Resident geologist, Ont. Dept. Mines, 63-68; ASSOC. PROF. GEOL, WINONA STATE COL, 68- Geol. Soc. Am; Soc. Econ. Geol. Study of iron formations—sedimentary deposits of Archean age, Precambrian areas of Canadian shield. Address: Dept. of Geology, Winona State College, Winona, MN 55987.

DONOVAN, JOHN JOSEPH, b. Lynn, Mass; m. 63; c. 5. COMPUTER SCIENCE, ELECTRICAL ENGINEERING. B.S, Tufts Univ, 63; B.S, Mass. Inst. Technol, 63; M.Eng, Yale, 64, M.S, 65, M.Ph. & Ph.D.(comput), 66. Group mgr, IBM Corp, 65-66; ASSOC. PROF. ELEC. ENG, MASS. INST. TECHNOL, 66- Ford fel, Mass. Inst. Technol, 66; consult, med. sch, Yale, Pan Am, Honeywell, Inc, U.S. Underwater Systs. Ctr, Olivetti & Ciba-Corp. 66-; pres, Int. Comput. Inc, 67-69; adj. prof, Tex. Tech Univ, 68-71; lectr, Lowel Sch, 68-71; chmn. bd, MITROL, 70-71; mem. adv. bd, Honeywell, Inc, 70-71; lectr, Univ. R.I, 71. Asn. Comput. Mach. Programming languages and linguistics; computers and medicine. Address: Dept. of Electrical Engineering, Massachusetts Institute of Technology, Cambridge, MA 02139.

DONOVAN, JOHN LEO, b. Rochester, N.Y, Apr. 1, 29; m. 53; c. 4. PHYSICS, NUCLEAR SCIENCE. B.S, Rochester, 51; M.S, Pittsburgh, 53; Atomic Energy Cmn. & Owens-Corning Fiberglas fels. & Ph.D.(nuclear sci), Michigan, 64. Instr, N.Y. Univ, 53-56; SR. RES. PHYSICIST, Curtiss-Wright Corp, 56-59; EASTMAN KODAK CO, 64- Assoc. lectr, Rochester, 66- U.S.P.H.S.R, 54-, Scientist. AAAS; Am. Nuclear Soc; Am. Phys. Soc; Soc. Photog. Sci. & Eng. Nonsilver image forming systems and their application to radiography, including measurement of intrinsic efficiency of phosphors irradiated with x-rays. Address: Eastman Kodak Co, Physics Research Lab, Kodak Park, Rochester, NY 14650.

DONOVAN, JOHN W, b. Boston, Mass, June 7, 29; m. 61; c. 4. PHYSICAL CHEMISTRY. B.S, Boston Col, 50; M.S, Col. Holy Cross, 53; Ph.D.(chem), Cornell, 59. Fel. chem, Rochester, 59-61; trainee molecular biol, virus lab, California, Berkeley, 61-63; res. assoc. chem, Oregon, 63-65; MEM. STAFF, WEST. REGIONAL RES. LAB, U.S. DEPT. AGR, 65- Physical chemistry of proteins. Address: Western Regional Research Lab, U.S. Dept. of Agriculture, Berkeley, CA 94710.

DONOVAN, LEO F(RANCIS), b. East Orange, N.J, Apr. 12, 32; m. 60; c. 2. CHEMICAL ENGINEERING. B.S, Lehigh, 54; M.Ch.E, Rensselaer Polytech, 57, Ph.D.(chem. eng), 65. Chem. engr, res. lab, Mobil Oil Co, 57-59; nuclear chem. engr, nuclear power eng. dept, Alco Prod. Inc, 59-62; AEROSPACE ENGR, LEWIS RES. CTR, NASA, 65- Summer, chem. engr, silicone prod. dept, Gen. Elec. Co, 62. U.S.A, 54-56. Am. Inst. Chem. Eng. Fluid mechanics; numerical analysis; numerical flow visualization; computer time sharing. Address: 155 Kraft St, Berea, OH 44017.

DONOVAN, RICHARD C, b. McKees Rocks, Pa, May 15, 41; m. 64; c. 2. MECHANICAL ENGINEERING. B.S, Pittsburgh, 62, M.S, 64, Nat. Sci. Found. fels, 64-65, 65-66, Ph.D.(mech. eng), 67. Asst. prof. mech. eng, Pittsburgh, 67-68; mem. res. staff, ENG. RES. CTR, WEST. ELEC. CO, 68-71, RES. LEADER, 71- Am. Soc. Mech. Eng; Soc. Rheol; Soc. Plastics Eng. Rheology and heat transfer; polymer processing. Address: 192 Rice Dr, Morrisville, PA 19067.

DONOVAN, ROSS G(RANT), b. Niagara Falls, Ont, Sept. 20, 30; m. 52; c. 2. BIOCHEMISTRY. B.A, Toronto, 52, M.A, 54, Ph.D.(biochem), 65. Chief chemist, Collis Leather Co, Ltd, Ont, 53-60; GROUP LEADER, RES. & DEVELOP. LABS, CAN. PACKERS, LTD, TORONTO, 63- Am. Sci. Affiliation; Am. Leather Chem. Asn; fel. Chem. Inst. Can; Can. Biochem. Soc; Brit. Soc. Leather Trades Chem; Brit. Chem. Soc. Leather; proteins of connective tissue; proteolytic enzymes. Address: 17 Markland Dr, Etobicoke, Ont, Can.

DONOVAN, TERENCE M, b. Chicago, Ill, Dec. 7, 31; m. 55; c. 3. SOLID STATE PHYSICS. B.S, San Jose State Col, 56; M.S, Stanford Univ, 61; Ph.D, 70. Physical chemist, chem. div, U.S. Naval Ord. Test Sta, 56-60, CHEM. PHYSICIST, PHYSICS DIV, MICHELSON LAB, NAVAL WEAPONS CTR, 61-, assoc. chemist, Shockley Transistor Corp, 60-61. U.S.M.C, 50-51. Thermochemistry; epitaxial semiconductor film, growth; electrochemistry; optical properties of solids; optical properties and photoemission; electronic structure of solids. Address: Physics Division, Michelson Lab, Naval Weapons Center, China Lake, CA 93555.

DONOVAN, THOMAS A(RNOLD), b. Galesburg, Ill, July 11, 37; m. 60; c. 3. INORGANIC CHEMISTRY. B.A, Knox Col. (Ill), 59; Nat. Sci. Found. fel, Univ. Ill, 61-62, Ph.D.(inorg. chem), 62. Asst. prof. CHEM, Ind. State Col, 62-64; Knox Col.(Ill), 64-68; STATE UNIV. N.Y. COL. BUFFALO, 68-70, ASSOC. PROF, 70- AAAS; Am. Chem. Soc. Preparation, characterization and properties of new coordination compounds; biological applications of coordination chemistry. Address: Dept. of Chemistry, State University of New York College at Buffalo, 1300 Elmwood Ave, Buffalo, NY 14222.

DONOVICK, PETER JOSEPH, b. Champaign, Ill, Jan. 14, 38; m. 62; c. 2. PHYSIOLOGICAL PSYCHOLOGY. B.A, Lafayette Col, 61; M.S, Wisconsin, 63, Ph.D.(psychol), 67. ASST. PROF. PSYCHOL, HARPUR COL, STATE UNIV. N.Y. BINGHAMTON, 66- Nat. Inst. Ment. Health res. grants, 67-72, spec. res. fel. anat. & vis. asst. prof, Hershey Med. Ctr, Pa. State Univ, 70-71; consult, Life Sci. Inc. Prog. on Alcohol Toxicity & Psychopharmacol. Effects, 71. AAAS; Am. Psychol. Asn; Animal Behav. Soc; N.Y. Acad. Sci; Psychonomic Soc. The role of various central nervous system structures, particularly those in the limbic system, in regulation of homeostatic mechanisms. Address: Dept. of Psychology, Harpur College, State University of New York at Binghamton, Binghamton, NY 13901.

DONOVICK, RICHARD, b. Minneapolis, Minn, July 8, 11; m; c. 4. BACTERIOLOGY. B.A, California, Los Angeles, 34, M.A, 36; Ph.D.(bact), Illinois, 40. Asst. bact, California, Los Angeles, 34-36; Illinois, 36-40; res. fel, col. physicians & surg, Columbia, 40-41; pathologist, virus div, Lederle Labs, N.Y, 41-42; sr. bacteriologist & head typhus dept, Reichel Labs, Pa, 42-44; res. assoc. div. microbiol, Squibb Inst. Med. Res, 44-46, assoc. mem, 46-49, head dept. microbiol. res. & develop, 49-50, dir. div, 50-69; RES. PROJ. DIR. & MEM. EXEC. COMT, LIFE SCI, INC, 69- Mem. Sci. Adv. Bd, U.S. Air Force. With Off. Res. & Develop; U.S.A; U.S.N, 44. Dipl, Am. Bd. Microbiol. Fel. AAAS; Am. Soc. Microbiol.(treas, 62-64); Soc. Exp. Biol. & Med; Am. Chem. Soc; fel. N.Y. Acad. Sci; fel, Am. Acad. Microbiol. Experimental infections of virus and rickettsial diseases; several aspects for antibiotics; fermentation; chemotherapy of number of experimental bacteriological infections; various biosynthesis including biosynthesis of steroids. Address: Life Sciences, Inc, 2900 72nd St. N, St. Petersburg, FL 33710.

DONSKER, MONROE D(AVID), b. Burlington, Iowa, Oct. 17, 24; m. 46. MATHEMATICS. B.A, Minnesota, 44, M.A, 46, Ph.D.(math), 49. Asst. MATH, Minnesota, 44-46, instr, 46-48; Cornell, 48-50; asst. prof, Univ. Minn, 50-53, assoc. prof, 53-56, prof, 56-59; Fulbright sr. res. scholar, Denmark, 59-61; PROF, COURANT INST. MATH. SCI, N.Y. UNIV, 62- Mem, Comt. Int. Exchange of Persons; chmn. postdoctoral comt, Off. Naval Res; chmn, Fulbright Screening Panel in Math. Civilian with U.S.N; Nat. Bur. Standards. Am. Math. Soc; Math. Asn. Am. Stochastic processes; analysis. Address: Courant Institute of Mathematical Sciences, New York University, 251 Mercer St, New York, NY 10012.

DOO, V(EN) Y(OUNG), b. Kiangsu, China, Mar. 31, 22; m. 51; c. 4. METALLURGY. B.S, Col. Ord. Eng, China, 44; M.S, Illinois, 55, Ph.D.(metall), 58. Res. assoc. phys. metall, Univ. Ill, 57-58; adv. metallurgist, COMPONENTS DIV, IBM CORP, 58-67, SR. METALLURGIST, 67- Chinese Army, 44-52, Maj. Am. Soc. Metals; Am. Inst. Mining, Metall. & Petrol. Eng; Electrochem. Soc; Am. Phys. Soc. Growth and property of various thin films of semiconductors and insulators; their application in microelectronic circuits. Address: IBM Corp, Components Division, Dept. 10C, Bldg. 300-94, Hopewell Junction, NY 12533.

DOOB, HUGO, JR, b. New York, N.Y, May 24, 10; m. 36; c. 3. CHEMISTRY. A.B, Cornell, 30, Ph.D.(chem), 37; Munich, 30-31. Asst. dairy indust, Cornell, 37; chemist, Brown-Lipe-Chapin Div, Gen. Motors Corp, N.Y, 37-38; asst. dairy indust, Cornell, 38-42, res. assoc, 42-43; res. chemist, N.Am. Rayon Corp, 43-46, sect. leader, 46-55; proj. mgr. prod. develop, Owens Corning Fiberglas Corp, 55-61, specifications, 61-64, specifications supvr, 64-67; asst. prof. CHEM, WARREN WILSON COL, 67-70, ASSOC. PROF, 70- Am. Chem. Soc. Electrochemistry of deposition; catalytic poisoning and metal overvoltage; physical chemistry of dairy products; fiber chemistry; reinforced plastics; glass fiber technology. Address: Dept. of Chemistry, Warren Wilson College, Swannanoa, NC 28778.

DOOB, J(OSEPH) L(EO), b. Cincinnati, Ohio, Feb. 27, 10; m. 31; c. 3. MATHEMATICS. A.B, Harvard, 30, A.M, 31, Ph.D.(math), 32. Nat. Res. fel. math, Columbia, 32-34, assoc. theoret. statist. & Carnegie Corp. fel, 34-35; assoc. MATH, UNIV. ILL, URBANA-CHAMPAIGN, 35-37, asst. prof, 37-43, assoc. prof, 43-45, PROF, 45- With U.S.N, 41-45. Nat. Acad. Sci; Am. Math. Soc.(pres, 63-64); fel. Inst. Math. Statist.(v.pres, 45, pres, 50). Probability. Address: Dept. of Mathematics, University of Illinois-Urbana-Champaign, Urbana, IL 61801.

DOODY, EDWARD, b. Chicago, Ill, Mar. 30, 25. PHYSICAL CHEMISTRY. B.S, St. Mary's Col, 46; M.S, St. Louis, 50, Ph.D.(phys. chem), 53. Teacher, mil. high sch, Mo, 46-53; instr. CHEM, CHRISTIAN BROS. COL, 53-54, PROF, 54- Cottrell res. grant, 54; Nat. Sci. Found. grant, 54, res. grant, 62; Atomic Energy Cmn. res. grant, 55-; Tenn. heart res. grant, 62, 63; Am. Chem. Soc. Petrol. res. grant, 63. Summers, res. participant, Duquesne & Pittsburgh, 54, 55; instr, summer inst, Oak Ridge, Tenn, 56; Ft. Lewis, Colo, 59; res. participant, N.Y. Univ, 61, 62; participant, summer inst, Ohio State, 63; Utah & Florida, 64; ed, South. Chemist. Am. Chem. Soc; Am. Inst. Chem. Heavy metal ions; transport across membranes and reactions with nucleic acids and derivatives; effect of industrial wastes on biotic community. Address: Dept. of Chemistry, Christian Brothers College, 650 E. Pkwy, Memphis, TN 38104.

DOODY, THOMAS C(LARE), b. San Rafael, Calif, Oct. 13, 01; m. 39. CHEMISTRY. B.S, California, 24, M.S, 25, Ph.D.(chem), 38. Chem. engr. Barium Prod, Inc, Calif, 26-29; Termite Invests. Cmt, California, 29-34; chemist, Paraffin Co, 34; prof. indust. chem. & physics, Polytech. Col, Oakland, 38-39; from instr. to prof. CHEM. ENG, N.C. State Col, 39-47; assoc. prof, PURDUE UNIV, 47-65, prof, 65-70, EMER. PROF, 70- Exchange prof, Taiwan Prov. Col. Eng, 54-55. AAAS; Am. Chem. Soc; assoc. Am. Inst. Chem. Eng; Am. Soc. Eng. Educ. Chemical equilibria and reaction rates; mannite-arsenious acids. Address: Dept. of Chemical Engineering, Purdue University, Lafayette, IN 47907.

DOOLAN, PAUL DELOHERY, b. New Haven, Conn, Jan. 21, 24; m. 49; c. 4. MEDICINE. M.D, Georgetown, 47. Dir. clin. invest. ctr, U.S. Naval Hosp, Oakland, Calif, 58-61; res. collab, Brookhaven Nat. Lab, 61-67; PROF. MED, MED. COL. VA, VA. COMMONWEALTH UNIV, 67- Dir. dept. clin. invest, nat. naval med. ctr, Naval Med. Res. Inst, Md, 64-65, exec. off, 65-67. Dipl, Am. Bd. Internal Med, 55. U.S.N, 43-46, 48-, Capt. AAAS; Soc. Mil. Surg. U.S; Am. Col. Physicians; Am. Heart Asn; Am. Fedn. Clin. Res; Soc. Exp. Biol. & Med. Kidney physiology and disease. Address: Dept. of Medicine, Medical College of Virginia, Virginia Commonwealth University, Richmond, VA 23219.

DOOLEY, D(ONALD) A(LLEN), b. Los Angeles, Calif, Apr. 30, 27; m. 51; c. 3. AERONAUTICS. B.S, Notre Dame, 49; M.S, Calif. Inst. Technol, 50, Guggenheim fel, 52-54, Ph.D.(aeronaut, physics), 56. Res. engr. opers. res, N.Am. Aviation, Inc, 50-52; res. engr. combustion, jet propulsion lab, Calif. Inst. Technol, 53-55; res. specialist missile preliminary anal, N.Am. Aviation, Inc, 55-56; asst. prof. aeronaut. eng, Michigan, 56-57; chief missile anal. sect, Aeronutronic Systs, Inc, 57, mgr. reentry tech. proj, 57-58, chief propulsion sect, Titan Prog. Off, Space Tech. Labs, Inc, Thompson Ramo Wooldridge, Inc, 58-60; dir. spacecraft sci. subdiv, Aerospace Corp, 60-61, tech. dir. Titan III, 61-63, v.pres. & gen. mgr. eng. div, 63-64, weapon systs. div, Calif, 63-65; asst. to chief scientist, United Aircraft Corp, Conn, 65-66; v.pres. & gen. mgr. systs. planning div, Aerospace Corp, 66-68, v.pres. & assoc. opers. gen. mgr. systs. eng. opers, El Segundo, 68-70; v.pres. & prog. dir. space shuttle prog, Convair Aerospace Div, Gen. Dynamics Corp, 70-71; V.PRES. RES. & DEVELOP, SYST. DEVELOP. CORP, 71- Consult, Ramo-Wooldridge Corp, 56-57. U.S.A, 44-47. Am. Inst. Aeronaut. & Astronaut; Am. Ord. Asn. Space sciences; aerothermochemistry and reentry technology; advanced rocket engines; systems management of ballistic and space vehicle projects; combustion phenomena; chemistry and reentry technology; systems management of space and ballistic systems. Address: 4780F La Villa Marina, Marina Del Rey, CA 90291.

DOOLEY, ELMO S, b. Davidson, Tenn, Feb. 23, 24; m. 45; c. 3. BIOLOGY, MICROBIOLOGY. B.S, Tenn. Polytech, 52; M.S, Tennessee, 55, Ph.D.(bact), 57. Consult. microbiol, Cumberland Med. Center, 57-58; chief microbiol. br, U.S. Army Med. Res. Lab, 58-61; sr. scientist microbiol, U.S. Aerospace Med. Res. Lab, 61-63; chmn. DEPT. BIOL, TENN. TECHNOL. UNIV, 64-66, MEM. STAFF, 66- U.S.A.F.R, 42-, Lt. Col. Aerospace Med. Asn; Am. Soc. Microbiol; Am. Fedn. Clin. Res; fel. Royal Soc. Health. Aerospace and life support systems. Address: Dept. of Biology, Tennessee Technological University, Cookeville, TN 38501.

DOOLEY, GEORGE JOSEPH, III, b. Greenwich, Conn, Aug. 8, 41; m. 63; c. 3. MATERIALS SCIENCE. B.S, Univ. Notre Dame, 63; U.S. Atomic Energy Comn. assistantship, Iowa State Univ, 63-66, M.S, 66; Bur. Mines fel, Ore. State Univ, 66-68, Ph.D.(mat. sci), 69. Res. metallurgist, Albany Metall. Res. Ctr, Bur. Mines, 66-68; RES. SCIENTIST, AEROSPACE RES. LABS, U.S. AIR FORCE SYSTS COMMAND, 68- U.S.A.F, 68-72, Capt. Am. Soc. Metals; Am. Inst. Mining, Metall. & Petrol. Eng. Surface chemistry and surface physics of both single crystal and polycrystalline materials using the techniques of low energy electron diffraction and auger electron spectroscopy. Address: Aerospace Research Labs, U.S. Air Force Systems Command, ARL/LJ-Bldg. 450, Wright-Patterson Air Force Base, OH 45433.

DOOLEY, GLENN, b. South Haven, Kans, May 18, 05; m. 36; c. 2. ANALYTICAL CHEMISTRY. B.S, Southwest Mo. State Col, 28; M.S, Iowa, 32, Ph.D. (anal. chem), 35. Res. assoc, Iowa, 35-36; prof. CHEM. & head dept, Huron Col, 36-37; instr. Agr. & Mech. Col. Texas, 37-40, asst. prof, 40-42; West. Ky. Univ, 42-46, assoc. prof, 46-60, prof, 60-70; RETIRED. Am. Chem. Soc; Am. Crystallog. Asn. Crystal structure analysis by x-rays; optical crystal analysis by polarized light organic reagents in analytical chemistry; analytical chemistry of vanadium. Address: Box 266, College Heights, Bowling Green, KY 42101.

DOOLEY, J(OHN) RAYMOND, JR, b. Denver, Colo, Dec. 12, 25; m. 52; c. 5. PHYSICS. B.S, Regis Col.(Colo), 49; M.S, Univ. Denver, 51. Engr, Colo. State Hwy. Dept, 49-51; instr. physics, guided missile training, Lowry AFB, Colo, 51-52; staff mem. nuclear physics, Sandia Corp, 52-63; PHYSICIST, ISOTOPE GEOL. BR, U.S. GEOL. SURV, 53- U.S.A.A.F, 44-45. Am. Chem. Soc; Geochem. Soc; Health Phys. Soc; Am. Soc. Mass Spectrometry. Natural radioactivity and uranium geochemistry; autoradiography; uranium and thorium disequilibrium; health physics; uranium-234 fractionation and fission tracks. Address: Isotope Geology Branch, U.S. Geological Survey, Denver Federal Center, Denver, CO 80225.

DOOLEY, JOSEPH FRANCIS, b. N.Y.C, Oct. 3, 41; m. 63; c. 1. BIO-ORGANIC CHEMISTRY. B.S, Fordham Univ, 63; univ. fel, Univ. Minn, Minneapolis, 65-66, E.I. du Pont de Nemours & Co, Inc. fel, 65-67, Ph.D. (org. chem), 67. Res. chemist, E.I. du Pont de Nemours & Co, Inc, 67-70; STAFF SCIENTIST, MED. RES. LABS, PFIZER INC, 70- AAAS; Am. Chem. Soc. Development of new diagnostic tests; application of immune response to detection of disease; development of clinical instrumentation; radio-labeling techniques; lipid analysis; diagnostic chemistry. Address: Medical Research Labs, Pfizer Inc, Groton, CT 06340.

DOOLEY, SAMUEL, b. Bloomington, Ill, Mar. 4, 13; m. 38; c. 4. PEDIATRICS, PUBLIC HEALTH. B.S, Ill. Wesleyan, 34; M.D, Hopkins, 38. Intern med. & surg, Bellevue Hosp, New York, 38-39; intern & res. pediat, New York Hosp, 39-42; asst. prof, med. col, Cornell, 45-50; child health, sch. pub. health, Harvard, 50-54; health assoc, Community Serv. Soc, New York, 54-56; exec. dir, Nat. Cancer Found, 56-60; assoc. dir. welfare pediat, New York Hosp, 60-64; PROF. MATERNAL & CHILD HEALTH, SCH. PUB. HEALTH, UNIV. CALIF, BERKELEY, 64- U.S. Dept. State specialty exchange consult, Ger, 52-53; mem. pediat. adv. cmt, New York Dept. Health,

54-57, orthop. adv. cmt, 57-60. U.S.A, 42-46, Maj. Fel. Am. Pub. Health Asn. General pediatrics; maternal and child health. Address: Dept. of Maternal & Child Health, School of Public Health, University of California, Berkeley, CA 94720.

DOOLEY, THOMAS JOSEPH, b. Jackson Heights, N.Y, Jan. 12, 40. ORGANIC CHEMISTRY. B.S, Queens Col.(N.Y), 61; M.A, Univ. Ore, 64; Am. Hoechst fel, Univ. R.I, 65-66, Ph.D.(org. chem), 67. Res. asst, Univ. Ore, 62-63; Nat. Insts. Health res. assoc, Univ. Wis, Madison, 67; res. chemist, Dexter-Midland Corp, Ill, 68-69, dir. resin lab, 69; res. lab, Keystone Aniline & Chem. Co, 69; DIR, ORION, 70- Am. Chem. Soc; Soc. Study Alchemy & Early Chem. Organic photochemistry; unique unsaturated systems; non-benzenoid aromatic systems; ultraviolet spectroscopy; strained organic systems; photoreduction. Address: ORION, P.O. Box 949, Westhampton Beach, NY 11978.

DOOLEY, THOMAS PRICE, b. Elberton, Ga, Oct. 12, 04; m. 42; c. 2. GENETICS, CYTOLOGY. A.B, Morehouse Col, 27; Detroit, 29; M.S, Iowa, 31; Ph.D.(zool), Iowa, 39; Columbia, 43. PROF. BIOL, Ark. State Col, 29-31; PRAIRIE VIEW AGR. & MECH. COL, 34-, head dept. nat. sci, 41-49, dean sch. arts & sci, 49-68. Sci. workshop fel, Columbia Univ, 44; mem. conf. col. teachers genetics, Colo. State Univ, summer 62; vis. scientist, Nat. Sci. Found. & Tex. Acad. Sci, 65- AAAS; Genetics Soc. Am; Am. Micros. Soc; Nat. Asn. Res. Sci. Teaching; Nat. Inst. Sci. Antibiosis; experimental biology; influence of colchicine on the germ cells of insects. Address: Dept. of Biology, Prairie View Agricultural & Mechanical College, Prairie View, TX 77445.

DOOLEY, WALLACE T, b. Conway, Ark, June 15, 17; m. 39; c. 4. ORTHOPEDIC SURGERY. A.B, Kansas, 39, M.A, 41; M.D, Meharry Med. Col, 47. Rockefeller Found. fel, 51-52; Nat. Polio Found. fel, 52-55; DIR. PHYS. MED, GEORGE W. HUBBARD HOSP, 55-, PROF. ORTHOP. SURG, MEHARRY MED. COL, 67-, assoc. prof, 60-67, HEAD DIV, 60-, prog. dir. rehab. med, 63-67. Chief orthop. surg, Riverside Sanitarium & Hosp, 55- U.S.A. Am. Cong. Rehab. Med. Address: Dept. of Surgery, Meharry Medical College, Nashville, TN 37208.

DOOLEY, WILLIAM PAUL, b. Richmond, Va, Aug. 2, 15; m. 41; c. 2. CHEMISTRY, CHEMICAL ENGINEERING. B.S, Richmond, 38; S.M, Mass. Inst. Tech, 40. Tech. & admin. asst. to gen. mgr, Am. Viscose Corp, 40-45, asst. supt, staple develop. plant, 45-46, supt, 46-50, head develop. serv. dept, 50-55, corp. prod. tech. supvr, 55-58, proj. engr. & sr. technologist, 58-60; mkt. specialist, COMMERCIAL DEVELOP, SUN OIL CO, 60-67, asst. to dir, 67-70, PROJ. MGR, 70- Am. Chem. Soc; Am. Inst. Chem. Eng; Am. Asn. Textile Chem. & Colorists; Am. Asn. Textile Technol; Chem. Mkt. Res. Asn. Manufacture of viscose and viscose rayon products; technical support of sales programs; petrochemicals market research and development. Address: Sun Oil Co, 1608 Walnut St, Philadelphia, PA 19103.

DOOLIN, PAUL F, b. Jacksonville, Ill, May 17, 26. CELL BIOLOGY. A.B, Ill. Col, 50; M.S, Illinois, 53; Ph.D.(chem. cytol), Western Reserve, 58. Res. asst. cytol. & histol, Illinois, 50-53; res. assoc. cytochem, Inst. path, Western Reserve, 53-58; asst. prof, Washington & Jefferson Col, 59-60; assoc. prof. zool, Illinois State, 60-64; path, STRITCH SCH. MED, LOYOLA UNIV.(ILL), 64-69, ASSOC. PROF. ANAT. & PATH, 69-; RES. CHEMIST, NEUROPATH. RES. STA, VET. ADMIN. HOSP, 67-, res. biologist & chief electron micros. lab, 64-67. U.S.N.R, 44-46. AAAS; Am. Soc. Zool; Am. Soc. Cell Biol; Soc. Cryobiol; Electron Micros. Soc. Am. Cell growth and differentiation; histochemistry and ultrastructure. Address: Neurological Ultrastructure, Veterans Administration Hospital, Hines, IL 60141.

DOOLING, J(OHN) STUART, O.S.F.S, b. Philadelphia, Pa, June 27, 13. PHYSICAL CHEMISTRY. A.B, Catholic Univ, 36, Ph.D.(physics), 50; hon. LL.D, Muhlenberg Col, 71. Instr. physics, Catholic Univ. 48-50, chem, 50-54, asst. prof, 54-57, assoc. prof, 57-63; PRES, ALLENTOWN COL, 64- Mem. bd. trustees, DeSales Hall Sch. Theol; bd. dirs, Lehigh Valley Asn. Independent Cols. Am. Phys. Soc; Am. Chem. Soc; Am. Asn. Physics Teachers. Molecular structure; internal friction in metals. Address: Allentown College, Center Valley, PA 18034.

DOOLITTLE, ARTHUR K(ING), b. Oberlin, Ohio, Nov. 15, 96; m. 23; c. 2. CHEMISTRY. A.B, Columbia, 19, B.S, 20, Ch.E, 23. Res. engr, Dorr Co, 23-25; plant engr, Sherwin-Williams Co, Ill, 25-29, chief lacquer div, N.J, 29-31; develop. engr, Bowen Res. Corp, 31; dir. lacquer res, Bradley & Vrooman Co, 31-32; tech. head coatings res, Carbide & Carbon Chems. Corp, 32-44, asst. dir. res, Union Carbide Corp, 44-55, sr. scientist, 55-61; PRES, ARCADIA INST. SCI. RES, 59- Prof. chem, Drexel. Inst, 61-64. Consult, 58-; partner, Dorr Consults, 59-61. Mem. adv. bd, chem. eng. dept, Princeton, 55-58, ed. adv. bd. appl. polymer sci, 59-64; chmn. bd. trustees, Gordon Res. Conf, Am. Asn. Adv. Sci, 55. U.S.A, 17-19, 2nd Lt. AAAS; Am. Inst. Chem. Eng.(v.pres, 55); Am. Chem. Soc. Surface coatings; solvents; plasticizers; resins; theory of solvent action; theory of viscosity; theory of liquids; liquid state physics; paint technology. Address: 406 Osborne Lane, Wallingford, PA 19086.

DOOLITTLE, DONALD P(RESTON), b. Torrington, Conn, May 14, 33; m. 57; c. 2. GENETICS. B.S, Connecticut, 54; M.S, Cornell, 56, Ph.D.(animal genetics), 59. Asst, Cornell, 54-58; fel, Roscoe B. Jackson Mem. Lab, 58-60; asst. res. prof. biomet, grad. sch. pub. health, Univ. Pittsburgh, 60-65; asst. prof. genetics & asst. geneticist, W.Va. Univ, 65-67, ASSOC. PROF, ANIMAL SCI, PURDUE UNIV, 67- AAAS; Am. Genetics Asn; Am. Soc. Animal Sci; Poultry Sci. Asn. Population genetics; mammalian genetics; biometry. Address: Dept. of Animal sciences, Purdue University, Lafayette, IN 74907.

DOOLITTLE, DORTHA B(AILEY), b. Oberlin, Ohio, Apr. 16, 96; m. 23; c. 2. CHEMISTRY. A.B, Oberlin Col, 18; Michigan, 18; M.S, Illinois, 20; Richards fel, Mass. Inst. Technol, 21-22; Hall fel, Oberlin Col, 44-45. Instr. CHEM, Oberlin Col, 18-19; Illinois, 19-21; prof, Oxford Col. Women, 22-23; asst, Yale, 23; instr, Barnard Col, Columbia, 24-25, 28-29; prof, Kanawha Col, 32-39; assoc. prof, Morris Harvey Col, 39-54; asst, Union Carbide Corp, 54-58; assoc. prof, W.Va. Inst. Tech, 58-62; adj. prof, Drexel Inst, 62-65; ASST. PROF. CHEM, PMC COLS, 65- Trustee, Arcadia Inst. Sci. Res, 59- Am. Chem. Soc. Antidimmers for gas masks; midriatic compounds; energy output of women in walking experiments; vitamin C; viscosity; liquid-state physics. Address: 406 Osborne Lane, Wallingford, PA 19086.

DOOLITTLE, HOWARD D(ANIEL), b. Willimantic, Conn, Feb. 18, 10; m. 33. PHYSICS. B.S, Trinity Col.(Conn), 31; Ph.D.(physics), Chicago, 36. Instr. physics, Trinity Col.(Conn), 31-32, 35-40, asst. prof, 40-41; staff mem, radiation lab, Mass. Inst. Tech, 41-46; physicist, MACHLETT LABS, INC, 46-48, assoc. dir. eng, 58-62, DIR. TECHNOL, 62- Fel. Am. Phys. Soc. Nuclear physics; radio pulse modulators; electronic tubes. Address: Machlett Labs, Inc, Stamford, CT 06907.

DOOLITTLE, J(ESSE) S(EYMOUR), b. Bethany, Conn, Sept. 20, 03; m. 27. MECHANICAL ENGINEERING. B.S, Tufts, 25; M.S, Pa. State, 37. Student engr, Gen. Elec. Co, Mass, 25-27; instr. MECH. ENG, Case, 27-31; from instr. to assoc. prof, Pa. State Univ, 31-47; PROF. & DEPT. GRAD. ADMINSTR, N.C. STATE UNIV, 47- G. Edwin Burks Award, 70. AAAS; fel. Am. Soc. Mech. Eng; Am. Soc. Eng. Educ. Thermodynamics; heat transfer; power. Address: Dept. of Mechanical Engineering, North Carolina State University, Raleigh, NC 27607.

DOOLITTLE, JOHN H(ENRY), b. Foster, Mo, Feb. 8, 20; m. 41; c. 4. ELECTRONICS. B.S, Kansas, 42. From jr. electronics engr. to head phys. systs. sect, Cornell Aeronaut. Lab, N.Y, 46-57; from dept. head to dir. res. div, Radiation, Inc, Fla, 57-61; from asst. dept. head to ASSOC. DIR. ELECTRONICS DIV, CORNELL AERONAUT. LAB, INC, BUFFALO, 61- Sig.C, U.S.A, 42-46, Capt. Sr. mem. Inst. Elec. & Electronics Eng. Radar; electron circuits; remote control systems for aircraft and guided missiles; navigation; data links; space navigation and control man-machine interface. Address: 8754 Greiner Rd, Williamsville, NY 14221.

DOOLITTLE, ROBERT E, b. New Haven, Conn, May 22, 36; m. 59; c. 3. ORGANIC CHEMISTRY. B.S, Connecticut, 58, Ph.D.(chem), 63. Res. assoc. org. chem, Duke, 63-64; Washington (St. Louis), 64-65; RES. CHEMIST, PESTICIDE CHEM. RES. BR, AGR. RES. CTR, U.S. DEPT. AGR, 65- Am. Chem. Soc; The Chem. Soc. Natural products; insect pheremones; sex attractants. Address: 3211 Dunnington Rd, Beltsville, MD 20705.

DOOLITTLE, ROBERT F(REDERICK), II, b. Chicago, Ill, Dec. 21, 25; m. 55; c. 2. PHYSICS. A.B, Oberlin Col, 48; M.S, Michigan, 50, Ph.D.(physics), 58. Asst, Michigan, 50-58; asst. prof. physics, San Diego State Col, 58-60; MEM. TECH. STAFF, space physics dept, TRW Space Tech. Labs, 60-66, space sci. lab, TRW SYSTS, 66-70, STAFF SCIENTIST, INSTRUMENT SYSTS. LAB, REDONDO BEACH, 70- U.S.N.R, 44-46, 52-54, Lt.Comdr. AAAS; Am. Phys. Soc; Am. Inst. Aeronaut. & Astronaut; Am. Geophys. Union. High energy and cosmic ray physics. Address: 1290 Monument St, Pacific Palisades, CA 90272.

DOOLITTLE, RUSSELL F, b. New Haven, Conn, Jan. 10, 31; m. 55; c. 2. BIOCHEMISTRY. B.A, Wesleyan, Univ, 52; M.A, Trinity Col.(Conn), 57; Nat. Sci. Found. fel, Harvard, 60-61, Ph.D.(biochem), 62. Instr. biol, Amherst Col, 61-62; Nat. Heart Inst. fel, 62-64; asst. res. biologist, UNIV. CALIF, SAN DIEGO, 64-65, asst. prof. CHEM, 65-67, ASSOC. PROF, 67- Mem. corp, Marine Biol. Lab; career develop. award, U.S. Pub. Health Serv, 69- U.S.A, 52-54, Sgt. Soc. Gen. Physiol; Am. Soc. Biol. Chem. Evolution of protein molecules, particularly comparative biochemistry of blood coagulation proteins. Address: Dept. of Chemistry, University of California at San Diego, La Jolla, CA 92037.

DOOLITTLE, WARREN T(RUMAN), b. Webster City, Iowa, July 24, 21; m. 42; c. 3. FORESTRY. B.S, Iowa State Univ, 46; M.F, Duke Univ, 50; Ph.D, Yale, 55. Res. forester, southeast. forest & range exp. sta, U.S. FOREST SERV, 46-57, Wash. D.C, 57-59, asst. dir, NORTHEAST. FOREST EXP. STA, 59-70, DIR, 70- U.S.A.F, 42-45, 51-52, Res, Lt. Col. AAAS; Soc. Am. Foresters; Soil Conserv. Soc; Am; Am. Forestry Asn. Silviculture; forest management and soils. Address: 1142 Waterloo Rd, Berwyn, PA 19312.

DOOMES, EARL, b. Washington, La, Feb. 8, 43; m. 65; c. 1. ORGANIC CHEMISTRY. Nat. Sci. Found. Trainee, Univ. Nebr, 67, Merck Sharp & Dohme fel, 68, Ph.D.(chem), 69. Fel, CHEM, Northwest. Univ, 68-69; ASST. PROF, MACALESTER COL, 69- Am. Chem. Soc. Small-ring heterocycles; azetidinyl ketones; episulfones; mechanisms of allylic substitution reactions; mechanisms of 1,3-elimination reactions—the stereochemistry of alpha-sulfonyl carbanions; annulenes, bridged and nonbenzonoid aromatics. Address: Dept. of Chemistry, Macalester College, St. Paul, MN 55101.

DOORENBOS, HAROLD E, b. Morrison, Ill, Oct. 4, 25; m. 49; c. 2. ORGANIC CHEMISTRY. B.S, Cent. Col.(Iowa), 49; M.S, Arkansas, 56; Smith Kline & French fel. & Ph.D.(chem), Delaware, 62. Instr. chem, Pa. State, 55-56; CHEMIST, U.S. Dept. Agr, Md, 58; E.I. du Pont de Nemours & Co, 61-62; DOW CHEM. CO, 62- U.S.N.R, 43-46. AAAS; Am. Chem. Soc; Sci. Res. Soc. Am. Organic synthesis; pharmaceutical, polymer, radioactive tracer, chlorine and fluorine chemistry. Address: 2102 Sylvan Lane, Midland, MI 48640.

DOORENBOS, NORMAN J(OHN), b. Flint, Mich, May 13, 28; m. 51; c. 7. PHARMACOGNOSY, MEDICINAL CHEMISTRY. B.S, Univ. Mich, 50, M.S, 51, Ph.D.(chem), 53. Sr. res. chemist sensitizing dyes, Ansco, 53-56; asst. prof. pharmaceut. chem, Univ. Md, 56-57, assoc. prof, 58-63, prof, 63-65; med. chem, UNIV. MISS, 65-67, PROF. PHARMACOG. & CHMN. DEPT, 67- Vis. scientist, Am. Asn. Cols. Pharm, 63-; Merck Sharp & Dohme lectr, W.Va. Univ, 64. Consult, Malinckrodt Chem. Works, 63-; Nat. Sci. Found. Sci. Curr. Proj, Univ. Ill, 64. AAAS; Am. Chem. Soc.(treas, 49, chmn, 50); Am. Pharmaceut. Asn; Am. Cols. Pharm; Am. Soc. Pharmacog; Soc. Econ. Bot. Medical chemistry; steroids; heterocyclic steroids; heterocyclic compounds; alkaloids, natural products; biopharmaceutics; pharmacology; drug abuse; marijuana and phytochemistry. Address: Dept. of Pharmacognosy, University of Mississippi School of Pharmacy, University, MS 38677.

DOPPMAN, JOHN LEO, b. Springfield, Mass, June 14, 28; m. 66; c. 1. RADIOLOGY. B.A, Col. of Holy Cross, 49; M.D, Yale, 53. Dep. chief RADIOL, Nat. Insts. Health, Md, 64-70; PROF, UNIV. CALIF, SAN DIEGO, 70- Address: Dept. of Radiology, University of California, San Diego, Box 109, La Jolla, CA 92037.

DORAIN, PAUL B(RENDEL), b. New Haven, Conn, Aug. 30, 26; m. 50; c. 2. PHYSICAL CHEMISTRY. B.S, Yale, 50; Du Pont fel, Indiana, 53-54, Ph.D, 54. Mem. inst. nuclear studies, Chicago, 54-56; Aeronaut. Res. Lab, Ohio, 56-58; asst. prof. CHEM, BRANDEIS UNIV, 58-60, assoc. prof, 60-67, PROF, 67-, CO-CHMN. DEPT, 71- U.S.N.R, 44-46. Paramagnetic resonance; optical spectra of 4d and 5d transition metal ions; solid state. Address: Dept. of Chemistry, Brandeis University, Waltham, MA 02154.

DORAN, D(AVID) J(AMES), b. Bemidji, Minn, Mar. 23, 23; m. 50. PARASITOLOGY. B.A, California, Los Angeles, 48, M.A, 49, Ph.D.(parasitol, protozool), 52. Instr. biol, exten. div, California, Los Angeles, 50-52; PARASITOLOGIST, ANIMAL DISEASE & PARASITE RES. DIV, AGR. RES. SERV, U.S. DEPT. AGR, 52- Infantry, U.S.A, 43-46. Am. Soc. Parasitol; Soc. Protozool; Tissue Cult. Asn; Am. Soc. Zool. Protozoan diseases of domesticated animals; tissue culture. Address: National Animal Parasite Lab, Veterinary Science Research Division, Agricultural Research Center, Beltsville, MD 20705.

DORAN, DONALD GEORGE, b. Los Angeles, Calif, Oct. 2, 29; m. 50; c. 4. PHYSICS. B.S, Washington State, 51, M.S, 55, Ph.D.(physics), 60. Eng. asst, Hanford Works Div, Gen. Elec. Co, 51-53; aeronaut. res. scientist, Ames Aeronaut. Lab, Nat. Adv. Cmt. Aeronaut, 55; physicist, Poulter Res. Labs, Stanford Res. Inst, 55-58, 60-62, sr. physicist, 62-64, head solid state group, 64-65, dir. shock wave physics div, 65-67; res. assoc. mat. res. sect, Pac. Northwest Lab, Battelle Mem. Inst, 67-70; RES. ASSOC, MAT. TECHNOL. DEPT, WADCO CORP, 70- Am. Phys. Soc; Am. Nuclear Soc. Materials behavior in fast nuclear reactors; computer modeling of radiation effects in solids; shock waves in solids. Address: 1853 Mahan Court, Richland, WA 99352.

DORAN, THOMAS J, JR, b. Brooklyn, N.Y, Dec. 31, 42; m. 64; c. 3. ORGANIC CHEMISTRY. B.S, Case Inst. Tech, 62; Ph.D.(chem), Western Reserve, 67. SR. RES. CHEMIST, CHEM. DIV, PPG INDUSTS, INC, 66- Am. Chem. Soc. Organic synthesis; nuclear magnetic resonance spectroscopy; natural products chemistry. Address: 496 Parkway Dr, Norton, OH 44203.

DORAN, WILLIAM THOMAS, b. New York, N.Y, July 31, 10; m. 32, 50; c. 4. OCCUPATIONAL MEDICINE, PUBLIC HEALTH. A.B, Dartmouth Col, 30; M.D, Cornell, 34; Nat. Found. Infantile Paralysis fel, Hopkins, 50-51, M.P.H, 51. Intern med. & surg, Bellevue Hosp, New York, 34-36; res. surg, Lawrence Hosp, Bronxville, 36-37; practicing surgeon, 37-42; chief ed, dept. med. & surg, Vet. Admin, 46-50; med. dir. occup. health, soc. security admin, Bur. Old Age & Survivors Ins, 51-56; U.S. Army Engr. Center. & Develop. Labs, 56-62; chief physician oper. health & safety, U.S. Atomic Energy Comn, 62-66, chief occup. med. staff, div. oper. health & safety, 66-71; CHIEF OCCUP. HEALTH & EMPLOYEE HEALTH, ST. ELIZABETHS HOSP, NAT. INST. MENT. HEALTH, DEPT. HEALTH, EDUC. & WELFARE, 71- Lectr, sch. hyg. & pub. health, Hopkins, 52-54. Consult, div. prev. med, Army Surgeon Gen. Off, 50-51. Mem, President's Cmt. Med. Records, Bur. Budget, 47-50; chmn. arrangements, Am. Indust. Health Conf, 64, chmn. prog, 65, mem. long range prog. planning cmt, 64-66. Dipl, Am. Bd. Prev. Med, 59. Med.C, 42-46, Res, 46-50, Lt. Col. Fel. Am. Col. Prev. Med; fel. Indust. Med. Asn; fel. Am. Pub. Health Asn. National medical program planning in fields of medical administration, public health, occupational health, nuclear medicine, medical education and medical care. Address: Employee Health, St. Elizabeths Hospital, 2700 Martin Luther King Ave. S.E, Washington, DC 20032.

DORATO, PETER, b. New York, N.Y, Dec. 17, 32; m. 56; c. 3. ELECTRICAL ENGINEERING. B.E.E, City Col. New York, 55; M.S.E.E, Columbia, 56; Nat. Sci. Found. faculty fel, Polytech. Inst. Brooklyn, 60-61, D.E.E, 61. Instr. ELEC. ENG, City Col. New York, 56-57; ASSOC. PROF, POLYTECH. INST. BROOKLYN, 57- Vis. prof, Univ. Colo, Boulder, 69-70. Soc. Indust. & Electronics Eng; Am. Math. Soc. Control theory; stability; network synthesis. Address: Dept. of Electrical Engineering, Polytechnic Institute of Brooklyn Graduate Center, Rt. 110, Farmingdale, NY 11735.

D'ORAZIO, VINCENT T, b. Joliet, Ill, Dec. 28, 29; m. 54; c. 2. ORGANIC CHEMISTRY. B.S, Illinois, 52; Ph.D.(org. chem), Mich. State, 63. Supv. chemist, U.S. Rubber Co, 52-54; SR. RES. CHEMIST, S.C. JOHNSON & SON, INC, 63- Sig.C, U.S.A, 53-55. AAAS; fel. Am. Inst. Chem; Am. Chem. Soc; Brit. Chem. Soc. Synthesis of optically active tetrazole analogs of amino acids as antimetabolites; synthesis of analogs of pyrethrin—a naturally occurring insecticide. Address: S.C. Johnson & Son, Inc, Racine, WI 53403.

DORCHESTER, JOHN E(DMUND) C(ARLETON), b. Vancouver, B.C, Aug. 18, 17; nat; m. 44; c. 3. PHYSIOLOGY, BIOCHEMISTRY. B.A, British Columbia, 47, M.A, 48; fel, Toronto, 48-49, Ph.D.(physiol, biochem), 52. Asst, Toronto, 49-52; instr. physiol, Jefferson Med. Col, 53-56, asst. prof, 56-60; PROF. SCI, WEST CHESTER STATE COL, 60-, v.chmn, dept, 65-67. R.C.A.F, 40-41, Can. Army, 42-46, Lt. Am. Physiol. Soc. Thermal tolerance in fish; gastrointestinal hormones; hormonal assay methods; gastrointestinal innervation and relation to structure and hormones; effects of tranquilizers on gastrointestinal motility. Address: 301 Westtown Way, West Chester, PA 19380.

DORCHEUS, SAMUEL HOWARD, b. Ashton, Idaho, Mar. 14, 35; m. 60; c. 3. CHEMICAL ENGINEERING. B.S.Ch.E, Idaho, 57; M.S, Lawrence Col, 59, Ph.D.(chem. eng), 62. Sr. proj. engr, Weyerhaeuser Co, 62-63; sr. res. engr, Ecusta Paper Div, Olin Mathieson Chem. Corp, 63-66; RES. ASSOC, CONSOLIDATED PAPERS, INC, 66- Tech. Asn. Pulp & Paper Indust. Functional properties of a variety of paper products; water pollution abatement. Address: Consolidated Papers, Inc, Research & Development Division, P.O. Box 50, Wisconsin Rapids, WI 54494.

DORDICK, HERBERT S(HALOM), b. Phila, Pa, Oct. 20, 25; m. 48; c. 2. ELECTRICAL ENGINEERING, SYSTEMS ANALYSIS. B.S.E.E, Swarthmore Col, 49; M.S.E.E, Pennsylvania, 57. Res. & develop. engr, Leeds & Northrup Co, Pa, 49-54; systs. engr. & mgr. adv. proj, Radio Corp. Am, 54-62; dir. eng, electronic instruments div, Burroughs Corp, 62-64; group leader & sr. mem. res. staff, Rand Corp, 64-68; dep. dir. res. & spec. projs, Syst. Develop. Corp, 68-69; PRES, INFO. TRANSFER CORP, 69- Consult, Rand Corp, Off. Econ. Opportunity, Off. Telecommun. Planning, Dept. of Justice, 61-; contrib. researcher, President's Task Force Telecommun. Policy. U.S.A, 44-46. AAAS; Inst. Elec. & Electronics Eng; Am. Inst. Aeronaut. & Astronaut; Opers. Res. Soc. Am. Mechanization of electronic manufacturing; micro electronics; missile and space vehicle support systems and operations analysis; automatic testing instrumentation; biomedical engineering; corporate and engineering management; continuing education systems and products for the health care industry; audiovisual education and training systems; information systems design. Address: Information Transfer Corp, 1505 Fourth St, Santa Monica, CA 90401.

DORDICK, ISADORE L, b. Riga, Latvia, June 14, 11; nat. GEOGRAPHY. A.B, Pennsylvania, 33, A.M, 37; Ph.D.(geog), Hopkins, 51. Res. assoc, Mt. Sinai Hosp, 38-39; res. & editing, 40-42; librn, Library of Cong, 42-44; biologist, Off. QM Gen, U.S. Dept. War, 44-45; res. analyst, U.S. Dept. State, 45-47; climatologist, Am. Meteorol. Soc, 51-57; consult. bioclimatologist, Sales Prod. Serv, 58-62; CONSULT, AM. METEOROL. SOC, 62- Asn. Am. Geog; Am. Meteorol. Soc. Physiological, agricultural and applied climatology; cultural and economic geography. Address: 900 N. Lake Shore Dr, Apt. 1804, Chicago, IL 60611.

DORE, JACKSON (IRA), b. Ottawa, Ont, Jan. 18, 06; m. 35; c. 2. INORGANIC CHEMISTRY. B.S, Queen's (Can), 30. Asst. ore dressing & metall. div, Dept. Mines, Can, 25-26; chem. engr, fireproofing timber, Forest Prods. Labs, 30-33; chemist, McGill, 34; inspector, sewer explosions cmt, Corp. City of Ottawa, 35; jr. chemist animal nutrit. studies, Ottawa Dept. of Agr, 36; res. off. appl. chem. div, Nat. Res. Coun, 43-55; sr. adv. chemist & asst. chief customs-excise chem. lab, Dept. Nat. Revenue, 55-68, head inorg. sect, 68-71; CONSULT. CHEMIST & CHEM. ENGR, 71- Mem. adv. cmt. pub. utilities sect, Civil Defense Servs, 40-45. Fel. Chem. Inst. Can; Prof. Inst. Pub. Serv. Can; Can. Soc. Chem. Indust. Address: 43 Grosvenor Ave, Ottawa, Ont. K1S 4S1, Can.

DORE, WILLIAM G(EORGE), b. Ottawa, Ont, April 17, 12; m. 42; c. 3. BOTANY. B.A, Queen's(Can), 33; M.Sc, McGill, 35; scholar, Ohio State, 40-41, fel, 42-43, Ph.D.(bot), 48. Asst. agron, Macdonald Col, McGill, 33-35; bot, dept. agr, Ottawa, 35-37; lectr, Dalhousie, 37-43, asst. prof, 43-45; Ont. Agr. Col, 46-47; assoc. botanist, PLANT RES. INST, CAN. DEPT. AGR, OTTAWA, 47-56, SR. BOTANIST, 56- Am. Soc. Plant Taxon; Can. Soc. Agron; Int. Asn. Plant Taxon. Systematic studies of grasses; ecology of grazing lands. Address: Plant Research Institute, Research Branch, Dept. of Agriculture, Ottawa, Ont, Can.

DOREMUS, ROBERT H(EWARD), b. Denver, Colo, Sept. 16, 28; m. 56; c. 4. PHYSICAL CHEMISTRY. B.S, Colorado, 50; fel, Illinois, 50-51, M.S, 51, Firestone Co. fel, 51-53, Ph.D.(phys. chem), 53; Ramsay & Fulbright fel, Cambridge, 53-55, Ph.D.(phys. chem), 56. Phys. chemist, res. lab, Gen. Elec. Co, 55-71; PROF. GLASS & CERAMICS, RENSSELAER POLYTECH. INST, 71- Summer, metallurgist, Los Alamos Sci. Lab, 52, phys. chemist, Gen. Elec. Co, 53. AAAS; Am. Ceramic Soc. Glass science; crystallization from solution; optical properties of metals; diffusion; precipitation in metals; ionic binding to polyelectrolytes. Address: Materials Science Dept, Rensselaer Polytechnic Institute, Troy, NY 12181.

DORENBUSCH, WILLIAM E(DWIN), b. Hamilton, Ohio, Mar. 14, 36; m. 64. NUCLEAR PHYSICS. B.S, Notre Dame, 58, Nat. Sci. Found. summer fel. & Ph.D.(nuclear physics), 62; Woodrow Wilson fel, Wisconsin, 58-59. Instr. PHYSICS, Notre Dame, 62-63; Mass. Inst. Tech, 63-65, asst. prof, 65-69; ASSOC. PROF, WAYNE STATE UNIV, 69- Am. Phys. Soc. Measurement of nuclear reaction Q-values; charged particle spectroscopy with nuclear reactions. Address: Dept. of Physics, Wayne State University, Detroit, MI 48202.

DORENFELD, ADRIAN C, b. Brooklyn, N.Y, Dec. 16, 19; m. 42; c. 3. METALLURGICAL & MINING ENGINEERING. B.S, Columbia, 40, E.M, 41. Operator, Utah Copper Co, 41; metallurgist, U.S. Vanadium Co, 41-42; mill supt, Callahan Zinc-Lead Co, 42; chief metallurgist, Mammoth-St. Anthony Co, 42-43; metallurgist, Combined Metals Co, 43-45; foreman, Phelps Dodge Corp, 45-50; asst. prof. mineral eng, Alabama, 51-52, assoc. prof, 52-54; sr. mineral engr, C.F. Braun & Co, 54-56; gen. mgr. mines, Roberts & Assocs, 56-60; assoc. prof. mineral eng, Univ. Minn, Minneapolis, 60-70; PRES, MINERALS TECH. CORP, 66- Pres. Subsidiary Mex. Minerals & Metals, Mex; consult, Pac. Uranium Inc, 55-60; Israel Mining Industs, 56-; Gen. Mills, Inc, 62- Am. Inst. Mining, Metall. & Petrol. Eng; Can. Inst. Mining & Metall. Examination, management and design of mineral projects; application of statistics to mineral processing; treatment of oxidized ores. Address: 115 Hennepin Ave, Minneapolis, MN 55401.

DORER, FREDERIC E(DMUND), b. Cleveland, Ohio, Aug. 24, 33; m. 61; c. 3. BIOCHEMISTRY. A.B, Western Reserve, 55, M.S, 56; Ph.D.(biochem), State Univ. N.Y, 61. Fel. biochem, sch. med, Wisconsin, 61-63; chemist, radioisotope serv, VET. ADMIN. HOSP, 63-68, RES. CHEMIST, 68-, SR. INSTR. BIOCHEM, HOSP, CASE WEST. RESERVE UNIV, 69- Am. Chem. Soc; The Chem. Soc. Intermediary metabolism; amino acid, peptide, and protein chemistry. Address: Veterans Administration Hospital, 10701 East Blvd, Cleveland, OH 44106.

DORF, ERLING, b. Nysted, Nebr, July 19, 05; m. 34; c. 4. GEOLOGY, PALEOBOTANY. B.S, Chicago, 25, Ph.D.(geol), 30. Asst. instr, Chicago, 25-26; instr. GEOL, PRINCETON, 26-30, asst. prof, 30-40, assoc. prof, 40-46, PROF, 46- CURATOR PALEOBOT, 36- Lectr, Pennsylvania, 38-42; summer lectr, California, 40; curator, Acad. Nat. Sci, Phila, 40-49; prof, Wagner Free Inst, 48- Lectr, Villanova, 61-67; Rutgers, 66-70; Consult, Gulf Oil Co, Venezuela, 40; Life & Time Mag; World Book; U.S. Nat. Mus. Mem. cmn. paleobot, Nat. Res. Coun, 35-46, v.chmn, 41, chmn, 42-46, mem. adv. comt, 46-50. AAAS; Int. Asn. Plant Taxon; Bot. Soc. Am; fel. Geol. Soc. Am; Nat. Asn. Geol. Teachers (Neil Miner Teaching Award, 63); Am.

Geol. Inst; Am. Inst. Biol. Sci; Int. Orgn. Paleobot; Paleobot. Soc. India; Danish Acad. Sci. & Letters; fel. Paleont. Soc.(v.pres, 43). Devonian, Cretaceous and Tertiary paleobotany; Mesozoic stratigraphy; Pliocene floras of California; geologic climates. Address: Dept. of Geology & Geophysical Sciences, Princeton University, Princeton, NJ 08540.

DORF, RICHARD C, b. N.Y.C, Dec. 27, 33; m. 56; c. 2. ELECTRICAL ENGINEERING. B.S.E.E, Clarkson Tech, 55; M.S.E.E, Colorado, 57; Ph.D.(elec. eng), U.S. Naval Postgrad. Sch, 61. Instr. ELEC. ENG, Clarkson Tech, 56-58; res. assoc, New Mexico, 58-59; instr, U.S. Naval Postgrad. Sch, 59-61; lectr, Edinburgh, 61-62; assoc. prof, U.S. Naval Postgrad. Sch, 62-63; assoc. prof, Univ. Santa Clara, 63-67, prof, 67-69, chmn. dept, 63-69; dean col. eng. & technol, OHIO UNIV, 69-, V.PRES. EDUC. SERV, 69- U.S.A.R, 56-63. Inst. Elec. & Electronics Eng; Am. Soc. Eng. Educ. Analysis and design of automatic control systems; design of digital control systems; analysis of biological systems. Address: Cutler Hall, Ohio University, Athens, OH 45701.

DORFF, ERVIN K, b. Biwabik, Minn, June 5, 32; m. 55; c. 3. MATHEMATICS, PHYSICS. B.A, Minnesota, 53; M.S, Lehigh, 55, Ph.D.(math), 59. Asst. math, Lehigh, 53-55, instr, 55-59; asst. prof, Minnesota, Duluth, 59-61; sr. engr, Control Data Corp, 61-65, dept. mgr. systs. anal, 65-66; sr. comput. scientist, COMPUT. COMMUN, INC, 66-68, V.PRES, 68- Asn. Comput. Mach; Am. Math. Soc; Math. Asn. Am. Algebraic and topological systems; symbolic logic; electronic digital computing systems; advanced operating systems; remote terminals; time-sharing; remote conversational consoles. Address: Computer Communications, Inc, 5933 W. Slauson Ave, Culver City, CA 92030.

DORFMAN, A(BRAHAM) L(EO), b. New York, N.Y, Feb. 26, 16; m. 43; c. 2. ORDNANCE ENGINEERING. B.M. E, Cooper Union, 41; Stevens Inst. Tech. Asst. prod. mgr, Masell Mfg. Corp, 35-37; designer machines, Chiplets, Inc, 37-38; mech. engr, exp. lab, Remington Rand, Inc, 38-41; ord. engr, U.S. Army, PICATINNY ARSENAL, U.S. ARMY MUNITIONS COMMAND, 41-52, chief pyrotech. lab, 52-54, chief bomb, warhead, mine & grenade sect, 54-56, eng. res. lab, 56-59, nuclear & adv. systems lab, 59-60, tech. asst. to commanding officer, 60-69, TECH. ASST. TO TECH. DIR, 69- U.S. Army adv, joint air standardization coord. cmt, Working Party on Air Pyrotech, London, 51, mem. Ottawa & London, 52-53; U.S. Army mem, pyrotech. cmt, Mil. Agency for Standardization, NATO, London, 53. Meritorious civilian serv. award, U.S. War Dept, 45; mem. Army-Air Force invest. team, Japan & Korea, 51; res. liaison cmt. Off. Ord. Res, 56-59. Indust. Adv. Bd, Col. Sci. & Eng, Fairleigh Dickinson, 64- AAAS; Am. Ord. Asn. Development and engineering of conventional, special and nuclear munitions; physical and engineering sciences and technology associated with ordnance weaponry; research, development and engineering management and administration. Address: Picatinny Arsenal, U.S. Army, Dover, NJ 07801.

DORFMAN, ALBERT, b. Chicago, Ill, July 6, 16; m. 40; c. 2. BIOCHEMISTRY. B.S, Chicago, 36, Ph.D.(biochem), 39, M.D, 44. Asst. biochem, UNIV. CHICAGO, 37-40, res. assoc, 40-43, instr. pediat, SCH. MED, 48, asst. prof, 48-53, assoc. prof, 53-57, prof, 57-64, pediat. & biochem, 64-65, RICHARD T. CRANE DISTINGUISHED SERV. PROF. PEDIAT, 65-, CHMN. DEPT, 62-; DIR. JOSEPH P. KENNEDY, JR. MENT. RETARDATION RES. CTR, 65- Dir. La Rabida-Univ. Chicago Inst, 57-69. With Off. Sci. Res. & Develop, 44; chief biochem, U.S. Army Med. Dept. Res. & Grad. Sch, 46-48; dir. res, La Rabida Jackson Park Sanitarium, 50-; mem. coun. rheumatic fever, Am. Heart Asn; mem. Comt. Genetics. Mead Johnson Award, 57; Borden Award, 70. U.S.A, 43-46. Am. Chem. Soc; Soc. Exp. Biol. & Med; Am. Soc. Biol. Chem; Am. Pediat. Soc; Am. Acad. Arts & Sci. Bacterial nutrition and metabolism; respiratory enzymes; mechanism of drug action; chemistry of connective tissue; growth factors for dysentery bacilli; rheumatic fever. Address: Dept. of Pediatrics, University of Chicago, 920 E. 59th St, Chicago, IL 60637.

DORFMAN, BEN-ZION, b. New York, N.Y, Sept. 3, 23; m. 45; c. 2. GENETICS. B.A, Brooklyn Col, 60; univ. fel, Yale, 60-61, M.A, 61, Nat. Sci. Found. fel, 61-62, Nat. Insts. Health fel, 62-64, Ph.D.(genetics), 64. Fel. GENETICS, Washington (Seattle), 64-65; ASST. PROF, ALBERT EINSTEIN COL. MED, 65- U.S.A, 43-46. AAAS; Am. Soc. Microbiol. Genetics and biochemistry of purine biosynthesis in yeast; complementation and fine structure at specific loci. Address: Albert Einstein College of Medicine, Yeshiva University, Eastchester Rd, & Morris Park Ave, Bronx, NY 10461.

DORFMAN, DONALD, b. Bronx, N.Y, Mar. 5, 34; m. 54; c. 4. FRESH WATER & MARINE BIOLOGY. B.S, Monmouth Col. N.J, 66; M.S, Univ. Conn, 68; Ph.D.(environ. sci), Rutgers Univ, 70. Res. asst. fisheries, Univ. Conn, 66-68; environ. sci, Rutgers Univ, 68-70; ASST. PROF. BIOL, MONMOUTH COL.(N.J), 70- Am. Fisheries Soc. Effect of lead on growth of brook trout; responses of anadromous fishes to increased temperature and decreased oxygen concentration; fish scrum proteins. Address: Dept. of Biology, Monmouth College, West Long Branch, NJ 07764.

DORFMAN, EDWIN, b. Phila, Pa, Sept. 18, 21; m. 48; c. 2. ORGANIC & POLYMER CHEMISTRY. B.S, Pa. State, 44; Ph.D.(chem), Columbia, 53. Chemist, HOOKER CHEM. CORP, 53-64, SR. CHEMIST, 64- U.S.N, 44-46. Am. Chem. Soc. Fluoro-carbon, organo-silicon and chlorocarbon chemistry; herbicides; organic reaction mechanisms; fire retardant polymers. Address: 2515 Stony Point Rd, Grand Island, NY 14072.

DORFMAN, HOWARD DAVID, b. N.Y.C, July 20, 28; m. 52; c. 3. PATHOLOGY. B.A, N.Y. Univ, 47; M.D, State Univ. N.Y, 51. Intern, Maimonides Hosp. Brooklyn, 51-52; resident path. & microbiol, Mt. Sinai Hosp, N.Y.C, 52-54; surg. path, Columbia Presby. Med. Ctr, 54-58; pathologist & dir. labs, Sharon & New Milford Hosps, Conn, 58-59; asst. pathologist, Sinai Hosp. Baltimore, 59-61, assoc. pathologist, 62-64; DIR. LABS. & PATHOLOGIST, HOSP. JOINT DISEASES & MED. CTR, 64-; PROF. CLIN. PATH, MT. SINAI SCH. MED, 68-, assoc. prof, 67-68. Asst. surgery, col. physicians & surgeons, Columbia Univ, 57-58, asst. prof, 65-67; med. sch, Johns Hopkins Univ, 63-64; staff pathologist, Johns Hopkins Hosp, 63-64. Med.C, U.S.A, 54-56, Capt. Fel. Col. Am. Path; fel. N.Y. Acad. Med; Int. Acad. Path; fel. Am. Soc. Clin. Path; Am. Med. Asn. Pathology of bone tumors

and joint diseases with particular reference to rheumatoid arthritis, neoplasms, secondary to pre-existing bone disease, osteoblastic tumors and vascular tumors of the bone. Address: Hospital for Joint Diseases & Medical Center, 1919 Madison Ave, New York, NY 10035.

DORFMAN, J(AY) ROBERT, b. Pittsburgh, Pa, May 20, 37; m. 60; c. 3. THEORETICAL PHYSICS, STATISTICAL MECHANICS. B.A, Hopkins, 54, Ph.D.(physics), 61. Res. assoc. PHYSICS, Rockefeller Inst, 61-64; asst. prof, DEPT. PHYSICS & ASTRON. & INST. FLUID DYNAMICS & APPL. MATH, UNIV. MD, COLLEGE PARK, 64-67, ASSOC. PROF, 67- Vis. assoc. prof, Rockefeller Univ, 69-70. Am. Phys. Soc. Kinetic theory; theory of transport processes. Address: Dept. of Physics & Astronomy, University of Maryland, College Park, MD 20742.

DORFMAN, LEON M(ONTE), b. Winnipeg, Man, Can, June 9, 22; nat; m. 48; c. 3. PHYSICAL CHEMISTRY. B.Sc, Manitoba, 44; Nat. Res. Coun. Can scholar, Toronto, 44-46, M.A, 45, Ph.D.(chem), 47. Fel, Rochester, 47-48, instr. chem, 48-50; res. assoc, Knolls Atomic Power Lab, Gen. Elec. Co, 50-55, res. lab, 55-57; sr. chemist, Argonne Nat. Lab, 57-64; PROF. CHEM, OHIO STATE UNIV, 64-, CHMN. DEPT, 68- Consult, Argonne Nat. Lab, 64-65; Gen. Dynamics Corp, 64-67; prof, Univ. Toronto, 67; vis. res. prof, Hebrew Univ. Jerusalem, 69; Guggenheim fel, 71-72; vis. scientist, Royal Inst. London, 71-72. Am. Chem. Soc; Am. Phys. Soc; Radiation Res. Soc. Radiation chemistry; photochemistry; fast reaction; spectroscopy of transient species. Address: Dept. of Chemistry, Ohio State University, 140 W. 18th Ave, Columbus, OH 43210.

DORFMAN, RALPH I(SADORE), b. Chicago, Ill, June 30, 11; m. 33; c. 2. BIOCHEMISTRY. B.S, Univ. Ill, 32; Ph.D.(physiol. chem, pharmacol), Univ. Chicago, 34. Asst. physiol. chem, Chicago, 33-35; instr. pharmacol, sch. med, La. State, 35-36; physiol. chem, Yale, 36-39, asst. prof, 39-41; biochem, Western Reserve & chemist, Brush Found, 41-49, assoc. prof, 49-51; assoc. dir, Worcester Found. Exp. Biol, 51-56, dir, 56-64; SR. V.PRES. SYNTEX RES. DIV, 64-, dir. inst. hormone biol, 64-69. Res. prof, Boston Univ, 51-67; prof, Clark Univ, 56-64; vis. prof, sch. med, Stanford Univ, 67- Consult. adv. panel metab. biol, div. biol. & med. sci, Nat. Sci. Found; sub-chmn. cmt. standardization of androgens, U.S. Pharmacopoeia; mem. endocrinol. panel, Cancer Chemother. Nat. Serv. Center, U.S. Pub. Health. Serv, chmn, subcmt. biol. activity, endocrinol panel; mem. sci. adv. cmt, Nat. Better Bus. Bur, Inc; exec. & prog. cmts, 2nd Int. Cong. Endocrinol. Distinguished serv. award, med. alumni, Univ. Chicago, 67. With Off. Sci. Res. & Develop; U.S.P.H.S. Fel. AAAS; fel. Am. Acad. Arts & Sci; Am. Chem. Soc; Soc. Exp. Biol. & Med; Endocrine Soc; Am. Soc. Biol. Chem; Am. Statist. Asn; Am. Asn. Cancer Res; fel. N.Y. Acad. Sci; hon. mem. Arg. Soc. Endocrinol. & Nutrit; Danish Soc. Endocrinol; Pan-Am. Med. Asn; Mex. Endocrine Soc; hon. fel. Chilean Med. Asn; affiliate mem. Royal Soc. Med; hon. fel. Port. Endocrinol. Soc; for. cor. mem. Fr. Soc. Endocrinol; Int. Soc. Res. Reproduction; hon. mem. Mex. Nat. Acad. Med; hon. mem. Peruvian Endocrine Soc. Steroid biochemistry; bioassay; endocrinology; reproductive physiology. Address: Syntex Research Division, Stanford Industrial Park, Palo Alto, CA 94304.

DORFMAN, S(TEVEN) D(AVID), b. Brooklyn, N.Y, Sept. 26, 35; div; c. 1. ELECTRICAL ENGINEERING. B.S.E.E, Florida, 57; Howard Hughes fel, Southern California, 57-59, M.S.E.E, 59. Mem. tech. staff, HUGHES AIRCRAFT CO, 57-61, staff engr, 62, sect. head, 62-64, proj. mgr, 65-67, mgr. earth observation systs, advan. proj. labs, space systs. div, 67-69, MGR. ADVAN. PROG, SPACE & COMMUN. GROUP, NASA PROG. DIV, 69- Management of technical projects; systems design analysis and engineering; infrared sensing systems. Address: NASA Programs Division, Hughes Aircraft Co, El Segundo, CA 90245.

DORGAN, W(ILLIAM) E, b. Chicago, Ill, Oct. 27, 14; m. 51; c. 1. MATHEMATICS. B.Ed, Ill. State Norm. Univ, 42; M.S, Iowa, 51. Instr. high sch, Ill, 45-47; asst. MATH, Iowa, 48-51; asst. prof, WEST. STATE COL. COLO, 51-59, assoc. prof, 59-66, PROF, 66- Math. Asn. Am. Application of mathematic computers. Address: 9 Dorchester, Gunnison, CO 81230.

DORGAN, WILLIAM J(OSEPH), b. Davenport, Iowa, Dec. 27, 38; m. 65; c. 2. DEVELOPMENTAL & CELL BIOLOGY. B.A, St. Ambrose Col, 61; M.S, Creighton Univ, 63; Nat. Sci. Found. fel, Wash. Univ, 64-65; univ. fel, Univ. Colo, 65-66, Nat. Insts. Health fel, 66-68, Ph.D.(anat), 68. ASST. PROF. ZOOL, MONT. STATE UNIV, 68- AAAS; Soc. Develop. Biol. Programmed death in embryonic development and abnormal development; programmed death in rat placental giant cells in vitro studies on the photodynamic action of vital dyes in embryonic systems. Address: Dept. of Zoology, Montana State University, Bozeman, MT 59715.

DORI, ZVI, b. Haifa, Israel, Oct. 21, 34; U.S. citizen; m. 61; c. 3. INORGANIC CHEMISTRY. B.S, Columbia, 64, M.S, 65, Ph.D.(chem), 67. Asst. prof. chem, Temple Univ, 67-69, assoc. prof, 69-70; MEM. CHEM. STAFF, ISRAEL INST. TECHNOL, 70- Am. Chem. Soc. Photochemistry of coordination compounds; molecular and electronic structure of transition metal complexes. Address: Dept. of Chemistry, Israel Institute of Technology, Technion City, Haifa, Israel.

DORINSON, AMOS, b. Sioux City, Iowa, May 22, 13; m. 40; c. 1. INORGANIC CHEMISTRY. S.B, Chicago, 37, Ph.D.(chem), 46. Res. chemist, Pittsburgh Plate Glass Co, 38-40; Armour Labs, 40-48; sect. leader FUNDAMENTALS LUBRICATION, SINCLAIR RES, INC, ATLANTIC RICHFIELD CO, 51-69, RES. ASSOC, 69- AAAS; Am. Soc. Lubrication Eng. Lubrication theory; metal cutting and cutting fluids; fatty acids and derivatives. Address: 1746 Idlewild Lane, Homewood, IL 60430.

DORION, GEORGE H(ENRY), b. N.Y.C, Apr. 16, 29; m. 57; c. 4. ORGANIC CHEMISTRY. M.A, Williams Col, 53; Ph.D.(chem), Yale, 58. Scientist, Wright Air Develop, Center, 53-55; asst, Yale, 57-58; res. chemist, Am. Cyanamid Co, 58-62, sr. res. chemist, 62, group leader, 62-69; pres, Environ. Resources, Inc, 69-70; DIR. ADVAN. PROJ, BACARDI CORP, 70- U.S.A.F, 53-55, Res, 55- Am. Chem. Soc; Chem. Soc. London. Photochemistry; organic reaction mechanisms; monomer-polymer studies. Address: Bacardi Corp, P.O. Box 26368, Jacksonville, FL 32218.

DORITY, GUY HIRAM, b. Canandaigua, N.Y, Jan. 2, 33. ORGANIC CHEMISTRY. B.S, Oglethorpe, 54; M.A, North Carolina, 59; Ph.D.(chem), Hawaii, 65. Instr. CHEM, UNIV. HAWAII, HILO, 63-65, asst. prof, 65-71, ASSOC. PROF, 71- Summer instr, Oglethorpe Col, 56 & Campbell Col, 59; vis. scientist, Nat. Biol. Inst, Indonesia, 70-71; leader, training course natural prod. chem, S.E. Asian Ministries of Educ. Orgn. AAAS; Am. Chem. Soc. Aromatic and heterocyclic fluorine compounds; natural products from Polynesian and southeast Asian medicinal plants. Address: Dept. of Chemistry, University of Hawaii, Hilo, Hawaii 96720.

DORKO, ERNEST A, b. Detroit, Mich, Sept. 16, 36. ORGANIC & PHYSICAL CHEMISTRY. B.Ch.E, Detroit, 59; M.S, Chicago, 61, Ph.D.(org. chem), 64. Res. chemist, phys. sci. lab, U.S. Army Missile Command, Redstone Arsenal, Ala, 64-67; asst. prof. CHEM, AIR FORCE INST. TECHNOL, 67-70, ASSOC. PROF, 70- Consult, aerospace res. lab, Wright-Patterson Air Force Base, 68- U.S.A, 64-66, Capt. AAAS; Am. Chem. Soc. Synthesis of small ring organic compounds; infrared and normal coordinate analysis; electron diffraction analysis; shock-tube kinetics of small-ring isomerizations; kinetics of reactions occuring in solid-state organic compounds. Address: AFIT/ENM, Air Force Institute of Technology, Wright-Patterson Air Force Base, OH 45433.

DORLAND, RODGER M(ALONE), b. Wellington, Ont, July 13, 13; m. 39; c. 2. WOOD CHEMISTRY. B.A, Western Ontario, 35; Ph.D.(chem), McGill, 39. Res. chemist, Masonite Corp, Miss, 40-43, asst. dir. res, 43-47; DIR. RES, ABITIBI POWER & PAPER CO, LTD, 47-62, DIR. TECH. DEVELOP, 63- Dir, Tech. Asn. Pulp & Paper Indust; pres, Sheridan Park Res. Asn; chmn, Can. Res. Mgt. Asn. Pulp, paper, hardboard, particle board, pollution abatement. Address: 11 Harrison Rd, Willowdale, Ont, Can.

DORMAAR, JOHAN F(REDERIK), b. Djakarta, Indonesia, Feb. 16, 30; Can. citizen; m. 55; c. 3. SOIL CHEMISTRY. B.S.A, Univ. Toronto, 57, M.S.A, 58; Ph.D.(soil chem), Univ. Alta, 61; Ctr. Pedology, Nancy, France, 68-69. Asst. soil chem, Univ. Alta, 58-61, lectr, 61-62; RES. SCIENTIST, AGR. RES. STA, CAN. DEPT. AGR, 62- Netherlands Army, 53. Soil Sci. Soc. Am; Agr. Inst. Can; Can. Soc. Soil Sci; Int. Asn. Quaternary Res; Int. Soc. Soil Sci; Fr. Asn. Study Soil. Organic matter of chernozemic soils, formation and present properties as influenced by parent material and transformation or change towards organic matter of podzolic soils; lignin chemistry as related to soil organic matter; palaeosols; soil organic chemistry. Address: Soil Science Section, Canada Agriculture Research Station, Lethbridge, Alta, Can.

DORMAN, GERALD, b. U.S.A, Jan. 10, 34; m. 68. THEORETICAL PHYSICS. B.S, Brooklyn Col, 57; Ph.D.(physics), N.Y. Univ, 63. Instr. PHYSICS, Pratt Inst, 59-61; Cooper Union, 61-62; math. physicist, Stanford Res. Inst, 63-64; asst. prof, Polytech. Inst. Brooklyn, 64-69, assoc. prof, 69-71; mgr. regional educ, data processing div, RCA Corp, 69-71; DIR. COMPUT. CTR, TEACHERS COL, COLUMBIA UNIV, 71- Consult, Stanford Res. Inst, 64- Am. Phys. Soc. Electromagnetic and weak interactions of elementary particles; interaction of relativistic electron beams with plasmas; resonance oscillations and landau damping in inhomogeneous plasmas; computer science education. Address: Computer Center, Teachers College, 525 W. 120th St, New York, NY 10027.

DORMAN, HENRY JAMES, b. Chicago, Ill, Mar. 21, 28; m. 57; c. 2. GEOPHYSICS. B.A, Carleton Col, 49; M.S, Northwestern, 51; Stanolind fel, Columbia, 52-54, Union Carbide fel, 56-57, Ph.D.(geophys), 61. Res. asst. geophys, LAMONT-DOHERTY GEOL. OBSERV, COLUMBIA UNIV, 57-60, res. scientist, 60-63, sr. res. scientist, 63-64, sr. res. assoc, 64-65, ASST. DIR, 65- Mem. solid earth panel, geophys. res. bd, Nat. Acad. Sci, 61-64; vis. lectr, Univ. Wis, 63. U.S.A, 54-56. Seismol. Soc. Am; Am. Geophys. Union; Geol. Soc. Am. Long-period seismic waves; upper mantle of the earth; oceanic and continental crust; theory of seismic wave propagation; computer applications. Address: Lamont-Doherty Geological Observatory, Columbia University, Palisades, NY 10964.

DORMAN, HOMER L(EE), b. Denton, Tex, Sept, 23, 30; m. 54; c. 4. PHYSIOLOGY. B.A, North Texas State, 50, fel, 50-51, M.A, 51; Ph.D. Illinois, 57. Asst. prof. & res. assoc. PHYSIOL, COL. DENT, BAYLOR UNIV, 57-64, PROF, 64-, CHMN. DEPT, 70- Am. Physiol. Soc; Int. Asn. Dent. Res. Cardiovascular physiology; blood supply to oral tissue as related to metabolism; oral tissue edema; C-AMP in gingiva. Address: Physiology Dept, College of Dentistry, Baylor University, 800 Hall St, Dallas, TX 75226.

DORMAN, KEITH WILLIAM, b. Perry, Iowa, Feb. 9, 10; m. 37; c. 3. FORESTRY. B.S, Iowa State Col, 34; California, 37-38. Asst. ranger, Ottawa Nat. Forest, U.S. FOREST SERV, 34-37, jr. forester, lake states forest exp. sta, 39, south. forest exp. sta, 40-47, forester & asst. to chief div. forest mgt, SOUTHEAST. FOREST EXP. STA, 47-53, leader, Hitchiti Res. Center, 53-54, ASST. CHIEF DIV. FOREST MGT. RES, 55- AAAS; Soc. Am. Foresters. Forest genetics; forest tree planting. Address: Southeastern Forest Experiment Station, Post Office Bldg, Asheville, NC 28802.

DORMAN, LEROY MYRON, b. Virginia, Minn, Oct. 15, 38; m. 59; c. 3. GEOPHYSICS. B.S, Ga. Inst. Tech, 60; M.S, Wisconsin, 69, Ph.D.(geophys), 70. Asst. res. physicist, Ga. Inst. Tech, 63-66; res. asst. GEOPHYS, Wisconsin, 66-69; Carnegie fel, Carnegie Inst, 69-71; RES. GEOPHYSICIST, ATLANTIC OCEANOG. & METEOROL. LAB, NAT. OCEANOG. & ATMOSPHERIC AGENCY, 71- U.S.N, 60-63, Lt. Am. Geophys. Union; Seismol. Soc. Am; Soc. Explor. Geophys. Theoretical and experimental seismology; isostasy; exploration geophysics. Address: Atlantic Oceanographic & Meteorological Lab, 901 S. Miami Ave, Miami, FL 33130.

DORMAN, LINNEAUS CUTHBERT, b. Orangeburg, S.C, June 28, 35; m. 58; c. 2. ORGANIC CHEMISTRY. B.S, Bradley, 56; Dow Chem. Co. fel, Indiana, 59-60, Ph.D.(org. chem), 61. Res. chemist, DOW CHEM. CO, 60-62, EDGAR C. BRITTON RES. LAB, 62-68, SR. RES. CHEMIST, 68- AAAS; Am. Chem. Soc; Sci. Res. Soc. Am. Organic synthesis; pharmaceutical chemistry; synthesis of heterocyclic compounds; peptide synthesis. Address: Chemical Biology Research, Bldg. 438, Dow Chemical Co, Midland, MI 48640.

DORMAN, STEPHEN CHARLES, b. San Bernardino, Calif, May 19, 10; m. 36; c. 3. BIOCHEMISTRY. B.S, Calif. Inst. Tech, 31; Ph.D.(entom), California, 37. Lab. asst, citrus exp. sta, California, 31-33; sr. res. chemist, Shell Oil Co, 34-43; Shell Develop. Co, 44-47, sr. entomologist, Shell Oil Co, 47-52; ASST. TO DIR, AGR. RES. LAB, STAUFFER CHEM. CO, 52- Am. Chem. Soc; Entom. Soc. Am. Insect toxicology; blowfly repellents. Address: Stauffer Chemical Co, P.O. Box 760, Mountain View, CA 94040.

DORMANT, LEON M, b. Paris, France, Oct. 1, 40; U.S. citizen. PHYSICAL CHEMISTRY. B.S, Drexel Inst, 64; Stauffer fel, Southern California, 65, NASA fel, 66, Ph.D.(phys. chem), 69. SR. SCIENTIST, chem. div, 3M Co, 68-70; AEROSPACE CORP, 71- Unilever fel, Bristol Univ, 70-71. Am. Chem. Soc. Surface and colloid chemistry; lubrication; environmental pollution. Address: Aerospace Corp, Bldg. 120, Station 2117, P.O. Box 95085, Los Angeles, CA 90045.

DORMINEY, ROBERT WINSTON, b. Douglas, Ga, Jan. 19, 43; m. 64; c. 2. POULTRY PHYSIOLOGY. B.S, Florida, 64, M.S, 65; Ph.D.(physiol), Auburn, 68. ASST. PROF. POULTRY SCI, ORE. STATE UNIV, 68- Poultry Sci. Asn. Poultry environmental physiology and endocrinology, particularly as related to heat stress. Address: Dept. of Poultry Science, Oregon State University, Corvallis, OR 97331.

DORN, C(HARLES) RICHARD, b. London, Ohio, June 12, 33; m. 64; c. 3. VETERINARY PUBLIC HEALTH, EPIDEMIOLOGY. D.V.M, Ohio State, 57; M.P.H, Harvard, 62; California, Berkeley, 62-63. Staff vet, Stark Animal Hosp, Canton, Ohio, 57-58; vet. inspector, Cincinnati Health Dept, 60-61; U.S. Pub. Health Serv. trainee, 61-62; res. specialist cancer, Calif. State Dept. Pub. Health, 62-68; ASSOC. PROF. VET. MICROBIOL. & COMMUNITY HEALTH & MED. PRACTICE, UNIV. MO-COLUMBIA, 68- Lectr. vet. med, California, Davis, 67-68; consult, Calif. State Dept. Pub. Health, Berkeley, Calif, 68-; mem. exec. bd, Mo. Pub. Health Asn. Dipl, Am. Bd. Vet. Pub. Health. U.S.A.F, 58-60, Maj. Am. Vet. Med. Asn; fel. Am. Pub. Health Asn; Conf. Pub. Health Vets; Asn. Teachers Prev. Med. Cancer morbidity in dogs, cats, and man; temporal and spatial distribution of leukemia and other malignancies; heavy metal contamination of foods; epidemiology of salmonellosis and other zoonoses; interrelationship of animal and human behavior. Address: Dept. of Veterinary Microbiology, University of Missouri-Columbia, Columbia, MO 65201.

DORN, CONRAD PETER, JR, b. Baltimore, Md, Jan. 15, 37; m. 60; c. 3. PHARMACEUTICAL CHEMISTRY. B.S, Maryland, 58, Found. Pharmaceut. Ed. fel, 59-60, Nat. Sci. Found. fel, 60-61, M.S, 61, U.S. Pub. Health Serv. fel, 61-62, Ph.D.(pharmaceut. chem), 63; Yale, 58-59. RES. FEL, MERCK, SHARP & DOHME RES. LABS, MERCK & CO, 62- Synthesis of heterocyclic steroids and non-steroid anti-inflammatory agents. Address: 972 Fernwood Ave, Plainfield, NJ 07062.

DORN, DAVID W, b. Detroit, Mich, June 25, 30; m. 54; c. 4. PHYSICS. B.S, Purdue, 52, univ. res. found. fel. & Ph.D.(physics), 59. Res. physicist, LAWRENCE LIVERMORE LAB, 59-60, group leader physicist, 60-69, STAFF ASST. TO ASSOC. DIR. NUCLEAR DESIGN, 69- U.S.N, 52-55, Lt. Am. Phys. Soc. Symmetry studies in j-j coupling; astrophysics; fission processes; superheavy nuclei; nuclear device design to accomplish extreme neutron irradiations. Address: Lawrence Livermore Lab, P.O. Box 808, University of California, Livermore, CA 94550.

DORN, GORDON L, b. Chicago, Ill, June 8, 37; m. 59; c. 1. GENETICS. B.S, Purdue, 58, M.S, 60, Ph.D.(genetics), 61. Nat. Sci. Found. fel, 61-63; univ. res. fel. genetics, Albert Einstein Col. Med, 63, asst. prof, 64-68; chmn. dept. microbiol, Baylor Univ, 68-69; CHMN. DEPT. MICROBIOL. & DIR. CLIN. MICROBIOL. LABS, WADLEY INST. MOLECULAR MED, 69- AAAS; Am. Genetic Asn; Genetics Soc. Am. Phosphatases-esterases; gene-enzymes; fine genetic analysis; fermentation and antibiotics; microbiology. Address: Dept. of Microbiology, Wadley Institute of Molecular Medicine, 9000 Harry Hines Blvd, Dallas, TX 75235.

DORN, HERMAN WILLIAM, b. N.Y.C, Sept. 14, 11; m. 34; c. 4. ORGANIC & BIOLOGICAL CHEMISTRY. B.A, Clark Univ, 35, scholar, 35-36, M.A, 36, fel, 36-38, Ph.D.(org. chem), 38. Instr. chem. & physics, schs, Mass, 38-39; res. chemist & chem. prod. supt, Amino Prods. Co, 39-42; sr. res. chemist, Int. Minerals & Chem. Corp, 42-45; supvr. dept. nutrit. & biochem, Owens-Ill. Glass Co, Ohio, 45-48; dir. res, Irwin, Neisler Co, 48-51; dep. dir. res, U.S. Army Chem. Res. & Develop. Labs, 59-67; chief nuclear biol. & chem. div, Third U.S. Army, 67-70; CONSULT, DORN & CO, 51- Res. assoc. & Int. Mineral & Chem. Corp. fel. biochem. eng, Univ. Iowa, 43-44; lectr, Univ. Toledo, 45. Pres. & dir. res. Frozen Food Inst, N.Y, 46-56; pres, Mills Pharmaceut, Inc, Mo, 62-71; Physicians' Med. Lab, Inc, 62-71; Glencoe Res, Inc, 62-71. Assoc. ed, Food Tech. Chem.C, 42-45, Res, 45-, Col. Fel. AAAS; Am. Chem. Soc; Inst. Food Tech; Nat. Soc. Prof. Eng; Soc. Am. Mil. Eng; fel. Am. Inst. Chem; fel. N.Y. Acad. Sci; Am. Inst. Biol. Sci. Specializing in food technology and pharmaceuticals; food freezing, canning, harvesting, storage, and deterioration; clinical chemistry; synthesis of anti-asthmatics, cardioactive compounds, antipasmodics, curaremimetics, blood depressors, quaternaries, steroids, vitamins, cinchonoids, adrenergics, cholinergics, botanicals, amino acids, and proteins; biochemical engineering, research and development production management; pharamceutical manufacturing and formulations. Address: Dorn & Co, 7 Sona Lane, St. Louis, MO 63141.

DORN, WILLIAM S, b. Pittsburgh, Pa, July 12, 28; m. 52; c. 3. MATHEMATICS. B.S, Carnegie Inst. Tech, 51, Ph.D.(math), 55. Mgr. mech. & eng. syst. comput, Gen. Elec. Co, 55-57; res. scientist, N.Y. Univ, 57-59; mathematician, IBM Corp, 59-65, mgr. comput. ctr, 65-67, asst. dir. math. sci, 67-68; PROF. MATH. & DIR. COMPUT. EDUC, UNIV. DENVER, 68- U.S.A, 46-47, 52-53. AAAS; Asn. Comput. Mach.(ed-in-chief, Comput. Surveys, 68-); Soc. Indust. & Appl. Math.(secy, 64); Math. Asn. Am. Educational technology; digital computers and their application; numerical analysis; linear and non-linear programming; computer-assisted instruction. Address: Dept. of Mathematics, University of Denver, Denver, CO 80210.

DORNBUSCH, WILLIAM KETTE, JR, b. Vicksburg, Miss, July 14, 28; m. 54; c. 1. GEOMORPHOLOGY. B.S, Miss. State, 51. Logging engr. supvr,

Hycalog, Inc, La, 51-56; RES. GEOLOGIST, U.S. ARMY ENGR. WATERWAYS EXP. STA, 56- Dept. of Army Off. Commendation, 68. U.S.A, 46-47, Sgt. Geol. Soc. Am; Am. Soc. Photogram. Remote imagery interpretation; quantitative geomorphological studies in world environments; mobility studies involving description of terrain in terms amenable to vehicle performance; application of remote sensing systems to geologic and engineering soil studies. Address: U.S. Army Engineer Waterways Experiment Station, P.O. Box 631, Vicksburg, MS 39180.

DORNE, ARTHUR, b. Philadelphia, Pa, Apr. 6, 17; m. 39; c. 1. ENGINEERING. B.A, Pennsylvania, 38, B.S, 39. Radio engr, Glenn D. Gillett, consult. radio engr, Wash, D.C, 40-42; engr, Fed. Tel. & Tel. N.J, 42-43; antenna group leader & res. assoc, radio res. lab, Harvard, 43-45; supvr. engr. antenna group, Airborne Inst. Lab, N.Y, 45-47; PRES, Dorne & Margolin, Inc, 47-69; Granger Asn, 69-70; DORNE CONSULT, 71- Civilian with Off. Sci. Res. & Develop, 44. AAAS; fel. Inst. Elec & Electronics Eng; Mineral. Soc. Am. Telecommunications; radio navigation; antennas. Address: Dorne Consulting, P.O. Box 624, Setauket, NY 11733.

DORNER, ROBERT W(ILHELM), b. Bern, Switzerland, Oct. 22, 24; nat; m. 54; c. 2. BIOCHEMISTRY. Dipl, Lausanne, 48; Ph.D.(biochem), California, 53. Asst. biochem, California, 49-51, virus lab, 51-53; res. assoc. zool, Southern California, 53-54; jr. res. botanist, California, Los Angeles, 55-56, asst. res. botanist, 56-57; asst. insect toxicol. entom, citrus exp. sta, Riverside, 57-62, ASST. PROF. BIOCHEM, SCH. MED, ST. LOUIS UNIV, 62- Spec. investr, Arthritis Found, 64-67. AAAS; Am. Chem. Soc; Am. Rheumatism Asn. Biochemistry of connective tissues and their diseases. Address: Section of Arthritis, School of Medicine, St. Louis University, St. Louis, MO 63104.

DORNETTE, WILLIAM H(ENRY) L(UEDERS), b. Cincinnati, Ohio, June 22, 22; m. 45; c. 2. ANESTHESIOLOGY. B.S, Cincinnati, 44, M.D, 46, J.D, 69. Fel. anesthesiol, med. ctr, Georgetown, 49-51; instr, Wisconsin, 52-54, asst. prof, 54-55; California, Los Angeles, 55-57; prof. & chmn. dept, col. med, Univ. Tenn, Memphis, 58-65; chief anesthesiol, VET. ADMIN. HOSP, Cincinnati, Ohio, 65-71; DIR. EDUC, DIV. ANESTHESIOL, CLEVELAND CLIN, 72- Anesthesiologist-in-chief, John Gaston Hosp; asst. clin. prof, col. med, Univ. Cincinnati, 65-71. Med.C, 47-49, Capt. Am. Soc. Anesthesiol; Am. Med. Asn; fel. Am. Col. Legal Med; Nat. Fire Protection Asn; Int. Anesthesia Res. Soc. Instrumentation in anesthesiology; pathology of anesthetic complications; anatomy related to anesthesia; legal problems related to medicine. Address: Division of Anesthesiology, Cleveland Clinic, 2020 E. 93rd St, Cleveland, OH 44106.

DORNEY, ROBERT S(TARBIRD), b. Milwaukee, Wis, Apr. 1, 28; m. 50; c. 5. PARASITOLOGY B.S, Univ. Wis, 49, M.S, 52, Ph.D, 59; fel, Mont. State Univ, 51. Conserv. biologist, Wis. Conserv. Dept, 49-57; asst. dept. vet. sci, Univ. Wis, 57-58, instr. parasitol, 58-59, asst. prof. biol, biol. exten, 59-62, assoc. prof, 63-64; sci. adv, Pan Am. Union, 64-67; assoc. prof. biol, UNIV. WATERLOO, 67-69, PROF, SCH. URBAN & REGIONAL PLANNING & DEPT. BIOL, 69- Pres, Ecoplans Ltd. Wildlife Soc; Am. Soc. Mammal; Am. Soc. Parasitol; Soc. Protozool; Ecol. Soc. Am. Epizootiology of protozoan and helminth diseases; ecology of game birds and mammals; ecology of human settlements and impact of development activities on temperate ecosystems. Address: School of Urban & Regional Planning, University of Waterloo, Waterloo, Ont, Can.

DORNFELD, CLINTON A(LVIN), b. Winona, Minn, Feb. 17, 18; m. 41; c. 4. CHEMISTRY. B.S, Winona State Teachers Col, 40; fel, State Col. Wash, 40-43, M.S, 43; Allied Chem. & Dye Corp. fel. & Ph.D.(org. chem), Iowa, 46. Asst, Iowa, 43-44, asst. Office Sci. Res. & Develop. contract, 44-46; RES. CHEMIST, G.D. SEARLE & CO, 46- Bartow prize, 46. Am. Chem. Soc. Synthetic organic chemistry; synthesis of drugs; organonitrogen compounds. Address: G.D. Searle & Co, P.O. Box 5110, Chicago, IL 60680.

DORNFELD, ERNST J(OHN), b. Milwaukee, Wis, Apr. 6, 11; m. 45; c. 5. ZOOLOGY. B.S, Marquette, 33; Marquette scholar, Wisconsin, 34-35, A.M, 35, Ph.D.(zool), 37. Asst. zool, Wisconsin, 35-37; instr. histol. & embryol, sch. med, Oklahoma, 37-38; ZOOL, ORE. STATE UNIV, 38-42, asst. prof, 42-45, assoc. prof, 45-50, PROF, 50-, CHMN. DEPT, 52- AAAS; Am. Soc. Zool; Am. Soc. Cell Biol; Am. Soc. Gen. Physiol. Experimental cytology of the adrenal gland; cytology and embryology of the ovary; role of nucleic acids in cell growth and differentiation; cytochemistry; physiology of mitosis; comparative vertebrate histology. Address: Dept. of Zoology, Oregon State University, Corvallis, OR 97331.

DORNFEST, BURTON S, b. New York, N.Y, Oct. 31, 30; m. 54; c. 2. HEMATOLOGY, ANATOMY. B.A, N.Y. Univ, 52, M.S, 54, Ph.D.(physiol), 60; fel, Nat. Insts. Health, Nat. Heart Inst, 58-60. Mem. staff biostatistics, Mem. Hosp. Cancer & Allied Diseases, New York, 52-53; asst. biol, N.Y. Univ, 53-54, 56-58, instr. gen. sci, 58-63; ANAT, N.Y. Med. Col, 63-64; STATE UNIV. N.Y. DOWNSTATE MED. CTR, 64-67, ASST. PROF, 67- Leukemia Soc. fel, 60-61; fel, Nat. Heart Inst, 61-63, res. grant, Nat. Inst. Arthritis & Metab. Diseases, 64-71. Summers, res. consult, Warburg Respirometry, Creedmoor State Hosp, New York, 57, tech. collab, dept. biol, Brookhaven Nat. Lab, 59, 60. U.S.A, 54-56. AAAS; N.Y. Acad. Sci; Reticuloendothelial Soc; Am. Soc. Hemat; Am. Asn. Anat; Soc. Exp. Biol. & Med. Problems relating to hemopoiesis; roles of the bone marrow and spleen and the effect of various stimuli and depressors on blood cell production, release and destruction in the rat. Address: Dept. of Anatomy, State University of New York, Downstate Medical Center, 450 Clarkson Ave, Brooklyn, NY 11203.

DORNHEIM, F(REDERICK) R(OBERT), b. Brooklyn, N.Y, June 6, 32. CHEMICAL ENGINEERING, MATHEMATICS. B.Che.E, Cooper Union, 53; M.A, DePaul, 59. Chem. engr, Sinclair Res. Labs, 53-54, computer programmer, 56-63, mgr. comput. center, Sinclair Oil Co, 63-65, coordinator tech. comput, 65-67, mgr. systs. & comput. planning dept, 67-68; MGR. planning, scheduling & tech. serv, ATLANTIC RICHFIELD CO, 68-71, PROF. SERV, 71- U.S.A, 54-56. Process design, construction and economic evaluation. Address: Atlantic Richfield Co, Box 2451, Houston, TX 77001.

DORNHOFF, LARRY LEE, b. Minden, Nebr, Apr. 13, 42; m. 68; c. 1. MATHEMATICS. B.S, Univ. Nebr, Lincoln, 62; M.S, Univ. Chicago, 63, Nat. Sci. Found. fel, 62-66, Ph.D.(math), 66. Instr. MATH, Yale, 66-68; ASST. PROF, UNIV. ILL, URBANA, 68- Math. Asn. Am; Am. Math. Soc. Finite group theory; group representations; representations of finite groups, especially solvable groups; solvable permutation groups. Address: Dept. of Mathematics, University of Illinois, Urbana, IL 61801.

DORNING, JOHN J(OSEPH), b. Bronx, N.Y, Apr. 17, 38; m. 63; c. 3. MATHEMATICAL PHYSICS. B.S, U.S. Merchant Marine Acad, 59; M.S, Columbia, 63, Atomic Energy Cmn. fels, 63-66, Ph.D.(nuclear sci. & eng), 67. Marine engr, U.S. Merchant Marine, 60-62; asst. physicist, Brookhaven Nat. Lab, 67-69, assoc. physicist, 69-70; ASSOC. PROF. NUCLEAR ENG, UNIV. ILL, URBANA-CHAMPAIGN, 70- U.S.N, 59-60, Ens. Am. Nuclear Soc.(Mark Mills Award, 67); Soc. Indust. & Appl. Math; Am. Phys. Soc. Neutron transport theory and thermalization; reactor physics, special functions; plasma physics; kinetic theory of gases. Address: 204 Nuclear Engineering Lab, University of Illinois, Urbana-Champaign, Urbana, IL 61801.

DORNSEIFER, THEODORE, b. Philadelphia, Pa, Aug. 20, 33; m. 60; c. 2. FOOD SCIENCE, ORGANIC CHEMISTRY. B.S, Del. Valley Col, 58; Nat. Sci. Found. fel, Georgia, 60-61, Ph.D.(food sci), 63. Chemist res. & develop, Thomas J. Lipton Co, 58-60; res. asst. food sci, Georgia, 60-63, asst. prof, 63-65; head food technologist, Polak's Frutal Works, 65-68; from sr. scientist to SUPVR. RAW MAT. RES, FRITO-LAY, 68- U.S.A, 53-55. Inst. Food Tech. Isolation and identification of chemical components responsible for food flavors; improvement and development of new processes for food industry. Address: Frito-Lay, 900 N. Loop 12, Irving, TX 75060.

DORNTE, RALPH W(ILLIAM), b. Ft. Wayne, Ind, Nov. 27, 05; m. 31. PHYSICAL CHEMISTRY. B.S, Purdue, 27; M.S, Cornell, 29; Ph.D.(chem), Princeton, 31. Nat. Res. fel. chem, California, 31-33; res. chemist, Gen. Elec. Co, 33-42; chemist, Esso Labs, Standard Oil Develop. Co, 42-48; res. supvr, plastics div, Allied Chem. Corp, 48-50, chief res. chemist, 50-57, lab. dir, 57-62; res. scientist Elec. Storage Battery Co, C.F. Nordberg Res. Center, 62-70; RETIRED. AAAS; Am. Chem. Soc. Kinetics; molecular structure; electron diffraction; polymerization; dielectric polarization; alkylation; plastics. Address: 2764 Arrowhead Dr, Langhorne, PA 19047.

DORNY, CARL NELSON, b. Washington, D.C, Jan. 20, 37; m. 60; c. 4. ELECTRICAL ENGINEERING. B.E.S, Brigham Young, 61; Nat. Sci. Found. fel, Stanford, 61-63, M.S.E.E, 62, Westinghouse fel, 64-65, Ph.D.(elec. eng), 65. Engr, Westinghouse Res. Labs, 63-64; asst. prof. ELEC. ENG, UNIV. PA, 65-69, Winterstein asst. prof, 69-70, ASSOC. PROF, 70- White House fel, spec. asst. to the Secy, U.S. Dept. Agr, 69-70; Nat. Sci. Found. res. initiation grant, 67-69; summers, asst. engr, Lawrence Radiation Lab, California, 60, mem. tech. staff, Boeing Co, 61 & Bell Tel. Labs, 62. Consult, Westinghouse Res. Labs, Pa, 66- Inst. Elec. & Electronics Eng. Computer optimization; applied mathematics; mathematical programming; numerical analysis; control theory; system engineering; operations research; optimization of distributed systems. Address: 126 Moore School, University of Pennsylvania, Philadelphia, PA 19104.

DORON, VERA F, b. Bratislava, Czech, Oct. 3, 29; U.S. citizen; m. 52; c. 2. INORGANIC CHEMISTRY. B.S, Israel Inst. Tech, 52, prof. engr, 53; M.S, Wayne State, 57, univ. fel, Union Carbide fel. & Ph.D.(inorg. chem), 59. Res. scientist, sci. lab, Ford Motor Co, 59-61; asst. prof. INORG. CHEM. Israel Inst. Tech, 61-63; lectr, grad. div, Adelphi, 64-65; ASST. PROF, Hunter Col, 65-67; RUTGERS UNIV, 67-, res. coun. fel, 67-70. Res. grant, City Col. New York, 66-67. Am. Chem. Soc. Coordination chemistry; organometallic compounds; characterization and stereochemistry of new compounds; differential thermal techniques applied to kinetic problems in coordination chemistry. Address: Dept. of Chemistry, Rutgers University, Newark, NJ 07102.

DOROTHY, ROBERT GLENN, b. Canton, Ill, June 27, 40; m. 67. CHEMICAL PHYSICS. B.S, Iowa State, 62; M.S, Wyoming, 64; Ph.D.(physics), British Columbia, 67. Res. physicist, E.I. DU PONT DE NEMOURS & CO, INC, 67-69, SR. RES. PHYSICIST, 69- Am. Phys. Soc. Optical properties of metals and semi-conductors; nuclear magnetic resonance in gases; molecular spectroscopy of polymers. Address: 13 Thornhollow Rd, Meadowood, Newark, DE 19711.

DOROUGH, GUS D(OWNS), JR, b. Los Angeles, Calif, March 5, 22; m. 70; c. 3. CHEMISTRY. B.S, California, 43, Ph.D.(chem), 47. Asst. chem, California, 43-44; res. chemist, Manhattan Atomic Bomb Proj, 44-46; Nat. Res. fel, Wash, D.C, 46-47; instr. chem, Wash. Univ, 47-49, asst. prof, 49-54; chemist & div. leader, Lawrence Radiation Lab, Univ. Calif, 54-67; head dept. chem, 67-71; DEP. DIR. RES. & TECHNOL, DEFENSE RES. & ENG, WASH, D.C, 71- Am. Chem. Soc; Am. Inst. Chem. Chemical explosives; material research and development. Address: Office of the Secretary of Defense/Office of Director of Defense Research & Engineering, Rm. 3E144, The Pentagon, Washington, DC 20301.

DOROUGH, H(ENDLEY) WYMAN, b. Elba, Ala, Dec. 23, 36; m. 57; c. 5. INSECT TOXICOLOGY, ENTOMOLOGY. B.S, Auburn Univ, 59, M.S, 60; Ph.D.(entom), Univ. Wis, 64. Lab. asst. ENTOM, Auburn Univ, 56-59, res. asst, 59-61; Univ. Wis, 61-63; asst. prof, Tex. A&M Univ, 63-67, assoc. prof, 67-69; UNIV. KY, 69-70, PROF, 70- U.S. Pub. Health Serv. res. grant, 65-71. AAAS; Entom. Soc. Am; Am. Chem. Soc. Chemistry and toxicology of pesticides as related to their interactions with animals and plants. Address: Dept. of Entomology, University of Kentucky, Lexington, KY 40506.

DORR, JOHN A(DAM), JR, b. Grosse Pointe Park, Mich, Oct. 25, 22; m. 43; c. 3. VERTEBRATE PALEONTOLOGY. B.S, Michigan, 47, M.S, 49, Ph.D.(vert. paleont), 51; Kentucky. Asst. vert. paleont, Michigan, 48-51; asst. curator, Carnegie Mus, Pittsburgh, 51-52; instr. HIST. GEOL, UNIV. MICH, 52-59, assoc. prof, 59-64, PROF, 64-, chmn. dept, 66-71. Dir.

geol. expeds. & summer camp; res. assoc, Mus. Paleont, Univ. Mich. C.Eng, 43-46, 1st Lt. Soc. Vert. Paleont.(past pres); Geol. Soc. Am. Mammalian vertebrate paleontology; Cenozoic stratigraphy; Tectonic history of the Middle Rockies. Address: Dept. of Geology & Mineralogy, University of Michigan, Ann Arbor, MI 48104.

DORR, JOHN VAN N(OSTRAND), II, b. New York, N.Y, May 16, 10; m. 46; c. 3. GEOLOGY. B.S, Harvard, 32; Geol.E, Colo. Sch. Mines, 37; hon. D.Sc, Univ. Minas Gerais, 66. Geologist, Superior Oil Co, Calif, 37-38; jr. geologist, U.S. GEOL. SURV, 38-41, asst. geologist, 41-46, staff geologist, OFF. INT. GEOL, 46-71, ACTING CHIEF, BR. LATIN AM. & AFRICAN GEOL, 71- V.pres, working group manganese, Int. Asn. Genesis Ore Deposits, 70. Medal, State of Minas Gerais, Brazil, 62. Fel. AAAS; fel. Geol. Soc. Am; Soc. Econ. Geol; fel. Brazilian Geol. Soc.(v.pres, 56, Bonifacio medal, 64); Geol, Mining & Metall. Soc. India. Economic geology; ore deposits; tungsten; nickel; manganese; iron. Address: Office of International Geology, U.S. Geological Survey, Washington, DC 20242.

DORRANCE, WILLIAM HENRY, b. Highland Park, Mich, Dec. 3, 21; m. 46; c. 4. AERODYNAMICS. B.S, Michigan, 47, M.S, 48. Res. engr, aeronaut. res. center, Michigan, 47-49, aerodyn. group leader, 49-51; sr. aerodyn. engr, Convair Div, Gen. Dynamics Corp, 51-53, aerodyn. group supvr. astronaut. div, 53-55, asst. to dir. sci. res, gen. off, 55-58, sr. staff scientist, 58-61; head gas dynamics dept, Aerospace Corp, 61-62, group dir. adv. planning div, 62-64; v.pres, Conductron Corp, 64-69, group exec, 64-67, mem. bd. dirs, 65-67, 68-69; chmn. bd. dirs. Interface Systs. Corp, 67-69, chmn. & chief exec, 69-70; PRES. & MEM. BD. DIRS, ORGN. CONTROL SERV, INC, 71-; PRES, ENG. & CONSULT. CO, 70- U.S.A.F.R, 45-, Maj. Am. Inst. Aeronaut. & Astronaut. Weapon system planning; systems and operations analysis; high speed aerodynamics; compressible gas dynamics; hypersonic flow; nonsteady flow phenomena; thermal protection systems; high performance missile design. Address: 11 Heatheridge, Ann Arbor, MI 48104.

DORRELL, WILLIAM W(OODROW), b. Morgantown, W.Va, May 15, 17; m. 42; c. 3. BACTERIOLOGY. A.B, West Virginia, 38, M.S, 41; fel, Wisconsin, 41-42, Ph.D.(bact), 48. Lab. asst. bact, West Virginia, 38-41; asst. fungi physiol, Wisconsin, 46-47; microbiologist, U.S. ARMY, Ft. Detrick, 47-53, biol. sci. adminstr, 53-58, dir. tech. serv, 58-63, sci. adv, Army Staff, DEPT. ARMY, WASH, D.C, 64-70, BIOL. SCI. ADMINR, ARMY RES. OFF, 70- U.S.A, 42-46. Am. Soc. Microbiol. Fungi physiology and fermentations; plant pathology; oxidative respiration of Fusarium graminearum; aerobiology. Address: Route 6, Pinecliff, Frederick, MD 21701.

DORRENCE, SAMUEL M(ICHAEL), b. Rock Springs, Wyo, May 21, 39; m. 60; c. 3. ORGANIC CHEMISTRY. B.A, Utah, 61, Ph.D.(org. chem), 64. Res. chemist, Celanese Chem. Co, 64-67, group leader, 67; RES. CHEMIST, Laramie Petrol. Res. Center, U.S. BUR. MINES, 67-70, LARAMIE ENERGY RES. CTR, 70- Am. Chem. Soc. Nucleophilic displacement reactions of sulfonate esters of carbohydrates; hydrocarbon oxidation in vapor and liquid phases; reactions of formaldehyde; functional group determinations of asphalt. Address: Laramie Energy Research Center, Box 3395, University Station, Laramie, WY 82070.

DORRER, EGON, b. Munich, West Germany, Feb. 14, 34; m. 64; c. 2. GLACIOLOGY, PHOTOGRAMMETRY. Dipl. Ing, Munich Tech, 59, Dr. Ing. (geod), 66. Asst. photogram, Munich Tech, 60-62; asst. geodesist, Univ. Michigan, 62-63; res. asst. photogram, Munich Tech, 63-65; field geodesist, Grand Valley State Col, 65-66; chief engr, Munich Tech, 66-67; ASSOC. PROF. SURV, UNIV. N.B, 67- Mem. subcomt. glaciers, Nat. Res. Coun. Am. Polar Soc; Int. Soc. Photogram; Am. Soc. Photogram; Glaciol. Soc; Can. Inst. Surv; Ger. Soc. Photogram; Ger. Surv. Asn; Ger. Soc. Polar Res. Stereoplotters in conjunction with digital computers; movement determination of vast ice sheets by geodetic methods; aerotriangulation; adjustment computations; testing of instruments; hybrid stereoplotters; computers; glacier movement determinations; glacier cartography; computer simulation; holography; mathematics; numerical analysis; glacier mechanics. Address: Dept. of Surveying Engineering, University of New Brunswick, Fredericton, N.B, Can.

DORRIS, JOHN C, b. Providence, Ky, Jan. 8, 35; m. 59. FOOD & PROTEIN CHEMISTRY. B.S, Murray State Univ, 57; Nat. Insts. Health fel, Mich. State Univ, 64-68, M.S, 67, Ph.D.(food sci), 68. Assoc. scientist nutrit. prod. develop, Mead Johnson & Co, 58-59, scientist, 61-64; MEM. SCI. STAFF, RALSTON PURINA CO, 68- U.S.A, 59-61. Inst. Food Technol; Am. Chem. Soc. Protein interactions in food systems; flavor chemistry; protein food analogs; protein functionality as affected by various food processing parameters; nutritional snack foods; convenience foods. Address: Ralston Purina Co, Checkerboard Square, St. Louis, MO 63188.

DORRIS, KENNETH LEE, b. Baytown, Tex, Sept. 26, 35; m. 57; c. 1. PHYSICAL CHEMISTRY. B.S, Texas, 61; Ph.D.(microwave spectros), 66. Asst. prof. CHEM, LAMAR UNIV, 65-69, ASSOC. PROF, 69- Res. assoc, Savannah River Lab, Atomic Energy Comn, summer 66; Robert A. Welch res. grant, 67-70. Med.C, U.S.A, 54-57. Am. Chem. Soc. Spectroscopic studies of heterocyclic and N-acyl compounds, especially structure, symmetry and forces in the molecule. Address: Dept. of Chemistry, Lamar University, Beaumont, TX 77704.

DORRIS, PEGGY RAE, b. Holly Bluff, Miss, Feb. 27, 33. ZOOLOGY. B.S, Miss. Col, 56; M.S, Univ. Miss, 63, Ph.D.(zool), 67. Asst. BIOL, Univ. Miss, 63-66; asst. prof, HENDERSON STATE COL, 66-70, ASSOC. PROF, 70- Spiders of Mississippi and Arkansas. Address: 125 Evonshire Dr, Arkadelphia, AR 71923.

DORRIS, TROY C(LYDE), b. West Frankfort, Ill, Apr. 6, 18; m. 43; c. 2. LIMNOLOGY, WATER POLLUTION. Ph.D.(zool, limnol), Univ. Ill, 53. Assoc. prof. biol. sci, Quincy Col, 47-56; assoc. prof. ZOOL, OKLA. STATE UNIV, 56-61, PROF, 61-, DIR. RESERVOIR RES. CTR, RES. FOUND, 67- Biological effects of oil refinery effluents; biological parameters for water quality criteria; primary productivity of tropical waters. Address: Reservoir Research Center, Oklahoma State University, Stillwater, OK 74075.

DORROH, JAMES R(OBERT), b. Marion, Ala, Apr. 20, 37; m. 59; c. 1. MATHEMATICS. B.A, Texas, 58, M.A, 60, Nat. Sci. Found. fel, 60-62, Ph.D.(math), 62. Asst. prof. MATH, LA. STATE UNIV, BATON ROUGE, 62-67, assoc. prof, 67-71, PROF, 71- Am. Math. Soc; Math. Asn. Am. Functional analysis; semigroups of linear and nonlinear transformations. Address: Dept. of Mathematics, Louisiana State University, Baton Rouge, LA 70803.

DORROH, J(OE) L(EE), b. Rosebud, Tex, Sept. 22, 04; m. 31; c. 2. MATHEMATICS. A.B, Texas, 26, A.M, 27, Ph.D, 30. Instr. math, Texas, 26-30; Nat. Res. fel, Calif. Inst. Tech, 30-31; Princeton, 31-32, asst, 32-33; instr, Hopkins, 33-35, scholar biostatist, sch. hyg, 35-36; assoc. prof. math, Judson Col, 36-38; prof, Ouachita Baptist Col, 38-41; asst. prof, La. State Univ, 42-46; assoc. prof, Ill. Inst. Technol, 46-47; prof, Tex. A&I Univ, 47-70, chmn, dept, 52-66; RETIRED. Am. Math. Soc; Math. Asn. Am. Point-set theory; foundations of geometry; abstract algebras. Address: Box 967, Kingsville, TX 78363.

DORROUGH, DOUGLAS C(HARLES), b. Honolulu, Hawaii, Jan. 13, 27. MATHEMATICAL LOGIC. B.S, Dayton, 49; M.A, Hawaii, 53; Williams fel, North Carolina, 54-55, Ph.D.(math. logic), 64. Asst. prof. math. & logic, Jackson Col, 53-54; lectr. logic & sci. method, North Carolina, 55-58; opers. analyst, Tech. Opers, Inc, 58-59; opers. res. scientist, Syst. Develop. Corp, 59-60; staff res. engr, A.C. Spark Plug Div, Gen. Motors Corp, 60-63; sr. scientist, Douglas Aircraft Co, Calif, 64-67; assoc. prof. philos. & comput. sci, La. State Univ, 67-69; MEM. TECH. STAFF, N.AM. ROCKWELL CORP, 69- Lectr, Univ. Calif, Los Angeles, 65-67; Opers. Res. Around the World, 69. Asn. Symbolic Logic; Am. Math. Soc. Multivalued logics and statistical decision theory; application of both deterministic and stochastic finite mathematical techniques to the structuring of self-organizing systems; investigation of logical and epistemological bases for artificially intelligent mechanisms. Address: P.O. Box 6362, Anaheim, CA 92806.

DORSCHNER, KENNETH P(ETER), b. Appleton, Wis, Sept. 7, 21; m. 51; c. 2. AGRONOMY. B.S, Wisconsin, 49, M.S, 51, Ph.D, 54. Res. asst, Wisconsin, 49-51, 52-54; asst. plant physiologist, Miss. State Col, 51-52; biologist, Niagara Chem. Div, FMC Corp, 54-59, supvr. biol. labs, 59-62, prod. mgr. herbicides, 62-67; res. supvr. pesticides, W.R. Grace & Co, Md, 67-69; MGR. AGR. CHEM. RES, GLIDDEN-DURKEE DIV, SCM CORP, 69- Ord. Dept, U.S.A, 42-45. Weed Sci. Soc. Am. Synthetic plant hormones as herbicidal compounds. Address: Glidden-Durkee Division, SCM Corp, P.O. Box 389, Jacksonville, FL 32201.

DORSCHU, KARL E(DWARD), b. Collingswood, N.J, Aug. 16, 30; m. 56; c. 3. METALLURGICAL ENGINEERING. B.S, Drexel Inst. Tech, 53; M.Met.E, Rensselaer Polytech. Inst, 57; Ph.D.(metall. eng), Lehigh, 60. Engr. welding metall, aviation gas turbine div, Westinghouse Elec. Corp, 53-54; Frankford Arsenal, 54-55; instr. & res. asst, Rensselaer Polytech. Inst, 55-57; instr, Lehigh, 57-59; sr. engr, res. lab, Air Reduction Co, 59-63, proj. supvr, 63-65, supvr, 65-67, asst. dir. welding res, 67-71; V.PRES. & GEN. MGR, ELECTROTHERM CORP, 71- U.S.A, 54-55. Am. Welding Soc.(1st nat. prize, 53, Lincoln Gold Medal, 69); Am. Soc. Metals. Metallurgy and heat transfer in welding. Address: Electrotherm Corp, 1500 S. 50th St, Philadelphia, PA 19143.

DORSETT, HENRY GRADY, JR, b. Chapel Hill, N.C, Dec. 28, 12; m. 33; c. 3. PHYSICS, MATHEMATICS. B.S, Wake Forest Col, 33; fel, Duke, 34; M.S, North Carolina, 37; Maryland, 47-52. Physicist, North Carolina, 35-39; Duke Power Co, 39-41; U.S. Bur. Standards, 41-45; U.S. Naval Ord. Lab, 45-52; Ralph M. Parsons Co, 52-55; Vitro Corp. Am, 55-57; chief dust exp. res. sect, U.S. Bur. Mines, Pa, 57-66; physicist, exp. res. & develop. labs, U.S. Army Night Vision Lab, Va, 66-67; FIRE RES. DIR. OFF. CIVIL DEFENSE & SECY. ARMY, 67- Mem. dust hazards cmt, Nat. Fire Protection Asn, 60-; chmn. cmt. dust explosions, Int. Electrotech. Cmn, 63- AAAS; Acoust. Soc. Am; Am. Geophys. Union; Instrument Soc. Am. Dust explosions; acoustics, particularly underwater sound; optics; development of infrared components and detectors for more effective night vision. Address: 1E543, Office of Civil Defense & Secretary of the Army, The Pentagon, Washington, DC 20310.

DORSETT, JOHN O(REM) F(ILLMORE), b. Indianapolis, Ind, June 25, 07; m. 40; c. 4. PHYSICS. B.S, U.S. Naval Acad, 31; M.S, Mass. Inst. Tech, 40; M.S, Ohio State, 52. Lectr, U.S. Naval War Col, 52-55, head dept. res. & anal, 53-55; res. analyst, opers. res. off, Hopkins, 57-62; prin. scientist, Booz-Allen Appl. Res, 62-64; SR. OPERS. ANALYST, STANFORD RES. INST, 64- U.S.N, 31-57, Capt. Am. Meteorol. Soc; Opers. Res. Soc. Am; assoc. fel. Am. Inst. Aeronaut. & Astronaut. Ducting of radar propagation over sea surfaces; elastic scattering of protons using Van de Graaff; operational analysis of weapons systems and military operations; computer simulation of military operations. Address: Stanford Research Institute, 333 Ravenswood Ave, Menlo Park, CA 94025.

DORSEY, CLARK L(AWLER), JR, b. Lakota, Va, Apr. 22, 23; m. 45; c. 4. CHEMICAL ENGINEERING. B.S, Va. Polytech. Inst, 45, M.S, 46; Ph.D. (chem. eng), Purdue Univ, 49. Mem. staff, textile fibers dept, acetate & orlon div, E.I. DU PONT DE NEMOURS & CO, INC, 49-56, nylon div, 57-60, new prod. div, 61-64, develop. dept, 65-67, PLANNING MGR. ORG. CHEM. DEPT, 68- Venture analysis and development; corporate planning; societal systems; management sciences. Address: 501 Wooddale Rd, Wilmington, DE 19807.

DORSEY, GEORGE F(RANCIS), b. Chattanooga, Tenn, Dec. 15, 42; m. 66; c. 1. ORGANIC CHEMISTRY. A.B, Chattanooga, 64; Ph.D.(chem), Tennessee, 69. DEVELOP. CHEMIST, NUCLEAR DIV, UNION CARBIDE CORP, 69- Am. Chem. Soc. Organic mass spectrometry; mechanism of ester hydrolysis; polymers; adhesives. Address: Union Carbide Corp, Nuclear Division, P.O. Box Y, Oak Ridge, TN 37830.

DORSEY, HERBERT G(ROVE), JR, b. East Orange, N.J, Sept. 15, 12; m. 39; c. 3. POLAR, HYDRO-METEOROLOGY. B.S, Harvard, 38; M.S, Mass. Inst. Tech, 49. Meteorologist, U.S. Antarctic exped, 39-41; U.S. Weather Bur, 41-43; Lt, arctic opers, U.S. Army Air Force, 43-44, Capt, Air

Weather Serv, 45-48; Maj, arctic projs, U.S. Dept. Air Force, 50-54; consult. Water Resources, 54-62; CYCLES ANALYSIS, 62- Special congressional medal; Air Medal. Am. Meteor. Soc; Arctic Inst. N.Am. Local heavy winter precipitation; Arctic and Antarctic meteorology; long range forecasts; Arctic glaciation; water resources development. Address: P.O. Box 652, Ojai, CA 93023.

DORSEY, JOHN M, b. Streator, Ill, Mar. 25, 06; m. 38; c. 3. SURGERY. B.S, Univ. Chicago, 26, M.D, 30. Fel. SURG, Mayo Grad. Sch, Univ. Minn, 32-35; PROF, MED. SCH, NORTHWEST. UNIV, 55- Am. Surg. Asn; Am. Asn. Thoracic Surg; Int. Soc. Surg; Am. Col. Surg. Gastrointestinal disease; thoracic surgery. Address: Dept. of Surgery, Evanston Hospital, 2650 Ridge Ave, Evanston, IL 60201.

DORSEY, JOHN M(ORRIS), b. Clinton, Iowa, Nov. 19, 00; m. 26; c. 2. PSYCHIATRY, PSYCHOLOGY. M.D, Iowa, 25, A.B, 26, M.S, 28. Intern, State Psychopathic Hosp, Iowa, 25-26, sr. res. physician, 26-27, acting asst. dir, 27-28; ment. hygienist & lectr. sociol, Michigan, 28-38, sr. instr. psychiat, 28-31, prof, 31-34, assoc. prof, 34-38, lectr. post-grad. med, med. sch, 38-46; prof. psychiat. & chmn. dept, col. med, WAYNE STATE UNIV, 46-61, univ. prof, 61-71, EMER. UNIV. PROF, 71- Rockefeller fel, Vienna, 35-37; dir. child guid. div, Children's Fund, Mich, 42-; med. dir, McGregor Ctr, 47-; spec. lectr, Purdue; chief consult, Vet. Admin. Hosp, Dearborn, 47-; staff physician, Harper Hosp; trustee, Hannan Mem. Home & Scudder Found. Old People, 53- Dipl, Am. Bd. Neurol. & Psychiat. Am. Med. Asn; Am. Psychiat. Asn; Am. Psychol. Asn; Am. Psychosom. Soc; Am. Psychopath. Asn; Asn. Mil. Surg; Am. Psychoanal. Asn; Am. Orthopsychiat. Asn; Acad. Psychoanal. Psychoanalysis; application of psychiatry to general practice of medicine. Address: 756 Mackenzie Hall, Wayne State University, Detroit, MI 48202.

DORSEY, ROBERT T, b. Cleveland, Ohio, Feb. 28, 18; m. 45; c. 1. ELECTRICAL ENGINEERING. S.B, Mass. Inst. Tech, 40. Supvr. ord, Naval Ord. Lab, 40-43, mine test sta, 43-45; lighting appln, GEN. ELEC. CO, 48-66, MGR. LIGHTING DEVELOP, 66- Mem, Int. Comn. Illum, 57-, v.pres, 67; chmn, U.S. Comt. Appln, 64- Fel. AAAS; fel. Illum. Eng. Soc.(pres-elect, 71). Illuminating engineering; new lighting techniques; design and application of new lamps; development on vision and visual performance. Address: Lamp Dept, General Electric Co, Nela Park, Cleveland, OH 44112.

DORSEY, WILLIAM RAOUL, b. St. Louis, Mo, Oct. 4, 18; m. 44; c. 2. CHEMICAL ENGINEERING. B.S, Univ. Calif, 40; U.S. Navy Postgrad. Sch, 44-45. Chem. engr, Basic Veg. Prod, Inc, 49; chief chemist, Vacu-Dry Co, 49-53, dir. res, 53-59, v.pres. res. & develop. div, 59-65; PRES, Chelan Packing Co, 65-71; COLUMBIA PROD. INC, 71- Bur. aeronaut, U.S.N, 43-46, Lt. Assoc. Am. Chem. Soc; assoc. Inst. Food Technol. Food process engineering. Address: Columbia Products Inc, P.O. Box 94, Wenatchee, WA 98801.

DORSEY, W(ILLIAM) SMITH, b. Revelstoke, B.C, Dec. 28, 19. COMPUTER & INFORMATION SCIENCE. B.S, Iowa State Univ, 40; Ph.D.(org. chem), Calif. Inst. Technol, 50. MEM. TECH. STAFF, ELECTRONICS GROUP, AUTONETICS DIV, N.AM. ROCKWELL CORP, 68- U.S.N.R, 43-46, Lt. Asn. Comput. Mach; Am. Chem. Soc; Am. Inst. Chem. Eng; Am. Soc. Info. Sci. Applications of computer processing and information science to literature problems of research and engineering. Address: HA08, Autonetics, Box 4173, Anaheim, CA 92803.

DORSKY, JULIAN, b. New York, N.Y, May 11, 16; m. 40; c. 3. CHEMISTRY. A.B, Brooklyn Col, 36; M.S, Pa. State, 37; Indust. fel, Purdue, 37-39, Ph.D. (org. chem), 39. Group leader, develop. sect, Ethyl Corp, La, 39-47; sr. fel, Mellon Inst, 47-51; chemist, GIVAUDAN CORP, 51-59, res. assoc, 59-64, res. adminstr, 64-66, asst. res. dir, 66-67, assoc. res. dir, 67-69, dir. res, 69-71, V.PRES. RES, 71- AAAS; Am. Chem. Soc. Organic chemistry. Address: 125 Delawanna Ave, Clifton, NJ 07014.

DORSON, WILLIAM JOHN, JR, b. Nashua, N.H, May 9, 36; m. 58; c. 2. CHEMICAL & BIOMEDICAL ENGINEERING. B.Ch.E, Rensselaer Polytech, 58, M.Ch.E, 60; Ph.D.(chem. eng, biomed), Cincinnati, 67. Coop. engr, Gen. Elec. Co, 56-58, develop. engr, Knolls Atomic Power Lab, 58-64, res. & develop. engr, space power & propulsion dept, 64-65; instr. chem. eng, Cincinnati, 65-66; assoc. prof. BIOMED. ENG, ARIZ. STATE UNIV, 66-71, PROF, 71- Consult, Gen. Elec. Co; Randam Electronics, Inc; Hunkar Instrument Develop. Labs, Inc; mem, Int. Conf. Med. & Biol. Eng, 67. Am. Chem. Soc; Am. Soc. Mech. Eng; Am. Inst. Chem. Eng; Asn. Advan. Med. Instrumentation. Development of medical diagnostic and prosthetic methods; body fluid rheology; transport phenomena; radioactive tracer techniques; two-phase flow and heat transfer; nucleonics. Address: Dept. of Chemical Engineering, Arizona State University, Tempe, AZ 85281.

DORST, JOHN PHILLIPS, b. Cincinnati, Ohio, July 8, 26; m. 50; c. 4. MEDICINE, RADIOLOGY. Pomona Col, 48-49; M.D, Cornell, 53. Intern, Univ. Iowa Hosps, 53-54, resident radiol, 55-58; fel. pediat. radiol, Childrens Hosp, Univ. Cincinnati, 58-59, asst. prof. radiol, univ. 59-63, assoc. prof, 63-66, asst. prof. pediat, 65-66; assoc. prof. RADIOL, JOHNS HOPKINS UNIV, 66-69, PROF, 70-, ASSOC. PROF. PEDIAT, 68- C.Eng, 44-46, Sgt. Soc. Pediat. Radiol; fel. Am. Col. Radiol; Radiol. Soc. N.Am; Am. Roentgen Ray Soc. Pediatric radiology; functional craniology; choudrodysplasias. Address: Dept. of Radiology, Johns Hopkins Hospital, Baltimore, MD 21205.

DORT, WAKEFIELD, JR, b. Keene, N.H, July 16, 23; m. 54, 67; c. 1. GEOLOGY, GEOMORPHOLOGY. B.Sc, Harvard, 44; M.Sc, Calif. Inst. Tech, 48; Ph.D.(geol), Stanford, 55. Field geologist, Bunker Hill & Sullivan, Idaho, 47, 49; U.S. Geol. Surv, 48; instr. geomorphol. & econ. geol, Duke, 48-50; geomorphol, Stanford, 50-52; asst. prof. GEOL, Pa. State. 52-57; assoc. prof, UNIV. KANS, 57-70, PROF, 70- Consult. eng. geol, 50-52, ground water & petrol. geol, 52-57. Geol. ed, Petrol. & Natural Gas Digest, 53-56; assoc. ed, Monitor, 56-59; Oil & Gas Abstracts, 59-61; Mining Abstracts, 59-61. Mem. visual ed. cmt, Am. Geol. Inst, 55-63, earth sci. curriculum proj, 63-64. Antarctic expeds, U.S, 65, 66 & 69, Japan, 67. U.S.M.C, 44-47. AAAS; Geol. Soc. Am; Am. Asn. Petrol. Geol; Am. Geog. Soc; Asn. Am. Geog; Nat. Asn. Geol. Teachers (treas, 61-65); Glaciol. Soc; Soc. Am. Archaeol; Swed. Soc. Anthrop. & Geog. Geomorphology; glacial and Pleistocene geology; late Cenozoic paleoclimatology; geology of Idaho; engineering geology; geology of archaeological sites; educational films; geomorphology of Antarctica. Address: Dept. of Geology, University of Kansas, Lawrence, KS 66044.

DORWARD, DONALD L, b. Peoria, Ill, Dec. 5, 24; m. 50; c. 2. ORGANIC CHEMISTRY, INFORMATION SCIENCE. B.S, Univ. Ill, 48; M.S, Ore. State Univ, 50; Atomic Energy Comn. fel, Wayne State Univ, 50-53; LL.B, Franklin Univ, 61; J.D, Capital Univ, 66. Res. chemist, Pabst Brewing Co, Ill, summer 50; develop. chemist, U.S. Rubber Co, Mich, 51; assoc. ed, org. indexing, chem. abstr. serv, Am. Chem. Soc, 53-62; sr. info. scientist, info. storage & retrieval, Battelle Mem. Inst, 62-67, info. res. sect, 67-68; ATTORNEY & RES. CONSULT, LaCour Dorward & Rickman, 68-70; DAVIS, DORWARD, GIFFORD & LURIE, 70- Mem. comt. mod. methods handling chem. info, Nat. Acad. Sci-Nat. Res. Coun, 61-64; attorney at law, 61-; chief, tech. serv. div, Ohio Law Enforcement Planning Agency, 69-71. U.S.A.F, 43-45, Res, 45-; Maj. Am. Chem. Soc; Am. Soc. Info. Sci; Sci. Res. Soc. Am. Synthetic organic chemistry; physiological activity-chemical structure correlation; computer storage and retrieval of scientific and technical information; information and communication theory; scientific and technical applications to law enforcement and criminal justice. Address: Davis, Dorward, Gifford & Lurie, 83 S. High St, Suite 312, Columbus, OH 43215.

DORWARD, RALPH C(LARENCE), b. Viking, Alta, July 31, 41; m. 64; c. 2. METALLURGY, MATERIALS SCIENCE. B.Sc, Alberta, 62, M.Sc, 64; Ph.D. (metall), McMaster, 67. Res. assoc. metall, Alberta, 64; RES. METALLURGIST, KAISER ALUMINUM & CHEM. CORP, 67- Am. Inst. Mining, Metall. & Petrol. Eng; Am. Soc. Metals. Alloy solidification; thermodynamics of solutions, phase transformations and phase equilibria; diffusion in metals and semiconductors; deformation structures in metals; physical metallurgy of aluminum alloys. Address: Fabrication & Applications Research Dept, Kaiser Center for Technology, Pleasanton, CA 94566.

DORWART, HAROLD L(AIRD), b. Greenville, Pa, Aug. 27, 02; m. 33; c. 1. MATHEMATICS. A.B, Washington & Jefferson Col, 24, Sc.D, 68; Ph.D. (math), Yale, 31. Asst. instr. MATH, Yale, 24-27, instr, 27-28; Williams Col, 28-30, 31-35; asst. prof, Washington & Jefferson Col, 35-43, assoc. prof, 43-47, prof, 47-49; Seabury prof. & chmn. dept, TRINITY COL.(CONN) 49-67, dean col, 67-68, EMER. PROF, 67- Am. Math. Soc; Math. Asn. Am. Address: 54 Willieb St, Glastonbury, CT 06033.

DORY, ROBERT A(LLAN), b. St. Paul, Minn, June 7, 36; m. 67; c. 2. MATHEMATICAL PHYSICS. B.S, North Dakota, 58; fel, Wisconsin, 58-60, M.S, 60, Ph.D.(physics), 62. Res. asst. physics, Midwest. Univ. Res. Asn, 60-62; instr, Wisconsin, 62-64; PHYSICIST, OAK RIDGE NAT. LAB, 64- Am. Phys. Soc. High energy accelerators; thermonuclear research; plasma theory. Address: Oak Ridge National Lab, P.O. Box Y, Oak Ridge, TN 37830.

DOSANJH, DARSHAN S(INGH), b. Sultanwind, India, Feb. 21, 21; m. 57; c. 2. AERONAUTICAL ENGINEERING. B.Sc, Punjab, 44, M.Sc, 45; M.S.E, Michigan, 48; Ph.D.(aeronaut), Hopkins, 53. Jr. instr. mech. eng, Hopkins, 49-50, asst, aeronaut. dept, 50-54; res. assoc, inst. fluid dynamics & appl. math, Maryland, 55-56; assoc. prof. mech. eng, SYRACUSE UNIV, 56-62, PROF. MECH. & AEROSPACE ENG, 62- Vis. prof, Col. Aeronaut. Eng, 61-62; NATO sr. fel, 67; Fulbright-Hays sr. faculty res. fel. & vis. prof, Southampton Univ, 71-72. Acoust. Soc. Am; assoc. fel. Am. Inst. Aeronaut. & Astronaut; Am. Phys. Soc; Am. Soc. Mech. Eng; assoc. fel. Royal Aeronaut. Soc. High speed gas dynamics; aerodynamics; aerodynamic noise; bioacoustics; plasma dynamics. Address: Dept. of Mechanical & Aerospace Engineering, Syracuse University, Syracuse, NY 13214.

DOSCHEK, GEORGE A, b. Pittsburgh, Pa, Sept. 3, 42; m. 68. ASTROPHYSICS. B.S, Univ. Pittsburgh, 63, NASA traineeship, 65-68, Ph.D.(physics), 68. Teaching asst. physics, Pittsburgh, 63-64, res. assoc. astrophys, Univ. Pittsburgh at E.O. Hulburt Center Space Res, U.S. NAVAL RES. LAB, 68-70, RES. ASTRONOMER, E.O. HULBURT CTR. SPACE RES, 70- Am. Astron. Soc. Solar x-ray astronomy; solar flares. Address: E.O. Hulburt Center for Space Research, U.S. Naval Research Lab, Washington, DC 20390.

DOSCHER, MARILYNN SCOTT, b. New York, N.Y, July 1, 31. BIOCHEMISTRY. B.A, Cornell, 53; Ph.D.(biochem), Washington(Seattle), 59. Chemist, Schering Corp, N.J, 53-55; fel. BIOCHEM, Yale, 60-64; Am. Cancer Soc. res. assoc. grant, Brookhaven Nat. Lab, 64-67; ASST. PROF. BIOCHEM, SCH. MED, WAYNE STATE UNIV, 67- Nat. Insts. Health fel, Yale, 60-62. Am. Chem. Soc. Protein structure. Address: Dept. of Biochemistry, Wayne State University School of Medicine, 1400 Chrysler Freeway, Detroit, MI 48207.

DOSCHER, NATHAN, b. New York, N.Y, June 13, 08; m. 33; c. 2. HEALTH, PHYSICAL EDUCATION. B.S, City Col, 29, A.M, Columbia, 32; LL.B, Fordham, 32; Ph.D.(ed), N.Y. Univ, 39. PROF. HYGIENE, City Col, 29-39; BROOKLYN COL, 29-, ADULT ED, 47-, GRAD. DIV, 52-, SUPVR. STUDENT TEACHING, 51-, DEPT. CHMN. GRAD. COURSES, 64- Accident investr, Citizens Budget Cmn, New York, 47; lectr, N.Y. Univ, 48, res. assoc, 49. Am. Asn. Health, Phys. Ed. & Recreation; Phys. Ed. Asn. Camping; mental hygiene of handicapped college students; accidents in municipal departments; safety; health and hygiene; testing; critical analysis of visual aides used in teaching safety on city streets. Address: Dept. of Graduate Courses, Brooklyn College, Brooklyn, NY 11210.

DOSHAN, HAROLD DAVID, b. N.Y.C, Oct. 30, 41; m. 63; c. 1. METABOLISM, ORGANIC CHEMISTRY. B.A, Cornell Univ, 62; Nat. Sci. Found. fel, Stanford Univ, 62-63, Nat. Insts. Health fel, 63-67, Ph.D.(org. chem), 67. Res. assoc. org. chem, Johns Hopkins Univ, 67-68, Nat. Insts. Health fel. pharmacol, sch. med, 68-70; RES. SCIENTIST, MED. RES. LABS, CHAS. PFIZER & CO, INC, 70- Am. Chem. Soc. Drug metabolism; natural products; biosynthetic pathways; strained ring systems and their reactions. Address: Drug Metabolism Dept, Medical Research Labs, Chas. Pfizer & Co, Inc, Groton, CT 06340.

DOSHI, PRATAP KILACHAND, b. Rangoon, Burma, Dec. 15, 38. NUCLEAR & ELECTRICAL ENGINEERING. B.S, Univ. Rangoon, 61; M.S, Univ. Ill, 63, Ph.D.(nuclear eng), 68. Prin. physicist, Babcock & Wilcox Co, 67-68, lead engr, 69; ADV. ENGR, UNITED NUCLEAR CORP, ELMSFORD, 70- Am. Nuclear Soc. Reactor physics; kinetics; methods development; reactor pulse and wave propagation; reactor heat transfer; xenon oscillation; direct energy conversion. Address: Amberlands Bldg. 3, Apt. A, Albany Post Rd, Croton-on-Hudson, NY 10520.

DOSKOTCH, RAYMOND W(ALTER), b. Husiatyn, West. Ukraine, May 23, 32; Can. citizen; m. 55; c. 2. PHARMACOGNOSY, BIOCHEMISTRY. B.Sc, McMaster, 55, M.S, Wisconsin, 57, Du Pont fel, 58, Ph.D.(biochem), 59. Res. assoc, Enzyme Inst, Wisconsin, 59-60; unit head, Mich. Dept. Health Labs, 60-61; asst. prof. res, sch. pharm, Wisconsin, 61-63; asst. prof. pharmacog, col. pharm, OHIO STATE UNIV, 63-66, assoc. prof, 66-70, PROF. BIOCHEM, COL. BIOL, SCI. & PROF. NATURAL PROD. CHEM, COL. PHARM, 70- Am. Soc. Pharmacog; Am. Chem. Soc; The Chem. Soc. Isolation of biologically active natural products and structure determination biosynthesis of natural products. Address: Ohio State University College of Pharmacy, 500 W. 12th Ave, Columbus, OH 43210.

DOS PASSOS, CYRIL F(RANKLIN), b. New York, N.Y, Feb. 7, 87; m. 27; c. 1. ENTOMOLOGY. LL.B, N.Y. Law School, 09; hon. Sc.D, Wittenberg, 65. Res. assoc, dept. insects & spiders, Am. Mus. Natural Hist, 36-70; Carnegie Mus, 52-70; RETIRED. Entom. Soc. Am; Soc. Syst. Zool; Lepidop. Soc; Entom. Soc. Can; Royal Entom. Soc. London. Lepidoptera; Rhopalocera; Satyridae. Address: Washington Corners, Mendham, NJ 07945.

DOSS, DEVA CHITHA, b. Sattur, Madras, India, Jan. 1, 39. MATHEMATICS. B.S, Madras, 58; M.S, Poona, 60, Ph.D.(math. statist), 63. Instr. MATH, Spicer Mem. Col, India, 58-59; asst. prof, Oakwood Col, 64-65; Univ. Sask, 65-69; ASSOC. PROF, UNIV. ALA, HUNTSVILLE, 69- Am. Statist. Asn. Truncated and censored samples; parametric estimation. Address: P.O. Box 1247, University of Alabama, Huntsville, AL 35807.

DOSS, MILDRED A(NN), b. Lewistown, Ill, Sept. 2, 03. PARASITOLOGY. A.B, New Mexico, 25; B.L.S, Illinois, 28. Parasitologist in charge index-catalogue med. & vet. zool, animal parasites lab, animal disease & parasite res. div, Agr. Res. Serv, U.S. Dept. Agr, 36-60; RES. ASSOC. ZOOL, UNIV. MD, COLLEGE PARK, 61- Superior serv. award, U.S. Dept. Agr, 53. Fel. AAAS; Am. Soc. Parasitol. Zoological nomenclature; bibliography of animal parasites. Address: 109 Park Valley Rd, Silver Spring, MD 20910.

DOSS, NAGIB A, b. Cairo, Egypt, May 17, 28; U.S. citizen; m. 59; c. 6. ORGANIC CHEMISTRY. B.Sc, Cairo, 50, M.Sc, 54, Ph.D.(org. chem), 58. Instr. chem, Cairo, 50-55, lectr, teachers col, 55-56; instr, Ohio State, 56-58; chemist, Toms River Chem. Corp, 58-63; Gen. Aniline & Film Corp, 63-70; RES. ASSOC, ALLIED CHEM. CORP, BUFFALO, 70- Am. Chem. Soc; Am. Asn. Textile Chem. & Colorists. Dyes, intermediates and chemicals. Address: 16 Eastwick Dr, Williamsville, NY 14221.

DOSS, RAOUF, b. Cairo, Egypt, Sept. 9, 15; m. 52; c. 3. MATHEMATICS. Lic es sc, Paris, 38; Ph.D.(math), Cairo, 44. Lectr. MATH, Alexandria, 43-50, assoc. prof, 50-54; prof, Cairo, 54-65; vis. prof, Illinois, Urbana, 65-66; PROF, STATE UNIV. N.Y. STONY BROOK, 66- Mem, Inst. Adv. Study, 49-50. State prize sci, Egypt, 51, 64; Prix France-Egypte, 52. Abstract harmonic analysis. Address: Dept. of Mathematics, State University of New York at Stony Brook, Stony Brook, NY 11790.

DOSSEL, WILLIAM E(DWARD), b. St. Louis, Mo, Apr. 16, 20; m. 55; c. 2. HISTOLOGY, EMBRYOLOGY. B.A, Ill. Col, 48; M.S, Marquette, 50; Bruce fel, Hopkins, 54, Ph.D.(zool), 54. Asst. zool, Marquette, 48-50; jr. instr, Hopkins, 50-53; instr. ANAT, sch. med, North Carolina, 54-57, asst. prof, 57-60; assoc. prof, SCH. MED, CREIGHTON UNIV, 60-69, PROF, 69-, CHMN. DEPT, 70-, acting chmn, 69-70. Asst, Marine Biol. Lab, Woods Hole, Mass, 52-54. U.S.A, 42-46, Res, 46-57, Capt. Am. Asn. Anat; Electron Micros. Soc. Am. Functional and morphological development of chick endocrine organs; fine structure chick embryonic organs. Address: Dept. of Anatomy, Creighton University School of Medicine, 657 N. 27th St, Omaha, NE 68131.

DOSSETOR, JOHN BEAMISH, b. Bangalore, India, July 19, 25; Can. citizen; m. 57; c. 4. TRANSPLANTATION IMMUNOLOGY, NEPHROLOGY. B.A, Oxford, 46, M.A. & B.M, B.Ch, 50; Ph.D, McGill Univ, 61. Asst. prof. med. & exp. surg, McGill Univ, 61-69; PROF. MED, HEAD DIV. NEPHROLOGY & CHMN. MED. RES. COUN. TRANSPLANTATION GROUP, 69- Fel, Royal Col. Physicians Can, 57. R.A.M.C, 51-53, Maj. Am. Soc. Artificial Internal Organs; fel. Am. Col. Physicians; Can. Physiol. Soc; Can. Soc. Chemother; Am. Soc. Nephrology; Can. Soc. Immunol; Transplantation Soc. Address: Clinical Sciences Bldg, University of Alberta, Edmonton, Alta, Can.

DOSSO, HARRY WILLIAM, b. Gull Lake, Sask, Jan. 9, 32; m. 56; c. 4. NUCLEAR PHYSICS, GEOPHYSICS. B.A, British Columbia, 55, Nat. Res. Coun. Can. fel, 56-57, M.Sc, 57, Ph.D, 67. Instr. PHYSICS, UNIV. VICTORIA (B.C), 57-58, asst. prof, 59-65, assoc. prof, 66-69, PROF. & HEAD DEPT, 69- Res. tech. officer, Pac. Naval Lab, Defence Res. Bd. Can, 58-63; Nat. Res. Coun. & Defence Res. Bd. Can. grants, 65- Can. Asn. Physicists; Am. Geophys. Union. Low energy nuclear physics; underwater acoustics; electromagnetic fields; geomagnetic micropulsations and magnetotelluric modelling; analytical and analogue methods of studying electromagnetic variations at the earth's surface. Address: Dept. of Physics, University of Victoria, Victoria, B.C, Can.

DOST, FRANK NORMAN, b. Seattle, Wash, Mar. 24, 26; m. 50; c. 2. PHYSIOLOGY, TOXICOLOGY. B.S. & D.V.M, Wash. State Univ, 51; M.S, Kans. State Univ, 59. Private practice, 51-56; instr. physiol. & pharmacol, Kans. State Univ, 56-59; Mark L. Morris Found. fel. & jr. vet, dept. vet. physiol. & pharmacol, Wash. State Univ, 59-62; asst. prof. chem, pharmacol. & vet. med, ORE. STATE UNIV, 62-67; ASSOC. PROF. VET. MED, ENVIRON. HEALTH SERV. CTR, 67- Consult, adv. comt, Environ. Protection Agency, 70-; mem. ad hoc panel toxicol. hydrazines, Nat. Acad. Sci-Nat. Res. Coun, 71- Soc. Toxicol; Am. Soc. Vet. Physiol. & Pharmacol; Am. Asn. Lab. Animal Sci. Effects of intoxicants on biochemical and physiological mechanisms and metabolic fate of intoxicants. Address: Environmental Health Science Center, Oregon State University, Corvallis, OR 97331.

DOSTAL, HERBERT C, b. Ludington, Mich, Oct. 9, 30; m. 51; c. 6. PLANT PHYSIOLOGY, HORTICULTURE. B.S, Mich. State, 60, M.S, 62, Ph.D.(hort), 63. Asst. prof. HORT, Idaho, 63-64; PURDUE UNIV, 64-70, ASSOC. PROF, 70- U.S.A.F, 51-55. Am. Soc. Hort. Sci. Biochemistry and physiology of ripening and senescence of fruit tissues. Address: Dept. of Horticulture, Purdue University, Lafayette, IN 47907.

DOTEN, ROBERT K(INGSLAND), b. Boston, Mass, Dec. 8, 05; m. 31. GEOLOGY. B.S. Mass. Inst. Tech, 27, M.S, 29; Ph.D.(geol), Princeton, 36. Instr. mineral, Mass. Inst. Tech, 29-32; consult, Nat. Recovery Admin, 33-34, geologist, 36-41; private practice, 47-50; from assoc. prof. to prof. geol, Univ. Vt, 51-69; RETIRED. U.S.A, 42-46, Lt.Col. Geol. Soc. Am; Mineral. Soc. Am; Am. Geochem. Soc; Mineral. Asn. Can. Origin and interrelationships of igneous and metamorphic rock through study of physical chemical reactions and geochemical data. Address: 8335 Garden Home Rd, Portland, OR 97223.

DOTO, IRENE L(OUISE), b. Wilmington, Del, May 7, 22. STATISTICS. B.A, Pennsylvania, 43; M.A, Temple, 48; Columbia, 54. Instr. math, Temple Univ, 46-53; statistician, epidemiology br, U.S. PUB. HEALTH SERV, 54-55, Kansas City Field Sta, 55-66, CHIEF STATIST. & PUB. SERV, ECOL. INVEST. PROG, CTR. DISEASE CONTROL, 66- Lectr, med. sch, Univ. Kans, 62; adj. assoc. prof, Kans. State Univ, 71- Am. Statist. Asn; Inst. Math. Statist; Biomet. Soc; Int. Statist. Inst; Am. Pub. Health Asn; Royal Soc. Health; Am. Thoracic Soc; Wildlife Soc; Soc. Epidemiol. Res; Sci. Res. Soc. Am. Biostatistics; epidemiology; cooperative clinical trials. Address: Center for Disease Control, U.S. Public Health Service, 2002 W. 39th St, Kansas City, KS 66103.

DOTSON, G(EORGE) KENNETH, b. Kingman, Ind, Jan. 16, 18; m. 49; c. 2. AGRICULTURE, AGRONOMY. B.Sc, Illinois, 40. Soil scientist, U.S. Soil Conserv. Serv, 42-52; soil technician IV, div. lands & soils, Ohio Dept. Natural Resources, 53-55, asst. chief, 55-57, chief, 57-68; RES. SOIL SCIENTIST, R.A. TAFT WATER RES. CTR, ENVIRON. PROTECTION AGENCY, 68- Am. Soc. Agron; Soil Sci. Soc. Am; Soil Conserv. Soc. Am. Use of land surface for utilization and recycle of wastes. Address: R.A. Taft Water Research Center, Environmental Protection Agency, 4676 Columbia Pkwy, Cincinnati, OH 45226.

DOTT, ROBERT H(ENRY), b. Sioux City, Iowa, Jan. 8, 96; m. 22; c. 2. GEOLOGY. B.S.F, Michigan, 17, A.M, 20. Asst. mineral, Michigan, 16-17, geol, 19-20; geologist, Empire Gas & Fuel Co, 17-19; for. prod. dept, Standard Oil Co. of N.J, 20-22; Carter Oil Co, 22-26; Mid-Continent Petrol. Corp, 26-29; chief geologist, Sunray Oil Co, 29-31; consult. geologist, 31-35; dir, Okla. Geol. Surv, 35-52; exec. dir, AM. ASN. PETROL. GEOL, 52-63, ED. CONSULT, 63-, distinguished lectr, 51, 57. Mem, Int. Geol. Cong, 33, 56, 60. U.S.A.A.F, 18-19. Hon. mem. Am. Asn. Petrol. Geol.(assoc. ed, 31-51, secy-treas, 51); fel. Geol. Soc. Am; hon. mem. Asn. Am. State Geol. Economic geology of petroleum and industrial minerals; stratigraphy, especially of mid-continent region; structure of the Arbuckle Mountains and other parts of Oklahoma; groundwater of Oklahoma and the southwest. Address: American Association of Petroleum Geologists, P.O. Box 979, Tulsa, OK 74101.

DOTT, ROBERT H(ENRY), JR, b. Tulsa, Okla, June 2, 29; m. 51. GEOLOGY. B.S, Univ. Mich, 50, M.S, 51; Atomic Energy Comn. fel, Columbia Univ, 51-53, Ph.D, 55. Field asst, U.S. Geol. Surv, 47-48; asst. struct. geol, Univ. Mich, 50-51; geologist, Humble Oil & Ref. Co, 54-58; assoc. prof. GEOL, UNIV. WIS, MADISON, 58-66, PROF, 66- With Cambridge Res. Ctr, U.S. Air Force, 56-57; mem, Comn. on Educ. in Geol. Sci, 67-69; consult, Roan Selection Trust, Zambia, 67; vis. prof, Univ. Calif, Berkeley, 69; lectr, Tulsa Univ, 69. U.S.A.F.R, 50-64, Capt; Commendation Ribbon. Geol. Soc. Am; Am. Asn. Petrol. Geol.(pres. award, 56); Am. Soc. Paleont. & Mineral; Int. Asn. Sedimentol. Sedimentology and tectonics of mobile belts, particularly Pacific Northwest, Southern Chile, Antarctic Peninsula and Lake Superior-Precambrian; Pennsylvania age rocks of Nevada; submarine sliding; clastic intrusions. Address: Dept. of Geology & Geophysics, University of Wisconsin, Madison, WI 53705.

DOTTERWEICH, FRANK H(ENRY), b. Baltimore, Md, Dec. 11, 05; m. 46. CHEMICAL ENGINEERING. B.E, Hopkins, 28, Ph.D.(chem. eng), 37. From cadet engr. to asst. gen. supt. gas opers, Consol. Gas, Elec. Light & Power Co, 28-34; instr. & coach, Hopkins, 34-37; assoc. prof. ENG, TEX. A&I UNIV, 37-41, PROF, 41-, dean eng, 64-71, dir. div, 46-64. Tech. consult, Petrol. Admin. War, 42-45; Nat. Gas & Gasoline. Am. Chem. Soc; Am. Inst. Mining, Metall. & Petrol. Eng; Am. Inst. Chem. Eng; Am. Gas. Asn. Processing of gas-condensate reservoirs; chemicals from gas. Address: School of Engineering, Texas A&I University, Kingsville, TX 78363.

DOTTI, L(OUIS) B(ASIL), b. New York, N.Y, Aug. 13, 03; m. 32; c. 2. PHYSIOLOGY. B.S, Columbia, 29, A.M, 31, Ph.D.(physiol), 36. Asst. res, col. physicians & surgeons, Columbia, 29-31, physiol, 31-34, instr, 34-36; asst. prof. physiol. & biochem, N.Y. Med. Col, 36-43, assoc, 43-44; chemist, ST. LUKE'S HOSP, NEW YORK, N.Y, 42-68, CONSULT. CLIN. CHEMIST, 68-, asst. dir. labs, 52-68. Lectr, N.Y. Med. Col, 44-62; consult. biochemist, dept. health, St. Luke's hosp, N.Y.C; Continental Ins. Co. Dipl, Am. Bd. Clin. Chem, 51. AAAS; Harvey Soc; Am. Chem. Soc; Am. Physiol. Soc; Am. Asn. Clin. Chem.(treas, 48-59); Soc. Exp. Biol. & Med; N.Y. Acad. Sci. Carbohydrate and calcium metabolism; liver function tests; cholesterol metabolism and atherosclerosis. Address: 80 W. Oakdene Ave, Palisades Park, NJ 07650.

DOTY, COY WILLIAM, b. Cleveland, Ala, Sept. 18, 31; m. 51; c. 4. AGRICULTURAL ENGINEERING. B.S.A.E, Auburn Univ, 58; M.S.A.E, S.Dak. State Univ, 68. Res. agr. engr, sedimentation lab, soil & water conserv. res. div, Agr. Res. Serv, U.S. DEPT. AGR, Miss, 58-64, S.Dak, 64-68, AGR. ENGR, COASTAL PLAINS SOIL & WATER CONSERV. RES. CTR, 68-

U.S.A, 52-54, Sgt. Am. Soc. Agr. Eng; Soil Conserv. Soc. Am. Investigations on sediment yield and delivery, soil erosion, runoff, moisture conservation, tillage, irrigation and drainage on agricultural lands. Address: Coastal Plains Soil & Water Conservation Research Center, U.S. Dept. of Agriculture, P.O. Box 3039, Florence, SC 29501.

DOTY, D(ELBERT) M(ALCOLM), b. Union Co, Ind, Apr. 27, 08; m. 30; c. 2. AGRICULTURAL BIOCHEMISTRY. B.S.A, Purdue, 29, M.S, 32, Ph.D.(agr. chem), 41. Asst. chemist, exp. sta, Purdue, 29-41, acting head dept. agr. chem, 41-43, asst. chief dept. & assoc. prof. biochem, 43-48; chemist & asst. dir. res. & educ, Am. Meat Inst. Food, 48-56, assoc. dir. res. & educ, 56-61, dir, 61-64; TECH. DIR, FATS & PROTEINS RES. FOUND, INC, 64- Am. Chem. Soc; Inst. Food Technol; Am. Oil Chemists' Soc; Am. Meat Sci. Asn. Plant biochemistry; enzyme chemistry; chemistry of meat; protein chemistry. Address: Fats & Proteins Research Foundation, Inc, 3150 Des Plaines Ave, Des Plaines, IL 60018.

DOTY, J(OHN) ROY, b. Stuttgart, Ark, Feb. 13, 06; m. 30; c. 1. PHYSIOLOGY, BIOCHEMISTRY. B.S, Monmouth Col, 27; Ph.D.(biochem), Illinois, 33. Instr. chem, Monmouth Col, 28-30; asst, Illinois, 33-35; instr. physiol, sch, med, La. State, 35-41, asst. prof, 41-43; sr. chemist, bur. chem, Am. Dent. Asn, 43-48, secy. coun. dent. therapeut, 49-69, asst. secy. asn. res. & therapeut, 61-71; CONSULT, 71- Mem, Nat. Avd. Dent. Res. Coun, 55-59. Am. Dent. Asn; Am. Chem. Soc; Am. Soc. Biol. Chem; Int. Asn. Dent. Res. Intestinal absorption; metabolism of amino acids; renal tubular reabsorption of amino acids and related compounds; chemical procedures; analysis of pharmaceutical products. Address: 411 Taylor Ave, Glen Ellyn, IL 60137.

DOTY, MAXWELL STANFORD, b. Portland, Ore, Aug. 11, 16; m. 40; c. 3. BOTANY. B.S, Ore. State Col, 40, M.S, 42; Ph.D.(biol), Stanford, 45. Asst. bot, Ore. State Col, 39-41; biol, Stanford, 41-45; instr. BOT, Northwestern, 45-46, asst. prof, 46-50; assoc. prof, UNIV. HAWAII, 50-54, PROF. & CHMN. DEPT, 54- Head dept. bot, marine biol. lab, Woods Hole Oceanog. Inst, 46-51. AAAS; Am. Soc. Limnol. & Oceanog; Bot. Soc. Am; Ecol. Soc. Am; Phycol. Soc. Am. Marine algae; primary productivity and ecology. Address: Dept. of Botany, University of Hawaii, Honolulu, HI 96822.

DOTY, MITCHELL E(MERSON), b. Clarksville, Iowa, Aug. 18, 31; m. 59; c. 1. INORGANIC CHEMISTRY. B.A, Mankato State Col, 56; M.S, Nebraska, 59; Ph.D.(inorg. chem), Kansas State, 63. Res. chemist, Phillips Petrol. Co, 63-64; INVESTR, N.J. ZINC CO, PALMERTON, 64- U.S.A, 54-55. Am. Chem. Soc; Faraday Soc. Inorganic-physical chemistry. Address: P.O. Box 51, Archbald, PA 18403.

DOTY, PAUL M(EAD), b. Charleston, W.Va, June 1, 20; m. 42, 54; c. 4. BIOCHEMISTRY. B.S, Pa. State, 41; M.A, Columbia, 43, Ph.D.(chem), 44. Instr. chem, Polytech. Inst. Brooklyn, 43-45, asst. prof, 45-46; Notre Dame, 46-48; asst. prof. phys. chem, HARVARD, 48-50, assoc. prof. chem, 50-56, PROF, 56-68, BIOCHEM. & MOLECULAR BIOL, 68-, chmn. dept, 67-70. Ed, J. Polymer Sci, 45-61; Rockefeller fel, Cambridge Univ, 46-47; Harvey Lectr, 59-60; ed, J. Molecular Biol, 59-63; chmn. sci. adv. cmt. Soviet-Am. exchanges, Nat. Acad. Sci, 61-63; mem, President's Sci. Adv. Cmt, 61-65; consult, U.S. Arms Control & Disarmament Agency, 61-; chmn. cmt. rev. gen. ed, Harvard, 62-64; mem, Coun. For. Relations, 62- Fel. Nat. Acad. Sci; Am. Chem. Soc.(pure chem. award, 56); Fedn. Am. Sci; Am. Soc. Biol. Chem; fel. Am. Acad. Arts & Sci; Fedn. Am. Socs. Exp. Biol. Molecular biology; structure, properties and function of nucleic acids and proteins. Address: Dept. of Biochemistry & Molecular Biology, Harvard University, Cambridge, MA 02138.

DOTY, ROBERT BRUCE, b. Ironton, Ohio, Apr. 16, 28; m. 58; c. 3. BACTERIOLOGY. B.S, Maryland, 50; M.S, Florida, 56; Ph.D.(bact), Pa. State, 62. Lab. technician, U.S. Pub. Health Serv, 50-51; asst. bact, Florida, 56-57; instr. MICROBIOL, PA. STATE UNIV, 62-67, ASST. PROF, 67- A.U.S, 51-53, Sgt. AAAS; Am. Soc. Microbiol; Am. Inst. Biol. Sci. Early laboratory diagnosis of caseous lymphadenitis in sheep and goats. Address: Dept. of Microbiology, Pennsylvania State University, University Park, PA 16802.

DOTY, ROBERT L, b. Missouri Valley, Iowa, Aug. 2, 18. ELECTRICAL ENGINEERING. B.S, Univ. Iowa, 48; Ph.D, Iowa State Univ, 55. Instr. elec. eng, Iowa State Univ, 53-55, asst. prof, 55-59; sect. chief preliminary eng, data systs. div, AUTONETICS DIV, N.Am. Aviation, Inc, 59-62, chief engr, 62-65, DIR. ADVAN. ANAL, N.AM. ROCKWELL CORP, 65- U.S.N, 42-45. Control theory; inertial navigation; digital computers. Address: Autonetics Division, North American Rockwell Corp, 3370 Miraloma Ave, Anaheim, CA 92803.

DOTY, ROBERT W(ILLIAM), b. New Rochelle, N.Y, Jan. 10, 20; m. 41; c. 4. NEUROPHYSIOLOGY, NEUROPSYCHOLOGY. B.S, Chicago, 48, M.S, 49, Ph.D.(physiol), 50. U.S. Pub. Health Serv. fel, neurophysiol, neuropsychiat. inst, Illinois, 50-51; asst. prof. PHYSIOL, col. med, Utah, 51-56; med. sch, Michigan, 56-57, assoc. prof, 58-61, PROF, CTR. BRAIN RES, SCH. MED, UNIV. ROCHESTER, 61- Mem, Nat. Eye Inst. Visual Sci. Study Sect, 68-72; Int. Brain Res. Orgn; Ed, Neurosci. Transl; Exp. Neurol; Acta Neurobiologiae Experimentalis; Conditional Reflex. U.S.A, 41-46, Capt. Am. Physiol. Soc; Pavlovian Soc. N.Am; Soc. Neurosci; Am. Psychol. Asn; Psychonomic Soc. Visual cortex; reflex deglutition; conditioned reflexes. Address: Center for Brain Research, University of Rochester School of Medicine, Rochester, NY 14620.

DOTY, STEPHEN BRUCE, b. DeKalb, Ill, Nov. 20, 38; m. 60. BIOLOGY. B.A, Rice, 61, M.A, 63, Ph.D.(biol), 65. Instr. radiol. sci, SCH. HYG. & PUB. HEALTH & orthop. surg, UNIV. HOSP, JOHNS HOPKINS UNIV, 65-67, asst. prof. radiol. sci, sch. & orthop. surg, hosp, 67-69, ASSOC. PROF. RADIOL. SCI, SCH. & ORTHOP. SURG, HOSP, 69- Bowles Found. res. grant, 65-69. Electron microscopy and histochemistry of bone cells and bone matrix as found in the normal, the external and internally irradiated, and after hormonal treatments. Address: Dept. of Orthopedic Surgery, Johns Hopkins Hospital, Baltimore, MD 21205.

DOTY, W(ILLIAM) D'ORVILLE, b. Rochester, N.Y, March 11, 20; m. 45; c. 2. METALLURGY. B.Met.E, Rensselaer Polytech, 42, M.Met.E, 44, Ph.D.(metall), 46. Welding res. fel. & asst, Rensselaer Polytech, 42-46, supvr, 46-47; welding metallurgist, Carnegie-Illinois Steel Corp, 47-52, U.S. STEEL CORP, 52-57, div. chief bar, plate & forged prods, 58-66, RES. CONSULT. STEEL PROD. DEVELOP, APPL. RES. LAB, 66- With Off. Sci. Res. & Develop, 44; chmn. pressure vessel res. comt, Welding Res. Coun; mem. heavy sect. steel technol. comt, Atomic Energy Comn-Oak Ridge Nat. Lab; adv. comt, ship hull res. comt, Nat. Res. Coun. Am. Inst. Mining, Metall. & Petrol. Eng; Am. Soc. Metals; Am. Welding Soc; Am. Soc. Mech. Eng; Brit. Inst. Welding. Development and application of new and improved carbon, high-strength low-alloy and high-yield-strength alloy steels; weldability of steels, especially quenched and tempered carbon and alloy steels; design, material selection and fabrication of pressure vessels and structures. Address: Applied Research Lab, U.S. Steel Corp, Monroeville, PA 15146.

DOTY, WILLIAM EARL NEAL, b. Webb City, Mo, Apr. 2, 26; m. 47; c. 4. GEOPHYSICS. B.S, Okla. Agr. & Mech. Col, 48; Sloan fel, 62; S.M, Mass. Inst. Tech, 63. Develop. engr, CONTINENTAL OIL CO, 48-50, res. geophysicist, 50-51, sr. res. geophysicist, 51-53, res. group leader, 53-55, supvry. res. geophysicist, 55-60, dir. explor. res, 60-64, mgr. explor, 64-66, V.PRES, 66-70, NEW BUS. DEVELOP, ADMIN. DEPT, WEST. HEMISPHERE PETROL. DIV, 70- U.S.N, 46-47, Lt.(jg), Soc. Explor. Geophys.(award); Am. Geophys. Union. Methods and instrumentation related to seismic exploration of earth. Address: Administration Dept, Western Hemisphere Petroleum Division, Continental Oil Co, P.O. Box 2197, Houston, TX 77001.

DOTZENKO, ALEXANDER D(ANIEL), b. Sandpoint, Idaho, Feb. 8, 20; m. 41; c. 4. AGRONOMY. B.Sc, Idaho, 41; Ph.D.(crops), Rutgers, 50. Asst, Rutgers, 49-50; asst. prof. & asst. agronomist, New Mexico State, 50-52; assoc. prof. agron. & assoc. agronomist, COLO. STATE UNIV, 52-67, PROF. AGRON. & AGRONOMIST, 67- U.S.A, 43-46, 1st Lt. Am. Soc. Agron. Forage crops; production, genetics and physiological factors related to forage grasses and legumes. Address: Dept. of Agronomy, Colorado State University, Ft. Collins, CO 80521.

DOUB, W(ILLIAM) B(LAKE), b. Rocky Mt, N.C, Dec. 10, 24; m. 64. NUCLEAR PHYSICS. Ph.D.(nuclear physics), California, Los Angeles, 56. SR. SCIENTIST, BETTIS ATOMIC POWER LAB, WESTINGHOUSE ELEC. CORP, WEST MIFFLIN, 57- U.S.A.F, 43-45. Am. Phys. Soc; Am. Nuclear Soc. Nucleon-nucleon low energy scattering; reactor physics. Address: 628 Rolling Green Dr, Bethel Park, PA 15102.

DOUBLES, JAMES A(RTHUR), b. Richmond, Va, Jan. 9, 14. MYCOLOGY. A.B, North Carolina, 35, M.A, 38, Ph.D.(bot), 40. Instr. bot, Campbell Jr. Col, 41-42; asst. prof. BIOL, W.Ga. Col, 42-46; assoc. prof, Birmingham-Southern Col, 47-60, prof, 60-69; ASSOC. PROF, TROY STATE UNIV, 69- Fel. AAAS; assoc. Bot. Soc. Am; assoc. Mycol. Soc. Am; Am. Fern Soc. Taxonomy of seed plants of Georgia and Alabama; taxonomic study of myxomycetes of Southeastern United States. Address: Dept. of Biology, Troy State University, Troy, AL 36081.

DOUDNEY, C(HARLES) O(WEN), b. Dallas, Tex, Nov. 5, 25; div; c. 1. BIOCHEMISTRY, GENETICS. Ph.D.(genetics), Texas, 53. Res. biologist, Texas, 51-53; assoc. biologist, Oak Ridge Nat. Lab, 53-55; res. assoc, Pennsylvania, 55-56; assoc. biologist, Univ. Tex. M.D. Anderson Hosp. & Tumor Inst, 56-60, biologist, 60-67, chief sect. genetics, 56-67, assoc. prof. biol, post-grad. sch. med, 57-67, assoc, grad. sch. biomed. sci, 63-67; HEAD DEPT. GENETICS, ALBERT EINSTEIN MED. CTR, 67- U.S.A, 43-45. Genetics Soc. Am; Am. Soc. Microbiol. Biochemistry and genetics of neurospora; radiation protection and recovery of microorganisms; mutation; macromolecular synthesis; ultraviolet effects on microorganisms; human genetics; medical genetics; mutation in mammalian cell lines and carcinogenesis. Address: 364 Williams Rd, Wynnewood, PA 19096.

DOUDOROFF, MICHAEL, b. Petrograd, Russia, Nov. 14, 11; nat; m. 52; c. 1. MICROBIOLOGY. A.B, Stanford, 33, A.M, 34, Ph.D.(microbiol), 39. Asst, Stanford, 34-39; instr. BACT, UNIV. CALIF, BERKELEY, 40-43, asst. prof, 43-47, assoc. prof, 47-52, PROF, 52-, MOLECULAR BIOL, 64- Guggenh2im fel, 49-50; res. prof, Miller Inst, 59-61; Nat. Insts. Health sr. res. fel, 62. Sugar Res. Found. Prize, 46. Nat. Acad. Sci; Am. Soc. Microbiol; Soc. Gen. Physiol; Am. Soc. Biol. Chem. Nutritional requirements and metabolism of bacteria; bacterial enzymes; carbohydrate metabolism; bacterial taxonomy and phylogeny. Address: Dept. of Bacteriology, University of California, Berkeley, CA 94720.

DOUDOROFF, PETER, b. Libau, Russia, June 22, 13; nat; m. 38, 48, 68; c. 1. ZOOLOGY. A.B, Stanford, 35; Ph.D.(zool), California, 41. Asst. biologist, U.S. Bur. Fisheries, 34; asst. biol, Stanford, 34-35; oceanog, Scripps Inst, California, 35-41; biologist, La. State Dept. Conserv, 41-45; aquatic biologist, U.S. Fish & Wildlife Serv, Wash. & Ore, 46-47; biologist, U.S. Pub. Health Serv, Ohio, 47-50, fisheries res. biologist, 50-53, supvry. fishery res. biologist, Ore, 53-65; PROF. FISHERIES, ORE. STATE UNIV, 54- AAAS; Am. Fisheries Soc; Am. Soc. Ichthyol. & Herpet; Am. Soc. Limnol. & Oceanog; Water Pollution Control Fedn; Int. Asn. Theoret. & Appl. Limnol. Ecology, physiology and toxicology of fresh-water and marine fishes; inland fisheries biology; water pollution and sanitation. Address: Dept. of Fisheries & Wildlife, Oregon State University, Corvallis, OR 97331.

DOUGAL, ARWIN A(DELBERT), b. Dunlap, Iowa, Nov. 22, 26; m. 51; c. 4. ELECTRICAL ENGINEERING. B.S, Iowa State Col, 52; M.S, Illinois, 55, Ph.D.(elec. eng), 57. Engr, Collins Radio Co, 52; asst. ELEC. ENG, Illinois, 52-56, res. assoc, 56-57, asst. prof, 57-59, assoc. prof, 59-61; PROF, UNIV. TEX, AUSTIN, 61-, DIR. ELECTRONICS RES. CTR, 71-, dir. labs, electronics & rel. sci. res, 64-67. Asst. dir. defense res. & eng. for res, Dept. of Defense, D.C, 67-69. U.S.A.F, 46-49. Am. Phys. Soc; Inst. Elec. & Electronics Eng; Soc. Eng. Sci. Electrical gaseous discharge and plasma physics; magnetohydrodynamics; controlled thermonuclear fusion; electron physics of the gaseious state; ionization phenomena and physics of the earth-

earth's upper atmosphere; science and technology and lasers and coherent electro-optics; holography; scientific research administration. Address: Dept. of Electrical Engineering, University of Texas at Austin, Austin, TX 78712.

DOUGALL, DONALD K, b. Perth, West. Australia, Dec. 3, 30; m. 56, 69. BIOCHEMISTRY, CELL PHYSIOLOGY. Scholar, Australian Nat. Univ, 53-56; M.Sc, Western Australia, 54; D.Phil, Oxford, 56. Nat. Res. Coun. Can. fel, 56-57; proj. assoc. biochem, Wisconsin, 57-59; lectr, Sydney, 59-63; asst. prof, Ohio State Univ. & Agr. Exp. Sta, 63-67, assoc. prof. bot. & biochem, univ, 67-71; SCIENTIST & ASSOC. DIR, W. ALTON JONES CELL SCI. CTR, 71- Am. Soc. Plant Physiol; Soc. Develop. Biol; Int. Asn. Plant Tissue Cult.(secy, 70-); N.Y. Acad. Sci. Biosynthesis of amino acids; control of metabolism in plants; growth and morphogenesis in plant cell cultures. Address: W. Alton Jones Cell Science Center, P.O. Box 631, Lake Placid, NY 12946.

DOUGALL, RICHARD S(TEPHEN), b. Schenectady, N.Y, Apr. 22, 37; m. 67; c. 3. HEAT TRANSFER, FLUID MECHANICS. B.S.M.E, Union Col. (N.Y), 59; Gen. Elec. Found. fel, Mass. Inst. Technol, 59, S.M, 60, M.E. & Sc.D, 63. Res. asst, heat transfer lab, Mass. Inst. Technol, 60-63; asst. prof. MECH. ENG, UNIV. PITTSBURGH, 63-68, ASSOC. PROF, 68- Consult, adv. bd. on hardened elec. power systs, Nat. Acad. Sci, 64-66; Westinghouse Nuclear Energy Systs, 67- Am. Soc. Mech. Eng; Am. Soc. Eng. Educ; Am. Nuclear Soc; Soc. Natural Philos. Boiling heat transfer and two-phase flow in engineering systems; convection and radiation heat transfer. Address: Dept. of Mechanical Engineering, University of Pittsburgh, 4200 Fifth Ave, Pittsburgh, PA 15213.

DOUGH, ROBERT LYLE, b. Ft. Lauderdale, Fla, Aug. 5, 31; m. 53; c. 5. SCIENCE EDUCATION. B.S, Guilford Col, 53; fel, Vanderbilt, 53-54; M.S, N.C. State, 56, Ph.D.(appl. physics), 62. Instr. physics, N.C. State Col, 56-60; assoc. nuclear engr, Astra, Inc, 60-61; asst. prof. physics, N.C. State Univ, 62-68; ASSOC. PROF. SCI. EDUC, E.CAROLINA UNIV, 68- Summer designer nuclear eng, Newport News Shipbldg. & Dry Dock Co, 56; vis. asst. prof, ctr. res. in col. instr. sci. & math, Fla. State Univ, 67-68. Health Phys. Soc; Am. Asn. Physics Teachers. Introductory physics education. Address: Dept. of Science Education, East Carolina University, Greenville, NC 27834.

DOUGHERTY, CHARLES ROBERTS GRAFLY, b. Glenside, Pa, Dec. 29, 15; m. 38; c. 2. MECHANICAL ENGINEERING. B.S, Pennsylvania, 37; Iowa State. Asst. supt, Atlas Asbestos Co, Pa, 37-38; instr. MECH. ENG, Iowa State, 38-45, asst. prof, 45-46; RUTGERS UNIV, 46-47, assoc. prof, 47-58, PROF, 58- Summers, asst. res. engr, Boeing Airplane Co, 54; sr. res. engr, Rocketdyne Div, N.Am. Aviation, Inc, 56-57; asst. proj. engr, Pratt & Whitney Aircraft, summers, 58, 59, 61, 64, 65, 67. Am. Soc. Mech. Eng; Am. Soc. Eng. Educ; Am. Inst. Aeronaut. & Astronaut; Combustion Inst. Thermodynamics; combustion; gas dynamics; heat transfer. Address: College of Engineering, Rutgers University, New Brunswick, NJ 08903.

DOUGHERTY, ELLSWORTH, III, b. Phila, Pa, Nov. 29, 18; m. 42; c. 2. CYTOLOGY. B.S, Rutgers, 40; V.M.D, Pennsylvania, 43; M.S, Cornell Univ, 66, Ph.D, 70. Asst. res. specialist poultry, Rutgers, 47-48; asst. prof, Cornell, 49-50, dir. lab, 50-64; leader cytol. invests, Plum Island Animal Disease Lab, U.S. Dept. Agr, 64-66; SR. RES. ASSOC, SPEC. VIRUS CANCER PROG, NAT. CANCER INST, ONCOL. LAB, STATE UNIV. N.Y. VET. COL, CORNELL UNIV, 66- Consult, L.I. Duck Farmers Mkt. Co-op, Inc, 50-64; N.Y. State Dept. Health, 58-64; Smith Kline & French, Pa, 60-64; Food & Drug Res. Lab, 60-64. Mem. res. coun, Inst. Am. Poultry Industs, 55-64. Vet.C, 43-47, Maj. Tissue Culture Asn; Conf. Res. Workers Animal Diseases; Inst. Food Technol; Am. Vet. Med. Asn; N.Y. Acad. Sci. Cytological investigations; pathology; virology; bacteriology. Address: Oncology Lab, State University of New York Veterinary College, Cornell University, Ithaca NY 14850.

DOUGHERTY, HARRY L, b. San Jose, Costa Rica, Sept. 22, 26; U.S. citizen; m. 52; c. 4. ANATOMY, ORTHODONTICS. A.B, California, Berkeley, 51, fel, 51-53, M.A, 53, D.D.S, San Francisco, 57. Fel, inst. exp. biol, California, Berkeley, 51-53; assoc. clinician, Children's Hosp, Los Angeles, 58-60; chief sci, Orthop. Hosp, 60-64; ASSOC. PROF. ORTHOD. & CHMN. DEPT, SCH. DENT, UNIV. SOUTH. CALIF, 60- U.S.N.R, 44-46. AAAS; Am. Asn. Orthod. Cleft palate research. Address: Dept. of Orthodontics, University of Southern California School of Dentistry, Los Angeles, CA 90007.

DOUGHERTY, HARRY W(ILLIAM), b. N.Y.C, Mar. 17, 34; m. 55; c. 2. BIOCHEMISTRY. B.S, City Col. N.Y, 57; Nat. Sci. Found. fels, Columbia Univ, 59-61, Ph.D.(biochem), 62. Instr. biochem, Columbia Univ, 61-62; fel, Duke Univ, 62-64; BIOCHEMIST, MERCK & CO, INC, 64- U.S.A, 53-55. Am. Chem. Soc. Enzymology; biochemistry of parasites; oxidative phosphorylation. Address: Dept. of Biochemistry, Merck & Co, Inc, Rahway, NJ 07016.

DOUGHERTY, JAMES G(REGG), JR, b. N.Y.C, Jan. 13, 26; m. 49; c. 2. ELECTRICAL ENGINEERING. B.S.E.E, Princeton, 48, M.S.E.E, 49. Engr. & sect. leader, VITRO LABS, 48-55, group leader systs. eval, 55-57, acoustics res. group, 57-59, head dept. res. & studies, 59-67, develop. eng. dept, 67-69, asst. head res. dept, 69-71, SR. STAFF ENGR, RES. & DEVELOP. BR, 71- U.S.N, 44-46. Inst. Elec. & Electronics Eng. Electronics; acoustics; operations research; data processing. Address: Vitro Labs, 14000 Georgia Ave, Silver Spring, MD 20910.

DOUGHERTY, JEAN HAY, b. Minneapolis, Minn, Nov. 3, 19; m. 41. HEMATOLOGY. B.S, Minnesota, 40, M.A, 42; M.D, Yale, 47. Asst. anat, med. sch, Minnesota, 41-42; instr. clin. micros, sch. med, Yale, 44-47; lectr. anat, COL. MED, UNIV. UTAH, 47-48, instr. path, 48-52, HEMATOLOGIST, RADIOBIOL. LAB, 52-, ASSOC. RES. PROF. PATH, 70-, asst. res. prof, 63-70. Am. Asn. Cancer Res; Radiation Res. Soc. Cancer biology; bacteriology. Address: Radiobiology Lab, University of Utah College of Medicine, Salt Lake City, UT 84112.

DOUGHERTY, JOHN E, b. Lindsay, La, Feb. 2, 22; m. 44; c. 4. PHYSICS. B.S, La. State, 42; Ph.D.(physics), Michigan, 50. Radio physicist, U.S. Naval Res. Lab, 42-43; instr. physics, La. State, 43-44; mem. staff electronics, California, 44-45; physics lab, Hopkins, 45-46; asst. Michigan, 46-50; MEM. STAFF PHYSICS, LOS ALAMOS SCI. LAB, UNIV. CALIF, 50- Am. Phys. Soc. Nuclear and neutron physics; ferroelectrics; mechanics. Address: 3548 Arizona Ave, Los Alamos, NM 87544.

DOUGHERTY, JOHN JOSEPH, b. Paterson, N.J, Oct. 16, 23; m. 53; c. 4. SYSTEMS ANALYSIS, COLLEGE ADMINISTRATION. B.S, U.S. Naval Acad, 45; Stevens Inst. Tech, 40-42; B.S, U.S. Naval Postgrad. Sch, 52, M.S, 53; Univ. N.Mex, 67; M.S, Univ. Notre Dame, 70. Asst. electronics mat. officer, staff Atlantic Destroyer Force, R.I, 55-57, asst. planning & estimating supt, Mass, 57-60, prog. mgr. res. & develop. commun, Navy Bur. Ships, D.C, 60-62, br. head res. & develop. command support, 62-63, acting dir. res. & develop. warfare systs, 63, asst. dir. Comsat progs, NASA, 63-65; dir. personnel & contracts, sr. res. engr. & mgt. consult, Dikewood Corp, 65-67; opers. analyst, Joint Task Force II, 67-69; dir. systs. anal, Univ. Notre Dame, 69-70; prof. systs. & chmn. systs. ctr, PRESCOTT COL, 70-71, PRES, 71- Consult. long haul commun, Sec. Navy, 60-61; mem. Polaris Command Commun. Comt, 60-63; tech. comt. commun. satellite, NASA-Dept. Defense, 61-65; consult, advan. res. & develop. mgt. prog, Pa. State Univ, 61-63; Blue Ribbon Astronaut, 62; guest lectr, Univ. N.Mex, 65-66. Award, U.S. Navy Bur. Ships, 62. U.S.N, 42-65, Comdr.(Ret). Assoc. fel, Am. Inst. Aeronaut. & Astronaut; sr. mem. Inst. Elec. & Electronics Eng. Communications satellite systems and their sociological impact; education of the engineer and scientist in the humanities; optimization of their organization and efforts. Address: Prescott College, Prescott, AZ 86301.

DOUGHERTY, JOHN WILLIAM, b. Jerome, Ariz, Oct. 13, 25; m. 47; c. 4. SYSTEMS ANALYSIS. B.S, California, Berkeley, 47; Ph.D.(syst. sci), Polytech. Inst. Brooklyn, 69. Test engr, GEN. ELEC. CO, SCHENECTADY, 47-48, design engr, medium steam turbine, generator & gear dept, 48-55, design anal. engr, 55-58, design methods engr, 58-60, consult. eng. ed, corp. eng, 60-71, SR. ENGR. TEST FACILITIES, TURBINE DIV. FACILITIES PLANNING, 71- U.S.N, 44-46. Inst. Elec. & Electronics Eng; Nat. Soc. Prof. Eng. Synchronous generator design; computerated design; Chebyshev approximation theory; engineering education. Address: 3 Frank St, Ballston Lake, NY 12019.

DOUGHERTY, P(ATRICK) H(ENRY), b. Dayton, Ky, Mar. 24, 09; m. 41; c. 1. CHEMISTRY. B.S, Iowa, 30, scholar, 30-31, M.S, 31; Ph.D.(org. chem), Yale, 33. Plant prod, du Pont Rayon Co, 30; lab. instr, Yale, 31-33; chemist, Calco Chem. Co, 33-34; patent specialist, rayon div, E.I. du Pont de Nemours & Co, 34-39; patent attorney, Breisen & Schrenk, 39-40; spec. asst. to v.pres. in charge new prods, Merck & Co, Inc, 40-41; res. chemist & spec. asst, Upjohn Co, 41-43; pres, Dougherty Chem, 45-64; LAB. DIR, FLA. RACING CMN. LAB, 64- Am. Chem. Soc; N.Y. Acad. Sci. Synthesis of organics and biochemicals, particularly pyrimidines and purines; cinchophen analogues and aminoalcohol esters thereof; organic synthesis and organic analysis. Address: 451 N.E. 134th St, North Miami, FL 33161.

DOUGHERTY, RALPH C, b. Dillon, Mont, Jan. 31, 40; m. 60; c. 1. PHYSICAL ORGANIC & BIOLOGICAL CHEMISTRY. B.S, Mont. State Col, 60; Woodrow Wilson fel, Chicago, 60-61, Nat. Sci. Found. fel, 61-63, Ph.D. (phys. org. chem), 63. Resident res. assoc, Argonne Nat. Lab, 63-65; asst. prof. CHEM, Ohio State Univ, 65-69; ASSOC. PROF, FLA. STATE UNIV, 69- AAAS; Am. Chem. Soc; Brit. Chem. Soc. Biogenesis of pyrrole pigments; reactivity of porphyrins and chlorins; organic mass spectrometry; photochemistry; environmental chemistry; prostaglandins. Address: Dept. of Chemistry, Florida State University, Tallahassee, FL 32306.

DOUGHERTY, RICHARD H(AINES), b. Hanover, Pa, Apr. 14, 41; m. 63; c. 1. FOOD SCIENCE, HORTICULTURE. B.S, Univ. Md, College Park, 63, M.S, 66; Ph.D.(food sci), N.C. State Univ, 70. ASST. PROF. FOOD SCI, UNIV. FLA, 69- Inst. Food Technol; Am. Soc. Hort. Sci. Flavors of citrus and tropical fruits; processing and utilization of tropical and subtropical fruits and leguminous vegetables. Address: Dept. of Food Science, University of Florida, Gainesville, FL 32601.

DOUGHERTY, ROBERT M(ALVIN), b. Long Branch, N.J, May 25, 29; m. 50; c. 2. MICROBIOLOGY, VIROLOGY. B.S, Rutgers, 52, M.S, 54, Ph.D.(microbiol), 57. Instr. microbiol, sch. med. & dent, Rochester, 57-60; Nat. Cancer Inst. spec. res. fel. virol, Imp. Cancer Res. Found, London, Eng, 60-62; assoc. prof. MICROBIOL, STATE UNIV, N.Y. UPSTATE MED. CTR, 62-69, PROF, 69- U.S.A, 46-47. AAAS; Am. Soc. Microbiol; N.Y. Acad. Sci; Soc. Exp. Biol. & Med; Am. Asn. Immunol; Brit. Soc. Gen. Microbiol. Virology; virus immunology; viral oncology. Address: Dept. of Microbiology, State University of New York Upstate Medical Center, Syracuse, NY 13210.

DOUGHERTY, R(OBERT) W(ATSON), b. Newcomerstown, Ohio, Feb. 5, 04; m. 48; c. 2. VETERINARY MEDICINE. B.S, Iowa State, 27; D.V.M, Ohio State, 36; M.S, Oregon State, 42. Instr. vet. med, Oregon State, 37-39, asst. prof, 39-42; assoc. prof, State Col. Wash, 46-48; prof, State Univ. N.Y. Vet. Col, Cornell, 48-61, acting head dept. vet. physiol, 53-54; LEADER PHYSIOPATH. INVESTS, NAT. ANIMAL DISEASE LAB, 61- Fulbright scholar, New Zealand, 56-57; prof, Iowa State, 62- Chmn. orgn. & ed. comt, Int. Symposium Physiol. Digestion in Ruminant, 64. Distinguished Alumnus award, Ohio State, 65. U.S.A, 42-46, Lt. Col. AAAS; N.Y. Acad. Sci; Conf. Res. Workers Animal Diseases (pres, 71); Am. Vet. Med. Asn.(Borden Award, 63); Soc. Exp. Biol. & Med; Am. Physiol. Soc. Reproductive physiology in ruminants; bovine spermatozoa and the vaginal pH of the female; formation and absorption of toxins from the bovine rumen; hematological changes in certain pathological conditions in ruminants; physiological studies of acute tympanites in ruminants; including blood and cerebrospinal fluid pressure changes, blood gas changes and cardiac output; cineradiographic studies of eructation in sheep; physiological studies of acute indigestion in ruminants; isotopic studies of the physiologic disposition of inhaled eructated gas in sheep and goats. Address: National Animal Disease Lab, P.O. Box 70, Ames, IA 50010.

DOUGHERTY, THOMAS ANTHONY, b. Wichita, Kans, Dec. 31, 37; m. 63; c. 4. PHYSICAL CHEMISTRY. B.S, Wichita, 60, M.S, 62; Ph.D.(phys. chem), Iowa State, 67. Asst. x-ray crystallog, Ames Lab, Atomic Energy Comn, Iowa State Univ, 62-66; SR. ENGR, BOEING CO, 66- Am. Chem. Soc; Am. Soc. Test. & Mat; Soc. Aerospace Mat. & Process Eng. Development studies on adhesive bonding and advanced composites. Address: Boeing Co, CAG, P.O. Box 3707, Seattle, WA 98124.

DOUGHERTY, THOMAS F(RANCIS), b. Forman, N.Dak, Mar. 27, 15; m. 42; c. 2. CYTOLOGY, ANATOMY. B.S, Minnesota, 36, M.A, 37, Ph.D.(hemat), 42; fel, Oklahoma, 37-39. Asst. anat, Minnesota, 39-42; Int. Cancer Found. fel, Yale, 42-43, instr. anat. & hemat, 43-47; PROF. ANAT, COL. MED, UNIV. UTAH, 47-, CHMN. DEPT, 49-, DIR. RADIOBIOL, LABS, 58- Spec. consult. to Surgeon Gen, U.S. Army. With off. Sci. Res. & Develop, 44. AAAS; Am. Asn. Anat; Am. Physiol. Soc; Soc. Exp. Biol. & Med; Am. Asn. Cancer Res; Endocrine Soc; N.Y. Acad. Sci. Estrogen induced leukemia; site of antibody formation; endocrine control of release of antibodies and growth and physiology of lymphoid tissue; relation of morphology to function of lymphocytes; adrenal cortex; inflammation; allergic phenomenon. Address: 2C109 Medical Center, University of Utah, Salt Lake City, UT 84112.

DOUGHERTY, T(HOMAS) J(OHN), b. Buffalo, N.Y, Aug. 2, 33. ORGANIC CHEMISTRY. B.S, Canisius Col, 55; Nat. Sci. Found. summer fel. & Ph.D. (org. chem), Ohio State, 59. Res. chemist, film dept, Yerkes Res. & Develop. Lab, E.I. du Pont de Nemours & Co, Inc, 59-67, staff scientist, 67-70; CANCER RES. SCIENTIST, ROSEWELL PARK MEM. INST, 70- AAAS; Am. Chem. Soc. Physical-organic chemistry, especially free radical chemistry; photochemistry; radiation chemistry. Address: Rosewell Park Memorial Institute, 666 Elm St, Buffalo, NY 14203.

DOUGHERTY, WILLIAM J, b. Brooklyn, N.Y, June 3, 34; m. 58; c. 2. CELL BIOLOGY, HISTOLOGY. B.S, St. Joseph's Col.(Pa), 56; Long Island, 56-58; M.A, Princeton, 61, Lapham fel, 61-62, Nat. Insts. Health fel, 62-63, Ph.D.(biol), 63. Biochemist, State Univ. N.Y. Downstate Med. Center, 56-59; U.S. Pub. Health Serv. fel, Harvard, 63-64; asst. prof. ANAT, MED. UNIV. S.C, 64-69, ASSOC. PROF, 69- Summers, asst, Marine Biol. Lab, Woods Hole, Mass, 61, res. assoc, 63. U.S.A, 59. Am. Soc. Cell Biol; Am. Soc. Zool; Electron Micros. Soc. Am; Am. Asn. Anat; Histochem. Soc. Cytochemical and electron microscope study of cells and tissues, especially mechanisms of mitosis and cytokinetics and effects of heavy metals and other poisons on mitochondrial structure and function; muscle ultrastructure and cytochemistry. Address: Dept. of Anatomy, Medical University of South Carolina, 80 Barre St, Charleston, SC 29401.

DOUGHTY, CHARLES C(ARTER), b. Alamosa, Colo, Dec. 12, 15; m. 44; c. 2. HORTICULTURE. B.S, Kansas State, 52; Ph.D.(hort), Washington State, 59. Acting supt. HORT, Coastal Wash. Res. & Exten. Unit, WASH. STATE UNIV, 54-65, ASSOC. HORTICULTURIST, WEST. WASH. RES. & EXTEN. CTR, 65- Dow Chem. Co. award, 68. U.S.A.A.F, 41-45, S/Sgt. AAAS; Am. Soc. Hort. Sci. Effects of growth regulators on hardiness and freeze injury in small fruits, herbicide activity and nutrition of horticultural crops. Address: Western Washington Research & Extension Center, Washington State University, Puyallup, WA 98371.

DOUGHTY, CLYDE C(ARL), b. Hutchinson, Kans, July 21, 24; m. 51; c. 4. BIOCHEMISTRY. B.A, Kansas, 48, M.A, 50; Ph.D.(microbiol. biochem), Ill. Inst. Tech, 56. Asst, rheumatic fever res. inst, Northwestern, 51-53; Ill. Inst. Tech, 53-56; res. biochemist, Charles F. Kettering Found, 56-59; res. assoc. biol. chem, COL. MED, UNIV. ILL, CHICAGO CIRCLE, 59-62, from asst. prof. to ASSOC. PROF. BIOL. CHEM. & PREV. MED, 62- U.S.A, 45-47. AAAS; Am. Soc. Microbiol; Am. Soc. Biol. Chem. Enzymology; microbial cell wall; microbial metabolism; immunochemistry. Address: Dept. of Biological Chemistry, University of Illinois at Medical Center, 1853 W. Polk, Chicago, IL 60612.

DOUGHTY, J(OSEPH) BAYNE, b. Ronceverte, W.Va, Jan. 16, 12; m. 35; c. 5. CHEMISTRY. A.B, West Virginia, 33, M.S, 34, Ph.D.(chem), 43. Sanitarian, State Health Dept, W.Va, 34-35; instr. sci. & math, Greenbrier Col, 36-41; asst. instr. chem, West Virginia, 41-43; res. chemist, W.VA. PULP & PAPER CO, 43-51, res. assoc, 51-57, ASST. DIR. RES, 57- Analyst, W.Va. Geol. Surv, 42. Am. Chem. Soc; Forest Prods. Res. Soc; Am. Forestry Asn. Am. Tech. Asn. Pulp & Paper Indust. Chemistry of ethyleneimine; production, properties and uses of lignin and tall oil manufacturing saturating papers, laminates and corrugated board. Address: Research Lab, West Virginia Pulp & Paper Co, N. Charleston, SC 29406.

DOUGHTY, JULIAN O, b. Tuscaloosa, Ala, June 11, 33; m. 56; c. 2. FLUID MECHANICS, RHEOLOGY. B.S, Miss. State, 56, M.S, 60; Ph.D.(eng. sci), Tennessee, 66. Design engr, McDonnell Aircraft Co, 56-57; instr. eng. graphics, Miss. State, 57-60; instr. & res. asst. basic. eng. & eng. mech, Tennessee, 60-66; asst. prof. AEROSPACE ENG, UNIV. ALA, TUSCALOOSA, 66-70, ASSOC. PROF, 70- Participant, NASA-Am. Soc. Eng. Educ. summer faculty fel. prog, Marshall Space Flight Ctr, 67, 70; NASA res. grant, 71. Mem, educ. & student affairs comt, Am. Inst. Aeronaut. & Astronaut, 69, 70. Am. Inst. Aeronaut. & Astronaut; Soc. Natural Philos. Aerodynamics; viscoelastic fluids. Address: Dept. of Aerospace & Mechanical Engineering & Engineering Mechanics, Box 6307, University of Alabama, University, AL 35486.

DOUGHTY, MARK, b. Hull, Eng, Dec. 20, 21; m. 49; c. 7. ORGANIC CHEMISTRY. B.Sc, London, 49, Ph.D.(org. chem), 51. Res. dir. org. chem. lab, Fothergill & Harvey, Eng, 51-54; lectr. chem, Mt. St. Mary's Col, Eng, 54-61; chem. & physics, Staffordshire Col. Tech, Eng, 62-63; from asst. prof. to ASSOC. PROF. CHEM. & CHMN. DEPT, LOYOLA COL.(CAN), 63- R.A.F, 42-46, Warrant Officer. Stereochemistry; cellulose derivatives; mechanism of organic reactions. Address: Dept. of Chemistry, Loyola College, Montreal 262, Can. P.Q.

DOUGHTY, RICHARD MORRISON, b. Sewickley, Pa, Dec. 5, 21. PHARMACOGNOSY. B.S, Pittsburgh, 48, M.S, 54. Asst. chem, Pittsburgh, 48-49, PHARMACOG, 49-51; instr, UNIV. KY, 51-54, ASST. PROF, 54-, ASST. TO DEAN STUDENT ALUMNI AFFAIRS, 69-, acting chmn. materia medica dept, 66-69. Fel, Ind. Univ, 58-59. U.S.A, 42-45. AAAS; Am. Soc. Pharmacog. Allergenic pollen morphology; natural product biosynthesis; medicinal herbs; coumarins; toxic plants. Address: College of Pharmacy, University of Kentucky, Lexington, KY 40506.

DOUGHTY, SAMUEL PRESTON, JR, b. Corpus Christi, Tex, May 31, 40; m. 62; c. 1. MECHANICS, APPLIED MATHEMATICS. B.E.S, Texas, Austin, 63, M.S, 65, Ph.D.(mech. eng), 68. Instr. math. & physics, Southwestern (Tex), 64-65; res. engr, Tracor, Inc, 65-66; asst. prof. mech. eng, Univ. Tex, Austin, 68-69; N.C. State Univ, 69-70; sr. staff physicist, Hamilton Watch Co, 70-71; ASST. PROF. PHYSICS, TEX. LUTHERAN COL, 71- Am. Soc. Mech. Eng. Classical mechanics; engineering applications of elasticity, vibration theory, rigid body dynamics; dynamics of mechanisms, stability. Address: Dept. of Physics, Texas Lutheran College, Seguin, TX 78155.

DOUGLAS, ALEXANDER EDGAR, b. Melfort, Sask, Apr. 12, 16; m. 45; c. 3. PHYSICS. B.A, Saskatchewan, 39, M.A, 40; Ph.D.(physics), Pa. State, 48. Res. physicist, acoustics, NAT. RES. COUN, 41-46, spectros. lab, PHYSICS DIV, 48-70, DIR, 70- Am. Phys. Soc; Can. Asn. Physicists; Royal Soc. Can; fel. Royal Soc. Spectroscopic investigation of molecular structure. Address: Division of Physics, National Research Council, Ottawa, Ont, Can. K1A OS1

DOUGLAS, ALLAN G(LOVER), b. Salt Lake City, Utah, Mar. 9, 12; m. 42; c. 3. ZOOLOGY. B.S, Utah State, 34; Thompson fel, California, 37, Ph.D. (protozool), 40. Asst. zool, California, 34-37; prof. biol, Southwest Mo. State Col, 42-48; asst. prof, Calif. State Polytech. Col, 48-49; PROF. BIOL. SCI, CHICO STATE COL, 49- Cytology and taxonomy of gregarines parasitic in centipedes and millipedes. Address: Dept. of Biological Sciences, Chico State College, Chico, CA 95926.

DOUGLAS, ALLAN STANLEY, b. Boston, Mass, Dec. 27, 39; m. 62; c. 3. CHEMICAL ENGINEERING, POLYMER CHEMISTRY. S.B, Mass. Inst. Technol, 61, S.M, 63, Sc.D.(chem. eng), 66. Proj. engr, Dynatech Corp, Mass, 62-65; fel. eng. & asst. prof. chem. engr, Mass. Inst. Technol, 66-68; staff assoc, Gulf Gen. Atomic. Inc, Calif, 68-70; DIR. MEMBRANE DEVELOP, MILLIPORE CORP, BEDFORD, 70- Lect, San Diego State Col, 68-69. Am. Inst. Chem. Eng. Structure-property relations of polymers; controlled porosity polymer membranes; reverse osmosis; air pollution control. Address: 11 Gallup Dr, Chelmsford, MA 01824.

DOUGLAS, A(LVIN) G(ENE), b. Crowley, La, Feb. 24, 31; m. 59; c. 2. AGRONOMY, PLANT BREEDING. B.S, Miss. State, 53; M.S, Texas A&M, 58, Nicholson fel, 59, Ph.D.(plant breeding), 59. Asst. prof. AGRON, Univ. Ga, 59-67; assoc. prof, MISS. STATE UNIV, 67-70, PROF, 70- U.S.A, 53-55, 1st Lt. Am. Soc. Agron. Cotton breeding, especially heterosis, disease, and insect resistance. Address: Dept. of Agronomy Crops, Mississippi State University, Box 5248, State College, MS 39762.

DOUGLAS, BEN HAROLD, b. Wesson, Miss, Feb. 20, 35; m. 53; c. 2. PHYSIOLOGY. B.S, Miss. Col, 56; univ. fel, Mississippi, 60-64, Ph.D. (physiol), 64. Instr. basic electronics, Keesler Air Force Base, Miss, 56-57; teacher physics, Copiah-Lincoln Jr. Col, 57-60; chief instr, sch. nursing, St. Dominics Hosp, Miss, 62-63; instr. med. & physiol, SCH. MED, UNIV. MISS, 64-65, asst. prof, 65-68, ASSOC. PROF. MED. & PHYSIOL, 68- AAAS; Am. Heart Asn; Am. Physiol. Soc; Am. Fedn. Clin. Res; Am. Soc. Study Reproduction. Hypertension and hypertension effects on pregnancy. Address: Dept. of Medicine, Medical Center, University of Mississippi, Jackson, MS 39216.

DOUGLAS, BEVERLY, b. Nashville, Tenn, Sept. 23, 91; m. 24; c. 2. SURGERY. Litt.B, Princeton, 14; M.D, Hopkins, 18; M.S, Yale, 21; Nat. Res. Coun. fel, Lyons, 21-23, D.Sc, 25. Instr. surg, Yale, 19-22, asst, 21-22; asst. prof, sch. med, Vanderbilt Univ, 25-28, assoc. prof, 28-70, vis. surgeon, hosp, 26-70, asst. dean, univ, 26-50; RETIRED. Med.C, U.S.A, 18, 1st Lt; Med.C, Tenn. State Militia, Col. Fel. Am. Col. Surg; Am. Asn. Plastic Surg; Am. Soc. Plastic & Reconstruct. Surg. Healing of arteries. Address: 425 Sunnyside Dr, Nashville, TN 37205.

DOUGLAS, BODIE E(UGENE), b. New Orleans, La, Dec. 31, 24; m. 45; c. 4. INORGANIC CHEMISTRY. B.S, Tulane, 44, M.S, 47; fel, Illinois, 47-49, Ph.D.(chem), 49. Asst, Tulane, 46-47; res. assoc. CHEM, Pa. State, 49-50, asst. prof, 50-52; UNIV. PITTSBURGH, 52-56, assoc. prof, 56-63, PROF, 63- Fulbright lectr, Leeds, 54-55; vis. prof, Osaka Univ, 70. U.S.N.R, 43-46, Lt. AAAS; Am. Chem. Soc. Coordination compounds; spectroscopy. Address: Dept. of Chemistry, University of Pittsburgh, Pittsburgh, PA 15213.

DOUGLAS, BRUCE L, b. New York, N.Y, July 14, 25; m. 54; c. 3. DENTISTRY. A.B, Princeton, 47; D.D.S, N.Y. Univ, 48; cert, Columbia, 51, M.A, 55, dipl, 57; M.P.H, California, 62. Intern dent, Queens Gen. Hosp, Jamaica, N.Y, 48-49, res. oral surg, 53-54; private practice, 54-59; Fulbright prof. dent, col. dent, Okayama, 59-61; assoc. prof. oral med. & soc. aspects dent, COL. DENT, UNIV. ILL, 61-66, oral diag, 66-67, PROF. COMMUNITY DENT, 67-, DENT. & ORAL SURG, RUSH MED. COL, 71-, assoc. prof. prev. med. & community health, col. med, Univ. Ill, 66-67, prof. prev. med, 67-71. Consult, Hemophilia Found. U.S.N, 51-53. Am. Dent. Asn; fel. Am. Med. Writers' Asn; Am. Pub. Health Asn; Int. Asn. Dent. Res. Oral surgery. Address: Dept. of Dental & Oral Surgery, Rush Medical College, 1725 W. Harrison St, Chicago, IL 60612.

DOUGLAS, BRYCE, b. Glasgow, Scotland, Jan. 6, 24; m. 55; c. 3. ORGANIC CHEMISTRY. B.S, Glasgow, 44; Ph.D.(chem), Edinburgh, 48. Res. chemist, J.F. MacFarlan & Co, Scotland, 44-46; asst, Royal Col. Physicians Lab, 47-49; dept. biol. chem, Aberdeen, 49; Nat. Res. Coun. Can. fel, 49-51; fel, Harvard Med. Sch, 52-53; res. assoc. natural prod, Indiana, 53-56, vis. res. assoc, Malaya, 56-58; sect. head, SMITH KLINE & FRENCH LABS, 56-67, dir. res. macrobiol, 67-71, V.PRES. RES. & DEVELOP, PHARMACEUT. PROD, 71- AAAS; Am. Chem. Soc; Am. Soc. Pharmacog; Soc. Chem. Indust; fel. Royal Inst. Chem; The Chem. Soc. Alkaloids; chemotherapy; heterocyclic compounds. Address: Research & Development Division, Smith Kline & French Labs, 1500 Spring Garden St, Philadelphia, PA 19101.

DOUGLAS, CARROLL R(EECE), b. Knoxville, Tenn, Sept. 3, 32; m. 51; c. 1. POULTRY NUTRITION. B.S, Tennessee, 55, Ph.D.(animal nutrit), 66; M.S.A, Florida, 59. Asst. poultry nutrit, Tennessee, 56-57; interim asst, Florida, 57-59; farm mgr, Am. Develop. Corp, Fla, 60; asst. mgr. & mgr. chick hatchery, Fla. State Hatcheries, 60-62; nutritionist & supvr, Loret Mills, Tenn, 62; asst. poultry nutrit, Tennessee, 62-66, poultryman & leader exten. poultry, agr. ext. serv, 66-69; ASST. PROF. POULTRY MGT. & ASST. SCIENTIST, UNIV. FLA, 69- U.S.A, 56, res, 56-68, Capt. AAAS; Poultry Sci. Asn; World Poultry Sci. Asn. Protein, amino acid, energy and mineral requirements of broilers and laying hens; xanthophyll utilization by the chicken; management systems for growing chickens. Address: Dept. of Poultry Science, University of Florida, Gainesville, FL 32601.

DOUGLAS, CHARLES F(RANCIS), b. Tucson, Ariz, July 16, 30; m. 52; c. 2. AGRONOMY. B.S, Illinois, 56, M.S, 57; Ph.D.(agron), Purdue, 61. Agr. consult, Tenn. Valley Authority, 61-65, supvr. agr. & indust. educ. progs. on fertilizer mfr. & use, Midwest. & New Eng. States, 65-69; HEAD DEPT. AGRON, COASTAL PLAIN EXP. STA, UNIV. GA, 69- U.S.A.F, 51-54, S/Sgt. Am. Soc. Agron. Crop physiology and ecology; fertilizer education; experimental fertilizer use. Address: Dept. of Agronomy, Coastal Plain Experiment Station, University of Georgia, Tifton, GA 31794.

DOUGLAS, CHARLES HERBERT, b. Loughman, Fla, Dec. 2, 26; m. 49; c. 2. RESEARCH ADMINISTRATION. B.M, Converse Col, 49, M.M, 58; Wofford Col, 47-49; Ph.D.(music), Fla. State, 65. Teacher pub. schs, S.C, 49-50; instr, U.S. Vet. Rehab. Sch, La, 50-51; teacher parochial & private schs, La, 53-57; asst. prof. music, Converse Col, 57-61; UNIV. GA, 61-66, assoc. prof, 66-67, asst. dean arts & sci, 67-68, asst. v.pres. all areas, 68-71, ASST. V.PRES. RES. & DIR. GEN. RES, 71- Mem, Nat. Coun. Univ. Res. Adminr. & Nat. Conf. Admin. Res, 68- U.S.N, 43-45 & 51-53. Am. Soc. Cybernet; Am. Soc. Info. Sci; Nat. Oceanog. Asn. Developing research programs in natural and social sciences, humanities, and fine arts. Address: Office of the Vice President for Research, University of Georgia, Athens, GA 30601.

DOUGLAS, CLARENCE J(OSEPH), b. Redford, N.Y, May 5, 07; m. 34. CIVIL ENGINEERING. B.S, Vermont, 29, C.E, 46. Engr, John F. Casey Co, Pa, 29-33; asst. prof. struct, Vermont, 46-47; proj. engr. & mgr. construct, John F. Casey Co, 47-52; consult. engr, 52-56; pres, McKeesport Eng. & Construct. Co, Inc, Pa, 56-57; assoc. prof. struct, NORWICH UNIV, 57-68, PROF. CIVIL ENG, 68-, acting head dept, 63-64. C.Eng, 33-36, 40-45, Col. Fel. Am. Soc. Civil Eng; Am. Soc. Eng. Educ; Nat. Soc. Prof. Eng. Structural design; construction management; mechanics; protective construction. Address: 7 Winter St, Northfield, VT 05663.

DOUGLAS, DAVID L(EWIS), b. Seattle, Wash, Jan. 22, 20; m. 48; c. 2. PHYSICAL CHEMISTRY. B.S, Calif. Inst. Tech, 47, fel, 50-51, Ph.D.(phys. chem), 51. Res. assoc, Knolls Atomic Power Lab, Gen. Elec. Co, 51-55, phys. chemist, res. lab, 55-60, mgr. fuel cell eng, aircraft accessory turbine dept, 60-62, tech. planning, direct energy conversion oper, 62-64; dir. res. & develop, Gould-Nat. Batteries, Inc, 64-66, v.pres. res, 66-70, V.PRES. & DIR. ENERGY TECH. LAB, GOULD INC, 70- U.S.A.A.F, 42-45, 1st Lt. Fel. AAAS; fel. Am. Inst. Chem; Am. Phys. Soc; Am. Chem. Soc; Electrochem. Soc; Am. Inst. Aeronaut. & Astronaut; Am. Mgt. Asn. Electrochemistry; fuel cells; batteries. Address: Gould Inc, Gould Labs-Energy Technology, P.O. Box 3140, St. Paul, MN 55165.

DOUGLAS, DEXTER RICHARD, b. Benton, Ohio, Nov. 14, 37; m. 62; c. 2. PLANT PATHOLOGY, BOTANY. B.S, Kent State, 62; M.S, Wyoming, 65; Ph.D.(plant path), Minnesota, 68. RES. PATHOLOGIST, U.S. DEPT. AGR, BRANCH EXP. STA, UNIV. IDAHO, 68- U.S.A, 62-64. Am. Phytopath. Soc. Control of potato diseases through host resistance, emphasis on nature of disease resistance. Address: Branch Experiment Station, Box AA, University of Idaho, Aberdeen, ID 83210.

DOUGLAS, DONALD AINSLIE, JR, b. Washingtonville, N.Y, Nov. 28, 21; m. 46; c. 2. METALLURGICAL ENGINEERING. B.S, Alabama, 46; Houston & Tennessee, 46-65. Mem. staff, Hughes Tool Co, Tex, 46-52; sect. chief res, metals & ceramics div, Oak Ridge Nat. Lab, 52-66; mgr. powder prod, mat. systs. div, Union Carbide Corp, 66-70; MEM. TECH. STAFF, STELLITE DIV, CABOT CORP, 70- U.S.M.C, 42-46, Capt. Am. Soc. Mech. Eng; Am. Soc. Metals; Soc. Nondestructive Test. Nuclear fuels and materials; administration; service environment and complex stress states on flow and fracture of metals; economics of fabrication and quality control; gaseous and liquid metal corrosion of reactor materials. Address: Stellite Division, Cabot Corp, P.O. Box 746, Kokomo, IN 46901.

DOUGLAS, DONALD S(TEPHENS), b. Acme, Wash, Nov. 29, 10; m. 35; c. 2. BOTANY. B.S, State Col. Wash, 34. Asst. agron, State Col. Wash, 34-35; agronomist, SOIL CONSERV. SERV, U.S. DEPT. AGR, 35-48, nursery agronomist, Wash, 48-50, nursery mgr, Idaho, 50-54, plant mat. specialist, Idaho, Utah & Nev, 54-60, regional plant mat. specialist, cornbelt states, 61-63, head plant mat. specialist, 64-70, REGIONAL PLANT MAT. SPECIALIST, PAC. STATES, 70- U.S.A, 42-46, Capt. Am. Soc. Range Mgt; Soil Conserv. Soc. Am. Plants for soil conservation; seed production of grasses; forage crops; rangeland reseeding. Address: Soil Conservation Service, U.S. Dept. of Agriculture, Portland, OR 97209.

DOUGLAS, DONALD STERLING, b. Baltimore, Md, June 11, 35; m. 63; c. 2. COMPARATIVE PHYSIOLOGY. A.B, Oberlin Col, 57; James B. Duke fels, Duke, 57-59, Ph.D, 63. Nat. Sci. Found. res. grant, U.S. Antarctic Res. Prog, 59-61; asst. prof. physiol, Rutgers, 62-65; assoc. prof. zool, George Washington Univ, 65-70; PROF. ZOOL. & DIR. ACAD. DEVELOP, GOV. STATE UNIV, 70- Nat. Sci. Found. teaching equip. grant, 67-69, res. grant, 67-70. AAAS; Am. Physiol. Soc; Am. Soc. Zool; N.Y. Acad. Sci. Salt and water metabolism. Address: Governors State University, Park Forest South, IL 60466.

DOUGLAS, GEORGE F, b. Fayetteville, Ark, Feb. 3, 15; m. 37; c. 4. CIVIL ENGINEERING. B.S, Arkansas, 40. Mem. staff, Consol. Aircraft, Calif, 40-42; chief engr, Interstate Eng. Corp, Ill, 42-46; proj. engr, N.Am. Aviation, Inc, 46-53; from asst. chief proj. engr. to asst. gen. mgr, NORTHROP CORP, 53-57, v.pres. eng, Norair Div, 57-62, v.pres, corp. & gen. mgr, Ventura Div, 62-69, pres, Northrop Carolina, Inc, 67-69, SR. V.PRES. ADMIN, CORP, 69- Assoc. fel. Am. Inst. Aeronaut. & Astronaut; Aerospace Indust. Asn. Am; Soc. Automotive Eng; Armed Forces Mgt. Asn; Am. Ord. Asn. Design and project coordination of advanced weapon and space landing systems. Address: Northrop Corp, 1800 Century Park E, Los Angeles, CA 90067.

DOUGLAS, GORDON WATKINS, b. Midlothian, Va, June 2, 21; m. 45; c. 4. OBSTETRICS, GYNECOLOGY. A.B, Princeton, 42; M.D, Hopkins, 45. Asst. OBSTET. & GYNEC, SCH. MED, N.Y. UNIV, 49-52, asst. prof, 53-56, PROF. & CHMN. DEPT, 56- Markle scholar, 52. Dir, Am. Bd. Obstet. & Gynec, 64- Med.C, 46-48, Capt. Am. Col. Obstet. & Gynec; Am. Col. Surg; Asn. Profs. Gynec. & Obstet; Harvey Soc; Am. Gynec. Soc; Am. Asn. Obstet. & Gynec. Immunology. Address: Dept. of Obstetrics & Gynecology, New York University School of Medicine, New York, NY 10016.

DOUGLAS, H(OWARD) C(LARK), b. Los Angeles, Calif, July 4, 10; m. 36; c. 3. MICROBIOLOGY. A.B, California, 36, Ph.D.(microbiol), 49. Instr. MICROBIOL, UNIV. WASH, 41-43, asst. prof, 43-50, assoc. prof, 50-58, PROF, 58- Am. Soc. Microbiol; Brit. Soc. Gen. Microbiol. Bacterial taxonomy and biochemistry; physiology genetics of yeast. Address: Dept. of Genetics, University of Washington, Seattle, WA 98105.

DOUGLAS, HUGH, b. Salisbury, S.Rhodesia, Oct. 28, 27; m. 53; c. 4. NATURAL RESOURCES ECONOMICS. A.B, Amherst Col, 49; M.A, Columbia, 51. Geologist, U.S. Atomic Energy Cmn, 51; Tex. Gulf Sulphur Co, 51-55; sr. geologist & asst. to mgr, Am. Overseas Petrol. Ltd, Turkey, 55-59, Libya, 59-62; consult, Oil Shale Corp. & Swan Petrol. Ltd, 62-63; secy. treas, Thermonetics, Inc, 63-65; indust. economist energy & natural resources & mgr. mining & mineral economics, Stanford Res. Inst, 65-71; MGR. MINERAL PLANNING, UTAH CONSTRUCT. & MINING, 71- Geol. Soc. Am; Am. Inst. Mining, Metall. & Petrol. Eng; Am. Asn. Petrol. Geol. Address: 83 Lupin Lane, Atherton, CA 94025.

DOUGLAS, JAMES, b. Uvalde, Tex, Oct. 1, 14; m. 41; c. 4. CIVIL ENGINEERING. B.S, U.S. Naval Acad, 38; B.C.E. & M.C.E, Rensselaer Polytech, 43; Armed Forces Staff Col, 54; Naval War Col, 59-60; Ph.D.(civil eng), Stanford, 63. Instr. CONSTRUCT, STANFORD UNIV, 61-63, ASSOC. PROF, 63- Chmn. comt. construct. mgt, Hgwy. Res. Bd, 70. Civil Eng.C, U.S.N, 34-61, Capt. Fel. Am. Soc. Civil Eng.(Thomas Fitch Rowland prize, 69); Am. Soc. Eng. Educ. Economics of construction equipment ownership, obsolescence, depreciation, standardization; simulation of construction equipment operations using statistical-computer solution. Address: Dept. of Civil Engineering, School of Engineering, Stanford University, Stanford, CA 94305.

DOUGLAS, J(AMES) M(ERRILL), b. Aurora, Ill, July 27, 33; m. 58; c. 2. CHEMICAL ENGINEERING. B.E, Hopkins, 54; Ph.D.(chem. eng), Delaware, 60. Res. chem. engr, Atlantic Ref. Co, Pa, 60-62, res. assoc, 62-65; asst. prof. CHEM. ENG, Delaware, 65; assoc. prof, Univ. Rochester, 65-68; PROF, UNIV. MASS, AMHERST, 68- Atlantic Ref. Co. res. grant, Imp. Col, London, 64. Chem.C, 60, 1st Lt. Am. Inst. Chem. Eng. Process dynamics and control; optimization theory; reaction kinetics; reactor design. Address: Dept. of Chemical Engineering, University of Massachusetts, Amherst, MA 01003.

DOUGLAS, JAMES NATHANIEL, b. Dallas, Tex, Aug. 14, 35; m. 56; c. 3. RADIO ASTRONOMY. B.S, Yale, 56, M.S, 58, Ph.D.(astron), 61. Instr. ASTRON, Yale, 60-61, asst. prof, 61-65; assoc. prof, UNIV. TEX, AUSTIN, 65-71, PROF, 71- Mem. Cmn. 5, Int. Sci. Radio Union, 63-; Int. Astron, Union, 64- Fel. AAAS; Am. Astron. Soc; Am. Geophys. Union. Studies of decametric radiation from Jupiter and from discrete radio sources. Address: Dept. of Astronomy, University of Texas, Austin, TX 78712.

DOUGLAS, JAMES R(USSELL), b. Los Angeles, Calif, Sept. 29, 12; m. 34; c. 2. VETERINARY PARASITOLOGY. B.S, California, 35, Ph.D.(entom parasitol), 39. Asst, California, 35-37, Hooper Found. Med. Res, 40-42; asst. prof. parasitol. & asst. entomologist, exp. sta, col. agr, UNIV. CALIF, DAVIS, 46-51, assoc. prof. parasitol. & assoc. parasitologist, SCH. VET. MED, 51-57, PROF. PARASITOL. & PARASITOLOGIST, 57-, ASSOC. DEAN, 66- Med.C, U.S.N, 42-45, Lt. Comdr. Am. Soc. Parasitol; Entom. Soc. Am. Transmission of plague; pathogenesis and control of parasites affecting man and animals. Address: School of Veterinary Medicine, University of California, Davis, CA 95616.

DOUGLAS, JIM, JR, b. Austin, Tex, Aug. 8, 27; m. 50; c. 2. MATHEMATICS. B.S, Texas, 46; M.A, Rice Inst, 50, Ph.D.(math), 52. Instr. eng. mech, Texas, 47-48; asst. math, Rice Inst, 48-52; asst. res. engr, Humble Oil & Ref. Co, 52-53, res. engr, 53-57; asst. prof. MATH, Rice Univ, 57-59, assoc. prof, 59-61, prof, 61-64, W.L. Moody, Jr. Prof, 64-67; PROF, UNIV. CHICAGO, 67- Ferguson Medal, Am. Inst. Mining, Metall. & Petrol. Eng. Am. Math. Soc; Math. Asn. Am; Soc. Indust. & Appl. Math. Partial differential equations; numerical analysis. Address: Dept. of Mathematics, University of Chicago, Chicago, IL 60637.

DOUGLAS, J(OCELYN) F(IELDING), b. Delta, Utah, Jan. 25, 27; m. 51; c. 3. BIOCHEMISTRY. B.S, Univ. Ill, 48; M.A, Columbia Univ, 50, Ph.D.(chem), 53. Asst. chem, Columbia Univ, 48-52; res. chemist, Johnson & Johnson, 52-54, proj. leader, 54-58; DIR. BIOCHEM, WALLACE LABS, 58- U.S.A, 44-46. AAAS; Am. Soc. Pharmacol. & Exp. Therapeut; Am. Chem. Soc; Int. Soc. Biochem. Pharmacol; N.Y. Acad. Sci; Soc. Exp. Biol. & Med. Metabolism; enzymes; hypocholestermic agents; biochem. pharmacology; clinical chemistry; drug analysis. Address: 164 Balcort Dr, Princeton, NJ 08540.

DOUGLAS, JOHN E(DWARD), b. Normal, Ill, June 29, 26; m. 51; c. 3. PHYSICAL CHEMISTRY. B.S, Chicago, 47, M.S, 48; Ph.D.(chem), Washington (Seattle), 52. Instr. chem, Wyoming, 52-56; phys. chemist, Stanford Res. Inst, 56-60; assoc. prof. CHEM, EAST. WASH. STATE COL, 60-66, PROF, 66- Am. Chem. Soc. Gas phase kinetics; energetics of complex formation; application of molecular orbital methods to chemical reactivity. Address: Dept. of Chemistry, Eastern Washington State College, Cheney, WA 99004.

DOUGLAS, JOHN G(RAY), b. Baltimore, Md, Aug. 1, 00; m. 36. PALEONTOLOGY. A.B, Hopkins, 21, Ph.D.(geol, paleont), 28. Geologist, Venezuela Gulf Oil Co, 24-25, 26-27; paleontologist, Lago Petrol. Corp, 28-31; assoc. prof. geol. & paleont, North Carolina, 31-34; geologist, Venezuela Gulf Oil Co, 34-36; Mene Grande Oil Co, 36-55; assoc. prof. GEOL, UNIV. MISS, 55-56, prof, 56-70, chmn. dept, 56-65, EMER. PROF, 70- AAAS; Am. Asn. Petrol. Geol; fel. Geol. Soc. Am. Miocene mollusks from northwestern Venezuela. Address: Box 52, University, MS 38677.

DOUGLAS, JOSEPH FRANCIS, b. Indianapolis, Ind, Oct. 31, 26; m. 50; c. 4. ELECTRICAL ENGINEERING. B.S.E.E, Purdue, 48; M.S.E.E, Missouri, 62. Proj. Engr. elec. eng, U.S. Dept. Agr, 48-56; asst. prof, Southern Univ, 56-62, assoc. prof. & head dept, 62-64; training coordinator, atomics div, Am. Mach. & Foundry Co, 64-66; asst. prof. ENG, PA. STATE UNIV, YORK CAMPUS, 66-70, ASSOC. PROF, 70-, GROUP LEADER ELEC. TECHNOL. & ENG, 66- U.S.A.A.F, 45. Sr. mem. Inst. Elec. & Electronics Eng. Low speed with reasonable torque output from electrical induction motors of the wound roter class. Address: Faculty Office K, Pennsylvania State University, 1031 Edgecomb Ave, York, PA 17403.

DOUGLAS, LARRY J(OE), b. Oklahoma City, Okla, Mar. 3, 37; m. 69; c. 2. PHYSICAL CHEMISTRY, ELECTROCHEMISTRY. B.S, Univ. Denver, 58, univ. fels, 65, 68-70, NASA traineeship, 65-68, Ph.D.(phys. chem), 70. Assoc. res. engr, Nat. Cash Register Co, Calif, 58-61, res. engr, 62-64; RES. SCIENTIST, DENVER RES. CTR, MARATHON OIL CO, 70- AAAS; Am. Chem. Soc; Sci. Res. Soc. Am; Electrochem. Soc. Mass transport mechanisms in oxide crystals; electrochemistry of alloy deposition; liquid/liquid and liquid/solid interfacial properties; adsorption into and from micellar solutions; electrokinetic behavior of non-electrolytic fluids. Address: Denver Research Center, Marathon Oil Co, P.O. Box 269, Littleton, CO 80122.

DOUGLAS, LEE T(HOMAS), b. Springfield, Mo, May 5, 27; m. 46, 63; c. 5. QUANTITATIVE GENETICS. A.B, Lewis & Clark Col, 49; Ph.D.(zool), California, 53; Cert, Oak Ridge Inst. Nuclear Studies, 55; Ind. Univ, 69-70; Univ. Tex, 70. Lectr. bot, Portland, 49-50; asst, California, 50-52; asst. prof. BIOL, Emory & Henry Col, 52-55, assoc. prof, 55-58, prof. & chmn. dept, 58-59; assoc. prof, Puget Sound, 59-60; res. assoc, Hopkins, 60-63; ASSOC. PROF. GENETICS, UNIV. NIJMEGEN, 63- Grantee, U.S. Pub. Health Serv, 58-63. DeFriece Medal, 57. U.S.N.R, 45-46. Am. Soc. Parasitol; fel. Am. Physiol. Soc; Genetics Soc. Am; N.Y. Acad. Sci. Population genetics; Drosophila genetics; computer simulation of Markov processes; meiosis-mechanics and relationship to recombination. Address: Dept. of Genetics, University of Nijmegen, Nijmegen, Holland.

DOUGLAS, LOWELL A(RTHUR), b. Durango, Colo, June 17, 26; m. 53; c. 2. MINERALOGY, SOIL GENESIS. B.S, Utah State, 52, M.S, 59; Ph.D.(soils), Rutgers, 61. Soil chemist, U.S. Salinity Lab, Calif, 54-56; instr. SOILS, RUTGERS UNIV, 59-61, asst. prof, 61-65, assoc. prof, 65-69, PROF, 69- Assoc. ed, Soil Sci, 68- U.S.A.A.F, 44-45. Soil Sci. Soc. Am; Clay Minerals Soc; Mineral. Soc. Am; Int. Soc. Soil Sci. Clay mineralogy; soil chemistry; polar soils; clay mineral genesis and alteration; environmental studies. Address: Dept. of Soils & Crops, Rutgers, The State University, New Brunswick, NJ 08903.

DOUGLAS, NEIL H(ARRISON), b. Moorefield, W.Va, Feb. 17, 32; m. 58; c. 2. ICHTHYOLOGY, HERPETOLOGY. B.S, Okla. State, 55, M.S, 59, Ph.D.(zool), 62. Asst. zool, Okla. State, 57-59, water pollution, 59-62; asst. prof. ZOOL, NORTHEAST LA. UNIV, 62-65, ASSOC. PROF, 65-, CURATOR MUS. ZOOL, 70- U.S.A, 55-57, 1st Lt. Am. Fisheries Soc; Am. Soc. Icthyol. & Herpet. Taxonomy of freshwater fishes; herpetology; fresh water fishes of Louisiana. Address: Dept. of Biology, Northeast Louisiana University, Monroe, LA 71201.

DOUGLAS, R(ICHARD) H(ERBERT), b. Edmonton, Alta, Sept. 20, 19; m. 44; c. 2. METEOROLOGY. B.Sc, Alberta, 41; M.A, Toronto, 45; Ph.D.(meteorol), 57. Meteorologist, Meteorol. Serv. Can, 41-51, res. meteorologist, 51-60; res. assoc. meteorol, McGill Univ, 57-60, assoc. prof, 60-65; PROF. AGR. PHYSICS & CHMN. DEPT, MACDONALD COL, 65- Field dir, Alta. Hail studies, 56-65, sci. dir, 65-69. Am. Meteorol. Soc; fel. Royal Meteorol. Soc. Cloud and precipitation physics; severe storms, particularly hail; agrometeorology. Address: Dept. of Agricultural Physics, Macdonald College, Quebec, Que, Can.

DOUGLAS, ROBERT ALDEN, b. High Point, N.C, Dec. 4, 25; m. 48; c. 3. MECHANICS, MATERIALS SCIENCE. B.S, Purdue, 51, M.S, 52, Ph.D.(mech), 56. Mgr. res. & develop, Danly Mach. Specialties, 56-58; assoc. prof. MECH, N.C. STATE UNIV, 58-63, PROF, 63-, ASSOC. HEAD DEPT. ENG. MECH. & MGR. THEMIS RES. PROG, 67- Dep. dir, U.S. Eng. Team, Afghanistan, 64-66. U.S.A, 43-47, 1st Lt. Am. Soc. Mech. Eng; Am. Soc. Metals; Soc. Exp. Stress Anal; Am. Soc. Eng. Educ. The behavior of materials at extremely high deformation rates. Address: Dept. of Engineering Mechanics, 349 Reddick Bldg, North Carolina State University, Raleigh, NC 27607.

DOUGLAS, R(OBERT) GORDON, b. Winnipeg, Man, Apr. 14, 98; U.S. citizen; m. 30; c. 3. MEDICINE. M.D, C.M, McGill, 24; hon. LL.D, Alberta, 63. House officer med, Montreal Gen. Hosp, Que, 24-26; res. OBSTET. & GYNEC, Johns Hopkins Hosp, Baltimore, Md, 26-30; assoc, MED. COL, CORNELL UNIV, 30-32, asst. prof, 32-37, assoc. prof, 37-48, acting prof, 48-49, prof, 49-65, EMER. PROF, 65-; DIR. MED. EDUC, PROVIDENCE LYING-IN HOSP, 67- Consult, New York Hosp, 65, Roosevelt Hosp, N.Y. & St. Lukes Hosp, N.Y, 66, Providence Lying-In Hosp, R.I. & R.I. Hosp, Providence, 68 & perinatal res. comt, Nat. Inst. Neurol. Diseases & Stroke. Proj. dir, Maternal & Infant Care Proj, N.Y.C, 65-67. Dipl, Am. Bd. Obstet. & Gynec, 40, v.pres, 60-64. Can. Army, 17-19, Sgt. Am. Med. Asn; Am. Col. Obstet. & Gynec.(pres, 56-58); Am. Asn. Obstet. & Gynec.(pres, 61-62); Am. Gynec. Soc. Prevention and control of infection in obstetrics and gynecology; early detection and control of pelvic cancer; control of perinatal mortality. Address: Providence Lying-In Hospital, 50 Maude St, Providence, RI 02908.

DOUGLAS, ROBERT GORDON, JR, b. New York, N.Y, Apr. 17, 34; m. 56; c. 3. INTERNAL MEDICINE, INFECTIOUS DISEASES. A.B, Princeton, 55; M.D, Cornell Univ, 59. Intern med, N.Y. Hosp, 59-60, asst. resident, 60-61; Johns Hopkins Hosp, 61-62; chief res, N.Y. Hosp, 62-63; clin. assoc. & clin. investr, lab. clin. invest, Nat. Inst. Allergy & Infectious Diseases, 63-66; instr. microbiol. & med, col. med, Baylor Univ, 66-67; asst. prof, 67-69, assoc. prof, 69-70; ASSOC. PROF. MED. & MICROBIOL. & HEAD INFECTIOUS DISEASES UNIT, SCH. MED. & DENT, UNIV. ROCHESTER, 70- AAAS; Soc. Exp. Biol. & Med; Infectious Diseases Soc. Am; Am. Fedn. Clin. Res; fel. Am. Col. Physicians; Am. Soc. Microbiol. Pathogenesis of respiratory viral and mycoplasma infections; herpes simplex; vaccines; antiviral chemotherapy; secretory antibody; clinical virology. Address: Dept. of Medicine, University of Rochester School of Medicine & Dentistry, 260 Crittenden Blvd, Rochester, NY 14642.

DOUGLAS, ROBERT JAMES, b. Seattle, Wash, Dec. 4, 37. MATHEMATICS. B.S, Washington (Seattle), 61, M.S, 66, Ph.D.(math), 68. Res. Assoc. MATH, Univ. N.C, Chapel Hill, 68-69; ASST. PROF, SAN FRANCISCO STATE COL, 69- U.S.A.R, 56-64. Am. Math. Soc; Math. Asn. Am. Combinatorial analysis; graph theory. Address: Dept. of Mathematics, School of Natural Sciences, San Francisco State College, 1600 Holloway Ave, San Francisco, CA 94132.

DOUGLAS, R(OBERT) J(OHN), b. Toronto, Ont, May 3, 25; m. 47; c. 3. MICROBIOLOGY. B.S.A, Toronto, 49, M.S.A, 50; Ph.D, Mich. State, 55. Lectr. bact, ONT. AGR. COL, UNIV. GUELPH, 50-56, from asst. prof. to assoc. prof. RES, DEPT. MICROBIOL, 56-70, PROF, 70- R.C.N.V.R, 44-45. Am. Soc. Microbiol; Can. Soc. Microbiol; Can. Fedn. Biol. Sci. Physiology and serology of streptomyces; immunology. Address: Dept. of Microbiology, Ontario Agricultural College, University of Guelph, Guelph, Ont, Can.

DOUGLAS, R(OBERT) J(OHN) W(ILSON), b. Southampton, Ont, Aug. 3, 20; m. 47; c. 3. GEOLOGY. B.Sc, Queen's (Can), 42; Ph.D.(geol), Columbia, 50. Geologist, GEOL. SURV. CAN, 47-56, head geol. fuels, 56-64, CHIEF regional geol. div, 64-67, SPEC. PROJS, 67- R.C.A.F, 43-45. Am. Asn. Petrol. Geol; Geol. Soc. Am; fel. Royal Soc. Can.(Miller medalist, 65); Geol. Asn. Can. Structural and petroleum geology; geology of Canada; geotectonics. Address: Geological Survey of Canada, Dept. of Energy, Mines & Resources, Ottawa, Ont, Can. K1A OE8.

DOUGLAS, R(ONALD) G(EORGE), b. Osgood, Ind, Dec. 10, 38; m. 60; c. 3. MATHEMATICS. B.S, Ill. Inst. Tech, 60; Ph.D.(math), La. State, 62. Res. instr. MATH, Michigan, 62-64, asst. prof, 64-66, assoc. prof, 66-69; PROF, STATE UNIV. N.Y. STONY BROOK, 69-, CHMN. DEPT, 71- Mem, Inst. Advan. Study, 65-66; Sloan fel, 68- Am. Math. Soc; Math. Asn. Am. Operator theory; functional analysis; measure theory; abstract harmonic analysis. Address: Dept. of Mathematics, State University of New York at Stony Brook, Stony Brook, NY 11790.

DOUGLAS, ROY RENÉ, b, Chicago, Ill, Oct. 8, 38; m. 66; c. 1. TOPOLOGY, MATHEMATICS. B.A, Northwestern, 60; Nat. Sci. Found. fel, California, Berkeley, 60-62; M.A, 63, Ph.D.(math), 65. Res. asst. MATH, Univ. Calif, Berkeley, 63-65; asst. prof, UNIV. B.C, 65-69, ASSOC. PROF, 69- Nat. Res. Coun. Can. grant, 67- Am. Math. Soc; Can. Math. Cong. Algebraic topology; H-spaces. Address: Dept. of Mathematics, University of British Columbia, Vancouver 8, B.C, Can.

DOUGLAS, THOMAS B(ASIL), b. Elkins, W.Va, May 15, 09; m. 49. PHYSICAL CHEMISTRY. B.S, North Carolina, 31, fel, 31-32, M.S, 32; du Pont fel, Ohio State, 36-37, Ph.D.(chem), 38. Asst, North Carolina, 32-33; Ohio State, 33-36, Comly fel. surg. res, 39; instr. phys. chem, Mont. State Col, 39-42, asst. prof, 42-46; Western Reserve, 46-47; chemist, NAT. BUR. STANDARDS, 47-57, SUPVR. PHYSICIST, 57- Res. assoc, Manhattan Proj, Ohio State, 43. AAAS; Am. Phys. Soc; Am. Chem. Soc. Thermodynamics; statistical mechanics; calorimetry; high-temperature phase equilibria. Address: National Bureau of Standards, Washington, DC 20234.

DOUGLAS, W. J. MURRAY, b. Briercrest, Sask, Feb. 15, 27; c. 1. CHEMICAL ENGINEERING. B.Sc, Queen's (Ont), 48; M.S.E, Michigan, 52, Visking Corp. & Dow Chem. Co. fels. & Ph.D.(chem. eng), 58. Develop. engr, Polymer Corp, Ont, 48-51; asst. prof. CHEM. ENG, McGILL UNIV, 58-62, assoc. prof, 62-69, PROF, 69- Consult, Pulp & Paper Res. Inst. Can, 62- AAAS; Am. Inst. Chem. Eng; Chem. Inst. Can. Transport processes, including transport of heat, mass and momentum; chemical reaction and diffusion; mixing. Address: Dept. of Chemical Engineering, McGill University, Montreal, Que, Can.

DOUGLAS, WALTER S, b. Cranford, N.J, 22, 12; m. 38; c. 3. CIVIL & TRANSPORTATION ENGINEERING. B.A, Dartmouth Col, 33; M.S, Harvard, 35. Jr. engr, Nashville Bridge Co, Tenn, 35-37; asst. to chief engr, N.Y. World's Fair of 1939, Inc, 37-39; struct. engr, Parsons, Klapp, Brinckerhoff & Douglas, 39-40; asst. to chief engr, Caribbean Architect Engrs, 40-41; proj. dir. mil. construct, Parsons, Brinckerhoff, Hall & Macdonald, 46-51, partner, PARSONS, BRINCKERHOFF, QUADE & DOUGLAS, 52-66, SR. PARTNER, 66- U.S.N, 41-45, Lt. Comdr. Nat. Acad. Eng; fel. Am. Soc. Civil Eng; Am. Inst. Consult. Eng; Soc. Am. Mil. Eng. Address: Parsons, Brinckerhoff, Quade & Douglas, 111 John St, New York, NY 10038.

DOUGLAS, W(ILLIAM) A(LVIN), b. Maben, Miss, May 6, 06; m. 29; c. 2. ENTOMOLOGY. B.S, Miss. State Col, 28, M.S, 34. Jr. entomologist, bur. entom. & plant quarantine, U.S. Dept. Agr, rice exp. sta, La, 28-38, asst. entomologist, 38-43, Miss, 43-46, assoc. entomologist, 46-52, entomologist, entom. res. br, Agr. Res. Serv, 52-62, sta. leader, south. grain insects invests, 62-70; RETIRED. Assoc. Am. Entom. Soc. Life history, cultural and artificial control of sugarcane and rice insects; corn breeding for resistance to the corn earworm. Address: P.O. Box 182, State College, MS 39762.

DOUGLAS, WILLIAM KENNEDY, b. Estancia, N.Mex, Sept. 5, 22; m. 46; c. 1. MEDICINE, AEROSPACE MEDICINE. B.S, Col. Mines & Metal, Texas, 46; M.D, Texas, 48; M.P.H, Hopkins, 54. U.S. AIR FORCE, 49-, command flight surgeon, hq, Northeast Air Command, 50-52, base surgeon, Harmon Air

Force Base, Newf, 52-53, res. aviation med, Hopkins & Langley Air Force Base, 53-55, chief prfnl. serv, hq, mil. air transport serv, 55-57, chief air-crew effectiveness br, Off. Surgeon Gen, 57-59, flight surgeon, Proj. Mercury Astronauts, NASA, 59-62, from asst. dep. bioastronaut. hq, Air Force Missile Test Center to dir. bioastronaut, hq, Air Force East. Test Range, Patrick Air Force Base, Fla, 62-66, asst. dep. chief staff bioastronaut. & med, Hq, systs. command, 66-68, chief cent. aeromed. serv, Hq, Europe, 68-71, V.COMDR. AEROSPACE MED. DIV, SYSTS. COMMAND, 71- Cert. aviation med, Am. Bd. Prev. Med, 56. U.S.A.F, 49-, Col. AAAS; fel. Am. Col. Physicians; Am. Med. Asn; fel. Aerospace Med. Asn.(Louis H. Bauer Found. award, 64); Asn. Mil. Surg. U.S; Am. Inst. Aeronaut. & Astronaut. (John Jefferies Award, 65); Int. Acad. Astronaut. Address: Headquarters, AMD/CV, Brooks Air Force Base, TX 78235.

DOUGLAS, W(ILLIAM) W(ILTON), b. Glasgow, Scotland, Aug. 15, 22; m. 54; c. 2. NEUROPHARMACOLOGY, NEUROENDOCRINOLOGY. M.B, Ch.B, Glasgow, 46, M.D, 49. Houseman, Glasgow West Infirmary, 46; Law Hosp, Carluke, 47; lectr. physiol, Aberdeen Univ, Scotland, 47-48; staff mem. med. res. coun, physiol. & pharmacol. div, Nat. Inst. Med. Res, Eng, 50-56; vis. assoc. PHARMACOL, col. physicians & surg, Columbia, 52-53; assoc. prof, Albert Einstein Col. Med, 56-58, PROF, 58-68; SCH. MED, YALE, 68- R.A.M.C, 48-50, Maj. Am. Physiol. Soc; Soc. Pharmacol. & Exp. Therapeut; Pharmacol. Soc. Can; Brit. Pharmacol. Soc; Brit. Physiol. Soc; Can. Physiol. Soc. Pharmacology and physiology of the neurohumoral transmission; cellular mechanisms of release of nervous and neuroendocrine secretions. Address: Dept. of Pharmacology, Yale University School of Medicine, 333 Cedar St, New Haven, CT 06510.

DOUGLASS, CARL D(EAN), b. Little Rock, Ark, Apr. 27, 25; m. 46; c. 2. BIOCHEMISTRY. B.S, Hendrix Col, 47; M.S, Oklahoma, 49, Ph.D.(chem), 52; fel, Oak Ridge Inst. Nuclear Studies, 50-51. Asst, Oklahoma, 47; instr. biochem, sch. med, Arkansas, 52-53, asst. prof, 53-57, assoc. prof, 57-59; chief nutrit. res. br, U.S. Food & Drug Admin, 59-61; nutrit. prog. officer, Nat. Inst. Arthritis & Metab. Diseases, 61-64; chief res. & training div, Nat. Libr. Med, 64-66, chief facilities & resources div, 66-67; assoc. dir. prog. develop, div. res. facilities & resources, NAT. INSTS. HEALTH, 67-69, assoc. dir, div. res. resources, 69-70, assoc. dir. statist, anal. & res. eval, DIV. RES. GRANTS, 70-71, ACTING DEP. DIR, 71- U.S.N.R, 43-46. AAAS; Am. Chem. Soc; Soc. Exp. Biol. & Med; Am. Inst. Nutrit; Am. Inst. Biol. Sci. Intermediary metabolism of drugs; metabolism of plant pigments. Address: Division of Research Grants, Room 452, Westwood Bldg, National Institutes of Health, Bethesda, MD 20014.

DOUGLASS, DAVID H(OLMES), JR, b. Bangor, Maine, Feb. 12, 32; m. 53; c. 3. PHYSICS. B.S, Univ. Maine, 55; Ph.D.(physics), Mass. Inst. Technol, 59. Res. scientist PHYSICS, Lincoln Lab, Mass. Inst. Technol, 59-61, instr, 61-62; asst. prof, Univ. Chicago, 62-65, assoc. prof, 65-67, PROF, 67-68; UNIV. ROCHESTER, 68- Alfred P. Sloan res. fel, 62-66. AAAS; Am. Phys. Soc; Am. Asn. Physics Teachers; Am. Astron. Soc. Liquid helium; superconductivity; low temperature and solid state physics; gravitation. Address: Dept. of Physics, University of Rochester, Rochester, NY 14627.

DOUGLASS, DAVID L(ESLIE), b. Newark, N.J, Sept. 28, 31; m. 52; c. 4. METALLURGY. B.S, Pa. State, 53, M.S, 55; Ph.D.(metall), Ohio State, 58. Metallurgist, Savannah River Lab, E.I. du Pont de Nemours & Co, 53-54; Battelle Mem. Inst, 55-57; mgr. alloy studies, Knolls Atomic Power Lab, Gen. Elec. Co, 58-60, tech. specialist metall, Vallecitos Atomic Lab, 60-66; sr. scientist, Stanford Res. Inst, 66-67, head corrosion sci. sect, 67-68; PROF. MAT. SCI, UNIV. CALIF, LOS ANGELES, 68- Instr, Ohio State, 56-58; adj. lectr, Rensselaer Polytech, 58-60; Lawrence Radiation Lab, California, Livermore, 60-61; consult, Europ. Atomic Energy Cmn-Atomic Energy Cmn. Joint Prog, Nuclear Studies Ctr, Belg, 63-65; ed, J. Oxidation of Metals. Am. Soc. Metals; Am. Inst. Mining, Metall. & Petrol. Eng; Am. Ceramic Soc. Corrosion and oxidation mechanisms; physical metallurgy; electron microscopy. Address: Dept. of Metallurgy, 6531 Boelter Hall, University of California, Los Angeles, CA 90024.

DOUGLASS, DEAN C(ARLTON), b. Rochester, N.Y, Nov. 13, 29; m. 54; c. 1. PHYSICAL CHEMISTRY. B.S, Rochester, 51; U.S. Rubber Co. fel, Cornell, 54-55; Ph.D.(phys. chem), 57. Asst. gen. chem, Cornell, 51-53; MEM. TECH. STAFF, BELL TEL. LABS, 57- Fel. Am. Phys. Soc. Nuclear quadruple and nuclear magnetic resonance application to molecular structure and motions. Address: Bell Telephone Labs, Murray Hill, NJ 07971.

DOUGLASS, DONALD W(ICKWARE), b. Los Angeles, Calif, Sept. 21, 08; m. 33; c. 1. ZOOLOGY. A.B, Grinnell Col, 30; M.A, Univ. Mich, 32, Ph.D. (zool), 34. Instr. biol, Tex. Technol. Col, 34-39; game exec, game div, MICH. STATE DEPT. NATURAL RESOURCES, 39-49, 50-67, chief game div, 67-70, SPEC. ASST. TO DIR, 70- Assoc. prof, Mich. State Col, 49-50. Assoc. Am. Ornith. Union; Wilson Ornith. Soc; Wildlife Soc. Address: Michigan State Dept. of Natural Resources, Lansing, MI 48926.

DOUGLASS, IRWIN B(RUCE), b. Des Moines, Iowa, Sept. 2, 04; m. 31; c. 2. ORGANIC CHEMISTRY. B.S, Monmouth Col, 26; Ph.D.(org. chem), Kansas, 32; D.Sc, Monmouth Col, 58. Teacher, high sch, Ill, 26-28; instr. chem, Kansas City Jr. Col, 30-31; asst. instr, Kansas, 29-32; acting assoc. prof, N.Dak, Col, 32-33; asst. prof, North. Mont. Col, 33-37, 38-40; asst, Yale, 37-38; asst. prof, UNIV. MAINE, 40-42, assoc. prof, 42-46, prof, 46-70, acting head dept, 41-46, head dept, 46-52, PLANNING OFF, UNIV, 69-, EMER. PROF. CHEM, 70- AAAS; Am. Chem. Soc; Tech. Asn. Pulp & Paper Indust; Air Pollution Control Asn. Kraft pulping odor control; organic sulfur compounds; potato starch; wood chemistry. Address: 4 Summer St, Orono, ME 04473.

DOUGLASS, JAMES E(DWARD), b. Bessemer, Ala, Nov. 3, 28; m. 53; c. 2. FORESTRY. B.S, Auburn Univ, 51; M.S, Mich. State Univ, 55; Clemson Univ, 68-69; Univ. Ga, 69-71. Conserv. forester, Int. Paper Co, 53-54; RES. FORESTER, SOUTHEAST. FOREST & RANGE EXP. STA, U.S. FOREST SERV, ASHVILLE, 56-; MEM. STAFF, COWEETA HYDROLOGIC LAB, 71- U.S.A, 51-53, 1st Lt. Soc. Am. Foresters; Soil Sci. Soc. Am. Soil moisture-vegetative relations; forest hydrology using control and treatment experimental watershed approach. Address: Coweeta Hydrologic Lab, Box 601, Franklyn, NC 28734.

DOUGLASS, JAMES E(DWARD), b. Corpus Christi, Tex, May 18, 30; m. 55; c. 2. ORGANIC CHEMISTRY. B.A, Rice, 52; Procter & Gamble fel, Texas, 57-58, Ph.D.(chem), 59. Hickrill Chem. Res. Found. res. fel, 58-59; asst. prof. CHEM, Univ. Ky, 60-65; assoc. prof, MARSHALL UNIV, 65-68, PROF, 68- U.S.N.R, 52-55, Lt. AAAS; Am. Chem. Soc. Organometallic chemistry; pyridinium ylide chemistry; heterocyclic synthesis. Address: Dept. of Chemistry, Marshall University, Huntington, WV 25701.

DOUGLASS, JOHN R(ICHMOND), b. Hwai Yuan, Anhwei, China, Feb. 16, 25; m. 70. ORGANIC CHEMISTRY, BOTANY. B.S, Hamilton Col, 45; Am. Cyanamid fel, Colorado, 49-50, Ph.D.(chem), 52. Asst. gen. & anal. chem, Colorado, 47-48, 50-51, org. chem, 48, 50-53; instr. biochem. & asst. chemist, exp. sta, Colorado State, 52; instr. inorg. & org. chem, Colo. Sch. Mines, 53-55; Colorado State, 55-62; park guide, Carlsbad Caverns Nat. Park, 62; park naturalist, Petrified Forest Nat. Park, 62-64; White Sands Nat. Monument, 64-67; west. dist. naturalist, Yellowstone Nat. Park, 67-71; ASST. CHIEF PARK NATURALIST, ROCKY MT. NAT. PARK, 71- Summers, nat. park ranger, Colorado, 56, naturalist, 57-62. Sand dune movement; structures produced during dune movement. Address: Box 1363, Estes Park, CO 80517.

DOUGLASS, JOSEPH DARRELL, JR, b. Cleveland, Ohio, May 30, 35; m. 62; c. 1. OPERATIONS RESEARCH. B.E.E, Cornell, 58, M.S, 60, Ph.D.(networks math), 62. Asst. prof. elec. eng, Cornell, 61-62; mem. staff weapons res, Sandia Corp, 62-63; sr. analyst, Res. Triangle Inst, N.C, 63-66; mem. res. staff, Inst. Defense Anal, D.C, 66-69; PROG. MGR. SPEC. STUDIES DIV, SERENDIPITY, INC, 69- Consult, Gen. Elec. Co, 61-62. Network theory; system theory; weapons strategy; civil defense operations. Address: Special Studies Division, Serendipity Inc, 2001 Jefferson-Davis Hwy, Arlington, VA 22202.

DOUGLASS, MATTHEW McCARTNEY, b. Port of Spain, Trinidad, Sept. 21, 26; U.S. citizen; m. 54; c. 4. CIVIL ENGINEERING. B.Eng, McGill, 52; M.S.E, George Washington, 62; nat. Sci. Found. fel, & Ph.D.(civil eng), Okla. State, 66. Jr. engr, Kilborn Eng. Co, Ont, 52; asst. engr, dept. works & hydraul, Trinidad, 53-55, exec. engr, 55-57; asst. designer, E. Lionel Pavlo, Consult. Engrs, 57; instr. CIVIL ENG, Howard, 57-62, asst. prof, 62-66; ASSOC. PROF, SIR GEORGE WILLIAMS UNIV, 66- Am. Soc. Civil Eng; Am. Soc. Eng. Educ; Eng. Inst. Can. Elastic-plastic buckling of columns; application of complementary potential energy to the analysis of space frameworks; curved-girder orthotropic bridges. Address: Faculty of Engineering, Sir George Williams University, Montreal 107, Que, Can.

DOUGLASS, P(RITCHARD) C(ALKINS), b. Jamestown, N.Y, Mar. 22, 13; m. 38; c. 3. ANALYTICAL CHEMISTRY. B.S, Houghton Col, 35; Cornell; Pittsburgh. Chemist, G.C. Murphy Co, Pa, 37-42; Bausch & Lomb Optical Co, 42-48; fel, Mellon Inst. Indust. Res, 48-51; microscopist cotton properties, Coats & Clark Res. Labs, N.J, 51-53; chemist & head anal. chem. & controls, BAUSCH & LOMB, INC, 53-63, CHEMIST SPECIALIST, 63- Am. Chem. Soc; Electrochem. Soc; fel. Am. Inst. Chem; Am. Soc. Test. & Mat. Application of analytical and electrochemistry to chemical processes and materials; microscopy; instrumentation applied to metal finishing, glass, lubrication and polycrystalline materials. Address: Materials Application Research Lab, Bausch & Lomb, Inc, Rochester, NY 14602.

DOUGLASS, RAYMOND C(HARLES), b. San Francisco, Calif, Mar. 30, 23; m. 48; c. 2. INVERTEBRATE PALEONTOLOGY. B.S, Stanford, 50, Ph.D, 57; Shell fel, Nebraska, 51-52, M.S, 52. Field asst, U.S. GEOL. SURV, 47-48, GEOLOGIST, 52- Asst, Nebraska, 50-51; mem. faculty, U.S. Dept. Agr. Grad. Sch, 57- Dir, Cushman Found Foraminiferal Res, 61-, pres, 64-66. U.S.A, 43-46, Res, 46-49. Paleont. Soc; Soc. Econ. Paleont. & Mineral. Evolution, ecology and distribution of large foraminifera; Pennsylvanian and Permian Fusulinidae. Address: U.S. Geological Survey, E501, U.S. National Museum, Washington, DC 20242.

DOUGLASS, RAYMOND D(ONALD), b. Gorham, Maine, Dec. 29, 94; m. 18; c. 3. MATHEMATICS. B.A, Maine, 15, M.A, 16, hon. Sc.D, 43; Ph.D. (math), Mass. Inst. Tech, 31. Prin, high sch, Mass, 16-17; sub-master, high sch, N.H, 17-18; instr. MATH, MASS. INST. TECHNOL, 19-30, asst. prof, 30-34, assoc, 34, 39, PROF, 39- Univ. exten. lecturer, 25- Camouflage sect, Nat. Defense Research Council, 43-45. Citation, Army Sig. Corp; Commendation, Nat. Defense Res. Council; Charles F. Park Gold Medal. With Office Sci. Res. & Develop; Chem. Warfare Serv; U.S. Navy, 44. U.S.N, 18-19, Ens. Summation of series; definite integrals; elements of nomography; calculus and its applications; analytical geometry; graphical mathematics. Address: 18 Oak Ave, Belmont, MA 02178.

DOUGLASS, ROBERT L, b. Weiser, Idaho, July 25, 21; m. 45; c. 2. SPEECH PATHOLOGY. A.B, Redlands, 46, M.A, 48; Ph.D, Southern California, 51. Speech therapist, Children's Hosp, Los Angeles, Calif, 50-51; asst. prof. SPEECH, CALIF. STATE COL, LOS ANGELES, 51-56, assoc. prof, 56-60, PROF, 60-, chmn. dept. speech & drama, 66-69. Res. consult, Children's Speech & Hearing Center, 60-; speech consult, Lawrence Sch. Except. Children, 62- U.S.A.A.F, 41-45, T/Sgt. Am. Psychol. Asn; Am. Speech & Hearing Asn. Speech pathology and audiology; clinical psychology. Address: Dept. of Speech & Drama, California State College at Los Angeles, 5151 State College Dr, Los Angeles, CA 90032.

DOUGLASS, ROBERT M(ARSHALL), b. Burbank, Calif, Sept. 29, 28; m. 50, 64. CRYSTALLOGRAPHY. B.A, Pomona Col, 50; Ph.D.(geol), California, 54. Asst. geol. sci, California, 50-54, mem. staff chem. & metall. div, Los Alamos Sci. Lab, 54-69; RETIRED. Fel. Am. Inst. Chem; Mineral Soc. Am; Am. Crystallog. Asn; Geochem. Soc. X-ray, optical and morphological crystallography; mineralogy; microscopy; crystal chemistry. Address: P.O. Box 619, Las Vegas, NM 87701.

DOUGLASS, ROGER LEIGH, b. Grinnell, Iowa, Jan. 29, 31; m. 53; c. 2. PHYSICS. B.S, Colorado, 54; Ph.D.(physics), California, Berkeley, 62.

Lectr. PHYSICS, California, Berkeley, 61-62; asst. prof, Am. Univ, Beirut, 62-69; ASSOC. PROF, MERRILL COL, UNIV. CALIF, SANTA CRUZ, 69- Nat. Sci. Found. fel, 62. Sig.C, U.S.A, 54-56. Am. Phys. Soc. Low temperature physics; spin-wave heat transport; quantized vortices in superfluid helium. Address: Dept. of Physics, 315 Natural Science II, Merrill College, University of California, Santa Cruz, CA 95060.

DOUGLASS, ROGER THACKREY, b. Mullinville, Kans, Apr. 27, 38; m. 62; c. 2. MATHEMATICS. B.A, Kansas, 60, Ph.D.(math), 67; M.A, Michigan, 61. Instr. MATH, Kent State, 61-63; ASST. PROF, UNIV. MASS, AMHERST, 67- Am. Math. Soc; Math. Asn. Am. Point-set topology, particularly relation theory. Address: Dept. of Mathematics, University of Massachusetts, Amherst, MA 01002.

DOUGLASS, TERRY DEAN, b. Jackson, Tenn, Oct. 26, 42; m. 64; c. 2. ELECTRICAL ENGINEERING. B.S, Tennessee, 65, M.S, 66, Nat. Defense Ed. Act fel, 67, Ph.D, 68. SR. SCIENTIST, LIFE SCI. DEPT, ORTEC, INC, 68- Optimization of time measurement in nuclear instrumentation; electronic instrumentation in neurophysiology; scanning and integrating microdensitometry. Address: Ortec, Inc, 100 Midland Rd, Oak Ridge, TN 37830.

DOUGLIS, AVRON, b. Tulsa, Okla, Mar. 14, 18; m. 41; c. 2. MATHEMATICS. A.B, Chicago, 38; M.S, N.Y. Univ, 48, Ph.D.(math), 49. Res. fel, Calif. Inst. Tech, 49-50; instr. MATH, N.Y. Univ, 50-51, asst. prof, 51-54, assoc. prof, 54-56; assoc. res. prof, UNIV. MD, COLLEGE PARK, 56-58, PROF, 58- U.S.A, 42-46. Am. Math. Soc; Math. Asn. Am. Partial differential equations. Address: Dept. of Mathematics, University of Maryland, College Park, MD 20742.

DOUKAS, GEORGE, b. Baltimore, Md, Dec. 31, 17; m. 47; c. 3. MECHANICAL ENGINEERING. B.E, Hopkins, 40. Engr. org. chemicals, E.I. DU PONT DE NEMOURS & CO, N.J, 40-42, plastics, W.Va, 47-48, tech. supvr, N.J, 49-52, neoprene, Ky, 52-58, res. & develop, acetylene, 58-60, SUPT, elastomers, Tex, 60-69, RES. & DEVELOP. LAB, 69- U.S.N, 42-46, Lt. Comdr. Am. Soc. Mech. Eng. Process for manufacture of monomers; polymerization processes for production of synthetic rubbers and plastics. Address: Research & Development Lab, E.I. du Pont de Nemours & Co, P.O. Box 3269, Beaumont, TX 77704.

DOUKAS, HARRY M(ICHAEL), b. Washington, D.C, July 30, 19; m. 47; c. 4. ORGANIC CHEMISTRY, BIOCHEMISTRY. B.S, Maryland, 42; M.S, Georgetown, 52, Ph.D.(chem), 53. Asst, Maryland, 46-48; chemist, bur. agr. & indust. chem, biol. active compounds div, U.S. Dept. Agr, 48-52, res. chemist, east. utilization res. br, Phila, 53-55; sr. investr, Georgetown, 52-53; head org. sect, chem. crops biol. lab, U.S. Army, 55-58; prog. dir. fels, Nat. Sci. Found, 58-65; ASST. CHIEF FELS, CAREER DEVELOP. REV. BR, DIV. RES. GRANTS, NAT. INSTS. HEALTH, 65- U.S.A.A.F, 42-45. Am. Chem. Soc; Sci. Res. Soc. Am. Natural and synthetic plant growth hormones; unsaturated naphthylenic acids; isolation and characterization of plant alkaloids; substituted pyridine compounds; science administration. Address: 9920 Brixton Lane, Bethesda, MD 20034.

DOULL, JOHN, b. Baker, Mont, Sept. 13, 23; m. 58. PHARMACOLOGY. B.S, Mont. State Col, 44; Ph.D.(pharmacol), Chicago, 50, M.D, 53. Asst, toxicity lab, Chicago, 46-51, res. assoc, 51-53, asst. prof. pharmacol, univ, 53-57, assoc. prof, 57-67; res. assoc, U.S. Air. Force Radiation Lab, 53-54, asst. dir, 54-67; PROF. PHARMACOL. & TOXICOL, MED. CTR, UNIV. KANS, 67- U.S.N, 44-46. AAAS; Soc. Exp. Biol. & Med; Am. Soc. Pharmacol. & Exp. Therapeut; Am. Chem. Soc. Radiation Res. Soc; Am. Indust. Hyg. Asn. Pesticides; hibernation; biological aspects of ionizing radiation; toxicology. Address: Dept. of Pharmacology & Toxicology, University of Kansas Medical Center, Rainbow Blvd. at 39th, Kansas City, KS 66103.

DOUMANI, GEORGE ALEXANDER, b. Acre, Palestine, Apr. 16, 29; U.S. citizen; m. 57; c. 3. PETROLEUM GEOLOGY, STRATIGRAPHY. B.A, California, Berkeley, 56, M.A, 57. Petrol. inspector, Arabian Am. Oil Co, Saudi Arabia, 50-52; exploitation engr, Shell Oil Co, Calif, summer 56; geologist, Hersey Inspection Bur, 57-58; geologist & glaciologist, Nat. Acad. Sci. & Nat. Sci. Found, Antarctic, 58-60; res. assoc. geol, Inst. Polar Studies, Ohio State, 60-63; sect. head arctic & antarctic bibliog, cold regions sect, sci. & technol. div, LIBR. CONG, 63-66, SPECIALIST EARTH SCI. & OCEANOG, SCI. POLICY RES. DIV, CONG. RES. SERV, 66- Doumani Peak & Mount Doumani in Antarctica named by Nat. Bd. Geog. Names; Antarctic Serv. Medal, U.S. Dept. Defense; Knight, Nat. Order of Cedars, Lebanon Repub. Am. Asn. Petrol. Geol; fel. Geol. Soc. Am; Geosci. Info. Soc; Am. Polar Soc. Stratigraphic paleontology; earth sciences and oceanography; national science policy issues; antarctic geology. Address: Science Policy Research Division, Congressional Research Service, Library of Congress, Washington, DC 20540.

DOUMAS, A(RTHUR) C(ONSTANTINOS), b. Fredericksburg, Va, Jan. 31, 32; m. 51; c. 3. CHEMICAL ENGINEERING. Fel, Va. Polytech, 52-53, Weirton scholar, 53-55, Ph.D.(chem. eng), 55. Proj. leader, DOW CHEM, CO, FREEPORT, 55-70, MGR, 70- Am. Chem. Soc. Am. Soc. Metals; Am. Soc. Qual. Control; Am. Chem. Soc; Inst. Chem. Eng. Chemical process; applications; electrochemistry; heat transmission; engineering statistics; unit operations. Address: 217 Narcissus, Lake Jackson, TX 77566.

DOUMAS, BASIL T, b. Argos Orestikon, Greece, July 16, 30; U.S. citizen; m. 57; c. 3. CLINICAL CHEMISTRY. B.S, Thessaloniki, 52; M.S, Tennessee, 60, Ph.D.(biochem), 62. Consult. path, Baptist Mem. Hosp, Memphis, Tenn, 60-62, head dept. clin. chem, 62-64; asst. prof. path, med. col, Univ. Ala. & asst. dir. clin. chem, univ. hosp, 64-65; assoc. dir. clin. chem, univ. hosp, Univ. Ala, 65-70, ASSOC. PROF. PATH, 68-70; MED. COL. WIS, 70- Instr, Univ. Tenn, 63-64. Greek Army, 52-54, 2nd Lt. AAAS; Am. Asn. Clin. Chem; Am. Chem. Soc; N.Y. Acad. Sci; Acad. Clin. Lab. Physicians & Scientists. Electrophoresis of serum proteins and dye binding; bacterial metabolism pyrimidines; clinical chemistry methodology, standards, instrumentation and quality control. Address: Dept. of Pathology, Medical College of Wisconsin, 8700 W. Wisconsin Ave, Milwaukee, WI 53226.

DOUMAS, MENELAOS, b. Greece, Jan. 26, 23; nat; m. 51; c. 2. MECHANICAL ENGINEERING. B.S.M.E, City Col, 47; M.S.M.E, Columbia, 49. Sect. head, cent. res. labs, Gen. Foods Corp, 47-55, fel. engr, 55-58, supvr. thermal hydraulic & mech. design nuclear reactors, 58-59; MGR. IRRADIATIONS, BETTIS ATOMIC POWER LAB, WESTINGHOUSE ELEC. CORP, 55- U.S.A, 42-45. Am. Soc. Mech. Eng; Am. Nuclear Soc; Am. Inst. Chem. Eng. Development work on food processing and equipment; spray drying; atomization of liquids; thermal, hydraulic and mechanical design of nuclear reactors; design of high pressure and temperature irradiation facilities; remote handling and examination equipment. Address: 354 Southridge Dr, Pittsburgh, PA 15241.

DOUMAUX, ARTHUR ROY, JR, b. Little Neck, N.Y, Mar. 15, 38; m. 62; c. 2. ORGANIC CHEMISTRY. B.S, Lehigh, 61; Ph.D.(org. chem), Yale, 66. RES. & DEVELOP. CHEMIST, UNION CARBIDE CORP, 66- Am. Chem. Soc. Photosensitized autoxidation of heterocyclic dienes, especially those relating to naturally found substances; metal-ion catalyzed oxidations with peroxidic materials; chemistry of ethylene oxide adducts. Address: 1401 Wilkie Dr, Charleston, WV 25314.

DOUNCE, ALEXANDER L(ATHAM), b. Syracuse, N.Y, Dec. 7, 09; m. 37; c. 3. BIOCHEMISTRY. Hamilton Col, 26-28; A.B, Cornell, 30, Ph.D.(org. chem), 35. Chemist, Continental Can Co, 35-36; instr. biochem, Cornell, 36-41; SCH. MED. & DENT, UNIV. ROCHESTER, 41-43, assoc, Manhattan Dist. Proj, 43-46, asst. prof. BIOCHEM, 46-54, assoc. prof, 54-65, PROF, 65- Consult, Rochester Div, Atomic Energy Proj, 46-54. AAAS; Am. Chem. Soc; Am. Soc. Biol. Chem; Soc. Exp. Biol. & Med; Am. Asn. Cancer Res; Am. Soc. Cell Biol. Enzyme research; indirect cancer research; cytochemistry; applied protein chemistry; nucleoprotein chemistry. Address: Dept. of Biochemistry, University of Rochester School of Medicine & Dentistry, 260 Crittenden Blvd, Rochester, NY 14642.

DOUNDOULAKIS, GEORGE J, b. Detroit, Mich, Oct. 19, 21; m. 48; c. 3. PHYSICS. B.S, Brooklyn Col, 50; M.S, Polytech. Inst. Brooklyn, 53. Sr. electronics scientist, Mat. Lab, N.Y, 50-55; dir. res, Gen. Bronze Corp, 55-60; pres, Advancement Devices, Inc, 56-62; dir. electronics, Continental Copper & Steel Industs, Inc, 62-65; v.pres. & secy, Codafile, Inc, 65-67; mgr. adv. microwave eng, defense electronic prod, RCA Corp, 67-68; DIR. RES. & DEVELOP, W.J. CASEY ENTERPRISES, GREENVALE, 68- Instr, RCA Corp, 53-56. Brit. Intel, 41-43; O.S.S, U.S.A, 43-45; King's Medal of Courage; Legion of Merit. Inst. Elec. & Electronics Eng. Antennas; narrow band television; analog computers; information retrieval systems. Address: 2498 Kayron Lane, North Bellmore, L.I, NY 11710.

DOUPNIK, BEN L(EE), JR, b. Agenda, Kans, Aug. 13, 39; m. 61; c. 3. PHYTOPATHOLOGY. A.B, Kans. Wesleyan Univ, 62; M.S, Univ. Nebr, 64; Ph.D.(plant path), La. State Univ, 67. ASST. PROF. PLANT PATH, COASTAL PLAIN EXP. STA, UNIV. GA, 67- AAAS; Am. Phytopath. Soc; Am. Inst. Biol. Sci; Am. Soc. Microbiol. Host-parasite physiology; mycotoxins and their effects on warm-blooded animals and plants. Address: University of Georgia Coastal Plain Experiment Station, Tifton, GA 31794.

DOUROS, JOHN D(RENKLE), b. Reading, Pa, Dec. 26, 30; m. 54; c. 2. MICROBIOLOGY. B.A, Duke, 52; M.S, Rutgers, 55; Ph.D.(bact), Pa. State, 58. Assoc. microbiologist, Parke, Davis & Co, 57-60; Sun Oil Co, 60-63; sr. chemist & microbiologist, Esso Res. & Eng, 63-68; MGR. MICROBIOL. RES. & DEVELOP, GATES RUBBER CO, 68- Med.C, U.S.A, 52-54. Am. Soc. Microbiol; Am. Chem. Soc; Soc. Indust. Microbiol; N.Y. Acad. Sci. Mechanism of action of antibiotics; degradation of organic compounds by microorganisms. Address: Gates Rubber Co, Denver, CO 80127.

DOUSA, THOMAS PATRICK, b. Prague, Czech, Dec. 13, 37; m. 66; c. 2. INTERNAL MEDICINE, PHYSIOLOGY. M.D, Charles Univ, Prague, 62; Ph.D.(biochem), Czech. Acad. Sci, 68. From intern to resident & res. assoc, Inst. Cardiovasc. Diseases, Prague, 62-65; attending physician, Community Med. Ctr, 65-68; clin. investr. & attending physician, dept. med. I, Charles Univ, 68-69; Am. Med. Asn. fel. molecular endocrinol, Inst. Biomed. Res, Chicago, 69-70; ASST. PROF. PHYSIOL, MED. SCH, NORTHWEST. UNIV, 70- Czech. Acad. Sci. Prize, 69. Am. Fedn. Clin. Res; Czech. Med. Soc; Europ. Soc. Clin. Invest. Cellular action of ADH in the kidney; hormonal regulation of sodium excretion. Address: Dept. of Physiology, Northwestern University Medical School, 303 E. Chicago Ave, Chicago, IL 60611.

DOUSLIN, DONALD RAYMOND, b. Paynesville, Mich, Dec. 7, 16; m. 42; c. 2. PHYSICAL CHEMISTRY. B.S, Michigan Tech, 40; A.M, Iowa, 41; Ph.D.(phys. chem), Mass. Inst. Tech, 48. Chem. engr, Phillips Petrol. Co, 41-43; phys. chemist THERMODYN, U.S. BUR. MINES, 43-46, sect. leader, 52-63, PROJ. COORD, 63- Phys. chemist, Shell Develop. Co, 48-52. AAAS; Am. Chem. Soc; Am. Inst. Chem. Eng. Compressibility of gases; intermolecular forces; vapor-liquid equilibria; thermochemistry; vapor pressure. Address: 3309 Woodland Rd, Bartlesville, OK 74003.

DOUTHART, RICHARD J(AMES), b. Chicago, Ill, June 11, 35; m. 59; c. 2. BIOPHYSICAL CHEMISTRY. B.S, Little Rock Univ, 61; Ph.D.(phys. chem), Univ. Ill, Urbana, 68. Chemist, IIT Res. Inst, 62-64; SR. BIOPHYSICIST, LILLY RES. LABS, 68- AAAS; Am. Chem. Soc. Physical chemistry of nucleic acids and virus; interferon induction; DNA replication, interaction of nucleic acids with small molecules. Address: Lilly Research Labs, 307 E. McCarty St, Indianapolis, IN 46206.

DOUTHETT, DOANE, b. Easton, Pa, July 19, 28. PHYSICS. A.B, Vassar Col, 48; M.S, Carnegie Inst. Tech, 49, Am. Asn. Univ. Women nat. fel, 56, Ph.D.(physics), 58. Instr. physics, Woman's Col, North Carolina, 50-51; mem. tech. staff, Ramo Wooldridge Corp, 58-59, Space Tech. Corp, 59-61; assoc. prof. physics & astron, Vassar Col, 61-62; mem. tech. staff, Space Gen. Corp, Aerojet Gen. Corp, 64-66; electronics div, TRW Systs, Calif, 66-67, sect. staff engr, 67-70; self-employed, 71- Low temperature solid state physics; ferrimagnetism; microwave electronics; optics; nonlinear effects in semiconductors; millimeter wave radiometry. Address: Route 1, Box 391, Cambridge, MD 21613.

DOUTHETT, E(LWOOD) M(OSER), b. Pottstown, Pa, Oct. 4, 15; m. 49; c. 5. NUCLEAR CHEMISTRY. B.S, Pa. State Col, 36; M.S, Ohio State, 47; Ph.D. (nuclear chem), California, 51. Engr, Gen. Elec. Co, 36-39; Gen. Steel Castings Co, 39-41; U.S. Air Force, 41-69, air tech. liaison officer, Am. Embassy, The Hague, 47-48, Mem. Tech. Appln. Center, U.S. Air Force, Wash, D.C, 51-54, dir. McClellan Cent. Lab, 54-58, chief weapons develop. br, hq, 59-60, res. div, 60-61, dir. geophys. res. directorate, Cambridge Res. Labs, 61-62, mgr, SNAP-50 nuclear auxiliary space power prog, U.S. Atomic Energy Comn, 62-65, comdr, Air Force Rocket Propulsion Lab, Edwards Air Force Base, Calif, 65-69; DIR. EFFECTS EVAL. DIV, U.S. ATOMIC ENERGY COMN, 69- U.S.A.F, 41-69, Col.(Ret). Ranges of fission products; radiochemistry of fission products. Address: Effects Evaluation Division, Nevada Operations Office, U.S. Atomic Energy Commission, 2753 S. Highland Dr, Las Vegas, NV 89114.

DOUTHIT, HARRY ANDERSON, JR, b. Raymondville, Tex, June 18, 35; m. 59; c. 1. MOLECULAR BIOLOGY. B.A, Texas, 61, Ph.D.(bot), 65. Fel. molecular biol, Wisconsin, 64-67; ASST. PROF. BOT, UNIV. MICH, 67- U.S.A, 56-59. AAAS; Am. Soc. Microbiol. Enzymology, including the nature and relevance of thiaminase I; differentiation including the contributions and interactions of nucleic acids in bacterial differentiation. Address: Dept. of Botany, University of Michigan, Ann Arbor, MI 48104.

DOUTHIT, THOMAS D. N(ATHAN), b. Lubbock, Tex, July 9, 18; m. 48; c. 2. GEOPHYSICS. B.S, Tex. Tech. Col, 51; M.S, St. Louis, 59; M.B.A, Chicago, 62. Geophysicist, Air Force Cambridge Res. Labs, U.S. Air Force, 56-61, prog. coord, 62-64, dir. space physics lab, 64-68, dir. ionospheric physics lab, 68-69; geophysicist, Weston Observ, 69-70; PROG. COORD, AIR FORCE CAMBRIDGE RES. LABS, 70- Chmn. working group, Int. Years Quiet Sun, 63-66, del, Madrid, Spain, 65, London, Eng, 67; mem. comt. solar-terrestrial res, Nat. Acad. Sci, 64-69; del, Int. Years Active Sun, London, Eng, 69. U.S.A.F, 42-45, 51-69, Lt.Col. (Ret). Soc. Explor. Geophys; Am. Geophys. Union; Am. Geol. Inst; Seismol. Soc. Am; N.Y. Acad. Sci. Engineering management; seismology; space physics; ionospheric physics; arctic terrain research. Address: 24 Raymond Rd, Chelmsford, MA 01824.

DOUTT, J. KENNETH, b. Steubenville, Ohio, Mar. 24, 05; m. 30; c. 1. MAMMALOGY. B.S, Pittsburgh, 29; M.A, California, 31; hon. Sc.D, Waynesburg Col, 49. Asst, sect. mammal, CARNEGIE MUS, 31-37, CURATOR MAMMAL, 38-, leader of numerous world expeds, 24-70. Am. Soc. Mammal; Soc. Study Evolution; Wildlife Soc; Soc. Syst. Zool; Soc. Vert. Paleont. Mammalian fauna of Utah, Arizona, Hudson Bay region, northeast Canada and Pennsylvania; seals of the genus Phoca; white-tailed deer of eastern North America. Address: Carnegie Museum, 4400 Forbes Ave, Pittsburgh, PA 15213.

DOUTT, RICHARD L(EROY), b. La Verne, Calif, Dec. 6, 16; m. 42; c. 2. ENTOMOLOGY. B.S, California, 39, M.S, 40, Ph.D.(entom), 46, LL.B, 59. Jr. entomologist, DIV. BIOL. CONTROL LABS. AT ALBANY, UNIV. CALIF, BERKELEY, 46-48, asst. prof. BIOL. CONTROL & ENTOM, 48-54, assoc. prof, 54-60, PROF, 60-, chmn. dept, 64-69, acting dean col. agr. sci. & acting assoc. dir. agr. exp. sta, 69-70. U.S.N, 41-45, Lt. Comdr. Am. Entom. Soc; Ecol. Soc. Am. Taxonomy of Chalcidoidea; biology of entomophagous insects. Address: Division of Biological Control, University of California 9240 S. Riverbend Ave, Parlier, CA 93648.

DOUTY, RICHARD T, b. Williamsport, Pa, June 12, 30; m. 59; c. 4. STRUCTURAL ENGINEERING. B.S, Lehigh, 56; M.S, Ga. Inst. Tech, 57; Ph.D. (struct. eng), Cornell, 64. Engr. trainee, Bethlehem Steel Co, 57-58; res. assoc, Cornell, 61-62; asst. prof. CIVIL ENG, UNIV. MO-COLUMBIA, 62-65, assoc. prof, 65-68, PROF, 68- Participant, Nat. Sci. Found. proj. use of computers & math optimization tech. in eng. design, 65; sr. fel, Univ. Pa, 69-70; mem. eval. panel, associateship prog, Nat. Res. Coun, 71. U.S.N, 50-54. AAAS; Am. Soc. Civil Eng; Int. Asn. Bridge & Struct. Eng. Computer techniques in engineering design. Address: College of Engineering, University of Missouri-Columbia, Columbia, MO 65201.

D'OUVILLE, EDMOND L(AWRENCE), b. Phila, Pa, June 10, 09; m; c. 7. ORGANIC CHEMISTRY. B.S, Villanova Col, 32; M.S, Pennsylvania, 34, Ph.D.(org. chem), 37. Instr. chem, Villanova Col, 33-37; from res. chemist to dir. tech. info. & liaison, Standard Oil Co, 37-62, tech. liaison, res. & develop, PATENTS & LICENSING DEPT, Am. Oil Co, 62-66, DIR. TECH. LIAISON, STANDARD OIL CO.(IND), 66- Chemist, Mellon Inst. Indust. Res, 42-44. Organic synthesis; reactions of hydrocarbons. Address: Patents & Licensing Dept, Standard Oil Co.(Indiana), 910 S. Michigan Ave, Chicago, IL 60680.

DOUVILLE, PHILLIP RAOUL, b. Hartford, Conn, June 24, 36; m. 59; c. 3. PHYSICAL CHEMISTRY. B.A, Univ. Conn, 59, Ph.D.(phys. chem), 69; Univ. Maine, 59-61. Asst. instr. CHEM, Univ. Conn, 63-65; asst. prof, CENT. CONN. STATE COL, 65-70, ASSOC. PROF, 70- AAAS; Am. Chem. Soc; The Chem. Soc; New Eng. Asn. Chem. Teachers. Effect of gases on surface tension of liquids. Address: Dept. of Chemistry, Central Connecticut State College, New Britain, CT 06050.

DOUVRES, FRANK WILLIAM, b. N.Y.C, Apr. 16, 27; m. 53. PARASITOLOGY. B.S, Maryland, 48, M.S, 51, Ph.D, 58. Asst. zool, Maryland, 48-53, 55-56; PARASITOLOGIST, regional animal disease res. lab, AGR. RES. SERV, U.S. DEPT, AGR, 53-55, ANIMAL PARASITE DIV, 56- U.S.N.R, 45-47. Am. Soc. Parasitol; Am. Micros. Soc; Am. Astron. Soc. Veterinary helminthology. Address: Animal Parasite Division, Agricultural Research Service, U.S. Dept. of Agriculture, Beltsville, MD 20705.

DO-VAN-QUY, DOMINIC, b. Nam-Dinh, North Vietnam, Jan. 19, 27. ENTOMOLOGY, PARASITOLOGY. B.A, St. Joseph Sem. & Col, Yonkers, N.Y, 51; M.S, Fordham Univ, 57, Ph.D.(biol), 60. Chief entom. sect, admin. gen. malaria eradication, Ministry Health, Saigon, 60-63; chief entom-parasitol. & plague labs, Pasteur Inst. Vietnam, 63-68; asst. prof. genetics & cell physiol, Fairleigh Dickinson Univ, 69-70; RES. ADMINR, AM. CANCER SOC, INC, 70- Prof. zool, Univ. Hue, 62-68; parasitol, Univ. Saigon, 66-68, entom, sch. agr, 66-68; zool, Univ. Can-tho, 67-68. Am. Inst. Biol. Sci. Mosquito taxonomy of Vietnam, particularly mosquito genetics, ecology and control; insecticide resistance studies of mosquitoes and fleas; plague and infectious diseases in Vietnam. Address: Dept. of Research, American Cancer Society, Inc, 219 E. 42nd St, New York, NY 10017.

DOVE, A(LLAN) B(URGESS), b. Ayr, Scotland, Apr. 9, 09; m. 34, 63; c. 3. CHEMICAL & METALLURGICAL ENGINEERING. B.Sc, Queen's Univ. (Ont), 32. Chem. engr, STEEL. CO. CAN. LTD. 32-38, engr, Montreal Plants, 38-40, supt. Lachine Plant, 46-53, develop. & res, 53-67, SR. DEVELOP. METALLURGIST, WIRE & FASTENER DIV, 67- Awards, Am. Iron & Steel Inst, 60, Wire Asn, 37, 49, 55, 64, 69 & 70. R.C.E, 40-46, Res, 46-65, Lt. Col. Am. Soc. Metals; fel. Chem. Inst. Can; Eng. Inst. Can; N.Y. Acad. Sci. Wood fastenings; corrosion of metals; scale formation and removal; concrete reinforcing; cold working of metals. Address: Wire & Fastener Divisions, Steel Co. of Canada Ltd, 334 Wellington St. N, Hamilton 21, Ont, Can.

DOVE, D(EREK) B(RIAN), b. Middlesex, Eng, Jan. 12, 32; m. 54; c. 2. PHYSICS. B.Sc, Imp. Col, London, 53, Ph.D.(crystallog), 56. Sci. officer, Atomic Energy Res. Estab, Eng, 55-59, sr. sci. officer, 59; fel, Nat. Res. Coun. Can, 59-61; mem. tech. staff, Bell Tel. Labs, Inc, 61-67; ASSOC. PROF. METALL, MAT. & ELEC. ENG, UNIV. FLA, 67- Electron Micros. Soc. Am. Electron diffraction and microscopy; magnetic films; magneto-optic effects; structure of glasses and amorphous semiconductors. Address: Dept. of Metallurgical & Materials Engineering, University of Florida, Gainesville, FL 32601.

DOVE, J(OHN) E(DWARD), b. Minneapolis, Minn, Aug. 11, 30; m. 62; c. 3. PHYSICAL CHEMISTRY. B.A, Oxford, 52, B.Sc, 54, M.A. & D.Phil.(chem), 59. Laming traveling fel. from Queen's Col, Oxford, Göttingen, 57-58; sr. sci. officer, div. chem. eng, atomic energy res. estab, U.K. Atomic Energy Authority, 58-60; asst. prof. CHEM, UNIV. TORONTO, 62-66, ASSOC. PROF, 66- Commonwealth Fund Harkness fel, Harvard, 60-62; vis. scientist, Univ. Göttingen, 69-70. R.A.F, 54-56, Flying Officer. AAAS; Am. Phys. Soc; Combustion Inst; Chem. Inst. Can; Brit. Chem. Soc; Faraday Soc. Kinetics of high temperature reactions in gases; ionization in gases; chemistry and physics of shock waves and detonations; mass spectroscopy. Address: Dept. of Chemistry, University of Toronto, Toronto 5, Ont, Can.

DOVE, LEWIS DUNBAR, b. Savannah, Ga, Oct. 8, 34; m. 58; c. 1. PLANT PHYSIOLOGY & BIOCHEMISTRY. B.S, Univ. Md, 57, M.S, 59; summers, Nat. Sci. Found. fels, Duke Univ, 60 & 61, Ph.D.(bot), 64. Phys. sci. aid, plant indust. sta, U.S. Dept. Agr, Md, 57; instr. bot, Newcomb Col, Tulane Univ, 61-65, asst. prof. BIOL, 65-69; ASSOC. PROF, WEST. ILL. UNIV, 69- Soc. Sigma Xi res. grant in aid, 65-66; res. grants, Nat. Sci. Found, 67-69 & Ill. State Acad. Sci, 71-72. Am. Soc. Plant Physiol; Bot. Soc. Am; Am. Soc. Agron. Effects of environmental stress on protein and nucleic acid metabolism in plants; effects of drought on ion absorption by roots. Address: Dept. of Biological Sciences, Western Illinois University, Macomb, IL 61455.

DOVE, RAY ALLEN, b. Rockmart, Ga, Aug. 17, 21; m. 47; c. 4. CHEMISTRY. B.S, Akron, 47, M.S, 53. Chemist, GOODYEAR TIRE & RUBBER CO, 53-58, jr. res. chemist, 58-61, SR. RES. CHEMIST, 61- U.S.A, 42-45, Sgt. Am. Chem. Soc. Polarography; ultraviolet spectrophotometry; nonaqueous titrimetry; solid-liquid, gas and ion-exchange chromatography; flame photometry; atomic absorption spectroscopy. Address: Dept. 455B, Research Bldg, Goodyear Tire & Rubber Co, Akron, OH 44316.

DOVE, WILLIAM FRANCIS, b. Wash, D.C, July 30, 33; m. 61; c. 2. PLASMA PHYSICS. B.S, Pa. State Univ, 56; Ph.D.(physics), Univ. Calif, Berkeley, 68. RES. ASSOC. PHYSICS & ASTRON, UNIV. MD, 68- U.S.N, 56-61, Lt. Am. Phys. Soc. High Mach number plasma flow, magnetic diffusion, shock wave propagation and turbulent ion heating; non-equilibrium plasma transport properties and measurement of thermoelectric coefficient. Address: Dept. of Physics & Astronomy, University of Maryland, College Park, MD 20742.

DOVE, W(ILLIAM) FRANKLIN, b. Marion, Iowa, April 11, 97; m. 33; c. 5. BIOLOGY, GENETICS. B.S, Iowa State Col, 22; M.S, Wisconsin, 23, Ph.D. (genetics), 27. Asst. genetics, Wisconsin, 23-26; assoc. biologist, exp. sta, Maine, 26-31, biologist & head dept, 31-43; biologist & head food acceptance br, QM Subsistence Res. & Develop. Lab, Chicago, 44-46, biologist & technologist, QM Food & Container Inst. for Armed Forces, 46-48; COL. MED, DEPT. PUB. HEALTH, UNIV. ILL. COL. MED, 50-66, EMERITUS BIOLOGIST & TECHNOLOGIST, 66- Biochemist, State Dept. Pub. Health, Ill, 52-55. Vis. scientist, Nat. Insts. Health, 50-51; coordinator food acceptance, cmt. on food acceptance, Office QM-Gen, 45-48, consult, mil. planning div, 44. Mem. adv. bd, U.S. Soil, Plant & Nutrit. Lab, Cornell, 39-42. AAAS; Soc. Develop. Biol; Genetics Soc. Am; Am. Soc. Human Genetics; Biomet. Soc; Inst. Food Tech. Food acceptability, its determination and evaluation; basic foods and the nutrition of populations; transplantation of tissues; behavior toward subsistence; water and the consumer. Address: 339 N. Grove Ave, Oak Park, IL 60302.

DOVE, WILLIAM F(RANKLIN), JR, b. Bangor, Maine, June 20, 36; m. 64. MICROBIAL GENETICS, PHYSICAL CHEMISTRY. A.B, Amherst Col, 58; Woodrow Wilson fel, Calif. Inst. Tech, 58-59, Nat. Sci. Found. fel, 58-61, Noyes fel, 61-62, Ph.D.(chem), 62. Nat. Sci. Found. fel, molecular genetics, Med. Res. Coun, Eng, 62-63; Nat. Insts. Health fel. biochem, Stanford, 64-65; asst. prof. ONCOL, SCH. MED, UNIV. WIS, MADISON, 65-70, ASSOC. PROF, 70- Am. Chem. Soc. Biochemical genetics; structure of nucleic acids and proteins. Address: Dept. of Oncology, University of Wisconsin School of Medicine, Madison, WI 53706.

DOVENMUEHLE, ROBERT H(ENRY), b. St. Louis, Mo, July 10, 24; m. 45; c. 5. PSYCHIATRY. Valparaiso, 42-44; M.D, St. Louis, 48. Res. physician, Hastings State Hosp, 49-51; chief open sect. psychiat, William Beaumont Army Hosp, 51-53; resident & chief res. psychiat, Duke Hosp, 54-55, chief in-patient serv, 55-57, asst. prof. psychiat, sch. med, Duke, 57-63, assoc. prof, 63-65, res. coord. ctr. study aging, 57-65; dir. ment. health progs, West. Interstate Comn. Higher Educ, 65-66; prof. psychiat, Univ.

Mo, Kansas City, 66-69; dir. geriat. progs, Kansas City Gen. Hosp. & Med. Ctr, 66-69; CLIN. PROF. PSYCHIAT, UNIV. TEX. SOUTHWEST. MED. SCH, 69-; EXEC. DIR, DALLAS COUNTY MENT. HEALTH & MENT. RETARDATION CTR, 69- Consult, Keeley Inst, 54-65; attend, Vet. Admin. Hosp, Durham, N.C, 55-65, Roanoke, Va, 59-64; adj. prof, N. Tex. State Univ, 69-; spec. lectr. occup. ther, Tex. Woman's Univ, 70- Dipl. psychiat, Am. Bd. Psychiat. & Neurol, 63. Med.C, 51-53, 1st Lt. Geront. Soc; fel. Am. Psychiat. Asn; Am. Med. Asn. Psychiatric problems of older people; criteria of effective psychiatric nursing therapy. Address: Dallas Co. Mental Health Center, 414 S. Thornton Freeway, Suite 120-D, Dallas, TX 75203.

DOVER, JAMES H, b. Phila, Pa. STRUCTURAL GEOLOGY, METAMORPHIC PETROLOGY. B.A, Wesleyan Univ, 60; M.Sc, Univ. Wash, 62, Ph.D. (geol), 66. Fel, Wesleyan Univ, 66-68; ASST. PROF. GEOL, COLO. SCH. MINES, 68- Antarctic serv. medal, U.S. Dept. Interior, 70. Geol. Soc. Am. Geology of central Idaho—igneous, metamorphic and structural development; major fault patterns in central Nova Scotia; geology of the Patuxent Mountains, Antarctica. Address: Dept. of Geology, Colorado School of Mines, Golden, CO 80401.

DOVERSPIKE, LYNN D, b. Cumberland, Okla, Mar. 1, 34; m. 54; c. 3. ATOMIC & MOLECULAR PHYSICS. B.S, Okla. State Univ, 58; M.S, Univ. Calif, Los Angeles, 60; Ph.D.(physics), Univ. Fla, 66. ASST. PROF. PHYSICS, COL. WILLIAM & MARY, 67- Am. Phys. Soc. Experimental low energy atomic and molecular physics. Address: Dept. of Physics, College of William & Mary, Williamsburg, VA 23185.

DOVIAK, RICHARD J, b. Passaic, N.J, Dec. 24, 33; m. 57; c. 3. ELECTROMAGNETICS, METEOROLOGY. B.S.E.E, Rensselaer Polytech. Inst, 56; M.S.E.E, Univ. Pa, 59, Ph.D.(elec. eng), 63. Instr. elec. eng, Moore Sch. Elec. Eng, Univ. Pa, 60-61, assoc, 62-64, asst. prof, 65-70, supvr, acad. labs, 67-71; METEOROLOGIST, NAT. SEVERE STORMS LAB, NAT. OCEANIC & ATMOSPHERIC AGENCY, 71- Prin. investr, Nat. Sci. Found. res. grant, 69-71; consult, A.R.K. Electronics Corp, 70-71. AAAS; Am. Geophys. Union; Inst. Elec. & Electronics Eng. Radar meteorology— antennas, propagation and scattering; electromagnetic interference; nonionizing radiation of biological tissues; atmospheric probing. Address: National Severe Storms Lab, National Oceanic & Atmospheric Agency, Norman, OK 73069.

DOW, DANIEL G(OULD), b. Ann Arbor, Mich, Apr. 26, 30; m. 54; c. 4. ELECTRICAL ENGINEERING. B.S.E, Michigan, 52, M.S.E, 53; Bel. Tel. Labs. fel. & Ph.D.(elec. eng), Stanford, 58. Asst. prof, Calif. Inst. Tech, 58-61; dir. res. tube div, Varian Assocs, 61-65, mgr. microwave semiconductor task force, cent. res. labs, 65-68; CHMN. DEPT. ELEC. ENG, UNIV. WASH, 68- U.S.A.F, 53-55, 1st Lt. Am. Phys. Soc; Inst. Elec. & Electronics Eng. Microwave tubes; solid state devices; plasma physics; physical electronics. Address: Dept. of Electrical Engineering, University of Washington, Seattle, WA 98105.

DOW, GARNETT McCORMICK, b. Biddeford, Maine, Aug. 5, 34; m. 61; c. 3. GEOLOGY. B.A, Maine, 59; M.S, Illinois, 62, Ph.D.(geol), 65. Res. asst. geol, Ill. State Geol. Surv, 62-64; res. scientist, Pan-Am. Petrol. Corp, 64-68, SR. RES. SCIENTIST, AMOCO PROD. CO, 68- Sig.C, 54-56, Res, 56-59. Mineral. Soc. Am; Electron Probe Anal. Soc. Am. Igneous and metamorphic petrology; structural geology; mineralogy; origin of pillow structures; mineral diagenesis and paleoenvironments; petroleum geology; geotectonics in relation to world oil distribution; feldspars in sedimentary rocks. Address: Amoco Production Co, Box 591, Tulsa, OK 74102.

DOW, JAMES W, b. Worcester, Mass, Sept. 8, 17; m. 67; c. 2. MEDICINE, BIOMEDICAL ENGINEERING. B.S, Harvard, 41; M.D, Tufts, 44. Res. fel, Nat. Heart Inst, 47-49; instr. med. med. sch, Harvard, 49-51; asst. prof, med. sch, Tufts, 53-58; adj. prof. med. sci, Drexel Inst, 60-62; exec. secy, bioeng, training br, Nat. Inst. Gen. Med. Sci, 63-65, head biophys. sci. sect, 65-66; PROF. MED. & BIOENG, UNIV. ILL, CHICAGO & MED. CTR, 66-, HEAD PROG. BIOENG, UNIV, 68-; ACTING CHMN. BIOMED. ENG, PRESBY. ST. LUKE'S HOSP, 68- Consult, biomed. eng. training comt, training br, Nat. Inst. Gen. Med. Sci, 62-63, training comt. on eng. in biol. & med, 69-; spec. consult, Bur. Health Serv, 67-68. Cardiovascular control systems; analysis of health service systems. Address: Dept. of Bioengineering, University of Illinois at Chicago Circle, Box 4348, Chicago, IL 60680.

DOW, NORRIS F(ITZ), b. Exeter, N.H, Apr. 17, 17; m. 41; c. 3. AERONAUTICAL ENGINEERING. B.S, Mass. Inst. Tech, 39. Draftsman, Lockheed Aircraft Co, 39; head airframe components br, Nat. Adv. Comt, Aeronaut, Va, 39-55; consult. engr, space sci. lab, Gen. Elec. Co, 55-69; PRES, DOWEAVE, INC, 69- Mem. heat protection panel, mat. adv. bd, Nat. Acad. Sci, 58-59, comt. design brittle mat, 63; res. adv. comt. struct. design, Nat. Aeronaut. & Space Admin, 59-60, missile & space vehicle struct, 63. Am. Inst. Aeronaut. & Astronaut; Soc. Exp. Stress Anal. Combination of structural design with other sciences into a structural system. Address: Doweave, Inc, 200 Eagle Rd, Strafford, PA 19087.

DOW, O(RVILLE) E(LTON), b. Glenwood Springs, Colo, Feb. 11, 06; m. 29; c. 2. ELECTRICAL ENGINEERING. B.S, Colorado, 28. Student engr, Radio Corp. Am, 28-29, radio engr, commun, 29-42, proj. engr, David Sarnoff Res. Center, 42-57; head systs. & radio design groups, C. Stellarator Assocs, 57-61; mem. tech. staff, David Sarnoff Res. Ctr, RCA Corp, 61-71; RETIRED. With Off. Sci. Res. & Develop; U.S.A, 44. Sr. mem. Inst. Elec. & Electronics Eng. Design of microwave transmitters and pulse communication circuits; plasma physics. Address: 1704 Dale Ct, Fort Collins, CO 80521.

DOW, PAUL C(ROWTHER), JR, b. Melrose, Mass, Mar. 31, 27; m. 50; c. 4. AERONAUTICAL ENGINEERING. B.S, U.S. Mil. Acad, 49; M.S.E.(aeronaut. eng) & M.S.E.(instrumentation eng), Michigan, 54, Ph.D.(aeronaut. eng), 57. Mgr. guid, control & commun. dept, Avco Res. & Adv. Develop. Div, AVCO CORP, 60-68, PROG. DIR, 68- U.S.A.F, 49-60, Capt. Assoc. fel. Am. Inst. Aeronaut. & Astronaut. Project management; penetration aids; reentry systems. Address: 19 Strawberry Hill Rd, Andover, MA 01810.

DOW, PHILIP, b. Ann Arbor, Mich, June 20, 05; m. 36. PHYSIOLOGY. B.S, Michigan, 27; Ph.D.(physiol), Yale, 35. Asst. chem, Michigan, 24-27; phys-

iol. chem, Yale, 28-30, reader appl. physiol, 29-32; res. fel. PHYSIOL, sch. med, Georgia, 35-39, instr, 36-39, asst. prof, 39-41, assoc. prof, 41-50; PROF, MED. COL. GA, 50-, chmn. dept, 60-71. Sr. instr. sch. med, Western Reserve, 39-40. Mem. cardiovasc. study sect, Nat. Insts. Health, 60-64; physiol. test comt, Nat. Bd. Med. Exam, 62-65. Am. Physiol. Soc.(exec. ed, Handbook Physiol); Am. Heart Asn. Physical chemistry of proteins; hemodynamics; energy metabolism; statistical analysis of clinical data; adsorption of egg albumin collodion membranes; spectrophotometry of vital dyes; cardiac output by dye dilution. Address: Dept. of Physiology, Medical College of Georgia, Augusta, GA 30902.

DOW, R(ICHARD) B(URT), b. Willimantic, Conn, Sept. 3, 04; m. 44. PHYSICS. A.B, Clark, 27, A.M, 28; Ph.D.(physics), Harvard, 33. Asst. physics, Clark, 27-28; instr, Worcester Polytech, 28-32; res. assoc. geophys, Harvard, 33-35; asst. prof. physics & chem, Pa. State, 35-39, assoc. prof, 39-41; ballistician, Aberdeen Proving Ground, 41-46; physicist, bur. ord, Navy Dept, 46-57; aero sci. adminstr, Air Force Off. Sci. Res, 57-60; chief systs. criteria, Martin Co, Md, 60-61; sr. engr, Bendix Radio Div, 61-66; v.pres, sci. & tech. serv, Md. Equities, Ltd, 66-67; prof, Towson State Col, 67-70; RETIRED. U.S.N.R, 41-46, Lt. Comdr. Fel. AAAS; Am. Soc. Mech. Eng; fel. Am. Phys. Soc; assoc. fel. Am. Inst. Aeronaut. & Astronaut. Physical and chemical properties at very high pressures; interior ballistics; rockets and combustion; guided missiles; systems analysis; technical management and control; fundamentals of advanced missiles. Address: 611 St. Francis Rd, Towson, MD 21204.

DOW, RICHARD P(HELPS), b. Reading, Mass, May 14, 07; m. 45; c. 2. ENTOMOLOGY. A.B, Harvard, 28, M.S, 29, Ph.D.(entom), 35. Lab. asst, Harvard & Radcliffe Col, 29-35; asst. curator insects, Boston Soc. Natural Hist, 32-35, curator, 35-41, ed, 39-41; spec. res. assoc, Nat. Defense Res. Cmt, Harvard, 41-42; entomologist, commun. disease ctr, U.S. Pub. Health Serv, 46-47, sr. asst. scientist, 47-49, scientist, 49-57, sr. scientist, 57-62; CHIEF ETHOLOGY SECT, ENTOM. RES. CTR, FLA DIV. HEALTH, 62- U.S.A, 42-45, Capt. Am. Entom. Soc; Am. Soc. Trop. Med. & Hyg; Am. Mosquito Control Asn. Aculeate wasps; Hippelates eye gnats; mosquito biology, especially traps, attractants, host selection, dispersal. Address: Box 1232, Vero Beach, FL 32960.

DOW, ROBERT S(TONE), b. Wray, Colo, Jan. 4, 08; m. 34; c. 2. ANATOMY, PHYSIOLOGY. B.S, Linfield Col, 29; A.M. & M.D, Oregon, 34, Ph.D.(anat), 35; hon. D.Sc, Linfield Col, 63. Asst. anat, med. sch, Oregon, 30-35; intern, Wis. Gen. Hosp, Madison, 35-36; Nat. Res. Coun. fel. physiol, sch. med, Yale, 36-37; Belgian-Am. Ed. Found. fel, Brussels & Nat. Hosp, London, 37-38; fel, Rockefeller Inst, 38-39; clin. instr. neurol, MED. SCH, UNIV. ORE, 39-42, asst. prof. anat, 39-42, assoc. prof, 42-46, asst. clin. prof. MED, DIV. NEUROL, 46-52, assoc. clin. prof, 52-69, CLIN. PROF, 69-; DIR. LAB. NEUROPHYSIOL, GOOD SAMARITAN HOSP, 66- Fulbright scholar, Pisa, Italy, 53-54. Am. Asn. Anat; Am. Physiol. Soc; fel. Am. Col. Physicians; Am. Asn. Neurol. Surg; Am. Neurol. Asn; Am. Acad. Neurol; Am. Electroencephalog. Soc.(pres, 57-58); Am. Epilepsy Soc.(pres, 64). Neurological anatomy and physiology; innervation of the lung; comparative anatomy of the cerebellum; anatomy and physiology of the cerebellum and vestibular systems; pathology of multiple sclerosis; action potentials in central nervous system. Address: Lab. of Neurophysiology, Good Samaritan Hospital, Portland, OR 97210.

DOW, W(ILLIAM) G(OULD), b. Faribault, Minn, Sept. 30, 95; m. 24, 68; c. 2. ELECTRICAL ENGINEERING. B.S, Univ. Minn, 16, E.E, 17; M.S.E, Univ. Mich, 29. Diversified eng. & bus. experience, 19-26; instr. elec. eng, UNIV. MICH, 26-30, asst. prof, 30-38, assoc. prof, 38-45, prof, 45-66, chmn. dept, 58-65; EMER. PROF. ELEC. ENG. & SR. RES. SPACE GEOPHYSICIST, 66- Res. engr, radio res. lab, Nat. Defense Res. Comt, proj, Harvard, 43-45; electronics eng. consult, Nat. Bur. Standards, 45-53. C.Eng, 17-19, Lt. AAAS; Inst. Elec. & Electronics Eng; Am. Soc. Eng. Educ; Am. Welding Soc; Am. Phys. Soc; Am. Inst. Aeronaut. & Astronaut; Am. Geophys. Union; Am. Astronaut. Soc. Aeronomy; physical electronics; controlled nuclear fusion; space research and exploration; microwave devices; radar and radar countermeasures; plasmas of all kinds. Address: 915 Heatherway, Ann Arbor, MI 48104.

DOWALIBY, MARGARET S(USANNE), b. Dover, N.H, Mar. 5, 24. OPTOMETRY. D.Optom, Los Angeles Col. Optom, 50. Clin. supvr, LOS ANGELES COL. OPTOM, 48-53, assoc. prof. clin. optom, 53-66, PROF. OPTOM, 66- Am. Acad. Optom. Cosmetic effect of lenses and frames; optics of lenses; impact resistant lenses. Address: Los Angeles College of Optometry, 950 W. Jefferson Blvd, Los Angeles, CA 90007.

DOWBEN, ROBERT M(ORRIS), b. Phila, Pa, Apr. 6, 27; m. 50; c. 3. PHYSIOLOGY. A.B, Haverford Col, 46; M.S, Univ. Chicago, 47, M.D, 49; hon. A.M, Brown Univ, 49. Fel, Inst. Atomenergi, Oslo, 50-51; dept. med, Johns Hopkins Univ, 51-52; instr, Univ. Pa, 52-53; dir. radioisotope unit, Vet. Admin. Hosp, Phila, Pa, 53-55; asst. prof. med, Northwest. Univ, 56-62; assoc. prof. biol, Mass. Inst. Technol, 62-68; PROF. MED. SCI, BROWN UNIV, 68- Lalor fel, 60; lectr, Harvard, 63-68; mem, Marine Biol. Lab. U.S.A.F, 55-56, Capt. AAAS; Am. Chem. Soc; Soc. Exp. Biol. & Med; Am. Physiol. Soc; Biophys. Soc; Faraday Soc; Am. Soc. Clin. Invest; Am. Soc. Biol. Chem; Brit. Biochem. Soc. Muscle; biological membranes; protein structure; contractile proteins. Address: Division of Biological & Medical Sciences, Brown University, Providence, RI 02912.

DOWBENKO, R(OSTYSLAW), b. Ukraine, Jan. 8, 27; nat; m. 51; c. 1. ORGANIC CHEMISTRY. Ph.B, Northwestern, 54, Weyerhaeuser found. fel. & Ph.D.(org. chem), 57. Res. chemist, Wrigley Co, 54; sr. res. chemist, Pittsburgh Plate Glass Co, 57-64, res. assoc, 64-67, sr. res. assoc, PPG INDUSTS, INC, 67-69, ASST. DIR. RESIN RES, 69- Am. Chem. Soc; Am. Inst. Chem; The Chem. Soc. Organic polymer chemistry. Address: PPG Industries, Inc, P.O. Box 127, Springdale, PA 15144.

DOWD, JOHN P, b. New Bedford, Mass, Feb. 1, 38; m. 61; c. 2. HIGH ENERGY PHYSICS. S.B, Mass. Inst. Technol, 59, Ph.D.(physics), 66. Res. asst. physics, Mass. Inst. Technol, 59-66; vis. scientist, Ger. Electron Synchrotron, Hamburg, 66-67; ASST. PROF. PHYSICS, SOUTHEAST. MASS. UNIV, 67- Am. Phys. Soc; Am. Asn. Physics Teachers. Experimental High energy physics; meson photoproduction. Address: Dept. of Physics, Southeastern Massachusetts University, North Dartmouth, MA 02747.

DOWD, LIONEL E(ARLE), b. Squamish, B.C, Can, Oct. 30, 15; U.S. citizen; m. 38; c. 4. PAPER & ANALYTICAL CHEMISTRY. B.S, Washington (Seattle), 40. Chemist, WEYERHAEUSER CO, 41-43, res. chemist, 43-53, asst. chief chem. sect, 53-57, supvr. anal. lab, 57-59, mgr. anal. & test lab, 59-69, MGR. ANAL. & TEST RES, 69- Am. Chem. Soc; Forest Prod. Res. Soc; Am. Soc. Test. & Mat. Materials analysis and testing; wood and bark chemistry; analytical methods. Address: Research Division, Weyerhaeuser Co, Longview, WA 98632.

DOWD, PAUL, b. Brockton, Mass, Apr. 11, 36; m. 60; c. 3. ORGANIC CHEMISTRY. A.B, Harvard, 58; M.A, Columbia Univ, 59, Ph.D.(chem), 62. Lectr. CHEM, Harvard, 63-64, instr, 64-66, lectr, 66-67, asst. prof, 67-70; ASSOC. PROF, UNIV. PITTSBURGH, 70- Alfred P. Sloan Found. fel, 70- Am. Chem. Soc. Reactive intermediates in organic chemistry. Address: Dept. of Chemistry, University of Pittsburgh, Pittsburgh, PA 15213.

DOWDELL, RODGER B(IRTWELL), b. Portsmouth, N.H, Mar. 18, 25; m. 46; c. 8. ENGINEERING, FLUID MECHANICS. B.E, Yale, 45; M.S, Brown, 52, Nat. Sci. Found. fel, 62-63; Ph.D, Colo. State Univ, 66. Fluid mech. engr, B-I-F Industs, R.I, 52-59; assoc. prof. mech. eng. & chmn. dept, Univ. Bridgeport, 59-66; assoc. prof. MECH. ENG. & APPL. MECH, UNIV. R.I, 66-71, PROF, 71- Mem. & del, Int. Standards Orgn, 59- U.S.N, 43-46, Lt. Am. Soc. Mech. Eng. Flow measurement and control; hydrodynamics; aerodynamics; heat transfer; propulsion. Address: Dept. of Mechanical Engineering & Applied Mechanics, University of Rhode Island, Kingston, RI 02881.

DOWDEN, BOBBY FLOYD, b. Florien, La, Jan. 2, 32; m. 55; c. 4. WATER POLLUTION. B.S, Northwest. State Univ, 55; Indust. Res. fels, La. State Univ, Baton Rouge, 59 & 63, M.S, 61, Ph.D.(zool), 66. Teacher, high sch, La, 57-59; aquatic biologist, div. water pollution control, La. Wildlife & Fisheries Comn, 61-62; instr. BIOL, Univ. South. Miss, 62-63; asst. prof, Miss. State Col. Women, 66-67; LA. STATE UNIV, SHREVEPORT, 67-71, ASSOC. PROF, 71- Vis. asst. prof, La. State Univ, Baton Rouge, Gulf Coast Res. Lab, Miss, summer 69. U.S.M.C, 51-52, Res, 52-69. AAAS; Am. Soc. Limnol. & Oceanog; Am. Fisheries Soc; Am. Inst. Biol. Sci. Toxicity and other physiological effects of pollutants on the physiology of aquatic animals. Address: Dept. of Biological Sciences, Louisiana State University in Shreveport, 8515 Youree Dr, Shreveport, LA 71105.

DOWDLE, JOSEPH C(LYDE), b. July 3, 27; U.S. citizen; m. 56; c. 3. ELECTRICAL ENGINEERING. B.E.E, Ala. Polytech, 52, M.E.E, 58; Ford Found. fel, Nat. Sci. Found. fel, & Ph.D.(elec. eng), N.C. State Col, 62. Instr. elec. eng, Ala. Polytech, 53-57; asst. proj. engr, Radiation, Inc, 57-58; instr. ELEC. ENG, N.C. State Col, 58-62; assoc. prof, UNIV. ALA, HUNTSVILLE, 62-65, PROF, 65-, EXEC. ASST. TO V.PRES. HUNTSVILLE AFFAIRS, 69-, dir. grad. prog, 62-63, chmn. dept. eng, 66-69. Consult, Troxler Elec. Labs, 58-63; vis. scholar, Univ. Mich, 68-69. U.S.N, 45-46. Am. Soc. Eng. Educ; Inst. Elec. & Electronics Eng; Am. Math. Soc. High frequency electromagnetics wave phenomena; dielectric materials; powdered dielectrics at millimeter frequencies; magnetic field effect on gyros. Address: Dept. of Engineering, University of Alabama in Huntsville, Huntsville, AL 35807.

DOWDLE, WALTER R, b. Irvington, Ala, Dec. 11, 30; m. 53; c. 2. VIROLOGY. B.S, Univ. Ala, 55, M.S, 57; Ph.D.(microbiol), Univ. Md, 60. MEM. RES. STAFF, VIROL. SECT, CTR. DISEASE CONTROL, 60-, CHIEF, RESPIRATORY VIROL. UNIT, 70- Vis. prof, Univ. N.C; dir. regional reference ctr. respiratory diseases, WHO, dir. Int. Influenza Ctr. Americas. U.S.A.F, 48-52, S/Sgt. Am. Soc. Microbiol; Soc. Exp. Biol. & Med. Bacteriophage; human respiratory disease viruses; mycoplasma agents of man. Address: Respiratory Virology Unit, Center for Disease Control, 1600 Clifton Rd, Atlanta, GA 30333.

DOWDS, RICHARD E, b. Cuyahoga Falls, Ohio, Feb. 25, 30; m. 50; c. 2. MATHEMATICS. B.S, Kent State, 51; M.S, Purdue, 54, Socony-Mobil fel, 55, Ph.D.(math), 59. Asst. prof. MATH, Purdue, 58-59; assoc. prof, Butler, 59-64, prof, 64-65; ASSOC. PROF, STATE UNIV. N.Y. COL. FREDONIA, 65- Am. Math. Soc; Math. Asn. Am. Functional analysis; topological vector spaces; measure theory. Address: Dept. of Mathematics, State University of New York College at Fredonia, Fredonia, NY 14063.

DOWDY, ANDREW H(UNTER), b. Longwood, Mo, Nov. 24, 04; m. 30; c. 2. RADIOLOGY. A.B, Cent. Col.(Mo), 29, hon. D.Sc, 57; M.D, Washington (St. Louis), 31. Intern, Henry Ford Hosp, 31-32, res. internal med, 32-34, radiol, 34-37; instr. med. & radiol, sch. med. & dent, Rochester, 37-38, asst. prof. radiol, 39-42, assoc. prof, 42-43, asst. radiologist, Strong Mem. Hosp, 37-43, dir, Manhattan Dist. proj, 43-46, prof. radiol, 46-48, dir, Atomic Energy Cmn. proj, 46-48, chmn. dept. radiol, 47-48; PROF. RADIOL, MED. SCH, UNIV. CALIF, LOS ANGELES, 48-, chmn. dept, 48-70. Responsible investr. on grants, Am. Cyanamid Corp, 41-57; Off. Sci. Res. & Develop, 41. Med. consult, Atomic Energy Cmn, 48-59. Dipl, Am. Bd. Radiol, 39, cert. appreciation, 63. With U.S.A, 44; U.S.P.H.S, 49-56, U.S.A.F, 55-58. AAAS; dipl, Pan-Am. Med. Asn; fel. Am. Med. Asn; Am. Soc. Cancer Res; Am. Cancer Soc; Am. Col. Radiol. (Gold Medal, 70); Am. Roentgen Ray Soc. Experimental clostridial infection in dogs; treating deaf children with small amounts of radium; constructing and testing new type radium loading device; cancer and infection. Address: Dept. of Radiology, University of California Medical School, Los Angeles, CA 90024.

DOWDY, EDWARD J(OSEPH), b. San Antonio, Tex, Sept. 25, 39; m. 61; c. 5. NUCLEAR ENGINEERING. B.A. & B.S, St. Mary's Univ.(Tex), 61; M.E, Tex. A&M Univ, 63, NASA fel, 63-65, Ph.D.(nuclear eng), 65. Asst. prof. NUCLEAR ENG, Univ. Mo-Columbia, 65-67; TEX. A&M UNIV, 67-70, ASSOC. PROF, 70- Faculty res. fel, Univ. Mo-Columbia, summer 66. AAAS; Am. Nuclear Soc; Am. Phys. Soc. Radiation detection instrumentation; reactor physics. Address: Dept. of Nuclear Engineering, College of Engineering, Texas A&M University, College Station, TX 77843.

DOWDY, ROBERT H, b. Union, W.Va, June 28, 37; m. 58; c. 1. SOIL SCIENCE. B.S, Berea Col, 59; M.S, Kentucky, 62; Ph.D.(soil sci), Mich. State, 66. RES. SOIL SCIENTIST, SOIL & WATER CONSERV. RES. DIV, AGR. RES. SERV, U.S. DEPT. AGR, 66- Asst. prof, Minnesota, St. Paul, 66- Am. Soc. Agron; Soil Sci. Soc. Am; Clay Minerals Soc. Clay-chemical phenomena; clay-organic interactions and the significance of such associations on the binding together of soil masses. Address: Soil Science Bldg, University of Minnesota, St. Paul, MN 55101.

DOWDY, W(ILLIAM) W(ALLACE), b. Eastover, S.C, Oct. 10, 90; m; c. 1. BIOLOGY. A.B, Iowa State, 23; M.S, Cornell, 28; Ph.D.(ecol), Western Reserve, 42. Prof. biol, Shaw, 23-26; Langston, 27; LINCOLN UNIV, 28-60, RESEARCHER ECOL. & ENTOMOL, 60- Address: Dept. of Biology, Lincoln University, Jefferson City, MO 65101.

DOWE, THOMAS W(HITFIELD), b. Eagle Pass, Texas, Jan. 26, 19; m. 43; c. 3. ANIMAL HUSBANDRY. B.S, Agr. & Mech. Col. Texas, 42; M.S, Kans. State Col, 47, Ph.D.(animal nutrit, biochem), 52. Animal husbandman, S.Dak. State Col, 47-48; asst. prof. animal husb, col. agr, Nebraska, 48-57; DIR. AGR. EXP. STA, UNIV. VT, 57-, DEAN, COL. AGR, 65- Dir, Univ. Nebr. Agr. Mission, U.S. Agency Int. Develop, Colombia, S.Am, 70-72. U.S.A, 42-46, Res, 46-67, Lt. Col. Am. Soc. Animal Sci; Am. Soc. Range Mgt. Ruminant nutrition; non-protein nitrogen utilization; roughage utilization; nutrient requirements of ruminants. Address: College of Agriculture, University of Vermont, Burlington, VT 05401.

DOWELL, ARTHUR M(AULTSBY), JR, b. Birmingham, Ala, Aug. 14, 22; m. 43; c. 3. PHYSICAL ORGANIC CHEMISTRY. B.S, Howard Col, 43; M.S, Ga. Inst. Tech, 47, Nat. Sci. Found. fel, 52-53, Ph.D.(chem), 54. Instr, Ga. Inst. Tech, 47-48; asst. prof, Hampden-Sydney Col, 48-51; head, appln. res. sect, Buckeye Cellulose Corp, 53-67, HEAD, DIV. PHYSICS, FLA. COL, TEMPLE TERRACE, 67- U.S.N.R, 44-46. Am. Chem. Soc; Brit. Chem. Soc. Synthesis of quinoline acids by the Pfitzinger reaction; mechanism of the basic hydrolysis of haloforms; chemistry of cellulose. Address: 8712 Elmdale, Rt. 6, Tampa, FL 33617.

DOWELL, CLIFTON E(NDERS), b. McKinney, Tex, Dec. 12, 32; m. 55; c. 2. MICROBIOLOGY. B.S, Tex. Christian Univ, 55, M.A, 57; Nat. Insts. Health fel, Univ. Tex, Dallas, 57-62, Ph.D.(microbiol), 62. Nat. Insts. Health res. fel, biophys, Calif. Inst. Technol, 62-64; asst. prof. microbiol, sch. med, Tulane Univ, 64-66; bact, Univ. Calif, Davis, 66-69; ASSOC. PROF. MICROBIOL, UNIV. MASS, AMHERST, 69- Am. Soc. Microbiol. Bacteriophage; microbial genetics. Address: Dept. of Microbiology, University of Massachusetts, Amherst, MA 01002.

DOWELL, DOUGLAS C, b. Tacoma, Wash, May 31, 24; m. 45; c. 1. ENGINEERING MECHANICS, NUCLEAR ENGINEERING. B.S, Univ. Iowa, 49; M.S, U.S. Air Force Inst. Technol, 56; Ph.D.(eng. mech), Iowa State Univ, 64. Proj. engr, Armed Forces spec. weapons proj, U.S. Air Force, Sandia Base & Los Alamos Sci. Lab, 50-54, U.S. Atomic Energy Comn, Idaho, 56-60, instr. physics & math, U.S. Air Force Acad, 60-62, asst. prof. eng. mech, 64-65, assoc. prof, 65-68, dep. head dept, 66-68; assoc. dean sch. eng, CALIF. STATE POLYTECH. COL, KELLOGG-VOORHIS, 68-70, DIR. EDUC. SERV, 70- U.S.A, 42-45, T/Sgt; U.S.A.F, 49-68, Lt. Col. AAAS; Am. Acad. Mech; Am. Soc. Eng. Educ; Soc. Am. Mil. Eng. Engineering education; effect of shock waves on buried structures. Address: Office of Educational Services, California State Polytechnic College, Kellogg-Voorhis, 3801 W. Temple Ave, Pomona, CA 91768.

DOWELL, EARL HUGH, b. Macomb, Ill, Nov. 16, 37; m. 63; c. 1. AEROSPACE SCIENCES. B.S, Univ. Ill, 59; S.M, Mass. Inst. Technol, 61, Sc.D.(aeronaut. eng), 64. Res. engr, aerospace div, Boeing Co, 62-63; res. asst. aeronaut. & astronaut, Mass. Inst. Technol, 63-64, asst. prof, 64-65, AEROSPACE & MECH. SCI, PRINCETON, 65-68, ASSOC. PROF, 68- Am. Inst. Aeronaut. & Astronaut. Structural dynamics; aeroelasticity; unsteady aerodynamics. Address: Dept. of Aerospace & Mechanical Sciences, Princeton University, Forrestal Campus, Princeton, NJ 08540.

DOWELL, FRANK H(ERBERT), b. Birmingham, Ala, Aug. 27, 26; m. 51; c. 3. PARASITOLOGY, MEDICAL ENTOMOLOGY. A.B, Birmingham-South. Col, 48; M.S, Univ. Tenn, 49, Ph.D.(parasitol, entom), 64; Air Command & Staff Col, 53. Instr, Univ. of the South, 50; U.S. Air Force Sch. Aviation Med, 51-55, entomologist & parasitologist, 5th epidemiol. flight, 55-58, chief environ. res. br, entom. div, U.S. Army Biol. Labs, 58-59, entomologist, spec. aerial spray flight, 59-62, chief entomologist, 5th epidemiol. flight, 64-66; sr. res. entomologist, Olin Res. Ctr, 66-67, mgr. pesticides, 67-68; MGR. PLANT SCI. RES, DOW CHEM. CO, 68- Mem. Armed Forces Pest Control Bd, 58-62, v.chmn, 61-62; mem, Interdept. Comt. Pest Control, 59-62; adj. assoc. prof, South Conn. State Col, 67-68. U.S.A, 44-46, U.S.A.F, 51-66, Maj. AAAS; Am. Mosquito Control Asn; Entom. Soc. Am; Weed Sci. Soc. Am; Sci. Res. Soc. Am. Experimental parasitology; experimental entomology. Address: AG-Organics Dept, Dow Chemical Co, Walnut Creek, CA 94598.

DOWELL, MICHAEL BRENDAN, b. Bronx, N.Y, Nov. 18, 42; m. 68; c. 1. INORGANIC & PHYSICAL CHEMISTRY. B.S, Fordham, 63; Ph.D.(inorg. chem), Pa. State, 67. Physicist, Pitman-Dunn Res. Labs, U.S. Army Frankford Arsenal, 67-69; RES. SCIENTIST, PARMA TECH. CENTER, UNION CARBIDE CORP, 69- Ord.C, U.S.A, 67-69, Capt. AAAS; Am. Chem. Soc; Am. Phys. Soc. Kinetics and thermodynamics of phase transformations in solids; solid state phase transformations particularly in ferroelectrics; vaporization of solids; effects of neutron irradiation on solids. Address: 6105 W. Ridgewood Dr, Parma, OH 44129.

DOWELL, VIRGIL E(UGENE), b. Melvern, Kans, June 3, 26; m. 61; c. 4. FISHERY BIOLOGY. B.S, Kans. State Teachers Col, 51, M.S, 52; Ph.D.(zool), Univ. Okla, 57. Asst, Kans. State Teachers Col, 50-52; Univ. Okla, 52-53; Okla. Biol. Surv, 53-56; asst. prof. BIOL, UNIV. NORTH. IOWA, 56-62, assoc. prof, 62-68, PROF, 68- U.S.A.A.F, 44-46. Am. Inst. Biol. Sci; Am. Fisheries Soc; Am. Soc. Ichthyol. & Herpet. Aquatic biology. Address: 1609 Grandview Ct, Cedar Falls, IA 50613.

DOWELL, VULUS RAYMOND, JR, b. Mt. Vernon, Ky, July 27, 27; m. 48; c. 4. MICROBIOLOGY, BACTERIOLOGY. B.S, Univ. Ky, 61; M.S, Univ. Cincinnati, 62, Ph.D.(microbiol), 66. Instr. microbiol. & res. surg, Univ. Cincinnati, 65-66; res. microbiologist in charge anaerobic bact. lab, CTR. DISEASE CONTROL, 66-71, CHIEF ENTEROBACT. UNIT, 71- Asst. prof, Ga. State Univ, 71-; assoc. prof, sch. pub. health, Univ. N.C; Registry of Med. Technologists, Am. Soc. Clin. Path. U.S.A, 45-46. Am. Soc. Microbiol; Sci. Res. Soc. Am; Brit. Soc. Gen. Microbiol; N.Y. Acad. Sci. Characterization of anaerobic bacteria and enterobacteriaceae; improving diagnostic procedures; botulism; Clostridium perfringens; foodborne disease; salmonellosis; shigellosis; miscellaneous enteric diseases; polymicrobic infections; host-parasite relations. Address: Enterobacteriology Unit, Lab. Division, Center for Disease Control, 1600 Clifton Rd, Atlanta, GA 30333.

DOWER, GORDON E(WBANK), b. Brit, Nov. 16, 23; m. 47; c. 4. ELECTROCARDIOLOGY. M.B, B.S, St. Bartholomew's Hosp. Med. Col, 49. Instr. PHARMACOL, UNIV. B.C, 54-58, asst. prof, 58-64, ASSOC. PROF, 64- Fel, Can. Life Ins. Co, 54-57; Heart Found. Can, 57- Consult, Shaughnessy Hosp; res. consult, Vancouver Gen. Hosp. Biophys. Soc; N.Y. Acad. Sci; fel. Am. Col. Cardiol; Can. Physiol. Soc. Polarcardiography; techniques in electrocardiographic diagnosis. Address: Dept. of Pharmacology, University of British Columbia, Vancouver, B.C, Can.

DOWLER, CLYDE CECIL, b. Moundsville, W.Va, Jan. 12, 33; m. 56; c. 4. CROP PRODUCTION, PLANT PHYSIOLOGY. B.S, West Virginia, 54, M.S, 56; Ph.D.(agron), Ohio State, 58. RES. AGRONOMIST, AGR. RES. SERV, U.S. DEPT. AGR, N.C, 59-63, P.R, 63-67, GA. COASTAL PLAIN EXP. STA, 67- Weed Sci. Soc. Am. Use of herbicides in crop production and the effect of herbicides on weed ecology. Address: Georgia Coastal Plain Experiment Station, Tifton, GA 31794.

DOWLER, LLOYD, b. Chugwater, Wyo, Nov. 1, 11; m. 35. AGRICULTURE. B.S, Univ. Wyo, 35, M.S, 41. Instr. voc. agr, high sch, Wyo, 35-43; teacher trainer agr. educ, Univ. Nev, 46-48; asst. prof. poultry husb, FRESNO STATE COL, 48-51, dean sch. agr, 51-69, PROF. AGR. EDUC, 69- State supvr. agr. educ, Carson City, Nev, 46-48; mem, Agency Int. Develop. Surv. Team, Sudan, summer 61; Calif. State Bd. Agr, 64-67; Stanford Res. Inst-U.S. Dept. Agr-Agency Int. Develop. Educ. Task Force Team, Chile, 65. U.S.N.R, 43-45, Lt. Secondary agricultural education, including careers in agribusiness, curriculum, advisory committees, school farm laboratories; administration of college agricultural programs. Address: School of Agricultural Sciences, Fresno State College, Fresno, CA 93710.

DOWLER, WILLIAM M(INOR), b. Birch Tree, Mo, Nov. 10, 32; m. 58; c. 3. PLANT PATHOLOGY, MICROBIAL PHYSIOLOGY. B.S, Missouri, 54, M.S, 58; Ph.D.(plant path), Illinois, 61. RES. PLANT PATHOLOGIST, CROPS RES. DIV, U.S. DEPT. AGR, 61- U.S.A, 54-56, Res, 56-, Maj. Am. Phytopath. Soc; Am. Soc. Microbiol; Am. Soc. Hort. Sci. Diseases of fruit trees, especially control of bacterial diseases of peaches; physiology of pathogens and etiology of diseases. Address: Dept. of Plant Pathology, U.S. Dept. of Agriculture, Clemson University, Clemson, SC 29631.

DOWLEY, MARK WILLIAM, b. Dundalk, Ireland, Apr. 28, 34; nat; m. 67; c. 2. PHYSICS. B.Sc, Nat. Univ. Ireland, 56; M.A, Univ. Toronto, 57, McKee-Gilchrist fel, 57-59, Ph.D.(low temperature physics), 59. Res. asst, Off. Naval Res. grant & lectr. nuclear magnetic resonance, Univ. Calif, Berkeley, 59-61; staff scientist, solid state low temperature physics, Int. Bus. Mach. Corp, 61-67; sr. res. physicist; MGR, ION LASER DEVELOP. SYSTS. & APPLN, COHERENT RADIATION INC, 69- Am. Phys. Soc; Am. Asn. Physics Teachers. Low temperature physics; hydrodynamics of liquid helium; nuclear magnetic resonance in metals; superconducting solenoids; physics of polymers, laser physics, non-linear optics. Address: Coherent Radiation Inc, 932 E. Meadow Dr, Palo Alto, CA 94303.

DOWLING, EDMUND AUGUSTINE, b. Waterford, Ireland, July 26, 27; U.S. citizen; m. 53; c. 4. PATHOLOGY. M.B,B.Ch. & B.A.O, Nat. Univ. Ireland, 51. Instr. PATH, MED. COL. ALA, 54-57, asst. prof, 57-62, assoc. prof, 62-67, PROF, 67- Consult, Birmingham Baptist Hosps, 58-; Vet. Admin. Hosp, Tuskegee, Ala, 60-; dir, surg. path, Univ. Hosp, 62- Dipl, Am. Bd. Path, 59. Am. Med. Asn; Brit. Med. Asn; Inst. Acad. Path; Am. Soc. Cytol; Int. Acad. Cytol. Neoplastic diseases; exfoliative cytology. Address: 619 S. 19th St, Birmingham, AL 35233.

DOWLING, FORREST LEROY, b. Boscobel, Wis, Aug. 30, 34; m. 60; c.2. GEOPHYSICS. B.S, Univ. Wis, Madison, 60, Nat. Sci. Found. grants, 64-68, Ph.D.(geophys), 68. Res. asst, Univ. Wis, Madison, 64-68, res. assoc, geophys. & polar res. ctr, 68-70; GEOPHYSICIST, NEWMONT EXPLOR. LTD, 70- U.S.N, 52-56. Am. Geophys. Union; Soc. Explor. Geophys. Magnetotelluric resistivity soundings across the Wisconsin Arch; galvanic, magnetic and electromagnetic methods of mineral exploration. Address: Newmont Exploration Ltd, 44 Briar Ridge Rd, Danbury, CT 06810.

DOWLING, HARRY F(ILMORE), b. Washington, D.C, Nov. 11, 04; m. 31; c. 3. MEDICINE. A.B, Franklin & Marshall Col, 27, hon. Sc.D, 53; M.D, George Washington, 31. Intern & asst. res, Baltimore City Hosps, 31-32; teaching fellow, med, Harvard, 33-34; clin. instr, sch. med, George Washington, 34-40, clin. prof, 40-50, dir. cent. lab, univ. hosp, 34-41; prof. prev. med, MED. CTR, UNIV. ILL, 50-51, prof. MED. & head dept, 51-69; EMER. PROF, 69- Asst. sch. med, Hopkins, 32-33; asst. res, Thorndike Mem. lab, Boston City Hosp, 33-34; chief George Washington med. div, Gallinger Munic. Hosp, 40-50. Am. Soc. Clin. Invest; Am. Fedn. Clin. Res; fel. Am. Col. Physicians; Asn. Am. Physicians; Am. Asn. Hist. Med. Infectious diseases; sulfonamides; antibiotics; medical history. Address: 208 Bliss Lane, Great Falls, VA 22066.

DOWLING, HERNDON G(LENN), (JR), b. Cullman, Ala, Apr. 2, 21; m. 43; c. 4. HERPETOLOGY. B.S, Alabama, 42; M.S, Florida, 48; summer, Mexico City Col, 48; Ph.D.(zool), Michigan, 51. Instr. biol, Florida, 47-48; mus. asst, Michigan, 48-51; instr. biol, Haverford Col, 51-52; asst. prof. zool, Arkansas, 52-56, assoc. prof, 56-59; assoc. curator reptiles, N.Y. Zool. Park, 59-60, curator, 60-67; DIR. GENERA OF REPTILES PROJ, AM. MUS. NATURAL HIST, 68- Fel, Florida, 56-57; assoc, dept. amphibians & reptiles, Am. Mus. Natural Hist, 57-; adj. prof, Rhode Island, 64-; N.Y. Univ, 65-; summer, asst. prof. zool, Mt. Lake Biol. Sta, Virginia, 54; gen. ed, Catalogue Am. Amphibians & Reptiles, 66-; ed, Amphibian & Reptile Sect, Biol. Abstr, 68-; Herpet. Rev, 69- U.S.M.C, 42-46, Capt. Fel. AAAS; Am. Inst. Biol. Sci; Am. Soc. Ichthyol. & Herpet; Am. Soc. Zool; Soc. Study Evolution; Coun. Biol. Educ; Soc. Study Amphibians & Reptiles; Soc. Syst. Zool; Soc. Vert. Paleont; fel. Indian Acad. Zool; Brit. Herpet. Soc. Systematic herpetology; taxonomic studies of colubrid snake genera; higher categories of Serpentes; zoogeographic studies of amphibians and reptiles. Address: Dept. of Herpetology, American Museum of Natural History, Central Park West at 79th St, New York, NY 10024.

DOWLING, J. THOMAS, b. Seattle, Wash, May 11, 26; m. 68; c. 3. INTERNAL MEDICINE. B.Sc, Washington (Seattle), 48; nat. scholar, Harvard Med. Sch, 48-52, M.D, 52. Intern MED, Boston City Hosp, Mass, 52-53, asst. res, 53-54, res, 54-55, res. fels, 55-56, 57-58, chief res, 56-58; asst. clin. prof, sch. med, California, Los Angeles, 58-60, assoc. prof, 61; SCH. MED, UNIV. WASH, 61-65, PROF, 65-; MEM. ATTEND. STAFF, DESERT HOSP, PALM SPRINGS, 69- Asst, Harvard Med. Sch, 53-58, tutor, 57-59; res. fel, Thorndike Mem. Lab, Mass, 55-56; Am. Cancer Soc. fel, 55-56, cancer res, 56-57; Am. Col. Physicians Hutton traveling scholar, 64; civilian consult, U.S. Army Madigan Gen. Hosp, 64-; physician-in-chief, King County Hosp, Seattle, 64-69; Tomlin Mem. lectr, 65. Dipl, Am. Bd. Internal Med, 63. U.S.A.A.F.R, 44-46. Am. Soc. Clin. Invest; Am. Physiol. Soc; Endocrine Soc; fel. Am. Col. Physicians; Soc. Nuclear Med. Endocrinology and metabolism; clinical teaching; consultation practice; investigation and basic physiological chemistry in metabolism. Address: 36-969 Palomino Lane, Cathedral City, CA 92234.

DOWLING, JEROME M, b. Chicago, Ill, July 9, 31; m. 56; c. 4. PHYSICS, SPECTROSCOPY. B.S, Ill. Inst. Tech, 53, M.S, 55, Ph.D.(physics), 57. Asst. prof. physics, Arizona State, 57-59, assoc. prof, 59-61; MEM. TECH. STAFF, AEROSPACE CORP, 61- Fel, div. pure physics, Nat. Res. Coun. Can, 57-59. Fel. Am. Phys. Soc; Am. Asn. Physics Teachers; Optical Soc. Am. Infrared and Raman spectroscopy; molecular structure and dynamics; interferometry. Address: 30637 Rue Valois, Palos Verdes Peninsula, CA 90274.

DOWLING, JOHN, JR, b. Ashland, Ky, Sept. 12, 38; m. 63; c. 2. PHYSICS. B.S, Univ. Dayton, 60; M.S, Ariz. State Univ, 62, Ph.D.(physics), 64. Res. assoc. molecular spectros, Ariz. State Univ, 64; atmospheric & space physics, Univ. Fla, 64-66; Univ. N.H, 66-70; ASSOC. PROF. PHYSICS, MANSFIELD STATE COL, 70- Physicist, res. inst, Univ. Dayton, summers 60, 61. Am. Phys. Soc; Am. Asn. Physics Teachers. Molecular spectroscopy; computer aided instruction. Address: Dept. of Physics, Mansfield State College, Mansfield, PA 16933.

DOWLING, JOHN ELLIOTT, b. Pawtucket, R.I, Aug. 31, 35; m. 61; c. 2. NEUROBIOLOGY. A.B, Harvard, 57, Ph.D.(biol), 61. Instr. biol, Harvard, 60-61, asst. prof, 61-64; assoc. prof. ophthal. & biophys, sch. med, Johns Hopkins Univ, 64-71; PROF. BIOL, HARVARD, 71- AAAS; Asn. Res. Vision & Ophthal.(Friedenwald Award, 70); Soc. Gen. Physiol. Visual physiology, chemistry and anatomy; nervous system, fine structure and function. Address: Biological Labs, Harvard University, 16 Divinity Ave, Cambridge, MA 02138.

DOWLING, JOHN J, b. Webster Groves, Mo, Dec. 8, 34; m. 58; c. 5. GEOPHYSICS. B.S, St. Louis, 57, Ph.D.(geophys), 64; M.S, Tulsa, 60. Res. engr, Jersey Prod. Res. Inc, 57-60; asst. to dean inst. tech, St. Louis, 60-63, instr. eng, 60-64, res. asst. geophys, 63-64; res. assoc. geosci, Southwest Ctr. Adv. Studies, 64-67; asst. prof. geophys, Tex. Tech Col, 67-68; MEM. MARINE SCI. INST, S.E. BR, UNIV. CONN, 68- AAAS; Am. Geophys. Union; Seismol. Soc. Am; Soc. Explor. Geophys; Am. Soc. Eng. Educ. Interior of the earth from elastic waves; marine geophysics; crustal structure in deep oceans and at continental margins. Address: Marine Sciences Institute, S.E. Branch, University of Connecticut, Groton, CT 06340.

DOWLING, JOSEPH F(RANCIS), b. N.Y.C, June 19, 33; m. 58; c. 2. CARBOHYDRATE CHEMISTRY, FOOD TECHNOLOGY. B.A, Adelphi Univ, 55, M.S, 66. Asst. chief chemist, CORN INDUST. DIV, CPC INT. INC, 64-67, chief chemist, 67-69, LABS. MGR, 69- Secy, Cane Sugar Ref. Res. Proj, 65-; v.chmn, U.S. Nat. Comt. Uniform Methods Sugar Anal, 70- U.S.A, 55-57. Sugar Indust. Tech.(George & Eleanor Meade Award, 68); Am. Chem. Soc; Am. Soc. Sugar Beet Technol; Inst. Food Technol. Sugar chemistry, development of analytical methods and improved means of refining sugar; applications of sugars in the food industry; gas liquid chromatography of sugar and related sugar impurities. Address: Corn Industrial Division, CPC International Inc, 1 Federal St, Yonkers, NY 10702.

DOWLING, MARIE AUGUSTINE, b. Baltimore, Md, Aug. 19, 24. MATHEMATICS. B.A, Col. Notre Dame (Md), 45; Catholic Univ, 58; Hopkins, 61-63; summers, Nat. Sci. Found. grants, Stanford, 60, American Univ, 64 & Minnesota, 68. Teacher, St. Marys High Sch, Md, 46-48; Notre Dame Prep. Sch, 48-59; ASSOC. PROF. MATH, COL. NOTRE DAME (MD), 59-, CHMN. DEPT, 65- Am. Math. Soc; Math. Asn. Am. Teaching mathematics on the undergraduate level. Address: Dept. of Mathematics, College of Notre Dame of Maryland, Baltimore, MD 21210.

DOWLING, PATRICK J, b. Oklahoma City, Okla, Apr. 29, 37; m. 63; c. 3. PHYSICS. B.S, Loyola (La), 59; M.S, Indiana, 61, Ph.D.(physics), 63. Res. assoc. physics, Univ. Minn, 63-65; mem. tech. staff, Gen. Res. Corp, Calif, 65-67; PROJ. NUCLEAR PHYSICIST, CONVAIR AEROSPACE DIV, GEN. DYNAMICS CORP, 67- Consult, Socony-Mobil field res. lab, Tex, 63-64. Am. Phys. Soc. Theoretical physics; electrodynamics, scattering theory. Address: Convair Aerospace Division, General Dynamics, P.O. Box 748, Ft. Worth, TX 76101.

DOWNER, J(OHN) L(ESLIE) de C(OURCY), b. London, Eng, Mar. 16, 22; m. 43; c. 2. NEUROPHYSIOLOGY. B.Sc, McGill, 52, Carnegie fel. & M.Sc, 53; fel, Hopkins, 54-57, Ph.D.(physiol), 57. Jr. instr. psychol, Hopkins, 53-54, instr. anat. & physiol, 56-57; instr. physiol, med. sch, Harvard, 57-59, assoc, 59-60; hon. res. assoc, anat. dept, Univ. Col, London, 60-63, dir. cerebral functions res. group, 63-66; PROF. OPHTHAL, SCH. MED, UNIV. WASH, 66-, RES. AFFILIATE, REGIONAL PRIMATE RES. CTR, 66- Mem. sci. staff, Med. Res. Coun, U.K, 60-63. Can. Army, 39-46. Am. Physiol.

Soc; N.Y. Acad. Sci; Anat. Soc. Gr. Brit. & North. Ireland. Central nervous system and behavior. Address: Dept. of Ophthalmology, School of Medicine, H.S.B. RR 801-SN 10, University of Washington, Seattle, WA 98105.

DOWNER, ROGER GEORGE HAMILL, b. Belfast, North. Ireland, Dec. 21, 42; m. 66; c. 1. INSECT PHYSIOLOGY, ENDOCRINOLOGY. B.S, Queen's Univ. Belfast, 64, M.S, 67; Prov. Ont. fel, Univ. West. Ont, 68-70, Ph.D.(zool), 70. ASST. PROF. BIOL, UNIV. WATERLOO, 70- Dept. Univ. Affairs, Prov. Ont. res. grant, 70; Nat. Res. Coun. Can. res. grant, 70-73. AAAS; Am. Soc. Zool; Can. Soc. Zool. Regulation of lipid metabolism in insects; biochemical changes associated with development of insects. Address: Dept. of Biology, University of Waterloo, Waterloo, Ont, Can.

DOWNES, ALFRED W, b. Fostoria, Ohio, July 3, 07; m. 33; c. 2. PLASTICS. A.B, Oberlin Col, 29; A.M, Western Reserve, 30; Ph.D.(phys, inorg. chem), Wisconsin, 32. Fel, Wisconsin, 32-33; chemist, works lab, Carbide & Carbon Chem. Co, 33-35, group leader, process develop. lab, 35-42, supvr, 42-47, asst. dir. plant labs, 47-53, asst. dir. develop, Union Carbide Plastics Co, 53-54, assoc. dir, 54-56, prod. gen. mgr, 57-59, dir. food packaging admin, 59-67; RETIRED. Am. Chem. Soc. Plastics; use of hydrogen peroxide in vinyl polymerization; chemistry of indium. Address: 566 S. Third Ave, Sturgeon Bay, WI 54235.

DOWNES, J(OHN) A(NTONY), b. Wimbledon, Eng, Feb. 14, 14; m. 53; c. 5. ENTOMOLOGY. B.Sc, London, 35; Commonwealth Fund fel, California, 37-39. Demonstr. zool, London, 39-40; from lectr. to sr. lectr. entom, Glasgow, 40-53; entomologist, sci. serv, CAN. DEPT. AGR, 53-58, head vet. & med. entom, 58-59, SR. ENTOMOLOGIST, RES. BR, 59- Sr. sci. inspector, Ministry Food, Gt. Britain, 41-45; hon. sci. inspector, Dept. Agr, Scotland, 45-47. Del, Med. Res. Coun, Can, 50; secy, Int. Cong. Entom. 56. Entom. Soc. Am; Soc. Study Evolution; Entom. Soc. Can; Royal Entom. Soc. London; Brit. Soc. Exp. Biol. Systematics, behavior and physiology of insects, especially diptera and lepidoptera; arctic insects. Address: 877 Riddell Ave, Ottawa 13, Ont, Can. K2A 2V8

DOWNES, JOHN D, b. Buckhannon, W.Va, Feb. 27, 19; m. 40; c. 4. HORTICULTURE. B.S, West Virginia, 42, M.S, 51; Ph.D.(hort), Mich. State, 55. Instr. & asst. hort, West Virginia, 43-51; asst, Mich. State, 51-54; asst. horticulturist, Malheur Br. Exp. Sta, Ore. State Col, 54-55; assoc. prof. hort, Mich. State Univ, 55-70; PROF. AGRON, TEX. TECH UNIV, 70- Crop specialist, IRI Res. Inst, Brazil, 67-68. U.S.N.R, 45-46. Am. Soc. Hort. Sci. Plant physiology, nutrition, breeding, and genetics; biometry. Address: Dept. of Agronomy, Texas Tech University, Lubbock, TX 79409.

DOWNES, KENNETH WILLIAM, b. Winnipeg, Man, Aug. 31, 10; m. 37; c. 1. PHYSICAL CHEMISTRY. B.Sc, Manitoba, 32, M.Sc, 34; Nat. Res. Coun. fel, McGill, 46, Can. Indust. Ltd. fel. & Ph.D.(phys. chem), 47. Metallurgist, Hudson Bay Mining & Smelting Co, Ltd, 34-40; res. officer EXTRACTION METALL, MINES BR, CAN. DEPT. MINES & TECH. SURVS, 47-54, CHIEF DIV, 54- R.C.A.F, 40-45, Squadron Leader. Chem. Inst. Can; Can. Inst. Mining & Metall. Hydrometallurgy. Address: Extraction Metallurgy Division, Mines Branch, Dept. of Mines & Technical Surveys, 300 LeBreton St, Ottawa 1, Ont, Can.

DOWNES, WILLIAM A(RTHUR), b. Providence, R.I, Nov. 15, 11; m. 39. ELECTRONICS. B.S, Rhode Island, 33, B.Ed, R.I. Col, 37; Mass. Inst. Tech, 43; Brown, 47. Teacher, pub. sch, R.I, 38-42; proj. engr. radar, radiation lab, Mass. Inst. Tech, 42-45; electronic engr. sonar, U.S. Navy Underwater Sound Lab, 46-48, sect. head sonar develop, 48-51, br. head, 51-61, div. head anti-submarine warfare sonar div, 61-70, HEAD SURFACE SHIP & SURVEILLANCE SONAR DEPT, NEW LONDON LAB, NAVAL UNDERWATER SYSTS. CTR, 70- U.S. Navy Commanding Officer & Dir. annual award, 63. Radar beacons; sonar equipment and systems. Address: 987 River Rd, Mystic, CT 06355.

DOWNEY, BERNARD J(OSEPH), b. Philadelphia, Pa, Jan. 18, 17; m. 55; c. 1. PHYSICAL CHEMISTRY. B.A, Catholic Univ, 38, M.S, 45, Ph.D.(phys. chem), 52. Instr. chem, De La Salle Col, 44-49; asst. prof, La Salle Col, 49-52, assoc. prof, 52-54; asst. prof, Seton Hall, 54-59; assoc. prof, VILLANOVA UNIV, 59-61, PROF. CHEM, 61-, ASSOC. DEAN GRAD. STUDIES, 70-, chmn. dept. chem, 60-69. Vis. res. prof, Imp. Col, Univ. London, 69-70. Am. Chem. Soc. Kinetics of metallic film oxidation; diffusion in ionic crystals; kinetics; thermodynamics. Address: Dept. of Chemistry, Villanova University, Villanova, PA 19085.

DOWNEY, H(ARRY) FRED, b. Hagerstown, Md, Aug. 6, 39; m. 65; c. 2. PHYSIOLOGY, BIOPHYSICS. B.S, Univ. Md, College Park, 61, M.S, 64; Nat. Insts. Health fel. & Ph.D.(biophys), Univ. Ill, Urbana, 68. ASST. PROF. VET. PHYSIOL. & PHARMACOL, UNIV. ILL, URBANA, 68-, PHYSIOL. & BIOPHYS, 71- Vis. asst. prof, Cornell Univ, winter 71. Coronary circulation, especially control and distribution of coronary blood flow; transcapillary exchange; mammary blood flow, especially its control and relationship to lactation. Address: Dept. of Veterinary Physiology & Pharmacology, University of Illinois, Urbana, IL 61801.

DOWNEY, JOHN A, b. Regina, Sask, Can, Sept. 16, 30; m. 53; c. 4. MEDICINE, PHYSIOLOGY. B.Sc. & M.D, Manitoba, 54; Ph.D.(physiol), Oxford, 62. Intern, Vancouver Gen. Hosp, B.C, 53-54; resident phys. med. & rehab, Presby. Hosp, New York, 54-56, 57-58, res. assoc. 58-59; resident internal med, Peter Bent Brigham Hosp, Boston, Mass, 56-57, 59-60; vis. worker, Christ Church Col, Oxford, 60-62; vis. fel. phys. med, COL. PHYSICIANS & SURGEONS, COLUMBIA UNIV, 62-63, asst. prof. med, 63-70, asst. prof. phys. med. & rehab, 63-64, assoc. prof, 64-70, PROF, REHAB. MED, 70- Life Inst. Med. Res. Fund fel, 61-62. Attend. phsiatrist, Blythedale Children's Hosp, Vahalla, 63-; asst. attend. physician, Presby. Hosp, 63-64, assoc. attend. physician, 64- Dipl, Am. Bd. Phys. Med. & Rehab. Am. Rheumatism Asn; Am. Acad. Phys. Med. & Rehab; Am. Cong. Rehab. Med. Physiology of temperature regulation; control of respiration; peripheral circulation; clinical care of patients with chronic disabling illness. Address: Dept. of Rehabilitation Medicine, Columbia University College of Physicians & Surgeons, New York, NY 10032.

DOWNEY, JOHN C(HARLES), b. Eureka, Utah, Apr. 12, 26; m. 49; c. 5. ENTOMOLOGY. Fel, Utah, 47-50, B.S, 49, M.S, 50; Ph.D.(entom), California, 57. Instr. biol, Utah, 50-52; assoc. zool, California, 52-56; asst. prof, Southern Illinois, 56-61, assoc. prof, 61-66, prof, 66-68; PROF. BIOL. & HEAD DEPT, NORTH. IOWA UNIV, 68- U.S.A.F, 44-45. Entom. Soc. Am; Soc. Syst. Zool; Lepidop. Soc; Am. Soc. Zool. General variation and evolution; taxonomy and morphology Lycaenidae; ecology and behavior of insects. Address: Dept. of Biology, University of Northern Iowa, Cedar Falls, IA 50613.

DOWNEY, PAUL M(ILTON), b. Nashua, N.H, Apr. 28, 15; m. 40; c. 1. INDUSTRIAL ENGINEERING. B.S, Worcester Polytech, 36; M.S, New Hampshire, 38; Ph.D, Florida, 56. Chem. analyst, Monsanto Chem. Co, 38-39, rubber technician, 39-42, res. chemist, 45-49, group res. leader, 49-51, coord. rubber chem. res, 51-53; asst, Univ. Fla, 53-55, Du Pont fel, 55-56, assoc. prof. indust. eng, 56-61, prof, 61-64, prof. indust. & systs. eng. & chmn. dept, 64-69; PROF. ENG, UNIV. S.FLA, 69- U.S.A.A.F, 42-45, Maj. Am. Chem. Soc; fel. Am. Inst. Chem; Inst. Indust. Eng; Am. Soc. Eng. Educ; Opers. Res. Soc. Am; Inst. Mgt. Sci; fel. The Chem. Soc. Systems engineering; operations research; quality control. Address: Dept. of Engineering, University of South Florida, Tampa, FL 33620.

DOWNEY, R(ICHARD) K(EITH), b. Saskatoon, Sask, Jan. 26, 27; m. 52; c. 5. AGRICULTURE. B.S.A, Univ. Sask, 50, M.Sc, 52; Ph.D, Cornell Univ, 61. RES. SCIENTIST. Exp. Farm, Lethbridge, Alta, 52-57; CROPS SECT, CAN. AGR. RES. STA, 57- Nat. dir, Agr. Inst. Can. Bond Medal, Am. Oil Chemists' Soc, 63; merit award, Pub. Serv. Can, 68. Can. Soc. Agron.(past pres). Oil seed and forage crop improvement. Address: Crops Section, Canadian Agricultural Research Station, University Campus, Saskatoon, Sask, Can.

DOWNEY, RONALD J, b. Manitowoc, Wis, Apr. 8, 33; m. 57; c. 5. CELL PHYSIOLOGY. B.S, Regis Col.(Colo), 55; M.S, Creighton Univ, 58; U.S. Pub. Health Serv. fel, Univ. Nebr, 60-61, Ph.D.(microbiol), 61. Res. assoc. cell metab, U.S. Dept. Agr, D.C, 61-62; asst. prof. biol, UNIV. NOTRE DAME, 62-66, assoc. prof. MICROBIOL, 66-70, PROF, 70- U.S. Pub. Health Serv. career develop. award. Am. Soc. Microbiol; Soc. Exp. Biol. & Med; Am. Soc. Cell Biol; Am. Soc. Exp. Path. Oxidative metabolism; electron transport; metabolism of reticuloendothelial cells; synthesis of respiratory enzymes. Address: Dept. of Microbiology, University of Notre Dame, Notre Dame, IN 46556.

DOWNEY, R(ONALD) S(TUART), b. Smithfalls, Ont, Nov. 9, 38; m. 62; c. 3. VETERINARY MEDICINE. D.V.M, Ont. Vet. Col, 61, M.S, 68. Res. asst. VET. MED, Univ. Calif, Davis, 61-65; ASSOC. PROF, ONT. VET. COL, UNIV. GUELPH, 65-, CHIEF STAFF SMALL ANIMAL MED. & SURG, 70- Clinical medicine; cardiovascular physiology. Address: Dept. of Clinical Studies, Ontario Veterinary College, University of Guelph, Guelph, Ont, Can.

DOWNEY, VINCENT M, b. Kansas City, Kans, Mar. 22, 12; m. 42. MEDICINE. A.B, Stanford Univ, 33, M.D, 38. Staff scientist, LOCKHEED MISSILES & SPACE CO, 63-66, CONSULT. AEROSPACE MED, 66- Lectr, sch. med, Stanford Univ, 63-; mem. comt. hyperbaric oxygenation, Nat. Acad. Sci-Nat. Res. Coun, 65-67. Med.C, 42-62, Col. Aerospace Med. Asn.(Tuttle Award, 64); Am. Col. Physicians. Decompression sickness. Address: Dept. of Community & Preventive Medicine, Stanford University Medical Center, Stanford, CA 94305.

DOWNHOWER, JERRY F, b. Indianapolis, Ind, Oct. 25, 40; m. 64; c. 1. POPULATION ECOLOGY. B.A, Occidental Col, 62; M.A, Kansas, 64, Ph.D. (zool), 68. Res. asst, State Biol. Surv. of Kans, 62-64; zool, Univ. Kans, 64-68; lectr. biol, Cornell Univ, 68-70; ASST. PROF. ZOOL, OHIO STATE UNIV, 70- Mem. faculty of orgn. for trop. studies, 71; steering comt, biol. sci. curriculum studies, 71. AAAS; Soc. Syst. Zool; Am. Soc. Mammal. Behavior; adaptive significance of vertebrate; social organizations. Address: Dept. of Zoology, Ohio State University, Columbus, OH 43210.

DOWNIE, CURRIE S, b. Detroit, Mich, May 10, 22; m. 47; c. 2. INFORMATION SCIENCES, METEOROLOGY. B.S, Detroit Inst. Tech, 42; Mass. Inst. Tech, 42-43; M.S, Chicago, 50, M.B.A, 60. U.S. Air Force, 42-70, weather officer, Air Weather Serv, 43-52, dep. dir. high altitude weather res. proj, 52-55, chief cloud physics div, Air Force Cambridge Res. Labs, 55-59, geophys. planning div, off. aerospace res, 60-61, resources planning div, 61-63, phys. sci. div, European off, 63-66, dir. sci. & tech. info, 66-69, dir. plans, 69-70; CONSULT, 70- Chmn. task group dissemination of info. for comt. sci. & tech. info, Fed. Coun. Sci. & Tech, 67-69. Am. Meteorol. Soc; Air Pollution Control Asn; Water Pollution Control Fedn; Am. Soc. Info. Sci. Address: 1007 Priscilla Lane, Alexandria, VA 22308.

DOWNIE, HARRY G, b. Toronto, Ont, June 11, 26; m. 50; c. 4. PHYSIOLOGY, EXPERIMENTAL SURGERY. D.V.M, Ont. Vet. Col, 48, M.V.Sc, 52; fel, State Univ. N.Y. Vet. Col, Cornell Univ, 49-51, M.S, univ, 51; Nat. Res. Coun. scholar, Univ. West. Ont, 52-55, Ph.D.(physiol), 59. Lectr. PHYSIOL, ONT. VET. COL, UNIV. GUELPH, 48-49, asst. prof, 51-52, assoc. prof, 55-56, PROF, 56-, CHMN. DEPT. BIOMED. SCI, 69-, head dept. res, 56-58, head dept. physiol. sci, 58-69. Fel. coun. arteriosclerosis, Am. Heart Asn. Fel. AAAS; Conf. Res. Workers Animal Diseases(pres, 62-63); Can. Vet. Med. Asn; N.Y. Acad. Sci; Am. Soc. Vet. Physiol. & Pharmacol. Animal physiology, especially liver physiology and surgery; cardiovascular surgery; blood coagulation; blood flow and vascular disease in man and animals. Address: Dept. of Biomedical Sciences, Ontario Veterinary College, University of Guelph, Guelph, Ont, Can.

DOWNIE, JOHN, b. Glasgow, Scotland, Dec. 12, 31; Can. citizen; m. 59; c. 3. CHEMICAL ENGINEERING. B.Sc, Glasgow, 53; M.A.Sc, Toronto, 56, Shell Oil fel, 57, Ph.D.(chem. eng), 59. Res. engr, reservoir mech, Gulf Res. & Develop. Co, 59-62; asst. prof. CHEM. ENG, QUEEN'S UNIV.(ONT), 62-64, assoc. prof, 64-71, PROF, 71- Chem. Inst. Can; Can. Soc. Chem. Eng. Chemical kinetics and reactor design. Address: Dept. of Chemical Engineering, Queen's University, Kingston, Ont. Can.

DOWNING, ARTHUR COVINGTON, JR, b. Kearny, N.J, Mar. 24, 25; m. 46; c. 3. MATHEMATICS. B.A, Princeton, 47; M.S, Michigan, 48, fels, 49-53, Ph.D.(math), 60. Instr. physics, Princeton, 47; asst. math. eng. res. inst, Michigan, 49, asst, 51-53; mathematician math. panel, Oak Ridge Nat. Lab, 53-60, asst. dir, math. div, 60-64; mgr. TECH. APPLN. DEVELOP, CONTROL DATA CORP, 64-65, dir, 65-66, 3000 lower prog. develop, 66-68, GEN. MGR, software review & test div, 68-69, SOFTWARE DESIGN REV, 69- Assoc. prof. Univ. Tenn, 63-64; mem. adv. bd, Sch. Math. Study Group, 63-66; nat. lectr, Asn. Comput. Mach, 65-66. U.S.N.R, 43-45. Am. Math. Soc; Asn. Comput. Mach.(ed, Commun, 62-65). Numerical analysis; convergence for partial differential equations; characteristic value problems for symmetric matrices; programming techniques for digital computers; protection of computer programs. Address: Corporate Development, Control Data Corp, 8100 34th Ave. S, Minneapolis, MN 55440.

DOWNING, CARL G, b. Coeur d'Alene, Idaho, July 29, 29. CHEMICAL ENGINEERING. B.S, Univ. Wash, 53; M.S, Univ. Wis, 56, Ph.D.(chem. eng), 59. Res. engr, Weyerhaeuser Co, Wash, 59-62; asst. prof. chem. eng, San Jose State Col, 62-64, Ore. State Univ, 64-69; CONSULT. ENGR, 69- U.S.A, 53-55. Am. Inst. Chem. Eng. Address: 5630 N.E. 42nd, Apt. E, Portland, OR 97218.

DOWNING, C(HARLES) G(LENN) E(LDRICK), b. Sceptre, Sask, May 4, 14; m. 40; c. 4. AGRICULTURAL ENGINEERING. B.E, Univ. Sask, 40; M.Sc, Iowa State Univ, 48. Design engr, Dom. Exp. Sta, Sask, 39-42; head dept. eng, Ont. Agr. Col, Guelph, 46-65; dir. sch. agr. eng, Univ. Guelph, 65-67; DIR. AGR. ENG, RES. BR, CAN. DEPT. AGR, OTTAWA, 67- R.C.E.M.E, 42-46, Capt. Fel. Am. Soc. Agr. Eng; Am. Soc. Eng. Educ; Can. Soc. Agr. Eng; fel. Eng. Inst. Can; Agr. Inst. Can. Mobile power and machinery; engineering education. Address: Research Branch, Canada Dept. of Agriculture, Ottawa, Ont. K1A 0C6, Can.

DOWNING, C(HARLES) R(UPERT), b. Gloversville, N.Y, Aug. 18, 26; m. 54; c. 3. ECONOMIC BOTANY, PLANT PHYSIOLOGY. B.S, Union (N.Y), 50; M.S, Cornell, 54. Asst. pharmacol, Albany Med. Col, Union (N.Y), 50-52; sci. aide bot, N.Y. State Mus, 54-55; plant physiologist, chem. corps, U.S. Army, Md, 55-57; sr. biologist & group leader, V-C Chem. Corp, div. Socony Mobil Co, Inc, 58-70, MEM. RES. & DEVELOP. DEPT, MOBIL OIL CO, 70- Aide aquatic weed control, Tenn. Valley Auth, Wilson Dam, Ala, summer 53. U.S.N, 44-46. Weed Sci. Soc. Am; Am. Soc. Plant Physiol; Am. Soc. Hort. Sci. Herbicides; defoliants; plant growth regulators; pollen analysis; mammalian toxicology. Address: Research & Development Dept, Mobil Oil Co, P.O. Box 631, Ashland, VA 23005.

DOWNING, D(ANIEL) F(RANCIS), b. Moosup, Conn, Aug. 21, 16; m. 45; c. 4. CARDIOLOGY. B.A, Holy Cross Col, 37; M.A, Columbia, 38; M.D, Boston, 44. Assoc. pediat, Hahnemann Med. Col, 48-49, asst. prof, 49-53, assoc. prof, 53-69; CHIEF PEDIAT. CARDIOL, DEBORAH HOSP, BROWNS MILLS, N.J, 69- Med.C, 45-46, Lt.(jg). AAAS; Am. Col. Cardiol; Am. Heart Asn; Am. Fedn. Clin. Res; Am. Acad. Pediat; Am. Col. Physicians; Am. Col. Chest Physicians; Int. Cardiovasc. Soc. Cardiovascular physiology; pediatric cardiology. Address: Deborah Hospital, Brown Mills, NJ 08015.

DOWNING, DONALD G(RAHAM), b. Worcester, Mass, Jan. 8, 05; m. 25; c. 1. MECHANICAL ENGINEERING. B.S, Worcester Polytech, 26, M.S, 37, hon. D.E, 61. Instr. civil eng, Lehigh, 26-27; struct. draftsman, East. Bridge & Struct. Co, Mass, 27; instr. mech. eng, Worcester Polytech, 27-37, asst. prof, 37-43, prof, 43-54, dir. admissions, 54-55, dean students & admissions, 55-64; RETIRED. Am. Soc. Eng. Educ. Experimental stress analysis. Address: 21 Dean St, Worcester, MA 01609.

DOWNING, DONALD L(EONARD), b. Willoughby, Ohio, Apr. 2, 31; m. 59; c. 2. FOOD SCIENCE. B.S.A, Georgia, 57, S.C. Prescott fel, 61-62, Ph.D. (food sci), 63. Instr. food sci, Georgia, 61-63; food scientist, Beech-Nut Life Savers, Inc, 63-67; ASST. PROF. FOOD SCI, CORNELL UNIV, 67- U.S.A, 52-55. Inst. Food Tech; Int. Asn. Milk, Food & Environ. Sanit. Science and technology related to food preservation and environmental quality. Address: Dept. of Food Science & Technology, Cornell University, Geneva, NY 14456.

DOWNING, DONALD T(ALBOT), b. Perth, West. Australia, Mar. 11, 29; m. 52; c. 6. BIOCHEMISTRY. B.Sc, Western Australia, 51, Ph.D.(org. chem), 55. Res. chemist, Kiwi Polish Co. Ltd, Australia, 54-55; res. officer wax chem, Commonwealth Sci. & Indust. Res. Orgn, 55-63, sr. res. officer, 63-64, sr. res. scientist, 64-66; asst. res. prof. dermat. & biochem, SCH. MED, BOSTON UNIV, 66-69, ASSOC. PROF. BIOCHEM. & ASSOC. RES. PROF. DERMAT, 69- Nat. Insts. Health res. career develop. award, 69- Am. Chem. Soc; Am. Oil Chemists' Soc; Soc. Invest. Dermat. Chemical composition and biosynthesis of lipids. Address: Dept. of Dermatology, Boston University School of Medicine, 80 E. Concord St, Boston, MA 02118.

DOWNING, D(OUGLAS) C(RAWFORD), b. Brandon, Man, Aug. 3, 18; m. 47; c. 4. ORGANIC CHEMISTRY. B.A, McMaster, 38; M.A, Toronto, 40, Nat. Res. Council Can. student, 41-42, Ph.D, 42. Asst. chem, Toronto, 38-40; res. chemist, Nat. Res. Council Can, 42-44; SHAWINIGAN CHEM. DIV, GULF OIL CAN. LTD, 46-55, DIR. RES, 55- R.C.A.F, 44-46. Am. Chem. Soc; Chem. Inst. Can. Organomercurials; high explosives; organic chemicals from acetylene and petroleum. Address: 302 Parkwood Circle, Dorval, Que, Can.

DOWNING, GEORGE V, JR, b. Salem, Va, July 29, 23; m. 51; c. 5. PHYSICAL CHEMISTRY. B.A, Haverford Col, 47; Shell fel, Cornell, 50-51, Ph.D.(phys. chem), 52. Chemist, Off. of Sci. Res. & Develop. Malaria Res. Proj, N.Y. Univ, 44-46; res. chemist, natural prod. develop. group, MERCK & CO, INC, 51-56, group leader, anal. methods develop, 56-62, mgr. process controls res, 62-65, DIR. PHYS. & ANAL. RES, 65- AAAS; Am. Chem. Soc; N.Y. Acad. Sci. Purity characterization of organic compounds; analytical methods development; trace methods in biological materials; chromatographic methods; ion-exchange technology. Address: 26 Skyline Dr, Warren, NJ 07060.

DOWNING, HAROLD E(UGENE), b. Floris, Iowa, Sept. 18, 18; m. 64; c. 2. VETERINARY MEDICINE. D.V.M, Iowa State Univ, 51. Unit head, infectious diseases, Chas. Pfizer Co, Ind, 51-55; exec. v.pres, Myzon Labs, Ill, 55-61; MGR. AGR-VET. ACTIVITIES, UPJOHN INT. INC, 61- U.S.A.A.F, 42-46, T/Sgt. Animal disease control; food preservation; pesticide research; rodent control. Address: Upjohn International Inc, Kalamazoo, MI 49001.

DOWNING, JEAN F(ERRIS), b. Point-Isabel, Ind, Mar. 7, 18; m. 62. BACTERIOLOGY, BIOCHEMISTRY. B.S, Purdue, 41; M.A, Indiana, 45; Ph.D. (bact), Pa. State, 51. Eng. staff, Purdue, 41-43; chief chemist, Hoosier Soybean Mills, 46-48; DIR. res, Specifide Inc, 51-53; agr. res, ELI LILLY & CO, 53-66, ANIMAL SCI, GREENFIELD LABS, 66- Mem. bd. dirs, agr. res. inst, Nat. Acad. Sci-Nat. Res. Coun, 60-63. AAAS; Animal Health Inst; Am. Soc. Animal Sci. Virology; animal nutrition; parasitology. Address: Greenfield Labs, Eli Lilly & Co, Box 708, Greenfield, IN 46140.

DOWNING, J(OHN) SCOTT, b. Phila, Pa, July 31, 40. MATHEMATICS, TOPOLOGY. A.B, Princeton Univ, 62; M.S, Mich. State Univ, 66, Ph.D. (math), 69. Teacher, high sch, Venezuela, 62-65; ASST. PROF. MATH, UNIV. NEBR, OMAHA, 69- Am. Math. Soc; Math. Asn. Am. Topology of manifolds. Address: Dept. of Mathematics, University of Nebraska at Omaha, Omaha, NE 68101.

DOWNING, JOSEPH R(ICHARD), b. New Florence, Mo, May 20, 15; m. 38, 66, 68; c. 2. CHEMISTRY. A.B, Cent. Col.(Mo), 37; Ph.D.(phys. chem), Univ. Ill, 40. CHEMIST, E.I. DU PONT DE NEMOURS & CO, INC, 40- AAAS. Molecular structure and properties. Address: Experimental Station, E.I. du Pont de Nemours & Co, Inc, Wilmington, DE 19898.

DOWNING, MANCOURT, b. Denver, Colo, May 25, 25; m. 48; c. 4. BIOCHEMISTRY. S.B, Chicago, 52, Ph.D.(biochem), 55. Res. assoc, Am. Meat Inst. Found, 52-55; instr. CHEM, UNIV. COLO, BOULDER, 55-57, asst. prof, 57-64, ASSOC. PROF, 64- U.S.N, 43-46. Fel. AAAS; Soc. Biol. Chem. Thermodynamic properties of biological macromolecules; biological and physical properties of vitamin B_{12} and DNA; intermediary metabolism of nucleic acids; cytokinins. Address: Dept. of Chemistry, University of Colorado, Boulder, CO 80302.

DOWNING, RALPH C(HARLSON), b. Torrington, Wyo, Feb. 26, 15; m. 46; c. 4. ORGANIC CHEMISTRY. B.S, Monmouth Col. N.J, 36; Ph.D.(chem), Univ. Va, 42. CHEMIST, E.I. DU PONT DE NEMOURS & CO, INC, 41- Civilian with Manhattan Dist. Proj, 42-45. Am. Chem. Soc. Reactions of alpha and gamma unsaturated diketones; chemistry of fluorine. Address: 111 Rockingham Dr, Windsor Hills, Wilmington, DE 19803.

DOWNING, R(EGINALD) H(ORTON), b. New Germany, N.S, Nov. 19, 08; nat; m. 49; c. 1. MATHEMATICS. B.A, Acadia, 30; M.S, West Virginia, 32; Ph.D.(math), 34. Asst. math, West Virginia, 30-34, instr, 34-38; res. assoc, Bur. Govt. Res, W.Va, 34-38; instr. math, Purdue, 38-42; eng. mathematician, Kaiser Fleetwings, Inc, 42-47; assoc. prof. math. AIR FORCE INST. TECHNOL, 47-49, prof. & head dept, 49-51, dean resident col, 51-56, dir. resident instruction, 56-58, dean faculty, 58-61, dean eng, 61-69, DIR. ACAD. AFFAIRS, 69- Sigma Xi Award, 34. AAAS; Am. Math. Soc; Am. Soc. Eng. Educ; Math. Asn. Am; Am. Inst. Aeronaut. & Astronaut. Engineering education. Address: Air Force Institute of Technology, Wright Patterson Air Force Base, OH 45433.

DOWNING, S(HIRLEY) EVANS, b. Meredith, N.H, June 29, 30; m. 55; c. 2. PATHOLOGY. B.S, New Hampshire, 52; M.D, Yale, 56. Intern path, Grace New Haven Community Hosp, 56-57; U.S. Pub. Health Serv. fel, sch. med, Yale, 57-58, Life Ins. Med. Res. Fund fel, 59-60, Nuffield Inst. Med. Res, Eng, 58-59; scientist, Nat. Heart Inst, 60-62; assoc. physiol, George Washington, 62; asst. prof. PATH, SCH. MED, YALE, 62-65, ASSOC. PROF, 65- James Hudson Brown fel, 55; Keese prize, sch. med, Yale, 56; res. career develop. award, U.S. Pub. Health Serv, 62-67. U.S.P.H.S, 60-62, Sr. Asst. Surg. AAAS; Am. Heart Asn; Am. Fedn. Clin. Res; Am. Med. Asn; Am. Soc. Exp. Path; Am. Physiol. Soc. Cardiovascular physiology; pathophysiology. Address: Alden Dr, Gulford, CT 06437.

DOWNING, W(ILLIAM) C(HAPPELL), JR, b. Terre Haute, Ind, Dec. 6, 02; m. 33; c. 4. ENGINEERING. B.S, Yale, 24. Instr. mech. & elec. eng, Yale, 24-27; chief engr, Lincoln Meter Div, Sangamo Elec. Co, 27-53; asst. chief engr, 53-62, dir. power equip. eng, 62-68; ENG. CONSULT, 68- AAAS; Inst. Elec. & Electronics Eng. Electric metering. Address: 1416 S. Park Ave, Springfield, IL 62704.

DOWNING, WILLIAM L(AWRENCE), b. Des Moines, Iowa, Oct. 2, 21; m. 46; c. 3. BIOLOGY. B.A, Iowa, 43, M.S, 48, Ph.D.(zool), 51. Instr. biol, Iowa, 49-51; prof. BIOL. & head dept, Jamestown Col, 51-63; PROF, HAMLINE UNIV, 63- U.S.N.R, 43-45, 49, Lt. AAAS; Am. Soc. Zool; Soc. Protozool; fel. Royal Soc. Trop. Med. & Hyg. Morphogenesis of ciliates; undergraduate education in biology and biological curricula. Address: Dept. of Biology, Hamline University, St. Paul, MN 55101.

DOWNS, B(ERTRAM) W(ILSON), JR, b. St. Paul, Minn, Dec. 11, 25; m. 56; c. 3. THEORETICAL PHYSICS. B.S, Calif. Inst. Technol, 46; M.S, Univ. Minn, 49; Ph.D.(physics), Stanford Univ, 56. Res. fel, Univ. Birmingham, 55-56; res. assoc, lab. nuclear studies, Cornell Univ, 56-59; asst. prof. PHYSICS, UNIV. COLO, BOULDER, 59-60, assoc. prof, 60-65, PROF, 65-, assoc. dean grad. sch. & acting dir. comput. ctr, 65-67. Consult, Atomic Power Develop. Assocs, Mich, 57-58; vacation consult, Atomic Energy Res. Estab, Eng, 63-64; mem. staff, Oxford, 63-64. U.S.N, 43-46, 50-53, Res, 46-50, 53-61, Lt. Fel. Am. Phys. Soc. Hyperon-nucleon interactions and hypernuclei. Address: Dept. of Physics, University of Colorado, Boulder, CO 80302.

DOWNS, DAVID S, b. Woodbury, N.J, Jan. 4, 41; m. 67. SOLID STATE PHYSICS. B.A, Gettysburg Col, 62; M.S, Univ. Del, 64, Ph.D.(physics), 69. Nat. Res. Coun. res. assoc. physics, PICATINNY ARSENAL, 68-69, RES. PHYSICIST, FELTMAN RES. LAB, SOLID STATE BR, 69- Am. Phys. Soc; Am. Asn. Physics Teachers. Electron spin resonance of transition metals in

II-VI compounds; electrical and optical properties of metallic azides. Address: Feltman Research Lab, Picatinny Arsenal, Dover, NJ 07801.

DOWNS, HAROLD ROBERT, b. Wellington, Kans, Feb. 18, 19; m. 42; c. 2. GEOLOGY, PALEONTOLOGY. B.A, Wichita, 42; M.S, Iowa, 47, Ph.D. (paleont), 49. DIV. PALEONTOLOGIST, SHELL OIL CO, 49- U.S.A.A.F, 42-45. Correlation of the Pennsylvanian and Permian in the mid-continent; micropaleontology of the mid-continent, Ordovician-Permian, principally fusulinids and conodonts. Address: Shell Oil Co, 1700 Broadway, Denver, CO 80202.

DOWNS, JAMES J(OSEPH), b. St. Joseph, Mo, Jan. 31, 28. PHYSICAL & INORGANIC CHEMISTRY. B.S, St. Benedicts Col, 49; M.S, Notre Dame, 52; Ph.D.(chem), Fla. State, 54. PRIN. CHEMIST, MIDWEST RES. INST, 56- U.S.A, 54-56. AAAS; Am. Chem. Soc; Am. Statist. Asn. Computer data processing; mass spectroscopy; electron paramagnetic resonance spectroscopy; nuclear magnetic resonance spectroscopy; kinetics; structural chemistry. Address: 4019 W. 93rd Terr, Prairie Village, KS 66207.

DOWNS, JAMES PATE, b. Savannah, Ga, July 17, 31; m. 54; c. 3. GEOPHYSICS. B.S, Ga. Inst. Tech, 56; Nat. Sci. Found. fel, Mass. Inst. Tech, 58-59, Ph.D.(geophys), 60. Mem. tech. staff, Bell Tel. Labs, 60-62; head dept. opers. anal, BELLCOMM INC, 62-64, spec. asst. to pres, 64-65, head dept. systs. anal, 65-66, planetary studies, 66-68, Bell Syst. Studies, 69-70, DIR. BELL SYST. STUDIES CTR, 70- U.S.A.F, 49-52, S/Sgt. Am. Geophys. Union. Impact of technology; economics and structure of organizations. Address: 8304 Fenway Rd, Bethesda, MD 20034.

DOWNS, LESLIE E, b. Glidden, Iowa, Nov. 6, 00; m. 27; c. 2. CHEMISTRY, PHYSICS. B.S, Iowa State Col, 26; M.S, Wisconsin, 32. Res. engr, U.S. Gypsum Co, Iowa & Ill, 26-28; jr. physicist, Nat. Bur. Standards, 28; chem. engr, forest prod. lab, U.S. Forest Serv, Wis, 28-59; res. engr, Trionics Corp, 61-62; mem. staff, Madison Res, Inc, Middleton, 62-67; RES. ENGR, Madison Res. Ctr, Gilford Instrument Labs, 67-70; W.M. GRENGG & ASSOCS, 70- Adhesives; thermoluminescence radiation exposure meters; thermal conductivity of building materials; paint and other protective coatings; control of shrinkage of wood; water repellents; bleaching of wood; electric heating of veneer logs; incendiary effects of thermal radiation at very high temperatures; protection of wood against fire. Address: W.M. Grengg & Assocs, 4605 W. Beltline Hwy, Madison, WI 53711.

DOWNS, L(LOYD) E(UGENE), b. Weston, Ore, Apr. 17, 02; m. 30; c. 2. GENETICS. B.A, Pacific Union Col, 33; M.A, 45; Ph.D.(genetics of Protozoa); Southern California, 57. Teacher prep. sch, Pacific Union Col, 33-35; Brazil Jr. Col, 36-41, pres, 37-39; teacher sci, Loma Linda Acad, 42-44; prof. biol, La Sierra Col, 44-71; RETIRED. AAAS; Soc. Protozool; Am. Soc. Naturalists. Genetics of protozoa. Address: 830 Bluebell St, Placerville, CA 95667.

DOWNS, M(ARTIN) L(UTHER), b. Reading, Pa, March 12, 10; m; c. 2. CHEMISTRY. B.S, Pa. State, 31; M.S, Lawrence Col, 32, Ph.D.(pulp, papermaking), 34. Develop. dept, Mead Corp, 34-37; from chief chemist to tech. dir, Thilmany Pulp & Paper Co, 37-70, v.pres, 64-70; OWNER & MGR, PAPER CONCEPTS CONSULT, 70- Am. Chem. Soc; Tech. Asn. Pulp & Paper Indust. Paper chemistry; paper sizing; stock processing; specialty and technical papers; paper recycling. Address: Paper Concepts, 1000 Greengrove Rd, Appleton, WI 54911.

DOWNS, ROBERT J(ACK), b. Sapulpa, Okla, June 25, 23; m. 45; c. 1. BOTANY. B.S, George Washington, 50, M.S, 51, Ph.D.(bot), 54. Student asst. physics & bot, George Washington, 49-50, asst. bot, 50-51; phys. sci. aide, astrophys. observ, Smithsonian Inst, 51-52; plant physiologist photoperiod proj, plant indust. sta, hort. crops res. br, agr. res. serv, U.S. Dept. Agr, 52-59, mem. pioneering res. group, plant physiol. lab, crops res. div, plant indust. sta, 59-65; PROF. BOT. & HORT. SCI. & DIR. PHYTOTRON, N.C. STATE UNIV, 65- U.S.N, 41-47. Am. Soc. Hort. Sci; Instrument Soc. Am; Int. Soc. Biometeorol; Am. Soc. Agr. Eng; Am. Soc. Plant Physiol. Phytochrome and the regulatory effects of light on plants; taxonomy of South American plants, especially Xyridaceae and Bromeliaceae; bioengineering and environmental physiology. Address: Southeastern Plant Environment Labs, Room 2003, Gardner Hall, North Carolina State University, Raleigh, NC 27607.

DOWNS, THEODORE, b. Chicago, Ill, July 1, 19; m. 45; c. 2. VERTEBRATE PALEONTOLOGY. B.S, Kans. State Teachers Col, 41; Kansas, 41, 46; M.A, California, 48, Ph.D.(vert. paleont), 51. Curator vert. paleont, LOS ANGELES COUNTY MUS, 52-61, CHIEF CURATOR EARTH SCI. DIV, 61- Nat. Res. fel, 51-52; vis. prof, Southern California. Med.C, U.S.A, 42-43, U.S.A.A.F, 43-46. AAAS; Geol. Soc. Am; Soc. Vert. Paleont; Am. Soc. Mammal; Soc. Study Evolution; Soc. Syst. Zool; Paleont. Soc. Paleomammalogy; evolution; paleoecology; paleogeographic distribution of middle to late Cenozoic vertebrates; field operations in Nevada, Oregon, California and Mexico. Address: Los Angeles County Museum of Natural History, 900 Exposition Blvd, Los Angeles, CA 90007.

DOWNS, THOMAS D, b. Kalamazoo, Mich, Aug. 28, 33; m. 62; c. 1. BIOSTATISTICS. B.S, West. Mich. Univ, 60; M.P.H, Univ. Mich, 62, Ph.D. (biostatist), 65. Asst. prof. BIOMET, Case West. Reserve Univ, 65-70, ASSOC. PROF, UNIV. TEX. SCH. PUB. HEALTH, HOUSTON, 70- U.S.A, 53-56, Res, 56-62, Sgt. Math. Asn. Am; Am. Statist. Asn; Am. Pub. Health Asn; Biomet. Soc. Applied statistics and mathematics in public health. Address: Dept. of Health Science, University of Texas School of Public Health, Houston, TX 77025.

DOWNS, THOMAS L(UTHER), JR, b. Revere, Mass, Jan. 26, 06; m. 43; c. 1. MATHEMATICS. A.B, Bowdoin Col, 27, A.M, Harvard, 30, Ph.D.(math), 34. Instr. math. & German, Franklin & Marshall Col, 27-29; instr. MATH, Harvard, 32-34, 35-36; Sweet Briar Col, 34-35; Trinity Col.(Conn), 36-42; assoc. prof, U.S. Naval Acad, 46-47; WASH. UNIV, 47-48, PROF, 58- U.S.N.R, 42-46. Am. Math. Soc. Differential geometry; planar points of analytic surfaces. Address: Dept. of Mathematics, College of Arts & Sciences, Washington University, St. Louis, MO 63130.

DOWNS, W(ILBUR) G(EORGE), b. Perth Amboy, N.J, Aug. 7, 13; m. 40; c. 4. VIROLOGY. A.B, Cornell, 35, M.D, 38; M.P.H, Hopkins, 41. Mem, State Biol. Surv, N.Y, 35-37; intern & res. med, New York Hosp, 38-40; mem. field staff, div. med. & pub. health, Rockefeller Found, 41-62, assoc. dir. div. biomed. sci, 62-71; MEM. STAFF, ARBOVIRUS RES. UNIT, YALE, 71-, dir. unit & prof. epidemiol, sch. med, 64-71. Mem. expert adv. panel malaria, WHO, 50-57, virus diseases, 57-; standing adv. cmt. med. res, Brit. West Indies, 56-; bd. virus reference reagents & panel arthropod-borne virus reference reagents, Nat. Insts. Health, 63-68; mem. comn. on malaria, Armed Forces Epidemiol. Bd, 65- Med.C, 42-46, Lt.Col. AAAS; Am. Soc. Trop. Med. & Hyg; Am. Soc. Parasitol; Am. Pub. Health Asn; Am. Mosquito Control Asn; Royal Soc. Trop. Med. & Hyg. Malaria; insecticides; arthropod transmitted virus disease. Address: Arbovirus Research Unit, Yale University, 60 College St, New Haven, CT 06510.

DOWNSBROUGH, GEORGE ATHA, b. Firthcliffe, N.Y, Feb. 14, 10; m. 48; c. 2. PHYSICS. B.S, Rutgers, 31, M.S, 33, Ph.D.(physics), 36. Asst. Rutgers, 31-36; physicist & sr. physicist, res. lab, Johns-Manville Corp, 36-40; sr. physicist, bur. ord, U.S. Navy Dept, 40-42; gen. mgr, Boonton Radio Corp, 42-44, v.pres. & dir, 44-50, treas, 50-59, pres. & dir, 50-64; MEM. STAFF, Am-Standard Corp, 63-65; SINGER CO, 65- Consult, War Prod. Bd. & Bus. & Defense Serv. Admin, 42-44, 50-53. AAAS; Am. Phys. Soc; Instrument Soc. Am; Sci. Apparatus Makers Asn.(past pres); Inst. Elec. & Electronics Eng. Photoelectric threshold of aluminum; damping of torsional oscillations in quartz fibers. Address: 495 Pepperidge Tree Terr, Smoke Rise, Butler, NJ 07405.

DOWS, DAVID A(LAN), b. San Francisco, Calif, July 25, 28; m. 50; c. 3. PHYSICAL CHEMISTRY. B.S, Univ. Calif, 52, Dow Chem. fel, 52-53, Ph.D. (chem), 54. Instr. CHEM, Cornell Univ, 54-56; UNIV. SOUTH. CALIF, 56-57, asst. prof, 57-59, assoc. prof, 59-63, PROF, 63-, CHMN. DEPT, 66- Nat. Sci. Found. sr. res. fel, Oxford, 62-63; NATO vis. prof, Univ. Florence, 70; consult, Los Alamos Nat. Lab. U.S.A, 46-48. Am. Chem. Soc; Am. Phys. Soc. Molecular electronic and infrared spectroscopy; molecular structure; crystal spectroscopy and intermolecular forces in crystals. Address: Dept. of Chemistry, University of Southern California, Los Angeles, CA 90007.

DOWSON, JOHN, b. Auburn, N.Y, Jan. 14, 16; m. 41; c. 2. DENTISTRY. B.S, Eastern Michigan, 38; D.D.S, Michigan, 45, M.S, 47. Asst. prof. ENDODONTICS, SCH. DENT, UNIV. MICH, 53-65, assoc. prof, 65-69, PROF, 69-, CHMN. DEPT, 67- Dipl, Am. Bd. Endodontics, secy, 69- U.S.A.F, 51-53, Capt. Am. Asn. Endodont. Address: Dept. of Endodontics, University of Michigan School of Dentistry, Ann Arbor, MI 48104.

DOWTY, EARL LEONARD, b. Webb City, Mo, Apr. 14, 39. MECHANICAL ENGINEERING. B.S, Okla. State, 60, Ph.D.(mech. eng), 64; M.S, Calif. Inst. Tech, 61. Lectr. fluid mech, Nottingham, 64-65; mem. staff, propulsion res. sect, Martin Co, 65-67; asst. prof. mech. eng, Okla. State Univ, 67-69; BR. MGR, THERMAL & FLUID MECH. BR, BASIC ENG. DEPT, GULF GEN. ATOMIC, 69- Am. Soc. Mech. Eng. Boundary layer flows; heat conduction and convection. Address: 13434 Calais Dr, Del Mar, CA 92014.

DOXTADER, KENNETH G(UY), b. San Francisco, Calif, June 22, 38; m. 62; c. 2. SOIL MICROBIOLOGY. B.S, Univ. Calif, Berkeley, 61; M.S, Cornell Univ, 63, Ph.D.(agron), 65. Res. asst. soil microbiol, Cornell Univ, 61-65; asst. prof. AGRON, COLO. STATE UNIV, 65-69, ASSOC. PROF, 69- AAAS; Am. Soc. Microbiol; Am. Soc. Agron; Int. Soc. Soil Sci. Physiology and ecology of soil microorganisms; microbial biogeochemistry; microbial transformations of pesticides and minerals. Address: Dept. of Agronomy, Colorado State University, Ft. Collins, CO 80521.

DOXTATOR, CHARLES W(ILLIAM), b. Winnipeg, Man, June 8, 02; nat; m. 32; c. 6. PLANT GENETICS, PHYTOPATHOLOGY. B.S.A, Manitoba, 28; M.S, Minnesota, 31, Ph.D, 36. Field asst. plant breeding, Manitoba, 29-30; instr. plant genetics, Minnesota, 30-36; PLANT BREEDER, SUGAR BEETS, AM. CRYSTAL SUGAR CO, 36- Am. Soc. Sugar Beet Technol. Biochemistry; genetics in crop plants, especially in breeding of sugar beets for improvement in agronomic character, development of superior chemical characteristics. Address: American Crystal Sugar Co, Rocky Ford, CO 81067.

DOYLE, DARRELL J(OSEPH), b. Allentown, Pa, July 26, 39; m. 64; c. 1. BIOCHEMISTRY. B.A, Lehigh Univ, 61, M.S, 63; Nat. Insts. Health fel, Johns Hopkins Univ, 65-67, Ph.D.(biochem), 67. Nat. Insts. Health fel, Stanford Univ, 67-69; ASST. PROF. ANAT. & CELL BIOL, MED. SCH, UNIV. PITTSBURGH, 69- Vis. prof, Univ. Chile, 71. AAAS. Developmental biology; biochemical genetics; regulatory mechanisms in eukaryotic cells. Address: Dept. of Anatomy & Cell Biology, University of Pittsburgh Medical School, 4200 Fifth Ave, Pittsburgh, PA 15213.

DOYLE, EUGENIE F, b. N.Y.C, Oct. 19, 21; m. 44; c. 5. PEDIATRIC CARDIOLOGY. M.D, Johns Hopkins Univ, 46. Intern pediat, Johns Hopkins Hosp, 46-47; resident, Bellevue Hosp, 47-49; fel. PEDIAT. CARDIOL, MED. CTR, N.Y. UNIV, 49-53, DIR. DEPT, 59-, PROF. PEDIAT, SCH. MED, 70-, asst. prof, 53-58, assoc. prof, 59-70. Am. Pediat. Soc; Am. Heart Asn; fel. Am. Col. Cardiol; fel. Am. Acad. Pediat. Treatment of acute rheumatic fever and rheumatic heart disease; natural history of congenital heart disease, especially aortic stenosis and the types of congenital cardiovascular defects associated with intrauterine rubella infection. Address: Dept. of Pediatric Cardiology, New York University, Medical Center, 550 First Ave, New York, NY 10016.

DOYLE, F(RANK) L(AWRENCE), b. San Antonio, Tex, Oct. 16, 26; m. 62; c. 1. HYDROLOGY, GEOLOGY. B.S, Univ. Tex, 50; M.S, La. State Univ, 55; fel, Univ. Ill, 54-55, Ph.D.(geol), 58. Instr. geol, St. Mary's Univ. San Antonio, 50-53; asst. geologist, Ill. State Geol. Surv, 56-58; asst. prof. geol, St. Mary's Univ. San Antonio, 58-60, assoc. prof, 60-62, chmn. dept, 61-62; geologist, water resources div, U.S. Geol. Surv, Colo. & Ariz, 62-63; assoc. prof. geol, Univ. Conn, 63-65; CONSULT. HYDROGEOLOGIST, 65-; ADJ. PROF, DIV. NATURAL SCI. & MATH, UNIV. ALA, HUNTSVILLE, 71- Consult, Int. Resources & Geotech, Inc, 65-68; Tex. Instruments Inc, 68-70; Int. Ctr. Arid & Semi-Arid Land Studies, Tex. Tech Univ, 70-71; Ala.

State Geol. Surv, 71-; ctr. environ. studies, Univ. Ala, Huntsville, 71- Petrol. geologist, Seeligson Eng. Comt, 52-53; fuels br, U.S. Geol. Surv, Mont, 55; asst, Ill. State Geol. Surv, 55-56, assoc. geologist, 58-62. U.S.A, 45-46. Fel. AAAS; fel. Geol. Soc. Am; Am. Inst. Prof. Geol; Am. Asn. Petrol. Geol; Am. Water Resources Asn. Geomorphology; environmental geology and hydrology; Quaternary, areal and subsurface geology; applications of remotely-sensed data; hydrology and geology of volcanic terranes, tropics, deserts and semi-arid areas. Address: c/o Center for Environmental Studies, University of Alabama in Huntsville, Huntsville, AL 35807.

DOYLE, FREDERICK JOSEPH, b. Oak Park, Ill, Apr. 3, 20; m. 55; c. 4. PHOTOGRAMMETRY, GEODESY. B.C.E, Syracuse, 51; Fulbright fel, Netherlands, 51-52. With, Inter-Am. Geod. Surv, S.Am, 46-47; instr. surv. & photogrammetry, Syracuse, 48-51, lectr. photogrammetry, 52-53, asst. prof, 53-56, assoc. prof, 56-59; chmn. dept. geod. sci, Ohio State, 59-60; dir. intel. systs, Broadview Res. Corp, 60-61; chief res. engr, Raytheon-Autometric, 61-67, chief scientist, 67-69; RES. SCIENTIST, U.S. GEOL. SURV, 69- U.S.A, 43-48, 1st Lt. Am. Cong. Surv. & Mapping; Am. Geophys. Union; Soc. Photog. Sci. & Eng; Soc. Photo-Optical Instrument Eng; Am. Soc. Photogram; Can. Inst. Surv. Photogrammetric system design and analysis. Address: U.S. Geological Survey, 1340 Old Chain Bridge Rd, McLean, VA 22101.

DOYLE, GEORGE J(OSEPH), b. San Jose, Calif, Aug. 4, 18; m. 64. PHYSICAL CHEMISTRY. B.A, San Jose State Col, 40; M.Sc, Calif. Inst. Tech, 48; Ph.D.(phys. chem), Indiana, 55. Nat. Defense Res. Cmt. res. asst. chem, Northwestern, 42-45 & Calif. Inst. Tech, 45-46; res. asst. phys. chem, Indiana, 47-52; jr. res. chemist, California, 52-54; PHYS. CHEMIST, Stanford Res. Inst, 54-71; STATEWIDE AIR POLLUTION RES. CTR, UNIV. CALIF, RIVERSIDE, 71- Am. Chem. Soc; Am. Phys. Soc. Properties of aerosols by their interaction with light or sound; kinetics and mechanisms of thermal and photochemical reactions. Address: University of California Statewide Air Pollution Research Center, Riverside, CA 92502.

DOYLE, GREGORY GEORGE, b. Lewiston, Idaho, Mar. 29, 32; m. 64; c. 2. CYTOGENETICS, BOTANY. B.S, Washington (Seattle), 54; M.S, Washington State, 56; Floyd fel, Indiana, 59-60; Ph.D.(bot), Illinois, 60. Asst. cytogenetics, Washington State, 54-56; bot, Illinois, 56-59; biol, Indiana, 59; RES. GENETICIST, AGR. RES. SERV, U.S. DEPT. AGR, 60-; ASSOC. PROF. CYTOGENETICS, UNIV. MO-COLUMBIA, 70-, asst. prof, 60-70. Genetics Soc. Am; Am. Genetic Asn. Cytogenetics of maize; preferential pairing; chromosome aberrations; polyploidy; non-homologous pairing and crossing over; synthesis of artificial allotetraploid maize strains. Address: 103 Curtis Hall, University of Missouri-Columbia, Columbia, MO 65201.

DOYLE, JAMES E, b. Champaign, Ill, Apr. 21, 30; m. 50; c. 4. PHYSICS. B.S, San Diego State Col, 58. Physicist, Lawrence Radiation Lab, California, Livermore, 58-62; sr. scientist, EG&G INC, 62-64, sci. exec, 64-69, MGR. WEAPONS MEASUREMENTS, 69- Detector instrumentation design and development; nuclear weapons testing. Address: EG&G Inc, P.O. Box 98, Goleta, CA 93017.

DOYLE, JAMES M, b. Lawler, Iowa, Apr. 30, 34; m. 58; c. 3. ENGINEERING MECHANICS, APPLIED MATHEMATICS. B.S, Iowa State Univ, 56, M.S, 60; Ph.D.(mech), Univ. Ill, 63. Asst. prof. eng. sci, Univ. Notre Dame, 63-65; ENG. MECH, UNIV. ILL, CHICAGO CIRCLE, 65-70, ASSOC. PROF, 70- C.Eng, 57-59, Res, 59- Am. Soc. Civil Eng; Am. Soc. Mech. Eng. Structural engineering; biomedical engineering. Address: Dept. of Materials Engineering, University of Illinois at Chicago Circle, Chicago, IL 60680.

DOYLE, J(OHN) R(OBERT), b. Norwood, Mass; Dec. 18, 24; m. 56; c. 4. INORGANIC CHEMISTRY. B.S, Mass. Inst. Technol, 49, M.S, 52; Ph.D, Tulane, 55. Chemist, Mass. Inst. Technol, 49-52; instr. INORG. CHEM, UNIV. IOWA, 55-57, asst. prof, 58-60, assoc. prof, 60-65, PROF, 65- U.S.N.R, 43-46, Lt.(jg). AAAS; Am. Chem. Soc; Am. Crystallog. Asn. Hydrides of boron and other group III elements; structures of metalolefin compounds. Address: Dept. of Chemistry, University of Iowa, Iowa City, IA 52240.

DOYLE, JOSEPH T(HEOBALD), b. Providence, R.I, June 11, 18; m. 44; c. 2. CARDIOLOGY. A.B, Harvard, 39, M.D, 43. Asst. med, Harvard Med. Sch, 48-49; asst. physiol. & Whitehead res. fel, sch. med, Emory, 49-50; instr. physiol. & asst. med, Grady Mem. Hosp, Atlanta, Ga, 50-51, dir. electrocardiographic lab, 50-52, instr. med. & physiol. & asst. coordinator, cardiovascular training prog, 51-52; assoc. MED, sch. med, Duke, 52; asst. prof, ALBANY MED. COL, 52-54, assoc. prof, 54-61, HEAD, DIV. CARDIOL, 60-, PROF, 61-, DIR. CARDIOVASCULAR HEALTH CTR, 52- Dir. private diagnostic clin, 57-; cardiac catheterization unit, 57-63; attend. staff, Albany Hosp. & Albany Vet. Admin. Hosp, 53- Consult, U.S. Vet. Admin. Regional Off, Atlanta, 51-52. Fel. coun. arteriosclerosis & coun. clin. cardiol. & epidemiol, Am. Heart Asn. Dipl, Am. Bd. Internal Med, 52 & Am. Bd. Cardiovasc. Diseases, 59. Med.C, 44-45, 1st Lt. Am. Fedn. Clin. Res; fel. Am. Col. Physicians. Cardiovascular physiology and epidemiology. Address: Division of Cardiology, Albany Medical College, New Scotland Ave, Albany, NY 12208.

DOYLE, LAWRENCE EDWARD, b. Cincinnati, Ohio, Mar. 12, 09; m. 39; c. 3. MECHANICAL & INDUSTRIAL ENGINEERING. B.S.M.E, Yale, 30; M.E, Univ. Ill, 50. Engr, Cincinnati Milling Mach. Co, 35-40; supvr. mfg. eng, Allison Div, Gen. Motors Corp, 41-43; mech. engr, Norman E. Miller & Assoc, 43-45; asst. prof. MECH. ENG, UNIV. ILL, URBANA, 46-50, assoc. prof, 50-55, PROF, 55- Am. Soc. Metals; Am. Soc. Mech. Eng; Soc. Mfg. Eng.(Nat. Educ. Award, 61). Establishment and development of a scientific basis for process design in manufacturing. Address: Mechanical Engineering Bldg, University of Illinois, Urbana, IL 61801.

DOYLE, MARGARET D(AVIS), b. Chelsea, Okla, Sept. 23, 14; m. 47; c. 1. NUTRITION. B.Sc, Univ. Ark, 34; S.M, Univ. Chicago, 38, Home Econ. Alumnae fel, 44, Ph.D.(nutrit), 45. Instr. foods, Univ. Minn, 38-40; foods & nutrit, Conn. Col, 40-42; Univ. Chicago, 45-49, asst. prof, 49-53; NUTRIT, UNIV. MINN, ST. PAUL, 60-62, assoc. prof, 62-70, PROF, 70- Dipl, Am. Bd. Nutrit. Fel. AAAS; Am. Inst. Nutrit; Am. Dietetic Asn; Am. Home Econ. Asn. Protein-calorie interrelation in young adults; food habits and dietary intake patterns of obese women and of young adults. Address: Dept. of Nutrition, College of Home Economics, University of Minnesota, St. Paul, MN 55101.

DOYLE, MICHAEL P, b. Minneapolis, Minn, Oct. 31, 42; m. 64; c. 2. PHYSICAL ORGANIC CHEMISTRY. B.S, Col. St. Thomas, 64; Nat. Insts. Health fel, Iowa State, 66-67, Ph.D.(org. chem), 68. Instr. ORG. CHEM, Illinois, Chicago Circle, 68; asst. prof, HOPE COL, 68-71, ASSOC. PROF, 71- AAAS; Am. Chem. Soc. Free radical rearrangements; reactions of nitrosonium and nitronium ions; production and reactions of carbonium ions: synthetic intermediates and new aromatic compounds; silane reductions; oxidative organic chemistry; solvolytic displacements. Address: Dept. of Chemistry, Hope College, Holland, MI 49423.

DOYLE, MILES L(AWRENCE), b. Ashland, Ohio, July 14, 27; m. 55; c. 2. BIOCHEMISTRY. A.B, Ashland Col, 49; fel, St. Louis, 51-55, Ph.D.(biochem), 55. Instr. biochem, Vanderbilt, 55-58; asst. prof. chem, Quincy Col, 58-61; asst. res. biochemist, California, Davis, 61-62; ASSOC. PROF. CHEM, Wis. State Col, Eau Claire, 62-64; Col. St. Teresa (Minn), 64-66; ARK. STATE UNIV, 66- Res. biochemist, Thayer Vet. Admin. Hosp, Tenn, 55-58; summer, Nat. Sci. Found. res. partic, La. State Univ, 63, Ind. Univ, 65. U.S.N, 45-46. Fel. AAAS; Am. Chem. Soc; Brit. Biochem. Soc. Enzymology. Address: Dept. of Physical Science, Arkansas State University, State University, AR 72467.

DOYLE, OWEN W, b. Buffalo, N.Y, May 12, 23; m. 49; c. 3. MEDICINE, RADIOLOGY. B.S, Univ. Notre Dame, 43; M.D, Yale, 47. Intern, Millard Fillmore Hosp, Buffalo, N.Y, 47, asst. resident surg, 48, path, 49; RADIOL, Univ. Mich, 50, resident, 51, 52-53, instr, 52-56; assoc, MED. CTR, DUKE UNIV, 56-58, asst. prof, 58-59, ASSOC. PROF, 59- Chief radiol, Moses H. Cone Hosp, Greensboro, 68-, pres. med. staff, 70-; consult, Vet. Hosp, N.C. U.S.N.R, 43-45, 53-54. AAAS; Am. Col. Radiol; Am. Col. Physicians; Am. Roentgen Ray Soc; Radiol. Soc. N.Am. Radiology; isotopes. Address: 1013 Professional Village, Greensboro, NC 27401.

DOYLE, PATRICK H, b. Mich, Nov. 21, 27; m. 49; c. 3. MATHEMATICS, TOPOLOGY. B.S, Univ. Mich, 50, M.S, 51; Ph.D.(math), Univ. Tenn, 57. Instr. MATH, West. Mich. Univ, 53-54; Univ. Tenn, 54-57, acting asst. prof, 57-58; asst. prof, Mich. State Univ, 58-61, assoc. prof, 61-62; PROF, Va. Polytech. Inst. & State Univ, 62-65; MICH. STATE UNIV, 65- Am. Math. Soc; Math. Asn. Am. Topological n-manifolds; embedding problems. Address: Dept. of Mathematics, College of Natural Science, Michigan State University, East Lansing, MI 48823.

DOYLE, RICHARD ROBERT, b. Camden, N.J, July 29, 37; m. 63; c. 2. ORGANIC CHEMISTRY, BIOCHEMISTRY. B.S, Drexel Univ, 60; M.S, Univ. Mich, 63, Ph.D.(org. chem), 65. Nat. Insts. Health fel. & res. assoc. biochem, Univ. Mich, 65-67; ASST. PROF. ORG. CHEM, DENISON UNIV, 67- AAAS; Am. Chem. Soc. Amino acid synthesis; mushroom chemistry. Address: 14 Sunset Hill, Granville, OH 43023.

DOYLE, ROBERT O, b. Fall River, Mass, June 19, 36; m. 64; c. 1. ASTROPHYSICS. Sc.B, Brown, 58; A.M, Harvard, 62, Ph.D.(astrophys), 68. Res. assoc. & instr, astrophys. inst, Brandeis, 64-66; consult. astron. ed, private practice, 66-68; sci. asst. to dir, HARVARD COL. OBSERV, 68-71, RES. FEL, 71- Secy, NASA Astron. Missions Bd, 68-70. AAAS; Am. Astron. Soc. Quantum calculations of continuous molecular spectra and applications to astrophysics; astronomy education materials. Address: Harvard College Observatory, 60 Garden St, Cambridge, MA 02138.

DOYLE, ROGER WHITNEY, b. Halifax, N.S, Mar. 7, 41; m. 64. ECOLOGY, GENETICS. B.S. & Nat. Res. Coun. Can. fel, Dalhousie Univ, 62, M.S, 63; Sheffield fel, Yale, 65, Cullman fel, 66, Ph.D.(biol), 67. Asst. prof. zool. & Nat. Insts. Health biol. sci. support grant, Duke Univ, 67-71; ASSOC. PROF. BIOL, DALHOUSIE UNIV, 71- Am. Soc. Limnol. & Oceanog; Ecol. Soc. Am; Soc. Study Evolution. Oxidation- reduction processes in aquatic environments; population ecology and ecological genetics of marine benthic animals. Address: Dept. of Biology, Dalhousie University, Halifax, N.S, Can.

DOYLE, T(HOMAS) C(ARLSON), b. Seattle, Wash, Oct. 1, 08. MATHEMATICS. B.S, Washington(Seattle), 31; Ph.D.(math), Princeton, 39. Asst. math, Washington(Seattle), 33-35; instr, Princeton, 35-39; Wyoming, 39-40; Stanford, 40-45; asst. prof, Dartmouth Col, 45-51, mathematician, Naval Res. Lab, 51-55; STAFF MEM, LOS ALAMOS SCI. LAB, 55- Am. Math. Soc. Differential invariant theory; optimization of a continuous n-parameter system with application to automatic lens design by a digital computer. Address: Los Alamos Scientific Lab, C-6, Los Alamos, NM 87544.

DOYLE, THOMAS D(ANIEL), b. N.Y.C, June 29, 38; m. 63; c. 4. ORGANIC & PHARMACEUTICAL CHEMISTRY. B.S, Fordham Univ, 60; Ph.D.(chem), George Wash. Univ, 71. Tech. asst. chem, Mass. Inst. Technol, 60-62; RES. CHEMIST, DIV. DRUG CHEM, FOOD & DRUG ADMIN, WASH, D.C, 63- AAAS; Am. Chem. Soc. Orbital symmetry control of photochemical reactions; theory and application of partition chromatography in pharmaceutical analysis; spectrochemical analysis; computer applications in chemistry. Address: 7704 Poplar Tree Lane, Falls Church, VA 22042.

DOYLE, WALTER M, b. Utica, N.Y, Sept. 26, 37; m. 62. ATOMIC PHYSICS. B.A, Syracuse, 59; Ph.D.(physics), California, 63. Physicist, Hughes Aircraft Co, 63-64; sr. scientist, Philco Corp, Ford Motor Co, 64-66, prin. scientist, Aeronutronic Div, 66-69; V.PRES. & DIR. RES. & DEVELOP, LASER PRECISION CORP, 69- Am. Phys. Soc. Solid state physics; optics; quantum electronics. Address: Laser Precision Corp, 5 W. Whitesboro St, Yorkville, NY 13495.

DOYLE, W(ILLIAM) CARTER, JR, b. Fairfield, Ala, May 9, 29; m. 55; c. 2. ORGANIC CHEMISTRY. B.S, New Mexico, 51, Ph.D.(chem), 55. Asst, New Mexico, 52-55; res. chemist, agr. chem, Naugatuck Chem. Div, U.S. Rubber Co, 56-57; Newport Industs. Div, Heyden-Newport Chem. Corp, 57-63, group leader, 63-64; res. chemist, Spencer Chem. Div, Gulf Oil Corp, 64-69, SR. RES. CHEMIST, AGR. CHEM. DIV, GULF RES. & DEVELOP. CO, 69- Am. Chem. Soc. Organic synthesis; herbicides; fungicides; insecticides; heterocyclic chemistry. Address: Agricultural Chemicals Division, Gulf Research & Development Co, 9009 W. 67th St, Merriam, KS 66202.

DOYLE, WILLIAM CLETUS, S.J, b. St. Louis, Mo, Apr. 27, 02. MATHEMATICS. A.B, St. Louis, 26, A.M, 27, Ph.D.(math), 38. Instr. MATH, CREIGHTON, 27-30; asst. prof, ROCKHURST COL, 38-42, assoc. prof, 42-51, prof, 51-68, EMER. PROF, 68- Am. Math. Soc; Math. Asn. Am. Generalization of Lambert's series; infinite series; vectorial geometry. Address: Dept. of Mathematics, Rockhurst College, Kansas City, MO 64110.

DOYLE, W(ILLIAM) D(AVID), b. Boston, Mass, June 5, 35; m. 58; c. 3. SOLID STATE PHYSICS. B.S, Boston Col, 57, M.S, 59; Ph.D.(physics), Temple, 64. Sr. physicist, magnetics, Franklin Inst. Res. & Develop, 59-64; proj. leader, UNIVAC DIV, SPERRY RAND CORP, 64-67, mgr. physics sect, 67-70, SR. STAFF SCIENTIST, 71- Mem, adv. comt. magnetism, Am. Inst. Physics, 64-; sr. res. fel, Univ. York, Eng, 70-71. Am. Phys. Soc. Magnetic properties of thin films and fine particles; magnetization processes; domain theory. Address: UNIVAC Division, Sperry Rand Corp, Blue Bell, PA 19422.

DOYLE, W(ILLIAM) L(EWIS), b. Brooklyn, N.Y, May 19, 10; m. 37; c. 1. CELL BIOLOGY. A.M, Hopkins, 32, Ph.D.(zool), 34. Bruce fel, Hopkins, 34-35; Rockefeller fel, Cambridge, 35-36, Carlsberg Lab, Copenhagen, 36-37; asst. prof. biol, Bryn Mawr Col, 37-42; res. assoc. & asst. prof. pharmacol, UNIV. CHICAGO, 42-44, assoc. prof. pharmacol, 44-45, ANAT, 45-50, PROF, 50-, dir. toxicity lab, 45-56, assoc. dean div. biol. sci, 58-61, coord. basic med. sci. curriculum, 69-71. Dir, Mt. Desert Island Biol. Lab, 64-67, v.pres, 67-68, pres, 70- Consult, Chem. Corps, U.S. Army, 46-59; reserve officer & sci. attaché, U.S. For. Serv, Stockholm, 51-52. With Off. Sci. Res. & Develop, 42-46. AAAS; Am. Asn. Anat; Histochem. Soc.(pres, 61-62); Soc. Develop. Biol; Am. Physiol. Soc; Am. Soc. Zool; Am. Soc. Cell Biol; Electron Micros. Soc. Am. Enzyme histochemistry; cellular fine structure. Address: Dept. of Anatomy, University of Chicago, Chicago, IL 60637.

DOYLE, W(ILLIAM) P(ATRICK), b. Seattle, Wash, Feb. 15, 32; m. 57; c. 4. CHEMISTRY, BIOCHEMISTRY. B.S, Seattle Univ, 55; Ph.D.(chem), Ore. State Univ, 60. Chemist, TEXACO, INC, 59-60, sr. chemist, 60-63, res. chemist, 63-64, group leader chem. prod. develop, 64-67, asst. supvr. res, 67-69, asst. to mgr. petrochem. dept, 69-71, ASST. TO SR. V.PRES, 71- Chemical product development and chemical processing; petroleum refining processing. Address: 135 E. 42nd St, New York, NY 10017.

DOYLE, WILLIAM T, b. Coalinga, Calif, June 1, 29; m. 53; c. 4. CRYPTOGAMIC BOTANY. B.A, Univ. Calif, Berkeley, 57, Nat. Insts. Health fel, 59, Ph.D.(bot), 60. Instr. BIOL, Northwest. Univ, 60-61, asst. prof, 61-65; COWELL COL, UNIV. CALIF, SANTA CRUZ, 65-67, ASSOC. PROF, 67- U.S.A.F, 49-52. AAAS; Soc. Develop. Biol; Am. Bryol. & Lichenological Soc; Bot. Soc. Am; Phycol. Soc. Am. Development, morphology and cytology of lower plants; developmental physiology of bryophytes and algae. Address: Dept. of Biological Sciences, University of California, Santa Cruz, CA 95060.

DOYLE, WILLIAM T(HOMAS), b. New Britain, Conn, Dec. 5, 25; m. 51; c. 2. PHYSICS. B.Sc, Brown, 51; M.Sc, Yale, 52, Nat. Sci. Foun. fel, 52-54, Ph.D.(physics), 55. Instr. PHYSICS, DARTMOUTH COL, 55-57, asst. prof, 57-60, assoc. prof, 60-64, PROF, 64- Nat. Sci. Found. fel, 58-59. U.S.N.R, 43-46. Am. Phys. Soc; Am. Asn. Physics Teachers. Experimental nuclear physics; nuclear reactions; solid state physics; optical and magnetic properties of defects in solids; magnetic resonance. Address: Dept. of Physics, Dartmouth College, Hanover, NH 03755.

DOYLE, WORTHIE L(EFLER), (JR), b. Phila, Pa, Feb. 12, 22. MATHEMATICS. B.A, Washington (Seattle), 43, Ph.D, Calif. Inst. Technol, 50. Res. engr, radar systs. anal, Hughes Aircraft Co, 51-58; Lincoln Lab, Mass. Inst. Technol, 58-60; Aeronutronic Div, Ford Motor Co, 60-61; Rand Corp, 61-64; COMMUN. CONSULT, 64- U.S.A.A.F, 44-46. Am. Math. Soc. Algebra; noise theory; digital simulations. Address: 1120 Bethel Ave, Port Orchard, WA 98366.

DOYNE, THOMAS H(ARRY), b. Pottsville, Pa, Sept. 21, 27; m. 55; c. 1. BIOCHEMISTRY. B.S, Pa. State, 50, M.S, 53, Ph.D.(biochem), 57; Fulbright fel, Osaka Univ, 53-54. Asst. x-ray crystallog. & chem, Pa. State Univ, 50-57; asst. prof. CHEM, VILLANOVA UNIV, 57-60, assoc. prof, 60-65, PROF, 65-, CHMN. DEPT, 70- U.S.A, 45-47. Am. Chem. Soc; Am. Crystallog. Asn; Brit. Chem. Soc. Determination of the absolute configuration of molecules by means of x-ray analysis; structure of divalent cation salts of amino acids and peptides. Address: Dept. of Chemistry, Villanova University, Villanova, PA 19085.

DOZIER, JAMES BUCHANAN, JR, b. Montgomery, Ala, May 14, 20; m. 41; c. 2. PHYSICS, MATHEMATICS. B.S, Auburn, 50, M.S, 51; Ph.D.(physics), Alabama, 61. Res. engr. PHYSICS, N.Am. Aviation, Inc, 51-52; asst. prof, Southern Mississippi, 52-53; instr, Alabama, 53-60, asst. prof, 60-61; SPACE SCIENTIST, MARSHALL SPACE FLIGHT CTR, NASA, 61- Mem. astron. sub-comt, Space Sci. Steering Comt, 61-64; assoc. prof, Univ. Ala, Huntsville, 61- U.S.A, 1st Lt. Am. Astron. Soc. Radio astronomy; electromagnetic propagation; atmospheric physics; celestial mechanics; meteoroid physics. Address: Marshall Space Flight Center, NASA, Huntsville, AL 35812.

DOZIER, LEONARD C(AMPBELL), JR, b. Norfolk, Va, May 22, 21; m. 44; c. 3. ELECTROMECHANICAL ENGINEERING. B.S, Tufts, 42. Res. engr, servomechanisms lab, Mass. Inst. Tech, 42-46; engr, Martin-Hubbard Corp, 47-48; tech. specialist guid. & control, N.Am. Aviation, Inc, 48-61, asst. to gen. mgr. navig. systs, Autonetics Div, 61-67, mgr. qual. & reliability, N.AM. ROCKWELL CORP, 67-69, MGR. ADVAN. TECHNOL, AUTOMOTIVE TECH. CTR, 69- Naval Ord. develop. award, 45. Civilian with U.S.A.A.F; U.S.N, 44. Servomechanisms; automatic computers; automatic control of aircraft; inertial navigation; instrumentation; automation. Address: Automotive Technical Center, North American Rockwell Corp, 2445 W. Maple Rd, Troy, MI 48084.

DOZOIS, K. PIERRE, b. Helena, Mont, Sept. 20, 12; m. 32; c. 2. MICROBIOLOGY, PUBLIC HEALTH. B.S, Mont. State Col, 27; fel. & M.S, Pa. State, 30; fel. & Ph.D.(med. bact), Maryland, 37. Independent res. microbiol. raw foods, 40-62; ASSOC. PROF. MICROBIOL. & PUB. HEALTH, CALIF. STATE COL, LOS ANGELES, 62- Res. consult, Canteen Co. Am, 63-; consult, Calif. State Dept. Health. AAAS; Am. Pub. Health Asn; Nat. Asn. Sanit. Microbial flora of raw and prepared foods; microbial standardization of sanitizing agents and disinfectants; food plant sanitation. Address: Dept. of Public Health, California State College at Los Angeles, 5151 State College Dr, Los Angeles, CA 90032.

DOZSA, LESLIE, b. Budapest, Hungary, May 25, 24; m; c. 2. VETERINARY MEDICINE. D.V.M, Univ. Budapest, Hungary, 46. Asst. prof. obstet. sterility, clinic. obstet, Vet. Col, Hungary, 47-51; field veterinarian sterility, Artificial Insemination Ctr, 51-56; assoc. prof. ANIMAL HUSB. & PATH, W.VA. UNIV, 57-71, PROF, 71- Sterility of cattle, particularly histopathology. Address: Dept. of Animal Industry & Veterinary Science, West Virginia University, Morgantown, WV 26506.

DRACH, JOHN CHARLES, b. Cincinnati, Ohio, Sept. 25, 39; m. 64; c. 2. BIOCHEMICAL PHARMACOLOGY. B.S, Univ. Cincinnati, 61, M.S, 63, Ph.D.(biochem), 66. Assoc. res. biochemist, Parke, Davis & Co, 66-68, res. biochemist, 69-70; ASST. PROF. DENT. & MEM. INTERDEPT. GRAD. PROG. MED. CHEM, UNIV. MICH, 70- AAAS; Am. Chem. Soc. Function and metabolism of nucleic acids; metabolism and mechanism of action of Antineoplastic and antiviral drugs. Address: Dept. of Oral Biology, School of Dentistry, University of Michigan, Ann Arbor, MI 48104.

DRACHMAN, DANIEL BRUCE, b. New York, N.Y, July 18, 32; m. 60; c. 3. NEUROLOGY, EMBRYOLOGY. A.B, Columbia, 52; M.D, N.Y. Univ, 56. Intern med, Beth Israel Hosp, Boston, Mass, 56-57; asst. res, Harvard neurol. unit, 57-58; res. neurol, Boston City Hosp, 58-59, neuropath, 59-60; clin. assoc. neurol, Nat. Insts. Health, 60-62, res. assoc. neuroembryol, 62-63; asst. prof. NEUROL, Tufts-New Eng. Med. Center, 63-69; ASSOC. PROF, SCH. MED, JOHNS HOPKINS UNIV, 69- Teaching fel, Harvard, 57-60; clin. instr, Georgetown Univ, 61-63. U.S.P.H.S, 60-63, Surg. AAAS; Am. Acad. Neurol; Am. Med. Asn; N.Y. Acad. Sci; Royal Soc. Med. Neuroembryology; congenital neuromuscular defects; diseases of muscle; development and trophic relationship of nerve & muscle; histopathology; physiology. Address: Dept. of Neurology, Johns Hopkins School of Medicine, Baltimore, MD 21205.

DRACHMAN, DAVID A, b. New York, N.Y, July 18, 32; m. 59; c. 3. NEUROLOGY, PHYSIOLOGICAL PSYCHOLOGY. A.B, Columbia Col, 52; M.D, N.Y. Univ, 56. Intern med, hosp, Duke, 56-57; res. neurol. & teaching fel. neurol. & neuropath, Harvard Med. Sch, 57-60; instr, sch. med, Georgetown, 61-63; asst. prof. NEUROL, MED. SCH, NORTHWEST. UNIV, 63-67, assoc. prof, 67-71, PROF, 71- Clin. assoc. neurol, Nat. Inst. Neurol. Diseases & Blindness, 60-63; consult, Vet. Admin. Hosp, Hines, Ill, 63-70; vis. scientist, med. sch, Georgetown, 66-; lectr, Food & Drug Admin, 68- U.S.P.H.S, 60-63, Surg. AAAS; fel. Am. Acad. Neurol; Am. Neurol. Asn; N.Y. Acad. Sci. Neurology of memory; neuroophthalmology; human spatial orientation. Address: Dept. of Neurology, Northwestern University Medical School, Chicago, IL 60611.

DRACHMAN, RICHARD J(ONAS), b. New York, N.Y, June 2, 30; m. 64; c. 2. THEORETICAL PHYSICS. A.B, Columbia Col, 51; Nat. Sci. Found. fel, Columbia, 53-56, A.M, 54, Ph.D.(physics), 58. Asst. physics, Columbia, 51-53; physicist, Naval Res. Lab, 56-58, Nat. Res. Coun. res. assoc, 58-59, physicist, 59-63; asst. prof. physics, Brandeis Univ, 59-63; MEM. STAFF, LAB. SPACE PHYSICS, GODDARD SPACE FLIGHT CTR, NASA, 63- Consult, United Aircraft Res. Labs, 61-62; mem. faculty, U.S. Dept. Agr. Grad. Sch, 66- Am. Phys. Soc. Quantum theory; positron systems; atomic scattering. Address: Lab. for Space Physics, Code 641, Goddard Space Flight Center, Greenbelt, MD 20771.

DRACUP, JOHN ALBERT, b. Seattle, Wash, July 14, 34; m. 56; c. 4. CIVIL ENGINEERING, SYSTEMS ANALYSIS. B.S, Washington (Seattle), 56; M.S, Mass. Inst. Tech, 60; Ph.D.(civil eng), California, Berkeley, 66. Engr, Shell Oil Co, Tex, 56-57; Boeing Aircraft Co, Wash, 58-59; res. asst. eng, Mass. Inst. Tech, 59-60; engr, Hill & Ingman, Wash, summer 60; asst. prof. eng, Oregon State, 60-62; teaching fel, California, Berkeley, 62-65; ASSOC. PROF. ENG. SYSTS, UNIV. CALIF, LOS ANGELES, 65- Summer grants, Nat. Sci. Found, 61, 63 & Ford Found, 62; Univ. California & U.S. Govt. grants, 66- Consult, U.S. Govt. Water Resources Coun, 66-67; Lockheed Aircraft Int, Inc, Calif, 67; Rocketdyne, Inc, 67-; TRW Systs, Inc, 67-; Environ. Dynamics, Inc, 67- Mem. U.S. del, Int. Conf. Water for Peace, 67. C.Eng, U.S.A, 57-58, Res, 59-65, Capt. Am. Soc. Civil Eng; Am. Water Resources Asn; Am. Geophys. Union. Water resources. Address: School of Engineering & Applied Sciences, 7620 Boelter Hall, University of California, Los Angeles, CA 90024.

DRACY, ARTHUR E, b. Virgil, S.Dak, May 12, 17; m. 43; c. 1. DAIRY HUSBANDRY. B.S, Minnesota, 43, M.S, 46, Ph.D, 49. Herdsman, Minnesota, 45, asst. dairy husb, 46-48; PROF, S.DAK. STATE UNIV, 48-67, ANIMAL HUSB, 67- UN Spec. Fund, Costa Rica, 66-67. U.S.A, 43-44. Am. Dairy Sci. Asn. Ova transfer in cattle; bloat in ruminants; immunized milk. Address: Dept. of Animal Husbandry, South Dakota State University, Brookings, SD 57006.

DRAEGER, ARTHUR A(NDREW), b. Seguin, Tex, Mar. 23, 11; m. 37; c. 2. PHYSICAL CHEMISTRY, CHEMICAL ENGINEERING. B.S.Ch.E. & M.S.Ch.E, Texas, 32, Ph.D.(phys. chem), 35. Jr. engr, HUMBLE OIL & REF. CO, 35-37, sr. res. chemist, 37-38, new proj. engr, 38-42, sr. proj. engr, 42-45, asst. div. head, 45-47, head res. & develop, 47-50, tech. asst. to mgr. opers, 50-51, head tech. serv. div, 51-52, acting mgr. tech. & res. div, 53-54, head res. & develop, 54-58, mgr. gen. off, sales mkt. dept, 58-59, mgr. N.Tex. area mkt, 59-60, asst. mgr. N.Y. mkt. area, 60-61, MGR.

mkt. res, mkt. hq, 61-63, econ. & planning dept. hq, 64-66, CORP. PLANNING DEPT. HQ, 66- Am. Chem. Soc; Am. Inst. Chem. Eng. Chemicals; corporate planning; technological and economic applications. Address: 5406 Tilbury, Houston, TX 77027.

DRAEGER, SIDNEY S, b. Seguin, Tex, Feb. 14, 13; m. 42; c. 4. MATHEMATICS. B.A, Texas, 32, M.A, 35. PROF. MATH, PAN AM. COL, 46-, HEAD DEPT, 64-, dean sch. technol, 55-64. Sig.C, 42-46, Maj. Math. Asn. Am. Analysis; training of elementary teachers. Address: Dept. of Mathematics, Pan American College, Edinburg, TX 78539.

DRAEMEL, FREDERICK CLISE, b. Seattle, Wash, Sept. 21, 13; m. 44; c. 3. CHEMICAL ENGINEERING. B.S, Mass. Inst. Technol, 35, M.S, 36. Chem. engr, PHILLIPS PETROL. CO, 36-48, supvr. pilot plant develop, 48-53, supvr. develop, 53-61, supvr. technol, 61-67, ASST. CHIEF PROCESS ENGR, 67- Am. Inst. Chem. Eng. Development, pilot plant and process engineering on catalytic cracking; coking; reforming; desulphurization and hydrocracking. Address: Phillips Petroleum Co, Martinez, CA 94553.

DRAGO, RUSSELL S(TEPHEN), b. Turners Falls, Mass, Nov. 5, 28; m. 50; c. 3. INORGANIC CHEMISTRY. B.S, Univ. Mass, 50; Ph.D.(chem), Ohio State Univ, 54. Fel, Ohio State Univ, 54-55; instr. INORG. CHEM, UNIV. ILL, URBANA-CHAMPAIGN, 55-57, asst. prof, 57-62, assoc. prof, 62-65, PROF, 65- U.S.A.F, 51-52. Am. Chem. Soc.(award for res. inorg. chem, 69). Lewis acid-base interactions; physical inorganic chemistry; spectroscopy; transition metals; non-aqueous solvents; semiempirical molecular orbital calculations. Address: 3308 Lakeshore Dr, Champaign, IL 61820.

DRAGOUN, FRANK J, b. Omaha, Nebr, Sept. 21, 29; m. 54; c. 3. HYDROLOGY, CIVIL ENGINEERING. B.S, Nebraska, 53; M.S, Colorado State, 66. Civil engr, Soil Conserv. Serv, U.S. Dept. Agr, 53-55, hydraul. engr, Agr. Res. Serv, 55-62, res. hydraul. engr, 62-70; ASST. GEN. MGR, CENT. NEBR. PUB. POWER & IRRIG. DIST, 70- U.S.M.C, 47-51, Sgt. Am. Soc. Civil Eng; Nat. Soc. Prof. Eng; Soil Conserv. Soc. Am; Int. Asn. Sci. Hydrol; Am. Geophys. Union; Am. Water Resources Asn. Removal and transport of sediment from small agricultural watersheds; hydrologic systems of small agricultural watersheds. Address: Central Nebraska Public Power & Irrigation District, P.O. Box 356, Holdrege, NE 68949.

DRAGOVICH, ALEXANDER, b. Podgorica, Yugoslavia, Feb. 26, 23; U.S. citizen; m. 48; c. 1. MARINE ECOLOGY. B.S, Munich Tech, 47; M.S, Miss. State Col, 50; Hawaii, 50-51. Lab. instr. aquatic biol, Miss. State Col, 50; zool, Hawaii, 50-51; res. asst. diseases of pineapples, Calif. Packing Corp, 51; tuna ecol, Calif. Fish & Game Dept, 54-55; FISHERY RES. BIOLOGIST, BUR. COMMERCIAL FISHERIES, 55-65, TROP. ATLANTIC BIOL. LAB, 66- Occasional consult, Fla. Bd. Conserv. & Fla. univs. AAAS; Ecol. Soc. Am; Gulf & Caribbean Fisheries Inst. Ecology and taxonomy of marine phytoplankton and invertebrates; ecology of tunas. Address: Tropical Atlantic Biological Lab, 75 Virginia Beach Dr, Miami, FL 33149.

DRAGSDORF, R(USSELL) DEAN, b. Detroit, Mich, Nov. 21, 22; m. 48; c. 2. SOLID STATE PHYSICS. S.B, Mass. Inst. Technol, 44, fel, 45-48, Ph.D. (physics), 48. Asst. prof. PHYSICS, KANS. STATE UNIV, 48-51, assoc. prof, 51-56, PROF, 56-, assoc. dean & acting dean grad. sch, 65-66. Res. physicist, metals res. lab, Union Carbide Corp, 56-57; Lawrence Radiation Lab, 68. Am. Phys. Soc; Am. Crystallog. Asn; Fr. Soc. Mineral. & Crystallog. X-ray diffraction; small angle x-ray scattering; small particle properties; crystal imperfections. Address: Dept. of Physics, Cardwell Hall, Kansas State University, Manhattan, KS 66502.

DRAGSTEDT, LESTER R(EYNOLD), b. Anaconda, Mont, Oct. 2, 93; m. 22; c. 4. SURGERY, PHYSIOLOGY. B.S, Chicago, 15, M.S, 16; Ph.D.(physiol), 20, M.D, Rush, 21; hon. Dr, Guadalajara, 53; Lyon, France, 59; hon. D.Sc, Univ. Fla, 69. Assoc. physiol, Chicago, 15-16; instr. pharmacol, Iowa, 16-17, asst. prof. physiol, 17-19; Chicago, 19-23; prof. physiol. & pharmacol, Northwestern, 23-25; assoc. prof. SURG, Chicago, 25-30, prof. 30-53, Jones prof, 53-59, chmn. dept, 48-59; RES. PROF. COL. MED, UNIV. FLA, 59-, PROF. PHYSIOL, 66- Hon. prof, Guadalajara, 53. Gold medal, Miss. Valley Med. Soc, 59; Bigelow Medal, Boston Surg. Soc, 64; hon. fel, Royal Col. Physicians & Surgeons, Can, 64; hon. fel, Royal Col. Surgeons, Eng, 64; Royal Order of the North Star, Sweden, 67. Sanit.C, 18-19, Lt. Nat. Acad. Sci; fel. AAAS; Am. Surg. Asn.(distinguished serv. award & gold medal, 69); Soc. Clin. Surg; Am. Med. Asn.(silver medal, 45, gold medal, 53, distinguished serv. award, 63); Am. Physiol. Soc; Soc. Exp. Biol. & Med; Am. Gastroenterol. Asn.(Friedenwald Medal, 64); Am. Col. Physicians; Am. Col. Surg; hon. mem. Asn. Mex. Gastroenterol; hon. mem. Mex. Nat. Acad. Med. Physiology of the stomach, pancreas, parathyroid glands; pathogenesis of peptic ulcer, intestinal obstruction and parathyroid tetany; discovery of lipocaic; introduction of vagotomy in treatment of peptic ulcer. Address: Dept. of Surgery, University of Florida College of Medicine, Gainesville, FL 32601.

DRAGSTEDT, LESTER REYNOLD, II, b. Chicago, Ill, Oct. 20, 28; m. 58; c. 6. SURGERY. B.S.Med.Sc, Northwestern, 50, M.D, 53. Instr. surg, Chicago, 60-61; CHIEF GRADE SURGEON, U.S. VET. ADMIN, 61- Clin. assoc. prof, Iowa, 68- Med.C, U.S.A.F, 55-57, Capt. Am. Med. Asn; Am. Col. Surg; Soc. Surg. Alimentary Tract. Surgical research in gastrointestinal diseases. Address: 2601 Glennor Rd, Des Moines, IA 50310.

DRAGT, A(LEXANDER) J(AMES), b. Lafayette, Ind, Apr. 7, 36; m. 57; c. 3. PHYSICS. A.B, Calvin Col, 58; Ph.D.(physics), California, Berkeley, 64. Sr. scientist, Lockheed Missiles & Space Co, 61-62; staff scientist, Aerospace Corp, 63; mem. dept. PHYSICS, Inst. Adv. Study, 63-65; asst. prof, UNIV. MD, COLLEGE PARK, 65-68, ASSOC. PROF, 68- Am. Phys. Soc; Am. Geophys. Union. Theoretical elementary particle physics; space physics. Address: Dept. of Physics & Astronomy, University of Maryland, College Park, MD 20742.

DRAGT, GERRIT, b. Grand Rapids, Mich, Aug. 28, 08; m. 34; c. 3. ANALYTICAL CHEMISTRY. A.B, Calvin Col, 31; M.S, Purdue, 33, Ph.D.(anal. chem), 37. Asst. chem, Purdue, 31-37; res. chemist, E.I. du Pont de Nemours & Co, 37-50; in charge anal. lab, Gen. Elec. Chem. Prod. Lab, 50-71; CONSULT. ENVIRON. CONTROL, 71- With Atomic Energy Comn; Off. Sci. Res. & Develop, 44. Am. Chem. Soc; Electrochem. Soc. Instrumental methods of analysis; polarograph; ultraviolet and infrared spectroscopy; orthotolidine methods for the determination of chlorine in drinking water; analytical chemistry of phosphors. Address: 1337 Beach Ave, Lakewood, OH 44107.

DRAGUN, HENRY L, b. Philadelphia, Pa, Feb. 24, 32; m. 59. PHYSICAL & ORGANIC CHEMISTRY. A.B, Pennsylvania, 53; Ph.D.(phys. chem), Rutgers, 60. Res. phys. chemist, mech. res. lab, E.I. du Pont de Nemours & Co, Del, 59-62; sr. chemist, Elkton Div, Thiokol Chem. Corp, 62-65; PROF. CHEM, ANNE ARUNDEL COMMUNITY COL, 65-, CHMN. DIV. SCI, 69- AAAS; Am. Chem. Soc; Am. Ord. Asn. High energy propellant development; investigation of relationship between microstructure of polymeric materials and their macroscopic electrical and mechanical properties. Address: Division of Science, Anne Arundel Community College, Arnold, MD 21012.

DRAISIN, W(ILBURT) M(ILTON), b. N.Y.C, Nov. 19, 16; m. 42; c. 2. MINERALOGY, CRYSTALLOGRAPHY. A.B, Univ. Wis, 36; A.M, Harvard, 40. Asst. to curator mineral. mus, Harvard, 39-40, asst, x-ray lab, 40-41; inspector, U.S. Naval Gun Factory, 42; crystallographer, Majestic Radio & TV Corp, 42-44; res, Polaroid Corp, Mass, 45; res. physicist, Baird Assocs, 47-58; V.PRES. & GEN. MGR, CRYSTAL RES. INC, 58- AAAS; Mineral. Soc. Am; Am. Crystallog. Asn; Optical Soc. Am; Soc. Appl. Spectros. Piezoelectric oscillators; physico-chemical relations in minerals; mineral synthesis; narrow band optical filters; piezoelectric pressure gauges. Address: 10 Ashmont Dr, Saxonville, MA 01701.

DRAKE, ALVIN WILLIAM, b. Bayonne, N.J, Sept. 21, 35; m. 57. OPERATIONS RESEARCH. S.B. & S.M, Mass. Inst. Technol, 58, E.E, 61, Sc.D. (elec. eng), 62. Asst. prof. ELEC. ENG, MASS. INST. TECHNOL, 62-67, ASSOC. PROF, 67-, ASSOC. DIR. OPERS. RES. CTR, 66- Consult, strategic studies group, Raytheon Corp, summer 62; Ford fel, Mass. Inst. Technol, 64- Sig.C, 62-64, Res, 64-, Capt. Opers. Res. Soc. Am; Inst. Elec. & Electronics Eng. Statistical communication theory; probabilistic systems; public administration. Address: Dept. of Electrical Engineering, Massachusetts Institute of Technology, Cambridge, MA 02139.

DRAKE, ARTHUR E(DWIN), b. Elmwood Place, Ohio, Sept. 17, 18; m. 41; c. 3. ELECTROCHEMISTRY. A.B, Miami Univ, 40; M.S, West. Reserve Univ, 42, Ph.D.(electrochem), 43. Res. chemist, Hercules, Inc, 43-45, sales rep, 45-48, sales supvr, 48-55, sales mgr, 55-61, dir. develop, 61-66; PRES, DRACO, INC, GREENVILLE, 66- Electromotive force measurements on molten binary alloys. Address: 2 Swallow Hill Rd, Wilmington, DE 19807.

DRAKE, AVERY A(LA), JR, b. Kansas City, Mo, Jan. 17, 27; m. 63; c. 2. GEOLOGY. B.S, Mo. Sch. Mines, 50, M.S, 52. Asst, Mo. Sch. Mines, 50-52; GEOLOGIST, U.S. GEOL. SURV, 52- Geologist, Nat. Lead Co, 51. Mem, Nat. Sci. Found-U.S. Navy Exped, Bellingshausen Sea, Antarctica, 61. U.S.A, 45-46, C.Eng.Res, 46-, Maj. Geol. Soc. Am; Soc. Econ. Geol; Geochem. Soc. Structural geology of central Appalachians; Precambrian geology; Antarctic geology. Address: U.S. Geological Survey, Bldg. 10, Washington, DC 20242.

DRAKE, B(ILLY) BLANDIN), b. Warsaw, Mo, Dec. 18, 17; m. 41; c. 3. BIOCHEMISTRY. A.B, Cent. Methodist Col.(Mo), 39; M.S, Pittsburgh, 41. Buhl Jr. res. fel, 39-43, Ph.D.(biochem), 43. Sr. scientist, ROHM & HAAS CO, 43-68, head enzyme technol. serv. lab, 68-71, HEAD ENZYME LAB, 71- Am. Chem. Soc. Production and properties of enzymes; separation and oxidation of amino acids; microbial fermentations. Address: Enzyme Lab, Rohm and Haas Co, Bristol, PA 19007.

DRAKE, CHARLES H(ADLEY), b. Waterloo, Iowa, Feb. 8, 16; m. 42; c. 2. BACTERIOLOGY. B.A, Minnesota, 37, M.S, 39, Ph.D.(bact), 42. Teaching asst. BACT, Minnesota, 36-42, instr. med. bact, exten. div, 42; sch. lib. arts & sch. med, Kansas, 42-44; asst. prof, WASH. STATE UNIV, 44-48, assoc. prof, 48-53, PROF, 53- Agent, bur. biol. surv. & bur. plant indust, U.S. Dept. Agr, 36-42. Am. Soc. Microbiol; Am. Pub. Health Asn. Medical mycology and bacteriology; immunology; public health; pathogenicity and allergic properties of Nocardia asteroides; Pseudomonas deruginose; bacterial limnology. Address: Dept. of Bacteriology & Public Health, Washington State University, Pullman, WA 99163.

DRAKE, CHARLES L(UM), b. Ridgewood, N.J, July 13, 24; m. 50; c. 3. GEOPHYSICS. B.S.E, Princeton, 48; Ph.D.(geol), Columbia Univ, 58. Lectr. GEOL, Columbia Univ, 53-55, instr, 58-59, asst. prof, 59-62, assoc. prof, 62-67, acting asst. dir, Lamont Geol. Observ, 63-65; prof. & chmn. dept, 67-69; PROF, DARTMOUTH COL, 69- Nat. Sci. Found. sr. fel, Cambridge, 65-66; Condon lectr, Univ. Ore, 69; pres, inter-union comt. on geodynamics, Int. Coun. Sci. Unions, 70-; chmn. comt. on geodynamics, Nat. Acad. Sci, 70-; comt. adv. to Envir. Sci. Serv. Admin, 70-, mem. Ocean Affairs Bd. & Geophys. Res. Bd; exec. bd, Law of Sea Inst. U.S.A, 43-46. AAAS; Am. Asn. Petrol. Geol; Geol. Soc. Am; Marine Tech. Soc; Soc. Explor. Geophys; Am. Geophys. Union; Royal Astron. Soc; Seismol. Soc. Am. Marine geology and geophysics; tectonics; structural geology; seismology. Address: R.D. 1, East Thetford, VT 05043.

DRAKE, CHARLES R(OY), b. Cromwell, Ky, Apr. 27, 18; m. 49; c. 2. PLANT PATHOLOGY. B.S, West. Ky. State Col, 52; Ph.D.(plant path), Wisconsin, 56. Asst, Wisconsin, 52-56; plant pathologist, crops res. div, Agr. Res. Serv, U.S. Dept. Agr, Va. Agr. Exp. Sta, 56-62, ASSOC. PROF. PLANT PATH, VA. POLYTECH. INST. & STATE UNIV, 62- U.S.A, 42-46, 50-51. Am. Phytopath. Soc; Am. Inst. Biol. Sci. Diseases of fruit, with special interest in apple rots, fire blight and peach brown rot; plant pathological histochemistry. Address: Dept. of Plant Pathology & Physiology, Virginia Polytechnic Institute & State University, College of Agriculture, Blacksburg, VA 24061.

DRAKE, CHARLES W(HITNEY), b. South Portland, Maine, Mar. 8, 26; m. 52; c. 3. PHYSICS. B.S, Maine, 50; M.A, Wesleyan, 52; Socony-Vacuum fel, Yale, 56-57, Ph.D, 58. Intermediate scientist, Westinghouse Elec. Corp,

52-53; instr. PHYSICS, Yale, 57-60, asst. prof, 60-66; ASSOC. PROF, ORE. STATE UNIV, 66- U.S.N, 44-46. Am. Phys. Soc. Atomic and molecular beams; polarized particles for nuclear reactions; beam foil spectroscopy. Address: Dept. of Physics, Oregon State University, Corvallis, OR 97331.

DRAKE, EDGAR N(ATHANIEL), II, b. Springfield, Mo, May 18, 37; m. 59; c. 3. PHYSICAL & ANALYTICAL CHEMISTRY. B.S, Houston, 60; M.S, Colorado, 62; Ph.D.(chem), Texas A&M, 69. Instr. CHEM, Texas A&I, 62-63; asst. prof, Howard Payne Col, 63-65; ASSOC. PROF, ANGELO STATE UNIV, 65- Am. Chem. Soc. Chemistry of coordination compounds; stability of complexes; mechanisms of complex ion reactions. Address: Dept. of Chemistry, Angelo State University, San Angelo, TX 76901.

DRAKE, E(DWARD) LAWSON, b. Charlottetown, P.E.I, Apr. 9, 30; m. 56; c. 2. INVERTEBRATE PATHOLOGY, ENTOMOLOGY. B.Sc, McGill Univ, 50; M.S, Cornell Univ, 59; Ph.D.(biol), Dalhousie Univ, 69. Entomologist, Govt. of Nyasaland, 52-56; experimentalist, Cornell Univ, 56-57; lectr. BIOL, Prince of Wales Col, 59-66, asst. prof, 66-69, ASSOC. PROF, UNIV. PRINCE EDWARD ISLAND, 69- Virus diseases of insects; insect fine structure; insect taxonomy. Address: Dept. of Biology, University of Prince Edward Island, Charlottetown, P.E.I, Can.

DRAKE, ELISABETH M(ERTZ), b. N.Y.C, Dec. 20, 36; m. 57. CRYOGENICS, CHEMICAL ENGINEERING. S.B, Mass. Inst. Technol, 58, Sc.D.(chem. eng), 66. Engr, ARTHUR D. LITTLE, INC, 58-64, SR. ENGR, 66- Vis. lectr, dept. chem. eng, Univ. Calif, Berkeley, spring 71. AAAS; Am. Inst. Chem. Eng; Am. Chem. Soc. Liquefied natural gas technology; design and development of special cryogenic equipment; contributor to design and production of lunar heat flow experiment for Apollo missions. Address: Engineering Sciences Section, Arthur D. Little, Inc, 20 Acorn Park, Cambridge, MA 02140.

DRAKE, F(RANK) D(ONALD), b. Chicago, Ill, May 28, 30; m. 53; c. 3. ASTRONOMY. B.E.P, Cornell, 52; M.A, Harvard, 56, Nat. Sci. Found. fel, 55-56, Rice fel, Gen. Elec. Co, 56-57, Ph.D.(astron), 58. Dir, astron. res. group, Ewen Knight Corp, 57-58; asst. astronomer, Nat. Radio Astron. Observ, W.Va, 58-59, assoc. astronomer, 59-63; chief, lunar & planetary sci. sect, Jet Propulsion Lab, Calif, 63-64; assoc. prof. astron, Cornell Univ, 64-66; dir, Arecibo Ionospheric Observ, P.R, 66-68; PROF. ASTRON. & ASSOC. DIR. CTR. RADIOPHYSICS & SPACE RES, CORNELL UNIV, 68-, CHMN. DEPT, 69- Mem, Int. Astron. Union; Int. Sci. Radio Union; astron. facilities panel of comt. on sci. & pub. policy, Nat. Acad. Sci. U.S.N, 52-55. Am. Astron. Soc; Inst. Elec. & Electronics Eng. Radio astronomy, particularly of solar system; 21 centimeter line research; radio telescope development. Address: Center of Radiophysics & Space Research, Space Science Bldg, Cornell University, Ithaca, NY 14850.

DRAKE, GEORGE M(ARSHALL), JR, b. Goodlettsville, Tenn, July 25, 32; m. 58; c. 4. CHEMICAL ENGINEERING. B.S, Tennessee, 55, M.S, 57, Phillips Petrol. fel, 57-59, Du Pont fel, 59-60, Ph.D.(chem. eng), 61. RES. ENGR, SPRUANCE FILM RES. & DEVELOP. LAB; E.I. DU PONT DE NEMOURS & CO, INC, 61- U.S.N, 57. AAAS; Am. Chem. Soc; Am. Inst. Chem. Eng; Am. Soc. Eng. Educ. Plastic films; film coatings; laminate structures; packaging films. Address: 5716 Boynton Pl, Richmond, VA 23225.

DRAKE, G(EORGE) WILSON, b. Beattie, Kans, Jan. 13, 08; m. 35; c. 2. CHEMISTRY. B.S, Texas Tech. Col, 30, A.M, 32; Ph.D.(physical chem), Texas, 36. Instr. CHEM, Texas Tech. Col, 30-33; Texas, 33-36; prof, UNIV. HOUSTON, 36-70, EMER. PROF, 70- Am. Chem. Soc. Preparation and physical properties of gallium; parachor of some hydrazine derivatives; specific heat of gaseous hydrogen cyanide and hydrogen sulfide. Address: 5626 Newport, Houston, TX 77023.

DRAKE, GORDON WILLIAM FREDERIC, b. Regina, Sask, Aug. 20, 43; m. 66; c. 1. ATOMIC PHYSICS, ASTROPHYSICS. B.Sc. & Nat. Res. Coun. Can. bursary, McGill Univ, 64; M.Sc, Univ. West. Ont, 65; Nat. Res. Coun. Can. stud, York Univ.(Ont), 65-67, Ph.D.(physics), 67. Nat. Acad. Sci. res. fel. PHYSICS, Smithsonian Astrophys. Observ, Mass, 67-69; ASST. PROF, UNIV. WINDSOR, 69- Am. Phys. Soc. Theory of atomic processes, including relativistic effects, radiative transitions, electron-atom and atom-atom scattering; precision calculations for two-electron systems and applications to astrophysical problems. Address: Dept. of Physics, University of Windsor, Windsor, Ont, Can.

DRAKE, HUBERT M(UNSON), b. Brooklyn, N.Y, Nov. 25, 21; m. 43; c. 3. AERODYNAMICS. B.S.E, Univ. Mich, 43. Jr. aeronaut. engr, Langley Lab, NASA, 43-44, aeronaut. engr, 44-47, aeronaut. res. scientist, Muroc Flight Test Unit, 47-52, chief stability & control br, high speed flight sta, 52-56, asst. chief res. div, 56-61, chief progs. off, flight res. ctr, 61-62, advan. planning off, 62-65, asst. dir. aeronaut. missions, mission anal. div, Off. Advan. Res. & Technol, 65-70, CHIEF AERONAUT. DIV, AMES RES. CTR, 70- Mem. res. adv. comt. on stability & control, NASA, 57-58, ad hoc comt. on human factors & training, spec. comt. on space technol, 58, res. adv. comt. on control guid. & navig, 59-60, res. adv. comt. on missile & space vehicle aerodyn. & X-15 Flight Test Steering Comt, 60-65, ad hoc comt. on manned lunar landing by rendezvous tech, 61, res. & technol. adv. comt. on aeronaut, 68-70. X-15 Group Achievement Award, NASA, 64, Apollo Group Achievement Award, 69. Am. Inst. Aeronaut. & Astronaut. Stability and control of unusual aircraft; transonic and supersonic handling qualities; development of flight research procedures; operational problems of manned spacecraft; mission analysis of aircraft in transportation systems. Address: 5529 Castle Glen Ave, San Jose, CA 95129.

DRAKE, JOHN E(DWARD), b. Simla, India, Apr. 20, 36; m. 60; c. 2. INORGANIC CHEMISTRY, SPECTROSCOPY. B.Sc, Univ. Southampton, 57, Ph.D.(chem), 60. Chemist, Lawrence Radiation Lab, Univ. Calif, Berkeley, 60-62; asst. lectr. CHEM, Univ. Hull, 62-63; lectr, Univ. Southampton, 63-69; assoc. prof, UNIV. WINDSOR, 69-71, PROF, 71- The Chem. Soc; Chem. Inst. Can. Spectroscopic and synthetic studies of main group organometalloids and hydrides; application of electrical discharges to preparative problems. Address: Dept. of Chemistry, University of Windsor, Windsor, Ont, Can.

DRAKE, JOHN W, b. Detroit, Mich, Feb. 10, 32; m. 60; c. 2. GENETICS, VIROLOGY. B.S, Yale, 54; Ph.D.(biol), Calif. Inst. Technol, 58. Res. assoc. bact, UNIV. ILL, URBANA-CHAMPAIGN, 58-59, instr. MICROBIOL, 59, asst. prof, 59-64, assoc. prof, 64-69, PROF, 69- Fulbright fel, Weizmann Inst, 57-58; Guggenheim fel, 64-65; U.S. Pub. Health Serv. spec. res. fel, 71-72; chmn. biol. sect, grad. fel. panel, Nat. Sci. Found-Nat. Res. Coun, 71- Genetics Soc. Am; Am. Soc. Microbiol; Environ. Mutagen Soc. (ed. newsletter). Replication and genetics of bacterial viruses; molecular mechanisms of mutation. Address: Dept. of Microbiology, University of Illinois, Urbana, IL 61801.

DRAKE, KENNETH, b. N.Y.C, July 19, 25; m. 55. POLYMER CHEMISTRY. B.S, Columbia, 50; Ph.D, Mass. Inst. Tech, 55. CHEMIST, Texas Co, 55-56; S.D. Warren Co, 56-60; UNION CARBIDE CORP, 62. U.S.A.A.F, 43-46. Address: Union Carbide Co, Box 8361 Technical Center, Bldg. 701, South Charleston, WV 25303.

DRAKE, ROBERT L, b. Bradford, Pa, June 24, 26; m. 50; c. 4. ELECTRICAL ENGINEERING. B.S.E.E, Tulane, 50, M.S.E.E, 57; California, Los Angeles, 59-61; Ph.D.(elec. eng), Miss. State, 65. Plant engr, Buckeye Cellulose Corp. Div, Procter & Gamble Co, 50-54; instr. elec. eng, Tulane, 54-57, asst. prof, 57-59; mem. tech. staff, Space Tech. Labs, Inc. Div, Thompson-Ramo-Wooldridge, Inc, 59-61, proj. engr, 61-62; asst. prof. ELEC. ENG, TULANE UNIV, 62-66, assoc. prof, 66-70, PROF, 70- Nat. Sci. Found. sci. faculty fel, 63-64; partner, Systs. Technol. Inst. Control, information and adaptive control systems; engineering applications of information theory. Address: Dept. of Electrical Engineering, Tulane University, New Orleans, LA 70118.

DRAKE, ROBERT M, JR, b. Eagle Cliff, Ga, Dec. 13, 20; m. 44; c. 2. MECHANICAL ENGINEERING. B.S.M.E, Kentucky, 42; M.S.M.E, California, Berkeley, 46, Ph.D.(eng), 50. From instr. to assoc. prof. heat transfer, fluid mech. & thermodyn, California, Berkeley, 47-55; prof. mech. eng. & chmn. dept, Princeton, 56-63; prof, Univ. Ky, 64-71, dean col. eng, 66-71, chmn. dept. mech. eng, 66-67; V.PRES. RES. & DEVELOP, COMBUSTION ENG, INC, 71- Engine design specialist & supvr. turbine air design, Gen. Elec. Co, 54-56, consult, 56-57; McGraw-Hill Book Co, 58-68; Rand Corp, 60-63; Air Preheater Co, 62; consult. & dir, Intertech Corp, 62; consult, Nat. Sci. Found, 62-63; Arthur D. Little, Inc, 63, sr. staff consult, 63-64. U.S.A.A.F, 42-47, Capt. Am. Soc. Mech. Eng; Am. Soc. Eng. Educ; assoc. fel, Am. Inst. Aeronaut. & Astronaut; Nat. Soc. Prof. Eng. Heat transfer; thermodynamics; fluid mechanics. Address: Combustion Engineering, Inc, 1000 Prospect Hill Rd, Windsor, CT 06095.

DRAKE, ROGER FIELD, b. St. Paul, Minn, Mar. 1, 30; m. 50, 69; c. 3. ELECTROCHEMISTRY, BIOMEDICAL ENGINEERING. B.S, Wisconsin, 54. Proj. engr, Ray-O-Vac Div, Elec. Storage Battery Co, 55-61, group leader battery res. & develop, 61-64; sr. res. chemist, Boston Lab, Monsanto Res. Corp, Everett, Mass, 64-66, res. group leader fuel cell & electrochem. res, 66-69; task group leader electrochem. & biomed. res, biomed. res. labs, AM. HOSP. SUPPLY CORP, 69-70, DIR, CORP. TECHNOL. CTR, SANTA ANA, 70- AAAS; Am. Chem. Soc; Electrochem. Soc. Miniature battery systems; fuel cells; biological fuel cells; reactor kinetics and catalysis; gas adsorption. Address: 26716 La Sierra Dr, Mission Viejo, CA 92675.

DRAKE, RONALD LEWIS, b. Mehoopany, Pa, Mar. 25, 32; m. 67; c. 4. FLUID MECHANICS, APPLIED MATHEMATICS. B.S, Drexel Inst, 55; M.A, Pa. State, 59; Pennsylvania, 59-62; Nat. Sci. Found. fel, Colorado State, 65-67, Ph.D.(fluid mech), 67. Instr. civil eng, Pa. State Univ, 56-57; aeronaut. engr, Nat. Adv. Cmt. Aerospace, Ohio, 57-58; instr. math, Drexel Inst, 58-60, asst. prof, 60-65, 67-68; STAFF SCIENTIST, NAT. CTR. ATMOSPHERIC RES, 68- Hydraulics; stability theory; porous flow theory; potential flow; wind-water waves; integro-differential equations; mesoscale and Cumulus modeling of atmospheric phenomena. Address: National Center for Atmospheric Research, Boulder, CO 80302.

DRAKE, STEVENS S(TEWART), b. Seattle, Wash, Mar. 30, 17; m. 41; c. 1. ORGANIC CHEMISTRY. B.S, Northwestern, 39, M.S, 41; Ph.D.(org. chem), Illinois, 43. Instr. chem, Northwestern, 39-41, Illinois, 41-43; from chemist to asst. lab. dir, DOW CHEM. CO, 43-51, lab. dir, 53-56, dept. personnel adminstr, 56-58, lab. dir, 58-64, dept. patent coord, 64-69, SR. RES. CHEMIST, 69- Civilian with Nat. Defense Res. Cmt, 44. AAAS; Am. Chem. Soc. Product development; plastics copolymerization; asymmetric polymerization; synthetic rubber; pigmentation of plastics; personnel administration; patent coordination. Address: Dow Chemical Co, Midland, MI 48642.

DRALEY, JOSEPH EDWARD, b. Wash, D.C, Jan. 26, 19; m. 43; c. 2. CHEMISTRY. B.App.Chem, Catholic Univ, 39, Ph.D.(phys. chem), 47. Chemist & group leader, metall. lab, Chicago, 42-45; engr, Kellex Corp, 45-46; asst. proj. engr, Appl. Physics Lab, Md, 46-47; sr. chemist & sect. chief, Oak Ridge Nat. Lab, 47-48; SR. CHEMIST, ARGONNE NAT. LAB, 48- Whitney award, Nat. Asn. Corrosion Engrs, 61. Am. Chem. Soc; Electrochem. Soc; Sci. Res. Soc. Am; Am. Nuclear Soc; N.Y. Acad. Sci; Am. Inst. Min, Metall. & Petrol. Eng. Aqueous corrosion of light metals; aqueous complex ions; gas-metal reactions; colloidal hydrous oxide behavior; heat transfer from hot surface to air stream; liquid sodium-metal reactions; sodium technology. Address: Argonne National Lab, Argonne, IL 60439.

DRANCE, S. M, b. Bielsko, Poland, May 22, 25; Can. citizen; m. 52; c. 3. OPHTHALMOLOGY. M.B, Ch.B, Edinburgh, 48; dipl. ophthal, Royal Col. Surg, 53. Res. assoc. ophthal, Oxford, 55-57; assoc. prof. ophthal, Saskatchewan, & dir. glaucoma clin, 57-63; assoc. prof. OPHTHAL, UNIV. B.C, 63-68, PROF, 68-, DIR. GLAUCOMA SERV, 63- Mem. subcomt. ophthal, Can. Dept. Health & Welfare Res. Grants, 64; Med. Res. Coun. Can, 67-; ed, Can. J. Ophthal. Fel. Royal Col. Surg, 56. R.A.F, 49-51, Squadron Leader. Asn. Res. Vision & Ophthal; Can. Med. Asn; Can. Ophthal. Soc; Brit. Med. Asn; Ophthal. Soc. U.K. Behavior of visual function under conditions of raised intraocular pressure; pharmacology of glaucoma medication; natural history of glaucoma. Address: Dept. of Ophthalmology, University of British Columbia, Vancouver, B.C, Can.

DRANCHUK, PETER MICHAEL, b. Poland, Sept. 4, 28; Can. citizen. PETROLEUM ENGINEERING. B.Sc, Univ. Alta, 52, M.Sc, 59. Sessional instr. PETROL. ENG, UNIV. ALTA, 52-53, lectr, 53-59, from asst. prof. to ASSOC. PROF, 59- AAAS; Am. Inst. Mining, Metall. & Petrol. Eng; Can. Inst. Mining & Metall. Petroleum production and reservoir mechanics. Address: Dept. of Chemical & Petroleum Engineering, University of Alberta, Edmonton, Alta, Can.

DRANE, CHARLES JOSEPH, JR, b. Boston, Mass, Nov. 21, 27; m. 71. MATHEMATICAL PHYSICS. B.S, Boston Col, 50; S.M, Mass. Inst. Technol, 53, M.S, 66. Physicist radiation, Nat. Bur. Standards, 52; THEORET. RES. PHYSICIST, AIR FORCE CAMBRIDGE RES. LABS, 55- U.S.A, 53-55, Res, 55-61. Sci. Res. Soc. Am; Inst. Elec. & Electronics Eng; assoc. mem. Int. Sci. Radio Union. Electromagnetic theory; applied mathematics; communication theory; antenna theory; array theory; electromagnetic scattering Address: Microwave Physics Lab, Air Force Cambridge Research Labs, Laurence G. Hanscom Field, Bedford, MA 01731.

DRANE, JOHN WANZER, b. Forest, La, June 26, 33; m. 55; c. 3. STATISTICS, BIOMETRY. B.S, Northwest. State Col.(La), 55; M.S, Florida, 57; Ph.D.(biomet), Emory, 67. Nuclear engr, Newport News Shipbldg. & Dry Dock Co. Va, 56-61; assoc. prof. math, Randolph-Macon Col, 60-64; instr. & spec. fel. statist. & biomet, Emory, 63-65, ASSOC. PROF, 65-68; STATIST, SOUTH. METHODIST UNIV, 68-; BIOSTATIST. & CHMN. DIV. BIOMATH. & BIOSTATIST, UNIV. TEX. SOUTHWEST. MED. SCH, 70- U.S.A.F, 51-52. AAAS; Soc. Indust. & Appl. Math; Biomet. Soc; Inst. Math. Statist; Math. Asn. Am; Am. Pub. Health Asn. Theory and application of nonlinear regression methods in statistical inference; application of theory of automatic control systems of problems in biology. Address: Dept. of Statistics, Southern Methodist University, Dallas, TX 75222.

DRANOFF, JOSHUA S(IMON), b. Bridgeport, Conn, June 30, 32; m. 53; c. 3. CHEMICAL ENGINEERING. B.E, Yale, 54; Gen. Elec. Coffin fel, Princeton, M.S.E, 56, Nat. Sci. Found. fel, Ph.D.(chem. eng), 60. Asst. prof. CHEM. ENG, Yale, 57-58, Northwestern, 58-62; assoc. prof, Columbia, 62-63; NORTHWEST. UNIV, 63-67, PROF, 67-, CHMN. DEPT, 71- Am. Chem. Soc; Am. Inst. Chem. Eng. Chemical reactor analysis; ion exchange; adsorption on molecular sieves. Address: Dept. of Chemical Engineering, Northwestern University, Evanston, IL 60201.

DRAPALIK, DONALD J(OSEPH), b. Chicago, Ill, Dec. 10, 34. PLANT TAXONOMY. B.A, South. Ill. Univ, Carbondale, 59, M.A, 62; Nat. Sci. Found. fel, Univ. N.C, Chapel Hill, summer 63, William Chambers Coker fel, 64 & summer 68, univ. fel, summer 67, Ph.D.(bot), 70. ASST. PROF. BIOL, GA. SOUTH. COL, 68-, MEM. GRAD. FACULTY, 71-, faculty res. grant, 70-71. Partic, Nat. Sci. Found. summer inst. syst, Smithsonian Inst, 70. Int. Asn. Plant Taxon; Am. Soc. Plant Taxon; Bot. Soc. Am; Asn. Southeast. Biol; Wilderness Soc. Taxonomy, morphology and evolution of the North American milkweeds. Address: Dept. of Biology, Georgia Southern College, Statesboro, GA 30458.

DRAPANAS, THEODORE, b. Buffalo, N.Y, Feb. 20, 30; m. 54; c. 3. SURGERY. M.D, Buffalo, 52. Intern med, E.J, Meyer Mem. Hosp, Buffalo, N.Y, 52-53, res. SURG, 53-58; assoc, State Univ. N.Y. Buffalo, 58-60, Buswell res. fel, 59-63, asst. prof, 60-64; prof, sch. med, Pittsburgh & sr. staff mem, Presby-Univ. Hosp, 64-68; PROF. & CHMN. DEPT, SCH. MED, TULANE UNIV, 68- U.S. Pub. Health Serv. spec. res. fel. surg, 58-59. Attend. surg, E.J. Meyer Mem. Hosp, 58-64; consult, U.S. Vet. Admin. Hosp, Pittsburgh, 64- U.S. Jr. Chamber Commerce distinguished serv. award, 61. Dipl, Am. Bd. Surg, 59, Am. Bd. Thoracic Surg, 61. Med.C.Res, 52-62, Maj. Fel. Am. Col. Surg; Am. Surg. Asn; Soc. Clin. Surg; Soc. Univ. Surg; Am. Asn. Surg. of Trauma, Soc. Surg. Alimentary Tract. Surgery of liver and gastrointestinal tract. Address: Dept. of Surgery, Tulane University School of Medicine, 1430 Tulane Ave, New Orleans, LA 70112.

DRAPER, ARLEN D, b. Pima, Ariz, Dec. 6, 30; m. 55; c. 6. CROP BREEDING. B.S, Arizona State, 57; M.S, Arizona, 59; Ph.D.(crop breeding), Iowa State, 64. RES. GENETICIST, field lab. tung invests, U.S. DEPT. AGR, 64-65, FRUIT & NUT CROPS RES. BR, 65- U.S.A, 53-55, Sgt. Am. Soc. Hort. Sci; Crop Sci. Soc. Am. Study of optimum plot size and shape for safflower yield trials; recurrent selection for seed size in birdsfoot trefoil; strawberry breeding; blueberry breeding; cytogenetics. Address: Fruit & Nut Corps Research Branch, Plant Industry Station, Beltsville, MD 20705.

DRAPER, ARTHUR L(INCOLN), b. Philadelphia, Pa, Feb. 20, 23; m. 46; c. 3. PHYSICAL CHEMISTRY. B.A, Rice, 48, Procter & Gamble fel, 48-50, M.A, 49, Humble Oil & Ref. Co. fel, 50-51, Ph.D.(chem), 51. Res. chemist, Jersey Prod. Res. Co, Okla, 51-57; res. assoc. dept. chem, Rice, 58-59; asst. prof. CHEM, TEX. TECH UNIV, 59-61, ASSOC. PROF, 61- U.S.A.A.F, 43-46. Fel. AAAS; Geochem. Soc; Am. Geophys. Union; Am. Chem. Soc. Physical and colloid chemistry; kinetics; solid state; structure; surface chemistry; oxides and mixed oxides; adsorption; catalysis; cosmochemistry. Address: Dept. of Chemistry, Texas Tech University, Lubbock, TX 79409.

DRAPER, C(ARROLL) I(SAAC), b. Maroni, Utah, Sept. 27, 14; m. 39; c. 6. POULTRY NUTRITION. B.S, Utah State Univ, 39; fel, Iowa State Col, 39-41, Ph.D, 42. Asst. prof. poultry husb, State Col. Wash, 41-43; head poultry dept, Univ. Hawaii, 43-45; assoc. prof. poultry husb, UTAH STATE UNIV, 45-48, head poultry dept, 48-70, PROF. ANIMAL SCI, 70- Poultry Sci. Asn. Value of protein feeds in poultry diets. Address: Dept. of Animal Science, Utah State University, Logan, UT 84321.

DRAPER, C(HARLES) S(TARK), b. Windsor, Mo, Oct. 2, 01; m. 38; c. 4. AERONAUTICAL ENGINEERING. A.B, Stanford, 22; B.S, Mass. Inst. Tech, 26, M.S, 28, Sc.D.(physics), 38; hon. Dr, Eidgenossische Tech, Zurich, 67. Asst. AERONAUT. ENG, MASS. INST. TECHNOL, 29-30, res. assoc. 30-35; asst. prof, 35-38, assoc. prof, 38-39, prof, INSTRUMENT LAB, 39-66, INST. PROF, 66-, dir, 39-69, head dept. aeronaut. & astronaut, 51-66. Wright mem. lectr, Royal Aeronaut. Soc, London, 55; Wright Bros. lectr, 65. Consult. Reed award; medal merit & ord. develop. award, U.S. Navy, 46, distinguished serv. award, 56, Distinguished Pub. Serv. award, 61; exceptional civilian serv. award, U.S. Air Force, 51-60, Commander's award, 64; airpower award, Mass. wing, Air Force Asn, airpower trophy; Magellan medal, Am. Philos. Soc, 59; Procter prize, Sci. Res. Soc, 59; Potts medal, Franklin Inst, 60; award, Nat. Soc. Prof. Engr, 62; space flight award, Astron. Soc, 62; Presidential Nat. Medal Sci, 65; Bendix Award, 66. Civilian with Off. Sci. Res. & Develop; Nat. Defense Res. Comt; U.S.A; U.S.A.A.F; U.S.N; Nat. Adv. Comt. Aeronaut, 44. Nat. Acad. Sci; AAAS; fel. Am. Soc. Mech. Eng.(testimonial appreciation, 51, Holly Medal, 57); fel. Am. Inst. Aeronaut. & Astronaut.(Louis W. Hill Space Transportation Award, 62); Soc. Automotive Eng; Am. Soc. Eng. Educ; Am. Inst. Consult. Eng; fel. Inst. Elec. & Electronic Eng; Int. Acad. Astronaut.(pres, 64); Am. Ord. Asn. (Blandy Medal, 58); fel. Am. Phys. Soc; fel. Am. Acad. Arts & Sci; N.Y. Acad. Sci. Gyroscopic instrumentation; computing systems; control systems; measurement systems. Address: Dept. of Aeronautical Engineering, Instrumentation Lab, Massachusetts Institute of Technology, Cambridge, MA 02139.

DRAPER, EDGAR, b. St. Louis, Mo, Feb. 5, 26; m. 49; c. 3. PSYCHIATRY. A.B, Washington (St. Louis), 46, M.D, 53; Duke, 46-47; B.D, Northwestern, 49; grad, Inst. Psychoanal, Chicago, 66. Intern internal med, St. Louis City Hosp, 53-54; res. physician psychiat, Cincinnati Gen. Hosp, 54-55; staff psychiatrist, U.S. Pub. Health Serv. Hosp, Ft. Worth, Tex, 55-57; res. physician, Cincinnati Gen. Hosp, 57-59; instr. psychiat, Univ. Chicago, 59-60, asst. prof, 60-66, assoc. prof, 66-68; PROF. PSYCHIAT. & DIR. RESIDENCY EDUC. PSYCHIAT, MED. CTR, UNIV. MICH, ANN ARBOR, 68- Consult, Child & Family Serv. Agency, Ill, 60-62; Ment. Health Ctr, Bloomington, 62- U.S.P.H.S, 55-57, Sr. Asst. Surg. Soc. Sci. Study Relig; Acad. Relig. & Ment. Health; fel. Am. Psychiat. Asn. Clinical psychiatric study of the meaning of religious ideation. Address: 3020 Provincial Dr, Ann Arbor, MI 48108.

DRAPER, E(RNEST) LINN, JR, b. Houston, Tex, Feb. 6, 42; m. 62; c. 4. PHYSICS, NUCLEAR ENGINEERING. B.A, Rice, 64, B.S, 65; Nat. Sci. Found. trainee, Atomic Energy Cmn. fel. & Ph.D.(nuclear sci), Cornell, 70. ASST. PROF. MECH. ENG, UNIV. TEX, AUSTIN, 69-, DIR. NUCLEAR REACTOR LAB, 71-, assoc. dir, 70-71. Am. Nuclear Soc; Am. Phys. Soc; Am. Inst. Chem. Eng. Neutron and reactor physics. Address: Dept. of Mechanical Engineering, University of Texas at Austin, Austin, TX 78712.

DRAPER, H(AROLD) H(UGH), b. Manitoba, Can, Apr. 11, 24; nat; m. 47; c. 2. NUTRITIONAL BIOCHEMISTRY. B.S.A, Manitoba, 45; M.Sc, Alberta, 48; Ph.D.(animal nutrit), Illinois, 52. Lectr. animal nutrit, Manitoba, 45-46; Alberta, 48-49; asst, Illinois, 49-51; nutritionist, vet. res. dept, Merck & Co, Inc, 52-54; asst. prof. animal nutrit, UNIV. ILL, URBANA, 54-58, assoc. prof. NUTRIT. BIOCHEM, 58-65, PROF, 65- Orgn. European Economic Co-op. fel, Liverpool, 61. Can. Army, 45. AAAS; Soc. Exp. Biol. & Med; Am. Soc. Animal Sci; Am. Inst. Nutrit. Vitamin E function and metabolism; biochemical aspects of aging. Address: Dept. of Food Science, University of Illinois, Urbana, IL 61801.

DRAPER, JAMES E(DWARD), b. Kansas City, Mo, Sept. 14, 24; m. 48; c. 4. NUCLEAR PHYSICS. B.A, Williams Col, 44; Ph.D.(physics), Cornell, 52. Instr. & asst. PHYSICS, Williams Col, 46-47; asst, Cornell, 47-52, res. assoc, 52; assoc. physicist, Brookhaven Nat. Lab, 52-56; asst. prof, Yale, 56-59, assoc. prof, 59-62, sr. res. assoc, 62-63; PROF, UNIV. CALIF, DAVIS, 64-, chmn. dept, 66-71. Res. assoc, nuclear physics div, Atomic Energy Res. Estab, Harwell, Eng, 71. U.S.N.R, 44-46. Fel. Am. Phys. Soc. Nuclear physics, especially neutron physics experimental; neutron spectroscopy; photonuclear and particle reactions. Address: Dept. of Physics, University of California, Davis, CA 95616.

DRAPER, JOHN DANIEL, b. Hagerstown, Md, June 13, 19; m. 46; c. 4. ORGANIC CHEMISTRY. B.S, Franklin & Marshall Col, 41; Ph.D.(org. chem), Maryland, 48. Asst. gen. chem, Maryland, 41-43, res. chemist, Cmt. Med. Res. contract, 43-45, asst. inorg. quant. anal, univ, 45-46; sr. res. chemist, Phillips Petrol. Co, 47-49; res. chemist, J.T. Baker Chem. Co, 49-51; asst. prof. CHEM, BETHANY COL, 51-53, assoc. prof, 53-54, PROF. & HEAD DEPT, 54- Consult, Stoner-Midge Corp, Pa, 54-63. Am. Chem. Soc. Synthesis and analysis of antimalarials; synthetic lubricating oil additives; kinetics of organic reactions. Address: Dept. of Chemistry, Bethany College, Bethany, WV 26032.

DRAPER, LAURENCE R(ENE), b. New York, N.Y, Apr. 14, 30; m. 54; c. 2. IMMUNOLOGY, RADIATION BIOLOGY. A.B, Middlebury Col, 52; univ. fel, Chicago, 52-54, William H. Wilder, Jr. fel, 53-54, Ph.D.(microbiol), 56. Res. assoc. microbiol, Chicago, 56-57, asst. prof, 59-60; res. assoc. immunol, Argonne Nat. Lab, 57-59; res. biologist, physiol. lab, Nat. Cancer Inst, 60-68; ASSOC. PROF. MICROBIOL, UNIV. KANS, 68- Logal fel. microbiol, Univ. Chicago, 60. Am. Asn. Immunol; Radiation Res. Soc; Am. Soc. Microbiol. Radiation & cellular immunology. Address: Dept. of Microbiology, University of Kansas, Lawrence, KS 66044.

DRAPER, NORMAN R(ICHARD), b. Southampton, Eng, Mar. 20, 31. STATISTICS. B.A, Cambridge, 54, Fulbright travel scholar, U.S. Govt. & dipl, 55, Bell Tel. fel, 57, M.A, 58; Ph.D.(math. statist), North Carolina, 58. Statistician. plastics div, Imperial Chem. Indust, Eng, 58-60, mem. math. res. ctr, 60-61; asst. prof. STATIST, UNIV. WIS, MADISON, 61-62, assoc. prof, 62-66, PROF, 66- Summers, statist. asst. dyestuffs div, Imperial Chem. Indust, Eng, 55, Am. Cyanamid Co, N.Y, 56; res. asst, statist. tech. res. group, Princeton, 57; vis. prof, Imperial Col, London, falls 67 & 68; indust. consult. auth. & lectr. Inst. Math. Statist; Am. Statist. Asn; Biomet. Soc; Royal Statist. Soc; Am. Soc. Qual. Control. Experimental statistics; design and analysis of experiments; statistical theory; regression analysis; nonlinear estimation; response surface methodology. Address: Dept. of Statistics, University of Wisconsin, 1210 W. Dayton St, Madison, WI 53706.

DRAPER, ROY D(OUGLAS), b. Fresno, Calif, May 30, 33; m. 60; c. 2. BIOCHEMISTRY. B.S, Sacramento State Col, 55, B.A, 59; Nat. Insts. Health fel, California, Davis, 59-64, Ph.D.(biochem), 64. Clin. technician, Suttar Hosp, Sacramento, 55-56; Hotel Dieu Hosp, El Paso, Tex, 57; ASST. PROF. CHEM, SACRAMENTO STATE COL, 64- U.S.A, 56-58. Am. Chem. Soc. Enzyme mechanism and general biochemistry. Address: Dept. of Chemistry, Sacramento State College, Sacramento, CA 95819.

DRASIN, DAVID, b. Philadelphia, Pa, Nov. 3, 40; m. 63; c. 2. MATHEMATICS. A.B, Temple, 62; Ph.D.(math), Cornell, 66. Instr. MATH, Rutgers, 62; asst. prof, PURDUE UNIV, 66-69, ASSOC. PROF, 69- Math. Asn. Am; Am. Math. Soc. Functions of a complex variable; Tauberian theorems. Address: Dept. of Mathematics, Purdue University, Lafayette, IN 47907.

DRATZ, ARTHUR F(REDERICK), b. Lynbrook, N.Y, Dec. 25, 23; m. 49; c. 1. NUCLEAR MEDICINE. B.A, Duke Univ, 47, Ph.D.(biochem), 53. ASST. CHIEF SCI, NUCLEAR MED. SERV, VET. ADMIN. HOSP, 52- Instr, Emory Univ, 53-65, asst. prof, 65- U.S.N.R, 43-46, Res, 46-64, Lt.(jg). Soc. Nuclear Med; Health Physics Soc. Nuclear medicine. Address: Nuclear Medicine Service, Veterans Administration Hospital, P.O. Box 29457, Atlanta, GA 30329.

DRAUGLIS, EDMUND, b. Phila, Pa, May 21, 33; m. 64; c. 2. THEORETICAL CHEMISTRY. B.S, Pennsylvania, 55; Cornell, 55-57; M.S, Yale, 59, Ph.D. (phys. chem), 61. Phys. chemist, semiconductor prod. dept, Gen. Elec. Co, N.Y, 61; res. scientist, United Aircraft Res. Lab, Conn, 62-63; SR. PHYSICIST, BATTELLE MEM. INST, 64- Am. Phys. Soc. Semiconductors; theory of surface states; theory of energy exchange between gases and surfaces; theory of liquid crystals; theory of boundary layer lubrication. Address: Division of Solid State Physics, Battelle Memorial Institute, 505 King Ave, Columbus, OH 43201.

DRAUS, FRANK JOHN, b. Dupont, Pa, Oct. 30, 29; m. 56; c. 4. BIOCHEMISTRY. B.S, Alliance Col, 51; M.S, Duquesne Univ, 53, Ph.D.(biochem), 57. Asst. BIOCHEM, SCH. DENT. MED, UNIV. PITTSBURGH, 56, res. assoc, 58, asst. prof, 59-61, assoc. prof, 61-65, PROF, 65-, HEAD DEPT, 67- Temporary adv, WHO, 69; indust. consult. AAAS; assoc. Am. Dent. Asn; fel. Am. Inst. Chem; Am. Chem. Soc; Int. Asn. Dent. Res; N.Y. Acad. Sci. Mechanism for the formation of synthetic calculus; isolation and characterization of mucoproteins and mycopolysaccharides from salivary glands. Address: 1024 Dale Dr, Pittsburgh, PA 15220.

DRAVNIEKS, ANDREW, b. Petersburg, Russia, Oct. 3, 12; nat; m. 39; c. 2. PHYSICAL CHEMISTRY. Chem. Eng, Latvia, 38; UNRRA scholar, Marburg, 46; Ph.D, Ill. Inst. Tech, 49. Subasst. chem, Latvia, 36-38, asst, 38-40, lectr, 40-41; sci. assoc, 41-44; analyst, Berlin, Ger, 45; res. dept, Continental Can Co, 47; res. assoc, Ill. Inst. Tech, 47-49; sect. head corrosion sect, eng. res. dept, Standard Oil Co. Ind, 49-60; SR. SCI. ADV, ILL. INST. TECHNOL. RES. INST, 60-, TECH. DIR. ODOR SCI. CTR, 60- Lectr, Riga State Tech, Latvia, 39-44; tech. mgr, Riga Paint & Chem. Factory, 41-44. Latvian Army, 38. AAAS; Am. Chem. Soc; Electrochem. Soc; Nat. Asn. Corrosion Eng.(Speller Award, 71); N.Y. Acad. Sci; Am. Soc. Test. & Mat; Inst. Food Technol. Polargraphy; technology of paints and lacquers; reactions between gases and metals at high temperatures; corrosion, especially in nonelectrolytes; electrochemistry; fuel cells; olfaction; olfactronics; odor measurements. Address: Odor Science Center, Illinois Institute of Technology Research Institute, 10 W. 35th St, Chicago, IL 60616.

DRAWBAUGH, DONALD W, b. Miles City, Mont, Dec. 9, 23; m. 49; c. 2. PHYSICS. A.B, Kansas, 48, A.M, 53, fel, 56-57, Ph.D.(physics), 57. Asst. instr. physics, Kansas, 48-56; physicist, Combustion Eng, Inc, 57-60; WESTINGHOUSE ASTRONUCLEAR LAB, 60-62, MGR. PHYSICS, 62- Sig.C, 42-46. Am. Phys. Soc; Am. Nuclear Soc. Neutron transport theory; reactor physics. Address: Westinghouse Astronuclear Lab, P.O. Box 10864, Pittsburgh, PA 15236.

DRAY, SHELDON, b. Chicago, Ill, Nov. 20, 20; m. 53; c. 2. MEDICINE, IMMUNOCHEMISTRY. B.S, Chicago, 41; M.D, Illinois, 46, M.S, 47; Ph.D.(phys. biochem), Minnesota, 54. Intern, res. & ed. hosps, Illinois, 46-47; med. off, nutrit. sect, Bur. State Serv, U.S. Pub. Health Serv, 47-49; phys. biol. lab, Nat. Inst. Arthritis & Metab. Diseases, Nat. Insts. Health, 49-54, immunol. lab, Nat. Inst. Allergy & Infectious Diseases, 55-65; PROF. MICROBIOL. & HEAD DEPT, UNIV. ILL. MED. CTR, 65- Coun. mem, Int. Union Immunol. Socs; consult, WHO. U.S.A, 43-46. AAAS; Am. Chem. Soc; Am. Med. Asn; Am. Soc. Microbiol; Am. Soc. Human Genetics; Am. Asn. Immunol.(secy-treas, 64-70); Soc. Exp. Biol. & Med. Biocolloids; physical chemistry of membranes; immunochemistry; serum proteins; immunogenetics; maternal-fetal incompatibility. Address: Dept. of Microbiology, University of Illinois at the Medical Center, Chicago, IL 60612.

DRAY, WALTER LAWRENCE, b. Boston, Mass, Jan. 31, 17; m. 41; c. 8. ENGINEERING. B.S, Univ. Notre Dame, 40. Asst. chief engr, Bendix Corp, Ind, 40-50; asst. eng. mgr, Elgin Nat. Watch Co, Ill, 50-52; exec. engr, BENDIX CORP, 52-68, dir. qual. assurance, 68-70, DIR. ENG, 70- Pres. & bd. chmn, Quad-Cities Tech. Adv. Coun, Iowa, 66-68, mem. bd. dirs, 68-; mem. indust. adv. bd, Black Hawk Col, 66-; eng. col. bd. consult, Univ. Iowa, 67-68; chmn, East. Iowa Res. Adv. Coun, 67-68; mem. eng. col. adv. coun, Iowa State Univ, 67- Soc. Automotive Eng; Am. Ord. Asn. Directing research and development of company products, including aerospace instrumentation, life support equipment, aerospace fuel management, industrial sonic equipment and medical products. Address: Instruments & Life Support Div, Bendix Corp, 2734 Hickory Grove Rd, Davenport, IA 52808.

DRAYER, DENNIS EUGENE, b. Frankfort, S.Dak, June 24, 28; m. 50; c. 2. CHEMICAL ENGINEERING. B.S, S.Dak. Sch. Mines & Technol, 52; M.S, Kans. State Univ, 54; Ph.D.(chem. eng), Univ. Colo, Boulder, 61. Instr. chem. eng, Kans. State Univ, 53-54; chem. engr, Dow Chem. Co, 54-58; chem. engr, cryogenic eng. lab, Nat. Bur. Standards, 59-61; res. engr, MARATHON OIL CO, 61-65, advan. res. engr, 65-68, SR. RES. ENGR, 68- Adj. assoc. prof, Univ. Denver, 66- U.S.N, 46-48. Am. Chem. Soc; Am. Inst. Chem. Eng. Heat transfer in cryogenic systems; liquid phase hydrocarbon oxidations; economic evaluation techniques; project evaluation. Address: Marathon Oil Co, Denver Research Center, P.O. Box 269, Littleton, CO 80122.

DRAYSON, SYDNEY ROLAND, b. Buckhurst Hill, Eng, Dec. 21, 37; m. 63; c. 2. ATMOSPHERIC PHYSICS. B.Sc, Univ. London, 60; NATO stud, Univ. Chicago, 60-62, M.S, 61; Ph.D.(meteorol), Univ. Mich, 67. Asst. res. mathematician, UNIV. MICH, 63-66, res. assoc, 66-67, lectr. meteorol. & assoc. res. engr, 68-69, ASST. PROF. METEOROL, 70- AAAS; Am. Meteorol. Soc; Am. Geophys. Soc. Atmospheric radiative transfer, including radiative heating rates, remote sounding of the atmosphere and molecular spectroscopy; numerical methods and computer applications. Address: 2577 Bunker Hill Rd, Ann Arbor, MI 48105.

DRAZIN, MICHAEL P(ETER), b. London, Eng, June 5, 29. MATHEMATICS. B.A, Cambridge, 50, fel, 52-53, M.A, 53, Ph.D.(math), 53. Fel. Trinity Col, Cambridge, 52-53; sci. off, Admiralty Res. Lab, Teddington, Eng, 53-55; fel. Trinity Coll, Cambridge, 55-57; vis. lectr, Northwestern, 57-58; sr. scientist, Res. Inst. Adv. Study, 58-62; ASSOC. PROF. MATH, PURDUE UNIV, 62- Smith's Prize of University of Cambridge, 52; Prize fel. of Trinity Col, 55-57. Am. Math. Soc; Soc. Indust. & Appl. Math. Non-commutative ring theory; abstract algebra; combinatorial problems; matrix theory; applied mathematics. Address: Dept. of Mathematics, Purdue University, Lafayette, IN 47907.

DREA, JOHN JAMES, JR, b. New London, Conn, July 27, 28; m. 57; c. 3. ENTOMOLOGY. B.S, Boston Col, 50; B.S, California, Berkeley, 52, Ph.D. (entom), 57. RES. ENTOMOLOGIST, ENTOM. RES. DIV, U.S. DEPT. AGR, 56- AAAS; Entom. Soc. Am; Am. Entom. Soc; Entom. Soc. Can; Soc. Phys. & Natural Sci. Morocco. Foreign exploration and research directed toward the introduction into the United States of insects for use in the biological control of noxious weeds and insect pests; release, recovery and evaluation of insects introduced into the United States. Address: European Parasite Lab, U.S. Dept. of Agriculture, 47 Rue des Fontenelles, 92-Sevres, France.

DREBUS, RICHARD W(ILLIAM), b. Oshkosh, Wis, Mar. 30, 24; m. 47; c. 3. PSYCHOLOGY. B.S, Wisconsin, 47, M.S, 50, fel. & Ph.D, 52. Asst, Wisconsin, 49-51; training mgr, Ansul Chem. Co, 52-55, asst. to v.pres. sales, 55-57, dir. sales admin. servs, 57-58, mkt, 59; mgr. tech. personnel develop, Mead Johnson & Co, 60-63, dir. personnel develop, 63-65, v.pres. corp. planning, 65-66, pres. int. div, 66-68; V.PRES. HQ. OPERS, INT. DIV, BRISTOL-MYERS CO, 68- U.S.A, 43-45. Am. Psychol. Asn; N.Y. Acad. Sci. International business management; adult education and development. Address: Bristol-Myers Co, International Division, 345 Park Ave, New York, NY 10022.

DREBY, EDWIN C(HRISTIAN), III, b. Haddonfield, N.J, Sept. 2, 15; m. 40; c. 5. PHYSICAL & ORGANIC CHEMISTRY. Ph.D.(phys. chem), Yale, 39. Res. asst, Am. Soc. Testing & Mat, 39-41; res. chemist, SCHOLLER BROS, INC, 41-54, DIR. LAB, 54- Am. Chem. Soc; Am. Asn. Textile Chem. & Colorists; Am. Soc. Test. & Mat. Development of chemical products to assist in the scouring and dyeing of textile yarns, fabrics and garments and to alter their hand for ease of manufacture and consumer requirements. Address: 3110 W. Coulter St, Philadelphia, PA 19129.

DRECHSEL, DIETER, b. Wittgensdorf, Ger, Feb. 25, 37; m. 61; c. 3. NUCLEAR PHYSICS. Dipl, Darmstadt Tech, 61, Dr. rer. nat.(physics), 64. Asst. PHYSICS, Inst. Theoret. Physics, Darmstadt Tech, 61-65, Frankfurt, 65-66 & 68-69; guest worker, Nat. Bur. Standards, Wash, D.C, 66-67; res. assoc. prof, Catholic Univ, 67-68; assoc. prof, Virginia, 69-70; inst. theoret. physics, Univ. Frankfurt, 70-71; PROF, INST. NUCLEAR PHYSICS, UNIV. MAINZ, 71- Am. Phys. Soc; German Phys. Soc. Elastic and inelastic electron scattering; fine structure of giant resonances in nuclei; nucleon-nucleon bremsstrahlung; pion production processes. Address: Institute of Nuclear Physics, University of Mainz, Mainz, Ger.

DRECHSEL, PAUL D(AVID), b. Newark, N.J, Oct. 24, 25; m. 50; c. 4. PHYSICAL CHEMISTRY. B.S, Rutgers Univ, 46; Ph.D.(phys. chem), Cornell Univ, 51. Sr. res. chemist, Allegany Ballistics Lab, Hercules, Inc, 51-57, res. supvr, 57-58, group supvr, 58-61, asst. dept. supt, 61-62, dept. supt, 62-70, res. scientist, HERCULES RES. CTR, 70-71, RES. ASSOC, 71- Am. Chem. Soc. Physical chemistry and mechanical properties of polymers; solid rocket propellants; ablative insulations; diffusion; heat transfer. Ad dress: 127 Westgate Dr, Wilmington, DE 19808.

DRECHSLER, CHARLES, b. Butternut, Wis, May 1, 92; m. 30; c. 3. BOTANY. B.S, Wisconsin, 13, M.S, 14; Ph.D.(biol, mycol), Harvard, 17. Asst, Agr. Exp. Sta, Conn, 16; field asst, bur. plant indust, soils & agr. eng, U.S. Dept. Agr, 17-18, sci. asst, 19-20, asst. pathologist, 20-24, assoc. pathologist, 24-29, pathologist, 29-53, mycologist, hort. crops res. br, Agr. Res. Serv, 53-62, collab, 62-69; RETIRED. Distinguished Serv. Award, U.S. Dept. Agr, 58. U.S.A, 17-19. AAAS; Bot. Soc. Am; Am. Phytopath. Soc; Mycol. Soc. Am; Micros. Soc. Am.(v.pres, 45); Torrey Bot. Club; Soc. Econ. Bot; German Bot. Soc. Taxonomy of oomycetes causing root rot of crop plants; description of predacious and parasitic fungi subsisting on soil animalcules; readily culturable Entomophthoraceae. Address: 6915 Oakridge Rd, Hyattsville, MD 20780.

DRECKTRAH, H(AROLD) GENE, b. La Crosse, Wis, Nov. 1, 38; m. 62; c. 2. ENTOMOLOGY, INSECT MORPHOLOGY. B.S, Wis. State, La Crosse, 62; M.S, Iowa State, 64, Ph.D.(entom), 66. Res. asst, Iowa Dept. Agr, 62-66; ASST. PROF. BIOL, WIS. STATE UNIV-OSHKOSH, 66- Entom. Soc. Am; Am. Entom. Soc. Insect morphology, especially the internal reproductive organs of both sexes. Address: Dept. of Biology, Wisconsin State University-Oshkosh, Oshkosh, WI 54901.

DREEBEN, ARTHUR (B), b. N.Y.C, Feb. 15, 22; m. 50; c. 2. INORGANIC CHEMISTRY. B.S, Polytech. Inst. Brooklyn, 48, fel, 48-50, M.S, 50. Asst. chem, res. lab, Gen. Elec. Co, 50-52; Knolls Atomic Power Lab, 52-53; assoc. res. eng, res. dept. lamp div, Westinghouse Elec. Corp, 53-58; MEM. TECH. STAFF, DAVID SARNOFF RES. CTR, RCA CORP, 58- U.S.A, 42-45. Am. Chem. Soc; Electrochem. Soc; Am. Asn. Crystal Growth. Solid state chemistry; luminescence; photoconduction; crystal growth and imperfections. Address: 75 Dodds Lane, Princeton, NJ 08540.

DREES, DAVID T, b. Dyersville, Iowa, Nov. 23, 33; m. 56; c. 4. PATHOLOGY, VETERINARY MEDICINE. D.V.M, Iowa State, 57; M.S, Mich. State, 66, Ph.D.(path), 69. Instr. anat, Mich. State, 64-68, Nat. Insts. Health fel. path, 68-69; HEAD ANIMAL HEALTH & PATH, WARREN-TEED PHARMACEUT, INC, 69- Am. Vet. Med. Asn. Cytology of inflammation; colibacillosis in germ free swine; animal models. Address: 1461 Bridgeton Dr, Columbus, OH 43220.

DREESE, E(RWIN) E(RNEST), b. Millbrook, Mich, Sept. 10, 95; m. 20, 47; c. 2. ELECTRICAL ENGINEERING. B.S, Michigan, 20, M.S, 22, E.E, 29. Instr. elec. eng, Michigan, 20-25; chief engr, Lincoln Elec. Co, Cleveland, 25-30; prof. elec. eng. & chmn. dept, OHIO STATE UNIV, 30-70, EMER. PROF. ELEC. ENG, 70- Ed, textbooks, Int. Textbook Co. Mem. coun. exec. bd, Argonne Nat. Lab, 50-54, chmn, 54-; chmn. bd. trustees & juries of award comt, Lincoln Arc Welding Found. U.S.A, 17-19, 1st Lt. Fel. Inst. Elec. & Electronics Eng; Am. Soc. Eng. Educ. Electric machine analysis. Address: Dept. of Electrical Engineering, Ohio State University, Columbus, OH 43210.

DREESZEN, VINCENT H(AROLD), b. Palmyra, Nebr, July 23, 21; m. 44; c. 3. GEOLOGY, HYDROLOGY. A.B, Nebr. State Teachers Col, Peru, 42; M.Sc, Nebraska, 50. Geologist, CONSERV. & SURV. DIV, UNIV. NEBR, LINCOLN, 47-59, asst. dir. div, 59-67, acting dir, 67-69, DIR. DIV, 69-, ASSOC. PROF. GEOL, 70- U.S.N, 42-45, Lt. Am. Water Works Asn; Asn. Am. State Geol; Geol. Soc. Am. Optimum use of water resources; conservation of other natural resources; study and correlation of Pleistocene sediments and their land forms. Address: Conservation & Survey Division, 113 Nebraska Hall, University of Nebraska, Lincoln, NE 68508.

DREGNE, HAROLD E(RNEST), b. Ladysmith, Wis, Sept. 25, 16; m. 43; c. 4. SOIL CHEMISTRY. B.S, Wis. State, 38; M.S, Wisconsin, 40; Ph.D.(soil chem), Oregon State, 42. Asst, Oregon State, 40-42; jr. soil scientist, Soil Conserv. Serv, U.S. Dept. Agr, 42-43, 46; asst. prof. agron, Idaho, 46-47; asst. soil scientist, Washington State, 47-49; prof. agron. & agronomist, exp. sta, N.Mex. State Univ, 49-50, prof. soils, 50-69; PROF. AGRON. & CHMN. DEPT, TEX. TECH UNIV, 69- Head, Inter Col. Exchange Prog, Pakistan, 55-57; mem, U.S. Soil Salinity Del, Soviet Union, 60; soil fertil. expert, Food & Agr. Orgn, UN, Chile, 61; del, Latin Am. Arid Lands Conf, Arg, 63; prog. chmn, Int. Arid Lands Conf, Tucson, Ariz, 69. U.S.N, 42-46, Lt. AAAS; assoc. Am. Soc. Agron; assoc. Am. Soil Sci. Soc. Chemistry and fertility of arid region soils; saline and sodium soils; irrigation water quality. Address: Dept. of Agronomy, Texas Tech University, Lubbock, TX 79409.

DREHER, JOHN JAMES, b. Flint, Mich, Apr. 11, 20; m. 47; c. 1. PSYCHOACOUSTICS, LINGUISTICS. A.B, Michigan, 45, M.A, 47, Ph.D.(instrumental phonetics), 51. Prin. investr. psycholing, univ. res. found, Ohio State, 51-57; res. engr, Lockheed Calif. Co, 57-58, res. specialist, 58-60, group engr, 60-63, dept. mgr. life sci, 63-65; res. scientist, Douglas Advan. Res. Labs, 65-68, dir. info. sci, 68-70; SCI. CONSULT, 70- Tech. consult, Hoover Inst. War, Peace & Revolution, Stanford Univ, 67- U.S.A, 42-46, Res, 46-49; U.S.A.F.R, 51-63, Capt. Acoust. Soc. Am; Am. Inst. Physics; Aerospace Med. Asn; Phonetic Soc. Japan. Linguistics research and target recognition techniques basic to antisubmarine warfare application. Address: 12 S. Old Ranch Rd, Arcadia, CA 91006.

DREICER, HARRY, b. Bad Lausick, Ger, Oct. 6, 27; U.S. citizen; m. 50; c. 3. PHYSICS. B.S, Mass. Inst. Tech, 51, Radio Corp. Am. fel, 52-53, Ph.D. (physics), 55. MEM. STAFF PHYSICS, LOS ALAMOS SCI. LAB, UNIV. CALIF, 54- Part-time prof, New Mexico, 60; European Atomic Energy Community fel, Lab. Gas Ionizzati, Frascati, Italy, 64-65 & Saclay Nuclear Res. Center, France, 65. Consult, Boeing Sci. Res. Labs, 59-; Martin Co, 61. Fel. Am. Phys. Soc. Effect of coulomb interactions and radiation field on plasma distribution functions; runaway electrons in plasmas; measurement of plasma microwave emission and transmission; anomalous high frequency electrical resistivity of plasmas. Address: Los Alamos Scientific Lab, P.O. Box 1663, Los Alamos, NM 87544.

DREIDING, ANDRE S(AMUEL), b. Zurich, Switz, June 22, 19; nat; m. 47, 71; c. 2. CHEMISTRY. B.S, Columbia, 41, A.M, 43; univ. fel, Michigan, 45, Monsanto fel, 45-47, Ph.D.(chem), 47; hon. Ph.D, Univ. Clermont-Ferrand, 65. Res. chemist, Hoffmann-LaRoche, Inc, N.J, 43-45; Lloyd fel, Univ. Mich, 47-48, Rackham fel, 48-49; asst. prof, Wayne State Univ, 49-54; docent, ORG. CHEM, UNIV. ZURICH, 55-63, PROF, 63- Consult. eng. res, 48-50; res. assoc, Detroit Inst. Cancer Res, 49-54; vis. prof, Univ. Mich, 51-52; Univ. Tex, Austin, 66; Israel Inst. Technol, 67; Weizmann Inst. Sci, 71. Ruzicka Medal, Swiss Fed. Inst. Technol, 62. Swiss Chem. Soc.(Werner Medal, 58); hon. mem. Chem. Soc. Belg.(Stas Medal, 71); Am. Chem. Soc; The Chem. Soc; Swiss Soc. Natural Sci. Organic reactions; mechanisms; synthesis; natural products; biosynthesis; chemical taxonomy; stereochemistry; conformational analysis; mathematical treatment of structure. Address: Dept. of Organic Chemistry, University of Zurich, Rämistrasse 76, 8001 Zurich, Switz.

DREIER, WILLIAM MATTHEWS, JR, b. Omaha, Nebr, Mar. 20, 37; m. 61; c. 1. CHEMICAL ENGINEERING. B.S, Wisconsin, 59, M.S, 60; Ph.D.(chem. eng), Minnesota, 64. Aerospace engr, Lewis Res. Ctr, NASA, 63-64; sr. res. chem. engr, GEN. MILLS, INC, 64-68, SECT. LEADER, JAMES FORD BELL RES. CTR, 68- Am. Inst. Chem. Eng. Thermodynamics of cryogenic fuels; microwave heating; dehydration. Address: James Ford Bell Research Center, General Mills, Inc, 9000 Plymouth Ave. N, Minneapolis, MN 55427.

DREIFKE, GERALD E(DMOND), b. St. Louis, Mo, June 21, 18; m. 51; c. 4. ELECTRICAL ENGINEERING, APPLIED MECHANICS. B.S. & M.S, Wash. Univ, 48, Nat. Sci. Found. faculty fel, 60-61, D.Sc, 61. Layout & drafting, Curtiss Wright Corp, 36-39; design engr, 39-44; layout engr, Douglas Aircraft, 39; instr. eng, St. Louis, 48-50, asst. prof, 50-54, assoc. prof, 54-61, prof. elec. eng, 61-70, secy. dept, 51-54, dir. dept, 54-70; MGR. RES. & DEVELOP, UNION ELEC. CO, 70- Consult, Emerson Elec. Co, 51; Monsanto Co, 61-; mem. tech. staff, Bell Tel. Labs, 63; ed-in-chief, Instrument Soc. Am, 67- Cert. merit, U.S. War Prod. Bd, 42. U.S.N.R, 44-45. Inst. Elec. & Electronics Eng; Am. Soc. Eng. Educ. Automatic controls; linear and non-linear systems; system dynamics. Address: Research & Development Dept, Union Electric Company, P.O. Box 149, St. Louis, MO 63166.

DREIFUS, DAVID W(ALTER), b. Cincinnati, Ohio, Nov. 25, 43; m. 67. PHYSICAL CHEMISTRY. B.Sc, Univ. Cincinnati, 66; Ph.D.(chem), McGill Univ, 71. RES. SCIENTIST, UNION CAMP CORP, 70- Penetration of fluids into porous media; role of free volume in polymer solution thermodynamics; glass transition temperatures of polymer-diluent systems. Address: Research & Development Labs, Union Camp Corp, P.O. Box 412, Princeton, NJ 08540.

DREIFUS, LEONARD S, b. Phila, Pa, May 27, 24; m. 58. CARDIOLOGY. B.A, Pennsylvania, 47; M.D, Hahnemann Med. Col, 51. Instr. MED, HAHNEMANN MED. COL, 56-61, CLIN. ASSOC. PROF, 61-, RES. ASSOC. PROF. PHYSIOL. & BIOPHYS. & ACTING DIR. CARDIOL, 69- Chief of cardiol, Valley Forge Army Hosp, 56-59; asst. vis. physician, Philadelphia Gen. Hosp, 56- U.S.A.A.F, 42-46. Am. Soc. Clin. Invest; fel. Am. Col. Physicians. Cardiovascular research; electro cardiology; medicine. Address: 1415 Hagys Ford Rd, Narbeth, PA 19072.

DREIFUSS, FRITZ EMANUEL, b. Dresden, Ger, Jan. 20, 26; U.S. citizen; m. 54; c. 2. MEDICINE. M.B, Ch.B, New Zealand, 50. House physician & res. neurol officer, Nat. Hosp, London, Eng, 54-57; asst. prof. NEUROL, SCH. MED, UNIV. VA, 59-64, assoc. prof, 64-68, PROF, 68-, NEUROLOGIST; UNIV. HOSP, 59- Neurologist, Commonwealth of Va. Child Neurol. Prog, 59- AAAS; Am. Acad. Neurol; Asn. Res. Nerv. & Ment. Diseases; Am. Med. Asn; N.Y. Acad. Sci. Brit. Med. Asn. Neurological sciences, especially pediatric neurology; epilepsy and mental retardation. Address: Dept. of Neurology, University of Virginia Hospital, Charlottesville, VA 22903.

DREIKORN, BARRY ALLEN, b. Norristown, Pa, Sept. 15, 39; m. 62. ORGANIC CHEMISTRY. B.A, Rutgers, 61; Nat. Inst. Ment. Health fel, Pennsylvania, 63-66, Ph.D.(org. chem), 66. SR. ORG. CHEMIST, GREENFIELD LABS, ELI LILLY & CO, 66- AAAS; Am. Chem. Soc. Synthetic organic chemistry. Address: Eli Lilly & Co, Greenfield Labs, Greenfield, IN 46140.

DREIKORN, RUSSELL E, b. Kearny, N.J, Sept. 15, 16; m. 45; c. 2. PHYSICAL CHEMISTRY. A.B, Drew Univ, 42; Ph.D.(x-ray diffraction), Polytech. Inst. Brooklyn, 51. Mem. staff, res. div, United Shoe Mach. Corp, Mass, 50-57; metall. div, Sylvania Elec. Corp, N.Y, 57-58; lead scientist, res. & develop. div, Avco Corp, Mass, 58-64; DEVELOP. ENGR, COMPONENTS DIV, IBM CORP, Oswego, N.Y, 64-67, ENDICOTT, 67- Am. Crystallog. Asn; Am. Chem. Soc. Fabrication of high density multi-layer copper-epoxy electronic components and achievement of high density interconnections; influence of manufacturing and environmental factors on corrosion and reliability; high temperature x-ray diffractometry of refractory materials. Address: 701 Catalina Blvd, Endwell, NY 13760.

DREILING, DAVID A, b. N.Y.C, June 5, 18; m. 46; c. 1. SURGERY. B.A, Cornell, 38; M.D, N.Y. Univ, 42. Dazian fel. exp. surg. & anat, N.Y. Med. Col, 45-46; Ralph Colp fel. exp. surg. & gastroenterol, 46-47; Guggenheim fel. exp. gastroenterol, 47-49; DIR. DEPT. SURG, Greenpoint Hosp, 62-64; ELMHURST GEN. HOSP, 64- DIR. EXP. GASTROINTESTINAL SURG. & ANIMAL RES. FACILITIES, Mt. SINAI HOSP, 63-, PROF. SURG, MT. SINAI SCH. MED, 66- Mem. bd. trustees, Nat. Digestive Disease Found, 70-; Am. Fedn. Digestive Disease, 70-; Dipl, Am. Bd. Surg. AAAS; fel. Am. Med. Asn; fel. Am. Col. Surg; Am. Physiol. Soc; Am. Fedn. Clin. Res; Am. Gastroenterol. Asn; Am. Col. Gastroenterol.(ed, Jour, 71-); fel. World Med. Asn; fel. Int. Col. Surg. Gastroenterology physiology; diagnosis of pathophysiologic evaluation of pancreatic inflammation; mechanics of secretion of the pancreas. Address: 171 W. 57th St, New York, NY 10019.

DREILING, MARK JEROME, b. Kansas City, Mo, Nov. 27, 40; m. 68; c. 2. PHYSICS. B.S, Kans. State Univ, 62, M.S, 64, NASA fel, 66-67, Ph.D.(physics), 68. RES. PHYSICIST, PHILLIPS PETROL. CO, 67- Am. Inst. Phys; Am. Crystallog. Asn. X-ray diffraction; small-angle x-ray scattering. Address: 100 Forrest Park Rd, Bartlesville, OK 74003.

DREIMANIS, A(LEKSIS), b. Valmiera, Latvia, Aug. 13, 14; Can. citizen; m. 42; c. 2. GEOLOGY. Mag. rer. nat, Latvia Univ, 38, habil, 41; hon. D.Sc, Univ. Waterloo, 69. Asst. GEOL, inst. geol, Latvia Univ, 38-40, lectr, 41, privat-docent, 42-44; assoc. prof, Baltic Univ, 46-48; lectr, UNIV. WEST. ONT, 48-51, asst. prof, 51-56, assoc. prof, 56-64, PROF, 64- Consult, Inst. Res. Mineral Resources of Latvia, 42-44; Ont. Dept. Planning & Develop, 50-53; various Can. & U.S. govt. agencies, explor. & eng. consult. companies, 50-; Can. del, Int. Geol. Cong, 60; Int. Asn. Quaternary Res, 65, 69; mem, Can. Nat. Adv. Comt. Res. in Geol. Sci. & chmn. subcomt. quaternary geol, 67-71; mem, Baltic Res. Inst. Gold Medal, Univ. Latvia, 36. Latvian Army, 39-40, Latvian Legion, 44-45, 2nd Lt. Geol. Soc. Am; Soc. Econ. Paleont. & Mineral; Int. Asn. Sedimentol; Geol. Asn. Can; Can. Inst. Mining & Metall; Ger. Quaternary Union; Swedish Geol. Soc; Int. Asn. Gt. Lakes Res. Pleistocene and glacial geology; lithology and fabric of glacial deposits; pollen analysis; Pleistoc stratigraphy of Latvia and eastern Great Lakes region, North America; indicator trains. Address: Dept. of Geology, University of Western Ontario, London 72, Ont, Can.

DREISBACH, PAUL F(RANKLIN), b. Allentown, Pa, Oct. 22, 10; m. 39. ORGANIC CHEMISTRY. B.S, Muhlenberg Col, 31; Ph.D.(org. chem), N.Y. Univ, 37. Asst. chem, Univ. Heights Col, N.Y. Univ, 32-36; org. res. chemist, Pyridium Corp, 36-38; G.W. Carnrick Co, 38-44; Calco Chem. Div, AM. CYANAMID CO, BOUND BROOK, 44-50, GROUP LEADER pharmaceut. res, 50-54, RES. SERV. DEPT, 54- AAAS; Am. Chem. Soc; fel. Am. Inst. Chem; N.Y. Acad. Sci. Cholines and thio derivatives; local anesthetics of pyridine series; steroids; pharmaceuticals; chemotherapy; staining compounds; oncology; chemical literature; protection of scientific developments. Address: 173 W. High St, Somerville, NJ 08876.

DREISBACH, ROBERT H(ASTINGS), b. Baker, Ore, Mar. 29, 16; m. 41; c. 2. MEDICINE. A.B, Stanford, 37; Ph.D.(pharmacol) & M.D, Chicago, 42. Asst. pharmacol, Chicago, 39-42; intern, St. Mary's Hosp, 42-43; instr. PHARMACOL, SCH. MED, STANFORD UNIV, 43-44, asst. prof, 46-49, assoc. prof, 49-55, PROF, 55- Med.C, 44-46, Capt. Toxicology; environmental pollution. Address: Stanford University School of Medicine, Stanford, CA 94305.

DREISS, GERARD J(ULIUS), b. West New York, N.J, July 11, 28; m. 59; c. 2. THEORETICAL PHYSICS. B.A. & Henry Rutgers scholar, Rutgers Univ,

58; Nat. Sci. Found. fel, Harvard, 58-59; M.S, Univ. Pa, 64, NASA trainee, 64-67, Ph.D.(physics), 68. Mathematician, Avco-Everett Res. Lab, 59-63; vis. instr. physics, Northeast. Univ, 68-69, asst. prof, 69-71; ASST. ED, PHYS. REV, 71- U.S.N, 50-54. Am. Phys. Soc. Theoretical nuclear physics; collective motion in nuclei. Address: The Physical Review, Brookhaven National Lab, Upton, NY 11973.

DREIZEN, PAUL, b. N.Y.C, Oct. 23, 29. BIOPHYSICS, MEDICINE. A.B, Cornell, 51; M.D, N.Y. Univ, 54. Intern. med, N.Y. Univ-Bellevue Med. Center, 54-55, asst. resident, 55-56, asst. med, 58-59; cardiologist, U.S. Naval Hosp, Nat. Naval Med. Center, 56-58; res. assoc. biol, Mass. Inst. Technol, 59-62; asst. prof. med, STATE UNIV. N.Y. DOWNSTATE MED. CTR, 62-67, assoc. prof, 67-71, PROF. MED. & BIOPHYS, 71- Nat. Res. fel, 59-63; career scientist, N.Y. City Health Res. Coun, 63- Med.C, 56-58, Lt. AAAS; Biophys. Soc; Am. Fedn. Clin. Res; Harvey Soc; Am. Chem. Soc; Am. Soc. Clin. Invest; Faraday Soc; Am. Phys. Soc. Physical chemistry of contractile proteins; mechanism of muscular contraction. Address: State University of New York Downstate Medical Center, 450 Clarkson Ave, Brooklyn, NY 11203.

DREIZEN, SAMUEL, b. N.Y.C, Sept. 12, 18; m. 56; c. 1. NUTRITION. B.A, Brooklyn Col, 41; D.D.S, Western Reserve, 45; M.D, Northwestern, 58. Res. assoc, Cincinnati, 45-47; instr, NUTRIT. & METAB, Northwestern, 47-48, asst. prof, 48-59, assoc. prof, 59-66; PROF, INST. DENT. SCI, DENT. BR, UNIV. TEX, 66- Asst. sci. dir, nutrit. clinic, Hillman Hosp, 48-60; Clayton Found. fel, 49-54; consult. nutrit, Am. Dent. Asn, 64-; M.D. Anderson Hosp. & Tumor Inst, Univ. Tex, 67-, prof, grad. sch. biomed. sci, 68- Edgar Martin Mem. Award, Odontographic Soc. Chicago, 70. U.S.A, 43-44. AAAS; Am. Asn. Phys. Anthrop; Am. Dental Asn; Int. Asn. Dental Res; Soc. Res. Child Develop; N.Y. Acad. Sci. Dental caries; nutritional deficiency diseases; child growth and development. Address: Institute for Dental Science, University of Texas Dental Branch, P.O. Box 20068, Houston, TX 77025.

DRELICH, ARTHUR (HERBERT), b. Jersey City, N.J, Mar. 26, 20; m. 49; c. 5. ORGANIC CHEMISTRY. B.A, N.Y. Univ, 40; M.S, Univ. Pa, 42. Jr. chemist protective agents, Edgewood Arsenal, 42-43; supvr. chem. res, CHICOPEE MFG. CO, 43-67, SR. SCIENTIST, RES. DIV, 67- AAAS; Am. Chem. Soc; Royal Micros. Soc. Bonding of non-woven fabrics; viscose chemistry; properties of polymer latexes; fiber and chemical microscopy and scientific photography. Address: 60 Parkside Rd, Plainfield, NJ 07060.

DRELL, SIDNEY D(AVID), b. Atlantic City, N.J, Sept. 13, 26; m. 52; c. 3. THEORETICAL PHYSICS. A.B, Princeton, 46; A.M, Illinois, 47, Ph.D. (physics), 49. Res. assoc. PHYSICS, Illinois, 49-50; instr, Stanford, 50-52; res. assoc, Mass. Inst. Technol, 52-53, asst. prof, 53-56; assoc. prof, STANFORD UNIV, 56-60, PROF, 60-, DEP. DIR. LINEAR ACCELERATOR CTR, 70- Consult, Los Alamos Sci. Labs, 56-64, 68-; Off. Sci. & Technol, 60-; Inst. Defense Anal, 60-; Guggenheim fel, 61-62, 71-72; Loeb lectr. & vis. prof, Harvard, 62, 70; mem, President's Sci. Adv. Comt, 66-70; consult, U.S. Arms Control & Disarmament Agency, 69- Nat. Acad. Sci; fel. Am. Phys. Soc; Am. Acad. Arts & Sci; Fedn. Am. Sci. Quantum field theory; elementary particle physics. Address: Stanford Linear Accelerator Center, Stanford University, Stanford, CA 94305.

DRELL, WILLIAM, b. Chicago, Ill, Jan. 26, 22; m. 43; c. 3. BIOCHEMISTRY. A.B, California, Los Angeles, 43, Nutrit. Found. fel, 44, M.A, 46, U.S. Pub. Health Serv. fel, 47-49, Ph.D.(chem), 49. Teaching asst. chem, California, Los Angeles, 43; chemist, Shell Chem. Corp, 44-46; asst. chem, California, Los Angeles, 46-47; res. fel, Calif. Inst. Tech, 49-51; asst. res. physiol. chemist, California, Los Angeles, 51-54; ESTAB. INVESTR, Am. Heart Asn, 54-59; CALBIOCHEM, 59- Instr, Los Angeles City Col, 47. Am. Chem. Soc; Soc. Exp. Biol. & Med; Am. Soc. Biol. Chem; Brit. Chem. Soc. Amino acid and vitamin microassay; antivitamins; animal nutrition; purine and pyrimidine metabolism; chromatography; catecholamine biosynthesis and metabolism; clinical chemistry. Address: 10933 N. Torrey Pines Rd, La Jolla, CA 92037.

DRENAN, JAMES W(ARNER), b. Middletown, N.Y, Nov. 16, 20; m. 51; c. 2. PHYSICAL CHEMISTRY. Ph.D.(chem), Rochester, 49. Technician, med. sch, Harvard, 41-42; fel, Illinois, 49-51; asst. prof. CHEM, Kentucky, 51-55; prof. & head dept, Lincoln Mem. Univ, 55-57; ASSOC. PROF, MILLIKIN UNIV, 57- U.S.A, 42-45. Am. Chem. Soc. Physical chemistry and statistical mechanics of liquids and solutions. Address: Dept. of Chemistry, Millikin University, Decatur, IL 62522.

DRENCHKO, JOHN, b. N.Y.C, June 1, 24; m. 51; c. 1. ORGANIC CHEMISTRY. B.Sc, Univ. Ill, 51; fel, Univ. Ky, 53-58, Ph.D.(org. chem), 58. Lab. asst. azo dye res, Am. Cyanamid Corp, 42-43, 46-47, chemist, 51-53; instr. chem, Univ. Ky, 53-58; chemist vat dye res, Gen. Aniline & Film Corp, 58-65; DIR. RES. & DEVELOP, VERONA-PHARMA CHEM. CORP, 65- Chemist, Gen. Aniline & Film Corp, summers 55-56. U.S.A.A.F, 43-46. Am. Chem. Soc. New dyes for use in colored films. Address: Hillsborough Rd, Belle Mead, NJ 08502.

DRENICK, R(UDOLF) F, b. Vienna, Austria, Aug. 20, 14; nat; m. 46; c. 3. APPLIED MATHEMATICS. Ph.D.(theoret. physics), Vienna Univ, 39. Asst. prof. math. & physics, Villanova Col, 39-44; engr. anal, Gen. Elec. Co, 46-49; mgr. anal. group, Radio Corp. Am, 49-57; res. mathematician, Bell Tel. Labs, Inc, 57-61; PROF. ELEC. ENG, POLYTECH. INST. BROOKLYN, 61-, chmn. dept, 66-67. Nat. Sci. Found. fel, 64-65. Consult. mathematician, Princeton, 62-; Res. Triangle Inst, Durham, 62- U.S.A, 45-46. Am. Math. Soc; fel. Inst. Elec. & Electronics Eng; Soc. Indust. & Appl. Math; Inst. Math. Statist; Opers. Res. Soc. Am. Application of mathematical methods to engineering problems. Address: 1165 Long Hill Rd, Millington, NJ 07946.

DRENNAN, JAMES E(LLIOTT), b. Salem, Ohio, Nov. 21, 26; m. 50; c. 2. PHYSICS, MATHEMATICS. B.A, Ohio Wesleyan, 49. Physicist, BATTELLE MEM. INST, 49-52, prin. physicist, 52-56, proj. leader reliability eng, 56-62, SR. PHYSICIST reliability & environ. effects, 62-66, ADVAN. ELECTRONICS DIV, DEPT. PHYSICS & METALL. 66- U.S.A.F, 45-46. Sr. mem. Inst. Elec. & Electronics Eng. Gaseous electronics; thermionic emission; reliability engineering; test design; radiation and environmental effects. Address: Advanced Electronics Division, Battelle Columbus Labs, 505 King Ave, Columbus, OH 43201.

DRENNAN, OLLIN J(UNIOR), b. Kirksville, Mo, Apr. 11, 25; m. 53; c. 3. HISTORY OF SCIENCE. A.B, Northeast Mo. State Teachers Col, 49; B.S, Mo. Valley Col, 50; Gen. Elec. Co. fel, Case, 52; M.S, Bradley, 55; Ph.D. (hist. sci), Wisconsin, 61. Prog. dir. & engr, Radio Sta. KMMO, 49; teacher, high sch, Mo, 51-52; instr. physics & chem, Mo. Valley Col, 52-53; asst. prof. physics, Evansville Col, 53-55; instr, Northeast Mo. State Teachers Col, 55-64; assoc. prof. physics, WEST. MICH. UNIV, 64-67, PROF. NATURAL SCI, 67-, ASSOC. DEAN, COL. GEN. STUDIES & AREA CHMN, GEN. STUDIES SCI, 71-, dir, 64-67. U.S.N.R, 44-46. Am. Asn. Physics Teachers; Hist. Sci. Soc. 19th and 20th century physical science; general education science. Address: 2419 Pine Ridge Rd, Kalamazoo, MI 49008.

DRESCH, F(RANCIS) W(ILLIAM), b. Sharon, Pa, Sept. 21, 13; m. 39. MATHEMATICAL ECONOMICS. A.B, Stanford, 32, A.M, 34; Ph.D.(math), California, 37. Asst, California, 35-37, Florence Noble traveling fel. math, Cambridge & Paris, 37-38; instr. math, California, 38-41; asst. dir. comput. & ballistics, U.S. Naval Proving Ground, 46-51, dir, 51-52; sr. statistician, STANFORD RES. INST, 52-57, mgr. indust. opers. res. & electronic data processing, 57-61, math. economist, 62-70, SR. MATH. ECONOMIST, 70- U.S.N.R, 41-46. AAAS; Am. Math. Soc; Inst. Math. Statist; Economet. Soc; Inst. Mgt. Sci; Brit. Oper. Res. Soc. Econometrics; ballistics; statistics; computing techniques; operations research. Address: Stanford Research Institute, 333 Ravenswood, Menlo Park, CA 94025.

DRESCHER, ROBERT F(REDERICK), b. Hibbing, Minn, Apr. 24, 25; m. 50; c. 4. PLANT PATHOLOGY. B.A, Minnesota, 50, M.S, 53, Ph.D.(plant path), 56. Chief microbiologist, paper sect, Buckman Labs, Tenn, 56-64; v.pres, Sharpley Labs, Va, 64-66; scientist, Rohm and Haas Co, Pa, 66-70; PROD. MGR, NOPCO CHEM. DIV, DIAMOND SHAMROCK CORP, 70- U.S.A, 43-46. AAAS; Am. Phytopath. Soc; Soc. Indust. Microbiol; Tech. Asn. Pulp & Paper Indust. Microbiology of pulp, paper, paints and petroleum; corrosion of metals by microorganisms, foods and textiles. Address: 977 Queens Dr, Yardley, PA 19067.

DRESCHER, W(ILLIA)M J(AMES) b. Craig, Colo, Aug. 20, 18; m. 41; c. 2. CIVIL ENGINEERING, GEOLOGY. B.S.E, Colorado, 40; M.S, Wisconsin, 56. Engr, Am. Bridge Co. Ind, 40-41; hydraul. engr, U.S. GEOL. SURV, Fla, 41-42, La, 42-44, WIS, 46-51, dist. engr, 51-57, br. area chief, 57-62, hydraul. res. engr, 62-66, RES. HYDROLOGIST, 66- Lectr, Univ. Wis; U.S. chmn. steering comt, Int. Field Year Great Lakes, Int. Hydrol. Decade. U.S.N.R, 44-46, Ens. Am. Geophys. Union; Am. Soc. Civil Eng; Geol. Soc. Am; Am. Water Works Asn; Am. Asn. Petrol. Geol; Am. Water Resources Asn. Ground-water hydrology. Address: 1815 University Ave, Madison, WI 53706.

DRESDEN, CARLTON F, b. Dodgeville, Wis, Oct. 17, 31; m. 55; c. 3. BIOCHEMISTRY, ORGANIC CHEMISTRY. B.S, Wisconsin State, Platteville, 53; M.S, Wisconsin, 57, Ph.D.(org. chem, biochem), 59. Assoc. prof. chem, Slippery Rock State Col, 59-61; asst. prof. biochem, La. State, 61-62; PROF. CHEM, SLIPPERY ROCK STATE COL, 62-, chmn. sci. div, 62-70. U.S.A, 53-55. AAAS; Am. Chem. Soc. Biochemistry of the myxomycetes; mechanism of action of bacterial toxins. Address: Dept. of Chemistry, Slippery Rock State College, Slippery Rock, PA 16057.

DRESDEN, MARC H(ENRI), b. Hague, Netherlands, July 21, 38; U.S. citizen; m. 60; c. 2. BIOCHEMISTRY, DEVELOPMENTAL BIOLOGY. B.S, Yale, 60; Nat. Insts. Health fels. & Ph.D.(bact. immunol), Harvard, 66. Atomic Energy fel. med, Mass. Gen. Hosp, 66-68; ASST. PROF. BIOCHEM, BAYLOR COL. MED, 68- AAAS; Soc. Develop. Biol; Am. Chem. Soc; Am. Inst. Biol. Sci. Collagen metabolism; limb regeneration in vertebrates. Address: Dept. of Biochemistry, Baylor College of Medicine, Houston, TX 77025.

DRESDEN, MAX, b. Amsterdam, Netherlands, Apr. 23, 18; U.S. citizen; m. 48; c. 2. THEORETICAL PHYSICS. Amsterdam, 35-38; Leyden, 38-39; Ph.D.(physics), Michigan, 46. Asst. PHYSICS, Michigan, 41-46; asst. prof, Kansas, 46-48, assoc. prof, 48-51, prof, 51-57, prof. & chmn. dept, Northwestern, 57-60; PROF, Iowa, 60-64; STATE UNIV. NEW YORK STONY BROOK, 64-, EXEC. OFF, INST. THEORET. PHYSICS, 66- Vis. prof, Hopkins, 57-58; vis. lectr, Am. Inst. Physics, 57-; summers, lectr, Inst. Theoret. Physics, 59, Bergen Summer Sch. Weak Interactions, 62 & Brandeis Summer Sch, 63. Consult, Argonne Nat. Lab, 57-; vis. sr. scientist, Brookhaven Nat. Lab, 64- Mem, bd. dirs, Midwest Univs. Res. Asn, 56-64; sci. bd. dirs, Midwest Res. Inst, 62- Fel. Am. Phys. Soc. Statistical mechanics; superconductivity; quantum field theory; behavior of positrons; parastatistics; symmetrics and S matrix theory; particle physics. Address: Dept. of Physics, State University of New York at Stony Brook, Stony Brook, NY 11790.

DRESDNER, RICHARD DAVID, b. New York, N.Y, Feb. 20, 18; m. 50; c. 2. CHEMISTRY. B.A, N.Y. Univ, 41; scholar, Pa. State, 41-42, fel, 42-47, M.S, 44, Ph.D.(phys. chem), 47. Res. engr, Battelle Mem. Inst, Ohio, 47-50; Picatinny Arsenal, 50-51; Micrometallic Corp, N.Y, 51-53; assoc. res. prof. chem, UNIV. FLA, 53-59, assoc. prof. CHEM, 59-66, PROF. & CHMN. DIV, 66- Consult, fluorine chem. With Off. Sci. Res. & Develop, 44. AAAS; Am. Chem. Soc. Electrolytic fluorinations; viscosity; low temperature air rectification; analytical photochemistry; kinetics; pyrotechnics; plastic filters; synthetic reactions; fluorochemicals; photochemical fluorinations. Address: Dept. of Chemistry, University of Florida, Gainesville, FL 32601.

DRESEL, PETER E, b. Ulm, Germany, Feb. 27, 25; nat; m. 47; c. 3. PHARMACOLOGY. B.S, Antioch Col, 48; Ph.D.(pharmacol), Rochester, 52. Instr. pharmacol, Cincinnati, 52; Emory, 53-54; res. pharmacologist, Wm. S. Merrell Co, 54-56; asst. prof. PHARMACOL. & THERAPEUT, UNIV. MANITOBA, 56-62, assoc. prof, 62-65, PROF, 65- Vis. scientist, Gothenburg, 63-64; Univ. Col, London, 70-71. U.S.A, 43-45. AAAS; Cardiac Muscle Soc; Am. Soc. Pharmacol. & Exp. Therapeut; Pharmacol. Soc. Can. Heart and circulation. Address: Dept. of Pharmacology, Faculty of Medicine, University of Manitoba, Winnipeg, Man, R3E 0W3, Can.

DRESHER, WILLIAM H(ENRY), b. Phila, Pa, Mar. 15, 30; m. 58; c. 2. CHEMICAL METALLURGY. B.S, Drexel Inst, 53; Ph.D.(metall), Utah, 56. Assoc. metallurgist, Union Carbide Nuclear Co, 56-60, group leader, nuclear div, Union Carbide Corp, 60-64, asst. dir. res, mining & metals div, 64-65, group leader, Union Carbide Res. Inst, 65-67, proj. mgr, fibrous ceramic mat, corp. res. dept, 67-71; DEAN COL. MINES, UNIV. ARIZ, 71-; DIR, ARIZ. BUR. MINES, 71- Am. Inst. Min, Metall. & Petrol. Eng; Am. Chem. Soc; Am. Soc. Test. & Mat. Extractive metallurgy of non-ferrous metals; mechanical and chemical properties of metals and ceramics; fibrous ceramic materials; new venture management. Address: College of Mines, University of Arizona, Tucson, AZ 85721.

DRESHFIELD, ARTHUR C(HARLES), b. Brooklyn, N.Y, Oct. 19, 01; m. 25; c. 4. CHEMISTRY. A.B, Columbia, 22, Ch.E, 24. Chemist, Taylor Chem. Co, 24-25; tech. dir, Paper Makers Chem. Corp, Mich, 25-37; dir. opers, Hercules Powder Co, Del, 37-44; mgr. res, H.P. Smith Paper Co, Ill, 44-46; mgr. spec. div, Chicago Testing Lab, 46-59; dir. paper res. & develop. dept, Glidden Co, 59-61, mgr. tech. serv, 61-62, res. & develop, chem. group, 62-68; TEACHER DEPT. SCI, SEVERN SCH, 68- Consult. chem. engr, 46-59; staff consult, Chicago Paper Testing Lab, 68- Emer. mem. Tech. Asn. Pulp & Paper Indust; emer. mem. Am. Inst. Chem. Eng. Manufacture of dry rosin size, casein, wax emulsions, paper and board. Address: Severn School, Water St, Severna Park, MD 21146.

DRESHFIELD, ARTHUR C(HARLES), JR, b. Kalamazoo, Mich, Nov. 9, 29; m. 57; c. 3. CHEMICAL ENGINEERING. B.S, Illinois, 51; M.S, Lawrence Col, 53, Ph.D, 56. Res. engr. papermaking processes, Scott Paper Co, 55-57; from res. group mgr. pulping & paperboard to dir. res, Fibreboard Paper Prod, 57-68, DIR. PROD. DEVELOP, FIBREBOARD CORP, 68- Chmn. indust. adv. coun, forest prods. lab, California, 64-65. Steele Medal, Inst. Paper Chem, 56. U.S.A.R, 51-, 1st Lt. Tech. Asn. Pulp & Paper Indust. Alkaline pulping; papermaking; packaging. Address: Fiberboard Corp, 55 Francisco St, San Francisco, CA 94133.

DRESKA, NOEL, b. Kankakee, Ill, Dec. 24, 28. PHYSICS. A.B, Col. St. Francis (Ill), 50; Nat. Sci. Found. summer fels, 59, 60 & 61; Arthur Schmitt fel, 61-64; Ph.D.(physics), Ohio State, 64. Instr. PHYSICS, Col. St. Francis (Ill), 64-66; asst. prof, LEWIS COL, 66-70, ASSOC. PROF. & CHMN. DEPT, 70- Am. Asn. Physics Teachers. High resolution, infrared and molecular spectroscopy. Address: Dept. of Physics, Lewis College, Lockport, IL 60441.

DRESKIN, SANFORD A, b. Newark, N.J, June 30, 36; m. 59; c. 2. PHYSICS, MATHEMATICS. B.S, Muhlenberg Col, 58; M.S, Stevens Inst. Tech, 61. Jr. scientist, Feltman Res. Lab, Picatinny Arsenal, N.J, 58-59; res. engr, Gulton Industs. Inc, 59-61; engr, astro electronics div, RCA, 61-62, mem. tech. staff, David Sarnoff Res. Center, 62-65; res. scientist, Nat. Cash Register Co, 65-66; SR. SCIENTIST, AM. CAN RES. LABS, 66- Am. Phys. Soc. Piezoelectricity; piezoresistance; photoconductivity; transport phenomena in thin films; holography; information storage and retrieval; thin film deposition; physical optics. Address: American Can Co, Princeton Lab, P.O. Box 50, Princeton, NJ 08540.

DRESNER, JOSEPH, b. Belgium, Feb. 11, 27; nat; m. 57. PHYSICS. B.S.E, Michigan, 49, M.S, 50; Ph.D.(physics), N.Y. Univ, 58. Physicist Hosp. Joint Diseases, N.Y, 50-53; asst, N.Y. Univ, 54-58; MEM. TECH. STAFF, DAVID SARNOFF RES. CTR, RCA CORP, 58- Consult, Hosp. Joint Diseases, N.Y, 53-54; vis. prof, sch. engr. Sao Carlos, Univ. Sao Paulo, 71-72. U.S.A, 46-47. Am. Phys. Soc. Luminescence and photoconductivity of solids; medical radiation physics; solid state physics. Address: David Sarnoff Research Center, RCA Corp, Princeton, NJ 08540.

DRESNER, LAWRENCE, b. Brooklyn, N.Y, Sept. 16, 29; m. 52; c. 4. THEORETICAL PHYSICS. B.S, City Col, 50; M.A, Princeton, 52, Ph.D.(physics), 59. PHYSICIST, OAK RIDGE NAT. LAB, 54- Sci. Res. Soc. Am. Reactor physics; nuclear physics; water desalination; shock waves. Address: Oak Ridge National Lab, P.O. Box X, Oak Ridge, TN 37831.

DRESS, WILLIAM J(OHN), b. Buffalo, N.Y, June 9, 18. TAXONOMIC BOTANY. B.A, Buffalo, 39; Ph.D.(bot), Cornell Univ, 53. Asst, L.H. BAILEY HORTORIUM, CORNELL UNIV, 47-53, asst. prof. bot, 53-57, taxonomist, 57-60, assoc. prof. BOT, 60-68, PROF, 68- Ed, Baileya; Gentes Herbarum. U.S.A.A.F, 42-45. Am. Soc. Plant Taxon; Int. Asn. Plant Taxon. Plant taxonomy, especially of cultivated plants; revision of genus Chrysopsis. Address: L.H. Bailey Hortorium, Cornell University, Ithaca, NY 14850.

DRESSEL, F(RANCIS) G(EORGE), b. Hart, Mich, Sept. 22, 04; m. 32; c. 2. MATHEMATICS. B.S, Mich. State Col, 28; fel, Michigan, 28-29, M.S, 29; Chicago, 30, 38; Ph.D.(math), Duke 33; Brown, 39-40. Instr. MATH, DUKE UNIV, 29-41, asst. prof, 41-45, assoc. prof, 45-52, PROF, 52- Mem. N.C. Stand-by Unit, U.S. Air Force, 51-; asst. math. sci. div, off. ord. res, U.S. Army, 51-; teacher, civil aeronaut. admin, Duke, 42-43. Am. Math. Soc; Math. Asn. Am. Integral equations; Stieltjes integrals; partial differential equations. Address: 2502 Frances St, Durham, NC 27707.

DRESSEL, HERMAN OTTO, b. N.Y.C, Jan. 15, 26; c. 1. ELECTROOPTICS. B.S, Dartmouth Col, 47, M.S, 48. Jr. engr, physics lab, Sylvania Elec. Prod. Inc, 48-54, sr. engr, 54-60; res. engr, GTE LABS, INC, 60-61, advan. res. engr, 62-65, eng. specialist, 65-67, mem. tech. staff, 67-69, GROUP MGR. ELECTRON OPTICS, 69- U.S.N, 44-46. Inst. Elec. & Electronics Eng; Sci. Res. Soc. Am. Electron tube research and electron optics of devices for operation at centimeter, millimeter and submillimeter wavelengths; system and propagation studies at millimeter wavelengths; research in electron beam accessed imaging, storage and display devices. Address: GTE Labs, Inc, 208-20 Willets Point Blvd, Bayside, NY 11360.

DRESSEL, PAUL L(EROY), b. Youngstown, Ohio, Nov. 29, 10; m. 32; c. 3. MATHEMATICS, STATISTICS. A.B, Wittenberg Col, 31; A.M, Mich. State, 34; Ph.D.(statist), Michigan, 39. Instr. math, MICH. STATE UNIV, 34-40, asst. prof, 40-44, prof. & head bd. exam, 44-54, prof. & dir. eval. servs, 54-59, instr. res, 59-64, PROF. UNIV. RES. & DIR. INST. RES, 64-, ASST. PROVOST, 60-, dir. comp. study eval, 49-53, counseling, 44-54. Gen. Ed. Bd. fel, 39-40. With U.S.A, 44. AAAS; fel. Am. Psychol. Asn; Psychomet. Soc. Educational research; higher education; evaluation in general education. Address: Michigan State University, East Lansing, MI 48823.

DRESSEL, R(ALPH) W(ILLIAM), b. Buffalo, N.Y, Mar. 3, 22; m. 45; c. 4. PHYSICS. B.S, Union Col, 44; Atomic Energy Comn. fel, Univ. Ill, 49-50; Ph.D.(physics), 50. Asst. instr, Union Col, 42-44; mem. staff, radiation lab, Mass. Inst. Technol, 44-46; asst, Univ. Ill, 46-49; asst. prof. physics, N.MEX. STATE UNIV, 50-52, assoc. prof, 52-56, prof, 56-61, assoc. physicist, phys. sci. lab, 52-56, physicist, 56-61, head dept. physics, univ, 57-61, PROF. PHYSICS, 56-; PHYSICIST, NUCLEAR EFFECTS BR, WHITE SANDS MISSILE RANGE, 61- AAAS; Am. Asn. Physics Teachers; Am. Phys. Soc; Philos. Sci. Asn. Electromagnetic radiation; interaction of high energy quanta, electrons with matter. Address: 1740 Imperial Ridge, Las Cruces, NM 88001.

DRESSELHAUS, G(ENE) (FREDERICK), b. Ancon, C.Z, Nov. 7, 29; m. 58; c. 4. SOLID STATE PHYSICS. A.B, California, 51, Ph.D.(physics), 55. Instr. physics, Chicago, 55-56; asst. prof, Cornell, 56-60; MEM. STAFF, LINCOLN LAB, MASS. INST. TECHNOL, 60- Consult, Gen. Elec. Res. Lab, 56-60; Oak Ridge Nat. Lab, 58-60. Fel. Am. Phys. Soc. Electronic energy bands in solids; surface impedance of metals; excitons in insulators. Address: Lincoln Lab, Massachusetts Institute of Technology, Lexington, MA 02173.

DRESSELHAUS, MILDRED S, b. Brooklyn, N.Y, Nov. 11, 30; m. 58; c. 4. SOLID STATE PHYSICS. A.B, Hunter Col, 51; Fulbright fel, Cambridge, 51-52; A.M, Radcliffe Col, 53; Bell fel, Chicago, 56-57, Ph.D.(physics), 58. Nat. Sci. Found. fel, Cornell, 58-60; mem. staff, Lincoln Lab, MASS. INST. TECHNOL, 60-67, Abby Rockefeller Mauze vis. prof, DEPT. ELEC. ENG, 67-68, PROF, 68- Am. Phys. Soc. Semimetals and semiconductors; optical properties of solids; electronic band structure of solids. Address: Dept. of Electrical Engineering, Massachusetts Institute of Technology, 77 Massachusetts Ave, Cambridge, MA 02139.

DRESSER, HUGH W, b. Utica, N.Y, Jan. 31, 30; m. 51; c. 2. GEOLOGY, PALEONTOLOGY. B.S, Cincinnati, 50, M.S, 51; Ph.D.(geol), Wyoming, 60. Jr. geologist, Carter Oil Co, 51-52, field geologist, 52-54; geologist II, Humble Oil & Ref. Co, 59-64, res. geologist, Esso Prod. Res. Co, 64-65; asst. prof. GEOL, MONT. COL. MINERAL SCI. & TECHNOL, 65-68, ASSOC. PROF, 68- U.S.A, 54-56. Am. Asn. Petrol. Geol; Geol. Soc. Am; Am. Inst. Prof. Geol; Soc. Econ. Paleont. & Mineral; Paleont. Soc. Environmental stratigraphy and palichnology. Address: Dept. of Geology, Montana College of Mineral Science & Technology, Butte, MT 59701.

DRESSER, MILES JOEL, b. Spokane, Wash, Dec. 19, 35; m. 59; c. 3. PHYSICS. B.A, Linfield Col, 57; Ph.D.(physics), Iowa State, 64. Asst. prof. PHYSICS, WASH. STATE UNIV, 63-70, ASSOC. PROF, 70- Am. Phys. Soc; Am. Vacuum Soc; Am. Asn. Physics Teachers. Ultra high vacuum surface physics; surface ionization; thermionic and field emission; mass spectrometry; surface and solid diffusion. Address: Dept. of Physics, Washington State University, Pullman, WA 99163.

DRESSER, THORPE, b. Garfield, Utah, March 2, 11; m. 41; c. 3. CHEMICAL ENGINEERING. B.S, Mo. Sch. Mines, 33; scholar, Rensselaer Polytech, 33-34, M.S, 34, fel, 34-36, D.Ch.E, 36. Technologist, Sinclair Ref. Co, 36-40, process engr, 40-49, asst. div. dir, res. labs, 49-69; SR. RES. CHEM. ENGR, ATLANTIC RICHFIELD CO, 69- AAAS; Am. Chem. Soc; Am. Inst. Chem. Eng; fel. Am. Inst. Chem. Phase pressure, volume and temperature; phase equilibria; distillation calculations; thermodynamics; computerized calculations. Address: 15740 S. Spaulding Ave, Harvey, IL 60426.

DRESSLER, BYRON B(ROWN), b. Shelbyville, Ill, Aug. 30, 15, m. 41; c. 3. MATHEMATICS. A.B, Illinois, 37, A.M, 38; Ohio State, 46-48. Instr. math, Ala. Polytech, 40-46; asst, Ohio State, 46-48; asst. prof. MATH, KENT STATE UNIV, 48-59, assoc. prof, 59-68, PROF, 68- DIR. COMPUT. CTR, 63- Data Processing Mgt. Asn. Differential equations; computer science. Address: 621 Crain Ave, Kent, OH 44240.

DRESSLER, HANS, b. Vienna, Austria, July 21, 26; nat; m. 56; c. 1. ORGANIC & BIOCHEMISTRY. Vienna Univ, 49; A.M, Columbia, 51, Ph.D.(chem), 54. Asst. chem, Columbia, 51-52, asst, 53; fel, monomer synthesis, Mellon Inst, 54-56; sr. chemist, Verona Res. Center, KOPPERS CO, INC, 56-62, GROUP MGR, MONROEVILLE RES. CENTER, 62- Am. Chem. Soc; Am. Inst. Chem; N.Y. Acad. Sci; The Chem. Soc. Organic synthesis; product and process development. Address: Koppers Co, Inc, Monroeville Research Center, 440 College Park Dr, Monroeville, PA 15146.

DRESSLER, MITCHELL LLOYD, b. Providence, R.I, Jan. 11, 43; m. 70. ORGANIC CHEMISTRY. B.S, Univ. R.I, 64; Allied Chem, Busch, Nat. Insts. Health, Harrison, Socony Mobil & univ. fels, Nat. Sci. Found. summer fel. & Ph.D.(org. chem), Univ. Pa, 69. SR. RES. CHEMIST, ARCO CHEM. CO, GLENOLDEN, 69- Am. Chem. Soc. Chemical reactivities of thienopyridines; chemical treatment of cellulosic material to improve durable press and flame retardant properties. Address: 220 Locust St, Philadelphia, PA 19106.

DRESSLER, ROBERT L(OUIS), b. Marquette, Kans, Aug. 12, 23. ORGANIC CHEMISTRY. B.S, Univ. Denver, 56, M.S, 57; Shell Oil fel, Univ. Colo, Boulder, 61-62, Ph.D.(org. chem), 62. Res. assoc. org. chem, Fla. State Univ, 62-63; res. chemist, Denver Res. Inst, Univ. Denver, 64-66; res. assoc. org. chem, Univ. Colo, 66-67; asst. prof. CHEM, FT. HAYS KANS. STATE COL, 67-71, ASSOC. PROF, 71- Nat. Insts. Health fel, 62-63. Am. Chem. Soc; The Chem. Soc. Chemistry and synthesis of polynuclear aromatic compounds, diterpenes, fluoro-organic and heterocyclic compounds. Address: Dept. of Chemistry, Ft. Hays Kansas State College, Hays, KS 67601.

DRESSLER, RUSSELL G(EORGE), b. Mishawaka, Ind, Dec. 17, 07; m. 32; c. 1. CHEMICAL ENGINEERING. B.S, Southern California, 31, M.S, 34, Ph.D.(chem), 39. Chief chemist, Procter & Gamble, Calif, 31-32; chem. engr, Globe Grain & Milling Co, 32-37; res. chem. engr, Colgate-Palmolive-Peet Co, N.J, 39-40; sr. chem. engr, Chem. Warfare Serv, Edgewood

Arsenal, 40-41, Mich, 41-42, Colo, 42-44; dir. pilot plants, Calif. Res. Corp, 44-46; chief gas synthesis demonstration plant, U.S. Bur. Mines, 46-53; tech. asst. to pres, Atlas Powder Co, 53-55; PROF. CHEM, TRINITY UNIV, 58-, chmn. dept, 58-69. Chem. process consult, 55- Am. Chem. Soc; Am. Inst. Chem. Eng. Hydrogenation of organic chemicals; organic unit synthesis reactions; chemical and petroleum process development; synthetic liquid fuels development; engineering economics; chemical plant design and construction; reservoir evaporation control. Address: 204 Carolwood Dr, San Antonio, TX 78213.

DREVDAHL, ELMER R(ANDOLPH), b. Marquette, Mich, Aug. 24, 26; m. 49; c. 2. MINING ENGINEERING, COMPUTER SCIENCE. B.S, Mich. Col. Min. & Tech, 48; Colo. Sch. Mines, 50; fel, Washington (Seattle), 50-51, M.S, 51. Min. engr, Jones & Laughlin Ore Co, Mich, 48-50; asst. prof. MINING ENG, S.Dak. Sch. Mines & Tech, 51-55; Arizona, 55-58, assoc. prof, 58-63; head div. tech, Ariz. West. Col, 63-65; dir. tech. ed, CLARK COL, 65-66, dean occup. educ, 66-69, ASSOC. PROF, 69- Instr. & exam, U.S. Bur. Mines First Aid Training; summers, seaman, Pittsburg Steamship Co, 43, engr, Mont. Dakota Utilities Co, 52, asst. rock drill engr, Homestake Mining Co, 53, explor. engr, Rushmore Clareton Oil Co, 54, resident engr, U.S. Pub. Health Serv, 56, sanit. engr, 57, Nat. Park Serv, 58, analyst, Steep Rock Iron Mines, Ltd, Can, 61. U.S.N, 44-46. Am. Inst. Mining, Metall. & Petrol. Eng; Nat. Soc. Prof. Eng; Am. Soc. Civil Eng; Am. Soc. Eng. Educ. Analysis of equipment systems and application of computers to mining operations. Address: Dept. of Engineering & Technology, Clark College, Vancouver, WA 98663.

DREVES, ROBERT G(EORGE), b. Brooklyn, N.Y, Oct. 24, 14; m. 38; c. 2. AERONAUTICAL ENGINEERING. N.Y. Univ, 32-38. Coordinator prod. control aircraft prods, Sperry Gyroscope Co, 41-43, asst. aircraft flight instruments, 43-44; mil. training specialist, U.S. NAVAL TRAINING DEVICE CTR, 46-52, head aerospace syst. trainers dept, 60-65, assoc. tech. dir, maintenance eng, 65-69, DIR. LOGISTICS & FIELD ENG, 70- U.S.N, 43-46, Lt. AAAS; Soc. Logistics Eng; Am. Inst. Aeronaut. & Astronaut. Design, development, test and utilization of air weapon system simulators for training of pilots and air crews. Address: 1215 Ensenada Rd, Orlando, FL 32807.

DREW, DAN DALE, b. Abilene, Tex, Sept. 29, 26; m. 49; c. 5. COMPUTER SCIENCE, MATHEMATICS. B.S, North Texas State, 50, M.S, 51; Ph.D. (eng), Tex. A&M Univ, 66. Mathematician, U.S. Naval Ord. Test Sta, Calif, 51-53; analyst digital comput, Gen. Dynamics/Convair, Tex, 53-56, group engr, 56-59; appl. sci. rep, Int. Bus. Mach. Corp, Tex, 59-60; comput. specialist, TEX. A&M UNIV, 60-62, assoc. dir, 62-68, assoc. prof. INDUST. ENG, 66-68, PROF. & DIR. COMPUT. & INFO. SCI. DIV, 68- U.S.N, 44-46. Asn. Comput. Mach; Soc. Indust. & Appl. Math. Digital computing; numerical analysis in the field of structural mechanics. Address: Teague Bldg, Texas A&M University, College Station, TX 77840.

DREW, DAVID A(BBOTT), b. Philadelphia, Pa, Sept. 19, 16; m. 43; c. 2. CHEMICAL ENGINEERING. B.S, Pennsylvania, 37, Ph.D.(chem. eng), 44. Mem. staff, Elec. Storage Battery Co, 37-39; chem. engr, HERCULES INC, 43-51, supvr. pilot plant div, 51-55, MGR. GEN. SERV. DIV, 55- Inst. Chem. Eng. Address: Research Center, Hercules Inc, Wilmington, DE 19899.

DREW, DAVID P, b. Birmingham, Eng, Mar. 28, 43. GEOMORPHOLOGY, HYDROLOGY. B.A, Univ. Nottingham, 64; Ph.D.(geog), Bristol Univ, 67. Demonstr, GEOG, Bristol Univ, 64-68; ASST. PROF, UNIV. SASK, REGINA, 68- Mem, Brit. Cave Res. Group, 60-; Brit. Geomorphol. Res. Group, 64- Am. Geophys. Union. Morphometric analysis of tropical land forms and drainage nets in Jamaica; badland development and piping in southern Saskatchewan. Address: Dept. of Geography, University of Saskatchewan, Regina, Sask, Can.

DREW, FRANCES L, b. Pittsburgh, Pa, Apr. 30, 17; m. 36; 49; c. 3. PUBLIC HEALTH. Vassar Col, 34-36; M.D, McGill, 42; M.P.H, Pittsburgh, 61. Res. assoc. med, McGill, 43-48; instr. med, UNIV. PITTSBURGH, 48-61, clin. asst. prof. PREV. MED, 61-69, CLIN. ASSOC. PROF, 69- Psychosomic Soc; Am. Pub. Health Asn; Asn. Teachers Prev. Med. Hypertension; epidemiology of chronic diseases; social determinants of disease. Address: Dept. of Preventive Medicine, M200 Scaife Hall, University of Pittsburgh, Pittsburgh, PA 15213.

DREW, HOWARD DENNIS, b. Newark, Ohio, June 7, 39; m. 65. PHYSICS. B.S, Pittsburgh, 62; Ph.D.(physics), Cornell, 68. Res. assoc. SOLID STATE PHYSICS, UNIV. MD, COLLEGE PARK, 67-70, ASST. PROF, 70- Am. Phys. Soc. Electrodynamics of metals and superconductors at millimeter and submillimeter wavelengths; infrared detectors and lasers. Address: Dept. of Physics, University of Maryland, College Park, MD 20740.

DREW, HOWARD F(ELSHAW), b. Lyons Falls, N.Y, Oct. 22, 23; m. 44; c. 2. ORGANIC CHEMISTRY. B.A, Amherst Col, 44, M.A, 47; Ph.D.(chem), Univ. Minn, 51. Res. chemist, PROCTER & GAMBLE CO, 51-57, head org. synthesis sect, 57-58, org. res. dept, 58-59, assoc. dir, 59-69, DIR. res. div, 69-71, FOODS & COFFEE TECHNOL. DIV, 71- U.S.A.A.F, 43-46. Am. Chem. Soc. Address: 69 Reily Rd, Cincinnati, OH 45215.

DREW, JAMES V(AN), b. Flushing, N.Y, Sept. 21, 30; m. 56; c. 3. SOIL SCIENCE. B.S, Rutgers, 52, Ph.D.(soil sci), 57. Asst. arctic soils, Rutgers Univ, 55-57; asst. prof. AGRON, UNIV. NEBR, LINCOLN, 57-61, assoc. prof, 61-64, PROF, 64-, ASST. DEAN GRAD. COL, 70- U.S.A.F, 52-53. AAAS; Am. Soc. Agron; Int. Soc. Soil Sci. Soil genesis, classification, survey and mineralogy; remote sensing of soil resources. Address: 412 Administration Bldg, University of Nebraska, Lincoln, NE 68508.

DREW, JOHN H, b. Cleveland, Ohio, Nov. 7, 43; m. 69. MATHEMATICS. B.S, Case Inst. Technol, 65; Ph.D.(math), Univ. Minn, 70. ASST. PROF. MATH, COL. WILLIAM & MARY, 70- Math. Asn. Am. Study of ordinary differential equations for a forced second order system subject to hysteresis. Address: Dept. of Mathematics, College of William & Mary, Williamsburg, VA 23185.

DREW, LAWRENCE JAMES, b. Astoria, N.Y, Dec. 18, 40; m; c. 1. STATISTICS, GEOLOGY. B.S, Univ. N.H, 62; M.S, Pa. State Univ, 64, Ph.D, 66. Fel, Pa. State Univ, 66-67; res. geologist, U.S. Bur. Mines, 67; res. scientist, Geotech Div, Teledyne Inc, 67-69; SR. RES. GEOLOGIST, CITIES SERV. OIL CO, 69- Int. Asn. Math. Geol; Am. Statist. Asn; Opers. Res. Soc. Am. Statistical analysis of geological data; quantitative mapping procedures and stratigraphy; exploration drilling strategies; economic analysis of exploration data; statistical design and analysis of hydrogeology experiments; petrography; mineralogy; petrology. Address: Exploration Production Research, Cities Service Oil Co, Box 50408, Tulsa, OK 74150.

DREW, LELAND OVERBEY, b. Charleston, S.C, June 13, 23; m. 44; c. 1. AGRICULTURAL ENGINEERING. B.S, Clemson Col, 43; Repub. Steel Co. fel. & M.S, Iowa State Col, 45; California, Davis, 50-51; Nat. Sci. Found. fel. & Ph.D.(agr. eng), Mich. State, 63. Instr. agr. eng, Clemson Col, 43-44; asst. agr. engr, Edisto Br, S.C. Agr. Exp. Sta, 45-47; asst. prof. AGR. ENG, Georgia, 47-50, assoc. prof, 50-56; adv, Int. Co-op. Admin, Lebanon, 56-59 & Pakistan, 59-60; ASSOC. PROF, Clemson, 63-68; OHIO STATE UNIV, 68- Adv. to dean col. technol. & agr. eng, Univ. Udaipur, India. Am. Soc. Agr. Eng. Agricultural machinery, including tillage and seedling mechanics, harvesting and post-harvest handling of fruits and vegetables. Address: Dept. of Agricultural Engineering, College of Agriculture & Home Economics, Ohio State University, Columbus, OH 43210.

DREW, PHILIP GARFIELD, b. Dedham, Mass, Jan. 25, 32; m. 61; c. 2. SYSTEMS ENGINEERING. B.S, Carnegie Inst. Tech, 54; S.M, Harvard, 59, Ph.D.(eng), 64. Res. asst. control systs. eng, Harvard, 61-64; MEM. PROF. STAFF ENG, ARTHUR D. LITTLE, INC, 64- Summer consult. engr, Rand Corp, 60, 61; lectr, Harvard Summer Sch, 65. C.Eng, 54-58, 1st Lt. Inst. Elec. & Electronics Eng. Systems analyses; hospital design. Address: Arthur D. Little, Inc, 35 Acorn Park, Cambridge, MA 02140.

DREW, PHIL(IP) W(ARNER), b. Salem, Ore, Feb. 28, 04; m. 28; c. 3. CHEMISTRY. B.S, Knox Col, 25. Compounder, Goodyear Tire & Rubber Co, 25-35, foreman in process dept, 35-39, chief chemist, 39-46, tech. supt, 46-50, mgr. fabric develop, 50-57, mgr. auto tire design, 57-66, dir. develop. ctr, Goodyear S.A, Luxembourg, 66-70; RETIRED. Am. Chem. Soc; Soc. Automotive Eng. Rubber chemistry. Address: 2737 Weymouth Rd, Medina, OH 44256.

DREW, ROBERT DANIEL, b. Bridgeport, Conn, Dec. 2, 16; m. 41; c. 5. CHEMICAL ENGINEERING. B.E, Yale, 39. Res. engr, Paulsboro Res. Lab, MOBIL OIL CORP, 39-50, supvry. engr, 50-58, supvr. eng. & construct, 58-59, supvr. tech. serv, 59-62, MGR. AIR & WATER CONSERV. MFG, N.AM. DIV, N.Y, 62- Am. Inst. Chem. Eng; Am. Chem. Soc. Process and catalyst development in catalytic cracking and reforming; technical service to petroleum refining operations. Address: Mobil Oil Corp, North American Division, 150 E. 42nd St, New York, NY 10017.

DREW, ROBERT T(AYLOR), b. Red Bank, N.J, Apr. 22, 36; m. 62; c. 3. HEALTH PHYSICS. B.S, Rensselaer Polytech, 58; M.S, N.Y. Univ, 62, Ph.D. (radiation health), 68. Sanit. chem. trainee, N.Y. State Dept. Health, 58-59; chemist, N.J. Dept. Health, 60; res. asst, inst. environ. med, N.Y. Univ. Med. Ctr, 60-67, assoc. res. scientist, 67-69, instr, 69-70; SR. STAFF FEL, NAT. INST. ENVIRON. HEALTH SCI, 70- Health Physics Soc; Am. Indust. Hyg. Asn. Inhalation toxicology, especially effects of short and long term exposures to environmental agents and combinations of agents; environmental radiation. Address: National Institute of Environmental Health Sciences, P.O. Box 12233, Research Triangle Park, NC 27709.

DREW, RUSSELL C(OOPER), b. Chicago, Ill, Aug. 16, 31; m. 53; c. 5. PHYSICS. B.S, Colorado, 53; Ph.D.(physics), Duke, 61. TECH. ASST. reentry vehicles, U.S. Naval Spec. Proj. Off, 63-66; SPACE SCI. & TECHNOL, OFF. SCI. & TECHNOL, EXEC. OFF. PRESIDENT, 66- U.S.N, 53-, Capt. Am. Inst. Aeronaut. & Astronaut. Electron spin resonance; radiation damage studies; missile reentry systems; space science and technology; aeronautical systems. Address: Office of Science & Technology, Executive Office, The White House, Washington, DC 20506.

DREW, RUTH M(IRIAM), b. Providence, R.I, Dec. 11, 11. BACTERIOLOGY. A.B, Marietta Col, 34, hon. D.Sc, 58; M.S, Cincinnati, 35; Ph.D.(med. scis), Radcliffe Col, 50. Med. technologist, Good Samaritan & Holmes Hosps, Ohio, 35-41; instr. & lectr. bacter, Cincinnati, 38-41; bacteriologist, Parke-Davis Co, 42-43; Harvard, 43-45; instr. med. bacter, 45-47, Ernst fel, 47-49; assoc. med. bacteriologist, BROOKHAVEN NAT. LAB, 49-58, assoc. scientist, 58-59, SCIENTIST, 59- AAAS; Am. Soc. Microbiol; Am. Asn. Immunol. Pathogenic bacteriology; tissue culture. Address: Medical Dept, Brookhaven National Lab, Upton, NY 11973.

DREW, THOMAS B(RADFORD), b. Medford, Mass, Feb. 9, 02; m. 30; c. 3. CHEMICAL ENGINEERING. B.S, Mass. Inst. Tech, 23, M.S, 24. Asst, Mass. Inst. Tech, 24-25; instr. chem. eng, Drexel Inst, 25-28; Mass. Inst. Tech, 28-34; chem. engr, exp. sta, E.I. du Pont de Nemours & Co, 34-40; lectr. CHEM. ENG, Columbia, 36-40, assoc. prof, 40-45, prof, 45-65, head dept, 48-57; prof, MASS. INST. TECHNOL, 65-67, EMER. PROF, 67- Dir. eng, substitute alloy mat. labs, Manhattan Dist, Columbia, 42-43; bd. sr. reviewers, U.S. Atomic Energy Cmn, 52-57; vis. prof, Mass. Inst. Tech, 59-60; Ford Found. prog. specialist, Birla Inst. Tech, India, 63-65. Consult, E.I. du Pont de Nemours & Co, 43-44, 51-62; Brookhaven Nat. Lab, 46-; ed, Advan. in Chem. Eng, 56- Max Jakob Mem. Award, Am. Soc. Mech. Engrs. & Am. Inst. Chem. Engrs, 67. With Off. Sci. Res. & Develop, 41. AAAS; Am. Inst. Chem. Eng.(Walker Award, 37, inst. lectr, 51); hon. mem. Am. Soc. Mech. Eng; Am. Chem. Soc; fel. N.Y. Acad. Sci. Flow of fluids; heat transmission; mass transfer and diffusion; combustion; nuclear engineering. Address: Temple, NH 03084.

DREW, WILLIAM A(RTHUR), b. Grosse Pointe, Mich, Apr. 29, 29; m. 57; c. 1. ENTOMOLOGY. A.B, Marietta Col, 51; Ph.D.(entom), Mich. State Univ, 58. Asst. prof. ENTOM, OKLA. STATE UNIV, 58-63, assoc. prof, 63-68, PROF, 68-, CURATOR, 58- U.S.A, 52-53. Entom. Soc. Am; Entom. Soc. Can. Curator insect collection Oklahoma; taxonomy of Hemiptera and spiders. Address: Dept. of Entomology, Oklahoma State University, Stillwater, OK 74074.

DREW, WILLIAM B(ROOKS), b. Greenwich, Conn, Dec. 11, 08; m. 30; c. 2. PLANT ECOLOGY. S.B, Mass. State Col, 30; A.M, Harvard, 31, Ph.D. (taxon. bot), 34; Michigan, 36. Asst, Gray Herbarium, Mass, 31-35; prof. biol, Cambridge Sch. Lib. Arts, 34-35; prof. biol. & geol, Am. Int. Col, 35-36; vis. asst. prof. bot, Tennessee, 36-37; Missouri, 37-38; vis. assoc. prof. & acting head dept, Carleton Col, 38-39; asst. prof, Missouri, 39-43; botanist, Cinchona Missions, Ecuador, Colombia, 43-45; forest ecologist, U.S. Forest Serv, Mont, 45; assoc. prof. BOT, MICH. STATE UNIV, 45-48, PROF, 48-, CHMN. DEPT. BOT. & PLANT PHYSIOL, 62-, head dept, 48-62. Botanist, Boyd exped, E.Greenland, 33. With For. Econ. Admin; Soil Conserv. Serv. Fel. AAAS; Bot. Soc. Am; Ecol. Soc. Am; Am. Soc. Plant Taxon; Am. Bryol. & Lichenological Soc; Am. Soc. Nat. Plant ecology; floristics of prairie vegetation; taxonomy; flora of Michigan. Address: Dept. of Botany & Plant Physiology, Michigan State University, East Lansing, MI 48823.

DREWES, HARALD D, b. Ger, Nov. 22, 27; nat; m. 57; c. 2. GEOLOGY. B.A, Wash. Univ, 51; Binney fel, Yale, 51-52, M.A, 52, Stanolind fel, 52-53, Ph.D, 54. GEOLOGIST, U.S. GEOL. SURV, 54- U.S.A, 46-48. Am. Geol. Soc; Ger. Geol. Asn. Thrust tectonics of the basin and range geologic province, especially southeastern California, eastern Nevada and southeastern Arizona, related problems of faulting, gneiss dome development, magmatism, sedimentation and mineralization. Address: U.S. Geological Survey, Federal Center, Bldg. 25, Denver, CO 80225.

DREWES, PATRICIA ANN, b. Chicago, Ill, Jan. 12, 32. BIOLOGICAL CHEMISTRY. B.A, Immaculate Heart Col, 53; Ph.D.(biol. chem), Univ. Calif, Los Angeles, 65. Control chemist, Vitaminerals, Calif, 53-59; res. biochemist, dept. neurochem. & neuropharmaceut. res, Vet. Admin. Hosp, Sepulveda, Calif, 59-60; res. fel, med, Harvard Med. Sch. & Beth Israel Hosp, 65-67; RES. SCIENTIST, BIO-SCI. LABS, 67- AAAS; Am. Chem. Soc; N.Y. Acad. Sci; Am. Asn. Clin. Chem. Pharmaceutical analysis; serotonin metabolism; metabolic response of transplantable murine tumors and leukemia cells to radio- and chemotherapy; clinical chemistry, enzymology and immunochemistry. Address: Bio-Science Labs, 7600 Tyrone Ave, Van Nuys, CA 91405.

DREWES, WOLFRAM U(LRICH), b. Ger, Jan. 9, 29; nat; m. 50; c. 3. GEOGRAPHY. B.A, Colorado, 51; M.A, Syracuse, 51, N.Y. State Veterans scholar, 52-54, univ. fel, 53-54, Watson fel. & Ph.D.(geog), 57. Res, Cent. Am, 52; asst, Syracuse, 52-53, geogr, Planning Comn, Anchorage, Alaska, 54; res. assoc. climatic res. in Peru, Syracuse Res. Inst. & U.S. Army Qm. Proj, 55-57; econ. geo, Int. Coop. Admin, Agency Int. Develop, 57-61; geog. attaché, S.Am, U.S. State Dept, 61, India, Pakistan, Afghanistan, Nepal, 62, chief natural resource unit, Orgn. Am. States, 63-66, asst. dir. Dept. Econ. Affairs, Latin Am, 66-70; REGIONAL DEVELOP. SPECIALIST, SPEC. PROJ. DEPT, INT. BANK RECONSTRUCT. & DEVELOP, 70- U.S.M.C, 46-48. Asn. Am. Geog; Am. Geog. Soc. Natural resource evaluation in underdeveloped areas; regional planning; transport analysis. Address: 5014 River Hill Rd, Washington, DC 20016.

DREWRY, WILLIAM ALTON, b. Dyess, Ark, Oct. 23, 36; m. 59; c. 3. ENVIRONMENTAL ENGINEERING. B.S, Univ. Ark, 59, M.S, 61; Ph.D.(environ. eng), Stanford Univ, 68. Instr. civil eng, Univ. Ark, 60-62; res. asst. ENVIRON. ENG, Stanford Univ, 62-65; asst. prof, Univ. Ark, 65-68; ASSOC. PROF, UNIV. TENN, KNOXVILLE, 68- Am. Soc. Civil Eng; Am. Soc. Eng. Educ; Am. Asn. Prof. Sanit. Eng; Am. Water Works Asn; Water Pollution Control Fedn. Water quality control; virus removal from water by various treatment processes; virus movement through groundwater. Address: Dept. of Civil Engineering, University of Tennessee, Knoxville, TN 37916.

DREWS, HARALD J(OACHIM), b. Waldhausen, Ger, Nov. 19, 19; m. 55; c. 3. ORGANIC CHEMISTRY. M.S, Greifswald, 51, Ph.D.(org. chem), 53. Instr. org. chem, Greifswald, 50-54; res. chemist, Degussa, Germany, 55-57; petrochem, Amoco Chem. Corp, Ind, 57-62; MEM. RES. STAFF, Stauffer Chem. Co, 62-67; Vivonex Corp, 68-70; ALTA BATES HOSP, 71- Am. Chem. Soc; Soc. Ger. Chem. Drug synthesis for animal health application; solid phase peptide synthesis; analytical instrumentation for amino acid determination; clinical biochemistry. Address: Clinical Lab, Alta Bates Hosp, Berkeley, CA 94705.

DREWS, REINHOLD E(LDOR), b. Mellowdale, Alta, Can, Sept. 23, 32; m. 57; c. 2. PHYSICS. B.A, British Columbia, 55, M.Sc, 57; Ph.D.(physics), California, Berkeley, 62. Sr. physicist, Gen. Dynamics/Astronautics Div, Calif, 61-63, staff scientist, 63-64; SCIENTIST RES. & ENG. DIV, XEROX CORP, ROCHESTER, 64- Am. Phys. Soc. Optical and electrical properties of semiconductor materials; electroluminescent, photoconductive, laser and positive-negative junction devices; paramagnetic resonance properties of solids. Address: Xerox Corp, Research & Engineering Division, Xerox Square, Rochester, NY 14644.

DREWS, UDO WILHELM, b. Danzig, Ger, Oct. 30, 39; m. 67; c. 2. SOLID STATE PHYSICS, OPTICS. B.S, Univ. Cologne, 63, M.S, 66, Ph.D.(physics), 69. Res. asst. solid state physics, Univ. Cologne, 66-69; STAFF ENGR, REMOTE SENSING DEPT, AEROSPACE SYSTS. DIV, BENDIX CORP, 69- Ger. Phys. Soc; Optical Soc. Am. Kerr and Faraday effect in ferro- and ferri-magnetic materials; evaporation techniques for metals and alloys; optical design and performance analysis of airborne multiband spectrometers-radiometers, cryogenic detector cooling in satellite borne multispectral scanners. Address: 1016 Michigan, Ann Arbor, MI 48104.

DREXEL, R(OGER) E(DWARD), b. Rochester, N.Y, Feb. 10, 20; m. 50; c. 1. CHEMICAL ENGINEERING. B.S, Rochester, 41; Sc.D.(chem. eng), Mass. Inst. Tech, 46. Res. assoc, Mass. Inst. Tech, 42-44; INDUST. & BIOCHEM. DEPT, E.I. DU PONT DE NEMOURS & CO, INC, 44-65, mgr. planning div, 65-66, dir. mfg. div, 66-67, asst. gen. mgr. dept, 67-69, GEN. MGR. DEPT. 69- Am. Inst. Chem. Eng; Am. Chem. Soc. Heat transfer; process development. Address: Industrial & Biochemical Dept, E.I. du Pont de Nemours & Co, Inc, Room 5038 du Pont Bldg, Tenth & Market St, Wilmington, DE 19898.

DREXHAGE, KARL HEINZ, b. Herford, W.Ger, Feb. 25, 34; m. 61; c. 2. PHYSICAL CHEMISTRY. Dipl. chem, Univ. of Marburg, 59, Ph.D.(phys. chem), 64. Res. assoc. phys. chem, Univ. Marburg, 64-67, asst. prof, 67-68; fel, IBM Res. Lab, Calif, 68-69; RES. SCIENTIST, RES. LABS, EASTMAN KODAK CO, 69- Quantum chemistry; monomolecular layers; optics of thin films; energy transfer; luminescence of organic dyes; laser physics; ultrashort light pulses; laser dyes. Address: Eastman Kodak Co, Research Labs, Physics Division, 343 State St, Rochester, NY 14650.

DREXLER, EDWARD J(AMES), b. Cincinnati, Ohio, Feb. 9, 38; m. 63; c. 4. ANALYTICAL CHEMISTRY. B.S, Xavier (Ohio), 59, M.S, 62; Ph.D.(zirconium chem), Wayne State, 65. Asst. CHEM, Xavier (Ohio), 59-61; assoc, Wayne State, 61-64; asst. prof, WIS. STATE UNIV, WHITEWATER, 64-68, ASSOC. PROF, 68- Am. Chem. Soc. Analytical chemistry of zirconium and hafnium; specific ion electrodes. Address: Dept. of Chemistry, 244 Upham Hall, Wisconsin State University, Whitewater, WI 53190.

DREXLER, HENRY, b. Carnegie, Pa, June 24, 27; m. 57; c. 2. MICROBIOLOGY. B.S, Pa. State, 54; Ph.D.(microbiol), Rochester, 60. Technician clin. chem, Brookhaven Nat. Lab, 54-56; instr. microbiol, sch. med, Southern California, 60-62; U.S. Pub. Health Serv. fel. microbial genetics, Karolinska Inst, Sweden, 62-64; asst. prof. MICROBIOL, BOWMAN GRAY SCH. MED, 64-69, ASSOC. PROF, 69- U.S.A, 45-46. Am. Soc. Microbiol. Microbial genetics, especially bacteriophage-host cell relationships and transduction. Address: Dept. of Microbiology, Bowman Gray School of Medicine, Winston-Salem, NC 27103.

DREXLER, R(OBERT) V(IRGIL), b. Morton, Ill, Sept. 19, 10; m. 37; c. 4. BRYOLOGY. B.S, Bradley, 34; M.S, Illinois, 36, Ph.D.(bot), 40. Asst. bot, Illinois, 35-40; instr. BIOL, COE COL, 40-43, asst. prof, 43-46, assoc. prof, 46-47, PROF. & HEAD DEPT, 47- Dir, Assoc. Cols. Midwest Wilderness Field Sta, 61-69. Am. Inst. Biol. Sci; Am. Bryol. & Lichenological Soc; Bot. Soc. Am; Torrey Bot. Club. Taxonomy and ecology of Bryophyta. Address: Dept. of Biology, Coe College, Cedar Rapids, IA 52402.

DREYER, DAVID, b. Snoqualmie Falls, Wash, Dec. 22, 30; m. 53; c. 2. ORGANIC CHEMISTRY. B.S, Washington (Seattle), 54, Ph.D.(org. chem), 60. Nat. Insts. Health fel, 60-61; chemist, fruit & veg. chem. lab, U.S. Dept. Agr, 61-68; ASSOC. PROF. CHEM, SAN FRANCISCO STATE COL, 68- U.S.A, 54-56. Am. Chem. Soc; The Chem. Soc; Soc. Ger. Chem. Natural products chemistry. Address: Dept. of Chemistry, San Francisco State College, San Francisco, CA 94132.

DREYER, DONALD A(LLEN), b. San Antonio, Tex, Nov. 26, 21. VIROLOGY. B.S, Trinity (Tex), 51, M.S, 53; Ph.D.(prev. med), Texas, 58. Instr. biol, Trinity (Tex), 53-55; res. assoc. path, sch. med, Pittsburgh, 59-60; asst. prof. virol. & epidemiol, col. med, Baylor, 60-61; asst. biologist, Univ. Tex. M.D. Anderson Hosp. & Tumor Inst, 61-66; assoc. res. prof. virol, inst. microbiol, Rutgers Univ, New Brunswick, 66-68; proj. dir, Life Sci, Inc, 68-71; DIR. GRAY RES. INST. MOLECULAR BIOL. & DIR. MICROBIOL, GRAY INDUSTS, INC, 71- Fel. microbiol, Univ. Tex. Med. Br. Galveston, 58-59; consult. med. parasitologist, 61- U.S.A.A.F, 42-45. AAAS; Am. Soc. Trop. Med. & Hyg; Tissue Cult. Asn. Virology; oncology; tissue culture; medical parasitology. Address: Gray Industries, Inc, P.O. Box 23518, Ft. Lauderdale, FL 33307.

DREYER, ROBERT M(ARX), b. Chicago, Ill, Jan. 6, 14. ECONOMIC GEOLOGY. B.S, Northwestern, 34; M.S, Calif. Inst. Tech, 37, Ph.D.(geol), 39. Asst. geol, Northwestern, 34-35; teaching fel, Calif. Inst. Tech, 36-39; instr, Kans, 39-41, asst. prof, 42-46, assoc. prof, 46-48, prof. & chmn. dept, 48-53; supvry. geologist, Kaiser Aluminum & Chem. Corp, 53-59; asst. chief geologist, Reynolds Metals Co, 59-61; pres, West. Mineral Assocs, 62-64; mgr. mineral div, Assoc. Oil & Gas Co, 64-65; PRES, WEST. MINERAL ASSOC, 65- Soil surveyor, U.S. Soil Conserv. Serv, 36; geologist, U.S. Geol. Surv, 38. U.S.N.R, 42-46. Fel. Geol. Soc. Am; Soc. Econ. Geol; Am. Inst. Mining, Metall. & Petrol. Eng; fel. Mineral. Soc. Am. Petrography; economic geology; mineralogy; geophysics; geochemistry. Address: Suite 605, 1255 Post St, San Francisco, CA 94109.

DREYER, WILLIAM A(LBERT), b. Chicago, Ill, Mar. 7, 04; m. 31; c. 2. ZOOLOGY. A.B, Illinois, 26; Ph.D.(zool), Chicago, 31. Lab. asst, Chicago, 28-31; instr. ZOOL, UNIV. CINCINNATI, 31-37, asst. prof, 37-45, assoc. prof, 45-54, PROF, 54- Fel, Huyck Preserv. AAAS; Int. Asn. Ecol; Wilderness Soc; Am. Soc. Zool; Ecol. Soc. Am.(secy, 42-47, v.pres, 48, pres, 57); Soc. Study Evolution; Am. Inst. Biol. Sci. Insect ecology and physiology; distribution of ant mounds; ornithology; microhabitat ecology. Address: Dept. of Biological Sciences, University of Cincinnati, Cincinnati, OH 45221.

DREYER, WILLIAM J, b. Kalamazoo, Mich, Aug. 11, 28; m. 52; c. 3. BIOLOGICAL CHEMISTRY. B.A, Reed Col, 52; fels, Washington (Seattle), 53-56, Ph.D.(biochem), 56. Fel. Polio Found. Nat. Insts. Health, 56-57, res. biochemist, 57-63; PROF. BIOL, CALIF. INST. TECHNOL, 63- Biophys. Soc; Genetics Soc. Am. Chemical genetics; protein structure; mechanism of control of protein synthesis. Address: Biology Division, California Institute of Technology, Pasadena, CA 91109.

DREYFUS, MARC G(EORGE), b. Brooklyn, N.Y, Mar. 5, 26; m. 54; c. 2. PHYSICS. A.B, Harvard, 47, S.M, 49; Mass. Inst. Tech, 49-50. Asst. spectros, Mass. Inst. Tech, 49-50; physicist, Am. Optical Co, 50-54; Librascope, Inc, 54-59; Barnes Eng. Co, 59-63; Bulova Watch Co, 64; Philips Labs, 65-67; CHIEF SCIENTIST, BAI CORP, 67- U.S.A.F, 44-45. Optical Soc. Am; Soc. Appl. Spectros. Optics; spectroscopy; optical information processing. Address: BAI Corp, 28 Magee Ave, Stamford, CT 06902.

DREYFUS, PIERRE MARC, b. Geneva, Switz, Oct. 14, 23; U.S. citizen; m. 47; c. 3. NEUROCHEMISTRY, NUTRITION. B.S, Tufts Col, 47; M.D, Columbia Univ, 51. Intern & asst. resident med, N.Y. Hosp, 51-53; asst. & chief resident neurol, Harvard Med. Sch, 53-55; res. fel. neuropath, 55-58, asst. NEUROL, 58-59, instr, 59-62, assoc, 62-66; asst. prof, 66-68; PROF. & CHMN. DEPT, UNIV. CALIF, DAVIS, 68-; DIR, SACRAMENTO MED. CTR, 68- Clin. assoc, McLean Hosp, 62-67. Dipl, Am. Bd. Psychiat. & Neurol, 58. Mil. Intel, U.S.A, 43-46, M/Sgt. Am. Soc. Clin. Nutrit; Am. Inst. Nutrit; Int. Soc. Neurochem. Am. Soc. Neurochem; Am.

Asn. Neuropath; Asn. Univ. Prof. Neurol. Address: Dept. of Neurology, School of Medicine, University of California, Davis CA 95616.

DREYFUS, RUSSELL W(ARREN), b. Michigan City, Ind, Dec. 23, 29; m. 52; c. 2. SOLID STATE PHYSICS. B.S, Purdue, 51, M.S, 53; Jr. Sterling fel, Yale, 57, M.S, 58, Ph.D.(physics), 60. Tech. staff mem. semiconductor res, Hughes Aircraft Co, 53-54; guest assoc. scientist, Brookhaven Nat. Lab, 54-56; RES. STAFF MEM. LASER PHYSICS, INT. BUS. MACH. CO, 58- Guest scientist, Swiss Fed. Inst. Tech, 64. Ord.C, U.S.A, 54-56. Am. Phys. Soc. Defects in ionic and semiconductor crystals by electrical, optical and mechanical properties; crystal growing;dynamical measurements using lasers. Address: Thomas J. Watson Research Center, IBM Corp, P.O. Box 218, Yorktown Heights, NY 10598.

DREYFUS, STUART E(RNEST), b. Ind, Oct. 19, 31. MATHEMATICS. A.B, Harvard, 53, Ph.D.(appl. math), 64. Actuarial clerk, Metropolitan Life Ins. Co, 53-54; numerical analyst, Gen. Elec. Co, 54-55; mathematician, Rand Corp, 55-67, ASSOC. PROF. INDUST. ENG. & OPERS. RES, UNIV. CALIF, BERKELEY, 67- Mathematical methods of optimization; operations research; computational aspects of dynamic programming and variational problems. Address: Dept. of Industrial Engineering & Operations Research, University of California, Berkeley, CA 94720.

DREYFUSS, JACQUES, b. St. Gall, Switz, Jan. 20, 37; U.S. citizen; m. 64; c. 2. BIOCHEMISTRY. B.S, Beloit Col, 58; Ph.D.(biochem), Hopkins, 63. Fel. biochem, Princeton, 63-64; GROUP LEADER DRUG METAB, E.R. SQUIBB & SONS, INC, 64- Am. Soc. Pharmacol. & Exp. Therapeut; N.Y. Acad. Sci. Drug metabolism; central nervous system and cardiovascular agents. Address: Squibb Institute for Medical Research, New Brunswick, NJ 08903.

DREYFUSS, M(AX) PETER, b. Frankfurt, Ger, Sept. 24, 32; nat; m. 54; c. 2. ORGANIC CHEMISTRY. B.S, Union Col, 52; Allied Chem. & Dye fel, Cornell, 55-56, Ph.D.(chem), 57. Res. chemist, RES. CTR, B.F. GOODRICH CO, 56-60, sr. res. chemist, 60-67, RES. ASSOC, 67- Imp. Chem. Indust. fel, Liverpool, 63-65. Am. Chem. Soc. Polymerization of cyclic ethers; polytetrahydrofuran; polymer chemistry; organic synthesis. Address: Research Center, B.F. Goodrich Co, Brecksville, OH 44141.

DREYFUSS, PATRICIA, b. Reading, Pa, Apr. 28, 32; m. 54; c. 2. POLYMER CHEMISTRY. B.S, Rochester, 54; Sohio fel, Akron, 60-61, Nat. Sci. Found. fels, 61-63, Ph.D.(polymer sci), 64. Am. Asn. Univ. Women Marie Curie int. fel, Liverpool, 64-65; res. chemist, B.F. Goodrich Res. Ctr, 65-71; RES. ASSOC. CHEM, CASE WEST. RESERVE UNIV, 71- Am. Chem. Soc. Crystallization kinetics and morphology of polymers; polytetrahydrofuran; structure-property relations of plastics. Address: 506 West Point Dr, Akron, OH 44313.

DREYFUSS, PAUL D(ANIEL), b. Wuppertal, Germany, Dec. 4, 06, nat. 47; m. 36; c. 2. CHEMISTRY. Ph.D.(chem), Bonn, 33, Justus Liebig Gesell. fel, 33; Ph.D.(chem), Cagliari, Italy, 35. Asst. chem, Cagliari, Italy, 33-35; Catania, Italy, 35-37; Pavia, 37; RES. CHEMIST, Gaspacolor, Inc, 37-51; Ciba, 51-54; Cincinnati Chem. Works, Inc, 54-57; Ciba States Ltd, 59-67, CIBA PHOTOCHEM. LTD, SWITZ, 67- Am. Chem. Soc. Constitution and color; constitution of natural organic compounds; color photography; olivile; photographic chemistry; dyes; organic chemistry. Address: Ciba Photochemical Ltd, Fribourg, Switzerland.

DREYFUSS, ROBERT G(EORGE), b. Frankfurt-Main, Ger, Sept. 6, 31; nat; m. 56. INORGANIC CHEMISTRY. B.S, Union Col, 52. Mgr. res. & develop. control lab, Thatcher Glass Mfg. Co, Inc, 52-61; asst. dir. res. & eng, Glass Containers Corp, 61-65; TECH. DIR, METRO CONTAINERS, KRAFTCO CORP, 66- Am. Chem. Soc; Am. Ceramic Soc; Air Pollution Control Asn; German Soc. Glass Tech. Glass technology and manufacturing. Address: Metro Containers, Kraftco Corp, 107 West Side Ave, Jersey City, NJ 07305.

DRIBIN, DANIEL MACCABAEUS, b. Chicago, Ill, Dec. 10, 13; m. 36; c. 1. ALGEBRA. S.B, Chicago, 33, S.M, 34, fel, 34-36, Ph.D.(math), 36. Nat. Res. fel, Inst. Adv. Study, & Yale, 36-38; instr. math, Nebraska, 38-42; jr. res. analyst, U.S. War Dept, 42; ANALYST, NAT. SECURITY AGENCY, 46- Lectr. math, George Washington, 46-58, assoc. prof. lectr, 58-60, PROF. LECTR, 60- U.S.A, 42-46, Res, 48-50, Capt; Legion of Merit. Am. Math. Soc; Math. Asn. Am.. Algebraic number fields; algebraic number theory; projective geometry; history of modern mathematics. Address: 1016 Kathryn Rd, Silver Spring, MD 20904.

DRICKAMER, HARRY G(EORGE), b. Cleveland, Ohio, Nov. 19, 18; m. 42; c. 5. CHEMICAL ENGINEERING. B.S.E, Univ. Mich, 41, M.S, 42, Ph.D.(chem. eng), 46. Res. group leader, Pan Am. Ref. Corp, Tex, 42-46; asst. prof. CHEM. ENG. & PHYS. CHEM, UNIV. ILL, URBANA, 46-49, assoc. prof, 49-53, PROF, 53- Nat. Acad. Sci; Am. Geophys. Union; Am. Chem. Soc.(Ipatieff Prize, 56); Am. Inst. Chem. Eng.(Colburn Award, 47, Alpha Chi Sigma Award, 66); Am. Phys. Soc.(Buckley Solid State Physics Prize, 67); Faraday Soc; Am. Soc. Eng. Educ.(Bendix Res. Award, 68). Physical chemistry; properties of matter at high pressure. Address: 105-E Chemistry Bldg, School of Chemical Sciences, University of Illinois, Urbana, IL 61801.

DRICKEY, DARRELL J, b. Rapid City, S.Dak, June 20, 34; m. 57; c. 3. PHYSICS. B.S, S.Dak. Sch. Mines & Tech, 56; M.S, Stanford, 60, Ph.D.(physics), 63. Res. assoc. physics, Stanford, 62-63; lab. linear accelerator, Univ. Paris, 63-64; mem. staff, res. div, Stanford Linear Accelerator Ctr, 64-68; ASSOC. PROF. PHYSICS, UNIV. CALIF, LOS ANGELES, 68- Am. Phys. Soc. High energy and particle physics. Address: Dept. of Physics, University of California, Los Angeles, CA 90024.

DRIES, WILLIAM CHARLES, b. Milwaukee, Wis, Nov. 4, 30; m. 57; c. 3. MECHANICAL & METALLURGICAL ENGINEERING. B.S, Wisconsin, 53, M.S, 56, Ph.D.(metall. eng), 62. Consult. mech. engr, Lofte & Fredericksen, 56-59; res. asst. metall. eng, UNIV. WIS, MADISON, 60-62, PROJ. ASSOC. MECH. ENG, 62-; PRES, DRIES JACQUES ASSOCS, INC, 62- U.S.A, 53-55. Am. Soc. Mech. Eng; Nat. Soc. Prof. Eng; Am. Soc. Heat, Refrig. & Air Conditioning Eng; Am. Soc. Metals; Brit. Inst. Metals. Physical metallurgy of iron; protective construction for nuclear weapons; environmental engineering; computer applications to engineering problems. Address: 6226 N. Highlands Ave, Madison, WI 53705.

DRIESCH, A(LBERT) J(OHN), b. Pittsburgh, Pa, Sept. 2, 20. ORGANIC CHEMISTRY. B.A, St. Francis Col.(Pa), 43; M.S, Notre Dame, 51. Asst. prof. CHEM, ST. FRANCIS COL.(PA), 56-63, PROF, 63-, HEAD DEPT, 52- Am. Chem. Soc. General organic chemistry. Address: Dept. of Chemistry, St. Francis College, Loretta, PA 15940.

DRIESENS, ROBERT J(AMES), b. Redford, Mich, Jan. 12, 18; m. 53; c. 3. BACTERIOLOGY. A.B, Calvin Col, 39; M.S, Mich. State Col, 49, Ph.D.(bact), 52. Bacteriologist, labs, Mich. Dept. Health, 52-60; head bact. prod. develop. dept, Corvel, Inc, Omaha, 60-64, develop. assoc, 64-65; sr. bacteriologist, vaccines develop, ELI LILLY & CO, 65-69, SR. MICROBIOLOGIST, BIOL. PROD. DEVELOP, 69- U.S.A, 42-46, 2nd Lt. Am. Soc. Microbiol. Bacterial biologicals; mass culture of microbes; microbial nutrition; prophylactic immunization; microbial conversions of chemicals. Address: Dept. G780, Biological Products Development, Eli Lilly & Co, Box 708, Greenfield, IN 46140.

DRIEVER, CARL WILLIAM, b. Chicago, Ill, Mar. 4, 38; m. 64; c. 1. BIOCHEMICAL PHARMACOLOGY. B.S, Purdue, 61, M.S, 63; Ph.D.(pharmacol), 65. Teaching asst. pharm, sch. pharm, Purdue, 61-62, U.S. Pub. Health Serv. fel, PHARMACOL, 62-65; asst. prof, sch. pharm, Maryland, 65-67; COL. PHARM, UNIV. HOUSTON, 67-68, ASSOC. PROF, 68- Summer lab. asst, Abbott Labs, Ill, 61. AAAS; Am. Pharmaceut. Asn; N.Y. Acad. Sci. Drug metabolism; enzyme induction; drug dependence and tolerance. Address: College of Pharmacy, University of Houston, Cullen Blvd, Houston, TX 77004.

DRIGGERS, F(RANK) E(DGAR), b. El Paso, Texas, Dec. 14, 19; m. 45; c. 2. REACTOR PHYSICS. A.B, California, 40; A.M, Michigan, 48, Atomic Energy Cmn. fel, 50-51, Ph.D.(physics), 51. Jr. astronomer, Naval Observ, Washington, D.C, 40-41; res. physicist, Eng. Res. Inst, Michigan, 46-50; reactor physicist, E.I. DU PONT DE NEMOURS & CO, INC, 51-64, MEM, STAFF ADV. OPER. PLANNING, 64- Army Ord, 41-51. Reactor physics; isotope technology; operations research. Address: Savannah River Lab, E.I. du Pont de Nemours & Co, Inc, Aiken, SC 29801.

DRIGGERS, J(AMES) CLYDE, b. Ft. Green, Fla, Jan. 10, 17; m. 40; c. 4. COLLEGE ADMINISTRATION. B.S.A, Florida, 38, Ph.D, 49. Instr. poultry husb, Florida, 39-40, asst. prof, 46-49, assoc. prof, 49-55, prof, 55-57; chmn. poultry div, Georgia, 57-64; PRES, ABRAHAM BALDWIN AGR. COL, 64- U.S.A, 42-45, Res, 45-, Col. Poultry Sci. Asn.(pres, 63-64); World Poultry Sci. Asn. Preservation of egg quality; minerals in poultry feeding; feeds indigenous to Florida for poultry feeding; high-efficiency feeds for layers; radioactive isotope studies in poultry metabolism. Address: Abraham Baldwin Agriculture College, Tifton, GA 31794.

DRIGGS, F(RANK) H(OWARD), b. Clinton, Mo, Oct. 25, 95; m. 24; c. 3. INORGANIC CHEMISTRY, METALLURGY. A.B, Baker, 17, hon. LL.D, 58; M.S, Illinois, 21, Ph.D.(inorg. chem), 24. Asst. chem, Illinois, 19-24, instr, 24-27, res. chemist, Westinghouse Lamp Co, N.J, 27-34; FANSTEEL METALL. CORP, 34-52, pres, 52-64, mem. bd. dirs, 64-67, CONSULT, 67- C.Eng, U.S.A, 17-19. Am. Chem. Soc; Am. Inst. Mining, Metall. & Petrol. Eng; Soc. Mining Eng. Rare metals; atomic weight of lanthanum and holmium; purification of hafnium; preparation of ductile uranium, thorium, tantalum and tungsten. Address: 971 Rancho Santa Fe, CA 92067.

DRILL, VICTOR A(LEXANDER), b. Sunderland, Eng, June 10, 16; nat. 25; m. 40; c. 3. PHARMACOLOGY. B.S, Long Island, 38; Ph.D.(physiol), Princeton, 41; M.D, Yale, 48. Asst. chemist, Fleischmann Labs, N.Y, 37-38; Jacobus fel, Princeton, 41-42; Nat. Res. Coun. fel, Northwestern, 42-43; instr. pharmacol, col. physicians & surg, Columbia, 43-44; med. sch, Yale, 44-47, asst. prof, 47-48; prof, Wayne, 48-54; dir. biol. res, G.D. SEARLE & CO, 54-70, DIR. SCI. & PROF. AFFAIRS, 70- Dir. ed. & assoc. physician, Detroit Receiving Hosp, 49-54; prof. lectr, Univ. Ill, Chicago-Circle, 54-; lectr, Northwest. Univ, 54- Mem. U.S. Comn, World Med. Asn; mem, drug res. bd, Nat. Res. Coun. Am. Fertility Soc; Am. Soc. Pharmacol. & Exp. Therapeut; Am. Physiol. Soc; Soc. Exp. Biol. & Med; Am. Fedn. Clin. Res; Am. Chem. Soc; Asn. Am. Med. Cols; Am. Asn. Study Liver Diseases; Soc. Toxicol.(pres, 72-73); fel. N.Y. Acad. Sci; fel. Royal Soc. Med; Int. Soc. Res. Reproduction; Family Planning Asn. Americas; hon. mem. Venezuelan Soc. Pharmacol. Pharmacology; endocrinology, oral contraceptives. Address: G.D. Searle & Co, P.O. Box 5110, Chicago, IL 60680.

DRILLIS, RUDOLFS J(OHN), b. Grostona, Latvia, May 10, 93; U.S. citizen; m. 18; c. 2. BIOMECHANICS. Polytech. Inst, Riga, 14-16; Latvia, 24-29; Herder Inst, Latvia, 28-30; Ph.D.(appl. psychol), Leipzig, 31. Mgr, Psychotech. Inst, Riga, 24-34; consult. human eng, Chamber Indust. & Trade, 36-40; from asst. lectr. to asst. prof. psychol, Latvia, 37-44; teacher, gymnasium, Germany, 45-49; scientist biomech. & human eng, res. div, sch. eng. & sci, N.Y. Univ, 49-54, sr. res. scientist, 54-71. Mem. comt. job redesign, Nat. Welfare Coun, 53-57. Russian Air Force, 16-18; Latvian Air Force, 19-21, Wing Comdr. Human Factors Soc; N.Y. Acad. Sci. Human engineering; biomechanics and psychomotorics of work and sport movements; evaluation of tools and prostheses; design of proper tools and equipment. Address: 88 Prospect Park W, New York, NY 11215.

DRIMMER, BERNARD E, b. New York, N.Y, July 31, 17; m. 66. PHYSICAL CHEMISTRY. B.S, City Col. New York, 38; George Washington, 43-44; Maryland, 47-49. Chemist, Naval Gun Factory, D.C, 41-43; U.S. Bur. Mines, Md, 43-44; Carbide & Carbon Chem. Corp, Columbia, 44; maj. prod. supvr, Oak Ridge Nat. Lab, 44-46; phys. scientist, Naval Ord. Lab, Md, 46-50; ammunition engr, U.S. Dept. Army, D.C, 50-52; prod. engr, Atomic Energy Comn, 52-53; ammunition engr, Naval Purchasing Off, Belg, 53-56, supvr. chemist, Naval Ord. Lab, Md, 56-63, phys. sci. adminr, Bur. Naval Weapons, WASH, D.C, 63-66, DIR. ENERGY CONVERSION & MAT. DIV, NAVAL ORD. SYSTS. COMMAND, 66- AAAS; Am. Phys. Soc. Detonation phenomena; shock hydrodynamics; shaped explosive charges; high-speed photography; propellants and propulsion; energy conversion systems; gaseous diffusion. Address: 4841 S. Ninth St, Arlington, VA 22204.

DRINKARD, RUSSELL D(REW), b. Richmond, Va, Nov. 13, 00; m. 31; c. 4. PHYSICAL CHEMISTRY. B.S, Richmond, 23: Ph.D.(chem), Hopkins, 27. Res. chemist, Standard Oil Co. of N.Y, 27-28; Columbia Eng. & Mgt. Corp, 28-32; instr, Kanawha Jr. Col, 32-33; res. chemist, Citro Chem. Co, 33-49; Chas. Pfizer & Co, 49-66; CONSULT, WAVERLY CHEM. CO, GUILFORD, 66- General organic synthesis on fine chemicals, vitamins; antibiotics, drugs. Address: 8 Gallup Lane, Waterford, CT 06385.

DRINKARD, W(ILLIAM) C(HARLES), JR, b. Eufaula, Ala, May 11, 29. INORGANIC CHEMISTRY. B.A, Huntingdon Col, 50; M.S, Ala. Polytech. Inst, 52; Ph.D.(inorg. chem), Illinois, 56. Chemist, Food Mach. & Chem. Corp, 52-53; E.I. du Pont de Nemours & Co, 55; asst. prof. chem, California, Los Angeles, 56-60; MEM. STAFF, EXP. STA, E.I. DU PONT DE NEMOURS & CO, INC, 60- Am. Chem. Soc. Complex inorganic compounds; ligand reactivity; homogeneous catalysis by metal ions. Address: 1337 Kynlyn Dr, Wilmington, DE 19803.

DRINKER, PHILIP ALDRICH, b. Brookline, Mass, Apr. 7, 32; m. 53; c. 4. FLUID DYNAMICS, BIOENGINEERING. B.S, Yale, 54; Ph.D.(hydrodyn), Mass. Inst. Technol, 61. Res. asst. hydrodyn, Mass. Inst. Technol, 57-61, Ford Found. fel. eng, 61-63, asst. prof. civil eng, 61-65; res. assoc, DEPT. SURG, HARVARD MED. SCH, 65-69, PRIN. ASSOC. SURG. & CHIEF BIO-ENG. DIV, 69- Consult. surg, Peter Bent Brigham Hosp, 65-; lectr, Mass. Inst. Technol, 65- U.S.P.H.S, 54-57, Asst. Sanitarian. AAAS; Am. Soc. Civil Eng; Am. Soc. Eng. Educ; Int. Asn. Hydraul. Res; Biomed. Eng. Soc; Am. Soc. Artificial Internal Organs. Fluid dynamics and mass transport studies in circulatory and pulmonary physiology; blood oxygenation; equipment design for respiratory care. Address: Dept. of Surgery, Peter Bent Brigham Hospital, 721 Huntington Ave, Boston, MA 02115.

DRINKWATER, W(ILLIAM) DALE, b. Minneapolis, Minn, May 23, 20; m. 43; c. 6. AERONAUTICAL ENGINEERING. B.Ae.E, Minnesota, 42, M.S, 47; M.B.A, Sacramento State Col, 71. Jr. engr, Twin Cities Aircraft Corp, Minn, 41; instr. aeronaut. eng, Minnesota, 42-44, navig. exten. div, 42-44, aeronaut. eng, 46-47; Notre Dame, 47-48; asst. prof, 48-50; consult, U.S. Naval Ord. Test. Sta, 50-57; asst. to mgr. eng. & res. div, liquid rocket plant, Aerojet-Gen. Corp, 57-61, mgr, develop. fabrication div, 61-64; asst. mgr, contract & prog. admin, rocket engine opers-nuclear, 64-68, mgr. prog. mgt, comput. sci, 68-69; RETIRED. Civilian with Nat. Adv. Comt. Aeronaut, 41. U.S.N.R, 44-46, Res, 48-57, Lt. Comdr. Assoc. fel. Am. Inst. Aeronaut. & Astronaut; Am. Soc. Eng. Educ. Ultimate strength of stiffened D-tubes; high velocity hotwire anemometer; electronic pressure-cell for use in high speed fluid flow; combustion in rocket motors; transition in supersonic boundary layer. Address: 1338 42nd St, Sacramento, CA 95819.

DRINKWATER, WILLIAM O(THO), b. Providence, R.I, Sept. 29, 19; m. 49; c. 2. HORTICULTURE. B.V.A, Massachusetts, 47, fel, 47-49, M.S, 49; Ph.D.(hort), Rutgers, 54. Asst. veg. crops, Rutgers, 51-52; instr, Connecticut, 49-52, asst. prof, 52-56; RUTGERS UNIV, 56-57, assoc. prof, 57-63, PROF, 63-68, HORT. & FORESTRY, 68- U.S.C.G, 42-46. Am. Soc. Hort. Sci; Am. Soc. Plant Physiol; Am. Inst. Biol. Sci. Soil and plant water relationships; irrigation. Address: Blake Hall, Rutgers University, New Brunswick, NJ 08903.

DRINNAN, ALAN J(OHN), b. Bristol, Eng, Apr. 6, 32; U.S. citizen; m. 56; c. 2. ORAL PATHOLOGY. B.D.S, Bristol, 54, M.B, Ch.B, 62; D.D.S, State Univ. N.Y. Buffalo, 64. Tutor oral surg, Bristol, 57-58; vis. asst. prof. oral path, SCH. DENT, STATE UNIV. N.Y. BUFFALO, 62-65, assoc. prof. ORAL DIAG. & CLIN. PATH, 65-70, PROF. & CHMN. DEPT, 70- Consult. dentist & chief dent. serv, Buffalo Gen. Hosp, 66-; WHO consult, Port Moresby Dent. Col, Papua, New Guinea, 71. Fel, Royal Col. Surgeons, Eng, 62. Brit. Army, 55-57, Capt. Int. Asn. Dent. Res; fel. Am. Acad. Oral Path; Am. Dent. Asn. Experimental carcinogenesis; dental education; medical-dental relationships. Address: School of Dentistry, State University of New York at Buffalo, Buffalo, NY 14214.

DRIPPS, ROBERT D(UNNING), b. Phila, Pa, June 19, 11; m. 39; c. 2. MEDICINE. A.B, Princeton, 32; M.D, Univ. Pa, 36. Instr. pharmacol, UNIV. PA, 38-40, assoc, 42-45, assoc. prof. surg, 45-47, ANESTHESIOL, SCH. MED. & GRAD. SCH. MED, 48-50, PROF. & CHMN. DEPT, 51- Civilian consult, U.S. Naval Hosp. Phila, 45-; mem. comt. on rev, U.S. Pharmacopeia, 50-60; comn. anesthesiol, Nat. Res. Coun, 50-62, comn. metab. & trauma, 56-62; surg. study sect, U.S. Pub. Health Serv, 52-59, res. training grant comt, 58-63, nat. adv. comn. res. resources & facilities, 63-67, chmn. comt. res. training anesthesia, 67-71; trustee, Princeton, 67-71. John F. Lewis Award, Am. Philos. Soc, 65; hon. fel, Royal Col. Surgeons, Ireland, 70. With Off. Sci. Res. & Develop, 44. Asn. Am. Physicians; Am. Soc. Anesthesiol. (distinguished serv. award, 66); Am. Physiol. Soc; Am. Soc. Pharmacol; fel. Am. Med. Asn; Am. Soc. Clin. Invest; Am. Surg. Asn. Respiratory and circulatory physiology; physiology of anesthesia. Address: University of Pennsylvania Hospital, Philadelphia, PA 19104.

DRISCOLL, DENNIS MICHAEL, b. Warren, Pa, July 10, 34; m. 69. METEOROLOGY. B.S, Pa. State Univ, 59, M.S, 61; Nat. Insts. Health fel. & Nat. Sci. Found. fel, 65; Ph.D.(meteorol), Univ. Wis, 71. Res. assoc. meteorol, Travelers Res. Ctr, 61-62; instr. geog, Univ. Wis-Milwaukee, 62-64, teaching asst. meteorol, 65-66, instr. geog, Univ. Wis. Ctr. Syst, 64-65; ASST. PROF. METEOROL, TEX. A&M UNIV, 69- Am. Meteorol. Soc; Int. Soc. Biometeorol. Human biometeorology; statistical meteorology-climatology; hydrometeorology. Address: Dept. of Meteorology, Texas A&M University, College Station, TX 77843.

DRISCOLL, DOROTHY H, b. Boston, Mass, May 30, 24. BIOPHYSICS. B.S, Radcliffe Col, 46; fel, Smith Col, 47-48, M.A, 49; Boston, 50. Instr. sci, Northampton Sch. for Girls, 46-47; asst. biol. sci, Smith Col, 48-49, instr. zool, 49-50; technician, biophys. lab, Harvard Med. Sch, 51-53, res. asst. clin. isotopes, 53-55; res. assoc. & health safety off, atomic bomb casualty comn, Nat. Acad. Sci, 54-56; jr. tech. specialist, med. physics div, Brookhaven Nat. Lab, 56-61; res. assoc. radiol, MED. COL, THOMAS JEFFERSON UNIV, 61-67, asst. prof. radiol, 67-71, ASSOC. PROF. MED. PHYSICS, 71- Investr, Marine Biol. Labs, Woods Hole, 49-50; adj. lectr. radiol. health prog, physics div, Manhattan Col, 65-69; consult. clin. radioisotopes, Sacred Heart Hosp, Allentown, 66-68; dept. oncol, Children's Hosp, Phila, 71- Am. Ornith. Union; Health Physics Soc; Soc. Nuclear Med; Am. Asn. Physicists in Med; N.Y. Acad. Sci; Radiol. Soc. N.Am; Radiation Res. Soc. Clinical isotopes; biomedical physics. Address: 561 Judson St, Philadelphia, PA 19130.

DRISCOLL, EGBERT G(OTZIAN), b. Indianapolis, Ind, Nov. 10, 29. GEOLOGY, INVERTEBRATE PALEONTOLOGY. B.A, Oberlin Col, 52; M.S, Nebraska, 56; Fulbright fel, Australia, 58-59; Ph.D.(geol), Michigan, 62. Asst. geol, Nebraska, 55-56; teaching fel, Michigan, 56-57, instr. geol, 60-63, asst, mus. paleont, 57-58, asst. curator, 60-63; asst. prof. GEOL, WAYNE STATE UNIV, 63-65, assoc. prof, 65-71, PROF, 71- U.S.A, 53-55. Soc. Econ. Paleont. & Mineral; Brit. Palaeont. Asn; Australian Geol. Soc. Paleozoic pelecypods; marine benthic ecology; sediment-fauna relations. Address: Dept. of Geology, Wayne State University, Detroit, MI 48202.

DRISCOLL, GARY L(EE), b. Campbellsville, Pa, Mar. 30, 40; m. 59; c. 3. ORGANIC CHEMISTRY. B.S, Pa. State Univ, 62; Wis. Alumni Res. Found. fel, Univ. Wis, Madison, 62-63, Nat. Sci. Found. fel, 63-64; Ph.D.(org. chem), Univ. Del, 68. Res. chemist, res. & develop, SUN OIL CO, 64-70, SR. RES. CHEMIST, CORP. RES, 70- Am. Chem. Soc. Development of synthetic lubricants; synthesis and characterization of polymers and oligomers; organic syntheses via photochemistry and electrochemistry; organic synthesis and reaction mechanisms. Address: 3505 Bethel Rd, Boothwyn, PA 19061.

DRISCOLL, GEORGE C(LARENCE), JR, b. Mineola, N.Y, Jan. 26, 27; m. 57; c. 1. CIVIL ENGINEERING. B.S, Rutgers Univ, 50; M.S, Lehigh Univ, 52, Ph.D.(civil eng), 58. Asst. civil eng, LEHIGH UNIV, 50-52, asst. engr. tests, Fritz Eng. Lab, 52-57, res. instr. CIVIL ENG, 57-58, res. asst. prof, 58-60, res. assoc. prof, 60-65, PROF, 65-, ASSOC. DIR, FRITZ ENG. LAB, 69- Citation, Eng. News-Record, 66. U.S.A.A.F, 45-46. Am. Soc. Civil Eng.(Huber Res. Prize, 66); Am. Welding Soc.(Davis Silver Medal Award, 58, Adams Mem. Award, 70); Nat. Soc. Prof. Eng. Plastic analysis and design of welded continuous frames and their components; plastic design of multistory steel frames; computer-aided design. Address: Dept. of Civil Engineering, Lehigh University, Bethlehem, PA 18015.

DRISCOLL, GEORGE FRANCIS, b. North Baltimore, Ohio, Jan. 3, 03; m. 29; CIVIL ENGINEERING. B.S, Notre Dame, 25, C.E, 29. Asst. engr, Ohio State Hwy. Dept, 25-26, asst. div. engr, 26-29; surv. transitman, City of Chillicothe, 30-31, city engr, 31-34; exec. secy, Nat. Recovery Admin. Code, Aggregates Industs, 34-35; sales mgr, South. Ohio Quarries Co, 35-44; assoc. prof. civil eng, Notre Dame, 44-53; v.pres, H.&S. Asphalt Contracting Co, 53-58; PROF. CIVIL ENG, UNIV. DAYTON, 58- Asphalt Inst. grant, Cornell, 59-; Automotive Safety Found. grant, Texas A&M, 64- Traffic eng. consult, Cities of Xenia, Ohio, 62 & Oakwood, 63-65; Monsanto Chem. Labs, 65. Mem. Hwy. Res. Bd, Nat. Acad. Sci-Nat. Res. Coun, 62. Nat. Soc. Prof. Eng; Am. Rd. Builders Asn; Am. Soc. Civil Eng. Highway and traffic engineering; construction; surveying. Address: Dept. of Civil Engineering, University of Dayton, Dayton, OH 45409.

DRISCOLL, JOHN G, b. New York, N.Y, Apr. 17, 33. MATHEMATICS. B.S, Iona Col, 54; M.S, St. Johns, 57, Nat. Sci. Found. fel, Columbia, 63, Ph.D. (math), 69. Teacher, St. Joseph's Acad, W.I, 57-61, Power Mem. Acad, N.Y, 61-65; asst. prof. math, IONA COL, 65-71, PROF. MATH. & PRES, 71-, asst. to pres, 69-71. Math. Asn. Am. Algebraic integration theory; mathematical education; mathematical analysis for the behavioral sciences. Address: Iona College, New Rochelle, NY 10801.

DRISCOLL, JOHN S(TANFORD), b. Olean, N.Y, May 31, 34; m. 62; c. 3. ORGANIC CHEMISTRY. B.S, Mich. State Univ, 56; Parke-Davis fel, Princeton, 57-58, M.A, 58, Monsanto fel, 58-59, Nat. Sci. Found. summer fel, 59, Ph.D.(org. chem), 60. Sr. res. chemist, Boston Lab, Monsanto Res. Corp, 60-64, res. group leader, 64-68; RES. CHEMIST, NAT. CANCER INST, 68- Am. Chem. Soc; The Chem. Soc. Cancer chemotherapy; medicinal chemistry; structure-activity relationships; heterocyclic synthesis; central nervous system antitumor drugs. Address: Drug Development Branch, National Cancer Institute, Bethesda, MD 20014.

DRISCOLL, MICHAEL JOHN, b. Peekskill, N.Y, Sept. 8, 34; wid; c. 1. NUCLEAR ENGINEERING. B.S, Carnegie Inst. Tech, 55; Nat. Sci. Found. fel. & M.S, Florida, 62; Nat. Sci. Found. fel. & Nucl.E, Mass. Inst. Tech, 64, Atomic Energy Cmn. fel. & Sc.D.(nuclear eng), 66. Eng. analyst, Phillips Petrol. Co, 55-56; nuclear propulsion engr, naval reactor br, Atomic Energy Cmn. & nuclear propulsion div, bur. ships, U.S, Navy, 57-60; asst. prof. NUCLEAR ENG, MASS. INST. TECHNOL, 66-69, ASSOC. PROF, 69- U.S.N, 56-60, Lt. Am. Nuclear Soc; Am. Soc. Eng. Educ. Fast reactor physics; experimental reactor physics; reactor design and analysis; nuclear propulsion. Address: Dept. of Nuclear Engineering, Massachusetts Institute of Technology, 138 Albany St, Cambridge, MA 02139.

DRISCOLL, RAYMOND L(EVERING), b. Va, Oct. 11, 05; m. 35; c. 3. PHYSICS. B.S, Col. of William & Mary, 28; fel, North Carolina, 34-36, M.A, 36. Physicist, Gen. Elec. Co, N.Y, 28-30; cryogenic lab, U.S. Bur. Mines, Texas, 30-33; asst, North Carolina, 34-36; physicist, Nat. Bur. Standards, 36-71; RETIRED. Stratton award, 62. Am. Phys. Soc. Dielectrics; gas laboratory techniques; absolute electrical measurements; atomic constants. Address: 10139 Cedar Lane, Kensington, MD 20795.

DRISCOLL, RICHARD J(AMES), b. Chicago, Ill, Aug. 14, 28. ANALYTICAL MATHEMATICS. B.S, Loyola (Ill), 50, A.M, 51; Ph.D.(math), Northwestern, 59. Instr. MATH, Northwest. Univ, 57-58; LOYOLA UNIV, CHICAGO, 58-60, asst. prof, 60-66, ASSOC. PROF, 66- Sig.C, U.S.A, 54-56. Am. Math. Soc; Math. Asn. Am. Ordinary differential equations; calculus of variations. Address: Dept. of Mathematics, Loyola University, Chicago, IL 60626.

DRISCOLL, RICHARD S(TARK), b. Denver, Colo, Sept. 16, 28; m. 54; c. 2. RANGE MANAGEMENT, REMOTE SENSING. B.S, Colo. State Univ, 51, M.S, 57, Ph.D.(range ecol. & soils), 62. Range conservationist, Pac. N.W. Forest & Range Exp. Sta, U.S. FOREST SERV, 52-56, proj. leader range mgt. & wildlife habitat res, 56-60, wildlife habitat res, 60-62, range mgt. res, div. watershed, recreation & range res, 62-65, PRIN. RANGE ECOLOGIST, ROCKY MT. FOREST & RANGE EXP. STA, 65- Lectr, Oregon State, 58-60; spec. instr, Univ. Denver, 71. Ecol. Soc. Am; Am. Soc. Range Mgt. Range ecology including ecosystem analysis; remote sensing of range, wildlife habitat and watershed resources. Address: Rocky Mountain Forest & Range Experiment Station, Ft. Collins, CO 80521.

DRISCOLL, WALTER G(ERARD), b. Boston, Mass, Apr. 21, 17; m. 41; c. 4. PHYSICS, ENGINEERING. B.S, Boston Col, 38, fel, 38-40, M.S, 40; Rockefeller scholar, Brown, 46-51, Ph.D.(eng), 51. Spec. asst. prod. mgr, Gen. Foods Corp, 40; spec. agent & physicist, Fed. Bur. Invest, 40-46; res. assoc. appl. math. & eng, Brown, 46-51; chief of appl. physics div, Dept. Defense, 51-55; v.pres. & res. dir, Baird-Atomic, Inc, 55-63; dir. univ. res, Boston Col, 63-67; DIR. RES. FACILITY DEVELOP. & BIOMED. ENG, ST. VINCENT HOSP, 67- Consult, Inst. Defense Anal, 64- Optical Soc. Am; Am. Phys. Soc; Electron Micros. Soc. Am; Inst. Elec. & Electronics Eng. Spectroscopy acoustical information; optical instrumentation. Address: 28 Westwood Rd, Shrewsbury, MA 01545.

DRISCOLL, WILLIAM T(HORVALD), b. Pagoda, Colo, Jan. 5, 20; m. 46; c. 2. ZOOLOGY. B.A, Denver, 42, M.S, 48; Ph.D.(zool), California, 54. Teacher, high sch, Colo, 43-44; instr. ZOOL, Denver, 44-48; asst, California, 48-50, assoc, 50-51; asst. prof, UNIV. DENVER, 51-56, assoc. prof, 56-64, PROF, 64-, ASSOC. DEAN COL. ARTS & SCI, 68-, chmn. dept. biol. sci, 58-68. Summers, vis. prof, Univ. Calif, Berkeley, 53 & 62; ranger naturalist, Yellowstone Nat. Park, 54-58, lectr, Nat. Sci. Found. Inst, Colo. Col, 61, assoc. dir, 63 & 64; mem. comt. exam, natural sci. test col. level exam. prog, Educ. Test. Serv, 71. Fel. AAAS; Am. Soc. Zool; Nat. Asn. Biol. Teachers; Asn. Am. Med. Cols. Experimental embryology; amphibian hypophysis and thyroid; teaching by closed circuit television. Address: 2234 S. Madison St, Denver, CO 80210.

DRISKO, R(ICHARD) W(ARREN), b. San Mateo, Calif, Nov. 16, 25; m. 53; c. 2. ORGANIC CHEMISTRY. B.S, Stanford, 47, M.S, 48, Schweitzer & Rosenberg, fel, Ph.D.(chem), 50. SR. PROJ. SCIENTIST CHEM, U.S. NAVAL CIVIL ENG. LAB, 50- Meritorious civilian serv. award, U.S. Navy, 53. U.S.A, 54-56. Am. Chem. Soc; Nat. Asn. Corrosion Eng; Marine Technol. Soc; Sci. Res. Soc. Am; Am. Soc. Test. & Mat. Isolation and identification of alkaloids; determination of amino acid sequence in proteins; analysis of creosote; paints, protective coatings and corrosion control; pollution; ecology. Address: Code L52, U.S. Naval Civil Engineering Lab, Port Hueneme, CA 93043.

DRISKO, RONALD LEE EVANS, b. Gardiner, Maine, Sept. 8, 42. PHYSICAL ORGANIC CHEMISTRY. B.S, East. Nazarene Col, 64; Du Pont fel, Johns Hopkins Univ, 65-67, M.A, 66, Ph.D.(phys. org. chem), 68. Res. assoc. photochem, McCollum-Pratt Inst. Microbiol, Johns Hopkins Univ, 68-69; RES. CHEMIST, WASH. RES. CTR, W.R. GRACE & CO, CLARKSVILLE, 69- Am. Chem. Soc. Mechanistic organic photochemistry; mechanism of the photodimerization of acenaphthylene; external heavy-atom effects on photochemical reactions; photo-oxidation; photopolymerization. Address: 108 W. 39th St, Baltimore, MD 21218.

DRISTY, FORREST E, b. Eakin, S.Dak, Oct. 23, 31; m. 58; c. 2. MATHEMATICS. B.S, S.Dak. Sch. Mines & Tech, 53, M.S, 59; Fulbright fel, New South Wales, 53-54; Ph.D.(math), Florida State, 62. Indust. engr, Eastman Kodak Co, 54; instr. MATH, S.Dak. Sch. Mines & Tech, 57-59; asst. prof, Fla. Presby. Col, 62-65; assoc. prof, 65-66; Clarkson Col. Technol, 66-68; PROF, STATE UNIV. N.Y. COL. OSWEGO, 68- Vis. fel, Princeton, 67-68. U.S.A, 55-56. Am. Math. Soc; Math. Asn. Am. Applications of linear algebra to geometry and topology. Address: Dept. of Mathematics, State University of New York College at Oswego, Oswego, NY 13126.

DRIVER, CHARLES H(ENRY), b. Orlando, Fla, Oct. 12, 21; m. 43; c. 3. FOREST PATHOLOGY, RANGE MANAGEMENT. B.S, Georgia, 47, fel, 47-48, M.S, 50; fel, La. State, 52-54, Ph.D, 54. Res. technician forest path, U.S. Dept. Agr, 46-47; instr. biol, Emory, 49-52; res. botanist, Int. Paper Co, 54-57, dir. forest res, 57-65; PROF. FOREST PATH, COL. FOREST RESOURCES, UNIV. WASH, 65- U.S.A, 43-46. Mycol. Soc. Am; Tech. Asn. Pulp & Paper Indust. Pathology of intensely managed forest; forest products pathology; management of wildlands range resources. Address: College of Forest Resources, University of Washington, Seattle, WA 98105.

DRIVER, E(DGAR) S(TEWARD), b. Pittsburgh, Pa, July 12, 21. GEOPHYSICS. A.B, Dartmouth, 43; M.Litt, Pittsburgh, 59. Geophysicist, Gulf Res. Develop. Co, 45-51; seismic party chief, Mene Grande Oil Co, Venezuela, 51-52; geophysicist, Gulf Res. & Develop. Co, 52; chief geophysicist, Mene Grande Oil Co, 53-56; res. geophysicist, Gulf Res. & Develop. Co, 56-61, supvr. seismic interpretation & develop. sect, 61-67, mgr. marine explor. proj, 67-70, GEOPHYS. ADV. EXPLOR. & PROD. DEPT, GULF OIL CORP, 70- Mem. Order Brit. Empire. Am. Field Serv. with Brit. Army, 43-45. Soc. Explor. Geophys; Am. Asn. Petrol. Geol. Seismic systems; marine geology; geology of continental margins; seismic noise analysis. Address: Exploration & Production Dept, Gulf Oil Corp, P.O. Box 1166, Pittsburgh, PA 15230.

DRIVER, GARTH EDWARD, b. Waterville, Wash, Aug. 18, 23; m. 48; c. 5. CONTROL ENGINEERING. B.S, Kansas, 47, M.S, 48. Engr, Hanford Labs, 49-59, sr. engr, 59-65; res. assoc. control systs, PAC. NORTHWEST LAB, BATTELLE MEM. INST, 65 (mgr. digital systs. sect, 65-68, mgr. control & instrumentation dept, 68-70, MGR. COMPUT. & CONTROL DEPT, 70- U.S.N.R, 43-46. Inst. Elec. & Electronics Eng. Transistor circuits; radiation telemetry; nuclear reactor instrumentation; computer process control; process simulation. Address: Pacific Northwest Lab, Battelle Memorial Institute, P.O. Box 999, Richland, WA 99352.

DRIVER, RODNEY D(AVID), b. London, Eng, July 1, 32; U.S. citizen; m. 55; c. 3. MATHEMATICS. B.S, Minnesota, 53, M.S, 55, Ph.D.(math), 60. Instr. math, Minnesota, 56-60; fel, Res. Inst. Adv. Study, 60-61; staff mem, math. res. center, U.S. Army, Wisconsin, 61-62; Sandia Corp, 62-69; ASSOC. PROF. MATH, UNIV. R.I, 69- Am. Math. Soc. Functional-differential equations; two-body problem of classical electrodynamics. Address: Dept. of Mathematics, University of Rhode Island, Kingston, RI 02881.

DRNEC, JAMES, b. Joliet, Ill, Nov. 30, 40; m. 64; c. 1. BIOCHEMISTRY. A.B, Millikin Univ, 63; Ph.D.(biochem), St. Louis Univ, 68. SR. INVESTR, SEARLE DIAGNOSTIC, INC, 68- Protein purification; enzymology; clinical chemistry. Address: 9450 N. Washington, Niles, IL 60648.

DRNEVICH, VINCENT PAUL, b. Wilkinsburg, Pa, Aug. 6, 40; m. 66. CIVIL ENGINEERING. B.S.C.E, Notre Dame, 62, M.S.C.E, 64; Ph.D.(civil eng), Michigan, 67. Instr. field surv, Notre Dame, summer 62, res. asst. soil dynamics, 62-64; Michigan, 64-65; soils engr, Ove Arup & Partners, London, summer 65; res. asst. soil dynamics, Michigan, 65-67; ASST. PROF. CIVIL ENG, UNIV. KY, 67- Univ. Kentucky summer faculty res. award, 68; Nat. Sci. Found. eng. res. initiation grant, 68-69; mem, Int. Soc. Soil Mech. & Found. Eng, 64-, mem. soil dynamics cmt. & preconf. pub. subcmt, 68-69. Am. Soc. Civil Eng; Am. Soc. Test. & Mat.(prize, 66). Behavior of soils due to dynamic loading such as caused by machines and earthquakes; improvement of soil testing techniques and equipment. Address: Dept. of Civil Engineering, University of Kentucky, Lexington, KY 40506.

DROBECK, HANS P(ETER), b. Bavaria, Germany, Oct. 3, 23; nat; m. 48; c. 4. TOXICOLOGY, EXPERIMENTAL PATHOLOGY. B.S, Delaware, 48; M.S, Syracuse, 51, univ. fel, 51-52, Ph.D.(zool), 53. Asst. Syracuse, 48-51; assoc. res. pathologist, Parke, Davis & Co, 53-56; res. pathologist, STERLING WINTHROP RES. INST, N.Y, 56-63, SECT. HEAD, 63- U.S.A, 43-45. AAAS; Soc. Toxicol; Am. Soc. Parasitol. Toxicology. Address: Pine Ave, R.D. 1, Rensselaer, NY 12144.

DROBNIES, SAUL I(SAAC), b. New York, N.Y, June 8, 33; m. 52; c. 1. MATHEMATICS, OPERATIONS RESEARCH. B.S, Texas, 55, M.A, 58, fel, 60, Ph.D.(math), 61. Fel. math, Rice, 61-62; sr. opers. analyst, Gen. Dynamics Corp, 62-63; asst. prof. MATH, SAN DIEGO STATE COL, 63-67, assoc. prof, 67-70, PROF, 70- Am. Math. Soc; Math. Asn. Am; Soc. Indust. & Appl. Math. Mathematical analysis; continued fractions; operations research. Address: Dept. of Mathematics, San Diego State College, San Diego, CA 92115.

DROBNYK, JOHN WENDEL, b. Trenton, N.J, Sept. 30, 35; m. 61; c. 2. GEOLOGY. B.A, Amherst Col, 57; M.S, Rutgers, 59, Ph.D.(geol), 62. Asst. instr. geol, Rutgers, 57-61, res. asst, 61-62; geologist, Pan-Am. Petrol. Corp, 62-64; instr. GEOL, SOUTH. CONN. STATE COL, 64-65, asst. prof, 65-68, ASSOC. PROF, 68-, CHMN. DEPT. EARTH SCI, 67- Instr, Rutgers Univ, summers 60-61. Am. Asn. Petrol. Geol; Soc. Econ. Paleont. & Mineral; Geol. Soc. Am. Geology of modern clastic sediments; interpretation of ancient depositional environments. Address: Tuttles Point, Guilford, CT 06437.

DROBOT, STEFAN, b. Cracow, Poland, Aug. 7, 13; U.S. citizen; m. 41; c. 3. MATHEMATICS. M.A, Jagiellonian, 37; Warsaw Tech, 35-36; Ph.D.(math), Wroclaw, 47. Asst. theoret. mech, Lwow Polytech. Inst, Poland, 39-40; lectr, Siberian Metall. Inst. U.S.S.R, 41-46; asst. prof. MATH, Wroclaw Univ. & Polytech. Inst, 46-49, assoc. prof, 49-59; res. assoc. prof, Chicago, 59-60; assoc. prof, Notre Dame, 60-62, PROF, 62-63; OHIO STATE UNIV, 63- Head dept. appl. math, math. inst, Polish Acad. Sci, 49-58. Am. Math. Soc; Math. Asn. Am. Mechanics of continua; dimensional analysis; operational calculus; variational principles. Address: Dept. of Mathematics, Ohio State University, Columbus, OH 43210.

DROBOT, VLADIMIR, b. Novokuznetsk, U.S.S.R, Oct. 30, 41; U.S. citizen; m. 68. MATHEMATICS. B.S, Univ. Notre Dame, 63; M.S, Univ. Ill, 64, Ph.D.(math), 67. ASST. PROF. MATH, STATE UNIV. N.Y. BUFFALO, 67- Am. Math. Soc. Topological dynamics; ergodic theory. Address: Dept. of Mathematics, State University of New York at Buffalo, 4246 Ridge Lea Rd, Amherst, NY 14226.

DROEGE, J(OHN) W(ALTER), b. Seymour, Ind, Sept. 7, 21. PHYSICAL CHEMISTRY. A.B, Indiana, 42; Ph.D.(chem), Ohio State, 53. PRIN. CHEMIST PHYS. CHEM, BATTELLE MEM. INST, 53- C.W.S, U.S.A.A.F, 43-45. AAAS; Am. Chem. Soc. Thermodynamics; calorimetry; physical properties of materials; solid propellants; high temperature chemistry. Address: Battelle Memorial Institute, 505 King Ave, Columbus, OH 43201.

DROESSLER, EARL G(EORGE), b. Dubuque, Iowa, Jan. 14, 20; m. 44; c. 1; m. 57; c. 4. METEOROLOGY. A.B, Loras Col, 42, hon. D.Sc, 58; U.S. Naval Post Grad. Sch, 43-44; Oslo, 50-51. Meteorologist, Off. of Naval Res, 46-50, head geophys. br, 50; exec. dir. cmt. geophys. & geog, Res. & Develop. Bd, 52-53; exec. secy, coord. cmt. gen. sci, Off. of Asst. Secy. Defense for Res. & Develop, 54-58; prog. dir. atmospheric sci, Nat. Sci. Found, 58-66; prof. atmospheric sci. & v.pres. res, State Univ. N.Y. Albany, 66-71; PROF. GEOSCI. & ADMIN. DEAN RES, N.C. STATE UNIV, 71- Mem, Adv. Cmt. Weather Control, 53-57; U.S. Nat. Cmt. for Int. Geophys. Year, 55-64; chmn, Interagency Conf. Weather Modification, 59-; vis. res. fel, Commonwealth Sci. & Indust. Res. Orgn, Australia, 63-64; chmn. bd. trustees, Univ. Corp. Atmospheric Res, 71. U.S.N, 42-47, Lt. Comdr. Am. Meteorol. Soc; fel. Am. Geophys. Union. Cloud physics; weather modification. Address: North Carolina State University, Raleigh, NC 27607.

DROGIN, I(SAAC), b. Bialystok, Poland, Dec. 10, 90; U.S. citizen; m. 35. CHEMISTRY. B.A, City Col, 13; M.Sc, Pittsburgh, 17, fel, 17-19, Ph.D.(chem), 19. Fel, Mellon Inst, 19-22; chief chemist, J.M. Huber, Inc, 22-40; dir. res, United Carbon Co, Inc, 40-58, v.pres, 55-62, sr. tech. adv, 62-68; consult, 68-70; RETIRED. V.pres, United Rubber & Chem. Co, 57-62. AAAS; Am. Chem. Soc; Am. Inst. Chem; Am. Soc. Test. & Mat; Soc. Plastics Eng; Tech. Asn. Pulp & Paper Indust; N.Y. Acad. Sci; fel. Brit. Inst. Rubber Indust. Carbon blacks; rubber technology; halogens in organic compounds; inversion of cane sugar; distillation; gasoline; natural gas. Address: 411 E. 53rd St, New York, NY 10022.

DROLL, HENRY ANDREW, b. N.Y.C, Sept. 2, 26; m. 52; c. 5. INORGANIC CHEMISTRY. B.S, George Washington, 52, M.S, 53; U.S. Naval fel, Pa. State, 53-54, Ph.D.(chem), 56. Atomic Energy Cmn. asst, George Washington, 52-53; Pa. State, 54-55; sr. scientist, atomic power div, Westinghouse Elec. Corp, Pa, 55-56; asst. prof. CHEM, UNIV. MO-KANSAS CITY, 56-62, assoc. prof, 62-71, PROF, 71- Summer, chemist, elec. div, electrochem. sect, U.S. Nat. Bur. Standards, 52. U.S.N.R, 44-46, Res, 46-50. AAAS; Am. Chem. Soc. Chemistry of less familiar elements; chemical equilibrium, especially study of complex ions in aqueous systems; preparation of coordination compounds. Address: Dept. of Chemistry, University of Missouri-Kansas City, Kansas City, MO 64110.

DROLSOM, P(AUL) N(EWELL), b. Martell, Wis, July 15, 25; m. 50; c. 2. PLANT BREEDING, PATHOLOGY. B.S, Univ. Wis, 49, M.S, 50, Ph.D. (agron, plant path), 53. Asst. agron, Univ. Wis, 49-52; pathologist, Agr. Res. Serv, U.S. Dept. Agr. & N.C. State Col, 53-58; asst. prof. AGRON, UNIV. WIS, MADISON, 58-61, assoc. prof, 61-66, PROF, 66- Mem, U.S. Agency Int. Develop. Prog, Brazil, 64-66. U.S.A, 43-46. AAAS; Am. Soc. Agron; Am. Phytopath. Soc; Am. Inst. Biol. Sci. Grass breeding; disease resistance. Address: Dept. of Agronomy, University of Wisconsin, Madison, WI 53706.

DROMGOLD, LUTHER D, b. Newport, Pa, Apr. 20, 25; m. 50; c. 4. CHEMICAL ENGINEERING. B.S, Pa. State, 49. Engr, KENDALL REF. CO. DIV, WITCO CHEM. CORP, 49-54, sales engr, 55-62, MGR. NEW PROD. DEVELOP, 62- U.S.A, 43-45. Am. Chem. Soc; Am. Soc. Lubrication Eng. Petroleum, especially specialized and process lubricants, automotive underbody coatings; rust preventives, petroleum resins, adhesives, emulsions and hydraulic fluids. Address: 21 McKune Ave, Bradford, PA 16701.

DROMMOND, FRED G(EORGE), b. Sanborn, Nebr, Mar. 5, 11. PHARMACY, PHARMACEUTICAL CHEMISTRY. Ph.C. & B.S, Colorado, 33, res. fels, 33-38, M.S, 34; Am. Found. Pharm. Ed. fel, Purdue, 50, Ph.D.(pharm), 51. Instr. PHARM, UNIV. COLO, BOULDER, 38-42, 46-50, asst. prof, 51-54, assoc. prof, 54-60, PROF, 60- C.Eng, 42-46, 1st Lt. AAAS; Am. Pharmaceut. Asn; Am. Soc. Hosp. Pharmacists; Am. Chem. Soc. Toxicology; emulsion stability; oral pharmaceuticals; organoleptic testing; suspending agents; organic medicinal synthesis. Address: School of Pharmacy, University of Colorado, Boulder, CO 80302.

DRONAMRAJU, KRISHNA RAO, b. Pithapuram, India, Jan. 14, 37; m. 62; c. 1. EVOLUTIONARY THEORY & GENETICS. B.Sc, Andhra, India, 55; M.Sc, Agra, 57, Ph.D.(human genetics), 64; Indian Statist. Inst, Calcutta, 58-61. Consult, Univ. Grants Comn, Govt. India, 59-61; res. fel, Glasgow, 61-62; asst. prof. genetics, State Univ. N.Y. Buffalo, 65-66; vis. fel, Alberta, 66-68; vis. prof. med. genetics, Saskatchewan, 68-69; CHIEF GENETICIST, LANCASTER CLEFT PALATE CLIN, 69- Assoc, Columbia Univ. Seminars, 64-; ed, Haldane & Mod. Biol, Johns Hopkins Press & Oxford Univ. Press, 68. AAAS; Am. Soc. Human Genetics; Genetics Soc. Am; N.Y. Acad. Sci; Am. Asn. Phys. Anthrop; Brit. Genetical Soc; Brit. Soc. Cell Biol; Brit. Soc. Study Human Biol. Speciation and theory of evolution; human genetics and evolution; population genetics and polymorphic systems. Address: 148 Lepore Dr, Lancaster, PA 17602.

DROOZ, ARNOLD T, b. Albany, N.Y, Nov. 17, 21; m. 55; c. 2. FOREST ENTOMOLOGY. B.S, N.Y. State Col. Forestry, 48, M.S, 49. ENTOMOLOGIST, bur. entomol. & plant quarantine, U.S. Dept. Agr, 49-53, forest serv, 53-57, state dept. forests & waters, Pa, 57-60; U.S. FOREST SERV, 60-68, PROJ. LEADER BIOL. CONTROL, SOUTHEAST. FOREST EXP. STA, 68- Consult, Food & Agr. Orgn, Columbia Forest Entom, summer 69. U.S.A.A.F, 43-46. Soc. Am. Foresters; Entom. Soc. Am; Entom. Soc. Can; Int. Orgn. Biol. Control. Forest insect parasites; ecology of forest insects. Address: Forestry Sciences Lab, U.S. Forest Service, P.O. Box 12254, Research Triangle Park, NC 27709.

DROPESKY, BRUCE J(OSEPH), b. Phila, Pa, Apr. 29, 24; m. 48; c. 2. NUCLEAR CHEMISTRY. B.S, Rensselaer Polytech, 49; Ph.D.(phys. chem), Rochester, 53. Mem. staff, LOS ALAMOS SCI. LAB, 53-70, ASSOC. GROUP LEADER, 70- U.S.A.A.F, 43-45. AAAS; Am. Chem. Soc; Am. Phys. Soc. High energy nuclear reactions; nuclear decay scheme studies; nuclear spectroscopy; electromagnetic isotope separation. Address: Los Alamos Science Lab, P.O. Box 1663, Los Alamos, NM 87544.

DROPKIN, DAVID, b. Vitebsk, Russia, Sept. 13, 08; nat; m. 40; c. 2. ENGINEERING. M.E, Cornell Univ, 33, McMullen res. scholar, 34-37, M.M.E, 35, Ph.D.(psychromet), 38. Westinghouse res. assoc, CORNELL UNIV, 37-43, instr. MECH. ENG, 41-43, asst. prof, 43-46, assoc. prof, 46-57, prof, 57-70, JOHN EDSON SWEET PROF. ENG, 70- Vis. engr, Brookhaven Nat. Lab, 49-50; sr. scientist, Avco Res. & Adv. Develop, Div, 57, consult, 57-64, sr. consult, 64-; vis. prof, Cardiff Univ, 71. AAAS; Am. Soc. Heat, Refrig. & Air Conditioning Eng; Am. Soc. Eng. Educ; Am. Soc. Mech. Eng. Heat transfer in confined spaces with and without rotation; diagnostics of high temperature; high velocity gases; heat transfer to boiling liquids and ablating objects. Address: Dept. of Engineering, Upson Hall, Cornell University, Ithaca, NY 14850.

DROPKIN, JOHN J(OSEPH), b. Bobruisk, Russia, Feb. 22, 10; U.S. citizen; m. 33, 57; c. 4. PHYSICS. A.B, Columbia, 30; M.S, Polytech. Inst. Brooklyn, 47, Ph.D.(physics), 48. Asst. physics, Polytech. Inst. Brooklyn, 47-48; Columbia, 30-35; teacher, high sch, N.Y, 36-48; asst. prof. PHYSICS, POLYTECH. INST. BROOKLYN, 48-51, assoc. prof, 51-55, PROF, 55-, head dept, 57-65. AAAS; fel. Am. Phys. Soc; Am. Asn. Physics Teachers. Stimulated phosphorescence and photoconduction in infrared sensitive phosphors; infrared photoconduction in zinc sulfide; solid state physics, especially conduction, photoconduction and luminescence. Address: Dept. of Physics, Polytechnic Institute of Brooklyn, Brooklyn, NY 11201.

DROPKIN, VICTOR H(ARRY), b. New York, N.Y, Mar. 21, 16; m. 41; c. 1. ZOOLOGY. B.A, Cornell, 36; Ph.D.(zool), Chicago, 40. Instr, Chicago, 40-41; U.S. Air Force, 41-45; from instr. to assoc. prof. biol, Roosevelt, 46-51; fel, Naval Med. Res. Inst, 51-53; nematologist, plant indust. sta, U.S. Dept. Agr, 53-69; PROF. PLANT PATH, UNIV. MO-COLUMBIA, 69- Nat. Sci. Found. travel grant, Rothamsted Exp. Sta, Eng, summer 58; vis. prof, Univ. Wis, 66-67. U.S.A.F, 43-46, Capt. Soc. Nematol.(treas, 62-63, v.pres, 64-65); Am. Phytopath. Soc; Europ. Soc. Nematol. Nematodes parasitic on plants. Address: Dept. of Plant Pathology, 108 Waters Hall, University of Missouri-Columbia, Columbia, MO 65201.

DROPP, JOHN JEROME, b. Monessen, Pa, Dec. 2, 40; m. 62; c. 2. BIOLOGY, HISTOLOGY. B.A, Wash. & Jefferson Col, 62; M.S, Ohio Univ, 64; Ph.D. (zool), Ore. State Univ, 69. Neurophysiologist, Walter Reed Army Inst. Res, Wash, D.C, 68-70; ASST. PROF. BIOL, WILSON COL, 70- Med.Serv.C, U.S. Army, 68-70, Capt. AAAS; Am. Soc. Zool. Behavioral stress and its effects on various organ systems of the body—effects at the histological level; trophic effects of neurons. Address: Dept. of Biology, Wilson College, Chambersburg, PA 17201.

DROSDOFF, MATTHEW, b. Chicago, Ill, Dec. 15, 08; m. 35; c. 2. SOIL SCIENCE. B.S, Illinois, 30; M.S, Wisconsin, 32; Ph.D.(soil chem), 34. Asst. soils, Wisconsin, 30-35; jr. soil surveyor, soil chem. div, U.S. Dept. Agr, 38-40, assoc. soil technologist, Tung Lab, Bur. Plant Indust, 40-42, bur. plant indust, soil & agr. eng, 42-53, soil technologist, 45-50, sr. soil scientist, 50-, hort. crops res. br, agr. res. serv, 53-55, Soils Adv, Int. Coop. Admin, Peru, 55-60; food & agr. officer, Agency for Int. Develop, Vietnam, 60-64; adminstr, Int. Agr. Develop. Serv, U.S. Dept. Agr, 64-66; PROF. SOIL SCI, CORNELL UNIV, 66- Adv, Point IV Agr. Mission to Colombia, 51-53, Bolivia, 54. AAAS; Am. Soc. Agron; Soil Sci. Soc; Am. Agr. Econ. Asn. Chemical studies of colloidal clays; field and laboratory research on genesis and morphology of soils; soil chemistry and fertility related to tung production; mineral nutrition of tung trees including minor elements; foliar analysis of tropical tree crops; soil survey; agricultural development. Address: Dept. of Agronomy, Cornell University, Ithaca, NY 14850.

DROSSMAN, MELVYN M(ILES), b. Brooklyn, N.Y, June 30, 37; m. 58; c. 3. BIOMEDICAL ENGINEERING, COMPUTER SCIENCE. B.E.E. & fel, Polytech. Inst. Brooklyn, 57, M.E.E, 59, Ph.D.(elec. eng), 67. Instr. elec. eng, Polytech. Inst. Brooklyn, 58-66; res. assoc. psychophysiol, State Univ. N.Y. Downstate Med. Ctr, 66-68; assoc. prof. ELEC. & COMPUT. TECHNOL, N.Y. INST. TECHNOL, 68-70, PROF, 70-, CHMN. DEPT. ELECT. TECHNOL, 68- Consult, res. ctr, Rockland State Hosp, 63-66. AAAS; Computer analysis of averaged evoked electroencephalographic responses in human subjects using visual and auditory stimuli to determine relationship between electroencephalogram and cerebral information processing. Address: Dept. of Electrical Technology, New York Institute of Technology, 268 Wheatley Rd, Old Westbury, NY 11568.

DROST-HANSEN, W(ALTER), b. Chicago, Ill, Sept. 29, 25; m. 50; c. 2. CHEMICAL PHYSICS. Magister scientiarium, Copenhagen, 50. Asst. mass spectros. invest, Inst. Theoret. Physics, Copenhagen, 46-50; Carlsberg Found. fel, Inst. Phys. Chem, 50; spec. asst, Ill. Inst. Tech, 50-51; res. phys. chemist, Bjorksten Res. Labs, 51-52; assoc. prof. chem. physics & sr. chem. physicist, N.Mex. Inst. Min. & Tech, 53-56; sr. res. engr, Pan-Am. Petrol. Corp, 56-61; sr. res. chemist, Jersey Prod. Res. Co, 61-64; assoc. prof. chem. physics, inst. marine sci, UNIV. MIAMI, 64-66, prof, 66-70, PROF. CHEM. & DIR. LAB. WATER RES, 70-, chmn. div. chem. oceanog, 69-70. AAAS; Am. Chem. Soc; N.Y. Acad. Sci; Denmark Chem. Soc. Chemical physics; theory of reaction rates; structure and properties of water and aqueous solutions; surface phenomena; physical chemistry of biological systems. Address: Lab. for Water Research, Dept. of Chemistry, University of Miami, Coral Gables, FL 33124.

DROSTE, JOHN B(ROWN), b. Hillsboro, Ill, Nov. 23, 27; m. 51; c. 2. SEDIMENTOLOGY. B.S, Illinois, 51, M.S, 53, Ph.D.(geol), 56. Instr. geol. & dir. of gen. studies, Illinois, 56-57; instr. GEOL, IND. UNIV, BLOOMINGTON, 57-59, asst. prof, 59-61, assoc. prof, 61-68, PROF, 68- Assoc. prog. dir, inst. sect, Nat. Sci. Found, D.C, 63-64. U.S.A, 46-48, C.Eng, 48-, 1st Lt. Geol. Soc. Am; Soc. Econ. Paleont. & Mineral. Clay mineralogy; sedimentation; sedimentary petrography, particularly the origin and distribution of clay minerals in sedimentary rock, including origin and occurrence of clay minerals in soils and clay mineral diagenesis. Address: Dept. of Geology, Indiana University, Bloomington, IN 47401.

DROUET, FRANCIS, b. Philadelphia, Pa, Mar. 1, 07. BOTANY. A.B, Missouri, 28, A.M, 29, Ph.D.(bot), 31. Asst. bot, Missouri, 28-31, herbarium, 31-35; Missouri fel, Woods Hole, 30; tech. consult, Bur. Fisheries, 30-31; asst. to state plant pathologist, Mo, 31-35; botanist, Cmn. Tech. Piscicult, Brazil, 35; Seessel fel. bot, Yale, 36-38; curator cryptogamic herbarium, Chicago Nat. Hist. Mus, 38-58; res. assoc, N.Mex. Highlands, 58-59; res. prof. dept. bot, Arizona, 59-62; RES. FEL, ACAD. NATURAL SCI, PHILA, 62- Instr, Marine Biol. Lab, Woods Hole, 34, 36-38; res. assoc, Northwestern, 46-49. Bot. Soc. Am; Am. Micros. Soc; Am. Soc. Plant Taxon; Torrey Bot. Club; Int. Asn. Plant Taxon. Systematics and floristics of Myxophyceae. Address: Academy of Natural Sciences, 1900 Parkway, Philadelphia, PA 19103.

DROUGARD, MAURICE E(MILE), b. Algiers, Apr. 9, 20; nat; m. 59; c. 2. PHYSICS. M.S, Syracuse Univ, 58. Tech. engr, res. lab, IBM Corp, 52-54, assoc. physicist, 54-56, mem. staff, 56-67; La Radiotechnique, 67-69; STAFF ENGR, LABORATOIRE D'ELECTRONIQUE ET DE PHYSIQUE, 69- French Army, 45-52, Capt. Am. Phys. Soc. Ferroelectricity, especially dielectric properties and switching; electroluminescence and phosphors research; switching transistor design; optical properties of semiconductors. Address: Laboratoire d'Electronique et de Physique, 91, Limeil-Brevannes, France.

DROUGAS, JOHN, b. Boston, Mass, Aug. 7, 30; m. 59; c. 2. ORGANIC & POLYMER CHEMISTRY. B.S, Northeastern, 53, M.S, 55; Archer Daniels Midland Co. fel, Mich. State, 56-58, Ph.D.(org. chem), 59. Chemist res. & develop, Arthur D. Little, Inc, 59-61; res. chemist textile fibers, E.I. DU PONT DE NEMOURS & CO, INC, 61-67, SUPVR, 67- AAAS; Am. Chem. Soc. Fiber properties; high polymers. Address: 327 Hampton Rd, Sharpely, Wilmington, DE 19803.

DROULAND, KENNETH EARL, b. Detroit, Mich, Feb. 11, 22; m. 50; c. 3. PATHOLOGY, MEDICINE. Pittsburgh Haverford Col; M.D, George Washington, 49. Intern, U.S. Naval Hosp, Calif, 49-50; resident pathologist, St. Elizabeth's Hosp, Ind, 50-52; asst. pathologist, U.S. Naval Hosp, Ill, 52-53, dir. labs. ward. med. officer, C.Z, 53; asst, Univ. Hosp, Michigan, 54; PATHOLOGIST, HOSPS, ORE. & IDAHO, 54- Mem. bd. & exec. cmt, Med. Serv. Bur, 63- U.S.A, 42-46; U.S.N, 49-50, 52-53, Lt. Fel. Am. Soc. Clin. Path; Am. Med. Asn; fel. Col. Am. Path. Clinical and anatomical pathology. Address: Route 4, Nampa, ID 83651.

DROZDA, WILLIAM, b. Canton, Ohio, June 17, 28; m. 58; c. 3. MATHEMATICS. B.S, Antioch Col, 51. Prin. mathematician opers. res, Battelle Mem. Inst, 53-59; consult. opers. analyst, comput. dept, Gen. Elec. Corp, 59-62; mgr. opers. anal, Del. E. Webb Corp, 62-65; consult, 65-67; SR. SYSTS. ANALYST, BATTELLE MEM. INST, 67- Chem.C, U.S.A, 51-53. Am. Statist. Asn; Inst. Mgt. Sci. Operations research; applications of scientific methods to problems of management; statistical and probability analysis; data processing systems analysis and design; application of data processing techniques to management and technical problems. Address: Battelle Memorial Institute, 505 King Ave, Columbus, OH 43201.

DROZIN, V. G, b. Boguchar, Russia, Feb. 3, 14; U.S. citizen; m. 59; c. 2. PHYSICS, CYBERNETICS. B.S, Teachers Inst, Russia, 41; M.S, Göttingen, 50; Ford Found. fel, Columbia, 51-52, Ph.D.(appl. mech), 56. Res. Asst, Max Planck Inst. Phys. Chem, 50-51; res. assoc. phys. chem, Columbia, 52-56; from asst. prof. to PROF. PHYSICS, BUCKNELL UNIV, 56- Vis. prof, Missouri-Columbia, 66-67. Am. Asn. Physics Teachers. Electrical properties of liquid dielectrics; application of cybernetics to the teaching-learning process. Address: 616 Ikler St, Lewisburg, PA 17837.

DRUCKENBROD, WILLIAM F, b. Cleveland, Ohio, Sept. 21, 14; m. 41; c. 1. OPERATIONS RESEARCH, TRANSPORTATION ENGINEERING. B.S, Fenn Col, 36. Design engr, Bell Aircraft Corp, 38-39; proj. engr, Taylorcraft Aviation Corp, 39-41; proj. flight test engr, Glenn L. Martin Co, 41-46, commercial design analyst, 46-49; opers. analyst, opers. res. off, Hopkins, 49-55; chief systs. anal, aircraft div, Fairchild Aircraft & Engine Corp, 55-61; proj. scientist, Booz Allen Appl. Res, Inc, 61-62; chief anal. br, Fed. Aviation Agency, 62-66; PROG. MGR. SYSTS. ENG. STUDIES, NAT. BUR. STANDARDS, 66- Am. Inst. Aeronaut. & Astronaut. Operational and cost effectiveness analysis of transportation systems; air traffic control and communications problems; cost-benefit studies; cargo handling in marine terminal areas, airport delay problems; highway safety and maintenance problems; automated mail processing and handling systems; modular housing systems; mine safety analysis. Address: 9921 Silver Brook Ct, Rockville, MD 20850.

DRUCKER, ARNOLD, b. Brooklyn, N.Y, Mar. 18, 32; m. 57; c. 2. POLYMER & ORGANIC CHEMISTRY. B.S, City Col. New York, 53; M.S, Polytech. Inst. Brooklyn, 56, Am. Cyanamid Co. & Nat. Insts. Health fels, 61-63, Ph.D. (polymer & org. chem), 64. Res. chemist, Merck & Co, 56-58; Am. Cyanamid Co, Conn, 58-71; TEACHER GEN. CHEM, RIDGEFIELD HIGH SCH, 71- Lectr, City Col. New York, 66- AAAS; Am. Chem. Soc. Keratin chemistry; stereospecific polymerization; epoxy resins; triazine polymers; steroids; water soluble polymers; paper chemistry. Address: 40 Duke Dr, Stamford, CT 06905.

DRUCKER, BERTRAM MORRIS, b. New York, N.Y, Oct. 6, 19. MATHEMATICS. A.B, North Carolina, 40, A.M, 46, Ph.D.(math), 53; fel, Oak Ridge Inst. Nuclear Studies, 51-53. Instr. MATH, North Carolina, 43-49; asst. prof, GA. INST. TECHNOL, 53-56, assoc. prof, 56-62, PROF, 62-, asst. dir. sch. math, 58-59, assoc. dir, 59-62, dir, 62-70. Am. Math Soc; Math. Asn. Am; Asn. Comput. Mach. Numerical analysis; digital computers. Address: Apt. 1811, 620 Peachtree St, N.W, Atlanta, GA 30308.

DRUCKER, DANIEL CHARLES, b. N.Y.C, June 3, 18; m. 39; c. 2. ENGINEERING. B.S, Columbia, 37, scholar, C.E, 38, fel, Ph.D.(eng), 40. Eng. asst, Tunnel Auth, New York, 37; asst, Columbia, 38-39; instr. mech. eng, Cornell, 40-43; supvr. mech. solids, Armour Res. Found, Ill. Inst. Technol, 43-45, asst. prof. mech, 46-47; assoc. prof. eng, Brown, 47-50, prof, 50-64, Ballou prof, 64-68, chmn. phys. sci. coun, 61-63; DEAN COL. ENG, UNIV. ILL, URBANA, 68- Guggenheim fel, 60-61; NATO sr. sci. fel, 68; Fulbright travel grant, 68; mem. exec. comt, Surv. Mat. Sci. & Eng. Lamme Medal, Am. Soc. Eng. Educ, 67. U.S.A.A.F, 45-46. Nat. Acad. Eng; AAAS; assoc. fel. Am. Inst. Aeronaut. & Astronaut; sci. fel. Am. Acad. Arts & Sci; Am. Soc. Civil Eng.(von Karman Medal, 66); fel. Am. Soc. Mech. Eng; hon. mem. Soc. Exp. Stress Anal.(pres, 61). Photoelasticity; plasticity; mechanics of metal cutting and deformation processing; stress analysis; soil mechanics; materials engineering. Address: 106 Engineering Hall, College of Engineering, University of Illinois, Urbana, IL 61801.

DRUCKER, E(UGENE) E(LIAS), b. New York, N.Y, Dec. 11, 24; m. 46; c. 3. MECHANICAL ENGINEERING. B.S, Mass. Inst. Tech, 49, M.S, 50. Asst. MECH. ENG, Mass. Inst. Tech, 49-50; instr, U.S. Naval Postgrad. Sch, 50-51, asst. prof, 51-55, assoc. prof, 55-56; SYRACUSE UNIV, 56-62, PROF, 62- Engr, Babcock & Wilcox Co, 51, Westinghouse Atomic Power Div, 54; Fulbright lectr, Delft, 65-66. Consult, Materials Adv. Bd, Nat. Acad. Sci, 57-58, Int. Bus. Mach, 58. U.S.A.A.F, 43-46, Capt. Am. Soc. Mech. Eng; Am. Soc. Eng. Educ; Am. Nuclear Soc; Am. Soc. Heating, Refrig. & Air Conditioning Eng. Thermodynamics, heat transfer, fluid mechanics, applications of these to nuclear power. Address: 228 Lockwood Rd, Syracuse, NY 13214.

DRUCKER, HARRIS, b. Brooklyn, N.Y, July 28, 43; m. 66; c. 2. ELECTRICAL ENGINEERING. B.S.E.E, Pa. State, 64; Ford fel, Pennsylvania, 65-66, M.S.E, 66, Ph.D.(elec. eng), 67. Jr. engr, Philco Corp, Ford Motor Co, Pa, part-time, 64-67; engr, Radio Corp. Am, N.J, 67-68; ASST. PROF. ELECTRONIC ENG, MONMOUTH COL.(N.J), 68- Inst. Elec. & Electronics Eng; Am. Soc. Eng. Educ. Pattern recognition, particularly as applied towards speech recognition. Address: Dept. of Electronic Engineering, Monmouth College, West Long Branch, NJ 07764.

DRUCKER, HARVEY, b. Chicago, Ill, Jan. 1, 41; m. 65. MICROBIOLOGY, BIOCHEMISTRY. B.S, Illinois, 63, Ph.D.(microbiol), 67. Fel. microbiol, cardiovascular res. inst, med. center, California, San Francisco, 67-69; SR. RES. INVESTR. MOLECULAR BIOL, BATTELLE MEM. INST, 69- Am. Soc. Microbiol; Am. Chem. Soc. Applications of physical measurements of biological macromolecules to new systems. Address: Dept. of Biology, Battelle Memorial Institute, P.O. Box 999, Richland, WA 99352.

DRUCKER, WILLIAM D, b. New York, N.Y, Mar. 30, 29; m. 56; c. 2. MEDICINE, ENDOCRINOLOGY. B.A, N.Y. Univ, 50, M.D, 54. Nat. Insts. Health fel, 59-62; instr. MED, SCH. MED, N.Y. UNIV, 62-64, asst. prof, 64-70, ASSOC. PROF, 70- Career scientist, Health Res. Coun. City of New York, 62- Med.C, 57-59, Capt. AAAS; Endocrine Soc; Am. Fedn. Clin. Res. Steroid hormone metabolism, especially steroid conjugates, biologic action of adrenal androgens and effect of steroid hormones on brain; testis in myotonic dystrophy, Klinefelter syndrome; Cushing's syndrome; acromegaly. Address: New York University School of Medicine, 550 First Ave, New York, NY 10016.

DRUCKER, WILLIAM R(ICHARD), b. Chicago, Ill, Apr. 5, 22; m. 47; c. 4. MEDICINE. B.S, Harvard, 43; M.D, Hopkins, 46. Instr. surg, Western Reserve, 54-57, asst. prof, 57-61, assoc. prof, 61-66, prof, 66; PROF. SURG. & CHMN. DEPT, UNIV. TORONTO & SURGEON-IN-CHIEF, TORONTO GEN. HOSP, 66- Charles O. Finley scholar, 54-57; Markle scholar, 58-63. Fel, Royal Col. Surgeons, Can. Med.C, U.S.N.R, 47-49, Lt.(jg). Am. Surg. Asn; Fedn. Am. Socs. Exp. Biol; Can. Soc. Clin. Invest; fel. Am. Col. Surg. Nutrition and intermediary metabolism in surgical patients; hemorrhagic shock. Address: Banting Institute, 100 College St, Toronto 2, Ont, Can.

DRUCKMAN, RALPH, b. Montreal, Can, Nov. 16, 24; U.S. citizen; m. 57; c. 3. NEUROLOGY. B.Sc, McGill, 46, M.D, C.M, 48. Acad. registr, Nat. Hosp, Queen Sq, 52; fel, dept. neurol. & neurosurg, McGill, 53-54; asst. prof, dept. physiol. & neurol, Baylor, 55-59, assoc. prof, 59; neurol, Univ. Colo, 59-68; prof. & chmn. dept, med. ctr, sch. med, Univ. Okla, 68-71; NEUROLOGIST, LONG BEACH NEUROL. MED. GROUP, INC, 71- AAAS; Am. Med. Asn; Am. Acad. Neurol; Am. Epilepsy Soc. Epilepsy. Address: Long Beach Neurological Medical Group, Inc, 2865 Atlantic Ave, Suite 104, Long Beach, CA 90806.

DRUDGE, J(UNIOR) HAROLD, b. Bremen, Ind, Feb. 7, 22; m. 46; c. 1. VETERINARY PARASITOLOGY. D.V.M, Mich. State Univ, 43; Vet. Med. Asn. Res. Coun. fel, Johns Hopkins Univ, 47-50, Sc.D.(parasitol), 50. VET. PARASITOLOGIST, agr. exp. sta, Miss. State Col, 50-51; AGR. EXP. STA, UNIV. KY, 51-, CHMN. DEPT. VET. SCI, 68-, acting chmn. dept, 63-68. Vet.C, U.S.A, 44-46. Am. Vet. Med. Asn; Am. Soc. Parasitol. Nematode parasites of cattle, sheep and horses. Address: Dept. of Veterinary Science, University of Kentucky, Lexington, KY 40506.

DRUDING, LEONARD F, b. Orange, N.J, July 11, 35; m. 62; c. 3. INORGANIC CHEMISTRY. B.S, Mass. Inst. Technol, 56; Ph.D.(inorg. chem), Iowa State Univ, 60. Fel. CHEM, Northwest. Univ, 60-61; asst. prof, RUTGERS UNIV, 61-64, assoc. prof, 64-71, PROF, 71- Fulbright lectr, Tunghai Univ, 67-68. Am. Chem. Soc. Unusual oxidation states; inorganic thin layer chromatography; amine complexes of cobalt (III). Address: 49 Hedges Ave, Chatham, NJ 07928.

DRUEHL, LOUIS D, b. San Francisco, Calif, Oct. 9, 36; m. 64; c. 2. MARINE ECOLOGY, PHYCOLOGY. B.Sc, Washington State, 59; fel, Bonn, 58-59; M.Sc, Washington (Seattle), 61; Nat. Res. Coun. studentship, British Columbia, 63-65, Ph.D.(bot, oceanog), 65. Lectr. bot, British Columbia, 65-66; asst. prof. BIOL, SIMON FRASER UNIV, 66-71, ASSOC. PROF, 71- Nat. Res. Coun. Can. grants, 66-; vis. asst. prof, Friday Harbor Marine Lab, Washington (Seattle), summer 66. AAAS; Int. Phycol. Soc; Phycol. Soc. Am; Can. Bot. Asn; Brit. Phycol. Soc. Marine algal distribution ecology; biology of the Laminariales; monitoring of on-shore oceanographic conditions. Address: Dept. of Biological Sciences, Simon Fraser University, Burnaby 2, B.C, Can.

DRUELINGER, MELVIN L, b. South Bend, Ind, Dec. 7, 40; m. 59; c. 2. ORGANIC CHEMISTRY, PHOTOCHEMISTRY. B.S, Ind. Univ, Bloomington, 62; Wis. Alumni Res. Found. fel, Univ. Wis, Madison, 62-63, Nat. Insts. Health fel, 63-67, Ph.D.(org. chem), 67. Nat. Insts. Health res. fel. ORG. CHEM, Iowa State Univ, 67-68; ASST. PROF, IND. STATE UNIV, TERRE HAUTE, 68- Am. Chem. Soc; The Chem. Soc; Int. Soc. Heterocyclic Chem. Organic photochemistry; highly reactive organic species; organic reaction mechanisms; heterocyclic compounds, especially small strained polyheterocyclic systems. Address: Dept. of Chemistry, Indiana State University, Terre Haute, IN 47809.

DRUFENBROCK, DIANE, O.S.F, b. Evansville, Ind, Oct. 7, 29. MATHEMATICS. B.A, Alverno Col, 53; M.S, Marquette, 59; Ph.D.(math), Illinois, 61. Asst. prof. MATH, ALVERNO COL, 61-67, ASSOC. PROF, 67- Lectr, grad. sch, Marquette. Am. Math. Soc; Math. Asn. Am. Theory of prime power metabelian groups. Address: Dept. of Mathematics, Alverno College, 3401 S. 39th St, Milwaukee, WI 53215.

DRUGAN, JAMES RICHARD, b. Detroit, Mich, May 5, 38; m. 57; c. 3. SYSTEMS ENGINEERING, STATISTICS. B.S, Univ. Calif, Los Angeles, 60, M.S, 63, Ph.D.(eng), 69. Engr. kinematics, Singer-Librascope, 58-62, consult. engr, 62-63; sr. engr. systs. dynamics, Singer-Librascope, 63-64; res. group supvr, Jet Propulsion Lab, 64-66; staff engr. systs. anal, SINGER-LIBRASCOPE, 66-70, SUPVR. APPL. ANAL, 70- Staff consult. large scale systs, DHA, 68-71. Systems analysis; pattern recognition; detection theory; experimental design; computer software systems; information theory; estimation theory; controls; kinematics; systems simulation; dynamic programming; human factors; signal processing; involutometry; dynamics and acoustics. Address: 10410 Arnwood Rd, Lake View Terrace, CA 91342.

DRUGER, MARVIN, b. Brooklyn, N.Y, Feb. 21, 34; m. 57; c. 3. GENETICS. B.S, Brooklyn Col, 55; M.A, Columbia, 57, Nat. Insts. Health fel, 59, Ph.D.(genetics), 61. Asst. prof. zool. & sci. teaching, SYRACUSE UNIV, 61-66, assoc. prof, 66-71, PROF. BIOL. & SCI. EDUC, 71- Nat. Insts. Health fel, Sydney,

Australia, 61-62; Nat. Insts. Health res. grant, 62-66; Fulbright lectr, Sydney, Australia, 69-70. U.S.C.G.R, 57-65. AAAS; Genetics Soc. Am; Soc. Study Evolution; Am. Soc. Zool; Am. Asn. Biol. Teachers; Nat. Sci. Teachers Asn; Am. Inst. Biol. Sci; Nat. Asn. Res. Sci. Teaching. Evolutionary genetics; individualized instruction; genetic basis for selection. Address: Dept. of Biology, Syracuse University, Syracuse, NY 13210.

DRUGG, WARREN S(OWLE), b. Sitka, Alaska, Jan. 29, 29; m. 58; c. 3. BOTANY, PALYNOLOGY. B.S, Univ. Wash, 52, M.S, 58; Ph.D.(bot), Claremont Grad. Sch, 66. Geologist, Calif. Explor. Co, STANDARD OIL CO. CALIF, 58-60, assoc. res. geologist, Calif. Res. Corp, 60-66, res. geologist, Chevron Res. Co, 66-68, SR. RES. GEOLOGIST, CHEVRON OIL FIELD RES. CO, 68- U.S.A.F, 52-56, 1st Lt. Bot. Soc. Am; Soc. Econ. Paleont. & Mineral. Fossil spores, pollen and dinoflagellates of Mesozoic and Tertiary Age. Address: Chevron Oil Field Research Co, P.O. Box 446, La Habra, CA 90631.

DRUI, ALBERT BURNELL, b. St. Louis, Mo, Aug. 31, 26; m. 49; c. 2. INDUSTRIAL & MECHANICAL ENGINEERING. M.S, Washington (St. Louis), 57, B.S, 49. Planning & design engr, McDonnell Aircraft Corp, 49-53; prod. engr, Army Ord. Corps, 53; tech. economist, Olin Mathieson Chem. Corp, 54; plant indust. engr, metals div, Dow Chem. Co, 55-58; sr. supvr. div. planning staff, Boeing Co, 58-60; asst. prof. MECH. ENG, UNIV. WASH, 60-70, ASSOC. PROF, 70- Consult. indust. & mech. engr, 60-; U.S. Dept. Health, Educ. & Welfare res. grant radiol. opers. efficiency, 67-70, co-investr, res. grant Medex doctors' asst. prog, 69-71. Am. Inst. Indust. Eng; Inst. Mgt. Sci. Work measurement and plant layout; effective delivery of health care by examining radiologists, anesthesiologists, general practitioners and mid medical care professions. Address: Dept. of Mechanical Engineering, University of Washington, Seattle, WA 98105.

DRUKEY, D(ONALD) L(EON), b. Great Falls, Mont, July 23, 22; m. 45. THEORETICAL PHYSICS. B.Ch.E, Minnesota, 43, res. fel, 46-49, M.S, 47, Atomic Energy Cmn. fel, 49-50, Ph.D.(physics), 50. Engr. instrumentation, Kellex Corp, 43-44; tech. engr, Carbide & Carbon Chem. Corp, 44-46; theoret. physicist, radiation lab, California, 50; radar eng, Hughes Aircraft Co, 51-54; Thompson-Ramo-Wooldridge, Inc, 54-63; mgr. res. & tech. div, Systs. Develop. Corp, 63-66, v.pres, 66-67; Comput. & Software, Inc, 67-69; INDEPENDENT CONSULT, 69- System design; radar engineering; research management. Address: 27234 Escondido Beach, Malibu, CA 90265.

DRUKKER, A(LEXANDER) E(MANUEL), b. Zaandam, Netherlands, Feb. 27, 23; nat; m. 48; c. 4. CHEMISTRY. Drs, Amsterdam, 48. Res. chemist, N.V. Polak en Schwarz, Netherlands, 48-53; from sr. res. chemist to group leader, LAKESIDE LABS. INC, DIV. COLGATE-PALMOLIVE CO, 53-66, ASSOC. RES. SCIENTIST, 66- Am. Chem. Soc; Am. Soc. Info. Sci. Organic synthesis; medicinal chemistry; information science. Address: 1104 W. Montclaire Ave, Milwaukee, WI 53217.

DRUM, C(HARLES) M(ONROE), b. Richmond, Va, Sept. 17, 34; m. 58; c. 3. SOLID STATE PHYSICS. B.S, Washington & Lee, 57; M.S, Virginia, 61, Ph.D.(physics), 63. Nat. Sci. Found. fel, Atomic Energy Res. Estab, Eng, 63-64; MEM. TECH. STAFF, BELL TEL. LABS, INC, 64- U.S.A, 57-59. Am. Phys. Soc. Imperfections in crystals; electron diffraction; crystal growth. Address: Bell Telephone Labs, 555 Union Blvd, Allentown, PA 18103.

DRUM, I(AN) M(ONDELET), b. Ottawa, Ont, Oct. 22, 13; m. 44; c. 2. CHEMICAL ENGINEERING. Carleton Von Monk scholar & Dipl, Royal Mil. Col, Can, 35; Leonard mem. scholar, Queen's(Can), 36, B.Sc, 37. Exec. v.pres, Dye & Chem. Co. Can, Ltd, 48-51; mgr. special projs, HOME OIL CO, LTD, 51-66, V.PRES. SPEC. PROJS, 66- Fel. Chem. Inst. Can. Processing, transporting and marketing of natural gas and crude oil. Address: 304 Sixth Ave. S.W, Calgary, Alta, Can.

DRUM, RYAN WILLIAM, b. Milwaukee, Wis, Sept. 25, 39. BIOLOGY. B.Sc, Iowa State, 61, Ph.D.(phycol), 64. NATO fel, Univs. Bonn & Leeds, 64-65; ASST. PROF. BOT, Arkansas, 66; Massachusetts, Amherst, 66-70; FAIRHAVEN COL, 70- Vis. asst. prof, Univ. Calif, Los Angeles, 69-70. AAAS; Am. Soc. Cell Biol; Bot. Soc. Am; Phycol. Soc. Am; Int. Phycol. Soc. Cytoplasmic ultrastructure of diatoms; biogenesis of silica in diatoms; grasses and sponges; single-cell ecology; synthetic petrification; silica replication of cell lumens; multi-media teaching. Address: Dept. of Botany, Fairhaven College, Bellingham, WA 98225.

DRUMHELLER, CARL E(UGENE), b. Earlville, Pa, Apr. 14, 21; m. 44; c. 5. PHYSICS. B.S, Pa. State, 42, M.S, 45, Ph.D.(physics), 53. Instr. physics, Pa. State, 43-46, asst, ord. res. lab, 46-48, res. assoc, 48-50; res. asst. prof. elec. eng, Illinois, 50-57; sr. res. physicist, Kemet Co, Ohio, 57-60; MGR. phys. electronics lab, GEN. DYNAMICS/ELECTRONICS, 60-65, APPL. PHYSICS LAB, ROCHESTER, 65- Am. Vacuum Soc. Tunnel emission phenomena in thin films; thin film microelectronics; silicon oxygen films; conduction in polycrystal-line metal films; infrared detectors. Address: 265 Thornell St, Pittsford, NY 14534.

DRUMHELLER, JOHN E(ARL), b. Walla,Walla, Wash, Dec. 19, 31; m. 56; c. 3. PHYSICS. B.S, Washington State, 53; M.S, Colorado, 58, Ph.D.(physics), 62. Engr, Douglas Aircraft Co, Calif, 53-54; Kaiser Aluminum Co, Wash, 54; res. assoc, Zurich, 62-64; asst. prof. PHYSICS, MONT. STATE UNIV, 64-67, ASSOC. PROF, 67- U.S.A.F, 55-57, 1st Lt. Am. Phys. Soc; Am. Asn. Physics Teachers. Electron paramagnetic resonance in dilute impurity crystals; dielectric and magnetic susceptibility studies. Address: Dept. of Physics, Montana State University, Bozeman, MT 59715.

DRUMHELLER, KIRK, b. Walla Walla, Wash, Jan. 14, 25; m. 50; c. 4. AERONAUTICAL ENGINEERING. S.B, Mass. Inst. Tech, 45; Harvard, 47-48. Instr. math, Whitman Col, 46-47; engr, Gen. Elec. Co, 51-53, supvr. fuel element prod, 53-55, supvr. tool & equip. eng, 56-57, mgr. design & projs, 58-62, adv. fuel develop, 62-65; ceramic mat. develop, PAC. NORTHWEST LABS, BATTELLE MEM. INST, 65-66, MGR. MAT. DEVELOP, 66- U.S.N.R, 43-59, Lt.(jg). Am. Nuclear Soc. Nuclear fuel element, materials, radioistope process and equipment development. Address: Dept. of Materials Development, Battelle Memorial Institute, P.O. Box 999, Richland, WA 99352.

DRUMKE, JOHN STEPHEN, b. Chicago, Ill, Nov. 2, 36. BOTANY. B.S, Loyola (Ill), 57; M.S, Chicago, 60; Ph.D.(bot), Tennessee, 64. Res. asst. plant physiol, Chicago, 60-61; ASSOC. PROF. BOT, NORTHLAND COL, 65-, CHMN. DEPT, 68- Mem. tech. rev. panel, High Ed. Act, State of Wis, 66- Plant taxonomy; taxonomy and ecology of Corylus in North America; nutrition; soil fertility. Address: Dept. of Biology, Northland College, Ashland, WI 54806.

DRUMM, M(ANUEL) F(ELIX), b. St. Louis, Mo, June 21, 22; m. 42; c. 6. ORGANIC CHEMISTRY. B.S, Manmouth Col, 45; M.S, Nevada, 48; Du Pont fel, Missouri, 49-50, Ph.D.(org. chem), 51. Res. chemist, plastics div, MONSANTO CO, 50-52, res. group leader, 52-58, res. sect. leader, 58-60, MGR. RES, 60-65, PLASTIC PROD. & RESINS DIV, 65- Summer instr, Univ. Nev, 48. U.S.M.C, 43-46, 2nd Lt. Am. Chem. Soc. Thermosetting polymers; compounding and processing polyvinylchloride; polymer foams; coatings. Address: 730 Worcester St, Indian Orchard, MA 01051.

DRUMMETER, LOUIS F(RANKLIN), JR, b. Minersville, Pa, Dec. 27, 21; m m. 44; c. 4. PHYSICS. B.A, Hopkins, 43, Ph.D.(physics), 49. Jr. instr. physics, Hopkins, 42-44, instr, 44, asst, 44-48; physicist, U.S. NAVAL RES. LAB, 48-52, SUPV. PHYSICIST, 52- AAAS; Optical Soc. Am. Radiometry; atmospheric optics; radiative heat transfer; infrared. Address: 5503 Belfast Dr, Rosecroft Park, Washington, DC 20022.

DRUMMOND, ANDREW JAMIESON, b. Bellshill, Scotland, Sept. 5, 17; U.S. citizen; m. 42; c. 2. PHYSICS, SPACE SCIENCE. B.Sc, St. Andrews, 37. Head meteorol. div, Kew Observ, London, 41-49; head radiation serv, S.African Weather Bur, 49-56; CHIEF SCIENTIST, EPPLEY LAB. INC, 56- Consult, U.S. Air Force, 58; U.S. Army, 64; Jet Propulsion Lab, 64. Ed-in-chief, Solar Energy, 67. Mem. cmn. instruments & methods observ, World Meteorol. Orgn, 51-56; int. radiation cmn, Int. Union Geol. & Geophys, 54-63. Fel. Am. Phys. Soc; Am. Geophys. Union; Am. Inst. Aeronaut. & Astronaut; fel. Brit. Inst. Physics & Phys. Soc; fel. Royal Meteorol. Soc. Thermal radiation. Address: Eppley Lab. Inc, 12 Sheffield Ave, Newport, RI 02840.

DRUMMOND, GEORGE I, b. Alta, Jan. 19, 25; m. 50; c. 3. BIOCHEMISTRY, PHARMACOLOGY. B.Sc, Alberta, 49, M.Sc, 51; Ph.D, Wisconsin, 55. Fel. biochem, Wisconsin, 55; PHARMACOL, Western Reserve, 55-57; asst. prof, UNIV. B.C, 58-62, assoc. prof, 62-66, PROF, 66- Can. Army, 43-46. AAAS; Am. Soc. Biol. Chem; Am. Soc. Pharmacol; Am. Chem. Soc. Enzymes; carbohydrate, fat and nucleotide metabolism. Address: Dept. of Pharmacology, University of British Columbia, Vancouver, B.C, Can.

DRUMMOND, JAMES, b. Warm Springs, Mont, Feb. 9, 21; m. 50; c. 3. ANIMAL SCIENCE. B.S, Mont. State Col, 48; M.S, Wyoming, 56. Instr. ANIMAL SCI, MONT. STATE UNIV, 48-51, asst. prof, 51-62, PROF. & SHEEP SPECIALIST, 62-, SUPVR. WOOL LAB, 51- Mem, Nat. Lamb & Wool Indust. Cmt, 64- U.S.A.F, 42-45, 1st Lt. Wool growth; physical characteristics. Address: Wool Lab, Montana State University, Bozeman, MT 59715.

DRUMMOND, J(AMES) E(DGAR), b. Portland, Ore, Dec. 7, 24; m. 50; c. 3. PLASMA PHYSICS. B.S, Oregon State Col, 48, M.S, Stanford, 49, Ph.D.(physics), 56. Physicist Nucleonics, Hanford Works, General Electric Co, 48, 50-52; Calif. Res. & Develop. Co, 53; Sr. Engr, Plasmas, Sylvania Microwave Physics Lab, 53-57; Poulter Res. fel, Stanford Res. Inst, 57-58; head plasma physics lab, Boeing Sci. Res. Labs, 58-70; DIR. TECHNOL, PERSONAL COMPUT. CO, 70- U.S.N, 42-46. Am. Phys. Soc; Sci. Res. Soc. Am. Classical and quantum plasma physics. Address: 2616 171st Ave. S.E, Bellevue, WA 98008.

DRUMMOND, KEITH N, b. Halifax, N.S, Can, May 6, 31; m. 55; c. 5. PEDIATRICS. B.A, McGill, 53; M.D, C.M, 55. Instr. PEDIAT, Minnesota, 62-63, asst. prof, 63-64; McGILL UNIV, 64-66, ASSOC. PROF, 66- Fel. Royal Col. Physicians Can, 62. Am. Fedn. Clin. Res; Soc. Pediat. Res; Am. Soc. Nephrology; Can. Soc. Clin. Invest; Can. Urol. Asn; Int. Soc. Nephrology; Am. Soc. Exp. Path. Pediatric nephrology; pathogenesis of glomerular injury. Address: Dept. of Pediatrics, McGill University, Montreal, Que, Can.

DRUMMOND, KENNETH H(ERBERT), b. Riverside, Calif, Jan. 19, 22; m. 55; c. 3. OCEANOGRAPHY. B.S, Arizona, 49; Texas A&M, 50-57. Marine res. technician, Scripps Inst. California, 49-50; asst. oceanog. & chief technician, res. found, Texas A&M, 50-52, assoc. oceanog. & proj. dir, 53-57; oceanogr, U.S. Navy Oceanog. Off, 52-53; exec. officer, satellite tracking prog, Smithsonian Astrophys. Observ, 57-58, administr, 58-59, asst. dir. mgt, 59-60; asst. to chancellor admin, California, San Diego, 60-62; Wash. rep. earth sci, sci. servs. div, Tex. Instruments Inc, 62-69; dir. prog. develop, Teledyne Inc, 69-70, ASSOC. DIR, ALEXANDRIA LABS, TELEDYNE GEOTECH CORP, 71- Consult, Smithsonian Inst, 60-61; participating scientist, Int. Indian Ocean Exped, 62; instr, Naval Reserve Off. Sch, 63-67; exec. secy. indust. investment panel, Comn. Marine Resources & Eng. Develop, Exec. Off. of President, 67-68. U.S.N, 43-46. Fel. AAAS; Am. Geophys. Union; Marine Technol. Soc; Am. Astron. Soc; Am. Astronaut. Soc. Scientific administration in the earth sciences; satellite tracking. Address: Alexandria Labs, Teledyne Geotech Corp, 314 Montgomery St, Alexandria, VA 22313.

DRUMMOND, MARGARET C(RAWFORD), b. Tulsa, Okla, Dec. 4, 22. BIOCHEMISTRY. A.B, Agnes Scott Col, 44; M.S, Emory, 46, Ph.D.(bact), 57. Instr. biochem, nursing sch, Emory, 46; biochemist, U.S. Pub. Health Serv, 47-49; res. biochemist, tuberc. res. Veterans Admin. Hosp, 49-53; chief res. & clin. biochem. labs, Gravely Sanatorium, N.C, 53-54; instr. bact. med. sch, & res. assoc. div. basic health sci, EMORY UNIV, 57-60, asst. prof. MICROBIOL, 60-66, ASSOC. PROF, 66- AAAS; Am. Soc. Microbiol. Host-parasite interrelationships; host resistance factors in tuberculosis; purification and study of mechanism of action of staphylococcal coagulase. Address: Dept. of Microbiology, 505 Woodruff Research Bldg, Emory University, Atlanta, GA 30322.

DRUMMOND, PAUL E(DWARD), b. Boston, Mass, Sept. 25, 30; m. 58; c. 3. ORGANIC CHEMISTRY. B.S, Boston Col, 52, M.S, 55; Tech. Asn. Pulp & Paper Indust. fel. & Ph.D.(org. chem), Vanderbilt, 58. Res. assoc, Mass. Inst. Tech, 58-59; res. chemist ORG. SYNTHESIS, NIAGARA CHEM. DIV, FMC CORP, 59-60, supvr, 61-62, mgr, 62-66, ASST. DIR. RES. & DEVELOP, 66- Am. Chem. Soc. Synthesis of insecticides, fungicides and herbicides. Address: Niagara Chemical Division, FMC Corp, 100 Niagara St, Middleport, NY 14105.

DRUMMOND, PAUL LINWOOD, b. Woodbridge, N.J, Aug. 20, 26. GEOLOGY, MINERALOGY. B.A, Waynesburg Col, 49; Ph.D.(geol), Columbia Univ, 55. Petrol. geologist, Texaco Inc, Texas, 55-57, Tex. Co, Inc, 57-62; PROF. GEOL, WAYNESBURG COL, 62- U.S.A, 44-46, S/Sgt. Geol. Soc. Am; Mineral Soc. Am; Am. Asn. Petrol. Geol. Address: P.O. Box 546, R.D. 5, Waynesburg, PA 15370.

DRUMMOND, R(OGER) O(TTO), b. Peoria, Ill, Aug. 11, 31; m. 53; c. 2. ENTOMOLOGY, ACAROLOGY. A.B, Wabash Col, 53; Ph.D, Univ. Md, 56. Med. entomologist, res. div, U.S. DEPT. AGR, 56-70, INVESTS. LEADER, LIVESTOCK INSECTS LAB, ENTOM. RES. DIV, 70- Fel. AAAS; Am. Entom. Soc; Am. Soc. Parasitol. Animal systemic insecticides; livestock parasites. Address: Livestock Insects Lab, U.S. Dept. of Agriculture, P.O. Box 232, Kerrville, TX 78028.

DRUMMOND, WILLIAM E(CKEL), b. Portland, Ore, Sept. 18, 27; m. 53; c. 3. THEORETICAL PHYSICS. B.S, Stanford, 51; Wiess fel, 55-56, Nat. Sci. Found. fels, 56-58, Ph.D.(physics), 58; Stanford. Physicist, Hanford Labs, Gen. Elec. Co, 51-52; Calif. res. & develop, 52-54; radiation lab, California, 54; Stanford Res. Inst, 55-58; prin. scientist, res. lab, Avco Mfg. Co, 58-59; physicist, Gen. Atomic Div, Gen. Dynamics Corp, 59-65; PROF. PHYSICS, UNIV. TEX, AUSTIN, 65-, DIR, CTR. PLASMA PHYSICS & THERMONUCLEAR RES, 66- Lectr, Stanford Univ, 55. U.S.N, 45-46. AAAS; fel. Am. Phys. Soc. Plasma physics; supersonic flow and shock waves; shock waves in solids; nuclear reactor theory. Address: Dept. of Physics, University of Texas at Austin, Austin, TX 78712.

DRURY, A(LBERT) R(OOKS), b. Athol, Mass, Dec. 9, 20; m. 45; c. 2. VETERINARY MEDICINE. D.V.M, Mich. State Col, 44, M.S, 52. Veterinarian City Health Dept, Pontiac, Mich, 44-47; practicing veterinarian, 47-49; prof. res, dept. surg. & med, COL. VET. MED, MICH. STATE UNIV, 49-69, ASST. PROF. LARGE ANIMAL SURG. & MED, 69- U.S.A, 43-44, Capt. Am. Vet. Med. Asn. Mastitis of dairy cows. Address: 2011 Pawnee Trail, Okemos, MI 48864.

DRURY, HORACE F(EATHERSTONE), b. Columbus, Ohio, June 4, 15; m. 35; c. 5. BIOCHEMISTRY. B.S, George Washington, 37; Thayer fel, Harvard, 37, A.M, 38, Ph.D.(biol), 40. Asst. zool, George Washington, 35-37; biol, Radcliffe Col, 38-40; instr, Suffolk, 40-41; tutor, Brooklyn Col, 41-45, instr, 45-48, asst. prof, 48-54; biochemist, Arctic Aeromed. Lab, 54-59, tech. dir, 59-61, dir. res, 61-67; DIR. INST. AGR. SCI, UNIV. ALASKA, 67- U.S.A.A.F, 43-46, 51-54. AAAS; Arctic Inst. N.Am; Soc. Develop. Biol; N.Y. Acad. Sci. Experimental embryology; high energy phosphorus compounds; night vision; nutrition; emergency survival diets. Address: Institute of Agricultural Sciences, University of Alaska, College, AK 99701.

DRURY, LISTON NATHANIEL, b. Jacksonville, Fla, Oct. 5, 24; m. 52; c. 2. AGRICULTURAL ENGINEERING. B.S.A.E, Georgia, 50, M.S, 61; Tennessee, 54; Iowa State, 63. Electrification adv, Suwannee Valley Elec. Coop, 50-51; Talquin Elec. Coop, 51-53; instr, Tennessee, 53-54; RES. AGR. ENGR, AGR. RES. SERV, U.S. DEPT. AGR, 55- U.S.N, 42-46. Am. Soc. Agr. Eng. Poultry environmental research. Address: Southeast Poultry Research Lab, U.S. Dept. Agriculture, 934 College Station Rd, Athens, GA 30601.

DRURY, WILLIAM H(OLLAND), b. Newport, R.I, Mar. 18, 21; m. 51; c. 4. ECOLOGY. B.A, Harvard, 42, M.A, 48, fel, 49-52, Ph.D, 52. Asst. prof. biol. & gen. ed, Harvard, 52-56; DIR. RES, MASS. AUDUBON SOC, 56-; LECTR. BIOL, HARVARD, 56- U.S.N, 42-46. Ecol. Soc. Am; Am. Ornith. Union; Wilson Ornith. Soc; Arctic Inst. N.Am; Cooper Ornith. Soc; Finnish, German & Brit. Ecol. Socs. Bird ecology and behavior; plant ecology relative to geological process. Address: R.F.D. 1, Codman Rd, Lincoln, MA 01773.

DRUSHEL, HARRY (VERNON), b. Evans City, Pa, Feb. 2, 25; m. 46; c. 3. ANALYTICAL CHEMISTRY. B.S, Pittsburgh, 49, Ph.D, 56. Fel, Mellon Inst, 51-58; chemist, ESSO RES. LABS, 58-66, res. assoc, 66-68, SR. RES. ASSOC, 68- U.S.A, 43-46, Sgt. Am. Chem. Soc; fel. Am. Inst. Chem. Absorption spectroscopy, ultraviolet, visible, infrared; polarography; instrumental analyses; sulfur and nitrogen compounds in petroleum; luminescence spectroscopy; gas chromatography; microcoulometry. Address: 10787 Goodwood Blvd, Baton Rouge, LA 70815.

DRUTOWSKI, RICHARD C, b. Hamtramck, Mich, Jan. 22, 23; div; c. 2. PHYSICS. B.Eng, Michigan, 44, M.S, 46. Jr. physicist, U.S. Naval Res. Lab, 44-45; res. physicist, RES. LAB, GEN. MOTORS CORP, 48-53, SR. RES. PHYSICIST, 53- Vis. scientist, Cambridge, 59-60. U.S.N, 45, Ens. Physical properties of elastomers; characterization of elastomer deterioration. Address: General Motors Corp, Research Lab, 12 Mile & Mound Rd, Warren, MI 48090.

DRYDEN, HUGH L(ATIMER), JR, b. Wash, D.C, July 1, 23; m. 64; c. 2. ORGANIC CHEMISTRY. A.B, Hopkins, 43; Ph.D.(chem), Mass. Inst. Tech, 50. Chemist, rubber sect, Bur. Standards, 43-46; asst, Illinois, 50-51; instr. chem, Northwestern, 51-54, asst. prof, 54-56; res. chemist, G.D. SEARLE & CO, 56-61, head, chem. process res, 61-68, mgr, 68-71, RES. FEL, 71- AAAS; Am. Chem. Soc. Synthetic organic chemistry; carbocyclic compounds; molecular rearrangements; steroid chemistry. Address: G.D. Searle & Co, P.O. Box 5110, Chicago, IL 60680.

DRYDEN, LESLIE P(OWELL), b. Baltimore, Md, Dec. 25, 14; m. 39; c. 3. BIOCHEMISTRY. B.S, George Washington, 47; M.S, American Univ, 61. Biol. aide, Bur. of Dairy Indust, U.S. DEPT. AGR, BELTSVILLE, MD, 36-44, chemist, DAIRY CATTLE RES. BR, 44-62, RES. BIOCHEMIST, 62- AAAS; Am. Dairy Sci. Asn; Am. Inst. Nutrit. Nutrition; vitamins. Address: 6112 43rd St, Hyattsville, MD 20781.

DRYDEN, (ABRAHAM) LINCOLN (JR), b. Baltimore, Md, Dec. 30, 03; m. 33. GEOLOGY. A.B, Hopkins, 25; from assoc. to prof. GEOL, BRYN MAWR COL, 30-69; EMER. PROF, 69- Summer geologist, Md. Geol. Surv, 27-30. With U.S.N, 42-44; U.S. Geol. Surv, 44-46, 52-54. U.S.A, 44. Am. Asn. Petrol. Geol; fel. Geol. Soc. Am. Sedimentation, particularly heavy minerals as applied to stratigraphy of the Atlantic Coastal Plain. Address: Port Republic, MD 20676.

DRYDEN, WARREN A(RNOLD), b. Brooklyn, N.Y, Dec. 29, 26; m. 58; c. 2. METEOROLOGY. B.S, N.Y. Univ, 52, fel, 52-53, M.S, 53, Ph.D, 56. Asst. meteorologist, N.Y. Univ, 52-55; asst. prof. meteorol, Fla. State, 55-59; data reduction analyst, MISSILE TEST PROJ, RCA INT. SERV. CORP, 59-62, sr. engr, 62-68, mgr. satellite orbital anal, 68-69, data reduction, 69-71, MGR. DATA SYSTS. PROCESSING, 71- U.S.N, 44-46. Am. Meteorol. Soc. Atmospheric turbulence and refraction and their effects on optic and microwave propagation; astrodynamics and orbit determination of earth satellites and space probes. Address: RCA International Service Corp, Missile Test Project Bldg. 989, MU 811, Patrick Air Force Base, FL 32925.

DRYER, ROBERT L(EONARD), b. N.Y.C, July 30, 21; m. 44; c. 3. BIOCHEMISTRY. B.S, Univ. Iowa, 43, M.S, 47, Ph.D.(biochem), 49. Anal. chemist, Harvard, 43-45; instr. BIOCHEM, med. sch, Univ. Ind, 49-51, asst. prof, 51-54; UNIV. IOWA, 55-57, assoc. prof, 57-68, PROF, 68- Consult, Camp Atterbury Hosp, 51-53; Thornton-Haymord Labs, Ind, 53-54; Mattox & Moore, Inc, 54-58; mem. comt. clin. chem, Nat. Res. Coun, 69-; vis. prof, Wenner-Gren Inst, 70-71. Dipl, Am. Bd. Clin. Chem, dir, 69- AAAS; Am. Chem. Soc; Soc. Exp. Biol. & Med; Am. Asn. Clin. Chem; Am. Soc. Biol. Chem. Lipid and clinical biochemistry; chemistry of brown adipose tissue. Address: Dept. of Biochemistry, University of Iowa, Iowa City, IA 52240.

DRYHURST, GLENN, b. Birmingham, Eng, Sept. 15, 39; m. 65. ANALYTICAL CHEMISTRY, ELECTROCHEMISTRY. B.Sc, Univ. Aston, 62; Ph.D. (anal. chem), Univ. Birmingham, 65. Res. assoc. electrochem, Univ. Mich, 65-67; asst. prof. CHEM, UNIV. OKLA, 67-70, ASSOC. PROF, 70- Lectr, Univ. Mich, 66-67. Young author award, Electrochem. Soc, 70. Am. Chem. Soc; Brit. Soc. Anal. Chem; Royal Inst. Chem. Electrochemistry of biologically important n-heterocyclic compounds and correlation with biological transformations of these compounds; instrumental methods of organic microanalysis; periodate oxidations in organic chemistry. Address: Dept. of Chemistry, University of Oklahoma, 620 Parrington Oval, Norman, OK 73069.

DRYNAN, W(ALTER) RONALD, b. Toronto, Ont, Jan. 14, 32; m. 56; c. 6. ENVIRONMENTAL HEALTH, ENGINEERING. B.A.Sc, Toronto, 54; M.S, Texas, 56, Ph.D.(sanit. eng), 61. Res. SANIT. ENG, Texas, 54-61; asst. prof, UNIV. WATERLOO, 61-63, assoc. prof, 63-65, PROF, 65- Am. Water Works Asn.(resources div. award, 59); Water Pollution Control Fedn. Biological waste treatment; environmental radioactivity; water resources management. Address: Dept. of Civil Engineering, University of Waterloo, Waterloo, Ont, Can.

DRYSDALE, JOHN J(AY), b. Springfield, Ill, July 13, 27; m. 52; c. 3. ORGANIC CHEMISTRY. B.S, Mass. Inst. Tech, 50; Ph.D.(chem), Illinois, 53. Res. chemist, E.I. DU PONT DE NEMOURS & CO, 53-58, res. supvr, 58-60, div. head, 60-67, res. mgr, 67-70, RES. DIR, 70- U.S.N.R, 45-46. Am. Chem. Soc. Free radical chemistry; reverse osmosis; new product development; organic fluorine chemistry; high temperature synthesis. Address: Horseshoe Hill, Box 295, Hockessin, DE 19707.

D'SOUZA, ANTHONY FRANK, b. Bombay, India, May 9, 29. MECHANICS, MECHANICAL & AEROSPACE ENGINEERING. B.E, Poona, 54; M.S, Notre Dame, 60; Ph.D.(eng), Purdue, 63. Jr. engr. design, Mahindra & Mahindra Ltd, India, 54-55; asst. supt, Air-India Int. Corp, 55; consult. indust. mgt, Ibcon Ltd, 55-57; trainee, Ransomes & Rapier Ltd, Eng, 57-58; asst, Notre Dame, 58-60; Purdue, 60-63; asst. prof. DYNAMICAL SYSTS. & CONTROL, ILL. INST. TECHNOL, 63-67, ASSOC. PROF, 67- Res. grant, Nat. Sci. Found, 63-65, lab. develop. grant, 64-66. Am. Soc. Mech. Eng. Optimal and adaptive control of distributed parameter systems; stability theory, blood flow, hydrodynamic stability. Address: Dept. of Mechanics, Mechanical & Aerospace Engineering, Illinois Institute of Technology, Chicago, IL 60616.

DU, JULIE (YI-FANG) T(SAI), b. Tsingtao, China; m. 64. BIOCHEMISTRY, NUTRITION. B.S, Nat. Taiwan Univ, 59; M.S, Tex. Tech Univ, 63; Ph.D. (phys. chem), Ohio State Univ, 70. NAT. INSTS. HEALTH FEL. PATH, UNIV. LOUISVILLE, 70- Am. Chem. Soc. Address: 3506 Rems Ct, Louisville, KY 40222.

DU, LI-JEN, b. Harbin, China, Sept. 27, 35; m. 64. ELECTRICAL ENGINEERING, APPLIED PHYSICS. B.S, Nat. Taiwan Univ, 58; dipl. Chinese Air Force Electronics & Commun. Sch, 60; M.S, Ohio State Univ, 62, Ph.D. (elec. eng), 65. Res. assoc. ELEC. ENG, electro sci. lab, Ohio State Univ, 64-68; ASST. PROF, UNIV. LOUISVILLE, 68- Nat. Sci. Found. res. fel, Stanford Univ, summer 70. Chinese Air Force, 2nd Lt. AAAS; Inst. Elec. & Electronics Eng; Optical Soc. Am. Applied electromagnetics; antenna and wave propagation; coherent optics and laser technology. Address: Dept. of Electrical Engineering, University of Louisville, Louisville, KY 40208.

DUA, P(REM) NATH, b. Bhera, India, Nov. 15, 35; m. 61; c. 2. VETERINARY MEDICINE, ANIMAL NUTRITION. D.V.M, Punjab Univ, 56; M.S, Miss. State Univ, 63, Ph.D.(nutrit. & biochem), 67. Vet. surgeon, Punjab Vet. Dept, India, 56-59; instr. vet. med, Punjab Vet. Col, 57-61; res. asst. poultry sci, Miss. State Univ, 61-67; res. assoc. nutrit. & biochem, Vanderbilt Univ, 67-69, assoc. veterinarian, 69-70; VETERINARIAN, STATE LAB, VA. DEPT. AGR, 70- Ralston Purina Co. res. fel, 66. Poultry Sci. Asn; Am. Inst. Nutrit; Am. Vet. Med. Asn. Vitamins A and K; carotenoid and lipid metabolism; thiamine metabolism. Address: State Lab, Virginia Dept. of Agriculture, Harrisonburg, VA 22801.

DUANE, DAVID B(IERLEIN), b. Port Jervis, N.Y, June 4, 34; m. 57; c. 2. MARINE GEOLOGY, COASTAL ENGINEERING. A.B, Dartmouth Col, 57; M.S, Univ. Kans, 59, Shell Oil fel, 61, Ph.D.(geol), 63. Explor. geologist, Magnolia Petrol. Co, 57; Mobil Oil Co, 62-64; res. phys. scientist, U.S. Lake Surv, CORPS ENGRS, U.S. ARMY, 64-65, supvry. res. phys. scientist, 65-66, CHIEF. GEOL. BR, COASTAL ENG. RES. CTR, 66- Instr, bur. correspondence study, Univ. Kans, 60-68. Geol. Soc. Am; Soc. Econ. Paleont. & Mineral. Geologic processes and history as related to coastal engineering, mineral exploration and exploitation; impact of ocean waste disposal on the environment; shore processes, sediment transport, coastal geomorphology, regional geology. Address: 6202 Wilmett Rd, Bethesda, MD 20034.

DUANE, J(EROME) J(AY), b. Brooklyn, N.Y, May 26, 17; m. 40; c. 2. PHYSICAL CHEMISTRY. B.Ch, Cornell, 38; fel, Polytech. Inst. Brooklyn, 41-42, M.S, 42, fel, 42-43, Ph.D.(inorg-phys. chem), 43. Chemist, Peerless Paint & Varnish Corp, 38-41; Manhattan Proj, substitute alloy mat. lab, Columbia & Carbide & Carbon Chem. Corp, 43-46; res. chemist, res. labs, Eastman Kodak Co, N.Y, 46-62; sr. staff mem, lab, United-Carr Inc, 63-68, head chem. div, 68-69; sr. chemist, Itek Corp, 69-70; TECH. DIR, PAVELLE CORP, 70- AAAS; Am. Chem. Soc; Soc. Photog. Sci. & Eng. Photographic chemistry; coatings; polymers; colloids. Address: Pavelle Corp, 8 Henderson Dr, West Caldwell, NJ 07006.

DUANE, THOMAS DAVID, b. Peoria, Ill, Oct. 10, 17; m. 44; c. 4. OPHTHALMOLOGY. B.S, Harvard, 39; M.D, Northwest. Univ, 43, M.S, 44; Ph.D.(physiol), Univ. Iowa, 48. PROF. OPHTHAL. & CHMN. DEPT, MED. COL, THOMAS JEFFERSON UNIV, 62- U.S.N.R, 50-53, Lt. Am. Ophthal. Soc; Am. Acad. Ophthal. & Otolaryngol; Am. Asn. Res. Vision & Ophthal; Am. Med. Asn. Biophysics of the eye, especially retinal circulation. Address: Dept. of Ophthalmology, Jefferson Medical College, Thomas Jefferson University, 1025 Walnut St, Philadelphia, PA 19107.

DUANY, LUIS F, JR, b. Santiago de Cuba, Cuba, Dec. 26, 19; m. 48; c. 1. DENTAL EPIDEMIOLOGY, PREVENTIVE DENTISTRY. D.D.S, Univ. Havana, 44; M.P.H, Univ. N.C, Chapel Hill, 65, Dr.P.H.(epidemiol), 70. Private practice, Cuba, 44-61; asst. prof. oral cancer, sch. dent, Univ. Havana, 45-46; scientist adminr. res. grants, Nat. Inst. Dent. Res, 61-63; Nat. Inst. Dent. Res. fel, Univ. Miami & Univ. N.C, 63-66; asst. prof. epidemiol. & prev. dent, sch. dent, Univ. P.R, San Juan, 66-67; CHIEF EPIDEMIOL. SECT, INST. ORAL BIOL, UNIV. MIAMI, 67- Consult, div. oral biol, Univ. Miami, 65-67, div. family med, 68-69; Pan-Am. Health Organ, WHO, 68-; lectr, sch. dent, univ. Antioquia, Colombia, 68-; sch. dent, Univ. El Salvador, 70-; Nat. Inst. Dent. Res, 71- Dipl. Asn. Oral Surgeons Cuba 47; P.R. Pub. Health Dept, 67. Am. Dent. Asn; Int. Asn. Dent. Res; Am. Pub. Health Asn. Epidemiology of dental caries, especially microbiology, dietary regimes, dental plaque extent, oral hygiene, fluoride exposure and their relationship to caries status; studies of caries, particularly free and carie active students. Address: P.O. Box 875, Biscayne Annex, Miami, FL 33152.

DUAX, WILLIAM L(EO), b. Chicago, Ill, Apr. 18, 39; m. 65; c. 4. X-RAY CRYSTALLOGRAPHY, BIOCHEMISTRY. B.A, St. Ambrose Col, 61; NASA res. fel, Univ. Iowa, 64-66, Ph.D.(phys. chem), 67. Res. fel. inorg. x-ray crystallog, Ohio Univ, 67-68; res. assoc. steroid struct. & x-ray crystallog, MED. FOUND. BUFFALO, 68-69, HEAD CRYSTALLOG. LAB, 69- Co-prin. investr, Nat. Cancer Inst. grant, 71-; del, NATO Advan. Study Inst, York, Eng, fall 71. Am. Crystallog. Asn; Am. Chem. Soc. Conformational analysis of crystal structure data for steroids and steroid complexes; elucidation of structural-functional relationships among steroids; development and application of direct methods of crystal structure determination of large biologically import molecules. Address: Medical Foundation of Buffalo, 73 High St, Buffalo, NY 14203.

DUB, MICHAEL, b. Opaka, Ukraine, Mar. 11, 17; U.S. citizen; m. 49; c. 1. CHEMISTRY. M.S, Vienna, 44; Innsbruck, 45-46; B.S, City Col. New York, 55. Res. chemist N.Y. Quinine & Chem. Works, 52-55; Monsanto Chem. Co, 55-60, SR. RES. CHEMIST, MONSANTO CO, 61- Am. Chem. Soc. Organometallic chemistry; organic synthesis. Address: 1060 Orchard Lakes Dr, St. Louis, MO 63141.

DUBACH, HAROLD W, b. St. Joseph, Mo, Nov. 25, 20; m. 46; c. 4. OCEANOGRAPHY, METEOROLOGY. A.B, Baker, 42; Chicago, 42-43; Hopkins, 49-51; summers, N.Y. Univ, 56, Mass. Inst. Tech, 59 & 66. Res. meteorologist to chief upper air sect, thunderstorm proj, Weather Bur, Ill, 46-48; res. oceanogr, div. oceanog, Naval Hydrographic Off, Wash, D.C, 48-54, dep. dir. oceanog. anal. div, 54-60; acting dir, Nat. Oceanog. Data Ctr, 60-61, dep. dir, 61-68, sci. staff asst. to dep. oceanogr, 68-69; Dept. Defense rep, Marine Environ. Prediction Staff, ENVIRON. SCI. SERV. ADMIN, 69, ASST. DIR, CTR. MARINE DEVELOP. SERV, 69- Mem. Civil Serv. Cmn. exam. panel oceanog, 54-61, panel meteorol, 57-60; mem. men's cmt, Int. Christian Univ, Tokyo, 64-; chmn, Am. Soc. Test. & Mat. & subcmt. natural environ. testing, 65- U.S.A.F, 42-46, Res, 46-62, Maj; Navy-Cent. Intel. Agency Commendation, 59; Navy Superior Accomplishment award, 62. AAAS; Am. Meteorol. Soc; Am. Soc. Limnol. & Oceanog; Marine Technol. Soc; Am. Soc. Test. & Mat; Oceanog. Soc. Japan; Australian Marine Sci. Asn. Design & development of automated processing systems for oceanographic observations; marine meteorological research, especially air-sea interaction; upper-air studies; design subsurface temperature sensor for rough seas; documentation and information sciences applied to coastal environment. Address: Coastal Plains Center for Marine Development Services, Box 3643, Wilmington, NC 28401.

DuBAR, JULES R, b. Canton, Ohio, June 30, 23; m. 64; c. 2. INVERTEBRATE PALEONTOLOGY. B.S, Kent State, 49, Illinois, 50-51; M.S, Oregon State, 50; Duke, 52; Ph.D, Kansas, 57. Asst. geol, Kent State, 47-48; Oregon State, 49-50; Illinois, 50-51; instr, Southern Illinois, 51-53; Kansas, 53-54; from instr. to asst. prof, Southern Illinois, 54-57; Houston, 57-59, assoc. prof, 59-62; Duke, 62-64; sr. geologist, res. lab, Esso Prod. Res. Co, 64-67; assoc. prof. GEOSCI, MOREHEAD STATE UNIV, 67-69, PROF, 69-, CHMN. DEPT, 67- Nat. Sci. Found. grants, 59-64, 68-70. Consult, Fla. Geol. Surv, 53-59; Int. Minerals & Chem. Corp, 63-64, Summers, mem, geophys. crew, U.S. Geol. Surv, 51; proj. geologist, S.Carolina Div. Geol, 62-64. U.S.C.G, 43-46. AAAS; Am. Asn. Petrol. Geol; Geol. Soc. Am; Am. Soc. Oceanog; Am. Malacol. Union; Int. Paleont. Union; Am. Soc. Syst. Zool; Paleont. Soc; Soc. Econ. Paleont. & Mineral. Stratigraphy; paleontology and paleoecology of Neogene of eastern seaboard and gulf coastal region; Neogene mollusca. Address: Dept. of Geoscience, Moorehead State University, Morehead, KY 40351.

DuBARD, JAMES L(EROY), b. Atlanta, Ga, Mar. 13, 37; m. 60; c. 3. NUCLEAR PHYSICS. B.E.E, Ga. Inst. Technol, 59, Ph.D.(physics), 66; M.S, Mass. Inst. Technol, 61; NASA trainee, 62. Res. assoc. PHYSICS, nuclear res. lab, Fla. State Univ, 66-68; ASST. PROF, UNIV. LOUISVILLE, 68- Am. Phys. Soc. Nuclear structure physics; nuclear reaction and decay scheme spectroscopy. Address: Dept. of Physics, University of Louisville, Louisville, KY 40208.

DUBAY, GEORGE H(ENRY), b. Chicago, Ill, May 26, 14; m. 46; c. 5. MATHEMATICS. B.S, Loyola (Ill), 36, M.A, 38. Salesman, Midcontinent Chem. Corp, 38-39; purchase agent McKesson & Robbins, Inc, 39-40; teacher, pub. schs, Ill, 46, 47-48; instr. MATH, Marquette, 46-47; asst. prof, UNIV. ST. THOMAS, 48-61, assoc. prof, 61-69, PROF, 69-, CHMN. DEPT, 52- Minnie Piper Prof. award, 58; cert, data processing, 64. Asn. Comput. Mach; Math. Asn. Am; Soc. Indust. & Appl. Math; Data Processing Mgt. Asn. (tech. ed, Jour. Data Mgt); Asn. Educ. Data Systs. Computing. Address: 6407 Thrush Rd, Houston, TX 77017.

DUBBE, RICHARD F, b. Minneapolis, Minn, Jan. 9, 29; m. 50; c. 4. ELECTRONICS. B.E.E, Minnesota, 53. Tech. serv. engr, MINN. MINING & MFG. CO, 53-58, res. engr, 58-63, proj. supvr. electron beam recording, 63-65, proj. mgr, 65-66, RES. MGR. MINCOM DIV, 66- Soc. Motion Picture & TV Eng; Inst. Elec. & Electronics Eng; Soc. Photog, Sci. & Eng. Electron beam, magnetic and sound recording; television; motion picture technology. Address: Mincom Division, Minnesota Mining & Manufacturing Co, 300 S. Lewis Rd, Camarillo, CA 93010.

DUBBELDAY, PIETER STEVEN, b. Surakarta, Indonesia, Dec. 23, 28; nat; m. 58; c. 2. NUCLEAR PHYSICS. Candidatus, Free Univ, Amsterdam, 50, Drs, 53, Ph.D.(nuclear physics), 59; Mass. Inst. Tech, summer 56. Asst. physics, Free Univ, Amsterdam, 51-53, 54-56, chief asst, 56-59; proj. assoc. & instr, nuclear physics lab, Wisconsin, 59-61; engr, missile test proj, RCA Serv. Co, 61-63, sr. engr, 63-66; assoc. prof. physics, FLA. INST. TECHNOL, 66-70, PROF. PHYSICS & OCEANOG, 70-, instr. physics, 60-66. Am. Geophys. Union; Marine Technol. Soc; Am. Asn. Physics Teachers; Am. Phys. Soc; Netherlands Phys. Soc. Neutron physics, especially polarization of neutrons; problems in missile tracking; survey and error analyses of atmospheric refraction. Address: Dept. of Physics, Florida Institute of Technology, Country Club Rd, Melbourne, FL 32910.

DUBBS, CLYDE A(NDREW), b. Mar Vista, Calif, Aug. 25, 20. BIOCHEMISTRY. B.S, Calif. Inst. Tech, 43, fel, 43-46, Ph.D.(bio-org. chem), 46. Asst. biol, Calif. Inst. Tech, 46; res. assoc. bact. & parasitol, sch. med. Southern California, 47-48; biochemist, res. serv, U.S. Vet. Admin. Center, Los Angeles, 48-54, chief biochemist, 54-60; asst. clin. prof. physiol. chem, SCH. MED, UNIV. CALIF, LOS ANGELES, 55-61, ASST. RES. CHEMIST, 60-; RES. CHEMIST, ST. JOHN'S HOSP, SANTA MONICA, 61- Dipl, Am. Bd. Clin. Chem, 52. AAAS; Am. Inst. Chem; N.Y. Acad. Sci; Am. Chem. Soc; Am. Asn. Clin. Chem; Bot. Soc. Am; Soc. Appl. Spectros; Coblentz Soc. Clinical chemistry; protein subfractionation; isoenzymes; electrophoresis; design of microapparatus. Address: 1814 West Blvd, Los Angeles, CA 90019.

DUBBS, DEL ROSE M, b. Vesta, Minn, Feb. 10, 28. VIROLOGY, BIOCHEMISTRY. B.A, Minnesota, 50, M.S, 57, Ph.D.(bact), 61. Res. asst. bact, Minnesota, 53-60; res. assoc. biochem, Univ. Texas M.D. Anderson Hosp. & Tumor Inst, 60-62; asst. prof. VIROL, BAYLOR COL. MED, 62-69, ASSOC. PROF, 69- U.S. Pub. Health Serv. res. career develop. award, 65-70. Am. Soc. Microbiol. Studies of the biochemical alterations in virus infected cells and to relate these changes to transformation of normal cells to malignant cells. Address: Dept. of Biochemical Virology, Baylor College of Medicine, Houston, TX 77025.

DUBE, HARVEY A(LBERT), b. Chicopee, Mass, April 19, 18; m. 43; c. 3. CHEMISTRY. B.S, Niagara, 41; M.S, Detroit, 43; Ph.D.(plant chem), Iowa State Col, 47. Asst. CHEM, Iowa State Col, 43-45; instr, XAVIER UNIV. (OHIO), 47-48, asst. prof, 48-53, assoc. prof, 53-59, PROF, 59- Am. Chem. Soc. Thermodynamic properties of organic compounds; electro chemistry of molten salts; high polymers; atomic and molecular structure. Address: Dept. of Chemistry, Xavier University, Cincinnati, OH 45207.

DUBE, MAURICE A(NDREW). BOTANY. B.S, Washington State, 50; M.S, Oregon State, 58, Ph.D.(bot), 63. Asst. prof. bot, WEST. WASH. STATE COL, 63-68, ASSOC. PROF. BIOL, 68- U.S.A, 50-52. Life history of marine algae. Address: Dept. of Biology, Western Washington State College, Bellingham, WA 98225.

DUBECK, LEROY W, b. Orange, N.J, Mar. 1, 39. SOLID STATE PHYSICS. B.A, Rutgers, 60, M.A, 62, fel, 62-65, Ph.D.(physics), 65. Teaching asst. PHYSICS, Rutgers, 60-62; asst. prof. TEMPLE UNIV, 65-69, ASSOC. PROF, 69- Am. Phys. Soc; Am. Asn. Physics Teachers. Thermal conductivity; magnetization and flux motion properties of superconductors; nuclear magnetic resonance of superconductors. Address: Dept. of Physics, Temple University, Philadelphia, PA 19122.

DUBECK, M(ICHAEL), b. Brantford, Ont, Can, Feb. 16, 26; nat; m. 57; c. 2. ORGANIC CHEMISTRY. B.S, McMaster, 51, M.S, 52; Ph.D, Purdue, 58. SUPVR. CHEM. RES, ETHYL CORP, 58- Am. Chem. Soc. Organic reaction mechanisms; organo metallic synthesis. Address: Ethyl Corp, 1600 W. 8 Mile Rd, Ferndale, Detroit, MI 48220.

DUBERG, JOHN E(DWARD), b. N.Y.C, Nov, 30, 17; m. 43; c. 2. AERONAUTICAL ENGINEERING. B.S, Manhattan Col, 38; M.S, Va. Polytech. Inst, 40; Ph.D.(struct. eng), Illinois, 48. Field engr, Caldwell Wingate Builders, 38-39; asst, Talbot Lab, Illinois, 40-43; aeronaut. res. scientist, Nat. Adv.

Cmt. Aeronaut, Va, 43-46; asst. chief res. engr, Standard Oil Co. Ind, 46-48; aeronaut. res. scientist, Nat. Adv. Cmt. Aeronaut, 48-52, chief, struct. res. div, 52-56; res. engr, Aeronautronics Systs, Inc, 56-57; prof. struct. eng, Illinois, 57-59; tech. asst. to chief, THEORET. MECH. DIV, LANGLEY RES. CTR, NASA, 59-61, tech. asst. to assoc. dir, 61-64, asst. dir, 64-68, ASSOC. DIR, 68- Mem. panel guided missiles mat, minerals & metals adv. bd, Nat. Acad. Sci. Fatigue of joints in steel structures; stress analysis of stiffened shells; space environmental effects. Address: Langley Research Center, NASA, Hampton, VA 23365.

DUBES, GEORGE R(ICHARD), b. Sioux City, Iowa, Oct. 12, 26; m. 64; c. 4. GENETICS. B.S, Iowa State, 49; Atomic Energy Cmn. fel. & Ph.D.(genetics), Calif. Inst. Tech, 53. Res. assoc, inst. co-op. res, McCollum-Pratt Inst, Hopkins, 53-54; sect. virus res, med. center, Kansas, 54-56, asst. prof. pediat, 56-60, assoc. prof, 60-64; ASSOC. PROF. MICROBIOL, COL. MED. UNIV. NEBR, 64-, head viral genetic sect, Eugene C. Eppley Inst. Res. Cancer & Allied Diseases, 64-68. U.S.A, 45-46. AAAS; Genetics Soc. Am; Am. Genetic Asn; Am. Inst. Biol. Sci; Am. Soc. Microbiol; Am. Asn. Cancer Res; N.Y. Acad. Sci; Biomet. Soc. Genetics of animal viruses; transfection; amoebic cysts. Address: Dept. of Medical Microbiology, University of Nebraska College of Medicine, 42nd & Dewey, Omaha, NE 68105.

DUBES, RICHARD C, b. Chicago, Ill, Oct. 7, 34; m. 59; c. 1. COMPUTER SCIENCE. B.S.E.E, Illinois, 56; M.S, Mich. State, 58, Nat. Sci. Found. summer fels, 60, 61, Gen. Tel. & Elec. Found. fel, 61-62, Ph.D.(elec. eng), 62. Mem. tech. staff, Hughes Aircraft Co, 56-57; asst. ELEC. ENG, MICH STATE UNIV, 57-58, asst. instr, 58-61, asst. prof, 62-65, assoc. prof, 65-70, PROF, 70- AAAS; Inst. Elec. & Electronics Eng. Pattern recognition in electroencephalography; information theory; statistical computing. Address: Dept. of Computer Science, Michigan State University, East Lansing, MI 48823.

DUBEY, GEORGE A, b. Kansas City, Kans, Aug. 24, 22; m. 46; c. 5. BIO-CHEMISTRY. B.S, Iowa, 44, M.S, 45. Biochemist, Norwich Parmacal Co, 45-46; Sulphite Pulp Mfrs. Res. League, Inc, 46-63, RES. ASSOC, 63-66, Pulp Mfg. Res. League, 66-70, EFFLUENT PROCESSES GROUP, DIV. IN-DUST. & ENVIRON. SYSTS, INST. PAPER CHEM, 70- Am. Chem. Soc. Utilization of spent sulfite liquor from the manufacture of sulfite pulp; utilization of organics. Address: Effluent Processes Group, Division of Industrial & Environmental Systems, Institute of Paper Chemistry, 1043 E. South River St, Appleton, WI 54911.

DUBEY, RAJENDRA NARAIN, b. Bihar, India, Nov. 2, 38; m. 67; c. 3. ME-CHANICAL ENGINEERING, APPLIED MATHEMATICS. B.Sc, Patna, 57; B.Sc, Ranchi, 61; Ph.D.(civil eng), Waterloo, 66. Asst. lectr. civil eng, Regional Inst. Tech, Jamshedpur, India, 61-62; asst. engr, M.M. Bilaney & Co, India, 63-64; fel. civil eng, UNIV. WATERLOO, 66-67, ASST. PROF. MECH. ENG, 67- Assoc. mem. Am. Soc. Mech. Eng. Plastic instabilities in solids; convective instabilities in fluids; boundary layer flow; dynamic instabilities. Address: 618 Mount Anne Dr, Waterloo, Ont, Can.

DUBEY, SATYA D(EVA), b. Sakara Bajid, India, Feb. 10, 30; U.S. citizen; m. 60; c. 1. STATISTICS, MATHEMATICS. B.S, Patna Univ, 51; dipl, Indian Statist. Inst, Calcutta, 53; Ph.D.(statist), Mich. State Univ, 60. Tech. asst. statist, Indian Inst. Technol, 53-56; res. asst. math, Carnegie Inst. Technol, 56-57; instr. statist. & res. asst, Mich. State Univ, 57-60; sr. math. statistician, Procter & Gamble Co, Ohio, 60-65, head statist. sect, 65-66; prin. statistician & group leader statist. & opers. res, Ford Motor Co, Mich, 66-68; ASSOC. PROF. INDUST. ENG. & OPERS. RES, N.Y. UNIV, 68- Consult, Mich. State Budget Div, 58; Dept. Health, Educ. & Welfare, 63-65; Dept. Defense, 68-70; Del, Int. Statist. Inst, 71; prin. investr. & dir. res. contract on statist. procedures in reliability eng, Dept. Army, 71- AAAS; fel. Royal Statist. Soc; Am. Statist. Asn; Inst. Math. Statist; Biomet. Soc; Am. Soc. Qual. Control; Indust. Math. Soc. Statistical inference procedures applicable to engineering, physical, social, mathematical and computer sciences. Address: Dept. of Industrial Engineering & Operations Research, New York University, 181st St. & University Ave, Bronx, NY 10453.

DUBIN, ALVIN, b. Russia, Jan. 23, 14; nat; m. 38; c. 2. BIOLOGICAL CHEMISTRY. B.A, Brooklyn Col, 40, M.S, 42. Asst. dir. labs, Beth-El Hosp, 38-46; ASST. PROF. BIOCHEM, COL. MED, UNIV. ILL, 60-; DIR. DEPT. BIOCHEM, HOKTOEN INST. MED. RES, COOK COUNTY HOSP, 53-, chief biochemist, 47-53. Consult, Oak Forest Hosp, 56-; Woodlawn Hosp, 56; MacNeal Mem. Hosp, 58-; asst. prof, Cook County Grad. Sch, 60- Am. Asn. Clin. Chem; Soc. Exp. Biol. & Med; Am. Chem. Soc. Biochemistry and its relationship to liver and kidney disease; synthesis and degradation of proteins and the excretion of proteins as related to renal damage; relationship of uric acid and calcium metabolism to such diseases as gout and parathyroid diseases. Address: Dept. of Biochemistry, Hoktoen Institute for Medical Research, Cook County Hospital, 627 S. Wood St, Chicago, IL 60612.

DUBIN, DONALD T, b. Brooklyn, N.Y, Mar. 23, 32; m. 65; c. 6. BIOCHEM-ISTRY, BACTERIOLOGY. A.B, Harvard, 53; M.D, Columbia, 56. Intern med, Bronx Munic. Hosp, N.Y, 56-57; res, 59-60; sr. asst. surgeon biochem. Nat. Insts. Health, 57-59; res. fel. bact, Harvard Med. Sch, 60-62, instr, 62-63, assoc, 63-66, asst. prof, 66-67; assoc. prof. MICROBIOL, RUTGERS MED. SCH, COL. MED. & DENT. N.J, 67-71, PROF, 71- Am. Soc. Microbiol; Am. Soc. Biol. Chem. Nucleic acid metabolism; mitochondrial biogenesis. Address: Dept. of Microbiology, Rutgers Medical School, College of Medicine & Dentistry of New Jersey, New Brunswick, NJ 08903.

DUBIN, I(SADORE) N(ATHAN), b. Montreal, Que, July 13, 13; nat; div; c. 3. PATHOLOGY. B.Sc, McGill, 35, M.D.C.M, 39. Intern med, Royal Victoria Hosp, Can, 39-40; asst. res. & res. path, St. Luke's Hosp, Cleveland, 40-42; asst, Duke, 42-43; instr, 43-44, assoc, 44-45; asst. prof, col. med, Tennessee, 45-48, assoc. prof, 48-49; spec. res. fel, Nat. Cancer Inst, 49-50; chief hepatic path. sect, Armed Forces Inst. Path, 51-55; PROF. PATH, MED. COL. PA. & CHIEF PATHOLOGIST, HOSP, 55-, chmn. dept. path, col, 55-69. Spec. lectr, Univ. Miss. 48-49; spec. consult, 56-62; consult. & lectr. path, U.S. Naval Hosp, 61-; adj. prof. med. sci, Drexel Inst. Technol,

62-65; consult, Nat. Res. Coun, 63-67; Nat. Heart Inst. spec. res. fel. & vis. prof, Univ. Berne, 70; mem. ad hoc comt. isoniazid & liver disease, Ctr. Disease Control, U.S. Pub. Health Serv, 71. Asst. res, Duke Univ. Hosp, 42-44, asst. pathologist, 44-45; attend. pathologist, John Gaston Hosp, Memphis, Tenn, 45-49; Vet Admin. Hosp, 47-49; chief serv. path, Phila. Gen. Gen. Hosp, Pa, 55-66; consult, Vet. Admin. Hosp, Phila, 55- Dipl, pathologic anat, Am. Bd. Path, 45. Med.C, A.U.S, 51-53, Maj. Fel. AAAS; Am. Asn. Path. & Bact; Am. Soc. Exp. Path; fel. Am. Col. Physicians; Soc. Exp. Biol. & Med; Int. Acad. Path. Tissue culture; malaria; Hodgkin's disease; liver diseases; cytology. Address: Dept. of Pathology, Medical College of Pennsylvania, Philadelphia, PA 19129.

DUBIN, MAURICE, b. Boston, Mass, Dec. 29, 26; m. 60; c. 3. PHYSICS, ASTROPHYSICS. B.S, Michigan, 48; A.M, Harvard, 49. Physicist, Cornell Aeronaut. Res. Lab, 48-50; geophys. res. directorate, Air Force Cambridge Res. Labs, Mass, 50-59; Goddard Space Flight Center, NASA, Md, 59, head aeronomy prog, off. space sci, hqs, DC, 59-64, CHIEF INTERPLANETARY DUST & COMETARY PHYSICS, 64- Mem, synoptic rocket panel working group II, Cmt. Exten. to Standard Atmosphere, 60-; mem. tech. panel on satellites, Int. Geophys. Year. U.S.N.R, 45-46. Am. Phys. Soc; Sci. Res. Soc. Am; Am. Inst. Aeronaut. & Astronaut; Am. Geophys. Union. Space research in atmospheric physics, astrophysical research on interplanetary dust and comets; experimental research with sounding rockets and satellites for investigations of the airglow, the upper atmosphere and micrometeorites. Address: NASA, Code SGM, Washington, DC 20546.

DUBINS, LESTER E(LI), b. Wash, D.C, Apr. 27, 20. MATHEMATICS. B.S, City Col. New York, 42; M.S, Chicago, 50, Ph.D.(math), 55. Mathematician, inst. air weapons res, Chicago, 51-55; asst. prof. math, Carnegie Inst. Tech, 55-57; Nat. Sci. Found. fel, Inst. Adv. Study, 57-59; UNIV. CALIF, BERKELEY, 59-60, asst. prof, 60-61, from asst. prof. MATH. & STATIST. to PROF, 61- Consult, inst. air weapons res, Chicago, 55-60. Sig.C, 42-48, 1st Lt. Am. Math. Soc; Math. Asn. Am. Probability theory; differential geometry; game theory; functional analysis. Address: Dept. of Mathematics & Statistics, University of California, Berkeley, CA 94720.

DUBINS, M(ORTIMER) IRA, b. Boston, Mass, Mar. 24, 19; m. 51; c. 1. SCI-ENCE EDUCATION, GEOLOGY. B.S, Tufts Col, 40; Army Air Force Sch. Meteorol, 43; M.S, Kansas, 48; Harvard, 48-49; Ed.M, Boston, 49, Ed.D. (sci. ed), 53. Instr. chem. & sci, Boston, 48-49; teacher & head dept. sci, high sch, Foxboro, 49-53, teacher, 53-54; instr. sci. ed, Castleton Teachers Col, 54-55; asst. prof, Northwestern, 55-57; PROF. GEOL. & METEOROL, STATE UNIV. N.Y. COL. ONEONTA, 57- Instr, Boston, 50-51; dir, Nat. Sci. Found. Earth Sci. Inst, 61-63. Summers, Nat. Sci. Found. fel, Texas, 59; vis. prof, North Dakota, 65, 69; Physicist, Permafrost, U.S. Corps Army Engrs. U.S.A.F, 42-46, 51-53, Capt. Fel. AAAS; Am. Meteorol. Soc; Mineral. Soc. Am; Nat. Sci. Teachers Asn; Nat. Asn. Res. Sci. Teaching; Nat. Asn. Geol. Teachers. Meteorology; economic geology; earth science; mineralogy; crystallography. Address: Dept. of Earth Science, State University of New York College at Oneonta, Oneonta, NY 13820.

DUBINSKY, BARRY, b. Phila, Pa, Nov. 23, 40. PHARMACOLOGY. B.S, Temple, 62; U.S. Pub. Health Serv. summer fels, Pittsburgh, 64-66, M.S, 65, Am. Found. Pharmaceut. Ed. fel, 66-68, Ph.D.(pharmacol), 68. Asst. pharmacol, Pittsburgh, 62-66; SCIENTIST, DEPT. PHARMACOL, WARNER-LAMBERT RES. INST, MORRIS PLAINS, 68- AAAS. Neuropharmacology; psychopharmacology. Address: Apt. 3, 195 N. Beverwyck Rd, Lake Hiawatha, NJ 07034.

DUBINSKY, EDWARD LEONARD, b. Phila, Pa, Feb. 7, 35. MATHEMATICS. B.A, Temple, 56; M.A, Pennsylvania, 58; Ph.D.(math), Michigan, 62. Lectr. MATH, Univ. Col. Sierra Leone, 62-63; Ghana, 63-64; asst. prof, Tulane Univ, 64-67, assoc. prof, 67-70; vis. prof, inst. math, Polish Acad. Sci, 70-72; PROF, CLARKSON COL. TECHNOL, 72- Am. Math. Soc; Math. Asn. Am. Locally convex spaces; sequence spaces; nuclear spaces; partial differential equations. Address: Dept. of Mathematics, Clarkson College of Technology, Potsdam, NY 13676.

DUBISCH, ROY, b. Chicago, Ill, Feb. 5, 17; m. 39; c. 3. MATHEMATICS. B.S, Chicago, 38, scholar, 38-40, M.S, 40, fel, 40-41, Ph.D.(math), 43. Asst. physics, Wilson Jr. Col, 38-40; instr. MATH, Ill. Inst. Tech, 40-41; Montana, 42-46; asst. prof. & chmn. dept, Triple Cities Col, 46-48; assoc. prof, Fresno State Col, 48-54, prof. & chmn. dept, 55-61; PROF, UNIV. WASH, 61- Am. Math. Soc; Math. Asn. Am. Mathematical education. Address: Dept. of Mathematics, University of Washington, Seattle, WA 98105.

DUBISKI, STANISLAW, b. Warsaw, Poland, Aug. 21, 29; Can. citizen; m. 55; c. 1. IMMUNOCHEMISTRY, IMMUNOGENETICS. M.D, Wroclaw, 53; M.D. (microbiol), Silesian Med. Acad, 57. Res. asst. microbiol, med. sch, Wroclaw, 51-54; Silesian Med. Acad, 54-57, asst. prof, 57-59; head dept. serol, Inst. Hemat, Poland, 59-61; res. fel. med. biophys, Univ. Toronto, 61-63, res. assoc. & clin. teacher, 63-67, asst. prof. path. & med, 67-70, ASSOC. PROF. PATH. CHEM, 70-, MEM. INST. IMMUNOL, SCH. GRAD. STUDIES, 71-; HEAD IMMUNOL. RES. LAB, TORONTO WEST. HOSP, 63- Training scholar, Cambridge & Lister Inst, Eng, 58. Brit. Soc. Immunol; N.Y. Acad. Sci; Am. Asn. Immunol; Can. Soc. Immunol.(secy, 67-68, v.pres, 71-72). Polymorphism of serum proteins; mechanism and regulation of antibody formation; genetics and immunochemistry of rabbit immunoglobulin allotypes. Address: Immunology Labs, Connaught Medical Research Bldg, One Spadina Crescent, Toronto 179, Ont, Can.

DUBLE, RICHARD LEE, b. Galveston, Tex, May 31, 40; m. 69. AGRONOMY, PLANT PHYSIOLOGY. B.S, Tex. A&M Univ, 62, M.S, 65, Ph.D.(plant & soil sci), 67. ASST. PROF. forage physiol, agr. res. & exten. ctr, TEX. A&M UNIV, Overton, 67-70, TURF RES, COLLEGE STATION, 70- Am. Soc. Agron. Address: Dept. of Soil & Crop Science, Texas A&M University, College Station, TX 77843.

DUBLIN, THOMAS D(AVID), b. N.Y.C, Jan. 18, 12; m. 39; c. 2. MEDICAL RESEARCH. A.B, Dartmouth Col, 32; M.D, Harvard, 36; M.P.H, Hopkins, 40, Dr.P.H, 41. Intern, Boston City Hosp, 36-38; asst. res. physician,

Rockefeller Inst. Hosp, 38-39; epidemiologist-in-training, State Dept. Health, N.Y, 39-40, asst. dist. state health off, '40, epidemiologist, 41-42; assoc. prof. prev. med. & community health, L.I. Col. Med, 42-43, prof. & exec. off. dept, 43-48; exec. dir, Nat. Health Coun, 48-53, med. consult, Nat. Found. Infantile Paralysis, 53-55; med. dir. community serv. prog, off. of dir, Nat. Insts. Health, 55-60, acting chief, geog. disease studies, 60, chief, epidemiol. & biomet. br, Nat. Inst. Arthritis & Metab. Diseases, 60-66; res. adv. health serv, off. tech. coop. & res, Agency Int. Develop, 66-67, Off. War on Hunger, 67-68; DIR. OFF. HEALTH MANPOWER, DEPT. HEALTH, EDUC. & WELFARE, 68- Dipl, Am. Bd. Prev. Med, 49, mem. bd, 61-, v.chmn. prev. med, 65- AAAS; fel. Am. Pub. Health Asn; Am. Med. Asn; Am. Epidemiol. Soc; fel. N.Y. Acad. Med. Epidemiology; medical research and education. Address: Office of the Assistant Secretary for Health & Scientific Affairs, Dept. of Health, Education & Welfare, 330 Independence Ave. S.W, Room 4059 North, Washington, DC 20201.

DUBLIN, WILLIAM B(ROOKS), b. Little Rock, Ark, Dec. 10, 09; m. 42; c. 1. PATHOLOGY. A.B, California, Los Angeles, 29; Southern California, 29-31; M.A, California, 33, M.D, 36. Fel. path, Mayo Found, Minnesota, 37-40; PATHOLOGIST, West. State Hosp, Wash, 40-44; Emery Clinic, 44-45; Indianapolis Gen. Hosp, 45-49; vet. admin. hosp, Ft. Logan, Colo, 49-54; Daniel Freeman Mem. Hosp, 54-65; Laurel Grove Hosp, 65-70; CHIEF, LAB. SERV, VET. ADMIN. HOSP, 70- Assoc. clin. prof. path, Calif. Col. Med; clin. assoc. prof. otolaryngol, sch. med, Stanford Univ, 67- Fel. Am. Med. Asn; Am. Soc. Clin. Path; fel. Am. Col. Physicians; fel. Col. Am. Path. Neuropathology; ophthalmic pathology; histology; anatomy; surgical pathology; otolaryngologic pathology. Address: Lab. Service, Veterans Administration Hospital, Martinez, CA 94553.

DUBNAU, DAVID, b. N.Y.C, July 4, 37; m. 58; c. 3. MOLECULAR BIOLOGY. B.A, Lafayette Col, 56; M.A, Columbia Univ, 58, Ph.D.(zool), 61. Nat. Insts. Health fel. bact. physiol, Nat. Inst. Med. Res, Eng, 61-64; fel. biochem, Albert Einstein Col. Med, 64-65; ASSOC. MICROBIOL, PUB. HEALTH RES. INST, CITY OF NEW YORK, 66- Nat. Insts. Health res. grant, 66-69; Nat. Sci. Found. res. grant, 70-72. AAAS; Am. Soc. Microbiol. Synthesis of ribosomes; control of protein synthesis; microbial genetics; mechanism of genetic recombination. Address: The Public Health Research Institute, 455 First Ave, New York, NY 10016.

DUBNAU, EUGENIE, b. Brussels, Belg, Nov. 1, 38; U.S. citizen; m. 59; c. 3. MICROBIAL GENETICS. B.A, Columbia Univ, 60, M.A, 61; Ph.D.(microbial genetics), Univ. London, 63. Fel. MICROBIAL GENETICS, sch. med, N.Y. Univ, 64-68; RES. ASSOC, PUB. HEALTH RES. INST, 68- Address: Dept. of Genetics, Public Health Research Institute, 455 First Ave, New York, NY 10016.

DUBNER, RONALD, b. N.Y.C, Oct. 12, 34; m. 58; c. 3. NEUROPHYSIOLOGY, NEUROANATOMY. B.A, Columbia Univ, 55, D.D.S, 58; Ph.D.(physiol), Univ. Mich, Ann Arbor, 64. Intern, clin. dent, Pub. Health Serv. Hosp, Baltimore, Md, 58-59, staff dentist, clin. ctr, Nat. Insts. Health, 59-61, investr. physiol, NAT. INST. DENT. RES, 61-64, neurophysiol, 65-68, CHIEF, NEURAL MECHANISMS SECT, 68- Vis. assoc. prof, sch. dent, Howard Univ, 68-; co-chmn, Conf. Oral-Facial Mechanisms, Honolulu, 70; vis. scientist, dept. anat, Univ. Col, London, 70-71. U.S.P.H.S, 58- AAAS; Am. Physiol. Soc; Am. Asn. Anat; Int. Asn. Dent. Res; Soc. Neurosci. Mechanisms of oral facial sensation and movement, especially mechanisms of pain, touch and temperature sensation; cortical and subcortical mechanisms of sensation. Address: Neural Mechanisms Section, Bldg. 30, Room B-2, National Institute of Dental Research, Bethesda, MD 20014.

DUBNICK, BERNARD, b. Brooklyn, N.Y, May 29, 28; m. 52, 66; c. 2. PHARMACOLOGY. B.S, City Col. New York, 49; Ph.D.(chem), Illinois, 53. SR. RES. ASSOC, WARNER-LAMBERT RES. INST, 53- AAAS; Am. Chem. Soc; fel. N.Y. Acad. Sci; Am. Soc. Pharmacol. Biochemical pharmacology; central nervous system; cardiovascular; allergy. Address: Warner-Lambert Research Institute, Morris Plains, NJ 07950.

DUBNOFF, JACOB W(ILLIAM), b. Los Angeles, Calif, Jan. 26, 09; m. 32; c. 2. BIOCHEMISTRY. A.B, California, Los Angeles, 31; M.A, California, 33; Ph.D.(biochem), Calif. Inst. Tech, 44. Lab. technician, dept. agr, California, 33-34; res. biochemist, Kazan (Russia), 34-36; sr. res. fel, Calif. Inst. Tech, 36-62; assoc. res. prof. NEUROSURG, sch. med, Loma Linda, Univ, 62-69; ADJ. PROF, SCH. MED, UNIV. SOUTH. CALIF, 69- Am. Soc. Biol. Chem. Transmethylation in animal tissues; intermediary nitrogen metabolism; development of chemical analytical methods; apparatus for incubation of tissue slices and homogenates; medical biochemistry; plant physiology; physiological biochemistry; nutritional biochemistry; protein biochemistry; vitamins. Address: School of Medicine, University of Southern California, 1200 State St, Box 323, Los Angeles, CA 90033.

DUBO, SARA, b. Winnipeg, Man, Aug. 30, 16; nat; m. 47; c. 2. PSYCHIATRY. M.D, Manitoba, 39, B.Sc, 42. Resident med, St. Boniface Hosp, 39-40; St. Boniface Sanatarium, 40-41; fel, Manitoba, 41-42; path, Banting Inst, 42-43; resident psychiat, Toronto Psychiatric Inst, 43-44; Bellevue Hosp, 46-49; asst. dir. children's unit & asst. prof. psychiat, Michigan, 49-56; ASSOC. DIR. HAWTHORN CTR, 56- R.C.A.M.C, 44-46, Capt. Am. Psychiat. Asn; Am. Orthopsychiat. Asn. Psychiatric residential treatment techniques; asthma in children; child psychiatry. Address: Hawthorn Center, 18471 Haggerty Rd, Northville, MI 48167.

DuBOIS, ARTHUR BROOKS, b. New York, N.Y, Nov. 21, 23; m. 50; c. 3. PHYSIOLOGY. M.D, Cornell, 46. Intern med, N.Y. Hosp, 46-47; Life Ins. med. res. fel. physiol, sch. med, Rochester, 49-51; asst. res. med, Peter Bent Brigham Hosp, 51-52; asst. prof. PHYSIOL, SCH. MED, UNIV. PA, 52-55, assoc. prof, 55-60, PROF, 60-, MED, 62-, assoc. prof, 57-62. Investr, Am. Heart Asn, 55-63; Bowditch lectr, Am. Physiol. Soc, 58; consult, U.S. Naval Hosp, Phila, Pa, 58-; mem, Nat. Res. Coun. panel rev. Nat. Sci. Found. fel. appln, 59-62; Am. Inst. Biol. Sci. adv. comt. physiol, Off. Naval Res, 61-; consult, Phila. Gen. Hosp, 62-; chmn. comt. gaseous environ. manned spacecraft, space sci. bd, Nat. Acad. Sci, 62-63; Jackson lectr, Am. Col. Chest Physicians, Nat. Insts. Health. res. career award, 63-, mem. cardiovasc. study sect, 64-68; Nathanson lectr, Univ. South. Calif, 64; chmn. comt. on biol. effects atomspheric pollutants, Nat. Res. Coun, 68-; panel for selection of lung ctr, Nat. Heart & Lung Inst, 71. Med.C.Res, 49-51, Lt.(jg). Am. Physiol. Soc; Am. Soc. Clin. Invest; Asn. Am. Physicians. Physiology of respiration and pulmonary circulation; normal and clinical function of the lungs. Address: 22 E. Springfield Ave, Philadelphia, PA 19118.

DuBOIS, CLARENCE W, b. New Paltz, N.Y, Oct. 16, 09; m. 36; c. 3. FOOD TECHNOLOGY. B.S, Cornell, 35. Inspector, State Fruit & Veg. Inspection Serv, N.Y, 35; asst. county agent, State Agr. Exten. Serv, 35-38; investr, N.Y. Exp. Sta, Geneva, 38-41; assoc. prof. food preserv. & head dept, exp. sta, Louisiana, 42-45; consult, D.K. Tressler & Assocs, 45-49; chief food technol. sect, res. & develop. dir, Minute Maid Corp, PLYMOUTH, 50-61, Minute Maid Co. Div, COCA COLA CO, 61-64, MGR. FOOD TECHNOL. SECT, CITRUS RES. & DEVELOP. DEPT, FOODS DIV, 64- Vis. prof, sch. fisheries, Laval Univ, 45, 47 & 49. Inst. Food Technol. Use of ascorbic acid as anti-browning agent in frozen fruits, particularly peaches. Address: 926 Maxwell Ave, Orlando, FL 32804.

DU BOIS, D(ONALD) F(RANK), b. Little Falls, N.Y, Jan. 4, 32; m. 55; c. 3. THEORETICAL PHYSICS. B.A, Cornell, 54; Rand Corp. fel, Calif. Inst. Tech, 56-57, Inst. Bus. Mach. Corp. fel, 57-58, Ph.D.(physics, math), 59. Instr. physics, Calif. Inst. Tech, 58-59; res. physicist, Rand Corp, Calif, 59-62; SR. STAFF PHYSICIST, HUGHES AIRCRAFT CO, 62- Consult, Rand Corp, 58-59. Phys. Soc. Many-particle theory; quantum and statistical mechanics; plasma and solid state physics; electron correlations in metals; interaction of radiation with plasma; transport in semiconductors. Address: Hughes Research Labs, 3011 Malibu Canyon Rd, Malibu, CA 90265.

DuBOIS, DONALD W, b. Denver, Ind, Oct. 20, 43; m. 62; c. 1. INORGANIC CHEMISTRY, ELECTROCHEMISTRY. B.A, McMurry Col, 65; Nat. Sci. Found. fel. & Ph.D.(chem), Kansas, 69. SR. RES. CHEMIST, PPG INDUSTS, 69- Am. Chem. Soc. Non-aqueous solvents. Address: PPG Industries, Corpus Christi, TX 78408.

DUBOIS, DONALD W(ARD), b. Oklahoma City, Okla, Jan. 31, 23; div. MATHEMATICS. M.A, Oklahoma, 50, Ph.D.(math), 53. Instr. MATH, Oklahoma, 52-53; Ohio State, 53-55; from asst. prof. to assoc. prof, UNIV. N.MEX, 63-68, PROF, 68- U.S.N.R, 44-46, Lt.(jg). Am. Math. Soc. Abelian groups; real fields and varieties. Address: Dept. of Mathematics, University of New Mexico, Albuquerque, NM 87106.

DUBOIS, ERNEST P(AUL), b. Waterloo, Iowa, May 27, 17; m. 42; c. 1. PETROLEUM GEOLOGY, STRATIGRAPHY. B.S, Univ. Chicago, 38, Ph.D. (geol, paleont), 42. Geologist, Empresa Colombiana de Petroleos, 51-55; mgr. explor. geol, C.A. Bays, Consult, 55-57; GEOLOGIST, Standard-Vacuum Oil Co, 57-62; ESSO MID.E, STANDARD OIL CO.(N.J), 62- Address: Esso Middle East, 30 Rockefeller Center, New York, NY 10020.

DuBOIS, FREDERICK W(ILLIAMSON), b. Newburgh, N.Y, Nov. 6, 23; m. 46; c. 3. INORGANIC CHEMISTRY. B.S, St. Lawrence, 46; fel, Idaho, 46; fel, Michigan, 47-50, M.S, 49, Ph.D.(chem), 52. Instr. chem, Idaho, 46-47; qual. anal, Michigan, 51; MEM. STAFF, LOS ALAMOS SCI. LAB, 52- Am. Chem. Soc. Complex ions in solution; military high explosives; detonation theory; plastics and elastomers. Address: GMX-3, Los Alamos Scientific Lab, Los Alamos, NM 87544.

DuBOIS, JOHN R(OGER), b. Eau Claire, Wis, Aug. 16, 34; m. 54; c. 3. ELECTRICAL ENGINEERING. B.S, Wisconsin, 57, M.S, 59, Ph.D.(elec. eng), 63. Supvr. transmitter eng, TV. Wis, Inc, 57-63; sr. electronics engr, North Star Res. & Develop. Inst, 63-65, dir. electronics res, 65-71; DIR. COMMUN, HENNEPIN COUNTY, MINN, 71- Instr. elec. eng, Wisconsin, 57-63. Inst. Elec. & Electronics Eng. Solid state devices and applications; electronics technology in law enforcement; electronic countermeasures; very high frequency and ultra-high frequency communications systems. Address: 7005 Heatherton Trail, Edina, MN 55435.

DuBOIS, KENNETH P(ATRICK), b. Aberdeen, S.Dak, Aug. 9, 17; m. 58; c. 3. PHARMACOLOGY. B.S, S.Dak. State Col, 39; M.S, Purdue, 40; Ph.D.(physiol), Wisconsin, 43. Asst. PHARMACOL, UNIV. CHICAGO, 43-45, res. assoc, 45-46, instr, 46-47, asst. prof, 47-51, assoc. prof, 51-56, PROF, 56-, DIR. TOXICITY LAB, 53- Consult, U.S. Pub. Health Serv, 56-; Nat. Bd. Med. Exam. Assoc. ed, J. Toxicol. & Appl. Pharmacol, 58-60, managing ed, 60-64. With Nat. Defense Res. Cmt; Chem. C, U.S.A, 44. AAAS; Am. Soc. Pharmacol. & Exp. Therapeut.(assoc. ed, Jour, 53); Radiation Res. Soc.(assoc. ed, Radiation Res, 54-56); Am. Chem. Soc; Soc. Exp. Biol. & Med; Am. Indust. Hyg. Asn; N.Y. Acad. Sci; Soc. Toxicol.(merit award, 71). Toxicity and action of selenium; toxicity of chemical warfare agents; enzyme methods; analytical biochemistry methods; drug metabolism; mechanism of action of drugs and poisons; biological effects of radiation; toxicity and metabolism of radioactive isotopes. Address: Toxicity Lab, University of Chicago, 930 E. 58th St, Chicago, IL 60637.

DU BOIS, ROBERT L(EE), b. Omaha, Nebr, Jan. 25, 24; m. 47. GEOPHYSICS. B.S, Univ. Wash, 49, M.S, 50, Ph.D.(geol), 54. Asst. prof. geol, Univ. Ariz, 52-58, assoc. prof, 58-64, prof, 64-67; KERR McGEE PROF. GEOL. & GEOPHYS. & DIR. EARTH SCI. OBSERV, UNIV. OKLA, 67- Consult. econ. geol, 53- AAAS; Am. Geophys. Union; fel. Geol. Soc. Am. Ord.C, U.S.A, 43-46. Archeomagnetism; paleomagnetism; rock magnetism. Address: School of Geology & Geophysics, University of Oklahoma, Norman, OK 73069.

DUBOIS, RONALD JOSEPH, b. Lawrence, Mass, Jan. 3, 42. ORGANIC CHEMISTRY. B.S, Lowell Tech. Inst, 64; Ph.D.(org. chem), Clarkson Tech, 69. Res. chemist, E.I. du Pont de Nemours & Co, Inc, 68-71; MEM. STAFF CANCER RES, MICROBIOLOGICAL ASSOCS, INC, BETHESDA, 71- Am. Chem. Soc. Synthesis of agricultural chemicals for use as herbicides, fungicides and insecticides. Address: 3027 Hewitt Ave, Apt. 468, Silver Spring, MD 20906.

DuBOIS, THOMAS DAVID, b. Mexico, Ind, Nov. 15, 40; m; c. 1. INORGANIC CHEMISTRY. B.A, McMurry Col, 62; M.S, Ohio State, 65, Ph.D.(inorg.

chem), 67. ASSOC. PROF. CHEM, UNIV. N.C, CHARLOTTE, 67- Am. Chem. Soc. Coordination compounds; magnetochemistry; coordinated ligand reactions. Address: Dept. of Chemistry, University of North Carolina at Charlotte, Charlotte, NC 28205.

DUBOS, RENE (JULES), b. Saint-Brice, France, Feb. 20, 01; nat; m. 34, 46. PATHOLOGY. B.S, Inst. Nat. Agronomique, Paris, 22; Ph.D, Rutgers Univ, 27; hon. Sc.D, Univ. Rochester, 41, Harvard, 42, Rutgers Univ, 49, Univ. Paris, 50, Univ. Col. Dublin, 55, New Sch. for Social Res, 56; Univ. Rio de Janiero, 56, Dartmouth Col, 56; hon. M.D, Univ. Liege, 47, Yeshiva Univ, 61, Univ. Alta, 63, Univ. Pa, 65, Univ. Calif, 65; hon. degrees, Colby Col. & Carleton Col, 66, St. John's Univ, 68; plus ten others. Asst. soil microbiol, N.J. Exp. Sta, 24-27; fel, ROCKEFELLER UNIV, 27-28, asst, 28-30, assoc, 30-38, assoc. mem, 38-41, mem, 41-42, 44-71, prof. PATH, 57-71, EMER. PROF, 71- Fabyan prof. comp. path. & prof. trop. med, Harvard Med. Sch, 42-44; ed, J. Exp. Med, 46-71; mem, President's Citizens' Adv. Comt. on Environ. Qual, 70- Phillips award, Am. Col. Physicians, 40; Wilson Medal, Am. Clin. & Climat. Asn, 46; Trudeau Medal, Nat. Tuberc. Asn, 51; award, Pharmaceut. Indust, 52; Triennial award, Mass. Gen. Hosp, 53; Hitchcock Award, Univ. Calif, 54; Howard Taylor Ricketts Award, Univ. Chicago, 58; Robert Koch Centennial Award, Robert Koch Inst, Berlin & Passano Found. Award, 60; Mod. Med. Award for Distinguished Achievement, 61; Phi Beta Kappa Award, 63 & 65; Arches of Sci. Award, Pac. Sci. Ctr, 66; Pulitzer Prize, 69; Harold Terry Clark Award, 70. Nat. Acad. Sci; Am. Acad. Pediat.(Johnson Award, 40); Am. Pub. Health Asn.(Lasker Award, 48); Am. Philos. Soc; Harvey Soc.(pres, 51); Am. Soc. Microbiol.(pres, 51); Am. Med. Asn.(award, 64). Cellulose decomposition by aerobic bacteria; oxidations and reductions in bacterial cultures; decomposition of capsular polysaccharides of pneumococcus by bacterial enzymes and their use in the study of infections; use of specific bacterial enzymes in biochemistry; antibacterial agents of biological origin; bacterial toxins; bacillary dysentery; bacteriology; tuberculosis; nutrition and infection; effects that environmental forces exert on human life. Address: Rockefeller University, 66th St. & York Ave, New York NY 10021.

DuBOSE, LEO EDWIN, b. Gonzales, Tex, Apr. 22, 31; m. 51; c. 3. ANIMAL SCIENCE. B.S, Abilene Christian Col, 52; M.S, S.Dak. State Col, 54; Ph.D. (animal breeding), Texas A&M, 65. Asst. prof. ANIMAL SCI, S.Dak. State Col, 54-57; teacher, San Angelo Col, 57-63; ASSOC. PROF, ABILENE CHRISTIAN COL, 65- Am. Soc. Animal Sci; Am. Soc. Range Mgt. Digestability of feeds by ruminants; heritability estimates of carcass traits and production traits in beef cattle; correlations between traits in beef cattle. Address: Dept. of Agriculture, Abilene Christian College, Box 7986, Abilene, TX 79601.

DUBOSE, ROBERT T(RAFTON), b. Dallas, Tex, Oct. 17, 19; m. 44; c. 3. VETERINARY MEDICINE & VIROLOGY. B.S. & D.V.M, Texas A&M, 56, M.S, 58. Instr. VET. MICROBIOL, Texas A&M, 56-59; PROF, VA. POLYTECH. INST. & STATE UNIV, 59- Ord. Dept, 40-46, Capt. Am. Vet. Med. Asn; Am. Asn. Avian Path; Am. Soc. Microbiol; Wildlife Disease Asn. Propagation of turkey hemorrhagic enteritis virus in cell cultures; pathogenicity of quail bronchitis virus and chicken embryo lethal orphan virus in birds and cells; modification of infectious bronchitis virus. Address: Dept. of Veterinary Science, Virginia Polytechnic Institute & State University, Blacksburg, VA 24061.

DUBOWSKI, KURT M(AX), b. Berlin, Ger, Nov. 21, 21. BIOCHEMISTRY, TOXICOLOGY. A.B, N.Y. Univ, 46; M.Sc, Ohio State, 47, Nat. Res. Coun. fel, 48-49, Ph.D.(chem, toxicol), 49. Biochemist & asst. dir. labs, Norwalk Hosp, 50-53; dir. chem, Iowa Methodist Hosp, 53-58; assoc. prof. clin. chem. & dir. labs, hosp. & clins, Univ. Fla, 58-61; assoc. prof. clin. chem. & toxicol, SCH. MED, UNIV. OKLA, 61-64, PROF. BIOCHEM, CLIN. CHEM. & TOXICOL, 64-, DIR. TOXICOL. LABS, MED. CTR, 61-, dir. clin. chem, 61-65. Lectr, N.Y. Univ. & Northwestern, 50-56; Iowa, 54-58; Ind. Univ, 58- Toxicologist to coroner, Fairfield County, Conn, 50-53; chief dep. coroner & toxicologist, Polk County, Iowa, 53-58; state criminalist, Iowa State Dept. Pub. Safety, 53-58; dir. chem. tests for alcoholic influence, State of Okla, 70- Spec. consult, U.S. Pub. Health Serv, 57-62, 67-; consult, U.S. Vet. Admin, 59-; Oklahoma City Police Dept, 61-; Okla. State Bur. Invest, 66-; Okla. Med. Res. Found. & Okla. State Med. Exam, 67-; U.S. Dept. Transportation, 68-; Okla. Dept. Pub. Safety, 69-; U.S. Social Security Admin, 70-; Nat. Inst. Ment. Health, 71-; Okla. Comnr. Narcotics & Drug Abuse Control, 71- Mem. comt. alcohol & drugs, Nat. Safety Coun, 50-, chmn, 69-71; dir. Am. Bd. Clin. Chem, secy-treas, 58- Dipl, Am. Bd. Clin. Chem. U.S.A, 42-46, 1st Lt. Fel. AAAS; fel. Am. Asn. Clin. Chem; fel. Am. Acad. Forensic Sci; Am. Med. Asn; Am. Chem. Soc; fel. Asn. Clin. Sci; fel. Am. Inst. Chem; N.Y. Acad. Sci; Sci. Res. Soc. Am; Soc. Med. Jurisp; Soc. Toxicol; Biomed. Eng. Soc; Brit. Medico-Legal Soc; fel. Indian Acad. Forensic Sci; Soc. Exp. Biol. & Med. Effects and determination of alcohol in biologic materials; clinical chemical and toxicological methodology; blood pH and blood gas measurements; fluid and electrolyte abnormalities; evaluation of trace evidence in criminal investigations; forensic chemistry. Address: Toxicology Labs, University of Oklahoma Medical Center, 800 N.E. 13th St, Oklahoma City, OK 73104.

DUBRAVCIC, MILAN FRANE, b. Gospic, Croatia, July 25, 22; m. 53; c. 4. FOOD SCIENCE, ANALYTICAL CHEMISTRY. B.S, Univ. Zagreb, 48; Muscular Dystrophy Asn. & univ. fel, Univ. B.C, 64-65; Atomic Energy Comn. fel. & Ph.D.(food sci), Univ. Mass, Amherst, 68. Chemist, Dept. Health, Cent. Inst. Hyg, Zagreb, Yugoslavia, 48-53; chief chemist, Lifeguard Milk Prod. Ltd, Australia, 54-56; res. chemist, Imp. Chem. Industs, 56-61; Commonwealth Sci. & Indust. Res. Orgn, 62-63; ASST. PROF. CHEM. TECHNOL, UNIV. AKRON, 68- Dir. Nat. Sci. Found. grant for instructional sci. equip, Univ. Akron, 69-71. AAAS; Am. Chem. Soc; Croatian Chem. Soc; Inst. Food Technol. Food technology; methodology for analysis of foods and plastics; mechanisms of enzymatic, oxidative, thermal and radiolytic degradation of organic materials. Address: Dept. of Chemical Technology, University of Akron, Akron, OH 44304.

du BREUIL, FELIX L(EMAIGRE), b. Paris, France, Feb. 11, 21; nat; m. 49; c. 7. MINERAL ENGINEERING. Ing.c.Mines, Nat. Sch. Mines, Paris, 45; M.S, Pa. State, 47, Ph.D.(elec. eng), 49. From instr. to assoc. prof. mineral eng, Pa. State, 49-56; field engr, Jeffrey Mfg. Co, 56-58; PROJ. ENGR, BITUMINOUS COAL RES, INC, 58- Inst. Elec. Eng; French Soc. Mineral Indust; Instrument Soc. Am. Mine mechanization; bulk materials handling; automatic control problems; coal gasification. Address: 1365 Foxwood Rd, Monroeville, PA 15146.

DUBREUIL, ROBERT, b. Montreal, Que, Sept. 18, 26; m. 53; c. 4. VIROLOGY, CANCER. B.Sc, Univ. Montreal, 50, M.Sc, 52, Ph.D.(virol), 70; Can. Res. Coun. fel, Col. de France, 53-54. Res. asst. VIROL, INST. MICROBIOL. & HYG. MONTREAL, 54-63, res. assoc, 63-70, RES. MEM, 71- AAAS; Can. Soc. Microbiol. Human and animal virus vaccines; SV_{40}-virus tumors. Address: Dept. of Virology, Institute of Microbiology, P.O. Box 100, Laval-des-Rapides, Que, Can.

DuBRIDGE, LEE A(LVIN), b. Terre Haute, Ind, Sept. 21, 01; m. 25; c. 2. PHYSICS. A.B, Cornell Col.(Iowa), 22, Sc.D, 40; A.M, Wisconsin, 24, Ph.D. (physics), 26; hon. Sc.D, Polytech. Inst. Brooklyn, 46, Wesleyan, 46, British Columbia, 47, Washington (St. Louis), 48, Occidental Col, 52, Maryland, 55, Columbia, 57, Indiana, 57, Wisconsin, 57, Pa. Mil. Col, 62, DePauw, 62, Pomona Col, 65, Carnegie Inst. Technol, 65, Syracuse Univ, 69, Tufts Univ, 69, Rensselaer Polytech. Inst, 70; hon. LL.D, California, 48, Rochester, 53, Southern California, 57, Northwestern, 58, Loyola (Calif), 63, Notre Dame Univ, 67, Ill. Inst. Technol, 68; hon. L.H.D, Univ. Judaism, 58, Redlands, 58; hon. D.C.L, Union (N.Y), 61; hon. D.Sc, Rockefeller Inst, 65. Instr. physics, Wisconsin, 25-26; Nat. Res. Coun. fel, Calif. Inst. Tech, 26-28; asst. prof, Washington (St. Louis), 28-33, assoc. prof, 33-34; prof. & chmn. dept, Rochester, 34-46, dean faculty arts & sci, 38-42; dir. radiation lab, Mass. Inst. Technol, 40-45; pres, CALIF. INST. TECHNOL, 46-69, EMER. PRES, 69- With phys. sci. div, Nat. Res. Coun, 36-42; assoc. ed, Am. Physics Teacher, 35-38; Phys. Rev, 36-39; Rev. Sci. Instruments, 36-42. Trustee, Rand Corp, 48-61; Rockefeller Found, 56-67; Mellon Inst, 58-66. Mem, gen. adv. comt, Atomic Energy Comn, 46-52; sci. adv. comn, Off. Defense mobilization 51-56; Nat. Sci. Bd, 58-64; Nat. Merit Scholar. Corp, 63-69; Distinguished Civilian Serv. Awards Bd, 63-67; bd. dirs, Nat. Educ. TV, 64-69; sci. adv. to President, 69-70; mem, Presidents' Sci. Adv. Comt, 69- Brit. Royal Medal, 46; Medal for Merit, 46; Res. Corp. Award, 47. Nat. Acad. Sci; AAAS; fel. Am. Phys. Soc.(v.pres, 46, pres, 47); Am. Philos. Soc; fel. Am. Acad. Arts & Sci. Biophysics; nuclear disintegration; photoelectric and thermionic emission; direct current amplification; energy distribution of photoelectrons; theory of photoelectric effect; radar. Address: Apt. 3A, 2355 Via Mariposa West, Laguna Hills, CA 92653.

DUBROVIN, KENNETH P, b. Chicago, Ill, Oct. 24, 31; m. 54; c. 5. SOIL CHEMISTRY, PLANT PHYSIOLOGY. B.S, Illinois, 53; Fulbright scholar, Wageningen, 53-54; Ph.D.(soil chem), Wisconsin, 56; M.BA, Missouri, 66. Res. biologist, Spencer Chem. Div, Gulf Oil Corp, 56-66, sr. res. biologist, Gulf Res. & Develop. Co, 66-69, sect. supvr, pesticide res. & develop, 69-71; DIR. RES, GREAT WEST. SUGAR CO, 71- Am. Chem. Soc; Am. Soc. Agron; Soil Sci. Soc. Am; Int. Soc. Soil Sci. Improved fertilizers; development of new and unique herbicides, fungicides, insecticides and nematicides; mechanism of action of herbicides. Address: P.O. Box 539, Longmont, CO 80501.

DUBROW, DAVID L(AWRENCE), b. Brooklyn, N.Y, Jan. 8, 30; m. 55; c. 3. FOOD TECHNOLOGY, BIOCHEMISTRY. B.S, Univ. Miami, 56; M.S, Univ. Md, College Park, 68, Ph.D.(food sci), 71. Food technologist, inst. marine sci, Univ. Miami, 56-63; Bur. Commercial Fisheries, Dept. Interior, 63-66, res. food technologist, 66-69; SUPVRY. RES. FOOD TECHNOLOGIST, NAT. MARINE FISHERIES SERV, DEPT. COMMERCE, 69- U.S.A.F, 51-55, Sgt. Inst. Food Technol. Evaluation of fish and fishery products; process development and quality control of protein concentrates by solvent extraction of fish; factors affecting protein quality of fish proteins. Address: Fishery Products Technology Lab, National Marine Fisheries Service, College Park, MD 20740.

DuBRUL, E. LLOYD, b. N.Y.C, Apr. 5, 09; m. 56. ANATOMY. D.D.S, N.Y. Univ, 37; M.S, Univ. Ill, 49, Ph.D, 55. Instr. oral & maxillofacial surg, UNIV. ILL. MED. CTR, 46-47, asst. prof, 47-55, asst. prof. in charge oral anat, COL. DENT, 47-56, assoc. prof, 56-59, prof, 59-64, PROF. ORAL ANAT, 64-, HEAD DEPT, 66-, PROF. ANAT, COL. MED, 59-, assoc. prof, 58-59, asst. prof. post grad. studies, col. dent, 48-51, acting head. dept. oral anat, 64-66. Vis. prof, Nat. Sci. Found. Summer Inst. Col. Teachers of Comparative Anat, Harvard, 62, Univ. Wash, 68. U.S.A, 42-46, Maj. Fel. AAAS; Am. Soc. Zool; Am. Asn. Anat; Am. Asn. Phys. Anthrop; N.Y. Acad. Sci. Comparative anatomy; neuroanatomy; anthropology. Address: Dept. of Oral Anatomy, Colleges of Medicine & Dentistry, University of Illinois at the Medical Center, 808 S. Wood St, Chicago, IL 60612.

DuBRUL, ERNEST, b. Wooster, Ohio, Mar. 2, 43; m. 66; c. 2. BIOCHEMISTRY, DEVELOPMENTAL BIOLOGY. H.A.B, Xavier Univ.(Ohio), 64; Ph.D. (biol), Wash. Univ, 69. FEL, BIOL. DIV, OAK RIDGE NAT. LAB, 69- Soc. Develop. Biol. Nucleic acids and protein synthesis in development. Address: Biology Division, Oak Ridge National Lab, Oak Ridge, TN 37830.

DUBS, M(ARNE) A(RTHUR), b. Baltimore, Md, Feb. 15, 22; m. 44; c. 3. CHEMICAL ENGINEERING. B.S, Hopkins, 43. Div. head ENG. LAB, Linde Co, Div, Union Carbide Corp, 48-51, from asst. to supt. 51-54, asst. mgr, 54-57, mgr, 57-62, gas prod. develop, 62-64, tech. dir. cryogenic prod, 64-65, prod. mgr. new prod, 65-67, div. dir, Ocean Systs. Inc, 67, gen. mgr, 67-69; DIR. OCEAN RESOURCES, KENNECOTT COPPER CORP, 69- Processes and equipment for producing and distributing cryogenic fluids, atmospheric gases, hydrogen, synthesis gas; cryogenic equipment; food preservation; cryobiology; underwater development. Address: Kennecott Copper Corp, 161 E. 42nd St, New York, NY 10017.

DUBUC, SERGE, b. Montreal, Que, Apr. 16, 39; m. 62; c. 3. MATHEMATICS. B.Sc, Univ, Montreal, 62, Nat. Res. Coun. Can. fel, 62-63, M.Sc, 63; Erastus Brooks fel, Cornell Univ, 63-64, Ph.D.(math), 66. Asst. MATH, Cornell Univ, 64-66; asst. prof, Univ. Montreal, 66-71; ASSOC. PROF, UNIV. SHERBROOKE, 71- Ford Motor Co. fel, 68-69. Can. Math. Cong. Functional analysis, especially extreme points theory; mathematical analysis, especially iteration of functions; probability theory, especially branching processes; plane geometry. Address: Dept. of Mathematics, University of Sherbrooke, Sherbrooke, Que, Can.

DUBY, JOHN, b. Alta, Can, June 10, 30; m. 60; c. 2. ENGINEERING. Rhodes scholar. & B.Sc, Alberta, 52; Nat. Res. Council special scholar. & Edgell Shepper scholar, Oxford, 55, B.A, M.A. & Ph.D, 56. Inspection & field engr. equipment, Brown & Roote, 52; tutor sch. eng, sci, Oxford, 55-56; special lectr. elec. eng, Alberta, 56-57, assoc. prof. civil eng, 57-59, mech. eng, 59-64; pres, Digital Anal. & Tech. Assistance, Ltd, 64-70; PARTNER, BLAIN BINNIE ASSOC. ENG. LTD, 70- Spec. lectr. civil eng, Univ. Alta, 64-65; spec. consult, Dept. Pub. Works, Govt. Alta, 71-72. R.C.A.F, 49-53; R.A.F.R, 53-56. Chem. Inst. Can; Eng. Inst. Can. Engineering. Address: Blain Binnie Associates Engineering Ltd, 631-7th Ave. S.W, Calgary, Alta, Can.

DUBY, PAUL F(RANÇOIS), b. Brussels, Belg, Dec. 16, 33; m. 59; c. 3. METALLURGY. Mech. & Elec. E, Brussels, 56; Belg-Am. Ed. Found. fel, Columbia, 58-60, William Campbell fel, 60-61, Eng.Sc.D.(mineral eng), 62. Temp. res. assoc, center nuclear sci, Royal Mil. Sch, Brussels, 57-58; res. assoc. mineral eng, Henry Krumb Sch. Mines, Columbia, 61-63; asst. prof. metall. eng, sch. metall. eng, Pennsylvania, 63-65; MINERAL ENG, HENRY KRUMB SCH. MINES, COLUMBIA UNIV, 65-68, ASSOC. PROF, 68- Sig.C, Belg. Army, 56-58, 2nd Lt. Am. Inst. Mining, Metall. & Petrol. Eng; Electrochem. Soc. Extractive metallurgy; transport properties of fused salts; applied electrochemistry; hydrometallurgy; surface chemistry; corrosion. Address: Henry Krumb School of Mines, Columbia University, New York, NY 10027.

DUBY, ROBERT T, b. Ludlow, Mass, July 10, 40; m. 61; c. 2. ANIMAL & REPRODUCTIVE PHYSIOLOGY. B.S, Massachusetts, 62, M.S, 65, Ph.D. (animal physiol), 67. Nat. Insts. Health fel, 67-68; ASST. PROF. reproductive physiol, Cornell Univ, 68-70; VET. & ANIMAL SCI, UNIV. MASS, AMHERST, 70- Soc. Study Reproduction. Mink physiology, especially problems faced by the mink industry; utero ovarian relationships in domestic animals. Address: Dept. of Veterinary & Animal Sciences, University of Massachusetts, Amherst, MA 01002.

DUCE, ROBERT ARTHUR, b. Midland, Ont, Can, Apr. 9, 35; U.S. citizen. ATMOSPHERIC CHEMISTRY. B.A, Baylor, 57; Nat. Insts. Health fel. & Ph.D.(inorg. & nuclear chem), Mass. Inst. Tech, 64. Res. assoc. geochem, Mass. Inst. Tech, 64-65; asst. prof. chem. & asst. meteorologist, inst. geophysics, Univ. Hawaii, 65-68, assoc. prof. & assoc. geochemist, 68-70; ASSOC. PROF. OCEANOG, UNIV. R.I, 70- U.S.A.F, 57-61, Res, 61-, Capt. Am. Chem. Soc; Am. Meteorol. Soc; Geochem. Soc; Am. Geophys. Union. Atmospheric chemistry of the halogens and lead; chemical oceanography; chemical fractionation at the air-sea interface; global transport of atmospheric particulate matter; chemistry of sea surface films; neutron activation analysis. Address: Graduate School of Oceanography, University of Rhode Island, Kingston RI 02881.

DUCH, MICHAEL WILLIAM, b. Newark, N.J, Mar. 22, 41; m. 66; c. 3. PHYSICAL & ANALYTICAL CHEMISTRY. B.S, Rutgers Univ, 63; Ph.D. (phys. chem), Univ. Utah, 70. Res. asst. anal. chem, Union Carbide Corp, 63-64; RES. CHEMIST, E.I. DU PONT DE NEMOURS & CO, INC, 70- AAAS; Am. Chem. Soc. Carbon-13 nuclear magnetic resonance studies of polybutadienes, polyisoprenes and saturated nitrogen heterocyclic molecules; gel permeation chromatography and high pressure liquid chromatography. Address: 101 King William St, Newark, DE 19711.

DUCHAMP, DAVID JAMES, b. St. Martinville, La, Oct. 15, 39; m. 64; c. 2. PHYSICAL CHEMISTRY, X-RAY CRYSTALLOGRAPHY. B.S, Southwestern Louisiana, 61; Ph.D.(phys. chem), Calif. Inst. Tech, 65. RES. SCIENTIST, UPJOHN CO, 65- AAAS; Am. Chem. Soc; Am. Crystallog. Asn; Am. Asn. Comput. Mach. Molecular structure studies by x-ray diffraction; application of mathematics and computers to chemical problems; data acquisition and control, via computer, of physical measurement instruments. Address: Physical & Analytical Division, Upjohn Co, Kalamazoo, MI 49001.

DuCHARME, DONALD WALTER, b. Saginaw, Mich, June 14, 37; m. 58; c. 3. PHARMACOLOGY. A.B, Central Michigan, 59; U.S. Pub. Health Serv. grant & Ph.D.(pharmacol), Michigan, 65. RES. ASSOC. CARDIOVASC. DISEASES, UPJOHN CO, 65- Adj. asst. prof. biol, West. Mich. Univ. Am. Heart Asn; Am. Soc. Pharmacol. & Exp. Therapeut. Cardiovascular physiology and pharmacology, particularly the autonomic control of the capacity vessels and the role of these vessels in the etiology of arterial hypertension. Address: Cardiovascular Diseases Research, Upjohn Co, Kalamazoo, MI 49001.

DuCHARME, ERNST P(ETER), b. St. Paul, Minn, July 15, 16; m. 47; c. 1. PLANT PATHOLOGY. B.Sc, St. Mary's Col. (Minn), 38; M.S, De Paul, 43; Ph.D.(plant path), Minnesota, 49. Instr, high sch, 38-43; asst. plant path, Minnesota, 43-46; PLANT PATHOLOGIST, AGR. RES. & EDUC. CTR, UNIV. FLA, 46- AAAS; Am. Soc. Nat. Am. Phytopath. Soc; Bot. Soc. Am; Mycol. Soc. Am. Root diseases of citrus; soil microbiology in relation to the citrus root disease complex; root parasitizing nematodes; soil ecology. Address: Agricultural Research & Education Center, University of Florida, Box 1088, Lake Alfred, FL 33850.

DUCHARME, JACQUES R, b. Montreal, Que, Jan. 1, 28; m. 55; c. 5. PEDIATRICS, BIOCHEMISTRY. B.A, Montreal, 48, M.D, 54; Pennsylvania, 54-55, M.Sc, 61. Res. PEDIAT, Children's Hosp. Phila, 55-57; lectr, Columbia, 57-59; UNIV. MONTREAL, 59-61, asst. prof, 61-66, assoc. prof, 66-69, PROF. & CHMN. DEPT, 69-; DIR. PEDIAT. ENDOCRINE RES. LAB, L'HÔPITAL SAINTE-JUSTINE, 60- Res. fel, Babies' Hosp, Columbia-Presby. Med. Center, New York, 57-59; res. grants, Med. Res. Coun. Can, 60- Am. Pediat Soc; fel. Am. Acad. Pediat; Endocrine Soc; Soc. Pediat. Res; Can. Soc. Clin. Invest; Can. Pediat. Soc. Steroid biochemistry; steroid metabolism in premature, newborn infants, infancy and children. Address: Dept. of Pediatrics, L'Hopital Sainte-Justine, University of Montreal, Montreal, Que, Can.

DUCHESNEAU, EUGENE A(LFRED), JR, b. Quebec, Que, Nov. 16, 30; U.S. citizen; m. 61. BIOLOGY. B.S, St. Joseph's Col.(Pa), 52. Chemist, Monomer-Polymer-Dajac Inc, 52-57; POLYMER CHEMIST & PROJ. LEADER, polyvinyl chloride dept, BORDEN, INC, 57-70, CHEM. DIV. THERMOPLASTICS GROUP, 70- Am. Chem. Soc. High polymer chemistry; suspension, emulsion and graft polymerization and copolymerization of monomers like vinyl chloride; acrylic and methacrylic esters; acrylonitrile, butadiene, styrene and vinylidene. Address: Borden, Inc, Chemical Division Thermoplastics Group, 511 Lancester St, Leominster, MA 01453.

DUCK, B(OBBY) N(EAL), b. Reagan, Tenn, Sept. 6, 39; m. 62; c. 1. CYTOGENETICS, GENETICS. B.S, Univ. Tenn, 61; M.S, Auburn Univ, 63, Nat. Defense Educ. Act fel, 61-64, Ph.D.(agron), 64. Asst. agronomist, agr. exp. sta, Univ. Fla, 64-66, asst. prof. AGRON, UNIV. TENN, MARTIN, 66-70, ASSOC. PROF. & ASST. DEAN SCH. AGR, 70- Am. Soc. Agron; Crop Sci. Soc. Am; Am. Genetic Asn. Breeding and management of forage crops. Address: School of Agriculture, University of Tennessee at Martin, Martin, TN 38237.

DUCK, IAN MORLEY, b. Kamloops, B.C, Can, Oct. 4, 33; m. 63; c. 2. NUCLEAR PHYSICS. B.Sc, Queen's (Ont), 55; Ph.D.(theoret. nuclear physics), Calif. Inst. Tech, 61. Res. assoc. PHYSICS, Southern California, 61-63; RICE UNIV, 63-65, asst. prof, 65-67, assoc. prof, 67-69, PROF, 69- Weak interactions; nuclear reaction mechanisms; few nucleon problems. Address: Dept. of Physics, Rice University, Houston, TX 77001.

DUCK, WILLIAM N, JR, b. Millheim, Pa, Feb. 9, 20; m. 44; c. 2. BIOCHEMISTRY, PHYSICAL CHEMISTRY. B.S, Pa. State, 42; dipl. chem. eng, Drexel Inst, 44; M.S, Franklin & Marshall Col, 64. Quality control supvr, Nat. Dairy Prods, Inc, 42-50; res. & develop. chemist. Am. Stores Co, Inc, 50-54; res. dir, Pa. Mfrs. Confectioners Asn, 54-64; RES. CHEMIST, GEN. CIGAR CO, 64- Am. Chem. Soc. Studies of moisture relations of sugar glasses and fat crystalization of chocolate and other fats. Address: 607 Capri Rd, Lancaster, PA 17603.

DUCKETT, JAMES W(ILLIAM), b. Greenwood, S.C, July 8, 11; m. 36; c. 3. ORGANIC CHEMISTRY. B.S, The Citadel, 32; fel, Georgia, 32-34, M.S, 34; Michigan, 36; fel, North Carolina, 40-41, Ph.D.(org. chem), 41. Asst. prof. chem, THE CITADEL, 34-41, assoc. prof, 41-53, prof, 53-54, dean admissions & records, 54-62, col, 62-68, v.pres, 68-70, PRES, 70- Consult, U.S. Chem, Biol. & Radiol. Adv. Coun, 59- Chem.C, 42-46, Res, 46-, Col. Am. Chem. Soc. Drug chemistry; resene in Pinus cerabea; general chemistry; medicinal agents; organic solvents; chemical warfare; new n'-isocyclic sulfanilamides. Address: The Citadel, Charleston, SC 29409.

DUCKETT, KERMIT EARL, b. Asheville, N.C, Mar. 27, 36; m. 65; c. 2. PHYSICS. B.S, Ga. Inst. Tech, 58; M.S, Colorado, 61; Ph.D.(physics), Tennessee, 64. Res. assoc. fiber physics, Am. Enka Corp, 58-59; ASST. PROF. PHYSICS, UNIV. TENN, KNOXVILLE, 65- Nat. Sci. Found. res. assoc, U.S. Dept. Agr, 65-66. Am. Phys. Soc; Am. Asn. Physics Teachers. Infrared lasers and spectroscopy; physical properties of cellulosic fibers; x-ray diffraction. Address: Dept. of Physics, University of Tennessee, Knoxville, TN 37916.

DUCKSTEIN, LUCIEN, b. Paris, France, Aug. 25, 32; U.S. citizen; m. 58; c. 3. OPERATIONS RESEARCH. M.Sc, Toulouse, 55, M.Sc, 56, dipl, Nat. Polytech. Inst. Elec. Eng. & Hydraul, 56; Ph.D.(fluid mech), 62. Engr, Régie Nat. Renault, France & Germany, 58-60; jr. civil engr. aerodyn, Colorado State, 61-62; PROF. SYSTS. ENG, UNIV. ARIZ, 62- Sci. Adv, Metra-Int. Inst. Mgt. Sci; Opers. Res. Soc. Am. Systems engineering; mathematical models of traffic flow; optimization techniques; economic calculus; hydrology and water resources. Address: Dept. of Systems & Industrial Engineering, University of Arizona, Tucson, AZ 85721.

DUCKWORTH, DONNA HARDY, b. Baltimore, Md, Sept. 12, 35; m. 64; c. 1. BIOCHEMISTRY, GENETICS. B.A, Fla. State, 57; Ph.D.(biochem), Hopkins, 66. Nat. Insts. Health fel. physiol. chem, sch. med, Hopkins, 66-67; instr. MICROBIOL, SCH. MED, UNIV. VA, 67-68, ASST. PROF, 68- AAAS; Am. Soc. Microbiol. Biochemistry and physiology of bacteriophage infection; control of cell replication. Address: Dept. of Microbiology, University of Virginia School of Medicine, Charlottesville, VA 22901.

DUCKWORTH, H(ENRY) E(DMISON), b. Brandon, Man, Can, Nov. 1, 15; m. 42; c. 2. PHYSICS. B.A, Manitoba, 35, B.Sc, 36; Sheldon fel, Chicago, 41, fel, 41-42, Ph.D.(physics), 42; hon. D.Sc, Ottawa, 66, McMaster, 69, Laval, 71. Lectr. physics, United Col, 38-40; jr. physicist, Nat. Res. Coun. Can, 42-44, asst. res. chemist, 44-45, asst. prof. PHYSICS, Manitoba, 45-46; assoc. prof, Wesleyan, 46-51; prof, McMaster, 51-65, chmn. dept, 56-61, dean grad. studies, 61-65; v.pres. develop, Manitoba, 65-66, acad.v.pres, 66-71; PRES, UNIV. WINNIPEG, 71- Nuffield fel, 55; ed, Can. J. Physics, 56-62; mem. comn. atomic masses, Int. Union Pure & Appl. Physics, secy, 60-66, chmn, 66-69; mem. Nat. Res. Coun. Can, 61-67; Defence Res. Bd, 65-71; hon. fel, United Col, 66. Manitoba Jubilee Award, 61. Fel. Am. Phys. Soc; fel. Royal Soc. Can.(pres. sect. III, 64, Tory Medal, 65, pres, 71); Can. Asn. Physicists (pres, 60, medal, 64). Mass spectroscopy. Address: 49 Oak St, Winnipeg 9, Man, Can.

DUCKWORTH, JOHN KELLY, b. Hazard, Ky, July 31, 28; m. 53; c. 5. PATHOLOGY. B.S, U.S. Merchant Marine Acad, 49; Memphis State, 52-53; M.D, Tennessee, 56. Design engr, Rotary Lift Corp, 49-50; B.F. Shaw & Co, 51-52; intern, Greenville Gen. Hosp, S.C, 56-57; gen. practice, Mo, 57-60; res. path, col. med, Tennessee, 60-64, asst. prof, 64-65; DIR. LABS, METHODIST HOSP, 65- Louis Levy award, 56; Am. Cancer Soc. Clin. fel, 62-64. U.S.N.R, 50-63, Lt.(jg). Col. Am. Path; Am. Soc. Clin. Path; Am. Med. Asn; Aerospace Med. Asn. Surgical pathology; aerospace medicine; tumors of paraganglia tissues. Address: 1390 Farrow Rd, Memphis, TN 38116.

DUCKWORTH, WALTER DONALD, b. Athens, Tenn, July 19, 35; m. 55; c. 3. ENTOMOLOGY. B.Sc, Middle Tenn. State, 57; M.Sc, N.C. State, 60, Ph.D. (entom), 62. ASSOC. CURATOR ENTOM, SMITHSONIAN INST, 62- Asn. Trop. Biol.(secy-treas, 67-71); Entom. Soc. Am; Soc. Syst. Zool. Biosystematics of the Microlepidoptera, particularly tropical groups. Address: Dept. of Entomology, Smithsonian Institution, Washington, DC 20560.

DUCKWORTH, WILLIAM C(APELL), b. Jackson, Tenn, Oct. 31, 19; m. 51; c. 3. B.S, Univ. of the South, 40; M.S, Ga. Inst. Tech, 54. Chem. engr, Am. Cyanamid Co, 46-47; chem. technologist, Tenn. Corp, 47-61; mkt. res. engr, Enjay Chem. Co, 61-63; sr. chem. economist, South. Res. Inst, 63-66; sr. proj. engr, Gulf Res. & Develop. Co, 66-71; SR. ENGR, VELSICOL CHEM. CORP, 71- Am. Chem. Soc; Am. Inst. Chem. Eng; Am. Asn. Cost Eng; Chem. Mkt. Res. Asn. Polymer properties and economics; pesticides; chemical economics. Address: 3077 Eagle Dr, Memphis, TN 38118.

DUCKWORTH, WINSTON H(OWARD), b. Greenfield, Ohio, Oct. 15, 18; m. 41; c. 2. CERAMIC ENGINEERING. B.Ch.E, Ohio State, 40, Res. Found. fel, 40-41, M.S, 41. Asst. supvr, BATTELLE MEM. INST, 46-52, chief ceramic div, 52-66, FEL, 66-, FOUNDING DIR. DEFENSE CERAMIC INFO. CTR, 71- With Atomic Energy Comn; U.S.N, 44. U.S.A.A.F, 41-46, Lt. Col. AAAS; fel. Am. Ceramic Soc; Nat. Inst. Ceramic Eng.(pres); Nat. Soc. Prof. Eng; Am. Soc. Test. & Mat; Can. Ceramic Soc. Processing and behavior of ceramic materials; brittle behavior; aircraft and nuclear ceramics; research management. Address: Battelle Memorial Institute, 505 King Ave, Columbus, OH 43201.

DUCLOS, DONALD P(AUL), b. Detroit, Mich, June 16, 31; m. 60; c. 3. AEROSPACE ENGINEERING. B.M.E, Detroit, 54; M.S, Northwestern, 55, univ. transportation ctr. fel, 57-58, R.E. Cabell fel, 58-59, J.M. Barker fel, 59-60, Ph.D.(mech. eng), 60. Specialist sci. res. engr, power conversion div, Repub. Aviation Corp, N.Y, 60-63; sr. scientist, fluid physics div, Electro-optical Systs, Inc, Calif, 63-66; mem. tech. staff, REENTRY SYSTS. DIV, AEROSPACE CORP, 66-68, MGR. DATA INTERPRETATION, 68- U.S.A, 55-57. Am. Inst. Aeronaut. & Astronaut; Am. Phys. Soc. Combustion; real gas effects in hypersonic flows; plasma thermodynamics; instrumentation; plasma diagnostics; reentry simulation; pulsed plasma accelerators; crossed-field plasma accelerators; hypersonic wakes; radar signature. Address: Reentry Systems Division, Aerospace Corp, 1111 E. Mill St, San Bernardino, CA 92408.

DUCLOS, LEO ALBERT, b. Manila, Ark, July 12, 34; m. 58; c. 5. PLANT BREEDING. B.S, Arkansas, 58; M.S, Purdue, 64, Ph.D.(plant genetics, breeding), 66. RES. GENETICIST, UNIV. MO, 66- Nat. Guard, 52-, Capt. Am. Soc. Agron; Crop Sci. Soc. Am; Am. Soybean Asn. Plant genetics; agronomy; statistics. Address: Delta Center, University of Missouri, Portageville, MO 63873.

DUCLOS, ZACHARY M(ARK), b. Manila, Ark, Jan. 9, 31; m. 58; c. 4. PLANT GENETICS & BREEDING. B.S, Arkansas, 57, M.S, 58; Ph.D.(plant genetics & breeding), Purdue, 62. Res. asst. maize genetics, Purdue, 60-62; res. agronomist, DeKalb AgRES, INC, 62-64, dir. cotton res, 64-67, RES. AGRONOMIST, CORN DIV, 67- U.S.A, 57, 1st Lt. Development of hybrid corn varieties for the south and southeast. Address: DeKalb AgResearch, Inc, Route 3, Box 132, Leesburg, GA 31763.

DUCOFF, HOWARD S, b. N.Y.C, May 5, 23; m. 46; c. 4. RADIATION BIOLOGY. B.S, City Col. New York, 42; Ph.D.(physiol), Chicago, 53. Jr. biologist, Argonne Nat. Lab, 46-51, assoc. biologist, 51-57; asst. prof. PHYSIOL, UNIV. ILL, URBANA, 57-59, assoc. prof, 59-65, PROF, 65- U.S. Pub. Health Serv. spec. fel, Cambridge, 64-65. Consult, Argonne Nat. Lab, 57-63; staff consult, Argonne Univs. Assoc, 69- Med.C, U.S.A, 43-46. AAAS; Am. Soc. Protozool; Radiation Res. Soc; Am. Soc. Cell Biol; Soc. Invert. Path; Am. Soc. Zool; Soc. Gen. Physiol. Physiology of cell division; cellular radiobiology; insect physiology; biology of aging. Address: Dept. of Physiology & Biophysics, 524 Burrill Hall, University of Illinois, Urbana, IL 61803.

DUCOFFE, ARNOLD L, b. Montreal, Can, Mar. 22, 21; U.S. citizen; m. 43; c. 4. AEROSPACE ENGINEERING. B.Aero Eng, Ga. Inst. Tech, 43, M.S, 47; Ph.D.(gas dynamics), Michigan, 52. Asst. prof. aerodyn, GA. INST. TECHNOL, 45-48, assoc. prof, 51-55, prof, 55-63, acting dir. AEROSPACE ENG, 63-64, DIR, 64- Consult, aerodyn. div, Sandia Corp, N.Mex, 54-63; dir, Universal Co. Ltd, Que, Rich's Inc, Ga. & Unitron Int. Systs, Inc, Calif. Am. Inst. Aeronaut. & Astronaut. Low speed aerodynamics of helicopters; high speed gas dynamics and heat transfer; laminar and turbulent viscous boundary layer flow; slip flow; stability and control. Address: Dept. of Aerospace Engineering, Georgia Institute of Technology, Atlanta, GA 30332.

DUDA, EDWARD J(OHN), b. Northampton, Mass, Aug. 30, 24; m. 55; c. 2. ENTOMOLOGY. B.S, Syracuse, 48; M.S, Massachusetts, 53, Ph.D.(entom), 62; Minnesota. Jr. entomologist, Main Forest Serv, 48-51; asst. entomologist, Bartlett Tree Res. Labs, 51-55, assoc. entomologist, 55-57, entomologist, 57-60, acting dir, 60-62, dir, 62-65, ASSOC. PROF. IN CHARGE, BARTLETT ARBORETUM, UNIV. CONN, 65- U.S.A, 44. Entom. Soc. Am; Am. Inst. Biol. Sci; Am. Asn. Bot. Gardens & Arboretums. Biology; ecology; control of forest and shade tree insects. Address: Bartlett Arboretum, University of Connecticut, Brookdale Rd, Stamford, CT 06903.

DUDA, EDWIN, b. Donora, Pa, Oct. 15, 28; m. 55; c. 4. MATHEMATICS. B.A, Washington & Jefferson Col, 51; M.S, West Virginia, 53; Ph.D.(math), Virginia, 61. Instr. MATH, West Virginia, 53, 55-57; Virginia, 60-61; from asst. prof. to ASSOC. PROF, UNIV. MIAMI, 61-, ACTING CHMN. DEPT. 67- U.S.A, 53-55. Am. Math. Soc; Math. Asn. Am. Transformations; topological analysis. Address: Dept. of Mathematics, University of Miami, Coral Gables, FL 33124.

DUDA, JOHN J, b. Herbert, Pa, Jan. 25, 31; m. 57; c. 2. MEDICAL MICROBIOLOGY, ELECTRON MICROSCOPY. B.A, Wash. & Jefferson Col, 61; Nat. Insts. Health fel, W.Va. Univ, 64-68, M.S, 65, Ph.D.(med. microbiol), 68. CLIN. LAB DIR, BROWNSVILLE GEN HOSP, 57- Sig.C, U.S.A, 53-55. Am. Soc. Microbiol; N.Y. Acad. Sci; Am. Acad. Microbiol; Am. Asn. Clin. Chem. Ultrastructure studies of Clostridium botulinum and actinomyces utilizing immuno-cytochemical methods, specifically immuno-ferritin methods. Address: 130 Creek Rd, Brownsville, PA 15417.

DUDA, J(OHN) L(ARRY), b. Donora, Pa, May 11, 36; m. 62; c. 4. CHEMICAL ENGINEERING. B.S, Case Inst. Tech, 58; M.Ch.E, Delaware, 61, Ph.D. (chem. eng), 63. Res. engr, process fundamentals lab, Dow Chem. Co, 63-

71; ASSOC. PROF. CHEM. ENG, PA. STATE UNIV, 71- Am. Inst. Chem. Eng; Am. Chem. Soc. Transport phenomena; molecular diffusion; fluid mechanics; polymer processing; arctic engineering. Address: Dept. of Chemical Engineering, Pennsylvania State University, University Park, PA 16802.

DUDA, RICHARD OSWALD, b. Evanston, Ill, Apr. 27, 36; m. 68; c. 1. ELECTRICAL ENGINEERING. B.S, California, Los Angeles, 58, M.S, 59; Space Tech. Labs. fels, Mass. Inst. Tech, 60-61, Ph.D.(elec. eng), 62. SR. RES. ENGR, INFO. SCI. LAB, STANFORD RES. INST, 62- AAAS; Asn. Comput. Mach; Inst. Elec. & Electronics Eng. Electronic computers and artificial intelligence, especially pattern recognition and machine learning; information, control and network theory. Address: 590 Vine St, Menlo Park, CA 94025.

DUDA, SEWERYN JOZEF, b. Chorzow, Poland, Apr. 20, 33; m. 55; c. 3. GEOPHYSICS, SEISMOLOGY. Magister geofizyki, Warsaw, 55; filosofie licentiat, Uppsala, 61, filosofie doktor & docent, 67. Asst. geophys. inst, Warsaw Univ, 55-58; scientist, Seismos Inc, Hannover, Germany, 58-60; asst. proj. scientist, seismol. inst, Uppsala, 60-61, 62-65; vis. prof, DEPT. EARTH & ATMOSPHERIC SCI, ST. LOUIS UNIV, 66-67, asst. prof, 67-69, ASSOC. PROF, 69- Res. fel, seismol. lab, Calif. Inst. Tech, 64; UNESCO expert in seismol, Int. Inst. Seismol. & Earthquake Eng, Tokyo, Japan, 70. Seismol. Soc. Am; Soc. Explor. Geophys; Ger. Geophys. Soc; European Asn. Explor. Geophys; Polish Geophys. Soc; Am. Geophys. Union. Earthquake seismology; computational methods in geophysics; time series analysis. Address: Dept. of Earth & Atmospheric Sciences, St. Louis University, 3507 Laclede Ave, St. Louis, MO 63156.

DUDAR, JOHN S, b. Weyburn, Sask, Sept. 3, 28; m. 56; c. 4. GEOLOGY. B.Sc, Saskatchewan, 54; M.S, Michigan, 57, Ph.D.(geol, minerals), 60. Mine geologist, Eldorado Mining & Ref, Sask, 54-55; prod. geologist, Shell Oil Co, Tex, 58, field engr. & res. geologist, Shell Can. Ltd, Alta, 59-64; asst. prof. geol, Eastern Michigan, 64-65; geologist, Pan Am. Petrol, 65-69; mgr. explor. prod, Uravan Minerals, 69-70; CONSULT, OIL & GAS EXPLOR, METAL DEPOSITS, 70- Can. Govt. grant, uranium mine study, Sask, 55-58. Summers, student engr, Am. Yellowknife Mines, Northwest Territories, 52, student geologist, Consol. Mining & Smelting, B.C, 53, mine geologist, Eldorado Mining & Ref, 54-57. Am. Asn. Petrol. Eng; Eng. Inst. Can. Uranium; Smackover & Wilcox formations of Texas; sulphur; metallic minerals; sandstone & carbonate environments & exploitation for hydrocarbons. Address: 8102 Mobud, Houston, TX 77036.

DUDAS, JOSEPH H, b. Pittsburgh, Pa, May 20, 33; m. 56; c. 5. METALLURGICAL ENGINEERING. B.S, Pittsburgh, 56, M.S, 61. Res. engr. metall, Pittsburgh, 56, 57-60; welding & brazing, res. lab, ALUMINUM CO. AM, 61-68, GROUP LEADER, ATOMIZING & P/M, ALCOA TECH. CTR, 68- C.Eng, 56-57, Res, 57-64, Capt. Am. Soc. Metals; Am. Soc. Test. & Mat; Sci. Res. Soc. Am. Investigation of gases in steel; development of processes and aluminum alloys for welding, brazing and soldering; development of processes and alloys for aluminum powder metal products. Address: Alcoa Technical Center, P.O. Box 2970, Pittsburgh, PA 15230.

DUDDEY, JAMES E, b. Dayton, Ky, Aug. 11, 41; m. 65; c. 2. ORGANIC & POLYMER CHEMISTRY. A.B, Thomas More Col, 61; Petrol. Res. Fund fels, St. Louis Univ, 61-62 & 65-66, M.S, 65, Ph.D.(org. chem), 67. Chemist, appl. res. lab, U.S. Steel Corp, 66-68; SR. RES. CHEMIST, POLYESTER RES. & DEVELOP, GOODYEAR TIRE & RUBBER CO, 68- Am. Chem. Soc. Reactions of trifluoroacetic acid with alkynes, substituted alkynes and substituted alkyl tosylates; reactions of carbon monoxide; modifications of polyesters. Address: 705 San Moritz Dr, Akron, OH 44313.

DUDECK, ALBERT EUGENE, b. West Hazleton, Pa, Oct. 16, 36; m. 59; c. 3. AGRONOMY. B.S, Pa. State, 58, Ph.D.(agron), 64. ASST. PROF. turf res, Nebraska, 64-70; ORNAMENTAL HORT, INST. FOOD & AGR. SCI, UNIV. FLA, 70- Am. Soc. Agron; Crop Sci. Soc. Am. Turfgrass phase of highway and fine turf research; grass breeding; turfgrass breeding and genetics. Address: Agricultural Research Center, Institute of Food & Agricultural Sciences, University of Florida, 3205 S.W. 70th Ave, Ft. Lauderdale, FL 33314.

DUDEK, EMILY PITCHER, b. Boston, Mass, Jan. 21, 37; m. 62. INORGANIC CHEMISTRY. B.A, Smith Col, 58; M.A, Radcliffe Col, 60, Ph.D.(chem), 62. Instr. CHEM, Simmons Col, 62-63; Wellesley Col, 63-68; ADJ. ASST. PROF, BRANDEIS UNIV, 68- Brit. Chem. Soc. Spectroscopic studies of organometallic compounds; synthesis and properties of metal chelates. Adress: Dept. of Chemistry, Brandeis University, Waltham, MA 02154.

DUDEK, GERALD, b. Binghamton, N.Y, Oct. 15, 32; m. 62. ORGANIC CHEMISTRY. B.S, Calif. Inst. Tech, 54; Ph.D.(chem), Harvard, 59. RES. ASSOC. CHEM, HARVARD, 60- Am. Chem. Soc. Address: Dept. of Chemistry, Harvard University, Cambridge, MA 02138.

DUDEK, R(ICHARD) A(LBERT), b. Clarkson, Nebr, Sept. 3, 26; m. 54; c. 2. INDUSTRIAL ENGINEERING. B.S, Nebraska, 50; univ. fel, Iowa, 50, M.S, 51, Ph.D.(indust. eng, mgt), 56. Plant indust. engr, Fairmont Foods Co, Sioux City, Iowa, 51-52, div. indust. engr, Nebr, 52-53; asst. instr, Iowa, 53-54; asst. prof. mech. eng, Nebraska, 54-56; assoc. prof. indust. eng. & res. assoc. schs. health professions, Pittsburgh, 56-58; PROF. INDUST. ENG. & CHMN. DEPT, TEX. TECH UNIV, 58-, HON. PROF, 70-, DIR. CTR. BIOTECHNOL. & HUMAN PERFORMANCE, 69- Consult. U.S.N.R, 44-46. Am. Soc. Eng. Educ; Am. Soc. Mech. Eng; Am. Inst. Indust. Eng.(Spec. Serv. award, 62, appreciation award, 71); Inst. Mgt. Sci; Nat. Soc. Prof. Eng. Application of statistical and mathematical techniques involved in operations research; sequencing/scheduling; systems analysis; work analysis and design of biotechnology. Address: Dept. of Industrial Engineering, Texas Tech University, Lubbock, TX 79409.

DUDERSTADT, EDWARD C(HARLES), b. Kansas City, Kans, Dec. 20, 28; m. 50; c. 2. CERAMIC ENGINEERING. B.S, Missouri, Rolla, 58, M.S, 59. Tech. engr, aircraft nuclear propulsion dept, GEN. ELEC. CO, CINCINNATI, 59-61, sr. engr, nuclear mat. & propulsion oper, 61-66, PRIN. ENGR,

NUCLEAR SYSTS. PROGS, 66- U.S.A, 51-54, 1st Lt. Am. Ceramic Soc. Physical and mechanical properties of ceramics, refractory metals and cermets; ceramic materials fabrication processes; rates and mechanisms of gas transport in solids. Address: 5327 Dee Alva Dr, Fairfield, OH 45014.

DUDERSTADT, JAMES JOHNSON, b. Ft. Madison, Iowa, Dec. 5, 42; m. 64; c. 2. APPLIED PHYSICS. B.Eng, Yale, 64; M.S, Calif. Inst. Tech, 65, Ph.D.(eng. sci, physics), 68. Atomic Energy Cmn. res. fel. eng. sci, Calif. Inst. Tech, 68; ASST. PROF. NUCLEAR ENG, UNIV. MICH, 69- Am. Nuclear Soc; Am. Phys. Soc. Nuclear reactor physics; statistical physics; plasma physics; applied mathematics. Address: Dept. of Nuclear Engineering, University of Michigan, Ann Arbor, MI 48105.

DUDEWICZ, EDWARD JOHN, b. Jamaica, N.Y, Apr. 24, 42; m. 63; c. 3. STATISTICS. S.B, Mass. Inst. Technol, 63; Nat. Sci. Found. fels, Cornell Univ, summers 64 & 65, 66-67, M.S, 66, univ. fel, 66-67, Ph.D.(statist), 69. Summers, eng. res. asst, RAD div, Avco Corp, 62 & asst. engr, 63; res. asst. STATIST, Cornell Univ, 65-66; ASST. PROF, UNIV. ROCHESTER, 67- Reviewer, Math. Rev, 66-; prin. investr. grant, Off. Naval Res-Ctr. Naval Anal, 67-72; consult, Graflex Inc, Singer Co, 69; Gleason Works, 69; myocardial infarction res. unit, Strong Mem. Hosp, 70-72; reviewer, Zentralblatt für Mathematik, 70- Inst. Math. Statist; Am. Statist. Asn; Math. Asn. Am. Statistical selection and ranking procedures; estimation of ordered parameters; statistical inference with unknown and unequal variances; nonparametric techniques. Address: Dept. of Statistics, University of Rochester, Rochester, NY 14627.

DUDEY, NORMAN, b. Wichita, Kans, May 18, 37; m. 63; c. 2. NUCLEAR CHEMISTRY. A.B, Univ. Kans, 59; Ph.D.(nuclear chem), Clark Univ, 64. Fel, Columbia Univ, 64-65; head nuclear detector sect, Isotopes, Inc. Div, Teledyne Inc, 65-67; asst. chemist, ARGONNE NAT. LAB, 67-68, ASSOC. CHEMIST, 69- Am. Phys. Soc; Am. Nuclear Soc. Development and production of germanium and gas detectors; development of radio assay techniques; determination of neutron cross sections, fission yields and fast-reactor neutron spectral measurement techniques; studies of nuclear reaction. Address: Bldg. 205, Argonne National Lab, Argonne, IL 60439.

DUDGEON, EDNA, b. Sweetwater, Tex, Feb. 25, 13. GENETICS. B.S, Southwest. Tex. State Col, 37; M.A, Texas, 50, Ph.D.(genetics), 55. Instr. biol, Texas Tech. Col, 48-49; asst. prof, Mississippi, 53-54; assoc. prof, Col. Ozarks, 55; asst. prof. zool, Southern Illinois, 55-60; assoc. prof, biol, SOUTHEAST MO. STATE COL, 60-64, PROF. ZOOL, 64- U.S.N.R, 43-46. Genetics Soc. Am; Soc. Study Evolution; Am. Soc. Zool. Genetics and evolution of drosophila; radiation genetics. Address: 1502 Dunklin, Cape Girardeau, MO 63701.

DUDLEY, ALDEN WOODBURY, JR, b. Lynn, Mass, May 15, 37; m. 59; c. 3. NEUROPATHOLOGY. A.B, Duke, 58, M.D, 62. Nat. Insts. Health training fel. neuropath, Duke, 65-67, ASST. PROF. neurol. & path, 67-68; PATH, UNIV. WIS, MADISON, 68- Neuropathologist, Center for Cerebrovascular Res, Durham, N.C, 67-68. Consult, Nat. Biomed. Res. Found, Silver Spring, Md. & Vet. Admin. Hosps, Madison & Tomah, Wis, 68-; Mendota & Cent. Colony State Hosps, Madison, 69- Res. assoc, lab. exp. neuropath, Nat. Inst. Neurol. Diseases & Strokes, U.S.P.H.S. AAAS; N.Y. Acad. Sci; Am. Asn. Neuropath. Computer analysis of histologic sections of brain; herbicide toxicology on Primates; mechanism of strokes and related diagnostic procedures; neuropathology of mental retardation, alcoholism and related areas. Address: 2805 Post Rd, Madison, WI 53713.

DUDLEY, BEVERLY, b. Chicago, Ill, Apr. 2, 06; m. 39. ELECTRONIC ENGINEERING. S.B, Mass. Inst. Tech, 35; M.Sc, Columbia, 53. Electronics engr, RCA Mfg. Co, 35-36; ed. electronics, McGraw-Hill Publ. Co, 36-45; tech. & res, Mass. Inst. Tech, 45-59, asst. to dir. res. & ed, Lincoln Lab, 59-60; staff mem. adv. res, Lab. for Electronics, Inc, 60-63; weapons syst. eval. div, Inst. Defense Anal, 63-71; CONSULT, ED. & WRITER, 71- Consult. prof, Newark Col. Eng, 41-43. Sr. mem. Inst. Elec. & Electronics Eng; Acoust. Soc. Am; Optical Soc. Am. Communications. Address: 5423 Cathedral Ave. N.W, Washington, DC 20016.

DUDLEY, DARLE W, b. Salem, Ore, Apr. 8, 17; m. 41; c. 2. MECHANICAL ENGINEERING. B.S, Oregon State, 40. Engr, Gen. Elec. Co, 40-48, sect. head gear develop, 48-57, mgr. adv. gear eng, 57-64; mech. transmissions, Mech. Tech. Inc, 64-65, tech. dir, 65-67; CHIEF GEAR TECHNOL, SOLAR DIV, INT. HARVESTER CO, 67- Edward P. Connell award, 58; Golden Gear Award, Power Transmission Design, 66. Am. Soc. Mech. Eng; Am. Gear Mfrs. Asn. Fatigue strength; friction and wear; gear arrangements. Address: 6355 Lake Shore Dr, San Diego, CA 92119.

DUDLEY, FRANK MAYO, b. Umatilla, Fla, Dec. 27, 20; m. 41; c. 2. PHYSICAL SCIENCE, CHEMISTRY. A.B, Oglethorpe Univ, 44; B.S, Univ. Ga, 47; M.A, Ohio State Univ, 50, Ph.D.(sci. educ), 62. Clin. chemist, Downey Hosp, Gainesville, Ga, 46-47; Theresa-Holland Clin, Leesburg, Fla, 47-48; instr, high sch, Ohio, 50-53, head dept. sci, 53-55; asst. sci. educ, Ohio State Univ, 56-57; instr. chem, Palm Beach Jr. Col, 57-60; eval. serv. phys. sci, Univ. S.Fla, 60-61; clin. lab. off, U.S. Army Hosp, Fort Polk, La, 61-62; asst. prof. PHYS. SCI, UNIV. S.FLA, 62-69, ASSOC. PROF, 69- Consult. summer insts, Agency Int. Develop, India, Bhubaneswar, Orissa, 66; Nat. Sci. Found, Punjab Univ, 67. Dept. Army Nat. Defense Medal, 69. Med.Serv.C, U.S.A.R, 50-, Maj. AAAS. Improvised equipment in teaching the biological sciences; relationship of preparation and professional status to the decisions of science teachers; selected electrolytes for the separation of colloidal components in electrophoresis and chromatography methods. Address: College of Basic Studies, 342 Physics Bldg, University of South Florida, Tampa, FL 33620.

DUDLEY, HOMER WALTER, b. Oranda, Va, Nov. 14, 96; m. 23; c. 3. ELECTRICAL ENGINEERING. B.S, Pa. State, 21; A.M, Columbia, 24. Mem. tech. staff, Bell Tel. Labs, 21-61; COMMUN. SYSTS, INT. TEL. & TEL. CORP, 62-64, CONSULT, 64- Stuart Ballantine Medal, Audio Eng. Soc, 65. Med.C, U.S.A, 18-19. Fel. AAAS; Inst. Elec. & Electronics Eng; Acoust. Soc. Am. Acoustics; communication circuit research and development; analysis and synthesis of speech; distortion in transmitting speech; voice operation circuits; visible speech; ultrasonics; underwater sound. Address: 150 Ashland Rd, Summit, NJ 07901.

DUDLEY, HORACE C(HESTER), b. St. Louis, Mo, June 28, 09; m. 35, 54; c. 4. PHYSICS, RADIOBIOLOGY. A.B, Mo. State Teachers Col, 31; Maryland, 31-34; Hopkins, 35-36; Ph.D, Georgetown, 41. Lab. asst, U.S. Bur. Standards, 31-32; jr. chemist, bur. chem, U.S. Dept. Agr, 33-34; med. res. div, Chem. Warfare Serv, 34-36; biochemist, U.S. Pub. Health Serv, 36-42; head allied sci. sect, Med. Serv. Corps, U.S. Navy, 49-52, in charge biochem. div, Naval Med. Res. Inst, 47-52, head radioisotope lab, Naval Hosp, St. Albans, N.Y, 52-62; prof. physics & chmn. dept, Southern Mississippi, 62-69; PROF. RADIATION PHYSICS, UNIV. ILL. MED. CTR, 69- Res. collab, Brookhaven Nat. Labs, 52-57; consult, Oak Ridge Inst. Nuclear Studies, 48-57; L.I. Jewish Hosp, 57-61. Dipl. Am. Bd. Health Physics, 60. U.S.A.R, 31-42; U.S.N, 42-62, Capt; Bronze Star, 45, Navy Commendation Medal, 46. Fel. AAAS; Health Physics. Soc; Am. Phys. Soc; Am. Asn. Physics Teachers; Am. Asn. Physicists Med. Biochemistry; radioactive isotopes; nuclear theory; theory of neutrinoflux as generalized sub-quantic medium; radio biology. Address: Dept. of Radiology, University of Illinois at the Medical Center, Box 6998, Chicago, IL 60680.

DUDLEY, J(AMES) DUANE, b. Twin Falls, Idaho, Sept. 8, 28; m. 50; c. 5. PHYSICS. B.S, Brigham Young, 52; M.A, Rice Inst, 53; Ph.D.(physics), Utah, 59. Instr. physics, Idaho State Col, 53-54; physicist, Hughes Aircraft Co, 54-55; instr. physics, Brigham Young, 56-58, asst. prof, 58-59; physicist, Sandia Corp, 59-61; asst. prof. PHYSICS, BRIGHAM YOUNG UNIV, 61-63, assoc. prof, 63-69, PROF, 69- Am. Asn. Physics Teachers. High pressure pheonomena; theoretical mechanics; thermal physics. Address: Dept. of Physics, Brigham Young University, Provo, UT 84601.

DUDLEY, JAMES R(OBERT), b. St. Paul, Minn, Apr. 23, 17; m. 42; c. 3. ORGANIC CHEMISTRY. A.B, Carleton Col, 36; M.S, Iowa, 38, Ph.D.(org. chem), 40. Res. chemist & group leader, Am. Cyanamid Co, 40-48, supvr. new prod. develop, 48-52; v.pres, Carwin Co, 52-55; dir. res. & develop, Richardson Co, 55-65, v.pres, 57-65; exec. v.pres, Marine Colloids, Inc, 65-68; pres, Encanto Prod, Inc, 68-70; TECH. COORD, AJAX INT. CORP, 70- AAAS; Am. Chem. Soc; fel. Am. Inst. Chem; Commercial Chem. Develop. Asn.(exec. secy, 54-56, pres, 60-61); Chem. Mkt. Res. Asn; N.Y. Acad. Sci. Synthetic resins and elastomers. Address: P.O. Box 4565, Santa Barbara, CA 93103.

DUDLEY, JOHN HENDERSON, b. Oakland, Calif, Sept. 25, 07; m. 31. CIVIL ENGINEERING. B.S, U.S. Mil. Acad, 30; M.S, Mass. Inst. Tech, 39; U.S. Army War Col, 50-51; Ford Found. grant, Harvard, 66. Asst. commandant, U.S. Army Engr. Sch, 58-60; PROF. CIVIL ENG, CALIF. STATE COL. LONG BEACH, 60- Lectr, Armed Forces Staff Col, 58-60; res. grant, Calif. State Col. Found, 66-67; summer engr, Converse Found. Engrs, Calif, 63 & L.T. Evans, Inc, 64. Mem, Cmt. Int. Affairs, Engrs. Joint Coun, 58-61. U.S.A, 30-60, Brig. Gen. Fel. Am. Soc. Civil Eng; Am. Soc. Eng. Educ; Nat. Soc. Prof. Eng; Soc. Am. Mil. Eng. Open channel flow; mechanics of desiccated soils. Address: Dept. of Civil Engineering, California State College, Long Beach, CA 90801.

DUDLEY, JOHN M(INOT), b. Boston, Mass, July 17, 26; m. 60; c. 3. PHYSICS. S.B, Mass. Inst. Tech, 46; Ph.D.(physics), California, Berkeley, 60. Instr. physics, Pomona Col, 55-56; prin. physicist, Aerojet-Gen. Nucleonics Div, Gen. Tire & Rubber Co, 60-63, staff specialist, 63-64; ASSOC. PROF. PHYSICS, COLBY COL, 64- Lectr, Joe Berg Found, California, Davis, 60; consult, thermonuclear div, Oak Ridge Nat. Lab, 70-71. Am. Phys. Soc; Am. Inst. Aeronaut. & Astronaut. Plasma and nuclear physics. Address: Dept. of Physics, Colby College, Waterville, ME 04901.

DUDLEY, JOHN W(ESLEY), b. Huntsville, Ind, Sept. 29, 31; m. 51; c. 4. PLANT BREEDING, GENETICS. B.S, Purdue, 53; M.S, Iowa State, 55, Ph.D.(crop breeding), 56. Plant geneticist, sugar beet sect, agr. res. serv, U.S. Dept. Agr, 57-59; alfalfa sect, crop sci. dept, N.C. State Univ, 59-65; assoc. prof. AGRON, UNIV. ILL, URBANA, 65-69, PROF, 69- Biomet. Soc; Am. Soc. Agron; Am. Genetics Asn; Crop Sci. Soc. Am.(ed, Crop Sci, 71). Quantitative genetics; plant breeding methods. Address: Dept. of Agronomy, University of Illinois, Urbana, IL 61801.

DUDLEY, KENNETH HARRISON, b. Hagerstown, Md, Nov. 12, 37; m. 66; c. 2. ORGANIC & MEDICINAL CHEMISTRY. B.S, Elon Col, 59; Ph.D.(org. chem), North Carolina, 63. Nat. Sci. Found. fel, inst. inorg. chem, Univ. Basel, 63-64; chemist, chem. & life sci. lab, Res. Triangle Inst, N.C, 64-67; ASST. PROF, CTR. FOR RES. PHARMACOL. & TOXICOL, SCH. MED, UNIV. N.C, CHAPEL HILL, 67- Am. Chem. Soc. Syntheses of condensed heterocyclic systems, naphthoquinone compounds, model riboflavin analogs and isoflavonoids; drug metabolism. Address: Center for Research in Pharmacology & Toxicology, University of North Carolina School of Medicine, Chapel Hill, NC 27514.

DUDLEY, MICHAEL ALAN, b. Strawberry Hill, Eng, May 22, 42; m. 68. POLYMER SCIENCE. A.I.R.I. & Assoc. Nat. Col. Rubber Technol, London, 64, Fel. & Ph.D.(ablation), 67. Res. chemist, DuPont of Can, 67-70; assoc. scientist, NORANDA RES. CTR, 70-71, GROUP LEADER POLYMER RES. & NEW PROD. DEVELOP, 71- Assoc. Brit. Inst. Rubber Indust; affiliate Am. Chem. Soc. Thermal degradation of polymers; molecular weight and rheological characterization of polymers; electrodeposition of water soluble resins; compounding of polyvinyl chloride. Address: Chemistry Dept, Noranda Research Centre, 240 Hymus Blvd, Pointe Claire, Que, Can.

DUDLEY, PATRICIA, b. Denver, Colo, May 22, 29. INVERTEBRATE ZOOLOGY. B.A, Colorado, 51, M.A, 53; Nat. Sci. Found. fel, Washington (Seattle), 56, Ph.D.(zool), 57. Res. assoc. ZOOL, Washington (Seattle), 57-59, acting instr, 59; instr, BARNARD COL, COLUMBIA UNIV, 59-62, asst. prof, 62-65, ASSOC. PROF, 66- Summer vis. instr, marine labs, Univ. Wash, 60-61, Nat. Sci. Found. fel, 65-66. Am. Soc. Zool; Marine Biol. Asn. U.K; Soc. Syst. Zool. Systematics, development and histology of copepods symbiotic in marine animals; electron microscopy of crustacea. Address: Dept. of Biological Sciences, Barnard College, Columbia University, New York, NY 10027.

DUDLEY, PRISCILLA PERKINS, b. Glens Falls, N.Y, Oct. 26, 40; m. 62. GEOLOGY. B.A, Bryn Mawr Col, 62; Nat. Sci. Found. fels, California, Berkeley, 62-66, Ph.D.(geol), 67. Instr. GEOL, BOSTON COL, 67-68, ASST. PROF, 68- AAAS; Geol. Soc. Am; Mineral Soc. Am; Geochem. Soc; Am. Geophys. Union; Geol. Soc. London; Mineral. Soc. Gt. Brit. & Ireland. Metamorphic petrology. Address: Dept. of Geology & Geophysics, Boston College, Chestnut Hill, MA 02167.

DUDLEY, RICHARD H(ARRISON), b. Los Angeles, Calif, Mar. 31, 31; m. 55; c. 2. PHYSICAL METALLURGY. B.A, Columbia Univ, 54, M.S, 55; Ph.D. (phys. metall), Rensselaer Polytech. Inst, 62. Res. asst. welding, Rensselaer Polytech. Inst, 58-62; mem. tech. staff, BELL TEL. LABS, INC, 62-68, supvr. silicon device technol, 68-70, SUPVR. METALS GROUP, 70- U.S.N.R, 55-58, Lt.(jg). Inst. Elec. & Electronics Eng. Metallization for silicon integrated circuits. Address: Bell Telephone Labs, Inc, 555 Union Blvd, Allentown, PA 18103.

DUDLEY, RICHARD M(ANSFIELD), b. East Cleveland, Ohio, July 28, 38; m. 62. MATHEMATICS. A.B, Harvard, 59; Nat. Sci. Found. fels, Princeton, 59-62, Ph.D.(math), 62. Instr. MATH, California, Berkeley, 62-63, asst. prof, 63-67, ASSOC. PROF, MASS. INST. TECHNOL, 67- A.P. Sloan fel, 66-68. Inst. Math. Statist; Am. Math. Soc. Probability theory; Schwartz distributions; abstract analysis; statistics. Address: Dept. of Mathematics, Massachusetts Institute of Technology, Cambridge, MA 02139.

DUDLEY, R(OBERT) A(UGUR), b. Kodaikanal, India, May 7, 26; U.S. citizen; m. 58. PHYSICS. B.A, Pennsylvania, 46; Nat. Cancer Inst. fel. & Ph.D. (physics), Mass. Inst. Tech, 51. Fulbright scholar, London, 51-53; consult. radioisotope techniques, Egyptian Atomic Energy Comn, 55-56; res. assoc. dept. physics, Mass. Inst. Tech, 56-60; SR. OFF, DIV. RES. & LABS, INT. ATOMIC ENERGY AGENCY, 60- U.S.N.R, 43-46, 53-55, Lt. AAAS; Am. Phys. Soc. Nuclear physics and radioactivity in biological problems; autoradiography and other radiation measurement techniques; fallout; radium toxicity. Address: International Atomic Energy Agency, Vienna 1, Austria.

DUDLEY, THEODORE, b. Boston, Mass, Dec. 31, 36; m. 60; c. 2. PLANT TAXONOMY. B.S, Massachusetts, 58; Cornell, 60; Ph.D.(plant taxon), Edinburgh, 63. Asst. taxonomist, arnold arboretum, Harvard, 59-60, hort. taxonomist, 63-66; RES. BOTANIST, U.S. NAT. ARBORETUM, 66- Bot. Soc. Am; Am. Soc. Plant Taxon; Am. Asn. Bot. Gardens & Arboretum. Generic and specific limits of groups in the Cruciferae and the Carprifoliaceae; taxonomic research in the cultivated species of Ilex in Aquifoliaceae; plant exploration in Turkey, the Peruvian Andes, Tierra del Fuego and Oceanic Islands. Address: Herbarium, U.S. National Arboretum, Washington, DC 20002.

DUDLEY, UNDERWOOD, b. N.Y.C, Jan. 6, 37; m. 63; c. 2. MATHEMATICS. B.S, Carnegie Inst. Technol, 57, M.S, 58; Ph.D.(math), Univ. Mich, 65. Asst. prof. MATH, Ohio State Univ, 65-67; DePAUW UNIV, 67-69, ASSOC. PROF, 69- Am. Math. Soc; Math. Asn. Am; Soc. Indust. & Appl. Math. Number theory; recreational mathematics. Address: Dept. of Mathematics, DePauw University, Greencastle, IN 46135.

DUDLEY, WINSTON M(ANSFIELD), b. Swissvale, Pa, Feb. 21, 12; m. 36; c. 3. ENGINEERING MECHANICS. B.S, Swarthmore Col, 32; M.S, Michigan, 33, univ. fel, 33-34, Sc.D.(mech), 38. Instr. appl. mech, Case, 34-41, asst. prof, 41-45, assoc. prof. mech, 45-47; assoc. dir, eng. res. dept, Standard Oil Co, Ind, 47-58, sr. consult. engr, 58-63; assoc. prof. MECH. ENG, SACRAMENTO STATE COL, 63-66, PROF, 66- Consult, Euclid Rd. Mach. Co, 42-46; Thompson Prods, Inc, 43-47; Aerojet Corp, 63-65. Am. Soc. Mech. Eng.(jr. award, 42). Machine design; cam design; vibration; stress analysis; analog and digital computation. Address: 50 Sandburg Dr, Sacramento, CA 95819.

DUDOCK, BERNARD S, b. New York, N.Y, Nov. 17, 39; m. 64; c. 2. BIOCHEMISTRY, MOLECULAR BIOLOGY. B.S, City Col. New York, 61; Ph.D. (org. chem), Pa. State, 66. Nat. Insts. Health fel. biochem, Cornell, 66-68; ASST. PROF. BIOCHEM, STATE UNIV. N.Y. STONY BROOK, 68- Nat. Cancer Inst. grant, 68- AAAS; Fedn. Am. Socs. Exp. Biol. Primary structure of nucleic acids; role of nucleic acids in cellular differentiation and development. Address: Dept. of Biochemistry, State University of New York at Stony Brook, Stony Brook, NY 11790.

DUDZIAK, DONALD JOHN, b. Alden, N.Y, Jan. 6, 35; m. 59; c. 2. NUCLEAR PHYSICS, APPLIED MATHEMATICS. B.S, U.S. Merchant Marine Acad, 56; Atomic Energy Cmn. fel. & M.S, Rochester, 57; Westinghouse-Bettis fel. & Ph.D.(appl. Math), Pittsburgh, 63. From assoc. engr. to sr. engr. reactor physics, Bettis Atomic Power Lab, Westinghouse Elec. Corp, 57-65; STAFF MEM, LOS ALAMOS SCI. LAB, UNIV. CALIF, 65- Summer asst. nuclear engr, shipbuilding div, Bethlehem Steel Corp, Mass, 56; prof, Univ. N.Mex, 66; vis. prof, Univ. Va, 68-69; mem, Nat. Cross Sect. Eval. Working Group. U.S.N.R, 52-, Lt. Comdr. Am. Nuclear Soc; Soc. Indust. & Appl. Math; Health Phys. Soc. Radiation shielding analysis and nuclear hazards evaluation; application of stochastic process theory to nuclear reactor kinetics; nuclear reactor analysis for development of design models; radiological physics and radiation biology. Address: 318 Navajo Rd, Los Alamos, NM 87544.

DUDZIAK, WALTER FRANCIS, b. Adams, Mass, Jan. 7, 23; m. 54; c. 4. PHYSICS, COMPUTER SCIENCE. B.S. & M.S, Rensselaer Polytech, 48; Case, 48-49; Ph.D.(math, physics), California, Berkeley, 54. Engr, Manhattan Dist. Proj, Oak Ridge Nat. Lab, 44-46; instr. physics, Rensselaer Polytech, 47-48; aeronaut. res. scientist, Nat. Adv. Cmt. Aeronaut, Ohio, 48-49; mem. res. staff, Lawrence Radiation Lab, California, 49-58; tech. mil. planning oper, Gen. Elec. Co, 58-60, mgr. comput. sci. oper, 60-64, tech. mil. planning oper, 64-65; dir. info. sci. inst. & exec. v.pres. res. & develop, PAN-FAX, INC, 65-68, CONSULT. & MEM. BD, 65-; PRES, INFO. SCI, INC, 68- Lectr, California, Santa Barbara, 58-59. U.S.A, 43-44, C.Eng, 44-46, T/Sgt. Am. Phys. Soc; Am. Asn. Comput. Mach; Am. Geophys. Union. Leads; application of computer sciences to various scientific disciplines; effects of nuclear detonations; propagation of electromagnetic radiation; optical scanning; digitizing techniques as applied to rapid data transmission. Address: Information Science, Inc, 123 W. Padre St, Suite 3, Santa Barbara, CA 93105.

DUECHS, DIETHELM F(RANZ), b. Schweinfurt, Ger, Sept. 9, 38; m. 63; c. 3. THEORETICAL PHYSICS. Dipl, Munich, 63, dr. rer. nat.(plasma physics), 67. Physicist, Inst. Plasma Physics, Ger, 63-67; res. assoc. plasma physics, Univ. Md, College Park, 67-69; res. physicist, Naval Res. Lab, 69-71; MEM. SCI. STAFF, MAX PLANCK INST. PLASMA PHYSICS, 71- Consult, plasma physics lab, Princeton, 70- Ger. Phys. Soc; Am. Phys. Soc. Plasma dynamics; breakdown processes; stability of plasma configurations; applied mathematics; solution of partial differential equations; numerical methods; simulation of plasmas by computer codes. Address: Max Planck Institute for Plasma physics, 8046, Garching, Ger.

DUECKER, H(EYMAN) C(LARKE), b. Seville, Ohio, July 18, 29; m. 49; c. 2. INORGANIC CHEMISTRY. B.S, Marion Col, 50; Inst. Silicate Res. fel, Univ. Toledo, 54-55, M.S, 56; Ph.D, Univ. Md, 64. Res. chemist, Radio Corp. Am, 51-54; sci. lab, Ford Motor Co, 55-58; phys. chemist, Nat. Bur. Standards, 58-66; inorganic chemist, W.R. GRACE & CO, 66-67, mgr, INORG. RES, 67-69, DIR, 69- Assoc. prof. chem, Marion Col, Ind, 68-69. AAAS; Am. Chem. Soc; Am. Ceramic Soc. Inorganic oxides, preparation, properties and identification; silicates, zeolites; catalytic materials and processes; surface and colloid chemistry; inorganic construction materials. Address: Research Division, W.R. Grace & Co, Clarksville, MD 21029.

DUEKER, JAMES E(DSON), b. Falls City, Nebr, June 17, 22; m. 48; c. 2. PHYSICS. B.S, Mo. Sch. Mines, 44, M.S, 48; Ph.D.(physics), Missouri, 60. Asst. prof, physics, Wittenberg, 48-56; asst. phys. electronics, Missouri, 56-59; res. scientist, astrophys. lab, res. div, McDonnell Aircraft Corp, 59-61, assoc. scientist, electrooptics lab, 61-62, sr. scientist & head lab, 62-70, BR. MGR. OPTOELECTRONIC TECH, McDONNELL DOUGLAS ASTRONAUT. CO-E, 70- U.S.A.A.F, 42-46, 1st Lt. Am. Phys. Soc; Optical Soc. Am. Physical electronic and optical properties; electrooptical and photoelectric devices. Address: McDonnell Douglas Astronautics Co-East, Dept. E413, P.O. Box 516, St. Louis, MO 63166.

DUELL, PAUL M(ERWYN), b. Goodland, Kans, Dec. 11, 24; m. 48; c. 4. INORGANIC CHEMISTRY. B.A, Ft. Hays Kans. State Col, 50, M.S, 51; Ph.D.(chem), Kansas State, 58. Instr. phys. sci, Garden City Jr. Col, 51-52; instr. CHEM, Washburn, 52-53; Kans. State, 53-57; asst. prof. WILLAMETTE UNIV, 57-58, assoc. prof, 58-59, PROF. & CHMN. DEPT, 59- Summers, Nat. Sci. Found. grant, Utah, 59, Oregon State, 61; vis. prof, Nat. Sci. Found. Summer Inst, Kans. State Col, Pittsburg, 60. U.S.A, 44-47. AAAS; Am. Chem. Soc. Physical properties of mixed aqueous salt solutions, including magnetic susceptibilities, conductivities, partial molal volumes; physical properties of binary aqueous salt solutions; ligand field effects on complex ions in aqueous and non-aqueous solutions. Address: Dept. of Chemistry, Willamette University, Salem, OR 97301.

DUELL, ROBERT WILLIAM, b. New York, N.Y, Feb. 24, 29; m. 56; c. 3. AGRONOMY, CROPS. B.A, Connecticut, 50, M.S, 54; Ph.D, Rutgers, 57. Res. assoc, RUTGERS UNIV, 55-57, asst. res. specialist, 57-60, assoc. res. specialist, 60-67, ASSOC. RES. PROF, DEPT. SOILS & CROPS, 67- With Agency Int. Develop, Brazil, 65-67. Med.C, U.S.A, 51-53. Am. Soc. Agron. Pasture production; forage quality; crop establishment; mineral uptake and fertilizer efficiency; roadside vegetation research. Address: Dept. of Soils & Crops, College of Agriculture, Rutgers University, New Brunswick, NJ 08902.

DUELLMAN, WILLIAM E(DWARD), b. Dayton, Ohio, Sept. 6, 30; m. 53; c. 3. HERPETOLOGY. M.S, Univ. Mich, 53. Asst. herpet, mus. zool, Univ. Mich, 52-56, teaching fel. zool, univ, 54-56; instr, dept. biol, Wayne State Univ, 56-59; asst. prof. zool, UNIV. KANS, 59-63, assoc. prof, 63-68, PROF, 68-70, DEPT. SYSTS. & ECOL, 70-, CURATOR, MUS. NATURAL HIST, 70-, ASSOC. DIR, 71-, asst. curator herpet, 59-63, assoc. curator, 63-70. Am. Soc. Ichthyol. & Herpet; Soc. Study Evolution; Am. Soc. Syst. Zool; Ecol. Soc. Am; Brit. Herpet. Soc. Systematics; zoogeographic patterns; evolution; zoogeography of New World herpetofauna; evolutionary biology of reptiles and amphibians. Address: Museum of Natural History, University of Kansas, Lawrence, KS 66044.

DUELTGEN, RONALD REX, b. Salem, Ore, Sept. 21, 40; m. 62; c. 2. MEDICINAL CHEMISTRY. B.A, Oregon State, 62; Ph.D.(org. chem), Michigan, 67. RES. INVESTR, CHEM, G.D. SEARLE & CO, 67- AAAS; Am. Chem. Soc. Synthetic organic chemistry; natural products, steroids, alkaloids and terpenes. Address: Division of Chemical Research, G.D. Searle & Co, P.O. Box 5110, Chicago, IL 60680.

DUER, WAYNE CARLTON, b. Lubbock, Tex, Feb. 8, 43; m. 63; c. 3. PHYSICAL CHEMISTRY. B.A, Ft. Hays Kans. State Col, 65; M.S, Univ. Mo-Rolla, 67, Nat. Sci. Found. summer fel, Nat. Defense Educ. Act fel. & Ph.D.(phys. chem), 70. Instr. CHEM, Univ. Mo-Rolla, 70; RES. ASSOC, UNIV. FLA, 70-, interim vis. assoc. prof, 70-71. Am. Chem. Soc; The Chem. Soc. Solution chemistry; hydrogen-deuterium isotope effects on heats of solution of nonelectrolytes; conductance and thermodynamic properties of electrolyte solutions. Address: Dept. of Chemistry, University of Florida, Gainesville, FL 32601.

DUERIG, WILLIAM H(ENRY), b. New York, N.Y, Sept. 10, 21; m. 44; c. 3. PHYSICS. B.S, N.Y. Univ, 43; Ph.D.(physics), Maryland, 52. Asst. physics, N.Y. Univ, 43-44; jr. physicist, radiation lab, California, 44-45; prin. staff physicist & group supvr. telemetering, appl. physics lab, Hopkins, 45-51, solid state physicist, 51-53, supvr, transistor group, 52-53; sr. res. physicist, Electro. Mech. Res. Inc, 53-57, mgr. res. & develop, 57-58; v.pres. res. & eng, Midwest. Instruments, Inc, 58-59; v.pres. & gen. mgr, Oliver Shepherd Industs, Inc, 59-61; dir. res. & advan. develop, aerospace div, Gen. Precision, Inc, 61-67; pres, E.S.R, INC, 67-70, TECH. & FINANCIAL CONSULT, 71- Assoc. Am. Phys. Soc; Inst. Elec. & Electronics Eng; Instrument Soc. Am. Telemetering; computers; children's educational products; color centers in alkali halides. Address: E.S.R, Inc, 60 Austin Blvd, Commack, NY 11725.

DUERKSEN, JACOB D(IETRICH), b. Alta, Can, Nov. 29, 29; U.S. citizen; m. 57; c. 2. CELL BIOLOGY, BIOCHEMISTRY. B.S, Univ, B.C, 53, B.C. Sugar Ref. Co. fel, 53-55, M.S, 55; Am. Soc. Microbiol. fel, Univ. Ill, 56; Ph.D.(bact), Univ. Wis, 58. Asst. microbiol, Univ. B.C, 53-55; Univ. Mich, 55-56; bact, Univ. Wis, 56-58; asst. prof. microbiol, Univ. Kans, 60-64, assoc. prof, sch. med, 64-70; PROF. BIOL, UNIV. CALGARY, 70- Nat. Insts. Health res. grant, 61-67, spec. res. fel, 69-70; Kans. Cancer Inst. res. grant, 67-69; Can. Nat. Res. Coun, grant, 70- Am. Soc. Microbiol; Am. Soc. Cell Biol; Can. Soc. Cell Biol; Can. Soc. Biochem; Can. Soc. Microbiol. Genetic regulatory mechanisms in biosynthesis, growth and development in both procaryotic and encaryotic cells. Address: Dept. of Biology, University of Calgary, Calgary 44, Alberta, Can.

DUERKSEN, JOHN HUGO, b. Chilliwack, B.C, Dec. 23, 34; m. 60; c. 2. CHEMICAL ENGINEERING. B.A.S, Univ. B.C, 58; Athlone fel, Eng, 58-60; dipl, Imp. Col. Sci. & Technol, Univ. London, 60; Ph.D.(chem. eng), McMaster Univ, 68. CHEM. RES. ENGR, Atomic Energy of Can, 61-64; CHEVRON RES. CO, STANDARD OIL CO. CALIF, 67- Am. Inst. Chem. Eng; Am. Chem. Soc. Polymerization kinetics and reactor modeling; petroleum hydrocracking—process and catalyst research and development. Address: Process Research Dept, Chevron Research Co, 576 Standard Ave, Richmond, CA 94802.

DUERR, FREDERICK G, b. St. Paul, Minn, May 17, 35; m. 54; c. 3. ZOOLOGY, COMPARATIVE PHYSIOLOGY. B.A, Minnesota, 56, Ph.D.(zool), 65. ASSOC. PROF. zool, South Dakota, 61-67; BIOL, Univ. Sask, Regina, 67-68; UNIV. N.DAK, 68- AAAS; Am. Soc. Zool; Am. Soc. Parasitol. Comparative physiology of digenetic trematode parasitism; physiology of respiration and nitrogen excretion. Address: Dept. of Biology, University of North Dakota, Grand Forks, ND 58202.

DUERRE, JOHN A, b. Webster, S.Dak, Aug. 21, 30; m. 57; c. 3. MICROBIAL BIOCHEMISTRY, PHYSIOLOGY. B.S, S.Dak. State Col, 52, M.S, 56; Ph.D. (bact), Minnesota, 60. Atomic Energy Comn. fel, Argonne Nat. Lab, 60-61; res. bacteriologist, Rocky Mt. Lab, Nat. Inst. Allergy & Infectious Diseases, 61-63; asst. prof. MICROBIOL, SCH. MED, UNIV. N.D, 63-65, assoc. prof, 65-71, PROF, 71- Nat. Sci. Found. res. grant, 68-71; vis. scientist, neuropsychiat. res. unit, Med. Res. Coun. Labs, Eng, 69-70; Nat. Insts. Health career develop. award, 70-, res. grant, 71- Sulfur amino acid metabolism in mammalian systems; methylation of brain histones; microbiology. Address: Dept. of Microbiology, University of North Dakota, Grand Forks, ND 58201.

DUERST, RICHARD WILLIAM, b. Rice Lake, Wis, Aug. 18, 40; m. 64; c. 2. PHYSICAL & ANALYTICAL CHEMISTRY. B.A, St. Olaf Col, 62, Nat. Insts. Health Summer grant, 62; Ph.D.(chem), California, Berkeley, 66. Fel. phys. chem, Lawrence Radiation Lab, California, 66-67; Nat. Res. Coun-Nat. Bur. Standards res. fel, Nat. Bur. Standards, Md, 67-69; ASST. PROF, DEPT. CHEM, WIS. STATE UNIV, EAU CLAIRE, 69- Summers, tech. student, Union Carbide Chem. Co, 61 & res. asst, Lawrence Radiation Lab, California, 63-66. Am. Chem. Soc; The Chem. Soc; Am. Phys. Soc. Nuclear magnetic resonance studies of inorganic systems; dissociation of strong acids; hydration of ionic species in aqueous solution; metal-metal pair interactions; effect of isotopic substitution on physical properties. Address: Dept. of Chemistry, Wisconsin State University, Eau Claire, WI 54701.

DUESEL, BERNARD F(RANCIS), b. Webster, Mass, June 18, 07; m. 38; c. 4. CHEMISTRY. A.B, Clark, 29, A.M, 30. Res. chemist, Pyridium Corp, 30-43, asst. dir. develop, 43-46; sr. res. chemist, Nepera Chem. Co. Div, Warner-Lambert Pharm, 46-57, chief develop. chemist, 57-59, sr. develop. chemist, 59-61, res. mgr, 61-69; RETIRED. Am. Chem. Soc. Pharmaceuticals; sulfa drugs; vitamins; pharmaceutical chemistry. Address: 512 Valley Ave, Yonkers, NY 10703.

DUESING, CONSTANTIN MICHAEL, b. Berlin, Ger, Dec. 15, 32; m. 59. PETROLOGY, MINERALOGY. B.Sc. & M.Sc, Munich, 54, Ph.D.(geol), 59. NATO fel. geol, McGill, 60-62; RES. GEOLOGIST, J. ROY GORDON RES. LAB, INT. NICKEL CO. CAN, LTD, 62- Can. Inst. Min. & Metall; Mineral. Asn. Can; German Geol. Asn; German Mineral. Soc. Igneous and metamorphic petrology; economical geology of ore deposits. Address: J. Roy Gordon Research Lab, International Nickel Co. of Canada, Ltd, Clarkson, Ont, Can.

DUESTERHOEFT, WILLIAM CHARLES, JR, b. Austin, Tex, Dec. 10, 21; m. 49; c. 1. ELECTRICAL ENGINEERING. B.S, Texas, 43, M.S, 49; Ph.D. (elec. eng), Calif. Inst. Tech, 53. Elec. engr, Gen. Elec. Co, 43-46; instr. elec. eng, Texas, 46-48, asst. prof, 48-49; instr, Calif. Inst. Tech, 49-52; aerophysics engr, Gen. Dynamics/Convair, 52-54; assoc. prof. ELEC. ENG, UNIV. TEX, AUSTIN, 54-60, PROF, 60- Corp. consult, 54- Inst. Elec. & Electronics Eng; Am. Soc. Eng. Educ; Am. Phys. Soc. Plasma dynamics; geophysics; power and energy conversion systems. Address: Dept. of Electrical Engineering, University of Texas at Austin, Austin, TX 78712.

DUFF, DALE THOMAS, b. Ross Co, Ohio, Dec. 26, 30; m. 58; c. 1. CROP PHYSIOLOGY. B.S, Ohio State Univ, 57, M.S, 64; Ph.D.(crop sci), Mich. State Univ, 67. Trainee, Soil Conserv. Serv, U.S. Dept. Agr, 55-57; agronomist, Clinton County Farm Bur. Coop Asn, Ohio, 58-61; asst. instr. agron, Ohio State Univ, 61-64; teaching asst. crop sci, Mich. State Univ, 64-67; ASST. PROF. PLANT & SOIL SCI, UNIV. R.I, 67- U.S.N, 49-52. AAAS; Am. Soc. Agron; Crop Sci. Soc. Am; Am. Inst. Biol. Sci. Stress physiology of turf grasses, especially high temperature and low temperature effects upon growth. Address: Dept. of Plant & Soil Science, University of Rhode Island, Kingston, RI 02881.

DUFF, DAVID CECIL BUCHANAN, b. Edinburgh, Scotland, Oct. 15, 01; m. 32; c. 1. BACTERIOLOGY, IMMUNOLOGY. B.A, Toronto, 26, M.A, 27, Ph.D, 30. From instr. to prof. bact. & immunol, British Columbia, 29-70; RETIRED. Consult. pathologist, Pac. Biol. Sta, 30-40; investr, Atlantic Biol. Sta, 26; Fisheries Exp. Sta, Prince Rupert, 29. R.C.A.F, 43-44, Flight Lt. Brit. Soc. Gen. Microbiol. Microbial physiology; marine microbiology; roles of marine micro-organisms in relation to the turnover of elements in the seas. Address: 4687 W. 5th Ave, Vancouver 8, B.C, Can.

DUFF, FRATIS L, b. Randlett, Okla, July 7, 10; m. 37; c. 2. MEDICINE. B.S, Oklahoma, 33, M.D, 39; M.P.H, Hopkins, 50; D.P.H, 53. U.S. Air Force, 40-68, dir. training & chief trop. med. dept, U.S. Air Force Sch. Aerospace Med, 43-47, wing surgeon & chief prfnl. serv. br, Far East Air Force, Japan, 47-49; prof. mil. sci. & tactics, Hopkins, 49-51, mem. staff, hqs, Surgeon General's Off, 51-53, commandant, U.S. Air Force Sch. Aerospace Med, 53-59, dep. surgeon, Germany, 59-62, command surgeon, Air Force Systs. Command, 62-64, Tactical Air Command, 64-68; DEP. COMNR, PROG. PLANNING, TEX. STATE DEPT. HEALTH, 68- U.S.A.F, 40-68, Brig. Gen. Am. Med. Asn; Am. Pub. Health Asn; fel. Am. Col. Physicians; Am. Col. Prev. Med; Aerospace Med. Asn; Am. Soc. Parasitol; Royal Soc. Trop. Med. & Hyg. Military preventive and aviation medicine. Address: State Dept. of Health, 1100 W. 49th St, Austin, TX 78756.

DUFF, G(EORGE) F(RANCIS) D(ENTON), b. Toronto, Ont, July 28, 26; m. 51; c. 5. MATHEMATICS. B.A, Toronto, 48, M.A, 49; Ph.D.(math), Princeton, 51. Moore instr, Mass. Inst. Tech, 51-52; asst. prof. MATH, UNIV. TORONTO, 52-57, assoc. prof, 57-61, PROF, 61-, CHMN. DEPT, 68- Ed, Can. J. Math, 57-61. Am. Math. Soc; Can. Math. Cong.(pres, 71-73). Differential equations. Address: 20 Buckingham Ave, Toronto 317, Ont, Can.

DUFF, (JAMES) GORDON, b. Rosetown, Sask, Apr. 3, 30. PHARMACEUTICAL CHEMISTRY. B.S.P, Saskatchewan, 53, M.Sc, 55; Ph.D.(pharmceut. chem), Florida, 58. Instr. pharm, Saskatchewan, 58-59, spec. lectr, 59-61; DIR, COL. PHARM, DALHOUSIE UNIV, 61-, PROF. PHARMACEUT. CHEM, 63- Am. Asn. Cols. Pharm. Synthesis of organic medicinal compounds. Address: College of Pharmacy, Dalhousie University, Halifax, N.S, Can.

DUFF, IVAN F(RANCIS), b. Pendleton, Ore, July 20, 15; m; c. 2. INTERNAL MEDICINE. A.B, Oregon, 38; M.D, Michigan, 40. Intern, univ. hosp, UNIV. MICH, 40-41, asst. resident INTERNAL MED, 41-42, resident, 42-46, instr, MED. SCH, 46-48, asst. prof, 48-53, assoc. prof, 53-60, PROF, 60-, PROF. IN CHARGE ARTHRITIS DIV, UNIV. HOSP, 60-, asst. physician, 48-53. Dir, Regional Arthritis Control Prog, Mich, 69-71. Med.C, 42-46, Comdr. Am. Fedn. Clin. Res; Am. Rheumatism Asn; fel. Am. Col. Physicians. Rheumatic and thromboembolic diseases. Address: Arthritis Division, Bldg. 9, Room 920, University Hospital, Ann Arbor, MI 48104.

DUFF, J(ACK) E(RROL), b. Baltimore, Md, May 17, 18; m. 47. ELECTRONICS. B.S, Case Inst. Technol, 39. Jr. engr, HOOVER CO, 39-41, sr. engr, 41-45, dir. elec. sect, 45-54, res. coord, 54-55, DIR. RES, 55- With Off. Sci. Res. & Develop; U.S.N, 44. Inst. Elec. & Electronics Eng. Small series motor design; industrial electronic control and inspection equipment design; analysis of multivibrator circuits; electrostatic heating-thermal control; frequency multiplier. Address: Engineering Dept, Hoover Co, 101 Eastern St, North Canton, OH 44720.

DUFF, JAMES T(HOMAS), b. Sandusky, Ohio, Jan. 23, 25. MICROBIOLOGY. B.S, Ohio State, 47, M.S, 49; Ph.D, Texas, 60. Microbiologist, immunol. br, med. invest. div, U.S. Army Biol. Lab, Ft. Detrick, 49-56, 59-65; microbiologist, NAT. CANCER INST, 65-66, ASSOC. CHIEF, VIRAL CARCINOGENESIS BR, 66- Res. scientist, dept. bact, Univ. Tex, 57-59. U.S.N, 43-46, Res, 46-, Comdr. AAAS; N.Y. Acad. Sci; Tissue Culture Asn; Am. Soc. Microbiol; Sci. Res. Soc. Am; Brit. Soc. Gen. Microbiol. Azotobacter bacteriophage; Clostridium botulinum toxins and toxoids; tissue culture; psittacosis group vaccines; viral oncology. Address: Viral Carcinogenesis Branch, National Cancer Institute, Bethesda, MD 20014.

DUFF, M(cGEE) A, b. Moran, Tex, Aug. 22, 26; m. 51; c. 2. ANALYTICAL CHEMISTRY. B.S, Southern Methodist, 50, M.S, 52; Ph.D.(anal. chem), La. State, 56. Res. anal. chemist, CELANESE CHEM. CO, 55-58, GROUP LEADER, 58- U.S.N, 44-46. Am. Chem. Soc. Process development. Address: Celanese Chemical Co, P.O. Box 9077, Corpus Christi, TX 78408.

DUFF, RAYMOND STANLEY, b. Hodgdon, Maine, Nov. 2, 23; m. 45; c. 3. PEDIATRICS, SOCIOLOGY. B.A, Maine, 48; M.D, Yale, 52, M.P.H, 59. Intern & res. pediat, Yale-New Haven Hosp, 52-55; dir. bur. med. serv, New Haven Health Dept, 55-56; instr. pediat. & pub. health, sch, YALE, 56-59, asst. prof. pediat. & sociol, 59-67, ASSOC. PROF. PEDIAT, SCH. MED, 67- Asst. dir. ambulatory serv, Yale-New Haven Hosp, 56-59. U.S.A, 43-46, 2nd Lt. AAAS; fel. Am. Pub. Health Asn; fel. Am. Acad. Pediat; Am. Sociol. Asn. Behavioral aspects of health, especially health or illness care in large hospitals as influenced by patients, families, physicians, nurses, administrators and others. Address: Dept. of Pediatrics, School of Medicine, Yale University, New Haven, CT 06520.

DUFF, ROBERT H(ODGE), b. Durand, Mich, Oct. 21, 29; m. 58; c. 3. INORGANIC & PHYSICAL CHEMISTRY. B.S, Mich. State, 51; Ph.D.(inorg. chem), Indiana, 61. Control chemist, Am. Agr. Chem. Co, Mich, 51-53; asst, Indiana, 53-59; electron microscopist & phys. chemist, Nat. Bur. Standards, 59-61; staff scientist electron micros, Avco Corp, Wilmington, 61-66; res. assoc, LEDGEMONT LAB, KENNECOTT COPPER CORP, LEXINGTON, 66-70, ANAL. CHEMIST, 70- AAAS; Am. Chem. Soc; fel. Am. Inst. Chem; Electron Micros. Soc. Am; Int. Soc. Stereology; Int. Metallographic Soc. Use of electron microscopy in all phases of material science; use of x-rays for elemental analysis with the electron microscope. Address: 21 Robin Hood Rd, Arlington, MA 02174.

DUFF, RUSSELL E(ARL), b. Grand Rapids, Mich, Nov. 28, 26; m. 47; c. 5. PHYSICS. B.S.E, Michigan, 47, M.S, 48, Ph.D.(physics), 51. Res. assoc, eng. res. inst, Michigan, 47-51; mem. staff, Los Alamos Sci. Lab, 51-61; Inst. Defense Anal, 61-62; proj. leader, Lawrence Radiation Lab, 62-64, div. leader, 64-67; DIR, SYSTS, SCI. & SOFTWARE & GEN. MGR, APPL. NUCLEAR DIV, 67- U.S.N.R, 44-46. Am. Nuclear Soc; Am. Phys. Soc. Shock and detonation hydrodynamics; high temperature chemistry. Address: Applied Nuclear Division, Systems, Science & Software, P.O. Box 1620, La Jolla, CA 92037.

DUFF, WILLARD MOYLE, b. Canon City, Colo, July 20, 39; m. 63; c. 1. PHYSIOLOGY. B.S, Midland Col, 61; M.S, Nebraska, 63, U.S.P.H.S. fel, 65-67, Ph.D.(physiol), 67. Res. assoc. physiol, sch. med, Creighton, 63-65, assoc. instr, 64-65; asst. prof. BIOL, UNIV. HARTFORD, 67-70, ASSOC.

PROF, 70-, MED. INSTR, HARTFORD HOSP, 70-, DIR. GRAD. STUDIES, UNIV, 71- Instr, Nebraska, summer 65. AAAS; Asn. Am. Med. Cols; Am. Soc. Zool; N.Y. Acad. Sci. Physiological action of the posterior pituitary hormones at both the gross renal system and membrane levels; organophosphates and cell metabolism. Address: Dept. of Biology, University of Hartford, 200 Bloomfield Ave, West Hartford, CT 06117.

DUFFEE, RICHARD A(NTHONY), b. Boston, Mass, Dec. 25, 30; m. 52; c. 5. BIOMETEOROLOGY. B.S, Boston Col, 52; B.S, Pa. State, 53; Ohio State. Prin. meteorologist, Battelle Mem. Inst, 56-62, sr. biometeorologist, 62-68; res. engr, Travelers Res. Corp, 68-70; DIR. ODOR ENG. & ASST. MKT. DIR, RES. CORP. NEW ENG, 70- U.S.A.F, 52-56, 1st Lt. Am. Chem. Soc; Am. Meteorol. Soc; Air Pollution Control Asn. Atmosphere diffusion; air pollution; atmospheric chemistry; physical environmental psychology; pollution control. Address: TRC-The Research Corp. of New England, 210 Washington St, Hartford, CT 06106.

DUFFELL, STANLEY, b. Port Moody, B.C, Aug. 3, 08; m. 41; c. 2. GEOLOGY. Ph.D.(geol), Toronto, 35. Mining geologist, mining consult, 35-40; GEOLOGIST, GEOL. SURV. CAN, 45- R.C.A.F, 41-45. Geol. Soc. Am; Royal Soc. Can; Geol. Asn. Can; Can. Inst. Min. & Metall. Economic geology. Address: Geological Survey of Canada, Ottawa, Ont, Can.

DUFFER, WILLIAM RILEY, b. Ada, Okla, Mar. 27, 34; m. 55; c. 4. LIMNOLOGY, ZOOLOGY. B.S, Okla. State Univ, 55, Nat. Sci. Found. fel, & M.S, 59, Nat. Insts. Health fel. & Ph.D.(zool, limnol), 65; Nat. Sci. Found. fel, Northwest. State Col.(La), 58. RES. AQUATIC BIOLOGIST, ROBERT S. KERR WATER RES. CTR, WATER QUAL. OFF, ENVIRON. PROTECTION AGENCY, 65- Am. Soc. Limnol. & Oceanog. Water pollution; water quality control; ecology. Address: Route 1, Roff, OK 74865.

DUFFETT, WALTER N, b. San Diego, Calif, Mar. 10, 30; m. 52; c. 3. PHYSICAL GEOGRAPHY, CARTOGRAPHY. B.A, San Diego State Col, 53; M.A, Ohio State Univ, 59; Ph.D, Univ. Colo, 69. U.S. AIR FORCE, 53-, cartog. geod. off, 53-63, asst. prof. GEOG, U.S. AIR FORCE ACAD, 63-70, ASSOC. PROF, 70- U.S.M.C, 50-51, U.S.A.F, 53-, Lt. Col. Asn. Am. Geog. Cartographic materials; Latin American geography. Address: DFG, U.S. Air Force Academy, CO 80840.

DUFFEY, DICK, b. La Fontaine, Ind, Aug. 26, 17. NUCLEAR ENGINEERING. B.S, Purdue Univ, 39; M.S, Univ. Iowa, 40; Ph.D.(nuclear eng), Univ. Md, 56. Engr. nuclear proj, Union Carbide, 40-42; nuclear engr, U.S. Atomic Energy Comn, 47-54; head nuclear eng. prog, UNIV. MD, 54-65, assoc. prof. NUCLEAR ENG, 56-59, PROF, 59-, nuclear reactor dir, 58-68. Nuclear Engr, Mass. Inst. Technol, summer 54; tech. sect. adv. comt. on reactor safeguards, Atomic Energy Comn, 59-66. U.S.A, 42-47. Am. Nuclear Soc; Am. Phys. Soc; Am. Geophys. Union; Am. Inst. Chem. Eng. Nuclear reactor design and operation; nuclear reactor safety; neutron uses; californium 252 uses. Address: Nuclear Engineering Program, University of Maryland, College Park, MD 20740.

DUFFEY, DONALD CREAGH, b. Winchester, Va, Feb. 9, 31. PHYSICAL & ORGANIC CHEMISTRY. B.S, Va. Polytech, 53; M.A, Rice, 55; Ph.D.(chem), Ga. Inst. Tech, 59. Res. fel, Pa. State Univ, 59-60; asst. prof. CHEM, MISS. STATE UNIV, 60-61, assoc. prof, 62-67, PROF, 67- Johnson Res. Found. fel, Univ. Pa, 64-65; vis. prof, Univ. Cincinnati, 68. Am. Chem. Soc. Reaction mechanisms; chemical spectroscopy. Address: Dept. of Chemistry, Mississippi State University, P.O. Box 35, State College, MS 39762.

DUFFEY, GEORGE H(ENRY), b. Manchester, Iowa, Dec. 24, 20; m. 45; c. 3. THEORETICAL PHYSICS. B.A, Cornell Col, 42; Brown Univ, 42; A.M, Princeton, 44, Ph.D.(chem. physics), 45. Asst, Princeton, 42-45; asst. prof. chem, S.Dak. State Col, 45-49, assoc. prof, 49-55, PROF, 55-58; chem. & physics, Univ. Miss, 58-59; PHYSICS, S.DAK. STATE UNIV, 59- Am. Phys. Soc; Am. Chem. Soc. Alpha-particle nuclear models; symmetry arguments; polarographic theory; valence theory; molecular-orbital calculations; detonation-wave theory. Address: Dept. of Physics, South Dakota State University, Brookings, SD 57006.

DUFFEY, L(OWELL) M(YERS), b. Seaman, Ohio, Oct. 25, 28; m. 51; c. 3. EXPERIMENTAL EMBRYOLOGY. B.S, Maryville Col, 51; M.S, Kans. State, 53; Nat. Inst. Health Res. fel, 56-57; Ph.D.(zool), Indiana, 58. Instr. biol, Lewis & Clark Div, Univ. Idaho, 57; anat, med. ctr, Univ. Ark, 58-60; asst. prof, Med. Col. Ala, 60-61; biol, Birmingham-South. Col, 62-63; ASSOC. PROF. zool, Univ. S.Dak, 63-68; BIOL, N.TEX. STATE UNIV, 68- AAAS; Am. Soc. Zool; Am. Asn. Anat. Avian cardiogenesis. Address: Dept. of Biology, North Texas State University, Denton, TX 76203.

DUFFIE, JOHN A(TWATER), b. White Plains, N.Y, Mar. 31, 25; m. 47; c. 3. CHEMICAL ENGINEERING. B.Ch.E, Rensselaer Polytech, 45, M.Ch.E, 48; Ph.D.(chem. eng), Wisconsin, 51. Res. engr, electrochems. dept, E.I. du Pont de Nemours & Co, 51-52; sci. liaison off, Off. Naval Res, 52-53; PROF. CHEM. ENG, UNIV. WIS, MADISON, 69-, DIR. SOLAR ENERGY LAB, 54-, DIR. UNIV-INDUST. RES. PROG. & ASSOC. DEAN, GRAD. SCH, 65-, asst. dir. eng. exp. sta, 57-65. Consult, U.S.N, 43-46, 52-53. Am. Inst. Chem. Eng; Am. Soc. Eng. Educ. Spray drying; solar energy research. Address: 5710 Dorsett Dr, Madison, WI 53711.

DUFFIELD, ALAN M, b. Perth, W. Australia, Dec. 16, 36; m. 60; c. 2. ORGANIC CHEMISTRY, MASS SPECTROMETRY. B.S, Western Australia, 58, Ph.D.(org. chem), 62. Fel. org. chem, STANFORD UNIV, 62-65, RES. ASSOC. mass spectrometry, 65-68, DEPT. GENETICS, HEAD MASS SPECTROMETRY LAB, 69- Consult, chem. evolution lab, exobiol. div, NASA Res. Center, Calif, 69- AAAS; Am. Chem. Soc; The Chem. Soc. Applications of mass spectrometry to organic chemical problems, especially natural products; structural assignments to ions formed on electron impact in a mass spectrometer; applications of mass spectrometry to biological problems; computer interpretation of mass spectra. Address: Dept. of Genetics, Stanford University Medical School, Stanford, CA 94305.

DUFFIELD, JACK JAY, b. Long Beach, Calif, Nov. 7, 33; m. 58; c. 2. ANALYTICAL CHEMISTRY. B.A, Pomona Col, 55; Ph.D.(anal. chem), Mass. Inst. Technol, 60. PROJ. ENGR. INSTRUMENT DESIGN, Appl. Physics Corp, 60-66, CARY INSTRUMENTS, 66- Am. Chem. Soc; N.Y. Acad. Sci; Soc. Appl. Spectros. Optical and electronic instrument design. Address: Cary Instruments, 2724 S. Peck Rd, Monrovia, CA 91016.

DUFFIELD, JOHN W(ARREN), b. Brooklyn, N.Y, June 5, 12; m. 39; c. 3. FORESTRY. B.S, Cornell, 34; M.F, Harvard, 35; Ph.D.(genetics), California, 51. Jr. forester, U.S. Forest Serv, 35-36, jr. forest ecologist, 39-42, forest geneticist, 46-53; asst. prof. forestry, col. forestry, Washington, 53-54; forester, Indust. Forest Asn, 54-56, tech. dir, 56-63; PROF. SILVICULTURE, N.C. STATE UNIV, 63- U.S.A, 42-46, Maj. Bot. Soc. Am; Soc. Am. Foresters; Ecol. Soc. Am. Forest genetics and forest tree breeding; silviculture. Address: School of Forest Resources, North Carolina State University, Raleigh, NC 27607.

DUFFIELD, ROBERT B(ROKAW), b. Trenton, N.J, Oct. 15, 17; m. 43; c. 2. CHEMISTRY. A.B, Princeton, 40; Ph.D.(chem), Univ. Calif, Berkeley, 43. Mem. staff, Manhattan Dist, Los Alamos Lab, 43-46; from asst. prof. chem. to assoc. prof. physics & chem, Univ. Ill, Urbana, 46-56; asst. lab. dir, John J. Hopkins lab, Gen. Atomic Div, Gen. Dynamics Corp, 56-67; PROF. CHEM, UNIV. CHICAGO & DIR, ARGONNE NAT. LAB, 67- Consult, Brookhaven Nat. Lab. & Los Alamos, 46-56; del, Int. Conf. Peaceful Uses Atomic Energy, Geneva, 58 & 64; mem. bd. trustees, Scripps Clin. & Res. Found, 59- Fel. Am. Phys. Soc; Am. Chem. Soc. Power reactors; radioactivity; photonuclear reactions; photofission of uranium; neutron-binding energies; radioactive decay processes; design and operation of nuclear reactors. Address: Argonne National Lab, 9700 S. Cass Ave, Argonne, IL 60440.

DUFFIELD, ROGER C, b. Kansas City, Kans, Apr. 7, 37; m; c. MECHANICAL & AEROSPACE ENGINEERING. B.S.M.E, Univ. Kans, 60, M.S.M.E, 64, Ph.D, 68. Jr. draftsman, Great Lake Pipe Line Co, summer 57; stud. engr, U.S. Army Corps Eng, summers 58 & 59; design engr, LFM Mfg. Co. Div, Rockwell Mfg. Co, 60-62; asst. instr. eng. mech, Univ. Kans, 64-66; asst. prof. MECH. & AEROSPACE ENG, UNIV. MO-COLUMBIA, 66-70, ASSOC. PROF, 70- Am. Soc. Mech. Eng. Structural dynamics. Address: 1005 Plymouth Dr, Columbia, MO 65201.

DUFFIELD, WENDELL A(RTHUR), b. Sisseton, S.Dak, May 10, 41; m. 64. PETROLOGY, STRUCTURAL GEOLOGY. B.A, Carleton, 63; M.S, Stanford, 65, Ph.D.(geol), 67. GEOLOGIST, U.S. GEOL. SURV, 66- Geol. Soc. Am; Mineral Soc. Am. Igneous and metamorphic petrology; structural geology; mineralogy. Address: Volcano Observatory, Hawaii National Park, HI 96718.

DUFFIN, JOHN H, b. Easton, Pa, June 18, 19; m. 54. CHEMICAL ENGINEERING. B.S, Lehigh, 40; Ohio State, 53-54; Ph.D.(chem. eng), California, Berkeley, 59. Lab. analyst & chief chemist, Hercules Powder Co, N.J. & Utah, 40-44; tech. adv. & prod. foreman, uranium isotope prod, Tenn. Eastman Corp, 44-45; res. engr, Allied Chem. & Dye Corp, N.Y, 45-53; res. scientist, Battelle Mem. Inst, 53-54; instr. chem. eng, California, Berkeley, 54-59; asst. prof. chem. eng; & dir. comput. center, San Jose State Col, 59-62; ASSOC. PROF. CHEM. ENG, U.S. NAVAL POSTGRAD. SCH, 62-, CHMN, DEPT MAT. SCI. & CHEM, 69- Consult, Kaiser Aluminum & Chem. Co, 57-58; Int. Bus. Mach. Corp, 60- Fel. Am. Inst. Chem; Am. Inst. Chem. Eng. Mathematical modeling of chemical engineering processes and use of models to investigate control problems for purposes of obtaining optimum control and designing equipment based on dynamic behavior. Address: Dept. of Material Science & Chemistry, U.S. Naval Postgraduate School, Monterey, CA 93940.

DUFFIN, R(ICHARD) J(AMES), b. Chicago, Ill, Oct. 13, 09; m. 47; c. 2. MATHEMATICS, PHYSICS. B.S, Illinois, 32, Coffin fel, 32-33, Ph.D.(physics), 35. Instr. math, Purdue, 36-40; assoc, Illinois, 40-42; physicist, Carnegie Inst, 42-46; prof. math, CARNEGIE-MELLON UNIV, 46-70, UNIV. PROF. MATH. SCI, 70- Dir. appl. math. res, Duke, 58-59. Vis. prof, Purdue, 49-50; Dublin Inst. Adv. Studies, 59-60; distinguished vis. prof, State Univ. N.Y. Stonybrook, 67; Tex. A&M Univ, 68. Consult, Westinghouse Res. Labs, 56- Am. Math. Soc; Soc. Natural Philos; Soc. Indust. & Appl. Math. Thermal and magnetic effects in conductors; quantum theory; Fourier type integrals and series; functional inequalities; navigational devices; partial difference equations; elasticity; electrical network theory; linear and nonlinear programming. Address: Dept. of Mathematics, Carnegie-Mellon University, Pittsburgh, PA 15213.

DUFFUS, H(ENRY) J(OHN), b. Vancouver, B.C, Aug. 27, 25; m. 48. PHYSICS. B.Ap.Sc, British Columbia, 48, B.A, 49; D.Phil.(physics), Oxford, 53. Lectr. physics, Carleton Col, 48-51; physicist & defence sci. serv. Officer, Defence Res. Bd, 54-59; PROF. PHYSICS, ROYAL RDS. MIL. COL, 59-, HEAD DEPT, 59- Nat. Res. Coun. Can. spec. overseas scholar, 52-53. Paramagnetism at low temperatures; microwave spectroscopy; geomagnetism; infrared sensing. Address: Dept. of Physics, Royal Roads Military College, Victoria, B.C, Can.

DUFFUS, JAMES E(DWARD), b. Detroit, Mich, Feb. 11, 29; m. 52; c. 3. PLANT PATHOLOGY. B.S, Mich. State Col, 51; Ph.D.(plant path), Univ. Wis, 55. PLANT PATHOLOGIST, U.S. DEPT. AGR, 55-, acting supt, Agr. Res. Sta, 69-70. Assoc, exp. sta, Univ. Calif, Davis, Berkeley, 62- Superior Serv. award, Sugarbeet Invests Unit, U.S. Dept. Agr. Am. Soc. Sugar Beet Technol; Am. Phytopath. Soc. Virus diseases of sugarbeets and vegetable crops; interrelationships of yellowing type virus diseases; virus-vector relations; insect feeding through membranes, infectivity neutralization; role of wild hosts in virus epidemiology. Address: U.S. Agricultural Research Station, P.O. Box 5098, Salinas, CA 93901.

DUFFY, BENEDICT J, JR, b. Rochester, N.Y, July 26, 20; m. 53; c. 3. PREVENTIVE MEDICINE. A.B, Princeton, 41; M.D, Rochester, 54. Asst. prof. med, sch. med, Georgetown, 54-58, dir. center of pop. res, 62-64; fel. epidemiol, London Sch. Hyg, Eng, 58-59; prof. prev. med, Seton Hall Col. Med. & Dent, 59-62; consult. pop, Latin Am. Bur, Agency Int. Develop, U.S. Dept. State, 64-66; PROF. prev. med, SCH. MED, TUFTS UNIV, 66-69,

COMMUNITY HEALTH & SOCIAL MED, 69- Mem. cmt. on pop, Nat. Acad. Sci, 62-69. Med.C, U.S.N, 44-46, 53-54. Am. Pub. Health Asn; Asn. Teachers Prev. Med. Analysis and epidemiology of radiation cancer; medical care delivery studies; population and family planning. Address: 49 Bennet St, Boston, MA 02111.

DUFFY, BERNARD J(OSEPH), JR, b. Kansas City, Mo, Aug. 30, 23; m. 52; c. 2. CHEMICAL ENGINEERING. B.S, Mass. Inst. Tech, 47, M.S, 48. Sr. chem. engr, tech. serv, res. dept, Sugar Creek Ref, Standard Oil Co, 48-54, group leader, 54-55, asst. supt, 55-58, res. supvr. mfg. dept, 58-61; mgr, ref. div, J.F. PRITCHARD & CO, 61-64, V.PRES, 64- U.S.N.R, 43-46, Lt.(jg). Sci. Res. Soc. Am; Am. Inst. Chem. Eng. Petroleum refining. Address: J.F. Pritchard & Co, 4625 Roanoke Pkwy, Kansas City, MO 64112.

DUFFY, CARL E(DWARD), b. Corning, Ohio, June 15, 06; m. 42. MICROBIOLOGY. A.B, Ohio (Athens), 34; M.S, Cincinnati, 38, Ph.D.(bact), 40. Teaching fel. zool, Ohio (Athens), 35-36; res. bacteriologist, contagious div, Cincinnati Gen. Hosp, 36-39; res. asst. pediat, Childrens Hosp. Res. Found, 36-39, res. assoc, 40-43; virologist, Sharp & Dohme, Inc, 43; asst. prof. BACT, col. med, Wayne, 43-45, asoc. prof, 45-48; PROF. MICROBIOL. & HEAD DEPT, SCH. MED, UNIV. ARK, LITTLE ROCK, 48- Spec. investr, Rockefeller Inst, 44-45; AAAS; Am. Soc. Microbiol; Soc. Exp. Biol. & Med; Am. Asn. Path. & Bact; fel. Am. Pub. Health Asn; Am. Asn. Immunol; N.Y. Acad. Sci. Rabies; diphtheria; vesicular stomatitis; nutrition; arthropod-borne viral encephalitides; interference phenomenon, age and susceptibility to viral infections. Address: Dept. of Microbiology, University of Arkansas School of Medicine, Little Rock, AR 72204.

DUFFY, DANIEL J(OSEPH), b. New York, N.Y, Apr. 30, 24; m. 52; c. 4. OPERATIONS RESEARCH, INDUSTRIAL ENGINEERING. B.S, Columbia, 49, M.S, 55; Eng. Sc.D.(indust. eng), N.Y. Univ, 65. Asst. prof. indust. eng, Rutgers, 54-56; asst. div. mgr, Am. Mgt. Asn, 56-57; assoc. prof. indust. eng, Polytech. Inst. Brooklyn, 57-65, prof, 65-67, admin. off, 57-67; V.PRES. ACAD. AFFAIRS, STATE UNIV. N.Y. MARITIME COL. FT. SCHUYLER, 67- Mem, Eng. Manpower Comn, 57-58. U.S.N, 43-46, Lt. (jg). Opers. Res. Soc. Am; Am. Inst. Indust. Eng. Man-machine systems; measurement in managerial systems, simulation. Address: State University of New York Maritime College, Ft. Schuyler, NY 10465.

DUFFY, FRANK HOPKINS, b. Honolulu, Hawaii, Jan. 22, 37; m. 64; c. 4. NEUROPHYSIOLOGY, NEUROLOGY. B.S.E.(elec. eng) & B.S.E.(math), Michigan, 58; M.D, Harvard, 63. Internship, Yale New Haven Hosp, 63-64; res. neurol. surg, Mass. Gen. Hosp, 64-66; neurol, Peter Bent Brigham & Children's Hosp. Med. Ctr, 66-68; res. fel. neurol, HARVARD MED. SCH, 66-68, instr. NEUROL, 70-71, ASST. PROF, 71-, NEUROLOGIST, PETER BENT BRIGHAM HOSP, BETH ISRAEL HOSP. & LAB. BASIC NEUROPHYSIOL, CHILDREN'S HOSP, 70- Mem. comt. on vision, Nat. Acad. Sci-Nat. Res. Coun, 69-70. Med.C, U.S.A, 68-70, Maj. Computer analysis of the EEG and evoked potentials; single cell microelectrode studies of visual and somatosensory systems of primates. Address: 4 Bryden Rd, Weston, MA 02193.

DUFFY, JACQUES WAYNE, b. Nimes, France, July 1, 22; m. 50; c. 3. MECHANICAL ENGINEERING. B.A, Columbia, 47, B.Sc, 48, M.S, 49, Ph.D. (appl. mech), 57. Res. engr. dynamics of aircraft, Grumman Aircraft Eng. Corp, 49-51; asst. prof. ENG, BROWN UNIV, 53-60, assoc. prof. 60-65, PROF, 65-, CHMN, CTR. BIOPHYS. SCI. & BIOMED. ENG, 69- John Simon Guggenheim Mem. Found. fel, 64-65. U.S.A.A.F, 42-45. Soc. Exp. Stress Anal; Am. Soc. Mech. Eng; Soc. Rheol. Dynamic plasticity; biomechanics. Address: Dept. of Engineering, Brown University, Providence, RI 02912.

DUFFY, JAMES V, b. New York, N.Y, Jan. 12, 33; m. 59; c. 3. ORGANIC & POLYMER CHEMISTRY. B.S, Queens Col.(N.Y), 54; M.S, Maryland, 57. CHEMIST, Am. Viscose Corp, 57-58; Atlantic Res. Corp, 58-63; U.S. NAVAL ORD. LAB, 63- U.S.A.F, 58. Am. Chem. Soc. Chemistry of the interface in reinforced plastics; chemistry of high temperature silicone polymers; chemistry of high modulus reinforcements, such as graphite and silicon carbide fibers. Address: 13102 Ivy Dr, Beltsville, MD 20705.

DUFFY, JOHN PAUL, b. N.Y.C, Dec. 23, 27; m. 52; c. 3. ENTOMOLOGY, ZOOLOGY. B.S, St. Francis Col.(N.Y), 50; M.S, St. John's (N.Y), 52; fel, Rutgers, 54-57, Ph.D.(entom), 58. Med. entomologist, U.S. Pub. Health Serv, Ga, 58-59, S.C, 59; teacher BIOL, Loyola Col.(Md), 59; asst. prof, St. John's Univ.(N.Y), 59-68; ASSOC. PROF, ST. BONAVENTURE UNIV, 68- Entom. Soc. Am; Am. Soc. Zool; Am. Mosquito Control Asn. Insect physiology, use of paper chromatography to demonstrate substances to ascertain their role in mosquito nutrition and biochemistry functions. Address: 4 Mile Rd, Alleghany, NY 14706.

DUFFY, NORMAN V(INCENT), JR, b. Washington, D.C, Nov. 1, 38; m. 62; c. 4. INORGANIC CHEMISTRY. B.S, Georgetown, 61, Ph.D.(chem), 66. NATO fel, 65-66; vis. asst. prof. CHEM, KENT STATE UNIV, 66-67, asst. prof, 67-70, ASSOC. PROF, 70- Am. Chem. Soc. Mechanisms of nucleophilic substitution reactions of octahedral transition metal complexes; mass spectrometry and arsine complexes of metal carbonyls. Address: Dept. of Chemistry, Kent State University, Kent, OH 44242.

DUFFY, PHILIP, b. Nimes, France, July 22, 23; U.S. citizen; m. 49; c. 2. NEUROLOGY, NEUROPATHOLOGY. B.A, Columbia, 43, M.D, 47. Instr. neuropath, Columbia, 54-55; asst. prof. neurol, State Univ. N.Y, 55-64; assoc. prof. NEUROPATH, COL. PHYSICIANS & SURGEONS, COLUMBIA UNIV, 64-68, PROF, 68- U.S.A, 50-54. Am. Acad. Neurol; Am. Asn. Neuropath; Asn. Res. Nerv. & Ment. Disease. Central nervous system tumors. Address: Division of Neuropathology, College of Physicians & Surgeons, Columbia University, 630 W. 168th St, New York, NY 10032.

DUFFY, REGINA M(AURICE), b. Jersey City, N.J. PLANT MORPHOLOGY. B.A, Col. of New Rochelle, 41; M.S, Fordham, 44; Ph.D.(bot), Columbia, 50. Instr. biol, N.J. State Teachers' Col, 41-42, 43-44, 46; teacher, pub. sch, 45-46; teaching asst. bot, Columbia, 47-50, research assoc, 50-55; asst. prof. biol, Long Island, 51-52, 53-55; Jersey City State Col, 55-59; lectr, Hunter Col, 59; chmn, sci. dept, Nanuet Schs, Nanuet, N.Y, 59-67; admin. head, NORTHWEST. CONN. COMMUNITY COL, 67-68, PRES, 68- Bot. Soc. Am; Torrey Bot. Club. Cellular morphology; liverworts. Address: Northwestern Connecticut Community College, Winsted, CT 06098.

DUFFY, RICHARD JAMES, b. Yonkers, N.Y, Jan. 7, 37; m. 60; c. 3. LOW TEMPERATURE & SOLID STATE PHYSICS. M.E, Stevens Inst. Tech, 58, M.S, 60, Ph.D.(physics), 64. Nat. Sci. Found. fel, PHYSICS, Nat. Ctr. Sci. Res, Grenoble, France, 64-65; Nat. Res. Coun-Nat. Bur. Standards res. assoc, Nat. Bur. Standards, Colo, 65-66; ASST. PROF, AMHERST COL, 66- Am. Phys. Soc. Superconductivity of thin metallic films; density of superfluid helium. Address: Dept. of Physics, Amherst College, Amherst, MA 01002.

DUFFY, ROBERT E(DWARD), b. Scranton, Pa, May 27, 30; m. 53; c. 3. AERONAUTICAL ENGINEERING. B.A.E, Rensselaer Polytech, 51, M.A.E, 54, Ph.D, 65. Aeronaut. engr, U.S. Govt, 51-52; instr. AERONAUT. ENG, RENSSELAER POLYTECH INST, 53-55, asst. prof, 55-65, ASSOC. PROF, 65- Consult, Grumman Aircraft Eng. Corp, 58-; Gen. Elec. Co; G.C. Dewey Corp; N.Y. State Bur. Educ; dir, Panaflight Corp; Burden Lake Holding Corp. Assoc. fel. Am. Inst. Aeronaut. & Astronaut. Flight mechanisms; experimental aerodynamics. Address: Dept. of Aeronautical Engineering, Rensselaer Polytechnic Institute, Troy, NY 12181.

DUFFY, WAYNE E(DWARD), b. Boise, Idaho, Dec. 28, 20; m. 51; c. 1. ORGANIC CHEMISTRY. A.Sc, Boise Jr. Col, 40; B.A, Col. of Idaho, 47; M.S, Idaho, 48; J.D, Lincoln Univ.(Calif), 72. Chief chemist, feed & fertilizer testing lab, Idaho State Dept. Agr, 49; supvr. mass spectrometry lab, chem. processing plant, nat. reactor testing sta, Am. Cyanamid Co, 51-53; Phillips Petrol. Co, 53-55; sr. engr, anal. dept, x-ray fluorescence lab, Bettis field plant, Westinghouse Elec. Co, 55-56; sr. res. engr, org. moderated reactor group, Atomics Int, Calif, 56-59; mgr, mass spectrometry, Vallecitos Nuclear Ctr, Gen. Elec. Co, 59-68; sr. staff engr, Martin-Marietta Corp, Colo, 69-70; CONSULT. CHEMIST, 70- U.S.A, 42-46, Sgt. AAAS; fel. Am. Inst. Chem; Am. Chem. Soc; N.Y. Acad. Sci; Am. Soc. Mass Spectrometry; Am. Bar Asn. Mass spectrometry; analytical instrumentation; high vacuum technology; clean room technology; law. Address: 5515 Fremont St, Boise, ID 83704.

DUFFY, WILLIAM THOMAS, JR, b. San Francisco, Calif, June 30, 30; m. 59; c. 3. SOLID STATE PHYSICS. B.E.E, Santa Clara, 53; M.S, Stanford, 54, Ph.D.(physics), 59. Asst. prof. PHYSICS, UNIV. SANTA CLARA, 59-63, assoc. prof, 64-68, PROF, 68- Nat. Sci. Found. fel, State Univ. Leiden, 61-62; res. assoc. & vis. scientist, Stanford Univ, 68-69. U.S.N, 48-49, Res, 49-55. Inst. Elec. & Electronic Eng; Am. Phys. Soc. Nuclear magnetic resonance; antiferromagnetism; magnetism of organic free radicals; superconductivity; electronics in science. Address: Dept. of Physics, University of Santa Clara, Santa Clara, CA 95053.

DUFLOT, LEO SCOTT, b. Mayfield, Ky, June 24, 19; m. 51; c. 5. ANESTHESIOLOGY. B.A, Texas, 39, M.D, 43. Instr. ANESTHESIOL, MED. BR, UNIV. TEX, 51-52, asst. prof, 52-65, ASSOC. PROF, 65- Res. assoc, Pennsylvania, 51. Dipl, Am. Bd. Anesthesiol, 54. Med.C, 44-46, Lt. Am. Med. Asn; Am. Soc. Anesthesiol; Am. Col. Anesthesiol; Int. Anesthesia Res. Soc. Address: Dept. of Anesthesiology, University of Texas Medical Branch, Galveston, TX 77550.

DUFORT, NORMAND, b. St. Lin, Que, Dec. 30, 34; m. 62; c. 2. ORGANIC CHEMISTRY. B.A, Univ. Montreal, 56, B.Sc, 59, M.Sc, 60, Nat. Res. Coun. Can. fel, 59-63, Ph.D.(org. chem), 63. Asst. prof. ORG. CHEM, UNIV. MONTREAL, 63-68, ASSOC. PROF, 68- Chem. Inst. Can. Reactions of Friedel-Crafts; synthesis of aliphatic, cyclic and bicyclic sulfones and their reduction by complex metal hydrides. Address: Dept. of Sciences, University of Montreal, Montreal, Que, Can.

DUFOUR, DIDIER, b. Baie St-Paul, Que, Feb. 7, 26; m. 54; c. 4. BIOLOGY, EXPERIMENTAL MEDICINE. B.A, Laval, 47, Ph.D, 56; V.M.D, Montreal, 52. Res. asst, inst. exp. med. & surg, Montreal, 52-53; inst. human biol, Laval, 53-56; asst. prof. biol, Ottawa (Can), 56-57; BIOCHEM, FACULTY MED, LAVAL UNIV, 57-63, assoc. prof, 63-67, PROF, 67-, DIR. BIOMED. CTR, 64- Res. consult, Ministry Health, Prov. Que, 63-, mem. Med. Res. Coun. Cancer, 64-; Sanit. Comt. Can, 63-; Colloquium on Protides of Biol. Fluids, Belgium, 63-; dir, Health Res. Inst, Univ. Que, 71- Col. Vet. Med. Can; Can. Biochem. Soc; Can. Fedn. Biol. Soc; Int. Asn. Documentalists. Immunopathology; immunochemistry of experimental carcinogenesis. Address: Faculty of Medicine, Laval University, Quebec, Que, Can.

DUFOUR, ROBERT E, b. Chicago, Ill, Sept. 11, 02. CHEMICAL ENGINEERING. B.S, Armour Inst. Tech, 25. Asst. chem. engr, UNDERWRITERS' LABS, INC, CHICAGO, 25-49, assoc, 49-56, sr. assoc. managing engr, 56-62, managing engr, 62-67, CONSULTING ENGR, 67- Civilian with U.S.N, 44. AAAS; fel. Am. Inst. Chem; Am. Chem. Soc. Combustion and flame as related to fire and explosion hazards; toxicity of combustion and thermal decomposition products. Address: 1801 Oak Ave, Northbrook, IL 60062.

DuFRESNE, ANN (HEDBERG), b. Kirksville, Mo, Aug. 27, 30; m. 49; c. 1. ANALYTICAL CHEMISTRY. A.B, Chicago, 47, S.M, 54, Bernard, Lowenthal & Viol fels, 54-57, Ph.D.(anal. chem), 57. Res. assoc. meteorites, Enrico Fermi Inst. Nuclear Studies, Chicago, 57-59, spectrographer geochem, dept. geol, 59-61; asst. biochemist heme proteins, Am. Meat Inst. Found, 61-64; asst. prof. anal. chem, Georgetown, 64-69; EXPERT, BASIC CHEM, UNESCO & VIS. PROF. ANAL. CHEM, UNIV. BRASILIA, 69- AAAS; Am. Chem. Soc. Ion exchange; metal chelate compounds; polarography; chemical analysis of meteorites; emission spectrochemical analysis of rocks and minerals; heme proteins and porphyrins; chromatography of myoglobin; gas chromatography; Mössbauer spectrometry. Address: Project UNESCO BRA/9, Dept. of Chemistry, University of Brasilia, Brasilia D.F, Brazil.

DUFTY, JAMES W, b. Freeport, N.Y, May 5, 40; m. 64. PHYSICS. A.B, Williams Col, 62; M.S, Lehigh, 64, Armstrong Cork fel. & Ph.D.(physics), 67. Fel. physics, Lehigh Univ, 67-68; UNIV. FLA, 68-70, ASST. PROF. PHYS-

ICS & CHEM. ENG, 70- Am. Phys. Soc. Non-equilibrium statistical mechanics. Address: Dept. of Physics, University of Florida, Gainesville, FL 32601.

DUGA, J(ULES) J(OSEPH), b. Bellaire, Ohio, Mar. 21, 32; m. 55; c. 2. PHYSICS. B.Sc, Ohio State, 53, M.Sc, 55, Ph.D, 60. From prin. physicist, phys. chem. div. to sr. res. physicist, solid state res. div, Battelle Mem. Inst, 56-70; TECH. & SCI. CONSULT; 70- AAAS; Am. Phys. Soc; Am. Inst. Mining, Metall. & Petrol. Eng; Am. Ceramic Soc. Semiconductors; thermo and galvanomagnetic effects; scattering by lattice imperfections; quantum theory of solids; transport phenomena; automatic data acquisition system design; adhesion; conduction in liquids; dislocations in solids; biomaterials; solid surface energies. Address: 2605 Bryden Rd, Bexley, OH 43209.

DUGAL, HARDEV SINGH, b. Bareilly, India, Feb. 1, 37; m. 68. PHYSICAL & ORGANIC CHEMISTRY. B.Sc, Agra Univ, 55; M.S, Harcourt Butler Technol. Inst, India, 58; Inst. Cellulose Chem. scholar, Darmstadt Tech. Univ, 62-63, Dr. Ing.(cellulose chem), 63. Stud. apprentice, distillery dept, Daurala Sugar Works, India, 55-66; pool off, Coun. Sci. & Indust. Res, New Delhi, 66-68; dir. new projs, Punj Sons Ltd, 68; res. fel. phys. chem, INST. PAPER CHEM, 68-69, res. fel. phys. chem. & proj. leader, 69-70, ASST. PROF. CHEM, 70- Chemist, Gwalior Rayon Silk Mfg. Co. Ltd, Nagda, India, 58-59; stud. apprentice, Adam Opal, Russelsheim am Main, W.Ger, 60; fel, Inst. Paper Chem, 64-66; mem. del, Tech. Asn. Pulp & Paper Indust. Conf. on Air & Water Environ, Jacksonville, Fla, 69, Minneapolis, 70 & Boston, 71; consult, pulp & paper indust. Tech. Asn. Pulp & Paper Indust; Indian Tech. Asn. Pulp & Paper Indust. Pulping, bleaching and paper making; wet-end additives; carbohydrate chemistry; physical and chemical aspects of aqueous environment in pulp and paper industry. Address: Institute of Paper Chemistry, P.O. Box 1048, Appleton, WI 54911.

DUGAL, L(OUIS) P(AUL), b. Quebec, Que, Oct. 1, 11; m. 37; c. 3. BIOLOGY, PHYSIOLOGY. B.A, Laval, 31, M.Sc, 34; Ph.D.(biol), Pennsylvania, 39. From asst. prof. to prof. biol, Montreal, 35-45; exp. physiol, Laval, 45-55; biol, Ottawa, 55-65, chmn. dept, 55-60, dean, faculty pure & appl. sci, 60-65; dep. dir, sci. secretariat, Privy Coun. Can, 65-66; v.dean, med. sch, UNIV. SHERBROOKE, 66-67, V.RECTOR, 67- Assoc. dir, Inst. Hyg. & Human Biol, 45-55; Guggenheim fel, Columbia, 54-55; summer, lectr, sch. geog, McGill, 48. Consult, Royal Can. Air Force, 48. Mem, Nat. Res. Coun. Can, 44-50; mem. adv. comt. & chmn. arctic med. res, Defense Res. Bd. Can, 47-58. Officer, Order Brit. Empire, 46; laureate, French Acad. Sci, Montyon prize, 52. Can. Physiol. Soc.(pres, 51-52); fel. Royal Soc. Can. Resistance and acclimatization of mammal to cold environment; respiration at high altitudes. Address: University of Sherbrooke, Sherbrooke, Que, Can.

DUGAN, ALLAN EDWARD, b. Rochester, N.Y, Mar. 2, 41; m. 62; c. 4. SOLID STATE PHYSICS, ELECTRONICS. B.Sc, Univ. Toronto, 62; Ph.D. (physics), Pa. State Univ, 67. Sr. res. physicist, WEST. ELEC. CO, 67-68, mem. res. staff, 68-70, RES. LEADER, DEVICE TECHNOL, 70- Am. Phys. Soc; Inst. Elec. & Electronic Eng. Optical, photoconductive, dielectric and luminescent properties of III-V and II-VI semiconductors; liquid phase and vapor phase growth of epitaxial III-V material; electroluminescent device fabrication; electron beam inspection of semiconductor and thin film devices; ion implantation; ion and electron optics. Address: Engineering Research Center, Western Electric Co, P.O. Box 900, Princeton, NJ 08540.

DUGAN, CHARLES HAMMOND, b. Baltimore, Md, Apr. 2, 31; m. 54; c. 5. CHEMICAL & ATMOSPHERIC PHYSICS. B.S, Kentucky, 51; M.A, California, Los Angeles, 54; Ph.D.(appl. physics), Harvard, 63. Physicist, U.S. Navy Electronics Lab, 51-52; Smithsonian Astrophys. Observ, 61-67; asst. prof. DEPT. PHYSICS, YORK UNIV, 67-69, ASSOC. PROF, 69- U.S.A, 54-56. AAAS; Am. Phys. Soc. Atomic and molecular processes. Address: Dept. of Physics, York University, Downsview 463, Ont, Can.

DUGAN, JOHN PHILIP, b. Darby, Pa, Apr. 23, 42; m. 64; c. 3. MECHANICAL ENGINEERING. B.S, Pa. Mil. Col, 64; M.S, Northwestern, 66, NASA fel. & Ph.D.(theoret. & appl. mech), 67. Nat. Sci. Found. & Off. Naval Res. Funds fel. mech, Hopkins, 67-69; asst. prof. mech. eng. Univ. Toronto, 69-71; RES. PHYSICIST, OCEAN SCI. DIV, NAVAL RES. LAB, 71- Mem, Int. Oceanog. Found, 66- Am. Soc. Mech. Eng. Waves in fluids. Address: Ocean Sciences Division, Naval Research Lab, Washington, DC 20390.

DUGAN, KIMIKO H(ATTA), b. Kyoto City, Japan, Oct. 21, 24; U.S. citizen; m. 47. MICROSCOPIC ANATOMY. B.A, Okla. Col. Women, 61; M.S, Univ. Okla, 65, fel, 65-70, Ph.D.(med. sci), 70. Instr. ANAT, SCH. MED. & GRAD. COL, UNIV. OKLA, 69-71, ASST. PROF, 71- Electron Micros. Soc. Am; Am. Soc. Zool; Am. Chem. Soc. Electron microscopy; histology; embryology; histochemistry; cytochemistry. Address: Dept. of Anatomical Sciences, University of Oklahoma Medical Center, 801 N.E. 13th St, Oklahoma City, OK 73104.

DUGAN, LE ROY, JR, b. Petersburgh, Ind, Aug. 18, 15; m. 38; c. 3. ORGANIC CHEMISTRY. B.S, Indiana, 37; fel, Washington (Seattle), 37-42, Ph.D.(org. chem), 42. Assoc. org. chem, Am. Meat Inst. Found, 46-48, org. chem, 48-49, chief div. org. chem, 49-61; assoc. prof. DEPT. FOOD SCI, MICH. STATE UNIV, 61-66, PROF. FOOD SCI. & HUMAN NUTRIT, 66-, ASST. DEAN ADVAN. GRAD STUDIES, 71- Chem.C, U.S.A, 42-46, Res, Col. Am. Chem. Soc; Am. Oil Chem. Soc; Soc. Chem. Indust; Inst. Food Technol. Autoxidation of fats; antioxidants for fats and foods; lipid composition, phospholipid studies; lipid-protein interactions; lipid browning; pesticide distribution in foods; lipid nutrition; food chemistry. Address: Dept. of Food Science & Human Nutrition, Michigan State University, East Lansing, MI 48823.

DUGAN, PATRICK R, b. Syracuse, N.Y, Dec. 14, 31; m. 56; c. 4. MICROBIOLOGY, BIOCHEMISTRY. B.S, Syracuse, 56, M.S, 59, Ph.D.(microbiol), 63. Res. asst. microbiol. & biochem, Syracuse Univ. Res. Corp, 56-58, res. assoc, 58-61, assoc. res. scientist, 61-63; asst. prof. MICROBIOL, OHIO STATE UNIV, 63-67, assoc. prof, 67-70, PROF. & CHMN. DEPT, 70- AAAS; Am. Soc. Microbiol; Soc. Indust. Microbiol; Water Pollution Control Fedn. Microbial physiology, particularly aquatic organisms; microbial metabolism of inorganic compounds; analytical chemistry. Address: Dept. of Microbiology, Ohio State University, 484 W. 12th Ave, Columbus, OH 43210.

DUGAN, RICHARD E, b. Rockford, Ill, Oct. 28, 30; m. 66; c. 2. BIOCHEMISTRY. B.S, Northwestern, 52; Ph.D.(biochem), Iowa State, 60. Asst. prof. chem, Ill. Benedictine Col, 60-62, assoc. prof. & chmn. dept, 62-65; RES. CHEMIST, LIPID METAB. LAB, VET. ADMIN. HOSP, 65- Res. Corp. res. grant, 61-62; consult. & res. assoc, Argonne Nat. Lab, 61-64; dir, Nat. Sci. Found. undergrad. res. partic. grant, 62-64; Nat. Insts. Health res. grant, 63-64; mem. carotenoid subcomt, Nat. Res. Coun. Comt. Specification & Criteria for Biochem. Compounds. AAAS; Am. Chem. Soc; N.Y. Acad. Sci. Biochemistry and spectrophotometry of vitamin A and carotenoids; enzymatic synthesis of fats and steroids; protein synthesis; enzymology, particularly biosynthesis, purification, mechanism of action, and regulation of enzymes of lipid metabolism. Address: Lipid Metabolism Lab, Veterans Administration Hospital, Madison, WI 53705.

DUGAS, HERMANN, b. Baie-Comeau, Que, Nov. 21, 42; m. 66. BIOPHYSICS, ORGANIC CHEMISTRY. B.Sc, Montreal, 64; Ph.D.(org. synthesis), New Brunswick, 67. FEL. org. synthesis, New Brunswick, 67-68; protein chem, biochem. lab, Nat. Res. Coun. Can, 68-69, biophys, 69-70, ASST. PROF, DEPT. CHEM, UNIV. MONTREAL, 70- Am. Chem. Soc; Chem. Inst. Can; Can. Biochem. Soc. Mechanism of enzyme action; utilization of electron spin resonance and nuclear magnetic resonance for the study of biological systems. Address: Dept. of Chemistry, University of Montreal, Montreal, Que, Can.

DUGDALE, MARION, b. Bellavista, Callao, Peru, Oct. 7, 28; U.S. citizen; m. 55; c. 2. INTERNAL MEDICINE, HEMATOLOGY. A.B, Bryn Mawr Col, 50; M.D, Harvard Med. Sch, 54. Intern & res. med, North Carolina, Chapel Hill, 54-57; fel. hemat, Duke Hosp, N.C, 57-58; res, UNIV. TENN, 58-59, instr. MED, 59-62, asst. prof, 62-67, ASSOC. PROF, 68- Mem. coun. on cerebrovasc. disease & coun. on thrombosis, Am. Heart Asn. Am. Med. Asn; Am. Soc. Hemat. Hemostasis. Address: 800 Madison Ave, Memphis, TN 38103.

DUGDALE, RICHARD C(OOPER), b. Madison, Wis, Feb. 6, 28; m. 53; c. 2. BIOLOGICAL OCEANOGRAPHY, LIMNOLOGY. B.S, Wisconsin, 50, M.S, 51, Ph.D.(zool), 55. Fel, Georgia, 56; instr. zool, Kentucky, 57; Pittsburgh, 58-60, asst. prof, 60-62; assoc. prof. marine sci, Alaska, 62-64, prof, 65-67; RES. PROF. OCEANOG, UNIV. WASH, 67- Sig.C, 52-53, 2nd Lt. Fel. AAAS; Am. Soc. Limnol. & Oceanog; Ecol. Soc. Am. Nitrogen cycle in the sea; biological nitrogen fixation in sea and lakes; vitamins and microorganic constituents; mechanisms of nutrient limitation. Address: Dept. of Oceanography, University of Washington, Seattle, WA 98105.

DUGDALE, VERA A, Limnol, see ALEXANDER, VERA.

DUGGAN, DANIEL E(DWARD), b. N.Y.C, June 29, 26; m. 56; c. 3. BIOCHEMICAL PHARMACOLOGY. B.S, St. Johns, 51; M.S, Maryland, 53; fel, Georgetown, 53-55, Ph.D.(biochem), 55. Asst, Maryland, 51-53; Am. Instrument Co. fel, Nat. Heart Inst, 55-56, biochemist, 56-62; res. assoc, MERCK INST. THERAPEUT. RES, 62-70, SR. RES. FEL, 70- U.S.N.R, 43-46. Am. Chem. Soc; Am. Soc. Pharmacol. & Exp. Therapeut. Drug metabolism; pharmacokinetics; applications of spectrophotometric, fluorometric and isotope techniques to biochemical analysis; biochemistry of active transport; inflammation. Address: Merck Institute Therapeutic Research, West Point, PA 19486.

DUGGAN, DENNIS E, b. Calgary, Alta, July 13, 30; m. 54; c. 4. BACTERIAL GENETICS. B.Sc, Alberta, 53; M.Sc, Oregon State, 57, Ph.D.(bact), 61. Sr. res. bacteriologist, H.J. Heinz Co, 58-61; Midwest Res. Inst, 61-62; fel. bact, sch. med, Kansas, 62; genetics, Oak Ridge Nat. Lab, 63-64; sch. med, Yale, 64-67; ASSOC. PROF. BACT, UNIV. FLA, 67- Am. Soc. Microbiol. Freezing preservation of bacteria; mass culture and concentration of lactobacilli; radiation & thermal preservation of foods; radiation resistant bacteria; mechanisms of radiation resistance; gene action; transduction. Address: Dept. of Microbiology, McCarty Hall, University of Florida, Gainesville, FL 32601.

DUGGAN, H(ECTOR) E(WART), b. Medicine Hat, Alta, July 3, 15; m. 40; c. 3. RADIOLOGY. M.D, Alberta, 38. Instr. radiol, faculty med, Alberta, 47-52, lectr, 53-57, prof, 57-65; DIR. DEPT. RADIOL, FOOTHILLS HOSP, 65- John S. MacEachern fel. radiother, Europe, 52. Mem. staff radiol, univ. hosp, Alberta, 46-49, co-dir. dept, 49-52, dir, 53-65; prof. diag. radiol, Univ. Calgary, 69- R.C.A.M.C, 41-46, Maj. Fel. Am. Col. Radiol; Radiol. Soc. N.Am; Soc. Nuclear Med; Can. Med. Asn; Can. Asn. Radiol. Basic effects of radiation; measurement of radiation dosage from radioisotopes and diagnostic radiography; therapeutic radiology; information, storage and retrieval. Address: Dept. of Radiology, Foothills Hospital, Calgary 42, Alta, Can.

DUGGAN, HELEN ANN, O.P, b. Essex, Ont, Jan. 11, 21; U.S. citizen. CHEMISTRY. B.S, Siena Heights Col, 41; Ph.D.(chem), Catholic Univ, 48. Teacher, Catholic schs, Ill, 41-43, Mich, 54-56; instr. chem, Barry Col, 47-53, asst. prof, 53-54; asst. prof. chem. & physics, Siena Heights Col, 56-62, assoc. prof. chem. & biol, 62-63; prof. chem. & biol. & chmn. div. natural sci, St. Dominic Col, 63-68; PROF. CHEM, BARRY COL, 68- Mem, Cath. Round Table Sci, 49. Am. Chem. Soc; Am. Inst. Chem. Chemical genetics; thermal decomposition of hydrocarbons. Address: 810 N. Olive Ave, West Palm Beach, FL 33401.

DUGGAN, JEROME L, b. Columbus, Ohio, Aug. 4, 33; m. 51; c. 3. PHYSICS. M.S, North Texas State, 56; Ph.D.(physics), La. State, 61. Asst. prof. PHYSICS, Georgia, 61-63; MEM. SR. STAFF, SPEC. TRAINING DIV, OAK RIDGE ASSOC. UNIVS, 63- Am. Phys. Soc. Low energy nuclear physics. Address: Oak Ridge Associated Universities, Special Training Division, P.O. Box 117, Oak Ridge, TN 37831.

DUGGAN, MICHAEL J, b. Boulder, Colo, May 21, 31; m. 58; c. 2. PHYSICS. S.B, Mass. Inst. Tech, 52; M.S, Ohio State, 53; Ph.D.(physics), Stanford, 64. ASST. PROF. PHYSICS, SAN JOSE STATE COL, 64- U.S.A.F, 52-56, 1st Lt. Theoretical physics. Address: 3768 Laguna Ave, Palo Alto, CA 94306.

DUGGAN, REO E(LDRED), b. Ragley, La, Aug. 23, 16; m. 39; c. 2. ANALYTICAL CHEMISTRY. B.S, La. State, 37, M.S, 38. Chemist, foods & drugs develop. anal. methods, FOOD & DRUG ADMIN, 39-48, asst. to dist. chief, admin, 48-50, chief chemist, New Orleans Dist, 50-60, bur. field admin, D.C, 60-64; asst. dir. sci, Bur. Regulatory Compliance, 64-67, DEP. ASSOC. COMNR. COMPLIANCE, 67- Am. Chem. Soc; Asn. Off. Anal. Chem. Analytical methods for detection and estimation of adulteration; decomposition in foods and drugs. Address: 6319 Anneliese Dr, Falls Church, VA 22044.

DUGGER, CORTLAND OTIS, b. Boston, Mass, Apr. 26, 26; m. 56; c. 2. INORGANIC CHEMISTRY. B.S, Tufts, 50; Howard, 55-56; Northeastern, 58-60; Mass. Inst. Technol, 65. RES. CHEMIST, Lincoln Labs, Mass. Inst. Technol, 56-59; U.S. AIR FORCE CAMBRIDGE RES. LABS, L.G. HANSCOM FIELD, BEDFORD, 59- Consult, Semi-Elements, Inc, Pa, 68-; mem. staff, Northeast. Univ, 70-71. Hosp.C, U.S.N, 44-46, 51. Am. Inst. Physics; Am. Ceramic Soc. New ferrite materials; new laser and acoustic materials. Address: 118 Fayerweather St, Cambridge, MA 02138.

DUGGER, G(ORDON) L(ESLIE), b. Winter Haven, Fla, Nov. 13, 23; m. 45; c. 3. CHEMICAL ENGINEERING. B.Ch.E, Florida, 44, M.S.E, 47; Ph.D. (chem. eng), Case, 53. Aeronaut. res. scientist flame res, Nat. Adv. Comt. for Aeronaut, 47-54; supvr. chem. process develop. res. div, Int. Minerals & Chem. Corp, 54-57; group supvr. APPL. PHYSICS LAB, JOHNS HOPKINS UNIV, 57-63, SUPVR. HYPERSONIC PROPULSION GROUP, 63- Award eng. sci, Washington Acad. Sciences, 64. C.Eng, 44-46, Sgt. Fel, AAAS; Combustion Inst; fel. Am.Inst. Aeronaut. & Astronaut.(tech. ed, Am. Astronaut. & Aerospace Eng, 63, ed-in-chief, J. Spacecraft & Rockets, 64-71, v.pres, publ, 71-). Flame propagation; flame stability; fuels and propellants; supersonic aerodynamics; heat transfer; supersonic combustion; ramjet and other advanced air breathing engine cycles. Address: 1023 Kathryn Rd, Silver Spring, MD 20904.

DUGGER, GORDON SHELTON, b. Vilas, N.C, July 17, 21; m. 58. NEUROSURGERY. A.B, North Carolina, 41; M.D, Hopkins, 45. Demonstr. neuropath, McGill, 50-51; instr. neurosurg, UNIV. N.C, CHAPEL HILL, 54-55, asst. prof, 55-58, assoc. prof, 58-64, PROF.SURG, 64-, CHIEF DIV. NEUROSURG, 57- Consult, Watts Hosp, N.C; Vet. Admin. Hosp. Dipl, Am. Bd. Neurosurg. Am. Med. Asn; N.Y. Acad. Sci; Am. Asn. Neurol. Surg; Cong. Neurol. Surg. Ultrastructure of the hypothalamus and pituitary role of the nervous system in endocrine regulation. Address: Dept. of Neurosurgery, University of North Carolina, Chapel Hill, NC 27514.

DUGGER, HARRY A, b. Oklahoma City, Okla, June 28, 36; m. 65; c. 1. ORGANIC CHEMISTRY. A.B, Oklahoma Baptist, 58; univ. fels, Michigan, 58-62, M.S, 60, Nat. Sci. Found. fels, 60-61, Ph.D.(chem), 62. Nat. Insts. Health fel, Zurich, 62-64; SR. CHEMIST, SANDOZ PHARMACEUT, INC, 64- Summer chemist, Sun Oil Co, 59. AAAS; Am. Chem. Soc; Am. Inst. Chem; N.Y. Acad. Sci. Organic synthesis; reaction mechanisms; drug metabolism; synthesis with isotopic labels. Address: Sandoz Pharmaceuticals, Inc, Route 10, Hanover, NJ 07936.

DUGGER, W(ILLIE) M(ACK), JR, b. Adel, Ga, July 28, 19; m. 46; c. 2. PLANT PHYSIOLOGY. B.S.A, Georgia, 41; M.S, Wisconsin, 42; Ph.D, N.C. State Col, 50. Asst, Wisconsin, 41-42; asst. prof. bot, Georgia, 46; asst, N.C. State, 46-50; asst. prof. plant physiol, Maryland, 50-55; assoc. plant physiologist, dept. bot, agr. exp. sta, Florida, 55-60; res. plant physiologist, agr. air res. ctr, UNIV. CALIF, RIVERSIDE, 60-63, PROF. BOT, 63-, DEAN, COL. BIOL. & AGR. SCI, 68-, ASSOC. DIR. AGR. EXP. STA, 70-, chmn. dept. life sci, 64-68. U.S.A, 42-46, Capt. AAAS; Am. Soc. Plant Physiol. Organic transport and minor element nutrition in plants; desert plant physiology; smog effect on plants. Address: College of Biological & Agricultural Sciences, University of California, Riverside, CA 92502.

DUGGINS, OLIVER H(ERVEY), b. St. Louis, Mo, Feb. 22, 13; m. 36; c. 2. BIOLOGY. B.S, Northwest. Univ, 34-35; teacher, pub. sch, 36-41; agent, Fed. Bur. Invest, 41-43, lab. supvr, 43-46; prof. zool, Harris Teachers Col, 47-64; assoc. prof. BIOL, ST. LOUIS DIST. JR. COL, 64-66, PROF, 66-, CHMN. LIFE SCI. DIV, FOREST PARK COMMUNITY COL, 66- Res. asst, Wash. Univ, 47; grants, Fed. Security Agency, 49-53; Wennergren Found, 53-59; consult, Procter & Gamble, 53-55; chmn, interinstitutional comt. allied health, Bi State Regional Med. Prog; bd. dir, Alliance for Regional Community Health. Am. Asn. Phys. Anthrop. Age changes in hair; racial characteristics of hair; general ecology; field exercises. Address: 10 Alden Lane, Creve Coeur, MO 63141.

DUGGINS, WILLIAM E(DGAR), b. Phila, Pa, Aug. 3, 20; m. 47; c. 2. ORGANIC CHEMISTRY. A.B, LaSalle Col, 43; Swift fel. & Ph.D, Mass. Inst. Tech, 49. Res. chemist, Gen. Aniline & Film Corp, 49-52, sr. develop. engr, 52-59, supvr. new prod. develop, 59-60, proj. mgr, 61; asst. to v.pres. res. & develop, COLLIER CARBON & CHEM. CORP, 61-62, mgr. mkt. res. & develop, 62-70, TECH. MGR, 70- Am. Chem. Soc; Commercial Develop. Asn; Chem. Mkt. Res. Asn. Dyes; intermediates; resins; amino acids; high-pressure acetylene chemicals; petrochemicals; fertilizers; pesticides; petroleum coke; carbon; graphite. Address: 3427 Corinna Dr, Palos Verdes Peninsula, CA 90274.

DUGLE, DAVID L, b. Chicago, Ill, Dec. 21, 34; m. 56. RADIATION BIOLOGY & CHEMISTRY. B.A, South Dakota, 58, summer, Nat. Sci. Found. fel, 59, M.A, 60; summers, Nat. Res. Coun. Can. fels, Alberta, 61-64, Ph.D. (chem), 64. Res. technician, G. Barr & Co, Chicago, 56-57; field geologist, S.Dak. State Geol. Surv, 57; lectr, South Dakota, 59; Nat. Res. Coun. Can. fel. chem, Alberta, 64-65; Nat. Insts. Health fel. molecular biophys, Yale, 65-67; RES. OFFICER MED. BIOPHYS, WHITESHELL NUCLEAR RES. ESTAB, ATOMIC ENERGY CAN, LTD, 67- Biophys. Soc. Radiation chemistry of nucleic acids and organic compounds; radiation biology of microorganisms. Address: Whiteshell Nuclear Research Establishment, Atomic Energy of Canada, Ltd, Pinawa, Man, Can.

DUGLE, JANET MARY ROGGE, b. Pierre, S.Dak, June 7, 34; m. 56. PLANT TAXONOMY. B.A. & scholar, Carleton Col, 56; M.A. & Nat. Sci. Found. fel, South Dakota, 60; univ. fel, Alberta, 60-61, Nat. Res. Coun. studentship, 62-64, Ph.D.(bot), 64. Secy, Hotpoint Co, Chicago, 56; teacher, high sch, S.Dak, 57-58; instr. bot, South Dakota, 59-60, curator, 58-60; instr, Alberta, 64-65; lectr. biol, Yale, 65-67, secy. biophys, 66-67; RES. OFFICER BOT, ATOMIC ENERGY CAN. LTD, WHITESHELL NUCLEAR RES. ESTAB, 67- Univ. res. fel. biol, Yale, 65-66; res. assoc, 67; lectr, Manitoba, 68. Sum-

mers, playground supvr, Sioux Falls Recreation Dept, S.Dak, 50-55. AAAS; Bot. Soc. Am; Am. Soc. Plant Taxon; Can. Bot. Asn; Ecol. Soc. Am; Soc. Study Evolution; Int. Asn. Plant Taxon. Plant systematics and ecology; evolutionary biology. Address: Whiteshell Nuclear Research Establishment, Pinawa, Man. R0E 1L0, Can.

DUGLISS, CHARLES H(OSEA), b. Staatsburg, N.Y, Oct. 12, 21; m. 46; c. 2. CHEMICAL ENGINEERING. B.Ch.E, Pratt Inst, 43. Chem. engr, STAMFORD RES. LABS, AM. CYANAMID CO, 43-64, SR. RES. SCIENTIST, resins res. group, 64-68, CHEM. ENG. DIV, 68- Am. Inst. Chem. Eng; Am. Chem. Soc. Thermosetting and thermoplastic polymers and processes; reinforced plastics; polymer processing. Address: 2792 Hickory St, Yorktown Heights, NY 10598.

DUGOFF, HOWARD, b. Yonkers, N.Y, Nov. 23, 36; m. 58; c. 3. MECHANICAL ENGINEERING, PHYSICS. M.E, Stevens Inst. Tech, 58, Curtis Wright fel, 58-60, M.S, 60. Res. asst. underwater weapons, Davidson Lab, Stevens Inst. Tech, 59-60, assoc. res. engr, 60-63, res. engr, 63-65, chief vehicle res, 65-67; asst. head phys. factors, hwy. safety res. inst, Univ. Mich, 67-71; CHIEF, ANAL. & SIMULATION BR, MOBILITY SYSTS. LAB, U.S. ARMY TANK-AUTOMOTIVE COMMAND, 71- Mem. driving simulation comt, Hwy. Res. Bd, Nat. Acad. Sci-Nat. Res. Coun, 68-; mem. comt. F-9 on tires, Am. Soc. Test. & Mat. Am. Soc. Mech. Eng; Soc. Automotive Eng; Int. Soc. Terrain-Vehicle Systs. Hydrodynamics and mechanics of submerged vehicles; hydrodynamics performance of amphibious craft; mechanics of off-road vehicles; stability and control of pneumatic tired vehicles; analysis of driver-vehicle-highway systems. Address: 2680 Lowell Rd, Ann Arbor, MI 48103.

DUGUAY, MICHEL ALBERT, b. Montreal, Que, Sept. 12, 39; m. 63; c. 2. PHYSICS. B.S, Montreal, 61; Ph.D.(physics), Yale, 66. MEM. TECH. STAFF LASERS, BELL TEL. LABS, 66- Optical Soc. Am; Am. Phys. Soc; Inst. Elec. & Electronics Eng; Sci. Res. Soc. Am. Laser frequency shifting; laser pulse compression; x-ray lasers; ultrashort laser pulse displays; optical sampling; ultrafast Kerr cells; picosecond lifetime measurements; ultrahigh-speed photography. Address: Bell Telephone Labs, Murray Hill, NJ 07974.

DUGUNDJI, JAMES, b. New York, N.Y, Aug. 30, 19; m. 44. MATHEMATICS. B.A, N.Y. Univ, 40; fel, North Carolina, 40-42; Nat. Res. fel, Mass. Inst. Tech, 46-47, M.S, 47, Off. Naval Res, fel, 47-48, Ph.D.(math), 48. Asst. prof. MATH, UNIV. SOUTH. CALIF, 48-51, assoc. prof, 51-58, PROF, 58- Res. assoc, Mass. Inst. Technol, 47-48; mem, Inst. Advan. Study, 51-53; Ed, Pac. J. Math, 63-; vis. prof, Univ. Frankfurt, 64-65; Univ. Pisa, 65; Rice Univ, 66-67. U.S.A.A.F, 42-46, 1st Lt. Am. Math.Soc. Deformation topology; information theory. Address: Dept. of Mathematics, University of Southern California, Los Angeles, CA 90007.

DUGUNDJI, JOHN, b. New York, N.Y, Oct. 25, 25; m. 65; c. 2. AERONAUTICAL ENGINEERING. B. of A.E, N.Y. Univ, 44; M.S, Mass. Inst. Tech, 48, Sc.D.(aeronaut. eng), 51. Res. engr. aerodynamics, Grumman Aircraft Eng. Corp, 48-49; asst. aeroelasticity, Mass. Inst. Tech, 50-51; prin. dynamics engr, Repub. Aviation Corp, 51-56; asst. prof. AERONAUT. & ASTRONAUT, MASS. INST. TECHNOL, 57-62, assoc. prof, 62-70, PROF, 70- U.S.N.R, 44-46; U.S.A.F.R, 50-52, 2nd Lt. Am. Inst. Aeronaut. & Astronaut. Aeroelasticity; structural dynamics. Address: 71 Babcock St, Brookline, MA 02146.

DUHL, DAVID N, b. Staten Island, N.Y, Apr. 20, 39; m. 63; c. 2. METALLURGY. B.Met.E, Rensselaer Polytech, 60; S.M, Mass. Inst. Tech, 63, Ph.D.(metall), 64. Res. asst. metall, Mass. Inst. Tech, 60-64; res. assoc, adv. mat. res. & develop. lab, PRATT & WHITNEY AIRCRAFT DIV, UNITED AIRCRAFT CORP, 64-70, SR. RES. ASSOC, MAT. ENG. & RES. LAB, 70- Am. Inst. Min, Metall. & Petrol. Eng; Am. Soc. Metals. High temperature alloy development and evaluation; phase stability and equilibra. Address: Pratt & Whitney Aircraft, Materials Engineering & Research Lab, J Mezzanine, 400 Main St, East Hartford, CT 06118.

DUHL, LEONARD J, b. New York, N.Y, Mar 24, 26; m. 51; c. 4. PSYCHIATRY. A.B, Columbia, 45; M.D, Albany Med. Col, 48. Intern, Jewish Hosp, Brooklyn, N.Y, 48-49; res. psychiat, Vet. Admin. Hosp, Winter, 49-54; psychiatrist, prfnl. serv. br, Nat. Inst. Ment. Health, 54-64, chief, planning staff, 64-65, off. planning, 65-66; spec. asst. to secy, Dept. Housing & Urban Develop, 66-68; PROF. CITY & REGIONAL PLANNING, COL. ENVIRON. DESIGN & PROF. PUB. HEALTH, SCH. PUB. HEALTH, UNIV. CALIF, BERKELEY, 68-; PSYCHIAT, MED. CTR, UNIV. CALIF, SAN FRANCISCO, 68- Fel, sch. psychiat, Menninger Found, 49-54; sr. asst. surgeon, U.S. Pub. Health Serv-Contra Costa County Health Dept, Calif, 51-53; clin. instr, George Wash. Univ, 58-61, assoc. 61-63, asst. clin. prof, 63-68; mem. recreation comt, U.S. Dept. Health, Educ, Welfare, 56, res. adv. comt, Off. Ed, 56-57, joint task force serv. & housing, 61-, comn. subcomt. cultural deprivation-poverty, 63; consult, Peace Corps, 61-65; adv. comt. migratory labor, U.S. Pub. Health Serv, 62; mem. bd. trustees, Park Forest Col, 65-68; bd. dirs, Human Interaction Res. Inst, Calif, 68-; mem. sci. & technol. adv. comt, Calif. State Legis, 70; consult, Man/Machine Interface Corp, Minn, 71- Dipl. psychiat, Am. Bd. Psychiat. & Neurol, 56. U.S.P.H.S, 51-53, Res, 54-, Med. Dir. Fel. AAAS; Int. Asn. Sci. Study Ment. Deficiency; fel. Am. Orthopsychiat. Asn; fel. Am. Psychiat. Asn; fel. Am. Pub. Health Asn; fel. Soc. Appl. Anthrop; Int. Asn. Child Psychiat.(asst. secy. gen, 62-66); assoc. Royal Soc. Med; Am. Acad. Psychiat. Public health psychiatry; community development and organization; urban planning; mental retardation; alcoholism; mental health aspects of education; psychoanalytic concepts. Address: Dept. of City Planning, 228 Wurster Hall, University of California, Berkeley, CA 94720.

DUICH, JOSEPH M, b. Farrell, Pa, June 7, 28; m. 53; c. 3. AGRONOMY. B.S, Pa. State Univ, 52, Ph.D.(agron), 57. Instr. AGRON, PA. STATE UNIV, 54, from asst. prof. to assoc. prof, 57-67, PROF, 67- U.S.M.C, 46-48. Fel. AAAS; Am. Soc. Agron; Crop Sci. Soc. Am; Weed Sci. Soc. Am. Agronomic research in turfgrass field; breeding, weed control and fertility research. Address: College of Agriculture, Dept. of Agronomy, Pennsylvania State University, 21 Tyson Bldg, University Park, PA 16802.

DUING, WALTER, b. Saarbrücken, Germany, Feb. 11, 35; m. 59; c. 1. PHYSICAL OCEANOGRAPHY. Eng, Karlsruhe Tech, 59; Dr. rer. nat, Kiel, 64. Engr, Naples, Italy, 60; asst. prof. oceanog, Kiel, 64-66; Hawaii, 67-69; assoc. prof, INST. MARINE SCI, UNIV. MIAMI, 69-71, PROF. PHYS. OCEANOG, 71-, CHMN. DIV, 70- Problems of the oceanic water movements especially the monsoonal circulation of the Indian Ocean; investigations into the three dimensional distribution of motion fields in the ocean. Address: Institute of Marine Sciences, University of Miami, Miami, FL 33149.

DUISBERG, PETER CASPAR, b. Philadelphia, Pa, Dec. 31, 19; m. 46; c. 2. NATURAL RESOURCES. B.S, Pa. State Col, 40, M.S, 42; Ph.D.(agr. chem, soils), Arizona, 45. Food chemist, Swift & Co, Ill, 41-43; asst. supt, Port Reading Creosoting Plant, N.J, 45-46; asst. prof. chem, Haverford Col, 46-47; New Mexico State, 47-51; res. dir, Desert Prods, Co, 51-52; Farmers Co-op. Oil Mill & Southwest Irrigated Cotton Growers Asn, Tex, 52-58; Fulbright prof, Cath. Univ. Chile, 58-59; UNESCO consult, Latin Am, 60-63; chief natural resources div, Inter-Am. Geod. Surv, 64-71; CONSULT, 71- Wiley award, 40; hon. prof, Cath. Univ. Chile, 59. AAAS (award, 64); Argentine Sci. Soc. Natural resource surveys; geography; agricultural chemistry; soils; desert plant utilization; hydrology. Address: Route 1, Box 526, Englewood, FL 33533.

DUISMAN, JACK A(RNOLD), b. Ft. Knox, Ky, Mar. 14, 37; m. 61; c. 2. PHYSICAL CHEMISTRY. B.A, Augustana Col, 59; Ph.D.(phys. chem), California, Berkeley, 66. Nat. Sci. Found. fel. phys. chem, Univ. Kansas, 66-67; res. chemist, LINDE DIV, UNION CARBIDE CORP, 67-70, PROJ. SCIENTIST, 70- Am. Chem. Soc. Chemical thermodynamics; solid state chemistry; critical phenomena; zeolite catalysis. Address: Linde Division, Union Carbide Corp, Tarrytown Technical Center, Tarrytown, NY 10591.

DUJOVNE, CARLOS A, b. Resistencia, Arg, July 9, 37; m. 63; c. 1. CLINICAL PHARMACOLOGY, INTERNAL MEDICINE. M.D, Buenos Aires, 61. Instr. pharmacol. & med, Buenos Aires, 62-63; intern, Mt. Sinai Hosp, Chicago, Ill, 63-64, res. internal med, 64-66; Vet. Admin. Hosp, Wash, D.C, 66-67; Nat. Insts. Health fel. liver & metab, George Washington, 67-68; fel. clin. pharmacol, Johns Hopkins Hosp, 68-70; ASST. PROF. MED. & PHARMACOL, SCH. MED, UNIV. KANS, 70- Instr, sch. med, Loyola Univ. (Ill), 65; clin. asst, Chicago Med. Sch, 65-66. Hepatotoxicity; drug toxicity and adverse reactions; clinical therapeutic trial; effects of drugs in tissue culture. Address: Clinical Pharmacology & Toxicology Center, University of Kansas Medical Center, Kansas City, KS 66103.

DUKE, C. MARTIN, b. Wellsville, N.Y, Oct. 25, 17; m. 42; c. 1. CIVIL ENGINEERING. B.S, California, Berkeley, 39, M.S, 41. Asst. eng. aid, U.S. Bur. Pub. Rd, Calif, 39; assoc. civil eng, California, Berkeley, 39-41, instr, 41-45, res. engr, 44; struct. designer, Austin Co, 45-46; sr. testing engr, Pac. Islands Engrs, Guam, 46-47; asst. prof. ENG, UNIV. CALIF, LOS ANGELES, 47-50, assoc. prof, 50-56, PROF, 56- Fulbright res. award, Japan, 56-57; mem. panel consult, Air Force Spec. Weapons Proj, 61-62; bd. dam consult, Los Angeles Dept. Water & Power, 63-; vis. prof, Univ. Chile, 67; pres, Earthquake Eng. Res. Inst, 70- Am. Soc. Civil Eng; Seismol. Soc. Am; Am. Soc. Eng. Educ; Soc. Explor. Geophys. Earthquake engineering; soil mechanics, structures; effects of site conditions on seismic intensity. Address: Dept. of Mechanics & Structures, University of California, Los Angeles, CA 90024.

DUKE, C(HARLES) B(RYAN), b. Richmond, Va, Mar. 13, 38; m. 61; c. 2. PHYSICS. B.S, Duke Univ, 59; Ph.D.(physics), Princeton, 63. Staff mem. physics, Gen. Elec. Co, 63-69; PROF. PHYSICS, UNIV. ILL, URBANA, 69-, RES. PROF, COORDINATED SCI. LAB, 69- Chmn. steering comt, Int. Conf, Solid Surfaces, 71; consult, Gen. Elec. Co. Fel. Am. Phys. Soc; Am. Vacuum Soc. Scattering theory; many-body theory; electron tunneling in solids; low-energy electron-solid-scattering; surface crystallography; chemisorption; catalysis. Address: Dept. of Physics, University of Illinois, Urban, IL 61801.

DUKE, CHARLES E(DWARD), b. Williamsport, Pa, Nov. 26, 21; m. 44; c. 3. AERONAUTICAL ENGINEERING. B.S, Pa. State, 43, M.S, 48, Ph.D.(aeronaut. eng), 53; fel, Ord. Res. Lab, 49. Flight test engr, east. aircraft div, Gen. Motors Corp, 43-45; proj. engr, dept. eng. res, Pa. State, 46-47, asst. prof. aeronaut. eng, 47-55; sr. engr, intel. dept, Haller Raymond & Brown, Inc, 55-57, v.pres, res. dept, 57-63; exec. v.pres, HRB Singer, Inc, 63-68; DIR. PLANNING, MITRE CORP, 68- U.S.A.A.F, 45-46. Am. Inst. Aeronaut. & Astronaut. Automatic control; aircraft propulsion; analytical studies of internal friction in solids. Address: Mitre Corp, P.O. Box 208, Bedford, MA 01730.

DUKE, CHARLES L(EWIS), b. Asheville, N.C, Sept. 7, 40; m. 65; c. 2. NUCLEAR PHYSICS. B.S, N.C. State Univ, 62; Ph.D.(physics), Iowa State Univ, 67. Atomic Energy Comn. fel. PHYSICS, Ames Lab, Iowa, 67-68; instr, inst. physics, Aarhus Univ, 68-69; ASST. PROF, GRINNELL COL, 69- Am. Phys. Soc. Production and study of nuclei far from stability through on-line isotope separator techniques; beta-strength function and delayed neutron measurements. Address: Dept. of Physics, Grinnell College, Grinnell, IA 50112.

DUKE, DAVID ALLEN, b. Salt Lake City, Utah, Nov. 26, 35; m. 55; c. 4. MINERALOGY, MATERIALS SCIENCE. B.S, Utah, 57, M.S, 59, Ph.D.(geol. eng, ceramics), 62. Jr. scientist, Kennecott Copper Res. Ctr, 60-61; res. mineralogist, CORNING GLASS WORKS, 62-67, mgr. adv. mat. res, 67-70, MGR. BUS. DEVELOP, TECH. PROD. DIV, 70- Mineral. Soc. Am; Am. Ceramic Soc; fel. Am. Inst. Chem. Geochemical and instrumental analysis of rocks and minerals; crystal chemistry; crystallization of glass and the properties of glass-ceramic materials; chemical strengthening of glass-ceramics. Address: Corning Glass Works, Main Plant, Corning, NY 14830.

DUKE, DOUGLAS, b. Phila, Pa, Aug. 7, 23; m. 44; c. 2. ASTRONOMY, ASTROPHYSICS. A.B, California, 47; Ph.D.(astron), Chicago, 50. Asst, Yerkes Observ, Wisconsin, 47-50; asst. prof. astron, North Carolina, 50-51; astron. & phys. sci, Florida, 51-53, assoc. prof, 54; head visibility br, U.S. Naval Electronics Lab, 54-55; res. engr, Convair Astronaut, 55-57;

sr. engr, Atlantic Missile Range, Eng. Radio Corp. Am, 57-59; mem. tech. staff, Inst. Defense Anal, D.C, 59-62; staff scientist to v.pres, res, Autonetics Div, N.Am. Aviation, Inc, 62-64; dir. aerospace prog, Data Dynamics, Inc, 64-65; PROF. ASTRON, UNIV. MIAMI, 66- Asst. dir, Morehead Planetarium, Chapel Hill, N.C, 50-51; consult, Commanding Gen, N.Am. Air Defense Command, 61-62. Fel. AAAS; Am. Astron. Soc; Optical Soc. Am. Observational astrophysics; astrometry; missile and satellite tracking instrumentation; data reduction; satellite and interplanetary orbits; celestial navigation; atmospheric optics; planetarium operation. Address: Dept. of Physics, University of Miami, Box 8284, Coral Gables, FL 33124.

DUKE, EDWARD EUDEL, Bus. Mgt, Eng. Sci, see 12th ed, Soc. & Behav. Vols.

DUKE, EVERETTE L(ORANZA), b. Goochland Co, Va, June 28, 29; m. 53; c. 2. SOIL SCIENCE. B.S, Va. State Col, 49; scholar. & M.S, Mich. State, 50, Alumni fel. & Ph.D.(soil sci), 55; summer, Syracuse, 63. Instr. hort, Va. State Col, 50-51, assoc. prof. sci, Norfolk Div, 55-63, prof. biol, NORFOLK STATE COL, 63-71, ASSOC. DEAN ACAD. AFFAIRS, 71- Dir, thirteen-col. curriculum prog, Norfolk State Col, 67-71. U.S.A, 51-53. Farm crops; land utilization in relation to land character in rural-urban fringe areas in Southern Michigan. Address: Dept. of Biology, Norfolk State College, 2401 Corprew Ave, Norfolk, VA 23504.

DUKE, FREDERICK R(OBERT), b. Unityville, S.Dak, Mar. 17, 17; m. 41; c. 6. PHYSICAL CHEMISTRY. A.B, South Dakota, 37; Smith fel, Illinois, 37-40, Ph.D.(anal. chem), 40. Res. fel, Illinois, 40-41; res. chemist, rayon dept, E.I. du Pont de Nemours & Co, 41-42; instr. anal. chem, Princeton, 42-45; asst. prof, Mich. State, 45-48, assoc. prof. phys. chem, Iowa State, 48-54, prof, 54-63; Robert A. Welch prof. CHEM, Texas A&M, 63-65; prof, Purdue Univ, 65-68; PROF. & CHMN. DEPT, UNIV. IOWA, 68- With Off. Sci. Res. & Develop, 44. Am. Chem. Soc; Electrochem. Soc. Mechanism of oxidation-reduction reactions and phase changes; thermodynamics and kinetics of fused salts; enzyme kinetics and mechanisms. Address: Dept. of Chemistry, University of Iowa, Iowa City, IA 52240.

DUKE, GARY EARL, b. Galesburg, Ill, Dec. 16, 37; m. 61. AVIAN PHYSIOLOGY & ECOLOGY. B.A, Knox Col.(Ill), 59; M.S, Mich. State, 64, Ph.D, 67. ASST. PROF. AVIAN & VET. PHYSIOL, UNIV. MINN, ST. PAUL, 68-, grad. sch. & agr. exp. sta. res. grants, 67-69. U.S.A, 60-62. Am. Ornith. Union; Poultry Sci. Asn; Cooper Ornith. Soc; Wildlife Soc. Chromium 51 passage rate studies in birds; comparison of gastrointestinal motility and absorption in healthy turkeys and those with contagious enteritis; studies of intraluminal pressures and smooth muscle electrical potentials in the turkey gastrointestinal tract. Address: Dept. of Veterinary Physiology & Pharmacology, University of Minnesota, St. Paul, MN 55101.

DUKE, JAMES A, b. Birmingham, Ala, Apr. 4, 29; m. 50; c. 1. BOTANY. A.B, North Carolina, 52, M.A, 55, Ph.D.(bot), 59. Lab. asst. BOT, North Carolina, 54-59; res. asst, Mo. Bot. Garden, 59-61, asst. curator, 61-63; asst. prof. bot, Univ. Wash, 61-62; res. botanist, U.S. Dept. Agr, 63-65; ecologist, Battelle Mem. Inst, 65-71; SUPVY. BOTANIST, NEW CROPS RESEARCH BRANCH, U.S. DEPT. AGR, 71- Chem.C, U.S.D.A, 55-57. Am. Soc. Photogram; Asn. Trop. Biol; Int. Oceanog. Found; Inst. Caribbean Studies; Am. Forestry Asn; Int. Soc. Plant Taxon; Soc. Econ. Bot; Am. Ornith Union; Am. Soc. Agron. Taxonomy and ecology in Panama and Puerto Rico. Address: Plant Industry Sta, Agricultural Research Service, Beltsville, MD 20705.

DUKE, JOHN W(ALTER), b. Ballinger, Tex, Oct. 30, 37; m. 57; c. 3. MATHEMATICS. B.A, North Texas State, 59; M.S, Texas Tech, 61; Ph.D.(math), Colorado, 68. Instr. MATH, Texas Tech, 61-64, asst. prof, 66-68; ASSOC. PROF, ANGELO STATE UNIV, 68- Instr, Auburn, summer 66. Am. Math. Soc; Math. Asn. Am. Matrices over division algebras; general ring theory. Address: Dept. of Mathematics, Angelo State University, San Angelo, TX 76901.

DUKE, J(OSEPH) A, S.J, b. Cleveland, Ohio, Jan. 18, 14. PHYSICAL BIOCHEMISTRY. A.B, Georgetown, 39; Ph.L, Woodstock Col.(Md), 40, S.T.L, 47; M.S, Fordham, 43, Ph.D.(chem), 52. Asst. prof. chem, Loyola Col.(Md), 40-41; Fordham, 41-43; Woodstock Col.(Md), 44-46; assoc. prof, Georgetown, 52-57; prof. & chmn. dept, Wheeling Col, 57-68; RES. BIOCHEMIST, CARDIOVASC. RES. INST, MED. CTR, UNIV. CALIF, SAN FRANCISCO, 68- AAAS; Am. Chem. Soc. Amphoteric properties of enzymes; fractionation and composition of proteins; enzyme kinetics. Address: Cardiovascular Research Institute, University of California Medical Center, San Francisco, CA 94122.

DUKE, JUNE TEMPLE, b. Cambridge, Ohio, June 18, 22. ORGANIC & POLYMER CHEMISTRY. Night Schs, Akron, 44-56; Buffalo & Canisius Col, 56-59. Technician, Off. Rubber Reserve, Govt. Labs, Univ. Akron, 44-45, lab. supvr. rubber res, 45-50, chemist supvr, 50-56; res. chemist, energy div, Olin Mathieson Chem. Corp, 56-59; sr. chemist, STANDARD OIL CO. (OHIO), 59-60, sr. res. chemist & proj. leader polymer res, 60-68, RES. ASSOC, 68- AAAS; Am. Chem. Soc; Fedn. Socs. Paint Technol. Polymerization and structure of synthetic rubber; organo-boron polymers; synthetic coatings; emulsion polymerization; resins and plastics. Address: 28649 Jackson Rd, Chagrin Falls, OH 44022.

DUKE, KENNETH L(INDSAY), b. Heber City, Utah, Feb. 22, 12; m. 34; c. 3. ANATOMY. A.B, Brigham Young, 36; fel, Duke, 39-40, Ph.D.(cytol), 40. Asst. zool, Brigham Young, 36-37; Duke Univ, 37-39, instr. ANAT, SCH. MED, 40-43, assoc, 43-46, asst. prof, 46-51, ASSOC. PROF, 51- Vis. instr, sch. med, Missouri, 44; sch. med, North Carolina, 46, vis. assoc. prof, 55; vis. asst. prof. sch. med, Tennessee, 49; China Med. Bd. N.Y. travel. fel, Malaya, 61; summers, vis. assoc. prof, Brigham Young, 59, 65. Am. Asn. Anat; Am. Soc. Mammal. Histology; cytology; mammalian reproductive tract; germ cells of mammals. Address: Dept. of Anatomy, Duke University Medical Center, Durham, NC 27710.

DUKE, MARY ELEANOR, b. Marfa, Tex, Apr. 12, 18; m. 39. BIOLOGY. B.A, Tex. West. Col, 39; M.A, Univ. Tex, Austin, 45, Ph.D, 67. Technician, Turner's

Clin. Lab, 38; El Paso Med. & Surg. Clin, 39; assoc. prof. & instr. biol. sci, Tex. West. Col, 40-41, 43, 45; res. technician endocrinol, Ochsner Clin, La, 46; ASSOC. PROF. BIOL. SCI, UNIV. TEX, EL PASO, 47- Fel. AAAS; N.Y. Acad. Sci; Soc. Protozool; Nat. Asn. Biol. Teachers; Biol. Photog. Asn; Ecol. Soc. Am; Am. Micros. Soc; Am. Soc. Limnol. & Oceanog. Electron microscopy of diatoms; biological deposition of silicon compounds. Address: Dept. of Biological Sciences, University of Texas at El Paso, El Paso, TX 79968.

DUKE, MICHAEL B, b. Los Angeles, Calif, Dec. 1, 35; m. 58; c. 4. GEOLOGY, COSMOCHEMISTRY. B.S, Calif. Inst. Tech, 57, Standard Oil Co. Calif. fel, 58-59, Stauffer Found. fel, 59-60, Nat. Sci. Found. fel, 60-62, M.S, 61, Ph.D.(geochem), 63; Pa. State, 57-58. Geologist, astrogeol. br, U.S. Geol. Surv, 63-70; LUNAR SAMPLE CURATOR, MANNED SPACECRAFT CTR, NASA, 70- Summer vis. lectr. planetary sci, Calif. Inst. Technol, 64. Nininger Meteorite Award, Ariz. State Univ, 63. AAAS; Mineral. Soc. Am; Am. Geophys. Union. Mineralogy, petrology and chemical composition of extraterrestrial materials; techniques of micro-mineralogical analysis. Address: 18314 Point Lookout Dr, Houston, TX 77058.

DUKE, PHILLIP S, b. Chicago, Ill, Aug. 27, 33. EXPERIMENTAL PATHOLOGY, BIOCHEMISTRY. B.S, Univ. Calif, Los Angeles, 56; Ph.D.(exp. path), 67. Fel. biochem, med. sch, Univ. Nebr, 67-68; PRES. & DIR. TOXICOL, DUKE LABS, 68-, DUKE RES. FOUND, INC, 70- Soc. Toxicol; Am. Acad. Clin. Toxicol; Soc. Cosmetic Chem; Am. Chem. Soc; Am. Water Works Asn. Cancer research; drug urinalysis methodology. Address: Duke Labs, 4846 W. Chicago Ave, Chicago, IL 60651.

DUKE, ROY B(URT), JR, b. Houston, Tex, Sept. 20, 32; m. 50; c. 3. ORGANIC CHEMISTRY. B.S, Houston, 56, M.S, 60; Ph.D.(chem), Ga. Inst. Tech, 67. Res. chemist, Am. Oil Co, 56-60; Tex. Eastman Co, 60-62; instr, Ga. Inst. Tech, 62-65; ADV. RES. CHEMIST, MARATHON OIL CO, 66- U.S.N.R, 52-56. Am. Chem. Soc. Catalysis; dehydrogenation; mechanism of the Grignard reaction; kinetics and mechanism of the reaction of alkoxides with methylene halides; aldol and related condensations. Address: Marathon Oil Co, Box 269, Littleton, CO 80121.

DUKE, THOMAS W, b. Archer City, Tex, Sept. 15, 31; m. 54; c. 2. OCEANOGRAPHY. B.S, Texas A&M, 53, M.S, 60, Ph.D.(oceanog), 62; res. scientist, Res. Found, Texas A&M, 60-61; supvry. fishery biologist, radiobiol. lab, Bur. Commercial Fisheries, 61-68, chief, biol. field sta, 68-70; DIR. ENVIRON. PROTECTION AGENCY LAB, 70- Adj. asst. prof. zool, N.C. State Univ, 65-66; Univ. W.Fla, 68-71. U.S.A.F, 53-56, 1st Lt. AAAS; Am. Soc. Limnol. & Oceanog; Ecol. Soc. Am. Pollution ecology, including cycling of pesticides and radioactive materials in the estuarine environment. Address: Environmental Protection Agency, Gulf Breeze Lab, Sabine Island, Gulf Breeze, FL 32561.

DUKE, VICTOR HAL, b. Kamas, Utah, Jan. 15, 25; m. 49; c. 3. PHARMACOLOGY, PHARMACOGNOSY. B.S, Idaho State, 49, B.S, 50; Ph.D.(pharm), Univ. Utah, 61. Asst. prof. PHARMACOL, Univ. N.Mex, 61-65; assoc. prof, col. pharm, Univ. Wyo, 65-68; UNIV. MONT, 68-70, PROF, 70- Dir. drug abuse seminar educators, Univ. Mont, 69, 70, 71; mem, Nat. Adv. Coun. Health Manpower Educ, 71-72. U.S.A, 43-46. Am. Pharmaceut. Asn. Effect of drugs on analgesic threshold in animals; drug action in obesity and the evaluation of anorexigenics; research in neuro and behavioral pharmacology of psychotogens. Address: School of Pharmacy, University of Montana, Missoula, MT 59801.

DUKE, WILLIAM MENG, b. N.Y.C, May 20, 16; m. 50; c. 4. SPACE TECHNOLOGY. B.S, N.Y. Univ, 35; Sc.M, 36; M.E, State Univ. N.Y, 47; Ph.D. (math. & appl. mech), Univ. Calif, Los Angeles, 58; Eng.D, Clarkson Col. Technol, 63; hon. Sc.D, Univ. Tampa, 67. Struct. engr, Keyport Aeromarine Corp, N.Y, 35; aerodynamicist, Wilford Gyroplane Co, 36; stress analyst, Curtiss Wright Corp, 36-39, aeronaut. engr, 39-42; design res. engr, Vultee Aircraft Corp, 42-43; chmn. res. div, head aerodyn, dept. & asst. dir, aeronaut. lab, Cornell Univ, 43-50, v.pres, tech. opers, 50-55; prog. dir, Titan weapon syst, Space Technol. Labs, Calif, 56-57, v.pres. & dir. eng. & tech. div. Atlas, Thor, Titan & Minuteman progs, 58-59, sr. v.pres. res, eng. & fabrication, 60-62; pres, ITT Fed. Labs. & v.pres, ITT Mil. & Space Group, 62-64; pres, Whittaker Corp, 64-70; CHMN. BD. & CHIEF EXEC. OFF, DYNASCIENCES CORP, 70-; TASKER INDUSTS, 70-; KHD SCIENCES, INC, 70- Sr. stress analyst, Douglas Aircraft Co, 39; mem. Los Angeles, bus. & indust. coun, League Women Voters U.S; eng. adv. coun, Univ. Calif; comt. accelerated utilization of new mat, Nat. Mat. Adv. Bd. Naval Ord. develop. award, 45; U.S. Navy commendation letter; NASA Apollo achievement award; centennial citation, Soc. Plastics Indust. AAAS; assoc. fel. Am. Inst. Aeronaut. & Astronaut; Newcomen Soc; N.Y. Acad. Sci. Applied mechanics and mathematics; missile technology; research and development direction; corporate management. Address: Dynasciences Corp, 11661 San Vicente Blvd, Los Angeles, CA 90049.

DUKELOW, DONALD A(LLEN), b. Ellwood City, Pa, June 13, 32; m. 56; c. 3. METALLURGY. B.S, Geneva Col, 54; M.S, Carnegie Inst. Tech, 56, Union Carbide & Chem. fel, 56-57, Ph.D.(metall), 57. Res. engr, Jones & Laughlin Steel Corp, 57-64; asst. prof. metall. eng, Pittsburgh, 64-67; ASSOC. RES. CONSULT, U.S. STEEL CORP, MONROEVILLE, 67- Am. Inst. Min, Metall. & Petrol. Eng. Physical chemistry of metallurgy. Address: 719 Pinetree Rd, Pittsburgh, PA 15243.

DUKELOW, W. RICHARD, b. Princeton, Minn, Oct. 23, 36; m. 58; c. 3. REPRODUCTIVE PHYSIOLOGY, BIOCHEMISTRY. B.S, Minnesota, 57, M.S, 58, Ph.D.(physiol), 62. Instr. animal husb, Minnesota, Grand Rapids, 60-62, asst. prof, 62-64; res. assoc. BIOCHEM, Univ. Ga, 64-65, asst. res. prof, 65-69; ASSOC. PROF, ENDOCRINE RES. UNIT, CTR. LAB. ANIMAL RESOURCES, MICH. STATE UNIV, 69- Nat. Insts. Health biomed. grant, 66-67, spec. fel, 67-68 & res. career develop. award, 70; Lalor Found. res. grant & Pop. Coun. grant, 67-68; vis. scientist, Ore. Regional Primate Res. Ctr, 67-68. Am. Fertil. Soc; Am. Soc. Animal Sci; Brit. Soc. Study Fertil; Am. Physiol. Soc. Biochemistry and physiology of reproduction, especially spermatozoa capacitation, intrauterine devices and embryonic mortality before and after nidation; primatology. Address: Endocrine Research Unit, Center for Lab. Animal Resources, Michigan State University, East Lansing, MI 48823.

DUKES, GEORGE H(OUSTON), JR, b. Flora, Miss, June 12, 31; m. 55. BOTANY, PARASITOLOGY. B.S, Miss. Col, 53, M.A, 59; Ph.D.(bot), La. State, 61; dipl, Oak Ridge Inst. Nuclear Studies, 62; U.S. Dept. Health Ed. & Welfare grant, Univ. N.C, 63-64, M.S.P.H, 64; dipl. appl. parasitol. & entom, Univ. London, 67; grad, fish disease lab, Auburn Univ, 70. Teacher, high sch, Miss, 55-58; instr. bot. & bact, Miss. Col, 58-59; lab. instr. bot, La. State Univ, 59-61; assoc. prof. BIOL, Union Univ.(Tenn), 61-63; PROF, McNEESE STATE COL, 64-, head dept, 64-70. U.S.A, 53-55. Fel. AAAS; Am. Soc. Trop. Med. & Hyg; life fel. Royal Soc. Trop. Med. & Hyg. Dehydrogenation activities in Helminthosporium victoriae; silicified tertiary fossil woods; etiology of Microsporum canis; taxonomy of the Myxomycetes; life cycle studies of Sarcocystis species and Sebekia oxycephala. Address: Dept. of Biology, McNeese State College, Lake Charles, LA 70601.

DUKES, JOHN R, b. Findlay, Ohio, Oct. 9, 30; m. 53; c. 2. NUCLEAR PHYSICS, ELECTRICAL ENGINEERING. B.S.(physics) & B.E.E, Ohio State, 54, M.B.A, 71; B.S.(lib. arts), Bowling Green State, 54. Elec. engr, INDUST. NUCLEONICS CORP, 56-57, physicist, 57-58, physics supvr, 58-61, MGR. APPL. PHYSICS, 61-, radiol. safety off, 60-69. Mem. faculty, Franklin, 57-65; mem. comt. N43.3, Am. Nat. Standards Inst, 62- U.S.A, 54-56, 1st Lt. Health Physics Soc; Am. Nuclear Soc; Inst. Elec. & Electronics Eng. Development of peaceful uses of atomic and nuclear energy directed toward measurement of material properties for industrial applications. Address: Industrial Nucleonics Corp, 650 Ackerman Rd, Columbus, OH 43202.

DUKES, PETER P(AUL), b. Vienna, Austria, June 27, 30; U.S. citizen; m. 61; c. 2. BIOCHEMISTRY. Graz Univ, 53; Ph.D.(biochem), Chicago, 58. Res. asst. biochem, Univ. Chicago, 54-55, instr, 58-63, asst. prof, 63-67; BIOCHEM. & PEDIAT, SCH. MED, UNIV. SOUTH. CALIF, 67-71, ASSOC. PROF, 71- Res. assoc, Argonne Cancer Res. Hosp, 58-67; U.S. Pub. Health Serv. spec. fel, physiol. chem. inst, Univ. Marburg, 64-65; mem. erythropoietin comt, Nat. Heart & Lung Inst, 70-74. AAAS; Am. Soc. Biol. Chem; Am. Soc. Hemat; Ger. Soc. Biol. Chem. Erythropoietin; regulation of hematopoiesis; control of cell differentiation by hormones; mechanism of action of hormones. Address: Hematology Research Labs, Childrens Hospital of Los Angeles, 4650 Sunset Blvd, Los Angeles, CA 90027.

DUKES, P(HILIP) D(USKIN), b. Reevesville, S.C, Jan. 16, 31; m. 56; c. 2. PLANT PATHOLOGY. B.S, Clemson Univ, 53; M.S, N.C. State Univ, 60, Ph.D.(plant path), 63. Plant chief clerk, Davison Chem. Corp, W.R. Grace & Co, 53-54; asst. county agent, S.C. Exten. Serv, 56-58; asst. plant pathologist & asst. prof. plant path, Coastal Plain Exp. Sta, Univ. Ga, 62-67, assoc. prof. plant path, 67-70; RES. PLANT PATHOLOGIST, VEG. BREEDING LAB, AGR. RES. SERV, U.S. DEPT. AGR, 70- Nat. Guard, 49-53; Sig.C, U.S.A, 54-56. Am. Phytopath. Soc; Bot. Soc. Am; Mycol. Soc. Am. Physiology of phytopathogenic fungi; physiology of parasitism of root and stem pathogens; breeding disease resistant vegetables; sweet potato diseases; physiology and genetics of Fusarium oxysporum f. sp. batatas. Address: Vegetables Breeding Lab, U.S. Dept. of Agriculture, P.O. Box 3348, Charleston, SC 29407.

DUKES-DOBOS, FRANCIS N, b. Budapest, Hungary, June 7, 20; U.S. citizen; m. 47; c. 1. ENVIRONMENTAL PHYSIOLOGY, ERGONOMICS. M.D, Eötvös Lóránd, Budapest, 51. Res. assoc. environ. physiol, Nat. Inst. Occup. Health, Budapest, 49-56; pathophysiol. allergy, Johns Hopkins Univ, 57-61; ASST. CHIEF LAB. PHYSIOL. & ERGONOMICS, NAT. INST. OCCUP. SAFETY & HEALTH, 61- Asst. clin. prof, grad. sch. environ. health, Univ. Cincinnati, 66-; environ. physiologist, WHO, Geneva, Switz, 67-69. AAAS; Am. Indust. Hyg. Asn; Am. Conf. Govt. Indust. Hygienists; Am. Physiol. Soc; Brit. Ergonomics Res. Soc. Environmental physiology; measurement of workers' industrial heat exposure, analysis of their physiological responses to heat stress and physical work; physiological assessment of fatigue; effect of food on autonomic nervous reactivity; human factors. Address: 7840 Glenorchard Dr, Cincinnati, OH 45237.

DUKLER, A(BRAHAM) E(MANUEL), b. Newark, N.J, Jan. 5, 25; m. 48; c. 3. CHEMICAL ENGINEERING. B.E, Yale, 45; M.S, Delaware, 50, Ph.D, 51. Develop. engr, Rohm Haas Co, 45-48; res. engr, Shell Oil Co, 50-52; asst. prof. CHEM. ENG, UNIV. HOUSTON, 52-54, assoc. prof, 54-60, PROF, 60-, CHMN. DEPT, 65-, TECH. DIR. HOUSTON RES. INST, 68- Vis. prof, Univ. Brazil, summer 63; Nat. Sci. Found. sr. fel, Eng, 67-68; consult, Shell Oil Co; off. saline water, U.S. Dept. Interior; Dow Chem. Co; NASA; U.S. Atomic Energy Comn. Am. Inst. Chem. Engrs-Alpha Chi Sigma res. award, 70. AAAS; Am. Chem. Soc; Am. Inst. Chem. Eng; Am. Soc. Eng. Educ. Fluid mechanics; multiphase flow; boundary layer; heat and mass transfer; turbulence. Address: Dept. of Chemical Engineering, University of Houston, Houston, TX 77004.

DULANEY, EUGENE L(AMBERT), b. Garbor, Okla, June 2, 19; m. 62; c. 1. MICROBIOLOGY. B.S, Texas Tech. Col, 41; M.A, Texas, 43; fel, Wisconsin, 43-44, 46, Ph.D.(bot), 46. Asst. biol, Texas Tech. Col, 39-41; tutor bot, Texas, 41-43; res, Off. Prod. Res. & Develop. proj, 44-45; sr. microbiologist, MERCK & CO, INC, 46-60, res. assoc, 60-65, SR. RES. FEL, MICROBIOL. RES. LABS, 65- Can. Nat. Res. Coun. fel, 55-56. Fel. AAAS; Bot. Soc. Am; Mycol. Soc. Am; Am. Soc. Microbiol; Torrey Bot. Club; fel. Am. Acad. Microbiol; Soc. Indust. Microbiol.(v.pres, 61-62, pres, 62-63); fel. N.Y. Acad. Sci; Can. Soc. Microbiol; Brit. Mycol. Soc; Brit. Soc. Gen. Microbiol; Mycol. Soc. France. Genetics and physiology of microorganisms; biology of streptomyces; mycology; industrial microbiology. Address: Merck Institute for Therapeutic Research, Rahway, NJ 07065.

DULBECCO, RENATO, b. Catanzaro, Italy, Feb. 22, 14; nat; m. 40, 63; c. 3. VIROLOGY. M.D, Univ. Turin, 36; hon. D.Sc, Yale, 68; hon. LL.D, Univ. Glasgow, 70. Asst. path, Univ. Turin, 40-45, histol. & embryol, 45-47; res. assoc. bact, Univ. Indiana, 47-49; sr. res. fel, Calif. Inst. Technol, 49-52, assoc. prof. BIOL, 52-54, prof, 54-63; SR. FEL, SALK INST. BIOL. STUDIES, 63- Albert & Mary Lasker Basic Med. Res. Award, 64; Howard Taylor Ricketts Award, 65; Paul Ehrlich-Ludwig Darmstaedter Adj. Prize,

67. Nat. Acad. Sci; AAAS; Am. Acad. Arts & Sci; Genetics Soc. Am; Am. Asn. Cancer Res; Tissue Cult. Asn. Radiations biology. Address: Salk Institute for Biological Studies, P.O. Box 1809, San Diego, CA 92112.

DULGEROFF, CARL R(ICHARD), b. Wood River, Ill, Dec. 26, 29; m. 57; c. 2. PHYSICS. A.B, Cent. Methodist Col, 53; Ph.D.(physics), Washington (St. Louis), 59. Asst. physics, Washington (St. Louis), 53-58, res. assoc, 58-59; sr. physicist, Rocketdyne Div, N.Am. Aviation, Inc, 59-60, prin. scientist, 60-63, sr. tech. specialist physics, 63-67; SECT. HEAD, HUGHES RES. LABS, MALIBU, 67- U.S.N, 48-49. Am. Phys. Soc; Am. Inst. Aeronaut. & Astronaut; Inst. Elec. & Electronics Eng. Beta and gamma ray spectroscopy; positron annihilation; electron polarization; ion propulsion; ultra high vacuum; thermal radiation. Address: 23110 Erwin St, Woodland Hills, CA 91364.

DULIN, WILLIAM E, b. Md, Jan. 25, 25; m. 48; c. 2. ZOOLOGY. B.S, Wash. Col.(Md), 47; Ph.D, Indiana, 52. Res. scientist, UPJOHN CO, 52-57, head res. sect, 57-68, MGR. DIABETES RES, 68- U.S.N.A.F, 43-45. Am. Diabetes Asn; Am. Physiol. Soc; Endocrine Soc; Soc. Exp. Biol. & Med. Carbohydrate metabolism; mechanism of action of hypoglycemic agents and exercise; fat metabolism; physiology of fat deposition and mobilization; steroid and protein hormone assays; studies on experimental diabetes. Address: Upjohn Co, Kalamazoo, MI 49001.

DULING, BRIAN R, b. Pueblo, Colo, May 27, 37; m. 56; c. 3. PHYSIOLOGY. A.B, Univ. Colo, Boulder, 62; Ph.D.(cardiovasc. physiol), Univ. Iowa, 67. U.S. Pub. Health Serv. fel. PHYSIOL, 67-68; instr. SCH. MED, UNIV. VA, 68-69, ASST. PROF, 69- Va. Heart Asn. jr. fel. physiol, 68-69. U.S.A.F, 55-58. AAAS; Am. Physiol. Soc. Investigation of the mechanisms active in controlling blood flow to tissues, especially relation between blood flow and tissue metabolic activity. Address: Dept. of Physiology, School of Medicine, University of Virginia, Charlottesville, VA 22901.

DULING, I(RL) N(OEL), b. Huntington, W.Va, Jan. 12, 29; m. 52; c. 2. ORGANIC & POLYMER CHEMISTRY. B.S, Mass. Inst. Tech, 50; M.S, Delaware, 58; Sun Oil Co. fel, Pennsylvania, 58-61, Ph.D.(org. chem), 61. Chemist, SUN OIL CO, 50-54, asst. res. chemist, 56-60, assoc. res. chemist, 60-66, res. chemist & sect. chief polymer & new chem. develop, 66-70, TECH. PLANNING ADV, 70- Mil. Intel, 54-56. Am. Chem. Soc. Constitution and physical properties of petroleum waxes; petrochemicals related to polymer technology; new polymers based on adamantane and naphthalene; properties of polymers and oils; synthetic lubricants. Address: Sun Oil Co, 1608 Walnut St, Philadelphia, PA 19103.

DULIS, EDWARD J(OHN), b. Brooklyn, N.Y, Oct. 30, 19; m. 45; c. 3. PHYSICAL METALLURGY. B.S, Alabama, 42; M.S, Stevens Inst. Tech, 50. Asst. metallurgist, U.S. Naval Air Sta, 42-45; res. metallurgist, U.S. Steel Res. Lab, N.J, 45-52, supv. technologist, appl. res. lab, Pa, 52-55; res. supvr, Crucible Steel Co. Am, 55-59, mgr. prod. res, 59-64, dir. prod. res. & develop, 64-65, res, 65-69, managing dir, CRUCIBLE MAT. RES. CTR, 69-71, PRES, 71- Am. Soc. Metals; Am. Inst. Min, Metall. & Petrol. Eng. Development of new stainless steels, valve steels, high temperature alloys, powder metallurgy products and processes; technical management toward commercial application of scientific developments. Address: Crucible Materials Research Center, P.O. Box 88, Pittsburgh, PA 15230.

DULK, GEORGE A, b. Denver, Colo, May 21, 30; m. 58; c. 1. RADIO ASTRONOMY, ASTROPHYSICS. B.S, U.S. Mil. Acad, 55; M.S, Purdue, 59; Nat. Sci. Found. fel. & Ph.D.(astro-geophys), Colorado, 65. Res. assoc. ASTRO-GEOPHYS, UNIV. COLO, BOULDER, 65-66, asst. prof, 66-70, ASSOC. PROF, 70- Vis. fel, Commonwealth Sci. & Indust. Res. Orgn, Australia, 69-70. Ord.C, U.S.A, 55-63, Capt. Am. Geophys. Union; Am. Astron. Soc; Int. Astron. Union; Astron. Asn. Australia. Ionospheric and magnetospheric physics; radio astronomy; satellite-planet relationships; Jupiter's radio emission; solar radiophysics; coronal structure. Address: Dept. of Astro-Geophysics, University of Colorado, Boulder, CO 80302.

DULKIN, S(OL) I, b. Chicago, Ill, Dec. 17, 15; m. 36; c. 2. PHYSIOLOGICAL CHEMISTRY. B.S, Lewis Inst, 40; M.S, Illinois, 47; Ph.D.(biochem), Northwestern, 51. Biochemist, Cook County Hosp, Ill, 39-41; consult. chemist, Dr. F. Hartman & Assocs, 41-44; nutrit. chemist, U.S. Army Qm. Food & Container Inst, 44-51; TECH. DIR, CHEM-TECH. LABS, 52- AAAS; Am. Chem. Soc; Am. Asn. Clin. Chem; Inst. Food Technol; Am. Asn. Bioanalysts; N.Y. Acad. Sci. Vitamins; assay procedures, stability studies and requirements; foods and nutrition; Browning reaction; army rations, analytical and adequacy; clinical methodology; metabolism; cancer research. Address: 236½ S. Robertson Blvd, Beverly,Hills, CA 90211.

DULL, GERALD G, b. Laurel, Mont, Aug. 20, 30; m. 53; c. 2. BIOCHEMISTRY. B.S, Mont. State Col, 52; Ph.D.(chem), Mich. State, 56. Head biochem. dept, Pineapple Res. Inst, Hawaii, 56-66; plant prod. qual. invest. leader, human nutrit. res. div, AGR. RES. SERV, U.S. DEPT. AGR, 66-69, CHIEF, FRUIT & VEG. LAB, RICHARD B. RUSSELL AGR. RES. CTR, 69- AAAS; Am. Chem. Soc; Inst. Food. Technol. Plant biochemistry; plant composition; post harvest fruit physiology; fruit and vegetable processing. Address: Richard B. Russell Agricultural Research Center, U.S. Dept. of Agriculture, Box 5677, Athens, GA 30604.

DULL, MALCOLM F(ELDHEISER), b. Chattanooga, Ohio, Feb. 17, 05; m. 34. ORGANIC CHEMISTRY. A.B, Hope Col, 26; M.S, Massachusetts, 28; Ph.D. (org. chem), Northwestern, 31. Instr. chem, DePaul, 32-33; chemist, Universal Oil Prods. Co, 33-34; prof. chem. & chmn. dept. chem. & physics, DePaul, 34-43; asst. prof, CHEM, UNIV. PITTSBURGH, 43-48, ASSOC. PROF, 48- Am. Chem. Soc. Organic chemistry of ketene; nitroparaffins; diphenylmethane derivatives; cyclohexylbenzene; plant enzymes; free radicals; browning reaction; carbene reactions; cyclopropanone derivatives; aliphatic nitroso compounds. Address: Dept. of Chemistry, University of Pittsburgh, Pittsburgh, PA 15213.

DULL, MARTIN H(ONER), b. Passaic, N.J, Dec. 21, 41; m. 69; c. 1. MATHEMATICS. B.A, Boston Col, 63; Schmitt fel, Univ. Notre Dame, 63, Danforth Found. fel, 63-69, M.S, 66, Nat. Sci. Found. traineeship, 68, Ph.D. (math), 69. Vis. asst. prof. MATH, West. Mich. Univ, 69-70; ASST. PROF, UNIV. PITTSBURGH, 70- Am. Math. Soc; Math. Asn. Am. Characterization of the automorphisms of the two-dimensional linear groups over integral domains. Address: Dept. of Mathematics, University of Pittsburgh, 4200 Fifth Ave, Pittsburgh, PA 15213.

DULL, RAYMOND B(ROADWELL), b. White Cloud, Mich, Oct. 15, 08; m. 39; c. 3. PHYSICS. A.B, Kalamazoo Col, 32; M.S, Chicago, 35; Ph.D.(physics), Pa. State, 38. Res. physicist, Nat. Carbon Co. Div, UNION CARBIDE CORP, 39-43, develop. engr, 43-55, tech. serv. mgr. arc carbons, 55-61, MEM. STAFF, CARBON PROD. DIV, PARMA TECH. CTR, 61- Physical testing; developmental engineering; spectroscopy; reserve and dry batteries; arc carbons; oxidation of graphite. Address: Carbon Products Division, Union Carbide Corp, P.O. Box 6116, Cleveland, OH 44101.

DULLAGHAN, MATTHEW EDWARD, b. New York, N.Y, Feb. 4, 24; m. 55; c. 3. ORGANIC & ANALYTICAL CHEMISTRY. B.S, Fordham, 47, M.S, 49, Ph.D.(synthetic org. chem), 53. Proj. leader, Evans Res. & Develop. Corp, 52-54; res. chemist, TEXTILE FIBERS DEPT, E.I. DU PONT DE NEMOURS & CO, Del, 54-60, SR. RES. CHEMIST, BENGER LAB, 60- Asst. prof, sch. ed, Fordham, 53-55. U.S.A, 42-46. AAAS; Am. Chem. Soc; Am. Asn. Textile Chem.& Colorists. Thiophene chemistry; explosives; natural products; textile fibers, polymerization, preparation and evaluation; dyeing and finishing of textiles. Address: E.I. du Pont de Nemours & Co, Benger Lab, P.O. Box 948, Waynesboro, VA 22980.

DULLER, NELSON M, JR, b. Houston, Tex, Mar. 6, 23; m. 55; c. 1. NUCLEAR PHYSICS. B.S, Texas A&M, 48; M.A, Rice, 51, Ph.D, 53. Asst. prof. PHYSICS, Texas A&M, 53-54; Missouri, 54-60, ASSOC. PROF, 60-62; TEX. A&M UNIV, 62- Sloan Found. fel, 56-58. U.S.A, 43-45. Am. Phys. Soc; Am. Asn. Physics Teachers; Ital. Phys. Soc. High energy nuclear and cosmic ray physics. Address: Dept. of Physics, Texas A&M University, College Station, TX 77843.

DULLIEN, FRANCIS A. L, b. Budapest, Hungary, Dec. 14, 25. CHEMICAL ENGINEERING, PHYSICAL CHEMISTRY. Chem.E, Budapest Tech, 50; Eldorado Mining & Ref. Co. fel, British Columbia, 57-58, M.Appl.Sci, 58, Ph.D.(chem. eng), 60. Asst. prof. phys. chem, Budapest Tech, 50-56; chem. eng, Okla. State, 60-62; sr. res. engr, Jersey Prod. Res. Co, 62-65; Esso Prod. Res. Co, 65-66; PROF. CHEM. ENG, UNIV. WATERLOO, 66- Vis. prof, Purdue Univ, 71-72. Am. Inst. Chem. Eng; Am. Chem. Soc; Soc. Petrol. Eng; Chem. Inst. Can; Can. Soc. Chem. Eng; N.Y. Acad. Sci. Diffusion and flow through porous media; determination of structure of porous media; mixing of liquids; air cleaning; diffusion in gaseous and liquid systems; surface chemistry. Address: R.R. 1, St. Agatha, Ont, Can.

DULMAGE, HOWARD T(AYLOR), b. Bridgeport, Conn, July 13, 23; m. 53; c. 2. MICROBIOLOGY. B.S, Illinois, 47; fel, Rutgers, 47-50, Ph.D.(microbiol), 51. Res. microbiologist, Abbott Labs, Ill, 50-62; Nutrilite Prod, Calif, 62-63, dir. biol. res. & develop, 63-67; RES. MICROBIOLOGIST, COTTON INSECT RES. BR, U.S. DEPT. AGR, 67- U.S.A, 43-46. Am. Chem. Soc; Am. Soc. Microbiol; Soc. Invert. Path; Entom. Soc. Am. Nutrition and strain studies actinomycetes; microbial fermentations; antitumor antibiotics; microbiological insect control. Address: 8 Edgewater Pl, Brownsville, TX 78520.

DULMAGE, W(ILLIAM) J(AMES), b. Winnipeg, Man, June 9, 19; nat; m. 42; c. 3. PHYSICAL CHEMISTRY. B.Sc, Manitoba, 46; Ph.D.(chem), Minnesota, 51. Lectr. chem, Manitoba, 46-47; res. & develop. chemist, Elec. Reduction Co, Can, Ltd, 51-52; res. assoc, RES. LABS, EASTMAN KODAK CO, 52-70, ASST. HEAD PHOTOMAT. DIV, 70- Can. Sig.C, 42-45. Am. Chem. Soc. X-ray crystallography; molecular structure; structure and properties of high polymers; phase rule studies; unconventional photoreproduction systems. Address: Research Labs, Eastman Kodak Co, Rochester, NY 14615.

DULOCK, VICTOR A, JR, b. Waco, Tex, Feb. 26, 39; m. 59; c. 4. PHYSICS. B.A, St. Thomas, 60; Ph.D.(physics), Florida, 64. Res. assoc. physics, Florida, 64-65; asst. prof, La. State Univ, New Orleans, 65-67; mem. prof. staff, TRW SYSTS, INC, 67-69, sect. head, 69-70, LAB. STAFF ENGR, 70- Am. Phys. Soc; Am. Asn. Physics Teachers. Analytical mechanics; quantum mechanics; group theory; electron scattering. Address: TRW Systems, Inc, One Space Park Dr, Houston, TX 77058.

DULZ, GÜNTHER, b. Hamburg, Ger, Apr. 25, 31; m. 60; c. 2. PHYSICAL CHEMISTRY. M.S, Kiel, 59; Fulbright fel, Columbia, 59-63, Ph.D.(chem), 63. Asst. chem, Columbia, 59-60; jr. res. assoc, Brookhaven Nat. Lab, 60-62, res. assoc, 62-63; res. chemist, E.I. DU PONT DE NEMOURS & CO, INC, 63-66, SR. RES. CHEMIST, TEXTILE RES. LAB, 66- Am. Chem. Soc; Ger. Chem. Soc. Kinetics of inorganic oxidation-reduction reactions; polymer chemistry; kinetics and thermodynamics of polyamidation. Address: Textile Research Lab, E.I. Du Pont de Nemours & Co, Inc, Chestnut Run, Wilmington, DE 19898.

DUM, CHRISTIAN T(HOMAS), b. Saalfelden, Austria, June 14, 39. PLASMA & THEORETICAL PHYSICS. Dipl. appl. math, Vienna Tech. Univ, 63, Dipl. Ing, 64; U.S. Dept. State Fulbright travel grant, 64-66; Ph.D.(physics), Mass. Inst. Technol, 68. Teaching asst, Mass. Inst. Technol, 64-67, res. asst, 67-68; res. assoc. plasma physics, CORNELL UNIV, 68-70, instr. elec. eng, 69-70, ASST. PROF. APPL. PHYSICS, 70- Int. Atomic Energy Agency-UN Educ. Sci. & Cult. Orgn. scientist, Int. Ctr. Theoret. Physics, Italy, 70; staff scientist, Max Planck Inst. Plasma Physics, 71- Am. Phys. Soc. Plasma physics, especially nonlinear phenomena, plasma turbulence and transport processes; statistical mechanics. Address: Lab. of Plasma Studies, Cornell University, Ithaca NY 14850.

DUMAN, M(AXIMILIAN) G(EORGE), b. Nicktown, Pa, Feb. 21, 06. SYSTEMATIC BOTANY. A.B, St. Vincent Col, 32; M.S, Catholic Univ, 37, Ph.D. (bot), 41. Instr. BIOL, St. Vincent Col, 32-36, 37-39, assoc. prof, 41-56; Catholic Univ, 57-61, PROF, ST. VINCENT COL, 61-, pres. col, 62-63. Instr, Latrobe Hosp, 46-58. Mem, Arctic exped, Catholic Univ, 39, Hudson Bay, 38, 39, North Quebec, 50, Ungava, 51, James Bay, 52, 53, 54, 55, 56,

Yukon, 70, N.W. Territories, 71. Arctic field trip, Int. Bot. Cong. 59. AAAS; assoc. Bot. Soc. Am; assoc. Am. Soc. Plant Taxon; Int. Asn. Plant Taxon. Taxonomic and distributional studies of arctic and subarctic carices. Address: Dept. of Biology, St. Vincent College, Latrobe, PA 15650.

DUMAS, DAVID HOWARD, Youngstown, Ohio, June 4, 42; m. 65; c. 1. ORGANIC & PAPER CHEMISTRY. B.S, Youngstown State Univ, 64; Ph.D.(org. chem), Univ. Pittsburgh, 68. RES. CHEMIST, HERCULES INC, 68- Am. Chem. Soc. Organic synthesis of natural products; chemistry of paper additives. Address: Hercules Research Center, Wilmington, DE 19899.

DUMAS, HERBERT M, JR, b. El Dorado, Ark, Dec. 16, 27; m. 53; c. 1. SOLID STATE PHYSICS, OPTICS. A.B, Arkansas, 54, B.S, 55, M.S, 56. Tech. staff mem. physics, SANDIA CORP, 56-60, supvr. tech. sect, 60-65, seismic systs. div, 65-69, SUPVR. SATELLITE SENSORS DIV, 69- U.S.N, 46-49, Sig.C, 52-54, 2nd Lt. Optical Soc. Am. Detection instrumentation and diagnostic measurements of atomic detonations; seismic systems development; energy conversion devices. Address: 1304 Florida N.E, Albuquerque, NM 87110.

DUMAS, JEAN, b. Montreal, Que, June 4, 25; m. 53; c. 5. ELECTRICAL ENGINEERING. B.Eng, McGill, 48; S.B, Mass. Inst. Tech, 51, S.M, 52. Res. scientist, Can. Armament Res. & Develop. Estab, 52-55; asst. prof. ELEC. ENG, LAVAL UNIV, 55-58, assoc. prof, 58-68, PROF, 68-, asst. head dept, 66-69. Ford fel, Carnegie Inst. Technol, 61-62. Inst. Elec. & Electronics Eng. Measurements; circuits; standards; lines. Address: Dept. of Electrical Engineering, Laval University, Quebec, Que, Can.

DUMAS, KENNETH J, b. New York, N.Y, Oct. 26, 26; m. 52; c. 3. MEDICINE. A.B, Drew, 48; M.D, N.Y. Med. Col, 52. Assoc. dir. clin. res, Chas. Pfizer & Co, Inc, 54-59, dir, 59-61; dir. clin. res, Syntex Labs, Inc, 61-62, med. dir, 62-64, SYNTEX RES, 64-66, V.PRES. & DIR. INST. CLIN. MED, 66- U.S.N, 44-46. Am. Med. Asn; N.Y. Acad. Sci. Direct multi-disciplinary clinical and biological group responsible for animal toxicology, experimental pharmacology and clinical research with both steroidal and nonsteroidal compounds. Address: Institute of Clinical Medicine, Syntex Research, Stanford Industrial Park, Palo Alto, CA 94304.

DUMAS, LAWRENCE B(ERNARD), b. Plainwell, Mich, Mar. 2, 41; m. 65; c. 2. MOLECULAR BIOLOGY, BIOCHEMISTRY. B.S, Mich. State Univ, 63; M.S, Univ. Wis, Madison, 65, U.S. Pub. Health Serv. fel, 65-68, Ph.D.(biochem), 68. U.S. Pub. Health Serv. res. fel. biol, Calif. Inst. Technol, 68-70; ASST. PROF. BIOL. SCI, NORTHWEST. UNIV, 70- AAAS. Mechanism and control of the replication of nucleic acids. Address: Dept. of Biological Sciences, Northwestern University, Evanston, IL 60201.

DUMAS, PHILIP C(ONRAD), b. Wash, Apr. 9, 23; m. 46; c. 3. VERTEBRATE ZOOLOGY. B.S, Oregon State, 48, M.A, 49, Ph.D.(zool), 53. Instr. biol, Idaho, 53-55, asst. prof, 55-65; assoc. prof. ZOOL, CENT. WASH. STATE COL, 65-70, PROF, 70-, CHMN. DEPT. BIOL, 66- U.S.A, 43-46. Zoogeography; herpetology; ecology. Address: Dept. of Biological Science, Central Washington State College, Ellensburg, WA 98926.

DUMBAUGH, WILLIAM H(ENRY), JR, b. Butler, Pa, Dec. 12, 29. INORGANIC & PHYSICAL CHEMISTRY. B.S, Rochester, 51; Res. Corp. fel. & Ph.D.(chem), Pa. State, 59. Sr. chemist, CORNING GLASS WORKS, 58-66, MGR. GLASS CHEM. RES, 66- U.S.N, 51-54, Res, 54-60, Lt. Am. Chem. Soc; Brit. Soc. Glass Technol; Am. Ceramic Soc. Glass composition; high temperature chemistry. Address: Research & Development Dept, Corning Glass Works, Sullivan Park, Corning, NY 14830.

DUMBAULD, RICHARD K(EITH), b. Somerset, Pa, Mar. 23, 32; m. 53; c. 3. METEOROLOGY. B.S, Pittsburgh, 54; N.Y. Univ, 54-55; M.S, Michigan, 59. Res. asst, Indust. Hyg. Found. Am, 53-54; res. meteorologist, U.S. Weather Bur, 59-62; STAFF SCIENTIST, GCA TECHNOL. DIV, GCA CORP, 63- U.S.A.F, 54-58, Capt. Am. Geophys. Union; Am. Meteorol. Soc; Royal Meteorol. Soc; Air Pollution Control Asn. Development and application of atmospheric diffusion and transport models to applied problems in air pollution; hazard-safety analysis for weapons tests; reactor operations; design and analysis of atmospheric measurement programs. Address: GCA Technology Division, GCA Corp, P.O. Box 15009, Salt Lake City, UT 84115.

DUMBROFF, ERWIN B(ERNARD), b. Newark, N.J, Mar. 20, 32; m. 51; c. 3. PLANT PHYSIOLOGY, BIOSTATISTICS. B.S.F, Georgia, 56, M.F, 58, Ph.D.(bot, plant physiol), 64. Res. forester, U.S. Forest Serv, Fla, 57-60, Ga, 60-64, plant physiologist, 64-65; asst. prof. BIOL, UNIV. WATERLOO, 65-68, ASSOC. PROF, 68- U.S.M.C, 50-52, Res, 52-57, S/Sgt. AAAS; Am. Soc. Plant Physiol; Can. Soc. Plant Physiol; Am. Inst. Biol. Sci. Mineral nutrition and mechanisms of ion uptake; seed physiology; dormancy mechanisms in plants; mechanisms of salt tolerance. Address: Dept. of Biology, University of Waterloo, Waterloo, Ont, Can.

DUMENIL, LLOYD C, b. Argyle, Iowa, July 23, 20; m. 44; c. 1. SOIL FERTILITY. B.S, Iowa State, 42, M.S, 51, Ph.D.(soil fertil), 58. Res. assoc. SOILS, IOWA STATE UNIV, 46-50, asst. prof, 50-58, ASSOC. PROF, 58- Sig.C, U.S.A, 42-43. Am. Soc. Agron. Response of field crops to fertilization; soil and crop management; climatic factors affecting corn yields. Address: Dept. of Agronomy, Iowa State University, Ames, IA 50010.

DUMEY, ARNOLD I, b. N.Y.C, Nov. 30, 06; m. 39; c. 1. ELECTRONICS. A.B, Columbia Univ, 27, J.D, 29. Analyst, Armed Forces Security Agency, 46-52; systs. designer electronics, Potter Instrument Co, Inc, 52-54; CONSULT, 54- Consult, Nat. Security Agency, U.S. Dept. Defense, 53-, mem. sci. adv. bd, 58-70; consult, Inst. Defense Anal, 59-, mem. tech. staff, 67-69, adv. comt, commun. res. div, 62-; consult, Proj. MAC, Mass. Inst. Technol, 63. U.S.A, 42-46, Res, 46-70, Lt.Col.(Ret). AAAS; Inst. Elec. & Electronics Eng; Asn. Comput. Mach. Data handling by electronic and electromechanical means; computers. Address: 641 Mt. Lucas Rd, Princeton, NJ 08540.

DUMIN, DAVID J(OSEPH), b. Westfield, Mass, Oct. 6, 35; m. 64. SOLID STATE PHYSICS. B.S, Hopkins, 57; M.S, Purdue, 61; Ph.D.(elec. eng), Stanford, 65. Cryogenics engr, Int. Bus. Mach. Corp, 57-60; asst. electromagnetic theory, Purdue, 60-61; SOLID STATE PHYSICS, Stanford, 61-64; MEM. TECH. STAFF, RCA CORP, 64- Outstanding achievement award, RCA Labs, 66. Sig.C.Res, Capt. AAAS. Materials science in solid state physics. Address: RCA Labs, David Sarnoff Research Center, Princeton, NJ 08540.

DUMITRU, EARL TRAIAN, b. Hamilton, Ont, Mar. 4, 28; m. 50; c. 5. PHYSICAL & POLYMER CHEMISTRY. B.Sc, McMaster, 50, M.Sc, 52; Ph.D. (phys. chem), Cornell, 57. Res. chemist, polymer res. lab, plastics dept, Dow Chem. Co, 57-68; sr. staff mem, Am. Cement Co, 68-70, group leader polymers, 70-71; SUPVR. POLYMER SYNTHESIS, HOOKER CHEM. & PLASTICS DIV, OCCIDENTAL PETROL. CORP, 71- Am. Chem. Soc. Composites of polymers with cement; impact-resistant plastics; flame-retardant plastics; synthesis and evaluation of polymers. Address: Occidental Petroleum Corp, Hooker Research Center, M.P.O. Box 8, Niagara Falls, NY 14302.

DUMKE, WALTER H(ENRY), b. Sleepy Eye, Minn, July 12, 04; m. 30. PHYSICAL CHEMISTRY. B.S, Minnesota, 27; fel, Colo. Sch. Mines, 27-29, M.S, 29; fel, Iowa, 29-31, Ph.D, 31. Res. chemist, Gates Rubber Co, Colo, 32-33; res. engr, Bur. Reclamation, U.S. Dept. Interior, 33-37; from asst. prof. CHEM. to assoc. prof, COLO. SCH. MINES, 37-57, prof. & head dept, 57-70, EMER. PROF, 71- Am. Chem. Soc. Sulfur compounds in oil-shale; gasometric determination of oxygen in coals; dielectric constants and electric moments of fatty acids; particle size analysis of Portland and pozzolana cement; oil aerosols; metal complexes in oil crudes. Address: 3320 W. 46th Ave, Denver, CO 80211.

DUMKE, WARREN LLOYD, b. Milwaukee, Wis, Oct. 26, 28; m. 63. CHEMICAL PHYSICS, PHYSICAL CHEMISTRY. B.S, Wisconsin, 51; Off. Naval Res. fel, Utah, 51-53; M.S, Iowa State, 56; Ph.D.(phys. chem), Nebraska, 65. Res. asst. phys. chem, Atomic Energy Cmn-Iowa State, 53-56; instr. chem. physics & sci, Mankato State Col, 56-58; asst. chem, Nebraska, 58-64; asst. prof, Kent State, 64-65; NASA res. assoc. neutron diffraction, 65-67; asst. prof. PHYSICS, MARSHALL UNIV, 67-71, ASSOC. PROF, 71- Am. Chem. Soc; Am. Crystallog. Asn. X-ray and neutron diffraction; quantum mechanical calculations. Address: Dept. of Physics, Marshall University, Huntington, WV 25703.

DUMM, MARY E(LIZABETH), b. Newark, N.J, Dec. 9, 16. BIOCHEMISTRY. A.B, Swarthmore Col, 38; M.A, Bryn Mawr Col, 40, Ph.D.(biochem), 43; Harvard Med. Sch, 41-42. Instr. biol, Bryn Mawr Col, 42-44; chem. col. med, N.Y. Univ, 44-47, asst. med, 47-50, adj. asst. prof, 50-56, asst. prof, 56-59; lectr. BIOCHEM, VELLORE CHRISTIAN MED. COL, 59-60, assoc. prof, 60-64, PROF, 64- Adj. prof, Teachers Col, Columbia Univ, 71- Am. Physiol. Soc; Endocrine Soc; Soc. Exp. Biol. & Med; Diabetes Asn; N.Y. Acad. Sci. Endocrinology and metabolism; medical, clinical and nutritional biochemistry. Address: 13 Samson Ave, Madison, NJ 07940.

DUMMEL, ROBERT J(OSEPH), b. San Francisco, Calif, June 19, 30; m. 57; c. 2. ORGANIC CHEMISTRY. B.S, San Francisco, 52; M.S, Stanford, 54, Ph.D.(chem), 58. Res. assoc. med. colloids proj, Palo Alto Med. Res. Found, 58-60; Hazleton Nuclear Sci. Corp, Palo Alto, 60-61; Alberta, 61-63; acting asst. prof. pharm, SCH. MED, UNIV. CALIF, SAN FRANCISCO, 63-65, RES. CHEMIST PHARMACOL, 65- Am. Chem. Soc; The Chem. Soc. Organic synthesis; biochemistry; teaching. Address: Dept. of Pharmacology, School of Medicine, University of California, San Francisco Medical Center, San Francisco, CA 94122.

DUMMETT, CLIFTON O(RRIN), b. Georgetown, British Guiana, May 20, 19; nat; m. 43; c. 1. PERIODONTOLOGY. B.S, Roosevelt Col, 41; D.D.S, Northwestern, 41, M.S.D, 42; Rosenwald fel, Michigan, 46-47, M.P.H, 47. Prof. periodont, oral path. & pub. health & dean & dir. dent. ed, sch. dent, Meharry, 45-49; chief dent. serv. & exec. secy. res. & educ, Vet. Admin. Hosp, Tuskegee, 49-64; prof. dent, sch. vet. med, Tuskegee Inst, 64-66; assoc. prof. periodont, sch. dent, Univ. Ala, 65-66; dent, Northwest. Univ, 66; chief dent. serv, Vet. Admin. Res. Hosp. & chmn. res. study group oral diseases, 66; prof. & chmn. dept. community dent. & dent. dir. multipurpose health serv. ctr, UNIV. SOUTH. CALIF, 66-68, ASSOC. DEAN EXTRAMURAL AFFAIRS, 68- Mem. comt, pub. health surv. dent, Am. Coun. Educ; del, nat. citizen comt, World Health Org, 53. Dipl, Am. Bd. Periodont; Am. Bd. Oral Med. U.S.A.F, 55-57, Maj. AAAS; fel. Am. Pub. Health Asn; Am. Dent. Asn; Nat. Dent. Asn.(award, 52, ed. bull. 53-); Am. Asn. Endodontists; Int. Asn. Dent. Res.(v.pres, 67, pres. elect, 68). Oral pathology; public health dentistry; dental education; oral diagnosis. Address: School of Dentistry, University of Southern California, Los Angeles, CA 90007.

DU MOND, JESSE W(ILLIAM) M(ONROE), b. Paris, France, July 11, 92; U.S. citizen; m. 19, 44; c. 2. PHYSICS. B.S, Calif. Inst. Tech, 16; fel, 21-29, Ph.D. (physics), 29; M.S, Union (N.Y), 19; hon. Dr, Royal Univ. Uppsala, 66; hon. D.Sc, Univ. Man, 67. With testing dept, Gen. Elec. Co, N.Y, 16-17, consult. eng. dept, 17-18; designer, turbo alternator dept, French Thomson-Houston Co, Paris, 19-20; asst. elec. engr, Nat. Bur. Standards, 20-21; res. fel. PHYSICS, CALIF. INST. TECHNOL, 29-31, res. assoc, 31-38, assoc. prof, 38-46, prof, 46-63, EMER. PROF, 63- Acting assoc. prof, Stanford, 31. Mem. cmt. fundamental phys. constants & conversion factors, Nat. Res. Coun. With Off. Sci. Res. & Develop; U.S.A.A.F; U.S.N, 44. C.Eng, U.S.A, 18-19. Nat. Acad. Sci; Am. Phys. Soc; Fr. Phys. Soc. Complex quantity sliderule; stereofluoroscope; Compton modified line structure; linear momenta of structure electrons in solid and gaseous matter; multi-crystal spectrograph; curved crystal x-ray spectrograph; precision two crystal x-ray spectrometer; high intensity x-ray tube; precision measurements of the atomic constants, e, h/e, h/m; new consistency diagram for the atomic constants; ballistics; acoustics; solid state; gamma-ray spectroscopy; beta-ray spectroscopy; point-focusing monochromators for low-angle x-ray diffraction; least squares evaluations of the atomic constants. Address: Dept. of Physics, West Norman Bridge Lab, Room 163, California Institute of Technology, Pasadena, CA 91109.

DUMONT, ALLAN E, b. New York, N.Y, Oct. 8, 24; m. 49; c. 3. SURGERY, PHYSIOLOGY. B.A, Hobart Col, 45; M.D, N.Y. Univ, 48. Instr. SURG, MED. SCH, MED. CTR, N.Y. UNIV, 55-59, asst. prof, 59-62, assoc. prof, 62-68, PROF, 68- A.A. Berg fel. exp. surg, 55-59; investr, N.Y. Health Res. Coun, 59-61; U.S. Pub. Health Serv. fel, 61-62, res. career develop. award, 61-71. Med.C.Res, 51-53, Lt.(jg). AAAS; Am. Physiol. Soc; Soc. Exp. Biol. & Med; Soc. Univ. Surg; Am. Surg. Asn. Function of the lymphatic system; wound healing. Address: Dept. of Surgery, Medical School, New York University Medical Center, 550 First Ave, New York, NY 10016.

DUMONT, JAMES NICHOLAS, b. Sigourney, Iowa, Sept. 19, 35; m. 61; c. 2. ZOOLOGY, CYTOLOGY. B.S, State Univ. Iowa, 57, M.S, 60; Ph.D.(zool), Massachusetts, 64. Instr. biol, Rockford Col, 61-62; res. assoc. zool, Massachusetts, 64-65, lectr. electron micros, 65-66; RES. BIOLOGIST, OAK RIDGE NAT. LAB, 66- Lectr, Univ. Tenn-Oak Ridge Grad. Sch. Biomed. Sci, 71- Am. Soc. Zool; Electron Micros. Soc. Am; Am. Soc. Cell Biol; Am. Asn. Anat; Soc. Study Reproduction. Electron microscopy; oocyte development. Address: Biology Division, Oak Ridge National Lab, Oak Ridge, TN 37830.

DuMONT, PHILIP A(TKINSON), b. Rochester, Minn, July 9, 03; m. 35; c. 4. ORNITHOLOGY. B.S, Drake, 26; California, 32; Iowa, 32-33. Mem, Am. Mus. Natural Hist. Franco-Anglo-Am. mission, Madagascar, 29-31; wildlife technician, State Fish & Game Cmn, Iowa, 33-35; Malheur Nat. Wildlife Refuge, U.S. Fish & Wildlife Serv, Ore, 35; refuge mgr, Sand Lake Nat. Wildlife Refuge, S.Dak, 36-39; biologist, DIV. NAT. WILDLIFE REFUGES, U.S. FISH & WILDLIFE SERV, 39-59, chief sect. pub. use, 59-64, CHIEF BR. INTERPRETATION, 64- Am. Ornith. Union; Wilson Ornith. Soc; Cooper Ornith. Soc; Wildlife Soc. Bird migration and distribution, particularly in Iowa and Madagascar; national wildlife refuge system; albatrosses on Midway Islands. Address: U.S. Fish & Wildlife Service, Interior Bldg, Room 2350, Washington, DC 20240.

DuMONTELLE, PAUL B(ERTRAND), b. Kankakee, Ill, June 22, 33; m. 55; c. 5. GEOLOGY. B.A, DePauw Univ, 55; M.S, Lehigh Univ, 57. Geologist, Homestake Mining Co, 57-63; ASSOC. GEOLOGIST, ILL. STATE GEOL. SURV, 63- Am. Inst. Mining, Metall. & Petrol. Eng; Geol. Soc. Am; Am. Inst. Prof. Geol. Engineering and environmental geology; topographic and computer mapping. Address: 2020 Burlison Dr, Urbana, IL 61801.

DUN, F(WU) T(ARNG), b. China, May 9, 10; nat; m. 28; c. 3. NEUROPHYSIOLOGY. B.Sc, Tsing Hua Univ, China, 33; China Found. Res. Fel. physiol, Cambridge, 37-39; D.rer. nat, Jena, 39. Asst. psychol, Tsing Hua Univ, 33-35; res. fel. neurophysiol, Peiping Union Med. Sch, 39-42; prof. physiol. psychol, Tsing Hua Univ, 42-48; lectr. physiol, Otago Med. Sch, New Zealand, 49-52; asst. res. neurophysiologist, Washington (Seattle), 52-53, assoc. prof. PHYSIOL, KIRKSVILLE COL. OSTEOPATH. MED, 53-59, PROF, 59- Am. Physiol. Soc; N.Y. Acad. Sci; Fedn. Am. Soc. Exp. Biol. Synaptic and neuromuscular transmission of impulses; interaction between nerve fibers; conduction of impulses along branched nerve fibers; chemical processes accompanying the afterpotentials; nodes of Ravier in fibers of different diameters and at points of branchings. Address: Dept. of Physiology, Kirksville College of Osteopathic Medicine, Kirksville, MO 63501.

DUNAGAN, T(OMMY) T(OLSON), b. Hamilton, Tex, Oct. 17, 31; m. 56; c. 2. PHYSIOLOGY. B.S, Texas A&M, 53, M.S, 55; Ph.D.(zool), Purdue, 60. Parasitologist, Arctic Aeromed Lab, 55-57; Nat. Insts. Health res. fel, Purdue, 58-62; asst. prof. PHYSIOL, SOUTH. ILL. UNIV, 62-66, assoc. prof, 66-71, PROF, 71- U.S.A.F, 55-57, Lt. Am. Soc. Parasitol; N.Y. Acad. Sci. Physiological parasitology; biochemistry; tissue culture of helminths. Address: Dept. of Physiology, Southern Illinois University, Carbondale, IL 62901.

DUNATHAN, H(ARMON) C(RAIG), b. Celina, Ohio, July 25, 32; m. 56; c. 2. ORGANIC CHEMISTRY. B.A, Ohio Wesleyan, 54; M.S, Yale, 55, Ph.D, 58. Asst. prof. CHEM, HAVERFORD COL, 57-63, assoc. prof, 63-68, PROF, 68- Organic reaction mechanisms; mechanism of enzyme action. Address: Dept. of Chemistry, Haverford College, Haverford, PA 19041.

DUNAVANT, BILLY G(LENN), b. Hot Springs, Ark, Oct. 4, 25; m. 49. BIONUCLEONICS. B.S, George Peabody Col, 50, M.A, 53; Ph.D, Purdue, 59. Instr. biol. & chem, Freed-Hardeman Col, 50-54; tech. reviewer & tech. asst. to dir. isotopes div, U.S. Atomic Energy Comn, 54-56; radiological control off. & radiobiologist, Purdue, 56-59, asst. prof. health physics, 59-60; assoc. prof. RADIATION BIOL, COL. MED, UNIV. FLA, 60-67, PROF, 67-, DIR. NUCLEAR SCI, UNIV, 66-, univ. radiation control off, 60-64, asst. dir. nuclear sci, 64-66. Consult, Atomic Energy Comn. U.S.N, 43-46. Fel. AAAS; Soc. Nuclear Med; Health Physics Soc; Am. Asn. Physicists in Med. Radiation biophysics; radioisotope tracers in biological research; environmental radioactivity. Address: 317 Nuclear Sciences Center, University of Florida, Gainesville, FL 32601.

DUNAVIN, LEONARD SYPRET, JR, b. Algood, Tenn, Dec. 17, 30; m. 62; c. 1. AGRONOMY. B.S, Tenn. Polytech, 52; M.S.A, Florida, 54, Nat. Plant Food Inst. fel, 57-59, Ph.D.(agron), 59. Asst. agronomist, AGR. RES. CTR, JAY, UNIV. FLA, 59-67, ASSOC. AGRONOMIST, 67- U.S.A, 54-56. Am. Soc. Agron; Crop Sci. Soc. Am. Production and management of pasture and forage crops, their physiological responses to environment with emphasis on microclimate. Address: Agricultural Research Center, Jay, Route 3, Box 575, Jay, FL 32565.

DUNAWAY, PAUL B(URNETT), b. Decherd, Tenn, May 16, 24; m. 49; c. 3. ZOOLOGY. B.A, Tennessee, 50, M.S, 54. Tech. ed, OAK RIDGE NAT. LAB, UNION CARBIDE CORP, 55-58, VERT. ECOLOGIST, 58- U.S.M.C.R, 42-45, Sgt. AAAS; Am. Soc. Mammal; Radiation Res. Soc. Effects of ionizing radiation on vertebrate populations; mammalian population dynamics; biological cycling of radionuclides; environmental impact of nuclear reactors. Address: Ecological Sciences Division, Oak Ridge National Lab, Oak Ridge, TN 37830.

DUNBAR, BURDETT S(HERIDAN), b. Kewanee, Ill, Dec. 6, 38; m. 71. MEDICINE, ANESTHESIOLOGY. B.S, Illinois, Urbana, 60, M.D, 63. Intern, Springfield City Hosp, Ohio, 63-64; resident ANESTHESIOL, Hosp. Univ. Pa, 64-66, Nat. Insts. Health res. fel, dept. physiol, grad. sch. med, Pennsylvania, 66-67; clin. asst. prof, med. sch, Texas, San Antonio, 68-69; ASST. PROF, Univ. Chicago, 69-71; GEORGE WASH. UNIV, 71-, STAFF ANESTHESIOLOGIST, UNIV. HOSP, 71- Attend. staff physician, Michael Reese Hosp. & Med. Ctr, 69-71. U.S.A.F, 67-69, Capt. AAAS; Am. Med. Asn; Am. Soc. Anesthesiol. Respiratory physiology. Address: Dept. of Anesthesiology, George Washington University Hospital, Washington, DC 20037.

DUNBAR, CARL O(WEN), b. Hallowell, Kans, Jan. 1, 91; m. 15; c. 2. PALEONTOLOGY. A.B, Kansas, 13; Ph.D.(paleont), Yale, 17. Dana res. fel, Yale, 17-18; instr. geol, Minnesota, 18-20; asst. curator invert. paleont, PEABODY MUS, YALE, 20-26, curator, 26-59, dir, 42-59, asst. prof. hist. geol, UNIV, 20-27, assoc. prof, 27-30, prof. PALEONT. & STRATIG, 30-59, EMER. PROF. & EMER. DIR, 59- Civilian scientist observer, Oper. Crossroads, 46. Assoc. ed, J. Paleont, 30-38; Am. J. Sci, 39- Mem. staff exped, Newf. & Labrador. Del, Int. Geol. Cong, Moscow, 37. Hayden medal, Phila. Acad. Sci; distinguished serv. citation, Kansas. Nat. Acad. Sci; Am. Philos. Soc; fel. Geol. Soc. Am.(v.pres, 52); fel. Paleont. Soc.(treas, 24-37, 43-46, pres, 40; medal); hon. mem. Soc. Econ. Paleont. & Mineral; Am. Asn. Petrol. Geol; Am. Geophys. Union; Am. Acad. Arts & Sci; for. cor. mem. Am. Geol. Soc. London; hon. mem. Mex. Geol. Soc. Historical geology; paleontology and stratigraphy of the late Paleozoic; Fusulinidae; Brachiopoda; general biology; administration of scientific acitivity; invertebrate zoology. Address: 1615 Santa Barbara Dr, Dunedin, FL 33528.

DUNBAR, HOWARD S(TANFORD), b. Jersey City, N.J, Sept. 30, 19; m. 44; c. 3. NEUROLOGICAL SURGERY. A.B, Cornell, 41, M.D, 44. Ledyard fel, MED. COL, CORNELL UNIV, 51-52, asst. prof, neurosurg, 52-64, ASSOC. PROF. NEUROL. SURG, 64- Dir. neuro-surg, Roosevelt Hosp; consult, Montrose Vet. Hosp. Fel. Am. Col. Surg; Harvey Soc. Radioisotopes in localization of brain lesions; stereotoxin surgery. Address: 430 E. 63rd St, New York, NY 10021.

DUNBAR, JEAN M(EAD), b. Avon, Ill, Nov. 25, 03; m. 25. CHEMISTRY. B.Ed, West. Ill. State Teachers Col, 24; M.S, Northwestern, 36, Ph.D.(biochem), 38. Instr. chem, Lewis Inst, 30-40; biochemist, Armour & Co, 38-41; lab. mgr, Benvenue Lab, Ohio, 41-42; chem. engr. & asst. chief chemist, Kingsbury Ord. Plant, Ind, 42-43; supvr. Pepsodent div, Lever Bros, 43-52; tech. dir, Lanteen Labs, 52-53; mem. tech. sales dept, Algin Corp, 53-54; instr. col. pharmacy, Illinois, 56-61; PROF. MFG. PHARM, SAMFORD UNIV, 61- Instr, Northwestern, 40-41, 44-45. Characterization of gastic mucin and its resistance to enzymatic degradation; dentifrice manufacturing; manufacturing pharmacy. Address: School of Pharmacy, Samford University, Birmingham, AL 35209.

DUNBAR, JOHN SCOTT, b. Toronto, Ont, Aug. 16, 21; m. 49; c. 3. RADIOLOGY. M.D, Toronto, 45. Dir. radiol. dept, Montreal Children's Hosp, 52-71, assoc. prof. med, McGill Univ, 63-71; PROF. DIAG. RADIOL. & CHMN. DEPT, UNIV. B.C. & DIR. DEPT. DIAG. RADIOL, VANCOUVER GEN. HOSP, 71- Can. Army, 43-46, Capt. Am. Roentgen Ray Soc; Soc. Pediat. Radiol; Asn. Univ. Radiol; Am. Col. Radiol; Radiol. Soc. N.Am; Can. Asn. Radiol; Can. Med. Asn. Diagnostic radiology. Address: Dept. of Diagnostic Radiology, University of British Columbia, Vancouver, B.C, Can.

DUNBAR, JOSEPH E(DWARD), b. Bristol, Conn, Feb. 9, 24; m. 51; c. 5. ORGANIC CHEMISTRY. B.S, Rensselaer Polytech, 49; M.S, Illinois, 52, Ph.D.(chem), 56. Asst. org. res. chemist, Ill. Geol. Surv, 49-53; org. res. chemist, DOW CHEM. U.S.A, 55-62, sr. res. chemist, 62-66, group leader, E.C. BRITTON RES. LAB, 66- U.S.A, 42-46. AAAS; Am. Chem. Soc; Am. Inst. Chem. Correlation of chemical structure with biological activity; chemistry of organic sulfur compounds; bioalkylating agents. Address: 5813 Sturgeon Creek Pkwy, Midland, MI 48640.

DUNBAR, M(AXWELL) J(OHN), b. Edinburgh, Scotland, Sept. 19, 14; m. 45. ZOOLOGY. B.A, Oxford, 37, M.A, 39; Henry fel, Yale, 37-38; Nat. Res. Coun. Can. fel, McGill, 40-41, Ph.D.(zool), 41. Can. consul, Dept. External Affairs, Greenland, 41-46; asst. prof, ZOOL, McGILL UNIV, 46-48, assoc. prof, 48-59, PROF, 59-, CHMN, MARINE SCI. CENTRE, 63- Guggenheim fel, Denmark, 52-53; convenor, Int. Biol. Prog, 70- Bruce Medal for polar exploration, Royal Soc. Edinburgh. AAAS; hon. fel. Am. Geog. Soc; fel. Royal Soc. Can; fel. Royal Geog. Soc. Marine biology and oceanography; arctic regions; breeding cycles in the arctic plankton; production in arctic water; development of arctic marine resources; history of biology. Address: Marine Sciences Centre, McGill University, Montreal 110, Que, Can.

DUNBAR, PHYLLIS M(ARGUERITE), b. Bronxville, N.Y. PHYSICAL CHEMISTRY. B.A, Columbia, 45, scholar, 46-47, M.A, 47, fel, 47-49, Ph.D.(chem), 49. Asst. CHEM, Barnard Col, Columbia, 43-45, lectr, 45-46; fel, med. col, Cornell, 49-50; ASSOC. PROF, DOUGLASS COL, RUTGERS UNIV, 50- Asst, Babies Hosp, Col. Physicians & Surgeons, Columbia Univ. Am. Chem. Soc. Reaction mechanisms; structure and reactivity. Address: Dept. of Chemistry, Douglass College, Rutgers, The State University, New Brunswick, NJ 08901.

DUNBAR, ROBERT C(OPELAND), b. Boston, Mass, June 26, 43; m. 69; c. 1. PHYSICAL CHEMISTRY. A.B, Harvard, 65; Ph.D.(chem. physics), Stanford Univ, 70. Res. assoc. CHEM, Stanford Univ, 70; ASST. PROF, CASE WEST. RESERVE UNIV, 70- Am. Phys. Soc; Am. Chem. Soc. Ion-molecule reaction processes in gas phase; properties of gas-phase ions; ion cyclotron resonance spectroscopy. Address: Dept. of Chemistry, Case Western Reserve University, Cleveland, OH 44106.

DUNBAR, R(OBERT) S(TANDISH), JR, b. Providence, R.I, Nov. 30, 21; m. 41; c. 2. ANIMAL GENETICS. B.S, Rhode Island, 49; M.S, Cornell, 50, Ph.D. (animal breeding), 52. Assoc. prof. dairy husb, W.VA. UNIV, 52-57, assoc. statistician, 57-62, chmn. dept. animal indust. & vet. sci, 62-64, DEAN COL. AGR. & FORESTRY, 64- U.S.A, 42-46. Statistical analysis and design of biological experiments. Address: College of Agricultural & Forestry, West Virginia University, Morgantown, WV 26506.

DUNBAR, ROBERT WILFRID, b. Hamilton, Ont, Feb. 9, 30; m. 60; c. 2. CYTOTAXONOMY. B.A, Univ. Toronto, 51, M.A, 58, Ph.D.(cytol), 62. Med. Res. Coun. Eng. sr. res. fel. cytotaxon, Univ. Durham, 62-65; asst. prof. GENETICS, Univ. Sask, Regina, 65-68; ASSOC. PROF, UNIV. WEST. ONT, 68- Nat. Res. Coun. Can. grant, 65-; WHO grant, 69- Giant chromosome cytotaxonomy of palaearctic Simuliidae and the Ethiopian simuliid complexes included in Simulium damnosum and Simulium neavei. Address: Dept. of Zoology, University of Western Ontario, London 72, Ont, Can.

DUNBROOK, RAYMOND F(REDERICK), b. Grand Rapids, Mich, May 9, 96; m. 19; c. 3. ORGANIC CHEMISTRY. B.S, Michigan, 17; M.S, Pittsburgh, 21, Ph.D.(org. chem), 23. Res. & plant control chemist, Holland Aniline Co, Mich, 17-20; instr. org. chem, Pittsburgh, 20-23; assoc. prof, Wittenberg Col, 23-27; prof, 27-29; res. chemist, org. res. div, Firestone Tire & Rubber Co, 29-38, asst. res. dir, 38-60; chmn. comt. elastomers, adv. bd. mil. personnel suppliers & consult, Nat. Acad. Sci-Nat. Res. Coun, 60-70; CONSULT, 70- With U.S.A; U.S.N; chief polymer res. br, Rubber Reserve Co, 44. Am. Chem. Soc; fel. Am. Inst. Chem. Synthetic organic chemicals for the rubber industry; polymerization applied to synthetic rubber and plastics. Address: 2326 Alpine Ave, South Gate, Sarasota, FL 33580.

DUNCALF, DERYCK, b. York, Eng, Nov. 14, 26; U.S. citizen; m. 50; c. 2. MEDICINE, ANESTHESIOLOGY. M.B, Ch.B, Leeds, 50. House physician, St. James Hosp, Leeds, Eng, 50, jr. anesthetic officer, 50-51; anesthetic officer, Gen. Infirmary, 51-52; res. surg. officer, Clayton Hosp, Wakefield, 52-53; registr. anesthetist, United Leeds Hosp, 53-54; sr. registr, dept. anesthetics, Welsh Nat. Sch. Med, Univ. Wales, 54-56; exchange fel. anesthesiol, Mercy Hosp, Pittsburgh, Pa, 56-57; clin. fel. anesthesia, Montreal Children's Hosp, Que, 57-58; asst. prof. anesthesiol, State Univ. N.Y. Downstate Med. Center, 58-61; asst. clin. prof, col. physicians & surgeons, Columbia, 62-64; ASSOC. PROF. CLIN. ANESTHESIOL, ALBERT EINSTEIN COL. MED, 65- Vis. instr, sch. med, Pittsburgh, 56-57. Assoc. attend. anesthesiologist, Kings County Hosp, Brooklyn, N.Y, 59-61; assoc. dir. anesthesia res, Mercy Hosp, Pittsburgh, 61-62; acting chief dept. anesthesia, Vet. Admin. Hosp, 61-62; assoc. attend. anesthesiologist, Montefiore Hosp. & Med. Center, Bronx, N.Y, 62-64, attend. anesthesiologist, 64-; assoc. vis. anesthesiologist, Morrisania City Hosp, 63-; assoc. vis. anesthesiologist, Bronx Munic. Hosp. Center, 65-; consult, Wyckoff Heights Hosp, Brooklyn, 66- Dipl. anesthetics, Royal Col. Physicians London, 53; Royal Col. Surgeons Eng, 53, fel. faculty anaesthetists, 54; dipl, Am. Bd. Anesthesiol, 60. AAAS; Am. Med. Asn; Am. Soc. Anesthesiol; fel. Am. Col. Anesthesiol; N.Y. Acad. Sci; Asn. Anaesthetists Gt. Brit. & North. Ireland; Int. Anesthesia Res. Soc; dipl. mem. Pan. Am. Med. Asn. Pharmacology of muscle relaxants and narcotics; anesthesia in ophthalmology; physiology of respiratory insufficiency; mechanical ventilation. Address: Dept. of Anesthesiology, Albert Einstein College of Medicine, 1300 Morris Park Ave, Bronx, NY 10461.

DUNCAN, A(LBERT) B(ENJAMIN) F(ORD), b. Memphis, Tenn, June 26, 03; m. 39; c. 1. PHYSICAL CHEMISTRY. B.S, Virginia, 24; Ph.D.(chem), Hopkins, 29. Instr. CHEM, Tennessee, 24-26; Hopkins, 28-30, assoc, 30-33; asst, Brown Univ, 34-35, instr. 35-38; asst. prof, UNIV. ROCHESTER, 38-46, assoc. prof, 46-50, prof, 50-70, EMER. PROF, 70-; VIS. PROF. ASTRON, UNIV. VA, 70- Am. Chem. Soc.(former asst. ed, jour); Am. Phys. Soc. Molecular structure; spectroscopy. Address: Dept. of Astronomy, University of Virginia, P.O. Box 3818 University Station, Charlottesville, VA 22903.

DUNCAN, ALLEY H(UGH), b. Rosenberg, Tex, Aug. 19, 11; m. 38; c. 4. MECHANICAL ENGINEERING. B.S, Kans. State Col, 37; M.S, 49. Sales engr, Westinghouse Elec. Corp, 37-43; instr. elec. eng, Kansas State Col, 43-44, mech. eng, 44; engr. designer, Consol. Vultee Aircraft Corp, 44-45; instr. MECH. ENG, KANS. STATE UNIV, 45-47, asst. prof, 47-49, assoc. prof, 49-52, PROF, 52- Am. Soc. Mech. Eng; Am. Soc. Eng. Educ. Thermodynamics; heat power engines; engineering economics; turbomachinery. Address: 1209 Bertrand, Manhattan, KS 66504.

DUNCAN, ANDREW A, b. Pencaitland, Scotland, Mar. 13, 21; U.S. citizen; m. 44; c. 4. HORTICULTURE. B.S, Maryland, 50, M.S, 52, Ph.D.(physiol), 56. Exten. specialist veg. crops, Maryland, 52-58; Oregon State, 58-70; PROF. HORT. SCI. & HEAD DEPT, UNIV. MINN, ST. PAUL, 70- U.S.A, 41-45. Am. Soc. Hort. Sci. Commercial vegetable production extension. Address: Dept. of Horticultural Science, University of Minnesota, St. Paul, MN 55101.

DUNCAN, ARCHIBALD, b. St. Paul, Minn, Jan. 31, 14; m. 37; c. 3. INORGANIC ANALYTICAL CHEMISTRY. B.A, Macalester Col, 36; M.S, Mont. Sch. Mines, 38. Shift foreman, res. dept, Cerro de Pasco Copper Corp, Peru, 38-40, supvr. cent. res. anal. lab, 41-42; group supvr. inorg. anal. res, MINN. MINING & MFG. CO, 45-64, MGR. INORG. ANAL. CHEM, CENT. RES. LABS, 3M CTR, 64- U.S.A, 42-45, Capt. Am. Chem. Soc. Chemical and instrumental methods for inorganic analysis. Address: Minnesota Mining & Manufacturing Co, Central Research Labs, 3M Center, St. Paul, MN 55101.

DUNCAN, BETTIE, b. Ashland, Miss, June 21, 33. MICROBIOLOGY. A.B, Judson Col, 55; M.S, Birmingham-South. Col. 61; Ph.D.(microbiol), Arkansas, 66. Assoc. biologist, South. Res. Inst, Ala, 57-62; asst. prof. MICROBIOL, KANS. STATE COL. PITTSBURG, 66-68; ASSOC. PROF, 68- Am. Soc. Microbiol; N.Y. Acad. Sci. Rare earth metal effects on microorganisms; pigment production in fungi; microbial ecology of the strip pits of south eastern Kansas. Address: Dept. of Microbiology, Kansas State College, Pittsburg, KS 66762.

DUNCAN, BLANTON C(HARLES), b. Greenwood, Miss, Feb. 2, 28; m. 50; c. 3. PHYSICAL CHEMISTRY. B.A, Vanderbilt, 50; Ph.D.(chem), Washington State, 57. CHEMIST colloidal electrolytes, NAT. BUR. STANDARDS, 50-52, MEMBRANE PHENOMENA, 57- U.S.A, 46-47. Am. Chem. Soc; Asn. Comput. Mach. Machine processing of chemical data; chemical data automation. Address: National Bureau of Standards, Gaithersburg, MD 20760.

DUNCAN, BUDD LEE, b. Thief River Falls, Minn, Nov. 15, 36; m. 58; c. 3. PHYSICAL CHEMISTRY, MOLECULAR SPECTROSCOPY. B.A, Macalester Col, 58; M.S, S.Dak. State, 60; Ph.D, Univ. Tenn, 70. Assoc. prof. CHEM, TENN. WESLEYAN COL, 61-70, PROF, 70- Am. Chem. Soc; Coblentz Soc. Kinetics of Diels-Alder reactions; infra-red spectroscopy; force fields of dimethyl compounds. Address: Dept. of Chemistry, Tennessee Wesleyan College, Athens, TN 37303.

DUNCAN, C(ECIL) E(UGENE), b. Atascadero, Calif, Oct. 21, 21; m. 43; c. 3. MATHEMATICS. B.S, Richmond, 47; Ph.D.(math), Stanford Univ, 57. Sr. mem. staff, res. labs, Lockheed Missiles & Space Co, Lockheed Aircraft Corp, 57-69, MGR, INFO. SCI. LAB, LOCKHEED PALO ALTO RES. LABS, 69- U.S.A.A.F, 39-46, Res, 46-55. AAAS; Am. Math. Soc; Am. Phys. Soc; Inst. Elec. & Electronics Eng; Soc. Indust. & Appl. Math. Asymptotics. Address: Information Science Lab, Lockheed Palo Alto Research Labs, 3251 Hanover St, Palo Alto, CA 94304.

DUNCAN, CHARLES LEE, b. Waynesboro, Tenn, Oct. 10, 39; m. 68. BACTERIOLOGY. B.S, Tennessee, 61; M.S, La. State, Baton Rouge, 63; Ph.D. (bact), Wisconsin, Madison, 67. ASST. PROF. BACT, UNIV. WIS, MADISON, 68- Am. Soc. Microbiol. Clostridium perfringens food poisoning; sporulation of anaerobic bacteria and germination of their spores. Address: Food Research Institute, University of Wisconsin, Madison, WI 53706.

DUNCAN, DAVID B(EATTIE), b. Sydney, Australia, June 16, 16; nat; m. 48; c. 3. STATISTICS. B.Sc, Agr. Sydney Univ, N.S.W, 38, B.A, 41, Pawlett scholar, 45-47; Ph.D.(math. statist), Iowa State Col, 47. Lectr. agr. biomet, Sydney Univ, N.S.W, 38-40; sr. lectr. statist. methods, 47-50; assoc. prof. STATIST, Va. Polytech, 50-52, prof, 52-54; prof, Florida, 55-56; res. assoc, Univ. N.C, 56-60; PROF. STATIST. & BIOSTATIST, JOHNS HOPKINS UNIV, 61- Statist. consult, Air Force East. Test Range, 57-69. Horsley Award, Va. Acad, 51. R.A.A.F, 41-45. Fel. Inst. Math. Statist; fel. Am. Statist Asn; Biomet. Soc. Multiple comparisons; linear theory and methods; time series; recursive estimation. Address: Dept. of Biostatistics, Johns Hopkins University, 615 N. Wolfe St, Baltimore, MD 21212.

DUNCAN, DAVID R(OBARDSON) L(INCOLN), b. Denver, Colo, Feb. 12, 09; m. 37; c. 2. PUBLIC HEALTH. B.S, Denver, 29; Gen. Ed. Bd. fellow, Western Reserve, 37-40; Ph.D.(biochem), Chicago, 41; M.D, Colorado, 46. Assoc. prof. chem, Denver, 41-43; examining physician, Denver Pub. Schs, 47-48; med. dir, Las Animas-Huerfano Dist. Health Dept, 49-50; Tri-County Dist. Health Dept, 51-54; sr. surgeon, U.S. Pub. Health Serv, 54-58; chief maternal & child health & crippled children's serv, Alaska Dept. Health, 58-62, med. dir, Greater Anchorage Area Borough-Health Dept, 62-70; SERV. UNIT DIR, U.S. PUB. HEALTH SERV-INT. HEALTH SERV, 70- U.S.A, 44-46. Am. Med. Asn; Am. Sch. Health Asn; Am. Pub. Health Asn. (Ross Award, west. br, 70); Am. Thoracic Soc. Male sex hormones; growth during childhood and adolescence; fertility and sterility in human female. Address: Public Health Service Hospital, Tanana, AK 99777.

DUNCAN, DON DARRYL, b. Mayfield, Ky, Sept. 9, 39; m. 58; c. 2. PHYSICS. B.S, Murray State, 61; M.S, Kentucky, 63, Ph.D.(physics), 68. Asst. prof. PHYSICS, MURRAY STATE UNIV, 67-70, ASSOC. PROF, 70- Am. Phys. Soc. Angular correlation studies in nuclear physics. Address: Dept. of Physics, Murray State University, Murray, KY 42071.

DUNCAN, D(ONAL) B(AKER), b. Altus, Okla, May 16, 25; m. 46; c. 4. PHYSICS. B.S, Calif. Inst. Tech, 45, Atomic Energy Cmn. fel, 49-50, Ph.D, 51. Mgr. eng, Autonetics Div, N.Am. Aviation, Inc, 50-59; asst. gen. mgr. Aeronutronic Div, Ford Motor Co, Calif, 59-66; pres. guid. & control systs. div, Litton Industs, 66-68; v.pres. & chief tech. off, SINGER CO, N.Y, 68, v.pres. defense & space systs. group, 68-70, V.PRES. INFO. SYSTS. GROUP, 70- U.S.N.R, 42-52, Lt. Am. Phys. Soc; Inst. Elec. & Electronics Eng; Am. Inst. Aeronaut. & Astronaut. Systems engineering; management and development of systems for tactical weapons, reentry, space, reconnaissance and propulsion. Address: Singer Co, 2350 Washington Ave, San Leandro, CA 94577.

DUNCAN, DONALD, b. Marietta, Minn, Jan. 31, 03; m. 24; c. 3. ANATOMY. A.B, Carleton Col, 23; A.M, Minnesota, 27, Ph.D.(anat), 29. Asst. prof. ANAT, Utah, 29-30; Buffalo, 30-32; assoc. prof, sch. med, Texas, 32-41, prof, 41-42; prof. & head dept, sch. med, Buffalo, 42-43; prof, La. State Sch. Med, 43-46; prof. & chmn. dept, MED. BR, UNIV. TEX, 46-68, assoc. dean grad. sch, 52-69, ASHBEL SMITH PROF, 68- Am. Asn. Anat.(managing ed, jour, 60-68, 1st v.pres, 61, pres, 67, Henry Gray Award, 71); Soc. Exp. Biol. & Med; Am. Asn. Phys. Anthrop; Am. Acad. Neurol. Degeneration and regeneration of nerve fibers; myelination; structure of spinal nerve roots; action of oil anesthetics; pathology of the spinal cord and cerebellum; electron microscopy of nervous system. Address: Dept. of Anatomy, University of Texas, Medical Branch, Galveston, TX 77550.

DUNCAN, DONALD G(ORDON), b. Lincoln, Nebr, Apr. 21, 20. MATHEMATICS. B.A, British Columbia, 42, M.A, 44; fel, Michigan, 47-50, Ph.D.(math), 51. Res. engr, Nat. Res. Coun. Can, 43-44; lectr. physics, McGill, 44-45; MATH, British Columbia, 45-47; asst. prof, Arizona, 50-54; San Jose State Col, 54-58, assoc. prof, 58-60, PROF, 60-63; SONOMA STATE COL, 63- Consult, Off. Naval Res, 57- Am. Math. Soc; Math. Asn. Am; London Math. Soc. Theory of groups; lattice theory; aerodynamics; numerical analysis. Address: 5440 Montecito Ave, Santa Rosa, CA 95404.

DUNCAN, DONALD LEE, b. Farmington, Mo, June 7, 30; m. 55. MATHEMATICS, CHEMICAL ENGINEERING. B.S, Missouri, Rolla, 52, M.S, Missouri, Columbia, 57; Ph.D.(math), Florida, 62. Chem. engr. design & develop, Union Carbide Nuclear Co, Tenn, 52-53; tech. sales & serv, Enjay Chem. Co. Div, Standard Oil Co. N.J, N.Y, 57-59; assoc. prof. MATH, Ga. State Univ, 62-67; HEAD DEPT, VALDOSTA STATE COL, 67- Sr. res. scientist, Ga. Inst. Technol, 66- Chem.C, U.S.A, 63-66, 1st Lt. Am. Math. Soc; Math. Asn. Am. Ordinary and partial differential equations; orthogonal polynomials; complex variables; applied mathematics; biomathematics. Address: 2410 Georgia Ave, Valdosta, GA 31601.

DUNCAN, DONALD P(ENDLETON), b. Joliet, Ill, Feb. 24, 16; m. 56; c. 3. FORESTRY. B.S.F, Michigan, 37, M.S, 39; Ph.D.(forestry, bot), Minnesota, 51. Shelterbelt supvr, U.S. Forest Serv, Kans, 39-40, jr. forester, South. Forest Exp. Sta, La, 40-41; instr. forestry & forester, exp. sta, Kans. State Col, 41-42, asst. prof, exten, 45-47; instr. FORESTRY, Minnesota, 47-51, asst. prof, 51-54, assoc. prof, 54-59, prof, 59-65, asst. dir. sch. 64-65; PROF. & DIR. SCH, UNIV. MO-COLUMBIA, 65- Consult, Minn. Natural Resources Coun, 61-63; vis. scientist, Nat. Sci. Found, 64-65, 68 & 69; consult, Ford Found. Latin-Am. Fel. Prog, 68 & 70; Coop. State Res. Serv, 69; Coun. Grad. Schs, 70. U.S.A, 42-45. AAAS; Soc. Am. Foresters; Ecol. Soc. Am. Forest ecology; forest influences; forest recreation. Address: School of Forestry, University of Missouri-Columbia, Columbia, MO 65201.

DUNCAN, DONALD STUART, b. Brooklyn, N.Y, Aug. 3, 15; m. 46; c. 2. PHYSICS. B.S, Mass. Inst. Tech, 37; Michigan, 46; M.S, N.Y. Univ, 48. Instr. math. & physics, Pratt Inst, 38-44; res. engr, substitute alloy material labs, Columbia, 44-45; Carbide & Carbon Chems. Corp, 45-46; from instr. to PROF. PHYSICS, PRATT INST, 46- Am. Inst. Physics; Am. Asn. Physics Teachers; Am. Soc. Mech. Eng; Am. Soc. Eng. Educ. Mechanical vibrations; automatic process control; applied mechanics. Address: Dept. of Physics, Pratt Institute, Brooklyn, NY 11205.

DUNCAN, DOUGLAS WALLACE, b. Vancouver, B.C, Sept. 7, 34; m. 58; c. 1. APPLIED MICROBIOLOGY. B.S.A, Univ. B.C, 57; Ph.D.(food technol), Mass. Inst. Technol, 61. Mem. res. staff, Knorr Forschungs Inst, Corn Prod. Co, Switz, 61-62; B.C. RES. COUN, 62-65, GROUP LEADER, 65- Hon. prof, Univ. B.C; mem. mining subcomt, Nat. Adv. Comt. on Mining & Metall. Res. Brit. Soc. Gen. Microbiol. Microbiological leaching of sulfide minerals; occurance of false-positive coliforms in industrial effluents; deterioration of wood chips. Address: Division of Applied Biology, British Columbia Research Council, 3650 Wesbrook Crescent, Vancouver 8, B.C, Can.

DUNCAN, ELWIN R(AYMOND), b. Clay Co, Iowa, Feb. 14, 13; m. 40; c. 2. AGRONOMY. B.S, Iowa State, 39, M.S, 43, Ph.D, 54. Exten. specialist agron. & farm mgt, Iowa State, 40-43; asst. prof. soils & exten. specialist, Minnesota, 46-53; PROF. AGRON. & EXTEN. AGRONOMIST, COOP. EXTEN. SERV, IOWA STATE UNIV, 53- Consult, Ford Found, Brazil, 64-65; corn prod. probs, Argentina, 65- U.S. Dept. Agr. superior serv. award, 58, meritorious serv. award, Epsilon Sigma Phi, 65; distinguished serv. award, Gamma Sigma Delta, 69. U.S.A, 43-46. Fel. Am. Soc. Agron; Soil Sci. Soc. Am; Soil Conserv. Soc. Am. Corn grain quality; determination of genotype response to harvesting, drying and subsequent handling; crop production; soil management; plant development. Address: Dept. of Agronomy, Iowa State University, Ames, IA 50010.

DUNCAN, GEORGE THOMAS, b. Chicago, Ill, Aug. 7, 42; m. 69. STATISTICS. B.S, Univ. Chicago, 63, M.S, 64; Ph.D.(statist), Univ. Minn, 70. Statistician, Texaco Res. Labs, 64-65; vol, U.S. Peace Corps, Philippines, 65-67; ASST. PROF. MATH, UNIV. CALIF, DAVIS, 70- AAAS; Inst. Math. Statist; Am. Statist. Asn; Math. Asn. Am. Foundations of statistical inference. Address: Dept. of Mathematics, University of California, Davis, CA 95616.

DUNCAN, GERALD R, b. Windsor, Ont, Feb. 22, 34; m. 55; c. 2. ORGANIC CHEMISTRY. B.Sc, Toronto, 57, John H.H. Jury scholar. & Poulenc award, 57-58, Nat. Res. Coun. Can. stud, 58-59, M.Sc, 59; Can. Found. Adv. Pharm. scholar, Basel, 59-62, D.Phil.(chem), 62. Asst. prof. PHARMACEUT. CHEM, UNIV. TORONTO, 62-68, ASSOC. PROF, 68-, CHMN. GRAD. DEPT, 69- Chmn. grants comt. for pharmaceut. sci, Med. Res. Coun, 71. Chem. Inst. Can; Swiss Chem. Soc. Isolation of natural products, chiefly steroids and alkaloids; structure elucidation of natural products; steroid synthesis and biochemistry. Address: Faculty of Pharmacy, University of Toronto, Toronto 181, Ont, Can.

DUNCAN, GORDON D(UKE), b. Clayton, N.C, May 25, 26; m. 51; c. 3. BIOCHEMISTRY. B.S, N.C. State Col, 49; Ph.D.(biochem), 53. Asst, U.S. plant, soil & nutrit. lab, Cornell, 49-53; biochemist, biochem. res. lab, Elgin State Hosp, 53-57; clin. biochem, Charlotte Mem. Hosp, 57-67; PROF. CHEM, QUEENS COL.(N.C), 67- Assoc. dir. clin. chem, Diag. Labs; chmn. bd. dirs, AquAir Labs. Inc. U.S.A.A.F, 44-46, Res, 46-59, 1st Lt. AAAS; Am. Chem. Soc; Am. Asn. Clin. Chem; N.Y. Acad. Sci. Clinical biochemistry. Address: 1900 Selwyn Ave, Charlotte, NC 28207.

DUNCAN, GORDON W, b. Weehawken, N.J, July 3, 32; m. 55; c. 4. ENDOCRINOLOGY. B.S, Cornell, 54; M.S, Iowa State, 55, Ph.D.(reprod. physiol), 60. Res. assoc. & asst. prof. animal physiol, Iowa State, 59-60; SR. RES. SCIENTIST, Upjohn Co, 60-71; BATTELLE SEATTLE RES. CTR, 71- Lectr, West. Mich. Univ, 60-71. U.S.A.F, 55-58, Capt. AAAS; Am. Soc. Animal Sci; Endocrine Soc; Am. Physiol. Soc; Brit. Soc. Study Fertil. Basic and applied research in physiology of reproduction. Address: Battelle Seattle Research Center, Seattle, WA 98105.

DUNCAN, HARRY ERNEST, b. Hartford, W.Va, Nov. 20, 36; m. 58; c. 3. PLANT PATHOLOGY. B.S, West Virginia, 59, M.S, 61, Ph.D.(plant path), 66. Exten. instr. plant path, N.C. STATE UNIV, 65-66, exten. asst. prof, 66-70, EXTEN. ASSOC. PROF. PLANT PATH. & IN CHARGE EXTEN, 70- Am. Phytopath. Soc. Diseases of vegetable crops; pesticides in plant disease control; extension plant pathology. Address: 1409 Gardner Hall, North Carolina State University, Raleigh, NC 27607.

DUNCAN, I. B. R, b. Kilmarnock, Scotland, Oct. 10, 26; Can. citizen; m. 57; c. 2. MEDICAL MICROBIOLOGY. M.B, Ch.B, Glasgow, 51, M.D, 62. Asst. lectr. bact, Glasgow, 52-55, lectr, 57-60; res. bacteriologist, Hosp. Sick Children, Toronto, Ont, 55-57; asst. prof. bact, Univ. West. Ont, 60-65, assoc. prof, 65-67; PROF. MED. MICROBIOL, UNIV. TORONTO & DIR. MICROBIOL, SUNNYBROOK HOSP, 67- Dir. microbiol, St. Joseph's Hosp, London, Ont, 60-67. Fel. Royal Col. Physicians & Surgeons Can, 62. Col. Path. Eng; Infectious Diseases Soc. Am; Can. Soc. Microbiol.(v.pres, 69-70); Can. Asn. Med. Microbiol.(secy-treas, 62-67); Path. Soc. Gt. Brit. & Ireland. Echoviruses; staphylococcal epidemiology; antibiotics and gram-negative bacilli. Address: Dept. of Microbiology, Sunnybrook Hospital, Toronto 315, Ont, Can.

DUNCAN, IRA J(ERIAH), b. Carroll Co, Ga, Feb. 16, 06; m. 32; c. 4. AGRICULTURAL CHEMISTRY. B.S, Georgia, 30; M.S, West Virginia, 33; Ph.D. (agr. chem), 36. Asst. agr. chem, exp. sta, West Virginia, 30-36, asst. chemist, 36-42; chief chemist, Axton-Fisher Tobacco Co, Ky, 42-44; res. chemist, Detrex Corp, 44-60, DIR. RES, OXFORD CHEM. DIV, CONSOL. FOODS CORP, 60- Spec. instr, Wayne, 46-47. Am. Chem. Soc; Am. Oil Chem. Soc. Coumarin investigation in sweet clover; anthocyan pigments of apples; vegetable oil extraction equipment; paint bonding; cold forming and rust proofing of metals; industrial floor maintenance products; metal cleaning and conversion coatings; aluminum etchants; emulsion cleaners and degreasers; paint strippers. Address: Oxford Chemical Division, Consolidated Foods Corp, P.O. Box 80202, Atlanta, GA 30341.

DUNCAN, IRMA W(AGNER), b. Buffalo, N.Y, Jan. 30, 12; m. 37; c. 2. BIOCHEMISTRY. M.S, Chicago, 35, Ph.D.(biochem), 50. Prof. sci, Colo. Woman's Col, 44-48; asst. prof. chem, Denver, 51-59; BIOCHEMIST, ARCTIC HEALTH RES. CTR, U.S. PUB. HEALTH SERV, 60- U.S. Pub. Health Serv. grant, 57. Fel. AAAS; Am. Chem. Soc. Serum proteins; enzymes, metabolic diseases, nutrition and genetics. Address: Arctic Health Research Center, U.S. Public Health Service, College, AK 99701.

DUNCAN, JAMES F(RANCIS), b. Mears, Mich, Apr. 28, 00; m. 28; c. 2. PHYSICS. A.B, Kalamazoo Col, 23; A.M, Michigan, 27, Ph.D.(physics), 30. Instr. PHYSICS, Kalamazoo Col, 24-25; asst, Yale, 26-27; PROF, Lombard Col, 28-29; Hastings Col, 29-30; WIS. STATE UNIV, 30-, V.PRES. BUS. AFFAIRS, 62-, dean instruction, 45-55, dean col, 55-62. AAAS; Am. Phys. Soc; Am. Asn. Physics Teachers. Certain electronic bands of carbon dioxide; electronics; spectroscopy. Address: Dept. of Physics, Wisconsin State University, Oshkosh, WI 54901.

DUNCAN, JAMES L(OWELL), b. West Plains, Mo, Dec. 14, 37; m. 63; c. 3. MICROBIOLOGY. A.B, Drury Col, 59; D.D.S, St. Louis, 63; Ph.D.(microbiol), Washington (Seattle), 67. U.S. Pub. Health Serv. fel, 63-67; ASST. PROF. MICROBIOL, MED. & DENT. SCHS, NORTHWEST. UNIV, 67- AAAS; Am. Soc. Microbiol. Bacterial toxins and their effects on mammalian tissues. Address: Dept. of Microbiology, Northwestern University, Chicago, IL 60611.

DUNCAN, JAMES M(OYER), b. Frostproof, Fla, Jan. 25, 21; m. 47; c. 2. SYSTEMS ENGINEERING. B.Ch.E, Florida, 43; M.S, Wisconsin, 44; Cert, Oak Ridge Sch. Reactor Tech, 55. Chem. engr, Tenn. Eastman Corp, 44-46; Nat. Distillers Prod. Corp, 46; develop. engr, Ramie Mills, Fla, 47; asst. prof. chem. eng, Florida, 48-53; chief chem. engr, Patchen & Zimmerman Engrs, 53-58; assoc. prof. nuclear eng, Florida, 58-59; nuclear engr, Gen. Nuclear Eng. Corp, 59-61; br. chief, nuclear reactor lab, Northrop Corp, 61-63; mgr. nuclear eng, HOLMES & NARVER, INC, 63-68, systs. & planning, 68-70, ASST. TO V.PRES. TECHNOL, 70- Consult, Univ. Fla, 55-58; Univ. Mass, 59; Phillips Petrol. Co, 59; AMF Atomics, 60. Prof. designations in value eng, Univ. Calif, Los Angeles, 67 & systs. & prog. planning & control, 70. Chem.C, U.S.A, 46-47; Nat. Soc. Prof. Eng; Am. Nuclear Soc; Am. Inst. Chem. Eng. Nuclear and process engineering; materials handling; management systems development. Address: Holmes & Narver, Inc, 400 E. Orangethorpe, Anaheim, CA 92801.

DUNCAN, JAMES PLAYFORD, b. Adelaide, S.Australia, Nov. 10, 19; m. 42; c. 4. MECHANICAL ENGINEERING. B.E, Adelaide, 41, M.E, 54; Turner & Newall fel, Manchester, 55-56, D.Sc.(sci. pub), 64. Develop. engr, Richards Industs. Ltd, 41-47; lectr. mech. eng, Adelaide, 47-51, sr. lectr, 53-54; turbine engr, Metrop. Vickers Elec. Co, Manchester, 52; PROF. MECH. ENG. & HEAD DEPT, Sheffield, 57-66; UNIV. B.C, 66- Consult, Firth Brown Tools Ltd, Eng, 61-66; Perkin-Elmer Corp, 66-68; Caterpillar Tractor Co, 67- V.chmn. adv. cmt, Royal Engrs. Eng, 62-66. Soc. Exp. Stress Anal; assoc. Inst. Eng, Australia; Brit. Inst. Mech. Eng; Brit. Inst. Prod. Eng; Brit. Inst. Physics & Phys. Soc. Design and production of automobile and aircraft sheet metal; stress analysis by optical means of steam power plant components; surface generation by numerical control. Address: Dept. of Mechanical Engineering, University of British Columbia, Vancouver, B.C, Can.

DUNCAN, JAMES T(HAYER), b. Chicago, Ill, Apr. 15, 32; m. 61; c. 1. DEVELOPMENTAL BIOLOGY. A.B, Wabash Col, 54; Ph.D.(biol), Stanford Univ, 60. Asst. prof. zool, Univ. Calif, Riverside, 60-62; asst. prof. BIOL, SAN FRANCISCO STATE COL, 62-66, ASSOC. PROF, 66- Am. Cancer Soc. res. grant, 61-63; Nat. Sci. Found. res. grants, 63-65, 68-71; Nat. Sci. Found. sci. faculty fel, 65-66. AAAS; Am. Soc. Zool; Soc. Develop. Biol. Embryonic induction and the developmental control of cellular differentiation in Amphibians. Address: Dept. of Cell and Molecular Biology, San Francisco State College, San Francisco, CA 94132.

DUNCAN, JOHN L(EASK), b. Adelaide, S. Australia, Dec. 20, 32; m. 61; c. 3. MECHANICAL ENGINEERING. B.M.E, Univ. Melbourne, 55; M.S.T, Univ. Manchester, 63, Ph.D.(eng), 68. Trainee, Caterpillar Tractor Co, 56-58; planning supvr, Caterpillar of Australia Proprietary Ltd, 58-60; asst. field engr, Vacuum Oil Co, 60-61; asst. lectr. ENG. EDUC, inst. sci. & technol, Univ. Manchester, 62-63, lectr, 63-68, sr. lectr, 68-70; PROF, McMASTER UNIV, 70- Assoc. Brit. Inst. Mech. Eng.(T.B. Hall prize, 68). Engineering plasticity; sheet metal technology; manufacturing and production processes. Address: Dept. of Mechanical Engineering, McMaster University, Hamilton, Ont, Can.

DUNCAN, KATHERINE, b. Tamaroa, Ill, Oct. 14, 13; m. 39; c. 2. INTERNAL MEDICINE. B.S, Illinois, 35, M.D, 38. Intern, Hurley Hosp, Flint, Mich, 37-38; private practice, Ill, 38-41; staff physician, Crab Orchard Defense Plant, Ill, 43; asst. med. dir, Nutrit. Res. Lab, 43-45; attend. physician pediat. & maternity, Montgomery County Health Dept, Md, 52-53; med. off. pharmacol, bur. biol. & phys. sci, Food & Drug Admin, DEPT. HEALTH EDUC. & WELFARE, 60-61, ADMIN. MED. OFF, career develop. rev. br, DIV. RES. GRANTS, NAT. INSTS. HEALTH, 61-70, INSTNL. RELS. SECT.

70- Rheumatoid diseases; allergy; medical administartion. Address: Institutional Relations Section, Division of Research Grants, National Institutes of Health, Bethesda, MD 20014.

DUNCAN, LEONARD C(LINTON), b. Owensboro, Ky, Dec. 28, 36; m. 63; c. 2. INORGANIC CHEMISTRY. A.B, Wabash Col, 58; M.A, Wesleyan, 61; Ph.D.(chem), Washington (Seattle), 64. Asst. INORG. CHEM, Purdue, 64-65; asst. prof, CENT. WASH. STATE COL, 65-67, ASSOC. PROF, 67-, chmn. dept. chem, 66-68. Res. Corp. & Nat. Sci. Found. res. grants, 69. Am. Chem. Soc. Synthesis of highly fluorinated compounds of the lighter elements. Address: Dept. of Chemistry, Central Washington State College, Ellensburg, WA 98926.

DUNCAN, LEROY E(DWARD), JR, b. Norfolk, Va, July 30, 17; m. 42; c. 2. INTERNAL MEDICINE. A.B, Duke, 39; M.D, Hopkins, 42. Intern, Hopkins Hosp, 42-43, asst. res, 43-44; Vanderbilt Hosp, 47-48, res, 48-49; sr. investr, Nat. Heart Inst, 49-65, CHIEF ADULT DEVELOP. & AGING BR, NAT. INST. CHILD HEALTH & HUMAN DEVELOP, 65- Mem. coun. on arteriosclerosis, Am. Heart Asn. Dipl. Am. Bd. Internal Med. Med.C, 44-46, Capt. AAAS; Am. Med. Asn; Am. Heart Asn; Am. Fedn. Clin. Res; fel. Am. Col. Physicians; Am. Physiol. Soc. Heart failure; atherosclerosis; aging. Address: National Institute of Child Health & Human Development, Bethesda, MD 20014.

DUNCAN, MARGARET CAROLINE, b. Salt Lake City, Utah, June 9, 30; m. 58; c. 4. PEDIATRIC NEUROLOGY. B.A, Texas, 52, M.D, 55. Fel. PEDIAT. NEUROL, Hopkins, 60-61; instr, SCH. MED, LA. STATE UNIV, NEW ORLEANS, 61-63, asst. prof, 63-66, ASSOC. PROF, 66- Consult, Handicapped Children's Prog, La. State Bd. Health, 64- Dipl, Am. Bd. Pediat, 62; cert. neurol, Am. Bd. Psychiat. & Neurol, 65 & child neurol, 69. Am. Acad. Neurol; Am. Epilepsy Soc. Reflex epilepsy; infantile neuroaxonal dystrophy; cerebral edema in infants and children. Address: Dept. of Neurology, Louisiana State University in New Orleans, 1542 Tulane Ave, New Orleans, LA 70112.

DUNCAN, MARION M, JR, b. Bloomfield, Mo, June 24, 27; m. 48; c. 2. THEORETICAL PHYSICS. B.S, Ala. Polytech, 49, Humble Oil fel, 52-53, M.S, 53, univ. fel, Duke, 53-54, Shell Oil fel, 54-55, Ph.D.(physics), 56. Instr, North Carolina, 56; vis. asst. prof. PHYSICS, Duke, 56-60; asst. prof, Texas A&M, 60-61; assoc. prof, UNIV. GA, 61-66, PROF, 66-, HEAD DEPT. PHYSICS & ASTRON, 68- U.S.N, 45-46. Am. Phys. Soc. Low energy nuclear physics. Address: Dept. of Physics & Astronomy, University of Georgia, Athens, GA 30601.

DUNCAN, R(ICHARD) D(ALE), b. Alhambra, Calif, Apr. 1, 41; m. 70; c. 1. MATHEMATICS. B.Sc, Univ. Calif, Berkeley, 63, M.A, 65; Ph.D, Univ. Calif, San Diego, 70. Asst. MATH, Univ. Calif, Berkeley, 63-65; Univ. Calif, San Diego, 65-70; ASST. PROF, UNIV. MONTREAL, 70- Probability; functional analysis; Markov processes and potential theory. Address: Dept. of Mathematics, University of Montreal, Box 6128, Montreal 101, Que, Can.

DUNCAN, RICHARD H(ENRY), b. St. Louis, Mo, Aug. 13, 22; m; c. 2. PHYSICS, ELECTRICAL ENGINEERING. B.S.E.E, Univ. Mo, 49, M.S, 51, Ph.D.(physics), 54. Prof. elec. eng. & physicist, phys. sci. lab, N.Mex. State Univ, 54-65, v.pres. res, 65-69; TECH. DIR. & CHIEF SCIENTIST, WHITE SANDS MISSILE RANGE, 69- Am. Soc. Eng. Educ; Inst. Elec. & Electronics Eng. Integral equations occurring in electromagnetic radiation problems; antenna engineering. Address: STEWS-SC, White Sands Missile Range, NM 88002.

DUNCAN, ROBERT L(EE), b. Johnstown, Pa, July 3, 28; m. 57; c. 3. MATHEMATICS. B.A, Pa. State, 52, M.A, 56. Asst, ord. res. lab, Pa. State, 52-53; asst. math, Pa. State, 53-55, instr, 55-61; res. mathematician, Hercules Powder Co, 61-62; ASSOC. PROF. MATH, Lock Haven State Col, 62-67; KING OF PRUSSIA GRAD. CTR, PA. STATE UNIV, 67- U.S.A, 46-48. Am. Math. Soc; Math. Asn. Am; Soc. Indust. & Appl. Math. Density of sequences; arithmetical functions; distribution of sequences of real numbers modulo one. Address: King of Prussia Graduate Center, Pennsylvania State University, Guelph & Henderson Rds, King of Prussia, PA 19406.

DUNCAN, ROBERT LOUIS, JR, b. Petersburg, Va, Dec. 4, 36; m. 58; c. 2. MEDICINAL & ORGANIC CHEMISTRY. B.S, Randolph-Macon Col, 58; Ph.D.(med.chem), Med. Col. Va, 67. Control chemist, A.H. ROBINS CO, INC, 58-62, SR. RES. CHEMIST, 66- Air Nat. Guard, 58-66; U.S.A.F, 61-62. Am. Chem. Soc. Indoles. Address: 2414 Poates Dr, Richmond, VA 23228.

DUNCAN, RONALD IAN, b. Winnipeg, Man, Apr. 30, 33; m. 55; c. 2. BIOPHYSICS. B.S, Oklahoma, 60, M.S, 62, Nat. Insts. Health fel. & Ph.D.(neurophysiol), 65. Fel. & lectr. BIOPHYS, UNIV. WEST. ONT, 65-67, ASST. PROF, 67- Am. Biophys. Soc. Cellular communication; bioelectricity; membrane transport. Address: Dept. of Biophysics, University of Western Ontario Faculty of Medicine, London 72, Ont, Can.

DUNCAN, STEWART, b. Danvers, Mass, Apr. 18, 26; m. 54; c. 2. ZOOLOGY. A.B, Boston, 49, A.M, 50, Ph.D.(parasitol), 57. Instr. BIOL, BOSTON UNIV, 50-57, asst. prof, 58-63, assoc. prof, 63-69, PROF, 69- Vis. prof, Ceylon, 65. U.S.A, 44-46. Am. Soc. Parasitol; Am. Ornith. Union; Am. Soc. Zool; Soc. Protozool; Wildlife Disease Asn. Parasitology, bird parasities; entomology; ornithology. Address: Dept. of Biology, Boston University, Boston, MA 02215.

DUNCAN, THOMAS O, b. Wash, D.C, June 5, 28; m. 56; c. 4. ZOOLOGY. B.S, Okla. State, 53. Fishery aide, biol. lab, U.S. FISH & WILDLIFE SERV, Wash, 53-54, fishery biologist, Bur. Commercial Fisheries, 54-60, exec. secy, Am. Fisheries Adv. Comt, D.C, 60-62, CHIEF CENT. RESERVOIR INVESTS. FISHERY BIOL, BUR. SPORT FISHERIES & WILDLIFE, 62- U.S.M.C, 46-49, Am. Fisheries Soc; Am. Soc. Limnol. & Oceanog. Sport fisheries in reservoirs; North Pacific salmon. Address: Bureau of Sport Fisheries & Wildlife, 113 S. East St, Fayetteville, AR 72701.

DUNCAN, WALTER E(DWIN), b. Red Lodge, Mont, Apr. 30, 10; m. 39; c. 3. METALLURGY. B.S, Mont. State Col, 33; fel, Mont. Sch. Mines, 33-34, M.S, 34, Min. Dr. E, 60; fel, Mo. Sch. Mines, 35-39. Asst. to A.M. Gaudin, Mont, 34-35; mill man, Mont. Coal & Iron Co, 35; res. metallurgist, Mo. Sch. Mines, 37-39; metallurgist, Mahoning Min. Co, Ill, 39-46, Ozark-Mahoning Co, 46-49; assoc. prof. CHEM. ENG, NAT. RESOURCES RES. INST, UNIV. WYO, 49-60, PROF, 60-, DIR. INST, 71-, asst. dir, 60-65, assoc. dir, 65-71. Consult, Peruvian Govt, 51- Am. Chem. Soc; Am. Inst. Mining, Metall. & Petrol. Eng. Mineral and chemical processing, testing and beneficiation; phosphate rock treatment and processing; submerged combustion. Address: Natural Resources Research Institute, University of Wyoming, Box 3038 University Station, Laramie, WY 82070.

DUNCAN, WILBUR H(OWARD), b. Buffalo, N.Y, Oct. 15, 10; m. 41; c. 3. TAXONOMY. A.B, Univ. Ind, 32, M.A, 33; Ph.D.(bot), Duke Univ, 38. Instr. BOT, UNIV. GA, 38-40, asst. prof, 40-42, assoc. prof, 46-52, PROF, 52- U.S.P.H.S.R, 42-46, 48-53, Lt. Comdr. Bot. Soc. Am; Am. Soc. Plant Taxon; Asn. Trop. Biol; Int. Asn. Plant Taxon. Plant taxonomy; floristics; biosystematics. Address: Dept. of Botany, University of Georgia, Athens, GA 30601.

DUNCAN, WILLIAM GRAHAM, b. Greenville, Ky, Mar. 3, 09; m. 30; c. 4. PLANT PHYSIOLOGY. B.S, Purdue Univ, 30, M.S, 56, Ph.D.(soils, plant nutrit), 58. Assoc. prof. AGRON, UNIV. KY, 59-70, PROF, 70- AAAS; Crop Sci. Soc. Am; Int. Soc. Soil Sci. Physiology of crop yield; computer simulation of crop growth and yield, and of photosynthesis in plant canopies. Address: Dept. of Agronomy, University of Kentucky, Lexington, KY 40506.

DUNCKHORST, F(AUSTINO) T, b. Mogollon, N.Mex, July 1, 31. CHEMICAL ENGINEERING. B.S, New Mexico State, 57; M.S, Pittsburgh, 59, Ph.D.(adsorption chromatography), 64. Jr. engr, BETTIS ATOMIC POWER LAB, WESTINGHOUSE ELEC. CORP, 57-58, assoc. engr, 58-61, engr. 61-64, sr. engr, 64-70, FEL. ENGR, 70- U.S.A.F, 50-54, S/Sgt. N.Y. Acad. Sci; Am. Inst. Chem. Eng. Heat transfer and fluid flow problems in nuclear reactor design. Address: Westinghouse Electric Corp, Bettis Atomic Power Lab, P.O. Box 79, West Mifflin, PA 15122.

DUNCOMBE, E(LIOT), b. Bahamas, May 30, 16; nat; m. 44; c. 3. ENGINEERING MECHANICS. B.A, Cambridge, 37, M.A, 42; M.E.E, Delaware, 56; Ph.D.(controls), Pittsburgh, 65. Prod. engr, J. Lucas Ltd, Eng, 37-46; sr. scientist, Nat. Gas Turbine Estab, 46-47; res. engr, Nat. Res. Coun. Can, 47-51; sect. engr, aircraft power plants, WESTINGHOUSE ELEC. CORP, 51-57, ENGR, BETTIS ATOMIC POWER LAB, 57- Am. Nuclear Soc; Inst. Elec. & Electronics Eng. Gas dynamics; aviation gas turbines; nuclear power plants; fuel elements; control theory. Address: Westinghouse Electric Corp, Bettis Atomic Power Lab, Fuel Element Dept, P.O. Box 79, West Mifflin, PA 15122.

DUNCOMBE, R(AYNOR) L(OCKWOOD), b. Mt. Vernon, N.Y, Mar. 3, 17; m. 48; c. 1. ASTRONOMY. B.A, Wesleyan, 40; M.A, Iowa, 41; Ph.D, Yale, 56. Jr. astronr, U.S. Naval Observ, 42-43, asst. astronr, 43-45, assoc. astronr, 45-48; res. assoc, Yale Observ, 48-49; astronr, U.S. NAVAL OBSERV, 49-63, DIR. NAUTICAL ALMANAC OFF, 63- AAAS; Am. Inst. Aeronaut. & Astronaut; Am. Astron. Soc; Asn. Comput. Mach; Am. Inst. Navig; Int. Astron. Union. Elements of Venus; variable stars; dynamical astronomy; computing machinery. Address: 2335 King Pl. N.W, Washington, DC 20007.

DUNDEE, DOLORES SAUNDERS, b. Topeka, Kans, Aug. 7, 27; m. 51. ZOOLOGY. B.S, Washburn, 49; M.A, Kansas, 51; Ph.D, Michigan, 56. Asst, Kansas, 49-51; res. asst. malacol, Univ. Mich, 52-56; Paterson State Teachers Col, 57; asst. prof, LA. STATE UNIV, 58-62, assoc. prof, 63-67, PROF. BIOL. SCI, 67- Am. Soc. Zool; Am. Malacol. Union. Gastropod ecology and anatomy; freshwater mussel anatomy. Address: Dept. of Biology, Louisiana State University, New Orleans, LA 70122.

DUNDEE, HAROLD A, b. Tulsa, Okla, Aug. 23, 24; m. 51. HERPETOLOGY. B.S, Oklahoma, 48; fel, Michigan, 55-56, M.S, 57, Ph.D, 58. Asst. prof, Montclair State Teachers Col, 56-57; instr. ZOOL, TULANE UNIV, LA, 58-60, asst. prof, 60-66, ASSOC. PROF, 66-, ed, Tulane Studies Zool, 63-68. Dir. Meade Natural Hist. Libr, 65-68. Med.C, U.S.A, 45-46. Am. Soc. Ichthyol. & Herpet; Ecol. Soc. Am; fel. Soc. Study Amphibians & Reptiles. Aggregative behavior and habitat selection by snakes; ecology and endocrinology of neotenic salamanders. Address: Dept. of Biology, Tulane University of Louisiana, New Orleans, LA 70118.

DUNDON, ROBERT W, S.J, b. Iron Mountain, Mich, Aug. 4, 32. PHYSICAL & INORGANIC CHEMISTRY. A.B. & Ph.L, St. Louis Univ, 60; M.A, Johns Hopkins Univ, 63, Ph.D.(chem), 65; B.D, Woodstock Col.(Md), 68. ASST. PROF. CHEM, MARQUETTE UNIV, 69- Meteoritical Soc; Am. Chem. Soc; Geochem. Soc. Kinetics of Ag(II) reactions; thermodynamics of NO_3 radical; cation disorder in pyroxenes which have been shocked or heated; Mössbauer absorption spectroscopy. Address: Dept. of Chemistry, Marquette University, 1131 W. Wisconsin Ave, Milwaukee, WI 53233.

DUNDURS, J(OHN), b. Riga, Latvia, Sept. 13, 22; m. 52; c. 3. MECHANICS. B.S.M.E, Northwestern, 51, M.S, 55, Cabell fel, 57-58, Ph.D, 58. Designer diesel engines, Int. Harvester Co, 52-53; res. engr. hydraul. lab, NORTHWEST. UNIV, 53-54, instr. CIVIL ENG, 55-57, asst. prof, 58-60, assoc. prof, 61-66, PROF, 66- Am. Soc. Mech. Eng; Am. Soc. Civil Eng. Theory of elasticity; micromechanics. Address: Dept. of Civil Engineering, Northwestern University, Evanston, IL 60201.

DUNEER, ARTHUR GUSTAV, JR, b. Brooklyn, N.Y, Aug. 29, 24; m. 51; c. 3. RADIATION PHYSICS. B.S, Rensselaer Polytech, 49, M.S, 54, Ph.D.(physics), 59. Scientist, Assoc. Nucleonics, 56-59; prin. physicist, Repub. Aviation Corp, 59-64; sr. tech. specialist, space & info. div, N.Am. Aviation, Inc, 64-66, MEM. TECH. STAFF, AUTONETICS DIV, N.AM. ROCKWELL CORP, 66- U.S.N, 46-49. Am. Phys. Soc. Electromagnetic theory applied to antennas and shielding; application of computers to electromagnetic interaction calculations; nuclear radiation shielding applied to reactor and space physics; nuclear radiation effects; plasma physics. Address: 519 E. Las Palmas Dr, Fullerton, CA 92632.

DUNEGAN, HAROLD L, b. Eufaula, Okla, Feb. 25, 31; m. 58; c. 2. MATERIALS SCIENCE. B.S, San Jose State Col, 61. Proj. engr, Lawrence Radiation Lab, 61-70; PRES, DUNEGAN RES. CORP, 70- Chmn, Acoust. Emission Working Group, 67. U.S.C.G, 51-54. Am. Soc. Metals; Soc. Nondestructive Test. Acoustic emission and fracture mechanics characterization of materials and structures for nondestructive detection of fatigue crack growth, hydrogen embrittlement and stress corrosion cracking; incipient failure diagnosis of structures. Address: Dunegan Research Corporation, 2044 Research Dr, Livermore, CA 94550.

DUNELL, B(ASIL) A(NDERSON), b. Vancouver, B.C, Apr. 5, 23. PHYSICAL CHEMISTRY. B.A.Sc, British Columbia, 45, M.A.Sc, 46; Textile Res. Inst. fel, Princeton, 46-49, M.A, 48, Ph.D.(chem), 49. Asst. CHEM, UNIV. B.C, 45-46, asst. prof, 49-61, assoc. prof, 61-65, PROF, 65- Faraday Soc; fel. Chem. Inst. Can; The Chem. Soc. Solid state nuclear magnetic resonance. Address: Dept. of Chemistry, University of British Columbia, Vancouver 8, B.C, Can.

DUNFORD, HUGH BRIAN, b. Oyen, Alta, Oct. 25, 27; m. 52; c. 4. PHYSICAL CHEMISTRY. M.Sc, Univ. Alta, 52; Ph.D.(chem), McGill Univ, 54. Chem. Inst. Can. fel. CHEM, McMaster Univ, 54-55; asst. prof, Dalhousie Univ, 55-57; UNIV. ALTA, 57-60, assoc. prof, 60-68, PROF, 68- Am. Chem. Soc; Chem. Inst. Can; Faraday Soc. Rapid reaction kinetics; mechanisms of enzyme reactions. Address: Dept. of Chemistry, University of Alberta, Edmonton 7, Alta, Can.

DUNFORD, JAMES MARSHALL, b. Seattle, Wash, Oct. 13, 15; m. 41; c. 8. NUCLEAR & MARINE ENGINEERING. B.S, U.S. Naval Acad, 39; S.M, Mass. Inst. Tech, 44. Design supt. marine eng, Norfolk Naval Shipyard, 54-55, dep. asst. chief nuclear power, bur. ships, Dept. Navy, Wash, D.C, 55-61; v.pres. naval nuclear power, N.Y. Shipbuilding Corp, 61-65; prof. mech. eng, Univ. Pa, 65-67; TECH. DIR, NAVAL AIR ENG. CTR, 67- Secy. Navy letter commendation. U.S.N, 39-61, Capt. Soc. Naval Archit. & Marine Eng; Am. Soc. Naval Eng; Am. Soc. Mech. Eng. Nuclear power plants for naval submarine and surface vessels; application of nuclear power of undersea research vessels. Address: Naval Air Engineering Center, Philadelphia, PA 19112.

DUNFORD, MAX P(ATTERSON), b. Bloomington, Idaho, June 17, 30; m. 54; c. 6. GENETICS, BOTANY. B.S, Brigham Young, 54, M.S, 58; Ph.D.(genetics), Univ. Calif, Davis, 62. ASST. PROF. BIOL, Mills Col, 62-63; N.MEX. STATE UNIV, 63- U.S.A, 54-56. Bot. Soc. Am. Cytotaxonomy and biosystematics. Address: Dept. of Biology, New Mexico State University, University Park, NM 88001.

DUNFORD, RAYMOND A, b. Bristol, Eng, June 19, 14; Can. citizen; m. 40; ANALYTICAL CHEMISTRY. B.Sc, Univ. London, 37. Chemist, Brit. Drug Houses Ltd, 37-39, chief chemist, Can, 39-53, prod. mgr, 53-58, plant mgr, 58-64, dir, 64-69; V.PRES. PROD, GLAXO CAN. LTD, 70- Fel. Royal Inst. Chem; fel. Chem. Inst. Can. Determination of steroid hormones and vitamin E. Address: Glaxo Canada Ltd, Queensway, Toronto 550, Ont, Can.

DUNGAN, KENDRICK WEBB, b. Science Hill, Ky, Jan. 7, 28; m. 51; c. 3. PHARMACOLOGY, PHYSIOLOGY. B.S, Kentucky, 51. Assoc. pharmacologist, William S. Merrell Co, Ohio, 51-54; PRIN. INVESTR. PHARMACOL, MEAD JOHNSON & CO, 54- U.S.N, 46-48. AAAS; N.Y. Acad. Sci; Am. Soc. Pharmacol. & Exp. Therapeut; Soc. Exp. Biol. & Med. Respiration; uterus; gut; autonomic nervous system. Address: Mead Johnson & Co, 2404 Pennsylvania St, Evansville, IN 47721.

DUNGWORTH, DONALD L, b. Hathersage, Eng. July 16, 31; nat; m. 62; c. 2. VETERINARY PATHOLOGY. B.V.Sc, Univ. Liverpool, 56; Ont. Vet. Col, 56-57; Ph.D.(vet. path), Univ. Calif, Davis, 61. Lectr. VET. PATH, Univ. Calif, Davis, 59-61; Univ. Bristol, 61-62; asst. prof, UNIV. CALIF, DAVIS, 62-66, assoc. prof, 66-70, PROF. & CHMN. DEPT, 70- WHO fel, Inst. Diseases of Chest, Brompton, London, Eng, 68-69. Dipl, Am. Col. Vet. Path. Royal Col. Vet. Surg; Int. Acad. Path; Am. Asn. Path. & Bact. Pulmonary pathology, especially response to infections and allergic conditions; neoplasia, especially lymphoma/leukemias and myeloproliferative disorders. Address: Dept. of Pathology, School of Veterinary Medicine, University of California, Davis, CA 95616.

DUNHAM, B(RADFORD), b. Jan. 29, 23. SYMBOLIC LOGIC. B.A, Col. William & Mary, 43; M.A, Harvard, 48, fel, 49-50, Ph.D.(symbolic logic), 50. Asst. philos, Harvard, 47-48; Sheldon traveling fel, 48-49; instr. philos. & logic, Duke, 50-53; ADV. LOGICIAN, THOMAS J. WATSON RES. CTR, IBM CORP, 57- Lectr, Oxford, 58. U.S.N, 43-46, Lt.(jg). Asn. Symbolic Logic. Interrelationship of logic and computing machines. Address: Research Center, IBM Corp, P.O. Box 218, Yorktown Heights, NY 10598.

DUNHAM, CHARLES BURTON, b. Port Alberni, B.C, Jan. 25, 38. MATHEMATICS. B.A, Univ. B.C, 59, M.A, 63; Univ. Toronto, 63-64; Ph.D.(math), Univ. West. Ont, 68. Res. asst. COMPUT. SCI, UNIV. WEST. ONT, 64-65, lectr, 65-69, ASST. PROF, 69- Asn. Comput. Mach. Approximation theory; numerical analysis; best approximation, with emphasis on Chebyshev approximation; subroutines for mathematical functions; computational arithmetic. Address: Dept. of Computer Science, University of Western Ontario, London, Ont, Can.

DUNHAM, CHARLES L(ITTLE), b. Evanston, Ill, Dec. 28, 06; m. 32; c. 3. MEDICINE. B.A, Yale, 29; M.D, Chicago, 34. Asst. med, Chicago, 36-42, instr, 42-46, asst. prof, 46-49; asst. chief med. br, biol. & med. div, Atomic Energy Comn, 49-50, chief, 50-54, dep. dir, 54-55, dir. div. biol. & med, 55-67; CHMN. DIV. MED. SCI, NAT. RES. COUN, 67- Distinguished serv. award, Atomic Energy Comn, 57. Med.C, 43-46, Capt. AAAS; Am. Pub. Health Asn; Am. Med. Asn; Radiation Res. Soc; Am. Rheumatism Asn; Indust. Med. Asn; Soc. Nuclear Med; Health Phys. Soc; Am. Nuclear Soc. Allergy, arthritis; radiation biology and health. Address: 5302 Carvel Rd, N.W, Washington, DC 20016.

DUNHAM, CHARLES W, b. Norwich, Vt, May 9, 22; m; c. 3. HORTICULTURE. B.S, Massachusetts, 46; M.S, Wisconsin, 48; Ph.D.(hort), Mich. State, 54. Asst. hort, Wisconsin, 46-48; instr. floricult, Massachusetts, 48-52; asst. hort, Mich. State Univ, 52-54; asst. prof, UNIV. DEL, 54-58, ASSOC. PROF, PLANT SCI, 58- Alex Laurie award, 57. U.S.A, 43-46. Am. Soc. Hort. Sci; Am. Hort. Soc. Plant nutrition, especially ornamental plants; plant propagation and physiology applied to growth of ornamental plants. Address: Dept. of Horticulture, University of Delaware, Newark, DE 19711.

DUNHAM, D(ONALD) W(EST), b. Stuyvesant Falls, N.Y, Dec. 2, 08; m. 35; c. 1. ZOOLOGY. B.S, Muskingum Col, 34; M.A, Ohio State, 36, Ph.D.(zool), 41. Asst. zool, Ohio State, 37-41; instr. BIOL, UNIV. EVANSVILLE, 41-43, asst. prof. 43-44, assoc. prof, 44-45, acting head dept, 43-45, PROF. & HEAD DEPT, 45- Freshwater Coelenterata; taxonomy of the Ixodidae. Address: Dept. of Biology, University of Evansville, Evansville, IN 47714.

DUNHAM, JEWETT, b. Anaheim, Calif, Feb. 6, 24; m. 51; c. 3. ZOOLOGY, PHYSIOLOGY. B.A, Iowa, 48, M.S, 52, Ph.D.(zool), 57. Instr. biol. chem, Chadwick Sch, Calif, 50-53; asst. prof. ZOOL, IOWA STATE UNIV, 57-63, assoc. prof, 63-69, PROF, 69- U.S.A, 42-45. AAAS; Am. Soc. Zool; Am. Inst. Biol. Sci. Biological barriers. Address: Dept. of Zoology, Iowa State University, Ames, IA 50010.

DUNHAM, JOHN MALCOLM, b. San Jose, Calif, June 27, 23; m. 51; c. 4. ANALYTICAL CHEMISTRY. B.S, California, Los Angeles, 48; Ph.D.(anal. chem), 57. Chemist agr. res, Dow Chem. Co, Calif, 48-51; asst, California, Los Angeles, 52-56; instr. chem, Occidental Col, 56-57, asst. prof, 57-58; res. chemist, Sterling-Winthrop Res. Inst, N.Y, 58-62; sr. anal. chemist, Pitman-Moore Div, Dow Chem. Co, 62-66, proj. leader, Dow Human Health Res. & Develop, 66-67; SECT. HEAD ANAL. CHEM, SQUIBB INST. MED. RES, 68- U.S.N, 43-46. Am. Chem. Soc. Determination of drugs in pharmaceutical dosage forms and biological systems; coulometric titrations; separations; organic polarography; nonaqueous titrations; identity and purity of organic compounds. Address: Squibb Institute for Medical Research, New Brunswick, NJ 08903.

DUNHAM, KENNETH ROYAL, b. Rochester, N.Y, Feb. 5, 23; m. 48; c. 2. ORGANIC & POLYMER CHEMISTRY. B.A, Hobart Col, 43; Oswego State Teachers Col, 44; Denver, 47-48; Rochester, 50-55. Chemist, Eastman Kodak Co, 45-47; Genesee Res. Corp, 48-50; res. chemist, EASTMAN KODAK CO, 50-64, RES. ASSOC. PHOTORESISTS, 64- U.S.A.A.F, 43-45, 2nd Lt. Soc. Photog. Eng. & Sci. Polycarbonates; polyesters; photoresists; metal organics; stereoregular polymers; organic synthesis. Address: Eastman Kodak Co, Research Lab, 343 State St, Rochester, NY 14650.

DUNHAM, MILTON L(EON), JR, b. Phila, Pa, May 19, 22; m. 44; c. 2. CHEMICAL ENGINEERING. B.S, Carnegie Inst. Tech, 42. Res. & develop. engr, Linde Air Prod. Co. Div, UNION CARBIDE CORP, 45-46, supvr. prod. develop. silicones div, 56-63, prod. mgr, 63-64, mgr. tech. serv, 64-67, tech. mgr. CHEM. & PLASTICS, 67-70, INT. MGR, 70- U.S.A.A.F, 42-45, 1st Lt. AAAS; Am. Chem. Soc; Am. Inst. Chem. Eng. Silicone rubber technology and fluids. Address: Union Carbide Corp, 270 Park Ave, New York, NY 10017.

DUNHAM, PHILIP BIGELOW, b. Columbus, Ohio, Apr. 26, 37. PHYSIOLOGY. B.A, Swarthmore Col, 58; Ph.D.(zool), Chicago, 62. U.S. Pub. Health Serv. fel, 62-63; asst. prof. zool, SYRACUSE UNIV, 63-67, assoc. prof, 67-71, PROF. BIOL, 71- Vis. assoc. prof, sch. med, Yale, 68-70. Soc. Gen. Physiol; Am. Physiol. Soc; Biophys. Soc. Active transport of Na and K in red blood cells in humans and HK and LK in sheep; regulation of solutes and water in protozoa. Address: Dept. of Biology, Syracuse University, Syracuse, NY 13210.

DUNHAM, R(OBERT) J(ACOB), b. Red Rock, Okla, Aug. 15, 24; m. 46; c. 4. GEOLOGY. B.S, Oklahoma, 49, M.S, 51; Nat. Sci. Found. fel. & M.S, Yale, 52, Nat. Sci. Found. fel. & Ph.D.(geol), 61. Jr. geologist, Calif. Co, 49; instr, Oklahoma, 49-50; geologist, U.S. Geol. Surv, 50-55; SR. RES. ASSOC. GEOL, SHELL DEVELOP. CO, 55- U.S.A, 43-45. Geol. Soc. Am; Am. Asn. Petrol. Geol; Geochem. Soc; Am. Petrol. Inst; Soc. Econ. Paleont. & Mineral (councilor, 68-70). Structural geology; geology of fuels; sedimentation and diagenesis of carbonate rocks. Address: Shell Development Co, P.O. Box 481, Houston, TX 77001.

DUNHAM, THEODORE, JR, b. New York, N.Y, Dec. 17, 97; m. 26; c. 2. ASTRONOMY, BIOPHYSICS. A.B, Harvard, 21; M.D, Cornell, 25; Ph.D, Princeton, 27. Nat. Res. Coun. fel. physics, Mt. Wilson Observ, Carnegie Inst, 27-28, asst. astronr, 28-36, astronr, 36-47; SCI. DIR, FUND ASTROPHYS. RES, 36-; CONSULT PHYSICS, 66-; HON. ASSOC. HARVARD OBSERV, 71- Assoc. prof, Princeton, 34-36; res. assoc, Oxford, 38-39; mem. sect. instruments, Nat. Defense Res. Comt, 40-42; chief sect. optical instruments, Off. Sci. Res. & Develop, 42-46; Henry E. Warren fel, Harvard Med. Sch. & assoc, Peter Bent Brigham Hosp, 46-48; res. assoc, Mass. Inst. Tech, 47-48; Harvard Observ, 47-52; res. assoc, inst. optics & fel. med, Rochester, 48-57; reader, Australian Nat. Univ, 57-61, personal prof, 61-64; sr. res. fel, Tasmania, 65-70; sr. fel, Nat. Sci. Found, 67-68. Mem. comt. vision, Armed Forces-Nat. Res. Coun; Nat. Geog. Soc-U.S. Navy Eclipse Exped, Canton Island, 37. C.W.S, U.S.A, 19. Am. Phys. Soc; Am. Astron. Soc; Optical Soc. Am; Royal Astron. Soc. Interpretation of stellar spectra; stellar spectrographs; photoelectric spectrophotometry; planetary atmospheres; material of interstellar space; ultraviolet spectrophotometry of cells. Address: P.O. Box 135, Chocorua, NH 03817.

DUNHAM, THOMAS E(SCHMAN), b. North Canton, Ohio, Aug. 24, 41; m. 63; c. 2. PHYSICAL METALLURGY. B.A, Ohio Wesleyan Univ, 63; B.Met.E, Ohio State Univ, 65, Ph.D.(metall), 68. RES. METALLURGIST, REFRACTORY METALS LAB, GEN. ELEC. CO, 68- Am. Soc. Metals; Metall. Soc. Effect of solutes and dispersed phases on mechanical, physical and microstructural properties of refractory metals, particularly tungsten; powder metallurgy of refractory metals. Address: Lamp Metals & Components Dept, Refractory Metals Lab, General Electric Co, 21800 Tungsten Rd, Cleveland, OH 44117.

DUNHAM, VALGENE L(OREN), b. Jamestown, N.Y, Oct. 6, 40; m. 62. PLANT PHYSIOLOGY & BIOCHEMISTRY. B.S, Houghton Col, 62; Nat. Sci. Found. fel, Syracuse Univ, 64-65, M.S, 65, Nat. Defense Educ. Act fel, 65-68, Ph.D.(bot), 69. Teacher, pub. sch, N.Y, 62-63, head dept. biol, 63-64; teaching asst. bot, Syracuse Univ, 68-69; RES. ASSOC. HORT, PURDUE UNIV, 69- AAAS; Bot. Soc. Am; Am. Inst. Biol. Sci; Am. Soc. Plant Physiol. Effects of amino acids on growth and development of Marchantia polymorpha gemmalings; effects of gamma irradiation on various aspects of RNA synthesis including alterations of RNA polymerase and the DNA template. Address: Dept. of Horticulture, Purdue University, Lafayette, IN 47907.

DUNHAM, WOLCOTT B(ALESTIER), b. Boston, Mass, June 15, 00; m. 40; c. 2. VIROLOGY. A.B, Columbia, 24, M.D, 28. Asst. bacteriologist, N.Y. Post-Grad. Med. Sch. Hosp, Columbia, 36-46, res. fel, 39-40; res. biologist, Vet. Admin. Hosp, 46-61, dir. gen. med. res. lab, 49-56, asst. dir. prfnl. serv. res, 56-61, assoc. chief of staff, 61-68; VIS. INVESTR, JACKSON LAB, 68- Assoc, Squibb Inst. Med. Res, 42-46; assoc. prof, med. col, Univ. Tenn, 52-68. Dipl, Am. Bd. Microbiol. With Off. Sci. Res. & Develop, 44. AAAS; Am. Acad. Microbiol; Am. Asn. Immunol; Am. Fedn. Clin. Res; Soc. Exp. Biol. & Med; Am. Col. Physicians; N.Y. Acad. Sci; fel. N.Y. Acad. Med. Penicillin therapy in experimental syphilis; infectious hepatitis; virus hemagglutination; granuloma inguinale antigens; tissue cultures; leukemia. Address: Jackson Lab, Bar Harbor, ME 04609.

DUNHOLTER, H(OWARD) F(RANK), b. Cincinnati, Ohio, Oct. 21, 11; m. 50; c. 2. PHYSICS. A.B, Cincinnati, 35, scholar, 36, Ph.D.(physics, math), 39. Aeronaut. engr, Vultee Aircraft, 39-40; fire control engr, armament div, Sperry Gyroscope, 40-42; head thermodyn. group, Convair Div, Gen. Dynamics Corp, 42-45, chief develop. engr, Atlas prog, 55-59, asst. chief engr. develop, Convair-Astronaut, 59-62, dir. res, Astro Div, 62-65; CHIEF SCIENTIST, SPACE SYSTS. DIV, HUGHES AIRCRAFT CO, 65- Am. Inst. Aeronaut. & Astronaut. Electron diffraction; aerodynamics; thermodynamics. Address: 1732 Via Boronada, Palos Verdes Estates, CA 90274.

DUNHOLTER, RUSSEL (JOHN), b. Cincinnati, Ohio, Feb. 28, 08; m. 38; c. 2. MATHEMATICS, MECHANICS. C.E, Cincinnati, 30, Ph.D.(math), 39. Instr. math, UNIV. CINCINNATI, 30-36, asst. prof, 37-45, assoc. prof. MECH, 46-53, PROF, 54- Res. engr. & consult, U.S. Air Force & aircraft indust; consult, Wright-Patterson Air Force Base, 42-46, 53; Aeroprod. Div, Gen. Motors Corp, 49-51; Gen. Dynamics/Convair, 51; Aircraft Nuclear Propulsion, Gen. Elec. Co, 54-60; Cincinnati & Suburban Bell Tel. Co, 59. Am. Math. Soc; Am. Soc. Eng. Educ. Rational mechanics; discrete field theory; diakoptics. Address: Dept. of Engineering Analysis, University of Cincinnati, Mail Location 112, Cincinnati, OH 45221.

DUNICZ, B(OLESLAW) L(UDWIK), b. Lwow, Poland, Feb. 13, 12; nat. PHYSICAL CHEMISTRY. M.Sc, King John Casimir Univ, Poland, 35; Ph.D. (phys. chem), King's Col, London, 47. Asst. to prof. qual. anal. chem, Lwow, 34-39; asst. lectr, Polish Univ. Col, London, 47; asst. photochem, Colorado, 48; res. fel, Minnesota, 49; asst. chem. thermodyn, Chicago, 50-52; instr. phys. chem, Chicago Undergrad. Div, Illinois, 52-53; res. assoc. chem. thermodyn, col. eng, N.Y. Univ, 53-55; instr. phys. & gen. chem, Long Island, 55-56, asst. prof, 56-59; inorg. qual. anal. & phys. chem, The Citadel, 59-60; physical chemist, U.S. Naval Radiol. Defense Lab, 60-68; lectr. physics, Col. Notre Dame (Calif), 69-71; DIR. CHEM. LABS, UNIV. SAN FRANCISCO, 70- Res. worker, U.S. Naval Radiol. Defense Labs, summers 58-59. Polish Army, 40; Brit. Home Guard, 42-43. Fel. AAAS; Am. Chem. Soc; fel. Am. Inst. Chem. Photochemistry; kinetics; thermodynamics; fused salts; surface phenomena. Address: Apt. 1H, Sunset Towers, 8 Locksley Ave, San Francisco, CA 94122.

DUNIGAN, EDWARD P, b. Marshfield, Wis, June 16, 34; m. 61; c. 2. SOIL MICROBIOLOGY. B.S, Wis. State, Stevens Point, 58; M.S, Mich. State, 61; Ph.D.(agr. chem, soils), Arizona, 67. Res. chemist, U.S. Rubber Co; Gen. Motors Res. Labs, 62-64; res. assoc. herbicides, Arizona, 64-67; ASST. PROF. SOIL MICROBIOL, LA. STATE UNIV, BATON ROUGE, 67- U.S.A, 52-54. Am. Soc. Agron; Soil Sci. Soc. Am; Crop Sci. Soc. Am. Soil organic matter; herbicide-nodulation of soybean interactions; physical chemistry of herbicide adsorption; herbicide-soil organic matter interactions; fertilizer runoff; water quality. Address: Dept. of Agronomy, Louisiana State University, Baton Rouge, LA 70803.

DUNIHUE, F(RED) W(ILLIAMS), b. Bowling Green, Ky, June 9, 06; m. 34; c. 3. ANATOMY. A.B, Wabash Col, 29; M.Sc, N.Y. Univ, 31, Ph.D.(histol, embryol), 34. Asst. biol, N.Y. Univ, 29-35; neuroanat, histol. & embryol, COL. MED, UNIV. VT, 36-38, asst. prof. HISTOL. & EMBRYOL, 38-44, assoc. prof, 44-49, prof, 49-71, EMER. PROF, 71- AAAS; Am. Asn. Anat; Am. Soc. Exp. Biol; Am. Soc. Zool; Electron Micros. Soc. Am. Histology; anatomy of the kidney. Address: 2 Park Ave, Essex Junction, VT 05452.

DUNIPACE, DONALD W(ILLIAM), b. Bowling Green, Ohio, May 24, 07; m. 28; c. 2. PHYSICS. B.A, Ohio State, 29, M.A, 30. Asst. physics, Ohio State, 29-32; fel, 32-33; physicist, Libbey-Owens-Ford Glass Co, 35-62; staff scientist, Ball Bros. Res. Corp, 62-69; SR. SCIENTIST, LIBBY-OWENS-FORD CO, 69- AAAS; Sci. Res. Soc. Am; Am. Phys. Soc; Optical Soc. Am. Investigation of glass and glass production problems; optical instrumentation; radiative heat transfer phenomena. Address: Libbey-Owens-Ford Co, 1701 E. Broadway St, Toledo, OH 43605.

DUNIPACE, KENNETH ROBERT, b. Bowling Green, Ohio, Sept. 26, 29; m. 63; c. 2. CONTROL SYSTEMS. B.S, Ohio State, 51; S.B, Mass. Inst. Technol, 56; M.E, Florida, 65; Ph.D.(elec. eng), Clemson, 68. Staff engr, Permaglass, Inc, 53-54; exec. officer aerophys. res, Mass. Inst. Technol, 56-58, staff engr. Polaris guid, 58-60, test mgr, 60-63, sr. rep. Apollo guid. & navig, 63-65; res. asst. elec. eng, Florida, 66; Clemson, 66-68; ASSOC. PROF. ELEC. ENG. & RES. ASSOC, TRANSPORTATION INST, UNIV. MOROLLA, 68- Consult, instrumentation lab, Mass. Inst. Technol, 68-71. U.S.N, 51-53, Lt. Inst. Elec. & Electronics Eng; Simulation Coun. Development of guidance and navigation systems for aerospace and highway application; application of contemporary control theory to transportation problems. Address: Dept. of Electrical Engineering, University of Missouri-Rolla, Rolla, MO 65401.

DUNIWAY, JOHN M(ASON), b. San Francisco, Calif, Nov. 6, 42; m. 65; c. 1. PLANT PATHOLOGY & PHYSIOLOGY. B.A, Carleton Col, 64; Ph.D.(plant pathol), Univ. Wis, Madison, 69. Nat. Sci. Found. fel. plant physiol, res. sch. biol. sci, Australian Nat. Univ, 69-70; LECTR. PLANT PATH. & ASST. PLANT PATHOLOGIST, UNIV. CALIF, DAVIS, 70- AAAS; Am. Phytopath. Soc; Am. Soc. Plant Physiol. Water relations and photosynthesis in diseased plants; water relations of microorganisms. Address: Dept. of Plant Pathology, University of California, Davis, CA 95616.

DUNK, A(LLAN) C(ARLTON), b. Woodford, Ont, Apr. 18, 21; nat; m. 50; c. 4. MECHANICAL ENGINEERING. B.A.Sc, Toronto, 50; M.S.M.E, Purdue, 51, Ph.D.(mech. eng), 55. Instr. mech. eng, Purdue, 52-55, asst. prof, 55-59, assoc. prof, 59-64; eng. supvr. planetology instruments group, space sci. div, jet propulsion lab, Calif. Inst. Technol, 64-68; prof. mech. eng, Drexel Inst. Technol, 68-69; STAFF ENGR, BIOSCI. SECT, JET PROPULSION LAB, CALIF. INST. TECHNOL, 69-, sr. res. engr, summers 59-64, consult, 63-64. Adj. prof, Univ. South. Calif, 69-71. Can. Army, 42-46, S/Sgt. Am. Soc. Mech. Eng.(ed, Bull. Mach. Design, 59-61); Am. Soc. Eng. Educ. Kinematics; machine design; optical-mechanical instrument design. Address: 2225 E. Midwick Dr, Altadena, CA 91001.

DUNKEL, MORRIS, b. Brooklyn, N.Y, Dec. 4, 27; m. 57; c. 3. ORGANIC CHEMISTRY. B.S, Long Island, 50; M.S, Brooklyn Col, 54; Ph.D.(org. chem), Arkansas, 56. Res. chemist, Norda Essential Oil & Chem. Co, 51-53, group leader, 56-58; res. chemist, Nopco Chem. Co, 58-59, head org. fine chem. res, 59-61; group leader, UOP CHEM. DIV, UNIVERSAL OIL PROD. CO, 61-66, DIR. APPL. RES, CHEM. DIV, 66- U.S.A, 46-47, Res, 54-58, 2nd Lt. Am. Chem. Soc; The Chem. Soc. Organic synthesis; aroma and flavor chemistry; natural products; vitamins; catalytic hydrogenation; stereochemistry; reactions at elevated temperatures and pressures; flame retardancy; polymer stabilization. Address: UOP Chemical Division, Route 17, East Rutherford, NJ 07073.

DUNKELBERG, WILBUR E(UGENE), JR, b. San Antonio, Tex, Mar. 30, 28; m. 55; c. 4. MICROBIOLOGY. B.S, Maryland, 52; M.S, Kentucky, 56; Ph.D. (microbiol), Vanderbilt, 68. Microbiologist, Ky. State Dept. Pub. Health, 54-55; City Hosp, Springfield, Ohio, 55-57; MED. SERV. CORPS, U.S. ARMY, 57-, virologist, Second Army Med. Lab. Ft. Meade, Md, 57-59, microbiologist, Army Hosp, Frankfurt, Ger, 59-62, Valley Forge Gen. Hosp, Pa, 62-64, microbiologist & lab. dir, Army Med. Res. Team, Vietnam, 67-68, MICROBIOLOGIST, THIRD ARMY MED. LAB, 68- Guest researcher, venereal disease res. lab, Nat. Commun. Disease Ctr, Atlanta, 69-70. Med.Serv.C, U.S.A, 57-, Maj. Am. Soc. Microbiol; Asn. Mil. Surg. U.S. Microbial nutrition; microbiology of venereal diseases; epidemiology of Corynebacterium vaginale and determination of its growth requirements and methods of isolation; plague in Vietnam. Address: Microbiology Dept, Third U.S. Army Medical Lab, Ft. McPherson, GA 30330.

DUNKELBERGER, TOBIAS H(ENRY), b. Paxinos, Pa, Nov. 4, 09; m. 41; c. 2. PHYSICAL CHEMISTRY, MICROCHEMISTRY. Sc.B, Dickinson Col, 30; Ph.D.(phys. chem), Pittsburgh, 37. Teacher, high sch, Pa, 30-31; asst. CHEM, Pittsburgh, 31-36; asst. prof, N. Texas Agr. Col, 36-37; Idaho, 37-38; Duquesne, 38-41; N.Y. State Col. Ceramics, Alfred, 41-44; prof. & head dept, Duquesne, 44-52; PROF. CHEM, UNIV. PITTSBURGH, 52-, ASSOC. DEAN COL. ARTS & SCI, 69- Prof, Univ. Pittsburgh faculties in Ecuador, Agency Int. Develop. contract, 63-67, chief-of-party, faculties in Guatemala, 67-69. AAAS; Am. Chem. Soc.(Pittsburgh award, 70). Thermodynamics of solutions; microchemistry; chemical education. Address: College of Arts & Science, University of Pittsburgh, Pittsburgh, PA 15213.

DUNKELMAN, LAWRENCE, b. Paterson, N.J, June 28, 17; m. 50; c. 2. PHYSICS, ASTRONOMY. B.E.E, Cooper Union, 38, E.E, 49. Jr. marine engr, U.S. Naval Shipyard, N.H, 39-41; elec. engr, U.S. Bur. Ships, U.S. Dept. Navy, 41-43, electronics engr, 43-48; physicist, U.S. Naval Res. Lab, 48-58; aeronautics & space scientist & head ultraviolet detection systs. & planetary optics, Goddard Space Flight Ctr, NASA, Md, 59-64; mem. sr. staff, Inst. Defense Anal, Arlington, Va, 64-65; head planetary optics, GODDARD SPACE FLIGHT CTR, NASA, 65-69, HEAD ASTRON. SYSTS. BR, 69- Consult, univ. & indust. labs; staff specialist, astron. orbiting observ, NASA, 59-61, mem. comt. astronaut. training & exp, 62-64; proj. scientist, U.K-U.S. Ariel II satellite, 61-64; mem. eclipse exped, U.S. Navy, Sweden, 54, Peru, 65. AAAS; fel. Optical Soc. Am; Int. Astron. Union; Sci. Res. Soc. Am. Atmospheric attenuation of ultraviolet, visible and near infrared; ultraviolet technology; electrooptics; low light level photography; spectrophotometric instrumentation for space research; planetary atmospheres; solar research; manned space sciences. Address: Lab. for Optical Astronomy (673), Goddard Space Flight Center, Greenbelt, MD 20771.

DUNKER, ALAN KEITH, b. New Orleans, La, Mar. 16, 43; m. 65. BIOPHYSICS. B.S, California, Berkeley, 65; M.S, Wisconsin, Madison, 67, Nat. Inst. Health grant, 67-69, Ph.D.(biophys), 69. FEL. BIOPHYS, YALE, 69- Structure and process of assembly of viruses, especially picornaviruses, other animal viruses and the bacteriovirus fd; theory of molecular sieving with applications to gel electrophoresis. Address: Dept. of Molecular Biophysics & Biochemistry, 1937 Yale Station, Yale University, New Haven, CT 06520.

DUNKER, CARL F(REDERICK), b. Willimansett, Mass, July 18, 14; m. 42; c. 3. CHEMISTRY, FOOD TECHNOLOGY. B.S, Mass. State Col, 36, M.S, 37, Ph.D.(food tech), 39. Supvr. water anal. lab, Mass. Dept. Pub. Health, 38; res. chemist, exp. sta, Mass. State Col, 39; biol. dir. vitamin div, LaWall & Harrisson, Pa, 40; supvr. meat dehydration, exp. res. pilot plant, U.S. Dept. Agr, 40-42; res. dir, Surdik Food Prod. Corp, 45; mem. staff, Wirthmore Res. Lab, 47-48; res. technologist, U.S. Dept. Agr, 48-53; res. leader, Gaines Div, Gen. Foods Corp, 53-57; faculty mem. & dir. seafood processing lab, Univ. Md, 57-59; tech. dir, Perk Foods Co, Ill, 61-69; MEM. STAFF, SWIFT & CO, 69- AAAS; Inst. Food Technol. Seafood processing; foods development; chemical biological and microbiological vitamins; dehydration of vegetables and meats and method of storing them; biassay of poultry feeds; water analysis; dog food; meat curing and freezing. Address: Swift & Co, 1919 Swift Dr, Oak Brook, IL 60521.

DUNKER, MELVIN F(REDERICK) W(ILLIAM), b. Baltimore, Md, June 12, 13; m. 41; c. 3. PHARMACEUTICAL CHEMISTRY. Ph.G, Maryland, 33, B.S, 34, M.S, 36, Ph.D.(pharmaceut. chem), 39, Warner fel, 39-40. Asst, sch. pharm, Maryland, 34-39; Rockefeller Found. assoc, Northwestern, 40-41; instr. pharm, Wisconsin, 41-42, asst. prof, 42-45; assoc. prof. PHARMACEUT. CHEM, COL. PHARM, WAYNE STATE UNIV, 45-49, PROF, 49- AAAS; Am. Chem. Soc; Am. Pharmaceut. Asn. Replacement of diazonium boro-fluoride by mercury; aliphatic amines; steroids; the i-ethers of 3-hydroxy-5-cholenic acid; fluorine substituted phenols; phenobarbital. Address: College of Pharmacy, Wayne State University, 5501 Second Ave, Detroit, MI 48202.

DUNKIN, JOHN WILLIAM, b. Fayette Co, Ind, Dec. 2, 27; m. 49; c. 5. ENGINEERING SCIENCES. B.S, Purdue, 53, M.S, 54, Ph.D.(eng. sci), 61. Instr. eng. mech, Purdue, 54-61; sr. res. engr, Jersey Prod. Res. Co, Standard Oil Co. N.J, 61-64; SR. RES. ASSOC, ESSO PROD. RES. CO, 64- Soc. Explor. Geophys; Am. Geophys. Union; Soc. Eng. Sci. Elastodynamics; transient response of layered elastic media; wave propagation in electromagnetic elastic media and in randomly inhomogeneous media; exploration seismology. Address: Esso Production Research Co, P.O. Box 2189, Houston, TX 77001.

DUNKL, CHARLES F(RANCIS), b. Vienna, Austria, Sept. 16, 41; Can. citizen; m. 65. MATHEMATICS. B.Sc, Toronto, 62, M.A, 63; Ph.D.(math), Univ. Wisconsin, 65. Instr. MATH, Princeton, 65-67; asst. prof, UNIV. VA, 67-70, ASSOC. PROF, 70- Am. Math. Soc. Harmonic analysis; special functions. Address: Dept. of Mathematics, University of Virginia, Charlottesville, VA 22903.

DUNKLE, DAVID H(OSBROOK), b. Winnipeg, Man, Sept. 9, 11; m. 30; c. 1. VERTEBRATE PALEONTOLOGY. B.A, Kansas, 35; Ph.D.(zool), Harvard, 39. Teaching asst. comp. anat, Harvard, 36-39; assoc. curator in charge dept. paleont, Cleveland Mus. Nat. Hist, 39-46; assoc. curator, div. vert. paleont, U.S. Nat. Mus, 46-60; tech. adv. paleont. & stratig, U.S. Geol. Surv-U.S. Opers. Mission, Pakistan, 60-62; assoc. curator, div. vert. paleont, U.S. Nat. Mus, 62-68; CURATOR PALEONT, CLEVELAND MUS. NATURAL HIST, 68- Adj. prof, Case West. Reserve Univ, 68- Soc. Vert. Paleont. Morphology and stratigraphic significances of fossil fishes. Address: Cleveland Museum of Natural History, Wade Oval, University Circle, Cleveland, OH 44106.

DUNKLE, JOHN ROBERT, b. Jacksonville, Fla, June 30, 24; m. 50; c. 2. GEOGRAPHY. B.A.E, Florida, 48; M.A, California, Los Angeles, 50; Ph.D. (geog), Clark, 55. Observer, U.S. Weather Bur, Fla, 42-49; assoc. prof. PHYS. SCI. & GEOG, UNIV. FLA, 49-65, PROF, 65-, ASST. DEAN, UNIV. COL, 69- U.S.A.A.F, 43-46. Asn. Am. Geog. Cultural and historical geography; Africa; cartography. Address: 206 Benton Hall, University of Florida, Gainesville, FL 32601.

DUNKLE, MICHAEL PATRICK, b. Dover, N.J, Oct. 15, 32; m. 61; c. 3. PHYSICAL CHEMISTRY. B.S, Fordham Univ, 54; Seton Hall Univ, 57-58; Ph.D.(phys. chem), Purdue Univ, 64. Lab. technician, Picatinny Arsenal, 54-55; res. chemist, photo prods. res. lab, E.I. DU PONT DE NEMOURS & CO, 63-66, PROCESS CHEMIST, PHOTO PRODS. DEPT, 66- U.S.A, 55-56, Res, 57-63. Am. Chem. Soc; Am. Inst. Chem; Soc. Photog. Sci. & Eng. Photographic chemistry; graphic arts; silver halide and polymer photosensitive systems; ultraviolet, infrared and Raman spectroscopy; gas chromatography; thermal analysis. Address: R.D. 1, Towanda, PA 18848.

DUNKLEY, WALTER L(EWIS), b. Olds, Alta, Feb. 15, 18; nat; m. 43; c. 3. FOOD SCIENCE. B.Sc, Univ. Alta, 39, M.Sc, 41; Ph.D.(dairy indust, biochem), Univ. Wis, 43. Lectr. & asst. prof, dairying, Univ. Alta, 43-46; res. chemist, Golden State Co, Ltd, Calif, 46-48; asst. prof. food sci. & technol, UNIV. CALIF, DAVIS, 48-50, assoc. prof, 50-58, PROF. FOOD SCI. & TECHNOL, 58-, CHMN. DIV. FOOD & CONSUMER SCI, 70- Fulbright Awards, Fats Res. Lab, New Zealand, 56-57, Agr. Inst. Ireland, 63-64, faculty chem. eng, Univ. Guayaquil, 69. Am. Dairy Sci. Asn.(Borden Award, 68); Inst. Food Technol; Int. Asn. Milk, Food & Environ. Sanit. Chemistry and processing or dairy products; oxidative and hydrolytic rancidity; processing by ultrafiltration and reverse osmosis. Address: Dept. of Food Science & Technology, University of California, Davis, CA 95616.

DUNLAP, ALBERT A(TKINSON), b. Bowdoinham, Maine, Oct. 31, 02; m. 34; c. 4. PLANT PATHOLOGY & PHYSIOLOGY. A.B, Bates Col, 23; M.S, Yale, 27; Ph.D.(plant path), 29. Instr. forest path, Yale, 27-29; fel, Nat. Res. Coun, 29-30; mycologist plant path, Conn. Agr. Exp. Sta, 30-38; chief plant path. & physiol, Tex. Agr. Exp. Sta, 38-47; head, Tex. A&M Col. Syst, 47-50; leader plant path, Ill. Inst. Technol, 50; CHMN. BIOL, FITCHBURG STATE COL, 67- Fel. AAAS; Am. Inst. Biol. Sci. Physiological effects of plant viruses, seedling diseases, phymatotrichum root rot of cotton, cotton boll-shedding, and weed killers; water pollution effects on certain algae. Address: 430 Marsh Hill Rd, Dracut, MA 01826.

DUNLAP, BOBBY DAVID, b. Post, Tex, Mar, 21, 38; m. 65; c. 2. PHYSICS. B.S, Tex. Tech. Col, 59; Ph.D.(physics), Washington (Seattle), 66. Assoc. mem. tech. staff physics, Bell Tel. Labs, Inc, 62-63; resident res. assoc, ARGONNE NAT. LAB, 66-70, ASSOC. PHYSICIST, 70- Solid state physics by application of the Mössbauer effect. Address: Argonne National Lab, Argonne, IL 60439.

DUNLAP, CHARLES E(DWARD), b. New York, N.Y, June 8, 08; m. 37; c. 4. PATHOLOGY. A.B, Harvard, 30, M.D, 34. Intern, Chicago, 34-35, asst. res. path, 36-37, res. & asst. path, 37; Littauer fel. path, Harvard Cancer Comn, 37-39, asst, Harvard Med. Sch, 39-40, instr, 40-43; asst. prof. PATH, SCH. MED, TULANE UNIV, 43-44, assoc. prof, 44-45, PROF. & CHMN. DEPT, 45- Asst. res, Presby. Hosp, Chicago, 35; res. fel, Collis P. Huntington Hosp, 39-43; vis. pathologist, Charity Hosp, New Orleans, 43-46, sr. vis. pathologist, 46-; consult, Armed Forces Inst. Path, 52-; path. study sect, U.S. Pub. Health Serv, 54-57, training grants comt, 57-58, mem. path. training comt, 58-62, cancer training comt, 62-64, clin. cancer training comt, 65-67, radiation biol. effects adv. comt, 66-70; comt. on path. effects of radiation, Nat. Res. Coun, 55-58; mem. bd. dirs, Oak Ridge Inst. Nuclear Studies, 55-62; Urban Maes Res. Found, 57-61; adv. comt, President's Comn. Heart Disease & Cancer, 64. Am. Asn. Cancer Res; Am. Soc. Exp. Path.(v.pres, 62-63, pres, 63-64); Soc. Exp. Biol. & Med; Am. Asn. Path. & Bact; fel. Col. Am. Path; Int. Acad. Path; Am. Med. Asn; Am. Soc. Clin. Path; Asn. Am. Med. Col; Radiation Res. Soc. Carcinogenic hydrocarbons; biologic effects of radiation; human cancer. Address: Tulane University School of Medicine, 1430 Tulane Ave, New Orleans, LA 70112.

DUNLAP, DONALD G(ENE), b. Bend, Ore, Sept. 21, 26; m. 56; c. 1. VERTEBRATE ZOOLOGY. B.S, Oregon State, 49, M.A, 51; Ph.D.(zool), Washington State, 55. Asst. zool, Oregon State, 49-51, Washington State, 51-55; jr. physiologist, col. vet. med, 55-56; asst. prof. biol, Ripon Col, 56-59; ZOOL, UNIV. S.DAK, 59-60, assoc. prof, 60-63, PROF, 64- Vis. prof, Coe Col, 57. AAAS; Am. Soc. Ichthyol. & Herpet; Soc. Syst. Zool; Am. Soc. Zool; Ecol. Soc. Am; Am. Inst. Biol. Sci; Soc. Study Amphibians & Reptiles. Biology of the amphibians and reptiles; environmental physiology; animal ecology. Address: Dept. of Biology, University of South Dakota, Vermillion, SD 57069.

DUNLAP, DUANE SHERBERT, b. Elgin, Ill, Feb. 28, 24; m. 47. OPERATIONS RESEARCH. B.S.E.E, Illinois, 49; Vanderbilt, 43-44; Yale, 44. Electronic engr, armament lab, WRIGHT-PATTERSON AIR FORCE BASE, U.S. AIR FORCE, 53-55, gen. engr, weapons guid lab, 55-57, physicist, 57-60, gen. engr, aeronaut. systs. div, 60-61, chief mission anal. div, DEP. FOR STUDIES & ANAL, 61-66, tech. dir, directorate of opers. res, 66-69, DIR, ADVAN. SYST. ANAL, 69- Lectr, air staff, Japan Air Self Defense Force, 67; v.chief of staff & staff mems, Royal Swedish Air Force, 67. Outstanding performance awards, 58, 61, 62, 64, 69, 70 & 71. U.S.A, 43-46, 1st Lt. Opers. Res. Soc. Am. Technical direction of an Air Force operations research organization; quantitative analysis of major Air Force weapons development decision alternatives. Address: 1720 Ruskin Rd, Dayton, OH 45406.

DUNLAP, EUGENE W, b. Memphis, Tenn, Sept. 14, 20; m. 60. BIOLOGICAL SCIENCES. B.S, St. Louis, 50, M.Ed, 52; Ed.D, Wayne State, 62. Instr. eng, Inst. Tech, St. Louis Univ, 52-55, asst. prof, 55-61, assoc. prof, 61-70; SUPT, SCOTLAND COUNTY PUB. SCHS, 70- Electronics & space consult, 70- U.S.A.A.F, 43-46, Instr. Am. Soc. Eng. Educ. Cryogenic study of metal cutting and strength of behavior of metals; toxic metals and their effect on living organisms; industrial fatigue of worker and effect on production. Address: Office of the Superintendent, Scotland Co. Public Schools, Memphis, MO 63555.

DUNLAP, G(EORGE) WESLEY, b. Gardnerville, Nev, Apr. 13, 11; m. 35, 68; c. 5. ELECTRICAL ENGINEERING. A.B, Stanford, 31, Ryan High Voltage Res. Lab. fel, 32-35, Ph.D.(elec. eng), 36. Student engr, GEN. ELEC. CO, 35-36, develop. engr. high voltage & impulse sect, gen. eng. lab, 36-45, asst. div. engr, high voltage & nucleonics div, gen. eng. & consult. lab, 45-51, div. engr, 51-53, mgr. instrument & nuclear radiation eng. servs. dept, 53-55, eng. physics & anal. lab, 55-61, sr. engr, Adv. Tech. Labs, 61-66, CONSULT. ENGR, RES. & DEVELOP. CTR, 66- Vis. Webster prof, Mass. Inst. Technol, 55-56. Alfred Noble Prize, 42. Am. Phys. Soc; Nat. Soc. Prof. Eng; Marine Technol. Soc; fel. Inst. Elec. & Electronics Eng; Am. Nuclear Soc. High voltage phenomenon; circuit interruption; particle accelerators; radiation and electronic instruments; electrical measurements; nuclear engineering; energy conversion; electron physics; oceanology. Address: General Electric Research & Development Center, 1 River Rd, Schenectady, NY 12305.

DUNLAP, HENRY F(RANCIS), b. Ennis, Texas, Oct. 4, 16; m. 42; c. 3. GEOPHYSICS. B.A, Rice Inst, 38, M.A, 39, fel, 39-41, Ph.D.(physics), 41. Asst. physicist, dept. terrestrial magnetism, Carnegie Institution, 41-42; physicist, New Mexico, 42-45, lectr. physics, 43-44; maj. physicist, Atlantic Ref. Co, 45-66, head, long range res. sect, ATLANTIC RICHFIELD CO, 66-69, RES. SCIENTIST, 69- Res. assoc, inst. meteoritics, New Mexico. With Office Sci. Res. & Develop, 44. Am. Phys. Soc; Soc. Explor. Geophys. (v.pres, 64-65); Am. Asn. Petrol. Geol; Am. Inst. Min, Metall. & Petrol. Eng. Nuclear physics; internal and external ballistics; geophysics; instrumentation in supersonic aerodynamics; meteorites; well logging. Address: Atlantic Richfield Co, Box 2819, Dallas, TX 75221.

DUNLAP, JACK S(HERWIN), b. Reno, Nev, Apr. 27, 16; m. 45; c. 2. VETERINARY PARASITOLOGY. A.B, California, 38; M.S, Mich. State Col, 49, D.V.M.(vet. med), 50. Case aid worker, State Relief Admin, Calif, 40; Poultry Lab, Calif, 40-41; asst. PARASITOL, Mich. State Col, 46-48; asst. prof, DEPT. PATH, COL. VET. MED, WASH. STATE UNIV, 50-54, assoc. prof, 54-61, PROF, 61- U.S.A, 41-46, 1st Lt. AAAS; Am. Soc. Parasitol; Am. Vet. Med. Asn; Soc. Exp. Biol. & Med. Parasite physiol; coccidiosis; mammalian. Address: 2107 Orion Dr, Pullman, WA 99163.

DUNLAP, JANIS L(UNDY), b. Mobile, Ala, Nov. 5, 40; m. 68; c. 2. PHYSIOLOGICAL PSYCHOLOGY. B.A, Ala. Col, 63; Nat. Defense Educ. Act fel, Tulane Univ, 63-66, M.S, 66, Ph.D.(psychol), 68. Asst. prof. PSYCHOL, TULANE UNIV, 68-69, Newcomb Col, 69-70, RES. ASSOC, PHYSIOL. LAB, 70- AAAS; Am. Psychol. Asn. Prenatal and postnatal determinants of reproductive function; development of ovarian responsiveness in rats; hormonal factors related to aging of the reproductive system. Address: Dept. of Psychology, Physiological Lab, Tulane University, New Orleans, LA 70118.

DUNLAP, JULIAN L(EE), b. LaGrange, Ga, Jan. 27, 32; m. 60; c. 2. PHYSICS. B.E.E, Ga. Inst. Technol, 54; Nat. Sci. Found. fel, Vanderbilt, 56-58, Ph.D.(physics), 59. PHYSICIST, THERMONUCLEAR DIV, OAK RIDGE NAT. LAB, 59- Am. Phys. Soc. Infrared spectroscopy; plasma physics and controlled thermonuclear research. Address: Thermonuclear Division, Oak Ridge National Lab, P.O. Box Y, Oak Ridge, TN 37830.

DUNLAP, LAWRENCE H(ALLOWELL), b. Madison, Wis, Oct. 23, 10; m. 41; c. 2. ORGANIC CHEMISTRY. A.B, Missouri, 31, B.S, 33, M.A, 35; Ph.D. (chem), Illinois, 39. Res. chemist, ARMSTRONG CORK CO, 39-46, head resins sect, 46-52, asst. mgr. Chem. Dept, 52-55, gen. mgr. chem. div, 55-62, SR. RES. ASSOC, 62- U.S.N.R, 42-45. Adj. prof. chem, grad. div, Franklin & Marshall Col, 47-48. Mem, XII Int. Cong. Pure & Appl. Chem.

AAAS; Am. Chem. Soc; Am. Oil Chem. Soc; fel. Am. Inst. Chem; Am. Ord. Asn; Brit. Chem. Soc. Oxidation and polymerization of drying oils; polymerization of resins; research administration; thermodynamic properties of polymers; fire and smoke retardant compositions of polymers. Address: 1315 Quarry Lane, Lancaster, PA 17603.

DUNLAP, PAUL R, b. Chungsha, China, Nov. 21, 25; U.S. citizen; m. 47; c. 3. STATISTICS. B.A, Pa. State Univ, 48, M.Ed, 50; Ph.D.(statist), Am. Univ. D.C, 68. Teacher, high schs, Pa, 48-53; group leader, Ralph M. Parsons Co, Md, 53-55; sr. engr, Martin Marietta Co, 55-56; sr. statistician, res. & develop. div, Avco, Del, 56-60; mem. tech. staff, Mitre Corp, Mass, 60-67; ASSOC. PROF. QUANT. METHODS, COL. BUS. ADMIN, OHIO UNIV, 67- Summers, consult, United Tel. of Ohio, 69 & NASA-Am. Soc. Eng. Educ. faculty fel, 70. U.S.A.A.F, 43-45. Inst. Math. Statist; Am. Statist. Asn; Am. Inst. Decision Sci. Biometrics, equipment reliability and quality control; systems engineering and information management; multidisciplinary approach to problem solving through applications of statistical methods—for example communication—speed listening, price theory, urban blight and teaching effectiveness. Address: 47 Charles St, Athens, OH 45701.

DUNLAP, PEGGY M(AYFIELD), b. Austin, Tex, Mar. 24, 27; wid. PHYSICAL CHEMISTRY. B.S, Texas, 48, Ph.D.(chem), 52. Spec. instr. chem, Texas, 52-53; sr. res. technologist, MOBIL RES. & DEVELOP. CORP, 53-67, RES. ASSOC, 67- State Republican Committeewoman, 71- Am. Chem. Soc. Catalysis; solid fluid kinetics; interfacial tension and contact angles. Address: Mobil Research & Development Corp, P.O. Box 900, Dallas, TX 75221.

DUNLAP, RALPH I(RVIN), JR, b. Jacksonville, Ill, Oct. 2, 18; m. 44; c. 2. CHEMISTRY. A.B, Swarthmore Col, 40; Ph.D.(phys. chem), Columbia, 45. Chemist, Wis. Steel Works, Ill, 40; lab. asst, Columbia, 40-42, 45; res, Manhattan proj, Nat. Defense Res. Cmt, 42; res. chemist, MONSANTO CO, 43-46, res. group leader, 46-51, prod. supt, 51-52, asst. dir. res. 52-56, assoc. dir, 57-58, prod. tech. serv. mgr, 58-64; asst. res. dir, 64-67, ASSOC. RES. DIR, 67- AAAS; Am. Chem. Soc. Ultracentrifuge; starch chemistry; process development of phenolic; alkyd, polystyrene and silicone plastics; ultracentrifugal behavior of synthetic polysaccharides. Address: Polymers Research, Monsanto Co, 730 Worcester St, Indian Orchard, MA 01051.

DUNLAP, RICHARD M(ORRIS), b. Columbia, Mo, Sept. 5, 17; m. 46, 69; c. 5. MECHANICAL ENGINEERING. B.S. & M.S, Mass. Inst. Tech, 41. Trainee engr, United Shoe Mach. Corp, 38-39; jr. engr, Sperry Prod. Co, 41; proj. engr, Res. Construct. Co, 41-45; teacher, Robert Col, 45-48; mech. engr, U.S. Naval Underwater Ord. Sta, 48-59, head appl. sci. dept, 59-61; assoc. dir. res, U.S. Naval Underwater Weapons Res. & Eng. Sta, 61-71; ASSOC. DIR. LONG RANGE PLANNING, U.S. NAVAL UNDERWATER SYSTS. CTR, NEWPORT, 71- Am. Soc. Mech. Eng; Am. Inst. Aeronaut. & Astronaut; Acoust. Soc. Am; Inst. Elec. & Electronics Eng. Underwater weapons systems. Address: 452 Mitchell Lane, Middletown, RI 02840.

DUNLAP, ROBERT (D), b. Carbondale, Pa, Apr. 5, 22; m. 53; c. 3. PHYSICAL CHEMISTRY. B.A, Colgate, 43; M.S, Pa. State, 44, Ph.D.(chem), 49. Asst. CHEM, Pa. State, 43-49; instr, UNIV. MAINE, ORONO, 49-51, asst. prof, 51-54, assoc. prof, 54-59, PROF, 59- Am. Chem. Soc. Physical chemistry; fluorocarbon of solutions. Address: Dept. of Chemistry, Aubert Hall, University of Maine, Orono, ME 04473.

DUNLAP, W(ILLIAM) CRAWFORD, b. Denver, Colo, July 21, 18; m. 40; c. 1. PHYSICS. B.S, New Mexico, 38; Ph.D.(physics), California, 43. Asst. physics, California, 38-42; res. physicist, U.S. Dept. Agr, 42-45; res. assoc, Gen. Elec. Res. Lab, 45-55; consult. semiconductors, Gen. Elec. Electronics Lab, 55-56; supvr. solid state res, Bendix Res. Labs, 56-58; dir. semiconductors res. & solid state electronic res, Raytheon Res. Div, 58-64; asst. dir. electronic components res, electronics res. ctr, NASA, 64-68, dir. res, 68-70; SCI. ADV, TRANSPORT SYSTEMS CTR, U.S. DEPT. TRANSPORTATION, CAMBRIDGE, 70- Assoc. prof, evening session, Siena Col, 52-54; ed-in-chief, Solid State Electronics, 59- Fel. Am. Phys. Soc; fel. Inst. Elec. & Electronics Eng. Cosmic rays; dielectrics; color and spectrophotometry; semiconductors; solid state physics. Address: 126 Prince St, West Newton, MA 02165.

DUNLAP, WILLIAM J(OE), b. Wichita Falls, Tex, Oct. 9, 29; m. 57; c. 1. BIOCHEMISTRY. B.S, Texas A&M Univ, 52; Ph.D.(chem), Univ. Okla, 61. Food technologist, Mrs. Tuckers Foods, Tex, 52-55; res. assoc. chem, Univ. Oklahoma, 60-62; biochemist, Kerr-McGee Oil Indust, Inc, Okla, 62-63; res. chemist, res. inst, Univ. Okla, 63-67; RES. CHEMIST, ROBERT S. KERR WATER RES. CTR, ENVIRON. PROTECTION AGENCY, 67- U.S.A, 52-54, Res, 54-64, Capt. Am. Chem. Soc. Flavonoids and related polyphenolic compounds; chromatography; hydrocarbon fermentations; food chemistry; chemistry of water pollution; sub-surface biochemistry; anaerobic degradation of organic compounds; chromatography. Address: Robert S. Kerr Water Research Center, Environmental Protection Agency, P.O. Box 1198, Ada, OK 74820.

DUNLEAVY, JOHN M, b. Omaha, Nebr, June 6, 23; m. 47; c. 4. PLANT PATHOLOGY. Ak-sar-ben fel, Nebraska, Ph.D.(plant path), 53. Asst. prof. PLANT PATH, IOWA STATE UNIV, 53-56, assoc. prof, 56-61, PROF, 61-; SOYBEAN DISEASE RES. COORD, U.S. DEPT. AGR, 59-, plant pathologist, 53-59. U.S.A.A.F, 42-46. AAAS; Am. Phytopath. Soc; Am. Soc. Microbiol; Am. Soybean Asn; Brit. Soc. Gen. Microbiol. Diseases of soybeans. Address: 1118 Michigan Ave, Ames, IA 50010.

DUNLOP, ANDREW P, b. Balloch, Scotland, Nov. 26, 14, nat. 31; m. 38; c. 3. CHEMISTRY. B.S, Chicago, 38; Ill. Inst. Tech, 42-43. Lab. asst, QUAKER OATS CO, 31-38, res. chemist, 38-47, asst. dir. chem. res, 47-59, assoc. dir, 59-69, DIR. CHEM. RES. & DEVELOP, 69- AAAS; fel. Am. Inst. Chem; Am. Chem. Soc; N.Y. Acad. Sci. Furfural and its derivatives; levulinic acid; furan chemistry. Address: Chemical Research & Development, Quaker Oats Co, 617 W. Main St, Barrington, IL 60010.

DUNLOP, D. L, b. Medicine Hat, Alta, Feb. 15, 25; m. 52; c. 5. OBSTETRICS, GYNECOLOGY. B.Sc. & M.D, Manitoba, 52; M.S, Nebraska, 66. Teaching fel. OBSTET. & GYNEC, Manitoba, 62; asst. instr, Nebraska, 65-66; assoc. prof, FACULTY MED, UNIV. ALTA, 67-70, PROF, 70- Nat. Insts. Health fel, 65-66. Fel, Royal Col. Physicians & Surgeons Can, 63. R.C.N.V.R, 44-46. Can. Med. Asn; fel. Am. Col. Obstet. & Gynec. Vasopressor substances in amniotic fluid and serum. Address: Faculty of Medicine, 5-123 Clinical Science Bldg, University of Alberta, Edmonton, Alta, Can.

DUNLOP, DOUGLAS W(AYNE), b. Milwaukee, Wis, Jan. 27, 15; m. 38; c. 1. BOTANY. Ph.B, Wisconsin, 37, Ph.M, 38, Ph.D.(bot), 40. Asst. instr. bot, Wisconsin, 37-40; instr. biol, Brooklyn Col, 40-46; asst. prof. BOT, UNIV. WIS-MILWAUKEE, 46-59, assoc. prof, 59-66, PROF, 66-, CHMN. DEPT, 69- U.S.A.F, 43-46, Res, 46-, Lt. Col. AAAS; Bot. Soc. Am; Am. Fern Soc; Soc. Econ. Bot; Int. Soc. Plant Morphol. Biomagnetics; cytology; morphology. Address: Dept. of Botany, University of Wisconsin-Milwaukee, Milwaukee, WI 53201.

DUNLOP, E(DWARD) C(LARENCE), b. Center, Mo, Jan. 18, 16; m. 45; c. 2. CHEMISTRY. A.B, Westminster Col.(Mo), 36; M.S, Illinois, 38, Ph.D. (chem), 42. Instr. chem, Westminster Col.(Mo), 36-37; asst, Buswell & Rodebush, Ill, 38-41; asst. water analysis, State of Ill, 41-42; chemist, E.I. DU PONT DE NEMOURS & CO, DEL, 42-43, Wash, 43-45, asst. head PHYS. & ANAL. DIV, CENT. RES. DEPT, 46-63, HEAD, 63- Am. Chem. Soc; Optical Soc. Am; Soc. Appl. Spectros; Am. Soc. Test. & Mat. Analytical chemistry. Address: E.I. du Pont de Nemours & Co, Wilmington, DE 19898.

DUNLOP, ROBERT ANDREW, Mgt. Comput. Systs, see Suppl. I to 11th ed, Soc. & Behav. Vols.

DUNLOP, ROBERT H(UGH), b. London, Eng, Apr. 16, 29; Can. citizen; m. 58; c. 6. VETERINARY PHARMACOLOGY & PHYSIOLOGY. D.V.M, Toronto, 56; Am. Vet. Med. Asn. fel, Minnesota, 56-57; Ph.D.(vet. physiol. & pharmacol), 61. Res. fel. vet. physiol. & pharmacol, Minnesota, 56-61; clin. pathologist vet. med, W.B. Cartmell, Eng, 61-62; assoc. prof. vet. pharmacol, State Univ. N.Y. Vet. Col, Cornell, 62-65; PROF. VET. PHYSIOL. & HEAD DEPT, UNIV. SASK, 65- Co-chmn. conf. chem. & metab. of L- & D- lactic acids, N.Y. Acad. Sci-Nat. Inst. Health, 64; dean faculty vet. sci, Makerere Univ, Uganda, 71-73; mem. comt, Livestock Pesticides, Lethbridge, 67-71; mem, Can. Comt. Pesticide Use in Agr, 69-71; mem. sub-comt. metals, Nat. Res. Coun. Comt. Sci. Criteria Environ. Qual, 70-71. Borden Award, 56. Am. Vet. Med. Asn; Am. Soc. Vet. Physiol. & Pharmacol; Royal Col. Vet. Surg; Can. Vet. Med. Asn. Pathophysiology of ruminant disease, particularly the syndrome resulting from excessive ingestion of feeds rich in starch and sugar; toxicology of lactic isomers, histamines and catecholamines; thiamin inadequacy in ruminants and polioencephalomalacia; toxicology of mercury and lead. Address: Faculty of Veterinary Science, Makerere University, P.O. Box 7062, Kampala, Uganda.

DUNLOP, STUART G(EORGE), b. Chicago, Ill, Nov. 19, 07; m. 41; c. 2. BACTERIOLOGY. Ph.C, Illinois, 28; B.S, Colorado, 39, M.S, 41, Ph.D. (bact), 47. Asst. pharmacist, Chicago Drug & Surg. Co, 26-28, registered pharmacist, 28-30; engr, West. Battery & Supply Co, Colo, 30-42; teaching fel, SCH. MED, UNIV. COLO, DENVER, 46-47, instr. BACT, 47-48, asst. prof, 48-51, assoc. prof, 51-64, PROF, 64- Lehn & Fink Medal, 39. Qm.C, U.S.A, 42-46. Am. Soc. Microbiol; Am. Soc. Exp. Biol; Am. Pub. Health Asn. Milk, water and food sanitation; metabolism; enterics; virology to enterics; virology; clinical microbiology; sanitation. Address: Dept. of Microbiology, School of Medicine, University of Colorado, Denver, CO 80220.

DUNLOP, WILLIAM ROBERT, b. Mt. Pleasant, Ont, Can, Aug. 2, 16. AVIAN PATHOLOGY, CELL BIOLOGY. D.V.M, Toronto, 38. Dir, D&B Labs, 38-48; lectr. histol. & embryol, Ont. Vet. Col, Toronto, 48, poultry pathologist, 49-50; asst. poultry pathologist, UNIV. N.H, 50-51, RES. PATHOLOGIST & PROF. POULTRY SCI, 51- Am. Vet. Med. Asn; Poultry Sci. Asn; Am. Soc. Microbiol; Am. Pub. Health Asn; Am. Soc. Cell Biol; Tissue Cult. Asn; N.Y. Acad. Sci. Avian virology; cancer research. Address: Kendall Hall, University of New Hampshire, Durham, NH 03824.

DUNN, A(NDREW) F(LETCHER), b. Sydney, N.S, Jan. 17, 22; m. 43; c. 2. EXPERIMENTAL PHYSICS. B.Sc, Dalhousie, 42, M.Sc, 47; Ph.D.(physics), Toronto, 50. Jr. res. off. PHYSICS, Atlantic Fisheries Exp. Sta, 46-47; asst. res. off, NAT. RES. COUN. CAN, 50-54, assoc. res. off, 54-63, SR. RES. OFF, 63-, HEAD ELEC. SECT, 71- Can. Army, 42-45, Capt. Fel. Inst. Elec. & Electronics Eng; Can. Asn. Physicists. Precision electrical measurements; national primary standards; absolute determination of electrical quantities. Address: Division of Physics, National Research Council of Canada, Montreal Rd, Ottawa, Ont, K1A 0S1, Can.

DUNN, ARNOLD S(AMUEL), b. Rochester, N.Y, Jan. 31, 29; m. 52; c. 2. PHYSIOLOGY, ENDOCRINOLOGY. B.S, George Washington, 50; Harrison fel. & Ph.D.(physiol), Pennsylvania, 55. Res. assoc. metab. & endocrinol, Michael Reese Hosp. Res. Inst, 55-56; instr. pharmacol, sch. med, N.Y. Univ, 56-58, asst. prof, 58-62; asst. prof. BIOL. SCI, UNIV. SOUTH. CALIF, 62-67, assoc. prof, 67-70, PROF, 70- Endocrine Soc; Am. Physiol. Soc; Fedn. Am. Socs. Exp. Biol; Am. Soc. Biol. Chem. Physiology of cell division; endocrine control of metabolism; carbohydrate metabolism. Address: Dept. of Biological Sciences, University of Southern California, Los Angeles, CA 90007.

DUNN, ARTHUR L(OVELL), b. Omaha, Nebr, Sept. 7, 08; m. 44; c. 3. MEDICAL ELECTRONICS. B.A, Omaha, 30; M.A, Nebraska, 31, Toni Co. fel, 48-49, Ph.D.(med. sci), 49. Tech. asst. physiol. & pharm, med. col, Nebraska, 43-48, asst. res. prof, 49, asst. prof, 49-53; lab. dir. & prin. scientist, radioisotope unit, VET. ADMIN. HOSP, 56-63, CHIEF ELECTRONICS RES. UNIT, 63-; ASST. PROF. BIOCHEM. & BIOPHYS, COL. MED, UNIV. NEBR, 54- AAAS; Am. Physiol. Soc; Am. Chem. Soc; Inst. Elec. & Electronics Eng; Am. Nuclear Soc; Soc. Nuclear Med; N.Y. Acad. Sci. Electrophysiology; biophysics; medical instrumentation. Address: Dept. of Biochemistry, University of Nebraska College of Medicine, Omaha, NE 68105.

DUNN, BERNARD JOSEPH, b. N.Y.C, May 26, 24; m. 52; c. 4. PHYSICS. B.S, Fordham, 47, Ph.D, 58; M.A, Columbia, 49. Instr. physics, Fordham, 49-53, asst. prof, 53-60; PRES, BRADDOCK, DUNN & McDONALD, INC, 60- Research rare earths spectros, Hopkins, 57-58. U.S.A.A.F, 43-45, 2nd Lt. Am. Inst. Aeronaut. & Astronaut. Aerospace science; missile systems. Address: 773 Bittersweet Pl, El Paso, TX 79922.

DUNN, CECIL GORDON, b. Chatham, Mass, Feb. 28, 04; m. 34; c. 2. FOOD TECHNOLOGY, INDUSTRIAL MICROBIOLOGY. S.B, Mass. Inst. Technol, 30, Ph.D.(food tech, indust. microbiol), 34. Instr. biol. & pub. health, MASS. INST. TECHNOL, 34-39, asst. prof, 39-41, assoc. prof, 46-69, EMER. ASSOC. PROF. INDUST. MICROBIOL, 69- Consult, Carnation Co. U.S.A, 41-46, Res, 51-60, Col. Fel. AAAS; fel. Am. Acad. Microbiol; fel. Am. Pub. Health Asn; Inst. Food Technol; Am. Chem. Soc. Food science; industrial and food microbiology; fermentations; food preservation. Address: Bald Hill Rd, R.F.D, New Gloucester, ME 04260.

DUNN, CECIL G(ORDON), b. Wenatchee, Wash, Nov. 13, 07; m. 29, 44; c. 4. PHYSICS. B.A, Montana, 31; M.S, Illinois, 33, Ph.D.(physics), 37. Asst. physics, Illinois, 31-37; res. physicist. metall, GEN. ELEC. CO, Pittsfield, Mass, 37-55, PHYSICIST, PHYS. CHEM. LAB, GEN. ELEC. RES. & DEVELOP. CTR, N.Y, 55- AAAS; Electrochem. Soc; Am. Phys. Soc; Am. Inst. Min, Metall. & Petrol. Eng.(Mathewson gold medal). Recrystallization and grain growth in metals; development of magnetic material; dielectric oxide films. Address: Physical Chemistry Lab, General Electric Research & Development Center, Schenectady, NY 12301.

DUNN, CHARLES L, b. Cleveland, Ohio, Feb. 16, 20; m. 45; c. 3. CHEMISTRY. A.B, Oberlin Col, 42. Chemist, Hercules Res. Center, 42-44; shift supvr, rocket propellant prod, Sunflower Ord. Works, 44-45; res. chemist, Res. Ctr, Hercules Powder Co, 47-60, tech. coordinator, 60-63, MGR. pesticide control servs, 63-65, AGR. CHEM. DEVELOP, SYNTHETICS DEPT, HERCULES INC, WILMINGTON, 65- U.S.A, 45-47. Am. Chem. Soc; Sci. Res. Soc. Am; Entom. Soc. Am. Analytical chemistry; agricultural chemicals; pesticide composition; residue behavior; metabolic fate. Address: 712 Ashford Rd, Wilmington, DE 19803.

DUNN, CHARLES NORD, b. Elk River, Minn, Oct. 25, 36; m. 58; c. 4. SOLID STATE PHYSICS. B.S, Minnesota, 58, Nat. Defense Ed. Act. fel, 59-62, M.S.E.E, 60, Ph.D.(elec. eng), 64. MEM. TECH. STAFF MICROWAVE DIODES, BELL TEL. LABS, INC, 64- U.S.N.R, 54-62. Inst. Elec. & Electronic Eng; Am. Phys. Soc. Development of microwave diodes; oxide-coated-cathode; charge transport in non-ionized gases. Address: Bell Telephone Labs, Inc, 2525 N. 11th St, Reading, PA 19604.

DUNN, CLARK A(LLAN), b. Stickney, S.Dak, Sept. 9, 01; m. 28; c. 2. CIVIL ENGINEERING. B.S, Wisconsin, 23; C.E, Okla. State, 34, M.S, 37; McMullen scholar, Cornell, 40-41, Ph.D, 41. Engr, bridge div, S.Dak. State Hwy. Comn, 23-27; assoc. with J.E. Kirkham, Consult. Engr, 27; construct. engr, bridge div, Ark. State Hwy. Dept, 27-29; asst. prof. CIVIL ENG, OKLA. STATE UNIV, 29-36, assoc. prof, 36-41, PROF. & HEAD GEN. ENG, 41-, DIR. ENG. RES. & HEAD SCH. GEN. ENG, 45-, observer, task force frigid opers, Fairbanks, Alaska. Fel. AAAS; Am. Soc. Civil Eng; Am. Soc. Eng. Educ; Nat. Soc. Prof. Eng.(dir, 51-55, v.pres, 55-57, pres, 58-59). Electric welding inspection. Address: 317 N. Husband St, Stillwater, OK 74075.

DUNN, DARREL E(UGENE), b. Clay Center, Kans, July 15, 32; m. 65; c. 1. GEOLOGY. B.S, Univ. Ill, Urbana, 55, Ph.D.(geol), 67. Geologist, Pure Oil Co, 57-61; groundwater geologist, Alta. Res. Coun, Edmonton, Can, 66-67; asst. prof. GEOL, Mont. State Univ, 67-71, ASSOC. PROF, 71-; UNIV. TOLEDO, 71- U.S.A, 55-57. Geol. Soc. Am; Am. Water Resources Asn; Am. Asn. Petrol. Geol. Hydrogeology. Address: Dept. of Geology, University of Toledo, Toledo, OH 43606.

DUNN, DAVID BAXTER, b. Mustang, Okla, Jan. 10, 17; m. 42; c. 6. BOTANY. B.A, California, Los Angeles, 40, M.A, 43, Ph.D.(bot), 48. Asst. bot, California, Los Angeles, 40-42, 46-47; instr. bot. & genetics, Calif. State Polytech. Col, 47-48; asst. bot, atomic energy proj, California, Los Angeles, 48-50; biol, N.Mex. Agr. & Mech. Col, 50-53; vis. lectr, Minn, 54; vis. botanist, Rancho Santa Ana Bot. Garden, 53-55; Occidental Col, 55-56; asst. prof. BOT, UNIV. MO, 56-66, assoc. prof, 66-70, PROF. & CURATOR HERBARIUM, 70- Ed, Trans, Mo. Acad. Sci, 66-; ed, Mus. Contrib. Monographic Series, 70- U.S.A.F, 42-46. Fel. AAAS; Soc. Study Evolution; Am. Soc. Plant Taxon; Bot. Soc. Am; Ecol. Soc. Am; Int. Asn. Plant Taxon. Lupinus, the taxonomy, breeding systems, genetics, ecological races, intersterility and interfertility between colonies as well as races; desert ecology. Address: 1306 Hinkson, Columbia, MO 65201.

DUNN, DAVID E(VAN), b. Dallas, Tex, Oct. 13, 35; m. 58; c. 2. GEOLOGY. B.S, Southern Methodist, 57, M.S, 59; Pan Am. Petrol. Found. fel, Texas, 60-61, univ. fel, 61-62, Ph.D.(geol), 64. Asst. prof. STRUCT. GEOL, Tex. Tech. Col, 62-63; vis. asst. prof, UNIV. N.C, CHAPEL HILL, 63-64, asst. prof, 64-67, ASSOC. PROF, 67-, ACTING CHMN. DEPT. GEOL, 67-, asst. chmn, 66-69. Summers, jr. geologist, Pan Am. Petrol. Corp, Tex, 57, N.Mex, 59, consult. geologist, 60, 61; consult, Lawrence Radiation Lab, 70- Am. Geophys. Union; Am. Inst. Prof. Geol; Am. Asn. Petrol. Geol; Geol. Soc. Am; Nat. Asn. Geol. Teachers. Deformation in orogenic belts; rock mechanics. Address: Dept. of Geology, University of North Carolina, Chapel Hill, NC 27514.

DUNN, DONALD A(LLEN), b. Los Angeles, Calif, Dec. 31, 25; m. 48; c. 2. COMMUNICATIONS. B.S, Calif. Inst. Tech, 46; M.S, Stanford, 47, E.E, 50, LL.B, 51, Ph.D.(elec. eng), 56. Res. assoc. elec. eng, Stanford, 51-59; dir. res, Eitel-McCullough, Inc, 59-61; dir, electron devices lab, STANFORD UNIV, 61-64, dir. plasma physics lab, 65-68, ASSOC. PROF. ENG-ECON. SYSTS, 69- Mem. 20th Century Fund task force on int. satellite commun; consult, Nat. Acad. Eng. comn on telecommun. U.S.N, 44-46, Lt.(jg). Inst. Elec. & Electronics Eng; Am. Phys. Soc; Inst. Mgt. Sci. Telecommunications systems; public policy analysis. Address: Dept. of Engineering-Economic Systems, Stanford University, Stanford, CA 94305.

DUNN, D(ONALD) W(ILLIAM), b. Kingston, Ont, Apr. 10, 23. MATHEMATICS. B.A, Queen's (Ont), 48; Ph.D.(math), Mass. Inst. Tech, 53. Asst. math, Mass. Inst. Tech, 52-53, res. assoc, 53-54; res. fel. aeronaut, Hopkins, 54-57; asst. res. off, Nat. Res. Coun. Can, 57-65; MATH CONSULT, 65- Can. Army, 41-46. Am. Math. Soc; Soc. Indust. & Appl. Math; Can. Math. Cong. Applied mathematics; fluid dynamics. Address: 280 Laurier Ave. E, Apt. 61, Ottawa, Ont. K1N 6P5, Can.

DUNN, DORIS F(RANKEL), b. N.Y.C, July 9, 27; m. 52; c. 2. BIOCHEMISTRY. B.S, Brooklyn Col, 47; M.S, Rochester, 52; Inst. Cancer Res. fel, Temple, 52-55, Ph.D.(biochem), 56. Asst. biochem, sch. hygiene, Hopkins, 49-50; Atomic Energy Cmn, Rochester, 50-52; res. assoc, metab. & endocrinol, res. inst, Michael Reese Hosp, 55-56; res. fel, Sloan-Kettering Inst. Cancer Res, 56-57, res. biochemist, pharmacol, sch. med, Univ. South. Calif, 63-66; INFO. ANALYST, BRAIN INFO. SERV, BIOMED. LIBR, UNIV. CALIF, LOS ANGELES, 70- Am. Chem. Soc. Neuroendocrinology. Address: 1272 Monument St, Pacific Palisades, CA 90272.

DUNN, DOROTHY FAY, b. Sidney, Ill. PUBLIC HEALTH. B.S, Illinois, 39; M.S.P.H, North Carolina, 46; Minnesota, 57; Ph.D, Purdue, 62; North Carolina, 64. Home economist, U.S. Dept. Agr, 39-43; Wisconsin, 44-45; pub. health ed. consult, State Dept. Pub. Health, Ill, 46-50; instr. hyg, Illinois, 51-52, asst. prof, 52-54, assoc. prof. hyg. & pub. health, 55-67; prof. home econ. & chmn. dept, West. Ky. Univ, 67-68; prof. family econ. & home mgt. & chmn. dept, Stout State Univ, 68-71; ASST. TO REGIONAL DIR. CONSUMER AFFAIRS, FOOD & DRUG ADMIN, U.S. DEPT. HEALTH, EDUC. & WELFARE, CHICAGO, 71- Fel. AAAS; fel. Am. Pub. Health Asn; Am. Col. Health Asn; Am. Sch. Health Asn. Domestic water consumption; level of tuberculosis knowledge and smoking habits of university freshmen. Address: 504 E. Chalmers, Champaign, IL 61820.

DUNN, EDWIN E(RVIN), b. Cody, Wyo, Oct. 4, 07. BIOCHEMISTRY. B.A, Wyoming, 29; M.S, Cincinnati, 30, Ph.D.(biochem), 32. Chemist, Texas Co, Wyo, 29-30; res. biochemist Agr. Res. Labs, Inc, N.J, 32-33; instr. biochem, col. med, Nebraska, 33-35; res. biochemist, res. lab, DOW CHEM. CO, 35-39, ASST. DIR. biochem. res. lab, 39-70, CHEM. BIOL RES, 70- Am. Chem. Soc; Sci. Res. Soc. Am. Fermentation; enzymology; microbiology; toxicology and industrial hygiene; preservatives; information storage and retrieval. Address: Dow Chemical Co, 1701 Bldg, Midland, MI 48640.

DUNN, FLOYD, b. Kansas City, Mo, Apr. 14, 24; m. 50; c. 2. BIOPHYSICS. B.S, Illinois, 49, M.S, 51, Ph.D.(elec. eng), 56. Asst. elec. eng, bioacoustics lab, UNIV. ILL, URBANA, 49-54, res. assoc, 54-57, res. asst. prof, dept. elec. eng. & biophys. res. lab, 57-61, assoc. prof. ELEC. ENG. & BIOPHYS, 61-65, PROF, 65- Nat. Insts. Health spec. res. fel, dept. microbiol, Univ. Col. S. Wales, 68-69. Sig.C, U.S.A, 43-46. AAAS; fel. Acoustical Soc. Am; Am. Inst. Physics; Biophys. Soc. Ultrasonics; ultrasonic biophysics, ultrasonic absorption microscopy and spectroscopy; physical mechanism of the action of ultrasound on biological systems; transmission line theory; electrical engineering; infrasonics; bioengineering. Address: Bioacoustics Research Lab, University of Illinois, Urbana, IL 61801.

DUNN, FLOYD W(ARREN), b. Huntington, Ark, Dec. 15, 20; m. 44; c. 3. BIOCHEMISTRY. B.S, Abilene Christian Col, 44; M.S, Colorado, 46, Ph.D. (biochem), 50. Prof. chem, Abilene Christian Col, 46-60; assoc. prof. BIOCHEM, med. units, Tennessee, 60-63, PROF, 63-65; col. med, Univ. Ill, assigned to faculty med, Chiengmai Univ, Thailand, 65-68; DEPT. CHEMISTRY, ABILENE CHRISTIAN COL, 68- U.S. Int. Co-op. Admin. tech. adv. chem, Chulalongkorn, Bangkok, 58-59. Am. Chem. Soc; Am. Soc. Biol. Chem; Soc. Exp. Biol. & Med. Synthesis of amino acids and peptides; amino acid antagonists; proteolytic enzymes; microbiological assay. Address: Dept. of Chemistry, Abilene Christian College, Abilene, TX 79601.

DUNN, FRANK J(ACK), b. Columbia, S.C, Aug. 26, 21; m. 44; c. 2. PHYSICAL CHEMISTRY. A.B, Columbia, 42, M.A, 47, U.S. Pub. Health Serv. fel, 47-49, Ph.D.(chem), 49. GROUP LEADER, LOS ALAMOS SCI. LABS, CALIFORNIA, 49- U.S.N.R, 42-45. AAAS. Instrumentation; heterogeneous reactions; isotope effects. Address: 103 Catron, Santa Fe, NM 87501.

DUNN, F(RANK) LOWELL, b. Erie, Pa, Mar. 26, 98; m. 30, 51; c. 2. B.S, Chicago, 20; M.D, Harvard, 24; M.A, Univ. Nebr, 31. Dir. clin. invest, COL. MED, UNIV. NEBR, 26-34, asst. prof. clin. physiol, 35-47, assoc. prof, 47-69, prof, MED, 48-69, EMER. PROF, 69-, dir. cardiovasc. res, 51-63. Clin. dir. lab, Clarkson Hosp, 30-40; chief div. biophys, Eppley Inst, 63- Dipl, Am. Bd. Internal Med. Fel. Am. Med. Asn; fel. Am. Col. Physicians; Am. Rheumatism Asn; Am. Diabetes Asn; Am. Fedn. Clin. Res. Electrophysiology; heart and lung sounds; radiation measurements; biomedical engineering. Address: 847 Fairacres Rd, Omaha, NE 68132.

DUNN, FREDERICK L(ESTER), b. Seneca Falls, N.Y, Dec. 24, 28; m. 69; c. 2. EPIDEMIOLOGY, ANTHROPOLOGY. A.B, Harvard, 51, M.D, 56; D.T.M.&H, Univ. London, 60. Intern, King Co. Hosp, Seattle, Wash, 56-57; asst. chief, influenza surveillance unit, Commun. Disease Ctr, U.S. Pub. Health Serv, Ga, 57-58, chief, 58-59; from asst. res. epidemiologist & asst. clin. prof. trop. med. to assoc. res. epidemiologist & assoc. clin. prof, UNIV. CALIF, SAN FRANCISCO, 60-67, assoc. prof. epidemiol, 67-69, PROF. EPIDEMIOL. & ANTHROP, 69-, CHMN. GRAD. GROUP IN ANTHROP, 71- Lectr, sch. pub. health, Univ. Calif, Berkeley, 65- U.S.P.H.S, 57-59, Sr. Asst. Surg. AAAS; Am. Pub. Health Asn; Am. Anthrop. Asn; Am. Soc. Trop. Med. & Hyg; Soc. Am. Archaeol; Am. Soc. Parasitol; Royal Soc. Trop. Med. & Hyg; Royal Anthrop. Inst. Gt. Brit. & Ireland. Medical anthropology and behavioral epidemiology; epidemiology of infectious and parasitic diseases; parasitism in non-human primates; cultural evolution in Southeast Asia; comparative medical systems in Asia. Address: Dept. of International Health, University of California, San Francisco, CA 94122.

DUNN, GEORGE LAWRENCE, b. Groton, Conn, May 5, 36; m. 59; c. 3. ORGANIC CHEMISTRY. B.A, Connecticut, 58; Nat. Defense Ed. Act fel, Maine, 59-62, M.S, 60, Ph.D.(org. chem), 62. Sr. med. chemist, SMITH KLINE & FRENCH LABS, 62-69, SR. INVESTR, 69- Am. Chem. Soc; Brit. Chem. Soc. Steroid synthesis; heterocyclic and polycyclic cage compounds; antibiotics; semisynthetic penicillins and cephalospories. Address: Smith Kline & French Labs, 1500 Spring Garden St, Philadelphia, PA 19101.

DUNN, G(ERALD) E(MERY), b. Hampton, N.S, Can, May 12, 19; m. 45; c. 3. ORGANIC CHEMISTRY. B.S, Acadia, 43; M.A, Toronto, 46; Ph.D.(chem), Iowa State Col, 50. Asst. prof. CHEM, UNIV. MAN, 51-54, assoc. prof, 54-60, PROF, 60- Corp. fel, Harvard, 50-51. Am. Chem. Soc. Mechanisms; organosilicon compounds. Address: Dept. of Chemistry, University of Manitoba, Winnipeg 19, Man, Can.

DUNN, G(ERALD) M(ARVIN), b. Canfield, W.Va, Sept. 4, 19; m. 55; c. 4. PLANT BREEDING, GENETICS. B.S, West Virginia, 48; M.S, Purdue, 50, Ph.D.(plant breeding & genetics), 51. Asst. plant breeding, Purdue, 48-51; asst. prof. AGRON, UNIV. N.H, 51-55, assoc. prof, 55-62, PROF, 62- U.S.A, 41-45. Am. Soc. Agron; Am. Genetic Asn. Genetic studies on chemical composition and diseases of corn; breeding and genetics of perennial grasses and legumes. Address: 35 Bagdad Rd, Durham, NH 03824.

DUNN, GORDON HAROLD, b. Montpelier, Idaho, Oct. 11, 32; m. 52; c. 8. ATOMIC & MOLECULAR PHYSICS. B.S, Washington, 55, Ph.D.(physics), 61. Nat. Bur. Standards-Nat. Res. Coun. fel, ATOMIC COLLISIONS, NAT. BUR. STANDARDS, 61-62, PHYSICIST, JOINT INST. FOR LAB. ASTRO-PHYS, 62- Lectr, Dept. physics & astrophys, Univ. Colo, 62-; mem. gen. comt, Int. Conf. on Physics of Electronic & Atomic Collisions, 69-73; chmn, Gaseous Electronics Conf, 71, 72. Gold Medal, Dept. Commerce, 70. Fel. Am. Phys. Soc. Investigation of collisions of electrons, photons and ions with simple atomic and molecular systems. Address: Joint Institute for Lab. Astrophysics, University of Colorado, Boulder, CO 80302.

DUNN, HENRY A(RTHUR), b. Shirley, Mass, July 15, 11; m. 39; c. 1. ENTO-MOLOGY. B.S, New Hampshire, 34; Ph.D.(entomol), Rutgers, 52. Field aide entomol, U.S. Dept. Agr, 36-41; technician, U.S. Army, 41-42; entomologist, Merck & Co, Inc, N.J, 47-48; asst, Rutgers, 48-52; chief entomologist, res. & develop. dept, Diamond Black Leaf Co, Va, 52-55; prin. entomologist, COOP. STATE RES. SERV, U.S. DEPT. AGR, 56-66, asst. to adminstr, 66-71, DEP. ASST. ADMINSTR, 71- Sanit.C, U.S.A, 42-47. Am. Entom. Soc. Agricultural entomology; insecticides. Address: Cooperative State Research Service, U.S. Dept. of Agriculture, Washington, DC 22206.

DUNN, HENRY G(EORGE), b. Leipzig, Germany, Apr. 18, 17; m. 54; c. 2. PEDIATRICS. M.B. & B.Ch, Cambridge, 42, M.A, 43; M.R.C.P, Royal College of Physicians, England, 48, D.C.H, 50. Registr, children's dept, London Hosp, England, 49-51; Hosp. Sick Children, London, England, 51-52; asst. pathologist, Babies Hosp, Columbia-Presby. Med. Center, 52-53; chief resident PEDIAT, Vancouver Gen. Hosp, 53-54; fel, UNIV. B.C, 54-55, asst. prof, 56-63, assoc. prof, 63-68, PROF, 68- Holt fel, Columbia, 52-53; res. assoc, med. sch, Harvard, 59; Children's Med. Center, 59. Consult, Woodlands Sch. retarded. Am. Asn. Ment. Deficiency; Can. Med. Asn; Can. Pediat. Soc; Can. Neurol. Soc; Royal Soc. Med; Brit. Med. Asn. R.A.M.C, 44-46, Maj. Pediatric neurology, mental retardation; hemolytic disease of newborn; metabolic disorders in children. Address: 715 W. 12th Ave, Vancouver 9, B.C, Can.

DUNN, HOWARD EUGENE, b. Kansas City, Mo, Apr. 14, 38; m. 61; c. 2. ORGANIC CHEMISTRY. A.B, William Jewell Col, 60; Ph.D.(org. chem), Illinois, 65. Res. chemist, res. ctr, Phillips Petrol. Co, 65-69; ASST. PROF, DEPT. CHEM, IND. STATE UNIV, EVANSVILLE, 69- Summers, chemist, Argonne Nat. Lab, 60, res. chemist, Eli Lilly & Co, 61; res. grant, South. Ill. Univ, 71. Am. Chem. Soc. Organoboron, sulfoxide and sulfone chemistry; reactions in liquid ammonia; homogeneous catalysis. Address: Dept. of Chemistry, Indiana State University, Evansville, IN 47712.

DUNN, HOWARD J, b. Los Angeles, Calif, Aug. 10, 11; m; c. 2. FOOD CHEMISTRY. A.B, California, Los Angeles, 36. Jr. cereal chemist, State Dept. Agr, Calif, 36-38, field rep, 38-44; anal. chemist, LABS, VAN CAMP SEA FOOD CO, INC, RALSTON PURINA CO, 44-53, chief chemist, 53-59, MGR. byprod. control, 59-68, MARINE PROD. RES. & DEVELOP, 68- AAAS; Am. Chem. Soc; Inst. Food Tech. Development of powdered vitamin A and D products; water soluble carotene; condensed fish solubles; stabilized fish meals; spray dried amino acids; ultraviolet spectrophotometry; partition chromatography; bile acids; amino acids; vitamin microbiological assays; fermentation chemistry; food plant technology. Address: Ralston Purina Co, 302 Terminal Way, Terminal Island, CA 90731.

DUNN, J. STANLEY, b. Corrine, Utah, Oct, 17, 17; m. 46; c. 3. INORGANIC CHEMISTRY. B.S, Utah State, 39, M.S, 41; Purdue, 41-42, 46-47; Res. Corp. N.Y. fel, Syracuse, 48-49, Ph.D.(chem), 50. Instr. chem, Syracuse, 49-50; res. chemist, Monsanto Chem. Co, 50-53; sr. chemist, navy ord. div, EASTMAN KODAK CO, 53-59, PHOTOG. RES. LABS, 59-64, RES. ASSOC, 64- U.S.N, 42-46, Lt. AAAS; Am. Chem. Soc. Photographic chemistry; coordination compounds. Address: Photographic Research Labs, Eastman Kodak Co, 343 State St, Rochester, NY 14650.

DUNN, JAMES E, II, b. Pittsburgh, Pa, June 1, 34; m. 54, 69; c. 3. AEROSPACE MEDICINE. A.B, Hopkins, 56; M.D, Maryland, 60. Intern med, Pa. Hosp, 60-61; aerospace physiologist, Sch. Aerospace Med, 61-65; resident, gen. surg, sch. med, Duke Univ, 65-66, neurosurg, 66-71; ASST. PROF. NEURO-SURG. & CLIN. DIR. SHOCK TRAUMA UNIT, UNIV. MD, BALTIMORE, 71-U.S.A.F.R, 59-, Maj. Hypercalcemia; hypothermia; rapid decompression; altitude acclimatization; closed head trauma; hyperbaric oxygen therapy and toxicity. Address: Shock Trauma Unit, University of Maryland, Baltimore, MD 21201.

DUNN, JAMES ELDON, b. Fairbury, Nebr, Jan. 8, 36; m. 64; c. 2. MATHE-MATICAL STATISTICS. B.Sc, Univ. Nebr, 57, M.Sc, 61; Ph.D.(statist), Va. Polytech. Inst, 63. Asst. prof. MATH, UNIV. ARK, FAYETTEVILLE, 63-67, ASSOC. PROF, 67- Statist. consult, Ark. State Judiciary Comn, 63-65; Bur. Sport Fisheries & Wildlife, 65-71 & Sport Fishing Inst, 68-71; Nat. Sci. Found. sci. faculty fel, Stanford Univ, 71-72. Am. Statist. Asn; Biomet. Soc. Statistical applications in biology. Address: Computing Center, University of Arkansas, Fayetteville, AR 72701.

DUNN, JAMES ROBERT, b. Sacramento, Calif, Oct. 18, 21; m. 46; c. 4. GE-OLOGY. A.B, California, 43, Ph.D.(geol), 50. Asst, California, 46-50; assoc. prof. GEOL, RENSSELAER POLYTECH. INST, 50-66, PROF, 66-;

CHMN. BD, JAMES R. DUNN & ASSOCS, 71-, pres, 60-71. Geologist, New Idria Quicksilver Mining Co, 46; Iron Ore Co, Can, 51; indust. & govt. consult, 53- U.S.N.R, 43-46, Lt.(jg). Am. Inst. Prof. Geol; Asn. Eng. Geol; Soc. Econ. Geol; Am. Inst. Planners; Am. Soc. Test. & Mat; Am. Concrete Inst; Nat. Asn. Geol. Teachers; fel. Geol. Soc. Am; Am. Inst. Mining, Metall. & Petrol. Eng; Clay Minerals Soc. Physical and chemical characteristics of rock aggregate for concrete; economic and industrial geology of mineral deposits; engineering geology; socio-economic applications of geology, including environmental geology, conservation and planning; computer simulation techniques in planning for mineral resource development. Address: James R. Dunn & Associates, Box 158, Averill Park, NY 12018.

DUNN, JOHN EDWARD, JR, b. Greenville, Iowa, Sept. 30, 06; m. 34; c. 3. PUBLIC HEALTH. B.S, South Dakota, 28, A.B, 29; M.D, Washington (St. Louis), 31; M.S.P.H, Michigan, 38; Harvard, 39-40. Rotating intern, Letterman Gen. Hosp, San Francisco, Calif, 31-32; asst. res, St. Luke's Hosp, 33-34; ward surgeon, U.S. Marine Hosp, 34-36; epidemiologist in training, State Health Dept, N.Y, 36-37; in charge health dept. survs, U.S. Pub. Health Serv, 38-39, field invests, dermatosis invest. sect, Nat. Insts. Health, 40-44, head skin physiol. unit, indust. hyg. res. lab, 44-46, 47-48, med. dir. & chief field invests. sect, Nat. Cancer Inst, 48-53; mem. staff cancer epidemiol. studies, STATE HEALTH DEPT, CALIF, 53-60, CANCER CONSULT, BUR. CHRONIC DISEASES, 60- Mem. adv. comt. epidemiol, diagnosis & therapy, Am. Cancer Soc, 70- Dipl, Am. Bd. Prev. Med. U.S.P.H.S, 34-60. Am. Med. Asn; N.Y. Acad. Sci; fel. Am. Pub. Health Asn. Immunologic mechanism of allergic skin sensitivity; occupational dermatitis; photo sensitization of the skin by petroleum solvents; cancer epidemiology. Address: California Dept. of Public Health, 2151 Berkeley Way, Berkeley, CA 94704.

DUNN, JOHN FREDERICK, JR, b. Passaic, N.J, May 13, 30; m. 53; c. 5. MECHANICAL ENGINEERING. S.B, Mass. Inst. Tech, 51, S.M, 53, Sc.D. (mech. eng), 57. Proj. engr, dynamic anal. & control lab, Mass. Inst. Tech, 51-57; res. div, Walworth Co, 57-58, asst. dir. valve res, 58-59, chief engr. design & prod. control res, 59-62; assoc. prof. MECH. ENG, NORTHEAST. UNIV, 62-63, PROF, 63- Mem. exec. comt, Mfrs. Standardization Soc. Valve & Fitting Indust, 61-62. Am. Soc. Mech. Eng; Am. Soc. Eng. Educ. Components for high-performance electro-hydraulic and electro-pneumatic control systems. Address: Dept. of Mechanical Engineering, Room 75-RI, Northeastern University, Boston, MA 02115.

DUNN, J(OHN) HOWARD, b. Omaha, Nebr, Aug. 29, 09; m. 35; c. 3. MECHANI-CAL ENGINEERING. B.S, Iowa State Univ, 31. Asst. mgr, Dunn Mfg. Co, 31-34; develop. engr, ALUMINUM CO. AM, 34-41, asst. to mgr. prod. planning, 41-44, automotive develop. mgr, 44-49, asst. mgr. develop. div, 49-53, mgr, 53-59, process develop. labs, 59-67, dir. develop, 67-70, V.PRES. RES. & DEVELOP, 70- Prof. achievement award in eng, Iowa State Univ, 71. Soc. Automotive Eng; Sci. Res. Soc. Am; Am. Ord. Asn; Am. Soc. Metals. Applications of aluminum alloys and products, especially in the automotive field. Address: Alcoa Research & Development Dept, Aluminum Co. of America, 1501 Alcoa Bldg, Pittsburgh, PA 15219.

DUNN, JOHN ROBERT, b. Andover, Eng, May 12, 30; m. 55; c. 4. PHYSI-CAL ORGANIC CHEMISTRY. B.Sc, London, 51; D.Phil.(phys. org. chem), 53. Nat. Res. Coun. Can. fel, 53-55; sr. chemist, Natural Rubber Producers' Res. Asn, 55-62; sr. res. chemist, POLYMER CORP, LTD, 62-66, SUPVR. COMPOUNDING RES, 66- Am. Soc. Test. & Mat; fel. Chem. Inst. Can. Rubber technology; oxidation and antioxidants in rubber and aldehydes; vulcanization of rubber; physical properties of polymers; photolysis of ketones; flame retardancy. Address: Polymer Corp. Ltd, Vidal St, Sarnia, Ont, Can.

DUNN, JOHN THORNTON, b. Washington, D.C, Oct. 27, 32; m. 62; c. 3. ENDOCRINOLOGY. A.B, Princeton, 54; M.D, Duke, 58. Intern med, N.Y. Hosp-Cornell, 58-59; res, Univ. Utah Hosps, 59-61; fel. thyroid, Mass. Gen. Hosp-Harvard, 61-62 & 63-64; Presby. Hosp-Columbia, 62-63; biochem, Harvard Med. Sch, 64-66; asst. prof. MED, SCH. MED, UNIV. VA, 66-70, ASSOC. PROF, 70- Nat. Inst. Arthritis & Metab. Disease res. grant, 66-; U.S. Pub. Health Serv. res. career develop. award, 71-; consult, Pan Am. Health Orgn. U.S.P.H.S, 62-64, Surg. AAAS; Am. Thyroid Asn.(Van Meter prize, 68); Endocrine Soc; Am. Fedn. Clin. Res. Thyroglobulin structure; endemic goiter. Address: School of Medicine, University of Virginia, Charlottesville, VA 22901.

DUNN, L(ESLIE) C(LARENCE), b. Buffalo, N.Y, Nov. 2, 93; m. 18; c. 2. ZOOLOGY, GENETICS. B.S, Dartmouth Col, 15, hon. D.Sc, 52; M.S, Harvard, 17, Sc.D.(genetics), 20. Asst. zool, Harvard, 15-17, 19; geneticist, Storrs Exp. Sta, Connecticut, 20-28; prof. ZOOL, COLUMBIA UNIV, 28-62, EMER. PROF. & RES. ASSOC, 62- Exec. officer dept. zool, Columbia, 40-46. Managing ed, Genetics, 36-41; ed, Columbia Biol. Series, 36- U.S.A, 17-19, 1st Lt. Nat. Acad. Sci; Genetics Soc. Am.(pres, 32); Am. Soc. Naturalists (v.pres, 42, pres, 61, ed, Am. Naturalist, 51-60); Am. Soc. Human Genetics (pres, 61); Am. Soc. Zool; Am. Philos. Soc; Norweg. Acad. Sci. History of genetics; genetics and gene distribution in human and animal populations; effects of mutations on development in mammals. Address: Nevis Biological Station, Columbia University, Irvington on Hudson, NY 10533.

DUNN, MARVIN I, b. Topeka, Kans, Dec. 21, 27; m. 56; c. 2. INTERNAL MEDICINE, CARDIOLOGY. B.A, Kansas, 50, M.D, 54. Instr. med. & fel. cardiovasc. disease, KANSAS, 58-60, assoc. MED, 60-62, asst. prof, 62-65, assoc. prof, 65-71, PROF, 71- DIR. CARDIOVASC. LAB, 63- Consult, Vet. Admin. Hosp, Kansas City, Mo, 60-; Menorah Hosp, 61-; Bethany & Providence Hosps, Kansas City, Kans, 65-; U.S. Air. Force; Fel. coun. clin. cardiol, Am. Heart Asn, 66- Dipl, Am. Bd. Internal Med, 63, Am. Bd. Cardiovasc. Disease, 65. U.S.A, 46-47. Am. Med. Asn; fel. Am. Col. Cardiol; fel. Am. Col. Physicians; Am. Fedn. Clin. Res; N.Y. Acad. Sci. Clinical cardiovascular problems and hemodynamics. Address: Cardiovascular Lab, University of Kansas Medical Center, 39th & Rainbow, Kansas City, KS 66103.

DUNN, MARVIN R(ICHARD), b. Lubbock, Tex, Nov. 12, 31; m. 58; c. 3. MEDICINE, PATHOLOGY. B.A, Hardin-Simmons, 51; M.D, Texas, 55.

Intern PATH, St. John's Hosp, Tulsa, Okla, 55-56; Am. Cancer Soc. fel, southwest. med. sch, Texas, 56-57; asst, MED. COL. PA, 57-59, instr, 59-60, assoc, 60-61, asst. prof, 61-64, ASSOC. PROF, 64-, ASSOC. DEAN, 65- Adj. prof, Drexel Univ, 62-; spec. consult, Nat. Cancer Inst, 60-62; chief of physician educ. br, Bur. Health Manpower Educ, Nat. Insts. Health, 69- Dipl, Am. Bd. Path, 60; Christian R. & Mary E. Linback Award, 62. U.S.P.H.S, 57-59, Sr. Asst. Surg. Int. Acad. Path. Synthesis, metabolism and control of connective tissues; tissue transplantation; histochemistry. Address: Dept. of Pathology, Medical College of Pennsylvania, 3300 Henry Ave, Philadelphia, PA 19129.

DUNN, MARY C(ATHERINE), b. Iva, S.C, Apr. 29, 24. ZOOLOGY. B.S, Winthrop Col, 45; M.S, Michigan, 47; U.S. Pub. Health fel. & Ph.D.(zool), Georgia, 57. Analyst chem, Tenn. Eastman Corp, 45-56; instr. biol, Culver-Stockton Col, 47-48; asst. res. parasitologist, Parke Davis & Co, 48-51; asst. prof. zool, Phila. Col. Pharm, 57-58; res. assoc. parasitol, Columbia, 58-63; ASSOC. PROF. BIOL, Shorter Col, 63-65; MID. TENN. STATE UNIV, 65- AAAS; Am. Soc. Parasitol; Am. Soc. Trop. Med. & Hyg; Am. Micros. Soc. General zoology; cytology of trematodes; general parasitology. Address: Dept. of Biology, Middle Tennessee State University, Murfreesboro, TN 37130.

DUNN, MICHAEL F, b. Greeley, Colo, July 11, 39; m. 58; c. 4. BIOCHEMISTRY, ENZYMOLOGY. P.R.E, Colo. Sch. Mines, 61; M.S, Ga. Inst. Technol, 63, Ph.D.(phys. org. chem), 66. Res. assoc. enzym, Inst. Molecular Biol, Univ. Ore, 66-69; physics & chem. inst, Tech. Univ. Denmark, 69-70; ASST. PROF. BIOCHEM, UNIV. CALIF, RIVERSIDE, 70- Nat. Insts. Health fel, 66-67; U.S. Pub. Health Serv. trainee, 67-69; NATO fel, 69-70, Am. Cancer Soc. grant, 71-72. Am. Chem. Soc. Enzyme structure, function and catalytic mechanism via rapid kinetic techniques; dehydrogenases; aldolases; growth factor proteins. Address: Dept. of Biochemistry, University of California, Riverside, CA 92502.

DUNN, OLIVE JEAN, b. Can, Sept. 1, 15; m. 36, 52; m. 3. BIOSTATISTICS. A.B, Univ. Calif, Los Angeles, 36, M.A, 51, Ph.D.(math), 56. Asst. prof. statist, Iowa State Univ, 56-57; BIOSTATIST, SCH. PUB. HEALTH, UNIV. CALIF, LOS ANGELES, 57-64, assoc. prof, 64-70, PROF, 70- AAAS; Inst. Math. Statist; Am. Statist. Asn; Biomet. Soc; Am. Pub. Health Asn. Confidence interval estimation. Address: School of Public Health, University of California, Los Angeles, CA 90024.

DUNN, PAUL M(ILLARD), b. Lennox, S.Dak, Oct. 15, 98; m. 26; c. 2. FORESTRY. B.S, Iowa State Col, 23, fel, 23-26, M.S, 33. Dist. forester & assoc. forester, State Forestry Dept, Mo, 26-31; asst. prof. forestry, Utah State Col, 31-32, assoc. prof, 32-35, prof, 35-42, exten. forester, 31-35, in charge sch. forestry, 35-38, dean, 38-42; PROF. FORESTRY, ORE. STATE UNIV, 42-, dean sch. forestry, 42-55. Adv. forest educ, Univ. Chile, 52-53; dir. forestry, St. Regis Paper Co, 55-62, v.pres, 62-68. U.S.A, 17-19. AAAS; Soc. Am. Foresters(pres, 62-63); Am. Forestry Asn.(pres, 68-70); Forest Hist. Soc.(pres, 69-70). Silviculture; nursery practices; forest management; forest practices; wood utilizations. Address: School of Forestry, Oregon State University, Corvallis, OR 97331.

DUNN, RICHARD B, b. Baltimore, Md, Dec. 14, 27; m. 51. MECHANICAL ENGINEERING, ASTRONOMY. B.M.E, Univ. Minn, 49, M.S, 50; Ph.D, Harvard, 61. PHYSICIST SOLAR ASTRON, SACRAMENTO PEAK OBSERV, 53- Am. Astron. Soc. Solar astronomy; instrumentation. Address: Sacramento Peak Observatory, Sunspot, NM 88349.

DUNN, R(ICHARD) H(UDSON), b. Lancaster, Ky, Apr. 7, 20; m. 43; c. 2. BIOLOGY, BOTANY. B.S, Wilberforce, 42; M.S, Ohio State, 45, Ph.D.(bot, hort), 53; Cornell, 56. Instr. biol, Fla. Agr. & Mech. Univ, 45-46; hort, VA. STATE COL, 46-48, asst. prof, 48-52, assoc. prof. biol. & plant sci, 52-62, PROF. BIOL, 62-, DIR. SCH. ARTS & SCI, 67- Consult. Va. Teachers Asn, 57-; State Dept. Educ. Va, 58; dir, Nat. Sci. Found. Inst. High Sch. Sci. Teachers, Va. State Col, summers, 58-61, 64-66; assoc. prog. dir, inst. sect, Nat. Sci. Found; dir, Acad. Year Inst. High Sch. Teachers Biol, 65-66; biol. ed. specialist, U.S. Agency Int. Develop-Ohio State Univ, India Proj, summer 66. AAAS; Nat. Asn. Biol. Teachers; Nat. Sci. Teachers Asn; Bot. Soc. Am. Plant nutrition; science teaching; biological science. Address: School of Arts & Sciences, Virginia State College, Petersburg, VA 23803.

DUNN, ROBERT GARVIN, b. Lake Village, Ark, July 30, 17; m. 50; c. 3. AEROSPACE & CHEMICAL ENGINEERING. B.S, La. State, 42; M.S, Ohio State, 49, Ph.D.(chem. eng), 64. Chem. analyst, Esso Labs, Standard Oil Co. La, 40-43; proj. engr, power plant lab, U.S. AIR FORCE, Ohio 44-49, unit chief, 49-51, res. engr, propulsion res. br, aeronaut. res.lab, 51-54, res. group chief FLUID DYNAMICS FACILITIES RES. LAB. AEROSPACE RES. LABS, 54-61, proj. scientist, 61-65, br. chief, 65-67, DEP. LAB. DIR, 67- U.S.A.F, 43-46 & 51-53, Res, 53-56, 1st Lt. Combustion Inst; Am. Inst. Aeronaut. & Astronaut; Am. Chem. Soc; fel. Am. Inst. Chem. Fluid dynamics; propulsion; supersonic combustion; aeromechanics simulation techniques; gaseous detonation; aircraft engine testing at extreme temperatures. Address: 121 Redder Ave, Dayton, OH 45405.

DUNN, SAMUEL L, b. Tipton, Ind, Apr. 17, 40; m. 63; c. 2. MATHEMATICS. B.A, Olivet Nazarene Col, 61, B.S, 62; M.S, Univ. Wis-Milwaukee, 64, univ. fel, 66-68, Ph.D.(math), 69; Nat. Sci. Found. summer fels, Univ. Wis-Madison, 64 & 65. Teacher, high sch, Ill, 61-62; asst. prof. MATH, SEATTLE PAC. COL, 68-71, ASSOC. PROF, 71-, COORD. CURRICULUM MATH. ECON, 70- Summers, Nat. Sci. Found. fel, Pa. State Univ, 69, res. partic, Univ. Okla, 70. Am. Math. Soc; Math. Asn. Am. Ring theory, particularly quasi-Frobenius quotient rings; quotient rings and their topologies. Address: Dept. of Mathematics, Seattle Pacific College, Seattle, WA 98119.

DUNN, STANLEY A(USTIN), b. Long Beach, Calif, Nov. 13, 21; m. 44; c. 3; m. 57; c. 1. PHYSICAL CHEMISTRY. B.S, Calif. Inst. Tech, 43; M.A, Hopkins, 48, Ph.D.(chem), 51. Chemist, Jackson Lab, E.I. du Pont de Nemours & Co, 50-54; from res. assoc. to head anal. dept, Rhodia, Inc, 54-59; ASSOC. DIR. INORG. & HIGH TEMPERATURE DIV, BJORKSTEN RES. LABS, INC, 59- U.S.N.R, 43-46, Ens. Am. Ceramic Soc; Am. Chem. Soc; Am. Inst. Chem. Materials science; reaction kinetics; thermodynamics; rheology. Address: Inorganic & High Temperature Division, Bjorksten Research Labs, Inc, P.O. Box 265, Madison, WI 53701.

DUNN, STUART, b. Amboy, Minn, Aug. 12, 00; m. 40; c. 2. BOTANY. B.S, Minnesota, 23, Ph.D.(plant physiol), 31; M.S, Iowa State Col, 25. Asst. plant physiol, Minnesota, 23-24; teaching fel, Iowa State Col, 24-25, instr, 25-26; BOT, UNIV. N.H, 26-37, asst. prof, 37-47, assoc. prof, 47-60, prof, 60-70, EMER. PROF, 70-, plant physiologist, 47-70. Res. fel, Calif. Inst. Technol, 52-53. AAAS; Am. Soc. Plant Physiol; Weed Sci. Soc. Am. Effects of light quality on plant growth and metabolism; weed life cycles and growth. Address: 24 Woodman Rd, Durham, NH 03824.

DUNN, S(TUART) THOMAS, b. Rock Island, Ill, Aug. 27, 40; m. 61; c. 3. THERMODYNAMICS. B.S.M.E, Mo. Sch. Mines, 62; Nat. Defense Ed. Act fel, Okla. State, 62-64, M.S.M.E, 63, Ph.D.(mech. eng), 65. Group leader thermoradiative properties, Nat. Bur. Standards, 64-66; pres, Dunn Assocs, Inc, 66-69; v.pres, Dunn Anal. Instruments Div, BLOCK ENG, INC, 69-70, PRES, DIGILAB, INC, 70- Am. Inst. Aeronaut. & Astronaut; Am. Soc. Mech. Eng; Optical Soc. Am. Air Pollution Control Asn; Marine Tech. Soc. Thermal radiative properties of solids and powders; thermal control surfaces for space crafts; optics; use of interferometers and spectrometers for absolute property measurements; conduction heat transfer; lasers. Address: Digilab, Inc, 237 Putnam Ave, Cambridge, MA 02139.

DUNN, THELMA B(RUMFIELD), b. Pittsylvania Co, Va, Feb. 6, 00; m. 29; c. 3. PATHOLOGY. A.B, Cornell, 22; M.D, Virginia, 26; hon. D.M.S, Woman's Med. Col. Pa, 62; hon. degree, Univ. Perugia, 69. Intern, Bellevue Hosp, New York, 26-27; instr. path, Virginia, 27-28, asst. prof, 28-29, acting head dept, 29-30; volunteer lab. asst, George Washington, 36-38, asst, 38-42; fel, NAT. CANCER INST, 42-47, pathologist, 47-70, CONSULT, REGISTRY EXP. CANCERS, 70- Federal Women's award & Distinguished Serv. medal, Dept. Health, Ed. & Welfare, 62. Am. Soc. Path. & Bact; fel. Am. Col. Physicians; fel. Col. Am. Path; Am. Asn. Cancer Res.(pres, 61). Pathologic anatomy of laboratory mice; cancer. Address: 1604 Jamestown Dr, Charlottesville, VA 22901.

DUNN, THOMAS GUY, b. Livingston, Mont, Jan. 31, 35; m. 60; c. 2. REPRODUCTIVE PHYSIOLOGY, ENDOCRINOLOGY. B.S, Mont. State Univ, 62; M.S, Univ. Nebr, Lincoln, 65; Nat. Insts. Health fel, 65-68; Ph.D.(physiol), Colo. State Univ, 69. ASST. PROF. animal sci, Purdue Univ, 68-70; ANIMAL PHYSIOL, UNIV. WYO, 70- U.S.A, 56-58. AAAS; Am. Soc. Animal Sci; Soc. Study Reproduction. Influence of nutrition on reproductive performance and endocrinology of beef cattle; influence of environmental temperature on endocrinology of chickens; glucose biokinetics in sheep. Address: Division of Animal Science, University of Wyoming, Box 3354, University Station, Laramie, WY 82070.

DUNN, THOMAS HENRY, b. Eldorado Springs, Colo, May 19, 02; m. 30. CHEMISTRY. B.A, Colorado, 26; Mass. Inst. Tech, 39. Chemist, Midwest Ref. Co, 26-33; chief chemist, Stanolind Oil & Gas Co, 33-47, res. group supvr, 47-63, staff res. scientist, Pan-Am. Petrol. Corp, 63-67; RETIRED. Am. Chem. Soc; Rheol. Soc; Am. Inst. Min, Metall. & Petrol. Eng. Collodial chemistry of clay drilling fluids; corrosion of oil field equipment; geochemical analysis of gases and solids; rheology of drilling fluids. Address: 2515 Grape Ave, Boulder, CO 80302.

DUNN, THOMAS M, b. Sydney, Australia, Apr. 25, 29; m. 53; c. 3. PHYSICAL CHEMISTRY. B.Sc, Sydney, 49, M.Sc, 51; 1851 Exhib. scholar, London, 52-54, Ph.D.(phys. chem), 57. Teaching fel. chem, Sydney, 50-52; asst. lectr, PHYS. CHEM, Univ. Col, London, 54-56, lectr, 56-63; PROF, UNIV. MICH, ANN ARBOR, 63- Plenary lectr, Int. Conf. Co-ord. Chem, Stockholm, Sweden, 62. Am. Chem. Soc; fel. Brit. Chem. Soc; Faraday Soc. High resolution vapour phase spectra of organic and inorganic molecules in the visible and ultraviolet regions; electronic spectra at 4°K of both organic and inorganic crystals. Address: Dept. of Chemistry, University of Michigan, Ann Arbor, MI 48104.

DUNN, WENDELL E(ARL), JR, b. Baltimore, Md, Aug. 30, 22; m. 44; c. 4. CHEMICAL ENGINEERING. B.E, Hopkins, 43, Ph.D.(chem. eng), 50- Instr, Hopkins, 47-50; Res. supvr, E.I. du Pont de Nemours & Co, 50-68; RES. DIR, RUTILE & ZIRCON MINES, AUSTRALIA, 68- U.S.A.A.F, 43-46. Inst. Chem. Eng; Inst. Mech. Eng. X-ray bone densitometry; heat and mass transfer; diffusion; reaction kinetics of high temperature reactions; chlorine metallurgy; fluidization. Address: Rutile & Zircon Mines (Newcastle) Ltd, 68 Arthur St, North Sydney, N.S.W. 2060, Australia.

DUNN, WILLIAM LAWRIE, b. London, Ont, Can, Oct. 23, 27; m. 56; c. 3. PATHOLOGY. B.Sc, Western Ontario, 50, M.D, 54; Ph.D.(exp. path), London, 63. Teaching fel. path, Western Ontario, 57-59; Harvard, 59-60. Asst. prof. PATH, UNIV. B.C, 63-67, assoc. prof, 67-69, PROF. & HEAD DEPT, 69-; DIR. LABS, VANCOUVER GEN. HOSP, 69- Consult, Can. Tumor Reference Ctr. Cert. path, Royal Col. Physicians & Surgeons Can, 64, exam. gen. surg, 70- AAAS; N.Y. Acad. Sci; Int. Acad. Path; Can. Asn. Path. Liver disease; tumor biology; diagnostic pathology. Address: Dept. of Pathology, University of British Columbia, Vancouver 8, B.C, Can.

DUNN, WILLIAM L(EWIS), b. Lake Village, Ark, Oct. 18, 14; m. 40; c. 2. ANALYTICAL CHEMISTRY. A.B, Illinois, 36; Ph.D.(anal. & inorg. chem), Wisconsin, 41. Asst. chem, Wisconsin, 36-38, instr, exten. div, 38, asst, 38-41; instr, Cornell Col, 41-43; asst. prof, 43-45, instr. math, 43-44; prof. chem, Colo. State Col. Educ, 45-49, acting chmn. div. scis, 47-48; dean, LAKE FOREST COL, 49-62, PROVOST & DEAN FACULTY, 62- Polarography; water treatment; science teaching. Address: Lake Forest College, Lake Forest, IL 60045.

DUNN, WILLIAM R(YDER), JR, b. Hollywood, Calif, Apr. 18, 35; m. 57; c. 3. ELECTRICAL ENGINEERING. A.B, Univ. Calif, Berkeley, 58; M.S, Univ. Santa Clara, 68, Ph.D.(elec. eng), 70. Proj. engr, Lockheed Aircraft Corp, 62-70; ASST. PROF. ELEC. ENG, UNIV. SANTA CLARA, 70- NASA res. grant, 71-72. Inst. Elec. & Electronics Eng. Network topology; computer aided design; microelectronics. Address: Dept. of Electrical Engineering, University of Santa Clara, Santa Clara, CA 95053.

DUNN, WILLIAM W(ILEY), b. Abilene, Tex, Sept. 13, 42; m. 66. MATERIALS SCIENCE, METALLUGY. B.S, Tex. Technol. Col, 66; Ph.D.(mat. sci), Rice Univ, 70. RES. METALLURGIST, REFRACTORY METALS LAB, GEN. ELEC. CO, 70- Am. Soc. Metals; Metall. Soc. Equilibrium solubility of carbon in iron, nickel and cobalt; powder metallurgy research of tungsten alloys. Address: General Electric Co, Refractory Metals Lab, 21800 Tungsten Rd, Cleveland, OH 44117.

DUNNAM, F(RANCIS) E(UGENE), b. Alexandria, La, Jan. 29, 31; m. 65. PHYSICS. B.S, La. State, 52, M.S, 54, fel, 57-58, Ph.D.(physics), 58. Asst. PHYSICS, La. State, 54-56, instr, 56-57; asst. prof, UNIV. FLA, 58-67, ASSOC. PROF, 67- Consult, Oak Ridge Nat. Lab, 61-63. AAAS; Am. Phys. Soc; Am. Asn. Physics Teachers. Experimental nuclear physics; charged particle acceleration; vacuum techniques; ion sources; nuclear instrumentation. Address: Dept. of Physics, University of Florida, Gainesville, FL 32603.

DUNNAVANT, WILLIAM R(EXFORD), b. Sidney, Ohio, Aug. 2, 31; m. 56; c. 2. ORGANIC & POLYMER CHEMISTRY. B.S, Miami (Ohio), 53, M.S, 54; Allied Chem. & Dye Corp. fel, Duke, 58-59, Ph.D.(org. chem), 60. Instr. chem, Mercy Hosp. Sch. Nursing, Hamilton, Ohio, 54-55; res. chemist, aeronaut. res. lab, Wright Air Develop. Center, 55-57; sr. res. chemist polymers, Standard Oil Co, Ohio, 60-63; BATTELLE-COLUMBUS LABS, 63-70, CHIEF POLYMER CHEM. DIV, 70- U.S.A.F.R, 55-57, Capt. Am. Chem. Soc. Acrylic lattices; molding resins; inorganic and semi-organic polymers; polymer—films and fibers, structure-property relationships, processing, pilot-planting and thermal stability. Address: Dept. of Biology, Environment & Chemistry, Polymer Chemistry Division, Battelle-Columbus Labs, 505 King Ave, Columbus, OH 43201.

DUNNE, BRIAN BORÚ, JR, b. Santa Fe, N.Mex, Jan. 8, 24; m. 54; c. 2. PHYSICS. B.S, Calif. Inst. Tech, 45; M.A, California, Los Angeles, 52, Ph.D.(physics), 55. Res. assoc. physics, California, Los Angeles, 54-56; sr. staff mem, J.J. Hopkins Lab. Pure & Appl. Sci, Gen. Atomic Div, Gen. Dynamics Corp, 57-67, founder, Systs, Sci. & Software, 67-69; MEM. STAFF, Sci. Applns, Inc, 69-71; SHIP SYSTS, INC, 71- U.S.N.R, 41-46, Lt. AAAS; Am. Phys. Soc; Am. Geophys. Union. Shock and detonation waves; heavy metal plasma guns; reactor critical assemblies; underwater sound generators; underwater explosions; explosive reconstitution. Address: Ship Systems, Inc, 11750 Sorrento Valley Rd, La Jolla, CA 92037.

DUNNE, HOWARD W(ALTER), b. Omaha, Nebr, March 19, 13; m. 34; c. 4. VETERINARY PATHOLOGY & BACTERIOLOGY. D.V.M, Iowa State Col, 41; Am. Vet. Med. Asn. fel, Mich. State, 46-48, Ph.D.(animal path), 51. Asst. prod. mgr, The Corn States Serum Co, 42-44, mgr, 44-46; res. veterinarian, state foot & mouth disease labs, Bur. of Animal Indust, U.S. Dept. Agr, Netherlands, 48-50; asst. prof. path, Mich. State, 50-51, assoc. prof. bacter, 51-52; deputy chief vet. microbiol, biol. warfare labs, U.S. Army Chem. Corps, 52-53; PROF. VET. SCI, PA. STATE UNIV, 53- Consult, Chem. Corps, U.S. Army, 54-59; Food & Agr. Org, U.N; mem. Secy. Nat. Comt. for Eradication of Hog Cholera, U.S. Dept. Agr; West. Hemisphere Virus Classification Comt. Dipl, Am. Col. Vet. Path; Am. Col. Vet. Microbiol; 12th Int. Vet. Cong. Award, 71. Fel. Am. Acad. Microbiol; Am. Vet. Med. Asn; Am. Soc. Microbiol; N.Y. Acad. Sci. Veterinary virology; swine diseases; bovine mucosal diseases; enteroviruses. Address: Animal Disease Lab, Pennsylvania State University, University Park, PA 16802.

DUNNE, THOMAS G(REGORY), b. Los Angeles, Calif, Oct. 10, 30. PHYSICAL INORGANIC CHEMISTRY. B.S, California, Los Angeles, 52; fel, Washington (Seattle), 52-54, Ph.D.(chem), 57. Assoc. chemist, Int. Bus. Mach. Corp, 57-61; res. assoc, Mass. Inst. Tech, 61-63; asst. prof. CHEM, REED COL, 63-69, ASSOC. PROF, 69- Coordination complex studies; oxidation-reduction mechanisms. Address: Dept. of Chemistry, Reed College, Portland, OR 97202.

DUNNEBACKE, THELMA H(UDSON), Embryol, Zool, see DIXON, THELMA H(UDSON) DUNNEBACKE.

DUNNER, EDWARD, b. Brooklyn, N.Y, Oct. 4, 10; m. 39; c. 2. INTERNAL MEDICINE. A.B, Syracuse, 31; M.D, Bern, 36. Chief tuberc. serv, Vet. Admin. Hosp, Calif, 46-50; area chief tuberc, Mo, 50-54; chief training & standards, CENT. OFF, VET. ADMIN, 54-55, chief tuberc. res. & exec. secy, Vet. Admin. Armed Forces Co-op. Study Tuberc, 55-58, assoc. dir. & chief, clin. studies div, res. serv, 58-62, dir, 62-66, SPEC. ASST. FOR RES. & EDUC, 66- Vet. Admin. Meritorious Serv. Award, 59. Med.C, 42-46, Maj. N.Y. Acad. Sci; Am. Med. Asn; Am. Thoracic Soc; fel. Am. Col. Chest Physicians (hon. gov); Asn. Mil. Surg. U.S. Chemotherapy of tuberculosis; clinical studies in sarcoidosis; cooperative studies. Address: Research & Education in Medicine, U.S. Veterans Administration, Washington, DC 20420.

DUNNETT, CHARLES W(ILLIAM), b. Windsor, Ont, Can, Aug. 24, 21; m. 47; c. 3. STATISTICS. B.A, McMaster, 42; M.A, Toronto, 46; D.Sc, Aberdeen, 60; Columbia. Instr. math, Columbia, 46-48; Maritime Col, 48-49; biometrician, Can. Dept. Nat. Health & Welfare, 49-52; res. assoc. statist, Cornell, 52-53; STATISTICIAN, LEDERLE LABS, AM. CYANAMID CO, 53- Mem. Order British Empire. R.C.N, 42-45. Fel. Am. Statist. Asn; Biomet. Soc; Royal Statist. Soc; Int. Asn. Statist. Phys. Sci. Application of statistics to design and analysis of experiments in biological and physical sciences, statistical methodology; programing methods for electronic computers. Address: 19 Edsall Ave, Nanuet, NY 10954.

DUNNIGAN, JACQUES, b. St. Jerome, Que, May 1, 35; m. 63; c. 4. PHYSIOLOGY. B.A, St. Laurent Col, 56; B.Sc, Ottawa (Ont), 60, Ph.D, 63. Res. asst. med, Laval, 63-64; adj. prof. SCI, UNIV. SHERBROOKE, 64-68, ASSOC. PROF, 68- Nat. Res. Coun. Can. grants, 64-70; mem. res. comn, Univ. Que. Can. Physiol. Soc. Gastrointestinal physiology; gastroenterology; pancreas; digestion. Address: Faculty of Science, University of Sherbrooke, Sherbrooke, Que, Can.

DUNNING, CHARLES A(LEXANDER), b. Baltimore, Md, March 5, 16; m. 39; c. 5. ORGANIC CHEMISTRY. A.B, Hopkins, 37, Ph.D.(chem), 40. Res. chemist, HYNSON, WESTCOTT & DUNNING, 40-50, SECY-TREAS, 50- Am. Chem. Soc. Pharmaceutical chemicals. Address: Charles & Chase Sts, Baltimore, MD 21201.

DUNNING, D(OROTHY) COVALT, b. Wash, D.C, Jan. 1, 37; m. 60. BIOLOGY, ANIMAL BEHAVIOR. B.A, Middlebury Col, 58; M.A, Mt. Holyoke Col, 60; Nat. Insts. Health fel. & Ph.D.(biol), Tufts Univ, 66. Teaching fel. biol, Tufts Univ, 66-67; scholar. animal behav, Max Planck Inst. Physiol. of Behav, 67; instr. zool, Duke Univ, 68-69; ASST. PROF. BIOL, W.VA. UNIV, 69- AAAS; Am. Soc. Zool; Am. Soc. Mammal. Physiological mechanisms of animal behavior. Address: Dept. of Biology, West Virginia University, Morgantown, WV 26506.

DUNNING, ERNEST LEON, b. Ky, Nov. 13, 20; c. 2. MECHANICAL ENGINEERING. B.S.M.E, Univ. Rochester, 46; M.S.M.E, Univ. Ky, 50; Ph.D, Univ. Houston, 67. Instr. physics & math, Pikeville Col, 47-49; ASSOC. PROF. MECH. ENG, Evansville Col, 50-54; La. Polytech, 55-57; SOUTH. ILL. UNIV, CARBONDALE, 57- Summer, res. engr, Am. Mach. & Foundry Co, N.Y, 55; sch. indust. prog, Hughes Aircraft Co, 59. Consult, Schnacks Refrig. Co, 53-54; Christopher Unitemp Heating Co, 46-57. U.S.N, 42-46. Nat. Soc. Prof. Eng; Am. Soc. Mech. Eng; Am. Soc. Eng. Educ. Thermodynamics; heat transfer; refrigeration and air conditioning. Address: School of Engineering & Technology, Southern Illinois University, Carbondale, IL 62901.

DUNNING, GORDON MERRILL, b. Cortland, N.Y, Sept. 11, 10; m. 36; c. 2. HEALTH PHYSICS, SCIENCE EDUCATION. State Univ. N.Y. Col. Cortland, 29-32, 34-35; M.S, Syracuse, 41, Ed.D.(sci. ed), 48. Teacher, pub. schs, N.Y, 32-41; physics, N.Y. State Agr. & Tech. Inst, 47-48; Pa. State Teachers Col, 48-51; biophys. res. analyst, div. biol. & med, U.S. Atomic Energy Cmn, 51-57, chief radiation effects weapons br, 57-59; sci. adv, div. radiol. health, U.S. Pub. Health Serv, 59-60; asst. dir. off. health & safety, U.S. ATOMIC ENERGY COMN, 60-61, dep. dir. div. oper. safety, 61-68, tech. adv, 68-70, SR. SCIENTIST, OFF. ENVIRON. AFFAIRS, 70- Mem. U.S. del, Int. Conf. Peaceful Uses Atomic Energy, Switz, 55; faculty affiliate, Colo. State Univ, 67-68. Cert, Am. Bd. Health Physics, 60. U.S.A, 42-46, Lt. Col. Fel. AAAS; Health Physics Soc; Am. Asn. Physics Teachers; Nat. Asn. Res. Sci. Teaching; Nat. Sci. Teachers Asn. Developing criteria for radiation protection. Address: Office of Environmental Affairs, U.S. Atomic Energy Commission, Washington, DC 20545.

DUNNING, H(ENRY) A(RMITT) BROWN, JR, b. Baltimore, Md, Oct. 5, 09; m. 45, 52; c. 2. CHEMISTRY. Ph.D.(org. chem), Hopkins, 34. Res. chemist, HYNSON, WESTCOTT & DUNNING, 34-39, chief chemist & dir. chem. res. & control labs, 39-49, V.PRES, 49- Am. Chem. Soc. Organic medicinal chemicals; relation of physical to physiological properties. Address: 1912 Old Court Rd, Baltimore, MD 21204.

DUNNING, HENRY S(HANKLAND), b. Syracuse, N.Y, April 18, 05; m. 33; c. 2. CLINICAL NEUROLOGY. A.B, Cornell, 27, M.D, 30. Intern med, N.Y. Hosp, 30-32, asst. res. pathologist, 32-34; Nat. Res. Coun. fel, MED. COL, CORNELL UNIV, 34-35, instr. neurol, 36-37, 39-42, asst. prof. CLIN. NEUROL, 42-48, assoc. prof, 48-61, PROF, 61- Asst. res. neurologist, N.Y. Hosp, 35-36, neurologist to out-patients, 36-37, res. psychiatrist, 37-39, asst. attend. neurologist, 39-50, assoc. attend. neurologist, 50-63, attend. neurologist, 63- Dipl, Am. Bd. Psychiat. & Neurol. Am. Med. Asn; Am. Acad. Neurol. Neurology; neurohistology; neuropathology. Address: Cornell University Medical College, 1300 York Ave, New York, NY 10021.

DUNNING, H(ERBERT) NEAL, b. Hazard, Nebr, June 2, 23; m. 46; c. 1. PHYSICAL CHEMISTRY. B.S, Nebr. State Teachers Col, 44; Avery fel, Nebraska, 47-48, M.S, 48, du Pont fel, 48-49, Standard Oil Co. fel, 49-50, Ph.D.(phys. chem), 50. Asst. chem, Nebraska, 46-47; res. chemist, Standard Oil Co. Ind, 50-51; phys. chemist, petrol. exp. sta, sec. recovery br, U.S. Bur. Mines, 51-52; chief fundamental res. sect, region VI, 52-56, surface chem. sect. & nat. gas res. sect, prod. br, region IV, 56-60; head, chem. res. dept, GEN. MILLS, INC, 60-64, res. dir. explor. food processing, 64-70, TECH. DIR. QUAL. CONTROL, 70- Meritorious Serv. Award, U.S. Dept. Interior, 60. U.S.N.R, 44-46. AAAS; Am. Inst. Chem. Eng; Nat. Asn. Corrosion Eng; Am. Inst. Mining, Metall. & Petrol. Eng; Am. Chem. Soc. Surface and colloid chemistry; detergency; diffusion in aqueous media; hydrocarbon isomerization; physiochemical properties of porphyrins; fluid flow in porous media; gas-well behavior; gas flow and properties; irradiation damage; sedimentation; corrosion; textile finishes; natural gums; proprietary chemicals; ion exchange; food processing; chemical modification of foodstuffs; microwave energy; food engineering. Address: Quality Control Dept, General Mills, Inc, 9200 Wayzata Blvd, Minneapolis, MN 55440.

DUNNING, J(AMES) H(ENRY), FITZGERALD, b. Baltimore, Md, Aug. 26, 02; m. 26; c. 2. CHEMISTRY. A.B, Hopkins, 24, Ph.D.(chem), 27. Res. chemist, HYNSON, WESTCOTT & DUNNING, INC, 25-28, dir. chem. res, 28-35, secy-treas, 32-45, GEN. MGR, 41-, PRES, 45- Dir, Am. Found. Pharmaceut. Ed, 61-; mem, bd. dir, Keswick Home Incurables, 63- Trustee, Hopkins, 60-, chmn. vis. comt. sch. hyg. & pub. health. AAAS; Am. Chem. Soc; Am. Pharmaceut. Asn; Pharmaceut. Mfrs. Asn.(pres, Am. Drug Mfrs. Asn, 56-58). Chemotherapy; pharmaceutical and biological activity of chemicals; slow absorption of drugs. Address: Hynson, Westcott & Dunning, Inc, Charles & Chase Sts, Baltimore, MD 21201.

DUNNING, JAMES M(ORSE), b. New York, N.Y, Oct. 16, 04; m. 35; c. 2. DENTISTRY, PUBLIC HEALTH. A.B, Harvard, 26; D.D.S, Columbia, 30; M.P.H, Harvard, 47. Asst. oper. dent, dent. sch, Columbia, 30-35; dental dir, Metrop. Life Ins. Co, 35-45; dean, SCH. DENT. MED, HARVARD, 47-52, lectr. pub. health dent, 52-60, asst. clin. prof, 60-63, clin. prof. ECOL. DENT, 63-65, PROF, 65-, dir. dent. health serv, univ. health serv, Harvard-Radcliffe, 55-65. Private practice, 30-42, 52-65; pres, Dent. Health Serv, Inc, 41-45; consult, U.S. Pub. Health Serv. Hosp, Brighton, Mass, 60- Mem. comn. dent, Nat. Res. Coun, 47-51. Lemuel Shattuck Award, Mass. Pub. Health Asn, 62. U.S.N.R, 42-45, Lt. Comdr. Am. Dent. Asn; fel. Am. Col. Dent; fel. Am. Pub. Health Asn. Principles of dental public health; epiedemiology of dental caries; dental education; industrial dental service. Address: 23 Buckingham St, Cambridge, MA 02138.

DUNNING, JOHN R(AY), b. Shelby, Nebr, Sept. 24, 07; m. 30; c. 2. PHYSICS. A.B, Nebr. Wesleyan, 29, hon. Sc.D, 45; fel, Columbia, 32-33, Ph.D. (physics), 34; hon. LL.D, Adelphi Col, 51, Phila. Col. Osteop, 61; hon. Sc.D, Temple, 55, Whitman Col, 58, Trinity Col, 58; hon. D.Sc.Ed, Col. Puget Sound, 57. Asst. physics, COLUMBIA UNIV, 29-32, instr, 33-35, asst. prof, 35-38, assoc. prof, 38-46, prof, 46-69, dean faculty eng. & appl. sci, 50-69, THAYER LINDSLEY PROF. APPL. SCI. & PRES. INST, 69- Cutting traveling fel, Columbia, 35-36, off. investr, Ofr. Sci. Res. & Develop, 41, dir. div. I, Substitute Alloy Mat. Labs, 42-45, res, Div. War Res, 45-46, sci. dir, 46-50, dir. sci. res, 50- Pres, Hall Sci. City of New York, 65-; Atomic Pioneers, Inc, Chmn. cmt. nuclear energy glossary, Am. Soc. Mech. Engrs. & Nat. Res. Coun, 47-; chmn, Basic Sci. Found; mem. sci. adv. panel, U.S. Dept. Army; div. cmt. math, phys. eng. sci, Nat. Sci. Found, 58; chmn, Empire State Atomic Develop. Assocs, 63-; N.Y. State Sci. Adv. Coun. to Legis, 63-; President's Cmt. Super Sonic Transport-Sonic Boom, 64- Spec. rep, Manhattan Dist, Bikini, 46. Mem. bd. dirs, Oak Ridge Inst. Nuclear Studies, 50-; Vitro Corp, 50-; City Invest. Co, 57; Sci. Serv, 58. With Nat. Bur. Standards, 44. Nat. Acad. Sci; fel. AAAS; fel. Am. Phys. Soc.(v.pres, 51); Am. Soc. Eng. Educ; Inst. Elec. & Electronics Eng; Am. Optical Soc; Am. Asn. Physics Teachers; N.Y. Acad. Sci; Am. Soc. Mech. Eng; Am. Inst. Mining, Metall. & Petrol. Eng. Matter, energy and radiation; nuclear physics; production of high energy particles; neutrons; energy release in uranium fission. Address: 164 Engineering Terr, Columbia University, 520 W. 120th St, New York, NY 10027.

DUNNING, JOHN RAY, JR, b. N.Y.C, Nov. 26, 37. PHYSICS. B.S, Yale, 60, Carnegie fel. & M.S, 61; Nat. Sci. Found. fel, Harvard, 61-65, Ph.D.(physics), 65. Lectr. PHYSICS, Harvard, 65-66, instr, 66-68, res. fel. & lectr, 68-69; ASST. PROF, SONOMA STATE COL, 69- AAAS; Am. Phys. Soc. High energy experimental physics, especially the electromagnetic structure of nucleons and mesons. Address: Dept. of Physics, Sonoma State College, 265 College View Dr, Rohnert Park, CA 94928.

DUNNING, JOHN W(ALCOTT), b. Ottumwa, Iowa, Dec. 20, 12; m. 39; c. 3. ORGANIC CHEMISTRY. B.S, Iowa State Col, 35, Parke, Davis & Co. fel, 35-37; Ph.D.(biophys. chem), 38. Lab. & pilot plant dir, Anderson Clayton & Co, 37-42; chemist, north. regional res. lab, bur. agr. & indust. chem, U.S. Dept. Agr, 42-44, in charge synthetic liquid fuels proj, 44-48; dir. res, V.D. ANDERSON CO, 48-53, v.pres, 53-64, PRES, 64- Am. Chem. Soc; Am. Oil Chem. Soc. Saccharification; industrial fermentation; pyrolysis; esterification; pulping; pilot plant developments; bacterial oxydations; vitamin C synthesis; vegetable oils; vegetable seed processing; finish drying of synthetic rubber. Address: V.D. Anderson Co, 19699 Progress Dr, Strongsville, OH 44136.

DUNNING, K(ENNETH) L(AVERNE), b. Yale, Iowa, Sept. 24, 14; m. 41; c. 4. NUCLEAR & ATOMIC PHYSICS. B.E.E, Univ. Minn, 38; M.S, Univ. Md, 50; Ph.D, Cath. Univ. Am, 68. Communications engr, West. Union Tel. Co, 38-41; electron. scientist, NAVAL RES. LAB, 45-50, physicist, 50-51, HEAD VAN DE GRAAFF BR, NUCLEAR SCI. DIV, 51- Sig.C, 41-45, Maj. Am. Phys. Soc; Sci. Res. Soc. Am. Centimeter and millimeter wave guide components; Cockroft-Walton accelerators; nuclear weapons tests; Van de Graaff accelerators; nuclear interactions; ion-induced x-rays; charged particle energy loss; surface analysis; computer programming; nuclear instrumentation. Address: Code 6670, Nuclear Sciences Division, Naval Research Lab, Washington, DC 20390.

DUNNING, RANALD G(ARDNER), b. Thornton, Ohio, Oct. 6, 02; m. 37; c. 2. CHEMICAL ENGINEERING. B.S, Princeton, 24, A.M, 25; S.M, Mass. Inst. Tech, 27. Chem. engr, Roessler & Hasslacher Chem. Co, N.J, 26-31; develop. engr, Barber Asphalt Co, 31-38; chem. engr, Merck & Co, Inc, 38-40, process develop. head, 40-45, res. proj. analyst, 45-49, tech. asst, office of sci. dir, 49-53, sci. admin. div, 53-57; mgr. res. & develop, Metalwash Mach. Co, N.J, 57; chief engr, Chemirad Corp, 59-66; CONSULT. CHEM. ENGR, 66- Am. Chem. Soc; Am. Inst. Chem. Eng; Chem. Mkt. Res. Asn. Equilibrium in the synthesis and decomposition of methanol. Address: 227 Tuttle Pkwy, Westfield, NJ 07090.

DUNNING, ROBERT L(EWIS), b. Portland, Ore, Jan. 18, 31; m. 52; c. 4. PHYSICAL CHEMISTRY, RHEOLOGY. B.S, Lewis & Clark Col, 54; fel, Ore. State Univ, 55, M.S, 56. Asst. chem, Ore. State Univ, 54; res. chemist, rubber div, Shell Chem. Corp, 56-62; sr. engr, Nortronics Div, Northrop Corp, 62; sales engr, Instron Eng, 62-63; mgr. spec. proj, res. & develop. dept, DOUGLAS OIL CO, PARAMOUNT, 63-64, mgr. appl. res, 64-66, mgr. res. & develop, 66-70, coord. profit optimization, planning dept, 70-71, PROJ. COORD, RES. & DEVELOP. DEPT, 71- U.S.A.F, 51-52, Res, 54-60, Capt.(Ret), Am. Chem. Soc; Soc. Rheol; Asn. Asphalt Paving Technol; Opers. Res. Soc. Am. The rheology and other physical properties of viscoelastic materials, especially elastomers and asphalt; the rheology and colloid chemistry of aqueous emulsions of asphalt and of latices of elastomers; kinetics of oxidation of asphalt. Address: 2743 W. Broadway, Anaheim, CA 92804.

DUNNING, THOM(AS) H(AROLD), JR, b. Jeffersonville, Ind, Aug. 3, 43; m. 61; c. 2. THEORETICAL CHEMISTRY. B.S, Univ. Mo-Rolla, 65; Woodrow Wilson fel, Calif. Inst Technol, 65-66, Nat. Sci. Found. fel, 66-69, Ph.D.(chem), 70. Scientist, Monsanto Co, summers 65, 66 & 67; fel, Battelle Mem. Inst, 70-71; RES. FEL, A.A. NOYES LAB. CHEM. PHYSICS, CALIF. INST. TECHNOL, 71- Am. Phys. Soc. Molecular quantum mechanics; electronic structure of atoms and molecules; interaction of atomic and molecular systems. Address: 631 Palm View Pl, Pasadena, CA 91101.

DUNNING, W(ILHELMINA) F(RANCES), b. Topsham, Maine, Sept. 12, 04. PATHOLOGY. A.B, Maine, 26, hon. D.Sc, 60; M.A, Columbia, 28, Ph.D. (zool), 32. Asst, inst. cancer res, Columbia, 26-30, assoc, 30-41; instr. path, col. med. Wayne, 41-48, asst. prof. oncol, 48-50, res. assoc, 45-50; Detroit Inst. Cancer Res, 46-50; prof. zool, UNIV. MIAMI, 50-52; RES. PROF. EXP. PATH, 52-65, DEPT. MED, 65-; RES. ASSOC, PAPANICOLAOU CANCER RES. INST, 71- AAAS; Am. Asn. Cancer Res; Genetics Soc. Am; Am. Soc. Zool; N.Y. Acad. Sci. Mammalian genetics; experimental pathology; nutrition and cancer; endocrinology and genetics in experimental cancer. Address: Papanicolaou Cancer Research Institute, 1155 14th St, Miami, FL 33136.

DUNNINGAN, ARTHUR PAUL, b. Pylesville, Md, Feb. 3, 08; m. 46; c. 1. BACTERIOLOGY. B.S, Maryland, 30, M.S, 32, Ph.D.(bact), 36; fel, Harvard, 39-40, M.P.H, 40. Asst. bact, Maryland, 30-36; asst, bur. animal indust, U.S. Dept. Agr, 36; bacteriologist, State Dept. Health, Minn, 36-42; assoc. microbiologist & acting chief, BACT. BR, DIV. MICROBIOL, FOOD & DRUG ADMIN, FED. SECURITY AGENCY, 46-, DEPT. HEALTH, ED. & WELFARE, 53-70, LAB. SURV. OFF, LAB. DEVELOP. PROG, 70- Sanit.C, 42-46, Capt. Assoc. Am. Soc. Microbiol; assoc. Am. Pub. Health Asn. Dairy and food bacteriology; public health; communicable diseases; factors affecting growth of Lactobacilli; anaerobes; microbiology of cosmetics. Address: Division of Microbiology, Food & Drug Administration, 200 C St. S.W, Washington, DC 20204.

DUNNINGTON, BRUCE (WILLARD), b. Lore City, Ohio, Nov. 26, 24; m. 49; c. 2. METALLURGY. B.Met, Ohio State, 48, Met.E, 49, Ph.D.(metall), 51. Sr. res. supvr, Savannah River Plant Proj, E.I. du Pont de Nemours & Co, 51-57; consult. physics dept, Battelle Mem. Inst, 57-63; mem. res. staff, E.I. du Pont de Nemours & Co, 63-68; PRES, GLENNEL CORP, 68- U.S.A.A.F, 42-45, 2nd Lt. Am. Soc. Metals. Materials studies of nuclear and space systems; new applications of explosives. Address: Glennel Corp, 908 Chickadee Lane, West Chester, PA 19380.

DUNNINGTON, FRANK G(LASS), b. Colorado Springs, Colo, May 7, 03; m. 44; c. 2. PHYSICS. B.S, California, 29, Ph.D.(physics), 32. Nat. Res. fel. PHYSICS, Calif. Inst. Tech, 32-35, res. fel, 35-37; asst. prof, RUTGERS UNIV, 37-45, assoc. prof, 45-46, prof, 46-68, chmn. dept, 46-52, proj. dir, radiol. health training prog, 61-68, dir. radiation sci. ctr, 66-68, EMER. PROF, 68- Mem. staff, radiation lab, Mass. Inst. Tech, 41-45. V.chmn, Governor's Adv. Cmt. Radiation Protection, N.J, 55-57; chmn, N.J. Comn. Radiation Protection, 58-69; mem, Conf. Radiol. Health. With Nat. Defense Res. Comt, 41-44. Fel. Am. Phys. Soc; Am. Asn. Physics Teachers; Health Phys. Soc. Electro optical shutters; spark breakdown; specific charge of electron; atomic constants; low temperature and nuclear physics. Address: 445 Wedgewood Dr, Port Richey, FL 33568.

DUNNY, STANLEY, b. Northampton, Mass, Aug. 2, 39. ORGANIC & ORGANOMETALLIC CHEMISTRY. B.S, Univ. Mass, 61; M.S, Univ. Wis, 63; Ethyl Corp fel, Purdue Univ, 66-67, Ph.D.(chem), 67. Instr. CHEM, St. Michael's Col.(Vt), summer 67; asst. prof, HOLYOKE COMMUNITY COL, 69-70, ASSOC. PROF, 70- Am. Chem. Soc. Hydrosilylation of acetylenes via amine catalysis; organosilicon chemistry; synthesis of rings containing silicon atoms. Address: 142 Crescent St, Northampton, MA 01060.

DUNPHY, DONAL, b. Northampton, Mass, Feb. 24, 17; m. 44; c. 3. PEDIATRICS. B.A, Col. Holy Cross, 39; M.D, Yale, 44. Instr. pediat, sch. med, Yale, 47-50; attend. pediatrician, Bridgeport Gen. Hosp, 50-53; assoc. pediatrician, sch. med, Buffalo, 55-56, asst. prof. PEDIAT, Buffalo Children's Hosp, 56-59, assoc. prof, 59-61; PROF. & HEAD DEPT, COL. MED, UNIV. IOWA, 61- Fel. cardiol, dept. pediat, sch. med, Yale, 50-52. Dir, pediat. out-clin, Buffalo Children's Hosp, 55-61, child develop. study, 55-59, Nat. Insts. Health Collab. Proj, 58-61. Pediat. consult, Nat. Insts. Neurol. Diseases & Blindness, 60-61. Med. Dept, 53-55, Capt. AAAS; Am. Pediat. Soc; N.Y. Acad. Sci; Am. Acad. Pediat; Asn. Am. Med. Cols. Cord blood gas analysis in twins; factors affecting neurological status of children and methods for early recognition; plasmin in the therapy of hyaline membrane disease. Address: Dept. of Pediatrics, University of Iowa, College of Medicine, Iowa City, IA 52240.

DUNPHY, EDWIN B(LAKESLEE), b. Newark, N.J, Dec. 26, 95; m. 23; c. 2. OPHTHALMOLOGY. A.B, Princeton, 18; M.D, Harvard, 22. Asst. instr, HARVARD MED. SCH, 25-35, instr, 35-40, prof, 40-47, Williams clin. prof, 47-49, Williams prof. OPHTHAL, 49-62, head dept, 40-62, EMER. WILLIAMS PROF, 62-, OPHTHALMOLOGIST, HEALTH SERV, 63-; CHIEF OPHTHAL, MASS. EYE & EAR INFIRMARY, 40-, clin. asst, 24-27, asst. surgeon, 27-32, surgeon, 32-40. Mem. cmt. ophthal, Nat. Res. Coun, 47-; ophthal. postgrad. training grant cmt, Nat. Insts. Health, 56-60; secy, Am. Bd. Ophthal, 47-55. U.S.N.R, 42-45, Capt. Pan-Am. Med. Asn; Royal Soc. Med; Am. Med. Asn.(ophthal. res. medal); Am. Ophthal. Soc.(v.pres, 59-60, pres, 60, Howe Medal); Am. Acad. Ophthal. & Otolaryngol.(pres, 64-75); Am. Col. Surg; Am. Orthoptic Coun.(secy-treas, 38-40). Management of ocular malignancy; use of radioactive isotopes in ocular tumor diagnosis. Address: 75 Mt. Auburn St, Cambridge, MA 02138.

DUNPHY, J. ENGLEBERT, b. Northampton, Mass, Mar. 31, 08; m. 36; c. 4. MEDICINE, SURGERY. A.B, Col. Holy Cross, 29, hon. D.Sc, 64; M.D, Harvard Med. Sch, 33; hon. L.H.D, Seton Hall, 64. Clin. prof. SURG, Harvard, 53-55, prof, 55-59; PROF. SURG. & CHMN. DEPT, med. sch, Oregon, 59-64; SCH. MED, UNIV. CALIF, SAN FRANCISCO, 64- Consult, U.S. Vet. Admin. Hosps, 46-; Surgeon Gen, U.S. Army, 54-; dir, Sears Surg. Lab. & Fifth surg. serv, Boston City Hosp, 55-59. Dipl, Am. Bd. Surg; hon. fel, Royal Col. Surg. Med.C, U.S.A, 42-46. Asn. Am. Med. Cols; fel. Am. Col. Surg; Soc. Univ. Surg; Am. Surg. Asn; Am. Med. Asn; Am. Acad. Arts & Sci; Royal Soc. Med; Int. Soc. Surg. Studies of sound healing; biology of cancer; pancreatic and biliary pathophysiology. Address: Dept. of Surgery, University of California School of Medicine, San Francisco, CA 94122.

DUNPHY, JAMES F(RANCIS), b. Boston, Mass, May 16, 30; m. 61; c. 3. ORGANIC CHEMISTRY. B.S, Boston Col, 51; Ph.D.(org. chem), Illinois, 60. Chemist, Nat. Starch & Chem. Corp, 52-57; res. chemist, film dept, Yerkes Res. & Develop. Lab, E.I. DU PONT DE NEMOURS & CO, INC, 59-67, STAFF SCIENTIST, 67-70, TECUMSEH FILM PLANT, 70- U.S.A, 53-55. AAAS; Am. Chem. Soc. Organic chemistry of high polymers; monomer synthesis; preparation and characterization of addition and condensation polymers; development of thermally stable polymers; adhesives; polymerization catalysis. Address: Tecumseh Film Plant, E.I. du Pont de Nemours & Co, Inc, P.O. Box 481, Topeka, KS 66601.

DUNSHEE, BRYANT R, b. Des Moines, Iowa, Mar. 13, 21; m. 49; c. 3. BIOCHEMISTRY. B.S, Michigan, 42; Ph.D.(biochem), Wisconsin, 49. Supvr. prods, Hercules Powder Co, 42-45; instr. physiol. chem, Minnesota, 49-52; sr. biochemist food res, cent. res. lab, GEN. MILLS, INC, 52-57, sect. leader food develop. dept, 57-62, RES. ASSOC. FOOD DEVELOP. ACTIV-

ITY, JAMES FORD BELL RES. CTR, 62- Am. Chem. Soc; Inst. Food Tech. Packaged food mixes; ingredient testing, formulation and baking evaluation. Address: James Ford Bell Research Center, General Mills, Inc, 9000 Plymouth Ave. N, Minneapolis, MN 55427.

DUNSKI, NAPHTALI (NEIL), b. Tel Aviv, Israel, Jan. 18, 38; U.S. citizen; m. 63; c. 2. ORGANOMETALLIC & POLYMER CHEMISTRY. B.S, Univ. Louisville, 64, Ph.D.(phys. org. chem), 68. Asst. chem, Univ. Louisville, 67-68; RES. CHEMIST, UNION CARBIDE CORP, 68- Israeli Army, 55-60, Lt. Am. Chem. Soc. Investigation of new inorganic coordination polymers; new catalysts for the polymerization of unsaturated alpha-olefins; acrylate rubbers; ethylene-propylene diene monomer rubber; urethane elastomers. Address: Chemicals & Plastics Research & Development, Union Carbide Corp, P.O. Box 8361, South Charleston, WV 25303.

DUNSMORE, HERBERT J, b. Ionia, Mich, Sept. 9, 10; m. 33; c. 2. ENVIRONMENTAL HEALTH. B.S, Mich. State, 33; M.P.H, Michigan, 47. Asst. soils engr, Mich. State Hwy. Dept, 35-38; pub. health engr, Calhoun County Health Dept. & W.K. Kellogg Found, 38-48; chief environ. health, health dept, City of Pittsburgh, 48-56; environ. health eng, Health Dept, Allegheny County, 57-60, bur. air pollution control, 60-65; asst. to admin. v.pres. eng, U.S. STEEL CORP, 65-69, DIR. ENVIRON. CONTROL, 69- Chmn, Munic. Conf. Pub. Health Eng, 50; mem. bd. consult, Nat. Sanit. Found, Univ. Mich, 50; consult, Pub. Health Serv. Adv. Comt. Food Sanit, 57-61; mem. coun. tech. adv, Air Pollution Comn. Pa, 63-64; President's Task Force on Air Pollution, 70. U.S.P.H.S, 55-, Sanit. Eng. Dir. Air Pollution Control Asn. Environmental engineering; air and stream pollution control. Address: 9 New Brighton Rd, Pittsburgh, PA 15202.

DUNSON, WILLIAM ALBERT, b. Cedartown, Ga, Dec. 17, 41; m. 63; c. 2. COMPARATIVE PHYSIOLOGY, MARINE BIOLOGY. B.S, Yale, 62; Nat. Insts. Health trainee, Michigan, 63-65, M.S, 64, Nat. Insts. Health fel. & Ph.D.(zool), 65. Teaching fel. zool. & cell physiol, Michigan, 62-63; ASSOC. PROF. BIOL, PA. STATE UNIV, 65- Sr. scientist, Stanford Univ, 68; Nat. Sci. Found. grants, 68-; chief scientist Res/Vessel Alpha Helix, Scripps Inst. Oceanog, 70. AAAS; Am. Physiol. Soc; Cooper Ornith Soc; Am. Soc. Ichthyol. & Herpet; Am. Soc. Zool; Am. Soc. Limnol. & Oceanog. Comparative and environmental physiology, particularly in relation to ionic and osmotic regulation and ion transport; salt glands; active transport across epithelia; hereditary fluid imbalances in chickens and axolotls. Address: Dept. of Biology, Life Sciences Bldg, Pennsylvania State University, University Park, PA 16802.

DUNSTON, JOYCE M(ARILYN REDDOCH), b. Toronto, Ont, Dec. 27, 38; m. 70. ORGANIC CHEMISTRY. B.Sc, Toronto, 61, M.A, 62, Ph.D.(org. chem), 66. Res. assoc, Cornell, 66, fel, Carleton (Can), 66-67, fel. & spec. lectr, 67-68, asst. prof. chem, 68-69; vis. scientist, div. biol, NAT. RES. COUN, 69, fel. DIV. CHEM, 69-71, GUEST WORKER, 71- Structural and synthetic organic chemistry and photochemistry. Address: Division of Chemistry, National Research Council, Ottawa, Ont, K1A 0R6, Can.

DUNTLEY, SEIBERT Q(UIMBY), b. Bushnell, Ill, Oct. 2, 11; m. 37; c. 3. PHYSICS. B.S, Mass. Inst. Tech, 33, Sc.D.(physics), 39; M.S, Calif. Inst. Tech, 35. Asst. physics, Calif. Inst. Tech, 33-34; teaching fel, Mass. Inst. Tech, 37-39, instr, 39-42, asst. prof, 42-52; assoc. res. physicist & dir, VISIBILITY LAB, SCRIPPS INST, UNIV. CALIF, 52-54, RES. PHYSICIST & DIR, 54-, PROF, 66- Consult & physicist, Work Projs. Admin, 40-42; consult, Gen. Elec. Co, 46-51; bur. ships, U.S. Dept. Navy, 49-68. Consult, U.S.A.F, 42; tech. aide, Nat. Defense Res. Comt. & Off. Sci. Res. & Develop, 42-46. Army Navy cert. appreciation. Illum. Eng. Soc; fel. Optical Soc. Am.(dir, 58-61; Ives Medalist, 61; pres, 65 & 66). Design of optical instruments; spectrophotometry; goniophotometry; colorimetry; photometry; optical properties of diffusing materials; spectrophotometry of living human skin; atmospheric optics; visibility; hydrologic optics; vision in space; remote sensing. Address: Scripps Institution of Oceanography, University of California, La Jolla, CA 92037.

DUNTON, ERNEST MAPP, JR, b. Exmore, Va, Jan. 30, 12; m. 59. AGRONOMY. B.S, Va. Polytech, 33, M.S, 37; Ph.D.(soil fertility), Cornell, 42. Instr, high sch, Va, 33-35; asst. agronomist, Tenn. Valley Authority, exp. sta, Va. Polytech, 36-38; asst. soils, Cornell, 38-42; agronomist, East. States Farmers Exchange, Mass, 42; soil technologist, VA. TRUCK & ORNAMENTALS RES. STA, 46-66, SCIENTIST IN CHARGE, 66- U.S.A, 42-45. AAAS; Am. Soc. Agron; Soil Sci. Soc. Am. Fertilizers; soil testing; liming vegetable corps. Address: Virginia Truck & Ornamentals Research Station, Painter, VA 23350.

DUNTON, H(ENRY) L(ANKFORD), b. Exmore, Va, Sept. 17, 08; m. 34; c. 2. AGRONOMY. B.S, Va. Polytech, 29; M.S, Mich. State Col, 33, Ph.D.(soils), 49. County agent, Va. Polytech, 29-31; asst. crop management, Mich. State Col, 31-34; erosion specialist, U.S. Dept. Agr, 34-35; asst. prof. exten. agron, VA. POLYTECH INST, 35-39, assoc. prof. exten. conserv, 39-43, prof, emergency farm labor prog, 43-45, exten. agron, 46-47, prof. AGRON. & head dept, 48-70, EMER. PROF, 70- Crop management. Address: Dept. of Agronomy, Virginia Polytechnic Institute, Blacksburg, VA 24060.

DUNTON, MARGUERITE ELIZABETH, b. Underhill, Wis, July 8, 25; m. 58. MATHEMATICS. Ph.B, Wisconsin, 47; M.A, Radcliffe Col, 54; Ph.D.(math), Colorado, 60. Asst. math, Wisconsin, 47-48; analyst, U.S. Dept. Defense, 50-53; mathematician, Gen. Dynamics/Convair, 53; asst. prof, MATH, Univ. Colo, 60-61; SACRAMENTO STATE COL, 61-69, ASSOC. PROF, 69- Summer staff mem, Lincoln Lab, 57-58. Am. Math. Soc; Math. Asn. Am. Diophantine equations; cubic congruences; number theory. Address: Division of Science & Mathematics, Sacramento State College, 6000 J. St, Sacramento CA 95819.

DUNTON, MYRON L, b. Smith Center, Kans, Nov. 15, 30; m. 53; c. 2. ANALYTICAL CHEMISTRY. B.S, Kansas State, 52; M.S, Ohio State, 53, Ph.D. (anal. chem), 56. Res. chemist anal. geochem, Jersey Prod. Res. Co, Okla, 58-65; SR. RES. SCIENTIST ANAL. CHEM, AMOCO PROD. CO, 65- U.S.A.F, 56-58, Capt. Am. Chem. Soc; Geochem. Soc. Gas chromatographic and spectrophotometric methods development applied to geochemical petroleum exploration. Address: Amoco Production Co, P.O. Box 591, Tulsa, OK 74102.

DUNWORTH, W(ILLIAM) P(AUL), b. N.Y.C, Jan. 19, 25; m. 47; c. 3. ORGANIC CHEMISTRY. B.S, Fordham Univ, 47, M.S, 49, Ph.D.(phys. chem), 52. Fel, Mellon Inst, 52-54; chemist, E.I. DU PONT DE NEMOURS & CO, 54-70, SR. RES. CHEMIST, 70- U.S.A.A.F, 43-46. Dyes; petroleum additives. Address: 1416 Drake Rd, Wilmington, DE 19803.

DUPERTUIS, C(LARENCE) WESLEY, b. Yacolt, Wash, June 2, 07; m. 34; c. 2. ANTHROPOLOGY. B.S, Harvard, 29, M.A, 31, Ph.D.(phys. anthrop), 40. Asst. anthrop, Harvard, 32-34, dir. racial surv, Ireland, 34-36; res. assoc. constitutional med, col. physicians & surgeons, Columbia, 36-48; assoc. prof. CLIN. ANTHROP, SCH. MED, CASE WEST. RESERVE UNIV, 48-67, PROF, 67- Consult, U.S. Air Force, 51- Am. Asn. Phys. Anthrop. Clinical anthropology; constitutional medicine; somatotyping. Address: Room 143-7, School of Medicine, Case Western Reserve University, 2119 Abington Rd, Cleveland, OH 44106.

DUPLER, DONALD A, b. Chicago, Ill, Nov. 19, 14; m. 43; c. 2. MEDICINE. B.S, Juniata Col, 36; M.D, Harvard, 40. ASST. PROF. CARDIOL, SCH. MED, UNIV. PA, 53-, CHIEF MED. & CLIN. CARDIOL, PRESBY. HOSP, 60-; CHIEF CARDIOL, LANKENAU HOSP, 70- Med.C, U.S.N, 43-47. Am. Col. Physicians; Am. Col. Cardiol; Am. Soc. Internal Med. Cardiology. Address: 4028 Walnut St, Philadelphia, PA 19104.

DUPONT, CLAIRE HAMMEL, b. Wash, D.C, Apr. 27, 33; m. 66; c. 2. BIOCHEMISTRY, PEDIATRICS. Cornell Univ, 51-54; M.D, George Washington Univ, 58; Ph.D.(biochem), Univ. Md, 64. Intern, Phila. Gen. Hosp, Pa, 58-59; resident pediat, Children's Hosp. D.C, 59-61; spec. fel, Nat. Inst. Neurol. Diseases & Blindness extra-mural prog, sch. med, Univ. Md, 61-64, asst. prof. pediat. res, 64-66, pediat. & biochem, summer 66; biochem, faculty med, Univ. Montreal, 66-71; ASST. DIR. BIOCHEM, MONTREAL CHILDREN'S HOSP, 71- Asst, sch. med, George Washington Univ, 60-61. AAAS; Soc. Pediat. Res; fel. Am. Acad. Pediat; Can. Biochem. Soc. Nuclear protein synthesis; hemoglobin synthesis and its regulation by heme and oxygen. Address: Dept. of Biochemistry, Montreal Children's Hospital, Montreal, Que, Can.

DUPONT, JACQUELINE (LOUISE), b. Plant City, Fla, Mar. 4, 34. NUTRITION, BIOCHEMISTRY. B.S, Fla. State, 55, Mead Johnson award & Nat. Sci. Found. fel, 61, Ph.D.(nutrit), 62; M.S, Iowa State, 59. Home economist, human nutrit. res. div, U.S. Dept. Agr, 55-56, nutrit. specialist, 56-62, res. nutrit. specialist, 62-64; asst. prof. biochem, col. med, Howard, 64-66; FOOD SCI. & NUTRIT, COLO. STATE UNIV, 66-69, ASSOC. PROF, 69- Am. Dietetic Asn; Am. Oil Chem. Soc; Am. Inst. Nutrit. Effects of dietary fat upon metabolism of cholesterol and fatty acids; bio-oxidation of unsaturated fatty acids. Address: 3625 Terry Ridge Rd, Ft. Collins, CO 80521.

DU PONT, JOHN ELEUTHERE, b. Phila, Pa, Nov. 22, 38. ORNITHOLOGY, MALACOLOGY. B.S, Univ. Miami, 62; hon. Sc.D, Villanova Univ, 71. DIR, DEL. MUS. NATURAL HIST, 57- Nat. Audubon Soc; Am. Ornith. Union; Brit. Ornith. Union; Am. Soc. Mammal. Taxonomy and zoogeography of birds, with emphasis on those from the Philippines and southeast Asia; taxonomy of marine mollusks, with emphasis on the family Volutidae. Address: Delaware Museum of Natural History, P.O. Box 3937, Greenville, DE 19807

DUPONT, PAUL E(MILE), b. Chicopee, Mass, Aug. 21, 41; m. 63; c. 2. ORGANIC CHEMISTRY. B.S, Massachusetts, 63; Ph.D.(chem), Rensselaer Polytech, 68. Asst. res. chemist, STERLING-WINTHROP RES. INST, 63-68, ASSOC. RES. CHEMIST, 68- Am. Chem. Soc. Organic reaction mechanisms; synthesis of heterocyclic compounds. Address: Sterling-Winthrop Research Institute, Rensselaer, NY 12144.

DUPONT, TODD, b. Houston, Tex, Aug. 29, 42; m. 64; c. 2. NUMERICAL ANALYSIS. B.A, Rice Univ, 63, Ph.D.(math), 69. Res. mathematician, Esso Prod. Res. Co, 67-68; instr. MATH, UNIV. CHICAGO, 68-69, ASST. PROF, 69- Am. Math. Soc; Soc. Indust. & Appl. Math. Numerical solution of partial differential equations; nonlinear boundary-value problems. Address: Dept. of Mathematics, University of Chicago, Chicago, IL 60637.

DuPRAW, ERNEST J(OSEPH), b. Los Angeles, Calif, May 16, 31; m. 55; c. 5. CELL & MOLECULAR BIOLOGY. B.S, Notre Dame, 53; M.A, Columbia, 55, univ. fel, 55-56, U.S. Pub. Health Serv. fel, 56-57, Ph.D.(zool), 58. Asst. prof. biol, Florida, 57-61; U.S. Pub. Health Serv. fel, 60-61; asst. prof. zool, California, Davis, 61-66; Nat. Sci. Found. sr. fel, Stanford Univ, 66-67; assoc. prof. cell biol, SCH. MED, Univ. Md, 67-69; fel, STANFORD UNIV, 69-71, ASSOC. PROF. ANAT, 71-, Chmn, Cell & Molecular Biol. Coun, 70- Am. Soc. Cell Biol; Int. Soc. Cell Biol; Soc. Gen. Physiol; Soc. Develop. Biol. Ultrastructure of chromosomes and nuclei; nuclear transplant; non-Linnean taxonomy. Address: Dept. of Anatomy, Stanford University School of Medicine, Stanford, CA 94305.

DU PRE, DONALD BATES, b. Houston, Tex, Mar. 17, 42; m. 64; c. 1. CHEMICAL PHYSICS. B.A, Rice Univ. 64; M.A, Princeton, 66, Woodrow Wilson Found. fel, 64-65, Nat. Insts. Health fel, 65-68, Ph.D.(chem), 68. Fel. chem. physics, sci. ctr, N.Am. Rockwell Corp, 68-69; ASST. PROF. CHEM, UNIV. LOUISVILLE, 69- Grants, Res. Corp. & Petrol. Res. Fund. Am. Phys. Soc. Laser light scattering spectroscopy; chemical physics of polymers and liquid crystals. Address: Dept. of Chemistry, University of Louisville, Louisville, KY 40208.

DUPRE, EDMUND J, b. New Bedford, Mass, Aug. 13, 12; m. 60. POLYMER CHEMISTRY. B.S, N.C. State Col, 48; M.Ed, Boston, 59; Manchester Tech. Col, 59. Colorist, Jeandors Dye & Print Works, 34-36; asst. dyer, U.S. Finishing Co, 36-38; textile chemist, Fruit of the Loom, Inc, 38-42; instr. textile chem, New Bedford Inst. Tech, 42; chemist, Better Fabrics Testing Bur, 43-45; instr. CHEM, SOUTHEAST. MASS. UNIV, 45-46, ASSOC. PROF, 48- U.S.A, 42-43, S/Sgt. Am. Asn. Textile Chem. & Colorists; Am. Soc.

Eng. Educ; fel. Am. Inst. Chem. Practical uses of synthetic polymeric hydrophilic colloids in the paper and textile industries. Address: Dept. of Textile Chemistry, Southeastern Massachusetts University, North Dartmouth, MA 02747.

DU PRE, F(RITS) K(AREL), b. The Hague, Holland, Oct. 21, 12; nat; m. 47; c. 2. PHYSICS. Ph.D.(physics), Leyden Univ.(Holland). RES. PHYSICIST, Philips Res. Labs, Eindhoven, Holland, 40-46, PHILIPS LABS, BRIARCLIFF MANOR, 46- Am. Phys. Soc. Cryogenics. Address: 14 Hazelton Dr, White Plains, NY 10605.

DUPRE, GERALD DENNIS, b. Central Falls, R.I, Apr. 16, 37; m. 61; c. 3. ANALYTICAL CHEMISTRY. B.S, Providence Col, 59; Ph.D.(org. chem), Univ. Conn, 63. From chemist to sr. res. chemist, anal. res. div, Esso Res. & Eng. Co. Inc, N.J, 62-69; sr. scientist, autolab div, Vidar Corp, Calif, 70; GROUP LEADER, AGR. CHEM. DIV, CIBA-GEIGY CORP, ARDSLEY, 71- Am. Chem. Soc. Petroleum resin and polymer studies; product quality and technical service; petroleum and petrochemical characterization by chromatographic techniques; method development for pesticides and their metabolites; compound characterization by instrumental methods; lab automation and data reduction from analytical instruments. Address: 5 Twin Peg Dr, New York, NY 10956.

DUPREE, DANIEL (EDWARD), b. Coushatta, La, Dec. 1, 32; m. 54; c. 1. MATHEMATICS. B.S, La. Polytech, 54; M.S, Auburn, 59, Ph.D.(math), 60. Asst. prof. math, Auburn, 60-61; chmn. dept, NORTHEAST LA. UNIV, 61-64, DEAN, COL. PURE & APPL. SCI, 64- Res. grants, Nat. Sci. Found, 63-64, Sigma Xi, 64-65. Consult, Marshall Space Flight Ctr, 61-62. U.S.A.F, 54-57, 1st Lt. Am. Math. Soc; Math. Asn. Am. Interpolation theory and multivariable approximation. Address: College of Pure & Applied Sciences, Northeast Louisiana University, Monroe, LA 71201.

DUPREE, LARTIUS TRESCOTT, b. Sumter, S.C, June 15, 26; m. 52; c. 6. BIOLOGY, PHYSIOLOGY. B.S, Morgan State Col, 55; Howard, 55-56; George Washington, 57-58. Training officer, Ord. Sch, Aberdeen Proving Grounds, Md, 56-57; biologist, lab. biol, Nat. Cancer Inst, 57-64; sr. biologist, Melpar, Inc, Va, 64-66; CELL BIOLOGIST, DEPT. MED. MICROBIOL, GULF SOUTH RES. INST, 67- Instr, La. State Univ, 67- U.S.A.F, 49-53, S/Sgt. Am. Soc. Trop. Med. & Hyg. Cell biology of mammalian and insect cells, tissue and organs in vitro, especially establishing primary and continuous cell lines, differentiation of normal from neoplastic cells and tissue and hormone production in vitro. Address: Gulf South Research Institute, 5010 Leroy Johnson Dr, New Orleans, LA 70126.

DuPUIS, ROBERT N(EWELL), b. Indianapolis, Ind, June 4, 10; m. 35; c. 2. CHEMISTRY. A.B, Illinois, 31; Ph.D.(org. chem), N.Y. Univ, 34. Res. chemist, Miner Labs, 35-45, asst. dir, 45-47; mgr. res. & develop, S.C. Johnson & Son, Inc, 47-52; dir. & res. v.pres, Philip Morris, Inc, 52-60; v.pres, Gen. Foods Corp, 60-67; INDUST. CONSULT, 67- Dir, Barrow Res. Labs, Inc, 68-71; rep, Coun. Libr. Resources; mem, Indust. Res. Inst. Am. Chem. Soc. Synthesis and uses of glycerine and derivatives; alkyd resins; waxes and wax products; paints, varnishes and enamels; tobacco, smoke and filters; food products and processes; permanence and durability of paper. Address: 3902 Exeter Rd, Richmond, VA 23221.

DUPUY, HAROLD P(AUL), b. Lockport, La, Sept. 10, 22. BIOCHEMISTRY. B.S, La. State, 50, M.S, 53, Ph.D.(biochem), 56. RES. CHEMIST, FATS & OILS, SOUTH. REGIONAL RES. LAB, 56- U.S.A.F, 43-45. Am. Chem. Soc; Am. Oil Chemists' Soc; Inst. Food Technol; Am. Inst. Chem. Lathyrism; fats and oils. Address: Southern Regional Research Lab, 1100 Robert E. Lee Blvd, New Orleans, LA 70119.

DUPUY, JOHN L, b. Paris, France, Jan. 10, 35; m; c. 1. MARINE SCIENCE. B.S, Oglethorpe Univ, 57; M.S, Rutgers Univ, 63; Ph.D, Univ. Wash, 68. Asst. gen. biol, Rutgers Univ, 60-62; res. assoc, col. fisheries, Univ. Wash, 63-68; ASSOC. MARINE SCIENTIST, VA. INST. MARINE SCI, 68-; ASST. PROF. MARINE SCI, COL. WILLIAM & MARY, 68-; UNIV. VA, 68- U.S. Pub. Health Serv. grant, 63-68; Shellfish Sanitation grant, 65-68. Marine ecology and culture. Address: Virginia Institute of Marine Science, Gloucester Point, VA 23062.

DUQUESNOY, RENE J, b. The Hague, Netherlands, May 24, 38; U.S. citizen; m. 68. IMMUNOLOGY. Ingenieur, Delft Technol. Univ, 63; Ph.D.(exp. path), Univ. Tenn, Memphis, 67. Res. assoc. path, med. units, Univ. Tenn, Memphis, 63-67; fel. pediat, Univ. Minn, 68-70; ASST. PROF. MICROBIOL, MED. COL. WIS, 70- Am. Soc. Exp. Path; Am. Asn. Immunol; Soc. Exp. Biol. & Med. Endocrine relationships of the immune system, particularly pituitary influences of thymus; effect of milk in the development and function of the lymphoid system. Address: Dept. of Microbiology, Medical College of Wisconsin, 561 N. 15th St, Milwaukee, WI 53233.

DUQUET, ROBERT THEODORE, b. Sherbrooke, Que, Can, Sept. 17, 29; nat; m. 52; c. 5. METEOROLOGY. B.Sc, Loyola (Can), 50; M.A, Toronto, 52; Ph.D, N.Y. Univ, 61. Meteorologist, meteorol. div, Can. Dept. Transport, 51-55; asst, N.Y. Univ, 55-58; asst. prof. meteorol, Pa. State, 58-64, assoc. prof, 64-68, COMPUT. SCI, State Univ. N.Y. Albany, 68-71; PROF. & COORD. COMPUT. ACTIVITIES, BOWLING GREEN STATE UNIV, 71- Am. Meteorol. Soc; Am. Geophys. Union; Royal Meteorol. Soc. Synoptic meteorology; numerical weather prediction. Address: Dept. of Computer Science, Bowling Green State University, Bowling Green, OH 43402.

DUQUETTE, ALFRED L, b. Troy, Vt, Oct. 14, 23; div. PHYSICAL SCIENCES, MATHEMATICS. B.S, Massachusetts, 48; A.M, Columbia, 50; Ph.D, Colorado, 60; Michigan, 63. Instr. math, Montana State, 50-52; asst. prof, St. John's, 52-54; instr, Colorado, 54-55; off. naval res. asst, Illinois, 58-60; asst. prof, Kentucky, 60-61; sr. scientist, Jet Propulsion Lab, 61-62; sr. mem. tech. staff, ITT Fed. Labs, Calif, 62-64; adv. engr, future comput. technol, IBM Space Guidance Ctr, 64-66; PROF. MATH, W.GA. COL, 66- Am. Math. Soc; Math. Asn. Am. Advanced computer development. Address: Dept. of Mathematics, West Georgia College, Carrollton, GA 30117.

DUQUETTE, DAVID J(OSEPH), b. Springfield, Mass, Nov. 4, 39; m. 61; c. 2. METALLURGY, MATERIALS SCIENCE. B.S, U.S. Coast Guard Acad, 61; Ph.D.(metall), Mass. Inst. Technol, 68. Res. asst. metall, corrosion lab, Mass. Inst. Technol, 65-68; res. assoc, adv. mat. res. & develop. lab, Pratt & Whitney Div, United Aircraft Corp, 68-70; ASST. PROF. MAT. SCI, RENSSELAER POLYTECH. INST, 70- U.S.C.G, 61-65, Lt. Am. Soc. Metals; Am. Inst. Min, Metall. & Petrol. Eng; Nat. Asn. Corrosion Eng. Corrosion science and engineering including the effect of environment on mechanical properties of crystalline materials; structure and properties of metallic meteorites. Address: Materials Division, Rensselaer Polytechnic Institute, Troy, NY 12181.

DURACHTA, CHESTER W(ILLIAM), b. Chicago, Ill, Dec. 22, 25; m. 55; c. 5. BIOLOGY, MICROBIOLOGY. B.S, Northwestern, 50, M.S, 53, Ph.D.(parasitol), 57. Lab. instr. biol, Northwestern, 54-56; technician toxicol, cardiovasc. physiol. & hemat, G.D. Searle & Co, 52-57; sr. scientist res. & develop, Smith Kline & French, Phila, 57-61; DIR. TECH. INFO. SERVS, MEAD JOHNSON & CO, 61- U.S.N, 44-46, Res, 49-52, Sgt. AAAS; Am. Soc. Info. Sci; Am. Med. Writers' Asn; N.Y. Acad. Sci; Am. Soc. Zool. Electronic data processing, especially pharmacology, medicine, nutrition; develop and maintain computer applications for processing, correlating and retrieving biomedical and chemical data; relate electronic data processing applications to integrated management information system. Address: 115 Nunning Rd, Evansville, IN 47712.

DURAN, BENJAMIN S, b. Tularosa, N.Mex, Nov. 25, 39; m. 59; c. 4. MATHEMATICS, STATISTICS. B.S, Albuquerque, 61; M.S, Colorado State, 64, Ph.D.(statist), 66. ASST. PROF. MATH, Eastern New Mexico, 66-69; col. med, Baylor Univ, 69-71; TEX. TECH UNIV, 71- Asst. prof, div. biomath, Tex. Inst. Rehab. & Res, 70-71; adj. asst. prof. math. sci, Rice Univ, 70-71. Inst. Math. Statist; Am. Statist. Asn; Math. Asn. Am. Nonparametric statistics; renewal theory; stochastic processes. Address: Dept. of Mathematics, Texas Tech University, Lubbock, TX 79409.

DURAN, RUBEN, b. Calif, Sept. 30, 24; m. 43; c. 5. PLANT PATHOLOGY. B.S, Calif. State Polytech. Col, 54; Ph.D.(plant path), Washington State, 58. Res. asst. plant path, Washington State, 54-58, instr. gen. plant path, 58-59; plant pathologist, agr. mkt. serv, U.S. Dept. Agr, 59-61; asst. prof. PLANT PATH, WASH. STATE UNIV, 61-64, assoc. prof, 64-71, PROF, 71- U.S.N, 42-48. Am. Phytopath. Soc; Bot. Soc. Am; Mycol. Soc. Am. Taxonomy and biology of the Ustilaginales; teaching at the post-graduate level. Address: Dept. of Plant Pathology, Washington State University, Pullman, WA 99163.

DURAN, SERVET A(HMET), b. Kutahya, Turkey, Jan. 2, 20; nat; m. 46; c. 3. PHYSICAL METALLURGY, MATERIALS SCIENCE. B.S, Mo. Sch. Mines, 43; A.M, Stanford, 45, Engr, 46, Ph.D.(mat. sci), 63. Asst. metallog, Stanford, 46; instr. PHYS. METALL, WASH. STATE UNIV, 47-49, asst. prof, 49-53, assoc. prof, 53-61, PROF, 61-, chmn. dept, 59-70. Vis. assoc. prof, Stanford Univ, 56-58; consult, Mid. E. Tech. Univ, Turkey, 69. Am. Soc. Metals; assoc. Am. Inst. Min, Metall. & Petrol. Eng; Am. Soc. Eng. Educ. Solid-state reactions; creep of metals; engineering education. Address: Dept. of Materials Science & Engineering, Washington State University, Pullman, WA 99163.

DURAND, DONALD P, b. New York, N.Y, Oct. 18, 29; m. 51; c. 4. MICROBIOLOGY. A.B, Guilford Col, 55; M.S, Kansas State, 57, Ph.D.(microbiol), 60. Asst. prof. microbiol, sch. med, Missouri, 59-64, ASSOC. PROF, 64-68; BACT, IOWA STATE UNIV, 68- Nat. Insts. Health grant, 60-66 & spec. fel, Cambridge, 66-67. U.S.A, 52-54. AAAS; Am. Soc. Microbiol; Brit. Soc. Gen. Microbiol; Tissue Cult. Asn. Animal viruses in conjunction with their physical and biochemical properties as they relate to virus-host cell interaction. Address: Dept. of Bacteriology, Iowa State University, Ames, IA 50010.

DURAND, EDWARD A(LLEN), b. Duluth, Minn, Dec. 20, 19; m. 49; c. 5. INORGANIC CHEMISTRY. B.S, St. Mary's Col.(Minn), 41; M.S, Creighton, 43; Ph.D.(chem), Wisconsin, 50. Chemist, Martin-Nebr. Aircraft Co, 43-45; assoc. inorg. chemist, Armour Res. Found, 45-46; res. engr, res. labs. Aluminum Co. Am, 50; sr. res. chemist, Ekco Prods. Co, Ill, 51-61; STAFF CHEMIST, IBM CORP, 62- Assoc. ed, Metals Handbook, Am. Soc. Metals, 66-70, sr. ed, 70- AAAS; Am. Chem. Soc; Nat. Asn. Corrosion Eng; Am. Electroplaters Asn. Chemical and electrochemical surface treatment of metals; corrosion. Address: 7002 Fox Hill Dr, Solon, OH 44139.

DURAND, JAMES B(LANCHARD), b. Cranford, N.J, June 13, 29; m. 52; c. 3. BIOLOGY. B.Sc, Rutgers, 51; M.A, Harvard, 54, Ph.D.(biol), 55. Instr. ZOOL, RUTGERS, 55-57, asst. prof, 57-60, assoc. prof, 60-67, PROF, 67- Am. Soc. Zool. Arthropods and molluscs; field work in marine biology. Address: Dept. of Zoology, Rutgers University, Camden, NJ 08102.

DURAND, LOYAL, III, b. Madison, Wis, May 19, 31; m. 54, 70; c. 3. THEORETICAL PHYSICS. B.S, Yale, 53, M.S, 54, Ph.D.(physics), 57. Vis. mem. PHYSICS, Inst. Advan. Study, 57-59; res. assoc, Brookhaven Nat. Lab, N.Y, 59-61; asst. prof, Yale, 61-65; PROF, UNIV. WIS, MADISON, 65-, chmn. dept, 69-71. Nat. Sci. Found. fel, 57-59; summers, vis. prof, physics inst, Univ. Colo, 60, 61; mem. physics. adv. comt, Nat. Accelerator Lab, 68-71; trustee & chmn. exec. comt, Aspen Ctr. Physics, Colo, 68- Am. Phys. Soc. Theoretical physics, mainly high energy particle physics; phenomenology and scattering theory. Address: Dept. of Physics, University of Wisconsin, Madison, WI 53706.

DURAND, MARC L, b. Ware, Mass, Sept. 24, 40; m. 63; c. 3. ORGANIC CHEMISTRY. B.S, Holy Cross Col, 62; Ph.D.(chem), New Hampshire, 67. Asst. prof. CHEM, Alliance Col, 66-68; assoc. prof, WEST CHESTER STATE COLLEGE, 68-71, PROF, 71- Summer asst. prof, New Hampshire, 67. Am. Chem. Soc. Synthetic organic chemistry; natural products with experience in infrared, ultraviolet, nuclear magnetic resonance spectroscopy and optical rotatory dispersion. Address: Dept. of Chemistry, West Chester State College, West Chester, PA 19380.

DURANDETTA, DONALD W, b. Clearfield, Pa, Jan. 12, 42. ORGANIC & POLYMER CHEMISTRY. B.S, Loch Haven State Col, 63; B.F. Goodrich assistantship, Cornell Univ, 65-67, Ph.D.(org. chem), 67. RES. CHEMIST, EXP. STA, E.I. DU PONT DE NEMOURS & CO, INC, 67- Am. Chem. Soc. Organic and polymer chemistry of fluorinated monomers, polymers, polyethylene and copolymers. Address: Bldg. 323, Experimental Station, E.I. du Pont de Nemours & Co, Inc, Wilmington, DE 19898.

DURANT, FREDERICK C(LARK), III, b. Ardmore, Pa, Dec. 31, 16; m. 47; c. 3. ASTRONAUTICS. B.S, Lehigh, 39; Phila. Mus. Sch. Indust. Arts, 46-47. Asst. area engr, E.I. du Pont de Nemours & Co, N.J, 39-41; rocket engr, Bell Aircraft Corp, N.Y, 47-48; dir. eng, U.S. Naval Air Rocket Test Sta, 48-51; consult, Wash, D.C, 51-54; sr. staff mem, Arthur D. Little, Inc, Mass, 54-57; exec. asst. to dir, Avco-Everett Res. Lab, 57-59, dir. pub. & govt. rels, res. & develop. div, Avco Corp, 59-61; sr. rep. aerospace-rockets, Bell Aerosysts. Co, Wash, D.C, 61-64; consult. astronaut, 64-65; ASST. DIR. ASTRONAUT, NAT. AIR & SPACE MUS, SMITHSONIAN INST, 65- Consult, U.S. Dept. Defense Res. & Develop. Bd, 53-54; pres, Int. Astronaut. Fedn, 53-56. U.S.N.R, 41-46, 48-52, Res, 52-70, Comdr. Fel. Am. Inst. Aeronaut. & Astronaut.(pres, Am. Rocket Soc, 53); Am. Astronaut. Soc; Brit. Interplanetary Soc. History of rockets and spaceflight; rocket engineering; national and international astronautical societies; public communications of astronautics. Address: National Air & Space Museum, Smithsonian Institution, Washington, DC 20560.

DURANT, JOHN ALEXANDER, III, b. Lynchburg, S.C, Jan. 20, 39; m. 58. ENTOMOLOGY. B.S, Clemson, 61, M.S, 63; NASA fel, Auburn, 65-66, Ph.D. (entom), 66. ASST. PROF. ENTOM, CLEMSON UNIV, 65- Entom. Soc. Am. Corn insects ecology and control. Address: Pee Dee Experiment Station, Clemson University, Florence, SC 29501.

DURANT, JOHN RIDGWAY, b. Ann Arbor, Mich, July 29, 30; m. 54; c. 3. INTERNAL MEDICINE, ONCOLOGY. B.A, Swarthmore Col, 52; M.D, Temple, 56. Spec. fel. med. neoplasia, Mem. Hosp, New York, 62-63; instr, MED, sch. med, Temple, 63-65, asst. prof, 65-67; assoc. prof. SCH. MED, UNIV. ALA, 68-70, PROF, 70-, DIR. DIV. HEMATOL. & ONCOL, 69-, DIR. CANCER RES. & TRAINING PROG, 70- Am. Cancer Soc. adv. clin. fel, 64-67, mem. prof. educ. comt, 70-; consult, Vet. Admin. Hosp, Tuskegee, 70- Dipl, Am. Bd. Internal Med, 63. U.S.N, 58-60, Lt. AAAS; fel. Am. Col. Physicians; Am. Fedn. Clin. Res; Am. Asn. Cancer Educ; Am. Asn. Cancer Res. Cancer chemotherapy; cytogenetics; immunology. Address: University of Alabama School of Medicine, 1919 Seventh Ave. S, Birmingham, AL 35233.

DURANT, THOMAS MORTON, b. Evanston, Ill, Nov. 19, 05; m. 29; c. 3. CLINICAL MEDICINE. B.S, Michigan, 28, M.D, 30; hon. D.Sc, Franklin & Marshall Col, 64. Intern, univ. hosp, Michigan, 30-32, instr. internal med, med. sch, 32-35; assoc. physician, Desert Sanatorium, Ariz, 35-36; asst. prof. med, SCH. MED, TEMPLE UNIV, 36-37, assoc. prof, 37-46, prof. clin. med, 46-56, prof. internal med. & chmn. dept, 56-66, PROF. MED, 66- Asst. vis. physician, Phila. Gen. Hosp, 41-46, vis. physician, 46-; mem. exam. bd, Am. Bd. Internal Med, 51-59, chmn, 57-59; consult, Vet. Admin. Hosp, Phila; consult. & lectr, U.S. Naval Hosp, Phila, 53-; consult. int. med, U.S.N. Hosp; U.S.A.F; chmn, drug res. bd, Nat. Res. Coun. Strittmatter award, Phila. County Soc, 65; Am. Fedn. Clin. Res.(secy, 40-43, v.pres, 44, pres, 45); Am. Heart Asn; Am. Clin. & Climat. Asn; Asn. Am. Physicians. Electrocardiology; air embolism; myotonia dystrophica; pleurisy and empyema; effect of carbon dioxide and other gases on electrocardiogram of the right ventricle; use of intravenous carbon dioxide for cardiovascular diagnosis. Address: 1242 Lafayette Rd, Gladwynne, PA 19035.

DURANT, W. S, b. Mobile, Ala, Sept. 5, 32; m. 59; c. 2. REACTOR PHYSICS. B.S, Auburn, 53, M.S, 55. Res. engr. HEAT TRANSFER & HYDRAULICS, SAVANNAH RIVER LAB, E.I. DU PONT DE NEMOURS & CO, 55-70, SR. RES. ENGR, 70- Mem, Oak Ridge traveling lect. prog, 64-67. U.S.A, 55-57, Capt. Burnout heat flux; improvement of heat transfer with rough surfaces; fluid flow instability in nuclear reactors; containment of fission products from nuclear reactors; reactor safety. Address: Savannah River Lab, E.I. du Pont de Nemours & Co, Aiken, SC 29802.

DURANTE, ANTHONY J(OSEPH), b. N.Y.C, Apr. 8, 43. ORGANIC CHEMISTRY. B.S, Iona Col, 64; univ. fel, Fordham Univ, 64, Geigy chem. res. fel, 66, Ph.D.(organic chem), 71. Res. asst. organic chem, Lederle Div, Am. Cyanamid Co, summer 65; RES. & DEVELOP. CHEMIST, UNION CARBIDE CORP, TARRYTOWN, 68- Am. Chem. Soc. Synthesis of natural products; synthesis of pesticide synergists; silicone chemistry, especially synthesis and evaluation of silicone resins in high performance protective coatings. Address: 631 Minneford Ave, Bronx, NY 10464.

DURANTE, RAYMOND W, b. Union City, N.J, June 8, 28; m. 50; c. 3. NUCLEAR ENGINEERING. M.E, Stevens Inst. Tech, 50, M.S.I.E, 55; cert. nat. defense mgt, Indust. Col. Armed Forces, 66. Proj. engr, Savannah River H-bomb Proj, Am. Machine & Foundry Co, 50-52, resident consult, atomic submarine prog, 52-55, mgr. eng, 55-56; asst. mgr. mkt. & planning, Allis Chalmers Co, 56-59; mgr. opers. nuclear res. & develop, Aerojet Gen. Corp, Wash, D.C, 59-62, dir. planning, Calif, 62-66; proj. mgr. nuclear desalting, U.S. Dept. Interior, 66-69; EXEC. DIR, WATER RESOURCES INST, INC, 69- Mem, U.S. Planning Cmt, Geneva Conf, 57; subgroup, U.S.-Mex. Border Comn, 67. Am. Nuclear Soc; Am. Ord. Asn; Inst. Aeronaut. & Astronaut. Development and application of water resource projects for the improvement or augmentation of water supplies, especially technology involving the application of nuclear energy. Address: Water Resources Institute, Inc, 1703 N. Hampshire Ave, N.W, Washington, DC 20009.

DURAY, JOHN R, b. Whiting, Ind, Jan. 28, 40; m. 66; c. 2. PHYSICS. B.S, St. Procopius Col, 62; Boston Col, 62-63; Ph.D.(physics), Univ. Notre Dame, 68. From res. assoc. to INSTR, PHYSICS, Ohio State Univ, 68-70; PRINCETON, 70- Am. Phys. Soc. Experimental nuclear physics. Address: Dept. of Physics, Jadwin Hall, Princeton University, Princeton, NJ 08540.

DURBECK, ROBERT C(HARLES), b. Poughkeepsie, N.Y, Apr. 26, 35; m. 63; c. 2. CONTROL SYSTEMS, MECHANICAL ENGINEERING. B.S.M.E. & Daniel F. Pullman award, Union Col.(N.Y), 56; M.S, Cornell Univ, 58; IBM fel. & Ph.D.(control systs), Case Inst. Technol, 65. Assoc. design engr, data systs div, IBM CORP, 58-61, res. staff mem. control systs, RES. DIV, 64-68, mgr. power systs. studies, 68-69, MGR. mech. technol, 69-71, APPL. TECHNOL, 71- Outstanding contribution award, IBM Corp, 68. Am. Soc. Mech. Eng; Inst. Elec. & Electronics Eng; Instrument Soc. Am. Design and control of large scale physical and information systems; high performance mechanical and electro-mechanical systems. Address: IBM Research Lab, Monterey & Cottle Rds, San Jose, CA 95114.

DURBETAKI, PANDELI, b. Istanbul, Turkey, May 31, 28; nat; m. 54; c. 3. MECHANICAL ENGINEERING. B.S, Robert Col, Turkey, 51; M.S, Rochester, 54; Ph.D.(mech. eng), Michigan State, 64. Asst. mech. eng, Rochester, 51-52; drafting & design, Anstice Co. & Rochester Button Co, N.Y, 52-53; instr. MECH. ENG, Rochester, 53-56, asst. prof, 56-60; instr. Michigan State, 60-61, Nat. Sci. Found. sci. faculty fel, 61-63, instr, 63-64; ASSOC. PROF, GA. INST. TECHNOL, 64-, COORD. GRAD. STUD, 68- Am. Soc. Mech. Eng; Am. Soc. Eng. Educ; Combustion Inst. Classical, statistical and non-equilibrium thermodynamics; combustion; particle combustion; combustion in stratified charge mixtures; stratified charge operation of spark ignition engines. Address: School of Mechanical Engineering, Georgia Institute of Technology, Atlanta, GA 30332.

DURBIN, ENOCH JOB, b. New York, N.Y, Sept. 6, 22; m. 45; c. 3. AEROSPACE & MECHANICAL SCIENCES. B.S, City Col. New York, 43; Delaware, 43-44; M.S, Rensselaer Polytech, 47. Mem. res. staff, appl. physics lab, Hopkins, 44-45; A.D. Cardwell Mfg. Co, 46; lectr. transient anal. linear syst, Virginia, 47-48; head appl. physics sect, aerophys. lab, N.Am. Aviation, Inc, 51-53; DIR. INSTRUMENT & CONTROL LAB, PRINCETON, 53-, PROF. AEROSPACE & MECH. SCI, 65- Consult, various U.S. Corp, 50-; NATO, 53-; SUD Aviation, France, 59-65; dir. res. & labs, U.S. Army, Wash, 66-67, electronics command, Ft. Monmouth, 66- Mem. exec. bd, Found. Instrumentation, Educ. & Res; mem, Army Sci. Adv. Panel; Sci. Adv. Group for Aviation Systs. Fel. AAAS. Analysis of dynamic engineering data and physical transducer principles. Address: Dept. of Aerospace & Mechanical Sciences, Princeton University, Princeton, NJ 08540.

DURBIN, JOHN R(ILEY), b. Elk City, Kans, Nov. 18, 35; m. 58; c. 3. MATHEMATICS. B.A, Wichita, 56, fel. & M.A, 58; univ. fel, Michigan, 59-60; univ. fel, Kansas, 60-62, Nat. Sci. Found. fel, 62-63, Ph.D.(math), 64. Asst, Kansas, 63-64; asst. prof. MATH, UNIV. TEX, AUSTIN, 64-69, ASSOC. PROF, 69- On leave, Cambridge, 66-67. U.S.A, 59, Res, 59-, Capt. Am. Math. Soc; Math. Asn. Am. Group theory. Address: Dept. of Mathematics, University of Texas, Austin, TX 78712.

DURBIN, LEONEL DAMIEN, b. Riviera, Tex, Nov. 13, 35; m. 63; c. 1. CHEMICAL ENGINEERING. B.S, Tex. Col. Arts & Indust, 57; Am. Oil Co. & Nat. Sci. Found. fels. & Ph.D.(chem. eng), Rice, 61. Asst. prof. CHEM. ENG, TEX, A&M UNIV, 61-69, PROF, 69- Summer prof, Humble Prod. Res. Center, Tex, 62-64. Am. Inst. Chem. Eng; Am. Chem. Soc. Chemical process dynamics; analog and digital simulation with feedback, adaptive, and optimal control; dynamics of distributed flow systems; optimal design methods. Address: Dept. of Chemical Engineering, Texas A&M University, College Station, TX 77840.

DURBIN, PATRICIA WALLACE (MRS. JAMES T. HEAVEY), b. Oakland, Calif, Apr. 7, 27; m. 58; c. 1. BIOPHYSICS. B.S, California, 48, Ph.D. (biophys), 53. Asst, UNIV. CALIF, 50, PHYSIOLOGIST, LAWRENCE BERKELEY LAB, 51-, asst, 52, res. fel, 54-56, lectr, 57-59. Mem. comt, II, Nat. Coun. Radiation Protection, 57, comts. 30 & 34, 69- AAAS; Radiation Res. Soc; Health Physics Soc. Biological effects of radiation; radioactive tracers; bone metabolism; biology of the transuranic elements. Address: Lawrence Berkeley Laboratory, University of California, Berkeley, CA 94720.

DURBIN, RICHARD D(UANE), b. Santa Ana, Calif, Sept. 6, 30; m. 54; c. 3. PLANT PATHOLOGY. B.S, California, 52, Ph.D, 58. Res. asst, California, 53-54, sr. lab. tech, 54-57; Nat. Sci. Found. res. fel, 57-58, asst. prof. PLANT PATH, Minnesota, 58-62; assoc. prof, UNIV. WIS, MADISON, 62-67, PROF, 67-; LAB. CHIEF, PIONEERING RES. LAB, U.S. DEPT. AGR, 65-, plant pathologist, oat invests, 62-65. Am. Phytopath. Soc; Bot. Soc. Am; Am. Soc. Plant Physiol. Physiology of plant parasitism; soil microbiology. Address: Dept. of Plant Pathology, University of Wisconsin, Madison, WI 53706.

DURBIN, RICHARD P(AUL), b. Columbus, Ohio, June 3, 23; m. 44; c. 4. BIOPHYSICS. Ph.D.(physics), Columbia, 53. Instr. physics, Columbia, 53; fel, Harvard Med. Sch, 54-56, assoc, 56-59, asst. prof. biophys, 60; assoc. res. biophysicist, CARDIOVASC. RES. INST, MED. CTR, UNIV. CALIF, SAN FRANCISCO, 60-65, res. biophysicist, 65-70, PROF. PHYSIOL. IN RESIDENCE, 70- Estab. investr, Am. Heart Asn, 58-63. U.S.N.R, 43-44. Biophys. Soc; Am. Physiol. Soc. Ion and water transport in biological tissue. Address: Cardiovascular Research Institute, University of California Medical Center, San Francisco, CA 94122.

DURBIN, RONALD PRIESTLEY, b. Bement, Ill, Jan. 23, 39; m. 61; c. 2. ANALYTICAL CHEMISTRY. B.A, MacMurray Col, 61; Ph.D.(anal. chem), Univ. Ill, Urbana, 66. Res. chemist, HERCULES, INC, 65-70, SR. RES. CHEMIST, 70- Am. Chem. Soc. Chromatography; thermodynamics of solute-solvent interactions; solvent effects in organic chemistry; analytical application of complex metal hydride reducing agents; spectrochemical methods of analysis. Address: Research Center, Hercules, Inc, Wilmington, DE 19899.

DURDALLER, CORNELIUS GERARD, b. Brooklyn, N.Y, Nov. 17, 33; div; c. 1. METALLURGY, MATERIALS SCIENCE. B.S, Carnegie-Mellon Univ, 57, Gen. Elec. fel, 59-61, M.S, 60, Ph.D.(metall), 62. Lectr. metall, Pennsylvania, 61-62, asst. prof, 62-64; chief metallurgist, HOEGANAES CORP, 64-68, DIR. RES, 68- Mem, Powder Metall. Res. Adv. Bd, 68-, chmn, 70-72. AAAS; Am. Inst. Mining, Metall. & Petrol. Eng; Am. Ceramic Soc; Brit. Inst. Metals. Powder metallurgy, including consolidation of iron, low and high alloy powder for structural part applications. Address: 338 S. Third St, Philadelphia, PA 19106.

DURDEN, CHRISTOPHER JOHN, b. London, Eng, Feb. 25, 40; Can. citizen; m. 63; c. 2. PALEONTOLOGY, SYSTEMATIC ENTOMOLOGY. B.Sc, McGill, 61; Binney-Twenhofel fel, Schuchert-univ. fel. & M.S, Yale, 68. Asst. park naturalist, Algonquin Park Nature Mus, Ont. Dept. of Lands & Forests, 55-56; asst. entom, entom. res. inst, res. br, Can. Dept. Agr, 57-58; geol. asst. Sudbury Basin Proj, Int. Nickel Co, 59; asst. reconnaissance mapping, Geol. Surv. Can, 60; asst. party chief, bedrock stratig. mapping, Geol. Serv, Ministry of Natural Resources, Que, 61; teaching asst. geol, Yale, 62-64, biol, 64-65; curatorial asst. invert. paleont. & entom, Peabody Mus. Natural Hist, 62-66; res. asst. invert. paleont, Carnegie Mus, Pa, 66-68; CURATOR GEOL, TEX. MEM. MUS, 68- AAAS; Paleont. Soc; Lepidop. Soc; fel. Geol. Asn. Can. Paleozoic insect evolution; speciation ecology in modern and fossil Lepidoptera, Orthoptera, Collembola, corals and woody plants; Paleozoic coral evolution; Carboniferous and Silurian biostratigraphic correlation; biotic provinciality; ecosystem dynamics evolution; natural selection. Address: Texas Memorial Museum, 24th & Trinity St, Austin, TX 78705.

DURDEN, JOHN APLING, JR, b. Phoenix, Ariz, July 7, 28; m. 55; c. 5. PHARMACEUTICAL & ORGANIC CHEMISTRY. B.S, Arizona State, 50; M.S, Mississippi, 52; Parke-Davis fel, Kansas, 52-56, Ph.D.(pharm. & org. chem), 57. Instr. org. & phys. chem, Midwestern, 54-56; res. chemist, UNION CARBIDE CORP, 57-67, RES. SCIENTIST, CHEM. & PLASTICS OPERATING DIV, 67- U.S.A.A.F, 54-56, 1st Lt. Am. Chem. Soc. Organic synthesis; reaction mechanisms; agricultural chemistry; structure-activity correlations. Address: Chemical & Plastics Operating Division, Technical Center, Union Carbide Corp, South Charleston, WV 25303.

DURDING, W(ILLIAM) WALTER, b. Baltimore, Md, Dec. 25, 11; m. 38; c. 1. PHYSICS, MATHEMATICS. A.B, Gettysburg Col, 34; Ph.D.(physics), Hopkins, 46. Jr. instr. physics, Hopkins, 34-38, asst, 36-38; instr. math, Gettysburg Col, 38-40; sr. physicist, APPLIED PHYSICS LAB, JOHNS HOPKINS UNIV, 46-50, PRIN. PROF. STAFF, 50-68, DIR, 68- Legion of Merit award. U.S.A, 40-45, Col. Am. Ord. Asn. Design and development of heavy military vehicles and gun mounts; guidance components and systems for guided missles. Address: Applied Physics Lab, Johns Hopkins University, 8621 Georgia Ave, Silver Spring, MD 20910.

DURE, LEON S, III, b. Macon, Ga, Jan. 19, 31; m. 58; c. 4. BIOCHEMISTRY. B.A, Virginia, 53, M.A, 57; Ph.D.(biol), Texas, 60. Fel. BIOCHEM, GEORGIA, 60-62, asst. prof, 62-66, assoc. prof, 66-69, PROF, 69- Nat. Sci. Found. grant, 63-; Atomic Energy Cmn. contract, 64-; career develop. award, U.S. Pub. Health Serv, 67-72; consult, biol. div, Oak Ridge Nat. Lab, 63- U.S.M.C, 53-55, Res, 55-, Lt. Col. Am. Soc. Biol. Chem; Am. Soc. Plant Physiol. Developmental biochemistry; nucleic acid and protein biosynthesis. Address: Dept. of Biochemistry, University of Georgia, Athens, GA 30601.

DURELL, JACK, b. New York, N.Y, July 5, 28; m. 55. PSYCHIATRY, BIOCHEMISTRY. A.B, Harvard, 49; Brown Jr. fel, Yale, 50, M.D, 53. Intern, U.S. Pub. Health Serv. Hosp, Baltimore, Md, 53-54; res. biochemist, Nat. Inst. Ment. Health, 54-57; clin. assoc. psychiat. inst, Maudsley Hosp, London, Eng, 57-59; res. psychiatrist, Nat. Inst. Ment. Health, 60-63, chief sect. psychiat, lab. clin. sci, 63-67; DIR. MED. AFFAIRS, PSYCHIAT. INST. WASH, D.C. & DIR. CTR. STUDIES BEHAV. BIOL, FOUND, 67- Med. dir, U.S. Pub. Health Serv, 53-67; consult, Nat. Inst. Ment. Health. Am. Psychiat. Asn; Asn. Res. Nerv. & Ment. Diseases; Am. Col. Psychiat; Psychiat. Res. Soc; Am. Col. Neuropsychopharmacol. Biological and social dynamics of psychiatric illness; biochemical mechanisms of neural activity; mechanisms of enzyme action; milieu therapy of schizophrenia and effective disorders. Address: Psychiatric Institute of Washington, 2141 K St. N.W, Washington, DC 20037.

DURELLI, AUGUST JOSE, b. Buenos Aires, S.Am, Apr. 30, 10; m. 43; c. 3. ENGINEERING. C.E, Buenos Aires, 32; D.E. & D.Soc.S, Paris, 36. Designer, Cia. Gral. Construcciones, Argentina, 33, engr, 38-39; Argentine Asn. Adv. Sci. fel, Mass. Inst. Tech, 40, Guggenheim Mem. Found. fel, 41; vis. prof, Tech. Sch, Montreal, 42-43; head, city lab, Buenos Aires, 44-46; res. engr, Armour Res. Found, 46-51, supvr. mech. eng, 51-61; PROF. civil eng, Ill. Inst. Tech, 56-61; MECH, CATH. UNIV. AM, 61- Vis. lectr, Princeton, 63-65. Adv, State Lab, Buenos Aires, 44-46. Mem, Argentine Center Eng. With Can. Res. Coun, 44. Am. Soc. Mech. Eng. Pre-stressed reinforced concrete; photoelasticity; brittle material and coating method of stress analysis; strain gages; elasticity; moire; dynamic stress analysis; holography. Address: Dept. of Civil Engineering, Catholic University of America, Washington, D.C. 20017.

DUREN, PETER LARKIN, b. New Orleans, La, Apr. 30, 35; m. 57; c. 2. MATHEMATICS. A.B, Harvard, 56; Ramo-Wooldridge Corp. fel, Mass. Inst. Tech, 57-59, Nat. Sci. Found. fel, 59-60, Ph.D.(math), 60. Instr. MATH, Stanford, 60-62; asst. prof, UNIV. MICH, 62-66, assoc. prof, 66-69, PROF, 69- Alfred P. Sloan Found. fel, 64-66; mem. Inst. Advan. Study, Princeton, N.J, 68-69; res. assoc, eval. panel, Nat. Res. Coun, 71. Am. Math. Soc; Math. Asn. Am; London Math. Soc. Complex analysis; schlicht functions; Hardy spaces of analytic functions; harmonic analysis. Address: Dept. of Mathematics, University of Michigan, Ann Arbor, MI 48104.

DUREN, W(ILLIAM) L(ARKIN), JR, b. Macon, Miss, Nov. 10, 05; m. 31; c. 3. MATHEMATICS. B.A, Tulane, 26, M.A, 28; fel, Chicago, 28-30, Ph.D. (math), 30. Asst. MATH, Tulane, 25-26, instr, 26-28; Col. City of Detroit, 30-31; asst. prof, Tulane, 31-37, assoc. prof, 37-42, prof, 42-44, head dept, 46-55, Univ. chmn, 48-55; UNIV. PROF, UNIV. VA, 55-, dean col. arts & sci, 55. Mem, Inst. Adv. Study, 36-37. Prog. dir. math, Nat. Sci. Found, 52, consult, 53-54; mem. comt. regional develop. & predoctoral fel. panel, Nat. Res. Coun, 52, postdoctoral fel. bd, 53, mem. comt. educ. policy, math. div, 57-59, chmn, 59-60. Opers. analyst, U.S.A.A.F, 44-45. Civilian with Nat. Defense Res. Comt; Off. Naval Res, 44-47. AAAS; Am. Math. Soc; Math. Asn. Am.(v.pres, 53, pres, 55-56). Differential equations; calculus of variations; quantum mechanics. Address: Dept. of Mathematics, College of Arts & Sciences, University of Virginia, Charlottesville, VA 22903.

DURET, M(AURICE) F(RANCIS), b. Gainsborough, Sask, Jan. 27, 22; m. 53; c. 2. MATHEMATICS, PHYSICS. B.Sc, Queen's (Ont), 49, M.Sc, 50; Ph.D. (math, physics), Toronto, 53. Res. officer, ATOMIC ENERGY OF CAN, LTD, 53-61, BR. HEAD REACTOR RES, 61- R.C.N, 40-45. Am. Nuclear Soc. Reactor design and operation. Address: Atomic Energy of Canada, Ltd, Chalk River, Ont, Can.

DURFEE, RAPHAEL B, b. Bisbee, Ariz, Apr. 7, 18; m. 43; c. 2. OBSTETRICS, GYNECOLOGY. A.B, Stanford, 39, M.D, 44. Asst. prof. OBSTET. & GYNEC, MED. SCH, UNIV. ORE, 57-58, assoc. prof, 58-66, PROF, 66- Regent for State of Ore, Int. Col. Surgeons. U.S.A, 55-57, Maj. Fel. Am. Col. Surg; fel. Am. Col. Obstet. & Gynec; fel. Am. Soc. Abdominal Surg; fel. Int. Col. Surg; fel. Pan-Am. Med. Asn. Clinical research and investigation in gynecologic surgery. Address: Dept. of Obstetrics & Gynecology, University of Oregon Medical School, Portland, OR 97201.

DURFEE, ROBERT LEWIS, b. Farmville, Va, May 5, 36; m. 60; c. 2. CHEMICAL ENGINEERING. B.S, Va. Polytech, 57; M.S, 59, Ph.D.(radiation chem), 61. Res. engr. chem. systs, Atlantic Res. Corp, 61-69; dir. life sci, VERSAR INC, 69-71, V.PRES, 71- Solid state radiation chemistry; projects on advanced fuels, non-Newtonian flow, cryogenic systems, and boiling heat transfer; life sciences and environmental systems; new product development. Address: Versar Inc, 6621 Electronic Dr, Springfield, VA 22150.

DURFEE, WAYNE K(ING), b. North Scituate, R.I, Oct. 1, 24; m. 51. POULTRY SCIENCE. B.S, Rhode Island, 50, M.S, 53; Ph.D, Rutgers Univ, 63. ASSOC. PROF. POULTRY SCI, UNIV. R.I, 51- U.S.N.R, 43-45. AAAS; Poultry Sci. Asn; N.Y. Acad. Sci. Avian physiology. Address: Dept. of Animal Science, University of Rhode Island, Kingston, RI 02881.

DURFEE, WILLIAM H(ETHERINGTON), b. Montague, Mass, Apr. 12, 15; m. 39; c. 4. MATHEMATICS. A.B, Harvard, 36, M.A. 40; Ph.D.(math), Cornell, 43. Instr. math, Cornell, 40-43; Yale, 43-45; math. physicist, Nat. Defense Res. Coun, Northwestern, 45-46; instr. math, Dartmouth Col, 46-47, asst. prof, 47-51; mathematician, Nat. Bur. Standards, 51-53; Opers. Res. Off, 53-55; assoc. prof. MATH, MT. HOLYOKE COL, 55-61, PROF, 61- Am. Math. Soc; Math. Asn. Am. Algebra. Address: Dept. of Mathematics, Mount Holyoke College, South Hadley, MA 01075.

DURFLINGER, ELIZABETH W(ARD), b. Ft. Wayne, Ind, July 8, 13; m. 49. INVERTEBRATE ZOOLOGY. B.A, Western Col, 33; M.A, Cincinnati, 34, Ph.D.(zool), 39. Instr. ZOOL, BUTLER UNIV, 40-41, asst. prof, 41-47, assoc. prof, 47-54, PROF, 54-, dean women, 40-65. Sci. Res. Soc. Am. Ecology of entomostraca; aquatic invertebrates. Address: 1010 Oakwood Trail, Indianapolis, IN 46260.

DURGAN, ELFORD S(TURTEVANT), b. Portland, Maine, May 22, 05. PHYSICAL CHEMISTRY. A.B, Clark, 26; A.M, Princeton, 27, Ph.D.(phys. chem), 30. Asst, Am. Petrol. Inst, Princeton, 26-29; instr. chem, Maine, 29-30; res. chemist, Godfrey L. Cabot Co, 30-33; sales dept, Grasselli Chem. Dept, E.I. du Pont de Nemours & Co, 34-39; res. chemist, Chem. & Pigment Co, 39-40; chemist, Merck & Co, 40-68; PROF, DEPT. CHEM, THOMAS NELSON COMMUNITY COL, 68- Instr, Union Jr. Col, 56-68. Am. Chem. Soc. Equilibria and kinetics of gas reactions; hydrocarbons. Address: Dept. of Chemistry, Thomas Nelson Community College, Hampton, VA 23366.

DURGIN, WILLIAM W, b. Framingham, Mass, Apr. 26, 42; m. 64; c. 2. FLUID MECHANICS. B.S, Brown Univ, 64, Ph.D.(fluid dynamics), 69; M.S, Univ. R.I, 66. Asst, Univ. R.I, 64-65; Narragansett Marine Lab, 65-66; res. asst, Univ. R.I, 65-66; Brown Univ, 68-70; asst. prof. eng. sci. & mech, Univ. Fla, 70-71; ASST. PROF. DEPT. MECH. ENG. & RES. ENG, ALDEN RES. LABS, WORCESTER POLYTECH. INST, 71- Am. Inst. Aeronaut. & Astronaut; Am. Soc. Mech. Eng. Turbulence; geophysical fluid mechanics; instrumentation. Address: Alden Research Labs, Worcester Polytechnic Institute, Worcester, MA 01609.

DURHAM, CLARENCE O(RSON), JR, b. Victoria, Tex, Oct. 20, 20; m. 59; c. 2. GEOLOGY. B.S, Texas, 42; cert. meteorol, Chicago, 43; fel, Columbia, 50-51, Ph.D.(geol), 57. Lab. asst. geol, Texas, 46-47, lab. instr, 47-48; asst, Bur. Econ. Geol, Tex, 48-49; Columbia, 49-50; instr. struct. geol, LA. STATE UNIV, 51-53, asst. prof. GEOL, 53-58, assoc. prof, 58-63, PROF, 63-, CHMN. DEPT, 65-, DIR. SCH. GEOL, 66- Instr. summer camp, Univ. Tex, 48-52; res. geologist, La. Geol. Surv, 55-57, dir. res, 57-63. U.S.A.A.F, 42-46, Capt. AAAS; Am. Asn. Petrol. Geol; Soc. Econ. Paleont. & Mineral; Am. Geophys. Union. Mesozoic and Cenozoic stratigraphy; structural geology; geology of Gulf of Mexico region; sedimentary iron ores. Address: Dept. of Geology, Louisiana State University, Baton Rouge, LA 70803.

DURHAM, FORREST, b. Ithaca, N.Y, Dec. 11, 15; m. 44; c. 2. GEOLOGY. A.B, Cornell, 38, M.A, 47; Ph.D.(geol), Syracuse, 54. Instr. geol, N.Y. State Teachers Col, Cortland, 48-51; instr. & res. assoc, Syracuse, 51-54; assoc. prof. GEOL, N.Y. State Teachers Col, New Paltz, 54-55; Col. of Puget Sound, 55-56; St. Lawrence, 56-57; ASSOC. PROF. & CHMN. DEPT, HOFSTRA UNIV, 57- C.Eng, 41-46, 1st Lt. Fel. Geol. Soc. Am; Nat. Asn. Geol. Teachers. Pleistocene and ground water geology; sedimentation; environmental geomorphology. Address: Dept. of Geology, Hofstra University, Hempstead, NY 11550.

DURHAM, FRANK EDINGTON, b. Jonesboro, La, July 12, 35; m. 56; c. 3. NUCLEAR PHYSICS. B.S, La. Polytech, 56; M.A, Rice, 58, Anderson fel, 58-60, Ph.D.(physics), 60. Asst. prof, PHYSICS, TULANE UNIV, 60-64, assoc. prof, 64-67, PROF, 67- Summers, res. assoc. physics, Rice, 60; res. participant, Oak Ridge Inst. Nuclear Studies, 61, 62; temporary physicist, Oak Ridge Nat. Lab, 63, 64; mem. La. Nuclear & Space Auth, 68-; consult, Gulf S. Res. Inst, 70- Am. Phys. Soc. Experimental studies of nuclear structure at low energies. Address: Dept. of Physics, Tulane University, New Orleans, LA 70118.

DURHAM, FRANKLIN P(ATTON), b. Wiley, Colo, Dec. 22, 21; m. 43; c. 3. AERONAUTICAL ENGINEERING. B.S, Colorado, 43, M.S, 49, Aero.Eng,

53. Exp. test engr, Pratt & Whitney Aircraft, 43-47; instr. aeronaut. eng, Colorado, 47-49, asst. prof, 49-53, assoc. prof, 53-55, prof, 55, head dept, 56; group leader, LOS ALAMOS SCI. LAB, 57-61, ALTERNATE DIV. LEADER, 61- Am. Inst. Aeronaut. & Astronaut. Nuclear rocket propulsion; thermodynamics; heat transfer. Address: 3100 Arizona Ave, Los Alamos, NM 87544.

DURHAM, GEORGE S(TONE), b. Portland, Ore, Dec. 26, 12; m. 35; c. 2; m. 58. PHYSICAL CHEMISTRY. B.A, Reed Col, 35; Ph.D.(phys. chem), N.Y. Univ, 39. Asst. chem, N.Y. Univ, 35-39; res. chemist, Weyerhaeuser Timber Co, Wash, 39-40; instr. CHEM, Ore. State Col, 40-41; Illinois, 41-43; SMITH COL, 43-45, asst. prof, 45-53, assoc. prof, 53-59, PROF, 59-, chmn. dept, 58-66. Vis. asst. prof, Massachusetts, 44-45, vis. lectr, 57-62, mem. grad. faculty, 61-; res. grants & res. contracts, Sigma Xi, Nat. Sci. Found, Off. Naval Res, Air Force Off. Sci. Res, Off. Ord. Res. & Army Res. Off; summers, vis. asst. prof, N.Y. Univ, 45-46. Am. Chem. Soc. Solid solutions of inorganic salts; solid state theory of the alkali halides. Address: 160 South St, Northampton, MA 01060.

DURHAM, HARVEY RALPH, b. Perry, Fla, Feb. 25, 38; m. 63; c. 3. MATHEMATICS. B.S, Wake Forest Univ, 59; M.A, Univ. Ga, 62, Ph.D.(math), 65. ASSOC. PROF. MATH, APPALACHIAN STATE UNIV, 65-, ASSOC. DEAN FACULTIES, 71-, chmn. dept, 67-71. Partic, Am. Coun. Educ. Acad. Admin. Internship Prog, 69-70. AAAS; Am. Math. Soc; Math. Asn. Am. Combinatorial topology. Address: Office of Academic Affairs, Appalachian State University, Boone, NC 28607.

DURHAM, J(OHN) WYATT, b. Okanogan, Wash, Aug. 22, 07; m. 35; c. 1. INVERTEBRATE PALEONTOLOGY. B.Sc, Univ. Wash, 33; M.A, Univ. Calif, 36, Ph.D.(paleont), 41. Asst. geol, Univ. Calif, 35-36; geologist, Standard Oil Co. Calif, 36-39; asst, mus. paleont, Univ. Calif, 41-42; geologist & chief paleontologist, Tropical Oil Co, Colombia, 43-46; assoc. prof. PALEONT, Calif. Inst. Technol, 46-47; UNIV. CALIF, BERKELEY, 47-53, PROF, 53-, chmn. dept, 56-58. Guggenheim fel, 54-55, 65-66; mem. Paleont. Res. Inst; U.S. Nat. Comt. Geol, 66-70. AAAS; Am. Soc. Syst. Zool; fel. Paleont. Soc.(v.pres, 52-53, pres, 65-66); Soc. Econ. Paleont. & Mineral; Brit. Palaeontograph. Soc; fel. Geol. Soc. Am; Am. Asn. Petrol. Geol; Brit. Palaeont. Asn; Palaeont. Soc. Japan. Tertiary Molluscan paleontology; Tertiary stratigraphy; Tertiary and recent corals and echinoids; Cretaceous ammonites; paleoclimates; paleobiogeography; lower Cambrian, Pre Cambrian fossils. Address: Dept. of Paleontology, University of California, Berkeley, CA 94720.

DURHAM, LEONARD, b. Glen Carbon, Ill, Aug. 27, 25; m. 48; c. 4. ZOOLOGY. B.S, Illinois, 49, M.S, 50, Ph.D.(zool), 55. Lab. & field asst, Ill. Natural Hist. Surv, 47-49, tech. asst, 49-50; fishery biologist, Ill. Dept. Conserv, 50-55; PROF. ZOOL, EAST. ILL. UNIV, 55-, DIR, DIV. LIFE SCI, 67- Mem. Ill. Nature Preserves Comn, 70- U.S.N, 43-46. AAAS; Am. Soc. Ichthyol. & Herpet; Am. Fisheries Soc; Wildlife Soc. Fishery biology; ecology of fishes and fish management; conservation; water pollution. Address: Division of Life Sciences, Eastern Illinois University, Charleston, IL 61920.

DURHAM, LOIS J(EAN), b. Oakland, Calif, Dec. 21, 31. ORGANIC CHEMISTRY. B.S, California, 54; Lilly fel, Stanford, 55-56, Du Pont fel, 56-57, Ph.D.(org. chem), 59. Instr. org. chem, Stanford, 59-60; sr. res. chemist, Stanford Res. Inst, 60-61; NUCLEAR MAGNETIC RESONANCE SPECTROSCOPIST, STANFORD UNIV, 61- AAAS; Am. Chem. Soc. Application of nuclear magnetic resonance spectroscopy in determination of organic structural analysis; organic reaction mechanisms, organic peroxides. Address: Dept. of Chemistry, Stanford University, Stanford, CA 94305.

DURHAM, NORMAN N(EVILL), b. Ranger, Tex, Feb. 14, 27; m. 52; c. 4. BACTERIOLOGY. B.S, North Texas State, 49, M.S, 51; fel, Texas, 51-52, Ph.D.(bact), 54. Lab. asst. bot. & bact, North Texas State, 46-49, student instr, 49-51; res. scientist, Texas, 52-54; asst. prof. BACT, OKLA. STATE UNIV, 54-57, assoc. prof, 57-60, PROF, 60-, DEAN, GRAD. COL, 68- Vis. lectr, sch. med, Univ. Okla, 63; Kans. State Univ, 65; consult. biol. sci, NASA, 63-69; with div. biol. & med, U.S. Atomic Energy Comn, 66-68; mem. coun. manpower planning, U.S. Off. Educ, 70- U.S.N, 45-46. AAAS; Am. Acad. Microbiol; Am. Soc. Microbiol; Brit. Soc. Gen. Microbiol; Biochem. Soc. Radiations; bacterial metabolism and metabolic pathways; genetics; agricultural bacteriology; protein and enzyme synthesis; mechanism of antibiotic action; metabolic regulations, cell growth and reproduction; genetic transformation. Address: Dept. of Microbiology, Oklahoma State University, Stillwater, OK 74074.

DURHAM, RALPH M(ARION), b. Bristol, Colo, Dec. 20, 23; m. 46; c. 8. GENETICS, ANIMAL HUSBANDRY. B.S, Colo. Agr. & Mech. Col, 48; M.S, Wisconsin, 49, Ph.D, 51. Asst. animal breeding, Wisconsin, 48-51; asst. prof. genetics & animal breeding, N.Mex. Col, 51-53; animal husbandman, swine sect, Animal & Poultry Husb. Res. br, agr. res. serv, U.S. Dept. Agr, 54-55; exten. animal breeding specialist & assoc. prof, Iowa State Col, 55-59; PROF. ANIMAL HUSB, TEX. TECH UNIV, 59-, head dept, 59-65. U.S.N.R, 44-46. AAAS; Am. Soc. Animal Sci; Poultry Sci. Asn. Genetics of growth and reproduction in cattle, sheep and swine; heterosis and carcass improvement in swine; performance testing methods in beef and swine. Address: Dept. of Animal Husbandry, Texas Tech University, Lubbock, TX 79409.

DURHAM, RAY W(ILSON), b. Darlington, Eng, Apr. 6, 23; Can. citizen; m. 48; c. 5. RADIOCHEMISTRY. B.Sc, Durham, 47, Ph.D.(radiochem), 50. Res. asst. radiochem, Londonderry Lab. Radiochem, Durham, 49-50; fel. photochem, Nat. Res. Coun. Can, 50-52; asst. res. off. radiochem, Atomic Energy Can. Ltd, 52-54, group leader, Ont, 54-71; HEAD RADIOCHEM. LAB, CAN. CENTRE INLAND WATERS, 71- R.A.F, 43-44. Chem. Inst. Can. Neutron activation analysis in pollution studies; radioactive age determinations of sediments. Address: Canada Centre for Inland Waters, 867 Lakeshore Rd, P.O. Box 5050, Burlington, Ont, Can.

DURHAM, ROSS M, b. Toronto, Ont, Sept. 19, 30; U.S. citizen; m. 55; c. 3. NEUROPHYSIOLOGY, SPACE BIOLOGY. A.B, California, Los Angeles, 62, Ph.D.(zool), 68. Proj. biologist, space biol. labs, brain res. inst, Univ. Calif, Los Angeles, 68-70, asst. res. psychologist, 70-71; ASST. PROF. BIOL, UNIV. TENN, CHATTANOOGA, 71- Vis. prof, Univ. South. Calif, 70-71; consult, Vet. Admin. Hosp, Sepulveda, Calif, 70-71. U.S.A.F, 50-54, Sgt. Water balance in vertebrates; thirst, its cause and control; renal physiology; physiological psychology; electrophysiological recording from units in subcortical nucleii. Address: Dept. of Biology, University of Tennessee at Chattanooga, Chattanooga, TN 37403.

DURHAM, WILLIAM F(AY), b. Cedartown, Ga, Apr. 19, 22; m. 47; c. 3. BIOCHEMISTRY. A.B, Emory Univ, 43, M.S, 48, Ph.D.(biochem), 50. Biochemist, toxicol. sect, tech. br, Communicable Disease Ctr, U.S. Pub. Health Serv, 50-57, CHIEF, Wenatchee Field Sta, 57-67, pesticide res. lab, 67-70, PERRINE PRIMATE LAB, ENVIRON. PROTECTION AGENCY, 70- Clin. assoc. prof. pharmacol, sch. med, Univ. Miami, 67- U.S.N.R, 44-46. Fel. AAAS; Soc. Toxicol; Am. Soc. Pharmacol. & Exp. Therapeut; Am. Chem. Soc; Sci. Res. Soc. Am. Toxicology of insecticides. Address: Perrine Primate Lab, Environmental protection Agency, P.O. Box 490, Perrine, FL 33157.

DURIEUX, CHARLES W(OGAN), b. Havana, Cuba, Dec. 26, 20; U.S. citizen; m. 51; c. 2. DATA PROCESSING. B.S, La. State, 42; M.S, Stanford, 50; Harvard & Mass. Inst. Tech, 42. Physicist, Nat. Bur. Standards, 50-53; Diamond Ord. Fuze Lab, 53-56; assoc. mathematician, Rand Corp, 56-57; comput. syst. specialist, Syst. Develop. Corp, 57-59, br. head mgt. comput. prog. develop, 59-61, asst. dept. head mgt. info. syst. develop, 61-65, dept. mgr, 65-68; br. mgr. comput. sci. div, Comput. Sci. Corp, 68-69; sr. ADP res. & develop. specialist, Defense Commun. Agency, 69-70; MEM. EXEC. STAFF, EAST. REGION, SYSTS. DIV, COMPUT. SCI. CORP, 70- U.S.A.A.F, 42-46, Maj. Asn. Comput. Mach; Inst. Elec. & Electronics Eng. Development of computer based information processing systems; automatic data processing. Address: Computer Sciences Corp, 6565 Arlington Blvd, Falls Church, VA 22046.

DURIG, JAMES ROBERT, b. Washington County, Pa, Apr. 30, 35; m. 55; c. 3. PHYSICAL CHEMISTRY. B.A, Washington & Jefferson Col, 58; Woodrow Wilson fel, Mass. Inst. Tech, 58-59, Union Carbide Corp. fel, 60-61, Ph.D. (phys. chem), 62. Asst. prof. CHEM, UNIV. S.C, 62-65, assoc. prof, 65-68, prof, 68-70, EDUC. FOUND. PROF, 70- Russel Award for res, 68. Chem.C, 63-64, 1st Lt. Fel. Am. Phys. Soc; Am. Chem. Soc; Soc. Appl. Spectros; Coblentz Soc.(award, 70). Infrared, Raman and microwave spectra of polyatomic molecules, especially molecules having low frequency vibrations; torsional barriers; molecular structure of organometallic molecules. Address: Dept. of Chemistry, University of South Carolina, Columbia, SC 29208.

DURIO, WALTER O'NEAL, b. Arnaudville, La, Jan. 17, 38. PARASITOLOGY. B.Sc, Southwestern Louisiana, 59, M.S, 60; Ph.D.(zool, physiol), Nebraska, Lincoln, 66. ASST. PROF. BIOL, UNIV. SOUTHWEST. LA, 66- Am. Soc. Parasitol; Am. Micros. Soc. Helminthology; taxonomy of digenetic trematodes. Address: Dept. of Biology, University of Southwestern Louisiana, Lafayette, LA 70501.

DURKAN, JAMES P, b. Baltimore, Md, Jan. 13, 34; m. 58; c. 4. MEDICINE, OBSTETRICS & GYNECOLOGY. A.B, Loyola Col.(Md), 55; M.D, Maryland, 59. Internship, Mercy Hosp, Baltimore, Md, 59-60; res. OBSTET. & GYNEC, hosp, UNIV. MD, 60-64, asst. prof, 64-71, ASSOC. PROF, 71-; HEAD DEPT. OBSTET. & GYNEC, MERCY HOSP, 68- Dipl, Am. Bd. Obstet. & Gynec, 67. Fel. Am. Col. Obstet. & Gynec. Neurologic influence on menstrual function; clinical oncology; clinical family planning. Address: Dept. of Obstetrics & Gynecology, Mercy Hospital, Baltimore, MD 21202.

DURKEE, EDWARD FLEMING, b. Midwest, Wyo, Nov. 27, 28; m. 49; c. 5. PETROLEUM & ECONOMIC GEOLOGY. B.S, Univ. Wyo, 52, Husky Oil scholar, 52, M.A, 53. Geologist, Gulf Oil Corp, 53-56; field geologist, Am. Overseas Petrol, Ltd, Philippines, 56-58; proj. geologist, Caltex Pac. Oil Co, Indonesia, 58-59; regional geologist, Am. Overseas Petrol, Ltd, Turkey, 59-60, exploration supvr, 60-62, Australia, 62-68, mgr, 68-69; Texaco Overseas Petrol. Co, 69; V.PRES. & CHIEF GEOLOGIST, BASIC EARTH SCI. SYSTS, INC, 69- Acting lectr, dept. geol, Univ. Queensland, 68. U.S.M.C, 46-48. AAAS; Am. Asn. Petrol. Geol; Soc. Econ. Paleont. & Mineral; Paleont. Soc. Am; Australian Geol. Soc; Philippines Geol. Soc; Geol. Soc. Am. Field surveys and library research to provide syntheses of stratigraphy, structure and natural resources of geological basins; the assessment of their economic potential; planning operations to evaluate same. Address: Basic Earth Science Systems, Inc, 500 Gulf Bldg, 1780 S. Bellaire, Denver, CO 80222.

DURKEE, L(aVERNE) H, b. Darien, N.Y, June 23, 27; m. 56; c. 2. BOTANY. B.S, Syracuse, 51, M.S, 54, col. fel, 56-58, Ph.D, 60. Asst. prof. BIOL, Grove City Col, 58-61; Parsons Col, 61; GRINNELL COL, 62-65, assoc. prof, 65-70, PROF, 70- U.S.A, 45-47. AAAS; Bot. Soc. Am; Ecol. Soc. Am. Palynology; plant systematics. Address: Dept. of Biology, Grinnell College, Grinnell, IA 50112.

DURKIN, DOMINIC J, b. St. Johnsbury, Vt, Dec. 24, 30; m. 58; c. 4. HORTICULTURE, PLANT PHYSIOLOGY. B.S, New Hampshire, 52; M.S, Ohio State, 58, Helena Chamberlain fel, 58-60, Ph.D.(hort), 60. Asst. prof. hort, Purdue, 60-65, assoc. prof, 65-69; PROF. FLORICULT, RUTGERS UNIV, 69-, CHMN. DEPT. HORT. & FORESTRY, 71- U.S.A.F, 52-56, 1st Lt. Am. Soc. Hort. Sci. Bud dormancy in the rose; florist crop physiology; post harvest physiology; cut flowers. Address: Dept. of Horticulture & Forestry, Rutgers University, New Brunswick, NJ 08903.

DURLAND, JOHN R(OYDEN), b. Chicago, Ill, Mar. 7, 14; m. 36; c. 4. CHEMICAL ENGINEERING. B.S, Mich. Col. Min. & Tech, 35; Ph.D.(org. chem), Wisconsin, 39. Res. chemist, MONSANTO CO, 39-40, res. chemist & leader group, Nitro, 41-45, develop. supt, 46, plant mgr, 47-52, asst. prod. mgr, org. chems. div, 52-53, plant mgr, J.F. Queeny, 53-55, tech. prod. mgr, org. chem. div, 55-60, prod. dir, 60-65, mgr. int. & interdivisional mfg, 65-67, V.PRES, MITSUBISHI MONSANTO CHEM. CO, 67- Am. Chem. Soc; Am.

Inst. Chem. Eng. Hydrogenation; process research in production of organic chemicals. Address: Mitsubishi Monsanto Chemical Co, 4, 2-Chome, Marunouchi, Chiyoda-Ku, Tokyo, Japan.

DURLAND, M(ERRILL) A(UGUSTUS), b. Centralia, Kans, Jan. 6, 97; m. 20; c. 2. MECHANICAL ENGINEERING. B.S, Kans. State Col, 18, M.E, 22, M.S, 23; London, 19; Pittsburgh, 28. Instr. appl. math. & mach. design, KANS. STATE UNIV, 19-21, asst. prof. mach. design, 21-25, assoc. prof, 25-28, prof, 28-62, mech. eng, 62-67, asst. dean, sch. eng. & archit, 28-49, dean, 49-62, dir, eng. exp. sta, 49-62, EMER. PROF. MECH. ENG. & EMER. DEAN & DIR, 67- Apprentice stud, Westinghouse Elec. & Mfg. Co, 28. C.Eng, U.S.A, 18-19. Am. Soc. Mech. Eng; Am. Soc. Eng. Educ; Nat. Soc. Prof. Eng. Design of gear teeth for maximum strength; characteristics of Portland cement. Address: Dept. of Mechanical Engineering, Kansas State University, Manhattan, KS 66502.

DURLING, ALLEN E(DGAR), b. Summitt, N.J, Dc. 21, 34; m. 60; c. 3. ELECTRICAL ENGINEERING. B.S, Lafayette Col, 60; M.E.E, Syracuse, 62, Ph.D.(elec. eng), 64. Elec. engr, prod. develop. lab, Int. Bus. Mach. Corp, 60-61; asst. ELEC. ENG, Syracuse Univ, 61-62, instr, 62-64; asst. prof, UNIV. FLA, 64-66, assoc. prof, 66-70, PROF, 70- Consult, Int. Bus. Mach. summer 63. U.S.N, 54-58, Res, 58-, Lt. Comdr. Inst. Elec. & Electronics Eng; Am. Soc. Eng. Educ. Analog, digital and hybrid computation; discrete systems. Address: Dept. of Electrical Engineering, University of Florida, Gainesville, FL 32601.

DURLING, FREDERICK CHARLES, b. Detroit, Mich, July 31, 31. MATHEMATICAL STATISTICS, MATHEMATICS. B.A, Arlington State Col, 65; Nat. Insts. Health fels, South. Methodist Univ, 65-69, M.S, 67, Ph.D.(statist), 69. Asst. prof. MATH. STATIST, Med. Univ. S.C, 69-71; LECTR, UNIV. WAIKATO, N.Z, 71- U.S.A, 52-54 & 55-57, Sgt. AAAS; Inst. Math. Statist; Am. Statist. Asn; Am. Acad. Arts & Sci. Multivariate distributional theory; bivariate Burr distribution—development and investigation of theoretical and empirical properties; bivariate imput—quantal response data analysis; nonlinear estimation. Address: Dept. of Mathematics, University of Waikato, Hamilton, N.Z.

DURNEY, CARL H(ODSON), b. Blackfoot, Idaho, Apr. 22, 31; m. 53; c. 6. ELECTRICAL ENGINEERING. B.S, Utah State, 58; Nat. Defense Ed. Act fel, Utah, 59-62, M.S, 61, Gen. Tel. & Electronics fel, 62-63, Ph.D.(elec. eng), 64. Assoc. res. engr. control systs, Boeing Airplane Co, Wash, 58-59; asst. res. prof. ELEC. ENG, UNIV. UTAH, 63-68; ASSOC. PROF, 68- On leave, mem. tech. staff, Crawford Hill Lab, Bell Tel. Labs, N.J, 65-66. U.S.A.F, 50-54. Inst. Elec. & Electronics Eng; Am. Soc. Eng. Educ. Electromagnetic field theory; microwave theory and devices; engineering pedagogy; interaction of electromagnetic fields and living systems. Address: Dept. of Electrical Engineering, University of Utah, Salt Lake City, UT 84112.

DURNEY, HARRY AUGUSTINE, b. Dec. 21, 24; U.S. citizen; m. 57. METALLURGICAL & PHYSICAL CHEMISTRY. B.Ch.E, Hopkins, 47, M.A. & Ph.D.(chem), 50. Res. chemist, Catalyst Res. Corp, Md, 48-53; Kennecott Copper Corp, N.Y, 53-56; proj. supvr, Kennecott Titanium Develop. Corp, Ohio, 56-60, mgr. opers, Que. Iron & Titanium Corp, 60-67; GEN. MGR, QUE. METAL POWDERS LTD, 67- Summer jr. chem. engr, West. Elec. Co, Md, 47. U.S.N, 44-46. Am. Chem. Soc; Am. Inst. Min, Metall. & Petrol. Eng; Electrochem. Soc; Am. Soc. Test. & Mat. Electrochemistry; high temperature metallurgy, especially titanium, zirconium and iron. Address: Quebec Metal Powders Ltd, Box 500, Sorel, Que, Can.

DURNFORD, A(NDREW) M(ONTAGUE) I(SAACSON) A(LEXANDER) W(ILLIAM), b. Sarnia, Ont, Aug. 04; m. 33; c. 4. PHYSICS. B.A, Western Ontario, 25, M.A, 26; Nat. Res. Coun. Can. bursary, Toronto, 26-27, student, 27-28, fel, 28-29, Ph.D, 31. Asst. PHYSICS, Toronto, 29-30; from instr. to assoc. prof, UNIV. WEST. ONT, 30-66, prof, 66-70, EMER. PROF. 70- Am. Phys. Soc; Can. Asn. Physicists. Zeeman effect of spectral lines; thermionic valve as a voltage amplifier; voltage amplifier using a pre-saturation diode as load; coulomb-energy radii from isobaric mass parabolas. Address: Dept. of Physics, University of Western Ontario, London 72, Ont, Can.

DURNFORD, ROBERT F(RED), b. Carlton, Mont, June 29, 22; m; c. 2. ELECTRICAL ENGINEERING. B.S, Mont. State Col, 44, M.S, 49; Ph.D, Ohio State Univ, 65. Assoc. prof. ELEC. ENG, MONT. STATE UNIV, 47-66, PROF, 66- Sig.C, 44-46, Res, 42-44, 46-52, 1st Lt. Am. Soc. Eng. Educ; Inst. Elec. & Electronics Eng. Industrial electronics; control; energy conversion. Address: Dept. of Electrical Engineering, Montana State University, Bozeman, MT 59715.

DURNICK, THOMAS JACKSON, b. Ft. Leavenworth, Kans, Mar. 1, 46. PHYSICAL CHEMISTRY, SPECTROSCOPY. B.S, Rensselaer Polytech. Inst, 67, Ph.D.(phys. chem), 71. RES. ASSOC, RES. FOUND, STATE UNIV. N.Y. BINGHAMTON, 71- Am. Chem. Soc. Molecular spectroscopy of large organic molecules of potential biological interest; ultraviolet, infrared and raman investigations of ground and excited states, including computer calculation and analysis of spectra. Address: Dept. of Chemistry, State University of New York at Binghamton, Binghamton, NY 13901.

DURNO, WILLIAM H(ENRY), b. Pittsburgh, Pa, Aug. 28, 14; m. 43. CHEMISTRY. B.S, Pittsburgh, 37. Chemist, FED. LABS, INC, 37-39, plant supt, 39-44, chief chemist, 44-60, asst. sales mgr, 60-64, QUAL. CONTROL MGR, 64- With Off. Sci. Res. & Develop, 44. Fel. Am. Inst. Chem; Am. Chem. Soc. Chemical explosives; electrochemistry; pyrotechnics. Address: Federal Labs, Inc, Saltsburg, PA 15681.

DUROCHER, G(ILLES), b. Montreal, Que, Nov. 28, 40; m. 64; c. 2. PHYSICAL CHEMISTRY. B.Sc, Univ. Montreal, 62, M.Sc, 63, Ph.D.(spectros), 65. Fel, Univ. Paris, 65-67; Nat. Res. Coun. Can, 68; asst. prof. MOLECULAR SPECTROS. & QUANTUM CHEM, UNIV. MONTREAL, 68-71, ASSOC. PROF, 71- London Chem. Indust. Medal, 62. Chem. Inst. Can. Molecular spectroscopy of the organic solid state, especially absorption, fluorescence and phosphorescence of molecules in solid matrices at temperatures ranging

from 300° K to 4.2° K. Address: Dept. of Chemistry, University of Montreal, P.O. Box 6128, Montreal 101, Que, Can.

DURR, ALBERT M(ATTHEW), JR, b. Nebraska City, Nebr, May 22, 23; m. 45 c. 2. ORGANIC CHEMISTRY. B.S, Okla. State, 50, cities serv. fel. & M.S, 51. Res. chemist, chem. dept, Beacon Res. Labs, Tex. Co, 51-55; lubricants group, DEVELOP. & RES. DEPT, CONTINENTAL OIL CO, 55-56, sr. res. chemist, 56-58, acting res. group leader, 58-59, RES. GROUP LEADER, 59- U.S.A.F, 42-46. Am. Chem. Soc; Sci. Res. Soc. Am; Am. Soc. Lubrication Eng; Int. Soc. Gen. Semantics. Fundamental organic chemistry; petroleum lubricants. Address: 111 Glenside Ave, Ponca City, OK 74601.

DURR, F(RIEDRICH) (E), b. Poughkeepsie, N.Y, July 28, 33; m. 57; c. 4. MICROBIOLOGY. B.S, St. John's, 55; M.S, Wisconsin, 58, Ph.D.(med. microbiol), 60. Instr. microbiol, col. med. & dent, Seton Hall Univ, 60-63; RES. VIROLOGIST, J.L. SMITH MEM. CANCER RES, PFIZER, INC, 63- Am. Soc. Microbiol. Effect of viruses on transplantable mouse tumors; bioassay of murine leukemia viruses; purification and concentration; oncogenic activity of Rous sarcoma virus for mammals; virological and immunological studies with human lymptomas and leukemias. Address: Pfizer, Inc, 199 Maywood Ave, Maywood, NJ 07607.

DURRANI, SAJJAD H(AIDAR), b. Jalalpur, Pakistan, Aug. 27, 28; U.S. citizen; m. 59; c. 3. ELECTRICAL ENGINEERING. B.A, Govt. Col, Lahore, Pakistan, 46; B.Sc.Eng, Eng. Col, Lahore, 49; Govt. Punjab fel, Manchester, 51-53, M.Sc.Tech, 53; Sc.D.(elec. eng), New Mexico, 62. Lectr. elec. eng, Eng. Col, Lahore, 49-56, asst. prof, 56-59; instr. & res. assoc, New Mexico, 59-62; engr, commun. prod. dept, Gen. Elec. Co, Va, 62-64; prof. elec. eng. & chmn. dept, pres. teaching staff asn. & dir. res, Eng. Univ, Lahore, 64-65; assoc. prof. elec. eng, Kans. State Univ, 65-66; sr. engr, Space Ctr, RCA, 66-68, systs. eng. eval. & res, 68; mem. tech. staff, COMMUN. SATELLITE CORP, 68-69, br. mgr, systs. anal. lab, 69-71, STAFF SCIENTIST, ADV. STUDIES LAB, 71- Mem. U.S. Comn. II, Int. Sci. Radio Union. Sr. mem. Inst. Elec. & Electronics Eng; Brit. Inst. Elec. Eng; assoc. fel, Am. Inst. Aeronaut. & Astronaut. Electromagnetic theory; communications systems; antennas and propagation; space communications. Address: COMSAT Labs, P.O. Box 115, Clarksburg, MD 20734.

DURRANT, S(TEPHEN) D(AVID), b. Salt Lake City, Utah, Oct. 11, 02; m. 33; c. 2. ZOOLOGY. A.B, Utah, 29, fel, 29-31, M.A, 31; fel, Minnesota, 31-32; California, 38-39; Ph.D, Kansas, 50. Instr. ZOOL, UNIV. UTAH, 32-42, asst. prof, 42-46, assoc. prof, 46-51, PROF, 51- Instr, Kansas, 45. Naturalist, U.S. Park Serv, 31; biologist, U.S. Bur. Fisheries, 34; supvr. in charge mosquito abatement, Utah, 35; field supvr. ecol. res, Upper Colo. River Develop. Proj, Glen Canyon, 58, Flaming Gorge, 59, Navajo, 60, Curecanti, 61. Am. Soc. Mammal (v.pres, 55-60, pres, 60-62); Wildlife Soc; Soc. Study Evolution; Am. Soc. Syst. Zool. Taxonomic and anatomical studies of Utah mammals; vertebrate anatomy. Address: Dept. of Biology, University of Utah, Salt Lake City, UT 84112.

DURRELL, CORDELL, b. San Francisco, Calif, Aug. 7, 08; m. 37. GEOLOGY. A.B, California, 31, Ph.D.(geol), 36. Instr. geol, California, 36-37; field geologist, 37-38; instr. GEOL, UNIV. CALIF, Los Angeles, 38-41, from asst. prof. to assoc. prof, 41-51, PROF, 51-63, DAVIS, 63- Assoc. geologist, U.S. Geol. Surv, 43-47; prof, Petroleo Brasileiro, Salvador, Bahia, Brazil, 58 & 59. Am. Geophys. Union; Am. Asn. Petrol. Geol; fel. Geol; Soc. Am. Geologic structure; ore deposits; stratigraphy; metamorphism; petrology. Address: Dept. of Geology, University of California, Davis, CA 95616.

DURRELL, R(ICHARD) H(USTON), b. Cincinnati, Ohio, Dec. 1, 14; m. 46. GEOLOGY. B.A, Cincinnati, 36. Asst, UNIV. CINCINNATI, 46-47, instr. GEOL, 47-54, acting chmn. dept, 54-55, asst. prof, 55-62, ASSOC. PROF, 63-, acting chmn. dept, 62-63. V.pres, Cincinnati Mus. Natural Hist. AAAS; Am. Soc. Photogram; Nat. Asn. Geol. Teachers; Geol. Soc. Am; N.Y. Acad. Sci; Am. Geophys. Union. Geomorphology; glaciology; physiography; aerial photography. Address: Dept. of Geology, University of Cincinnati, Cincinnati, OH 45221.

DURRELL, WILLIAM S, b. Miami, Fla, Oct. 14, 31; m. 53; c. 5. ORGANIC & POLYMER CHEMISTRY. B.S, Florida, 53, Ph.D.(org. chem), 61; Ohio State, 56-57. Chemist, Peninsular Chem. Res, Fla, 53-55, coord. res. & develop, 61-64; res. chemist, Ethyl Corp, La, 55-56; res. assoc, Burke Res. Co, 64-65; group leader, Geigy Chem. Corp, Ala, 65-68, asst. develop. mgr, 68-69, develop. mgr, R.I, 69-70, DIR. RES, PLASTICS & ADDITIVES DIV, CIBA-GEIGY LTD, ARDSLEY, 70- U.S.A.F, 56-58. Am. Chem. Soc. Fluorine compounds; organic synthesis, particularly of polymer additives; polymers for engineering plastics and high temperature service. Address: 56 High Way, Chappaqua, NY 10514.

DURRENBERGER, JOHN A, b. Perham, Minn, Aug. 22, 20; m. 46; c. 3. AERONAUTICAL ENGINEERING, OPERATIONS ANALYSIS. B.Aero.E, Minnesota, 42; Miami (Fla), 45. Supvry. physicist, Hq. Air Proving Ground Command, Eglin Air Force Base, Fla, 54-58; supvry. opers. analyst, Hq. Air Defense Command, Ent Air Force Base, Colo, 58-61; dep. dir. opers. anal, Hq. U.S. Air Forces Europe, Germany, 61-64; chief scientist & chief opers. anal, U.S. Air Force Tactical Air Warfare Ctr, Eglin Air Force Base, 64-67, DIR. OPERS. ANAL, HQ, U.S. AIR FORCES, EUROPE, 67- Secy. Air Force decoration except. serv, 65; Presidential citation, 65. U.S.N, 42-46, Res, 46-, Comdr. Opers. Res. Soc. Am; Am. Ord. Asn. Military operations research. Address: Headquarters, U.S. Air Forces in Europe, Box 8418, APO New York 09633.

DURRETT, LARRY RANDALL, b. Kenedy, Tex, July 21, 36; m. 55; c. 3. ANALYTICAL & ORGANIC CHEMISTRY. B.S, Texas, 57. Chemist, Houston Ref. Lab, SHELL OIL CO, 57-60, res. chemist, Houston Res. Lab, 60-65, res. group leader petrol. process develop, 65-66, asst. mgr, distilling dept, HOUSTON REF, 66-68, asst. mgr, CATALYTIC CRACKING DEPT, 68-69, MGR, 69- AAAS; Am. Chem. Soc; Am. Soc. Test. & Mat. Catalytic cracking; hydrotreating; alkylation; catalytic reforming; methylene and iodine chemistry; gas chromatography; mass spectrometry. Address: Shell Oil Co, Houston Refinery, Catalytic Cracking Dept, P.O. Box 100, Deer Park, TX 77536.

DURRILL, PRESTON LEE, b. Ft. Madison, Iowa, Apr. 4, 36; m. 66. CHEMISTRY, CHEMICAL ENGINEERING. S.B, Mass. Inst. Tech, 57, S.M, 59; Ph.D.(chem. eng), Va. Polytech, 66. Chem. engr, Esso Res. Labs, La, 59-60; from assoc. prof. to PROF. CHEM, RADFORD COL, 65- AAAS; Am. Chem. Soc; Am. Inst. Chem. Eng; Soc. Plastics Eng. Diffusion of gases in solids and molten polymers. Address: Radford College Station, P.O. Box 639, Radford, VA 24141.

DURRUM, EMMETT L(EIGH), b. Spokane, Wash, May 4, 16; m. 41; c. 3. BIOCHEMISTRY. B.S, Harvard, 39; M.D, Stanford, 46. Engineer, Shell Develop. Co, San Francisco, 39-42; med. officer, field research lab, med. dept, U.S. Dept. Army, 46-51, chief biochem. sect, cardio-respiratory disease dept, army med. serv. grad. sch, 51-52, dept. Pharmacol, 52-54, ASSOC. CLIN. PROF, SCH. MED, STANFORD UNIV, 54-; assoc. dir. res, Spinco Div, Beckman Instruments, Inc, 55-62; CHMN. BD. & RES. DIR, DURRUM INSTRUMENT CORP, 62- U.S.A, 42-46. AAAS; Am. Chem. Soc; Am. Soc. Biol. Chem; N.Y. Acad. Sci. Electrophoresis, separations by physical methods for proteins; amino acid; atherosclerosis; computerized amino acid analyzers. Address: Durrum Instrument Corp, 3950 Fabian Way, Palo Alto, CA 94303.

DÜRSCH, FRIEDRICH, b. Dresden, Ger, June 10, 30; m. 51. ORGANIC CHEMISTRY. B.S, Dresden Tech, 52; M.S, Darmstadt Tech, 55, Ph.D.(org. chem), 56. Res. assoc. natural prods, Virginia, 57-60; sr. chemist PHARMACEUTS, Wallace Labs. Div, Carter Prods. N.J, 60-62, asst. dir, 62-63; SR. SCIENTIST, SQUIBB INST. MED. RES, 64- Am. Chem. Soc. Synthetic organic chemistry; derivatives of hydroxylamine; alkaloids; pharmaceuticals; antibiotics; process development. Address: Squibb Institute for Medical Research, New Brunswick, NJ 08903.

DURSCH, H(ARRY) ROBERT, b. Phila, Pa, Sept. 25, 23; m. 50; c. 3. BIOCHEMISTRY, OCEANOGRAPHY. B.S, Pa. State, 47; M.S, Oregon, 50. Asst. instr, Pa. State, 47-48; asst, Oregon, 48-50; instr, Skagit Valley Jr. Col, 50-55; asst, Washington (Seattle), 55-56; CHMN. DIV. NATURAL SCI, SKAGIT VALLEY COL, 56-, Nat. Sci. Found. faculty fel, 64-65. Summers, vis. asst. prof, Summer Inst. Oceanog, 60-65, assoc. dir, 61-64, co-dir, 65. AAAS; Am. Chem. Soc; Am. Asn. Physics Teachers; Nat. Sci. Teachers Asn; Am. Geophys. Union. Trace elements concentration in the sea. Address: Division of Natural Sciences, Skagit Valley College, Mt. Vernon, WA 98273.

DURSO, D(ONALD) F(RANCIS), b. Youngstown, Ohio, Jan. 30, 25; m. 48; c. 5. CELLULOSE CHEMISTRY. B.S, Case, 47; M.S, Purdue, 49, Ph.D.(biochem), 51. Asst, Purdue, 47-48, 48-51; res. chemist, Buckeye Cellulose Corp, Tenn, 51-53, org. group leader, 53-56, assoc. dir. res, 56-64, mgr. res. dept, 64-71; PROF. FOREST SCI, TEX. A&M UNIV, 71- U.S.N.R, 44-46. Building panels derived from agricultural residues; carbon column chromatography of sugars; structure of guar polysaccharide through acid hydrolysis; cellulose composition; structure and preparation of cellulose derivatives; chemistry of pulping and bleaching. Address: Dept. of Forest Science, Texas A&M University, College Station, TX 77843.

DURSO, JOHN WILLIAM, b. Brooklyn, N.Y, Feb. 1, 38; m. 59; c. 4. THEORETICAL PHYSICS. A.B, Cornell, 59; Ph.D.(theoret. physics), Pa. State, 64. Res. asst. physics, Pa. State, 60-64; res. assoc, Inst. Theoret. Physics, Naples, 64-65; theoret. physics, Mich. State, 65-67; ASST. PROF. PHYSICS & COMPUT. STUDIES, MT. HOLYOKE COL, 67- Am. Phys. Soc. Elementary particle physics, especially analytic properties of scattering amplitudes; electromagnetic structure of hadrons. Address: Dept. of Physics, Mount Holyoke College, South Hadley, MA 01075.

DURST, HAROLD EVERETT, b. Morrowville, Kans, Feb. 18, 24; m. 49; c. 1. BIOLOGY, ENVIRONMENTAL SCIENCES. B.S, Kansas State, 48; M.Ed, Colorado, 53; Ph.D.(sci. ed), Oregon State, 67. Teacher, Ness City Pub. Schs, Kans, 48-54, prin, 53-54; off. mgr, Firestone Tire & Rubber Co, 54-57; buyer, Boeing Airplane Co, 57-58; teacher, Wichita Pub. Schs, Kans, 58-61 & 62-63; consult-writer, Biol. Sci. Curriculum Study, 61-62; instr. BIOL, KANS. STATE TEACHERS COL, 63-65, asst. prof, 67-70, ASSOC. PROF, 70- Area consult, Biol. Sci. Curriculum Study, 62-65; dir, sci. workshop, Peace Corps, India, 68; Nat. Sci. Found. In-Serv. Inst. for Sec. Teachers of Sci. & Math, 68-, Summer Inst. Environ. Biol. & Human Ecol, 70. U.S.A, 44-45. AAAS; Am. Inst. Biol. Sci; Am. Educ. Res. Asn. Curriculum evaluation; college biology; affective behavior and assessment of postgraduate needs of high school biology teachers. Address: Dept. of Biology, Kansas State Teachers College, Emporia, KS 66801.

DURST, JACK ROWLAND, b. Stow, Ohio, June 22, 26; m. 48, 67; c. 5. BIOCHEMISTRY, NUTRITION. B.S, Ohio, 48; M.S, Ohio State, 53; fel, Purdue, 53-56, Ph.D.(biochem), 56. Chemist, Goodyear Tire & Rubber Co; res. asst, Kettering Res. Found, Ohio State, 49-53, res. assoc, 53; res. chemist, Swift & Co, 56-57; sr. res. chemist, PILLSBURY CO, 57-60, sr. scientist, 60-66, tech. mgr, 66-68, RES. ASSOC. APPL. RES, 68- U.S.A, 44-46, Qm.C, 48-51, 2nd Lt. Am. Chem. Soc; Inst. Food Technol; Am. Pub. Health Asn. Natural products and their degradation into components; preparation and controlled nutrition of foods; invention of new food forms through control of structure; formulation and fabrication of nutritionally controlled foods for astronauts; proteins; dietary studies. Address: Applied Research, Pillsbury Co, 311 Second St. S.E, Minneapolis, MN 55414.

DURST, LINCOLN KEARNEY, b. Santa Monica, Calif, Aug. 5, 24; m. 56; c. 3. MATHEMATICS. B.A, California, Los Angeles, 45; B.S, Calif. Inst. Tech, 46, fel, 46-51, Ph.D.(math), 52. Instr. math, Rice Univ, 51-55, asst. prof, 55-60, assoc. prof, 60-67; prof, Claremont Men's Col, 67-70; DEP. EXEC. DIR, AM. MATH. SOC, 70- Mem. bd. dirs, Nat. Fedn. Sci. Abstracting & Indexing Serv, 71- AAAS; Am. Math. Soc; Math. Asn. Am; Can. Math. Cong; Soc. Indust. & Appl. Math. Number theory; algebra. Address: American Mathematical Society, P.O. Box 6248, Providence, RI 02904.

DURST, RICHARD A(LLEN), b. New Rochelle, N.Y, Dec. 27, 37; m. 64; c. 3. ANALYTICAL CHEMISTRY. B.S, Rhode Island, 60; Nat. Sci. Found. fel, Mass. Inst. Tech, 61-63, Ph.D.(anal. chem), 63. Nat. Acad. Sci-Nat. Res. Coun. resident res. assoc. CHEM, Nat. Bur. Standards, 63-64; vis. asst. prof, Pomona Col, 64-65; asst. prof, Boston Col, 65-66; res. chemist, ANAL. CHEM. DIV, NAT. BUR. STANDARDS, 66-70, CHIEF ELECTROCHEM. ANAL. SECT, 70- Assoc. mem. comn. electrochem, Int. Union Pure & Appl. Chem, 71-73. AAAS; Am. Chem. Soc; Am. Asn. Clin. Chem. Electroanalytical chemistry; instrumental analysis; electrochemistry; voltammetry; ion-selective electrodes. Address: Analytical Chemical Division, Bldg. 222, Room A219, National Bureau of Standards, Washington, DC 20234.

DURST, RICHARD E(DWARD), b. Warren, Ohio, March 22, 06; m. 31; c. 2. CHEMICAL ENGINEERING. B.S, Otterbein Col, 29; Ph.D.(chem. eng), Ohio State, 48. Instr. chem, Otterbein Col, 29-30; ref. chemist, Capital City Prods. Co, 30-44; res. assoc, Res. Found, Ohio State 44-49; prof. CHEM. ENG, UNIV. MAINE, 49-71, EMER. PROF, 71- Am. Inst. Chem; Am. Inst. Chem. Eng; Tech. Asn. Pulp & Paper Indust; Nat. Soc. Prof. Eng. Vegetable oil refining; boiler water scale formation; recovery of potassium from the mineral polyhalite; flow of non-Newtonian materials; solid-liquid separations. Address: 40 Myrtle St, Orono, ME 04473.

DURY, ABRAHAM, b. New York, N.Y, May 12, 15; m. 40; c. 2. PHYSIOLOGY. B.A, Brooklyn Col, 36; M.Sc, N.Y. Univ, 40; Ph.D.(physiol), George Washington, 47. Physiologist, U.S. Dept. Agr, 40-46; asst. prof. physiol, sch. med, George Washington, 46-49; dir. Dorn Lab. Med. Res, Bradford Hosp, 49-59; tech. dir. geront. lab, Vet. Admin. Hosp, 59-63; head biochem. sci. sect, Nat. Inst. Gen. Med. Sci, 63-66, assoc. chief res. grants br, 66-68; CHIEF RES. BASIC SCI, VET. ADMIN. CENT. OFF, 68- U.S. del, Int. Cong. Geront, 57. U.S.N.R, 43-46, Lt. Fel. AAAS; Endocrine Soc; Am. Physiol. Soc; Soc. Exp. Biol. & Med; fel. Geront. Soc; fel. N.Y. Acad. Sci. Physiology of metabolism; endocrine-nutritional roles in cardiovascular diseases; processes of aging. Address: Veterans Administration Central Office, 810 Vermont Ave. N.W, Washington, DC 20420.

DURY, GEORGE H, b. Hellidon, Eng, Sept. 11, 16. GEOMORPHOLOGY. B.A, Univ. London, 37, M.A, 44, Ph.D.(geomorphol), 51, hon. D.Sc, 71. Lectr. in charge geog. & geol, Enfield Tech. Col, Middlesex, Eng, 46-48; lectr. geog, Birkbeck Col, Univ. London, 49-62; McCaughey prof, Univ. Sydney, 62-69, dean faculty sci, 67-68; PROF. GEOG. & GEOL, UNIV. WIS, MADISON, 69-, CHMN. DEPT. GEOG, 71- Div. staff scientist, water resources div, U.S. Geol. Surv, 60-61; vis. prof, dept. geol, Fla. State Univ, 67. R.A.F, 40-46, Res, 46-58. Australian & N.Z. Asn. Advan. Sci; Royal Geog. Soc; Geol. Soc. London; Australian Geol. Soc; Asn. Am. Geog; Am. Geog. Soc; Inst. Brit. Geog. General theory of meandering valleys; deep weathering and duricrusting; glacial diversions of surface drainage; pedimentation; paleoclimatology. Address: Dept. of Geography & Geology, University of Wisconsin, Madison, WI 53706.

DURYEA, WILLIAM R, b. Port Jervis, N.Y, July 29, 38; m. 61; c. 4. BOTANY, ECOLOGY. B.S, St. Bernardine Siena Col, 62; Ph.D.(biol), St. Bonaventure Univ, 67. ASSOC. PROF. BIOL, ST. FRANCIS COL.(PA), 66- AAAS; Bot. Soc. Am; Ecol. Soc. Am; Animal Behavior Soc; Nat. Wildlife Fedn. Bryophyte morphogenesis; coelenterate regeneration; animal behavior; zoological and botanical taxonomy. Address: Dept. of Biology, St. Francis College, Loretto, PA 15940.

DURYEE, A(BRAM) WILBUR, b. North Hackensack, N.J, July 5, 99; m; c. 3. MEDICINE. B.Sc, Rutgers, 21; M.D, Columbia, 25. PROF. CLIN. MED, POST-GRAD. MED. SCH, N.Y. UNIV, 49-, attend. physician, univ. hosp. Consult; private practice. Dipl, Am. Bd. Internal Med, 37. Fel. Am. Med. Asn; fel. Am. Therapeut. Soc.(pres, 47); fel. Am. Heart Asn.(v.pres, 58, award, 60); fel. N.Y. Acad. Med. Diseases of peripheral blood vessels. Address: 140 E. 54th St, New York, NY 10022.

DURYEE, WILLIAM R(ANKIN), b. Saranac Lake, N.Y, Nov. 11, 05; m. 31; c. 1. CELL PHYSIOLOGY. B.A, Yale, 27, Ph.D.(zool), 33; Bern, Munich, & Copenhagen, 35-36. Asst. biol, Yale, 27-28; instr. zool, Northwestern, 30-35; asst. prof. biol, N.Y. Univ, 36-40; prof. assoc. cmt. on growth, Nat. Res. Coun, 45-46; cytologist, Nat. Cancer Inst, Nat. Insts. Health, U.S. Pub. Health Serv, 47-55; res. prof. EXP. PATH, SCH. MED, GEORGE WASH. UNIV, 55-71, EMER. PROF, 71- Staff assoc, dept. terrestrial magnetism, Carnegie Inst, 47-55; mem. panel cell physiol, Nat. Res. Coun, 52-54; exec. comt, Am. Inst. Biol. Sci, 55-57; sci. adv. comt, Damon Runyon Mem. Fund, 61-68; corp, Marine Biol. Lab, Woods Hole. U.S.A, 40-46, Maj. AAAS; Am. Asn. Anat; Soc. Gen. Physiol.(secy-treas, 51-53); Am. Asn. Cancer Res; Radiation Res. Soc; Am. Soc. Cytol; Am. Inst. Biol. Sci; Int. Soc. Cell Biol; Royal Soc. Med. Physiology of the nucleus; nucleolar origin of cancer; micrurgy; tissue culture of amphibian tumors; cine-photomicrography. Address: 3241 N. Woodrow St, Arlington, VA 22207.

DURZAN, D(ONALD) J(OHN), b. Hamilton, Ont, Aug. 4, 37; m. 59; c. 1. PLANT PHYSIOLOGY, BIOCHEMISTRY. B.Sc, McMaster Univ, 59; Ph.D.(plant physiol), Cornell Univ. 64. Res. off. physiol, Can. Dept. Forestry, 59-68, RES. SCIENTIST & HEAD BIOCHEM. SECT, FOREST ECOL. RES. INST, DEPT. ENVIRON, 68- Res. asst, Cornell Univ, 60-63. AAAS; Am. Soc. Plant Physiol; Can. Soc. Plant Physiol; The Chem. Soc; Can. Soc. Cell Biol; Prof. Inst. Pub. Serv. Can. Metabolism of nitrogenous compounds in relation to growth and development of forest trees. Address: Biochemistry Lab, Forest Ecology Research Institute, Dept. of the Environment, Ottawa, Ont, K1A 0H3, Can.

DUS, KARL M, b. Vienna, Austria, Jan. 2, 32; m. 71. BIOCHEMISTRY. Ph.D.(chem), Univ. Vienna, 58. Res. fel. med, Harvard Med. Sch. & Mass. Gen. Hosp, 58-60; res. assoc. biochem, Brandeis Univ, 60-61; asst. res. chem, Univ. Calif, San Diego, 61-65, assoc. res. chemist I, 65-67, assoc. res. chemist II, 67-68; ASST. PROF. BIOCHEM, UNIV. ILL, URBANA, 68- Investr. genetics & physiol, Nat. Ctr. Sci. Res, Gif-sur-Yvette, France, 65-66; co-prin. investr, NASA grant, 66-68. AAAS; Am. Chem. Soc; Am. Soc. Biol. Chem; Instrument Soc. Am. Protein structure-function; protein sequence; monoxygenases and drug detoxification; evolution of proteins;

bacterial photosynthesis; nitrogen fixation. Address: Dept. of Biochemistry, 390A E. Chemistry, University of Illinois, Urbana, IL 61801.

DUSANIC, DONALD G, b. Chicago, Ill, Dec. 15, 34; m. 71; c. 5. PARASITOLOGY. S.B, Univ. Chicago, 57, S.M, 59, Ph.D.(microbiol), 63. Instr. MICROBIOL, Univ. Chicago, 63-64; asst. prof, UNIV. KANS, 64-68, assoc. prof, 68-71, PROF, 71- Vis. asst. prof. parasitol, Univ. Philippines, 64; Nat. Taiwan Univ, 71; med. consult, Naval Med. Res. Unit No. 2, Taipei, Taiwan. Am. Soc. Parasitol; Soc. Protozool; Am. Soc. Trop. Med. & Hyg; N.Y. Acad. Sci. Immunology and physiology of animal parasites. Address: Dept. of Microbiology, University of Kansas, 2900 Chisholm Dr, Lawrence, KS 66044.

DUSCHATKO, ROBERT W(ILLIAM), b. N.Y.C, Mar. 9, 28; m. 57; c. 4. PETROLEUM GEOLOGY. A.B, Columbia, 49, M.A, 56. Jr. geologist, Meyer & Achtschin, Tex, 54-55; geologist, Pan Am. Petrol. Corp, La, 56-60, sr. geologist, Okla, 60-63, sr. res. scientist, 63-68, RES. GROUP SUPVR, 68-71, AMOCO PROD. CO, 71- AAAS; Soc. Econ. Paleont. & Mineral; Geol. Soc. Am; Am. Asn. Petrol. Geol. Rock fracture orientation; igneous petrology; Deltaic sedimentation; diagenesis of quartzose sandstones; Lacustrine sedimentation. Address: Amoco Production Co, P.O. Box 591, Tulsa, OK 74102.

DUSCHINSKY, ROBERT C(HARLES), b. Vienna, Austria, Oct. 25, 00; nat; m. 32. CHEMISTRY. Ph.D.(chem), Vienna, 26. Chemist, Soc. Indust. Res. & Develop, France, 27-28; Mfrs. Pure Chem. Prod, Paris, 28-29; res. fel, Hoffman-La Roche, Inc, 30-40; N.J, 40-65; assoc. scientist, Sloan-Kettering Inst. Cancer Res, N.Y.C. & Inst. Chem. Natural Substances, Gif-sur-Yvette, France, 65-67; CHEMIST, SWISS INST. EXP. CANCER RES, 67- Am. Chem. Soc; N.Y. Acad. Sci; Am. Asn. Cancer Res. Amino acids in particular resolutions; sugars; synthesis of desthiobiotin and analogs; biotin analogs; medicinal chemistry; synthesis of 5-fluorouracil and derivatives for cancer chemotherapy. Address: Swiss Institute for Experimental Cancer Research, Rue Bugnon 21, 1011 Lausanne, Switz.

DUSENBERRY, JAMES E, b. Beaver City, Nebr, June 29, 21; m. 45; c. 1. PHARMACOGNOSY. B.S, Univ. Nebr, 49, M.S, 52; Am. Found. Pharmaceut. Educ. fel, Univ. Connecticut, 53-55, Ph.D.(pharmacog), 56. Instr. pharmacog, Univ. Nebr, 49-52; asst. prof, MED. CTR, UNIV. ARK, 55-57, assoc. prof, 57-59, PROF. PHARMACEUT. SCI, 65- Grant, Am. Acad. Arts & Sci, 56-57; Eli Lilly Co, 57-58; U.S. Pub. Health Serv, 58-65. U.S.M.C, 42-45. Am. Asn. Cols. Pharm. Natural product chemistry; biosynthesis of simple lysergic acid derivatives by ergot fungus parasitizing Paspalum dilitatum. Address: Dept. of Pharmaceutical Sciences, University of Arkansas Medical Center, Little Rock, AR 72204.

DUSENBURY, JOSEPH H(OOKER), b. Troy, N.Y, Nov. 18, 23; m. 47. PHYSICAL CHEMISTRY. B.S, Union Col, 47; Ph.D.(chem), California, Berkeley, 50. Res. chemist, Am. Cyanamid Co, 47, 50-53; asst. chem, California, 47-50; from head phys. org. chem. sect. to assoc. res. dir, Textile Res. Inst, N.J, 53-61; sect. leader, CHEM. DEPT, DEERING MILLIKEN RES. CORP, 61-64, DEPT. MGR, 64- Mem, Textile Res. Inst. U.S.A, 42-45. Fel. AAAS; Am. Chem. Soc; Fiber Soc; Soc. Rheol; fel. Am. Inst. Chem; fel. Brit. Textile Inst. Reactions of nitrous acid; dyeing and finishing of textiles; polymerization; physical properties and chemical modification of fibers. Address: 413 Overland Dr, Spartanburg, SC 29302.

DU SHANE, JAMES W(ILLIAM), b. Madison, Ind, Apr. 17, 12; m. 39; c. 2. PEDIATRICS, CARDIOLOGY. A.B, DePauw Univ, 33; M.D, Yale, 37. Instr. PEDIAT, MAYO GRAD. SCH. MED, UNIV. MINN, 47-52, asst. prof, 52-57, assoc. prof, 57-61, PROF, 61-, HEAD PEDIAT. CARDIOL. SECT, MAYO CLIN, 69-, head pediat. sect, 57-69. Chmn, coun. rheumatic fever & congenital heart disease, Am. Heart Asn, 59-61; mem. bd. gov, Mayo Clin, 60-; bd. trustees, Mayo Found, 65- Dipl, Am. Bd. Pediat, chmn. sub-bd. cardiol, 60-65. U.S.N.R, 43-46, Lt. Am. Pediat. Soc; Am. Heart Asn; Am. Col. Chest Physicians. Congenital heart disease; pathology; symptomatology; electrocardiology. Address: Mayo Clinic, 200 First St. S.W, Rochester, MN 55901.

DUSHNIK, BEN, b. Minsk, Russia, Aug. 15, 97; nat; m. 30. MATHEMATICS. A.B, Michigan, 25, A.M, 26, Ph.D.(math), 31. Instr. MATH, UNIV. MICH, 25-36, asst. prof, 36-47, assoc. prof, 47-64, prof, 64-67, EMER. PROF, 67- Am. Math. Soc. Transfinite numbers; point-set theory; elementary number theory. Address: 354A West Engineering Bldg, University of Michigan, Ann Arbor, MI 48103.

DUSI, JULIAN L(UIGI), b. Columbus, Ohio, Nov. 10, 20; m. 47. BIOLOGICAL SCIENCES. B.S, Ohio State, 43, M.S, 46, Ph.D.(zool), 49. Asst, Ohio State, 46-49; PROF. ZOOL. & ENTOM, AUBURN UNIV, 49- U.S.A.A.F, 43-45, 2nd Lt. AAAS; Am. Soc. Mammal; Wilson Ornith. Soc; Am. Ornith. Union. Rabbit food habits; bird and mammal behavior and ecology. Address: Dept. of Zoology-Entomology, Auburn University, Auburn, AL 36830.

DUSSEAU, JERRY W(ILLIAM), b. Toledo, Ohio, July 30, 41; m. 66. VERTEBRATE PHYSIOLOGY, ENDOCRINOLOGY. B.A, Earlham Col, 63; M.S, La. State Univ, Baton Rouge, 66, Nat. Insts. Health fel, 67-69, Ph.D.(vert. physiol), 69. ASST. PROF. BIOL, Earlham Col, 69-70; HOPE COL, 70- AAAS. Biological rhythms; endocrine basis for biological clock mechanisms. Address: Dept. of Biology, Hope College, Holland, MI 49423.

DUSTMAN, EUGENE HENRY, b. Poland, Ohio, May 5, 17; m. 40; c. 2. ZOOLOGY. B.Sc, Ohio State, 41, M.S, 43, Ph.D, 49. Field biologist, Ohio State, 40; State Div. Conserv, Ohio, 41; fel, Ohio Div. Conserv, Fish & Wildlife Serv, Wildlife Mgt. Inst. & Ohio State Univ, 41-43, 46-49; leader, Ohio Co-op. Wildlife Res. Unit, Ohio State Univ, 49-59; asst. chief, br. wildlife res, BUR. SPORT FISHERIES & WILDLIFE, D.C, 59-63, DIR. PATUXENT WILDLIFE RES. CTR, 63- U.S.A, 42-45. Wildlife Soc; Am. Soc. Mammal. Ecology and animal behavior. Address: Patuxent Wildlife Research Center, Bureau of Sport Fisheries & Wildlife, Laurel, MD 20810.

DUSTMAN, JOHN HENRY, b. Buffalo, N.Y, Apr. 18, 40; m. 63; c. 2. ZOOLOGY, ENDOCRINOLOGY. B.S, Canisius Col, 61; Ph.D.(zool), Indiana, 66. Asst. prof. ZOOL. & asst. chmn. dept, IND. UNIV. NORTHWEST, 66-70, ASSOC. PROF. & CHMN. DEPT. BIOL, 70-, DIR. NORTHWEST CTR. MED. EDUC, 70- Consult, water pollution, Boise Cascade Corp, 70- Biol. Photog. Asn; Am. Soc. Zool; Soc. Study Reproduction; Nat. Asn. Biol. Teachers; Am. Inst. Biol. Sci; N.Y. Acad. Sci. Chemical nature and biological activity of synthetic steroids on the reproductive system of fowl. Address: Dept. of Zoology, Indiana University Northwest, Gary, IN 46408.

DUSTMAN, ROBERT EARL, b. Caldwell, Idaho, May 14, 25; m. 49; c. 2. PSYCHOLOGY. B.A, Idaho, 51; M.A, Utah, 62, Ph.D.(psychol), 63. Prin, grade sch, Idaho, 51-58; physiol. trainee psychol. VET. ADMIN. HOSP, 61-63, res. assoc, 63-64, RES. PSYCHOLOGIST, 65-; ASSOC. RES. PROF. PSYCHOL. & RES. INSTR. NEUROL, UNIV. UTAH, 65- U.S.N, 43-46. AAAS; Am. Psychol. Asn. Relationship of electrical activity of the brain to behavior. Address: Dept. of Psychology, University of Utah, Salt Lake City, UT 84112.

DUSTO, ARTHUR R, b. Libertyville, Ill, Oct. 22, 29; m. 54; c. 2. MECHANICS, AERONAUTICAL ENGINEERING. B.S, Purdue, 51; M.S, Washington (Seattle), 61, Ph.D.(aeronaut, astronaut), 63. Stress analyst, Northrop Aircraft, 52-55; instr. aeronaut. & astronaut, Washington (Seattle), 60-63; res. specialist AERONAUT. ENG, Boeing Co, 58-64; assoc. prof, Arizona, 64-65; RES. SPECIALIST, BOEING CO, 65- U.S.N. Civil Eng.C, 55-58, Lt. (jg). Am. Inst. Aeronaut. & Astronaut. Matrix formulation of aircraft structural problems; singularities in otherwise continuous media; hypersonic boundary layers and atmospheric flight mechanics. Address: Boeing Co, 20403 68th Ave. & S. Kent, Seattle, WA 98178.

DUSWALT, ALLEN A(INSWORTH), JR, b. N.Y.C, Nov. 18, 32; m. 54; c. 2. ANALYTICAL CHEMISTRY. B.S, Queens Col.(N.Y), 54; M.S, Purdue, 56, Ph.D.(anal. chem), 59. Asst, Purdue, 54-57; RES. CHEMIST, HERCULES, INC, 58- Am. Chem. Soc. Differential thermal analysis; thermal gravimetric analysis; analytical instrumental design; general methods development; gas chromatography. Address: 809 Denton Hollow Rd, R.D. 6, West Chester, PA 19380.

DUSWALT, JOAN M, b. N.Y.C, Mar. 31, 33; m. 54; c. 2. ANALYTICAL CHEMISTRY. B.S, Queens Col.(N.Y), 54; M.S, Purdue Univ, 57; Ph.D.(anal. chem), 62. RES. ANAL. CHEMIST, SUN OIL CO, 60- Am. Chem. Soc. Separation chemistry; analytical applications and molecular structure studies in infrared, nuclear magnetic resonance and ultraviolet spectroscopy. Address: Research & Development Dept, Sun Oil Co, Box 426, Marcus Hook, PA 19061.

DUSZA, JOHN PAUL, b. Bondsville, Mass, Sept. 30, 31; m. 59; c. 4. ORGANIC CHEMISTRY. B.S, Massachusetts, 53, M.S, 55; Ph.D, Yale, 58. Res. chemist, METAB. DISEASE THER. SECT, LEDERLE LAB. DIV, AM. CYANAMID CO, 58-71, SR. RES. CHEMIST, 71- AAAS; Am. Chem. Soc; The Chem. Soc. Steroid and synthetic organic chemistry. Address: Metabolic Disease Therapy Section, Lederle Labs, Pearl River, NY 10965.

DUSZYNSKI, DONALD WALTER, b. Chicago, Ill, July 28, 43; m. 70. PARASITOLOGY, ECOLOGY. B.S, Wis. State Univ-River Falls, 66; univ. assistantship, Colo. State Univ, 66-67, M.S, 68, Ph.D.(zool), 70; Nat. Sci. Found-Ford Found. fel, Univ. Costa Rica, summer 67; Nat. Sci. Found. stipend, Univ. of the Pac, summer 68. ASST. PROF. BIOL, UNIV. N.MEX, 70- Am. Inst. Biol. Sci; Am. Soc. Parasitol; Soc. Protozool; Wildlife Disease Asn. Protozoan parasites of Southwestern animals; intra- and interspecific interactions which take place between parasites inhabiting the same host. Address: Dept. of Biology, University of New Mexico, Albuquerque, NM 87106.

DUTCH, STEPHEN JOHN, JR, b. Trenton, N.J, May 26, 25; m. 53; c. 6. NEUROLOGY. B.A, Pennsylvania, 48, M.D, 52. Resident NEUROL, Jefferson Med. Col, 53-56; resident & fel, sch. med, Pittsburgh, 56-58; assoc, COL. MED, UNIV. NEBR, OMAHA, 58-60, asst. prof, 60-62, ASSOC. PROF, 62-, PEDIAT, 69-, asst. prof, 61-69. U.S.A, 43-46. Am. Acad. Neurol; Am. Psychiat. Asn; Am. Electroencephalog. Soc. Neurologic problems of infancy and childhood. Address: 416 Doctors Bldg, Omaha, NE 68131.

DUTCHER, CLINTON HARVEY, JR, b. Vallejo, Calif, Apr. 28, 32. SOLID STATE PHYSICS, COMMUNICATIONS. B.S, Florida, 59, M.S, 61, Ph.D. (physics), 68. Mem. tech. staff, Bell Tel. Labs, 61-63; instr. physics, Florida, 63-68; GROUP LEADER APPL. RES. ELECTRONIC COMMUN, INC, 68- Ord.C, U.S.A, 53-56. Inst. Elec. & Electronics Eng. Statistical physics; communications theory; information theory. Address: Electronic Communications, Inc, P.O. Box 12248, 1501 72nd St. N, St. Petersburg, FL 33733.

DUTCHER, JAMES D(EAN), b. Denver, Colo, Oct. 15, 12. BIOCHEMISTRY. B.S, Denver, 33, M.S, 35; Rutgers, 35-36; Ph.D.(biochem), Columbia, 40. Instr. biochem. col. physicians & surgeons, Columbia, 39-40; res. biochemist, Squibb Inst, E.R. Squibb & Sons, 41-68; PRIVATE RES, 68- Du Pont fel, Cornell, 39-41. With Off. Sci. Res. & Develop, 44. AAAS; Am. Chem. Soc; Am. Soc. Biol. Chem. Chemistry of steroid hormones; isolation of natural products such as alkaloids, antibiotics and vitamins; determination of molecular structure of natural products; chemistry of amino sugars; biochemistry of nucleic acids. Address: 15 Mine St, New Brunswick, NJ 08901.

DUTCHER, RAY M(ARVIN), b. Jersey City, N.J, Oct. 1, 26; m. 56; c. 1. BACTERIOLOGY. B.S, Fla. South. Col, 49; M.S, Kentucky, 57; Ph.D.(bact), Massachusetts, 60. Cancer res. fel, South. Bio-Res. Inst, Fla, 49-50; biologist & res. assoc, Lederle Labs, N.Y, 50-53; bacteriologist, Ky. Vet. Lab, Inc. & Del-Tor Vet. Clin, 56-57; instr. virol, Massachusetts, 57-60; asst. res. prof. virol, sch. vet. med, Univ. Pa, 60-64, assoc. res. prof, 64-68, assoc. res. prof. microbiol. & chief sect. viral oncol, 68-69; ASST. TO DIR. BIOL. & CHEM. PROD. DEVELOP. DIV, RES. & DEVELOP. DEPT, WYETH LABS, INC, 69- Nat. Insts. Health grant, 60-65; vis. biologist, Am. Inst. Biol. Sci, 62-65; researcher, South. Bio-Res. Inst. & A.P. Cooke Mem. Cancer Res. Lab, Fla. South. Col, 63-65; mem, Int. Comt. Comp. Leukemia, 63-65; head dept. virol, S.Jersey Med. Res. Found, 64-69; chmn, World Comt. Comp. Leukemia Res, 69-71; trustee,

Leukemia Soc, Inc, v.chmn, med. adv. comt. U.S.A.A.F, 44-46, Med.Serv.C. Res, 50-63, Capt. AAAS; Am. Soc. Microbiol; fel. Am. Pub. Health Asn; N.Y. Acad. Sci; U.S. Livestock Sanit. Asn; Electron Micros. Soc. Am; Am. Asn. Cancer Res; Am. Hemat. Soc; Royal Soc. Health; Soc. Exp. Biol. & Med. Virology; immunology; oncology. Address: Research & Development Dept, Wyeth Labs, Inc, Philadelphia, PA 19101.

DUTCHER, RUSSELL R(ICHARDSON), b. Brooklyn, N.Y, Oct. 28, 27; m. 52; c. 2. GEOLOGY. B.A, Connecticut, 51; M.S, Massachusetts, 53; Ph.D. (geol), Pa. State, 60. Instr. geol, Massachusetts, 52-53; res. asst, Pa. State Univ, 56-60, res. assoc, 60-63, asst. prof, 63-66, assoc. prof. 66-70, asst. dir. coal res. sect, 60-70; PROF. GEOL. & CHMN. DEPT, SOUTH. ILL. UNIV, 70- Geol. Soc. Am; Am. Asn. Petrol. Geol; Am. Inst. Mining, Metall. & Petrol. Eng. Coal petrology, petrography and stratigraphy; alteration of coals by igneous intrusives; industrial minerals. Address: Dept. of Geology, Southern Illinois University, Carbondale, IL 62901.

DUTÉ, JOHN C, b. Columbus, Ohio, Sept. 1, 28; m. 50; c. 3. INSTRUMENTATION, ENGINEERING. B.S, Va. Polytech, 50; M.S.E, Michigan, 55. Engr, inst. sci. & tech, Michigan, 51, 53-55; res. engr, Chicago Aerial Industs, Ill, 55-56; engr, inst. sci. & technol, Univ. Mich, Ann Arbor, 56-61; RES. ENGR, INSTRUMENTS, INC, 61- Sig.C, U.S.A, 51-53, 1st Lt. Sr. mem. Inst. Elec. & Electronics Eng.(pres, 70); Instrument Soc. Am. Measurement systems; application of analog and digital computers; infrared scanning systems; data transmission; digital data processing; data acquisition systems; industrial process control; computer interfacing. Address: Information Instruments, Inc, 62 Enterprise Dr, Ann Arbor, MI 48103.

DuTEMPLE, OCTAVE J, b. Hubbell, Mich, Dec. 10, 20; m. 51; c. 2. NUCLEAR & CHEMICAL ENGINEERING. B.S, Michigan Tech, 48, M.S, 49; M.B.A, Northwestern, 55. Assoc. chem. engr. fuel reprocessing, Argonne Nat. Lab, 49-58; EXEC. SECY, AM. NUCLEAR SOC, 58- U.S.A.A.F, 45. AAAS; Am. Nuclear Soc; Am. Inst. Chem. Eng; Am. Chem. Soc. Administration of scientific society; economics of nuclear industry; archeology, prehistoric copper. Address: American Nuclear Society Inc, 244 E. Ogden Ave, Hinsdale, IL 60521.

DUTHIE, HAMISH, b. Aberdeen, Scotland, Aug. 30, 38; m. 62; c. 4. FRESHWATER BIOLOGY, LIMNOLOGY. B.Sc, Univ. Col. N.Wales, 60, Ph.D. (biol), 64. Lectr. BIOL, UNIV. WATERLOO, 63-65, asst. prof, 65-68, ASSOC. PROF, 68- Phycol. Soc. Am; Am. Soc. Limnol. & Oceanog; Can. Bot. Asn. Primary production of phytoplankton and relation to physical and chemical factors; biology of reservoirs; biological aspects of reservoir management; taxonomy of diatoms. Address: 241 Park Lawn Pl, Waterloo, Ontario, Can.

DUTHIE, W(ILLIAM) D(WIGHT), b. Pullman, Wash, June 30, 12. METEOROLOGY. B.A, Washington (Seattle), 35, fel, 35-38, M.S, 37; J.S.K. fel, Princeton, 38-40, Ph.D.(math), 40. Instr. math, Michigan, 40-46; aerol, NAVAL POSTGRAD. SCH, 45-46, prof, 46-63, chmn. dept, 47-63, prof. METEOROL, 63-71, distinguished prof, 64-70, EMER. PROF, 71- Instr, Midshipmen's Sch, Chicago, Ill, 40-42, U.S.N.R, 40-46. Am. Math. Soc; Am. Geophys. Union. Abstract algebra; synoptic meteorology; dynamic meteorology; lattice theory; mathematical logic. Address: Route 1, 62 Mt. Devon Rd, Carmel, CA 93921.

DUTINA, DRAGOMIR, b. New York, N.Y, May 26, 25; m. 46; c. 5. ANALYTICAL CHEMISTRY, RADIOCHEMISTRY. B.S, City Col. New York, 48; M.S, Rutgers, 49. Anal. chemist, U.S. Pub. Health Serv, 50-51; Knolls Atomic Power Lab, GEN. ELEC. CO, 51-57, chemist radiochem, 57-63, anal. chemist, power tube dept, 63-64, VALLECITOS ATOMIC LAB, 64-70, MGR, LIQUID METALS DEVELOP, 70- U.S.A, 43-46, Sgt. Am. Chem. Soc; Am. Soc. Test. & Mat. Analysis of nuclear reactor materials, particularly liquid metals; radiochemical studies of nuclear reactor coolants including water, liquid metals and organics; sodium chemistry and technology. Address: Vallecitos Atomic Lab, General Electric Co, P.O. Box 846, Pleasanton, CA 94566.

DUTKA, BERNARD J, b. Ft. William, Ont, Oct. 5, 32; m. 57; c. 2. MICROBIOLOGY. B.A, Queen's Univ.(Ont), 55, Hons, 57, M.Sc.(microbiol. & immunol), 64; Duke Univ, 64. Lab. supvr, Kingston Gen. Hosp, Ont, 57-66; pub. health eng. div, Dept. Nat. Health & Welfare, 66-71; HEAD MICROBIOL. SECT, CAN. CTR. INLAND WATERS, DEPT. ENVIRON, 71- Int. Asn. Great Lakes Res. Development of water pollution methodology; role of microorganisms in recycling of nutrients from the sediment and sediment-water interface; taxonomy of bacteria in sediments and water. Address: Microbiology Lab, Canada Centre for Inland Waters, Dept. of Environment, 867 Lakeshore Rd, Box 5050, Burlington, Ont, Can.

DUTKA, JACQUES, b. N.Y.C, Dec. 29, 19; m. 45; c. 2. MATHEMATICS. B.S, City Col, 39; A.M, Columbia, 40, Ph.D.(math), 43; George Washington, 40-41. Asst. statistician, U.S. War Dept, 42; asst. res. mathematician, applied math. panel, Columbia, 43; instr. math, Princeton, 46-47; asst. prof, Rutgers, 47-53; mathematician, Norden-Ketay Corp, 53-56; sr. engr, Radio Corp. of Am, 56-59, leader, 59-61, mgr, 61-63; staff scientist, Ford Instrument Co, 64-66, systs. anal. & eval. mgr, 66-67; STAFF SCIENTIST, Sperry-Rand Corp, 67; Riverside Res. Inst, 67-70; AM. TEL. & TEL. CO, 71- Adj. assoc. prof. elec. eng, Columbia, 54-59, adj. prof, 59- Consult, opers. res. group, U.S. Dept. Navy, 44-45. Consult, with Off. of Naval Res, 46-47. Am. Math. Soc; Inst. Math. Statist. Probability; statistics; system analysis; communication theory; numerical analysis and computer applications. Address: 39 Claremont Ave, New York, NY 10027.

DUTRA, FRANK ROBERT, b. Sacramento, Calif, Jan. 7, 16; m. 46. PATHOLOGY. A.B, Northwestern, 40, M.S, 41, M.D, 42. Intern, City Hosp, Cleveland, Ohio, 41-42; res. pathologist, hosp, Western Reserve, 42-43; Rocke Legal Med. fel, Harvard, 43-44; asst. prof. indust. & forensic path, Kettering Lab, Cincinnati, 47-48, assoc. prof, 49-52; asst. clin. prof. PATH, MED. SCH, UNIV. CALIF, SAN FRANCISCO, 53-62, ASSOC. CLIN. PROF, 62-; PATHOLOGIST. & DIR. LABS, EDEN HOSP, 54- Pathologist, Sutter Hosp, Sacramento, 53-54; consult, San Francisco Vet. Admin. Hosp, 53-; Martinez Vet. Admin. Hosp, Oakland, 59-; U.S. Naval Hosp, 63-; Santa Clara County Med. Ctr, 63- Civilian with Off. Sci. Res. & Develop, 44; Med.C, U.S.A, 44-47. Fel. Am. Med. Asn; Am. Soc. Clin. Path; Am. Asn. Path. & Bact; fel. Am. Col. Path. Pathogenic aspects of certain metals; carcinogenesis; physiologic aspects of heat; toxicology of some industrial substances; surgical and clinical pathology. Address: Eden Hospital 20103 Lake Chabot Rd, Castro Valley, CA 94546.

DUTRA OLIVEIRA, JOSE EDUARDO, b. São Paulo, Brazil, Dec. 10, 27; m. 53; c. 6. NUTRITION, INTERNAL MEDICINE. M.D, Univ. São Paulo, 51. Asst, Vanderbilt Univ, 53-55; Rockefeller Found. fel, Tulane Univ, La. & Univ. Cincinnati, 55; Pan. Am. Health Orgn. fel, Inst. Nutrit. of Cent. Am. & Panama, 62-63; PROF. NUTRIT, MED. SCH. RIBEIRAO PRETO, UNIV. SAO PAULO, 65-, ASST. PROF. MED, 68- Latin Am. Nutrit. Soc.(1st pres, 66); Brazilian Med. Asn. Protein foods for infant feeding; metabolic studies in normal and malnourished children; experimental nutrition; studies on soya, rice, common beans and corn, including aspects of agriculture, animal nutrition and human nutrition. Address: Faculty of Medicine, Medical School of Ribeirão Prêto, University of São Paulo, 14100 Ribeirão Prêto, São Paulo, Brazil.

DUTRA, RAMIRO C(ARVALHO), b. Ponta Delgada, Portugal, Sept. 27, 31; U.S. citizen; m. 58; c. 2. ORGANIC & FOOD CHEMISTRY. B.S, California, Davis, 54, M.S, 56, Ph.D.(agr. chem), 59. Jr. specialist dairy indust, Calif. Agr. Exp. Sta, 54-57, asst. specialist food chem, 57-59; asst. prof. chem, CALIF. STATE POLYTECH. COL, 59-64, assoc. prof, 64-69, PROF. FOODS & NUTRIT. & CHMN. DEPT, 69- Inst. Food Technol; Soc. Nutrit. Educ. Isolation and identification of organoleptic compounds; non-enzymatic browning of foods; fortification of cereal proteins; technology of proteins from unconventional sources. Address: Dept. of Foods & Nutrition, California State Polytechnic College, Pomona, CA 91766.

DUTRO, J(OHN) THOMAS, JR, b. Columbus, Ohio, May 20, 23; m. 48; c. 3. PALEONTOLOGY. A.B, Oberlin Col, 48; scholar, Yale, 49-50, M.S, 50, Ph.D.(geol), 53. GEOLOGIST, U.S. GEOL. SURV, 48-; RES. ASSOC, SMITHSONIAN INST, 62- Mem. geol. panel, Bd. Civil Serv. Exam, 58-65; chief paleont. & stratig. br, U.S. Geol. Surv, 62-68, mem. geol. names comt, 62-68, 70-; secy-treas, Am. Geol. Inst, 66-71. U.S.A.A.F, 43-46. AAAS; Geol. Soc. Am; Arctic Inst. N.Am; Paleont. Soc; Brit. Palaeont. Asn; Am. Geol. Inst. Devonian, Carboniferous and Permian brachiopods; late Paleozoic stratigraphy; paleogeography of Alaskan Paleozoic. Address: Room E-325, U.S. National Museum, Washington, DC 20242.

DUTT, GORDON R(ICHARD), b. Choteau, Mont, Oct. 25, 29; m. 54; c. 2. SOIL CHEMISTRY. B.S, Mont. State Col, 56; M.S, Purdue, 59, Ph.D.(soil chem), 60. Asst. res. irrigationist, California, 60-64; assoc. prof. SOIL & WATER CONSERV, UNIV. ARIZ, 64-68, PROF, 68- U.S.N, 48-52. AAAS; Soil Sci. Soc. Am; Soil Conserv. Soc. Am. Physical chemistry of soil and water systems; water quality and ground water hydrology. Address: Dept. of Agricultural Chemistry & Soils, University of Arizona, Tucson, AZ 85721.

DUTT, RAY H(ORN), b. Bangor, Pa, Aug. 26, 13; m. 46; c. 2. ANIMAL SCIENCE. B.S, Pa. State, 41; M.S, Wisconsin, 42, Ph.D.(genetics), 48. Asst. animal husbandman, UNIV. KY, 48-51, assoc. animal husbandman, 51-58, PROF. ANIMAL SCI, 58- Ed, Jour. Animal Sci, 64-66. U.S.M.C, 43-46, Maj. Fel. AAAS; Biomet. Soc; Genetics Soc. Am; Am. Dairy Sci. Asn; Am. Soc. Animal Sci.(pres, 67-68). Physiology of reproduction in farm animals. Address: 437 Bristol Rd, Lexington, KY 40502.

DUTTA, SARADINDU, b. Dacca, Brit. India, Jan. 28, 31; m. 62; c. 3. PHARMACOLOGY. B.Sc, Calcutta, 52, G.V.Sc, 53; M.S, Wisconsin, 57; Ph.D. (pharmacol), Ohio State, 62. Res. asst. animal physiol, Indian Vet. Res. Inst, 54-57; res. assoc. PHARMACOL, OHIO STATE UNIV, 63-64, instr, 64-65, asst. prof, 65-70, ASSOC. PROF, 70- Res. grants, Nat. Heart Inst, 65-68, Cent. Ohio Heart Asn, 66-68. Determining the relationship between the uptake and subcellular partitioning of radio-labeled cardiac drugs, such as ouabain, quinidine and digoxin and the development of the pharmacological effects. Address: 220 Hamilton Hall, Ohio State University, 1645 Neil Ave, Columbus, OH 43210.

DUTTA, SHIB PRASAD, b. Calcutta, India, Nov. 27, 35; m. 69. ORGANIC & MEDICINAL CHEMISTRY. B.Sc, Univ. Calcutta, 55, M.Sc, 58, Coun. Sci. & Indust. Res. Govt. India fel, 65-67, Ph.D.(org. chem), 67. Chemist, Alkali & Chem. Corp. India, Ltd, 57-60; sr. chemist, Union Carbide India, Ltd, 60-62; res. chemist, Jadavpur Univ, 62-64; res. fel, Bose Inst, Calcutta, 65-67; res. assoc. med. chem, sch. pharm, State Univ. N.Y. Buffalo, 67-69; CANCER RES. SCIENTIST, ROSWELL PARK MEM. INST, 69- Chemistry of natural products; chemistry and synthesis of modified nucleosides in t-RNA. Address: Roswell Park Memorial Institute, General Clinical Research Center, 666 Elm St, Buffalo, NY 14203.

DUTTA, S(ISIR) K(AMAL), b. Bengal, India, Aug. 28, 28; m. 55; c. 1. GENETICS. B.S, Dacca, 49; M.S, Kans. State, 58, Ph.D.(genetics), 60. Lectr. biol, K.N. Col, Calcutta Univ, 49-50; asst. plant sci, Agr. Res. Inst, Calcutta, 50-56; exp. sta, Kans. State, 56-59; res. assoc. bot, Chicago & Columbia, 59-61; dir, Pineapple Res. Sta, Malaya, 61-64; res. assoc. biol, Rice Univ, 64-65; asst. prof, Tex. South. Univ, 65-66; chmn. div. sci. & math, Jarvis Christian Col, 66-67; PROF. MOLECULAR GENETICS, HOWARD UNIV, 67- AAAS; Genetics Soc. Am; Am. Soc. Microbiol. Molecular biology; microbial genetics. Address: Dept. of Botany, Howard University, Washington, DC 20001.

DUTTON, A(RTHUR) M(ORLAN), b. Des Moines, Iowa, July 28, 23; m. 45; c. 2. STATISTICS. B.S, Iowa State, 45, Ph.D.(statist), 51. Instr. & res. assoc. statist, Iowa State, 47-51; instr. radiation biol, Univ. Rochester, 51-53, asst. prof, 53-61, assoc. prof, 61-68, lectr. math, 51-57; PROF. MATH. SCI, FLA. TECHNOL. UNIV, 68-, CHMN. DEPT, 69- U.S.N.R, 43-51, Lt. (jg). AAAS; Am. Statist. Asn; Biomet. Soc; Inst. Math. Statist; Am. Math. Soc. Statistical techniques; mathematics and statistics education. Address: Florida Technological University, Box 25000, Orlando, FL 32816.

DUTTON, CARL E(VANS), b. Dunkirk, Ohio, Jan. 24, 04; m. 30; c. 2. GEOLOGY. A.B, DePauw, 26; A.M, Illinois, 28; Ph.D.(geol), Minnesota, 31. Asst. geol, Illinois, 26-28; instr, Minnesota, 28-36; asst. prof. geog. & geol, Wayne, 36-42; vis. asst. prof. geol, Michigan, 42-43; geologist, U.S. GEOL. SURV, 43-46, regional geologist, N.Cent. Region, 46-62, RES. GEOLOGIST, 62- Comt. iron ore resources, U.N, 53-54. Geol. Soc. Am; Soc. Econ. Geol. Economic and structural geology in Lake Superior region; iron-ore deposits. Address: 222 Science Hall, University of Wisconsin, Madison, WI 53706.

DUTTON, DAVID B, b. Asheville, N.C, Nov. 19, 26. PHYSICS. B.S, Case, 47; Ph.D.(physics), Illinois, 52. Res. assoc. OPTICS, UNIV. ROCHESTER, 53-56, asst. prof, 56-59, sr.res.assoc, 59-61, assoc.prof, 61-63, SR. TECH. ASSOC, 63- Fulbright fel, Ecole Normale Superieure, Paris, 52-53. U.S.N.R, 45-46. AAAS; fel. Am. Phys. Soc; Optical Soc. Am. Optics; solid state physics. Address: Institute of Optics, University of Rochester, Rochester, NY 14627.

DUTTON, DONNELL W(AYNE), b. St. Louis, Mo, Sept. 24, 13; m. 40; c. 3. AEROSPACE ENGINEERING. B.S, Missouri, 35, M.E, 59; M.S, Ga. Inst. Tech, 40. Designer, Allis-Chalmers Mfg. Co, Ill, 35-38; chief engr, Monocoupe Aircraft Co, Mo, 39; stress analyst, Curtiss-Wright Aircraft Corp, 40; asst. prof. AERONAUT. ENG, GA. INST. TECHNOL, 40-43, PROF, 43-, dir. Guggenheim Sch. Aeronaut, 43-63, PROF, 63- Sci. adv. res. & develop. div, gen. staff, U.S. War Dept, 46-47. Consult, Nat. Adv. Comt. Aeronaut; res. & develop. div, dept. army, 50-58; Asst. Secy. Defense for Res. & Eng, 56- Assoc. fel. Am. Inst. Aeronaut. & Astronaut; Am. Soc. Eng. Educ; Am. Helicopter Soc. Structural analysis; design; helicopter; aircraft. Address: School of Aerospace Engineering, Georgia Institute of Technology, Atlanta, GA 30332.

DUTTON, FREDERIC B(OOTH), b. Cleveland, Ohio, Dec. 24, 06; m. 30; c. 2. INORGANIC CHEMISTRY. A.B, Oberlin Col, 28, A.M, 32; Ph.D.(chem), Western Reserve, 37. Teacher, high sch, Ohio, 30-31; instr. chem, Baldwin-Wallace Col, 31-34, asst. prof, 34-39; instr, Yale, 39-40; prof, Olivet Col, 41; assoc. prof, Baldwin-Wallace Col, 41-47; MICH. STATE UNIV, 47-49, prof, 50-57, head sci. & math. teaching ctr, 57-64, 65-67, PROF. CHEM. & DEAN LYMAN BRIGGS COL, 67- Prog. dir, Nat. Sci. Found, 64-65. AAAS; Am. Chem. Soc. Nat. Asn. Res. Sci. Teaching (pres, 64). Science education. Address: 931 Wick Ct, East Lansing, MI 48823.

DUTTON, GUY G(ORDON) S(TUDDY), b. London, Eng, Feb. 26, 23; m. 51; c. 3. ORGANIC CHEMISTRY. B.A, Cambridge, 43, M.A, 46; M.Sc, London, 52; Ph.D.(agr. biochem), Minnesota, 55. Jr. sci. officer, United Kingdom Govt, 43-45; lectr. org. & inorg. chem, Sir John Cass Col, 45-49; asst. prof. ORG. CHEM, UNIV. B.C, 49-59, assoc. prof, 59-64, PROF, 64- Vis. prof, Univ. Grenoble, 65-66; NATO lectr, Tech. Univ. Denmark & Max Planck Inst, Freiburg, 68. Fel. Brit. Chem. Soc; fel. Chem. Inst. Can. Carbohydrate chemistry, particularly structures of polysaccharides. Address: Dept. of Chemistry, University of British Columbia, Vancouver, B.C, Can.

DUTTON, HERBERT J(ASPER), b. Evansville, Wis, May 30, 14; m. 37; c. 3. CHEMISTRY. B.A, Wisconsin, 36, M.A, 38, Ph.D.(plant physiol), 40. Asst. bot. & chem, Wisconsin, 39-41; assoc. chemist, west. regional res. lab, bur. agr. & indust. chem, U.S. DEPT. AGR, 41-45, chemist, 45-48, HEAD CHEM. & PHYS. PROPERTIES INVESTS, NORTH.UTILIZATION RES. & DEVELOP. DIV, 53- Superior serv. award, U.S. Dept. Agr, 56, res. award, 57; Can. res. award, 61. Am. Chem. Soc; Am. Oil Chemists' Soc; Simulation Coun. Quantum efficiency of carotenoid-sensitized photosynthesis; instrumental methods of lipid separation and characterization of lipids; fatty acid biosynthesis; kinetics and mechanism of heterogeneous and homogeneous catalytic hydrogenation; analog simulation. Address: Northern Utilization Research & Development Division, U.S. Dept. of Agriculture, 1815 N. University, Peoria, IL 61604.

DUTTON, JOHN A(LTNOW), b. Detroit, Mich, Sept. 11, 36; m. 62; c. 2. METEOROLOGY. B.S, Univ. Wis, 58, M.S, 59, Ph.D.(meteorol), 62. Asst. prof. METEOROL, PA. STATE UNIV, 65-68, assoc. prof, 68-71, PROF, 71- Expert, systs. eng. group, res. & tech. div, Air Force Systs. Command, 65- U.S.A.F, 62-65, 1st Lt. Am. Meteorol. Soc; Math. Asn. Am. Theoretical fluid mechanics; atmospheric dynamics and energetics of the general circulation; turbulence. Address: Dept. of Meteorology, Pennsylvania State University, 503 Deike Bldg, University Park, PA 16802.

DUTTON, RICHARD W, b. London, Eng, May 16, 30; U.S. citizen; m. 54; c. 2. CELL BIOLOGY, IMMUNOLOGY. B.A, Cambridge, 52, M.A, 55; Ph.D.(biochem), London, 55. Fel, med. sch, London, 55-56; vis. lectr. biochem, Med. Col. Va, 57-58; res. instr. biochem. & med, sch. med. & dent, Rochester, 58-59; asst. lectr. chem. path, med. sch. London, 59-62; assoc. exp. path, Scripps Clin. & Res. Found, 62-68; assoc. prof. BIOL, UNIV. CALIF, SAN DIEGO, 68-70, PROF, 70- Am. Cancer Soc. Dernham fel, 63-68. Am. Soc. Immunol; Fedn. Am. Socs. Exp. Biol; Am. Soc. Exp. Path; Brit. Biochem. Soc; Brit. Soc. Immunol. Cellular immunology; molecular basis of antigen stimulation. Address: Dept. of Biology, University of California, San Diego, P.O. Box 109, La Jolla, CA 92037.

DUTTON, ROBERT E(DWARD), JR, b. Milford, N.H, Aug. 11, 24; m. 58; c. 2. PHYSIOLOGY, INTERNAL MEDICINE. Gettysburg Col, 42-43; The Citadel, 43-44; Hopkins, 44-45; M.D, Med. Col. Va, 49. Instr. med, State Univ. N.Y. Upstate Med. Center, 56-59; Nat. Heart Inst. fel. environ. med, sch. hyg. & pub. health. & med, sch. med, Hopkins, 59-61, instr. environ. med, sch. hyg. & pub. health, 61-64, asst. prof, 64-68; ASSOC. PROF. PHYSIOL, ALBANY MED. COL, 68-, MED, 70- Clin. investr, U.S. Vet. Admin, 61-64; asst. chief phys. med. & rehab, Baltimore City Hosp, Md, 64-68; consult. pulmonary diseases, Vet. Admin. Hosp, Baltimore, 67-68; attend. physician, Albany Med. Ctr. Hosp, 70-; Vet. Admin. Hosp, Albany, 70-; adj. prof, Rensselaer Polytech. Inst, 71- U.S.A, 43-46; U.S.A.F, 51-53. Am. Fedn. Clin. Res; Am. Thoracic Soc; Am. Physiol. Soc. Pulmonary physiology, particularly control of respiration; pulmonary diseases. Address: Dept. of Physiology, Albany Medical College, Albany, NY 12208.

DUTTON, WALTER ARTHUR, b. Montreal, Que, Feb. 27, 39; m. 69. INORGANIC CHEMISTRY. B.Sc, McGill, 60, Prov. Que. studentship, 60-61, Nat. Res. Coun. Can. fel, 62-65, Ph.D.(inorg. chem), 65. Res. fel, organogermanium compounds, Sussex, 65-67; RES. CHEMIST, NORANDA RES. CTR, 68- Brit. Chem. Soc; Chem. Inst. Can; Am. Chem. Soc. Information retrieval; applications of computers to process control; chemistry of selenium and tellurium. Address: Noranda Research Center, 240 Hymus Blvd, Pointe Claire, Que, Can.

DUTTWEILER, DAVID W(ILLIAM), b. Buffalo, N.Y, Sept. 15, 27; m. 53; c. 5. SANITARY ENGINEERING. B.S.E, Michigan, 48; M.S.E, Hopkins, 57, Ph.D. (sanit. eng), 63. Designer struct. eng, T.H. McKaig, Consult. Engr, N.Y, 48-49; instr. sanit. eng, Army Eng. Sch, Med. Serv. Corps, U.S. Army, 49-51, Med. Field Serv. Sch, 52-53, sanit. engr, Hq, Austria, 53-55, Med. Lab, Europe, 55-56, Environ. Hyg. Agency, 57-58, chief sanit. eng. div, 58-60, dept. sanit. eng, Walter Reed Army Inst. Res, 62-65, sanit. eng. res. sect, Army Med. Res. & Develop. Command, D.C, 65-66, chief sanit. engr, surg, Army Viet Nam, 67, instr, Army Med. Field Serv. Sch, 68-69; DIR. SOUTHEAST WATER LAB, ENVIRON. PROTECTION AGENCY, 69- Res. assoc, Univ. Ga, 69-; mem. comn. environ. health, Armed Forces Epidemiol. Bd, 70- Med.Serv.C, U.S.A, 49-69, Lt. Col.(Ret). AAAS; Am. Soc. Civil Eng; Am. Pub. Health Asn; Nat. Soc. Prof. Eng; Water Pollution Control Fedn; Am. Conf. Govt. Indust. Hygienists; Am. Acad. Environ. Eng; N.Y. Acad. Sci; Conf. Fed. Environ. Eng. Mathematical models in sanitary engineering; research management; water quality control; heat exchange in natural waters; environmental health. Address: Southeast Water Lab, Environmental Protection Agency, College Station Rd, Athens, GA 30601.

DUTY, ROBERT C, b. Morrison, Ill, Sept. 28, 31; m. 58; c. 2. ORGANIC & PHYSICAL CHEMISTRY. B.S, Illinois, 53; cert. meteorol, St. Louis, 54; M.Ed, Midwestern, 56; Ph.D.(org. chem), Iowa, 61. Sr. chemist, petrol. prod. lab, Humble Oil & Refining Co, La, 60-61; assoc. prof. CHEM, West. State Col. Colo, 61-63; ILL. STATE UNIV, 63-67, PROF, 67- U.S.A.F, 53-57, Res, 57-, Capt. AAAS; Am. Chem. Soc. Organic polarography; gas chromatography; inductive and field effects of quaternization reactions and organophosphorus chemistry. Address: Dept. of Chemistry, Illinois State University, Normal, IL 61761.

DUVAL, ADDISON (McGUIRE), b. Va, July 1, 02; m. 30; c. 2. MEDICINE, PSYCHIATRY. M.D, Med. Col. of Va, 29. Intern & res. psychiat, St. Elizabeths Hosp, D.C, 29-32, med. officer, 32-53, asst. supt, 53-59; from instr. to clin. prof. psychiat, sch. med, George Washington, 34-59; dir, Mo. Div. of Mental Diseases, 59-62; clin. prof. psychiat, sch. med, Missouri, 59-62; DIR, training & res, Eastern State Hosp, Va, 62-63; DIV. MENTAL HEALTH, GA. DEPT. PUB. HEALTH, 63-; CLIN. PROF. PSYCHIAT, SCH. MED, EMORY UNIV, 63- Dipl, Am. Bd. Psychiat. & Neurol; cert, Ment. Hosp. Admin. Fel. Am. Col. Psychiat; fel. Am. Med. Asn; fel. Am. Psychiat. Asn.(v.pres, 64-65); fel. Am. Pub. Health Asn. Clinical and administrative psychiatry. Address: Division of Mental Health, Georgia Dept. of Public Health, 47 Trinity Ave. S.W, Atlanta, GA 30334.

DUVAL, ANNA MARIE, b. Denver, Colo, Nov. 1, 13. BIOCHEMISTRY. A.B, Denver, 34, M.A, 36; Child Res. Council fel, Colorado, 36-43, Ph.D.(biochem), 42. Instr. chem, Cent. Sch. of Nursing, 34-36; asst. prof. CHEM, Colorado, 43-48; sch. nursing, Denver, 48-52; instr, UNIV. MINN, DULUTH, 52-54, asst. prof, 54-61, assoc. prof, 61-70, PROF, 70- Am. Chem. Soc. Acclimatization to Hypoxia. Address: 1122 Chester Park Dr, Duluth, MN 55812.

DUVAL, CLAIBORNE ALEXANDER, JR, b. Austin, Tex, Jan. 12, 19; m. 39; c. 2. CHEMICAL ENGINEERING. B.S, Texas, 42. Process engr, Beaumont Tech. Dept, Mobil Oil Corp, 41-48, supvr. res. & develop, Beaumont Labs, 49-55, chief process engr, 56-58, sr. technologist, 58-59, mgr. process res. & develop, MOBIL CHEM. CO, Tex, 60-66, tech. dir. res. & develop, N.Y, 66-67, asst. mgr. res. & develop, N.J, 67-68, MGR, RES. & DEVELOP. LABS, TEX, 68- Am. Chem. Soc; Am. Inst. Chem. Eng. Research management and organization; process development; petrochemicals. Address: 1230 Nottingham, Beaumont, TX 77706.

DU VAL, MERLIN K(EARFOTT), b. Montclair, N.J, Oct. 12, 22; m. 44; c. 3. MEDICINE, SURGERY. A.B, Dartmouth Col, 43; M.D, Cornell, 46. Instr. surg, sch. med, State Univ. N.Y, 54-55, asst. prof, 55-56; assoc. prof, sch. med, Oklahoma, 57-60, prof. & asst. dir. med. center, 61-63; dean col. med, Univ. Ariz, 64-71; ASST. SECY. HEALTH & SCI. AFFAIRS, DEPT. HEALTH, EDUC. & WELFARE, 71- Asst. attend. surgeon, U.S. Vet. Admin. Hosp, N.Y, 55-56; U.S. Naval Hosp, N.Y, 55-56. Markle scholar, 56-61. Dipl, Nat. Bd. Med. Exam, 47; Am. Bd. Surg. Med.C, U.S.N, 47-49. Am. Surg. Asn; Soc. Univ. Surg; Am. Med. Asn; Am. Col. Surg. Address: Dept. of Health, Education & Welfare, 330 Independence Ave. S.W, Washington, DC 20201.

DUVALL, ARNDT JOHN, III, b. St. Paul, Minn, Jan. 14, 31; m. 56; c. 4. OTOLOGY, OTOLARYNGOLOGY. B.A, Minnesota, 52, M.D, 55, M.S, 62. Nat. Insts. Health spec. fel, Iowa, 61-62; Karolinska Hosp. & Karolinska Inst, Sweden, 62-63; asst. prof. OTOLARYNGOL, UNIV. MINN, MINNEAPOLIS, 63-67, assoc. prof, 67-70, PROF, 70- Res. asst, Minn. Vet. Hosps, 63- Med.C, 56-58, Capt. AAAS; Soc. Head & Neck Surg; Am. Laryngol, Rhinol. & Otol. Soc; Am. Acad. Ophthal. & Otolaryngol; Am. Acad. Facial Plastic & Reconstruct. Surg; Am. Col. Surg; Am. Med. Asn. Anatomy, pathology and physiology of the ear, particularly the use of electron microscopy. Address: Dept. of Otolaryngology, University of Minnesota, 412 Union St. S.E, Minneapolis, MN 55445.

DUVALL, DAVID SCOTT, b. Denver, Colo, Sept. 20, 40; m. 61; c. 4. PHYSICAL METALLURGY. B.S, Colo. Sch. Mines, 62; M.S, Rensselaer Polytech, 69. Metall. engr, mat. develop. lab, Fla. Res. & Develop. Center, PRATT & WHITNEY AIRCRAFT, 62-63, RES. ASSOC, adv. mat. res. & develop. lab, 63-70, MAT. ENG. & RES. LAB, 71- Chmn. wrought nickel alloys subcomt. & mem. high alloys comt. & brazing res. cubcomt, Welding Res. Coun, 68- Am. Welding Soc.(William Spraragen Award, 66 & 69); Am. Inst. Mining, Metall. & Petrol. Eng; Am. Soc. Metals. Behavior of metals during joining operations; characteristics and properties of heat-resistant nickel alloys; mechanisms and characteristics of fusion-welding, brazing, and diffusion-bonding processes. Address: Materials Engineering & Research Lab, Pratt & Whitney Aircraft, Bldg. 260, Middletown, CT 06457.

DUVALL, GEORGE E(VERED), b. Leesville, La, Feb. 6, 20; m. 41; c. 2. PHYSICS. B.S, Oregon State Col, 46; Ph.D.(physics), Mass. Inst. Tech, 48. Assoc. physicist, underwater sound, div. war res, California, 41-46; res. assoc. electron, res. lab. electron, Mass. Inst. Tech, 46-48; physicist, Gen. Elec. Co, 48-50, head theoretical group, 50-53, reactor physics, 53-54; sr. physicist, Poulter Labs, Stanford Res. Inst, 54-57, sci. dir, 57-62, dir, 62-64; PROF. PHYSICS, WASH. STATE UNIV, 64- AAAS; Am. Phys. Soc; Combustion Inst. Underwater sound; stochastic processes; reactor physics; shock and detonation phenomena; equations of state of solids; finite amplitude wave propagation. Address: Dept. of Physics, Washington State University, Pullman, WA 99163.

DUVALL, HARRY M(AREAN), b. Lanham, Md, Oct. 27, 10. ORGANIC CHEMISTRY. B.S, Maryland, 32, Ph.D.(org. chem), 36. E.R. Squibb & Sons fel, Virginia, 36-38; res. chemist, Jackson Lab, E.I. du Pont de Nemours & Co, Inc, 38-50; Thiokol Chem. Corp, 50-53; Masonite Corp, 54-58; PROF. CHEM. & HEAD DEPT, VALDOSTA STATE COL, 58- Am. Chem. Soc. Process development of dyestuffs; rubber chemicals; organic chemicals; synthetic rubber; liquid polymers; wood products. Address: Dept. of Chemistry, Valdosta State College, Valdosta, GA 31601.

DUVALL, JACQUE L, b. Rensselaer, Ind, July 17, 24; m. 48; c. 7. PHYSICAL & ORGANIC CHEMISTRY. B.S, California, 50. Asst. chief engr, Excello Mfg. Co, 51-53; res. staff mem, indust. & aircraft Labs, J.B. Ford Div, Wyandotte Chems. Corp, 53-57; supvr. specification develop, Turco Prods. Co, 57; supvr, Los Nietos Res. Labs, J.B. Ford Div, Wyandotte Chems. Corp, 57-63, dir. res, 63-66, RES. ASSOC, 66-70, CHEM. SPECIALTIES DIV, BASF WYANDOTTE CORP, 70- U.S.A.A.F, 42-46. Am. Chem. Soc; Am. Oil Chem. Soc; Am. Soc. Test. & Mat; Chem. Specialties Mfrs. Asn. Colloidal and surface chemistry; detergency. Address: Chemical Specialities Division, BASF Wyandotte Corp, P.O. Box 2147, Los Nietos, CA 90606.

DUVALL, JOHN J(OSEPH), b. Sedro-Woolley, Wash, Oct. 20, 36; m. 56; c. 5. PHYSICAL ORGANIC CHEMISTRY. B.S, Brigham Young, 58, Ph.D.(org. chem), 63. Teaching assoc, Brigham Young, 59-60; RES. CHEMIST, LARAMIE ENERGY RES. CTR, BUR. MINES, 63- Am. Chem. Soc. Radiation chemistry of shale oil components; shale oil analysis; organic reaction mechanisms and kinetics. Address: Box 3331, University Station, Laramie, WY 82070.

DUVALL, PAUL FRAZIER, JR, b. Atlanta, Ga, Aug. 19, 41; m. 63; c. 1. TOPOLOGY, DYNAMICS. B.S, Davidson Col, 63, Woodrow Wilson fel, spring 63; Nat. Defense Educ. Act fels, Univ. Ga, fall 63 & summer 66, M.A, 65, Nat. Sci. Found. fel, 66-67, Ph.D.(math), 67. Asst. prof. MATH, Univ. Ga, 67-68; Va. Polytech. Inst. & State Univ, 70-71; ASSOC. PROF, OKLA. STATE UNIV, 71- Consult, Dept. Defense, 70- U.S.A, 68-70, Capt. Am. Math. Soc; Math. Asn. Am. Geometric topology; topological dynamics; actions of discrete groups on manifolds; embedding of complexes in manifolds. Address: Dept. of Mathematics, Oklahoma State University, Stillwater, OK 74074.

DUVALL, R(ONALD) N(ASH), b. Needham, Mass, June 17, 24; m. 53; c. 3. PHARMACEUTICAL CHEMISTRY. B.S, Mass. Col. Pharm, 49, col. fel, 49-51, M.S, 51, Eli Lilly fel, 55-56, Ph.D.(pharmaceut. chem), 57; Boston, 53-55. Asst. pharmaceut. chem, Mass. Col. Pharm, 52-54, instr, 54-57, asst. prof, 57-62; sect. head corp. pharmaceut. res. lab, MILES LABS, INC, 62-63, acting dir, 63-64, dir, 64-70, ASST. DIR. PHARMACEUT. RES. & DEVELOP. LAB, 70- Consult, Muro Pharmacal Labs, Mass; Chester A. Baker, Inc; Hoyt Pharmaceut. Co, 59-62. U.S.A, 43-46, S/Sgt. Am. Pharmaceut. Asn; Am. Chem. Soc. Pharmaceutical analysis; metal chelates of medicinal agents; antiradiation compounds; drug dosage form stability; carbohydrate browning mechanisms; salicylamide metabolism; industrial pharmacy. Address: Pharmaceutical Research & Development Lab, Miles Labs, Inc, 1127 Myrtle St, Elkhart, IN 46514.

DUVALL, VINSON L(AMAR), b. Godley, Texas, Sept. 5, 18; m. 41; c. 3 RANGE MANAGEMENT. B.S, Agr. & Mech. Col, Texas, 41; M.S, Texas Tech. Col, 49; Ph.D.(range mgt), Agr. & Mech. Col, Texas, 59. Instr. agr, Midwestern, 48-50, asst. prof, 50-53, chmn. dept. agr. & dir. farm opers, 53-59; range conservationist, SOUTH. FOREST EXP. STA, U.S. FOREST SERV, 59-66, prin. range scientist, 66-68, ASST. DIR, 68- U.S.A.A.F, 43-46. Am. Soc. Range Mgt. Research administration; forest range ecology. Address: 6405 Boutall St, Metairie, LA 70003.

DUVALL, WILBUR I(RVING), b. Gaithersburg, Md, Jan. 3, 15; m. 45; c. 4. PHYSICS. B.S, Maryland, 36, fel, 37-38, M.S, 38, 47-48; Amherst Col, 38-39; George Washington, 46. Instr. high sch, Md, 36-37; lab. instr, Amherst Col, 38-39; jr. phys. sci. aide, U.S. BUR. MINES, 39-40, jr. physicist, 40-42, asst. physicist, 42-43, assoc. physicist, 43-47, physicist, 47-49, supvr. physicist, 49-52, supvry. physicist, blasting res, Md, 52-65, SUPVRY. RES. PHYSICIST, ROCK MECH. 65- With Off. Sci. Res. & Develop, 44; adj. prof. rock mech, Colo. Sch. Mines, 69- AAAS; Am. Inst. Mining, Metall. & Petrol. Eng; Seismol. Soc. Am; Am. Geophys. Union. Experimental stress analysis; stresses in underground mining structures; generation and propagation of explosive waves; electronics; rock mechanics. Address: Denver Mining Research Center, U.S. Bureau of Mines, Bldg. 20, Federal Center, Denver, CO 80225.

DuVARNEY, RAYMOND CHARLES, b. Clinton, Mass, Oct. 11, 40; m. 63; c. 2. SOLID STATE PHYSICS. B.A, Clark, 62, Ph.D.(physics), 68; M.S, New Hampshire, 64. ASST. PROF. PHYSICS, EMORY UNIV, 68- Am. Phys. Soc. Investigations of the pyroelectric and ferroelectric properties of solids using the techniques of magnetic resonance. Address: Dept. of Physics, Emory University, Atlanta, GA 30322.

DUVENDECK, JERRY P(AUL), b. Kalamazoo, Mich, Dec. 11, 21; m. 44; c. 3. WILDLIFE MANAGEMENT. B.Sc, Alma Col, 43; Chicago, 46-47; M.S, Mich. State Univ, 52, Ph.D.(fisheries, wildlife), 64. Game biologist, Houghton Lake Wildlife Exp. Sta, MICH. DEPT. CONSERV, 53-61, Rose Lake Wildlife Res. Ctr, 61-63, game res. biologist, 63-65, BIOLOGIST IN CHARGE, HOUGHTON LAKE WILDLIFE RES. STA, 65- U.S.N.R, 43-46, Lt.(jg). Am. Wildlife Soc. Food habits and nutritional requirements of white-tailed deer; cottontail rabbit habitat; effects of pesticides on wildlife. Address: Houghton Lake Wildlife Research Station, Box 158, Houghton Lake Heights, MI 48630.

DUVICK, DONALD N(ELSON), b. Sandwich, Ill, Dec. 18, 24; m. 50; c. 3. GENETICS, PLANT BREEDING. B.S, Illinois, 48; Ph.D.(bot), Washington (St. Louis), 51. Corn breeder, maize genetics & physiol, PIONEER HI-BRED INT, INC, 51-71, DIR. DEPT. PLANT BREEDING, 71- U.S.A, 43-46. AAAS; Genetics Soc. Am; Am. Soc. Plant Physiol; Bot. Soc. Am; Am. Soc. Agron. Cytoplasmic inheritance of pollen sterility in maize; immunological identification of plant proteins; developmental morphology and anatomy of maize endosperm. Address: Dept. of Plant Breeding, Pioneer Hi-Bred International, Inc, Johnston, IA 50131.

DU VIGNEAUD, VINCENT, b. Chicago, Ill, May 18, 01; m. 24; c. 2. BIOCHEMISTRY. B.S, Univ. Ill, 23, M.S, 24; Ph.D, Univ. Rochester, 27; hon. Sc.D, N.Y. Univ. & Yale, 55, Univ. Ill, 60, St. Louis Univ. & Univ. Rochester, 65, George Washington Univ, 68. Asst. biochemist, Phila. Gen. Hosp. & grad. sch. med, Pennsylvania, 24-25; asst. vital econ, sch. med, Rochester, 25-27; Nat. Res. Coun. fel. pharmacol, sch. med, Hopkins, 27-28; Kaiser Wilhelm Inst, Ger. & med. sch, Edinburgh, 28-29; assoc. physiol. chem, Illinois, 29-30, asst. prof, 30-32; prof. biochem. & head dept, sch. med, George Washington, 32-38; med. col, CORNELL UNIV, 38-67, EMER. PROF. BIOCHEM, MED. COL. & PROF. CHEM, UNIV, 67- Foster lectr, Buffalo, 39; Harvey Soc. Lectr, N.Y, 42 & 54; Hitchcock lectr, California, 44; vis. lectr, Am-Swiss Found. Sci. Exchange, Switz, 47; Stieglitz Mem. lectr, Chicago, 48; Eastman lectr, Rochester, spec. univ. lectr, London & Liversidge lectr, Cambridge, 49; Messenger lectr, Cornell, 50; Herter lectr, N.Y. Univ, 52; Goldforb lectr. & Remsen Mem. lectr, 54; Edsel B. Ford lectr, Henry Ford Hosp, Detroit, Mich, 54; Hanna lectr, sch. med, Western Reserve, 55; Dakin Mem. lectr, Adelphi Col. & Nieuwland lectr, Notre Dame, 56; Edgar Fahs Smith lectr, Pennsylvania, 58; Martland Mem. lectr, Seton Hall Col. Med. & Mayo lectr, col. med, Iowa, 59; Hogg lectr, post-grad. sch. med, Texas, 60, Bodanska lectr, med. br, 63; Mellon lectr, sch. med, Pittsburgh, 62; Burger lectr, Virginia & Iddles lectr, New Hampshire, 64. Trustee, Rockefeller Univ. Mem. fel. bd. natural sci, Nat. Res. Coun, 51-52; Lilly fel. bd, 51-53; adv. coun, Children's Hosp. Res. Found, Cincinnati; health res. adv. coun, N.Y.C, 58-62; adv. coun. Nat. Inst. Arthritis & Metab. Diseases, 60-64; past chmn. bd, Fedn. Am. Socs. Exp. Biol. Hillebrand Prize, Chem. Soc. Wash, 36; Borden Award, Asn. Am. Med. Cols, 47; Lasker Award, Am. Pub. Health Asn. & award of merit war res, 48; Osborne & Mendel Award, 53; Scott Award, 54; sci. award, Am. Pharmaceut. Mfg. Asn, 54; Chandler Medal, Columbia, 55; Passano Award, 55; Nobel Prize chem, 55; achievement award, Illinois, 59; Twentieth Anniversary Award, Nutrit. Found, 61; 7th annual hon. lect. award, Albany Med. Col, 63; medalist, Pirquet Soc. Clin. Med, 64; Am. Col. Physicians Award, 65; Eli Lilly Lect. Award, Endocrine Soc, 67. Nat. Acad. Sci.(chmn, biochem. sect, 58-60); Am. Chem. Soc.(Nichols Medal, 45, Willard Gibbs Medal, 56); hon. mem. Argentine Biol. Soc; fel. Am. Acad. Arts & Sci; Am. Philos. Soc; hon. mem, Royal Soc. Edinburgh; hon. mem. The Chem. Soc; hon. mem. Royal Inst. Chem; hon. mem. Sweden Royal Soc. Sci. Chemistry of insulin and posterior pituitary hormones: biotin, choline and transmethyation; intermediary sulfur metabolism; amino acid peptide and protein chemistry; penicillin. Address: Dept. of Chemistry, Cornell University, Ithaca, NY 14850.

DUVIVIER, JEAN FERNAND, b. Rio de Janeiro, Brazil, Dec. 17, 26; U.S. citizen; m. 56; c. 5. AERONAUTICAL ENGINEERING. B.Sc, Boston, 55; S.M, Mass. Inst. Tech, 58, E.A.A, 66. Teaching asst. aircraft design, Tech. Inst. Aeronaut, Sao Paulo, Brazil, 51-53; res. staff aeroelasticity, Mass. Inst. Tech, 55-58, proj. leader aerodyn, 58-61; sci. staff opers. res, Center Naval Anal, 61-66; sr. res. engr, Elec. Boat Div, Gen. Dynamics Corp, 66-68; MGR. SYSTS. EVAL, VERTOL. DIV, BOEING CO, 68- Consult, Res. Anal. Corp, 66. Brazilian Army, 44-45. Assoc. fel. Am. Inst. Aeronaut. & Astronaut; Am. Helicopter Soc; Inst. Strategic Studies. Aerodynamics and wind tunnel testing; aeroelasticity; fluid mechanics and boundary layer control; structural dynamics; operations research; systems analysis; simulation of transportation systems; risk analysis. Address: 181 Woodhill Lane, Media, PA 19063.

DUVOISIN, ROGER C, b. Towaco, N.J, July 27, 27; m. 48; c. 4. NEUROLOGY. M.D, New York Med. Col, 54. Intern, Lenox Hill Hosp, N.Y.C, 54-55, resident NEUROL, 55-56; Presby. Hosp, Columbia Presby. Med. Ctr, N.Y.C, 56-58; res. assoc, COL. PHYSICIANS & SURGEONS, COLUMBIA UNIV, 62-65, asst. prof, 65-69, ASSOC. PROF, 69- Mem, Nat. Insts. Health Study Group Encephalitis, 63; Parkinson's Disease Found. Clin. res. fel, 63-64; consult, N.Y.C. Bd. Educ, 63-; consult. adminr, Fed. Aviation Admin, 65- U.S.A.F, 56-62, Maj. AAAS; Am. Med. Asn; fel. Am. Col. Physicians; Am. Neurol. Asn; fel. Am. Acad. Neurol. Neurological complications of achondroplastic dwarfs; cerebral vascular disease; syncopal mechanisms; convulsive syncope; infectious polyneuritis; clinical features, natural history, epidemiology, pathology, clinical pharmacology and treatment of Parkinson's disease and post-encephalitic Parkinsonism. Address: Dept. of Neurology, College of Physicians & Surgeons, Columbia University, 710 W. 168th St, New York, NY 10032.

DUWE, ARTHUR E(DWARD), b. Saginaw, Mich, July 17, 22; wid; c. 3. IMMUNOLOGY, EMBRYOLOGY. B.S, Alma Col, 49; M.S, Ohio State, 50, Ph.D.(zool), 53. Asst. instr. zool, Ohio State, 52; asst. prof, North State Teachers Col, 53-54; Superior, Wis. State Col, 54-59, assoc. prof, 59-64; PROF. BIOL, Waynesburg Col, 64-68, LAKE SUPERIOR STATE COL, 68- Sigma Xi grant, 59; Nat. Insts. Health grants, 60-65; summers, Am. Soc. Physiologists fel, Michigan, 58, 59. U.S.A, 42-45; Croix de Guerre. AAAS; Am. Soc. Ichthyol. & Herpet; Am. Soc. Parasitol. Comparative immunology. Address: Dept. of Biology, Lake Superior State College, Sault Sainte Marie, MI 49783.

DUWELL, ERNEST J(OHN), b. Chicago, Ill, Mar. 12, 29; m. 50; c. 4. PHYSICAL CHEMISTRY. B.S, Iowa, 50, Atomic Energy Cmn. fel, 52-54, Ph.D.(chem), 54; M.S, Purdue, 52. Asst, Purdue, 50-52; sr. res. chemist, Jones & Laughlin Steel Corp, 54-56; res. specialist, MINN. MINING & MFG. CO, 56-66, RES. MGR. ABRASIVES DIV, 66- Am. Chem. Soc. Metal cutting and finishing; corrosion; ceramics. Address: 904 Seventh St, Hudson, WI 54016.

DUWEZ, POL EDGARD, b. Mons, Belgium, Dec. 11, 07; nat; m. 35; c. 1. METALLURGY, PHYSICS. Met.E, Mons (Belgium), 32, fel, 35-40; Sc.D.(physics & math), Brussels, 33; Belgium Am. Ed. Found. fel, Calif. Inst. Tech, 33-35. Prof, sch. mines, Mons (Belgium), 38-40; res. engr, CALIF. INST. TECHNOL, 41-47, assoc. prof. mech. eng, 47-52, PROF, 52-66, MAT. SCI, 66- Mem. sci. adv. bd. to Chief of Staff, U.S.A.F, 45-55. Dudley award, Am. Soc. Test. & Mat, 51; Francis J. Clamer Medal, Franklin Inst, 68. AAAS; Am. Inst. Min, Metall. & Petrol. Eng.(Mathiewson Gold medal, 64); Am. Phys. Soc; Solar Energy Soc; Soc. Civil Eng. France. Physics of metals; high temperature materials; powder metallurgy. Address: W.M. Keck Lab. of Engineering Materials, California Institute of Technology, Pasadena, CA 91109.

DUX, J(AMES) P(HILIP), b. N.Y.C, July 15, 21; m. 48; c. 2. PHYSICAL CHEMISTRY. B.S, Queens Col.(N.Y), 42; M.A, Columbia, 47; Ph.D.(phys. chem), Polytech. Inst. Brooklyn, 55. Anal. chemist, Gen. Chem. Co, 42-44; res. chemist, phys. & anal. chem, Merck & Co, Inc, 47-50; group leader phys. chem, cellulose sect, AM. VISCOSE DIV, FMC CORP, 54-59, group head anal. chem, 59-61, SECT. LEADER, acetate fibers, 61-70, SYNTHETIC STAPLE & INDUST. YARNS, 70- U.S.A, 44-46. Fiber Soc; Am. Chem. Soc. Analytical and physical chemistry in polymers; polyelectrolytes; reaction kinetics; cellulose chemistry; statistics; radiochemistry; diffusion problems; fiber physics and chemistry. Address: American Viscose Division, FMC Corp, Marcus Hook, PA 19061.

DUXBURY, ALYN CRANDALL, b. Olympia, Wash, Dec. 1, 32; m. 56; c. 3. OCEANOGRAPHY. B.S, Washington (Seattle), 55, M.S, 56; United Gas Pipeline Co. fel, Texas A&M, 59-60, Ph.D.(phys. oceanog), 63. Res. assoc. & lectr. PHYS. OCEANOG, Bingham Oceanog. Lab, Yale, 60-64; RES. ASST. PROF, UNIV. WASH, 64- Chem.C, U.S.A, 56-58. AAAS; Am. Soc. Limnol. & Oceanog; Am. Geophys. Union. Descriptive physical oceanography, hydrographic survey work. Address: Dept. of Oceanography, University of Washington, Seattle, WA 98105.

DUXBURY, D(EAN) D(AVID), b. Tripoli, Wis, Dec. 20, 34; m. 60; c. 3. FOOD TECHNOLOGY. B.S, Univ. Wis, Madison, 56, M.S, 57. Qual. control supvr, Libby, McNeill & Libby, Ill, summer 56; res. asst, Univ. Wis, Madison; 56-57; food technologist, RES. & DEVELOP. CTR, SWIFT & CO, 59-61, sect. head canned meats, 61-65, group leader, 65-69, RES. MGR, 69- Sub-comt. chmn. comt. on container integrity, Nat. Canners Asn, 70- U.S.A, 57-59. Inst. Food Technol. Storage life studies for fresh packaged cranberries; irradiated canned beef studies for sterility and flavor acceptance; canned foods new product development; development of flexible packaged foods. Address: Swift & Co, Research & Development Center, 1919 Swift Dr, Oak Brook, IL 60521.

DUYSEN, MURRAY E, b. Henderson, Iowa, July 27, 36; m. 56; c. 2. PLANT PHYSIOLOGY. B.A, Univ. Omaha, 59; M.Sc, Univ. Nebr, 62, Ph.D.(bot), 66. Asst. prof. BOT, N.DAK. STATE UNIV, 65-69, ASSOC. PROF, 69- AAAS; Am. Soc. Plant Physiol; Bot. Soc. Am. Plant growth and development; physiology of cell division; water relations and plant growth. Address: Dept. of Botany, North Dakota State University, Fargo, ND 58102.

DVONCH, WILLIAM, b. Chicago, Ill, June 22, 15; m. 52; c. 4. ORGANIC BIOCHEMISTRY. B.S, Illinois, 39; M.S, Purdue, 48, Ph.D.(biochem), 50. Asst, Wright Jr. Col, Chicago, 39-40; chemist, starch & dextrose sect, north. regional res. lab, bur. agr. & indust. chem, U.S. Dept. Agr, 41-46, BIOCHEMIST, fermentation sect, north. utilization res. br, Agr. Res. Serv, 50-54; RES. DIV, WYETH LABS, 54- Am. Chem. Soc. Carbohydrate chemistry; isolation of antibiotics; enzymes. Address: 75 Ivywood Lane, Radnor, PA 19087.

DVORACEK, L(OUIS) M(ARTIN), b. Grant Co, N.Dak, Dec. 1, 27; m. 53; c. 2. CHEMICAL ENGINEERING. B.S, Washington (Seattle), 50, M.S, 51, Univ. fel. & Standard Oil fel, 52-53, Ph.D, 53. SR. DESIGN ENGR, UNION OIL CO. CALIF, 54- Nat. Asn. Corrosion Eng; Am. Inst. Chem. Eng; Am. Inst. Mech. Eng. Corrosion and metallurgy. Address: Research Dept, Union Oil Co. of California, P.O. Box 76, Brea, CA 92621.

DVORACEK, MARVIN JOHN, b. Penelope, Tex, July 16, 32; m. 57; c. 2. AGRICULTURAL ENGINEERING. B.S, Texas A&M, 53 & 59; M.S, California, Davis, 62. Soil conservationist, Soil Conserv. Serv, U.S. Dept. Agr, 53 & 56; instr. eng. graphics, Texas A&M, 57-59, AGR. ENG, 59; lectr. & jr. specialist California, Davis, 60-62; asst. prof, TEX. TECH UNIV, 62-67, ASSOC. PROF, 67- Nat. Sci. Found. fac. fel, dept. hydrol. & water resources, Univ. Ariz, 70- U.S.A, 53-55, Res, 55-, Maj. Am. Soc. Agr. Eng; Am. Soc. Civil Eng; Nat. Soc. Prof. Eng. Ground water recharge; irrigation; water conservation; evaporation; ground water pollution; runoff; hydrologic cycle. Address: Dept. of Hydrology & Water Resources, University of Arizona, Tucson, AZ 85721.

DVORAK, HENRY R(UDOLPH), b. Houston, Tex, Nov. 28, 22; m. 51; c. 5. NUCLEAR PHYSICS. B.S, Houston, 47; M.A, Texas, 52, Ph.D.(physics), 53. Mech. engr, Manhattan Proj, Oak Ridge Nat. Lab, 44-46; instr. physics, Houston, 46-47; lab. asst, Texas, 47-49, res. scientist II, 49-53; sr. nuclear engr, GEN. DYNAMICS/FT. WORTH, 53-55, chief nuclear radiation effects, 55-59, nuclear res. & develop, 59-63, dir, 63-65, CHIEF SCIENTIST, NUCLEAR & APPL. RES, 65- Consult, Nat. Acad. Sci, 63- U.S.A, 43-46. Am. Phys. Soc; Am. Nuclear Soc. Non-destructive test methods; optical holography; acoustic emission monitoring and research; powder metallurgy; diffusion bonding; laser applications. Address: 4805 Hilldring Dr. E, Ft. Worth, TX 76109.

DVORAK, VERNE I, b. Barneston, Nebr, Apr. 2, 25; m. 56; c. 3. HYDROLOGY, HYDRAULIC ENGINEERING. B.S, Nebraska, 56, M.S, 64. Civil engr. flood control, soil conserv. serv, U.S. DEPT. AGR, 56, hydrologist flood prev, 56-57, RES. HYDRAUL. ENGR, AGR. RES. SERV, 57- U.S.N, 44-46. AAAS; Am. Soc. Agr. Eng. River channel behavior as related to soils, climate and agriculture, processes of erosion and deposition in flood water reservoirs. Address: 2407 Cheshire S, Lincoln, NE 68512.

DVORETZKY, ISAAC, b. Houston, Tex, Jan. 24, 28; m. 58; c. 3. ORGANIC CHEMISTRY. B.A, Rice Inst. fel, 48, M.A, 50, Humble Oil & Ref. Co. fel, 51-52, Ph.D.(chem), 52. Res. chemist, Houston Res. Lab, SHELL OIL CO, 52-56, group leader, 56-62, res. supvr, SHELL DEVELOP. CO, 62-69, MGR, UNCONVENTIONAL RAW MAT. DEPT, 69- Spec. assignment Royal Dutch/Shell-Lab, Holland, 58-59; mfg. res. dept, Shell Oil Co, N.Y, 67-68. Am. Chem. Soc. Synthesis of heterocyclic compounds; local anesthetics; high-molecular-weight hydrocarbons; lubricating oil processing; alkylation; constitution of petroleum; catalysis and hydrocarbon chemistry. Address: Shell Development Co, 1400 53rd St, Everyville, CA 94608.

DVORNIK, D(USHAN) M(ICHAEL), b. Mezica, Yugoslavia, Oct. 23, 23; Can. citizen; m. 51; c. 1. BIOCHEMISTRY, ORGANIC CHEMISTRY. Chem.Eng, Zagreb, 48, Ph.D.(chem), 54. Res. chemist, Pliva Chem. Works, Yugoslavia, 46-49, head dept. synthetic chem, 50-52, res. scientist, 52-54; fel. natural prods, lab. org. chem, Swiss Fed. Inst. Tech, 54-55; fel. alkaloids, Nat. Res. Coun. Can, 55-58, synthetic chem, Ottawa (Can), 58-59; res. chemist, AYERST RES. LABS, 59-64, ASSOC. DIR. RES, 64-, DIR. BIOCHEM. DEPT, 64- Fel. coun. arteriosclerosis, Am. Heart Asn, 63- Am. Chem. Soc; Am. Soc. Biol. Chem; Soc. Exp. Biol. & Med; fel. Chem. Inst. Can; Can. Biochem. Soc. Lipid metabolism; drug metabolism; biochemical pharmacology. Address: Biochemistry Dept, Ayerst Research Labs, P.O. Box 6115, Montreal, Que, Can.

DVOSKIN, SAMUEL, b. Bronx, N.Y, Feb. 17, 17; m. 44. INTERNAL MEDICINE. B.S, City Col. New York, 37, M.S, 39; fel, Columbia, 43, Ph.D.(anat). & M.D, 45. Jr. biologist, City Col. New York, 37-40; instr. anat, COL. PHYSICIANS & SURGEONS, COLUMBIA UNIV, 40-42, Ayerst, McKenna & Harrison fel. of Am. Asn. Study Int. Secretions, 47, ASST. MED, 48-51, 53- Intern & res. med, Presby. Hosp, 45-48, asst. physician, 48-51, 51-59; internist, Pack Med. Group, 48-51, 53-69. Med.C, U.S.N.R, 42-44; U.S.A, 51-53. Endocrine Soc; Am. Asn. Anat; Thyroid Asn; Am. Col. Physicians; Am. Med. Asn; Am. Fedn. Clin. Res; N.Y. Acad. Sci. Spermatogenesis; endocrine control; pituitary regulation of thyroid cytology; hormonal effects of iodine; local maintenance of spermatogenesis by intratesticular implants in hypophysectomized rats; clinical reports and tests for cancer; operative risk in aged patients undergoing major surgery for cancer; cancer chemiotherapy. Address: 180 Cabrini Blvd, New York, NY 10033.

DWASS, MEYER, b. New Haven, Conn, Apr. 9, 23; m. 49; c. 2. MATHEMATICAL STATISTICS. A.B, George Washington, 48; A.M, Columbia, 49; Ph.D.(math. statist), North Carolina, 52. Math. statistician, Bur. Census, 49-52; asst. prof. MATH, Northwest. Univ, 52-57, assoc. prof, 57-61; PROF, Univ. Minn, 61-62; NORTHWEST. UNIV, 62- Artil.C, U.S.A, 43-46. Am. Math. Soc; Inst. Math. Statist; Am. Statist. Asn. Nonparametric statistics; renewal theory; probability theory. Address: Dept. of Mathematics, Northwestern University, Evanston, IL 60201.

DWIGGINS, CLAUDIUS W(ILLIAM), JR, b. Amity, Ark, May 11, 33. PHYSICAL CHEMISTRY. B.S, Arkansas, 54, M.S, 56, Am. Oil Co. fel, Coulter-Jones fel. & Ph.D.(chem), 58. PROJ. LEADER, PETROL. COMPOSITION RES, U.S. BUR. MINES, 58- AAAS; N.Y. Acad. Sci; Am. Chem. Soc. X-ray diffraction and structure determination; x-ray fluorescence and absorption; trace elements in petroleum; structural chemistry of transition elements; colloid physics. Address: Energy Research Center, U.S. Bureau of Mines, Bartlesville, OK 74003.

DWIGHT, CHARLES HARRISON, b. Closter, N.J, July 9, 97; m. 34. PHYSICS. B.A, Bellevue Col, 19; M.S, Chicago, 25; Ph.D.(physics), Cincinnati, 31. Asst. PHYSICS, Oklahoma, 19-21; instr, Illinois, 21-22; demonstr, Chicago, 22-23; instr, COL. ENG, UNIV. CINCINNATI, 23-41, asst. prof, 41-59, assoc. prof, 59-70, EMER. ASSOC. PROF, 70- Mem, U.S. Nat. Comt. of Int. Comn. Illumination. With Office Sci. Res. & Develop; U.S.A, 44. Atmospheric electricity; effects of soft x-rays on viscosity of agar and apple pectin; solarization of glass; heat; spectrophotometry. Address: Dept. of Physics, University of Cincinnati, Cincinnati, OH 45221.

DWIGHT, LESLIE ALFRED, b. Wayne, Okla, Aug. 22, 07; m. 34; c. 2. MATHEMATICS. B.S, Oklahoma Baptist, 29; M.A, Oklahoma, 35; Texas, 48-49; Ph.D.(math), Peabody Col, 52. Teacher, high schs, Okla, 29-34; Tenn, 34-39; asst. prof. MATH, SOUTHEAST. STATE COL, 39-51, PROF. & HEAD DEPT, 52- Analyst math, U.S. Artil. Ctr, 53-54. U.S.N, 43-46, Lt. Math. Asn. Am. Mathematics education. Address: Dept. of Mathematics, Southeastern State College, Durant, OK 74701.

DWINELL, LEW DAVID, b. Albuquerque, N.Mex, Mar. 24, 38; m. 61; c. 3. PLANT PATHOLOGY. B.S, Colorado State, 61; M.S, Denver, 63; Ph.D.(plant path), Cornell, 67. PLANT PATHOLOGIST, FORESTRY SCI. LAB, U.S. FOREST SERV, 66- Am. Phytopath. Soc; Asn. Comput. Mach. Forest tree diseases, particularly rusts, hardwood, and nursery diseases. Address: Forestry Sciences Lab, U.S. Forest Service, Carlton St, Athens, GA 30601.

DWINGER, PHILIP, b. The Hague, Netherlands, Sept. 25, 14. MATHEMATICS. Ph.D.(math), Leiden, 38. Prof. MATH. & head dept, Indonesia, 53-56; asst. prof, Purdue, 56-58, assoc. prof, 58-60, PROF, 60-62; Delft, 62-65, UNIV. ILL, CHICAGO, 65- Am. Math. Soc; Netherlands Math. Soc. Algebra, particularly ordered sets and lattices; Boolean algebras. Address: Dept. of Mathematics, Box 4348, University of Illinois, Chicago, IL 60680.

DWIVEDY, RAMESH C, b. Etawah, India, Mar. 15, 43; m. 67; c. 1. AGRICULTURAL ENGINEERING, BIOENGINEERING. B.S, Univ. Allahabad, 63; M.S, Univ. Guelph, 65; Ph.D.(agr. eng), Univ. Mass, Amherst, 70. Lectr.

agr. eng, Univ. Udaipur, India, 63-64; teacher, high sch, Ont, Can, 66-67; ASST. PROF. AGR. ENG, UNIV. DEL, 70- Assoc. Am. Soc. Agr. Eng. Stress analysis in grain mass inside a bin; electrophysiological research to develop a non-chemical device of insect control; aquacultural engineering. Address: Dept. of Agricultural Engineering, University of Delaware, Newark, DE 19711.

DWORETZKY, MURRAY, b. N.Y.C, Aug. 18, 17; m. 43; c. 2. ALLERGY, IMMUNOLOGY. B.A, Pennsylvania, 38; M.D, L.I. Col. Med, 42; M.S, Minnesota, 50. Intern, City Hosp, New York, 42-43, asst. res. path, 43, fel, 46; res, Chicago, 47; fel. med, Mayo Found, 48-51; asst. med, MED. COL, CORNELL UNIV, 51, instr, 52-56, asst. prof. clin. med, 56-61, clin. pub. health & prev. med, 57-62, clin. assoc. prof. MED, 61-66, CLIN. PROF, 66- Attend. physician, Manhattan Eye, Ear & Throat Hosp, 52-62; asst. physician, New York Hosp, 51, physician, 51-56, asst. attend. physician, 56-61, assoc. attend. physician, 61-66, attending physician, 66-, physician-in-charge, allergy clin, 61- Dipl, Am. Bd. Internal Med, 52, exam, 68-71; dipl, Am. Bd. Allergy, 54, exam, 71- Med.C, 43-46, Capt. AAAS; Soc. Exp. Biol. & Med; Am. Med. Asn; fel. Am. Acad. Allergy (pres, 68); fel. Am. Col. Allergists; fel. Am. Col. Physicians; Am. Fedn. Clin. Res; Am. Asn. Immunol; fel. N.Y. Acad. Med. Anaphylaxis; toxic and allergic reactions to staphylococcal fractions; management of asthma. Address: 115 E. 61st St, New York, NY 10021.

DWORJANYN, LEE O(LEH), b. Lviv, Ukraine, Feb. 18, 34; m. 58; c. 4. CHEMICAL ENGINEERING. B.Sc, Univ. Sydney, 55, B.E, 57; Leverhulme scholar, Univ. London, 60-62, Ph.D.(diffusion), Imp. Col, 62. Chem. engr, Imp. Chem. Industs. Australia & N.Z, 57-59; res. engr. prod. develop, E.I. DU PONT DE NEMOURS & CO, Del, 62-69, SR. RES. ENGR, ORLON-LYCRA TECH. DIV, 70- Am. Chem. Soc; Royal Australian Chem. Inst. Textile fibers; acrylic fibers technology; economic evaluations; venture analysis; market research; non-wovens; disposables; hydraulic jets; flow through orifices and nozzles. Address: 234 Welsh St, Camden, SC 29020.

DWORKEN, HARVEY J, b. Cleveland, Ohio, Aug. 1, 20; m. 49; c. 2. INTERNAL MEDICINE, GASTROENTEROLOGY. B.A, Dartmouth Col, 41; M.D, Western Reserve, 44. Intern, Michael Reese Hosp, Chicago, Ill, 44-45; res. psychiat, New Eng. Med. Ctr, Boston, Mass, 47-48; asst. res. med, Mt. Sinai Hosp, Cleveland, Ohio, 48-49, chief res, 49-50; fel. gastroenterol, Hosp. Univ. Pa, 50-52; clin. instr. med, CASE WEST. RESERVE UNIV, 52-57, sr. clin. instr, 57-59, asst. clin. prof, 59-62, asst. prof, 62-65, ASSOC. PROF. MED, 66-, PHYSICIAN-IN-CHARGE GASTROINTESTINAL LABS, UNIV. HOSPS, CLEVELAND, 62-, chmn. curriculum revision comt, univ, 66-70. Med.C, U.S.A, 45-47, Capt. Am. Col. Physicians; Am. Gastroenterol. Asn; Am. Med. Asn. Curriculum planning; clinical investigation on gastric secretion and inflammatory diseases of the intestinal tract. Address: Dept. of Medicine, Case Western Reserve University, University Circle, Cleveland, OH 44106.

DWORKIN, MARTIN, b. N.Y.C, Dec. 3, 27; m. 57; c. 2. MICROBIOLOGY. A.B, Indiana, 51; Nat. Sci. Found. fels, Texas, 53-55, Ph.D.(bact), 55. Res. scientist bact, Texas, 52-53; res. fel, California, 55-57; asst. prof. MICROBIOL, med. center, Indiana, 57-61, assoc. prof, 61-62; UNIV. MINN, MINNEAPOLIS, 62-69, PROF, 69- Nat. Insts. Health fels, 55-57, career develop. award, 64, 69. U.S.A, 46-48. Am. Soc. Microbiol; Brit. Soc. Gen. Microbiol. Microbial physiology; myxobacteria; developmental microbiology. Address: Dept. of Microbiology, University of Minnesota, Minneapolis, MN 55455.

DWORNIK, JULIAN JONATHAN, b. Colonsay, Sask, Mar. 11, 38; m. 63; c. 1. ANATOMY. B.A, Andrews, 61; M.Sc, Manitoba, 64, fels, 65-67, Ph.D.(anat, neuroanat), 69. Demonstr. microanat, Manitoba, 63-64, teaching asst. ANAT, 65-66, teaching fel, 66-67; instr, Louisville, 67-69, ASST. PROF, 69-70; COL. MED, UNIV. S.FLA, 70- Pan Am. Asn. Anat; Can. Asn. Anat. Gross anatomy and teratology. Address: Dept. of Anatomy, University of South Florida College of Medicine, Tampa, FL 33620.

DWORNIK, STEPHEN E, b. Buffalo, N.Y, July 3, 26; m. 51; c. 3. GEOLOGY, GEOPHYSICS. B.A, Buffalo, 50, M.A, 51. Chief, geo-eng. br, eng. res. & develop. labs, U.S. Army, Ft. Belvoir, Va, 51-65; Surveyor Prog. scientist, OFF. SPACE SCI. & APPLNS, NASA, 65-68, PLANETOLOGY PROG. MGR, 68- U.S.A, 44-46. AAAS; Am. Soc. Photogram; Soc. Am. Mil. Eng; Sci. Res. Soc. Am. In-situ spectroscopy; spectral zonal aerial photography; lunar-terrestrial geology analogs; environmental test site selection; remote sensing of the terrain; anti-intrusion devices. Address: Office of Space Sciences & Applications, NASA, Washington, DC 20546.

DWORSCHACK, ROBERT G(EORGE), b. Milwaukee, Wis, Feb. 26, 20; m. 45; c. 4. FERMENTATION CHEMISTRY. B.S, Wisconsin, 42; M.S, Bradley, 49. CHEMIST, Kurth Malting Co, 41; north. regional res. lab, bur. agr. & indust. chem, U.S. Dept. Agr, 42-44, 45-51, north. utilization res. div, agr. res. serv, 51-60; Columbia Malting Co, 60-64; CLINTON CORN PROCESSING CO, 64- Am. Soc. Microbiol. Process and product development in microbiology; starch chemistry; enzymology. Address: Clinton Corn Processing Co, 1251 Beaver Channel Pkwy, Clinton, IA 52732.

DWYER, DENNIS MICHAEL, b. Passaic, N.J, Feb. 26, 45; m. 69. PARASITOLOGY, PROTOZOOLOGY. B.A, Montclair State Col, 67; M.S, Univ. Mass, Amherst, 70, Nat. Inst. Allergic & Infectious Diseases traineeship & Ph.D.(zool), 71. NAT. INST. ALLERGIC & INFECTIOUS DISEASES FEL. PARASITOL, ROCKEFELLER UNIV, 71- Soc. Protozool; Am. Soc. Parasitol. Cultivation, cryopreservation, some aspects of pathogenicity and immunology of various parasitic protozoan groups; mechanisms and etiology of protozoan diseases. Address: Rockefeller University, 66th St. & York Ave, New York, NY 10021.

DWYER, DON D, b. Hugoton, Kans, Dec. 28, 34; m. 56; c. 2. RANGE MANAGEMENT, ECOLOGY. B.S, Ft. Hays Kans. State Col, 56, M.S, 58; Ph.D. (range mgt), Texas A&M, 60. Asst. prof. forestry, Ariz. State Col, 59-60; agron & bot, Oklahoma State, 60-64; assoc. prof. range mgt, New Mexico State, 64-67, prof, 67-71; PROF. RANGE SCI. & HEAD DEPT, UTAH STATE UNIV, 71- Soc. Range Mgt; Ecol. Soc. Am; Am. Soc. Agron. Grazing management on native rangeland; ecology of native range plants. Address: Dept. of Range Science, Utah State University, Logan, UT 84321.

DWYER, FRANCIS GERARD, b. Philadelphia, Pa, June 13, 31; m. 61; c. 5. CHEMICAL ENGINEERING. B.Ch.E, Villanova, 53; M.S, Pennsylvania, 63, Mobil fel, 63-66, Ph.D.(chem. eng), 66. Jr. engr, MOBIL RES. & DEVELOP. CORP, 53-54, chem. engr, 56-62, sr. chem. engr, 62-69, ENGR. ASSOC, 69- Chem.C, U.S.A, 54-56. Am. Inst. Chem. Eng. Development of cracking, zeolite and oxidation catalysts; physical and chemical mechanisms of catalysis via hydrogen-deuterium exchange. Address: Mobil Research & Engineering Corp, Paulsboro NJ 08066.

DWYER, JAMES MICHAEL, b. Paterson, N.J, Nov. 16, 31. PHYSICAL CHEMISTRY, HISTORY OF SCIENCE. A.B, Princeton, 53; Columbia, 57-58; Ph.D.(nuclear chem), Rochester, 63. Res. assoc. radiochem, Brookhaven Nat. Lab, 62-63; asst. prof. CHEM, Adelphi Univ, 63-67; ASSOC. PROF, C.W. POST COL, L.I. UNIV, 67- Summer res. assoc, Los Alamos Nat. Lab, 60. U.S.N, 53-56, Lt.(jg). Am. Chem. Soc; The Chem. Soc. Electrochemistry and spectra of aromatic selenium compounds; parallelisms in history of music and mathematics. Address: Dept. of Chemistry, C.W. Post College, Long Island University, Greenvale, NY 11548.

DWYER, JOHN B, b. N.Y.C, May 4, 18; m. 42. CHEMICAL ENGINEERING. S.B, Mass. Inst. Tech, 40, S.M, 41. Staff mem, M.W. KELLOGG CO, 41-55, mgr. admin. eng, 55-57, design eng, 57-62, comput. dept, 62-64, chief engr, 64-65, dir. eng, 65-69, V.PRES. & DIR. RES. & ENG. DEVELOP, 69- Am. Inst. Chem. Eng; Sci. Res. Soc. Am. Chemical engineering; computer management and development. Address: M.W. Kellogg Co, 1300 Three Greenway Plaza E, Houston, TX 77046.

DWYER, J(OHN) D(UNCAN), b. Newark, N.J, Apr. 26, 15; m. 42; c. 4. SYSTEMATIC BOTANY. A.B, St. Peter's Col, 36; M.S, Fordham, 38, fel. & Ph.D.(bot), 41. Instr. BIOL, St. Francis Col.(N.Y), 42; prof, Albany Col. Pharm, 42-47; Siena Col, 47-53; assoc. prof, ST. LOUIS UNIV, 53-59, PROF, 58-, head dept, 53-63. Nat. Acad. Sci. res. grant, Mus. Natural Hist, Paris, 52; Off. Naval Res. grant, Panama, 59; U.S. Agency Int. Develop-Univ. Tenn. Unit, Univ. Panama, summers, 61-63; curator trop. S.Am. Phanerogams, Mo. Bot. Gardens, 64-; consult, U.S. Army Tropic Test Ctr, Panama, 65; Ciba Pharm. Co; Cent. Am. Inst. Res. & Indust. Technol, Guatemala, 70- AAAS; Torrey Bot. Club; Am. Soc. Plant Taxon; Asn. Taxon. Study Trop. African Flora. American species of Ochnaceae and Leguminosae; general flora of Central America and Peru. Address: Dept. of Biology, St. Louis University, St. Louis, MO 63103.

DWYER, ORRINGTON E(MBRY), b. Western Bay, Newf, May 22, 12; U.S. citizen; m. 42; c. 3. CHEMICAL ENGINEERING. B.S, Northeast. Univ, 34; M.S, Mass. Inst. Technol, 36; Garland scholar, Yale, 38-39, D.Eng, 40. Chemist, Mass. Gas Soc, 34-35; chem. engr, Boston Woven Hose & Rubber Co, 36-37; instr. chem. eng, Univ. Rochester, 39-41, asst. prof, 41-47, assoc. prof. & chmn. dept, 47-51; mem. staff, BROOKHAVEN NAT. LAB, 51-52, head chem. eng. div, nuclear eng. dept, 52-67, GROUP LEADER HEAT TRANSFER, ENG. DEPT, 67- Sr. chem. engr, Off. Rubber, 43-44; supvr. develop. sect, Fercleve Corp, Oak Ridge, Tenn, 44-45; vis. prof, Univ. Minn, 59. Fel. AAAS; Am. Inst. Chem. Eng; Am. Soc. Mech. Eng; fel. Am. Nuclear Soc. Liquid metal heat transfer; nuclear engineering; reactor fuel reprocessing. Address: Dept. of Applied Science, Brookhaven National Lab, Upton, NY 11973.

DWYER, PAUL S(UMNER), b. Chester, Pa, Dec. 8, 01; m. 32; c. 2. STATISTICS. A.B, Allegheny Col, 21; A.M, Pa. State, 23; Ph.D, Michigan, 36. Instr. math, Pa. State, 21-26; asst. prof, Antioch Col, 26-29, assoc. prof, 29-33, prof, 33-36; asst. prof. math, UNIV. MICH, ANN ARBOR, 37-42, assoc. prof, 42-46, PROF, 46-67, STATIST, 67-, CONSULT. & DIR, STATIST. RES. LAB, 46-, asst. & assoc. ed. invests, 36-45. Consult, Princeton, 42; Dept. Army, 50-53. Fel. AAAS; Am. Math. Soc; Math. Asn. Am; fel. Am. Statist. Asn; Fel. Inst. Math. Statist.(secy-treas, 44-49, pres, 51); Psychomet. Soc; Economet. Soc; Biomet. Soc. Mathematical and applied statistics; computational techniques; linear programming. Address: Box 663, Mackinaw City, MI 49701.

DWYER, R(OBERT) F(RANCIS), b. Utica, N.Y, Feb. 20, 30; m. 53; c. 2. ANALYTICAL & PHYSICAL CHEMISTRY. B.S, Syracuse, 51; M.S, Pa. State, 53. Res. chemist, Linde Div, UNION CARBIDE CORP, 53-61, sr. res. chemist, 61-62, group leader, low temperature measurement & radiation serv, 62-66, supvr. anal. servs, 66-69, MGR. ANAL. SERV, REALTY DIV, 69- Mem. sampling & anal. panel, group on composition exhaust gases, Co-ord. Res. Coun, 61-67. Am. Chem. Soc. Instrumental methods of analysis; research applications of radioisotopes; radiation chemistry; blood preservation; low-temperature measurements of physical properties; rheologic and thermodynamics properties of slush and solid hydrogen. Address: Realty Division, Union Carbide Corp, Tarrytown Technical Center, P.O. Box 65, Tarrytown, NY 10591.

DWYER, ROBERT J(OSEPH), b. Norwood, Ohio, Jan. 11, 07. PHYSICS. A.B, Cincinnati, 29; A.M, Harvard, 37, Coffin fel, 39-41, Ph.D.(physics), 41. Instr. radio eng, RCA Inst, Inc, 37-39; physics, Lafayette Col, 41-42; Trinity Col.(Conn), 42-43, asst. prof, 43-45; physicist, Ray Control Co, 45-46; Lane-Wells Co, Calif, 46-52; sr. scientist, Beckman Instruments, Inc, 52-56; asst. prof. PHYSICS, Purdue, 56-60; PROF, WAGNER COL, 60-, chmn. dept. math. & physics, 60-69. AAAS; Am. Phys. Soc; Inst. Elec. & Electronics Eng; Optical Soc. Am; Am. Asn. Physics Teachers. Atomic physics; spectroscopy; electronics; instrumentation. Address: Dept. of Physics, Wagner College, Staten Island, NY 10301.

DWYER, SAMUEL J, III, b. San Antonio, Tex, June 8, 32; m. 53; c. 6. ELECTRICAL ENGINEERING. B.S, Texas, 57, M.S, 59, Ph.D.(elec. eng), 63. Instr. ELEC. ENG, Texas, 57-63; asst. prof, UNIV. MO-COLUMBIA, 63-69, assoc. prof, 69-70, PROF, 70- Res. engr, Defense Res. Lab, 60-61; Nat. Inst. Ment. Health, res. grant, 65- Intel.C, 51-53, Sgt. Inst. Elec. & Electronics Eng; Asn. Comput. Mach; Inst. Math. Statist; Am. Statist. Asn. Application of statistics and information theory to electroencephalograph; statistical communication theory. Address: Dept. of Electrical Engineering, University of Missouri-Columbia, Columbia, MO 65201.

DWYER, SEAN G, b. N.Y.C, Mar. 12, 45; m. 68; c. 2. PHYSICAL ORGANIC & POLYMER CHEMISTRY. B.S, Univ. N.Dak, 66, NASA traineeship, 66-69, N.Dak. State Bd. Higher Educ. scholar, 69-70, Ph.D.(org. chem), 70. RES. CHEMIST, S.C. JOHNSON & SONS, INC, 70- Am. Chem. Soc. Arsonium ylides and imines; attempted synthesis of stable carbenes; product development. Address: S.C. Johnson & Sons, Inc, 1525 Howe St, Station 54, Racine, WI 53403.

DWYER, THOMAS A, b. New York, N.Y, Nov. 18, 23. COMPUTER SCIENCE, APPLIED MATHEMATICS. B.S, Dayton, 45; M.S, Case, 51, Ph.D.(math), 60. Chmn. math. dept, Cathedral Latin Sch, 47-57; ASSOC. PROF. COMPUT. SCI, Dayton, 60-67; UNIV. PITTSBURGH, 68- Nat. Sci. Found. fel, Case; summers, res. assoc. numerical anal, Argonne Nat. Lab, 62 & 63, Mich. State Univ, 65, optimization theory, 66; prin. investr, Proj. SOLO, 69-71. Am. Math. Soc; Soc. Indust. & Appl. Math; Asn. Comput. Mach. Nonlinear networks and boundary value problems; optimization; computers in education; computer assisted instruction; man-machine systems. Address: Dept. of Computer Science, University of Pittsburgh, 800 Cathedral of Learning, Pittsburgh, PA 15213.

DWYER, WENDELL A(RTHUR), b. Randolph, Nebr, Mar. 25, 09; m. 31; c. 4. MATHEMATICS, OPERATIONS RESEARCH. B.S, Creighton, 30, M.S, 32; summers, Wisconsin, 31 & 33, Minnesota, 32; Ph.D.(math), Nebraska, 37. From asst. to prof. math. & statist. & asst. to pres, Creighton, 30-48; from opers. analyst to chief eval. div, opers. anal. off, Hq. Strategic Air Command, 49-57; exec. asst. adv. planning, Westinghouse Elec. Corp, 57-62; chief syst. anal, aerospace div, Boeing Co, 62-66; CHIEF OPERS. ANAL, MIL. AIRLIFT COMMAND, 66- Consult, Omaha City Planning Comn, 41-45; Nebr. unit, U.S. Pub. Health Serv, 42-45; U.S. Air Force, 62- AAAS; Am. Math. Soc; Math. Asn. Am; Am. Statist. Asn; Opers. Res. Soc. Am. Development of operations research tools and their application in the weapons system and business management areas. Address: Military Airlift Command, Scott Air Force Base, IL 62225.

DY, KIAN SENG, b. Philippines, June 28, 40; m. 67. SOLID STATE PHYSICS. B.Sc, Ohio State, 61; Ph.D.(physics), Cornell, 67. Res. assoc. PHYSICS, Univ. Ill, Urbana, 67-68; ASST. PROF, UNIV. N.C, CHAPEL HILL, 68- Quantum statistical mechanics; transport properties of fluids; lattice dynamics. Address: Dept. of Physics, University of North Carolina at Chapel Hill, Chapel Hill, NC 27514.

DYAL, PALMER, b. Odon, Ind, Oct. 27, 33; m. 55; c. 2. PHYSICS, ASTROPHYSICS. B.A, Coe Col, 55; Ph.D.(chem, physics), Univ. Ill, Urbana-Champaign, 59. Proj. scientist, U.S. Air Force, Kirtland AFB, 61-66; RES. SCIENTIST, AMES RES. CTR, NASA, 66- Sci. achievement award, Air Force Systs. Command, 62; Apollo achievement award, NASA, 69. U.S.A.F, 59-61, Capt. AAAS; Am. Phys. Soc; Am. Geophys. Union. Magnetic field research on the moon in the Apollo Program; magnetic field and particle experiments on high altitude nuclear bursts; photo production of pions from complex nuclei. Address: 26405 Ascension Dr, Los Altos Hills, CA 94022.

DYAR, JAMES JOSEPH, b. Marietta, Ohio, Nov. 1, 31; m. 58; c. 3. PLANT PHYSIOLOGY. A.B, West Virginia, 54, M.S, 57; Ph.D.(bot), Ohio State, 60. Asst. prof. biol, West Virginia, 60-61; researcher tobacco, Brown & Williamson Tobacco Corp, 61-62; asst. prof. BIOL, BELLARMINE COL, 62-65, assoc. prof, 65-70, PROF, 70-, CHMN. DEPT, 69- Tobacco Indust. Res. Comt, grant, 63-64; Nat. Sci. Found. res. grant, 64-65. Med.C, U.S.A, 54-56. AAAS; Am. Soc. Plant Physiol; Am. Inst. Biol. Sci. Organic translocation in plants; molecular research in tobacco. Address: Dept. of Biology, Bellarmine College, 2000 Norris Pl, Louisville, KY 40205.

DYAR, ROBERT, b. De Smet, S.Dak, Nov. 15, 09. MEDICINE. B.A, Minnesota, 30, M.B. & M.D, 34; M.P.H, Hopkins, 37, Dr.P.H, 38. Practicing physician, S.Dak, 35-36; assoc. epidemiol, sch. hygiene & pub. health, Hopkins, 37-39; res. proj. dir, San Joaquin Local Health Dist, State Dept. Pub. Health, Calif, 40-42; chief div. prev. med, 45-59, div. res, 59-68; dean grad. sch. med. sci, Univ. of the Pac. & exec. dir. Pac. Inst. Med. Sci, 68-71; RETIRED. Lectr. sch. pub. health, California, 46-; spec. consult. adv. comt. epidemiol. & biomet, Nat. Insts Health, 56-59, chmn, 60-64; mem, U.S. Nat. Comt. Vital & Health Statists, 60-63, chmn, 63-; Nat. Adv. Comt. Chronic Diseases & Health of Aged, 57-59. U.S.A.A.F, 42-45. Fel. Am. Col. Prev. Med; fel. Am. Pub. Health Asn; Am. Epidemiol. Soc; Asn. Teachers Prev. Med. Epidemiology; research administration and training. Address: 614 Santa Barbara Rd, Berkeley, CA 94707.

DYAR, R(OBERT) M(ATTHEW), b. Lowell, Ohio, Sept. 6, 15; m. 40; c. 2. CHEMISTRY. A.B, Marietta Col, 37; M.S, Detroit, 39. Chemist, Marietta Dyestuffs Co, 39-44; Marietta-Harmon Chem. Co, 44-46; develop. chemist, AM. CYANAMID CO, 46-51, group leader, 51-55, chief develop. chemist, 55-59, TECH. DIR, MARIETTA PLANT, 59- AAAS; Am. Chem. Soc. Dyestuffs and intermediates; organic specialties. Address: 631 Fifth St, Marietta, OH 45750.

DYAS, HAROLD EUGENE, b. Butte, Mont, Dec. 18, 14; m. 44; c. 1. CHEMISTRY. B.S, Wisconsin, 36; Manchester, 37-38; Ph.D.(chem), Duke, 41. Chief chemist, Badger Ord. Works, Wis, 41-44; group leader, Metall. Lab, Ill, 44-45; res. chemist, Sherwin-Williams Co, 45-50; chief chemist, Weber Costello Co, 50-64; tech. & gen. mgr. plant opers, John G. Carlsen Co, 64-67; TECH. DIR, MUNRO ADHESIVE CO, LYONS, 67- With Atomic Energy Comn; Off. Sci. Res. & Develop; U.S.A, 44-47. Am. Chem. Soc. Powder explosives; radioactive materials; dry colors; kinetics of fast reactions. Address: 401 N. High Ridge Rd, Hillside-Berkeley, IL 60162.

DYBA, RAYMOND V(ICTOR), b. Yonkers, N.Y, July 3, 21; m. 49; c. 2. PHYSICS. B.S, Mass. Inst. Technol, 50; M.S, Yale, 51, Ph.D.(physics), 54. Res. physicist, E.I. du Pont de Nemours & Co, 54-67, staff scientist, 67-68; SR. SCIENTIST, TEXTILE RES. INST, 69- U.S.A, 42-46, Sig.C.Res, 46-65, Maj. AAAS; Am. Phys. Soc. Physical properties of polymers. Address: Textile Research Institute, P.O. Box 625, Princeton, NJ 08540.

DYBALSKI, JACK N(ORBERT), b. Chicago, Ill, Oct. 19, 24; m. 51; c. 3. ORGANIC & SURFACE CHEMISTRY. Ph.B, Chicago, 51; Northwestern. 51-52. Chemist, ARMOUR INDUST. CHEM. CO, 53-54, res. chemist, 54-60, sect. leader asphalt res, 60-64, proj. mgr. water conserv, 62-71, RES. MGR, HWY. CHEM. DIV, 71-, COMMERCIAL DEVELOP, 64- Mem. Hwy. Res. Bd, Nat. Acad. Sci-Nat. Res. Coun, 60- U.S.A, 43-45, S/Sgt. Am. Chem. Soc; Asn. Asphalt Paving Technol; Am. Soc. Test. & Mat; Am. Soc. Civil Eng. Bituminous research and development based on cationic concept pertaining to hydrological uses for water conservation and industrial uses in building and paving. Address: 4754 S. Wood St, Chicago, IL 60609.

DYBBS, ALEXANDER, b. Boston, Mass, Jan. 4, 43; m. 70. HEAT TRANSFER, FLUID MECHANICS. B.S, Tufts Univ, 64; S.M, Mass. Inst. Technol, 66; Ph.D.(eng), Univ. Pa, 70. Assoc. engr, appl. physics lab, Johns Hopkins Univ, 66-68; ASST. PROF. ENG, CASE WEST. RESERVE UNIV, 70- Am. Soc. Mech. Eng. Surface tension phenomena; heat transfer in rarefield gases; fluid mechanics of corneal contact lenses; heat transfer in porous media; laser Doppler flow meter measurements in porous media. Address: Dept. of Fluid, Thermal & Aerospace Sciences, Case Western Reserve University, Cleveland, OH 44016.

DYBCZAK, Z(BIGNIEW) W(LADYSLAW), b. Zaleszczyki, Poland, June 27, 24; U.S. citizen; m. 57; c. 2. MECHANICAL & NUCLEAR ENGINEERING. B.Sc, London, 50; summer fels, Toronto, 56, 57, Ph.D.(mech. eng), 59. Indust. design engr, Eng, 49-51; demonstr. & res. asst. mech. eng, Toronto, 52-54, instr, 54-56, lectr, 56-59; assoc. mech. engr. res. & develop, Argonne Nat. Lab, 60; PROF. & DEAN ENG, TUSKEGEE INST, 60- Consult, Can. & U.S. Govt, Industs. & Founds; summers, resident res. assoc. nuclear eng, Argonne Nat. Lab, 61- Polish Br, R.A.F, 41-47. Am. Soc. Mech. Eng; Am. Nuclear Soc; Am. Soc. Eng. Educ. Photoelastic stress analysis; design and vibration analysis; nuclear reactor shielding; experimental reactor physics. Address: School of Engineering, Tuskegee Institute, AL 36088.

DYBING, C(LIFFORD) DEAN, b. Deadwood, S.Dak, Nov. 6, 31; m. 53; c. 4. PLANT PHYSIOLOGY. B.S, Colo. Agr. & Mech. Col, 53, M.S, 55; Ph.D. (plant physiol), California, Davis, 59. Asst. bot. & plant path, Colo. Agr. & Mech. Col, 53-55; bot, California, Davis, 55-58; PLANT PHYSIOLOGIST, OILSEEDS & INDUST. CROPS RES. DIV, U.S. DEPT. AGR, 60- Vis. Scientist, Prairie Regional Lab, Nat. Res. Coun. Can, Sask, 67-68; prof, S.Dak. State Univ, 71- U.S.A.F, 58-60, Admin. Off. Am. Soc. Plant Physiol; Am. Soc. Agron; Weed Sci. Soc. Am. Lipid metabolism; plant growth regulators; weed control. Address: Agricultural Research Service, Plant Science Dept, South Dakota State University, Brookings, SD 57006.

DYBVIG, DOUGLAS HOWARD, b. Bemidji, Minn, Feb. 14, 35; m. 57; c. 4. ORGANIC CHEMISTRY. B.A, St. Olaf Col, 57; Ph.D.(org. chem), Illinois, 61. Sr. res. chemist, MINN. MINING & MFG. CO, 60-70, MGR. LAB, 70- Asst. prof. chem, St. Olaf Col, 64-65. Am. Chem. Soc; The Chem. Soc. Organic reaction mechanisms; synthesis and chemistry of fluorine compounds; chemistry of rocket fuels; color reproduction; optics; development of color-in-color process. Address: Minnesota Mining & Manufacturing Co, Bldg. 235-3F, 3M Center, St. Paul, MN 55101.

DYBWAD, JENS PETER, b. Leipzig, Ger, July 27, 35. SURFACE CHEMISTRY. Diplom, Karlsruhe Tech, 59; Ph.D.(mineral), Univ. Tübingen, 66. RES. SCIENTIST, AIR FORCE CAMBRIDGE RES. LABS, 66- AAAS; Crystal growth; radiation effects on crystal surfaces. Address: Air Force Cambridge Research Labs, L.G. Hanscom Field, Bedford, MA 01730.

DYCE, ROLF BUCHANAN, b. Guelph, Ont, Oct. 12, 29; U.S. citizen; m. 59; c. 2. RADIOPHYSICS. B.S, Cornell, 51, Ph.D.(elec. eng), 55. Res. engr. radio propagation, Stanford Res. Inst, 57-63, staff scientist, 63-64; res. assoc. planetary radar, ARECIBO OBSERV, CORNELL UNIV, 64-65, ASSOC. DIR, 65- Mem. comn. III, IV, U.S. Nat. Comt, Int. Sci. Radio Union, 53-; res. assoc, radiosci. lab, Stanford Univ, 66-68. U.S.A.F, 55-57, Res, 51-55, 57-62, Capt. Inst. Elec. & Electronics Eng.(propagation ed, Trans. Group Antennas & Propagation, 64-69). Experimental studies of the ionosphere employing low frequency radar, satellite or cosmic signals; radar exploration of the moon and planets. Address: Arecibo Observatory, Box 995, Arecibo, PR 00612.

DYCK, ARNOLD WOLFF JAN, b. Ekaterinoslav, Russia, Dec. 13, 06; nat; m. 48; c. 3. ORGANIC & AGRICULTURAL CHEMISTRY. A.B, Bluffton Col, 30; M.A, Saskatchewan, 33; Ph.D.(org. & agr. chem), McGill, 35. Asst, McGill, 33-35; res. soil chemist, Dept. Agr, Ottawa, 35-37; res. & adv. work, Rubber Res. Inst, Malaya, 37-41; head chem. div, Inst. Agron. do Norte, Brazil, 41-43; sr. chemist, Rubber Develop. Corp, Brazil, 43-45; tech. information, Nat. Res. Coun. Can, 46; ed, Can. Chem. & Process Industs, 46-51; ED. DIR, Paper Indust, Chicago, 52-64; PAPER INDUST. MGT. ASN, 64- Can. Pulp & Paper Asn; Am. Chem. Soc; Tech. Asn. Pulp & Paper Indust. Organic nitrogen compounds; plant nutrition; spectrographic analysis; soil chemistry; rubber chemistry; insecticides; vegetable oils; technical writings. Address: Paper Industry Management Association, 2570 Devon Ave, Des Plaines, IL 60018.

DYCK, G(ERALD) W(AYNE), b. Borden, Sask, July 11, 38; m. 66; c. 2. REPRODUCTIVE PHYSIOLOGY. B.S.A, Univ. Sask, 60; M.Sc, Univ. Man, 63; Ph.D.(reproductive physiol), Iowa State Univ, 66. RES. SCIENTIST, CAN. DEPT. AGR, 66- Hon. prof, Univ. Man, 69- Agr. Inst. Can; Can. Soc. Animal Prod; Brit. Soc. Study Fertil; Soc. Study Reproduction; Am. Soc. Animal Sci; Prof. Inst. Pub. Serv. Can. Reproductive physiology, especially female swine embryonic survival and litter size, nutritional and environmental effects, ovulation rate, and uterine function; nature of estrus—post weaning and puberty; neural control of corpus luteum function. Address: Canada Dept. of Agriculture, Research Station, Box 610, Brandon, Man, Can.

DYCK, PETER LEONARD, b. Man, Mar. 31, 29; m. 58; c. 2. GENETICS. B.S.A, Univ. Man, 56, M.Sc, 57; Ph.D.(genetics), Univ. Calif, Davis, 60. RES. SCIENTIST, CAN. DEPT. AGR, 60- Genetics Soc. Can. Genetics of wheat, particularly leaf and stem rust resistance. Address: Canada Dept. of Agriculture, Research Station, 25 Dafoe Rd, Winnipeg 19, Man, Can.

DYCK, RUDOLPH H(ENRY), b. Pasadena, Calif, Apr. 17, 31; m. 55; c. 3. PHYSICAL CHEMISTRY. B.S, Univ. Calif, 52, Ph.D.(chem), 56. Mem. tech. staff, RCA Labs, 55-62; FAIRCHILD RES. & DEVELOP. LAB, 62-67, SECT. MGR, OPTOELECTRONICS, 67- AAAS; Am. Phys. Soc; Soc. Photog. Sci. & Eng. Photosensitive devices, arrays and subsystems; light emitting diodes, arrays and subsystems. Address: 160 Ely Place, Palo Alto, CA 94306.

DYCK, WALTER PETER, b. Winkler, Man, Dec. 7, 35; m. 65; c. 3. INTERNAL MEDICINE, GASTROENTEROLOGY. B.A, Bethel Col.(Kans), 57; M.D, Kansas, 61. Intern. & res. med, Henry Ford Hosp, Detroit, Mich, 61-63, 65-66; Nat. Insts. Health training fel. gastroenterol, Mt. Sinai Sch. Med, 66-68; INVESTR. EXP. PHYSIOL, SCOTT & WHITE MEM. HOSP, 68-, SR. STAFF CONSULT. GASTROENTEROL, SCOTT & WHITE CLIN, 68-, CHMN, DEPT. RES, 70- Res. fel. gastroenterol, Univ. Zurich, 63-64; gastrointestinal enzym, Univ. Toronto & Hosp. for Sick Children, Toronto, Ont, 64-65; consult, Vet. Admin. Ctr, Temple, Tex, 68-; clin. instr. internal med, southwest. med. sch, Univ. Tex, 70- Am. Med. Asn; Am. Fedn. Clin. Res; Am. Gastroenterol. Asn; Am. Col. Physicians; Am. Physiol. Soc. Hormonal control of pancreatic secretion; factors influencing gastric mucosal permeability. Address: Dept. of Research, Scott & White Clinic, 2401 S. 31st St, Temple, TX 76501.

DYCUS, A(UGUSTUS) M(AHON), b. Paducah, Ky, Sept. 21, 17; m. 43; c. 2. PLANT PHYSIOLOGY. B.S, Akron, 46, Ph.D.(plant physiol), Cornell, 52. Instr. natural sci, Akron, 46-48; asst. bot, Cornell, 48-52; plant physiologist, rubber plant invest, U.S. Dept. Agr, 52-54; assoc. prof. biol, State Univ. N.Y. Teachers Col, New Paltz, 54-55; asst. prof. BOT, Oberlin Col, 55-59; ASSOC. PROF, ARIZ STATE UNIV, 59-, HEAD DEPT, 61- U.S.N, 42-46. Am. Soc. Plant Physiol; Am. Soc. Hort. Sci; Bot. Soc. Am. Biosynthesis of rubber in plants; enzyme systems relating to plant respiration. Address: Dept. of Botany, Life Science Center, Arizona State University, Tempe, AZ 85281.

DYCUS, DALE W(YATT), b. Cincinnati, Ohio, Mar. 8, 39; m. 63; c. 1. PHYSICAL & ORGANIC CHEMISTRY. B.A, Hanover Col, 62; univ. assistantship, Tulane Univ, 64, Nat. Sci. Found. fel, 65, Ph.D.(phys. chem), 70. RES. CHEMIST, SUN OIL CO, 69- AAAS; Am. Chem. Soc; Soc. Petrol. Eng. Cosolvent effects on the rates of reaction of some substituted benzoyl chlorides in alcohol-benzene solutions; physical chemistry and mechanisms of petroleum recovery from reservoirs. Address: Sun Oil Co, 503 N. Central Expressway, Richardson, TX 75080.

DYE, DAVID L, b. Seattle, Wash, Aug. 5, 25; m. 52; c. 3. PHYSICS. B.S, Washington (Seattle), 45, Ph.D.(physics), 52. Res. assoc, radiol. lab, med. center, California, 54-55, 58-59; chmn. physics, Gordon Col, Rawalpindi, 55-58; res. specialist, Aero-Space Div, Boeing Co, 59-62, chief radiation effects lab, 62-64, chief radiation effects unit, 64-68; sr. scientist, Air Force Spec. Weapons Ctr, 68-70; CHIEF RADIATION EFFECTS UNIT, AEROSPACE DIV, BOEING CO, 70- U.S.N, 42-45, Res, 52-53, Lt. AAAS; Am. Phys. Soc; Inst. Elec. & Electronics Eng. Radiation dosimetry and health physics; radiation effects on electronics components and systems; space radiation and nuclear physics; system survivability. Address: 12825 S.E. 45th Pl, Bellevue, WA 98006.

DYE, FRANK J, b. Bronx, N.Y, Jan. 12, 42; m. 67; c. 1. CYTOLOGY. B.S, Danbury State Col, 63; Nat. Insts. Health fel, Fordham Univ, 65, M.S, 66, Ph.D.(cytol), 69; fel, New Eng. Inst, 67. Instr. BIOL, WEST. CONN. STATE COL, 67-70, ASST. PROF, 70-; ADJ. PROF, NEW ENG. INST, 70-, res. assoc, 68-70. AAAS; Tissue Cult. Asn; Am. Inst. Biol. Sci; Am. Soc. Zool; N.Y. Acad. Sci. Origin of tissue culture populations; morphogenesis; gene activation; in vitro movement of epithelial cells. Address: Dept. of Biology, Western Connecticut State College, 181 White St, Danbury, CO 06810.

DYE, H(ENRY) A(BEL), b. Dunkirk, N.Y, Feb. 14, 26; m. 50; c. 2. MATHEMATICS. M.S, Chicago, 47, Atomic Energy Cmn. fel, 49-50, Ph.D.(math), 50. Bateman fel, Calif. Inst. Tech, 50-52; instr, 52-53; mem. sch. math, Inst. Adv. Study, 53-54; asst. prof. MATH, Iowa, 54-56; assoc. prof, Southern California, 56-59; Iowa, 59-60; PROF, UNIV. CALIF, LOS ANGELES, 60- Sig.C, U.S.A, 44-46. Am. Math. Soc. Functional analysis. Address: Dept. of Mathematics, 6364 Mathematical Sciences Bldg, University of California, Los Angeles, CA 90024.

DYE, JAMES E(UGENE), b. Rock Springs, Wyo, Oct. 17, 39; m. 67. CLOUD PHYSICS, ATMOSPHERIC SCIENCES. B.S, Univ. Wash, 62, Ph.D.(atmospheric sci), 67. Res. assoc, dept. atmospheric sci, Univ. Wash, 62-67; inst. meterol, Univ. Stockholm, 67-68; asst. prof, atmospheric simulation lab, dept. mech. eng, Colo. State Univ, 69-70; ASST. PROG. SCIENTIST, LAB. ATMOSPHERIC SCI, NAT. CTR. ATMOSPHERIC RES, 70- Fulbright travel grant, Comt. on Int. Exchange of Persons, Fulbright-Hays prog. with Sweden, 67-68. U.S.A, 57, Res, 57-66. Am. Meteorol. Soc. Cloud and precipitation physics including weather modification; aerosol physics; aeronomy, particularly with relevance to the formation of noctilucent clouds; meteorological instrumentation. Address: Lab. of Atmospheric Sciences, National Center for Atmospheric Research, Box 1470, Boulder, CO 80302.

DYE, JAMES L(OUIS), b. Soudan, Minn, July 18, 27; m. 48; c. 3. PHYSICAL CHEMISTRY. A.A, Va. Jr. Col, Minn, 48; A.B, Gustavus Adolphus Col, 49; Ph.D.(chem), Iowa State Col, 53. Asst. PHYS. CHEM, Inst. Atomic Res. & DEPT. CHEM, Iowa State Col, 49-53; PROF, MICH. STATE UNIV, 53- Nat. Sci. Found. Sci. Faculty fel, Max Planck Inst, Göttingen, Ger, 61-62; vis. scientist, Ohio State Univ, 68-69. U.S.A, 45-46. AAAS; Am. Chem. Soc. Electrochemistry spectra e.s.r. of metal-amine solutions; kinetics of fast electron and proton transfer reactions in non-aqueous media; solvated electron properties in pure and mixed solvents. Address: Dept. of Chemistry, Michigan State University, East Lansing, MI 48823.

DYE, RICHARD W(ILBUR), b. Franklin, N.J, Nov. 11, 21. PHYSICAL CHEMISTRY. B.S, Mich. State Col, 43. Res. chem, Nat. Dairy Res. Labs, 46-48; res. lab, chem-pigments-metals div, Glidden Co, 48-57, res. group leader, 57-65, MGR. ANAL. DEPT, PIGMENTS & COLOR GROUP, GLIDDEN-

DURKEE DIV, SCM CORP, 65- U.S.N.R, 43-46, Lt.(jg). Electron Micros. Soc. Am. Light and electron microscopy; x-ray and electron diffraction; emission spectroscopy; spectrophotometry, pigment and inorganic chemistry. Address: Analytical Dept, Pigments & Color Group, Glidden-Durkee Division, SCM Corp, 3901 Hawkins Point Rd, Baltimore, MD 21226.

DYE, ROBERT F(ULTON), b. Gloster, Miss, Oct. 18, 20; m. 47; c. 3. CHEMICAL ENGINEERING. B.S, Miss. State, 43; M.S, Ga. Inst. Tech, 51, Shell fel, 51-52, Ph.D.(chem. eng), 53. Chem. engr, inorg. & org. res, Monsanto Chem. Co, 46-49; asst. chem. eng, Ga. Inst. Tech, 50-51, 52-53; sr. process & design proj. engr, process develop. div, Phillips Petrol. Co, 53-62; dir. Miss. Res. & Develop. Ctr, 62-68; PROCESSING ENGR, SHELL DEVELOP. CO, SHELL OIL CO, INC, 68- Artil.C, 43-46, U.S.A.R, 46-, Maj. AAAS; Am. Chem. Soc; Am. Inst. Chem. Eng; N.Y. Acad. Sci. Gas diffusion; diffusional processes; chemical technology; applied economics. Address: Shell Develop. Co, Shell Oil Co, Inc, 1400 53rd St, Emeryville, CA 94608.

DYE, WILLIAM THOMSON, JR, b. Chattanooga, Tenn, July 8, 18; m. 44; c. 2. ORGANIC CHEMISTRY. B.S, North Carolina, 40, Ph.D.(org. chem), 44. Res. chemist, Naval Res. Lab, D.C, 44-46; Monsanto Chem. Co, 47-52; Chemstrand Corp, 52-58, group leader, 60, Chemstrand Res. Ctr, Inc, Monsanto Co, 60-70; MGR. PATENT LIAISON, BURLINGTON INDUSTS. RES. CTR, 71- Am. Chem. Soc. Organic phosphorus compounds; synthetic fibers; textiles; patent liaison. Address: Burlington Industries Research Center, P.O. Box 21327, Greensboro, NC 27420.

DYEN, MARTIN E, b. Phila, Pa, July 11, 34; m. 60; c. 2. ORGANIC CHEMISTRY. B.A, Temple Univ, 55, NASA fel, 65-67, Ph.D.(chem), 67. SR. ORG. CHEMIST, SMITH KLINE & FRENCH LABS, 67- U.S.A, 60-62, 1st Lt. AAAS; Am. Chem. Soc. Synthesis of organic compounds and scale-up problems. Address: 1109 Hedgerow Lane, Philadelphia, PA 19115.

DYER, ALBERT J(OSEPH), b. Amity, Mo, Mar. 23, 10; m. 35; c. 2. NUTRITION. B.S, Missouri, 33, M.S, 39, Ph.D.(nutrit), 49. County exten. agent, Missouri, 35-38, instr. animal husb, 38-43, from instr. to prof, 46-54; mkt. counsr, Kansas City Livestock Exchange & Yard Co, 54-55; PROF. ANIMAL HUSB, UNIV. MO, 55-, chmn. dept, 57. Consult. beef cattle prog, Int. Coop. Admin. & Agency Int. Develop, Chile, 61. Chief mil. nutrit. br, Off. Surgeon Gen, U.S.A, 45-46, Capt. Am. Soc. Animal Sci. Production and management of beef cattle and sheep. Address: 125 Mumford Hall, University of Missouri, Columbia, MO 65201.

DYER, A(LLAN) E(DWIN), b. Toronto, Ont, Aug. 23, 23; m. 44; c. 4. PHARMACOLOGY. Phm.B, Univ. Toronto, 49, Ph.D.(pharmacol), 55, M.D, 67; B.Sc, Univ. Buffalo, 51. Can. Life Ins. Off. Asn. fel, Univ. Toronto, 54-56, univ. fel, 55-56; res. assoc. & head bioassay dept, Connaught Med. Res. Labs, 56-67; intern, Toronto West. Hosp, 67-68; CHIEF DRUGS & BIOL, ONT. DEPT. HEALTH, 68- R.C.A.F, 43-45, 51-57, Res, 57- Pharmacol. Soc. Can; Can. Fedn. Biol. Soc. Methodology for screening and assessing pharmacological and toxicological activity. Address: Drugs & Biologicals, Ontario Dept. of Health, SW 968 Hepburn Block, Parliament Bldgs, Toronto, Ont, Can.

DYER, DANIEL SINCLAIR, b. Salt Lake City, Utah, Nov. 7, 37; m. 64; c. 2. INORGANIC & PHYSICAL CHEMISTRY. B.A, Colorado, 60; Ph.D.(chem), Utah, 67. Res. asst, Utah, 60-67; RES. CHEMIST, U.S. AIR FORCE MAT. LAB, 67- Engr, Hercules Powder Co, Utah, 63. Am. Chem. Soc; Sci. Res. Soc. Am. Fluorine-19 nuclear magnetic resonance studies of metalfluorine complexes to elucidate stereochemistry, kinetics of exchange reactions and the nature of the metal-fluorine bonds; application of digital computers to chemical instrumentation; computer specialization. Address: Air Force Materials Lab, LPA, Wright Patterson Air Force Base, OH 45433.

DYER, DENZEL L(EROY), b. McCool Jct, Nebr, Oct. 12, 29; m. 52; c. 3. BIOCHEMISTRY. B.S, York Col, 50; M.S, Univ. Nebr, 53, Ph.D.(chem), 55. Chemist, Dow Chem. Co, 55-59; assoc. res. scientist, life sci. dept, Martin-Marietta Corp, 59-64; prin. scientist, life sci. dept, Northrop Corp. Labs, 64-69; CONSULT. CHEMIST, 69- U.S.A.R, Capt. Am. Chem. Soc; Am. Soc. Microbiol; Soc. Indust. Microbiol; N.Y. Acad. Sci; Asn. Consult. Chemists & Chem. Eng. Microbiology; microbial physiology; microbial chemistry. Address: 6008 Flambeau Rd, Palos Verdes Peninsula, CA 90274.

DYER, DONALD CHESTER, b. Great Bend, Kans, July 8, 39; m. 59; c. 2. PHARMACOLOGY. B.S, Kansas, 61, Ph.D.(pharmacol), 65. Fel. PHARMACOL, Manitoba, 65-67; ASST. PROF, Oregon State, 67-68; SCH. MED, UNIV. WASH, 68- AAAS; N.Y. Acad. Sci. Polypeptides; smooth muscle stimulating lipids; autonomic drugs; fetal pharmacology. Address: Dept. of Pharmacology, School of Medicine, University of Washington, Seattle, WA 98105.

DYER, (SHERMAN) ELDON, b. Corpus Christi, Tex, June 19, 29; m. 50; c. 2. MATHEMATICS. B.A. & B.S, Texas, 47, Ph.D.(math), 52. Instr. pure math, Texas, 49-51; asst. prof. MATH, Georgia, 52-55; Hopkins, 55-56; mem, Inst. for Adv. Study, 56-57; res. lectr, Chicago, 57-59, assoc. prof, 59-63, PROF, 63-64; Rice Univ, 64-70; GRAD. MATH. CTR, CITY UNIV. NEW YORK, 70- Nat. Sci. Found. fel, 56-57; Sloan Found. fel, 60-62; ed, Proceedings, Am. Math. Soc, 62-67; mem. math. div, Nat. Res. Coun, 64-66. Am. Math. Soc. Topology. Address: Graduate Mathematics Center, City University of New York, 33 W. 42nd St, New York, NY 10036.

DYER, ELIZABETH, b. Haverhill, Mass, May 10, 06. ORGANIC CHEMISTRY. A.B, Mt. Holyoke Col, 27, A.M, 29; Ph.D.(chem), Yale, 31. Asst. chem, Mt. Holyoke Col, 27-29; Yale, 29-31. Chem. Found. fel, 31-33; instr. CHEM, UNIV. DEL, 33-40, asst. prof, 40-47, assoc. prof, 47-51, prof, 51-71, EMER. PROF, 71- AAAS; Am. Chem. Soc. Polymers; isocyanates; pyrimidines and purines. Address: 232 Cheltenham Rd, Newark, DE 19711.

DYER, FRANK FALKONER, b. Webbers Falls, Okla, Nov. 18, 31; m. 57; c. 2. INORGANIC & PHYSICAL CHEMISTRY. B.S, Oklahoma State, 53, M.S, 55; Union Carbide Nuclear fel, Tennessee, 56, Ph.D.(chem), 58.

CHEMIST, Pan Am. Petrol. Corp, 58-60; OAK RIDGE NAT. LAB, 60- Chem.C, 58, 1st Lt. Am. Chem. Soc. Thermodynamics of electrolytic solutions; stability constants of metal complexes; solvent extraction; relations between physical properties and molecular structure of polymers; nucleonics. Address: Oak Ridge National Lab, P.O. Box X, Oak Ridge, TN 37831.

DYER, HUBERT J(EROME), b. Daylesford, Australia, June 4, 14; U.S. citizen; m. 41; c. 2. BOTANY. S.B, Chicago, 39, S.M, 40, Ph.D.(plant physiol), 46; Ohio State, 40-41. Qual. control res, Libby, McNeill & Libby, Ill, 43-47, head res. dept, 47-48; instr. BOT, BROWN UNIV, 48-50, asst. prof, 50-59, ASSOC. PROF, 59- AAAS; Am. Soc. Plant Physiol; Bot. Soc. Am; Soc. Exp. Biol. & Med; Scandinavian Soc. Plant Physiol; Japanese Soc. Plant Physiol. Mineral nutrition; photoperiodism; effects of ultrasound. Address: Division of Biological & Medical Science, Brown University, Providence, RI 02912.

DYER, HUGH N(ELSON), JR, b. Martinsville, Va, Mar. 24, 13; m. 40; c. 1. PHYSICAL CHEMISTRY. B.S, Va. Polytech, 33, M.S, 34; Du Pont fel, Virginia, 36-37, Ph.D.(phys. chem), 38. Res. chemist, Behr-Manning Corp, 37-50, dir. prod. testing, 50-58, asst. mgr. prod. eng. dept, 58-62, tech. dir. coated abrasives opers, 62-69; SECURITY ANALYST, FIRST ALBANY CORP, 71- Instr, Rensselaer Polytech. Inst, 45-46. Am. Chem. Soc. Thermodynamics; statistical quality control and design of experiments; cutting fluids and theory of metal cutting; investment securities analysis. Address: 361 Shaker Rd, Loudonville, NY 12211.

DYER, IRA, b. Brooklyn, N.Y, June 14, 25; m. 49; c. 2. ACOUSTICS. S.B, Mass. Inst. Tech, 49, S.M, 51, Ph.D.(acoustics), 54. Asst. physics, Mass. Inst. Tech, 49-51; acoust. scientist, Bolt Beranek & Newman Inc, 51-61, v.pres. & dir. phys. sci, 61-71, dir. prog. advan. study, 64-67; PROF. & HEAD DEPT, OCEAN ENG, MASS. INST. TECHNOL, 71- U.S.A.A.F, 44-45. Fel. Acoust. Soc. Am.(biennial award, 60). Acoustic waves and vibrations; acoustic scattering and diffraction; noise of aerodynamic origin; structure-borne sound; underwater acoustics; blast waves; combustion. Address: 26 Valleyspring Rd, Newton, MA 02158.

DYER, IRWIN (ALLEN), b. Dahlonega, Ga, Feb. 8, 21; m. 43; c. 3. ANIMAL SCIENCE. B.S.A, Georgia, 46, M.S.A, 47; Ph.D, Illinois, 50. Assoc. prof. animal sci, Georgia, 50-52; adv. ministry of agr, El Salvador, Cent. Am, 52-54; assoc. prof. ANIMAL SCI, WASH. STATE UNIV, 55-61, PROF, 61-, ASSOC. DEAN GRAD. SCH, 70-, chmn. grad. prog. nutrit, 68-70. Nutrit. consult. U.S.N, 42-45, Res, 45-60, Lt. Comdr.(Ret). AAAS; Am. Inst. Biol. Sci; Am. Inst. Nutrit. Ruminant nutrition. Address: Graduate School, Washington State University, Pullman, WA 99163.

DYER, JAMES ARTHUR, b. San Antonio, Tex, Feb. 10, 32; m. 53. MATHEMATICS. B.S, Texas, 52, M.A, 54, Ph.D.(math), 60. Res. scientist physics, defense res. lab, Texas, 54-58, asst. prof. MATH, univ, 60-61; Arizona, 61-62; South. Methodist Univ, 62-64, assoc. prof, 64-65; IOWA STATE UNIV, 66-70, PROF, 70- Am. Math. Soc; Math. Asn. Am; London Math. Soc; Math. Soc. France. Integration; functional analysis; integral equations. Address: Dept. of Mathematics, Iowa State University, Ames, IA 50010.

DYER, JAMES LEE, b. Long Beach, Calif, Sept. 2, 34; m. 60. ENGINEERING. B.S, California, Los Angeles, 57, M.S, 60, Ph.D.(eng), 65. Teaching fel. eng, California, Los Angeles, 65; mem. tech. staff, TRW Systs, 65-66; asst. prof. MECH. ENG, CALIF. STATE COL. LONG BEACH, 66-70, ASSOC. PROF. & CHMN. DEPT, 70- Chem.C, Nat. Guard, 57-65, Capt. AAAS. Thermodynamics of phase changes and irreversible processes. Address: Dept. of Engineering, California State College, 6101 E. Seventh St, Long Beach, CA 90801.

DYER, JOAN L, b. Brooklyn, N.Y, Aug. 4, 41; m. 67. MATHEMATICS. A.B, Barnard Col, Columbia, 61; Nat. Sci. Found. fels, N.Y. Univ, 61-62 & 63-65, univ. fel, 62-63, Ph.D.(math), 65. Vis. lectr, sch. gen. studies, Australian Nat. Univ, 65; Ritt instr. MATH, Columbia, 65-67; asst. prof, LEHMAN COL, 67-71, ASSOC. PROF, 71-, GRAD. CTR, CITY UNIV. NEW YORK, 71- Am. Math. Soc. Residual properties of polycyclic groups and generalized free products with amalgamations; nilpotent Lie algebras and their automorphisms; nil- and solv-manifolds. Address: Dept. of Mathematics, Herbert H. Lehman College, Bedford Park Blvd. W, Bronx, NY 10468.

DYER, JOHN N(ORVELL), b. Norfolk, Va, July 19, 30; m. 51; c. 2. PHYSICS. A.B, California, Berkeley, 56, Ph.D.(physics), 61. Asst. prof. PHYSICS, NAVAL POSTGRAD. SCH, 61-64, assoc. prof, 64-69, PROF, 69- Consult, Lawrence Radiation Lab, California, 61-; Aerospace Corp, Calif, 63-64. U.S.A, 51-53, 1st Lt. Am. Phys. Soc. Electron scattering; linear accelerators; nuclear structure; electron energy loss in matter; radiation effects. Address: 270 Mar Vista Dr, Monterey, CA 93940.

DYER, JOHN R(OBERT), b. Springfield, Mo, Jan. 31, 29. ORGANIC CHEMISTRY. B.S, Northwestern, 50; Upjohn Co. fel. Illinois, Ph.D.(chem), 54. Proj. assoc. Wisconsin, 54-56; asst. prof. CHEM, GA. INST. TECHNOL, 56-59, assoc. prof, 59-66, PROF, 66- Am. Chem. Soc. Chemistry of natural products. Address: School of Chemistry, Georgia Institute of Technology, Atlanta, GA 30332.

DYER, LAWRENCE D, b. Los Angeles, Calif, Sept. 3, 30; m. 52; c. 3. PHYSICAL CHEMISTRY. B.S, Calif. Inst. Tech, 51; Gen. Motors fel, Virginia, 54-56, Du Pont fel, 56-57, Ph.D.(phys. chem), 57. Eng. asst, Helipot Corp, 49-50; chem. asst. org. chem, U.S. Naval Ord. Test Sta, Calif, 51; jr. chemist fused hydroxide corrosion, Oak Ridge Nat. Lab, 51-53; sr. res. phys. chemist, res. labs, Gen. Motors,Corp, 57-66; MEM. TECH. STAFF, TEX. INSTRUMENTS INC, 66- Electrochem. Soc; Am. Asn. Crystal Growth; Am. Chem. Soc. Surface physics and chemistry; friction and wear; fused salts and hydroxides; crystal growth of copper and silicon; silicon epitaxial growth; plastic deformation in copper and silicon. Address: Texas Instruments, 13500 N. Central Expressway, Dallas, TX 75222.

DYER, M(ELVIN) I, b. Havre, Mont, Oct. 18, 32; m. 57; c. 2. ZOOLOGY. B.S, Univ. Idaho, 55; M.S, Univ. Minn, 61, Ph.D.(zool), 64. Asst. prof. ZOOL, Univ. Guelph, 64-67; ASSOC. PROF, OHIO STATE UNIV, 67-; BIOLOGIST-SUPVR, PATUXENT WILDLIFE RES. CTR, U.S. BUR. SPORT FISHERIES & WILDLIFE, 67- Med.C, U.S.A, 55-57, Res, 60- Am. Ornith. Union; Wilson Ornith. Soc. Avian zoogeography and ecology. Address: Box 2097, Sandusky, OH 44870.

DYER, R. F, b. Framingham, Mass, Dec. 21; m. 44; c. 3. MECHANICAL ENGINEERING. B.S, Worcester Polytech, 43; East Tenn. State, 63. Mech. engr, SYNTHETIC FIBER DEVELOP, TENN. EASTMAN CO. DIV, EASTMAN KODAK CO, 46-55, sr. mech. engr, 55-66, CHIEF MECH. ENGR, FIBER SPINNING DEVELOP. LAB, 66- U.S.N, 42-46, Lt. Comdr. AAAS; Am. Soc. Mech. Eng; Am. Asn. Textile Technol. Development, design and invention in manufacture and use of synthetic fibers, cigarette filters, textured yarns and nonwovens. Address: Fiber Development Division, B112, Tennessee Eastman Co, Kingsport, TN 37662.

DYER, RANDOLPH H, b. Ft. Smith, Ark, Oct. 31, 40; m. 64; c. 1. BIOCHEMISTRY. A.B, Transylvania Col, 62; American Univ, 62-63. CHEMIST, Melpar Inc, Va, 63-66; ALCOHOL, TOBACCO & FIREARMS LAB, U.S. TREASURY DEPT, 66- Asn. Off. Anal. Chem. Analytical chemistry and biochemistry, especially enzymes and fermentation processes and products. Address: Alcohol, Tobacco & Firearms Lab, U.S. Treasury Dept, Internal Revenue Service Bldg, Washington, DC 20224.

DYER, ROBERT F(RANK), b. Sewickley, Pa, Apr. 21, 37; m. 60; c. 3. ANATOMY, CELL BIOLOGY. B.S, Geneva Col, 59; U.S. Pub. Health Serv. fel, Univ. Pittsburgh, 63-66, Ph.D.(anat, cell biol), 66. Instr, ANAT, SCH. MED, MED. CTR, LA. STATE UNIV, 66-69, ASST. PROF, 69- Consult, cell biol, U.S. Pub. Health Serv. Hosp, Carville; Edward G. Schlieder Educ. Found. grant, 70- Am. Asn. Anat; Electron Micros. Soc. Am; Pan Am. Asn. Anat. Ovarian development; ultrastructural relationship of mycobacteria to cultured cells; effects of constant light on retinal morphology. Address: Dept. of Anatomy, Louisiana State University, School of Medicine, 1542 Tulane Ave, New Orleans, LA 70112.

DYER, ROLLA McINTYRE, JR, b. Elizabethtown, Ky, Dec. 30, 22; m. 47; c. 3. ANALYTICAL & ORGANIC CHEMISTRY. Ohio State Univ, 46-49; Ph.D, Univ. Louisville, 63. Instr. CHEM, Campbellsville Col, 59-60; vis. instr, Univ. Louisville, 60-63; asst. prof, Northeast La. Univ, 63-67; asst. prof, IND. STATE UNIV, EVANSVILLE, 67-68, assoc. prof, 68-71, PROF, 71-, CHMN. DIV, 68- Separation and identification of components of complex mixtures; design and preparation of instructional models especially three dimensional magnetic field maps. Address: Division of Science & Mathematics, Indiana State University, Evansville, IN 47712.

DYER, WILLIAM G(ERALD), b. Boston, Mass, Oct. 27, 29; m. 65; c. 2. HELMINTHOLOGY. A.B, Boston Univ, 57, A.M, 58; Ph.D.(parasitol), Colo. State Univ, 65. Res. asst. endocrinol, Worcester Found. Exp. Biol, 58-60, biochem, Harvard Med. Sch, 60-62, prof. zool, head biol. dept, Minot State College, 65-69; ASST. PROF, SOUTH. ILL. UNIV, 69- Hosp.C, U.S.N, 48-52. Am. Soc. Parasitol; Wildlife Disease Asn; Am. Inst. Biol. Sci. Endocrinology; helminthology; immunology. Address: Dept. of Zoology, Southern Illinois University, Carbondale, IL 62901.

DYER, WILLIAM J(OHN), b. Antigonish, N.S, Oct. 30, 13; m. 44; c. 4. BIOCHEMISTRY. B.Sc, St. Francis Xavier, 34; M.Sc, McGill, 37, Ph.D, 40. Analyst soil surv, soil anal, N.S. Agr. Col, 34-35; asst. soil res, Nat. Res. Coun. Can, Macdonald Col, McGill, 36-39, analyst gen. res, 39-40; jr. biochemist, forest prod. lab, Dept. Mines & Forests, Ottawa, 40; biochemist, FISHERIES RES. BD. CAN, 40-64, PRIN. BIOCHEMIST, 64- Fel. Chem. Inst. Can. Quality changes in frozen fish; antemortem and postmortem biochemical changes relating to product quality. Address: Fisheries Research Board of Canada, Box 429, Halifax, N.S, Can.

DYER-BENNET, JOHN, b. Leicester, Eng, Apr. 17, 15; nat; m. 51; c. 2. MATHEMATICS. A.B, California, 36, Kraft scholar, A.M, 37, Howison fel, 37-40; M.A, Harvard, 39, Ph.D.(math), 40. Asst. MATH, California, 36-37; instr, Vanderbilt, 40-41, 45-46; Purdue, 46-47, asst. prof, 47-56, assoc. prof, 56-60; CARLETON COL, 60-65, PROF, 65-, chmn. dept. math. & astron, 64-66. Nat. Sci. Found. faculty fel, Switz, 58-59. U.S.A, 41-45, 51-52, Ord.C, U.S.A.R, Lt. Col.(Ret). Am. Math. Soc; Math. Asn. Am.(vis. lectr, 63-64). Abstract algebra. Address: Dept. of Mathematics, Carleton College, Northfield, MN 55057.

DYKE, BENNETT, U.S. citizen. BIOLOGICAL ANTHROPOLOGY, HUMAN GENETICS. B.A, Trinity Col, 55; Univ. Chicago, 59-62; Ph.D, Univ. Mich, 68. Instr. ANTHROPOL, Bucknell Univ, 64-70; ASST. PROF, PA. STATE UNIV, 70- Population Coun. fel, 69-70. AAAS; Am. Soc. Human Genetics; Am. Asn. Phys. Anthropol; Brit. Soc. Study Human Biol. Genetic demography; computer simulation of human populations; population genetics. Address: Dept. of Anthropology, Pennsylvania State University, University Park, PA 16802.

DYKE, RICHARD WARREN, b. Chicago, Ill, Oct. 22, 22; m. 47; c. 6. MEDICINE, HEMATOLOGY. A.B, Ind. Univ, 44, M.D, 46. Intern, Marion County Gen. Hosp, Indianapolis, Ind, 46-47, resident, 49-53; instr, SCH. MED, IND. UNIV-PURDUE UNIV, INDIANAPOLIS, 53-54; asst. prof. MED, 55-63, ASSOC. PROF, 63-; DIR. POISON CONTROL CTR, MARION COUNTY GEN. HOSP, 55-, CLIN. DIR. INTERNAL MED, 59-, CHMN. FORMULARY COMN, 63-, dir. med. educ, 53-59. Dipl, Am. Bd. Internal Med, 55. Med.C, U.S.A, 47-49, Capt. Fel. Am. Col. Physicians; Am. Med. Asn; Am. Soc. Internal Med; Am. Soc. Hemat. Clinical research in cancer chemotherapy. Address: 542 W. 83rd St, Indianapolis, IN 46260.

DYKE, W(ALTER) P(AYNE), b. Forest Grove, Ore, Dec. 9, 14; m. 45; c. 4. PHYSICS. B.A, Linfield Col, 38; Ph.D.(physics), Washington (Seattle), 46. Staff mem, radiation lab, Mass. Inst. Tech, 42-45; prof. physics, head dept. & dir. res, Linfield Col, 46-55, dir. res. inst, 55-61; PRES, FIELD EMISSION CORP, 58- Presidential cert. of merit, 46. Fel. Am. Phys. Soc; fel. Inst. Elec. & Electronics Eng.(electronic achievement award, Inst. Radio Eng, 58, David Sarnoff award, 68); Am. Asn. Physics Teachers. Electron physics solid state; field emission and its applications. Address: Field Emission Corp, Box 58, McMinnville, OR 97128.

DYKEN, MARK LEWIS, b. Laramie, Wyo, Aug. 26, 28; m. 51; c. 6. MEDICINE, NEUROLOGY. B.S, Indiana, 51, M.D, 54. Res. NEUROL, med. center, Indiana, 55-58; clin. dir. & dir. res, New Castle State Hosp, 58-61; from asst. to assoc. prof, SCH. MED, IND. UNIV, 61-69, PROF, 69-, PRIN. INVESTR. & DIR, CEREBRAL VASCULAR CLIN. RES. CTR, 66-, CHMN. DEPT. NEUROL, 71- Med. dir, Ind. Multiple Sclerosis Soc. Clin, 61-; asst. dir, multicategorical clin. res. facility, Indiana, 62-66; consult, Cerebral Palsy Clin, 61-70; dir, Ind. Regional Med. Stroke Prog, 68; mem. clin. mgt. study group & epidemiol. study group, Joint Comt. Stroke Facilities, 70- Mem. adv. comt, neurol. sensory disease serv. prog, Bur. State Servs, Pub. Health Serv, 64-67; bd. dirs, Ind. Neuromuscular Res. Lab, 65- U.S.A, 46-48. Am. Med. Asn; fel. Am. Acad. Neurol; Asn. Res. Nerv. & Ment. Diseases. Cerebrovascular disease; epilepsy; muscle disease; changes in brain and vasculature following injury early in life; demyelinating diseases. Address: Dept. of Neurology, Indiana University School of Medicine, Indianapolis, IN 46202.

DYKEN, PAUL R, b. Casper, Wyo, Mar. 14, 34; m. 61; c. 3. PEDIATRICS, NEUROLOGY. B.S, Indiana, 56, M.D, 59. Intern, Phila. Gen. Hosp, Pa, 59-60; res. neurol, Ind. Univ. & Affiliated Hosps, 60-63; fel. neurophysiol, Barnes Hosp, Washington (St. Louis), 63-64; pediat. neurol, Chicago, 64-65; asst. prof, med. ctr, Ind. Univ-Purdue Univ, Indianapolis, 65-68, ASSOC. PROF, 68-69; NEUROL. & PEDIAT, MED. COL. WIS, 69-, CHMN. DEPT. NEUROL, 71-; CHIEF NEUROLOGIST, MILWAUKEE CHILDREN'S HOSP, 69- Consult, South. Wis. Colony, 69-; Milwaukee County Gen. Hosp, 69-; Woods Vet. Hosp, 71- Dipl, Am. Bd. Psychiat. & Neurol, 66. AAAS; Asn. Res. Nerv. & Ment. Diseases; Am. Acad. Neurol; Am. Med. Asn; Am. Acad. Pediat; Pan Am. Med. Asn. Neural degenerative diseases; disorders of amino acid metabolism and skeletal muscle. Address: 1700 W. Wisconsin Ave, Milwaukee, WI 53233.

DYKINS, JUSTIN EUGENE, b. Beach, N.Dak, July 23, 20; m. 49; c. 3. CIVIL ENGINEERING. B.S, Wyoming, 50. Off. & field engr, J.T. Banner & Assoc, Wyo, 50; struct. detailer, Lanc & Raugland Architect & Engr, Minn, 50-51; N.Am. Aviation Inc, Calif, 51-52; civil engr, struct. div, NAVAL CIVIL ENG. LAB, PORT HUENEME, 53-56, RES. CIVIL ENGR, POLAR DIV, 56- Distinguished civilian serv. award, U.S. Dept. Navy, 62. U.S.N.A.F, 42-45, Lt.(jg). Am. Soc. Civil Eng. Polar problems; materials research of physical and mechanical properties of ice and snow with overall objective to develop and structural theories describing elastic and viscoelastic behavior. Address: 102 Corsicana Dr, Oxnard, CA 93030.

DYKMAN, ROSCOE A, b. Pocatello, Idaho, Mar. 20, 20; m. 44; c. 4. PHYSIOLOGICAL PSYCHOLOGY. Ph.D.(human develop), 49. Instr. psychol, Ill. Inst. Technol, 47-50; U.S. Pub. Health Serv. fel, Hopkins, Hosp, 50-52, instr. psychiat, 52-53; asst. dir. studies, Asn. Am. Med. Cols, 53-55; assoc. prof. PSYCHOL, MED. CTR, UNIV. ARK, 55-61, PROF, 61- U.S.A, 42-45. Am. Psychol. Asn; Soc. Psychophysiol. Res. Physiological, experimental and child psychology; psychophysiology and learning. Address: Dept. of Psychiatry, University of Arkansas Medical Center, Little Rock, AR 72201.

DYKSTERHUIS, E(DSKO) J(ERRY), b. Hospers, Iowa, Dec. 27, 08; m. 33; c. 3. ECOLOGY. B.S, Iowa State Col, 32; Ph.D.(bot), Nebraska, 45. Field asst, Powell Nat. Forest, Utah, 30; jr. forester, Nat. Forests, N.Mex, 33-34; Southwest. Forest & Range Exp. Sta, U.S. Forest Serv, 34; jr. range exam. & sr. forest ranger, Crook Nat. Forest, Ariz, 34-35; asst. range exam, Carson Nat. Forest, New Mex, 35-38; assoc. range exam, South. Forest Exp. Sta, Texas, 38-39; sr. flood control rep, U.S. Forest Serv, Kans. & Ozarks, 39-41; range conservationist, U.S. Soil Conserv. Serv, Tex, Okla, La. & Ark, 43-49, head range conservationist, Mont, Wyo, N.Dak, S.Dak. & Nebr, 49-64; prof. RANGE ECOL, TEX, A&M UNIV, 64-70, EMER. PROF, 71- Vis. prof, Montana State, 50; Kansas State, 62; exten. range specialist, S.Dak. State, 64; mem, Nat. Resources Coun, 51-52. Fel. AAAS; Am. Inst. Biol. Sci; Soil.Conserv. Soc. Am; Ecol. Soc. Am.(Mercer Award, 49, bot. assoc. ed, Ecol. Monogr, 59-61); Am. Soc. Range Mgt.(pres, 68). Prairie and savanna rangelands in relation to soils, climate, fire and grazing. Address: Dept. of Range Science, Texas A&M University, College Station, TX 77843.

DYKSTRA, K(ENNETH) G, b. Pella, Iowa, May 23, 11; m. 38; c. 3. BIOPHYSICAL CHEMISTRY. B.S, Cent. Col.(Iowa), 33; Ph.D.(biophys. chem), Iowa State Col, 38. Chemist, Am. Can Co, 37-42; chief chemist, Snider Packing Corp, 42-43, plant mgr, Birdseye Div, GEN. FOODS CORP, 44-47, dir. labs, 47-58, res. mgr, 58-71, DIR. CTR. NUTRIT, 71- AAAS; Inst. Food Technol. Chemistry of enzymes; food preservation and packaging. Address: General Foods Corp. Center of Nutrition, 250 North St, White Plains, NY 10625.

DYKSTRA, RICHARD L(YNN), b. Des Moines, Iowa, Oct. 19, 42; m. 64; c. 2. MATHEMATICAL STATISTICS. B.A, Cent. Col.(Iowa), 65; Ph.D. (statist), Iowa, 68. ASST. PROF. STATIST, UNIV. MO-COLUMBIA, 68- Am. Statist. Asn; Inst. Math. Statist. Probability theory; stochastic processes. Address: Dept. of Statistics, University of Missouri-Columbia, Columbia, MO 65201.

DYKSTRA, STANLEY J(OHN), b. Eddyville, Iowa, Apr. 27, 24; m. 49; c. 2. ORGANIC CHEMISTRY. A.B, Calvin Col, 49; Ph.D.(chem), Wayne, 53. Asst, Wayne, 52, teaching fel, 52-53; res. assoc, Stanford, 53-54; sr. res. chemist, MEAD JOHNSON & CO, 54-61, group leader, 61-68, sect. leader CHEM. DEVELOP, MEAD JOHNSON RES. CTR, 68-70, DIR, 70- U.S.A.A.F, 43-45. Am. Chem. Soc; Sci. Res. Soc. Am; N.Y. Acad. Sci. Epoxyethers; primary aliphatic hydroperoxides, medicinals. Address: Mead Johnson Research Center, 2404 Pennsylvania, Evansville, IN 47721.

DYKSTRA, THOMAS KARL, b. Grand Rapids, Mich, May 9, 35; m. 59; c. 3. ORGANIC & POLYMER CHEMISTRY. B.A, Calvin Col, 57; Ph.D.(org. chem), Illinois, 61. Res. chemist, EASTMAN KODAK CO, 61-65, RES. ASSOC. CHEM, 66- AAAS; Am. Chem. Soc. Application of organic and polymer chemistry to electrophotography. Address: Eastman Kodak Co, Research Lab, Bldg 81, Kodak Park, Rochester, NY 14650.

DYM, CLIVE L, b. Leeds, Eng, July 15, 42; U.S. citizen; m. 64; c. 2. APPLIED MECHANICS & MATHEMATICS. B.C.E, Cooper Union, 62; M.S, Polytech. Inst. Brooklyn, 64; Ph.D.(aeronaut. eng), Stanford, 67. Asst. prof. eng, State Univ. N.Y. Buffalo, 66-69; mem. res. staff, Inst. Defense Analyses, 69-70; ASSOC. PROF. CIVIL ENG. & BIOTECHNOL, CARNEGIE-MELLON UNIV, 70- Consult, Bell Aerospace Corp, 67-69; assoc. prof. lectr, George Washington, 69-70; consult, Dravo Corp, 71- AAAS; Am. Acad. Mech; Am. Soc. Civil Eng; Am. Soc. Mech. Eng; Am. Inst. Aeronaut. & Astronaut; Acoust. Soc. Am. Stability and vibrations of elastic systems; variational and pertubation methods; systems analysis; science policy; acoustics, sound transmission and noise pollution; biomechanics. Address: Dept. of Civil Engineering, Carnegie-Mellon University, Pittsburgh, PA 15213.

DYME, HARRY C(HAIM), b. Toronto, Ont, Apr. 26, 12; nat; m. 44; c. 3. BIOCHEMISTRY. B.S.A, Ont, Agr. Col, 34; fel, Iowa State Col, 35-39, Ph.D. (physiol. chem, nutrit. chem), 39. Demonstr. & lab. asst. chem, Ont. Agr. Col, 34-35; in charge qual. control lab, Kraft Cheese Co, 40-41; supt. & chief chemist, Afral Corp, 41-43; proj. leader, Nat. Oil Prod. Co, N.J, 43-45; consult. chemist, New York, 45-46; chief chemist & chmn. chem. res, Found. Appl. Res, 46-49; chief nutrit. sect, aero med. lab, Wright Air Develop. Ctr, 49-60; biol. sci. adminstr, aeronaut. syst. div, AIR FORCE SYST. COMMAND, 60-64, OPERS. RES. ANALYST, RES. & TECH. DIV, 64- AAAS; Am. Chem. Soc; Sci. Res. Soc. Am. Physiological and nutritional chemistry; meat curing; flavoring and processing; food preservation; new product development; purification and factionation of biological preparations; treatment of industrial waste effluents; nutritional physiology of men in flight and in emergency situations; foods and feeding methods to meet flight and emergency feeding requirements; operations research analysis of the human component of systems in advanced systems studies. Address: 1935 Philadelphia Dr, Dayton, OH 45406.

DYMENT, JOHN CAMERON, b. Hamilton, Ont, June 7, 38; m. 63; c. 3. SOLID STATE PHYSICS. B.Sc, McMaster, 60; M.Sc, British Columbia, 62; Ph.D. (physics), McGill, 65. MEM. TECH. STAFF, BELL TEL. LABS, MURRAY HILL, 65- Am. Inst. Physics. Paramagnetic resonance; injection laser diodes, including problems of mode control, heat sinking and various delay time phenomena. Address: 61 Tallmadge Ave, Chatham, NJ 07928.

DYMICKY, MICHAEL, b. Ukraine, Oct. 1, 20; nat; m. 43; c. 2. ORGANIC & PHYSICAL CHEMISTRY. Chem. Tech, Polytech. Lwiw, Ukraine, 43; dipl. chem, Innsbruck, 47, Doctorandum, 49; fel, Pennsylvania, 52-53; Ph.D, Temple, 60. Res. chemist, Wyeth Inst, 53-56, 59-62; U.S. Agr. Res. Serv, 56-59; assoc. prof. chem, Kutztown State Col, 62-65; Gwynedd-Mercy Col, 65-66; MEM. STAFF, SMOKE INVESTS. TOBACCO LAB, EAST. UTILIZATION RES. & DEVELOP. DIV, AGR. RES. SERV, U.S. DEPT. AGR, 66- Am. Chem. Soc. Chemistry of plants; physiological compounds occurring in nature; organic syntheses; spectroscopy. Address: 9653 Dungan Rd, Philadelphia, PA 19115.

DYMON, JOSEPH J(OHN), b. New York Mills, N.Y, Mar. 2, 26. PHYSICAL CHEMISTRY. B.S, Syracuse, 48, Procter & Gamble fel, 48-51, Ph.D. (chem), 53. Eng. specialist phys. chem, Gen. Tel. & Electronics Labs, Inc, N.Y, 51-69; SR. PHYSICIST, GEN. TIME RES. CTR, 69- Am. Chem. Soc; Am. Crystallog. Asn; Sci. Res. Soc. Am; Electrochem. Soc. Crystallography; solid state physics. Address: General Time Research Center, 58 Progress Dr, Stamford, CT 06902.

DYMSZA, HENRY A, b. Newton, N.H, Jan. 14, 22; m. 56; c. 4. NUTRITION, BIOCHEMISTRY. B.S, Pa. State, 43, Ph.D.(agr. & biochem), 54; M.S, Wisconsin, 50. Res. nutritionist, Gen. Foods Corp, 54-59; sr. res. assoc. nutrit, Mass. Inst. Tech, 59-64; head metab. sect, food div, U.S. Army Natick Labs, 64-66; assoc. prof. FOOD & NUTRIT. SCI, UNIV. R.I, 66-70, PROF, 70-, CHMN. DEPT, 66- U.S.M.C, 43-46. AAAS; Am. Chem. Soc; Am. Inst. Nutrit; Inst. Food Technol; Am. Asn. Lab. Animal Sci; Am. Home Econ. Asn; Am. Dietetic Asn; Environ. Mitagen Soc. Food science; nutritional biochemistry; infant animal nutrition; synthetic and unusual nutrients and diets; energy metabolism; psychological and gnotobiotic nutrition; intestinal flora; military and space nutrition; food preservation & safety; fish nutrition. Address: Dept. of Food & Nutritional Science, University of Rhode Island, Kingston, RI 02881.

DYNE, PETER JOHN, b. London, Eng, Sept. 14, 26; Can. citizen; m. 53; c. 2. RADIATION CHEMISTRY. B.Sc, London, 46, Ph.D.(phys. chem), 49. Asst. lectr. phys. chem, King's Col, London, 49, lectr, Imp. Col, 49-50; fel. physics, Nat. Res. Coun. Can, 50-52; chem, jet propulsion centre, Calif. Inst. Technol, 52-53; sci. off, ATOMIC ENERGY CAN, LTD, 53-65, head mat. sci. br, WHITESHELL NUCLEAR RES. ESTAB, 65-71, DIR. CHEM. & MAT. SCI. DIV, 71- Fel. Chem. Inst. Can; Faraday Soc. Photochemistry; molecular spectroscopy; radiation chemistry; problems in pure and applied chemistry and in materials relevant to reactor technology. Address: Atomic Energy of Canada Ltd, Pinawa, Man, R0E 1L0, Can.

DYNES, J. ROBERT, b. Miller, S.Dak, Oct. 18, 22; m. 47; c. 2. ANIMAL SCIENCE. B.S, S.Dak. State Col, 49, M.S, 50; Ph.D, Tex. A&M Univ, 68. Instr, high sch, 50-51; instr. MEATS, MONT. STATE UNIV, 51-56, asst. prof, 56-62, ASSOC. PROF, 62- U.S.A, 43-45, S/Sgt. Am. Soc. Animal Sci; Am. Meat Sci. Asn; Inst. Food Tech. Meats research; carcass and red meat development in live animals. Address: Dept. of Animal Science, Montana State University, Bozeman, MT 59715.

DYRENFORTH, W(ILLIAM) P(HILLIP), b. Denver, Colo, Nov. 20, 20; m. 49; c. 4. MINERALS BENEFICIATION. B.S, Colorado, 43; Diesel Eng, N.C. State Col, 44. Power plant prod. engr, Stearns Roger Mfg. Co, 46-49; res. engr, Dorr Co, 49-52; sr. res. engr. & group leader, ore processing, res. div, Int. Minerals & Chem. Corp, 52-55, sect. leader, process eval, 55-56; sales mgr, Carpco Mfg. Inc. & gen. mgr, Carpco Export Corp, 56-59, TECH. DIR, CARPCO RES. & ENG, INC, 59-, V.PRES, 61- U.S.N.R, Lt.(jg). Am. Inst. Mining, Metall. & Petrol. Eng. General mineral beneficiation by gravity, high intensity magnetics and electrostatics. Address: Box 3272, Carpco Research & Engineering, Inc, Jacksonville, FL 32206.

DYRNESS, CHRISTEN THEODORE, b. Chicago, Ill, June 4, 33; m. 62; c. 3. FOREST SOILS. B.S, Wheaton Col.(Ill), 54; M.S, Oregon State, 56, Ph.D. (soil sci), 60. ASSOC. PROF. SOIL SCI, ORE. STATE UNIV, 59-; SOIL SCIENTIST WATERSHED MGT. RES, PAC. NORTHWEST FOREST & RANGE EXP. STA, U.S. FOREST SERV, 59- AAAS; Soil Sci. Soc. Am; Am. Soc. Agron. Physical and morphological properties of soil and plant soil relationships; physical properties of forest soils as affected by management practices; plant-soil relationships on pumice soils. Address: Forestry Sciences Lab, Pacific Northwest Forest & Range Experiment Station, U.S. Forest Service, 3200 Jefferson Way, Corvallis, OR 97331.

DYROFF, DAVID R(AY), b. St. Louis, Mo, Feb. 16, 40; m. 61; c. 3. PHYSICAL CHEMISTRY. B.S, Illinois, 62; Nat. Sci. Found. fel, Calif. Inst. Technol, 62-64, Ph.D.(chem), 65. Sr. res. chemist, MONSANTO CO, 65-67, RES. GROUP LEADER INORG. DIV, 67- Sci. Res. Soc. Am. X-ray crystallography; phosphate chemistry; industrial process research and development; alkylbenzene; detergent builders. Address: Inorganic Research Dept, Monsanto Co, 800 N. Lindbergh Blvd, St. Louis, MO 63166.

DYRUD, JARL E(DVARD), b. Maddock, N.Dak, Oct. 20, 21; m. 52; c. 3. PSYCHIATRY. A.B, Concordia Col.(Moorhead, Minn), 42; M.D, Hopkins, 45. Intern, Hopkins, 45-46; Vet. Admin. Ment. Hyg. Clin, D.C, 48-49; resident psychiat, Chestnut Lodge, Inc, 49-51, staff psychiatrist, 51-56; resident & U.S. Pub. Health Serv. fel, Spring Grove State Hosp, 52-53; private practice, 56-68; prin. investr. behav. anal, Inst. Behav. Res, 63-68; PROF. PSYCHIAT, SCH. MED, UNIV. CHICAGO & DIR. CLIN. SERV. PSYCHIAT, UNIV. HOSPS, 68- Consult, Md. State Hosps, 56-68; dir. psychiat, Chestnut Lodge Res. Inst, 67-68; consult, lab. adult psychiat, Nat. Inst. Ment. Health, 67-68, mem. clin. projs. res. rev. comt. U.S.N.R, 46-48, Lt.(jg). AAAS; Am. Psychiat. Asn; Am. Psychoanal. Asn; Acad. Psychoanal. Ego psychology; operant analyses of behavior in the study of schizophrenia; minimal brain dysfunction; normal child development within the framework of psychoanalytic ego psychology. Address: Dept. of Psychiatry, University of Chicago Hospitals, 950 E. 59th St, Chicago, IL 60637.

DYSART, GORDON, b. Dallas, Tex, Nov. 20, 27; m. 51; c. 2. PETROLEUM ENGINEERING. B.S, Texas, 61. Plant mgr, Dysart Mfg. Co, Tex, 49-57; res. asst, Tex. Petrol. Res. Comt, 57-61; petrol. engr, Standard Oil Co. Tex, 61-66; res. engr, West Co, 66-70; CONSULT. PETROL. ENGR, INT. DIV, DeGOLYER & MacNAUGHTON, 70- Soc. Petrol. Eng; Am. Petrol. Inst. Heat exchange in oilwell tubing and fractured formations; hydraulic and explosive fracturing of rock to stimulate oil and gas production. Address: 5625 Daniels Ave, Dallas, TX 75206.

DYSART, RICHARD J(AMES), b. Chicago, Ill, May 6, 32. ENTOMOLOGY. B.S, Illinois, 54, Ph.D.(entom), 61. Asst. entomologist, Ill. Natural Hist. Surv, 60-63, assoc. entomologist, 63-65; RES. ENTOMOLOGIST, EUROP. PARASITE LAB, U.S. DEPT. AGR, FRANCE, 65- U.S.A.R, 54-56, 1st Lt. Entom. Soc. Am. Ecology of insect pests of forage and pasture crops; biological control of insects. Address: U.S. Dept. of Agriculture, European Parasite Lab, 47 rue des Fontanelles, 92-Sèvres, France.

DYSINGER, PAUL WILLIAM, b. Burns, Tenn, May 24, 27; m. 58; c. 4. TROPICAL MEDICINE, PUBLIC HEALTH. B.A, South. Missionary Col, 51; M.D, Loma Linda, 55; M.P.H, Harvard, 62. Med. attaché, Am. Embassy, Phnom Penh, Cambodia, 58-60; res. assoc. prev. med, sch. med, Loma Linda, 61; dir. pub. health & trop. med, field sta, Tanganyika, E.Africa, 62-64; asst. prof. pub. health, LOMA LINDA UNIV, 64-67, chmn. dept. trop. health, 67-71, ASSOC. DEAN ACAD. AFFAIRS & INT. HEALTH, 71-, PROF. INT. HEALTH, 71- World Health Orgn. traveling fel, 69; consult, New Guinea, 64-; TRW, Inc, 67-; Vocational Rehab, Calif, 67- U.S.P.H.S, 56-58, Sr. Surg. AAAS; fel. Am. Pub. Health Asn; Am. Soc. Trop. Med. & Hyg; Am. Geog. Soc; fel. Royal Soc. Trop. Med. & Hyg; Soc. Int. Develop. Statistical epidemiology, especially mortality studies in emphysema and accidents; manpower studies in East Africa. Address: School of Health, Loma Linda University, Loma Linda, CA 92354.

DYSON, DEREK C(HARLESWORTH), b. San Eduardo, Arg, Dec. 23, 32; m. 61; c. 2. CHEMICAL ENGINEERING. B.A, Cambridge, 55; Ph.D.(chem. eng), London, 66. Develop. engr, Du Pont of Can, 58-60; res. engr, Pennsalt Chem. Corp, 60-62; res. asst. CHEM. ENG, Imp. Col, London, 62-65; asst. prof. RICE UNIV, 66-69, ASSOC. PROF, 69- Arg. Army, 57-58. Am. Inst. Chem. Eng. Optimization of chemical processes; theory of interfacial stability in the capillary regime. Address: Dept. of Chemical Engineering, Rice University, Box 1892, Houston TX 77001.

DYSON, FREEMAN J(OHN), b. Crowthorne, Eng, Dec. 15, 23; nat; m. 50; c. 6. THEORETICAL PHYSICS. B.A, Cambridge, 45. Res. fel, Trinity Col, Cambridge, 46-49; Univ. Birmingham, 49-51; PROF. PHYSICS, Cornell, 51-53; INST. ADVAN. STUDY, 53- Heineman Prize, Am. Inst. Physics, 65; Lorentz Medal, Royal Netherlands Acad, 66; Max Planck Medal, Ger. Phys. Soc, 69; J. Robert Oppenheimer Mem. Prize, Ctr. Theoretical Studies, 70. Nat. Acad. Sci; fel. Royal Soc.(Hughes Medal, 68); Am. Phys. Soc. Quantum field theory. Address: Institute for Advanced Study, Princeton, NJ 08540.

DYSON, IAN FRASER, b. Leeds, Eng, Apr. 5, 40; m. 63; c. 2. ORGANIC CHEMISTRY. B.Sc, Leeds, 60, Ph.D.(org. chem), 63. Res. chemist, ORG. CHEM. DEPT, E.I. DU PONT DE NEMOURS & CO, 63-68, supvr, 68-69, DIV. HEAD, 69- Am. Chem. Soc; The Chem. Soc. Natural products; petroleum chemistry; synthetic organic chemistry. Address: E.I. du Pont de Nemours & Co, Jackson Lab, Orchem Div, Deepwater, NJ 08023.

DYSON, JAMES E(VERETT), JR, b. Des Moines, Iowa, Jan. 18, 26; m. 47, 68. MEDICAL EDUCATION. B.A, Drake Univ, 47; M.S, Univ. Iowa, 50; Ph.D.(microbiol), Univ. Mich, 55; M.Ed, Univ. Ill, 71. Instr. biol, Drake Univ, 47-48; asst. bact, Univ. Iowa, 49-50; Univ. Mich, 51-54; asst. prof, Colo. State Univ, 54-58; med. ctr, W.Va. Univ, 58-62, assoc. prof, 62, assoc. prof. microbiol. & dir. div. acad. commun, 63-66; educ. commun. specialist, regional med. progs. serv, Health Serv. & Ment. Health Admin, Wash, D.C, 66-67; fel, ctr. educ. develop, Univ. Ill. Med. Ctr, 67-68; chief biomed. educ. sect, Colo-Wyo. Regional Med. Prog, med. ctr, Univ. Colo, Denver, 68-69, assoc. dir. continuing educ, 69-71; ASST. PROF. MED. EDUC, CTR. EDUC. DEVELOP, COL. MED, UNIV. ILL. MED. CTR, 71- Med. commun. fel, med. ctr, Univ. Kans, 62-63. U.S.N.R, 43-46, Lt(jg). Am. Educ. Res. Asn; Asn. Am. Med. Cols; Asn. Educ. Commun. & Technol; Nat. Asn. Educ. Broadcasters. Factors in effective continuing education for health professionals; educational technology in learner-centered curricula. Address: Center for Educational Development, College of Medicine, University of Illinois Medical Center, 835 S. Wolcott, Chicago, IL 60612.

DYSON, JOHN E(DGAR), b. Leeds, Eng, Dec. 27, 29. BIOCHEMISTRY. B.Sc, London, 63; Ph.D.(biochem), California, Riverside, 66. Res. biochemist, California, Riverside, 66-67; res. assoc, MED. SCH, UNIV. N.DAK, 67-68; ASST. PROF. BIOCHEM, 68- Nat. Sci. Found. res. grant, 69- AAAS; Am. Chem. Soc. Isolation of enzymes; relationship of the physical and chemical properties of enzymes to their structure and function; enzyme kinetics and mechanisms. Address: Dept. of Biochemistry, University of North Dakota Medical School, Grand Forks, ND 58201.

DYSON, PETER JOHN, b. Weston, Ont, Can, Feb. 23, 23; m. 52; c. 3. FORESTRY, ECONOMICS. B.S.A, Toronto, 52; Brigham Young, 53-54; M.S.F, Univ. Mont, 57, 57-59; Ph.D.(econ, forestry), N.C. State, 63. Teacher, Tooele Bd. Ed, 54-55; asst. forestry mgt. & entom, Univ. Mont, 55-57, instr. finance & mensuration, 57-59; instr. ECON, FINANCE & MENSURATION & exten. specialist, N.C. State, 59-63, asst. prof, 63-65; ASSOC. PROF, UNIV. GA, 65- Soc. Am. Foresters; Forest Prod. Res. Soc; Am. Farm Econ. Asn; Can. Farm Econ. Asn. Economic analysis; wood science. Address: School of Forest Resources, University of Georgia, Athens, GA 30601.

DYSON, ROBERT DUANE, b. Minneapolis, Minn, May 18, 39; m. 61; c. 3. BIOPHYSICS, PHYSICAL BIOCHEMISTRY. B.S, Oregon, 61; Nat Insts. Health fel, Illinois, Urbana, 62-65, M.S, 63, Ph.D.(biophys. chem), 65. Nat. Insts. Health fel. & res. assoc. molecular biol, California, Berkeley, 65-67; asst. prof. BIOPHYSICS, ORE. STATE UNIV, 67-71, ASSOC. PROF, 71- AAAS; Am. Chem. Soc. The behavior of macromolecules in solution and applications to metabolic control. Address: Dept. of Biochemistry & Biophysics, Oregon State University, Corvallis, OR 97331.

DYSON, VERENA H, b. Naples, Italy, May 6, 23; U.S. citizen; c. 3. MATHEMATICS. Ph.D.(math), Univ. Zurich, 47. Instr. math, Goucher Col, 49-50; Cornell Univ, 51-53; asst. prof, San Jose State Col, 59-61; lectr, Univ. Calif, Berkeley, 61-63; asst. prof, Adelphi Univ, 63-64; lectr. philos, Univ. Calif, Los Angeles, 64-65; MATH, Mills Col, 65-66; ASST. PROF, UNIV. ILL, CHICAGO CIRCLE, 66- Am. Math Soc; Math Asn. Am; Asn. Symbolic Logic. Intuitionism; decision problems; theory of infinite groups. Address: Dept. of Mathematics, University of Illinois at Chicago Circle, Box 4348, Chicago, IL 60680.

DZIDIC, ISMET, b. Derventa, Yugoslavia, June 14, 39. PHYSICAL CHEMISTRY, ANALYTICAL BIOCHEMISTRY. Dipl. Eng, Univ. Zagreb, 63; Ph.D. (phys. chem), Univ. Alta, 70. Res. chemist, Res. Inst. Org. Chem. Industs, 63-64; teaching asst. phys. chem, Univ. Alta, 65-70; FEL, INST. LIPID RES, BAYLOR COL. MED, 71- Am. Chem. Soc; Am. Soc. Mass Spectrometry. Mass spectrometric study of gaseous ion-molecule reactions, solvation of ions in the gas phase; proton affinities of organic molecules; application of the chemical ionization mass spectrometry for structural studies of biological compounds. Address: Institute for Lipid Research, Baylor College of Medicine, Houston, TX 77025.

DZIECIUCH, MATTHEW A(NDREW), b. Edmonton, Alta, Can, Oct. 11, 31; m. 58; c. 2. PHYSICAL CHEMISTRY, ELECTROCHEMISTRY. B.Sc, Alberta, 57, M.Sc, 58; Ph.D.(electrochem), Ottawa, 62. RES. SCIENTIST ELECTROCHEM, FORD MOTOR CO, 60- AAAS; Sci. Res. Res. Soc. Am; Electrochem. Soc. Electrode kinetics; double layer; energy conversion; gas phase kinetics. Address: Scientific Lab, Ford Motor Co, P.O. Box 2053, Dearborn, MI 48121.

DZIERZANOWSKI, FRANK J(OHN), b. Plains, Pa, Aug. 28, 29; m. 54; c. 2. INORGANIC CHEMISTRY. B.S, Rutgers, 56. Jr. res. chemist, Minerals & Chem. Corp. Am, 56-60, res. chemist, Minerals & Chem. Philipp Corp, 60-64, sr. res. chemist, 64-66; RES. SUPVR. FUNDAMENTAL RES, ENGELHARD MINERALS & CHEM. CORP, 66- Med.C, U.S.A, 51-53. Catalysis Soc; Am. Chem. Soc; Clay Minerals Soc. Synthesis and properties of inorganic compounds; hydothermal synthesis of minerals; clay mineralogy; adsorption and catalysis. Address: 8 Norfolk Rd, Somerset, NJ 08873.

DZIEWIATKOWSKI, DOMINIC D(ONALD), b. Chicago, Ill, Feb. 20, 15; m. 42; c. 1. BIOLOGICAL CHEMISTRY. A.B, West. State Teachers Col, Mich, 39; M.S, Michigan, 41, scholar, Ph.D.(biol. chem), 43. Instr. biochem, sch. med, Vanderbilt, 43-46; asst. prof, Hopkins, 46-48; assoc, Rockefeller Inst. Hosp, 48-57, assoc. prof, Rockefeller Univ, 57-67; PROF. DENT. & CHMN. DEPT. ORAL BIOL, SCH. DENT, DIR. DENT. RES. INST. & PROF. BIOCHEM, SCH. MED, UNIV. MICH, ANN ARBOR, 67- Harvey Soc; Am. Soc. Biol. Chem; Am. Chem. Soc; Fedn. Am. Socs. Biol. Chem. Detoxication, ossification; mineral metabolism; metabolism of muscle. Address: Dept. of Oral Biology, University of Michigan School of Dentistry, Ann Arbor, MI 48104.

DZIEWONSKI, ADAM M(ARIAN), b. Lwow, Poland, Nov. 15, 36; m. 67. SEISMOLOGY, GEOMAGNETISM. M.S, Univ. Warsaw, 60; Dr. Tech. Sci.(appl. geol), Acad. Mining & Metall, Cracow, 65. Res. asst. seismol, inst. geophys, Polish Acad. Sci, 61-65, res. assoc, 65; Southwest Ctr. Advan. Studies, 65-69, asst. prof. seismol. & geomagnetism, Univ. Tex, Dallas, 69-71; ASSOC. PROF. GEOPHYS. & ASSOC, CTR. EARTH & PLANETARY PHYSICS, HARVARD, 72- Mem, Polish Sci. Exped. to N. Vietnam, Int. Geophys. Year, 58-59; del, Int. Cong. Int. Asn. Seismol. & Physics of the Earth's Interior-Int. Asn. Geomagnetism & Aeronomy, Madrid, 69; prin. investr, Nat. Sci. Found. res. grant, 69 & prin. co-investr, 70. Seismol. Soc. Am; Am. Geophys. Union; Soc. Explor. Geophys. Physical properties of the earth's interior from observations of seismic wave propagation; electrical and thermal properties of the crust and upper mantle from geomagnetic deep soundings. Address: Hoffman Lab, Harvard University, 20 Oxford St, Cambridge, MA 02138.

DZIMIANSKI, JOHN W(ILLIAM), b. Baltimore, Md, Dec. 13, 24; m. 52; c. 3. ELECTRICAL ENGINEERING. B.E, Hopkins, 47, Dr. Eng, 52. Asst. high frequency insulation, Hopkins, 47-52; group leader, elec. res. sect. Allis-Chalmers Mfg. Co, 52-56; ADV. ENGR, SYSTS. DEVELOP. DIV, WESTINGHOUSE ELEC. CORP, 56- C.Eng, U.S.A, 44-46. Inst. Elec. & Electronics Eng; Electrochem. Soc. Molecular electronics; semiconductor reliability physics. Address: 412 Forest Lane, Catonsville, MD 21228.

DZIUK, HAROLD EDMUND, b. Foley, Minn, Apr. 27, 30; m. 52; c. 5. VETERINARY PHYSIOLOGY. B.S, Minnesota, 51, D.V.M, 54, M.S, 55, Ph.D.(vet. physiol), 60. Instr. VET. PHYSIOL, col. vet. med, Minnesota, 51-54, 57-60; scientist, Hanford Prod. Oper, Gen. Elec. Co, Wash, 60-61; assoc. prof, Iowa State Univ, 61; asst. prof, COL. VET. MED, UNIV. MINN, ST. PAUL, 61-64, assoc. prof, 64-69, PROF, 69- Vet.C, 55-56, Res, 56-63, 1st Lt. Conf. Res. Workers Animal Diseases; Am. Vet. Med. Asn; assoc. Am. Physiol. Soc. Comparative gastrointestinal physiology; pathogenesis of diseases of the gastrointestinal tract. Address: Dept. of Veterinary Physiology, College of Veterinary Medicine, University of Minnesota, St. Paul, MN 55101.

DZIUK, PHILIP J, b. Foley, Minn, Mar. 24, 26; m. 51; c. 7. REPRODUCTIVE PHYSIOLOGY, ENDOCRINOLOGY. B.S, Univ. Minn, 50, M.S, 52, fel, 53-55, Ph.D.(dairy husb), 55. Asst. prof. ANIMAL PHYSIOL, UNIV. ILL, URBANA, 55-62, assoc. prof, 62-67, PROF, 67- Lalor fels, 58-59, 61-62; vis. investr, R.B. Jackson Lab, 59; Pig Indust. Develop. Auth. fel, Cambridge, Eng, 61-62; mem. comt. on hormones, Nat. Acad. Sci-Nat. Res. Coun, 62-; indust. consult. Upjohn Award, Am. Fertil. Soc, 70. U.S.N, 45-46. AAAS; Am. Asn. Anat; Am. Soc. Animal Sci.(physiol. & endocrinol. award, 71); Brit. Soc. Study Fertil; Soc. Study Reproduction. Egg transfer in cattle and swine; control of ovulation in cattle, sheep and swine; superovulation; artificial insemination; early stages of fertilization of eggs; embryonal mortality; sperm transport in male and female. Address: Dept. of Animal Science, 111 Animal Genetics, University of Illinois, Urbana, IL 61801.

DZOANH, NGUYEN T, b. Vietnam, Mar. 4, 30; m. 53; c. 3. PLASMA PHYSICS. Lic.ès sc, Sorbonne, 57, Dr. ès Sc.(physics), 61. Nat. Sci. Found. fel. physics, Sorbonne, 61-62; res. assoc. chem. physics, Indiana, 62-64; asst. prof. physics, Ill. Inst. Technol, 64-68; ASSOC. PROF. ELECTROPHYS, UNIV. NOTRE DAME, 68- Am. Phys. Soc. Electrostatics and gaseous discharges. Address: Dept. of Electrical Engineering, University of Notre Dame, Notre Dame, IN 46556.

DZOMBAK, WILLIAM C(HARLES), b. McKeesport, Pa, Dec. 4, 21; m. 53. PHYSICAL CHEMISTRY. B.Sc, Pittsburgh, 43; Purdue Res. Found. fel, Purdue, 43-46, 49-50, Ph.D.(chem), 50. Assoc. prof, Providence Col, 50-52; assoc. chemist, Argonne Nat. Lab, 52-53; assoc. prof. PHYS. CHEM, ST. VINCENT COL, 53-64, PROF, 64- Physical chemistry. Address: Dept. of Physical Chemistry, St. Vincent College, Latrobe, PA 15650.

DZWONS, GEORGE S(TANLEY), b. Rosholt, Wis, Nov. 12, 08; m. 36; c. 1. ELECTRICAL ENGINEERING. B.S, Wisconsin, 32. Technician audio visual develop, Teachers Col, Columbia, 33-38; head sales & develop, audio equipment, 39-42; engr, Nat. Defense Res. Cmt. Proj, Columbia, 42-44; head develop. portable uranium detector, Can. Govt, 44; engr, Chem. Warfare Div, U.S. Govt, 44-45; consult. engr, Oil Field Serv, Co, Colo, 46-69; PRES, SCIMITAR CORP. DIV, MILES SPECIALTY CO, 69- Soc. Explor. Geophys. Electro-mechanical devices; radio active detectors and devices; telemetering and measuring instrumentation; geophysical and Borehole instrumentation and development. Address: Scimitar Corp. Division of Miles Specialty Co, 4747 S. 83rd East Ave, Tulsa, OK 74115.

E

EACHUS, ALAN CAMPBELL, b. Champaign, Ill, July 11, 39; m. 61; c. 2. ORGANIC CHEMISTRY. B.S, Syracuse, 60; Nat. Sci. Found. coop. fel, State Univ. N.Y. Col. Forestry, Syracuse, 63-64, Ph.D.(org. chem), 64. Fel. abstraction kinetics, State Univ. N.Y. Col. Forestry, Syracuse, 64; res. chemist, Dow Chem. Co, 66-67, develop. specialist, 67-69, res. chemist, 69-70; SR. RES. CHEMIST, ALBERTO-CULVER CO, MELROSE PARK, 70- U.S.A, 64-66, Capt. Am. Chem. Soc; N.Y. Acad. Sci; fel. Am. Inst. Chem. Development of personal care items and toiletries; disinfectant/detergent formulations; flame fuels; chemical specialty items. Address: 644 S. Michigan Ave, Villa Park, IL 60181.

EACHUS, JOSEPH J(ACKSON), b. Anderson, Ind, Nov. 5, 11; m. 45; c. 2. MATHEMATICS. A.B, Miami (Ohio), 33; A.M, Syracuse, 36; Ph.D.(math, physics), Illinois, 39. Asst. math, Syracuse, 34-36; Illinois, 36-39; instr, Purdue, 39-42; elec. engr, U.S. Dept. Defense, 46-55; systs. dir, DATAmatic Corp, Minneapolis-Honeywell Regulator Corp, 55-62, prin. staff. scientist, electronic data processing div, Honeywell Inc, 62-70, GROUP DIR, APPL. RES. DIV, HONEYWELL INFO. SYSTS, 70- Mem. info. systs. panel, comput. sci. & eng. bd, Nat. Acad. Sci, 70- U.S.N, 42-46. Am. Math. Soc; Asn. Comput. Mach; fel. Inst. Elec. & Electronics. Eng; fel. N.Y. Acad. Sci. Differential equations; q-difference equations; orthogonal functions; computing machinery, communications, electronics. Address: Applied Research Division, Honeywell Information Systems Inc, 200 Smith St, Waltham, MA 02154.

EADE, K(ENNETH) E(DGAR), b. Ft. William, Ont, Jan. 16, 26; m. 56; c. 2. GEOLOGY. B.Sc, Queen's Univ.(Ont), 48; M.Sc, McGill Univ, 50, Ph.D.(geol), 55. GEOLOGIST, Geol. Surv. Can, 51-53; Port. W.Africa Proj, 53-54; GEOL. SURV. CAN, 55- Geol. Soc. Am; Soc. Econ. Geol; Arctic Inst. N.Am; Can. Geol. Soc; Can. Inst. Min. & Metall. Precambrian geology in northern Canada. Address: Geological Survey of Canada, Geological Survey Bldg, 601 Booth St, Ottawa, Ont, Can.

EADE, N(ORMAN) R(USSEL), b. Hawarden, Sask, Jan. 4, 29. PHARMACOLOGY. B.Sc, Saskatchewan, 52, M.Sc, 54; Independent Order Daughters of Empire scholar, Oxford, 54-56, D.Phil.(pharmacol), 57; M.D.C.M, McGill, 64. Hosmer fel, pharmacol, McGill, 57-58, lectr, 58-59, asst. prof, 59-65; fel. med, Johns Hopkins Hosp, 65-66; ASSOC. PROF. CLIN. PHARMACOL, McGILL UNIV, 66-, PEDIAT, MONTREAL CHILDREN'S HOSP, 68-, med, Royal Victoria Hosp, 66-68. Charles-Oscar Monat scholar, McGill Univ; Lederle med. faculty award, 59-63. Can. Pharmacol. Soc; Can. Physiol. Soc. Autonomic nervous system; biogenic amines. Address: Dept. of Pharmacology & Therapeutics, McGill University, Montreal 2, Que, Can.

EADES, C(HARLES) H(UBERT), JR, b. Dallas, Tex, July 19, 16; m. 42; c. 3. BIOCHEMISTRY. B.S, Southern Methodist, 38; M.A, Texas, 40; Ph.D.(biochem), Illinois, 48. Instr. sci, Paris Jr. Col, Tex, 40-42; supvr. sect. anal. lab, Pan Am. Ref. Corp, 42-45; spec. res. asst, Illinois, 45-48; instr. biochem, Tennessee, 48-49, asst. prof, 50-55; sr. chemist, Mead Johnson & Co, 55-56, group leader, 56-57, sect. leader, 57-59; sr. scientist, WARNER LAMBERT RES. INST, 59-64, sr. res. assoc, 64-70, SR. CLIN. RES. ASSOC, 70- Consult, dept. path, Booth Mem. Hosp, Flushing, N.Y, 63-70; mem. coun. arteriosclerosis & coun. high blood pressure res, Am. Heart Asn. AAAS; N.Y. Acad. Sci; Soc. Exp. Biol. & Med; Fedn. Am. Socs. Exp. Biol; Am. Soc. Biol. Chem; Am. Chem. Soc; Am. Inst. Nutrit; Am. Med. Writers Asn. Amino acid requirements of man; nutrition of lactic acid bacteria; amino acid metabolism in stress; health and disease; automatic instrumentation; human nutrition; lipid and cholesterol metabolism; arteriosclerosis and cardiovascular disease; use of radioisotopes in metabolic and biochemical studies. Address: Warner Lambert Research Institute, Morris Plains, NJ 07950.

EADES, DAVID C(LUTHE), b. Evansville, Ind, Feb. 3, 35; m. 59; c. 4. TAXONOMY. A.B, Wabash Col, 55; M.B.A, Michigan, 56, M.S, 59; Ph.D.(zool), Indiana, 62. Asst. curator insects, Acad. Natural Sci. Phila, 60-61; asst. prof. biol, State Univ. Col. Oneonta, 62-63, assoc. prof, 63-64; res. assoc. microbiol, UNIV. ILL, URBANA, 64-65, asst. prof. zool, 65-69, ASSOC. PROF. ZOOL. & LIFE SCI, 69-, Nat. Insts. Health res. fel, 64-65. AAAS; Soc. Syst. Zool; Am. Entom. Soc. Computer-based education—computer programs for biology education and computer taxonomy; taxonomy of Orthoptera. Address: 252 Engineering Research Lab, University of Illinois, Urbana, IL 61801.

EADES, JAMES B(EVERLY), JR, b. Bluefield, W.Va, July 22, 23; m. 50; c. 3. AEROSPACE ENGINEERING, ENGINEERING MECHANICS. B.S, Va. Polytech, 44, M.S, 49, Ph.D.(eng. mech), 58. Instr. aeronaut. eng, Va. Polytech, 47-48, asst. prof, 48-51, 53-57, prof. aerospace eng, 57-69, head dept, 61-69; SR. ANALYST, ANAL. MECH. ASSOC, INC, SEABROOK, 69- Aeronaut. res. specialist, Naval Ord. Lab, White Oak, Md, 63- Summers, aeronaut. res. scientist, Nat. Adv. Comt. Aeronaut, Langley Field, Va, 58, NASA, 59; dir. conf. lunar explor, Blacksburg, Va, 62; v.pres, Celestial Mech. Inst, Inc; Nat. Acad. Sci. sr. fel, Goddard Space Flight Ctr, 67-69; consult, U.S. Army Transportation Corps, Naval Ord. Lab. & Res. Anal. Corp. U.S.N.R, 44-46, 51-53, Comdr. Sr. mem. Am. Astron. Soc; assoc. fel. Am. Inst. Aeronaut. & Astronaut. Transonic flow phenomenon; high speed aerodynamics, flight and control; wind-tunnel testing of structures and vehicles; space flight, space mechanics and celestial mechanics. Address: 1603 Peacock Lane, Silver Spring, MD 20904.

EADES, JAMES L, b. Charlottesville, Va, Apr. 21, 21; m. 41; c. 2. MINERALOGY. B.A, Univ. Va, 50, M.A, 53; Ph.D.(geol), Univ. Ill, 62. Soils res. engr, Va. Coun. Hwy. Invest. & Res, 52-58; res. asst, Univ. Ill, Urbana, 58-62, res. asst. prof. GEOL, 62-70; ASSOC. PROF, UNIV. FLA, 70- Nat. Lime Asn. res. grant, 58-; mem. hwy. res. bd, Nat. Acad. Sci-Nat. Res. Coun; consult, Lime Indust. and Hwy. Depts; mem. staff, U.S. Agency Int. Develop. projs, Africa. U.S.N, 43-46. Am. Soc. Test. & Mat; Clay Minerals Soc; Geol. Soc. Am. Clay mineralogy; calcium silicate reactions at ambient and elevated temperatures; SO_2 reactions. Address: Dept. of Geology, University of Florida, Gainesville, FL 32601.

EADIE, GEORGE ROBERT, b. Eldorado, Ill, Sept. 24, 23; m. 43; c. 2. MINING ENGINEERING. B.S, Illinois, 49, M.S, 56, E.M, 57. Asst. prof. mining eng, Illinois, 54-59, assoc. prof, 59-63; mem. staff, Freeman Coal Mining Corp, 63-65; assoc. ed, Coal Mining & Processing, 65-68; ADMIN. ENGR, ILL. STATE GEOL. SURV, 68- Prof, Univ. Ill, Urbana. U.S.A.A.F, 42-45; U.S.A.F.R, Lt. Col.(Ret). Am. Inst. Mining, Metall. & Petrol. Eng. Mine ventilation and safety. Address: Illinois State Geological Survey, Natural Resources Bldg, Urbana, IL 61801.

EADS, EWIN A(LFRED), b. Rockdale, Tex, Jan. 24, 15; m. 42; c. 2. INORGANIC CHEMISTRY. B.S, North Texas State, 40, M.S, 42; Nat. Sci. Found. faculty fel, 60-61; Ph.D.(inorg. chem), Tulane, 62. Instr. sci, North Texas State, 44-46; PROF. CHEM, LAMAR UNIV, 46-, DIR. ENVIRON. STUDIES, 69- Instr, Tulane, 58-60; State of Tex. res. grant, boron nitrogen heterocycles, 61- AAAS; Am. Chem. Soc. Boron nitrogen heterocycles; flame reactions of organohalogens in presence of methane, air and copper oxide. Address: 915 E. Lavaca, Beaumont, TX 77705.

EADS, JAMES H(ARVEY), JR, b. Kansas City, Mo, July 27, 18; m. 47. MAMMALOGY, BACTERIOLOGY. A.B, Kansas, 41; M.S, Alabama, 49, Graham prize scholar, 49-50, fel, 50-53. Asst. Alabama, 48-50, acting asst. prof. BIOL, 54-55; prof. & acting head dept, Huntingdon Col, 53-54; ASST. PROF, Middle Tenn. State Col, 55-58; MEREDITH COL, 58- South. Fels. Fund award, 55-56. Med.C, U.S.A, 43-46. AAAS; Am. Soc. Mammal; Am. Soc. Clin. Path. Microtechnique; ecology; distribution taxonomy; food habits of family Cricetidae. Address: Dept. of Biology, Meredith College, Box 373, Raleigh, NC 27611.

EADS, RICHARD B(AILEY), b. Bonham, Tex, Feb. 17, 19; m. 39; c. 1. MEDICAL ENTOMOLOGY. B.S, Tex. A&M Univ, 39, Ph.D.(entom), 49. Prin. entomologist, State Dept. Health, Tex, 39-60; SCIENTIST DIR, U.S. PUB. HEALTH SERV, 60- Med.Serv.C, U.S.N.R, 43-60, Lt. Comdr. Am. Soc. Trop. Med. & Hyg; Am. Soc. Parasitol; Am. Mosquito Control Asn. Regulatory work in foreign quarantine program; formulation and implementation of measures to prevent the introduction of insects or other arthropods of known or suspected public health importance into the United States by international carriers. Address: U.S. Public Health Service, 1838 El Camino Real, Suite 213, Burlingame, CA 94010.

EAGAN, CHARLES J, b. Tottenham, Ont, Sept. 25, 21; m. 53; c. 7. PHYSIOLOGY, BIOPHYSICS. B.A, Western Ontario, 49, M.Sc, 56; fel, Washington (Seattle), 57-59, Ph.D.(physiol, biophys), 61. Asst. biophys, Western Ontario, 49-53; sci. off. physiol, Defence Res. Bd. Can, 54-57; res. physiologist, arctic aeromed. lab, U.S. Air Force, Alaska, 59-67; ASSOC. PROF. PHYSIOL. & BIOPHYS, COLO. STATE UNIV, 67- Gen. chmn, Alaskan Sci. Conf, 64. R.C.A.F, 41-45; Can. Army, 50-54, Lt. Fel. AAAS (pres. Alaska div, 64); Am. Physiol. Soc; Am. Soc. Zool; fel. Arctic Inst. N.Am; Soc. Gen. Physiol; Metric Asn; Can. Physiol. Soc; Can. Soc. Zool; Int. Soc. Biometeorol; Am. Inst. Biol. Sci. Effect of level of physical fitness and altitude acclimatization on cold tolerance; habituation to environmental stress; seasonal acclimatization versus genetic adaptation; peripheral blood flow; bioenergetics; aerospace physiology; factors affecting endurance fitness; canine physiology. Address: Dept. of Physiology & Biophysics, Colorado State University, Ft. Collins, CO 80521.

EAGER, GEORGE SIDNEY, JR, b. Baltimore, Md, Sept. 5, 15; m. 45; c. 3. ELECTRICAL ENGINEERING. B.E, Hopkins, 36, Dr. Eng.(elec. eng), 41. Physicist, Armstrong Cork Co, Pa, 45-47; asst. dir. res, GEN. CABLE CORP, 48-66, DIR. RES, 66- U.S.A, 42-45. Inst. Elec. & Electronics Eng; Int. Conf. Large Elec. Systs. Electrical wires and cables; dielectrics; electrical transmission; high voltage testing. Address: 14 Bellegrove Dr, Montclair, NJ 07043.

EAGER, R(ICHARD) L(IVINGSTON), b. Kenaston, Sask, Aug. 27, 17; m. 49; c. 2. PHYSICAL CHEMISTRY. B.E, Saskatchewan, 43, M.Sc, 45, Nat. Res. Coun. Can. stud. & fel, 45, 46; Ph.D.(chem), McGill Univ, 49. Asst. prof. CHEM, UNIV. SASK, 47-55, assoc. prof, 55-65, PROF, 65- Vis. lectr, Univ. Leeds, 64-65. AAAS; Chem. Inst. Can. Radiation chemistry. Address: Dept. of Chemistry & Chemical Engineering, University of Saskatchewan, Saskatoon, Sask, Can.

EAGER, ROBERT PAUL, b. Beecher,City, Ill, July 13, 31; m. 61. ANATOMY, NEUROANATOMY. A.B, Washington (St. Louis), 56; Ph.D.(anat), Pennsylvania, 61. U.S. Pub. Health Serv. fel, Northwestern, 61-62; instr. ANAT, SCH. MED, YALE, 62-64, asst. prof, 64-67, ASSOC. PROF, 67- U.S.N, 48-52. AAAS; Am. Asn. Anat. Experimental neuroanatomical studies of intracerebellar pathways; electron microscopic studies of degeneration in the cerebellum. Address: Dept. of Anatomy, Yale University School of Medicine, 333 Cedar St, New Haven, CT 06511.

EAGER, SHERMAN W(ESLEY), b. Vincennes, Ind, Jan. 28, 88; m; c. 6. PHYSICS. A.B, Indiana, 23, Ph.D.(physics, math), 38; M.S, Okla. Agr. & Mech. Col, 26. Asst. prof. PHYSICS, OKLA. STATE UNIV, 23-29, assoc. prof, 29-41, prof, 41-54, head dept, 46-54, EMER. PROF, 54-; PROF, PAN AM. COL, 60- Acting prof, Tulsa, 55-56; prof, Stephen F. Austin State Col, 56-60, acting head dept, 57-58. U.S.A, 17-19, 42-46, Lt. Col. (Ret); Silver Star Medal. Am. Asn. Physics Teachers. Photoelectricity; effect of ionization on the velocity of sound waves at ultrasonic frequencies; unconventional sources of electric power. Address: 1711 Charles Circle, Edinburg, TX 78539.

EAGLE, DONALD F(ROHLICHSTEIN), b. St. Louis, Mo, Jan. 30, 33; m. 61; c. 2. PHYSICS. B.S, Yale, 54; M.S, Ga. Inst. Tech, 56, Ph.D.(physics), 62. Asst. res. physicist, eng. exp. sta, Ga. Inst. Tech, 56-61; sr. physicist, magnetic tape lab, Ampex Corp, 62-67; sr. res. physicist, Dikewood Corp, 67-69; MEM. TECH. STAFF, SANDIA LABS, 69- Am. Phys. Soc. Microwave spectroscopy and molecular structure; magnetic materials and magnetism; systems analysis; neutron transport. Address: Sandia Labs, Division 1715, P.O. Box 5800, Albuquerque, NM 87115.

EAGLE, EDWARD, b. Baltimore, Md, Nov. 27, 08; m. 42; c. 4. PHYSIOLOGY, TOXICOLOGY. A.B, Hopkins, 29; Du Pont fel, Virginia, 29-31, M.S, 31; univ. fel, Chicago, 35-36, Ph.D.(physiol), 40. Asst. physiol, Chicago, 36-38, res. asst, 38-42; res. physiologist, RES. LABS, SWIFT & CO, 46-49, HEAD DIV. PHYSIOL. & TOXICOL, 49- Mem. coun. arteriosclerosis, Am. Heart Asn. U.S.A.A.F, 42-46, Maj. AAAS; Am. Physiol. Soc; Am. Soc. Pharmacol. & Exp. Therapeut; Soc. Exp. Biol. & Med; Soc. Toxicol. Adrenal extracts; conditioned reflexes; choline; metabolism; cottonseed physiology; nutrition; chemicals in foods. Address: Research & Development Center, Swift & Co, 1919 Swift Dr, Oak Brook, IL 60521.

EAGLE, HARRY, b. New York, N.Y, July 13, 05; m. 28; c. 1. MEDICINE. A.B, Hopkins, 23, M.D, 27, fel, 28-29; hon. M.S, Yale, 48; hon. D.Sc, Wayne State, 65. Intern, Hopkins Hosp, 27-28, asst, med. sch, Hopkins, 29-30, instr, 30-32; res. fel, Harvard Med. Sch, 32-33; assoc. bact, sch. med, Pennsylvania, 33-35, asst. prof, 35-36; dir. venereal disease res. lab, Hopkins & U.S. Pub. Health Serv, 36-46; sci. dir. res. br, Nat. Cancer Inst, 47-49, chief exp. therapeut, microbiol. inst, Nat. Insts. Health, 49-58, exp. ther, Nat. Inst. Allergy & Infectious Disease, 58-59, lab. cell biol, 59-61; PROF. CELL BIOL, ALBERT EINSTEIN COL. MED, 61-, ASSOC. DEAN. SCI. AFFAIRS, 70-, chmn. dept. cell biol, 61-70. Lectr, sch. med, Hopkins, 36-47; trustee, Microbiol. Found, Rutgers. Lilly Bronze Medal, 36; Alvarenga Prize, Col. Physicians Phila, 36; Presidential Cert. Merit, 48; Borden Award, Asn. Am. Med. Col, 64; Einstein Commemorative Award, 69. With Off. Sci. Res. & Develop, 44; U.S.P.H.S, 36-61, Med. Dir. Nat. Acad. Sci; Am. Acad. Arts & Sci; Am. Soc. Biol. Chem; Am. Soc. Clin. Invest; Asn. Am. Physicians; Am. Asn. Immunol; Am. Soc. Cell Biol; Am. Asn. Cancer Res; Am. Soc. Microbiol. Immunochemistry; antigen-antibody reaction; serodiagnosis and chemotherapy of syphilis; blood coagulation; trypanosomiasis and tropical diseases; detoxification of metal poisoning; mode of action of antibiotics; cell and tissue culture. Address: Dept. of Cell Biology, Albert Einstein College of Medicine, 1300 Morris Park Ave, Bronx, NY 10461.

EAGLE, JOHN EDWIN, b. St. Anthony, Idaho, Aug. 14, 09; m. 37; c. 1. MATHEMATICS. B.S, Mont. State Col, 30; Chicago, 33; Univ. Mont, 36; M.A, Stanford, 40, Ed.D.(math), 47; Ore. State Col, 43-44. Part-time instr, Mont. State Col, 30-31; teacher, high sch, Mont, 31-37 & Calif, 38-43; asst. prof, Army Spec. Training Prog, Ore. State Col, 43-46; asst. prof. MATH, SAN DIEGO STATE COL, 46-49, assoc. prof, 49-52, PROF, 52- Teacher, Menlo Sch. Boys, 44-45; lectr, Stanford Univ, 45-46; ed, Calif. Math. Coun. Bull, 47-54; summers, lectr, Mont. State Col, 53 & Univ. Colo, 55; dir, Nat. Sci. Found. Insts, 59-61, assoc. dir, 62-65, dir. summer inst, 65; partic, Inst. Math. Pedag, Brussels, Belg, spring 70. Relationship of reading abilities to sucess in mathematics. Address: Dept. of Mathematics, San Diego State College, San Diego, CA 92115.

EAGLE, J(OHN) FREDERICK, b. New York, N.Y, July 16, 17; m. 43; c. 6. PEDIATRICS. B.A, Yale, 40; M.D, Columbia, 43. Intern, St. Luke's Hosp, 44; asst. res. pediat, Babies Hosp, 48-49; from asst. res. to res, Children's Hosp, 49-51; from asst. to asst. prof, Buffalo, 51-56; asst. clin. prof, Columbia, 56-63, assoc. prof. pediat. & asst. dean, col. physicians & surgeons, 63-67; DEAN & EXEC. V.PRES, N.Y. MED. COL, 67- Asst. attend. pediatrician, E.J. Meyer Mem. Hosp, 55-56; attend. pediatrician & dir. pediat, St. Luke's Hosp, 56-63. Med.C, 44-47, Capt. Soc. Pediat. Res; Am. Acad. Pediat. Pediatric endocrinology. Address: New York Medical College, Flower & Fifth Ave. Hospitals, Fifth Ave. at 106th St, New York, NY 10029.

EAGLE, SAM, b. St. Anthony, Idaho, July 11, 12; m. 41; c. 6. CHEMICAL ENGINEERING. B.S, Mont. State Col, 34; fel, Carnegie Inst. Tech, 34-37, M.S, 35, D.Sc.(chem), 38. Night sch. instr, Carnegie Inst. Tech, 37-38; res. chemist, res. & develop. sect, STANDARD OIL CO. CALIF, 38-41, asst. foreman, cracking div, Richmond Ref, 41-43, foreman, 43-45, res. chemist, Calif. Res. Corp, 46-49, sr. res. chemist, 49-56, tech. asst. chem, 56-61, RES. ENGR, CHEVRON RES. CO, RICHMOND, 62- Am. Inst. Chem. Eng; Am. Chem. Soc. Process development in oil refining; adsorption; petrochemicals; catalyst research. Address: 7769 Baron Ct, El Cerrito, CA 94530.

EAGLE, THOMAS McCAULEY, b. U.S, May 28, 13; m. 38; c. 4. VETERINARY MEDICINE. D.V.M, Colorado State, 38. Jr. vet, bur. animal indust, agr. res. serv, U.S. Dept. Agr, 38-40; owner, Eagle Animal Hosp, Kansas City, Mo, 46-64; ASSOC. PROF. VET. MED. & SURG, SCH. VET. MED, UNIV. MO-COLUMBIA, 64- Vet.C, U.S.A, 40-46, Lt. Col. Am. Vet. Med. Asn; Am. Asn. Vet. Clinicians. Small animal hospital management; small animal surgery & medicine. Address: School of Veterinary Medicine, University of Missouri-Columbia, Columbia, MO 65201.

EAGLE, WATT WEEMS, b. Statesville, N.C, Mar. 14, 98; m. 30; c. 1. OTOLARYNGOLOGY. A.B, North Carolina, 18; M.D, Hopkins, 25; Pennsylvania, 30. Asst. curator, N.C. State Mus, 19-20; from asst. to instr. OTOLARYNGOL, Sch. med, Hopkins, 27-30; from instr. to prof, SCH. MED, DUKE UNIV, 30-69, EMER. PROF. & EMER. CHIEF DIV, 69-, chief univ. hosp, 30-69. Consult, Church Home Hosp, 25-26; Hopkins Hosp, 26-30. U.S.A, 18-19, 2nd Lt. Fel. Am. Acad. Ophthal. & Otolaryngol; fel. Am. Laryngol. Asn; fel. Am. Laryngol, Rhinol. & Otol. Soc.(v.pres, 49); fel. Am. Med. Asn. Address: 703 Professional Dr, New Bern, NC 28560.

EAGLEMAN, JOE R, b. Howell Co, Mo, Oct. 9, 36; m. 60; c. 3. METEOROLOGY, SOIL PHYSICS. B.S, Missouri, 59, M.S, 61, Ph.D.(meteorol), 63. Asst. prof. METEOROL, UNIV. KANS, 63-67, ASSOC. PROF, 67- Am. Meteorol. Soc; Am. Soc. Agron. Methods of measuring and calculating evapotranspiration; surface energy budget and water balance; soil moisture movement and methods of measurement; microclimatology; structure of thunderstorms and tornadoes; tornado damage to buildings. Address: Dept. of Geography & Meteorology, University of Kansas, Lawrence, KS 66044.

EAGLES, BLYTHE A(LFRED), b. New Westminster, B.C, Apr. 23, 02; m. 30. DAIRYING. B.A, Univ, B.C, 22, hon. D.Sc, 68; M.A, Univ. Toronto, 24, Ph.D, 26. Teaching fel, Univ. Toronto, 22-26; Sterling fel, Yale, 26-28; asst. biochem, Nat. Inst. Med. Res, Univ. London, 28-29; asst. prof. dairying, UNIV. B.C, 29-30, assoc. prof, 30-36, prof. & head dept, 36-67, chmn. div. animal sci, 55-67, dean faculty agr, 49-67, EMER. DEAN FACULTY AGR. & LECTR. BIOCHEM, FACULTY MED, 67- Inst. Food Technol; fel. Agr. Inst. Can; fel. Royal Soc. Can; hon. mem, Can. Soc. Microbiol.(pres, 68-69); Can. Physiol. Soc; fel. Chem. Inst. Can; Brit. Biochem. Soc. Creatine and uric acid metabolism; ergothioneine and glutathione in blood; constitution of glutathione; ripening of cheese; nutrition of bacteria; bios. Address: Dept. of Biochemistry, Faculty of Medicine, University of British Columbia, Vancouver, B.C, Can.

EAGLES, ELDON LEWIS, b. Moncton, N.B, Mar. 9, 11; U.S. citizen; m. 57. MEDICINE, PUBLIC HEALTH ADMINISTRATION. Mt. Allison, 28-30; M.D, C.M, Dalhousie, 36; dipl, Toronto, 40; Dr.P.H, Hopkins, 58. Gen. practice med. & surg, N.S, Can, 36-39; div. med. health officer, Dept. Pub. Health, N.S, 40-54, dir. child & maternal health, 54-56; res. fel, sch. hyg. & pub. health, Hopkins, 56-57; assoc. res. prof, grad. sch. pub. health, Pittsburgh, 57-64; asst. dir. ADMIN. & RES, NAT. INST. NEUROL. DISEASES & STROKE, 64-70, DEP. DIR, 70- Mem. adv. cmt. neurol. & sensory disease serv, U.S. Pub. Health Serv, 62-63, grants review panel & communicative disorders res. training cmt, Nat. Inst. Neurol. Diseases & Blindness, 62-64. Fel. AAAS; fel. Am. Speech & Hearing Asn; Am. Acad. Ophthal. & Otolaryngol; fel. Am. Pub. Health Asn. Neurological and sensory diseases, especially hearing, language and speech. Address: 5905 Aberdeen Rd, Bethesda, MD 20034.

EAGLES, JAN, b. Sept. 24, 38; U.S. citizen. HISTOLOGY, ANATOMY. B.S, Samford, 61; M.S, Alabama, 63, Ph.D.(anat), 68. Teacher, jr. high sch, Ala, 60-61; instr. anat. med. ctr, Alabama, 66-68; ASST. PROF. BIOL, UNIV. MONTEVALLO, 69- Am. Asn. Phys. Anthrop. Histological structure of ligaments of human arch; joint development; age changes in ligaments and tendons; aging in the knee joint of rats and other animals; ultrastructure of connective tissues. Address: Dept. of Biology, University of Montevallo, Montevallo, AL 35115.

EAGLESON, HALSON V(ASHON), b. Bloomington, Ind, Mar. 14, 03; m. 32, 41; c. 3. PHYSICS. A.B, Indiana, 26, A.M, 31, Gen. Ed. Bd, fel, 35-36, Ph.D. (physics), 39. Prof. math. & physics, Morehouse Col, 27-35, head dept. PHYSICS, 35-47; PROF, HOWARD UNIV, 47- Head dept, Clark Col, 40-47.

Acoust. Soc. Am; Am. Asn. Physics Teachers; Nat. Inst. Sci.(pres, 48). Architectural acoustics; sound transmission; design of optical instruments; musical acoustics; ultrasonics; shock waves. Address: Dept. of Physics, Howard University, Washington, DC 20001.

EAGLESON, PETER STURGES, b. Phila, Pa, Feb. 27, 28; m. 49; c. 3. HYDROLOGY. B.S, Lehigh Univ, 49, M.S, 52; Sc.D.(civil eng), Mass. Inst. Technol, 56. Asst. fluid mech, Lehigh Univ, 50-51; MASS. INST. TECHNOL, 52-54, instr, 54-55, asst. prof. hydraul. eng, 55-61, assoc. prof. CIVIL ENG, 61-65, PROF, 65-, HEAD DEPT, 70- C.Eng, 49-50, 2nd Lt. Am. Soc. Civil Eng.(res. prize, 63); Am. Geophys. Union; Int. Asn. Hydraul. Res; Int. Asn. Sci. Hydrol. Coastal processes and hydrologic systems. Address: Dept. of Civil Engineering, Room 1-290, Massachusetts Institute of Technology, Cambridge, MA 02139.

EAGLETON, LEE C(HANDLER), b. Vallejo, Calif, July 27, 23; m. 53; c. 3. CHEMICAL ENGINEERING. S.B, Mass. Inst. Tech, 47, S.M, 48; Res. Corp. grant in aid & D.Eng, Yale, 51. Res. assoc. chem. eng, Columbia, 50-51; develop. engr, Rohm & Haas Co, 51-56; assoc. prof. CHEM. ENG, Univ. Pa, 56-66, prof, 66-70; PROF. & HEAD DEPT, PA. STATE UNIV, 70- Consult, Rohm & Haas Co, 56- U.S.A.R, 42-46. Am. Chem. Soc; Am. Soc. Eng. Educ; Am. Inst. Chem. Eng. Heat and mass transfer to packed beds; adsorption; thermodynamics; kinetics; process optimization; mixing in liquid phase reactors; evaporation. Address: Dept. of Chemical Engineering, 160 Chemical Engineering Bldg, Pennsylvania State University, University Park, PA 16802.

EAGLETON, ROBERT DON, b. Ladonia, Tex, Aug. 19, 37; m. 63; c. 2. SOLID STATE PHYSICS. Nat. Sci. Found. fel, Okla. State Univ, 59, M.S, 62, Ph.D.(physics), 69. Instr. PHYSICS, U.S. Naval Nuclear Power Sch, Calif, 62-65; ASST. PROF, CALIF. STATE POLYTECH. COL, KELLOGG-VOORHIS, 68- U.S.N, 62-65, Lt. Am. Asn. Physics Teachers. Temperature dependence of positronium annihilation in solids; thermally stimulated luminescence in stannic oxide single crystals and ceramics. Address: Dept. of Physics, California State Poytechnic College, Kellogg-Voorhis, Pomona, CA 91768.

EAGON, JOHN A(LONZO), b. Portsmouth, N.H, May 5, 32; m. 57; c. 2. MATHEMATICS. B.A, Princeton, 54; M.S, Chicago, 58, Ph.D.(math), 61. NATO fel. MATH, Sheffield, 61-62; asst. prof, Univ. Ill, Urbana, 62-67; ASSOC. PROF, UNIV. MINN, MINNEAPOLIS, 67- U.S.A, 54-56. Am. Math. Soc. Commutative rings; linear graphs. Address: Dept. of Mathematics, University of Minnesota, Minneapolis, MN 55455.

EAGON, ROBERT G(ARFIELD), b. Salesville, Ohio, Oct. 29, 27; m. 52; c. 1. MICROBIOLOGY. B.Sc, Ohio State Univ, 51, M.Sc, 52, fel, 52-54, Ph.D. (bact), 54. Fulbright scholar, Pasteur Inst, Paris, 54-55; asst. prof. bact, UNIV. GA, 55-59, assoc. prof. MICROBIOL, 59-66, PROF, 66- Med.C, U.S.A, 46-49, Res, 49- AAAS; Am. Soc. Microbiol; fel. Am. Acad. Microbiol. Bacterial metabolism; physiology. Address: Dept. of Microbiology, University of Georgia, Athens, GA 30601.

EAKER, CHARLES MAYFIELD, b. Bonne Terre, Mo, Aug. 3, 19; m. 43; c. 3. CHEMISTRY. A.B, Cent. Col, 41; Ph.D.(org. chem), Maryland, 46. Asst, Off. Sci. Res. & Develop, Md, 43-45; res. chemist, MONSANTO CO, 46-52, group leader, 52-69, RES. GROUP LEADER, 69- Am. Chem. Soc. Synthetic organic chemistry; rubber antioxidants and vulcanization agents; agricultural chemicals. Address: Monsanto Co, 260 Springside Dr, Akron, OH 44313.

EAKIN, BERTRAM E, b. Jerome, Idaho, Oct. 9, 28; m. 52; c. 3. CHEMICAL ENGINEERING, GAS DYNAMICS. B.S, Mass. Inst. Tech, 51; M.S, Ill. Inst. Tech, 57, Ph.D.(gas tech), 62. Lab. technician, Chem. & Geol. Labs, Casper, Wyo, 51-53; inst. gas technol, Ill. Inst. Technol, 53-54, asst. chem. engr, 54-57, assoc. chem. engr, 57-62, chem. engr, 62-64, sr. chem. engr, 64-71; DIR. RES, P-V-T INC, 71- Adj. instr, Ill. Inst. Tech, 53-57, adj. asst. prof, 57-71. Am. Inst. Chem. Eng. Experimental measurement of thermodynamic and transport properties of gases and liquids at cryogenic temperatures and elevated pressures. Address: P-V-T, Inc, P.O. Box 36272, Houston, TX 77036.

EAKIN, JAMES (HENRY), JR, b. Byesville, Ohio, Nov. 13, 22; m. 47; c. 2. AGRONOMY. B.S, Ohio State, 47, M.S, 49. Instr. AGRON, Ohio State, 47-49; from asst. prof. to PROF, PA. STATE UNIV, 49-, HEAD AGRON. EXTEN, 61- Consult, Tenn. Valley Auth, 64-; Tenn. Corp. U.S.A, 43-46. Fel. Am. Soc. Agron; Soil Sci. Soc. Am; Crop Sci. Soc. Am. Soil technology. Address: Agronomy Extension, 317 Tyson Bldg, Pennsylvania State University, University Park, PA 16802.

EAKIN, RICHARD M(ARSHALL), b. Florence, Colo, May 5, 10; m. 35; c. 2. ZOOLOGY. A.B, California, 31, fel, 34-35, Ph.D.(zool), 35. Asst. zool, California, 31-34; Nat. Res. Coun. fel, Erlangen & Freiburg, Ger, 35-36; instr. zool, UNIV. CALIF, BERKELEY, 36-39, asst. prof, 39-42, asst. dean col. letters & sci, 40-43, assoc. prof. ZOOL, 43-49, PROF, 49-, chmn. dept. zool, 42-48 & 52-57, Miller Res. Prof, Miller Inst. Basic Res. Sci, 61-62 & 69-70; chmn. inst, 61-67. Guggenheim fel, Stanford Univ, 53; Nat. Sci. Found. fel, Univ. Berne, 57; U.S. del, Sem. on Retina, Fukuoka, Japan, 66; chmn. sessions, Cong. Electron Micros, Kyoto, 66 & Grenoble, 70. Sr. citation for distinguished teaching, Univ. Calif, Berkeley, 62; assoc. stud. distinguished teaching award, 68. AAAS; Am. Soc. Zool; Soc. Develop. Biol; Soc. Exp. Biol. & Med; Int. Soc. Develop. Biol; Electron Micros. Soc. Am; fel. Inst. Embryol. Determination and regulation in amphibian development; fine structure of photoreceptors and of amphibian embryo. Address: Dept. of Zoology, University of California, Berkeley, CA 94720.

EAKIN, RICHARD R, b. New Castle, Pa, Aug. 6, 38; m. 60. MATHEMATICS. B.A, Geneva Col, 60; Nat. Defense Ed. Act fel, Washington State, 60-63, M.A, 62, Nat. Sci. Found. fel, 63-64, Ph.D.(math), 64. Asst. prof. MATH, BOWLING GREEN STATE UNIV, 64-69, ASSOC. PROF. & ASST. DEAN GRAD. SCH, 69- Am. Math. Soc; Math. Asn. Am. Combinatorial mathematics. Address: Dept. of Mathematics, Bowling Green State University, Bowling Green, OH 43403.

EAKIN, RICHARD TIMOTHY, b. Birmingham, Ala, May 25, 42. BIOCHEMISTRY, MOLECULAR BIOLOGY. B.S, Univ. Tex, Austin, 63; Nat. Insts. Health fel. & Ph.D.(biochem), Calif. Inst. Technol, 68. Nat. Insts. Health fel, Stanford Univ, 68-71; RES. ASSOC. CHEM, UNIV. TEX, AUSTIN, 71- AAAS; Am. Chem. Soc. Genetics and biochemistry of isoleucine and valine biosyntheses in Neurospora; biochemistry of mitochondria in Neurospora; mitochondrial oxidase systems; respiratory-deficient cytoplasmic mutants of Neurospora. Address: Dept. of Chemistry, University of Texas, Austin, TX 78712.

EAKIN, ROBERT E(DWARD), b. LaGrande, Ore, Jan. 23, 16; m. 40; c. 4. BIOCHEMISTRY. B.S, Oregon State Col, 37, M.S, 39; Standard Brands fel, Texas, 39-41, Ph.D.(biochem), 42. Res. biochemist, nutrit. clin, Hillman Hosp, Ala, 41-43; asst. prof. BIOCHEM, UNIV. TEX. AUSTIN, 46-47, assoc. prof, 47-57, PROF, 57- U.S.N.R, 43-46, Lt. Am. Chem. Soc; Am. Soc. Biol. Chem. Factors promoting growth of yeast; microbiological methods for B vitamins; avidin; chemical phenomena associated with biological development. Address: Dept. of Chemistry, University of Texas at Austin, Austin, TX 78712.

EAKIN, THOMAS E(MORY), b. Detroit, Mich, Nov. 9, 14; m. 43; c. 2. GEOLOGY, HYDROLOGY. A.B, California, Los Angeles, 41. Geologist, U.S. GEOL. SURV, Calif, Nev, Ore. & Wash, 42-50, in-charge tech. assistance & for. training prog, Wash, D.C, 51-57, admin. geologist & chief for. hydrol. sect, 57-60, HYDROLOGIST, NEV, 60- Water resources tech. assistance adv, Iran, 51-52; UN tech. adv, W.Indies, 53. Am. Geophys. Union; Geol. Soc. Am. Ground water geology and hydrology; water resources investigations, quantitative reconnaissance and program planning. Address: U.S. Geological Survey, Survey Water Resources Division, 705 N. Plaza St, Carson City, NV 89701.

EAKINS, PETER RUSSELL, b. Montreal, Que, May 17, 27; m. 50, 62; c. 3. GEOLOGY. B.Sc, McGill, 48, M.Sc, 49, Ph.D,(geol), 52. Geochemist, Cerro de Pasco Corp, 52-55; explor. geologist, Malartic Gold Fields, Ltd, 55-57; chief geologist, Mineral Mgt. Ltd, 57-58; lectr. GEOL, McGILL UNIV, 58-59, asst. prof, 59-64, ASSOC. PROF, 64- Summers, geologist, Que. Dept. Nat. Resources, 59, 62, 68, 70, 71, Consol. Zinc Corp, 60, Geol. Surv. Can, 61, consult. geologist, Norque Copper Mines, Ltd, 63, 64; prof. off. & geo-sci. consult, Expos. of 67, 65; consult. geologist, Mkuski Copper Mines, Zambia, Africa, 67-68; chmn. exhibits comt, Georama 72, Int. Geol. Cong. Montreal, 69- Geol. Soc. Am; Geochem. Soc. fel. Royal Geog. Soc; fel. Geol. Asn. Can.(ed, Newsletter, 62-); Can. Inst. Min. & Metall. Structural geology; mineral exploration; Malartic gold deposits, Quebec; structures in the Quebec Appalachians; volcanic rock types of Northwestern Quebec; geochemical prospecting techniques for copper deposits in Peru. Address: Dept. of Geological Sciences, McGill University, Montreal, Que, Can.

EAKMAN, JAMES MILTON. b. Cedar, Minn, Dec. 26, 37; m. 62; c. 3. CHEMICAL ENGINEERING, COMPUTER SCIENCE. B.S, Minnesota, 60, Ph.D.(chem. eng), 66. Res. engr, Archer Daniels Midland Co, 60-66; Ashland Chem. Co. Div, Ashland Oil & Ref. Co, Inc, 66-68; asst. prof. CHEM. ENG, UNIV. NEBR, LINCOLN, 68-71, ASSOC. PROF, 71- Consult, Indust. Res. & Info. Serv, State of Nebr, 68-; Ashland Chem. Co, 69-70; North. Natural Gas Co, 70- Am. Inst. Chem. Eng; Am. Chem. Soc; Asn. Comput. Mach. Computer aided chemical process design; numerical analysis; chemical process development; biochemical engineering; statistical computations; optimization. Address: Dept. of Chemical Engineering, University of Nebraska, Lincoln, NE 68508.

EAKS, IRVING L(ESLIE), b. Sawtelle, Calif, May 24, 23; m. 48; c. 3. PLANT PHYSIOLOGY, BIOCHEMISTRY. B.S, Colo. Agr. & Mech. Col, 48; M.S, California, Davis, 50, Ph.D.(plant physiol), 53. Asst, UNIV. CALIF, Davis, 48-52, jr. plant physiologist, citrus exp. sta, RIVERSIDE, 52-54, asst. plant physiologist, 54-58, assoc. plant physiologist, 58-62, PLANT PHYSIOLOGIST, 62- U.S.A, 43-46. Am. Soc. Plant Physiol; Am. Soc. Hort. Sci. Postharvest physiology, handling and chemical composition of fruits and vegetables; chilling injury of cold-sensitive crops. Address: Dept. of Biochemistry, University of California, Riverside, CA 92502.

EALES, JOHN GEOFFREY, b. Wolverhampton, Eng, Sept. 9, 37; m. 63; c. 1. ANIMAL PHYSIOLOGY, ENDOCRINOLOGY. B.A, Oxford, 59; M.Sc, British Columbia, 61, Ph.D.(zool), 63. Asst. prof. biol, New Brunswick, 63-67; ZOOL, UNIV. MAN, 67-69, ASSOC. PROF, 69- Can. Soc. Zool. Thyroid function in fish. Address: Dept. of Zoology, University of Manitoba, Winnipeg, Man, Can.

EALY, ROBERT P(HILLIP), b. Kay County, Okla, July 6, 14; m. 39. ORNAMENTAL HORTICULTURE. B.S, Okla. State, 41; M.S, Kans. State Col, 46; Ph.D, La. State, 55. Asst. hort, Kans. State Col, 41-42; asst. prof, Okla. State, 46-55, assoc. prof, 55-58, prof, 58-61; prof. & head dept, KANS. STATE UNIV, 61-63, prof. hort. & landscape archit. & head dept, 63-66, PROF. LANDSCAPE ARCHIT, 66-, HEAD DEPT, 69-, ASSOC. DEAN COL. ARCHIT. & DESIGN, 67-, dir. landscape archit, 66-69. U.S.A, 42-46, 1st Lt. Am. Soc. Landscape Archit. Landscape Architecture; outdoor recreation; plant ecology; ornamental planning; ornamental landscape plant materials; dwarfing rootstocks; herbaceous perennial flowers; chlorosis of ornamentals; graft unions; container grown nursery stock; radioactive tracers; landscape architecture. Address: 1925 Vermont St, Manhattan, KS 66502.

EAMES, ARNOLD C, b. West Paris, Maine, Feb. 10, 30; m. 54; c. 3. PAPER CHEMISTRY. B.M.E, Rensselaer Polytech, 51; M.S, Inst. Paper Chem, Lawrence, 57, Ph.D.(paper chem), 59. Res. engr, S.D. Warren Co, 53-54; proj. engr, Container Corp. Am, 57; res. engr, S.D. WARREN CO, 59-61, ASST. RES. DIR. NEW PROD. DEVELOP, 62- Summers, res. engr, Kimberly Clark Corp, 55, proj. engr, Scott Paper Co, 56. U.S.M.C.R, 51-53, Res, 53-60, Capt. Tech. Asn. Pulp & Paper Indust. Coated paper technology for printing and other special uses. Address: S.D. Warren Co, Cumberland Mills, ME 04092.

EAMES, M(ICHAEL) C(URTIS), b. Birmingham, Eng, Feb. 6, 31; m. 56; c. 2. NAVAL ARCHITECTURE. B.Sc, Durham, 50 & 51; M.E, N.S. Tech. Col, 57.

Shipbldg. apprentice, R. & W. Hawthorn-Leslie & Co, Ltd, Eng, 47-52; sci. officer, hydrodyn, CAN. DEFENCE RES. ESTAB. ATLANTIC, 52-58, group leader, appl. math, 58-60, HEAD spec. studies team, 60-63, FLUID MECH. SECT, 63- R.A.F.V.R, 50-53; R.C.N.R, 54-59, Lt. Soc. Naval Archit. & Marine Eng; Am. Inst. Aeronaut. & Astronaut; Am. Soc. Naval Eng; Can. Aeronaut. & Space Inst; Royal Inst. Naval Archit; Brit. Inst. Marine Eng; Royal Aeronaut. Soc. Applied hydrodynamics and aerodynamics; naval architecture; aeronautical engineering; ocean engineering. Address: 49 Murray Hill Dr, Dartmouth, N.S, Can.

EAMES, WILLIAM, b. Minnedosa, Man, Sept. 21, 29; m. 62; c. 4. MATHEMATICAL ANALYSIS. B.Sc, Brandon, 50; B.Sc, Manitoba, 52, M.Sc, 53; Ph.D.(math), Queen's (Ont), 56. Nat. Res. Coun. fel, Univ. Col, London, 56-57; asst. prof. MATH, New Brunswick, 57-58; lectr, Sir John Cass Col, Eng, 58-63, sr. lectr, 63-66; ASSOC. PROF, LAKEHEAD UNIV, 66- Am. Math. Soc; Can. Math. Cong; London Math. Soc. Measure theory. Address: Dept. of Mathematics, Lakehead University, Thunder Bay, Ont, Can.

EAMES, WILMER B, b. Kansas City, Mo, May 8, 14; m. 39; c. 2. DENTISTRY. D.D.S, Kansas City-West. Dent. Col, 39. Prof. oper. dent, dent. sch. Northwest. Univ.(Ill), 61-67, assoc. dean, 64-67; PROF. OPER. DENT, SCH. DENT, EMORY UNIV, 67- Dent.C, 41-45, Maj. Am. Dent. Asn; Int. Asn. Dent. Res; Am. Acad. Restorative Dent. Research in dental materials and operative techniques; clinical studies comparing dental materials. Address: Emory University School of Dentistry, Atlanta, GA 30322.

EANDI, RICHARD D, b. San Francisco, Calif, Oct. 14, 36; m. 68. COSMIC RAY & ELEMENTARY PARTICLE PHYSICS. B.S, Univ. San Francisco, 58; Ph.D.(physics), Univ. Calif, Berkeley, 63. PHYSICIST, Lawrence Radiation Lab, Univ. Calif, Berkeley, 63-67; MANNED SPACECRAFT CTR, NASA, 67- NATO fel, Deutsches Electronen-Synchrotron, Ger, 65-66. Am. Phys. Soc. Elementary particle experimental physics; pi-meson interactions with nucleons. Address: Code TN2, NASA Manned Spacecraft Center, Houston, TX 77058.

EANES, EDWARD DAVID, b. Rochester, N.Y, Sept. 2, 34; m. 61; c. 2. PHYSICAL CHEMISTRY. B.S, Col. William & Mary, 57; Nat. Sci. Found. fel, Hopkins, 57-59, M.A, 59, Ph.D.(crystal struct), 61. Phys. chemist, Nat. Bur. Standards, 60-61; asst. prof. phys. chem, med. col. Cornell Univ, 63-67; CHIEF MOLECULAR STRUCT. SECT, LAB. BIOL. STRUCT, NAT. INST. DENT. RES, 67- U.S.P.H.S, 61-63. Am. Chem. Soc; Am. Crystallog. Asn. Calcium phosphate chemistry; biological calcification. Address: Lab. of Biological Structure, National Institute of Dental Research, Bethesda, MD 20014.

EANES, R(ONALD) D(EAN), b. Polk Co, Iowa, Dec. 24, 16; m. 36; c. 2. ELECTROCHEMISTRY. B.S, Antioch Col, 40; M.S, Pennsylvania, 46. From sr. res. technologist to sect. head prod. eng. div, LEEDS & NORTHRUP CO, 42-63, dir. eng, 63-68, V.PRES. INSTRUMENT GROUP, 68- Am. Chem. Soc; Electrochem. Soc; Instrument Soc. Am; Sci. Apparatus Makers Asn. Address: Leeds & Northrup Co, Sumneytown Pike, North Wales, PA 19454.

EARDLEY, A(RMAND) J(OHN), b. Salt Lake City, Utah, Oct. 25, 01; m; c. 1. GEOLOGY. A.B, Utah, 27; hon. D.Sc, 70; Ph.D.(geol), Princeton, 30. Jr. geologist, U.S. Geol. Surv, 29-31; instr. econ. geol, Michigan, 30-34, asst. prof, 34-38, assoc. prof, 38-43, prof, 43-49; dir. div. earth scis, UNIV. UTAH, 49-54, dean col. mines & mineral industs, 54-65, prof. GEOL, 65-70, EMER. PROF, 70- Reynolds lectr, Utah, 55; pres, Am. Geol. Inst, 64-65. Talmadge sci. achievement award, Brigham Young Univ, 63. Am. Inst. Min, Metall. & Petrol. Eng; Nat. Asn. Geol. Teachers (pres, 62-63); fel. Geol. Soc. Am; Am. Asn. Petrol. Geol. (ed, 53, distinguished lectr, 51); Am. Geophys. Union. Tectonics of North America; structural geology of the Rocky Mountains; aerial photographs; sedimentation; petroleum geology. Address: 2618 Skyline Dr, Salt Lake City, UT 84108.

EARECKSON, WILLIAM M(ILTON), III, b. Phila, Pa, Oct. 10, 22; m. 48; c. 4. ORGANIC & POLYMER CHEMISTRY. B.S, Maryland, 43, fel, 48-50, Ph.D. (chem), 50. Asst. phys. chem, Maryland, 46-48; res. chemist, textile fibers dept, pioneering res. lab, E.I. DU PONT DE NEMOURS & CO, INC, Del, 50-56, res. supvr, 56-61, SR. RES. CHEMIST, SPRUANCE RES. & DEVELOP. LAB, 61- Guest lectr, Univ. Richmond, spring 68. U.S.M.C, 43-46, Res, 48-50. AAAS; Am. Chem. Soc; Sci. Res. Soc. Am. Synthetic fiber and cellulosic papers; spun bonded fabric products; polymer synthesis, stabilization and characterization. Address: 8409 Freestone Ave, Richmond, VA 23229.

EARGLE, G(EORGE) MARVIN, b. Salisbury, N.C, Sept. 29, 39. APPLIED MATHEMATICS. M.A, N.C. State Univ, 63, NASA grant, 64, Ph.D.(math), 68. ASST. PROF. MATH, N.C. State Univ, 66-69; APPALACHIAN STATE UNIV, 69- Soc. Indust. & Appl. Math; Am. Math. Soc; Math. Asn. Am. Applications of mathematics; elasticity theory. Address: Dept. of Mathematics, Appalachian State University, Boone, NC 28607.

EARHART, CHARLES FRANKLIN, JR, b. Melrose Park, Ill, Oct. 26, 41. MOLECULAR BIOLOGY, MICROBIAL PHYSIOLOGY. A.B, Knox Col.(Ill), 62; Nat. Insts. Health fel, Purdue Univ, 63, Ph.D.(molecular biol), 67. Fel. biol, Purdue Univ, 66-67; Nat. Insts. Health fel, sch. med, Tufts Univ, 67-68; faculty assoc. MICROBIOL, UNIV. TEX, AUSTIN, 68-70, ASST. PROF, 70- Nat. Insts. Health res. grant, 70- AAAS; Am. Soc. Microbiol. Physiological and biochemical changes which occur after bacteriophage infection; studies on the association of DNA with membrane in infected and uninfected cells. Address: Dept. of Microbiology, University of Texas at Austin, Austin, TX 78712.

EARHART, J. RONALD, b. Hershey, Pa, July 29, 41; m. 63; c. 1. SPACE SCIENCE, IONOSPHERIC PHYSICS. B.S, Lebanon Valley Col, 63; M.S, Univ. N.H, 66, NASA fel, 68-69, Ph.D.(physics), 69. SR. PHYSICIST, ITT ELECTRO-PHYSICS LABS, 68- Am. Geophys. Union. Space physics, especially ionospheric physics and radio-physics with ground based riometer systems and more elaborate radio propagation techniques. Address: ITT Electro-Physics Labs, 9140 Old Annapolis Rd, Columbia, MD 21043.

EARHART, ROBERT W(AYNE), b. Clarinda, Iowa, Mar. 19, 21. PLANT PATHOLOGY. B.S, Iowa State, 42; M.S, Wisconsin, 47, Ph.D.(plant path. & breeding), 49. Plant pathologist, cereal crops sect, U.S. Dept. Agr, 49-54; assoc. prof. bot, Clemson, 55-57, prof, 57-59; res. biologist, CHEMAGRO CORP, KANSAS CITY, MO, 59-61, ASST. SUPVR. FIELD RES, 61- Plant pathologist, Florida, 51-54. U.S.A, 42-46, Chem.C.Res, 46-, Lt. Col. AAAS; Am. Soc. Agron; Am. Phytopath. Soc. Pesticide development; control of plant diseases of economic crops; diseases caused by seed and soil-borne pathogens and nematodes; variability within species of plant pathogens; industrial research and development. Address: 7200 Woodward, Overland Park, KS 66204.

EARING, M(ASON) H(UMPHRY), b. Albany, N.Y, Oct. 23, 21; m. 49; c. 4. ORGANIC CHEMISTRY. Ph.D.(chem), Rensselaer Polytech, 50. Mem. staff org. res, Wyandotte Chem. Corp, 50-60, sr. res. chemist, 60-63; SR. CHEMIST, BALLAST DEPT, GEN. ELEC. CO, 63- U.S.A.A.F, 43-45, 2nd Lt. Fel. AAAS; Am. Chem. Soc; fel. Am. Inst. Chem. Industrial and polymer chemistry; polyethers and urethane polymers; dielectric and acoustic properties of polymers. Address: 1510 N. Gilbert Ave, Danville, IL 61832.

EARL, ALFRED E(LLSWORTH), b. Mt. Vernon, N.Y, June 8, 19; m. 41; c. 4. TOXICOLOGY. D.V.M, Cornell, 41. Private practice, 41-48; sr. res. veterinarian, admin. comt. macrobiol. res, Ciba Pharmaceut. Co, 48-54, dir. vet. res, 54-62, toxicol. & path. res, 62-69; HEAD VET. RES, ANIMAL HEALTH DIV, AYERST RES. LABS, 69- Mem. sci. adv. comt, Animal Health Inst. Am. Vet. Med. Asn; Soc. Toxicol; Pharmaceutical Mfrs. Asn; Pan-Am. Med. Asn; Am. Asn. Lab. Animal Sci. Pathology; experimental surgery; lab animal care; biologic quality control; pharmacology. Address: Animal Health Division, Ayerst Research Labs, Chazy, NY 12921.

EARL, BOYD L, b. Pa, July 20, 27; m. 49; c. 4. MATHEMATICS. B.S, Wilkes Col, 52; M.S, Bucknell, 57. Teacher, high sch, Pa, 52-56; instr. MATH, Bucknell, 56-61; ASSOC. PROF, WILKES COL, 61- Nat. Sci. Found. sci. faculty fel, Pa. State, 62-63. U.S.A.A.F, 45-46. Math. Asn. Am; Am. Math. Soc. Topology; algebra. Address: Dept. of Mathematics, Wilkes College, Wilkes-Barre, PA 18703.

EARL, CHARLES RILEY, b. San Diego, Calif, Oct. 27, 33; m. 60; c. 2. POLYMER & PHYSICAL CHEMISTRY. A.B, Whittier Col, 55; Ph.D. (polymer chem), Polytech. Inst. Brooklyn, 70. Chemist, U.S. Food & Drug Admin, 55-56; Aerojet-Gen. Corp, 56-59; res. fel, Jewish Hosp. Brooklyn, 59-61; sr. res. fel, Polytech. Inst. Brooklyn, 62-68; SR. RES. CHEMIST, DEERING MILLIKEN RES. CORP, 68- Instr, Spartanburg Tech. Educ. Ctr, 71- Am. Chem. Soc. Adsorption, adhesion of polymers to textile fibers; relationship of polymer structure and properties; polyelectrolytes. Address: 440 Harrell Dr, Spartanburg, SC 29302.

EARL, FRANCIS L(EE), b. Jasper, Mo, Dec. 12, 24; m. 50; c. 2. VETERINARY TOXICOLOGY. D.V.M, Mich. State Col, 47; Maryland, 50-59. Vet, State Vet. Off, State Mo, 47-48; sta. vet, animal husb. div, bur. animal indust, U.S. Dept. Agr, Md, 48-52, vet. path. div, 52-61; DIV. TOXICOL, FOOD & DRUG ADMIN, 61-63, VET. MED. OFF, SPEC. PHARMACOL. ANIMAL LAB, BUR. FOODS, 64- Am. Vet. Med. Asn; Am. Col. Vet. Toxicol; Am. Asn. Lab. Animal Sci; Teratology Soc. Atrophic rhinitis in swine; swine erysipelas; use of swine on drug toxicity research; comparative toxicology of dogs and swine; diseases and housing of miniature swine; clinical laboratory values of dogs and swine; occular toxicity in dogs; teratogenic effects of compounds in dogs and miniature swine. Address: Division of Toxicology, Special Pharmacology Animal Lab, BF 158, Food & Drug Administration, Washington, DC 20204.

EARL, JAMES A(RTHUR), b. Omaha, Nebr, Aug. 14, 32; m. 55; c. 2. PHYSICS. B.S, Mass. Inst. Tech, 53, Ph.D.(physics), 57. Physicist, Ft. Monmouth, 58; lectr. PHYSICS, Minnesota, 58-61, asst. prof, 61-65; ASSOC. PROF, UNIV. MD, 65- U.S.A.R, 53-59, 1st Lt. Am. Phys. Soc; Am. Geophys. Union. Cosmic ray extensive air showers; solar cosmic rays; effects of geomagnetism on cosmic rays; primary cosmic ray electrons. Address: Dept. of Physics, University of Maryland, College Park, MD 20740.

EARLE, ALVIN MATHEWS, b. Topeka, Kans, Mar. 20, 31; m. 54; c. 3. ANATOMY. B.S, Loyola (Ill), 54; M.S, Colorado, 58, Nat. Insts. Health fel, 59-60, Ph.D.(zool), 62. Assoc. prof. biol. & chmn. dept, Regis Col.(Colo), 60-66; Nat. Insts. Health spec. res. fel, med. ctr, Kansas, 66-68; ASSOC. PROF. ANAT, COL. MED, UNIV. NEBR, 68- Med.Serv.C, U.S.N.R, 51-, Lt. Comdr. AAAS; Am. Asn. Anat; Am. Soc. Zool; Am. Soc. Ichthyol. & Herpet. Comparative anatomy; vertebrate embryology; herpetology; comparative neuroanatomy. Address: Dept. of Anatomy, University of Nebraska Medical Center, Omaha, NE 68105.

EARLE, CLIFFORD J(OHN), JR, b. Racine, Wis, Nov. 3, 35; m. 60; c. 1. MATHEMATICS. B.A, Swarthmore Col, 57; Nat. Sci. Found. fel, Harvard, 57-61, M.A, 58, Ph.D.(math), 62. Instr. & res. fel. MATH, Harvard, 62-63; mem, Inst. Adv. Study, 63-65; asst. prof, CORNELL UNIV, 65-66, assoc. prof, 66-69, PROF, 69- AAAS; Am. Math. Soc. Functions of a complex variable; Riemann surfaces; quasiconformal mappings; automorphic forms. Address: Dept. of Mathematics, Cornell University, Ithaca, NY 14850.

EARLE, DAVID P(RINCE), JR, b. Englewood, N.J, May 23, 10; m. 36; c. 4. MEDICINE. A.B, Princeton, 33; M.D, Columbia, 37, Med.Sc.D.(int. med), 42. Intern, St. Luke's Hosp, New York, 37-39; res, Columbia, res. serv, Goldwater Hosp, 39-41; instr. MED, sch. med, N.Y. Univ, 41-43, asst. prof, 43-47, assoc. prof, 47-54; PROF, MED. SCH, NORTHWEST. UNIV, 54-, CHMN. DEPT, 65- Res. assoc, N.Y. Univ. res. serv, Goldwater Hosp, 41-46, dir, 46-47; consult, Surgeon Gen, 52-56. Mem. cardiovasc. study sect, U.S. Pub. Health Serv, 58-62; metab. training grants comt, Nat. Inst. Arthritis & Metab. Diseases, 64-67, chmn, 66-67, mem. urol. res. training grants comt, 67-69, chmn, 68-69, mem, Nat. Adv. Arthritis & Metab. Diseases Coun, 70- With Off. Sci. Res. & Develop, 44. Am. Soc. Clin. Invest; Am. Physiol. Soc; Soc. Exp. Biol. & Med; fel. Am. Col. Physicians; Asn. Am. Physicians. Clinical and experimental renal disease; chemotherapy of human malaria; water and electrolyte metabolism; hemorrhagic fever. Address: Northwestern University Medical School, 303 E. Chicago Ave, Chicago, IL 60611.

EARLE, ERNEST L, JR, b. Cambridge, Mass, May 24, 22; m. 56; c. 2. CHEMICAL ENGINEERING. B.S.Ch.E, Northeastern, 47, Jr. technologist, CORP. RES. DEPT, Gen. Foods, Inc, 47-48, asst. technologist, 48-50, assoc. technologist, 50-52, proj. leader, 52-54, sect. head, 54-60, LAB. MGR, GEN. FOODS CORP, 60- U.S.A.A.F, 42-46, Capt. Am. Inst. Chem. Eng; Inst. Food Technol. Engineering process development in food industry; extraction; heat transfer; dehydration processes and economic evaluations. Address: Technical Center, General Foods Corp, 250 North St, White Plains, NY 10605.

EARLE, F(ONTAINE) R(ICHARD), b. Fayetteville, Ark, Sept. 8, 06; m. 38. CHEMISTRY. B.Ch.E, Arkansas, 27; Cornell, 27-28; M.S, Okla. Agr. & Mech. Col, 32. Chemist, Atlantic Ref. Co, Pa, 28-29; Columbia Rope Co, N.Y, 29-30; teacher, high sch, Ark, 33-34; engr, U.S. Engrs, Tenn, 34; seafood inspector, U.S. DEPT. AGR, 34-36, res. chemist, soybean indust. prods. lab, 36-40, NORTH. REGIONAL RES. LAB, 40-56, LEADER NEW CROPS SCREENING UNIT, 56- Am. Chem. Soc; Am. Oil Chemists' Soc; Soc. Econ. Bot. Chemical composition of oilseeds and cereal grains; plant materials to discover potential new crops for the production of new industrial raw materials. Address: Northern Regional Research Lab, Agriculture Research Service, U.S. Dept. of Agriculture, Peoria, IL 61604.

EARLE, K(ENNETH) M(ARTIN), b. Jacksonville, Tex, Dec. 29, 19; m. 44; c. 3. PATHOLOGY, NEUROPATHOLOGY. B.A, Rice, 42; M.D, Texas, 45; Montreal Neurol. Inst. fel, McGill, 49-51, M.Sc, 51. Intern, John Sealy Hosp, 45-46; fel. path, McGill, 51-52; instr, sch. med, California, Los Angeles, 52-53; from assoc. prof. to prof. path, med. br. hosp, sch. med, Texas, 53-62, from asst. dean to dean med, 58-62; CHIEF NEUROPATH. BR, ARMED FORCES INST. PATH, 62- Consult. neuropath. & Am. Bd. Path; proj. secy, Int. Soc. Neuropath, 70- Dipl, Am. Bd. Path. U.S.N, 46-49. Am. Asn. Path. & Bact; Int. Acad. Path; Am. Soc. Exp. Path; Am. Asn. Neuropath.(pres, 67); Am. Crystallog. Asn; Soc. Appl. Spectros. Brain tumors; epilepsy; x-ray diffraction; spectroscopy; biological effects of laser radiation. Address: Armed Forces Institute of Pathology, Washington, DC 20305.

EARLE, MARSHALL D(ELPH), b. Greenville, S.C, July 28, 13; m. 43; c. 4. PHYSICS. B.S, Furman, 33; M.A, Cornell, 35; Sherwin-Williams fel, Pennsylvania, 40-41, Corning Glass Works fel, 41-42, Ph.D.(physics), 42. Teacher, sch, N.C, 36; Wash, D.C, 37-38; demonstr, Elgin Watch Co. exhibit, World's Fair, 39; instr. physics, Pennsylvania, 41-42; physicist, Am. Viscose Corp, Pa, 46-47; res. physicist, Franklin Inst, 47-51; res. scientist, radiation lab, Hopkins, 51-57, prin. res. scientist, 57-61; staff scientist, AEROSPACE CORP, 61-62, MGR. INFRARED SECT, 62- U.S.N.R, 42-45, 53-, Comdr. Am. Phys. Soc. Theory of solids; electrical conductivity of semiconductors; photoconductivity; infrared techniques. Address: Aerospace Corp, Bldg. A-2, Room 1243, P.O. Box 95085, Los Angeles, CA 90045.

EARLE, NORMAN W(ILLISTON), b. San Juan, P.R, Sept. 7, 27. ENTOMOLOGY. B.S, Illinois, 49, M.S, 50, indust. fel, 50-52, Ph.D.(entom), 52. Chemist, org. synthesis, Julius Hyman & Co, 49; ENTOMOLOGIST, Rocky Mt. Arsenal, Shell Develop. Co, 52-57; ENTOM. RES. DIV, AGR. RES. SERV, U.S. DEPT. AGR, 57- U.S.A, 46-47. Entom. Soc. Am. Insect toxicology; mode of action of pyrethrum synergists; microbioassay of insecticidal residues on food crops; insect physiology and toxicology. Address: Cotton Insects Research Branch, Agricultural Research Service, U.S. Dept. of Agriculture, 4115 Gourrier Ave, Baton Rouge, LA 70808.

EARLE, RALPH H(ERVEY), JR, b. Cranston, R.I, Apr. 15, 28. ORGANIC CHEMISTRY. Sc.B, Brown, 49; M.S, Ga. Inst. Tech, 50; Hooker fel, Purdue, 54-55, Res. Found. grant, 55-56, Continental Oil Co, fel, 56-57, Ph.D. (org. chem), 57. Chemist, Hercules Powder Co, 50, 52-54, res. chemist, 57-68, SUPVR. COMMERCIAL DEVELOP. ADV. PLANNING, PINE & PAPER CHEM. DEPT, HERCULES INC, 68- Fel. chem, Univ. Canterbury, 66-67. U.S.A, 51-52. Am. Chem. Soc. Chemistry of wet strength resins; nitrogen-containing heterocycles; amine-epichlorohydrin reactions, retention and flocculation. Address: Pine & Paper Chemicals Dept, Hercules, Inc, 910 Market St, Wilmington, DE 19801.

EARLE, ROBERT W(ALLACE), b. Battle Creek, Mich, Jan. 7, 14. PHARMACOLOGY. B.A, California, 40; M.S, Idaho, 41; Ph.D, Southern California, 59. Asst. prof. chem, Kemper Mil. Sch, 41-42; res. chemist, Don Baxter, Inc, Glendale, Calif, 42-46; prof. pharmacol, UNIV. CALIF, IRVINE-CALIF. COL. MED, 46-66, SR. LECTR, 66-69, MED. PHARMACOL. & THERAPEUT, 69-, ASST. DEAN STUD. AFFAIRS, 70- Vis. prof, Calif. State Col, Los Angeles, 64-; Los Angeles Col. Optom, 66- AAAS. Fundamental properties of heart muscle; effects of various drugs on the properties of heart muscle; nature of local anesthetic action; monaminergic nerve tracts in the brain. Address: University of California, Irvine-California College of Medicine, Irvine, CA 92664.

EARLE, SYLVIA ALICE, b. Gibbstown, N.J, Aug. 30, 35; m; c. 6. MARINE BOTANY. B.S, Fla. State, 55; Nat. Sci. Found. scholar, Virginia, 55; Nat. Sci. Found. scholar, Gen. Foods fel. & M.A, Duke, 56, Ph.D.(bot), 66; Florida, 59-60. Fisheries res. biologist, U.S. Fish & Wildlife Serv, N.C, 57; instr. biol, St. Petersburg Jr. Col, 63-64; res. assoc. marine biol, Cape Haze Marine Lab, 64-65, resident dir, 66-67; sr. res. assoc. marine biol, 67-68; RES. ASSOC. BOT, UNIV. CALIF, BERKELEY, 69-; LOS ANGELES COUNTY MUS. NATURAL HIST, 70- Phycologist, cruises, Int. Indian Ocean Exped. & Southeast. Pac. Biol. Oceanog. Prog, 64-66; instr, Tulane Univ, 66; consult, Mote Sci. Found, 66; res. fel, Farlow Herbarium, Harvard, 67-; res. scholar, Radcliffe Inst. Independent Study, 67-69; consult, Smithsonian-Link Man-In-Sea Prog, 68-; assoc. scientist, marine sci. inst, Univ. S.Fla, 69-; aquanaut- scientist & team leader, Tektite II Proj, 70- Dept. Interior Conservation Serv. Award, 70. Phycol. Soc. Am; Am. Soc. Ichthyol. & Herpet; Am. Fisheries Soc; Bot. Soc. Am; Int. Phycol. Soc. Systematics, ecology and distribution of benthic marine algae, especially island floras and plants of deep water; interrelationships among marine animals and plants. Address: Dept. of Botany, Los Angeles County Museum of Natural History, Los Angeles, CA 90007.

EARLE, T(HOMAS) E(VANS), b. Pa, Apr. 28, 25; m. 67; c. 2. INDUSTRIAL CHEMISTRY. B.S, Kentucky, 45. Chemist, res. dept, Standard Oil Co, 45-54, technologist, develop. & patent dept, 54-57, patent adv, res. dept, 57-61; res. & develop. dept, Am. Oil Co, 61-68; SR. FOR. PATENT CORRESPONDENT, PATENTS & LICENSING DEPT, STANDARD OIL CO, 68- Am. Chem. Soc. Chemicals; petrochemicals; patents. Address: 5542 Blackstone Ave, Chicago, IL 60637.

EARLE, T(HOMAS) T(HERON), b. Greenville, S.C, July 23, 05; m. 38. BOTANY. B.S, Furman, 28; Ph.D.(bot), Minnesota, 37. Instr. biol, Furman, 30-32; teaching asst. bot, Minnesota, 33-37; instr. biol, Newcomb Col, TULANE UNIV, 38-41, asst. prof, 41-43, assoc. prof, 43-45, prof, 45-47, BOT, 47-49, RICHARDSON PROF, 49-, DIR. SUMMER SCH, 47- Mem, Univ. Minn. bot. exped, Australia & N.Z, 34-35; consult, water hyacinth control exps, corps engrs, U.S. Dept. Army, 48-50. AAAS; Bot. Soc. Am; Am. Fern. Soc; Torrey Bot. Club. Plant morphology; aquatic plant control; embryology. Address: Dept. of Botany, Tulane University, New Orleans, LA 70118.

EARLEY, ERNEST BENTON, b. Orangeburg, S.C, Dec. 19, 06; m. 31; c. 2. PLANT PHYSIOLOGY. B.S, Clemson Col, 28; M.S, Va. Polytech, 29; Ph.D. (agron), Illinois, 41. Teaching fel, Va. Polytech, 28-29; asst. agron, Illinois, 29-37; asst. agronomist, regional soybean lab, bur. plant indust, soils & agr. eng, U.S. Dept. Agr, 37-44; asst. prof. AGRON, UNIV. ILL, URBANA, 44-49, assoc. prof, 49-55, PROF, 55- Am. Soc. Agron; Am. Soc. Plant Physiol. Ear shoot development of corn; effect of light and chemicals on growth and yield of corn. Address: 211 Davenport Hall, University of Illinois, Urbana, IL 61801.

EARLEY, JAMES W(ILLIAM), b. Adelaide Twp, Ont, Can, July 6, 22; U.S. citizen; m. 46; c. 3. GEOCHEMISTRY. B.Sc, Western Ontario, 45; M.A, Queen's (Ont), 47; Ont. Res. Found. fel, Toronto, 47-49, Ph.D.(mineral), 50. Mineralogist, Gulf Res. & Develop. Co, 49-50, head, chem. mineral. sect, 50-57, asst. dir. div. geol. & geochem, 57-62, supvr. geochem. sect, 62-66, training mgr, Gulf Res. & Develop. Co, 66-67, mgr. explor, nuclear fuels div, Gulf Oil Corp, 67-68, V.PRES, GULF MINERAL RESOURCES CO, 68- Summers, geologist, Int. Nickel Co. Can, 45-48. R.C.N, 41-45. Fel. Mineral Soc. Am; Geochem. Soc; Geol. Soc. Am; Am. Asn. Petrol. Geol; Can. Mineral. Asn; Mineral Soc. Gt. Britain & Ireland. Geochemical and mineralogical processes involved in deposition of sediments; formation of rocks; origin, migration and accumulation of oil. Address: Gulf Mineral Resources Co, 1780 S. Bellaire St, Denver, CO 80222.

EARLEY, JOSEPH E(MMETT), b. Providence, R.I, April 6, 32; m. 56; c. 3. INORGANIC CHEMISTRY. B.S, Providence Col, 54; Dow Chem. Co. fel, Brown, 56-57, Ph.D.(phys. chem), 57. Res. assoc, inorg. chem, Chicago, 57-58; asst. prof. CHEM, GEORGETOWN UNIV, 58-63, assoc. prof, 63-69, PROF, 69- Consult, U.S. Air Force Off. Sci. Res, 61-; vis. assoc, Calif. Inst. Technol, 67-68. Potter Prize, Brown Univ, 57. Chem.C, 57, Res, 57-, Capt. AAAS; Am. Chem. Soc. Reactions of coordination compounds and oxyanions; mechanisms of oxidation reactions in aqueous solution. Address: Dept. of Chemistry, Georgetown University, Washington, DC 20007.

EARLEY, LAURENCE E, b. Ahoskie, N.C, Jan. 23, 31; m; c. 3. INTERNAL MEDICINE. B.S, North Carolina, 53, M.D, 56. Instr. MED, Harvard Med. Sch, 63-64, assoc, 64-67, asst. prof, 67-68; assoc. prof, UNIV. CALIF, SAN FRANCISCO, 68-69, PROF, 69- Boston Med. Found. grant, 61-63; Nat. Insts. Health career develop. award, 67-68; mem. training grants comt, Nat. Inst. Arthritis & Metab. Diseases, 68- Mem. drug efficacy study, Nat. Res. Coun-Nat. Acad. Sci, 67-68; sci. adv. coun, Nat. Kidney Found, 68, fel. comt, 69; exec. comt. renal sect, Am. Heart Asn, 69- U.S.P.H.S, 57-58. Am. Fedn. Clin. Res; Am. Soc. Clin. Invest; Am. Physiol. Soc; Am. Soc. Nephrology. Physiology and pathophysiology of renal function and electrolyte physiology; physio-pharmacology of diuretic agents; physiology and pathophysiology of regulation of extracellular fluid volume; clinical renal diseases. Address: Dept. of Medicine, 1315 Moffitt Hospital, University of California, San Francisco, CA 94122.

EARLL, FRED.NELSON, b. Berkeley, Calif, Mar. 5, 24; m. 46; c. 3. GEOLOGY. B.S, Southern California, 54; Ph.D.(geol), Utah, 57. Geologist, West. Consult. Serv, Utah, 54-57; asst. prof. GEOL, MONT. COL. MINERAL SCI. & TECHNOL, 57-58, assoc. prof, 58-64, HEAD DEPT, 58-, PROF, 64- U.S.A.A.F, 42-46. Geol. Soc. Am; Am. Inst. Prof. Geol; Soc. Econ. Geol. Base and precious metal mining districts; geochemical prospecting; ore mineralogy. Address: Dept. of Geology, Montana College of Mineral Science & Technology, Butte, MT 59701.

EARLOUGHER, ROBERT CHARLES, JR, b. Tulsa, Okla, June 26, 41; m. 70. PETROLEUM ENGINEERING. B.S, Stanford, 63, Nat. Sci. Found. fel, 63-66, M.S, 64, Ph.D.(petrol. eng), 66. Res. engr, MARATHON OIL CO, 66-69, ADV. RES. ENGR, 69- Am. Soc. Petrol. Eng; Sci. Res. Soc. Am. Thermal and miscible water flooding methods of petroleum recovery; reservoir engineering; transient testing methods; hazards associated with transporting liquefied natural gas by ship. Address: Marathon Oil Co, Box 269, Littleton, CO 80122.

EARLS, LESTER T(HOMAS), b. Solon, Ohio, Nov. 14, 06; m. 34; c. 2. PHYSICS. A.B, Wisconsin, 27, M.S, 29, Ph.D.(physics), Michigan, 34. Asst. physics, Wisconsin, 27-29, instr. physics & math, exten. center, Milwaukee, 29-33; prof, Col. Ozarks, 34-36; assoc. prof. PHYSICS, Centenary Col, 36-38; IOWA STATE UNIV, 38-51, PROF, 51- Am. Phys. Soc; Am. Asn. Physics Teachers; Optical Soc. Am. Spectroscopy; spectrochemical analysis; underwater acoustics. Address: Dept. of Physics, Iowa State University, Ames, IA 50010.

EARLY, JACK D(ENT), b. Florence, S.C, Feb. 28, 29; m. 54; c. 2. ENTOMOLOGY. B.S, Clemson Col, 53, M.S, 54; Ph.D.(entomol), N.C. State Col, 58. Asst. entomol, Clemson Col, 53-54; N.C. State Col, 54-57; res. entomologist, MONSANTO CO, 58-61, sr. res. chemist, 61-64, TECH. REP, WASHINGTON, D.C, 64- U.S.A, 57-58, 2nd Lt. Entom. Soc. Am. Insecticidal structure and activity correlation; insect toxicology; organic insecticide. Address: Monsanto Co, 1101 17th St. N.W, Washington, DC 20036.

EARLY, JAMES G(ARLAND), b. Wash, D.C, Nov. 8, 37; m. 61; c. 2. METALLURGY. B.S, Lehigh Univ, 59; Ph.D.(metall), Rensselaer Polytech. Inst, 63. METALLURGIST, NAT. BUR. STANDARDS, 63- Am. Soc. Metals; Am. Inst. Min, Metall. & Petrol. Eng; Brit. Inst. Metals. Kinetics of melting-freezing process in metals; characterization of perfect metal crystals and origin of defects in metal crystals; sintering of pure metals. Address: Metallu gy Division, National Bureau of Standards, Washington, DC 20234.

EARLY, JAMES M, b. Syracuse, N.Y, July 25, 22; m. 48; c. 8. PHYSICS. B.Sc, N.Y. State Col. Forestry, Syracuse, 43; M.Sc, Ohio State, 48, Ph.D. (elec. eng), 51. Instr. & res. assoc. elec. eng, Ohio State, 46-51; mem. tech. staff, Bell Tel. Labs, 51-56, dept. head, 56-62, dir, 62-69; V.PRES. & DIR. RES, FAIRCHILD CAMERA & INSTRUMENT CORP, 69- C.Eng, U.S.A, 43-45. AAAS; Am. Phys. Soc; Inst. Elec. & Electronics Eng. Anisotropic dielectric waveguides; junction transistor physics; semiconductor physics technology and engineering. Address: Fairchild Camera & Instrument Corp, 4001 Miranda Ave, Palo Alto, CA 94304.

EARLY, JOSEPH E, b. Williamsburg, Ky, Jan. 14, 40; m. 63; c. 1. MATHEMATICS & EDUCATION. B.S, Cumberland Col.(Ky), 63; Nat. Sci. Found. fel, Univ. Tenn, Knoxville, 65, M.Math, 66, Nat. Defense Educ. Act fel, 66-69, Ed.D.(math. educ), 69. Teacher, elem. sch, Ohio, 59-60; high sch, Ky, 63-65; PROF. MATH. & CHMN. DEPT, CUMBERLAND COL.(KY), 69- Math. Asn. Am. Grade level teaching preferences of prospective elementary teachers with respect to their attitudes toward arithmetic and achievements in mathematics. Address: Dept. of Mathematics, Cumberland College, Williamsburg, KY 40769.

EARNEST, CHARLES MANSFIELD, b. Goodsprings, Ala, June 7, 41. ANALYTICAL CHEMISTRY. B.S, Univ. Ala, Tuscaloosa, 64, Nat. Sci. Found. grant, 67-69, Ph.D.(chem), 70. LECTR. CHEM, STILLMAN COL, 69- Am. Chem. Soc. Chromatographic separations; thermodynamics of separations; thermal methods of analysis. Address: Dept. of Chemistry, Stillman College, Tuscaloosa, AL 35401.

EARNEST, SUE W, b. Grand Forks, N.Dak, Sept. 19, 07; m. 28; c. 3. SPEECH PATHOLOGY. B.A, San Diego State Col, 29; M.A, Southern California, 37, Ph.D, 47. Instr. eng, Louisville, 45-46; asst. prof, SAN DIEGO STATE COL, 47-48, assoc. prof. speech, 48-54, PROF. SPEECH PATH. & AUDIOL, 54-, chmn. dept, 54-61. Mem. west. regional ed. comn, United Cerebral Asns, 63-66. Fel. Am. Speech & Hearing Asn; Int. Soc. Rehab. Disabled. Aphasia; cerebral palsy; geriatrics and speech. Address: Dept. of Speech Pathology & Audiology, San Diego State College, San Diego, CA 92115.

EARNSHAW, JOHN W, b. Toronto, Ont, July 22, 39; m. 65. ELECTRON PHYSICS. B.A.Sc, Toronto, 61; Ph.D.(electron physics), Cambridge, 65. Asst. sci. res. off. electron physics, Nat. Res. Coun. Can, 65-67; asst. prof. PHYSICS, TRENT UNIV, 67-70, ASSOC. PROF, 70- Am. Vacuum Soc. Ultra high vacuum electron optics. Address: Dept. of Physics, Trent University, Peterborough, Ont, Can.

EARP, UNUS F(ULLER), b. Halifax Co, Va, Jan. 25, 15; m. 46; c. 2. AGRICULTURAL ENGINEERING. B.S, Va. Polytech, 39, M.S, 50. Instr. agr. eng, Va. Polytech, 39-42; engr, Aircraft Radio Labs, Wright Field, 42-45; from instr. to assoc. prof. AGR. ENG, VA. POLYTECH. INST. & STATE UNIV, 45-56, PROF, 56- Am. Soc. Agr. Eng; Am. Soc. Eng. Educ. Rural electrification; processing agricultural products; farm refrigeration; ultraviolet radiation; ultrasonic energy. Address: Dept.of Agricultural Engineering, Seitz Hall, Virginia Polytechnic Institute & State University, Blacksburg, VA 24061.

EARSHEN, JOHN J(AMES), b. Ladgene, Bulgaria, Jan. 27, 28; U.S. citizen; m. 54; c. 3. ACOUSTICS, ELECTRONIC ENGINEERING. S.B, Mass. Inst. Tech, 51; M.S, Buffalo, 59. Jr. engr, Cornell Aeronaut. Lab, 51-52, asst. engr, 52-54, assoc. engr, 54-57; tech. asst, systs. div, Bendix Corp, 57-59, head acoustics sect, 59-61; tech. asst, electronics div, CORNELL AERONAUT. LAB, 61-64, HEAD, APPL. SCI. BR, PHYSICS DIV, 64- Lectr, undergrad. div, State Univ. N.Y. Buffalo, 52-57, grad. sch. eng, 64-, consult, med. sch, 54-57. Indust. acoustics consult, 64- Mem, antisubmarine warfare adv. cmt, Nat. Security Indust. Asn, 59-; panel ocean wide surv, Nat. Acad. Sci, June 62. Acoust. Soc. Am; Inst. Elec. & Electronics Eng; Audio Eng. Soc. Undersea warfare; biomedical instrumentation; system engineering; oceanographic instrumentation; analog simulation; man-machine systems. Address: Cornell Aeronautical Lab, 4455 Genesee St, Buffalo, NY 14221.

EASH, JOHN T(RIMBLE), b. Albany, Ind, Sept. 1, 06; m. 27; c. 2. METALLURGY. B.S, Purdue, 28; M.S, Michigan, 29, Ph.D.(metall), 32. Asst, Michigan, 29-31; res. metallurgist, RES. LAB, INT. NICKEL CO, 31-35, sect. supvr, 35-50, metall. supvr, 50-54, asst. mgr, 54-62, mgr, 62-70, MGR. RES, 70- Am. Inst. Mining, Metall. & Petrol. Eng; Am. Soc. Metals; Am. Foundrymen's Soc; Brit. Inst. Metals. Copper-nickel-tin alloys constitution and properties; platinum and palladium dental alloys; nickel alloys; cast iron melting; high strength low alloy steels; elevated temperature alloys; maraging steels. Address: Paul D. Merica Research Lab, Internickel Co, Sterling Forest, Suffern, NY 10901.

EASLEY, ELIZA (LILA) WALLER, b. Martinsville, Va, Mar. 26, 28. BIOCHEMISTRY. B.S, Longwood Col, 50; M.S, Florida, 57; Ph.D.(biol), N.Y. Univ, 67. Technician biochem, Va. Polytech, 52-55; Boyce Thompson Inst, 59-61; biochemist, Rockland State Res. Facility, 62-63; bacteriologist, Mt. Morris Tuberc. Hosp, 64-65; res. asst. biochem, Worchester Found, 65-66; Woods Hole Marine Biol. Lab, 66-67; res. assoc. cell physiol, Rockefeller Univ, 67-70; ASST. PROF. BIOL, ST. PAUL'S COL.(VA), 70- Fel. Am. Inst. Chem; Am. Chem. Soc; Harvey Soc; N.Y. Acad. Sci. Cellular metabolism. Address: Dept. of Natural Science, St. Paul's College, Lawrenceville, VA 23868.

EASLEY, J(AMES) W, b. Los Angeles, Calif, Nov. 17, 22; m. 46; c. 2. PHYSICS. B.A, California, Berkeley, 50, Ph.D.(physics), 55. Mem. tech. staff, Bell Tel. Labs, 54-60, mgr. radiation effects dept, Sandia Lab, 60-62, dir. radiation physics res. orgn, 62-64, DIR. mil. digital systs. lab, BELL TEL. LABS, 64-70, DIR. OCEAN SYSTS. DESIGN CTR, 70- Consult, Off. Dir. of Defense Res. & Eng, 66- U.S.A, 42-48, Maj. Sr. mem. Inst. Elec. & Electronics Eng; Am. Phys. Soc. High Energy nucleon-nucleon scattering; semiconductor device physics; radiation damage in semiconductors; ocean acoustics; information processing. Address: Ocean Systems Design Center, Bell Labs, Whippany, NJ 07981.

EASLEY, JOHN T, b. Cass Co, Mo, Jan. 20, 33; m. 53; c. 6. ENGINEERING MECHANICS. B.S, Kansas, 59, M.S, 61, Ph.D.(eng. mech), 64. ASST. PROF. ENG. MECH, UNIV. KANS, 64- Consult, Butler Mfg. Co, Mo, 64- U.S.A, 53-56. Stress and stability analysis of orthotropic plates and shells; mechanics of granular solid media. Address: Dept. of Mechanics & Aerospace Engineering, University of Kansas, Lawrence, KS 66045.

EASLEY, RONALD L, b. Fulton Co, Ill, Dec. 31, 34; m. 57; c. 3. PHYSICS. B.S, Illinois, 56; M.S, Mass. Inst. Tech, 60; Ph.D.(physics), Alabama, 63. Physicist missile develop, U.S. Army Missile Command, 58-63; sr. res. weapon systs. anal. & asst. dir, Stanford Res. Inst, 63-65; asst. dir. strategic systs. rev. & anal, off. dir. defense res. & eng, Dept. Defense, 65-70; PRES, SYST. PLANNING CORP, 70- Ord.C, U.S.A, 56-58, 1st Lt. Microwave diagnostics of electron plasmas; analysis of military weapon systems. Address: 7916 Fenway Rd, Bethesda, MD 20034.

EASLEY, WARREN C, b. Monterey Park, Calif, June 18, 41; m. 67; c. 1. PHYSICAL CHEMISTRY. B.A, Univ. Calif, Riverside, 63; Ph.D.(chem), Univ. Calif, Berkeley, 67. Fel. chem, Univ. Fla, 67-69; RES. CHEMIST, EXP. STA, E.I. DU PONT DE NEMOURS & CO, INC, 69- AAAS; Am. Chem. Soc. Electron spin resonance of matrix isolated molecules; bonding in ground and excited states of small, reactive molecules; solid state chemistry; matrix-molecule interactions. Address: 1401 Delaware Ave, Wilmington, DE 19806.

EASLEY, WILLIAM KENNETH, b. Morristown, Tenn, July 19, 21; m. 44; c. 4. CHEMISTRY. B.S, Carson-Newman Col, 44; M.S, Richmond, 47; Ph.D.(chem), Georgetown, 51. Chemist, Tenn. Eastman Corp, Oak Ridge, 46; instr. chem, Arkansas, 47-48; asst. prof. org. chem, Carson-Newman Col, 48-49; res. chemist, Chemstrand Corp, 51-55; prof. chem, Arkansas State Teachers Col, 55-57; East Tennessee State Col, 57-59; prof, Northeast La. State Col, 59-69, chmn. dept, 59-66, dean grad. sch, 66-69; DEAN COL. ARTS & SCI, WINTHROP COL, 69- U.S.N, 44-46. Am. Chem. Soc. Esters of plant growth hormones; quaternary salts of heterocyclic nitrogen compounds; synthesis of monomers and catalysts for condensation polymers. Address: College of Arts & Science, Winthrop College, Rock Hill, SC 29730.

EASON, ROBERT G(ASTON), b. Bells, Tenn, May 15, 24; m. 50; c. 2. PHYSIOLOGICAL PSYCHOLOGY. B.A, Univ. Mo, 50, M.A, 52, Ph.D.(psychol), 56. Res. assoc. electrophysiol, Univ. Calif, Los Angeles, 56-57; res. psychologist, U.S. Navy Electronics Lab, 57-60; asst. prof. PSYCHOL, San Diego State Col, 60-63, assoc. prof, 63-66, prof, 66-67; PROF. & HEAD DEPT, UNIV. N.C, GREENSBORO, 67- AAAS; Am. Psychol. Asn; Psychonomic. Soc; Soc. Psychophysiol. Res; Soc. Neurosci. Electrophysiological correlates of arousal, motivation, emotion, attention and perception. Address: Dept. of Psychology, University of North Carolina, Greensboro, NC 27412.

EASON, WALTER E(DWARD), JR, b. Ridley Park, Pa, May 29, 20; m. 44; c. 2. CHEMICAL ENGINEERING. B.S, Drexel Inst, 43; M.S, Hopkins, 56. Proj. engr, Barrett Div, Allied Chem. & Dye Corp, 46-51; chem. engr, Davison Chem. Co, 51-52, develop. engr, 52-57; mgr. res. eval, res. div, W.R. GRACE & CO, 57-63, asst. to pres, 63-64, dir. cent. serv, 64-68, dir. develop, 68-70, DIR. ADMIN, 70- Chem.C, 43-46, Capt. Am. Inst. Chem. Eng; Commercial Develop. Asn. Process and product development; economic evaluations. Address: Research Division, Washington Research Center, W.R. Grace & Co, Clarksville, MD 21029.

EAST, CONRAD, S.J, b. Quebec, Que, Can, Feb. 12, 23. METEOROLOGY, ATMOSPHERIC PHYSICS. B.A, Montreal, 48; L.Phil, Col. Immaculate Conception, 49, L.Th, 58; B.Appl.Sc, Laval, 53; M.A, Toronto, 59; Ph.D. (meteorol), McGill, 64. Lectr. physics, Jesuit Col, Que, 51-53; ASST. DIR. GEOPHYS. OBSERV. & LECTR. METEOROL, JEAN-DE-BREBEUF COL, 64-; ASST. DIR, ECOL. RES. CTR. MONTREAL, 71- Lectr, sch. hyg, Univ. Montreal, 66-67, asst. prof, sch. pub. health, 67-70, assoc. prof, 70-71. Can. Meteorol. Soc; French-Can. Asn. Advan. Sci; Am. Meteorol. Soc; Am. Geophys. Union; Air Pollution Control Asn; Royal Meteorol. Soc. Atmospheric electricity; solar radiation; air pollution. Address: Ecological Research Center of Montreal, 4101 Sherbrooke St. E, Montreal 406, Que, Can.

EAST, DOUGLAS A(LFRED), b. Newark, N.J, Oct. 26, 32; m. 55; c. 2. FLUID DYNAMICS. A.B, Middlebury Col, 55; S.B, Mass. Inst. Tech, 55, S.M, 57, Mech.E, 59, Ph.D.(fluid dynamics), 64. Instr, Mass. Inst. Tech, 56-61, admin. asst. to pres, 61-63; sr. proj. engr, Joseph Kaye & Co, Inc, 64-65, dir. res, 65-67; mgr. fluid & thermal eng. dept, Dynatech Corp, 68-70; DIR. MAINTENANCE & REPAIRS DIV, RILEY STOKER CORP, 70- Am. Soc. Mech. Eng. Address: Riley Stoker Corp, 9 Neponset St, Worcester, MA 01606.

EAST, JAMES LINDSAY, b. Senatobia, Miss, Nov. 5, 36; m. 63; c. 1. VIROLOGY. B.S, Memphis State Univ, 63, M.S, 67; Ph.D.(microbiol), Univ. Tenn, 70. Spec. technologist virol, St. Jude Childrens Res. Hosp, 63-67, U.S. Pub. Health Serv. trainee, 67-70; proj. investr, UNIV. TEX. M.D. ANDERSON HOSP. & TUMOR INST, 70-71, ASST. VIROLOGIST, 71- U.S.A, 58-60. Am. Soc. Microbiol; Am. Asn. Cancer Res. Replication of paramyxoviruses and tumor viruses. Address: Dept. of Virology, University of Texas M.D. Anderson Hospital and Tumor Institute, Houston, TX 77025.

EAST, LARRY VERNE, b. Apr. 16, 37; U.S. citizen; m. 59; c. 1. PHYSICS. B.S, Wichita, 58, M.S, 60; Ph.D.(physics), Case Inst. Tech, 65. Part-time instr, Case Inst. Tech, 62-65; STAFF MEM. PHYSICS, LOS ALAMOS SCI. LAB, UNIV. CALIF, 67- U.S.A, 65-67, Res, 67-68, Capt. Am. Asn. Phys. Teachers; Am. Phys. Soc. Gamma-ray and x-ray spectroscopy; fission neutrons; nuclear physics instrumentation. Address: Los Alamos Scientific Lab, Los Alamos, NM 87544.

EAST, T(HOMAS) W(ILLIAM) R(USSELL), b. Swansea, Wales, Apr. 21, 22; m. 44; c. 2. PHYSICS. B.A, Cambridge, 43; Ph.D.(physics), McGill, 55. Exp. officer radar, Telecommun. Res. Estab, 42-51; asst. cloud physics, McGill, 51-57, asst. prof. physics, 57-58; head electronics sect, RAYTHEON CAN, LTD, 58-66, DIR. ADVAN. DEVELOP, 68- Darton prize, 58. Inst. Elec. & Electronics Eng; Can. Asn. Physicists; Royal Meteorol. Soc. Electronic circuit design; weather radar. Address: Raytheon Can, Ltd, 400 Phillip St, Waterloo, Ont, Can.

EASTBURN, FRANCIS J(OSEPH), b. Wilmington, Del, July 9, 38; m. 60. CHEMICAL ENGINEERING. B.Ch.E, Delaware, 60; Texaco fel, Stevens Inst. Tech, 60-64, M.S, 63, D.Sc,(chem. eng), 66. Sr. res. engr, cent. res. labs, Gen. Mills, Inc, 65-67; asst. prof. CHEM. ENG, UNIV. LOUISVILLE, 67-71, ASSOC. PROF, 71- Am. Inst. Chem. Eng. Reaction kinetics; exploratory food processing; educational techniques. Address: Dept. of Chemical Engineering, University of Louisville, Louisville, KY 40208.

EASTER, DONALD P(HILIPS), b. Washington, D.C, Aug. 10, 19; m. 50; c. 4. PHYSICAL CHEMISTRY. B.S, Maryland, 42. Anal. chemist, U.S. Dept. Agr, 42; res. chemist org. chem. res, Celanese Corp. Am, 42-45; phys. chem. res. & mass spectrom, appl. physics lab, Hopkins, 45-52; sr. scientist gen. res. lab, Olin Indust, Inc, 52-56, prin. proj. chemist, basic res. group, U.S. Army Eng. Res. & Develop. Labs, Va, 56-59, chief mass spectrometry segment, 59-62; PROG. SCIENTIST, OFF. LUNAR & PLANETARY PROGS, NASA, 62- Fel. AAAS; Sci. Res. Soc. Am; Am. Chem. Soc. Synthetic organic chemistry; physical chemistry;of fuels for jet propulsion; mass spectrometry; extraterrestrial planetary atmospheres; instrumentation for unmanned landings on the moon and planets. Address: 1405 N. Cleveland St, Arlington, VA 22201.

EASTER, STEPHEN SHERMAN, (JR), b. New Orleans, La, Feb. 12, 38; m. 63; c. 2. PHYSIOLOGY, BIOPHYSICS. B.S, Yale, 60; Harvard Med. Sch, 60-61; Ph.D.(biophys), Johns Hopkins Univ, 67. U.S. Pub. Health Serv. fel. physiol, Cambridge, 67-68; Miller Inst. Basic Res, Univ. Calif, Berkeley, 68-69; Wilmer Ophthal. Inst, Johns Hopkins Univ, 69; ASST. PROF. ZOOL, UNIV. MICH, ANN ARBOR, 70- Asn. Res. Vision & Ophthal. Physiology of vision and eye movements, particularly in fish. Address: Dept. Zoology, University of Michigan, Ann Arbor, MI 48104.

EASTERBROOK, DON J, b. Sumas, Wash, Jan. 29, 35; m. 57. GEOLOGY. B.S, Washington (Seattle), 58, M.S, 59, Nat. Sci. Found. grant, 61-63, Ph.D. (geol), 62. Instr. GEOL, WEST. WASH. STATE COL, 59-62, asst. prof, 62-65, assoc. prof, 65-66, PROF, 66-, CHMN. DEPT, 65- Nat. Sci. Found. res. grant, 64-66. AAAS; Geol. Soc. Am; Am. Asn. Quarternary Environ; Int. Asn. Quarternary Res. Glacial geology; geomorphology; sedimentation; environmental geology. Address: Dept. of Geology, Western Washington State College, Bellingham, WA 98225.

EASTERBROOK, ELIOT KNIGHTS, b. Dudley, Mass, Oct. 28, 27; m. 57; c. 2. POLYMER & ORGANIC CHEMISTRY. B.S, New Hampshire, 48, M.S, 50; Ph.D.(phys. org. chem), Ohio State, 53. Sr. res. chemist, CHEM. DIV, U.S. Rubber Co, 52-62, group leader stereo polymer res, 62-67, RES. SCIENTIST, UNIROYAL INC, 67- Am. Chem. Soc. Polymerization of butadiene and acrylonitrile; nonaqueous polymerization of ethylene and propylene elastomers. Address: Chemical Division, UniRoyal Inc, Naugatuck, CT 06770.

EASTERBROOK, KENNETH BRIAN, b. Ilford, Eng, June 4, 35; m. 56; c. 3. VIROLOGY. B.Sc, Bristol, 56; Ph.D.(virol), Australian Nat. Univ, 62. Lectr. virol, Western Australia, 61-63; res. fel, Australian Nat. Univ, 63-65; U.S. Pub. Health Serv. int. res. fel. electron micros, Calif. Inst. Tech, 65-66; res. fel, Ont. Cancer Inst, 66-67; ASSOC. PROF. VIROL, DALHOUSIE UNIV, 67- Electron Micros. Soc. Am; Can. Soc. Cell Biol. Ultrastructure of viruses; morphology of virus cell interaction; electron microscopy. Address: Dept. of Microbiology, Dalhousie University, Halifax, N.S, Can.

EASTERDAY, B(ERNARD) C(ARLYLE), b. Hillsdale, Mich, Sept. 16, 29; m. 52; c. 1. VETERINARY SCIENCE, COMPARATIVE MEDICINE. D.V.M, Mich. State Univ, 52; M.S, Univ. Wis, 58, Ph.D.(vet. microbiol, path), 61. Gen. practice, Mich, 52; veterinarian, Ft. Detrick, Md, 55-56, 58-61; asst, UNIV. WIS, MADISON, 56-58, assoc. prof. VET. SCI, 61-66, PROF, 66-, CHMN. DEPT, 68- Mem. expert panel on zoonoses, WHO; res. resources comt. & subcomt. Influenza, Nat. Insts. Health. Am. Col. Vet. Microbiol. Vet.C, U.S.A, 53-54, 1st Lt. Am. Vet. Med. Asn; Conf. Res. Workers Animal Diseases. Infectious diseases, viral; pathogenesis; influenza; epidemiology. Address: Dept. of Veterinary Science, University of Wisconsin, Madison, WI 53706.

EASTERDAY, HARRY T(YSON), b. Sault Ste. Marie, Mich, Oct. 6, 22; m. 47; c. 2. NUCLEAR PHYSICS. A.B, California, 47; Ph.D, 53. Physicist, radiation lab, California, 53-55; asst. prof. PHYSICS, Oregon, 55-60; assoc. prof, ORE. STATE UNIV, 60-67, PROF, 67- Mem. staff, Lawrence Radiation Lab, Berkeley, 63-64. Ord. Dept, U.S.A, 42-46. Am. Phys. Soc. Low energy experimental nuclear physics. Address: Dept. of Physics, Oregon State University, Corvallis, OR 97331.

EASTERDAY, JACK L(EROY), b. Crestline, Ohio, Mar. 24, 28. ELECTRICAL ENGINEERING. B.S, Toledo, 52. Assoc. engr, Sperry Rand Corp, 52-55; elec. engr, reliability eng. div, BATTELLE MEM. INST, 57-60, proj. leader, 60-62, sr. engr, 62-64, asst. dir. adv. electronics group, 64, ASSOC. CHIEF ADV. ELECTRONICS DIV, 65- Sig.C, U.S.A, 55-57. Inst. Elec. & Electronics Eng. Reliability engineering; reliability, maintainability, safety, electronic packaging and semiconductor applications, including design reviews, computerized circuit analyses, construction-packaging studies and parts evaluations. Address: Physics & Metallurgy Dept, Battelle Memorial Institute, 505 King Ave, Columbus, OH 43201.

EASTERDAY, KENNETH E, b. Kirksville, Ind, June 27, 33; m. 59; c. 1. MATHEMATICS. B.S, Indiana, 55, Lilly fel, 58, M.A, 60; Gen. Elec. Co. fel, Purdue, 59; Ed.D, Western Reserve, 63. Teacher, pub. sch, Ohio, 57, 59-63; Ind, 57-59; assoc. prof. math, State Univ. N.Y, 63-64; asst. prof. MATH. IN SEC. EDUC, AUBURN UNIV, 64-70, ASSOC. PROF, 70- Med.C, U.S.A, 55-57. Construction of mathematics programs in grades seven through twelve; methods of teaching mathematics at all levels; modern algebra. Address: Dept. of Mathematics Education, 5064 Haley Center, Auburn University, Auburn, AL 36830.

EASTERDAY, OTHO D(UNREATH), b. Allen Co, Ind, Oct. 3, 24; m. 49; c. 4. PHARMACOLOGY, RADIATION BIOLOGY. B.A, Ball State, 48; M.S, Iowa, 50, U.S. Pub. Health Serv. fel, 51-53, Ph.D.(pharmacol), 53. Res. asst. pharmacol, Iowa, 48-51; assoc. pharmacologist, Brookhaven Nat. Lab, 53-62; pharmacologist & radiobiologist, Hazleton Labs, Inc, 62-66; dir. dept. pharmacol. & radiation, Gulf S. Res. Inst, La, 66-68; HEAD, TOXICOL. & PHARMACOL. RES, RES. & DEVELOP. CTR, INT. FLAVORS & FRAGRANCES, INC, 68- U.S.N, 43-46, Ens. Fel. AAAS; fel. N.Y. Acad. Sci; Am. Soc. Pharmacol. & Exp. Therapeut; Soc. Toxicol; Biomet. Soc; Am. Asn. Lab. Animal Sci; Coblentz Soc; Radiation Res. Soc; Soc. Nuclear Med; Am. Nuclear Soc; Pan-Am. Med. Asn. Chemical structure and activity; pharmacodynamics; toxicology; biometry; radiation; radioactive tracers; spectroscopy; chemical synthesis; boron and lithium pharmacology and toxicology; natural products; radio respirometry and pharmacology. Address: Research & Development Center, International Flavors & Fragrances, Inc, 1515 Hwy. 36, Union Beach, NJ 07760.

EASTERLING, G(EORGE) R(ILEY), b. Guernsey Co, Ohio, Oct. 15, 05; m. 39; c. 3. ZOOLOGY. A.B, Ohio Univ, 27, M.A, 33; M.S, Case West. Reserve Univ, 65. Teacher, rural sch, Ohio, 24-26, high sch, 27-40; teaching fel. BIOL, Ohio Univ, 31-33; from asst. prof. to assoc. prof, KENT STATE UNIV, 47-67, EMER. PROF, 67- U.S.A, 35-36, 42-47, 50-52, Maj.(Ret). Human heredity. Address: 223 Highland Ave, Kent, OH 44240.

EASTERLING, RONALD E, b. Benton Harbor, Mich, Apr. 14, 32; m. 54; c. 5. INTERNAL MEDICINE, NEPHROLOGY. M.D, Univ. Mich, Ann Arbor, 57. Instr. internal med, Univ. Mich, Ann Arbor, 66-67, asst. prof, 67-68; chief hemodialysis unit, Vet. Admin. Hosp, Ann Arbor, Mich, 68-70; ASSOC. PROF. INTERNAL MED, UNIV. MICH, ANN ARBOR, 70- Mem. sci. adv. bd, Kidney Found. Mich, 67- U.S.A, 56-66, Maj. Fel. Am. Col. Physicians; Am. Soc. Artificial Internal Organs; Am. Fedn. Clin. Res; Am. Soc. Nephrology; Asn. Advan. Med. Instrumentation. Treatment of renal failure by dialysis methods; in vivo evaluation of hemodialyzers; estimation of the natural history of renal diseases through a longitudinal regional data bank. Address: 907B Terrace Bldg. 9, University of Michigan Medical Center, Ann Arbor, MI 48104.

EASTERLING, WILLIAM EWART, JR, b. Raleigh, N.C, Oct. 8, 30. OBSTETRICS, GYNECOLOGY. Angier P. Duke scholar. & A.B, Duke, 52; Fordham award & M.D, North Carolina, 56. Intern med, N.C. Mem. Hosp, 56-57, res. obstet. & gynec, 57-61, instr, 60-61; fel. reprod. physiol, California, 63-64; asst. prof. OBSTET. & GYNEC, UNIV. N.C. MEM. HOSP, 64-67, ASSOC. PROF, 67- Fordham Award, 61. Chief obstet. & gynec, 839th Tactical Air Command Hosp, Stewart AFB, Tenn, Med.C, U.S.A.F, Capt. AAAS; Am. Med. Asn; Am. Col. Obstet. & Gynec; Endocrine Soc; Soc. Gynec. Invest. Endocrinology of obstetrics and gynecology. Address: Dept. of Obstetrics & Gynecology, University of North Carolina School of Medicine, Chapel Hill, N.C. 27514.

EASTERLY, W(ILLIAM) D(ELMON), JR, b. Sheridan, Ark, May 16, 26; m. 53; c. 2. PHARMACY. B.S.Ph, Georgia, 50, M.S, 52; Am. Found. Pharmaceut. Ed. fel, 52-54; Ph.D, Florida, 54. Instr. pharmaceut. chem, Georgia, 50-51; asst. prof. pharm, Mississippi, 54; SCH. PHARM, UNIV. ARK, LITTLE ROCK, 54-58, assoc. prof. PHARM. & PHARMACEUT. CHEM, 58-64, PROF, 64-, CHMN. DEPT. PHARMACEUT, 70- U.S.N.R, 44-46. Am. Pharmaceut. Asn; Acad. Pharmaceut. Sci; Am. Chem. Soc. Amides of dichloroacetaldehyde; permeability of red corpuscles to urea derivatives and immunological diseases. Address: School of Pharmacy, University of Arkansas Medical Center, Little Rock, AR 72201.

EASTES, FRANK E(LISHA), b. Wilson Co, Tenn, July 31, 24; m. 53; c. 6. ORGANIC CHEMISTRY. B.S, Tenn. Polytech, 49; M.S, Vanderbilt, 51, Ph.D, 55. Staff scientist, E.I. du Pont de Nemours & Co, 53-62; sr. proj. leader, CRY-O-VAC DIV, W.R. GRACE & CO, 62-66, SECT. HEAD FILM COATINGS, 66- Am. Chem. Soc. Reactions of thiophthalic anhydride; resolutions of racemic amines; cellulose chemistry; film coating and adhesion. Address: 729 Otis Blvd, Spartanburg, SC 29302.

EASTES, JOHN W(ESLEY), b. Greenfield, Ind, Apr. 4, 10; m. 41; c. 2. CHEMISTRY. B.S, Butler, 31; M.A, Cincinnati, 33, fel, 33-36, Ph.D.(chem), 36. Res. chemist, Rohm & Haas Co. & Resinous Prod. & Chem. Co, 36-42; res. chemist, Calco Chem. Div, Am. Cyanamid Co, 45-53; proj. leader, chem. res. dept, Scott Paper Co, 53-56, res. assoc, 56-60; DIR. PULP & PAPER SECT, RES. & DEVELOP. DEPT, ECUSTA PAPER DIV, OLIN CORP, 60- C.W.S, 42-46, Capt. Am. Chem. Soc; Tech. Asn. Pulp & Paper Indust. Sanitary papers; specialty papers; long fiber papers; chlorination of carbonsulfur compounds; Friedel-Crafts reactions; ion-exchange resins; chemical warfare agents and chemical propellants; textile finishing agents; pigments; wet strength resins and chemicals for paper; pulp and paper making; fine papers; cigarette papers. Address: Research & Development Dept, Ecusta Paper Division, Olin Corp, Pisgah Forest, NC 28768.

EASTHAM, A(RTHUR) M(IDDLETON), b. Vancouver, B.C, Feb. 15, 17; m. 46; c. 3. ORGANIC CHEMISTRY. B.A, British Columbia, 37, M.A, 39; Ph.D. (chem), McGill, 42. RES. CHEMIST, Polymer Corp, 45-48; NAT. RES. COUN. CAN, 42-45, 48- Asst. ed, Can. Jour. Chem. Am. Chem. Soc; Chem. Inst. Can; The Chem. Soc. Physical organic chemistry; catalysis by Friedel-Crafts reagents. Address: 265 Crestview Rd, Ottawa KIH 5G4, Ont, Can.

EASTHAM, JAMES N(ORMAN), b. Cumberland, R.I, Dec. 10, 03; m. 40; c. 3. MATHEMATICS. B.S, Providence Col, 26; M.A, Catholic Univ, 28, Ph.D. (math), 31. Instr. math, Providence Col, 30-31; head dept. math. & physics, Nazareth Col.(N.Y), 31-46; asst. prof. MATH, Cooper Union, 46-51, assoc. prof, 51-60, PROF, 60-61; QUEENSBOROUGH COMMUNITY COL, 61-, DEAN OPEN ADMISSIONS SERV. & SUMMER SESSION, 71-, chmn. dept, 61-69; dean summer session, 66-71. Instr. Rochester, 40-42. Consult, Rheem Mfg. Co, 50-52. Math. Asn. Am; Am. Soc. Eng. Educ. Quartic curves; vibration theory. Address: Summer Session Office, Queensborough Community College, City University of New York, Bayside, NY 11364.

EASTHAM, JEROME F(IELDS), b. Daytona Beach, Fla, Sept. 22, 24; m. 49; c. 3. ORGANIC CHEMISTRY. B.S, Kentucky, 48; Ph.D.(chem), California, 51. Asst. California, 48-51; U.S. Atomic Energy Cmn. Fel, London Univ, 51-52, Wisconsin, 52-53; asst. prof. CHEM, UNIV. TENN, KNOXVILLE, 53-58, assoc. prof, 58-62, PROF, 62- U.S.A, 42-46. AAAS; Am. Chem. Soc; Brit. Chem. Soc. Chemistry of steroids and related natural products; mechanisms of organic reactions; organometallic chemistry. Address: Dept. of Chemistry, University of Tennessee, Knoxville, TN 37916.

EASTIN, EMORY FORD, b. Picayune, Miss, Nov. 27, 40; m. 61; c. 2. BOTANY. B.S, Miss. State, 62, M.S, 63; Ph.D.(bot, plant physiol), Auburn, 66. Asst. prof. weed sci, Miss. State, 66-67; AGRON, TEX. A&M UNIV, 67-71, ASSOC. PROF, 71- Am. Soc. Plant Physiol; Weed Sci. Soc. Am; Am. Soc. Agron; Crop Sci. Soc. Am. Mode of action of herbicides in plants and absorption, translocation and metabolism of herbicides by plants. Address: Dept. of Soil & Crop Science, Texas A&M University, College Station, TX 77843.

EASTIN, JERRY D(EAN), b. Madrid, Nebr, Jan. 18, 31; m. 57; c. 3. AGRONOMY. B.Sc, Nebraska, 53, M.Sc, 55; Ph.D.(crop physiol), Purdue, 60. Nat. Acad. Sci-Nat. Res. Coun. res. assoc, Army Biol. Labs, Ft. Detrick, Md, 60-61; asst. prof. agron, UNIV. NEBR, 61-64, res. plant physiologist, crops res. div, Agr. Res. Serv, U.S. Dept. Agr, 64-70, ASSOC. PROF. AGRON, 70- AAAS; Am. Soc. Agron; Crop Sci. Soc. Am; Am. Soc. Plant Physiol. Carbon dioxide fixation in Bacillus anthracis; characterization of wheat gluten proteins by chemical and physical methods; physiology of the grain sorghum plant. Address: 102 KCR, University of Nebraska, Lincoln, NE 68503.

EASTIN, JOHN A, b. Grant, Nebr, June 13, 34; m. 61. AGRONOMY, PLANT PHYSIOLOGY. B.S, Nebraska, 58; M.S, Purdue, 61, Ph.D.(crop physiol, biochem), 63. Res. asst. crop physiol, Purdue, 58-63; asst. prof. agron, Wisconsin, 63-68; RES. AGRONOMIST, DeKALB AGR. RES. INC, 68- U.S.A, 54-56. AAAS; Crop Sci. Soc. Am; Am. Soc. Agron; Am. Soc. Plant Physiol. Crop physiology and production. Address: DeKalb Agricultural Research Inc, Sycamore Rd, DeKalb, IL 60115.

EASTLAND, DAVID MEADE, b. Meridian, Miss, Nov. 27, 22; m. 44. THERMODYNAMICS, AIR CONDITIONING. B.S, Miss. State, 44, M.S, 50. Instr. MECH. ENG, MISS. STATE UNIV, 46-50, asst. prof, 50-53, assoc. prof, 53-58, PROF, 58- Am. Soc. Mech. Eng; Nat. Soc. Prof. Eng; Am. Soc. Eng. Educ. Thermodynamics; fluid flow; instruments. Address: Dept. of Mechanical Engineering, Drawer ME, Mississippi State University, State College, MS 39762.

EASTLAND, GEORGE WARREN, JR, b. Omaha, Nebr, Sept. 5, 39, m. 67; c. 1. INORGANIC & PHYSICAL CHEMISTRY. B.S, Wittenberg Univ, 61; Ph.D. (inorg. chem), S.Dak. State Univ, 69. Teacher, high sch, Ohio, 61-63; lab. asst. CHEM, Wittenberg Univ, 63-64; asst, S.Dak. State Univ, 64-69; ASST. PROF, SAGINAW VALLEY COL, 69- Am. Chem. Soc; The Chem. Soc. Preparation and investigation of properties of novel coordination compounds of transition metals, such as rhenium and rhodium. Address: Dept. of Chemistry, Saginaw Valley College, 2250 Pierce Rd, University Center, MI 48710.

EASTLER, THOMAS E(DWARD), b. Boston, Mass, Oct. 10, 44; m. 65; c. 1. ENVIRONMENTAL GEOLOGY. Sc.B, Brown Univ, 66; Geol. Soc. Am. Penrose Bequest grant, Columbia Univ, 67-69, M.A, 68, Nat. Sci. Found. fel, summer 68, Ph.D.(geol), 71. ASST. PROF. GEOPHYSICS, U.S. AIR FORCE INST. TECHNOL, 70- Vis. lectr, Univ. Dayton, 70-; prin. investr, Nat. Sci. Found. Res. Applicable to Nat. Needs Grant, 71- U.S.A.F, 70-, Capt. AAAS; Am. Geophys. Union; Geol. Soc. Am; Nat. Asn. Geol. Teachers; Soc. Econ. Paleont. & Mineral; Am. Soc. Photogram. Impact of engineering endeavours on the environment; utility of tools of remote sensing in total environmental studies—ecosystems analysis—and their limitation. Address: Dept. of Mechanics, U.S. Air Force Institute of Technology, Wright-Patterson Air Force Base, Dayton, OH 45433.

EASTLICK, HERBERT L(EONARD), b. Platteville, Wis, Apr. 24, 08; m. 35. ZOOLOGY. A.B, Montana, 30; M.S, Washington (St. Louis), 32, Ph.D.(zool), 36. Asst, Washington (St. Louis), 31-34, instr. zool, 34-35, asst, 35-36, instr, univ. col, 35-36; Stephens Col, 36-37; Missouri, 37-39; Nat. Res. Coun. fel, Chicago, 39-40; asst. prof. ZOOL, WASH. STATE UNIV, 40-44, assoc. prof, 44-47, PROF, 47-, chmn. dept, 47-64. Phi Sigma scholar, Marine Biol. Lab, Woods Hole, 32, Collecting Net scholar, 33. AAAS; fel. Am. Soc. Nat; Soc. Develop. Biol; Am. Asn. Anat; Am. Soc. Zool; Am. Micros. Soc. Experimental embryology and carcinogenesis; cytology; histology; interspecies incompatibility; feather character and pathology in transplanted limbs; cytology of invertebrate and vertebrate muscle and adipose tissue; orgin of avian melanoblasts. Address: Dept. of Zoology, Washington State University, Pullman, WA 99163.

EASTLUND, BERNARD J, b. Salem, Ore, Aug. 7, 38; m. 64; c. 1. PHYSICS. B.S, Mass. Inst. Tech, 60, Ph.D.(physics), Columbia, 65. Res. fel. plasma physics, Columbia, 65-66; PHYSICIST, U.S. ATOMIC ENERGY COMN, 66- Consult, Bell Tel. Labs, N.J, 66. Am. Phys. Soc; Am. Astrophys. Soc. Basic plasma physics; controlled thermonuclear research. Address: 12312 Village Square Terr, Rockville, MD 20852.

EASTMAN, ARTHUR A(LLEN), b. Lawrence, Kans, Nov. 12, 07; m. 33; c. 1. ELECTRICAL ENGINEERING. B.S, Kansas, 30; E.E, 53. Lab. asst, LAMP DIV, GEN. ELEC. CO, 30-34, physicist, 34-57, res. specialist, 57-61, VISUAL RES. ENGR, 61- Lectr. Case, 50-56. Fel. Illum Eng. Soc. Light and vision; evaluation of flicker from light sources and measurement of visibility of visual tasks; chromatic contrast and evaluation of color rendering qualities of light sources; development of contrast threshold visibility meter. Address: 1939 Green Rd, Apt. 412, Cleveland, OH 44121.

EASTMAN, DANIEL (ROBERT) P(EDEN), b. Semans, Sask, Can, Jan. 23, 33; m. 55; c. 2. PHYSICS. B.S, Houghton Col, 55; M.S, Pa. State, 57, Ph.D. (physics), 61. Optical engr, Plummer & Kershaw, Pa, 61-62; asst. prof. PHYSICS, Houghton Col, 62-63, prof, 63-65; asst. prof, PA. STATE UNIV, 65-69, ASSOC. PROF, 69- Optical Soc. Am; Am. Asn. Physics Teachers. Vibration rotation spectra; high precision spectroscopy; brillouin spectroscopy. Address: S-6 Osmond Lab, Pennsylvania State University, University Park, PA 16802.

EASTMAN, FRED S(COVILLE), b. Seattle, Wash, Feb. 10, 04; m. 28; c. 2. AERONAUTICAL ENGINEERING. B.S, Washington (Seattle), 25; M.S, Mass. Inst. Tech, 29. Test engr, Gen. Elec. Co, N.Y, 25-26; asst, UNIV. WASH, 26-27, instr. gen. eng, 27-30, instr. AERONAUT. ENG, 30-34, asst. prof, 34-39, assoc. prof, 39-44, PROF, 44-, exec. off, 46-52. With U.S.N, 44. Assoc. fel. Inst. Aeronaut. Sci. Electromagnetic type wind tunnel balance; flexure pivots; cyclogiro type and miscellaneous other moving wing systems; use of special jet configurations for energizing and controlling lifting surfaces in ornithoid motion for purposes of high lift and thrust. Address: Dept. of Aeronautical Engineering, University of Washington, Seattle, WA 98105.

EASTMAN, JOHN W, b. Charleston, Ill, May 10, 35; m. 66; c. 1. PHYSICAL CHEMISTRY, SPECTROSCOPY. B.S, Pa. State, 57; Monsanto fel, California, Berkeley, 59, Ph.D.(chem), 61. Teaching asst. chem, California, Berkeley, 57-58; Nat. Sci. Found. fel, 61-62; res. asst. quantum chem, Uppsala, 62-63; chemist, Shell Develop. Co, 63-71; CHEMIST, MED. CTR, UNIV. CALIF, SAN FRANCISCO, 71- Alexander Von Humboldt res. fel. phys. chem, Mainz, 68-69. AAAS; Am. Chem. Soc; Am. Phys. Soc. Electronic structure of molecules; quantum chemistry; electron spin resonance; luminescence of molecules; photochemistry; clinical chemistry. Address: Dept. of Clinical Pathology & Lab. Medicine, University of California Medical Center, San Francisco, CA 94122.

EASTMAN, JOSEPH T(HORNTON), b. Minneapolis, Minn, Nov. 2, 44; m. 70. COMPARATIVE ANATOMY. B.A, Univ. Minn, Minneapolis, 66, M.S, 68, Nat. Sci. Found. trainee, 69-70, Ph.D.(zool), 70. Instr. ANAT. SCI, MED. CTR, UNIV. OKLA, 70-71, ASST. PROF, 71- AAAS; Am. Asn. Anat; Am. Inst. Biol. Sci; Am. Soc. Zool; Am. Soc. Ichthyol. & Herpet. Pharyngeal bones and teeth in cyprinoid fishes, especially morphology, inter- and intraspecific variation and taxonomic significance; fish anatomy. Address: Dept. of Anatomical Sciences, University of Oklahoma Medical Center, 800 N.E. 13th St, Oklahoma City, OK 73104.

EASTMAN, LESTER F(UESS), b. Utica, N.Y, May 21, 28; m. 48; c. 3. ELECTRICAL ENGINEERING. B.E.E, Cornell, 53, Sperry Gyroscope Co. fel. & M.S, 55, Gen. Elec. Co. fel. & Ph.D.(elec. eng), 57. Instr. ELEC. ENG, CORNELL UNIV, 54-56, asst. prof, 57-59, assoc. prof, 59-66, PROF, 66- Vis. assoc. prof. electronics, Chalmers Tech, Sweden, 60-61; vis. mem. tech. staff, RCA Res. Labs, Princeton, 64-65; co-founder & consult, Cayuga Assoc, 67-, pres, 70- Consult, Westinghouse Elec. Co, 55-64, Sylvania Elec. Co, 56, Cornell Aero Lab, 57-64, Int. Bus. Mach. Corp, 61-64; Raytheon Mfg. Co, 61-64. U.S.N, 46-48. Fel. Inst. Elec. & Electronics Eng. Physical electronics and semiconductor devices, especially in the microwave frequencies. Address: 316 Phillips Hall, Cornell University, Ithaca, NY 14850.

EASTMAN, MICHAEL PAUL, b. Lancaster, Wis, Apr. 14, 41; m. 63; c. 2. PHYSICAL CHEMISTRY. B.A, Carleton Col, 63; Ph.D.(phys. chem), Cornell Univ, 68. Fel, Los Alamos Sci. Lab, 68-70; ASST. PROF. CHEM, UNIV. TEX, EL PASO, 70- Am. Chem. Soc. Magnetic resonance. Address: Dept. of Chemistry, University of Texas at El Paso, El Paso, TX 79968.

EASTMAN, P(HILIP) C(LIFFORD), b. Port Hope, Ont, May 28, 32; m. 56; c. 2. SOLID STATE PHYSICS. B.Sc, McMaster, 55, M.Sc, 56; Ph.D.(physics), British Columbia, 60. NATO fel. & Rutherford Mem. Award, Bristol, 60-61; sr. sci. officer, Defence Res. Telecommun. Estab, Ottawa, 61-63; asst. prof. PHYSICS, UNIV. WATERLOO, 63-65, ASSOC. PROF, 65- Can. Asn. Physicists. Galvanomagnetic and optical properties of metals; semimetals, semiconductors and insulators in single crystal, polycrystal and thin film forms. Address: Dept. of Physics, University of Waterloo, Waterloo, Ont, Can.

EASTMAN, RICHARD H(ALLENBECK), b. Erie, Pa, Oct. 30, 18; m. 42; c. 3. ORGANIC CHEMISTRY. A.B, Princeton, 41; fel, Harvard, 42-44, A.M, 43, Thayer fel, & Ph.D.(org. chem), 44. Asst, Harvard, 44-46; instr. ORG. CHEM, STANFORD UNIV, 46-48, asst. prof, 48-51, assoc. prof, 51-58, PROF, 59- Nat. Sci. Found. fel, 58-59. Am. Chem. Soc. Chemistry of natural products; ultraviolet and infrared spectroscopy; organic photochemistry. Address: Dept. of Chemistry, Stanford University, Stanford, CA 94305.

EASTMAN, ROBERT M(ERRIAM), b. Dayton, Ohio, Apr. 17, 18; m; c. 3. INDUSTRIAL ENGINEERING. A.B, Antioch Col, 40; M.S, Ohio State, 48; Ph.D, Pa. State, 55. Asst. instr. eng. drawing, Ohio State, 47-48; instr. INDUST. ENG, Pa. State, 48-51; assoc. prof. & res. assoc, eng. exp. sta, Ga. Inst. Technol, 51-55; PROF, UNIV. MO-COLUMBIA, 55-, chmn. dept, 55-68. Fulbright lectr, Indust. Univ. Santander, 62-63; consult area redevelop. admin, U.S. Dept. Commerce, 62-65; U.S. Off. Educ, 68-69; vis. prof, Mid. East Tech. Univ, Ankara, 69-71; consult, Dept. Health, Educ. & Welfare, 71, mem. steering comt, Nat. Ctr. Health Serv. Res. & Develop, Health Serv. & Ment. Health Admin, 71- U.S.A.A.F, 42-46, Capt. Am. Inst. Indust. Eng; Am. Soc. Quality Control; Oper. Res. Soc. Am; Am. Soc. Eng. Educ; Soc. Int. Develop. Engineering economy; technical aid to Point Four countries; operations research; regional development and planning. Address: 600 S. Glenwood Ave, Columbia, MO 65201.

EASTMAN, WILLARD L, b. Watertown, N.Y, Apr. 5, 32; m. 60; c. 2. APPLIED MATHEMATICS. A.B, Cornell, 53; M.A, Harvard, 55, Ph.D. (econ), 59. Staff mem, comput. lab, Harvard, 55-62, instr. APPL. MATH, 60-62; RES. STAFF MEM, SPERRY RAND CORP, 62- Operations research; mathematical programming; coding theory; maximal length sequences; computational methods for best approximation; data base organization; information storage and retrieval. Address: Sperry Rand Research Center, Sudbury, MA 01776.

EASTMOND, E(LBERT) JOHN, b. San Francisco, Calif, July 6, 15; m. 37; c. 4. PHYSICS. A.B, Brigham Young, 37; Thompson Mem. scholar, California, 39-41, Ph.D.(physics), 43. Physicist, west. regional res. lab, Bur. Agr & Indust. Chem, U.S. Dept. Agr, 42-50; asst. prof. PHYSICS, BRIGHAM YOUNG UNIV, 51-53, assoc. prof, 53-57, PROF, 57- Tech. staff, Space Tech. Labs, Los Angeles, 58; Aerospace Corp, 63-64; Nat. Sci. Found. sci. faculty fel, Univ. Calif, Irvine, summers 71, 72. Am. Asn. Physics Teachers; Optical Soc. Am. Diatomic molecular spectroscopy; spectrochemical analysis; spectrophotometry and colorimetry; rotational analysis of a band system attributed to ionized nitric oxide. Address: Dept. of Physics, Brigham Young University, Provo, UT 84601.

EASTON, ARCHIE H(ARTER), b. Ottawa Co, Mich, Sept. 14, 13; m. 42; c. 2. MECHANICAL ENGINEERING. B.S, Michigan, 35, M.E, 55. Mech. engr, Andersen Sand & Gravel Co, Mich, 36-37; jr. engr, Nat. Bur. Standards, Wash, D.C, 37-41; proj. engr. automotive div, Aberdeen Proving Grounds, Md, 41-46; dir. truck res. proj, COL. ENG, UNIV. WIS, MADISON, 46-53, PROF. MECH. & CIVIL ENG, 53- Summers, sr. proj. engr, Gen. Motors Proving Ground, Mich, 59. Consult. Chmn. cmt. winter driving hazards, Nat. Safety Coun, 56- Soc. Automotive Eng; Nat. Soc. Prof. Eng; Am. Soc. Test. & Mat. Automotive testing and behavior; automobile accident reconstruction. Address: Dept. of Mechanical Engineering, University of Wisconsin, Madison, WI 53705.

EASTON, DEXTER M(ORGAN), b. Rockport, Mass, Sept. 13, 21; m. 53; c. 4. NEUROPHYSIOLOGY. B.A, Clark, 43; fel, Harvard, 43-47, M.A, 44, Ph.D. (biol), 47. Asst, Clark, 42-43; Harvard, 45; instr. zool, Washington (Seattle), 47-50, res. physiologist, med. sch, 52-55; asst. prof. physiol, FLA. STATE UNIV, 55-58, ASSOC. PROF. BIOL. SCI, 58- Fulbright scholar, Otago Med. Sch, New Zealand, 50-51. Fel. AAAS; Am. Soc. Zool; Soc. Gen. Physiol; Am. Physiol. Soc. Neuromuscular transmission; spinal cord physiology; microelectrode analysis of cell potentials and excitability; electrical activity of peripheral nerve. Address: Dept. of Biological Science, Florida State University, Tallahassee, FL 32306.

EASTON, ELMER C(HARLES), b. Newark, N.J, Dec. 23, 09. ELECTRICAL ENGINEERING. B.S, Lehigh, 31, fel, 31-33, M.S, 33, hon. D.Eng, 65; Sc.D. (elec. eng), Harvard, 42. Mem. faculty, Newark Col. Eng, 35-42; grad. sch. eng, Harvard, 42-48, asst. dean, 46-48; DEAN COL. ENG, RUTGERS UNIV, 48- AAAS; Am. Soc. Eng. Educ.(pres, 64-65); Nat. Soc. Prof. Eng; Inst. Elec. & Electronics Eng. Conduction of electricity through gases. Address: College of Engineering, Rutgers, The State University, New Brunswick, NJ 08903.

EASTON, GENE DOUGLAS, b. Rupert, Idaho, Apr. 1, 28; m. 55; c. 2. PLANT PATHOLOGY. B.S, Idaho, 52, M.S, 54; Ph.D.(plant path), Wisconsin, 57. Asst. prof. plant path, Maine, 59-63; asst. plant pathologist, WASH. STATE UNIV, 63-71, ASSOC. PLANT PATHOLOGIST, IRRIGATED AGR. RES. & EXTEN. CTR, 71- U.S.A.F, 57-59, Capt. Am. Phytopath. Soc; Potato Asn. Am. Plant virology; soil microbiology; general potato pathology; experimental soil fungicide investigations. Address: Irrigated Agriculture Research & Extension Center, Washington State University, Prosser, WA 99350.

EASTON, IVAN G(EORGE), b. Sweden, Nov. 20, 16; nat; m. 41; c. 4. ELECTRICAL ENGINEERING. B.S, Northeastern, 38; M.S, Harvard, 39. Instr. physics, Harvard, 39-40; mgr. ENG, GEN. RADIO CO, 40-64, v.pres, 64-68, SR. V.PRES, 68- Am. Soc. Test. & Mat; fel. Inst. Elec. & Electronics Eng. Electrical measurement and standards, particularly impedance measurement techniques and dielectric measurements. Address: General Radio Co, 300 Baker Ave, West Concord, MA 01742.

EASTON, NELSON R(OY), b. Craftsbury, Vt, Oct. 8, 19; m. 44; c. 3. ORGANIC CHEMISTRY. A.B, Middlebury Col, 41; Ph.D.(org. chem), Illinois, 46. Chemist, Merck & Co, N.J, 41-43; asst. org. chem, Illinois, 43-44, asst, 44-46; sr. chemist, J.T. Baker Chem. Co, N.J, 46-47; asst. prof. org. chem, Lehigh, 47-53; res. chemist, LABS, ELI LILLY & CO, 53-62, res. assoc, 62-64, asst. dir. CHEM. RES, 64-66, dir, 66-69, ASSOC. DIR. RES, 69- With Off. Sci. Res. & Develop, 44. Am. Chem. Soc. Hypotensive agents; reactions of acetylenes; heterocyclic compounds from acetylenic amines. Address: Eli Lilly & Co, Indianapolis, IN 46206.

EASTON, RICHARD J, b. Beaver, Utah, July 12, 38; m. 62; c. 2. MATHEMATICS. B.S, Univ. Utah, 60, M.S, 63, Ph.D.(math), 66. Asst. prof. MATH, Weber State Col, 65-67; IND. STATE UNIV, 67-70, ASSOC. PROF, 70- Lectr, Hill Air Force Base, 66-67. Am. Math. Soc; Math. Asn. Am. Vector measures; integration theory; functional analysis. Address: Dept. of Mathematics, Indiana State University, Terre Haute, IN 47809.

EASTON, ROBERT WALTER, b. Chicago, Ill, Dec. 8, 41; m. 65. MATHEMATICS. B.S, Univ. Wis, 63, M.S, 65, Ph.D.(math), 67. ASST. PROF. APPL. MATH, BROWN UNIV, 67- Am. Math. Soc. Differential equations; celestial mechanics. Address: Dept. of Applied Mathematics, Brown University, Providence, RI 02912.

EASTON, THOMAS W, b. Bridgton, Maine, Oct. 6, 21; m. 43; c. 4. CYTOLOGY, EVOLUTION. B.A, Univ. Maine, 43, M.A, 48; Ph.D.(cytol), Brown Univ, 51. Instr. anat, sch. med, Johns Hopkins Univ, 51-52; Brown Univ. pres. fels, France, 53-54; res. coord, U.S. Dept. Defense, 55-60; asst. prof. BIOL, COLBY COL, 60-63, ASSOC. PROF, 64- Mil. Intel. Res, 42-46. AAAS. Fine structure of ciliary apparatus and relation to functions other than motility; origin and function of mammalian macrophages. Address: Dept. of Biology, Colby College, Waterville, ME 04901.

EASTON, WILLIAM BIGELOW, b. Portsmouth, Va, Mar. 8, 39; m. 61; c. 2. COMPUTER SCIENCE. B.Eng.Phys, Cornell, 61; Nat. Sci. Found. fel, Princeton, 61-64, Ph.D.(math), 64. Consult, APPL. LOGIC CORP, 62-65, sr. mathematician, 65-67, tech. dir, 67-69, DIR. ADVAN. SYSTS, 69- Instr, Princeton, 64-65; vis. lectr, Rutgers Univ, 65- Am. Math. Soc; Asn. Symbolic Logic; Asn. Comput. Mach. Operating systems; axiomatic set theory. Address: Applied Logic Corp, 1 Palmer Square, Princeton, NJ 08540.

EASTON, W(ILLIAM) H(EYDEN), b. Bedford, Ind, Jan. 14, 16; m. 40; c. 2. GEOLOGY. B.S, George Washington, 37, A.M, 38; fel, Chicago, 38-39, Ph.D.(geol), 40. Asst, U.S. Nat. Mus, 36-38; Chicago, 39-40; asst. geologist, Ill. Geol. Surv, 40-42, assoc. geologist, 42-44; asst. prof. GEOL, UNIV. SOUTH. CALIF, 44-48, assoc. prof, 48-51, PROF, 51-, chmn. dept, 63-67. Asst, George Washington, 37-38; U.S. Geol. Surv, 52-53; Guggenheim fel, 59-60. U.S.N.R, 44-46. Paleont. Soc; fel. Geol. Soc. Am; Soc. Econ. Paleont. & Mineral; Am. Asn. Petrol. Geol. Paleozoic paleontology and stratigraphy; oil and gas exploration; Carboniferous corals; Hawaiian reefs. Address: Dept. of Geological Sciences, University of Southern California, Los Angeles, CA 90007.

EASTWOOD, BASIL R, b. Argyle, Wis, Dec. 17, 36; m. 63; c. 2. ANIMAL SCIENCE, POPULATION GENETICS. B.S, Wis. State Univ, Platteville, 58; M.S, S.Dak. State Univ, 60; Ph.D.(dairy cattle breeding), Mich. State Univ, 67. Exten. dairyman, Univ. Mass, 63-65; asst. prof. ANIMAL SCI, IOWA STATE UNIV, 65-71, ASSOC. PROF, 71-, EXTEN. DAIRYMAN, 65- Am. Dairy Sci. Asn. Use of records in genetic improvement of dairy cattle. Address: Dept. of Animal Science, 4 Kildee Hall, Iowa State University, Ames, IA 50010.

EASTWOOD, DeLYLE, b. Upper Darby, Pa, Nov. 19, 32; m. 66. PHYSICAL CHEMISTRY. M.S, Chicago, 55, Charles H. Viol fel, 57, Nat. Sci. Found. summer fel, 59, Ph.D.(phys. chem), 64. Res. asst. chem, res. insts, Chicago, 54-56, teaching asst, 57-59, phys. chemist, 59-60, res. asst, inst. study metals, 61-64; res. fel. phys. chem. & spectros, Harvard, 64-66; res. assoc, Univ. Wash, 66-69; Northeast. Univ, 70-71; SR. CHEMIST, BAIRD-ATOMIC, INC, 71- AAAS; Am. Phys. Soc; Am. Chem. Soc. Electronic spectroscopy including luminescence of porphyrins, dyes and aromatic compounds; photoelectron spectroscopy; environmental and pollution research; paramagnetism and antiferromagnetism of transition metal halides. Address: Dept. 75, Baird-Atomic, Inc, 125 Middlesex Turnpike, Bedford, MA 01730.

EASTWOOD, DOUGLAS WILLIAM, b. Ellsworth, Wis, Sept. 17, 18; m. 43; c. 4. ANESTHESIOLOGY. A.B, Coe Col, 40; M.D, Iowa, 43, M.S, 49. Intern, Receiving Hosp, Detroit, Mich, 44; instr. internal med, Wayne, 44-45; asst. res. ANESTHESIOL, univ. hosps, Iowa, 47-48, res, 48-49, instr, col. med, 49-50, assoc. prof, 54-55; asst. prof. & chief, sch. med, Washington (St. Louis), 50-54; PROF, SCH. MED, UNIV. VA, 55-, chmn. dept, 55-71. Asst. res. internal med, Receiving Hosp, Detroit, 44-45; on leave, Lister Hill Ctr. Nat. Libr. Med, 71- U.S.A, 45-47. Am. Soc. Anesthesiol; Int. Anesthesia Res. Soc. Educational resources; evaluation of educational methods. Address: Dept. of Anesthesiology, University of Virginia School of Medicine, Charlottesville, VA 22901.

EASTWOOD, G(EORGE) E(DMUND) PETER, b. Spiritwood, Sask, June 4, 23. GEOLOGY. B.Sc, Saskatchewan, 44; Ph.D.(geol), Minnesota, 50. Chief of field party, Geol. Surv. Can, 47-48; asst. prof. mineral. & struct. geol, Alabama, 49-50; assoc. geologist, B.C. DEPT. MINES & PETROL. RESOURCES, 51-, GEOLOGIST, 63- Geol. Soc. Am; Geol. Asn. Can. Mineralogy; hard-rock geological mapping; economic geology. Address: Dept. of Mines & Petroleum Resources, Victoria, B.C, Can.

EASTWOOD, JUDITH JANSSEN, b. Englewood, N.J, Mar. 18, 44; m. 68. MARINE BIOLOGY, ECOLOGY. B.A, Denison Univ, 66; Bermuda Biol. Sta, summer 67; Nat. Sci. Found. trainee, Lehigh Univ, 66-68, M.S, 68, Sigma Xi grant-in-aid, 71-72, Ph.D.(biol), 72. Instr. ecol. & bot, Cedar Crest Col, 68-69; ADJ. LECTR. BIOL, YORK COL.(N.Y), 71- AAAS; Am. Inst. Biol. Sci. Development and light related behavior of Echinoplutei larvae. Address: 275 Engle St, J-5, Englewood, NJ 07631.

EASTWOOD, La VERNE W(INFIELD), b. Wiota, Wis, May 12, 04; m. 44. METALLURGY. B.S, Wisconsin, 29, M.S, 30, fel, 30-31, Ph.D.(metal), 31. Instr. phys. metal, Michigan, 31-34, asst. prof, 34-35; res. metallurgist, lab, Aluminum Co, Am. 35-42; chief metallurgist, Md. Sanit. & Mfg. Co, 43-44; supvr, Battelle Mem. Inst, 44-51; asst. dir. res, Kaiser Aluminum & Chem. Corp, 51-57; mgr. res. planning, Olin Mathieson Chem. Corp, 57-asst. to v.pres. sales & tech. mgr. sheet & plate opers, Olin Corp, Ohio, 57-69; NONFERROUS METALL. CONSULT, 69- Supvr. res, Nat. Adv. Comt. Aeronaut, 44; Atomic Energy Comn; Off. Sci. Res. & Develop; U.S. Air Force; U.S. Navy. Am. Inst. Mining, Metall. & Petrol. Eng; Am. Soc. Metals; Am. Foundrymen's Soc; Brit. Inst. Metals. Physical and foundry metallurgy of nonferrous alloys; aluminum; magnesium; beryllium; titanium; copper. Address: Route 2, Woodsfield, OH 43793.

EASTWOOD, RAYMOND L, b. Pawnee City, Nebr, Aug. 27, 40. GEOCHEMISTRY, PETROLOGY. B.S, Kans. State Univ, 62, M.S, 65; Ph.D.(geol), Univ. Ariz, 70. Res. asst. geol, Univ. Ariz, 64-68; res. mineralogist geochem, res. & develop. dept, Phillips. Petrol. Co, Okla, 68-70; ASST. PROF. GEOL, NORTH. ARIZ. UNIV, 70- AAAS; Am. Geophys. Union; Geochem. Soc; Geol. Soc. Am. Isotope geology; strontium isotope ratios; igneous and metamorphic petrology; sedimentary geochemistry; thermodynamics and kinetics; geochronology; mineralogy; geochemistry and petrology of volcanic rocks. Address: Dept. of Geology, Northern Arizona University, Flagstaff, AZ 86001.

EASTWOOD, SYLVANDER CECIL, b. Cicero, N.Y, Sept. 12, 16; m. 37; c. 2. CHEMICAL ENGINEERING. B.S.Ch.E, Syracuse, 37. Chem. engr, West. Elec, N.J, 37-38; chemist, Ross & Rowe, New York, 38-39; chem. engr. develop. div, Socony Mobil Oil Co, 39-42, group leader, 42-47, res. assoc, 47-52, asst. supvr. appl. catalyst res. oper, 52-58, supvr, 58-64, mgr. process res. sect, appl. res. & develop. div, 64-67, mgr. process sect, tech. serv. div, MOBIL RES. & DEVELOP. CORP, 67-69, RES. ADV, PROCESS SECT, APPL. RES. & DEVELOP. DIV, 69- Am. Chem. Soc; Am. Inst. Chem. Eng. Applied research and development of petroleum and petrochemical processes including catalysts; development of new reforming, hydrocracking and catalytic cracking catalysts. Address: Research Dept, Mobil Research & Development Corp, Paulsboro, NJ 08066.

EASTWOOD, T(HOMAS) A(LEXANDER), b. London, Ont, Nov. 27, 20; m. 49; c. 4. PHYSICAL CHEMISTRY. B.A, Western Ontario, 42, Nat. Research Council Can. bursar & M.A, 43; Can. Industs. Ltd. fel. & Ph.D.(chem), McGill, 46; Nat. Research Council Can. fel, Oxford, 49-50, D.Phil.(chem), 51. Control chemist, Imperial Oil Ltd, 43-44; RES. OFF. CHEM, atomic energy proj, Nat. Research Coun. Can, 47-49; ATOMIC ENERGY OF CAN. LTD, 51- Hon. lectr, McGill, 46-47; chemist, UK Atomic Energy Authority, Eng, 64-65. Carnegie res. award, Oxford, 50-51. Am. Phys. Soc; sr. mem. Am. Chem. Soc; fel. Chem. Inst. Can. Radio chemistry; nuclear physics; kinetics of chemical reactions. Address: Atomic Energy of Canada Ltd, Chalk River Nuclear Labs, Chalk River, Ont, Can.

EASTY, DWIGHT B(UCHANAN), b. Lakewood, Ohio, Mar. 8, 34; m. 58; c. 3. ANALYTICAL CHEMISTRY. B.A, Ohio Wesleyan Univ, 56; M.S, Lawrence Col, 58, Ph.D.(paper chem), 61. Develop. engr, paper sect, res. & develop. lab, Nat. Vulcanized Fibre Co, 61-62, group leader, 62-66; vis. asst. prof. CHEM, Ohio Wesleyan Univ, 66-67; res. assoc, Univ. Wis, Madison, 67-68, lectr, 68-69; ASST. PROF, INST. PAPER CHEM, 69- AAAS; Am. Chem. Soc. Bioanalytical chemistry; continuous analysis; determination of trace elements and compounds in the environment; radiochemical methods; analysis of paper. Address: 2101 Clover Lane, Appleton, WI 54911.

EATHERLY, W(ALTER) P(ASOLD), b. Washington, D.C, June 23, 23; m. 44; c. 3. PHYSICS. B.S, Calif. Inst. Tech, 48, M.S, 49; Illinois. Jr. physicist gas kinetics, Carbide & Carbon Chem. Co, 44-46; engr. vacuum eng, Consol. Eng. Corp, 47-49; supvr. solid state physics, Atomics Int, 49-54; asst. dir. res, carbon prod. div, Union Carbide Corp, 57-62, gen. mgr. nuclear fuels dept, 63-67, consult, OAK RIDGE NAT. LAB, 67-70, HEAD, CARBON DEVELOP. LAB, 70- U.S.A, 43-46. AAAS; Am. Phys. Soc; Am. Nuclear Soc. Nuclear materials engineering; solid state physics. Address: Carbon Development Lab, Oak Ridge National Lab, P.O. Box X, Oak Ridge, TN 37830.

EATON, ALVIN RALPH, b. Toledo, Ohio, Mar. 13, 20; m. 70; c. 2. PHYSICS, AERODYNAMICS. A.B, Oberlin Col, 41; M.S, Calif. Inst. Technol, 43. Asst. aeronaut. eng, Calif. Inst. Technol, 41-42, engr. aerodyn. res, 42-43, S.Calif. coop. wind tunnel, 44-45; ENGR. & SUPVR. GUIDED MISSILE PROG, APPL. PHYSICS LAB, JOHNS HOPKINS UNIV, 45-, SUPVR. MISSILE SYSTS. DIV, 65- Meritorious pub. serv. citation, U.S. Dept. Navy, 57. Weapon system integration; missile systems engineering; missile guidance and control. Address: 6701 Surrey Lane, Clarksville, MD 21029.

EATON, D(ONALD) R(EX), b. Leicester, Eng, July 20, 32; m. 59; c. 4. PHYSICAL CHEMISTRY. B.A, Oxford, 55, M.A, 59, D.Phil.(chem), 58. Fel, div. pure physics, Nat. Res. Coun. Can, 58-60; res. chemist, cent. res. dept, E.I. Du Pont de Nemours & Co, 60-64, res. supvr, 64-68; assoc. prof. CHEM, McMASTER UNIV, 68-71, PROF, 71- Am. Chem. Soc; Can. Inst. Chem; The Chem. Soc. Transition metal chemistry; magnetic resonance. Address: Dept. of Chemistry, McMaster University, Hamilton, Ont, Can.

EATON, GEORGE T(HOMAS), b. Edmonton, Alta, Can, Apr. 18, 10; nat; m. 36; c. 3. CHEMICAL ENGINEERING. B.A, McMaster, 31, M.A, 33; B.S, Acadia, 33. Chemist, photog. chem, KODAK RES. LABS, 37-43, staff asst, 43-46, supvr, indust. sales studio, sales div, 46-51, ed, sales serv. div, 51-53, staff asst, APPLIED PHOTOG. DIV, 53-56, ASST. DIV. HEAD, 57-, HEAD, PHOTOG. CHEM. DEPT, 56- Lectr, Rochester Inst. Tech, 52- Fel. Photog. Soc. Am; Soc. Photog. Sci. & Eng.(pres, 57-61); Soc. Motion Picture & TV. Eng. Chemistry of photographic processing; photoreproduction; engineering drawings; microfilming; editorial work on photographic yearbooks and encyclopedia; teaching. Address: 699 Heritage Rd, Rochester, NY 14615.

EATON, G(EORGE) W(ALTER), b. Upper Canard, N.S, Sept. 4, 33; m. 56; c. 2. HORTICULTURE, BOTANY. B.S.A, Toronto, 55; Ph.D.(pomol), Ohio State, 59. Exten. specialist POMOL, Ont. Dept. Agr, 55-58, res. scientist, 58-64; asst. prof, UNIV. B.C, 64-66, ASSOC. PROF, 66- Am. Soc. Hort. Sci; Can. Soc. Hort. Sci; Agr. Inst. Can; Genetics Soc. Can; Am. Statist. Asn. Reproductive physiology and morphology of fruit crops; mineral nutrition; biometrics. Address: Dept. of Plant Science, University of British Columbia, Vancouver 8, B.C, Can.

EATON, GORDON P(RYOR), b. Dayton, Ohio, Mar. 9, 29; m. 51; c. 2. PHYSICAL GEOLOGY. B.A, Wesleyan Univ, 51; M.S, Calif. Inst. Technol, 53, Ph.D.(geol, geophys), 57. Instr. geol, Wesleyan Univ, 55-57, asst. prof, 57-59; Univ. Calif, Riverside, 59-63, assoc. prof, 63-67, chmn. dept. geol. sci, 66-67; GEOLOGIST, U.S. GEOL. SURV, 67- Res. geologist, U.S. Geol. Surv, 63-65. Geol. Soc. Am; Am. Geophys. Union; Soc. Explor. Geophys. Applied geophysics; general physical geology. Address: 1955 Hoyt St, Lakewood, CO 80215.

EATON, H(AMILTON) D(EAN), b. Elmhurst, N.Y, Nov. 24, 16; m. 46; c. 3. ANIMAL NUTRITION. B.S, Iowa State, 39; M.S, Rutgers, 41; Ph.D.(animal husb), Cornell, 47. Asst. dairy husb, Rutgers, 39-41; animal husb, Cornell, 41-42, 46-47; asst. prof. animal nutrit, UNIV. CONN, 47-50, assoc. prof, 50-56, PROF, 57-70, NUTRIT. SCI, 70- U.S.A, 42-45. AAAS; Am. Soc. Animal Sci; Am. Dairy Sci. Asn.(awards, 52, 62); Am. Chem. Soc; Biomet. Soc; Am. Inst. Nutrit. Nutrition; vitamin A metabolism. Address: Dept. of Nutritional Sciences, University of Connecticut, Storrs, CT 06268.

EATON, J(AMES) E(DMONDS), b. N.Y.C, Mar. 27, 12; m. 39; c. 1. ALGEBRA. B.S, Yale, 36, Ph.D.(math), 39. Asst. prof. math, Hofstra Col, 39-40, assoc. prof. & chmn. dept, 40-41; instr, Queens Col.(N.Y), 41-46; mathematician, Naval Res. Lab, 46-47; instr. MATH, QUEENS COL.(N.Y), 47-49, asst. prof, 49-53, assoc. prof, 53-61, PROF, 61- Mem. staff, radiation lab, Mass. Inst. Tech, 44-46; mathematician, Naval Res. Lab, 47-57. With Off. Sci. Res. & Develop, 44. Am. Math. Soc; Math. Asn. Am. Group theory. Address: 166-25 Powells Cove Blvd, Beechhurst, NY 11357.

EATON, J(AMES) H(OWARD), b. Woodland, Calif, Nov. 28, 33; m. 56; c. 3. ELECTRICAL ENGINEERING. B.S, California, Berkeley, 58, M.S, 60, Ph.D.(elec. eng), 62. Asst. prof. systs. theory, California, Berkeley, 62-64; mgr. systs. dept, IBM RES. LAB, 64-71, DIR. TECH. PLANNING, 71- Consult, IBM Res, 63-64. U.S.A, 54-55. Inst. Elec. & Electronics Eng. Theory of optimal control; systems theory and its application to the design and analysis of computer systems. Address: IBM Research Center, P.O. Box 218, Yorktown Heights, NY 10598.

EATON, J(AMES) R(OBERT), b. Bluffton, Ind, Nov. 1, 02; m. 29; c. 1. ELECTRICAL ENGINEERING. B.S.E.E, Purdue, 25, Ph.D.(elec. eng), 42; M.S.E.E, Wisconsin, 38. Transmission engr, Consumers Power Co, Mich, 25-37; instr. ELEC. ENG, Wisconsin, 38-40; from instr. to prof, PURDUE UNIV, 40-71, EMER. PROF, 71- Inst. Elec. & Electronics Eng; Am. Soc. Eng. Educ. High voltage; effect of lightning on power systems; instrument for measuring capacitance and resistance of power system insulation in place; impulse characteristics of electrical connections to the earth; nuclear power and instrumentation. Address: 175 Drury Lane, West Lafayette, IN 47906.

EATON, JEROME F, b. Newark, N.J, Jan. 7, 41; m. 64; c. 2. GEOPHYSICS. B.S, Lehigh Univ, 63; NASA trainee, Princeton, 63-65, M.A, 65, Ph.D.(geophys), 68. RES. GEOPHYSICIST, GULF RES. & DEVELOP. CO, 68- Soc. Explor. Geophys; Am. Geophys. Union. Steady and transient states of strain in igneous rocks at high temperature; relationships between continental margins and ocean basins; seismic response of trapped fluids. Address: Exploration Division, Gulf Research & Development Co, P.O. Drawer 2038, Pittsburgh, PA 15230.

EATON, JERRY P(AUL), b. Fresno Co, Calif, Dec. 11, 26; m. 47; c. 4. SEISMOLOGY. A.B, California, 49, Ph.D.(geophys), 53. Asst. seismol, California, 50-53; geophysicist, Hawaiian Volcano Observ, U.S. GEOL. SURV, 53-61, crustal studies br, 61-65, res. geophysicist, OFF. EARTHQUAKE RES. & CRUSTAL STUDIES, 65-70, CHIEF, 70- Lectr, Univ. Calif, Berkeley, 60-61. AAAS; Seismol. Soc. Am; Soc. Explor. Geophys; Geol. Soc. Am; Am. Geophys. Union. Mechanics of earthquake generation; detailed studies of seismicity; geophysics of volcanoes; structure of the continental crust. Address: Office of Earthquake Research & Crustal Studies, U.S. Geological Survey, 345 Middlefield Rd, Menlo Park, CA 94025.

EATON, JOHN LeROY, b. Decatur, Ill, Sept. 21, 39; m. 61; c. 2. ENTOMOLOGY, PHYSIOLOGY. B.S, Illinois, 62, U.S. Pub. Health Serv. fel, 63-65, Ph.D.(entom), 66. Kettering Found. teaching intern biol, Kalamazoo Col, 66-67, ASST. PROF, 67-69; DEPT. ENTOM, VA. POLYTECH. INST, 69- Upjohn Co. res. grant, 66-67. U.S.A.R, 57-65. AAAS; Entom. Soc. Am. Insect sensory reception; insect behavior. Address: Dept. of Entomology, Virginia Polytechnic Institute, Blacksburg, VA 24061.

EATON, LAFAYETTE CLAUD, b. Memphis, Tenn, Nov. 14, 43; m. 63; c. 2. POPULATION BIOLOGY & GENETICS. A.B, Univ. Calif, Berkeley, 65, M.A, 66; Nat. Sci. Found. fels, Univ. Costa Rica, summers 68 & 70; Nat. Insts. Health grant & Ph.D.(pop. biol), Stanford Univ, 71. ASST. PROF. BIOMET. & PLANT TAXON, Ind. State Univ, Terre Haute, 69-71; UNIV. CINCINNATI, 71- AAAS; Am. Inst. Biol. Sci; Bot. Soc. Am. Biosystematics; population variability; gene flow in natural populations. Address: Dept. of Biological Sciences, University of Cincinnati, Cincinnati, OH 45221.

EATON, MAX LEON, b. Syracuse, Nebr, July 7, 09; m. 33; c. 3. APPLIED MATHEMATICS. B.S, Kans. State Col, 32, M.S, 33; LL.B, LaSalle Exten. Univ, 50; Navy scholar, California, Los Angeles, 57-58. Mem. tech. dept, Sinclair Oil Co, 33-36; technologist, Shell Oil Co, 36-38; chem. engr, Richfield Oil Co, 38-50; private consult. appl. math, 50; mathematician, Naval Air Missile Center, 50-51, 52-54, statistician, 51-52, math. statistician, 54-55; phys. sci. adminstr, 55-56, aero res. engr. flight systs, 56-59; analyst opers. res, Pac. Missile Range, 59-64; MATH. STATISTICIAN RES. EXP. DESIGN, U.S. NAVAL CIVIL ENG. LAB, 64- Instr, exten. courses, California, 52- U.S.A, 41-46, Capt. Sci. Res. Soc. Am. Chemical engineering; analysis of physical systems; mathematics; statistics; system modelling and analysis; prediction uncertainties; probability; error analysis; problem formulation; design of experiments; analysis of neutron penetration and Poisson processes. Address: 225 E. Hemlock St, Oxnard, CA 93030.

EATON, MERRILL T(HOMAS), JR, b. Howard Co, Ind, June 25, 20; m. 42; c. 3. PSYCHIATRY. A.B, Indiana, 41, M.D, 44. Intern, St. Elizabeth's Hosp, 44-45; res. physician, Colo. State Hosp, 47-48; Sheppard-Pratt Hosp, 48-49; assoc. PSYCHIAT, sch. med, Kansas, 49-51, asst. prof, 51-54, assoc. prof, 54-60; COL. MED, UNIV. NEBR, OMAHA, 60-62, PROF, 62-, CHMN. DEPT, 68-; DIR, NEBR. PSYCHIAT. INST, 68- Dipl, Am. Bd. Psychiat. & Neurol. Med.C, 45-47, Capt. Am. Psychiat. Asn; Asn. Am. Med. Cols; Am. Med. Asn. Psychotherapy; medical education. Address: 602 S. 44th Ave, Omaha, NE 68105.

EATON, MONROE D(AVIS), b. Stockton, Calif, Dec. 2, 04; m. 33; c. 4. MICROBIOLOGY. A.B, Stanford, 27, A.M, 28; M.D, Harvard, 30. Asst. bact, Harvard Med. Sch. & instr. biochem. sci, Harvard, 30-33, res. tutor, 31-33; instr. bact, sch. med, Yale, 33-36; asst. prof. bact. & immunol, Washington (St. Louis), 36-37; mem. staff, int. health div, Rockefeller Found, 37-47; assoc. prof. BACT. & IMMUNOL, HARVARD MED. SCH, 47-68, prof, 68-71, EMER. PROF, 71-; SR. SCIENTIST, DEPT. MED. MICROBIOL, MED. SCH, STANFORD UNIV, 71- Dir. res. lab, State Dept. Pub. Health, Calif, 39-47. Consult, U.S.A. AAAS; Am. Soc. Microbiol; Am. Asn. Immunol; Soc. Exp. Biol. & Med; Am. Acad. Arts & Sci. Bacterial variation; bacterial toxins; immunology of malaria; influenza and virus pneumonia; chemotherapy of virus diseases; virus and tumors. Address: Dept. of Medical Microbiology, Stanford University Medical School, Stanford, CA 94305.

EATON, MORRIS LEROY, b. Sacramento, Calif, Aug. 10, 39; m. 64; c. 1. MATHEMATICAL STATISTICS. B.S, Washington (Seattle), 61. M.S, Stanford, 63, Ph.D.(statist), 66. Res. assoc. STATIST, Stanford, 66; asst. prof, UNIV. CHICAGO, 66-70, ASSOC. PROF, 70- Fel. Am. Statist. Asn; fel. Inst.

Math. Statist. Multivariate analysis; decision theory ranking procedures; invariance in statistical problems. Address: Dept. of Statistics, University of Chicago, Chicago, Ill. 60637.

EATON, NORMAN RAY, b. Turlock, Calif, June 30, 26; m. 51; c. 2. MICROBIOLOGY. B.A, California, 51; fel, Washington (Seattle), 51-55, M.S, 53, Ph.D, 55. Instr. bact, California, 55-57; res. instr. med. & microbiol, Washington (Seattle), 57-63; asst. prof. BIOL, BROOKLYN COL, 63-66, assoc. prof, 66-70, PROF, 70-; RES. BIOCHEMIST, VET. ADMIN. HOSP, 57- Summer, res. instr, Washington (Seattle), 56. U.S.A, 44-46. AAAS; Am. Soc. Microbiol; Genetics Soc. Am. Catabolic processes of microbial metabolism; microbial biosynthesis of lipids. Address: Dept. of Biology, Brooklyn College, Brooklyn, NY 11210.

EATON, PAUL BERNARD, b. Elkhart, Ind, May 21, 17. INDUSTRIAL & METALLURGICAL ENGINEERING. B.S, Notre Dame, 48; M.S, Purdue, 52. Instr. gen. eng, PURDUE UNIV, 48-52, asst. prof. METALS PROCESSING, 52-62, ASSOC. PROF, 62- Consult, indust. orgns, 55- Mem, Foundry Educ. Found, 60- Ord.C, 40-47, Sgt. Am. Soc. Metals; Am. Inst. Mining, Metall. & Petrol. Eng; Am. Soc. Eng. Educ; Am. Foundrymen's Soc. Physical and process metallurgy of ferrous metals. Address: School of Metallurgical Engineering, Purdue University, Lafayette, IN 47907.

EATON, PHILIP EUGENE, b. Brooklyn, N.Y, June 2, 36. ORGANIC CHEMISTRY. A.B, Princeton, 57; M.A, Harvard, 60, Ph.D.(chem), 61. Asst. prof. CHEM, California, Berkeley, 60-62; UNIV. CHICAGO, 62-65, ASSOC. PROF, 65- Alfred P. Sloan Found. res. fel, 63-69; consult, E.I. du Pont de Nemours & Co, Inc; Nat. Insts. Health. Chemistry of small ring compounds, cubane and dodecahedrane; photochemistry. Address: Dept. of Chemistry, University of Chicago, Chicago, IL 60637.

EATON, STEPHEN W(OODMAN), b. Geneva, N.Y, Dec. 22, 18; m. 46; ORNITHOLOGY. Ph.D.(zool), Cornell, 49. Asst. prof. BIOL, ST. BONAVENTURE, 49-53, assoc. prof, 53-57, PROF, 57-; ED, SCI. STUDIES, 66- U.S.A.A.F, 42-46, 1st Lt. AAAS; Am. Ornith. Union; Wilson Ornith. Soc; Cooper Ornith. Soc; Am. Soc. Mammal; Ecol. Soc. Am. Vertebrate zoology; faunal studies; biology of Parulidae and of the wild turkey; Canandaigua Lake as an ecosystem; Allegheny River, aquifer and reservoir, a study of a water resource. Address: Dept. of Biology, St. Bonaventure University, St. Bonaventure, NY 14778.

EATON, THEODORE H(ILDRETH), JR, b. Boston, Mass, Nov. 16, 07; m. 34; c. 3. ZOOLOGY. A.B, Cornell, 30; fel, California, 30-33, Ph.D.(zool), 33. Res. zoologist, Cornell, 33-34; wildlife technician, Nat. Park Serv, 34-35; instr. zool, Union (N.Y), 37-40; asst. agron, Cornell, 40-42; asst. prof. biol, Buffalo, 42-45; instr. physiol, med. sch, Georgetown, 45-46; managing ed, Washington Inst. Med, 46-47; prof. biol, Southwestern Col.(Kans), 47-50; East. Carolina Col, 50-58; assoc. prof. ZOOL, UNIV. KANS, 58-62, PROF, 62-, CURATOR, LOWER VERT. FOSSILS, MUS. NATURAL HIST, 62-, assoc. curator, 58-62. Mem. exped, Rainbow Bridge-Monument Valley, 33; res. Barro Colo. Island, C.Z, 39; Fulbright lectr. zool, Univs. Saigon & Hue, Viet-Nam, 65-66; summers, vis. prof, Univ. Kans, 54, 57. vis. assoc. prof, Univ. Calif, 58, res, Highlands Biol. Sta, 56, Mt. Lake Biol. Sta, 63, Rocky Mt. Biol. Lab, 67, 68, 71. Am. Soc. Zool; Am. Soc. Ichthyol. & Herpet; Soc. Vert. Paleont; fel. N.Y. Acad. Sci. Evolution; vertebrate morphology; vertebrate paleontology. Address: Dept. of Systematics & Ecology, Museum of Natural History, University of Kansas, Lawrence, KS 66045.

EATON, WILLIAM THOMAS, b. Long Beach, Calif, Feb. 22, 38; m. 61; c. 2. MATHEMATICS. B.S, Univ. Utah, 61, M.S, 63; Ph.D.(math), 67. Asst. prof. MATH, Univ. Tenn, Knoxville, 67-70; ASSOC. PROF, UNIV. TEX, AUSTIN, 70- Mem. Inst. Advan. Stud, 69-70; Alfred P. Sloan fel, 69-71. Am. Math. Soc. Topology of manifolds, particularly embeddings of manifolds in three-manifolds; piecewise linear topology and combinatories; statistics and probability theory. Address: 8408 Silver Ridge Dr, Austin, TX 78759.

EATOUGH, HARRY, b. Fall River, Mass, Sept. 10, 06; m. 30; c. 2. CHEMISTRY. B.S, Brown, 26, M.S, 27, Ph.D.(org. chem), 29. Res. chemist, exp. sta, E.I. du Pont de Nemours & Co, 29-68; RETIRED. Francis Wayland scholar. Fel. AAAS; Am. Chem. Soc; Sci. Res. Soc. Am. Organic-inorganic compounds of nitrogen and silicon; cellulose derivatives; chemotherapy of cancer; radiological safety. Address: 206 N. Brownleaf Rd, Hillside Heights, Newark, DE 19711.

EATOUGH, NORMAN L, b. Bingham Canyon, Utah, Oct. 18, 33; m. 56; c. 4. PHYSICAL CHEMISTRY. B.S, Brigham Young, 57, B.E.S, 58, M.S, 59, Nat. Sci. Found. fel, 66-68, Ph.D.(phys. chem), 68; M.S.Ch.E, Washington (Seattle), 60. Sr. develop. engr, Hercules Powder Co, 60-64; asst. prof. chem, Dixie Jr. Col, 64-65; instr. chem. eng, Brigham Young, 65-66; asst. prof. CHEM, CALIF. STATE POLYTECH. COL, 68-70, ASSOC. PROF, 70- Consult, Hercules Powder Co, 64-65. U.S.A, 53-55. Am. Chem. Soc. High pressure chemistry. Address: Dept. of Chemistry, California State Polytechnic College, San Luis Obispo, CA 93401.

EAVES, DAVID MAGILL, b. N.Y.C, Dec. 7, 33; m. 57, 66; c. 3. MATHEMATICS. B.Sc, Mass. Inst. Tech, 56; M.Sc, Washington (Seattle), 63, Ph.D. (math), 66. Instr. MATH, SIMON FRASER UNIV, 65-66, ASST. PROF, 66- U.S.N.R, 56-60, Lt.(jg). Am. Math. Soc; Math. Asn. Am. Probability theory. Address: Dept. of Mathematics, Simon Fraser University, Burnaby 2, B.C, Can.

EAVES, EDGAR D(EWEY), b. Johnson County, Tex, May 27, 04; m. 39; c. 2. MATHEMATICS. B.S, Univ. Okla, 28, M.A, 30; Ph.D.(math), Univ. Tex, 39. Instr. MATH, UNIV. TENN, KNOXVILLE, 30-35, asst. prof, 36-41, assoc. prof, 41-47, PROF, 47- Am. Math. Soc; Math. Asn. Am. The doubleslot, salient fieldpole problem of the dynamo electric machine. Address: Dept. of Mathematics, University of Tennessee, Knoxville, TN 37916.

EAVES, GEORGE N(EWTON), b. Athens, Tenn, Mar. 12, 35. MEDICAL MICROBIOLOGY. B.A, Chattanooga, 57; M.S, Tennessee, 59; Ph.D.(med. microbiol), Wayne State, 62. Asst. prof. biol, Washington & Jefferson Col, 62-63; fel. microbiol, Bryn Mawr Col, 63-65; grants assoc, div. res. grants, NAT. INSTS. HEALTH, 65-66, div. res. resources, 66-67, EXEC. SECY. MOLECULAR BIOL. STUDY SECT, DIV. RES. GRANTS, 67- Guest investr, Rockefeller Univ, 70-71. AAAS; Am. Soc. Cell Biol; Coun. Biol. Ed. Exocellular enzymes of bacteria; metabolic effects of bacterial endotoxins. Address: National Institutes of Health, Westwood Bldg, Room 204, Bethesda, MD 20014.

EAVES, J(AMES) C(LIFTON), b. Hillside, Ky, June 26, 12; m. 38; c. 2. MATRIX ALGEBRA; A.B, Kentucky, 35, Haggin trust fel, 40-41, M.A, 41; Ph.D.(matrix algebra), North Carolina, 49. Asst. prof. math, Alabama, 49-50; assoc. prof, Ala. Polytech, 50-51, res. assoc. prof, 51-52, prof. math. & admin. asst, 53-54, prof. math. & res. assoc, Auburn Res. Found, 52-53; prof. math. & astron, Univ. Ky, 54-67, head dept, 54-63; CENTENNIAL PROF. MATH. & CHMN. DEPT, W.VA. UNIV, 67- U.S.N.R, 43-46, Lt. Am. Math. Soc; Math. Asn. Am; Soc. Indust. & Appl. Math. Matrices; simultaneous reductions; inverse approximations; computer analysis; patents and patent law; space trajectories and transformations; higher dimensional matrices. Address: Dept. of Mathematics, West Virginia University, Morgantown, WV 26506.

EBACH, EARL A, b. Saginaw, Mich, May 13, 28; m. 53; c. 4. CHEMICAL ENGINEERING. B.S, Michigan, 51, M.S, 52, Ph.D.(chem. eng), 57. CHEM. ENGR, DOW CHEM. CO, 57-, GROUP LEADER, 69-, proj. leader, 57-69. Am. Inst. Chem. Eng. Research and development in organic chemicals. Address: 4610 Andre, Midland, MI 48640.

EBADI, MANUCHAIR SAFARALI, b. Shahmirzad, Iran, Sept. 6, 35; m. 59; c. 3. NEUROPHARMACOLOGY, NEUROCHEMISTRY. B.S, Park Col, 60; M.S, Univ. Mo-Kansas City, 62; Ph.D.(pharmacol), Univ. Mo-Columbia, 66. Res. asst. pediat, sch. med, Univ. Mo-Columbia, 64-66, res. assoc. pediat. & instr. pharmacol, 66-67; asst. prof. pediat, SCH. MED, UNIV. NEBR, OMAHA, 67-68, PHARMACOL, 68-69, assoc. prof, 69-71, PROF. & CHMN. DEPT, 71-, acting chmn. dept, 70-71. Nat. Inst. Ment. Health int. prof. fel, 69-70; mem, U.S. Pharmacopoeial Conv, 70; Dreyfus Med. Found. fel. Stud. Am. Med. Asn. Golden Apple Award, 71. AAAS; Am. Chem. Soc; Am. Soc. Pharmacol. & Exp. Therapeut; Am. Soc. Neurochem; Am. Soc. Clin. Pharmacol. & Chemother. Developmental pharmacology; neurochemical and pharmacological aspects of central nervous system drugs; relationship between coenzyme B_6 and neurotransmitters in the central nervous system; the biochemistry of cyclic 3', 5'-adenosinemonophosphate in the central nervous system. Address: Dept. of Pharmacology, University of Nebraska School of Medicine, Omaha, NE 68105.

EBAUGH, FRANKLIN G, JR, b. Philadelphia, Pa, Dec. 25, 21; m. 71; c. 4. ADMINISTRATION, HEMATOLOGY. B.A, Dartmouth Col, 44; M.D, Cornell, 46. Intern med, N.Y. Hosp, 46-47, asst. res, 48-49, res. hemat, 49-50; asst. med, sch. med, Boston, 50-53, instr, 53; surgeon, Nat. Insts. Health, U.S. Pub. Health Serv, 53-55; asst. prof. hemat, med. sch, Dartmouth, 55-58, assoc. prof. clin. path, 58-64; dean, med. sch, Boston, 64-69, PROF. MED. & DEAN, MED. SCH, MED. CTR, UNIV. UTAH, 69- Asst, med. sch, Cornell, 48-50; res. assoc, Mass. Mem. Hosp, 50-53. AAAS; Am. Soc. Clin. Invest; fel. Am. Col. Physicians; Col. Am. Path; Am. Soc. Hemat; Am. Soc. Exp. Path. Measurement of red cell survival in vivo; nature of interaction of hemoglobin and red cells with the chromate iron. Address: Office of the Dean, University of Utah Medical Center, 50 N. Medical Dr, Salt Lake City, UT 84112.

EBAUGH, PAUL, b. Salt Lake City, Utah, Aug. 17, 14; m. 38; c. 4. PHYSICS, ENGINEERING. A.B, Denison, 35. Res. chemist, Owens Corning Fiberglas Corp, 35-42; Basic Refractories Inc, 42-43; res. assoc, underwater sound lab, Harvard, 43-45; proj. engr. & prof. eng. res, ord. res. lab, PA. STATE UNIV, 45-52, asst. dir. eng. res, 52-57, asst. dean, res, col. eng. & archit, 57-65, DIR. SPACE SCI. & ENG. LAB, COL. ENG, 65-, ASSOC. DEAN RES, 67- AAAS; Am. Chem. Soc; Acoustical Soc. Am; Inst. Elec. & Electronics Eng; Am. Soc. Eng. Educ. Surface chemistry of glass; underwater transducer calibration techniques; underwater homing weapon system research and development; underwater sound; acoustic noise reduction. Address: College of Engineering, 105 Hammond Bldg, Pennsylvania State University, University Park, PA 16802.

EBBERT, ARTHUR, JR, b. Wheeling, W.Va, Aug. 25, 22. INTERNAL MEDICINE. B.A, Virginia, 44, M.D, 46. Instr. & asst. to dean, sch. med, Virginia, 52-53; instr. & asst. dean MED, SCH. MED, YALE, 53-54, asst. prof. & asst. dean, 54-63, assoc. prof, 63-71, PROF, 71-, ASSOC. DEAN, 60- Physician, Univ. Va. Hosp, 52-53; assoc. physician, Grace-New Haven Hosp, 53-60, asst. attend. physician, 60-68; attend. physician, Yale-New Haven Hosp, 68- Consult, Waterbury Hosp, 57- Med.C, 47-49, Capt. Asn. Am. Med. Cols. Medical education. Address: School of Medicine, Yale University, 333 Cedar St, New Haven, CT 06510.

EBBESSON, SVEN O. E, b. Backaby, Sweden, Oct. 14, 37; U.S. citizen; m. 62; c. 2. NEUROANATOMY. B.A, Southwestern Col.(Kans), 57; Tulane, 57-60; Ph.D.(anat), Maryland, 64. Asst. anat, Tulane, 58-60; neuroanatomist, Walter Reed Army Med. Center, 62-65; asst. neuroanat, sch. med, Maryland, 63-64, instr, 64-65; neuroanatomist, lab. perinatal physiol, Nat. Inst. Neurol. Diseases & Blindness, 65-69; ASSOC. PROF. NEUROSURG. & ANAT, MED. SCH, UNIV. VA, 69- Vis. asst. prof, sch. med, Puerto Rico & hon. mem, inst. marine biol, 66-70. Med.Serv.C, 61-65; U.S.P.H.S.R, 65-69, Lt. Comdr. AAAS; Am. Asn. Anat; Int. Soc. Stereol. Comparative neurology; stereology. Address: Dept. of Neurosurgery, University of Virginia Medical School, Charlottesville, VA 22901.

EBBIGHAUSEN, EDWIN G, b. Crookston, Minn, June 28, 11; m. 37; c. 2. ASTRONOMY. B.A, Minnesota, 36; Ph.D.(astron), Chicago, 40. Instr. math. & astron, Wilson Col, 39-41; asst. prof, Allegheny Observ, Pittsburgh, 41-44; res. engr, Westinghouse Res. Labs, 44-45; assoc. prof. PHYSICS, UNIV. ORE, 46-58, PROF, 58- Lectr, Buhl Planetarium, Pa, 42-44; Carnegie intern fel, Harvard, 55-56; Dom. Astrophys. Observ, 58-59; Kitt Peak Nat. Observ, 65-66. Coordinator, Ore. Center Sci. Teaching Improvement Prog,

Am. Asn. Adv. Sci, 56-58. AAAS; Am. Astron. Soc; Royal Astron. Soc. Spectroscopic binaries; eclipsing binary photometry. Address: Dept. of Physics, University of Oregon, Eugene, OR 97403.

EBBING, DARRELL D(ELMAR), b. Peoria, Ill, July 1, 33; m. 55; c. 3. PHYSICAL CHEMISTRY. B.S, Bradley, 55; Ph.D.(phys. chem), Indiana, 60. Res. assoc. CHEM, Indiana, 60-62; asst. prof, WAYNE STATE UNIV, 62-65, assoc. prof, 65-69, PROF, 69- Am. Chem. Soc; Am. Phys. Soc. Quantum mechanical study of molecular properties and chemical binding. Address: Dept. of Chemistry, Wayne State University, Detroit, MI 48202.

EBBS, J. HARRY, b. Notts, Eng, Sept. 18, 06; Can. citizen; m. 35; c. 3. MEDICINE, PEDIATRICS. M.D, Toronto, 31; M.D, Birmingham, 38. Res, Hosp. Sick Children, Ont, Can, 31-33; Columbia-Presby. Med. Ctr, 33-34; Birmingham Children's Hosp, Eng, 34-35, pathologist. & res. dir, 35-38; PHYSICIAN, HOSP. SICK CHILDREN, 38-; assoc. prof. PEDIAT, UNIV. TORONTO, 46-67, PROF, 67- Mem. Food & Nutrit. Adv. Bd, Can, 40-45; adv. coun, Duke Edinburgh awards, 64; mem. Nat. Adv. Coun. Fitness & Amateur Sport, 62-; mem. health comt, Sci. Coun. Can, 69-; pres, Brora Res. Ctr, 69- Dipl. child health, Royal Col. Physicians, 35, fel, 49; fel. Royal Col. Physicians & Surgeons Can, 49; Can. Medal, 67. Can. Army, Capt. Am. Pediat. Soc.(v.pres, 65); Soc. Pediat. Res; Can. Pediat. Soc.(pres, 55); Brit. Paediat. Asn. Nutrition of infants and pregnancy; nutrition surveys in Canada; height and weight surveys of children. Address: School of Physical and Health Education, University of Toronto, Toronto 181, Ont, Can.

EBBS, JANE C(OTTON), b. Newport, R.I, May 11, 12. PHYSIOLOGY, NUTRITION. B.S, Rhode Island, 35, M.S, 37; fel, Chicago, 40-41. Asst. instr. nutrit, Rhode Island, 38-39; asst. home econ, U.S. Dept. Agr, 42; nutrit. adv, Off. Qm. Gen, Dept. Army, 42-49, spec. feeding & nutrit. adv, 49-62; spec. asst. to dir, Defense Supply Agency, 62-65; from adv. to CHIEF PROG. PLANNING & EVALUATION, NUTRIT. DIV, FOOD & AGR. ORGN, UN, 65- Am. Chem. Soc; Am. Inst. Nutrit; assoc. fel. Am. Astronaut. Soc; fel. Am. Pub. Health Asn; Am. Dietetic Asn; Am. Home Econ. Asn; sr. mem. Royal Soc. Health. Vitamin A requirement of young adults; space nutrition; food processing methods; world food problems and new foods; feeding the armed forces. Address: Food & Agriculture Organization of the United Nations, Rome, Italy 00100.

EBCIOGLU, IBRAHIM K(UTSI), b. Istanbul, Turkey, Dec. 30, 21; m. 54; c. 3. APPLIED MECHANICS. M.S, Tech. Univ. Istanbul, 45; fel, Minnesota, Minneapolis, 53-54, Ph.D.(aero. eng), 58. Engr, Turkish Air League Aircraft Factory, Turkey, 45-46, asst. head sect. res. lab, 46-47, head sect, 47; 48-52; res. engr, Univ. Minnesota, Minneapolis, 58-60; res. mats. engr, directorate of mats. & processes, Wright-Patterson Air Force Base, Ohio, 60-61; asst. res. prof. dept. eng. mech, UNIV. FLA, 61-64, assoc. res. prof. DEPT. ENG. SCI. & MECH, 64-66, PROF, 66- Consult, Turkish Air Force Hq, Ankara, Turkey, 48, vis. prof, Air Force Inst. Tech, Wright-Patterson Air Force Base, Ohio, 61. Spec. award, Eighth Annual Air Force Syst. Command Sci. & Eng. Symp, 61. Soc. Eng. Sci. Aircraft structural design and static test planning; theory of plasticity; theory of similitude for supersonic vehicles; theory of creep; thermo-plasticity and dynamics of layered plates and shells. Address: Dept. of Engineering Science & Mechanics, University of Florida, Gainesville, FL 32601.

EBDON, DAVID WILLIAM, b. Detroit, Mich, Apr. 9, 39; m. 67; c. 2. PHYSICAL CHEMISTRY. B.S, Michigan, Ann Arbor, 61; Ph.D.(phys. chem), Maryland, 67. Lectr. chem, Maryland, 67-68; ASST. PROF. PHYS. CHEM, EAST. ILL. UNIV, 68- Sr. res. scientist, Nat. Biomed. Res. Found, 67-68. Am. Chem. Soc; Faraday Soc. Thermodynamic and kinetic properties of electrolyte solutions; ultrasonic relaxation spectroscopy; specific solvent interaction; theory of electrolytes; chemical oceanography. Address: Dept. of Chemistry, Eastern Illinois University, Charleston, IL 61920.

EBEL, ALFRED, b. Biala, Austria, Apr. 5, 07; U.S. citizen; m. 36; c. 2. REHABILITATION MEDICINE, ELECTROMYOGRAPHY. B.S, N.Y. Univ, 33; M.D, L.I. Col. Med, 36. PHYSICIAN, Vet. Admin. Hosp, Fayetteville, N.C, 40-47, REHAB. MED, Vet. Admin. Hosp, Bronx, N.Y, 47-67; MONTEFIORE HOSP. & MED. CTR, 67-; PROF. REHAB. MED, Albert Einstein Col. Med, 67- Consult, Vet. Admin. Hosp, Bronx, N.Y, 67- Med.C, U.S.A.R, 44-46, Res. 57-67, Col. Am. Col. Physicians; Am. Acad. Phys. Med. & Rehab; Am. Cong. Rehab. Med. Various areas in rehabilitation medicine, including education, exercise therapy, orthotics, spinal cord injury and electromyography. Address: Dept. of Rehabilitation Medicine, Montefiore Hospital and Medical Center, 111 E. 210th St, New York, NY 10467.

EBEL, MARVIN E(MERSON), b. Waterloo, Iowa, Sept. 23, 30; m. 60; c. 4. THEORETICAL PHYSICS. B.S, Iowa State, 50, M.S, 52, Ph.D.(physics), 53. Nat. Sci. Found. fel, Inst. Theoret. Physics, Copenhagen, 53-54; instr, Yale, 54-56; asst. prof, 56-57; UNIV. WIS, MADISON, 57-59, assoc. prof, PHYSICS, 59-64, PROF, 64- Sloan Found. fel, 57-62. Fel. Am. Phys. Soc. Field theory; high energy physics; solid state physics. Address: Dept. of Physics, University of Wisconsin, Madison, WI 53706.

EBEL, ROBERT H(ENRY), b. New Haven, Conn, Oct. 18, 16; m. 56; c. 4. ORGANIC CHEMISTRY. B.S, Yale, 38, Ph.D.(chem), 41. From res. chemist to develop. mgr, ORG. CHEM. DIV, AM. CYANAMID CO, 41-55, dir. process develop. res. div, 56-60, MGR. REFINERY CHEM. RES. & DEVELOP, 60- Mem. Platinum-Palladium Comt. AAAS; Am. Inst. Chem. Eng; Am. Chem. Soc; Am. Inst. Chem; N.Y. Acad. Sci. Reaction of diamines with iminoesters; rubber chemicals; pharmaceutical chemicals; mineralogy; catalysts. Address: American Cyanamid Co, 1937 W. Main St, Stamford, CT 06904.

EBELING, ALFRED W, b. Anaheim, Calif, Mar. 30, 31; m. 56; c. 2. ZOOLOGY. B.S, California, Los Angeles, 54, fel. & Ph.D.(zool), 60. Asst. prof. biol, Yale, 60-63; ZOOL, UNIV. CALIF, SANTA BARBARA, 63-66, ASSOC. PROF, 66-, contracts & grants off, 66-67. Nat. Sci. Found. grants, 61-65, 66-68. AAAS; Am. Soc. Icthyol. & Herpet; Am. Soc. Limnol. & Oceanog. Ichthyology; marine ecology. Address: Dept. of Biological Sciences, University of California, Santa Barbara, CA 93106.

EBELING, DOLPH G, b. N.Y.C, Aug. 1, 20; m. 42; c. 2. METALLURGY. B.S, Rensselaer Polytech, 40, M.S, 48, Ph.D.(metal), 50; Carnegie Inst. Tech, 40-41; Union Col, 50-54. Metal. asst, Carnegie Il. Steel Corp, 40-41; ord. specialist, U.S. Naval Proving Ground, 41-46; develop. metallurgist, chem. dept, GEN. ELEC. CO, 46-47, metallurgist, carboloy dept, 50-51, res. assoc, res. lab, 51-53, mgr. metal. unit, turbine div, 53-60, consult, Knolls Atomic Power Lab, 60-61, mat. eng. serv, 61-66, MGR. ENG. EDUC, 66- Pres, Ebeling Assoc, Inc, 70- Am. Soc. Metals; Am. Soc. Mech. Eng; N.Y. Acad. Sci; Am. Inst. Min, Metall. & Petrol. Eng; Brit. Iron & Steel Inst. Permanent magnets; high temperature alloys; fracture of metals and ductile-brittle transitions; alloy embrittlement and long time phase stability at high temperature; structure-property relationships; alloy design and process development for large forgings and castings. Address: 2063 Coolidge Pl, Schenectady, NY 12309.

EBELING, WALTER, b. San Bernardino, Calif, Nov. 26, 07; m. 30; c. 1. ENTOMOLOGY. B.S, California, 28, M.S, 29, Ph.D.(entom), 35. Asst. entom, California, 29; agent, U.S. Dept. Agr, 30; jr. entomologist, grad. sch. trop. agr. & citrus exp. sta, California, Riverside, 30-36, asst. entomologist, 36-42, assoc. entomologist, 42-48, ENTOMOLOGIST, UNIV. CALIF, LOS ANGELES, 48-, PROF. ENTOM, 54-, assoc. prof, 48-54. Fulbright prof, Univ. Cairo, 60-61; partic, Int. Termite Conf, UNESCO, Kinsasha, Congo, 64; summer sci. inst, Poona Univ, India, 68; lectr, Food & Agr. Orgn, Food Technol. Training Centre, Mysore, India, 69. Fel. AAAS; Entom. Soc. Am; Am. Inst. Biol. Sci; hon. fel. Indian Acad. Pest Control Sci. Biology and control of citrus and avocado insects and mites; biology and control of structural and household pests; insecticides. Address: Dept. of Agricultural Sciences, University of California, Los Angeles, CA 90024.

EBELING, WILLIAM CHARLES, b. Jersey City, N.J, Jan. 22, 28; m. 51; c. 3. ELECTRICAL ENGINEERING. B.E.E, Cooper Union, 49; M.E.E, Stevens Inst. Tech, 55. Engr, elevator div, Otis Elevator Co, 49-53, staff engr, electronic div, 53-54, proj. engr, 54-55, sect. head, 55-58, chief engr, 58-59; Photronics Corp, 59-62, v.pres. & secy, 62; staff asst. link group, Gen. Precision Inc, 62-63, mgr. develop. eng, 63-67, tech. dir, 67-69; DIR. ENG, REFLECTONE, INC, 69- Design and development of simulation systems of visual scenes and airborne radar systems. Address: Reflectone, Inc, 2051 W. Main St, Stamford, CT 06904.

EBENS, RICHARD JOHN, b. Berwyn, Ill, Jan. 13, 39; m. 61; c. 3. GEOLOGY. B.S, Beloit Col, 61; Nat. Defense Educ. Act fel, Univ. Wyo, 61-64, M.A, 64, Ph.D.(geol), 66. Asst. prof. geol, Emory Univ, 66-70; GEOLOGIST, U.S. GEOL. SURV, DENVER, 70- Geol. Soc. Am. Sedimentary petrology of Upper Tertiary rocks of Rocky Mountains and Great Plains; geochemical survey of bedrock units of Missouri; sampling designs and geostatistics. Address: U.S. Geological Survey, Federal Center, Denver, CO 80225.

EBER, GERHARD R, b. Leipzig, Germany, Aug. 7, 07; nat; m. 37; c. 3. AEROPHYSICS. B.S, Hannover Tech, 30, Dr. Ing, 42; M.S, Dresden Tech, 33. Instr. thermodyn, Danzig Tech, 34-37; br. chief, aerodyn. inst, Army Res. Center, 37, div. chief, supersonic aerodyn, 39-45; consult, aerothermodyn, Naval Ord. Lab, Md, 45-46, chief aerophys. div, aerophys. res, 51-53; sci. adv. aerodyn. tech. anal. div, Holloman Air Develop. Center, HOLLOMAN AFB, 53-55, tech. dir. res. & develop, 55-58, chief sci. & eng. staff, Air Force Missile Develop. Center, 59-60, TECH. DIR, off. res. analyses, Off. Aerospace Res, 60-70; OFF. ASST. STUDY SUPPORT, AIR FORCE SYSTS. COMMAND, KIRTLAND AIR FORCE BASE, N.MEX, 71- Mem. tech. comt. aircraft heat transfer, 53-54. Meritorious civilian serv. cert. & emblem, 51; Off. Aerospace Res. outstanding achievement award, 70. AAAS; assoc. fel. Am. Inst. Aeronaut. & Astronaut; Am. Ord. Asn; Sci. Res. Soc. Am; Ger. Soc. Aeronaut. & Astronaut. Aerothermodynamics, boundary layer structure and stability; design of supersonic and hypersonic wind tunnels and high speed tracks; advanced technology applications; Air Force systems synthesis and analysis. Address: 1812 Embudo Dr. N.E, Albuquerque, NM 87112.

EBER, LAURENCE E(LWIN), b. Kirk, Nebr, Sept. 14, 22; m. 49; c. 2. METEOROLOGY. A.B, California, Los Angeles, 49, M.A, 52. Asst. meteorol, California, Los Angeles, 50-52; assoc. meteorologist, Pineapple Res. Inst, Hawaii, 52-56; res. meteorologist, California, Los Angeles, 56; METEOROLOGIST, U.S. Bur. Commercial Fisheries, 56-70, FISHERY OCEANOG. CTR, NAT. MARINE FISHERIES SERV, NAT. OCEANIC & ATMOSPHERIC ADMIN, 70- U.S.A, 42-45. Am. Meteorol. Soc; Am. Geophys. Union. Cloud physics; synoptic meteorology; interaction of sea and atmosphere; data processing. Address: Fishery Oceanography Center, La Jolla, CA 92037.

EBERHARD, ANATOL, b. Istanbul, Turkey, Nov. 13, 38; U.S. citizen; m. 64. ORGANIC CHEMISTRY, BIOCHEMISTRY. B.A, California, Berkeley, 59; Woodrow Wilson fel. & M.A, Harvard, 60, Nat. Insts. Health fel & Ph.D. (chem), 64. Nat. Insts. Health fel, California, Berkeley, 64-66; asst. prof. biol, Harvard, 66-71; ASSOC. PROF. CHEM, FAIRLEIGH DICKINSON UNIV, 71- AAAS; N.Y. Acad. Sci; Am. Chem. Soc. Physical-organic chemistry of organic phosphonates; developmental biochemistry. Address: Dept. of Chemistry, Fairleigh Dickinson University, Teaneck, NJ 07666.

EBERHARD, EVERETT, b. Topeka, Kans, Mar. 15, 15; m. 41; c. 2. ELECTRICAL ENGINEERING. B.S, Kansas, 36; M.E, Yale, 38. Instr. elec. eng, S.Dak. State Col, 39-40; elec. engr, Hobart Bros. Co, 40; instr, U.S. Air Force Radio & Radar Schs, 40-42; sr. engr, Victor Div, Radio Corp. of Am, 46-50; sr. engr. & proj. leader, systs. develop, MOTOROLA, INC, 50-, sect. head in charge integrated circuit sect, WEST. MIL. ELECTRONIC CTR, 60-67, SR. ELEC. ENGR, TACTICAL ELECTRONICS DEPT, 67- U.S.A.A.F, 42-46, Capt. Sr. mem. Inst. Elec. & Electronics Eng. Automation in field of test equipment; design of transistor oscillator circuits; application of all types of integrated circuits to military equipment. Address: 30 E. Colter, Phoenix, AZ 85012.

EBERHARD, WILLIAM GRANVILLE, b. Boston, Mass, Sept. 15, 43; m. 67; c. 2. BIOLOGY. A.B, Harvard, 65, Ph.D.(biol), 69. ASST. PROF. BIOL, UNIV. VALLE, COLOMBIA, 69- Animal behavior and evolution; natural history of insects; web forms of spiders. Address: Depto. Biologia, Universidad del Valle, Cali, Colombia.

EBERHARDT, J(OHN) E(RNST), b. Ames, Iowa, Dec. 5, 11; m. 40; c. 2. CHEMICAL ENGINEERING. Ch.E, Cincinnati, 33; Sc.D.(chem. eng), Mass. Inst. Tech, 36. Instr. chem. eng, Mass. Inst. Tech, 35-36, dir. Buffalo Sta, sch. chem. eng, practice, 36-38, asst. prof, 37-38; res. engr, BETHLEHEM STEEL CO, 38-56, asst. mgr. res, 56-64, gen. mgr, HOMER RES. LABS, 64-69, ASST. V.PRES. RES, 69- Am. Inst. Chem. Eng; Am. Chem. Soc; Am. Inst. Mining, Metall. & Petrol. Eng. Metallurgy of iron and steel; heat transfer combustion of fuels; furnace design. Address: R.D. 4, Bethlehem, PA 18015.

EBERHARDT, L(ESTER) L(EE), b. Valley City, N.Dak, Oct. 15, 23; m. 44; c. 3. BIOLOGY. B.S, N.Dak. State Teachers Col, 46; Mich. State Col, 48-52; Ph.D.(wild life mgt), Mich. State, 60; California, Berkeley, 61-62. Biometrician, game div, State Dept. Conserv, Mich, 52-61; ECOLOGIST, PAC. NORTHWEST LAB, BATTELLE MEM. INST, 62- Med. Dept, U.S.A, 43-46. AAAS; Wildlife Soc; Biomet. Soc; Ecol. Soc. Am; Am. Statist. Asn. Animal population research; statistical studies in ecology. Address: 2528 W. Klamath Ave, Kennewick, WA 99336.

EBERHARDT, MANFRED KARL, b. Heidenheim, Ger, Dec. 5, 30. ORGANIC CHEMISTRY. Ph.D.(org. chem), Univ. Tübingen, 57. Res. assoc, Univ. Chicago, 57-59; Univ. Ark, 59-60; Univ. Notre Dame, 60-62; fel. radiation chem. & org. chem, Mellon Inst, 62-64; SCIENTIST, Munich Tech, 65-67; P.R. NUCLEAR CTR, 67- Am. Chem. Soc. Mechanism of organic reactions, free radicals, quantum chemistry and radiation chemistry. Address: Puerto Rico Nuclear Center, Caparra Heights Station, San Juan, PR 00935.

EBERHARDT, NIKOLAI, b. Rakvere, Estonia, July 2, 30; m. 56; c. 4. MICROWAVE ELECTRONICS, ELECTROMAGNETICS. Dipl. physics, Univ. Munich, 57; Ph.D.(physics), Munich Inst. Technol, 62. Res. engr, Siemens und Halske A.G, Ger, 56-62; assoc. prof. ELEC. ENG, LEHIGH UNIV, 62-70, PROF, 70- Consult, Bell Tel. Labs, 63- Physics of magnetically confined electron beams; color display tubes; theoretical and experimental investigations in the area of passive microwave devices, especially ferrite devices and filters. Address: Dept. of Electrical Engineering, Lehigh University, Bethlehem, PA 18015.

EBERHARDT, ROBERT LOUIS, b. Ames, Iowa, June 22, 20; m. 43; c. 3. MARINE ECOLOGY. A.B, California, Berkeley, 49; M.S, Utah State, 50; California, Los Angeles, 63-65. Food & drug inspector, State of Calif, 50, aquatic biologist, 50-54; design engr, Todd Shipyards Corp, 54-57; admin. scientist exobiol, Space Tech. Corp, 57-60; res. scientist, marine lab, Lockheed Aircraft Corp, 60-69; INSTR. MARINE TECHNOL, SAN DIEGO COMMUNITY COLS, 69- Lectr, exten. div, California & U.S. Naval Res. Officers Sch, 61-66. Consult. bioacoustics, U.S. Naval Oceanog. Off, 64-65, oceanog. technician training, U.S. Naval Training Devices Center, Calif, 64-66; coastal resources; state & private groups, 69- U.S.N, 38-45, Res, 46-70, Lt. Comdr. Fisheries Soc.(exec. v.pres, 66); Wildlife Soc; fel. Geog. Soc. Am. Biogeography; distribution patterns and behavior of marine organisms of importance in commercial programs and naval warfare; training methods and curriculum development for marine technicians. Address: San Diego Community Colleges, 835 12th Ave, San Diego, CA 92101.

EBERHARDT, WILLIAM HENRY, b. Montclair, N.J, Feb. 11, 20; m. 46; c. 3. PHYSICAL CHEMISTRY. A.B, Hopkins, 41; Ph.D.(phys. chem), Calif. Inst. Tech, 45. Asst, Calif. Inst. Tech, 41-44, instr, 44-46; asst. prof, GA. INST. TECHNOL, 46-50; assoc. prof, 50-55, PROF, 55- Summer lectr, Illinois, 56. Hon. fel, Minnesota, 53; vis. prof, Harvard, 64. AAAS; Am. Chem. Soc. Visible and ultraviolet spectroscopy; molecular structure. Address: School of Chemistry, Georgia Institute of Technology, Atlanta, GA 30332.

EBERHART, BRUCE MACLEAN, b. San Jose, Calif, Oct. 14, 27; m. 51; c. 3. BIOCHEMICAL GENETICS. A.B, San Jose State Col, 50; Ph.D. Stanford, 56. Instr. GENETICS, Princeton, 56-58, asst. prof, 58-63; PROF. BIOL. & HEAD DEPT, UNIV. N.C, GREENSBORO, 63- U.S.N.R, 46-50. Genetics Soc. Am. Genetic control of enzyme synthesis in microbes, particularly Neurospora; role of enzymes in cellular metabolism and differentiation. Address: Dept. of Biology, University of North Carolina at Greensboro, Greensboro, NC 27412.

EBERHART, DALE R(AYMOND), b. Savannah, Ohio, Dec. 6, 06; m. 28; c. 7. CHEMISTRY. A.B, Ohio State, 29, M.S, 33, Ph.D.(chem), 35. Res. chemist, E.I. du Pont de Nemours & Co, 29-31; mem. jr. staff, Ohio State, 31-35; res. chemist, Calco Chem. Co, 35-46, res. fel, 46-50, develop. group leader, Am. Cyanamid Co, 50-55, sr. chemist, 55-70; RETIRED. Fel. Am. Inst. Chem; Am. Chem. Soc. Azo dyes and intermediates; absorption spectroscopy; thioindigo and anthraquinone dyes and intermediates; triazine compounds; optical bleaching agents; synthetic plant growth materials; identification of diverse commercial organic compounds. Address: 319 Beechwood Ave, Middlesex, NJ 08846.

EBERHART, GLENN H, b. Loveland, Colo, Dec. 11, 34; m. 71. PHARMACOLOGY, CLINICAL PHARMACY. B.S, Univ. Denver, 56; M.S, Univ. Calif, San Francisco, 64, Ph.D.(pharmacol), 66. Fel. pharmacol, Univ. Minn, 66-68; asst. prof, UNIV. MO-KANSAS CITY, 68-71, LECTR. MED, MED. SCH, 71- U.S.N.R.R, 57-60, Lt. AAAS; Am. Pharmaceut. Asn; Am. Asn. Cols. Pharm. Effects of drugs in neonatal animals; mechanism of analgesia of morphine. Address: Dept. of Pharmacology, University of Missouri-Kansas City, Kansas City, MO 64110.

EBERHART, H(OWARD) D(AVIS), b. Lima, Ohio, Aug. 16, 06; m. 61; c. 2. CIVIL ENGINEERING. B.S, Oregon, 29; M.S, Ore. State Col, 35. Coach & instr, high sch, 29-33; jr. topog. engr, U.S. Geol. Surv, 34; mem. staff, U.S. Eng. Off, Bonneville Dam, 35-36; instr. CIVIL ENG, UNIV. CALIF, BERKELEY, 36-39, asst. prof, 39-43, assoc. prof, 43-48, PROF, 48-, RES. ENGR. & V.CHMN, BIOMECH. LAB, UNIV. HOSP, SAN FRANCISCO, 70-, chmn. dept, univ, 59-63. Fulbright lectr, Assiut, 64-65. Consult, Consol. Vultee Aircraft Corp, 43-44; in charge res. concrete pavement invests, Hamilton Field, 44; res. proj, cmt. prosthetic res. & develop, Nat. Res. Coun, 45-, mem-at-large, div. eng. & indust. res, 60-66. Fel. Am. Soc. Civil Eng; Am. Soc. Eng. Educ; Am. Concrete Inst; Soc. Exp. Stress Analysis. Structural engineering; biomechanics; experimental stress analysis. Address: Dept. of Civil Engineering, University of California, Berkeley, CA 94708.

EBERHART, JAMES G, b. Columbus, Ohio, Feb. 6, 36; m. 58; c. 2. PHYSICAL CHEMISTRY. B.S, Ohio State Univ, 57, Kettering Found. fel, 62; Ph.D.(phys. chem), 63. Tech. staff mem, surface chem. & physics, Sandia Corp, 63-68; ASSOC. CHEMIST, CHEM. ENG. DIV, ARGONNE NAT. LAB, 68- Am. Chem. Soc; Am. Inst. Mining, Metall. & Petrol. Eng; Am. Vacuum Soc. Surface chemistry; adsorption; catalysis; isotope separation; gas plating; thin film adhesion; surface tension; wetting by liquid metals; critical properties; grain boundary groove growth; nucleation; estimation of thermodynamic properties. Address: Chemical Engineering Division, Argonne National Lab, Argonne, IL 60439.

EBERHART, PAUL, b. Douglas Co, Kans, May 21, 06; m. 40; c. 2. MATHEMATICS. B.S, Washburn, 28; M.A, Kansas, 29; Chicago, 34; Ph.D.(math), Brown, 43. Asst. instr. MATH, Kansas, 29-30; instr, Brown, 30-37; instr, WASHBURN UNIV, 37-38, asst. prof, 38-42, assoc. prof, 42-43, PROF, 43-, HEAD DEPT, 42- Am. Math. Soc; Math. Asn. Am. Fourier series; summability; summability of derived and conjugate derived Fourier series. Address: Dept. of Mathematics, Washburn University, Topeka, KS 66621.

EBERHART, ROBERT J, b. Lock Haven, Pa, Sept. 9, 30; m. 53; c. 4. PHYSIOLOGY, VETERINARY MEDICINE. A.B, Cornell, 52; V.M.D, Pennsylvania, 59; Ph.D.(physiol), Pa. State, 66. Instr. vet. sci, Pa. State, 59-63; fel, Am. Vet. Med. Asn, 63-65; asst. prof. VET. SCI, PA. STATE UNIV, 66-71, ASSOC. PROF, 71- U.S.N, 52-53, Lt.(jg). Am. Vet. Med. Asn. Bovine mastitis; adrenal cortical physiology in cattle. Address: Dept. of Veterinary Science, Pennsylvania State University, University Park, PA 16802.

EBERHART, STEVE A, b. Keya Paha, S.Dak, Nov. 11, 31; m. 53; c. 4. GENETICS, STATISTICS. B.Sc, Nebraska, 52, M.Sc, 58; Ph.D.(genetics, statist), N.C. State, 61. RES. GENETICIST, Iowa State, U.S. DEPT. AGR, 61-64, Nat. Agr. Res. Sta, Kenya, 64-68, AGR. RES. SERV, 68- Arthur S. Flemming Award, 70. U.S.A.F, 52-56, 1st Lt. Am. Soc. Agron; Biomet. Soc. Statistical genetics of maize, including estimation of additive, dominance and epistatic variances; development of a model to study gene action in diallels of fixed varieties and to predict variety and variety cross performance. Address: Dept. of Agronomy, Iowa State University, Ames, IA 50010.

EBERL, J(AMES) J, b. Dunkirk, N.Y, Oct. 7, 16; m. 44. PHYSICAL CHEMISTRY. B.A, Buffalo, 38, Ph.D.(phys. chem), 41; Adv. Mgt. Prog, Harvard, 55. Instr. chem, Delaware, 41-42; mgr. paper makers chem. div, Hercules Powder Co, 42-43; sr. res. fel, Mellon Inst, 43-44; dir. spec. prod. lab, Johnson & Johnson, 44-48; res. dir, Scott Paper Co, 48-60, asst. v.pres. res, Pa, 60-71; PRES. & CHIEF EXEC. OFF, NEWBOLD, INC, 71- Spec. lectr, Univ. Del, 42-43; trustee, res. fund, Phila. Gen. Hosp, 63-; mem. bd. mgrs, Franklin Inst, mem. labs. comt, finance comt, personnel policy comt; mem. bd. mgrs, Bartol. Res. Found; res. mgt, group Phila. Jessie Ketcham Medal, City of Buffalo, 30. Am. Chem. Soc; Tech. Asn. Pulp & Paper Chem; Am. Inst. Chem. Proteins; cellulose; synthetic fibers; high polymers; paper coatings; plastic fabrication; inorganic cements; sterilization; biological active compounds; adhesives; plasticizers; rosin sizing; hydrocarbons; magnetic susceptibility; wax; pulping; bleaching; papermaking; sanitary paper products; specialty papers. Address: Room 410, Franklin Institute Research Labs. Bldg, 20th & Race Sts, Philadelphia, PA 19103.

EBERLE, HELEN I, b. Oakland, Calif, Mar. 2, 32; m. 58; c. 3. MOLECULAR BIOLOGY, BIOPHYSICS. B.S, Calif. State Col, Los Angeles, 56; Ph.D. (microbiol), Univ. Calif, Los Angeles, 65. Pub. Health microbiologist, Los Angeles Co. Health Dept, 56-60; Nat. Insts. Health fels, Kans. State Univ, 65-67; UNIV. ROCHESTER, 67-68, instr. RADIATION BIOL. & BIOPHYS, 68-69, ASST. PROF, 70- Am. Cancer Soc. grant, 70-72. Faculty res. award, Am. Cancer Soc, 69. AAAS; Am. Soc. Microbiol; Biophys. Soc. Mechanism and regulation of DNA replication. Address: Dept. of Radiation Biology & Biophysics, University of Rochester, Rochester, NY 14620.

EBERLE, JON W(ILLIAM), b. Chillicothe, Ohio, Aug. 28, 34; m. 56; c. 4. BIOMEDICAL ENGINEERING, ELECTROMAGNETICS. B.S, Ohio State Univ, 57, M.S, 60, Ph.D.(elec. eng), 64. Res. assoc. phased arrays, antenna lab, Ohio State Univ, 57-61, assoc. supvr, 61-65; mem. tech. staff, Tex. Instruments Inc, 65-66, mgr. advan. radar develop. br, 66, surface systs. dept, 66-68, corp. mkt, 68-69; v.pres. biomed, Intermed Corp, 69-70; consult. to dean, BIOMED. & ELEC. ENG, SOUTH. METHODIST UNIV, 70-71, ASSOC. PROF, 71- Fel, dept. bus. admin, Ohio State Univ, 64-65; res. scientist, div. thoracic & cardiovasc. surg, dept. of surg, med. sch, Univ. Tex, 70-; mem, subpanel on elec. safety, Am. Nat. Standards Inst, 70-; elec. engr, Vet. Hosp, Dallas, 71- Inst. Elec. & Electronics Eng; Asn. Advan. Med. Instrumentation. Membrane oxygenators having heparin ionically bound to their surfaces; continuous monitoring of pH of blood and partial pressures of O_2 and CO_2 in blood; computerized medical records; x-ray holography. Address: Electronic Sciences Center, Institute of Technology, Southern Methodist University, Dallas, TX 75222.

EBERLE, MARCEL KARL, b. Schaenis, Switz, May 5, 34; m. 63; c. 2. ORGANIC CHEMISTRY. B.S, State Univ. St. Gallen, Switz, 54; dipl, Swiss Fed. Inst. Technol, 58, Ph.D.(org. chem), 62. Nat. Insts. Health grant, synthetic org. chem, Yale, 62-64; res. asst, Univ. Basel, 64-65; RES. CHEMIST, Eastman Res, Zurich, Switz, 65-66; SANDOZ PHARMACEUT. INC, 67- Am. Chem. Soc. Structure and biosynthesis of natural products; synthesis in heterocyclic chemistry. Address: Sandoz Pharmaceutical Inc, Route 10, East Hanover, NJ 07936.

EBERLEIN, G(EORGE) DONALD, b. New Brunswick, N.J, Nov. 21, 20; m. 69; c. 1. GEOLOGY. B.S, Yale, 42; Claremont Cols, 46; Stanford, 46-49. Geologist, Big Sandy Mine, Inc, Ariz, 41; metals sect, U.S. GEOL. SURV, 42-47, BR. ALASKAN MINERAL RESOURCES, 47-53, staff geologist, mineral deposits, 53-57, asst. br. chief, 57-59, br. chief, 59-63, RES. GEOLOGIST, 63- Teaching fel. & asst, Stanford; Binney fel. & Penfield prize, Yale. U.S.N, 44-46. Fel. Geol. Soc. Am; Mineral. Soc. Am; Soc. Econ. Geol; Mineral. Asn. Can. fel. Geol. Soc. London. Petrology of igneous and metamorphic rocks; mineral resources of Alaska; optical crystallography. Address: Branch of Alaskan Mineral Resources, U.S. Geological Survey, 345 Middlefield Rd, Menlo Park, CA 94025.

EBERLEIN, PATRICIA JAMES, b. Wash, D.C, July 15, 25; m. 46, 56; c. 7. MATHEMATICS. B.S, Chicago, 44; Ph.D.(math), Mich. State, 55. Instr. math, Wayne, 55-56; mathematician, Inst. Adv. Study, 56-57; res. assoc, comput. ctr, Univ. Rochester, 57-61, asst. dir. anal, 61-68; ASSOC. PROF. MATH. & COMPUT. SCI, STATE UNIV. N.Y. BUFFALO, 68- Am. Math. Soc; Soc. Indust. & Appl. Math; Asn. Comput. Mach. Applied mathematics; numerical analysis; linear algebra. Address: Dept. of Mathematics, State University of New York at Buffalo, 4246 Ridge Lea Rd, Amherst, NY 14226.

EBERLEIN, WALTER R(ATHER), b. Shawano, Wis, Aug. 29, 21. PEDIATRICS, ENDOCRINOLOGY. Harvard Col, 39-42, M.D, Harvard, 45. Fel. pediat, Mayo Found, 49-51; asst, Kinderspital, Zurich, 51-52; fel. pediat. endocrinol, Johns Hopkins Hosp, 52-53; res. fel, Mass. Gen. Hosp, 53-54; instr. PEDIAT, SCH. MED, UNIV. PA, 54-55, assoc, 55-56, asst. prof, 56-60, assoc. prof, 60-67, PROF, 67-, DIR. CHEM. LABS, CHILDREN'S HOSP. PHILA, 58-, ENDOCRINOLOGIST, 64-, assoc. endocrinologist, 54-63. Mead Johnson Award, Am. Acad. Pediat, 57. Med.C, 46-48, Capt. AAAS; Soc. Pediat. Res; Endocrine Soc; Am. Soc. Clin. Invest. Pediatric endocrinology; steroid metabolism and laboratory methodology. Address: Children's Hospital of Philadelphia, 1740 Bainbridge St, Philadelphia, PA 19146.

EBERLEIN, W(ILLIAM) F(REDERICK), b. Shawano, Wis, June 25, 17; m. 43, 56; c. 7. MATHEMATICS. A.B, Harvard, 38, Ph.D.(math), 42; M.A, Wisconsin, 39. Propeller res. analyst, Bur. Ships, 41-42, instr. math, Purdue, 46; Michigan, 46-47; mem, Inst. Adv. Study, 47-48; asst. prof. math, Wisconsin, 48-54, assoc. prof, 54-55; vis. prof, Wayne State, 55-56; mem. inst. math. sci, N.Y. Univ, 56-57; PROF. MATH, UNIV. ROCHESTER, 57- Mem, ergodic theory panel, Int. Cong. Mathematicians, 50; vis. prof, Oxford Univ, fall, 70. U.S.N.R, 43-46, Res, 46-54. Am. Math. Soc; Math. Asn. Am; Swiss Math. Soc. Functional analysis; mathematical physics. Address: Dept. of Mathematics, University of Rochester, Rochester, NY 14627.

EBERLY, JOSEPH H(ENRY), b. Carlisle, Pa, Oct. 19, 35; m. 60; c. 3. THEORETICAL PHYSICS. B.S, Pa. State, 57; M.S, Stanford, 59, Ph.D.(physics), 62. Res. physicist, Stanford Linear Accelerator Ctr, 62; resident res. assoc, nuclear physics div, U.S. Naval Ord. Lab, Md, 62-65; vis. res. assoc. QUANTUM OPTICS, UNIV. ROCHESTER, 65-66, res. assoc-asst. prof, 66-67, asst. prof, 67-69, ASSOC. PROF, 69- Nat. Acad. Sci-Nat. Res. Coun. resident res. associateship, 62-64; lectr, Univ. Md, 64-65; Nat. Acad. Sci. vis. lectr, east. Europe, 70; vis. mem. dept. physics & Stanford Linear Accelerator Ctr, Stanford Univ, 71-72; consult, Eastman Kodak Res. Labs. U.S. Navy Civilian Serv. Award, 64. Am. Phys. Soc. Electromagnetic interactions of atomic particles; theory of high intensity photon beams; quantum electrodynamics; quantum optics. Address: Dept. of Physics & Astronomy, University of Rochester, Rochester, NY 14627.

EBERLY, WILLIAM R(OBERT), b. North Manchester, Ind, Oct. 4, 26; m. 46; c. 3. ZOOLOGY. A.B, Manchester Col, 48; M.A, Indiana, 55, Ph.D.(zool), 58. Sci. instr, pub. schs, Ind, 47-52; asst. zool, Indiana, 52-55; asst. prof. BIOL, MANCHESTER COL, 55-59, assoc. prof, 59-67, PROF, 67- Vis. scientist, Uppsala, 63-64. Phycol. Soc. Am; Am. Soc. Limnol. & Oceanog; Int. Asn. Theoret. & Appl. Limnol; Int. Phycol. Soc. Oxygen production in lakes and lake typology; systematics and ecology of fresh water and terrestrial crustacea; ecology and taxonomy of blue-green algae. Address: 1515 Sunset Dr, North Manchester, IN 46962.

EBERSOLE, A(LVIN) J(AMES), b. Filer, Idaho, Apr. 10, 21; m. 47; c. 3. CHEMICAL ENGINEERING. B.S, Wisconsin, 44. Res. engr, Calif. Res. Corp, 44-50; sr. res. engr, FLUOR CORP, LTD, 50-57, comput. engr, 57-66, CHIEF COMPUT. ENGR, 66- Am. Inst. Chem. Eng. Treating of gasoline and refining oils; investigation of bubble cap performance; gas treating; sulfur dioxide recovery; application of digital computer to engineering problems. Address: Fluor Corp, Ltd, 2500 S. Atlantic Blvd, Los Angeles, CA 90022.

EBERSOLE, GEORGE DAVID, b. Plattsmouth, Nebr, July 11, 36; m. 57; c. 2. ENGINEERING. B.S, Milwaukee Sch. Eng, 61; Caterpillar Tractor fel. & M.S, Univ. Wis, Madison, 63; Ph.D.(chem. eng), Univ. Tulsa, 71. Res. engr, mfg. opers, Falk Corp, 61-63; consult. engr, 63; GROUP LEADER, FUELS & LUBRICANTS, PHILLIPS PETROL. CO, 63- Mem. faculty, Univ. Tulsa, 71- AAAS; Soc. Automotive Eng. Relationships between hydrocarbon fuel composition and lubricants and engine performance, including air pollution. Address: 1424 Arbor Dr, Bartlesville, OK 74003.

EBERSON, FREDERICK, b. N.Y.C, Feb. 10, 92; m. 25; c. 2. BACTERIOLOGY, PREVENTIVE MEDICINE. B.S, City Col. New York, 12; fel, Iowa State, 14, M.S, 15; M.A, Columbia, 16, Ph.D, 18; Hennepin Co. Tuberc. Soc. fel, Minnesota, 22-23, M.B. & M.D, 24. Asst, Mass. Inst. Tech, 12-13; instr. bact, Iowa State, 14; res. bacteriologist in charge dept. res. bact. & path, N.Manchurian Plague Prev. Serv, China, 16-17; asst. path. & bact, Rockefeller Inst, 17-19; assoc. dermat. & in charge syphilis res. lab, Washington (St. Louis), 19-21; assoc. dermat. res. & in charge lab, Mayo Clin, 22-23; instr. med, med. sch, California, 24-26, asst. prof, 26-33, physician, univ. hosp. & chest clin, 24-33, epidemiologist, 26-31; bur. commun. diseases, Dept. Pub. Health, Calif, 34-38; pathologst & chief lab. serv, U.S. Vet. Admin. Facility, 38-40; pathologist & dir. labs, Gallinger Hosp, Wash, D.C, 40-42; pathologist & chief lab, serv, Vet. Admin. Hosps, 42-52; assoc. prof. path. & bact, col. med. Tennessee, 52-54; tri-county health dir, State Dept. Health, Ky, 54-56; assoc. prof. bact. & prev. med. & dir. health & clin. serv, West. Ky. Univ, 56-62, emer. prof, 62-70; RETIRED. Mem. comt. standardization Wasserman technol, 21-22; physician-in-chief, children's tuberc. dept, San Francisco Hosp, 27-28; dir. clin. labs. & res. & chief epidemiologist, Mt. Zion Hosp, 29-32; assoc. clin. prof. community med, med. ctr, Univ. Ky, 64-67, clin. prof, 67-70; instr, Rockefeller Inst. Army Med. Sch; Army Lab, Yale. U.S.A, 17-19. Fel. AAAS; Am. Med. Asn; Am. Soc. Microbiol; Soc. Exp. Biol. & Med; fel. Am. Pub. Health Asn; fel. Col. Am. Path. Pathology; immunology; tuberculosis; bacterial strains; syphilis; poliomyelitis; plague; infectious diseases; epidemiology; antibiotics; bacterial variation; medical history; community medicine; pathology. Address: 3262C 67th Terr. S, St. Petersburg, FL 33712.

EBERSPACHER, WARREN A(RTHUR), b. St. Paul, Minn, June 8, 29; m. 52; c. 2. AERONAUTICAL ENGINEERING. B.A.E, Minnesota, 52. Aeronaut. engr, Naval Missile Center, 52-53, supvry. aero. res. engr, 55-58; sr. engr, Lockheed Missiles & Space Co, 58-59; head space res. div, NAVAL MISSILE CTR, 59-66, ocean eng. br, 66-68, tech. consult, SYST. INTEGRATION DIV, 68-69, ASSOC. HEAD, DIV. & CHMN. NAVY INDUST. FUNDING WORKING GROUP, 69-; PRES, SYST. SYNTHESIS INC, OJAI, 69- Aeronaut. engr, Cessna Aircraft Co, 53; mem, Creative Educ. Found, 67- U.S.N, 53-55, Res, 55-70, Comdr.(Ret). AAAS; Soc. Res. Adminr; World Future Soc. System engineering; engineering management; organizational development. Address: 1357 McNell Rd, Ojai, CA 93023.

EBERSTEIN, ARTHUR, b. Chicago, Ill, Apr. 23, 28; m. 61; c. 2. BIOPHYSICS. B.S, Ill. Inst. Technol, 50; M.S, Univ. Ill, 51; Ph.D.(biophys), Ohio State Univ, 57. Nat. Sci. Found. fel, Copenhagen Univ, 57-58, Nat. Insts. Health fel, 58-59; res. scientist biophys, Inst. Muscle Disease, 59-61; physics, Am. Bosch Arma Corp, 61-63; head med. electronics dept, Lundy Electronics & Systs, Inc, 63-64; ASST. PROF. BIOPHYS, SCH. MED, N.Y. UNIV, 64-, ASSOC. PROF. REHAB. MED, 70- U.S.A, 54-56. Biophys. Soc; Am. Physiol. Soc. Muscle physiology. Address: Institute of Rehabilitation Medicine, New York University Medical Center, 400 E. 34th St, New York, NY 10016.

EBERT, ANDREW G(ABRIEL), b. Brooklyn, N.Y, Jan. 5, 36; m. 61; c. 3. PHARMACOLOGY, BIONUCLEONICS. B.S, Long Island, 57; M.S, Purdue, 61, Ph.D.(pharmacol), 62. Sr. res. scientist, Squibb Inst. Med. Res. Div, Olin Mathieson Chem. Corp, 61-65; supvr. pharmacol, INT. MINERALS & CHEM. CORP, 65-68, mgr. pharmacol. & govt. registrn, 68-70, MGR. PROD. SAFETY EVAL, 70- Am. Pharmaceut. Asn; Am. Soc. Pharmacol. & Exp. Therapeut; Soc. Toxicol. Metabolic fate of drugs; biochemical pharmacology; mechanisms of drug tolerance; young animal sensitivity to drugs; tracer methodology; metabolic fate of barbiturates; phenothiazines; safety evaluation of food, food components, and agricultural chemicals; toxicology. Address: Growth Sciences Center, International Minerals & Chemical Corp, Libertyville, IL 60048.

EBERT, EARL ERNEST, b. Oakland, Calif, Sept. 28, 31; m. 57; c. 3. FISHERIES BIOLOGY. B.A, San Jose State Col, 59; Calif. State Col. Long Beach, 65. Aquatic biologist, marine resources lab, CALIF. DEPT. FISH & GAME, 60-63, asst. marine biologist, 63-66, assoc. marine biologist, Menlo Park, 66-70, SR. MARINE BIOLOGIST & DIR. SHELLFISH CULT. LAB, MARINE CULT. LAB, MONTEREY, 70- U.S.M.C, 51-54, Sgt. Marine biology-diving; development of underwater sampling techniques; environmental studies in regard to marine submarine outfall effluents; fish and invertebrate behavior; population and ecological studies of abalones; mariculture feasibility studies. Address: Shellfish Culture Lab, Marine Culture Lab, California Dept. of Fish & Game, Granite Canyon, Coast Route, Monterey, CA 93940.

EBERT, IAN O, b. Mingo, Iowa, Mar. 13, 20; m. 45; c. 2. ELECTRICAL ENGINEERING. B.S, Iowa State Col, 42; M.S, Illinois, 47. Electronic res. engr, Naval Res. Lab, 43-46, 47-48; asst, Illinois, 46-47; asst. prof. ELEC. ENG, MICH. STATE UNIV, 48-54, ASSOC. PROF, 54- Adv, eng. col, Poona, 63-64; vis. engr, eng. summer insts, India, 65, 66, 70. U.S.N.R, 45-, Comdr. AAAS; Am. Soc. Eng. Educ; Inst. Elec. & Electronics Eng. Semiconductor physics and electronics; audio circuits and acoustical systems; electronic circuits; communication system development. Address: Dept. of Electrical Engineering, Michigan State University, East Lansing, MI 48823.

EBERT, JAMES D(AVID), b. Bentleyville, Pa, Dec. 11, 21; m. 46; c. 3. EXPERIMENTAL EMBRYOLOGY. A.B, Washington & Jefferson Col, 42, hon. Sc.D, 69; Bruce fel, Hopkins, 49-50, Ph.D.(biol), 50. Jr. instr. biol, Hopkins, 46-49; instr, Mass. Inst. Tech, 50-51; asst. prof. zool, Indiana, 51-54, assoc. prof, 54-55; DIR. DEPT. EMBRYOL, CARNEGIE INST, 56- Vis. scientist, Brookhaven Nat. Lab, 53-54; hon. prof, Hopkins, 56-; Philips vis. prof, Haverford Col, 60-61; Patten vis. prof, Indiana, 62-63; dir. embryol. training. prog, Marine Biol. Lab, Woods Hole, 62-, trustee, 64-, pres. & dir, 70- Mem. adv. panel, comt. growth, Nat. Res. Coun, 53-55, genetic & develop. biol, Nat. Sci. Found, 55-56, div. comt. biol. & med. sci, 63-67; mem. comt. basic res. aging, Am. Inst. Biol. Sci, 55-60, pres. inst, 63; mem. cell biol. study sect, U.S. Pub. Health Serv, 58-62, Comn. Undergrad. Ed. Biol. Sci, 63-67; bd. sci. coun, Nat. Cancer Inst, 67-71; bd. sci. overseers, Jackson Lab, 67-; bd. dir, Oak Ridge Assoc. Univs, 67-71; vis. comts, Mass. Inst. Technol, 59-68; Case West. Reserve Univ, 64-68; Univ. Pa, 67-69; Columbia Univ, 67-69; Univ. Ore, 67-; Harvard, 69-; Princeton, 70-; Nat. Insts. Health lectr, 67; Yamagiwa Mem. lectr, Tokyo, 68. First Distinguished Serv. Award, Wash. & Jefferson Col, 65; Wisdom Award of Honor, 70. U.S.N.R, 42-52, Lt. Nat. Acad. Sci; AAAS; Soc. Develop. Biol.(pres, 57-58); Am. Soc. Nat; Am. Soc. Zool.(pres, 70); Soc. Gen. Physiol; Am. Asn. Anat; fel. Am. Acad. Arts & Sci; N.Y. Acad. Sci; fel. Int. Inst. Embryol. Acquisition of biological specificity; protein synthesis and interactions in development; heart development; graft versus host reactions; viruses as tools in developmental biology; melanogenesis; amino acid and vitamin metabolism in development; tumorigenic viruses; viral oncogenic sequences; cell replicating mechanisms. Address: Dept. of Embryology, Carnegie Institution of Washington, Baltimore, MD 21210.

EBERT, LYNN J, b. Sandusky, Ohio, Apr. 17, 20; m. 43; c. 4. METALLURGICAL ENGINEERING. B.S, Case, 41, M.S, 43, Ph.D.(metall), 54. From asst. to res. assoc, CASE WEST. RESERVE UNIV, 41-51, sr. res. assoc, 51-54, asst. prof. METALL. ENG, 54-57, assoc. prof, 57-65, PROF, 65- Am. Soc. Metals; Am. Inst. Mining, Metall. & Petrol. Eng. Mechanical and physical behaviors of ferrous and non-ferrous metals and alloys. Address: Dept. of Metals & material Science, Case Western Reserve University, Cleveland, OH 44106.

EBERT, PAUL A(LLEN), b. Columbus, Ohio, Augl 11, 32; m. 54; c. 3. CARDIOVASCULAR SURGERY, PHYSIOLOGY. B.S, Ohio State Univ, 54,

M.D, 58. Intern SURG, Johns Hopkins Hosp, 58-59, asst. resident, 59-60; sr. resident, clin. of surg, Nat. Heart Inst, 60-62; asst. resident, Johns Hopkins Hosp, 62-65, chief resident, 65-66; asst. prof. med. ctr, Duke Univ, 66-68, assoc. prof, 68-71; PROF. & CHMN. DEPT, MED. COL, CORNELL UNIV, 71-, CHIEF SURGEON, N.Y. HOSP-CORNELL MED. CTR, 71- Nat. Cancer Inst. fel, 62-63; Mead Johnson scholar, 64; Markle scholar, 67. U.S.P.H.S, 60-62. Am. Med. Asn; Asn. Acad. Surg; Am. Heart Asn; Am. Col. Surg; Int. Cardiovasc. Soc; Soc. Univ. Surg; Soc. Vascular Surg; Am. Surg. Asn. Address: Dept. of Surgery, New York Hospital-Cornell Medical Center, 525 E. 68th St, New York, NY 10021.

EBERT, PAUL J, b. New Orleans, La, Jan. 11, 36; m. 57; c. 4. PHYSICS. B.S, La. State, 57, M.S, 59, Ph.D.(physics), 62. PHYSICIST, U.S. Air Force Sch. Aerospace Med, 61-64; LAWRENCE LIVERMORE LAB, UNIV. CALIF, 64- U.S.A.F, 61-64, 1st Lt. Am. Phys. Soc. Characteristics of nuclear radiation detectors; interaction of radiation with matter. Address: Lawrence Livermore Lab, P.O. Box 808, Livermore, CA 94550.

EBERT, PHILIP E, b. Milwaukee, Wis, Sept. 4, 29; m. 57; c. 2. ORGANIC & POLYMER CHEMISTRY. B.S.Ch.E, Purdue, 51; Ph.D.(org. polymer chem), Pennsylvania, 60. Chem. engr. res. & develop, Hercules Powder Co, 51-55; res. chemist textile fibers, E.I. DU PONT DE NEMOURS & CO, 60-64, tech. serv. rep. DYEING & FINISHING, 64-66, TECH. SERV. SUPVR, 66- U.S.M.C.R, 51-54, Res, 54-60, 1st Lt. Am. Chem. Soc; Am. Asn. Textile Chem. & Colorists. Manmade fibers; applications of dyeing, finishing and textile chemistry; acidcatalyzed polymerization of epoxides. Address: 611 Andover Rd, Edenridge, Wilmington, DE 19803.

EBERT, RICHARD VINCENT, b. St. Paul, Minn, Oct. 25, 12; m. 47. CLINICAL MEDICINE. B.S, Chicago, 33, M.D, 37. Intern, Boston City Hosp, Mass, 37-39; asst. res. med, Peter Bent Brigham Hosp, Boston, 39-41, jr. assoc, 41-42; chief med. serv, Vet. Admin. Hosp, 46-52, 53-54; prof. MED, med. sch, Minnesota, 49-52, Clark prof, 52-53; prof, Northwestern, 53-54; PROF. & CHMN. DEPT, SCH. MED, Univ. Ark, 54-66; UNIV. MINN, MINNEAPOLIS, 66- Fel, Harvard Med. Sch, 40-42. Med.C, U.S.A, 42-45. Am. Med. Asn; Am. Col. Physicians; Am. Soc. Clin. Invest.(pres, 58); Soc. Exp. Biol. & Med; Asn. Am. Physicians. Pulmonary and cardiovascular physiology; cardiac catheterization in humans; blood volume and peripheral circulation in humans. Address: Dept. of Medicine, University of Minnesota School of Medicine, 412 Union St. S.E, Minneapolis, MN 55455.

EBERT, ROBERT H, b. Minneapolis, Minn, Sept. 10, 14; m. 39; c. 3. INTERNAL MEDICINE. B.S, Chicago, 36, M.D, 42; Rhodes scholar, Oxford, 36-39; D.Phil, 39; hon. A.M, Harvard, 64; hon. D.Sc, Northeast. Univ, 68, Univ. Md, 70; hon. LL.D, Univ. Toronto, 70. Asst. prof. MED, Chicago, 49-52; assoc. prof, 52-55, prof, 55-56; Hanna-Payne prof, Western Reserve, 56-58, John H. Hord prof, 58-64; Jackson prof, HARVARD MED. SCH, 64-65, PROF, 65-, DEAN, FACULTY MED, 65- Markle scholar, 48-; dir. med, univ. hosps, Cleveland, 56-64; mem. spec. adv. group, Vet. Admin, Wash. D.C, 59-63; chief med. serv, Mass. Gen. Hosp, 64-65; pres, Harvard Community Health Plan, 68-; mem. inst. med, Nat. Acad. Sci. Dipl, Am. Bd. Internal Med, 52, mem, 61; distinguished serv. award, Chicago, 62. U.S.N.R, 44-46, Lt. Am. Soc. Clin. Invest; Am. Thoracic Soc.(pres, 61); Asn. Am. Physicians (v.pres, 71-72); Am. Clin. & Climat. Asn; fel. Am. Col. Physicians; fel. Am. Acad. Arts & Sci; fel. Am. Pub. Health Asn. Tuberculosis and mechanisms of inflammation. Address: Faculty of Medicine, Harvard Medical School, 25 Shattuck St, Boston, MA 02115.

EBERT, THOMAS A, b. Appleton, Wis, July 10, 38; m. 60; c. 2. ECOLOGY. B.S, Wisconsin, Madison, 61; M.S, Oregon, 63, Ph.D.(biol), 66. Instr. biol, Univ. Ore, 66-67; ASST. PROF. ZOOL, Univ. Hawaii, 67-69; SAN DIEGO STATE COL, 69- AAAS; Ecol. Soc. Am. Marine ecology; population ecology of echinoderms. Address: Dept. of Biology, San Diego State College, San Diego, CA 92115.

EBERT, WESLEY W, b. Maple Grove Twp, Minn, Mar. 22, 26; m. 54; c. 5. GENETICS, BOTANY. B.S, Minnesota, 61; M.S, California, Davis, 63, Ph.D.(genetics), 64. Asst. prof. BIOL, SONOMA STATE COL, 64-67, assoc. prof, 67-71, PROF, 71-, CHMN. DEPT, 69- U.S.A, 45-46, Res, 46-69. Am. Soc. Agron. Genetics and anatomical development of Carthamas tinctorius. Address: Dept. of Biology, Sonoma State College, 1801 E, Cotati Ave, Rohnert Park, CA 94928.

EBERT, WILLIAM R(OBLEY), b. Philadelphia, Pa, Aug. 2, 22; m. 54; c. 3. PHARMACEUTICAL CHEMISTRY. B.S, Michigan, 52, M.S, 54, Smith Kline & French Labs. fel, 54-56, Ph.D.(pharmaceut, chem), 56. Teaching fel. drug anal. & master pharmacist, Michigan, 52-56; res. fel. pharmaceut, Sterling-Winthrop Res. Inst, 56-58; chief chemist, Vick Chem. Co, 58-59; dir. pharmaceut. res. & develop, Lemmon Pharmacal Co, 59-60; sci. dir. pharmaceut. res, PHILLIPS ROXANNE LABS, 60-61, dir, 61-62, asst. dir. res. & develop, 62-64, dir, 64-68, V.PRES. PHARMACEUT. RES, 68- U.S.N, 42-45. Am. Pharmaceut. Asn; Am. Soc. Hosp. Pharmacists; fel. Am. Inst. Chem; Am. Chem. Soc; Drug Info. Asn; N.Y. Acad. Sci. Study and development of graded release oral pharmaceuticals utilizing radioactive tracers; unit dose pharmaceuticals for hospital use. Address: 2259 Haverford Rd, Columbus, OH 43221.

EBERTS, F(LOYD) S(AMUEL), JR, b. Easton, Pa, Dec. 24, 24; m. 49; c. 2. BIOCHEMISTRY. B.S, Pa. State Col, 48; M.S, Wisconsin, 50, Ph.D.(biochem), 52. Asst. biochem, Wisconsin, 48-52; SR. RES. SCIENTIST, UPJOHN CO, 52- U.S.A, 43-45. Am. Chem. Soc; N.Y. Acad. Sci. Nitrogen metabolism of plant tumor tissues and tissue culture; steroid biosynthesis; drug metabolism; mechanism of drug action; biochemical pharmacology; analytical methods development; isolation techniques. Address: Dept. of Physical & Analytical Chemistry, 7261-126-2, Upjohn Co, Kalamazoo, MI 49001.

EBERTS, ROBERT EUGENE, b. Columbus, Ohio, May 30, 31; m. 53; c. 5. INORGANIC CHEMISTRY. B.S, Dayton, 53; Ph.D.(phys. chem), Iowa State, 57. Asst, Ames Lab, U.S. Atomic Energy Cmn, 53-57; inorg. res. chemist, Wyandotte Chem. Corp, 57-62; product develop. chemist, metals div, Nat. Res. Corp, 62-63, sr. chemist, 63-69; metall. eng. staff, Arthur D. Little, Inc, 69-70; MEM. STAFF, MEARL CORP, 71- U.S.A.R, 53-61, Chem.C, 57, 1st Lt. Am. Chem. Soc; Electrochem. Soc. Physical chemistry; industrial chemical research; tantalum chemistry; rare earth metals and compounds; pigments. Address: The Mearl Corp, 1057 Lower South St, Peekskill, NY 10566.

EBERWEIN, JOHN ARMAND, b. Pittsfield, Mass, Jan. 28, 33; m. 61; c. 2. ORGANIC CHEMISTRY. B.S, Vermont, 55, M.S, 57; Ph.D.(org. chem), Ohio State, 63. Res. chemist, Circleville Res. & Develop. Lab, FILM DEPT, E.I. DU PONT DE NEMOURS & CO, Ohio, 62-64, S.C, 64-69, STAFF SCIENTIST, 69- Assoc. res. dir, United Merchants & Mfrs. Res. Ctr, 67- AAAS; Am. Chem. Soc. Rearrangement reactions of cyclohexadienones and cyclohexadienols containing the trichloromethyl group; polyesters composition, properties and catalysis; films. Address: E.I. du Pont de Nemours & Co, P.O. Box 3000, Florence, SC 29501.

EBETINO, FRANK F(REDERICK), b. Rye, N.Y, Jan. 12, 27; m. 50; c. 2. ORGANIC CHEMISTRY. B.S, Ohio, 49; William S. Merrell Co. fel, Lehigh, 51-53, M.S, 53. Res. chemist, Eaton Labs. Div, Norwich Pharmacal Co, 49-51; Johns-Manville Corp, 53-55; sr. res. chemist, chem. res. div, NORWICH PHARMACAL CO, 55-60, unit leader, 60-61, chief chem. sect, 61-68, asst. dir. CHEM. DIV, 68-69, DIR, 69- U.S.A, 44-46, 1st Lt. Fel. Am. Inst. Chem; N.Y. Acad. Sci; Am. Chem. Soc; Soc. Chem. Indust. Organic synthesis in field of heterocyclic chemistry; chemical structure-biological activity relationships. Address: Research & Development Dept, Norwich Pharmacal Co, P.O. Box 191, Norwich, NY 13815.

EBIN, DAVID G, b. Los Angeles, Calif, Oct. 24, 42; m. 71. MATHEMATICS. A.B, Harvard, 64; Ph.D.(math), Mass. Inst. Technol, 67. Nat. Sci. Found. fel, 67-68; lectr. MATH, Univ. Calif, Berkeley, 68-69; ASSOC. PROF, STATE UNIV. N.Y. STONY BROOK, 69- Speaker, Int. Cong. Mathematicians, Nice, France, 70. Am. Math. Soc. Differential geometry; infinite dimensional manifolds; nonlinear partial differential equations; mathematical theory of fluid mechanics. Address: Dept. of Mathematics, State University of New York at Stony Brook, Stony Brook, NY 11790.

EBINGER, JOHN E(DWIN), b. Cincinnati, Ohio, June 2, 33; m. 56; c. 1. BOTANY, TAXONOMY. A.B, Miami (Ohio), 55; M.A, Yale, 59, Ph.D.(bot), 61. Res. asst, Conn. Agr. Exp. Sta, 61-62; ASST. PROF. BOT, Roanoke Col, 62-63; EAST. ILL. UNIV, 63- U.S.A.F, 55-58, Capt. Am. Soc. Plant Taxon; Bot. Soc. Am; Int. Asn. Plant Taxon. Monographic studies in the family Juncaceae and introgressive hybridization studies in Digitaria Gramineae. Address: Dept. of Botany, Eastern Illinois University, Charleston, IL 61920.

EBLE, JOHN NELSON, b. St. Louis, Mo, May 19, 27; m. 50; c. 3. BIOCHEMISTRY. B.S, Missouri, 49; M.S, Wisconsin, 52, Ph.D.(biochem), 54. Instr. pharmacol. & physiol, Kirksville Col, 54-56, asst. prof, 56-60; pharmacologist, DOW CHEM. CO, 60-64, ASSOC. SCIENTIST, 64-66, HUMAN HEALTH RES. LAB, 66- AAAS; Am. Physiol. Soc; Soc. Exp. Biol. & Med; Am. Soc. Pharmacol. & Exp. Therapeut; Brit. Pharmacol. Soc; Int. Soc. Biochem. Pharmacol. Warfarin; blood coagulation; interchange between somatic and autonomic nervous systems; autonomic and central nervous system pharmacology. Address: Human Health Research Labs, Dow Chemical Co, P.O. Box 10, Zionsville, IN 46077.

EBLE, T(HOMAS) E(UGENE), b. Toledo, Ohio, Sept. 15, 23; m. 45; c. 6. BIOCHEMISTRY. B.Sc, Loyola (Ill), 44; fel, Georgetown, 44-45, M.S, 46, Ph.D.(biochem), 48. Chemist, Bur. Standards, 45; Food & Drug Admin, 45-48; Harris Res. Labs, 48; res. chemist, UPJOHN CO, 48-59, SECT. HEAD, 59- AAAS; Am. Chem. Soc; Am. Oil Chem. Soc. Antibiotics; chromatographic separation methods; isolation, characterization and identification of antibiotics; biosynthesis of antibiotics; structure of antibiotics; chemical and biochemical modification of antibiotics. Address: Upjohn Co, Kalamazoo, MI 49001.

EBLIN, LAWRENCE P(OWELL), b. Rutland, Ohio, Oct. 28, 09; m. 38; c. 1. CHEMISTRY. B.S, Ohio Univ, 31; Ph.D.(phys. chem), Ohio State Univ, 35. Asst. CHEM, Ohio State Univ, 31-35; instr, OHIO UNIV, 35-41, asst. prof, 41-44, assoc. prof, 44-51, PROF, 51-, chmn. dept, 52-58, dir. summer sci. insts, 57-64, dir. freshman chem, 58-64. With Nat. Defense Res. Comt. AAAS; fel. Am. Inst. Chem; Am. Chem. Soc. Vapor pressures; dialysis; eutectic mixtures; viscosity; chemical education. Address: Dept. of Chemistry, Ohio University, Athens, OH 45701.

EBNER, CHARLES ARTHUR, b. Willimantic, Conn, Aug. 24, 40. LOW TEMPERATURE PHYSICS. A.B, Cornell, 62; M.S, Illinois, 63, Nat. Sci. Found. fels, 63-66, Ph.D.(physics), 67. Nat. Sci. Found. fel. LOW TEMPERATURE PHYSICS, Paris, 67-68; ASST. PROF, OHIO STATE UNIV, 68- Theory of dilute solutions of helium-three in helium-four at low temperatures; intermediate state of type-one superconductors. Address: Dept. of Physics, Ohio State University, 174 W. 18th Ave, Columbus, OH 43210.

EBNER, FORD FRANCIS, b. Colfax, Wash, Feb. 10, 34; m. 60; c. 2. NEUROSCIENCE. B.S, Wash. State Univ, 54, D.V.M, 58; Ph.D.(neuroanat), Univ. Md, 65; hon. M.S, Brown Univ, 69. Nat. Insts. Health fel, physiol, Johns Hopkins Univ, 60-63; spec. fel, anat, Univ. Md, 63-65, asst. prof. anat. & physiol, 65-66; NEUROSCI, BROWN UNIV, 66-69, ASSOC. PROF, 69- Vet.C, U.S.A, 58-60, Res, Capt. AAAS; Am. Asn. Anat; Am. Asn. Neuropath; Am. Physiol. Soc; Neurosci. Soc; Biol. Stain Comn. Problems in neuroanatomy, neurophysiology and physiological psychology. Address: Division of Biological & Medical Sciences, Neurosciences Section, Brown University, Providence, RI 02912.

EBNER, HERMAN GEORGE, b. Chicago, Ill, Apr. 1, 31. POLYMER & ORGANIC CHEMISTRY. B.S, Loyola (Ill), 53, M.S, 55; Ph.D.(org. chem), Carnegie-Mellon Univ, 59. Asst. proj. chemist, Standard Oil Co.(Ind), 59-61, proj. chemist, Am. Oil Co, 61-63; sr. proj. chemist, AMOCO CHEM. CORP, 63-69, GROUP LEADER, 69- Am. Chem. Soc. Polymer characterization; polymer products; petroleum additives. Address: Amoco Chemicals Corp, P.O. Box 400, Naperville, IL 60540.

EBNER, KURT E, b. New Westminster, B.C, Mar. 30, 31; m. 57; c. 3. BIOCHEMISTRY. B.S.A, British Columbia, 55, M.S.A, 57; Ph.D.(dairy biochem), Illinois, 60. Can. Overseas Nat. Res. Coun. fel, Nat. Inst. Res. Dairying, Reading, Eng, 60-61; instr. physiol. chem. & fel, Minnesota, 61-62; asst. prof. BIOCHEM, OKLA. STATE UNIV, 62-65, assoc. prof, 65-69, PROF, 69-, Sigma Xi lectr, 70. Nat. Insts. Health career develop. award, 69. Am. Chem. Soc.(Borden Award, 69); Am. Soc. Biol. Chem. Mechanism of hormone action at the enzyme level; enzyme mechanisms. Address: Dept. of Biochemistry, Oklahoma State University, Stillwater, OK 74075.

EBNER, STANLEY GADD, b. Lincoln, Nebr, Oct. 29, 33; m. 56; c. 2. ENGINEERING MECHANICS, AEROSPACE ENGINEERING. B.S, Univ. Nebr, Lincoln, 55; B.S, Univ. Colo, Boulder, 63, M.S, 64, Ph.D.(eng. mech), 68. U.S. AIR FORCE, 56-, instr. ENG. MECH, U.S. AIR FORCE ACAD, 64-66, asst. prof, 66-68, assoc. prof, 68-70, DEP. HEAD DEPT, 70- Hon. lectureship, Univ. Colo, Colorado Springs, 65-71, partic, Nat. Sci. Found. Summer Insts. Struct. Mech, 65 & 66; NASA-Am. Soc. Eng. Educ. summer faculty fel, 69. U.S.A.F, 56-, Maj. Dynamics and vibrations. Address: Dept. of Engineering Mechanics, U.S. Air Force Academy, CO 80840.

EBY, CHARLES J, b. Detroit, Mich, May 29, 29; m. 51; c. 4. ORGANIC CHEMISTRY. B.S, Michigan, 51; fel, Dartmouth Col, 51-53, M.A, 53; fel, Off. Ord. Res, Duke, 53-56, Monsanto fel, 54-55, Ph.D.(org. chem), 56. Res. chemist, Monsanto Chem. Co, 56-63, mem. staff govt. rels, MONSANTO RES. CORP, 63-66, MGR. RES. & DEVELOP. MKT, 66- Summers, res. chemist, Dow Chem. Co, 52-53. Am. Chem. Soc; Am. Inst. Aeronaut. & Astronaut. Materials and systems; organic chemistry; condensations; eliminations; substitutions; rearrangements; cyclizations. Address: 1101 17th St. N.W, Washington, DC 20006.

EBY, DENISE, S.C, b. Baltimore, Md, Dec. 8, 17. CHEMISTRY. B.S, St. Joseph Col.(Md), 39; M.S, Cath. Univ. Am, 53; Ph.D, Univ. Md, 70. Teacher, high schs, Md, 39-41, 46-50; N.Y, 42-45; W.Va, 45-46; asst. prof. CHEM, ST. JOSEPH COL.(MD), 50-63, assoc. prof, 63-70, PROF, 70- AAAS; Am. Chem. Soc. Chemical education; enzyme kinetics and studies of Glyceraldehyde-3-phosphate dehydrogenase, including the interaction of nicotinamide adenine dinucleotide. Address: Dept. of Natural Sciences, St. Joseph College, Emmitsburg, MD 21727.

EBY, EDWARD S(TUART), b. Chicago, Ill, Oct. 3, 34; m. 65. MATHEMATICS. B.S, Illinois, 56, M.S, 57, Ph.D.(math), 64. Mathematician, U.S. NAVY UNDERWATER SOUND LAB, 57-64, RES. MATHEMATICIAN & RES. ASSOC, 64- Lectr, dept. elec. eng, Connecticut, 65- AAAS; Am. Math. Soc; Math. Asn. Am; Acoust. Soc. Am. Underwater acoustics; signal processing. Address: U.S. Navy Underwater Sound Lab, Ft. Trumbull, New London, CT 06321.

EBY, FRANK S(HILLING), b. Kansas City, Mo, Apr. 6, 24; m. 58; c. 3. NUCLEAR PHYSICS. B.S, Illinois, 49, M.S, 50, Eastman Kodak fel, 52-53, Ph.D.(physics), 54. Res. assoc. physics, Illinois, 54; mem. proj. Sherwood Res, LAWRENCE LIVERMORE LAB, UNIV. CALIF, 54-58, atomic weapons design, 58-67, DIV. LEADER DEVICE DESIGN, 67- U.S.A.A.F, 43-46, 1st Lt. AAAS; Am. Phys. Soc. Nuclear reactions; scintillation crystals; plasma physics; high explosives; weapons design. Address: Lawrence Livermore Lab, Bldg. 111, Livermore, CA 94550.

EBY, HAROLD H(ILDENBRANDT), b. Platteville, Colo, Mar. 3, 18; m. 42; c. 3. ORGANIC CHEMISTRY. B.S, Colo. State Col, 40; M.A, Nebraska, 47, fel, 47-48, Ph.D.(org. chem), 49. Asst, Nebraska, 40-42, 46-48; res. chemist, CONTINENTAL OIL CO, 48-52, sr. res. chemist & acting group leader, 52-54, res. group leader, 54-58, supvry. res. chemist, 58-69, SUPVR. TECH. INFO. SERV, RES. & DEVELOP. DEPT, 69- U.S.A, 42-45, Res, 45-50, Chem.C. Res, 50-52, Capt. AAAS; Spec. Libraries Asn; Am. Soc. Info. Sci; Am. Chem. Soc. Lubricants; fuels; waxes; specialty petroleum products; technical information. Address: 2108 Meadowbrook Dr, Ponca City, OK 74601.

EBY, JOHN E(DSON), b. Wabash, Ind, Mar. 18, 33; m. 53; c. 5. SOLID STATE PHYSICS, OPTICS. B.A, Col. Wooster, 54; Ph.D.(physics), Rochester, 59. ENGR. PHYSICS, Sylvania Elec. Prod, Inc, GEN. TEL. & ELECTRONICS CORP, 59-69, GTE SYLVANIA, INC, 69- Optical Soc. Am; Am. Phys. Soc; Electrochem. Soc. Optical properties of solids; radiometry; high temperature interactions of gases with refractory metals. Address: GTE Sylvania, Inc, 100 Endicott St, Danvers, MA 01923.

EBY, JOHN MARTIN, b. Reading, Pa, Dec. 8, 39; m. 62; c. 3. ORGANIC CHEMISTRY. B.A, Goshen Col, 60; Nat. Sci. Found. fel, Delaware, 62-63, Ph.D.(org. chem), 65. RES. CHEMIST, RES. & DEVELOP. CTR, ARMSTRONG CORK CO, 65- Brit. Chem. Soc. Organic synthesis; heterocyclic nitrogen compounds; organotin compounds; vinyl degradation reactions. Address: Root Manor, R.D. 1, Manheim, PA 17545.

EBY, LAWRENCE THORNTON, b. South Bend, Ind, May 3, 16; m. 41; c. 2. ORGANIC CHEMISTRY. B.S, Notre Dame, 38, M.S, 39, Ph.D.(org. chem), 41. Res. chemist, Standard Oil Develop. Co, 41-55; Esso Res. & Eng. Co, 55-57; sr. mkt. develop. eng, Enjay Co, Inc, 57-58, asst. mgr. mkt. develop. div, 58-64; pres, Protective Treatments, Inc, Aeroplast Corp. & Dellrose Industs, Helene Curtis Industs, Inc, 64-65; res. dir, chem. div, Chrysler Corp, Mich, 65-67; MGR. POLYMER DIV, U.S. GYPSUM CO, 67- AAAS; Chem. Mkt. Res. Asn; Commercial Develop. Asn; Am. Ord. Asn; Am. Chem. Soc; Soc. Plastics Eng; Asn. Iron & Steel Eng; fel. Am. Inst. Chem.(Honor Scroll, 61); Tech. Asn. Pulp & Paper Indust; Am. Asn. Textile Chem. & Colorists; Soc. Automotive Eng. Adhesives; sealants; lubricating oil additives; antioxidants for synthetic rubber; vulcanization of butyl rubber; toxicity of petroleum products; synthesis of petrochemicals; polymerization; diesel fuel additives; chemicals for paper and textiles; market development of petrochemicals; paints, coatings and building materials. Address: Polymer Division, Research Dept, U.S. Gypsum Co, 1000 E. Northwest Hwy, Des Plaines, IL 60016.

EBY, ROBERT L, b. Montgomery County, Ohio, Nov. 19, 28; m. 50; c. 3. DAIRY INDUSTRY. B.S, Ohio State Univ, 51. Instr, agr. exten, Ohio State Univ, 51-53; instr. & farm mgr, Ohio Agr. Exp. Sta, 53-68, SUPT. OUTLYING BRANCHES, OHIO AGR. RES. & DEVELOP. CTR, 68- Dairy herd management. Address: 106 Miller Rd, Wooster, OH 44691.

EBY, ROBERT NEWCOMER, b. Pittsburgh, Pa, July 17, 31; m. 55; c. 2. CHEMICAL ENGINEERING. B.S.E, Princeton, 52; Dow Chem. Co. fel, Illinois, 52-53, Shell Oil Co. fel, 53-55, Ph.D.(chem. eng), 58. Res. engr, plastics div, Union Carbide Corp, 55-56, group leader, 56-62, prod. supvr, mfg. dept, 62-64, area supvr. eng. & qual. control, 64-66, prod. supt, 66-67, prod. supt. & mgr, vinyl fabrics dept, 67-69; PROD. MGR. FILM MFG, POLAROID CORP, NORWOOD, 69- Am. Chem. Soc; Am. Inst. Chem. Eng. Polyolefin, vinyl and condensation polymerization processes; non-Newtonian flow; heat and mass transfer from high viscosity fluids; optimization of capital expenditures for process modification and expansion. Address: 20 Baskin Rd, Lexington, MA 02173.

EBY, RONALD K(RAFT), b. Reading, Pa, May 7, 29; m. 52; c. 2. PHYSICS. B.S, Lafayette Col, 52; M.S, Brown, 55, Ph.D.(physics), 58. Asst, Brown, 52-57; physicist, polychems. dept, exp. sta, E.I. du Pont de Nemours & Co, 57-63; polymers div, NAT. BUR. STANDARDS, 63-67, chief polymer crystal physics sect, 67-68, CHIEF POLYMERS DIV, 68- Acoustical Soc. Am; Am. Phys. Soc; Electron. Micros. Soc. Am. Polymer physics; physical acoustics; ultrasonic propagation. Address: Polymer Division, National Bureau of Standards, Washington, DC 20234.

ECANOW, BERNARD, b. Chicago, Ill, Nov. 22, 23; m. 65; c. 2. PHARMACEUTICAL SCIENCES, MEDICAL SCIENCES. B.Ch.E, Univ. Minn, 47, B.S, 51, Am. Found. Pharmaceut. Educ. fel, 53-54, Ford Found. fel, 55, Ph.D. (pharmaceut. chem), 55. Asst. prof. MFG. PHARM, Butler Univ, 56-57, assoc. prof, 57-58; asst. prof, UNIV. ILL, 58-63, assoc. prof, 64-69, PROF, 70- Consult, McGraw Hill-Air Force Proj, 59-60; Ctr. Drug & Cosmetic Co, 62-; Presby-St. Lukes Hosp, 67-; Rush Med. Col, 70- U.S.A, 44-46, Med.Serv.C.Res, 51-55. AAAS; Am. Pharmaceut. Asn. Drug-biological membrane interactions; surfactants of biological interests; physical-chemical and biological aspects of pharmaceutical formulation; toxic effects of environmental pollutants; physical chemistry of biological phenomena. Address: College of Pharmacy, University of Illinois, 833 S. Wood St, Chicago, IL 60612.

ECCLES, JOHN, b. Melbourne, Australia, Jan. 27, 03; m. 29, 68; c. 9. PHYSIOLOGY. M.B, B.S, Melbourne, 25; M.A. & D.Phil.(physiol), Oxford, 29; hon. Sc.D, Cambridge, 60; hon. D.Sc, Tasmania, 64, British Columbia, 66, Gustavus Adolphus, 67, Marquette, 67; Loyola, 69; LL.D, Melbourne, 65; M.D, Charles, Prague, 69, Yeshiva, 69. Demonstr. physiol, Oxford, 30-37; dir. med. sci, Sydney Hosp, Australia, 37-43; prof. physiol, Otago, N.Z, 44-51; Australian Nat. Univ, 51-66; mem, Am. Med. Asn. Ed. & Res. Found. Inst. Biomed. Res, 66-68; prof. physiol, SCH. MED, STATE UNIV. N.Y. BUFFALO, 68, DISTINGUISHED PROF. PHYSIOL. & BIOPHYS, LAB. NEUROBIOL, 68- Herter lectr, Hopkins, 55. Knight Bachelor, Queen Elizabeth's Birthday Honours, 58; Baly Medal, Royal Col. Physicians, 61; Royal Medal, Royal Soc, 62; Cothenius Medal, Leopold Carol German Acad. Res. Natural Sci, 63; Nobel Prize in Med, 63. For. assoc. mem. Nat. Acad. Sci; for. hon. mem. Am. Acad. Arts & Sci; hon. mem. Am. Col. Physicians; hon. mem. Electroencephalographic Soc; Am. Neurol. Asn; Am. Philos. Soc; hon. mem. N.Y. Acad. Sci. Physiology of nerve cells and of their synaptic functions; operational principles of the nervous system. Address: Dept. of Physiology, School of Medicine, State University of New York at Buffalo, Buffalo, NY 14214.

ECCLES, SAMUEL FRANKLIN, b. Reno, Nev, Sept. 19, 30; m. 53; c. 2. NUCLEAR PHYSICS. B.S, Nevada, 52; M.S, La. State, 54; Ph.D.(physics), Washington (Seattle), 58. Res. physicist, Inst. Nuclear Physics, Amsterdam, Holland, 58-59; asst. prof. gen. physics, Nevada, 59-62; RES. PHYSICIST, LAWRENCE RADIATION LAB, UNIV. CALIF, 62- U.S.A.R, 62, 1st Lt. Am. Inst. Physics; Am. Phys. Soc. Medium energy nuclear physics including scattering and reaction experiments; nuclear structure physics; sub-critical reactor and neutron physics; transuranium heavy element production in nuclear devices; fission processes; astrophysics. Address: Lawrence Radiation Lab, University of California, P.O. Box 808, Livermore, CA 94550.

ECCLES, WILLIAM J, b. Owatonna, Minn, Apr. 18, 32; m. 67. ELECTRICAL ENGINEERING, COMPUTER SCIENCE. S.B, Mass. Inst. Tech, 54, S.M, 57; Ph.D.(elec. eng), Purdue, 65. Instr. elec. eng, Purdue, 59-65; ASST. PROF. ELEC. ENG. & DIR. COMPUT. CTR, UNIV. S.C, 65- Sig.C, U.S.A, 57-59, Lt. Asn. Comput. Mach; Inst. Elec. & Electronics Eng; Am. Soc. Eng. Educ. Address: Computer Center, University of South Carolina, Columbia, SC 29208.

ECCLESTON, BARTON H(ENRY), b. Anadarko, Okla, Aug. 31, 15; m. 40; c. 6. CHEMISTRY. A.B, Col. Emporia, 38; Kansas, 38-39. Tester, Bay Oil Co, Kans, 40; city filter operator, Wichita, Kans, 40-42; jr. technologist, BARTLESVILLE ENERGY RES. CTR, U.S. BUR. MINES, 42-43, asst. technologist, 43-44, assoc. chemist, 44-46, chemist, 46-57, asst. chief, br. chem. & ref, 57-59, PROJ. LEADER develop. anal. methods, 59-66, FUELS COMBUSTION RES, 66- AAAS; fel. Am. Inst. Chem; Am. Chem. Soc. Relationship of fuel composition to air pollution; smog forming potential of automotive emissions, exhaust and evaporation. Address: Fuels Combustion Research, Bartlesville Energy Center, U.S. Bureau of Mines, Box 1398, Bartlesville, OK 74003.

ECHANDI, EDDIE, b. San José, Costa Rica, Nov. 21, 27; m. 52; c. 2. PLANT PATHOLOGY. Ing. Agr, Costa Rica, 51; Inter-Am. Inst. Agr. Sci, 53; Ph.D. (plant path), Wisconsin, 55. Prof. plant path, Costa Rica, 55-61; Inter-Am. Inst. Agr. Sci, 61-62, head plant indust. & soils dept, 62-64, basic food crops prog, 64-67; PROF. PLANT PATH, N.C. STATE UNIV, 67- Vis. scientist, California, Berkeley, 65; co-leader, nat. bean prog, N.C. State Univ. Agr. Mission to Peru, Lima, 67-; vis. prof, Agrarian Univ, Peru, 68- Am. Phytopath. Soc; Latin Am. Asn. Phytopath. Diseases of tropical plants; host-parasite relations; ecology of plant disease and plant pathogens; cultivation and production of beans and pulses. Address: Dept. of Plant Pathology, North Carolina State University, Raleigh, NC 27607.

ECHELBERGER, WAYNE F, JR, b. Pierre, S.Dak, Oct. 23, 34; m. 60; c. 2. ENVIRONMENTAL HEALTH & ENGINEERING. B.S, S.Dak. Sch. Mines & Tech, 56; M.S, Michigan, 59, M.P.H, 60, U.S. Pub. Health Serv. fel, 61-64, Ph.D.(civil eng), 64. Civil engr, City of Milwaukee, Wis, 56; pub. health engr, State of S.Dak, 56-60; res. asst. civil eng, Michigan, 60 & 61, teaching fel, 60-61, instr, 64-65; asst. prof, UNIV. NOTRE DAME, 65-67, ASSOC. PROF. ENVIRON. HEALTH ENG, 67- Nat. Sci. Found. res. grant, 66-67 & res. equip. grant, 67-68; Fed. Water Pollution Control Admin. demonstration grant, 66-69; Environ. Protection Agency Water Qual. Off. res. & demonstration grant, 71-; consult. & secy-treas, Tennech, Inc. AAAS; Am. Soc. Civil Eng; Water Pollution Control Fedn; Am. Water Works Asn; Am. Soc. Limnol. & Oceanog; Am. Soc. Eng. Educ; Am. Asn. Prof. Sanit. Eng; Am. Inst. Chem. Biological and chemical treatment of water and wastewater; industrial waste treatment; studies and control of freshwater eutrophication. Address: Dept. of Civil Engineering, University of Notre Dame, Notre Dame, IN 46556.

ECHELLE, ANTHONY A(LLAN), b. McAlester, Okla, Sept. 9, 40; m. 69. ICHTHYOLOGY, HERPETOLOGY. B.S, Southeast. State Col, 63; Okla. Fish & Game Coun. fel, Univ. Okla, 65-67, M.S, 67, Ph.D.(zool), 70; Nat. Sci. Found. fel, Cameron State Agr. Col, 68. Instr. biol, Cameron State Agr. Col, 68-69; RES. BIOLOGIST, BIOL. STA, UNIV. OKLA, 69-, ADJ. ASST. PROF. ZOOL, UNIV, 71- Am. Fisheries Soc; Am. Soc. Ichthyol. & Herpet; Am. Inst. Biol. Sci; Am. Soc. Zool; Soc. Study Amphibians & Reptiles. Ecology and behavior; ecology, behavior and systematics of Cyprinodon; aggressive displays in Anolis, phylogenetic implications; reproductive cycles in fishes. Address: University of Oklahoma Biological Station, Willis, OK 73462.

ECHLIN, F(RANCIS) A(SBURY), b. Ottawa, Ont, June 12, 06; nat; m. 38; c. 3. NEUROSURGERY. M.D, C.M, McGill, 31, M.Sc, 39; Med. Sc.D, Columbia, 38. CLIN. PROF. NEUROSURG, MED. CTR, N.Y. UNIV, 64- Res. fel, Royal Soc. Can, 35; attend. & consult. neurosurgeon, Lenox Hill Hosp, N.Y.C; attend. neurosurgeon, Bellevue Hosps; N.Y. Eye & Ear Infirmary. Dipl, Am. Bd. Neurosurg. Med.C, 42-45, Maj. Fel. Am. Col. Surg; Am. Asn. Neurol. Surg; Am. Neurol. Asn; Am. Acad. Neurosurg; Am. Med. Asn; Asn. Res. Nerv. & Ment. Disease; Am. Electroencephalog. Soc. Neurophysiology; neuropathology. Address: 100 E. 77th St, New York, NY 10021.

ECHOLS, CHARLES E(RNEST), b. Alderson, W.Va, Dec. 5, 24; m. 60; c. 4. CIVIL ENGINEERING. B.C.E, Univ. Va, 49, M.C.E, 55, LL.B, 54. Instr. civil eng, Mich. State Univ, 55-57; ASST. PROF. CIVIL & APPL. MECH, UNIV. VA, 57- V.pres. construction & eng, A.B. Torrence & Co. Inc, 50-; v.pres, Willson Finance Serv. Inc, Staunton; dir. Monticello Bank, Charlottesville; mem. Hwy. Res. Bd, Nat. Acad. Sci-Nat. Res. Coun. U.S.A, 43-45; U.S.N, 45-46. Am. Soc. Civil Eng. Economics and construction. Address: Route 3, Box 47, Charlottesville, VA 22901.

ECHOLS, DOROTHY JUNG, b. N.Y.C, Sept. 9, 16; m. 41; c. 4. GEOLOGY. B.A, Wash. Sq. Col, N.Y. Univ, 36; M.A, Columbia, 38. Subsurface geologist & micropaleontologist, Am. Republics Corp, 38-41; gen. geologist, for. div, Texas Co, 41-42; consult, Pond Fork Oil & Gas Co, 46-51; ASST. PROF. GEOL, WASH. UNIV, 51- AAAS; Paleont. Soc; fel. Geol. Soc. Am; Geochem. Soc; Am. Asn. Petrol. Geol; Soc. Econ. Paleont. & Mineral. Micropaleontology; biological and morphological studies of microorganisms; some emphasis on Forminifera and Ostracoda; biostratigraphy; subsurface geology. Address: 218 Calverton Rd, Ferguson, MO 63135.

ECHOLS, JOSEPH TODD, JR, b. Raleigh, N.C, July 5, 36; m. 63. PHYSICAL CHEMISTRY. B.A, Belhaven Col, 59; Nat. Defense Ed. Act fel, 59-62; Nat. Insts. Health fel, 62-63; Ph.D.(phys. chem), Mississippi, 63. Assoc. prof. CHEM, E.Carolina Col, 63-64; vis. asst. prof. & fel, La. State, 64-65; prof, Belhaven Col, Miss, 65-67; ASSOC. PROF, PFEIFFER COL, 67-, CHMN. DEPT, 70- Am. Chem. Soc. Kinetics; free radical reactions. Address: Dept. of Chemistry, Pfeiffer College, Misenheimer, NC 28109.

ECHOLS, R(OBERT) E(UGENE), b. Santa Ana, Calif, Dec. 4, 18; m. 40; c. 2. PHYSICAL CHEMISTRY. B.S, California, 40. Chemist, Calif. Cap Co, 40-47; assoc. res. chemist, Calif. Res. Corp, 47-51; tech. rep. prod. develop, Oronite Chem. Co, 51-52, tech. serv. mkt, 52-53, tech. sales rep, 53-55, prod. specialist, 55-57; supvr. prod. develop, 57-59, mgr. prod. develop. & mkt. res, 59-62; V.PRES, Calif. Chem. Int. Inc, Switz, 62-67, CHEVRON CHEM. INT. INC, 67- U.S.N.R, 44-46, Res, 46-54, Lt.(jg), Am. Chem. Soc. Commercial chemical development. Address: Chevron Chemical International Inc, 200 Bush St, San Francisco, CA 94120.

ECHOLS, ROBERT M, b. College Heights, Ark, Aug. 31, 19; m. 42; c. 2. GENETICS. B.S, Ark. Agr. & Mech. Col, 53; M.F, Yale, 54, Union Bag & Paper Corp. fel, 54-55, John A. Hartford Found. fel, 55-56, Ph.D, 57. Prof. forestry, Ark. Agr. & Mech. Col, 56-57; proj. leader genetics, south. inst. forest genetics, U.S. FOREST SERV, Miss, 57-60, prin. res. forester, co-op. state res. serv, D.C, 60-62, proj. leader silvicult, Pac. Southwest Forest & Range Exp. Sta, CALIF, 62-63, genetics, Inst. Forest Genetics, 63-69, PRIN. RES. FORESTER, PAC. SOUTHWEST EXP. STA, 69- U.S.N.A.F, 41-46, 51-52, Lt.Comdr. AAAS; Soc. Am. Foresters. Genetics of forest trees; inheritance of physical and anatomical characters of wood; silviculture. Address: Pacific Southwest Experiment Station, U.S. Forest Service, P.O. Box 245, Berkeley, CA 94701.

ECHTERNACHT, ARTHUR C(HARLES), b. Indianapolis, Ind, Sept. 3, 39; m. 62; c. 2. VERTEBRATE ZOOLOGY, ECOLOGY. B.A, Univ. Iowa, 61; M.S, Ariz. State Univ, 64; Ph.D.(zool), Univ. Kans, 70. ASST. PROF. BIOL, BOSTON UNIV, 68- AAAS; Am. Soc. Ichthyol. & Herpet; Soc. Study Amphibians & Reptiles; Soc. Syst. Zool; Asn. Trop. Biol. Systematics and ecology of macroteiid lizards of the genera Ameiva and Cnemidophorus; systematics and ecology of tropical reptiles and amphibians. Address: Dept. of Biology, Boston University, Boston, MA 02215.

ECK, C(HARLES) F(REDERICK), b. Kenosha, Wis, Aug. 12, 12; m. 42; c. 2. CHEMICAL ENGINEERING. B.S, Wisconsin, 40; M.S, Va. Polytech, 41. Pilot plant engr, styrene monomer, Monsanto Chem. Co, Ohio, 41, priority supvr, govt. priorities for equip, Tex, 42, shift supvr, styrene monomer, 43-45, process engr, petrochems, Tex. & Mo, 46-48, chem. eng. group leader, Tex, 48-51, asst. dir. process eng, 51-53, mgr. process design, 53-55, planning engr, plastics econ, Mass, 55-58, sr. res. chemist, 58-62, GROUP LEADER, MOUND LAB, MONSANTO RES. CORP, 62- AAAS; Am. Chem. Soc; Am. Inst. Chem. Eng. Gas separation; thermal diffusion; process evaluation; stable isotope distribution. Address: Mound Lab, Monsanto Research Corp, Miamisburg, OH 45342.

ECK, DAVID LOWELL, b. Bagely, Minn, Nov. 21, 41; m. 64; c. 1. ORGANIC CHEMISTRY. B.A, Montana, 63; Ph.D.(chem), Washington State, 67. Anal. chemist, Anaconda Co, 63; Petrol. Res. Fund res. fel, California, Santa Cruz, 67-69; Sloan Found. vis. asst. prof. CHEM, Reed Col, 69-70; ASST. PROF, SONOMA STATE COL, 70- Elucidation of mechanisms in bimolecular elimination reactions involving weak bases; mechanistic considerations involving the formation of small ring oxygen and sulfur heterocycles. Address: Dept. of Chemistry, Sonoma State College, Rohnert Park, CA 94928.

ECK, HAROLD V(ICTOR), b. Newkirk, Okla, Nov. 14, 24; m. 47; c. 5. SOIL FERTILITY. B.S, Okla. Agr. & Mech. Col, 48; Ph.D.(agron), Ohio State Univ, 50; Univ. Ill, 69-70. Asst. prof. agron, Okla. Agr. & Mech. Col, 51-57; RES. SOIL SCIENTIST, SOUTH. PLAINS BR, SOIL & WATER CONSERV. RES. DIV, AGR. RES. SERV, U.S. DEPT. AGR, 57- U.S.A, 43-46. Am. Soc. Agron; Soil Sci. Soc. Am; Soil Conserv. Soc. Am; Am. Soc. Plant Physiol. Soil management; soil fertility; plant physiology. Address: Southwestern Great Plains Research Center, Bushland, TX 79012.

ECK, J(OHN) C(LIFFORD), b. Livingston, Mont, Dec. 2, 09; m. 35; c. 3. CHEMISTRY. B.S, Mont. State Col, 31; M.S, Illinois, 32, Ph.D.(org. chem), 35. Asst. animal chem. & nutrit, Exp. Sta, Iowa State Col, 35-40, res. assoc, 40-41; res. chemist Air Reduction Co, 41-45; proj. leader, Allied Chem. Corp, 45-71; SPEC. REP. HYDROTECHNIC CORP, 71- Fel. AAAS; N.Y. Acad. Sci; Am. Chem. Soc; fel. Am. Inst. Chem; assoc. Am. Inst. Chem. Eng. Amino acids; sterols; basic organic raw materials, acetylene; ethylene; soil conditioners; product development; water pollution control; incineration of solid wastes. Address: Kitchell Road, Convent Station, NJ 07961.

ECK, JOHN STARK, b. West Hempstead, N.Y, Mar. 18, 41; m. 64; c. 3. NUCLEAR & SOLID STATE PHYSICS. B.S, Polytech. Inst. Brooklyn, 62; Gilman fel, univ. fel. & Ph.D.(physics), Johns Hopkins Univ, 67. Jr. instr. PHYSICS, Johns Hopkins Univ, 62-65, res. asst, 65-67; res. assoc, Fla. State Univ, 67-69; ASST. PROF, KANS. STATE UNIV, 69- Res. physicist, Univ. Munich, summer 71. Am. Phys. Soc. Nuclear and solid state properties from coulomb excitation Mössbauer studies; nuclear heavy ion interactions from elastic and inelastic scattering of ^{16}O and ^{4}He from medium weight nuclei; optical model interpretation of nuclear scattering of protons, alphas and heavy ions; nuclear instrumentation. Address: Dept. of Physics, Kansas State University, Manhattan, KS 66502.

ECK, PAUL, b. Elizabeth, N.J, Sept. 3, 31; m. 55; c. 4. HORTICULTURE, SOILS. B.S, Rutgers, 53; M.S, Massachusetts, 55; Ph.D.(soils), Wisconsin, 57. Asst. prof. floricult, Massachusetts, 57-60; assoc. prof. POMOL, RUTGERS UNIV, 60-70, PROF, 70- Am. Soc. Hort. Sci; Am. Soc. Agron. Physiology and nutrition of floricultural and fruit crops especially carnation, blueberry, and cranberry cultures. Address: Dept. of Horticulture, Rutgers University, New Brunswick, NJ 08903.

ECK, THOMAS G, b. Genoa, N.Y, Oct. 19, 29; m. 59. PHYSICS. B.A, Buffalo, 51; Ph.D.(physics), Columbia, 58. Asst. prof. PHYSICS, CASE WEST. RESERVE UNIV, assoc. prof, 62-69, PROF, 69- Am. Phys. Soc. Low temperature physics; solid state physics; atomic spectroscopy. Address: Dept. of Physics, Case Western Reserve University, Cleveland, OH 44106.

ECKARD, WILLIAM ELMER, b. Pittsburgh, Pa, Apr. 29, 25; m. 59; c. 3. PETROLEUM ENGINEERING. B.S, Pittsburgh, 49. Trainee, U.S. BUR. MINES, Pa, 48, petrol. res. engr, field eng. br, 49-55, natural gas res. engr, 55-56, res. mgt. training, D.C, 56, asst. to chief, petrol. res. lab, W.Va, 56-58, asst. chief, 58-63, PROJ. COORD. petrol. eng. res. group, Petrol. Res. Ctr, 63-70, CHIEF, ALASKA FIELD OPER. CTR, 70- Mem. comt. underground storage, Am. Gas Asn, 63-70; sec. recovery & underground gas storage comt, east. dist, Am. Petrol. Inst, 55-63. Meritorious Serv. award, U.S. Dept. Interior. U.S.A, 43-46, C.Eng.Res, 46-65, Capt. Am. Soc. Petrol. Eng; Nat. Soc. Prof. Eng. Fluid flow through porous media; oil recovery methods; performance of underground natural gas storage reservoirs; management of mineral and fuels development and research programs. Address: Alaska Field Operation Center, P.O. Box 550, Juneau, AK 99801.

ECKARDT, R(OBERT) E, b. Fanwood, N.J, May 1, 16; m. 65; c. 4. BIOCHEMISTRY, TOXICOLOGY. B.S, Antioch Col, 37; M.S, West. Reserve Univ, 39, Ph.D.(biochem), 40, M.D, 43. Intern, N.Y. Hosp, 43-44, asst. res. med, 44, 47-48; spec. res. physician, Standard Oil Co, N.J, 48-50, asst. dir. med. res. sect, 50, DIR. MED. RES. DIV, ESSO RES. & ENG. CO, 51- Asst. attending physician, out patient dept, N.Y. Hosp, 48-70, physician to outpatients, 70-; instr. med, med. col, Cornell Univ, 43-70, assoc. clin. prof, 70-; post-grad. med. sch, N.Y. Univ-Bellevue Med. Ctr, 53-; secy. gen, XIII Int. Cong. on Occup. Health; mem. exec. bd, Am. Bd. Prev. Med. Dipl, Am. Bd. Internal Med, 50; Am. Bd. Prev. Med, 55. Med.C, 44-47, Maj. Fel. Am. Col. Physicians; Am. Med. Asn; Am. Indust. Hyg. Asn; Indust. Med. Asn.(v.pres, 57-59, pres, 60); N.Y. Acad. Med. Medicine; industrial hygiene. Address: Esso Research & Engineering Co, P.O. Box 45, Linden, NJ 07036.

ECKART, CARL (HENRY), b. St. Louis, Mo, May 4, 02; m. 26, 58. PHYSICS, GEOPHYSICS. B.S, Washington (St. Louis), 22, M.S, 23; Edison Lamp Works fel, Princeton, 23-25, Ph.D.(physics), 25. Fel, Washington (St. Louis), 22-23; nat. res. fel, Calif. Inst. Tech, 25-27; Guggenheim Mem. Found. fel, 27-28; asst. prof. physics, Chicago, 28-31, assoc. prof, 31-46; asst. dir. to dir. div. war res, UNIV. CALIF, 42-46, dir. marine phys. lab, SAN DIEGO, 46-52, Scripps Inst. Oceanog, 48-65, VICE CHANCELLOR ACAD. AFFAIRS, 65-, PROF. GEOPHYS, 67- Nat. Acad. Sci; AAAS; fel. Am. Phys. Soc; fel. Acoustical Soc. Am; Am. Acad. Arts & Sci. Hydrodynamics; thermodynamics. Address: University of California at San Diego, La Jolla, CA 92037.

ECKE, GEORGE G(RAFF), b. Pittsburgh, Pa, May 11, 21. ORGANIC CHEMISTRY. B.S, Carnegie Tech, 42; M.S, Pa. State Col, 47, Ph.D.(chem), 49.

Jr. chemist, Shell Develop. Co, 43-46; chemist, Ethyl Corp, 49-58; group mgr, Koppers Co, 58-62; fel, Wayne, 62-63; RES. ASSOC, PPG INDUSTS, INC, 64- Am. Chem. Soc. Reaction mechanisms; aromatic alkylations; acylation of olefins; interception reactions; organo metallic catalysis; epoxide reactions; agricultural chemicals. Address: Chemical Division, PPG Industries, Inc, P.O. Box 31, Barberton, OH 44203.

ECKEL, EDWARD F, b. Brooklyn, N.Y, Dec. 28, 19; m. 45; c. 1. PHYSICAL CHEMISTRY, PHYSICS ENGINEERING. B.S, Florida, 41, fel, 52-53, Ph.D. (chem), 53. Res. chemist, Tidings Corp. Am, 46-47; asst, Florida, 47-53; res. chemist & staff adminstr, U.S. Naval Ord. Lab, 53-54; prin. chemist & mgr, Nicac Chem. Corp, 54-56; sr. res. engr. & specialist, Rocketdyne Div, N.Am. Aviation, Inc, 57-60; specialist & supvr. adv. systs, space & info. systs. div, 61-62; mem. staff adv. planning, guided missile range div, Pan Am. World Airways, 62-64; assoc. prof. aerospace, Miami Dade Col, 65-67; PROF. CHEM. & PHYSICS & HEAD DEPT, PALM BEACH ATLANTIC COL, 67- Vis. lectr, Brevard Eng. Col, 62-64. Chem.C, U.S.A, 41-70, Lt. Col.(Ret). Fel. AAAS; Am. Inst. Aeronaut. & Astronaut; Am. Chem. Soc; Combustion Inst. Aero and fluid thermo chemistry and physics; chemical and nuclear rocketry; kinetics, space and particle physics; combustion; spectroscopy, instrumentation and adaptive computer processes. Address: P.O. Box 2234, Ft. Lauderdale, FL 33303.

ECKEL, EDWIN B(UTT), b. Washington, D.C, Jan. 27, 06; m. 31; c. 3. GEOLOGY. B.S, Lafayette Col, 28; fel, Arizona, 28-30, M.S, 30. Geologist, U.S. Geol. Surv, 30-42, in charge investigations domestic quicksilver deposits, 42-43, asst. chief mil. geol. unit, 44-45, chief eng. geol. br, 45-61, spec. proj. br, 62-65, res. geologist, 65-68; ed, GEOL. SOC. AM, 68-71, EXEC. SECY, 70- Chmn, comt. landslide invest, Hwy. Res. Bd, 51-62; mem. comt. Alaska earthquake, Nat. Acad. Sci, 64-71; part time res. geologist, U.S. Geol. Surv, 68- Merit award, Univ. Arizona, 60; Distinguished Serv. award, U.S. Dept. Interior, 65. Fel. Geol. Soc. Am; fel. Mineral. Soc. Am; Soc. Econ. Geol; Asn. Eng. Geol.(pres, 65); Am. Inst. Prof. Geol; Asn. Earth Sci. Ed. Engineering geology; ore deposits; German underground factories; Italian quicksilver industry; geology of Paraguay; geology of underground nuclear explosions; geology of Alaska earthquake. Address: Geological Society of America, 3300 Penrose Pl, Boulder, CO 80301.

ECKEL, FREDERICK MONROE, b. Philadelphia, Pa, Mar. 25, 39; m. 63; c. 1. PHARMACY. B.Sc, Phila. Col. Pharm, 61; M.Sc, Ohio State, 63. Resident pharm, Ohio State, 61-63, supvr. pharmacists, univ. hosp, 63-65, asst. dir. pharm, 63-66; instr. HOSP. PHARM, UNIV. N.C, CHAPEL HILL, 66-67, ASST. PROF, 67- Pharm. consult, St. Ann's Hosp. for Women, 64-66; dir, Plan of Pharm. Assistance, 66-, Duke Endowment & Reynolds Found. Plan of Pharm. Assistance grant, 66-; dir. pharm. serv, N.C. Mem. Hosp, 68- Am. Soc. Hosp. Pharmacists; Drug Info. Asn; Am. Pharmaceut. Asn. Development, improvement and implementation of professional pharmaceutical services; application of electronic data processing to hospital pharmacy practice; pharmacy service to small hospitals and nursing homes. Address: 713 Churchill Rd, Chapel Hill, NC 27514.

ECKEL, JOHN F(RIEND), b. Leon, Kans, Jan. 24, 03; m. 29; c. 2. METALLURGY. A.B, Kansas, 25; M.S, Carnegie Inst. Tech, 28, fel. & D.Sc. (metall), 32. Still inspector, Sinclair Ref. Co, 25; chemist, Skelly Oil Co, Kans, 25-26; chemist & compounder, B.F. Goodrich Co, Ohio, 26; metallurgist, Bell Tel. Labs, 28-30; sales engr, Gulf Ref. Co, 33-34; instr. metall, Iowa, 34-35; engr, Nat. Supply Co, 35; West. Elec. Co, N.J, 35-39; assoc. prof. metall, Purdue, 39-45; res. metallurgist, Gen. Elec. Co, 45-51, mat. engr, 51-56; prof. metall. eng, VA. POLYTECH. INST, 56-68, head dept, 56-64, metals & ceramic eng, 64-68, EMER. PROF. METALL ENG, 68- U.S. Bur. Mines fel. With Atomic Energy Comn; U.S.A, 44. Am. Soc. Metals (Howe Medal). Metallurgy of steels; non-ferrous and high temperature alloys; lead alloys; cable sheath construction; apparatus for covering cable core; method for inhibiting stress corrosion; effect of carbon on ten per cent ironmanganese alloys; influence of aging on stress corrosion of stainless steels. Address: 1101 Highland Circle S.E, Blacksburg, VA 24060.

ECKEL, ROBERT E(DWARD), b. Buffalo, N.Y, Mar. 17, 18; m. 47; c. 3. MEDICINE. B.A, Dartmouth Col, 38; M.D, Harvard, 42. Fel. med, SCH. MED, CASE WEST. RESERVE UNIV, 48-49, Am. Cancer Soc. fel. biochem, 49-51, Nat. Found. Infantile Paralysis fel, 51-53, asst. prof. MED, 53-60, assoc. prof, 60-70, PROF, 70- Fedn. Am. Soc. Exp. Biol. Med.C, U.S.N.R, 43-46. Mechanism of ion transport; renal disease. Address: Dept. of Medicine, Case Western Reserve University School of Medicine, Cleveland, OH 44106.

ECKELMAN, CARL A, b. Columbus, Ind, Feb. 14, 33; m. 61; c. 1. WOOD SCIENCE, STRUCTURAL ENGINEERING. B.S, Purdue, 59, M.S, 62, Ph.D. (wood sci), 68. Asst, PURDUE, 59-63, instr. WOOD SCI, 63-68, ASST. PROF, 68- U.S.A, 53-55, Sgt. Furniture engineering; wood moisture relations; basic fiber science. Address: Dept. of Forestry, Purdue University, Lafayette, IN 47907.

ECKELMAN, WILLIAM CHARLES, b. Houston, Tex, July 30, 41; m. 69; c. 2. INORGANIC & PHARMACEUTICAL CHEMISTRY. B.S, St. Louis Univ, 63; M.A, Wash. Univ, 65, Ph.D.(chem), 68. Group leader RADIOPHARMACEUT, Mallinckrokt Chem. Works, 68-69; ASSOC. CHEMIST, BROOKHAVEN NAT. LAB, 69- Am. Chem. Soc; Soc. Nuclear Med. Development of diagnostic radiopharmaceuticals including thyroid function tests, generator systems, and in vivo organ imaging agents. Address: Brookhaven National Lab, BLD 801, Upton, NY 11973.

ECKELMANN, F(RANK) DONALD, b. Englewood, N.J, May 25, 29; m. 53; c. 2. GEOLOGY. B.S, Wheaton Col.(Ill), 51; M.S, Columbia, 54, James Furman Kemp fel, 55-56, Ph.D, 56. Asst. geochem, Lamont-Doherty Geol. Observ, Columbia, 51-52, asst. geol, 52-55, res. assoc. geochem, 56-57; asst. prof. geol, BROWN UNIV, 57-60, assoc. prof, 60-64, PROF. GEOL. SCI, 64-, chmn. dept, 61-68, dean col, 68-71. Geol. Soc. Am; Geochem. Soc; Mineral. Soc. Am; Am. Geophys. Union. Petrology; petrology of metamorphic and igneous rocks; Precambrian terrains. Address: Dept. of Geological Sciences, Brown University, Providence, RI 02912.

ECKELMANN, WALTER R, b. Englewood, May 25, 29; m. 51; c. 3. GEOCHEMISTRY. B.S, Wheaton Col.(Ill), 51; M.A, Columbia, 54, Ph.D.(geochem), 56. Res. asst. GEOCHEM, Columbia, 51-55, res. assoc, 55-57; res. chemist, Jersey Prod. Res. Co, 57-59, sr. res. chemist, 59-62, sect. head, 62-64, res. mgr, European Lab, ESSO PROD. RES. CO, STANDARD OIL CO.(N.J), 64-66, dist. prod. geologist, Okla. & oper. mgr, New Orleans, Humble Oil & Refining Co, 66-70, GEN. MGR, GEOL. RES, 70- AAAS; Geol. Soc. Am; Am. Geochem. Soc; Am. Chem. Soc. Isotope geochemistry; mass spectrometry; low level radiation; research and operations. Address: Esso Production Research Co, P.O. Box 2189, Houston, TX 77001.

ECKELS, ARTHUR R(AYMOND), b. New Haven, Conn, Nov. 16, 19; m. 44; c. 4. ELECTRICAL ENGINEERING. B.S, Connecticut, 41; M.S, Harvard, 42; D.Eng, Yale, 50. Elec. engr, bur. ships, U.S. Navy, 42-43; from marine engr. to chief engr, U.S. Merchant Marine, 43-46; instr. ELEC. ENG, Yale, 47-49; prof, N.C. State Col, 49-56; PROF. & chmn. dept, Vermont, 56-61; N.C. STATE UNIV, 61- Res. participant, Oak Ridge Inst. Nuclear Studies, 53; opers. analyst, U.S. Air Force, 54-; Fulbright lectr, Chiao Tung Univ, 60; vis. prof, Japan Nat. Defense Col, 64. Consult, NASA, 63-64. Am. Soc. Eng. Educ; Inst. Elec. & Electronics Eng. Electrical instrumentation and control. Address: Dept. of Electrical Engineering, North Carolina State University, Raleigh, NC 27607.

ECKENFELDER, WILLIAM WESLEY, JR, b. N.Y.C, Nov. 15, 26; m. 50; c. 2. SANITARY ENGINEERING. B.C.E, Manhattan Col, 46; N.C. State Col, 47; M.S, Pa. State, 48; M.C.E, N.Y. Univ, 56. Sanit. engr, Atlantic Ref. Co, 48-49; res. assoc, N.Y. Univ, 49-50; asst. prof. civil eng, Manhattan Col, 55-58, assoc. prof, 58-65; prof. environ. health eng, Univ. Tex, 65-70; DISTINGUISHED PROF. ENVIRON. & WATER RESOURCES ENG, VANDERBILT UNIV, 70- V.pres, Weston, Eckenfelder & Assocs, 52-56; consult, 56-; pres, Hydrosci. Inc; Assoc. Water & Air Resources Engrs, Tenn. Allen Mem. Award, N.Y. State Sewage & Indust. Wastes Asn, 59. Am. Soc. Civil. Eng; Am. Chem. Soc; Am. Inst. Chem. Eng; Water Pollution Control Fedn; Am. Soc. Eng. Educ. Biological treatment of sewage and industrial wastes; mass transfer and aeration in waste treatment; process design of industrial waste treatment plants; water quality management. Address: Dept. of Environmental & Water Resources Engineering, Vanderbilt University, Nashville, TN 37203.

ECKENHOFF, JAMES E(DWARD), b. Easton, Md, Apr. 2, 15; m. 38; c. 4. ANESTHESIA. B.S, Kentucky, 37; M.D, Pennsylvania, 41; hon. D.Sc, Transylvania Univ, 70. Harrison fel. anesthesiol. & asst. instr. pharmacol, sch. med, Pennsylvania, 45-47, asst. instr. surg, 44-47, instr, 48-49, assoc, 49-50, asst. prof, 50-52, assoc. prof. anesthesiol. in surg, 52-55, prof, 55-66, asst. dir. dept, 53-66, assoc. clin. pharmacol, 48-66; PROF. ANESTHESIA, MED. SCH, NORTHWEST. UNIV, 66-, DEAN, 70-, chmn. dept. anesthesia, 66-70. Asst. surgeon, anesthesiol, Children's Hosp, Pa, 49-53, consult, 53-; Anesthesiol. Center, WHO, Denmark, 52; Valley Forge Army Hosp, Pa, 49-58; Vet. Admin. Hosp, Pa, 53-; U.S. Naval Hosp, Pa; consult. to surgeon gen, U.S. Navy. Mem. surg. study sect, Nat. Insts. Health, 62-66, anesthesia training grants comt, 66-70; dir, Am. Bd. Anesthesiol, 65- Dipl, Am. Bd. Anesthesiol; fel. Royal Col. Surg.(Hunterian Prof, 65). Med.C, 42-45, Capt. Am. Soc. Anesthesiol.(assoc. ed, Anesthesiol, 55-58, ed, 58-62); Am. Physiol. Soc; Am. Med. Asn; fel. Am. Col. Anesthesiol; Am. Col. Physicians; Royal Soc. Med. Physiological and pharmacological problems pertaining to coronary circulation; effects of opiates and antagonists upon normal and anesthetized man and the effect of changing carbon dioxide tensions upon the heart and circulation; deliberate hypotension; clinical anesthesiological problems. Address: Northwestern University Medical School, 303 E. Chicago Ave, Chicago, IL 60611.

ECKENRODE, ROBERT T, b. Harrisburg, Pa, Nov. 12, 27; m. 51; c. 4. CHEMICAL ENGINEERING, EXPERIMENTAL PSYCHOLOGY. B.Ch.E, Villanova, 51; Drexel Inst, 51-52; Pennsylvania, 52-55; M.A, Fordham, 64. Ord. engr, Frankford Arsenal, Pa, 49-56; sr. engr. & sr. v.pres, Dunlap & Assocs, Inc, Conn, 56-69; V.PRES, AM. STOCK EXCHANGE, 69- U.S.N, 46-47. Sci. Res. Soc. Am; Inst. Mgt. Sci; Opers. Res. Soc. Am. Research, analysis and development on military and industrial systems; operations research; information sciences; research management; management information and control systems. Address: 5 Little Brook Rd, Wilton, CT 06897.

ECKER, EDWIN D, b. Grovertown, Ind, Mar. 26, 34; m. 55; c. 3. MATHEMATICS. B.S, Ball State, 56; M.S, Illinois, Urbana, 59; Nat. Sci. Found. fel, Okla. State, summer 62; Ph.D.(math), Iowa State, 66. Instr. MATH, MacMURRAY COL, 59-63, asst. prof, 63-68, ASSOC. PROF, 68- Vis. prof, Univ. Okla, summer 65; Nat. Sci. Found. summer res. Inst, 67; vis. lectr, Univ. Ill, Urbana, 70-71. Math. Asn. Am; Am. Math. Soc. Group theory. Address: Dept. of Mathematics, MacMurray College, Jacksonville, IL 62650.

ECKER, HARRY ALLEN, b. Athens, Ga, Oct. 22, 35; m. 59; c. 3. ELECTRICAL ENGINEERING. B.E.E, Ga. Inst. Tech, 57, M.S.E.E, 59; Ph.D.(elec. eng), Ohio State, 65. Res. asst, Ga. Inst. Tech, 57-59; proj. engr, navigation & guid. lab, Wright-Patterson Air Force Base, U.S. Air Force, 59-60, syst. prog. off, 60-61, electronics engr, opers. anal. br, synthesis & anal. div, 61-62, acting chief, 62-63, aerospace engr, directorate of synthesis, dep. for studies & anal, 63-65, chief opers. anal. group, 65-66; sr. res. engr, radar lab, eng. exp. sta, GA. INST. TECHNOL, 66-69, HEAD, RADAR BR, ELECTRONICS DIV, 69- Air Force spec. act of serv. award, 63, Air Force Asn. award, 63. U.S.A.F, 59-62, Res, 62-, Capt. Inst. Elec. & Electronics Eng. Antennas; radar; systems analyses; bio-engineering. Address: Electronics Division, Georgia Institute of Technology, Atlanta, GA 30332.

ECKER, RICHARD EUGENE, b. Waverly, Iowa, Mar. 13, 30; m. 53; c. 5. DEVELOPMENTAL & MOLECULAR BIOLOGY. B.S, Iowa State, 58, Nat. Sci. Found. fel, 58-60, Ph.D.(bact), 61. Instr. bact, Iowa State, 60-61; microbiol, col. med, Florida, 62-64; asst. biologist, ARGONNE NAT. LAB, 64-66, ASSOC. BIOLOGIST, 66- Nat. Cancer Inst. fel, 61-62; Nat. Insts. Health res. grant, 62-64; distinguished vis. prof, Morehouse Col, 69-70. U.S.A, 50-53, Res, 53-59, 1st Lt. Soc. Develop. Biol. Biochemistry of development. Address: Biological & Medical Research Division, Argonne National Lab, Argonne, IL 60439.

ECKERD J(AMES) W(ILSON), b. New Bloomfield, Pa, Jan. 14, 16; m. 39; c. 2. CHEMICAL ENGINEERING. B.A, Gettysburg Col, 38; M.S, Pa. State 45, F.E, 50. Asst. chemist, testing labs, State Dept. Hwys, Pa, 39-41; asst, Pa. State, 41-46, sr. resident engr, lab. Anthracite Inst, 46-54; supt, Bonnie Burns Briquet Div, Reading Anthracite Co, 54-55; chief, br. of utilization & preparation, anthracite res. ctr, U.S. BUR. OF MINES, 55-64, res. dir, 64-65, proj. coord, Morgantown Coal Res. Ctr, 65-68, RES. DIR, 68-70, MORGANTOWN ENERGY RES. CTR, 70- Am. Chem. Soc; Am. Inst. Mining, Metall. & Petrol. Eng; Am. Gas Asn; Nat. Soc. Prof. Eng; Am. Soc. Test. & Mat. Kinetics of combustion; agglomeration of fine sizes of fuels; thermal stabilization of fuels; gasification kinetics and techniques; chemical constitution, irradiation, size reduction and preparation of solution fuels; non-fuel uses of carbonaceous minerals; pilot-plant design and operation. Address: Morgantown Energy Research Center, P.O. Box 880, Collins Ferry Rd, Morgantown, WV 26505.

ECKERLE, KENNETH LEE, b. Jasper, Ind, Oct. 18, 36. PHYSICS, MATHEMATICS. B.S, Indiana State, 58; M.S, Maryland, 62. Asst. physics, Maryland, 58-60, solid state physics, 60-62; atomic physicist, NAT. BUR. STANDARDS, 62-67, PHYSICIST, 67- Summers, physicist, U.S. Naval Res. Lab, 59-61. Am. Asn. Physics Teachers. Standards and measurements of transmittance and reflectance in the ultraviolet, visible, and infrared spectral regions; plasma spectroscopy; high pressure effects on color centers in alkali halides. Address: Room B306 Metrology Bldg, National Bureau of Standards, Washington, DC 20234.

ECKERMAN, JEROME, b. Brooklyn, N.Y, Nov. 18, 25; m. 48; c. 2. PHYSICS. B.S, Worcester Polytech, 48; M.S, Catholic Univ, 56, Ph.D.(physics), 58. Res. scientist, Nat. Adv. Comt. Aeronaut, 48-51; physicist & br. chief, U.S. Naval Ord. Lab, 51-59; sr. staff scientist, Avco, 59-65, assoc. sect. chief appl. physics, Avco Corp, 65-68; physicist, NASA Electronics Res. Ctr, Mass, 68-70, PHYSICIST/TECH. MGR, GODDARD SPACE FLIGHT CTR, 70- Meritorious civilian serv. award, 56. U.S.A.A.F, 44-45. Am. Phys. Soc; Am. Inst. Aeronaut. & Astronaut. Ballistics range research; chemical kinetics in air and alkali metal plasmas; laminar wake transition behind hypervelocity models; turbulent wake growth; laboratory studies of flow field observables; flow analysis by interferometry; light gas gun development. Address: 11817 Hunting Ridge Ct, Potomac, MD 20854.

ECKERSLEY, ALFRED, b. Manchester, Eng, Dec. 2, 28; nat; m. 57; c. 2. ELECTRICAL ENGINEERING. B.Sc, Col. Tech, England, 49; M.S.E.E, Pennsylvania, 54. Assoc. elec. eng, Pennsylvania, 49-57; lectr. & res. assoc, New Mexico, 57-59; elec. engr, Ark Electronics Corp, 59-61; res. engr, United Control Corp, 61-64; RES. ENGR, AEROSPACE GROUP, BOEING CO, 64- U.S. del, Spec. Int. Comt. Radioelec. Perturbations. Sr. mem. Inst. Elec. & Electronics Eng. Electronics; avionics; radio noise; interference measurement; electromagnetic compatibility. Address: 616-166 Ave. N.E, Bellevue, WA 98008.

ECKERT, ALFRED C(ARL), JR, b. Newark, N.J, June 12, 20; m. 44; c. 4. ANALYTICAL CHEMISTRY. B.S, Wheaton Col, 41; Ph.D.(anal. chem), Illinois, 45. Lab. asst. chem, Wheaton Col, 39-41; asst, Illinois, 41-44; jr. chemist, Chicago, 44-45; res. chemist, chem. div, Union Carbide Corp, Tenn, 45-48; res. engr, Battelle Mem. Inst, 48-52; tech. personnel off. rep, chem. div, Union Carbide Corp, Tenn, 52-53, asst. personnel adminstr, Tonawanda Labs, Linde Div, 53-56, tech. serv. group coord. chem. & spectros, speedway labs, 56-58; sr. exp. res. chemist, Allison Div, Gen. Motors Corp, 58-65; MGR. MAT. TESTING LAB, APPL. RES. GROUP, GLOBE-UNION INC, 65- Lectr, Univ. Tenn, 47-48. Am. Chem. Soc; Soc. Appl. Spectros; fel. Am. Sci. Affiliation; fel. Am. Inst. Chem. Mesomorphic state with special reference to carbon blacks; effects of magnetism on dislocation movements in nickel foil; quantative analysis of lead alloys by x-ray fluorescence. Address: Material Testing Lab, Applied Research Group, Globe-Union Inc, P.O. Box 591, Milwaukee, WI 53201.

ECKERT, CHARLES, b. Denver, Colo, Nov. 22, 14; m. 43; c. 2. SURGERY. M.D, Washington, 39. Asst. SURG, Washington (St. Louis), 41-44, instr, 44-48, asst. prof, 48-53, assoc. prof, 53-56; PROF. & CHMN. DEPT, ALBANY MED. COL, 56- Asst. surgeon, Barnes & St. Louis Children's Hosps, 44-56; attend. surgeon, St. Louis City Hosp, 46-56; surgeon-in-chief, Albany Med. Center Hosp, 56-; consult, Albany Vet. Admin. Hosp; Vassar Bros. Hosp, Poughkeepsie, N.Y; Mary McClellan Hosp, Cambridge; mem. bd. visitors, Roswell Park Mem. Inst, Buffalo, N.Y. Dipl, Am. Bd. Surg, 45, mem. bd, 64-70, v.chmn, 68-69, chmn, 69-70. U.S.A, 44, 1st Lt. AAAS; fel. Am. Col. Surg; Am. Med. Asn; Soc. Univ. Surg; Am. Surg. Asn. Cancer; surgical research. Address: Dept. of Surgery, Albany Medical Center, Albany, NY 12208.

ECKERT, CHARLES ALAN, b. St. Louis, Mo. Dec. 13, 38; m. 61; c. 2. CHEMICAL ENGINEERING. S.B, Mass. Inst. Tech, 60, Coffin fel. & S.M, 61; Woodrow Wilson fels, California, Berkeley, 61-63, Nat. Sci. Found. fel, 63-64, Ph.D.(chem. eng), 65. NATO fel. high pressure physics, high pressure lab, Nat. Ctr. Sci. Res, Bellevue, France, 64-65; asst. prof. CHEM. ENG, UNIV. ILL, URBANA, 65-69, ASSOC. PROF, 69- NATO fel, 64-65; consult, Phillips Petrol. Co, 67-; Guggenheim fel, 71; vis. prof, Stanford Univ, 71-72. AAAS; Am. Chem. Soc; Am. Inst. Chem. Eng; Am. Soc. Eng. Educ; Faraday Soc. Molecular thermodynamics and applied chemical kinetics; effects of high pressure on reactions in solution. Address: Dept. of Chemical Engineering, 213 E. Chemistry Bldg, University of Illinois, Urbana, IL 61801.

ECKERT, CHARLES F(RANKLIN), b. Moline, Kans, Jan. 2, 17; m. 42; c. 2. PHYSICAL CHEMISTRY. A.B, Baker, 38; Ph.D.(phys. chem), Northwestern, 42. Res. chemist, U.S. Rubber Co, 42-67; RES. ASSOC, UNIROYAL RES. CTR, 67- Am. Chem. Soc. Applied electron microscopy; latex and polyurethane foams; high polymer chemistry; synthetic rubber. Address: 3 Kathleen Ct, Wayne, NJ 07470.

ECKERT, EDWARD A(RTHUR), b. N.Y.C, July 2, 20; m. 59. VIROLOGY. B.A, Brooklyn Col, 40; M.S, Mass. Inst. Technol, 47; Nat. Cancer Inst. fel, Duke Univ, 49-51, Ph.D.(biol), 51. Res. assoc. surg, Duke Univ, 51-55, Am. Cancer Soc. res. scholar, 52-55, instr. BACT, 53-55; assoc. prof, State Univ. N.Y. Med. Ctr, 55-64; SCH. PUB. HEALTH, UNIV. MICH, 64-70, PROF, 70- U.S.A, 42-46. Soc. Exp. Biol. & Med; Am. Asn. Immunol; Am. Asn. Cancer Res. Properties of animal viruses; electron microscopy; immunology; biometry. Address: Dept. of Epidemiology, School of Public Health, University of Michigan, Ann Arbor, MI 48104.

ECKERT, ERNST R(UDOLF) G(EORG), b. Prague, Czech, Sept. 13, 04; nat; m. 31; c. 4. THERMODYNAMICS. Dipl. Ing, German Inst. Technol, Prague, 27, Dr. Ing, 31; Dr. habil, Inst. Technol, Danzig, 38; Dr. Ing. E.H, Munich Tech. Univ, 68; hon. Dr. Eng, Purdue Univ, 68; hon. D.Sc, Univ. Manchester, 68. Asst, German Inst. Technol, Prague, 28-34; lectr, Inst. Technol, Danzig, 35-38; sect. chief, Aeronaut. Res. Inst, Braunscheig; consult, power plant lab, U.S. Air Force, Wright-Patterson AFB, 45-49; turbine & compressor div, Lewis Res. Ctr, NASA, 49-51; PROF. MECH. ENG, UNIV. MINN, MINNEAPOLIS, 51-, DIR. THERMODYN. & HEAT TRANSFER DIV. & HEAT TRANSFER LAB, 55- Docent, Inst. Technol, Braunschweig, 39-40; prof. & dir. inst. thermodyn, German Inst. Technol, Prague, 43-45; Fulbright award, 62-63; vis. prof, Purdue Univ. U.S. rep. aerodyn. panel, Int. Comt. Flame Radiation; chmn. Am. Div, Commonwealth & Int. Libr. Sci; v.chmn. sci. coun, Int. Ctr. Heat & Mass Transfer, Yugoslavia; U.S. rep, Int. Heat Transfer Conf; mem, Nat. Comn. Fire Prev. & Control, 70- Max Jakob Award, 61. Fel. Am. Inst. Aeronaut. & Astronaut; Am. Soc. Mech. Eng; fel. N.Y. Acad. Sci; German Soc. Aeronaut. & Astronaut. Heat transfer; thermodynamics; gas turbines; jet propulsion. Address: Dept. of Mechanical Engineering, 125 Mechanical Engineering Bldg, University of Minnesota, Minneapolis, MN 55455.

ECKERT, GEORGE F(RANK), b. Akron, Ohio, Feb. 21, 24; m. 48; c. 3. PHYSICAL CHEMISTRY. B.S, Akron Univ, 44; univ. fel, Ohio State Univ, 48, 50, Ph.D.(chem), 50. Instr. phys. chem, Capital Univ, 47-48; res. chemist, E.I. du Pont de Nemours & Co, 51-54; assoc. prof. CHEM, CAPITAL UNIV, 54-60, PROF, 60- U.S.A, 44-46, Lt. Am. Chem. Soc. Low temperature thermodynamics; homogeneous catalysis; peroxide oxidations. Address: 867 Pleasant Ridge Ave, Columbus, OH 43209.

ECKERT, HANS ULRICH, b. Danzig, Ger, Apr. 20, 16; nat; m. 46; c. 2. AERODYNAMICS, PHYSICS. Cand.Phys, Danzig Tech. Univ, 38; Dipl.Eng, Tech. Univ, Berlin, 41. Sci. assoc, Ger. Inst. for Sci. Photog, Berlin, 41-42; test group leader, Aerodyn. Inst. Ger. Army Ord, 43-45; task scientist, aeronaut. res. lab, Wright Air Develop. Ctr, Ohio, 46-54; sr. aerodyn. engr, Convair, 54-56, staff scientist, sci. res. lab, 56-62; phys. & life sci. lab, Lockheed-Calif. Co, 62-63, head, plasma physics lab, 63-67; MEM. TECH. STAFF, PLASMA RES. LAB, AEROSPACE CORP, 67- AAAS; Am. Inst. Aeronaut. & Astronaut; Am. Phys. Soc. Electrical discharges in gases; plasma flow. Address: Plasma Research Lab, Aerospace Corp, P.O. Box 95085, Los Angeles, CA 90045.

ECKERT, HERBERT L, b. Lansdale, Pa, Aug. 21, 27; m. 67; c. 4. PEDIATRICS, INFECTIOUS DISEASES. B.S, Univ. Md, 50, M.D, 52. Res. assoc. pediat, sch. med, Univ. South. Calif, 62-65, asst. prof, 65; col. med, Univ. Calif, Los Angeles, 65-68; ASSOC. PROF. PREV. MED. & PEDIAT, MED. CTR, W. VA. UNIV, 68-; CHIEF INFECTIOUS DISEASE BR, APPALACHIAN LAB OCCUP. RESPIRATORY DISEASE, U.S. PUB. HEALTH SERV, 68- Med.C, 54-62, Lt. Comdr; U.S.P.H.S, Med. Dir. AAAS; Am. Acad. Pediat; fel. Am. Col. Physicians; Am. Soc. Microbiol; Am. Pub. Health Asn. Applied and clinical research in infectious diseases; epidemiology; occupational respiratory diseases with emphasis on virology. Address: Division of Preventive Medicine, West Virginia University Medical Center, Morgantown, WV 26506.

ECKERT, JOHN ANDREW, b. Rochester, N.Y, Apr. 12, 41; m. 64. ELECTROCHEMISTRY. B.S, Rochester Inst. Technol, 64; Nat. Insts. Health fel, Mass. Inst. Technol, 65-68, Ph.D.(chem), 70. Chemist, Bausch & Lomb, N.Y, 60-61; Eastman Kodak Co, 61-64; res. assoc, Mass. Inst. Technol, 69-70; RES. CHEMIST, ESSO RES. CTR, 70- Am. Chem. Soc. Solar energy conversion; physical organic chemistry; energy storage; ion selective membranes; ceramics. Address: Esso Research Center, Bldg. 1, Room 3008, Linden Ave, Linden, NJ 07036.

ECKERT, J(OHN) PRESPER, b. Phila, Pa, Apr. 9, 19; m. 44, 62; c. 4. ELECTRICAL ENGINEERING. B.S, Pennsylvania, 41, M.S, 43, hon. D.Sc. (eng), 64. Elec. engr, Moore Sch. Elec. Eng, Pennsylvania, 42, chief engr. Eniac, 44-46, Edvac, 45-46; chief engr. & v.pres, Eckert-Mauchly Comput. Corp, 46-51, dir. engr, Univac-Eckert-Mauchly Div, Remington Rand, Inc, 51-52, V.PRES. Remington Rand Div, SPERRY RAND CORP, 55-62, UNIVAC DIV, 62- Potts medal, Franklin Inst, 49; Scott Medal, City of Phila, 61; Pa. awards excellence, 68; Nat. Medal of Sci, 68. Civilian with U.S.A; Off. Sci. Res. & Develop; Nat. Bur. Standards; U.S. Bur. Census, 44. Nat. Acad. Eng; fel. Inst. Elec. & Electronics Eng.(Phila. sect. award, 65). Design and construction of large and small scale electronic digital computing devices. Address: Univac Division, Sperry Rand Corp, P.O. Box 500, Blue Bell, PA 19422.

ECKERT, JOHN S, b. Delta, Ohio, June 29, 10; m; c. 1. PHYSICAL & BIOLOGICAL SCIENCES. B.Ch.E, Ohio State, 33. Jr. chem. engr, Goodyear Tire & Rubber Co, 33-37; area supvr, E.I. du Pont de Nemours & Co, 37-42; plant processing engr, B.F. Goodrich Co, 42-44; plant mgr, U.S. Stoneware Co, 44-50, DIR. ENG, NORTON CO, 50- Adj. assoc. prof, Ohio State, 63- Am. Inst. Chem. Eng; Am. Soc. Metals; Am. Soc. Mech. Eng; Instrument Soc. Am; Nat. Asn. Corrosion Eng; Nat. Soc. Prof. Eng. Mass transfer and performance of packed beds for distillation; absorption and stripping processes. Address: 3000 Millboro Rd, Cuyahoga Falls, OH 44224.

ECKERT, JOSEPH N(ICOLAUS), b. Perth Amboy, N.J, Feb. 13, 14. BIOCHEMISTRY, PHYSIOLOGY. B.S, Rutgers, 36, Ph.D.(biochem), 48, M.S, 61. Chemist, E.R. SQUIBB & SONS, INC, 36-39, chemist group leader, 41-42, head dept. chem. control, 42-46, asst. dir. biol. prod, 46-47, head dept. formula, standards & off. filing, 47-48, cent. control, 48-52, MGR. QUAL. CONTROL, OVERSEAS, 52- AAAS; Am. Chem. Soc; Am. Soc. Qual. Control; N.Y. Acad. Sci. Nutritional biochemistry; protein hydrolysate; bacterial metabolism; assay methods; statistical analysis; quality control. Address: 1040 Amboy Ave, Edison, NJ 08817.

ECKERT, J(OSEPH) W(EBSTER), b. St. Louis, Mo, Mar. 27, 31; m. 57; c. 3. PLANT PATHOLOGY. B.S, Univ. Calif, Los Angeles, 52, Ph.D.(plant path), 58; fel, Rutgers Univ, 52-53, M.S, 53. Asst. plant path, UNIV. CALIF, RIVERSIDE, 55-57, jr. plant pathologist, 57-58, asst. plant pathologist, 58-62, asst. prof, PLANT PATH, 62-64, assoc. prof, 64-70, PROF, 70- Chem. Corps, U.S.A, 53-55. Am. Phytopath. Soc. Post harvest fruit and vegetable decays; physiology of fungi, fungicides. Address: Dept. of Plant Pathology, University of California, Riverside, CA 92502.

ECKERT, RICHARD E(DGAR), JR, b. Kansas City, Mo, July 24, 29; m. 51; c. 6. ECOLOGY. B.S, Univ. Calif, 52; M.S, Univ. Nev, 54; Ph.D.(farm crops), Ore. State Univ, 57. Range scientist, crops res. div, agr. res. serv, U.S. Dept. Agr, 57-70; MEM. STAFF, RENEWABLE RESOURCE CTR, UNIV. NEV, RENO, 70- Soc. Range Mgt. Range weed control and seeding; plant competition; ecological resource inventory. Address: Renewable Resource Center, University of Nevada, 920 Valley Rd, Reno, NV 89502.

ECKERT, ROGER E(ARL), b. Lakewood, Ohio, Aug. 8, 26; m. 51; c. 3. CHEMICAL ENGINEERING. B.S.E, Princeton, 48; M.S, Illinois, 49, Ph.D. (chem. eng), 51. Sr. engr, E.I. du Pont de Nemours & Co, 51-64; ASSOC. PROF. CHEM. ENG, PURDUE UNIV, 64- Consult, Glidden Co, 64- U.S.A, 46-47. Am. Inst. Chem. Eng; Soc. Rheol. Design and statistical analysis of experiments; rheology of viscoelastic polymer melts; organic and inorganic process development; diffusion in solids; mechanochemistry; biomedical engineering; scientific data processing and information retrieval. Address: 153 Indian Rock Dr, West Lafayette, IN 47906.

ECKERT, ROGER O(TTO), b. N.Y.C, Dec. 12, 34; m. 57; c. 4. ZOOLOGY, PHYSIOLOGY. B.A, Atlantic Union Col, 56; Nat. Sci. Found. fel, Columbia Univ, 56-59, M.A, 57, Nat. Insts. Health fel, 59-60, Ph.D.(zool), 60. Univ. res. fel. & Nat. Insts. Health fel, Harvard, 61-62; asst. prof. ZOOL, Syracuse Univ, 62-65, assoc. prof, 65-68; PROF, UNIV. CALIF, LOS ANGELES, 68- Nat. Insts. Health spec. postdoctoral fel, Univ. Saarlandes, 66-67; mem, Marine Biol. Lab. Am. Soc. Zool; Soc. Gen. Physiol; Am. Physiol. Soc; Am. Soc. Cell Biol; Biophys. Soc; Soc. Neurosci; N.Y. Acad. Sci. Cellular electrophysiology; invertebrate neurophysiology; regulatory functions of cell membrane; bioelectric phenomena and behavior in protozoa; genetic factors in membrane function. Address: Dept. of Zoology, University of California, Los Angeles, CA 90024.

ECKFELD, EDWARD LEWIS, b. Schoenbrunn, Ohio, June 23, 32; m. 57; c. 2. ANALYTICAL CHEMISTRY. B.S, Ohio, 55; East Tenn. State, 64-66. Jr. tech. man indust. chem, Goodyear Atomic Corp, 57-59, tech. man anal. chem, 59-61, develop. chemist, 61-64; NUCLEAR FUEL SERV, INC, 64-67, lab. sect. mgr, 67-70, LAB. MGR, PLUTONIUM FUELS PLANT, 70- U.S.A.F, 55-57, Capt. Am. Chem. Soc; Am. Vacuum Soc. Address: Plutonium Fuels Plant, Nuclear Fuel Service, Inc, West Valley, NY 14171.

ECKFELDT, EDGAR LAWRENCE, b. Norristown, Pa, Feb. 28, 15; m. 41; c. 4. CHEMISTRY. B.S, Univ. Pa, 36, M.S, 39, du Pont fel, 40-41, Ph.D. (phys. chem), 42. Asst. instr. chem, Univ. Pa, 36-40; chem. engr, W.Va. Pulp & Paper Co, 41-42; chemist, LEEDS & NORTHRUP CO, 42-68, PRIN. SCIENTIST, CORP. RES. DEPT, TECH. CTR, 68- With Off. Sci. Res. & Develop; U.S.A; U.S.N, 44. AAAS; Am. Chem. Soc; Electrochem. Soc; Instrument Soc. Am; fel. Am. Inst. Chem. Phase equilibria; pH equipment; electrochemical analytical methods; chemical instrumentation; coulometric analysis. Address: Corporate Research Dept, Technical Center, Leeds & Northrup Co, North Wales, PA 19454.

ECKHARDT, CARL J(OHN), b. Yorktown, Tex, Oct. 28, 02; m. 27; c. 2. MECHANICAL ENGINEERING. B.S, Texas, 25, M.S, 30. Student, Westinghouse Elec. & Mfg. Co, Pa, 25-26; instr. MECH. ENG, UNIV. TEX, AUSTIN, 26-29, adj. prof. & supt. power plants, 29-36, PROF, 36-, DIR. PHYS. PLANT, 50-, supt. utilities, 36-50. Consult. Fel. AAAS; fel. Am. Soc. Mech. Eng.(v.pres, 48-52; 75th Anniversary medal, 55); Am. Soc. Eng. Educ. Design, construction and operation of institutional heating and power plants. Address: Dept. of Mechanical Engineering, University of Texas, Box 7477, University Station, Austin, TX 78712.

ECKHARDT, CRAIG J(ON), b. Rapid City, S.Dak, June 26, 40. PHYSICAL CHEMISTRY. B.A, Colorado, 62; M.S, Yale, 64, Nat. Insts. Health fel, 65, univ. fel. & Ph.D.(chem), 67. ASST. PROF. PHYS. CHEM, UNIV. NEBR, LINCOLN, 67- Consult, Appl. Sci. Knowledge, Inc, Nebr, 68-; adv, Nebr. State Dept. Ed. Phys. Sci. Proj, 68-69; Am. Chem.Soc-Petrol. Res. Fund Type G grant, 68-70. Am. Inst. Physics; Faraday Soc. Experimental and theoretical study of the electronic structure of molecules and crystals, molecular complexes and molecules of biological importance; applications of specular reflection of light; magnetic and natural dichroism. Address: Dept. of Chemistry, University of Nebraska, Lincoln, NE 68508.

ECKHARDT, DONALD HENRY, b. Flushing, N.Y, Dec. 20, 32; m. 55; c. 4. GEOPHYSICS. B.S, Mass. Inst. Technol, 55, Standard Oil Co. Calif. fel, 60, Ph.D.(geophys), 61. Geologist, Magnolia Petrol. Co, Socony Mobil Oil Co, 55-56, seismic interpreter, Socony Mobil Oil Co. Venezuela, 56-58; res. assoc, Ohio State Univ. Res. Found, 60-61, selenodesy, lunar & planetary lab, Univ. Ariz, 61-63; RES. PHYSICIST, AIR FORCE CAMBRIDGE RES. LABS, 63- Res. assoc, div. sponsored res, Mass. Inst. Technol, 61-62; consult. mem. comn. 17, Int. Astron. Union; mem. working group one, Comt. Space Res, Int. Coun. Sci. Unions. AAAS; Am. Geophys. Union; Am. Astron. Soc. Geomagnetic induction; geodesy; selenodesy; planetary physics; lunar librations. Address: 3 Princess Pine Dr, Bedford, MA 10730.

ECKHARDT, EILEEN T(HERESA), b. Passaic, N.J, May 17, 28. PHARMACOLOGY. B.A, Caldwell Col, 49; M.S, Tulane Univ, 60, Ph.D.(pharmacol), 62. Asst. pharmacologist, Schering Corp, N.J, 49-54, assoc. pharmacologist, 54-58; teaching asst, PHARMACOL, Tulane Univ, 58-62; instr, Univ. Vt, 62-64, ASST. PROF, 64-67; N.J. COL. MED, 67- Liver hemodynamics; liver function; bromsulphalein excretion; role of the liver in drug metabolism. Address: Dept. of Pharmacology, New Jersey College of Medicine, 100 Bergen St, Newark, NJ 07103.

ECKHARDT, G(ISELA) (MARION), b. Frankfurt, Ger; m. 57. PHYSICS. Dipl, Frankfurt, Ger, 52, Dr. Phil. nat.(physics), 58. Engr. adv. mat. group, semiconductor & mat. div, Radio Corp. Am, 58-60; mem. tech. staff, quantum electronics dept, HUGHES RES. LABS, 60-66, plasma physics dept, 66-69, SR. STAFF PHYSICIST, 69- Am. Phys. Soc; German Phys. Soc. Plasma and gas discharge physics; spectroscopy; nonlinear optics; solid state physics. Address: Hughes Research Labs, Malibu, CA 90265.

ECKHARDT, RICHARD D(ALE), b. DeKalb, Ill, June 24, 18; m. 46; c. 4. INTERNAL MEDICINE. A.B, Univ. Ill, 40; M.D, Harvard, 43. Fel, Harvard Med. Sch, 44-45, asst, 45-46, res. fel, 46-49; assoc. int. med, Col. Med, Univ. Iowa, 49-52; res. assoc, Harvard Med. Sch, 52; clin. asst. prof. INT. MED, COL. MED, UNIV. IOWA, 52-53, 55-56, clin. assoc. prof, 56-57, 58-60, CLIN. PROF, 60-, ASST. DEAN VET. HOSP. AFFAIRS, 68-; CHIEF OF STAFF, VET. ADMIN. HOSP, IOWA CITY, 68-, chief, med. serv, 57-68, asst. chief, 52-57. Intern & resident, Harvard Med. Serv, Boston City Hosp, 44-46, fel. & assoc, Thorndike Mem. Lab, 46-49; dir. Hepatitis Surv. Group, Kyoto, Japan, 52; chief, med. serv, West Side Hosp. & attend. physician, med. serv, Res. & Ed. Hosps, Chicago, Ill, 57-58; assoc. prof. int. med, col. med, Univ. Ill, 57-58. Dipl, Am. Bd. Int. Med, 50. U.S.N.R, Naval Hosps, 46, 53-55, Lt.Comdr. AAAS; Am. Fedn. Clin. Res.(coun, 51-53); fel. Am. Med. Asn; Am. Asn. Study Liver Diseases; Soc. Exp. Biol. & Med; fel. Am. Col. Physicians; N.Y. Acad. Sci. Liver disease; protein and amino acid metabolism; nutrition. Address: Veterans Administration Hospital, Iowa City, IA 52240.

ECKHARDT, W(ILFRIED) O(TTO), b. Frankfurt, Ger, Mar. 30, 28; m. 57. PHYSICS. Dipl, Univ. Frankfurt, 52, Dr. phil. nat.(physics), 58. Asst, phys. inst, Frankfurt, 53-57; mem. staff, microwave & plasma electronics group, Radio Corp. Am, 58-60; mem. tech. staff, plasma physics dept, HUGHES RES. LABS, 60-63, sr. staff physicist & sect. head, 63-68, SR. SCIENTIST & HEAD LM CATHODE DEVICES PROJ, 68- Am. Phys. Soc; assoc. fel. Am. Inst. Aeronaut. & Astronaut; German Phys. Soc. Plasma and gas discharge physics; high voltage and high power technology; electric propulsion; direct energy conversion; microwave and infrared physics. Address: Hughes Research Labs, 3011 Malibu Canyon Rd, Malibu, CA 90265.

ECKHART, RICHARD A(LLEN), b. Franklin Twp, Pa, May 28, 35; m. 59; c. 3. CHEMICAL ENGINEERING. B.S, Lehigh Univ, 57; Univ. Mich, 57-58; M.S, Pa. State Univ, 61, Ph.D.(chem. eng), 64. Engr, Monsanto Chem. Co, 58-59; instr. chem. eng, Pa. State Univ, 59-62; engr, Esso Res. & Eng. Co, 63-66; asst. prof. chem. eng, Villanova Univ, 66-69; appl. scientist, Simulation Sci, Inc, 69-71; SR. APPLN. ENGR, BECKMAN INSTRUMENTS, 71- Lectr, Naval Air Eng. Ctr, Pa, 66 & 67. Am. Inst. Chem. Eng. Automatic control systems, including computer control; mathematical modelling and simulation; analog and digital computer applications. Address: 132 Santa Rosa Way, Placentia, CA 92670.

ECKHART, WALTER, b. Yonkers, N.Y, May 22, 38; m. 65. MOLECULAR BIOLOGY, VIROLOGY. B.S, Yale, 60; Nat. Sci. Found. fel, Univ. Calif, Berkeley, 61-65, Ph.D.(molecular biol), 65. Res. assoc. TUMOR VIROLOGY, SALK INST, 65-69, MEM. STAFF, 70-, Nat. Sci. Found. fel, 65-67, Am. Cancer Soc. fel, 67-70. Mechanism of cell transformation by DNA tumor viruses; genetics of polyoma virus; control of gene expression on mammalian cells. Address: Salk Institute, P.O. Box 1809, San Diego, CA 92112.

ECKHAUSE, MORTON, b. N.Y.C, May 17, 35; m. 68; c. 1. PHYSICS. A.B, N.Y. Univ, 57; M.S, Carnegie Inst. Technol, 61, Ph.D.(physics), 62. Res. assoc. PHYSICS, Carnegie Inst. Technol, 62; instr, Yale, 62-64; asst. prof, COL. WILLIAM & MARY, 64-67, ASSOC. PROF, 67- Am. Phys. Soc. Experimental high-energy nuclear physics; muon lifetimes; structure of muonium; cyclotron physics; pionic x-rays; muon capture gamma rays. Address: Dept. of Physics, College of William & Mary, Williamsburg, VA 23185.

ECKHOFF, NORMAN DEAN, b. Meade, Kans, Apr. 10, 38; m. 59; c. 2. NUCLEAR & INDUSTRIAL ENGINEERING. B.S, Kans. State Univ, 61, Atomic Energy Cmn. fel, 61-62, M.S, 63, Nat. Sci. Found. summer fels, 65 & 66 Ph.D.(nuclear eng), 68. Res. engr, Boeing Co, Kans, 62-63; process engr, Litwin Eng. Corp, 63; reactor engr, Atomic Energy Comn, Tenn, 63-64; instr. NUCLEAR ENG, KANS. STATE UNIV, 64-68, ASST. PROF, 68- Consult, Econ. Res. Serv, U.S. Dept. Agr, Systs. Res. Co, Kans, Comet Rice Mills, Tex, 68- & Kemin Indust, Iowa, 71- Am. Nuclear Soc. Neutron activation analysis; nuclear fuel management; linear statistical models; operations research; systems analysis. Address: Dept. of Nuclear Engineering, Kansas State University, Manhattan, KS 66502.

ECKIS, ROLLIN (POLLARD), b. Oakland, Calif, June 26, 05; m; c. 3. GEOLOGY. A.B, Pomona Col, 27, M.S, Calif. Inst. Tech, 30. Consult, Metrop. Water Dist. South. Calif, 30; engr-geologist, State Div. Water Resources, Calif, 30-34; petrol. geologist, Tex. Co, Calif, 34-37; dist. geologist, Richfield Oil Corp, 37-43, asst. chief geologist, 43-46, chief geologist, 46-54, v.pres. & mgr. explor, 54-56, exec. v.pres, 56-62, pres, 62-66, exec. v.pres, ATLANTIC RICHFIELD CO, 66-70, V.CHMN. BD, 69- Dir. Chubb Corp. Fel. Geol. Soc. Am; Am. Geophys. Union; Am. Asn. Petrol. Geol. Address: Atlantic Richfield Co, 445 S. Figueroa St, Los Angeles, CA 90017.

ECKLER, A(LBERT) ROSS, b. Boston, Mass, Aug. 29, 27; m. 51; c. 3. MATHEMATICAL STATISTICS. B.A, Swarthmore Col, 50; Ph.D.(math), Princeton, 54. Asst. statist, anal. res. group, James Forrestal Res. Ctr, Princeton, 52-54; mem. tech. staff, BELL TEL. LABS, 54-58, supvr, 58-62, HEAD APPL. MATH. & STATIST. DEPT, 62- Ed. & publ, Word Ways, J. Recreational Ling. U.S.A, 46-47. Nat. Speleol. Soc; Am. Statist. Asn; Int. Asn. Statist. in Phys. Sci. Mathematical models of missile offense and defense strategies; word-play and recreational linguistics; repair-vs-replace decisions applied to telephone equipment based on past history and environment. Address: Applied Mathematics & Statistics Dept, Bell Telephone Labs, Whippany, NJ 07960.

ECKLES, HOWARD, b. Porterville, Calif, July 3, 20; m. 43; c. 3. MARINE BIOLOGY. B.S, California, 42; Stanford, 46-48. Fishery res. biologist, U.S. Fish & Wildlife Serv, 48-53, chief br. marine fisheries, bur. commercial fisheries, 53-63, asst. to sci. adv, U.S. Dept. Interior, 63-67, prog.

mgr. marine resources develop, 67-71; SPEC. ASST. TO ADMINR. NAT. OCEANIC & ATMOSPHERIC ADMIN, U.S. DEPT. COMMERCE, 71-, ACTING DEP. ASST. ADMINR. FOR POLICY & PLANS, 71- U.S.N, 42-46, Lt. Am. Fisheries Soc; Marine Technol. Soc; Am. Inst. Fishery Res. Biol. Fishery research biology; oceanography. Address: Office of Special Assistant, National Oceanic & Atmospheric Administration, U.S. Dept. of Commerce, Rockville, MD 20852.

ECKLES, NYLENE E(LVIRA), (MRS. ARTHUR KIRSCHBAUM), b. Nora Springs, Iowa, Sept. 10, 08; m. 43; c. 2. INTERNAL MEDICINE. B.A, Carleton Col, 29; fel, Hopkins; M.S, Minnesota, 31; Ph.D.(physiol. chem), 43, B.M, 44, M.D, 45. Intern med, Western Reserve Lakeside Hosp, 44-45; resident, Presby. Hosp, Ill, 51; asst. dept. med, 52-53; res. intern, UNIV. TEX. M.D. ANDERSON HOSP. & TUMOR INST, 54-60, ASSOC. INTERNIST & ASSOC. PROF. MED, 60- Clin. asst. prof. anat, col. med, Baylor, 58- AAAS; Am. Soc. Clin. Oncol; Am. Asn. Cancer Res. Oncology; mammary cancer; experimental hypothalamic and pituitary physiology in human subjects; chemotherapy of breast cancer in mice and in humans. Address: Dept. of Medicine, M.D. Anderson Hospital & Tumor Institute, 6723 Bertner Dr, Houston, TX 77025.

ECKLUND, O(SCAR) F(REDERICK), b. Newton, Iowa, May 18, 13; m. 37; c. 2. FOOD TECHNOLOGY. B.S, Iowa State Col, 35. Chemist, Wis. Steel Works, 35-38; technologist res. dept, Am. Can Co, 38-57, group leader plastics & paper, 57-64, supvr. blow molding & thermoforming plastics res, 65-68, mgr. plastics tech. serv, 68-69; proprietor, O.F. Ecklund, Custom Thermocouples, 69- Inst. Food Technol; Soc. Plastic Eng. Food processing including process determination; aseptic canning; container development; plastics. Address: O.F. Ecklund, Custom Thermocouples, P.O. Box 279, Cape Coral, FL 33904.

ECKLUND, PAUL RICHARD, b. Denver, Colo, June 20, 41; m. 62; c. 2. PLANT PHYSIOLOGY. B.A, West. State Col. Colo, 64; Ph.D.(plant physiol), Ore. State Univ, 68. ASST. PROF. BIOL, VASSAR COL, 68- Am. Soc. Plant Physiol; Bot. Soc. Am; Am. Inst. Biol. Sci. Hormonal control of plant growth, development and senescence; biochemical and physiological changes associated with plant senescence. Address: Dept. of Biology, Vassar College, Poughkeepsie, N.Y. 12601.

ECKNER, FRIEDRICH A(UGUST) O(TTO), b. Plauen, Ger, Aug. 26, 26; U.S. citizen; m. 56; c. 3. PATHOLOGY. Dr.med, Univ. Cologne, 57. Asst. med, Univ. Cologne, 55, 56-57, path, 56, 57-58; resident path, Salem Hosp, Mass, 58-60; Univ. Chicago, 60-62; pathologist in training, congenital heart disease res. ctr, Hektoen Inst. Med. Res, 62-64, head sect. histochem, 64-70, assoc. pathologist, 67-70; ASSOC. PROF. PATH, UNIV. ILL. COL. MED, MED. CTR, CHICAGO, 70- Res. assoc. path, Univ. Chicago & lectr, Univ. Ill, 62-70. Pathology of congenital and acquired cardiac disease by qualitative and quantitative methods at the gross and microscopic level; experimental study of extracorporeal circulation and elective cardiac arrest by its tissue reactions. Address: Dept. of Pathology, University of Illinois College of Medicine, University of Illinois Medical Center, 1853 W. Polk St, Chicago, IL 60612.

ECKROAT, LARRY R(AYMOND), b. Bloomsburg, Pa, July 18, 41; m. 71. GENETICS, FISHERIES BIOLOGY. B.S, Bloomsburg State Col, 64; M.S, Pa. State Univ, 66, Ph.D.(zool), 69. ASST. PROF. BIOL, PA. STATE UNIV, BEHREND CAMPUS, 69- AAAS; Am. Fisheries Soc. Genetics of soluble protein polymorphisms in natural and hatchery populations of fishes. Address: Dept. of Biology, College of Science, Pennsylvania State University, Behrend Campus, Erie, PA 16510.

ECKROTH, CHARLES A(NGELO), b. Mandan, N.Dak, May 10, 34; m. 62; c. 2. PHYSICS. B.A, St. John's (Minn), 56; Ph.D.(physics), Iowa State, 66. Instr. PHYSICS, Missouri, Columbia, 65-66, ASST. PROF, 66-69; ST. CLOUD STATE COL, 69- Ord.C, U.S.A, 63-65, Res, 65-66, Capt. Am. Asn. Physics Teachers. Experimental and theoretical aspects of the Zeeman absorption spectra of rare earth compounds in the solid state at low temperatures; point symmetry groups; optics. Address: Dept. of Physics, St. Cloud State College, St. Cloud, MN 56301.

ECKROTH, DAVID R(AYMOND), b. Orwigsburg, Pa, Nov. 20, 39; m. 66. ORGANIC CHEMISTRY. A.B, Franklin & Marshall Col, 61; Nat. Insts. Health fel, Princeton, 62-65, M.A, 63, Ph.D.(org. chem), 66. Asst. instr. chem, Princeton, 61-62; assoc. res. chemist, Sterling-Winthrop Res. Inst, 65-66; asst. prof. CHEM, Wake Forest Univ, 66-69; vis. asst. prof, Iowa State Univ, 69-70; ASST. PROF, YORK COL.(N.Y), 70- AAAS; Am. Chem. Soc; The Chem. Soc. Determination of mechanisms of reactions leading to the formation of nitrogen heterocycles; C^{14} labeling studies; syntheses of biologically active materials; organic photochemistry. Address: Dept. of Chemistry, York College, 150-14, Jamaica Ave, Jamaica, NY 11432.

ECKSTEIN, BERNARD H(ANS), b. Ulm, Ger, Dec. 19, 23; nat; m. 58. PHYSICAL CHEMISTRY. A.B, Princeton, 48; Schluederberg fel, Procter & Gamble fel, Cornell Univ, 51-52, Ph.D.(phys. chem), 53. Res. assoc. chem, Cornell Univ, 52-54; RES. CHEMIST, textile fibers dept, E.I. du Pont de Nemours & Co, 54-57; PARMA TECH. CTR, UNION CARBIDE CORP, 57- U.S.A, 43-46. Am. Chem. Soc; N.Y. Acad. Sci. Reaction mechanisms; high temperature chemistry; composite and high performance materials. Address: 8930 Albion Rd, Cleveland, OH 44133.

ECKSTEIN, ELEANOR FOLEY, b. Chicago, Ill, Mar. 13, 40. NUTRITION. B.S, Univ. Calif, Los Angeles, 61; M.S, Univ. Wash, 66; Mead Johnson fel. & Ph.D, Kans. State Univ, 69. Admin. dietitian & head dietary dept, Burien Gen. Hosp, Seattle, Wash, 62-65; instr. inst. mgt, Carnegie-Mellon Univ, 66-67; ASST. PROF. FOOD MGT, UNIV. CALIF, BERKELEY, 69- Consult. opers. res. & systs. anal. off, U.S. Army Natick Labs, 70- Gen. Mills Award, 57. Am. Dietetic Asn; Inst. Food Technol. Institution management; menu planning by computer for institutional food service units; food habits and preferences of the American population. Address: Dept. of Nutritional Sciences, University of California, Berkeley, CA 94720.

ECKSTEIN, HERBERT P(HILIPP), b. Vienna, Austria, Aug. 4, 13; nat; m. 41; c. 1. PHYSICS. Cand.Phil, State Univ. Austria, 37. Chief technologist, chem. & sanit. eng, Can. Dry, Inc, 39-43; instr. physics, U.S. Air Force, Centenary Col, 43; asst. prof, Dayton, 46-47; physicist, optics, Nat. Adv. Comt. Aeronaut, Langley Field, 47-48; ballistics res. lab, Aberdeen Proving Ground, Md, 48-52; optics & electronics, Univ. Chicago Midway Labs, 52-56; Army Ballistics Missile Agency, Redstone Arsenal, Ala, 56-62; U.S. Army Eng. Res. & Develop. Labs, Ft. Belvoir, Va, 62-64; res. br, RSIC, REDSTONE ARSENAL, 64, chief translation br, 64-67, PHYSICIST, GE&M LAB, 68- U.S.A, 43-46, Ord.C.Res, Maj. Instrumental and atmospheric optics; low-density airflow; infrared communications; radio frequency propagation; night vision aids; specialized bibliographies; editorial work; translations. Address: 4017 Apollo Dr. S.W, Huntsville, AL 35805.

ECKSTEIN, JOHN W(ILLIAM), b. Central City, Iowa, Nov. 23, 23; m. 47; c. 5. INTERNAL MEDICINE. B.S, Loras Col, 46; M.D, Univ. Iowa, 50. Intern, Letterman Gen. Hosp, 50-51; asst. resident INTERNAL MED, univ. hosps, UNIV. IOWA, 51-52, resident, 52-53, asst, 53-54, instr, 54-55, assoc, 55-56, asst. prof, 56-60, assoc. prof, 60-65, PROF, 65-, DEAN, COL. MED, 70-, ESTAB. INVESTR, CARDIOVASC. LAB, UNIV. HOSPS, 58-, Am. Heart Asn. res. fel, 54-55, Rockefeller Found. fel, 53-54. Nat. Heart Inst. res. fel, Evans Mem. Hosp. & Mass. Mem. Hosps, 55-56. U.S.A.A.F, 43-45. Am. Med. Asn; Am. Heart Asn; Am. Col. Physicians; Am. Fedn. Clin. Res; Am. Soc. Clin. Invest; Soc. Exp. Biol. & Med; Am. Physiol. Soc; Am. Col. Chest Physicians. Internal medicine and cardiovascular physiology. Address: College of Medicine, University of Iowa, Iowa City, IA 52240.

ECKSTEIN, MARTIN CHRISTOF, b. Zirndorf, Ger, Mar. 17, 34. ASTRONOMY, PHYSICS. M.S, Munich, 59, Ph.D.(astron), 61. Res. asst. astron, Munich, 62; SCIENTIST, McDonnell Douglas Corp, Calif, 62-69; Europ. Space Opers. Ctr, 69-70; GER. EXP. ESTAB. AIR & SPACE RES, OBERPFAFFENHOFEN, 70- Hermann Oberth Soc. Development of improved methods of celestial mechanics; perturbation theory, particularly theory of satellite motion and earth-to-moon trajectories. Address: 8031 Neu-Gilching, Landsberger Str. 57, Germany.

ECKSTEIN, RICHARD W(ALDO), b. Tiro, Ohio, Oct. 9, 11; m. 37; c. 3. MEDICINE. B.S, Heidelberg Col, 33; fel, West. Reserve Univ, 35-36, M.A, 36, fel, 38-39, 41-46, M.D, 38. Intern med, Lakeside Hosp, CASE WEST. RESERVE UNIV, 39-40, asst. resident, 40-41, sr. instr. physiol, SCH. MED, 45-46, med, 46-49, asst. prof, 49-53, PHYSIOL. & MED, 53-60, ASSOC. PROF, 60- Estab. investr, Am. Heart Asn, 54. U.S.A, 42-45, Capt. AAAS; Am. Physiol. Soc; Soc. Exp. Biol. & Med; Am. Heart Asn; Am. Psychiat. Asn. Coronary artery blood flow; cardiovascular; limb blood flow in dogs during shock; coronary collateral circulation; coronary blood supply of chemoreceptors. Address: University Hospitals, Cleveland, OH 44106.

ECKWEILER, HOWARD J(ESSE), b. N.Y.C, July 11, 06; m. 42; c. 2. PHYSICS. B.S, N.Y. Univ, 28, M.S, 37, Ph.D.(math), 43. Physicist, Elec. Testing Lab, N.Y, 28-35; instr. math, N.Y. Univ, 37-43; dir. optical div, Kollsman Instrument Corp, 43-58; gen. mgr, Lyle Co, N.Y, 58-63; sr. staff scientist, space & info. systs. div, N.Am. Aviation, Inc, 63-67, Autonetics Div, 67-68; with Douglas Aircraft Co, 69-70; GEN. MGR, LYLE CO, CALIF, 71- Consult, Fairchild Camera & Instrument Corp, 28; Grumman Aircraft Eng. Corp, 61 & 62; mem, Franklin Inst. AAAS; Am. Phys. Soc; Am. Math. Soc; Optical Soc. Am; N.Y. Acad. Sci. Applied mathematics; optics; radiometry. Address: 667 Coate Rd, Orange, CA 92669.

ECOBICHON, D(ONALD) J(OHN), b. Lindsay, Ont, June 21, 37; m. 60; c. 2. BIOCHEMICAL PHARMACOLOGY. B.Sc.Phm, Univ. Toronto, 60, M.A, 62, Ph.D.(pharmacol), 64. Demonstr. pharmacol, faculty med, Univ. Toronto, 60-64; Nat. Res. Coun. Can. fel. protein chem, 64-65; asst. prof. PHARMACOL, Ont. Vet. Col, Univ. Guelph, 65-66, ASSOC. PROF, 66-69; DALHOUSIE UNIV, 69- Can. Biochem. Soc; Pharmacol. Soc. Can; N.Y. Acad. Sci; Soc. Toxicol. Study of drug hydrolysis by tissue esterases of various mammalian species; pharmacodynamics; mechanism of action; toxicology of chlorinated hydrocarbon insecticides. Address: Dept. of Pharmacology, Dalhousie University, Halifax, N.S, Can.

ECONOMOS, GEO(RGE), b. Haverhill, Mass, Aug. 22, 19; m. 47; c. 2. CERAMICS, INORGANIC CHEMISTRY. B.S, Northeast. Univ, 49; S.M, Mass. Inst. Technol, 51, Sc.D.(ceramics), 54. Asst. prof. metall, Mass. Inst. Technol, 54-61; ELECTRONICS CONSULT, RES. ADMIN, ALLEN-BRADLEY CO, MILWAUKEE, 61- Vis. prof, sch. appl. sci. & eng, Univ. Wis, Milwaukee. U.S.A.A.F, 41-45. AAAS; Am. Chem. Soc; Am. Ceramic Soc; N.Y. Acad. Sci; Am. Soc. Metals. Development of ceramic dielectrics, ferroelectrics and ferromagnetics; powder metallurgy; polymers. Address: 4476 N. Maryland Ave, Shorewood, WI 53211.

ECONOMOU, G(EORGE) A(RISTOTLE), b. Manchester, N.H, June 24, 23; m. 46, 69; c. 3. ASTRONOMY, OPTICS. S.B, Harvard, 46. Supvr. optical develop, Sandia Corp, 48-60; mem. staff optical instrumentation, Perkin-Elmer Corp, 56-60; dir. develop, Fecker Plant, Am. Optical Co, 60-70; V.PRES. INSTRUMENTATION, GOERZ OPTICAL CO, 70- U.S.A, 44-46, T/Sgt. Am. Optical Soc. Development of large diameter telescopes and optical systems; laser and electro-optical applications to instrumentation; metrology. Address: Goerz Optical Co, 301 Alpha Dr, Pittsburgh, PA 15238.

ECONOMOU, PETER, b. Ano-Ravenia, Greece, July 3, 30; U.S. citizen; m. 57; c. 3. PHYSICAL CHEMISTRY. Dipl, Univ. Thessalonika, 56; U.S. Pub. Health Serv. grant, Polytech. Inst. Brooklyn, 59-61, Ph.D.(phys. chem), 64. Res. chemist, Am. Cyanamid Co, 63-68; BILLERICA RES. CTR, CABOT CORP, 68-69, PAPER PROJ. MGR, 69- Greek Army, 56-57, 2nd Lt. Am. Chem. Soc. Colloids and polyelectrolytes; micellar systems; critical phenomena in aqueous solutions of long-chain quaternary ammonium salts; interactions of polyanions-polycations, simple and complex coacervation phenomena. Address: Billerica Research Center, Cabot Corp, Concord Rd, Billerica, MA 01821.

ECONOMOU, STEVEN GEORGE, b. Chicago, Ill, July 4, 22; m. 50; c. 3. MEDICINE. Chicago, 40-43; M.D, Hahnemann Med. Col, 47. Intern med, St. Francis Hosp, Evanston, Ill, 47-48, res. surg, 48-49, orthop, 50; fel. path, Cook County Hosp, Chicago, 49; res. SURG, Presby. Hosp, Chicago, 50-52, 54; asst. attend. surgeon, PRESBY-ST. LUKE'S HOSP, 54-60, assoc.

attend. surgeon, 60-64, dir. lab. surg. res, 64-70, ATTEND. SURGEON, 65-; ASSOC. PROF. SURG, COL. MED, UNIV. ILL, CHICAGO, 62-; PROF, RUSH MED. COL, 71- Asst. prof, Univ. Ill, Chicago, 54-62; ed, Presby-St. Luke's Hosp. Med. Bull, 62-69. U.S.A, 44-47. Am. Med. Asn; Am. Asn. Cancer Res; Nat. Geriat. Soc. Cancer surgery. Address: Presbyterian-St. Luke's Hospital, 1753 W. Congress Pkwy, Chicago, IL 60611.

ECONOMY, JAMES, b. Detroit, Mich, Mar. 28, 29; m. 61; c. 4. ORGANIC CHEMISTRY. B.S, Wayne State, 50; Off. Naval Res. fel, Maryland, 53-54, Ph.D.(chem), 54. Res. assoc. polymer res. & Marvel fel, Illinois, 54-56; gen. res. leader in charge res. Semet-Solvay Petrochem. Div, Allied Chem. Corp, 56-60; mgr. chem. dept, RES. DEVELOP. DIV, CARBORUNDUM CO, 60-70, MGR. RES. BR, 70- Lectr, Canisius Col, 61-62. AAAS; Am. Chem. Soc; fel. Am. Inst. Chem; N.Y. Acad. Sci. Inorganic fibers, flakes and whiskers; preparation characterization and applications of nitrides, borides, carbides and oxides; oxidation catalysis; preparation and evaluation of high temperature polymers; development of reinforced composites. Address: 465 Ruskin Rd, Buffalo, NY 14226.

EDAMURA, FRED Y, b. Vancouver, B.C, Jan. 25, 39; m. 62; c. 4. ORGANIC CHEMISTRY. B.S, Alberta, 60; M.A, Hopkins, 62, Esso Ed. Found. fel, 62-64, Ph.D.(org. chem), 65. RES. CHEMIST, HALOGENS RES. LAB, DOW CHEM. CO, 65- Am. Chem. Soc; Sci. Res. Soc. Am. Organic synthesis; terpene, carbene, and organic fluorine chemistry; synthesis of biologically active compounds. Address: Halogens Research Lab, 768 Bldg, Dow Chemical Co, Midland, MI 48640.

EDDINGER, RALPH TRACY, b. Wilkes-Barre, Pa, Feb. 5, 22; m. 45; c. 4. CHEMICAL ENGINEERING, FUEL TECHNOLOGY. B.S, Pa. State Univ, 42; N.W. Lord fel. & M.S, Ohio State Univ, 47, Ph.D.(metall), 48. Operating engr, Koppers Co, Inc, 42-46; res. engr, Consolidation Coal Co, 48-51; mgr. res. lab, East. Gas & Fuel Assocs, 51-61; sr. res. engr, FMC CORP, 61-66, MGR. PROJ. COED, 66- Chmn, Gordon Res. Conf. on Coal Sci, 69. Am. Chem. Soc; Am. Inst. Chem. Eng; Brit. Inst. Fuel; Am. Inst. Min, Metall. & Petrol. Eng. Industrial high-temperature and fluidized-bed low-temperature carbonization of coal; coal processing and utilization; chemical process research and development. Address: Process Research Dept, FMC Corp, P.O. Box 8, Princeton, NJ 08540.

EDDINGTON, CARL L(EE), b. Tulsa, Okla, Dec. 26, 32; m. 58; c. 3. BIOCHEMISTRY. B.S, Univ. Tulsa, 55; fel, St. Louis Univ, 62-66, Ph.D.(biochem), 68. Chemist, indust. serv. div, Dow Chem. Co, 58-62; RES. CHEMIST, SAMUEL ROBERTS NOBLE FOUND, 66- U.S.A, 55-57, Res, 57-61, Sgt. Tumor-host relationships, particularly leukocyte production of humoral factors, acute phase globulins, fever, iron metabolism, enzymes, endotoxins and immunology; biochemistry of lactation, particularly hormones, nucleic acid and protein biosynthesis. Address: Samuel Roberts Noble Foundation, Route 1, Ardmore, OK 73401.

EDDLEMAN, ELVIA ETHERIDGE, JR, b. Birmingham, Ala, Oct. 20, 22; c. 1. INTERNAL MEDICINE, CARDIOLOGY. B.S, Howard Col, 44; M.D, Emory Univ, 48. Intern MED, Grady Mem. Hosp, Atlanta, Ga, 48-49; resident, Parkland Hosp, Dallas, Tex, 49-50; fel, UNIV. ALA. SCH. MED, 52-53, instr, 53-54, asst. prof, 54-57, assoc. prof, 57-62, PROF, 62-; ASSOC. DIR. RES. & EDUC, VET. ADMIN. HOSP, 54-, asst. chief med. & chief cardiovasc. sect, 54-57, acting chief & chief med. serv, 57-62. Res. fel, Med. Col. Ala, 52-53. Dipl, Am. Bd. Internal Med, 56. Med.C, 50-52, Lt. Fel. Am. Col. Cardiol; fel. Am. Col. Physicians; Am. Fedn. Clin. Res; Am. Heart Asn; Am. Med. Asn; Ballistocardiographic Res. Soc. Cardiovascular research. Address: Dept. of Medicine, University of Alabama School of Medicine, 1919 Seventh Ave. S, Birmingham, AL 35233.

EDDOWES, EDWARD EVERETT, b. Phila, Pa, Mar. 29, 30; m. 56; c. 2. EXPERIMENTAL PSYCHOLOGY. A.B, Univ. Miami, 56; M.A, Univ. Fla, 58, Ph.D.(psychol. educ), 59. Eng. psychologist, Martin Co, Md, 59; air arm div, Westinghouse Elec. Corp, 59-60; sr. eng. psychologist, Aircraft Armaments, Inc, 60-62; proj. eng. psychologist, McDonnell Aircraft Corp, 62-65, mgr. advan. aircraft systs. sect, eng. psychol. dept, 66-68; assoc. prof. psychol, Univ. South. Ill, Edwardsville, 65-66; PROF. PSYCHOL. & CHMN. DEPT, LINDENWOOD COL, 68- U.S.N.R, 49-56, Lt.(jg). Am. Psychol. Asn; Human Factors Soc. Human learning and motivation; decision making, information, processing and problem solving; systematic and theoretical psychology; human engineering of displays and controls for equipment systems. Address: Dept. of Psychology, Lindenwood College, St. Charles, MO 63301.

EDDS, GEORGE TYSON, b. Heidenheimer, Tex, Jan. 9, 13; m. 31; c. 3. PHARMACOLOGY, VETERINARY MEDICINE. B.S. & D.V.M, Tex. A&M Univ, 36, M.S, 38; Ph.D.(pharmacol), Univ. Minn, 52. From instr. to prof. physiol. & pharmacol, Tex. A&M Univ, 35-50; v.pres. res, Ft. Dodge Labs, Iowa, 50-62; PROF. VET. SCI, UNIV. FLA, 62- Am. Vet. Med. Asn; U.S. Animal Health Asn. Pharmacology-toxicology drug actions on animals; anesthetics; analeptics; chemotherapy; anthelmintics; biologicals-attenuation by irradiation for vaccine production; physiology of laboratory and farm animals; aflatoxins as carcinogens; babesiosis control in horses. Address: Dept. of Veterinary Science, University of Florida, Gainesville, FL 32601.

EDDS, LOUISE LUCKENBILL, b. Lebanon, Pa, Nov. 19, 36; m. 71. EMBRYOLOGY. B.A, Oberlin Col, 58; Wash. Univ, 58-61; Ph.D.(biol), Brown Univ, 64. Arthritis Found. res. fel. arthritis & connective tissue diseases, sch. med, Boston Univ, 65-66, instr. res. dermat, 66-68; sci. fel, Hubrecht Lab, Royal Netherlands Acad. Sci. & Letters, 68-69; ASST. PROF. BIOL. SCI, SMITH COL, 69- AAAS; Am. Soc. Zool; Soc. Develop. Biol. Fine structure of amphibian egg; fine structure of wounded amphibian skin. Address: Clark Science Center-Smith College, Northampton, MA 01060.

EDDS, MAC V(INCENT), b. Newark, N.J, Mar. 25, 17; m. 40; div; m. 71; c. 3. EMBRYOLOGY. B.A, Amherst Col, 38, M.A, 40, hon. Sc.D, 68; Ph.D.(embryol), Yale 43. Asst. zool, Univ. Chicago, 43-45; instr. anat, sch. med, Univ. Pittsburgh, 45-46, asst. prof, 46-47; biol, Brown Univ, 47-51, assoc. prof, 51-56, prof, 56-71, chmn. dept, 60-63, div. med. sci, 63-65, dir. med, 65-68; PROF. ZOOL. & DEAN FACULTY NATURAL SCI. & MATH, COL. ARTS & SCI, UNIV. MASS, AMHERST, 71- In charge embryol. course, Marine Biol. Lab, Woods Hole, 56-60; managing ed, Develop. Biol, 58-71. With Off. Sci. Res. & Develop, 44. Am. Acad. Arts & Sci; Am. Asn. Anat; Am. Soc. Cell Biol; Am. Soc. Zool; Soc. Develop. Biol.(secy, 53-56); Int. Soc. Develop. Biol; Int. Soc. Cell Biol. Experimental embryology of amphibia and mammalia; nerve regeneration in mammals; development of collagen; development of nervous system. Address: Dept. of Zoology, University of Massachusetts, Amherst, MA 01002.

EDDY, BERNICE E(LAINE), b. Glendale, W.Va, Sept. 30, 03; m. 38; c. 2. BACTERIOLOGY. A.B, Marietta Col, 24; Taft fel, Cincinnati, 24-25, M.S, 25, Hogan fel, 25-28, Ph.D.(bact), 27. Asst. pediat. & bact, Cincinnati, 28-29, Davis teaching fel. bact, 29-30; laboratorian leprosy, Marine Hosp, La. U.S. PUB. HEALTH SERV, 31-35, assoc. bacteriologist, NAT. INSTS. HEALTH, 37-42, bacteriologist, 42-48, sr. bacteriologist, 48-54, prin. bacteriologist, 54-63, MICROBIOLOGIST, 63- Lectr, Cincinnati Col. Pharm, 29-30. Fel. AAAS; fel. Am. Pub. Health Asn; Am. Soc. Microbiol; Soc. Exp. Biol. & Med; Am. Asn. Immunol; Am. Soc. Trop. Med. & Hyg; Int. Leprosy Asn; Am. Acad. Microbiol; N.Y. Acad. Sci; Fedn. Am. Soc. Exp. Biol; Am. Asn. Cancer Res; Tissue Culture Asn. Classification of pneumococci; standardization of influenza virus vaccines and adenovirus vaccines; hemoglobinophilic bacilli; tuberculin; poliomyelitis virus; tumor viruses. Address: Division of Biologics Standards, National Institutes of Health, Bethesda, MD 20014.

EDDY, CHARLES E(LWYN), b. Weirton, W.Va, Mar. 4, 25; m. 46; c. 2. MECHANICAL ENGINEERING. B.S, Bucknell Univ, 45. Tool repairman serv. & maintenance, Weirton Steel Co, 46-47, test engr, fuel dept, 47-48, field engr. & draftsman, 48-53, mech. turn foreman, blooming mill, 53-55, mech. shop supt, 55-57; sr. res. engr, NAT. STEEL CORP, 57-59, asst. to dir. res. & develop, 59-64, mgr. spec. serv. res. & develop, 64, asst. dir, RAW MAT. DEPT, 65-66, DIR, 66- U.S.N, 43-46. Raw materials. Address: Raw Material Dept, National Steel Corp, 2800 Grant Bldg, Pittsburgh, PA 15219.

EDDY, C(HARLES) GRAHAM, b. Chicago, Ill, Oct. 27, 04; m. 29; c. 2. BACTERIOLOGY. B.A, Wayne State, 42; M.A, American Univ, 54. Photographer, Beidler-Viken Studio, 28-29; Underwood & Underwood, 29-30; med. photographer, Mayo Clin, 30-36; head photog. dept, Wayne County Gen. Hosp, 37-42; chief, med. illustration div, Vet. Admin, 46-58; Far East area officer, commun. media, Int. Coop. Admin, 58-60; commun. media off, U.S. AGENCY INT. DEVELOP. MISSION, Iran, 60-62, Pakistan, 63-64, Afghanistan, 64-65, instr. mat. proj. mgr, VIETNAM, 65-67, HEALTH EDUC. MAT. ADV, 67- Med.Serv.C, 42-45, Res, 45-64, Col.(ret). AAAS; fel. Biol. Photog. Asn.(Louis Schmidt Award, 55, v.pres, 49-51, pres, 51-53); N.Y. Acad. Sci; Am. Acad. Polit. & Soc. Sci; Soc. Photog. Sci. & Eng.(secy-treas, 59-60); Asn. Med. Illustrators; fel. Royal Photog. Soc. Gt. Brit. Photographic instrumentation; endoscopic photography; photomicrography. Address: U.S. Agency for International Development/Public Health, APO San Francisco, CA 96243.

EDDY, C(HARLES) ROLAND, b. Providence, R.I, Aug. 31, 14; m. 40; c. 4. PHYSICAL CHEMISTRY. Sc.B, Brown Univ, 35; Ph.D.(phys. chem), Univ. Ill, 38. Instr. phys. chem, Univ. Ill, 38-41; PHYS. CHEMIST, EAST. REGIONAL RES. LAB, EAST. UTILIZATION RES. & DEVELOP. DIV, U.S. DEPT. AGR, 41-; ADJ. PROF. PHYSICS, BEAVER COL, 66- AAAS; Am. Chem. Soc; Am. Asn. Physics Teachers. Infrared absorption spectroscopy; physical chemistry of starch and pectin; autoxidation of fats and oils; conversion of globular proteins to fibrous forms; dielectric properties; scientific applications of digital computers. Address: U.S. Dept. of Agriculture, 600 E. Mermaid Lane, Wyndmoor, PA 19118.

EDDY, CLIFFORD OTIS, JR, b. Henderson, Ky, July 6, 31; m. 53; c. 2. ORGANIC CHEMISTRY. A.B, Cornell Univ, 52; Ph.D.(org. chem), Univ. Rochester, 59. Sr. res. chemist, B.F. Goodrich Co, 57-60; Barberton Lab, Pittsburgh Plate Glass Co, 60-69; SCIENTIST, XEROX CORP, 69- AAAS; Am. Chem. Soc. Synthetic organic and polymer chemistry; organometallic, alkaloid and quinone chemistry. Address: Xerox Corp, Bldg. 139, 800 Phillips Rd, Webster, NY 14580.

EDDY, CORNELIA ANN, b. Oil City, Pa, Nov. 21, 06; m. 33, div. PUBLIC HEALTH, MEDICAL MICROBIOLOGY. B.A, Goucher Col, 27; Johns Hopkins Univ, 27-28, part-time 30-33; M.S, Tufts Univ, 48; Ph.D.(microbiol), Tulane Univ, 55. Technician pharmacol, sch. med, Johns Hopkins Univ, 28-29; med, Hill Sch. Infirmary, 29-30; asst. bacteriologist, Md. State Health Dept, 30-33; jr. microbiologist, Conn. State Health Dept, 35-37; technician, med, Children's Hosp. Boston, Mass, 37-38; bacteriologist, New Eng. Med. Ctr, 38-48; instr. microbiol, Sch. Med, Tulane Univ, 48-56, asst. prof, 56-61, assoc. prof, 61-71; RETIRED, JUNE 72. Asst. bact, sch. med, Tufts Univ, 43-48. Am. Soc. Microbiol; Am. Pub. Health Asn. Anonymous Mycobacteria; Hemophilus influenzae. Address: Dept. of Microbiology, School of Medicine, Tulane University, New Orleans, LA 70112.

EDDY, DONALD ARLINGTON, b. Sioux City, Iowa, Mar. 19, 06; m. 27; c. 1. AGRICULTURAL EDUCATION. B.S, S.Dak. State Col, 27, M.S, 45. Instr. agr, S.Dak. State Univ, 27-36, asst. prin, sch. agr, 36-41, dir, 41-61, asst. to dir. resident instr, 61-71; RETIRED. Development of Future Farmers of America in South Dakota. Address: 319 Ohio Dr, Brookings, SD 57006.

EDDY, EDWARD M(ITCHELL), b. Parsons, Kans, Feb. 9, 40; m. 63; c. 1. CELL & DEVELOPMENTAL BIOLOGY. B.S, Kans. State Univ, 62, M.S, 64; Nat. Insts. Health grant, Univ. Tex, 65-67, Ph.D.(anat), 67. Fel. anat, Harvard Med. Sch, 67-69, instr, 69-70; ASST. PROF. BIOL. STRUCT, UNIV. WASH, 70- Am. Soc. Cell Biol; Am. Asn. Anat; Soc. Develop. Biol; Am. Soc. Zool; Electron Micros. Soc. Am. Cell differentiation; nucleocytoplasmic interaction, formation and maturation of germ cells. Address: Dept. of Biological Structure, University of Washington, Seattle, WA 98105.

EDDY, G(EORGE) AMOS, b. Unity, Sask, June 8, 28; m. 50; c. 5. METEOROLOGY. B.A.Sc, Univ. B.C, 50; M.A, Univ. Toronto, 51; Ph.D.(meteorol), McGill Univ, 63. Asst. prof. atmospheric sci, Univ. Tex, Austin, 63-67, assoc. prof. biol, 67-68; PROF. METEOROL, UNIV. OKLA, 68- Vis. assoc. prof, Mass. Inst. Technol, 67-68. Am. Meteorol. Soc; Royal Meteorol. Soc.

Synoptic meteorology and weather forecasting; numerical weather prediction and analysis; statistical meteorology; ecosystem modeling; resource management modeling. Address: Dept. of Meteorology, University of Oklahoma, Norman, OK 73069.

EDDY, G(ERALD) E(RNEST), b. Lansing, Mich, Sept. 20, 07; m. 32; c. 2. GEOLOGY. B.S, Mich. State Col, 30; M.S, Michigan, 32. Compassman, MICH. GEOL. SURV, 29-30, asst. geologist, 30-31, geologist, 31-32, res. geologist, 32-33, petrol. geologist, 33-35, petrol. geologist & head petrol. geol. sect. surv, 35-36, mining geologist, 36-41, mine appraiser, 41-42, mining geologist, 45-46, state geologist & dir. geol. surv. div, 46-51, dir, DEPT. CONSERV, 51-64, state geologist, 64-71, EMER. STATE GEOL, 71- Consult, environ. & geol, 71- U.S.A, 42-45. Fel. Geol. Soc. Am; Am. Asn. Petrol. Geol; Asn. Am. State Geol. Limestone porosity and residues. Address: 2404 S. Logan St, Lansing, MI 48910.

EDDY, HUBERT ALLEN, b. Boston, Mass, June 2, 30; m. 59; c. 2. RADIATION BIOLOGY, PATHOLOGY. B.A, Boston Univ, 52, fel, 52-53, M.A, 54; Ph.D.(radiation biol), Univ. Rochester, 64. Instr. human ecol, Boston Univ, 53-54; res. asst. radiation biol, SCH. MED. & DENT, UNIV. ROCHESTER, 57-62, res. assoc, 62-63, instr, 64-68, ASST. PROF. RADIOL, 68- Mem, Late Effects Group N.Am. U.S.A, 54-56. AAAS; Radiation Res. Soc; Microcirculatory Soc. Study of mechanisms of effect of ionizing radiations of mammalian tissue and organ systems; tumor angiogenesis and the effect of ionizing radiations on tumor vasculature; comparative radiation oncology; radiation pathology. Address: Clinical Radiation Research Center, School of Medicine & Dentistry, University of Rochester, Rochester, NY 14642.

EDDY, JERRY K(ENNETH), b. Wheeling, W.Va, Aug. 17, 40; m. 62; c. 2. NUCLEAR PHYSICS. A.B, West Liberty State Col, 62; M.S, West Virginia, 64, Ph.D.(physics), 67. ASST. PROF. PHYSICS, INDIANA UNIV. PA, 67- Am. Asn. Physics Teachers; Am. Phys. Soc. Van de Graaff accelerators; nuclear spectroscopy; neutron induced charged particle reactions using the deuteron tritium reaction; activation analysis; neutron time of flight and polarization studies. Address: Dept. of Physics, Indiana University of Pennsylvania, Indiana, PA 15701.

EDDY, JOHN ALLEN, b. Pawnee City, Nebr, Mar. 25, 31; m. 53; c. 4. ASTROPHYSICS, SOLAR PHYSICS. B.S, U.S. Naval Acad, 53; Ph.D.(astrogeophys), Colorado, 62. Res. fel. radio astron, Nat. Bur. Standards, 62-63, physicist, 63; MEM. RES. STAFF ASTROPHYS, HIGH ALTITUDE OBSERV, 63- Lectr, Univ. Colo, 63-, consult, col. sci. improv. prog, 67-70. Boulder Scientist Award, Sci. Res. Soc. Am, 65. U.S.N, 53-57, Lt. Am. Astron. Soc; Int. Astron. Union. Infrared astronomy; history of astronomy. Address: High Altitude Observatory, Box 1558, Boulder, CO 80302.

EDDY, LOWELL P(ERRY), b. Portland, Ore, Nov. 25, 20; m. 46; c. 3. INORGANIC CHEMISTRY. B.S, Ore. State Col, 42, M.S, 48; Ph.D.(chem), Purdue, 52. Instr. chem, Wyoming, 50-51; res. assoc. & instr, Reed Col, 52-53; res. chemist. cellulose, Puget Sound Pulp & Timber Co, 53-57; asst. prof. CHEM, WEST. WASH. STATE COL, 57-64, ASSOC. PROF, 64- Petrol. Res. Fund, Am. Chem. Soc. int. faculty award & hon. res. asst, Univ. Col, Univ. London, 64; res. assoc, sch. chem, Univ. New South Wales, 69-70. U.S.A, 42-46, Chem.C.Res, 46-55, 1st Lt. Am. Chem. Soc. Analytical methods in the sulfite pulp industry; coordination compounds of transition elements. Address: 206 N. Garden St, Bellingham, WA 98225.

EDDY, NATHAN B(ROWNE), b. Glens Falls, N.Y, Aug. 4, 90; m. 13. PHYSIOLOGY, PHARMACOLOGY. M.D, Cornell, 11; hon. D.Sc, Michigan, 63. Instr. physiol, McGill, 16-20; asst. prof. physiol. & pharmacol, Alberta, 20-28, assoc. prof, 28-30; res. prof. pharmacol, dept. mat. med. & therapeut, Michigan, 30-39; prin. pharmacologist & med. off, NAT. INSTS. HEALTH, 39-60, consult. biologist, Mich, 30-39, NARCOTICS CONSULT, 60- Exec. secy, cmt. drug addiction, Nat. Acad. Sci-Nat. Res. Coun, 46-67, assoc. prof. 61-67; mem. expert cmt. drugs liable to produce addiction, WHO, 49-, chmn, 49, 51, 57, 58, 62, 63, consult, WHO, 61-; tech. adv, U.S. del, UN Narcotics Cmn, 57, 58; Lister Mem. lectr, Univ. Edinburgh, 59; mem. joint planning conf. for coop. res. on drug abuse, Nat. Sci. Found, Japan, 64; Kelynak Mem. Lect, Univ. London, 65; consult, Bur. Narcotics & Dangerous Drugs, 68-; Comt. Probs. of Drug Dependence, 71- Snow Medal for contribution to pub. health, Am. Social Health Asn, 67; WHO Medal meritorious serv. int. narcotics control, 68; gold medal, East. Psychiat. Res. Asn, 70. AAAS; Soc. Exp. Biol. & Med; Am. Soc. Pharmacol. & Exp. Therapeut. Drug addiction; analgesics; chemical structure and action; antimalarials; internal secretions; respiration; muscle. Address: 7055 Wilson Lane, Bethesda, MD 20034.

EDDY, NELSON W(ALLACE), b. Burford, Ont, Jan. 15, 39; m. 66; c. 1. NUCLEAR PHYSICS. B.A, McMaster Univ, 61; M.S, Univ. Mass, Amherst, 63; Ph.D.(nuclear physics), Ariz. State Univ, 69. ASST. PROF. PHYSICS, SIR GEORGE WILLIAMS UNIV, 68- Can. Asn. Physicists; Am. Phys. Soc; Am. Inst. Physics. Nuclear spectroscopy, especially of fission products and those produced by fast neutron reactions. Address: Dept. of Physics, Sir George Williams University, Montreal 107, Que, Can.

EDDY, ROBERT D(EVEREUX), b. Providence, R.I, Oct. 15, 14; m. 39; c. 3. INORGANIC CHEMISTRY. A.B, Brown Univ, 35; A.M. & Ph.D.(chem), Princeton, 38. Asst. CHEM, Princeton, 37-39; instr, Dartmouth Col, 39; TUFTS UNIV, 39-43, asst. prof, 43-49, assoc. prof, 49-53, PROF, 53- Consult, Educ. Testing Serv, 54- Civilian With Off. Sci. Res. & Develop, 44. Am. Chem. Soc. Phase rule studies; vapor pressure of water above solutions or salt hydrate systems; solubilities in ordinary water and deuterium water. Address: Dept. of Chemistry, Tufts University, Medford, MA 02155.

EDDY, SAMUEL, b. Decatur, Ill, Mar. 26, 97; m. 25; c. 2. BIOLOGY. B.A, James Millikin, 24; M.A, Illinois, 25, Ph.D.(zool, ecol), 29. Asst. prof. ZOOL, Millikin, 24-26; teaching asst, Illinois, 26-29; asst. prof, UNIV. MINN, MINNEAPOLIS, 29-38, assoc. prof, 38-44, prof, 44-64, EMER. PROF. & CURATOR FISHES, 64- Asst. biologist, State Natural Hist. Surv, Ill, 25-29; consult. for biol. survs, Minn. Div. Game & Fish, 37-40. Am. Micros. Soc; Ecol. Soc. Am.(v.pres, 53); Am. Soc. Ichthyol. & Herpet; Am. Fisheries Soc; Am. Soc. Limnol. & Oceanog. Ecological surveys; fish taxonomy and growth; limnology. Address: Museum of Natural History, University of Minnesota, Minneapolis, MN 55455.

EDDY, THOMAS A, b. Parsons, Kans, Dec. 31, 34; m. 64; c. 1. ENTOMOLOGY, WILDLIFE MANAGEMENT. B.S, Kans. State Univ, 57, Ph.D.(entom), 70; M.S, Univ. Ariz, 59. Instr. BIOL, KANS. STATE TEACHERS COL, 60-67, asst. prof, 67-71, ASSOC. PROF, 71- Wildlife Soc; Conserv. Educ. Asn. Hymenoptera ecology and behavior. Address: R.R. 1, Emporia, KS 66801.

EDE, ALAN WINTHROP, b. Stamford, Conn, Jan. 16, 33; m. 57; c. 3. MICROELECTRONICS. B.S, Worcester Polytech. Inst, 55; M.S, Univ. Maine, Orono, 63; Ph.D.(elec. eng), Ore. State Univ, 68. Engr, Raytheon Mfg. Co, 55-60; from instr. to ASSOC. PROF. ELEC. ENG, UNIV. MAINE, ORONO, 60- Inst. Elec. & Electronics Engr; Am. Soc. Eng. Educ. Electrofishing; underwater telemetry. Address: Dept. of Electrical Engineering, University of Maine, Orono, ME 04473.

EDEBURN, RALPH M(ILTON), b. Mercer, Pa, Jan. 4, 05; m. 33; c. 1. BIOLOGY. B.S, Pa. State Teachers Col, 28; M.S, Cornell Univ, 30, Ph.D.(ornith), 38. Teacher, high sch, Pa, 23-25, 28-45; prof. zool, Marshall Univ, 45-70; RETIRED. Assoc. Am. Ornith. Union; Wilson Ornith Soc. Breeding birds; population density; breeding distribution of birds in a typical upland area. Address: Box 42, R.D. 1, Mercer, PA 16137.

EDEIKEN, JACK, b. Phila, Pa, May 25, 23; m. 42; c. 5. RADIOLOGY. Villanova Univ, 41-43; M.D, Univ. Pa, 47. Asst. prof. RADIOL, sch. med, Univ. Pa, 51-58; assoc. prof, THOMAS JEFFERSON UNIV, 58-67, PROF, 67-, CHIEF DIAG. DIV, UNIV. HOSP, 69-, CHMN. DEPT. RADIOL, 71- Consult, Vet. Admin. Hosps, Wilmington, Del, 55- & Phila, Pa, 63-, U.S. Air Force. Dipl, Am. Bd. Radiol, 51. U.S.A, 51-53, 1st Lt. Radiol. Soc. N.Am; fel. Am. Col. Radiol; Am. Med. Asn. Address: Dept. of Radiology, Thomas Jefferson University Hospital, 11th & Walnut Sts, Philadelphia, PA 19107.

EDELBERG, ROBERT, b. N.J, Aug. 2, 21; m. 44; c. 4. PSYCHOPHYSIOLOGY. B.S, Rutgers, 42; Ph.D.(physiol), Pennsylvania, 49. Asst. prof. physiol, Long Island, 49-51; biophys. in psychiat, col. med, Baylor Univ, 56-59, assoc. prof, 59-63; prof. psychophysiol. & physiol, Med. Ctr, Univ. Okla, 63-70; PROF. PSYCHIAT, RUTGERS MED. SCH. & PROF. PSYCHOL, RUTGERS UNIV. GRAD. SCH, 70- Sr. res. fel, U.S. Pub. Health Serv, 58-62; consult, NASA, 62-63; mem. staff res. & develop, aero. med. lab, Wright Air Develop. Ctr, Wright-Patterson AFB; mem, exp. psychol. study sect, Nat. Insts. Health, 66-69. U.S.A.F, 42-46, 51-55, Maj. AAAS; Am. Physiol. Soc; N.Y. Acad. Sci; Soc. Psychophysiol. Res.(pres, 65-66); Am. Psychol. Soc; Am. Psychosom. Soc; Pavlovian Soc. N.Am. Cell permeability and membrane structure; electrophysiology; cardiovascular physiology; autonomic nervous activity; electrodermal physiology and psychophysiology. Address: Dept. of Psychiatry, Rutgers Medical School, New Brunswick, NJ 08903.

EDELBERG, SEYMOUR, b. Brooklyn, N.Y, Nov. 21, 23; m. 51; c. 2. OPTICAL PHYSICS. B.E.E, City Col. N.Y, 44; M.E.E, Polytech. Inst. Brooklyn, 47, sr. res. fel, 47-49, D.E.E, 53. Res. engr, Haskins Labs, 44-47; proj. engr, Sperry Gyroscope Co, 49-52; head, electronic div, Balco Res. Labs, 52-55; assoc. group leader, LINCOLN LAB, MASS. INST. TECHNOL, 55-69, GROUP LEADER LASER TECHNOL, 69- AAAS; Am. Phys. Soc; Inst. Elec. & Electronics Eng; Am. Inst. Aeronaut. & Astronaut. Antennas; radar scattering; reentry technology; electromagnetic and microwave theory; optics. Address: 89 Heath's Bridge Rd, Concord, MA 01742.

EDELEN, DOMINIC G(ARDINER) B(OWLING), b. Wash, D.C, Jan. 3, 33; m. 54; c. 6. APPLIED MATHEMATICS. B.E.S, Johns Hopkins Univ, 54, M.S.E, 56, Ph.D, 65. Jr. instr. math. & mech, Johns Hopkins Univ, 54-56; engr, Martin Co, Md, 56-59; mem. tech. staff, Hughes Aircraft Co, Calif, 59-60; mem. res. staff, Rand Corp, 60-66; PROF. math, Purdue Univ, 66-69; MATH. & ASTRON, LEHIGH UNIV, 69- Soc. Eng. Sci; Soc. Natural Philos; fel. Royal Astron. Soc; Tensor Soc. Application of general relativity and differential geometry to the study of the structure of galaxies; axiomatization of theoretical physics and the use of continuum mechanics and thermodynamics in relativity; non-local variational mechanics. Address: Center for the Application of Mathematics, Lehigh University, Bethlehem, PA 18015.

EDELHAUSER, HENRY F, b. Dover, N.J, Sept. 9, 37; m. 61; c. 2. PHYSIOLOGY, OPHTHALMOLOGY. B.A, Paterson State Col, 62; M.S, Mich. State Univ, 64, Nat. Insts. Health fel, 65, Ph.D.(physiol), 66. Lab. technician, Warner Lambert Pharmaceut. Res. Inst, 62; asst. physiol, Mich. State Univ, 62-65; instr, MED. COL. WIS, 66-68, asst. prof. PHYSIOL. & OPHTHAL, 68-71, ASSOC. PROF, 71-, fel. physiol, 66-67, res. assoc. ophthal, 67-68. Prin. investr, Wis. Dept. Natural Resources, grant, 69-71; Nat. Eye Inst. grant, 69-72; U.S.N, 55-58. Am. Soc. Biol. Sci; Am. Soc. Zool; Asn. Res. Vision & Ophthal; Am. Physiol. Soc. Membrane physiology; physiology and biochemistry of the eye; corneal cryopreservation; pathophysiology of the eye; fish physiology and eye disease; hydrophilic contact lens effects on the cornea. Address: Dept. of Physiology & Ophthalmology, Medical College of Wisconsin, 561 N. 15th St, Milwaukee, WI 53233.

EDELHOCH, HAROLD, b. N.Y.C, Oct. 25, 22; c. 2. PHYSICAL CHEMISTRY. B.A, N.Y. Univ, 43; M.A, Princeton, 46, Ph.D.(phys. chem), 47. Asst, Manhattan proj, Princeton, 43-47; Nat. Insts. Health fel, Harvard Med. Sch, 47-50; Univ. Wis, 50-51; asst. prof. oncol. & biochem, sch. med, Univ. Kans, 52-57; PHYS. CHEMIST, NAT. INST. ARTHRITIS & METAB. DISEASES, NAT. INSTS. HEALTH, 57- Prof. lectr, Georgetwon Med. Ctr, 64- U.S.A, 43-46. Am. Chem. Soc. Biophysics of macromolecules; biochemistry of proteins and enzymes; structure of hormones; thyroid proteins. Address: National Institute of Arthritis & Metabolic Diseases, National Institutes of Health, Bethesda, MD 20014.

EDELMAN, FRANZ, b. Breslau, Ger, Jan. 16, 22; nat; m. 47; c. 3. APPLIED MATHEMATICS. B.Sc, McGill Univ, 45; M.S, Brown Univ, 48, Ph.D.(appl. math), 50. Fel, McGill Univ, 45-46; res. asst, Brown Univ, 46-50; res. mathematician, RCA CORP, 50-57, opers. res. analyst, 57-61, DIR. OPERS. RES, 61- Opers. Res. Soc. Am; Inst. Mgt. Sci. Operations research; computer usage. Address: 19 Howe Circle, Princeton, NJ 08540.

EDELMAN, GERALD M(AURICE), b. New York, N.Y, July 1, 29; m. 51; c. 3. BIOCHEMISTRY. B.S, Ursinus Col, 50; M.D, Pennsylvania, 54; Ph.D.(biochem), Rockefeller Inst, 60. Med. house officer, Mass. Gen. Hosp, 54-55;

asst. physician, Rockefeller Inst, 57-60, asst. prof, 60-63, assoc. prof. BIO-CHEM. & assoc. dean grad. study, 63-66; PROF, ROCKEFELLER UNIV, 66- Mem, biophys. study sect, Nat. Insts. Health, 63-67; consult, Helen Haye Whitney Found, 63; sr. fel. prog, Nat. Sci. Found, 64; assoc, Neurosci. Res. Prog; mem, Sci. Coun. Inst. Theoret. Studies; Coun. Basel Inst. Immunol. Spencer Morris Award, Univ. Pa, 54. Med.C, 55-57, Capt. Nat. Acad. Sci; AAAS; Am. Chem. Soc.(Eli Lilly Award, 65); Am. Acad. Arts & Sci; Am. Soc. Biol. Chem; Am. Asn. Immunol. Protein chemistry; immunology; bio-physics; structure of antibodies; fluorescence spectroscopy; primary and three-dimensional structure of proteins. Address: Dept. of Biochemistry, Rockefeller University, New York, NY 10021.

EDELMAN, I(SIDORE) S(AMUEL), b. N.Y.C, July 23, 20; m. 42; c. 4. MED-ICINE. B.A, Ind. Univ, 41, M.D, 44. Intern, Greenpoint Hosp, 44-45; resident physician, Montefiore Hosp, 47-48, Dazian Found. fel, 48-49; Atomic Energy Comn. fel, med. sch, Harvard & Peter Bent Brigham Hosp, 49-50, Am. Heart Asn. fel, 50-52; asst. prof. med, SCH. MED, UNIV. CALIF, SAN FRANCISCO, 52-54, assoc. prof, 54-60, prof. med. & physiol, 60-67, SAM-UEL NEIDER RES. PROF. MED, 67-, PROF. BIOPHYS, 69-, faculty res. lectr, 66-67. Estab. investr, Am. Heart Asn, 52-57; chief med. serv, San Francisco Gen. Hosp, Univ. Calif, 56-58; sr. res. fel. chem, Calif. Inst. Technol, 58-59; John Punnett Peters mem. lectr, sch. med, Yale, 64; mem. Nat. Insts. Health study comt, Off. Sci. & Technol, 64; vis. scientist, Weizmann Inst. Sci, 65-66; res. career awards comt, Nat. Inst. Gen. Med. Sci, 69-73. Med.C, U.S.A, 45-47, Capt. Am. Fedn. Clin. Res; Endocrine Soc. (Eli Lilly Award, 69); Am. Physiol. Soc; Am. Soc. Clin. Invest; Biophys. Soc; Asn. Am. Physicians; Am. Soc. Nephrology; Am. Soc. Biol. Chem; Soc. Gen. Physiol. Body water and electrolyte metabolism; application of radio-active and stable isotopes to medicine; active transport across biological membranes; mechanism of action of steroid hormones, thyroid hormone and antidiuretic hormone; biophysics. Address: University of California School of Medicine, San Francisco, CA 94122.

EDELMAN, LEONARD E(DWARD), b. Scranton, Pa, July 16, 13; m. 43. CHEMISTRY. B.A, Hobart Col, 36; M.A, Univ. Cincinnati, 39, Laws fel, 40-41, Ph.D.(chem), 41. Chemist, Eastman Kodak Co, N.Y, 36, 39; Lake Erie Chem. Co, Ohio, 37-38, res. dir. & v.pres, 41-44; Amecco Chem. Co, 40; dir. tech. serv, Johnson & Johnson Co, N.J, 44; fel, Mellon Inst, 46-49; res. dir, Medaseal Co. & Med. Iodine Labs, 49-51; eng. mgr, Micarta Div, WESTINGHOUSE ELEC. CORP, 51-67, MGR. POLYMER CHEM, RES. & DEVELOP. CTR, 67- U.S.A, 44-46. AAAS; Am. Chem. Soc; Soc. Mfg. Eng. Polymers; coatings; laminates; nickel-organic compounds; metallo-organics; chemical warfare agents; reduction of organic halides in liquid ammonia solution with alkali and alkaline earth metals; iodine. Address: Research & Development Center, Westinghouse Electric Corp, Pittsburgh, PA 15235.

EDELMAN, ROBERT, b. Brooklyn, N.Y, Apr. 30, 42. ORGANIC & POLY-MER CHEMISTRY. B.S, Brooklyn Col, 63; Cities Serv. fel, Rutgers Univ, 67-68, Ph.D.(org. chem), 69. Fel, Univ. Fla, 68-69; RES. CHEMIST, CELANESE RES. CO, 69- Am. Chem. Soc. Polyacetal and polyurethane chemistry; organophosphorus chemistry; solvolysis of bicyclic derivatives. Address: Product Technology Section, Celanese Research Co, Morris Ct, Summit, NJ 07901.

EDELMAN, SEYMOUR, b. Jersey City, N.J, May 12, 14; m. 48; c. 4. ME-CHANICS, METEOROLOGY. B.S, N.Y. Univ, 46; Cooper Union, 32-35; U.S. Dept. Agr. Grad. Sch, 44-49. Observer meteorol, U.S. Weather Bur, 37-43, meteorologist, 44-46; physicist acoustics, NAT. BUR. STANDARDS, 46-64, chief, vibration measurements sect, 64-67, physicist, INSTRUMENTATION APPLN. SECT, 68-70, ACTING CHIEF, 70- Acoustical Soc. Am; Soc. Exp. Stress Anal; Inst. Environ. Sci. Use of optical methods to measure vibration; measurement of sound absorption and sound transmission; piezoelectric and pyroelectric effects in polymers. Address: 9115 Glenridge Rd, Silver Spring, MD 20910.

EDELMAN, WALTER E(UGENE), JR, b. Oregon, Ill, July 15, 33. MECHAN-ICAL ENGINEERING. B.M.E, Minnesota, 56, M.S,M.E, 58; Ph.D.(mech. eng), Oregon State, 67. Engr, Minneapolis Honeywell, Inc, 53-56; instr. mech. eng, Minnesota, 57-58; mem. tech. staff, Hughes Aircraft Co, 58-61; instr. MECH. ENG, Oregon State, 61-66; asst. prof, CALIF. STATE COL, LONG BEACH, 67-70, ASSOC. PROF, 70- Ralph R. Teetor Ed. Award, Soc. Automotive Eng. 68. Inst. Elec. & Electronics Eng; Am. Soc. Metals; Soc. Motion Picture & TV Eng; Am. Soc. Eng. Educ. Stresses in composite materials; properties and behavior of castable photoelastic materials. Address: 20822 Woodlea Lane, Huntington Beach, CA 92646.

EDELMANN, ABRAHAM, b. New York, N.Y, Sept. 5, 15; m. 42; c. 2. PHYS-IOLOGY. A.B, Johns Hopkins Univ, 36; fel, N.Y. Univ, 38-39, M.S, 39; fel, Ohio State Univ, 42-46, Ph.D.(physiol), 47. Nat. Res. Coun. asst, Ohio State Univ, 41-42, instr. physiol, 46-47; scientist, Brookhaven Nat. Lab, 47-55; mgr. dept. biol. & med, Nuclear Sci. & Eng. Corp, 55-60, v.pres, 60-64, consult, 64-67; WESTINGHOUSE ELEC. CORP, 66-70, MGR. REGIONAL HEALTH PLANNING, HEALTH SYSTS. DEPT, 70- Mem, Nat. Tech. Task Comt. Indust. Wastes, 57-; lectr, Univ. Pittsburgh, 62-; sr. lectr, Carnegie Inst. Technol, 64- AAAS; assoc. Aerospace Med. Asn; Am. Physiol. Soc; Endocrine Soc; Radiation Res. Soc.(secy, 52-57); Soc. Exp. Biol. & Med; Am. Fedn. Clin. Res; Harvey Soc; Am. Nuclear Soc; Soc. Nuclear Med; N.Y. Acad. Sci. Physiological effects of radiation; endocrinology; aviation physiology; respiration; metabolism. Address: 1634 Beechwood Blvd, Pittsburgh, PA 15217.

EDELMANN, CHESTER M, JR, b. N.Y.C, Dec. 26, 30; m. 53; c. 3. PEDIAT-RICS. A.B, Columbia, 51; Washington (St. Louis), 51-53; M.D, Cornell, 55. Asst. instr. PEDIAT, ALBERT EINSTEIN COL. MED, 57-59, instr, 59-62, asst. prof, 62-67, assoc. prof, 67-70, PROF, 70-, res. fel. renal physiol, 58-59 & 61-63. Nat. Insts. Health res. career develop. award, 63-68. Mem. med. adv. bd, Kidney Found. N.Y, 69-; kidney disease & nephrology index adv. comt, Nat. Insts. Health, 70-, gen. med. study sect. B, 71-74; coun. on circulation, Am. Heart Asn. U.S.N.R, 59-61, Lt. Comdr. AAAS; Am. Acad. Pediat; Harvey Soc; Am. Physiol. Soc; Soc. Pediat. Res; Am. Pediat. Soc; Am. Soc. Clin. Invest; Am. Soc. Nephrology; Am. Soc. Pediat. Nephrology; Am. Fedn. Clin. Res; N.Y. Acad. Sci; Am. Inst. Biol. Sci; Am.

Heart Asn; N.Y. Acad. Med; Soc. Exp. Biol. & Med; Royal Soc. Med. Developmental renal physiology; renal disease in infants and children. Address: Dept. of Pediatrics, Rose F. Kennedy Center, 1410 Pelham Pkwy. S, Bronx, NY 10461.

EDELSACK, EDGAR A(LLEN), b. N.Y.C, June 14, 24; m. 53; c. 1. PHYSICS. B.S, Southern California, 48. Asst, Southern California, 48-49; physicist, Emery Tumor Group, 49-53; head, Van de Graaff accelerator sect, U.S. Naval Radio Defense Lab, 53-56; PHYSICIST, OFF. NAVAL RES, Calif, 56-67, PHYSICS PROG, VA, 67- U.S.A, 43-45. AAAS; Am. Phys. Soc. Electrostatic accelerators; x-ray dosimetry; medical use of radioisotopes; bio-physics; superconducting devices. Address: Physics Program, Office of Naval Research, 800 N. Quincy, Arlington, VA 22217.

EDELSON, A. L, b. Los Angeles, Calif, Jan. 1, 40. MATHEMATICS. B.Sc, Univ. Calif, (Berkeley), 62; Ph.D, State Univ. N.Y. Stony Brook, 68. Instr. MATH, State Univ. N.Y. Stony Brook, 68-69; ASST. PROF, UNIV. CALIF, DAVIS, 69- AAAS; Am. Math. Soc. Algebraic topology; brain research instrumentation. Address: Dept. of Mathematics, University of California, Davis, CA 95616.

EDELSON, BURTON IRVING, b. New York, N.Y, July 31, 26; m. 52; c. 3. METALLURGY, SPACE TECHNOLOGY. B.S, U.S. Naval Acad, 47; M.S, Yale, 54, Ph.D.(metall), 60. Mgr. astronaut. res, Naval Bur. Ships, 59-62; staff mem. space technol, Nat. Aeronaut. & Space Coun, 62-65; Off. Naval Res, London, 65-67; ASST. DIR, COMSAT LABS, COMMUN. SATELLITE CORP, 68- Legion of Merit, 65. U.S.N, 47-67, Comdr. AAAS; assoc. fel. Am. Inst. Aeronaut. & Astronaut; Am. Soc. Metals (Henry M. Howe award, 63); sr. mem. Inst. Elec. & Electronics Eng; fel. Brit. Interplanetary Soc. Physical properties of two-phase alloys; communications satellite systems; navigation satellite systems. Address: Comsat Labs, Clarksburg, MD 20734.

EDELSON, DAVID, b. Brooklyn, N.Y, Nov. 27, 27; m. 53, 62; c. 4. PHYSICAL CHEMISTRY. B.S, Polytech. Inst. Brooklyn, 46; Ph.D.(chem), Yale, 49. Asst. chem, Yale, 46-49, Sterling res. fel, 49-50; MEM. TECH. STAFF, BELL TEL. LABS, 50- Am. Chem. Soc; Am. Phys. Soc. Gaseous electronics; chemical kinetics; aeronomy. Address: Physical Chemistry Research & Development Dept, Bell Telephone Labs, 600 Mountain Ave, Murray Hill, NJ 07974.

EDELSON, JEROME, b. N.Y.C, Nov. 17, 32; m. 56; c. 3. BIOLOGICAL CHEMISTRY. B.S, Brooklyn Col, 54; M.A, Univ. Tex, 57, Ph.D.(biol. chem), 60. Asst. prof. chem, Univ. Southwest. La, 60-63; SR. BIOCHEMIST, WAL-LACE LABS, CARTER-WALLACE, INC, 63- AAAS; Am. Chem. Soc; Am. Soc. Pharmacol. & Exp. Therapeut. Synthesis and biological activity of amino acid analogues; drug metabolism; biochemical pharmacology. Address: Wallace Labs, Carter-Wallace, Inc, Cranbury, NJ 08512.

EDELSON, SIDNEY, b. New York, N.Y, Aug. 24, 16; m. 47. MATHEMATICS, ASTRONOMY. B.A, Brooklyn Col, 38; M.A, N.Y. Univ, 49; M.A, George-town Univ, 53, Ph.D.(solar radiation), 61. Captain, China Waterways Transport, Shanghai, 46-47; mathematician, U.S. Naval Observ, D.C, 48-50, astronomer, 50-56; U.S. Naval Res. Lab, 56-62, res. astronomer proj. leader, 62-64; RES. SCIENTIST, solar studies, AMES RES. CTR, NASA, 64-66, optical physics & planetary atmospheres, 66-71, SOLAR MAGNETIC FIELDS & NON-THERMAL RADIATIVE PROCESSES, 71- U.S.N, 40-46, Lt. Comdr. Am. Astron. Soc; Sci. Res. Soc. Am; Math. Asn. Am. Latitude and time; radio astronomy; solar physics. Address: Physics Branch, N-230-1, Ames Research Center, Moffett Field, CA 94035.

EDELSTEIN, ALAN SHANE, b. St. Louis, Mo, June 27, 36; m. 63; c. 2. SOLID STATE PHYSICS. B.S, Wash. Univ, 58; Woodrow Wilson fel, 58; M.S, Stanford Univ, 59, Ph.D.(physics), 63. Res. assoc. physics, Stanford Univ, 63-64; Nat. Sci. Found. fel, Univ. Leiden, 64-65; res. assoc, IBM Corp, N.Y, 65-68; ASSOC. PROF. PHYSICS, UNIV. ILL, CHICAGO CIRCLE, 68- Am. Phys. Soc. Superconducting and normal state properties of Kondo alloys containing cerium as the magnetic impurity; modes of investigation including electron tunneling, resistivity, specific heat and susceptibility measurements. Address: Dept. of Physics, University of Illinois, Box 4348, Chicago, IL 60680.

EDELSTEIN, RICHARD M(ALVIN), b. Los Angeles, Calif, May 28, 30; m. 55; c. 3. PHYSICS. B.A, Pomona Col, 51; Ph.D.(particle physics), Columbia, 60. Res. physicist, CARNEGIE-MELLON UNIV, 60-62, asst. prof. PHYS-ICS, 62-65, assoc. prof, 65-69, PROF, 69- Weizmann Inst. fel, 70-71. Fel. Am. Phys. Soc. Mu meson physics; high energy proton and pi meson scattering. Address: Dept. of Physics, Carnegie-Mellon University, Schenley Park, Pittsburgh, PA 15213.

EDELSTEIN, STUART J, b. Perth Amboy, N.J, Sept. 6, 41; m. 64; c. 1. BIO-CHEMISTRY. B.S, Tufts Univ, 63; Woodrow Wilson fel, Univ. Calif, Berkeley, 63-64, Danforth fel, 63-67, Nat. Insts. Health fel, 66-67, Ph.D.(bio-chem), 67. Nat. Res. Coun. fel. cellular biochem, Pasteur Inst, Paris, 67-68; ASST. PROF. BIOCHEM. & MOLECULAR BIOL, CORNELL UNIV, 68- Physical biochemistry of proteins; quaternary structure of proteins, especially hemoglobin; ultracentrifugation. Address: Wing Hall, Cornell University, Ithaca, NY 14850.

EDEN, C. EDWARD, b. Waynesboro, Pa, Sept. 6, 37; m. 59; c. 2. PHARMA-COLOGY. B.S, Phila. Col. Pharm, 60, M.S, 62, Ph.D.(pharm), 65. Pharmacologist, Huntingdon Res. Ctr, Becton, Dickinson, Inc, 65-67, dept. chief toxicol. & pharmacol, Md, 68-70; MEM. STAFF, TOILETRIES DIV, GIL-LETTE CO, 70- Asst. prof, Univ. Md, 67-68. Cardiovascular pharmacology; toxicology. Address: Toiletries Division, Gillette Co, Boston, MA 02106.

EDEN, EDWIN W(INFIELD), JR, b. Highland Park, N.J, June 4, 11; m. 37; c. 3. WATER RESOURCES. B.S, Rutgers Univ, 33, C.E, 41; M.S, Univ. Iowa, 38; M.S, Univ. Mich, 53. Chief, hydraul. sect, Upper Miss. Valley Div, Corps Eng, 46-50, planning & reports br, Jacksonville Dist, 50-65; chief, Interoceanic Canal Studies, 65-70, SPEC. CONSULT ON WATER RE-SOURCE PROBS, 70- Mem. Permanent Int. Asn. Navig. Cong; coun. Wave Res; Int. Comn. Irrig. & Drainage; coord. comt, Interoceanic Canal Studies.

Exceptional Civilian Serv. Decoration, Dept. Army, 70. U.S.N, 42-46, Res, 46-53, Lt. Comdr. Am. Soc. Civil Eng.(Wellington Prize, 70); Am. Soc. Prof. Eng; Soc. Am. Mil. Eng; Am. Geophys. Union. Planning and design of facilities required for utilization of water resources; design of ports and harbors to fit needs of commercial navigation. Address: 5374 Sanders Rd, Jacksonville, FL 32211.

EDEN, H(ENRY) FRANCIS, b. Newcastle on Tyne, Eng, Dec. 23, 34. PHYSICS. B.Sc, Durham, 56, Ph.D.(physics), 59. Sci. officer, Nat. Phys. Lab, Eng, 59-60; sr. res. assoc. physics, King's Col, Durham, 60-62; res. assoc. geophys, Mass. Inst. Tech, 62-64; physicist, Arthur D. Little, Inc, Mass, 64-70; PROG. DIR. METEOROL, NAT. SCI. FOUND, 70- Am. Geophys. Union; fel. Royal Meteorol. Soc. Propagation of sound in air and water; model experiments in geophysical fluid dynamics relating to the atmosphere and oceans; atmospheric electricity. Address: National Science Foundation, Washington, DC 20550.

EDEN, JAMAL S(HAHAB), b. Jaffa, Palestine, Jan. 4, 25; m. 54; c. 1. ORGANIC CHEMISTRY. A.B, Washington (St. Louis), 49; M.A, Missouri, 52. Res. chemist, Diamond Alkali Co, 51-56, SR. RES. CHEMIST, B.F. GOODRICH RES. CTR, 56- AAAS; Am. Chem. Soc. Catalytic vapor phase reactions; organic synthesis. Address: B.F. Goodrich Research Center, Brecksville, OH 44141.

EDEN, MURRAY, b. Brooklyn, N.Y, Aug. 17, 20; m. 45; c. 3. INFORMATION SCIENCE. B.S, City Col. N.Y, 39; M.S, Univ. Md, 44, Ph.D.(phys. chem), 51. Phys. chemist, Nat. Bur. Standards, 43-49; biophysicist, Nat. Cancer Inst, 49-53; spec. fel. math. biol, U.S. Pub. Health Serv, Princeton, 53-55; biophysicist, Nat. Heart Inst, 55-59; PROF. ELEC. ENG, MASS. INST. TECHNOL, 59- Lectr, Am. Univ, 47-48; Harvard Med. Sch, 60-; consult. to dirgen, WHO, 63-; chmn, U.S. Nat. Comt. on Eng. in Med. & Biol, 67-; ed-in-chief, Info. & Control, 67- Am. Physiol. Soc; Biophys. Soc; Inst. Elec. & Electronics Eng. Instrumentation; physiological measurements; mathematical models for biology; pattern recognition; human cognitive processes. Address: Cognitive Information Processing Group, Room 20, D 219, Research Lab. of Electronics, Massachusetts Institute of Technology, Cambridge, MA 02139.

EDEN, RICHARD CARL, b. Anamosa, Iowa, July 10, 39; m. 64. SOLID STATE PHYSICS. B.S, Iowa State, 61; M.S, Calif. Inst. Tech, 62; Ph.D. (solid state physics), Stanford, 67. Test technician, Collins Radio Co, Iowa, summers 59 & 60; elec. engr, U.S. Naval Ord. Lab, Md, summer 61; res. asst. elec. eng, Calif. Inst. Tech, 61-62; design engr, adv. systs. develop. div, Int. Bus. Mach. Corp, Calif, summer 62; res. asst. elec. eng, Stanford, 62-67, res. assoc, 67-68; MEM. TECH. STAFF, SCI. CTR, N.AM. ROCKWELL CORP, 68- Am. Phys. Soc; Inst. Elec. & Electronics Eng. Investigation of the electronic structure of solids by means of such experimental techniques as photoemission and measurements of optical properties; solid state optical detector and other semiconductor device research. Address: Science Center, North American Rockwell Corp, 1049 Camino Dos Rios, Thousand Oaks, CA 91360.

EDEN, W(ILLIAM) G(IBBS), b. Talledega, Ala, May 3, 18; m. 40; c. 2. ECONOMIC ENTOMOLOGY. B.S, Auburn, 40, M.S, 47; Ph.D, Illinois, 50. Asst. county agr. agent, Geneva, Ala, 40-43, 46; asst. entomologist & asst. prof. ENTOM, Auburn Univ, 48-50, assoc. entomologist & assoc. prof, 50-53, entomologist & prof, 53-65; CHMN. DEPT, UNIV. FLA, 65- Med. Serv.C, Res, Capt. Entom. Soc. Am.(pres, 72). Research on biology and control of insects of corn, cotton, peanuts, vegetables, fruits; toxicology; teach insect toxicology; immature insects. Address: 4411 NW 17th Pl, Gainesville, FL 32601.

EDENS, WALTER W(ILLIAM), b. West Allis, Wis, Jan. 7, 10; m. 36; c. 2. METALLURGY. B.S, Marquette, 34; M.S, Wisconsin, 37. Mech. engr, Heil Co, 35-36; chief metallurgist, Ampco Metal, Inc, 37-45, tech. dir, 45-47; v.pres. & works mgr, Badger Brass & Aluminum Foundry Co, 47-51; assoc. proj. dir, Alloy Eng. & Casting Co, Ill, 51-52; res. supvr, Allis-Chalmers Mfg. Co, 52-60, asst. dir. res, 60-69; dir, product planning, AMPCO METAL INC, 69-71, MGR, RES. & DEVELOP, 71- Am. Soc. Metals; Am. Inst. Mining, Metall. & Petrol. Eng; Am. Soc. Test. & Mat; Am. Foundrymen's Soc. Physical and chemical metallurgy; alloying; melting; casting; extrusion; welding; fabrication. Address: AMPCO Metal Inc, P.O. Box 2004, Milwaukee, WI 53201.

EDER, HOWARD A(BRAM), b. Milwaukee, Wis, Sept. 23, 17; m. 54; c. 3. MEDICINE. B.A, Wisconsin, 38; M.D, Harvard, 42, fel, 43-46, Nutrit. Found. fellow, 44-46, M.P.H, 45. Intern, Peter Bent Brigham Hosp, Boston, 42-43, asst. res. physician, 43-44; asst. physician, Rockefeller Inst. Hosp, 46-50; asst. prof. med, med. col, Cornell, 50-54; investr, Nat. Heart Inst, Nat. Insts. Health, 54-55; assoc. prof. MED, col. med, State Univ. N.Y. Brooklyn, 55-57; ALBERT EINSTEIN COL. MED, 57-60, PROF, 60- Mem. task force arteriosclerosis, Nat. Heart & Lung Inst, 70-71. U.S.P.H.S, 52-55, Surg. Soc. Exp. Biol. & Med; Am. Soc. Clin. Invest; Am. Soc. Biol. Chem; Asn. Am. Physicians; Am. Physiol. Soc; Brit. Biochem. Soc. Lipid metabolism and atherosclerosis. Address: Albert Einstein College of Medicine, Eastchester Rd. & Morris Park Ave, New York, NY 10461.

EDER, WOLFGANG ERNST, b. Vienna, Austria, Sept. 29, 30; m. 61; c. 1. MECHANICAL ENGINEERING. M.Sc, Univ. Wales, 67. Detail designer, Motormuli K.G, Austria, 51-53; design engr, A.E.G. Union, Austria, 53-56; Ing. O. Ruthner K.G, Austria, 56-57; design draughtsman, Eng. Elec. Co, Liverpool, Gr. Brit, 57-60, design engr, Stafford, 60, develop. engr, Liverpool, 60-61; asst. lectr. MECH. ENG, Univ. Col. Swansea, Wales, 61-62, lectr, 62-67; ASSOC. PROF, UNIV. CALGARY, 68- Soc. Automotive Eng; Am. Soc. Eng. Educ; Brit. Design Res. Soc; Brit. Inst. Eng. Designers; Asn. Austrian Eng. & Archit. Systematic engineering design methods; psychological characteristics of engineering designers; moiré-replica method of creep strain detection and monitoring in pressure vessels. Address: Dept. of Mechanical Engineering, University of Calgary, Calgary 44, Alta, Can.

EDERER, FRED, b. Vienna, Austria, Mar. 5, 26; U.S. citizen; m. 58; c. 3. BIOSTATISTICS. B.S, City Col. New York, 49; M.A, Am. Univ, 59; N.Y.

Univ, 49-50; Columbia Univ, 50-51; Stanford Univ, 62. Jr. actuary, N.Y.C. Employees' Retirement Syst, 49-50; jr. statistician, N.Y.C. Health Dept, 50-52; statistician, U.S. Air Force, 52-55; Bur. Labor Statist, 55-57; Nat. Cancer Inst, 57-64, Nat. Heart & Lung Inst, 64-71, HEAD CLIN. TRIALS SECT, NAT. EYE INST, 71- Lectr, Am. Univ, 65-68; dir. statist ctr, Nat. Diet-Heart Study, 64-67; dir. coord. ctr, Urokinase-Pulmonary Embolism Trial, 68-71; exec. comt, Collab. Diabetic Retinopathy Study, 71-; mem. coun. epidemiology, Am. Heart Asn. Fel. Am. Pub. Health Asn; fel. Am. Heart Asn; Am. Statist. Asn; Biomet. Soc; Soc. Epidemiol. Res. Biometry; epidemiology; evaluation of therapeutic efficacy; cooperative study methodology. Address: National Eye Institute, 9000 Rockville Pike, Bethesda, MD 20014.

EDERSTROM, HELGE E(LLIS), b. Torsas, Sweden, Feb. 28, 08; nat. PHYSIOLOGY. B.S, Beloit Col, 37; M.S, Northwestern, 39, Ph.D.(zool), 41; Missouri, 44-45. Asst, Northwestern, 37-41; asst. prof. physiol. & pharmacol, sch. med, Missouri, 42-47; assoc. prof. PHYSIOL, sch. med, St. Louis, 47-52; PROF, SCH. MED, UNIV. N.DAK, 52- AAAS; Am. Physiol. Soc; Soc. Exp. Biol. & Med; Aerospace Med. Asn; Am. Soc. Zool. Temperature regulation; cardiovascular physiology. Address: Dept. of Physiology & Pharmacology, University of North Dakota, Grand Forks, ND 58201.

EDESKUTY, F(REDERICK) J(AMES), b. Minneapolis, Minn, Sept. 29, 23; m. 47; c. 4. CHEMICAL ENGINEERING. B.Ch.E, Minnesota, 44, Ph.D. (chem. eng), 50. Mem. res. staff, Los Alamos Sci. Lab, California, 50-53; consult. engr. air conditioning, J.V. Edeskuty & Assocs, 53-54; MEM. RES. STAFF, LOS ALAMOS SCI. LAB, UNIV. CALIF, 54- U.S.A, 44-46. Fel. Am. Inst. Chem; Int. Inst. Refrig. Adsorption kinetics; high pressure; cryogenics. Address: Los Alamos Scientific Lab, P.O. Box 1663, Los Alamos, NM 87544.

EDGAR, ALAN D, b. Glasgow, Scotland, July 5, 35; Can. citizen; m. 57. GEOCHEMISTRY, PETROLOGY. B.A, McMaster, 58; Nat. Res. Coun. studentship & M.Sc, 61; Ont. Res. Found. fel. & Ph.D.(geol), Manchester, 63. Lectr. GEOL, UNIV. WEST. ONT, 63-64, asst. prof, 64-68, ASSOC PROF, 68- Res. grants, Nat. Res. Coun, 63-71, Ont. Res. Found, 64-65, Geol. Surv. Can, 65-71 & NATO, 66-67. Mineral Soc. Am; Mineral. Asn. Can; fel. Brit. Geol. Asn; Mineral. Soc. Gt. Brit. & Ireland; fel. Geol. Asn. Can. Mineralogy and crystallography of feldspathoids; experimental studies of silicate systems pertinent to alkaline igneous rocks; petrology of alkaline undersaturated rocks. Address: Dept. of Geology, University of Western Ontario, London, Ont, Can.

EDGAR, ALBERT CORTLAND, b. Anadarko, Okla, Dec. 27, 08; m. 35; c. 2. CHEMICAL ENGINEERING. B.S, Iowa State Col, 33. Res. chemist, Wilson & Co, Inc, 34-47, asst. dir. res. & tech. div, 47-69, DIR. FOOD RES, WILSON CERT. FOODS, INC, 69- Am. Chem. Soc; Inst. Food Technol. Food research, principally meat; food technology and chemistry. Address: Wilson Certified Foods, Inc, 4545 Lincoln Blvd, Oklahoma City, OK 73105.

EDGAR, ARLAN L(EE), b. Gratiot Co, Mich, June 3, 26; m. 52; c. 3. ZOOLOGY. M.A, Michigan, 50, M.S, 57, Ph.D, 60. Instr. BIOL, ALMA COL, 50-51, asst. prof, 53-57, assoc. prof, 58-64, PROF, 65-, CHMN. DEPT, 71- Summer assoc. prof, Mich. State Univ, 61; vis. prof. biol. sta, Univ. Mich, 65- U.S.A, 51-53. AAAS; Am. Micros. Soc; Am. Soc. Zool. Proprioceptive organs of phalangids; physiological ecology and behavior of phalangids; taxonomy of phalangids in the Great Lakes region; effects of car exhaust on litter invertebrates. Address: Dept. of Biology, Alma College, Alma, MI 48801.

EDGAR, JAMES H, b. Richland, Tex, Aug. 6, 14; m. 38; c. 2. SCIENCE EDUCATION. B.S, E.Tex. State Col, 38, M.S, 46. Head dept. sci, NAVARRO JR. COL, 46-63, DIR. DIV. SCI. & MATH, 63- Consult, Tex. Miller Prod. U.S.A.A.F, 42-44, 2nd Lt. Am. Chem. Soc. Address: 1416 Ficklin Ave, Corsicana, TX 75110.

EDGAR, N. TERENCE, b. Bristol, Eng, Oct. 22, 33; m. 60; c. 2. MARINE GEOLOGY, GEOPHYSICS. B.A, Middlebury Col, 57; M.Sc, Fla. State, 60; Ph.D.(marine geol), Columbia, 68. Geologist, Shell Oil Co. Can. Ltd, 59-63; geophysicist, Lamont Geol. Observ, 63-68; coord. staff geologist, DEEP SEA DRILLING PROJ, SCRIPPS INST. OCEANOG, UNIV. CALIF, SAN DIEGO, 68-70, CHIEF SCIENTIST, 70- Mem, Atlantic adv. panel, Joint Oceanog. Inst. Deep Earth Sampling, 67-, chmn. site surv. panel, 69- AAAS; Am. Geophys. Union; Geol. Soc. Am. Sedimentology; stratigraphy; structural geology; marine seismology. Address: Deep Sea Drilling Project, Scripps Institution of Oceanography, University of California, San Diego, Box 109, La Jolla, CA 92037.

EDGAR, R(OBERT) S(TUART), b. Calgary, Alta, Sept. 15, 30; m. 57. GENETICS. B.Sc, McGill Univ, 53; Ph.D.(biol), Univ. Rochester, 57. Gosney & res. fels, biol. div, Calif. Inst. Technol, 57; fel. med. sci, Nat. Res. Coun, 57-59; asst. prof. biol, Calif. Inst. Technol, 60-63, assoc. prof, 63-66, prof, 66-70; PROVOST, KRESGE COL, UNIV. CALIF, SANTA CRUZ, 70- AAAS. Genetic recombination; bacteriophage. Address: Kresge College, University of California, Santa Cruz, CA 95060.

EDGAR, S(AMUEL) ALLEN, b. Stafford, Kans, Feb. 6, 16; m. 39; c. 2. MICROBIOLOGY, PATHOLOGY. A.B, Sterling Col, 37, hon. Sc.D, 62; M.S, Kansas State, 39; Ph.D.(zool), Wisconsin, 44. Asst. zool, Kansas State, 37-38, instr, 38-41; asst, Wisconsin, 41-44; PROF. POULTRY SCI. & POULTRY PATHOLOGIST, AUBURN UNIV, 47- Sr. scientist, U.S. Pub. Health Serv, Tahiti, 49-50. U.S.A, 44-47. Fel. AAAS; Am. Soc. Parasitol; Am. Micros. Soc; Poultry Sci. Asn; Am. Soc. Trop. Med. & Hyg; Am. Soc. Zool; Entom. Soc. Am; Am. Mosquito Control Asn; fel. N.Y. Acad. Sci; Philippine Malaria Soc. Resistance of animals to parasitic infections; virus, bacterial and parasitic diseases of poultry; development of the protozoan parasites Eimeria in domestic poultry; immunity of poultry to coccidial infections. Address: Dept. of Poultry Science, Auburn University, Auburn, AL 36830.

EDGCUMBE, CHARLES D(IEHL), b. Jersey City, N.J, Aug. 29, 14; m. 41; c. 6. CHEMICAL ENGINEERING. B.S, Lehigh, 36. Lab. asst, indust, chem. sales div, W.Va. Pulp & Paper Co, Pa, 36; chem. engr, res. & develop. div, Socony-Vacuum Oil Co, Inc, N.J, 36-43; process engr, Neches Butane Prods. Co, Tex, 43-45; SR. RES. CHEM. ENGR, RES. DEPT, MOBIL RES.

& DEVELOP. CORP, 45- Am. Chem. Soc; Am. Inst. Chem. Eng. Catalytic cracking process studies; application of new cracking catalysts. Address: 164 Delaware St, Woodbury, NJ 08096.

EDGE, ORLYN P, b. Platteville, Wis, Mar. 29, 39; m. 61; c. 3. MATHEMATICAL STASTISTICS. B.S, Wis. State, Platteville, 61; M.S, Iowa, 63, Ph.D.(math), 66. ASSOC. PROF. MATH, ILL. STATE UNIV, 66- Inst. Math. Statist; Am. Statist. Asn; Math. Asn. Am. Address: Dept. of Mathematics, Stevenson Hall, Illinois State University, Normal, IL 61761.

EDGE, RONALD (DOVASTON), b. Bolton, Eng, Feb. 3, 29; m. 56; c. 2. NUCLEAR PHYSICS. M.A, Cambridge, 52, fel. & Ph.D, 56. Res. fel. nuclear physics, Australian Nat. Univ, 54-58; asst. prof. PHYSICS, UNIV. S.C, 58-63, PROF, 64- Res. fel, Yale, 63. Russell Award. Am. Phys. Soc. Photonuclear disintegration at intermediate energies; neutron research and cosmic ray neutrons; low energy nuclear reactions; the operation of low and intermediate energy accelerators for nuclear particles; channeling in crystals. Address: Dept. of Physics, University of South Carolina, Columbia, SC 29208.

EDGELL, WALTER F(RANCIS), b. Logansport, Ind, July 26, 16; m. 37; c. 4. CHEMISTRY. B.S, California, 39; Minnesota, 39-40; M.S, Iowa, 41; Ph.D. (phys. chem), Harvard, 44. Chemist, div. eight, Nat. Defense Res. Cmt, Harvard, 43; instr. PHYS. CHEM, Iowa, 43-46, assoc. prof, 46-49; PROF, PURDUE UNIV, 49- Guggenheim fel, 56-57. Am. Chem. Soc; Am. Phys. Soc. Infrared and Raman spectroscopy; vibrational spectroscopy of electrolytic solutions; theory of spectra; exciton interactions in vibrational spectroscopy; metal carbonyls. Address: Dept. of Chemistry, Purdue University, Lafayette, IN 47907.

EDGERLEY, EDWARD, JR, b. Lancaster, Pa, Mar. 8, 31; m. 54; c. 4. CIVIL & SANITARY ENGINEERING. B.S, Pa. State, 52; S.M, Mass. Inst. Tech, 54; Ph.D.(sanit. eng), California, Berkeley, 68. Asst. prof. SANIT. ENG, WASH. UNIV, 57-62, ASSOC. PROF, 62-, asst. dean eng, 68-69. V.pres, Ryckman Edgerley Tomlinson & Assocs, Consult. Engrs, 57-71, sr. v.pres, 71-; mem. rev. comt. environ. health, Nat. Insts. Health, 69-71. Med.C, U.S.A.F, 54-57, Capt. Am. Soc. Civil Eng; Am. Water Works Asn.(pub. award, 62); Water Pollution Control Fedn; Am. Soc. Eng; Educ; Air Pollution Control Asn; Am. Indust. Hyg. Asn; Am. Chem. Soc. Industrial waste water treatment; water treatment; trace organics in water; air pollution abatement; noise control; ion exchange treatment of liquid and solids waste. Address: Dept. of Engineering, Washington University, St. Louis, MO 63130.

EDGERLEY, ROBERT H(OWARD), b. Johnstown, Ohio, Mar. 7, 16; m. 46; c. 3. ENVIRONMENTAL PHYSIOLOGY. B.Sc, Capital Univ, 37; M.Sc, Ohio State, 39, Ph.D.(zool), 42. Asst. zool, Ohio State, 38-42; asst. prof, Alabama, 46-47; res. scientist, col. physicians & surgeons, Columbia, 47-53; res. assoc, med. sch, Northwestern, 53-54; res. consult, Toni Res. Labs, 54-55; assoc. res. scientist, Martin-Marietta Corp, 55-61; res. specialist, space & info. systs. div, N.Am. Aviation, Inc, 62-66, sr. tech. specialist, N.Am. Rockwell Corp, 66-70; SECT. MGR, McDONNELL DOUGLAS ASTRONAUT. CO, 70- U.S.A.A.F, 43-46. Aerospace Med. Asn. Quantitative toxicology; radiobiology; biometrics. Address: 8435 Bridle Spur Dr, Hazelwood, MO 63042.

EDGERLY, CHARLES G(EORGE) M(ORGAN), b. Gilmanton, N.H, Nov. 29, 18; m. 44; c. 7. DAIRY HUSBANDRY. B.S, Univ. N.H, 48; M.S, Rutgers Univ, 50. Asst. prof. animal husb. & asst. animal husbandman, agr. exp. sta, Univ. Maine, 50-55; asst. prof. DAIRY HUSB, N.DAK. STATE UNIV, 55-65, ASSOC. PROF, 65-, ASSOC. ANIMAL HUSBANDMAN, AGR. EXP. STA, 65- U.S.A, 41-46, 51-52, Res, 52-, Maj. Am. Dairy Sci. Asn. Calf feeding; dairy cattle management. Address: 1317 Eighth Ave. S, Fargo, ND 58102.

EDGERTON, H(AROLD) E(UGENE), b. Fremont, Nebr, Apr. 6, 03; m. 28; c. 3. ELECTRICAL ENGINEERING. E.E, Univ. Nebr, 25, hon. D.Eng, 48; M.S, Mass. Inst. Technol, 27, D.Sc.(elec. eng), 31; hon. LL.D, Doane Col, 69, Univ. South. Calif, 69. Mem. test. lab, Gen. Elec. Co, 25-26; from instr. to prof. elec. eng, MASS. INST. TECHNOL, 26-66, INST. EMER. PROF, 66- With res. lab, Gen. Elec. Co, summer, 28. With Atomic Energy Comn; U.S.A.A.F, 46. Nat. Acad. Sci; Am. Acad. Arts & Sci; Nat. Acad. Eng; Am. Phys. Soc; fel. Inst. Elec. & Electronics Eng; fel. Photog. Soc. Am; Soc. Motion Picture & TV Eng. Electrical methods of producing flash lighting; angular transients of synchronous machines; stroboscopic motion pictures of rapidly moving mechanisms; sonar devices for instrumentation and exploration in the sub-bottom of the sea; underwater photography devices. Address: 100 Memorial Dr, Cambridge, MA 02142.

EDGERTON, JAMES HUBERT, b. Rutherford Co, N.C, Jan. 21, 13; m. 41. HEALTH PHYSICS, PHYSICAL & ANALYTICAL CHEMISTRY. B.S, Tusculum Col, 33; Tennessee, 47-56. Engr. textile processing, Elmore Corp, N.C, 35-37; supvr. & chem. engr, South. Kraft Div, Int. Paper Co, S.C, 37-42; lab. supvr. & sr. chemist, Oak Ridge Nat. Lab, Tenn, 46-56; aircraft nuclear scientist, in charge reactor chem. eng, Lockheed Aircraft Corp, 56-61, nuclear div. & process control engr, 61; chemist, E.I. du Pont de Nemours & Co, S.C, 61-64; HEALTH PHYSICIST WITH HDQ. DEPT. ARMY, 64- Mem. adv. comt, office U.S. Naval res. on molybdenum, 54-57; metall. adv. comt. titanium task force, U.S. Army, Mass, 56-57; Army Nuclear reactor systs. health & safety rev. comt, 64-; health physicist & dir. safety, mil. traffic mgt. & terminal serv, U.S. Army Transportation Eng. Agency, 68-; teacher, Army Nuclear Reactor Health & Safety Sch, Ft. Belvoir, Va; Dept. Defense mem, ASI Comt. Transportation & Packaging Radioactive Mat; transportation mem, Army Nuclear Reactor Systs. Health & Safety rev. comt. U.S.N, 42-46, Res, 47-54, Lt. Am. Nuclear Soc; Am. Chem. Soc; Health Physics Soc. Nuclear and inorganic chemistry; reactor technology; chemical engineering; chemistry; metallurgy; corrosion; decontamination; instrumentation; radioactive waste; radiochemistry and nuclear engineering; atomic, chemical, biological, radiological items and their characteristics during movement in transportation. Address: 7741 Donnybrook Center, Annandale, VA 22003.

EDGERTON, LOUIS J(AMES), b. Adena, Ohio, Jan. 28, 14; m. 46; c. 3. HORTICULTURE, POMOLOGY. B.S, Ohio State, 37; Ph.D.(pomol), Cornell, 41. Asst, Cornell, 37-41, instr. pomol, 41; res. assoc, Rutgers, 42-45; PROF. POMOL, CORNELL UNIV, 46-, HEAD DEPT, 70- Fulbright grant, Cairo Univ, 66. Am. Soc. Plant Physiol; Am. Soc. Hort. Sci. Studies on cold hardiness of fruit plants; chemical thinning and control of preharvest apple drop with plant growth regulators; absorption, translocation and metabolism of plant growth regulators by apple and peach trees. Address: Dept. of Pomology, Cornell University, Ithaca, NY 14850.

EDGERTON, MILTON T(HOMAS), JR, b. Atlanta, Ga, July 14, 21; m. 45; c. 4. PLASTIC SURGERY. A.B, Emory, 41; M.D, Hopkins, 44. Intern surg, Barnes Hosp, St. Louis, Mo, 44-45; asst. resident, Hopkins Hosp, 47-49, instr. PLASTIC SURG, sch. med, Hopkins, 49-51, asst. prof, 51-53, assoc. prof, 53-62, prof, 62-70; PROF. & CHMN. DEPT, SCH. MED, UNIV. VA, 70- Surgeon-in-charge, Johns Hopkins Univ. Hosp, 52-70; trustee, Cell Sci. Ctr, N.Y, 70-; consult, U.S.P.H.S, Vet. Admin, Baltimore City & Children's Hosps, Baltimore; Nat. Clin. Ctr, Nat. Insts. Health & Walter Reed Hosp, Bethesda; Vet. Admin. Hosp, Salem, Va; mem, Plastic Surg. Res. Coun; bd. trustees, Plastic Surg. Found. Dipl, Am. Bd. Surg. & Am. Bd. Plastic Surg, 51. Med.C, 45-47, Capt. Am. Med. Asn; fel. Am. Col. Surg; Am. Asn. Plastic Surg.(v.pres); Am. Soc. Plastic & Reconstruct. Surg; Am. Soc. Surg. of Hand; Soc. Univ. Surg; Am. Psychosom. Soc; Inst. Nuclear Eng; Nat. Soc. Med. Res. Head and neck cancer surgery; reconstructive surgery; congenital defects; hand surgery; tissue transplantation research. Address: Dept. of Plastic Surgery, University of Virginia Medical Center, Charlottesville, VA 22901.

EDGERTON, RICHARD O(LIVER), b. Rochester, N.Y, May 15, 14; m. 39; c. 2. ORGANIC CHEMISTRY. B.A, Rochester, 36; M.S, Michigan, 37, Ph.D.(org. chem), 40. Res. assoc, Mass. Inst. Tech, 40-41; chemist, EASTMAN KODAK CO, 41-52, sect. supvr, 52-56, supvr. photog. training, 56-66, training, 66-70, DIR. TRAINING, KODAK PARK DIV, 70- Am. Chem. Soc; Assoc. Photog. Soc. Am; Am. Soc. Training & Develop; sr. mem. Soc. Photog. Sci. & Eng. Synthetic organic research; vitamin synthesis; color photography; synthesis of polycyclic compounds. Address: 104 Alameda St, Rochester, NY 14613.

EDGERTON, ROBERT F(LINT), b. Rochester, N.Y, Oct. 16, 17; m. 42; c. 2. CHEMISTRY. B.A, Rochester, 40; M.S, Michigan, 41, Ph.D.(org. chem), 44. Fel. Army specialized training prog, Michigan, 41-44; res. chemist, Gen. Elec. Co, Mass, 44-45, tech. sales, 46-47; tech. staff, paper serv. div, EASTMAN KODAK CO, 47-53, group leader, prof. papers, 50-52, prod. improv, 52-53, tech. asst, Europ. & overseas orgn, 53-55, int. div, 55-57, Paris, France Off, 57-59, prod. mgr. graphic arts, 59-65, dir. int. advert. planning, int. mkt. div, 65-69, MGR. ADVERT. & CUSTOMER SERV, INT. PHOTOG. DIV, ROCHESTER, 69- Photog. Soc. Am. Synthesis of perhydrophenanthrene derivatives and antimalarials; dehydrogenation; emulsion polymerization; purification of phenolic materials; photographic paper fixation, toning and washing. Address: 1 Rollingwood Dr, Pittsford, NY 14534.

EDGERTON, ROBERT FRANK, b. Cambridge, Mass, May 10, 35; m. 59; c. 3. SOLID STATE PHYSICS, PHYSICAL OPTICS. B.S, Rochester, 57, Ph.D. (optics), 63. Res. assoc. solid state physics, inst. optics, Rochester, 63-64; asst. prof. PHYSICS, Carleton Col, 64-66; res. assoc, Cornell, 66-68; assoc. prof, Univ. Maine, 68-71; TEACHER, ROEPER CITY & COUNTRY SCH, 71- Vacuum ultraviolet spectroscopy in solids; luminescence of alkali halides at low temperatures. Address: Roeper City & Country School, 2190 N. Woodward Ave, Bloomfield Hills, MI 48013.

EDGERTON, ROBERT HOWARD, b. Canton, Conn, Dec. 27, 33; m. 55; c. 2. MECHANICAL ENGINEERING. B.S, Connecticut, 55, M.S, 57; Ph.D.(mech. eng), Cornell, 61. Asst. prof. ENG, Dartmouth Col, 62-67; ASSOC. PROF, OAKLAND UNIV, 67- Nat. Insts. Health Grant, 64-66. Summers, prod. engr, circuit breaker div, Gen. Elec. Co, 55, design engr, elec. boat div, Gen. Dynamics Corp, 56; Ford Found. fel, indust. prog, IBM Corp, 66-67. U.S.A.F, 60-62, Res, 62-, Capt. Am. Soc. Mech. Eng; Am. Soc. Eng. Educ; Am. Inst. Aeronaut. & Astronuat. Heat transfer, fluid mechanics and transport theory; flow and temperature measurements and instrumentation; biomedical engineering; blood flow; infra-red technology. Address: Dept. of Engineering, Oakland University, Rochester, MI 48063.

EDGERTON, WILLIAM H(OWARD), b. Bristol, Conn, June 7, 23; m. 47; c. 3. PHARMACEUTICAL CHEMISTRY. B.S, Connecticut, 45; Ph.D.(pharmaceut. chem), Kansas, 50. Head patent sect, Parke, Davis & Co, 50-55; SMITH KLINE & FRENCH LABS, 55-67, MGR. CORP. PATENTS, 67- Am. Chem. Soc. Chloramphenicol; penicillin; quinolines; phenothiazines; patent law. Address: 457 Maynard Dr, Strafford Wayne, PA 19087.

EDGETT, G(EORGE) L(EWIS), b. Moncton, N.B, Apr. 21, 00; m. 26; c. 2. MATHEMATICS, STATISTICS. B.A, Mt. Allison Univ, 23, M.A, 26; Ph.D, Univ. Ill, 30. Instr. MATH, Mt. Royal Col, 23-25; Univ. Ill, 25-30; PROF. QUEEN'S UNIV.(ONT), 30- Am. Soc. Qual. Control; Am. Statist. Asn; Inst. Math. Statist. Mathematical statistics. Address: Dept. of Mathematics, Queen's University, Kingston, Ont, Can.

EDGINGTON, L(LOYD) V(ERNON), b. Guthrie Center, Iowa, Nov. 13, 27; m. 50; c. 3. PLANT PATHOLOGY. B.S, California, 53; Ph.D.(plant path), Wisconsin, 56. Proj. asst. plant pathol, Wisconsin, 56-57; asst. plant pathologist, Conn. Agr. Exp. Sta, 57-60, assoc. plant pathologist, 60-65; assoc. prof. BOT, UNIV. GUELPH, 65-69, PROF, 69- U.S.A.F, 46-49. Translocation and fate of systemic fungicides in plants. Address: Dept. of Environmental Biology, University of Guelph, Guelph, Ont, Can.

EDGINGTON, THOMAS S, b. Los Angeles, Calif, Feb. 10, 32; m. 57; c. 2. PATHOLOGY, IMMUNOLOGY. A.B, Stanford, 53, M.D, 57. Intern, Hosp. Univ. Pa, 57-58; res. path, California, Los Angeles, 58-60; pathologist, Atomic Bomb Casualty Comn, Japan, 60-62; asst. prof. path, Univ. Calif, Los Angeles, 62-65; sr. res. fel, DEPT. EXP. PATH, SCRIPPS CLIN. & RES. FOUND, 65-68, ASSOC. MEM, 68-; ASSOC. ADJ. PROF. PATH, UNIV. CALIF, SAN DIEGO, 68- U.S.P.H.S, 60-62, Surg. AAAS; Am. Asn. Immunol; Am. Soc. Exp. Path; Am. Soc. Clin. Path; Col. Am. Path. Mechanisms of autoimmunity and the character of cell surfaces. Address: Dept. of Experimental Pathology, Scripps Clinic & Research Foundation, 476 Prospect St, La Jolla, CA 92037.

EDGREN, JAMES W, b. Iowa Falls, Iowa, Aug. 17, 29; m. 53; c. 2. PLANT PATHOLOGY. B.S, Iowa State, 57, M.S, 59. Plant pathologist, PAC. NORTHWEST FOREST & RANGE EXP. STA, U.S. FOREST SERV, 59-65, PLANT ECOLOGIST, 65- U.S.N, 51-54. Regeneration of forest stands; seedling morphology as influenced by nursery practices; forest ecology. Address: Pacific Northwest Forest & Range Experiment Station, U.S. Forest Service, P.O. Box 3141, Portland, OR 97208.

EDGREN, RICHARD A(RTHUR), b. Chicago, Ill, May 28, 25; m. 52; c. 2. BIOLOGY. Ph.D.(biol), Northwestern, 52. Asst. biol, Northwestern, 49-52; sr. investr, G.D. Searle & Co, 52-60; asst. mgr, nutrit. & endocrinol. sect, Wyeth Labs, 60-68, mgr. endocrinol. sect, 68-71; ASSOC. DIR. CLIN. RES, WARNER-LAMBERT CO, 71- Mem, coun. on arteriosclerosis, Am. Heart Asn. Sig.C, U.S.A. & U.S.A.A.F, 43-46. Ecol. Soc. Am; Am. Soc. Zool; Am. Soc. Ichthyol. & Herpet; Soc. Exp. Biol. & Med; Endocrine Soc; Royal Soc. Med. Endocrinology; gonadal physiology; steroid pharmacology; ecology; systematics and evolution; reptiles and amphibians. Address: Warner-Lambert Co, 170 Tabor Rd, Morris Plains, NJ 07950.

EDIDIN, MICHAEL AARON, b. Chicago, Ill, Mar. 31, 39; m. 64; c. 2. EMBRYOLOGY, IMMUNOLOGY. B.S, Chicago, 60; Nat. Sci. Found. fel, London, 60-63, Ph.D, 63. Nat. Sci. Found. fel. cell biol, Weizmann Inst, 63-64; Am. Heart Asn. res. fel. IMMUNOL, Harvard Med. Sch, 64-66; asst. prof, JOHNS HOPKINS UNIV, 66-71, ASSOC. PROF, 71- AAAS; Am. Asn. Immunol; Transplantation Soc. Transplantation biology; differentiation and chemistry of transplantation antigens. Address: Dept. of Biology, The Johns Hopkins University, Baltimore, MD 21218.

EDIE, R(ALPH) W(ILLIAM), b. Smoky Lake, Alta, Oct. 2, 21; m. 46; c. 3. GEOLOGY. B.Sc, Alberta, 45, Shell Oil fel, 48-49, M.Sc, 49; Ph.D.(geol), Mass. Inst. Tech, 52. Instr. geol, Alberta, 47-49; field geologist, Eldorado Gold Fields, Sask, 48-50; res. geologist, Texaco Explor. Co, 52-53; Shell Oil Co, 53-55; petrol. geologist, Alex McCoy Assocs, 55-56; consult. geologist, ANDRICHUK & EDIE CONSULT. GEOLOGISTS, 56-69, PARTNER, 69- Can. Inst. Mining & Metall. Trace elements in diabase; wall rock alteration associated with pitchblende; uranium mineralization; Mississippian sedimentation and oil fields in southeastern Saskatchewan; Devonian reefs in central Saskatchewan and Swan Hills area, Alberta. Address: Andrichuk & Edie Consulting Geologists, Third Floor, 205 Ninth Ave. S.E, Calgary 21, Alta, Can.

EDIGER, ROBERT I, b. Hutchinson, Kans, Apr. 2, 37; m. 58; c. 1. PLANT TAXONOMY & ECOLOGY. A.B, Bethel Col, 59; Nat. Sci. Found. fels, Kans. State Teachers Col, 63-64, M.S, 64; Ph.D.(bot), Kansas State, 67. Teacher, Ford Pub. Schs, 59-62; Hays Pub. Schs, 62-63; asst. prof. BOT, CHICO STATE COL, 67-70, ASSOC. PROF, 70-; DIR. BIOL, EAGLE LAKE BIOL, STA, 68- Bot. Soc. Am; Am. Soc. Plant Taxon; Int. Asn. Plant Taxon. Taxonomy of higher plants, especially the genus Senecio in the family Compositae. Address: Dept. of Biological Science, Chico State College, Chico, CA 95926.

EDING, HAROLD J(OHN), b. Blackfoot, Idaho, Sept. 4, 19; m. 42; c. 5. PHYSICAL CHEMISTRY. B.S, California, 41; M.A, Stanford, 44, Ph.D, 52. Chemist, Permanente Metals Corp, 41-48; sr. phys. chemist, Stanford Res. Inst, 48-68; STAFF CHEMIST, MEMOREX CORP, 68- Am. Chem. Soc. Process development; physical-inorganic chemistry; instrumentation; thermodynamics. Address: 59 Morton St, Palo Alto, CA 94303.

EDINGER, JAMES (G), b. Van Nuys, Calif, June 16, 18; m. 46; c. 2. METEOROLOGY. A.B, California, Los Angeles, 40, M.A, 48, Ph.D.(meteorol), 54. Res. asst. METEOROL, UNIV. CALIF, LOS ANGELES, 46-53, asst. prof, 53-61, ASSOC. PROF, 61- U.S.A.A.F, 40-46, Res, 46-50, Maj. Am. Meteorol. Soc. Air pollution; atmospheric diffusion. Address: 1433 Tigertail Rd, Los Angeles, CA 90024.

EDINGTON, CHARLES W, b. Knoxville, Tenn, Feb. 26, 25; m. 46; c. 2. GENETICS. A.B, Tennessee, 48, M.S, 49, Ph.D, 55; fel, Oak Ridge Inst. Nuclear Studies, 54-55. Head dept. sci, pub. sch, 51-52; asst, biol. div, Oak Ridge Nat. Lab, 52-54, assoc. biologist, 55-57; asst. prof. zool, Fla. State, 57-61, assoc. prof, 61-64; geneticist, DIV. BIOL. & MED, U.S. ATOMIC ENERGY COMN, 62-67, CHIEF BIOL. BR, 67- U.S.A, 44-46. Genetics Soc. Am. Radiation biology. Address: Division of Biology & Medicine, U.S. Atomic Energy Commission, Washington, DC 20545.

EDISEN, ADELE ELVIRA USKALI, b. N.Y.C, Mar. 11, 28; div; c. 3. NEUROPHYSIOLOGY. Ph.B, Chicago, 50, univ. scholar, 50-54, Ph.D, 54. Asst. physiol, Chicago, 53-54; Nat. Inst. Neurol. Diseases & Blindness res. fel, sch. med, Tulane, 54-56, res. assoc, 56-62; Nat. Inst. Neurol. Diseases & Blindness res. fel. physiol, sch. med, La. State, 62-64, res. assoc, 64-66; instr. biol, St. Mary's Dominican Col, 66-67, ASST. PROF, 67-68; Dillard, 68-69; PHYSIOL, ROCKEFELLER UNIV, 69- Res. asst, Ill. Neuropsychiatric Inst, 53-54; vis. investr, Rockefeller Inst. Med. Res, 55; res. assoc, sch. med, Tulane, 66; NASA fel. & Inst. Biol. Sci. colloquium on theoret. biophys. & biol. cell, 66-; consult, Tulane, 58-61. Electron Micros. Soc. Am; Am. Physiol. Soc; Int. Union Physiol. Sci. Cong. Electrophysiological studies of synaptic mechanisms of excitation and inhibition in the central nervous system; physical and chemical changes in nerve cells and their elements observed by microscopy; autonomic neuroeffector transmission. Address: Dept. of Physiology, Rockefeller University, 66th & York Ave, New York, NY 10021.

EDISON, ALLEN RAY, b. Plainview, Nebr, Sept. 21, 26; m. 49; c. 2. ELECTRICAL ENGINEERING. B.Sc, Nebraska, 50, M.Sc, 57; D.Sc.(elec. eng), New Mexico, 62. Instr. ELEC. ENG. UNIV. NEBR, LINCOLN, 53-57, asst. prof, 57-62, assoc. prof, 62-65, PROF, 65-, acting chmn. dept, 64-65, chmn, 65-70. Nat. Sci. Found. res. grant, 62-65. U.S.N, 44-46. Inst. Elec. & Electronics Eng; Am. Soc. Eng. Educ. Electromagnetic wave propagation; ultrasonics and instrumentation. Address: Dept. of Electrical Engineering, University of Nebraska, Lincoln, NE 68508.

EDISON, DAVID H, b. Wilmington, Del, Aug. 26, 33. ORGANIC CHEMISTRY. A.B, Oberlin Col, 55; Du Pont fel. & Ph.D.(chem), Rochester, 59. Res. chemist, textile fibers dept, E.I. DU PONT DE NEMOURS & CO, CHATTANOOGA, 58-68, SUPVR, 68- Am. Chem. Soc. Reaction mechanisms; isotopic labelling. Address: 1017 Crown Point Rd. E, Signal Mountain, TN 37377.

EDISON, JAMES ALLEN, b. Detroit, Mich, Jan. 19, 36; m. 63; c. 2. OPERATIONS RESEARCH, APPLIED MATHEMATICS. B.S, Detroit, 59; Notre Dame, 54-56; M.S, Wayne State, 60. Instr. math, Oklahoma, 60-62; mathematician, Apollo Proj, Gen. Elec. Co, 62-64; opers. analyst, Bunker-Ramo Corp, 64-65; exec. v.pres, INFO. RES. ASSOC, INC, 65-69, PRES, 69- Opers. Res. Soc. Am; Asn. Computing Mach. Operations research studies and project management in checkout of Apollo spacecraft; digital communication networks; computer simulation of anti-submarine warfare systems. Address: 17951 Aspen Tree Lane, Irvine, CA 92664.

EDISON, LARRY ALVIN, b. Aberdeen, Wash, Nov. 8, 36; m. 60; c. 4. MATHEMATICS. B.A, Whitman Col, 58; Ph.D.(math), Stanford, 65. Asst. prof. MATH, Reed Col, 64-70; ASSOC. PROF. & CHMN. DEPT, ALMA COL, 70- Am. Math. Soc; Math. Asn. Am. Harmonic analysis; almost periodic functions; functional analysis. Address: Dept. of Mathematics, Alma College, Alma, MI 48801.

EDISON, THEODORE M(ILLER), b. West Orange, N.J, July 10, 98; m. 25. PHYSICS. B.S, Mass. Inst. Tech, 23. Res. engr. & later mem. exec. bd. & tech. dir, Thomas A. Edison, Inc, 24-30; RES. ENGR. & PRES, CALIBRON PRODS, INC, 31-; DEVELOP. E-I MUTUAL ASN. AAAS; Acoust. Soc. Am; fel. Am. Geog. Soc; Am. Math. Soc; Math. Asn. Am; Inst. Elec. & Electronics Eng; Nat. Soc. Prof. Eng; Optical Soc. Am; Soc. Motion Picture & TV Eng. Applied physics; economics; special purpose calculating machines; remote control systems; mechanical and electrical engineering; ecology; nature preservation projects; planning and population problems. Address: Llewellyn Park, West Orange, NJ 07052.

EDLIN, ALBERT I(RVING), b. New York, N.Y, Apr. 21, 34. PHARMACOLOGY. B.S, Cincinnati, 56; M.S, Ohio State, 59; Ph.D.(pharmacol), Pittsburgh, 63. Asst, Ohio State, 58-59; Pittsburgh, 60-63; asst. res. biologist, Sterling-Winthrop Res. Inst, 63-64; asst. prof. PHARMACOL, Idaho State Univ, 64-69; ASSOC. PROF. & CHMN. DEPT, COL. PHARM, OHIO NORTH. UNIV, 69- AAAS; Am. Pharmaceut. Asn. Cardiovascular and autonomic pharmacology; experimental hypertension, studies in mechanism of action and drug screening methodology; antihypertensive therapy. Address: Dept. of Pharmacology, College of Pharmacy, Ohio Northern University, Ada, OH 45810.

EDLIN, FRANK E, b. Eskridge, Kans, Aug. 25, 09; m. 36; c. 2. INDUSTRIAL CHEMISTRY, ENGINEERING. B.S, Kansas State, 31. Field engr, indust. eng. div, E.I. Du Pont de Nemours & Co, 37-39, field supvr, 39-40, process engr, design div, 40-51, consult. engr, eng. serv. div, 51-60, engr, develop. dept, 60-62, sr. res. engr, eng. res. div, 62-65, lectr. eng, Ariz. State Univ, 65-71; PRES, WATER APPLNS, INC, 71- V.pres, Int. Plastics, Inc, Colwich, Kans, 67- AAAS; Am. Inst. Chem. Eng; Nat. Soc. Prof. Eng; Sci. Res. Soc. Am; Solar Energy Soc.(exec. secy, 65-67); Am. Soc. Mech. Eng. Solar radiation environment; high temperature reactions; water treatment. Address: Water Applications, Inc, 1036 W. 23rd St, Tempe, AZ 85281.

EDLIN, RAY L, b. Nara Visa, N.Mex, Apr. 16, 30. FOOD SCIENCE, BIOCHEMISTRY. B.S, Calif. State Polytech. Col, 51; M.S, Rutgers, 61, Ph.D. (food sci), 62. Asst. scientist, exp. sta, Texas A&M, 51-52; field rep, Gen. Motors Acceptance Corp, 52-54; asst. scientist, Warner-Lambert Res. Inst, 57-58; sr. chemist indust. gums, Kelco Co, Calif, 62-68; tech. dir, Gentry Corp, 68-69, mfg. mgr, 69-70; MEM. STAFF, FOODMAKER INC, 70- U.S.A, 54-57, Sgt. Inst. Food Technol; Am. Chem. Soc; Am. Oil Chem. Soc; N.Y. Acad. Sci. Causes and identification of rancidity and the end products or chemical substances involved; application of alginates and industrial gums to food applications; basic data of gums. Address: Foodmaker Inc, Box 783, San Diego, CA 92112.

EDLUND, MILTON C(ARL), b. Jamestown, N.Y, Dec. 13, 24; m. 45; c. 2. PHYSICS. M.S, Univ. Mich, 48, Ph.D, 66. Physicist reactor physics, gaseous diffusion plant, Oak Ridge Nat. Lab, 48-50, physicist & lectr, sch. reactor tech, 50-51, sr. physicist & sect. chief, 53-55; mgr. physics & math. dept, Babcock & Wilcox Co, 55-60, develop. dept, 60-62, appln. develop. dept, 62-65, asst. div. mgr, 65-66; prof. elec. eng, Univ. Mich, 66-67; consult, Union Carbide Corp, 67-70; CHMN. DEPT. NUCLEAR ENG, VA. POLYTECH. INST. & STATE UNIV, 70- Vis. lectr, Swedish Atomic Energy Cmn, 53. Ernest Orlando Lawrence award, 65. U.S.A, 43-46. Am. Phys. Soc; Sci. Res. Soc. Am; Am. Nuclear Soc. Neutron diffusion; nuclear reactor design. Address: 1103 Highland Circle, Blacksburg, VA 24060.

EDMAN, JAMES RICHARD, b. Kandiyohi Co, Minn, June 6, 36; m. 58; c. 3. ORGANIC CHEMISTRY. B.S, Gustavus Adolphus Col, 58; M.S, Univ. Nebr, 60, Nat. Insts. Health fel. & Ph.D.(chem), 63. Res. chemist, E.I. DU PONT DE NEMOURS & CO, 63-69, RES. SUPVR. PHOTOCHEM. CATALYSIS, 69- Am. Chem. Soc. Address: Film Dept, E.I. du Pont de Nemours & Co, Circleville, OH 43113.

EDMAN, JOHN DAVID, b. Jan. 20, 38; U.S. citizen; m. 59; c. 3. MEDICAL ENTOMOLOGY. B.Sc, Gustavus Adolphus Col, 59; Nat. Defense Ed. Act fel. & M.Sc, Nebraska, 61; Nat. Insts. Health fel. & Ph.D.(entom), Kansas State, 64. SR. SCIENTIST & ASST. DIR. ENTOM. RES. CTR, FLA. STATE DIV. HEALTH, 64- Nat. Insts. Health res. grant, 65-; consult, res. resources br, Nat. Inst. Allergy & Infectious Diseases, 67-; vector biol. br, WHO, 70- AAAS; Entom. Soc. Am; Am. Mosquito Control Asn. General biology, physiology and behavior of mosquitoes; immunological techniques. Address: Entomological Research Center, Florida State Division of Health, P.O. Box 520, Vero Beach, FL 32960.

EDMAN, THOMAS, b. Budapest, Hungary, Jan. 4, 23; U.S. citizen; m. 50; c. 4. TEXTILE TECHNOLOGY. B.S, Lowell Tech. Inst, 51; Leicester Col. Tech, Eng, 52; M.B.A, Drexel Inst, 58; D.Textile Sci, Phila. Col. Textiles & Sci, 60. PROF. KNITTING TECHNOL, PHILA. COL. TEXTILES & SCI, 54- Asst. prof, col. med, Baylor, 56; lectr, Fashion Inst. Tech, N.Y, 57-62. Ord. Dept, U.S.A, 43-46. Am. Soc. Test. & Mat. Textile engineering; development of textile fiber and fabric technology; research applications of medical-surgical textile fabrics. Address: Philadelphia College of Textiles & Science, School House Lane & Henry Ave, Philadelphia, PA 19144.

EDMAN, W(ALTER) W(ILLIAM), b. N.Y.C; m. 39; c. 3. CHEMISTRY. B.Ch.E, Cooper Union, 38; Polytech. Inst. Brooklyn, 38-39; Columbia Univ, 42-44. Anal. chemist, Colgate-Palmolive-Pete Co, N.J, 31-37; anal. res. chemist, M.W. Kellogg Co, 39-42; proj. leader, Evans Res. & Develop. Corp, 42-55, assoc. res. dir, 55-65; res. dir, ZOTOS INT, INC, 65-71, V.PRES, 71- Mem, Textile Res. Inst. Soc. Cosmetic Chem; Brit. Soc. Dyers & Colourists; Am. Asn. Textile Chem. & Colorists; Am. Inst. Chem; Cosmetic, Toiletry & Fragrance Asn. Emulsions; aerosols; hair cosmetics. Address: Zotos International, Inc, 100 Tokeneke Rd, Darien, CT 06820.

EDMARK, KARL W, b. Mar. 3, 24; U.S. citizen; m. 50; c. 6. CARDIOVASCULAR SURGERY. M.D, Colorado, 48. Fel. surg, Lahey Clin, Boston, Mass, 54-55; DIR. RES, PHYSIO-CONTROL CO. INC, DEL, 55-; CLIN. ASSOC. PROF. SURG, SCH. MED, UNIV. WASH, 64-, clin. instr, 57-64. Private practice, 56-; consult, adv. systs. develop. lab, IBM Corp, N.Y, 63-65; dir. cardiovasc. assoc. lab, Providence Hosp, 64- Dipl, Am. Bd. Surg. U.S.N, 52-54, Lt. Fel. Am. Col. Surg. Open heart surgery; coronary angiography; effects of electrokinetic energy on blood thrombus formation. Address: 715 Minor, Seattle, WA 98104.

EDMINSTER, TALCOTT W(HITE), b. E. Freetown, Mass, Oct. 1, 20; m. 44; c. 4. AGRICULTURAL ENGINEERING. B.S, Massachusetts, 42; M.S, Georgia, 43. Field construct. engr, Turner Construct. Co, 42; asst, Georgia, 42-43; asst. agr. engr, Va. Agr. Exp. Sta, Blacksburg, 43-44, agr. engr, state proj. supvr, Soil Conserv. Serv, U.S. DEPT. AGR, 44-53, East. Soil & Water Conserv. Res. Br, 53-61, assoc. dir, soil & water conserv. res. div, AGR. RES. SERV, 61-67, dep. administr, 67-70, assoc. adminstr, 70-71, ADMINSTR, 71- Vis. prof, California, 58. Mem, Int. Comn. Drainage & Irrig. Jump Award, 52; U.S. Dept. Agr. Serv. Award, 52. Soil Sci. Soc. Am; Am. Soc. Agron; Am. Soc. Agr. Eng; Soil Conserv. Soc. Am; Int. Soil Sci. Soc. Soil and water conservation; animal science; animal disease and parasitology; plant science; entomology; agricultural engineering; market quality; agricultural product transportation and storage; human nutrition; consumer and food economics and agricultural products utilization and industrial processing research. Address: Agricultural Research Service, U.S. Dept. of Agriculture, Rm. 302-Administration Bldg, Washington, DC 20250.

EDMISON, MARVIN T(IPTON), b. Lincoln, Nebr, July 21, 12; m. 39; c. 2. ORGANIC & INORGANIC CHEMISTRY. A.B, Nebraska, 33, M.Sc, 47; Ph.D. (chem), Okla. Agr. & Mech. Col, 52. Teacher, Shattuck Mil. Acad, 38-41; Wentworth Mil. Acad, 47-48; from asst. prof. to assoc. prof. chem, Arkansas, 51-55, asst. to v.pres. & provost, 55; DIR. RES. FOUND. & PROF. CHEM, OKLA. STATE UNIV, 55-, ASST. V.PRES. ACAD. AFFAIRS, 68- Proj. dir, Ordark Res. Proj, Arkansas, 52-53; res. adminr, Inst. Sci. & Tech, 54; mem. Nat. Coun. Univ. Res. Adminrs. U.S.A, 41-46, Res, 33-63, Col. AAAS; Am. Chem. Soc; Am. Inst. Chem. Radical substitution of aromatic nuclei; thermal decomposition of organic azides and inorganic oxidants; classified governmental research. Address: Research Foundation, Oklahoma State University, Stillwater, OK 74074.

EDMISTEN, W(ALTER) C(OLLINS), b. Cheyenne, Wyo, Feb. 11, 19; m. 46; c. 5. PHYSICAL CHEMISTRY. A.B, California, Los Angeles, 40, M.A, 42; Ph.D.(chem), Ohio State, 49. Chemist, Gen. Petrol. Corp, 41-42; Goodyear Synthetic Rubber Co, 42-44; res. chemist, Goodyear Tire & Rubber Co, 44-46; asst. proj. chemist, Standard Oil Co.(Ind), 49-53, group leader, 53-60; project mgr, Am. Oil Co, 60-64; SECT. LEADER, AMOCO CHEM. CORP, 64- Polymerization; kinetics; electron scattering; lubrication. Address: 20548 Attica Rd, Olympia Fields, IL 60461.

EDMISTER, W(AYNE) C(LINITE), b. Cleveland, Okla, Mar. 22, 09; m. 34; c. 3. MECHANICAL ENGINEERING. B.S, Okla. State, 32, Chem.E, 42; Telluride Asn. fel, & M.M.E, Cornell, 34. Res. engr, Sinclair Prairie Oil & Ref. Co, 33-34; res. & design chem. engr, Standard Oil Co.(Ind), 34-43; tech. asst, Rubber Reserve Co, 43-44; sr. process engr, Foster-Wheeler Corp, N.Y, 44-47; asst. dir. process develop, Hydrocarbon Res. Inc, 47-48; prof. chem. eng, Carnegie Inst. Tech, 48-51; sr. res. engr, Calif. Res. Corp, 52-56, eng. assoc, 57-59; prof. CHEM. ENG, OKLA. STATE UNIV, 58-71; EMER. PROF, 71-; CONSULT, 71- Adj. prof, N.Y. Univ, 47-48; Fulbright lectr, Kyoto & Tokyo, 65-66. Consult, Gen. Chem. Co, 48; L'Air Liquide, 51-52; Helium Res. Ctr, Bur. Mines; Phillip Petrol. Co, 60-63; Sinclair Res, Inc, 64; Commonwealth Oil Refining Co, P.R, 67-68; Eco-petrol, Colombia, 69; consult. & lectr, Univ. P.R, Mayaguez, 67-68; Indian Inst. Tech, Madras, 69. Richards Mem. Award, Am. Soc. Mech. Eng, 57; Hamlon award, Nat. Gas Processors Asn, 66. Am. Inst. Chem. Eng; Am. Chem. Soc. Thermodynamic properties of fluids; multicomponent fractionation; hydrocarbon and petroleum processing; chemical plant process design. Address: 75 Summit Ave, San Rafael, CA 94901.

EDMISTON, CLYDE, b. Greeley, Colo, June 4, 37; m. 58. PHYSICAL CHEMISTRY. B.A, Colo. State Col, 58; Ph.D.(chem), Iowa State, 63. Nat. Res. Coun. res. assoc. phys. chem, Nat. Bur. Standards, 63-64; asst. prof. CHEM, UNIV. WYO, 64-67, ASSOC. PROF, 67- Am. Chem. Soc. Petrol. Res. Fund grant, 64-65; Nat. Sci. Found. res. grant, 65-67 & sr. fel, Univ. Fla, 70-71. Am. Chem. Soc; Am. Phys. Soc. Quantum chemistry; molecular structure. Address: Dept. of Chemistry, University of Wyoming, Laramie, WY 82071.

EDMONDS, DEAN S(TOCKETT), JR, b. Brooklyn, N.Y, Dec. 24, 24; m. 51; c. 4. PHYSICS. B.S, Mass. Inst. Tech, 50, Ph.D.(physics), 58; M.A, Princeton, 52. Res. asst. physics, Mass. Inst. Tech, 52-56, guest physicist & res. fel, Cambridge Electron Accelerator, Mass. Inst. Tech. & Harvard, 59-61; asst. prof. PHYSICS, BOSTON UNIV, 61-67, ASSOC. PROF, 67- V.pres. & dir, Nuclide Corp, 58- U.S.A, 43-45, 45-47, T/Sgt. Am. Phys. Soc; Am. Asn. Physics Teachers. High energy accelerators; mass spectroscopy; molecular beam investigations; nuclear magnetic resonance; nuclear instrumentation; communication techniques; physical electronics. Address: Dept. of Physics, Boston University, Boston, MA 02215.

EDMONDS, FRANK N(ORMAN), JR, b. Minneapolis, Minn, Sept. 2, 19; m. 45; c. 2. THEORETICAL ASTROPHYSICS. A.B, Princeton, 41; Ph.D.(astron. & astrophys), Chicago, 50. Asst. prof. astron, Missouri, 50-52; math. & astron, UNIV. TEX, AUSTIN, 52-58, assoc. prof. ASTRON, 58-65, PROF, 65- Guggenheim fel, 62-63. U.S.A, 41-46, Capt. Am. Astron. Soc; Royal Astron. Soc; Int. Astron. Union. Radiative transfer theory; astronomical physics; stellar atmospheres; fluid dynamics; solar physics. Address: Dept. of Astronomy, University of Texas at Austin, Austin, TX 78712.

EDMONDS, JAMES D, JR, b. Texarkana, Tex, July 28, 39; m. 57; c. 4. PHYSICS. B.A, San Diego State Col, 62; Radio Corp. of Am. fel, Cornell Univ, 62, Ford Found. fel, 64, Ph.D.(appl. physics), 67. Appl. physics technician, Convair San Diego, 59-61, physicist, 61-62; asst. appl. physics, Cornell Univ, 63-67, res. assoc. electron micros, 67; mem. tech. staff, Hughes Res. Labs, 67-69; ASST. PROF. PHYSICS, U.S. INT. UNIV, 69- Lectr, Los Angeles Valley Col, 68; lectr, Calif. Luth. Col, 68-69. Am. Phys. Soc; Am. Asn. Physics Teachers. Thin film vacuum nucleation; x-ray diffratometry and structure analysis; transmission and scanning electron microscopy; ultrahigh vacuum; liberal arts-physics teaching; foundations of quantum field theory; electronic brain modeling. Address: Dept. of Physics, U.S. International University, California Western Campus, San Diego, CA 92106.

EDMONDS, MARY P, b. Racine, Wis, May 7, 22. BIOCHEMISTRY. B.A, Milwaukee-Downer Col, 43; M.A, Wellesley Col, 45, Ph.D.(biochem), Pennsylvania, 51. Instr. chem, Wellesley Col, 45-46; fel. BIOCHEM, Illinois, 50-52; res. assoc, cancer res. inst, Wisconsin, 52-55; Montefiore Hosp. Res. Inst, 55-65; asst. prof, grad. sch. pub. health, UNIV. PITTSBURGH, 65-67, assoc. res. prof, 67-71, ASSOC. PROF, FACULTY ARTS & SCI, 71- Intermediary metabolism and enzymology; chemistry and enzymology of nucleic acids and nucleotides. Address: Dept. of Biochemistry, A743 Crabtree Hall, University of Pittsburgh, Pittsburgh, PA 15213.

EDMONDS, PETER D(EREK), b. Tunbridge Wells, Eng, Mar. 29, 29; m. 63. PHYSICS, BIOPHYSICS. B.Sc, London, 52, dipl, Imp. Col. & Ph.D.(physics), 59. Asst. physics, phys. inst, Stuttgart Tech, 55-56; Physicist, Mullard Res. Labs, Eng, 56-58; Akers Res. Labs, Imp. Chem. Industs, Ltd, 58-61, plastics div. res. labs, 61-62; res. fel. chem. eng, Calif. Inst. Tech, 62-63; asst. prof. biomed. eng, UNIV. PA, 63-68, ASSOC. PROF. ELEC. ENG, 68- Sr. res. fel. biomed. eng, Univ. Wash, 69-70. Acoust. Soc. Am; Inst. Elec. & Electronics Eng; Am. Inst. Ultrasound Med; Biomed. Eng. Soc; fel. Brit. Inst. Physics & Phys. Soc. Ultrasonic measurements of absorption and velocity in liquids and liquid mixtures; kinetics of fast reactions; relaxation mechanisms; mesomorphic liquid states; aqueous solutions of proteins; biomaterials; bioeffects of ultrasound. Address: Dept. of Biomedical Engineering, Moore School of Electrical Engineering, University of Pennsylvania, Philadelphia, PA 19104.

EDMONDS, RICHARD H, b. Carbondale, Pa, May 10, 33; m. 53; c. 3. ANATOMY. B.S, State Univ, N.Y. Buffalo, 59, Ph.D.(anat), 65. Asst. prof. ANAT, ALBANY MED. COL, 65-69, ASSOC. PROF, 69- U.S.N, 51-55. Am. Asn. Anat; Am. Soc. Cell Biol. Cell Biology; developmental hematology; electron microscopy. Address: Dept. of Anatomy, Albany Medical College, Albany, NY 12208.

EDMONDS, SYLVAN M(ILTON), b. New York, N.Y, Nov. 29, 08; m. 44. CHEMISTRY. B.S, Col. City of N.Y, 29; fel, 29; M.A, Columbia, 31, Ph.D. (chem), 33. From tutor CHEM. to asst. prof, CITY COL NEW YORK, 29-59, PROF, 59- With U.S.A, 44. C.W.S, U.S.A, 42-45. Am. Chem. Soc. Oxidation potential indicators and their applications to analytical chemistry; oxidimetric methods for the determinations of iron and vanadium; qualitative and quantitative analysis; chemical equilibrium studies; instrumental methods of analysis, electrometric and polarographic studies; chemical instrumentation. Address: 413 Washington Terrace, Leonia, NJ 07605.

EDMONDSON, ANDREW JOSEPH, b. Leavenworth, Kans, May 11, 35; m. 56; c. 2. MECHANICAL ENGINEERING. B.S, Tex. Tech. Col, 57; M.S, Pa. State, 61; Ph.D.(mech. eng), Texas A&M, 64. Instr. mech. eng, Tex. Tech. Col, 57-59, 60-61; asst. prof. MECH. & AERO ENG, UNIV. TENN, KNOXVILLE, 64-69, ASSOC. PROF, 69- Summer res. participant, Oak Ridge Nat. Lab, 67, consult, 67- Am. Soc. Eng. Educ. Theoretical and experimental studies of shell problems; experimental investigations concerning the sealing mechanisms of mechanical face seals. Address: Dept. of Mechanical & Aerospace Engineering, University of Tennessee, Knoxville, TN 37916.

EDMONDSON, DALE EDWARD, b. Morris, Ill, Oct. 13, 42. BIOCHEMISTRY. B.S, North. Ill. Univ, 64; univ. fel, Univ. Ariz, 67-70, U.S. Pub. Health Serv. fel. & Ph.D.(chem), 70. RES. ASST. BIOCHEM, UNIV. MICH, 70-, U.S. PUB. HEALTH SERV. RES. FEL, 71- Am. Chem. Soc. Structure-function relations and mechanisms of action of flavoenzymes and metalloflavoenzymes. Address: Dept. of Biological Chemistry, University of Michigan, Ann Arbor, MI 48104.

EDMONDSON, DON E(LTON), b. Dallas, Tex, Sept. 6, 25; m. 51; c. 3. MATHEMATICS. B.S, Southern Methodist, 45, M.S, 48; Chicago; Ph.D. (math), Calif. Inst. Tech, 54. Res. instr. MATH, Tulane, 54-55; asst. prof, Southern Methodist, 55-57, assoc. prof, 57-60; UNIV. TEX, AUSTIN, 60-64, PROF, 64-, v.chmn. dept, 69-70. Consult, Tex. Instruments, Inc, 58-59; Tex. Ed. Agency, 62-64. U.S.N.R, 45-46, Ens. Am. Math. Soc; Soc. Indust. & Appl. Math; Math. Asn. Am. Abstract algebra, lattice theory; topological lattices; real and complex analysis. Address: Dept. of Mathematics, University of Texas at Austin, Austin, TX 78712.

EDMONDSON, FRANK K(ELLEY), b. Milwaukee, Wis, Aug. 1, 12; m. 34; c. 2. ASTRONOMY. A.B, Indiana, 33, M.A, 34, Lawrence fel, Lowell Observ, 33-34; Agassiz fel, Harvard, 35-36, Ph.D.(astron), 37. Asst, Indiana, 29-33; Lowell Observ, 34-35; Harvard, 36-37; instr. ASTRON, IND. UNIV, BLOOMINGTON, 37-40, asst. prof, 40-45, assoc. prof, 45-49, PROF, 49-, CHMN. DEPT, 44-, RES. ASSOC, McDONALD OBSERV, 41-, DIR, GOETHE LINK OBSERV, 48-, Kirkwood Observ, 45-48. Prog. dir. astron, Nat. Sci. Found, 56-57; mem. bd, Asn. Univs. for Res. in Astron, v.pres, 57-61, pres, 62-65; cor. mem, Am. Mus. Natural Hist, 58-; mem, Int. Astron. Union, chmn, U.S. Nat.

Comt, 62-64, v.pres. Comn. 20, 67-70, pres, 70- Order of Merit, Govt. of Chile, 64. AAAS (v.pres, 62); Am. Astron. Soc.(treas, 54-). Stellar motions and distribution; radial velocities of faint stars; rediscovery and observation of asteroids on the critical list; radio astronomy. Address: Dept. of Astronomy, 319 Swain Hall W, Indiana University, Bloomington, IN 47401.

EDMONDSON, HUGH A(LLEN), b. Maysville, Ark, Jan. 3, 06; m. 30; c. 4. PATHOLOGY. A.B, Oklahoma, 26; M.D, Chicago, 31. Instr. PATH, SCH. MED, UNIV. SOUTH. CALIF, 38-41, asst. prof, 41-43, assoc. prof, 43-48, PROF, 48-, CHMN. DEPT, 51-, DIR. LABS. & CHIEF PATHOLOGIST, LOS ANGELES COUNTY-UNIV. SOUTH. CALIF. MED. CTR, 68- Asst. pathologist, Los Angeles County Gen. Hosp, 38-39, attend. pathologist, 39-; asst. pathologist, St. Luke Hosp, Pasadena, 40-42, pathologist, 42-43. Consult, Santa Fe Hosp. & Children's Hosp; mem. bd. trustees, Estelle Doheny Eye Found, 71- Am. Med. Asn; Am. Asn. Path. & Bact; fel. Am. Col. Physicians; Am. Soc. Clin. Path; Am. Gastroenterol. Asn; Int. Acad. Path. Diseases of the liver, gallbladder and bile ducts; tumors of the liver, gallbladder and extrahepatic bile duct. Address: Dept. of Pathology, University of Southern California School of Medicine, 2025 Zonal Ave, Los Angeles, CA 90033.

EDMONDSON, J(OSEPH) E(MMETT), b. Springfield, Mo, Jan. 7, 18; m. 45; c. 5. DAIRY BACTERIOLOGY. B.S, Missouri, 39, A.M, 40; Ph.D, Iowa State Col, 53. Asst, UNIV. MO-COLUMBIA, 40-41, instr. dairy mfg, 41-43, prod. mgr, univ. creamery, 43-45, instr. dairy bact, 45-48, asst. prof. dairy bact. & chem, 48-53, assoc. prof, 53-58, prof, 58-67, PROF. FOOD SCI. & ACTING CHMN. DEPT, 67-, chmn. dept. dairy bact. & chem, 62-67. Mem, Nat. Adv. Pub. Health Training Coun. AAAS; Am. Dairy Sci. Asn; Int. Asn. Milk, Food & Environ. Sanit. Causative microorganisms of bovine mastitis; bacteriological quality of milk and milk products; sanitation as related to public health; factors affecting residue in milk and milk products; new food formulation; food sanitation and processing. Address: Dept. of Food Science & Nutrition, 1-74 Agriculture Bldg, University of Missouri-Columbia, Columbia, MO 65201.

EDMONDSON, LOCKE F(RANKLIN), b. New Edinburg, Ark, Mar. 4, 21; m. 44; c. 3. AGRICULTURAL CHEMISTRY. B.S, Arkansas, 42; M.S, Okla. Agr. & Mech. Col, 49; Ph.D.(agr. chem), California, Davis, 54. Instr. dairy mfg, Okla. Agr. & Mech. Col, 49; res. asst. dairy indust, Univ. Calif, Davis, 49-53, asst. specialist, 53-54; chemist, EAST. MKT. & NUTRIT. RES. DIV, AGR. RES. SERV, U.S. DEPT. AGR, 54-57, SUPVRY. CHEMIST, 57- U.S. Dept. Agr. group superior serv. award, 64. U.S.N, 42-46, Res, 46-, Lt. Comdr. Am. Chem. Soc; Am. Dairy Sci. Asn. Colloidal nature of milk proteins; ion exchange processes for removing radiostrontium and iodine-131 from milk; development of improved sterile milk concentrates; mineral and vitamin enrichment of milk products. Address: Eastern Marketing & Nutrition Research Division, Agriculture Research Service, U.S. Dept. of Agriculture, Washington, DC 20250.

EDMONDSON, MORRIS STEPHEN, b. San Antonio, Tex, Sept. 9, 41; m. 62; c. 2. ORGANIC CHEMISTRY. B.S, Southwest Tex. State Univ, 63; M.A, Univ. Tex. Austin, 66, Welch fel, 67-69, Ph.D.(org. chem), 70. RES. CHEMIST, Jefferson Chem. Co, 65-67; PETRO-TEX CHEM. CORP, 70- Welch Found. fel, 69-70. Am. Chem. Soc. Permanent press fabric treating agents and surfactants; liquid phase chlorination of dienes; heterogeneous catalysis. Address: 504 Portage, Friendswood, TX 77546.

EDMONDSON, W(ALLES) THOMAS, b. Milwaukee, Wis, Apr. 24, 16; m. 41. ECOLOGY. B.S, Yale, 38, Ph.D.(zool), 42; Wisconsin, 38-39. Asst. zool, Wisconsin, 39; biol, Yale, 39-41; asst. phys. oceanog, Naval Ord. Lab. Contract, Am. Mus. Natural Hist, 42-43; res. assoc, Bur. Ships Contract, Oceanog. Inst, Woods Hole, 43-46; lectr. biol, Harvard, 46-49; asst. prof. ZOOL, UNIV. WASH, 49-52, assoc. prof, 52-57, PROF, 57- Fel, Nat. Sci. Found, 59-60. AAAS; Am. Soc. Limnol. & Oceanog; Am. Micros. Soc; Am. Soc. Zool; Ecol. Soc. Am; Soc. Syst. Zool; Phycol. Soc. Am. Int. Limnol. Asn. Ecology and taxonomy of Rotifera; biology of plankton; lake productivity. Address: Dept. of Zoology, University of Washington, Seattle, WA 98195.

EDMONDSON, YVETTE HARDMAN, b. New York, N.Y, Sept. 20, 15; m. 41. BIOLOGY. B.A, Bennington Col, 36; M.S, Minnesota, 38; Ph.D.(bact), Wisconsin, 40. Teaching asst. bact, Minnesota, 37-38; asst. limnol. & bact, Wisconsin, 38-39, Works Progress Admin. proj, 39-40; teaching fel. sci, Bennington Col, 40-41, faculty mem. sci. dept, 41-45; res. asst, Oceanog. Inst, Woods Hole, 45-46; res. fel. biol, Harvard, 46-49; res. bot, Washington (Seattle), 49-56; ed. consult. biol, Barnhart Ref. Bks, 57-67; ED, LIMNOL. & OCEANOG, DEPT. ZOOL, UNIV. WASH, 67- Asst, res. proj, U.S. Dept. Navy, 43. Aquatic ecology and bacteria; anthocyanin biosynthesis; biological editing. Address: Dept. of Zoology NJ15, University of Washington, Seattle, WA 98105.

EDMONSON, GLENN VERNON, b. Blue Mound, Ill, June 19, 10; m. 35; c. 3. MECHANICAL ENGINEERING. B.S.E, Michigan, 32; M.E, 49. Spec. assignment, Kelvinator Corp, 32-37; staff engr, hydraul. coupling div, Am. Blower Corp, 37-47; assoc. prof. MECH. ENG, UNIV. MICH, ANN ARBOR, 47-54, PROF, 54-, DIR, BIOENG. PROG, 66- Mem. faculty, Wayne Univ, 46-47; Consult. Am. Soc. Eng; Educ; Am. Soc. Mech. Eng; Nat. Soc. Prof. Eng. Theory and performance of turbo-machinery; bioengineering. Address: 1434 Roxbury Rd, Ann Arbor, MI 48104.

EDMUND, A(LEXANDER) GORDON, b. Toronto, Ont, Aug. 11, 24; m. 51; c. 4. VERTEBRATE PALEONTOLOGY. B.A, Toronto, 51, M.A, 52; Ph.D, Harvard, 57. From asst. curator to CURATOR, DEPT. VERT. PALEONT, ROYAL ONT. MUS, 54- Med.C, Can. Army, 43-46. Soc. Vert. Paleont. Fossil reptiles and amphibians; tooth replacement in non-mammalian vertebrates; edentate mammals. Address: Royal Ontario Museum, 100 Queens Park, Toronto 5, Can.

EDMUND, R(UDOLPH) W(ILLIAM), b. Lockridge, Iowa, Mar. 9, 10; m. 39; c. 3. GEOLOGY. A.B, Augustana Col, 34; M.S, Iowa, 38, Ph.D.(struct. geol), 40. Instr. geol, Coe Col, 39-40; geologist, Shell Oil Co, Inc, 40-45; asst. div. geologist, Globe Oil & Ref. Co, Okla, 45-48; regional geologist, 51-53; assoc. prof. geol, Augustana Col, 48-50, prof, 50-51; v.pres. & gen. mgr, Sohio Petrol. Co, Okla, 53-60; prof. geol. & chmn. div. sci, Augustana Col, 60-69; V.PRES. ACAD. AFFAIRS, CALIF. LUTHERAN COL, 69- Fel. AAAS; fel. Geol. Soc. Am; Nat. Asn. Geol. Teachers; Soc. Explor. Geophys; Soc. Econ. Paleont. & Mineral. Structural geology; regional stratigraphy; stratigraphic oil traps; paleogeologic maps. Address: California Lutheran College, Thousand Oaks, CA 91360.

EDMUNDOWICZ, JOHN M(ICHAEL), b. Nanticoke, Pa, May 18, 38; m. 60; c. 2. BIOCHEMISTRY. B.S, Phila. Col. Pharm. & Sci, 60; M.S, Univ. Del, 63, Ph.D.(chem), 66. SR. BIOCHEMIST, ANTIBIOTIC MFG. & DEVELOP. DIV, ELI LILLY & CO, 66- AAAS; Am. Chem. Soc. Enzyme isolation and purification; carbohydrate metabolism; antibiotic isolation and purification; chemistry of beta-lactam antibiotics. Address: Dept. K418, Eli Lilly & Co, Kentucky Ave, Indianapolis, IN 46204.

EDMUNDS, GEORGE F(RANCIS), JR, b. Salt Lake City, Utah, Apr. 28, 20. BIOLOGY, ENTOMOLOGY. B.S, Univ. Utah, 43, M.S, 46; Ph.D.(entom), Univ. Mass, 52. Instr. biol, UNIV. UTAH, 45-52, asst. prof, 52-55, from assoc. prof. to PROF. ZOOL. & ENTOM, 55-, dept. environ. biol, 68-69, acting chmn. dept. biol, 69-70. Consult. air pollution agr. & forestry. Entom. Soc. Am; Soc. Syst. Zool; Air Pollution Control.Asn; Soc. Study Evolution; fel. Royal Entom. Soc. London; Soc. Entom. Uruguay. Evolution; taxonomy and biology of Ephemeroptera; evolution of insect wings; ecology of insect outbreaks in relation to air pollution. Address: 201 Biology Bldg, University of Utah, Salt Lake City, UT 84112.

EDMUNDS, LAFE R(EES), b. Salt Lake City, Utah, June 22, 24; m. 47; c. 3. ENTOMOLOGY. B.S, Utah, 47, fel, 47-48, M.S, 49; Ph.D, Ohio State, 52. Asst, Utah, 47-48; Ohio State, 50-52; sr. asst. scientist, U.S. Pub. Health Serv, 52-54; asst. prof. zool. & entom, Miss. State, 54-56; prin. entomologist, res. & develop. lab, Ft. Belvoir, Va, 56-59; prof. asst, NAT. SCI. FOUND, 59-61, assoc. prog. dir, 61-68, prof. assoc. & prog. coord, 69-71, EXP. PROJS. COORD. FOR EDUC, 71- Int. adv. to Mex, Pan Am. Health Orgn, WHO, 65-68. U.S.A, 43-46. Entom. Soc. Am. Culicidae; mosquitoes; Hymenoptera; Evaniidae; cockroach biology and parasites; insect ecology; science education. Address: National Science Foundation, 1800 G St, Washington, DC 20550.

EDMUNDS, LELAND NICHOLAS, JR, b. Aiken, S.C, Apr. 21, 39; m. 64; c. 3. BIOLOGICAL RHYTHMS. B.S, Davidson Col, 60; Woodrow Wilson fel, Princeton, 60-61, Nat. Insts. Health fel, 61-62, M.A, 62, John Dunlop fel. & Charlotte Elizabeth Procter fel, 62-63, Nat. Sci. Found. summer fel, 63, Nat. Insts. Health fel, 63-64, Ph.D.(biol), 64. Nat. Sci. Found-Orgn. Trop. Studies fel, Costa Rica, 64; instr. & res. asst. biol, Princeton, 64-65; asst. prof. BIOL. SCI, STATE UNIV. N.Y. STONY BROOK, 65-70, ASSOC. PROF, 70- Student trainee & biol. aide, insect physiol. lab, entom. res. div, agr. res. center, U.S. Dept. Agr, Md, 56-60; vis. invest. biophys, Carnegie Inst. Dept. Terrestrial Magnetism, 62. Nat. Sci. Found. res. grant, 65-72; res. found. grant, State Univ. N.Y, 69-70. AAAS; Am. Soc. Plant Physiol. Circadian rhythms; synchrony in cell division and growth; control and regulation of macromolecular aspects of the cell cycle; insect communication; adaptive polymorphism; sexual isolating mechanisms; oscillatory enzyme systems; cellular communication. Address: Division of Biological Sciences, State University of New York at Stony Brook, Stony Brook, NY 11790.

EDMUNDS, LEON K, b. Madison, Wis, Mar. 25, 29; m. 50; c. 9. PLANT PATHOLOGY. B.S, Wisconsin, 53, Ph.D.(plant path), 58. Res. assoc. plant path, Wisconsin, 58-60; RES. PLANT PATHOLOGIST, U.S. DEPT. AGR, AGR. RES. SERV, KANS. STATE UNIV, 60- Am. Phytopath. Soc. Diseases of grain sorghum in semihumid to semiarid areas of central United States. Address: Dickens Hall, Kansas State University, Manhattan, KS 66504.

EDMUNDS, LOUIS HENRY, JR, b. Seattle, Wash, Aug. 12, 31; c. 3. CARDIOTHORACIC SURGERY. B.S, Univ. Wash, 52; M.D, Harvard Med. Sch, 56. Intern, Mass. Gen. Hosp, 56-57, asst. resident surg, 57-59 & 61-63, resident, 63; teaching fel, Harvard Med. Sch, 63-64; clin. asst, Mass. Gen. Hosp, 64; sr. registrar, Leeds Gen. Infirmary, Eng, 64-65; assoc, Mason Clin, Seattle, Wash, 65-66; asst. prof. SURG, MED. CTR, UNIV. CALIF, SAN FRANCISCO, 66-68, ASSOC. PROF, 68-, DIR, EXP. SURG. LABS, 67-, assoc. cardiovascular res. inst, 66-67. Res. fel. thoracic surg, Leeds Univ, 64; investr, Virginia Mason Res. Ctr, Seattle, Wash, 65. Dipl, Am. Bd. Surg, 64; Am. Bd. Thoracic Surg, 65. U.S.N.R, 59-61, Lt. AAAS; Am. Heart Asn; Am. Col. Cardiol; Am. Soc. Artificial Internal Organs; Am. Asn. Thoracic Surg; Am. Thoracic Soc; Asn. Acad. Surg; N.Y. Acad. Sci; Soc. Univ. Surg; Am. Col. Surg. Address: Dept. of Surgery, University of California, San Francisco, Third & Parnassus, San Francisco, CA 94122.

EDMUNDSON, ALLEN B, b. Flat River, Mo, June 16, 32; m. 55; c. 3. BIOCHEMISTRY. A.B, Darmouth Col, 54; Ph.D.(biochem), Rockefeller Univ, 61. U.S. Pub. Health Serv. fel. biochem, unit molecular biol, Med. Res. Coun, Eng, 60-64; ASSOC. BIOCHEMIST, DIV. BIOL. & MED. RES, ARGONNE NAT. LAB, 64- Protein chemistry; determinations of structures and genetically controlled variations of proteins; correlation of structure and function. Address: Division of Biological & Medical Research, Argonne National Lab, Argonne, IL 60440.

EDMUNDSON, H(AROLD) P(ARKINS), b. Los Angeles, Calif, Dec. 13, 21; m. 63. MATHEMATICS. B.A, California, Los Angeles, 46, M.A, 48, Inst. Numerical Anal. fel, 50-51, Ph.D.(math), 53. Asst. math, California, Los Angeles, 49-50, 51-52; mathematician, Indust. Logistics Res. Proj, 53; U.S. Dept. Defense, 53-54; Rand Corp, 54-59; sr. assoc, Planning Res. Corp, 59-61; mem. sr. staff, Thompson-Ramo-Wooldridge, Inc, 61-64; sr. scientist, Syst. Develop. Corp, 64-67; PROF. MATH. & COMPUT. SCI, UNIV. MD, 67- Lectr, George Washington, 53-54; Southern California, 54-56; California, Los Angeles, 57-63, assoc. res. mathematician, 64- Sig.C, 42-46, Capt. Am. Math. Soc; Math. Asn. Am; Am. Soc. Info. Sci; Inst. Math. Statist; Asn. Comput. Mach; Asn. Symbolic Logic; sr. mem. Inst. Elec. & Electronics Eng. Mathematical statistics and logic; probability, matrix and information theories; stochastic processes; automatic translation; mathematical and computational linguistics. Address: Dept. of Mathematics, University of Maryland, College Park, MD 20740.

EDNEY, ERIC B, b. Bognor, Eng, Aug. 14, 13; m. 37; c. 2. ZOOLOGY. B.Sc, Rhodes Univ. Col, 34; Ph.D.(entom), London, 37; D.Sc.(zool), Birmingham, 51. Zoologist, Nat. Mus. South. Rhodesia, 37-40; lectr. biol, Makerere Univ. Col, Uganda, 41-46; ZOOL, Birmingham, 46-52, reader, 52-55; PROF, Univ. Col, Rhodesia, 55-64; UNIV. CALIF, RIVERSIDE, 65- Soc. Exp. Biol. & Med; fel. Royal Entom. Soc. London; fel. Brit. Inst. Biol. Physiology of arthropods; acclimation; taxonomy of African Chrysidae. Address: Dept. of Biology, University of California, Riverside, CA 92502.

EDNEY, NORRIS ALLEN, b. Natchez, Miss, July 17, 36; m. 59; c. 3. BIOLOGY. B.Sc, Tougaloo South. Christian Col, 57; M.Sc, Antioch Col, 62; Atlanta, 63; Ph.D.(conserv), Mich. State, 69. Prof. BIOL, Natchez Jr. Col, 57-62; instr, Alcorn Agr. & Mech. Col, 63-65, asst. prof, 65-66; teaching asst, Mich. State, 66-69, instr, summer 69; PROF, ALCORN AGR. & MECH. COL, 69- Res. conserv. aide, Dept. Natural Resources, State of Mich, 68-69; dir, Coop. Col-Sch. Sci. Prog. AAAS; Soc. Protozool; Mycol. Soc. Am; Soc. Econ. Bot; Bot. Soc. Am. Ecological succession of protozoa in pond and sewage water; histochemical study of certain enzyme systems in Trichomonas vaginalis; study of infections of fish by certain saprolegniaceous fungi. Address: Dept. of Biology, Alcorn Agricultural & Mechanical College, Box 174, Lorman, MS 39096.

EDNIE, NORMAN A(LEX), b. Leven, Scotland, July 5, 20; nat; m. 45; c. 4. CHEMICAL ENGINEERING. Ph.D.(chem. eng), Wisconsin, 51. RES. MGR, spunbonded prod. res. div, E.I. DU PONT DE NEMOURS & CO, 50-67, NYLON END-USE APPAREL, 67- Chem. Warfare Serv, U.S.A, 43-45. Am. Inst. Chem. Eng; Am. Chem. Soc; Sci. Res. Soc. Am. Synthetic fibers; synthetic fiber papers and non-woven fabrics; research and development management. Address: Textile Research Lab, E.I. du Pont de Nemours & Co, Chestnut Run, Wilmington, DE 19805.

EDSALL, GEOFFREY, b. Philadelphia, Pa, Jan. 28, 08; m. 35; c. 1. IMMUNOLOGY, MEDICINE. M.D, Harvard, 34. Med. intern, Mass. Gen. Hosp, 34-36; res. fel. med, Harvard Med. Sch, 36-37, pediat, 37-39; asst. dir. div. biol. labs, State Dept. Pub. Health, Mass, 39-42, dir, 42-49; prof. microbiol. sch. med, Boston, 49-52; dir. immunol. div, Walter Reed Army Inst. Res, 51-56; dir. div. communicable disease, 56-60; SUPT. STATE LAB. INST, MASS. DEPT. PUB. HEALTH, 60-; PROF. APPL. MICROBIOL, SCH. PUB. HEALTH, HARVARD, 60- Instr. sch. pub. health, Harvard, 40-47, asst. prof, 47-49, vis. lectr, 49-60; vis. prof, California, 55. Spec. consult, WHO, 53, 55, 59, consult, 63-; U.S. Army, 60-; U.S. Pub. Health Serv. & mem. adv. comt. immunization practices, 63- Trustee, Bergey Manual Trust, 57-65. Mem. comn. immunization, Armed Forces Epidemiol. Bd, 50-, dir, 52-64; mem. subcomt. blood, Off. Defense Mobilization, 51-52; revision comt, U.S. Pharmacopeia, 60-65; mem. immunol. panel, WHO, 62-; bd. sci. counsr, div. biologics standards, Nat. Insts. Health, 68- Del, U.S. Pharmacopeial Conv, 50; mem, U.S. del, 13th World Health Assembly, 60. Dipl, Am. Bd. Prev. Med; Am. Bd. Microbiol. Fel. AAAS; fel. Am. Acad. Arts & Sci; fel. Am. Pub. Health Asn; fel. Am. Acad. Microbiol; Am. Soc. Trop. Med. & Hyg; Am. Med. Asn; Epidemiol. Soc; Am. Soc. Microbiol; Am. Asn. Immunol.(ed, Jour, 48-54, pres, 50); Soc. Exp. Biol. & Med; Brit. Soc. Gen. Microbiol; fel. Royal Soc. Trop. Med. & Hyg. Biologic products; immunization; diphtheria and tetanus immunity; antibody response; typhoid fever. Address: State Lab. Institute, Massachusetts Dept. of Public Health, 375 South St, Boston, MA 02130.

EDSALL, JOHN T(ILESTON), b. Phila, Pa, Nov. 3, 02; m. 29; c. 3. BIOCHEMISTRY. A.B, Harvard, 23, M.D, 28; Cambridge, 24-26; hon. D.Sc, Univ. Chicago, 67, Case West. Reserve Univ, 67, N.Y. Med. Col, 67, Univ. Mich, 68. Tutor biochem. scis, HARVARD, 28-, instr, 28-32, asst. prof. BIOCHEM, 32-38, assoc. prof, 38-51, PROF, 51- Chmn. Bd. tutors biochem, scis, 31-57. Guggenheim Mem. Found. fel, Calif. Inst. Tech, 40-41, Harvard, 54-56; Fulbright vis. lectr, Cambridge, 52-56, Tokyo, 64; vis. prof, Col. France, 55-56; vis. fel, Australian Nat. Univ, 70; scholar, Fogarty Int. Ctr, Nat. Insts. Health, 70-71. Ed, Jour. Biol. Chem, 58-67. With Off. Sci. Res. & Develop; U.S. Pub. Health Serv, 44; mem, U.S. Nat. Comn. for UNESCO, 50-56; pres, Int. Cong. Biochem, N.Y, 64. Passano Found. award, 66. Nat. Acad. Sci; AAAS; Am. Chem. Soc; Am. Soc. Biol. Chem.(pres, 57-58); Am. Philos. Soc; Hist. Sci. Soc; Am. Acad. Arts. & Sci; Brit. Biochem. Soc; French Soc. Biol. Chem; Leopold Carol Ger. Acad. Res. Natural Sci; Royal Danish Acad. Sci. Physical chemistry of amino acids and proteins; Raman spectra of amino acids and peptides; double refraction of flow; muscle proteins; proteins involved in blood coagulation; light scattering in protein solution; dipolar ions and acid-base equilibria. Address: Biological Labs, Harvard University, Cambridge, MA 02138.

EDSBERG, R(OBERT) L(ESLIE), b. Seattle, Wash, Feb. 7, 22; m. 48; c. 3. ANALYTICAL CHEMISTRY. B.Chem, Minnesota, 44; M.S, Pennsylvania, 52. Res. chemist, Gen. Aniline & Film Co, 44-52; mgr. chem. sect, Burroughs Cent. Res. Labs, 52-55; chem. res, TODD CO. DIV, BURROUGHS CORP, 55-66, DIR. RES. & ENG, ROCHESTER, 66- Med.C, U.S.A, 44-46. Am. Chem. Soc. Graphic arts research as related to business machines, supplies. Address: 141 Butler Dr, Pittsford, NY 14534.

EDSE, RUDOLPH, b. Hamburg, Ger, Dec. 14, 13; nat; m. 39; c. 2. AERONAUTICAL ENGINEERING. Dipl. chem, Hamburg, 37, Dr.rer.nat.(phys. chem), 39. Res. phys. chemist, Inst. Aeronaut. Sci, Ger, 39-44, dep. head chem. dept, 44-46; sci. consult, Wright-Patterson AFB, U.S. Air Force, 45-51; asst. prof, AERONAUT. ENG, OHIO STATE UNIV, 51-54, assoc. prof, 54-57; PROF, 57-, DIR. ROCKET RES. LAB, 51- Consult, Allegany Ballistics Lab, Md, 57-63. Am. Inst. Aeronaut. & Astronaut. Propulsion; thermodynamics, combustion and high speed aerodynamics. Address: Dept. of Aeronautical & Astronautical Engineering, Ohio State University, Columbus, OH 43210.

EDSON, ALDEN P(OTTER), b. Kansas City, Mo, Nov. 3, 14; m. 48. METALLURGICAL ENGINEERING. B.S, Kansas, 37. Metallurgist, Int. Nickel Co, N.J, 37-43; sr. metallurgist, Hamilton Standard Div, United Aircraft Corp, 43, asst. chief metallurgist, 44-45, chief metallurgist, 45-51, chief mat. engr, 51-56; RES. ASSOC, INT. NICKEL CO, INC, 56- Am. Inst. Mining, Metall. & Petrol. Eng; Am. Soc. Metals; Inst. Elec. & Electronics Eng; Electrochem. Soc. Batteries; fuel cells; magnetostrictive materials; iron-nickel alloys; electrical and electronic alloys. Address: 199 Parkside Dr, Suffern, NY 10901.

EDSON, CHARLES GRANT, b. West Springfield, Mass, Dec. 16, 16; m. 42; c. 1. HYDRAULICS, MECHANICS. B.S, Massachusetts, 38; Mass. Inst. Tech, 42-43; M.S.E, Florida, 50. Engr, Corps Engrs, R.I, 38-40, Fla, 40-42, 46; asst. prof. HYDRAUL. & MECH, UNIV. FLA, 46-51, ASSOC. PROF, 51- Consult, Corps Engrs, Jacksonville, Fla, 48-49, D.C, 50-52, summer hydraul. engr, 63; summers hydraul. engr, cent. & south. flood control dist, West Palm Beach, Fla, 55, soil conserv. serv, U.S. Dept. Agr, 61; consult Brevard Eng. Co, 70. U.S.A.A.F, 42-46, 1st Lt. Fel. Am. Soc. Civil Eng. Open channel hydraulics; empirical relations in hydrology; three-body problem of mechanics; geometry; nomography and crystallography. Address: 2212 NW 15th Ave, Gainesville, FL 32601.

EDSON, FRANK GEORGE, b. St. Joseph, Mo, Feb. 21, 01; m; c. 1. CHEMISTRY. A.B, William Jewell Col, 25; fel, Colorado, 28-29, A.M, 29, Ph.D. (chem), 33. Sci. teacher, pub. sch, Mo, 24-25, 26-28; Ill, 25-26; asst. prof. chem, William Jewell Col, 29-32, assoc. prof, 32-36, prof. & head dept, 36-42; chief chemist, Jayhawk Ord. Works, 42-43; asst. prof. CHEM, Missouri, 43-44; PROF. & HEAD DEPT, WILLIAM JEWELL COL, 44-, dean of col, 49-59. Nat. Sci. Found. fel, Harvard, 57-58. Sanitary examination of water; colorimetric methods of analysis for quantitative determination of reducing sugars in food products. Address: Dept. of Chemistry, William Jewell College, Liberty, MO 64068.

EDSON, JAMES B(ROWN), b. Kansas City, Mo, July 29, 08; m. 37; c. 1. PHYSICS, ASTRONOMY. A.B, Kansas, 35, M.A, 38; Ph.D.(physics), Hopkins, 48. Asst, Lowell Observ, Calif. Inst. Tech, 35-38, leader planet group, 39-42, res. assoc, 41-44; ord. engr. rocket & guided missile res, ballistic res. labs, U.S. Dept. Army, 45-48, physicist tactical atomic weapons systs. develop, off. chief ord, 49-51, chief, west. regional off, admin. basic res, ord. res, 51-55, chief scientist, res. prog. mgt, res. & mat. br, off. chief ord, 55-57, asst. to dir. res. & develop. for tech. planning. Off. Secy. Army, 57-59, sr. adv. missiles to asst. chief. staff for intel, 59-61; tech. asst. to assoc. administr. for adv. res. & tech, NASA, 61-68; INDEPENDENT CONSULT, RES. & DEVELOP. MGT, 68- Consult, planetary atmospheres proj, Lowell Observ, 49-52. Mem. geophys. panel, Air Force Sci. Adv. Bd; chmn, Nat. Working Group Extraterrestrial Resources, 64- Karl Fairbanks Mem. Award, Soc. Photo-Optical Instrument. Eng, 68. Am. Astron. Soc; Am. Astronaut. Soc; Am. Soc. Cybernetics. Astronautics; rockets and missiles; planetary physics; international relation and strategic employment of Armed Forces. Address: Star Route 1156, Woodland Park, CO 80863.

EDSON, QUENTIN A, b. Burton, Wash, July 12, 26; m. 50; c. 2. FISHERIES BIOLOGY. B.S, Univ. Wash, 51. Biol. aide, Wash. Dept. Fisheries, 44-51, biologist, 51; jr. biologist, Alaska Dept. Fisheries, 51-53, biologist, 53-55; fisheries biologist, Wash. Dept. Fisheries, 55-64; City of Tacoma, 64-70; FISHERY BIOLOGIST, FED. POWER COMN, 70- U.S.A, 46-48. Am. Fisheries Soc. Research and management of Pacific Salmon; research and development of fish passage facilities at hydroelectric projects. Address: Federal Power Commission, 441 G St. N.W, Washington, DC 20426.

EDSON, SETON N(ORMAN), b. Quebec, Can, Aug. 2, 11; nat; m. 45. AGRICULTURAL CHEMISTRY, SOILS. B.S.A, Florida, 49, M.S, 50. Asst. Prof. SOILS, UNIV. FLA, 50-58, ASSOC. PROF, 58- Fla. Acad. award, 56. U.S.C.G, 31-34; U.S.N, 42-46, Res, Lt. Comdr. Am. Soc. Agron. Methods and procedures for soil analysis. Address: Dept. of Soils, Agricultural Experiment Station, University of Florida, Gainesville, FL 32601.

EDSON, WILLIAM A(LDEN), b. Burchard, Nebr, Oct. 30, 12; m. 42; c. 3. ELECTRICAL ENGINEERING. B.S, Kansas, 34, Summerfield scholar & M.S, 35; McKay fel. & Sc.D.(commun. eng), Harvard, 37. Mem. tech. staff, Bell Tel. Labs, 37-41, 43-44, supr, 44-45; asst. prof. elec. eng, Ill. Inst. Tech, 41-43; prof. physics, Ga. Inst. Tech, 45-46, elec. eng, 46-52, dir. sch. elec. eng, 51-52; vis. prof. & res. assoc, Stanford, 52-54; consult. engr, microwave lab, Gen. Elec. Co, 55-59, mgr. klystron subsect, 59-61; dir, Electromagnetic Technol. Corp, 61-62, pres, 62-70; sr. scientist, Vidar Corp, 70-71; SR. RES. ENGR, STANFORD RES. INST, 71- Consult, Nat. Bur. Standards, 51-64. Fel. Inst. Elec. & Electronics Eng; Am. Phys. Soc. Filters; electronic oscillators; cavity and quartz crystal resonators; broad band and microwave amplifiers. Address: Stanford Research Institute, 333 Ravenswood Ave, Menlo Park, CA 94025.

EDSTROM, RONALD D(WIGHT), b. Oakland, Calif, Mar. 21, 36; m. 59; c. 3. BIOCHEMISTRY. A.B, California, Berkeley, 58, Ph.D.(biochem), Davis, 62. Res. assoc. biochem, Michigan, 62-63; U.S. Pub. Health Serv. fel. physiol. chem, sch. med, Hopkins, 63-65; asst. prof. BIOCHEM, MED. SCH, UNIV. MINN, MINNEAPOLIS, 65-71, ASSOC. PROF, 71- AAAS; Am. Chem. Soc; Am. Soc. Biol. Chem; Am. Soc. Microbiol. Structure, degradation and biosynthesis of carbohydrate containing polymers, pectin, bacterial lipopolysaccharides and glycoproteins; biochemistry of carbohydrate polymers, especially bacterial polysaccharides, mammalian mucopolysaccharides, glycogen and glycoproteins; biochemistry of human polysaccharide storage diseases. Address: Dept. of Biochemistry, University of Minnesota School of Medicine, Minneapolis, MN 55455.

EDWARD, ALFRED GEORGE, b. Barre, Vt, Apr. 30, 19; m. 43; c. 1. ZOOLOGY. B.S, Colorado State, 48, D.V.M, 52. County agent, Colo. Exten. Serv, 52-55; veterinarian, Plum Island Animal Disease Lab, agr. res. serv, U.S. Dept. Agr, 55-60; Nat. Animal Disease Lab, 60-63; exp. animal resources, SCH. VET. MED, UNIV. CALIF, DAVIS, 63-70, PROF. LAB. ANIMAL MED, 70- Dipl, Am. Col. Lab. Animal Med. U.S.A.F, 42-46, 1st Lt. Am. Vet. Med. Asn; Am. Asn. Lab. Animal Sci. Laboratory animal facility design and management; mucoid enteritis in the rabbit. Address: Dept. of Clinical Sciences, School of Veterinary Medicine, University of California, Davis, CA 95616.

EDWARD, COSMAS, b. Baltimore, Md, Apr. 5, 26. BIOLOGY. B.A, Manhattan Col, 51; M.S, Fordham, 57, Ph.D.(biol), 62. Teacher, La Salle Acad, R.I, 47-49; St. Peter's High Sch, N.Y, 49-50, 54-58; Christian Bros. Acad, 50-54; Manhattan Col. High Sch, 58-59; instr. BIOL, MANHATTAN COL, 59-63, asst. prof, 63-68, ASSOC. PROF, 68- AAAS; Am. Inst. Biol. Sci. Regeneration in amphibians; antigenicity and homograft reactions in newts and other salamanders. Address: Dept. of Biology, Manhattan College, Bronx, NY 10471.

EDWARD, DEIRDRE WALDRON, b. Detroit, Mich, June 23, 23; Can. citizen; m. 53; c. 3. BIOCHEMISTRY. B.Sc, Univ. Birmingham, 44, fel, 49-53, Ph.D.(path. chem), 54. Staff res. off, Bakelite Corp, 44-46; clin. biochemist, Children's Hosp, Birmingham, Eng, 46-49; Lasdon res. fel, Trinity Col.(Dublin), 54-57; res. assoc. EXP. SURG, McGILL UNIV, 60-65, asst. prof, 65-67, ASSOC. PROF, 67- Can. Biochem. Soc; Brit. Biochem. Soc; N.Y. Acad. Sci. Structure and metabolism of polysaccharides, glycoproteins; absorption of metal ions and radionuclides by gastrointestinal tract; biosynthesis of glycoproteins. Address: Dept. of Experimental Surgery, Donner Bldg, McGill University, P.O. Box 6070, Montreal 101, Que, Can.

EDWARDS, ALAN KENT, b. Wichita, Kans, Apr. 29, 40; m. 62; c. 2. PHYSICS. A.B, Cent. Methodist Col, 62; M.S, Univ. Nebr, Lincoln, 64, Ph.D. (physics), 68. Res. assoc. PHYSICS, Univ. Wash, 67-70; ASST. PROF, UNIV. GA, 70- Am. Phys. Soc. Atomic and molecular physics. Address: Dept. of Physics, University of Georgia, Athens, GA 30601.

EDWARDS, ALAN M, b. Denver, Colo, Oct. 8, 33; m. 55; c. 3. AERONAUTICS, ASTRONAUTICS. B.S, U.S. Mil. Acad, 55; S.M, Mass. Inst. Tech, 61; Ph.D.(aeronaut. astronaut), Stanford, 65. U.S. AIR FORCE, 55-, asst. prof, eng. mech, U.S. Air Force Acad, 61-63, assoc. prof, 65-68, dep. dir. academics, Aerospace Res. Pilot Sch, 68-69, dir, 69-70, 614th Tactical Fighter Squadron, 70-71, AEROSPACE ASST, NAT. AERONAUT. & SPACE COUN, 71- Consult, Air Force Flight Test Sch, 66. Shell structures; aeroelasticity; flight dynamics. Address: Executive Office of The President, National Aeronautics & Space Council, Washington, DC 20502.

EDWARDS, A(LBERT) E(DWARD), b. Perth, N.B, Sept. 21, 15; m. 41; c. 3. PHYSICAL CHEMISTRY. B.Sc, New Brunswick, 36; M.S, Maine, 38; du Pont fel, Wisconsin, 40-41, Ph.D.(chem), 41. Asst. chem, Maine, 36-38; phys. chem, Wisconsin, 38-40; res. chemist, Aluminum Co. Can, Ltd, 41-45; Aluminum Labs, Ltd, 45-46, head dept. patents & contracts, 46-55, bus. mgr, 55-58, dir. res, Que, 58-69; MEM. STAFF, ALCAN RES. & DEVELOP. LTD, 69- Electrochemistry. Address: Alcan Research & Development Ltd, P.O. Box 6090, Montreal 101, Que, Can.

EDWARDS, ARTHUR L, b. Sacramento, Calif, Feb. 24, 33; m. 53; c. 3. CHEMICAL ENGINEERING, APPLIED MATHEMATICS. B.S, Washington (Seattle), 54; M.S, Illinois, 59, Ph.D.(chem. eng), 61. CHEM. ENGR. APPL. MATH. & COMPUT, LAWRENCE RADIATION LAB, UNIV. CALIF, 60- U.S.N, 54-57, Lt. Am. Inst. Chem. Eng; Am. Chem. Soc. High pressure solid state physics; application of computers to transient transport phenomena such as heat conduction, fluid flow and other potential flow problems. Address: Lawrence Radiation Lab, Box 808, Livermore, CA 94550.

EDWARDS, BEN E, b. Ross, Calif, Oct. 14, 35; m. 57, 66; c. 5. ORGANIC CHEMISTRY. S.B, Mass. Inst. Technol, 57; Ph.D.(org. chem), Ind. Univ, 62. Nat. Insts. Health fel. org. chem, Columbia Univ, 62-63; res. assoc, Southwest Found. Res. & Educ, 63-67; res. chemist, chem. sci. div, res. inst, Ill. Inst. Technol, 67-68; ASST. PROF, DEPT. CHEM, UNIV. N.C, GREENSBORO, 68- AAAS; Am. Chem. Soc; Brit. Chem. Soc. Organic synthesis; steroids; sulfur compounds; medicinal chemistry. Address: Dept. of Chemistry, University of North Carolina at Greensboro, Greensboro, NC 27412.

EDWARDS, BETTY F, b. Athens, Ga, Mar. 13, 15; m. 36; c. 2. ANATOMY. A.B, Agnes Scott Col, 35; Vanderbilt, 35-36; M.A, Emory, 51, Ph.D.(anat), 63. Instr. biol, Emory, 43-45, anat, 51-55; biol, Ga. State Col, 49-50, 55-61; anat, EMORY UNIV, 63-66, ASST. PROF. HISTOL. & EMBRYOL, 66- Am. Soc. Zool; Am. Inst. Biol. Sci; Am. Asn. Anat; Tissue Cult. Asn. Muscle and plant tissue culture; responses of animal and plant tissues to gravity; effects of weightlessness on growth. Address: Dept. of Anatomy, Emory University, Atlanta, GA 30322.

EDWARDS, BYRON N, b. Trinidad, Colo, Sept. 16, 32; m. 56; c. 3. APPLIED PHYSICS, ELECTRICAL ENGINEERING. B.S, California, Berkeley, 55, M.S, 57, Raytheon fel, 58, Ph.D.(elec. eng), 60. Assoc. elec. eng, California, Berkeley, 56-58; RES. SCIENTIST APPL. PHYSICS, aeronutronics div, FORD MOTOR CO, 59-62, PHILCO RES. LABS, 62- Lectr, Univ. Calif, Irvine, 70- Inst. Elec. & Electronics Eng; Am. Phys. Soc. Microwave engineering and applications of gas discharges; infrared engineering and physics, communication and tracking systems; electro-optical devices. Address: 847 S. Cedarwood Ave, Orange, CA 92667.

EDWARDS, CAROLYN T(ROWBRIDGE), b. N.Y.C, Dec. 5, 18; m. 46; c. 3. PHYSIOLOGY. B.A, Iowa, 39, M.A, 40; Ph.D.(physiol), Rochester, 45. Instr. PHYSIOL, Vassar Col, 43-46; asst. prof, Goucher Col, 46-48; assoc, MED. COL. OF VA, 48-49, ASST. PROF, 57- Chemical embryology of grasshoppers; chemistry of nerve and muscle; gastric secretion. Address: Dept. of Physiology, Medical College of Virginia, Virginia Commonwealth University, Richmond, VA 23219.

EDWARDS, CECILE HOOVER, b. East St. Louis, Ill, Oct. 20, 26; m. 51; c. 3. NUTRITION, BIOCHEMISTRY. B.S, Tuskegee Inst, 46, univ. fel, 46-47, M.S, 47; Gen. Educ. Bd. fel, Iowa State Univ, 47-49, Ph.D.(nutrit), 50. Res. assoc. nutrit, Iowa State Univ, 49-50; asst. prof. & res. assoc. foods & nutrit, Tuskegee Inst, 50-56, head dept, 52-56; PROF. NUTRIT, A&T STATE UNIV. N.C, 56- Collab, bur. home nutrit. & home econ, Agr. Res. Serv, U.S. Dept. Agr, 52-; guest scientist, Cent. Food Technol. Res. Inst, Mysore, India, 67-68; partic. distinguished scientists lect. series, Bennett Col, 70; vis. prof, Howard Univ, 71; adj. prof, Univ. N.C, Chapel Hill, 71; mem. exec. bd, Asn. Adminrs. Home Econ, mem. nat. adv. comt. long range res; comt. interpretation of recommended dietary allowances, Nat. Res. Coun; pres, Southeast. Col. Conf. Teachers of Food & Nutrit; chmn. panel community nutrit. educ, White House Conf. Food, Nutrit. & Health. Plaque for contributions to sci, Nat. Coun. Negro Women, 63; dipl. human nutrit, Am. Bd. Nutrit, 63; scroll & key for outstanding contribution to sci. & educ, City of East St. Louis, Ill. Am. Inst. Nutrit; Am. Home Econ. Asn; Soc. Nutrit. Educ; Am. Dietetic Asn; Nat. Inst. Sci. Nitrogen metabolism studies of adult rats; utilization of dietary supplements during growth and pregnancy; amino acid composition of foods; utilization of radioactive methionine; roles of methionine and vitamin B_{12} in metabolism; utilization of protein from vegetable sources; utilization of wheat by adult man. Address: Dept. of Home Economics, A&T State University of North Carolina, Greensboro, NC 27411.

EDWARDS, CHARLES, b. Wash, D.C, Sept. 22, 25; m. 51; c. 4. BIOPHYSICS. A.B, Hopkins, 45, M.A, 48, Nat. Found. Infantile Paralysis fel, 51-53, Ph.D. (biophys), 53. Hon. res. asst. biophys, University Col, London, 53-54, asst. lectr, 54-55; instr. physiol. optics, Hopkins 55-57, asst. prof, 57-58; asst. res. prof. physiol, Utah, 58-60; assoc. prof, Minnesota, 60-65, PROF, 65-67; BIOL. SCI, STATE UNIV. N.Y. ALBANY, 67-, DIR. NEUROBIOL. RES. CTR, 70- Nat. Found. Infantile Paralysis fel, 53-54; Lalor fel, Marine Biol. Lab, 57; Lederle fel, 59-60; mem. physiol. study sect, Nat. Insts. Health, 71- Soc. Gen. Physiol.(secy, 71-73); Am. Soc. Zool; Am. Physiol. Soc; Biophys. Soc. Membrane phenomena in excitable tissue; muscle contraction. Address: Dept. of Biological Sciences, State University of New York at Albany, Albany, NY 12203.

EDWARDS, CHARLES H(ENRY), JR, b. Pleasant Hill, Tenn, Sept. 27, 37; m. 58; c. 3. MATHEMATICS. B.S, Tennessee, 58, Ph.D.(math), 60. Asst. prof. MATH, Tennessee, 61; instr, Wisconsin, 61-62, asst. prof, 62-64; assoc. prof, UNIV. GA, 64-69, PROF, 69- Sloan res. fel, 64-66; mem, Inst. Adv. Study, 65-66. Am. Math. Soc. Topology of manifolds; embedding problems; combinatorial topology. Address: Dept. of Mathematics, University of Georgia, Athens, GA 30602.

EDWARDS, CHARLES MARTIN, b. Centralia, Ill, Oct. 18, 17; m. 41; c. 4. ELECTRICAL ENGINEERING. B.S. & M.S, Mass. Inst. Tech, 41. Engr, West. Elec. Co, Inc, 41-46; res. engr, Mass. Inst. Tech, 46-51; assoc. dir, Bendix Res. Labs, 51-60, staff asst. to exec. v.pres, 60-61, west. corp. rep, 61-62, gen. mgr. comput. div, 62-63, staff asst, v.pres, & group exec, UNITED GEOPHYS. CORP, BENDIX CORP, 63-67, V.PRES. & DIR. TECH. PROG, 67- Sr. mem. Inst. Elec. & Electronics Eng; Inst. Aeronaut. & Astronaut. Analog and digital computers; closed loop systems; electronics instrumentation; technical and general management. Address: United Geophysical Corp, P.O. Box M, Pasadena, CA 91109.

EDWARDS, DALE IVAN, b. Mattoon, Ill, Jan. 12, 30; m. 55; c. 4. NEMATOLOGY, PLANT PATHOLOGY. B.S, Eastern Illinois, 56; M.S, Illinois, 60, Ph.D.(plant path), 62. Asst. plant path, Illinois, 56-62; assoc. pathologist, Tela Railroad Co, 62-65; NEMATOLOGIST, PLANT SCI. RES. DIV, AGR. RES. SERV, U.S. DEPT. AGR, UNIV. ILL, URBANA, 65- U.S.A.F, 50-54, S/Sgt. Soc. Nematol. Host-parasite relationships and control of plant parasitic nematodes. Address: 107 F Horticulture Field Lab, University of Illinois, Urbana, IL 61801.

EDWARDS, D(ALLAS) CRAIG, b. Clearfield, Pa, Sept. 9, 39; m. 64. POPULATION ECOLOGY. B.A, Swarthmore Col, 61; Nat. Sci. Found. fel, Chicago, 61-65, Ph.D.(zool), 65. Nat. Sci. Found. fel, Scripps Inst. California, 65-66; ASST. PROF. ZOOL, MASSACHUSETTS, AMHERST, 66-, Res. Coun. faculty res. grants, 67, 69. AAAS; Ecol. Soc. Am; Brit. Ecol. Soc; Am. Soc. Zool; Am. Soc. Nat. Population ecology & behavior of benthic marine invertebrates. Address: Dept. of Zoology, University of Massachusetts, Amherst, MA 01002.

EDWARDS, DAVID F(RANKLIN), b. Ironton, Ohio, Mar. 2, 28; m. 54; c. 2. SOLID STATE PHYSICS. A.B, Miami (Ohio), 49; Hanna fel. & M.S, Cincinnati, 53, Laws fel. & Ph.D.(nuclear shell structure), 53. Solid state physicist, Battelle Mem. Inst, 53-55; Willow Run Lab, Michigan, 55-61; Lincoln Lab, Mass. Inst. Tech, 61-65; PROF. physics, COLO. STATE UNIV, 65-69, PHYSICS & ELEC. ENG, 69- Fulbright prof. physics, Univ. Rio Grande do Sul, Brazil, 70-71. Am. Phys. Soc. Solid state spectroscopy; nonlinear optical effects; second harmonic generation; mixing at optical frequencies. Address: Dept. of Physics, Colorado State University, Ft. Collins, CO 80521.

EDWARDS, D(AVID) O(LAF), b. Liverpool, Eng, Apr. 27, 32. PHYSICS. B.A, Oxford, 53, Sr. Hulme scholar, 53-56, M.A. & Ph.D.(physics), 57. Pressed Steel Co. res. fel. PHYSICS, Clarendon Lab, Oxford, 57-58; vis. asst. prof, OHIO STATE UNIV, 58-60, asst. prof, 60-62, assoc. prof, 62-65, PROF, 65- Mem. organizing comt, Int. Conf. Low Temperature Physics, 64. Am. Phys. Soc. Liquid and solid He^3 and He^4; superfluidity; cryogenics. Address: Dept. of Physics, Ohio State University, 174 W. 18th Ave, Columbus, OH 43210.

EDWARDS, DAVID OWEN, b. Buffalo, N.Y, Dec. 15, 30; m. 53; c. 3. CHEMICAL ENGINEERING, MANAGEMENT SCIENCE. B.S, Michigan, 53; Ph.D. (chem. eng), Wisconsin, 61. Instr. chem. eng, Wisconsin, 57-58; res. engr, film dept, E.I. DU PONT DE NEMOURS & CO, 60-69, CONSULT, CENT. SYSTS. & SERV. DEPT, SYSTS. & COMPUT. DIV, 69- U.S.N, 53-56, Lt.(jg). Am. Inst. Chem. Eng. Plastic film manufacture and processing; applications of computer techniques; venture modeling and computer applications. Address: Systems & Computer Division, Farmers Bank 11A7, E.I. du Pont de Nemours & Co, Wilmington, DE 19898.

EDWARDS, DONALD K, b. Richmond, Calif, Oct. 11, 32; m. 55; c. 2. THERMODYNAMICS. B.S, Univ. Calif, Berkeley, 54, fel, 54-55, M.S, 56, Ph.D. (mech. eng), 59. Thermodyn. engr, Lockheed Missile & Space Div, Calif, 58-59; asst. prof. ENG, UNIV. CALIF, LOS ANGELES, 59-63, assoc. prof, 63-68, PROF, 68- Faculty investr, Nat. Sci. Found. grants, 59-71; consult, TRW Systs, 62-71; pres. & chmn. bd, Gier Dunkle Instruments, Inc, Santa Monica, 63-66. Am. Soc. Mech. Eng; Optical Soc. Am; Solar Energy Soc; Am. Inst. Aeronaut. & Astronaut. Heat and mass transfer; thermal radiation; radiant energy transfer between solids and through absorbing, emitting, scattering media; molecular gas radiation; thermal radiation instrumentation; natural convection; radiation and convection. Address: Dept. of Energy & Kinetics, School of Engineering, University of California, Los Angeles, CA 90024.

EDWARDS, D(ONALD) K(EITH), b. Winnipeg, Man, Dec. 28, 30; m. 53; c. 3. ZOOLOGY, ENTOMOLOGY. B.A, British Columbia, 52, M.A, 54; Nat. Res. Coun. Can. stud. & Ph.D.(zool), McGill, 57. Res. scientist, Forest Res. Lab, 57-71; INSTR. BIOL. & HEALTH SCI. PHYSIOL, CAMOSUN COL, 71- Colombo Plan adv. to Panjab Agr. Univ, 66-67. Activity rhythms and physiological ecology of organisms. Address: Camosun College, Victoria, B.C, Can.

EDWARDS, DONALD M(ERVIN), b. Tracy, Minn, Apr. 16, 38; m. 64; c. 3. AGRICULTURAL ENGINEERING. B.S, S.Dak. State, 60, M.S, 61; Ph.D.(agr. eng), Purdue, 66. Mem. coop. educ. prog, Soil Conserv. Serv, U.S. Dept. Agr, 56-61; asst. AGR. ENG, S.Dak. State, 60-61; Purdue, 62-66; assoc. prof, UNIV. NEBR, LINCOLN, 66-70, PROF. & ASST. DEAN COL. ENG. & ARCHIT, 70- Consult. & collab. to several state & fed. agencies & industs. AAAS; Am. Soc. Agr. Eng; Am. Water Works Asn; Am. Soc. Eng. Educ; Nat. Soc. Prof. Eng. Water resources engineering, particularly irrigation; porous media; water pollution; engineering education as related to new teaching techniques and engineering educational programs. Address: Office of the Dean, College of Engineering & Architecture, University of Nebraska, Lincoln, NE 68508.

EDWARDS, DOYLE RAY, b. Dexter, Mo, Dec. 22, 38; m. 59; c. 4. NUCLEAR ENGINEERING. B.S, Mo. Sch. Mines, 59; Atomic Energy Comn. fel, Mass. Inst. Tech, 59-62, S.M, 61, Nat. Sci. Found. fel, 62-63, Sc.D.(nuclear eng), 63. Asst. prof. NUCLEAR ENG, UNIV. MO-ROLLA, 63-64, ASSOC. PROF, 64- Nat. Sci. Found. res. grant, 64-66; Atomic Energy Comn. equip. grant, 65, 66 & 68, traineeship grant, 65-71. AAAS; Am. Nuclear Soc; Am. Inst. Chem. Eng; Nat. Soc. Prof. Eng; Soc. Indust. & Appl. Math. Computer methods in nuclear engineering; fast neutron flux measurements by foil methods; computer simulation of radiation damage; economical recovery of waste heat; heat transfer in fuel bundles. Address: Nuclear Reactor Facility, University of Missouri-Rolla, Rolla, MO 65401.

EDWARDS, ERNEST P(RESTON), b. Landour, India, Sept. 25, 19; U.S. citizen; m. 55. ORNITHOLOGY. B.A, Virginia, 40; M.A, Cornell, 41, Denison fel, 41-42, Ph.D.(ornith), 49. Instr. biol, Kentucky, 49-50; civilian biologist, U.S. Army Chem. Corps, 52-54; asst. prof. biol, Hanover Col, 55-56; assoc. dir, Mus. Natural Hist. Houston, 57-60; PROF. BIOL, Univ. of the Pacific, 60-65; SWEET BRIAR COL, 65- Chem.C, 42-46, 51-52, 1st Lt. Cooper Ornith. Soc; Wilson Ornith Soc; Am. Ornith. Union. Ecology, distribution and taxonomy of tropical birds; ecology of the Blue Ridge Mountains; nomenclature and distribution of birds of the world. Address: Dept. of Biology, Sweet Briar College, Sweet Briar, VA 24595.

EDWARDS, EVAN A, b. East Cleveland, Ohio, Apr. 4, 15; m. 40; c. 4. ELECTRICAL ENGINEERING. B.S, Mass. Inst. Tech, 37, M.S, 38. Div. head eng, Taylor Instrument Co, 38-41; proj. engr, servomechanisms lab, Mass. Inst. Tech, 41-46; chief engr, Kryptar Corp, 46-48; asst. dir. eng, EASTMAN KODAK CO, 48-59, mem. bus. dynamics res. cmn, 59-60, ASST. DIR, FILM SERV. DIV, 60- Inst. Elec. & Electronics Eng; Am. Soc. Mech. Eng; Nat. Soc. Prof. Eng; Soc. Photog. Sci. & Eng. New photographic product development. Address: Film Services Division, Bldg. 56, Eastman Kodak Co, Kodak Park, Rochester, NY 14650.

EDWARDS, F(RANCES) KATHRYN, b. Auburn, Ala, Jan. 20, 23. PEDIATRICS, CARDIOLOGY. M.D, Med. Col, Ga, 50. Lab. technician, 4th Serv. Command Lab, Ga, 42-44; Grady Mem. Hosp, 44-46; intern, Crawford W. Long Hosp, Atlanta, 50-51, resident PEDIAT, 51-53; instr, Emory, 53-56; res. assoc. instr, Cincinnati, 58-59, asst. prof, 59-60; SCH. MED, EMORY UNIV, 60-63, ASSOC. PROF, 63-, FEL. DIAG. RADIOL, 69- U.S. Pub. Health Serv. trainee, 56-57, fel, 69-71. Am. Med. Asn; Am. Acad. Pediat; Am. Col. Cardiol. Cardiovascular physiology and pathology; extracorporeal circulation; congenital heart disease; diagnostic radiology. Address: Dept. of Radiology, Emory University, 80 Butler St, Atlanta, GA 30303.

EDWARDS, F(RANCIS) R(EES), b. Ottawa, Ohio, Mar. 31, 97; m. 31; c. 3. ANIMAL INDUSTRY. B.S, Florida, 18; M.S, Ohio State, 21; Iowa State Col, 23-24; Yale, 43-44. Asst. animal husb. & dairying, Florida, 18; prof, Puerto Rico, 21-23; teaching fellow animal husb, Iowa State College, 23-24; animal husbandman & head dept, exp. sta, Georgia, 21-41; veterans training agr, State Dept. Educ. Fla, 48-52; regional dir. civil defense, 52-53; asst. to dir, agr. exten. serv, 53-54, MANAGING DIR, AGR. SERV, 54- Soil surveyor, Isham Randolph Eng. Co, 19-20; agr. consult, Alliance for Progress, Chile, 63, agr. adv, 63-66; spec. consult. artificial insemination, Fla. Agr. Serv. Marine C, 18; U.S.A, 41-47. AAAS; assoc. Am. Soc. Animal Sci; Am. Agr. Econ. Asn. Animal feeding and breeding; effects of climatic factors on livestock; pasture management and use; effects of oils, fats and chlorophyl in diet; sweet potato and peanut feeding. Address: P.O. Box 1897, Plant City, FL 33566.

EDWARDS, FRANK C, b. Epworth, Iowa, May 7, 22. CHEMISTRY. B.S, Dubuque, 42; Ph.D.(phys. chem), Iowa State, 58. Jr. chemist, Manhattan Dist, Iowa, 44-46, Atomic Energy Cmn, 46-50; teaching & res. fel, Iowa State, 53-55; asst. prof. CHEM, Dubuque, 55-57, assoc. prof. & head dept, 57-61, chmn. sci. div, 59-61; vis. prof, AUSTIN COL, 61-62, PROF, CHMN. DEPT. & CHMN. AREA SCI. & MATH, 62- AAAS; Am. Chem. Soc. Surface chemistry, gravimetric adsorption studies; micro instrumentation, fused silica apparatus. Address: Dept. of Chemistry, Austin College, Sherman, TX 75090.

EDWARDS, FRANK WILLIAM, b. Williamsburg, Iowa, Aug. 10, 05; m. 28; c. 2. CIVIL ENGINEERING. B.S, Iowa, 28; M.S, 30, C.E, 44. Engr, Mgt. & Eng. Corp, Chicago, 28-32; asst. hydraulic invest, bur. agr. eng, U.S. Dept. Agr, Iowa City, 32-33; gauge reader hydraul. res, Waterways Exp. Sta, Miss, 33-34, asst. engr, 36; U.S. Corps Eng, Ohio, 34-35, Los Angeles, 35-36, assoc. engr, New Orleans, 36-39, chief mil. subdiv, N.C, 42-43, design br, Nebr, 45-56; from engr to sr. hydraul. engr, Panama Canal, C.Z, 39-42; asst. and later assoc. prof. eng, Pa. State Col, 43-45; prof. civil eng, Carnegie Inst. Tech, 46-48; dir, Dept, Ill. Inst. Tech, 48-53; mgr. Chicago off, Stanley Eng. Co, 53-64; pres, Limbaugh Eng. & Aerial Surveys, Inc, 64-65; pres. & dir, LIMBAUGH ENGRS, INC, 65-70, CONSULT, 70-; BOVAY ENGRS, INC, 70- Gen. mgr, Centennial Eng, 52; consult, St. Lawrence Seaway Develop. Corp; dir, Consult. Eng. Coun, 66-67, pres. N.Mex. chap, 67-68. Am. Soc. Civil Eng; Am. Soc. Eng. Educ; Am. Soc. Mech. Eng; Nat. Soc. Prof. Eng. Hydraulic model studies and design; direction of engineering design; water resources. Address: 7700 Gladden Ave. N.E, Albuquerque, NM 87110.

EDWARDS, FREDERICK H(ORTON), b. Can, June 23, 15; U.S. citizen; m. 51; c. 2. ELECTRICAL ENGINEERING. B.A.Sc, British Columbia, 49; M.Sc, N.S. Tech. Col, 55; Nat. Sci. Found. fel, Cambridge Math. Lab, 65-66. Design engr. apparatus div, Can. Westinghouse, 49-55; ASSOC. PROF. ELEC. ENG, UNIV. MASS, AMHERST, 55- R.C.A.F, 42-45. Inst. Elec. & Electronics Eng. Switching circuit theory and digital system design; energy conversion. Address: Dept. of Electrical Engineering, University of Massachusetts, Amherst, MA 01002.

EDWARDS, GAYLE D(AMERON), b. Alexandria, La, Mar, 8, 27; m. 55. ORGANIC CHEMISTRY. B.A, La. Col, 47; fel, Texas, 47-50, M.A, 48, Humble Ref. Co. fel, 50-51, Ph.D.(chem), 51. Res. chemist, Pan Am. Ref. Corp, 51-53; supvr, JEFFERSON CHEM. CO, 53-66, MGR. TECH. SERVS, NECHES PLANT, 66- U.S.A, 45-46. Am. Chem. Soc. Petrochemicals; surface active agents; organometallic compounds. Address: Neches Plant, Jefferson Chemical Co, P.O. Box 847, Port Neches, TX 77651.

EDWARDS, GEORGE, b. Glasgow, Scotland, June 28, 18; nat; m. 44; c. 3. CHEMISTRY. B.Sc, Glasgow, 41, Ph.D.(chem), 46. Exp. officer, chem. eng, S.W. Scotland br, Woolwich Arsenal, 41-46; lectr, Royal Col. Sci. & Tech, Scotland, 46-52; res. assoc. chem, Enrico Fermi Inst. Nuclear Studies, Univ. Chicago, 52-55; group leader, geol. age measurement, SHELL DEVELOP. CO, 55-64, MGR, ANAL. CHEM, 64- Sir James Bielby prize, 43. Geochem. Soc; Soc. Chem. Indust; Brit. Inst. Chem. Eng. Stable isotope absolute geologic age measurement; cosmic abundance of elements; analytical chemistry. Address: 3100 Mid Lane, Houston, TX 77027.

EDWARDS, GEORGE G(OODWIN), b. Albert Lea, Minn, Nov. 18, 14; m. 36; c. 2. FLUID MECHANICS, AERODYNAMICS. B.S, Univ. Minn, Minneapolis, 39; Stanford Univ, 58-60. Aeronaut. engr. wind tunnel design, NACA Ames Aeronaut. Lab, 40-45, aeronaut. res. scientist, 45-62, technol. utilization off, NASA AMES RES. CTR, 62-71, CHIEF FLIGHT PROGS. SUPPORT OFF, 71- U.S.N.R, 36-37. Assoc. fel. Am. Inst. Aeronaut. & Astronaut. Airflow about wings and bodies; performance, stability, and control of airplane configurations; fundamental investigations for space vehicles, including wingless, lifting-body types having airplane-like capabilities, including horizontal landing. Address: NASA Ames Research Center, Moffett Field, CA 94035.

EDWARDS, GERALD A(LONZO), b. Henderson, N.C, Nov. 22, 21; m. 51; c. 3. PHYSICAL CHEMISTRY. B.S, N.C. Col, 41; Ph.D.(chem), Buffalo, 51. Chemist, Lake Ontario Ord. Works, 42-43; chem. operator, Hooker Electrochem. Co, 43-45; chemist, Bell Aircraft Corp, 45-47; asst, Buffalo, 47-50; teacher, dept. chem, N.C. Col, 50-51; res. assoc, Carver Found. & asst. prof. CHEM, Tuskegee Inst, 51-55, assoc. prof, 55-56; PROF. & CHMN. DEPT, A&T STATE UNIV. N.C, 56-, CHMN, DIV. NATURAL SCI. & MATH, 68- Consult, Teachers Col, Columbia-U.S. Agency Int. Develop, prog. summer insts, India, 64, 65; phys. sci, Ohio State Univ-Agency Int. Develop. proj, Regional Col. Educ, Mysore, India, 67-68; assoc. prog. dir, Nat. Sci. Found. Am. Chem. Soc. Physical chemistry of polymers; copolymerization; electrical conductance; transport of amino acids. Address: 2711 McConnell Rd, Greensboro, NC 27401.

EDWARDS, GERALD ELMO, b. Gretna, Va, Sept. 17, 42; m. 69. PLANT SCIENCE & PHYSIOLOGY. B.S, Va. Polytech, 65; M.S, Illinois, 66; Nat. Sci. Found. traineeship & Ph.D.(plant sci), California, Riverside, 69. Fel. biochem, Univ. Ga, 69-71; ASST. PROF. HORT, UNIV. WIS, MADISON, 71- Am. Soc. Plant Physiol; Weed Sci. Soc. Am. Photosynthesis; biological energetics. Address: Dept. of Horticulture, University of Wisconsin, Madison, WI 53706.

EDWARDS, HARDY MALCOLM, JR, b. Ruston, La, Nov. 16, 29; m. 54; c. 1. NUTRITION, BIOCHEMISTRY. B.S.A, Southwest. La. Inst, 49; M.S.A, Florida, 50; Ph.D.(nutrit. biochem), Cornell, 53. Res. fel. animal nutrit, Florida, 49-50; res. asst. & nutrit. chemist, Cornell, 50-53; res. biochemist, Int. Minerals & Chem. Corp, 55-56, sr. res. biochemist, 56-57; asst. prof. NUTRIT. BIOCHEM, GEORGIA, 57-62, assoc. prof, 62-66, PROF, 66- Summer res. participant, Oak Ridge Inst. Nuclear Studies, 58; res. career develop. award, Nat. Insts. Health, 63-72; res. assoc, dept. physiol. chem, Univ. Lund, 64-65; Guggenheim Mem. Fel. & vis. prof, Tours, France, Cambridge, Eng. & Rowett Inst, Aberdeen, Scotland. Poultry Nutrit. Res. Award, Am. Feed Mfg. Asn, 62. Am. Soc. Animal Sci; Poultry Sci. Asn; Am. Inst. Nutrit; Soc. Exp. Biol. & Med. Lipid nutrition of aves; mechanism of divalent ion adsorption. Address: Dept. of Poultry Sciences, University of Georgia, Athens, GA 30601.

EDWARDS, H(AROLD) HERBERT, b. Milford, Mich, Oct. 31, 37; m. 62; c. 2. PLANT PHYSIOLOGY & BIOCHEMISTRY. B.A, Albion Col, 60; M.S, Wisconsin, 62, Ph.D.(bot), 65. Wis. Alumni res. fel, Wisconsin, 65; Nat. Insts. Health fel, Nebraska, 65-67; ASST. PROF. BIOL. SCI, WEST. ILL. UNIV, 67- Plant physiology and biochemistry of the obligate parasite-host complex of powdery mildewed barley. Address: Dept. of Biology, Western Illinois University, Macomb, IL 61455.

EDWARDS, HARRY W(ALLACE), b. Syracuse, N.Y, Oct. 6, 39; m. 66; c. 1. PHYSICAL CHEMISTRY. B.S, Nevada, 62; Gen. Elec. Found. fel, Arizona, 65-66, Ph.D.(phys. chem), 66. Lab. technician, Stauffer Chem. Co, summers 58, 59, 60; asst. chem, Am. Potash & Chem. Corp, summers 61, 62; asst. prof. MECH. ENG, COLO. STATE UNIV, 66-70, ASSOC. PROF, 70- Nat. Sci. Found. award, Lehigh, summer 67; res. grants, Nat. Sci. Found, 67-, Pub. Serv. Co. Colo, 67-70, Environ. Protection Agency, 70- Am.

Chem. Soc. Surface chemistry; physical chemistry of atmospheric phenomena. Address: Dept. of Mechanical Engineering, Colorado State University, Ft. Collins, CO 80521.

EDWARDS, HENRY L(EITNER), b. Micanopy, Fla, Mar. 12, 02; m. 23, 54. ANALYTICAL CHEMISTRY. B.S, Florida, 24; M.S, North Carolina, 34, Ph.D.(chem), 37. Sci. teacher, pub. sch, Fla, 24-26, prin, 26-36; instr. CHEM, Ga. Tech, 37-43, asst. prof, 43-46, assoc. prof, 46-51; PROF, GA. INST. TECHNOL, 51- Res. engr, chem. & metal, Lockheed Aircraft Corp, 54-55; mem. staff, Lockheed-Ga. Co, summers, 51-66. Am. Chem. Soc. Use of organic reagents in qualitative inorganic analysis. Address: Dept. of Chemistry, Georgia Institute of Technology, Atlanta, GA 30332.

EDWARDS, H(ERBERT) M(ARTELL), b. Brockville, Ont, Dec. 16, 21; m. 45; c. 3. CIVIL ENGINEERING. B.Sc, Queen's (Can), 44; M.S.C.E, Purdue, 54. Design engr. aircraft, Can. Ltd, 44; Douglas Aircraft, Inc, Calif, 44-45; stress analyst & designer, Can. Ltd, 45-46; lectr. CIVIL ENG, QUEEN'S UNIV.(ONT), 46-53, asst. prof, 54-57, assoc. prof, 57-67, PROF, 67-, ASSOC. DEAN, FACULTY APPL. SCI, 71- Assoc. dir, Ont. Joint Hwy. Res. Prog, 56- Consult, 55- Assoc. Hwy. Res. Bd; assoc. mem. Inst. Traffic Eng; Eng. Inst. Can. Traffic planning; mathematical explorations for traffic movements; soils engineering; highway pavement design. Address: Ellis Hall, Queen's University, Kingston, Ont, Can.

EDWARDS, HOWARD D(AWSON), b. Athens, Ga, Dec. 11, 23; m. 46; c. 4. AEROSPACE ENGINEERING. B.S, Georgia, 44; res. fel, Duke, 46-49, Ph.D.(physics), 50. Atmospheric physicist & chief, atmospheric composition sect, Air Force Cambridge Res. Labs, 49-51, Atmospheric Energy Br, 51-56; opers. res. scientist, Lockheed Aircraft, 56-59; res. assoc. prof. physics, GA. INST. TECHNOL, 59-64, assoc. prof. AEROSPACE ENG, 64-65, PROF, 65-; PRES, SYSTS. INSTRUMENTS RES. INC, 70- U.S.A, 44-46. Upper atmosphere research; data systems design and manufacture. Address: Systems Instruments Research Inc, 331 Luckie St, Atlanta, GA 30313.

EDWARDS, J. GORDON, b. Wilmington, Ohio, Aug. 24, 19; m. 46; c. 1. ENTOMOLOGY, SYSTEMATIC ZOOLOGY. B.S, Butler, 42; M.Sc, Ohio State, 46, Ph.D.(entomol), 49. Instr. entomol. & zool, SAN JOSE STATE COL, 49-52, asst. prof. ENTOMOL, 52-55, assoc. prof, 55-59, PROF, 59- Med.C, U.S.A, 42-45. Soc. Syst. Zool; Entom. Soc. Am; Nat. Audubon Soc. Coleoptera biology and taxonomy; high altitude biology; medical entomology; subspeciation; chemical pesticides and the environment. Address: Dept. of Biology, San Jose State College, San Jose, CA 95114.

EDWARDS, JAMES W(ESLEY), b. Evansville, Ind, Sept. 1, 38; m. 61; c. 1. ZOOLOGY, GENETICS. A.B, Evansville Col, 60; Nat. Defense Ed. Act fel, Utah State, 60-63, M.S, 62, Nat. Insts. Health fel, 63-64, Ph.D.(zool), 64. Asst. prof. BIOL, Saint Francis Col.(Pa), 64-65, assoc. prof, SALEM COL, 65-69, PROF, 69-, CHMN. DEPT, 65- AAAS; Genetics Soc. Am. Genetics of abnormal head development in Drosophila melanogaster, with special reference to eyelessness. Address: Dept. of Biology, Salem College, Winston-Salem, NC 27108.

EDWARDS, JESSE EFREM, b. Hyde Park, Mass, July 14, 11; m. 52; c. 2. PATHOLOGY. B.S, Tufts Col, 32, M.D, 35. Intern, Albany Hosp, N.Y, 36-37; res. path, Mallory inst. path, Boston City Hosp, 35-36, asst, 37-40, assoc. pathologist, 41-53; fel, Nat. Cancer Inst, 40-42; from asst. prof. to prof. path. anat, Mayo Found, UNIV. MINN, ST. PAUL, 46-60, CLIN. PROF. PATH, MED. SCH. & PROF. GRAD. SCH, 60-; DIR. LABS, CHARLES T. MILLER HOSP, 60- Instr. sch. med, Boston Univ, 38; Tufts Col, 39-40. Consult, Wash. Home Incurables, 40-42; Mayo Clin, 46-60; Surgeon Gen, Dept. Army; Hennepin County Hosp, Minneapolis, 64-; dept. med, Minneapolis Vet. Hosp, 66-; St-Paul Ramsey Hosp, 69- Distinguished Serv. award, Mod. Med, 64. Med.C, A.U.S, 46-60, Lt. Col.(Ret). Affiliate fel. Am. Acad. Pediat; fel. Am. Med. Asn; Am. Asn. Path. & Bact; Am. Soc. Exp. Path; fel. Col. Am. Path; Am. Heart Asn.(pres, 67-68); Int. Acad. Path.(pres). Congenital anomalies of heart and great vessels; pathology of cardiovascular diseases, congenital and acquired; induction of carcinoma in experimental animals; pathology of experimental and human cancer. Address: Charles T. Miller Hospital, St. Paul, MN 55102.

EDWARDS, JOHN AUERT, b. Middletown, N.Y, July 2, 30; m. 51; c. 2. HEAT TRANSFER, FLUID MECHANICS. B.S.M.E, N.C. State, 55, M.S, 57; Ph.D (mech. eng), Purdue, 62. Engr, Texaco, Inc, 57-58; res. assoc. heat transfer, Purdue, 58-61; assoc. prof. eng. mech, N.C. STATE UNIV, 62-70, PROF. ENG. MECH. & MARINE SCI, 70- Nat. Sci. Found. grants, 64-66; consult, Oak Ridge Nat. Lab, 66-68; Atomic Energy Comn. res. contract, 69- U.S.A, 51-53. Am. Soc. Eng. Educ; Am. Soc. Mech. Eng. Liquid metals lubrication; heat transfer with boiling alkali metals and dropwise condensation; fuels research; free convection and radiative heat transfer; turbulent lubrication; secondary turbulent flows; turbulent jets; fluidics. Address: Dept. of Engineering Mechanics, North Carolina State University, Raleigh, NC 27607.

EDWARDS, JOHN B, b. Brooklyn, N.Y, July 6, 39. CHEMICAL ENGINEERING. B.Ch.E, Pratt Inst, 61; M.S.E, Michigan, 62, M.S, 64, Ph.D.(chem. eng), 66. Res. asst. thermodyn, Michigan, 61-63, liquid metal res, 63-66; VEHICLE EMISSIONS SPECIALIST, CHRYSLER CORP, 66- Summers, engr, Interchem. Corp, 61, Babcock & Wilcox Corp, 63; adj. prof, dept. chem. eng, Univ. Detroit, 69- Electrochem. Soc; Soc. Automotive Eng; Am. Inst. Chem. Eng. Air pollution; liquid metal fuel cells; diffusion in liquid metals; thermodynamics. Address: 1809 Independence, Apt. 16, Ann Arbor, MI 48104.

EDWARDS, JOHN C, b. Petersburg, Va, Nov. 10, 13; m. 40; c. 4. ANALYTICAL CHEMISTRY. B.S, Richmond, 36. Asst. chemist, Solvay Process Co, Va, 36-41; assoc. chemist, Navy Dept, U.S. Govt, 41-46; anal. res. chemist, E.I. DU PONT DE NEMOURS & CO, 47-50, supvr. process control labs, MAY PLANT, 50-57, anal. res. dir, 57-66, DIR. ENVIRON. CONTROL, 66- Co-analyst, Nat. Bur. Standards. Am. Chem. Soc. Analytical research development of methods and techniques to identify, characterize and process acrylic fibers and related materials; application of instrumentation for analytical research; coordinator programs air and water pollution abatement. Address: 2000 Forest Dr, Camden, SC 29020.

EDWARDS, JOHN D, b. Hackensack, N.J, June 17, 25; m. 46; c. 5. PETROLEUM GEOLOGY. B.S, Cornell, 46; Ph.D.(geol), Columbia, 52. Field geologist, U.S. Geol. Surv, 49-50; geologist, special invests, SHELL OIL CO, 50-55, dist. geologist, 55-62, staff geologist, 62, div. explor. mgr, 62-64, area explor. mgr, 64-67, chief geologist, 67-68, asst. to v.pres. explor, 68-70, SR. STAFF GEOLOGIST, INT. VENTURES, 70- Lectr, Columbia Univ, 50. U.S.N.R, 43-46, Ens. AAAS; Geol. Soc. Am; Am. Inst. Mining, Metall. & Petrol. Eng; Am. Asn. Petrol. Geol. Stratigraphy; structural geology; petroleum exploration. Address: Shell Oil Co, Box 2463, 1 Shell Plaza, Houston, TX 77002.

EDWARDS, JOHN E(LZA), b. Rio Grande, Ohio, Jan. 23, 08; m. 36. PHYSICS. B.S, Ohio Univ, 30, A.M, 32; Univ. Chicago, summer 35; Ph.D.(physics), Ohio State Univ, 47. From instr. to assoc. prof. to PROF. PHYSICS, OHIO UNIV, 33-, chmn. dept. & distinguished prof. award, 62. Am. Phys. Soc; Am. Asn. Physics Teachers. X-rays; radioactivity; x-rays from radioactive sources. Address: Dept. of Physics, Ohio University, Athens, OH 45701.

EDWARDS, JOHN L(ESLIE), b. Grenola, Kans, Feb. 25, 19; m. 54; c. 2. GEOLOGY. B.S, Oklahoma, 41; M.A, Columbia, 53. Geologist, Carter Oil Co, 41-42, 46; Creole Petrol. Corp, 47-48; instr. geol, Oklahoma, 49; lectr, Columbia, 51-53; geologist, Am. Overseas Petrol. Corp, 53-60; ASST. PROF. PHYSICS, PATERSON STATE COL, 61- U.S.A.A.F, 42-46, Capt. Seismol. Soc. Am; Am. Asn. Petrol. Geol; Geol. Soc. Am; Am. Geophys. Union. Structural geology. Address: 10 Juniper Rd, Pines Lakes, Wayne, NJ 07470.

EDWARDS, JOHN O(ELHAF), b. Sewickley, Pa, July 21, 22; m. 50; c. 2. INORGANIC CHEMISTRY. A.B, Colgate Univ, 47; Inst. Paper Chem, Lawrence Col, 47-48; Ph.D.(chem), Univ. Wis, 51. Res. assoc. chem, Cornell Univ, 50-51; chemist, E.I. du Pont de Nemours & Co, 52; instr. CHEM, BROWN UNIV, 52-53, asst. prof, 53-56, assoc. prof, 56-63, PROF, 63- Consult, FMC Corp, 64-; fel, John Simon Guggenheim Mem. Found, 67-68. U.S.M.C, 42-45, T/Sgt. AAAS; Am. Chem. Soc. Chemistry of oxoanions and peroxides; kinetics and mechanisms of reactions. Address: Dept. of Chemistry, Brown University, Providence, RI 02912.

EDWARDS, JOHN R, b. Streator, Ill, Feb. 27, 37; m. 61; c. 3. BIOCHEMISTRY. B.S, Ill. Wesleyan Univ, 59; Ph.D.(biochem), Univ. Ill, 64. Nat. Insts. Health fel. microbiol, sch. med, Tufts Univ, 64-66; ASST. PROF, DEPT. CHEM, VILLANOVA UNIV, 66- Streptoccoccal L-forms; rhamnose polysaccharides; mode of action of penicillin on Staphylococcus; structure and synthesis of dextran from cariogenic Streptococcus. Address: Dept. of Chemistry, Villanova University, Villanova, PA 19085.

EDWARDS, JOHN ROY, b. Bingham Canyon, Utah, Oct. 5, 43; m. 63; c. 2. MATHEMATICS. B.A, Univ. Utah, 65, Nat. Defense Educ. Act fel, 65-68, Ph.D.(math), 68. ASST. PROF. MATH, UTAH STATE UNIV, 69- U.S.A, 70-72, Capt. Am. Math. Soc. Relationships between summation methods and integration theory; classical-type integral representations of linear operators in abstract settings; development and exploitation of new integral tools such as the v-integral by which to represent linear transformations in settings not addressed by ordinary integral techniques. Address: Dept. of Mathematics, Utah State University, Logan, UT 84321.

EDWARDS, JOHN S, b. Auckland, N.Z, Nov. 25, 31; m. 57; c. 4. ENTOMOLOGY. B.Sc, Auckland, 54, M.Sc, 56; Ph.D.(entom), Cambridge, 60. Sci. officer insect physiol, sch. agr, Cambridge, 60-61; res. assoc, Western Reserve, 61-62, asst. prof. biol, 62-67; assoc. prof. ZOOL, UNIV. WASH, 67-70, PROF, 70- Am. Soc. Zool; Soc. Develop. Biol; Brit. Soc. Exp. Biol; Royal Entom. Soc. Neurobiology; insect nervous system, development, aging and regeneration. Address: Dept. of Zoology, University of Washington, Seattle, WA 98105.

EDWARD, J(OHN) T(HOMAS), b. London, Eng, Mar. 23, 19; Can. citizen; m. 53; c. 3. ORGANIC CHEMISTRY. B.Sc, McGill, 39, Ph.D.(org. chem), 42; Iowa State Col, 42-43; D.Phil, Oxford, 49; M.A, Trinity Col. Dublin, 55, Sc.D, 71. Asst. res. scientist, Nat. Res. Coun. Can, 43-45; Can. Armaments Res. & Develop. Estab, Que, 45-46; lectr. CHEM, Manitoba, 46-47; Imp. Chem. Industs. res. fel, Birmingham, 49-52; lectr, Trinity Col, Dublin, 52-56; McGILL UNIV, 56-57, asst. prof, 57-62; assoc. prof, 62-66, PROF, 66- Exhib. of 1851 sci. scholar, 46-49. Am. Chem. Soc; Brit. Chem. Soc; fel. Royal Soc. Can; fel. Chem. Inst. Can. Explosives; heterocyclic compounds; strychnine; terpenes; steroids; paper electrophoresis; amino acids; reaction mechanisms and stereochemistry; acidity functions. Address: Dept. of Chemistry, P.O. Box 6070, McGill University, Montreal 101, Que, Can.

EDWARDS, J(OSEPH) D, JR, b. Alexandria, La, Nov. 25, 24; m. 60. ORGANIC CHEMISTRY. B.S, La. Col, 44; M.A, Texas, 48, Ph.D.(chem), 50. Chemist, Fercleve Corp, Tenn, 44; U.S. Naval Res. Lab, 45; fel, Texas, 46-50; asst. prof. chem, col. med, Baylor, 51-58; assoc. prof, Clemson, 59; sr. res. chemist, Monsanto Chem. Co, Tex, 59-60; assoc. prof. CHEM, Lamar State Col, 60-64, prof, 65-67; PROF. & HEAD DEPT, UNIV. SOUTHWEST. LA, 67- Fel, Illinois, 50-51; prin. scientist, res. div, U.S. Vet. Admin. Hosp, Houston, 51-58. Am. Chem. Soc; Brit. Chem. Soc. Alkaloids; plant pigments; synthetic organic chemistry. Address: Dept. of Chemistry, University of Southwestern Louisiana, Lafayette, LA 70501.

EDWARDS, JOSHUA LEROY, b. Jasper, Fla, Aug. 9, 18; m. 53; c. 3. PATHOLOGY, IMMUNOLOGY. B.S, Florida, 39; M.D, Tulane, 49. Intern, Baptist Hosp, New Orleans, La, 43-44; res, Touro Infirmary, 48-49; PATH, N.E. Deaconess Hosp, Boston, Mass, 49-50, chief res, 50-51; instr, Duke, 51-52, assoc. 52-53; asst, Rockefeller Inst, 53-54; prof. & chmn. dept, med. col, Univ. Fla, 55-67; prof. & dir. combined degree prog. med. sci, IND. UNIV, Bloomington, 67-69, PROF. & CHMN. DEPT, MED. CTR, INDIANAPOLIS, 69- Instr, Harvard, 49-51. Med.C, 44-46, Capt. Radiation pathology; cellular distribution of antigens; growth and development of cells and tissues; dynamics of antibody formation; cytology. Address: Indiana University Medical Center, 158 Medical Science Bldg, 1100 W. Michigan St, Indianapolis, IN 46202.

EDWARDS, KENNETH WARD, b. Ann Arbor, Mich, Jan. 18, 33; m. 56; c. 2. ANALYTICAL & PHYSICAL CHEMISTRY. B.S, Michigan, 54; M.A, Dartmouth Col, 56; Ph.D.(kinetics, calorimetry), Colorado, 63. Instr. phys. chem, Colo. Sch. Mines, 57-60; res. chemist, U.S. Geol. Surv, 61-66; ASST. PROF. ANAL. & RADIOCHEM, COLO. SCH. MINES, 66- Chmn. bd. dirs, Natural Resources Lab, Inc. Am. Chem. Soc. Analysis of trace concentrations of radionuclides in water and the physical chemistry and geochemistry of natural radionuclides in water, especially kinetics and mechanisms of solution, transport, and deposition; analytical and physical chemistry of trace metals and metalloids in the environment, especially problems in geochemical and pollution analysis and pollution abatement. Address: Dept. of Chemistry, Colorado School of Mines, Golden, CO 80401.

EDWARDS, KENNETH W(ESTBROOK), b. Lansing, Mich, July 22, 34; m. 60; c. 2. ELEMENTARY PARTICLE PHYSICS. B.S.E, Michigan, 56; Ph.D. (physics), Princeton, 61. Asst. PHYSICS, eng. res. inst, Michigan, 54-56; Princeton, 56-61, instr, 61; res. assoc, Iowa, 61-63, asst. prof, 63-67; ASSOC. PROF, CARLETON UNIV, 67- Summers, asst, Oak Ridge Nat. Lab, 56, Los Alamos Nat. Lab, 57, Brookhaven Nat. Lab, 59, res. assoc, Lawrence Radiation Lab, California, 61, mem. summer theoret. inst, Wisconsin, 64. Am. Phys. Soc. Scattering theory; elementary particle physics, particularly strong interaction cross sections. Address: Dept. of Physics, Carleton University, Ottawa, Ont, K1S 5B6, Can.

EDWARDS, LAWRENCE J(AY), b. Cornwall, N.Y, July 13, 40; m. 62; c. 3. PHYSIOLOGY, BIOCHEMISTRY. B.S, State Univ. N.Y. Albany, 62; N.Y. State Regents fels, Cornell, 63 & 64, M.S, 65, Ph.D.(insect physiol), 67. Res. asst. insect physiol, Cornell, 63-67; res. entomologist, U.S. Dept. Agr, Ga, 67-68; res. assoc. biochem, O'Donnell Res. Lab, N.Y, 68; ASST. PROF. INSECT PHYSIOL, TOXICOL, & APICULT, UNIV. MASS, AMHERST, 68- N.Y. Acad. Sci; Entom. Soc. Am. Anesthesia; carbon dioxide; carbonic anhydrase; succinic dehydrogenase; insect respiration and metabolism; endocrine organs; mode of action of naturally occurring biologically active compounds. Address: Dept. of Entomology, University of Massachusetts, Amherst, MA 01002.

EDWARDS, LAWRENCE K(NIGHT), b. Delaware, Ohio, July 10, 19; m. 45; c. 2. SYSTEMS ENGINEERING. A.B, Miami (Ohio), 40; Cornell, 41. Supvr. eng, Curtiss-Wright Corp, N.Y, 40-43; mgr. airplane & missile eng, McDonnell Aircraft Corp, Mo, 43-56; systs. eng, Polaris Prog, Lockheed Aircraft Corp, Calif, 56-59, vehicle develop, Agena Prog, 59-62, asst. chief engr, 62-65, mgr. adv. spacecraft progs, 66; pres, Tube Transit Corp, 67-70; SR. STAFF ENGR, SPACE SYSTS. DIV, LOCKHEED MISSILES & SPACE CO, 70- Assoc. fel. Am. Inst. Aeronaut. & Astronaut. Systems engineering; satellites; spacecraft; payloads; large structures; guidance and controls; dynamics; urban transportation and planning. Address: 301 Santa Rita Ave, Palo Alto, CA 94301.

EDWARDS, LEON ROGER, b. New Ulm, Minn, May 2, 40; m. 62; c. 2. SOLID STATE PHYSICS. B.Phys, Minnesota, 62; Ph.D.(physics), Iowa State, 67. STAFF MEM, orgn. 5131, SANDIA CORP, 67-69, PHYSICS SOLIDS RES, DIV, 5132, 69- Am. Phys. Soc. Low temperature physics; transport properties of rare earth metals and dilute alloys; equation of state. Address: Division 5132, Sandia Corp, Albuquerque, NM 87115.

EDWARDS, LESLIE E(RROLL), b. Montesano, Wash, Dec. 26, 14; m. 46; c. 3. PHYSIOLOGY. B.S, State Col. Wash, 37, M.S, 39; Ph.D.(physiol), Rochester, 44. Instr. PHYSIOL, Rochester, 43-46; Fels Res. Found, 46-47; assoc. MED. COL. OF VA, 47-49, asst. prof, 49-51, assoc. prof, 51-64, PROF, 64- AAAS; Am. Physiol. Soc; Soc. Gen. Physiol; Am. Chem. Soc. Lowering of ionic barriers in tissue; intermediary metabolism of carbohydrate and fat; biological value of proteins; gastric secretion; pancreatic function; muscle metabolism. Address: Dept. of Physiology, Medical College of Virginia, Health Sciences Division, Virginia Commonwealth University, Richmond, VA 23219.

EDWARDS, LEWIS HIRAM, b. Frederick, Okla, Nov. 6, 38; m. 60; c. 2. AGRONOMY, GENETICS. B.S, Okla. State, 61; Ph.D.(agron), N.Dak. State, 65. Res. geneticist, agr. res. serv, U.S. Dept. Agr, 65-67; asst. prof. GENETICS, OKLA. STATE UNIV, 67-70, ASSOC. PROF, 70-, GENETICIST-PLANT BREEDER, 67- Am. Soc. Agron; Crop Sci. Soc. Am. Genetic research in small grains, including mutation studies, quantitative genetic studies; barley and triticale breeding. Address: Dept. of Agronomy, Oklahoma State University, Stillwater, OK 74074.

EDWARDS, LOUIS LAIRD, JR, b. Bozeman, Mont, June 20, 36; m. 58; c. 2. CHEMICAL ENGINEERING. B.Ch.E, Rensselaer Polytech, 58; M.Ch.E, Delaware, 60; Ph.D.(chem. eng), Idaho, 66. Instr. CHEM. ENG, Idaho, 61-64, asst. prof, 64-66; Ford Found. resident, Union Carbide Corp, 66-67; ASSOC. PROF, UNIV. IDAHO, 67- Consult, Union Carbide Corp, 67- U.S.N. Civil Eng.C, 59-61, Lt. Am. Inst. Chem. Eng; Am. Soc. Eng. Educ. Mathematical modeling and optimization; design of polymerization reactors; ozone technology. Address: Dept. of Chemical Engineering, University of Idaho, Moscow, ID 83843.

EDWARDS, LYDIA B(OWMAN), b. Berkeley, Calif, June 3, 05. MEDICINE. Ecole Superieure, Brussels, 20-21; Rome, 22-23; B.A, Radcliffe Col, 27; Paris, 28; M.D, Hopkins, 32. Intern med, Hopkins Hosp, 32-33, pediat, 34-35, asst. res. pediat, 35-37, dir. pediat, outpatient dept, 37-38, from fel. to asst. prof. pediat. & prev. med, 39-43; asst. res. med, Strong Mem. Hosp, 33-34; with U.S. Pub. Health Serv, 43, Yugoslav mission, UN Relief & Rehab. Admin, 44-46; tuberc. res. off, WHO, 48-55; MED. DIR, TUBERC. PROG, U.S. PUB. HEALTH SERV, 55- Am. Thoracic Soc. Diagnostic skin testing of tuberculosis. Address: U.S. Public Health Service, 5600 Fishers Lane, Room 13A-44, Rockville, MD 20852.

EDWARDS, McIVER W(ILLIAMSON), JR, b. Darlington, S.C, Aug. 24, 35; m. 63; c. 2. PHYSIOLOGY, ANESTHESIA. B.S, Mass. Inst. Tech, 56; M.D, Pennsylvania, 62. Intern & instr. med, Johns Hopkins Hosp, 62-63; instr. PHYSIOL, MED. SCH, UNIV. PA, 63-64, assoc, 64-65, 67-68, ASST. PROF, 68-, ANESTHESIA, 71-, resident, 69-71. Pa. Plan fel, Iniv. Pa, 63-65, 67-68; U.S. Pub. Health Serv. fel, Middlesex Hosp. Med. Sch, Eng. 65-67. U.S.A, 56-58, 1st Lt. AAAS; Am. Soc. Anesthesiol. Respiratory physiology; neurophysiology; control of breathing; effects of anesthesia on respiration. Address: Depts. of Physiology & Anesthesia, University of Pennsylvania Medical School, B-403 Richards Bldg, Philadelphia, PA 19104.

EDWARDS, MARTIN A(RTHUR), b. Chautauqua, Kans, Mar. 22, 05; m. 24; c. 2. ELECTRICAL ENGINEERING. B.S.E.E, Kans. State Col, 28, B.S.M.E, 29, hon. M.E, 34, hon. D.Sc, 46. Asst. engr. in charge control systs. div, gen. eng. & consult. lab, GEN. ELEC. CO, 29-50, managing engr, gen. eng. lab, 50-52, x-ray dept, 52-60, mgr. adv. prod. planning oper, 60-69, CONSULT. SCIENTIST, ELEC. COMPONENTS DIV, 69- Asst. plant engr, Nat. Ref. Co. Kans. Coffin Award, 34, 40, 46. AAAS; fel. Inst. Elec. & Electronics Eng; Am. Ord. Asn. Servo systems; underwater ordnance; gas turbines; electrical control systems; x-ray equipment; electronic components. Address: General Electric Co, 1 River Rd, Schenectady, NY 12305.

EDWARDS, MARTIN H(ASSALL), b. St. Annes-on-Sea, England, Nov. 10, 27; nat. Can; m. 49; c. 2. PHYSICS. B.A, British Columbia, 49, M.A, 51; Ph.D.(physics), Toronto, 53. Res. assoc, Toronto, 53-54; asst. prof. PHYSICS, ROYAL MIL. COL, CAN, 54-56, assoc. prof, 56-61, PROF, 61- Res. assoc, Stanford, 64-65; Ont. Royal Comnr. ducks & pesticides, 69-70. Fel. Am. Phys. Soc; Am. Asn. Physics Teachers; Can. Asn. Physicists; Asn. Sci, Eng. & Technol. Community Can. Low temperature physics; low temperature properties of helium liquid and vapor; expansion coefficient; refractive index and density; lambda point and critical point; environmental impact of technology. Address: Dept. of Physics, Royal Military College, Kingston, Ont, Can.

EDWARDS, MARVIN B(ECTON), b. Forney, Tex, Nov. 22, 23; m. 46; c. 5. ORGANIC CHEMISTRY. B.S, Texas, 48, M.A, 50, Ph.D.(chem), 54. RES. CHEMIST, TEX. EASTMAN CO, 53-; Biochem. Inst. Tex, 51-53. U.S.A.A.F, 42-45. Am. Chem. Soc. Organic synthesis; polyolefins; synthetic resins. Address: Development Lab, Texas Eastman Co, Box 7444, Longview, TX 75601.

EDWARDS, MERRILL A(RTHUR), b. Amherst, N.S, May 12, 32; m. 56; c. 2. PHYSICS, BIOPHYSICS. B.Sc, New Brunswick, 53; Nat. Res. Coun. Can. bursar, Western Ontario, 53-54, M.Sc, 56, Ph.D, 60. ASSOC. PROF. PHYSICS, UNIV. N.B, 59- Nat. Res. Coun. Overseas fel, 66-67. R.C.A.F.R, 53- Biophys. Soc; Can. Asn. Physicists. Geophysics; peripheral circulation; use of radioactive clearance methods in determining the circulation; spectroscopy; surface physics of microspheres. Address: Dept. of Physics, University of New Brunswick, Fredericton, N.B, Can.

EDWARDS, MILES J(OHN), b. Portland, Ore, 1929; m. 56; c. 4. MEDICINE. B.A, Willamette, 51; M.S. & M.D, Oregon, 56. Nat. Insts. Health fel, cardiovasc. res. inst, med. center, California, San Francisco, 63-64; asst. prof. MED, MED. SCH, UNIV. ORE, 64-68, assoc. prof, 68-70, PROF. & CHIEF, DIV. CHEST DISEASES, 70- Dipl, Am. Bd. Internal Med, 64, Am. Bd. Pulmonary Diseases, 69. Med.C, U.S.A, 61-62, Capt. AAAS; Am. Thoracic Soc. Respiratory physiology, alterations in blood and oxygen affinity with various types of hypoxia. Address: Dept. of Medicine, University of Oregon Medical School, Portland, OR 97201.

EDWARDS, NANCY C(LAIRE), b. Montgomery, Ala, Oct. 16, 36. EMBRYOLOGY, DEVELOPMENTAL BIOLOGY. B.A, Agnes Scott Col, 58; Nat. Sci. Found. scholar, Bermuda, 62; univ. fels, Univ. N.C, Chapel Hill, 64 & 66, M.A, 66, Nat. Sci. Found. traineeship, 66-68, Ph.D.(zool), 71. Asst. dir. pub. rels. & develop, Agnes Scott Col, 58-59, dir. publicity, 59-61; instr. BIOL, UNIV. N.C, CHARLOTTE, 68-71, ASST. PROF, 71- AAAS; Am. Soc. Zool; Soc. Develop. Biol. Macromolecular patterns in coelenterate development; amphibian regeneration. Address: Dept. of Biology, University of North Carolina at Charlotte, Charlotte, NC 28213.

EDWARDS, O(GDEN) F(RAZELLE), b. Leslie, Mich, Apr. 26, 09; m. 32; c. 2. BACTERIOLOGY. B.S, Mich. State Col, 31, M.S, 33; Ph.D.(bact), Yale, 36. Asst. bact, Mich. State Col, 31-33; asst. bacteriologist, Yale, 33-36; instr, Illinois, 36-42; asst. prof. BACT, UNIV. KY, 46-47, ASSOC. PROF, 47- U.S.A, 42-46. Am. Soc. Microbiol; Electron Micros. Soc. Am. Electron microscopy of viruses; bacterial enzymes; actinomycetes. Address: Dept. of Microbiology, University of Kentucky, Lexington, KY 40506.

EDWARDS, OLIVER EDWARD, b. Wales, Jan. 8, 20; Can. citizen; m. 45; c. 2. ORGANIC CHEMISTRY. B.Sc, Alberta, 41; M.S, Northwestern, 43, Ph.D. (chem), 48. CHEMIST, ORG. CHEM. & ALKALOIDS, NAT. RES. COUN. CAN, 48- Can. Army, 43-46. Am. Chem. Soc; Can. Inst. Chem; fel. Royal Soc. Can. Reactions of dihydropyran and tetrahydropyran derivatives, electron deficient carbon and nitrogen; studies on the consitution of the Aconite alkaloids, chemistry of diterpenes; n-heterocyclics. Address: National Research Council, Sussex St, Ottawa, Ont, Can.

EDWARDS, O(SCAR) WENDELL, b. Marion, Ala, Jan. 2, 16; m. 43; c. 1. PHYSICAL CHEMISTRY. B.S, Birmingham-Southern, 36; M.S, Alabama, 41; Emory, 59. Teacher, pub. schs, 36-41, 43-44; chem. aide, TENN. VALLEY AUTHORITY, 41-42, jr. anal. chemist, 42-45, asst. anal. chemist, 45-46, res. chemist III, 46-56, RES. CHEMIST IV, 56- Am. Chem. Soc. Determination of phosphorus in phosphatic materials; microdetermination of phosphorus by an organic reagent; diffusion of phosphates and phosphoric acid by conductimetric and optical methods; measurement of dissocation and stability constants. Address: Tennessee Valley Authority, Fundamental Research Branch, Muscle Shoals, AL 35660.

EDWARDS, PALMER LOWELL, b. Enterprise, Ala, Mar. 9, 23; m. 64; PHYSICS. B.S, La. State, 44; S.M, Harvard, 47; Ph.D, Maryland, 58. Physicist, Naval Ord. Lab, 44-48, res. assoc, 49-55, solid state physicist, 55-60; assoc. prof. PHYSICS, Texas Christian, 60-64, prof, 64-67; PROF. & CHMN. PHYSICS FACULTY, UNIV. WEST FLA, 67- U.S.N.R, 44-45. Am. Phys. Soc. Magnetism; properties of materials. Address: 8866 Burning Tree Rd, Pensacola, FL 32504.

EDWARDS, PHYLLIS Q, b. Fresno, Calif, Dec. 19, 16. TUBERCULOSIS. A.B, California, Los Angeles, 37; M.D, California, 42; M.P.H, Harvard, 58.

Intern. med, Univ. California Hosp, 41-42; res. tuberc, Barlow Sanatarium, 45-48; med. off, tuberc. res, U.S. Pub. Health Serv, 48-50; tuberc. res. off, World Health Orgn, Denmark, 50-55; tuberc. res. sect, U.S. PUB. HEALTH SERV, D.C, 55-63, tuberc. consult, div. foreign quarantine, France, 63-66, asst. chief tuberc. prog, CTR. DISEASE CONTROL, 66-68, dep. chief, 68, CHIEF, TUBERC. BR, 68- Vis. lectr, sch. med, California, San Francisco, 63. Dipl, Am. Bd. Prev. Med, 59. Am. Pub. Health Asn; Am. Thoracic Soc. Epidemiology of tuberculosis and systemic fungus diseases; specificity of skin sensitivity to tuberculin and other mycobacterial antigens; histoplasmin, coccidioidin and other fungus antigens; planning and evaluation of tuberculosis control programs. Address: Tuberculosis Branch, Center for Disease Control, U.S. Public Health Service, 1600 Clifton Rd, Atlanta, GA 30333.

EDWARDS, RAYMOND R(ICHARD), b. Ft. Smith, Ark, Dec. 18, 17; m. 61. CHEMISTRY. A.B, Arkansas, 39; Ph.D.(inorg. chem), Mass. Inst. Tech, 48. Res. chemist, Lederle Labs, N.Y, 40-43; assoc. chemist, Clinton Labs, Oak Ridge, 43-46; res. assoc, Mass. Inst. Tech, 46-48; asst. prof. chem. & res. assoc. nuclear chem, Arkansas, 48-49, assoc. prof, 49-51, prof. & chmn. dept, 51-57; dir. grad. inst. tech, 57-60; tech. asst. to pres, Nuclear Sci. & Eng. Corp, 61-62, tech. dir, 62-65; sr. res. chemist, Carnegie Inst. Technol, 65-68; chmn. dept. CHEM, CHAPMAN COL, 68-70, RES. PROF, 70- Asst. dir. tech. prog, Div. Int. Affairs, Atomic Energy Comn, 56-57; chmn, subcmt. nuclear geophysics, Nuclear Sci. Comt-Nat. Res. Coun. AAAS; Am. Chem. Soc; Am. Geophys. Union; Am. Phys. Soc; Am. Nuclear Soc. Antibiotics; fission products; nuclear chemistry; chemical effects of nuclear transformations; nuclear geochemistry; application of radioactive tracers to biochemical and environmental problems. Address: 1192 Scherer Place, Tustin, CA 92680.

EDWARDS, RICHARD A(RCHER), b. Niagara Falls, N.Y, Apr. 24, 08; m. 31; PALEONTOLOGY. B.S, Michigan, 31, M.A, Cincinnati, 33; Ph.D.(paleont), North Carolina, 38. Asst. geol, Michigan, 29-31; Cincinnati, 31-34; fel, North Carolina, 34-35, instr, 35-38, 39-40; jr. geologist, U.S. Geol. Surv, 38-39; asst. prof. phys. sci, UNIV. FLA, 40-42, assoc. prof, 45-46, PROF, 46-47, GEOL, 47-, acting chmn. dept. geol, 66-69. Head dept. geol, Florida, 51-58. Head Ford Found. program from Univ. Florida to Univ. Mandalay, Burma, 58-62. U.S.N, 42-45, Lt. Soc. Vert. Paleont; Paleont. Soc; Am. Inst. Prof. Geol. Micropaleontology of ostracods; physiography of land forms in Florida. Address: Dept. of Geology, University of Florida, Gainesville, FL 32601.

EDWARDS, R(ICHARD) H(ARBIN), b. Carizozo, N.Mex, July 3, 17; m. 43; c. 4. APPLIED MATHEMATICS. A.B, California, Los Angeles, 40; Ph.D. (math), Ill. Inst. Tech, 49. Aerodynamicist, Goodyear Aircraft Corp, 42-45; mathematician, U.S. Naval Ord. Test Sta, 45-46; asst. math, Ill. Inst. Tech, 40-42, 46-48, instr, 48-49; SR. SCIENTIST, HUGHES AIRCRAFT CO, 49-; PROF. AEROSPACE ENG, UNIV. SOUTH. CALIF, 61- Am. Math. Soc; Math. Asn. Am. Elasticity; aerodynamics. Address: 4417 Via Pinzon, Palos Verdes, CA 90275.

EDWARDS, RICHARD M(ODLIN), b. Wilmington, Del, Sept. 6, 20; m. 43; c. 2. CHEMICAL ENGINEERING. B.S, Purdue, 41; M.S, Washington (Seattle), 48; Ph.D.(chem. eng), Arizona, 64. Chem. supvr, E.I. du Pont de Nemours & Co, 42-44; chem. engr, Mallinckrodt Chem. Works, 48-52, asst. to tech. dir, 52-54, asst. mgr. process develop, 54-56, mgr, 56-59; instr. CHEM. ENG, UNIV. ARIZ, 59-63, assoc. prof, 63-64, PROF, 64-, ASSOC. DEAN, COL. MINES, 71-, asst. to dean, 64-67, asst. dean, 67-70, acting dean, 70-71. Consult, Am. Potash & Chem. Co, 66-71. U.S.N.R, 44-46, Lt. AAAS; Am. Inst. Chem. Eng; Am. Soc. Eng. Educ; Am. Inst. Mining, Metall. & Petrol. Eng; Instrument Soc. Am; Am. Chem. Soc. Technology of uranium production; fluidized bed heat transfer; chemical separation processes; liquid-liquid extraction. Address: College of Mines, University of Arizona, Tucson, AZ 85721.

EDWARDS, ROBERT B(RYCE), b. Detroit, Mich, Jan. 13, 15; m. 39; c. 4. MICROBIOLOGY, IMMUNOLOGY. B.S, Mich. State, 38; Ph.D.(bact, immunol), Minnesota, 49. Bacteriologist, Mich. State Dept. Health, 38; Minnesota State Dept. Health, 38-40; res. scientist, Upjohn Co, 46-53; dir. microbiol. res, Lambert Pharmacal Co, 53-56; asst. sci. dir, Olin Mathieson Chem. Corp, Int, 56-58, new prod. mgr, 58-59; sci. dir, Julius Schmid, Inc, 59-62; V.PRES. & SCI. DIR, KREMERS-URBAN CO, 62- Sanit.C, 43-46, Capt. AAAS; Am. Soc. Microbiol; Reticuloendothelial Soc; Am. Pharmaceut. Asn; Acad. Pharmaceut. Sci; N.Y. Acad. Sci. Chemotherapy; antibiotics; microbiological conversions of corticoid steroids; microbial resistance. Address: Kremers-Urban Co, P.O. Box 2038, Milwaukee, WI 53201.

EDWARDS, R(OBERT) L(EE), b. Barnardsville, N.C, Jan. 21, 22; m. 51; c. 1. ANIMAL SCIENCE. B.S, Berea Col, 46; M.S, N.C. State Col, 54, Ph.D.(animal indust), 58. Teacher, pub. schs, N.C, 46-52; asst. agr. ed, N.C. State Col, 52-53, animal indust, 54-58; asst. prof. & asst. animal husbandman, Clemson Col, 58-64, ASSOC. PROF, CLEMSON UNIV, 64- U.S.A.A.F, 43-45. AAAS; Am. Soc. Animal Sci; Am. Inst. Biol. Sci. Nutrition of large animals; utilization of dietary lipids in ruminants; forage utilization by cattle and sheep. Address: Dept. of Animal Science, Clemson University, Clemson, NC 29631.

EDWARDS, ROBERT LOMAS, b. Phila, Pa, Aug. 24, 20; m. 42; c. 4. ECOLOGY. B.A, Colgate, 47; A.M, Harvard, 49, Ph.D.(biol), 51. Instr, Tufts, 49-50; in charge Arctic Res. Program, 50, 53, 54; instr, Air Staff & Command Col, Maxwell Field, Ala, 54; chief, indust. fishery invests, Fish & Wildlife Serv, 55-59; ASST. DIR, WOODS HOLE FISHERIES RES. LAB, 59- U.S.A.F, 41-45, Res, Maj. Soc. Am. Archaeol; Am. Soc. Mammal; Wilson Ornith. Soc. Vertebrate ecology, especially marine; ecology of arctic fishes and mammals; systematics and evolution of bird parasites; growth of fish. Address: Box 505, Woods Hole, MA 02543.

EDWARDS, ROBERT S(AMMIE), b. Andersonville, Ga, Nov. 3, 29; m. 60; c. 1. ORGANIC CHEMISTRY. B.Sc, Georgia, 51, M.E, 54, M.Sc, 57; Nat. Sci. Found. fel, Texas, 59, Ph.D.(chem), 61. Teacher, high sch, Ga, 54-55; instr. chem, Georgia, 56-57; SR. PROJ. CHEMIST, RES. & TECH. DEPT, TEXACO INC, 60- U.S.A, 51-53, Sgt. Am. Chem. Soc. Synthesis and structure-property relationships of nitrogen heterocyclics; mechanisms of photochemical reactions; dispersion of colloids in non polar media; polymerization; petroleum additives. Address: Research & Technical Dept, Texaco Inc, P.O. Box 1608, Port Arthur, TX 77640.

EDWARDS, ROBERT V(ALENTINO), b. Baltimore, Md, Dec. 15, 40; m. 62; c. 2. CHEMICAL ENGINEERING. A.B, Johns Hopkins Univ, 62, M.S, 64, Ph.D.(chem. eng), 68. Res. assoc. CHEM. ENG, CASE WEST. RESERVE UNIV, 68-69, sr. res. assoc, 69-70, ASST. PROF, 70- AAAS; Am. Inst. Chem. Eng. Gas phase photochemistry; measurement of the scalar transport properties of moving fluids and velocity measurements by light scattering; complex transport phenomena. Address: Dept. of Chemical Engineering, Case Western Reserve University, Cleveland, OH 44106.

EDWARDS, ROGER, b. Shrewsbury, Eng, Aug. 27, 29; m. 58; c. 3. PHYSICS. B.Sc, Birmingham, 50, Ph.D.(physics), 53. Sci. officer, electron devices, Serv. Electronic Res. Lab, Eng, 53-57; mem. tech. staff, BELL TEL. LABS, INC, 57-63, SUPVR, 63- Inst. Elec. & Electronics Eng. Semiconductor devices; silicon and germanium diodes and transistors; avalanche microwave diodes; digital integrated circuits. Address: Bell Telephone Labs, Inc, Mountain Ave, Murray Hill, NJ 07971.

EDWARDS, ROY L(AWRENCE), b. Southampton, Eng, Dec. 2, 22; Can. citizen; m. 49; c. 3. ECOLOGY. B.A, Oxford, 50, M.A, 52, Ph.D.(entom), 52. Lectr. entomol, Hull, England, 52-57; Nat. Res. Coun. Can. fel, 57-58; res. officer, Can. Agr. Res. Lab, 58-61; asst. prof. biol, Saskatchewan, 61-64; assoc. prof, BIOL, TRENT UNIV, 64-66, PROF, 66-, chmn. dept. biol, 66-69. R.A.F, 43-47, Flight Lt. Ecol. Soc. Am; Entom. Soc. Am; Am. Soc. Limnol. & Oceanog; Entom. Soc. Can; Can. Soc. Zool; Brit. Ecol. Soc; Royal Entom. Soc. London. Ecology and behavior of invertebrates. Address: Dept. of Biology, Trent University, Peterborough, Ont, Can.

EDWARDS, STEVE, b. Quincy, Fla, June 16, 30; m. 64; c. 2. THEORETICAL PHYSICS. B.S, Fla. State, 52, M.S, 54; Gen. Motors Corp. fel, Hopkins, 57-60, Ph.D.(theoret. physics), 60. Asst. prof. PHYSICS, FLA. STATE UNIV, 60-65, assoc. prof, 65-69, PROF, 69-, ASSOC. CHMN. DEPT, 65- Mem. adv. comt, Intermediate Sci. Curriculum Study. Am. Asn. Physics Teachers; Am. Phys. Soc. Group theoretic analysis of vibration problems; direct nuclear reaction theories, especially stripping and pick-up reactions of all types in low-energy nuclear physics. Address: Dept. of Physics, Florida State University, Tallahassee, FL 32306.

EDWARDS, TERRY WINSLOW, b. Sheboygan, Wis, Nov. 2, 35; m. 58; c. 1. ASTRONOMY. B.S, Univ. Wis, 58, M.S, 61, Ph.D.(astron), 68. Satellite observer, Astrophys. Obser, Smithsonian Inst, 58-59; res. asst. physics, Midwest. Univs. Res. Asn, 64-66; instr. PHYSICS & ASTRON, UNIV. MO, 66-67, asst. prof, 67-71, ASSOC. PROF, 71- Summer res. asst, Los Alamos Sci. Lab, Univ. Calif, 62; NASA res. grant, Space Sci. Res. Ctr, Univ. Mo, 66-69; NASA-Am. Soc. Eng. Educ. summer faculty fel, Ames Res. Ctr. & Stanford Univ, 70 & 71. AAAS; Am. Astron. Soc; Asn. Comput. Mach. Astrophysics; stellar thermodynamics; stellar structure; nucleosynthesis; celestial mechanics; binary and variable stars; digital computing. Address: Dept. of Physics & Astronomy, University of Missouri, Columbia, MO 65201.

EDWARDS, THOMAS F, b. Pittsfield, Ill, July 17, 27; m. 50; c. 3. CHEMISTRY, GEOLOGY. B.S, Illinois State, 51; M.A, Arizona State, 57; Nat. Sci. Found. fel, Mich. State, 60-61, Ed.D.(sci. educ), 66. Teacher, high schs, Ill, 51-57; instr. chem, ILLINOIS STATE, 57-59, asst. prof, 59-66, ASSOC. PROF, 67-70, ELEM. EDUC, 70- Instr, Mich. State, 65-66. Sci. consult, State Dept. Educ, Ill, 59-60; Springfield Pub. Sch. Syst, 63-64; Rand McNally Pub. Co, 67- U.S.A, 45-47. Nat. Sci. Teachers Asn; Nat. Asn. Res. Sci. Teaching. Development of a non-reading science content test for preschool children. Address: Dept. of Elementary Education, Illinois State University, Normal, IL 61761.

EDWARDS, T(HOMAS) HARVEY, b. Chilliwack, B.C, Feb. 12, 24; nat; m. 46; c. 4. PHYSICS. B.A, British Columbia, 47, M.A, 48; fel, Michigan, 48-51, Ph.D.(physics), 55. Instr, Michigan, 51-53, res. assoc, 53-54; asst. prof. PHYSICS, MICH. STATE UNIV, 54-59, assoc. prof, 59-65, PROF, 65- R.C.A.F, 43-45. Optical Soc. Am; Am. Phys. Soc. High-resolution infrared spectroscopy; molecular structure of asymmetric and symmetric top molecules. Address: Dept. of Physics, Michigan State University, East Lansing, MI 48823.

EDWARDS, VICTOR HENRY, b. Galveston, Tex, Oct. 17, 40; m. 63; c. 2. CHEMICAL ENGINEERING, MOLECULAR BIOLOGY. B.A, Rice Univ, 62; Ph.D.(chem. eng), Univ. Calif, Berkeley, 67. ASST. PROF. CHEM. ENG, CORNELL UNIV, 67- Assoc. prog. dir, eng. chem. prog, Nat. Sci. Found, 71, prog. mgr. advan. technol. appln, 71- Consult, Allied Chem. Corp, 70; Corning Glass Works, 70. Am. Chem. Soc; Am. Inst. Chem. Eng. Chemical synthesis using enzymes, microorganisms and tissue cultures; specialized separation techniques. Address: Advanced Technology Applications, National Science Foundation, 1800 G St. N.W, Washington, DC 20550.

EDWARDS, W. FARRELL, b. Logan, Utah, Oct. 5, 31; m. 55; c. 8. NUCLEAR PHYSICS. B.S, Univ. Utah, 55; Nat. Sci. Found. fel, Calif. Inst. Technol, 56-57, M.S, 57, Schlumberger Found. fel, 57-58, Ph.D.(physics), 60. From asst. prof. to PROF. PHYSICS, UTAH STATE UNIV, 59-, HEAD DEPT, 66- Nuclear spectroscopy; foundations of electromagnetism. Address: Dept. of Physics, Utah State University, Logan, UT 84321.

EDWARDS, W. STERLING, III, b. Birmingham, Ala, July 23, 20; m. 46; c. 4. SURGERY. B.S, Va. Mil. Inst, 42; M.D, Pennsylvania, 45. Intern, Mass. Gen. Hosp, 45-46, surg. res, 48-52; instr. surg, med. col. Ala, 52-53, asst. prof, 53-58, assoc. prof, 58-62, prof, 62-69; PROF. SURG. & CHMN. CARDIOTHORACIC DIV, SCH. MED, UNIV. N.MEX, 69- U.S. Pub. Health Serv. res. fel, West. Reserve Univ, 50-51; consult, Vet. Admin. Hosp, Albuquerque. Dipl, Am. Bd. Surg, 54; dipl, Am. Bd. Thoracic Surg, 59. Med.C, 46-48, Capt. Soc. Vascular Surg; Am. Med. Asn; Am. Col. Surg. Cardiovascular surgery and physiology; development of arterial and heart valve substitutes. Address: Dept. of Surgery, School of Medicine, University of New Mexico, Albuquerque, NM 87106.

EDWARDS, WALTER M(URRAY), b. Jacksonville, Fla, Sept. 29, 22; m. 42; c. 3. ORGANIC CHEMISTRY. B.S, Georgia, 44, M.S, 48; Ph.D.(org. chem), Ohio State, 52. Chemist, Tenn. Eastman Co, 44; Battelle Mem. Inst, 48-52; ELECTROCHEM. DEPT, sales tech. lab, E.I. DU PONT DE NEMOURS & CO, 52-70, RES. ASSOC, EXP. STA, 70- U.S.N.R, 44-52, Lt. Am. Chem. Soc. Condensation and vinyl polymers; polymeric binders; processing of thermoplastics. Address: Electrochemicals Dept, Experimental Station, E.I. du Pont de Nemours & Co, Wilmington, DE 19898.

EDWARDS, WALTON, b. Washington, D.C, Jan. 29, 10; m. 37; c. 3. PEDIATRICS. A.B, Stanford, 33; M.D, Cornell, 37. Instr. pediat, sch. med. & grad. sch. med, Pennsylvania, 39-40; chief pediat, Letterman Gen. Hosp, San Francisco, Calif, 46-49, 52-57, U.S. Army Tripler Gen. Hosp, Honolulu, 49-52, chief pediat. & med. serv, U.S. Army Hosp, Landstuhl, Germany, 57-60, chief pediat, Ireland Army Hosp, Ft. Knox, Ky, 60-63; ASSOC. PROF. PEDIAT, SCH. MED, UNIV. LOUISVILLE, 63- Consult, Surgeon Gen, U.S. Army, 57-60, 64- U.S.A, 40-63, Col. Assoc. Am. Col. Physicians; assoc, Asn. Hosp. Med. Educ. Cardiopulmonary disease. Address: Dept. of Pediatrics, University of Louisville School of Medicine, 226 E. Chestnut St, Louisville, KY 40202.

EDWARDS, WARRICK RIGELEY, (JR), b. Baltimore, Md, Oct. 9, 01; m. 33; c. 1. ORGANIC CHEMISTRY. B.S, Hopkins, 22, Ph.D.(org. chem), 28. Chemist, U.S. Indust. Chem. Co, Md, 22-23; James P. Hooper Mfg. Co, 23-24; instr. physics & chem, Mt. Vernon Collegiate Inst, 24-25; asst. prof. CHEM, LA. STATE UNIV, 28-32, assoc. prof, 32-42, PROF, 42- U.S.N.R, 43-45, Lt.Comdr. Am. Chem. Soc. Cyclopentyl, cyclohexyl, diphenyl and furfural derivatives; use of synthetic resins in water treatment; okra seed oil and meal; abnormal physical properties of certain series; reactions of nitroso compounds; reactions of mixed carboxylic anhydrides. Address: Dept. of Chemistry, Louisiana State University, Baton Rouge, LA 70803.

EDWARDS, WILLIAM BRUNDIGE, III, b. Phila, Pa, Oct. 10, 42. ORGANIC & MEDICINAL CHEMISTRY. B.A, Lehigh Univ, 64; Du Pont fels, Univ. Pa, 67 & 68, Allied Chem. fel, 67-68, Busch fel, 68-69, Ph.D.(org. chem), 69. Res. asst. org. chem, Wyeth Labs, Inc, 64-65; res. chemist, Ravdin Inst, 65-66; Arco Chem. Corp, Atlantic Richfield Co, 66; spectroscopist, Univ. Pa, 66-68; fel, Synvar Res. Inst, 69-70; ASSOC. PROF. ORG. RES, RES. CTR, PHILIP MORRIS INC, 71- Teaching asst, Univ. Pa, 65-67. AAAS; Am. Chem. Soc; The Chem. Soc. Synthesis and study of physical, chemical, and medicinal properties of nitrogen bridgehead, small ring, and partially saturated heterocyclic compounds; nuclear magnetic resonance and mass spectral studies or heterocyclic compounds. Address: Research Center, Philip Morris Inc, P.O. Box 26583, Richmond, VA 23261.

EDWARDS, WILLIAM CHARLES, b. Waukegan, Ill, May 17, 34; m. 61; c. 2. ECOLOGY. B.A, Carleton Col, 56; M.S, Wyoming, 58; Colo. State Col, 62; Ph.D.(bot), Univ. Nebr, 66. Teacher, high sch, Wyo, 58-63; from asst. prof. to ASSOC. PROF. BIOL, Mankato State Col, 66-70; LARAMIE COUNTY COMMUNITY COL, 70- AAAS; Bot. Soc. Am; Ecol. Soc. Am. Reproduction in antelope; growth pattern in birch. Address: Dept. of Biology, Laramie County Community College, Cheyenne, WY 82001.

EDWARDS, WILLIAM M(AXHAM), b. Du Quoin, Ill, Apr. 22, 36; m. 63; c. 3. SOIL PHYSICS. B.S, Illinois, 61, M.S, 62; Ph.D.(agron), Iowa State, 67. SOIL SCIENTIST, U.S. DEPT. AGR, 67- U.S.A, 56-58. Soc. Agron. Soil management; water pollution. Address: North Appalachian Experimental Watershed, Coshocton, OH 43812.

EDWARDSON, JOHN R(ICHARD), b. Kansas City, Mo, Apr. 17, 23; m. 48; c. 3. GENETICS. B.S, Agr. & Mech. Col. Tex, 48, M.S, 49; Ph.D.(biol), Harvard, 54. Asst. agronomist, UNIV. FLA, 53-61, assoc. agronomist, 61-66, AGRONOMIST, 66- U.S.A, 42-45. AAAS; Genetics Soc. Am; Am. Bot. Soc; Am. Genetic Asn; N.Y. Acad. Sci. Cytology and genetics of cytoplasmic characters in plants. Address: Agricultural Experiment Station, Institute of Food & Agricultural Science, University of Florida, Gainesville, FL 32601.

EELLS, JAMES, JR, b. Cleveland, Ohio, Oct. 25, 26; m. 50; c. 4. MATHEMATICS. B.A, Bowdoin Col, 47; A.M, Harvard, 51, Ph.D.(math), 54. Instr. MATH, Robert Col, Turkey, 47-48; Amherst Col, 48-50; teaching fel, Harvard, 51-53; instr, Tufts Col, 53-54; mem, Inst. Adv. Study, 54-56; asst. prof, California, Berkeley, 56-58; Columbia, 58-60, assoc. prof, 60-63; fel, Churchill Col, Cambridge, 63-64; PROF, Cornell Univ, 64-69; MATH. INST, UNIV. WARWICK, 69- Mem, Inst. Adv. Study, 62-63. Am. Math. Soc. Global topological and differential geometric properties of analysis; calculus of variations. Address: Mathematical Institute, University of Warwick, Coventry, England.

EER NISSE, ERROL P(ETER), b. Rapid City, S.Dak, Feb. 15, 40. ELECTRICAL ENGINEERING, PHYSICS. B.S.E.E, S.Dak. State, 62; Phi Kappa Phi fel, Purdue, 62, M.S.E.E, 63, Nat. Sci. Found. fel, 63-65, Ph.D.(elec. eng), 65. Staff mem. res, SANDIA CORP, 65-68, DIV. SUPVR, DEVICE PHYSICS RES. DIV, 68- Inst. Elec. & Electronics Eng. Ferroelectric, piezoelectric and semiconductor devices. Address: Division 5112, Sandia Corp, P.O. Box 5800, Albuquerque, NM 87115.

EERTMOED, GARY EUGENE, b. Pekin, Ill, Apr. 24, 39; m. 62; c. 2. ENTOMOLOGY. B.S. in Educ, Illinois State, 61, M.S, 63; Ph.D.(entom), Illinois, 69. Instr. biol, ILL. STATE UNIV, 63-64, ASST. PROF. BIOL. SCI, 69- Soc. Sigma Xi res. grant-in-aid, 67. Soc. Syst. Zool. Study of the order Psocoptera insecta using the methods of numerical taxonomy for arriving at estimates of phenatic resemblance between taxa of this group. Address: Dept. of Biological Sciences, Illinois State University, Normal, IL 61761.

EFFENBERGER, J(OHN) A(LBERT), b. Jersey City, N.J, Jan. 13, 34; c. 2. PHYSICAL CHEMISTRY. B.S, Fordham, 55; Ph.D.(phys. chem), Iowa State, 61. Res. assoc. biochem. Iowa State, 61-63; res. chemist, PLASTICS DEPT, E.I. DU PONT DE NEMOURS & CO, INC, 63-67, tech. rep, 67-68, PROD. SPECIALIST, TEFLON, 68- AAAS; Am. Chem. Soc; Am. Sci. Affiliation. Polymer science; natural and synthetic polymers; starch, starch-iodine complex; fluorocarbons and polymers derived from fluorocarbons; spectroscopy and physical properties of polymer systems; carbohydrates and enzymolysis of carbohydrates. Address: Plastics Dept, D-13127, E.I. du Pont de Nemours & Co,Wilmington, DE 19898.

EFFER, W. R, b. Warrington, Eng, Jan. 1, 27; Can. citizen; m. 53; c. 2. PLANT PHYSIOLOGY. B.Sc, Durham, 51; Ph.D.(plant physiol), Newcastle, 66. Res. chemist, Horlicks Ltd, Slough, Eng, 51-54; res. scientist, Ont. Res. Found, Toronto, 54-63 & 66-67; biologist, ONT. HYDRO-ELEC. COMN, 67-70, SUPVR. ENVIRON. STUDIES, 70- R.A.F, 44-48. Am. Soc. Plant Physiol; Can. Soc. Plant Physiol. Effects of air pollutants on vegetation and the biological changes associated with heat pollution. Address: Generation Projects Division, Ontario Hydro Research Labs, 620 University Ave, Toronto 2, Ont, Can.

EFFORD, IAN E(COTT), b. London, Eng, Jan. 4, 36; Can. citizen; m. 59; c. 4. ECOLOGY. B.Sc, Univ. London, 57; Nature Conservancy studentship & D.Phil.(pop. ecol), Oxford, 60. Royal Soc. Murray traveling studentship marine ecol, Scripps Inst, Univ. Calif, 60-61; demonstr. zool. & ecol, bur. animal pop, Oxford, 61-62; asst. prof. ECOL, UNIV. B.C, 62-65, assoc. prof, 65-71, PROF, 71- Summer asst. prof, marine biol. sta, Univ. Ore, 63; mem. Can. Med. Exped, Easter Island, 64-65; mem. freshwater comt, Can. Int. Biol. Prog, dir, Marion Lake Proj, 67- Ecol. Soc. Am; Int. Soc. Limnol; Brit. Ecol. Soc. Community structure and energy transfer in a lake; decision making in ecological and environmental problems. Address: Institute of Resource Ecology, University of British Columbia, Vancouver 8, B.C, Can.

EFFRON, EDWARD, b. Cincinnati, Ohio, Feb. 23, 30; m. 55; c. 2. CHEMICAL ENGINEERING. Ch.E, Cincinnati, 53; D.Sc.(chem. eng), Johns Hopkins Univ, 62. Engr, ESSO RES. & ENG. CO, 53-57, 62-65, SR. ENGR, 65- U.S.A, 54-56, 1st Lt. Reactor design; kinetics; transport phenomena; unit operations; fluid mechanics; catalysis; physical chemistry. Address: 45 Fernhill Rd, Springfield, NJ 07081.

EFFROS, EDWARD G(EORGE), b. N.Y.C, Dec. 10, 35. MATHEMATICS. S.B, Mass. Inst. Tech, 56; A.M, Harvard, 58, Ph.D.(math), 62. Instr. MATH, Columbia Univ, 61-64; asst. prof, UNIV. PA, 64-67, assoc. prof, 67-70, PROF, 70- Am. Math. Soc. Abstract analysis; representation theory of topological groups and C* algebras. Address: Dept. of Mathematics, University of Pennsylvania, Philadelphia, PA 19104.

EFRATY, AVI, b. Tel-Aviv, Israel, Dec. 7, 38. ORGANOMETALLIC CHEMISTRY. B.Sc, Bar-Ilan Univ, Israel, 63; Ph.D.(chem), McMaster Univ, 67. Teaching fel. CHEM, Univ. Waterloo, 67-68; res. assoc, Univ. Ga, 68-71; ASST. PROF, RUTGERS UNIV, 71- Med.C, Israeli Armed Forces, 56-59. Am. Chem. Soc; The Chem. Soc. Fluoroorganic, fluorohydrocarbon and organotin chemistry; π-bonded small ring transition metal complexes. Address: School of Chemistry, Rutgers University, New Brunswick, NJ 08903.

EFRON, DANIEL H, b. Warsaw, Poland, June 6, 13; U.S. citizen; m. 59. PHARMACOLOGY, PSYCHIATRY. Ph.D.(microbiol, chem), Univ. Warsaw, 38, M.D, 52. Adj, Nat. Inst. Health, Warsaw, 46-48, chief pharmacol. div, 48-52; chief pharmacol. dept, Nat. Inst. Drugs, 52-53; Nat. Inst. Mother & Child, 53-55; res. fel, Ciba Labs, Switz, 55-56; Univ. Basel, 56-58; chief pharmacol. dept, Nat. Drug Co, Pa, 58-61; spec. fel, Nat. Heart Inst, 61-64, prog. dir, psychopharmacol. serv. ctr, NAT. INST. MENT. HEALTH, 64-65, chief pharmacol. unit, 65-66, CHIEF PHARMACOL. SECT, 66- Clin. prof. psychopharmacol, sch. med, Maryland, 68- Exec. secy. pharmacol. & chem. comt, Nat. Inst. Ment. Health, 65-67 & comt. behav. pharmacol, 66-67; mem. toxicol. info. coord. comt, Nat. Libr. Med, Dept. Health, Educ. & Welfare, 67- Am. Soc. Pharmacol. & Exp. Therapeut; Am. Col. Neuropsychopharmacol.(secy-treas); Soc. Neurosci; Soc. Biol. Psychiat; Int. Col. Neuropsychopharmacol; European Soc. Study of Drug Toxicity. Methodology for evaluation and search for new drugs; drug metabolism; biochemical basis of psychiatric diseases. Address: Pharmacology Section, Psychopharmacology Research Branch, National Institute of Mental Health, Room 9-95, 5600 Fishers Lane, Rockville, MD 20852.

EFRON, ROBERT, b. N.Y.C, Dec. 22, 27; m. 67; c. 3. NEUROPSYCHOLOGY, NEUROPHYSIOLOGY. B.A, Columbia Col, 48; M.D, Harvard, 52. Med. house off, Peter Bent Brigham Hosp, Boston, Mass, 52-53; Moseley traveling fel, Harvard, 53-54; Nat. Found. Infantile Paralysis fel, Nat. Hosp, Queen Square, London, Eng, 56-60; chief neurophysiol-biophys. res. unit, VET. ADMIN. HOSP, Boston, Mass, 60-70; CHIEF NEUROPHYSIOL-BIOPHYS. RES. LAB, MARTINEZ & ASSOC. CHIEF STAFF, HOSP, 70- Mem. adv. bd, Int. Soc. Study Time, 66- Med.C, U.S.N.R, 54-56, Lt. AAAS; N.Y. Acad. Sci. Neurophysiology and neuropsychology of perception. Address: 1306 Ramsay Circle, Walnut Creek, CA 94596.

EFTHYMIOU, CONSTANTINE JOHN, b. Athens, Greece, Apr. 21, 30; m. 64; c. 3. MICROBIOLOGY. B.S, Athens Agr. Col, 52; M.S, Maryland, 58, Ph.D. (microbiol), 61. Asst. dairy tech, Maryland, 55-58, MICROBIOL, 58-61; asst. prof, Carnegie Inst. Technol, 61-64; GRAD. SCH, ST. JOHN'S UNIV. (N.Y), 64-68, ASSOC. PROF, 68-; RES. ASSOC, QUEENS HOSP. CTR. AFFILIATION, 68- Consult. microbiologist, Coca Cola Export Corp. Greek Nat. Army, 52-54, Lt. AAAS; Am. Soc. Microbiol. Microbiology and biochemistry of cheese ripening; microbial physiology and immunochemistry; dairy technology. Address: 84-63 126th St, Kew Gardens, NY 11415.

EGAN, B(ILLY) ZANE, b. Scott Co, Va, Aug. 31, 37; m. 57; c. 2. INORGANIC CHEMISTRY. A.B, Berea Col, 57; M.Sc, Ohio State, 60, Ph.D.(inorg. chem), 62. CHEMIST, OAK RIDGE NAT. LAB, UNION CARBIDE CORP, 62- Am. Chem. Soc. High vacuum inorganic synthesis; boranes and organo boron; solvent extraction; biochemical separations. Address: Oak Ridge National Lab, P.O. Box X, Oak Ridge, TN 37830.

EGAN, CLARK J(AMES), b. Oakland, Calif, Oct. 18, 10; m. 44; c. 2. CHEMISTRY. B.S, California, 31, Bruce Howard scholar, 31-32, Ph.D.(chem), 36. Instr. chem, California, 36-37; San Francisco, 37-40; San Mateo Jr. Col, 40-41; chem. engr, Nat. Defense Res. Comt, chem. dept, California, 41-44; chem. engr, plutonium proj, metal. lab, Chicago, 44-45; res. assoc, Calif. Res. Corp, 45-65, SR. RES. ASSOC, CHEVRON RES. CO, STANDARD OIL

CO, CALIF, 65- With Atomic Energy Comn, 46. Am. Chem. Soc. Low temperature calorimetry; thermodynamic calculations; heat transfer of fluids; petroleum refining process research; carbon dioxide; heat capacity and vapor pressure of the solid; heat of sublimation; thermodynamic and spectroscopic values of the entropy. Address: Chevron Research Co, Standard Oil Co. California, Richmond, CA 94803.

EGAN, FRANCIS P, b. N.Y.C, Oct. 17, 17; m. 40. MATHEMATICS. B.A, Manhattan Col, 37; M.S, Notre Dame, 51, Ph.D.(math. educ), 60. From instr. to assoc. prof. MATH, Niagara, 37-53, prof, 53-55; lectr, State Univ. N.Y. Buffalo, 55-59, PROF, STATE UNIV. N.Y. COL. ONEONTA, 59-, CHMN. DEPT, 62- Summers, lectr, Nat. Sci. Found. Inst. Math, 60, 66, dir, 65, 66. Math. Asn. Am; Asn. Symbolic Logic. Logic; metamathematics; teacher education. Address: Dept. of Mathematics, State University of New York College at Oneonta, Oneonta, NY 13820.

EGAN, HOWARD L, b. St. Louis, Mo, May 2, 38. MATHEMATICS. A.B, Washington (St. Louis), 60, A.M, 62, Ph.D.(group theory), 65. Asst. prof. MATH, Univ. Md, 65-71; ASSOC. PROF, GALLAUDET COL, 71- Am. Math. Soc. Infinite non-abelian group theory; algebraic coding theory. Address: Dept. of Mathematics, Gallaudet College, Washington, DC 20002.

EGAN, JAMES J(OHN), b. Oak Park, Ill, May 22, 27. PHYSICAL CHEMISTRY. B.S, Northwestern, 49; Ph.D.(phys. chem), Indiana, 54. Assoc. phys. chemist, BROOKHAVEN NAT. LAB, 53-60, CHEMIST, 60- U.S.N.R, 45-46. High temperature chemistry; molten salt chemistry; solid state chemistry; light scattering in aerosols. Address: Brookhaven National Lab, Upton, L.I, NY 11973.

EGAN, JAMES J(OSEPH), b. Covington, Ky, Nov. 7, 41; m. 64; c. 3. EXPERIMENTAL NUCLEAR PHYSICS. B.A, Thomas More Col, 63; NASA trainee, Univ. Ky, 65-67, M.S, 66, univ. fel, 68-69, Ph.D.(physics), 69. ASST. PROF. PHYSICS, LOWELL TECHNOL. INST, 69- Am. Phys. Soc. Low energy experimental nuclear structure physics; neutron scattering cross section measurements. Address: Dept. of Physics, Lowell Technological Institute, Lowell, MA 01854.

EGAN, KATHERINE SNOW, Speech Path, Audiol, see 12th ed, Soc. & Behav. Vols.

EGAN, RAYMOND D(AVIS), b. Honolulu, Hawaii, Aug. 22, 31; m. 55; c. 3. ELECTRICAL ENGINEERING. B.S, Stanford, 55, M.S, 56, Ph.D.(elec. eng), 60. Res. assoc, Stanford, 59-61; mgr. appl. res, GRANGER ASSOCS, 62-68, V.PRES, 68- Mem. U.S. Comn. 3, Int. Sci. Radio Union, 61- U.S.A.F, 51-54. Inst. Elec. & Electronics Eng; Am. Geophys. Union. Radio propagation; ionospheric physics; radio auroral studies; polar region propagation. backscatter and oblique incidence; ionosphere sounding. Address: Granger Associates, 1360 Willow Rd, Menlo Park, CA 94025.

EGAN, RICHARD L, b. Omaha, Nebr, Dec. 27, 17; m. 43; c. 2. MEDICINE. B.S.M, Creighton, 38, M.D, 40. Instr. med, sch. med, Creighton Univ, 41-46, asst. prof, 46-54, assoc. prof, 54-69, prof, 69-71, asst. dean, 54-59, dean, 59-70, asst. to pres. health sci, 70-71; ASST. DIR, DEPT. UNDERGRAD. MED. EDUC, AM. MED. ASN, 71- Consult, Vet. Admin. Hosps, Omaha & Lincoln, Nebr, 59-70. Am. Heart Asn; Asn. Am. Med. Cols; Am. Asn. Hist. Med; Am. Med. Writers Asn. Internal medicine; medical education. Address: Division of Medical Education, American Medical Association, 535 N. Dearborn St, Chicago, IL 60610.

EGAN, RICHARD STEPHEN, b. Chicago, Ill, Aug. 16, 41; m. 64; c. 3. PHARMACEUTICAL CHEMISTRY, NUCLEAR MAGNETIC RESONANCE. B.S, Univ. Ill. Med. Ctr, 63, Ph.D.(pharmaceut. chem), 71. ASSOC. RES. FEL, ABBOTT LABS, 66- AAAS; Am. Chem. Soc; Soc. Appl. Spectros. Nuclear magnetic resonance spectroscopy; structure and configuration and conformation assignments; macrolide antibiotics. Address: Chemical Physics Lab, Abbott Labs, North Chicago, IL 60064.

EGAN, ROBERT L, b. Morrilton, Ark, May 9, 20; m. 50; c. 5. RADIOLOGY. M.D, Pittsburgh, 50. Asst. radiologist, Univ. Texas M.D. Anderson Hosp. & Tumor Inst, 56-61, assoc. prof. radiol, post-grad. sch. med, Texas, 61-62; radiologist, Methodist Hosp. Ind, 62-65; assoc. prof. RADIOL, SCH. MED, EMORY UNIV, 65-68, PROF, 68- Chief sect. exp. diag. radiol. & assoc. radiologist, Univ. Texas M.D. Anderson Hosp. & Tumor Inst, 61-62. Spec. consult, cancer control prog, div. chronic diseases, bur. state serv, U.S. Pub. Health Serv, Dept. Health, Ed. & Welfare, 61-; consult, Health Ins. Plan of N.Y. Mammogarphy Surv. Prog, 62- Dipl, Am. Bd. Radiol, 56. U.S.N, 44-46, Med.C, 50-51, Lt.(jg). Radiol. Soc. N.Am; Roentgen Ray Soc; fel. Am. Col. Radiol; Am. Med. Asn. Cancer of the breast; teaching, evaluating and accumulating data on mammography and related procedures. Address: Dept. of Radiology, Emory University School of Medicine, Atlanta, GA 30322.

EGAN, THOMAS J, b. Winnipeg, Man, Can, Sept. 13, 25; m. 53; c. 3. MEDICINE, PEDIATRICS. B.A, British Columbia, 48; M.D, C.M, McGill, 52. Fel. res. med, Pittsburgh, 54-55, asst. instr. pediat, 57-59; instr, Western Reserve, 59-62; dir, res. lab, Children's Hosp. Akron, 59-62; asst. prof. PEDIAT, sch. med, Univ. Pittsburgh & dir. res. ctr, Children's Hosp, Pittsburgh, 62-65; ASSOC. PROF, SCH. MED, NORTHWEST. UNIV, 65-, MED. DIR. AMBULATORY SERV, CHILDREN'S MEM. HOSP, 70-, dir. clin. res. ctr, 65-70. R.C.N.V.R, 44-45. AAAS; Am. Fedn. Clin. Res; Soc. Pediatric Res. Inherited metabolic diseases; renal diseases; disorders of fluid and electrolyte balance. Address: Children's Memorial Hospital, 2300 Children's Plaza, Chicago, IL 60614.

EGAN, WALTER GEORGE, b. N.Y.C, Oct. 12, 23; m. 63. SOLID STATE PHYSICS, ELECTRICAL ENGINEERING. B.E.E, City Col. New York, 49; M.A, Columbia, 51; N.Y. Univ, 51-55; Ph.D.(solid state physics), Polytech. Inst. Brooklyn, 60. Engr, Egan Lab, N.Y, 46-50; nuclear physicist, nucleonics sect, Naval Mat. Lab, 50-56; prof. elec. eng, City Col. New York, 56-57; prin. res. engr, Ford Instrument Co. Div, Sperry-Rand Corp, 57-58, eng. proj. supvr, 58-60, asst. dir. res, 60-62, exec. asst. to v.pres. res, 62-63; STAFF SCIENTIST, GRUMMAN AIRCRAFT ENG. CO, 63- Mem. airlines electronic eng. comt, Air Lines Commun. Admin. Coun, 58-; adv. group aeronaut. res. & develop, NATO, 61- Sig.C, 42-45, Med.C, 45-46, Col. Am. Phys. Soc; Inst. Elec. & Electronics Eng; Sci. Res. Soc. Am; Am. Astron. Soc. Thin films; infrared; cryogenics; magnetics; microwaves and millimeter waves; lasers; masers; high vacuum; military and space sciences including guidance, navigation, oceanography, communications, countermeasures and antisubmarine warfare; astronomy; polarization properties of terrestrial and planetary surfaces. Address: Research Dept, Grumman Aircraft Engineering Co, Bethpage, L.I. NY 11714.

EGAR, JOSEPH MICHAEL, b. Jacksonville, Fla, Feb. 2, 30; m. 61; c. 4. GEOPHYSICS, MATHEMATICS. B.S, Oklahoma, 52; Ph.D.(geol, geophys, math), Texas A&M, 59. Eng. trainee, Savannah River Proj, E.I. du Pont de Nemours & Co, 52; instr. geol, Marietta Col, 55; asst. prof. geol. & math, Texas A&M, 57-59; Nat. Sci. Found. sci. faculty fel. math, 59-60; assoc. prof, Ball State Teachers Col, 60-63; Akron, 63-66; ASSOC. PROF. MATH. & ADJ. ASSOC. PROF. BIOL, CLEVELAND STATE UNIV, 66- Summer Woods Hole Oceanog. Inst. fel. geophys, 65. AAAS; Math. Asn. Am. Seismology, especially surface wave phenomena and underwater acoustics; applied mathematics; numerical analysis. Address: Dept. of Mathematics, Cleveland State University, Euclid Ave. & 24th St, Cleveland, OH 44115.

EGAR, MARGARET W(ELLS), b. Princeton, W.Va, July 25, 34; m. 61; c. 4. CYTOLOGY, GENETICS. B.S, Concord Col, 56; M.S, Emory, 58, Nat. Inst. Health fels. & Ph.D.(biol), 60. Asst. prof. biol, Ball State, 60-62; RES. ASSOC. REGENERATION, SCH. MED, CASE WEST. RESERVE UNIV, 65- AAAS. Cytochemical investigations of Tetrahymena macronucleus, especially in nucleolus; role of nerve in regeneration. Address: Dept. of Anatomy, Case Western Reserve University School of Medicine, Cleveland, OH 44106.

EGBERT, LARRE N, b. Smithfield, Utah, Apr. 3, 36; m. 55; c. 5. BIOCHEMISTRY, BIOPHYSICS. B.S, Utah State, 59, Nat. Sci. Found. & Nat. Insts. Health fels, 61-62; Nat. Insts. Health fel, Calif. Inst. Technol, 62-65, Ph.D. (biochem), 66. Assoc. mathematician, appl. physics lab, Hopkins, 59-60; staff mathematician, Los Alamos Sci. Lab, California, 60-61; ASST. PROF. zool, Brigham Young, 65-66; BIOL, Hopkins, 66-69; UTAH STATE UNIV, 69- AAAS; Am. Soc. Microbiol. Biophysical chemistry of nucleic acids and proteins; genetic coding; biochemical genetics; molecular biology; protein and nucleic acid structure. Address: Dept. of Bacteriology, Utah State University, Logan, UT 84321.

EGBERT, ROBERT B(ALDWIN), b. Chosica, Peru, S.Am, Dec. 13, 16; U.S. citizen; m. 41; c. 5. CHEMICAL ENGINEERING. B.Ch.E, Cooper Union, 38; Schweinburg fel, Mass. Inst. Technol, 39-40, M.Sc, 40, D.Sc.(chem. eng), 41. Asst, Mass. Inst. Technol, 39-41; prod. & design engr, Carbon & Carbide Chem. Corp, 41-47; chief engr. & v.pres. Sci. Design Co, Inc, 47-58; pres, Chem. Process Corp, 58-69; INDEPENDENT, CONSULT. ENGR, 69- AAAS; Am. Inst. Chem. Eng.(Walker Award); N.Y. Acad. Sci. Heat transmission by radiation from gases; development of commercial processes for the manufacture of ethylene oxide, maleic anhydride, phthalic anhydride; iso and terephthalic acids. Address: 8 Rip Rd, Hanover, NH 03755.

EGDAHL, RICHARD H, b. Eau Claire, Wis, Dec. 13, 26; m. 53; c. 4. SURGERY. M.D, Harvard, 50; Ph.D, Minnesota, 57. Instr. surg, Minnesota, 57-58; dir. surg. res. labs, Med. Col. Va, 58-64; PROF. SURG. & CHMN. DEPT, SCH. MED, BOSTON UNIV, 64- U.S. Pub. Health Serv. spec. res. fel, Minnesota, 57-58; Markle scholar, 58- Consult, Boston & Providence Vet. Hosps. U.S.N.R, 44-45, 52-55. Am. Soc. Clin. Invest; Soc. Univ. Surg; Am. Surg. Asn; Am. Physiol. Soc; Am. Soc. Exp. Path; Endocrine Soc.(Ciba award, 62). Experimental and clinical endocrinology; trauma; shock; pancreatitis. Address: University Hospital, 750 Harrison Ave, Boston, MA 02118.

EGE, SEYHAN N(URETTIN), b. Ankara, Turkey, Jan. 11, 31. ORGANIC CHEMISTRY. B.S, Am. Col. for Girls, Istanbul, 49; M.A, Smith Col, 52; univ. fels, Michigan, 52-54, 55-56, Rackham fel, 54-55, Ph.D.(org. chem), 56. Instr. CHEM, Michigan, 56-57; Am. Col. for Girls, Istanbul, 57-59; res. assoc, Boston, 59-61; asst. prof, Mt. Holyoke Col, 61-62; res. assoc. & part time lectr, Toronto, 62-65; lectr, UNIV. MICH, 65-67, asst. prof, 67-70, ASSOC. PROF, 70- AAAS; Am. Chem. Soc; The Chem. Soc. Molecular rearrangements; organic nitrogen compounds; synthesis of unsaturated fatty acids; organic photochemistry. Address: Dept. of Chemistry, 3301 Chemistry Bldg, University of Michigan, Ann Arbor, MI 48104.

EGEBERG, ROGER O, b. Chicago, Ill, Nov. 13, 03; m. 29; c. 4. INTERNAL MEDICINE, MEDICAL ADMINISTRATION. B.A, Cornell, 25; M.D, Northwestern, 29. Chief med. & prof. serv, Vet. Admin. Hosp, 46-56; med. dir, Los Angeles County Hosp, 56-58; med. dir, Los Angeles County Dept. Charities, 58-64; prof. med. & dean, sch. med, Univ. South. Calif, 64-69; asst. secy, health & sci. affairs, DEPT. HEALTH, EDUC. & WELFARE, 69-71, SPEC. ASST. TO SECY. FOR HEALTH POLICY & CONSULT. TO PRES. ON HEALTH AFFAIRS, 71- Med. consult, Armed Forces, 46; physician-in-residence, Vet. Admin. Hosps, 56- Mem. Nat. Adv. Cancer Coun, Nat. Cancer Inst, 64-; spec. med. adv. group, Vet. Admin, 65-; chmn, Governor's Cmt. Study Med. Aid & Health, Calif, 60; mem, President's Panel Spec. Study Narcotics, 62; Presidential Adv. Cmn. Narcotics & Drug Abuse, 63; mem. & past pres, Calif. State Bd. Health, 63. Fel. Am. Col. Physicians. Ecology of Coccidioides immitis, especially the reasons for spotty distribution in the soil of endemic areas; identification of antagonists and their susceptibility to high temperatures and high salinity. Address: Dept. of Health, Education & Welfare, Washington, DC 20201.

EGER, F. MARTIN, b. Lwów, Poland, May 31, 36; U.S. citizen. THEORETICAL PHYSICS. B.S, Mass. Inst. Tech, 58; Ph.D.(physics), Brandeis, 63. Res. assoc. theoret. physics, Brandeis, 63-64; fel. Lawrence Radiation Lab, Univ. Calif, 65-67; ASST. PROF. PHYSICS, RICHMOND COL, 67- AAAS; Am. Phys. Soc. Statistical mechanics and the many-body-problem; history and philosophy of science. Address: 2 Washington Square Village, New York, NY 10012.

EGER, WILBERT D(AVID), b. Buffalo, N.Y, Mar. 2, 25. ANALYTICAL CHEMISTRY. B.S, Canisius Col, 46, M.S, 48. Instr. chem, Canisius Col, 48-52; teacher, high sch, N.Y, 52-53; instr. CHEM, ROSARY HILL COL, 53-57, asst. prof, 57-67, ASSOC. PROF, 67- Am. Chem. Soc; Nat. Sci. Teachers Asn. Analytical and general chemistry. Address: 103 W. Northrup Place, Buffalo, NY 14214.

EGERMEIER, EDWARD R, b. Oklahoma City, Okla, Aug. 17, 31; m. 53; c. 2. DAIRY SCIENCE & BACTERIOLOGY. B.S, Okla. State, 53, M.S, 56. Instr. dairy bact, Okla. State, 56-57; chemist, res. labs, Carnation Co, Van Nuys, 57-60, group leader dairy res, 60-67; sr. scientist, Robert A. Johnston Co, 67; dairy res. mgr, BEATRICE FOODS CO, 67-70, DIR. PROD. DEVELOP, 70- U.S.N, 53-55. Am. Dairy Sci. Asn; Int. Food Tech. Soc. Product development in dairy and imitation dairy products as well as other food items in the dehydrated and frozen areas; bacteriophage in cheese cultures. Address: Research Dept, Beatrice Foods Co, 1526 S. State St, Chicago, IL 60605.

EGERMEIER, R(OBERT) P(AUL), b. Oklahoma City, Okla, Dec. 25, 27; m. 52; c. 2. MECHANICAL ENGINEERING. B.S, Oklahoma, 51; M.S, New Mexico State, 57. Asst. physicist, phys. sci. lab, New Mexico State, 53-57, asst. prof. mech. eng, 57-62; staff engr. & sect. mgr, Aerospace Corp, Calif, 62-67; staff. eng. scientist & mgr. ord. systs, Radio Corp. Am, 67-69; CONSULT, EGERMEIER ASSOCS, 69- Independent consult. Ord. Dept, U.S.A, 51-53. AAAS; Am. Inst. Aeronaut. & Astronaut; Am. Soc. Eng. Educ; Am. Soc. Mech. Eng; Nat. Soc. Prof. Eng; Inst. Elec. & Electronics Eng. Analog systems; automatic control and theory of measurement; thermodynamics and physical metallurgy; physics. Address: Egermeier Associates, 10037 Comanche Ave, Chatsworth, CA 91311.

EGERTON, JOHN R(ICHARD), b. Boulder, Colo, Dec. 3, 27; m. 51; c. 3. PARASITOLOGY. B.S, Colo. Agr. & Mech. Col, 51; M.S, Kans. State Col, 51, Ph.D.(parasitol), 53. Res. asst. parasitol, Kans. State Col, 50-53; instr. zool, Okla. Agr. & Mech. Col, 53-54, asst. prof, 54-55; res. assoc. PARASITOL, MERCK INST. THERAPEUT. RES, 55-58, res. assoc. & asst. to dir, 58-65, res. fel, 65-71, SR. RES. FEL, 71- Med.C, U.S.A, 45-47. Am. Soc. Parasitol; Biomet. Soc; World Asn. Adv. Vet. Parasitol. Nematode immunology; chemotherapy of helminth diseases; biometrics. Address: Merck Institute for Therapeutic Research, Merck Sharp & Dohme Research Labs, 400 E. Lincoln Ave, Rahway, NJ 07065.

EGGAN, L(AWRENCE) C(ARL), b. Fargo, N.Dak, Jan. 10, 35; div; c. 3. MATHEMATICS, LOGISTICS. B.A, Pacific Lutheran, 56; M.S, Oregon, 58, Nat. Sci. Found. fel, 59-60; Ph.D.(number theory), 60. Teaching fel. MATH, Oregon, 56-59; instr, Michigan, 60-62, asst. prof, 62-65; assoc. prof. & chmn. dept, Pac. Lutheran, 65-68; ASSOC. PROF, ILL. STATE UNIV, 68- Sigma Xi res. award, Oregon, 60; lectr, Imp. Col, London, 63-64; summer mathematician, Naval Ord. Lab, Calif, 58. Am. Math. Soc; Math. Asn. Am; London Math. Soc. Number theory, especially Diophantine approximations; logic, especially automata and finite automata. Address: Dept. of Mathematics, Illinois State University, Normal, IL 61761.

EGGE, ALFRED SEVERIN, b. Long Beach, Calif, Apr. 30, 33; m. 53; c. 3. ZOOLOGY. B.A, Long Beach, State Col, 57; M.S, Arizona, 59, Ph.D.(zool, biochem), 62. Asst. zool, Arizona, 57-61; asst. prof. physiol, Long Beach State Col, 61-64; asst. res. physiologist, sch. med, California, San Francisco, 64-66; assoc. prof, DEPT. BIOL, CALIF. STATE COL, SAN BERNARDINO, 66-70, PROF, 70-, CHMN, 68- Dent.C, U.S.A. Am. Soc. Zool; Am. Physiol. Soc. Neuroendocrinology; mechanism for aldosterone secretion. Address: Dept. of Biology, California State College, 5500 College Pkwy, San Bernardino, CA 92376.

EGGEN, DONALD T(RIPP), b. Hemet, Calif, Feb. 11, 22; m. 42; c. 4. NUCLEAR ENGINEERING & SCIENCE. B.A, Whittier Col, 43; Pa. State Col; Nat. Inst. Health fel, Ohio State, 47-48, Ph.D.(physics), 48. Res. physicist mass separation of uranium, Tenn. Eastman Corp, 44-45; res. asst. physics, Ohio State, 45-48; res. engr, exp. physics, N.Am. Aviation, Inc, 49-53, group engr, component develop, 53-57, res. specialist, exp. physics, 57-58, proj. engr, adv. epithermal thorium reactor, 59-63, proj. mgr. fast reactor & sodium components, 63-66; prog. mgr. fast reactor core design, Argonne Nat. Lab, 66-68; PROF. NUCLEAR ENG. & CHMN. NUCLEAR ENG. PROG, TECHNOL. INST, NORTHWEST. UNIV, 68- AAAS; Am. Phys. Soc; Am. Nuclear Soc. Fast reactor core design; safety; liquid metal technology and heat transfer. Address: Dept. of Engineering Science, Technological Institute, Northwestern University, Evanston, IL 60201.

EGGEN, DOUGLAS (AMBROSE), b. Rushford, Minn, Apr. 30, 25; m. 50; c. 3. BIOPHYSICS. Ph.B, Chicago, 47, B.S, 55, Nat. Sci. Found. fel, 55-57, Ph.D.(biophys), 57. Res. assoc, Chicago, 56-58; path, SCH. MED, LA. STATE UNIV, 58-60, instr, 60-63, asst. prof, 63-66, ASSOC. PROF. path. & chief sect. biophys, 66-70, PATH. & BIOMETRY, 70- Mem. Coun. Arteriosclerosis, Am. Heart Asn. Am. Soc. Exp. Path; Biophys. Soc. Medical biophysics; human and experimental atherosclerosis; computers in medical research; pathology. Address: Dept. of Pathology, Louisiana State University Medical Center, 1542 Tulane Ave, New Orleans, LA 70112.

EGGEN, OLIN J(EUCK), b. Orfordville, Wis, July 9, 19; m. 52; c. 2; div. ASTROPHYSICS. B.A, Wisconsin, 40, Ph.D.(astrophysics), 48. Res. assoc. astron, Lick Observ, California, 48-49, jr. astronomer, 49-50, asst. astronomer, 50-56; chief asst, Royal Greenwich Observ, 56-61; prof. astron, Calif. Inst. Technol, 61-66; DIR. MT. STROMLO OBSERV. & PROF. ASTRON, AUSTRALIAN NAT. UNIV, 66- Civilian with U.S.N, 48-49. U.S.A.A.F, 42-46. Am. Astron. Soc; Royal Astron. Soc. Visual double stars; photoelectric photometry; variable stars; stellar evolution; photoelectric magnitudes and colors of stars. Address: Mt. Stromlo Observatory, Australian National University, P.O. Box 4, Canberra, A.C.T, Australia 2600.

EGGENBERGER, ANDREW JON, b. Harlowton, Mont, May 8, 38. SPACE SCIENCE, APPLIED MECHANICS. B.S, Carnegie Inst. Tech, 61, Ph.D.(magnetohydrodyn), 67; Sc.M, Ohio State, 63. Assoc. res. engr, Boeing Co, 61-63; faculty fel. magnetohydrodyn, adv. res. inst, Lewis Res. Ctr, NASA, 67-68; ASST. PROF. ENG, UNIV. S.C, 67- Faculty fel. fluid turbulence, aero-astrodyn. lab, George C. Marshall Space Flight Ctr, NASA, 69. Am. Inst. Aeronaut. & Astronaut; Am. Soc. Civil Eng; Am. Soc. Test. & Mat; Am. Soc. Eng. Educ; Int. Soc. Biorheol. Fluid mechanics; magnetohydrodynamics. Address: College of Engineering, University of South Carolina, Columbia, SC 29208.

EGGENBERGER, DELBERT N(ORGAARD), b. Emington, Ill, May 28, 14; m. 35; c. 3. CHEMISTRY. B.Ed, Illinois State, 35; Illinois, 36; M.S, Ill. Inst. Tech, 47. Asst. phys. sci, Illinois State, 35-40; teacher, pub. sch, Ill, 42; asst. efficiency engr, Chicago Dist. Elec. Generating Corp, Ind, 42-46; res. chemist, Armour & Co, 46-56, head physics res, 56-60; ASSOC. PHYSICIST, ARGONNE NAT. LAB, 60-, HEAD PHYS. INSTRUMENTATION SECT, ELECTRONICS DIV, 61- Instr, Ill. Inst. Tech, 51-60. Instrument Soc. Am; Am. Sci. Affiliation (ed, 'Jour,' 51-61). Physical research instrument design and development; electrical conductance of colloidal solutions; light scattering; electron transit time; lasers. Address: Argonne National Lab, Argonne, IL 60439.

EGGENS, JACK LAMBERT, b. Ottawa, Ont, Mar. 2, 36; m. 62; c. 2. HORTICULTURE. B.Sc, Royal Mil. Col. Can, 60; B.S.A, Univ. Guelph, 65, M.Sc, 66, Ph.D.(hort), 70. Lectr. HORT, UNIV. GUELPH, 66-70, ASST. PROF, 70- R.C.A.S.C, 60-63, 1st Lt. Plant propagation; turf production and management. Address: Dept. of Horticultural Science, University of Guelph, Guelph, Ont, Can.

EGGER, CARL THOMAS, b. Monticello, Iowa, Feb. 5, 37; m. 57; c. 4. CHEMICAL ENGINEERING. B.S.Ch.E, Iowa, 59, M.S, 60, Nat. Sci. Found. fel, 60-62, Ph.D.(chem. eng), 62. Reservoir engr, Shell Develop, Co, Tex, 62; mgr. process develop, GRAIN PROCESSING CORP, 64-66, DIR. DEVELOP, 66- C.Eng, U.S.A, 62-64, Capt. Am. Inst. Chem. Eng. Secondary recovery; high vacuum; cryogenics; computer simulation; aerospace; fermentation technology; wet milling; distillation; waste treatment; enzymes; process control; evolutionary operations; solvent extraction; centrifugation; reverse osmosis. Address: 1304 Houser, Muscatine, IA 52761.

EGGER, MAURICE DAVID, b. Bakersfield, Calif, June 21, 36; m. 58; c. 3. NEUROPHYSIOLOGY. B.S, Stanford, 58; Fulbright fel, Hamburg, 58-59; M.S, Yale, 60, Ph.D.(physiol. psychol), 62. U.S. Pub. Health Serv. fel. psychiat, SCH. MED, YALE, 62-63, instr. ANAT, 65-66, asst. prof, 66-70, ASSOC. PROF, 70- Vis. scientist, Med. Res. Coun. Cerebral Function Res. Group, Univ. Col, Univ. London, 69-70. Am. Psychol. Asn; Am. Asn. Anat; Am. Physiol. Soc. Neural basis of behavior; organization of spinal reflexes; laser microscopy. Address: Dept. of Anatomy, Yale University, 333 Cedar St, New Haven, CT 06510.

EGGERS, A(LFRED) J(OHN), JR, b. Omaha, Nebr, June 24, 22; m. 50; c. 2. AERODYNAMICS. A.B, Omaha, 44; M.S, Stanford, 49, Ph.D.(eng. mech), 56. With NASA & predecessor, 44-71, chief vehicle environ. div, Ames Res. Ctr, 59-63, asst. dir. res. & dir. res. & develop. anal. & planning, 63-64, dep. assoc. adminstr. advan. res. & technol, NASA Hq, 64-68, asst. adminstr. policy, 68-71; ASST. DIR. RES. APPLN, NAT. SCI. FOUND, 71- Mem. sci. adv. bd, U.S. Air Force, 58- Arthur S. Flemming Award, 56; H. Julian Allen Award, NASA, 69. U.S.N.R, 42-46, Lt.(jg). AAAS; fel. Am. Inst. Aeronaut. & Astronaut; Am. Acad. Polit. & Soc. Sci; Am. Ord. Asn. Supersonic and hypersonic aerodynamics; aerodynamic heating, aerospace vehicles; aerospace research and development management, planning, and policy analysis and development. Address: Code RA, National Science Foundation, Washington, DC 20550.

EGGERS, DAVID F(RANK), JR, b. Oak Park, Ill, July 8, 22; m. 45; c. 3. PHYSICAL CHEMISTRY. B.S, Illinois, 43; fel, Minnesota, 47-50, Ph.D.(chem), 51. Asst, Minnesota, 43-44; chemist, Tenn. Eastman Corp, 44-47; instr. CHEM, UNIV. WASH, 50-52, asst. prof, 52-56, assoc. prof, 56-63, PROF, 63- Am. Chem. Soc; Optical Soc. Am. Absolute infrared intensities and electrical structure of molecules; vibrational spectra and molecular structure. Address: Dept. of Chemistry, BG-10, University of Washington, Seattle, WA 98195.

EGGERS, GEORGE WILLIAM NORDHOLTZ, JR, b. Galveston, Tex, Feb. 22, 29; m. 55; c. 2. MEDICINE, ANESTHESIOLOGY. B.A, Rice Inst, 49; M.D, Texas, 53. Instr. ANESTHESIOL, med. br, Texas, 56-59, asst. prof, 59-61; assoc. prof, SCH. MED, UNIV. MO-COLUMBIA, 61-67, PROF, 67-, CHMN. DEPT, 70- Grants, Med. Res. Found. Tex. & Galveston Heart Asn, 59-60, Tex. Heart Asn, 60-61, Nat. Insts. Health, 61-68; vis. res. prof, med. sch, Northwest. Univ, 68. Dipl, Am. Bd. Anesthesiol, 59. AAAS; fel. Am. Col. Anesthesiol; Am. Med. Asn; Am. Soc. Anesthesiol; Asn. Am. Med. Cols; Int. Anesthesia Res. Soc. Human pharmacology and physiology; cardiovascular dynamics; pulmonary circulation. Address: University of Missouri Medical Center, Columbia, MO 65201.

EGGERT, DEAN A, b. Petoskey, Mich, May 12, 38; m. 60; c. 3. PHYSIOLOGY. B.S, New Hampshire, 60; M.S, Mich. State, 61, Ph.D.(hort), 64. ASST. PROF. HORT, PURDUE UNIV, 65- U.S.A, 64-65, 1st Lt. Am. Soc. Hort. Sci. Physiological disorders of apple trees and fruits; prevention of freeze injury to low-growing crops by means of liquid foams. Address: Dept. of Horticulture, Purdue University, West Lafayette, IN 47907.

EGGERT, DONALD A, b. Cleveland, Ohio, May 13, 34. BOTANY, PALEOBOTANY. B.A, Western Reserve, 56; M.S, Yale, 58, Cullman fel, 58-59, Sheffield fel, 59-60, Ph.D.(bot), 60. Nat. Sci. Found. fel, Univ. Ill, 60-61; asst. prof. BOT, South. Ill. Univ, 61-65; prof. Univ. Iowa, 65-69; ASSOC. PROF, UNIV. ILL, CHICAGO CIRCLE, 69- Sigma Xi grant, 62-63; Nat. Sci. Found. grants, South. Ill. Univ, 63-65 & Univ. Iowa, 65-68; vis. lectr, Yale, 64-65. Morphology; anatomy; evolution of vascular land plants with emphasis upon the fossil forms of the late Paleozoic. Address: Dept. of Biological Sciences, University of Illinois at Chicago Circle, Chicago, IL 60680.

EGGERT, FRANKLIN P(AUL), b. Buffalo, N.Y, May 13, 20; m. 45; c. 4. HORTICULTURE. Ph.D.(pomol), Cornell Univ, 49. PROF. HORT, UNIV. MAINE, ORONO, 49-, DEAN GRAD. SCH, 62-, head dept, 49-62, dir. res, 62-69. U.S.M.C, 43-46. AAAS; Am. Soc. Hort. Sci; Bot. Soc. Am; Am. Pomol. Soc. Research administration. Address: Winslow Hall, University of Maine, Orono, ME 04473.

EGGERT, ROBERT G(LENN), b. Bennet, Nebr, Feb. 27, 27; m. 52; c. 2. ANIMAL NUTRITION, PHYSIOLOGY. B.S, Nebraska, 50, M.S, 52; Ph.D. (animal nutrit), Cornell, 54. Asst, Nebr. Exp. Substa, 50; animal husb. dept, Univ. Nebraska, 50-52; Cornell, 52-54; animal nutritionist, res. div, AM. CYANAMID CO, 54-59, group leader, agr. div, 59-68, SWINE PROG. MGR, 68- U.S.N, 45-46. Am. Soc. Animal Sci. Amino acid and trace mineral requirements of swine; non-protein nitrogen utilization by ruminants; antibiotics; hormones for growth and reproduction. Address: Jonathan Way, Washington Crossing, PA 18977.

EGGERT, RUSSELL, b. Niles, Mich, June 6, 05; m. 25; c. 3. HORTICULTURE, PLANT NUTRITION. B.S, Mich. State, 29, M.S, 39; Iowa State, 45-48. Instr. voc. agr, high schs, Mich, 29-42; appl. farming, New Hampshire, 42-43, asst. hort, 43-45; teaching fel. bot, Iowa State, 45-46, instr. HORT, 46-47, asst. prof, 47-48; assoc. prof, UNIV. N.HAMP, 48-64, prof, 64-70, acting chmn. dept, 61-64; EMER. PROF, 70- Northeast. Fertilizer Asn. res. grant, 53-55. Am. Soc. Hort. Sci. Nutrition of horticultural plants; problems of magnesium uptake and translocation in tree fruits. Address: 671 Wing Terrace, Deltona, FL 32763.

EGGERT, WILLIAM E(LMER), b. Wilkes-Barre, Pa, July 31, 27; m. 52; c. 3. METEOROLOGY. B.S, Pa. State, 49, M.S, 51. Instr. meteorol, Pa. State, 50-51; Fulbright scholars, Melbourne, 51-53; meteorologist, severe storms res, U.S. Weather Bur, 54-55, approach visibility proj, 55-56, meteorologist in charge, 56-59, aviation weather res. proj, 59-60; chief weather res. br, Fed. Aviation Agency, 60-63, meteorologist, syst. design team, 63-65; DIR. TEST & EVAL. LAB, NAT. WEATHER SERV, NAT. OCEANIC & ATMOS. ADMIN, 65- Am. Meteorol. Soc; Am. Geophys. Union. Aviation meteorology; meteorological optics, instrumentation and systems, mesometeorology. Address: Test & Evaluation Lab, National Weather Service, National Oceanic & Atmospheric Administration, Sterling, VA 22170.

EGGERTSEN, FRANK T(HOMAS), b. Provo, Utah, March 26, 13; m. 39; c. 3. CHEMISTRY. B.A, Utah, 34; Shevlin fel, Minnesota, 38-39, Ph.D.(phys. chem), 39. CHEMIST, Sherwin-Williams Co, Chicago, 39-43; SHELL DEVELOP. CO, SHELL OIL CO, 43- Am. Chem. Soc. Catalysts for petroleum refining processes and for manufacture of special chemicals from petroleum; general chemical and instrumental analysis; surface area of catalysts; gas chromatography; analysis of petroleum; air pollution; water pollution; thermal analysis. Address: Shell Development Co, P.O. Box 24225, Oakland, CA 94623.

EGGIMANN, WILHELM HANS, b. Zurich, Switz, Apr. 18, 29; m. 61; c. 2. ELECTRICAL ENGINEERING, SOLID STATE PHYSICS. Dipl, Swiss Fed. Inst. Tech, 54; M.S, Case, 59, Ph.D.(elec. eng), 61. Asst. microwave tech, Swiss Fed. Inst. Tech, 54-56; electromagnetic theory, Case, 56-61, asst. prof. ELEC. ENG, 61-64; ASSOC. PROF, WORCESTER POLYTECH. INST, 64- AAAS; Inst. Elec. & Electronics Eng. Electromagnetic theory; problems in diffraction theory; wave propagation and microwave techniques; plasma physics; collective interaction in solids; quantum electronics. Address: Dept. of Electrical Engineering, Worcester Polytechnic Institute, Worcester, MA 01608.

EGGLER, WILLIS A(LEXANDER), b. La Crosse, Wis, Mar. 28, 04; m. 29; c. 2. BOTANY. A.B, Northland Col, 27; M.S, Minnesota, 36, Ph.D.(bot), 39. Instr, high sch, Wis, 27-34; asst. bot, Minnesota, 35-39; instr. bot, zool. & geol, Gogebic Jr. Col, 39-42; prof. biol. & head dept, Alma Col, 42-45; assoc. prof, Cent. Mich. Col, 45-47; BOT, NEWCOMB COL, TULANE UNIV, 47-59, prof, 59-69, EMER. PROF, 69-; ASSOC. PROF. BIOL, WARREN WILSON COL, 69- AAAS; Ecol. Soc. Am. Ecology of deciduous forests; revegetation of volcanic areas; hardwoods of Mississippi river flood plains; Gulf Coast marshes; pinelands. Address: Dept. of Biology, Warren Wilson College, Swammanoa, NC 28778.

EGGLESTON, FORREST C(ARY), b. N.Y.C, Sept. 28, 20; m. 46; c. 2. MEDICINE, SURGERY. A.B, Princeton, 42; M.D, Cornell Univ, 45. Jr. attend. surgeon, first surg. div. & thoracic surg. dept, Bellevue Hosp, N.Y, 53; THORACIC SURGEON, CHRISTIAN MED. COL, INDIA, 54-, PROF. SURG, 55- Med. supt. & thoracic surgeon, Lady Irwin Sanatorium, 54- Dipl. Am. Bd. Surg. Med.C, U.S.N.R, 41-53. Fel. Am. Col. Surg. Address: Dept. of Surgery, Christian Medical College, Ludhiana, Punjab, India.

EGGLESTON, GLEN E, b. Salt Lake City, Utah, Aug. 20, 23; m. 44; c. 3. THERMODYNAMICS. B.S, Utah, 44; M.S, Washington, 49; Westinghouse fel. & ph.D.(mech. eng), Purdue, 53. Supvry. serv. engr, Westinghouse Elec. & Mfg. Co, 46-48; instr. mech. eng, Utah, 49-51; design engr, Douglas Aircraft Co, 53-58, rep. air conditioning sect, aircraft div, 58-59, asst. chief mech. sect, missiles & space systs. div, 59-62, sect. chief, 62, asst. chief vehicle design br, 62-64, br. chief, mech. sect, 64-67, asst. chief engr. crew systs, manned orbiting lab. prog, McDONNELL DOUGLAS CORP, 67-69, ASST. CHIEF ENGR. ENVIRON. ENG, 69- Instr, night sch, Carnegie Inst. Technol, 46-47; lectr, Univ. Calif, Los Angeles, 54-55. U.S.N, 44-46, Lt.(jg). Am. Soc. Mech. Eng. Heat transfer in the specific areas of aerodynamic heating. Address: 27161 Fond du Lac Rd, Palos Verdes Peninsula, CA 90274.

EGGLESTON, JOHN M, b. San Francisco, Calif, June 26, 26; m. 50; c. 4. AERONAUTICAL ENGINEERING. B.S, Va. Polytech. Inst, 49; M.S, Univ. Va, 54; Le Grange fel, Princeton, 56-57, M.S, 58; Sloan fel, Mass. Inst. Technol, 65-66, M.S, 66. Aeronaut. engr, high speed flight res. center, Nat. Adv. Cmt. Aeronaut, Edwards Air Force Base, 49-51, aeronaut. res. scientist, stability & control br, Langley Res. Center, 51-59, asst. head flight mech, NASA, 59-62, tech. asst, spacecraft tech. div, MANNED SPACECRAFT CTR, 62, asst. chief, space environ. div, 62-64, asst. chief space environ, advan. spacecraft tech. div, 64-66, assoc. chief, space sci. div, 66-67, dep. chief, lunar & earth sci. div, 67-69, ASST. TO DIR. ENG. & DEVELOP, 70- Instr, univ. exten, Univ. Va, 58-61. U.S.M.C, 44-46. Am. Inst. Aeronaut. & Astronaut; Am. Astronaut. Soc.(nat. dir, 64-). Space environment definition; scientific experiments in space; mission planning; space mechanics; guidance; navigation; stability and control; atmospheric turbulence. Address: 320 Lakeshore Dr, Seabrook, TX 77586.

EGGLETON, RICHARD E(LTON), b. Ann Arbor, Mich, Feb. 9, 32; m. 54; c. 2. GEOLOGY. B.S.E, Michigan, 54, M.S, 55; Arizona, 63-65. GEOLOGIST geol. names comt, U.S. GEOL. SURV, 55-57, eng. geol. br, 57-60, ASTROGEOL. BR, 60- AAAS; Am. Geophys. Union; Geol. Soc. Am; Am. Astronaut. Soc. Lunar geology; terrestrial impact structures. Address: Astrogeology Branch, U.S. Geological Survey, 601 E. Cedar Ave, Flagstaff, AZ 86001.

EGLAND, RICHARD JAMES, b. Portland, Ore, Mar. 18, 42. PHYSICAL CHEMISTRY. B.Sc, Western Michigan, 62; Ph.D.(phys. chem), Wisconsin, 68. Res. asst. phys. chem, Wisconsin, 66-68; sci. res. coun. fel, Univ. Leicester, 68-70; RES. FEL. DEPT. BIOCHEM, BRANDEIS UNIV, 70- Magnetic resonance studies of non-heme iron proteins; gas chromatographic method for field measurements of denitrifying bacteria. Address: 13 Dartmouth St, Waltham, MA 02154.

EGLE, DAVIS MAX, b. New Orleans, La, Jan. 31, 39; m. 63; c. 2. AEROSPACE & MECHANICAL ENGINEERING. B.S, La. State, 60; M.S, Tulane, 62, NASA fel, 63-65, Ph.D.(mech. eng), 65. Asst. prof. AEROSPACE & MECH. ENG, UNIV. OKLA, 65-69, ASSOC. PROF, 69- Okla. Regents Award, 68. Am. Soc. Mech. Eng; Am. Soc. Eng. Educ; Am. Inst. Aeronaut. & Astronaut. Theoretical and experimental structural dynamics; mechanical vibration. Address: Dept. of Aerospace & Mechanical Engineering, University of Oklahoma, Norman, OK 73069.

EGLE, JOHN LEE, b. Martinsbur, W.Va, July 13, 39; m. 61; c. 1. PHARMACOLOGY, PHYSIOLOGY. B.S, Shepherd Col, 61; M.S, West Virginia, 63, Ph.D.(pharmacol), 64. Asst, Univ. W.Va, 61-64; cardiovasc. training, Bowman Gray Sch. Med, 64-68; ASST. PROF. PHARMACOL, MED. COL. VA, VA. COMMONWEALTH UNIV, 68- Am. Col. Pharmacists. Effects of antibiotics on the flora and fauna of the rat cecum; mechanisms of the effects of hypoxia on the cardiovascular system and their alteration by drugs. Address: Medical College of Virginia, Virginia Commonwealth University, Richmond, VA 23219.

EGLER, FRANK E(DWIN), b. New York, N.Y, Apr. 26, 11; m. 68. PLANT ECOLOGY. B.S, Chicago, 32; M.S, Minnesota, 34; Eaton scholar, Yale, 35, univ. fel. & Ph.D.(plant ecol), 36; Sorbonne, 36. Res. fel, Yale & Bishop Mus, 36-37; asst. prof. forest bot, N.Y. State Col. Forestry, Syracuse, 37-44; dir. exp. sta, Chicle Develop. Co, 41-44; IN CHARGE ATON FOREST, 45- Assoc. prof, Connecticut, 47-48; tech. adv, R/W Maintenance Corp, 50-54; res. assoc, dept. conserv, Am. Mus. Natural Hist, 51-55; Guggenheim fel, 56-58; consult. vegetationist, 49-; vis. prof, Wesleyan Univ, 62 & Yale, 65. Fel. AAAS; Ecol. Soc. Am; fel. Am. Geog. Soc. Vegetation science and management; general ecology. Address: Aton Forest, Norfolk, CT 06058.

EGLI, DENNIS B, b. Fort Dodge, Iowa, Sept. 4, 42. AGRONOMY, CROP PHYSIOLOGY. B.S, Pa. State, 65; M.S, Illinois, 67, Ph.D.(agron), 69. ASST. PROF. AGRON, UNIV. KY, 69- Am. Soc. Agron; Crop Sci. Soc. Am. Crop production, ecology and physiology; soybean production. Address: Dept. of Agronomy, University of Kentucky, Lexington, KY 40506.

EGLITIS, IRMA, b. Riga, Latvia, Oct. 13, 07; nat; m. 38. ANATOMY. M.D, State Univ. Latvia, 31; cert, State Univ. N.Y. Buffalo, 68. From asst. instr. to instr. gross anat, histol, embryol, State Univ. Latvia, 31-44; instr. gross anat, Ernst Moritz Arndt Univ, 44-45; ANAT, COL. MED, OHIO STATE UNIV, 52-56, asst. prof, 56-62, assoc. prof, 62-67, PROF, 67-, COL. DENT, 56- Specialist in dermat. & syphilol. Am. Asn. Anat; Am. Med. Womens Asn. Integument; visual apparatus; blood vessels. Address: Dept. of Anatomy, Ohio State University College of Medicine, Columbus, OH 43210.

EGLITIS, JOHN A(RNOLD), b. Latvia, Dec. 16, 02; nat; m. 38. ANATOMY, OTOLARYNGOLOGY. M.D, State Univ. Latvia, 31, D.Sc.(med), 40, Dr. Habil, 42; fel, Strasbourg, 32, Innsbruck, 36-37; cert, Hamburg, 48. From asst. to assoc. prof. histol. & embryol. & chmn. dept. anat, Latvia, 27-44; assoc. prof. histol, Greifswald, 44-45; chmn. dept, Baltic Univ, Hamburg, 46-49; instr. ANAT, COL. MED, OHIO STATE UNIV, 51, asst. prof, 52-55, assoc. prof, 55-61, PROF, 61-, COL. DENT. & GRAD. SCH, 61- Prize, Latvian Culture Found, 40. Am. Asn. Anat. Glandular division; tissue cultures; blood vessels; metaplasia; spinal cord. Address: Dept. of Anatomy, Ohio State University College of Medicine, Columbus, OH 43210.

EGLOFF, DAVID ALLEN, b. Mason City, Iowa, Apr. 13, 35; m. 59; c. 2. AQUATIC ECOLOGY, INVERTEBRATE ZOOLOGY. B.A, Amherst Col, 57; M.S, Yale, 59; Nat. Insts. Health fel, Stanford, 63-66, Ph.D.(biol), 67. ASST. PROF. BIOL, OBERLIN COL, 66- Ecol. Soc. Am; Am. Soc. Zool; Am. Soc. Limnol. & Oceanog. Ecology of fresh-water and marine plankton; cyclomorphosis; sex ratio and population dynamics of copepods. Address: Dept. of Biology, Oberlin College, Oberlin, OH 44074.

EGLY, RICHARD S(AMUEL), b. Grabill, Ind, July 6, 14; m. 49; c. 4. CHEMICAL ENGINEERING. B.S, Purdue, 36; M.S, Illinois, 38, Ph.D.(chem. eng), 40. Asst. chem, Illinois, 36-40; chem. engr, COMMERCIAL SOLVENTS CORP, 40-43, chief chem. eng. group, 43-50, dir. chem. res, 50-55, dir. nitroparaffin develop, 55-57, assoc. sci. dir, 58-61, DIR. PROCESS DEVELOP, 62- With Off. Sci. Res. & Develop, 44. Am. Chem. Soc; Soc. Indust. Chem; Nat. Asn. Corrosion Eng; Am. Inst. Chem. Eng; Am. Soc. Test. & Mat. High pressure properties and techniques; heat transfer; manufacture of aliphatic amines; nitration of hydrocarbons and reactions of nitroparaffins; explosives; propellants; hazard potential of chemicals. Address: Commercial Solvents Corp, 1331 S. First St, Terre Haute, IN 47808.

EGNER, DONALD OTTO, b. Cleveland, Ohio, Apr. 18, 28; m. 50; c. 4. PHYSICS, OPERATIONS RESEARCH. B.A, West. Md. Col, 49; Delaware, 53-55. Chief surv. sect, health physics group, chem. center, U.S. ARMY, 49-51, physicist, spec. projs. div, chem. res. & develop. lab, 51, nuclear defense lab, 53-55, chief theoret. physics sect, 55-62, phys. scientist, LIMITED WAR LAB, ABERDEEN PROVING GROUND, 62-64, OPERS. RES. ANALYST, 64- Tech. dir, Tech. Assocs, Inc, 68- Chem.C, U.S.A, 51-53, 1st Lt. AAAS; Soc. Rheol; N.Y. Acad. Sci. Atmospheric physics; micrometeorology; air pollution. Address: Route 1, Box 70, Pine Hill Dr, White Marsh, MD 21162.

EGOLF, DONALD R, b. Osterburg, Pa, Aug. 27, 28; m. 64. PLANT BREEDING. B.Sc, Pa. State; Kroeger Agr. scholar; Morrell-Smith scholar; senatorial scholar; Skinner scholar; res. scholar; Shell fel; M.Sc, Cornell; Ph.D. (plant breeding). Asst. plant breeding dept, Cornell, 51-53, floriculture dept, 53-55; Fulbright scholar, London, 56-58; CYTOGENETICIST, U.S. NAT. ARBORETUM, 58- AAAS; Am. Genetic Asn; Royal Hort. Soc. Cytogenetical and cytotaxonomical studies of the genus Viburnum; cytogenetical studies in various woody ornamental groups to produce superior cultivars. Address: U.S. National Arboretum, Washington, DC 20250.

EGYÜD, LASZLO G(YORGY), b. Budapest, Hungary, Oct. 18, 27. BIOCHEMISTRY. Ford Found. scholar, London, 57-60, B.Sc, 59; Jr. Leverhulm fel, Ment. Res. Found, Eng, 60-63; Ph.D.(biochem), Lister Inst. Prev. Med, London, Eng, 63. Dept. Sci. & Indust. Res. fel. biochem, Lister Inst. Prev. Med, London, Eng, 63; independent investr, INST. CELL RES, MARINE BIOL. LAB, 63-68, CO-DIR. RES, 68- Christine & Alfred Sonntag Found. grant cancer res, 68-72. Corp. mem, Marine Biol. Lab, Woods Hole, 67- AAAS; N.Y. Acad. Sci; Brit. Biochem. Soc; Am. Acad. Ocean Sci. Enzymology; regulation of cell division and cancer; bioelectronics. Address: Institute of Cell Research, Marine Biological Lab, Woods Hole, MA 02543.

EHHALT, DIETER H(ANS), b. Heidelberg, Ger, May 11, 35; m. 57; c. 2. ATMOSPHERIC SCIENCES. B.S, Univ. Heidelberg, 56, M.S, 59, Ph.D.(physics), 63, Habil.(physics), 69. Asst. prof. physics, Univ. Heidelberg, 61-69, docent, 67-69; SR. SCIENTIST, LAB. ATMOSPHERIC SCI, NAT. CTR. ATMOSPHERIC RES, 69-, fel, 64-65, vis. scientist, 65-67. Am. Geophys. Union. Atmospheric chemistry; mass spectrometry; nuclear physics; isotope hydrology; isotope geochemistry and its application to the atmosphere; natural and man-made radioactivity; tritium; radiocarbon. Address: Lab. of Atmospheric Sciences, National Center for Atmospheric Research, Boulder, CO 80302.

EHLE, BYRON L(EONARD), b. Seattle, Wash, Jan. 18, 37; m. 58; c. 4. NUMERICAL ANALYSIS, COMPUTER SCIENCE. B.A, Whitman Col, 59; M.Sc, Stanford Univ, 61; Ph.D.(comput. sci), Univ. Waterloo, 69. Teaching asst, Stanford Univ, 59-61; instr. math, UNIV. VICTORIA (B.C), 61-69, ASST. PROF. MATH. & COMPUT. SCI, 69- Lectr, Univ. Waterloo, 66-69, res. assoc, 68-69. Asn. Comput. Mach; Am. Math. Soc; Math. Asn. Am; Can. Info. Processing Soc. Numerical methods for the solution of ordinary differential equations, particularly stiff equations; development of effective teaching tools for computer software. Address: Dept. of Mathematics, University of Victoria, Victoria, B.C, Can.

EHLER, ARTHUR WAYNE, b. Los Angeles, Calif, May 21, 22; m. 57; c. 2. PHYSICS. B.E, Southern California, 47, B.A, 48, M.S, 50, Ph.D.(physics), 55. Proj. engr, Aerophys. Develop. Corp, 54-56; asst. chief res. sect. PLASMA PHYSICS, Douglas Aircraft Co, 56-60; MEM. TECH. STAFF, Hughes Res. Labs, 60-70, AMES RES. CTR, 70- U.S.N.R, 42-46, Lt.(jg). AAAS; Am. Phys. Soc; Sci. Res. Soc. Am. Absorption of radiation by plasma; production of plasma by lasers magnetically driven shocks; electric field dissociation of molecular ions; analysis of proposed methods of producing hot, dense plasma; molecular laser research. Address: 1549 Canna Ct, Mountain View, CA 94040.

EHLERS, (FRANCIS) EDWARD, b. Portland, Oregon, Nov. 5, 16; m. 44; c. 4. APPLIED MATHEMATICS. B.S, Oregon State Col, 41; fel, Brown, 45-46, M.S, 47, Ph.D.(applied math), 49. Asst. math, Oregon State Col, 41-42, instr, 50-51; staff mem, radiation lab, Mass. Inst. Technol, 42-45; asst, grad. div. applied math, Brown, 47-49, assoc, 49-50; aerodynamicist, BOEING CO, 51-54, RES. SPECIALIST, math. serv. unit, phys. res. staff, 54-58, MATH. LAB, SCI. RES. LABS, 58- Am. Math. Soc; Soc. Indust. & Appl. Math; Am. Inst. Aeronaut. & Astronaut. Fluid mechanics; linearized theory; hodograph method; gas dynamics; mechanics; elasticity. Address: 2685 S.W. 172nd St, Seattle, WA 98166.

EHLERS, ERNEST G(EORGE), b. N.Y.C, Jan. 17, 27; m. 50; c. 2. MINERALOGY. M.S, Univ. Chicago, 50, Ph.D.(geol), 52. Asst. geol, Univ. Chicago, 50-51; geologist, N.J. Zinc Co, 52-54; asst. prof. MINERAL, OHIO STATE UNIV, 54-57, assoc. prof, 57-65, PROF, 65- Fulbright sr. lect. awards, State Univ. Utrecht, 66-67 & Univs. Athens, Patras & Thessaloniki, 71-72. U.S.N, 45. Fel. Mineral. Soc. Am; fel. Geol. Soc. Am; Geochem. Soc; Am. Ceramic Soc. Hydrothermal and high pressure equilibria; petrology; optical mineralogy. Address: Dept. of Mineralogy, Ohio State University, 104 W. 19th Ave, Columbus, OH 43210.

EHLERS, GERHARD FRIEDRICH LOUIS, b. Berlin, Ger, May 23, 13; U.S. citizen; m. 44; c. 2. ORGANIC & POLYMER CHEMISTRY. B.S, Brunswick Tech, 36, M.S, 38, Ph.D.(org. chem), 39. Res. chemist dyestuffs, I.G. Farbenindustrie A.G, Ger, 39-43; pilot plant mgr. poison gas, Anorgana G.m.b.H, 43-45; sr. res. chemist, Siemens-Schuckert Werke A.G, 48-57; RES. CHEMIST & GROUP LEADER POLYMERS, AIR FORCE MAT. LAB, WRIGHT-PATTERSON AFB, 57- Ger. Air Force. Am. Chem. Soc; Am. Soc. Test. & Mat. Polymer characterization; thermal stability, degradation mechanisms of polymers; phase transitions in polymers; structure-property correlations. Address: Air Force Materials Lab.(LNP), Wright-Patterson Air Force Base, OH 45433.

EHLERS, HERTHA, b. Brazil, May 25, 09; U.S. citizen; m. 37; c. 4. PEDIATRICS. B.S, Pacific Union Col, 33; M.D, Loma Linda, 34. Resident physician pediat. & contagion, Los Angeles County Hosp, Calif, 34-36; instr. PEDIAT, SCH. MED, LOMA LINDA UNIV, 37-39, from asst. prof. to assoc. prof, 39-61, PROF, 61- Fel. Am. Acad. Pediat; Am. Med. Asn. Renal diseases. Address: Dept. of Pediatrics, Loma Linda University School of Medicine, Loma Linda, CA 92354.

EHLERS, JÜRGEN LUDWIG, b. Hamburg, Germany, Dec. 29, 29; m. 58; c. 3. THEORETICAL PHYSICS. Dr. rer. nat.(gen. relativity), Hamburg, 58, Dr. habil.(relativistic mech), 61. Res. asst. theoret. physics, Hamburg, 59-61; res. assoc, Syracuse, 61-63; assoc. prof, Univ. Tex. Austin, 64-67, prof, 67-71; MEM. MAX PLANCK INST. PHYSICS & ASTROPHYS, 71- Vis. lectr, Kiel, 61; univ. docent, Hamburg, 63-66; vis. assoc. prof, Southwest Center for Adv. Studies, Dallas, Tex, 64-65; Flick Found. fel, 61-63. All aspects of general relativity theory and its relation to other branches of physics and to astrophysics, cosmology and differential geometry; basic conceptual and mathematical structure of physical theories. Address: Max Planck Institut für Physik und Astrophysik, 8 Munich 23, Fohringer Ring 6, W.Ger.

EHLERS, M(ELVIN) H, b. Twin Falls, Idaho, June 7, 18; m. 44; c. 2. ANIMAL BREEDING. B.S, Univ. Idaho, 43; M.S, State Col. Wash, 50, Ph.D. (animal sci), 54. Instr. & jr. dairy scientist, WASH. STATE UNIV, 52-55, asst. prof. DAIRY SCI, 59-61, assoc. prof, 61-67, PROF, 67- U.S.A, 43-46, 51-52, Capt. AAAS; Am. Soc. Animal Sci; Brit. Soc. Study Fertility; Am. Dairy Sci. Asn; Soc. Study Reproduction. Artificial insemination; semen metabolism; reproduction efficiency. Address: Dept. of Animal Sciences, Washington State University, Pullman, WA 99163.

EHLERS, VERNON JAMES, b. Pipestone, Minn, Feb. 6, 34; m. 58; c. 4. ATOMIC PHYSICS. A.B, California, Berkeley, 56, Ph.D.(physics), 60. Res. physicist, Lawrence Radiation Lab, Univ. Calif, 60-61; NATO fel, Heidelberg, 61-62; res. physicist, Lawrence Radiation Lab, Univ. Calif, 62-66; assoc. prof. PHYSICS, CALVIN COL, 66-68, PROF, 68- Lectr, Univ. Calif, Berkeley, 61-66; consult, Lawrence Radiation Lab, Univ. Calif, 66-; Nat. Sci. Found. vis. sci. faculty fel, Joint Inst. Lab. Astrophys, Univ. Colo, Boulder, 71-72. AAAS; Am. Phys. Soc; Nat. Sci. Teachers Asn; Am. Asn. Physics Teachers; Am. Sci. Affiliation. Atomic-beam, magnetic-resonance measurements of the spins and nuclear moments of radioactive nuclei. Address: Dept. of Physics, Calvin College, Grand Rapids, MI 49506.

EHLERT, THOMAS CLARENCE, b. Milwaukee, Wis, July 1, 31; m. 63; c. 4. PHYSICAL CHEMISTRY. B.S, Wisconsin, 57, M.S, 58, Ph.D.(chem), 63; Arizona, 60-62. Instr. chem, Wisconsin, Milwaukee, 57-60; U.S. Dept. Defense fel, 63-64; asst. prof. CHEM, MARQUETTE UNIV, 64-69, ASSOC. PROF, 69- U.S.A, 53-55. Am. Chem. Soc. High temperature chemistry; mass spectroscopy; fluorine chemistry. Address: Dept. of Chemistry, Marquette University, Milwaukee, WI 53233.

EHLIG, CARL F, b. Los Angeles, Calif, Apr. 2, 24; m. 57; c. 3. PLANT PHYSIOLOGY, BIOCHEMISTRY. B.S, California, 49, M.S, 50, Ph.D.(plant physiol), 54. Sr. lab. technician, California, 54-55; plant physiologist, U.S. Salinity Lab, 55-64; res. plant physiologist, U.S. Plant, Soil & Nutrit. Lab, N.Y, 64-67; PLANT PHYSIOLOGIST, IMPERIAL VALLEY CONSERV. RES. CTR, 67- Am. Soc. Agron; Soil Sci. Soc. Am; Crop Sci. Soc. Am; Am. Soc. Plant Physiol. Plant and soil water relations; plant response to saline and alkaline conditions; mineral nutrition. Address: Imperial Valley Conservation Research Center, 4151 Hwy. 86, Brawley, CA 92227.

EHLIG, PERRY L(AWRENCE), b. San Gabriel, Calif, May 23, 27; m. 51; c. 5. PETROLOGY, GEOLOGY. B.A, California, Los Angeles, 52, Humble Oil fel, 54-55, Nat. Sci. Found. fel, 55-56, Ph.D.(geol), 58. Assoc. prof. GEOL, CALIF. STATE COL, LOS ANGELES, 56-67, PROF, 67- U.S.A.F, 45-49, Res, 49-52. Geol. Soc. Am; Mineral. Soc. Am; Am. Asn. Petrol. Geol; Nat. Asn. Geol. Teachers. Metamorphic petrology, particularly the evolution of Pelona and similar schists in California; structural geology; mechanics of slow moving landslides. Address: Dept. of Geology, California State College, Los Angeles, CA 90032.

EHLMANN, ARTHUR J, b. St. Charles, Mo, May 18, 28; m. 56; c. 2. MINERALOGY. B.S, Missouri, 52, Calif. Co. fel. & M.A, 54; univ. fel. & Ph.D. (mineral), Utah, 58. Subsurface geologist, Shell Oil Co, 54-56; asst. prof. GEOL, TEX. CHRISTIAN UNIV, 58-63, assoc. prof, 63-70, PROF, 70- U.S.A, 46-48. Mineral. Soc. Am; Soc. Econ. Paleont. & Mineral. Mineralogy; genesis of clays; hydrothermal synthesis; trace studies; x-ray diffraction studies. Address: Dept. of Geology, Texas Christian University, Fort Worth, TX 76129.

EHMAN, DEWAYNE L(EE), b. Noblesville, Ind, Aug. 30, 43. ANALYTICAL CHEMISTRY. B.S, Purdue Univ, 65; Ph.D.(anal. chem), Univ. Calif, Riverside, 69. PROJ. ANALYST, CELANESE TECH. CTR, 69- AAAS; Am. Chem. Soc. Electrochemistry; gas chromatography; nuclear magnetic resonance of metal complexes. Address: Celanese Technical Center, 1901 Clarkwood Rd, Corpus Christi, TX 78408.

EHMAN, PHILIP JOHN, b. Bozeman, Mont, Aug. 29, 11; m. 38; c. 6. CHEMISTRY. B.S, Mont. State Col, 32; fel, Chicago, 34-35, Ph.D.(org. chem), 35. Res. chemist, Continental Can Co, 35-36; ANSUL CO, 36-50, mgr. chem. res, 50-57, chem. res. & develop, 57-59, res. mgr, chem. prod. div, 59-65, asst. to gen. mgr, 65-66, SPEC. PROJS. MGR, 66-69, Madison Res. Lab, 70- AAAS; Am. Chem. Soc; Soc. Chem. Indust. Refrigeration, fire protection; methylation; sulfur dioxide; heterocyclic nitrogen compounds; methyl ethers; organic arsenicals; herbicides; arsenic residues. Address: Ansul Co, P.O. Box 4325, Madison, WI 53711.

EHMANN, WILLIAM D(ONALD), b. Madison, Wis, Feb. 7, 31; m. 55; c. 4. RADIOCHEMISTRY. B.S, Wisconsin, 52, M.S, 54; Ph.D.(radiochem), Carnegie Inst. Tech, 57. Asst, Wisconsin, 52-54; Atomic Energy Cmn. proj. chemist, Carnegie Inst. Tech, 54-57, res. assoc, 57; Nat. Res. Coun-Nat. Acad. Sci. res. assoc, Argonne Nat. Lab, 57-58; asst. prof. CHEM, UNIV. KY, 58-63, assoc. prof, 63-66, PROF, 66-, distinguished prof, col. arts & sci, 68-69. Proj. dir, U.S. Atomic Energy Comn, Univ. Ky, 60-71, NASA, 68-, alumni res. award, 64; Fulbright res. scholar & hon. res. fel, inst. advan. studies, Australian Nat. Univ, 64-65; consult, Argonne Nat. Lab, 59-67; vis. prof, Ariz. State Univ, 69; invited lectr, advan. study inst, NATO, Oslo, 70. AAAS; Meteoritical Soc; Geochem. Soc; Am. Chem. Soc; Int. Asn. Geochem. & Cosmochem. Nuclear chemistry; geochemistry; cosmochemistry; low background counting techniques; activation analysis; lunar chemistry; trace elements in environmental health. Address: Dept. of Chemistry, University of Kentucky, Lexington, KY 40506.

EHNI, GEORGE (JOHN), b. Pekin, Ill, Feb. 18, 14; m. 39; c. 6. NEUROSURGERY. B.S, Northwestern, 38, M.D, 40; M.S, Minnesota, 43. Fel, Mayo Clin, Minn, 40-43, mem. sect. neurosurg, 43-44; neurosurgeon, Scott & White Clin, Temple, Tex, 46-49; assoc. prof. NEUROL. SURG, postgrad. med. sch, Texas, 49-59; PROF. & HEAD DEPT, COL. MED, BAYLOR UNIV, 59- Asst. prof, M.D. Anderson Hosp. Cancer Res, 49-59. U.S.N.R, 44-46.

Am. Med. Asn; Am. Col. Surg; Am. Asn. Neurol. Surg; Am. Neurol. Asn. Address: Dept. of Neurological Surgery, Baylor University College of Medicine, Houston, TX 77025.

EHRENBECK, RAYMOND, b. Hackensack, N.J, Oct. 13, 30; m. 58; c. 1. MECHANICAL ENGINEERING. B.S, Stevens Inst. Tech, 53; M.S, Northeastern, 60. Design engr, E.I. du Pont de Nemours & Co, 53; consult. mech. engr, Air Force Cambridge Res. Labs, 55-66; mech. engr, NASA Electronics Res. Ctr, 66-70; STAFF MECH. ENGR, TRANSPORTATION SYSTS. CTR, DEPT. TRANSPORTATION, 70- U.S.A.F, 53-55, 1st Lt. Am. Soc. Mech. Eng. Development of mechanical systems for advanced transportation systems. Address: Transportation Systems Center (TME), Dept. of Transportation, 55 Broadway, Cambridge, MA 02142.

EHRENBURG, FREDERICK KEATE, b. New York, N.Y, Apr. 13, 29; m. 55, 67; c. 4. PHYSICS, ORDNANCE. B.S, California, Berkeley, 56, M.S, 58. Prog. mgr, MB Assoc, 61-65; mem. tech. staff, Aerospace Corp, Calif, 65-67; sr. staff engr, MB Assoc, Calif, 67-70; INDUST. CONSULT. WEAPON SYST. DESIGN, DEVELOP. & MKT, 70- Res. asst. & instr, Univ. Calif, Berkeley, 58-61; consult. nuclear reactor experimentation, summer 61. U.S.A, 46-49, 50-52, S/Sgt. Am. Nuclear Soc; Am. Inst. Physics; Am. Phys. Soc; Inst. Elec. & Electronics Eng. Development of small rocket special weapons; high density, small volume data recorders; magnetohydrodynamic power sources for laser pumping; defense of strategic Inter-Continental Ballistic Missile force; command and control of strategic Inter-Continental Ballistic Missile defense forces; reentry decoys; tactical warfare ordnance; signals and markers. Address: P.O. Box 524, Blue Jay, CA 92317.

EHRENFELD, DAVID W, b. New York, N.Y, Jan. 15, 38; m. 70. ANIMAL PHYSIOLOGY & BEHAVIOR. B.A, Harvard, 59, M.D, 63; Nat. Insts. Health fel, 64; Ph.D (zool), Florida, 66. Interim asst. prof. BIOL. SCI, Florida, 67; asst. prof. BARNARD COL, COLUMBIA UNIV, 67-71, ASSOC. PROF, 71- N.Y. Acad. Sci; Ecol. Soc. Am. Orientation and navigation of sea turtles; supporting studies of visual and olfactory physiology of sea turtles; biological conservation. Address: Dept. of Biology, Barnard College, Columbia University, New York, NY 10027.

EHRENFELD, ELVERA, b. Phila, Pa, Mar. 1, 42. BIOCHEMISTRY. B.A, Brandeis Univ, 62; Ph.D.(biochem), Univ. Fla, 67. Fel, ALBERT EINSTEIN COL. MED, 67-69, ASST. PROF. CELL BIOL, 69- Nat. Sci. Found. res. grant, 70- RNA virus replication and inhibition of host-cell function; regulation of gene expression in animal cells. Address: Dept. of Cell Biology, Albert Einstein College of Medicine, 1300 Morris Park Ave, Bronx, NY 10461.

EHRENFELD, JOHN R(OOS), b. Chicago, Ill, May 16, 31; m. 56; c. 3. CHEMICAL ENGINEERING. Nat. Sci. Found. fel, B.S. & Sc.D.(chem. eng), 53. Proj. leader, Arthur D. Little Co, 57-61; staff engr, Prototech, Inc, 61-62; dep. dir, appl. sci. lab, GCA Tech. Div, GCA Corp, 62-65, dir, 65-66, dir. appl. res. opers, 66-68; PRES, WALDEN RES. CORP, 68- Lectr, Univ. Md, 59. Chem.C, 57-59, 1st Lt. AAAS; Am. Chem. Soc; Am. Inst. Chem. Eng; Air Pollution Control Asn. Radiative heat transfer; thermodynamics of phase equilibria; fuel cells; applied mathematics; air pollution control; combustion. Address: 359 Allston St, Cambridge, MA 02139.

EHRENFELD, LOUIS, b. Houston, Tex, Aug. 23, 00; m. 27; c. 2. CHEMISTRY. B.S, Rice Inst, 21; fel, Northwestern, 21-26, M.S, 22. Instr. chem, Northwestern, 26-27; consult. chemist, 26-30; curator chem, Mus. Sci. & Indust, Chicago, 30-37; asst. to mgr. & dean, Wahl-Henius Inst, Chicago, 33-38; mgr, Milwaukee Div, Pabst Brewing Co, 38-44; tech. dir, Red Top Brewing Co, Cincinnati, 44-53; ENG. CONSULT, 53- V.pres. res. & develop, Alex Fries & Bro, Inc, 55-66; instr, Ohio Mechanics Inst, 56-59; spec. lectr, Cincinnati Sci. Ctr, 67-69. Mem. ed. staff, Encycl. Britannica, 26-28. U.S.A, 17-19. Am. Chem. Soc; Inst. Food Tech. Alcoholic fermentation; humanization of chemistry; food technology. Address: 1617 E. McMillan St, Cincinnati, OH 45206.

EHRENFELD, ROBERT LOUIS, b. N.Y.C, Sept. 18, 21; m. 55; c. 3. ORGANIC CHEMISTRY. A.B, Cornell, 42. Sage fel. & Ph.D.(org. chem), 48. Asst, Cornell, 42-43; res. chemist, Off. Sci. Res. & Develop. & Manhattan Proj, Columbia, 43-46; res. assoc, Mass. Inst. Tech, 48-49; PRES. & GEN. MGR, HALOCARBON PRODS. CORP, 50- Am. Chem. Soc. Preparation, polymerization and depolymerization of organic fluorine compounds; reactions of free fluorine; photochemical chlorination of chlorofluoro ethylenes as related to their fluorination with elementary fluorine. Address: Halocarbon Products Corp, 82 Burlews Ct, Hackensack, NJ 07601.

EHRENFORD, FRANK A(LVIN), JR, b. New York, N.Y, Oct. 7, 15; m. 56; c. 2. VETERINARY & MEDICAL PARASITOLOGY. B.S, California, 47, Ph.D. (parasitol), 52. Asst. med. entom. & helminth, California, 47-49; biologist, mosquito surv. bur. vector control, U.S. Pub. Health Serv, 49; res. asst. vet. parasitol, California, 49-52; parasitologist, Pitman-Moore Co. Div. Dow Chem. Co, 52-66, group leader, parasitol, human health res. & develop. lab, 66-69, res. specialist, agr. dept, 69-70; RES. PARASITOLOGIST, AGR. VET. PROD. DEPT, ABBOTT LABS, 70- Vis. lectr, sch. pub. health, med. sch, Ind. Univ. U.S.A, 42-46, Maj. Am. Soc. Parasitol; Am. Soc. Trop. Med. & Hyg. Nutrition effect on host-parasite relationship; experimental chemotherapy of veterinary and medical helminths and protozoa; experimental host-parasite systems; parasite ecology. Address: Agricultural Veterinary Products Dept, Abbott Labs, Box 188, Long Grove, IL 60047.

EHRENHAFT, JOHANN L, b. Vienna, Austria, Oct. 10, 15; nat; m. 53; c. 1. SURGERY. Vienna; M.D, Iowa, 38. Intern surg, Hopkins Hosp, 38-39, Halsted fel, 39-40; res, COL. MED, UNIV. IOWA, 40-42, 45-47, instr, 47-48, assoc, 48-49; asst. prof. GEN. SURGERY, 49-51, assoc. prof, 51-53, PROF, 53-, CHMN. DIV. THORACIC SURG, 49- Fel, Barnes Hosp, St. Louis, Mo, 48-49. Med.C, 42-46, Maj. AAAS; Am. Med. Asn; fel. Am. Col. Surg; Asn. Thoracic Surg; Am. Col. Chest Physicians; Soc. Vascular Surg; Am. Surg. Asn; Am. Geriatrics Soc; Soc. Univ. Surg; Am. Heart Asn; Asn. Mil. Surg. U.S; Int. Cardiovasc. Soc. Thoracic and cardiac disease; subjects in cardiovascular surgery. Address: 325 Beldon Ave, Iowa City, IA 52240.

EHRENPREIS, L(EON), b. Brooklyn, N.Y, May 22, 30; m. 61; c. 2. MATHEMATICS. B.S, City Col, 50; M.A, Columbia, 51, Ph.D.(math), 53. Instr. MATH, Hopkins, 53-54; mem, Inst. Adv. Study, 54-57; assoc. prof, Brandeis, 57-59; Yeshiva Univ, 59-61; prof, Courant Inst. Math. Sci, N.Y. Univ, 62-68; PROF, YESHIVA UNIV, 68- Am. Math. Soc. Partial differential equations; lie groups; several complex variables; automorphic functions; theory of distributions; methodology in learning for students and researchers. Address: Dept. of Mathematics, Yeshiva University, Washington Heights, New York, NY 10033.

EHRENPREIS, S(EYMOUR), b. Brooklyn, N.Y, June 20, 27; m. 54; c. 3. BIOCHEMISTRY, NEUROCHEMISTRY. B.S, City Col, 49; fel, N.Y. Univ, 51-53, Ph.D, 54. Res. assoc. biochem, sch. med, Pittsburgh, 53-55; res. assoc. & instr. chem, Cornell, 55-57; res. assoc. & asst. prof. biochem, col. physicians & surgeons, Columbia, 57-61; assoc. prof. pharmacol, sch. med, Georgetown Univ, 61-68; assoc. prof. pharmacol. & head lab. molecular pharmacol, N.Y. Med. Col, 68-70; ASSOC. RES. SCIENTIST, N.Y. STATE RES. INST. NEUROCHEM. & DRUG ADDICTION, 71- Burger lectr, Univ. Va, 65; mem. vis. sci. prog, Am. Pharmaceut. Asn, 68-; ed. Neurosci. Res, 69- U.S.N, 45-46. Fel. AAAS; fel. Am. Inst. Chem; Am. Soc. Biol. Chem; Am. Soc. Pharmacol. & Exp. Therapeut; Am. Chem. Soc; Soc. Exp. Biol. & Med; assoc. mem. Am. Med. Asn. Protein interactions and modifications; kinetics and equilibria in the fibrinogen-thrombin system; mechanism of quaternary ammonium-macromolecular interactions; molecular mechanisms of nerve activity and neurotropic drug action; isolation of drug receptors; cholinesterase; smooth muscle pharmacology. Address: New York State Research Institute for Neurochemistry & Drug Addiction, Ward's Island, NY 10035.

EHRENREICH, HENRY, b. Frankfurt, Ger, May 11, 28; nat; m. 53; c. 3. THEORETICAL PHYSICS. A.B, Cornell, 50, Ph.D.(physics), 55. Theoret. physicist, res. lab, Gen. Elec. Co, 55-63; GORDON McKAY PROF. APPL. PHYSICS, HARVARD, 63-, vis. lectr, 60-61. Vis. prof, Brandeis Univ. & Univ. Paris, 69. Fel. Am. Acad. Arts & Sci; fel. Am. Phys. Soc. Solid state physics; optical properties of solids; transport and many particle theory; semiconductors; theory of metals; electronic properties of disordered systems. Address: Division of Engineering & Applied Physics, Harvard University, Cambridge, MA 02138.

EHRENREICH, JOHN H(ELMUTH), b. New London, Wis, Feb. 17, 29; m. 54; c. 2. FORESTRY, RANGE MANAGEMENT. B.S, Colorado State, 51, M.S, 54; Ph.D.(plant ecol), Iowa State, 57. Res. aide, Colorado State, 53-54; from asst. to instr. gen. bot, Iowa State, 55-57; proj. leader range & wildlife res, U.S. Forest Serv, 57; res. assoc. forestry, Missouri, 57-60, assoc. prof, 60-64; prof. range mgt, Univ. Ariz, 64-66, prof. watershed mgt. & head dept, 66-71; DEAN COL. FORESTRY, WILDLIFE & RANGE SCI, UNIV. IDAHO, 71- Summers, range aide, U.S. Forest Serv, 49, 53, res. aide, Colo. State, 50. U.S.A.F, 51-53, 1st Lt. Ecol. Soc. Am; Am. Soc. Range Mgt; Soc. Am. Foresters; Wildlife Soc. Ecological research in soil-plant relations. Address: College of Forestry, Wildlife & Range Sciences, University of Idaho, Moscow, ID 83844.

EHRENREICH, THEODORE, b. N.Y.C, July 30, 13. PATHOLOGY. M.D, Univ. Paris, 39. Littauer fel. path, Harvard, 42-44; pathologist, Bronx Vet. Admin. Hosp, 48-58; dir. labs, St. Francis Hosp, 58-66; assoc. prof. path. & clin. path, N.Y. Med. Col, 56-67, prof, 67-68; DIR. LABS, LUTHERAN MED. CTR, 68- Consult. cancer res, Bronx Vet. Admin. Hosp; lectr. forensic med, sch. med, N.Y. Univ, 67- Dipl, Am. Bd. Path. Med.C, U.S.A, 44-46. Am. Soc. Clin. Path; fel. Col. Am. Path; Am. Med. Asn; Am. Asn. Path. & Bact; N.Y. Acad. Med; Int. Acad. Forensic Med; Int. Acad. Path. Pathologic anatomy; cancer; nephropathology. Address: 400 E. 57th St, New York, NY 10022.

EHRENSON, STANTON J(AY), b. New York, N.Y, Oct. 13, 31; m. 60; c. 2. PHYSICAL CHEMISTRY. B.S, Long Island, 52; M.S, Wisconsin, 54; Tenn. Eastman fel, Ga. Inst. Tech, 56, Ph.D.(chem), 57. Fel. chem, Pa. State, 57-58, instr, 58-59; res. assoc, Chicago, 59-62; assoc. chemist, BROOKHAVEN NAT. LABS, 62-66, CHEMIST, 66- Fel. AAAS; Am. Chem. Soc; Fedn. Am. Scientists. Molecular structure; organic reaction mechanisms. Address: Dept. of Chemistry, Brookhaven National Lab, Upton, NY 11973.

EHRENSTEIN, GERALD, b. N.Y.C, Sept. 27, 31; m. 60; c. 3. BIOPHYSICS, MOLECULAR PHYSICS. B.E.E, Cooper Union, 52; M.A, Columbia, 58, Ph.D.(physics), 62. Asst. microwave spectros, Columbia Radiation Lab, 57-62; PHYSICIST, NAT. INSTS. HEALTH, 62- Mem. sci. technol. adv. comt, Wash. Tech. Inst; mem. corp, Marine Biol. Lab, Woods Hole, Mass. U.S.C.G, 52-54, Lt.(jg). Am. Phys. Soc; Biophys. Soc. Mechanism of nervous excitation; membrane phenomena; molecular structure. Address: Lab. of Biophysics, National Institutes of Health, Bethesda, MD 20014.

EHRENSTORFER, SIEGLINDE K. M, b. Regensburg, Ger, Oct. 24, 27; m; c. 1. INORGANIC & PHYSICAL CHEMISTRY. B.S, Univ. Munich, 54, M.S, 57, Ph.D.(phys. chem), 60. Res. chemist, Allied Chem. Corp, 60-66; Stauffer Chem. Corp, 66-68; sr. res. chemist, Armour Pharmaceut. Co, 68-70; V.PRES, RUIG APOCH INC, 70- Am. Chem. Soc; Soc. German Chem. Organic, clinical, analytical, medicinal chemistry; reactions in the solid state; zeolitic phosphates; gas hydrates; catalysis; colloids; antiperspirants; emulsions; clinical testing. Address: 1162 Tuxedo Square, Teaneck, NJ 07666.

EHRENTHAL, IRVING, b. N.Y.C, Sept. 22, 18; m. 46; c. 3. BIOCHEMISTRY. B.A, Yeshiva Univ, 39; M.S, Michigan, 40; Ph.D.(agr. biochem), Minnesota, 50. Org. chemist, org. med. res, Wm. R. Warner & Co, 46-47; sr. biochemist, Maimonides Hosp, 51; sr. chemist, vitamins, Nopco Chem. Co, 51-53; GROUP LEADER, CARBOHYDRATES, ANHEUSER-BUSCH, INC, 54- U.S.A, 42-45. Am. Chem. Soc. Carbohydrates; starch and starch hydrolyzates; polysaccharide structure. Address: 1003 Laval Dr, University City, MO 63132.

EHRET, ANNE, b. Belleville, Ill, Oct. 10, 37. PHYSICAL ORGANIC CHEMISTRY. B.S, Illinois, 59; M.S, California, Los Angeles, 62, Ph.D.(org. chem), 67. Asst. prof. CHEM, Drake Univ, 67-71; FEL, HARVARD, 71- Am. Chem. Soc. Organic reaction kinetics involving ion pairing phenomena. Address: Dept. of Chemistry, Harvard University, Cambridge, MA 02138.

EHRET, CHARLES F(REDERICK), b. New York, N.Y, Mar. 9, 23; m. 45; c. 6. ZOOLOGY. B.S, City Col. New York, 46; fel, Notre Dame, 46-48, M.S, 48, Ph.D, 51. Jr. biologist, ARGONNE NAT. LAB, 48-51, assoc. biologist, 51-66, SR. BIOLOGIST, 66- U.S. Pub. Health Serv. fel, inst. biophys, Geneva, 60-61; vis. prof, Indiana, 63; NASA fel, 66; vis. prof, Univ. Wis, 71. Consult, Atomic Energy Comn. & Nat. Sci. Found. Centennial medal award sci, Univ. Notre Dame, 65; distinguished scientist award, Argonne Univ. Asn, 71. U.S.A, 43-46. Am. Soc. Zool; Soc. Protozool; Am. Soc. Gen. Physiol. Photobiology; action spectroscopy; photoperiodism and cellular rhythmicity; microbial epigenetics; organelle theory of cell ultrastructure; electron microscopic autoradiography and organelle development; eukaryotic-circadian principle; circadian-infradian rule and chronon theory of biological clocks. Address: Biology Division, Argonne National Laboratory, Argonne, IL 60439.

EHRET, WILLIAM F(REDERICK), b. New York, N.Y, July 18, 02; m. 26; c. 2. PHYSICAL CHEMISTRY. B.S, Col. City of N.Y, 23, fel, 23-24; M.S, Columbia, 24, Ph.D.(chem), 27. Asst. CHEM, Columbia, 24-26; instr, N.Y. UNIV, 26-29, asst. prof, 29-32, assoc. prof, 32-36, PROF, 36- Exchange lectr, Edinburgh, 29-30; vis. prof, Columbia, 43-44; Hawaii, 50-51. AAAS; Am. Chem. Soc; fel. N.Y. Acad. Sci. Phase rule studies in alloy systems and aqueous solutions; the properties of inorganic substances. Address: Dept. of Chemistry, New York University, Washington Square, New York, NY 10003.

EHRHARDT, C(HARLES) H(ENRY), b. Plainfield, Wis, Dec. 21, 10; m. 39; c. 1. PHYSICS. B.S, Hillsdale Col, 33; Ph.D.(physics), Purdue, 39. Asst. physics, Purdue, 34-39, instr, 39-40; res. physicist, Universal Oil Prods. Co, Chicago, 40-47; Swift & Co, 47-49; AM. OIL CO, 49-53, GROUP LEADER, 53- Am. Phys. Soc; Am. Chem. Soc; Electron Micros. Soc. Am. X-ray diffraction and structure of materials; physical methods of analysis. Address: 8850 Idlewild Ave, Highland, IN 46322.

EHRHART, LLEWELLYN M(cDOWELL), b. Dallastown, Pa, Apr. 22, 42; m. 64; c. 2. MAMMALOGY. B.A, Franklin & Marshall Col, 64; Woodrow Wilson nat. fel, Cornell Univ, 64-65, Ph.D, 71. Instr. vertebrate zool, Cornell Univ, 67; ASST. PROF. BIOL. SCI, FLA. TECHNOL. UNIV, 69- AAAS; Am. Soc. Mammal; Ecol. Soc. Am; Soc. Study Evolution. Behavioral ecology of the cricetine rodent genus, Peromyscus; effects of aircraft noise on wildlife. Address: Dept. of Biological Sciences, Florida Technological University, Orlando, FL 32816.

EHRHART, WENDELL A, b. Dallastown, Pa, Nov. 12, 34; m. 58; c. 2. ORGANIC CHEMISTRY. B.S, Franklin & Marshall Col, 56; M.A, Princeton, 58, Parke, Davis & Co. fel, 58-59, Ph.D.(org. chem), 61. CHEMIST, flooring div, ARMSTRONG CORK CO, 60-64, CHEM. DIV, 64- Am. Chem. Soc. Synthesis and property studies of amidines, pyrimidines, pyrimido (4,5-d) pyrimidines, polyesters and polyurethanes; formulation and processing of polymers. Address: 160 School House Lane, Hellam, PA 17406.

EHRHORN, JACK M(ACFARLANE), b. Mountain View, Calif, Nov. 17, 02; m. 29, 67; c. 5. MINING ENGINEERING. A.B, Stanford, 25, E.M, 27; cert. adv. mgt. prog, Harvard, 55. From miner to shift boss in several mines, Ariz, Calif, Nev. & Utah, 27-32; shift boss, Idaho Md. Mines Corp, 32-35, mine supt, 35-38; consult. mining engr, 38-42; construct. supt, West. Knapp Engr. Co, 42-44; indust. relations engr, U.S. Smelting Refining & Mining Co, 44-45, supt, U.S. Mines, 45-51, asst. to mgr. mines, 51-52, dir. indust. develop, 52-71; CONSULT. MINING ENGR. & MINERAL ECONOMIST, 71- Chmn. & mem. adv. coun, col. mines & minerals industs, Univ. Utah, 60-70; adv. bd, Utah Geol. & Mineral. Surv, 63-70. Soc. Mining Eng.(pres, 65); Am. Inst. Mining, Metall. & Petrol. Eng.(v.pres, 65 & 66); Can. Inst. Mining & Metall. Mine production and management; industrial and engineering research; exploration and mineral development; mineral economy. Address: 1711 S. Eighth St, Las Vegas, NV 89104.

EHRICH, F(ELIX) FREDERICK, b. N.Y.C, Oct. 19, 19; m. 53; c. 3. ORGANIC CHEMISTRY. B.S, City Col. New York, 39; M.S, Iowa, 40; Ph.D.(org. chem), Maryland, 42. Asst. chem, Maryland, 40-42; org. res. chemist, Corn Prod. Ref. Co, 42; E.I. DU PONT DE NEMOURS & CO, INC, 46-58, res. supvr, 58-70, TECH. DIR, PIGMENTS DEPT, COLORQUIM S.A. DE C.V, 70- U.S.A.A.F, 43-46, chief test facility, eng. div, Air Force Materiel Command, 1st Lt. Am. Chem. Soc. Synthetic pigments; barbituric acids; molecular rearrangements; spiropyrimidine and heterocyclic syntheses; phthalocyanine and quinacridone pigments. Address: E.I. du Pont de Nemours & Co, Inc, International Dept, Wilmington, DE 19898.

EHRICH, FREDRIC F(RANKLIN), b. New York, N.Y, Dec. 17, 28; m. 55; c. 3. MECHANICAL ENGINEERING. B.S, Mass. Inst. Tech, 47, Shell fel, 49-51, M.E, 50, Sc.D.(mech. eng), 51; Netherlands Govt. fel, Tech. Inst, Delft, 47-48. Supvr. anal. & mech. develop. & tech. rep, Rolls Royce, Eng, Westinghouse Elec. Corp, 51-57; mgr. preliminary design, turbomachinery eng. oper. & T64 engine design, GEN. ELEC. CO, 57-66, mgr. preliminary design, turbomach. & mech. syst. eng. oper, AIRCRAFT ENGINE GROUP, 66-68, mgr. design tech. oper, 68-70, MGR. TECH. PLANS, 70- Am. Soc. Mech. Eng; Am. Inst. Aeronaut. & Astronaut. Aerodynamics; applied mechanics; mechanical design. Address: Aircraft Engine Group, General Electric Co, 1000 Western Ave, Lynn, MA 01910.

EHRICKE, KRAFFT ARNOLD, b. Berlin, Ger, Mar. 24, 17; U.S. citizen; m. 45; c. 3. AERONAUTICAL ENGINEERING. Tech. Univ, Berlin, 41-42; L.H.D, Nat. Col. Educ, Evanston, 61. Develop. engr, Ger, 42-45; jet propulsion engr, Dept. Army, Ft. Bliss, 47-50, chief gasdynamics sect, Army Ballistic Missile Ctr, Redstone Arsenal, 50-52; systs. engr, Bell Aircraft Corp, 52-54; design specialist, Convair Div, Gen. Dynamics Corp, 54-55, chief, design & systs. anal, 56-57, asst. to tech. dir, Convair-Astronautics, 57-58; originator & prog. dir, Centaur Space Vehicle, 58-62, dir. advan. studies dept, 62-65; asst. div. dir. Astrionics Div, N.Am. Aviation, 65-68; CHIEF SCI. ADV. SPACE SYSTS. & APPL, SPACE DIV, N.AM. ROCKWELL CORP, 68- Chmn, NASA adv. comt. elec. energy systs, 59-62; consult, Dept. Defense-U.S. Air Force, 58-61. Guenther Loeser Medal, Int. Astronaut. Fedn, 56. Fel. Am. Astron. Soc; Am. Inst. Aeronaut. & Astronaut. (Astronautics Award, 57; G. Edward Pendray Award, 61); Brit. Interplanetary Soc; Int. Acad. Astronaut; Ger. Soc. Space Res.(pres, 42-43). Address: Space Division, North American Rockwell Corp, 12214 Lakewood Blvd, Downey, CA 90241.

EHRIG, RAYMOND J(OHN), b. Jersey City, N.J, Dec. 31, 28; m. 50; c. 5. POLYMER CHEMISTRY. B.S, Seton Hall, 50; fels, Polytech. Inst. Brooklyn, 52-56, M.S, 53, Ph.D.(chem), 57. Anal. chemist, U.S. Testing Co, 50-52; res. chemist, Shell Chem. Corp, 57-60, sr. res. chemist, 60-62; res. supvr, W.R. Grace & Co, 62-66; mgr. polymerization res, Chemplex Co, 66-69; DIV. CHIEF, PLASTICS, APPL. RES. LAB, U.S. STEEL CORP, 69- Lectr, Univ. Calif, Long Beach, 57-59; Col. Immaculate Conception, 60-62; Col. Notre Dame (Md), 63-65; Elmhurst Col, 66-69. AAAS; Am. Chem. Soc; Soc. Plastics Eng; Soc. Plastics Indust. Ionic and radical polymerization and copolymerization; polymer kinetics and thermal decomposition studies; polymer chemistry; polystyrene; polyethylene. Address: 2360 Milgrove Rd, Pittsburgh, PA 15241.

EHRLE, ELWOOD B(ERNHARD), b. Paterson, N.J, Nov. 13, 33; m. 56; c. 3. PLANT TAXONOMY. B.S, Rutgers, 54; M.A, Columbia, 55; Ph.D.(bot), Pa. State, 58. Teaching asst. bot, Pa. State, 55-58; prof. biol. & acting chmn. dept, State Univ. N.Y. Col. Geneseo, 58-68; assoc. dir. off. biol. educ, Am. Inst. Biol. Sci, 68-71; DEAN SCH. ARTS & SCI, MANKATO STATE COL, 71- Partic, acad. year inst, Cornell Univ, 66; chmn. sci-technol. adv. bd, Wash. Tech. Inst; consult, Am. Inst. Biol. Sci; Consult. Bur. Facilities & Curriculum Design. AAAS; Bot. Soc. Am; Am. Soc. Plant Taxon; Int. Asn. Plant Taxon; Soc. Study Evolution; Am. Bryol. & Lichenological Soc; Am. Inst. Biol. Sci; Nat. Asn. Biol. Teachers. Bryology; organic evolution; biological education. Address: School of Arts & Science, Mankato State College, Mankato, MN 56001.

EHRLICH, ANNETTE, b. Brooklyn, N.Y, Mar. 23, 31. PHYSIOLOGICAL PSYCHOLOGY. B.S, Brooklyn Col, 54; M.A, City Col. New York, 56; Ph.D. (physiol. psychol), McGill, 60. Asst. psychol, McGill, 56-60; res. assoc, Chicago Wesley Mem. Hosp, Ill, 60-64; vis. scientist, primate ctr, Univ. Wash, 64-66; asst. prof. PSYCHOL, Bowling Green State Univ, 66-69; CALIF. STATE COL, LOS ANGELES, 69-71, ASSOC. PROF, 71- Lectr, Northwest. Univ, 63-64; Nat. Inst. Mental Health grants, 68-69, 70-72. AAAS; Am. Psychol. Asn; N.Y. Acad. Sci. Primate behavior. Address: Dept. of Psychology, California State College at Los Angeles, Los Angeles, CA 90032.

EHRLICH, EDWARD NORMAN, b. Detroit, Mich, Sept. 20, 28; m. 61; c. 3. INTERNAL MEDICINE. B.S, Michigan, 48, M.D, 52. Intern MED, Wayne County Gen. Hosp, 52-53, resident, 53-54; UNIV. CHICAGO, 57-60, instr, 60-61, asst. prof, 61-68, ASSOC. PROF, 68- U.S.N.R, 54-57, Lt.Comdr. AAAS; Am. Fedn. Clin. Res; Am. Polar Soc; Endocrine Soc. Adrenocortical regulation of salt metabolism in humans. Address: Dept. of Medicine, University of Chicago, Chicago, IL 60637.

EHRLICH, GEORGE EDWARD, b. Vienna, Austria, July 18, 28; U.S. citizen; m. 68; c. 1. INTERNAL MEDICINE. A.B, Harvard, 48; M.B. & M.D, Chicago Med. Sch, 52. Intern, Michael Reese Hosp, Chicago, Ill, 52-53; asst. res. surg. & path, Francis Delafield Hosp, New York, N.Y, 55-56; med, Beth Israel Hosp, Boston, Mass, 56-57; res, New Eng. Center Hosp, 57-58; train trainee, Nat. Inst. Arthritis & Metab. Diseases, Bethesda, Md, 58-59; instr. med, med. col, Cornell Univ, 59-64; asst. prof. med. & phys. med. & rehab, SCH. MED, TEMPLE UNIV, 64-66, ASSOC. PROF. PHYS. MED. & REHAB, 66-, MED, 67-; DIR, ARTHRITIS CTR. & SECT. RHEUMATOLOGY, ALBERT EINSTEIN MED. CTR. & MOSS REHAB. HOSP, 64-, SR. ATTEND. PHYSICIAN, 64- Fel, Hosp. Spec. Surg. N.Y, 59-60; Sloan Kettering Inst, 60-61; spec. fel, Arthritis & Rheumatism Found, 64; lectr, grad. sch. med, Univ. Pa, 64-; consult, U.S. Naval Hosp, Phila, 64-; Food & Drug Admin; Squibb-Olin fel, Mem. Ctr. Cancer & Allied Diseases, 68. Ed, Jour. Albert Einstein Med. Ctr; Arthritis & Rheumatic Diseases Abstracts, 68-70. Philip Hench Award, 71; Distinguished Serv. Award, Arthritis Found, 71. Med.C, 53-55, U.S.N.R, Comdr. Am. Col. Physicians; Am. Rheumatism Asn; Am. Med. Asn; Am. Med. Writers' Asn; Am. Fedn. Clin. Res; Royal Soc. Trop. Med. & Hyg; Am. Cong. Rehab. Med; Am. Pub. Health Asn; Am. Soc. Human Genetics; fel. Am. Geriat. Soc; hon. fel. Ecuador Rheumatism Soc; hon. mem. Ecuador Med. Asn; Pam-Am. Med. Asn. Rheumatology; investigations of the arthritis of joint dynamics; pathogenesis of arthritis manifestations. Address: Albert Einstein Medical Center, York & Tabor Rds, Philadelphia, PA 19141.

EHRLICH, GERT, b. Vienna, Austria, June 22, 26, nat; m. 57. PHYSICAL CHEMISTRY. A.B, Columbia, 48; fel. Harvard, 48-50, A.M, 50, Nat. Inst. Health fel, 51-52, Ph.D.(chem), 52. Res. assoc, physics, Univ. Mich, 52-53; metal res. dept, Gen. Elec. Res. Lab, 53-68; PROF. PHYS. METALL. & RES. PROF, COORD. SCI. LAB, UNIV. ILL, URBANA, 68- U.S.A, 45-47. Am. Chem. Soc; Faraday Soc; fel. Am. Phys. Soc; Am. Vacuum Soc. Polymer electrolytes; light scattering, infrared spectroscopy; physical chemistry of interfaces; surface processes; field and ion microscopy; ultra high vacuum techniques. Address: Coordinated Science Lab, University of Illinois, Urbana, IL 61801.

EHRLICH, GERTRUDE, b. Vienna, Austria, Jan. 7, 23; nat. MATHEMATICS. B.S, Ga. State Col. Women, 43; M.A, North Carolina, 45; Ph.D.(math), Tennessee, 53. Instr. MATH, Oglethorpe, 46-50; asst, Tennessee, 50-52, instr, 52-53; UNIV. MD, COLLEGE PARK, 53-56, asst. prof, 56-62, assoc. prof, 62-69, PROF, 69- Math. Asn. Am; Am. Math. Soc. Continuous geometry; ring theory. Address: 6702 Wells Pkwy, University Park, MD 20782.

EHRLICH, HENRY L(UTZ), b. Stettin, Ger, Aug. 31, 25; nat. MICROBIOLOGY. B.S, Harvard, 48; M.S, Wisconsin, 49, Ph.D.(agr. bact), 51. Alumni Res. Found. asst, Wisconsin, 48-50, asst, 50-51; asst. prof. BIOL, RENSSELAER POLYTECH. INST, 51-57, assoc. prof, 57-64, PROF, 64- AAAS; fel. Am. Acad. Microbiol; Am. Soc. Microbiol; Am. Inst. Biol. Sci; Soc. Indust. Microbiol. Geomicrobiology; microbial physiology; bacteriophage. Address: Dept. of Biology, Rensselaer Polytechnic Institute, Troy, NY 12181.

EHRLICH, HOWARD G(EORGE), b. Milwaukee, Wis, Nov. 9, 24; m. 55; c. 2. CYTOLOGY. B.S, Marquette, 48; Boyce-Edens res. scholar, Minnesota, 54, Conway MacMillan mem. fel, 54-55, Ph.D.(cytol), 56. Asst. bot, Marquette, 46-48; res. asst. plant path, Minnesota, 50-52, asst. bot, 52-54, 55-56, res. fel, Cancer Soc, 56-58, Dight Inst, 58, instr. bot, 59; asst. prof. BIOL, DUQUESNE UNIV, 59-63, assoc. prof, 63-68, PROF, 68-, CHMN. DEPT. BIOL. SCI, 71-, acting chmn, 70-71. Inf, U.S.A, 43-45. AAAS; Bot. Soc. Am; Mycol. Soc. Am. Mycology; electron microscopy; growth. Address: Dept. of Biological Sciences, Duquesne University, Pittsburgh, PA 15219.

EHRLICH, I(RA) ROBERT, b. Washington, D.C, Sept. 1, 26; m. 50; c. 2. MECHANICAL ENGINEERING. B.S, U.S. Mil. Acad, 50; M.S, Purdue, 56; Ph.D.(eng), Michigan, 60. Supvr. programming, Int. Elec. Corp, 60-62; MGR. TRANSPORTATION RES. GROUP, DAVIDSON LAB, STEVENS INST. TECHNOL, 62- Guest lectr, U.S. Mil. Acad, 63- Consult, Grumman Aircraft Corp, 60-; Midwest Appl. Sci. Corp, 62-65; Chrysler Corp, 65. Gen. secy, Int. Soc. Terrain-Vehicle Systs, 63- Ord.C, U.S.A, 45-60, Capt. Am. Soc. Mech. Eng; Soc. Automotive Eng; Am. Soc. Test. & Mat. Transportation research. Address: Davidson Lab, Stevens Institute of Technology, Castle Point Station, Hoboken, NJ 07030.

EHRLICH, JOHN, b. New York, N.Y, Dec. 13, 07; m. 36; c. 1. MICROBIOLOGY. B.S, Cornell, 28; fel, Duke, 28-29, A.M, 29; S.M, Harvard, 30, Ames scholar, 31-33, Ph.D.(biol), 33. Asst. Harvard & Radcliffe Col, 29-30, Austin teaching fel, Harvard, 30-31; Nat. Res. Coun. fel, Imp. Mycol. Inst, Kew, England, 33-34; res. grant, Royal Bot. Gardens, 35; asst. prof. forestry, Idaho, 35-40, assoc. prof, 40-44; res. assoc, Minnesota, 44; div. head res. labs, Parke, Davis & Co, 44-52; lab. dir. antibiotic res, 52-70; INSTR. BIOL, HIGHLAND PARK COL, 70- With War Prod. Bd, 44. AAAS; Mycol. Soc. Am; Am. Soc. Microbiol; Soc. Indust. Microbiol; Am. Acad. Microbiol. Beech bark disease; white pine blister rust; Armillaria rot; systematic mycology, especially Nectriaceae; microbiology of antibiotics; chloramphenicol; viomycin; azaserine; D.O.N; elaiomycin; griseoviridin; viridogrisein; actinobolin; paromomycin; streptimidone; chalcomycin; antiviral antibiotics. Address: 15601 Essex Dr, Grosse Pointe Park, MI 48230.

EHRLICH, JOSEPH CHARLES, b. New York, N.Y, Oct. 13, 04; m. 31; c. 3. MEDICINE. Columbia, 21-23; M.D, L.I. Col. Med, 27. Littauer fel. path. rheumatic fever, Mt. Sinai Hosp, New York, 30; dir. labs, Lebanon Hosp, 32-63; DIR. DEPT. PATH, BRONX-LEBANON HOSP. CTR, 64- Res. assoc, Mt. Sinai Hosp, New York, 33-47; assoc. clin. prof. path, Albert Einstein Col. Med, Yeshiva; consult, St. Vincent's Hosp, Staten Island, N.Y. Med.C, 42-45, Maj. Am. Asn. Path. & Bact; fel. Col. Am. Path; N.Y. Acad. Sci. General and surgical pathology. Address: Bronx-Lebanon Hospital Center, 1650 Grand Concourse, Bronx, NY 10457.

EHRLICH, JULIAN, b. N.Y.C. PHYSICAL & POLYMER CHEMISTRY. B.S, City Col. New York, 42; D.D.S, N.Y. Univ, 45; M.S, Stevens Inst. Technol, 63, Ph.D.(chem), 71. Private practice, N.Y.C, 47-60; head anal. div, Schwarz Bio-Res. Corp, N.Y, 60-62; res. chemist, M&T Chem, Inc, div, Am. Can Co, N.J, 62-65; fel, U.S. Pub. Health Serv, 65-70; RES. ASSOC, U.S. Dept. Navy, 70-71; POLYMER CHEM, STEVENS INST. TECHNOL, 71- Vis. dentist, North. Dispensary New York, 47-49; Jewish Mem. Hosp, 47-48; lectr, Plastics Inst. Am, 66-69. Dent.C, U.S.N.R, 45-47, Lt. Comdr. Am. Chem. Soc; N.Y. Acad. Sci. Characterization of polymers; biophysical chemistry; ultracentrifugation; polysaccharide chemistry; dental caries and dental plaque; computer programming. Address: Dept. of Chemistry, Stevens Institute of Technology, Castle Point Station, Hoboken, NJ 07030.

EHRLICH, KENNETH C(RAIG), b. N.Y.C, Sept. 23, 43; m. 66. ORGANIC CHEMISTRY. A.B, Columbia Col, 65; Nat. Insts. Health fel, State Univ. N.Y. Stony Brook, 66-69; Ph.D.(chem), 70. NAT. INSTS. HEALTH FEL, COLUMBIA UNIV, 70- Am. Chem. Soc. Trimethylene-methane-iron tricarbonyl complexes; organometallic complexes; anti-aromatic compounds; boron chelates. Address: Havemeyer Hall, Dept. of Chemistry, Columbia University, Box 554, New York, NY 10027.

EHRLICH, LOUIS WILLIAM, b. Baltimore, Md, Oct. 4, 27; m. 59; c. 3. MATHEMATICS. B.S, Maryland, 51, M.A, 56; Ph.D, Texas, 63. Proj. engr, Hercules Powder Co, 51-54; asst. math, Maryland, 54-56; numerical analyst, Space Tech. Labs, Ramo-Wooldridge Corp, 56-59; res. scientist, Texas, 59-62; NUMERICAL ANALYST, APPL. PHYSICS LAB, JOHNS HOPKINS UNIV, 62- U.S.A, 45-47. Am. Math. Soc; Math. Asn. Am; Asn. Comput. Mach; Soc. Indust. & Appl. Math. Numerical analysis, including linear algebraic systems, finite difference approximations to elliptic partial differential equations and nonlinear systems. Address: Applied Physics Lab, Johns Hopkins University, 8621 Georgia Ave, Silver Spring, MD 20910.

EHRLICH, MARGARETE, b. Vienna, Austria, Sept. 28, 15; nat. RADIATION PHYSICS. Ph.D.(physics), Cath. Univ. Am, 55. X-ray technician, Grady Mem. Hosp, Atlanta, 40-48; PHYSICIST, NAT. BUR. STANDARDS, 48- Consult, Int. Atomic Energy Agency, 60-61; partic, First Int. Cong. Radiation Protection, 66; Second Int. Conf. Luminescence Dosimetry, 67; Fourth Int. Cong. Radiation Res, 70. Meritorious serv. award, U.S. Dept. Commerce, 62. Am. Phys. Soc; Radiation Res. Soc; Am. Asn. Physicists in Med; Health Physics Soc. Thermoluminescence dosimetry of x- and gamma radiation and electrons; radiologic physics. Address: C-210 Radiation Physics Bldg, National Bureau of Standards, Washington, DC 20234.

EHRLICH, MARY A(NN), b. Buffalo, N.Y, July 12, 26; m. 55; c. 2. BOTANY, PLANT PATHOLOGY. Ph.B, Marquette, 47; Ph.D.(plant path), Minnesota, Minneapolis, 55. Instr. biol, Marquette, 53-57; ed. asst, J. Plant Physiol, 57-59; RES. ASSOC. BIOL, DUQUESNE UNIV, 59- AAAS; Bot. Soc. Am; Am. Phytopath. Soc. Electron microscopy of plant fungal parasitism. Address: Dept. of Biology, Duquesne University, Pittsburgh, PA 15219.

EHRLICH, MORRIS J(OSEPH), b. Baltimore, Md, May 8, 20; m. 41; c. 1. PHYSICAL OPTICS. B.E, Hopkins, 41; M.S, California, 47, Ph.D.(eng), 50. Res. physicist, Lawrence Radiation Lab, California, 46-48; res. engr, Antenna Lab, 48-50; res. physicist, Hughes Aircraft Co, 50-54; Microwave

Radiation Co, 54-63; mem. staff, Aerospace Corp, 63-67; Hughes Aircraft Co, 67-68; br. chief antenna, electronics res. ctr, NASA, Mass, 68-69; MGR. COMMUN. EQUIP, INFO. SYSTS. DIV, MARTIN MARIETTA CO, 69- Lectr, Univ. Calif, 48-50, Los Angeles, 53- U.S.N.R, 42-46, Lt. Am. Phys. Soc; Inst. Elec. & Electronics Eng. Microwave antennas; electromagnetic theory. Address: Information Systems Division, Martin Marietta Co, Orlando, FL 32802.

EHRLICH, PAUL, b. Vienna, Austria, Feb. 26, 23; nat; m. 49; c. 5. PHYSICAL CHEMISTRY. B.S, Queens (N.Y), 44; M.S, Wisconsin, 48, Ph.D, 51. Phys. chemist, Nat. Bur. Standards, 51-53; fel. chem, Harvard, 53-54; res. chemist, Monsanto Co, 55-59, res. specialist, 59-60, group leader, 60-61, scientist, 61-67; assoc. prof. CHEM. ENG, STATE UNIV. N.Y. BUFFALO, 67-70, PROF, 70- U.S.A, 44-46. AAAS; Am. Phys. Soc; Am. Chem. Soc. Physical chemistry of polymers; high pressure polymerization of ethylene; thermodynamics of critical region. Address: Dept. of Chemical Engineering, State University of New York at Buffalo, Buffalo, NY 14214.

EHRLICH, PAUL R(ALPH), b. Phila, Pa, May 29, 32; m. 54; c. 1. BIOLOGY. A.B, Pennsylvania, 53; M.A, Kansas, 55, univ. fel, 54-55, Nat. Sci. Found. fel, 55-57, Ph.D.(entom), 57; hon. D.H.A, Univ. Pac, 70. Asst. entom, Kansas, 53-54, assoc, 58-59; res. assoc, Chicago Acad. Sci, 57-58; asst. prof. BIOL, STANFORD UNIV, 59-62, assoc. prof, 62-66, PROF, 66- Soc. Syst. Zool; Ecol. Soc. Am; Am. Soc. Naturalists; Soc. Study Evolution; Lepidop. Soc.(secy, 57-63). Population biology. Address: Dept. of Biological Sciences, Stanford University, Stanford, CA 94305.

EHRLICH, RICHARD, b. N.Y.C, Dec. 25, 21; m. 45; c. 2. REACTOR PHYSICS. B.A, Harvard, 41; Ph.D.(theoret. physics), Cornell, 47. Asst. physics, Cornell, 41-43, nat. res. fel, 46; jr. scientist, California, Los Alamos, N.Mex, 43-46; res. assoc. physics, GEN. ELEC. CO, 47-54, supvr, theoretical physics, 54, MGR, 54-55, math. anal, 55-58, ADV. DEVELOP, 58- Mem. adv. comt. reactor physics, U.S. Atomic Energy Comn, 60-; chmn. adv. comt. nat. neutron cross sect. ctr, Brookhaven Nat. Lab, 67- Fel. AAAS; Am. Phys. Soc; fel. Am. Nuclear Soc; Asn. Comput. Mach. Theoretical physics work in atomic energy field; nuclear reactor design and analysis; digital computations; technical management. Address: General Electric Co, Knolls Atomic Power Lab, Schenectady, NY 12301.

EHRLICH, RICHARD, b. Bedzin, Poland, Jan. 19, 24; nat; m. 50; c. 2. BACTERIOLOGY. M.S, Munich Tech. Univ, 48, Ph.D.(dairy bact), 49. Res. asst, Munich Tech. Univ, 47-49; lab. dir, Am. Butter Inst, 49-52; assoc. bacteriologist, IIT RES. INST, 52-53, res. bacteriologist, 53-57, supvr. biol. res, 57-60, asst. dir, 60-62, assoc. dir, 62-63, DIR. LIFE SCI, 63- AAAS; Am. Soc. Microbiol; N.Y. Acad. Sci; Air Pollution Control Asn. Public health bacteriology; respiratory infections; bacterial aerosols; sterilization techniques; microdetection methods for microorganisms; infectious aerobiology; space biology; health effects of air pollution. Address: Life Sciences Research Division, IIT Research Institute, 10 W. 35th St, Chicago, IL 60616.

EHRLICH, ROBERT, b. St. Paul, Minn, Mar. 4, 36. GEOLOGY, SEDIMENTOLOGY. B.A, Univ. Minn, 58; M.S, La. State Univ, 61, Mobil fel. & Ph.D. (geol), 65. Asst. prof. GEOL, MICH. STATE UNIV, 65-70, ASSOC. PROF, 70- Geol. Soc. Am; Int. Asn. Math. Geol; Int. Asn. Sedimentol. Detrital sedimentology; geometrics; organic geochemistry; crustal dynamics as expressed in sediments. Address: Dept. of Geology, Michigan State University, East Lansing, MI 48823.

EHRLICH, ROBERT, b. Brooklyn, N.Y, Feb. 6, 38; m. 61; c. 1. PHYSICS. B.S, Brooklyn Col, 59; Ph.D.(physics), Columbia Univ, 64. Res. investr. PHYSICS, Univ. Pa, 63-66; ASST. PROF, RUTGERS UNIV, 66- Am. Phys. Soc. Experimental elementary particle research. Address: Dept. of Physics, Rutgers, The State University, New Brunswick, NJ 08903.

EHRLICH, ROBERT S(TARK), b. N.Y.C, Aug. 30, 40; m. 67; c. 1. PHYSICS. A.B, Columbia Univ, 62; M.S, Rutgers Univ, 64, Ph.D.(physics), 69. Writer, Crowell-Collier Publ, 62; asst. prof. physics, Muskingum Col, 69-70; instr, City Col. New York, 70-71; RES. ASSOC. BIOCHEM, MED. SCH, RUTGERS UNIV, 71- Am. Phys. Soc; Am. Asn. Physics Teachers. Nuclear magnetic resonance used to study self-diffusion in liquid and gaseous xenon; magnetic resonance in biological materials. Address: 9 Civic Center Dr, Apt. 3, East Brunswick, NJ 08816.

EHRLICH, SANFORD H(OWARD), b. N.Y.C, June 11, 31; m. 55; c. 2. CHEMICAL PHYSICS. B.S, N.Y. Univ, 53, M.S, 59; Ph.D.(chem. physics), Adelphi, 63. Chem. physicist, Air Prod. & Chem, Inc, 63-65; sr. scientist, Am. Optical Co, Mass, 65-70; MEM. STAFF, RES. LABS, EASTMAN KODAK CO, 70- Med.C, 53-55. Am. Chem. Soc; Am. Vacuum Soc; Am. Phys. Soc. Energy transfer in gases and solids; spectroscopy of surface adsorbed molecules; photochemistry; thermodynamics of nonaqueous solutions; transference phenomena in nonaqueous media; luminescence and energy transfer in organic molecules; infrared spectroscopy of polymers; polarized emission; electrooptical effects. Address: Research Labs, Eastman Kodak Co, 343 State St, Rochester, NY 14650.

EHRLICH, S(AUL) PAUL, JR, b. Minneapolis, Minn, May 4, 32; m. 59; c. 2. EPIDEMIOLOGY, PUBLIC HEALTH. B.A, Minnesota, 53, B.S, 55, M.D, 57; M.P.H, California, 61. Intern, U.S. PUB. HEALTH SERV, Staten Island, N.Y, 57-58, med. off, Coast Guard, 58-59, Nat. Heart Inst, 59-60, chief heart disease control prog, field & training sta, 61-66, asst. chief prog. develop, heart disease control prog, div. chronic diseases, 66-67, chief tech. resources, off. int. health, 67-70, ASST. SURGEON GEN, 70-, DIR. OFF. INT. HEALTH, OFF. OF SECY, U.S. DEPT. HEALTH EDUC. & WELFARE, 70-, dep. dir, 69-70. Resident, sch. pub. health, Univ. Calif, 61-63, lectr, 63-; rep. to exec. bd, WHO, 69-; assoc. prof, Georgetown Univ, 69-; adj. prof, sch. pub. health, Univ. Tex, Houston, 70-; fel. coun. epidemiol, Am. Heart Asn. Dipl. Am. Bd. Prev. Med. AAAS; fel. Am. Col. Prev. Med; Am. Med. Asn; fel. Am. Pub. Health Asn; Am. Geriat. Soc; N.Y. Acad. Sci; Int. Epidemiol. Asn. Epidemiology of cardiovascular diseases; chronic diseases in geriatric groups. Address: Office of International Health, Office of the Secretary, U.S. Dept. of Health, Education and Welfare, 330 C St. S.W, Washington, DC 20201.

EHRLICH, STANLEY L(EONARD), b. Newark, N.J, Jan. 7, 25; m. 49; c. 3. ACOUSTICS, SYSTEMS ENGINEERING. Sc.B, Brown, 44, Sc.M, 45; fel, Mass. Inst. Tech, 45-48; Connecticut, 51-53. Physicist, U.S. Navy Underwater Sound Lab, 48-53; sr. engr. transducer develop, SUBMARINE SIG. DIV, RAYTHEON CO, 53-57, SONAR SYSTS. DEVELOP, 57-59, sect. mgr, 59-62, prin. engr, 62-70, CONSULT. ENGR, 70- AAAS; Am. Phys. Soc; fel. Acoust. Soc. Am; sr. mem. Inst. Elec. & Electronics Eng.(del, Am. Nat. Standards Inst, 71); Nat. Security Indust. Asn. Magnetostriction; electrostriction; electroacoustics; design of transducers; development of sonar systems; normal modes in solids, especially cylinders. Address: 1 Acacia Dr, Middletown, RI 02840.

EHRLICH, W(ALTER) A(RNOLD), b. Canora, Sask, Aug. 24, 09; m. 30. SOILS, GEOLOGY. B.S.A, Univ. Man, 39, M.Sc, 46; Ph.D.(soils), Univ. Minn, 54. Sr. pedologist, CAN. DEPT. AGR, 39-64, soils correlator, West. Can, 64-67, RES. COORD. PEDOLOGY, RES. BR, 67- Hon. res. prof. soil sci, Univ. Man, 64- Can. Soc. Soil Sci.(pres, 58-59); fel. Agr. Inst. Can; Int. Soc. Soil Sci. Soil classification; soil correlation. Address: Canada Dept. of Agriculture Research Branch, K.W. Neatby Bldg, Central Experimental Farm, Ottawa, Ont. K1A 0C6, Can.

EHRLINGER, HENRY P, III, b. Kellogg, Idaho, Aug. 5, 25; m; c. 2. METALLURGICAL ENGINEERING. E.M, Colo. Sch. Mines, 50; M.S, Nevada, 57. Metall. engr, Mex. Mining Dept, Am. Smelting & Refining Co, 50-53, 57-59, mill supt, Charcas Unit, 60-64; metall. engr, Atomic Energy Comn. res. proj, Univ. Nevada, 53-57; mill engr, Pima Mining Co, 64-66; MINERALS ENGR, MINERALS ENG. SECT, ILL. STATE GEOL. SURV, 66- U.S.A, 43-46, T/Sgt. Am. Inst. Mining, Metall. & Petrol. Eng; Mining & Metall. Soc. Am. Minerals beneficiation and utilization, research, development and commercial application. Address: Minerals Engineering Section, Illinois State Geological Survey, Urbana, IL 61801.

EHRMAN, JOACHIM B(ENEDICT), b. Nuremberg, Germany, Nov. 12, 29; nat; m. 61; c. 1. THEORETICAL PHYSICS. A.B, Pennsylvania, 48; A.M, Princeton, 49, Ph.D.(physics), 54. Mem. dept. physics, atomic energy res. dept, N.Am. Aviation, Inc, 51-53; instr, Sloane Physics Lab, Yale, 54-55; physicist nucleonics div, U.S. Naval Res. Lab, 55-66, plasma physics div, 66-68; PROF. APPL. MATH, UNIV. WEST. ONT, 68- Assoc. prof. lectr. physics, George Washington, 56-57; lectr, Maryland, 63-64; consult, plasma physics div, U.S. Naval Res. Lab, 69-70. Am. Phys. Soc. Plasma physics; electron beams; electron penetration through matter; nuclear reactors; group theory; nuclear physics. Address: Dept. of Applied Mathematics, University of Western Ontario, London 72, Ont, Can.

EHRMAN, LEE, b. N.Y.C, May 25, 35; m. 55; c. 2. POPULATION GENETICS. B.S, Queens Col.(N.Y), 56; M.A, Columbia, 57, Ph.D.(genetics), 59. Lectr. zool, Barnard Col, 56-58, U.S. Pub. Health Serv. fels. genetics, Columbia, 59-62; res. assoc. POP. GENETICS, ROCKEFELLER UNIV, 62-64, ASST. PROF, 64-; ASSOC. PROF. NATURAL SCI, STATE UNIV. N.Y. PURCHASE, 71- Shirley Farr fel, Am. Asn. Univ. Women, 62-63; Sigma Xi grant-in-aid, 63; Nat. Inst. Child Health & Human Develop. res. career develop. award, 64-, tutor biol, Queens Col.(N.Y), 61 & summers, 58-60; summer lectr. zool, Columbia, 62. AAAS; Soc. Study Evolution; Genetics Soc. Am; Animal Behavior Soc; Am. Eugenics Soc; Am. Soc. Zool; Am. Soc. Nat. Reproductive isolating mechanisms, especially hybrid sterility and sexual behavioral isolation; cytoplasmic inheritance. Address: Division of Natural Sciences, State University of New York at Purchase, Purchase, NY 10577.

EHRMAN, LEONARD, b. New York, N.Y, Jan. 24, 32; m. 57; c. 1. ELECTRICAL ENGINEERING. B.S, Mass. Inst. Tech, 53, M.S, 55; Ph.D.(elec. eng), Northeastern, 67. Mem. tech. staff, Sandia Corp, N.Mex, 58-61; group leader, res. & adv. develop. div, Avco Corp, Mass, 61-63; RES. SCIENTIST, SIGNATRON, INC, 63- Sig.C, U.S.A, 56-58, 1st Lt. Sr. mem. Inst. Elec. & Electronics Eng. Digital communications; radar analysis; signal processing; computer usage; data processing; bandwidth compression; channel characterization. Address: Signatron, Inc, 27 Hartwell Ave, Lexington, MA 02173.

EHRMANN, ROBERT LINCOLN, b. Boston, Mass, Sept. 2, 22; m. 58; c. 2. CELL BIOLOGY, PATHOLOGY. A.B, Swarthmore Col, 44; M.D, N.Y. Univ, 46. Med. House officer, Beth Israel Hosp, Boston, Mass, 46-47; res. fel. tissue culture, Hopkins Hosp, 49-51, U.S. Pub. Health Serv. sr. asst. surgeon, 51-56; sr. asst. res. path, Peter Bent Brigham Hosp, Boston, Mass, 56-58; asst. res, Boston Lying-In Hosp, 58; PARKWAY DIV, BOSTON HOSP. WOMEN, 59, asst. pathologist, 59-70, PATHOLOGIST, 70- Teaching fel. path, Harvard Med. Sch, 58-59, instr, 59-62, clin. assoc, 62-71, asst. prof, 71-74; Nat. Cancer Inst. grants, 58-68; dir, Boston Sch. Cytotechnol, 69-; Am. Cancer Soc. grant, 70-71. U.S. Army, 47-49, Capt; U.S.P.H.S, 51-56, Sr. Surgeon. AAAS; Tissue Culture Asn; Col. Am. Path; N.Y. Acad. Sci. Invasive behavior of transplantable choriocarcinoma when inoculated into hamster tissues; factors that cause human endometrium to secrete in organ culture; stimulation of new blood vessel growth by tumor implants and extracts of choriocarcinoma in the hamster cheek pouch. Address: Parkway Division, Boston Hospital for Women, 245 Pond Ave, Brookline, MA 02146.

EHRMANTRAUT, HARRY C(HARLES), b. Wash, D.C, Nov. 25, 21; m. 48; c. 1. BIOPHYSICS, BIOCHEMISTRY. B.S, George Washington, 47; M.S, Georgetown, 48; Ph.D.(biophys), Illinois, 50. Asst. photosynthesis proj, Illinois, 48-50; exec. secy. panel med. aspects atomic warfare, Res. & Develop. Bd, Off. Secy. Defense, 50-51; asst. to dir. res, Toni Co, 51-52; res. biophysicist, Armour Res. Found, 52-54; sr. biophysicist, Stanford Res. Inst, 54-55; dir. applns. res. dept, Spinco Div, Beckman Instruments, Inc, 56-59; pres, Mechrolab, Inc, 59-66; sci. adv, Found. for Nutrit. & Stress Res, 66-68; pres, Gymnas Corp, 68-70; CHMN, IMPROVED COMMUN, INC, 70- Pres. & dir, Altos Ctr, Inc, 70-71; mem, Int. Oceanog. Found. AAAS; Am. Chem. Soc; N.Y. Acad. Sci; Inst. Elec. & Electronics Eng; Biophys. Soc. Medical and biophysical instrumentation. Address: 541 Hawthorne Ave, Los Altos, CA 94022.

EHRREICH, ALBERT LeROY, b. Pipestone, Minn, June 11, 23; m. 51; c. 2. GEOLOGY. B.A, California, Los Angeles, 50, M.A, 55, Ph.D.(geol), 65. Geologist, U.S. Bur. Reclamation, 51-53; asst. prof. GEOL, CALIF. STATE COL. LONG BEACH, 57-64, ASSOC. PROF, 65- U.S.N.R, Lt. Geol. Soc. Am; Geochem. Soc; Mineral. Soc. Am; Nat. Asn. Geol. Teachers. Igneous and metamorphic petrology. Address: Dept. of Geology, California State College, Long Beach, 6101 E. Seventh St, Long Beach, CA 90804.

EHRREICH, STEWART JOEL, b. Brooklyn, N.Y, Mar. 24, 36; m. 60; c. 2. PHARMACOLOGY. B.S, Queens Col.(N.Y), 57; M.S. State Univ. N.Y. Downstate Med. Ctr, 61, Ph.D.(pharmacol), 63. Asst. pharmacol, Downstate Med. Ctr, 58-63; U.S. Pub. Health Serv. fel, med. col, Cornell, 63-65; sr. pharmacologist, Smith Kline & French Labs, 65-67, sr. investr, 67-69; sect. head, Geigy Pharmaceut. Div, Ciba-Geigy Ltd, 69-71; PRIN. SCIENTIST, SCHERING CORP, 71- Lectr. biol, Queens Col.(N.Y), 63-65; Brooklyn Col, 64-65. Pharmacology, physiology and electro-physiology of smooth and cardiac muscle; autonomic pharmacology. Address: 7 Sunderland Pl, Suffern, NY 10901.

EHRSTEIN, JAMES R(OBERT), b. Rochester, N.Y, July 30, 40. SOLID STATE PHYSICS. B.S, St. John Fisher Col, 62; Ph.D.(physics), Catholic Univ, 68. PHYSICIST, NAT. BUR. STANDARDS, 68- Am. Phys. Soc. Transport properties and fermi surface of metals; electrical properties of semiconductor epitaxial layers. Address: Bldg. 225, National Bureau of Standards, Washington, DC 20234.

EIAN, GILBERT L(EE), b. Fergus Falls, Minn, Apr. 15, 43; m. 66; c. 1. ORGANIC CHEMISTRY. B.Chem, Univ. Minn, Minneapolis, 65; M.S, Iowa State Univ, 67, Ph.D.(chem), 69. SR. CHEMIST, 3M CO, 69- AAAS; Am. Chem. Soc. Organic synthesis; organic photochemistry and light sensitive systems; free radicals in organic chemistry; chemistry of organic nitrogen compounds. Address: Central Research Lab, 3M Co, P.O. Box 33221, St. Paul, MN 55101.

EIARDI, ANTHONY J(OSEPH), S.J, b. Holyoke, Mass, July 3, 09. MATHEMATICS. A.B, Boston Col, 35, M.A.(philos), 36, M.A.(math), 38; S.T.L, Weston Col, 42. Instr. MATH, Boston Col, 36-38, ASSOC. PROF, 42-54, chmn. dept, 48-53; FAIRFIELD UNIV, 54- Am. Math. Soc; Math. Asn. Am. Teaching analysis on a college level. Address: Dept. of Mathematics, Fairfield University, Fairfield, CT 06430.

EIBECK, RICHARD E(LMER), b. Cincinnati, Ohio, Feb. 17, 35; m. 62; c. 2. ORGANIC CHEMISTRY. B.S, Cincinnati, 57; M.S, Illinois, 59, Ph.D.(chem), 61. Res. chemist, gen. chem. div, ALLIED CHEM. CORP, 60-64, sr. res. chemist, 64-67, TECH. SUPVR. indust. chem. div, 67, SPECIALTY CHEM. DIV, 67- Fel. Am. Inst. Chem. Chemistry of nonmetals; fluorine compounds, including sulfur fluorides; nitrogen fluorides; fluorocarbons; dielectric materials; alkali metal polysulfides. Address: 23 Pine Terrace, Orchard Park, NY 14127.

EIBEN, GALEN J, b. Monticello, Iowa, May 23, 36; m. 56; c. 3. ENTOMOLOGY. B.A, Wartburg Col, 60; M.S, Iowa State, 62, Ph.D.(entom), 67. Instr. biol, Tex. Lutheran Col, 62-64; res. assoc. entom, Iowa State, 64-66; ASST. PROF. BIOL, WARTBURG COL, 67- Am. Entom. Soc. Methodology involved in screening corn for resistance to corn rootworms; corn root development and its relation to rootworm populations. Address: Dept. of Biology, Wartburg College, Waverly, IA 50677.

EIBEN, ROBERT M(ICHAEL), b. Cleveland, Ohio, July 12, 22; m. 46; c. 6. MEDICINE. B.S, Western Reserve, 44, M.D, 46. Instr. pediat, CASE WEST. RESERVE UNIV, 49-51, asst. clin. prof, 51-54, asst. prof, 54-65, ASSOC. PROF. PEDIAT, 65-, ASST. PROF. NEUROL, 63- Asst. med. dir, dept. contagious diseases, Cleveland City Hosp, 49-50, acting dir, 50-52, asst. dir. dept. pediat. & contagious diseases, 54-60, med. dir, Respirator Care & Rehabilitation Center, 54-60; asst. pediatrist, Univ. Hosps, 49-51, assoc. pediatrist, 51-; fel, Univ. Wash, 60-63; pediat. neurologist, Cleveland Metrop. Gen. Hosp, 63- Am. Acad. Neurol; Am. Soc. Human Genetics; Am. Acad. Pediat; Am. Pediat. Soc. Biochemical studies of heredofamilial disorders of the nervous system. Address: 13303 Lakeshore Blvd, Bratenahl, OH 44108.

EIBERT, JOHN, JR, b. St. Louis, Mo, Sept. 18, 18; div; c. 4. CHEMISTRY. B.S, Washington (St. Louis), 40, scholar. & M.S, 42, fel. & Ph.D.(chem), 44; Calif. Inst. Tech, 40-41. Chemist, Scullin Steel Co, St. Louis, 42-43; lectr. physics, Washington (St. Louis), 43-44; res. chemist, Pan Am. Ref. Corp, Tex, 44-45; Anheuser-Busch, Inc, Mo, 45-46; consult. chemist & secy-treas, SCI. ASSOCS, 46-61, PRES, 61- Am. Chem. Soc; assoc. Inst. Food Tech. Calorimetry; measurement of vapor pressure; catalysis; protein hydrolysis; thermodynamic properties of certain aromatic hydrocarbons. Address: Scientific Associates, 6200 S. Lindbergh Blvd, St. Louis, MO 63123.

EIBLING, JAMES A(LEXANDER), b. Marion, Ohio, Nov. 22, 17; m. 40; c. 2. MECHANICAL ENGINEERING. B.M.E, Ohio State, 39. Mech. engr, B.F. Goodrich Co, Akron, 40-42; res. engr, BATTELLE MEM. INST, 46-56, asst. div. chief, 56-60, CHIEF THERMAL SYSTS. DIV, 60- C.Eng, 42-46, Res, 46-60, Lt.Col. Fel. Am. Soc. Mech. Eng; Am. Soc. Heat, Refrig. & Air-Conditioning Eng; Solar Energy Soc; Int. Inst. Refrig. Refrigeration; air conditioning; thermal systems; solar energy; sea water conversion; energy conversion devices; heat transfer; thermal and flow models. Address: Thermal Systems Division, Battelle Memorial Institute, Columbus, OH 43201.

EICH, ROBERT, b. Ann Arbor, Mich, Oct. 4, 23; m. 51; c. 3. MEDICINE. A.B, Michigan, 47, M.D, 51. Asst. prof. MED, STATE UNIV. N.Y. UPSTATE MED. CTR, 57-58, assoc. prof, 58-71, PROF, 71- U.S.A, 43-46. Cardiovascular disease; internal medicine. Address: State University of New York, Upstate Medical Center, Syracuse, NY 13210.

EICH, STEPHEN (JOSEPH), b. New York, N.Y, Aug. 31, 24; m. 46; c. 2. BIOCHEMISTRY. B.S, Queens Col, 48; M.S, Fordham, 50, Ph.D.(biochem), 55. Asst, Fordham, 52-54; res. assoc. med. col, Cornell, 54-56, instr, 56-57; res. investr, G.D. SEARLE & CO, 57-68, sr. res. investr, 68-71, ASST. DIR. BIOCHEM. RES, 71- U.S.A, 43-46. AAAS; Am. Chem. Soc; N.Y. Acad. Sci. ►

Mode of action of thiamine antagonists; ergothioneine; polysaccharides; peptides; biochemistry of mammalian reproduction; protein chemistry. Address: Biochemistry Dept, G.D. Searle & Co, Box 5110, Chicago, IL 60680.

EICHBAUM, BARLANE R, b. New Brunswick, N.J, Sept. 1, 26; m. 50; c. 3. SOLID STATE PHYSICS, CERAMIC ENGINEERING. B.S, Rutgers, 51, Ph.D. (ceramic eng), 56; M.S, Texas, 53; Temple, 62-65. Prod. & control engr, Hercules Powder Co, 50-52; res. & develop. engr, Am. Rock Wool Corp, 52; Texas State scholar. & Edward Orton Jr. fel, 52-53; proj. engr, U.S. Signal Corps, Rutgers, 53-56; res. engr, Int. Bus. Mach. Corp, 56-57, develop. engr. & tech. consult, prod. develop. labs, 57-59; mgr. magnetic tech, Aeronutronic Comput. Div, Ford Motor Co, 59-60, solid state devices, aeronutronic res. labs, 60, eng, 60-62, asst. dir, Philco Res. Labs, 62-63, dir. phys. electronics, Philco Corp, 63-65; dir. corp. develop. & tech. asst. to v.pres. eng. & res, Amp, Inc, Pa, 65-67; dir. res. & asst. to v.pres. eng, Gulton Industs, Inc, N.J, 67-69; DIR. RES. & DEVELOP, LEAR MOTORS CORP, 69- U.S.A.A.F, 45-46. Electrochem. Soc; Am. Ceramic Soc; sr. mem. Inst. Elec. & Electronics Eng; Sci. Res. Soc. Am; Am. Soc. Test. & Mat; Nat. Inst. Ceramic Eng; Am. Phys. Soc; Electronic Indust. Asn. Chemistry; ceramics; crystallography; metallurgy; general, electronic and mechanical engineering; materials in advanced equipment; electronic systems technology. Address: Lear Motors Corp, 5910 Alpha Ave, Reno, NV 89506.

EICHBERG, JOSEPH, b. Oct. 5, 35; U.S. citizen; m. 64; c. 2. BIOCHEMISTRY. B.S, Mass. Inst. Technol, 57; Ph.D.(biochem), Harvard, 62. Res. assoc. BIOL. CHEM, HARVARD MED. SCH, 64-68, assoc, 68-69, ASST. PROF, 69- U.S. Pub. Health Serv. fel, 62-65; estab. investr, Am. Heart Asn, 68-73; mem. bd. tutors, Harvard, 69- Am. Soc. Neurochem; Int. Soc. Neurochem; Brit. Biochem. Soc; Am. Soc. Biol. Chem. Lipid biochemistry and metabolism; neurochemistry; membrane biochemistry. Address: Research Lab, McLean Hospital, 115 Mill St, Belmont, MA 02178.

EICHBERGER, LE ROY CARL, b. Chicago, Ill, Oct. 26, 27; m. 55; c. 3. MECHANICAL ENGINEERING. B.S, Illinois, 51, M.S, 55, Ph.D.(theoret. & appl. mech), 59. Layout draftsman, McCormick Works, Int. Harvester Corp, 51-53; res. asst. theoret. & appl. mech, Illinois, 53-55, res. assoc, 55-57, instr, 57-59; asst. prof. MECH. ENG, UNIV. HOUSTON, 59-63, ASSOC. PROF, 63- Tech. consult, Reed Roller Bit Co, Houston, 59-61; Houston Eng. Res. Co, 61-62; Humble Oil & Ref. Co, 68-; vis. prof, Univ. Mich, 61-62; summers, participant, Inst. Aerospace Mech, Univ. Ariz, 64, Inst. Probabilistic Mech, Univ. N.Mex, 65. U.S.C.G, 46-47. Soc. Exp. Stress Anal; Am. Soc. Mech. Eng; Sigma Xi (secy-treas, 64-65, pres-elect, 65-67). Applied mechanics, specifically in areas of elasticity, shell analysis, vibration, dynamics, mechanics of materials, photoelasticity and experimental stress analysis. Address: Dept. of Mechanical Engineering, University of Houston, 3801 Collen Blvd, Houston, TX 77004.

EICHEL, BERTRAM, b. Brooklyn, N.Y, Feb. 23, 21; m. 49; c. 3. BIOCHEMISTRY, ENZYMOLOGY. B.A, Brooklyn Col, 43; D.D.S, N.Y. Univ, 46. Asst. plant physiol. & biochem, Brooklyn Col, 38-42; physiol. & biochem, col. dent, N.Y. Univ, 45-46, res. assoc, 46-48; assoc. attend. periodont. disease & oral med, Chronic Disease Hosp. Brooklyn, 48-50; asst. res. specialist enzymol. & biochem, bur. biol. res, Rutgers Univ, 49-52; res. biochemist & enzymologist, Jewish Hosp. Brooklyn, 55-57; chief labs & assoc. dir, inst. stomatol. res, Brooks Hosp, Brookline, Mass, 58-64; DIR, SCI. RESOURCES FOUND, 64- Mem. corp, Marine Biol. Labs, Woods Hole, investr. & library reader, 46-52, 55; clin. asst. vis. dentist, Greenpoint Hosp. Brooklyn, 47-50; consult, Gen. Foods Corp, 51-52; res. assoc, sch. dent. med, Tufts Univ, 57-60; trustee, Sci. Resources Found, 64-; consult, Tufts Lung Sta, 68-U.S.A, 42-44; U.S.A.F, 52-55, Capt. AAAS; Am. Inst. Biol. Sci; Am. Dent. Asn; Am. Soc. Cell Biol; Soc. Cryobiol; N.Y. Acad. Sci; Int. Asn. Dent. Res. Respiratory enzymes; hydrogen and electron transport; tissue and cell metabolism; inflammatory cell mechanisms; metabolic, oral and respiratory diseases; biological and biochemical effects of tobacco smoke; biological and biochemical effects and identification of environmental pollutants. Address: Science Resources Foundation, 50 Hunt St, Watertown, MA 02172.

EICHEL, HERBERT J(OSEPH), b. New York, N.Y, Mar. 13, 24. BIOLOGICAL CHEMISTRY. B.A, N.Y. Univ, 47, M.S, 49; fel, Rutgers, 50-51, Ph.D. (biochem, physiol), 51. Asst. physiol, Rutgers, 48-50, res. assoc, HAHNEMANN MED. COL, 51-55, asst. prof, 55-58, ASSOC. PROF. BIOCHEM, 58-Mem, Woods Hole Marine Biol. Lab. U.S. Pub. Health Serv. res. career develop award, 62- Med.C, U.S.A, 43-46. Fel. AAAS; Am. Chem. Soc; Soc. Protozool; Am. Soc. Biol. Chem; Soc. Exp. Biol. & Med; N.Y. Acad. Sci; Brit. Biochem. Soc; Radiation Res. Soc. Biological oxidations; electron transport in protozoa; biochemistry of Tetrahymena; enzymes; biochemical cytology; metabolic biology of Neisseria; biochemical effects of radiation. Address: Dept. of Biochemistry, Hahnemann Medical College, 235 N. 15th St, Philadelphia, PA 19102.

EICHEL, HERMAN J(OSEPH), b. Toledo, Ohio, Aug. 2, 24; m. 49; c. 5. BIOCHEMISTRY & ORGANIC CHEMISTRY. B.S, Dayton, 48; M.S, DePaul, 56; Ph.D.(biochem), Cincinnati, 66. Res. chemist, Abbott Labs, 48-53; C.F. Kettering Found, 53-57; sr. res. chemist, Diamond Labs, 57-58; proj. leader microencapsulation, Nat. Cash Register Co, 58-62; asst. to dir. res, HOECHST PHARMACEUT. CO, 62-63, asst. res. dir, 63-64, dir. pharmaceut. res, 64-66, v.pres. pharmaceut. res. & prod, 66-68, EXEC. V.PRES, 68- U.S.A, 43-45, Sgt. Am. Chem. Soc; Pharmaceut. Mfrs. Asn; N.Y. Acad. Sci. Syntheses of organic compounds to be tested on use of tropical diseases, tuberculosis, thyroid disease and veterinary products; synthesis of photosynthetic intermediates, coacervation studies; molecular heterogeniety of D-amino acid oxidase; synthetic studies of pyran chemistry. Address: Hoechst Pharmaceuticals Co, Route 202-206 North, Somerville, NJ 08876.

EICHELBERGER, JOHN F(REDERICK), b. Dayton, Ohio, June 10, 09; m. 45; c. 2. PHYSICS. B.S, Case, 31; M.S, Ohio State, 32, Ph.D.(physics), 40. Asst. res. physicist, Chicago, 42; asst. prof, State Col, Wash, 42-44; physicist & group supvr, appl. physics lab, Hopkins, 44-46; sr. res. physicist & group leader, Mound Lab, Monsanto Res. Corp, 47, sect. chief, 48-51, sect.

supvr, 51-54, asst. dir. res, 54-55, dir, 55-62, tech. coord, 62-67; RETIRED. Am. Phys. Soc. Quantum mechanics; gas dynamics; calorimetry. Address: 327 Jenny Lane, Dayton, OH 45459.

EICHELBERGER, JOHN LOWELL, b. Wash, D.C, Aug. 3, 43; m. 69. ORGANIC & ORGANOMETALLIC CHEMISTRY. B.S, Univ. Va, 65; Ph.D. (chem), Univ. Iowa, 70. PROJ. LEADER, GULF S. RES. INST, 70- Am. Chem. Soc. Synthesis of organophosphorus, organometallic and organic monomers and polymers; strained heterocycles; flame retardance of cellulosics; applications and properties of polymers; epoxide coatings; thermally stable polymers. Address: 6246 Colbert St, New Orleans, LA 70124.

EICHELBERGER, LILLIAN (MRS. RALPH CANNON), b. Macon, Miss, Mar. 2, 97; m. 23. CHEMISTRY. B.S, Miss. State Col. Women, 14; M.S, Chicago, 19, Ph.D.(chem), 21. Res. instr, Chicago, 21-24; res. chemist, Munic. Tuberc. Sanitorium, Ill, 24-28; res. assoc, Lasker Found. Med. Res, UNIV. CHICAGO, 29-36, asst. prof. biochem, 36-44, assoc. prof. biochem. & med, 44-50, biochem. & surg, 50-58, prof, 58-68, EMER. PROF. BIOCHEM, 68- Assoc. investr, Off. Sci. Res. & Develop, 43-46. Res. grant, U.S. Pub. Health Serv, 46-47. Am. Chem. Soc; Am. Soc. Biol. Chem; Soc. Exp. Biol. & Med; Soc. Trop. Med. & Hyg. Chemotherapy in tuberculosis; acid-base balance and salt water exchange between body fluids and tissues; experimental edema; hydronephrosis; tissue electrolytes; mineral metabolism of tissues; malaria; histochemical characterization of cartilages; organ transplantation. Address: Dept. of Surgery, University of Chicago, Chicago, IL 60637.

EICHELBERGER, R(OBERT) J(OHN), b. Washington, Pa, Apr. 10, 21; m. 43; c. 4. PHYSICS. A.B, Washington & Jefferson Col, 42; M.S, Carnegie Inst. Tech, 48, Ph.D.(physics), 54. Instr. PHYSICS, Washington & Jefferson Col, 42; res. physicist, Carnegie Inst. Tech, 43-45, res. supvr, 45-55; supv. physicist, U.S. ARMY BALLISTIC RES. LABS, 55-62, assoc. tech. dir, 62-67, DIR, 67- AAAS; Am. Phys. Soc; Am. Inst. Aeronaut. & Astronaut. Effects of extremely high temperatures and pressures on solids; non-steady fluid dynamics at extreme pressures; hypervelocity ballistics; shock phenomena; brittle fracture in metals. Address: U.S. Army Ballistic Research Lab, Aberdeen Proving Ground, MD 21005.

EICHELBERGER, ROBERT L(ESLIE), b. Wichita, Kans, Jan. 18, 26; m. 47; c. 3. PHYSICAL CHEMISTRY. B.S, California, Los Angeles, 48, M.S, 49; Ph.D.(chem), Wyoming, 57. Supvr. anal. chem, Truesdail Labs, Calif, 49-52; instr. col. eng, Wyoming, 52-54; res. chemist liquid metals, ATOMICS INT. DIV, N.Am. Aviation, Inc, 54-57, supvr. liquid metal chem, 57-66, SR. TECH. SPECIALIST, N.AM. ROCKWELL CORP, 66- U.S.N, 44-46. Am. Chem. Soc. Liquid metal chemistry; metal-gas reactions; analytical methods; chemical engineering. Address 8750 Quartz Ave, Northridge, CA 91324.

EICHELBERGER, W(ILLIAM) H, b. Wichita, Kans, Dec. 5, 21; m. 43; c. 4. ELECTRICAL ENGINEERING. B.S, Colorado, 43. Elec. design engr, Radio Corp. Am, 43-46; asst. chief engr, Hathaway Instrument Co, 46-52; res. engr, res. inst, UNIV. DENVER, 52-62, MGR. COMPUT. CTR, 62-, DIR. SYSTS. DEVELOP, 70- Sr. mem. Inst. Elec. & Electronics Eng; Asn. Comput. Mach. Applications of digital computers; digital computer logic and circuit design; pulse and digital instrumentation; audio engineering; radio receivers; electronic instrumentation. Address: Computing Center, University of Denver, Denver, CO 80210.

EICHELBRENNER, ERNEST A, b. Rüstringen, Ger, June 28, 13; Can. citizen; m. 39; c. 4. FLUID MECHANICS, APPLIED MATHEMATICS. B.Sc, Hamburg, 38, dipl. math, 43; Dr.ès Sci.(appl. math), Sorbonne, 55, Lic. ès Lettres, 56. Engr, Deschimag, Germany, 38-46; asst. prof, Hamburg, 46; res. engr, Onera, France, 46-58; assoc. prof. fluid mech, Poitiers, 58-61, PROF, 62-65; FLUID MECH, LAVAL UNIV, 65-, Candair Res. Chair vis. prof, 60-61. Exchange vis. prof, Syracuse, 63-64. Mem. Int. Union Theoret. & Appl. Mech. comt. to Nat. Res. Coun. Can, 66. Prix Henry Bazin, French Acad. Sci, 65. Assoc. fel. Am. Inst. Aeronaut. & Astronaut; Soc. Mech. Eng; Am. Acad. Mech. Fluid Mechanics, especially boundary layer theory, particularly three-dimensional boundary layers; applied mathematics, especially partial differential equations, particularly of the second order. Address: Dept. of Mechanical Engineering, Laval University, Quebec, Que, Can.

EICHELMAN, BURR S, JR, b. Hinsdale, Ill, Mar. 20, 43; m. 64; c. 2. PHYSIOLOGICAL PSYCHOLOGY. S.B, Univ. Chicago, 64, M.D, 68; Ph.D.(biopsychol), 70. Intern, Pediat, Med. Ctr, Univ. Calif, San Francisco, 69-70; STAFF ASSOC. LAB. CLIN. PSYCHOBIOL, NAT. INSTS HEALTH, 70- Psychiatry; neural correlates of aggression. Address: National Institutes of Health, Bldg. 10, Room 3N222, 9000 Rockville Pike, Bethesda, MD 20014.

EICHEN, ERWIN, b. Woodhaven, N.Y, May 14, 27; m. 50; c. 2. PHYSICAL METALLURGY. B.Met.E, Rensselaer Polytech, 51; Ph.D.(metall), Ohio State, 56. Res. engr. METALL, Battelle Mem. Inst. 51-52; res. assoc, Res. Found, Ohio State, 52-59, asst. prof. univ, 54-59; staff assoc, res. lab, Allegheny Ludlum Steel Corp, 59-61; prin. scientist, SCI. LAB, FORD MOTOR CO, 61-66, STAFF SCIENTIST, SCI. RES. STAFF, 66- Nat. Sci. Found. fel, Birmingham, 58-59. Consult, alloy develop. div, Battelle Mem. Inst, 55-58. U.S.N, 45-46. Am. Soc. Metals; Am. Inst. Min, Metall. & Petrol. Eng; Electron Micros. Soc. Am; Brit. Inst. Metals; Brit. Iron & Steel Inst. Phase transformations in metals; strengthening mechanisms in steel; thermionic emission microscopy; transmission electron microscopy; electron diffraction; kinetics of the $\alpha-\gamma$ transformation in pure iron and iron alloys. Address: Ford Motor Co, P.O. Box 2053, Dearborn, MI 48123.

EICHENBERGER, HANS P, b. Fribourg, Switz, Dec. 29, 21; U.S. citizen; m. 66; c. 5. ENGINEERING SCIENCE, FLUID MECHANICS. Dipl, Swiss Fed. Inst. Tech, 46; M.S, Pa. State, 49; Sc.D.(mech. eng), Mass. Inst. Tech. 51. Asst. internal combustion eng, Swiss Fed. Inst. Tech, 46-48; res. asst. diesel eng, Pa. State, 48-49; instr. gas turbines fluid flow, Mass. Inst. Tech, 50-52; asst. chief aerodyn, Garret Corp, Calif. & Ariz, 52-56; chief eng. sci, TRW Inc, 57-62; dir. res, res. ctr, Ingersoll Rand Co, 63-68; dir.

res. lab, IBM, SWITZ, 68-71, ASST. TO CORP. DIR. RES, 71- Lectr, Case Inst. Technol, 57-59. Swiss Army, 41-46, Lt. Am. Soc. Mech. Eng; Am. Inst. Aeronaut. & Astronaut; Inst. Elec. & Electronics Eng. Internal flow in machinery; external flow of bodies; drag reduction. Address: 131 Alte Landstr, Kilchberg, 8802, Switz.

EICHENGREEN, JEFFREY M, b. Baltimore, Md, Feb. 23, 43; m. 64; c. 1. PSYCHOLOGY. B.A, Johns Hopkins Univ, 64; Nat. Sci. Found. fel, Univ. Pa, 65-66, M.A, 66, Nat. Insts. Health fel, 67-68, Ph.D.(psychol), 71. ASST. PROF. PSYCHOL, COLO. COL, 69- AAAS; Optical Soc. Am. Human and animal psychophysics, especially color vision; human sexual behavior and inadequacies. Address: Dept. of Psychology, Colorado College, Colorado Springs, CO 80903.

EICHENHOLZ, ALFRED, b. Dabrowa, Poland, Apr. 5, 27; U.S. citizen; m. 52; c. 1. INTERNAL MEDICINE, METABOLISM. M.D, Univ. Munich, 51; M.Sc, Univ. Minn, Minneapolis, 64. Staff physician pulmonary disease serv, Vet. Admin. Hosp, Minneapolis, 57-59, asst. chief, 59-61, chief clin. radioisotope sect, 61-67; chief radioisotope serv, VET. ADMIN. HOSP, PITTSBURGH, 67-70, CHIEF MED. SERV, 70-; ASSOC. PROF. MED, SCH. MED, UNIV. PITTSBURGH, 67- Instr, Univ. Minn, Minneapolis, 57-64, asst. prof, 64-67. Dipl, Am. Bd. Internal Med, 60. Med.C, 53-55, 1st Lt. Am. Med. Asn; Am. Fedn. Clin. Res; N.Y. Acad. Sci; Soc. Nuclear Med. Acid base, fluid and electrolyte balance; renal physiology; pulmonary disease. Address: Medical Service, Veterans Administration Hospital, University Dr. C, Pittsburgh, PA 15240.

EICHENLAUB, VAL L, b. Battle Creek, Mich, Feb. 15, 33; m. 59. GEOGRAPHY. A.B, Western Michigan, 55; A.M, Michigan, 57; Ph.D.(geog), Ohio State, 64. Instr. GEOG, WEST. MICH. UNIV, 62-64, asst. prof, 64-67, ASSOC. PROF, 67- Nat. Sci. Found. grant, summer inst. quant. methods, Ohio State, 65. Am. Meteorol. Soc; Asn. Am. Geog; Am. Geog. Soc. Climatology, particularly lake effect snowfall. Address: Dept. of Geography, Western Michigan University, Kalamazoo, MI 49001.

EICHENWALD, HEINZ F(ELIX), b. Germany, Mar. 3, 26; nat; m. 51; c. 3. PEDIATRICS, MICROBIOLOGY. A.B, Harvard, 46, M.D, Cornell Univ, 50. Instr. PEDIAT, Cornell Univ, 55, asst. prof, 56-57, assoc. prof, 58-61, prof, 61-64; PROF. & CHMN. DEPT, SOUTHWEST. MED. SCH, UNIV. TEX, 64- Consult, U.S. Pub. Health Serv, 55-; career res. investr. award, 63; chmn. antibiotics panel I, nat. drug study, Nat. Res. Coun-Nat. Acad. Sci, 67-70; vis. prof, faculty med, Univ. Saigon, 69-; dir. pediat. prog, Am. Med. Asn-Vietnam Med. Sch. Proj, 69-; mem. nat. adv. coun, Nat. Inst. Child Health & Human Develop, 69-; consult, Food & Drug Admin, 70-; mem. res. comt, United Cerebral Palsy Found, 70-; chief-of-staff, Children's Med. Ctr, Dallas; pediatrician in chief, Parkland Hosp, Dallas; consult, various hosps. Markle Award, 53. Am. Pediat. Soc; Infectious Diseases Soc. Am; Harvey Soc; Soc. Pediat. Res; Sci. Res. Soc. Am. Infectious diseases of children; host-parasite interaction. Address: Dept. of Pediatrics, Southwestern Medical School, University of Texas at Dallas, Dallas, TX 75235.

EICHER, DON L(AUREN), b. Lincoln, Nebr, Dec. 12, 30; m. 54. GEOLOGY. B.A, Colorado, 54, M.S, 55; Nat. Sci. Found. fel. & Ph.D.(geol), Yale, 58. From asst. prof. to assoc. prof, GEOL, UNIV. COLO, BOULDER, 58-70, PROF, 70- Geol. Soc. Am; Paleont. Soc. Cretaceous micropaleontology; stratigraphy; marine paleocology. Address: Dept. of Geological Sciences, University of Colorado, Boulder, CO 80302.

EICHER, EVA M(AE), b. Kalamazoo, Mich, Sept. 26, 39. GENETICS. B.A, Kalamazoo Col, 61; M.S, Univ. Rochester, 63, U.S. Pub. Health Serv. traineeship, 64-67, Ph.D.(genetics), 67; summer training prog, Jackson Lab, 66. Res. assoc, Univ. Rochester, 67-70; ASSOC. STAFF SCIENTIST, JACKSON LAB, 71- Lectr, Univ. Rochester, 68; investr, Oak Ridge Nat. Lab, 70-71. Donald R. Charles Mem. Award, Univ. Rochester, 64. AAAS; Genetics Soc. Am; Soc. Develop. Biol. Mammalian genetics; mouse cytogenetics; mammalian x-chromosome; neurological mutations. Address: Jackson Lab, Bar Harbor, ME 04609.

EICHER, GEORGE J, b. Bremerton, Wash, Aug. 27, 16; m. 51; c. 2. FISHERIES BIOLOGY. B.S, Oregon State, 41. Field party leader, U.S. Bur. Fisheries, 39-41; free lance writer, 41-43; chief fisheries biologist, Ariz. Game & Fish Cmn, 43-47; proj. leader, U.S. Fish & Wildlife Serv, 47-56; AQUATIC BIOLOGIST, PORTLAND GEN. ELEC. CO, 56- Consult, indust. & govt. orgn, U.S. & Can, 57- Am. Fisheries Soc.(1st & 2nd v.pres, 62-64, pres, 64); Wildlife Soc; Am. Soc. Limnol. & Oceanog; Am. Inst. Fishery Res. Biol; fel. Int. Acad. Fishery Sci; N.Y. Acad. Sci. Fish behavior; fish passage at dams; red salmon in Alaska; aquatic weed control. Address; Portland General Electric Co, 621 S.W. Alder St, Portland, OR 97205.

EICHER, JOHN H(AROLD), b. Dayton, Ohio, Mar. 30, 21; m. 57; c. 2. ORGANIC CHEMISTRY. B.S, Purdue, 42, Ph.D.(chem), 52. Asst. mineral, Purdue, 42, org. chem, 45-48, asst. instr, 48-51; Am. Petrol. Inst. asst, Ohio State, 43; chemist, Manhattan Proj, Carbide & Carbon Chem. Corp, s.a.m. labs, Columbia, 43-45; res. consult, Tungston Plantation, Newport Ships, 51-52; asst. prof. CHEM, MIAMI UNIV, 52-61, ASSOC. PROF, 61-, faculty res. fel, 58. AAAS; Am. Chem. Soc. Gas viscosities; natural products; organic nitrogen compounds; stereochemistry. Address: Dept. of Chemistry, 216 Hughes Labs, Miami University, Oxford, OH 45056.

EICHER, RALPH N, b. Ligonier, Pa, Feb. 23, 29; m. 60; c. 2. MATHEMATICS. B.S, Westminster Col.(Pa), 54; M.S, Pittsburgh, 57; American Univ, 58-60. Res. mathematician, glass res. lab, Pittsburgh Plate Glass Co, 55-56; mathematician, appl. physics lab, Hopkins, 57-58; U.S. GEOL. SURV, D.C, 58-62, supvry. mathematician, Colo, 62-66, chief br. sci. appln, COMPUT. CTR. DIV, D.C, 66-70, CHIEF OFF. TELEPROCESSING, 70- U.S.A, 46-49, 50-51. AAAS; Asn. Comput. Mach; Data Processing Mgt. Asn; Int. Asn. Math. Geol. Application of numerical and statistical methods leading to solution of problems in geologic processes by digital computation. Address: Computer Center Division, U.S. Geological Survey, Interior Bldg, Washington, DC 20242.

EICHHOLZ, ALEXANDER, b. Zagreb, Yugoslavia, Dec. 12, 27; U.S. citizen; m. 55. BIOCHEMISTRY. B.A, Blackburn Col, 54; M.S, Illinois, 60, Ph.D. (biochem), 62. Instr. biochem, Chicago Med. Sch, 62-65, asst. prof, 65-66; PHYSIOL, RUTGERS MED. SCH, 66-68, ASSOC. PROF, 68- Schweppe Found. fel, 63-; Chicago Med. Sch. bd. trustees res. award, 65; Nat. Insts. Health grant. AAAS; Fedn. Am. Soc. Exp. Biol; Am. Soc. Cell Biol; Brit. Biochem. Soc. Membrane structure and function; intestinal transport. Address: 103 De Mott Lane, Somerset, NJ 08873.

EICHHOLZ, G(EOFFREY) G(UNTHER), b. Hamburg, Ger, June 29, 20; U.S. citizen. PHYSICS. B.Sc, Leeds, 42, Ph.D.(physics), 47. Exp. officer radar develop, British Admiralty, 42-46; demonstr. physics, Leeds, 46-47, asst. prof, British Columbia, 47-51; head radiation lab & physics & radiotracer subdiv, Can. Bur. Mines, 51-63; PROF. NUCLEAR ENG, GA. INST. TECHNOL, 63- Lectr, Univ. Ottawa, 56-58; Int. Atomic Energy Agency regional adv, Southeast Asia, 68. Am. Phys. Soc; Health Physics Soc; Am. Nuclear Soc; Can. Asn. Physicists; Brit. Inst. Physics & Phys. Soc.(fel. Phys. Soc). Industrial applications of radioisotopes; radiation effects; ferromagnetism; activation analysis; semiconductors; nuclear radiation detectors; environmental aspects of nuclear technology; architectural acoustics. Address: 1784 Noble Dr, N.E, Atlanta, GA 30306.

EICHHORN, EDGAR L(EO), b. Weltevreden, Netherlands, June 14, 23; U.S. citizen; m. 57; c. 2. CHEMICAL PHYSICS. B.S, Amsterdam, 50, Ph.D. (chem), 54, D.Sc.(physics), 56. Res. assoc. crystallog, Pa. State, 54-55; res. fel, Calif. Inst. Tech, 55-57; staff scientist, Burroughs Corp, 57-58, sect. mgr. appl. math, 58-60, dept. mgr. sci. applns, 60-62, div. group mgr. prof. serv, 62-64; dir. opers, C-E-I-R, Inc, Va, 64-65; div. staff mem. space flight oper, JET PROPULSION LAB, CALIF. INST. TECHNOL, 65, software develop. chief, 65-67, CHIEF ADVANCE PLANNING & ADVAN. ENG. SYSTS, 67- Fulbright travel grant, 54-55; George Ellery Hale fel, 55-56; Arthur Noyes fel, 56-57. Consult. mem, comput. comn, Int. Union Crystallog, 61-64; consult, C-H Die Co, 62-65; C-E-I-R, Inc, 65; Adv. Group Aerospace Res. & Develop, NATO, 68-70, mem. avionics panel WG, 70-; consult, Diebold-Europe, 69- Royal Netherlands Navy, 41-47. Am. Crystallog. Asn; Am. Ord. Asn; Am. Mgt. Asn; Int. Oceanog. Found. Crystallographic structure research, including single crystal diffraction, carotenoid and pyridine derivatives; numerical analysis of trajectory ballistics; thermodynamics of interior ballistics; computer configuration control and management. Address: 12615 Darla Ave, Granada Hills, CA 91344

EICHHORN, GUNTHER L(OUIS), b. Frankfurt am Main, Germany, Feb. 8, 27; nat; m. 64; c. 2. INORGANIC BIOCHEMISTRY. A.B, Louisville, 47; M.S, Illinois, 48, Ph.D.(chem), 50. Asst. inorg. chem, Illinois, 47-49, asst, General Aniline stipend, 49-50; asst. prof. inorg. chem, Louisiana, 50-54, assoc. prof, 54-57; Georgetown, 57-58; CHIEF SECT. MOLECULAR BIOL, GERONTOL. RES. CTR, Nat. Heart Inst, Md, 58-66, NAT. INST. CHILD HEALTH & HUMAN DEVELOP, 66- Summer fel, Ohio State Univ, 51 & 52; sr. asst. scientist, Nat. Inst. Mental Health, U.S. Pub. Health Serv, 54-57; distinguished lectr, Mich. State Univ, 71. Fel. AAAS; Geront. Soc; Am. Chem. Soc; fel. Am. Inst. Chem; Am. Soc. Biol. Chem; N.Y. Acad. Sci. Function of metals in biological processes; enzyme models; hemoproteins; metal ion catalysis; coordination chemistry; nucleic acids; gerontology. Address: Gerontology Research Center, National Institute of Child Health & Human Development, National Institutes of Health, Baltimore City Hospital, Baltimore, MD 21224.

EICHHORN, J(ACOB), b. Sheboygan, Wis, Sept. 14, 24; m. 59; c. 3. CHEMICAL ENGINEERING. B.S, Michigan, 46, M.S, 47, Ethyl fel, 48, Dow fel, 49-50, Ph.D.(chem. eng), 50. Mem. staff, DOW CHEM. CO, 50-56, div. leader, 56-61, mgr. spec. proj, plastics dept, 61-62, develop. mgr, packaging dept, 62-66, mgr. spec. proj, 66-68, exec. asst, 68-71, VENTURES MGR, PLASTICS DEPT, 71- Instr, Univ. Mich, 52-54; mem. prog. mgt. develop, Harvard, 68. Am. Chem. Soc; Am. Inst. Chem. Eng. Research, development and venture operations. Address: 4501 Arbor Dr, Midland, MI 48640.

EICHHORN, ROGER, b. Slayton, Minn, Apr. 1, 31; m. 52; c. 5. FLUID MECHANICS. B.E.E, Minnesota, 53, M.S.M.E, 55, Ph.D.(mech. eng), 59. Instr. mech. eng, Minnesota, 55-59; asst. prof, Princeton, 59-61, assoc. prof, 61-63, aerospace & mech. sci, 63-67; PROF. MECH. ENG. & CHMN. DEPT, UNIV. KY, 67- Nat. Sci. Found. fel, Imp. Col, Univ. London, 63-64; consult, Intertech Corp, 63-; Pratt & Whitney Corp, 69- AAAS; Am. Soc. Mech. Eng; Am. Inst. Aeronaut. & Astronaut; Am. Soc. Eng. Educ. Heat transfer in natural connection; high speed flows; channel and boundary layer flows; multiphase flows. Address: Dept. of Mechanical Engineering, 242 Anderson Hall, University of Kentucky, Lexington, KY 40506.

EICHHORN-von WURMB, HEINRICH K(ARL), b. Vienna, Austria, Nov. 30, 27; nat; m. 52; c. 4. ASTRONOMY. Ph.D.(astron), Vienna, 49. Instr, Vienna, 50-56, asst. prof, 56; ASTRON, Georgetown, 56-59; assoc. prof, Wesleyan, 59-64; PROF. & CHMN. DEPT, UNIV. S.FLA, 64- Brit. Coun. scholar, Glasgow, 51-52; Int. Coop. Admin. fel, McCormick Observ, 54-56; sr. consult, Geonautics, Inc, 57-; consult, Radio Corp. Am. Serv. Co, 59, Perkin-Elmer Co, 62; Smithsonian Astrophys. Observ, 61-63; Yale Univ. Observ, 63-64; Minneapolis Honeywell Regulator Co, 64; Geo-Space Co, 65; U.S. Army Map Serv, 65-70; vis. prof, Univ. Vienna & Univ. Graz, 71; grants, Nat. Sci. Found, NASA, U.S. Army, U.S. Air Force & U.S. Naval Res. Lab; partic. & lectr, nat. & int. conf. astron. Am. Astron. Soc; Int. Astron. Union; Royal Astron. Soc; Ger. Astron. Soc. Photographic astrometry; positional astronomy; celestial mechanics; stellar dynamics. Address: Dept. of Astronomy, University of South Florida, Tampa, FL 33620.

EICHINGER, BRUCE EDWARD, b. Canby, Minn, Oct. 25, 41; m. 62; c. 3. PHYSICAL CHEMISTRY. B.Ch, Minnesota, 63; Nat. Insts. Health fel, Stanford, 65-67, Ph.D.(polymer solutions), 67. Fel. chem, Yale, 67-68; ASST. PROF. PHYS. CHEM, UNIV. WASH, 68- Am. Chem. Soc. Thermodyanmics of polymer solutions; conformations of macromolecules. Address: Dept. of Chemistry, University of Washington, Seattle, WA 98105.

EICHINGER, J(ACK) W(ALDO), JR, b. Ottumwa, Iowa, Sept. 11, 04; m. 26; c. 2. INORGANIC CHEMISTRY. B.S, Iowa State Col, 26, Ph.D.(chem), 31. Asst. & instr, Iowa State Col, 31-34; asst. prof. chem, Detroit, 34-37, assoc. prof, 37-41; Williams Col, 46-47; prof. & coordinator nuclear sci. program, Fla. State Univ, 48-62; PROF. CHEM, Baghdad, 62-64; FLA.

STATE UNIV, 64- Asst. dir. chem, U.S. Mil. Acad, 44-46. U.S.A, 26, 41-46, Res, 49-64, Col. Am. Chem. Soc. Levulose sugar; corrosion of metals; caramels; sour taste of acids; phosphorescence spectroscopy; electron configurations; electron chart. Address: 3284 Longleaf Rd, Tallahassee, FL 32304.

EICHLER, E(UGENE), b. Granite City, Ill, Sept. 14, 29; m. 51; c. 3. NUCLEAR CHEMISTRY. B.S, St. Louis, 51; Ph.D.(chem), Washington, 55. NUCLEAR CHEMIST, OAK RIDGE NAT. LAB, 54- Vis. prof, Israel Atomic Energy Comn, 62; vis. scientist, Niels Bohr Inst, 68-69. Chem.C, U.S.A, 55-57. Sci. Res. Soc. Am; Am. Phys. Soc; Am. Chem. Soc. Nuclear spectroscopy and reactions. Address: Oak Ridge National Lab, P.O. Box X, Oak Ridge, TN 37830.

EICHLER, JOHN ORAN, b. Brooklyn, N.Y, Sept. 1, 05; m. 36; c. 2. CIVIL ENGINEERING. B.S, N.Y. Univ, 31; M.C.E, Syracuse, 43. Engr. construction, John McKeefrey Co, New York, 31-39; asst. prof. civil eng, Syracuse, 39-46; asst. civil engr, State Dept. Hy, N.Y, 46-47; assoc. prof. civil eng, Cooper Union, 47-56; PROF. CIVIL ENG, PHOTOGRAMMETRY & SURV. DIV, GA. INST. TECHNOL, 56- Am. Soc. Civil Eng; Am. Soc. Eng. Educ; Am. Soc. Photogrammetry; Am. Cong. Surv. & Mapping. Photogrammetry; mathematics of spiral curves; surveying and mapping. Address: Photogrammetry & Surveying Division, Georgia Institute of Technology, Atlanta, GA 30332.

EICHLER, VICTOR B, b. Dixon, Ill, July 13, 41; m. 65; c. 1. ZOOLOGY, EMBRYOLOGY. B.S, Univ. Ill, 63, M.S, 64; Nat. Insts. Health fel, Univ. Iowa, 66-69, Ph.D.(zool, embryol), 69. Nat. Insts. Health fels. anat, Univ. Chicago, 69-71; ASST. PROF. BIOL, WICHITA STATE UNIV, 71- Danforth tutorship, 70. AAAS; Am. Soc. Zool; Soc. Study Amphibians & Reptiles. Experimental embryology; development, morphology, physiology of vertebrate visual systems and epithalamic structures; influence of environmental lighting on body growth and development; evolution of pineal structures and role in body functions. Address: Dept. of Biology, Wichita State University, Wichita, KS 67208.

EICHLING, JOHN O, b. Gore, Okla, Dec. 30, 36; m. 61. RADIATION BIOPHYSICS. B.S, Northeast. Okla. State Col, 58; Atomic Energy Comn. fel. & M.S, Univ. Okla, 59; Ph.D.(biophys), Wash. Univ, 69. Asst. prof. physics, Northeast. Okla. State Col, 61-63; res. assoc. RADIOL, MED. SCH, WASH. UNIV, 63-66, instr, 66-70, ASST. PROF, 70- Health Physics Soc; Am. Phys. Soc; Soc. Nuclear Med. Medical application of short-lived radioisotopes; cerebral hemodynamics and metabolism; gamma-ray spectroscopy. Address: Dept. of Radiology, Washington University, 510 S. Kingshighway, St. Louis, MO 63110.

EICHMAN, MARTIN L, b. N.Y.C, Dec. 6, 34; m. 62; c. 2. PHYSICAL PHARMACY. B.S, Columbia, 55; M.Sc, Ohio State, 57, Am. Found. Pharmaceut. Ed. fel, 57-60, Ph.D.(pharm), 61. Sr. scientist, Merck & Co, Inc, 60-63; asst. prof. pharm, col. pharm, Univ. Ill, 63-66; res. & prod. supvr, Smith Kline & French Labs, 66-69; SR. SCIENTIST & GROUP LEADER, DEPT. PHARMACEUT. DEVELOP. & ETHICALS, WARNER LAMBERT RES. INST, 69- Am. Pharmaceut. Asn; Acad. Pharmaceut. Sci. Pharmacy research and product development; formulation of parenteral products, suspensions and ointments; absorption of drugs from pharmaceutical vehicles; drug stability. Address: Dept. of Pharmaceutical Development & Ethicals, Warner Lambert Research Institute, 170 Tabor Rd, Morris Plains, NJ 07950.

EICHMAN, P(ETER) L, b. Phila, Pa, Nov. 18, 25; m; c. 4. NEUROLOGY, MEDICINE. B.S, St. Joseph's Col, 45; M.D, Jefferson Med. Col, 49. Intern, Fitzgerald-Mercy Hosp, 49-50; fel. & res, Walter Reed Army Hosp, 50-51; Jefferson Med. Col, 51-52; Mayo Found, 52-54; Wisconsin, 54-55; instr. neuropsychiat, MED. SCH, UNIV. WIS, 55-57, asst. prof. neurol, 57-62, assoc. prof. neurol. & med. & dir. student health, 62-65, asst. dean clin. affairs, 65, DEAN MED. SCH, DIR. MED. CTR & PROF. MED. & NEUROL, 65- Consult, Vet. Admin. Hosp, 60-65; State Dept. Pub. Welfare, 60-65. Am. Acad. Neurol; Am. Col. Physicians; Am. Med. Asn; Am. Col. Health Asn. Relationship of perinatal injury and central nervous system defects; trace mineral excretion in porphyria; immunological responses in liver disease; development of a university health service. Address: University of Wisconsin Medical School, Madison, WI 53706.

EICHMANN, GEORGE, b. Budapest, Hungary, Nov. 3, 36; U.S. citizen; m. 62; c. 1. ELECTRICAL ENGINEERING. B.E.E, City Col. New York, 61, M.E.E, 63; Ph.D.(eng), City Univ. New York, 68. Jr. engr. ELEC. ENG, data syst. div, I.B.M, 61-62; lectr, CITY COL. NEW YORK, 63-68, ASST. PROF, 68- Engr, Goddard Space Flight Center, NASA, summers, 66, 67. Nat. Sci. Found. grant, 69-71; City Univ. New York Res. Found. grant, 71-72. Am. Soc. Eng. Educ; Inst. Elec. & Electronics Eng; Optical Soc. Am. Electromagnetic theory; quantum electronics; plasmas. Address: Dept. of Electrical Engineering, City College of New York, New York, NY 10031.

EICHNA, LUDWIG W(ALDEMAR), b. Tallin, Estonia, May 9, 08; nat. MEDICINE. A.B, Pennsylvania, 29, M.D, 32. Asst. instr, sch. med, Pennsylvania, 34-35; instr. med. & fel, sch. med, Hopkins, 36-40; instr. MED, col. med, N.Y. Univ, 40, asst. prof, 41-42, assoc. prof, 46-57, PROF, 57-60; CHMN. DEPT, STATE UNIV. N.Y. DOWNSTATE MED. CTR, 60- Asst. physician & Commonwealth fel, Hopkins Hosp, 36-40; asst. vis. physician, 47-; vis. physician & dir. med. serv, Kings County Hosp, Brooklyn, 60- Mem. fel. sect, comt. on growth, Nat. Res. Coun, 53, comt. cardiovasc. syst, 54, chmn, 57, med. fel. bd, 56; mem. res. coun, Pub. Health Res. Inst, 57; mem. comt. clin. invest, Nat. Found, 58; med. scientist training comt, Nat. Insts. Health, 63; panel & review comt, Health Res. Coun, N.Y. City. Med.C, U.S.A, 42-46. Am. Soc. Clin. Invest; Am. Physiol. Soc; Soc. Exp. Biol. & Med; Am. Heart Asn; N.Y. Acad. Med; N.Y. Acad. Sci; Asn. Prof. Med. (pres, 69-70); Asn. Am. Physicians (pres. 70-71). Cardiovascular investigation involving hemodynamics of congestive heart failure. Address: State University of New York Downstate Medical Center, 450 Clarkson Ave, Brooklyn, NY 11203.

EICHNER, EDUARD, b. Cleveland, Ohio, Nov. 11, 05; m. 31; c. 2. OBSTETRICS, GYNECOLOGY. A.B, Western Reserve, 25, M.D, 29. Jr. vis. obstetrician & gynecologist, Mt. Sinai Hosp, 36-41, sr. vis. obstetrician & gynecologist, 42-48, assoc. vis. obstetrician & gynecologist, 49-69; ASST. CLIN. PROF, OBSTET. & GYNECOL, SCH. MED, CASE WEST. RESERVE UNIV, 54- Dir. ed, St. Ann Hosp, 49-56; dir. res. obstet. & gynecol, Mt. Sinai Hosp, 58-, asst. dir, div. obstet-gynec, 69- Consult, Cleveland State Hosp, 49- Gold Award, Ohio State Med. Asn, 55. Dipl, Am. Bd. Obstet. & Gynecol. Med.C, Res, 42-48, Lt. Comdr. AAAS; Endocrine Soc; Soc. Exp. Biol. & Med; Am. Col. Surg; Am. Col. Obstet. & Gynec; N.Y. Acad. Sci; Int. Col. Surg; Am. Fertil. Soc; Pan-Am. Med. Asn. Medicine; anatomy; pathology; physiology; pharmacology; gynecic lymphatics; physiology fertility, pregnancy and labor; internal and external genitalia; effects of drugs on mother and fetus in pregnancy, labor, and the neonatal period. Address: Severance Medical Arts Bldg, Suite 712, 5 Severance Circle, Cleveland, OH 44118.

EICHORN, PAUL A(NTHONY), b. Boston, Mass, Aug. 8, 16; m. 47; c. 4. CYTOLOGY, MANAGEMENT SCIENCES. A.B, Boston Col, 41, M.A, 42; Ph.L, Weston Col, 42; Ph.D.(biol), Fordham, 46. Lab. asst. biol, Fordham, 42-44; prof, Seton Hall Col, 46-47; clin. invest, Lederle Labs, 47-49, cytologist & biologist, Lederle Labs, 49-55; consult, 55-56, tech. dir. vet. div, Warner-Chilcott Labs, 56-57; dir. new prod. coord, Warner-Lambert Res. Inst, 57-66; MGR. TECH. PLANNING & INFO. DIV, PHILIP MORRIS RES. CTR, 66- Mem. adv. bd, Adelphi Univ. AAAS; N.Y. Acad. Sci; Am. Mgt. Asn; Inst. Mgt. Sci; Planning Exec. Inst. Tissue culture virology; cancer; nutrition; research administration; technical planning; relation of polysomaty to the three-dimensional cell shapes and cell volumes in the root tips of Spinacia oleracea; psychology; physiology; management information systems; patents. Address: Technical Planning & Information Division, Philip Morris Research Center, P.O. Box 26583, Richmond, VA 23261.

EICHWALD, ERIC, b. Castrop, Ger, July 10, 02; nat; m. 38. CHEMISTRY. Dp.Ch, Univ. Berlin, 28, Ph.D.(food chem), 32; Pochamer Inst, 38; Columbia Univ, 39-42. Chief chemist, Durham Chem. Corp, 39-40; CHIEF CHEMIST & V.PRES, ARROW LABS, INC, 40-; ADMIRAL FOODS, INC, DARBY FOOD CORP, 66- Chief chemist, Ultrasonic, Eng. & Derustit-Arrow, GmbH, Ger. Am. Chem. Soc; Am. Soc. Test. & Mat; Soc. Cosmetic Chem; Inst. Food Technol. Food seasonings; canning; automotive chemicals, detergents and cosmetics. Address: Arrow Labs. Inc, 31 Westmoreland Ave, White Plains, NY 10606.

EICHWALD, ERNEST J, b. Germany, Dec. 13, 13; nat; m. 41; c. 3. PATHOLOGY. M.D, Freiburg, Germany, 38; M.D, Utah, 53. Instr. path, med. sch, Harvard, 46-48; asst. prof, Utah, 48-49, assoc. prof, 50-54; dir. labs, Mont. Deaconess Hosp, 54-66; prof. microbiol, Mont. State Univ, 66-70; PROF. PATH. & SURG. & CHMN. DEPT. PATH, COL. MED, UNIV. UTAH, 70- Ed, Transplantation Bull, 53-61; ed. adv, Cancer Res, 54-57; chmn. comt. tissue transplantation, Nat. Acad. Sci-Nat. Res. Coun, 57-69; ed, Transplantation, 62-; dir, McLaughlin Res. Inst, Great Falls, Mont, 66-70. U.S.A, 44-46. Am. Soc. Exp. Path; Soc. Exp. Biol. & Med; Am. Asn. Cancer Res; Am. Asn. Path. & Bact. Transplantation immunity. Address: Dept. of Pathology, College of Medicine, University of Utah Medical Center, Salt Lake City, UT 84112.

EICK, HARRY A(RTHUR), b. Rock Island, Ill, Dec. 9, 29; m. 54; c. 8. PHYSICAL & INORGANIC CHEMISTRY. B.S, St. Ambrose Col, 50; Allied Chem. & Dye fel, Iowa, 54-55, Ph.D.(chem), 56. Asst. prof. CHEM, Kentucky, 56-57; res. assoc, Kansas, 57-58; asst. prof, MICH. STATE UNIV, 58-63, assoc. prof, 63-67, PROF, 67-, assoc. chmn. dept, 70-71, interim dir. comput. lab, 71-72. Asn. Comput. Mach; Am. Chem. Soc; Am. Crystallog. Asn. High temperature and x-ray diffraction studies on lanthanide compounds. Address: 6098 Skyline Dr, East Lansing, MI 48823.

EICKELBERG, E(LMER) W(ILLIAM), b. Cedar Falls, Iowa, Dec. 19, 11; m. 36; c. 2. FOOD CHEMISTRY. B.S, Iowa State Col, 33, M.S, 35, Ph.D. (food chem), 37. Asst, Iowa State Col, 33-37; lab. dir, Fairmont Canning Co, 37-40, res. dir, 40-50, v.pres. res, 50-53, prod. mgr, 53-56; mgr, Chun King Frozen Food, Ohio, 56-64, managing dir, Chun King of Can, Ltd, 65-66, mgr, Chun King Corp, Ohio, 66-67; plant mgr, R.J. REYNOLDS FOOD INC, Ohio, 67-68, COORD. NEW PRODS. MFG, N.Y, 68- V.pres, Welcome Agr. Chem. Co, 50-55. Inst. Food Tech. Frozen pastries; preservation of vegetables by canning and freezing; oriental American foods; fertilizer; convenience foods, syrups, puddings, Mexican foods. Address: R.J. Reynolds Food Inc, 750 Third Ave, New York, NY 10017.

EICKELBERG, W. WARREN B, b. N.Y.C, Jan. 19, 25; m. 52; c. 4. PHYSIOLOGY. A.B, Hope Col, 49; Dennison fel, Wesleyan Univ, 49-51, M.A, 51; Fordham Univ, 51-52. Assoc. prof. BIOL, ADELPHI UNIV, 52-69, PROF, 69-, dir. develop, 58-60, v.pres, 60-66. Res. consult, Human Resources Ctr; mem. biomech. consult. group, President's Comt. Employ the Handicapped, 70-71; chmn. premed. curriculum, Adelphi Univ, 70. U.S.A.A.F, 43-46, 1st Lt. AAAS; N.Y. Acad. Sci. Cell physiology; protein metabolism; neurophysiology. Address: Dept. of Biology, Adelphi University, Garden City, NY 11530.

EICKHOFF, THEODORE C, b. Cleveland, Ohio, Sept. 13, 31; m. 52; c. 3. MEDICINE. A.B, Valparaiso Univ, 53; M.D, West. Reserve Univ, 57. Res. fel. med, Harvard Med. Sch, 62-64; dept. chief invests. sect, epidemiol. br, Communicable Disease Ctr, U.S. Pub. Health Serv, 64-66, chief bact. diseases sect, 66-67; asst. prof. med, MED. CTR, UNIV. COLO, DENVER, 67-68, ASSOC. PROF. MED. & HEAD DIV. INFECTIOUS DISEASES, 68- Mem. comt. meningococcal infections, Armed Forces Epidemiol. Bd, 64-, assoc. mem. comn. acute respiratory disease, 65-, comn. influenza, 69-; clin. asst. prof. prev. med, sch. med, Emory Univ, 64-67; consult, Fitzsimons Army Hosp, 68-; consult. to med. dir, NASA, 69-; mem. adv. comt. immunization practices, U.S. Pub. Health Serv, 70- Dipl, Am. Bd. Internal Med, 66. U.S.P.H.S, 59-67, Sr. Surg. AAAS; Infectious Diseases Soc. Am; N.Y. Acad. Sci; Am. Soc. Microbiol; Am. Fedn. Clin. Res; Am. Epidemiol. Soc; fel. Am. Col. Physicians; Am. Hosp. Asn; Am. Soc. Clin. Invest. Internal medicine; infectious diseases. Address: Dept. of Medicine, University of Colorado Medical Center, 4200 E. Ninth Ave, Denver, CO 80220.

EICKHOLT, THEODORE HENRY, b. Springfield, Minn, July 17, 32. PHARMACOLOGY. B.S, Minnesota, 55, Samuel W. Melendy fels, 60-62, Ph.D.

(pharmacol), 62. Asst. prof. PHARMACOL, NORTHEAST LA. UNIV, 63-66, ASSOC. PROF, 66- Am. Pharmaceut. Asn. Iron absorption and its mechanisms of control; gastrointestinal activity of cathartics; activity studies in laboratory animals; analgesic studies of the phenothiazine compounds. Address: School of Pharmacy, Northeast Louisiana University, Monroe, LA 71201.

EICKNER, HERBERT W(AYNE), b. Two Rivers, Wis, Sept. 1, 17; m. 41; c. 4. CHEMICAL ENGINEERING. B.S, Wisconsin, 39. Chem. asst, Marathon Chem. Co, Wis, 40-41; jr. engr, FOREST PRODS. LAB, U.S. FOREST SERV, 41-43, asst. engr, 43-45, chem. engr, 45-52, sr. chem. engr, 52-56, SUPVR. CHEM. ENGR, 61- Naval Ord. Serv. award. Forest Prod. Res. Soc; Am. Soc. Test. & Mat. Fire research; adhesives for wood, metals and plastics; forest products. Address: U.S. Forest Products Lab, Walnut St, Madison, WI 53705.

EICKSTAEDT, LAWRENCE LEE, b. Davenport, Iowa, July 20, 39; m. 60; c. 2. ECOLOGY, MARINE BIOLOGY. B.S, Buena Vista Col, 61; Nat. Sci. Found. summer fel, Univ. Iowa, 63, M.S, 64; Nat. Sci. Found. summer fel, Stanford Univ, 64, Ph.D.(biol), 69; Nat. Insts. Health grant, Hopkins Marine Sta, Calif, 65, Nat. Insts. Health fel, 66. ASST. PROF. BIOL, Calif. State Col, Hayward & Moss Landing Marine Labs, 68-69; State Univ. N.Y. Col. Old Westbury, 69-70; EVERGREEN STATE COL, 70- AAAS. Ecological physiology; reproductive biology of marine invertebrates; environmental design. Address: Dept. of Biology, Evergreen State College, Olympia, WA 98505.

EICKWORT, GEORGE C(AMPBELL), b. New York, N.Y, June 8, 40; m. 65; c. 1. ENTOMOLOGY. B.S, Mich. State, 62, Nat. Sci. Found. fel, Woodrow Wilson fel. & M.S, 63; Nat. Sci. Found. fel, Danforth fel. & Ph.D.(entom), Kansas, 67. ASST. PROF. ENTOM, STATE UNIV. N.Y. COL. AGR, CORNELL UNIV, 67- Res. fel, Huyck Preserve, summers 69, 70; consult, Harvard Univ. Mus. Comp. Zool, spring 70. AAAS; Asn. Trop. Biol; Bee Res. Asn; Entom. Soc. Am; Soc. Study Evolution; Soc. Syst. Zool; Entom. Soc. Can. Systematics, morphology, behavior and ecology of wild bees; systematics and biology of mites associated with aculeate Hymenoptera. Address: Dept. of Entomology, State University of New York College of Agriculture at Cornell University, Ithaca, NY 14850.

EIDE, CARL J(OHN), b. Carrington, N.Dak, Aug. 20, 04; m. 30; c. 2. PLANT PATHOLOGY. B.S, Minnesota, 28, M.S, 29, Ph.D.(plant path), 34; La. State, 29-30. Instr. bot, UNIV. MINN, ST. PAUL, 28-29, PLANT PATH, 30-37, asst. prof, 37-44, assoc. prof, 44-47, PROF, 47- Instr. La. State, 29-30; spec. temporary sci. aide, Rockefeller Found. Colombia & Mex, 55; agr. officer, Food & Agr. Orgn, UN, Chile, 60. Am. Phytopath. Soc; Potato Asn. Am. Genetics of Gibberella saubinetii; fruit diseases; vegetable diseases; disease resistance. Address: Dept. of Plant Pathology, University of Minnesota, St. Paul, MN 55101.

EIDELBERG, EDUARDO, b. Lima, Peru, Apr. 30, 30; m. 56; c. 2. PHYSIOLOGY. M.D, Lima, 55. Assoc. res. prof. anat, California, Los Angeles, 57-61; res. prof. neurophysiol, Ariz. State Univ. 61-69; CHMN. DIV. NEUROBIOL, BARROW NEUROL. INST, 61-; ADJ. PROF. NEUROL, COL. MED, UNIV. ARIZ, 71- Physiology of the nervous system; neuropharmacology; development of nervous system. Address: Division of Neurobiology, Barrow Neurological Institute, 350 W. Thomas Rd, Phoenix, AZ 85003.

EIDINGER, DAVID, b. Montreal, Que, Jan. 4, 31; m. 57; c. 2. MICROBIOLOGY, IMMUNOLOGY. B.Sc, McGill, 52, Ph.D.(anat), 58; M.D, Columbia, 59. Fel, Banting Res. Found, Can, 53-54; demonstr. anat, Columbia, 55-56; res. assoc. allergy, Royal Victoria Hosp, Montreal, Que, 61-64; asst. prof. MICROBIOL, QUEEN'S UNIV.(ONT), 64-70, ASSOC. PROF, 70- Res. assoc. Can. Heart Found, 61-64; grants, Ont. Heart Found, 64-; Nat. Cancer Inst, 67-; Med. Res. Coun, 67- Brit. Soc. Immunol; Can. Soc. Immunol; Can. Soc. Microbiol. Mechanism of antigenic competition; cell cooperation in delayed hypersensitivity; effect of hormonal changes on immune response. Address: Dept. of Microbiology, Queen's University, Kingston, Ont, Can.

EIDINOFF, MAXWELL LEIGH, b. New York, N.Y, Feb. 16, 15; m. 38; c. 2. PHYSICAL CHEMISTRY, BIOCHEMISTRY. B.A, Brooklyn Col, 34; Ph.D. (phys. chem), Pa. State Col, 38. Asst. phys. chem, Pa. State Col, 34-38; instr. chem, Queens Col.(N.Y), 38-42; res. supvr. div. war res, Columbia, 42-43; res. group leader, metall. lab, Chicago, 43-44; asst. prof. CHEM, QUEENS COL.(N.Y), 45-50, assoc. prof, 50-59, PROF, 59- Assoc. mem, Sloan Kettering Inst. Cancer Res, N.Y, 49-66, assoc. scientist, 66-70. Civilian with Off. Sci. Res. & Develop, 44. Am. Chem. Soc; Am. Asn. Cancer Res; Am. Asn. Biol. Chem. Biochemistry of viruses; low temperature calorimetry; statistical mechanics; isotope exchange and separation; isotope mass effects in chemical reaction rates; radiochemical measurements; application of radioactive tracers in medical research; intermediary metabolism studies. Address: Dept. of Chemistry, Queens College, Flushing, NY 11367.

EIDMAN, RICHARD AUGUST LOUIS, b. Belleville, Ill, Sept. 19, 36; m. 59; c. 3. CHEMICAL ENGINEERING. B.S, Washington (St. Louis), 58, Sc.D. (chem. eng), 63; Rotary fel, Nancy, 58-59; NATO-Nat. Sci. Found. fel, Cambridge, 62-63. Engr. polyolefins res, Sabine River Works, E.I. DU PONT DE NEMOURS & CO, 63-66, TECH. REP, POLYOLEFINS DIV, PLASTICS DEPT, CHESTNUT RUN LABS, 66- Tech. Asn. Pulp & Paper Indust. Physical and chemical treatment of surfaces of high polymers; physical properties of polymers and relationships with molecular parameters; extrusion coatings. Address: Plastics Dept, E.I. du Pont de Nemours, Chestnut Run Labs, Wilmington, DE 19898.

EIDSNESS, F(REDERIC) ARNOLD, b. Wash, D.C, May 9, 13; m. 37; c. 3. CHEMICAL & SANITARY ENGINEERING. B.S, Col. William & Mary, 36; Ph.D.(chem. eng), Florida, 56. V.pres, BLACK, CROW & EIDSNESS, INC, 51-69, EXEC.V.PRES, 69- Consult, WHO, Peru, 60; state health off, Fla, 64-; mem, Am. Sanit. Eng. Intersoc. Bd. U.S.P.H.S.R, Sr. Scientist. Am. Soc. Civil Eng; Am. Inst. Chem. Eng; Am. Water Works Asn; Water Pollution Control Fedn. Water and sewage. Address: Black, Crow & Eidsness, Inc, P.O. Box 1300, Boca Raton, FL 33432.

EIDSNESS, L(ARS) M(ICHAEL), JR, b. Wash, D.C, Dec. 1, 17. AEROSPACE ENGINEERING. B.M.E, Cath. Univ. Am, 42. Proj. engr, res. & develop. air weapons, Bur. Ord, 42-57; HEAD ENGR. develop. air weapons, Naval Aviation Ord. Test Sta, Va, 57-59; PROG. PLANS, astronaut. div, Bur. Naval Weapons, 60-66; SPACE SYSTS. DIV, NAVAL AIR SYST. COMMAND, 66- Outstanding performance awards, U.S. Navy, 45, 47, 50, 58, superior achievement & sustained superior performance awards, 59, Secy. Navy commendation-navigation satellite, 60, superior accomplishment award, 64. Air weapons, including bombs, rockets, guided missile warheads and mines; data capsules for reentry vehicles; space systems, including satellites and other unmanned spacecraft. Address: 4736 Eastern Ave. N.E, Washington, DC 20017.

EIDSON, WILLIAM WHELAN, b. Indianapolis, Ind, July 22, 35; m. 60; c. 2. NUCLEAR PHYSICS. B.S, Tulane, 57; M.S, Indiana, 59, Nat. Sci. Found. fel, 59-61, Ph.D.(physics), 61. Teaching asst. PHYSICS, Indiana, 57-59, instr, 61-63, asst. prof, 63-66, assoc. prof, 66-67; PROF. & CHMN. DEPT, UNIV. MO-ST. LOUIS, 67- AAAS; Am. Asn. Physics Teachers; Am. Physics Soc; Inst. Elec. & Electronic Eng. Accelerator studies of nuclear structure and reaction mechanisms; nuclear instrumentation; solid state detectors; ion-electron recombination. Address: Dept. of Physics, University of Missouri-St. Louis, St. Louis, MO 63121.

EIDUSON, SAMUEL, b. Buffalo, N.Y, Dec. 15, 18; m. 42. BIOLOGICAL CHEMISTRY. Ph.D.(biochem), California, Los Angeles, 52. Res. asst. biochem, California, Los Angeles, 48-50, med. sch, 50-51; res. biochemist, U.S. Vet. Admin, 51-62; ASSOC. PROF. BIOL. CHEM. & PSYCHIAT. & CHIEF RES. BIOCHEM, NEUROPSYCHIAT. INST. UNIV. CALIF, LOS ANGELES, 62- Sig.C, 43-46, 1st Lt. AAAS; Am. Chem. Soc; Am. Soc. Biol. Chem; Am. Soc. Neurochem. Neurochemistry; biochemical studies of behavior. Address: 941 Stonehill Lane, Los Angeles, CA 90049.

EIFERT, ROBERT L(EE), b. West Frankfort, Ill, June 23, 27; m. 50; c. 4. ORGANIC CHEMISTRY. A.B, Millikin, 50; Davis fel, Nebraska, 52, Du Pont fel, 53, Ph.D.(chem), 54. Res. chemist, prod. & process develop, E.I. DU PONT DE NEMOURS & CO, 54-64, sr. res. chemist, PLASTICS DEPT, 64-68, SR. SUPVR. RES, 68- U.S.N.R, 45-46. Am. Chem. Soc. Product and process development in industrial organic chemicals and polymers. Address: Plastics Dept, Research Division, Washington Lab, E.I. du Pont de Nemours & Co, Inc, Parkersburg, WV 26105.

EIFLER, GUS K(EARNEY, JR), b. Taylor, Tex, Feb. 14, 08; m. 40; c. 2. GEOLOGY. B.A, Texas, 29, M.A, 30; Ph.D.(geol), Yale, 41. Instr. geol, Texas, 29-38; lab. asst, Yale, 38-39; asst. prof, Texas, 39-42; consult. geologist, 50-64; RES. SCIENTIST ASSOC, BUR. ECON. GEOL, UNIV. TEX, 64- Petrol. consult, Tex. Land Bd, 51- U.S.A.A.F, 42-45. Soc. Econ. Paleont. & Mineral; fel. Geol. Soc. Am; Am. Asn. Petrol. Geol. Stratigraphy, structural geology; petroleum geology; geology of trans-Pecos, Texas; Pleistocene history of Texas high plains. Address: 1901 Meadowbrook, Austin, TX 78703.

EIGEL, EDWIN GEORGE, JR, b. St. Louis, Mo, June 4, 32; m. 59; c. 2. MATHEMATICS. B.S, Mass. Inst. Technol, 54; Fulbright fel, Univ. Marburg, 54-55; fel, St. Louis Univ, 55-59, Ph.D.(math), 61. Asst. prof. MATH, ST. LOUIS UNIV, 61-64, assoc. prof, 64-69, PROF, 69-, ASSOC. ACAD. V.PRES, 71-, asst. to dean grad. sch, 65-67, acting dean, 67-68, dean, 68-71. Danforth assoc, 64- U.S.A, 59-61, Mil. Intel. Res, 61-66, Capt. Am. Math. Soc; Math. Asn. Am. Numerical applications of functional analysis; theory of approximation; analytic theory of numbers. Address: St. Louis University, 221 N. Grand Blvd, St. Louis, MO 63103.

EIGELSBACH, HENRY T(HOMAS), b. Oak Park, Ill, Jan. 4, 19; m. 45; c. 3. MEDICAL BACTERIOLOGY. B.S, Purdue, 41; M.S, Kentucky, 43; Ph.D. (bact), Cincinnati, 47. Lab. asst. bact. & sr. technician, Kentucky, 41-43; teaching fel. bact, Cincinnati, 43-44; proj. chief, U.S. ARMY BIOL. DEFENSE LABS, 46-48, BR. CHIEF & SUPVRY. BACTERIOLOGIST, 48- Dipl, Am. Bd. Microbiol. U.S.N.R, 44-, Comdr; meritorious civilian serv. award, 68. Am.Soc. Microbiol; Am. Asn. Immunol; N.Y. Acad. Sci; Soc. Exp. Biol. & Med; Sci. Res. Soc. Am; Am. Acad. Microbiol. Pathogenesis; aerobiology; immunology; cellular morphology and colony type variation of Francisella tularensis; chemotherapy of tularemia; development of live tularemia vaccine; prophylactic vaccination via the respiratory route. Address: U.S. Army Biological Defense Lab, Frederick, MD 21701.

EIGEN, EDWARD, b. New York, N.Y, June 29, 23; m. 45; c. 2. CHEMISTRY, MICROBIOLOGY. B.A, Brooklyn Col, 44, M.A, 55. Bacteriologist, Food Res. Labs, 44-46, microbiologist, 47-52; U.S. Vitamin & Pharmaceut. Corp, 52-53, asst. supvr. anal. labs, 53-59; sr. res. biochemist, COLGATE PALMOLIVE CO, 59-62, SECT. HEAD biochem, 62-70, HOUSEHOLD PROD. RES, 70- U.S.A, 46-47. Am. Chem. Soc; Int. Asn. Dent. Res. Isolation of materials from natural products; microbiology; chromatography; oral health and skin research. Address: Colgate Palmolive Co, 909 River Rd, Piscataway, NJ 08854.

EIGHME, LLOYD ELWYN, b. Wenatchee, Wash, Jan. 15, 27; m. 51. INVERTEBRATE ZOOLOGY, ENTOMOLOGY. B.A, Pac. Union Col, 51, M.A, 53; Ph.D.(entom), Oregon State, 65. Instr. biol, Pac. Union Col, 58-62; res. asst. entom, Oregon State, 62-65; asst. prof. BIOL, PAC. UNION COL, 65-66, ASSOC. PROF, 66- Entom. Soc. Am. Applied entomology; insects in stored grain; taxonomy of Hymenoptera; Sphecidae. Address: Dept. of Biology, Pacific Union College, Angwin, CA 94508.

EIGNER, JOSEPH, b. Swampscott, Mass, Dec. 13, 33; m. 63; c. 2. MICROBIOLOGY. A.B, Dartmouth Col, 55; Nat. Sci. Found. fel, Harvard, 55-58, A.M, 58, univ. fel, 58-59, Ph.D.(phys. chem), 60. Netherlands Orgn. Health Res. fel, Leiden, 60-62; Nat. Sci. Found. fel. biol. chem, Michigan, 62-64; ASST. PROF. MICROBIOL, SCH. MED, WASH. UNIV, 64- Nat. Sci. Found. summer fel, Inst. High Molecular Compounds, U.S.S.R, 61. Am. Soc. Microbiol. Physical properties of DNA; bacterials viruses and nucleases. Address: Dept. of Microbiology, Washington University School of Medicine, Box 8093, St. Louis, MO 63110.

EIGSTI, ORIE J(ACOB), b. Morton, Ill, July 23, 08; m. 36; c. 2. BOTANY. B.S, Goshen Col, 31; M.A, Illinois, 33, fel, 34-35, Ph.D.(bot), 35. Asst. bot, Illinois, 35-36; Carnegie Inst, 36-37; res. assoc, Triarch Bot. Prods, Ripon, Wis, 37; prof. biol. & head dept, Greenville Col, 37-38; PROF. plant sci, Oklahoma, 38-45; Northwestern, 45-50; BOT, CHICAGO STATE UNIV, 58-Dir, Colchicine Res. Found, Inc, 50-55; Fulbright lectr, Pakistan, 52-53; UNESCO lectr, S.E. Asia, 53; pres, Am. Seedless Watermelon Seed Corp, 54- Dustin medal, 52. AAAS; Bot. Soc. Am; Genetics Soc. Am; Am. Soc. Hort. Sci; Am. Soc. Nat; Int. Soc. Plant Geog. & Ecol; Pakistan Asn. Adv. Sci. Colchicine cytogenetics; seedless watermelon seed production; pollen tube research. Address: Dept.of Botany, Chicago State University, 6800 S. Stewart, Chicago, IL 60621.

EIKENBARY, RAYMOND DARRELL, b. Quay, Okla, Nov. 2, 29; m. 53; c. 5. ENTOMOLOGY, FORESTRY. B.S, Okla. State, 57; Nat. Defense fel, Clemson, 61-64, M.S, 63, Ph.D.(entom), 64. Dist. forester, Bur. Land Mgt, 57-59; exten. agent ed, OKLA. STATE UNIV, 59-61, asst. prof. FOREST ENTOM, 64-68, ASSOC. PROF, 68- U.S.A, 50-52, Sgt. Entom. Soc. Am. Ecology; biological control of insects. Address: Dept. of Entomology, Oklahoma State University, Stillwater, OK 74074.

EIK-NES, KRISTEN (BORGAR DAHLER), b. Sparbu, Norway, Sept. 28, 23. ENDOCRINE PHYSIOLOGY, STEROID BIOCHEMISTRY. B.S, Col. Steinkjer, Norway, 42; Am-Scandinavian Found. fel, 49; Nordisk Insulin travel grantee, 51; M.D, Oslo, 51. Res. assoc. physiol, sch. med, Oslo, 47-48; biochem, sch. med, Utah, 52-54, res. instr, 54-56, asst. res. prof, 56-59, assoc. prof. biochem, 59-68; PROF. BIOCHEM. & CHMN. DIV. BIOCHEM. & PHYSIOL. OF REPRODUCTION, SCH. MED, UNIV. SOUTH. CALIF, 68- Lectr, Scandinavian Cong. Lab. & Clin. Invest, Sweden, 54; Fulbright Exchange fel, 51-54; program dir. steroid biochem, U.S. Pub. Health Serv, 57-; consult. clin. endocrinol, Holy Cross Hosp, 58-61; biomed. adv, Nat. Aeronaut. & Space Admin, 60. Royal Norwegian Underground, 42-45, Comdr. Endocrine Soc; Am. Soc. Physiol; Royal Soc. Med. Steroid methodology; synthesis and metabolism in vivo of androgens; estrogens and progestins. Address: Division of Biochemistry & Physiology of Reproduction, University of Southern California School of Medicine, 2025 Zonal Ave, Los Angeles, CA 90033.

EIKREM, LYNWOOD O(LAF), b. Lansing, Mich, June 11, 19; m. 46; c. 4. PHYSICAL CHEMISTRY. B.S, Mich. State Col, 41; S.M, Mass. Inst. Tech, 48, 49. Spectrochemist, Diamond Alkali Co, 41-42; chief spectrochemist, Chrysler Evansville Ord. Plant, 42-44; field engr, spectros, Harry Dietert Co, 44; assoc. prof. chem, La. Polytech, 46-47; adv. fel, Mass. Inst. Tech, 47-49; tech. dir. spectros, Jarrell-Ash Co, 49-53; proj. engr, emission spectros, Baird-Atomic Inc, 53-59; staff engr, Geophys. Corp. Am, Inc, 59-60; prod. develop. mgr, David W. Mann Co, 60-63, dir. mkt, 64-65; V.PRES, APPL. RES. LABS, INC, 65- Lectr, Boston Col. U.S.N.R, 44-46, Lt. Optical Soc. Am; Am. Soc. Test. & Mat; N.Y. Acad. Sci. Design, testing and applications of spectroscopic analytical instrumentation; interferometry; metrological instrumentation; x-ray; spectrochemistry. Address: 9545 Wentworth St, Sunland, CA 91040.

EILAR, KENDRICK R(USSELL), b. Laramie, Wyo, June 27, 24; m. 45; c. 5. ORGANIC CHEMISTRY. B.S, Harvard, 44; Hyman fel, Colorado, 47-49; Ph.D, 49. Calco res. fel, Illinois, 49-50; res. assoc, N.Mex. Sch. Mines, 46; res. chemist, Gen. Mills, Inc, 50-52; mgr. indust. dept, Guarantee Reserve Ins. Co, 52-55; gen. mgr, Gamma Uranium Corp, 55-56; group leader, Am. Potash & Chem. Corp, 57, head, org. chem. sect, 58, asst. mgr, WHITTIER RES. LAB, 59-63, MGR. RES, 64-69, KERR McGEE CORP, 69- U.S.N.R, 43-46, Ens. AAAS; Am. Chem. Soc. Organic synthesis; fatty nitrogen compounds; surfactants; organophosphorus compounds; organoboron compounds; pesticides; polymers. Address: Whittier Research Lab, Kerr McGee Corp, 12519 E. Washington Blvd, Whittier, CA 90602.

EILBERG, RALPH G, b. Phila, Pa, Apr. 23, 33. BIOCHEMISTRY. B.S, Pa. State, 55; M.S, Purdue, 57; Nat. Sci. Found. fel, Pa. State, 62, Ph.D.(biochem), 62. Res. chemist, Colgate Palmolive Co, 62-63; res. assoc, Beth Israel Hosp, 63-64; biochemist, Phila. Gen. Hosp, 65; Beth Israel Hosp, 65-68; ASST. PROF. BIOCHEM, N.Y. UNIV, 68- U.S.A.R, 55-61. AAAS; Am. Chem. Soc; N.Y. Acad. Sci. Protein biosynthesis; calcification and calcifying catalysts; lipid metabolism; fibrinolysin inhibitors. Address: 46 Seventh St, Cresskill, NJ 07626.

EILENBERG, SAMUEL, b. Warsaw, Poland, Sept. 30, 13; nat. 48. MATHEMATICS. M.A, Warsaw, 34, Ph.D.(math), 36. Instr. MATH, Michigan, 40-41, asst. prof, 41-45, assoc. prof, 45-46; PROF, Indiana, 46-47; COLUMBIA UNIV, 47- Vis. lectr, Princeton, 45-46; vis. prof, Fulbright & Guggenheim fel, Paris, 50-51; vis. prof, Tata Inst, Bombay, 53-54, 56-57; Hebrew Univ, 54; Univ. Paris, 66-67. Nat. Acad. Sci; Am. Math. Soc.(coun, 47-60); Math. Asn. Am. Topology, algebra and computer mathematics. Address: Dept. of Mathematics, 522 Mathematics Bldg, Columbia University, New York, NY 10027.

EILER, JOHN J(OSEPH), b. Jacksonville, Fla, Jan. 25, 10; m. 44; c. 1. BIOCHEMISTRY. A.B, California, 33, Ph.D.(biochem), 37. Mem. enzymes res. staff, Cutter Labs, 37-38; instr. biochem. & pharm, MED. CTR, UNIV. CALIF, SAN FRANCISCO, 38-41, asst. prof, 41-45, assoc. prof, 45-51, PROF, 51-, ASSOC. DEAN COL. PHARM, 56-, CHMN. DEPT. PHARMACEUT. CHEM, 58-, asst. dean, 48-56. Consult, U.S. Army, 47-; U.S. Pub. Health Serv, 47. Mem, Int. Union Physiol. Sci. Am. Chem. Soc; Soc. Exp. Biol. & Med; Am. Pharmaceut Asn; Am. Soc. Biol. Chem; N.Y. Acad. Sci; Brit. Biochem. Soc. Chemistry and metabolism of purines and nucleic acids; metabolism of carbohydrates; thyroid hormone and renal and intestinal functions; action of drugs on aerobic phosphorylation; biological action of narcotics and stimulants; mode of action of antimitotic agents. Address: Dept. of Biochemistry, University of California Medical Center, San Francisco, CA 94122.

EILERS, LAWRENCE JOHN, b. Ireton, Iowa, May 21, 27; m. 49; c. 4. PLANT TAXONOMY, PHYTOGEOGRAPHY. B.S, State Col. Iowa, 49, M.A, 60; Ph.D. (bot), Iowa, 64. Instr, high schs, Iowa, 49-51; elec. engr, Collins Radio Co, 52-56, environ. engr, 56-57; Admiral Radio Corp, Ill, 57-58; instr. sci, Charles City Consol. Schs, Iowa, 58-59; forest bot, State Univ. N.Y. Col. Forestry, Syracuse, 64-65; asst. prof. life sci, Indiana State, 65-68; ASSOC. PROF. BIOL, UNIV. NORTH. IOWA, 68- U.S.N, 45-46. AAAS; Soc. Study Evol; Am. Soc. Plant Taxon; Bot. Soc. Am; Am. Inst. Biol. Sci. Biosystematics of the genus Sullivantia; flora and phytogeography of the Midwest. Address: Dept. of Biology, University of Northern Iowa, Cedar Falls, IA 50613.

EILERS, LOUIS K(ENNETH), b. Gillespie, Ill, Apr. 11, 07; m. 30; c. 5. ORGANIC CHEMISTRY. B.S, Illinois, 29; nat. res. jr. fel, Virginia, 29-30, M.S, 30; Am. Petrol. Inst. jr. fel, Northwestern, 30-32, Ph.D.(org. chem), 32. Res. chemist, Marsene Transparent Paper Co, 33; Van Cleef Bros, 33-34; res. chemist & supt. roll coating dept, Eastman Kodak Co, 34-51, supt. film base mfg, 46-53, asst. mgr. film mfg, 53-55, asst. gen. mgr, Kodak part works, 55-56, v.pres. & asst. gen. mgr, 56-58, 1st v.pres, Tenn. Eastman Co. & Tex. Eastman Co, 59-61, pres, 61-63, pres, Eastman Chem. Prod, Inc, 59-60, dir, 59-67, v.pres, 63-67, exec. v.pres. & dir, EASTMAN KODAK CO, 63-67, PRES, 67-, CHIEF EXEC. OFF, 69- Pres. & dir, Carolina Eastman, 61-63; dir, Holston Defense Corp, 61-, Faserwerke Huels, 61-, Lincoln Rochester Trust Co, 64- Am. Chem. Soc; Photog. Soc. Am; Soc. Photog. Sci. & Eng. Alkaloid chemistry; hydrocarbon chemistry; rubber; cellulose acetate; photographic film base. Address: Eastman Kodak Co, 343 State St, Rochester, NY 14650.

EILERS, RUSSELL J(AY), b. St. Paul, Minn, May 20, 25. CLINICAL PATHOLOGY. B.A, Univ. Minn, 49, B.S, 50, B.A, 52, M.D, 53. Assoc. PATH, MED. CTR, UNIV. KANS, 57-58, asst. prof, 58-61, assoc. prof, 61-65, PROF, 65-, DIR. CLIN. LABS, 58- Mem, Int. Comt. Standardization Hemat, 64-; bd. dirs, Nat. Comt. Clin. Lab. Standards. U.S.N, 43-46. AAAS; Am. Med. Asn; Am. Soc. Clin. Path; Col. Am. Path; Int. Acad. Path; Am. Pub. Health Asn. Creatin metabolism; renal function; blood banking practice; clinical laboratory methodology. Address: Clinical Labs, University of Kansas Medical Center, 39th & Rainbow, Kansas City, KS 66103.

EILERTS, C(HARLES) KENNETH, b. Charleston, Okla, Nov. 7, 04; m. 25; c. 3. PHYSICAL CHEMISTRY. B.S, Okla. Agr. & Mech. Col, 26; M.S, Tulsa, 63. Mem. staff, Indust. Process Co, Calif, 27-29; res. supvr, Apache Powder Co, Ariz, 29-30; U.S. BUR. MINES, 30-49, prin. phys. chemist, 49-58, res. supvr, 58-63, RES. SCIENTIST, 63- Lectr, French Inst. Petrol, 58; Okla. State, 59; Texas, 61; Miss. State, 62; Alta, 64. Excellence award, Dept. Interior, 44; distinguished serv. award, 58; Hanlon Award, Natural Gas Producers Asn, 69; Arno C. Fieldner Award, U.S. Bur. Mines, 69. Am. Gas Asn; Am. Chem. Soc; Am. Inst. Min, Metall. & Petrol. Eng; Soc. Petrol. Eng; Am. Inst. Mech. Eng. Cracking and polymerization of natural hydrocarbon mixtures; properties of nitroglycerine explosives; inhibitors and corrosion resistance of metals; phase relations of gas-condensate fluids; transient flow of natural gas, helium and condensate fluids in reservoirs; pressure-, saturation- and velocity-dependence of mobility of gas-condensate fluids. Address: 811 S.E. Crown Dr, Bartlesville, OK 74003.

EIME, LESTER O(SCAR), b. Sappington, Mo, June 22, 22; m. 64. CHEMISTRY. A.B, Missouri, 44, A.M, 47. Instr. chem, Christian Col, 44-47; res. chemist, res. labs, Aluminum Co. Am, 47-57; Petreco Div, Petrolite Corp, 57-62; sr. res. chemist, space & electronics div, Emerson Elec. Co, 62-65; ENGR, McDONNELL AIRCRAFT DIV, McDONNELL-DOUGLAS CORP, 65- Asst. chem, Univ. Mo, 46-47. Am. Chem. Soc. Purification of hydrocarbons and other chemicals through electrical and catalytic processes; aluminum organic compounds; pigments for paint, plastics, rubber and paper coating industries; petroleum catalyst preparations; ablative materials and high temperature polymers; electrochemical corrosion studies of metals; printed circuits. Address: 111 Pebble Acres Ct, St. Louis, MO 63141.

EINARSSON, ALFRED W, b. Berkeley, Calif, Apr. 13, 15; m. 47; c. 2. PHYSICS. Ph.D.(physics), Univ. Calif, 46. Asst. prof. PHYSICS, Univ. South. Calif, 46-50, SAN JOSE STATE COL, 50-57, PROF, 57- Am. Phys. Soc. General physics; physical optics; electrical conduction in gases. Address: 18851 Overlook Rd, Los Gatos, CA 95030.

EINBINDER, SEYMOUR K, b. Brooklyn, N.Y, Jan. 15, 25; m. 48; c. 5. SYSTEMS ANALYSIS, MATHEMATICAL STATISTICS. B.M.E, N.Y. Univ, 49, M.M.E, 51; M.S.M.E, Stevens Inst. Tech, 57. Ord. engr, PICATINNY ARSENAL, 50-56, CHIEF ANAL. SECT, 56- U.S.A, 46-47. Am. Statist. Asn; Inst. Math. Statist; Am. Ord. Asn. Methodology for weapon effectiveness; statistics of reliability. Address: Picatinny Arsenal, SMUPA-DW6, Dover, NJ 07801.

EINERT, ALFRED ERWIN, b. Kearny, N.J, Feb. 6, 39; m. 67; c. 1. ORNAMENTAL HORTICULTURE, PLANT PHYSIOLOGY. B.S.A, Ark. State Univ, 64; Nat. Sci. Found. summer fel, Miss. State Univ, 65, M.S, 66, Ph.D.(ornamental hort), 69. Res. assoc. ORNAMENTAL HORT, Mich. State Univ, 69-70; ASST. PROF, UNIV. ARK, FAYETTEVILLE, 70- Netherlands Flower-Bulb Inst. trainee, Mich. State Univ, 68-70. U.S.A.F, 58-61. Am. Soc. Hort. Sci; Am. Soc. Plant Physiol; Bot. Soc. Am. Growth and development of bulb flower crops; role of environmental factors and growth regulators on lilies, tulips, irises. Address: Dept. of Horticulture, University of Arkansas, Fayetteville, AR 72701.

EINSET, EYSTEIN, b. Geneva, N.Y, Mar. 19, 25; m. 54; c. 3. BIOCHEMISTRY, BACTERIOLOGY. B.S, Cornell, 50, M.S, 51, Ph.D.(biochem), 56. Chemist, bur. commercial fisheries, U.S. Fish & Wildlife Serv, 55-57, lab. dir, 57-60; asst. prof. biochem, agr. exp. sta, Cornell, 60-62; mgr. food res, Tectrol Div, WHIRLPOOL CORP, 62-64, sr. res. biochemist, RES. & ENG. DIV, 64-69, STAFF SCIENTIST, 69- AAAS; Am. Chem. Soc; Inst. Food Technol. Food chemistry and processing; biochemistry of storage life extension of fresh plant, animal, and fishery food products by control of environmental variables. Address: Dept. of Food Science, Whirlpool Corp. Research & Engineering Center, Monte Rd, Benton Harbor, MI 49022.

EINSET, JOHN, b. Norway, Aug. 15, 15; nat; m. 45; c. 4. POMOLOGY. B.S, Cornell, 38, Ph.D.(cytol), 42. Instr. POMOL, N.Y. STATE AGR. EXP. STA, 42-44, asst. prof, 44-47, assoc. prof, 47-51, PROF, 51-, HEAD DEPT, 60-, assoc. head, 53-60. Genetics Soc. Am; Bot. Soc. Am; Am. Soc. Hort. Sci. Cytology and genetics of fruits. Address: New York State Agricultural Experiment Station, Geneva, NY 14456.

EINSPAHR, DEAN WILLIAM, b. Sioux City, Iowa, May 24, 23; m. 46; c. 2. FOREST GENETICS, SOILS. B.S, Iowa State, 49, M.S, 50, Ph.D.(soils, silvicult), 55. Asst. wood tech, Gamble Bros, Inc, Ky, 50-51; res. assoc. soils & silvicult, Iowa Agr. Exp. Sta, 52-55; res. asst. FOREST GENETICS, INST. PAPER CHEM, LAWRENCE UNIV, 55-58, res. aide, 59-62, res. assoc. & chief genetics & physiol. group, 63-70, SR. RES. ASSOC. & GROUP COORD, DIV. NATURAL MAT. & SYSTS, 70- U.S.A.A.F, 42-46, 1st Lt. Tech. Asn. Pulp & Paper Indust; Soil Sci. Soc. Am; Soc. Am. Foresters. Forest soils; silviculture; wood quality-paper quality relationship. Address: Division of Natural Materials & Systems, Institute of Paper Chemistry, Lawrence University, Appleton, WI 54911.

EINSPRUCH, NORMAN G(ERALD), b. Brooklyn, N.Y, June 27, 32; m. 53; c. 3. SOLID STATE SCIENCE. B.A, Rice Inst, 53; fel. 54-55, M.S, Colorado, 55; Ph.D.(appl. math), Brown, 59. Asst, Colorado, 53-54; asst, metals res. lab, Brown, 56-59, res. assoc, 59-; mem. tech. staff, TEX. INSTRUMENTS INC, 59-62, head, electron transport physics br, physics res. lab, 62-68, dir. advan. technol. lab, corp. res. & eng, 68-69, DIR. CHEM. MAT. DIV, TECH. CTR, 69-, acting head, thin film physics br, 64-65. Summers, asst, Shell Oil Co, 52; physicist, Nat. Bur. Standards, Colo, 55. AAAS; fel. Am. Phys. Soc; fel. Acoust. Soc. Am; sr. mem. Inst. Elec. & Electronics Eng. Silicon materials technology; transport in solids; physical acoustics; ultrasonic wave propagation in solids. Address: Chemical Materials Division, Texas Instruments Inc, P.O. Box 5936, M.S. 144, Dallas, TX 75222.

EINSTEIN, ELIZABETH ROBOZ, b. Szaszvaros, Hungary; nat; m. 59. NEUROCHEMISTRY. Ph.D.(biochem), Univ. Budapest, 38. Res. asst. bioorg. chem, Calif. Inst. Technol, 41-45; assoc. prof. chem, Univ. Wyo, 45-48; res. assoc. enzyme & carbohydrate res, Stanford Univ, 48-52; assoc. prof. biochem, sch. med, Georgetown Univ, 52-58; neurochem, sch. med, Stanford Univ, 58-59; PROF. NEUROCHEM. & LECTR. BIOCHEM, SCH. MED, UNIV. CALIF, SAN FRANCISCO, 59- Res. consult, Sugar Res. Found. N.Y, 45-48; SEATO scholar & lectr, orient & advanced researcher, Bangkok, 61-62; grants, Nat. Insts. Health, Multiple Sclerosis Soc. & Hartford Found. Raskob Award, Georgetown Univ, 56; Medaglia d'oro di Milano, Int. Cong. Neurochem, Milan, Italy, 69. Am. Chem. Soc; Soc. Exp. Biol. & Med; Am. Acad. Neurol. Neurochemical investigations; chemistry of demyelinating diseases; developing brain; cerebrospinal fluid. Address: 1090 Creston Rd, Berkeley, CA 94708.

EINSTEIN, FREDRICK W. B, b. Auckland, N.Z, Nov. 7, 40; m. 65; c. 1. INORGANIC CHEMISTRY. B.Sc, New Zealand, 62; M.Sc, Canterbury, 63; Ph.D.(chem), 65. Fel. CHEM, British Columbia, 65-67; asst. prof, SIMON FRASER UNIV, 67-71, ASSOC. PROF, 71- Am. Crystallog. Asn; Chem. Inst. Can; The Chem. Soc. Crystal structure analysis; computer technology. Address: Dept. of Chemistry, Simon Fraser University, Burnaby 2, B.C, Can.

EINSTEIN, HANS ALBERT, b. Bern, Switzerland, May 14, 04; nat; m. 27, wid; c. 2; m. 59. HYDRAULICS. Dipl, Swiss Fed. Inst. Tech, 26, Ph.D. (civil eng), 37. Design & steel construct. engr, Aug. Kloenne, Dortmund, 27-31; first engr, hydraulic lab, Fed. Inst. Switzerland, 31-38; hydraulic engr, soil conservation serv, U.S. Dept. Agr, 38-47; assoc. prof. mech. eng, UNIV. CALIF, BERKELEY, 47-53, PROF. HYDRAUL, 53- Guggenheim fel, 53. Am. Geophys. Union; Am. Soc. Civil Eng. Movement of sediment by streams; intersection of shock waves; tidal flows. Address: 1090 Creston Rd, Berkeley, CA 94708.

EINSTEIN, J. RALPH, b. Providence, R.I, Oct. 17, 25; m. 60; c. 3. CRYSTALLOGRAPHY, BIOPHYSICS. B.S, Yale, 44, B.Mus, 47, M.Mus, 48, Ph.D. (biochem), Harvard, 59. Nat. Sci. Found. fel, 59-60; res. assoc. x-ray crystallog, col. physicians & surgeons, Columbia, 60-65; BIOPHYSICIST, BIOL. DIV, OAK RIDGE NAT. LAB, 65- U.S.N, 44-46. Am. Crystallog. Asn. X-ray crystallography; molecular and crystal structures of large molecules of biological interest. Address: Biology Division, Oak Ridge National Lab, P.O. Box Y, Oak Ridge, TN 37830.

EINSTEIN, LLOYD T(HEODORE), b. Providence, R.I, Mar. 6, 27; m. 55; c. 3. PHYSICS. B.S, Yale, 49; M.A, Univ. Calif, Berkeley, 51. Sr. Proj. engr, NAVAL UNDERWATER SYSTS. CTR, 51-64, res. assoc, 64-66, HEAD SONAR ANAL. BR, 66- Acoust. Soc. Am. Sonar system design and analysis. Address: Naval Underwater Systems Center, New London Lab, Ft. Trumbull, New London, CT 06320.

EINSTMAN, WILLIAM J(OSEPH), b. Brooklyn, N.Y, Dec. 4, 25; m. 53; c. 2. ORGANIC CHEMISTRY. B.S, St. John's,50; M.S, Polytech. Inst. Brooklyn, 52. Proj. leader, MAXWELL HOUSE DIV, GEN. FOODS CORP, WHITE PLAINS, 52-56, sect. head, 57-66, sr. group leader, 66-70, LAB. MGR, 70- U.S.N, 44-46. AAAS; Am. Chem. Soc; Inst. Food Technol. Coffee. Address: 105 Old Orchard Rd, Port Chester, NY 10573.

EIPPER, ALFRED W(ARD), b. Montague, Mass, Nov. 16, 19; m. 42; c. 3. FISHERY BIOLOGY. B.A, Reed Col, 41; B.S, Maine, 49; Ph.D.(fishery biol), Cornell, 53; Harvard, 38-40. Asst. fish. biol, Maine, 48-49; res. asst, CORNELL UNIV, 49-51, res. assoc, 52-63, ASSOC. PROF, 63-; LEADER, N.Y. COOP. FISHERIES UNIT, U.S. BUR. SPORT FISHERIES & WILDLIFE, 63- U.S.C.G, 41-45, Lt.(jg). AAAS; Am. Fisheries Soc; Ecol. Soc. Am. Biology and management of fish populations and water resources; environmental problems and policies. Address: Fernow Hall, Cornell University, Ithaca, NY 14850.

EIPPER, EUGENE B(RETHERTON), b. Heyburn, Idaho, Aug. 10, 12; m. 37; c. 3. MECHANICAL ENGINEERING. B.S, Colorado, 34; M.M.E, Chrysler Inst. Eng, 37. Draftsman, Gen. Motors Truck Co, Pontiac, Mich, 34-35, exp. engr, Detroit diesel eng. div, 37-42; student engr, Chrysler Corp, Detroit, 35-37; plant engr, DeSoto-Chrysler Corp, 37; asst. chief engr, Andover Motors Corp, N.Y, 42-45; Wilkening Mfg. Co, Pa, 45-47; automotive supvr, petrol. lab, E.I. DU PONT DE NEMOURS & CO, INC, 47-53, supt. petrol. lab, 53-57, lab. engr, 57-62, engr, 62-65, PATENT ENGR, JACKSON LAB, 65- Soc. Automotive Eng. Development of lubricating oil and gasoline additives. Address: 233 Grandview Ave, Pitman, NJ 08071.

EIRICH, FREDERICK ROLAND, b. Vienna, Austria, May 23, 05; m. 36; c. 2. CHEMISTRY. Ph.D.(phys. chem), Vienna, 29, D.Sc.(phys. chem), 38; hon. M.A, Cambridge, 39. Res. & assoc. colloid chem, Vienna, 28-32, first chem. inst, 33-38; res. assoc. colloid sci, Cambridge, 38-40, res. assoc. & lectr. phys. chem, 44-46; sr. res. office, Melbourne, 41-43, assoc. prof. POLYMER CHEM, POLYTECH. INST. BROOKLYN, 47-50, prof, 50-69, DISTINGUISHED PROF, 69-, dean res, 67-70. Vis. prof, Bristol Univ, 64-65; consult, major chem. companies. Fel. N.Y. Acad. Sci; Am. Chem. Soc; Soc. Rheol.(ed, 52-56, from v.pres. to pres, 70-73). Constitution of colloid gold; colloidal metals; colloidal solutions; serum proteins; rheology; ultracentrifuge; liquid explosives; polymer chemistry. Address: Polytechnic Institute of Brooklyn, 333 Jay St, Brooklyn, NY 11201.

EIS, F(REDERICK) G(EORGE), b. Humboldt, Nebr, Jan. 9, 17; m. 43; c. 5. CHEMICAL ENGINEERING. B.S, Nebraska, 46. Spec. analyst, Spreckels Sugar Co, Woodland, 38-42; res. chem. engr, 46-50, chief chemist, 51-54, head res. chemist, 54-68, GEN. CHEMIST DIR. CHEM. RES, SPRECKELS SUGAR DIV, AMSTAR CORP, 68- U.S.A.A.F, 42-46. Sugar processing; mathematics; statistics; electronics; research and development. Address: Amstar Corp, Spreckels Sugar Division, 2 Pine St, San Francisco, CA 94106.

EISAMAN, JACK L(ANGOHR), b. Columbia City, Ind, Oct. 28, 13; m. 37; c. 3. MEDICINE. B.S, Indiana, 36, M.D. 38. Consult, CARDIOVASC. DISEASES, DEPT. INTERNAL MED, CAYLOR-NICKEL CLIN. & CLIN. HOSP, 46-64, SR. CONSULT, 64-, HEAD DEPT, 57-64 & 66-, MEM. CLIN. HOSP. BD, 57-, bd. gov, 57-71. Med.C, 44-46, Capt. Am. Med. Asn; fel. Am. Col. Physicians; fel. Am. Col. Chest Physicians; fel. Am. Col. Cardiol; Am. Diabetes Asn; Am. Fedn. Clin. Res. Peripheral vascular diseases; cardiac arrhythmias during surgery; electrocardiography; vectorcardiography; echocardiography; Doppler flow studies. Address: 303 S. Main, Bluffton, IN 46714.

EISBERG, R(OBERT) M(ARTIN), b. Kansas City, Mo, July 1, 28; m. 51. NUCLEAR PHYSICS. B.S, Illinois, 49; Ph.D.(physics), California, 53. Res. asst. PHYSICS, California Radiation Lab, 51-53; res. assoc, Brookhaven Nat. Lab, 53-55, Minnesota, 55-56; physicist, Cavendish Lab, England, 56-57; asst. prof, Minnesota, 57-59, assoc. prof, 59-60; Fulbright & Guggenheim fel, Tokyo, 60-61; assoc. prof, UNIV. CALIF, SANTA BARBARA, 61-62, PROF, 63- Res. asst, Los Alamos Sci. Lab, summers 49, 50; physicist, cyclotron lab, Arg, 62; Rutherford Lab, Eng, 65; visitor, Europ. Coun. Nuclear Res, Switz, 69; Fulbright-Hays fel, Colombia, 70. Fel. Am. Phys. Soc; Am. Asn. Physics Teachers; Fedn. Am. Sci. Experimental research in nuclear scattering and reactions; phenomenological theory of scattering and reactions; passage of particles through matter; textbook writing and editing. Address: Dept. of Physics, University of California, Santa Barbara, CA 93106.

EISCH, JOHN J(OSEPH), b. Milwaukee, Wis, Nov. 5, 30; m. 53; c. 5. ORGANIC CHEMISTRY. B.S, Marquette Univ, 52; Procter & Gamble fel, Iowa State Univ, 55, Ph.D.(chem), 56. Union Carbide Corp, fel, Ger, 56-57; res. assoc, Europ. Res. Assocs, Belg, 57; asst. prof. CHEM, St. Louis Univ, 57-59; Univ. Mich, 59-63; assoc. prof, Cath. Univ. Am, 63-66, PROF. & CHMN. DEPT, 66-72; STATE UNIV. N.Y. BINGHAMTON, 9/72- Consult, Union Carbide Corp, Continental Oil Co. & Ethyl Corp. Am. Chem. Soc; Am. Inst. Chem. Synthesis and properties of organometallic compounds; reactive intermediates, particularly anions, radical-anions and charge-transfer complexes; mechanisms of organic reactions; stereoselectivity and regioselectivity of carbon-metal and hydrogen-metal bond additions; non-benzenoid aromatic rings. Address: Dept. of Chemistry, State University of New York at Binghamton, Binghamton, NY 13901.

EISELE, CAROLYN, b. N.Y.C, m. 43. MATHEMATICS. A.B, Hunter Col; A.M, Columbia; Chicago; Southern California. From instr. to PROF. MATH, HUNTER COL, 23- Res. grants, Am. Philos. Soc, 52-54, 64-67, Shuster Faculty Fel. Fund, 60 & Nat. Sci. Found, 64-67, Am. Coun. Learned Socs. travel grants, Italy, 58 & Spain, 59. Dir, George Sarton Mem. Found; chmn. adv. screening cmt, Fulbright & Smith-Mundt Awards, 60-68. Hunter Col. del. & participant, Int. Math. Cong. & Int. Cong. Hist. & Philos. Sci, 54; participant, Int. Symp. Hist. Math. & Phys. Sci, Italy, 58 & 64-69. Fel. AAAS; Am. Math. Soc; Math. Asn. Am; Hist. Sci. Soc; fel. N.Y. Acad. Sci. History of mathematics; logic, history and philosophy of science. Address: 215 E. 68th St, New York, NY 10021.

EISELE, C(HARLES) WESLEY, b. New Albany, Ind, Apr. 6, 06; m. 33, 63; c. 2. MEDICINE. B.A, N.Cent. Col, 28; M.S, Northwestern, 31, M.B, 32, M.D, 33. Asst. med, Chicago, 34-35, instr, 35-41, asst. prof, 41-45, assoc. prof, 45-51, secy. dept. med, 41-47, chief gen. med. clin, 41-51; assoc. prof. MED, SCH. MED, UNIV. COLO, DENVER, 51-67, PROF, 67-, PREV. MED. & COMPREHENSIVE HEALTH CARE, 69-, ASSOC. DEAN POSTGRAD. MED. EDUC, 55-, asst. dean, 51-55. Mem. staff & consult, various hosps; consult. surgeon gen, U.S. Pub. Health Serv, 60- Mem. cmn. prfnl. & hosp. activities, trustee, 55, pres, 60-62. Fel. Am. Col. Physicians; fel. Am. Med. Asn; Soc. Exp. Biol. & Med; hon. fel. Am. Col. Hosp. Adminr. Brucellosis; toxoplasmosis; salmonellosis; evaluation and control of quality of medical care. Address: University of Colorado School of Medicine, 4200 E. Ninth Ave, Denver, CO 80220.

EISELE, HAROLD F(RANK), b. Hastings, Nebr, Jan. 23, 08; m. 33; c. 2. BOTANY. A.B, Grand Island Col, 29; fel, Iowa State Col, 29-33; M.S, 31, Ph.D.(plant ecol), 33. Prof. biol. & head dept, Sioux Falls Col, 33-35; proj. forester & soil conservationist, soil conserv. serv, U.S. Dept. Agr, 35-43, head prfnl. & tech. training sect, office of personnel, 43-46, asst. dir, grad. sch, U.S. Dept. Agr, 46-51; chief plans & reports br, off. chief of bur. of state serv, U.S. PUB HEALTH SERV, 51-54, spec. asst, prog. off, 54-60, mem. staff, off. planning & anal, 60-67, chief reports anal. staff, bur. health manpower, 67-68, CHIEF, SPEC. PROJS. STAFF, BUR. HEALTH PROF. EDUC. & MANPOWER TRAINING, NAT. INSTS. HEALTH, 68- AAAS; Am. Pub. Health Asn; Am. Soc. Pub. Admin. Program planning, analysis and administration. Address: Bureau of Health Professions Education & Manpower Training, National Institutes of Health, 9000 Rockville Pike, Bethesda, MD 20014.

EISELE, J(OHN) A(LLAN), b. Chicago, Ill, Oct. 25, 29; m. 57; c. 2. NUCLEAR & THEORETICAL PHYSICS. Nat. Sci. Found. fel. & Ph.D.(physics), Ohio State, 59. Scientist, Westinghouse Atomic Power Dept, Bettis Plant, Pa, 56-57; asst. prof. physics & astron, South. Ill. Univ, Carbondale, 59-62; ASSOC. PROF, Tex. A&M Univ, 62-65; PHYSICS, UNIV. MD, 66- Nat. Sci. Found. res. grants, South. Ill. Univ, Carbondale, 61-62 & Tex. A&M Univ, 62-65; nuclear physicist, cyclotron br, nuclear physics div, U.S. Naval Res. Lab, 65-70, consult, satellite tech. br, space systs. div, 70- Am. Phys. Soc. Reactor, neutron and modern physics; quantum mechanics and astronomy. Address: Satellite Techniques Branch, Space Systems Division, U.S. Naval Research Lab, Code 7970, Washington, DC 20032.

EISELE, L(OUIS) J(OHN), S.J, b. Tampa, Fla, Aug. 1, 12. PHYSICS. A.B, St. Louis, 35, fel, 39-40, M.S, 40. Assoc. prof. PHYSICS, SPRING HILL COL, 40-41, from assoc. prof. to PROF, 46-, DIR. SEISMIC STA, 46- Am. Asn. Physics Teachers; Am. Geophys. Union. Photoelectricity. Address: Dept. of Physics, Spring Hill College, Spring Hill Station, Mobile, AL 36608.

EISELEY, LOREN C(OREY), Anthrop, Hist. of Sci, see 12th ed, Soc. & Behav. Vols.

EISEMAN, BEN, b. St. Louis, Mo, Nov. 2, 17; m. 46; c. 4. SURGERY. B.A, Yale, 39; M.D, Harvard, 43. Instr. & asst. prof. surg, sch. med, Washington (St. Louis), 50-53, asst. dean, 50-52; assoc. prof. & prog, sch. med, Colorado, 53-61; prof. SURG. & chmn. dept, col. med, Kentucky, 61-67; PROF, MED. SCH, UNIV. COLO, DENVER, 67- Chief surg. serv, Vet. Admin. Hosp, Denver, 53-61; chief surg, Denver Gen. Hosp, 68- Mem. cmt. trauma, Nat. Res. Coun, 60-68; surg. study sect, Nat. Insts. Health, 61-66; exec. coun. cardiovasc. surg, Am. Heart Asn, 62- Dipl, Am. Bd. Surg, 51, mem. bd, 64-70; dipl, Am. Bd. Thoracic Surg, 58; mem, Nat. Bd. Med. Exam, 64- Med.C, U.S.N, 43-46, Res, 46-, Rear Adm. Am. Col. Surg; Am. Surg. Asn; Soc. Clin. Surg; Soc. Univ. Surg.(pres, 62); Soc. Vascular Surg; Asn. Thoracic Surg; Am. Gastroenterol. Asn. General surgery; tracheostomy and trauma; experimental coronary arterial surgery; peptic ulcer; histamine metabolism; gastric hypersecretion; role of ammonia in production of hepatic coma; treatment of hepatic coma with extracorporeal liver. Address: Dept. of Surgery, University of Colorado Medical Center, 4200 E. Ninth Ave, Denver, CO 80220.

EISEMAN, FRED S, b. Atlanta, Ga, Sept. 10, 21; m. 46; c. 4. ORGANIC CHEMISTRY. B.Ch.E, Ga. Inst. Tech, 46; M.S, Tulane, 49. Res. chemist, Nat. Aniline Div, Allied Chem. Corp, N.Y, 51-57; group leader, org. chem. res. & develop, Maumee Chem. Co, Ohio, 57-63; res. specialist, Gen. Aniline & Firm Corp, 63-70; SR. DEVELOP. CHEMIST, STAUFFER CHEM. CO, 70- U.S.A, 43-46. Am. Chem. Soc. Synthesis of fine organic chemicals; intermediates for dyes and pharmaceuticals; surfactants, antistats and oil additives. Address: Stauffer Chemical Co, Meadow Rd, Edison, NJ 08817.

EISEMANN, KURT, b. Nuremberg, Ger, June 22, 23; U.S. citizen; m. 69; c. 1. APPLIED MATHEMATICS. B.A, Yeshiva, 50; scholar, & M.S, Mass. Inst. Tech, 52; Ph.D.(appl. math), Harvard, 62. Sr. mathematician, Int. Bus. Mach. Corp, N.Y, 52-56, res. mathematician, N.Y. & Mass, 56-61; mgr. math. res, Univac Div, Sperry Rand Corp, D.C, 61-63; assoc. prof, sch. eng. & dir. comput. ctr, Catholic Univ, 63-66; tech. dir, Comput. Usage Develop. Corp, Mass, 66-68; DIR. ACAD. COMPUT. SERV. & PROF. COMPUT. SCI, NORTHEAST. UNIV, 68- Lectr, Yeshiva, 53-55; Catholic Univ, 62-63. Soc. Indust. & Appl. Math. Applications of mathematics to concrete problems; linear programming; numerical analysis; effective use of computers; physical and engineering problems. Address: Northeastern University, 360 Huntington Ave, Boston, MA 02115.

EISEN, EDWIN OTTO, b. Newark, N.J, Mar. 12, 40; m. 64; c. 3. CHEMICAL & NUCLEAR ENGINEERING. B.S.Ch.E, Newark Col. Eng, 61, M.S.Ch.E, 62, Eng.Sc.D, 64. Asst. prof. CHEM. ENG, LAMAR UNIV, 64-68, ASSOC. PROF, 68- Am. Chem. Soc; Am. Inst. Chem. Eng. Chemical kinetics; salt effects in liquid-liquid equilibria; thermodynamics; physical properties of compounds. Address: Dept. of Chemical Engineering, Lamar University, P.O. Box 10053, Beaumont, TX 77710.

EISEN, EUGENE J, b. New York, N.Y, May 14, 38; m. 60; c. 3. GENETICS, STATISTICS. B.S.A, Georgia, 59; M.S, Purdue, 62, Ph.D.(genetics), 65. Asst. prof. ANIMAL GENETICS, N.C. STATE UNIV, 64-67, ASSOC. PROF, 67- Genetics Soc. Am; Biomet. Soc; Poultry Sci. Asn; Am. Soc. Animal Sci. Experimental quantitative genetical studies with mice, involving genetical aspects of dynamics of growth and maternal influences on quantitative traits, and effects on inbreeding and selection on these traits. Address: Dept. of Animal Science, North Carolina State University, Raleigh, NC 27607.

EISEN, FRED H(ENRY), b. Tulsa, Okla, June 2, 29; m. 54; c. 3. PHYSICS. B.S, Calif. Inst. Tech, 51; M.A, Princeton, 53, Ph.D.(physics), 56. Asst, Princeton, 51-56; from sr. physicist to res. specialist, Atomics Int. Div, N.AM. AVIATION, INC, 56-65, MEM. TECH. STAFF, SCI. CTR, 65- Vis. scientist, Inst. Physics, Aarhus Univ, 70-71. Am. Phys. Soc; Sci. Res. Soc. Am. Diffusion in solids; semiconductors; radiation damage; ion implantation in semiconductors; channeling. Address: 1049 Camino Dos Rios, Thousand Oaks, CA 91360.

EISEN, HENRY, b. Brooklyn, N.Y, Dec. 18, 21. PHARMACEUTICAL CHEMISTRY. B.S, St. John's (N.Y), 49; M.S, Rutgers, 51; Am. Found. Pharmaceut. Ed. fel, Connecticut, 52-54, Ph.D.(pharmaceut. chem), 54. Asst. prof. pharm, ST. JOHN'S UNIV.(N.Y), 54-58, assoc. prof, 58-61, PROF. PHARMACEUT. & CHMN. DEPT, 61- Med. Dept, U.S.A, 42-46, M/Sgt. Am. Pharmaceut. Asn; Acad. Pharmaceut. Sci. Pharmacy research and development. Address: Dept. of Pharmaceutics, St. John's University, Grand Central & Utopia Pkwys, Jamaica, NY 11432.

EISEN, HERMAN N(ATHANIEL), b. Brooklyn, N.Y, Oct. 15, 18; m. 48; c. 5. MICROBIOLOGY. A.B, N.Y. Univ, 39, M.D, 43. Asst. path, col. physicians & surgeons, Columbia, 44-46; Nat. Insts. Health fel, col. med, N.Y. Univ, 47-48, fel. chem, 48-49, asst. prof. indust. med, 49-53, assoc. prof, 53-55; prof. med, SCH. MED, WASH. UNIV, 55-61, PROF. MICROBIOL. & HEAD DEPT, 61- Consult to Surgeon Gen, U.S. Pub. Health Serv. & U.S. Army; mem. comn. immunization, Armed Forces Epidemiol. Bd, 60; allergy & immunol. study sect, Nat. Insts. Health, 56-60, 61-66, chmn, 65-66. Nat. Acad. Sci; Am. Soc. Clin. Invest.(v.pres, 65); Harvey Soc; Am. Asn. Immunol.(pres, 68-69); Soc. Exp. Biol. & Med; Asn. Am. Physicians; Am. Chem. Soc; Am. Acad. Arts & Sci; Biophys. Soc; Am. Soc. Biol. Chem. Antibody function and structure; antibody formation. Address: Dept. of Microbiology, Washington University School of Medicine, St. Louis, MO 63110.

EISEN, JAMES DAVID, b. Chicago, Ill, July 27, 32; m. 59; c. 2. BIOLOGY, CYTOGENETICS. B.S, Illinois, 53; M.S, Emory, 54, Ph.D.(cytol), 60; Nat. Sci. Found. summer fel, Marine Biol. Labs, 59. Nat. Insts. Health fels, Uppsala, 60-61, Univ. Lund, 61-62; ASSOC. PROF. HUMAN GENETICS, COL. MED, UNIV. NEBR, 62-, PEDIAT, 65-, DIR. GENETIC SERV, 68- U.S.A, 54-56. AAAS; Tissue Cult. Asn; Am. Soc. Human Genetics; Am. Asn. Mental Deficiency; N.Y. Acad. Sci. Human cytogenetics; cytogenetic basis for forms of mental retardation and congenital malformations; in utero detection of genetic abnormalities. Address: Division of Human Genetics, University of Nebraska Medical Center, Omaha, NE 68105.

EISEN, MARTIN, b. Toronto, Ont, Aug. 12, 32; m. 61; c. 3. MATHEMATICS. B.A, Univ. Toronto, 58, M.A, 59, Ph.D.(math), 61. Asst. prof. MATH, TEMPLE UNIV, 61-70, ASSOC. PROF, 70- Probability theory; functional analysis; logic. Address: Dept. of Mathematics, Temple University, Philadelphia, PA 19122.

EISENBERG, ADI, b. Breslau, Ger, Feb. 18, 35; U.S. citizen; m. 57; c. 1. PHYSICAL CHEMISTRY. B.S, Worcester Polytech, 57; Thiokol fel, Princeton, 58-59, M.A, 59, Procter & Gamble fel, 59-60, Ph.D.(phys. chem), 60. Res. assoc. polymer chem, Princeton, 60-61; NATO fel, Basel, 61-62; asst. prof. CHEM, Univ. Calif, Los Angeles, 62-67; ASSOC. PROF, McGILL UNIV, 67- Consult, Jet Propulsion Lab, 62-67; Owens-Ill, 64-68; Energy Conversion Devices, 70- Am. Chem. Soc; Soc. Rheol; fel. Am. Phys. Soc. Viscoelastic properties and relaxation mechanisms in organic and inorganic polymers and glasses; polymer equilibria; glass transition phenomena in amorphous materials; properties of ionic polymers; polymer chemistry. Address: Dept. of Chemistry, McGill University, Montreal, Que, Can.

EISENBERG, DAVID, b. Chicago, Ill, Mar. 15, 39; m. 63; c. 2. BIOPHYSICAL CHEMISTRY. A.B, Harvard, 61; Rhodes scholar, Oxford, 61-64, D.Phil. (theoret. chem), 64. Nat. Sci. Found. fel. CHEM, Princeton, 64-66; res. fel, Calif. Inst. Technol, 66-68; asst. prof, UNIV. CALIF, LOS ANGELES, 68-71, ASSOC. PROF, 71- Alfred P. Sloan fel. Study of biological macromolecules by x-ray diffraction; structure and properties of water. Address: Dept. of Chemistry, University of California, Los Angeles, CA 90024.

EISENBERG, EUGENE, b. Los Angeles, Calif, Oct. 10, 27; m. 57; c. 2. MEDICINE, ENDOCRINOLOGY. B.A, California, 47, M.S, 50; M.D, California, San Francisco, 50. Intern, Los Angeles County Gen. Hosp, 50-51; asst. res. med, Univ. California, Hosp, 51-52, res. endocrinol. & jr. res. endocrinologist, 52-53, 55; Nat. Insts. Health Res. fel, med. sch, London, 55-56; clin. instr. MED, SCH. MED, UNIV. CALIF, SAN FRANCISCO, 56-60, asst. prof, 60-64, assoc. prof, 64-70, CLIN. PROF, 70-, asst. res. physician, 57-60. Nat. Insts. Health res. fel, med. sch, Univ. Calif, 56-57; attending physician, San Francisco Hosp, 58-; vis. prof, Forsyth Res. Inst, 66-67. Med.C, 53-55, Capt. Am. Fedn. Clin. Res; Endocrine Soc; fel. Am. Col. Physicians. Anabolic effects of steroid hormones, developed assay; cerebral metabolism and steroid anesthesia; bone mineral metabolism. Address: 6500 Fairmount, El Cerrito, CA 94530.

EISENBERG, FRANK, JR, b. Philadelphia, Pa, Apr. 14, 20; m. 48; c. 4. BIOCHEMISTRY. B.S, Pennsylvania, 41, Nat. Insts. Health fel, 49-50, Ph.D, 51. Chemist, synthet. fiber res, Celanese Corp. Am, 41-43; org. chem, Gen. Foods Corp, 43-44; instr. biochem, Pennsylvania, 50-51; biochemist, gen. med. res, Vet. Admin, 51-52; asst. intermediary metab, Pub. Health Res. Inst. N.Y, 52-54; BIOCHEMIST, NAT. INST. ARTHRITIS & METAB. DISEASES, 54- U.S.A, 44-46. AAAS; Am. Soc. Biol. Chem. Mechanism of action of dextransucrase and levansucrase; biosynthesis of inositol; metabolism of glucuronic acid; biosynthesis of glucuronic acid; gas chromatography of sugars and sugar phosphates; glucuronic acid pathway. Address: National Institute of Arthritis & Metabolic Diseases, National Institutes of Health, Bethesda, MD 20014.

EISENBERG, JOHN F(REDERICK), b. Everett, Wash, June 20, 35; m. 57; c. 2. VERTEBRATE ZOOLOGY, ANIMAL BEHAVIOR. B.S, Washington State, 57; Nat. Sci. Found. fel, California, Berkeley, 58-59, M.A, 59, Nat. Acad. Sci. fel, 60-62, Ph.D.(zool), 62. Asst. prof. ZOOL, British Columbia, 62-64; UNIV. MD, COLLEGE PARK, 64-65, RES. ASSOC. PROF, 65-; RESIDENT SCIENTIST, NAT. ZOOL. PARK, SMITHSONIAN INST, 65- Am. Soc. Zool; Am. Soc. Mammal. Mammalian social behavior; analysis of social structure; determination of factors responsible for limiting population growth; philosphy of science. Address: National Zoological Park, Smithsonian Institute, Washington, DC 20009.

EISENBERG, JUDAH MOSHE, b. Cincinnati, Ohio, Dec. 17, 38; m. 61; c. 3. THEORETICAL PHYSICS. A.B, Columbia, 58; Nat. Sci. Found. fel, Mass. Inst. Technol, 58-62, Ph.D.(physics), 63. Asst. prof. PHYSICS, UNIV. VA, 62-65, assoc. prof, 65-68, PROF, 68-, CHMN. DEPT, 70- Fel. Am. Phys. Soc. Nuclear structure theory; medium-energy physics; pion-nucleus interactions. Address: 2514 Hillwood Pl, Charlottesville, VA 22901.

EISENBERG, LAWRENCE, b. New York, N.Y, Dec. 21, 19; m. 50; c. 2. ELECTRONIC ENGINEERING. B.S, City Col. New York, 40, B.E.E, 44; M.E.E, Polytech. Inst. Brooklyn, 52, Ph.D.(elec. eng), 66. Sr. instr. electronics, Sch. Indust. Tech, 50-52; proj. engr, Polytech. Res. & Develop. Corp, 52-56; sr. logician, Digitronics Corp, L.I, 56-58; lectr. elec. eng, City Col. New York, 58; res. assoc. electronics, ROCKEFELLER UNIV, 58-66, ASST. PROF, 66-, CO-HEAD DEPTS. ELECTRONICS & COMPUT. SCI. & AFFILIATE, 70- Instr. in charge, grad. dept. elec. eng, Polytech. Inst. Brooklyn, 56- U.S.A.F, 45-46, Sgt. Inst. Elec. & Electronics Eng. Electrical stimulation of tissue by radiofrequency methods, particularly the heart, bladder and phrenic nerve. Address: Depts. of Electronics & Computer Sciences, Rockefeller University, New York, NY 10021.

EISENBERG, LAWRENCE, b. N.Y.C, June 9, 33; m. 58; c. 3. ELECTRICAL ENGINEERING. B.S.E.E, Fairleigh Dickinson Univ, 60; M.S, N.Y. Univ, 61; Nat. Sci. Found. fel, Newark Col. Eng, 65-66, D.Eng.Sc, 66. Elec. engr, Syst. Develop. Corp, 60-61; instr. ELEC. ENG, Newark Col. Eng, 61-65, asst. prof, 66-67, assoc. prof, 67-68, ASST. PROF, MOORE SCH. ELEC. ENG, UNIV. PA, 68- Summers, engr, Int. Tel. & Tel. Co, 62; Gen. Precision, Inc, 63; Electronics Assocs. Inc, 64; Phila. Elec. Co, 70. Consult, elec. safety comt, Univ. Pa. hosp, 70; del, Am. Automatic Control Coun, 69- U.S.A.F, 52-55. Inst. Elec. & Electronics Eng; Instrument Soc. Am; Am. Soc. Eng. Educ; Franklin Inst. Linear and nonlinear automatic controls; lumped and distributed circuit theory; system theory applied to transportation problems; power system analysis. Address: 143 Thornhill Rd, Cherry Hill, NJ 08034.

EISENBERG, LEON, b. Phila, Pa, Aug. 8, 22; m. 47; c. 2. PSYCHIATRY. A.B, Pennsylvania, 44, M.D, 46; hon. A.M, Harvard, 67. Instr. physiol, med. sch, Pennsylvania, 47-48; asst. instr. neurophysiol, basic sci. course, Army Med. Dept. Research & Grad. Sch, 48-50; res. physician psychiat, Sheppard Pratt Hosp, Md, 50-52; asst. psychiatrist, childrens' psychiat. serv, hosp, Hopkins, 52-53, instr. psychiat. & pediat, med. sch, 53-55, asst. prof, 55-58, assoc. prof, 58-61, PROF. child psychiat, 61-67; PSYCHIAT, HARVARD MED. SCH, 67-; PSYCHIATRIST-IN-CHIEF, MASS. GEN. HOSP, 67- Dir, Glen Burnie Ment. Hyg. Clin, 53-54; psychiat. ed, Crownsville State Hosp, 53-57; psychiatrist, Hopkins Hosp, 54-57, asst-psychiatrist-in-charge, 57-59, psychiatrist-in-charge, childrens' psychiat. serv, 59- Consult, Rosewood State Training Sch, 56-58; Baltimore City Hosp, 58-; Sinai Hosp, 64- Ed, J. Orthopsychiat, 62-; consult. ed, J. Child Psychol. & Psychiat. Morris prize, med. sch, Pennsylvania, 46. Med.C, 48-50, Capt. AAAS; Am. Acad. Child Psychiat; Soc. Res. Child Develop; Am. Psychopath. Asn; Am. Psychiat. Asn; Asn. Res. Nerv. & Ment. Disease; Am. Orthopsychiat. Asn; Am. Pub. Health Asn; Am. Acad. Pediat; Am. Acad. Arts & Sci; Soc. Neurosci; Psychiat. Res. Soc; Am. Pediat. Soc. Child psychiatry, especially early infantile autism, school phobia, psychopharmacology and studies in the development of cognition; learning disorders. Address: Dept. of Psychiatry, Massachusetts General Hospital, Boston, MA 02114.

EISENBERG, M. MICHAEL, b. N.Y.C, Jan. 27, 31; m. 53; c. 3. SURGERY, GASTROENTEROLOGY. A.B, N.Y. Univ, 52; M.D, Harvard, 56. Instr, exp. surg, col. med, Univ. Fla, 62-64, asst. prof. SURG, 64-67, assoc. prof, 67-68; PROF, COL. MED, UNIV. MINN, MINNEAPOLIS, 68- Res. fel, col. med, Univ. Fla, 62-63; Univ. Calif, 65-66; sr. investr, Nat. Insts. Health res. projs, 66-; chief surg, Mt. Sinai Hosp, Minneapolis, 68-; attend. surgeon, Univ. Minn. Hosps, 68-; consult, Minneapolis Vet. Admin. Hosp, 69- Med.C, U.S.A, 58-60, Capt. Am. Col. Surg; Soc. Univ. Surg; Am. Gastroenterol. Asn; Soc. Exp. Biol. & Med; Am. Physiol. Soc; Soc. Surg. Alimentary Tract. Physiology of secretory and motor mechanisms in the pancreas, biliary tract and stomach and duodenum. Address: Dept. of Surgery, University of Minnesota, Minneapolis, MN 55455.

EISENBERG, MARTIN, b. Neptune, N.J, Oct. 27, 41; m. 63; c. 2. OPERATIONS RESEARCH. B.S. & M.S, Mass. Inst. Tech, 64, Ph.D.(opers. res), 67. MEM. TECH. STAFF, BELL TEL. LABS, AM. TEL. & TEL. CO, 67- Computer applications; queuing theory; telephone traffic studies. Address: Room 2C-432, Bell Telephone Labs, Holmdel, NJ 07733.

EISENBERG, MARTIN A(LLAN), b. Brooklyn, N.Y, Mar. 8, 40; m. 60. SOLID MECHANICS. B.Aero.E, N.Y. Univ, 60, M.S, 62; M.E, Yale, 64, D.Eng. (solid mech), 66. Asst. res. scientist, eng. res. div, N.Y. Univ, 60-61; struct. engr, Sikorsky Aircraft Div, United Aircraft Corp, 61-64; asst. instr. ENG. SCI. & MECH, Yale, 65-66; asst. prof, UNIV. FLA, 66-68, ASSOC. PROF, 68- AAAS; Am. Soc. Mech. Eng; Am. Acad. Mech; Am. Soc. Eng. Educ; Soc. Eng. Sci. Theory of plasticity; stress wave propagation in solids; continuum mechanics. Address: Dept. of Engineering Science & Mechanics, University of Florida, Gainesville, FL 32601.

EISENBERG, MAX A, b. New York, N.Y, Sept. 12, 17; m. 48; c. 2. BIOCHEMISTRY, MICROBIOLOGY. B.A, Brooklyn Col, 38; M.S, N.Y. Univ, 41; Ph.D. (biochem), Duke, 50. Lab. asst. biol, Brooklyn Col, 39-41, lectr, 41-47; U.S. Pub. Health fel, 50-52; res. assoc. neurochem, COL. PHYSICIANS & SURGEONS, COLUMBIA, 52-56, asst. prof. BIOCHEM, 56-64, assoc. prof, 64-70, PROF, 70- U.S. Pub. Health grant, 60- Consult, Vet. Admin. Hosp, 60- Sanit.C, 42-46, 1st Lt. AAAS; Am. Soc. Biol. Chem. Intermediary metabolism of carbohydrates and lipids; biosynthesis of biotin. Address: Dept. of Biochemistry, Columbia University College of Physicians & Surgeons, 630 W. 168th St, New York, NY 10032.

EISENBERG, MORRIS, b. Poland, Aug. 26, 21; nat; m. 50; c. 3. CHEMICAL ENGINEERING, ELECTROCHEMISTRY. B.S, California, 50, M.S, 51, Ph.D. (chem. eng), 53. Asst. plant mgr, Zgoda Tanneries, Poland, 39-42; instr. chem, California, 50-51, res. engr, 51-53; sr. electrochemist, Stanford Res. Inst, 53-56; v.pres. & dir. res, Thermo Mat, Inc, 56-57; MGR. ELECTROCHEM. LAB, LOCKHEED MISSILE & SPACE CO, 57-61; PRES. & DIR. RES, ELECTROCHIMICA CORP, 61- Lectr, Stanford, 54-56; California, 59-; chmn. bd, Elca Battery Co, 70- Electrochem. Soc; Sci. Res. Soc. Am; Am. Inst. Chem. Eng; Inst. Elec. & Electronics Eng. Nonaqueous electrochemistry; theoretical electrochemistry; mass transfer and hydrodynamics in relation to electrode reactions and their kinetics; electrochemical energy conversion; fuel cells, batteries; solid state chemistry; heterogeneous catalysts; long life alkaline Mercad batteries; high energy lithium organic batteries. Address: 1140 O'Brien Dr, Menlo Park, CA 94025.

EISENBERG, MURRAY, b. Phila, Pa, May 23, 39; m. 61; c. 2. MATHEMATICS. B.A, Univ. Pa, 60, M.A, 62; Ph.D.(math), Wesleyan Univ, 65. Asst. prof. MATH, UNIV. MASS, AMHERST, 65-69, ASSOC. PROF, 70- Nat. Sci. Found. grant, 66-70. Am. Math. Soc; Math. Asn. Am. Topological dynamics; dynamical systems; transformation groups; general topology. Address: Dept. of Mathematics & Statistics, University of Masschusetts, Amherst, MA 01002.

EISENBERG, PHILLIP, b. Detroit, Mich, Nov. 6, 19; m. 42; c. 2. MECHANICS. B.S, Wayne, 41; C.E, Calif. Inst. Technol, 48. Instr. civil eng, Iowa, 42; physicist, hydrodynamics, David Taylor Model Basin, 42-44, head fluid phenomena br, 45-53; mech. br, Off. Naval Res, 53-59; PRES, HYDRONAUTICS, INC, LAUREL, 59- Guest lectr, Hamburg, 53. Mem. cavitation comt, Int. Towing Tank Conf, 63. Meritorious civilian award, 44, superior accomplishment award, U.S. Navy, 58; distinguished alumnus citation, Wayne State Univ, 58. U.S.N.R, 44-45. AAAS; Am. Inst. Aeronaut. & Astronaut; Acoust. Soc. Am; Am. Phys. Soc; fel. Am. Soc. Mech. Eng.(first tech. award, 59); Soc. Naval Archit. & Marine Eng.(ed, J. Ship. Res, 61-71, v.pres, 70-72). Hydrodynamics, especially cavitation; structural mechanics. Address: 6402 Tulsa Lane, Bethesda, MD 20034.

EISENBERG, RICHARD, b. N.Y.C, Feb. 12, 43; m. 66; c. 2. INORGANIC CHEMISTRY. A.B, Columbia Col, 63; M.A, Columbia, 64, Nat. Sci. Found. fel, 64-66, Ph.D.(chem), 67. Asst. prof. CHEM, BROWN UNIV, 67-71, ASSOC. PROF, 71- Am. Chem. Soc; Am. Crystallog. Asn. Synthetic and structural studies of transition metal complexes containing new or unusual ligands; organo-transition metal chemistry; x-ray diffraction. Address: Dept. of Chemistry, Brown University, Providence, RI 02912.

EISENBERG, RITA B, b. Chicago, Ill, Mar. 25, 21. AUDIOLOGY, ENVIRONMENTAL MEDICINE. B.A, Brooklyn Col, 41; M.A, Columbia, 46; fel. & Sc.D.(audiol), Hopkins, 56. Audiologist, San Francisco Speech & Hearing Center, Calif, 56-58; chief audiol. serv, Cincinnati Speech & Hearing Center, Ohio, 58-61; DIR. BIOACOUSTIC LAB, ST. JOSEPH HOSP, 61- Nat. Inst. Neurol. Diseases & Blindness spec. res. fel, 61-64. Instr, sch. med. & Kettering Inst, Cincinnati, 59-61. Consult, Hamilton County Diag. Clin, Cincinnati Gen. Hosp, 58-61; Child Guid. Clin, Cincinnati, 58-61; Lancaster County Dept. Spec. Serv, 61-; Lancaster Cleft Palate Clin, 61-70; subcomt. commun. & its disorders, Nat. Adv. Comt, Nat. Inst. Dent. Res, 66; consult, ed, Child Develop, 68-71. AAAS; Int. Soc. Develop. Psychobiol; fel. Am. Speech & Hearing Asn; Soc. Res. Child Develop; Acoustical Soc. Am; Ontogeny of communicative functions, normal and aberrant; biochemical and bioelectrical correlates of behavior. Address: Bioacoustic Lab, Research Institute, St. Joseph Hospital, Lancaster, PA 17604.

EISENBERG, ROBERT C, b. Denison, Tex, Aug. 5, 38; m. 56; c. 2. MICROBIOLOGY. B.S, Northwest Mo. State Col, 60; M.S, N.C. State, 62, Nat. Defense Educ. Act fel, U.S. Pub. Health Serv. traineeship & Ph.D.(microbiol), 66. Res. assoc. MICROBIOL, Illinois, Urbana, 66-67; ASST. PROF, WEST. MICH. UNIV, 67- Nat. Sci. Found. teaching equip. grant, 67-69; Nat. Insts. Health res. grant, 70- AAAS; Am. Soc. Microbiol. Bacterial membranes and electron transport complexes; carbohydrate metabolism and regulation processes. Address: Dept. of Biology, Western Michigan University, Kalamazoo, MI 49001.

EISENBERG, ROBERT M(ICHAEL), b. Chicago, Ill, Mar. 11, 38; m. 62; c. 3. ECOLOGY. B.A, Chattanooga, 61; M.S, Michigan, 64, Ph.D.(zool), 65. ASST. PROF. BIOL, RICE UNIV, 65- Ecol. Soc. Am; Am. Soc. Limnol. & Oceanog. Factors determining population size and structure. Address: Dept. of Biology, Rice University, Houston, TX 77001.

EISENBERG, ROBERT S, b. New York, N.Y, Apr. 25, 42; m. 64; c. 1. ELECTROPHYSIOLOGY, BIOPHYSICS. A.B, Harvard, 62; Ph.D.(biophys), Univ. Col, London, 65. Assoc. PHYSIOL, Duke, 65-68; asst. prof, UNIV. CALIF, LOS ANGELES, 68-70, ASSOC. PROF, 70- Am. Physiol. Soc; Biophys. Soc; Soc. Gen. Physiol; Am. Soc. Cell Biol; Inst. Elec. & Electronics Eng. Electrophysiology of muscle; impedance measurements; properties of the sarcotubular system; three dimensional electrical field problems. Address: Dept. of Physiology, University of California, Los Angeles, CA 90024.

EISENBERG, ROSELYN J(ANE), b. N.Y.C, Apr. 26, 40; m. 61; c. 2. MICROBIOLOGY, BIOCHEMISTRY. A.B, Bryn Mawr Col, 60; Nat. Insts. Health trainee, Univ. Pa, 61-65, Ph.D.(microbiol), 65. U.S. Pub. Health Serv, fel, biochem, Princeton, 66-68, instr. biol, 68; lectr, UNIV. PA, 68, res. assoc. MICROBIOL, sch. med, 68-69, ASST. PROF, SCH. DENT. MED, 69- Nat. Inst. Dent. Res. grant, ctr. oral health res, Univ. Pa, 69- AAAS; Am. Soc. Microbiol. Microbial physiology, genetics; transcription, conjugation, DNA replication in Escherichia coli; DNA replication in lactic acid bacteria; lactic dehydrogenases of lactic acid bacteria, cell division in lactic acid bacteria, mechanism and control. Address: School of Dental Medicine, University of Pennsylvania, Philadelphia, PA 19104.

EISENBERG, SEYMOUR, b. Winston-Salem, N.C, Sept. 19, 18; m. 50; c. 2. MEDICINE. B.A, Univ. N.C, 40, M.D, Bowman Gray Sch. Med, 44. Clin. asst. prof. med, UNIV. TEX.(SOUTHWEST) MED. SCH, DALLAS, 50-59, assoc. prof, 59-65, PROF. INTERNAL MED, 65- Asst. chief, med. serv, Vet. Admin. Hosp, Dallas, 50-66, chief, 66- U.S.N, 46-47. Am. Fedn. Clin. Res; Am. Heart Asn. Cardiovascular medicine. Address: Dept. of Internal Medicine, University of Texas (Southwestern) Medical School, Dallas, TX 75230.

EISENBERG, SHELDON MERVEN, b. Phila, Pa, May 14, 42; m. 71. MATHEMATICS. A.B, Temple, 63; Nat. Defense Ed. Act fel, Lehigh, 63-65, M.S, 65, Ph.D.(math), 68. Instr. MATH, Temple, 65-68; asst. prof, UNIV. HARTFORD, 68-70, ASSOC. PROF, 70- Am. Math. Soc; Math. Asn. Am. Approximation theory. Address: Dept. of Mathematics, University of Hartford, West Hartford, CT 06117.

EISENBERG, SIDNEY E(DWIN), b. New Britain, Conn, Jan. 15, 13; m. 46; c. 2. MEDICINE. A.B, Wesleyan, 35; M.D, Rochester, 39. Clin. instr. internal med, sch. med, Yale, 45-54, asst. clin. prof, 54-60; dep. chief med, NEW BRITAIN GEN. HOSP, 64-67, ASSOC. CHIEF MED, 67- Sr. attend. physician & cardiologist, hosps, 45- Fel. Am. Col. Physicians. Anemia, cardiology. Address: 41 Brookside Rd, New Britain, CT 06052.

EISENBERG, SYLVAN, b. N.Y.C, Aug. 30, 13; m. 38; div; c. 3. THERMODYNAMICS. B.A, Pennsylvania, 34, M.S, 35; Ph.D.(chem), Stanford, 43. Dir. lab. & corp. consult, West Foods Lab, Lactol Corp, Calif, 36-41; DIR. & OWNER, ANRESCO, 41-; PRES, MICRO TRACERS, INC, 61- Asst. prof, Santa Clara, 46-48; lectr, San Francisco, 50-56. Consult, Vacudry Corp,

43-44; tech. dir. & co-owner, Desiccated Foods Co, N.Y, 43-47. Am. Chem. Soc; Am. Soc. Bakery Eng; Am. Asn. Cereal Chem; Inst. Food Technol; Nat. Soc. Prof. Eng; Am. Soc. Test. & Mat. Mixing of solids; foods; cleaning materials; corrosion. Address: ANRESCO, 381 11th St, San Francisco, CA 94103.

EISENBERG, WILLIAM V(ICTOR), b. N.Y.C, Feb. 4, 13; m. 41; c. 3. MICRO-BIOLOGY. B.A, Brooklyn Col, 34; Catholic Univ, 37; M.A, George Washington, 42. Lab. asst, Brooklyn Col, 34; bot. aide, bur. plant indust, soils & agr. eng, U.S. Dept. Agr, 36-37, microanalyst, FOOD & DRUG ADMIN, 37-40, Fed. Security Agency, 40-47, acting chief MICROANAL. BR, DIV. MI-CROBIOL, 47-50, CHIEF, 50- U.S. del, codex alimentarius comn. comt. food hyg, Food & Agr. Orgn/WHO, UN. Am. Chem. Soc; assoc. Asn. Off. Agr. Chem; Inst. Food Tech. Optical crystallography of drugs; microscopy of foods and drugs; mold mycelia count method for foods; sanitary biology of food and drug manufacturing establishments. Address: Division of Microbiology BF-216, U.S. Food & Drug Administration, 200 C St. S.W, Washington, DC 20204.

EISENBRANDT, L(ESLIE) L(EE), b. Chanute, Kans, June 23, 08; m. 36, 52; c. 4. PHARMACOLOGY. A.B, Col. Emporia, 32; M.S, Kans. State Univ, 34; Ph.D.(zool), Rutgers Univ, 36. Asst, Kans. State Univ, 32-34; Rutgers Univ, 34-36; instr. biol, Univ. Mo-Kansas City, 36-40, asst. prof, 40-42, physiol, sch. dent, 42-44, assoc. prof, 44-47, pharmacol, sch. pharm, 47-49, prof, 49-66, dean sch, 53-66; PROF. biol, Parsons Col, 66-67; PHARMACOL, SCH. MED, UNIV. MO-COLUMBIA, 67- Res. assoc, sch. med, Univ. Calif, 48-49; consult, Midwest Res. Inst, 55-62; mem. bd. trustees, U.S. Pharmacopeia, 70- AAAS; Am. Soc. Pharmacol. & Exp. Therapeut; Am. Soc. Pharmacol. & Exp. Therapeut; Am. Asn. Hist. Med; Soc. Exp. Biol. & Med; Am. Soc. Trop. Med. & Hyg; Sci. Res. Soc. Am. Drug metabolism and biliary excretion. Address: Dept. of Pharmacology, School of Medicine, University of Missouri-Columbia, Columbia, MO 65201.

EISENBRAUN, ALLAN A(LFRED), b. Lodz, Poland, Nov. 7, 28; m. 57; c. 2. ORGANIC CHEMISTRY. B.Sc, Innsbruck, 52; Gottesman fel, McGill, 57-58, Ph.D.(org. chem), 59. Res. chemist, Ogilvie Flour Mills Co, Ltd, 52-59, res. assoc, Diamond Labs, 59-60; sr. res. chemist, nitrogen div, Allied Chem. Corp, 60-66; polymer chemist, ETHYL CORP, 66-70, SR. POLYMER CHEMIST, 70- Am. Chem. Soc. Carbohydrates; amino acids; heterocyclic chemistry; polymerization kinetics; polymer stabilization; new polymers for packaging applications. Address: 12626 Parnell Dr, Baton Rouge, LA 70815.

EISENBRAUN, E(DMUND) J(ULIUS), b. Wewela, S.Dak, Dec. 10, 20; m. 49; c. 3. ORGANIC CHEMISTRY. B.S, Wisconsin, 50, M.S, 51, Wisconsin Alumni Res. fel, 52-54, Carbide & Carbon fel, 54-55, Ph.D, 55. Res. chemist, Monsanto Chem. Co, Ohio, 55-56; res. fel, Wayne State, 56-59; sr. res. assoc. chem, Stanford, 59-61; res. dir, Aldrich Chem. Co, Wis, 61-62; assoc. prof. CHEM, OKLA. STATE UNIV, 62-68, PROF, 68-, dir. res. proj. 58A, Am. Petrol. Inst, 62-68. Speaker, Gordon Res. Conf. Hydrocarbon Conf, 67. U.S.A, 41-46. Am. Chem. Soc; The Chem. Soc. Synthesis structure proof and reaction of hydrocarbons and methylcyclopentane monoterpenoids, metal-amine reactions; Favorskii reaction; catalytic hydrogenation, hydrogenolysis and dehydrogenation. Address: Dept. of Chemistry, Oklahoma State University, Stillwater, OK 74074.

EISENBUD, DAVID, b. N.Y.C, Apr. 8, 47. ALGEBRA. B.S, Univ. Chicago, 66, M.S, 67, Nat. Defense Educ. Act fel, 67-69, Nat. Sci. Found. fel, 69-70, Ph.D.(math), 70. LECTR. & RES. ASSOC. MATH, BRANDEIS UNIV, 70- Am. Math. Soc; Math. Asn. Am. Module theory over commutative and non-commutative rings and algebras; Dedekind Prime Rings; Artinian Rings; regular local rings; category theory and homological algebra. Address: Dept. of Mathematics, Brandeis University, Waltham, MA 02154.

EISENBUD, LEONARD, b. Elizabeth, N.J, Aug. 3, 13; m. 46; c. 1. THEO-RETICAL PHYSICS. B.S, Union (N.Y), 35; Ph.D.(theoret. physics), Princeton, 48. Physicist, Bartol Res. Found, Pa, 48-58; PROF. PHYSICS, STATE UNIV. N.Y. STONY BROOK, 58-, CHMN. DEPT, 68- Mem, Inst. Adv. Study, 41. Fel. Am. Phys. Soc. Nuclear physics; quantum mechanics. Address: Dept. of Physics, State University of New York at Stony Brook, Stony Brook, NY 11790.

EISENBUD, MERRIL, b. New York, N.Y, Mar. 18, 15; m. 39; c. 3. ENVIRON-MENTAL HEALTH. B.S.E.E, N.Y. Univ, 36, hon. Sc.D, 60. Indust. hygienist, Liberty Mutual Ins. Co, 36-47; assoc. prof. ENVIRON. MED, N.Y. UNIV. MED. CTR, 45-55, adj. prof, 55-59, PROF, 59- Dir. health & safety lab, U.S. Atomic Energy Cmn, 47-57, mgr. N.Y. Oper. Off, 54-59; mem, toxicol. cmt, Nat. Res. Coun, 52-62; atmospheric & indust. hyg. cmt, 52-; alternate U.S. rep, sci. cmt. effects atomic radiation, UN, 56-62; mem. cmt. meteorol. aspects of effects of atomic radiation, Nat. Acad. Sci, 56-64; expert adv. panel radiation, WHO, 57-; mem, Nat. Coun. Radiation Protection, 64-; adminr, Environ. Protection Admin, N.Y.C, 68-70; chmn. bd. dir, Environ. Analysts, Inc, 70- Fel. AAAS; Radiation Res. Soc; fel. Am. Nuclear Soc; Health Physics Soc.(pres, 64-66); Am. Indust. Hyg. Asn; Am. Pub. Health Asn. Environmental radioactivity; urban pollution; environmental effects of power generation; human ecology. Address: P.O. Box 837, Tuxedo, NY 10987.

EISENDRATH, ERNA R, b. St. Louis, Mo, June 24, 09; m. 34; c. 3. BOTANY. A.B, Bryn Mawr Col, 30; M.A, Washington (St. Louis), 60. Instr. BOT, WASH. UNIV, 60-63, asst. prof, 63-66, assoc. prof, 66-69, EMER. ASSOC. PROF, 69-; BOT. HISTORIAN, MO. BOT. GARDEN, 69- AAAS; Bot. Soc. Am. History of botany. Address: Dept. of Botany, Washington University, 4969 Pershing Pl, St. Louis, MO 63108.

EISENFELD, ARNOLD J(OEL), b. Pittsburgh, Pa, July 26, 36; m. 60; c. 2. PHARMACOLOGY, INTERNAL MEDICINE. A.B, Washington & Jefferson Col, 58; M.D, Yale, 62. Inter & res. med, Yale-New Haven Hosp. Center, Conn, 62-64; res. assoc, Nat. Insts. Health, 64-66; fel. pharmacol, SCH. MED, YALE, 66-67, asst. prof. PHARMACOL. & INTERNAL MED, 67-71, ASSOC. PROF, 71- U.S.P.H.S, 64-66, Surgeon. Am. Soc. Pharmacol. & Exp. Therapeut. Interaction of estrogens, androgens and progestins with

target organs; birth control; clinical pharmacology; hypertension. Address: Dept. of Pharmacology, Yale University School of Medicine, New Haven, CT 06510.

EISENFELD, JEROME, b. New York, N.Y, Oct. 13, 38; m. 62; c. 1. APPLIED MATHEMATICS. B.S, City Col. New York, 60; Indiana, 60-62; M.S, Chicago, 64, Ph.D, 66. Res. assoc. MATH, Chicago, 66; ASST. PROF, RENS-SELAER POLYTECH. INST, 66- Am. Math. Soc. Operator theory; hydro-dynamic stability; differential equations; control theory. Address: Dept. of Mathematics, Rensselaer Polytechnic Institute, Troy, NY 12181.

EISENHARDT, RUDOLF H(ERMANN), b. Berlin, Ger, Aug. 10, 24; m. 53; c. 3. PHYSICAL BIOCHEMISTRY. B.A, California, Berkeley, 52; Ben May fel, Chicago, 52-56, M.S, 54, Ph.D.(phys. & anal. chem), 62; Johnson Found. fel, Pennsylvania, 56-57. Engr, Westminster Co, Bolivia, 45-47, chief engr, 47-49; instr. chem, Illinois, 55-56; RES. ASSOC. PHYS. BIOCHEM, HARRI-SON DEPT. SURG. RES, SCH. MED, UNIV. PA, 57- Vis. prof, Wenner Gren Inst, Univ. Stockholm, 67-68; mem, Franklin Inst. AAAS; Biophys. Soc; Soc. Ger. Chem. Metabolic transients; energy-coupling mechanisms; stable and radioactive isotopes; isotope methodology; instrumentation; rapid mixing and sampling techniques; enzymology of pancreatitis. Address: 568 Dulles Bldg, University of Pennsylvania, Philadelphia, PA 19104.

EISENHART, CHURCHILL, b. Rochester, N.Y, Mar 11, 13; m. 39; c. 2. MATHEMATICAL STATISTICS. A.B, Princeton, 34, A.M, 35; Ph.D.(math. statist), London, 37. Instr. math, Wisconsin, 37-40, asst. prof, 40-45, assoc. prof, 45-47, statistician & biometrician, Exp. Sta, 37-47; chief statist. eng. lab, NAT. BUR. STANDARDS, 46-63, SR. RES. FEL, 63- Res. assoc, Tufts Col, 43; res. mathematician, appl. math. group, Columbia, 43-44, prin. math. statistician, statist. res. group, 44-45. Naval Ord. Develop. award, 46; U.S. Dept. of Commerce exceptional serv. award, 57; Rockefeller Pub. Serv. award, 58. Fel. AAAS; Biomet. Soc; Hist. Sci. Soc; fel. Inst. Math. Statist.(v.pres, 48); Math. Asn. Am; fel. Am. Statist. Asn.(v.pres, 58-59, pres, 71); Soc. Hist. Technol; fel. Royal Statist. Soc; Int. Statist. Inst. Mathematical statistics and its applications in the biological and physical sciences and in engineering and industry; history of statistical methodology. Address: National Bureau of Standards, MET A-123, Washington, DC 20234.

EISENHAUER, CHARLES M(ARTIN), b. New York, N.Y, Feb. 6, 30; m. 58; c. 2. NUCLEAR PHYSICS. B.S, Queens Col.(N.Y), 51. Jr. mathematician reactor physics, Brookhaven Nat. Lab, 51-52; nuclear physicist radiation penetration, Armed Forces Spec. Weapons Proj, 53-54; vis. scientist cold neutron exp, Brookhaven Nat. Lab, 56-57; RADIATION PHYSICIST, NAT. BUR. STANDARDS, 58- U.S.A, 52-54. Consult, Oak Ridge Nat. Lab, 64. Silver Medal, U.S. Dept. Commerce, 62. Am. Nuclear Soc. Penetration of nuclear radiation; experimental use of cold neutrons to study the dynamics of solids and liquids. Address: 12613 St. James Rd, Rockville, MD 20850.

EISENHAUER, HUGH R(OSS), b. Lethbridge, Alta, Oct. 11, 27; m. 50; c. 3. ORGANIC CHEMISTRY. B.A, Saskatchewan, 49, M.A, 50; Ph.D.(org. chem), Wisconsin, 53. Res. chemist, Can. Indust, Ltd, 53-54; Du Pont Co. Can, 54-62, sr. res. chemist, 62-66, res. scientist, pub. health eng. div, DEPT. EN-VIRON, 66-70, HEAD WATER SCI. SUBDIV, HYDROL. SCI. DIV, 70- Fel. Chem. Inst. Can; Water Pollution Control Fedn; Int. Asn. Water Pollution Res. Water pollution abatement and control; water science. Address: Hydrologic Sciences Division, Dept. of the Environment, 562 Booth St, Ottawa, Ont, Can.

EISENHUT, WOLFGANG O(TTO), b. Heidelberg, Ger, Jan. 13, 29; U.S. citizen; m. 54; c. 2. ORGANIC CHEMISTRY. Dr.rer.nat.(org. chem), Heidelberg, 55. Res. assoc, Stanford, 55-57; CHEMIST, SHELL DEVELOP. CO, 57- Am. Chem. Soc. Petroleum; natural products; resins; emulsion polymerization. Address: 306 La Questa Way, Woodside, CA 94061.

EISENLOHR, W(ILLIAM) S(TEWART), JR, b. Phila, Pa, Nov. 16, 07; m. 32; c. 3. ENGINEERING. B.S. in C.E, Pennsylvania, 28. Hydraul. engr, U.S. Geol. Surv, Mass, 28, Va, 28-29, Ala, 29-31, Ariz, 31-33, Wash, D.C, 33-61, Colo, 61-70; CONSULT, 71- Fel. Am. Soc. Civil Eng; Am. Geophys. Union; Nat. Soc. Prof. Eng. Hydraulics of natural channels; coefficients for velocity distribution in open channel flow; effect of water temperature on flow of natural streams; floods of North Central Pennsylvania; hydrology of prairie potholes. Address: 2550 Queen St, Lakewood, CO 80215.

EISENMAN, GEORGE, b. N.Y.C, May 6, 29; m. 52; c. 2. BIOPHYSICS. A.B, Harvard, 49, Nat. scholar, 49-53, M.D. 53. Res. fel, Harvard, 53-54, res. assoc, 54-55; sr. staff scientist, dept. basic res, East. Pa. Psychiat. Inst, 56-62; assoc. prof. physiol, col. med, Utah, 62-65; prof, Chicago, 65-69, biophys, 67-69; PROF. PHYSIOL, SCH. MED, UNIV. CALIF, LOS ANGE-LES, 69- Vis. prof, inst. physics, Univ. Genoa, summers 62 & 63; consult, Corning Glass Works, 62-; chmn, Gordon Conf. Ionic Movements & Interactions, 64-; mem. biophys. & biophys. chem. study sect, Nat. Insts. Health, 67-71. Am. Physiol. Soc; Biophys. Soc. Membrane biophysics; molecular biology; physical chemistry. Address: Dept. of Physiology, University of California Medical Center, Los Angeles, CA 90024.

EISENMAN, JOSEPH SOL, b. N.Y.C, Dec. 12, 30; m. 61; c. 2. PHYSIOLOGY. B.S, City Col. N.Y. 53; Inst. Neurol. Sci. fel, Univ. Pa, 55-58, Pa. Plan fel, 59-61, Ph.D.(physiol), 61. U.S. Pub. Health Serv. fel, 61-62; assoc. PHYS-IOL, Univ. Pa, 62-65, asst. prof, 65-70; ASSOC. PROF, MT. SINAI MED. SCH, 70- Med.Serv.C, U.S.A, 53-55. Am. Physiol. Soc; Soc. Neurosci. Neural control of body temperature; organization of trigeminal nucleus. Address: Dept. of Physiology, Mt. Sinai Medical School, New York, NY 10029.

EISENMAN, RICHARD L, b. Bridgeport, Conn, July 12, 28; m. 52; c. 2. AP-PLIED MATHEMATICS. A.B, Col. Holy Cross, 49; M.A, Connecticut, 50; Ph.D.(math), Michigan, 64. Instr. math, Fairfield, 49; Maryland, 50-52; U.S. AIR FORCE, 52-, res. mathematician, Wright Patterson AFB, 53-56, instr. math, U.S. Air Force Acad, 58-59, asst. prof, 59-63, assoc. prof, 63-68; chief, tactical anal, Tan Son Nhut AFB, Vietnam, 68-69; CHIEF, SYSTS. ANAL, PERSONNEL PLANS, HQ, U.S. AIR FORCE, D.C, 69- Consult, Air Battle Anal. Hqs, U.S. Air Force, 65; Kaman Nuclear Corp, 65-66; Holly

Sugar Corp, 68; staff asst. systs. anal, Off. Secy. Defense, D.C, 66-67; prof, George Wash. Univ, 69-70; Univ. Md, 70- U.S.A.F, 52-, Lt. Col. Math. Asn. Am; Opers. Res. Soc. Am. Theory and application of optimization models; game theory; personnel application of Operations research. Address: White Hall, Dunkirk, MD 20754.

EISENMANN, EUGENE, b. Panama City, Panama, Feb. 19, 06; U.S. citizen. ORNITHOLOGY. S.B, Harvard, 27, J.D, 30. RES. ASSOC. ORNITH, AM. MUS. NATURAL HIST, 57- Secy, Pan-Am. Sect, Int. Coun. Bird Preservation; chmn. standing comt. ornith. nomenclature, Int. Ornith. Cong; mem, Int. Comn. Zool. Nomenclature. Cooper Ornith. Soc; Wilson Ornith. Soc; Am. Ornith. Union (ed. Auk, 57-59, v.pres, 68-69). Neotropical birds, particularly in the Panama area; distribution and conservation of American birds. Address: American Museum of Natural History, 79th St. & Central Park W, New York, NY 10024.

EISENSON, JON, b. N.Y.C, Dec. 17, 07; m. 31; c. 2. HEARING & SPEECH SCIENCE. B.S.S, City Col. New York, 28; M.A, Columbia, 30, Ph.D.(educ, psychol), 35. Instr, schs, N.Y, 28-35; speech, Brooklyn Col, 35-42; dir. speech clin, Queens Col.(N.Y), 46-62; PROF. HEARING & SPEECH SCI. & DIR. INST. CHILDHOOD APHASIA, SCH. MED, STANFORD UNIV, 62- Lectr, col. physicians & surgeons, Columbia Univ; consult, U.S. Vet. Admin. Hosps, Calif, 62-; chmn. spec. educ. adv. comt. & mem. med. & sci. comt, United Cerebral Palsy Asn, 64-69; pres, Speech & Hearing Found, 65-70. Dipl, Am. Bd. Prof. Psychol. Asst. chief clin. psychologist, 44-45, dir. lang. rehab. clin, Army Gen. Hosp, 45-46, Med.C, Maj. Fel. AAAS; fel. Am. Speech & Hearing Asn.(pres, 58); fel. Am. Psychol. Asn; Speech Commun. Asn. Language; speech pathology with emphasis on stuttering and aphasia; psychology of speech; communication; psycholinguistics; confirmation and information in rewards and punishments. Address: Dept. of Hearing & Speech Science, Stanford University School of Medicine, 300 Pasteur, Palo Alto, CA 94305.

EISENSTADT, B(ERTRAM) J(OSEPH), b. New York, N.Y, Mar. 28, 23; m. 58; c. 1. MATHEMATICS. B.S, City Col. New York, 43; Sc.M, Brown, 46; fel, Michigan, 46-49; Ph.D.(math), 51. Res. assoc. physics, Nat. Adv. Comt. Aeronaut, 44-46; asst. prof. MATH, WAYNE STATE UNIV, 49-55, assoc. prof, 56-61, PROF, 62- Am. Math. Soc; Math. Asn. Am. Functional analysis. Address: Dept. of Mathematics, Wayne State University, Detroit, MI 48202.

EISENSTADT, JEROME M(ELVIN), b. Chicago, Ill, June 11, 26; m. 60. BIOCHEMISTRY, MICROBIOLOGY. B.S, Roosevelt, 52; M.A, Brandeis, 59, Ph.D.(biol), 60. Fel. biochem, Oak Ridge Nat. Labs, 60-62; asst. prof. MICROBIOL, SCH. MED, YALE, 62-66, ASSOC. PROF, 66- Nat. Insts. Health fel, 61-62. Consult, Oak Ridge Nat. Labs, 60-61, 62- Hosp.C, U.S.N, 44-46. Am. Soc. Microbiol. Cell-free synthesis of proteins and nucleic acids; isolation and characterization of ribonucleic acids; control mechanisms of protein and nucleic acid synthesis; biogenesis of cellular plastids. Address: Dept. of Microbiology, Yale University School of Medicine, 310 Cedar St, New Haven, CT 06510.

EISENSTADT, MAURICE, b. New York, N.Y, June 10, 31; m. 61. PHYSICS. B.C.E, City Col. New York, 52; A.M, Columbia, 53, Ph.D.(physics), 58. Asst. physics, Columbia, 54-58; PHYSICIST, Watson Labs, Int. Bus. Mach. Corp, 58-63; Hudson Labs, Columbia Univ, 63-69; ALBERT EINSTEIN COL. MED, 69- Am. Phys. Soc. Nuclear magnetic resonance; dielectric studies of macromolecules. Address: Dept. of Biochemistry, Albert Einstein College of Medicine, Bronx, NY 10461.

EISENSTADT, RAYMOND, b. Brooklyn, N.Y, May 13, 21; m. 57; c. 4. MECHANICAL ENGINEERING. B.S.M.E, City Col, 41; M.S.M.E, Columbia, 43, Trowbridge fel, 50-52, Ph.D.(mech. eng), 53. Construct. engr, Mediter. Theater, U.S. Govt. War Dept, 46; tech. consult. war surplus mat, Italy, 46-47; design engr. heat, vent. & air conditioning, P.M. Gussow, 48; Corgett-Tinghir, 48-49; engr. res. lubrication, Atomic Energy Cmn, Columbia, 52-53; wind tunnel proj. inst. res, Lehigh, 53-54, asst. prof. MECH. ENG, 53-54; assoc. prof, UNION COL.(N.Y), 54-69, PROF, 69- Nat. Sci. Found. faculty fel, Mass. Inst. Technol. & Univ. Mich, 60-61; summers, consult, Gen. Elec. Co, 55-57 & 65-68, Knolls Atomic Power Lab, 58-60, Watervliet Arsenal, 60, Nat. Sci. Found. fels, inst. mech. & dynamics, Yale, 63, Smith Inst. Solid State Sci. Res, 64; NASA Lewis Struct. Div. res. grant, 68-69, large steam turbine dept. res. grants, 69-71; mem. subcomt. plastic fatigue strength, pressure vessel res. comt, Welding Res. Coun. Ord. Dept, U.S.A, 43-46. Am. Soc. Mech. Eng; Am. Soc. Eng. Educ; Am. Soc. Metals; Soc. Exp. Stress Anal. Mechanical behavior of materials; fatigue of metals. Address: Dept. of Mechanical Engineering, Union College, Schenectady, NY 12308.

EISENSTARK, A(BRAHAM), b. Warsaw, Poland, Sept. 5, 19; nat; m. 48; c. 3. BACTERIOLOGY. A.B, Illinois, 41, A.M, 42, Ph.D.(bact), 48. Electron microscopist, Illinois, 46-48; asst. prof. BACT, Okla. Agr. & Mech. Col, 48-51; assoc. prof, KANS. STATE UNIV, 51-59, PROF, 59- Guggenheim fel, Inst. Microbiol, Copenhagen, Denmark, 59; Nat. Sci. Found. sr. fel, Univ. Leicester, 66; sect. head & prog. dir. molecular biol. sect, Nat. Sci. Found, Wash, D.C, 69-70. Med.C, U.S.A, 42-46. AAAS; Am. Soc. Microbiol; Electron Micros. Soc. Am. Bacteriophage and bacterial genetics. Address: Division of Biology, Kansas State University, Manhattan, KS 66502.

EISENSTATT, PHILLIP, b. Omaha, Nebr, Oct. 16, 22; m. 49; c. 3. GEOLOGY. B.Sc, Nebraska, 43. Geologist, EXPLOR. DEPT, SHELL OIL CO, 43-50, div. geologist, 50-62, STAFF GEOLOGIST, 62- Fel. Geol. Soc. Am; Am. Asn. Petrol. Geol. Subsurface and field geology assignments which could result in the discovery of oil and gas reserves; geological data processing applications. Address: Exploration Dept, Shell Oil Co, P.O. Box 60193, New Orleans, LA 70160.

EISENSTEIN, ALBERT B(ERNARD), b. Doniphan, Mo, Nov. 9, 20; m. 41; c. 5. INTERNAL MEDICINE, ENDOCRINOLOGY. A.B, Univ. Mo, 41; M.D, Wash. Univ, 44. Res. fel. nutrit, sch. med, Wash. Univ, 50-52, instr. prev. med. & med, 52-54, asst. prof, 54-58, assoc. prof, 58-66, chief endocrinol, med. serv, John Cochran Vet. Hosp, 66-68; DIR. DEPT. MED, CUMBERLAND

HOSP, 68- Dir. div. med, Jewish Hosp. St. Louis, 58-63, mem. dept. med, 63-66. U.S.A, 45-47, Capt. AAAS; Am. Soc. Clin. Invest; Am. Soc. Clin. Nutrit; Soc. Exp. Biol. & Med; Endocrine Soc; Am. Fedn. Clin. Res; Asn. Teachers Prev. Med. Adrenal cortical physiology and biochemistry; relationship of nutritional factors to endocrine function. Address: Dept. of Medicine, Brooklyn-Cumberland Medical Center, 39 Auburn Pl, Brooklyn, NY 11205.

EISENSTEIN, BOB I, b. New York, N.Y, Feb. 4, 39; m. 64. HIGH ENERGY PHYSICS. A.B, Columbia, 59, A.M, 61, Ph.D.(physics), 64. Res. assoc. PHYSICS, Columbia, 64; res. fel, Harvard, 64-67; asst. prof, UNIV. ILL, URBANA, 67-70, ASSOC. PROF, 70- Am. Phys. Soc. Muon depolarization in solids; wide-gap spark chambers; bubble chamber studies of strong interactions; streamer chambers. Address: Dept. of Physics, University of Illinois, Urbana, IL 61801.

EISENSTEIN, JULIAN (CALVERT), b. Warrenton, Mo, Apr. 3, 21; m. 48; c. 3. THEORETICAL PHYSICS. B.S, Harvard, 41, Ph.D.(physics), 48. Res. assoc. acoustics, Harvard, 42-45; instr. physics, Wisconsin, 48-52; asst. prof, Pa. State, 53-55; assoc. prof, 55-57; physicist, Nat. Bur. Standards, 57-66; PROF. PHYSICS, GEORGE WASH. UNIV, 66- Nat. Res. fel, 52-53. Am. Phys. Soc; Brit. Inst. Physics & Phys. Soc. Theoretical physics, particularly low temperature physics; paramagnetism; absorption spectra of complex ions. Address: 82 Kalorama Circle N.W, Washington, DC 20008.

EISENSTEIN, L(AURA) BEATRICE, b. N.Y.C, Nov. 9, 42; m. 64. PARTICLE PHYSICS. A.B, Columbia Univ, 63, Nat. Sci. Found. fel. & A.M, 64; Ph.D.(physics), Harvard, 69. RES. ASSOC. PHYSICS, UNIV. ILL, URBANA-CHAMPAIGN, 69- Am. Phys. Soc. Experimental high energy physics; nature and properties of elementary particles. Address: Dept. of Physics, University of Illinois, Urbana, IL 61801.

EISENSTEIN, REUBEN, b. Brooklyn, N.Y, May 3, 29; m. 59; c. 3. PATHOLOGY. B.S, Tulane, 49; M.D, La. State, 53. Asst. attend. PATH, PRESBY-ST. LUKE'S HOSP, 59-62, assoc. attend, 62-68, ATTEND, 68-; PROF, UNIV. ILL. COL. MED, 68-, assoc. prof, 66-68, asst. prof, 60-66. Med.C, 55-57, Capt. Am. Asn. Path. & Bact; Am. Soc. Exp. Path; Int. Acad. Path. Cytology; arteriosclerosis; calcification. Address: Dept. of Pathology, University of Illinois College of Medicine, 1853 W. Polk St, Chicago, IL 60680.

EISENSTEIN, SAM, b. Montreal, Que, Jan. 12, 36; m. 62; c. 2. BIOCHEMISTRY, VIROLOGY. B.Sc, Sir George Williams, 57; M.Sc, McGill, 59, Ph.D.(biochem), 63; dent, Tufts Univ, 69- Res. asst, dept. med, Royal Victoria Hosp, Montreal, 62-64; trainee nucleic acid & enzymol, Wistar Inst, 64-65; res. assoc. biochem. virol, dept. microbiol, med. ctr, Albert Einstein Col. Med, 65-66; biochem. & virol. of oncogenic viruses, Variety Children's Res. Found, 66-69. AAAS; Am. Soc. Microbiol. Enzymology of skeletal muscle and pancreatic proteolytic enzymes; biochemistry of nucleic acids; biochemical virology of oncogenic viruses. Address: 25 Littell Rd, Brookline, MA 02146.

EISENSTEIN, TOBY K(ARET), b. Phila, Pa, Sept. 15, 42; m. 63; c. 1. MICROBIOLOGY. B.A, Wellesley Col, 64; Nat. Insts. Health fel, Bryn Mawr Col, 66-69, Ph.D.(microbiol), 69. Instr. MICROBIOL, SCH. MED, TEMPLE UNIV, 69-71, ASST. PROF, 71- Summer fel, Stanford Univ, 69. AAAS; Am. Soc. Microbiol. Immunity to Salmonella infections; mechanisms of endotoxin toxicity. Address: Dept. of Microbiology & Immunology, Temple University School of Medicine, 3400 N. Broad St, Philadelphia, PA 19140.

EISENTHAL, KENNETH B, b. Brooklyn, N.Y, Mar. 23, 33; m. 57; c. 1. PHYSICAL CHEMISTRY. B.S, Brooklyn Col, 54; M.A, Harvard, 57, Ph.D. (chem. physics), 60. Fel. PHYS. CHEM, California, Los Angeles, 59-60, Nat. Insts. Health fel, 60-61, fel, 63-64; RES. SCIENTIST, Aerospace Corp, 61-63; RES. LAB, IBM CORP, 64- Am. Phys. Soc; Am. Chem. Soc. Electronic molecular spectroscopy; energy transfer; statistical mechanics. Address: Research Lab, IBM Corp, San Jose, CA 95114.

EISENTRAUT, KENT J(AMES), b. Troy, N.Y, July 31, 38; m. 64; c. 2. INORGANIC & ANALYTICAL CHEMISTRY. A.B, St. Michael's Col, 60; NASA fel, Rensselaer Polytech, 62-64, Ph.D.(anal. chem), 64. RES. SCIENTIST, silicone prod. dept, Gen. Elec. Co, summer 60; res. & develop. div, Jackson Lab, E.I. du Pont de Nemours & Co, Inc, summer 64; AEROSPACE RES. LABS, WRIGHT-PATTERSON AIR FORCE BASE, 64- U.S. Air Force Res. & Develop. award, 66. U.S.A.F, 60-67, Capt. Am. Chem. Soc; fel. Am.Inst. Chem; N.Y. Acad. Sci. Metal coordination chemistry; gas chromatography of volatile rare earth, transition and alkali metal chelates; atomic absorption spectroscopy; synthesis of volatile chelates; infrared and nuclear magnetic resonance spectrometry; differential thermal and thermal gravimetric analysis; metal analysis of Apollo 11, 12 & 14 lunar samples. Address: Chemistry Research Lab, Aerospace Research Labs, ARL/LJ, Wright-Patterson Air Force Base, OH 45433.

EISER, ARTHUR L, b. Geneva, Ill, Apr. 16, 28; m. 55; c. 3. PLANT TAXONOMY & ECOLOGY. B.A, Denver, 50; M.S, Iowa State, 52; Ph.D.(plant taxon. & ecol), Va. Polytech, 61. Asst. biol, Denver, 47-50; bot, Iowa State, 50-52; instr. hort, Va. Polytech, 54-56, asst, 56-58; asst. prof. sci, BALL STATE UNIV, 58-63, assoc. prof. BIOL, 63-69, PROF, 69- U.S.A, 52-54, 1st Lt. Ecol. Soc. Am. Plant taxonomy of flowering and ornamental plants; uses in landscaping. Address: Dept. of Biology, Ball State University, Muncie, IN 47306.

EISERLING, FREDERICK A, b. San Diego, Calif, May 8, 38; m. 63. MICROBIOLOGY. B.A, California, Los Angeles, 59, Ph.D.(microbiol), 64. U.S. Pub. Health Serv. fel. biophys, Geneva, 64-66; asst. prof. microbiol, UNIV. CALIF, LOS ANGELES, 66-70, ASSOC. PROF. BACT, 70- Am. Soc. Microbiol. Structure of bacteria and bacterial viruses. Address: Dept. of Bacteriology, University of California, Los Angeles, CA 90024.

EISING, LUCILE M(INELLA), b. Wood Co, Wis, Nov. 5, 08. MEDICINE. B.A, Carroll Col.(Wis), 29; M.D, Wisconsin, 33. Intern, Wis. Gen. Hosp, 33-34; asst. res. orthop. surg. & ear, nose & throat, Children's Hosp, San Francisco, 34-35; intern phys. med, univ. hosp, California, 35-36; asst.

res. orthop. surg. in charge phys. med, Children's Hosp, San Francisco, 36-42, exec. res. house staff, 41-42, res. orthop. surg. in charge phys. med, 42-44, res. in charge phys. med. & occup. ther, 44-46; ASST. CLIN. PROF. orthop. surg, SCH. MED, UNIV. CALIF, SAN FRANCISCO, 46-59, PHYS. MED, 59-, med. supvr. cerebral palsy prog, 46-48, curriculum phys. ther, 48-58, dir. phys. med, univ. hosp, 48-61. Lectr, Mills Col, 44-46; Stanford post-grad. course, Children's Hosp, 43, lectr. & clin. supvr, univ, 44-50; participant cerebral palsy workshop, San Francisco State Col, 52-53, students rehab. counseling prog, San Francisco State Col-Children's Hosp, 56; Arthritis & Rheumatism Found. grant, 60-63. Consult, Children's Hosp, 46-, asst. attend. staff orthop. surg, 46-54, attend. staff, 54-63, consult staff, 63-; active staff, Herbert C. Moffitt Hosp, 48-71, assoc. staff, 71-; consult, Rheumatic Disease Group, 48-69; phys. ther. dept, St. Joseph's Hosp, San Francisco, 69- Mem. qualifications appraisal bd, Calif. State Personnel Bd, 50-55; cerebral palsy adv. comt, May T. Morrison Ctr. Rehab, 51-52; dir, Inst. Neurol. Develop, Belmont, Calif, 67-71. Dipl, Am. Bd. Phys. Med. & Rehab, 56. Am. Phys. Ther. Asn; Am. Acad. Cerebral Palsy; Am. Med. Asn; Am. Cong. Rehab. Med; Am. Geriat. Soc; Am. Rheumatism Asn; Am. Heart Asn; Am. Inst. Ultrasonics in Med. Physical and rehabilitation medicine. Address: 1594 11th Ave, San Francisco, CA 94122.

EISINGER, JOSEF, b. Vienna, Austria, Mar. 19, 24; U.S. citizen; m. 63; c. 2. MOLECULAR BIOLOGY. B.A, Toronto, 47, M.A, 48; Ph.D.(physics), Mass. Inst. Tech, 51. Res. assoc, Mass. Inst, Tech, 51-52; Nat. Res. Coun. Can, 52-53; Rice Inst, 53-54; MEM. STAFF, BELL TEL. LABS, 54- Adj. assoc. prof. physics, N.Y. Univ, 60-63; Guggenheim fel, Switz, 63-64. Can. Army, 44-45. Fel. Am. Phys. Soc; Biophys. Soc. Excited states of nucleic acids; emission spectroscopy; structure of biological molecules. Address: Bell Telephone Labs, Murray Hill, NJ 07974.

EISLER, DANIEL M, b. Cleveland, Ohio, Dec. 19, 12; m. 37; c. 2. BACTERIOLOGY. B.S, Chicago, 35; M.S, Michigan, 39; Ph.D, Western Reserve, 50. Bacteriologist, St. Luke's Hosp, Ohio, 35-37; Mich. Dept. of Health, 39-41; Abbott Labs, Ill, 41-43, 46-47; lab. supt. clin. lab, Portland, Oregon, 50-52; RES. BACTERIOLOGIST, NAVAL BIOL. LAB, UNIV. CALIF, 52- Med.C, U.S.A, 43-46. Am. Soc. Microbiol. Studies in plague; anthrax; shigellosis. Address: Naval Biological Lab, Naval Supply Center, University of California, Oakland, CA 94625.

EISLER, RONALD, b. Brooklyn, N.Y, Feb. 23, 32; m. 63; c. 2. MARINE BIOLOGY. B.A, N.Y. Univ, 52; Miami (Fla), 52-53; M.S, Washington (Seattle), 57, Ph.D.(fisheries biol), 61. Asst, marine lab, Miami (Fla), 52-53; biol. aide, U.S. Army Med. Nutrit. Lab, Colo, 53-55; asst, col. fisheries, Washington (Seattle), 56; aquatic biologist, N.Y. State Conserv. Dept, 57-58; asst, lab. radiation biol, Washington (Seattle), 58-61; fishery res. biologist, Sandy Hook Marine Lab, U.S. Fish & Wildlife Serv, 61-66; RES. AQUATIC BIOLOGIST, NAT. MARINE WATER QUAL. LAB, U.S. ENVIRON. PROTECTION AGENCY, 66- Summers, fishery aide, U.S. Fish & Wildlife Serv, Alaska, 56, instr, inst. radiation biol, Univ. Wash, 59 & 60; adj. prof, grad. sch. oceanog, Univ. R.I, 70- Med.C, U.S.A, 53-55. Am. Fisheries Soc; Am. Soc. Ichthyol. & Herpet; Am. Soc. Limnol. & Oceanog; Marine Biol. Asn. U.K. Ecological aspects of coastal pollution; physiological ichthyology; marine toxicology. Address: U.S. Environmental Protection Agency, National Marine Water Quality Lab, P.O. Box 277, West Kingston, RI 02892.

EISLEY, JOE G(RIFFIN), b. Auglaize Co, Ohio, Apr. 7, 28; m. 56; c. 2. AEROSPACE ENGINEERING. B.S, St. Louis, 51; M.S, Calif. Inst. Tech, 52, Ph.D.(aeronaut, physics), 56. Asst. prof. AERONAUT. & ASTRONAUT. ENG, UNIV. MICH, 56-60, assoc. prof, 60-65, PROF, 65-, ASSOC. DEAN COL. ENG, 67- Nat. Sci. Found. faculty fel, 62-63; consult, Bendix Systs. Div, 59-60; Boeing Co, 61; Conductron Corp, 64. U.S.A, 46-47; U.S.A.F.R, 51-55. Am. Inst. Aeronaut. & Astronaut; Am. Soc. Eng. Educ; Am. Soc. Mech. Eng; Soc. Hist. Technol. Structural dynamics; nonlinear vibrations; aeroelasticity; stress analysis; engineering curriculum development; history of technology. Address: 2632 Park Ridge Dr, Ann Arbor, MI 48103.

EISMAN, LEON P(HILIP), b. Oklahoma City, Okla, July 9, 13; m. 43; c. 2. BACTERIOLOGY, PUBLIC HEALTH. Ph.B, Brown, 37; M.P.H, Mass. Inst. Tech, 40. Dir. labs, St. Louis County Health Dept. & Hosp, Mo, 40-41; MED. SERV. CORPS, U.S. NAVY, 41-, lab. & asst. sanit. off, Naval Air Sta, Tex, 41-43, instr. epidemiol, Naval Med. Sch, Bethesda, Md, 43, epidemiologist & lab. off, construct. training ctr, Va, 43-44, malaria & epidemic control unit 103, 5th Marine Div, 44-45, div. sanit. off, 45, off-in-charge epidemiol. unit 67, Naval Training Ctr, Md, 47, off-in-charge epidemiol. unit 24 & dist. sanit. off, Fifth Naval Dist, Norfolk, Va, 47-48, head field prev. med. lab, med. field res. lab, N.C, 48-50, div. sanit. off, 2nd Marine Div, 50-51, lab. & field prev. med. off, Fleet Epidemic Control Unit 2, U.S.S. Whidbey, 51-52, dist. sanit. off. & off-in-charge prev. med. unit 4, Ill, 53-55, head med. intel. sect, D.C, 55-59, lab. off, prev. med. unit 7, Italy, 59-62, commanding off, U.S. Naval Unit, Ft. Detrick, Md, 62-66, prev. med. off, 1st Marine Div, Fleet Marine Force, Vietnam, 66-67, head environ. health br, Naval Med. Sch, Nat. Naval Med. Ctr, Bethesda, Md, 67-68, force environ. health off, staff, Comdr. Naval Forces Marianas, 68-71; DEP. DIR. MIL. BLOOD PROG. AGENCY, DEPT. DEFENSE, WASH, D.C, 71- Med.Serv.C, U.S.N, 41-, Capt; Bronze Star Medal, 45; Commendation Medals, 45, 62. Am. Soc. Microbiol; Am. Pub. Health Asn; Sci. Res. Soc. Am. Epidemiology and bacteriology, especially preventive medicine coupled with developing new laboratory techniques and equipment design. Address: 4101 Cathedral Ave. N.W, Washington, DC 20016.

EISMANN, WILLIAM, JR, b. Chicago, Ill, June 15, 10; m. 49; c. 2. CHEMICAL ENGINEERING. B.S.(chem), Wisconsin, 32. Lab. asst, Pure Oil Co, 32-37; res. chemist, E.F. HOUGHTON & CO, 37, lubrication res. supvr, 37-55, asst. mgr. res, 55-58, MGR. lubrication prod, 59-68, tech. serv. lab, 68-71, PROD. LINE PLANNING, 71- Mem, Franklin Inst. Am. Soc. Lubrication Eng. Petroleum base lubricants and rust preventives; synthetic and preservative lubricants. Address: 303 W. Lehigh Ave, Philadelphia, PA 19133.

EISNER, ABNER, b. Phila, Pa, Dec. 10, 09; m. 41; c. 1. CHEMISTRY. B.S, Univ. Pa, 30, M.S, 31, Ph.D.(chem), 34. Asst. instr. chem, Univ. Pa, 31-35; RES. CHEMIST, U.S. Bur. Mines, 35-42; EAST. REGIONAL RES. LAB, AGR. RES. SERV, U.S. DEPT. AGR, 42- Adj. assoc. prof, eve. col, Drexel Univ. Am. Chem. Soc; Am. Oil Chemists' Soc. Fatty acids; fundamental chemistry of nicotine; chemistry of wool wax. Address: Eastern Regional Research Lab, U.S.Dept. of Agriculture, Chestnut Hill, Philadelphia, PA 19118.

EISNER, ELMER, b. Poughkeepsie, N.Y, Mar. 8, 19; m. 43; c. 3. PHYSICS. B.A, Brooklyn Col, 39; Ph.D.(physics), Hopkins, 44. Asst. physicist, Nat. Bur. Standards, 43-44; asst. prof. physics, Rutgers, 44-47; physicist, Argonne Nat. Lab, 47-50; TEXACO INC, 51-60, res. assoc, 60-69, SR. RES. ASSOC, 69- AAAS; Am. Phys. Soc; Am. Math. Soc. Analysis of nuclear scattering; design of electronic proximity fuses; analysis of pile behavior; geophysical exploration methods; numerical analysis. Address: Texaco Inc, Bellaire Lab, P.O. Box 425, Bellaire, TX 77401.

EISNER, HANS E(DWARD), b. Ger, Sept. 29, 92; nat; m. 25; c. 2. PHARMACEUTICAL CHEMISTRY. M.Ph, Berlin, 19; Ph.D.(chem), Munich & Berlin, 24. Asst. & fel, Kaiser Wilhelm Inst. Phys. Chem. & Electrochem, 21-33; tech. mgr, Inst. Andromaco, Spain, France & S.Am, 34-47; PRES, METROP. CONSULT. CHEMISTS, 47- Pres, Norvel Labs, 47-58; res, Cornell, 59- Ger. Army, 16-19. AAAS; Am. Chem. Soc. Biochemistry. Address: 301 Salem Dr, Ithaca, NY 14850.

EISNER, HOWARD, b. New York, N.Y, Aug. 8, 35; m. 57; c. 3. ELECTRICAL ENGINEERING, OPERATIONS RESEARCH. B.E.E, City Col. New York, 57; M.S, Columbia, 58; D.Sc.(eng. appl. sci), George Washington, 66. Eng. trainee, Ford Instrument Co, N.Y, summer 56; teaching asst. elec. eng, Columbia, 57; assoc. engr, Astronautics, Gen. Dynamics/Convair, summer 57; substitute teacher physics, Brooklyn Col, 57-59; res. engr, OPERS. RES. INC, SILVER SPRING, 59-63, prog. dir. eng. & opers. res, 64-66, assoc. dir. ENG. ANAL. DIV, 66-68, DIR. & V.PRES, 68- Lectr. physics, sch. gen. studies, Brooklyn Col, 58-59; lectr, sch. eng. & appl. sci, George Washington, 60-64, asst. prof. lectr, 64-66, col. gen. studies, 66-67. Inst. Elec. & Electronics Eng; Opers. Res. Soc. Am; Inst. Mgt. Sci; N.Y. Acad. Sci. Communications; information theory; systems. Address: 11313 Old Club Rd, Rockville, MD 20852.

EISNER, I(RA) (LEONARD), b. Poughkeepsie, N.Y, Jan. 31, 17; m. 42; c. 3. PHYSICS. B.A, Brooklyn Col, 36; univ. scholar, Quincy scholar, Hopkins, Ph.D.(physics), 48. Jr. instr. physics, Hopkins, 39-41; asst. physicist, aircraft radio lab, Wright Field, Ohio, 41-42; radio engr, Signal Corps, U.S. War Dept, 42-46; jr. instr. math, Hopkins, 46-47; asst. prof. physics, Pa. State Col, 48-51; physicist, Battelle Mem. Inst, 51-55; res. assoc. & asst. prof, Ohio State, 55-58; sr. physicist, instrument div, Barnes Eng. Co, 58-69; CONSULT. PHYSICIST, SCI. ASSOCS, 69- Lectr, vis. sci. prog, Nat. Sci. Found, 61-68; consult, Agency Int. Develop, summer sci. inst, India, 66-68; consult. physicist, electrooptics, radiometry, spectros, acoustics. AAAS; Optical Soc. Am; Am. Asn. Physics Teachers; Sci. Res. Soc. Am. Optics and infrared; atmospheric radiation; spectroscopy; radiometry; educational instruments; optical and electrical properties of solids; photoconductivity; music; non-destructive testing; medical instrumentation; thermography; remote sensing; physics pedagogy; light sources; optical materials and instruments. Address: 93 Woodridge Dr, Stamford, CT 06905.

EISNER, MARK JOSEPH, b. Poughkeepsie, N.Y, July 18, 38; m. 62; c. 1. OPERATIONS RESEARCH. B.A, Harvard, 60; Lanchester fel, Cornell Univ, 65, N.Y. State Regents fel, 66-68, Ph.D.(opers. res), 70. Opers. analyst, Res. Analysis Corp, 60-65; ASST. PROF. OPERS. RES, CORNELL UNIV, 69- Nat. Sci. Found. grant, 71- Opers. Res. Soc. Am; Inst. Mgt. Sci. Linear, nonlinear and stochastic programming; game theory; traffic control theory; military operations research; mathematical programming. Address: Dept. of Operations Research, College of Engineering, Upson Hall, Cornell University, Ithaca, NY 14850.

EISNER, MELVIN, b. Poughkeepsie, N.Y, Mar. 2, 22; m. 50; c. 4. PHYSICS. B.S, Brooklyn Col, 42; M.S, North Carolina, 47, Ph.D.(physics), 49. Assoc. prof. PHYSICS, Texas A&M, 48-54, PROF, 54-67; UNIV. HOUSTON, 67- U.S.N.R, 43-45, Lt.(jg). Fel. Am. Phys. Soc. Plasma physics; nuclear magnetic resonance; electron paramagnetic resonance. Address: Dept. of Physics, University of Houston, Cullen Blvd, Houston, TX 77004.

EISNER, PHILIP NATHAN, b. Springfield, Mass, Mar. 7, 34; m. 60; c. 1. PHYSICS. B.S, Mass. Inst. Technol, 55; Columbia Univ, 55-57; Ph.D.(physics), N.Y. Univ, 69. Sr. engr, ITT Labs, 57-61; res. assoc. PHYSICS RES, DEWEY ELECTRONICS CORP, 61-65, ASSOC. LAB. DIR, 68- Instr, N.Y. Univ, 69-70. AAAS; Am. Phys. Soc; Am. Geophys. Union. Ionospheric physics; ion-molecule interactions; atomic and molecular scattering of electrons; chemistry of the upper atmosphere. Address: 142 West End Ave, New York, NY 10023.

EISNER, ROBERT L(INDEN), b. Brooklyn, N.Y, June 21, 27; m. 53; c. 3. SOLID STATE PHYSICS. B.A, Brooklyn Col, 48; Ph.D.(physics), Iowa, 54. Asst. physics, Iowa, 48-51, res. asst, 51-53; res. engr, Westinghouse Res. Labs, 53-61, sr. engr, 61-66, semiconductor div, 66-67, SR. RELIABILITY ENGR, Westinghouse Astronuclear Lab, 67-71, WESTINGHOUSE TRANSPORTATION DIV, 71- U.S.N.R, 45-46. Am. Inst. Mining, Metall. & Petrol. Eng; Am. Phys. Soc; Electrochem. Soc. Semiconductor devices for high voltage and high power; device encapsulations; surface studies; reliability physics in special materials applications; systems safety and reliability analyses; physics of failure. Address: Westinghouse Transportation Division, Ave. A & West St, East Pittsburgh, PA 15112.

EISNER, THOMAS, b. Berlin, Ger, June 25, 29; nat; m. 52; c. 3. ZOOLOGY. B.A, Harvard, 51, Vaughn fel, 52-53, Gibb fel, 53-54, Lalor fel, 54-55, Ph.D, 55. Res. fel, Harvard, 55-57; asst. prof. BIOL, CORNELL UNIV, 57-62, assoc. prof, 62-66, PROF, 66- U.S. Pub. Health Serv. grant, 55-57, 59; Sigma Xi grant, 54, 58; Guggenheim fel, 64. Consult, U.S. Air Force, 53-54. Nat. Acad. Sci; AAAS. Insect physiology; comparative behavior; biocommunication; pheromones; defensive secretions. Address: Dept. of Entomology, Cornell University, Ithaca, NY 14850.

EISS, ABRAHAM L(OUIS), b. N.Y.C, Dec. 28, 34; m. 57; c. 2. METAL-LURGY, MATERIALS ENGINEERING. B.S, Purdue, 55, M.S, 56; N.Y. Univ, 56-59; M.S, Drexel Inst. Tech, 64. Engr, Sylcor Div, Sylvania Elec. Co, 56-59; eng. specialist, nuclear div, Martin Co, 59-63; proj. engr, Hittman Assocs, Inc, 63-65, chief mat. eng. & anal, 65-70; V.PRES. ENG, MAT. RESOURCES, INC, COCKEYSVILLE, 70- Sci. Res. Soc. Am; Am. Inst. Mining, Metall. & Petrol. Eng; Am. Soc. Metals. Powder metallurgy; materials recycling; reactor fuel elements and materials; materials for isotonic power and space applications; thermoelectrics; thermionics. Address: 6800 Hunt Ct, Baltimore, MD 21209.

EISS, ALBERT F(RANK), b. La Fargeville, N.Y, Feb. 2, 10; m. 34; c. 3. SCIENCE EDUCATION. A.B, Houghton Col, 33; M.A, St. Lawrence, 42; Ph.D.(sci. ed), N.Y. Univ, 54. Teacher, pub. schs, N.Y, 34-46; instr. chem, Clarkson Tech, 46-49; head physics dept, Paul Smith's Col, 49-57; prof. sci. ed, Indiana State Col.(Pa), 57-59; sci. ed. specialist, bur. curriculum serv, Dept. Pub. Instruction, 59-64; assoc. exec. secy, Nat. Sci. Teachers Asn, 64-71, EDUC. SYSTS. SPECIALIST, W. GA. EDUC. SERV. CTR, 71- AAAS; Nat. Sci. Teachers Asn; Nat. Asn. Res. Sci. Teaching. Improvement in the teaching of science. Address: 118 Alice Lane, Carrollton, GA 30117.

EISS, NORMAN SMITH, JR, b. Buffalo, N.Y, Mar. 13, 31; m. 57; c. 3. MECHANICAL ENGINEERING. B.M.E, Rensselaer Polytech, 53; M.S, Cornell, 59, Ph.D.(mech. eng), 61. Process engr, E.I. du Pont de Nemours & Co, 53-54; res. engr, Cornell Aeronaut. Lab, Inc, 56-66; ASSOC. PROF. MECH. ENG, VA. POLYTECH. INST. & STATE UNIV, 66- Nat. Sci. Found. sci. faculty fel, Imp. Col, London, 70-71. U.S.A.F, 54-56, 1st Lt. Am. Soc. Mech. Eng; Am. Soc. Lubrication Eng; Am. Soc. Eng. Educ. Friction; wear; lubrication; grinding with abrasives. Address: Dept. of Mechanical Engineering, Virginia Polytechnic Institute & State University, Blacksburg, VA 24061.

EISS, ROGER, b. Lowville, N.Y, Sept. 1, 37; m. 63. INORGANIC CHEMISTRY. B.S, Alfred, 58, M.S, 64; Union Carbide fel, Mass. Inst. Tech, 65-66, Nat. Sci. Found. fel, 66-67, Ph.D.(inorg. chem), 67. Res. chemist, AMP, Inc, Pa, 60-63; instr. math. & chem, Pittsburgh, 64; ASST. PROF. CHEM, ORE. GRAD. CTR, 67- AAAS; Am. Chem. Soc; Am. Inst. Chem; Am. Crystallog. Asn. Structure determination by x-ray techniques; transition metal chemistry; beta-diketone complexes; organic semiconducting materials. Address: Oregon Graduate Center, 19600 N.W. Walker Rd, Portland, OR 97005.

EISSENBERG, DAVID M(ARTIN), b. Brooklyn, N.Y, Aug. 5, 29; m. 53; c. 5. ENGINEERING. B.S, Col. William & Mary, 50; B.S, Mass. Inst. Tech, 52; M.S, Tennessee, 63. Mem. reactor operating group, homogeneous reactor exp, OAK RIDGE NAT. LAB, 52-53, assoc. develop. engr, 53-54, develop. engr. non-Newtonian fluid mech, 58-63, RES. ENGR. HEAT TRANSFER & FLUID FLOW, 64- U.S.N, 55-58, Lt.(jg). Fluid mechanics and heat transfer of non-Newtonian suspensions; nuclear reactor economics; nuclear desalination economics and engineering research. Address: Oak Ridge National Lab, P.O. Box X, Oak Ridge, TN 37830.

EISSLER, ROBERT L, b. Evansville, Ind, Feb. 8, 21; m. 48; c. 4. PHYSICAL CHEMISTRY. B.S, Evansville Col, 49; M.S, Illinois, 56, Ph.D.(chem), 60. Asst. chem. engr, Ill. State Geol. Surv, 52-60, assoc. chemist, 60-61; mgr. graphic arts res, Ball Bros. Res. Corp, 61-65; PRIN. CHEMIST, NORTH. REGIONAL LAB, AGR. RES. SERV, U.S. DEPT. AGR, 65- Vis. prof, Ball State Teachers Col, 62-63. U.S.A.F, 44-46, Res, 46-, Maj. Am. Chem. Soc. Surface chemistry; coal and petroleum; photoengraving and lithographing processes; organic and inorganic coatings; emulsions. Address: Northern Regional Lab, Agricultural Research Service, U.S. Dept. of Agriculture, 1815 N. University, Peoria, IL 61604.

EISSNER, ROBERT M, b. Newark, Del, Nov. 10, 26; m. 57; c. 3. MATHEMATICAL STATISTICS. B.A, Delaware, 48, M.A, 53. Mathematician, comput. lab, BALLISTIC RES. LABS, ABERDEEN PROVING GROUND, MD, 48-50, supvry. math. statistician, surveillance & reliability lab, 50-70, SUPVRY. PHYS. SCIENTIST, U.S. ARMY MAT. SYSTS. ANAL. AGENCY, 70- Inst. Math. Statist; Am. Statist. Asn. Perform reliability evaluations to evaluate the reliability and performance characteristics of nuclear and conventional ammunition systems in the U.S. Army's stockpile. Address: 49 Kells Ave, Newark, DE 19711.

EISTER, W(ARREN) K(ENNETH), b. Sunbury, Pa, Mar. 22, 19; m. 42; c. 2. CHEMICAL ENGINEERING. B.S, Bucknell, 40. Engr, smokeless powder mfg, E.I. du Pont de Nemours & Co, 40-43; atomic energy, radiochem. process develop, Oak Ridge Nat. Lab, 43-61; chief radioisotope prod. & mat, ATOMIC ENERGY COMN, 61-68, PROG. MGR. DIV.ISOTOPES DE-VELOP, 68- Lectr, Oak Ridge Sch. Reactor Technol, 49-52, Inst. Nuclear Studies, 48-54. Am. Chem. Soc; Am. Inst. Chem. Eng. Radiochemical process development; radioactive waste disposal. Address: 4 Holly Dr, Gaithersburgh, MD 20760.

EISZNER, JAMES R(ICHARD), b. Chicago, Ill, Aug. 12, 27; m. 50; c. 2. ORGANIC CHEMISTRY. B.S, Illinois, 50; Ph.D.(chem), Chicago, 52. Res. chemist, Standard Oil Co.(Ind), 52-54; mkt. analyst, Indoil Chem, 54-57; supvr. mkt. res. & develop, Amoco Chem. Corp, Standard Oil Co.(Ind), 57-58, dir. mkt. develop, 58-63; v.pres, mkt, Ott Chem. Co, Mich, 63-65, exec. v.pres, 65-67; V.PRES, CPC Develop. Co, 68-70, CPC INT, INC, 70-, PRES. INDUST. DIV, 70- Chmn. bd, Ott Chem. Co, Mich, 69-70, dir; Can. Starch Co, Ltd; Dural Prod. Ltd; CPC Develop. Co. U.S.A, 46-47. Am. Chem. Soc; Commercial Develop. Asn. New product development; petrochemicals; pharmaceuticals; agricultural chemicals. Address: CPC International, Inc, International Plaza, Englewood Cliffs, NJ 07632.

EITEL, MICHAEL J(OHANN) (EMIL) (RICHARD), b. Berlin, Ger, Nov. 8, 29; nat; m. 64; c. 2. PHYSICAL CHEMISTRY. B.S, Univ. Tenn, 50; Gen. Elec. Co. fel, Univ. Ill, 52-53, Ph.D, 54. Asst. chem, Univ. Ill, 50-51; res. chemist, film dept, E.I. du Pont de Nemours & Co, N.Y, 54-62; asst. prof. CHEM, Northeast. Univ, 62-67, assoc. prof, 67-69; ASSOC. PROF, DIV. INTER-DISCIPLINARY STUDIES, CLEMSON UNIV, 69- Am. Chem. Soc. Polyelectrolytes; kinetics of condensation and addition polymerization; determina-

tion of polymer molecular weights; statistical mechanics of rubber elasticity; polymer incineration. Address: Division of Interdisciplinary Studies, Clemson University, Clemson, SC 29631.

EITZMAN, DONALD V, b. Madison, Wis, June 6, 27; m. 54; c. 5. MEDICINE, PHYSIOLOGY. B.S, Northwest. Univ.(Ill), 50; M.D, Univ. Iowa, 54. Instr. PEDIAT, Univ. Minn, 56-57; southwest. med. sch, Univ. Tex, 57-58; asst. prof, UNIV. FLA, 58-62, assoc. prof, 62-68, PROF, 68- Nat. Insts. Health trainee immunol, 57-58, fel, 58-60; Daland fel. clin. med, 60-64; spec. fel. with Dr. K. Cross, 67-68. U.S.N, 45-46. Soc. Pediat. Res; Am. Pediat. Soc; Am. Physiol. Soc. Newborn physiology; ontogeny of the immune response in infants; comparative immunology in primates; perinatal physiology; acid base control; control of pulmonary blood flow. Address: College of Medicine, University of Florida, Gainesville, FL 32601.

EJRUP, BORJE E. V, b. Stockholm, Sweden, Aug. 19, 10; m. 37; c. 3. MEDICINE, CARDIOLOGY. A.B, Karolinska Inst, Sweden, 34, M.D, 41. First asst. to physician in charge, Stockholm City Hosp, 41-51; first asst. to head med. dept, Univ. Stockholm, Karolinska Inst, 51-61; res. fel. & res. assoc. MED. COL, CORNELL UNIV, 61-63, assoc. prof. MED, 63-67, CLIN. AS-SOC. PROF, 67- Assoc. prof, Karolinska Inst, Sweden, 49-61; res. grants, Karolinska Inst, Swedish Cancer Soc, Am. Cancer Soc. & Nat. Insts. Health, 41-67. Coordinator cerebral vascular disease res. study, Bellevue Hosp, 62-65; asst. attend. physician, N.Y. Hosp. & dir. tobacco withdrawal clin, N.Y. Hosp, 65-67; attend. physician, North Shore Hosp, 66-71. Med. Corps, Swed. Army, 39-45, Capt. Harvey Soc; N.Y. Acad. Sci. Peripheral vascular medicine; anti-smoking research. Address: 104 Hollywood Ave, Douglaston, NY 11363.

EK, ALAN R, b. Minneapolis, Minn, Sept. 5, 42; m. 64; c. 2. FORESTRY. B.S, Univ. Minn, 64, M.S, 65; Ph.D.(forestry), Ore. State Univ, 69. Res. off. FORESTRY, Can. Dept. Forestry & Rural Develop, 66-68; ASST. PROF, UNIV. WIS, MADISON, 68- Biomet. Soc; Soc. Am. Foresters; Am. Soc. Photogram. Mensuration; sampling; biomathematical modeling; aerial photo interpretation. Address: Dept. of Forestry, University of Wisconsin, Madison, WI 53706.

EKBERG, CARL E(DWIN), JR, b. Minneapolis, Minn, Oct. 28, 20; m. 44; c. 4. CIVIL ENGINEERING. B.C.E, Minnesota, 43, M.S, 47, Ph.D, 54. Instr. math. & mech, Minnesota, 46-51; asst. prof. CIVIL ENG, N.Dak. Agr. Col, 51-53; Lehigh, 53-55, assoc. prof, 55-59; PROF. & HEAD DEPT, IOWA STATE UNIV, 59- U.S.N.R, 43-46, Lt. Am. Soc. Civil Eng; Am. Concrete Inst; Am. Soc. Eng. Educ; Am. Rwy. Eng. Asn; Am. Soc. Prof. Eng; Int. Asn. Bridge & Struct. Eng. Structural engineering with particular emphasis on structural concrete; continuing study of composite floor system utilizing light-gage steel. Address: Dept. of Civil Engineering, Iowa State University, Ames, IA 50010.

EKBERG, DONALD ROY, b. Hinsdale, Ill, Dec. 23, 28; m. 61; c. 2. PHYSIOLOGY. B.S, Univ. Ill, 50, Ph.D.(physiol), 57; M.S, Univ. Chicago, 52. Instr. physiol, Univ. Ill, 55-58; physiologist, GEN. ELEC. CO, 58-65, MGR. LIFE SCI, 65- Fel. U.S. Pub. Health, Ger, 59-60; adj. prof, Drexel Univ, 69- U.S.A.F, 52-54, Res, 54-, Maj. Am. Physiol. Soc; Soc. Gen. Physiol; Am. Soc. Zool. Temperature adaptation; aviation and space medicine; environmental physiology. Address: General Electric Company, Box 8555, Philadelphia, PA 19101.

EKBLAW, GEORGE E(LBERT), b. Rantoul, Ill, June 1, 95; m. 31; c. 1. GEOLOGY. A.B, Illinois, 22, A.M, 23; fel, Stanford, 25-27, Ph.D, 27. Asst. State Geol. Surv, Ill, 20-21, asst. geologist, 21-22, 23-25, assoc. geologist, 25-26, 27-29, geologist in charge eng. geol, 29-31, head eng. & areal geol. div, 31-45, geol. ed, 29-45, div. eng. geol. & topog. mapping, 46-63, spec. res. geologist, 63-65; RETIRED. Qm.C, U.S.A, 17-19. AAAS; fel. Geol. Soc. Am; Nat. Soc. Prof. Eng. Kankakee and Alto Pass quadrangles in Illinois; gravel resources and road materials in Illinois; playa deposits in southwestern United States; glacial, stratigraphic, areal and engineering geology in Illinois; ornithology. Address: State Geological Survey, Urbana, IL 61803.

EKELUND-KAPPELER, BROR-SUNE (BRUCE), b. Lapland, July 2, 22; m. 49; c. 7. MATERIALS SCIENCE. B.S, Royal Inst. Tech, Stockholm, 48; dipl, Imp. Col, London, 52; F.L, Stockholm, 56; Cincinnati, 59-61. Dir. metall. & ceramics, Bjorksten Res. Labs, Trionics Corp, 56-58; assoc. prof. chem, S.Dak. State, 58-59; sr. res. assoc. ceramics, Cincinnati Milling Mach. Co, 58-61; prof. mat. sci, British Columbia, 61-; INDUST. CONSULT. MAT. TECHNOL. & APPL. RES, 64- Nat. Res. Coun. Can. associateship, 63-Consult, Boeing Co. & Bourns, Inc, 64-, Northwest Mines Develop. Corp. & MacMillan Bloedel, Ltd, 67- & Casco Industs. Ltd, 69- Am. Chem. Soc; Am. Ceramics Soc; Brit. Iron & Steel Inst; N.Y. Acad. Sci. Materials technology; metals; ceramics; composite and polymeric materials; high-temperature materials; surface treatments; corrosion; adhesion; protective systems; fire retardancy; water repellency. Address: 4194 W. 11th Ave, Vancouver 8, B.C, Can.

EKERN, FRANCES FLETCHER, b. Charleston, W.Va, Oct. 19, 35; m. 70. B.A, Wellesley Col, 57; M.S, Northwestern, 59, Nat. Insts. Health fels, 63 & 64, Ph.D.(biol. sci), 64. Teacher, Annie Wright Sem, 59-61; instr. natural sci, Mich. State Univ, 64-65, asst. prof, 65-69, assoc. prof, 69-70. AAAS; Bot. Soc. Am; Am. Inst. Biol. Sci. Vascular tissue differentiation and pattern development, especially in Lemna minor. Address: 309 Ivy St, Palatka, FL 32077.

EKERN, PAUL CHESTER, b. Ardmore, Okla, July 2, 20; m. 50, 56; c. 4. SOIL PHYSICS, HYDROLOGY. B.A, Westminster Col.(Mo), 42; cert, Chicago, 43; Ph.D, Wisconsin, 50. Instr. soils & meteorol, Wisconsin, 50-52, asst. prof, 52-55; soil physicist, Pineapple Res. Inst, 55-63; PROF. SOILS & AGRON, UNIV. HAWAII & HYDROLOGIST, WATER RESOURCES RES. CTR, 64- U.S.A, 42-46, 1st Lt. AAAS; Soil Sci. Soc. Am; Am. Meteorol. Soc; Soil Conserv. Soc. Am; Am. Geophys. Union; Am. Water Resources Asn; Int.Soc. Biometeorol. Consumptive use of moisture in evapotranspiration; micrometeorology of mulches and tillage; soil erosion. Address: 3133 Huelani Pl, Honolulu, HI 96822.

EKEY, DAVID C(LIFTON), b. Toronto, Ohio, Feb. 19, 23; m. 47; c. 2. INDUSTRIAL ENGINEERING. B.S.(indust. eng), Ohio State, 50, M.S, 50, B.S.(ed), 50; Foundry Ed. fel. & Ph.D.(indust. eng), 55. Chief clerk, Wierton Steel Co, 44-45; asst. prof. indust. eng, Pa. State, 51-55; dir. res, Lebanon Steel Foundry Co, 55-56, tech. dir, 56-57; prof. indust. eng, Ga. Inst. Tech, 57-61; CHMN. DEPT. INDUST. MGT, UNIV. RICHMOND, 61- Mgt. consult, Lynchburg Foundry Co, 59-61; Reynolds Metals Co, 61- Summers, consult, Ohio Malleable Iron Co, 50, Chamberburg Eng. Co, 52, Lebanon Steel Co, 55, Albert Remond & Assocs, 65. U.S.N, 43-44. Am. Foundrymen's Soc; Am. Soc. Metals; Am. Inst. Indust. Eng. Foundry methods; human engineering; operations research in industrial engineering. Address: Dept. of Industrial Management, School of Business Administration, University of Richmond, Richmond, VA 23220.

EKHOLM, WESLEY C, b. Dallas, Tex, Sept. 7, 13; m. 38; c. 2. CHEMISTRY. B.S, Rice Inst, 34, M.A, 36. Res. chemist, Columbian Carbon Co, 36-44, asst. dir. res, 44-49, asst. supt. carbon plants, 49-51, gen. supt, 51-52, gen. mgr. mfg. carbon black div, 52-56, carbon black & pigment div, 57-62, v.pres. pigments & elastomers div, 62-69; GROUP V.PRES. DIVERSE OPERS, CITIES SERV. CO, 70- Am. Chem. Soc; Am. Inst. Chem. Eng. Carbon black process development; combustion and pyrolysis of hydrocarbons; technology of pigments and rubber. Address: 29 Wesskum Wood Rd, Riverside, CT 06878.

EKLER, KURT, b. Hungary, Mar. 25, 22; nat. Can. PHYSICAL CHEMISTRY. B.Sc, McGill, 46, Int. Nickel Co. fel, 52-55, Ph.D.(chem), 55. Asst. res. chemist, Can. Copper Refiners, 46-51; res. chemist, Can. Marconi Co, 55-57; asst. prof. CHEM, LOYOLA COL.(QUE), 57-62, ASSOC. PROF, 62- Am. Chem. Soc; Electrochem. Soc; Can. Inst. Chem. Electrochemistry. Address: Dept. of Chemistry, Loyola College, Montreal, Que, Can.

EKLUND, CARL M(ILTON), b. Moorhead, Minn, Dec. 5, 03. EPIDEMIOLOGY. B.A, Minnesota, 25, M.D, 33. Anal. chemist, Minn. Grain Inspection Lab, 25-32; fel. med, med. sch, Minnesota, 33-36; med. off, Ft. Peck Hosp, 37; epidemiologist, State Dept. Health, Minn, 37-45; surgeon, NAT. INSTS. HEALTH, 45-47, sr. surgeon, 47-51, MED. DIR, 51- U.S. Pub. Health Serv. fel, int. health div. lab, Rockefeller Inst, 39-40. AAAS; Am. Chem. Soc; Am. Pub. Health Asn; Am. Soc. Microbiol. Western and St. Louis types encephalitis and Colorado tick fever; chronic virus diseases. Address: Rocky Mountain Lab, U.S. Public Health Service, Hamilton, MT 59840.

EKLUND, CURTIS EINAR, b. Austin, Tex, May 23, 31. MICROBIOLOGY. B.A, Texas, 53, M.A, 55, Ph.D.(microbiol), 63. Instr. bact, med. br, Texas, 54-55, bacteriologist, Imp. Sugar Co, Tex, 55-58; instr. biol, genetics & bact, Tex. Col. Arts & Indust, 58-60; asst. prof. bact, UNIV. TEX, Austin, 60-66, assoc. prof, MICROBIOL, EL PASO, 66-71, PROF, 71- Dir. tech. studies, Peace Corps Pub. Health Proj, Morocco, 64. U.S.A.R, 50-59, M/Sgt. Am. Soc. Microbiol. Petroleum microbiology; general and sugar bacteriology; bacteriophage, with emphasis on phage-induced enzymes. Address: Dept. of Biology, University of Texas at El Paso, El Paso, TX 79968.

EKLUND, KARL E, b. N.Y.C, July 3, 29; m. 67; c. 3. APPLIED PHYSICS. B.S, Mass. Inst. Tech, 50; M.A, Columbia, 56, Ph.D.(physics), 60. Physicist, Army Nuclear Defense Labs, 51-54; dir. res, Radiation Dynamics, Inc, 60-61; res. assoc. physics, Columbia, 62; asst. dir. nuclear struct. lab, Yale, 63-65; curator phys. labs, State Univ. N.Y. Stony Brook, 65-66, dir. phys. labs, 66-68, asst. to exec. v.pres. systs, 68-69, dir. budget, 70-71, asst. to exec. v.pres, 71; PRIN. ASSOC, EKLUND ASSOCS, 71- Assoc. prof, U.S. Merchant Marine Acad, 62. Consult, Parameters, Inc, 54-60; lectr, Stratos Div, Fairchild, 56-58; aerospace consult, 62-63. Chem.C, U.S.A, 51-53. Nuclear structure physics; electromagnetic transitions; accelerator design and ion optics; research management and administration; management systems; academic facilities planning; laboratory design; educational theory. Address: Eklund Associates, 66 Cliff Ave, Hempstead, NY 11550.

EKLUND, MELVIN W(ESLEY), b. Saco, Mont, July 16, 33; m. 60; c. 2. MICROBIOLOGY, FOOD SCIENCE. B.S, Washington State, 55, M.S, 57; Ph.D.(food sci, microbiol), Purdue, 62. MICROBIOLOGIST, TECHNOL LAB, NAT. MARINE FISHERIES SERV, U.S. DEPT. COMMERCE, 61- AAAS; Am. Soc. Microbiol; Inst. Food Technol. Irradiation preservation of fishery products; effect of antibiotics on psychrophilic bacteria; clostridium botulinum type E; incidence in fishing industry; heat destruction and factors affecting toxin production; yeasts in foods; relation of bacteriophages to toxigenicity of clostridium botulinum. Address: 18727 35th Ave. N.E, Seattle, WA 98155.

EKMAN, CARL FREDERICK W, b. Caribou, Maine, Feb. 13, 32; m. 59. INORGANIC & SOLID STATE CHEMISTRY. B.S, Northeastern, 55; Ph.D.(inorg. chem), Mass. Inst. Tech, 61. Sect. head inorg. chem. res, Itek Corp, 61-65, mgr. res. lab, 65-66; V.PRES. & DIR. RES. & DEVELOP, CARTER'S INK CO, 66- AAAS; Am. Chem. Soc; fel. Am. Inst. Chem. Physical inorganic chemistry of divalent silver; solid state photochemistry; chemical and physical consequences of actinic light on solids, particularly related to image forming systems. Address: Carter's Ink Co, 239 First St, Cambridge, MA 02142.

EKMAN, FRANK O(SCAR), b. London, Eng, Mar. 26, 17; U.S. citizen; m. 44; c. 3. CHEMICAL ENGINEERING. B.A.Sc, British Columbia, 44, M.A.Sc, 46; Ph.D.(chem. eng), Illinois, 50. Mem. staff, MacMillian Indust, Ltd, 44-45; asst, Illinois, 46-48; mem. staff, Howard Smith Paper Mills, Ltd, 49-51; Nat. Lead Co, 51-58; asst. mgr. res. & develop, Glidden Co, 58-59; mem. staff, Pittsburgh Plate Glass Co, 59-64; res. eng, Babcock & Wilcox Co, 64-66; TECH. DIR, ENVIRONEERING, INC, 66- Am. Chem. Soc; Tech. Asn. Pulp & Paper Indust; Air Pollution Control Asn. Aerosols. Address: Technology Dept, Environeering, Inc, 9933 N. Lawler, Skokie, IL 60076.

EKSTEDT, RICHARD D(EAN), b. East St. Louis, Ill, Nov. 13, 25; m. 55; c. 2. MICROBIOLOGY. A.B, Washington (St. Louis), 49; M.S, Michigan, 51, fel, 52-54, Ph.D.(bact), 55. Res. assoc. biochem, sch. med, Illinois, 54-55; med, MED. SCH, NORTHWEST. UNIV, 55-56, instr. MICROBIOL, 56-57, asst. prof, 57-62, assoc. prof, 62-71, PROF, 71- Helen Hay Whitney Found. fel, 58-61. Med.C, U.S.A, 44-46. Am. Soc. Microbiol; Am. Asn. Immunol; Brit. Soc. Gen. Microbiol; Reticuloendothelial Soc. Mechanisms of microbial pathogenicity; nonspecific host defense mechanisms; bacteriocidal activity of blood; immunity to staphylococci; host parasite relationships. Address: Dept. of Microbiology, Northwestern University Medical School, 303 E. Chicago Ave, Chicago, IL 60611.

EKSTROM, L(INCOLN), b. Providence, R.I, Aug. 21, 32; m. 57. PHYSICAL CHEMISTRY. Sc.B, Brown, 53; Nat. Sci. Found. fel, Mass. Inst. Tech, 53-56, Solar Energy fel, 56-57, Ph.D.(chem), 57. MEM. TECH. STAFF, LABS, RCA CORP, 57- David Sarnoff Outstanding Achievement Award, 63. AAAS; Am. Chem. Soc; Am. Phys. Soc; fel. Am. Inst. Chem. Thermoelectric materials; compound semiconductors; physical chemistry of compound semiconductors; absorption spectrophotometry of ionic solutions; magnetic recording materials. Address: RCA Corp, David Sarnoff Research Center, Princeton, NJ 08540.

EL-ABIAD, AHMED H(ANAFI), b. Mersa Matruh, Egypt, May 24, 26; U.S. citizen; m. 52; c. 2. ELECTRICAL ENGINEERING. B.Sc, Cairo, 48; Fulbright travel grant & U.S. Govt. scholar, Purdue Univ, 52-53, M.S.E.E, 53, Ph.D.(elec. eng), 56. Asst. engr, Egyptian State Tel. & Tel, 48-49; asst. ELEC. ENG, Cairo, 49-52; instr, PURDUE UNIV, 53-56, asst. prof, 58-62, assoc. prof, 62-65, PROF, 65- Lectr, Cairo Univ, 56-58; vis. asst. prof, Mass. Inst. Technol, 61-62. Consult, EBASCO Serv, N.Y, 56; Egyptian Electrification Comt, 56-58; Am. Elec. Power Serv. Corp, 59-64; Edison Elec. Inst, 63-64; Consumers Power Co, 66-68; partic, Int. Conf-Large High Tension Elec. Systs, France; mem. adv. comt, Elec. Power Res. & Develop. Ctr. Sr. mem. Inst. Elec. & Electronics Eng; Soc. Gen. Systs. Res; Tensor Soc; Japanese Res. Asn. Appl. Geom. Computer methods for power systems; power system security control; optimization and dynamics; large scale systems. Address: School of Electrical Engineering, Purdue University, Lafayette, IN 47907.

ELAM, EDWARD U(NDERWOOD), b. Pamplin, Va, Aug. 14, 22; m. 46; c. 4. ORGANIC CHEMISTRY. B.S, Va. Polytech, 42. Asst. res. chemist, RES. LABS, TENN. EASTMAN CO, 46-47, assoc. res. chemist, 47-50, res. chemist, 50-56, sr. res. chemist, 56-67, RES. ASSOC, 67- U.S.A, 42-46. AAAS; Am. Asn. Textile Chem. & Colorists; Am. Chem. Soc. Oxo and related reactions; catalytic hydrogenation; ketene chemistry. Address: Research Labs, Tennessee Eastman Co, P.O. Box 511, Kingsport, TN 37662.

ELAM, JACK G(ORDON), b. Glendale, Calif, Aug. 25, 21; m. 52; c. 4. GEOLOGY. A.B, California, Los Angeles, 43, M.A, 48; Ph.D.(geol), Rensselaer Polytech, 60. Geologist, Stanley & Stolz, Calif, 46-47; Richfield Oil Corp, 47-49; Cameron Oil Co, Calif. & Tex, 49-51; consult. geologist, 51-56; asst. prof. petrol. geol, Rensselaer Polytech, 56-60; CONSULT. GEOLOGIST, 60- Pres, Permian Basin Grad. Sch, 69- U.S.A, 43-46, Sgt. Am. Asn. Petrol. Geol; Geol. Soc. Am. Petroleum geology; sedimentology, particularly carbonate sedimentology. Address: 503 Gulf Bldg, Midland, TX 79701.

ELAM, JAMES O, b. Austin, Tex, May 31, 18; m. 46; c. 5. ANESTHESIOLOGY. A.B, Texas, 42; M.D, Hopkins, 45; Minnesota, 46-47; Washington (St. Louis), 47-48; Iowa, 49-51. Asst. prof. ANESTHESIOL, sch. med, Washington (St. Louis), 51-53; dir. dept, Roswell Park Mem. Inst, 53-63; PROF, Missouri, Kansas City Gen. Hosp, 64-66; PROF. ANESTHESIOL, UNIV. CHICAGO, 66- Contractor Res. & Develop. Command, Off. Surgeon Gen, Dept. Army, 54-64; consult, U.S. Army Chem. Center, 56-60. U.S.N, 43-45; Med.C, 55-56, Res, 45-46, 53-55, Maj. Am. Soc. Anesthesiol; Am. Med. Asn. Respiratory physiology in relation to anesthesia; emergency resuscitation; design and performance of anesthesia systems; obstetrical anesthesia. Address: Dept. of Anesthesiology, University of Chicago, Box 443, 950 E. 59th St, Chicago, IL 60637.

ELAM, LLOYD CHARLES, b. Little Rock, Ark, Oct. 27, 28; m. 57; c. 2. PSYCHIATRY. B.S, Roosevelt, 50; M.D, Washington (Seattle), 57. Intern, Illinois, 57-58; res. psychiat, Chicago, 58-61; staff psychiatrist, Billings Hosp, summer 61; prof. psychiat. & chmn. dept, MEHARRY MED. COL, 61-68, interim dean sch. med, 67-68, PRES, 68- Nat. Inst. Ment. Health fel, Riverside Hosp, Nashville, Tenn, 58-61, consult, 62-67; lectr, Univ. Tennessee, 63-67. U.S.A, 50-52. Group Advan. Psychiat; Am. Med. Asn; Am. Psychiat. Asn. Comprehensive health care. Address: Meharry Medical College, 1005 18th Ave. N, Nashville, TN 37208.

ELAM, WILLIAM WARREN, b. Alamo, Ga, May 1, 29; m. 54; c. 3. PLANT PHYSIOLOGY. B.S, Georgia, 61, Nat. Defense Ed. Act fel, 61, Ph.D.(plant sci), 65. Asst. prof. bot. & forestry, MISS. STATE UNIV, 65-70, ASSOC. PROF. FORESTRY, 70- U.S.M.C, 51-54, S/Sgt. Bot. Soc. Am. Response of plant tissue to physical forces, in vitro; tree physiology, especially growth and development in southern conifers. Address: Dept. of Forestry, Mississippi State University, P.O. Drawer FD, State College, MS 39762.

ELANDER, RICHARD P(AUL), b. Worcester, Mass, Sept. 17, 32; m. 58; c. 3. MICROBIOLOGY. B.S, Univ. Detroit, 55, fel, 55-56, M.S, 56; Ph.D.(bot), Univ. Wis, 60. Asst. bot, Univ. Wis, 56-60; sr. microbiologist, antibiotic mfg. & develop. div, Eli Lilly & Co, 60-65, res. scientist, res. labs, 65-67; mgr. process develop, Wyeth Antibiotic Labs, 67-68, mgr. bulk antibiotic prod. & process develop, WYETH LABS, INC, 68-71, ASSOC. DIR, PROD. & PROCESS DEVELOP, BULK PROD, 71- Fel, Univ. Minn, 66. Mycol. Soc. Am; Am. Chem. Soc; Soc. Indust. Microbiol.(secy, 66-67); Am. Soc. Microbiol. Fermentation, recovery and crystallization of natural and semi-synthetic penicillins; microbial genetics as applied to industrial fermentations; strain improvement via mutation and hybridization in penicillin and cephalosporin fungi. Address: Wyeth Labs, Inc, 611 E. Nield St, West Chester, PA 19380.

ELANDT-JOHNSON, REGINA C, b. Nowogrod, Poland, Nov. 22, 18; m. 64. MATHEMATICS, STATISTICS. Ph.M, Poznan, Poland, 46; Ph.D.(statist), Poznań Univ. Agr, 55. Asst. exp. statist, Poznan Univ. Agr, 46-53, lectr, 53-57, assoc. prof, 57-63, head dept. statist, 63-64; assoc. prof. BIOSTATIST, UNIV. N.C, CHAPEL HILL, 64-71, PROF, 71- Polish Acad. Sci.

scholar, Univ. Col, London, 58-59; fel, Case, 60-61. Statistics applied to agricultural experiments; statistical genetics; statistics in medical research. Address: Dept. of Biostatistics, University of North Carolina at Chapel Hill, Chapel Hill, NC 27514.

ELARDE, PAUL F(RANK), b. Ill, Aug. 16, 16; m. 40; c. 2. ENGINEERING PHYSICS. B.S, Illinois, 39. Asst. physicist, develop. nat. resources, State Geol. Surv, Ill, 39-42; degaussing program, Naval Ord. Lab, 42-43; DEVELOP. ENGR, test set design, WEST. ELEC. CO, 43-45, magnetics, 45-54, automation, 54-59, MAGNETICS, 59- AAAS; Inst. Elec. & Electronics Eng. Development of magnetic materials; test methods; equipment. Address: 9 S. 160 Modaff Rd, Naperville, IL 60540.

EL-ASSAR, RATEB JABER, b. Julis, Palestine, June 5, 37. FLUID MECHANICS, APPLIED MATHEMATICS. B.Sc, Cairo Univ, 60; fel. & M.Sc, Bucknell Univ, 64; Ph.D.(mech. eng), Univ. Ill, 68. Res. asst. fluid mech, Univ. Ill, 64-68; ASST. PROF. MECH. ENG, Rutgers Univ, 68-70; STEVENS INST. TECHNOL, 70- Am. Soc. Mech. Eng; Am. Inst. Aeronaut. & Astronaut; Am. Soc. Eng. Educ. Numerical methods. Address: Dept. of Mechanical Engineering, Stevens Institute of Technology, Hoboken, NJ 07030.

ELATTAR, TAWFIK MOHAMMED ALI, b. Cairo, Egypt, Nov. 6, 25; m. 56; c. 1. BIOCHEMISTRY. B.Sc, Cairo, 47, M.Sc, 55; Ph.D.(biochem), Missouri, 57. Biochemistr nutrit, agr. chem. dept, Ministry Agr, Egypt, 47-55; fel. biophys, California, Berkeley, 57-58; biochem, Worcester Found. Exp. Biol, Mass, 58-59; endocrinol, med. sch, Miami, 59-60; asst. prof. physiol. chem, Bonn, 61-64; asst. res. biochemist. med, med. sch. California, San Francisco, 64-68; assoc. prof, DEPT. BIOCHEMISTRY, SCH. DENT, UNIV. MO, 68-70, PROF. & DIR. HORMONE RES, 70- Metabolism and mode of action of steroid hormones; biochemistry of steroid hormones. Address: Dept. of Biochemistry, University of Missouri School of Dentistry, Kansas City, MO 64108.

EL-AWADY, ABBAS ABBAS, b. Dakahlia, U.A.R, Jan. 2, 39; m. 65; c. 1. PHYSICAL INORGANIC CHEMISTRY. B.Sc, Cairo, 58; Ph.D.(phys. inorg. chem), Minnesota, 65. Lab. instr. CHEM, faculty sci, Cairo, 58-59; res. assoc, California, Los Angeles, 65-66; asst. prof, WEST. ILL. UNIV, 66-71, ASSOC. PROF, 71- Am. Chem. Soc. Applications of physical methods to the study of inorganic reactions in solution; calorimetry, visible and ultraviolet spectra of transition metal complexes. Address: Dept. of Chemistry, Western Illinois University, Macomb, IL 61455.

EL-AZIZ, SHAWKY A. ABD, b. Baroud, Egypt, July 23, 39; m. 63; c. 2. INSECT TOXICOLOGY, ENTOMOLOGY. B.Sc, Alexandria, 60, M.Sc, 63; Ph.D. (insect toxicol), California, Riverside, 67. Teaching asst. insect toxicol, Alexandria, 60-63; res. asst, California, Riverside, 67-68; insect toxicologist, Boyce Thompson Inst, 68-70; asst. prof. insect toxicol, Ain Shams Univ, Cairo, 70-71; FEL. NEUROL, CORNELL UNIV, 71- Entom. Soc. Am; fel. Am. Inst. Chem. Metabolism of insecticides of enzymes present in the subcellular fractions of insects; relation between chemical structure and insecticidal activity of organophosphorous and carbamate compounds. Address: Dept. of Neurology, Cornell University, Ithaca, NY 14850.

ELBAUM, C(HARLES), b. May 15, 26; U.S. citizen; m. 56; c. 3. SOLID STATE PHYSICS. M.A.Sc, Univ. Toronto, 51, Ph.D.(appl. sci), 54; hon. M.A, Brown Univ, 61. Res. fel. metal physics, Univ. Toronto, 54-57; Harvard, 57-59; asst. prof. appl. physics, BROWN UNIV, 59-61, assoc. prof. PHYSICS, 61-63, PROF, 63- Fel. Am. Phys. Soc; Am. Inst. Min, Metall. & Petrol. Eng. Crystal defects; mechanical properties of solids; ultrasonic wave propagation; phonon and electron transport and interactions; phase transitions; biophysics. Address: Dept. of Physics, Brown University, Providence, RI 02912.

EL-BAYOUMI, MOHAMED ASHRAF, b. Cairo, Egypt, Dec. 7, 34; m. 56; c. 3. PHYSICAL CHEMISTRY, ELECTRONIC SPECTROSCOPY. B.Sc, Alexandria, 54; M.Sc, Fla. State, 57, Ph.D.(phys. chem), 61. Res. assoc. electronic spectra, Fla. State, 61; Mass. Inst. Tech, 61-62; lectr. phys. chem, faculty sci, Alexandria, 62-67; res. assoc. electronic spectra, Fla. State, 67-68; ASSOC. PROF. ELECTRONIC SPECTRA, MICH. STATE UNIV, 68- Am. Phys. Soc. Electronic spectra of organic and biological molecules; molecular exciton theory applied to dimers and aggregates; luminescence properties of weakly interacting molecular systems. Address: Dept. of Biophysics, Michigan State University, East Lansing, MI 48823.

ELBEIN, ALAN D, b. Lynn, Mass, Mar. 20, 33; m. 54; c. 3. MICROBIOLOGY, BIOCHEMISTRY. A.B, Clark, 54; M.S, Arizona, 56; Nat. Insts. Health fel, Purdue, 57-60, Ph.D.(microbiol), 60. Res. assoc. microbiol, Purdue, 60-61, Nat. Insts. Health fel, Michigan, 61-63; asst. res. biochemist, California, Berkeley, 63-64; asst. prof. biol, Rice, 64-67, assoc. prof, 67-69, DEPT. BIOCHEM, UNIV. TEX. MED. SCH, SAN ANTONIO, 69-70, PROF, 70- Nat. Insts. Health res. career develop. award, 65-69. Am. Soc. Biol. Chem; Am. Chem. Soc; Am. Soc. Microbiol. Biosynthesis of various microbiol products and structures, including antibiotics and cell walls; trehalose metabolism and biosynthesis; synthesis of glycolipids; effects of polyelectrolytes on enzymes. Address: Dept. of Biochemistry, University of Texas Medical School, San Antonio, TX 78229.

ELBEL, ROBERT E, b. Hannibal, Mo, July 8, 25; m. 60; c. 3. ENTOMOLOGY, ZOOLOGY. B.A, Kansas, 48, M.A, 50; Ph.D.(zool), Oklahoma, 64. Med. biol. technician typhus invests, Communicable Disease Ctr, U.S. Pub. Health Serv, 50, biol. aid dysentary studies, 50-51, typhus studies, 51; plague control adv, U.S. Opers. Mission Thailand, Int. Coop. Admin, 51-53, malaria control adv, 53-55; asst. zool, Norman & Willis Biol. Sta, Oklahoma, 56-60; trainee malaria eradication, career develop. div, Agency Int. Develop, Jamaica & Mex, 60-61, malaria specialist, U.S. Opers. Mission Thailand, 61-63; MED. ZOOLOGIST DISEASE ECOL, ECOL. & EPIDEMIOL. BR, DESERT TEST CTR, 63- Mem, Int. N.W. Conf. Diseases Nature Communicable Man. U.S.N.R, 43-45; U.S.P.H.S, 51-55, Lt. Comdr. Siam Soc; Am. Soc. Trop. Med. & Hyg; Am. Mosquito Control Asn; Soc. Syst. Zool. Taxonomy of Mallophaga of birds; comparative studies on flea larvae; fauna and animal-borne diseases of Thailand and west central Utah. Address: E and E Branch, Dugway Proving Ground, Dugway, UT 84022.

ELBERG, SANFORD S(AMUEL), b. San Francisco, Calif, Dec. 1, 13; m. 43; c. 2. BACTERIOLOGY. A.B, California, 34, Ph.D.(microbiol), 38; hon. D.H.L, Hebrew Union Col, 67. Asst. bact, Hooper Found, UNIV. CALIF, BERKELEY, 36-38, lectr. pub. health practice, 38-40, instr. BACT, 41-46, asst. prof, 46-47, assoc. prof, 47-51, PROF, 52-, DEAN GRAD. DIV, 61-, chmn. dept. bact, 52-57. Instr, State Col. Wash, 40; San Francisco Jr. Col, 40-41; Guggenheim fel, 57-58; Novy lectr, Michigan, 64. Consult, Naval Radiol. Defense Lab, 52-54; acting dir. & mem. adv. panel, Naval Biol. Lab, 56-57; consult, WHO, 57-58, mem. brucellosis panel, chmn. expert comt. brucellosis, 63- U.S.A; U.S.N, 42-46. AAAS; Am. Soc. Microbiol; Am. Asn. Immunol; Brit. Biochem. Soc. Cellular immunity; immunity in Brucella infections; biochemistry and physiology of Clostridia; air-borne respiratory infections; physiology and biochemistry of infection; bacteriology and immunity. Address: Division of Medical Microbiology & Immunology, School of Public Health, University of California, Berkeley, CA 94720.

ELBERT, DONALD LEE, b. Louisville, Ky, Nov. 30, 32; m. 54; c. 4. CHEMICAL ENGINEERING. B.Ch.E, Louisville, 55. Instr. physics, Louisville, 55-56; engr, Chemstrand Corp, 56-58, proj. leader nylon develop, 59-63, supvr, Chemstrand Co. Div, MONSANTO CO, 63-65, Astroturf, textiles div, 65-66, sr. res. engr, CHEMSTRAND RES. CENTER, 66-69, ENG. SPECIALIST, 69- Assoc. mem. Am. Inst. Chem. Eng. Astroturf recreational surface; nylon tire yarn; deep-dyeing nylon carpet yarn; Speckelon variable dyeing nylon; nylon yarn processes. Address: Textiles Division, Monsanto Co, P.O. Box 1507, Pensacola, FL 32502.

ELBERT, R(AYMOND) J(OHN), b. Waukesha, Wis, May 2, 22; m. 45; c. 4. ENGINEERING PHYSICS. B.S. & M.S, Wisconsin, 47. Asst. physics, substitute alloy mat. lab, Columbia, 44; design engr, Clinton Labs, E.I. du Pont de Nemours & Co, 44-46; res. supt. atomic energy, isotope separation, UNION CARBIDE CORP, 46-63, res. supt. refractory metals & fuel cell technol, 63-65, porous metals & fuel cell electrode technol, 65-69, proj. mgr. corp. res. dept, 69-70, MGR, POROUS MAT. TECHNOL, CARBON PROD. DIV, 70- Asst, Monsanto Chem. Co, 44-46. U.S.A, 43-46. Am. Soc. Metals. Refractory metals; fuel cell technology; investigation of cobalt, chromium, tungsten alloys; gaseous diffusion research; development of porous membranes; corrosion by fluorine and its compounds; research, development and production of abradable seals, filters, catalysts and porous metal products. Address: Union Carbide Corp, Parma Technical Center, 12900 Snow Rd, Parma, OH 44101.

ELBERTY, WILLIAM TURNER, JR, b. East Orange, N.J, Mar. 8, 30; m. 52; c. 3. GEOLOGY. B.S, St. Lawrence, 53; M.A, Dartmouth Col, 55; Ph.D. (geol), Indiana, 60. Instr. geol, ST. LAWRENCE UNIV, 58-60, asst. prof. GEOL. & GEOG, 60-65, ASSOC. PROF, 64- AAAS; Geochem. Soc. Mineralogy of Pleistocene sands and gravels; conservation and property zoning; mineralogy; geochemistry; economic geology. Address: Dept. of Geology & Geography, St. Lawrence University, Canton, NY 13617.

EL-BISI, HAMED M(OHAMED), b. El-Bagour, Menoufia, Egypt, Mar. 29, 26; nat; m. 52; c. 5. FOOD & INDUSTRIAL MICROBIOLOGY. B.Sc, Ain Shams, Cairo, 47; M.S, Illinois, 52, Ph.D.(food & indust. microbiol), 55. Instr, high sch, Egypt, 47-50; asst, Illinois, 54-55, res. assoc, 56-58; lectr, Ain Shams, Cairo, 55-56; asst. prof, Massachusetts, 58-62, mem. grad. faculty, 58-63, assoc. prof, 62-63; CHIEF MICROBIOL. DIV, FOOD LAB, U.S. ARMY NATICK LABS, 63- Mem. adv. comt, Egyptian Govt, 55-56; indust. adv. & consult, NASA, 60-63; summer study, Nat. Acad. Sci. Space Sci. Bd, 61; interdept. comt. food irradiation, 63-, interagency botulism res. coord. comt, 64- AAAS; Am. Inst. Biol. Sci; Soc. Indust. Microbiol; Sci. Res. Soc. Am; Am. Soc. Microbiol; Inst. Food Tech. Bacterial sporology; mode and kinetics of microbial death by heat, chemicals and ionizing irradiation; microbiology of foods; industrial fermentations. Address: Microbiology Division, Food Lab, U.S. Army Natick Labs, Natick, MA 01760.

ELBLING, IRVING N(ELSON), b. Salem, Mass, July 30, 20; m. 46; c. 2. ORGANIC CHEMISTRY. B.Sc, Northeastern, 43. From lab. asst. to instr, Northeastern, 40-43; student & engr, WESTINGHOUSE ELEC. CO, 43-44, res. chemist plastics & resins, res. lab, 44-50, chemist, org. coatings, paint & varnish dept, 50-52, res. chemist, RES. LAB, 52-53, supvr. insulation dept, 53-66, MGR. SPECIALTY COATINGS, 66- Roon Award Winner, 59. Am. Chem. Soc; Fedn. Socs. Paint Technol. Organic coatings; phenolic alkyd and epoxy resins; electrical insulating varnishes; insulating tapes; adhesives; fluidized bed powders. Address: Westinghouse Research Labs, Pittsburgh, PA 15235.

ELBOURN, ROBERT D(ARLING), b. Indianapolis, Ind, Oct. 5, 19. ELECTRICAL ENGINEERING. B.S, Purdue, 40, M.S, 49; Maryland, 46-47. Elec. engr, C.G. Conn, Ltd, Ind, 40-41; Naval Ord. Lab, D.C, 41-47; electronic scientist, NAT. BUR. STANDARDS, 47-59, chief components & techniques sect, info. tech. div, 59-70, ELECTRONIC ENGR, COMPUT. TECHNOL. DIV, 70- Sr. mem. Inst. Elec. & Electronics Eng; Asn. Comput. Mach; Asn. Symbolic Logic. Design of electronic digital computers; magnetic recording of digital data; electronic instrumentation. Address: Computer Technology Division, National Bureau of Standards, Washington, DC 20234.

ELCHLEPP, JANE G, b. St. Louis, Mo, May 26, 21. PATHOLOGY. B.A, Harris Teachers Col, 43; M.S, Iowa, 46, Ph.D.(zool), 48; M.D, Chicago, 55. Teacher, pub. sch, Mo, 43-44; asst. zool, Iowa, 45-48; instr. biol, Roosevelt, 48-51; asst. anat, Chicago, 51-53; pharmacol, Washington (St. Louis), 54; med, Chicago, 54-55; field investr, Nat. Cancer Inst, 55-62; asst. prof. PATH, MED. CTR, DUKE UNIV, 62-67, ASSOC. PROF, 67-, ASST. DEAN PLANNING, 65-, ASST. V.PRES. HEALTH AFFAIRS, 71-, asst. to v.pres. health affairs, 69-71. U.S.P.H.S.R, 55-, Sr. Surg. AAAS; N.Y. Acad. Sci. Address: Box 2901, Duke Hospital, Durham, NC 27706.

ELCRAT, ALAN ROSS, b. Chicago, Ill, Jan. 13, 42; m. 69. MATHEMATICS. B.S, New Mexico, 64; Nat. Defense Ed. Act. fel, Indiana, 65-67, M.A, 65, Ph.D, 67. Asst. prof. MATH, WICHITA STATE UNIV, 67-70, ASSOC. PROF, 70- Address: Dept. of Mathematics, Wichita State University, Wichita, KS 67208.

ELDEN, HARRY R, b. Miami, Fla, July 21, 28; m. 52; c. 5. PHYSICAL CHEMISTRY. Scholar, Miami, 46-50, B.S, 50, M.S, 53; investr. phys. chem. of aging, connective tissue, Howard Hughes Med. Inst, 56-65, assoc. prof, biochem. & med, 63-65; chief, biophys. sect, gerontol. br, Baltimore City Hosps, 65-69; ASSOC. PROF. CHEM, BARRY COL, 69- With U.S. Pub. Health Serv, 54-56. Consult, Warner Lambert Res. Inst, N.J, 63-65. Am. Chem. Soc; Biophys. Soc. Polymer chemistry; physical chemistry of aging connective tissue; mechanical properties of biological systems; physiology of aging. Address: Dept. of Chemistry, Barry College, Miami Shores, FL 33161.

ELDEN, RICHARD E(DWARD), b. Seneca Falls, N.Y, Feb. 25, 23; m. 55; c. 3. ANALYTICAL CHEMISTRY. S.B, Mass. Inst. Tech, 44; M.S, Washington (Seattle), 52. Chemist, Carbide & Carbon Chem. Co, Columbia, 44; INORG. CHEM. DIV, FMC CORP, 46-50, chief chemist, 51-56, prod. mgr, 56-59, resident mgr, Vancouver Plant, 59-63, mgr. spec. res. proj, 63-66, ASST. TO DIR, 67- U.S.N, 44-46. Am. Chem. Soc. Analytic instrumentation; administration. Address: Inorganic Chemicals Division, FMC Corp, P.O. Box 8, Princeton, NJ 08540.

ELDER, ALEXANDER S(TOWELL), b. Medford, Mass, July 29, 15; m. 47; c. 2. MATHEMATICS. B.A, Harvard, 38; M.Ed, Boston, 40; M.A, Delaware, 56. Elec. technician, Niagara, Lockport & Ont. Power Co, N.Y, 40-41; physicist, Watertown Arsenal, Mass, 46-49; from mech. engr. to chief, DYNAMICS SECT, ARMY BALLISTIC RES. LABS, 50-69, LEADER, SOLID PROPERTIES GROUP, 69- Eve. instr. math, Harford Jr. Col, 59-61. U.S.A, 42-46, T/Sgt. AAAS; Math. Asn. Am; Am. Math. Soc; Soc. Rheol. Mechanics of solids, including vibration theory, elasticity, and viscoelasticity; mechanical design of specialized apparatus and components. Address: U.S. Army Ballistic Research Labs, Aberdeen Research & Development Center, Aberdeen Proving Ground, MD 21005.

ELDER, FRANCIS B(EST), b. Chicago, Ill, Apr. 4, 06; m. 39; c. 1. SANITARY ENGINEERING. B.S, Rutgers, 30; M.S, Michigan, 40. Jr. traffic engr. & commercial rep, N.J. Bell Tel. Co, 30-34; storekeeper gauger, U.S. Treas. Dept, 34-36; sanit. inspector, N.J. State Dept. Health, 36-40; health officer, 40-41; eng. assoc, Am. Pub. Health Asn, 46-62; sanit. engr, U.S. Agency Int. Develop, Ethiopia, 62-69; RETIRED. Consult, Nat. Sanit. Found, 46-57; secy, Am. Sanit. Eng. Intersoc. Bd, 55-58. Instr. mil. sanit. & dir. dept, Supreme Hq, Allied Exped. Force, U.S.A, 41-46, Col. Am. Soc. Civil Eng; fel. Am. Pub. Health Asn; Inter-Am. Asn. Sanit. Eng. (U.S. sect. secy, 49-51, pres, 53). Public health administration. Address: Route 4, Marilyn Lane, Fort Myers, FL 33905.

ELDER, FRED A, b. Carrollton, Ohio, Dec. 4, 29; m. 55; c. 3. PHYSICAL CHEMISTRY. B.S, Muskingum Col, 54; M.S, Univ. Chicago, 62, Ph.D.(chem. phys), 68. Chemist, Nat. Bur. Standards, 54-55; lab. researcher, Calif. Res. Corp, 57-59; res. asst. mass spectros, Univ. Chicago, 62-69; ASST. PROF. CHEM, ROCHESTER INST. TECHNOL, 69- U.S.A, 51-54, S/Sgt. Mass spectroscopy. Address: Dept. of Chemistry, Rochester Institute of Technology, One Lomb Memorial Dr, Rochester, NY 14623.

ELDER, F(RED) KINGSLEY, JR, b. Coronado, Calif, Oct. 19, 21; m. 47; c. 8. PHYSICS. S.B, North Carolina, 41; M.S, Yale, 43, Ph.D.(physics), 47. Student asst, Nat. Bur. Standards, 41; lab. asst. physics, Yale, 41-43, res. asst, 43; instr, 43-44, asst. instruction, 46-47; physicist, Naval Res. Lab, D.C, 44-46; instr. physics, Pennsylvania, 47-49; asst. prof. Wyoming, 49-50; sr. physicist, appl. physics lab, Hopkins, 50-53; assoc. prof, Wabash Col, 53-55, prof. & chmn. dept, Belhaven Col, 55-59; physicist, antisubmarine warfare lab, Naval Air Develop. Center, 59-60, head res. br, 60-65; PROF. PHYSICS & CHMN. DEPT, ROCHESTER INST. TECHNOL, 65- Lectr, Vis. Sci. Prog, 58-59; summers, physicist, Nat. Bur. Standards, 49; Naval Ord. Lab, Md, 57-59. U.S.N.R, 44-46, Lt. Comdr. Am. Phys. Soc; Am. Asn. Physics Teachers; Netherlands Phys. Soc. Isotope separation by thermal diffusion; nuclear and atomic physics; separation and transmutation of neon isotopes; fluid dynamics; physics and geophysics of submarine detection. Address: Dept. of Physics, College of Science, Rochester Institute of Technology, Rochester, NY 14623.

ELDER, GLENN EARL, b. Ft. Wayne, Ind, Mar. 24, 14; m. 34; c. 4. PHYSICS, PHYSICAL METALLURGY. A.B, Evansville Col, 50; M.S, Tennessee, 52. Chemist, works lab, Gen. Elec. Co, Ind, 35-40, chief engr, Ohio, 45-47; res. asst. metall, Univ. Tennessee, 50-54; sr. metallurgist, Oak Ridge Nat. Lab, Tenn, 54-55; chief, environ. & gen. br, electro-mech. labs, White Sands Proving Ground, 55-56, dir. res & develop, 56-59, chief, nuclear effects lab, WHITE SANDS MISSILE RANGE, 59-66, DIR, NUCLEAR EFFECTS DIRECTORATE, 66- U.S.A, 40-45, Res, 45-, Lt. Col. Am. Nuclear Soc; Am. Ord. Asn. Fast burst reactor physics; radiation physics; linear electron accelerators; transient radiation effects. Address: Nuclear Effects Directorate, STEWS-TE-N, White Sands Missile Range, NM 88002.

ELDER, H. E, b. Eldorado, Ill, Nov. 5, 24; m. 48; c. 2. ELECTRONIC ENGINEERING. B.S, Illinois, 48; M.S, Newark Col, Eng, 54. Engr, AM. TEL. & TEL. CO, 48-51, mem. tech. staff, BELL TEL. LABS, INC, 51-57, SUPVR, 57- U.S.N, 44-46. Inst. Elec. & Electronics Eng. Microwave device development; magnetrons, traveling wave tubes, mixer and detector diodes, masers, klystrons and varactor diodes; solid state light-emitting diode development. Address: Bell Telephone Labs, Inc, 2525 N. 11th St, Reading, PA 19604.

ELDER, HOWARD A, b. Flushing, N.Y. COMPUTER SCIENCE. B.E.E, Cornell Univ, 61, M.S, 63, Ph.D.(comput. sci), 69. ASST. PROF. COMPUT. SCI, UNIV. N.C, CHAPEL HILL, 70- Programming systems. Address: Dept. of Computer Science, University of North Carolina at Chapel Hill, Chapel Hill, NC 27514.

ELDER, JAMES B(RUCE), b. Syracuse, N.Y, Nov. 15, 25; m. 51; c. 3. ZOOLOGY. A.B, Arizona, 51, fel, 51-53; M.S, 53; Ph.D.(wildlife mgt), Iowa State Col, 56. Asst. wildlife mgt, Iowa State Col, 53-56; instr. zool, Kansas State, 56-60; biol, Phoenix Col, 60-61; WILDLIFE BIOLOGIST, U.S. BUR. SPORT FISHERIES & WILDLIFE, 61- U.S.A, 44-46. Wildlife Soc; Soc. Range Mgt. Wildlife ecology and management. Address: 11140 Washburn Ave. S, Bloomington, MN 55431.

ELDER, J(OHN) PHILIP, b. London, Eng, Jan. 30, 31; m. 57; c. 2. PHYSICAL CHEMISTRY, ELECTROCHEMISTRY. B.Sc, Liverpool, 54, M.Sc, 56, Ph.D. (electrochem), 61. Fel, Royal Inst. Tech, Sweden, 61-63; Argonne Nat. Lab, 63-65; sr. electrochemist, mat. & control div, res. & develop. dept, Tex. Instruments, Inc, 65-70; GROUP LEADER, RES. CTR, ESB INC, 70- Am. Chem. Soc; Electrochem. Soc; Faraday Soc. Coordination chemistry; theoretical electrochemistry; electrode kinetics; electrochemical mass transfer; molten salts; fuel cells; batteries. Address: 9 Breece Dr, Yardley, PA 19067.

ELDER, JOHN T(HOMPSON), JR, b. Fall River, Mass, June 30, 27; m. 58; c. 2. PHARMACOLOGY. B.S, Mass. Col. Pharm, 53, M.S, 55; Ph.D.(pharmacol), Washington (Seattle), 59. Instr. PHARMACOL, Washington (Seattle), 57-63, asst. prof, 63-65; CREIGHTON UNIV, 65-67, ASSOC. PROF, 67- U.S.N, 45-47. Am. Soc. Pharmacol. & Exp. Therapeut. Psychopharmacology and autonomic pharmacology, especially as it applies to central nervous system function. Address: Dept. of Physiology & Pharmacology, Creighton University, Omaha, NE 68131.

ELDER, JOHN WILLIAM, S.J, b. Ann Arbor, Mich, June 27, 33. ORGANIC CHEMISTRY. B.S, Spring Hill Col, 58; M.S, Loyola (Ill), 60, Ph.D.(org. chem), 62. ASST. PROF. CHEM, Regis Col.(Colo), 67-69; FAIRFIELD UNIV, 69- Am. Chem. Soc. Organic chemistry—natural products. Address: Dept. of Chemistry, Fairfield University, Fairfield, CN 06430.

ELDER, JOSEPH D(ENISON), b. Denver, Colo, Aug. 20, 05; m. 36. PHYSICS. A.B, Princeton, 27, A.M, 28, 32-33; Columbia, 33-35. Instr. physics, Vermont, 28-32; Haverford Col, 37-39; asst. prof. physics & math, Lynchburg Col, 39-40, assoc. prof, 40-43, prof, 43-44; asst. prof. physics, Wabash Col, 44-47, assoc. prof, 47-48; SCI. ED, HARVARD UNIV. PRESS, 48- With Off. Sci. Res. & Develop, 42-46. AAAS; Am. Phys. Soc; Am. Asn. Physics Teachers. Atomic spectra; demonstration experiments in physics; semiconductors. Address: Harvard University Press, 79 Garden St, Cambridge, MA 02138.

ELDER, RICHARD C(HARLES), b. Ann Arbor, Mich, June 9, 39; m. 64. INORGANIC CHEMISTRY. B.S, St. Louis, 61; Nat. Insts. Health fel, Mass. Inst. Tech, 62-64, Ph.D.(chem), 64. Res. assoc. CHEM, Mass. Inst. Tech, 64-65; instr, Univ. Chicago, 65-67, asst. prof, 67-70; ASSOC. PROF, UNIV. CINCINNATI, 70- AAAS; Am. Chem. Soc. Structural chemistry of transition metal complexes; spin exchange in bridged polynuclear complexes; single crystal x-ray diffraction. Address: Dept. of Chemistry, University of Cincinnati, Cincinnati, OH 45221.

ELDER, ROBERT LEE, b. Louisville, Ky, Apr. 5, 31; m. 55; c. 2. RADIOLOGICAL PHYSICS. B.S, Indiana, 53; M.S, North Carolina, 55; fel, Oregon State, 55-58, B.S, 58; U.S. Pub. Health Serv. fel, Hopkins, 61-64, Sc.D.(biophys), 64. Asst. sanit. eng, North Carolina, 53-55; engr, U.S. PUB. HEALTH SERV, Nev, 58-60, sr. engr, 60-61, sr. scientist, Ala, 64-65, div. radiol health, 65-67, asst. to dir, Nat. Ctr. Radiol. Health, 67-69, assoc. dir, BUR. RADIOL. HEALTH, 69-70, DIR. DIV. ELECTRONIC PROD, 70- Res. lectr, Auburn, 64-65; assoc. prof, Oregon State, 65- AAAS; Am. Soc. Civil Eng; Am. Soc. Microbiol. Enzymatic repair mechanisms following exposure to ionizing radiation, and the response of cells following injury, especially the quantization of exposure dose with cellular damage. Address: Bureau of Radiological Health, U.S. Public Health Service, 12720 Twinbrook Pkwy, Rockville, MD 20850.

ELDER, S(AMUEL) A(DAMS), b. Baltimore, Md, July 13, 29; m. 55; c. 5. PHYSICS. B.S, Hampden-Sydney Col, 50; Sc.M, Brown, 53, Ph.D.(physics), 56. Asst. physics, Brown, 50-55; physicist assoc. staff, appl. physics lab, Hopkins, 56, sr. staff, 56-64; assoc. prof. PHYSICS, U.S. NAVAL ACAD, 64-68, PROF, 68- Acoust. Soc. Am; Can. Info. Processing Soc; Am. Asn. Physics Teachers; Am. Sci. Affiliation. Nonlinear acoustics; fluid dynamics; computer science; musical acoustics. Address: Dept. of Physics, U.S. Naval Academy, Annapolis, MD 21402.

ELDER, S(AMUEL) THOMAS, b. New Orleans, La, June 11, 29; m. 55; c. 2. EXPERIMENTAL & PHYSIOLOGICAL PSYCHOLOGY. B.A, Southwestern Louisiana, 56; M.A, Houston, 58; Ph.D.(psychol), La. State, 62. Res. assoc. psychiat. & neurol, sch. med, Tulane, 61-63, asst. prof, 63-64; assoc. prof. PSYCHOL, LA. STATE UNIV, NEW ORLEANS, 64-70, PROF, 70-, CHMN. DEPT, 66- Res. grants, Nat. Inst. Ment. Health, 61-64 & Nat. Sci. Found, 63-65. AAAS; Am. Psychol. Asn. Brain and behavior relationships; development and validation of automated teaching materials. Address: Dept. of Psychology, Louisiana State University in New Orleans, Lake Front, New Orleans, LA 70124.

ELDER, (JAMES) TAIT, b. Baltimore, Md, Mar. 9, 25; m. 47; c. 5. PHYSICS. A.B, North Carolina, 47; Ph.D.(physics), Hopkins, 52. Jr. instr. physics, Hopkins, 47-50, res. asst, 50-52; investr, res. dept. N.J. Zinc Co, 52-59; sr. res. physicist, cent. res. labs, MINN. MINING & MFG. CO, 59-62, head physics phenomena group, 62-64; mgr. gen. physics res, 64-67, tech. mkt. analyst, NEW BUS. VENTURES DIV, 67-70, MGR, DETECTION PROD, 71- U.S.N.R, 42-47, Lt.(jg). AAAS; Inst. Elec. & Electronics Eng; Am. Phys. Soc; Am. Asn. Physics Teachers. Infrared spectroscopy; mining geophysics; electrophotography; solid state physics; magnetic materials and measurements; research management; product and market development; security devices and techniques. Address: 748 Amber Dr, St. Paul, MN 55112.

ELDER, W(ILLIAM) H(ANNA), b. Oak Park, Ill, Dec. 24, 13; m. 41; c. 2. WILDLIFE CONSERVATION. B.S, Wisconsin, 36, Ph.M, 38, Ph.D.(zool), 42; Michigan, 37. Asst. zool, Wisconsin, 36-41; game technician, Nat. Hist. Surv, Ill, 41-43; asst. pharmacol, Chicago, 43-45; asst. prof. ZOOL, UNIV. MO-COLUMBIA, 45-47, assoc. prof, 48-51, prof, 51-54, RUCKER PROF, 54- Mem. staff, toxicol. lab, Chicago, 43-45; Guggenheim fel, 56-57; Fulbright fel, 65-66; Nat. Sci. Found. grant, Africa, 67-68. Am. Soc. Zool; Am. Soc. Mammal; Wildlife Soc; Wilson Ornith. Soc; Wilderness Soc. Physiology of reproduction; biology of the Canada goose; measures of productivity in wild populations; lead poisoning; biology of bats; avian chemosterilants; African elephant. Address: 108 Stephens Hall, University of Missouri-Columbia, Columbia, MO 65201.

ELDERFIELD, ROBERT C(OOLEY), b. Niagara Falls, N.Y, May 30, 04; m. 30; c. 2. ORGANIC CHEMISTRY. A.B, Williams Col, 26, hon. D.Sc, 52; Ph.D.(chem), Mass. Inst. Tech, 30. Instr. CHEM, Colby Col, 30; asst, Rockefeller Inst, 30-32, assoc, 32-36; asst. prof, Columbia, 36-37, assoc. prof, 37-41, prof, 41-52; UNIV. MICH, 52-70, EMER. PROF, 70- Vis. lectr, Buffalo, 48, lectr, Robert A. Welsh Found, 59; Nat. Res. Coun. Can. vis. scientist, 59-60. Consult, Eli Lilly & Co, 45-57; sci. consult, Sloan-Kettering Inst. Cancer Res, 52-55; Esso Res. & Eng. Co, 52-60; mem. staff trop. disease sect, Nat. Insts. Health, 46-50, 55- Mem. subcmt, chmn. div. chem. & chem. tech, Nat. Acad. Sci-Nat. Res. Coun, 60-62, mem, adv. bd. mil. personnel supplies, 64-; cmn. malaria, Armed Forces Epidemiol. Bd, & chem. adv. bd, Walter Reed Army Inst. Res, 64. Presidential Merit, 48; outstanding civilian serv. medal, U.S. Dept. Army, 71. With Off. Sci. Res. & Develop, 41-46; U.S. Pub. Health Serv; U.S.A, 44. Nat. Acad. Sci; AAAS; Am. Chem. Soc; Am. Soc. Biol. Chem. Synthetic organic chemistry; heteorcyclic compounds; chemotherapy; pharmacology; cardiac drugs; alkaloids. Address: 1800 Hermitage Rd, Ann Arbor, MI 48104.

ELDERS, M(INNIE) JOYCELYN, b. Schaal, Ark, Aug. 13, 33; m. 60; c. 2. PEDIATRICS, ENDOCRINOLOGY. B.A, Philander Smith Col, 52; cert. phys. ther, Brooke Army Med. Sch, 54; M.D, Univ. Ark, Little Rock, 60. Intern. PEDIAT, hosp, Univ. Minn, 60-61; resident, MED. CTR, UNIV. ARK, LITTLE ROCK, 61-64, instr, 64-67, asst. prof, 67-71, ASSOC. PROF, 71- Nat. Inst. Child Health & Human Develop. res. fel, med. ctr, Univ. Ark, Little Rock, 64-67, career develop. award, 67- Dipl, Am. Bd. Pediat, 64. U.S.A, 53-56, 1st. Lt. AAAS; Soc. Pediat. Res. Metabolism; effect of the thymus on growth and maturation; control of mucopolysaccharide synthesis and degradation; effect of nutritional manganese deficiency on lysosomal membranes. Address: Dept. of Pediatrics, University of Arkansas Medical Center, Little Rock, AR 72201.

ELDERS, WILFRED A(LLAN), b. Sunderland, Eng, Mar. 25, 33; m. 61. GEOLOGY. B.Sc, Durham, 57, Ph.D.(geol), 61; Pemberton studentship & Norweg. State scholar, Oslo, 57-59. Demonstr. petrol, Durham, 59-61; instr. GEOL, Chicago, 61-62, asst. prof, 62-68, ASSOC. PROF, Univ. Ill, Chicago Circle, 68-69; UNIV. CALIF, RIVERSIDE, 69- Louis Block Fund res. grant, Chicago, 62-63; Nat. Sci. Found. grants, 64-69. AAAS; Geol. Soc. Am; fel. Brit. Geol. Soc; Mineral. Soc. Gt. Brit. & Ireland; Norweg. Geol. Soc. Petrology and structure of granites and gneisses; mechanisms of emplacement of plutonic rocks; zoning in feldspars; origin of rapakivi granite; petrology and structure of Geothermal areas. Address: Dept. of Geological Sciences, University of California, Riverside, CA 92502.

ELDIB, IBRAHIM A(NDREW), b. Alexandria, U.A.R, Dec. 4, 29; m. 53; c. 3. CHEMICAL & SANITARY ENGINEERING. B.Sc, Fouad, Egypt, 50; Fulbright scholar, Tulsa, 50-51, M.Sc, 51; Tex. Co. fel, Oklahoma, 52-55, Ph.D.(chem. eng), 55. Petrol. technologist, Skelly Oil Co, Okla, 51-52; res. fel, Oklahoma, 52-55; sr. engr. process res. & develop, Esso Res. & Eng. Co, 56-62; PRES, ELDIB ENG. & RES, INC, 62-; NORTHEAST RES. INST, INC, 63- Lectr, Gordon Res. Conf, 60, 61, 62; proj. dir. renovation waste water, Dept. Health Ed. & Welfare, 61-62. Am. Chem. Soc; Nat. Soc. Prof. Eng; Am. Water Works Asn. Synthetic detergents development and manufacture; no-phosphate products; polymers and resins; water and air pollution control; design of sewage treatment and water works; design of sanitary landfills for disposal of domestic and industrial solid waste; solid waste recycling; international market development for government and industry. Address: Eldib Engineering & Research Inc, 170 Blanchard St, Newark, NJ 07105.

ELDIN, HAMED KAMAL, b. Cairo, Egypt, Dec. 31, 24; U.S. citizen; m. 51; c. 3. INDUSTRIAL ENGINEERING & MANAGEMENT. B.Sc, Cairo, 45; M.Sc, Calif. Inst. Tech, 48; Ph.D.(indust. eng), Iowa, 51. Asst. prof. indust. eng, Cairo, 51-52; employee & pub. rels. mgr, Esso Standard Near East Inc, 52-57; admin. mgr, Mobil Oil Egypt, 57-61; mem. bd. dirs, Nat. Inst. Mgt. Develop, 61-63; consult. comput. systs, Mobil Oil Corp, 63-65, Mobil Int, 65-66, rels. dept, 66-67; PROF. INDUST. ENG. & MGT, OKLA. STATE UNIV, 68- Vis. prof, Cairo, 52-63; gen. mgr, Ras Mallab Gypsum Co, 57-60; lectr, American Univ. Cairo, 58-60; vis. prof, Army Engr. Corps, 58-62. Award, Arab. Petrol. Conf, 61. Sr. mem. Am. Inst. Indust. Eng; Am. Soc. Eng. Educ; Inst. Mgt. Sci; Opers. Res. Soc. Am. Management science; software package library; computer oriented management information systems; simulation utility programs for production facilities design. Address: Dept. of Industrial Engineering & Management, Oklahoma State University, Stillwater, OK 74074.

ELDRED, EARL, b. Tacoma, Wash, Feb. 27, 19; m. 44; c. 3. NEUROPHYSIOLOGY. B.S, Washington (Seattle), 39; M.D. & M.S, Northwestern, 50. Intern, Virginia Mason Hosp, Seattle, Wash, 50-51; instr. anat, med. sch, California, Los Angeles, 51-52; mem. staff, Karolinska Inst, Sweden, 52-53; asst. prof. ANAT, MED. SCH, UNIV. CALIF, LOS ANGELES, 53-57, assoc. prof, 57-62, PROF, 62- Markle fel, 51-56. U.S.A, 41-46. AAAS; Am. Asn. Anat; Am. Physiol. Soc. Muscle receptors and motor control; effects of irradiation of the nervous system; muscle reflexology. Address: Dept. of Anatomy, University of California, Los Angeles, CA 90024.

ELDRED, NELSON R(ICHARDS), b. Oberlin, Ohio, Mar. 6, 21; m. 45; c. 5. ORGANIC CHEMISTRY. A.B, Oberlin Col, 43; M.S, Wayne, 47; Am. Petrol. Inst. fel, Pa. State Col, 46-50, Ph.D.(chem), 51. Asst, Parke Davis & Co, 43-46; res. chemist, Union Carbide Co, 50-68; asst. mgr. develop, Buckman Labs, Inc, 69; SUPVR. CHEM. DIV, GRAPHIC ARTS TECH. FOUND, 70- AAAS; Tech. Asn. Pulp & Paper Indust; Am. Chem. Soc. Synthetic resins and fibers; chemistry of papermaking; chemistry of paper and ink. Address: Chemistry Division, Graphic Arts Technical Foundation, 4615 Forbes Ave, Pittsburgh, PA 15213.

ELDREDGE, ARNOLD L(ORAINE), b. Cary, Idaho, Oct. 14, 24; m. 48. ELECTRICAL ENGINEERING. B.S, Utah State Agr. Col, 47; M.S, Stanford, 49, E.E, 50. Res. assoc, microwave res, Stanford Univ. & Varian Assocs, 50-54; consult. engr, Gen. Elec. Co, 54-58; mgr. parametric amplifier proj, Zenith Radio Res. Corp, 58-59; with Stanford Univ, 59-70; GEN. MGR, RADIATION DIV, VARIAN ASSOCS, 70- Consult, Helene Curtis, 51-52; Gen. Elec. Co, 54. Sr. mem. Inst. Elec. & Electronics Eng. Pulse forming networks; periodic microwave structures; microwave tube development. Address: 15 Upper Lake Rd, Woodside, Redwood City, CA 94062.

ELDREDGE, DONALD H(ERBERT), b. South Bend, Ind, July 5, 21; m. 47; c. 4. PHYSIOLOGY, BIOPHYSICS. S.B, Harvard, 43; M.D, Harvard Med. Sch, 46. Interne, Boston City Hosp, 46-47; asst. resident, Barnes Hosp, St. Louis, 52-53; RES. ASSOC. CENT. INST. DEAF, 53-; RES. PROF. OTOLARYNGOL, SCH. MED, WASH. UNIV, 64-, res. asst, 54-58, res. instr, 58-60, res. asst. prof, 60-61, res. assoc. prof, 61-64. Mem, comt. hearing & bioacoustics, Armed Forces-Nat. Res. Coun, 53-70. U.S.A.F, 47-51, Maj. Acoust. Soc. Am; Biophys. Soc. Normal and pathologic physiology and mechanical function of the ear. Address: Central Institute for the Deaf, 818 S. Euclid, St. Louis, MO 63110.

ELDREDGE, GEORGE (GILBERT), b. Vale, Oregon, July 16, 12; m. 42, 53; c. 4. CHEMICAL ENGINEERING. B.S, Oregon State Col, 36; Ph.D, Minnesota, 40. Corrosion Res, Aluminum Res. Labs, 40-45; SHELL DEVELOP. CO, 46-56, OPER. RES. APPLIED MATH. DEPT, 56- AAAS. Operations research; petroleum industry. Address: Applied Mathematics Dept, Shell Development Co, Emeryville, CA 94608.

ELDREDGE, JOHN C(ROSBY), b. Earlville, Iowa, Apr. 21, 86; m. 15; c. 2. AGRONOMY. B.S, Iowa State Col, 15, M.S, 24, Ph.D.(crop prod, plant physiol), 33. County agent, 15-20; asst. prof. farm crops, Iowa State Col, 21-36, assoc. prof, 37-70; RETIRED. Am. Soc. Agron. Genetics of corn; artificial injury simulating hail damage to corn, small grain and soybeans; popcorn breeding. Address: 602 Ash Ave, Ames, IA 50010.

ELDREDGE, K(ELLY) H(USBANDS), b. Salt Lake City, Utah, April 5, 21; m. 45, 54; c. 4. VIROLOGY. Univ. fels, Utah, 42-45, B.S, 43, M.S, 45; Newell scholar, Stanford, 45, Ph.D.(virol), 49. Asst, Utah, 42-45; instr. life sci, San Francisco State Col, 48-49; asst. prof. bacter, Arizona State, 49-52; lab. technologist, Mem. Med. Ctr, 53-54; teacher, pub. sch, 54-55; asst. prof. LIFE SCI, SACRAMENTO STATE COL, 55-60, assoc. prof, 60-70, PROF, 70- Consult, Friedlanders Labs; Sacramento County Hosp; Eskaton Health Care Ctr; Am. River Hosp. Am. Soc. Microbiol; Am. Pub. Health Asn. Effect of certain compounds on bacteriophage production; pathogenic fungi. Address: Dept. of Science, Sacramento State College, Sacramento, CA 95819.

ELDREDGE, LUCIUS G, b. East Greenwich, R.I, Mar. 1, 38; m. 58; c. 4. MARINE ZOOLOGY. B.S, Rhode Island, 59; Ph.D.(zool), Hawaii, 65. Res. assoc. marine zool, Bernice P. Bishop Mus, Hawaii, 64-65; assoc. prof. biol, UNIV. GUAM, 65-67, prof. & chmn. dept, 67-71, DIR. MARINE LAB, 71- Am. Soc. Zool; Soc. Syst. Zool; Asn. Trop. Biol; Int. Soc. Trop. Ecol; Marine Biol. Asn. U.K; Brit. Soc. Bibliog. Natural Hist; Hakluyt Soc. Taxonomy and ecology of ascidians, especially members of the family Didemnidae; taxonomy of Indo-Pacific lancelets; Indo-Pacific marine invertebrates; zoogeography; taxonomy; ecology. Address: Marine Lab, University of Guam, Box EK, Agana, GU 96910.

ELDREDGE, NILES, b. Brooklyn, N.Y, Aug. 25, 43; m. 64. PALEONTOLOGY. A.B, Columbia, 65, Nat. Sci. Found. fel, 66-68, Ph.D.(geol), 69. ASST. CURATOR INVERT. PALEONT, AM. MUS. NATURAL HIST, 69- Adj. asst. prof. geol, Columbia, 69- Paleont. Soc; Brit. Palaeont. Asn; Soc. Study Evolution; Soc. Syst. Zool. Paleozoic invertebrate evolution, particularly in arthropods and mollusks; biometrics and computer applications in paleontology. Address: Dept. of Invertebrate Paleontology, American Museum of Natural History, New York, NY 10024.

ELDRIDGE, ARTHUR C, b. Greenview, Ill, Jan. 20, 30; m. 54; c. 3. BIOCHEMISTRY. B.A, Blackburn Col, 52. Chemist, U.S. Dept. Interior, Utah, 52; RES. CHEMIST, NORTHERN REGIONAL RES. LAB, U.S. DEPT. AGR, 54- U.S.A, 52-54, Sgt. Am. Asn. Cereal Chem; Am. Chem. Soc; Inst. Food Tech. Isolation and characterization of plant proteins, particularly soybean; structure, physiological activity, nutritional and functional properties of plant proteins. Address: Northern Regional Research Lab, 1815 N. University, Peoria, IL 61604.

ELDRIDGE, BRUCE F(REDERICK), b. San Jose, Calif, Mar. 26, 33; m. 57; c. 3. MEDICAL ENTOMOLOGY. A.B, San Jose State, 54; M.S, State Col. Wash, 56; Ph.D.(entom), Purdue, 65. U.S. ARMY, 56-, instr, Army Med. Serv. Sch, Tex, 57-58, med. entomologist, Walter Reed Army Inst. Res, Wash, D.C, 58-60, 61-63, instr. med. entom, Med. Field Serv. Sch, 65-66, med. entomoloigst, Atlantic-Pac. Interoceanic Canal Study Comn, 68-69, entomologist, WALTER REED ARMY INST. RES, 68-69, CHIEF DEPT. ENTOM, 69- Acting chief entom. res. br, U.S. Army Med. Res. & Develop. Command, 69-70; chmn, Armed Forces Pest Control Bd, 71- U.S.A, 56-, Lt. Col. Entom. Soc. Am.(ed, misc. publ, 69-); Am. Mosquito Control Asn; Am. Soc. Trop. Med. & Hyg. Ecology and physiology of mosquitos. Address: Dept. of Entomology, Walter Reed Army Institute of Research, Washington, DC 20012.

ELDRIDGE, DAVID WYATT, b. Chattanooga, Tenn, Oct. 31, 40; m. 62; c. 2. MICROBIAL PHYSIOLOGY. B.S, Tenn. Polytech. Inst, 62; M.S, Auburn Univ, 64, Nat. Sci. Found. fel, 68, Ph.D.(bot), 69. Instr. bot, Auburn Univ, 64-66, res. asst, 66-68; ASST. PROF. BIOL, BAYLOR UNIV, 68- Am. Soc. Microbiol. Biochemistry and physiology of microbial toxins, especially aflatoxins produced by Aspergillus flavus; metabolism of sugar substitutes (cyclamates) by microorganisms. Address: Dept. of Biology, College of Arts & Sciences, Baylor University, Waco, TX 76703.

ELDRIDGE, F(RANCIS) R(EED), JR, b. Augusta, Ga, July 21, 16; m. 42; c. 1. PHYSICS. B.S, George Washington, 40; Hopkins, 49-50. Asst, Carnegie Inst, 38-39; assoc. physicist, U.S. Naval Ord. Lab, 39-43; physicist, Jones & Lamson Mach. Co, 43-47; spec. electronics engr, Martin Co, 47-48; asst. prof. physics, Hopkins, 48-52, dir. controls res. lab, 52-55; phys. scientist, Rand Corp, 55-62; spec. asst. to dep. asst. secy. defense for systs. anal, 62-66; asst. to spec. asst. to President, 66-67; v.pres, Kelly Sci. Corp, 67-68; mem. res. coun, Res. Anal. Corp, Va, 68-71; MEM. DIV. STAFF, MITRE CORP, 71- AAAS; Am. Phys. Soc. Cosmic rays; electromagnetic theory; servomechanisms; electronic computers; systems analysis; operations research; communications systems. Address: Mitre Corp, Westgate Research Park, McLean, VA 22101.

ELDRIDGE, FRANKLIN (ELMER), b. Fruitland, Idaho, June 14, 18; m. 41; c. 3. DAIRY HUSBANDRY. B.S,(agr), Idaho, 41; M.S, Kans, State Col, 42, Ph.D.(animal breeding), Cornell, 48. Asst. dairy husb, Kans. State Col, 41-42; Cornell, 42-43; animal res. investr, nat. resources sect, agr. div, gen. headquarters, Supreme Command Allied Powers, Japan, 46; asst. animal husb, Cornell, 46-48; assoc. prof, Kans. State Col, 48-54, PROF, 54; ANIMAL SCI, UNIV. NEBR, 54-, DIR. RESIDENT INSTR, 61-, ASSOC. DEAN, COL. AGR, 68-, assoc. dir, resident instr, 54-61. U.S.A, 43-46, 1st Lt. AAAS; Am. Dairy Sci. Asn; Am. Genetic Asn. Biological assay of vitamin A; genetics of conformation and production of dairy cattle. Address: College of Agriculture, University of Nebraska, Lincoln, NE 68508.

ELDRIDGE, FREDERIC L, b. Kansas City, Mo, July 8, 24; m. 51; c. 2. MEDICINE. A.B, Stanford Univ, 45, M.D, 48. Intern med, hosps, Stanford Univ, 47-48; resident pediat, med. br, Univ. Tex, 48-50; MED, hosps, STANFORD UNIV, 50-51, Irving fel, SCH. MED, 53, Neizer fel, 53-54, instr, 54-56, asst. prof, 56-62, ASSOC. PROF, 62-, HEAD DIV. RESPIRATORY MED, 64-; CHIEF RESPIRATORY DISEASE, PALO ALTO VET. HOSP, 69-, chief med. serv, 60-68. U.S. Pub. Health Serv. spec. res. fel. pulmonary physiol, St. Bartholomews Hosp, Univ. London, 54-55, neurophysiol, col. med, Univ. Utah, 68-69; Bank of Am-Giannini Found. fel, 55-56; Markle Found. scholar. med. sci, 56-61. U.S.A, 44-46; U.S.A.F, 51-53, Capt. Am. Fedn. Clin. Res; Am. Soc. Clin. Invest; Am. Col. Physicians; Am. Physiol. Soc; Am. Thoracic Soc. Cardiopulmonary and cardiac physiology; mechanics of respiration; metabolism of lactic acid; respiratory control mechanisms. Address: Dept. of Medicine, Stanford University Medical Center, Stanford, CA 94305.

ELDRIDGE, HUDSON BLUFORD, b. Linary, Tenn, Apr. 28, 33; m. 59; c. 3. PHYSICS. B.S, Tennessee, 58, M.S, 61; Ph.D.(physics), California, Los Angeles, 66. Assoc. mathematician, Union Carbide Nuclear Corp, 58-61; staff scientist, Aerospace Corp, 61-62; res. asst. physics, California, Los Angeles, 62-66; asst. prof, Univ. Wyo, 66-70; PRES, PPB INC. RES. REACTOR FACILITY, 70- Adj. prof, Univ. Wyo; vis. assoc. prof, Univ. Missouri-Columbia. Am. Phys. Soc. Nuclear structure; electronic methods; neutron activation analysis. Address: 105 Lindell, Columbia, MO 65201.

ELDRIDGE, JAMES S(AMUEL), b. Knoxville, Tenn, Sept. 14, 28; m. 51; c. 3. NUCLEAR & RADIO CHEMISTRY. B.S, Tennessee, 50, M.S, 56. Asst. scientist, health physics & radiochem, Oak Ridge Inst. Nuclear Studies, 50-56, CHEMIST NUCLEAR & RADIOCHEM, OAK RIDGE NAT. LAB, 56- Secy, Nat. Acad. Sci-Nat. Res. Coun. Subcmt. Use of Radioactivity Standards, 63- U.S.A.R, 50-51, 2nd Lt. Am. Chem. Soc; Am. Geophys. Union. Metrology of radionuclides; gamma-ray spectroscopy; analytical radiochemistry; decay scheme studies activation analysis. Address: Oak Ridge National Lab, P.O. Box X, Oak Ridge, TN 37830.

ELDRIDGE, JOHN E(MERSON), b. Great Barrington, Mass, Sept. 24, 19; m. 49; c. 4. PHYSICAL & CLINICAL CHEMISTRY. S.B, Harvard, 41; M.A, Dartmouth Col, 42; Ph.D.(chem), Univ. Wis, 48. Instr. chem, Dartmouth Col, 41-42; res. asst, Woods Hole Oceanog. Inst, 43-45; Univ. Wis, 46-48; res. chemist, E.I. du Pont de Nemours & Co, Inc, Del, 48-70; res. assoc, Univ. Del, 70-71; SUPVR, WASH. REFERENCE LAB, 71- Am. Chem. Soc; Soc. Rheol. Physical chemistry of high polymers. Address: Washington Reference Lab, Washington, DC 20007.

ELDRIDGE, JOHN W(ILLIAM), b. Nashua, N.H, Aug. 22, 21; m. 42; c. 3. CHEMICAL ENGINEERING. B.S, Maine, 42; M.S, Syracuse, 45; Ph.D. (chem. eng), Minnesota, 49. Student observer, Carnegie, Ill. Steel Corp, 42; chem. engr, Semet-Solvay Co, 42-46; Barrett Div, Allied Chem. & Dye Corp, 49-50; asst. prof. CHEM. ENG, Virginia, 50-53, assoc. prof, 53-62; HEAD DEPT, UNIV. MASS, AMHERST, 62-; V.PRES, GEN. AEROSOLS CORP, 55- Consult, Albemarle Paper Mfg. Co, 51-63; Holyoke Water Power Co, 62-64. Am. Chem. Soc; Am. Inst. Chem. Eng; Am. Soc. Eng. Educ. Continuous flow chemical reactor systems; thermodynamics; kinetics; polymerization. Address: Dept. of Chemical Engineering, University of Massachusetts, Amherst, MA 01002.

ELDRIDGE, KLAUS EMIL, b. Breslau, Ger, June 5, 38; U.S. citizen; m. 60; c. 2. MATHEMATICS. B.A, Hardin-Simmons, 60; M.S, Okla. State, 62; Ph.D.(math), Colorado, 65. Instr. math. & physics, Hardin-Simmons, 62; asst. prof. MATH, OHIO UNIV, 65-70, ASSOC. PROF, 70- Math. Asn. Am; Am. Math. Soc. Structures of fields, rings and algebras and their relations to the structure of groups. Address: Dept. of Mathematics, Ohio University, Athens, OH 45701.

ELDRIDGE, MARIE DELANEY, b. Baltimore, Md, June 1, 26; m. 61; c. 2. STATISTICS. A.B, Col. Notre Dame (Md), 48; Sc.M, Hopkins, 53. Methods statistician, Revere Copper & Brass, 48-50; asst, sch. hyg, Hopkins, 50-53; sr. statistician, Ralph M. Parsons Co, Md, 53-54; anal. statistician, U.S. Dept. Army, 54-55; asst. chief statist. br, Soc. Security Admin, 55-60; chief statist. opers, U.S. Off. Ed, 60-61, adv. & develop. servs, 61-62; statistician, Nat. Inst. Ment. Health, 62-65; dep. dir, OFF. STATIST. PROGS. & STANDARDS, U.S. POSTAL SERV, 65-70, DIR, 70- Lectr, Univ. Baltimore, 57-59. Fel. Am. Statist. Asn. Sample survey methodology; theory of sampling and quality checks on mass data; new analytical techniques. Address: 3201 E. Thornapple St, Chevy Chase, MD 20015.

ELDUMIATI, ISMAIL IBRAHIM, b. Damanhour, Egypt, Jan. 19, 40; m. 64; c. 2. ELECTRICAL ENGINEERING. B.Sc.E.E, Univ. Alexandria, 62; M.S, Univ. Mich, Ann Arbor, 66 & 68, fel, 67-68, Ph.D.(elec. eng), 70. Instr. elec. eng, Univ. Alexandria, 62-65; ASSOC. DIR. BIOPHYS, SENSORS INC, 70- AAAS; Inst. Elec. & Electronics Eng. Solid state materials and devices; microwaves; millimeter-wave detectors; non-chemical pest control and plant growth regulation. Address: 1135 McIntyre, Ann Arbor, MI 48105.

ELEFTHERIOU, BASIL E, b. Athens, Greece, Jan. 14, 34; U.S. citizen; m. 63; c. 4. ENDOCRINOLOGY, BIOCHEMISTRY. B.A, Maine, 56; Nat. Insts. Health summer fels, Massachusetts, 58, 59, M.A, 59; Ph.D.(biol. sci), 61. Nat. Insts. Health fel, R.B. Jackson Mem. Lab, 61-62; vis. asst. prof. biol. sci, Purdue, 62-63; asst. prof. zool, Kans. State Univ, 63-69; STAFF SCIENTIST, JACKSON LAB, 69- Lalor Found. summer fel, 63. AAAS; Am. Soc. Zool; N.Y. Acad. Sci; Brit. Soc. Study Fertil; Am. Physiol. Soc; Endocrine Soc; Am. Asn. Anat; Am. Inst. Biol. Sci; Animal Behav. Soc. Comparative endocrinology; behavior and hormones; behavior and neuroendocrinology. Address: Jackson Lab, Bar Harbor, ME 04609.

ELEHWANY, NAZMY E(LHAMY), b. Cairo, Egypt, Sept. 9, 27; U.S. citizen; m. 60; c. 3. HORTICULTURE. B.S, Cairo Univ, 50; M.S, Univ. Md, 53, Ph.D, 55. Qual. control mgr, HANOVER BRANDS INC, 57-63, dir. res. & qual. control, 63-69, V.PRES, AGR. & TECH. SERV, 70- Statistical quality control; food technology; food research. Address: Hanover Brands Inc, R.D. 3, Hanover, PA 17331.

ELEQUIN, FLORA TENGONCIANG, b. San Jose, Philippines, June 25, 32; m. 62; c. 1. CYTOGENETICS, ANIMAL GENETICS. B.A, Cent. Philippines Univ, 52; M.A, Silliman Univ, Philippines, 55; Fulbright scholar, Univ. Tex, Austin, 59, Nat. Insts. Health grant, 60, Ph.D.(zool), 65. Teacher biol, Filamer Christian Inst, Philippines, 55-56; instr, Cent. Philippine Univ, 56-59; asst. prof, Iloilo Col, Univ. Philippines, 66; res. geneticist, children's serv, Douglas Hosp, Verdun, Que, Can, 66-67; ASST. CYTOGENETICIST, METROPOLITAN HOSP, N.Y. MED. COL, 69- Environ. Mutagen Soc. Effects of chemicals on human chromosomes; diagnostic works on human patients; cultures of human cells; radiation genetics of Drosophila; human cytogenetics. Address: Cytogenetics Lab, Metropolitan Hospital, 97th St. & First Ave, New York, NY 10029.

ELEUTERIO, HERBERT S(OUSA), b. New Bedford, Mass, Nov. 23, 27; m. 51; c. 6. ORGANIC CHEMISTRY. B.S, Tufts Col, 49; Ph.D.(chem), Mich. State Univ, 53. Res. chemist, polychem. dept, exp. sta, E.I. DU PONT DE NEMOURS & CO, INC, 54-58, supvr, 58-59, supvr, indust. & biochem. dept, 59-62, res. sect. head, east. lab, EXPLOSIVES DEPT, 62-64, exp. sta. lab, 64-68, dir, 68-70, DIR, EAST. LAB, 70- Am. Chem. Soc. Reaction mechanisms; stereochemistry; polymer chemistry. Address: Eastern Lab, E.I. du Pont de Nemours & Co, Inc, Gibbstown, NJ 08027.

ELEY, H(ARRY) E(UGENE), b. Pittsburgh, Pa, Mar. 6, 21; m. 47; c. 3. CIVIL ENGINEERING. B.S, Miami (Fla), 42; B.S, Mass. Inst. Tech, 49; M.S, Fla. Inst. Tech, 67. Meteorologist forecasting & climat, U.S. Weather Bur, 42-43; construct. engr, Thomas P. Coogan Construct. Co, Fla, 49-50, construct. contracting partner, 50-51; construct. mgt. engr, U.S. Air Force, 51-56; mem. tech. staff, facilities & ground support missiles equip, Ramo Wooldridge Corp. & Space Tech. Labs, Inc, 56-61; MEM. STAFF, AEROSPACE CORP, 61- U.S.N, 43-45, Lt.(jg). Am. Inst. Aeronaut. & Astronaut. Building engineering and construction; facilities for handling, assembling, and launching guided missiles. Address: 969 Terry Dr, Eau Gallie, FL 32935.

ELEY, JAMES H, b. Montgomery, Ala, July 16, 40; m. 62; c. 2. BIOCHEMISTRY, PLANT PHYSIOLOGY. B.A, Univ. Tex, Austin, 62, M.A, 64, Ph.D. (physiol), 67. Nat. Insts. Health fel. biochem. of photosynthesis, Brandeis Univ, 67-68; ASST. PROF. BOT, UNIV. KY, 68- AAAS; Am. Soc. Plant Physiol; Am. Inst. Biol. Sci; Japanese Soc. Plant Physiol. Photosynthesis; algal physiology; electron transport in photosynthetic bacteria; glycolate metabolism by blue-green algae. Address: Dept. of Botany, University of Kentucky, Lexington, KY 40506.

ELFANT, ROBERT F, b. N.Y.C, Mar. 12, 36; m. 58; c. 2. ELECTRICAL ENGINEERING. B.S, Southern Methodist, 57; M.S, N.Y. Univ, 59; Minneapolis-Honeywell fel, Purdue, 59-60, Ph.D.(elec. eng), 61. Elec. Technician, Atlantic Ref. Co, 54-56; mem. tech. staff data commun, Bell Tel. Lab, 57-59; instr. elec. eng, Purdue, 59-61; mem. res. staff magnetics, Thomas J. Watson Res. Lab, INT. BUS. MACH. CORP, 61-66, mgr. memory res, 66-67, tech. plans & support, systs. develop. div, 67-68, memory prod. prog. mgr, COMPONENTS DIV, 68-69, FET prod. prog. mgr, 69-71, MGR. PACKAGING DEVELOP, EAST FISHKILL, 71- Inst. Elec. & Electronics Eng. Dynamic properties of ferromagnetic materials; new magnetic elements for computer memory applications. Address: Components Division, IBM Corp, East Fishkill Facility, Dept. 266, Bldg. 330-129, Hopewell Junction, NY 12533.

ELFBAUM, STANLEY GOODMAN, b. Boston, Mass, Sept. 24, 38; m. 70; c. 2. BIOCHEMISTRY. B.S, Northeastern, 61; Nat. Insts. Health fel, Northwestern, 64-65, Ph.D.(biochem), 66. Clin. chemist, Boston Med. Lab, Mass, 57-61; sr. biochemist, Gillette Med. Res. Inst, 65-67, proj. supvr. biomed. div, 67-70; DEPT. SUPVR, BOSTON MED. LAB, INC, 70- Am. Chem. Soc; Am. Asn. Clin. Chem. Radioimmunoassay of thyroid hormones; detection of abnormal hemoglobins; physical biochemistry of proteins. Address: 48 Williams Rd, Sharon, MA 02067.

ELFNER, LLOYD F, b. Manitowoc, Wis, Sept. 13, 23; m. 63; c. 3. EXPERIMENTAL PSYCHOLOGY, PSYCHOACOUSTICS. B.S, Univ. Wis, 58, M.S, 60, Ph.D.(exp. psychol), 62. Asst. prof. PSYCHOL, Kent State Univ, 62-66, assoc. prof, 66-67; FLA. STATE UNIV, 67-70, PROF, 70- Grants, Nat. Sci. Found, 64-66 & 67-69, Nat. Insts. Health, 64-66 & 69-72; mem. Evoked Audiometry Study Group. U.S.A.A.F, 42-47, S/Sgt. Am. Psychol. Asn; Acoust. Soc. Am; Psychonomic Soc. Temporal, intensive and spectral resolving powers of the human auditory system; auditory evoked potentials; effects of noise on behavior. Address: Dept. of Psychology, Florida State University, Tallahassee, FL 32306.

ELFORD, C(LARENCE) ROBERT, b. Boise, Idaho, Aug. 29, 12; m. 35; c. 2. METEOROLOGY. B.S, American Univ, 51. Observer meteorol, U.S. WEATHER BUR, Idaho, 30-36, radio operator, Mont, 36-37, forecaster, Calif, 37-45, meteorologist, D.C, 46-51, CLIMATOLOGIST, Iowa, 51-58, CALIF, 58- Am. Meteorol. Soc. Climatological summaries of local areas. Address: 50 Fulton St, Room 557, San Francisco, CA 94102.

ELFORD, HOWARD L(EE), b. Chicago, Ill, Sept. 2, 35; m. 62; c. 2. BIOCHEMISTRY. B.S, Univ. Ill, 58; Am. Meat Inst. fel, Cornell Univ, 58-62, Ph.D.(biochem), 63. Res. asst. biochem, Cornell Univ, 62; Nat. Insts. Health fel, Mass. Inst. Technol, 62-64; ASST. PROF, med. sch, Univ. Mich, Ann Arbor, 64-70; EXP. MED. & PHARMACOL, MED. SCH, DUKE UNIV, 70- Res. assoc, Argonne Nat. Lab, summer 59. AAAS; Am. Chem. Soc. Deoxyribonucleotide and DNA biosynthesis; biochemistry and pharmacology of cancer; mechanisms of vitamin B_{12} and its role in mammalian metabolism. Address: Dept. of Medicine, Lane Lab, Room 0564, Duke University Medical Center, Durham, NC 27710.

ELFTMAN, ALICE G, b. Byron, N.Y, Mar. 27, 04; m. 30; c. 2. ANATOMY. B.A, N.Y. State Col. Teachers, Albany, 26; M.A, Cornell, 29, Ph.D.(anat), 39. Instr. biol, N.Y. State Col. Teachers Albany, 26-28; from instr. to prof. BIOL. SCI, Hunter Col, 29-62, chmn. dept, 55-62; LEHMAN COL, 62-71, EMER. PROF, 72- Am. Asn. Anat. Histology of mammalian respiratory system; developmental anatomy of hypobranchial muscles; histochemistry of gold excretion; comparative anatomy of vertebrates. Address: 305 Cape Ct, Mill Valley, CA 94941.

ELFTMAN, HERBERT (OLIVER), b. Minneapolis, Minn, Oct. 31, 02; m. 30; c. 2. ANATOMY. A.B, California, 23, A.M, 25; Ph.D.(zool), Columbia, 29. Asst. paleont. & geol, California, 23-25; zool, COLUMBIA UNIV, 26-28, lectr, Seth Low Jr. Col, 28-29, asst. prof, 29-40, instr. ANAT, COL. PHYSICIANS & SURGEONS, 40-44, asst. prof, 44-48, assoc. prof, 48-61, prof, 61-71, EMER. PROF, 71- AAAS; Am. Asn. Anat; Am. Physiol. Soc; Histochem. Soc; Soc. Exp. Biol. & Med; N.Y. Acad. Sci. Biomechanics of human locomotion; histochemistry of phospholipids; cytochemistry of endocrine glands. Address: 305 Cape Court, Mill Valley, CA 94941.

ELGER, GERALD WILLIAM, b. Waukesha, Wis, May 16, 26; m. 52; c. 3. CHEMISTRY. B.S, Wisconsin, 51. Chemist, oil-shale demonstration plant, U.S. BUR. MINES, Colo, 51-53, ALBANY METALL. RES. CTR, 53-57, supvry. chemist, 57-59, supv. prod. metallurgist, 59-61, RES. CHEMIST, 61- U.S.N, 45-46. Am. Chem. Soc; Am. Inst. Mining, Metall. & Petrol. Eng; Sci. Res. Soc. Am. Zirconium-hafnium extraction technology; metallic reduction of rare metal halides; chlorination of minerals. Address: 3185 E. 14th Ave, Albany, OR 97321.

ELGERD, O(LLE) I(NGEMAR), b. Oxberg, Sweden, Mar. 31, 25; nat; m. 48; c. 3. ELECTRICAL ENGINEERING. B.S.E.E, Orebro Tech. Col, Sweden, 45; Dipl, Royal Inst. Tech, Sweden, 50; D.Sc.(elec. eng), Washington (St. Louis), 56. Designer relay & control of hydroplants, Swed. Elec. Co, Sweden, 48-51; asst. chief engr, Utility Co, 51-52; designer control windtunnels & steamplants, Sverdrup & Parcel, Consult. Engrs, Mo, 52-53; instr. ELEC. ENG, Washington (St. Louis), 53-56; PROF, UNIV. FLA, 56- Vis. prof, Colorado, 64-65; consult, Maloney Transformer Co; Gen. Elec. Co, Va; Hughes Aircraft Co, Calif; Martin Co, Fla; St. Regis Paper Co; Aerospace Corp. Swed. Army, 45-46. Sr. mem. Inst. Elec. & Electronics Eng; Swed. Soc. Eng. & Archit. Electromechanical componentry; general control theory with computer applications; electric energy conversion and automatic control. Address: Dept. of Electrical Engineering, University of Florida, Gainesville, FL 32603.

ELGHAMMER, H. WILLIAM, b. Stockholm, Sweden, Mar. 13, 94; U.S. citizen; m. 21; c. 2. PEDIATRICS. M.D, Loyola (Ill), 20. Prof. PEDIAT, STRITCH SCH. MED, LOYOLA UNIV. CHICAGO, 39-65, chmn. dept, 39-60, EMER. PROF, 65- Chief pediat. staff, Mercy Hosp, 39-58; prof. lectr, med. sch, Univ. Ill, 62; consult. pediatrician, Ill. Cent. Hosp; Presby-St. Luke's Hosp; Chicago Bd. Health. Dipl, Am. Bd. Pediat, 34. Med.C, U.S.A, 18. Am. Acad. Pediat; Am. Col. Physicians; Am. Med. Asn. Rheumatic fever; medical research; medical education. Address: 5844 Stony Island Ave, Chicago, IL 60637.

EL GHAMRY, MOHAMED TAWFIK, b. Meet Ghamr, U.A.R, Dec. 3, 37. ANALYTICAL & INORGANIC CHEMISTRY. B.S.Ag, Ain Shams Univ, Cairo, 59; Ministry of Agr. fel, Univ. London, 64, Ph.D.(anal. chem), Univ. & dipl, Imp. Col, 67. Teacher sci. & math, Ministry of Educ, Mecca, Saudi Arabia, 59-60; lab. supvr, agr. mus, Ministry of Agr, Cairo, U.A.R, 60-64; fel. anal. chem, Dalhousie Univ, 67-68; asst. prof. anal. & gen. chem, St. Mary's Univ. (N.S), 68-70; staff mem, chem. dept, Forsyth Dent. Ctr, Boston, 70-71; RES. ASSOC. ANAL. CHEM. & NUTRIT, SCH. PUB. HEALTH, HARVARD, 71- Mem, Nutrit. Found, 71. Sr. mem. Chem. Inst. Can; Am. Chem. Soc; Int. Asn. Dent. Res; Brit. Soc. Anal. Chem. Bioanalytical chemistry; dental chemistry; nutrition chemistry; spectroscopy; electrochemistry. Address: Dept. of Nutrition, Harvard University School of Public Health, 665 Huntington Ave, Boston, MA 02115.

ELGIN, JAMES H(ANSFORD), JR, b. Wash, D.C, Feb. 2, 42; m. 62; c. 2. PLANT GENETICS & BREEDING. B.S, Univ. Md, College Park, 64, M.S, 66; Ph.D.(alfalfa breeding), Pa. State Univ, 69. RES. AGRONOMIST, PLANT SCI. RES. DIV, AGR. RES. SERV, U.S. DEPT. AGR, 69- Am. Soc. Agron; Crop. Sci. Soc. Am; Genetics Soc. Can. Comparison of multiple trait selection methods in alfalfa breeding; development of laboratory techniques for screening alfalfa for stem nematode resistance; alfalfa genetics and breeding. Address: Agricultural Research Service, U.S. Dept. of Agriculture, IAREC, Prosser, WA 99350.

ELGIN, JOSEPH C(LIFTON), b. Nashville, Tenn, Feb. 11, 04; m. 29; c. 3; m. 60; c. 1. CHEMICAL ENGINEERING. Chem.E, Virginia, 24, fel, 24-25; du Pont fel, 25-26, M.S, 26; du Pont fel, Princeton, 27-28, Procter fel, 28-29, Ph.D.(phys. chem), 29. Acting asst. prof. phys. chem, Virginia, 26-27; instr. CHEM. ENG, PRINCETON, 29-31, asst. prof, 31-35, assoc. prof, 35-39, PROF, 39-, dean eng, 54-71, chmn. dept. chem. eng, 36-54, assoc. dean eng, 50-54. Am. Petrol. Inst. fel, Princeton, 29-31, Brooks fel, eng. sch, 31. Consult, indust. firms, 31-; Nat. Defense Res. Comt, 40-44; chief copolymer & copolymer equip. develop. br, Off. Rubber Dir, 42-44; chem. engr. & div. head, substitute alloy mat. lab, Columbia, 44-45; consult, Atomic Energy Comn, N.Y, 46-50. Trustee, Princeton, Assoc. Univs, Inc, 50-62 & 68-71, chmn. bd, 57-58; trustee, Procter Found, 62-66. Mem. div. chem. & chem. tech, Nat. Res. Coun, 47-58; grants comt, Res. Corp, 50-64, dir, 64-; Textile Res. Inst, 65-71. Am. Inst. Chem. Eng.(Walker Award, 57); Am. Chem. Soc; Am. Soc. Eng. Educ.(Lamme Award, 69). Solvent extraction; mechanics of countercurrent contacting towers and fluidized systems; chemical engineering separation methods; phase equilibria in nonideal systems; rubber reclaiming; hydrocarbon separation; polymerization. Address: School of Engineering & Applied Science, Princeton University, Princeton, NJ 08540.

ELGOT, CALVIN C, b. N.Y.C, Jan. 3, 22; m. 54; c. 6. MATHEMATICS. B.S, City Col, 48; A.M, Columbia, 49; Ph.D.(math), Michigan, 60. Elec. engr, Off. of Chief Engrs, 46; lectr. math, Columbia, 48-51; mathematician, Naval Ord. Lab, 51-54; asst. math, California, 54-55; res. assoc. & automata theory teaching, Michigan, 55-59; MGR. AUTOMATA & COMPUT, IBM CORP, 59- Vis. assoc. prof, Courant Inst. Math. Sci, N.Y. Univ, 63-65; vis. prof, Paris, 65-66. U.S.A, 43-45. Am. Math. Soc; Asn. Symbolic Logic; Asn. Comput. Mach; Inst. Elec. & Electronics Eng. Theory of finite automata; computability; foundation of programming theory; mathematical logic. Address: IBM Research, P.O. Box 218, Yorktown Heights, NY 10598.

EL GUINDY, M(AHMOUD) ISMAIL, b. Cairo, Egypt. INORGANIC CHEMISTRY, EXTRACTIVE METALLURGY. B.Sc, Ain Shams Univ, Cairo, 60; M.Sc, Rensselaer Polytech. Inst, 66, Ph.D.(inorg. chem), 68. Instr. chem, Assiut Univ, Egypt, 60-63; lectr, Siena Col.(N.Y), 66-67; res. assoc. metall, McGill Univ, 67-70; RES. GROUP LEADER CHEM, REFINERY DIV, ENGELHARD INDUSTS, NEWARK, 70- Spectroscopy of inorganic complexes; physical properties of inorganic compounds; electrochemistry; recovery of metals from ores; chemistry of rhenium and solvent extraction of precious metals. Address: 730 Sherman Ave, Plainfield, NJ 07060.

ELHILALI, M(OSTAFA) M, b. Minia, U.A.R, Nov. 3, 37; m. 69; c. 4. CANCER IMMUNOLOGY & ENZYMOLOGY. M.D, Univ. Cairo, 59, D.S, 62, D.U, 63, M.Ch, 64; Ph.D.(exp. surg), McGill Univ, 69. Intern med, Univ. Cairo Hosp, 60-61, resident urol, 61-63, clin. demonstrator, 63-65; clin. fel, Royal Victoria Hosp, Montreal, 65-67, resident surg, 67-68, clin. fel. urol, 68-69; resident, Ottawa Civic Hosp, 69; asst. prof. UROL, FACULTY MED, SHERBROOKE UNIV, 69-71, ASSOC. PROF, 71- Nat. Cancer Inst. Can. fel, 66-68; Med. Res. Coun. Can. grant, 69-72. Fel, Royal Col. Physicians & Surgeons Can, 69. Can. Med. Asn; Am. Urol. Asn; Can. Urol. Asn; Can. Soc. Immunol. Isoenzyme changes in prostatic cancer and of lactate dehydrogenase in bladder cancer; urodynamics; physicochemical changes in urinary lithiasis. Address: Dept. of Urology, Sherbrooke University, Sherbrooke, Que, Can.

ELIA, RAYMOND J, b. Farrell, Pa, Feb. 20, 25; m. 56; c. 4. ORGANIC CHEMISTRY. B.S, Duquesne, 50, Koppers fel, 51-52, M.S, 52; Cottrel fel, Mich. State Univ, 55-56, Ph.D.(phys. org. chem), 56. Sr. res. chemist, E.I. DU PONT DE NEMOURS & CO, 56-67, tech. serv. supvr, int. dept, Geneva, Switz, 67-70, RES. SUPVR, TEXTILE RES. LAB, 70- U.S.N, 43-46. Analyses of elastic fiber properties; methods of measuring and assessing; correlation with fabric behavior. Address: 714 Bristol Rd, Wilmington, DE 19803.

ELIA, VICTOR JOHN, b. Portland, Ore, May 11, 42; m. 66; c. 1. ORGANIC CHEMISTRY. B.S, Portland State Univ, 65; Ph.D.(chem), Univ. Nebr, Lincoln, 70. FEL. mech. org. chem, Notre Dame Univ, 69-71; ENVIRON. RES, KETTERING LAB, SCH. MED, UNIV. CINCINNATI, 71- Merck, Sharp & Dohme, Inc, outstanding res. award, 69. Am. Chem. Soc. Synthesis, reaction and mechanistic studies of organic nitrogen compounds; alkaline decomposition of organic disulfides; trace metals; isolation and biological studies of potential toxic environmental pollutants. Address: 3175 Bracken Rd, Cincinnati, OH 45211.

ELIAS, ARTHUR WILLIAM, b. N.Y.C, Feb. 21, 27; m. 54; c. 2. INFORMATION SCIENCE, BIOLOGY. B.S, Alabama, 50; Rutgers, 52-53. Pharmacologist, Maltbie Labs, 50-52; Warner-Chilcott Labs, 52-58; info. scientist, Warner-Lambert Res. Inst, N.J, 58-59, supvr. tech. info, 59; mgr, sci. info. serv, Warner-Lambert Res. Inst, 59-62; sci. info. sect, Wyeth Labs, Am. Home Prods. Corp, N.Y, 62-64; dir. pub. serv, Inst. Sci. Info, 64-68; ASSOC. PROF, INFO. SCI, DREXEL UNIV, 62-; PRES, INFO. CO. AM, 68- Mem, Am. Med. Asn-U.S. Pharmacopoeia Comn. Codes, 60-; mem. joint operating group, Spec. Libr. Asn-Am. Soc. Info. Sci, 64- U.S.N, 43-46, 50-52, Lt.(jg). AAAS; Am. Chem. Soc; N.Y. Acad. Sci; Am. Inst. Soc. Info. Sci. (ed. Jour, 63-). Pharmacology; lipid biochemistry; biological data processing. Address: Information Co. of America, 2101 Walnut St, Philadelphia, PA 19103.

ELIAS, (MICHAEL) HANS, b. Darmstadt, Ger, June 28, 07; nat. 45; m. 36; c. 2. MICROSCOPIC ANATOMY. Ph.D.(biol. math), Giessen, 31. Teacher, Schs, Ger, 31-34; res. fel, Fed. Polytechnicum, Zürich, 35; Padua, 36; chief, histol. lab. & sci. cinematography, Italian Nat. Res. Council, 37-38; Athenaeum Pontificium Lateranense, Rome, 39; biol. labs, Harvard, 39; prof. histol. & embryol, Middlesex Vet. Col, 39-45; proj. supvr. prod. med. films, U.S. Pub. Health Serv, 45-50; asst. prof. micros. anat, CHICAGO MED. SCH, 50-53, assoc. prof. ANAT, 53-55, PROF, 55- Consult, Inst. Ed. Cinematography, Rome. Fel. AAAS; Am. Asn. Anat; Am. Soc. Zool; Am. Med. Asn.(awards, 50, 55, 58); Am. Soc. Clin. Path; Int. Soc. Stereology (pres); German Anat. Soc; Italian Soc. Anat. Histology; embryology; surgical anatomy; cosmology; geometry of sectioning; four dimensional geometry; education; art; oncology. Address: 2670 Birchwood Lane, Deerfield, IL 60015.

ELIAS, JAMES A(NDREW), b. Pittsburgh, Pa, Oct. 3, 25; m. 47; c. 2. CHEMISTRY, PHYSICS. B.Sc, Ohio State, 46. X-ray analyst, res. labs, ARMCO STEEL CORP, 50-54, x-ray chemist, 54-56, res. engr, 56-64, sr. res. engr, 64-68, res. assoc, RES. & TECHNOL. DIV, 68-70, PRIN. RES. ASSOC, 70- Am. Inst. Mining, Metall. & Petrol. Eng; Am. Soc. Metals. General emission spectroscopy; special problems in x-ray and electron diffraction; orientation, drawability, internal friction and dislocations in low carbon steels; deformation of single crystal and polycrystalline materials. Address: Research & Technology Division, Armco Steel Corp, Middletown, OH 45042.

ELIAS, J(OEL) J(ESSE), b. Chicago, Ill, May 1, 25; m. 53; c. 4. ZOOLOGY, ANATOMY. B.S, Univ. Ill, 49; M.A, Univ. Calif, 51, Ph.D.(zool), 58. Instr. ANAT, SCH. MED, UNIV. CALIF, SAN FRANCISCO, 58-60, asst. prof, 60-66, ASSOC. PROF, 66- U.S.N, 43-46. AAAS; Am. Asn. Anat; Tissue Cult. Asn. In vitro studies of effects of hormones on mammary tissues. Address: Dept. of Anatomy, Medical Center, University of California School of Medicine, San Francisco, CA 94122.

ELIAS, M(AXIM) K(ONRADOVICH), b. Minsk, Russia, Aug. 12, 89; nat; m. 15; c. 3. PALEONTOLOGY, STRATIGRAPHY. E.Min, Mining Inst. St. Petersburg, 17; Ph.D.(paleont), Yale, 39. Geologist, Verk-Isetsk Mining Co, Russia, 17-18, chief geologist, 19-20; prof, Vladivostok Polytech. Inst, 20-23; geologist, Kans. Geol. Surv, 27-37; geologist in charge field explor. party, Socony-Vacuum Oil Co. Colombia, S.Am, 37-38; paleontologist, Nebr. Geol. Surv, UNIV. NEBR, 39-58, EMER. PALEONTOLOGIST, 58-; ADJ. PROF, RES. INST, UNIV. OKLA, 58- Docent, Ural Minign Inst, Russia, 17, assoc. prof, 17-20; geologist, Far East. sect, Geologicheski, 20-22; geologist in charge explor. party, Etnyre Syndicate, Colo, 27-28; consutl. paleontologist, Ch. Tomlinson, Okla, 45- Mem. comt. common problems genetics, paleont. & systs, Nat. Res. Coun. Marsh Fund Grant, Nat. Acad. Sci, 33; Carnegie Inst. New York grant, 33. AAAS; fel. Paleont. Soc; fel. Geol. Soc. Am; Bot. Soc. Am; Am. Asn. Petrol. Geol. Paleontology and stratigraphy; Permian, Pennsylvanian and Mississippian; grasses; algal-bryozoan symbiosis; goniatites; conodonts; paleoecology. Address: Research Institute, University of Oklahoma, Norman, OK 73068.

ELIAS, PETER, b. New Brunswick, N.J, Nov. 26, 23; m. 50; c. 3. ELECTRICAL ENGINEERING. S.B, Mass. Inst. Tech, 44; M.A, Harvard, 48, fel, 48-49, M.E, 49, fel, 49-50, Ph.D.(appl. sci), 50. Asst. appl. sci, Harvard, 48, 49; asst. prof. ELEC. ENG, MASS. INST. TECHNOL, 53-56, assoc. prof, 56-60, prof, 60-69, CECIL H. GREEN PROF, 69-, head dept, 60-66. Physicist, Baird Atomic, summer 50, consult, 53; Lowell fel, Harvard, 50-53; consult, E.I. du Pont de Nemours & Co, 53-57; Polaroid, 58; biophysics study sect, Nat. Inst. Health, 58; vis. lectr, Univ. Calif, 58; fel, Inst. Elec. & Electronics Eng, 59. U.S.N, 44-46. AAAS; Inst. Elec. & Electronics Eng; Inst. Math. Statist; Am. Acad. Arts & Sci; Am. Soc. Eng. Educ; Int. Sci. Radio Union. Information theory; communicating and computing reliably with unreliable elements channels and networks; economical description and processing of natural messages. Address: Dept. of Electrical Engineering, Massachusetts Institute of Technology, Cambridge, MA 02139.

ELIAS, THOMAS S, b. Cairo, Ill, Dec. 30, 42; m. 64; c. 1. SYSTEMATIC BOTANY, MORPHOLOGY. B.A, Southern Illinois, 64, univ. fel, summer 66, M.A, 66; grad. fel, St. Louis, 66-69, tuition scholar, 67-69, Nat. Sci. Found. traineeship, summer, 68, Ph.D.(biol), 69. Teaching asst, Southern Illinois, 64-66; lectr. gen. biol, St. Louis, summer 67, ASST. CURATOR BOT, ARNOLD ARBORETUM, HARVARD, 69- Am. Soc. Plant Taxon; Int. Asn. Plant Taxon. New world floristics; monographic studies in the Leguminosae and Rubiaceae; morphology of the woody angiosperms. Address: Arnold Arboretum, Harvard University, 22 Divinity Ave, Cambridge, MA 02138.

ELIAS, WILLIAM FRANK, b. Woodbridge, N.J, Aug. 1, 12; m. 32; c. 3. BACTERIOLOGY. B.S, Bucknell, 34; M.S, Pennsylvania, 40, Ph.D.(bact), 41. Bacteriologist, Nat. Drug Co, 34-40; Wyeth Labs, Inc, 40-44, Wyeth Inst, 45, tech. dir. antibiotic div, Wyeth Labs, Inc, 46-68, managing dir, 68-71; CONSULT, 71- AAAS; Am. Chem. Soc; Am. Inst. Biol. Sci; Am. Pharmaceut. Asn; Am. Soc. Microbiol; Soc. Indust. Microbiol. Synthetic media for bacterial culture; preparation of new allergens; antibiotics; antibiotic dosage forms and clinical testing; penicillin tablets; procaine penicillin for aqueous injection; alum toxoid prepared from diptherial toxin produced on a gelatinhydrolysate medium; benzathine penicillin G; penicillin V and other new synthetic penicillins. Address: 38 Windward Dr, Severna Park, MD 21146.

ELIASON, AFTON Y(EATES), b. Garland, Utah, Oct. 14, 06; m. 37; c. 3. PHYSICS. B.S, Utah State Col, 38; M.A, California, 30, Ph.D.(physics), 33. Teaching fel, California, 28-32, res. assoc, 33-34; ed. adv, U.S. Govt, 34-35; from instr. to PROF. PHYSICS, FRESNO STATE COL, 35- Summers, prof, California, Berkeley, 65, 66, California, Los Angeles, 48, 52, 60, 61, consult. physicist, Off. Ord. Res, Duke, 56; physicist, Edwards Air Force Base, 57-59, prof, Utah State, 59, adv. scientist, Lockheed Missile & Space Co, 61, sr. tech. specialist, N.Am. Aviation Co, Inc, 62, consult, 62-63; prof, Hawaii, 64, 68, 71. AAAS; Am. Inst. Physics; Am. Asn. Physics Teachers. Optics, spectroscopy; nuclear physics. Address: Dept. of Physics, Fresno State College, Fresno, CA 93726.

ELIASON, EVERETT J, b. Richmond, Ind, March 1, 01; m. 29; c. 2. FORESTRY. B.S, Purdue, 23, M.S, Syracuse, 25; Am-Scandinavian Found. fellow, Sweden, 27-28. Lab. asst. bot, N.Y. State Col. Forestry, Syracuse, 24-29; asst. forest pathologist, State Conserv. Dept, N.Y, 29-40, supervising forester, 45-49, asst. supt, tree nurseries, 49-56, supt, 56-61, head, forest res. unit, 61-69; RETIRED. U.S.A, 40-56, Lt. Col. Fel. Soc. Am. Foresters. Tree seed germination technique; forest nursery practice; forest improvement through forest genetics. Address: 75 McMaster St, Ballston Spa, NY 12020.

ELIASON, MORTON A, b. Fargo, N.Dak, Apr. 26, 32; m. 56; c. 4. PHYSICAL CHEMISTRY. B.A, Concordia Col.(Moorhead, Minn), 54; Nat. Sci. Found. fel, Wisconsin, 54-58, Ph.D.(phys. chem), 59. Asst. prof. CHEM, AUGUSTANA COL.(ILL), 58-63, assoc. prof, 63-69, PROF, 69-, CHMN. DIV. NATURAL SCI, 71- Vis. assoc. prof. chem, theoret. chem. inst, Univ. Wis, 66-67. Am. Chem. Soc. Quantum theory of small molecules; theory of reaction rates, liquids; solubility of inert gases in fused salts; collision processes and energy transfer in gases; theory of charge transfer complexes. Address: Dept. of Chemistry, Augustana College, Rock Island, IL 61201.

ELIASON, STANLEY B, b. McVille, N.Dak, Aug. 31, 39; m. 64. MATHEMATICS. B.A, Concordia Col.(Moorhead, Minn), 61; M.A, Univ. Nebr, Lincoln, 63, Ph.D.(math), 67. Instr. MATH, Univ. Nebr, Lincoln, 63-67; asst. prof, UNIV. OKLA, 67-71, ASSOC. PROF, 71- Summers, U.S. Army Res. Off-Durham grant, 70; U.S. Air Force res. joint grant, 71. Am. Math. Soc; Math. Asn. Am. Mathematical analysis; ordinary differential equations; distance between zeros; comparison theorems; eigenvalue problems; second order linear and nonlinear differential equations. Address: Dept. of Mathematics, 601 Elm Ave, Room 423, University of Oklahoma, Norman, OK 73069.

ELIASSEN, JOHN D(AVID), b. Yankton, S.Dak, Dec. 25, 35; m. 62. CHEMICAL ENGINEERING. B.S, Princeton, 57; Ph.D.(chem. eng), Minnesota, 63. Res. engr, Tenn. Eastman Co. div, Eastman Kodak Co, 58; E.I. du Pont de Nemours & Co, 63-66; ASST. PROF, DEPT. CHEM. ENG, UNIV. DEL, 66- U.S.A, 57. Am. Inst. Chem. Eng; Am. Chem. Soc. Interfacial and continuum mechanics; polymer science. Address: Dept. of Chemical Engineering, University of Delaware, Newark, DE 19711.

ELIASSEN, ROLF, b. N.Y.C, Feb. 22, 11; m. 41; c. 2. SANITARY ENGINEERING. B.S, Mass. Inst. Tech, 32, M.S, 33, Sc.D.(sanit. eng), 35. Sanit. engr, Dorr Co, Inc, Chicago, Los Angeles, 36-40; PROF. sanit. eng, N.Y. Univ, 40-49; Mass. Inst. Tech, 49-61; ENVIRON. ENG, STANFORD UNIV, 61-; PARTNER & SR. V.PRES, METCALF & EDDY, 61- Dir, Millipore Filter Corp, Mass, 58-62; consult, Int. Atomic Energy Agency, 57-62; Off. Sci. & Tech, Exec. Off. President, 61-; Calif. Dept. Water Resources, 64-; mem. gen. adv. comt, U.S. Atomic Energy Comn. C.Eng. U.S.A, 42-46, Maj. Nat. Acad. Eng; Am. Soc. Eng. Educ.(George Westinghouse Award, 50); fel. Am. Soc. Civil Eng; Am. Water Works Asn; Water Pollution Control Fedn; Am. Acad. Arts & Sci. Methods of water and sewage treatment; industrial and radioactive waste treatment processes. Address: Dept. of Civil Engineering, Stanford University, Stanford, CA 94305.

ELIASSON, SVEN G(USTAV), b. Malmo, Sweden, Apr. 16, 28; m. 51; c. 3. NEUROLOGY. Ph.D.(physiol), Lund, Sweden, 52; M.D, Royal Carolina Univ, Lund, 54. Asst. prof. physiol, Univ. of Lund, Sweden, 49-51, assoc. prof, 52, instr. neurol, 53; jr. res. anatomist, California, Los Angeles, 54-55, asst. res. anatomist, 55-56; asst. prof. NEUROL, Southwest. Med. Sch, Texas, 56-63; assoc. prof, SCH. MED, WASH. UNIV, 63-67, PROF, 67- Rotary Int. fel, 54-55. Am. Physiol. Soc; Am. Acad. Neurol; Am. Neurol. Asn; Am. Soc. Clin. Invest; Am. Fedn. Clin. Res. Gastrointestinal physiology; neurochemical and neurophysiological disturbances in peripheral nerves. Address: Dept. of Neurology, Washington University School of Medicine, 660 S. Euclid, St. Louis, MO 63110.

ELICEIRI, GEORGE L(OUIS), b. Buenos Aires, Arg, Oct. 27, 39; U.S. citizen; m. 66; c. 1. CELL BIOLOGY, BIOCHEMISTRY. M.D, Univ. Buenos Aires, 60; Ph.D.(biochem), Univ. Okla, 65. Trainee biochem, inst. sci. invest, Campomar Found, Buenos Aires, Arg, 60-61; fel, col. med, Baylor Univ, 61; Okla. Med. Res. Found, 61-65; Damon Runyon Mem. Fund fel, Argonne Cancer Res. Hosp, Univ. Chicago, 65-67; fel. cell biol, sch. med, N.Y. Univ, 67-68, instr, 68-69; ASST. PROF. PATH, SCH. MED, ST. LOUIS UNIV, 69- U.S. Pub. Health Serv. spec. fel, 67-69. Ribonucleic acids of mammalian cells; synthesis and its regulation; ribosomal,transfer and mitochondrial ribonucleic acids in mammalian cell cultures, including somatic cell hybrids. Address: Dept. of Pathology, St. Louis University School of Medicine, 1402 S. Grand Blvd, St. Louis, MO 63104.

ELICH, JOE, b. Tooele, Utah, Sept. 28, 18. MATHEMATICS. B.S, Utah State Agr. Col, 40; M.A, California, 42; California, Los Angeles, 48-50, 55-56, Berkeley, 61-62. Asst. prof. MATH, UTAH STATE UNIV, 46-58, PROF, 58- U.S.A, 42-46. Am. Math. Soc; Math. Asn. Am. Address: 102 N. Fifth St, Tooele, UT 84074.

ELIEL, ERNEST L(UDWIG), b. Cologne, Ger, Dec. 28, 21; U.S. citizen; m. 49; c. 2. ORGANIC CHEMISTRY. Univ. Edinburgh, 39-40; Dr. phys-chem. Sc, Univ. Havana, 46; Ph.D.(org. chem), Univ. Ill, 48. Instr. CHEM, UNIV. NOTRE DAME, 48-50, asst. prof, 50-53, assoc. prof, 53-60, PROF, 60-, head dept, 64-66. Sr. fel. Nat. Sci. Found, 58-59, 67-68; Arthur Kelly lectr, Purdue Univ, 61; E.C. Franklin Mem. lectr, Univ. Kans, 69. Teaching award, Mfg. Chem. Asn, 65; Morley Medal, 65; Laurent Lavoisier Medal, 68. AAAS; Am. Chem. Soc; fel. Brit. Chem. Soc. Stereochemistry; conformational analysis; heterocyclic chemistry; organosulfur chemistry; reductions with complex metal hydrides. Address: Dept. of Chemistry, University of Notre Dame, Notre Dame, IN 46556.

ELIEL, LEONARD P(AUL), b. Los Angeles, Calif, Sept. 14, 14; m. 43; c. 2. CANCER. B.S, Harvard, 36, M.D, 40. Res. fel. pediat. Harvard Med. Sch. & Children's Hosp, 46-47, Milton fel, Harvard Med. Sch, 47-48; instr. dept. med, Cornell Univ, 49-50, asst. prof, 50-51; assoc. prof. RES. MED, MED. SCH, UNIV. OKLA, 51-56, PROF, 56-, EXEC. V.PRES. MED. CTR. AFFAIRS & DIR. MED. CTR, 71-, interim exec. v.pres. med. ctr. affairs & interim dir, med. ctr, 70-71; v.pres-dir. res, Okla. Med. Res. Found, 65-70, head cancer res. sect, 51-64, exec. dir, 59-65. Clin. asst. physician, med. serv, Mem. Hosp, 48; asst, Sloan-Kettering Inst, 48-49, assoc, 49-51, Runyon sr. clin. res. fel, 49-51, chmn, clin. cancer training comt, Nat. Cancer Inst, Md, 69-71. U.S.N, 44-46, Lt. Am. Asn. Cancer Res; Am. Med. Asn; Am. Fedn. Clin. Res; Endocrine Soc; Am. Soc. Clin. Invest; fel. Am. Col. Physicians. Cancer endocrinology; parathyroid physiology. Address: Office of the Vice President for Medical Center Affairs, 800 N.E. 13th St, Oklahoma City, OK 73104.

ELIJAH, LEO MOSES, b. Nagpur, India, Mar. 30, 28; U.S. citizen; m. 61; c. 2. METALLURGICAL & INDUSTRIAL ENGINEERING. B.S, Bombay, 47; dipl, Nat. Foundry Col, Eng, 49; M.S, Wisconsin, 51. Metallurgist, Gen. Dynamics Corp, Can, 52-53; indust. & prod. engr, Ford Motor Co. Can, 53-57; sr. engr, Gen. Tel. & Electronics Corp, Pa, 57-58; metall. dir. & consult, George Sall Metals Co, Inc, 58-62; supvr. res. & develop, Beryllium Corp, 62-64; chief metall. & welding engr, opers. div, Am. Mach. & Foundry Co, Pa, 64-65; metall. & indust. eng. mgt. consult, 65-68; STAFF ENGR, IBM CORP, HOPEWELL JUNCTION, 68- Am. Soc. Metals; Am. Inst. Mining, Metall. & Petrol Eng. Engineering processes, materials and methods in fields of metallurgy, industry and chemistry; effective use of men and materials. Address: P.O. Box 101, Fishkill, NY 12524.

ELING, THOMAS EDWARD, b. Cincinnati, Ohio, Oct. 26, 41. PHARMACOLOGY, BIOCHEMISTRY. B.S, Cincinnati, 63, M.S, 64; Nat. Insts. Health fel, Alabama, 65-68, Ph.D.(biochem), 68. Fel. drug metab, Univ. Iowa, 68-69; SR. STAFF FEL, NAT. INST. ENVIRON. HEALTH SCI, 69- Am. Chem. Soc; N.Y. Acad. Sci. Synthesis and metabolism of labeled drugs; effect of drugs on microsomal drug metabolizing enzymes, factors controlling the development of these enzymes in newborn animals and man; prostaglandin biosynthesis by lungs and mechanism of drug uptake processes of the lung. Address: National Institute of Environmental Health Sciences, P.O. Box 12233, Research Triangle Park, NC 27709.

ELINGS, VIRGIL BRUCE, b. Des Moines, Iowa, May 9, 39; m. 62; c. 1. PHYSICS. S.B, Iowa State, 61; Ph.D.(physics), Mass. Inst. Tech, 65. Res. assoc. PHYSICS, Mass. Inst. Tech, 66; ASST. PROF, UNIV. CALIF, SANTA BARBARA, 66- Summers, res. engr, Autonetics Div, N.Am. Rockwell Corp, 62, staff mem, Bell Tel. Labs, 63; Atomic Energy Comn. grant, 66- Am. Phys. Soc. Elementary particle physics. Address: Dept. of Physics, University of California, Santa Barbara, CA 93106.

ELINS, HERBERT S(AMUEL), b. Lancaster, Pa, Nov. 24, 21; m. 49; c. 3. PHOTOGRAPHIC CHEMISTRY. B.S, Franklin & Marshall Col, 43; M.S, Illinois, 47, Ph.D.(chem), 49. Sr. res. chemist, EASTMAN KODAK CO, 49-57, res. assoc, RES. LABS, 57-69, lab. head, 69-71, SR. LAB. HEAD, 71- U.S.M.C.R, 43-46, Capt. AAAS; Soc. Photog. Sci. & Eng; Am. Chem. Soc. Color photography; photographic emulsions. Address: 30 Glen Ellyn Way, Rochester, NY 14618.

ELIOFF, THOMAS, b. Monroe, La, Dec. 11, 33; m. 56; c. 1. HIGH ENERGY PHYSICS. B.S, La. Polytech, 54; Ph.D.(physics), California, Berkeley, 60. PHYSICIST, LAWRENCE BERKELEY LAB, UNIV. CALIF, 60- Am. Phys. Soc. Experimental high energy physics concerning interactions of elementary particles; accelerator development. Address: Room 149, Bldg. 50, Lawrence Berkeley Lab, University of California, Berkeley, CA 94720.

ELION, GERTRUDE B(ELLE), b. New York, N.Y, Jan. 23, 18. BIOLOGICAL & ORGANIC CHEMISTRY. A.B, Hunter Col, 37; M.S, N.Y. Univ, 41; hon. D.Sc, George Wash. Univ. & hon. D.M.S, Brown Univ, 69. Lab. asst. biochem, sch. nursing, N.Y. Hosp, 37; asst. org. chem, Denver Chem. Co, 38-39; teacher chem. & physics, New York, 41-42; analyst food chem, Quaker Maid Co, 42-43; res. chemist org. chem, Johnson & Johnson, 43-44; sr. res. chemist, Wellcome Res. Labs, 44-67, asst. to dir, chemother. div, 63-67, HEAD EXP. THER, BURROUGHS WELLCOME CO, 67- Consult, chemother. study sect, U.S. Pub. Health Serv, 60-64. AAAS; Am. Asn. Cancer Res; Am. Soc. Hemat; Am. Chem. Soc.(Garvan Medal, 68); Am. Soc. Biol. Chem; N.Y. Acad. Sci; Brit. Chem. Soc. Chemistry of Purines, Pyrimidines and Pteridines; bacterial metabolism; metabolism of radioactive purines in bacteria and animals; chemotherapy; immunosuppression. Address: Burroughs Wellcome Co, 3030 Cornwallis Rd, Research Triangle Park, NC 27709.

ELION, HERBERT A(ARON), b. N.Y.C, Oct. 16, 23; m. 45; c. 4. PHYSICS. B.M.E, City Col. New York, 45; M.M.E, Polytech. Inst. Brooklyn, 49; Pa. State, 56; Mass. Inst. Tech, 60; Cambridge, 61; Rutgers, 63; Northeastern, 65; California, 67. Res. engr. & physicist, spec. proj. dept, M.W. Kellogg Co, 47-50; physicist, Airborne Instruments Lab, 50-51; proj. physicist, Freed Radio Corp, 51; chief engr, Paul Rosenberg Assocs, Consult. Physicists, 51-52; elec. engr, Farrand Optical Co, Inc, 52-53; res. elec. engr, Sperry Prods, Inc, 53-57; group leader physics, Radio Corp. Am, 57-59; pres. & dir. res, Elion Instruments, Inc, 59-64, Elion Princeton Assocs, 64-65; dir. instrumentation lab, GCA Corp, 65- SUPVRY. STAFF MEM, RES. & DEVELOP. DIV, ARTHUR D. LITTLE, INC, 67- Lectr, Polytech. Inst. Brooklyn, 55; Brown, 56; Stanford, 62; William Smith Col, 64. Consult, Radio Corp. Am, 58-59; ed, Pergamon Press, Eng, 64- Am. Am. Phys. Soc; sr. mem. Inst. Elec. & Electronics Eng; Am. Chem. Soc; Electron Micros. Soc; Am. Soc. Metals; Instrument Soc. Am. Electrons; charged particles; x-ray technology; ultrahigh vacuum; ultrasonics; magnetic resonance spectroscopy; heat transfer; solid state physics; gas kineics; electron optics; infrared detection; electro-optics; lasers; instruments. Address: Research & Development Division, Arthur D. Little, Inc, Acorn Park, Cambridge, MA 02140.

ELIOPOULOS, H(ERMES) A(NDREW), b. Salonica, Greece, Dec. 13, 25; nat; m. 58; c. 1. MATHEMATICS. B.Sc, Univ. Salonica, Greece, 46; M.Sc, McGill, 54; fel, Toronto, 54-56, Ph.D.(math), 56. Asst. MATH, McGill, 52-54; lectr, UNIV. WINDSOR, 56-57, asst. prof, 57-59; assoc. prof, 59-65, PROF, 65- Am. Math. Soc; Math. Soc. France. Differential geometry; classical and quantum field theories. Address: Dept. of Mathematics, University of Windsor, Windsor, Ont, Can.

ELIOT, ROBERT S, b. Oak Park, Ill, Mar. 8, 29; m. 57; c. 2. CARDIOLOGY, CHEMISTRY. B.S, New Mexico, 51; M.D, Colorado, 55. Intern, Evanston Hosp, Ill, 55-56; res. internal med, Colorado, 56-58, res. fel. cardiol, sch. med, Colorado, 58-60; med. fel. specialist cardiac path, Minnesota, 62-63, instr. MED, med. sch, 63-65, asst. prof, med. center, 65-67; assoc. prof. & cardiologist, SCH. MED, UNIV. FLA, 67-69, PROF, 69-; CHIEF CARDIOL. SECT, VET. ADMIN. HOSP, 69-, acting chief med. serv, 69-70. Acting chief cardiol, Vet. Admin. Hosp, Denver, Colo, 59; Nat. Heart Inst. fel. & res. trainee cardiovasc. path, Charles T. Miller Hosp, St. Paul, Minn, 62-63; consult. physician, Vet. Admin. Hosp, Minneapolis, Minn, 65-67. Kent award, 56. Med.C, 60-62, Capt. Am. Med. Asn; fel. Am. Col. Physicians; Am. Heart Asn; assoc. fel. Am. Col. Cardiol. Abnormal hemoglobin oxygen affinity in smokers and patients having signs of coronary insufficiency; myocardial proteins; cardiac pathology; vectorcardiography; electrocardiography. Address: Medical Service, Veterans Administration Hospital, Gainesville, FL 32601.

ELISBERG, BENNETT L(A DOLCE), b. N.Y.C, Nov. 11, 25; m. 64. INFECTIOUS DISEASES, INTERNAL MEDICINE. B.A, N.Y. Univ, 44; M.S, Tulane, 48, M.D, 50. Intern, St. Joseph's Mercy Hosp, 50-51; from jr. to sr. resident internal med, Kern County Gen. Hosp, 51-52, chief resident, 54-55; sr. med. officer, res. infectious diseases, U.S. Army Med. Res. Unit, Malaya, 55-58, DEP. DIR, 59-61; dept. virus diseases, WALTER REED ARMY INST. RES, 61-62, DEPT. RICKETTSIAL DISEASES, 62-, CHIEF, 63- Mem, Comn. Rickettsial Diseases, Armed Forces Epidemiol. Bd; exec. coun. viral & rickettsial registry comt, Am. Type Cult. Collection, adv. comt. human & animal viruses, Am. Type Cult. Collection, Div. Med. Sci, Nat. Acad. Sci. Dipl. Am. Bd. Med. Microbiol. Med.C, 52-54, 1st Lt. AAAS; Am. Soc. Microbiol; N.Y. Acad. Sci; Wildlife Disease Asn; Am. Soc. Trop. Med. & Hyg; Am. Asn. Immunol. Virus and rickettsial diseases of man. Address: Dept. of Rickettsial Diseases, Walter Reed Army Institute of Research, Washington, DC 20012.

ELISON, CHRISTIAN, b. Cebu, Philippines, Mar. 1, 21; nat; m. 44; c. 3. PHARMACOLOGY, TOXICOLOGY. B.S, Col. Puget Sound, 52; B.A, California, Berkeley, 57, M.S, San Francisco, 59, Ph.D.(pharmacol, toxicol), 61. Res. asst. pharmacol, California, San Francisco, 57-58, res. pharmacologist, 58-61, jr. res. pharmacologist, 61-62; ctr. health sci, Los Angeles, 61-62, asst. res. pharmacologist, 62-65; asst. prof. PHARMACOL, UNIV. SOUTH. CALIF, 65-66, ASSOC. PROF, 66- Med.Serv.C, 42-52, Sgt. Am. Soc. Pharmacol. & Exp. Therapeut; Int. Soc. Biochem. Pharmacol. Comparative pharmacology and toxicology; biochemical pharmacology; mechanism of drug action, primarily narcotic analgesics; biochemistry of contraction and relaxation of striated muscle. Address: School of Pharmacy, University of Southern California, Los Angeles, CA 90007.

ELIZAN, TERESITA S, b. Naga City, Philippines, Dec. 12, 31. NEUROLOGY, VIROLOGY. M.D, Philippines, 55. Intern, Philippine Gen. Hosp, Univ. Philippines, 54-55; asst. resident gen. path, St. Mary's Hosp, Waterbury, Conn, 55-56; neurol, sch. med, Yale & Grace-New Haven Hosp, Conn, 56-58; clin. clerk neurol. & neuropath, inst. neurol, Nat. Hosp, Univ. London, 58-59; chief resident neurol, Montreal Neurol. Inst, McGill, 59-60; res. asst, Mt. Sinai Hosp, New York, 60-61, res. assoc, 61-62; asst. prof. & head neurol. sect, col. med, Philippines, 62; vis. scientist & officer-in-charge, res. center, Nat. Inst. Neurol. Diseases & Blindness, Guam, 63-65, vis. scientist, epidemiol. br, Md, 65-66, res. neurologist, & neuropathologist, sect. infectious diseases, 66-68; asst. prof. neurol. & asst. attend. neurologist, MT. SINAI SCH. MED, 68-70, ASSOC. PROF. NEUROL. & ASSOC. ATTEND. NEUROLOGIST, 71-, HEAD, LAB. NEUROVIROL, 68- U.S. Pub. Health Serv. clin. fel. neurol, sch. med, Yale, 56-58; Dazian Found. Med. Res. fel, Mt. Sinai Hosp, New York, 60-61; clin. asst. prof. sch. med, Georgetown, 65- Dipl, Am. Bd. Psychiat. & Neurol, 63. AAAS; fel. Am. Acad. Neurol; Am. Asn. Neuropath; Asn. Res. Nerv. & Ment. Disease; Am. Neurol. Asn; Am. Soc. Microbiol; Soc. Neurosci; Teratology Soc; N.Y. Acad. Sci. Virological and immunological techniques in the study of central nervous system degenerations, neoplasma and infections; clinical neurology; epidemiology of neurological diseases; neurovirology. Address: Dept. of Neurology, Mt. Sinai School of Medicine, New York, NY 10029.

ELKAN, GERALD HUGH, b. Berlin, Ger, Aug. 3, 29. BACTERIOLOGY. A.B, Brigham Young Univ, 51; M.S, Pa. State Univ, 55; Ph.D.(bact), Va. Polytech, 59. Asst. Prof. BACT. N.C. STATE UNIV, 58-63, assoc. prof, 63-70, PROF, 70- Fulbright res. fel, Inst. Microbiol, Sweden, 63-64, Chem.C, U.S.A, 51-53, Res, 53-, Maj. AAAS; Am. Soc. Microbiol; fel. Am. Acad. Microbiol; Can. Soc. Microbiol; Brit. Soc. Gen. Microbiol; World Acad. Art & Sci; Netherlands Soc. Microbiol. Microbial physiology and metabolism; function and physiology of symbiotic nitrogen fixing bacteria. Address: Dept. of Microbiology, Institute of Biological Science, North Carolina State University, Raleigh, NC 27607.

EL-KAREH, AUGUSTE BADIH, b. Baabda, Lebanon, July 9, 32; U.S. citizen; m. 58; c. 2. ELECTRICAL ENGINEERING, APPLIED PHYSICS. Dip.Ing, Delft, 56, D.Sc, 62. Asst, res. labs, Europe, 53-55; asst. engr, Delft, 55-58; instr. elec. eng, New Mexico, 58-59; Pennsylvania, 59-60; mem. tech. staff, RCA Labs, N.J, 60-63; assoc. prof. elec. eng. & head electron physics lab, Pa. State, 63-66; prof. elec. eng, Clarkson Col. Technol, 66-67; Syracuse Univ, 67-71; PROF. ELEC. ENG. & DIR. ELECTRON BEAM LAB, UNIV. HOUSTON, 71- Chmn. Int. Electron Beam Symp, 64-65. Inst. Elec. & Electronics Eng. High power microwave tubes; electron beam techniques; millimeter wave generation; electron optics; electron physics; graduate courses on network synthesis. Address: Dept. of Electrical Engineering, University of Houston, Houston, TX 77004.

ELKES, JOEL, b. Germany, Nov. 12, 13; m. 43; c. 1. PSYCHIATRY, PSYCHOPHARMACOLOGY. London, 33-40; M.B, Ch.B, Birmingham, 47, M.D, 49. Sir Halley Stewart res. fel. pharmacol, Birmingham, 42-45, lectr, 45-48, sr. lectr. & acting dir. dept. pharmacol, 48-50, prof. exp. psychiat. & chmn. dept, 51-57; Fulbright traveling fel, 50-51; clin. prof. psychiat, sch. med, George Washington, 57-63; HENRY PHIPPS PROF. PSYCHIAT. & DIR. DEPT, JOHNS HOPKINS UNIV, 63-; PSYCHIATRIST-IN-CHIEF, JOHNS HOPKINS HOSP, 63- Vis. fel, New Eng. Hosp. Center, Boston, Mass. & Norwich State Hosp, Conn, 50-51; consult. psychiatrist, Birmingham United Hosp. & Birmingham Regional Hosp. Bd, 53-57; sci. dir, Birmingham Regional Psychiat. Early Treatment Center, 53-57; exam, Univ. London, 53-56; chief clin. neuropharmacol. res. center, Nat. Inst. Ment. Health, D.C, 57-63; dir. behav. & clin. studies center, St. Elizabeths Hosp, D.C, 57-63. Mem. psychopharmacol study sect, Nat. Inst. Ment. Health, 57-64; adv. comt. biol. sci, Air Force Off. Sci. Res, 64; dir, Found. Fund for Res. In Psychiat, 67- Fel. Am. Psychiat. Asn; Am. Soc. Pharmacol. & Exp. Therapeut; fel. Am. Psychopath. Asn.(pres. 69); fel. Am. Pub. Health Asn; Soc. Biol. Psychiat; Acad. Psychoanal; fel. Am. Acad. Arts & Sci; Am. Col. Neuropsychopharmacol.(1st pres, 61); N.Y. Acad. Sci; Brit. Physiol. Soc; Brit. Pharmacol. Soc; Royal Soc. Med; Royal Medico-Psychol. Asn; Brit. Psychol. Soc. Address: Dept. of Psychiatry & Behavioral Sciences, Johns Hopkins Hospital, 601 N. Broadway, Baltimore, MD 21205.

EL KHADEM, HASSAN S, b. Cairo, Egypt, Mar. 24, 23; m. 51; c. 2. ORGANIC & CARBOHYDRATE CHEMISTRY. B.Sc, Cairo Univ, 46; D.Sc.Tech, Swiss Fed. Inst. Technol, 49; Ph.D.(org. chem), Univ. London & dipl, Imp. Col, 52; hon. D.Sc, Univ. Alexandria, 63, Univ. London, 67. Lectr. CHEM, Univ. Alexandria, 52-58, asst. prof, 58-63, PROF, 63-71; MICH. TECHNOL. UNIV, 71- Fulbright scholar, Ohio State Univ, 63-66. Nat. Sci. Award, Egypt, 61. Carbohydrates; nitrogen heterocycles; metal chelates; polysaccharides; glycosides; plant chemistry. Address: Dept. of Chemistry & Chemical Engineering, Michigan Technological University, Houghton, MI 49931.

EL-KHAMY, SAID EL-SAYED, b. Sharkia, Egypt, Apr. 13, 44. COMMUNICATIONS. B.Sc, Univ. Alexandria, 65, M.Sc, 67; Univ. Calgary, 68; Ph.D.(elec. eng), Univ. Mass, Amherst, 71. Asst. elec. eng, Univ. Alexandria, 65-68; physics, Univ. Calgary, 68-69; ELEC. ENG, UNIV. MASS, AMHERST, 69-71, RES. ASSOC, 71- Inst. Elec. & Electronics Eng. Optimum transmission of information through dispersive, nonlinear and random media; wave propagation in plasmas; microwave engineering. Address: Dept. of Electrical Engineering, University of Massachusetts, Amherst, MA 01002.

ELKHOLY, HUSSEIN A, b. Elmansoura, Egypt, Oct. 30, 33; m. 61; c. 3. PHYSICS. B.Sc, Cairo, 57; Kandidat, Hungarian Acad. Sci, 61; Dr.rer.nat. (physics), Eötvös Lórand, Budapest, 61. Fel, Eötvös Lórand, Budapest, 61-62; asst. prof. physics, Cairo, 62-63; Khartoum, 63-64; FAIRLEIGH DICKINSON UNIV, 64-65, CHMN. DEPT. MATH. & PHYSICS, 67-, acting chmn. dept, 65-67. AAAS; Am. Phys. Soc; Am. Asn. Physics Teachers; Am. Math. Soc; Math. Asn. Am. Phase transformation; lattice defects; radiation effects in solids. Address: R.D. 1, Pitney Dr, Mendham, NJ 07945.

ELKIN, EUGENE M(ITCHELL), b. Poltava, Russia, May 9, 06, Can. citizen, 29; m. 39; c. 2. CHEMISTRY, CHEMICAL ENGINEERING. B.Sc, Manitoba, 29; B.E, M.Sc, McGill, 33, Ph.D, 35. Demonstr. physics, Manitoba, 28-31; asst. & demonstr. chem, McGill, 32-35; chemist, Donald-Hunt, Ltd, Montreal, 35; res. chemist & chem. engr, CAN. COPPER REFINERS, LTD, MONTREAL, 36-44, res. engr, 44-52, RES. SUPVR, 52- Chem. Inst. Can; Can. Soc. Chem. Eng; Air Pollution Control Asn. Refining of copper, precious metals, selenium and tellurium; extractive metallurgy; environmental control. Address: 5126 Chanranald Ave, Montreal 248, Que, Can.

ELKIN, LYNNE OSMAN, b. N.Y.C, June 10, 46; m. 67. PLANT PHYSIOLOGY, CYTOLOGY. A.B, Univ. Rochester, 67; N.Y. State Regents fel, Univ. Calif, Berkeley, 67, Nat. Insts. Health fel, 68-71, Ph.D.(bot), 72. Lectr. BIOL. SCI, CALIF. STATE COL, HAYWARD, 71-72, ASST. PROF, 72- Light reactions of photosynthesis; C_4 pathway of photosynthesis; fluorescence photomicroscopy; correlation of physiology and ultrastructure; scientific photography; science education; photorespiration; crassulacean acid metabolism. Address: Dept. of Biological Sciences, California State College, Hayward, CA 94742.

ELKIN, MILTON, b. Boston, Mass, Feb. 24, 16; m. 43; c. 3. RADIOLOGY. A.B, Harvard, 37; M.D, 41. Assoc. radiologist, Peter Bent Brigham Hosp, Boston, Mass, 51-52; asst. radiologist, New England Med. Center, Boston, 52-53; PROF. RADIOL. & CHMN. DEPT, ALBERT EINSTEIN COL. MED, YESHIVA UNIV, 54-; DIR. RADIOL, BRONX MUNIC. HOSP. CTR, 54- Assoc. radiologist, Cedars of Lebanon Hosp, Los Angeles, Calif, 53-54; Knox Lectr, London, Eng. & Holmes Lectr, Boston, Mass, 70; Rigler Lectr, Tel Aviv, Israel, 71; prog. dir, Nat. Inst. Gen. Med. Sci. training grant diag. radiol; prin. investr, Nat. Inst. Gen. Med. Sci. res. grant; spec. consult, U.S. Pub. Health Serv-Nat. Inst. Gen. Med. Sci. Gen. Med. Res. Prog-Proj. Comt. Med.C, U.S.A.F, 42-46, Maj. Fel. Am. Col. Radiol; Radiol. Soc. N.Am; Am. Roentgen Ray Soc; Am. Med. Asn; Asn. Univ. Radiol. Renal physiology; effects of radiation on tissue. Address: Dept. of Radiology, Albert Einstein College of Medicine, Yeshiva University, 1300 Morris Park Ave, Bronx, NY 10461.

ELKIND, JEROME I, b. New York, N.Y, Aug. 30, 29; m. 59; c. 3. INFORMATION SCIENCE. S.B. & S.M, Mass. Inst. Tech, 52, Sc.D, 56. Asst. elec. eng, Mass. Inst. Tech, 52-56, staff. mem. psychol, Lincoln Lab, 54-56; sr. scientist human eng, Radio Corp. of Am, 56-58; eng. psychol, BOLT, BERANEK & NEWMAN, 58-61, head dept, Mass, 61-65, v.pres, 65-69, sr. v.pres, 69-70; vis. prof. & mem. staff proj. Mac, Mass. Inst. Technol, 70-71; DIR. COMPUT. SCI. LAB, XEROX PALO ALTO RES. CTR, 71- Fel. Human Factors Soc; sr. mem. Inst. Elec. & Electronics Eng.(ed, Transactions, Inst. Radio Eng, 59-64); Asn. Comput. Mach. Interactive computer systems; man-machine systems; manual control. Address: Computer Science Lab, Xerox Palo Alto Research Center, 3180 Porter Dr, Palo Alto, CA 94304.

ELKIND, M(ICHAEL) J(OHN), b. Detroit, Mich, July 23, 22; m. 52; c. 4. INORGANIC CHEMISTRY. B.S, Detroit, 43, M.S, 48; Ph.D.(chem), Wayne, 51. Develop. chemist, pharmaceut. prods, R.P. Scherer Corp, 43-44; fel. chem, Detroit, 46-48; Wayne, 48-50, instr, 50-51; sr. res. & develop. chemist, photo prods. dept, E.I. du Pont de Nemours & Co, 51-52; Wyandotte Chem. Corp, 52-53; J.T. Baker Chem. Co, 53-56; MEM. TECH. STAFF, BELL TEL. LABS, 56- C.W.S, 44-46. Am. Chem. Soc. Inorganic fine and heavy chemicals; photographic chemistry; phase studies in non-aqueous media; chemistry of electron device materials and processing. Address: Bell Telephone Labs, Reading, PA 19604.

ELKIND, MORTIMER M, b. Brooklyn, N.Y, Oct. 25, 22; m. 60; c. 3. BIOPHYSICS. B.M.E, Cooper Union, 43; M.M.E, Polytech. Inst. Brooklyn, 49; M.S, Mass. Inst. Tech, 51, Ph.D, 53. Asst. proj. engr, Wyssmont Co, 43-44; proj. engr, Safe Flight Instrument Corp, 46-47; head instrumentation, Sloan-Kettering Inst. Cancer Res, 47-49; biophysicist, Nat. Cancer Inst, 49-69, SR. SCIENTIST, BIOL. DEPT, BROOKHAVEN NAT. LAB, 69-; MEM. STAFF, EXP. RADIOPATH. RES. UNIT, MED. RES. COUN, HAMMERSMITH HOSP, LONDON, ENG, 71- Mem. radiation study sect, Nat. Insts. Health, 61-65, molecular biol. study sect, 69-71. E.O. Lawrence Award, U.S. Atomic Energy Comn, 67; superior serv. award, Dept. Health, Educ. & Welfare, 69. U.S.N.R, 44-46, Lt.(jg). Biophys. Soc; Radiation Res. Soc. Van de Graaff accelerators; energy levels in light nuclei; radiobiology of microorganisms and mammalian cells in tissue culture. Address: Biology Dept, Brookhaven National Lab, Upton, NY 11973.

ELKINS, DONALD MARCUM, b. Woodville, Ala, Sept. 15, 40; m. 63; c. 2. AGRONOMY. B.S, Tenn. Polytech. Inst, 62; M.S, Auburn Univ, 64, NASA fel. & Ph.D.(agron), 67. Asst. prof. AGRON, SOUTH. ILL. UNIV, 67-71, ASSOC. PROF, 71- Am. Soc. Agron; Crop Sci. Soc. Am. Methods of achieving good establishment of forage legume crops; liming and fertilization procedures; herbicides; growth regulators; Rhizobium bacteria. Address: Dept. of Plant Industries, Southern Illinois University, Carbondale, IL 62901.

ELKINS, DOUGLAS A(LMA), b. Salt Lake City, Utah, Aug. 10, 12. METALLURGY. B.S, Univ. Utah, 33; M.S, Mass. Inst. Technol, 36. Draftsman, U.S. Dept. Agr, 36-40; mech. engr, BUR. MINES, U.S. DEPT. INTERIOR, 41-58, chief process eval, SALT LAKE CITY METALL. RES. CTR, 59-70, STAFF COORD, ENG. & PROCESS EVAL, 71- Plant engr, exp. alumina plant, Bur. Mines, 52-54. Am. Soc. Mech. Eng; Am. Asn. Cost Eng; Am. Inst. Chem. Eng. Magnesium production technology; evaluation of chemical and metallurgical processes; design of mining and metallurgical equipment. Address: 1875 E. 21st S, Salt Lake City, UT 84106.

ELKINS, EARL C(OOK), b. Spearfish, S.Dak, Sept. 19, 04; m. 35; c. 4. MEDICINE. B.S, Buena Vista Col, 27; M.D, George Wash. Univ, 33. Prof. PHYS. MED. & REHAB, MAYO GRAD. SCH. MED, UNIV. MINN, 53-69; EMER. PROF, 69-; head sect, Mayo Clin, 58-65, consult, 39-58. Secy-treas, Am. Bd. Phys. Med. & Rehab, 53. Dipl, Am. Bd. Phys. Med. & Rehab, 47. Am. Med. Asn; Am. Col. Physicians. Physical medicine and rehabilitation. Address: 1131 Seventh St. S.W, Rochester, MN 55901.

ELKINS, EARLEEN FELDMAN, b. South Bend, Ind, Mar. 20, 33; m. 54; c. 3. AUDIOLOGY. B.A, Maryland, 54, M.A, 56, Ph.D.(audiol), 67. Instr. speech, Maryland, 54-56; rehab. audiologist, Walter Reed Army Med. Ctr, 56-57; res. assoc, Electronic Teaching Labs, D.C, 60-61; asst. speech & hearing, UNIV. MD, 63-67, res. assoc, biocommun. lab, 67-70, RES. ASST. PROF, 70-; RES. AUDIOLOGIST, VET. ADMIN. HOSP, D.C, 67- Res. asst, Nat. Inst. Child Health & Human Develop, 64. Am. Speech & Hearing Asn; Acoust. Soc. Am. Speech intelligibility and perception. Address: 110 Lillian Lane, Silver Spring, MD 20904.

ELKINS, JOE C(HARLES), b. Waxahachie, Tex, Feb. 28, 22; m. 42; c. 3. ENTOMOLOGY. B.A, South. Methodist Univ, 47, M.S, 49. OWNER, RES. INSTRUMENTS CORP, 49-, PRES, 69-; S.I.A, INC, 71- U.S.A, 41-43. Am. Soc. Microbiol. Insect taxonomy; Hemiptera; Reduviidae; Harpactorinae of the Western hemisphere; Saicinae of the world; insect physiology and anatomy. Address: P.O. Box 55303, Houston, TX 77055.

ELKINS, JOHN RUSH, b. Beckley, W.Va, Nov. 16, 41; m. 63; c. 2. ORGANIC CHEMISTRY. B.S, W.Va. Inst. Tech, 63; Nat. Sci. Found. fels, West Virginia, 65-66 & summer 64-65, Ph.D.(org. chem), 66. Instr. CHEM, W.Va. Inst. Tech, 66-67; fel, Univ. Ky, 67-68; asst. prof, BLUEFIELD STATE COL, 68-70, ASSOC. PROF, 70-, CHMN. DEPT, 69- Mem, inst. polymer sci, Nat. Sci. Found, Univ. Akron, summer 71. Am. Chem. Soc. Catalytic hydrogenation of nitro groups; heterocyclic nitrogen chemistry; tobacco smoke; chestnut blight. Address: Dept. of Chemistry, Bluefield State College, Bluefield, WV 24701.

ELKINS, L(LOYD) E(DWIN), b. Golden, Colo, Apr. 1, 12; m. 34; c. 3. PETROLEUM ENGINEERING. P.P.E, Colo. Sch. Mines, 34; Harvard, 48; hon. Sc.D, Col. of Ozarks, 62. Roustabout to PROD. RES. DIR, Pan Am. Petrol. Corp, 34-71, AMOCO PROD. CO, 71- Citizens award, Tulsa, 61; distinguished achievement medal, Colo. Sch. Mines, 61; Engr. Hall Fame, Okla. State, 61. Am. Petrol. Inst; hon. mem. Am. Inst. Mining, Metall. & Petrol. Eng.(pres, 62, Lucas Gold Medal, 66); Am. Asn. Petrol. Geol. Oil field reservoir engineering; oil field drilling and well completion; oil field appraisals. Address: 2806 E. 27th St, Tulsa, OK 74114.

ELKINS, ROBERT H(IATT), b. Marion, Ind, Oct. 2, 18; m. 50; c. 5. CHEMISTRY. A.B, DePauw, 40; Standard Oil Co. fel. Western Reserve, 41-42, Ph.D.(chem), 45. Res. chemist, Standard Oil Co, Ohio, 40-43, Great Lakes Carbon Corp, 44-49; Sinclair Res. Lab, Inc, 49-56; mgr, org. & polymer. chem, Borg Warner Res. Ctr, 56-58, assoc. dir, chem. dept, 58-60; tech. mgr. commercial develop. & cent. res, Nalco Chem. Co, 60-66; SR. PROG. ADV, INST. GAS. TECHNOL, ILL. INST. TECHNOL, 66- AAAS; Am. Chem. Soc; Sci. Res. Soc. Am. Polymer chemistry; water soluble polymer applications; hydrocarbon processes; plastics; catalysis; petrochemicals; sulfur recovery from hydrogen sulfide; reactive carbon; air pollution control. Address: 119 N. Grant St, Hinsdale, IL 60521.

ELKINS, THOMAS A(NTHONY), b. Pittsburgh, Pa, Nov. 17, 06. MATHEMATICS. B.S, Carnegie Inst. Tech, 27, M.S, 31, Ph.D.(math), 56; A.M, Princeton, 35. Instr. math, night sch, Carnegie Inst. Tech, 25-28; draftsman, McClintic-Marshall Construct. Co, Rankin, Pa, 27-30; interpreter, GULF RES. & DEVELOP. CO, 30-35, res. mathematician, 35-69, SR. RES. MATHEMATICIAN, 69- Res. physicist, Gulf Res. & Develop. Co. contract, Off. Sci. Res. & Develop, 43-45. Am. Math. Soc; Soc. Explor. Geophys; Inst. Math. Statist; Am. Statist. Asn; Am. Geophys. Union. Mathematical and statistical analysis of geological and geophysical data; potential theory. Address: 3255 Parkview Ave, Pittsburgh, PA 15213.

ELKINS, WILLIAM L, b. Boston, Mass, Aug. 2, 32. EXPERIMENTAL PATHOLOGY. A.B, Princeton, 54; M.D, Harvard, 58. Intern surg, St. Vincents Hosp, New York, N.Y, 58-59; res. univ. hosp, UNIV. PA, 59-61, fel, Wistar Inst, 61-63, fel. PATH, SCH. MED, 65-66, instr, 66-68, asst. prof, 68-71, ASSOC. PROF, 71- Med.C.Res, 63-65, Lt. Comdr. AAAS. Transplantation immunology and immunopathology; tumor biology; endocrinology. Address: Dept. of Pathology, School of Medicine, University of Pennsylvania, Philadelphia, PA 19104.

ELKINTON, J(OSEPH) RUSSELL, b. Moylan, Pa, Oct. 12, 10; m. 40; c. 2. MEDICINE. A.B, Haverford, 32; M.D, Harvard, 37. Intern, hosp, Pennsylvania, 37-39, res. physician, 39-40, fel. med, 39-40, asst. instr, sch. med, 39-40; Nat. Res. Council fel. electrolyte physiol, sch. med, Yale, 40-42, instr. med, 42-45, asst. prof, 45-48; assoc. physician, New Haven Hosp, 42-48; asst. prof. CLIN. MED, UNIV. PA, 48-52, assoc. prof, 52-62, PROF, 62-, WARD PHYSICIAN, UNIV. HOSP, 48- Established investr, Am. Heart Asn, 49-59; consult, surg. gen, U.S. Pub. Health Serv, 54-58. Dipl, Am. Bd. Internal Med, 45; fel, Royal Col. Physicians, 68. Am. Med. Asn; Am. Soc. Clin. Invest; Am. Physiol. Soc; fel. & master Am. Col. Physicians (ed, Ann. Internal Med, 60-71, consult. ed, 71-); assoc. Asn. Am. Physicians. Electrolyte physiology; cardiovascular science; metabolic and renal diseases. Address: Hospital of University of Pennsylvania, Philadelphia, PA 19104.

ELLARD, JAMES A(LLEN), b. Vardaman, Miss, July 12, 28; m. 49; c. 3. ORGANIC CHEMISTRY. B.S, Miss. State Col, 49; Ky. Res. Found. fel, Kentucky, 53-55, Nat. Sci. Found, 55-56, Ph.D.(org. chem), 56. Analyst, Miss. State Chem. Regulatory, 49-51; res. chemist, MONSANTO CO, 56-61, sr. res. chemist, 61-67, GROUP LEADER ORG. SYNTHESIS, 67- Chem.C, 51-53, Lt. Am. Chem. Soc. Organic synthesis; physical organic chemistry; radiation chemistry. Address: 4055 Fleetwood Dr, Dayton, OH 45416.

ELLARSON, ROBERT S(COTT), b. Milwaukee, Wis, Sept. 21, 16; m. 54; c. 2. WILDLIFE MANAGEMENT. B.S, Wisconsin, 45, M.S, 46, Ph.D.(wildlife mgt), 56. Instr. wildlife mgt, UNIV. WIS, MADISON, 50-56, asst. prof, 56-61, AGR. EXTEN. SPECIALIST, 56-, assoc. prof, 61-68, PROF. WILDLIFE ECOL, 68- Wilson Ornith. Soc; Am. Soc. Mammal; Wildlife Soc; Am. Ornith. Union. Pesticide cycling in aquatic birds; wildlife conservation education. Address: Dept. of Wildlife Ecology, 215 Russell Labs, University of Wisconsin, Madison, WI 53706.

ELLE, GEORGE O, b. Falls City, Ore, May 22, 14; m. 42; c. 4. HORTICULTURE, VEGETABLE CROPS. B.S, Ore. State Col, 38; M.S, Tex. Tech. Col, 41; Ph.D.(veg. crops), Cornell, 51. Agr. census, U.S. Dept. Interior, 40; agr. mkt. admin, U.S. Dept. Agr, 42; asst. prof. hort, Tex. Tech. Col, 46-48; res. asst, Cornell, 48-51, PROF, TEX. TECH UNIV, 51-54, AGR. SCI, 69-, asst. dean sch. agr, 54-69. U.S.A, 42-46, Capt. AAAS; Am. Soc. Hort. Sci. Physiology and breeding of vegetable crops. Address: College of Agricultural Sciences, Texas Tech University, Lubbock, TX 79409.

ELLEBY, HOTTEN ARTHUR, b. Minneapolis, Minn, Sept. 11, 32; m. 62; c. 2. CIVIL ENGINEERING. B.C.E, Minnesota, 56, M.S.C.E, 57; Ph.D.(struct), Mich. State, 64. Asst. struct, Minnesota, 56-57; instr. CIVIL ENG, Mich. State, 57-65; asst. prof, IOWA STATE UNIV, 65-69, ASSOC. PROF, 69- Am. Soc. Civil Eng; Am. Concrete Inst; Am. Soc. Eng. Educ. Structures. Address: Dept. of Civil Engineering, Iowa State University, Ames, IA 50010.

ELLEFSEN, PAUL, b. Oak Park, Ill, June 20, 39; m. 62; c. 4. ANALYTICAL CHEMISTRY. B.A, Monmouth Col, 61; Ph.D.(chem), Case, 65. ASSOC. PROF. CHEM, HANOVER COL, 65- Am. Chem. Soc. Reaction mechanisms and analytical chemistry in nonaqueous solvents. Address: Dept. of Chemistry, Hanover College, Hanover, IN 47243.

ELLEFSON, CHARLES RAYMOND, b. Dawson, Minn, Sept. 14, 42. ORGANIC CHEMISTRY. B.A, Concordia Col.(Moorhead, Minn), 64; fel. & Ph.D.(org. chem), Univ. N.H, 68. Fel. med. chem, Univ. Mich, Ann Arbor, 68-69; RES. INVESTR. ORG. CHEM, DEPT. CHEM. RES, G.D. SEARLE & CO, 69- Am. Chem. Soc. Synthesis of tropane compounds, especially 3-aryltropidines and 3-aryl and 2 and 3-tropanols; conformational analysis of 3-aryltropidines and other tropanes and piperidines; synthesis of heterocyclic compounds of medicinal interest. Address: Dept. of Chemical Research, G.D. Searle & Co, Box 5110, Chicago, IL 60680.

ELLEFSON, RALPH D(ONALD), b. Glenwood, Minn, Jan. 25, 31; m. 55; c. 3. ORGANIC CHEMISTRY. B.A, Luther Col.(Iowa), 53; M.S, Iowa, 56, Ph.D.(chem), 58. Asst. chem, Luther Col.(Iowa), 52-53; Iowa, 53-57; Vet. Admin. Hosp, Iowa City, 57; instr. org. chem, Iowa Wesleyan Col, 57-58; instr. BIOCHEM, MAYO GRAD. SCH. MED, UNIV. MINN, 63-68, ASST. PROF, 68-, MEM. STAFF, MAYO CLIN, 63-, res. fel. biochem, Clin. & Found, 58-60, res. assoc, 60, asst. to staff, 60-63. AAAS; Am. Chem. Soc. Nitrogen heterocycles; lipid chemistry and metabolism; lipoproteins. Address: Dept. of Biochemistry, Mayo Graduate School of Medicine, University of Minnesota, Rochester, MN 55901.

ELLEM, KAY ADRIAN OSWALD, b. Sydney, Australia, May 4, 31; m. 62; c. 1. MOLECULAR BIOLOGY. B.Sc, Sydney, 53, M.B.B.S, 55; Ph.D.(microbiol), Pennsylvania, 61. Res. med. off, Royal Prince Alfred Hosp, Australia, 55-57; New S.Wales State Cancer Coun. res. fel. microbiol, Sydney, 57-58; traveling res. fel. virol. biochem, Wistar Inst, Pennsylvania, 58-61; sr. lectr. bact, Sydney, 61-63; assoc. prof. PATH, JEFFERSON MED. COL, THOMAS JEFFERSON UNIV, 64-68, PROF, 68- Fedn. Am. Socs. Exp. Biol. Biochemistry; virology; cell biology. Address: Dept. of Pathology, Jefferson Medical College, Thomas Jefferson University, Philadelphia, PA 19107.

ELLEMAN, DANIEL D(RAUDT), b. Lancaster, Ohio, Sept. 6, 31; m. 54; c. 3. PHYSICS. B.Sc. & M.Sc, Ohio State, 55, Ph.D.(physics), 59. RES. SPECIALIST, JET PROPULSION LAB, CALIF. INST. TECHNOL, 59- Low temperature physics with special emphasis in high field superconductivity; high resolution nuclear magnetic resonance and multiple irradiation experiments. Address: Jet Propulsion Lab, 4800 Oak Grove Dr, Pasadena, CA 91103.

ELLEMAN, THOMAS S(MITH), b. Dayton, Ohio, June 19, 31; m. 54; c. 3. PHYSICAL CHEMISTRY. B.S, Denison, 53; Ph.D.(chem), Iowa State Col, 57. Chemist, inst. atomic res, Ames Lab, 53-57; radiochemist, Battelle Mem. Inst, 57-64; assoc. prof. NUCLEAR ENG, N.C. STATE UNIV, 64-67, PROF, 67- Am. Chem. Soc; Am. Nuclear Soc. Radioisotopes applications; radiation effects; reactor chemistry. Address: Dept. of Nuclear Engineering, North Carolina State University, Raleigh, NC 27607.

ELLENBERGER, HERMAN A(LBERT), b. Annville, Pa, Mar. 24, 16; m. 50; c. 3. TOXICOLOGY. B.S, Lebanon Valley Col, 38; M.S, Pa. State Univ, 46, Ph.D.(agr. & biol. chem), 48. Plant chemist, Whitmoyer Labs, Pa, 39, asst. chemist, 41-43; lab. technician & asst. chemist, State Dept. Agr, Pa, 39-41; res. asst, Pa. State Univ, 43-45, fel, 45-48; biochemist, Lime Crest Res. Lab, N.J, 48-63; TOXICOLOGIST, Conn. State Dept. Health, 63-68; N.S. DEPT. PUB. HEALTH, 68- AAAS; Am. Chem. Soc; Am. Acad. Clin. Toxicol; Am. Asn. Clin. Chem; Asn. Clin. Sci; Can. Soc. Forensic Sci; Chem. Inst. Can. Analyses related to toxicological and occupational health work. Address: Pathology Institute, 5788 University Ave, Halifax, N.S, Can.

ELLENBOGEN, LEON, b. Brooklyn, N.Y, May 3, 27; m. 51; c. 3. BIOLOGICAL CHEMISTRY. B.S, City Col, 49; M.S, N.Y. Univ, 51; Ph.D.(chem), Indiana, 54. Anal. chemist, Novocol Chem. Co, 45; res. technician, 1st res. div, Columbia, Goldwater Mem. Hosp, 49-51; asst, Indiana, 51-52, res. asst, 52-53; chemist, LEDERLE LABS. DIV, AM. CYANAMID CO, 53-59, SR. RES. CHEMIST & GROUP LEADER, 59- U.S.N.R, 45-47. Am. Chem. Soc; Am. Soc. Hemat; Am. Soc. Biol. Chem; Soc. Exp. Biol. & Med.(ed, 61-62); N.Y. Acad. Sci; Am. Inst. Nutrit. Vitamin B_{12} and intrinsic factor; brain biochemistry; protein fractionation; absorption and metabolism of vitamin B_{12} and iron; gastrointestinal absorption; immunochemistry; nutrition; vitamins; radioisotopes; biochemical pharmacology; biogenic amines; catecholamine metabolism; coenzymes. Address: Lederle Labs, American Cyanamid Co, Pearl River, NY 10965.

ELLENBOGEN, W(ILLIA)M C(ROMWELL), b. Danville, Pa, Oct. 20, 17; m. 43. ANALYTICAL CHEMISTRY. B.S, Ursinus Col, 39; Pennsylvania, 39-40; M.S, St. Joseph's Col.(Phila), 56. Res. chemist, leather tanning & anal. chem, Wm. Amer Co, 40-43; sr. res. chemist, anal. chem. & refrig, York Corp, 43-47, sr. anal. chemist, pharmaceut. anal, res. & develop. anal. sect, Smith, Kline & French Labs, 47-48, head sect, 48-62, gen. lab. dept. mgr, 62-68; PROJ. DIR, UNIV. CITY SCI. CTR, 68- Am. Chem. Soc; Am. Pharmaceut. Asn; N.Y. Acad. Sci. Laboratory administration; analytical chemistry; pharmaceutical research and development; general project management. Address: University City Science Center, 3508 Market St, Philadelphia, PA 19104.

ELLENBURG, ARTHUR M(ARTIN), b. Anniston, Ala, Apr. 1, 12; m. 37; c. 2. CHEMISTRY. B.S, Ala. Polytech, 35. Chem. operator, Monsanto Co, Ala, 35, anal. chemist, 35-36, res. chemist, 36-37, Tenn, 38-42, Ala, 42-44, res. group leader, 44-54, St. Louis, 54-61, res. specialist, 61-69; PROD. TECHNOLOGIST, EDWIN COOPER, INC, 69- Am. Chem. Soc. Petroleum lubricant additives. Address: Edwin Cooper, Inc, 125 Lafayette Ave, St. Louis, MO 63104.

ELLENBURG, JANUS Y(ENTSCH), b. Linthicum, Md, Jan. 14, 22; m. 43. SPECTROSCOPY, FINE PARTICLE TECHNOLOGY. B.S, West. Md. Col, 42, Sc.D.(chem), 68; fel, N.Y. Univ, 42-43; fel, Univ. Tenn, Knoxville, 47-49. Asst. dir. res, Crown Cork & Seal Co, Md, 44-47; spectroscopist, Fairchild Engine & Aircraft Corp, Tenn, 49-52; sr. chemist, Oak Ridge Nat. Lab, 52-57; chemist, South. Res. Inst Ala, 57-58; spectroscopist, Hayes Int. Corp, 58-60; McWane Cast Iron Pipe Co, 60-61; sr. chemist, HAYES INT. CORP, 61-68, SR. SCIENTIST, 68- Adv, Bessemer State Technol. Inst, Ala, 71-72. Merit award, Inventions & Contrib. Bd, NASA, 70. Am. Inst. Aeronaut. & Astronaut; Am. Chem. Soc; Am. Asn. Contamination Control; Optical Soc. Am; Am. Inst. Phys; Soc. Appl. Spectros. Trace elements in matrices by emission spectroscopy; laminar sublayer effects in circulating fluids; dust particle blocking mechanisms; surface cleanliness of aerospace fluid systems; additives for dispersing fine particle clouds. Address: 1133 Lido Dr, Birmingham, AL 35226.

ELLENDER, RUDOLPH DENNIS, b. Houma, La, Nov. 10, 42; m. 68; c. 1. ENVIRONMENTAL & MARINE VIROLOGY. B.S, La. State Univ, Baton Rouge, 65, M.S, 66; Ph.D.(vet. microbiol), Tex. A&M Univ, 69. Fel, Tex. A&M Univ, 69-70; HEAD, DEPT. ENVIRON. VIROL, GULF SOUTH RES. INST, 70- World Maricult. Soc; Am. Soc. Microbiol; Int. Asn. Aquatic Animal Med. Quantitative detection of small amounts of enteric viruses in large volumes of water; detection and isolation of marine viruses causing diseases of fish; marine tissue culture; closed, artificial recirculated sea water systems. Address: Gulf South Research Institute, P.O. Box 26500, New Orleans, LA 70126.

ELLENDMAN, M(ERRILL), b. Phila, Pa, Dec. 6, 14; m. 45; c. 1. PHYSICAL CHEMISTRY. B.S, Pennsylvania, 36, M.S, 38. Anal. chemist, ord. metals, Frankford Arsenal, Pa, 40-43; res. chemist, Triumph Explosives Co, Md, 43-44; chief chemist, dent. alloys, J.B. Moyer, Pa, 44-48; res. chemist, Metro Smelting Co, 48-50; Quaker Chem. Prod, 50-51; asst. dir. res, Simonds Abrasive Co, 52-70; TECH. DIR, RED HILL ABRASIVE CORP, 70- Am. Chem. Soc. Chemistry of metals; lubrication; corrosion; abrasion; metal-forming; organic chemicals used in metal treatment. Address: 1531 Stevens St, Philadelphia, PA 19149.

ELLENTON, HAROLD K(ENNETH), b. Innisfail, Alta, Dec. 9, 26; m. 50; c. 5. PHYSICS. B.Sc, Western Ontario, 49; M.A, Toronto, 50. Meteorologist, Dept. Transport, 50-52; asst. prof. sci, UNIV. WATERLOO, 52-57, PHYSICS, 57-65, ASSOC. PROF, 65- Am. Asn. Physics Teachers; Am. Meteorol. Soc; Am. Geophys. Union; Can. Asn. Physicists. Geophysics; physical limnology and oceanography. Address: Dept. of Physics, University of Waterloo, Waterloo, Ont, Can.

ELLENTUCK, ERIK, b. New York, N.Y, May 13, 34. MATHEMATICAL LOGIC. A.B, N.Y. Univ, 56; Ph.D.(math), California, Berkeley, 62. Res. assoc. logic, Stanford, 61-62; mathematician, Shell Develop. Co, 62-63; staff mem, Inst. Adv. Study, 63-65, fel, 63-64; asst. prof. MATH, RUTGERS UNIV, 65-66, assoc. prof, 66-70, PROF, 70- Nat. Sci. Found. fel, 64-65; N.J. Res. Coun. faculty fel, 68-69, 71-72; vis. prof, Kyoto Univ, 68-69; staff mem. & inst. fel, Inst. Advan. Study, 71-72. Am. Math. Soc. Asn. Symbolic Logic. Theory of Dedekind finite cardinals. Address: Dept. of Mathematics, Rutgers, The State University, New Brunswick, NJ 08903.

ELLER, ANTHONY I(RVING), b. Detroit, Mich, June 30, 38; m. 68; c. 2. ACOUSTICS. A.B, Harvard, 60; M.S, Univ. Rochester, 63, Ph.D.(elec. eng), 66. Res. fel. acoust, Harvard, 66-69; ASST. PROF. PHYSICS, NAVAL POSTGRAD. SCH, 69- Acoust. Soc. Am; Inst. Elec. & Electronics Eng. Effects of bubbles on underwater sound; properties of nonlinear oscillations; ultrasonic cavitation of water. Address: Dept. of Physics, Naval Postgraduate School, Monterey, CA 93940.

ELLER, C(HARLES) HOWE, b. Bloomington, Ind, June 5, 04; m. 33; c. 2. EPIDEMIOLOGY, PUBLIC HEALTH ADMINISTRATION. A.B, Stanford, 27; M.D, Colorado, 30; Dr.P.H, Hopkins, 34. Health off, N.Mex. & Va, 32-36; assoc. prof. prev. med, sch. med, Virginia, 35-36; dir. rural health, State Dept. Health, Va, 36-37; dir. east. health dist, Baltimore, 37-46; assoc. prof. pub. health, Med. Col. of Va, 46-49; PROF. community health med. sch, Louisville, 49-59; PUB. HEALTH, SCH. MED, WASH. UNIV, 59-; COMNR. HEALTH, ST. LOUIS COUNTY, 59- Assoc. prof. sch. hyg. & pub. health & lectr, sch. med, Hopkins, 37-40; dir. pub. health, Richmond, 46; Louisville & Jefferson County Health Dept, Ky, 49-55; consult, Community Res. Assoc, N.Y, 55-; U.S. Pub. Health Serv. Fel. Am. Med. Asn; fel. Am. Pub. Health Asn. Diphtheria; medical care. Address: Dept. of Preventive Medicine & Public Health, Washington University School of Medicine, St. Louis, MO 63130.

ELLER, E(UGENE) R(UDOLPH), b. Centerville, Pa, May 17, 04; m. 34; c. 2. PALEONTOLOGY, GEOLOGY. B.S, Alfred, 30; Buffalo, 30-31; M.S, Pittsburgh, 33; hon. Sc.D, Waynesburg Col, 47. Asst. paleont, Pittsburgh, 31-33; asst. curator, CARNEGIE MUS, 33-45, CURATOR, 45- Lectr, Pittsburgh,

42-44, 48- AAAS; fel. Geol. Soc. Am; fel. Paleont. Soc; Soc. Study Evolution. Paleontology; stratigraphy; micropaleontological taxonomy; exploration and well cutting examination for fossile polychaete; mineralogy. Address: Carnegie Museum, 4400 Forbes St, Pittsburgh, PA 15213.

ELLER, J(AMES) G(ERALD), b. Robbinsville, N.C, Jan. 30, 21; m. 43; c. 3. ECOLOGY. B.S, West. Carolina Teachers Col, 43; Ph.D, North Carolina, 63. Instr. BIOL, WEST. CAROLINA COL, 47-53, asst. prof, 53-60, assoc. prof, 60-62, PROF, 60-, DEAN SCH. ARTS & SCI, 67- Mem, Am. Conf. Acad. Deans. U.S.N.R, 42-45, Lt.(jg). AAAS. Ecology of aquatic insects; seasonal regulation in Odonata and Ephemeroptera. Address: School of Arts & Sciences, Western Carolina University, Cullowhee, NC 28723.

ELLER, KENNETH L(OWELL), b. Noblesville, Ind, Apr. 14, 14; m. 37; c. 3. CHEMISTRY. B.S, Ind. Cent. Col, 36. Res. chemist, E.I. DU PONT DE NEMOURS & CO, INC, 37-40, prod. supvr, 40-50, serv. supt, 50-53, mgr. lab. serv, Niagara Falls Res. Lab, 54-59, indust. rels. supt, 60-67, mgr. indust. rels, photoprod. dept, 67-70, MGR. PERSONNEL & INDUST. RELS, EXPLOSIVES DEPT, 70- Personnel administration. Address: Explosives Dept, E.I. du Pont de Nemours & Co, Wilmington, DE 19898.

ELLERBROCK, HERMAN H(ENRY), JR, b. Baltimore, Md, Feb. 10, 06; m. 42. MECHANICAL ENGINEERING. B.E, Hopkins, 27; M.S, Case, 54; nuclear sch, Nat. Adv. Cmt. Aeronaut, 57. Engr, cooling internal combustion engines res, Nat. Adv. Cmt. Aeronaut, 30-42, asst. sect. head internal aerodyn. res, 42-46, chief turbine cooling br, 46-56, chief syst. design panel, nuclear rocket space vehicle res, NASA, 58-62, chief nuclear propulsion br, advan. develop. & eval. div, 62-66, CHIEF TURBINE COOLING BR, AIR BREATHING ENGINE DIV, 66- Teacher, Fenn Col, 57-67; Cleveland State Univ, 67-69. Assoc. fel. Am. Inst. Aeronaut. & Astronaut; N.Y. Acad. Sci. Heat transfer; gas turbine engines; nuclear reactors; space vehicles. Address: 3207 Rocky River Dr, Cleveland, OH 44111.

ELLERMEIER, ROBERT D(WIGHT), b. Swanton, Nebr, Mar. 26, 23; m. 48. ELECTRICAL ENGINEERING, APPLIED MATHEMATICS. B.S, Kansas, 54, M.S, 59, Ph.D.(elec. eng, math), 64. Elec. engr, Kans. Power & Light Co, 54-55; res. engr, Hughes Aircraft Co, 55-57; res. assoc, UNIV. KANS, 57, dir. vacuum tube res, electronics device lab, 57-61, res. engr. cryogenic systs, 61-64, instr. elec. eng, 63-64, asst. prof. elec. eng. & assoc. proj. leader satellite radar feasibility, ctr. res. eng. sci, 64-66, ASSOC. PROF. ELEC. ENG, 66-, ASSOC. DEAN GRAD. SCH, 69-, assoc. dir. remote sensing lab, 66-69. U.S.A.F, 43-46, 1st Lt. Inst. Elec. & Electronics Eng. Vacuum tube technology and semiconductor, design, construction and application; super conductivity and cryogenics; spatially periodic transmission line arrays of n-dimension; radar imaging and ground signature for remote sensing of unknown terrain. Address: Graduate School, University of Kansas, Lawrence, KS 66044.

ELLERS, ERICH WERNER, b. Berlin, Ger, Sept. 11, 28; m. 56; c. 2. GEOMETRY. Staatsexamen, Univ. Hamburg, 56, Dr. rer. nat, 59. Asst. prof. MATH, Univ. Hamburg, 58-63; Univ. Braunschweig, 63-64; reader, Flinders Univ. S.Australia, 66-68; ASSOC. PROF, Univ. N.B, 68-69; UNIV. TORONTO, 69- Vis. prof, Univ. Hanover, summer 71; Australian Math. Soc; Ger. Math. Asn; Am. Math. Soc; Math. Asn. Am; Can. Math. Cong. Foundations of geometry; metric geometry; collineation groups. Address: Dept. of Mathematics, University of Toronto, Toronto 181, Ont, Can.

ELLERSICK, FRED W(ILLIAM), b. Jersey City, N.J, May 12, 33; m. 58; c. 4. ELECTRICAL ENGINEERING. B.E.E, Rensselaer Polytech, 54; M.E.E, Syracuse, 61; Ph.D.(elec. eng), Maryland, 67. Engr, Int. Bus. Mach. Corp, 54-56, assoc. engr, mil. prods. div, 56-58, staff engr, fed. systs. div, 58-63, develop. engr, 63-69, sr. engr, 69; MEM. TECH. STAFF, COMMUN. SYSTS. DIV, MITRE CORP, BEDFORD, 69- U.S.A.F, 57-58. AAAS; sr. mem. Inst. Elec. & Electronics Eng. System engineering for computer-communications systems; communication theory; operations research. Address: 29 Fairland St, Lexington, MA 02173.

ELLERT, MARTHA SCHWANDT, b. Jersey City, N.J, Nov. 27, 40; m. 62. PHYSIOLOGY. B.S, Barry Col, 62; Ph.D.(physiol), Univ. Miami, 67. Lab. technician physiol, sch. med, Univ. Miami, 64-66; instr, SCH. MED, ST. LOUIS UNIV, 67-70, ASST. PROF. PHYSIOL. & DIR. SUMMER REFRESHER PROG, 70-, RES. GRANT, 68- Intestinal transport, particularly of sugars; effects of intestinal resection and dietary glucose on transport rates; effects of nicotine. Address: Dept. of Physiology, St. Louis University School of Medicine, 1402 S. Grand, St. Louis, MO 63104.

ELLERTSEN, BIRGER WALTHER, b. Brooklyn, N.Y, Feb. 7, 13; m. 39; c. 1. FORESTRY. B.S, Minnesota, 35; M.F, Michigan, 36. Forester, Civilian Conserv. Corps, 35; asst. forest path, Michigan, 35-38; jr. forester, tree crops res, TENN. VALLEY AUTH, 38-42, dist. forester, 42-44, staff asst, timber mgt, 44-49, staff forester, forest mgt. res, 49-53, chief forest mgt. investS. sect, 53-64, SUPVR, FOREST ECOL. & INFLUENCES SECT, 64- AAAS; Soil Conserv. Soc. Am; Soc. Am. Foresters; Am. Forestry Asn; Air Pollution Control Asn; Am. Water Resources Asn. Forestry-air pollution research; forest hydrology and management. Address: Division of Forestry, Fisheries & Wildlife Development, Tennessee Valley Authority, Norris, TN 37828.

ELLERTSON, MELVIN E(LROY), b. Minn, Oct. 16, 10; m. 42; c. 1. DAIRY CHEMISTRY. B.A, St. Olaf Col, 33. Chemist, CARNATION CO, 35-61, asst. dir. res, 61-66, DIR. PROCESS ENG, 66- AAAS; Am. Chem. Soc; Am. Dairy Sci. Asn; Inst. Food Technol. Proteins; food processing. Address: 17348 Stagg St, Northridge, CA 91324.

ELLESTAD, GEORGE A, b. Coalinga, Calif, Dec. 8, 34; m. 60; c. 2. ORGANIC CHEMISTRY. B.S, Oregon State, 56 & 57, M.S, 58; Ph.D.(chem), California, Los Angeles, 62. Nat. Insts. Health fel. with Prof. W.B. Whalley, sch. pharm, London, 62-64; CHEMIST, LEDERLE LABS, AM. CYANAMID CO, 64- Am. Chem. Soc; The Chem. Soc. Organic chemistry of natural products. Address: Lederle Labs, Pearl River, NY 10965.

ELLESTAD, R(EUBEN) B, b. Lanesboro, Minn, May 10, 00; m. 34; c. 3. CHEMISTRY. B.S, Minnesota, 22, M.S, 24, Ph.D.(anal. chem), 29. Asst, Harvard, 26-28; instr. chem, Tufts Col, 28-29; Minnesota, 29-42; res. dir, LITHIUM CORP. AM, 42-67, SR. SCIENTIST, 67-, V.PRES, 56- Chemist, Rock Anal. Lab, 29-42. U.S.A, 18. Am. Chem. Soc; Mineral. Soc. Am; Geochem. Soc. Inorganic and analytical chemistry. Address: Lithium Corp. of America, Box 795, Bessemer City, NC 28016.

ELLETT, C(LAYTON) W(AYNE), b. Northfield, Ohio, Nov. 12, 16; m. 54; c. 1. PLANT PATHOLOGY. B.S, Kent State Univ, 38; M.S, Ohio State, 40, Ph.D, 55. Asst. bot, OHIO STATE UNIV, 39-42, plant path, 42-44, instr. bot. & plant path, 46-55, asst. prof, 56-59, assoc. prof, 59-67, PROF. PLANT PATH, 67- Res. asst, Minnesota, 48; consult, Nat. Sci. Found, summers, 59 & 60; U.S. Agency Int. Develop, summer sci. inst. biol, India, 64 & 65. U.S.A, 44; U.S.N, 44-46, Res, 46-54. Am. Phytopath. Soc; Mycol. Soc. Am. Diseases of ornamentals and corn; parasitic fungi of Ohio; teaching; mycology. Address: Dept. of Plant Pathology, Ohio State University, 1735 Neil Ave, Columbus, OH 43210.

ELLETT, D. MAXWELL, b. Richmond, Va, July 1, 22; m. 58; c. 2. MECHANICAL ENGINEERING, APPLIED MECHANICS. B.M.E, Virginia, 43; M.Eng, Yale, 50, D.Eng, 52. Mem. staff mech. eng, Sandia Lab, 46-49; asst, Yale, 49-52; MEM. ENG. STAFF, SANDIA CORP, 52- U.S.A, 43-46, Res, 46-, Lt. Col. Am. Nuclear Soc; Soc. Am. Mil. Eng. Vibration and shock theory and analysis; operation of steady state and pulsed reactors; weapon system vulnerability and associated test methods; ground motion and building response from underground nuclear explosions. Address: 2000 Los Poblanos Pl. N.W, Albuquerque, NM 87107.

ELLETT, EDWIN WILLARD, b. Midlothian, Va, May 21, 25; m. 49; c. 1. VETERINARY MEDICINE & SURGERY. D.V.M, Georgia, 53; B.Sc, Va. Polytech, 54; M.S, Tex. A&M Col, 61. Vet, private practice, 53-56; asst. prof, VET. MED. & SURG, Okla. State, 56-58; TEX. A&M UNIV, 58-61, PROF. & CHIEF SMALL ANIMAL CLIN, 61- Consult, M.D. Anderson Hosp. & Tumor Inst, 61-; Alcon Labs, 64-; trainee comp. ophthal, sch. med, Stanford Univ, 70. U.S.C.G, 43-46. Am. Vet. Med. Asn; Am. Asn. Vet. Clinicians; Am. Soc. Vet. Ophthal. Surgery, especially ophthalmic and non-suture techniques; cataracts; evaluation of new drugs; ocular diseases of animals and their comparison with diseases of man. Address: Dept. of Veterinary Medicine & Surgery, Texas A&M University, College Station, TX 77843.

ELLETT, WILLIAM H, b. Alliance, Ohio, Oct. 10, 29; m. 65; c. 3. RADIATION BIOPHYSICS. B.S, Rensselaer Polytech, 53; M.S, N.Y. Univ, 58; Ph.D. (radiation physics), Univ. London, 68. Res. asst. radiol. physics, Sloan-Kettering Inst, 53-55; physicist, Hosp. for Joint Diseases, 55-57; asst. physicist, biophys, Mass. Gen. Hosp, Boston, 57-64; phys. sci. adminstr, U.S. Naval Radiol. Defense Lab, 64-66; hon. res. asst, Royal Post Grad. Med. Sch, Univ. London, 66-68; assoc. prof. radiation biophys, radiation ctr, Ore. State Univ, 68-71; SR. SCIENTIST, OFF. RES. & MONITORING, U.S. ENVIRON. PROTECTION AGENCY, 71- Attend. physicist, Manhattan Vet. Admin. Hosp, 56-57; fel, Harvard Med. Sch, 59-61, res, assoc, 61-64. AAAS; Am. Asn. Physicists in Med; Radiation Res. Soc. Radiation physics; radiation dosimetry; environmental health physics and hazard analysis. Address: Office of Research & Monitoring, U.S. Environmental Protection Agency, Washington, DC 20460.

ELLGAARD, ERIK G, b. Des Moines, Iowa, June 5, 39; m. 62; c. 2. GENETICS, DEVELOPMENTAL BIOLOGY. B.A, Drake Univ, 61; U.S. Pub. Health Serv. fel, Univ. Iowa, 66-68, Ph.D.(zool, genetics), 68. U.S. Pub. Health Serv. fel, Purdue Univ, 68-70; ASST. PROF. BIOL, TULANE UNIV, 70- Greater New Orleans Cancer Asn. grant, 71. AAAS; Genetics Soc. Am. Chromosomal puffing and its relationship to RNA and protein metabolism; role of histones in control of gene action; RNA and protein metabolism in the brain; high molecular weight RNAs. Address: Dept. of Biology, Tulane University, New Orleans, LA 70118.

ELLGEN, PAUL C, b. Osage, Iowa, Sept. 13, 44; m. 69. PHYSICAL & INORGANIC CHEMISTRY. B.A, Carleton Col, 63; Nat. Sci. Found. fel, Munich Tech. Univ, 67-68; Ph.D.(chem), Northwest. Univ, 68. ASST. PROF. CHEM, UNIV. CALIF, RIVERSIDE, 68- AAAS; Am. Chem. Soc. Kinetic and mechanistic investigations of the reactions of transition metal complexes. Address: Dept. of Chemistry, University of California, Riverside, CA 92502.

ELLIAS, LORETTA C(HRISTINE), b. Jacksonville, Fla, Sept. 3, 19. BACTERIAL METABOLISM. B.S, Fla. State Col. Women, 43; M.S, Kentucky, 46; Ph.D.(bact), Michigan, 58. Instr. BACT, FLA. STATE UNIV, 46-54, asst. prof, 54-63, ASSOC. PROF, 63- Dir, Tallahassee Regional Lab, State Bd. Health, 48-49. AAAS; Am. Soc. Microbiol. Purification of alpha-glucosidase and ascorbic acid oxidase; isolation and characterization of toxic factors of staphylococci; terminal oxidation and redox potential. Address: Dept. of Biological Sciences, Florida State University, Tallahassee, FL 32306.

ELLICKSON, BRUCE E, b. Chicago, Ill, Jan. 10, 17; m. 45; c. 4. MICROBIOLOGY, BIOCHEMISTRY. B.S, Illinois, 43, M.S, 46, Ph.D.(microbiol), 48; M.B.A, Chicago, 60. Chief chemist, animal feed lab, Consol. Prod. Co, 48-51, res. bacteriologist, Kraft Foods Co, 51-52, group leader in charge bact. lab, 52-58, assoc. mgr. fundamental res. lab, res. & develop. div, Nat. Dairy Prod. Corp, 58-59, mgr. patents & regulatory compliance, 59-64; prod. safety & microbiol, Armour Grocery Prod. Co, 64-67; asst. div. res. dir, res. & develop. div, NAT. DAIRY PROD. CORP, 67-68, MGR. REGULATORY COMPLIANCE, KRAFT FOODS CO, 68- Chmn. indust. adv. comt, food res. inst, Univ. Chicago, 59-; mem. tech. adv. comt, Fatty Acid Producer's Coun, 59-; Dairy Indust. Comt, 59-; consult, Res. & Develop. Assoc, 60- Med.C, 42-45, Sgt. Inst. Food Technol. Food bacteriology; antimycotics for food use; food chemistry and additives; food, drug and patent law. Address: 500 Peshtigo Ct, Chicago, IL 60690.

ELLIKER, P(AUL) R, b. La Crosse, Wis, Feb. 12, 11; div; c. 3. MICROBIOLOGY. B.S, Wisconsin, 34, M.S, 35, Ph.D.(dairy bact), 37. Asst, Wisconsin, 34-37, instr. dairy & food bact, 37-38; Nat. Elec. Mfrs. Asn. fel, Maryland, 38-39; instr. agr. bact, Wisconsin, 39-40; asst. prof. dairy bact, Purdue, 40-42, assoc. prof, 42-43, 45-47; PROF. MICROBIOL. & MICROBIOLOGIST IN CHARGE AGR. EXP. STA. ORE. STATE UNIV, 47-, CHMN.

DEPT. MICROBIOL, 52- Tech. dir, Dairy Soc. Int-U.S. exhibit, Madrid Int. Trade Fair, 59; U.S. State Dept. off. del, Int. Dairy Cong, Denmark, 62, Munich, 66. Sanit.C, 43-45, Capt. Int. Asn. Milk, Food & Environ. Sanit. (pres, 66-67); Am. Soc. Microbiol; Am. Dairy Sci. Asn; Am. Acad. Microbiol; Inst. Food Technol. Microbiology of dairy products; dairy farm and plant sanitation; germicides used in the food industries. Address: Dept. of Microbiology, Bioscience Bldg, Oregon State University, Corvallis, OR 97331.

ELLIN, ROBERT I(SADORE), b. Poland, Nov. 25, 25; nat; m. 50; c. 2. PHARMACEUTICAL CHEMISTRY. A.B, Hopkins, 46; Sharp & Dohme fel, Maryland, 47-48, Ph.D.(pharmaceut. chem), 50. Asst. chem, col. pharm, Maryland, 48-50; pharmaceut. chemist, med. div, Army Chem. Center, 50-51; prof. pharmaceut. chem. & chmn. dept. chem, R.I. Col. Pharm, 51-56; med. dir. pharmaceut. chem, EDGEWOOD ARSENAL, 56-65, supvry. res. chemist, clin. res. dept, 65-66, CHIEF, CLIN. LAB. BR, MED. RES. LAB, 66- AAAS; Am. Asn. Clin. Chem; Am. Pharmaceut. Asn; Am. Chem. Soc. Mechanism and kinetics of oxime degradation; toxicity of dimercaprol; automated pyridinium oxime and cholinesterase assay systems; nanogram levels of drugs in biological fluids; personnel detection analysis; conformation of chymotrypsin and cholinesterase. Address: Clinical Research Dept, Clinical Lab. Branch, Edgewood Arsenal, MD 21010.

ELLING, CARL H, b. Tacoma, Wash, Aug. 28, 17. ZOOLOGY. B.S, Washington State, 41; Washington, 49-50. Subprfnl. asst. herring pop. studies Alaska, U.S. FISH & WILDLIFE SERV, 46-49, proj. leader Alaska pink salmon invest, 50-51, Cook Inlet red salmon invest, 52-55, supv. fishway res, Bonneville Dam, BUR. COMMERCIAL FISHERIES, 56-60, ASST. DIR, fish passage res. prog, 61-64, FRESHWATER RES, BIOL. LAB, 65- U.S.A.A.F, 42-45. Am. Fisheries Soc; Am. Inst. Fishery Res. Biol. Migrations of salmon in southeastern and Cook Inlet, Alaska; fishway research, especially behavior and performance of Salmonids in fishways; migratory behavior and survival of Salmonids in impounded waters. Address: Biological Lab, Bureau of Commercial Fisheries, 2725 Mont Lake Blvd E, Seattle, WA 98102.

ELLING, LADDIE J(OE), b. Lawton, Okla, June 18, 17; m. 42; c. 3. PLANT BREEDING. B.S, Okla. Agr. & Mech. Col, 41; M.S, Univ. Minn, 48, Ph.D. (plant genetics), 50. Res. assoc. ALFALFA BREEDING & SEED PROD, UNIV. MINN, ST. PAUL, 50-53, asst. prof, 53-57, assoc. prof, 57-68, PROF, 68- U.S.A.A.F, 41-46, Capt. Am. Soc. Agron; Crop Sci. Soc. Am. Forage grass and legume seed production research. Address: Dept. of Agronomy & Plant Genetics, University of Minnesota, St. Paul, MN 55101.

ELLINGBOE, ALBERT H(ARLAN), b. Lakeville, Minn, Apr. 3, 31; m. 58; c. 2. PLANT PATHOLOGY, GENETICS. B.S, Univ. Minn, 53, M.S, 55, Ph.D.(plant path), 57. Asst. plant path, Univ. Minn, 54-57, res. fel, 57-58; BIOL, Harvard, 58-60; asst. prof. BOT. & PLANT PATH, MICH. STATE UNIV, 60-66, assoc. prof, 66-70, PROF, 70- Nat. Insts. Health spec. fel. & vis. assoc. prof. genetics, Univ. Wash, 66-67. AAAS; Genetics Soc. Am; Bot. Soc. Am; Am. Phytopath. Soc. Genetics and physiology of sexual incompatibility in fungi and plant parasitism. Address: Dept. of Botany & Plant Pathology, Michigan State University, East Lansing, MI 48823.

ELLINGBOE, E(LLSWORTH) K(NOWLTON), b. Menasha, Wis, Oct. 14, 09; m. 34; c. 3. ORGANIC CHEMISTRY. A.B, Lawrence Col, 30; A.M, Illinois, 32, Carr fel, 33-34, Ph.D.(org. chem), 34. CHEMIST, EXP. STA, E.I. DU PONT DE NEMOURS & CO, 34- With Office Sci. Res. & Develop, 44. AAAS; Am. Chem. Soc; Sci. Res. Soc. Am. Organic synthesis; vinyl polymers; Grignard reagent; cyclobutane derivatives. Address: Du Pont Experiment Station, Wilmington, DE 19898.

ELLINGBOE, J(ULES) K, b. Tucson, Ariz, March 18, 27; m. 48; c. 2. ELECTRICAL ENGINEERING. B.S.E.E, Arizona, 50; Southern California. Electronics engr, Radio Corp. of Am, 50-52; mem. tech. staff, Hughes Aircraft Co, 52-55; sr. proj. engr, Am. Electronics, 55-56; mem. tech staff, Space Tech. Labs, 56-66; proj. mgr, defense space systs. div, TRW SYSTS. GROUP, 66-71, MGR. ORBITAL OPERS, SPACE VEHICLES DIV, 71- U.S.N.R, 44-46. Inst. Elec. & Electronics Eng. Ballistic missile ground support equipment systems engineering; aerospace support equipment; spacecraft and ground station systems engineering; project management; spacecraft orbital operations. Address: 27033 Indian Peak Rd, Palos Verdes Peninsula, CA 90274.

ELLINGER, RUDOLPH H, b. Grand Rapids, Mich, Aug. 18, 20; m. 50; c. 2. ORGANIC CHEMISTRY, BIOCHEMISTRY. B.S, Mich. State, 50; M.S, Iowa State, 53, Ph.D.(biochem), 54. Biochemist, cent. res. labs, Pillsbury Co, Minn, 54-57, tech. mgr. prod. improv, refrig. prod. res. & develop. labs, Ky, 57-59; dir. res. prod. develop, J.D. Jewell, Inc, Ga, 59-61; supvr. tech. serv. labs, Durkee Famous Foods, Ill, 61-64; mgr. food prod. develop, Stauffer Chem. Co, N.Y, 64-69; dir. tech. serv, Stouffer Foods Corp, 70-71; MGR. REGULATORY COMPLIANCE, KRAFT FOODS DIV, KRAFTCO CORP, 71- AAAS; Am. Dairy Sci. Asn; Am. Chem. Soc; Am. Inst. Chem; Am. Asn. Cereal Chem; Inst. Food Technol. Baking and food technology; microbiology. Address: 500 Peshtigo Court, Chicago, IL 60690.

ELLINGHAUSEN, HERMAN C(HARLES), JR, b. Annapolis, Md, Nov. 3, 26; m. 51; c. 3. BACTERIOLOGY. B.S, Maryland, 50, Ph.D.(bact), 55; M.Sc, North Carolina, 52. Asst. bact, Maryland, 52-55; PRIN. RES. MICROBIOLOGIST, PROJ. LEADER LEPTOSPIROSIS RES, AGR. RES. SERV, ANIMAL DISEASE & PARASITE RES. DIV, BACTERIAL & MYCOTIC DISEASE INVESTS, NAT. ANIMAL DISEASE LAB, 55- Mem. staff, grad. sch, U.S. Dept. Agr. & lectr, Nat. Insts. Health, 55-60; mem, Leptospirosis Res. Workers Conf; West-North Cent. Interprof. Conf. on Diseases Common Animal & Man; adv. to grad. stud, Univ. N.C. & Colo. State Univ. U.S.A.A.F, 45-46. Am. Soc. Microbiol; Am. Acad. Microbiol; Conf. Res. Workers Animal Diseases. Microbial nutrition; bacterial metabolism; enzymes of pathogenic bacteria, visible and infrared spectrophotometry; electron microscopy. Address: U.S. Dept. of Agriculture, National Animal Disease Lab, P.O. Box 70, Ames, IA 50011.

ELLINGSON, HAROLD V(ICTOR), b. Parker, Idaho, Feb. 26, 13; m. 44. AEROSPACE MEDICINE, BACTERIOLOGY. B.S, Univ. Idaho, 35; fel, Univ. Wis, 35-41, M.S, 36, Ph.D.(med. bact), 39, M.D, 41; M.P.H, Johns Hopkins Univ, 45. Instr. bact, Univ. Wis, 41-42; chief mobile lab, Seventh Med. Lab, U.S. Army, 42-43, hosp. comdr, Ft. Detrick, Md, 43-45, 48-49, chief lab. serv, 34th Gen. Hosp, Korea, 46-48; head dept. prev. med, Sch. Aviation Med, U.S. Air Force, 50-54, dep. surgeon, Alaskan Air Command, 54-57, dir. educ, Sch. Aviation Med, 57-59, comdr, Med. Serv. Sch, 59-62, Sch. Aerospace Med, 62-66; PROF. PREV. MED. & CHMN. DEPT, OHIO STATE UNIV, 66- Trustee, Am. Bd. Prev. Med. Med.C, U.S.A.F, 49-66, Col; U.S. Army Commendation Medal, 51; U.S. Air Force Commendation, 59; Legion of Merit, 62. Am. Med. Asn; Asn. Mil. Surg. U.S; fel. Aerospace Med. Asn; fel. Am. Col. Physicians; fel. Am. Col. Prev. Med. Infectious diseases, medical education; research administration. Address: Dept. of Preventive Medicine, Ohio State University, 410 W. Tenth Ave, Columbus, OH 43210.

ELLINGSON, JOHN S, b. Rockford, Ill, Mar. 25, 40. BIOCHEMISTRY. B.S, Univ. Ill, Urbana, 62; M.S, Univ. Mich, Ann Arbor, 64, Ph.D.(biochem), 67. Trainee, Brandeis Univ, 67-70; ASST. PROF. BIOCHEM, MED. SCH, W.VA. UNIV, 70- Phospholipids and membranes; regulation of development in cellular slime molds. Address: Dept. of Biochemistry, School of Medicine, West Virginia University, Morgantown, WV 26506.

ELLINGSON, ROBERT J(AMES), b. Chicago, Ill, June 7, 23; m. 48; c. 2. PSYCHOLOGY. B.S, Northwest. univ, 47, M.A, 49, Ph.D.(psychol), 50; M.D, Univ. Nebr, 63. Res. assoc. psychol, Mooseheart Lab. Child Res, 48-50; assoc. MED. PSYCHOL, COL. MED, UNIV. NEBR, OMAHA, 50-51, asst. prof, 51-55, assoc. prof, 55-64, PROF, 64-, NEUROL, 70-, physiol, 68-70; CHIEF ELECTROENCEPHALOG. LAB, NEBR. PSYCHIAT. INST, 50-, ASSOC. DIR, 63- U.S.A.A.F, 43-46. AAAS; Am. Psychol. Asn; Am. Electroencephalog. Soc.(secy, 64-67, pres, 68-69); Int. Fedn. Socs. Electroencephalog. & Clin. Neurophysiol.(secy, 69-73); Asn. Res. Nerv. & Ment. Diseases; Soc. Neurosci; Int. Soc. Develop. Psychobiol; Asn. Psychophysiol. Study Sleep. Developmental psychobiology; electroencephalography. Address: Research Division, Nebraska Psychiatric Institute, 602 S. 44th Ave, Omaha, NE 68105.

ELLINGSON, R(UDOLPH) C(ONRAD), b. Madison, Wis, Mar. 8, 11; m. 39; c. 2. ORGANIC CHEMISTRY. B.A, St. Olaf Col, 33; Ph.D.(org. chem), Hopkins, 38. Lab. technician, Mass. Inst. Tech, 33-34; asst. chem, Hopkins, 34-38, instr, 38-39; res. chemist, MEAD JOHNSON & CO, 39-50, chief res. div, 50-53, asst. dir. res, 53-54, dir. nutrit. res. & prod. develop, 54-59, sr. res. scientist, prod. develop, 59-60, dir. sci. admin, 60-65, exec. dir. admin, RES. CTR, 65-66, DIR. clin. & med. res. admin, 66-68, PLANNING & COORD, 68- With Off. Sci. Res. & Develop, 44. AAAS; Am. Chem. Soc; Soc. Exp. Biol. & Med; N.Y. Acad. Sci; Am. Inst. Chem; Inst. Food Technol. Vitamins; pyrrole and porphyrin chemistry; pyrazine chemistry; chemotherapeutics; carbohydrates; nutrition. Address: 6921 Arcadian Highway, Evansville, IN 47715.

ELLINGTON, EARL FRANKLIN, b. Olympia, Ky, Nov. 15, 33; m. 53; c. 2. ANIMAL PHYSIOLOGY. B.S, Kentucky, 55, M.S, 56; Hart, Cole & Goss fel, California, 58-59, Ralston Purina fel, 59-61, Nat. Insts. Health fel, 61-62, Ph.D.(animal physiol), 62. Asst. prof. ANIMAL PHYSIOL, Oregon State, 62-68; ASSOC. PROF, UNIV. NEBR, LINCOLN, 68- Nat. Insts. Health res. grant, 64-67. Am. Dairy Sci. Asn; Am. Soc. Animal Sci. Physiology of reproduction. Address: Dept. of Animal Science, University of Nebraska, Lincoln, NE 68508.

ELLINGTON, JOE J, b. Yuma, Ariz, Dec. 3, 34. ENTOMOLOGY. B.S, Arizona, 56; M.S, Cornell, 58, Ph.D.(entom), 63. Field res. specialist, Calif. Chem. Co, 63-65; asst. prof. ENTOM, N.MEX. STATE UNIV, 65-69, ASSOC. PROF, 69- Entom. Soc. Am. Insects of economic importance, specifically onion and cotton insects. Address: Dept. of Botany & Entomology, New Mexico State University, University Park, NM 88070.

ELLINGTON, REX T(RUESDALE), JR, b. Gunnison, Colo, Apr. 20, 21; m. 49; c. 2. CHEMICAL ENGINEERING. B.S, Colo, 43; M.Gas Tech. & M.S, Ill. Inst. Tech, 49, Ph.D.(gas tech), 53. Opers. analyst, div. indust. co-op, Mass. Inst. Tech, 46-47; chem. engr, Boston Gas Co, 49-50; indust. engr, Chattanooga Gas Co, 52-54; supvr, combustion res, Inst. Gas Tech, 54-55, asst. res. dir, 55-63, chmn, ed. prog, 55-63; asst. dir. exploitation res, Sinclair Res, Inc, 63-64, dir, 64-65, dir. prod. res, Tulsa Res. Ctr, Sinclair Oil & Gas Co, 65-67, proj. mgr. shale oil develop, 66-68, gen. mgr. mineral resources develop, domestic oil & gas div, 68-69; MGR. SYNTHETIC CRUDE DEVELOP, SYNTHETIC CRUDE & MINERALS DEPT, ATLANTIC RICHFIELD CO, 69- Asst. prof, Ill. Inst. Tech, 54-58, adj. assoc. prof, 58-61, adj. prof, 61-64; lectr, Univ. Tulsa, 66 & 67; adv, Okla. State Univ, 67; mem. bd. dir, Okla. Univ. Res. Inst, 67; Colo. Sch. Mines Res. Inst, 70. U.S.N.R, 44-46, Lt. Am. Inst. Chem. Eng; Am. Inst. Mining, Metall. & Petrol. Eng. Hydrocarbon thermal and physical properties and phase behavior; gaseous combustion; radiant heat transfer; reservoir engineering; fluid flow; synthetic oil and gas processes; oil refining; hydrocarbon properties. Address: Synthetic Crude & Minerals Dept, Atlantic Richfield Co, Box 2819, Dallas, TX 75221.

ELLINWOOD, EVERETT HEWS, JR, b. Wilmington, N.C, June 27, 34; c. 3. PSYCHIATRY, NEUROPHARMACOLOGY. B.S, Univ. N.C, 56, U.S. Pub. Health Serv. fel, 56-58, univ. fel, 57-59, M.D, 59. Clin. instr. PSYCHIAT, Univ. Ky, 64-65; res. fel, MED. CTR, DUKE UNIV, 65-66, assoc, 66-67, asst. prof, 67-70, ASSOC. PROF, 70- U.S.P.H.S, 63-65, Lt. Comdr. AAAS; Am. Med. Asn; Am. Psychiat. Asn; Am. Psychopath. Asn; Soc. Biol. Psychiat. Analysis in cats and monkeys of the neuropharmacological and behavioral concomitants of chronic amphetamine intoxication which in humans is often associated with a psychosis. Address: Dept. of Psychiatry, Duke University Medical Ctr, Durham, NC 27706.

ELLINWOOD, H(OWARD) L(YMAN), b. Davenport, Iowa, Feb. 25, 26; m. 51; c. 5. GEOLOGY. B.A, Univ. Minn, 49, Ph.D.(geol), 53. Geologist, Bur. Econ. Geol, Tex, 49-50; CALIF. CO, 52-58, dist. geologist, 58-61, div. geologist, 61-68, div. supt, 68-70, CHIEF GEOLOGIST, 70- U.S.A, 44-45. Geol. Soc. Am; Am. Asn. Petrol. Geol. Petroleum geology. Address: California Co, 800 California Co. Bldg, New Orleans, LA 70003.

ELLION, M. EDMUND, b. Boston, Mass, Jan. 20, 23; m. 54; c. 2. MECHANICAL ENGINEERING, PHYSICS. B.S, Northeastern, 44; M.S, Harvard, 47; Ph.D.(physics, mech. eng), Calif. Inst. Tech, 53. Res. engr, Bell Aerospace Corp, 47-50, consult. aerospace indust, 53-60; exec. dir. appl. mech. & aerodyn, Nat. Eng. Sci. Co, 60-62; pres, Dynamic Sci. Corp, 62-65; MGR. PROPULSION & ELEC. POWER SYSTS, HUGHES AIRCRAFT CO, LOS ANGELES, 65- Lectr, California, Los Angeles, 55-56. U.S.N.R, 43-46, Lt. Am. Inst. Aeronaut. & Astronaut. Propulsion, flight control, structures and thermal control of missile and space craft systems. Address: 2152 Highland Oaks Dr, Arcadia, CA 91006.

ELLIOT, A(LFRED) J(OHNSTON), b. Calgary, Alta, Aug. 16, 11; m. 42; c. 4. OPHTHALMOLOGY. B.A, Univ. B.C, 32; M.D, Univ. Toronto, 37; Med.Sc.D, Columbia Univ, 41; dipl. ophthalmic med. & surg, Royal Col. Physicians & Surgeons, London, 45. Clin. teacher OPHTHAL, Univ. Toronto, 45-46, PROF. & HEAD DEPT, 46-61; UNIV. B.C, 61- Chief serv, Toronto Gen. Hosp. & Sunnybrook Vet. Admin. Hosp, 46-; consult, Hosp. for Sick Children, 46-; guest lectr, Univ. Mich, 55; head ophthal, Vancouver Gen. Hosp. & Shaughnessy Hosp, 61-; adv. to Dir. Gen, Can. Dept. Vet. Affairs, 66-; chmn. med. adv. bd, Shaughnessy Hosp. DVA, 68-70; Vancouver Gen. Hosp, 69- Dipl, Am. Bd. Ophthal, 41; fel, Royal Col. Physicians & Surgeons, Can, 57. R.C.A.F, 41-45, Wing Comdr. Am. Acad. Ophthal. & Otolaryngol; Am. Ophthal. Soc; Asn. Res. Vision & Ophthal; Can. Med. Asn; Can. Ophthal. Soc; Ophthal. Soc. U.K. Recurrent intraocular hemorrhage; carotid-cavernous fistulae; keratoconjunctivitis sicca. Address: Dept. of Ophthalmology, University of British Columbia, 2550 Willow St, Vancouver 9, B.C, Can.

ELLIOT, ARTHUR M(cAULEY), b. Minneapolis, Minn, May 13, 28; m. 54; c. 4. PLANT PATHOLOGY, MYCOLOGY. B.Sc, Univ. Minn, 53, M.Sc, 60, Ph.D.(plant path), 61. Asst. prof. BIOL, TEX. TECH UNIV, 62-66, ASSOC. PROF, 66- U.S.A, 46-47; U.S.A.F, 47-49. AAAS; Am. Phytopath. Soc; Mycol. Soc. Am; Am. Inst. Biol. Sci. Cotton seedling disease; ornamental tree diseases; vector transmission of plant pathogens; plant and insect phenology; ecology of Claviceps ranunculoides. Address: Dept. of Biology, Texas Tech University, Lubbock, TX 79409.

ELLIOT, ERIC CHARLES, b. Blenheim, Ont, Aug. 27, 23; U.S. citizen; m. 49; c. 3. CARDIOVASCULAR PHYSIOLOGY. M.D, Univ. Toronto, 47; B.Sc, Univ. Alta, 57, M.Sc, 61, Ph.D.(physiol), 68. Intern, 47-49; gen. practice, Can, 49-55; lectr. exp. surg, Univ. Alta, 58-61, sessional demonstr. physiol, 61-64; MED. OFF. RES, WALTER REED ARMY INST. RES, 64- Can. Life Ins. med. fel, 56-59; Can. Heart Found. fel, 59-64. Am. Physiol. Soc. Coronary circulation; cardiovascular. Address: Dept. of Cardiorespiratory Diseases, Walter Reed Army Institute of Research, Walter Reed Army Medical Center, Washington, DC 20012.

ELLIOT, JACK, JR, b. Oakland, Calif, May 12, 29; m; c. 4. PHYSICS, MATHEMATICS. A.B, California, Berkeley, 50; M.S, San Diego State Col, 62; Hopkins, 63. Prod. & qual. control engr, Crown Zellerbach Paper Co. & A.M. Gousha Map Co, Calif, 54-56; from res. physicist to PROJ. ENGR. SONAR SYSTS, U.S. NAVAL UNDERSEA RES. & DEVELOP. CTR, 56- U.S.A, 50-54, 1st Lt. Asn. Symbolic Logic; Philos. Sci. Asn. Application of modern theories of non-linear continuum mechanics, primarily to acoustics; transducer array design and analysis; development of equations of state. Address: 2067 Finch Lane, San Diego, CA 92123.

ELLIOT, JAMES I, b. Toronto, Ont, Aug. 21, 38; m. 63; c. 2. ANIMAL NUTRITION & MANAGEMENT. B.S.A, Univ. Toronto, 62; M.Sc, Univ. Alta, 65, Nat. Res. Coun. Can. scholar, 66-68, Ph.D.(animal nutrit), 69. Lectr. ANIMAL SCI, Univ. Alta, 68-69; ASST. PROF, MACDONALD COL, McGILL UNIV, 69- Agr. Inst. Can; Am. Soc. Animal Sci; Can. Soc. Animal Prod. Investigation of copper as a growth promotant in swine rations and its involvement in the synthesis of unsaturated fatty acids in the pig; nutritional evaluation of rapeseed meal for swine; neonatal and prenatal metabolism of methionine in the pig. Address: Dept. of Animal Science, Macdonald College, McGill University, Ste. Anne de Bellevue, Que, Can.

ELLIOT, JOE O(LIVER), b. Ames, Iowa, Feb. 8, 23; m. 50; c. 2. PHYSICS. B.S, Iowa State Col, 43; A.M, Columbia, 47; Ph.D.(physics), Maryland, 55. Res. physicist, Div. of War Res, Iowa State, 44; dept. terrestrial magnetism, Carnegie Inst, 45; lectr. & asst, Columbia, 46-49; res. nuclear physicist, NAVAL RES. LAB, 49-65, PHYS. SCI. ADMINR, 65- Sabbatical fel, inst. oceanog, Univ. B.C, 68-69. AAAS; Am. Phys. Soc; Am. Geophys. Union. Parameters of excited states of nuclei; neutron scattering; decay time of luminescence of phosphors; scintillation spectrometry; reactor technology; physical oceanography. Address: Naval Research Lab, Washington, DC 20390.

ELLIOT, J(OHN) M(URRAY), b. Can, Nov. 6, 27; nat; m. 51; c. 2. ANIMAL NUTRITION. B.Sc, McGill, 49; Gordon fel. & M.S, Vermont, 50; Danforth grant, Cornell, 56, Hood fel, 57, Ph.D.(animal nutrit), 58. Instr. animal husb, Massachusetts, 50-53, asst. prof. dairy & animal sci, 53-60; ANIMAL HUSB, CORNELL UNIV, 60-65, assoc. prof, 65-71, PROF, 71- Am. Soc. Animal Sci; Am. Dairy Sci. Asn; Am. Inst. Nutrit. Dairy cattle nutrition; vitamin B_{12} production and absorption. Address: Dept. of Animal Science, 262 Morrison Hall, Cornell University, Ithaca, NY 14850.

ELLIOTT, ALFRED M(ARLYN), b. Humboldt, S.Dak, June 19, 05; m. 28; c. 2. ZOOLOGY. B.A, Yankton Col, 28; M.S, N.Y. Univ, 31, Ph.D.(protozool), 34. Instr, high sch, S.Dak, 28-30; teaching fel, N.Y. Univ, 30-34; instr. biol, Minn. State Teachers Col, Bemidji, 34-38, prof. & chmn. sci. div, 38-47; asst. prof. ZOOL, UNIV, MICH, 47-51, assoc. prof, 51-55, prof, 55-71, EMER. PROF, 71- Trustee, Am. Type Culture Collection, 60-; dir, Acad. Year Inst, Nat. Sci. Found, 62-65; mem. corp, Marine Biol. Lab, Woods Hole. Fel. AAAS; Am. Micros. Soc.(v.pres, 56, pres, 60); Soc. Protozool. (v.pres, 56, pres, 60); fel. N.Y. Acad. Sci; Am. Soc. Zool; Am. Soc. Cell Biol; Electron Micros. Soc. Am; Soc. Study Evolution. Physiology of protozoa; protein, fat and carbohydrate utilization; intermediate metabolism; biochemical genetics; protozoan distribution; electron microscopy. Address: 2345 Tarpon Rd, Naples, FL 33940.

ELLIOTT, ALICE, b. Reece, Kans, Oct. 7, 19. ZOOLOGY, PARASITOLOGY. B.S, Kans. State Teachers Col, Emporia, 42; M.S, Kans. State, 47, Ph.D. (parasitol), 50. Asst. zool, Kans. State, 46-47, instr, 47-50; asst. prof, biol, Kans. State Teachers Col, Pittsburg, 50-51; Hope Col, 52-54, assoc. prof, 54-55; asst. prof. sci, Ball State Teachers Col, 55-59; prof. BIOL, Hope Col, 59-62; assoc. prof, CENT. MO. STATE COL, 62-66, PROF, 66- Res. assoc, inst. cellular res, Univ. Nebr, 58-59. AAAS; Am. Soc. Cell Biol; Am. Soc. Parasitol; Am. Micros. Soc; Tissue Cult. Asn. Taxonomy and ecology of fishes; helminthology; physiology of parasites; tissue culture. Address: 121 E. Hunt, Apt. 301, Warrensburg, MO 64093.

ELLIOTT, BERNARD B(URTON), b. Ottawa, Ont, Can, Nov. 10, 21; U.S. citizen; m. 45; c. 4. ENZYMOLOGY. B.S, McGill, 49, M.S, 50; fel, Purdue, 50-52, Ph.D, 52. Demonstr. plant physiol, McGill, 49-50; enzymologist, R.J. Reynolds Tobacco Co, 52-59; asst. dir. res. & develop, Froedtert Malt Corp, 59-62; pres. & managing dir, Brewing & Malting Res. Inst, 62-64; DIR. RES. & DEVELOP, FROEDTERT MALT CORP, 64- R.C.A.F, 40-45, Lt. AAAS; Am. Chem. Soc; Am. Soc. Brewing Chem; Master Brewers Asn. Am; Am. Asn. Cereal Chem; N.Y. Acad. Sci; fel. Am. Inst. Chem. Fermentations; isolation of natural products. Address: Froedtert Malt Corp, 3830 W. Grant, Milwaukee, WI 53201.

ELLIOTT, C(HARLES) G(EORGE), b. Comber, Ont, May 30, 28. BIOCHEMISTRY, FOOD CHEMISTRY. B.A, Toronto, 52, M.A, 58, Ph.D.(biochem), 62. ASST. PROF. CHEM, UNIV. GUELPH, 62- Fluoride metabolism in plants and animals; ascorbic acid metabolism and interrelations with other vitamins; leucocyte metabolism. Address: Dept. of Chemistry, University of Guelph, Guelph, Ont, Can.

ELLIOTT, DAN WHITACRE, b. Greenville, Ohio, Aug. 5, 22; m. 62; c. 2. SURGERY. M.D, Yale, 49; M.Sc, Ohio State Univ, 56. Asst. prof. SURG, Ohio State Univ, 57-59, assoc. prof, 59-63, PROF, 63-64; UNIV. PITTSBURGH, 64- Consult, Vet. Admin. Hosp, Dayton, Ohio, 57-64; Pittsburgh, Pa, 64-70, chief surg, 70- U.S.A.F, 51-53, Capt. Am. Surg. Asn; Soc. Univ. Surg; Am. Gastroenterol. Asn; Am. Burn Asn; Soc. Surg. Alimentary Tract; Int. Soc. Surg. Diseases of the pancreas; gastric acid secretion; peptic ulcer; gastrointestinal hemorrhage. Address: 657 Morewood Ave, Pittsburgh, PA 15213.

ELLIOTT, DAVID, b. Montreal, Que, Mar. 25, 38; m. 67; c. 1. STRUCTURAL GEOLOGY. B.Sc, McGill Univ, 60; Ph.D.(geol), Glasgow Univ, 64. Asst. lectr. STRUCT. GEOL, Imp. Col, Univ. London, 65-67; ASST. PROF, JOHNS HOPKINS UNIV, 67- Am. Geophys. Union; Geol. Soc. Am. Structures and mechanical properties in naturally deformed rocks. Address: Dept. of Earth & Planetary Science, Johns Hopkins University, Baltimore, MD 21218.

ELLIOTT, DAVID DUNCAN, b. Los Angeles, Calif, Aug. 4, 30; m. 62; c. 1. SPACE PHYSICS. B.S, Stanford, 51; M.S, Calif. Inst. Tech, 53, Ph.D,(physics), 59. Res. scientist space physics, Lockheed Missiles & Space Co, 59-61; mem, tech. staff, Aerospace Corp, 61-66, staff scientist, 66-67, dept. head physics, space radiation & atmospheric dept, 67-70; SCI. ADV, NAT. AERONAUT. & SPACE COUN, 70- AAAS; Am. Phys. Soc; Am. Geophys. Union. Optical emissions of the earth's atmosphere; instrumentation of earth satellites to make geophysical measurements. Address: National Aeronautics & Space Council, New Executive Office Bldg, Washington, DC 20502.

ELLIOTT, DAVID MEACHAM, b. Pensacola, Fla, Sept. 9, 36; m. 62; c. 3. MECHANICAL & NUCLEAR ENGINEERING. B.S, Kansas, 61, M.S, 62; Ph.D.(mech. eng), Texas A&M, 68. Res. engr, Atomics Int. Div, N.Am. Aviation, Inc, Calif, 62-64; DIR. NUCLEAR REACTOR LAB. & ASST. PROF. AEROSPACE, MECH. & NUCLEAR ENG, UNIV. OKLA, 67- Am. Nuclear Soc; Inst. Nuclear Mat. Mgt. Nuclear fuel management; nuclear methods in geophysics; nuclear analytical chemistry; instrumentation. Address: School of Aerospace, Mechanical & Nuclear Engineering, University of Oklahoma, Norman, OK 73069.

ELLIOTT, DENTON W, b. Bellefontaine, Ohio, Feb. 18, 14; m. 42; c. 3. CHEMISTRY. A.B, Otterbein Col, 37; M.A, Ohio State, 46. Instr, high schs, Ohio, 37-42; explosive chemist, Sanderson & Porter, Ill, 42-43; asst. prof. chem, Champlain Col, 46-52; res. admin, OFF. SCI. RES, U.S. AIR FORCE, 52-59, DEP. DIR. CHEM. SCI, 59- U.S.N, 43-46, Res, 46-, Lt. Comdr. AAAS; Am. Chem. Soc. Administration of research contracts. Address: 6312 Kirby Rd, Bethesda, MD 20034.

ELLIOTT, DONALD SANDFORD, b. Scottsbluff, Nebr, Mar. 9, 38; m. 58; c. 3. REPRODUCTIVE PHYSIOLOGY. B.S, Nebraska, 61; M.S, N.C. State, 66, Nat. Defense Educ. Act fel, 66-68, Ph.D.(reprod. physiol), 68. Asst. mgr, Elliott Ranch, Inc, 61-64; sr. res. toxicologist, Merck Inst. Therapeut. Res, 68-70, res. fel, 70-71; SR. STAFF FEL, PHARMACOL. & TOXICOL. BR, NAT. INST. ENVIRON. HEALTH SCI, 71- AAAS; N.Y. Acad. Sci; Am. Soc. Animal Sci; Soc. Study Reprod. Effects of environment on early embryonic development. Address: Pharmacology & Toxicology Branch, National Institute of Environmental Health Sciences, P.O. Box 12233, Research Triangle Park, NC 27709.

ELLIOTT, EDWARD S(UMNER), b. Bruceton Mills, W.Va, Feb. 8, 19; m. 42; c. 3. PLANT PATHOLOGY. B.A, W.Va. Univ, 41, M.S, 48, Ph.D.(plant path), 50. Res. asst. plant path, W.VA. UNIV, 47-50, asst. prof. plant path. & asst. plant pathologist, 53-61, assoc. prof. plant path. & assoc. plant pathologist, 61-67, PROF. PLANT PATH. & PLANT PATHOLOGIST, 67- C.Eng, 41-46, Chem.C, 51-52, Capt. Am. Phytopath. Soc. Diseases of forage crops; field crops and ornamentals. Address: Division of Plant Sciences, 401 Brooks Hall, West Virginia University, Morgantown, WV 26506.

ELLIOTT, EDWIN O(LIVER), b. Fargo, N.Dak, May 3, 28; m. 55; c. 4. MATHEMATICS. A.B, California, Berkeley, 49, M.A, 51, Ph.D.(math), 59. Analyst opers. res, sponsored res. div, Mass. Inst. Technol, 54-58; econs. div, Stanford Res. Inst, 58-59; asst. prof. math, Nevada, 59-60; MEM. TECH. STAFF, BELL TEL. LABS, INC, 60- Mem. security resources panel, Nat. Security Coun, 57. Opers. Res. Soc. Am; Am. Math. Soc; Inst.

Elec. & Electronics Eng. Measure theory; stochastic processes; applied probability. Address: Room 2B401, Dept. 3422, Bell Telephone Labs, Inc, Holmdel, NJ 07733.

ELLIOTT, EMMET R(OACH), b. Darlington Heights, Va, July 22, 08; m. 37. MATHEMATICS. B.S, Hampden-Sydney Col, 28; M.A, Duke, 29, fel, 32-34, Ph.D.(math), 35. Instr. math, N.C. State Col, 29-31; asst, Pennsylvania, 31-32; asst. prof, Hampden-Sydney Col, 34-35, assoc. prof, 35-42; civil serv, navig, Naval Air Sta, Corpus Christi, Tex, 42-43; prof. MATH, HAMPDEN-SYDNEY COL, 47-64, chmn. dept, 50-64, EMER. PROF, 64- U.S.N.R, 43-47, Lt. Comdr. Am. Math. Soc. Lebesque and Stieltjes integrals with reference to boundary value problems; mathematics analysis. Address: Hampden-Sydney College, Hampden-Sydney, VA 23943.

ELLIOTT, EUGENE W(ILLIS), b. Longmont, Colo, May 29, 16; m. 46; c. 2. CHEMISTRY, PLANT PHYSIOLOGY. B.A, Montana, 41; M.S, Iowa, 47, Ph.D.(mycol), 48. Res. asst. plant physiol, Wisconsin, 41-42; dir. microbiol. res. lab, Monsanto Chem. Co, Mo, 48-51; eng. draftsman, U.S. Bur. Reclamation, 51-52; sr. draftsman, Shell Oil Co, Mont, 52-58; instr. chem. & bot, EAST. MONT. COL, 58-60, asst. prof, 60-62, assoc. prof. chem. & plant physiol, 62-66, PROF. CHEM. & BOT, 66- Consult, Nat. Parks Asn, 62- U.S.A, 42-46, Res, 46-48. Effects of paradichlorobenzene on fungi; swarm-cells of Myxomycetes. Address: Division of Science & Mathematics, Eastern Montana College, Billings, MT 59101.

ELLIOTT, FRANK A, b. Capetown, S.Africa, Dec. 18, 10; m. 40; c. 2. NEUROLOGY. Lewis Mem. fel, 30; M.B, Ch.B, Capetown, 34; Hiddingh traveling fel, 35. Consult. neurol, Charing Cross Hosp, London Univ, 46-59; clin. prof. NEUROL, DIV. GRAD. MED, UNIV. PA, 59-65, PROF, 65-; CHIEF NEUROL. SERV, PA, 59-65, PROF, 65-; CHIEF NEUROL. SERV, PA. HOSP, 59-, DIR. DEPT. NEUROL, 66- Consult, Bryn Mawr Hosp, 60-; Children's Hosp. Phila, 61- Fel, Royal Col. Physicians, 48. R.A.M.C, 42-47, Lt. Col. Am. Acad. Neurol. Pathophysiology of pain; biochemical factors in cerebrovascular disease. Address: Pennsylvania Hospital, 807 Spruce St, Philadelphia, PA 19107.

ELLIOTT, FRED C(RAIG), b. Drayton, N.Dak, Aug. 19, 16; m. 42; c. 4. FARM CROPS. B.S, Iowa State Col, 45, M.S, 46, Ph.D.(crops breeding), 48. Res. sr. fel, Iowa State Col, 47-48; asst. prof. AGRON, Wash. State Col, 48-52, assoc. prof, 52-57; from assoc. prof. to PROF, MICH. STATE UNIV, 57- U.S.A.A.F, 42-45. Genetics Soc. Am. Cytogenetics; forage breeding. Address: Dept. of Farm Crops, Michigan State University, East Lansing, MI 48824.

ELLIOTT, F(RED) I(RVINE), b. New Concord, Ohio, Oct. 16, 15; m. 41; c. 3. DAIRY HUSBANDRY. B.S, Ohio State, 38; Ph.D.(animal husb), Cornell, 44. Exten. instr, Cornell, 41-44; dir. livestock work, Near East Found, 44-46; assoc. prof. dairy husb, N.C. State Col, 47-49; prof. dairy husb. & head dept. animal industs, Connecticut, 49-52; mgr, Am. Breeders Serv, N.C, 52-53; dir. res, AM. BREEDERS SERV, 53-65, prod. mgr, 56-65, DIR. LABS. & RES, 65- AAAS; Am. Soc. Animal Sci; Am. Dairy Sci. Asn; Soc. Study Reproduction; Soc. Cryobiol. Factors affecting reproductive processes; methods of evaluating fertility of bull semen samples; factors affecting functional sterility; extenders; freezing and thawing rates; processing techniques for frozen bovine semen. Address: American Breeders Service, DeForest, WI 53532.

ELLIOTT, GEORGE A(LGIMON), b. Trappe, Md, June 6, 25; m. 49; c. 3. PATHOLOGY. Va. Mil. Inst, 47-48; Maryland, 48-49; D.V.M, Georgia, 53; M.S, Pennsylvania, 57. Instr. vet. path, vet. sch, Pennsylvania, 55-58, assoc, 58-59, asst. prof, 59-60; sch. med, Vanderbilt Univ, 60-62; RES. ASSOC. PATH. & TOXICOL. RES, UPJOHN CO, 62- Dipl, Am. Col. Vet. Path. U.S.N, 45-46. Int. Acad. Path; N.Y. Acad Sci. Neuropathology; toxicology; virology; immunopathology. Address: Pathology & Toxicology Research, Upjohn Co, Kalamazoo, MI 49081.

ELLIOTT, G(EORGE) B(ALL), b. England, June 16, 18; nat; m. 45; c. 3. CLINICAL PATHOLOGY. M.B, B.S, Univ. Durham, 40; dipl, hon. cert, Alberta, 57. Asst. pathologist, Durham, England, 41-42; sr. indust. med. officer, Bristol Aero Co, 43-45; dir. clin. labs, Provincial Servs, 46-50, 52-53; dir. labs, Calgary Gen. Hosp, 53-65; CHIEF SURG. PATH, VANCOUVER GEN. HOSP, 65-; ASSOC. CLIN. PROF. PATH, UNIV. B.C, 65- Fel, Univ. Man, 50-51; consult. pathologist, Grace Hosp, 56- Dipl, Royal Col. Physicians & Surgeons, Can; fel. Royal Col. Path. R.C.N.R, 56-62, Surg. Lt. Comdr. Fel. Am. Col. Physicians; fel. Royal Soc. Med; Can. Soc. Clin. Chem. Histopathology; biochemistry. Address: Dept. of Surgical Pathology, Vancouver General Hospital, Vancouver 9, B.C, Can.

ELLIOTT, GUY R(UPERT) B(ETTS), b. Minneapolis, Minn, Nov. 22, 21; m. 56; c. 3. THERMODYNAMICS. B.S, Mont. State Col, 43; Ph.D.(chem), California, 52. CHEMIST, Oak Ridge Nat. Lab, 46-48; radiation lab, California, 48-52; Diamond Ord. Fuze Labs, 53-55; Argonne Nat. Lab, 55-57; LOS ALAMOS SCI. LAB, 57- Consult, U.S. Army Nuclear Defense Lab, Edgewood Arsenal, Md, 64-; vis. prof. metall, Univ. Utah, 70-71, adj. prof. & consult, 71- U.S.A, 43-46. Fel. AAAS; fel. Am. Inst. Chem; Am. Chem. Soc; Faraday Soc; Electrochem. Soc. Equilibrium kinetics; causes of solid and liquid alloy behavior; ordered defect microphases; solvent extraction of metals and ions; high temperature gaseous hydrate molecules; molten salt electrochemistry; contact electrification; radioactive fallout. Address: 103 Grand Canyon, Los Alamos, NM 87544.

ELLIOTT, H(AROLD) A(NDREW), b. Jarrow, Eng, Feb. 5, 20; m. 46; c. 5. MATHEMATICS, THEORETICAL PHYSICS. B.A, Jesus Col, Cambridge, 41, M.A, 44; Imp. Chem. Industs. fel, Bristol, 45-47, Ph.D.(physics), 47. Sci. off, Ministry Aircraft Prod, 41-45; asst. prof. math, McGill Univ, 47-49; prof, Royal Mil. Col. Can, 49-59, head dept, 59-67; ASSOC. DIR, SERV. FOR ADMISSION TO COL. & UNIV, 67- Am. Phys. Soc; Can. Math. Cong. Theory of the solid state; elasticity; electro-magnetic theory; mathematical education. Address: 151 Slater St, Ottawa, Ont. K1P 5N1, Can.

ELLIOTT, H(ELEN) MARGARET, b. Galveston, Tex, Aug. 16, 25; m. 70. MATHEMATICS. B.A, Rice Inst, 45; Genevieve McEnerney fel, California,

45-46, M.A, 46; Lansing fel, Radcliffe Col, 46-47, Whitney fel, 47-48, Ph.D. (math), 48. Asst, California, 46; Am. Asn. Univ. Women Hill fel, Harvard, 48-49; instr. MATH, Washington (St. Louis), 49-51, asst. prof, 51-55, assoc. prof, 55-64; acting prof, Col. William & Mary, 64-65; PROF, UNIV. BRIDGEPORT, 68-, CHMN. DEPT, 69- Nat. Sci. Found. faculty fel, Mass. Inst. Technol. & Harvard, 57-58. Am. Math. Soc; Math. Asn. Am; Nat. Coun. Teachers Math. Analysis; approximation theory. Address: Dept. of Mathematics, University of Bridgeport, Bridgeport, CT 06602.

ELLIOTT, HENRY HOWARD, b. Stuttgart, Ger, July 15, 25; U.S. citizen; m. 47; c. 3. INORGANIC CHEMISTRY. B.S, Oregon State, 51; Southern California, 55-58. Filtration engr, Dicalite Div, Great Lakes Carbon Corp, 53-56; res. engr, Los Angeles Chem. Plant, AM. POTASH & CHEM. CORP, 56-57, sr. res. engr, 57-59, WHITIER RES. LABS, 59-61, RES. PROJ. ENGR, 61- Process engr, gen. chem. div, Allied Chem. Corp, 55-56. U.S.A, 45-47; U.S.A.F, 51-53, Res, 51-66, Maj. Am. Inst. Chem. Eng. Development of process technology for inorganic chemical synthesis at high temperature; developed processes for boron trichloride, boron tribromide, titanium diboride, pigmentary titanium dioxide and rare earth chloride. Address: American Potash & Chemical Corp, 12519 E. Washington Blvd, Whittier, CA 90602.

ELLIOTT, HENRY W(OOD), b. Seattle, Wash, Apr. 10, 20; m. 47; c. 4. PHARMACOLOGY, ANESTHESIOLOGY. B.S, Washington (Seattle), 41, fel, 41-42, M.S, 43; Ph.D.(physiol), Stanford, 46; M.D, California, 53. Assoc. physiol, Washington (Seattle), 43; res. assoc, Stanford, 43-46; instr, Col. Physicians & Surgeons of San Francisco, 44-46; lectr. & res. assoc. pharmacol, med. ctr, California, San Francisco, 46-53, asst. prof, 53-55, asst. prof. pharmacol. & anesthesia, 55-58, assoc. prof. pharmacol, 58-64, prof, 64-68; PROF. MED. PHARMACOL. & THERAPEUT. & CHMN. DEPT, COL. MED, UNIV. CALIF, IRVINE, 68- Lederle med. faculty award, 55-57; ed, Annual Rev. Pharmacol, 65- AAAS; Am. Med. Asn; Am. Soc. Anesthesiol; Am. Soc. Pharmacol. & Exp. Therapeut; Soc. Exp. Biol. & Med; Am. Chem. Soc; Am. Fedn. Clin. Res; N.Y. Acad. Sci; Am. Soc. Clin. Pharmacol. & Therapeut.(past pres). Analgesics and anesthetics; tissue metabolism; hypothermia; drug addiction; drug development. Address: Dept. of Medical Pharmacology & Therapeutics, University of California College of Medicine, Orange County Medical Center, 101 S. Manchester Ave, Orange, CA 92668.

ELLIOTT, HOWARD C(LYDE), b. Birmingham, Ala, Sept. 21, 24; m. 58; c. 5. BIOCHEMISTRY. B.S, Birmingham-South. Col, 48; M.S, Alabama, 51, Ph.D.(biochem), 56. Chemist, cancer res. dept, MED. COL, UNIV. ALA, BIRMINGHAM, 49-50, asst. instr. biochem, 51-54, instr. CHEM, 55-56, asst. prof, 56-59, assoc. prof, 59-65, prof, 65-69, RES. PROF, 70-, ASST. PROF. BIOCHEM. MED, 66-; BIOCHEMIST, BAPTIST MED. CTR, 70- Med.C, 43-46. Soc. Exp. Biol. & Med; Am. Chem. Soc; Am. Diabetes Asn; Am. Soc. Nephrology. Biochemistry of benzoate congeners; renal transport mechanisms; electrolyte metabolism. Address: Chemistry Lab, Baptist Medical Center, 800 Montclair Rd, Birmingham, AL 35213.

ELLIOTT, IRVIN W(ESLEY), b. Newton, Kans, Oct. 21, 25; m. 52; c. 2. ORGANIC CHEMISTRY. B.S, Kansas, 47, M.S, 49, Ph.D.(chem), 52. Instr. CHEM, Southern Univ, 49-50; assoc. prof, Fla. Agr. & Mech. Col, 52-53, prof, 53-57; fel, Harvard, 57-58; PROF, FISK UNIV, 58- Am. Chem. Soc; Nat. Inst. Sci; The Chem. Soc. Synthetic organic chemistry; alkaloids. Address: Dept. of Chemistry, Fisk University, Nashville, TN 37203.

ELLIOTT, J. LELL, b. Warrensburg, Mo, Dec. 8, 08; m. 35. PHYSICAL ORGANIC CHEMISTRY. A.B, Univ. Colo, 30, A.M, 32, Ph.D.(chem), 35. Instr. CHEM, PAN AM. COL, 35-46, PROF, 46-, HEAD DEPT, 65-, head div. sci. & math, 46-52, dir. sci. div, 52-65, dir. res, 56-65. U.S.A.A.F, 42-46, Maj. Fel. AAAS; fel. Am. Inst. Chem; Am. Chem. Soc. Nuclear magnetic resonance; instrumentation and computer applications. Address: 930 W. Ebony Dr, Edinburg, TX 78539.

ELLIOTT, JACK C(ALKINS), b. Coldwater, Mich, July 27, 07; m. 31; c. 2. BOTANY. A.B, Albion Col, 39; M.A, Michigan, 46; Ph.D.(bot), Mich. State Col, 52. Teacher, pub. schs, Mich, 39-42; PROF. BOT, LYMAN BRIGGS COL, MICH. STATE UNIV, 46- U.S.A, 43-46, 1st Lt. Ecol. Soc. Am; Am. Inst. Biol. Sci. Plant ecology. Address: Lyman Briggs College, Michigan State University, East Lansing, MI 48823.

ELLIOTT, J(ACK) G(RESHAM), b. Detroit, Mich, June 16, 23; m. 45; c. 3. SYSTEMS & MATHEMATICAL ANALYSIS. B.S, Mich. State Univ, 48, M.A, 49, Ph.D.(math), 58. Instr. math, Ohio Univ, 53-54; MGR, SYSTS. SYNTHESIS DEPT, BENDIX RES. LABS, 54- Instr, appl. mgt. & technol. ctr, Wayne State Univ, 66- U.S.A, 42-46, 1st Lt. Math. Asn. Am. Dynamic analysis of aerospace and automotive vehicle systems, with emphasis on vehicle handling studies. Address: Bendix Research Labs, Bendix Center, Southfield, MI 48075.

ELLIOTT, J(AMES) A(NGUS), b. Wawota, Sask, Feb. 4, 23; m. 48. BACTERIOLOGY. B.S.A, Saskatchewan, 51; M.S, Wisconsin, 52, Ph.D.(dairy indust), 55. Res. officer, dairy res. inst, CAN. DEPT. AGR, 54-62, HEAD MICROBIOL. SECT, FOOD RES. INST, 62- Can. Army, 41-46. Am. Dairy Sci. Asn; Agr. Inst. Can; Can. Soc. Microbiol; Can. Inst. Food Technol. Microbiology of food products; role of bacteria in flavor development of cheese. Address: Food Research Institute, C.E.F, Canada Dept. of Agriculture, Ottawa, Ont. K1A 0C6, Can.

ELLIOTT, J(AMES) F(RANKLIN), b. Des Moines, Iowa, Mar. 10, 24; m. 46; c. 6. EXPERIMENTAL & MATHEMATICAL PHYSICS. B.S, Missouri, 48; Ph.D.(physics), Iowa State, 53. Asst, Ames Lab, Atomic Energy Comn, 48-53; PHYSICIST, ELECTRONICS LAB, GEN. ELEC. CO, 53- Gerald L. Phillippe Award distinguished pub. serv, 70. U.S.A.A.F, 43-46, Sgt. Am. Phys. Soc. Instrumentation; energy conversion; phosphors; ferroelectrics; magnetic properties of the rare earth metals; law enforcement systems. Address: Electronics Lab, General Electric Co, Electronics Park, Syracuse, NY 13201.

ELLIOTT, JAMES H, b. Hastings, Nebr, Jan. 15, 27; m. 48; c. 4. OPHTHALMOLOGY. B.A, Phillips, 49; M.D, Oklahoma, 52. Intern, Mercy Hosp,

Oklahoma City, Okla, 52-53; res. OPHTHAL, med. ctr, Oklahoma, 60-62; res. fel, Harvard Med. Sch, 62-65, instr. 65-66; assoc. prof, SCH. MED, VANDERBILT UNIV, 66-68, PROF. & CHIEF DIV, 68- Consult, Vet. Admin. Hosp, Nashville, 66- U.S.N, 45-46. Asn. Res. Vision & Ophthal; Am. Acad. Ophthal. Immunology as applied to ophthalmology, specifically immunosuppression of experimental corneal hypersensitivity and corneal graft rejection reactions. Address: Division of Ophthalmology, Vanderbilt Hospital, Nashville, TN 37203.

ELLIOTT, JAMES M(cFARLAND), b. Overton, Tex, Jan. 31, 19; m. 39; c. 3. SCIENCE EDUCATION. B.S, N.Tex. State Col, 42, M.S, 48; Ed.D, Mich. State, 53. Instr. biol, N.Tex. State Col, 46; biol. sci, MICH. STATE UNIV, 47-53, asst. prof. NATURAL SCI, 53-59, assoc. prof, 59-64, PROF, 64-, univ. col. dir. residence instr, east campus complex, 66. Hosp.C, U.S.N.R, 42-45. Science for general education. Address: Dept. of Natural Science, Michigan State University, East Lansing, MI 48823.

ELLIOTT, JOANNE, b. Providence, R.I, Dec. 5, 25. MATHEMATICS. B.A, Brown, 47, Emery fel, 47-48; M.A, Cornell, 49, Ph.D.(math), 50. Asst, Cornell, 47-50; instr. MATH, Swarthmore Col, 50-52; asst. prof, Mt. Holyoke Col, 52-55, asst. prof, Barnard Col, Columbia, 55-57, assoc. prof, 57-64; PROF, RUTGERS UNIV, 64- Vis. asst. prof, Brown, 54-55; Nat. Sci. Found. sr. fel, 61-62. Am. Math. Soc; Math. Asn. Am. Integral equations; applications of semigroups to integro-differential equations; differential equations. Address: Dept. of Mathematics, Rutgers The State University, New Brunswick, NJ 08903.

ELLIOTT, JOE C, b. Wis, Dec. 27, 42. PLANT MORPHOGENESIS & PHYSIOLOGY. B.S, Wis. State Univ, Eau Claire, 65; Nat. Defense Educ. Act fel, Univ. Mont, 65-68, Ph.D.(bot), 70. Fel, ctr. biol. natural systs, Wash. Univ, 69-70; LAB. COORD. BOT, UNIV. MONT, 70- Bot. Soc. Am; Am. Bryol. & Lichenological Soc. Morphogenesis of lower plants; distribution and ecology of bryophytes. Address: Dept. of Botany, University of Montana, Missoula, MT 59801.

ELLIOTT, JOHN, b. Bradford, Eng, Oct. 26, 37; m. 61; c. 2. COLOR CHEMISTRY. B.Sc, Leeds, 59, Int. Wool Secretariat scholar. & Ph.D.(colour & dyeing chem), 62. RES. & DEVELOP. CHEMIST, TOMS RIVER CHEM. CORP, 63- Am. Chem. Soc; Brit. Soc. Dyers & Colourists; assoc. Royal Inst. Chem. Physical and chemical modifications of fibrous proteins; application of polymers and dyestuffs to fibrous substrates; phthalocyanine and azo dye chemistry; dyeing technology. Address: 1005 Huntington Ave, Pine Beach, NJ 08741.

ELLIOTT, JOHN FRANK, b. St. Paul, Minn, July 31, 20; m. 46; c. 2. METALLURGY. B.Metall.E, Minnesota, 42; Nat. Res. fel. & Sc.D.(metall), Mass. Inst. Tech, 49. Phys. chemist, res. lab, U.S. Steel Corp, 49-51; sect. head, Inland Steel Co, 51-54, asst. supt, qual. control dept, 54-55; assoc. prof. METALL, MASS. INST. TECHNOL, 55-60, PROF, 60- Howe lectr, Am. Inst. Mining, Metall. & Petrol. Eng, 63; John Simon Guggenheim Mem. fel, 65; mem-at-large eng. div, Nat. Res. Coun-Nat. Acad. Sci. U.S.N.R, 42-46, Lt. Comdr. Am. Inst. Mining, Metall. & Petrol. Eng.(Hunt Award, 54); Am. Soc. Metals (White Award, 71); fel. Metall. Soc; Am. Inst. Chem; Am. Acad. Arts & Sci; Electrochem. Soc; Brit. Iron & Steel Inst. Physical chemistry of metals; chemical metallurgy. Address: Dept. of Metallurgy, Massachusetts Institute of Technology, Cambridge, MA 02139.

ELLIOTT, JOHN H(ABERSHAM), b. Baltimore, Md, July 20, 13; m. 41; c. 2. PHYSICAL CHEMISTRY. A.B, Haverford Col, 35; M.S, Pennsylvania, 37, Ph.D.(phys. chem), 40. Res. chemist, Phila. Lab, E.I. du Pont de Nemours & Co, 35-37; chief chemist, J.E. Rhodes & Sons, 37-42; res. chemist, RES. CTR, HERCULES INC, 42-43, SUPVR, 43- Am. Chem. Soc; Soc. Rheol. Acid strength studies; drag reduction and polymer rheology; effect of substituents on the acid strength of benzoic acid. Address: 305 Wilson Rd, Newark, DE 19711.

ELLIOTT, JOHN RAYMOND, b. Auburn, Nebr, Jan. 4, 16; m. 43; c. 2. ORGANIC CHEMISTRY. B.S, Iowa State Col, 37, Ph.D.(org. chem), Illinois, 43. Chemist, Gen. Elec. Co, Mass, 37-40, res. assoc, lab, 43-52, MGR. org. chem. res. sect, 52-65, org. chem. br, res. & develop. ctr, 65-68; RES. & DEVELOP, LOCTITE CORP, 69- AAAS; Am. Chem. Soc; Inst. Elec. & Electronics Eng. Organic reactions; silicones; organic polymers; metal hydride chemistry; oxidation chemistry; adhesives for metal fabrication industries; anaerobic and cyanoacrylote chemistry and adhesives. Address: Research & Development Dept, Loctite Corp, 705 N. Mountain Rd, Newington, CT 06111.

ELLIOTT, JOSEPH ROBERT, b. Kansas City, Kans, Dec. 11, 23; m. 53; c. 2. BIOCHEMISTRY. A.B, Kansas, 49; M.S, Missouri, 51, Ph.D.(biochem), 53. Fel. biochem, med. sch, Northwestern, 53-55; res. assoc. biol, Rice, 55-58; instr. biochem, col. med, Baylor Univ, 58-67; assoc. prof. lab. med. & dir. clin. chem. lab, med. sch, Univ. Okla, 67-70; CLIN. CHEMIST, ST. LUKE'S HOSP, 70- Mem. staff, Jefferson Davis Hosp, 57-59; biochemist, St. Luke's Episcopal Hosp, 59-67. U.S.A, 42-46. AAAS; Am. Physiol. Soc; Am. Asn. Clin. Chem; Soc. Exp. Biol. & Med. Clinical chemistry; hormone assay. Address: St. Luke's Hospital, 44th & Wornall Rd, Kansas City, MO 64111.

ELLIOTT, K(ENNETH) A(LLAN) C(ALDWELL), b. Kimberley, S.Africa, Aug. 24, 03; Can. citizen; m. 36; c. 3. BIOCHEMISTRY. M.Sc, Rhodes, S.Africa, 24; Ph.D.(biochem), Cambridge, 30, Sc.D, 50. Shift chemist, Rhodesia Broken Hill Develop. Co, 25; chemist, Modderfontein Dynamite Factory, S.Africa, 25-26; res. chemist, biochem. res. found, Franklin Inst, 33-39; in charge chem. res. lab, inst, Pa. Hosp, 39-44, asst. prof. biochem. in psychiat, Pennsylvania, 39-44; asst. prof. biochem, McGill Univ, 44-50, assoc. prof, 50-59, prof. & head dept, 59-68, Gilman Cheyney prof, 68-71; CAN. UNIV. SERV. OVERSEAS VOL. PROF. PHYSIOL. CHEM, UNIV. NIGERIA, ENUGU, 71- Beit Mem. fel, 29, fourth year fel, 32; fel, Cambridge, 33-36; assoc. neurochemist, Montreal Neurol. Inst, 44-51, neurochemist, 51-; ed, Can. J. Biochem. & Physiol, 56-59; Nat. Res. Coun. Can. sr. res. fel, 63; McGill Univ. Bethune exchange prof, Peking Chinese Med. Col, 64. AAAS; Am. Soc. Biol. Chem; Can. Physiol. Soc; Can. Neurol. Soc; Can. Biochem. Soc; Brit. Biochem. Soc; fel. Royal Soc. Can. Tissue metabolism, neurochemistry. Address: c/o Dept. of Biochemistry, McGill University, Montreal 2, Que, Can.

ELLIOTT, KENNETH McKELLER, b. Athens, Tenn, Nov. 8, 21; m. 59; c. 3. CHEMICAL ENGINEERING. B.S, Tennessee, 42. Group leader process develop, Magnolia Petrol. Co, 42-46; sr. res. engr, res. dept, Socony Mobil Oil Co, 46-50, res. assoc, 50-54, supvr. eng. & res. econ, 54-58, tech. dir. process develop, 58-59, mgr. appl. res. & develop, 59-64, mgr. eng. & prod, 64-65, gen. mgr, corp. eng. dept, 65-67, V.PRES. ENG, MOBIL OIL CORP, 67- Am. Inst. Chem. Eng. Process and product research and development for petroleum industry; design and construction of facilities for petroleum and chemical industries. Address: Mobil Oil Corp, 150 E. 42nd St, New York, NY 10017.

ELLIOTT, LARRY P, b. Fleming, Mo, Sept. 27, 38; m. 61; c. 3. BACTERIOLOGY, BIOLOGY. B.A, William Jewell Col, 60; M.S, Wisconsin, 62, Ph.D. (bact), 65. Asst. prof. BIOL, WEST. KY. UNIV, 65-68, ASSOC. PROF, 68- Nat. Sci. Found. res. partic, Univ. Iowa, summer 70. AAAS; Am. Sci. Affiliation; Am. Soc. Microbiol. Staphylococcal bovine mastitis, especially ecology in the dairy herd and environment; bacterial infections of the urinary tract. Address: Dept. of Biology, Western Kentucky University, Bowling Green, KY 42101.

ELLIOTT, LARRY P(AUL), b. Manhattan, Kans, Oct. 16, 31; m. 56; c. 2. RADIOLOGY. B.S, Univ. Fla, 54; M.D, Univ. Tenn, 57; Univ. Minn, 61-65. Assoc. prof. RADIOL, sch. med, Wash. Univ, 65-67; PROF, SHANDS TEACHING HOSP, COL. MED, UNIV. FLA, 67- Diagnostic radiology; congenital heart disease, especially roentgenographic and pathologic correlation. Address: Dept. of Radiology, Shands Teaching Hospital, College of Medicine, University of Florida, Gainesville, FL 32601.

ELLIOTT, LLOYD FLOREN, b. Clear Lake, S.Dak, July 7, 37; m. 58; c. 2. MICROBIOLOGY. B.S, S.Dak. State, 58; M.S, Kansas State, 61; Ph.D.(microbiol), Oregon State, 65. RES. MICROBIOLOGIST, SOIL & WATER CONSERV. RES. DIV, NORTH. PLAINS BR, AGR. RES. SERV, U.S. DEPT. AGR, 65- Am. Soc. Microbiol; Soil Conserv. Soc. Am; Am. Soc. Agron. Soil microbiology; sick alfalfa and the relationship of Rhizobium bacteria to this problem; energetics of bacterial oxidations; research on beef feedlot wastes; pollution control; waste disposal. Address: 141 Keim Hall, Dept. of Agronomy, University of Nebraska, Lincoln, NE 68503.

ELLIOTT, LOIS L(AWRENCE), b. Cincinnati, Ohio, July 3, 31; wid. EXPERIMENTAL PSYCHOLOGY. A.B, Bryn Mawr Col, 53; Nat. Sci. Found. fel, Cornell, 54-56, Ph.D, 56. RES. PSYCHOLOGIST, oper. lab, U.S. Air Force Personnel & Training Res. Lab, 56-58, personnel lab, Lackland Air Force Base, 58-60; audiol. lab, U.S. Air Force Sch. Aerospace Med, 60-63; Cent. Inst. for Deaf, 63-70, BUR. EDUC. FOR HANDICAPPED, U.S. OFF. EDUC, 70- Assoc. prof. psychol, Wash. Univ, 66-70. AAAS; Am. Psychol. Asn; Am. Statist. Asn; Am. Soc. Info. Sci; fel. Acoustical Soc. Am; Psychonomic Soc; Am. Speech & Hearing Asn. Psychoacoustics; perception; experimental design. Address: 4100 Cathedral Ave. N.W, Washington, DC 20016.

ELLIOTT, MARTIN A(NDERSON), b. Baltimore, Md, Feb. 21, 09; m. 34; c. 2. ENGINEERING. B.E, Hopkins, 30, Ph.D.(gas eng), 33. Instr, Hopkins, 30-34; gas engr, Consol. Gas, Elec. Light & Power Co, Md, 34-38; U.S. Bur. Mines, 38-41, chem. engr, 41-46, asst. chief res. & develop. br, 46-51, chief, 51-52; res. prof. mech. eng, Ill. Inst. Technol, 52-56, dir. inst. gas technol, 56-61, acad. v.pres, 61-67; SCI. ADV, TEX. EAST. TRANSMISSION CORP, 67- Distinguished serv. medal, U.S. Bur. Mines, 52; Percy Nicholls Award, Am. Soc. Mech. Engrs. & Am. Inst. Mining, Metall. & Petrol. Engrs, 67. Am. Inst. Chem. Eng; Am. Gas Asn; Am. Chem. Soc; Soc. Automotive Eng; Am. Soc. Mech. Eng; Am. Soc. Eng. Educ; Combustion Inst; Brit. Inst. Fuel. Performance of diesel engines; stability and sensitivity of explosives; coal hydrogenation and gasification; Fischer-Tropsch process; catalysis of steam-carbon reactions; combustion; long range energy supply. Address: Texas Eastern Transmission Corp, P.O. Box 2521, Houston, TX 77001.

ELLIOTT, MYRON A(NDREW), b. Taylorville, Ill, June 21, 10; m. 40. PHYSICS. B.S, Illinois, 35; Ph.D.(phys. chem), Wisconsin, 38. Asst, Wisconsin, 35-38; res. assoc, Nat. Bur. Standards, 38-40; physicist, Naval Res. Lab, 40-48; U.S. Navy Mine Defense Lab, 48-56, head acoust. br, minesweeping div, 56-60, mem. consult. staff, Naval Ship Res. & Develop. Lab, 60-70; RETIRED. AAAS; Am. Phys. Soc; Acoust. Soc. Am. Underwater acoustics; low-frequency transducers; instrumentation. Address: 2519 Cardwell Way, Sarasota, FL 33581.

ELLIOTT, NORMAN, b. Connah's Quay, Wales, Sept. 13, 07; nat; m. 31. PHYSICAL CHEMISTRY. B.A, Oberlin Col, 29, M.A, 30; Ph.D.(phys. chem), Calif. Inst. Tech, 38. Res. chemist, Dow Chem. Co, Mich, 30-32; instr, Pomona Col, 38-42, asst. prof, 42-46, phys. chem, Chicago, 46-48; SR. CHEMIST, BROOKHAVEN NAT. LAB, 48- Phys. chemist, Manhattan Proj, Chicago, 42-43, Oak Ridge Nat. Lab, 43-46. Crystal structure and magnetism. Address: Brookhaven National Lab, Upton, NY 11973.

ELLIOTT, PAUL M, b. Kingsville, Tex, Oct. 20, 22; m. 46; c. 3. PHYSICS. B.S, U.S. Naval Acad, 44; M.S, Tex. Col. Arts & Indust, 60; Ph.D.(physics), Tex. A&M Univ, 64. Instr. PHYSICS, TEX. A&I UNIV, 60-61, asst. prof, 64-66, assoc. prof, 66-69, PROF, 69- U.S.N, 41-48, Lt.(jg). AAAS; Am. Phys. Soc; Am. Asn. Physics Teachers. Molecular spectroscopy. Address: Dept. of Physics, Texas A&I University, Kingsville, TX 78363.

ELLIOTT, PAUL R(USSELL), b. Pueblo, Colo, Aug. 26, 33; div; c. 2. BIOCHEMISTRY, PHYSIOLOGY. B.A, Phillips, 55; univ. fel, Michigan, 55-57, M.S, 57, Nat. Insts. Health fel, 58-60, Ph.D.(zool), 60. Nat. Insts. Health fel. biochem, Johns Hopkins Univ, 60-63; asst. prof. zool, UNIV. FLA, 63-68, assoc. prof, 68-71, asst. dean preprof. educ, cols. arts & sci, dent. & med, 69-71, ASST. DEAN TALLAHASSEE PROGS, COL. MED, 71-; PROF. BIOL. SCI, FLA. STATE UNIV, 71-; DIR. PROG. MED. SCI, FLA. STATE UNIV, FLA. A&M UNIV. & UNIV. FLA, 71- Nat. Insts. Health res. grant, 64-67. Cytochemistry and physiology of the epididymis; bioluminescence in bacteria and ctenophrans; medical education research. Address: PIMS, Student Health Center, Florida State University, Tallahassee, FL 32306.

ELLIOTT, QUENTIN, b. Aurora, Nebr, Sept. 19, 19; div; c. 1. CHEMICAL ENGINEERING. B.S, Calif. Inst. Tech, 41, M.S, 42. Chem. engr, Texas Co, 42; res. assoc, Off. Sci. Res. & Develop, Calif. Inst. Tech, 42-45; chem. engr, West Cartridge Co, Ill, 45-46; U.S. Naval Ord. Test Sta, 46-56, head solid propellants div, 51-55, propellants & explosives dept, 55-56; proj. mgr. new prod. div, metal finishing, MINN. MINING & MFG. CO, 56-62, tech. & prod. mgr, mech plating prod, 62-63; mfg. mgr, indust. finishing dept, 64-68, PROD. COORD. NEW PROD, INDUST. MINERAL PROD. DIV, 68- Am. Inst. Chem. Eng. Chemical and mechanical manufacturing; metal plating; processing of explosives and thermoplastics; measurement of transient pressures; mechanical and chemical properties of plastics; internal ballistics of rocket motors. Address: Industrial Mineral Products Division, 3M Center, Minnesota Mining & Manufacturing Co, St. Paul, MN 55101.

ELLIOTT, RALPH B(ENJAMIN), b. Buffalo, N.Y, July 4, 07; m. 37; c. 2. PHYSICAL CHEMISTRY. A.B, Buffalo, 29; M.A, Princeton, 32, Ph.D. (chem), 34. Asst. dir. res. lab, Williams Gold Ref. Co, N.Y, 29-31; res. & develop. chemist, electrochem. dept, E.I. du Pont de Nemours & Co, Inc, 33-39, sales develop. peroxygens, 39-41, prod. supvr, 41-46, sales mgr, sodium prod, 46-47, prod. supt. peroxygens, 48-50, res. supvr, 52, plant supt, Dresden Plant, 53-59, Wash. rep, 60-63, mem. staff, mkt. res, 64-66, air-water pollution specialist, 66-70; TECH. CONSULT. AIR-WATER POLLUTION, UNIV. DEL, 70- Am. Chem. Soc. Physical and inorganic chemistry; electrochemical units of measurement; standard cells; peroxides. Address: 526 Ruxton Dr, Wilmington, DE 19809.

ELLIOTT, R(ALPH) F(RANCIS), b. Darke Co, Ohio, May 21, 15; m. 43; c. 3. ANIMAL NUTRITION. B.Sc, Ohio State, 41; M.Sc, Cornell, 47, Ph.D.(animal nutrit), 49. Asst. animal nutrit, Pa. State Col, 41-42, 43-45; Cornell, 45-49; asst. prof. dairy husb, Kentucky, 49-51; animal nutritionist, res. div. Am. Cyanamid Co, 51-56, dir. swine develop, farm & home div, 56-58, mgr. animal feed develop, agr. div, 58-62, nutrit. & physiol. sect, 62-64, animal indust. develop, 64-68; prof. animal sci. & nutrit, col. agr. & environ. sci, Rutgers Univ, 68-70; MGR. ANIMAL SCI, CORP. RES. & DEVELOP, ALLIED CHEM. CORP, 70- Med.C, U.S.A, 42-43. Am. Chem. Soc; Am. Dairy Sci. Asn; Am. Soc. Animal Sci; Animal Nutrit. Res. Coun. Vitamin A and carotene metabolism; antibiotics in animal nutrition; ruminant nutrition. Address: Allied Chemical Corp, P.O. Box 1021 R, Morristown, NJ 07960.

ELLIOTT, RICHARD LEE, b. Bethany, Mo, Oct. 12, 28; m. 59; c. 2. ORGANIC CHEMISTRY. B.S. & B.A, Northwest Mo. State Col, 50; M.A, Missouri, 56. SR. CHEMIST, MIDWEST RES. INST, 55- U.S.A, 51-53. Am. Chem. Soc; Sci. Res. Soc. Am. Organic synthesis; synthesis of silazane monomers; silicone and silazane polymers. Address: Midwest Research Institute, 425 Volker Blvd, Kansas City, MO 64110.

ELLIOTT, ROBERT A, b. Darke Co, Ohio, Dec. 29, 24; m. 46; c. 4. BACTERIOLOGY. A.B, Miami (Ohio), 49; M.S, Ohio State, 51, Ph.D.(bact), 53. Asst. & fel. dairy sci, Ohio State, 54-55; bacteriologist, biol. develop. dept, ELI LILLY & CO, GREENFIELD, 55-64, SR. BACTERIOLOGIST, biol. assay develop. dept, 64-69, BIOL. TECH. SERV. & QUAL. CONTROL, 69- U.S.A, 43-45, Res, 50-56. Am. Soc. Microbiol; N.Y. Acad. Sci. Development and testing of viral vaccines. Address: 9817 E. Michigan St, Indianapolis, IN 46229.

ELLIOTT, ROBERT D(ARYL), b. Nashville, Tenn, June 4, 35; m. 68; c. 3. ORGANIC CHEMISTRY. B.A, Vanderbilt, 57; Ph.D.(org. chem), Wayne State, 61. Sr. asst. scientist, tech. develop. labs, U.S. Pub. Health Serv, Ga, 60-63; SR. CHEMIST, SOUTH. RES. INST, 63- Synthesis of anticancer agents; antiradiation drugs and tritium labeled insecticides. Address: Southern Research Institute, 2000 Ninth Ave. S, Birmingham, AL 35205.

ELLIOTT, ROBERT D(UNSHEE), b. Yonkers, N.Y, Dec. 30, 14; m. 41; c. 5. METEOROLOGY. B.S, Calif. Inst. Tech, 36, M.S, 37. Meteorologist, East. Airlines, Ga, 37-39; Krick Weather Serv, Calif, 39-42; instr. meteorol, Calif. Inst. Tech, 40-42, asst. prof, 46-47; dir. res, Am. Inst. Aerological Res, Pasadena, 47-50; v.pres, N.AM. WEATHER CONSULT, 50-57, PRES, 57-; AEROMETRIC RES, INC, 56- Mem. adv. comt. weather serv, U.S. Dept. Commerce. U.S.N.R, 42-45. AAAS; Am. Meteorol. Soc.(co-ed, J. Appl. Meteorol, 60-67, appl. meteorol. award, 68); Am. Geophys. Union; Am. Soc. Civil Eng. Synoptic meteorology and weather modification. Address: North American Weather Consultants, Santa Barbara Airport, Goleta, CA 93103.

ELLIOTT, ROBERT H(ARE) E(GERTON), JR, b. Flushing, N.Y, Sept. 9, 06; m. 35; c. 3. PHYSIOLOGY, SURGERY. A.B, Princeton, 28; M.D, Columbia, 32, Med.Sc.D.(surg), 38. Instr. surg, COL. PHYSICIANS & SURGEONS, UNIV. COLUMBIA, 38-46, assoc, prof, 55-65, PROF, 65-, ASSOC. DEAN FACULTY MED, 66- Asst. surg, Vanderbilt Clin, 38-41, asst. chief clin, 41-46, chief, 46-50; asst. surg, Presby. Hosp, 41-46, asst. attend. surgeon, 46-50, assoc. attend. surgeon, 50-52, chief east surg, 52-66, attend. surgeon, 52-, asst. v.pres, 66-; Lewis Linn McArthur lectr, Frank Billings Found, Inst. Med, Ill, 47; assoc. attend. surgeon, Columbia div, Bellevue Hosp, 49-52; civilian consult, Sta. Hosp, U.S. Mil. Acad, 49-65; consult, Southampton Hosp; Harlem Hosp, N.Y, 64-66. Dipl, Nat. Bd. Med. Exam, 37; Am. Bd. Surg, 40. Civilian with Off. Sci. Res. & Develop, Nat. Res. Coun, 42-45. Am. Med. Asn; fel. Am. Col. Surg; Soc. Univ. Surg; Am. Thyroid Asn; N.Y. Acad. Med; Asn. Schs. Allied Health Professions. Physiology and surgery of the spleen and thyroid gland. Address: College of Physicians & Surgeons, Columbia University, 630 W. 168th St, New York, NY 10032.

ELLIOTT, ROBERT H(ENRY), b. Concord, N.H, July 26, 15; m. 41; c. 3. CHEMISTRY. B.S, New Hampshire, 36; M.S, Vermont, 37. Asst. chem, Gen. Chem. Co, New York, 37-45; res. chemist, Rumford Div, Heyden Chem. Corp, 45-50, Hulman Co, 50-66, dir. labs, 54-66; RES. ENGR, FRAM CORP. DIV, BENDIX CORP, 66- Am. Chem. Soc. Organic and inorganic process development; electrochemical process research; detergent formulation and testing; industrial waste treatment. Address: Fram Corp. Division, Bendix Corp, Pawtucket Ave, East Providence, RI 02916.

ELLIOTT, ROBERT M(EDILL), b. Chicago, Ill, Apr. 23, 12; m. 37; c. 2. PHYSICS. B.S, Mass. Inst. Tech, 34, fel. & scholar, 34-37; Ph.D.(physics), 37. Res. engr, Am. Thermos Bottle Co, Conn, 37-41; chief engr, 41; res. physicist, Mass. Inst. Tech, 41-43; mem. staff & sci. adv, Columbia, 43-45; res. engr, Am. Thermos Prods. Co, 45-49, chief engr, 49-60; ENG. MGR, THERMOS DIV, KING SEELEY THERMOS CO, 60- With Off. Sci. Res. & Develop, U.S.N, 44. Am. Soc. Test. & Mat; Am. Electroplaters Soc. Acoustics; operational research; vacuum technology; underwater ordnance. Address: Thermos Division, King Seeley Thermos Co, Thermos Ave, Norwich, CT 06360.

ELLIOTT, R(OBERT) PAUL, b. Brookings, S.Dak, Mar. 6, 18; m. 41; c. 1. FOOD BACTERIOLOGY. B.S, Washington (Seattle), 40, M.S, 49. Teaching fel. bact, Washington (Seattle), 40-41, 42; bacteriologist, State Pollution Comn, Wash, 41-42; bacteriologist & fishery technologist, fishery technol. res, U.S. Fish & Wildlife Serv, 42-50; Fulbright grant, Norway, 50-51; bacteriologist, U.S. Food & Drug Admin, Dept. Health, Educ. & Welfare, 51-59; chemist, west. utilization res. & develop. div, U.S. Dept. Agr, 59-64; microbiol. lab. coord, U.S. Food & Drug Admin, Dept. Health Educ. & Welfare, 64-66; head microbiol. group, tech. serv. div, CONSUMER & MKT. SERV, U.S. DEPT. AGR, 66-69, chief lab. br, 69-71, CHIEF CHEM. & MICROBIOL. BR, LAB. SERV. DIV, 71- Am. Soc. Microbiol; Inst. Food Technol. Microbiology of foods and drugs. Address: 1540 Live Oak Dr, Silver Spring, MD 20910.

ELLIOTT, ROBERT S(TRATMAN), b. New York, N.Y, Mar. 9, 21; m. 51; c. 4. ELECTRICAL ENGINEERING, ECONOMICS. A.B, Columbia, 42, B.S, 43; M.S, Illinois, 47, Ph.D.(elec. eng), 52; M.A, Univ. Calif. Santa Barbara, 71. Jr. engr. radar, Appl. Physics Lab, 43-46; asst. prof. elec. eng, Illinois, 46-52; res. physicist electromagnetic probs, Hughes Aircraft Co, 53-56; tech. dir. & v.pres, Rantec Corp, 56-59; PROF. ENG, UNIV. CALIF, LOS ANGELES, 59-, CHMN. DEPT, 69-, asst. dean grad. studies eng, 66-69. U.S.N.R, 52-53, Lt.(jg). Fel. Inst. Elec. & Electronics Eng. Electromagnetics; microwave tubes and antennas; electrical properties of materials; engineering economics. Address: School of Engineering & Applied Science, 7400 Boelter Hall, University of California, Los Angeles, CA 90024.

ELLIOTT, RODNEY P, b. Dayton, Ohio, Dec. 5, 26. PHYSICAL METALLURGY, CRYSTALLOGRAPHY. Met.E, Cincinnati, 50; M.S, Ill. Inst. Tech, 53, Ph.D.(metall. eng), 55. Asst. metallurgist, IIT Res. Inst, 52-54, assoc. metallurgist, 54-55, res. metallurgist, 55-58, sr. metallurgist, 58-65; assoc. prof. metall. eng, Univ. Cinn, 65-69; SR. METALLURGIST, IIT RES. INST, 69- Am. Soc. Metals; Am. Inst. Mining, Metall. & Petrol, Eng; Am. Crystallog. Asn. Alloy development; theory of alloy phases; crystallography of metal compounds; determination of metallurgical equilibrium. Address: 5201 S. Cornell Ave, Chicago, IL 60615.

ELLIOTT, ROSEMARY ESKRIDGE, b. Great Yarmouth, Eng, June 16, 34; m. 68; c. 5. BACTERIAL GENETICS, BIOCHEMISTRY. B.Sc, Birmingham, 55; M.A, Buffalo, 62; Ph.D.(biochem), State Univ. N.Y. Buffalo, 64. Cancer res. scientist, ROSWELL PARK MEM. INST, 64-66, SR. CANCER RES. SCIENTIST, 66- AAAS; Am. Soc. Microbiol. Reaction mechanisms in blood coagulation; host-controlled variation in bacteriophages; lysogenic association between bacteriophages and host cells. Address: Dept. of Biology, Roswell Park Memorial Institute, 666 Elm St, Buffalo, NY 14226.

ELLIOTT, RUSH, b. New Concord, Ohio, Apr. 21, 03; m. 27; c. 3. ZOOLOGY. A.B, Ohio, 24; A.M, Ohio State, 26; fel, Michigan, 28-30, Ph.D. (embryol), 30. Instr. biol, OHIO UNIV, 24-26, asst. prof, 26-28, 30-32, assoc. prof, 32-35, comp. anat, 35-38, prof. ANAT, 38-65, dean, col. arts & sci, 54-65, RUSH ELLIOTT PROF, 65-, dir. summer sch, 46-51, chmn, dept. zool, 49-54, dean, univ. col, 51-54. AAAS; Am. Asn. Anat; Am. Soc. Zool. Comparative histology, anatomy and neurology; embryology. Address: 3 Marietta Ave, Athens, OH 45701.

ELLIOTT, SHELDEN D(OUGLASS), JR, b. Anaheim, Calif, Feb. 3, 31; m. 54; c. 2. PHYSICS. B.S, Yale, 53, M.S, 54, Nat. Sci. Found fel, 54-56, Loomis fel, 56-57, Ph.D, 59. PHYSICIST, U.S. NAVAL WEAPONS CTR, 58- Am. Phys. Soc; Am. Astron. Soc; Weather Modification Asn. Low temperature physics; second sound in liquid helium isotope mixtures; atmospheric physics; astronomy; meteor physics; weather modification. Address: Code 602, U.S. Naval Weapons Center, China Lake, CA 93555.

ELLIOTT, S(HELDON) E(LLWOOD), b. Asunción, Paraguay, July 9, 25; U.S. citizen; m. 48; c. 3. MATHEMATICS. A.B, Phillips, 48; M.A, Michigan, 49. Fel, Michigan, 50-51, 55-56, jr. instr, 56-57; MATHEMATICIAN, PHILLIPS PETROL. CO, 51-55, 57-, MATH. GEOPHYSICIST, 69- U.S.A.A.F, 43-46, 1st Lt. Am. Math. Soc; Soc. Explor. Geophys. Seismology; operational calculus; differential equations; numerical methods; topology. Address: 1512 Macklyn Lane, Bartlesville, OK 74003.

ELLIOTT, STUART B(RUCE), b. Oakland, Calif, July 11, 27; m. 53; c. 2. PHYSICS. B.S, Stanford Univ, 49, M.S, 51, Ph.D.(physics), 60. Asst. prof. PHYSICS, Kenyon Col, 55-60; OCCIDENTAL COL, 60-67, ASSOC. PROF, 67-, CHMN. DEPT, 71- U.S.N.R, 45-46. Am. Asn. Physics Teachers; Optical Soc. Am.(sci. ed, Optics & Spectros, 68-). X-ray optics; effects of polishing imperfections on specular reflection of x-rays; holography. Address: Dept. of Physics, Occidental College, Los Angeles, CA 90041.

ELLIOTT, W(ILLARD) B(UFORD), b. Osborn, Mo, Jan. 5, 23; m. 68; c. 3. BIOCHEMISTRY. A.B, Northwest Mo. State Teachers Col, 43; M.S, Iowa, 48, Ph.D.(biochem), 50. Res. asst. BIOCHEM, IOWA, 47-50; instr, SCH. MED, STATE UNIV. N.Y. BUFFALO, 50-53, asst. prof, 53-62, assoc. prof, 62-67, PROF, 67- Consult, Erie Co. Lab, 51-58; Sisters of Charity Hosp, 59-61; U.S. Pub. Health Serv. res. career develop. award, 61-70. U.S.N.R, 43-46, Res, 46-55, Lt. Am. Chem. Soc; Am. Inst. Chem; Am. Soc. Biol. Chem. Enzyme systems and enzyme inhibitors; low temperature spectrophotometry; venom chemistry and immunology. Address: 38 E. Chateau Terr, Snyder, NY 14226.

ELLIOTT, W(ILLIA)M E(MERY), b. Minneapolis, Minn, Nov. 18, 21; m. 45; c. 5. PHYSICAL CHEMISTRY. B.S, Marquette, 44, M.S, 47; M.S, Wisconsin, 61. Asst. instr. chem, Marquette, 46-47; instr. chem. & math, Aquinas Col, 47-49; res. chemist, Allis Chalmers Mfg. Co, 49-63; scientist electrochem, Globe Union Inc, 63-67; asst. prof. CHEM, WIS. STATE UNIV-PLATTEVILLE, RICHLAND CAMPUS, 67-68, ASSOC. PROF, 68- Lectr. chem, Marquette Univ, 54. U.S.N.R, 44-46, Lt.(jg). Am. Chem. Soc. Electrical insulating materials and lubricants; electrochemical kinetics; thermodynamics; electrochemistry; nonaqueous electrolytes; batteries; fuel cells. Address: Dept. of Chemistry, Wisconsin State University-Platteville, Richland Campus, Richland Center, WI 53581.

ELLIOTT, WILLIAM H(UECKEL), b. St. Louis, Mo, June 4, 18; m. 49; c. 4. ORGANIC CHEMISTRY, BIOCHEMISTRY. B.S, St. Louis, 39, fel, 39-44, M.S, 41, Ph.D.(org. chem), 44. Asst. chem, Nat. Defense Res. Cmt. contract, Indiana, 44; instr. biol. chem, St. Louis, 44-47; res. assoc. chem, Mass. Inst. Tech, 47; sr. instr. biol. chem, ST. LOUIS UNIV, 47-50, asst. prof, 50-53, assoc. prof, 53-59, PROF. BIOCHEM, 59-, acting chmn. dept, 70-71. With comt. med. res, Off. Sci. Res. & Develop, 44; mem. res. career award comt, Nat. Inst. Gen. Med. Sci, 62-65; vis. investr, Karolinska Inst, Sweden, summer 65. AAAS; Am. Chem. Soc; Am. Soc. Biol. Chem; Soc. Exp. Biol. & Med; Am. Soc. Mass Spectrometry. Sterol and bile acid metabolism; mass spectrometry; chemistry and metabolism of fat-soluble substances. Address: Edward A. Doisy Dept. of Biochemistry, St. Louis University, 1402 S. Grand Blvd, St. Louis, MO 63104.

ELLIOTT, WILLIAM P(AUL), b. Geneva, Ill, June 16, 28; m. 52; c. 2. PHYSICAL OCEANOGRAPHY, METEOROLOGY. A.B, St. John's Col.(Md), 47; fel, Illinois, 47-49; M.S, Chicago, 52; Ph.D.(phys. oceanog), Texas A&M, 58. Res. assoc. meteorol, Texas A&M, 52-57, from instr. to asst. prof, 53-56; atmospheric physicist micrometeorol, U.S. Air Force Cambridge Res. Lab, 57-68; RES. ASSOC. OCEANOG, ORE. STATE UNIV, 68- AAAS; Am. Meteorol. Soc; Royal Meteorol. Soc. Micrometeorology; atmospheric turbulence and diffusion, especially wind and temperature structure and heat flux near the ground; air and water pollution; coastal processes. Address: Dept. of Oceanography, Oregon State University, Corvallis, OR 97331.

ELLIOTT, W(ILLIAM) W(HITEFIELD), b. Darlington Heights, Va, May 28, 98. MATHEMATICS. A.B, Hampden-Sydney Col; fel, Kentucky, 18-19, A.M; Chicago; fel, Cornell, 21-22, Ph.D.(math), 24. Head dept. MATH, Gordon Inst, 19-20; instr, Ga. Inst. Technol, 20-21; Cornell, 22-23; Yale, 23-25; asst. prof, DUKE UNIV, 25-27, prof, 27-67, EMER. PROF, 67- Am. Math. Soc; Math. Asn. Am. Differential and integral equations. Address: Dept. of Mathematics, Duke University, Durham, NC 27706.

ELLIS, ALAN F, b. New Wilmington, Pa, June 21, 36; m. 58; c. 1. ORGANIC CHEMISTRY. B.S, Westminster Col.(Pa), 58; Ph.D.(org. chem), Illinois, Urbana, 63. Res. chemist, GULF RES. & DEVELOP. CO, 62-68, sr. res. chemist, 68-69, SECT. SUPVR. ORG. RES, 69- Am. Chem. Soc; fel. Am. Inst. Chem. Petrochemical process development; specific hydrogenation techniques; nitrogen chemistry. Address: Gulf Research & Development Co, P.O. Drawer 2038, Pittsburgh, PA 19130.

ELLIS, ALBERT T(ROMLY), b. Atwater, Calif, Apr. 22, 17; m. 54. APPLIED MECHANICS. B.S, Calif. Inst. Tech, 43, M.S, 47, Ph.D.(mech. eng, physics), 53. Asst. physiol, Calif. Inst. Tech, 42-43; res. engr. electronics & instrumentation, Columbia, 44-46; electronics engr. & asst. head electronics hydrodyn. lab, Calif. Inst. Tech, 46-47; physicist, theory controls & servomechanisms, U.S. Naval Ord. Test Sta, 47-49; res. engr. hydrodyn, Calif. Inst. Tech, 49-54, sr. res. fel. eng, 54-57, assoc. prof. APPL. MECH, 58-67; PROF, UNIV. CALIF, SAN DIEGO, 67- Consult, Space Technol. Labs, 56-; Naval Undersea Ctr, San Diego; sr. vis. dept. appl. math. & theoret. physics, Cambridge, 64-65. Sig.C, U.S.A, 43-44. AAAS; Inst. Elec. & Electronics Eng; Am. Soc. Mech. Eng; Am. Phys. Soc; Acoustical Soc. Am; Int. Asn. Hydraul. Res; Int. Soc. Eng. Sci. Cavitation and drag reduction in dilute polymer flows; laser radiation interactions with solids and liquids; wave propagation in composite materials; high speed holography. Address: Dept. of Applied Mechanics, 6226 Urey Hall, University of California, San Diego, La Jolla, CA 92037.

ELLIS, BERNARD, b. Chicago, Ill, Dec. 25, 20; m. 42; c. 2. ENGINEERING. B.S, Ill. Inst. Tech, 42; California, Los Angeles, 50-52. Eng. trainee, Lockheed Aircraft Corp, 42; chief for. engine anal. br, Air Tech. Intel. Center, 45-46; purchasing agent, rocket div, Gen. Tire & Rubber Co, 46; thermodyn. analyst, Consol. Vultee Aircraft Corp, 47; sr. engr, heating and vent. sect, N.Am. Aviation, Inc, 47-48; head rocket br, Naval Air Missile Test Center, 48-53; proj. engr, Reaction Motors, Inc, 53-55; engr, flight sci. div, missile systs. div, LOCKHEED AIRCRAFT CORP, 55-57, mgr. propulsion dept, 57-62, prod. assurance, 62-63, CONSULT. ENGR, RES. ENG. DIV LOCKHEED MISSILES & SPACE CO, 63-, MGR. EAST. TECH. OFF, 70- U.S.A.A.F, 43-45. Assoc. fel. Am. Inst. Aeronaut. & Astronaut. Physical chemistry; propulsion physics; preliminary design and general performance. Address: Eastern Technical Office, Lockheed Missiles & Space Co, 6201 Greenbelt Rd, U-8B, College Park, MD 20740.

ELLIS, BOYD G, b. Havensville, Kans, Nov. 3, 32; m. 55; c. 3. SOIL CHEMISTRY. B.S, Kansas State, 54, M.S, 55; Ph.D.(soil chem), Michigan State, 61. Asst. prof. SOIL SCI, MICH. STATE UNIV, 61-63, assoc. prof, 63-68, PROF, 68- U.S.A.F, 54-56, 1st Lt. Am. Soc. Agron; Clay Minerals Soc. Soil fertility; chemistry of nutrients in the soil and their effect on plant growth; factors affecting availability of potassium, phosphorus, magnesium and zinc. Address: Dept. of Crop & Soil Sciences, Michigan State University, East Lansing, MI 48823.

ELLIS, BROOKS F(LEMING), b. Jonestown, W.Va, Aug. 2, 97; m. 20, 66. GEOLOGY. A.B, Marietta Col, 23, hon. Sc.D, 53; M.S, N.Y. Univ, 29, Ph.D. (geol), 32. Instr. sci, high sch, W.Va, 23-26; N.Y, 27-29; GEOL, N.Y. UNIV, 30-36, asst. prof, 36-43, assoc. prof, 43-46, prof, 46-66, chmn. dept, 43-57, head dept, 57-66, EMER. PROF, 66-; DIR, EQUITABLE PETROL. CORP, 70- Instr. evening sessions, Brooklyn Col, 33-39; dir. res. proj, Am. Mus. Nat. Hist, 30-41, curator micropaleont, 41-44, curator & chmn, 44-67, emer. curator, 67-; adj. prof, Rutgers Univ, 66-; pres. & dir, Petro-

therm, Inc. & United Arabian Petrol. Co. U.S.N, 17-19. AAAS; Am. Asn. Petrol. Geol; Paleont. Soc; Soc. Econ. Paleont. & Mineral; fel. Am. Geog. Soc; fel. Geol. Soc. Am; Am. Polar Soc; Am. Geophys. Union; Ger. Geol. Soc; Ger. Paleont. Soc; Swiss Paleont. Soc; Geol. Soc. France; Swiss Geol. Soc. Micropaleontology; microtechnique and instruments; taxonomy and nomenclature; Foraminifera; Ostracoda. Address: 72 Clarendon Rd, Scarsdale, NY 10583.

ELLIS, C(HARLES) H(ERBERT), b. Central City, Nebr, Nov. 28, 11; m. 38; c. 3. PHYSIOLOGY. A.B, Whittier Col, 34, M.S, 37; California, Los Angeles, 38-39; Ph.D.(animal physiol), Calif. Inst. Tech, 43. Instr. biol, Whittier Col, 37-39; teaching fel, physiol, Calif. Inst. Tech, 40-41, asst, 41-43; res. assoc, Gordon A. Alles Labs, 43-51; SR. PHARMACOLOGIST, WELLCOME RES. LABS, 51- With Off. Sci. Res. & Develop, 44. Am. Physiol. Soc; Soc. Exp. Biol. & Med; Am. Soc. Pharmacol. Nerve-muscle physiology of arthropods; anticonvulsant drugs; circulatory and respiratory actions of drugs; influence of drugs on central nervous system; influence of drugs on myoneural junction; physiology of the heart. Address: Wellcome Research Labs, 3030 Cornwallis Rd, Research Triangle Park, NC 27709.

ELLIS, CHARLES H(ERBERT), JR, b. Pasadena, Calif, Mar. 14, 41. BIOLOGY, DEVELOPMENTAL BIOLOGY. B.A, Swarthmore Col, 62; Nat; Insts. Health fel, Hopkins, 65-66, Ph.D.(biol), 66. Asst. prof. BIOL, Amherst Col, 66-71; ASSOC. PROF, NORTHEAST. UNIV, 71- AAAS; Am. Soc. Zool; Am. Soc. Nat; Soc. Develop. Biol. Echinoderm development, especially protein synthesis and genetic control of morphogenesis. Address: Dept. of Biology, Northeastern University, Boston, MA 02115.

ELLIS, C(HARLES) HOWARD, b. Milwaukee, Wis, May 17, 29; m. 52; c. 2. PALEONTOLOGY. B.S, Beloit Col, 51; fel, Colorado, 56-59, M.S, 58. Geologist paleont, Humble Oil & Ref. Co, 58-59; MARATHON OIL CO, 59-69, ADVAN. PALEONTOLOGIST, DENVER RES. CTR, 69- U.S.A, 51-54, Sgt. Soc. Econ. Paleont. & Mineral; Paleont. Soc. Invertebrate paleontology, primarily micropaleontology dealing with stratigraphic and paleontologic zonation, correlation, and paleoecology; palynology of Paleozoic, Cretacous and tertiary sediments. Address: Denver Research Center, Marathon Oil Co, P.O. Box 269, Littleton, CO 80120.

ELLIS, DANIEL B(ENSON), b. Rochdale, Eng, May 15, 37; U.S. citizen; m. 63; c. 2. BIOCHEMISTRY. B.Sc, Univ. Sheffield, 58; Ph.D.(biochem), McGill Univ, 61. Fel, Stanford Res. Inst, 61-62; res. assoc, Wistar Inst. Anat. & Biol, 62-64; biochemist, Stanford Res. Inst, 64-65; sr. biochemist, SMITH KLINE & FRENCH LABS, 66-70, SR. INVESTR, 71- AAAS; Am. Chem. Soc; Biochem. Soc; Sci. Res. Soc. Am. Control mechanisms; drug metabolism; biosynthesis of glycoproteins; biochemistry of nucleotides and nucleic acids; cancer chemotherapy. Address: Smith Kline & French Labs, 1500 Spring Garden St, Philadelphia, PA 19101.

ELLIS, DAVID A(LLEN), b. Seattle, Wash, Mar. 25, 17; m. 43; c. 1. PHYSICAL & INORGANIC CHEMISTRY. B.S, Washington (Seattle), 39; California, Los Angeles, 42-43; Chicago, 43; Res. Corp. fel, Southern California, 48-49, M.S, 48, Ph.D.(chem), 50. Chemist, Puget Sound Pulp & Timber Co, 40; observer, U.S. Weather Bur, 40-41; asst, Southern California, 45-48; res. chemist, Dow Chem. Co, 49-67; PROF. CHEM, AZUSA PAC. COL, 67-, CHMN. DIV. SCI. & MATH, 71- U.S.A.F, 42-45, Res, 45-, Lt. Col. Am. Chem. Soc. Solvent extraction; inorganic chemicals; ion exchange. Address: 1045 Bonner Ct, La Verne, CA 91750.

ELLIS, DAVID G(REENHILL), b. Marietta, Ohio, Mar. 9, 36; m. 69; c. 2. THEORETICAL PHYSICS. A.B, Marietta Col, 58; univ. fel, Cornell, 58-59, Nat. Sci. Found. fel, 59-62, Ph.D.(theoret. physics), 64. Res. assoc. theoret. physics, Indiana, 63-65; asst. prof. PHYSICS & ASTRON, UNIV. TOLEDO, 65-69, ASSOC. PROF, 69- Am. Phys. Soc; Am. Astron. Soc. Weak interactions at high energy; neutrino astrophysics; inelastic pion-nucleon scattering; inelastic atomic collisions. Address: Dept. of Physics & Astronomy, University of Toledo, Toledo, OH 43606.

ELLIS, DAVID JACK, b. Norristown, Pa, Feb. 1, 40; m. 63; c. 3. ORGANIC CHEMISTRY, BIOCHEMISTRY. B.S, Colorado State, 61; Ph.D.(org. chem), Univ. Calif, Berkeley, 65. Nat. Insts. Health fel, Marburg, Ger, 65-66; RES. BIOCHEMIST, INST. HORMONE BIOL, SYNTEX RES. DIV, 66- AAAS; Am. Chem. Soc; The Chem. Soc; German Soc. Biol. Chem. Synthetic organic chemistry; medicinal chemistry; molecular pharmacology; mechanisms of hormone action. Address: Institute of Hormone Biology, Syntex Research Division, Stanford Industrial Park, Palo Alto, CA 94304.

ELLIS, DAVID M, b. Ithaca, N.Y, Nov. 15, 37; m. 63; c. 2. ELECTRICAL ENGINEERING, SOLID STATE PHYSICS. B.S, Pa. State, 59; M.S, Washington (Seattle), 65, Ph.D.(elec. eng), 68. Res. engr, Burroughs Corp, Pa, 59-63; ASST. PROF. ELEC. ENG, UNIV. VT, 68- Consult. components div, IBM Corp, Vt, 68-70; Vertek Inc, 70- Inst. Elec. & Electronics Eng. Theory and applications of thin magnetic films; semiconductor electronics; nuclear magnetic resonance. Address: Dept. of Electrical Engineering, University of Vermont, Burlington, VT 05401.

ELLIS, DAVID REES, b. Nevin, N.Wales, Mar. 6, 41; m. 65; c. 2. ORGANIC & ANALYTICAL CHEMISTRY. B.S, Liverpool Col. Sci. & Technol, Eng, 65; Ph.D.(chem), Univ. Manchester, 68. Fel. radiation chem. sulphur compounds, Univ. S. Fla, 68-69; ANAL. CHEMIST, TOMS RIVER CHEM. CORP, 69- Am. Chem. Soc. Analysis of organosilicon compounds; radiation chemistry of sulfur compounds; analysis in the dye industry. Address: Toms River Chemical Corp, Toms River, NJ 08753.

ELLIS, DAVID WERTZ, b. Huntingdon, Pa, Feb. 8, 36; m. 61; c. 3. ANALYTICAL CHEMISTRY. A.B, Haverford Col, 58; du Pont fel, Mass. Inst. Technol, 60-61, Ph.D.(anal. chem), 62. Asst. prof. CHEM, UNIV. N.H, 62-67, ASSOC. PROF, 67-, ASSOC. ACAD. V.PRES, 70-, asst. dean, col. technol, 67-68, assoc. off. acad. v.pres, 68-69, acting acad. v.pres, 69. AAAS; Am. Chem. Soc; Soc. Appl. Spectros. Excited-state chemical reactions using fluorescence and phosphorescence; development of new methods of chemical analysis; analysis of water pollutants. Address: Thompson Hall, University of New Hampshire, Durham, NH 03824.

ELLIS, DEREK V, b. Windsor, Eng, July 26, 30; Can. citizen; m. 57; c. 3. BIOLOGY. B.Sc, Edinburgh, 51, Hons, 52; M.Sc, McGill, 54, Ph.D.(zool), 57; Nat. Res. Coun. Can. fel, Copenhagen, 55-56. Asst. scientist, Fisheries Res. Bd. Can, 57, assoc. scientist, 57-63; asst. prof. zool, Manitoba, 63-64; ASSOC. PROF. BIOL, UNIV. VICTORIA (B.C), 64- Ethology and ecology of aquatic animals. Address: Dept. of Biology, University of Victoria, Victoria, B.C, Can.

ELLIS, D(ON) E(DWIN), b. Ames, Iowa, Apr. 8, 08; m. 29; c. 1. PLANT PATHOLOGY. A.B, Nebr. Cent. Col, 28, B.S, 29; Iowa State Col, summers, 30, 31, 34; M.S, La. State, 32; Ph.D.(plant path), North Carolina, 45. Teacher, high sch, Nebr, 29-31; asst. plant path, exp. sta, La. State, 31-33; supv. technician forest path, state emergency conserv. work, Iowa, 33; asst. pathologist, div. forest path, bur. plant indust, U.S. Dept. Agr, 34-40; asst. plant pathologist, exp. sta, N.C. STATE UNIV, 40-44, assoc. prof. PLANT PATH, 44-50, PROF, 50-, HEAD DEPT, 54- Am. Phytopath. Soc. (pres, 70); Mycol. Soc. Am; Asn. Trop. Biol; Am. Inst. Biol. Sci. Diseases of vegetable crops. Address: Dept. of Plant Pathology, North Carolina State University, Box 5397, Raleigh, NC 27607.

ELLIS, DONALD EDWIN, b. San Diego, Calif, Feb. 20, 39; m. 65. SOLID STATE & MOLECULAR PHYSICS. S.B, Mass. Inst. Tech, 61, M.S, 64, Ph.D. (physics), 66. ASST. PROF. PHYSICS, Florida, 66-68; NORTHWEST. UNIV. (ILL), 68- Am. Phys. Soc; Asn. Comput. Mach. Electronic spectra of small molecules; transition metal complexes; ionic crystals. Address: Dept. of Physics, Northwestern University, Evanston, IL 60201.

ELLIS, EDWIN M, b. Watertown, S.Dak, Mar. 11, 14; m. 42; c. 3. MICROBI-OLOGY. B.S, Adrian Col; M.S, Wayne State; Ph.D.(microbiol), Mich. State, D.V.M. Asst, microbiol, Mich. State, 51-53, 54-56; animal pathologist, Ft. Detrick, Md, 53-54; IMMUNOLOGIST, Ga. Coastal Plain Exp. Sta, Dept. Animal Disease, U.S. Dept. Agr, 56-59; bacteriologist, Fla. State Dept. Agr, 59-60; CHIEF MICROBIOL, DIAG. SERV, NAT. ANIMAL DISEASE LAB, AGR. RES. SERV, U.S. DEPT. AGR, 60- Med.Admin.C.Res, 42, Lt. Am. Soc. Microbiol; Am. Vet. Med. Asn; fel. Am. Acad. Microbiol. Fluo-rescent antibody techniques applied to animal viruses; animal disease; tuberculosis; isolation and immunology. Address: Diagnostic Services, National Animal Disease Lab, U.S. Dept. of Agriculture, Box 70, Ames, IA 50011.

ELLIS, ELLIOT F, b. Englewood, N.J, Apr. 7, 29; m. 55; c. 4. PEDIATRICS. B.A, Kenyon Col, 50; M.D, Western Reserve, 54. Intern, Lenox Hill Hosp, New York, 54-55; res. Babies Hosp, Columbia-Presby. Med. Center, 57-59; fel, Children's Asthma Res. Inst. & Hosp, Denver, Colo, 62-63; fel. al-lergy & immunol. & instr. PEDIAT, col. med, Florida, 63-66; asst. prof. UNIV. COLO, DENVER, 66-70, ASSOC. PROF, 70-; CHIEF PEDIAT, NAT. JEWISH HOSP. & RES. CTR, 66- Bela Schick award, Am. Col. Allergists, 64; dipl, Am. Bd. Pediat. & Am. Bd. Pediat. Allergy. U.S.A.F, 55-62, Res, 63-, Lt. Col. Am. Acad. Pediat; Am. Acad. Allergy; Am. Col. Allergists; Am. Col. Physicians; Soc. Pediat. Res. Pediatric allergy and clinical im-munology. Address: 3800 E. Colfax Ave, Denver, CO 80206.

ELLIS, EMORY L(EON), b. Grayville, Ill, Oct. 29, 06; m. 30. CHEMISTRY. B.S, Calif. Inst. Tech, 30, fel, 31-34, M.S, 32, Ph.D.(chem, biochem), 34. Asst, Riverside Cement Co, 28-29; Calif. Inst. Tech, 30-31, 34-35, res. fel, 35-41; res. dir, Vita-Food Corp, Los Angeles, 41; asst. Calif. Inst. Tech, 42, supvr, test sect, 42-45; supvr. develop. div, U.S. Naval Ord. Test Sta, Calif, 45-46, asst. head rocket & exp. depts, 46-51, head rocket dept, 51-55; dir. ord. planning, Rheem Mfg. Co, 55-57; proj. leader, Inst. Defense Anal, D.C, 57-63; exec. dir. off. indust. assocs, Calif. Inst. Tech, 63-65; tech. consult, DEVCOM ASSOCS, 65, PARTNER, 65- Chemist, food & drug ad-min, U.S. Dept. Agr, 35-36. AAAS; Am. Chem. Soc; Sci. Res. Soc. Am; Inst. Strategic Studies. Thermochemistry; biochemistry of bacteria; physi-ological chemistry equilibria; entropies and free energies of substances of physiological interest. Address: P.O. Box 195, Kernville, CA 93238.

ELLIS, ERIC H(ANS), b. Mannheim, Ger, Aug. 25, 35; U.S. citizen; m. 58; c. 3. PHYSICS. B.S, Syracuse, 56, Ph.D.(physics), 65. Asst. PHYSICS, Syracuse, 56-64; instr, UNIV. OF THE SOUTH, 64-66, ASST. PROF, 66- Am. Asn. Physics Teachers. Infrared background radiation; atmospheric optical noise; fluorescence and spectroscopic analysis of bone. Address: Dept. of Physics, University of the South, Sewanee, TN 37375.

ELLIS, EVERETT LINCOLN, b. Kent, Wash, May 13, 19; m. 43; c. 4. WOOD SCIENCE & TECHNOLOGY. B.S, Univ. Wash, 41, Anderson fel, 51-52, Ph.D.(wood prod), 56; M.S, Mich. State Univ, 43. Asst, Mich. State Univ, 41-42; res. wood technologist, chem. div, Borden Co, 43-46; from asst. to assoc. prof. wood utilization, Univ. Idaho, 46-56; assoc. prof. wood technol, Univ. Mich, 56-65; prof. forest prod, forest res. lab, Ore. State Univ, 65-71, head dept, 65-70; N.Z. FOREST PROD. LTD. PROF. WOOD SCI, SCH. FOR-ESTRY, UNIV. CANTERBURY, 71- Summers, res. assoc, Calif. Forest Prod. Lab, 58, chemist, Packaging Corp. Am, 59 & res. assoc. Ore. Forest Res. Ctr, 60- Forest Prod. Res. Soc; assoc. Brit. Inst. Wood Sci; Soc. Wood Sci. & Technol. Wood and fiber anatomy and structure, including chemistry and mineral composition; factors of growth as related to wood structure and properties; education in wood science and technology. Ad-dress: School of Forestry, University of Canterbury, Christchurch 1, N.Z.

ELLIS, F(ORREST) ALBERT, b. Central City, Nebr, Nov. 28, 11; m. 38. PHYSIOLOGY. A.B, Whittier Col, 34, M.S, 36; Ph.D.(physiol), Stanford, 49. Prof. biol, William Penn Col, 37-42; teacher, high sch, Calif, 42-46; PROF. PHYSIOL, SAN JOSE STATE COL, 46- Res. asst, Stanford, 48-49. AAAS. Body temperature and respiratory physiology. Address: 1109 Steinway, Campbell, CA 95008.

ELLIS, FRANK R(USSELL), b. Celina, Ohio, Oct. 19, 15; m. 41; c. 4. CLINI-CAL PATHOLOGY. M.D, Michigan, 43. Resident asst. path, sch. med, Utah, 47-49; res. fel, Washington (Seattle), 49-50; pathologist, St. Anthony Hosp, Wash, 50-52; instr. path, sch. med, Colorado, 53-54; clin. pathologist, Wayne Co. Gen. Hosp, Eloise, Mich, 54-66; DIR, SOUTHEAST. MICH. RED CROSS BLOOD CTR, 66- Pathologist, DePaul Hosp, Wyo, 52-54; consult, Warren AFB, Wyo, 54; tech. adv. blood transfusion res. div, Army Med.

Res. Lab, Ky, 65- Dipl, Am. Bd. Path, 53. Med.C, 44-46, Res, 46-49, Col. (Ret). Fel. AAAS; Am. Acad. Forensic Sci; fel. Am. Soc. Clin. Path; Am. Med. Asn; Int. Soc. Blood Transfusion; Pan-Am. Med. Asn. Nature of blood group substance A in examples of weak subgroups of A, and its relation to anti-A antibody capable of detecting this antigen; detection and surveillance of the health carrier of hepatitis among volunteer blood doners. Address: Southeastern Michigan Red Cross Blood Center, 153 E. Elizabeth St, Detroit, MI 48232.

ELLIS, F(RANKLIN) HENRY, JR, b. Washington, D.C, Sept. 20, 20. THO-RACIC SURGERY. B.A, Yale, 41; M.D, Columbia, 44; Ph.D.(surg), Minne-sota, 51. Instr. SURG, Mayo Grad. Sch. Med, Univ. Minn, 53-56, from asst. prof. to prof, 64-70; LECTR, HARVARD MED. SCH, 70-; CHIEF CARDIOVASC. SURG, LAHEY CLIN. FOUND, 70- Dipl, Am. Bd. Surg, 53; Am. Bd. Thoracic Surg, 54. U.S.N.R, 45-48. Am. Med. Asn.(Billings Gold Medal, esophagitis, 55); Asn. Thoracic Surg; Am. Col. Surg; Soc. Vascular Surg; Int. Soc. Surg; Int. Cardiovasc. Soc; Soc. Clin. Surg; Soc. Univ. Surg. Thoracic and cardiovascular surgery. Address: Lahey Clinic Foundation, 605 Commonwealth Ave, Boston, MA 02215.

ELLIS, FRED E, b. Hutchinson, Kans, Apr. 22, 26; m. 58; c. 2. PHYSICS, ASTRONOMY. B.S, E.Tex. State Col, 54, M.S, 55; Ph.D.(physics), La. State, 65. Instr. physics, E.Tex. State Col, 55-58; asst. prof, Southern Missis-sippi, 64-65; res. collab, Nat. Radio Astron. Observ, 65; ASSOC. PROF. PHYSICS & ASTRON, PAN AM. UNIV, 66- U.S.N, 44-46, 51-52. Astrom-etry of extended radio sources; radio galactic spur. Address: Dept. of Physical Science, Pan American University, Edinburg, TX 78539.

ELLIS, FRED W(ILSON), b. Heath Springs, S.C, Apr. 24, 14; m. 40; c. 4. PHARMACOLOGY, BIOCHEMISTRY. B.S, South Carolina, 36; fel, Florida, 37-38, M.S, 38; fel, Maryland, 38-41, Ph.D.(pharmacol), 41; M.D, Duke, 51. Res. fel. pharmacol, Maryland, 41-42, supt. biochem. lab, univ. hosp, 41-42; assoc. PHARMACOL, Jefferson Med. Col, 42-43; from asst. to PROF, SCH. MED, UNIV. N.C, 43- AAAS; Am. Med. Asn; Am. Soc. Pharmacol; Soc. Exp. Biol. & Med. Adrenal function in experimental alcoholism; experi-mentally-induced physical dependence on ethanol in animals; development of animal models of alcoholism in monkeys and dogs. Address: School of Medicine, University of North Carolina, Chapel Hill, NC 27514.

ELLIS, GARLAND C(ECIL), b. Chatham Co, N.C, Aug. 27, 20; m. 52; c. 2. ORGANIC CHEMISTRY. B.S, High Point Col, 41. Chemist, Marietta Paint & Color Co, 41-42; Solvay Process Div, Allied Chem. & Dye Corp, 42-46, res. chemist, 46-52, sr. res. chemist, nitrogen div, 52-62, supvry. res. chemist, 62-66, tech. serv. supvr, plastics div, Allied Chem. Corp, 66-68; mgr. tech. serv, MATADOR CHEM. CO, 68, TECH. MGR, ORANGE PLANT, 68- Am. Chem. Soc; fel, Am. Inst. Chem. Organic synthesis; detergents; ethylene oxide and derivatives. Address: Matador Chemical Co, Inc, P.O. Box 216, Orange, TX 77630.

ELLIS, GEORGE FORBES, JR, b. Las Vegas, N.Mex, Feb. 23, 34; m. 54; c. 2. POPULATION GENETICS, STATISTICS. B.S, New Mexico State, 55; Ph.D.(animal breeding), Texas A&M, 63. Assoc. animal husbandman, Tex. Agr. Exp. Sta, 57-63; assoc. prof. animal husb, Tex. Tech. Col, 63, mgr, res. farm, 63-66; PARTNER, CORONADO CATTLE CO, 66- Consult, Coun. Rural Social, Caracas, Venezuela, 62-63. U.S.A.F, 55-56, 2nd Lt. Am. Soc. Animal Sci; Am. Soc. Range. Mgt. Beef cattle genetics and nutri-tion. Address: 2821 Marmon Dr, Midland, TX 79701.

ELLIS, GLEN E(DWARD), b. Merkel, Tex, May 6, 36; m. 64; c. 2. ACOUSTICS, COMPUTER SCIENCE. B.S, Univ. Tex, 58, M.A, 60. Eng. asst, Tex. Instru-ments, Inc, 58; res. scientist, APPL. RES. LABS, UNIV. TEX, AUSTIN, 58-64, supvr, oceanog. sect, 64-65, infrasonics res. sect, 65-67, HEAD COMPUT. SCI. DIV, 67- Acoust. Soc. Am. Ocean waves; harbor oscilla-tions; solion applications; infrasonics; underwater acoustics; signal pro-cessing; computer modeling; software development; computer facility man-agement. Address: P.O. Box 8029, Austin, TX 78712.

ELLIS, GORDON W(OODBURY), b. Berkeley, Calif, Dec. 28, 27; m. 49; c. 3. BIOPHYSICS, CYTOLOGY. A.B, California, Berkeley, 54, Ph.D.(zool), 61. Acting instr. zool, California, Berkeley, 58, res. zoologist, 59-61; asst. prof. molecular biol, Vanderbilt, 61-62; CYTOL, Dartmouth Med. Sch, 62-66; ASSOC. PROF, UNIV. PA, 66-, acting dir. prog. biophys. cytol, 71-72. Nat. Sci. Found. res. grant, 64-66. U.S.N, 46. Am. Soc. Zool; Soc. Gen. Physiol. Invention of piezoelectric micromanipulator; effects of mechanical injury to cell nucleus; measurement of mechanical properties of cell struc-tures; instrumentation for biological research; applied optics; holographic microscopy. Address: Dept. of Biology, University of Pennsylvania, Philadelphia, PA 19104.

ELLIS, HAL, b. New York, N.Y, Apr. 6, 18; m. 41; c. 2. INDUSTRIAL & MINING ENGINEERING. B.S, Cornell, 38; M.A, Harvard, 40; Ph.D.(entom, agr. chem), Minnesota, 42. Bacteriologist, Naval Med. Res. Inst, 42-43; entomologist res. & develop, Off. Qm. Gen, U.S. War Dept, 43-44; Pan-Am. Sanit. Bur, Guatemala, 44-45; med. dept, Standard Oil Co. N.J, S.Am, 45-47; consult. engr, Venezuela, 47-50; asst. prof. parasitol. & pub. health, Chicago Med. Sch, 50-55; res. dir, Colombian Inst. Tech. Invest, Bogota, Colombia, 55-57; sr. engr. & head Minuteman Rocket 1st Stage develop. & tech. specialist, Aerojet-Gen. Corp, Calif, 57-62; mgr. reliability, qual. control & eng. standards, Marquardt Corp, 62-65; PRES. & TECH. DIR, PAN-AM. INDUST. & MINING,CORP, MIAMI, 65- Res. fel, med. sch, Rochester, 38-39; recording sect, cmt. insecticides & insect repellents, Nat. Res. Coun. & Off. Sci. Res. & Develop, D.C, 42-44; consult. res. ana-lyst, Chicago. AAAS; Entom. Soc. Am; Am. Soc. Parasitol; Am. Chem. Soc; Am. Inst. Aeronaut. & Astronaut; Am. Soc. Trop. Med. & Hyg; Am. Micros. Soc; Am. Inst. Mining, Metall. & Petrol. Eng; Geol. Soc. Am; Am. Inst. Chem. Eng; Royal Soc. Trop. Med. & Hyg. Ecology and geography of parasitism and disease; biocide formulations; biological warfare; engi-neering economics; industrial microscopy; quality control; research man-agement; reliability; geology; ozone; water, sewage and waste pollution control. Address: P.O. Box 2158, Ocean View Branch, Miami Beach, FL 33140.

ELLIS, HAROLD BERNARD, b. Havre, Mont, Dec. 31, 17; m. 44; c. 4. CIVIL ENGINEERING. B.S, Washington State, 41; M.S, Mass. Inst. Tech, 47; Brown, 47-48; Ph.D.(civil eng), Iowa State, 63. Chief of schs. & training sect, engr. off, Hq. Cent. Pac. Area, U.S. Army, Hawaii, 44, commandant, hq. amphibious training ctr, 44-45, instr. & chief opers. & construct. sect, Engrs. Sch, Ft. Belvoir, Va, 45-46, unit instr, 118th engr. combat battalion, Nat. Guard, R.I, 47-50, asst. dist. engr, Dist. Engr. Off, Wash, D.C, 50-52; exec. off, hq. 931st engr. group, 52-53, staff off, aviation engr. force, Wolters AFB, Tex, 53-55, assoc. prof. mil. sci. & tactics, Army ROTC, Iowa State Univ, 55-59, dep. comdr. depot oper, Army Gen. Depot, France, 59-62; asst. prof. civil eng, IOWA STATE UNIV, 62-63, assoc. prof, 64-66, PROF, 66-68, civil eng. & construct. technol, 68-69, CIVIL ENG, 69-, HEAD TECH. INST, 62- U.S.A, 41-62, Lt. Col. Am. Soc. Civil Eng; Am. Soc. Eng. Educ; Am. Road Builders Asn; Nat. Soc. Prof. Eng. Address: Dept. of Civil Engineering, Iowa State University, Ames, IA 50010.

ELLIS, HOMER G(ODSEY), b. Paris, Tex, Sept. 29, 33; m. 57; c. 2. MATHEMATICS, PHYSICS. B.A, Texas, 55, M.A, 58, Ph.D.(math), 61. Asst. prof. math, Utah, 61-62; Washington, 62-65; vis. asst. prof. appl. math, UNIV. COLO, BOULDER, 65-67, asst. prof. MATH, 67-68, ASSOC. PROF, 68- Summers, res. asst, Autonetics Div, N.Am. Aviation, Inc, 56 & 57, 59-61. Am. Math. Soc; Math. Asn. Am. Relativity theory; differential geometry; mathematical physics. Address: 771 Crescent Dr, Boulder, CO 80303.

ELLIS, H(UBERT) W(HITFIELD), b. Port Maitland, N.S, Feb. 7, 18; m. 43; c. 1. MATHEMATICS. B.Sc, Acadia, 40, Nat. Res. Coun. Can, stud, 41, M.Sc, 42; M.A, Toronto, 46, Ph.D.(math), 47. Jr. res. physicist, Nat. Res. Coun. Can, 42-43; fel, Toronto, 46-47; lectr. & asst. prof. MATH, QUEEN'S UNIV.(ONT), 47-57, assoc. prof, 57-60, PROF, 60- Mem, Inst. Advan. Study, 56-57; res. assoc. & Nat. Res. Coun. Can. sr. res. award, res. assoc, Calif. Inst. Tech, 64-65. R.C.N.V.R, 43-45, Lt. Am. Math. Soc; Can. Math. Cong. Banach function spaces; vector lattices; integration and measure theory; non-absolutely convergent integrals; function spaces. Address: Dept. of Mathematics, Queen's University, Kingston, Ont, Can.

ELLIS, J. S, b. Kingston, Ont, Jan. 10, 27; m. 64. CIVIL ENGINEERING. B.Sc, Queen's (Ont), 48; M.Eng, McGill, 49; Ph.D.(civil eng), Cambridge, 57. Design engr, H.G. Acres & Co. Ltd, 49-54; struct. engr, J.D. Lee & Co. Ltd, 57-59; PROF. STRUCT. ENG, ROYAL MIL. COL. CAN, 59-, HEAD DEPT, 69- Defence Res. Bd. Can. res. grants, 62-64, 65; chmn. task group III, U.S. Column Res. Coun; trustee Road Safety Res. Fund, Eng. Inst. Can; vis. prof, Royal Mil. Col. Australia, 71. Eng. Inst. Can.(Duggan Medal, 65). Ultimate capacity of steel columns; automation and traffic control. Address: Dept. of Civil Engineering, Royal Military College, Kingston, Ont, Can.

ELLIS, JACK BARRY, b. Toronto, Ont, Jan. 4, 36; m. 61; c. 2. ELECTRICAL ENGINEERING. B.A.Sc, Toronto, 58; Athlone fel. & M.Sc, London & dipl, Imp. Col, 61; Ph.D.(elec. eng), Mich. State, 65. Engr, RCA Victor Ltd, Que, summer 58; lectr. elec. eng, Waterloo, 61-62; asst, Mich. State, 62-63, asst. instr. resource develop, 64-65; asst. prof. elec. eng, Univ. Waterloo, 65-66, assoc. prof, 66-70, dir. continuing res. prog. probs. urbanization, 68-70; PROF, FACULTY ENVIRON. STUDIES, YORK UNIV, 70- Consult, res. contract, Dept. Conserv, Mich, 65-66; Nat. Res. Coun. Can. oper. grant, 65-; summer overseas travel grant, 66; Dept. Hwy, Ont. res. grant, 65-; consult, res. contract, Dept. North. Affairs, Ont, summer 66. R.C.N, 54-58, Sub. Lt. Inst. Elec. & Electronics Eng. Nonlinear control systems; optimal control and systems theories; applications of systems theory and control theory to transportation networks, planning, economic and sociological systems. Address: Faculty of Environmental Studies, York University, Toronto, Ont, Can.

ELLIS, JAMES P(ERCY), JR, b. Palacios, Tex, Oct. 21, 27; m. 49; c. 5. BIOCHEMISTRY. B.S, Southwest Tex. State Col, 48, M.S, 49; fel, Texas, 49-50; Ph.D.(biochem), Tex. A&M Univ, 67. Asst. biochem, med. br, Texas, 50-52; RES. BIOCHEMIST, U.S. AIR FORCE SCH. AEROSPACE MED, 52- Med.C, U.S.N, 45-47. Development and use of biochemical methods for the assessment of physiologic function. Address: Environmental systems Branch, U.S. Air Force School of Aerospace Medicine, Brooks Air Force Base, TX 78235.

ELLIS, JAMES W(ATSON), b. Uruguaiana, Brazil, Aug. 16, 27; U.S. citizen; m. 51; c. 3. MATHEMATICS. A.B, Wofford Col, 48; Atomic Energy Cmn. fel, 49-52, M.S, Tulane, 51, Ph.D.(math), 52. Asst. prof. math, Fla. State, 52-57, assoc. prof, 57-58; assoc. prof, LA. STATE UNIV, NEW ORLEANS, 58-61, prof. & chmn. dept, 61-64, DEAN, JR. DIV, 64- U.S.A, 53-55. Am. Math. Soc; Math. Asn. Am. Linear topological spaces and topological algebras. Address: 2328 Lark St, New Orleans, LA 70122.

ELLIS, JASON A(RUNDEL), b. Newell, S.Dak, Dec. 22, 18; m. 52; c. 1. PHYSICS. B.S, S.Dak. Sch. Mines & Tech, 42; M.S, Iowa, 52, Ph.D.(physics), 62. Engr, Gen. Elec. Co, 42-45; physicist, U.S. Bur. Standards, 47; radiation res. lab, Iowa, 51-53; asst. prof. PHYSICS, North Texas State, 58-63; UNIV. TEX, ARLINGTON, 63-69, ASSOC. PROF, 69- Co-ed, Space-time. Sig.C, U.S.A, 45-46. AAAS; Am. Phys. Soc; Am. Asn. Physics Teachers; Optical Soc. Am; Int. Soc. Gen. Semantics. Theoretical physics; mathematical biophysics. Address: Dept. of Physics, University of Texas at Arlington, Arlington, TX 76010.

ELLIS, JERRY WILLIAM, b. Pittsburg, Kans, Aug. 22, 37; m. 58; c. 2. ORGANIC CHEMISTRY. B.S, Kans. State Col. Pittsburg, 59, M.S, 61; Nat. Insts. Health fel, Okla. State, 62-64, Ph.D.(org. chem), 65. Instr. chem, Kans. State Col. Pittsburg, 61; Okla. State, 61-62; asst. prof. ORG. CHEM, Wis. State, Whitewater, 65-66; asst. prof, EAST. ILL. UNIV, 66-69, ASSOC. PROF, 69- Consult, lamp div, Gen. Elec. Co, Ill, 60-, summer chemist, 66. U.S.A, 57, Res, 55-62. Am. Chem. Soc; The Chem. Soc. Total synthesis of terpenes; reactions of lead tetraacetate; conjugate Grignard additions. Address: Dept. of Chemistry, Eastern Illinois University, Charleston, IL 61920.

ELLIS, JOHN F(RANCIS), b. Torrington, Conn, July 29, 22; m. 46; c. 3. BIOLOGY. B.A, Amherst Col, 48, M.A, 50; Ph.D.(animal genetics), Edinburgh, 55. Teaching asst, Amherst Col, 48-50, instr. BIOL, 53-56, asst. prof, 56-58, res. assoc, 58-59; asst. prof, HAMILTON COL, 59-61, assoc. prof, 61-68, PROF, 68- U.S. Pub. Health Serv. trainee, State Univ. N.Y. Upstate Med. Ctr, 66-67; consult, N.Y. State Dept. Ment. Health, Marcy State Hosp. U.S.A, 43-45. Fel. AAAS; Genetics Soc. Am; Am. Inst. Biol. Sci. Human cytogenetics; genetics of mental retardation and mental illness; tissue culture and cell hybridization; Drosophila biochemical genetics. Address: 2 Stryker Lane, Clinton, NY 13323.

ELLIS, JOHN G(EORGE), b. Mass, Oct. 2, 24; m. 51; c. 2. BACTERIOLOGY. B.S, Massachusetts, 50, M.S, 51. Asst, Massachusetts, 51; chief bacteriologist, Diversey Corp, 51-56, head bact. control labs, Winthrop Labs, Div. Sterling Drug, N.Y, 56-66, assoc. res. biologist, Sterling-Winthrop Res. Inst, 66-67; microbiologist, CHESEBROUGH PONDS INC, 67-70, GROUP LEADER HOSP. PROD. RES, PROD. DEVELOP, 70- U.S.N.R, 43-46. Am. Soc. Microbiol. Sanitation in food and dairy industries; general sanitation; development of disinfectants; fermentations; pharmaceuticals; disinfectants; analytical microbiology. Address: Hospital Products Research, Product Development, Chesebrough Ponds Inc, Johns St, Clinton, CT 06413.

ELLIS, JOHN H, b. Almo, Ky, May 30, 29; m. 56; c. 4. SOIL CHEMISTRY. B.S, Murray State Univ, 55; M.S, Univ. Ky, 60, Ph.D.(soil sci), 70. Asst. chemist, agron. dept, UNIV. KY, 56-58, div. regulatory serv, 59-64, chemist, 64-66, sr. res. analyst, 66-69, ASST. PROF. SOIL CHEM. & SOILS ADV. NORTHEAST AGR. CTR, THAILAND, 70- U.S.A.F, 50-54, S/Sgt. Soil Sci. Soc. Am; Am. Soc. Agron; Asn. Off. Anal. Chem; Int. Soc. Soil Sci. Diffusion of plant mineral nutrients in soils; water movement in soils; pesticide pollution in soils and agricultural products. Address: University of Kentucky Team, USOM/Agriculture, APO San Francisco 96346.

ELLIS, JOHN J(AY), b. Michigan City, Ind, Feb. 2, 30; m. 53; c. 3. MYCOLOGY. A.B, Indiana, 52; M.S, Iowa, 56, Ph.D.(bot), 59. Asst. life sci, Iowa, 54-58; instr. bot, Omaha, 58-59; asst. prof. biol, Wartburg Col, 59-60; RES. MYCOLOGIST, NORTH. REGIONAL RES. LAB, AGR. RES. SERV, U.S. DEPT. AGR, 60- U.S.A, 52-54. AAAS; Mycol. Soc. Am; Bot. Soc. Am; Int. Asn. Plant Taxon; Brit. Mycol. Soc; Soc. Indust. Microbiol. Taxonomy and morphology of the Mucorales and Fungi Imperfecti; fermentation. Address: Northern Regional Research Lab, Agricultural Research Service, U.S. Dept. of Agriculture, Peoria, IL 61604.

ELLIS, J(OHN) MARSHALL, b. Midland, Ga, Sept. 24, 03; m. 41; c. 2. ZOOLOGY. A.B, Emory, 24, univ. fel, 24-25, M.S, 26; Ph.D.(zool), California, 34. Acting head biol. dept, Fla. South. Col, 25-26; prof. biol. & head dept, Jr. Col. Augusta, 26-43; sanitarian, U.S. Pub. Health Serv, 43-45, proj. review off. & exec. secy. surg. study sect, div. res. grants, Nat. Insts. Health, 46-56; res. admin, Am. Cancer Soc, 56-68; grants off, Mount Sinai Sch. Med, 68-71; RETIRED. Asst, Univ. Calif, 32-34; vis. prof, Univ. Tampa, 38-40; assoc. prof, Ala. Polytech. Inst, 46. AAAS; Am. Soc. Trop. Med. & Hyg; Am. Soc. Parasitol; Am. Micros. Soc; N.Y. Acad. Sci. Morphology and life cycles of protozoa; malaria parasitology and transmission; rearing of anopheline mosquitoes; experimental surgery; administration of biological and medical research grant programs. Address: 620 13th Ave. E, Cordele, GA 31015.

ELLIS, JOHN O(GBORN), b. Ithaca, N.Y, Dec. 25, 30; m. 53; c. 4. METEOROLOGY. A.B, Amherst Col, 52; S.M, Chicago, 54; Mass. Inst. Tech, 58-60. Res. meteorologist, U.S. Weather Bur, 55-64, gen. meteorologist, 64-66, Environ. Sci. Serv. Admin, 66-70, PHYS. SCIENTIST, ENVIRON. SCI. INFO. CTR, NAT. OCEANIC & ATMOSPHERIC ADMIN, 70- AAAS; Am. Meteorol. Soc; Am. Geophys. Union. Application of statistical methods and dynamical procedures to development of short range weather forecasting techniques; scientific publication review. Address: Environmental Science Information Center, National Oceanic & Atmospheric Administration, Rockville, MD 20852.

ELLIS, JOHN T(AYLOR), b. Lufkin, Tex, Dec. 27, 20; m. 42; c. 3. PATHOLOGY. B.A, Texas, 42; M.D, Northwestern, 45. Rotating intern, St. Luke's Hosp, 45-46; asst, William Buchanan Blood Cent, Baylor Hosp, 48; asst. PATH, col. med, Cornell, 48-49, instr, 49-50, asst. prof, 50-56, assoc. prof, 56-62; PROF. & CHMN. DEPT, sch. med, Emory Univ, 62-68; COL. MED, CORNELL UNIV, 68- Asst. res. pathologist, New York Hosp, 48-49, asst. attending pathologist, 50-55, assoc. attending pathologist, 55-; mem. cmt. blood, health resources adv. cmt, off. emergency planning, Exec. Off. President, 64-71; mem. path. study sect, Nat. Insts. Health, 65-69, chmn, 69-70; mem. sci. adv. bd. consult, Armed Forces Inst. Path, 70- Dipl, Nat. Bd. Med. Exam, 45; Am. Bd. Path, 51. Med.C, U.S.A, 46, 47-48, Capt. Am. Soc. Exp. Path; Soc. Exp. Biol. & Med; Harvey Soc; Am. Asn. Path. & Bact; Col. Am. Path; Int. Acad. Path. Nephrosis and experimental proteinuria; muscular dystrophy and experimentally induced diseases of muscle; iron metabolism; electron microscopy. Address: Dept. of Pathology, Cornell University Medical College, 1300 York Ave, New York, NY 10021.

ELLIS, KENNETH CARL, b. Centerville, Iowa, Feb. 8, 43; m. 65; c. 1. NEMATOLOGY. B.S, Northeast Mo. State Col, 65; Nat. Defense Educ. Act fel, Univ. Ariz, 65, M.S, 67, Ph.D.(plant path), 70. Res. asst. plant path, Univ. Ariz, 68-69; NEMATOLOGIST & PLANT PATHOLOGIST, AGR. RES. CTR, GREAT WEST. SUGAR CO, 69- Soc. Nematol; Am. Inst. Biol. Sci. General diseases of sugar beet and field crops; fungicidal treatment of seed; cercospora leaf spot control; rhizoctonia root rot control; chemical control of Heterodera schachtii and new product screening. Address: Agricultural Research Center, Great Western Sugar Co, P.O. Box 539, Longmont, CO 80501.

ELLIS, LeGRANDE C(LARK), b. Farmington, Utah, June 20, 32; m. 54; c. 6. PHYSIOLOGY, ENDOCRINOLOGY. B.S, Utah State, 54, M.S, 56; Ph.D. (physiol, endocrinol), Okla. State, 61. Instr. cellular physiol, Okla. State, 57-60, asst. prof, 60-62; fel. quant. biol, Utah, 62-64; asst. prof. physiol. & endocrinol, UTAH STATE UNIV, 64-66, assoc. prof, 66-71, PROF. PHYSIOL. & BIOCHEM, 71- Am. Physiol. Soc; Endocrine Soc; Soc. Exp. Biol. & Med; Soc. Study Reproduction; Radiation Res. Soc; Reticuloendothelial Soc. Steroid metabolism; conjugation and biosynthesis; effects of irradiation of steroid biotransformations by endocrine cells; environmental influences on endocrinology and reproduction. Address: Dept. of Zoology, Division of Biochemistry, Utah State University, Logan, UT 84321.

ELLIS, LEONARD C(ULBERTH), b. Portsmouth, Va, Dec. 13, 34; m. 54; c. 3. ORGANIC CHEMISTRY. B.S, Col. William & Mary, 56; Ph.D.(org. chem), Virginia, 62. RES. CHEMIST, VA. CHEM. INC, PORTSMOUTH, 61- Gas chromatographic analysis of amine mixtures; biogenetic mechanisms by tracer studies; amine derivatives; corrosion inhibitors; conformational analysis; stabilization of dithionites; groundwood pulp bleaching. Address: 2432 Taylorwood Blvd, Chesapeake, VA 23321.

ELLIS, LESLIE L(EE), JR, b. Norfolk, Va, Sept. 13, 25; m. 49; c. 4. ZOOLOGY. B.S, Tulane, 48, M.S, 49; Ph.D.(zool), Oklahoma, 52. Asst. zool, Tulane, 48; Oklahoma, 49-50, 51-52, spec. instr. & asst, univ. biol. sta. & state biol. surv, Okla, 50-51; res. aide, U.S. Pub. Health Serv, 52; asst. prof. zool. & entom, Miss. State Univ, 52-56, assoc. prof, 56-60, prof, 60-68, head dept. zool, 62-68; chmn. dept. biol. sci, FLA. TECHNOL. UNIV, 68-69, dir. GRAD. STUDIES & RES, 69-70, DEAN, 70- Nat. Sci. Found. panelist; indust. consult. Hosp.C, U.S.N.R, 44-46. Entom. Soc. Am. Aquatic biology; medical entomology and parasitology; bee diseases. Address: Office of Graduate Studies & Research, Florida Technological University, Orlando, FL 32816.

ELLIS, L(ILLIAN) N(ELSON), b. Haverhill, Mass, Mar. 15, 06; m. 29; c. 2; div. BIOCHEMISTRY. A.B, Mt. Holyoke Col, 27; Ph.D.(chem), Columbia, 32. Asst. food chem, Columbia, 27-39; from instr. to prof. chem, Adelphi Col, 39-56; prof, Douglass Col, Rutgers Univ, 56-71; RETIRED. Instr, Marymount Col, 36-38. AAAS; Am. Inst. Nutrit; Am. Chem. Soc; Am. Inst. Chem. Chemistry; enzymes; vitamins; minerals. Address: 6 Abbott St, Lebanon, NH 03766.

ELLIS, NATHAN KENT, b. Maple Rapids, Mich, Jan. 14, 09; m. 34; c. 3. HORTICULTURE. B.S, Mich. State Col, 32, M.S, 35, Ph.D.(hort), 50. In charge muck crops invests, PURDUE UNIV, 35-41, asst. prof. hort, 41-47, assoc. prof. & acting head dept, 47-50, prof. & head dept, 50-58, asst. dir, AGR. EXP. STA, 58-67, ASSOC. DIR, 67- Fel. AAAS; fel. Am. Soc. Hort. Sci; Am. Inst. Biol. Sci; Soc. Econ. Bot; Potato Asn. Am. Vegetable crop production on organic soils; production of essential oils from Mentha species; nutriculture systems and controlled environment. Address: 101 Agriculture Experiment Station Bldg, Purdue University, Lafayette, IN 47907.

ELLIS, N(ED) R(OYCE), b. Lancaster, Wis, Aug. 1, 94; m. 21; c. 2. BIOCHEMISTRY. B.S, Wisconsin, 18, M.S, 20. Asst, Exp. Sta, Wisconsin, 19-20; asst. biochemist, bur. animal indust, U.S. Dept. Agr, 20-24, assoc. biochemist, 24-30, chemist, 30-37, sr. biochemist, 37-42; in charge nutrit. invest, 42-55, chief animal & poultry husb. br, Agr. Res. Serv, 55-57, assoc. dir, animal husb. res. div, 57-64; RETIRED. Sanit.C, U.S.A, 17-19. AAAS; Soc. Exp. Biol. & Med; Am. Soc. Animal Sci; Am. Inst. Nutrit.(treas, 47-49); Am. Soc. Biol. Chem; Am. Chem. Soc. Biochemistry of animal fats; swine nutrition; vitamins; farm animal nutrition. Address: 4011 Van Buren St, West Hyattsville, MD 20782.

ELLIS, PHILIP PAUL, b. Saginaw, Mich, Oct. 30, 23. OPHTHALMOLOGY. West. Mich. Col, 41-43; Texas A&M, 43-44; M.D, Baylor, 48. Instr. OPHTHAL, col. med, Iowa, 54-55, asst. prof, 55-58; assoc. prof. & head dept, sch. med, Univ. Ark, 58-60; assoc. prof, SCH. MED, UNIV. COLO, 60-67, PROF, 67-, HEAD DEPT, 60- Dipl, Am. Bd. Ophthal, 55. Med.C, 43-46, 51-53, 1st Lt. Am. Med. Asn; Am. Acad. Ophthal. & Otolaryngol; Asn. Res. Vision & Ophthal; Am. Asn. Ophthal. Ocular pharmacology and toxicology; therapeutics; immunology. Address: Dept. of Ophthalmology, University of Colorado School of Medicine, 4200 E. Ninth Ave, Denver, CO 80220.

ELLIS, R(EED) HOBART, JR, b. Rangeley, Maine, Mar. 9, 18; m. 59. PHYSICS. A.B, Bowdoin Col, 39; A.M, Columbia, 48, Ph.D.(physics), 55. Res. physicist, radiol. res. labs, Columbia Med. Ctr, 50-54; assoc. ed, Nucleonics, 55-61, managing ed, 61-62; ed, Nuclear Fusion, 62-64; New York Off. Int. Atomic Energy Agency, 64-65; exec. ed, Physics Today, 65-66, chief ed, 66-69; MEM. STAFF, SMITHSONIAN INST, 69- Adj. assoc. prof, N.Y. Univ, 60-62. U.S.N.R, 43-46. Am. Phys. Soc; Am. Nuclear Soc; Health Physics Soc; Am. Asn. Physics Teachers. Radiation effects; dosimetry; nuclear technology. Address: Smithsonian Institution, Washington, DC 20560.

ELLIS, REX, b. Whiteville, N.C, Feb. 6, 29; m. 56. ORGANIC CHEMISTRY, BIOCHEMISTRY. B.S, A&T State Univ. N.C, 52; M.S, American Univ, 67. MEAT RES. CHEMIST, U.S. DEPT. AGR, 53- Am. Chem. Soc; Am. Oil Chem. Soc. Methods for determining stability of fats and oils. Address: Eastern Marketing & Nutrition Research Division, U.S. Dept. of Agriculture, 600 E. Mermaid Lane, Philadelphia, PA 19118.

ELLIS, RICHARD A(KERS), b. Brewster, Mass, May 5, 28. BIOLOGY. A.B, Massachusetts, 49; A.M, Harvard, 51, fel, 51-53, Ph.D, 54; A.M, Brown, 62. Instr. anat, sch. med, Harvard, 54; res. assoc, Bermuda Biol. Sta, 56; instr. BIOL, BROWN UNIV, 56-58, asst. prof, 58-61, assoc. prof, 62-67, PROF, 67- U.S.A, 54-56. AAAS; Am. Asn. Anat; Histochem. Soc; Am. Soc. Zool; Am. Soc. Cell Biol; Int. Soc. Cell Biol. Histochemistry and electron microscopy of salt-secreting epithelia and skin; innervation and vascularization of taste buds; histochemistry of the metrial gland in pregnancy and pseudopregnancy. Address: Division of Biological & Medical Sciences, Brown University. Providence, RI 02912.

ELLIS, RICHARD B(ASSETT), b. Abilene, Tex, May 12, 15; m. 40; c. 3. PHYSICAL CHEMISTRY. B.A, Vanderbilt, 36, M.S, 37, Ph.D.(anal. & phys. chem), 40. Supvr. anal. div, res. & develop. dept, Joseph E. Seagram & Sons, Ky, 40-42; res. chemist, Corning Glass Works, N.Y, 42-46; instr. chem, Florida, 46-47; asst. prof, Miami, 47-51; from sr. chemist to head inorg. sect, South. Res. Inst, 51-68; prof. physics & head dept, Huntingdon Col, 68-70; PROF. SCI, TROY STATE UNIV, MONTGOMERY, 70-, HEAD DEPT, 71- Lectr, Birmingham-South. Col, 54-66; Univ. Ala, Birmingham, 66-68. AAAS; Am. Asn. Physics Teachers; Am. Chem. Soc. Analysis distillery products; surface chemistry; electrochemistry; fused salt technology; high-temperature materials. Address: 3115 Partridge Rd, Montgomery, AL 36111.

ELLIS, RICHARD JOHN, b. New Castle, Ind, Apr. 11, 39; m. 62; c. 2. PLANT PHYSIOLOGY, MICROBIOLOGY. B.A, California, Santa Barbara, 60; Washington State, 60-61; NASA fel, California, Berkeley, 64-67, Ph.D. (bot), 67. ASST. PROF. BIOL, City Col. New York, 67-68; BUCKNELL UNIV, 68- Bot. Soc. Am; Phycol. Soc. Am; Am. Soc. Plant Physiol. Physiology of reproduction in algae and fungi; plant tissue culture; nutrition of algae and fungi. Address: Dept. of Biology, Bucknell University, Lewisburg, PA 17837.

ELLIS, ROBERT ANDERSON, JR, b. Kansas City, Mo, Oct. 16, 27; m. 54; c. 4. PHYSICS. B.A, Fisk, 48; M.S, Yale, 49; Ph.D.(physics), Iowa, 54. Instr. physics, Tennessee State, 49-50, asst. prof, 53-54, prof, 54-56; MEM. RES. STAFF, PLASMA PHYSICS LAB, PRINCETON, 56- U.S.A, 46-47. Am. Phys. Soc. Plasma physics. Address: Plasma Physics Lab, Princeton University, Princeton, NJ 08540.

ELLIS, ROBERT H(OMER), b. Madison, Wis, Apr. 13, 29; m. 52; c. 2. MICROBIOLOGY. B.A, Wisconsin, 51, M.S, 53, Ph.D.(microbiol), 57. Teaching asst, Wisconsin, 50-51; res. scientist, Aerospace Div, Boeing Co, 61-62; Scientist, sci. & tech. bur, U.S. Arms Control & Disarmament Agency, 62-64; dir. opers. res. div, Travelers Res. Ctr, 64-67, dep. dir. math. sci. dept, 67-68, dir. resource mgt. studies dept. & v.pres, 68-69, PRES, TRAVELERS RES. CORP, 69- Consult, U.S. Arms Control & Disarmament Agency, 64- U.S.A, 51-61; Army Commendation Medal, 61. AAAS; Am. Soc. Microbiol; Sci. Res. Soc. Am; Am. Geog. Soc; Brit. Soc. Gen. Microbiol. General and medical microbiology; human intestinal microbial flora; antibiotics and chemotherapy; biological and chemical weapons and defense planning and research; bioastronautics; operations research; systems analysis; complex environmental systems and their influence on man. Address: Travelers Research Corp, 250 Constitution Plaza, Hartford, CT 06103.

ELLIS, ROBERT J, b. Wash, D.C, May 1, 28; m. 57; c. 2. BACTERIOLOGY, MICROBIOLOGY. B.S, Maryland, 50; M.S, Rutgers, 52; Ph.D.(microbiol), Purdue, 55. Mem. staff, lab. br, bact. & diag. reagents sect, CTR. DISEASE CONTROL, U.S. PUB. HEALTH SERV, 54-58, chief reagents eval. unit, BIOL. REAGENTS SECT, 58-79, CHIEF IMMUNOBIOLOGICS ACTIVITY, 70- Am. Soc. Microbiol; Sci. Res. Soc. Am; Am. Pub. Health Asn. Standardization and evaluation of bacterial, viral, fungal and rickettsial diagnostic reagents and procedures used by various federal, state, local and international public health laboratories. Address: Center for Disease Control, U.S. Public Health Service, Atlanta, GA 30333.

ELLIS, ROBERT L, b. Richmond, Ind, July 26, 38; m. 62; c. 1. MATHEMATICS. A.B, Miami Univ, 60; James B. Duke fels, Duke Univ, 60-62, Nat. Sci. Found. fel, 62-63, Ph.D.(math), 66; Alexander von Humboldt fel, Univ. Mainz, 63-64. Instr. MATH, Duke Univ, 64-65, asst. prof, 65-66; UNIV. MD, COLLEGE PARK, 66-71, ASSOC. PROF, 71-, faculty res. award, summer 70. Nat. Sci. Found. grant, 67-69. Am. Math. Soc. Functional analysis and topology, particularly topological vector spaces over non-Archimedean fields and topology of zero-dimensional spaces. Address: Dept. of Mathematics, University of Maryland College of Arts & Sciences, College Park, MD 20742.

ELLIS, ROBERT MALCOLM, b. Meaford, Ont, Mar. 16, 36; m. 60; c. 2. GEOPHYSICS. B.A, Western Ontario, 57, M.Sc, 58; California, Los Angeles, 58-59; Ph.D.(physics), Alberta, 64. Instr. math, Western Ontario, 59-60; asst. prof. GEOPHYS, UNIV. B.C, 64-68, ASSOC. PROF, 68- Prin. fel, seismic proj, Arctic Inst. N.Am, 66; vis. scientist, Univ. Alta, 71-72. Am. Geophys. Union; Soc. Explor. Geophys. Seismology; geomagnetism. Address: Dept. of Geophysics, University of British Columbia, Vancouver 8, B.C, Can.

ELLIS, ROBERT WILLIAM JR, b. Richmond, Va, Oct. 16, 39; m. 60; c. 4. ENGINEERING MECHANICS. B.S, Va. Polytech, 62, Nat. Defense Ed. Act fel, 62-65, M.S, 63, Ph.D.(eng), 66. Asst. prof. eng, UNIV. S.FLA, 65-67, assoc. prof, 67-69, asst. dean col, 69-71, asst. dean acad. affairs for grad. studies, 71-, ASST. V.PRES. ACAD. AFFAIRS, 71- Metall. engr, polysci. div, Litton Indust, Inc, summer 62, consult, 62-63; instr, Va. Polytech. Inst, summer 65. Soc. Exp. Stress Anal; Nat. Soc. Prof. Eng; Am. Soc. Metals; Am. Soc. Eng. Educ. Engineering and composite materials; continuum mechanics. Address: University of South Florida, Tampa, FL 33620.

ELLIS, ROSCOE, JR, b. Havensville, Kans, Jan. 9, 20; m. 49; c. 4. SOIL CHEMISTRY. B.S, Kansas State, 48, M.S, 50; Ph.D.(soils), Wisconsin, 54. Instr. SOILS, KANS. STATE UNIV, 49-51, asst. prof, 52-55, assoc. prof, 55-60, PROF, 60- Vis. prof, Mich. State Univ, 61-62. U.S.A, 42-46, Capt. Am. Soc. Agron; Soil Sci. Soc. Am. Plant nutrition and clay mineralogy. Address: Dept. of Agronomy, Waters Hall, College of Agriculture, Kansas State University, Manhattan, KS 66502.

ELLIS, ROSS COURTLAND, b. McKinney, Tex, Feb. 23, 29; m. 51; c. 3. GEOLOGY. B.A, Occidental Col, 53; Ph.D, Washington (Seattle), 59. Asst. prof. GEOL, Washington (Seattle), 57-62; WEST. WASH. STATE COL, 62-65, ASSOC. PROF, 65- Structural geology; geomorphology; petrology. Address: Dept. of Geology, Western Washington State College, Bellingham, WA 98225.

ELLIS, ROY, b. Ky, June 30, 14; m. 43; c. 3. OCEANOGRAPHY. B.S, West. Ky. State, 37; M.A, Indiana, 39; cert, Chicago, 44; United Gas fel, Agr. & Mech. Col. Tex, 53-54, Ph.D, 59. Teacher, pub. sch, Miss, 39-42; radio instr, U.S. Army Air Force, 42-43; instr. math, Vanderbilt, 46; from asst. prof. PHYSICS to PROF. & CHMN. DEPT, CENTRE COL. KY, 46- U.S.N.R, 43-46, Lt. Comdr, 46- Am. Meteorol. Soc; Am. Asn. Physics Teachers. Gravity induced pressure variations in the presence of a submerged cylinder; physical oceanography. Address: Dept. of Physics, Centre College of Kentucky, Danville, KY 40422.

ELLIS, S(AMUEL) B(ENJAMIN), b. Reardan, Wash, 04; m. 29; c. 2. CHEMISTRY. B.S, Washington (Seattle), 26; Hart fel, Lafayette Col, 26-27: M.S, 27; fel, Columbia, 30, Ph.D.(phys. inorg. chem), 33. Asst, Columbia, 27-30, instr, 30-32; res. chemist, U.S. Rubber Prod, Inc, 33-37; Hellige, Inc, 37-49; New York Lab. Supply Co, 49-66; prof. chem, Dutchess Community

Col, 66-71; MEM. STAFF RES. & DEVELOP, DELTA SCI. CORP, 71- Am. Chem. Soc. Physical chemistry; rheology; electrical measurements; determination of hydrogen-ion concentration; general colorimetric analysis; instruments; laboratory equipment; electrostatics. Address: 64 Grove St, Lindenhurst, NY 11757.

ELLIS, STANLEY, b. California, Pa, Sept. 2, 23; m. 43; c. 2. BIOLOGICAL CHEMISTRY. B.S, Wayne, 47, M.S, 49, Ph.D.(biochem), 51. Res. assoc, inst. exp. biol, California, 51-55; asst. prof. biochem, sch. med, Emory, 55-60; sr. protein chemist, Cutter Labs, 60-62; res. scientist, BIOCHEM. ENDOCRINOL. BR, AMES. RES. CTR, NASA, 62-63, BR. CHIEF, 63- U.S. Pub. Health sr. res. fel, 59-60; mem. endocrinol. study sect, Nat. Insts. Health, 69-73. U.S.A, 43-46. Am. Soc. Biol. Chem; Endocrine Soc; Brit. Biochem. Soc. Chemistry of anterior pituitary hormones and proteolytic enzymes. Address: Biochemical Endocrinology Branch, Ames Research Center, NASA, Moffett Field, CA 94035.

ELLIS, SYDNEY, b. Boston, Mass, Apr. 20, 17; m. 42; c. 2. PHARMACOLOGY, BIOCHEMISTRY. S.B, Boston, 38, A.M, 39, Ph.D.(med. sci), 41. Asst. biochem, Boston, 39-41; res. fel. pharmacol, Harvard Med. Sch, 41-42; Nat. Defense Res. Cmt. toxicologist, N.Y. Univ, 42; asst. pharmacol, Harvard Med. Sch, 42-44; asst. prof, sch. med, Duke, 46-49; assoc. prof, sch. med, Temple, 49-57; prof. pharmacol. & chmn. dept, Woman's Med. Col. Pa, 57-67; PROF. PHARMACOL. & TOXICOL. & CHMN. DEPT, MED. BR, UNIV. TEX, 67- Consult, Smith Kline & French Labs, 57; Nat. Insts. Health Study Sects, PET, 60-64, Med. Chem. B, 64-68; Nat. Bd. Med. Exam, 64-68. Lindback Found. Award, 64. U.S.A, 44-46, Capt. AAAS; Am. Soc. Pharmacol; Am. Chem. Soc; Soc. Exp. Biol. & Med; N.Y. Acad. Sci. Enzymes; effects of enzyme inhibitors on tissues; chemistry and biochemistry of drug decomposition and metabolism; mechanism of action of neurohumoral agents; autonomic pharmacology; catecholamines on metabolism. Address: Dept. of Pharmacology & Toxicology, University of Texas Medical Branch, Galveston, TX 77550.

ELLIS, WADE, b. Chandler, Okla, June 9, 09; m. 32; c. 2. MATHEMATICS. B.S, Wilberforce Col, 28; M.S, New Mexico, 38; Ph.D.(math), Michigan, 44. Instr. math, Fisk, 38-40; Michigan, 43-45; staff mem, radiation lab, Mass. Inst. Tech, 45-46; physicist, U.S. Air Force Lab, Cambridge, 46-48; asst. prof. math, Oberlin Col, 48-50, assoc. prof, 50-54, prof, 54-67; PROF. MATH. & ASSOC. DEAN GRAD. SCH, UNIV. MICH, 67- Lectr. math, Boston, 47-48; faculty fel, India & France, 54-55; vis. prof, Nat. Univ. Eng, Peru, 64; dir. Nat. Sci. Found. summer insts. high sch. math. teachers, Oberlin Col, 58-61, 64. Mem, Entebbe Workshop, Africa, 62; vis. writing panels, Sch. Math. Study Group, 63 & 65, bd. adv, 64-67; mem. bd. trustees, Marygrove Col, 69-71, chmn. acad. affairs comt, 70-71; comt. int. educ, Asn. Grad. Schs, 70-72; mem. exec. bd, comn. insts. higher educ, N.Cent. Asn. Cols. & Secondary Schs, 70-75; mem. bd. trustees, Inst. Man & Sci, 70-; chmn. del, U.S-Japan Bi-Nat. Conf. Math. Educ, Tokyo, 71. Comdr, Orden de las Palmas Magisteriales del Peru, 64. Civilian with Off. Sci. Res. & Develop, 44. Math. Asn. Am; Am. Math. Soc. Electromagnetic theory; applications to radar; antennas; propagation; analytic mechanics; curriculum development; finite fields. Address: 1141 Chestnut Rd, Ann Arbor, MI 48104.

ELLIS, WALTER H(OLMAN), b. Nashville, Tenn, Aug. 18, 22; m. 66; c. 2. ORGANIC CHEMISTRY. B.A, Fisk, 44, M.A, 49; Nat. Sci. Found. fel, Wisconsin, 55-56. Instr. CHEM, FLA. A&M UNIV, 49-52, asst. prof, 52-55, ASSOC. PROF, 56- U.S.N, 44-46. Am. Chem. Soc; fel. Am. Inst. Chem. Phytochemistry; isolation of pharmacologically active compounds from plants; medicinal chemistry. Address: Dept. of Chemistry, Florida A&M University, Tallahassee, FL 32307.

ELLIS, WALTON P, b. Mammoth Spring, Ark, Aug. 25, 31; m. 56; c. 2. PHYSICAL CHEMISTRY. B.S, California, Berkeley, 53; Ph.D.(chem), Chicago, 57. STAFF MEM. CHEM. RES, LOS ALAMOS SCI. LAB, 57- AAAS; Am. Chem. Soc; Optical Soc. Am; Am. Vacuum Soc. Gas-solid reaction kinetics; optical and physical properties of surfaces and thin films; low energy electron diffraction; high energy electron diffraction; auger and loss spectra. Address: Los Alamos Science Lab, P.O. Box 1663, CMB-8, Los Alamos, NM 87544.

ELLIS, WARREN C(HASE), JR, b. Mexico, Mo, Sept. 15, 19; m. 42; c. 4. ORGANIC CHEMISTRY. B.S, Iowa State Col, 40; Ohio State, 48. Anal. chemist, U.S. Dept. Agr, Exp. Sta, Iowa State Col, 39-40; Monsanto Chem. Co, W.Va, 40-41, jr. res. chemist, 41-45; res. engr, BATTELLE MEM. INST, 45-47, asst. supvr, 48-54, div. chief, 54-60, asst. dept. mgr, 60-61, SR. ADMIN. ASST. & SR. PROJ. LEADER, 61- AAAS; Am. Chem. Soc; Am. Leather Chem. Asn. Agricultural chemicals; uses of organic chemicals; catalysts; lubricants; leather; wood preservation; advanced jet fuels; detergents; criminalistics; technology transfer. Address: Battelle Memorial Institute, 505 King Ave, Columbus, OH 43201.

ELLIS, WILLIAM C, b. Clay, La, Apr. 23, 31; m. 55; c. 1. ANIMAL NUTRITION. B.S, La. Polytech, 53; M.S, Missouri, 55, Ph.D, 59. Asst, Missouri, 53-55, instr. animal husb, 55-58, asst. prof, 58-61; ANIMAL SCI, TEX. A&M UNIV, 61-63, ASSOC. PROF, 63- N.Atlantic fel, 59-60. Fed. Am. Socs. Exp. Biol; Am. Soc. Animal Sci. Ruminant physiology; nutrition and metabolism; protein and energy metabolism by rumen microorganisms and the ruminants tissues. Address: Dept. of Animal Husbandry, Texas A&M University, College Station, TX 77843.

ELLIS, WILLIAM D(EE), b. Prineville, Ore, June 4, 43; m. 65. PHYSICAL & ANALYTICAL CHEMISTRY. B.A, Occidental Col, 65; Izaak Walton Killam Mem. fel, Univ. Alta, 67-68, Ph.D.(phys. chem), 68. PRIN. RES. SCIENTIST, HONEYWELL CORP. RES. CTR, 68- AAAS; Am. Chem. Soc; Instrument Soc. Am. Analytical instrumentation for pollution measurement; industrial process control and health services; minicomputer-instrument interfacing; fast reaction kinetics in solutions; physical chemical characterization of protein systems. Address: Honeywell Corporate Research Center, 500 Washington Ave. S, Hopkins, MN 55343.

ELLIS, WILLIAM H(AYNES), b. Cedar Hill, Tenn, Dec. 4, 31; m. 52. SYSTEMATIC BOTANY, PLANT ECOLOGY. B.S, Austin Peay State Col, 53, M.A, 56; Ph.D.(bot), Tennessee, 63. Teacher, high sch, Tenn, 55-56; instr. biol, Austin Peay State Col, 56-59, asst. prof, 59-60; investr. plant taxon, Oak Ridge Inst. Nuclear Studies, 61; Highlands Biol. Sta, 62; instr. bot, Tennessee, 62-63, vis. asst. prof, 62; assoc. prof. BIOL, AUSTIN PEAY STATE UNIV, 63-68, PROF, 68-, V.PRES. ACAD. AFFAIRS, 71-, dir. grad. studies, 66-67, assoc. dean faculties, 67-68, dean faculties, 68-71. Vis. scientist, Tenn. Acad. Sci, 64-65. Med.C, U.S.A, 53-55. AAAS; Am. Soc. Plant Taxon; Bot. Soc. Am; Nat. Asn. Biol. Teachers. Systematic revision of the genus Acer, section rubra, with emphasis on cytogenetics; pigment studies by chromatography, ecological considerations and morphological study; ecology of the woody flora of Kentucky and Tennessee. Address: Austin Peay State University, Clarkesville, TN 37040.

ELLIS, WILLIAM HOBERT, b. Albany, Ga, Dec. 28, 28; m. 50; c. 4. NUCLEAR CHEMISTRY & ENGINEERING. B.S, N.Ga. Col, 57; Ph.D.(nuclear & inorg. chem), Fla. State, 63. Asst. prof. NUCLEAR ENG. & CHEM, UNIV. FLA, 62-66, ASSOC. PROF, 66- U.S.N, 46-55, Res, 55-, Comdr. AAAS; Am. Nuclear Soc; Am. Chem. Soc. Nuclear and radio chemistry; nuclear instrumentation and spectrometry; activation analysis and direct energy conversion; inorganic chemistry. Address: Dept. of Nuclear Engineering Sciences, University of Florida, Gainesville, FL 32601.

ELLIS, WILLIAM N, b. Rangeley, Maine, Nov. 28, 20; m. 48; c. 4. SCIENCE POLICY. B.S, Univ. Maine, 43; M.S, Univ. Hawaii, 48. Asst. proj. engr, Sperry Gyroscope Co, 44-45; instr. physics, Univ. Alaska, 46-47; Univ. Hawaii, 47-49; Univ. B.C, 49-50; Univ. Edinburgh, 50-52; asst. prof, Univ. Vt, 52-54; physicist, U.S. Naval Res. Lab, 55-56; Nat. Sci. Found, 56-66; SCI. ADV, Dept. Commerce, 66-68; UNESCO, 68-70; DEPT. COMMERCE, 70- U.S.N, 45-47. Electronics; nuclear physics. Address: Office of the Assistant Secretary of Science & Technology, Dept. of Commerce, Washington, DC 20230.

ELLIS, WILLIAM W(ESLEY), b. Havre, Mont, Mar. 3, 27. NUTRITIONAL BIOCHEMISTRY. B.S, Mont. State Col, 47; Ph.D.(animal nutrit), Oregon State, 57. Asst, Iowa State, 47-49; Army Med. Res. Lab, Ky, 50-52; Oregon State, 53-55, instr, 55-56; asst. prof. BIOCHEM, UNIV. WYO, 56-60, assoc. prof, 60-65, PROF, 65- U.S.A.R, 50-56. Nutritional myopathy; blood coagulation; vitamin and mineral metabolism; lipid-hormone interrelationships; urolithiasis; selenium biochemistry. Address: Division of Biochemistry, University of Wyoming, Box 3944, University Station, Laramie, WY 82070.

ELLISON, ALFRED H(ARRIS), b. Quincy, Mass, Dec. 23, 23; m. 51; c. 5. SURFACE CHEMISTRY. B.S, Boston Col, 50; M.S, Tufts, 51; Ph.D.(surf. chem), Georgetown, 56. Chemist, U.S. Naval Res. Lab, 51-56; res. chemist, Texaco Res. Center, N.Y, 56-65; Harris Res. Labs, D.C, 65; Gillete Res. Inst, Inc, 65-69; ASST. DIR. DIV. CHEM. & PHYSICS, BUR. AIR POLLUTION SCI, ENVIRON. PROTECTION AGENCY, 69- U.S.A.A.F, 42-45, Res, 45-57. AAAS; Air Pollution Control Asn; Am. Chem. Soc. Administration of chemistry and physics research and development programs on atmospheric chemistry and on methods and instrumentation for measuring air pollutants in the air and in the emissions from sources. Address: Division of Chemistry & Physics, Environmental Protection Agency, Room Q-304, Technical Center, Research Triangle Park, NC 27711.

ELLISON, BART T, b. San Diego, Calif, Apr. 21, 42; m. 65; c. 2. CHEMICAL ENGINEERING, CORROSION. B.S, Univ. Calif, Berkeley, 64, M.S, 66, Ph.D.(mech. eng), 69. ENGR, SHELL DEVELOP. CO, 69- Am. Soc. Mech. Eng. The effects of fluid flow on corrosion. Address: Shell Development Co, P.O. Box 24225, Oakland, CA 94623.

ELLISON, FRANK O(SCAR), b. Omaha, Nebr, June 18, 26; m. 59; c. 2. PHYSICAL CHEMISTRY. B.S, Creighton, 49; Ph.D.(phys. chem), Iowa State, 53. Res. asst. spectros. & theoret. chem, Inst. Atomic Res, Iowa State, 50-53; instr. PHYS. CHEM, Carnegie Inst. Tech, 53-54, asst. prof, 54-65; assoc. prof, UNIV. PITTSBURGH, 65-68, PROF, 68- U.S.A, 44-46. AAAS; Am. Phys. Soc; Am. Chem. Soc. Theory of molecular spectra and electronic structure of molecules; chemical physics. Address: Dept. of Chemistry, University of Pittsburgh, Pittsburgh, PA 15213.

ELLISON, J(OHN) HOWARD, b. Lafayette, La, Feb. 25, 18; m. 44; c. 2. HORTICULTURE. B.S, Agr. & Mech. Col, Tex, 42; Ph.D.(veg. crops), Cornell, 48. Asst. prof. VEG. CROPS, Cornell, 48-53; assoc. res. specialist, RUTGERS UNIV, 53-61, RES. SPECIALIST, 61- Am. Soc. Hort. Sci. Asparagus breeding and culture. Address: Dept. of Horticulture & Forestry, Rutgers, The State University, New Brunswick, NJ 08903.

ELLISON, JOHN V(OGELSANGER), b. Cape Girardeau, Mo, Aug. 7, 19; m. 49; c. 4. PHYSICS. A.B, Southeast Mo. State Col, 39; Missouri, 39; Iowa, 40; Ill. Inst. Tech, 41. Instr, high sch, 39-41; physics, Ill. Inst. Tech, 41; instr. & dean physics & electronics, Am. TV Labs, 41-43; staff mem. underwater sound, div. war res, Columbia, 43-45; sect. head appl. electronics, sound div, Naval Res. Lab, 45-59; assoc. scientist, res. div, McDONNELL AIRCRAFT CO, McDONNELL DOUGLAS CORP, 59-62, proj. electronics engr, electronics systs. eng. dept, 62-65, MGR, RECONNAISSANCE LAB, 65- AAAS; Acoust. Soc. Am; Am. Soc. Photogram. Reconnaissance systems; antisubmarine warfare; remote sensing; sonar; underwater acoustics; information displays; radar; communications; optics; electro-optics. Address: 2 Douglass Lane, St. Louis, MO 63122.

ELLISON, LOIS TAYLOR, b. Ft. Valley, Ga, Oct. 28, 23; m. 45; c. 5. PHYSIOLOGY. B.S, Georgia, 43; M.D, Med. Col. Ga, 50. Asst. res. prof. physiol, MED. COL. GA, 51-65, surg, 60-65, assoc. res. prof. physiol. & surg, 65-68, assoc. prof. MED. & SURG, 68-71, PROF, 71-, DIR. CARDIOPULMONARY LAB, 56- Nat. Insts. Health res. career develop. award, 63-68. Am. Physiol. Soc; Am. Thoracic Soc; Am. Heart Asn. Pulmonary disease; preoperative and postoperative pulmonary function; heart and lung transplantation; lung surfactant; oxygen transport. Address: Dept. of Medicine & Surgery, Medical College of Georgia, Augusta, GA 30902.

ELLISON, MARLON L, b. Woodbine, Iowa, Dec. 18, 16; m. 49. BOTANY. B.S, Iowa State, 40; M.S, Trinity (Tex), 61; Ph.D.(bot), Kansas, 64. Instr. bot, Stephen F. Austin State Col, 63-64; asst. prof. BIOL, UNIV. TAMPA, 64-65, ASSOC. PROF, 65- U.S.A, 40-61, Lt. Col. Hepatic flora. Address: Dept. of Biology, University of Tampa, Tampa, FL 33606.

ELLISON, ROBERT ANDREW, b. St. John, N.B, July 9, 40; m. 64. ORGANIC CHEMISTRY. B.Sc, New Brunswick, 61, univ. demonstratorship, 61-62, Nat. Res. Coun. Can. studentship, 62-65, Ph.D.(org. chem), 65. Fel, Brandeis, 65-67; res. fel, Harvard, 67-68; ASST. PROF. CHEM, Boston, 68-69; SCH. PHARM, UNIV. WIS, MADISON, 69- Can. Army, Lt. Am. Chem. Soc; Chem. Inst. Can. Synthesis of organic molecules; development of new synthetic methods in organic chemistry. Address: School of Pharmacy, University of Wisconsin, 425 N. Charter St, Madison, WI 53706.

ELLISON, ROBERT G, b. Millen, Ga, Dec. 4, 16; m. 45; c. 5. CARDIOVASCULAR & THORACIC SURGERY. A.B, Vanderbilt, 39; M.D, Med. Col, Ga, 43. Instr. thoracic surg, MED. COL. GA, 47-49, asst. prof, 49-51, assoc. prof, 51-59, PROF. SURG, 59-, CHIEF DIV. THORACIC SURG, 55-, res. assoc. physiol, asst. res. prof, 53. Mem. surg. study sect, Nat. Insts. Health, 69-73; mem, Am. Bd. Thoracic Surg, 71-; consult, Crippled Children Serv, Atlanta; Vet. Admin. Hosp; Battey State Hosp, Rome, Ga. Dipl, Am. Bd. Surg. & Am. Bd. Thoracic Surg. Am. Med. Asn; Am. Col. Surg; Asn. Thoracic Surg; Am. Col. Cardiol; fel. Am. Col. Chest Physicians; Am. Physiol. Soc; Am. Thoracic Soc; Soc. Univ. Surg; Soc. Thoracic Surg.(pres, 71); Am. Surg. Asn. Address: Division of Thoracic Surgery, Medical College of Georgia, Augusta, GA 30902.

ELLISON, ROBERT L, b. Williamsport, Pa, Jan. 14, 30. GEOLOGY. A.B, Cornell, 52; Am. Asn. Petrol. Geologists grant & univ. scholar, Pa. State, 56, Mineral Indust. Exp. Sta. fel, 58, Ph.D.(geol), 61. Lab. asst, Pa. State, 55-58, instr. GEOL, 58-59; acting asst. prof, UNIV. VA, 59-61, asst. prof, 61-67, ASSOC. PROF, 67-, chmn. dept, 69-70, environ. sci, 71-72. Summers, asst, geol. field camp, 55, dir, 56, 57; Nat. Sci. Found. grants, 64-65, summers, 62, 63; assoc. faculty mem, Va. Inst. Marine Sci; Presidential appointee, Potomac River Fisheries Comn. U.S.N, 52-54. AAAS; Am. Asn. Petrol. Geol; Geol. Soc. Am; Am. Soc. Limnol. & Oceanog; Paleont. Soc; Nat. Asn. Geol. Teachers; Atlantic Estuarine Res. Soc. Distribution and ecology of Foraminifera; structure of benthic marine communities; estuarine geology and ecology. Address: Dept. of Environmental Sciences, University of Virginia, Charlottesville, VA 22903.

ELLISON, SAMUEL P(ORTER), JR, b. Kansas City, Mo, July 1, 14; m. 40; c. 3. GEOLOGY. A.B, Univ. Kansas City, 36; A.M, Missouri, 38, fel, 38-39, Ph.D.(geol), 40. Instr. geol, Mo. Sch. Mines, 39-43, asst. prof, 43-44; geologist, Stanolind Oil & Gas Co, 44-46, sr. geologist, 46-47, dist. geologist, 47-48; PROF. GEOL. SCI, UNIV. TEX, AUSTIN, 48-, DEAN COL. NATURAL SCI, 71-, chmn. dept. geol, 52-56, acting dean col. arts & sci, 70-71. Asst. geologist, U.S. Geol. Surv, 42-44; consult, Shell Oil Co, summers 53-56; Humble Oil & Ref. Co, 58-71; Fulbright sr. res. fel, Ger, 70. AAAS; Am. Asn. Petrol. Geol; Paleont. Soc; Soc. Econ. Paleont. & Mineral. (secy-treas, 53-58, pres, 59-60); fel. Geol. Soc. Am; Soc. Petrol. Eng; Nat. Asn. Geol. Teachers (v.pres, 63-64, pres, 64-65); Am. Inst. Prof. Geol. Micropaleontology; stratigraphy; petroleum geology; sedimentation; structural geology. Address: Dept. of Geological Sciences, University of Texas at Austin, Austin, TX 78712.

ELLISON, SOLON (ARTHUR), b. New York, July 13, 22; m. 46; c. 2. MICROBIOLOGY. B.S, City Col. New York, 42; D.D.S, Columbia, 46, U.S. Pub. Health Serv. fel, 50-51, Ph.D.(microbiol), 58. Instr. microbiol, col. physicians & surgeons, Columbia, 51-52, assoc, 52-58, asst. prof, 59-62; assoc. prof. ORAL BIOL, SCH. DENT, STATE UNIV. N.Y. BUFFALO, 62-64, PROF. & CHMN. DEPT, 64- U.S.A, 46-48. Am. Soc. Microbiol; Am. Asn. Immunol; Int. Asn. Dent. Res. Dentistry; immunology; salivary physiology. Address: Dept. of Oral Biology, State University of New York at Buffalo, 4510 Main St, Buffalo, NY 14226.

ELLISON, THEODORE, b. Milwaukee, Wis, July 15, 30; m. 53; c. 3. BIOCHEMISTRY. B.S, Wisconsin, 52, M.S, 56, Ph.D.(biochem, vet. sci), 59. Asst. vet. sci, Wisconsin, 52-59, sr. res. biochemist, Smith Kline & French Labs, 59-65; sr. biochemist & head drug metab. group, Riker Labs, 65, leader pharmacokinetics group, 65-69, sect. head pharmacokinetics, 69-71; HEAD BIOAVAILABILITY SECT, VICK DIVS. RES, 71- Qm.C, U.S.A, 54-56. AAAS; Am. Chem. Soc; N.Y. Acad. Sci; Am. Pharmaceut. Asn; Am. Soc. Pharmacol. & Exp. Therapeut; Soc. Exp. Biol. & Med; Int. Soc. Biochem. Pharmacol; Am. Nuclear Soc; Acad. Pharmaceut. Sci. Drug metabolism; radioisotopes; pharmacokinetics; biopharmaceutics; bioanalytical research; biochemical pharmacology; bioavailability. Address: Vick Divisions Research, One Bradford Rd, Mt. Vernon, NY 10553.

ELLISON, THOMAS M, b. Spartanburg, S.C, Nov. 26, 38; m. 60; c. 2. PHYSICAL & POLYMER CHEMISTRY. B.S, Wofford Col, 60; M.S, Clemson Univ, 62, Ph.D.(phys. chem), 64. Res. engr, Fiber Industs. Inc, summer 64; proj. supvr, RIEGEL PAPER CORP, MATTHEWS, 66-67, lab. supvr, 67-68, DIV. TECH. DIR, 68- Sig.C, U.S.A, 64-66, Capt. Am. Chem. Soc. Flexible laminations of plastic films and metal foils; adhesives and coatings; polyester chemistry; transport properties of synthetic membranes. Address: 3143 Champaign St, Charlotte, NC 28210.

ELLISON, WILLIAM LEE, b. Austin, Tex, Sept. 19, 23; m. 48; c. 4. PLANT TAXONOMY. B.S, Texas, 47, M.Ed, 53, Ph.D.(bot), 61. PROF. BIOL, Ark. Col, 61-63; Erskine Col, 63-66; Hardin-Simmons Univ, 66-67; ERSKINE COL, 67- U.S.N.R, 43-45, Lt.(jg). Am. Soc. Plant Taxon; Bot. Soc. Am. Taxonomy of Bahia and related genera; Compositae. Address: Dept. of Biology, Erskine College, Due West, SC 29639.

ELLITHORN, HAROLD E(DWARD), b. Detroit, Mich, Oct. 11, 11; m. 38; c. 1. ELECTRICAL ENGINEERING. B.S, Union (N.Y), 34; scholar, Harvard, 34-35, M.S, 35; Ph.D.(physics), Notre Dame, 45. Engr, Sylvania Elec. Prod, 35-36, dir. eng. lab, Salem Div, 36-38; instr. elec. eng, Notre Dame, 40-43, asst. prof, 43-46, assoc. prof, 46-54, prof. & head dept, 54-62; sr. staff eng. consult, Hughes Aircraft Co, 62-64; PROF. ELEC. ENG, MARQUETTE UNIV, 64-, chmn. dept, 64-69. Inst. Elec. & Electronics Eng; Nat. Soc. Prof. Eng. Microphones and head set receivers; antinoise characteristics of differential microphones; nonlinear networks. Address: Dept. of Electrical Engineering, Marquette University, Milwaukee, WI 53233.

ELLMAN, GEORGE L(EON), b. Chicago, Ill, Dec. 27, 23; m. 48; c. 1. BIOCHEMISTRY. B.S, Illinois, 48; M.S, State Col. Wash, 49; Ph.D.(chem), Calif. Inst. Tech, 52. Res. biochemist, Dow Chem. Co, 52-59; CHIEF RES. BIOCHEMIST, LANGLEY-PORTER INST, SAN FRANCISCO, 59- Res. assoc. pharmacol. & psychiat. & lectr. biochem, med. ctr, California, 59. U.S.A, 43-46. Soc. Pharmacol. & Exp. Therapeut. Drug action; cell growth; methodology. Address: 2090 Vistazo East, Tiburon, CA 94920.

ELLNER, PAUL D(ANIEL), b. New York, N.Y, May 2, 25; m. 48, 65; c. 3. MICROBIOLOGY. B.S, Long Island, 49; M.S, Southern California, 52; U.S. Navy fel. & Ph.D.(microbiol), Maryland, 56. Res. bacteriologist, Elenite Prod, Inc, 47-48; Foster D. Snell, Inc, 52; asst, Mt. Sinai Hosp, 53; Indiana, 53-54; instr. MICROBIOL, col. med, Florida, 56-60; asst. prof, col. med, Vermont, 60-63; COL. PHYSICIANS & SURGEONS, COLUMBIA UNIV, 63-66, assoc. prof, 66-70, PROF, 70-, DIR. DIAG. MICROBIOL. SERV, PRESBY. HOSP, 70-, staff microbiologist, 63-70. Dipl,;Am. Bd. Med. Microbiol. U.S.N, 43-44; U.S.P.H.S.R, 63, Sr. Asst. Scientist. AAAS; Am. Soc. Microbiol; fel. Am. Acad. Microbiol; Soc. Acad. Clin. Lab. Physicians & Scientists. Clinical bacteriology; infectious diseases; clostridia. Address: Columbia University College of Physicians & Surgeons, 630 W. 168th St, New York, NY 10032.

ELLS, C. E, b. Canard, N.S, Jan. 20, 23; m. 62; c. 2. PHYSICAL METALLURGY. B.A.Sc, Toronto, 50, M.A, 51; Ph.D.(metall), Birmingham, 57. Res. officer, METALL, Can. Dept. Mines & Tech. Survs, 51-53; engr, Westinghouse Elec. Corp, Can, 56-57; RES. OFF, ATOMIC ENERGY CAN. LTD, 57- R.C.A.F, 42-45. Am. Soc. Metals. Gases in metals; beryllium metallurgy; metallurgy of zirconium alloys. Address: Atomic Energy of Canada Ltd, Chalk River, Ont, Can.

ELLS, JAMES E, b. Cambridge, Mass, June 15, 31; m. 58; c. 1. HORTICULTURE. B.S, Massachusetts, 57; M.S, Mich. State, 58, Ph.D.(hort), 61. Asst. prof. HORT, EXP. STA, COLO. STATE UNIV, 61-69, ASSOC. PROF, 69-, PROCESSING CROPS SPECIALIST, EXTEN. SERV, 61- U.S.A, 52-54. Am. Soc. Hort. Sci; Inst. Food Technol. Culture and processing of horticultural crops. Address: Dept. of Horticulture, Colorado State University, Ft. Collins, CO 80521.

ELLS, VICTOR R(AYMOND), b. Benton Harbor, Mich, Dec. 7, 14, PHYSICAL CHEMISTRY. A.B, Kalamazoo Col, 35; M.S, Brown, 38; Ph.D.(phys. chem, photochem), Rochester, 39. Instr. chem. & spectros, Missouri, 39-43; res. phys. chemist, NORWICH PHARMACAL CO. & EATON LABS. DIV, 43-53, head phys. & anal. res. lab, 53-61, SR. PHYS. ANAL. CHEMIST, METHOD DEVELOP. RES, 61- AAAS; Am. Phys. Soc; Optical Soc; Am. Chem. Soc; Coblentz Soc; Soc. Appl. Spectros. N.Y. Acad. Sci. Spectrographic analysis; spectrophotometry and absorption spectra; photochemistry; application of physical chemical methods to drug development, characterization and analysis. Address: 119 S. Broad St, Norwich, NY 13815.

ELLSON, ROBERT A, b. N.Y.C, Dec. 15, 34; m. 58; c. 3. MECHANICAL ENGINEERING. B.S, City Col. N.Y, 57; M.S, Univ. Rochester, 63, Ph.D. (mech. eng), 66. Mech. engr, Gen. Elec. Co, N.Y, 57-58; jr. engr, N.Y.C. Housing Auth, 58-59; instr. mech. eng, Univ. Rochester, 59-64; engr, NASA, Lewis Res. Ctr, 65-68; ASSOC. PROF. MECH. ENG, ROCHESTER INST. TECHNOL, 68- Dow Chem. Co. Award, 70. U.S.A.R, 58-65. Am. Soc. Mech. Eng; Am. Soc. Eng. Educ.(Upper N.Y, Ont, Que. award, 69-70). Educational television; computer assisted instruction; engineering mechanics and thermodynamics. Address: Dept. of Mechanical Engineering, Rochester Institute of Technology, 1 Lomb Memorial Dr, Rochester, NY 14623.

ELLSPERMAN, LEWIS M, b. Evansville, Ind, Nov. 13, 11; m. 65; c. 5. CIVIL ENGINEERING. Denver Jr. Col, 31-32; Colorado, 34-35. Lab. technician, Corps Engrs, Colo, 41-43, mat. engr, 43; SUPVRY. MAT. ENGR. & HEAD MAT. SECT, DIV. RES, U.S. BUR. RECLAMATION, 46- Summer asphalt consult, U.S. Agency Int. Develop. & Repub. Sudan, Africa, 62; Agency Int. Develop. & Repub. Turkey, 66; consult, Repub. Arg, 70; mem, Int. Comn. Large Dams. Superior performance award, U.S. Bur. Reclamation, 62, meritorious serv. awards, 65 & 70. C.Eng, 43-46, 1st Lt. Am. Soc. Test. & Mat; Soc. Am. Mil. Eng. Asphalt technology; the use of asphaltic materials in hydraulic construction, particularly lower-cost canal and reservoir linings; petrochemicals; plastic and rubber linings. Address: U.S. Bureau of Reclamation, Denver Federal Center, Bldg. 56, Denver, CO 80225.

ELLSWORTH, ARTHUR C(HARLES), JR, b. Colo, Jan. 8, 19; m. 43; c. 4. CHEMICAL ENGINEERING. B.S.Ch.E, Denver. Res. & develop. engr, Columbia Chem. Div, Pittsburgh Plate Glass Co, 41-49, asst. dir. develop, Columbia South. Chem. Corp, 49-57, spec. projs. engr, 57-59, tech. dir, Pittsburgh Plate Glass Int, S.Am, 59-63; managing dir, Società Sviluppi Chimici S.P.A, Italy, 63-68; dir. for. activities, Asia & S.Am, CHEM. DIV, PPG INDUSTS, INC, 68-71, MGR. TECH. CTR, 71- Am. Inst. Chem. Eng. Synthetic resins; organic chlorinations; phosgenation; chlorobenzene and benzene hexachloride manufacture. Address: PPG Industries, Inc, Chemical Division, Box 4026, Corpus Christi, TX 78408.

ELLSWORTH, LOUIS D(ANIEL), b. Hamler, Ohio, Apr. 27, 17; m. 41; c. 2. PHYSICS. B.S, Case, 37; M.Sc, Ohio State, 38, fel, 40-41, Ph.D.(physics), 41. Asst. physics, Ohio State, 37-40; instr, Haverford Col, 41-42; staff mem. nat. defense res. comt, radiation lab, Mass. Inst. Technol, 42-45; assoc. prof. PHYSICS, KANS. STATE UNIV, 45-58, PROF, 58- Res. physicist, Rauland Corp, Ill, 45-46. Am. Phys. Soc; Am. Asn. Physics Teachers. X-ray diffraction analysis; mutations in bacteria by x-rays; electronics; nuclear reactor instrumentation; low energy nuclear physics; interactions of medium energy charged particles with matter. Address: Dept. of Physics, Kansas State University, Manhattan, KS 66502.

ELLSWORTH, ROBERT KING, b. Plattsburgh, N.Y, Nov. 22, 41; m. 63; c. 2. PLANT BIOCHEMISTRY. B.S, State Univ. N.Y. Col. Plattsburgh, 63, M.S,

66; Nat. Insts. Health fel, Iowa State, 67-68, Ph.D.(biochem), 68. Teacher, Lake Placid Cent. Sch, N.Y, 63-64; Beekmantown Cent. Sch, 64-65; instr. chem, State Univ. N.Y. Col. Plattsburgh, 65-66; trainee BIOCHEM, Iowa State, 66-67; asst. prof, STATE UNIV. N.Y. COL. PLATTSBURGH, 68-70, ASSOC. PROF, 70-, instr, summer 64. AAAS; Am. Chem. Soc; Am. Soc. Plant Physiol. Chlorophyll biosynthesis and enzymology; chloroplast physiology; analytical biochemistry; radio biochemical techniques. Address: Dept. of Chemistry, State University of New York College at Plattsburgh, Plattsburgh, NY 12901.

ELLWOOD, ERIC LOUIS, b. Melbourne, Australia, Sept. 8, 22; U.S. citizen; m. 47; c. 3. WOOD SCIENCE & TECHNOLOGY. B.Sc, Melbourne, 44, M.Sc, 51; Fulbright scholar. & Sheffield fel, Yale, 51-53, Ph.D.(wood tech), 53. Asst. forester, Victorian Forests Cmn, Australia, 45-47; res. off. wood tech, Commonwealth Sci. & Indust. Res. Orgn, 47-51, prin. res. off, 53-57; wood technologist & lectr, forest prod. lab, Univ. Calif, 57-61; prof. wood & paper sci. & head dept, N.C. STATE UNIV, 61-71, DEAN SCH. FOREST RESOURCES, 71- Forest Prod. Res. Soc; Tech. Asn. Pulp & Paper Indust; Soc. Wood Sci. & Technol.(pres, 65-66); Australian Inst. Foresters (secy-treas, 46); Int. Acad. Wood Sci. Wood physics, especially wood-fluid relations and its application to drying and treating processes; wood anatomy; relation between anatomy, wood and fiber properties. Address: School of Forest Resources, North Carolina State University, Raleigh, NC 27607.

ELLWOOD, PAUL M, JR, b. San Francisco, Calif, July 16, 26; m. 49; c. 3. REHABILITATION MEDICINE. B.A, Stanford Univ, 49, M.D, 53. Dir. inpatient serv, Elizabeth Kenny Inst, 53-58, med. adminr, Kenny Rehab. Inst, 58-62, EXEC. DIR, AM. REHAB. FOUND, 63- Fel. pediat, Univ. Minn, 53-55, neurol, 55-57, clin. assoc. prof. neurol. & pediat, 58-, clin. prof. phys. med. & rehab, 62-; consult, Arg. Ministry Pub. Health, 56; U.S. Dept. State Int. Coop. Admin, Nicaragua, 58; pres, mem. bd. dirs. & res. comt, Asn. Rehab. Ctrs, 60-62; mem, Surgeon Gen. Nat. Adv. Health Serv. Coun, 66; sci. & prof. adv. bd, Nat. Ctr. Health Serv. Res. & Develop, 68-; consult, Off. Asst. Secy. Health & Sci. Affairs, Dept. Health, Educ. & Welfare, 69-, Off. Secy, 69; mem. bd. dirs, Nat. Health Coun, 70. Award, Arg. Ministry Pub. Health, 57; Am. Acad. Neurol, 58; cert. merit, Am. Med. Asn, 59; President's Citation, President's Comt. Employ. Handicapped, 62. U.S.N.R, 44-46. Human resources policy research; health services research; pediatric neurology. Address: American Rehabilitation Foundation, Inc, 123 E. Grant St, Minneapolis, MN 55403.

ELLYIN, FERNAND, b. Rezaieh, Azerbaijan, Iran, Aug. 27, 38; Can. citizen; m. 66; c. 2. STRUCTURAL & SOLID MECHANICS. M.Sc, Univ. Tehran, 62; Nat. Res. Coun. Can, scholar, 65-66, Ph.D.(civil eng), Univ. Waterloo, 66. Engr, Beta Co, Iran, 62-63; res. asst. CIVIL ENG, Univ. Waterloo, 63-66; asst. prof, UNIV. SHERBROOKE, 66-69, ASSOC. PROF, 69-, HEAD STRUCT. & SOLID MECH. SECT, 70- Sr. res.off, dept. eng, Oxford, 68-69; vis. eng, div. theoret. studies & res, Ctr. Exp. Res. & Study Bldg. & Pub. Works, Paris, France, 69; proj. dir, subcomt. reinforced openings and external loads, Pressure Vessel Res. Comt, N.Y.C, 66- Am. Soc. Civil Eng; Can. Standards Asn; Am. Soc. Mech. Eng; Eng. Inst. Can; Am. Acad. Mech. Stress analysis and design of pressure vessels and piping systems; plastic design of structures; stress concentration in plates and shells; reliability of structures; high pressure technology. Address: Dept. of Civil Engineering, University of Sherbrooke, Sherbrooke, Que, Can.

ELLZEY, JOANNE TONTZ, b. Baltimore, Md, Mar. 23, 37; m. 69. BIOLOGICAL SCIENCES, MYCOLOGY. B.A, Randolph-Macon Woman's Col, 59; M.A, Univ. N.C, Chapel Hill, 63; Nat. Insts. Health grant, Univ. Tex. Austin, 64-69, Ph.D.(bot), 69. Teaching asst. BIOL, Univ. N.C, Greensboro, 62-63, instr, 63-64; ASST. PROF, UNIV. TEX. EL PASO, 69- AAAS; Bot. Soc. Am; Mycol. Soc. Am; Am. Inst. Biol. Sci. Utilization of electron microscopy and Nomarski interference microscopy to study the ultrastructure of gametogenesis and cell wall formation in saprolegniaceous fungi. Address: Dept. of Biological Sciences, University of Texas at El Paso, TX 79968.

ELLZEY, MARION LAWRENCE, JR, b. Shattuck, Okla, Apr. 13, 39; m. 69. PHYSICAL INORGANIC CHEMISTRY, APPLIED MATHEMATICS. B.A, Rice Univ, 61; Ph.D.(physics), Univ. Tex. Austin, 66. R.A. Welch fel, Univ. Tex. Austin, 66-68; ASST. PROF. chem. & math, UNIV. TEX. EL PASO, 68-70, CHEM, 70- R.A. Welch grant, Robert A. Welch Found, Tex, 71- Am. Inst. Physics, Am. Chem. Soc. Molecular quantum mechanics with emphasis on complexed transition metal ions and their electronic and magnetic properties; group theory and linear algebra. Address: Dept. of Chemistry, University of Texas at El Paso, El Paso, TX 79968.

ELLZEY, S(AMUEL) E(DWARD), JR, b. Mobile, Ala, May 16, 31; m. 60; c. 3. ORGANIC CHEMISTRY. B.S, Spring Hill Col, 54; M.S, Tulane, 57, Ph.D.(chem), 59. CHEMIST, SOUTH. REGIONAL RES. LAB, U.S. DEPT. AGR, 59- Am. Chem. Soc. Isocyanates and isocyanate generators; organic fluorine compounds; chemical modification of cotton; nuclear magnetic resonance. Address: 6335 Dwyer Rd, New Orleans, LA 70126.

ELM, ADOLF C(ASPAR), b. Sterbfritz, Ger, Sept. 25, 00; nat. 30; m. 24, 35; c. 1. CHEMISTRY. Ph.D.(org. chem), Marburg, 23. Paint chemist, E.I. du Pont de Nemours & Co, 24-26; paint technologist, Am. Asphalt Paint Co, Ill, 26-28; asst. tech. dir, McCloskey Varnish Co, 28-29; res. investr, N.J. Zinc Co, Pa, 29-43, chief org. mat. sect, 43-51, res. supvr, 51-70; RETIRED. Mattiello Mem. Lectr, 53. With U.S.N, 44. Am. Chem. Soc; fel. Am. Inst. Chem; Nat. Asn. Corrosion Eng; hon. mem. Fedn. Socs. Paint Technol.(George B. Heckel Award, 68). Drying oils; paints; pigments. Address: 475 Lafayette Ave, Palmerton, PA 18071.

ELMADJIAN, FRED, b. Aleppo, Syria, Oct. 5, 15; nat; m. 52. PHYSIOLOGY. B.S, Mass. Col. Pharm, 40, M.S, 42; M.A, Clark, 47; Ph.D.(physiol), Tufts Col, 49. Staff mem, Worcester Found, 44-62, sr. scientist, 55-62, res. assoc, Worcester State Hosp, 47-58, dir. biol. res, 58-62, dir. labs, 55-62; CHIEF BIOL. SCI. SECT, training & manpower resources br, NAT. INST. MENT. HEALTH, 62-66, BEHAV. SCI. TRAINING BR, 66- Asst. chemist, State Dept. Ment. Health, Mass, 45; physiologist, Mem. Found. Neuro-Endocrine Res, 46; res. assoc, med. sch, Tufts Col, 50-51; prof. lectr. & res. assoc, Mass. Col. Pharm, 50-53; physiologist, field sta, Nat.Inst. Ment. Health, Mass, 51-53; neurophysiologist, Mass. Dept. Ment. Health, 57-62; mem. revision comt, U.S. Pharmacopoeia, 55-60. Consult, opers. res. off, Hopkins, 52-61; dept. psychiat, New Eng. Med Ctr, 59-62; Worcester Found, 62-63. AAAS; Am. Physiol. Soc; Am. Pharmaceut. Asn; Endocrine Soc; N.Y. Acad. Sci; Soc. Biol. Psychiat; Royal Soc. Med. Stress physiology; adrenal cortical physiology; adrenal medulla; adrenaline and nonadrenaline, in normal and mental diseases. Address: 11508 Stonewood Lane, Rockville, MD 20852.

ELMENDORF, CHARLES HALSEY III, b. Los Angeles, Calif, July 1, 13; m. 45; c. 7. ELECTRICAL ENGINEERING. B.S, Calif. Inst. Tech, 35, M.S, 36. Mem. staff, Bell Tel. Labs, Inc, 36-55, asst. dir, submarine cable systs. dept, transmission systs. develop, 55-59, dir, 59-61, assoc. exec. dir, domestic systs, Mass, 61-66, ASST. V.PRES. ENG. DEPT, AM. TEL. & TEL. CO, 66- Fel. Inst. Elec. & Electronics Eng; Nat. Acad. Eng. Address: Engineering Dept, American Telephone & Telegraph Co, 195 Broadway, New York, NY 10007.

ELMER, CURTIS, b. Vienna, Austria, Dec. 25, 26; U.S. citizen; m. 46; c. 2. ORGANIC & POLYMER CHEMISTRY. A.B, Boston, 50, A.M, 51. Res. chemist, plastics div, MONSANTO CO, 51-55, res. group leader, thermoset resins, 55-60, tech. serv. mgr, 60-62, develop. assoc. plastics, 62-65, res. mgr. aerospace, Monsanto Res. Corp, 65-66, develop. mgr. plastics, cent. res. dept, 66-68, res. mgr. composites, new enterprise div, CHEMSTRAND RES. CTR, INC, 68-70, RES. MGR. TIRE CORD APPLN, 70- U.S.A, 45-48. Am. Chem. Soc; Soc. Plastics Eng; Soc. Plastics Indust. Combination of thermosetting polymers with reinforcements to form composites; fibrous combinations, including paper, glass, boron, quartz, carbon and graphite; application of fiber technology to reinforcement of automobile tires with inorganic fibers. Address: Chemstrand Research Center, Inc, Monsanto Co, P.O. Box 731, Durham, NC 27702.

ELMER, HAROLD S(TOUT), b. Ames, Iowa, Sept. 23, 22; m. 45; c. 2. ENTOMOLOGY. B.S, Kansas State, 48; M.S, California, Berkeley, 49. From jr. specialist to assoc. specialist, citrus res. ctr. & agr. exp. sta, UNIV. CALIF, RIVERSIDE, 49-69, SPECIALIST, KEARNEY HORT. FIELD STA, 69- U.S.N.A.F, Lt.(jg). Entom. Soc. Am. Biology, ecology and control of insects; mites on citrus and date palms. Address: Kearney Horticultural Field Station, P.O. Box 228, Reedley, CA 93654.

ELMER, OTTO C(HARLES), b. Vienna, Austria, Jan. 8, 18; nat; m. 45; c. 7. ORGANIC CHEMISTRY. B.A, Bluffton Col, 43; Ph.D.(org. chem), Minnesota, 48. Asst, Carleton Col, 43-44; Minnesota, 44-45, 46-48; chemist, Tex. Co, 48-53; from chemist to GROUP LEADER, GEN. TIRE & RUBBER CO, 53- Chemist, Rubber Reserve Co, 44-45, asst. scientist, 46. U.S.A, 45-46. Am. Chem. Soc; Am. Inst. Chem. Synthetic glycerides; autoxidation; reaction mechanisms; heterocycles; synthetic lubricants; lubricant additives; polymer chemistry; urethane elastomers and coatings; tire cord adhesives. Address: 720 Hillsdale Ave, Akron, OH 44303.

ELMER, WILLIAM ARTHUR, b. Bridgeton, N.J, May 12, 38; m. 62; c. 2. DEVELOPMENTAL GENETICS, BIOCHEMISTRY. A.B, Susquehanna Univ, 60; M.S, N.Mex. Highlands Univ, 63; Nat. Insts. Health trainee, Univ. Conn, 66-67, Ph,D, 67. Fel. BIOL, Oak Ridge Nat. Lab, 67-69; ASST. PROF. EMORY UNIV, 69- AAAS; Teratology Soc; Am. Soc. Zool. Genetic control of limb development; molecular aspects of hereditary skeletal anomalies; in vitro growth of genetically abnormal chondrocytes. Address: Dept. of Biology, Emory University, Atlanta, GA 30322.

ELMERGREEN, GEORGE L(ESTER), b. Elkhorn, Wis, July 19, 20; m. 46; c. 2. ELECTRICAL ENGINEERING. B.S.E.E, Wisconsin, 42, M.S, 49. Instr. ELEC. ENG, UNIV. WIS-MILWAUKEE, 47-49, asst. prof, 49-56, assoc. prof, 56-60, PROF, 60- U.S.A, 42-46, Capt. Inst. Elec. & Electronics Eng; Am. Soc. Eng. Educ; Simulation Coun. Electronic computers; automatic control theory; application of automatic control theory to biological feed back systems; electrical instrumentation. Address: College of Applied Science and Engineering, University of Wisconsin-Milwaukee, Milwaukee, WI 53201.

ELMGREN, JARL AVARD, b. New Britain, Conn, Oct. 28, 33; m. 56; c. 3. PHYSICS. B.S, New Hampshire, 55; Ph.D.(physics), Iowa State, 60. Assoc. physics, Iowa State, 60-61; instr, Swarthmore Col, 61-63, asst. prof, 63-67; staff physicist, MFG. RES. LAB, IBM CORP, 67-69, ADV. ENGR, 69- Am. Asn. Physics Teachers; Am. Phys. Soc. Optical and electrical properties of insulators; work function determinations for solids. Address: Dept. P68, C.D. Development, IBM Corp, Endicott, NY 13760.

ELMORE, CARROLL D(ENNIS), b. Pheba, Miss, Apr. 3, 40. PLANT PHYSIOLOGY, GENETICS. B.S, Miss. State Univ, 62; M.S, Univ. Ariz, 66; Ph.D.(agron), Univ. Ill, 70. PLANT PHYSIOLOGIST, DELTA STATES AGR. RES. CTR, U.S. DEPT. AGR, 70- U.S.A, 62-64, Capt. Am. Soc. Agron; Crop Sci. Soc. Am; Genetics Soc. Am; Am. Inst. Biol. Sci; Am. Soc. Plant Physiol. Adequacy of carbohydrate and mineral reserves for the developing cotton fruit; translocation patterns of reserve nutrients; genetic aspects of fruiting, fruit retention and fruit development in the cotton plant. Address: Cotton Physiology Lab, Plant Science Research Division, U.S. Dept. of Agriculture, Stoneville, MS 38776.

ELMORE, GLENN V(AN NESS), b. Topeka, Kans, Apr. 2, 16; m. 48; c. 1. PHYSICAL CHEMISTRY. B.S, Washburn, 38; M.S, Ga. Inst. Technol, 40. Instr. chem, Ga. Inst. Technol, 40-41; res. chemist, Tenn. Valley Auth, 41-47, 48-53; Oak Ridge Nat. Labs, 47-48; ELECTROCHEMIST, Kettering Found, 53-62; SYSTS. MFG. DIV, IBM CORP, 62- Am. Chem. Soc; Electrochem. Soc. Chemistry of phosphorus nitrides; radiation chemistry of decomposition of water; endothermic photochemical reactions; electrodeposition; fuel cells; adhesion of electroless metals. Address: IBM Corp, Systems Manufacturing Division, Dept. 093, 1701 North St, Endicott, NY 13760.

ELMORE, REX LYNN, b. Denison, Tex, July 26, 38; m. 63; c. 3. PHYSICAL ORGANIC CHEMISTRY. B.A, Austin Col, 60; Atomic Energy Comn. assistantship, Okla. State Univ, 61-64, Ph.D.(chem), 65. Chemist, PLASTICS DEPT, E.I. DU PONT DE NEMOURS & CO, INC, 65-71, SR. RES. CHEMIST,

71- Am. Chem. Soc. Structure and properties of ethylene polymers and copolymers versus synthesis, additives and processing characteristics; reaction mechanisms; kinetic isotope effects. Address: Plastics Dept, E.I. du Pont de Nemours & Co, Inc, P.O. Box 1089, POD-R, Orange, TX 77630.

ELMORE, ROBERT E, b. Oklahoma City, Okla, Sept. 28, 22; m. 55; c. 2. PHYSICS, MATHEMATICS. B.S, Tulsa, 53, M.S, 63. Chief engr, Radio KOME, Tulsa, 43-54; small bus. mgr, 54-64; CHIEF PARTICLE INSTRUMENTATION, AVCO ELECTRONICS DIV, AVCO CORP, 64- U.S.A.A.F, 43-46, Sgt. Am. Geophys. Union; Am. Inst. Aeronaut. & Astronaut; Am. Inst. Physics. Charged particle interaction with electric and magnetic fields; ultraviolet transmission absorption and generation; magnetic gradient measuring techniques; secondary electron emission and photoemission. Address: Avco Electronics Division, Avco Corp, 10700 E. Independence, Tulsa, OK 74115.

ELMORE, STANLEY MCDOWELL, b. Raleigh, N.C, Dec. 17, 33; m. 58; c. 4. MEDICINE, ORTHOPEDIC SURGERY. A.B, Vanderbilt, 55, M.D, 58. U.S. Pub. Health Serv. grant & instr. ORTHOP. SURG, sch. med, Vanderbilt, 65-66; ASSOC. PROF. & CHMN. DIV, MED. COL. VA, 66- Consult, McGuire Vet. Admin. Hosp, Richmond, Va, 66- Borden award, 57-58; dipl, Am. Bd. Orthop. Surg, 69. U.S.P.H.S, 60-62, Sr. Asst. Surg. Am. Acad. Orthop. Surg; Orthop. Res. Soc. Physical properties of articular cartilage; genetics of orthopedic diseases; bone changes in renal transplant patients. Address: Dept. of Orthopedic Surgery, Medical College of Virginia, Box 153, Richmond, VA 23219.

ELMORE, W(ILLIAM) C(RONK), b. Montour Falls, N.Y, Sept. 16, 09; m. 36; c. 4. PHYSICS. B.S, Lehigh, 32; Ph.D.(physics), Yale, 35. Asst. PHYSICS, Yale, 32-34; instr, Mass. Inst. Technol, 35-38; SWARTHMORE COL, 38-41, asst. prof, 41-46, assoc. prof, 46-51, PROF, 51-, head dept, 48-68. Fel, Bartol Res. Found, Pa, 42-43; staff mem, electronics group, Los Alamos Sci. Lab, 44-46, consult, 57-58; mem. physics adv. panel, Nat. Sci. Found, 52-53. With Off. Sci. Res. & Develop, 44. AAAS; Am. Phys. Soc; Am. Asn. Physics Teachers. Magnetic powder patterns; magnetic powders; electrolytic polishing; electronic instrumentation; ultrasonics; thermonuclear fusion. Address: Dept. of Physics, Swarthmore College, Swarthmore, PA 19081.

ELMS, JAMES C(ORNELIUS), b. East Orange, N.J, May 16, 16; m. 42; c. 4. PHYSICS. B.S, Calif. Inst. Tech, 48; M.A, California, Los Angeles, 50. Jr. stress analyst, Consol. Vultee Aircraft Corp, 40-41; chief develop. engr, G.M. Giannani Co, 48; res. assoc. geophys, California, Los Angeles, 49-50; res. engr. electronics, N. Am. Aviation Corp, 50-52, proj. engr. electromech. eng, 52, asst. sect. chief electronics, 53-55, mgr. fire control, 55-57; avionics dept, Martin Co, 57-59; v.pres. electronics systs, Crosley Div, AVCO Corp, 59, exec. v.pres, 59-60; gen. opers. mgr, Aeronutronic Div, Ford Motor Co, 60-63; dep. dir, Manned Spacecraft Center, NASA, Tex, 63-64; v.pres. & div. gen. mgr, space & info. systs. div, Raytheon Co, Mass, 64-65; dep. assoc. adminstr, off. manned space flight, Hq, NASA, 65-66, DIR Electronics Res. Ctr, 66-70; TRANSPORTATION SYSTS. CTR, U.S. DEPT. TRANSPORTATION, 70- Mem, space systs. comt, space prog. adv. coun, NASA, 70-; comt. fed. labs, 70-; Transportation Res. Forum. NASA spec. award, 64, except. serv. medal, 69, outstanding leadership medal, 70. U.S.A.A.F, 42-46, Capt. Am. Phys. Soc; assoc. fel. Am. Inst. Aeronaut. & Astronaut; fel. Inst. Elec. & Electronics Eng. Seismic investigation of earth's crustal structure: ordnance mechanisms; armament control; radar; missile guidance and control. Address: Transportation Systems Center, U.S. Dept. of Transportation, 55 Broadway, Cambridge, MA 02142.

ELMSLIE, J(AMES) S(TEWART), b. Quincy, Ill, Dec. 30, 30; m. 54; c. 2. ORGANIC CHEMISTRY. A.B, Grinnell Col, 52; Ph.D.(org. chem), Delaware, 59. Anal. chemist, Hercules Powder Co, 52-53, 55, sr. res. chemist, Allegany Ballistics Lab, HERCULES, INC, 58-69, TECH. SPECIALIST, MAGNA, 69- U.S.A, 53-55. Am. Chem. Soc. Encapsulation of solid particles; new ablative insulators; new sprayable insulation material; synthesis of high energy compounds for use in solid propellants; new binders for solid propellants. Address: 3733 Twinbrook St, Salt Lake City, UT 84109.

ELMSTROM, GARY WILLIAM, b. Chicago, Ill, Jan. 10, 39; m. 67; c. 2. PLANT PHYSIOLOGY, HORTICULTURE. B.S, Southern Illinois, 63, M.S, 64; Ph.D.(plant physiol), California, Davis, 69. ASST. PROF. HORT, UNIV. FLA, 69- AAAS; Am. Soc. Hort. Sci; Am. Soc. Plant Physiol; Scand. Soc. Plant Physiol; Japanese Soc. Plant Physiol. Nutritional and biochemical studies of soybean plants that differ with respect to iron nutrition; effect of nutrition, herbicides, growth regulators on cucurbits. Address: Agricultural Research Center, University of Florida, Box 388, Leesburg, FL 32748.

EL-NEGOUMY, ABDUL MONEM, b. Cairo, Egypt, May 23, 20; U.S. citizen; m. 51; c. 2. AGRICULTURAL BIOCHEMISTRY. B.S, Cairo, 43; M.S, Wisconsin, 48, Ph.D.(dairy chem), 51. Instr. bot, Alexandria, 43-46, lectr. food biochem, 51-57, assoc. prof, 57-58; res. assoc. & fel. dairy chem, Iowa State, 58-62; asst. prof. AGR. BIOCHEM, MONT. STATE UNIV, 62-65, assoc. prof, 65-69, PROF, 69- AAAS; fel. Am. Inst. Chem; Am. Dairy Sci. Asn; Inst. Food Technol. Dairy and food chemistry; autoxidation of food fats and oils; genetic variants and interactions of food proteins. Address: Dept. of Animal & Range Sciences, Montana State University, Bozeman, MT 59715.

ELNICK, MARVIN, b. N.Y.C, Oct. 14, 20; m. 44; c. 1. PHYSICS. B.S, U.S. Merchant Marine Acad, 44; B.A, Temple, 49, M.A, 51. Asst. physics & instr. phys. sci, Temple, 49-51; physicist, FRANKFORD ARSENAL, 51-58, chief microwave lab, 58-65, fire control lab, 65-66, CHIEF EXPLOR. DEVELOP. LAB, FIRE CONTROL DEVELOP. & EXPLOR. LABS, 66- Mem. Dept. Army Study Conf. Pisgah IV, Opers. Res. Off, Johns Hopkins Univ, 57; mem. ad hoc, Nike Zeus Radar Comt, 57-58; consult, Rocket & Guided Missile Agency, U.S. Army, 58-59, Missile Command, 61-63, 64-66; assoc. mem, Adv. Group Electronic Devices, 63-; U.S-U.K. Comt. High Power Laser Res, 64. U.S.N.R, 44-45, Res, 45-53, Ens. Sci. Res. Soc. Am. Acoustics; propagation of millimeter and submillimeter waves; development of Ruby Laser Rangefinder; target signatures at 5-15 microns; low light level image intensifiers; millimeter and submillimeter radiometry. Address: Exploratory Development Lab, Fire Control Development & Exploratory Labs, Frankford Arsenal, Bridge & Tacony Sts, Philadelphia, PA 19137.

ELOFSON, R(ICHARD) MACLEOD, b. Ponoka, Alta, June 14, 19; m. 41; c. 4. ORGANIC CHEMISTRY. B.Sc, Alberta, 41; Ph.D.(org. chem), Wisconsin, 44. Chemist, Defence Indust, Ltd, Can, 41; res. chemist, F.W. Horner, Ltd, 44-45, dir. res, 45-46; res. chemist, Gen. Aniline & Film Corp, 47-49; self employed, 49-53; SR. RES. CHEMIST, COAL RES. COUN, 53- Fel. Can. Inst. Chem; Am. Chem. Soc. Polarography and oxidation reduction potentials of organic compounds; protein hydrolysates; chemistry of acetylene; coalification; electron spin resonance spectroscopy. Address: Research Council of Alberta, Edmonton, Alta, Can.

ELOWE, LOUIS N, b. Baghdad, Iraq, Apr. 2, 22; U.S. citizen; m. 53; c. 3. PHARMACY, CHEMISTRY. Ph.C, Col. Pharm. & Chem, Iraq, 44; M.S, Univ. Wis, 52, Ph.D.(pharm, chem), 54. Managing dir, East. Wholesale Drug State, Iraq, 46-50; asst, Univ. Wis, 51-54; asst. prof. pharm, Univ. Toronto, 54-57; assoc. prof, Fordham Univ, 57-59; sr. pharmaceut. chemist, Schering Corp, 59; develop. chemist, Lederle Labs, Am. Cyanamid Co, 59-60, group leader, 60-64, mgr. pharmaceut. prod. develop, Cyanamid Int, 64-66; mgr. int. res. & control, CHESEBROUGH-POND'S, INC, 66-69, DIR. INT. RES. & CONTROL, 69- Am. Pharmaceut. Asn; Am. Chem. Soc; Can. Pharmaceut. Asn; Soc. Cosmetic Chem. Development of analytical methods in drug analysis; development in the field of pharmaceuticals, cosmetics, consumer products, hospital supplies, agriculturals. Address: 138 Wildcat Rd, Madison, CT 06443.

ELPERN, BILL, b. Wheeling, W.Va, June 28, 15; m. 42; c. 3. ORGANIC CHEMISTRY. A.B, California, 40; A.M, Stanford, 41; Ph.D.(chem), Nebraska, 45. Chemist, Nat. Defense Res. Cmt, Nebraska, 41-45; sr. chemist, Sterling-Winthrop Res. Inst, 45-57; group leader, Cutter Labs, 57-60; dir. chem. res. & control, Nat. Drug Co, 60-63; chem. res, U.S. Vitamin & Pharmaceut. Corp, 63-68, dir. labs, USV Pharmaceut. Corp, 68-71; DIR. RES. & DEVELOP, LIFE SCI. DIV, BECTON, DICKINSON & CO, 71- Am. Chem. Soc. Medicinal chemistry. Address: Mountain View Ave, Orangeburg, NY 10962.

ELRICK, D(AVID) E(MERSON), b. Toronto, Ont, Sept. 6, 31; m. 58; c. 4. SOIL PHYSICS. B.S.A, Ont. Agr. Col, 53; M.S, Wisconsin, 55, Ph.D.(soils), 57. Asst. prof. physics, Ont. Agr. Col, 57-60; res. off, div. plant indust, Commonwealth Sci. & Indust. Res. Orgn, Australia, 60-62; assoc. prof. SOIL SCI, UNIV. GUELPH, 62-65, PROF, 65-, chmn. dept, 71- Sr. fel, Grenoble, France, 68-69; mem. hydrol. subcomt, Nat. Res. Coun. Can. AAAS; Am. Geophys. Union; Soil Conserv. Soc. Am; Am. Soc. Agron; Agr. Inst. Can; Can. Soil Sci. Soc. Fluid flow in unsaturated media; miscible displacement. Address: Dept. of Land Resource Science, University of Guelph, Guelph, Ont, Can.

ELROD, ALVON CREIGHTON, b. Walhalla, S.C, Dec. 28, 28; m. 51; c. 6. MECHANICAL ENGINEERING. B.M.E, Clemson Univ, 49, M.M.E, 51; Gen. Elec. fel. & Ph.D.(mech. eng), Purdue Univ, 59. Instr. MECH. ENG, CLEMSON UNIV, 53-55, asst. prof, 55-58, ASSOC. PROF, 58- Nat. Sci. Found. res. grant, 60-62; Ford Found. indust. residency, mech. engr. appl. res. group, Gen. Elec. Flight Propulsion Div, 67-68. U.S.A.F, 51-53, Res, 53-, Lt. Col. Am. Soc. Mech. Eng. Heat transfer from dissociated gases and in boiling water situations; air and water pollution. Address: Dept. of Mechanical Engineering, Clemson University, Clemson, SC 29631.

ELROD, BRYANT D(ENNIS), b. Detroit, Mich, June 9, 34; m. 61; c. 4. ELECTRICAL ENGINEERING. B.E.E, Detroit, 57; M.Eng, Yale, 59, Ph.D.(elec. eng), 62; Göttingen, 61-62. Fulbright fel. math, Göttingen, 61-62; systs. scientist command & control systs, Air Force Electronic Systs. Div, 62-63; asst. prof. elec. eng, Air Force Inst. Tech, 63-65; MEM. TECH. STAFF SPACE TECHNOL, BELLCOMM, INC, 65- Summers, mem. tech. staff, res. labs, Bendix Corp, 60, Bell Tel. Labs, 61; consult, MB Electronics Div, Textron Inc, 62-63. U.S.A.F, 62-65, 1st Lt. Inst. Elec. & Electronics Eng. Optimal estimation and control theory; stability theory; space vehicle guidance and control systems. Address: 14724 Lake Terr, Rockville, MD 20853.

ELROD, HAROLD G(LENN), JR, b. Manchester, N.H, Nov. 19, 18; m. 42; c. 3. ENGINEERING SCIENCE. B.Sc, Mass. Inst. Technol, 42; Ph.D.(eng. sci), Harvard, 49. Instr. marine eng, U.S. Naval Acad, 42-45; res. engr. refrig, Clayton & Lambert Mfg. Co, 46; heat transfer & fluid flow, Babcock & Wilcox Co, 49-51; asst. prof. MECH. ENG, Case, 51-55; assoc. prof, Columbia, 55-58, PROF, 58-62; Mich. State Univ, 62-63; COLUMBIA UNIV, 63- Consult, Franklin Inst; Mech. Tech, Inc; Ampex Corp. U.S.N.R, 42-45; Lt. Comdr. Am. Soc. Mech. Eng; Am. Inst. Aeronaut. & Astronaut; N.Y. Acad. Sci. Fluid mechanics; heat transfer; lubrication; kinetic theory. Address: Dept. of Mechanical Engineering, Columbia University, New York, NY 10027.

ELROD, J(OHN) T(HOMPSON), b. Dallas, Tex, Oct. 4, 14; m. 39; c. 2. INDUSTRIAL ENGINEERING. B.S.M.E, Agr. & Mech. Col, Texas, 36; M.S.E, Purdue, 39; Ph.D.(indust. eng), Ohio State, 54. Engr, Allis-Chalmers Mfg. Co, 36-38; indust. engr, Gen. Motors Corp, 39-40; prod. control supvr, Continental Emsco Co, 46-47; asst. prof. mgt. eng, Agr. & Mech. Col, Texas, 46; INDUST. ENG, UNIV. HOUSTON, 47-49, assoc. prof, 49-67, PROF, 67-, chmn. dept, 49-67. Consult, 50-; vis. prof, Ford Found. Comput. Prog, Michigan, 61. U.S.A, 40-46, Res, 46-59, Lt. Col. Inst. Indust. Eng; Am. Soc. Eng. Educ; Am. Soc. Qual. Control. Work measurement; optimization of production systems; fundamental motions. Address: Dept. of Industrial Engineering, University of Houston, 3801 Cullen Blvd, Houston, TX 77004.

ELROD, L(LOYD) M(ELVIN), b. Nebraska City, Nebr, Aug. 6, 17; m. 45; c. 1. PHYSIOLOGY, ZOOLOGY. A.B, Nebr. Wesleyan, 48; M.S, Nebraska, 50, Ph.D.(zool, physiol), 59. Asst. physiol, Nebraska, 48-52, instr. physiol, 52-53; asst. prof. biol, Westminster Col.(Mo), 53-60, assoc. prof, 60-62, prof, 62-63; res. biologist path, med. sch, Northwest. Univ, 63-67; PROF. BIOL, DAVIS & ELKINS COL, 67- Summer instr, Univ. Nebr, 50. U.S.A, 41-44. AAAS; Soc. Protozool; Tissue Culture Asn; Am. Inst. Biol. Sci; Am. Soc.

Cell Biol. Protozoan respiration and metabolism; metabolism and cell division in tissue culture. Address: Dept. of Biology, Davis & Elkins College, Elkins, WV 26241.

EL-SADEN, MUNIR RIDHA, b. Baghdad, Iraq, Aug. 16, 28; U.S. citizen; m. 50; c. 3. THERMODYNAMICS. B.Sc, Denver, 51; M.S, Michigan, 53, Ph.D. (mech. eng), 57. Instr. eng. mech, Michigan, 55-57; unit engr, Daura Ref, Iraq, 57-58; lectr. mech. eng, Baghdad, 58-59; asst. prof, Texas, 59-61; assoc. prof, N.C. State Univ, 61-65, PROF, 65-66; ENG, CALIF. STATE COL, FULLERTON, 66- Nat. Sci. Found. res. fel, Stanford Univ, summer 61; res. engr, Avco Everett Res. Lab, summer 62; lectr, Ga. Inst. Tech, 62; E.I. du Pont de Nemours & Co, N.C, 64; Catholic Univ, 65; U.S. Air Force Off. Sci. Res. grant, 65-67. Am. Soc. Mech. Eng; Am.Inst. Aeronaut. & Astronaut; Am. Soc. Eng. Educ. Heat transfer; fluid mechanics; magnethohydrodynamics; energy conversion; nonequilibrium thermodynamics; thermomagnetic and galvanomagnetic devices. Address: Dept. of Engineering, California State College at Fullerton, 800 N. State College Blvd, Fullerton, CA 92631.

EL SAFFAR, ZUHAIR M, b. Baghdad, Iraq, Sept. 23, 34; m. 66; c. 3. CHEMICAL PHYSICS. B.S, Wales, 57, Ph.D.(physics), 60. Asst. prof. physics, Mich. State, 60-62; Baghdad, 62-65, assoc. prof, 66-67; res. assoc. solid state physics, Oak Ridge Nat. Lab, 65-66; chem, Hopkins, 67-68; asst. prof. PHYSICS, DePAUL UNIV, 68-70, ASSOC. PROF, 70- Consult, Argonne Nat. Lab, 69. Am. Phys. Soc; Am. Crystallog. Asn; Brit. Inst. Physics & Phys. Soc. Nuclear magnetic resonance in non-metallic solids, especially hydrocarbons, hydrates and ferroelectrics. Address: 613 Park Ave, River Forest, IL 60305.

ELSASSER, WALTER M, b. Mannheim, Ger, Mar. 20, 04; nat; m. 37, 64; c. 2. PHYSICS, GEOPHYSICS. Heidelberg; Munich; Ph.D.(physics), Göttingen, 27. Asst, Tech. Univ, Berlin, 28-30; instr. physics, Frankfurt, 30-33; res. fel, Inst. Henri Poincaré, Sorbonne, 33-36; asst. meteorol, Calif. Inst. Technol, 36-41; res. assoc, Blue Hill Meteorol. Observ, Harvard, 41-42; war res, Signal Corps Labs, 42-44; radio wave propagation comt, Nat. Defense Res. Comt, 44-45; indust. res. on electronics labs, Radio Corp. of Am, N.J, 45-47; assoc. prof. physics, Pennsylvania, 47-50; prof, Utah, 50-56; California, San Diego, 56-62; GEOPHYS, Princeton, 62-68; RES. PROF, INST. FLUID DYNAMICS & APPL. MATH, UNIV. MD, COLLEGE PARK, 68- Lectr, Sorbonne, 35 & 36; Mass. Inst. Technol, 38; acting head dept. physics, Univ. N.Mex, 60-61. German Phys. Soc. Prize, 32. Nat. Acad. Sci; fel. Am. Phys. Soc; Am. Geophys. Union (Bowie Medal, 59, Fleming Medal, 71). Theoretical physics; quantum theory; physics of the earth and atmosphere; geomagnetism; theoretical biology. Address: Institute for Fluid Dynamics & Applied Mathematics, University of Maryland, College Park, MD 20740.

EL-SAYED, MOSTAFA AMR, b. Zifta, Egypt, May 8, 33; m. 57; c. 5. PHYSICAL CHEMISTRY. B.Sc, Ain Shams, Cairo, 53; Ph.D.(phys. chem), Fla. State, 59. Instr. chem, Ain Shams, Cairo, 53-54; res. asst. spectros, Fla. State, 54-57, res. assoc, 58-59; res. fel, Harvard, 59-60; res. assoc, Calif. Inst. Technol, 60-61; asst. prof. CHEM, UNIV. CALIF, LOS ANGELES, 61-64, assoc. prof, 64-67, PROF, 67- Res. assoc, Yale, summer 57; Alfred P. Sloane fel, 65-67; John S. Guggenheim fel, 67; vis. prof, Am. Univ. Beirut, 67-68. Fresenius Award, 67; McCoy Award, 69. AAAS; Am. Chem. Soc; Am. Phys. Soc. Molecular spectroscopy; mechanisms of Phosphorescence, inter and intramolecular energy transfer; inter and intramolecular interactions, their effects on the spectra; vacuum ultraviolet spectra and photochemistry; photo-ionization potentials; nonlinear effects and laser spectroscopy; phosphorescence-microwave double resonance spectroscopy. Address: Dept. of Chemistry, University of California, Los Angeles, CA 90024.

ELSBACH, PETER, b. Zeist, Netherlands, Nov. 9, 24; m. 59; c. 2. MEDICINE, PHYSIOLOGY. M.D, Amsterdam, 50; Dr.(med. sci), Leiden, 64. Asst. res. MED, Bellevue Hosp, sch. med, N.Y. Univ, 53-55, res, 55-56; res. assoc. & asst. physician, Rockefeller Inst, 56-59; instr, SCH. MED, N.Y. UNIV, 59-61, asst. prof, 61-68, ASSOC. PROF, 68- N.Y. Heart Asn. sr. res. fel, 59-64; Health Res. Coun. career scientist award, N.Y, 64-; mem. coun. atherosclerosis, Am. Heart Asn, 63-; mem. ed. bd, J. Lipid Res, 67- Royal Dutch Army Res, 53, 1st Lt. Soc. Exp. Biol. & Med; Am. Physiol. Soc; Am. Soc. Clin. Invest. Biochemical and clinical investigation pertaining to transport and metabolism of lipids. Address: Dept. of Medicine, New York University School of Medicine, 550 First Ave, New York, NY 10016.

ELSBERND, HELEN, F.S.P.A, b. Calmar, Iowa, Jan. 15, 38. INORGANIC CHEMISTRY. B.A, Viterbo Col, 65; univ. fel, Univ. Ill, Urbana, 66-67, M.A, 67, Nat. Insts. Health fel, 67-69, Ph.D.(chem), 69. ASST. PROF. CHEM, VITERBO COL, 69- Res. assoc, Univ. Ill, Urbana, summers 70 & 71. AAAS; Am. Chem. Soc. Electron exchange reaction rates; studies of tris (ethylenediamine) ruthenium complexes; kinetic studies of ligand substitution reactions in complexes. Address: Dept. of Chemistry, Viterbo College, LaCrosse, WI 54601.

ELSBERRY, RUSSELL L(EONARD), b. Audubon, Iowa, Sept. 26, 41; m. 63; c. 2. METEOROLOGY. B.S, Colo. State Univ, 63, NASA trainee, 63-66, Ph.D.(atmospheric sci), 68. Jr. meteorologist, Colo. State Univ, 66-68; ASST. PROF. METEOROL, NAVAL POSTGRAD. SCH, 68- Am. Meteorol. Soc. Diagnosis and prediction of tropical weather disturbances; geophysical fluid dynamical model experiments as atmospheric analogues. Address: Dept. of Meteorology, Naval Postgraduate School, Monterey, CA 93940.

ELSDON, WILLIAM L(LOYD), b. Hughenden, Alta, Oct. 6, 21; m. 49; c. 4. PHYSICAL CHEMISTRY. B.Sc, Western Ontario, 51, M.Sc, 52; Ph.D.(phys. chem), McGill, 59. Asst. res. off, res. chem. br, Atomic Energy Can. Ltd, 54-58; asst. prof. PHYS. CHEM, UNIV. WATERLOO, 58-62, ASSOC. PROF, 62- Can. Army, 41-45. Fel. Chem. Inst. Can. Kinetics of photoaddition; kinetics and thermodynamics of polymerization; solubilities in fused salt systems. Address: Dept. of Chemistry, University of Waterloo, Waterloo, Ont, Can.

ELSEA, ARTHUR R(AY), b. Columbus, Ohio, Dec. 31, 14; m. 41; c. 3. METALLURGICAL ENGINEERING. B.Met.E, Ohio State Univ, 39. Res. engr, Battelle Mem. Inst, 39-50, asst. div. chief, FERROUS METALL, 50-65, assoc. div. chief, 65-67, DIV. CHIEF, BATTELLE COLUMBUS LABS, 67- Am. Inst. Mining, Metall. & Petrol. Eng; Am. Soc. Metals. Metallurgy of cobalt-chromium alloys; metallurgy of carbon and low alloy steels; physical and process metallurgy of cast irons; steel and ferrous alloy development and heat treatment; failure analysis; hydrogen embrittlement of ferrous alloys and steels. Address: Battelle Columbus Labs, 505 King Ave, Columbus, OH 43201.

ELSEA, JOHN R(OBERT), b. Alexandria, Va, Aug. 31, 25; m. 52; c. 4. TOXICOLOGY. B.S, Col. William & Mary, 47; M.S, Catholic Univ, 50, Ph.D. (biol), 53. Instr. sci, Emerson Inst, 47-53; toxicologist, Hazelton Labs, Inc, 53-60; dir. toxicol, Hill Top Res. Inst, Inc, 60-67, admin. v.pres, 67-68; TOXICOLOGIST, DEPT. PHARMACOL. RES, A.H. ROBINS CO, 68- Instr, Cath. Univ, 52. Med.C, U.S.A, 43-46. Am. Soc. Parasitol; Soc. Toxicol; N.Y. Acad. Sci. Toxicological techniques. Address: Dept. of Pharmacological Research, A.H. Robins Co, 1211 Sherwood Ave, Richmond, VA 23220.

ELSER, ARLON E, b. Litchfield, Mich, Aug. 12, 35; m. 53; c. 2. HORTICULTURE, PLANT PHYSIOLOGY. B.S, Mich. State Univ, 60, M.S, 61, Ph.D.(plant nutrit), 64. Asst. prof. ARTS & SCI, WEST. ILL. UNIV, 63-66, ASSOC. PROF, 66-, DIR. UNIV. PLANNING, 68-, chmn. dept. agr, 65-69, acting dean appl. sci, 67. Am. Coun. Educ. fel. acad. admin, Univ. N.C, 67-68; consult, Acad. Educ. Develop; bd. higher educ, N.C; Coun. Advan. Small Cols; Hail Ins. Adjusters Res. U.S.A, 55-57. AAAS; Am. Soc. Hort. Sci; Asn. Inst. Res; Int. Soc. Hort. Sci; Am. Soc. Planning Off; Am. Asn. Higher Educ. Academic planning, management and education modeling; simulation and forecasting; regional and statewide planning; educational and organizational programs, especially ecosystems and environmental protection. Address: Office of the President, Western Illinois University, Macomb, IL 61455.

ELSERMANN, EDI, b. Schwelm, W.Ger, May 25, 18; Can. citizen; m. 49. ANALYTICAL CHEMISTRY. Diplom, Tech. Univ. Aachen, 48, Dr. rer. nat, 51. Chemist, Badische, Anilin & Soda Fabrik, 51-53; res. fel, Ont. Res. Found, 54-55; from res. chemist to dir. lab. serv, res. & develop. div, Columbia Cellulose Co. Ltd, 55-68; TEACHING MASTER INSTRUMENTATION CHEM, ST. LAWRENCE COL. APPL. ARTS & TECHNOL, ONT, 68- Chem. Inst. Can; Am. Chem. Soc; Soc. Ger. Chem. Cellulose chemistry; chemical instrumentation. Address: 509 Shirley Ave, Cornwall, Ont, Can.

ELSEVIER, ERNEST, b. Amsterdam, Holland, Dec. 26, 14, nat; m. 44; c. 2. MECHANICAL ENGINEERING. B.S, Ala. Polytech, 49; M.S, Ga. Inst. Tech, 50. Instr. mech. eng, Ala. Polytech, 49; grad. asst. MECH. ENG, Ga. Inst. Tech, 50; instr, COL. OF ENG, DUKE UNIV, 50-51, asst. prof, 51-57, assoc. prof, 57-71, PROF, 71- Res. assoc, John D. Latimre & Assoc, 58- Consult, Pub. Serv. Co, N.C; Burlington Industs, 64-; partner, Gardner, Elsevier & Kline; mem. adv. bd, Fayetteville Tech. Inst; N.C. State Bd. Prof. Engrs. & Land Surveyors, 67-70, secy, 70. Gov. Award, 71. U.S.N.R, 40-46. AAAS; Am. Soc. Mech. Eng.(award, 62). Environmental sciences and fuels; thermodynamics; internal combustion; temperature; instantaneous temperature and pressures. Address: 2412 Wrightwood Ave, Durham, NC 27705.

ELSEY, JOHN C(HARLES), b. Salt Lake City, Utah, May 27, 35; m. 55; c. 4. ELECTRICAL ENGINEERING. B.S, Utah, 56; M.S, Mass. Inst. Technol, 60; Ph.D.(elec. eng), Illinois, 63. RES. SPECIALIST, AUTONETICS DIV, N.AM. ROCKWELL CORP, 63- Inst. Elec. & Electronics Eng. Digital computer technology; logical design; switching circuit theory; programing; numerical techniques; guidance and control of aerospace vehicles. Address: 1311 E. Adams Ave, Orange, CA 91767.

ELSEY, KENT D, b. Seattle, Wash, Sept. 20, 41; m. 65; c. 1. ENTOMOLOGY. B.S, Wash. State Univ, 63; M.S, N.C. State Univ, 66, Ph.D.(entom), 69. RES. ENTOMOLOGIST, OXFORD TOBACCO RES. STA, ENTOM. RES. DIV, AGR. RES. SERV, U.S. DEPT. AGR, 69- Entom. Soc. Am. Biology of the cabbage looper on tobacco; field mortality of the cabbage looper and biology of the tachinid Voria ruralis; behavior and effect of the predator Jalysus spinosus and the possibility of manipulating its population. Address: Oxford Tobacco Research Station, Oxford, NC 27565.

ELSEY, MARGARET GRACE, S.L, b. St. Louis, Mo, Aug. 16, 29. MATHEMATICS. A.B, Webster Col, 51; M.A, Catholic Univ, 60, Nat. Sci. Found. fel, 60-61, Ph.D.(math), 63. Instr, Loretto High Sch, 54-58; instr. MATH. & PHYSICS, LORETTO HEIGHTS COL, 62-63, asst. prof, 63-65, ASSOC. PROF, 65-, CHMN. DEPT, 62- Am. Math. Soc; Math. Asn. Am; Am. Asn. Physics Teachers; Asn. Comput. Mach; Nat. Coun. Teachers Math. Finitely compact spaces and convergence of normal Ritt series. Address: Dept. of Mathematics, Loretto Heights College, Denver, CO 80236.

EL-SHIEKH, ALY H, b. Rahmania, Egypt, Apr. 27, 31; m. 58; c. 2. POLYMER SCIENCE, MECHANICAL ENGINEERING. B.Sc, Univ. Alexandria, 56; Moscow State Univ, 58-59; M.S, Mass. Inst. Technol, 61, Mech.E, 64, D.Sc. (mech. eng), 65. Instr. workshop technol, Univ. Alexandria, 56-58, lectr. TEXTILE TECHNOL, 65-68; vis. lectr, N.C. STATE UNIV, 68-70, ASSOC. PROF, 70- Fiber Soc; fel. Brit. Textile Inst. Mechanics of textile structures; fiber crimp; processing dynamics; textured yarns; spindle vibration; journal bearings; carpet mechanics; fiber migration; snagging of knitted fabrics; dynamic properties of wool yarns; yarn forming systems. Address: Dept. of Textile Technology, North Carolina State University, Raleigh, NC 27607.

EL-SHIMI, A(HMED) FAYEZ, b. Alexandria, Egypt, May 18, 38. PHYSICAL CHEMISTRY. B.Sc, Univ. Alexandria, 60; U.A.R. govt. grant, Moscow State Univ, 62, Ph.D.(chem), 67. Instr. chem, Univ. Assiut, 60-62; asst. prof, faculty eng, Cairo Univ, 67-69; SR. RES. CHEMIST, RES. CTR, LEVER BROS. CO, EDGEWATER, 69- Am. Chem. Soc; Egyptian Chem. Soc; D.I. Mendeleyev All-Union Chem. Soc. Colloid stability, particularly stability of emulsions and foams; applied aspects of colloid chemistry in detergent, cosmetic and food areas. Address: 8700 Boulevard E, North Bergen, NJ 07047.

ELSHOFF, JAMES L(ESTER), b. Sidney, Ohio, Jan. 3, 44; m. 67. COMPUTER SCIENCE. B.A, Miami Univ, 66; M.S, Pa. State Univ, 69, Ph.D. (comput. sci), 70. Asst. comput. sci, Pa. State Univ, 66-69, elec. eng, 69-70; SR. ASSOC. RES. COMPUT. SCIENTIST, GEN. MOTORS RES. LABS, 70- Asn. Comput. Mach; Inst. Elec. & Electronics Eng. Computer operating systems; logical design; design of time sharing operating systems to support computer graphics; relations between computer hardware and software; design and use of digital differential analyzers. Address: Dept. of Computer Technology, General Motors Research Labs, 12 Mile & Mound Rd, Warren, MI 48090.

ELSLAGER, EDWARD F(AITH), b. Decatur, Ill, Oct. 7, 24; m. 46; c. 3. ORGANIC CHEMISTRY. B.S, James Millikin, 47; M.S, Illinois, 48, fel, 50-51; Ph.D.(chem), 51. Lab. asst, James Millikin, 46-47; Illinois, 48-50; assoc. res. chemist, PARKE, DAVIS & CO, 51-52, sr. res. chemist, 52-58, dir. lab. org. chem, 58-63, group dir, ORG. CHEM, 63-70, SECT. DIR, 70- V.pres, Third Int. Cong. Heterocyclic Chem, 71. U.S.A.A.F, 42-46. Am. Chem. Soc; Am. Soc. Trop. Med. & Hyg; Int. Soc. Heterocyclic Chem. Synthetic organic medicinals; chemistry of amebicides, anthelmintics, antimalarials, schistosomicides and other antiparasitic agents; synthesis of amines, dyes, heterocyclic compounds and quinones; antibacterial and antifungal drugs; antithrombotic and hypocholesteremic agents. Address: Dept. of Chemistry, Medical & Scientific Affairs Division, Parke, Davis & Co, 2800 Plymouth Rd, Ann Arbor, MI 48106.

ELSNER, NORBERT BERNARD, b. Queens Village, N.Y, Oct. 25, 33; m. 58; c. 2. METALLURGICAL ENGINEERING. B.S, Va. Polytech, 55. Res. assoc, solar div, Int. Harvester, 59-61; staff assoc. thermionic power conversion, GULF GEN. ATOMIC, INC, 61-64, BR. MGR, THERMOELEC. TECHNOL, 64- U.S.N.R, Res, Lt. Comdr. Am. Soc. Metals. Thermoelectric materials; alloy development; joining of semiconductors to conductors; high temperature testing; refractory metals; vapor deposition of W; mechanical forming; specialty braze alloys; diffusion bonding and welding; reentry PuO_2 fuel capsules; behavior of organic insulations in inert atmospheres. Address: 5656 Soledad Rd, La Jolla, CA 92037.

ELSNER, ROBERT W(ELLINGTON), b. Boston, Mass, June 3, 20; m. 46; c. 3. PHYSIOLOGY. B.A, N.Y. Univ, 50; Washington (Seattle), 53, M.S, 55, Ph.D. (physiol), 59. Observer, Mt. Washington Observ, N.H, 41-42; asst, Sloan Kettering Inst, 46-48; dept. pharmacol, med. col, Cornell, 49-50; jr. res. physiologist, sch. med, Washington (Seattle), 51-53; res. physiologist, Arctic Aeromed. Lab, 53-56; res. assoc, Washington, Seattle, 57-59, physiologist, Inst. Andean Biol, Peru, 59-61; inst. work physiol, Norweg. Res. Coun, Norway, 61; ASSOC. RES. PHYSIOLOGIST, SCRIPPS INST. OCEANOG, UNIV. CALIF, SAN DEIGO, 61- U.S. Pub. Health Serv. Res. Career Develop. Award, 65. Am. Field Serv, 42-44. AAAS; Fedn. Am. Socs. Exp. Biol; Am. Physiol. Soc; Arctic Inst. N.Am; Int. Soc. Biometeorol. Circulatory, environmental and marine physiology; exercise. Address: Physiological Research Lab, Scripps Institution of Oceanography, University of California, San Diego, La Jolla, CA 92037.

ELSOM, KENDALL ADAMS, b. Madison, Wis, Apr. 27, 04; m. 28; c. 2. MEDICINE. A.B, Wisconsin, 24; M.D, Pennsylvania, 27. Intern, grad. hosp, UNIV. PA, instr. pharmacol, SCH. MED, 28-35, assoc. med. & ward physician, univ. hosp, 35-42, assoc. prof. clin. med. & dir. med. outpatient dept, hosp, 46-50, dir. diag. clin, 50-61, prof. CLIN. MED, 50-62, VIS. PROF, 62-; MED. DIR, SCOTT PAPER CO, 61- Med.C, 42-46, Lt.Col. Fel. Am. Med. Asn; Am. Col. Physicians; Am. Soc. Clin. Invest; Am. Gastroenterol. Asn; Am. Clin. & Climat. Asn; Indust. Med. Asn; Am. Acad. Occup. Med. Renal physiology, gastrointestinal diseases and physiology; tropical diseases of gastrointestinal tract; techniques, yield and results of periodic health examinations. Address: Scott Paper Co, Scott Plaza, Philadelphia, PA 19113.

ELSON, CHARLES, b. Des Moines, Iowa, July 15, 34; m. 71; c. 4. NUTRITION. B.S, Iowa State, 56, M.S, 61; Ph.D.(food sci), Mich. State, 64. Res. fel. nutrit. sch. pub. health, Harvard, 64-66; ASST. PROF. NUTRIT. SCI, UNIV. WIS, MADISON, 66- Med.C, U.S.A, 57- AAAS; Am. Inst. Nutrit. Nutrient induced alterations in lipid metabolism. Address: Dept. of Nutritional Sciences, University of Wisconsin, Madison, WI 53706.

ELSON, ELLIOT, b. St. Louis, Mo, June 15, 37; m. BIOCHEMISTRY. A.B, Harvard, 59; Nat. Sci. Found. fel. & Ph.D.(biochem), Stanford Univ, 65. Fel. CHEM, Univ. Calif, San Diego, 65-68; ASST. PROF, CORNELL UNIV, 68- Physical chemistry of nucleic acids and proteins; thermodynamics and kinetics of conformational transitions. Address: Dept. of Chemistry, Cornell University, Ithaca, NY 14850.

ELSON, JESSE, b. Brooklyn, N.Y, Apr. 6, 10; m. 40; c. 2. PHYSICAL CHEMISTRY. B.S, Rutgers, 37, Ph.D, 53; M.S, N.C. State Col, 39; B.S, Va. Polytech, 43; Pennsylvania, 46-47. Soil surveyor, Soil Conserv. Serv, 38-39; soil technologist, exp. sta, Va. Polytech, 39-41, 42-43; proj. supvr, soil conserv. serv, U.S. Dept. Agr, 41-42; PROF. CHEM, DELAWARE VALLEY COL, 46- Res. fel, N.C. State Col. & Soil Conserv. Serv. U.S.N.R, 43-46, Lt. Fel. Am. Inst. Chem; Am. Chem. Soc. Relationship between atom size and ion size of element and its position in the periodic table; calculation of bonding parameters; derivation of empirical bond energy equations. Address: Dept. of Chemistry, Delaware Valley College of Science & Agriculture, Doylestown, PA 18901.

ELSON, JOHN A(LBERT), b. Kaiting, China, Mar. 2, 23; m. 57; c. 2. GEOLOGY. B.Sc, Western Ontario, 45; M.Sc, McMaster, 47; Stanolind Oil Co. fel, Yale, 48-50; M.S, 50, Ph.D, 56. Instr. geog, McMaster, 45-46; geologist, Geol. Surv, Can, 46-56; asst. prof. GEOL, McGILL UNIV, 56-64, assoc. prof, 64-68, PROF, 68- AAAS; fel. Geol. Soc. Am; fel. Geol. Asn. Can; Glaciol. Soc. Surficial geology in Southwestern Manitoba; deposition from glaciers; quaternary geology; photogeology, regional geomorphology of Canada; pleistocene stratigraphy; Glacial Lake Agassiz, Champlain Sea; freeze-thaw processes; denudation. Address: Dept. of Geological Sciences, McGill University, P.O. Box 6070, Montreal 101, Que, Can.

ELSON, ROBERT E(MANUEL), b. St. Louis, Mo, Feb. 17, 18; m. 43; c. 4. INORGANIC CHEMISTRY. B.S, Univ. Chicago, 39, M.S, 42. RES. CHEMIST, Pittsburgh Plate Glass Co, 42-46; Argonne Nat. Lab, 46-52; LAWRENCE RADIATION LAB, UNIV. CALIF, 52-, ASSOC. DIV. LEADER, 68-, chmn. phys. chem. sect, 64-68. Israel Atomic Energy Comn. fel, 61-62. AAAS; Am. Chem. Soc. Solution chemistry; chemistry of actinides and group V A elements. Address: Lawrence Radiation Lab, University of California, Livermore, CA 94550.

ELSON, WILLIAM O, b. Chicago, Ill, Feb. 1, 18; m. 42; c. 3. ORGANIC CHEMISTRY. B.S, Loyola (Ill), 40, M.S, 42; M.S, Armour Inst. Technol, 45. Instr. org. chem, Loyola (Ill), 42-43; res. chemist, Bauer & Black Co, 42-50, head med. res. div, 50-64; DIR. med. res, CHICAGO DIV, KENDALL CO, 64-70, HEALTH CARE RES, 70- Fel. Am. Chem. Soc; N.Y. Acad. Sci. Antimicrobial agents; keratolytic agents; percutaneous absorption. Address: Kendall Research Center, 411 Lake Zurich Rd, Barrington, IL 60010.

ELSPAS, B(ERNARD), b. New York, N.Y, July 26, 25; m. 51; c. 2. ELECTRONIC ENGINEERING. B.E.E, City Col. New York, 46; M.E.E, N.Y. Univ, 48; Ph.D.(elec. eng), Stanford, 55. Instr, City Col. New York, 46-49; from res. asst. to res. assoc, electronics lab, Stanford, 51-55; sr. res. engr, comput. tech. lab, STANFORD RES. INST, 56-58, STAFF SCIENTIST, 68- Sci. Res. Soc. Am; Inst. Elec. & Electronics Eng. Switching theory; logical design of digital computers; information theory; electronic computers. Address: Stanford Research Institute, 333 Ravenswood Ave, Menlo Park, CA 94025.

ELSTON, C(LAYTON) T(REVOR), b. Brandon, Man, Dec. 23, 27; m. 53; c. 2. POLYMER SCIENCE, ORGANIC CHEMISTRY. B.Sc, Univ. Man, 49, M.Sc, 51; Ph.D.(org. chem), Univ. Ill, Urbana, 54. Res. chemist, DU PONT OF CAN, 54-59, sr. res. chemist, 59-67, RES. ASSOC. POLYMER SYNTHESIS & RHEOLOGY, 67- Fel. Chem. Inst. Can. Mechanism of coordination catalysis and polymerization kinetics; polymer structure and relation to physical properties; effects of molecular weight distribution on polymer rheology. Address: 44 Westmoreland Rd, Kingston, Ont, Can.

ELSTON, COLIN, b. Prescot, Eng, Sept. 10, 42; m. 64; c. 3. RADIATION & PHYSICAL CHEMISTRY. B.Sc, Durham, 63; Sci. Res. Coun. scholar, & Ph.D.(radiation chem), Newcastle, 66. Res. assoc. chem, Univ. Kansas, 66-67; RES. CHEMIST, Dacron Res. Lab, 67-69; KIMBERLY CLARK CORP, 69- Gamma radiation effects on frozen aqueous systems studied by electron spin resonance; structure-property relationships of polymers; new fiber development; specialty nonwoven fabric development; novel applications for polymers and polymeric composites. Address: Pioneering Research Lab, Kimberly-Clark Corp, Neenah, WI 54956.

ELSTON, DONALD P(ARKER), b. Chicago, Ill, June 17, 26; m. 47; c. 4. GEOLOGY. A.B, Syracuse, 50, M.S, 51; Ph.D, Univ. Ariz, 68. GEOLOGIST, mineral deposits & fuels brs, U.S. GEOL. SURV, 53-62, BR. ASTROGEOL, FLAGSTAFF, 62- Res. assoc. geol, Univ. Ariz, 67-69. U.S.A, 44-46, 51-52, 1st Lt. AAAS; Geol. Soc. Am; Geochem. Soc; Am. Asn. Petrol. Geol. Geologic field investigations of salt structures and uranium deposits, Colorado Plateau; lunar geologic mapping; manned lunar exploration studies; Apollo 16 geologic support; paleomagnetic studies, volcanic and sedimentary rocks, Arizona. Address: Center of Astrogeology, U.S. Geological Survey, 601 E. Cedar Ave, Flagstaff, AZ 86001.

ELSTON, WOLFGANG E(UGENE), b. Berlin, Ger, Aug. 13, 28; nat; m. 52; c. 2. GEOLOGY. B.S, City Col. New York, 49; fel, N.Mex. Bur. Mines & Mineral Resources, 50-51; A.M. & Ph.D.(geol), Columbia Univ, 53. Lectr. GEOL, City Col. New York, 49-51; Columbia Univ, 51-52; asst. prof, Tex. Tech. Col, 55-57; UNIV. N.MEX, 57-63, assoc. prof, 63-67, PROF, 67- Summer geologist, N.Mex. Bur. Mines & Mineral Resources, 52-64; NASA res. grants, 64-; vis scientist, Am. Geophys. Union & vis. geol. scientist, Am. Geol. Inst, 68. U.S.A, 53-55, Res, 55-61. Fel. AAAS; fel. Geol. Soc. Am; Am. Asn. Petrol. Geol; Int. Astron. Union; Am. Inst. Prof. Geol; fel. Meteoritical Soc. Volcanotectonic processes of earth, moon and Mars; mineral deposits; volcanology. Address: Dept. of Geology, University of New Mexico, Albuquerque, NM 87106.

EL-SWAIFY, SAMIR A(LY), b. Port Said, U.A.R, July 14, 37; m. 61; c. 3. SOIL SCIENCE & CHEMISTRY. B.S, Univ. Alexandria, 57; Ph.D.(soil sci), Univ. Calif, Davis, 64. Asst. researcher, Soil Salinity Lab, Alexandria, U.A.R, 58-59; fel. soil chem, Univ. Calif, Riverside, 64-65; asst. prof. SOIL SCI, UNIV. HAWAII, 65-70, ASSOC. PROF, 70- Am. Soc. Agron; Soil Sci. Soc. Am; Int. Soc. Soil Sci. Soil and water salinity; irrigation water quality; physicochemical properties of tropical soils; clay-electrolyte interactions, including colloidal properties and rheology; swelling properties of clays; soil structural responses related to the chemistry of soil solution. Address: Dept. of Agronomy & Soil Science, University of Hawaii, Honolulu, HI 96822.

ELTGROTH, PETER GEORGE, b. Baltimore, Md, Sept. 17, 40; m. 67. ASTROPHYSICS. B.S, Calif. Inst. Tech, 62; A.M, Harvard, 63, Ph.D.(physics), 66. Nat. Res. Coun-Nat. Acad. Sci. res. fel. astrophysics, NASA, Tex, 66-67; PHYSICIST, LAWRENCE LIVERMORE LAB, UNIV. CALIF, 67- Hydrodynamics; plasma physics; general relativity. Address: L-71, Lawrence Livermore Lab, University of California, P.O. Box 808, Livermore, CA 94550.

ELTHERINGTON, LORNE, b. Calgary, Alta, June 2, 33; m. 60; c. 3. ANESTHESIOLOGY, PHARMACOLOGY. B.A, Univ. B.C, 57; M.Sc, Univ. Wash, 59, Ph.D.(pharmacol), 61; Nat. Insts. Health fel, Univ. Calif, San Francisco, 62-63, M.D, 67. Instr. pharmacol, Univ. Wash, 61-62; intern, San Francisco Gen. Hosp, 67-68; resident, dept. anesthesiol, med. ctr, Univ. Calif, San Francisco, 68-70; VIS. PROF. PHARMACOL, MAHIDOL UNIV, BANGKOK, 71- Nat. Insts. Health grant, 61-63. Influence of anesthesia on drug action. Address: Dept. of Pharmacology, Mahidol University, c/o The Rockefeller Foundation, G.P.O. 2453, Bangkok, Thailand.

ELTIMSAHY, ADEL H, b. Damanhoor, Egypt, June 10, 36; m. 67. ELECTRICAL ENGINEERING, CONTROL SYSTEMS. B.S, Cairo Univ, 58; U.S. Dept. Health, Educ. & Welfare scholar, Univ. Mich, Ann Arbor, 59, M.S, 61, fel, 64, Ph.D.(elec. eng), 67. Res. asst. elec. eng, Nat. Res. Ctr, Egypt, 58-59 & 62; consult. temperature control, Maxitrol Co, Mich, 66; ASST.

PROF. ELEC. ENG, Univ. Tenn, 67-68; UNIV. TOLEDO, 68- Summers, consult, Maxitrol Co, 68, Int. Fedn. Automatic Control, 69 & Eprad Co, 70. Inst. Elec. & Electronics Eng; Simulation Coun. Optimization of domestic and industrial heating systems; stability of nonlinear control systems. Address: Dept. of Electrical Engineering, University of Toledo, Toledo, OH 43606.

ELTING, E(RWIN) C(ECIL), b. Carthage, Mo, Aug. 18, 01; m. 26; c. 3. DAIRY HUSBANDRY. B.S, Missouri, 23, A.M, 25; hon. D.Sc, Clemson Col, 52. Asst. dairying, Missouri, 24-25, instr, 25-29; assoc. dairy husbandman, exp. sta, South Carolina, 29-36; exp. sta. adminstr, off. exp. sta, U.S. Dept. Agr, 36-46, asst. chief, 46-48, assoc. chief, 48-54, dep. asst. adminstr. for. exp. sta, Agr. Res. Serv, 54-55, dep. adminstr, 55-64, assoc. dir. res. prog. develop. & eval. staff, 64-67; RETIRED. AAAS. Animal physiology; research administration. Address: 3454 Gleneagles Dr, Silver Spring, MD 20906.

ELTON, EDWARD FRANCIS, b. Teaneck, N.J, Dec. 3, 35; m. 57; c. 5. CHEMICAL ENGINEERING. M.E, Stevens Inst. Tech, 57; M.S, Lawrence Col, 59, Ph.D.(chem. kinetics), 62. Asst. prof. chem. eng, Maine, 62-66, assoc. prof, 66-70; SUPVR, PULP PROCESSES RES. & DEVELOP, AM. CAN CO, 70- Nat. Sci. Found. eng. res. initiation grant, 64-66; Du Pont grants-in-aid, summers 62, 63. Tech. Asn. Pulp & Paper Indust; Am. Chem. Soc. Chemical kinetics; kinetics of delignification reaction; hydrogenolysis of lignin. Address: American Can Co, 1915 Marathon Ave, Neenah, WI 54956.

ELTON, RAYMOND C(ARTER), b. Baltimore, Md, May 30, 32; m. 53; c. 3. ATOMIC & PLASMA PHYSICS. B.S, Va. Polytech. Inst, 53; M.S, Maryland, 56, Ph.D.(physics), 63. Physicist ballistics, U.S. Naval Proving Ground, Va, 51-52; electronic engr. radar, Bendix Corp, Md, 53-54; asst. upper atmosphere physics, Maryland, 54-58; PHYSICIST ATOMIC & PLASMA PHYSICS, NAVAL RES. LAB, 58- Physicist missile guid, appl. physics lab, Hopkins, 55. Am. Phys. Soc; Sci. Res. Soc. Am. Spectroscopy on high temperature plasmas in vacuum ultraviolet region; solar and astrophysical spectroscopy; atomic physics as related to plasmas. Address: Naval Research Lab, Code 7720, Washington, DC 20390.

ELTON, RICHARD L(LOYD), b. Kalispell, Mont, Dec. 24, 27; m. 50; c. 4. PHYSIOLOGY, ENDOCRINOLOGY. B.A, Concordia Col.(Moorehead, Minn), 52; M.S, Kans. State, 53; Nat. Insts. Health fel, Purdue, 56-57, Ph.D.(zool), 57. ENDOCRINOLOGIST, G.D. Searle & Co, Ill, 57-65; RES. DEPT, SANDOZ PHARMACEUT, 66- U.S.A, 46-48. Endocrine Soc; Soc. Exp. Biol. & Med; Am. Inst. Biol. Sci. Physiology of reproduction stressing interactions of estrogens and progesterone on ovarian and uterine physiology. Address: Research Dept, Sandoz Pharmaceuticals, Hanover, NJ 07936.

ELTZ, ROBERT W(ALTER), b. Callicoon, N.Y, June 22, 32; m. 62; c. 3. BACTERIOLOGY. B.S, Rensselaer Polytech, 53; Ph.D.(bact), Cornell, 58. Asst, Cornell, 53-57; res. microbiologist, Chas. Pfizer & Co, Inc, 57-61; Sun Oil Co, Pa, 61-67, chief appl. microbiol. sect, 67-68, asst. to mgr, basic res. div, 69-70, tech. planning analyst, 70; DIR. BIOL. PROCESS DEVELOP. DEPT, SQUIBB INST. MED. RES, 70- Am. Chem. Soc; Am. Soc. Microbiol. Microbial metabolism; industrial production of antibiotics and organic chemicals by fermentation; research management. Address: Biological Process Development Dept, Squibb Institute for Medical Research, New Brunswick, NJ 08903.

ELTZE, ERVIN M(ARVIN), b. Crete, Nebr, May 9, 38; m. 63; c. 3. MATHEMATICS. B.A, Doane Col, 60; M.A, Univ. S.Dak, 62; Ph.D.(math), Iowa State Univ, 70. Instr. MATH, Creighton Univ, 62-65; Iowa State Univ, 68-70; ASST. PROF, FT. HAYS KANS. STATE COL, 70- Am. Math. Soc; Math. Asn. Am. Integration. Address: Dept. of Mathematics, Ft. Hays Kansas State College, Hays, KS 67601.

ELVEBACK, LILLIAN R(OSE), b. Sidney, Mont, Dec. 5, 15. BIOSTATISTICS. B.A, Minnesota, 41; M.A, Columbia, 48; fel, Mayo Clinic, 52; Ph.D.(statist), Minnesota, 55. Instr. math, Minnesota, 43-44; instr. biostatist, sch. pub. health, Columbia, 46-50; lectr, Minnesota, 50-55; assoc. prof, Tulane, 55-59, prof, 59-60; head statist. unit, dept. epidemiol, Pub. Health Res. Inst, 60-65; PROF. BIOSTAT, MAYO GRAD. SCH. MED, UNIV. MINN. & SECT. MED. STATIST, MAYO CLIN, 65- Inst. Math. Statist; Biomet. Soc; fel. Am. Statist. Asn. Statistical methods in the design, execution and evaluation of experimental research in the biological sciences, medicine and public health. Address: Section of Medical Statistics, Mayo Clinic, Rochester, MN 55901.

ELVERS, DOUGLAS J, b. Dannebrog, Nebr, Mar. 27, 35; m. 56; c. 3. GEOPHYSICS. B.Sc, Midland Col, 58; Nebraska, 59; Virginia, 66. Geophysicist, U.S. Navy Oceanog. Off, 60 & 61; SUPVRY. GEOPHYSICIST, FREDERICKSBURG GEOMAGNETIC OBSERV, U.S. COAST & GEOD. SURV, NAT. OCEANIC & ATMOSPHERIC ADMIN, 62- Am. Geophys. Union. Geomagnetism; oceanography; geology. Address: Fredericksburg Geomagnetic Observatory, U.S. Coast & Geodetic Survey, National Oceanic Atmospheric Administration, Corbin, VA 22446.

ELVERUM, GERARD WILLIAM, JR, b. Minneapolis, Minn, Sept. 29, 27; m. 48; c. 3. PHYSICS, MATHEMATICS. B.S, Minnesota, 49. Res. engr, jet propulsion lab, Calif. Inst. Tech, 49-54, group supvr. rocket engine combustion, 54-59; sect. head adv. propulsion, space tech. labs, TRW INC, 59-60, dept. mgr. propulsion res. & develop, 60-63, lab. dir. propulsion, TRW SYSTS, 63-65, MGR. ENG. OPERS, 66- U.S.A.A.F, 44-46. Am. Inst. Aeronaut. & Astronaut; Combustion Inst. Thermodynamics and physical-chemical properties of rocket propellants; combustion and combustion stability research; engineering and development of chemical, nuclear and electric powered propulsion systems. Address: 2220 Potrillo Rd, Rolling Hills Estates, CA 90274.

ELVIDGE, ARTHUR R(OLAND), b. London, Eng. NEUROSURGERY. M.D, McGill, 24, Cooper scholar, 24-26, M.Sc, 25, Ph.D, 27; hon. D.C.L, Bishop's, Can, 58. Demonstr. physiol, McGILL UNIV, 24-28, asst. demonstr. NEUROSURG, 31-32, lectr, 33-39, asst. prof, 39-59, ASSOC. PROF, 59-Res, Royal Victoria Hosp, 29-31, fel, 31-32, clin. asst, 32, assoc. neurosurgeon, 33-57, neurosurgeon, 57-59, neurologist & neurosurgeon-in-chief, 59-61, hon. neurosurgeon, 61-; jr. asst. neurosurg, Montreal Gen. Hosp, 30-31, asst, 31-33, traveling fel, 32-33, assoc, 33-48; Montreal Neurol. Inst, 34-54, neurosurgeon, 54-59, neurosurgeon-in-chief, 59-63, hon. neurosurgeon, 63-; sr. surgeon, Montreal Neurol. Spec. Treatment Center, 45-; head div. neurosurg, Queen Mary Vet. Hosp, 63-; consult. neurosurg, St. Mary's, Queen Elizabeth, Montreal Children's, Physicians, Alice Hyde Mem. & Brome Missisquoi Perkin's Hosps. Mem, Unitarian Serv. Cmt. Med. Mission, Greece & Italy, 48; participant med, voc. & social rehab. of brain injured, World Vet. Fedn-WHO, Helsinki, 58. Cert, Royal Col. Physicians & Surgeons Can, 46; Am. Bd. Neurol. Surg, 47; fel. Royal Col. Surg. Can. Army, 16-19; R.C.A.M.C, 42-46, Maj. AAAS; Am. Asn. Neuropath; Acad. Neurosurg.(v.pres, 45, 47, pres, 56); Am. Asn. Neurol. Surg; World Med. Asn; N.Y. Acad. Sci; Am. Neurol. Asn; Can. Neurol. Soc; Can. Med. Asn; Can. Physiol. Soc; Can. Neurol. Soc.(pres, 64); sr. mem. Soc. Neurol. Surg; Italian & Norwegian Neurosurg. Socs. Neurophysiology; neuropathology; hematology; immunology; blood coagulation and blood platelets; haematopoiesis and reticuloendothelial system; leucocyte reactions; opsonin and the reticuloendothelial system; hydrocephalus; acute anterior poliomyelitis; gliomata; pathology of psychosis; arteriography; head injuries; intracranial aneurysms. Address: Montreal Neurological Institute, McGill University, Montreal, Que, Can.

ELVING, PHILIP J(ULIBER), b. Brooklyn, N.Y, Mar. 14, 13; m. 37; c. 2. ANALYTICAL CHEMISTRY. A.B, Princeton, 34, fel, 34-36, A.M, 35, du Pont fel, 36-37, Ph.D.(chem), 37. Instr. chem, Pa. State Col, 37-39; anal. chem, Purdue, 39-41, asst. prof, 41-43; asst. dir. chem. res, Publicker Indust, Inc, Phila, 43-47; assoc. prof. chem, Purdue, 47-49; PROF. anal. chem, Pa. State Col, 49-52; CHEM, UNIV. MICH, 52- Vis. lectr, Harvard, 51-52; Hebrew Univ, Jerusalem, 66. Am. Chem. Soc.(Anachem Award, 57, Fisher Award, 60); Am. Soc. Test. & Mat; Electrochem. Soc. Polarography and electrochemistry of organic compounds; methods of inorganic and organic analysis. Address: Dept. of Chemistry, University of Michigan, Ann Arbor, MI 48104.

ELVIN-LEWIS, MEMORY P. F, b. Vancouver, B.C, May 20, 33; m. 57; c. 2. VIROLOGY, BACTERIOLOGY. B.A, Univ. B.C, 52; M.Sc, Univ. Pa, 57; M.Sc, Baylor Univ, 60; Ph.D.(microbiol), Univ. Leeds, 66. Med. technologist trainee, Shaughnessy Mil. Hosp, Vancouver, Can, 52-53; bacteriologist, Pearson Tuberc. Hosp, 54-55; med. tech, Am. Soc. Clin. Path, 55; asst. prof. MICROBIOL, SCH. DENT, WASH UNIV, 67-71, ASSOC. PROF, 71- Asst. clin. prof. oral path, sch. dent, Univ. St. Louis, 68-; mem. Am. Asn. Dent. Schs. Am. Soc. Microbiol; Int. Asn. Dent. Res. Studies in Chlamydia group of agents; caries bacteriology; recurrent aphthous stomatitis; endodontic microbiology; epidemiology of associated enterovirus diarrhea and aseptic meningitis; bacterial cytology. Address: 7915 Park Rd, St. Louis, MO 63117.

EL-WAKIL, M(OHAMED) M(OHAMED), b. Alexandria, Egypt, Mar. 9, 21; m. 50; c. 1. MECHANICAL & NUCLEAR ENGINEERING. B.S, Cairo Univ, 43; M.S, Univ. Wis, 47, Ph.D.(mech. eng), 49. Lectr. mech. eng, Univ. Alexandria, 50-52; res. assoc, Univ. Wis, 52-54; asst. prof, Univ. Minn, 54-55; assoc. prof, UNIV. WIS, MADISON, 56-61, PROF, 61-64, MECH. & NUCLEAR ENG, 64- Fulbright fel, 66. Am. Soc. Mech. Eng.(award, 51); Am. Nuclear Soc; Am. Soc. Eng. Educ.(West. Elec. award, 69, Benjamin Smith Reynolds award, 70; nuclear eng. award, 71). Heat and mass transfer; fuel vaporization studies; two-phase flow; nuclear power. Address: Dept. of Mechanical Engineering, University of Wisconsin, Madison, WI 53706.

EL WARDANI, S(AYED) A(LY), b. Alexandria, Egypt, Feb. 26, 27; m. 56; c. 3. OCEANOGRAPHY, GEOCHEMISTRY. B.S, Univ. Alexandria, 48; M.S, Scripps Inst. Oceanog, Univ. Calif, San Diego, 52, Ph.D.(chem, oceanog), 56. Sr. oceanogr, Univ. Wash, 56-57, res. asst. prof, 57-59; asst. prof, Portland State Col, 59-60; San Jose State Col, 60-63; res. oceanogr, U.S. Naval Radiol. Defense Lab, 63-64; staff scientist, Lockheed Ocean Lab, San Diego, 65-68, chief scientist, Gen. Ocean Sci. & Resources, San Diego, 68-70; CURRICULUM CONSULT, CITY & COUNTY DEPTS. OF EDUC, 70- Assoc. prof, U.S. Int. Univ, 65-66. AAAS; Am. Chem. Soc; Geochem. Soc; Am. Geophys. Union; Marine Technol. Soc; Am. Soc. Oceanog. General marine sciences; marine geochemistry and biogeochemistry; aquatic environmental pollution; environmental education. Address: 6416 La Jolla Scenic Dr. S, La Jolla, CA 92037.

ELWELL, ALBERT R, b. Winston, Mo, May 28, 06; m. 30. PHYSICS. A.B, Phillips, 28; M.A, Wyoming, 33, Ed.D, 51. Prin, high sch, Colo, 28-30; teacher, N.Mex, 30-33; prin, elem. & jr. high sch, Wyo, 33-37, supt, pub. sch, 37-43; instr. physics, Washington (Seattle), 43-44; communicator, Fed. Aviation Agency, Mont, 44-46; Idaho, 47-50; instr. physics, Purdue Exten, Ft. Wayne, Ind, 46-47; asst. prof, Wyoming, 50-52; staff mem, Sandia Corp, 52-67; INSTR. ALBUQUERQUE TECH. VOC. INST, 67- Am. Phys. Soc. Radiant heat; extremely high temperatures applied to various kinds of metal; determination of heat flow rates through different thicknesses and kinds of metal. Address: 504 Girard Blvd. S.E, Albuquerque, NM 87106.

ELWELL, DAVID LESLIE, b. Newton, N.J, Oct. 6, 40; m. 65; c. 2. LOW TEMPERATURE PHYSICS. B.A, Amherst Col, 62; Ph.D.(low temperature physics), Duke, 67. Res. asst. liquid helium, Duke, 62-67; ASST. PROF. PHYSICS, COL. WOOSTER, 67- Am. Phys. Soc; Am. Asn. Physics Teachers. Properties of liquid helium and the nature of the superfluid transition. Address: Dept. of Physics, College of Wooster, Wooster, OH 44691.

ELWELL, LEONARD H(UBERT), b. Climax, Mich, Dec. 20, 13; m. 41; c. 2. PHYSIOLOGY. A.B, Kalamazoo Col, 35; M.S, Kans. State Col, 37; M.S, Michigan, 41; Ph.D.(physiol), 51. Asst. genetics, Carnegie Inst, 39-40; PHYSIOL, Michigan, 46-51, asst. prof, sch. med, 51-59; assoc. prof, DENT. SCH, UNIV. ORE, 59-64, PROF, 64-, HEAD DEPT, 59- U.S.A, 42-46. AAAS; Am. Physiol. Soc. Blood flow in dental pulp; mammalian physiology; effect of curare on blood flow; effect of intrapulmonic pressure on muscular activity. Address: University of Oregon Dental School, Sam Jackson Park, 611 S.W. Campus Dr, Portland, OR 97201.

ELWELL, WALTER G, b. Stuart, Nebr, Feb. 23, 22; m. 47; c. 3. PHYSICS. B.A, Nebr. State Teachers Col, Peru, 48; M.A, Nebraska, 51. Instr. PHYS-

ICS, Nebr. State Teachers Col, Peru, 48-50; NEBR. WESLEYAN UNIV, 52-54, ASSOC. PROF, 56-, DIR. COMPUT. FACILITY, 63- U.S.N, 42-45. Asn. Comput. Mach; Asn. Systs. Mgt; Data Processing Mgt. Asn. Address: Computer Facility, Nebraska Wesleyan University, Lincoln, NE 68504.

ELWOOD, JAMES KENNETH, b. Ladysmith, Wis, Apr. 21, 36; m. 63; c. 1. ORGANIC CHEMISTRY. B.A, Wis. State Col, Eau Claire, 58; Nat. Sci. Found. fel, Mich. State, 61-62, Parke, Davis fel, 62-63, Ph.D.(org. chem), 63. Chemist, Minn. Mining & Mfg. Co, 61; sr. res. chemist, EASTMAN KODAK CO, 63-70, RES. ASSOC, 70- Am. Chem. Soc. Heterocyclic chemistry; spectroscopy; organic dyes; reaction mechanisms. Address: Eastman Kodak Co, Bldg. 82, Kodak Park, Rochester, NY 14650.

ELWOOD, JOHN CLINT, b. Beatrice, Nebr, Mar. 5, 30; m. 53; c. 2. BIOCHEMISTRY. B.S, Willamette, 56; M.S, Oregon, 58, Ph.D.(biochem), 60. U.S. Pub. Health Serv. res. fel, Cancer Res. Inst, Phila, Pa, 60-61; instr. BIOCHEM, STATE UNIV. N.Y. UPSTATE MED. CTR, 61-62, asst. prof, 62-67, ASSOC. PROF, 67- U.S. Pub. Health Serv. res. grants, 62-65. U.S.N, 48-52. AAAS. Fatty acid and cholesterol biosynthesis in normal and diabetic animals; relationship of glycolysis and respiration in tumor tissue. Address: Dept. of Biochemistry, State University of New York Upstate Medical Center, 766 Irving Ave, Syracuse, NY 13210.

ELWOOD, WILLIAM K, b. Ashtabula, Ohio, Oct. 15, 28; m. 56; c. 3. DENTISTRY. B.A, Ohio Wesleyan, 50; M.Sc, Ohio State, 53, D.D.S, 57; Ph.D. (anat), Wayne State, 65. Res. assoc. dent, Henry Ford Hosp, Detroit, Mich, 57-65; guest investr, Rockefeller Inst, 65-66; ASST. PROF. ANAT, MED. CTR, UNIV. KY, 66-, ORAL BIOL, 70- AAAS; Am. Asn. Anat; Am. Soc. Cell Biol; Int. Asn. Dent. Res; Electron Micros. Soc. Am; Am. Dent. Asn. Normal and abnormal development of dental tissues; anatomy. Address: 755 Bravington Way, Lexington, KY 40503.

ELWYN, ALEXANDER J(OSEPH), b. N.Y.C, May 14, 27; m. 52; c. 3. NUCLEAR PHYSICS. A.B, Grinnell Col, 51; Ph.D.(physics), Washington (St. Louis), 57. Res. assoc. physics, Brookhaven Nat. Lab, 56-59; from asst. scientist, to ASSOC. SCIENTIST, PHYSICS DIV, ARGONNE NAT. LAB, 59- U.S.A, 45-47. Am. Phys. Soc. Nuclear reaction mechanisms; neutron scattering and reactions; nuclear spectroscopy; neutron polarization in scattering and reactions. Address: Physics Division, Argonne National Lab, 9700 S. Cass Ave, Argonne, IL 60439.

ELWYN, DAVID HUNTER, b. N.Y, Jan. 9, 20; m. 41; c. 4. BIOCHEMISTRY. A.B, Columbia, 41, Ph.D.(biochem), 50. Life Ins. Med. Res. fel, Columbia, 50-53; instr. biochem, Harvard Med. Sch, 53-54, assoc, 54-57, asst. prof, 57-60; res. assoc. & asst. dir. dept. surg. res, Michael Reese Hosp. & Med. Center, 60-63; assoc. dir. dept. surg. res, Hektoen Inst. Med. Res, Cook County Hosp, 63-68; asst. prof. biol. chem, med. sch, Univ. Ill, 64-68; ASSOC. PROF. SURG, MT. SINAI SCH. MED, 68- U.S.A, 42-46. AAAS; Am. Soc. Biol. Chem; Am. Chem. Soc. Amino acid metabolism; phospholipid synthesis; in vivo reaction rates. Address: Dept. of Surgery, Mt. Sinai School of Medicine, Fifth Ave. & 100th St, New York, NY 10029.

ELY, CHARLES A, b. Washington, Pa, Dec. 11, 13. ANATOMY. A.B, Washington & Jefferson Col, 36; M.S, Univ. Hawaii, 40; Ph.D.(zool, anat), Univ. Wis, 48. Instr. ANAT, COL. PHYSICIANS & SURGEONS, COLUMBIA UNIV, 48-50, assoc, 50-51, asst. prof, 51-62, ASSOC. PROF, 62- AAAS; Am. Asn. Anat; Am. Asn. Cancer Res; Endocrine Soc; Soc. Exp. Biol. & Med; Harvey Soc; N.Y. Acad. Sci. Endocrinology; antigonadotrophins; experimental tumors of the gonads. Address: Dept. of Anatomy, College of Physicians & Surgeons, Columbia University, 630 W. 168th St, New York, NY 10032.

ELY, CHARLES ADELBERT, b. Wellsboro, Pa, Jan. 8, 33; m. 57; c. 2. VERTEBRATE ZOOLOGY. B.S, Pa. State, 55; M.S, Oklahoma, 57, Ph.D. (zool), 60. Asst. prof. ZOOL, FT. HAYS KANS. STATE COL, 60-63, assoc. prof, 63-67, PROF, 67- Field dir. Pac. proj. biol. res, div. birds, Smithsonian Inst, 63-66. Am. Ornith. Union; Cooper Ornith. Soc; Wilson Ornith. Soc. Avian distribution and taxonomy; speciation; birds of Mexico, High Plains area, United States and central Pacific. Address: Dept. of Zoology, Ft. Hays Kansas State College, Hays, KS 67601.

ELY, DONALD GENE, b. Hastings, Okla, Dec. 15, 37; m. 60; c. 2. ANIMAL SCIENCE. B.S, Okla. State, 61, M.S, 65; Ph.D.(amimal sci), Kentucky, 66. Asst, Okla. State, 61-63, res. asst, 63-66; asst. prof. ANIMAL SCI, Kansas State Univ, 66-68; UNIV. KY, 68-71, ASSOC. PROF, 71- Qm.C, U.S.A.R, 61-, Capt. Am. Soc. Animal Sci; Am. Soc. Range Mgt. Digestion and metabolism of protein and nonprotein nitrogen sources by ruminant animals. Address: Dept. of Animal Sciences, University of Kentucky, Lexington, KY 40506.

ELY, HAROLD M(ONROE), b. McRoberts, Ky, Feb. 11, 20; m. 42; c. 4. CHEMISTRY. B.S, Michigan, 43. Chemist, Shell Develop. Co, Calif, 43-46; Plywood Res. Found, 46-50; chief chemist, Coos Bay Lumber Co, Ore, 50-54; sr. res. assoc, Ore. Forest Prods. Lab, Oregon State Col, 54-55; sr. chemist res. dept, Potlatch Forests, Inc, 55-57; MGR. Allwood Div, hard board plant, Ore. Lumber Co, 57-67; BD. PLANT, POPE & TALBOT, INC, 67- Am. Chem. Soc; Forest Prods. Res. Soc; Tech. Asn. Pulp & Paper Indust. Controlled oxidization of hydrocarbons; alkylation; chlorination; hydrogenation; developing uses for wood waste; pulp and paper; hardboard. Address: 354 Hills, Oakridge, OR 97463.

ELY, JOHN FREDERICK, b. Chicago, Ill, Mar. 20, 30; m. 52; c. 5. SOLID MECHANICS. B.S.C.E, Purdue, 54; M.S, Northwestern, 58, Ph.D.(mech), 63. Struct. draftsman, Am. Bridge Div, U.S. Steel Corp, Ind, 47-50; part-time instr. civil eng, Northwestern, 56-58, lectr, 58-62, asst. prof. civil eng. & dir. truss bridge res. proj, 62-63; asst. prof. CIVIL ENG. & ENG. MECH, N.C. STATE UNIV, 63-66, ASSOC. PROF, 66- Nat. Sci. Found. res. grants, 64-66, 70-72; summers, res. asst, Purdue, 52, 53. C.Eng, 54-56, 1st Lt. Am. Soc. Civil Eng. Theory of elasticity; optimization of structural systems; non-linear stability analysis of trussed domes. Address: Dept. of Civil Engineering, North Carolina State University, Raleigh, NC 27607.

ELY, RALPH L(AWRENCE), JR, b. Roney's Point, W.Va, Nov. 26, 17; m. 48; c. 4. NUCLEAR PHYSICS. B.S, Washington & Jefferson Col, 40; M.S, Colorado, 44; Ph.D.(physics), Pittsburgh, 51. Asst. physics, Colorado, 40-42, instr, 42-44; assoc. physicist, U.S. Navy Radio & Sound Lab, 44-46; instr. physics, Pittsburgh, 46-48; res. assoc, Sarah Mellon Scaife Radiation Lab, 48-51; sr. scientist chem, Westinghouse Atomic Power Div, 51-54; tech. dir. & v.pres, Nuclear Sci. & Eng. Corp, 54-59; dir. measurement & controls lab, RES. TRIANGLE INST, 59-65, off. indust. serv, 65-69, ASSOC. FOR RES, OFF. V.PRES, 69- Am. Phys. Soc; Am. Nuclear Soc; Am. Soc. Test. & Mat. Application nuclear techniques to industry; nuclear instrumentation; isotope tracing; interdisciplinary research liaison, research administration. Address: Office of the Vice President, Research Triangle Inst, P.O. Box 12194, Research Triangle Park, NC 27709.

ELY, RAY E, b. Mich, Apr. 11, 14; m. 45; c. 4. ANIMAL NUTRITION. B.S, Mich. State Col, 41, Ph.D.(nutrit), 52; M.S, Missouri, 42. Asst. instr. dairy, Missouri, 41-42; asst. prof, dairy exp. sta, Mich. State Col, 44-48; dairy husbandman, dairy husb. res. br, U.S. Dept. Agr, 48-55; animal nutritionist, state exp. stas. div, 55-60; ASSOC. DIR, AGR. EXP. STA, UNIV. NEV, RENO, 60- U.S.A.A.F, 42-44. Sperm metabolism; cobalt nutrition in ruminants; effects of soil fertility on animal health; insecticide toxicity to animals; digestibility studies with ruminants; carbohydrate composition of forages; lignin metabolism. Address: Agriculture Experiment Station, University of Nevada, Reno, NV 89507.

ELY, RAYMOND L(OYD), b. Warren, Ohio, Sept. 12, 19; m. 42; c. 3. APPLIED MECHANICS. B.S, Carnegie Inst. Tech, 40, M.S, 44, D.Sc.(math), 51. Engr, design mil. aircraft, Grumman Aircraft Eng. Corp, 40-42; aeronaut. engr, high speed aerodyn, Wright-Patterson Air Force Base, 46-47; asst, Carnegie Inst. Tech, 47-50; engr, struct. steel res, Pittsburgh-Des Moines Co, 50-51; ENGR. & MEM. PRIN. STAFF, GUIDED MISSILES, APPL. PHYSICS LAB, JOHNS HOPKINS UNIV, 53- U.S.A.A.F, 42-46, 51-53, Res, 53-58, Maj. Am. Inst. Aeronaut. & Astronaut; Math. Asn. Am; Am. Ord. Asn. Technical supervision of engineers and scientists; vibration of beams; aircraft flutter; columns; supersonic aerodynamics; forced vibration of continuous beams under pulsating moving loads; guided missile design. Address: Applied Physics Lab, Johns Hopkins University, 8621 Georgia Ave, Silver Spring, MD 20910.

ELY, ROBERT P, JR, b. Freeport, Ill, Apr. 2, 30; m. 52; c. 4. PHYSICS. B.S, Mass. Inst. Technol, 52, M.S, 53, Ph.D.(physics), 60. Res. assoc, Lawrence Radiation Lab, UNIV. CALIF, BERKELEY, 59-62, asst. prof. PHYSICS, UNIV, 62-69, ASSOC. PROF, 69- U.S.A.F, 52-56, 1st Lt. Am. Phys. Soc. Elementary particle physics; bubble chambers in association with proton synchrotron accelerators. Address: Dept. of Physics, University of California, Berkeley, CA 94720.

ELY, T(HOMAS) S(HARPLESS), b. Philadelphia, Pa, Sept. 26, 24; m. 45; c. 5. MEDICINE. M.D, Georgetown, 48; M.S, Rochester, 61. Intern, U.S. Naval Hosp, Bethesda, Md, 48-49, res. proj. officer, Naval Med. Res. Inst, 49-52, 54-56, asst. med. officer, U.S.S. Kearsarge, 52-54; asst. chief med. br, div. biol. & med, U.S. Atomic Energy Cmn, 56-57, from asst. chief to chief health protection br, div. opera. safety, 57-61; asst. prof. prev. med & dir. occup. med. unit, sch. med. & dent, Univ. Rochester, 63-66; STAFF PHYSICIAN, LAB. INDUST. MED, EASTMAN KODAK CO, 66- U.S.N, 43-46, 48-56, Res, 56-, Comdr. AAAS; Indust. Med. Asn; Am. Acad. Occup. Med. Industrial medicine and toxicology; radiation health; biological effects of microwaves; nuclear weapon thermal burns. Address: Lab. of Industrial Medicine, Kodak Park Works, Eastman Kodak Co, Rochester, NY 14650.

ELY, WILLIAM TANDY, b. Hannibal, Mo, May 1, 32; m. 53; c. 3. ORGANIC CHEMISTRY. B.S, Missouri, 54; Smith Kline & French fel, Carnegie Inst. Technol, 59-60, inst. summer fel, 60, Ph.D.(chem), 61. Asst. chem, Carnegie Inst. Technol, 56-58, sr. asst, 58-59; assoc. res. chemist, Parke, Davis & Co, 60-64, res. chemist, 64-66, mgr. contact res, 66-68; HEAD DEPT. SCI, GREAT LAKES BIBLE COL, 68- U.S.A, 54-56. Am. Chem. Soc. Organic processes; heterocyclic chemistry; alkaloids; condensation reactions to form cyclic compounds. Address: Dept. of Science, Great Lakes Bible College, 106 E. North St, P.O. Box 5365, Lansing, MI 48905.

ELZAM, O. E, b. Haifa, Israel, May 18, 35; m. 69; c. 1. SOILS, PLANT NUTRITION. B.S, Univ. Calif, Davis, 61, M.S, 62, Ph.D.(plant nutrit), 66. Asst. prof. BIOL, CASE WEST. RESERVE UNIV, 68-69, ASSOC. PROF. & ASST. CHMN. DEPT, 69- Israeli Army, 55-57. AAAS; Am. Soc. Plant Physiol; Japanese Soc. Plant Physiol. Mechanisms of ion transport in plants; dynamics of nutrient cycling in nature; effect of pollution on the environment. Address: Dept. of Biology, Case Western Reserve University, Cleveland, OH 44106.

ELZAY, RICHARD PAUL, b. Lima, Ohio, Dec. 6, 31; m. 51; c. 1. DENTISTRY, ORAL PATHOLOGY. B.S, Indiana, 57, D.D.S, 60, M.S.D, 62. U.S. Pub. Health Serv. fel, Indiana, 60-62; instr. ORAL PATH, MED. COL. VA, 62-63, asst. prof, 63-66, ASSOC. PROF. & CHMN. DEPT, 66-, ASST. DEAN ACAD. AFFAIRS, 70- Consult, U.S. Navy Hosp, Portsmouth, Va, 62-; Vet. Admin. Hosp, Richmond, Va, 62- AAAS; Am. Acad. Oral Path; Am. Dent. Asn; Int. Asn. Dent. Res. Radiation effects on oral structure and oral carcinogenesis. Address: Dept. of Oral Pathology, Health Sciences Center, Medical College of Virginia School of Dentistry, Virginia Commonwealth University, Richmond, VA 23219.

ELZINGA, EUGENE ROBERT, b. Flint, Mich, Oct. 4, 28; m. 50; c. 4. CHEMICAL ENGINEERING. B.S, Michigan, 52, M.S, 54, Ph.D.(chem. eng), 57. Res. engr, ESSO RES. & ENG. CO, 57-59, sr. engr, 60-61, eng. assoc, 62-64, sect. head chem. eng, 65-66, SR. ENG. ASSOC, 66- U.S.N, 46-48. Heat and momentum transfer in two phase flow systems; kinetics and mechanisms of fermentation reactions. Address: Esso Research & Engineering Co, P.O. Box 111, Linden, NJ 07036.

ELZINGA, MARSHALL, b. Hudsonville, Mich, Mar. 25, 38; m. 60; c. 3. BIOCHEMISTRY, PHYSIOLOGY. A.B, Hope Col, 60; M.S, Univ. Ill, Urbana, 63, Wm. T. Porter fel, 63-64, Ph.D.(physiol), 64. Res. assoc. biol, Brookhaven Nat. Lab, 64-66, asst. biochemist, 66-67; res. assoc. BIOCHEM, Retina Found, Boston, 67-69; STAFF SCIENTIST, BOSTON BIOMEDICAL RES. INST, 69- Estab. investr, Am. Heart Asn, 68-; assoc, Harvard Med. Sch, 69- AAAS; Biophys. Soc; Am. Chem. Soc; Am. Soc. Biol. Chem. Structure and function of proteins; amino acid sequence of myosin, actin, digestive enzymes; hemoglobin; chemical modification of proteins; sequence techniques. Address: Boston Biomedical Research Institute, 20 Staniford St, Boston, MA 02114.

ELZINGA, RICHARD J(OHN), b. Salt Lake City, Utah, Apr. 23, 31; m. 57; c. 4. MEDICAL ENTOMOLOGY. B.S, Utah, 55, M.S, 56, Ph.D.(entom), 60. Nat. Acad. Sci. resident res. assoc, U.S. Army Biol. Warfare Lab, Md, 60-61; asst. prof. ENTOM, KANS. STATE UNIV, 61-66, ASSOC. PROF, 66- U.S.A, Sgt. Entom. Soc. Am. Acarology; ectoparasites of rodents; mites associated with army ants. Address: Dept. of Entomology, Kansas State University, Manhattan, KS 66502.

EMANUEL, ALAN S, b. Los Angeles, Calif, June 16, 36. CHEMICAL ENGINEERING, THERMODYNAMICS. B.S, Calif. Inst. Tech, 58, M.S, 59; Ph.D.(chem. eng), California, Berkeley, 63. RES. ENGR, CHEVRON RES. CORP, STANDARD OIL CO. CALIF, 62- Am. Inst. Chem. Eng. Mass transfer; computer applications. Address: Chevron Research Corp, Box 446, La Habra, CA 90631.

EMANUEL, GEORGE J(ACOB), b. N.Y.C, Apr. 3, 31; m. 58; c. 2. AERONAUTICAL ENGINEERING. B.A, California, Los Angeles, 52; AiResearch fels, Southern California, 55-57, M.S, 56; Ph.D.(gas dynamics), Stanford, 63. Res. assoc. GAS DYNAMICS, Stanford, 62-63; MEM. TECH. STAFF, AEROSPACE CORP, 63- AAAS; Am. Inst. Aeronaut. & Astronaut; Am. Phys. Soc. Gas dynamics; chemical nonequilibrium; thermal radiation; chemical lasers. Address: Aerophysics Lab, Aerospace Corp, Los Angeles, CA 90045.

EMANUEL, IRVIN, b. Baltimore, Md, Oct. 9, 26; m. 60; c. 2. EPIDEMIOLOGY. B.S, Rutgers, 51; fel, Arizona, 52-53, M.A, 56; M.D, Rochester, 60; M.S, Univ. Wash, 66. Asst. prof. anthrop. & asst. dir, U.S. Air Force Anthrop. Proj, Antioch Col, 53-55; phys. anthropologist, U.S. Dept. Air Force, Aerospace Med. Lab, 55-56, consult. anthrop, 57-60; intern pediat, Cleveland Metrop. Gen. Hosp, Ohio, 60-61; asst. res, UNIV. WASH, 61-62, fel. prev. med. & pediat, 62-64, sr. fel. & instr, 64-66, asst. prof, 66-70, ASSOC. PROF. EPIDEMIOL, INT. HEALTH & PEDIAT, 70- Guest investr, U.S. Naval Med. Res. Unit 2, Taipei, Taiwan, 64-66; U.S. Pub. Health Serv. res. career develop. award, Nat. Inst. Child Health & Human Develop, 66-71. Award, U.S. Dept. Air Force, 61. U.S.N, 45-46. Am. Pub. Health Asn. Epidemiology of abnormal fetal development; international health; public health; pediatrics. Address: Dept. of Epidemiology & International Health, School of Public Health & Community Medicine, University of Washington, Seattle, WA 98195.

EMANUEL, JACK HOWARD, b. Centerville, Iowa, Sept. 26, 21; m. 46; c. 2. STRUCTURAL ENGINEERING. B.S, Iowa State, 43, M.S, 60, Ph.D, 65. Weight control engr, Curtiss-Wright Corp, N.Y, 43-44; archit. designer, Early Lumber Store, Iowa, 47-51; mgr. & part-owner, Kingsley Lumber Co, 51-54; asst. to pres. & owner, H.F. Phelps, Oltmann and Phelps Bank, 54-58; instr, Iowa State, 58-61, asst. prof, 61-65; North Dakota, 65-66, ASSOC. PROF. CIVIL ENG, 66-68; UNIV. MO-ROLLA, 68- A.U.S, 44-46, C.Eng, 46-47, 2nd Lt. Am. Soc. Civil Eng; Am. Concrete Inst; Am. Soc. Eng. Educ; Nat. Soc. Prof. Eng. Prestressed steel beams; bridge supporting and expansion devices; dynamic behavior of rigid and elastomeric bearings; matrix methods of structural analysis; computer programming for structural design. Address: Dept. of Civil Engineering, University of Missouri-Rolla, Rolla, MO 65401.

EMANUEL, JOSEPH P(ATRICK), b. Keewatin, Minn, Jan. 26, 17; m. 43; c. 4. BOTANY. B.S, Minn. State Teachers Col, Duluth, 39; M.S, Minnesota, 47. Asst. prof. bot. & zool, Montana State, 47-49; bot, WINONA STATE COL, 49-56, ASSOC. PROF. BIOL. SCI, 56-, CHMN. DIV. SCI. & MATH, 64- U.S.A, 41-46, Lt. Col. Distribution of plants in northern Minnesota County. Address: Dept. of Botany, Winona State College, Winona, MN 55987.

EMARA, YEHIA ABDELAZIZ SALEH, b. Alexandria, Egypt, Oct. 23, 32; Can. citizen; m. 63; c. 3. GENETICS. B.Sc, Alexandria, 55; Cairo, 61; Ph.D.(genetics), Wales, 67. Lectr, Minia Inst. Agr, 55-56; res. off, crop res. dept, Ministry Agr, 56-67; ASST. PROF. GENETICS, MEM. UNIV. NEWF, 67- Nat. Res. Coun. Can. grant-in-aid, 68-69, 71-72. AAAS; Genetics Soc. Can; N.Y. Acad. Sci; Genetics Soc. Am. Inheritance of pathogenicity and resistance; quantitative and population genetics. Address: Dept. of Biology, Memorial University of Newfoundland, St. Johns, Newf, Can.

EMBER, GEORGE, b. Budapest, Hungary, Jan. 6, 30; U.S. citizen; m. 56. CHEMICAL ENGINEERING. Dipl, Budapest Tech, 53; M.Ch.E, Delaware, 61, Ph.D.(chem. eng), 62. Sr. proj. engr. res. & develop, Amoco Chem. Corp, 62-65; sr. res. engr, Halcon Int. Inc, 65-67; SR. PROCESS ENGR, HOFFMAN LA ROCHE CO, 67- Am. Inst. Chem. Eng. Distillation; combustion; transport properties; chemical reaction engineering. Address: Hoffman La Roche Co, Kingsland Rd, Nutley, NJ 07110.

EMBERSON, RICHARD M(AURY), b. Columbia, Mo, Apr. 2, 14; m. 47; c. 4. PHYSICS. A.B, Missouri, 31, A.M, 32, Ph.D.(physics), 36. Bemis fel, Harvard Observ, 36-39; instr. biophys, sch. med, Pittsburgh, 39-40; mem. staff radiation lab, Mass. Inst. Tech, 41-46; radio engr, Naval Res. Lab, 46; secretariat, res. & develop. bd, 46-51; asst. secy, Associated Univs, Inc, N.Y, 51-62; Inst. Radio Eng, 62, groups secy, INST. ELEC. & ELECTRONICS ENG, 63-64, DIR. TECH. SERV, 65- AAAS; Am. Astron. Soc; fel. Am. Phys. Soc; Am. Asn. Physics Teachers; Inst. Elec. & Electronics Eng; N.Y. Acad. Sci. Optical properties of metals; stellar radiometry; microwave radar; research administration; radio astronomy. Address: Institute of Electrical & Electronics Engineers, 345 E. 47th St, New York, NY 10017.

EMBLETON, TOM W(ILLIAM), b. Guthrie, Okla, Jan. 3, 18; m. 43; c. 5. HORTICULTURE. B.S, Arizona, 41; Ph.D.(pomol), Cornell, 49. Jr. sci. aide, bur. plant indust, soils & agr. eng, U.S. Dept. Agr, U.S. Date Garden, Indio, Calif, 42, sci. aide to horticulturist P-1, fruit & veg. crops & diseases, 46; asst. horticulturist, irrig. exp. sta, State Col. Wash, 49-50; CITRUS RES. CTR, UNIV. CALIF, RIVERSIDE, 50-56, assoc. horticulturist, 56-62, HORTICULTURIST, 62- U.S.A, 42-46, Maj. Fel. AAAS; Am. Soc. Hort. Sci; Am. Soc. Plant Physiol; Soil Sci. Soc. Am; Am. Soc. Agron. Soil acidification studies in northeastern apple orchards; citrus and avocado fertilization and field nutrition research; education. Address: Citrus Research Center, University of California, Riverside, CA 92502.

EMBLETON, T(ONY) F(REDERICK) W(ALLACE), b. Hornchurch, Eng, Oct. 1, 29; m. 53; c. 1. ACOUSTICS. B.Sc, Univ. London, 50, Royal scholar. & Ph.D.(physics), 52, D.Sc, 64. Fel, NAT. RES. COUN. CAN, 52-53, assoc. res. officer, 54-62, SR. RES. OFF, 62- Vis. lectr, Ottawa (Ont), 59-; Mass. Inst. Technol, 64 & 67. Acoust. Soc. Am.(award, 64). Acoustic radiation forces, standards; shock and explosion waves; industrial noise control. Address: Division of Physics, National Research Council of Canada, Ottawa, Ont, K1A 0S1, Can.

EMBODEN, WILLIAM ALLEN, JR, b. South Bend, Ind, Feb. 24, 35. SYSTEMATIC BOTANY. B.A, Purdue, 57; M.A, Indiana, 60; Vavra fel, California, Los Angeles, 64-65, Ph.D.(bot), 65. Asst. prof. BIOL, SAN FERNANDO VALLEY STATE COL, 65-70, ASSOC. PROF, 70- Mem. hon. faculty, Los Angeles County Mus. Natural Hist, 67-70. U.S.A.R, 55-61. Am. Soc. Plant Taxon; Int. Asn. Plant Taxon. Chemotaxonomy; cytogeography and chemogeography; chemical and cytological bases for distribution patterns in populations of Salvia and Bursera. Address: Dept. of Biology, San Fernando Valley State College, Nordhoff Ave, Northridge, CA 91324.

EMBODY, DANIEL R(OBERT), b. Ithaca, N.Y, July 10, 14; wid; c. 3. STATISTICS. B.S, Cornell, 38, M.S, 39. Sr. math. statistician, Arnold Bernhard & Co, Inc, 47-48; res. statistician, Wash. Water Power Co, 49-52; from head statist. sect. to coordinator electronic data processing, E.R. Squibb & Sons, Olin Mathieson Chem. Corp, 53-65; math. statistician, Bur. Ships, Dept. Navy, 65-67; BIOMETRICIAN, BIOMET. SERV. STAFF & PLANT PROTECTION DIV, AGR. RES. SERV, U.S. DEPT. AGR, 67- Consult, State Dept. Fish & Game, Idaho, 49-60; N.J, 55-65; U.S. Geol. Surv, 52-58. U.S.N.R, 42-46, Lt. Comdr. Am. Statist. Asn; Biomet. Soc; Soc. Indust. & Appl. Math; Entom. Soc. Am; Soc. Nematol. Application of statistical and biometric science to problems of naval engineering; medical research; fishery biology; entomology; pesticide monitoring; dynamics of insect trap operations; geology of landslides. Address: 5025 Edgewood Rd, College Park, MD 20740.

EMBREE, DOUGLAS GORDON, b. Wolfville, N.S, Apr. 19, 24; m. 48; c. 1. FOREST ENTOMOLOGY. B.Sc, New Brunswick, 50; M.S, State Univ. N.Y. Col. Forestry, Syracuse, 51; Ph.D.(zool), Ohio State, 61. RES. SCIENTIST, CAN. DEPT. FISHERIES & FORESTRY, 51- R.C.A.F, 42-45. Entom. Soc. Can; Can. Inst. Forestry. Population dynamics of forest insects, particularly evaluation of biological control agents. Address: Forest Research Lab, Canadian Dept. of Fisheries & Forestry, P.O. Box 4000, Fredericton, N.B, Can.

EMBREE, EARL OWEN, b. Alton, Ill, Feb. 17, 24; m. 62. MATHEMATICS. B.S, Morgan State Col, 50; M.S, Illinois, 52, Nat. Sci. Found. fel, 61, Ph.D.(math), 63. Mathematician, Ballistics Res. Labs, Md, 53-55; teacher MATH, MORGAN STATE COL, 55-58, asst. prof, 60-64, ASSOC. PROF, 64- U.S.A, 43-46. Am. Math. Soc; Math. Asn. Am. Ordinary linear differential equations involving distributions; symbolic logic; algebra. Address: Dept. of Mathematics, Morgan State College, Baltimore, MD 21212.

EMBREE, HARLAND D(UMOND), b. Monmouth, Ill, May 8, 23; m. 47; c. 4. ORGANIC CHEMISTRY. B.S, California, 48; Ph.D.(chem), Minnesota, 52. Res. chemist, Charles Pfizer & Co, 52-53; asst. prof. CHEM, Hamline, 53-57; assoc. prof, SAN JOSE STATE COL, 57-65, PROF, 65- Med.C, U.S.A, 42-45. Am. Chem. Soc. Chemical education. Address: 10500 Fleming Ave, San Jose, CA 95127.

EMBREE, M(ILTON) L(UTHER), b. Marceline, Mo, May 27, 24; m. 50; c. 2. ELECTRICAL ENGINEERING, ENGINEERING PHYSICS. B.S, Illinois, 49, M.S, 50; M.S, Lehigh, 57. Mem. res. staff, Illinois, 49-51; MEM. TECH. STAFF, SEMICONDUCTOR DEVICE & INTEGRATED CIRCUIT DEVELOP, BELL TEL. LABS, INC, 51- U.S.N, 43-46. Inst. Elec. & Electronics Eng. Address: Bell Telephone Labs, Inc, 2525 N. 11th St, Reading, PA 19604.

EMBREE, NORRIS D(EAN), b. Kemmerer, Wyo, Nov. 29, 11; m. 37; c. 3. CHEMISTRY. B.A, Wyoming, 31; Loomis fel, Yale, 33-34, Ph.D.(phys. chem), 34. Res. chemist, Distillation Prods. Industs, Eastman Kodak Co, 34-48, dir. res, 48-60, v.pres. in charge tech. opers, 60-68, ASST. DIR. RES, RES. LABS, TENN. EASTMAN CO, 68- Mem, oil & fat sect, Int. Union Pure & Appl. Chem, 61-; chmn, comt. fats & oils, div. chem. & chem. technol, Nat. Acad. Sci-Nat. Res. Coun, 63- Am. Chem. Soc; Am. Oil Chem. Soc.(pres, 59); Am. Inst. Chem. Eng; Am. Soc. Biol. Chem. High vacuum equipment and distillation; chemistry and technology of fats and oils; chemical products for use in nutrition and health care. Address: Research Labs, Tennessee Eastman Co, Kingsport, TN 37662.

EMBREE, ROBERT WILLIAM, b. Elliott, Iowa, Dec. 9, 32; m. 59; c. 3. BOTANY. B.A, Simpson Col, 54; M.S, Nebraska, 56; Nat. Insts. Health fel, California, Berkeley, 59-61, Ph.D.(bot), 62. Nat. Sci. Found. fel, Birkbeck Col, London, 61-63; vis. lectr. BOT, California, Berkeley, 63-64; asst. prof, Brown Univ, 64-68; ASSOC. PROF, UNIV. IOWA, 68- AAAS; Bot. Soc. Am; Mycol. Soc. Am; Phycol. Soc. Am; Torrey Bot. Soc; Brit. Mycol. Soc; Int. Phycol. Soc. Growth and development of fungi; ecology of coprophilous fungi; biology of mucoraceous fungi. Address: Dept. of Botany, University of Iowa, Iowa City, IA 52240.

EMBRY, BERTIS L(LOYD), b. Drummonds, Tenn, Nov. 23, 14; m. 41; c. 5. ELECTRICAL ENGINEERING. B.S, Utah State Univ, 41, M.S, 49; E.E, Stanford Univ, 54; Ph.D.(elec. eng), Univ. Mo, 66. Jr. engr, Rural Electrification Admin, 41-42, 46; electronics technician, radiation lab, Univ. Calif, 42-43; from asst. prof. to assoc. prof. agr. eng, UTAH STATE UNIV, 46-56, PROF. ELEC. ENG, 56- Am. Soc. Eng. Educ. fels, Atomic Energy Comn. Insts, summers 58-59, mem. prog, 64; adv. elec. & agr. eng, Utah State Contract, Iran, 60-62; consult, faculty eng, Univ. of the Andes, Venezuela, summer 68; consult. drainage, Colombia & Cent. Am, 71. U.S.N.R, 43-45, Lt. Inst. Elec. & Electronics Eng; Am. Soc. Eng. Educ; Nat. Soc. Prof. Eng. Electrical engineering in power and machinery; electronics; agricultural engineering; irrigation and drainage; direct energy conversion. Address: College of Engineering, Utah State University, Logan, UT 84321.

EMBRY, LAWRENCE B(RYAN), b. Morgantown, Ky, June 25, 18; m. 48. ANIMAL HUSBANDRY. B.S.A, Kentucky, 42; M.S.A, Cornell, 48, Ph.D, (animal husb), 50. Assoc. prof. ANIMAL SCI, S.DAK. STATE UNIV, 50-54, PROF, 54- U.S.A, 42-46, Res, Lt. Col. AAAS; Am. Soc. Animal Sci; Am. Inst. Nutrit; N.Y. Acad. Sci. Nutritive requirements of livestock; composition and nutritive value of feeds; feed additives. Address: Dept. of Animal Science, South Dakota State University, Brookings, SD 57006.

EMBRY, WALLACE ABNER, b. Quito, Tenn, Oct. 4, 42; m. 67; c. 2. ANALYTICAL CHEMISTRY. B.S, Memphis State Univ, 64; Ph.D, (anal. chem), Univ. Tex, Austin, 67. SR. ANAL. CHEMIST, MOBIL CHEM. CO, 67- Am. Chem. Soc; Soc. Appl. Spectros. Atomic absorption—flame emission spectroscopy; infrared and visible-ultraviolet spectroscopy. Address: 1850 Briarcliff, Beaumont, TX 77706.

EMBURY, JOHN DAVID, b. Grantham, Eng, July 12, 39; m. 63. PHYSICAL METALLURGY. B.Sc, Manchester, 60; Ph.D.(metall), Cambridge, 63. Res. scientist, U.S. Steel Res. Center, Pa, 63-65; sr. res. assoc. METALL, Univ. Newcastle, 65-66; asst. prof, McMASTER UNIV, 66-68, ASSOC. PROF, 68- Vis. fel, Battelle Mem. Inst, 71. Am. Soc. Metals; Am. Inst. Mining, Metall. & Petrol. Eng; Brit. Inst. Metals. Microstructure of deformed materials; mechanisms of deformation and fracture in metals; stress corrosion failure; mechanism of nucleation and growth processes in solids. Address: Dept. of Metallurgy & Materials Science, McMaster University, Hamilton, Ont, Can.

EMCH, G(EORGE) F(REDERICK), b. Wash, D.C, June 17, 25; m. 50; c. 2. PHYSICS. B.S, Trinity Col, 47. Assoc. physicist, APPL. PHYSICS LAB, JOHNS HOPKINS UNIV, 48-56, PHYSICIST, 56- U.S.N.R, 43-46, Lt. Am. Phys. Soc; Inst. Elec. & Electronics Eng. Simulation; search radar and weapon control system design and analysis. Address: 8621 Georgia Ave, Silver Spring, MD 20910.

EMCH, GERARD G, b. Geneva, Switz, July 21, 36; m. 59; c. 2. MATHEMATICAL PHYSICS. Maturité Sci, Col. Geneva, Switz, 55; Physics Dipl, Geneva, 59, Ph.D.(quant. mech, spec. relativity), 63. Asst. exp. physics, exp. physics res. lab, Geneva, 59-60, THEORET. PHYSICS, Univ, 59-63, chief, 63-64; res. assoc, Princeton, 64-65; Maryland, 65-66; ASST. PROF, UNIV. ROCHESTER, 66- Lectr, Boulder Sch. Theoret. Physics, summers 64 & 65; vis. fel, Colorado & Joint Inst. Lab. Astrophys, summer 65. Swiss Army. Swiss Phys. Soc. Experimental solid state physics; theoretical physics. Address: Dept. of Physics, University of Rochester, Rochester, NY 14627.

EMELE, JANE FRANCES, b. Phillipsburg, N.J, Nov. 14, 25. PHARMACOLOGY. B.S, Upsala Col, 47; M.S, Illinois, 49; Nat. Heart Inst. fel, Yale, 52-54, Ph.D.(pharmacol), 54. Res. asst, biol. div, Schering Corp, N.J, 47-48; physiol, Illinois, 49-50; microanal. chemist, Bell Tel. Labs, N.J, 51; chief sect. pharmacodynamics, div. pharmacol, Eaton Labs, Norwich Pharmacal Co, 54-55; SR. res. assoc. div. pharmacol, WARNER-LAMBERT RES. INST, 55-65, mgr. div. proprietary pharmacol, 65-66, dir. dept. pharmacol, CONSUMER PROD. RES. DIV, 66-70, ASSOC. DIR. BIOL. RES, 70- AAAS; Am. Soc. Pharmacol. & Exp. Therapeut; Am. Pharmaceut. Asn; Acad. Pharmaceut. Sci; Am. Therapeut. Soc; Int. Soc. Biochem. Pharmacol; N.Y. Acad. Sci. Neuropharmacology; analgesia, gastrointestinal and respiratory; cardiovascular neurophysiology. Address: Consumer Product Research Division, Warner-Lambert Research Institute, Morris Plains, NJ 07950.

EMERICH, DONALD WARREN, b. Schuylkill Haven, Pa, July 12, 20; m. 43; c. 3. ANALYTICAL CHEMISTRY. B.S, Pa. State, 42; Ph.D, Ohio State, 51. Chemist, Hercules Powder Co, N.J, 42-45; chem. engr, Badger Ord. Works, Wis, 45-47; res. chemist, Niacet Chem. Div, U.S. Vanadium Corp, 47-49; asst, Ohio State, 49-51; asst. prof. chem, Kansas State, 51-54; prof, Centenary Col, 54-60; PROF. ANAL. CHEM, MISS. STATE UNIV, 60-, HEAD DEPT, 66-, acting head dept, 64-66. AAAS; Am. Chem. Soc. Electrochemistry; nonaqueous titrimetry. Address: 2007 Pin Oak Dr, Starkville, MS 39759.

EMERICK, HAROLD B(URTON), b. New Brighton, Pa, July 6, 13; m. 38; c. 2. METALLURGICAL ENGINEERING. Carnegie Inst. Technol, 32-38. Supvr, JONES & LAUGHLIN STEEL CORP, 35-55, dir. tech. serv, 55-69, V.PRES. RES. & TECHNOL, 69- Am. Inst. Mining, Metall. & Petrol. Eng.(McKune Mem. Award, 42); fel. Am. Soc. Metals; fel. Metall. Soc.(pres, 65). Process metallurgy; iron and steel production technology. Address: Jones & Laughlin Steel Corp, 3 Gateway Center, Pittsburgh, PA 15230.

EMERICK, ROYCE J(ASPER), b. Tulsa, Okla, Jan. 1, 31; m. 53; c. 3. BIOCHEMISTRY, ANIMAL HUSBANDRY. B.S, Okla. State, 52; M.S, Wisconsin, 55, Ph.D.(biochem, animal husb), 57. PROF. BIOCHEM, S.DAK. STATE UNIV, 57- Res. fel, Univ. Wis, 65-66. Am. Chem. Soc; Am. Inst. Nutrit; Am. Soc. Animal Sci. Urinary calculi; nitrate and mineral metabolism. Address: Station Biochemistry Dept, South Dakota State University, Brookings, SD 57006.

EMERMAN, SIDNEY, b. Weehawken, N.J, Sept. 2, 29; m. 70. ORGANIC CHEMISTRY. B.S, Rutgers, 51; Ph.D.(org. chem), Cornell, 56. Instr. chem, Wells Col, 55; asst. prof. chem. & physics, Jarvis Christian Col, 56-58; res. assoc. ENDOCRINOL, sch. med, N.Y. Univ, 61-64, instr. & res. chemist, 64-68; ASST. PROF, KINGSBOROUGH COMMUNITY COL, CITY UNIV. NEW YORK, 68- Am. Chem. Soc. Organic reaction mechanisms; biosynthesis and metabolism of steroid hormones. Address: 333 E. 30th St, New York, NY 10016.

EMERSON, ALFRED EDWARDS, b. Ithaca, N.Y, Dec. 31, 96; m. 20, 50; c. 2. ZOOLOGY, ECOLOGY. B.S, Cornell, 18, M.A, 20, Ph.D.(entom), 25; hon. D.Sc, Mich. State, 61. Asst, Cornell, 16-18; res. asst. trop. res. sta, N.Y. Zool. Soc, 19-20, assoc, 20-21, asst. dir, 24; instr. ZOOL, Pittsburgh, 21-22, asst. prof, 22-24, assoc. prof, 25-29; UNIV. CHICAGO, 29-34, prof, 34-62, EMER. PROF, 62- Asst, Am. Mus. Natural Hist, 20, res. assoc, 40-; Guggenheim fel, 26-27; ed, Ecology, 32-39; res. assoc, Chicago Natural

Hist. Mus, 42-; Belgian Am. Ed. Found. fel, Belgian Congo, 48; mem, Bd. Natural Resources, Ill, 50-62; mem. panels systematics, Nat. Sci. Found, 52-57; vis. prof, Univ. Calif, summer 59; distinguished vis. prof, Mich. State Univ, 60; mem. bd. trustees, Biol. Info. Serv, 61-67; chmn. bd. dirs, Bache Fund, Nat. Acad. Sci, 65- Nat. Acad. Sci; AAAS (v.pres, 46); Am. Soc. Nat; Ecol. Soc. Am.(secy-treas, 31, pres, 40, citation as eminent ecologist, 67); Soc. Study Evolution (v.pres, 46, 48, pres, 60); fel. Am. Entom. Soc; Soc. Syst. Zool.(pres, 58); fel. Animal Behav. Soc. Ecology, taxonomy, zoogeography, development, behavior and evolution of termites; animal sociology; speciation. Address: Huletts Landing, NY 12841.

EMERSON, CHARLES PHILLIPS, b. Indianapolis, Ind, June 3, 12; m. 41; c. 5. MEDICINE. A.B, Princeton, 33; M.D, Harvard, 37. Intern, City Hosp, Boston, 38-39; res. fel. med, Harvard Med. Sch, 39-41, asst, 40-41; Am. Col. Physicians fel, Thorndike Mem. lab, City Hosp, Boston, 42, 46; asst. prof. med, SCH. MED, BOSTON UNIV, 46-50, assoc. prof, 50-71, PROF. MED, DIR. HEMAT. DIV, DEPT. MED. & CONSULT. CLIN. LABS, 71- Dir. labs, Evans Mem. Hosp. & Mass. Mem. Hosp, 57- U.S.A, 42-45. AAAS; Am. Soc. Hemat; fel. Am. Fedn. Clin. Res; Am. Soc. Clin. Invest; Int. Soc. Hemat. Internal medicine; hematology. Address: University Hospital, 750 Harrison Ave, Boston, MA 02118.

EMERSON, DAVID E(DWIN), b. Checotah, Okla, May 15, 32; m. 53; c. 3. ANALYTICAL CHEMISTRY. B.S, Southeast. State Col, 55. Chemist, HELIUM RES. CENTER, 58-61, supvry. chemist, 61-63, chief br. lab. serv, 63-71, CHIEF UNIT TECH. SERV, 71- U.S.A, 56, Res, 56-62, S/Sgt. Am. Chem. Soc. Development of gas analysis apparatus, especially helium and the impurities in helium; development methods in isotopic analysis, preparation of primary standards and sample preparation. Address: Helium Operations, Bureau of Mines, Box H 4372, Herring Plaza, Amarillo, TX 79101.

EMERSON, DAVID N, b. Ashland, Wis, Apr. 6, 35; m. 56; c. 3. ZOOLOGY, COMPARATIVE PHYSIOLOGY. A.B, California, Berkeley, 56; A.M, South Dakota, 63, Ph.D.(zool), 66. Asst. prof. zool, Univ. Alaska, 66-68; ASSOC. DIR. SCI. INFO. & REGULATORY AFFAIRS, MEAD JOHNSON & CO, 68- U.S.A, 57-59. AAAS. Comparative physiology of nitrogen metabolism of marine invertebrates during osmoregulation; developmental physiology of invertebrates. Address: Mead Johnson & Co, 2404 W. Pennsylvania, Evansville, IN 47721.

EMERSON, D(AVID) W(INTHROP), b. Littleton, Mass, Mar. 13, 28; m. 54; c. 3. ORGANIC CHEMISTRY. A.B, Dartmouth Col, 52; fel, Michigan, 53-55, M.S, 54, Allied Chem. & Dye Corp. fel, 55-56, Ph.D.(chem), 58. Res. chemist, Shell Oil Co, Tex, 57-63; asst. prof. CHEM, UNIV. MICH, DEARBORN CAMPUS, 63-66, assoc. prof, 66-69, PROF, 69-, chmn. div. lit, sci. & arts, 67-69. U.S.A, 46-47, 50-51. Am. Chem. Soc; The Chem. Soc. Mechanisms of organic reactions; reactive intermediates; organosulfur chemistry. Address: Dept. of Chemistry, University of Michigan, Dearborn Campus, Dearborn, MI 48128.

EMERSON, D(ONALD) O(RVILLE), b. Long Beach, Calif, July 19, 31; m. 57; c. 3. GEOLOGY, PETROLOGY. B.S, Calif. Inst. Tech, 53; M.S, Pa. State, 55, Ph.D.(mineral, petrol), 59. Asst. prof. geol, Univ. Calif, Davis, 57-65, assoc. prof, 65-69; GEOLOGIST, LAWRENCE LIVERMORE LAB, 69- Geol. Soc. Am; Mineral. Soc. Am; Am. Nuclear Soc. Applied geology and petrology. Address: Lawrence Livermore Lab, P.O. Box 808, Livermore, CA 94550.

EMERSON, ERNEST B(ENJAMIN), JR, b. Bridgewater, Mass, Apr. 29, 12; m. 38; c. 2. SURGERY. A.B, Williams Col, 34; M.D, Rochester, 38. Instr. SURG, DIV. OTORHINOLARYNGOL, SCH. MED. & DENT, UNIV. ROCHESTER, 41-53, ASST. PROF, 53-, BRONCHOSCOPIST, LAB. RES. DISEASES OF CHEST, DEPT. MED, 41-, jr. surgeon, hosp, 41-52. Asst. surgeon, Highland Hosp, 41-; Strong Mem. Hosp. & Rochester Munic. Hosp, 43-, courtesy staff, Genesee Hosp, 46-; consult, Canandaigua Vet. Admin. Hosp, 46-52; Batavia Vet. Admin. Hosp, 48-; chief staff, Town Webb Health Ctr, Old Forge. U.S.N, 43-46, Lt. Bronchoesophagology; development of new instruments; tonsil surgery; radium treatment of deafness. Address: Gray Lake, Old Forge, NY 13420.

EMERSON, FRANK H(ENRY), b. Kansas City, Mo, June 22, 21; m. 44; c. 4. HORTICULTURE, PLANT PATHOLOGY. A.B, Kansas, 47, M.A, 48; Ph.D, Cornell, 51. Asst. bot, Kansas, 47-48; plant path, Cornell, 48-51; asst. tech. dir, agr. chem, Stauffer Chem. Co, N.Y, 51-55; asst. prof. exten. horticulturist, PURDUE UNIV, 55-58, ASSOC. PROF. HORT. RES, 58- U.S.A, 44-46, Capt. Am. Soc. Hort. Sci; Am. Phytopath. Soc. Tree fruits; chemical growth regulators; winter hardiness; frost control; population density; training systems; chemical thinning, breeding and selection of new varieties resistant to apple scab. Address: Dept. of Horticulture, Purdue University, Lafayette, IN 47907.

EMERSON, FREDERICK B(EAUREGARD), JR, b. Wellsville, N.Y, Nov. 21, 35; m. 58; c. 3. INTERNAL MEDICINE. B.A, Alfred Univ, 57; Ph.D.(wildlife mgt), Cornell Univ, 61; M.D, Vanderbilt Univ, 70. Asst. wildlife mgt, Cornell, 57-61; Nat. Insts. Health fel. marine biol, Miami (Fla), 61-62; biologist wildlife mgt, Tenn. Valley Authority, 62-65; asst. prof. forestry, Univ. Tenn, 65-66; intern, MED. CTR, UNIV. COLO, DENVER, 70-71, RESIDENT MED, 71- Summers, biologist, N.Y. State Conserv. Dept, 55-57. Wildlife Soc. Medicine; ecology; conservation of natural resources. Address: 2371 Eudora, Denver, CO 80207.

EMERSON, GERALDINE M(ARIELLEN), U.S. citizen. BIOCHEMISTRY, MEDICAL PHYSIOLOGY. B.A, Univ. Miami, 49; Ph.D.(med, physiol, biochem, neuroanat), Univ. Ala, Birmingham, 60. ASST. PROF. BIOCHEM, MED. SCH, UNIV. ALA, BIRMINGHAM, 64. AAAS; Am. Physiol. Soc; Am. Inst. Chem. Endocrine factors in growth; aging in the Long-Evans rat; cancer immunotherapy; cell membrane potentials in situ; muscle diameters of different mammals and a comparison in the rat under different growth conditions. Address: Dept. of Biochemistry, University of Alabama Medical Center, Birmingham, AL 35233.

EMERSON, GLADYS ANDERSON, b. Caldwell, Kans, July 1, 03. NUTRITION, BIOCHEMISTRY. A.B. & B.S, Okla. Col. Lib. Arts, 25; M.A, Stanford, 26; fel, California, Los Angeles, 27-30, Ph.D.(nutrit, biochem), 32; Göttingen, 32-33. Asst, Stanford, 25-26; Iowa State Col, 30-31; res. assoc, inst. exp. biol, California, Los Angeles, 32-42; head dept. nutrit, Merck Inst. Therapeut. Res, 42-57; prof. NUTRIT. & head div, SCH. PUB. HEALTH, UNIV. CALIF, LOS ANGELES, 57-70, EMER. PROF. & NUTRITIONIST, 71- Lectr, sch. med, Univ. Calif, San Francisco, 45; lectr, Pa. State Col, 51; res. assoc, Sloan Kettering Inst. Cancer Res, 50-53; vis. lectr, Nebraska, 58. Mem. adv. bd, Qm. Food & Container Inst, 48-49; food & nutrit. bd, Nat. Res. Coun, 59-64; U.S. Nat. Comt, Int. Union Nutrit. Sci, 59-62; exec. comt, Am. Bd. Nutrit, 59-68; mem. bd, Meals for Millions, 70-; co-chmn, Calif. Comt. for WHO, 70-; v.chmn, panel new foods, White House Conf. Food Nutrit. & Health, 69 & 71; speaker, session chmn. & discussion leader, Int. Cong. Vitamin E, Japan, 70. With Off. Sci. Res. & Develop, 43-45. Fel. AAAS; Soc. Exp. Biol. & Med; Am. Inst. Nutrit; Am. Chem. Soc.(Garvan Medal, 52); fel. N.Y. Acad. Sci; Am. Inst. Chem. Amino acids; vitamin E; vitamin B complex; antimetabolites. Address: School of Public Health, University of California, Los Angeles, CA 90024.

EMERSON, JAMES L, b. Garrett, Ind, Jan. 23, 38; m. 62; c. 2. VETERINARY PATHOLOGY. D.V.M, Ohio State, 62; M.S, Purdue, 64, Ph.D, 66. Instr. path, sch. vet. sci. & med, Purdue, 62-66, asst. prof, 66; res. assoc. pathologist, Norwich Pharmacal Co, 66-69; PATHOLOGIST, HUMAN HEALTH RES. & DEVELOP. LABS, DOW CHEM. CO, 69- Assoc. mem. faculty, Ind. Univ-Purdue Univ, Indianapolis, 69- Am. Vet. Med. Asn; Am. Col. Vet. Path. Drug safety evaluation; mast cell distribution in pathologic conditions of animals; in utero hog cholera infection and its affect on the developing fetus; pathogenesis, gross and microscopic pathology of edema disease in swine. Address: 7229 Cranbrook Ct, Indianapolis, IN 46250.

EMERSON, JOHN WILFORD, b. Bloomington, Ind, Dec. 27, 33; m. 59; c. 3. GEOLOGY. B.S, New Mexico, 59, M.S, 61; Ph.D.(geol), Fla. State, 66. Geologist, Pan Am. Petrol. Corp, Colo, 66-67; asst. prof. GEOL, CENT. MO. STATE COL, 67-70, ASSOC. PROF, 70-, HEAD DEPT, 68- U.S.A, 53-55. Geol. Soc. Am; Am. Quaternary Asn. Sedimentology; sedimentary petrology; stratigraphy. Address: Dept. of Geology, Central Missouri State College, Warrensburg, MO 64093.

EMERSON, K(ARY) C(ADMUS), b. Sasakwa, Okla, Mar. 13, 18; m. 39; c. 3. MEDICAL ENTOMOLOGY, PARASITOLOGY. B.S, Okla. State, 39, M.S, 40, Ph.D.(entom), 49. U.S. Army, 40-66, med. entomologist, Philippines, 40-42, asst. prof, Okla. State, 46-49; tech. liaison, Off. Chief Res. & Develop, 59-60, SPEC. ASST. FOR RES. SECY. ARMY, 60- Res. assoc, Smithsonian Inst, 59-; summer instr, Far East Br, Maryland, 59. Consult, univs. & U.S. Depts. Agr. & Interior, 49-; U.S. mem, NATO Long-term Study Panel; mem, Defense Comt. Res; White House Panel Systs. & Taxon; White House Comt. Environ. Qual; res. assoc, mus, Okla. State Univ, adj. prof, 71- U.S.A, 40-66, Col.(Ret). Soc. Syst. Zool; fel. Entom. Soc. Am; Am. Soc. Trop. Med. & Hyg; Am. Soc. Parasitol; Wildlife Disease Asn; Entom. Soc. Can. Mallophaga; ectoparasites; arthropod-borne diseases. Address: 2704 N. Kensington St, Arlington. VA 22207.

EMERSON, KENNETH, b. Pasadena, Calif, Nov. 9, 31; m. 56; c. 3. PHYSICAL & INORGANIC CHEMISTRY. B.A, Harvard, 53; M.A, Oregon, 58; Ph.D.(chem), Minnesota, 61. Noyes fel, CHEM, Calif. Inst. Tech, 61-62; asst. prof, MONT. STATE UNIV, 62-65, assoc. prof, 65-70, PROF. CHEM, 70- U.S.A, 53-55. AAAS; Am. Chem. Soc; Am. Crystallog. Asn. Inorganic structure and its relation to the theory of the chemical bond; nature of isolated metal-metal bonds. Address: Dept. of Chemistry, Montana State University, Bozeman, MT 59715.

EMERSON, LEWIS COTESWORTH, b. Columbia, S.C, July 16, 25; m. 48; c. 3. PHYSICS. B.E.E, Ga. Inst. Tech, 49, Nat. Res. Coun. fel, 49-50; Oak Ridge Sch. Reactor Tech, 56-57; Ph.D.(physics), Tennessee, 63. Dept. head health physics, Union Carbide Nuclear Co, 50-56; HEALTH PHYSICIST, OAK RIDGE NAT. LAB, 57- Lectr, WHO, Belgium, 57, India, 58. U.S.A, 43-46. Health Physics Soc; Am. Phys. Soc. Hazard evaluation in nuclear industries; health physics; interaction of radiation with matter; radiation physics; optical properties of thin films; ellipsometry. Address: 101 Calvin Lane, Oak Ridge, TN 37830.

EMERSON, MARION P(RESTON), b. Washburn, Mo, Feb. 24, 18; m. 47; c. 3. ALGEBRA. B.S, Southwest Mo. State Col, 38; M.S, Wisconsin, 48; Ph.D. (math), Illinois, 52. Asst. prof. MATH, Harpur Col, 52-56; assoc. prof, Southwest Mo. State Col, 56-61; PROF. & HEAD DEPT, KANS. STATE TEACHERS COL, 61- U.S.A.A.F, 42-46, Res, 46-53, Capt. Am. Math. Soc; Math. Asn. Am. Modular lattices. Address: Dept. of Mathematics, Kansas State Teachers College, Emporia, KS 66801.

EMERSON, MERLE T, b. Spokane, Wash, Aug. 19, 30; m. 54; c. 2. PHYSICAL & ANALYTICAL CHEMISTRY. B.S, Whitworth Col.(Wash), 52; M.S, Wash. State Col, 58; Ph.D.(phys. chem), Washington (Seattle), 58. Res. assoc. CHEM, Fla. State, 58-60, asst, inst. molecular biophys, 60-62; asst. prof, Wayne State, 62-64, summer faculty fel, 63; asst. prof, Fla. State Univ, 64-69; ASSOC. PROF, UNIV. ALA, HUNTSVILLE, 69-, acting dir. natural sci. & math. div, 71. Nat. Insts. Health res. grant, 64-67; vis. assoc. prof, Univ. Hawaii, Hilo Campus, 68-69. Am. Chem. Soc. Molecular structure and kinetics of fast reactions using nuclear magnetic resonance spectroscopy; x-ray determination of crystal and molecular structures and instrumentation. Address: Dept. of Chemistry, University of Alabama in Huntsville, P.O. Box 1247, Huntsville, AL 35807.

EMERSON, RALPH, b. N.Y.C, Apr. 19, 12; m. 42; c. 2. MYCOLOGY. B.S, Harvard, 33, M.A, 34, Ph.D.(biol, mycol), 37. Nat. Res. Coun. fel. bot, Cambridge, 37-39; res. fel. biol, Harvard, 39-40; instr. BOT, UNIV. CALIF, BERKELEY, 40-44, asst. prof, 44-48, assoc. prof, 48-53, PROF, 53-, chmn. dept, 67-71. Guggenheim fel, Harvard, 48-49 & Univ. Costa Rica, 56-57; spec. univ. lectr, London, 50. Color photographer, Fleischmann Game-Fish Exped, Mex, 35; microbiologist, emergency rubber proj, U.S. Dept. Agr, Calif, 44-46. Nat. Acad. Sci; AAAS; Mycol. Soc. Am.(pres, 56); Bot. Soc. Am.(pres, 67); fel. Am. Acad. Arts & Sci; Am. Inst. Bio. Sci; Asn. Trop. Biol; Brit. Mycol Soc.(v.pres, 71). Fungi, cytogenetics, cytotaxonomy, sexuality, metabolism and nutrition, especially of water molds; microbiology of retting guayule; scientific color photography and phase-contrast cinemicrography. Address: Dept. of Botany, University of California, Berkeley, CA 94720.

EMERSON, ROBERT L, b. Corsicana, Tex, Nov. 13, 18; m. 44; c. 2. BACTERIOLOGY. B.S, North Texas State, 40, M.S, 41; Ph.D.(bact), Wisconsin, 44. Res. bacteriologist, Upjohn Co, 44-46; asst. prof. bact, Okla. State, 46-47; res. assoc, Wisconsin, 47-48; assoc. prof. bact, Florida, 48-52; chief lab. div, prod. develop. labs, PINE BLUFF ARSENAL, 52-59, DEP. DIR, BIOL. OPERS, 59- Am. Soc. Microbiol. Microbial fermentations. Address: Biological Operations, Pine Bluff Arsenal, Pine Bluff, AR 71603.

EMERSON, ROY EUGENE, b. Lockport, N.Y, Aug. 26, 12; m. 38; c. 4. AGRICULTURAL ENGINEERING. B.S, Cornell, 38, M.S, 46. Asst. prof. AGR. ENG, W.VA. UNIV, 46-58, ASSOC. PROF, 58- U.S.A, 41-45, Capt. Poultry housing; environmental factors affecting raising and production of poultry. Address: Dept. of Agricultural Engineering, West Virginia University, Morgantown, WV 26506.

EMERSON, STERLING (HOWARD), b. Lincoln, Nebr, Oct. 29, 00; m. 24; c. 2. GENETICS. B.Sc, Cornell, 22; A.M, Michigan, 24, Ph.D.(genetics), 28; Int. Educ. Bd. fel, Scandinavia, 25-26. Instr. bot, Michigan, 24-28; asst. prof. GENETICS, CALIF. INST. TECHNOL, 28-36, assoc. prof, 37-46, prof, 46-71; EMER. PROF, 71- Fulbright fel, Cambridge & Guggenheim fel, Cambridge & Univ. Paris, 51-52; geneticist, div. biol. & med, U.S. Atomic Energy Comn, 55-57; vis. prof, Univ. Wash, 63; Cornell Univ, 65; Copenhagen Univ, 66. Nat. Acad. Sci; AAAS; Genetics Soc. Am. Address: Dept. of Genetics, California Institute of Technology, Pasadena, CA 91109.

EMERSON, THOMAS E(DWARD), JR, b. Wilson, Okla, Feb. 3, 35; m. 55; c. 3. MEDICAL PHYSIOLOGY. B.S, Oklahoma, 58, Ph.D.(med. physiol), 64; M.Sc, Alberta, 61. Res. physiologist, Civil Aeromed. Res. Inst, Okla, 61-65; asst. prof. physiol. & res. asst. prof. med. surg, med. ctr, Univ. Okla, 65-66; ASSOC. PROF. PHYSIOL, MICH. STATE UNIV, 66- U.S.A, 58-59, Res, 59-61, Med.Serv.C.Res, 61-68, Capt. Soc. Exp. Biol. & Med; Am. Physiol. Soc; Am. Fedn. Clin. Res. Cardiovascular physiology; cardiovascular mechanisms during endotoxin and hemorrhagic shock; regulation of vasoactive agents and effects on peripheral blood flow; effects of vasoactive hormones on arteries and veins. Address: Dept. of Physiology, Michigan State University, East Lansing, MI 48823.

EMERSON, WILLIAM EDWARD, b. St. Louis, Mo, Sept. 21, 30; m. 62; c. 2. ORGANIC & POLYMER CHEMISTRY. A.B, Wash. Univ, 52; M.S, Duquesne Univ, 54, Ph.D.(chem), 62. Res. chemist, Hooker Chem. Corp, 62-69, sr. res. chemist, 69-70; GROUP LEADER CHEM, QUAKER OATS CO, 70- AAAS; Am. Chem. Soc. Fluorine chemistry; polymer chemistry; organic synthesis. Address: Chemical Research, Quaker Oats Co, 617 W. Main St, Barrington, IL 60010.

EMERSON, WILLIAM K(EITH), b. San Diego, Calif, May 1, 25. MALACOLOGY. A.B, San Diego State Col, 48; Hancock fel, Southern California, 48-50, M.S, 50; Ph.D.(paleont), California, Berkeley, 56. Mus. paleontologist, California, Berkeley, 51-55; asst. curator INVERT, AM. MUS. NATURAL HIST, 55-61, assoc. curator, 61-66, CURATOR, 66-, CHMN. DEPT. LIVING INVERT, 60- Res. assoc, San Diego Natural Hist. Mus, 62- Leader, Puritan-Am. Mus. Natural Hist. Exped, 57 & mem, Belvedere Exped, 62, Western Mexico; mem, Paleont. Res. Inst. Dorothy K. Palmer Award for Res, Univ. Calif, 54. Fel. AAAS; Paleont. Soc; Am. Malacol. Union (pres, 62); Soc. Syst. Zool. General invertebrate zoology; systematic malacology of Eastern Pacific faunas, especially Gastropoda and Scaphopoda; geographical distribution and ecology of Cenozoic marine mollusks. Address: American Museum of Natural History, New York, NY 10024.

EMERSON, WILLIAM S(TEVENSON), b. Boston, Mass, Mar. 25, 13; m. 58; c. 4. ORGANIC CHEMISTRY. A.B, Dartmouth Col, 34; Ph.D.(org. chem), Mass. Inst. Technol, 37. Du Pont fel, Illinois, 37-38, instr. chem, 38-41; res. chemist, Monsanto Chem. Co, 41-44, group leader, 44-51, asst. res. dir, 51-54, asst. dir. gen. develop. dept, 54-56; mgr. res, Whittier Lab, Am. Potash & Chem. Corp, 56-60; SR. STAFF ASSOC, ARTHUR D. LITTLE, INC, 60- AAAS; Am. Chem. Soc. Reductive alkylation; styrene chemistry; liquid phase oxidation; thiophene chemistry; dihydropyran chemistry; organometallic chemistry; applied organic chemistry; research management. Address: Arthur D. Little, Inc, 15 Acorn Park, Cambridge, MA 02140.

EMERY, ALAN ROY, b. Trinidad, B.W.I, Feb. 21, 39; Can. citizen; m. 62; c. 2. ICHTHYOLOGY, MARINE SCIENCES. B.Sc, Toronto, 62; M.Sc, McGill, 64; Cornell, 65; Ph.D.(marine sci), Miami (Fla), 68. Res. asst. biol. & oceanog. invest, Bellairs Res. Inst, McGill Univ, Barbados, W.I, 62-63; res. scientist in charge explor. fishing, St. Andrews Biol. Sta, Fisheries Res. Bd. Can, 64-65; RES. SCIENTIST IN CHARGE OF SMALLMOUTH BLACK BASS PROJ, MAPLE RES. STA, ONT. DEPT. LANDS & FOREST, 68- Res. assoc, Royal Ont. Mus, Toronto; sr. scientist, Sublimnos Proj, Ont. AAAS; Am. Soc. Ichthyol. & Herpet; Am. Fisheries Soc; Int. Asn. Prof. Diving Scientists. Pollution control; development of underwater research techniques; ichthyology, particularly ecology and systematics; ecology of coral reefs, particularly bioenergetics; behavior of fishes. Address: Ontario Dept. of Lands & Forests, Research Branch, Maple, Ont, Can.

EMERY, ALDEN H(AYES), b. Lancaster, N.H, June 2, 01; m. 24; c. 2. CHEMISTRY. A.B, Oberlin Col, 22; A.M, Ohio State, 23; hon. Sc.D, Dickinson, 57. With U.S. Bur. Mines, 23-36, asst. to chief engr, exp. sta. div, 27-35, asst. chief engr, 35-36; asst. mgr, Am. Chem. Soc, 36-45, asst. secy, 43-45, secy. & bus. mgr, 46-47, exec. secy, 47-65, hon. secy, 65-66; RETIRED. Asst. ed, Chem. Abstr, 30-37; sect. ed, Metall. Abstr, 31-39. AAAS; Am. Chem. Soc; Soc. Chem. Indust; Am. Inst. Chem. Administration. Address: 8101 Park Crest Dr, Silver Spring, MD 20910.

EMERY, ALDEN H(AYES), JR, b. Pittsburgh, Pa, May 2, 25; m. 52; c. 2. CHEMICAL ENGINEERING. B.S, Pa. State, 47; S.M, Mass. Inst. Tech, 49; Ph.D, Illinois, 55. Chem. engr, E.I. du Pont de Nemours & Co, 49-52; asst. prof. CHEM. ENG, PURDUE, 54-58, assoc. prof, 58-64, PROF, 64- U.S.N, 44-45. AAAS; Am. Chem. Soc; Am. Inst. Chem. Eng; Soc. Rheol. Thermal diffusion; mechanical properties of high polymers; enzyme engineering. Address: 815 N. Vine, West Lafayette, IN 47906.

EMERY, ALLAN R(USSELL), b. Detroit, Mich, Feb. 21, 30. COMPUTER SCIENCE, PHYSICAL CHEMISTRY. B.A, Ohio Wesleyan, 51; M.S, Michigan, 53, Ph.D, 57. Instr. chem, Michigan, 57-58; res. chemist, Socony Mobil Oil Co, 58-60; asst. prof. chem, DEARBORN CAMPUS, UNIV. MICH, 60-64, assoc. prof, 64-68, PROF. CHEM, 68-, ASST. DIR, COMPUT. CTR, 70-, res. assoc, 68-70. Am. Chem. Soc; Am. Phys. Soc; Asn. Comput. Mach. Molecular vibration spectroscopy; computer communications. Address: Computing Center, University of Michigan, Ann Arbor, MI 48105.

EMERY, ARTHUR J(AMES), JR, b. Middleburg, Pa, Dec. 1, 23; m. 48. BIOCHEMISTRY. B.S, Bucknell, 47; Cornell, 48-49; fel, Rochester, 50-54, Ph.D.(biochem), 54. Res. assoc. bact, N.Y. State Agr. Exp. Sta, Cornell, 47-48, asst, 48-49; res. chemist biol. stain comn, sch. med. & dent, Rochester, 49-51, from jr. scientist biochem, flash burn sect, atomic energy proj. to assoc. scientist & instr. biochem, 54-57; asst. prof. biol. chem, sch. med, Univ. Md, Baltimore City, 57-61, assoc. prof, 61-67, acting head dept, 62-63; sci. analyst, sci. anal. br, life sci. div, Off. Chief Res. & Develop, Army Res. Off, 67-70; PROG. DIR. MICROBIOL, BIOL. SCI. DIV, OFF. NAVAL RES, ARLINGTON, VA, 70- Hosp.C, U.S.N.R, 42-46. AAAS; Am. Chem. Soc; Am. Inst. Biol. Sci; Am. Soc. Microbiol. Nucleic acids and nucleoprotein complexes in protein synthesis; mechanisms of protein synthesis; chemistry and structure of nucleic acids and nucleoprotein complexes. Address: 9921 Evergreen Ave, Allview Estates, Ellicott City, MD 21043.

EMERY, ASHLEY F, b. San Francisco, Calif, Oct. 16, 34; m. 59; c. 2. MECHANICAL ENGINEERING. B.S, California, Berkeley, 56, M.S, 58, Ph.D. (mech. eng), 61. Res. engr, California, Berkeley, 55-60; assoc. prof. MECH. ENG, UNIV. WASH, 61-69, PROF, 69- Am. Soc. Mech. Eng. Heat transfer; gas dynamics; thermal stresses. Address: Dept. of Mechanical Engineering, University of Washington, Seattle, WA 98105.

EMERY, DONALD A(LLEN), b. South Berwick, Maine, Dec. 22, 28; m. 56; c. 2. PLANT BREEDING, GENETICS. B.S, New Hampshire, 50, M.S, 55; Ph.D.(agron), Wisconsin, 58. Asst. agron, New Hampshire, 53-55; Wisconsin, 55-58; asst. prof, N.C. STATE UNIV, 58-62, assoc. prof, 62-66, PROF. CROP SCI, 66- Med.C, 51-53. Selection and breeding for disease resistance in bromegrass; relation of seedling character to persistence in red clover; radiation genetics; breeding of peanuts. Address: Dept. of Crop Science, North Carolina State University, Raleigh, NC 27607.

EMERY, DONALD F, b. Amboy, Ill, Dec. 19, 28; m. 52; c. 2. BIOLOGICAL CHEMISTRY. B.A, Knox Col, 50; M.S, Purdue, 52, Ph.D.(biol. chem), 55. Proj. leader food res, GEN. MILLS, INC, 55-62, head mix develop. dept, 62-68, tech. dir. qual. control, 68-70, DIR. TECH. & QUAL. CONTROL SERV, 70- Am. Asn. Cereal Chem; Am. Chem. Soc; Inst. Food Technol. Food product analysis; microbiology; cereal product development; food chemistry; food preservation methods. Address: J.F. Bell Technical Center, General Mills, Inc, 9000 Plymouth Ave, Minneapolis, MN 55427.

EMERY, EDWARD M(ORTIMER), b. N.Y.C, Jan. 23, 26; m. 49; c. 4. PHYSICAL CHEMISTRY. B.S, Colorado, 48, Atomic Energy Comn. fel, 50-52, Ph.D.(chem), 52. Res. engr. res. dept, Servel, Inc, 52-54, sr. res. engr, 54-55; res. chemist, org. chem. div, MONSANTO CO, 55-60, res. proj. leader, 60-64, RES. GROUP LEADER, ORG. CHEM. DIV, 64- U.S.A, 44-45. Am. Chem. Soc; Instrument Soc. Am; Sci. Res. Soc. Am. Gas chromatography; physical analytical chemistry; absorption refrigeration; calorimetry; aliphatic fluorine chemistry. Address: Research Dept, Monsanto Co, 1700 S. Second St, St. Louis, MO 63177.

EMERY, GUY T(RASK), b. Manchester, N.H, May 22, 31; m. 55; c. 2. PHYSICS. A.B, Bowdoin Col, 53; Polaroid fel, Harvard, 53-54 & 56-57, A.M, 54, Ph.D.(physics), 59. Res. assoc. physics, Brookhaven Nat. Lab, 59-61, asst. physicist, 61-62, assoc. physicist, 62-66; assoc. prof. PHYSICS, IND. UNIV, 66-69, PROF, 69- Vis. assoc. prof, State Univ. New York Stony Brook, 65-66. U.S.A, 58-59, 1st Lt. Fel. Am. Phys. Soc; Am. Asn. Physics Teachers. Nuclear structure and spectroscopy; radioactive decay; neutron-capture gamma rays. Address: Dept. of Physics, Indiana University, Bloomington, IN 47405.

EMERY, JERRELL B(EMIS), b. Toledo, Ohio, Aug. 14, 29; m. 51; c. 3. BACTERIOLOGY, VIROLOGY. B.Ed, Toledo, 51, M.Sc, 52; Ph.D, Purdue, 60. Asst. virologist, Children's Hosp. Res. Found, 52-53; res. assoc, Pitman-Moore Co, 53-60, SR. VIROLOGIST, PITMAN-MOORE DIV, DOW CHEM. CO, 60-69, 70-, sr. res. virologist, human health res. & develop. dept, 69. U.S.M.C.R, 47-50. AAAS; Am. Soc. Microbiol; N.Y. Acad. Sci. Animal virology; immunology. Address: Pitman Moore Inc, P.O. Box 344, Washington Crossing, NJ 08560.

EMERY, JUEL F(RANCIS), b. Louisville, Ky, Dec. 9, 27; m; c. 1. ANALYTICAL CHEMISTRY, RADIOCHEMISTRY. B.S, Louisville, 51, M.S, 52. ANAL. CHEMIST, OAK RIDGE NAT. LAB, 52- U.S.A, 46-47. Am. Chem. Soc. Trace element analysis; gravimetric, volumetric, colorimetric techniques; neutron activation analysis; gamma-ray spectrometry. Address: Dept. of Chemistry, Oak Ridge National Lab, Oak Ridge, TN 37849.

EMERY, K(ENNETH) (ORRIS), b. Swift Current, Sask, Can, June 6, 14; U.S. citizen; m. 41; c. 2. MARINE GEOLOGY. B.S, Illinois, 37, scholar, 37-38, fel, 38-39, M.S, 39, fel, 39-40, Ph.D.(geol), 41. Assoc. geologist, Ill. State Geol. Surv, 41-43; marine geologist, div. war res, California, 43-45; asst. prof. geol, Southern California, 45-48, assoc. prof, 48-50, prof, 50-62; MARINE GEOLOGIST, WOODS HOLE OCEANOG. INST, 62- Guggenheim fel, Mid. East, 59. Geologist, U.S. Geol. Surv, 46-60; mem, Navy Res. & Develop. Bd; mem. cmt. paleoecol, Nat. Res. Coun. Del, Pac. Sci. Cong, N.Z, 49, Philippines, 53; oceanog. adv. to govts. of U.S, Israel & Rep. of China; spec. adv, comt. coord. offshore prospecting, Econ. Coun. Asia & Far East, 66-; mem. Nat. Acad. Sci. Comt. Oceanog, 71- Nat. Acad. Sci; Am. Acad. Arts & Sci; fel. Geol. Soc. Am; Soc. Econ. Paleont. & Mineral; Am. Asn. Petrol. Geol. Physiography, sediments and lithology of sea floor off California; general marine geology; marine geology of Bikini and nearby atolls, Guam, Persian Gulf; Dead Sea; eastern Mediterranean Sea; geological history of Atlantic continental shelf and slope; oil regions of continental margin off eastern Asia; structure of continental margin off western Africa. Address: Woods Hole Oceanographic Institution, Woods Hole, MA 02543.

EMERY, ROY S(ALTSMAN), b. Ill, Sept. 22, 28; m. 52; c. 4. ANIMAL NUTRITION, BIOCHEMISTRY. B.S, Colo. Agr. & Mech. Col, 50, M.S, 52; Ph.D.(nutrit, biochem), Mich. State, 55. Asst. DAIRY NUTRIT, MICH. STATE UNIV, 52-55, asst. prof, 55-62, assoc. prof, 62-67, PROF, 67- Am. Feed Mfrs. Award, 61; Sigma Xi Jr. Res. Award, 69. Am. Soc. Microbiol; Am. Inst. Nutrit; Am. Dairy Sci. Asn; Am. Soc. Animal Sci. Biochemistry and physiology of fermentation; digestion and nutrition in ruminants; intermediate and microbial metabolism. Address: Dairy Dept, Michigan State University, East Lansing, MI 48823.

EMERY, THOMAS FRED, b. Ross, Calif, July 31, 31; m. 62. BIOCHEMISTRY. B.S, Calif. Inst. Technol, 53; Du Pont fel, California, Berkeley, 58-59, Ph.D.(biochem), 60. Nat. Sci. Found. fel, Nat. Ctr. Sci. Res, France, 60-61; instr. biochem, sch. med, Yale, 61-62, asst. prof, 62-67, assoc. prof, 67-70; PROF. CHEM, UTAH STATE UNIV, 70- Brown Mem. grant, 61-62; prin. investr, U.S. Pub. Health Serv. res. grant, 62-73. U.S.A, 53-55. AAAS; Am. Chem. Soc; Fedn. Am. Socs. Exp. Biol. Isolation, structure, function and biosynthesis of naturally occurring hydroxamic acids. Address: Dept. of Chemistry, Utah State University, Logan, UT 84321.

EMERY, WILLIAM HENRY P(ERRY), b. Wickford, R.I, Feb. 10, 24; m. 46; c. 2. CYTOLOGY, TAXONOMY. B.S, R.I. State Col, 48; M.S, Connecticut, 50; Ph.D.(cyto-taxon), Texas, 56. Fel. cyto-taxon, SOUTHWEST TEX. STATE COL, 57, instr. BIOL, 57-58, asst. prof, 58-62, assoc. prof, 62-67, PROF, 67- U.S.M.C, 43-46, S/Sgt. AAAS; Am. Bot. Soc. Cyto-taxonomy of range grasses. Address: Dept. of Biology, Southwest Texas State College, San Marcos, TX 78666.

EMERY, W(ILLIS) L(AURENS), b. Salt Lake City, Utah, Nov. 23, 15; m. 41; c. 3. ELECTRICAL ENGINEERING. B.S, Utah, 36; M.S, Iowa State Col, 40, Ph.D.(elec. eng), 47. Instr. elec. eng, Utah, 36-37; sales engr, Campbell-Elsey Co, 37-38; instr. elec. eng, Utah, 38-39; Iowa State Col, 41-43, asst. prof, Iowa State Col, 46-47, radio engr, Naval Res. Lab, Washington, D.C, 43-45; assoc. prof. ELEC. ENG, Utah, 47-50; assoc. prof, UNIV. ILL, URBANA, 50-53, PROF, 53- Vis. prof, Indian Institute of Tech, Kharagpur, 60-62. Civilian with U.S.N, 44. AAAS; Inst. Elec. & Electronics Eng; Am. Phys. Soc; Am. Soc. Eng. Educ. Radiation from electric discharge in gases; microwaves. Address: Dept. of Electrical Engineering, University of Illinois, Urbana, IL 61801.

EMGE, ROBERT G(EORGE), b. San Diego, Calif, Sept. 13, 18; m. 45; c. 1. PLANT PATHOLOGY. B.S, Illinois, 46, Ph.D.(plant path), 50. Exten. plant pathologist, Arkansas, 49-51; PLANT PATHOLOGIST, Ft. Detrick, Md, 51-57; Taft Sanit. Eng. Ctr, U.S. Dept. Agr, Ohio, 57-59; Ft. Detrick, Md, 59-71; EPIPHYTOLOGY RES. LAB, U.S. DEPT. AGR, 71- U.S.A.A.F, 42-45. Am. Phytopath. Soc. Diseases of cereal crops; epiphytology of cereal rusts; host-pathogen relationships; microclimatology; air pollution. Address: 604 Biggs Ave, Frederick, MD 21701.

EMIGH, C(HARLES) ROBERT, b. Seattle, Wash, Apr. 7, 20; m. 46; c. 3. PHYSICS. B.S, Colorado, 42; M.S, Illinois, 48, Ph.D.)physics), 51. Jr. engr, res. & develop, Westinghouse Elec. Corp, 42-44; asst. physics, Illinois, 46-51; MEM. STAFF, LOS ALAMOS SCI. LAB, 51- Ford Found. sr. fel, European Ctr. Nuclear Res, Geneva, 57. Am. Phys. Soc; Soc. Nondestruct. Test; Inst. Elec. & Electronics Eng. Experimental and theoretical physics; design and development of apparatus used in experimental physics; solid state physics; accelerator physics and engineering. Address: 215 Barranca Rd, Los Alamos, NM 87544.

EMIGH, G. DONALD, b. Burley, Idaho, Jan. 21, 11; m. 38; c. 2. MINING, METALLURGY. B.S, Univ. Idaho, 32, M.S, 34; Ph.D.(geol), Univ. Ariz, 56. Mech. engr, Gen. Elec. Co, 36-37; U.S. Vanadium Corp, 37-48; DIR. MINING, MONSANTO CO, ST. LOUIS, 49- Am. Inst. Min, Metall. & Petrol. Eng; Soc. Econ. Geol; Geol. Soc. Am; Am. Inst. Prof. Geol; Can. Inst. Min. & Metall. Mineral industry and exploration. Address: 9334 Big Bend Blvd, Webster Groves, MO 63119.

EMIK, L(EON) OTIS, b. Columbus, Ind, Mar. 19, 13; m. 35; c. 2. STATISTICS, GENETICS. A.B, Stanford, 35; M.A, California, 37, Ph.D.(genetics), 43. Jr. animal husbandman, sheep exp. sta, bur. animal indust, U.S. Dept. Agr, 41-43, animal husbandman, 45-49; asst. chief statistics sect, communicable disease center, U.S. Dept. Health,Educ. & Welfare, 49-56, chief lab. med. & biol. sci, div. air pollution, 57-62, scientist adv, 62-67; RES. SCIENTIST, STATEWIDE AIR POLLUTION RES. CTR, UNIV. CALIF, RIVERSIDE, 67- Mem. vis. staff, air pollution res. center, California, Riverside, 62-67. U.S.N.R, 43-46; U.S.P.H.S, Scientist Dir. Am. Chem. Soc. Resistance genetics; medical biometry; experimental biological effects of air pollution. Address: Statewide Air Pollution Research Center, University of California, Riverside, CA 92502.

EMILIA, DAVID A, b. Danbury, Conn, Feb. 20, 42. GEOPHYSICS, PHYSICS. B.S, Fairfield Univ, 63; Nat. Defense Educ. Act fel, Northeast. Univ, 63-65, M.S, 65; NASA fel, Ore. State Univ, 66-68, Ph.D.(geophys), 68. RES. GEOPHYSICIST, DENVER RES. CTR, MARATHON OIL CO, 69- Soc. Explor. Geophys; Am. Geophys. Union; Am. Inst. Geol; Am. Inst. Physics; Royal Astron. Soc. Potential field and reflection-seismic interpretation theories; plate tectonics and ocean floor spreading. Address: Research Center, Marathon Oil Company, Box 269, Littleton, CO 80122.

EMILIUS (KRAMER), MARY, O.S.F, Biochem, see KRAMER, ELIZABETH, O.S.F.

EMIN, DAVID, b. N.Y.C, Oct. 2, 41; m. 63. SOLID STATE PHYSICS. B.A, Fla. State Univ, 62; NASA trainee, Univ. Pittsburgh, 63-66, Ph.D.(physics), 68. Asst. res. physicist, Univ. Calif, Los Angeles, 68-69; MEM. TECH. STAFF THEORET. PHYSICS, SANDIA LABS, 69- Am. Phys. Soc. Low-mobility electrical transport theory; small-polaron motion; polaron theory. Address: Division 5134, Sandia Labs, Albuquerque, NM 87115.

EMKEN, EDWARD ALLEN, b. Yates City, Ill, Aug. 12, 40; m. 64; c. 2. ORGANIC CHEMISTRY. B.S, Bradley Univ, 63; M.S, Univ. Iowa, 68, Nat. Sci. Found. fel. & Ph.D.(chem), 69. Sci. trainee, NORTH. REGIONAL RES. LABS, U.S. DEPT. AGR, 59-63, asst. res. chemist, 63-64, assoc. res. chemist, 64-69, RES. CHEMIST, 69- Teaching asst, Univ. Iowa, 66-69.

Am. Chem. Soc. Synthesis, characterization and mechanism of aryl carbonium ions; homogeneous catalytic hydrogenation and enzymatic oxidation of lipids; synthesis and metabolism of labeled lipids; methods developed for lipid analysis and separation. Address: 1530 W. Barker, Peoria, IL 61606.

EMLEN, JOHN MERRITT, b. Sacramento, Calif, Jan. 15, 38; m. 61. ECOLOGY. B.A, Wisconsin, 61; Ph.D.(zool), Washington (Seattle), 66. ASST. PROF. BIOL, Univ. Colo, Boulder, 66-68; State Univ. N.Y. Stony Brook, 68-71; IND. UNIV, BLOOMINGTON, 71- Nat. Sci. Found. grant, 67-69. AAAS; Ecol. Soc. Am. Theoretical and behavioral ecology; natural selection; human behavior. Address: Dept. of Zoology, Indiana University, Bloomington, IN 47401.

EMLEN, JOHN T(HOMPSON), JR, b. Phila, Pa, Dec. 28, 08; m. 34; c. 3. ZOOLOGY. B.S, Haverford Col, 31, hon. D.Sc, 70; Ph.D.(ornith), Cornell Univ, 34. Jr. biologist, bur. biol. surv, U.S. Dept. Agr, 34-35; instr. zool. & jr. biologist, exp. sta, California, 35-39, asst. prof. & asst. zoologist, 39-43; res. assoc, Rockefeller Inst, 43-46; assoc. prof. ZOOL, UNIV. WIS, MADISON, 46-50, PROF, 50-, chmn. dept, 51-53, 54-55. Guggenheim fel, Cent. Africa, 53-54; Nat. Sci. Found. res. fel, Africa, 59, Antarctica, 62-64. AAAS; Am. Ornith. Union; Am. Soc. Mammal; Wilson Ornith. Soc.(pres, 60); Ecol. Soc. Am. Population and behavior studies of birds and mammals. Address: Dept. of Zoology, University of Wisconsin, Madison, WI 53706.

EMLEN, STEPHEN THOMPSON, b. Sacramento, Calif, Aug. 21, 40; m. 62; c. 2. ANIMAL BEHAVIOR, ECOLOGY. B.A, Swarthmore Col, 62; M.S, Michigan, 64, Ph.D.(zool), 66. Asst. prof. ZOOL, CORNELL UNIV, 66-70, ASSOC. PROF, 70- AAAS; Animal Behav. Soc; Ecol. Soc. Am; Am. Ornith. Union; Cooper Ornith. Soc; Wilson Ornith. Soc; Am. Soc. Mammal; Brit. Ornith. Union. Orientation and navigation behavior; visual and acoustical communication systems; behavioral ecology of vertebrates. Address: Division of Biological Sciences, Cornell University, Ithaca, NY 14850.

EMLET, HARRY ELSWORTH, JR, b. New Oxford, Pa, Sept. 21, 27; m. 51; c. 2. AERONAUTICAL ENGINEERING. A.B, Princeton, 52. Systs. reviewer automatic data processing, Prudential Ins. Co, 55-56; aeronaut. engr, Martin Co, 56-57; res. analyst weapons systs. anal, Melpar, Inc, 57-58; aeronaut. engr. & proj. leader, ANAL. SERV. INC, 58-65, chief plans br, 65-67, tactical br, 67-70, MGR. TACTICAL DIV. & HEALTH SERV. STUDIES, 70- Summers, asst. aeronaut. lab, Princeton, 48, 50; mem, U.S. Air Force Keese Comt. Air Force Space Plan, 61 & Holzapple Comt. Air Force Space Prog, 62. U.S.A, 45-47. Opers. Res. Soc. Am; Soc. Advan. Med. Systs; Am. Inst. Aeronaut. & Astronaut. Military operational requirements analysis; research and development planning; weapons system analysis; planning techniques; philosophy; health systems analysis. Address: Analytic Services Inc, 5613 Leesburg Pike, Falls Church, VA 22041.

EMLET, LOGAN B(OND), b. New Oxford, Pa, Feb. 8, 13; m. 38; c. 2. CHEMISTRY. B.S, Dickinson Col, 35; Pennsylvania, 35-36; Rutgers & Delaware, 37-38. Supvr. dyestuff, E.I. du Pont de Nemours & Co, N.J, 36-41, explosives, Ill, 41-43, atomic energy, Tenn, 43-45; dir. opers, Monsanto Chem. Co, Tenn, 45-48; exec. dir, Oak Ridge Nat. Lab, Union Carbide Corp, 48-52, supt, Y-12 Plant, 52-53, mgr. prod, atomic energy plants, Oak Ridge & Paducah, Ky, 54-61, exec. v.pres. nuclear div, N.Y, 61-66, PRES. & MANAGING DIR, UNION CARBIDE S.AFRICA INC, 66- Address: 42 Cromartie Rd, Hurlingham, Johannesburg, S.Africa.

EMLING, BERTIN L(EO), b. Erie, Pa, July 9, 05. ORGANIC CHEMISTRY. A.B, St Vincent Col, 31; M.A, Hopkins, 38; Ph.D.(chem), Notre Dame, 41. Instr. ORG. CHEM, ST. VINCENT COL, 37-39, assoc. prof, 40-57, PROF, 57-, mem. bd. dirs, 57-65. Proj. dir, Nat. Coop. Undergrad. Chem. Res. Prog, 48-57. AAAS; Am. Chem. Soc; Soc. Indust. Chem; The Chem. Soc. Sulfonic acid esters; furyl amines; acetylenes; olefins; Schiff bases; polyester resins; autoxidation. Address: Dept. of Chemistry, St. Vincent College, Latrobe, PA 15650.

EMMANOUILIDES, GEORGE CHRISTOS, b. Drama, Greece, Dec. 17, 26; U.S. citizen; m. 59; c. 5. PEDIATRICS, CARDIOLOGY. M.D, Thessaloniki, 51; M.S, California, Los Angeles, 63. Fel. pediat. hemat, Children's Hosp of D.C, 59-60; Ont. Heart Asn. fel, Hosp. for Sick Children, Toronto, Ont, 60-61; U.S. Pub. Health Serv. trainee pediat. cardiol, med. ctr, UNIV. CALIF, LOS ANGELES, 61-63, asst. prof. PEDIAT, SCH. MED, 63-69, ASSOC. PROF, 69- Chief div. pediat. cardiol. & neonatology, Harbor Gen. Hosp, Torrance, Calif, 63-69, div. pediat. cardiol, 69-; mem. coun. congenital heart disease & rheumatic fever, Am. Heart Asn. Med.C, Greek Army, 1st Lt. AAAS; Soc. Pediat. Res; fel. Am. Col. Cardiol; N.Y. Acad. Sci; Am. Acad. Pediat; Am. Heart Asn. Cardiorespiratory adjustments of the newborn; fetal and neonatal physiology; pediatric cardiology. Address: Harbor General Hospital, 1000 W. Carson Ave, Torrance, CA 90509.

EMMANUEL, GEORGE, b. Tanta, Egypt, Sept. 19, 25; U.S. citizen; m. 59; c. 4. CARDIOPULMONARY PHYSIOLOGY. M.D, Nat. Univ. Athens, 52. Mem. faculty cardiopulmonary physiol, Belleview Hosp, Columbia, 57-59; instr. MED, STATE UNIV. N.Y. DOWNSTATE MED. CTR, 59-61, asst. prof, 61-67, ASSOC. PROF, 67- Greek Royal Navy, 44-55. Am. Physiol. Soc; Am. Soc. Clin. Invest; Am. Heart Asn; Harvey Soc. Cardiopulmonary physiology; teachings of medicine. Address: State University of New York Downstate Medical Center, Clarkson Blvd, Brooklyn, NY 11203.

EMMART, EMILY WALCOTT (MRS. CHARLES KINGSLEY TRUEBLOOD), b. Baltimore, Md; m. 49. CYTOLOGY. A.B, Goucher Col, 22; M.A, Hopkins, 24, Ph.D.(cytol, genetics), 30. Assoc. prof. biol, West. Md. Col, 24-28; assoc. entomologist, bur. entom, U.S. Dept. Agr, Mexico City, Mex, 30-31; instr. histol, Hopkins, 32-36; assoc. cytologist, div. pharmacol, Nat. Insts. Health, 36-40, Cytologist, 44-60, lab. exp. path, Nat. Inst. Arthritis & Metab. Diseases, 60-69; HON. FEL. BOT. DEPT, HARVARD, 70-; RES. FEL, HUNT BOT. LIBR, CARNEGIE MELLON UNIV, 70- Res. assoc, Smithsonian Inst, 70-71. Fel. AAAS; Soc. Exp. Biol. & Med; Am. Soc. Pharmacol. & Exp. Therapeut; Am. Soc. Microbiol; Soc. Indust. Microbiol; Am. Rheumatism Asn; Histochem. Soc; Fedn. Am. Soc. Exp. Biol. Cytology of chromosome pattern and induced liver cancer; chemotherapy of tuberculosis; antibiotics in therapy; fluorescence microscopy; cytological localization of antigens; cellular localization of streptococcal

hyaluronidase, glyceraldehyde 3-phosphate dehydrogenase in muscle and kidney and myosin in skeletal muscle and the conduction bundle of the heart; immunochemical studies with the hormone, prolactin and other hormones; historical ethnobotany of Mexico. Address: 7100 Armat Dr, Bethesda, MD 20034.

EMMATTY, DAVY A, b. Trichur, India, Sept. 29, 41; m. 68; c. 1. PLANT PATHOLOGY. B.S, Kerala, 61; M.S, Purdue, 66, Ph.D.(plant path), 68. SR. RES. PLANT PATHOLOGIST, H.J. HEINZ CO, 68- Development of tomatoes resistant to bacterial canker, tobacco mosaic virus, Verticillium, Fusarium race 1 & 2, bacterial spot and bacterial wilt; development of cucumbers resistant to Pseudomonas, cucumber mosaic virus, watermelon mosaic virus and Cladosporium. Address: Agricultural Research Dept, H.J. Heinz Co, 13737 Middleton Pike, Bowling Green, OH 43402.

EMMEL, THOMAS C, b. Inglewood, Calif, May 8, 41. POPULATION BIOLOGY, GENETICS. B.A, Reed Col, 63; Nat. Insts. Health fel. & Ph.D.(pop. biol), Stanford, 67. Lectr, entom, San Jose State Col, 65-66; course coord. & prof. trop. biol, Orgn. Trop. Studies, Inc, Costa Rica, 67-69; ASST. PROF. BIOL. SCI. & ZOOL, UNIV. FLA, 68- Nat. Insts. Health fel, genetics, Texas, Austin, 67-68. AAAS; Soc. Study Evolution; Asn. Trop. Biol; Ecol. Soc. Am; Lepidop. Soc. Population biology of tropical and Nearctic organisms; ecological genetics of natural populations, especially satyrid and nymphalid butterflies and land snails; territorial behavior. Address: Dept. of Biological Sciences & Zoology, University of Florida, Gainesville, FL 32601.

EMMEL, VICTOR M(EYER), b. St. Louis, Mo, Mar. 22, 13; m. 43; c. 4. HISTOLOGY. A.B, Brown, 35, M.S, 37, Ph.D.(biol), 39; M.D, Rochester, 47. Nat. Res. Coun. fel. med. scis, sch. med, Yale, 39-40; instr. ANAT, SCH. MED. & DENT, UNIV. ROCHESTER, 40-47, asst. prof, 48-50, assoc. prof, 50-62, PROF, 62- Intern, Strong Mem. Hosp, Rochester, 47-48. Trustee, Biol. Stain Cmn, secy, 55- Am. Asn. Anat; Soc. Exp. Biol. & Med; Histochem. Soc. Chemistry of sea-water; menstruation in the monkey; cytology and cytochemistry of the kidney and intestine; histopathology of kidney and intestine in vitamin E deficiency. Address: Dept. of Anatomy, University of Rochester, School of Medicine & Dentistry, Rochester, NY 14642.

EMMERICH, CLAUDE L(EON), b. Dusseldorf, Germany, Oct. 13, 22; nat; m. 47; c. 4. PHYSICS. M.E, Cincinnati, 43, fel, 46-49, M.S, 47, D.Sc, 49. Sr. physicist & res. dir, Martin-Hubbard Corp, 49-50; mem. staff, Mass. Inst. Tech, 50-56; head stabilization & navig. br, Norden Div, United Aircraft Corp, Conn, 56-63; prog. mgr, Aerospace Systs. Div, Gen. Precision, Inc, WAYNE, N.J, 63-71, SECT. MGR, KEARFOTT DIV, SINGER CO, 71- U.S.A, 43-46. Electromagnetic and thermal phenomena; navigation instrumentation; inertial navigation; gyroscopics; accelerometers. Address: 15 Hutchinson Ave, Scarsdale, NY 10583.

EMMERICH, W(ERNER) S(IGMUND), b. Duesseldorf, Germany, June 3, 21; nat; m. 53; c. 3. NUCLEAR PHYSICS. B.S, Ohio State, 49, M.S, 50, univ. fel, 51-52, Ph.D.(physics), 53. Res. eng. nuclear physics, WESTINGHOUSE RES. LABS, 53-57, adv. physicist, 57-64, MGR. ARC & PLASMA RES, 64- U.S.A, 42-46. AAAS; fel. Am. Phys. Soc; Combustion Inst; Am. Nuclear Soc. Optical model of atomic nucleus; beta, gamma and neutron spectroscopy; magnetohydrodynamics power generation; plasma physics. Address: 1883 Beulah Rd, Pittsburgh, PA 15235.

EMMERS, RAIMOND, b. Liepaja, Latvia, Apr. 19, 24; U.S. citizen; m. 56. MEDICAL PHYSIOLOGY, NEUROPHYSIOLOGY. B.A, E.Tex. Baptist Col, 53; M.A, North Carolina, 55; Ph.D.(neurophysiol), Syracuse, 58. Res. fel. neurophysiol, Wisconsin, 59-61; asst. prof. PHYSIOL, COLUMBIA UNIV, 61-71, ASSOC. PROF, 71- Nat. Inst. Neurol. Diseases & Blindness res. fel, 58-60, dir. res. proj, inst. grant, 61- Am. Asn. Anat. Neural mechanisms of taste and somesthesia; significance of taste in nutrition; sensory coding in the central nervous system. Address: Dept. of Physiology, Columbia University College of Physicians & Surgeons, New York, NY 10032.

EMMERSON, JOHN LYNN, b. Princeton, Ind, Nov. 21, 33; m. 57; c. 2. PHARMACOLOGY, TOXICOLOGY. B.S, Purdue, 58, Nat. Sci. Found. fel, 59-61, M.S, 60, Ph.D.(pharmacol), 62. Sr. pharmacologist, Eli Lilly & Co, 61-65; assoc. prof. toxicol, Purdue, 65-66; sr. toxicologist, ELI LILLY & CO, 66-67, HEAD METAB. DEPT, TOXICOL. DIV, 67- U.S.N, 51-54. AAAS; Am. Soc. Pharmacol. & Exp. Therapeut; Soc. Toxicol; Am. Pharmaceut. Asn. Biochemical mechanisms and metabolic aspects of drug toxicity. Address: Lilly Toxicology Labs, Eli Lilly & Co, Greenfield, IN 46140.

EMMERT, FRED H(ERBERT), b. Germany, May 5, 21; nat; m. 46; c. 1. PLANT NUTRITION. B.S, Massachusetts, 48, M.S, 49; Ph.D, Ohio State, 52; Oak Ridge Inst. Nuclear Studies, 56. Asst. prof. PLANT NUTRIT, UNIV. CONN, 52-57, assoc. prof, 57-61, PROF, 61- U.S.A, 42-46. Am. Soc. Plant Physiol; Scand. Soc. Plant Physiol. Function and behavior of nutrient ions in plant tissues. Address: Dept. of Plant Science, University of Connecticut, Storrs, CT 06268.

EMMERT, GELBERT A, b. Merced, Calif, June 2, 38; m. 64; c. 1. PLASMA PHYSICS. B.S, Univ. Calif, Berkeley, 61; M.S, Rensselaer Polytech. Inst, 64; Ph.D.(physics), Stevens Inst. Technol, 68. Anal. Engr, Energy Conversion Systs, United Aircraft Corp, 61-64; ASST. PROF. NUCLEAR ENG, UNIV. WIS, MADISON, 68- Am. Phys. Soc. Theoretical plasma physics; waves and instabilities in magnetically confined plasmas; guiding-center theory; controlled thermonuclear fusion. Address: Dept. of Nuclear Engineering, Engineering Research Bldg, University of Wisconsin, Madison, WI 53706.

EMMERT, LESLIE A(RTHUR), b. Kasson, Minn, Nov. 14, 16; m. 44; c. 2. ANATOMY. B.A, Carleton Col, 39; M.Ph, Wisconsin, 43, fel, 46-48, Ph.D. (zool), 53. Teaching asst. zool, Carleton Col, 39-41; Wisconsin, 41-46; instr. ANAT, Stritch Sch. Med, LOYOLA UNIV. CHICAGO, 48-51, assoc, 51-58, ASST. PROF. GRAD. SCH, 58- AAAS. Physiology of reproduction of cotton rat and other animals; morphology and histochemistry of fetal membranes. Address: Graduate School, Loyola University of Chicago, 820 N. Michigan Ave, Chicago, IL 60611.

EMMERT, R(ICHARD) E(UGENE), b. Iowa City, Iowa, Feb. 23, 29; m. 49; c. 3. CHEMICAL ENGINEERING. B.S, Iowa, 51; M.Ch.E, Delaware, 52,

Nat. Sci. Found. fel, 52, 54, Ph.D.(chem. eng), 54. Res. engr. chem. eng, E.I. DU PONT DE NEMOURS & CO, 54-58, res. proj. supvr, 58-61, sr. res. engr, 61, res. supvr, 61-63, mgr. indust. develop, 63-64, area supvr. mfg, 64-66, mfg. supt, 66-67, asst. plant mgr, 67-69, MGR. ENG. TECHNOL. & MAT. RES, 69- Lectr, Pennsylvania, 59- Chem.C, U.S.A, 54-56. Am. Inst. Chem. Eng; Am. Chem. Soc. Reaction kinetics; polymerization technology; mass transfer; gas absorption. Address: Engineering Technology & Materials Research, Experimental Station, E.I. du Pont de Nemours & Co, Wilmington, DE 19898.

EMMETT, JOHN L, b. Ogden, Utah, Aug. 3, 03; m. 32; c. 4. UROLOGY. A.B, Utah, 26; M.D, Northwestern, 30; M.S, Minnesota, 34. Intern, Passavant Mem. Hosp, Chicago, 30; fel, MAYO FOUND, UNIV. MINN, 31-34, first asst. UROL, 34-35, consult, 35, instr, 35-41, asst. prof, 41-45, assoc. prof, 45-53, PROF, 53- Dipl, Am. Bd. Urol, 37. Am. Med. Asn; Am. Urol. Asn; Am. Asn. Genito-Urinary Surg; Int. Soc. Urol; Brit. Asn. Urol. Surg; hon. mem. Mex. Soc. Urol; hon. mem. Chilean Soc. Urol. Address: Mayo Clinic, 200 First St. S.W, Rochester, MN 55902.

EMMETT, P(AUL) H(UGH), b. Portland, Ore, Sept. 22, 00; m. 30. PHYSICAL CHEMISTRY. B.S, Ore. State Col, 22, hon. D.Sc, 39; fel, Calif. Inst. Tech, 22-25, Ph.D.(phys. chem), 25; hon. Dr, Lyon, 64. Instr, Ore. State Col, 25-26; from asst. to sr. chemist, fixed nitrogen res. lab, bur. chem. & soils, U.S. Dept. Agr, 26-37; prof. chem. eng, Hopkins, 37-44; sr. fel, Mellon Inst, 44-55; W.R. Grace prof. chem, Johns Hopkins Univ, 55-71; INDUST, GOVT. & ACAD. CONSULT. & LECTR, 71- Lectr, George Washington, 27-29, 31-32, 33-34, 35-36; div. chief, Manhattan Proj, Columbia, 43-44. Mem. comt. contact catalysis, Nat. Res. Coun, 37-42; Coun. Sci. Res, Madrid, Spain, 64. With Off. Sci. Res. & Develop, 44. Catalyst Club Phila. Award, 70. Nat. Acad. Sci; Am. Chem. Soc.(Pittsburgh Award, 53, Kendall Award, 58, Md. sect. Award, 70). Contact catalysis; adsorption of gases on solids; heterogeneous gas-solid equilibria. Address: 600 Waverly Ct, Apt. 402, Milwaukie, OR 97222.

EMMI, SALVATORE, b. Syracuse, N.Y, May 6, 29; m. 62; c. 3. ORGANIC CHEMISTRY. B.S, Le Moyne Col, 51; Ph.D.(org. chem), State Univ. N.Y. Col. Forestry, 65. Anal. chemist, Syracuse Univ. Res. Corp, 58-60; res. chemist, PHOTOG. & REPROGRAPHIC DIV, GAF CORP, 64-70, SUPVR. NEW IMAGING PROCESSES RES. DEPT, 70- Am. Chem. Soc. Photographic chemistry; photochemistry; photopolymer systems; photoresist systems; ultramicroanalysis; polymer chemistry; biochemistry and organic synthesis; life processes, especially the role of catalysis in organic synthesis, the chemistry of aging and immunological mechanisms. Address: 23 St. John Ave, Binghamton, NY 13905.

EMMICK, ROBERT D, b. Holland, Mich, Aug. 13, 20; m. 45. ORGANIC CHEMISTRY. A.B, Hope Col, 42; Ph.D.(org. chem), Illinois, 46. Asst, Illinois, 42-44, Nat. Defense Res. Comt. & Off. Rubber Res. Contracts, 44-46; res. chemist, electrochem. dept, E.I. DU PONT DE NEMOURS & CO, 46-57, patent chemist, 57-59, supvr. patent sect, 59-62, patent agent, 62-63, sr. patent chemist, TEXTILE FIBERS DEPT, 63-66, PATENT SUPVR, 66- Am. Chem. Soc. Polymerization; nonwoven fabrics. Address: 39 Shellburne, Wilmington, DE 19803.

EMMONS, ARDATH HENRY, b. Albert Lea, Minn, Mar. 12, 24; m. 44; c. 5. NUCLEAR ENGINEERING. B.S, Dubuque, 48; M.S, Michigan, 54, Ph.D.(nuclear sci), 60. Jr. chemist, Oak Ridge Nat. Lab, 49-51; assoc. radiation safety officer, Michigan, 51-55, lab. supvr, Phoenix Lab, 55-60; dir. res. reactor, UNIV. MO-COLUMBIA, 60-70, V.PRES. RES, 70-, PROF. NUCLEAR ENG, 64- U.S.A, 43-46, Sgt. AAAS; Health Physics Soc; Am. Nuclear Soc; Am. Soc. Eng. Educ. Wavelength dependence of radiation effects; radiation and reactor applications; laboratory and reactor design; science and research administration. Address: 309 University Hall, University of Missouri-Columbia, Columbia, MO 65201.

EMMONS, D(OUGLAS) B(YRON), b. Can, May, 23, 30; m. 53; c. 4. AGRICULTURE, DAIRY INDUSTRY. B.S.A, Ont. Agr. Col, 52; M.S, Wisconsin, 53, Ph.D.(dairy indust), 57. Instr, Wisconsin, 55-57, asst. prof, 57-58; RES. OFFICER, CAN. DEPT. AGR, 58- Am. Dairy Sci. Asn.(Pfizer Paul-Lewis Award, 63); Agr. Inst. Can; Can. Inst. Food Technol. Cottage and cheddar cheese. Address: Food Research Institute, Canada Dept. of Agriculture, Ottawa, Ont, Can.

EMMONS, HAMILTON, b. London, Eng, Dec. 30, 30; U.S. citizen; m. 59; c. 3. OPERATIONS RESEARCH. A.B, Harvard Col, 52; M.S, Minnesota, 58; M.S, N.Y. Univ, 62; Ph.D.(opers. res), Hopkins, 68. Mem. tech. staff, Bell Tel. Labs, 58-64; ASST. PROF. OPERS. RES, CORNELL UNIV, 68- U.S.A, 54-56. AAAS; Inst. Mgt. Sci; Opers. Res. Soc. Am. Applied probability theory; inventory theory; scheduling theory; semi-Markov decision theory. Address: Dept. of Operations Research, Upson Hall, Cornell University, Ithaca, NY 14850.

EMMONS, HOWARD W(ILSON), b. Morristown, N.J, Aug. 30, 12; m. 35; c. 3. MECHANICAL ENGINEERING. M.E, Stevens Inst. Tech, 33, M.S, 35, hon. D.Eng, 63; Sc.D.(eng), Harvard, 38. Res. engr, Westinghouse Elec. Co, 37-39; asst. prof. MECH. ENG, Pennsylvania, 39-40; from asst. prof. to assoc. prof, HARVARD, 40-50, PROF, 50- Fulbright-Guggenheim fel, Eng, 52-53; Hunsaker vis. prof, Mass. Inst. Tech, 57-58. Consult, Pratt & Whitney Aircraft, 40-; Army Ord. Ballistics Res. Lab, Aberdeen Proving Ground, Md, 40-; Naval Ord. Lab, 46-52; mem. space sci. & technol. panel, Off. Sci. & Technol, 60-71; Gov. adv. comt. on Sci. & Technol, 65-71; chmn. Mass. Sci. & Technol. Found, 70- With Nat. Adv. Comt. Aeronaut, 44; Adv. Bd. Naval Ord. Test Sta, 49-55. Nat. Acad. Sci; Nat. Acad. Eng; AAAS; Am. Phys. Soc; Am. Soc. Mech. Eng; Math. Asn. Am; Am. Acad. Arts & Sci. Aerodynamics of combustion; supersonic aerodynamics; numerical solution of differential equations; fundamentals of gas dynamics. Address: 308 Pierce Hall, Harvard University, Cambridge, MA 02138.

EMMONS, LYMAN RANDLETT, b. Lawrence, Mass, June 14, 27; m. 71; c. 2. BIOLOGY. B.S, Trinity Col.(Conn), 51; M.A, Virginia, 59, Ph.D.(biol), 61. Master, Episocopal High Sch, Va, 51-57; asst. prof. BIOL, WASHINGTON & LEE UNIV, 61-65, assoc. prof, 65-69, PROF, 69- U.S.A, 45-47. Genetics Soc. Am; Am. Soc. Human Genetics; Am. Soc. Zool. Mammalian cytogenetics; biochemical and microbial genetics. Address: Dept. of Biology, Washington & Lee University, Lexington, VA 24450.

EMMONS, R(ICHARD) C(ONRAD), b. Winnipeg, Man, Can, Aug. 28, 98; nat; m. GEOLOGY. B.A, British Columbia, 19, M.A, 20; Ph.D.(geol), Wisconsin, 24. Instr. GEOL, Chicago, 24; UNIV. WIS, MADISON, 25, asst. prof, 26-30, assoc. prof, 30-37, PROF, 37- Geologist, Geol. Surv. Can, 20-28. Fel. Geol. Soc. Am.(v.pres, 45); fel. Mineral. Soc. Am.(pres, 44). Mineralogy; optical mineralogy; petrology; geology of the original Huronian area; the Ontario Pre-Cambrian; five axis universal stage; optical properties of feldspars; silicosis; geology of central Wisconsin; selected petrogenic aspects of plagioclase; steel penetration in foundry sand; genesis of geosynclinal granites; granites by recrystallization; gem stones. Address: Science Hall, University of Wisconsin, Madison, WI 53706.

EMMONS, WILLIAM D(AVID), b. Minneapolis, Minn, Nov. 18, 24; m. 49; c. 3. ORGANIC CHEMISTRY. B.S, Minnesota, 47; Ph.D.(chem), Illinois, 51. Sr. chemist, ROHM & HAAS CO, 51-52, group leader org. chem, 52-57, lab. head, 57-61, RES. SUPVR, 61- U.S.A.A.F, 43-46. Ed, Org. Syntheses, 61- U.S.A.A.F, 43-46. Am. Chem. Soc; Brit. Chem. Soc. Peracids; small ring heterocycles; organophosphorous chemistry; polymers and surface coatings. Address: 1411 Holcomb Rd, Huntingdon Valley, PA 19006.

EMON, DONALD E(DWARD), b. Seattle, Wash, Dec. 26, 37; m. 58; c. 3. NUCLEAR SCIENCE & ENGINEERING. B.S, Washington (Seattle), 60; Atomic Energy Comn. fel, Florida, 60-61, M.S, 61; Atomic Energy Comn. fels, Rensselaer Polytech, 62-64, Ph.D.(nuclear eng), 65. Eng. trainee, U.S. Naval Shipyard, Wash, 58; draftsman, Boeing Airplane Co, 59-60, assoc. engr, 60; student engr. adv. reactor eng. prog, Knolls Atomic Power Lab, Gen. Elec. Co, N.Y, 61-62, design physicist, 63; asst. prof. nuclear eng, Tex. A&M Univ, 64-67; nuclear engr, DIV. RES. & DEVELOP. TECHNOL, ATOMIC ENERGY COMN, 67-68, SR. REACTOR ENGR, 68- Am. Nuclear Soc; Am. Soc. Eng. Educ; Am. Soc. Mech. Eng. Buckling dependence of the extrapolation length; nuclear reactor research and design, especially neutron transport theory and thermal stress analysis. Address: P.O. Box 152, Germantown, MD 20767.

EMORI, RICHARD I(CHIRO), b. Tokyo, Japan, May 12, 24; m. 65; c. 1. APPLIED MECHANICS, MECHANICAL ENGINEERING. B.S, Tokyo, 49, Dr.Eng, 66; M.S, Michigan, 52 & 61. Stress analyst, Clark Equip. Co, 52-53; tech. rep. automotive, Toyota Motor Co, 54-55; proj. engr, Gen. Motors Corp, 55-61, res. engr. defense res. lab, 61-64; res. assoc. mech. eng, Tokyo, 64-66; staff engr, Int. Bus. Mach. Corp, 66-67; ASST. PROF. ENG. SYSTS, UNIV. CALIF, LOS ANGELES, 67- Lectr, Detroit, 57-58; Karlsruhe Tech, 66. Am. Soc. Mech. Eng; Soc. Automotive Eng; Japan Soc. Mech. Eng. Automotive transportation safety engineering; off-road locomotion and soil mechanics; experimental engineering by scale models; vehicle collision. Address: School of Engineering, University of California, Los Angeles, CA 90024.

EMPTAGE, MICHAEL ROLLINS, b. Jersey City, N.J, June 10, 39; m. 69. CHEMICAL PHYSICS. A.B, Middlebury Col, 60; Woodrow Wilson fel, Harvard, 60-61, Procter & Gamble fel, 61-62, Nat. Sci. Found. fel, 62-64, Ph.D.(chem), 65. NATO fel, Brussels, 64-65; res. assoc. CHEM, Brown, 65-66; ASST. PROF, Univ. Maryland, 66-68; SOUTH. ILL. UNIV, 68- AAAS; Am. Phys. Soc. Microwave spectroscopy; statistical mechanics of transport phenomena; chemical reactions in imperfect gases. Address: Dept. of Chemistry, Southern Illinois University, Carbondale, IL 62901.

EMRICH, GROVER H(ARRY), b. Englewood, N.J, Apr. 9, 29; m. 52; c. 3. GEOLOGY. B.S, Franklin & Marshall Col, 52; M.S, Fla. State, 57; Ph.D. (geol), Illinois, 62. Asst. geol, Fla. State, 54-55, 55-56; field surveyor, Fla. Geol. Surv, 55; asst, Ill. Geol. Surv, 56-58, asst. geologist, 58-63; ground water geologist, State Dept. Health, Pa, 63-71; MGR. ENVIRON. RESOURCES DEPT, A.W. MARTIN ASSOCS, 71- Fel. Geol. Soc. Am; Am. Water Resources Asn; Water Pollution Control Fedn. Ground water pollution and geology; stratigraphy and sedimentation; areal and ground water geology of Pennsylvania, Illinois and the Upper Mississippi Valley; development and management of programs for land disposal of wastes; ground water development. Address: A.W. Martin Associates, 900 W. Valley Forge Rd, King of Prussia, PA 19406.

EMRICH, RAYMOND J(AY), b. Denver, Colo, Nov. 30, 17; m. 42; c. 2. PHYSICS. A.B, Princeton, 38, A.M. & Ph.D.(physics), 46; Cambridge, 38-39; Cornell, 39-40. Asst, Nat. Defense Research Cmt, Princeton, 41-45; asst. prof. PHYSICS, LEHIGH UNIV, 46-49, assoc. prof, 49-55, PROF, 55-, DIR. FLUIDS RES. LAB, 48-, chmn. dept. physics, univ, 58-68. Vis. scientist, Ernst Mach Inst, Ger, 68; Nat. Acad. Sci. exchange vis, Siberia, 70-71; mem. comt. sci. & arts, Franklin Inst. AAAS; fel. Am. Phys. Soc.(secy, 58-65); Am. Soc. Eng. Educ; Am. Asn. Physics Teachers. Fluid dynamics; small scale and short time motions; fluctuations in non-equilibrium processes; small particle deposit and transport; shock tube. Address: Dept. of Physics, Lehigh University, Bethlehem, PA 18015.

EMRICH, WILLIAM OSCAR, b. Pittsburgh, Pa, Jan. 30, 42. ORGANIC CHEMISTRY. B.S, Bucknell, 63; M.S, Carnegie-Mellon Univ, 66, Ph.D.(chem), 68. SR. RES. CHEMIST, T.R. EVANS RES. CTR, DIAMOND SHAMROCK CORP, 67- AAAS; Am. Chem. Soc. Polyelectrolytes; wastewater treatment; flocculation, coagulation and sedimentation; organic synthesis; market research; new products; agricultural and biological chemistry. Address: 3 Meadowlawn Dr, Suite 4, Mentor, OH 44060.

EMRICK, DONALD D(AY), b. Waynesfield, Ohio, Apr. 3, 29. ORGANIC CHEMISTRY. B.S, Miami (Ohio), 51; M.S, Purdue, 54, Ph.D.(chem), 56. Asst, Purdue, 51-55; sr. chemist, Standard Oil Co.(Ohio), 55-56, tech. specialist, 56-61, RES. ASSOC, 61-65; NAT. CASH REGISTER CO, 65- Am. Chem. Soc. Organic sulfur chemistry; sterochemistry of ring compounds; lubricants; polymers; electronic absorption spectra; rare earths. Address: 4240 Lesher Dr, Kettering, OH 45429.

EMRICK, E(DWIN) ROY, b. Pittsburgh, Pa, Mar. 1, 29; m. 54; c. 2. ANALYTICAL CHEMISTRY. B.S, Duquesne, 51; Ph.D.(anal. chem), Pittsburgh, 59. Sr. chemist, Pratt & Whitney Aircraft Div, United Aircraft Corp, 59-61, proj. chemist, 61-63; ANAL. CHEMIST, NALCO CHEM. CO, 63-

Chem.C, 51-53, 1st Lt. Am. Chem. Soc; fel. Am. Inst. Chem. Polymer characterization; gel chromatography; thin-layer chromatography. Address: Nalco Chemical Co, 6216 W. 66th Pl, Chicago, IL 60638.

EMRICK, ROY M, b. Akron, Ohio, May 6, 32; m. 58; c. 3. SOLID STATE PHYSICS. A.B, Cornell, 54; M.S, Illinois, 58, Ph.D.(physics), 60. Res. assoc. PHYSICS, Illinois, 60; ASSOC. PROF, UNIV. ARIZ, 60- Am. Phys. Soc. Study of properties of lattice defects in solids by means of high temperature, high pressure and Mössbauer experiments. Address: Dept. of Physics, University of Arizona, Tucson, AZ 85721.

EMSHWILLER, MACLELLAN, b. Grand Rapids, Mich, Oct. 27, 27; m. 59. PHYSICS. B.S, Michigan, 52, M.S, 53; Ph.D.(physics), California, Berkeley, 59. MEM. TECH. STAFF PHYSICS, BELL TEL. LABS, 59- Instr, eve. sch, Fairleigh Dickinson, 60- U.S.C.G, 45-46; U.S.N, 46-48. AAAS; Am. Phys. Soc; Inst. Elec. & Electronics Eng. Signal processing techniques using optical techniques; nuclear magnetic resonance. Address: Bell Telephone Labs, Whippany, NJ 07981.

EMSLIE, A(LFRED) G(EORGE), b. Aberdeen, Scotland, Nov. 28, 07; nat. 41; m. 33; c. 2. PHYSICS. M.A, Aberdeen, 28; Commonwealth fellow, Cornell, 30-33, Ph.D.(physics), 33; Carnegie fel, Cambridge, 33-37, Ph.D.(physics), 38. Asst. physics, Aberdeen, 28-30; instr, Williams Col, 37-42, asst. prof, 42-43; staff mem, radiation lab, Mass. Inst. Tech, 43-46; res. lectr. electronics, Harvard, 46-47; assoc. prof. physics, Williams Col, 47-48, prof, 48-51; head physics group, ARTHUR D. LITTLE, INC, 51-61, STAFF ASSOC, 61-, consult, 46-50. Am. Phys. Soc. Classical theoretical physics; electromagnetic waves; underwater sound; physical optics; heat radiation and transmission; exotic inertial sensing; hydrodynamics of viscous fluids. Address: 14 Prospect Ave, Scituate, MA 02066.

EMSLIE, R(ONALD) F(RANK), b. Winnipeg, Man, Can, Feb. 27, 32; m. 60; c. 3. GEOLOGY. B.Sc, Manitoba, 56, M.Sc, 58; Ph.D, Northwestern, 61. Geologist, Geol. Surv. Can, 60-65; vis. asst. prof. geol, Queen's Univ.(Ont), 65-66, GEOLOGIST, GEOL. SURV. CAN, 66- Geol. Soc. Am. Igneous and metamorphic petrology. Address: Geological Survey of Canada, 601 Booth St, Ottawa 4, Ont, Can.

EMSON, H(ARRY) E(DMUND), b. Swinton, Lancashire, Eng, Nov. 16, 27; m. 53; c. 2. PATHOLOGY. B.A, Oxford, 48, B.M. & B.Ch, 52, M.A, 53; M.D, Saskatchewan, 59. Intern, Manchester Royal Infirmary, Eng, 52, res. clin. pathologist, 52-53; pathologist, Brit. Mil. Hosp, Germany, 53-55; registr. path, Birmingham Accident Hosp, 55-56; res, St. Paul's Hosp, 56-57; asst. res, univ. hosp, UNIV. SASK, 57-58, asst. pathologist, 58-60, LECTR. PATH, COL. MED, 58-; DIR. LABS, ST. PAUL'S HOSP, 60- Dipl, Royal Col. Physicians & Surg. Can, 58. R.A.M.C, 53-55, Capt; Regimental Med. Officer, R.C.A.M.C. Can. Med. Asn; Can. Asn. Path.(past pres); Brit. Med. Asn; Brit. Asn. Clin. Path. Diagnostic human pathology; genetic aspects and chromosomal structure in human neoplasia. Address: St. Paul's Hospital, Saskatoon, Sask, Can.

ENABNIT, ROBERT S(TERLING), b. Mason City, Iowa, Oct. 10, 19; m. 44; c. 3. PHYSICS, CHEMISTRY. B.A, Iowa, 41; California, Los Angeles; Southern California. Develop. engr. GOODYEAR TIRE & RUBBER CO, Calif, 41-43, res. physicist, RES. DIV, AKRON, 43-58, HEAD APPL. PHYSICS & ELECTRONICS SECT, 58- Electronic instrumentation; tire dynamics; noise and vibration; dynamic stability of vehicular motion; electrical properties of materials; transient wave-form phenomena; dielectric heating; ultrasonics; simulation. Address: 3125 Morewood Rd, Akron, OH 44313.

ENCE, ELMARS, b. Riga, Latvia, Oct. 16, 08; nat; m. 49. METALLURGY. M.S, Latvia, 34. Asst. prof, Latvia, 34-44; res. chemist, Heinkel Aircraft Works, Germany, 44-45; lectr. chem. & pharm. & head dept, Baltic Univ, Germany, 46-49; res. assoc, col. eng, N.Y. Univ, 51-57, res. scientist, 57-60; specialist res. engr, Repub. Aviation Corp, 60-65; ENGR. SPECIALIST, METALS RES. LABS, OLIN MATHEISON CHEM. CORP, 65- Inst. Mining, Metall. & Petrol. Eng; Am. Soc. Metals. Physical metallurgy; corrosion; x-ray crystallography. Address: Metals Research Labs, Olin Mathieson Chemical Corp, 91 Shelton Ave, New Haven, CT 06504.

ENCK, FRANK D(URRELL), b. Ephrata, Pa, Sept. 3, 26; m. 51; c. 1. PHYSICS. B.S, Franklin & Marshall Col, 50; M.S, Maryland, 52, Ph.D, 57. Asst, Maryland, 50-54; from instr. to PROF. PHYSICS & CHMN. DEPT, FRANKLIN & MARSHALL COL, 54- Instr, Wyomissing Polytech, 50. Physicist, U.S. Naval Ord. Lab, Md, 51. Sig.C, U.S.A, 44-46, T/Sgt. Am. Phys. Soc; Am. Asn. Physics Teachers; sr. mem. Inst. Elec. & Electronics Eng. Solid state physics; elastic constants, thermal expansion, compressibility, and superconductivity. Address: Dept. of Physics, Franklin & Marshall College, Lancaster, PA 17603.

ENDAHL, GERALD L(EROY), b. Lane, S.Dak, Dec. 16, 24; m. 54; c. 2. BIOCHEMISTRY. B.A, Augustana Col, 49; M.A, South Dakota, 53; Ph.D.(biochem), Oklahoma, 59. Res. assoc, Okla. Med. Res. Found, 53-57; res. fel, med. sch, Alabama, 57-60; asst. prof. physiol. chem. & surg, Ohio State Univ, 60-66, ASSOC. PROF, 66-70; PATH, UNIV. SOUTH. CALIF, 70- U.S.A, 45-46. AAAS; Am. Med. Asn; Am. Chem. Soc. Enzymes of carbohydrate metabolism; metabolism of steroid hormones; hormones of gastric acid secretion. Address: Dept. of Pathology, University of Southern California, 2825 S. Hope St, Los Angeles, CA 90007.

ENDE, NORMAN, b. Petersburg, Va, Apr. 5, 24; m. 48; c. 1. PATHOLOGY. B.S, Richmond, 45; M.D, Med. Col. Va, 47. Intern, Bronx Hosp, N.Y, 48; res. path. & surg, Vet. Admin. Hosp, New Orleans, La, 49-52, pathologist, Houston, Tex, 54-55, chief path, Fresno, Calif, 55-58; asst. clin. prof, Vanderbilt Univ, 58-61, asst. prof, 61-64, assoc. prof, 64-67; dir. path. labs, Grady Mem. Hosp, 67-69, chief path, 69-70; PROF. PATH. & CHIEF CLIN. PATH, N.J. COL. MED. & DENT, 70- Instr, col. med, Baylor Univ, 54-55, asst. prof, 55; chief, lab. serv. path, Vet. Admin. Hosp, Nashville, 58-67; Nat. Insts. Health res. grants, 61-; prof. path, Emory Univ, 67-69. Dipl, Am. Bd. Clin. Path, 53; Am. Bd. Anat. Path, 54. U.S.N, 52-54, Res, 54-65, Comdr. Soc. Nuclear Med; fel. Am. Col. Physicians; fel. Col. Am. Path; Am. Soc. Exp. Path; Am. Asn. Path. & Bact; fel. Am. Soc. Clin. Path. Mast cell, fibrinolysis and the hyper-coagulable state; carcinoma of the prostate and thromboangiitis obliterans; starvation; transplantation. Address: New Jersey College of Medicine & Dentistry, 100 Bergen St, Newark, NJ 07103.

ENDER, CLARENCE D, b. Hokah, Minn, May 20, 14; m. 50; c. 2. ORGANIC CHEMISTRY. B.Ch.E, Minnesota, 35. Engr, North. States Power Co, Wis, 36; chemist, Hercules Powder Co, Del, 36-39, mem. staff, tech. serv, Mich, 39-42, Del, 42, supvr. prod, Wis, 42-43, res. DEL, 43-47, mgr. res, 47-52, res. ctr, 52-55, dir. develop, 56-57, prod. sales mgr, 57-61, GOVT. LIAISON, HERCULES INC, 62- U.S.A.R, 35-41. AAAS; Am. Chem. Soc; Commercial Chem. Develop. Asn; Nat. Agr. Chem. Asn; Am. Ord. Asn. Bulk organic, inorganic and chemurgic chemicals; agricultural pesticides. Address: Hercules Inc, Wilmington, DE 19899.

ENDER, HANS H(ENRY), b. Vienna, Austria, Mar. 2, 96; U.S. citizen; m. 23. ORGANIC CHEMISTRY, PHYSICS. Ph.D.(chem), Vienna, 21. Asst. chem, Vienna, 20-21; Berlin, 21-22; plant mgr. & chief chemist, L. Marx Varnishes, Austria, 23-48; chief chemist, Vogel Varnishes, 48-50; Bacigalupo Co, Argentina, 50-53; res. assoc. chem, Polytech. Inst. Brooklyn, 53-56; chemist. res. & develop, silicones div, Union Carbide Corp, 56-66; res. chemist, Gaylord Assocs, 66-70; CONSULT, 70- Am. Chem. Soc; N.Y. Acad. Sci. Paints and varnishes; organo-silicon chemistry. Address: 3140 S. Ocean Dr, Hallandale, FL 33009.

ENDERBY, CHARLES ELDRED, b. Chicago, Ill, Nov. 15, 34; m. 57; c. 3. PHYSICS. B.S, Illinois, 57, M.S, 58, Ph.D.(elec. eng), 61. Asst. prof. elec. eng, Illinois, 60-61; mem. tech. staff, Gen. Elec. Co, 61-65; v.pres, ELECTRO OPTICS ASSOCS, 66-69, PRES, 69- Inst. Elec. & Electronics Eng. Optical modulation; millimeter wave generation; gas laser design. Address: 1852 Edgewood Dr, Palo Alto, CA 94303.

ENDERS, ALLEN C(OFFIN), b. Wooster, Ohio, Aug. 5, 28; m. 50; c. 4. ZOOLOGY. A.B, Swarthmore Col, 50; A.M, Harvard, 52, Ph.D, 55. Teaching fel. biol, Harvard, 52-53; Brandeis, 53-54; res. assoc, Rice, 54-55, asst. prof, 55-60, assoc. prof, 60-63; SCH. MED, WASH. UNIV, 63-69, PROF. ANAT, 69- Consult. Nat. Insts. Health, 64-; mem. anat. test comt, Nat. Bd. Med. Exam. AAAS; Am. Asn. Anat; Soc. Study Reproduction; Am. Soc. Cell Biol; Histochem. Soc; Soc. Develop. Biol. Fine structure of placenta and female reproductive tract; mechanisms of implantation. Address: Dept. of Anatomy, Washington University School of Medicine, St. Louis, MO 63110.

ENDERS, JOHN F(RANKLIN), b. West Hartford, Conn, Feb. 10, 97; m. 27; 51; c. 2. MICROBIOLOGY. A.B, Yale, 19, hon. D.Sc, 53; M.A, Harvard, 22, Ph.D.(bact, immunol), 30, hon. D.Sc, 56; hon. D.Sc, Trinity Col, 55, Northwestern, 56, Western Reserve, 58; Tufts, 60, Jefferson Med. Col, 62, Pennsylvania, 64, Univ. Ibadan, 68; hon. LL.D, Tulane, 58; D.L.H, Hartford, 60. Asst. BACT. & IMMUNOL, HARVARD MED. SCH, 29-30, instr, 30-35, asst. prof, 35-42, assoc. prof, 42-56, prof, CHILDREN'S HOSP, 56-62, UNIV. PROF, 62-67, EMER. UNIV. PROF, 67-, CHIEF RES. DIV. INFECTIOUS DISEASES, CHILDREN'S MED. CTR, 47- Civilian consult, Secy. War, 42-46; U.S. Pub. Health Serv. Mem, cmn, viral infections, Armed Forces Epidemiol. Bd; sci. adv. bd. of consults, Armed Forces Inst. Path; adv. panel on virus disease, WHO; correspondent, Acad. Sci. Inst. France, 71. For. mem, Royal Soc, 67. Passano Award, 53; Kimble res. award methodology, 54; Nobel Prize, med. & physiol, 54; Dyer Lectr. Award, U.S. Pub. Health Serv, 54; Chapin Medal, 55; Wilson Medal, 55; Bruce Mem. Lectr. Award, 56; Modern Med. Award, 56; Cameron Prize, Edinburgh, 60; Howard T. Ricketts Award, Chicago, 62; Diesel Gold Medal & Robert-Koch Medal, Ger, 62; sci. achievement award, Am. Med. Asn, 63; Presidential Medal of Freedom, 63; Commander, Repub. Upper Volta, 65. U.S.N.R, 17-18, Lt. Nat. Acad. Sci; AAAS; Soc. Exp. Biol. & Med.(ed, Virology); Am. Soc. Microbiol; Am. Philos. Soc; hon. mem. Brit. Soc. Gen. Microbiol; hon. mem. Harvey Soc; hon. fel. Am. Col. Surg; Am. Asn. Immunol.(ed, jour); Am. Pub. Health Asn.(Lasker Award, 54); assoc. Am. Acad. Pediat; fel. Am. Acad. Arts & Sci; hon. fel. Col. Am. Path; N.Y. Acad. Sci; cor. mem. Fr. Acad. Med; Royal Acad. Med, Belg; Leopold Carol Ger. Acad. Natural Sci. Virus disease of man and animal. Address: Children's Hospital, 300 Longwood Ave, Boston, MA 02115.

ENDERS, ROBERT K(ENDALL), b. Essex, Iowa, Sept. 22, 99; m. 23; c. 2. BIOLOGY. A.B, Michigan, 25, Hinsdale fel, 25-27, Ph.D.(zool), 27. Asst. prof. biol, Union Col.(N.Y), 27-28, prof, Mo. Valley Col, 28-30; Nat. Res. Coun. fel. zool, 30-32; asst. prof, Swarthmore Col, 32-38, from assoc. prof. to prof, 38-70, chmn. dept, 49-66; RETIRED. Chief instr, adv. intel. sch, Off. Strategic Servs, 43, chief schs. & training, Southeast Asia Command, 44; Fulbright fel, Pakistan, 52-53; res. fel, Acad. Natural Sci. Phila, 37-; dir, Rocky Mt. Biol. Lab, 59-68, pres, 69- Consult, Pac. Sci. Bd, 49-60; systematics panel, Nat. Sci. Found, 58-59, facility panel, 61-67. Trustee, Biol. Abstracts, 56-61, pres, 61-62; Sci. Invest. in Micronesia, 49. Leader, field trips, Panama, 29-71. U.S.A, 18-19. AAAS; Am. Soc. Mammal; Am. Asn. Anat; Am. Soc. Zool; Am. Paleont. Soc; Wildlife Soc; Soc. Syst. Zool. Physiology of reproduction in mustelids and other nondomesticated mammals; mammals of Central America. Address: 311 Elm Ave, Swarthmore, PA 19081.

ENDERSON, JAMES H, b. Sioux City, Iowa, Nov. 3, 36; m. 57; c. 1. ZOOLOGY. B.S. & M.S, Univ. Ill, 59; Ph.D.(zool), Univ. Wyo, 62. Asst. prof. ZOOL, COLO. COL, 62-68, ASSOC. PROF, 68- Nat. Sci. Found. faculty fel. systs. & ecol, Cornell Univ, 69-70. AAAS; Am. Inst. Biol. Sci; Am. Ornith. Union; Wilson Ornith. Soc; Cooper Ornith. Soc. Raptor ecology. Address: Dept. of Biology, Colorado College, Colorado Springs, CO 80903.

ENDERTON, HERBERT BRUCE, b. Hawaii, Apr. 15, 36; m. 61; c. 2. MATHEMATICAL LOGIC. B.S, Stanford, 58; M.A, Harvard, 59, Nat. Sci. Found. fel, 58-61, Ph.D.(math), 62. Instr. MATH, Mass. Inst. Tech, 62-64; asst. prof, UNIV. CALIF, Berkeley, 64-68, ASST. PROF. IN RESIDENCE, LOS ANGELES, & ASST. ED, J. SYMBOLIC LOGIC, 68- Am. Math. Soc; Asn. Symbolic Logic. Recursive function theory; definability theory; models of analysis; computational complexity. Address: Dept. of Mathematics, University of California, Los Angeles, CA 90024.

ENDICOTT, CLARENCE JAMES, b. Stoughton, Wis, May 6, 23; m. 46; c. 3. PHARMACEUTICAL CHEMISTRY. B.S, Wisconsin, 49, M.S, 50. Res. pharmacist, ABBOTT LABS, 50-56, group leader pharmaceut. res. & develop, 56-61, dept. mgr. pharmaceut. res, 61-63, dir. pharmaceut. res. & develop, 63-66, dir. hosp. prod. res. & develop, 66-68, sci. dir. hosp. prod. div, 68-71, V.PRES. SCI. AFFAIRS, 71- U.S.A, 42-46. AAAS; Am. Chem. Soc; Am. Pharmaceut. Asn. Tablet coatings; sustained release preparations; stability and combination compatibilities of drugs. Address: Abbott Labs, North Chicago, IL 60064.

ENDICOTT, JOHN F, b. Eugene, Ore, Aug. 1, 32. INORGANIC CHEMISTRY. B.A, Reed Col, 57; Ph.D.(phys. chem), Hopkins, 61. Res. assoc. inorg. chem, Stanford, 61-63; asst. prof. Boston Univ, 63-69; ASSOC. PROF. CHEM, WAYNE STATE UNIV, 69- U.S.A, 52-55, Sgt. Am. Chem. Soc; Am. Phys. Soc. Mechanisms of inorganic reactions; electron transfer reactions. Address: Dept. of Chemistry, Wayne State University, Detroit, MI 48202.

ENDICOTT, KENNETH M(ILO), b. Canon City, Colo, June 6, 16; m. 39; c. 3. PATHOLOGY. A.B, Colorado, 36, M.D, 39. Intern, U.S. Marine Hosp, Wash, 39-40; asst. surgeon, U.S. Pub. Health Serv, 40-42, div. path, Nat. Insts. Health, 42-52, sci. dir, div. res. grants, 52-55; chief, cancer chemother, Nat. Serv. Cent, 55-58; assoc. dir, Nat. Insts. Health, 58-60, dir, Nat. Cancer Inst, 60-69, DIR. BUR. HEALTH MANPOWER EDUC, NAT. INSTS. HEALTH, 69- Extern, St. Luke's Hosp, Denver, 38; Mt. Airy Sanitarium, 38-39; mem. res. proj, Med. Ctr. Fed. Prisoners, Mo, 42. AAAS; Biol. Stain Cmn; fel. Am. Med. Asn; Am. Asn. Path. & Bact; Am. Soc. Exp. Path; Soc. Exp. Biol. & Med. Pathologic physiology of blood-forming tissues; pathology of nutritional diseases; application of tracers in pathology; pathology of radiation injury; pathology of toxic substances; research administration. Address: Bureau of Health Manpower Education, National Institutes of Health, Bethesda, MD 20014.

ENDLICH, ROY M, b. Akron, Ohio, June 22, 24; m. 49; c. 3. METEOROLOGY. Akron, 41-42, 46; M.S, Chicago, 48; Mass. Inst. Tech, 53-58. Proj. scientist jet stream res, Air Force Cambridge Res. Labs, 51-60; HEAD WEATHER DYNAMICS GROUP, STANFORD RES. INST, 60- U.S.A.A.F, 42-46, 1st Lt. AAAS; Am. Geophys. Union; Am. Meteorol. Soc; Sci. Res. Soc. Am. Address: L-2104, Stanford Research Institute, Menlo Park, CA 94025.

ENDO, B(URTON) Y(OSHIAKI), b. Castroville, Calif, Feb. 5, 26; m. 54; c. 2. NEMATOLOGY. B.S, Iowa State, 51; M.S, N.C. State Col, 55, Ph.D.(plant path), 58. Asst. hort, N.C. State Col, 53-55; asst. nematologist, nematol. sect, U.S. DEPT. AGR, 55-58, nematologist, NEMATOL. INVESTS, W.Tenn. Exp. Sta, Tennessee, 58-63, RES. NEMATOLOGIST, PLANT INDUST. STA, 63- U.S.A, 51-53. AAAS; Am. Phytopath. Soc; Soc. Nematol.(secy, 68-71); Am. Inst. Biol. Sci. Host-parasite relations of nematode infected plants; plant disease resistance. Address: Nematology Investigations, Crops Protection Research Branch, Agricultural Research Service, Beltsville, MD 20705.

ENDO, R(OBERT) M(INORU), b. Mountain View, Calif, Mar. 30, 25; m. 50; c. 3. PLANT PATHOLOGY. B.S, Rutgers Univ, 50; M.S, Univ. Ill, 52, Ph.D.(plant path), 54. Res. asst. plant path, dept. hort, Univ. Ill, 51-54, agent sect. cereal crops & diseases, field crops res. br, agr. res. serv, U.S. Dept. Agr, 54-56, plant pathologist, 56-58; asst. prof. PLANT PATH. & asst. plant pathologist, UNIV. CALIF, Los Angeles, 59-61, RIVERSIDE, 61-65, assoc. prof. & assoc. plant pathologist, 65-71, PROF. & PLANT PATHOLOGIST, 71- U.S.A, 44-46. Am. Phytopath. Soc; Mycol. Soc. Am; Am. Inst. Biol. Sci. Diseases of turf grass and vegetables; yellow dwarf disease of cereals. Address: Dept. of Plant Pathology, University of California, Riverside, CA 92507.

ENDOW, NOBORU, b. Portland, Ore, Aug. 25, 22; m. 50; c. 4. PHYSICAL CHEMISTRY. B.S, Univ. Utah, 44; M.A, Univ. Wis, 48. CHEMIST, Gen. Elec. Co, 48-54; STANFORD RES. INST, 54- U.S.A, 44-46. AAAS; Am. Chem. Soc; fel. Am. Inst. Chem. Reactions of gases on clean metal films in ultrahigh vacuum; kinetics of fast reactions; photochemistry of nitrogen dioxide; atomic oxygen reactions; air pollution chemistry; corrosion of stainless steels and copper; fuel cells. Address: Stanford Research Institute, 333 Ravenswood Ave, Menlo Park, CA 94025.

ENDRES, GERARD F(RANCIS), b. New York, N.Y, Nov. 21, 28. ORGANIC CHEMISTRY. B.A, Hofstra Col, 50; Ph.D.(chem), Polytech. Inst. Brooklyn, 54. Res. assoc. chem, Polytech. Inst. Brooklyn, 54; org. chemist, res. lab, Gen. Elec. Co, 56-62; RES. ASSOC. CHEM, CORNELL UNIV, 62- U.S. Pub. Health Serv. spec. fel, 63-65, res. career develop. award, Nat. Heart Inst, 67- AAAS; Am. Chem. Soc; The Chem. Soc. Polymerization mechanisms; cationic vinyl polymerization; biopolymers; mechanism of blood clotting. Address: Dept. of Chemistry, Cornell University, Ithaca, NY 14850.

ENDRES, JOSEPH GEORGE, b. Chicago, Ill, Aug. 15, 32; m. 59; c. 3. CHEMICAL ENGINEERING, FOOD CHEMISTRY. B.S, Illinois, 55, Ph.D.(food chem), 61. Res. chemist, fat & oil chem, food res. div, Armour & Co, 61-62, sect. head, 62-64, asst. mgr, 64-70; V.PRES. CORP. RES. & ENG, CONTINENTAL COFFEE CO, 70- U.S.N, 55-58, Lt. Am. Oil Chemists' Soc; Inst. Food Technol; Am. Asn. Cereal Chem. Application of lipid chemistry to the analysis, synthesis and commercial use of fats and oils; application of food science to the food service industry. Address: 1440 Thornwood Dr, Downers Grove, IL 60515.

ENDRES, LELAND SANDER, b. Akron, Ohio, Mar. 31, 36; m. 59; c. 4. ORGANIC & PHYSICAL CHEMISTRY. A.B, Middlebury Col, 58; M.A, Univ. Ore, 63; Ph.D.(chem), Univ. Ariz, 67. Instr. & res. assoc. chem, Univ. Nebr, 66-67; sr. res. chemist, Minn. Mining & Mfg. Co, 67-69; ASST. PROF. CHEM, CALIF. STATE POLYTECH. COL, SAN LUIS OBISPO, 69- U.S.A, 58-60, Capt. Am. Chem. Soc. Reaction kinetics; carbonium ions; small ring heterocyclics; fluorocarbons. Address: 1351 Fernwood Dr, San Luis Obispo, CA 93401.

ENDRES, PAUL F(RANK), b. Peoria, Ill, Feb. 10, 42. PHYSICAL CHEMISTRY. B.S, Bradley Univ, 63; Ph.D.(chem), Univ. Rochester, 67. Fel. CHEM, Univ. Rochester, 67-69; ASST. PROF, BOWLING GREEN STATE UNIV, 69- Am. Phys. Soc. Energy transfer in molecular collisions; molecular beams. Address: Dept. of Chemistry, Bowling Green State University, Bowling Green, OH 43403.

ENDREY, ANDREW LASZLO, b. Hodmezovasarhely, Hungary, July 26, 27; U.S. citizen. ORGANIC CHEMISTRY. B.S, Western Reserve, 52, M.S, 54, Sherwin-Williams fel. & Ph.D.(org. chem), 56. Res. chemist, E.I. du Pont de Nemours & Co, 56-59; sr. res. chemist, Diamond Alkali Co, 59-61; consumer prod. div, UNION CARBIDE CORP, 61-68, PROJ. SCIENTIST, CHEM. & PLASTICS DIV, 68- AAAS; Am. Chem. Soc. Relative reactivity in organic chemistry; polymer synthesis and characterization. Address: Union Carbide Corp, P.O. Box 65, Tarrytown, NY 10591.

ENDRIZZI, JOHN E(DWIN), b. Wilburton, Okla, July 28, 23; m. 55; c. 5. CYTOGENETICS. B.S, Texas A&M, 49, M.S, 51; Ph.D.(bot), Maryland, 55. Asst. prof. cotton cytogenetics, Texas Agr. Exp. Sta, 55-63; PROF. PLANT BREEDING, UNIV. ARIZ, 63-, head dept, 63-71. Cotton genetics res. award, Nat. Cotton Coun. Am, 69. U.S.A, 43-46. AAAS; Am. Genetic Asn; Genetics Soc. Am; Soc. Study Evolution; Genetics Soc. Can; Am. Inst. Biol. Sci. Cytogenetics of Gossypium. Address: Dept. of Plant Breeding, College of Agriculture, University of Arizona, Tucson, AZ 85721.

ENDSLEY, L(OUIS) E(UGENE), JR, b. Lafayette, Ind, May 24, 12; m. 40; c. 3. MECHANICAL ENGINEERING. B.S, Purdue, 34, M.S, 36. Asst. instr. mech. eng, Purdue, 34-36; mech. eng, TEXACO, INC, 36-54, asst. to mgr. tech. servs, 54-56, dir, 56-58, asst. mgr, 58-60, planning dir. eng, 60-69, MGR. SCI. PLANNING, RES. & TECH. DEPT, 69- Mech. engr, Wright Field, U.S. Army Air Force, 39; consult to Asst. Secy. Defense, 50-54, 55-63. U.S.A, 42-46, Res, 34-64, Col. Sci. Res. Soc. Am; Soc. Automotive Eng. Petroleum fuels and lubricants; research and development. Address: Research & Technical Dept, Research Center, Texaco Inc, P.O. Box 509, Beacon, NY 12508.

ENELOW, ALLEN J(AY), b. Pittsburgh, Pa, Jan. 15, 22; m. 46; c. 6. PSYCHIATRY. A.B, West Virginia, 42; M.D, Louisville, 44. Fel, Menninger Found, 47-49; clin. instr. PSYCHIAT, sch. med, California, Los Angeles, 53-56, asst. clin. prof, 56-59; assoc. clin. prof, sch. med, Univ. South. Calif, 60-64, prof, 64-68; PROF. & CHMN. DEPT, COL. HUMAN MED, MICH. STATE UNIV, 68- Chief, psychosom. serv, Los Angeles County Gen. Hosp, 64-67. Dipl, Am. Bd. Psychiat. & Neurol. Med.C, 45-47, Capt. Am. Med. Asn; Am. Psychiat. Asn; Am. Psychoanal. Asn; fel. Am. Col. Physicians. Psychosomatic disorders; psychotherapy; postgraduate medical education. Address: Dept. of Psychiatry, College of Human Medicine, Michigan State University, East Lansing, MI 48823.

ENEMARK, JOHN HENRY, b. Lamberton, Minn, Aug. 24, 40; m. 62; c. 2. INORGANIC CHEMISTRY. B.A, St. Olaf Col, 62; Nat. Sci. Found. fel, Harvard, 63-65, A.M, 64, Nat. Insts. Health fel, 65-66, Ph.D.(chem), 66. Res. assoc. CHEM, Northwestern, 66-68; ASST. PROF. UNIV. ARIZ, 68- Nat. Sci. Found. res. fel, Northwest. Univ, 66-67. Am. Chem. Soc; Am. Crystallog. Asn. Transition metal compounds; x-ray crystallography. Address: Dept. of Chemistry, University of Arizona, Tucson, AZ 85721.

ENENSTEIN, NORMAN H(ARRY), b. Los Angeles, Calif, Nov. 2, 23; m. 43; c. 2. ELECTRICAL ENGINEERING. A.B, California, Los Angeles, 46; Cole scholar & M.S, Calif. Inst. Technol, 47, Ph.D.(elec. eng, physics), 49. Res. physicist, Hughes Aircraft Co, 49-54, proj. mgr, anti-airborne defense tactical data syst, U.S. Army, 54-56; v.pres. & dir. engr, Electro-Pulse, Inc, 56-58; dir. tactical systs. lab, Litton Industs, 58-62; mgr. systs. div, GROUND SYSTS. GROUP, HUGHES AIRCRAFT CO, 62-70, MGR. DATA PROCESSING PRODS. DIV, 70- U.S.A.A.F, 43-45, 2nd Lt. Inst. Elec. & Electronics Eng. Management of large scale military programs in the fields of data processing, radar, communications and weapon systems. Address: Data Processing Products Division, Ground Systems Group, Hughes Aircraft Co, Fullerton, CA 92643.

ENERSON, DANIEL M(ILTON), b. Glen Ellyn, Ill, Apr. 12, 22; m. 43; c. 4. SURGERY. B.S, Univ. Chicago, 44, M.D, 46. Resident SURG, Univ. Chicago Clins, 49-54, instr, 54-55; asst. prof, State Univ. N.Y. Upstate Med. Ctr, 56-62; SCH. MED, UNIV. PITTSBURGH, 63-66, CLIN. ASST. PROF, 66-; CHIEF SURG. RES, VET. ADMIN. HOSP, PITTSBURGH, 62-, chief cardiopulmonary surg, 62-68. Asst. attend, Univ. Hosp, Syracuse, 56-62; attend. surgeon, Vet. Admin. Hosp, Syracuse, 57-62; asst. surgeon, Syracuse Mem. Hosp, 57-62; assoc. attend. in thoracicovascular surg, West. Pa. Hosp, Pittsburgh, 66-; asst. in thoracic & cardiovasc. surg, Allegheny Valley Hosp, Natrona Heights, 66- Res. grants, Nat. Insts. Health, 57-66; Am. Heart Asn, 59-61. Dipl, Am. Bd. Surg, 56; Am. Bd. Thoracic Surg, 62. U.S.A, 43-46; U.S.P.H.S, 47-49, Maj. Am. Med. Asn; fel. Am. Col. Surg; Asn. Am. Med. Cols; Soc. Thoracic Surg. Effects of hypothermia and hypoxia on metabolism of kidney and other tissues in the maintenance of cell electrolyte gradients and cell size; energy balance in febrile surgical patients. Address: Veterans Administration Hospital, University Dr. C, Pittsburgh, PA 15240.

ENESCO, HILDEGARD ESPER, b. Seattle, Wash, June 16, 36; m. 64. CELL BIOLOGY. B.A, Reed Col, 58; Woodrow Wilson fel, Columbia, 58-59, M.A, 59, Nat. Sci. Found. fel, 59-62, Ph.D.(zool), 62. U.S. Pub. Health Serv. fel. anat, McGill, 62-63; Shirley Farr fel. biol, Montreal, 63-64; res. assoc. biochem, Allan Mem. Inst, McGill Univ, 64-67, lectr. psychiat, 67-68; asst. prof, SIR GEORGE WILLIAMS UNIV, 68-69, ASSOC. PROF. BIOL. SCI, 69- AAAS; Am. Soc. Zool; Am. Soc. Cell Biol; Genetics Soc. Am; Soc. Develop. Biol. Nucleic acids in embryology, cell function. Address: Dept. of Biological Sciences, Sir George Williams University, Montreal 107, Que, Can.

ENESCO, MIRCEA AARON, b. Roman, Romania, Apr. 20, 18; Can. citizen; m. 64; c. 1. BIOLOGY, ENDOCRINOLOGY. M.D, Med. Sch. Jassy, Romania, 42; Lic. ès Sci, Univ. Cleremont-Ferrand, 50; Ph.D.(histol), McGill Univ, 57. Resident, Verdun Gen. Hosp, Montreal, 52-54; Notre Dame Hosp, Montreal, 54-56; clin. fel. endocrinol, Mass. Gen. Hosp, 57-58; res. assoc. histol, McGill Univ, 58-63; MEM. DEPT. MED, SACRED HEART HOSP, 64-; CONSULT. INTERNAL MED, INST. ALBERT-PREVOST, 64- Consult, Verdun Gen. Hosp, 58-; Bellechasse Hosp, 60-66. Fel. Royal Col. Physicians & Surgeons Can, 57, cert. internal med, 57. Romanian Army, 42-44, Med. Off. Can. Med. Asn; Can. Fedn. Biol. Sci; N.Y. Acad. Sci; Asn. French Speaking Physiol; Geront. Soc; Int. Soc. Psychoneuroendocrinology. Growth and cell number; psychoendocrinology; biological gerontology, aging and cell population. Address: 3300 Falaise, Apt. 621, Montreal 301, Que, Can.

ENFIELD, FRANKLIN D, b. Woolstock, Iowa, Dec. 26, 33; m. 55; c. 3. ANIMAL BREEDING, GENETICS. B.S, Iowa State, 55; M.S, Okla. State, 57; Ph.D.(animal breeding), Minnesota, Minneapolis, 60. Asst. prof. animal breeding, UNIV. MINN, Minneapolis, 60-65, assoc. prof. animal sci, 65-66, GENETICS, 66-70, PROF, ST. PAUL, 70-; DIR. GRAD. STUDIES IN GENETICS, 71- Genetics Soc. Am; Am. Soc. Animal Sci. Effects of linkage and level of dominance in quantitative traits. Address: Dept. of Genetics & Cell Biology, College of Biological Sciences, University of Minnesota, St. Paul, MN 55101.

ENG, CHEE PING, b. Hong Kong, Oct. 29, 35; Can. citizen; m. 66. IMMUNOLOGY. B.Sc, Ottawa (Ont), 59; M.S.A, Toronto, 61; Ph.D.(microbiol), Minnesota, 66. Fel, Can. Nat. Cancer Inst, 66-67; lectr. tumor immunol, Univ. Sask, 67-69, asst. prof, 69-70; CHIEF, TUMOR IMMUNOL. SECT, DEPT. VIROL. & CELL BIOL, BIONETICS RES. LABS, 70- Address: 5510 Nicholson Lane, Bionetics Research Lab, Kensington, MD 20795.

ENG, LAWRENCE F, b. Spokane, Wash, Feb. 19, 31; m. 58; c. 4. BIOCHEMISTRY. B.S, Washington State, 52; M.S, Stanford, 54, Ph.D.(chem), 62. Res. scientist biochem. toxicol, aero med. lab, Wright Air Develop. Ctr, 54-57; asst. biochem, Stanford, 58-61; CHEMIST, PALO ALTO VET. ADMIN. HOSP, 61-; SR. SCIENTIST PATH, SCH. MED, STANFORD UNIV, 70- U.S.A.F, 52-57, Res, 57-, Capt. AAAS; Am. Chem. Soc; Int. Soc. Neurochem; Am. Soc. Neurochem; Soc. Neurosci; Am. Inst. Chem; Am. Soc. Biol. Chem. Clinical chemistry; biochemistry, development, and lipid chemistry of the brain; investigation of myelinating diseases of the central nervous system. Address: Lab. Service, Veterans Administration Hospital, Palo Alto, CA 94304.

ENG, SVERRE T(HORSTEIN), b. Skaanland, Norway, July 30, 28; U.S. citizen; m. 57; c. 3. SOLID STATE ELECTRONICS, ELECTROOPTICS. M.S, Chalmers Univ. Technol, Sweden, 53, Ph.D.(appl. physics), 67; Stanford Univ, 57-58; Howard Hughes fel, Univ. Calif, Irvine, 65-67. Res. engr, res. lab. electronics, Chalmers Univ. Technol, Sweden, 53-56; mem. tech. staff, semiconductor div, Hughes Aircraft Co, 56-57; asst. electronics, Stanford Univ, 57-58; sect. head. microwave & optical semiconductor physics & electronics, res. labs, Hughes Aircraft Co, 58-62, dept. head, 62-67; staff scientist & mem. tech. staff, Autonetics Div, N.Am. Rockwell Corp, 67-71; PROF. MICROWAVE & ELECTROOPTIC ELECTRONICS & HEAD INST. ELECTRONIC MEASUREMENTS, CHALMERS UNIV. TECHNOL, SWEDEN, 71- Norwegian Army, 48-49. Am. Phys. Soc; Inst. Elec. & Electronics Eng; Sci. Res. Soc. Am; Optical Soc. Am. Microwave semiconductor devices, especially high frequency transistors, parametric diodes, mixers, tunnel and backward diodes, integrated electronics, measurements and application studies; infrared detection; semiconductor and CO_2 lasers; superheterodyne instrumentation; laser radar. Address: Institute of Electronic Measurements, Chalmers University of Technology, Gibraltargatan 5 G, Gothenburg S, Sweden.

ENGBRING, NORMAN H, b. Milwaukee, Wis, Mar. 30, 25; m. 50; c. 3. MEDICINE. M.D, Marquette, 51. Intern, Milwaukee County Gen. Hosp, 51-52, resident, 52-55; instr. MED, SCH. MED, MARQUETTE UNIV, 55-59, asst. prof, 59-65, ASSOC. PROF, 65- Fel. metab, Milwaukee County Gen. Hosp, 55-58, dir. radioisotope lab, 58-67, chief metab. serv, 65- AAAS; Am. Fedn. Clin. Res; Am. Diabetes Asn; Endocrine Soc; Am. Med. Asn; Am. Col. Physicians. Endocrine and metabolic disorders. Address: 8700 W. Wisconsin Ave, Milwaukee, WI 53226.

ENGDAHL, RICHARD BOTT, b. Elgin, Ill, Apr. 16, 14; m. 40; c. 2. MECHANICAL ENGINEERING. B.S, Bucknell, 36; M.S, Illinois, 38. Asst, Illinois, 36-39, instr. mech. eng, 39-40; res. engr, Battelle Mem. Inst, 41-45, asst. supvr, 45-46, supvr. fuels, 47-50, chief fuels & air pollution div, 50-57, thermal eng. div, 57-58, staff eng, 58-65, FEL. ENVIRON. RES, BATTELLE-COLUMBUS LABS, 65- Fel. AAAS; Am. Indust. Hyg. Asn; Am. Soc. Mech. Eng; Am. Soc. Heat, Refrig. & Air-Conditioning Eng. Combustion of pulverized coal; steam ejector performance; gas turbine locomotive; meter for flow of pulverized coal suspended in air; air pollution; heat pump; environmental control; incineration. Address: Battelle-Columbus Labs, 505 King Ave, Columbus, OH 43201.

ENGE, HARALD ANTON, b. Fauske, Norway, Sept. 28, 20; nat; m. 47; c. 3. NUCLEAR PHYSICS. Eng. Dipl, Tech. Univ. Norway, 47; Dr. Philos, Bergen, 54. Lab. engr, Tech. Univ. Norway, 47; res. assoc. & lectr, Bergen, 48-55; instr. PHYSICS, MASS. INST. TECHNOL, 55-56, asst. prof, 56-59, assoc. prof, 59-63, PROF, 63- Co-founder & chmn, Deltaray Corp, 69- Fel. Am. Phys. Soc; Europ. Phys. Soc; Norweg. Phys. Soc. Low energy nuclear physics; nuclear energy levels studies through charged particle reactions. Address: Room 58-015, Massachusetts Institute of Technology, Cambridge, MA 02139.

ENGEBRECHT, RONALD HENRY, b. Oregon City, Ore, Jan. 18, 34; m. 54; c. 3. ORGANIC CHEMISTRY. B.S, Oregon State, 56, Nat. Sci. Found. fel. & Ph.D.(org. chem), 64; M.A, Mich. State, 59; Nat. Sci. Found. fel, Michigan, 59-60. Instr. high schs, Ore, 56-59; asst. prof. cancer res, Oregon State, 63-65; SR. RES. CHEMIST, EASTMAN KODAK CO, 65- Am. Chem. Soc. Organic photochemistry; synthesis of light-sensitive polymers; application of light-sensitive polymers for photoresists. Address: Research Lab, Eastman Kodak Co, Rochester, NY 14650.

ENGEBRETSON, GORDON R(OY), b. Milwaukee, Wis, June 15, 36; m. 58; c. 3. PHYSICAL CHEMISTRY. B.S, Carroll Col.(Wis), 58; Ph.D.(phys. chem), Iowa State, 62. Asst. crystallog. res, Ames Lab, 58-62; res. chemist, Sinclair Res, Inc, Ill, 62-66; asst. dir. dept. environ. health, Am. Med. Asn, 66-69; DEP. DIR, FLA. REGIONAL MED. PROG, 69- Adj. asst. prof, Univ. S.Fla; lectr. crystallog. U.S.A.R, 56-62, S/Sgt. Am. Chem. Soc; Am. Crystallog. Asn. Physico-chemical and structural investigations of solid state materials, solid state catalysts, and catalytic processes via modern instrumental techniques; health planning, program development and evaluation. Address: Florida Regional Medical Program, Suite 307, One Davis Blvd, Tampa, FL 33606.

ENGEL, A(DOLPH) JAMES, b. Erie, Pa, Oct. 13, 29; m. 52; c. 3. INORGANIC & ANALYTICAL CHEMISTRY. B.A, Columbia Union Col, 51; M.S, Maryland, 55. Lab. asst, Columbia Union Col, 48-51; asst, Maryland, 51-54; chemist, fertilizer sect, U.S. Dept. Agr, 54-56; instr. CHEM, Union Col, 56-58; Wis. State, Eau Claire, 58-64; ASST. PROF, COLUMBIA UNION COL, 64- Am. Chem. Soc. Micro methods of determination of metals; instrumental methods, including polarography. Address: 417 Boyd Ave, Takoma Park, MD 20012.

ENGEL, ALBERT E(DWARD) J(OHN), b. St. Louis, Mo, June 16, 16; m. 44; c. 2. GEOLOGY, GEOCHEMISTRY. B.A, Missouri, 38, M.A, 39; M.A, Princeton, 41, Ph.D.(geol), 42. Instr, Missouri, 38-40, asst. prof. geol, 42; GEOLOGIST, U.S. GEOL. SURV, 42-; asst. prof. GEOL, Calif. Inst. Tech, 48-49, assoc. prof, 49-54, PROF, 54-58; UNIV. CALIF, SAN DIEGO & SCRIPPS INST. OCEANOG, 58- Nat. Acad. Sci; fel. AAAS; Am. Acad. Arts & Sci; Geol. Soc. Am; Am. Geophys. Union; Am. Mineral. Soc. Crustal evolution. Address: Division of Geological Research, Scripps Institution of Oceanography, University of California at San Diego, P.O. Box 109, La Jolla, CA 92037.

ENGEL, ALFRED J, b. Munich, Ger, Mar. 30, 27; U.S. citizen; m. 53; c. 4. CHEMICAL ENGINEERING. B.Ch.E, Cornell, 52; Du Pont fel, Wisconsin, 56-57, Ph.D.(chem. eng), 61. Engr. petrochem, Calif. Res. Corp, 52-55; instr. CHEM. ENG, Wisconsin, 57-59; asst. prof, PA. STATE UNIV, 59-66, assoc. prof, 66-71, PROF, 71- Consult, Socony Mobil Oil Co, N.Y, 64. Mil. Intel, 45-47, Sgt. Am. Inst. Chem. Eng; Am. Chem. Soc. Chemical reaction kinetics and mass transfer; air pollution control and administration. Address: Dept. of Chemical Engineering, Pennsylvania State University, University Park, PA 16802.

ENGEL, ANDREW G, b. Budapest, Hungary, July 12, 30; U.S. Citizen; m. 58; c. 3. NEUROPATHOLOGY, BIOCHEMISTRY. B.S, McGill, 53, M.D, 55. Resident internal med. & neurol, Mayo Clin, 56-57, 60-62; clin. assoc. neurol, Nat. Inst. Neurol. Diseases & Blindness, 58-59; spec. fel. neuropath, Col. Physicians & Surgeons, Columbia, 62-65; instr. NEUROL, MAYO GRAD. SCH. MED, UNIV. MINN, 66-67, ASSOC. PROF, 67- Consult, Mayo Clin, 65- U.S.P.H.S, 57-59, Sr. Asst. Surg. Am. Soc. Cell Biol. Experimental neuropathology; muscle biochemistry; biochemical and ultrastructural studies of mechanisms of weakness in human and experimentally induced myopathies. Address: Dept. of Neurology, Mayo Clinic, Rochester, MN 55901.

ENGEL, CHARLES R(OBERT), b. Vienna, Austria, Jan. 28, 22; m. 51; c. 4. ORGANIC CHEMISTRY. B.S, Univ. Grenoble, 41; Chem.Eng, Swiss Fed. Inst. Tech, 47, Lunge scholar, 47-49, Ciba scholar, 49-50, D.Sc.(org. chem), 51; D.Sc, Univ. Paris, 70. Asst. prof. med. res, Univ. West. Ont, 51-54, assoc. prof, 54-58, hon. spec. lectr, 51-58; PROF. CHEM, LAVAL UNIV, 58- Can. Life Ins. Off. Asn. Med. fel, 52-58; ed, Steroids, 63-; vis. prof, Inst. Natural Chem. Substances, Nat. Ctr. Sci. Res, France, 66-67. Am. Chem. Soc; fel. Chem. Inst. Can; Can. Biochem. Soc; Swiss Chem. Soc; The Chem. Soc; Chem. Soc. France. Synthetic organic chemistry; steroids and related products; carbanionic rearrangements; chemical endocrinology; biologically active natural products. Address: Dept. of Chemistry, Laval University, Quebec 10, Que, Can.

ENGEL, ERIC, b. Geneva, Switz, Oct. 12, 25; m. 50; c. 3. MEDICINE. B.S, Geneva, 47, M.D, 51, Ph.D, 58. Instr. internal med, Geneva Univ. Hosp, 58-60; MED, Harvard Med. Sch, 60-63; asst. prof, SCH. MED, VANDERBILT UNIV, 63-67, ASSOC. PROF, 67- Clin. & res. fel. cytogenetics, Mass. Gen. Hosp, 60-63. Am. Soc. Clin. Invest. Address: Dept. of Medicine, Vanderbilt University School of Medicine, Nashville, TN 37203.

ENGEL, FRANK (AUGUST), JR, b. Steubenville, Ohio, July 29, 17; m. 40; c. 4. MATHEMATICS, PHYSICS; B.S, Pittsburgh, 38, M.S, 51. Sales & develop. engr, Speer Carbon Co, Pa, 39-41; design & test engr, Penn Elec. Co, 41-42; res. physicist, B.F. Goodrich Co, Ohio, 42-43, sr. physicist, Mine Safety Appliances, 43-51; supvr. gen. anal. & comput. sect, atomic power div, Westinghouse Elec. Corp, 51-55, adv. eng, anal. dept, eng. & serv. dept, 55-62; dir. comput. ctr, Harvard, 62-64; mgr. appl. sci. dept, electronic data processing div, Honeywell, Inc, 64-66; SUBDEPT. HEAD APPL. MATH, MITRE CORP, 66- Pres, SHARE, 56-57, v.pres, 60-61, mem. exec. bd, 57-58; chmn. comt. FORTRAN prog. lang. standards, Am. Nat. Standards Inst, 70- AAAS; Am. Math. Soc; Am. Nuclear Soc; Asn. Comput. Mach. Digital computer design; programming systems development, scientific and business data processing applications. Address: 179 Lewis Rd, Belmont, MA 02178.

ENGEL, FRED C, b. Hamburg, Ger, Mar. 12, 18; nat; m. 49; c. 3. MECHANICAL ENGINEERING. B.M.E, Ohio State, 43; M.Sc, Pittsburgh, 54. Test engr, Columbus McKinnon Chain Corp, 43-44; design engr, Cleveland Pneumatic Tool Co, 44-45; x-ray div, WESTINGHOUSE ELEC. CORP, 45-46, res. engr, res. labs, 46-57, SR. ENGR, ATOMIC POWER DEPT, 57- Am. Nuclear Soc; Am. Soc. Mech. Eng; Combustion Inst. Combustion; fuel atomization; hydraulics; 2 phase flow; liquid metal heat transfer. Address: Atomic Power Dept, Westinghouse Electric Corp, P.O. Box 158, Madison, PA 15663.

ENGEL, GEORGE L(IBMAN), b. New York, N.Y, Dec. 10, 13; m. 38; c. 2. MEDICINE, PSYCHIATRY. B.A, Dartmouth Col, 34; M.D, Hopkins, 38. Fel. med, Harvard Med. Sch, 41-42; instr. med. & psychiat, col. med, Cincinnati, 42-44, asst. prof, 45-46; SCH. MED. & DENT, UNIV. ROCHESTER, 46-49, assoc. prof, 49-57, PROF, 57-; PSYCHIATRIST & PHYSICIAN, STRONG MEM. HOSP, 57- Clinician, med. serv. Cincinnati Gen. Hosp, 42-44, asst. attend. psychiatrist, 43-44; consult, Off. Surgeon Gen; Fitzsimons Gen. Hosp, 48; res. studies sect, nat. adv. ment. health coun, U.S. Pub. Health Serv, 49-53; U.S. Pub. Health Serv. career res. award, 62. Civilian with Off. Sci. Res. & Develop, 44. AAAS; Am. Soc. Clin. Invest; Am. Psychosom. Soc; Am. Psychiat. Asn; Am. Psychoanal. Asn. Physiology of respiration and circulation; electroencephalography; syncope; delirium; migranine; decompression sickness; problems of clinical and psychosomatic medicine; psychoanalysis; medical education. Address: Strong Memorial Hospital, 260 Crittenden Blvd, Rochester, NY 14620.

ENGEL, GORDON RAY, b. Flesherton, Ont, Sept. 17, 36; m. 61; c. 2. PSYCHOLOGY. B.A, Queen's (Ont), 61, M.A, 62, Ph.D.(psychol), 64; Cambridge, 63-64. Scientist, Defence Res. Med. Labs, Toronto, Ont, 64-66; ASST. PROF. PSYCHOL, UNIV. WATERLOO, 66- Nat. Res. Coun. Can. award. Can. Psychol. Asn. Stereoscopic vision; electronic visual displays and processing; electronic simulation of neurological function. Address: Dept. of Psychology, University of Waterloo, Waterloo, Ont, Can.

ENGEL, I. M, Clin. Psychol, see 12th ed, Soc. & Behav. Vols.

ENGEL, JAN M(ARCIN), b. Danzig, May 1, 24; U.S. citizen; wid; c. 2. SOLID STATE PHYSICS. B.Sc, London, 46; Pennsylvania, 46-48; Temple, 49-50; California, Los Angeles, 56-57. Res. physicist, Socony-Vacuum Oil Co, N.J, 50-51; electronics lab, Gen. Elec. Co, N.Y, 51-53; sr. proj. engr, Motorola Inc, Ariz, 53-54; res. physicist, Pac. Semiconductors Inc, 54-57; assoc. physicist, res. lab, IBM CORP, 58-59, staff physicist, adv. systs. div, 59-60, ADV. PHYSICIST thin film devices, components lab, N.Y, 60-63, ELECTRON DEVICES, gen. prods. div, 64-65, DEVELOP. LAB, SYSTS. DEVELOP. DIV, 65- Lectr, dept. liberal arts, univ. exten, California, Los Angeles, 57-58, Berkeley, 58-60; voluntary ed. progs, Int. Bus. Mach. Corp, 62- Consult, Electro-Optical Systs. Inc, Calif, 57-58. Am. Inst. Physics; Am. Phys. Soc; Sci. Res. Soc. Am; fel. Brit. Inst. Physics & Phys. Soc; sr. mem. Inst. Elec. & Electronics Eng. Development of novel devices utilizing physical phenomena that are usually studied in the fields of solid state physics and utilizing semiconductor, thin film and/or electron beam technologies. Address: 2980 Cambridge Dr, San Jose, CA 95125.

ENGEL, JEROME, JR, b. Albany, N.Y, May 11, 38; m. 67; c. 2. NEUROPHYSIOLOGY, NEUROLOGY. B.A, Cornell, 60; M.D, Stanford, 65, Nat. Insts. Health fel, 64, Ph.D.(physiol), 66. Epilepsy Found. Am. grant, 65; Nat. Insts. Health fel. neurol, Stanford Univ. & Nat. Center Sci. Res, France, 65-66; intern med, Indiana Univ. Med. Center, 66-67; res. neurol, Albert Einstein Col. Med, 67-68; staff assoc. neurophysiol, lab. perinatal physiol, Nat. Inst. Neurol. Diseases & Stroke, 68-69, lab. neural control, 69-70; RESIDENT NEUROL, ALBERT EINSTEIN COL. MED, 70- Vis. asst. prof, sch. med, Univ. P.R, 68-69. U.S.P.H.S, 68-70, Surg. AAAS; Soc. Neurosci; Am. Physiol. Soc; Am. Acad. Neurol. Cortical neurophysiology; pathophysiology of epilepsy. Address: 100 Barberry Lane, New Rochelle, NY 10804.

ENGEL, JOHN HAL, JR, b. Detroit, Mich, Dec. 12, 30; m. 57; c. 3. ORGANIC & POLYMER CHEMISTRY. B.S, Detroit, 56, M.S, 58. Res. chemist, Gen. Motors Res. Labs, 58-62; sr. res. chemist, R.P. Scherer Corp, 62-63; res. scientist, CHRYSLER CORP, DETROIT, 63-66, sr. res. scientist, 66-67, GROUP LEADER polymer res, 67-70, EMISSIONS RES, 70- Adj. prof. chem, Marygrove Col, 68- Med.Serv.C, U.S.A, 53-55. Am. Chem. Soc. Solventless and aqueous paint and adhesive systems; polymer synthesis; infrared analysis of polymer systems; polyurethanes; conversion of emissions from engines and factories. Address: 705 Washington Rd, Grosse Pointe, MI 48230.

ENGEL, JOSEPH H(ENRY), b. N.Y.C, May 15, 22; m. 43; c. 3. MATHEMATICS, OPERATIONS ANALYSIS. B.S, City Col. New York, 42; Yale, 46; M.A, Univ. Wis, 47, Ph.D.(math), 49. Opers. analyst, opers. eval. group, Mass. Inst. Tech, 49-57, dep. dir, 57-62; dir, ctr. naval anal, Franklin Inst, 62-65, asst. chief scientist, prog. review, 65-67; spec. asst. to v.pres-technol, Commun. Satellite Corp, 67-68, dir. planning res. & serv, 68-70; HEAD, SYSTS. ENG. DEPT, UNIV. ILL, CHICAGO CIRCLE, 70- Chmn, adv. panel oper. res, NATO, 70- U.S.A, 42-44; U.S.A.A.F, 44-46; Distinguished Flying Cross. AAAS; Am. Math. Soc; Opers. Res. Soc. Am.(secy, pres, 68-69); Int. Fedn. Opers. Res. Soc. Operations research; stochastic processes; decision problems; symbolic logic; abstract group theory. Address: Systems Engineering Dept, University of Illinois at Chicago Circle, Box 4348, Chicago, IL 60680.

ENGEL, LAWRENCE J, b. St. Louis, Ill, May 10, 29; m. 52; c. 4. CHEMICAL ENGINEERING. B.Ch.E, Ga. Inst. Tech, 51, M.S.Ch.E, 54, Ph.D.(chem. eng), 56. Asst. instr. chem. eng, Ga. Inst. Tech, 53-56; engr, Esso Res. & Eng. Co, N.J, 56-59, sr. engr, spec. projs. unit, 59-63, chem. staff, 63-65, staff adv, Enjay Polymer Labs, 65-67, res. assoc, Enjay Additives Labs, 67-68, proj. coord, paramins div, Enjay Chem. Co, N.Y, 68-70; SR. ASSOC, ESSO RES. & ENG. CO, 70- Chem.C, U.S.A, 51-53, Res, 53-, Lt. Col. Am. Inst. Chem. Eng; Am. Chem. Soc. Petroleum and chemical process research from lab bench scale through design and operation of commercial unit; economics and staff planning and analysis of projects. Address: Esso Research & Engineering Co, P.O. Box 121, Linden, NJ 07036.

ENGEL, LEWIS L(IBMAN), b. N.Y.C, Sept. 2, 09; m. 38. BIOLOGICAL CHEMISTRY. B.S, Harvard, 30; fel, Columbia, 33-35, Ph.D.(biol. chem), 36; hon. LL.D, Glasgow, 69. Asst. biol. chem, Columbia, 31-33; fachhorer, Swiss Fed. Inst. Tech, 35-36; guest res. worker, res. inst, Royal Cancer Hosp, London, 36-37; John D. Archbold fel, Hopkins, 37-39, instr. med, 39-41; asst. biochem, Mayo Found, Minnesota, 42-43; res. assoc. biol. chem. & med, med. sch, HARVARD, 46-52, asst. prof. BIOL. CHEM, Mass. Gen. Hosp, 52-58, assoc. prof, MED. SCH, 58-66, AM. CANCER SOC. PROF, 66- Tutor biochem. sci, Harvard Col, 47-, chmn, 57-58, Am. Cancer Soc. faculty fel, 59-66, acting chmn, Bd. Tutors, 63-65; Macfarlane prof. exp. med, Univ. Glasgow, 67-68. Nat. Divisional Award, Am. Cancer Soc, 67. Sanit.C, U.S.A, 43-46. AAAS; Am. Chem. Soc; Am. Soc. Biol. Chem; Endocrine Soc. (v.pres, 62-63, Eli Lilly Lect. Award, 70); Am. Asn. Cancer Res; Am. Acad. Arts & Sci; N.Y. Acad. Sci; Brit. Biochem. Soc. Intermediary metabolism of steroids; terpenes and alkaloids; biochemistry of steroids and related compounds; cancer; endocrinology. Address: Huntington Labs, Massachusetts General Hospital, Boston, MA 02114.

ENGEL, MILTON BAER, b. Chicago, Ill, Aug. 7, 16; m. 42; c. 2. DENTISTRY. D.D.S, Illinois, 38, M.S, 40. Carnegie fel. ORTHOD, COL. DENT, UNIV. ILL, 41-42, res. assoc, 45-46, res. asst. prof, 46-53, assoc. prof, 53-57, PROF, 57- Practicing orthodontist. U.S.N, 42-45. AAAS; Am. Dent. Asn; Am. Asn. Orthodont; Soc. Exp. Biol. & Med; Am. Soc. Exp. Path; Int. Asn. Dent. Res. Experimental pathology; histochemistry; growth; orthodontics. Address: University of Illinois College of Dentistry, Chicago, IL 60612.

ENGEL, NIELS N(IKOLAJ), b. Bern, Switzerland, Nov. 21, 04; U.S. citizen; m. 34; c. 3. METALLURGY. B.S, Tech. Univ, Denmark, 25, M.S, 28; Cand. Phil, Copenhagen, 26; Dr. Ing.(metall), Aachen Tech, 31. Assoc. prof, Tech. Univ, Denmark, 36-51; METALL. ENG, Alabama, 51-59; PROF, GA. INST. TECHNOL, 59- Consult, Oak Ridge Nat. Lab, 64-; South. Saw, Ga, 66-; Southwire, Ga, 68- Adolf Martens Medal, Ger, 66. Am. Inst. Mining, Metall. & Petrol. Eng; Am. Soc. Metals. Basic conception of physical world; bonding between atoms; metallic properties; high and low temperature properties; nuclear and applied physical metallurgy. Address: Dept. of Chemical Engineering, Georgia Institute of Technology, Atlanta, GA 30332.

ENGEL, PAUL SANFORD, b. Pittsburgh, Pa, July 19, 42. PHOTOCHEMISTRY, ORGANIC CHEMISTRY. B.S, Univ. Calif, Los Angeles, 64; Woodrow Wilson Found. fel, Harvard, 64, Nat. Sci. Found. fel, 64-68, Ph.D.(chem), 68. Sr. asst. scientist, Nat. Insts. Health, 68-70; ASST. PROF. CHEM, RICE UNIV, 70- Am. Chem. Soc. Organic photochemistry; azo compounds; extrusion reactions; energy transfer; rearrangements of beta, gamma-unsaturated ketones; free radical chemistry. Address: Dept. of Chemistry, Rice University, Houston, TX 77001.

ENGEL, PAULINUS P, b. Grainfield, Kans, July 8, 31; m. 71. GENETICS. B.S, St. Benedict's Col.(Kans), 54; Philip Francis du Pont fel, Virginia, 58-60, M.A, 60; M.S, Yale, 61, Sterling fel, 61-62, Ph.D.(biol), 66. Instr. biol, St. Benedict's Col.(Kans), 66-70; ASST. PROF. MICROBIOL, VA. POLYTECH. INST. & STATE UNIV, 70- Genetics Soc. Am; Am. Soc. Microbiol. Induction and inheritance of biochemical mutations in bryophytes; gene-enzyme relationships in Streptomyces coelicolor. Address: Dept. of Biology, Virginia Polytechnic Institute & State University, Blacksburg, VA 24061.

ENGEL, R(ALPH) E, b. Hall Co, Nebr, Aug. 31, 15; m. 38; c. 1. AGRONOMY. A.B, Hastings Col, 37; M.S, Nebraska, 47; Ph.D, Rutgers, 51. With Bur. Standards, 42-45; from agronomist to PROF. TURF MGT, RUTGERS UNIV, 47- Fel. Am. Soc. Agron. Selection, fertilization, weed control and establishment of turfgrass management. Address: Dept. of Soils & Crops, College of Agriculture, Rutgers, The State University, New Brunswick, NJ 08903.

ENGEL, ROBERT DAVID, b. Los Angeles, Calif, Nov. 22, 32; m. 57; c. 2. COMPUTER SCIENCE. B.S, California, Los Angeles, 58, M.S, 59, Ph.D. (eng), 63. Res. engr. plasma properties, California, Los Angeles, 61-63, asst. prof. eng, 63-66, mem. staff, computer, opers. dept, Beckman Instrument Corp, 66-67; ASSOC. PROF. ENG, UNIV. REDLANDS, 67- Consult, electronics div, Rand Corp, 60-66. U.S.N, 51-55. Inst. Mgt. Sci; Inst. Elec. & Electronics Eng. Applied electromagnetic theory; microwaves; electronics; computers; simulation; systems. Address: Dept. of Engineering, University of Redlands, Redlands, CA 92373.

ENGEL, ROBERT HENRY, b. Mt. Vernon, N.Y, Mar. 10, 36; m. 57. BIOCHEMISTRY. B.S, Ursinus Col, 57; Purdue, 57-58; Ph.D.(biochem), Yale, 63. RES. BIOCHEMIST, Am. Cyanamid Co, 62-68; WILLIAM F. CLAPP LABS, BATTELLE MEM. INST, 68- Enzyme purification; phosphorus metabolism of brain; heparin and atherosclerosis; biochemical effects of environmental contaminants; marine bioadhesives; toxicity of oil-dispersing materials. Address: William F. Clapp Labs, Battelle Memorial Institute, Washington St, Duxbury, MA 02332.

ENGEL, ROBERT RALPH, b. Pittsburgh, Pa, Aug. 30, 42; m. 66. ORGANIC CHEMISTRY. B.S, Carnegie Inst. Tech, 63; Ph.D.(chem), Pa. State, 66. ASST. PROF. CHEM, QUEENS COL.(N.Y), 68- Chem.C, U.S.A, 66-68, Capt. Am. Chem. Soc; The Chem. Soc. Mechanism studies on reactions of organophosphorus compounds; paramagnetic nuclear magnetic resonance studies. Address: Dept. of Chemistry, Queens College, Flushing, NY 11367.

ENGEL, R(UBEN) W(ILLIAM), b. Shawano, Wis, July 10, 12; m. 39; c. 3. BIOCHEMISTRY. Ph.B, Wisconsin, 36, Ph.D.(biochem), 39. Asst, Wisconsin, 36-39; assoc. animal nutritionist, Ala. Polytech, 39-43, animal nutritionist, 46-52; head dept. biochem. & nutrit, VA. POLYTECH. INST. & STATE UNIV, 52-66, ASSOC. DEAN RES, COL. AGR, 66- Mem. panel on nutrit, comt. on growth, Nat. Res. Coun. & mem. food & nutrit. bd. & U.S. nat. comt. nutrit. Sanit.C, U.S.A, 43-46. Am. Asn. Cancer Res; Am. Chem. Soc; Am. Inst. Nutrit; Am. Dairy Sci. Asn. Chemical and pathological changes associated with B vitamin deficiencies; choline metabolism; relation of nutrition to cancer; minor elements in animal nutrition. Address: College of Agriculture, Virginia Polytechnic Institute & State University, Blacksburg, VA 24061.

ENGEL, RUDOLF, b. Bonn, Ger, Aug. 28, 04; nat; m. 33; c. 4. MEDICINE. M.D, Bonn, 29; Dr.med.habil, Berlin, 35; M.Sc. & M.D, Minnesota, 49. Resident, univ. hosp, Berlin, 29-30, 34-36; asst. pediat, Minnesota, 31; resident, univ. hosp, Heidelberg, 32-34; asst. prof, Hamburg, 36-38; assoc. prof. internal med, Berlin, 38-45; head dept, Luisen Hosp, Aachen, Germany, 46-48; from clin. asst. prof. to assoc. prof. pediat, Minnesota, 50-52; clin. instr. neurol, UNIV. ORE, 52-57, asst. prof. PEDIAT, MED. SCH, 57-59, assoc. prof, 59-68, PROF, 68- Fulbright lectr, Univ. Ceylon, 55-56; Univ. Hamburg, 62. AAAS; Am. Electroencephalog. Soc; Am. Acad. Cerebral Palsy; fel. Am. Col. Physicians. Causes of cerebral palsy; mental retardation and other malformations; biological sciences; neonatal electroencephalography; evoked potentials. Address: Dept. of Pediatrics, University of Oregon Medical School, Portland, OR 97201.

ENGEL, STANFORD L(OWELL), b. Phila, Pa, July 26, 24. PHARMACOLOGY. B.S, Phila. Col. Pharm, 44; Ph.D.(pharmacol), Columbia, 59. Res. bacteriologist, McNiel Labs, 46-51; asst. prof. pharmacol, Rutgers, 56-59; head pharmacol. & toxicol, Nopco Labs, 59-62; SR. RES. SCIENTIST, SQUIBB INST. MED. RES, 62- Med.C, U.S.N, 44-46. AAAS. Endocrinology; biochemistry and physiology of the neurophypophysis; pituitary regulation of metabolism; water and electrolyte balance; neuroendocrinology; mammalian reproduction. Address: Squibb Institute for Medical Research, Georges Rd, New Brunswick, NJ 08903.

ENGEL, W(ILLIAM) KING, b. St. Louis, Mo, Nov. 19, 30; m. 54; c. 3. NEUROLOGY. B.A, Hopkins, 51; M.D, McGill, 55. Intern neurol, Univ. Michigan Hosp, 55-56; clin. assoc. med. neurol. br, Nat. Inst. Neurol. Diseases & Blindness, 56-59; clin. clerk, Nat. Hosp, London, Eng, 59-60; assoc. neurologist, MED. NEUROL. BR, NAT. INST. NEUROL. DISEASES & BLINDNESS, 60-62; acting chief, 62-63, CHIEF, 63-, traineeship, 59-60. Mem. med. bd, Nat. Insts. Health, 68-69; clin. prof, George Wash. Univ. Sch. Med, 69-; mem. med. adv. bd, St. Judes Childrens Res. Hosp, Memphis, 70-; Myasthenia Gravis Found, 70-; exec. comt, res. group neuromuscular disorders, World Fedn. Neurol, 70-; assoc. exam, Am. Bd. Neurol. & Psychiat. Dipl, Am. Bd. Neurol. & Psychiat, 62. U.S.P.H.S, 56-59, 60-, Med. Dir. Fel. Am. Acad. Neurol.(S. Weir Mitchell Award, 62); Histochem. Soc; Am. Soc. Cell Biol; Am. Asn. Neuropath; hon. dipl. neurol. Pan-Am. Med. Asn; Am. Med. Asn; Asn. Univ. Prof. Neurol; hon. mem. French Neurol. Soc; Am. Neurol. Asn. Clinical neurology; histochemistry; neuromuscular diseases; tissue culture; electron microscopy; experimental pathology. Address: 4702 Broad Brook Dr, Bethesda, MD 20014.

ENGELBART, DOUGLAS C(ARL), b. Portland, Ore, Jan. 30, 25; m. 51; c. 4. ELECTRICAL ENGINEERING. B.S, Ore. State Col, 48; E.E, California, 53, Ph.D.(elec. eng), 55. Elec. engr, Nat. Adv. Comt. Aeronaut, Ames Aero Lab, Calif, 48-51; assoc. elec. eng, California, 54-55, asst. prof, 55-56; pres, tech. dir, Digital Tech, Inc, 56-57; from res. engr. to PROG. HEAD, MAN-MACH. INFO. SYSTS, STANFORD RES. INST, 57- Consult, Marchant Res, Inc, Calif, 55-56. U.S.N, 44-46. Digital computers; new device research with gas discharge and magnetics; man-computer on-line problem solving. Address: 89 Catalpa Dr, Atherton, CA 94025.

ENGELBERG, JOSEPH, b. Vienna, Austria, June 2, 28; nat; m. 54; c. 2. BIOPHYSICS. B.M.E, Cooper Union, 50; M.S, Pennsylvania, 53, Nat. Sci. Found. fel, 54-55, Pub. Health Serv. fel, 56-58, Ph.D.(physics), 58. Res. engr, surg. instrumentation, Pennsylvania, 50-53; bioeng, Franklin Inst, 53-54; instr. biophys, Colorado, 58-60; Am. Cancer Soc. fel, California, Berkeley, 60-61; asst. prof. PHYSIOL. & BIOPHYS, SCH. MED, UNIV. KY, 61-65, assoc. prof, 65-70, PROF, 70- Pub. Health Serv. fel, 58-60. Lederle Award, 63-66. Biophys. Soc; Am. Physiol. Soc. Design of artificial kidney and artificial heart-lung machines; respiratory mechanics; mechanics of pulmonary circulation; mammalian cells—physiology and effects of radiation; theoretical biology; development of health delivery systems. Address: Dept. of Physiology & Biophysics, University of Kentucky, Lexington, KY 40506.

ENGELBERT, LINCOLN E(DWIN), b. Mt. Vernon, Wis, June 1, 19; m. 49; c. 4. SOILS. B.S, Univ. Wis, 42, M.S, 47, Ph.D.(soils), 50. Instr. SOILS, UNIV. WIS, MADISON, 50-51, asst. prof, 51-55, assoc. prof, 55-59, PROF, 59-, chmn. dept, 58-69. Vis. scientist, Int. Atomic Energy Agency, Vienna, 63-64. U.S.M.C, 42-46, Res, 46-58, Maj. Am. Soc. Agron; Soil Sci. Soc. Am; Int. Soc. Soil Sci; Crop Sci. Soc. Am. Nitrogen efficiency studies; denitrification in soils; subsoil-plant relationships; effect of industrial waste disposal on soil and crops. Address: Dept. of Soils, University of Wisconsin, Madison, WI 53706.

ENGELBERT, VIBEKE ELISABETH, b. Kalo, Denmark, March 19, 01; Can. citizen. HISTOLOGY. M.S.A, Toronto, Ph.D.(biol, genetics). Res. asst. plant breeding, Ont. Agr. Col, 29-34; demonstr. zool, UNIV. TORONTO, 34-44, lectr, 44-49, asst. prof. HISTOL, 49-57, assoc. prof, 57-65, prof, 65-69, EMER. PROF, 69- Int. Soc. Hemat; Am. Soc. Hemat. Hemopoiesis differentiation; cell replacement. Address: c/o Mr. Erik Engelbert, R.R. 3, King City, Ont, Can.

ENGELBRECHT, HARLEN J, b. Marcus, Iowa, May 26, 20; m. 44; c. 3. VETERINARY MEDICINE. D.V.M, Iowa State Univ, 44. MEM. RES. STAFF, diag. lab, FT. DODGE LAB. DIV, AM. HOME PROD. CORP, 47-59, PROD. DEVELOP, 59- Am. Vet. Med. Asn; Am. Soc. Vet. Parasitol; Am. Soc. Parasitol. Veterinary parasitology and bacteriology. Address: Ft. Dodge Labs, Ft. Dodge, IA 50502.

ENGELBRECHT, R(ICHARD) S(TEVENS), b. Ft. Wayne, Ind, Mar. 11, 26; m. 48; c. 2. SANITARY SCIENCE, MICROBIOLOGY. A.B, Indiana, 48; M.S, Mass. Inst. Tech, 52, Sc.D.(sanit. sci), 54. Asst. microbiol, sch. med, Indiana, 48-50; civil & sanit. eng, Mass. Inst. Tech, 50-52, instr, 52-54; asst. prof. sanit. eng, UNIV. ILL. URBANA, 54-57, assoc. prof, 57-59, PROF. ENVIRON. ENG, 59- AAAS; Am. Soc. Microbiol; Am. Water Works Asn; Water Pollution Control Fedn.(Harrison P. Eddy Medal, 66). Water quality and stream pollution; water and wastewater treatment; solid waste management; environmental science. Address: Dept. of Civil Engineering, University of Illinois, Urbana, IL 61801.

ENGELDER, THEODORE C(ARL), b. Detroit, Mich, Aug. 31, 27; m. 52; c. 2. NUCLEAR PHYSICS. B.S, Michigan, 49; M.S, Yale, 50, Ph.D.(physics), 53. Proj. engr, Dow Chem. Co, 52-56; physicist, Chrysler Corp, 56; group supvr, atomic energy div, BABCOCK & WILCOX CO, 56-60; chief, exp. physics sect, res. & develop. div, 60-67, mgr. physics labs, 67-69, asst. dir. nuclear develop. ctr, 69-71, DIR, LYNCHBURG RES. CTR, 71- Am. Phys. Soc; Am. Nuclear Soc. Nuclear reactor design and development; experimental reactor physics. Address: 2236 Taylor Farm Rd, Lynchburg, VA 24503.

ENGELER, CARL O, b. Switz, Sept. 5, 24; m. 59; c. 2. ORGANIC CHEMISTRY. M.S, Swiss Fed. Inst. Tech, 48; Ph.D, Paris, 49. Chemist, GANE'S CHEM. WORKS, INC, 51-62, plant mgr, 62-66, V.PRES. PROD, 66- Swiss Army, 44-50. Am. Chem. Soc. Address: Gane's Chemical Works, Inc, 611 Broad St, Carlstadt, NJ 07072.

ENGELER, ERWIN, b. Switz, Feb. 13, 30; m. 56; c. 2. MATHEMATICS. Dipl, Swiss Fed. Inst. Tech, 55, Dr.Sc, 58. Vis. asst. prof. MATH, UNIV. MINN, MINNEAPOLIS, 58-60, asst. prof, 60-63, assoc. prof, 63-67, PROF, 67- Vis. asst. prof, California, Berkeley, 62-63; Privatdozent, Swiss Fed. Inst. Tech, 64. Res. mathematician, Int. Bus. Mach. Corp, Switz, 63-64. Am.

Math. Soc; Asn. Symbolic Logic. Mathematical logic and its applications to mathematics. Address: School of Mathematics, University of Minnesota, Minneapolis, MN 55455.

ENGELER, WILLIAM E, b. Brooklyn, N.Y, Nov. 13, 28; m. 55; c. 4. SOLID STATE PHYSICS. B.S, Polytech. Inst. Brooklyn, 51; M.S, Syracuse, 58, Ph.D.(physics), 61. PHYSICIST, GEN. ELEC. CO, 51-52, semiconductor prod. dept, 52-55, RES. LAB, 61- U.S.A, 55-56. Inst. Elec. & Electronics Eng; Electrochem. Soc; Phys. Soc. Semiconductors; infrared optical properties; junction lasers; surface properties; metal-oxide semiconductor devices; device physics. Address: Solid State Physics Lab, General Electric Co. Corporate Research & Development, P.O. Box 8, Schenectady, NY 12301.

ENGELFRIED, JOHN J(ACOB), b. N.Y.C, Sept. 16, 06; m. 35; c. 4. BIOCHEMISTRY, IMMUNOLOGY. B.S, Michigan, 32, M.S.P.H, 34, Dr.P.H.(immunol), 36. Technician in clin. chem. & bact, Michigan, 32-34, biochemist, dept. pediat, 34-36, instr, 36-41, Horace Rackham sch. grad. studies, 38-41, chemist, univ. hosp, 38-41; head, physiol. chem, U.S. Med. Sch, 41-46, serol, 47-50; clin. path, U.S. Naval Hosp, Oakland, 50-53, San Diego, 53-57; monitor, Dept. of Defense blood prog, 57-62; U.S. Naval Med. Res. Unit 1, California, Berkeley, 62-68; RETIRED. U.S.N, 41-68, Capt. AAAS; Am. Soc. Microbiol; Am. Pub. Health Asn. Biochemistry procedures for various determinations; immunology studies in sensitization; allergy; bacteriology methods; blood factors in serology; serological tests; distribution of the sulfonamide drugs in tissues and fluids of the body; blood bank procedures; military blood program. Address: 1704 Crescent Dr, Walnut Creek, CA 94598.

ENGELHARD, ARTHUR W(ILLIAM), b. Dayton, Ohio, Apr. 9, 28; m. 55; c. 3. PLANT PATHOLOGY. B.S, Ohio, 50; M.S, Yale, 52; Ph.D.(plant path), Iowa State, 55. Asst. plant sci, Yale, 50-51; plant path, Iowa State, 52-55; asst. plant pathologist, Ill. State Natural Hist. Surv, 55-56; res. plant pathologist, E.I. du Pont de Nemours & Co, 56-64, sr. sales res. biologist, 64-65, sr. res. biologist, 66; ASSOC. PROF. PLANT PATH. & ASSOC. PLANT PATHOLOGIST, RES. & EDUC. CTR, UNIV. FLA, 66- Am. Phytopath. Soc; Int. Soc. Plant Path. Cause and control of diseases of cut flower crops; foliage and soil fungicides. Address: 5306 Seventh Ave. Dr. W, Bradenton, FL 33505.

ENGELHARD, ROBERT J, b. Milwaukee, Wis, May 16, 27; m. 60; c. 2. FORESTRY. B.S, Utah State Univ, 50; M.S, Univ. Denver, 52; Ph.D.(forestry), Mich. State Univ, 69. Forester, U.S. Forest Serv, 52-56; Trees for Tomorrow, Inc, 56-65; instr. FORESTRY, WIS. STATE UNIV, 65-66, ASSOC. PROF, 67- U.S.A, 45-46 & 50-51, Sgt. Soc. Am. Foresters. Resource economics; forest policy; forest products acquisition and marketing. Address: 4309 Janick Circle N, Stevens Point, WI 54481.

ENGELHARDT, ALBERT GEORGE, b. Toronto, Can, Mar. 17, 35; m. 60; c. 3. PHYSICS, ELECTRICAL ENGINEERING. B.A.Sc, Toronto, 58; fels, Illinois, 58-60; M.S, 59, Ph.D.(elec. eng, math), 61. Asst. elec. eng, Illinois, 60-61; res. engr. physics & elec. eng, Westinghouse Elec. Corp, 61-62, sr. engr, 62-66, mgr. advan. plasma concepts, 66-70; SR. STAFF MEM, INST. RES, HYDRO-QUE, 70- Vis. prof, Univ. Que, 71- Am. Phys. Soc; Brit. Inst. Physics & Phys. Soc; Inst. Elec. & Electronics Eng. Plasma physics; collision phenomena in atomic and molecular gases; laser interaction with matter; electromagnetic wave propagation. Address: Institute of Research, Hydro-Quebec, 1800 Montee Ste. Julie, Varennes, Que, Can.

ENGELHARDT, DAVID MEYER, b. Austria, June 15, 12; nat; m. 52; c. 3. PSYCHIATRY. B.S, City Col. New York, 32; M.D, Vienna, 37. Assoc, L.I. Col. Med. & STATE UNIV. N.Y. DOWNSTATE MED. CTR, 48-49, assoc. prof. clin. psychiat, 49-50, clin. prof. PSYCHIAT, 50-53, assoc. prof, 53-62, PROF, 62-, DIR. PSYCHOPHARMACOL. TREATMENT & RES. UNIT, 56-, psychiat. treatment res. ctr, 64-67, exec. off. psychiat, 60-64, acting chmn. dept, 58-60. Consult, Northport Vet. Admin. Hosps, 49-; asst. dir, assoc. dir. & acting dir, Kings County Psychiat. Hosp, Brooklyn, 47-60, vis. psychiatrist hosp. ctr, 59-, dir. clin. servs, 60-64. Mem. comt. clin. drug eval, Nat. Inst. Ment. Health, 61-65, chmn. adv. coun. childhood ment. illness, 62-64; mem. psychopharmacol. study sect, Nat. Inst. Ment. Health, U.S. Pub. Health Serv, 65-67, ad hoc adv. comt. psychotomimetic drugs, 66-67, clin. psychopharmacol. res. rev. comt, 67-69, clin. projs. res. rev. comt, 70-74; panel on drugs used in psychiat, drug efficacy study, Nat. Res. Coun-Nat. Acad. Sci, 66-68; bd. trustees, Res. Fedn, Nat. Asn. Ment. Health, 63-65. Dipl, Am. Bd. Psychiat. & Neurol; cert, Ment. Hosp. Admin. U.S.A.A.F, 40-46, Lt. Col. Fel. AAAS; fel. Acad. Psychoanal; fel. Am. Col. Neuropsychopharmacol; fel. Am. Psychiat. Asn; Am. Med. Asn; Am. Psychopath. Asn; N.Y. Acad. Sci; Int. Col. Neuropsychopharmacol; Soc. Med. Psychoanal. Psychopharmacology; psychiatric treatment research. Address: Dept. of Psychiatry, State University of New York Downstate Medical Center, 450 Clarkson Ave, Brooklyn, NY 11203.

ENGELHARDT, DEAN L, b. Oak Park, Ill, Jan. 15, 40. MOLECULAR & CELL BIOLOGY. B.A, Amherst Col, 61, Atomic Energy Comn. fel, 61-62, M.A, 63; univ. fel, Rockefeller Univ, 62-67, Ph.D.(molecular biol), 67. Res. assoc. molecular biol, Rockefeller Univ, summer 67; Am. Cancer Soc. fel, Columbia, 67-68; cell biol, Lab. of R. Dulbecco, Salk Inst, 68; MICROBIOL, Albert Einstein Med. Sch, 68-69; ASST. PROF, UNIV. CONN, 69- Controls functioning at the level of translation of animal cell and viral messages from the point of view of their biochemical elucidation. Address: Biological Sciences Group, Life Sciences Bldg. U-44, University of Connecticut, Storrs, CT 06268.

ENGELHARDT, DONALD W(AYNE), b. Blue Island, Ill, Feb. 25, 35; m. 58; c. 3. PALEOBOTANY. A.B, Wabash Col, 57; M.A, Indiana, 61, Nat. Sci. Found. & Floyd Found. fels. & Ph.D.(paleobot), 62. Res. scientist PALYNOLOGY, PAN-AM. PETROL. CORP. RES. CTR, 61-67, STAFF PALEONTOLOGIST, 67- Mem. Inst. Org. Paleobot, Int. Union Biol. Sci. Soc. Econ. Paleont. & Mineral; Bot. Soc. Am; Am. Asn. Stratig. Palynologists (v.pres, 71). Pleistocene geology and palynology; palynology of Gulf Coast Tertiary; tertiary and Mesozoic sediments of Alaska. Address: Amoco Production Company Security Life Bldg, Denver, CO 80202.

ENGELHARDT, EDWARD L(OUIS), b. Paramaribo, Dutch Guiana, Aug. 22, 19; m. 47; c. 1. ORGANIC CHEMISTRY. B.S, Haverford Col, 41; Ph.D.(org. chem), Wisconsin, 44. Asst. org. chem, Wisconsin, 42-44; res. assoc, Sharp & Dohme, Inc, 44-53, Sharp & Dohme Div, Merck & Co, Inc, 53-56, MERCK SHARP & DOHME RES. LABS, 56-60, ASST. DIR, MED. CHEM. DEPT, 60- Fel. AAAS; Am. Chem. Soc; N.Y. Acad. Sci; The Chem. Soc; Soc. Chem. Indust. Chemistry of synthetic drugs; cardiovascular diseases; nervous and mental disorders; allergy. Address: Medicinal Chemistry Dept, Merck Sharp & Dohme Research Labs, West Point, PA 19486.

ENGELHARDT, HUGO TRISTRAM, b. Houston, Tex, Jan. 17, 12; m. 39; c. 2. INTERNAL MEDICINE. Texas; M.D, Tulane, 37. Asst. internal med, sch. med, Tulane, 40-41, instr, 41-45; clin. med, col. med, Baylor, 45-47, asst. prof, 47-51, assoc. prof, 51-64; lectr. med, sch. med, Tulane Univ, 64-67; CLIN. ASSOC. PROF. PHYSIOL. & MED, UNIV. TEX. MED. SCH, SAN ANTONIO, 67- Vis. physician, Charity Hosp, New Orleans & chief, White Diabetes Clin, Tulane Serv, 43-45; chief internist, Humble Oil & Ref. Co, 45-64; chief diabetes clin, Jefferson Davis Hosp, 47-57, assoc. physician, 48- Dipl, Am. Bd. Internal Med, 45. Fel. Am. Col. Physicians; Am. Med. Asn; Am. Diabetes Asn. Diabetes mellitus. Address: Star Route 2, New Braunfels, TX 78130.

ENGELHARDT, VAUGHN A(RTHUR), b. Chicago, Ill, Apr. 14, 18; m. 47; c. 3. ORGANIC CHEMISTRY. B.S, Northwestern, 40; M.S, Minnesota, 44, Nat. Defense Res. Comt, fel, 42-45, Am. Chem. Soc. fel, 46-48; Ph.D.(org. chem), 48. Jr. res. chemist, Commercial Solvents Corp, Ind, 40, 41; res. chemist, Nat. Defense Res. Comt, Columbia, 42; E.I. DU PONT DE NEMOURS & CO, 48-57, ASSOC. DIR, 57- U.S.N.R, 45-46. Am. Chem. Soc. Synthesis of organic compounds; cyclopropanes; acetone and chloracetone; acetylene; cyanocarbons. Address: Central Research Dept, Experiment Station, E.I. du Pont de Nemours & Co, Wilmington, DE 19898.

ENGELHART, JOHN E, b. Woodhaven, N.Y, Dec. 19, 35; m. 59; c. 4. ORGANIC & AGRICULTURAL CHEMISTRY. B.S, St. John's Univ, 57; Nat. Sci. Found. fel, 59-60; Ph.D.(org. chem), Mass. Inst. Technol, 61. Instr. chem, St. John's Univ.(N.Y), 61-62; res. chemist, Enjay Additives Lab, Esso Res. & Eng. Co, N.J, 62-66, sr. res. chemist, Esso Agr. Prod. Lab, 66-69, GROUP LEADER herbicide res, 69-70; CHEM. RES, UNION CAMP CORP, PRINCETON, 70- Am. Chem. Soc. Synthesis of pesticidal chemicals, largely in herbicide and fungicide areas; modification of structure of wood chemicals, particularly rosin, terpenes and fatty acids; synthesis of fuel oil and lube oil additives. Address: 815 Tice Pl, Westfield, NJ 07090.

ENGELKE, CHARLES E(DWARD), b. N.Y.C, July 26, 30; m. 55; c. 3. NUCLEAR & ATOMIC PHYSICS. B.S, Queens Col.(N.Y), 51; M.A, Columbia Univ, 53, Ph.D.(physics), 61. Asst. prof. PHYSICS, LEHMAN COL, 61-66, ASSOC. PROF, 66- Summers, res. assoc, Columbia Univ, 61-63, Yale, 64. U.S.A.F, 53-56, 1st Lt. Am. Phys. Soc. Neutron-proton interaction; Einstein-Podolsky-Rosen paradox; observation of linear and angular momentum correlations and interference effects involving systems whose wave functions have been reduced by observations on correlated systems. Address: Dept. of Physics & Astronomy, Herbert H. Lehman College, Bedford Park Blvd. W, Bronx, NY 10468.

ENGELKE, JOHN L(ELAND), b. Ancon, C.Z, Sept. 5, 30; m. 57, 70; c. 1. PHYSICAL CHEMISTRY. B.S, Mich. Col. Min. & Tech, 52, M.S, 54; Ph.D. (chem), California, 59. Resident student assoc, Argonne Nat. Lab, 52-54; asst, California, 54-55, radiation lab, 57-59; solid state chemist, Stanford Res. Inst, 59-62; mem. staff, Arthur D. Little, Inc, 62-68; ASSOC. PROF. CHEM, SALEM STATE COL, 68- Chem.C, U.S.A, 55-57. Am. Chem. Soc. High temperature chemistry; thermodynamics; molecular spectroscopy; solid state chemistry; refractory materials. Address: Dept. of Chemistry, Salem State College, Salem, MA 01970.

ENGELMAN, ARTHUR, b. N.Y.C, Mar. 17, 30; m. 55; c. 3. ATMOSPHERIC PHYSICS, METEOROLOGY. B.S, City Col. New York, 50; M.S, N.Y. Univ, 51; Syracuse, 55-56. Asst. meteorol, N.Y. Univ, 51-52, 54-55; physicist, Rome Air Develop. Ctr, 55-57; sect. head, radio propagation, missile div, Raytheon Co, 57-59; dept. mgr. atmospheric physics, GCA CORP, 59-70, DIV. V.PRES. & TECH. DIR, TECHNOL. DIV, 70- U.S.A, 52-53, 1st Lt. Am. Meteorol. Soc; Am. Geophys. Union. Micrometeorology; tropospheric and ionospheric radio propagation and military defense system analysis; upper atmosphere physics; nuclear weapons effects; physics of detonation-atmosphere interaction. Address: Technology Division, GCA Corp, Burlington Rd, Bedford, MA 01730.

ENGELMANN, F(RANZ), b. Kenzingen, Ger, Dec. 19, 28; m. 54; c. 2. ZOOLOGY. Ph.D.(zool), Bern, 57. Mem. staff, Albert Einstein Col. Med, 58-60; asst. ZOOL, Mainz, 60-63; asst. prof, UNIV. CALIF, LOS ANGELES, 63-65, assoc. prof, 65-69, PROF, 69- Privatdozent, Mainz, 62. Am. Soc. Zool; Entom. Soc. Am. Endocrinology of invertebrates; reproduction in insects. Address: Dept. of Zoology, University of California, Los Angeles, CA 90024.

ENGELMANN, MANFRED D(AVID), b. Chicago, Ill, June 1, 30; m. 54; c. 2. ANIMAL ECOLOGY. B.S, Northwestern, 53; Chicago, 53; M.S, Illinois, 55; Ph.D.(ecol), Michigan, 60. Instr. zool, Michigan, 59-60; NATURAL SCI, MICH. STATE UNIV, 60-64, from asst. prof. to PROF, 65- Nat. Sci. Found. grants, 63-65. Res. consult. to F.C. Evans, Univ. Michigan, 61. Fel. AAAS; Ecol. Soc. Am; Am. Soc. Zool. Ecology of arthopod fauna found in field or grass land; soils and physiology of soil arthropods, particularly oribatid mites. Address: Dept. of Natural Science, Michigan State University, East Lansing, MI 48823.

ENGELMANN, RICHARD H(ENRY), b. Cincinnati, Ohio, Jan. 6, 23; m. 47; c. 2. ELECTRICAL ENGINEERING. B.S, U.S. Naval Acad, 44; M.S, Univ. Cincinnati, 49. Instr. ELEC. ENG, UNIV. CINCINNATI, 48-52, asst. prof, 52-57, assoc. prof, 57-61, PROF, 61-, HEAD DEPT, 67- Guest prof, Bengal Eng. Col, India, 63-64; consult, Planet Prod. Corp; Midland Discount Co; Binns Mach. Prod; Avco Corp; Welco Indust, Inc. U.S.N, 44-46, 51-52, Lt. AAAS; Am. Soc. Eng. Educ; Inst. Elec. & Electronics Eng. Feedback control systems. Address: Dept. of Electrical Engineering, University of Cincinnati, Mail Location 30, Cincinnati, OH 45221.

ENGELMANN, RUDOLF J, b. Ward Co, N.Dak, Mar. 11, 30; m. 52; c. 6. METEOROLOGY. B.A, Augsburg Col, 50; N.Y. Univ, 52; Ph.D.(meteorol), Washington (Seattle), 64. Meteorologist, Gen. Elec. Co, Wash, 56-65; mgr. atmospheric sci, pac. northwest labs, Battelle Mem. Inst, 65-67; meteorologist, U.S. ATOMIC ENERGY COMN, 67-69, CHIEF, FALLOUT STUDIES BR, 69- U.S.A.F, 50-56, 1st Lt. Am. Meteorol. Soc. Scavenging of gases and particles from the atmosphere by clouds, rain and snow; cloud physics and weather modification; micrometeorology; turbulence and diffusion; weather analysis and forecasting. Address: Division of Biology & Medicine, U.S. Atomic Energy Commission, Washington, DC 20545.

ENGELS, WILLIAM L(OUIS), b. Green Bay, Wis, Oct. 28, 05; m. 45. ZOOLOGY. B.S, Notre Dame, 30; Munich, 32-33; Ph.D.(vert. zool), California, 37. Asst. biol, Notre Dame, 29-31, instr, 30-32; asst. paleont, California, 34, mus. vert. zool, 35, ZOOL, 35-37; instr, UNIV. N.C, CHAPEL HILL, 37-39, asst. prof, 39-41, assoc. prof, 41-52, prof, 52-71, EMER. PROF, 71- U.S.A.A.F, 42-46. Fel. AAAS. Adaptive anatomy of birds; distribution and differentiation of insular vertebrates; natural history of vertebrates, especially in North Carolina; avian photoperiodism; transequatorial migration. Address: Dept. of Zoology, University of North Carolina, Chapel Hill, NC 27515.

ENGELSTAD, ORVIS P, b. Fertile, Minn, Feb. 19, 28; m. 52; c. 3. SOIL SCIENCE. B.S, Minnesota, 52, M.S, 54; Ph.D.(soils), Iowa State, 60. Exten. soils agent, Minnesota, 53-55; res. assoc. soil fertil, Iowa State, 55-60; AGRONOMIST, TENN. VALLEY AUTH, 60- U.S.A, 46-47, Sgt. Am. Soc. Agron; Soil Sci. Soc. Am. Soil management; soil fertility; fertilizer evaluation and yield response to fertilizer as affected by climatic variables. Address: Soils & Fertilizer Research Branch, Tennessee Valley Authority, Muscle Shoals, AL 35660.

ENGEMANN, JOSEPH GEORGE, b. Belding, Mich, Nov, 27, 28; m. 64; c. 3. INVERTEBRATE ZOOLOGY. B.A, Aquinas Col, 50; M.S, Mich. State Univ, 56, Ph.D.(zool), 63. Instr. BIOL, WEST. MICH. UNIV, 60-64, asst. prof, 64-68, ASSOC. PROF, 68- Med.C, 50-52, Sgt. AAAS; Soc. Protozool; Am. Micros. Soc; Am. Soc. Syst. Zool; Am. Soc. Zool. Ecology of aquatic invertebrates; protozoan cytochemistry; aquatic isopods. Address: Dept. of Biology, Western Michigan University, Kalamazoo, MI 49001.

ENGEN, GLENN FORREST, b. Battle Creek, Mich, Apr. 26, 25; m. 52; c. 3. PHYSICS, ELECTRICAL ENGINEERING. B.A, Andrews Univ; Univ. Mich, 47-48; Univ. Md, 50-52; Ph.D, Univ. Colo, 69. Physicist instrumentation, U.S. Naval Ord. Lab, 50-52; electronics engr, Hopkins, 52-54; SR. RES. SCIENTIST, NAT. BUR. STANDARDS, 54- Mem, Int. Sci. Radio Union. U.S. Dept. Commerce silver medal for meritorious serv, 61. Microwave circuit theory, power and noise measurement. Address: 844 Spring Dr, Boulder, CO 80302.

ENGEN, RICHARD L(EE), b. Irene, S.Dak, Oct. 30, 32; m. 55; c. 3. PHYSIOLOGY, BIOMEDICAL ENGINEERING. B.S, Iowa State, 54, Ph.D.(physiol), 65; M.S, Colorado State, 58. Res. nutritionist, Morris Res. Lab, Kans, 58-62; asst. prof. PHYSIOL, COL. VET. MED, IOWA STATE UNIV, 65-68, ASSOC. PROF, 68- U.S.A, 54-56. Assoc. mem. Am. Physiol. Soc; assoc. mem. Soc. Exp. Biol. & Med; Am. Soc. Vet. Physiol. & Pharmacol. Nutritional physiology; cardiovascular dynamics; endocrinology. Address: Dept. of Physiology, College of Veterinary Medicine, Iowa State University, Ames, IA 50010.

ENGER, MERLIN DUANE, b. Williston, N.Dak, Dec. 8, 37; m. 58; c. 3. BIOCHEMISTRY. B.S, N.Dak. State, 59, M.S, 61; Nat. Insts. Health fel, Wisconsin, Madison, 61-64, Ph.D.(biochem), 64. STAFF MEM, BIOMED. RES. GROUP, LOS ALAMOS SCI. LAB, UNIV. CALIF, 64- AAAS; Am. Chem. Soc; Am. Inst. Chem. Isolation and characterization of cellulases and ribonucleic acid phages; investigation of synthesis and modification of ribonucleic acid in cultured mammalian cells. Address: Los Alamos Scientific Lab, H.4, Los Alamos, NM 87544.

ENGERMAN, RONALD L(ESTER), b. Chicago, Ill, May 4, 29; m. 51; c. 5. OPHTHALMOLOGY. B.S, Wisconsin, 51, M.S, 58, U.S. Pub. Health Serv. fel, 58-60, Ph.D.(zool, biochem), 64. Technician, Bjorksten Res. Labs, 51; rubber technologist, Army Engr. Res. & Develop. Labs, Va, 53-54; res. asst. zool, UNIV. WIS, MADISON, 54-58, Wis. Alumni Res. Found. fel. OPHTHAL, SCH. MED, 60-61, instr, 61-64, asst. prof, 64-68, ASSOC. PROF, 68- Fight for Sight Citation, Nat. Coun. Combat Blindness & Asn. Res. Ophthal, 64. C.Eng, U.S.A, 51-53. Asn. Res. Vision & Ophthal; Am. Diabetes Asn; Soc. Exp. Biol. & Med. Diabetic retinopathy and microangiopathy; biology of the microvasculature. Address: Dept. of Ophthalmology, University of Wisconsin School of Medicine, Madison, WI 53706.

ENGERT, MARTIN, b. Chicago, Ill, Nov. 6, 38; m. 71. MATHEMATICAL ANALYSIS. B.A, Carleton Col, 60; M.S, Stanford Univ, 62, Ph.D.(math), 65. Asst. prof. MATH, Univ. N.C, Chapel Hill, 65-67; staff mem, Aarhus Univ, 67-69; ASSOC. PROF, WIS. STATE UNIV, WHITEWATER, 69- Address: Dept. of Mathematics, Wisconsin State University, Whitewater, WI 53190.

ENGH, HELMER A, JR, b. Litchfield, Ill, May 21, 35; m. 60. GENETICS. A.B, Washington (St. Louis), 57; M.S, Southern Illinois, 59; Ph.D.(poultry sci), Maryland, 66. Asst. prof. BIOL, MANKATO STATE COL, 66-70, ASSOC. PROF, 70- C.Eng, U.S.A.R, 58-62. AAAS; Am. Inst. Biol. Sci; Poultry Sci. Asn. Biochemical genetics of serum enzymes. Address: Dept. of Biology, Mankato State College, Box 203, Mankato, MN 56001.

ENGH, ROBERT O(SWALD), b. New Rockford, N.Dak, Jan. 11, 24. PHYSICS. B.Chem, Minnesota, 48; Atomic Energy Comn. fel. & M.S, Oregon, 53. Res. chemist, Hanford Works, 48-51; from res. scientist to sr. res. scientist, HONEYWELL.RES. CTR, 53-68, PRIN. RES. SCIENTIST, 68- H.W. Sweat outstanding engr-scientist award, 68. U.S.A, 43-45. Gas discharge physics. Address: 16244 S. Temple Dr, Hopkins, MN 55343.

ENGIBOUS, J(AMES) C(HARLES), b. Norway, Mich, Aug. 12, 23; m. 47; c. 3. SOIL BIOCHEMISTRY. B.S, North. Mich. Col, 47; M.S, Oregon State Col,

50; Ph.D.(biochem), Ohio State, 52. Res. asst, Oregon State Col, 48-50; Ohio State, 50-52; soil biochemist, Monsanto Chem. Co, 52-54; group leader agron. res, Int. Minerals & Chem. Corp, 54-55, supvr. soils & plant nutrit. res, 55-59, mgr. agr. prod. res, 59-62, agr. servs, mat. dept, 62-63, tech. serv. dept, 63-70; CHMN. DEPT. AGRON. & SOILS, WASH. STATE UNIV, 71- U.S.N.R, 43-46. Soil chemistry, bacteriology and physics. Address: Dept. of Agronomy & Soils, Washington State University, Pullman, WA 99163.

ENGLAND, ALAN COULTER, b. Belleville, Ill, Mar. 1, 32; m. 58; c. 2. PHYSICS. B.S, Illinois, 54; Ph.D.(physics), Rochester, 61. PHYSICIST, THERMONUCLEAR DIV, OAK RIDGE NAT. LAB, 60- Vis. scientist, Inst. Plasma Physics, Munich, Ger, 67-68. U.S.N.A.F.R, 50-58. Sci. Res. Soc. Am; Am. Phys. Soc. High-energy nuclear physics; hot-electron plasmas. Address: Oak Ridge National Lab, P.O. Box Y, Oak Ridge, TN 37830.

ENGLAND, ANTHONY W, b. Indianapolis, Ind, May 15, 42; m. 62. GEOPHYSICS. S.B. & S.M, Mass. Inst. Tech, 65, Nat. Sci. Found. fel, 64-67, Ph.D.(geophys), 68. SCIENTIST-ASTRONAUT, MANNED SPACECRAFT CTR, NASA, 67- AAAS; Am. Geophys. Union; Soc. Explor. Geophys; Am. Inst. Geophys. Physics of geologically interesting solids; field heat flow; magneto-tellurics; rock mechanics; tectonophysics. Address: 1503 Mirror Lake, Seabrook, TX 77586.

ENGLAND, CHARLES BENNETT, b. Thomasville, Ga, Nov. 12, 30; m. 53; c. 3. SOIL SCIENCE, HYDROLOGY. B.S, Univ. Ga, 56, M.S, 58; Ph.D. (soil sci), N.C. State Univ, 65. Res. instr. soil sci, N.C. State Univ, 59-65; RES. SOIL SCIENTIST, HYDROGRAPH LAB, AGR. RES. SERV, U.S. DEPT. AGR, 65- Soil Sci. Soc. Am; Am. Soc. Agron; Soil Conserv. Soc. Am. Application of soil physics to streamflow predictions; effects of soil and crop practices on runoff, evapotranspiration, and soil water in agricultural watersheds. Address: Soil & Water Conservation, Agricultural Research Service, U.S. Dept. of Agriculture, Beltsville, MD 20705.

ENGLAND, C(HARLES) W(ALTER), b. Rising Sun, Md, Dec. 5, 99; m. 25; c. 1. DAIRY INDUSTRY. B.S, Maryland, 23; M.S, Cornell, 31, Ph.D.(bact), 33. Chemist & bacteriologist, Simpson's Dairy, Inc, D.C, 23-29; private dairy lab, Frederick, Md, 29-30; asst. bact, Cornell, 31-33; instr. dairy mfg, Maryland, 33-34, asst. prof, 34-35, assoc. prof, 35-38, prof, 38-44; tech. dir, C.Y. Stephens Dairy & Poultry Industs, D.C, 44-54; dir, England Labs, Md, 54-69; RETIRED. Bacteriologist, Inlet Valley Farms, Inc, N.Y, 31-32. Am. Dairy Sci. Asn; Inst. Food Technol. Ice cream; milk and milk products; foods and water. Address: 2030 Forest Hill Dr, Hillandale Forrest, Silver Spring, MD 20903.

ENGLAND, DAVID C(HARLES), b. Portland, Oregon, Mar. 5, 19; m. 45; c. 4. ORGANIC CHEMISTRY. A.B, Oregon State Col, 40; Ph.D.(org. chem), Wisconsin, 43. RES. CHEMIST, E.I. DU PONT DE NEMOURS & CO, 43- With Office Sci. Res. & Develop, 44. Am. Chem. Soc. Synthetic organic chemistry; catalytic dehydrogenation; hydrogenation; hydrocyanation; nitrilation, fluoroorganics. Address: Experimental Station, E.I. du Pont de Nemours & Co, Wilmington, DE 19898.

ENGLAND, DAVID C(HARLES), b. Myrtle, Mo, Jan. 4, 22; m. 46; c. 5. ANIMAL BREEDING. B.S, Washington State, 49; M.S, Minnesota, 50, Ph.D, 52. Asst. animal husbandman, Minnesota, 49-51, res. fel, 51-53, asst. prof. ANIMAL HUSB, 53-55; OREGON STATE UNIV, 55-61, assoc. prof, 61-69, PROF, 69- Mem. coop. state res. serv, U.S. Dept. Agr, 68-69. Am. Soc. Animal Sci. Genetics; swine production. Address: Dept. of Animal Science, Withycombe 112, Oregon State University, Corvallis, OR 97331.

ENGLAND, DON, b. Lyles, Tenn, Feb. 4, 37; m. 61; ORGANIC & PHARMACEUTICAL CHEMISTRY. B.S, Austin Peay State Col, 58; M.S, Arkansas, 61; Nat. Insts. Health fel. & Ph.D.(pharmaceut. chem), Mississippi, 66. Asst. prof. CHEM, HARDING COL, 60-63, ASSOC. PROF, 66- Summer res. assoc, sch. pharm, Mississippi, 66. AAAS; Am. Chem. Soc. Antihypertensive natural products and synthesis of potential antihypertensive agents. Address: Dept. of Chemistry, Box 543, Harding College, Searcy, AR 72143.

ENGLAND, JAMES WALTON, b. Newton, Kans, July 20, 38; m. 61; c. 1. MATHEMATICS. A.B, Kans. State Col. Pittsburgh, 60; M.A, Univ. Mo, 61, Ph.D.(math), 64. Asst. prof. MATH, Univ. Va, 64-68; SWARTHMORE COL, 68-69, ASSOC. PROF, 69- Am. Math. Soc; Math. Asn. Am. Topological dynamics, especially dynamic theory of transformation groups, with noncompact phase groups. Address: Dept. of Mathematics, Swarthmore College, Swarthmore, PA 19081.

ENGLAND, MILTON (W), b. Shamrock, Tex, Feb. 28, 17; m. 40; c. 2. ANIMAL BREEDING. B.S, Panhandle Agr. & Mech. Col, 42; M.S, Okla. Agr. & Mech. Col, 49. Asst. prof. ANIMAL HUSB, PANHANDLE STATE COL, 42-44, PROF, 44-, HEAD DEPT, 55- Am. Soc. Animal Sci. Performance testing of beef cattle; high concentrate rations for fattening beef cattle; grain preparation for feedlot cattle. Address: Box 186, Goodwell, OK 73939.

ENGLAND, RICHARD JAY, b. Springfield, Ill, Aug. 5, 26; m. 51; c. 3. POLYMER & ANALYTICAL CHEMISTRY. B.S, Bradley, 51. Chemist, explosives dept, E.I. DU PONT DE NEMOURS & CO, INC, N.J, 53-55, process chemist, 55-56, RES. CHEMIST, W.Va, 56-57, textile fibers dept, Va, 57, N.C, 57-59, FILM DEPT, 59- U.S.N.R, 44-46; U.S.A.F.R, 51-53, 1st Lt. Am. Chem. Soc. ϵ-Caprolactam; high explosives; polyester films and fibers; supervision; petroleum products. Address: E.I. du Pont de Nemours & Co, Inc, Film Dept, Technical Section, Circleville, OH 43113.

ENGLAND, WAYNE H, b. Phila, Pa, June 7, 37; m. 63; c. 2. PLANT ANATOMY, AGRICULTURAL MICROBIOLOGY. B.S, Waynesburg Col, 60; M.S, West Virginia, 62, Ph.D.(agr. microbiol), 65. Asst. prof. biol. & microbiol, SALEM COL.(W.VA), 65-70, chmn. dept. biol, 66-70, DEAN COL, 70- U.S.N, 56-58. Bot. Soc. Am; Am. Inst. Biol. Sci. Plant mycology, especially the anatomical aspects of the host-parasite complex associated with fungi which parasitize higher plants. Address: Salem College, Salem, WV 26426.

ENGLANDER, HAROLD R(OBERT), b. N.Y.C, Dec. 11, 23; m. 49; c. 1. DENTISTRY. D.D.S, Columbia, 48, M.P.H, 51. Prin. investr, U.S. Naval Dent. Res. Facility, Great Lakes, Ill, 53-58; assoc. prof. dent, dent. col, Illinois, 59-62; mem. staff, EPIDEMIOL. & BIOMET. BR, NAT. INST. DENT. RES, 62-67, DENT. DIR. & CHIEF FIELD TRIALS, 67- Vis. prof, Howard Univ; vis. lectr, Johns Hopkins Univ. Sch. Pub. Health; Univ. Md; consult, prev. dent, Surgeon Gen, U.S. Army. Dipl, Am. Bd. Dent. Pub. Health. U.S.N, 48-59, Lt. Comdr. AAAS; Am. Dent. Asn; fel. Am. Pub. Health Asn; Int. Dent. Fedn; Am. Pub. Health Asn; Int. Asn. Dent. Res; fel. Am. Col. Dent. Epidemiology; caries research in hamsters; clinical trials of anticaries agents. Address: National Institute of Dental Research, National Institutes of Health, Westwood Bldg, Room 528, Bethesda, MD 20014.

ENGLANDER, SOL WALTER, b. Baltimore, Md, Jan. 25, 30; m. 54; c. 3. BIOPHYSICS. B.S, Maryland, 51; M.S, Pittsburgh, 54, Ph.D.(biophys), 59. Biophysicist, Nat. Insts. Health, 59-61; instr. BIOCHEM, Dartmouth Med. Sch, 61-63, asst. prof, 63-67, ASSOC. PROF, SCH. MED, UNIV. PA, 67- Am. Cancer Soc. fel, 61-63. U.S.A, 54-55. Physical biochemistry; protein and nucleic acid structure and function; hydrogen exchange. Address: Dept. of Biochemistry, University of Pennsylvania School of Medicine, Philadelphia, PA 19104.

ENGLARD, SASHA, b. Antwerp, Belgium, June 28, 29; nat; m. 51; c. 3. BIOCHEMISTRY. B.S, City Col. New York, 49; Nat. Insts. Health fel, 51-53; Ph.D, Western Reserve, 53. Am. Heart Asn. fel, Pratt Inst, Hopkins, 53-55; assoc. prof. BIOCHEM, ALBERT EINSTEIN COL. MED, YESHIVA UNIV, 55-68, PROF, 68- Nat. Insts. Health spec. fel. & vis. prof, Hebrew Univ, Israel. Am. Soc. Biol. Chem; Brit. Biochem. Soc. Mechanism of enzyme reaction; stereospecificity of enzymatically catalyzed reactions; carbohydrate metabolism. Address: 1234 Pawnee Pl, New York, NY 10461.

ENGLE, A(LLEN) WENDELL, b. Sapulpa, Okla, Sept. 7, 17; m. 41; c. 1. ENGINEERING. B.S, Okla. Agr. & Mech. Col, 39, M.S, 53. Field engr, Well Surv, Okla, 39-41; Lane Wells Co, Houston, 41-42; instr. electronics, Okla. Agr. & Mech. Col, 42-45; res. engr, Well Surv, Inc, Okla, 45-59, proj. supvr, 59-61; SR. RES. ENGR, Lane-Wells Co, 61-68; Dresser Atlas, 68-70; DRESSER PETROL. SERV, 70- Am. Geophys. Union; Soc. Explor. Geophys; Acoust. Soc. Am. Design of nuclear measuring equipment; radioactivity and electrical well logging; acoustic well log systems; digital systems design. Address: 618 Diamond Leaf St, Houston, TX 77024.

ENGLE, CARL F(RANKLIN), b. Sunbury, Pa, Dec. 29, 30; m. 56; c. 4. AGRONOMY. B.S, Pa. State, 53, M.S, 55, Ph.D.(agron), 64. Instr. soil tech, Pa. State Univ, 57-64; asst. prof. agron. & genetics, W.Va. Univ, 64-70, exten. agronomist, 67-70; ASSOC. PROF. AGRON. & SOILS & EXTEN. SOIL SCIENTIST, WASH. STATE UNIV, 70- U.S.A, 55-57. Soil Conserv. Soc. Am; Am. Soc. Agron. Soil physics and characterization; soil fertility and soil management extension. Address: Dept. of Agronomy & Soils, 169 Johnson Hall, Washington State University, Pullman, WA 99163.

ENGLE, DAMON L(AWSON), b. Troy, W.Va, June 22, 19; m. 43; c. 4. POLYMER CHEMISTRY. B.S, Marshall, 41. Anal. chemist, chem. div, UNION CARBIDE CORP, 42-51, group leader synthetic fibers, 52-56, polymers, plastics div, 56-59, asst. dir. res. & develop, 59-66, dir, 66-69, ASST. PLANT MGR, CHEM. & PLASTICS DIV, 69- Am. Chem. Soc; Soc. Rheol; Am. Soc. Test. & Mat. Synthetic polymer technology. Address: Chemicals & Plastics Division, Union Carbide Corp, P.O. Box 8003, South Charleston, WV 25303.

ENGLE, EARL A(GARD), b. Litchfield, Mich, Oct. 11, 97; m. 34; c. 2. CHEMISTRY. B.A, Univ. Denver, 18, M.S, 19; Ph.D.(chem), Univ. Ill, 22; Univ. Mich, 37. Asst. & fel. chem, Univ. Ill, 19-21; from asst. prof. to prof. CHEM, UNIV. DENVER, 22-65, EMER. PROF, 65-, chmn. dept, 36-62, chmn. div. sci, 42-63. With Bur. Mines, 44. C.W.S, U.S.A, 17-19. AAAS; Am. Chem. Soc. Trace analysis; toxicology; pesticides; fertilizers. Address: 2233 S. Columbine St, Denver, CO 80210.

ENGLE, EDISON G(ROVE), JR, b. York, Pa, Oct. 14, 22; m. 45; c. 2. METEOROLOGY. B.S, Pa. State Teachers Col.(Millersville), 43; M.A, George Washington, 58. METEOROLOGIST, Capital Airlines, 46; U.S. Weather Bur, 46-50; U.S. GOVT, 50- U.S.A.A.F, 43-45. Am. Meteorol. Soc. Synoptic meteorology; urban climatology; physical geography. Address: 6207 Kellogg Dr, McLean, VA 22101.

ENGLE, JOHN E, b. Tampa, Fla, Sept. 14, 35; m. 57; c. 6. ORGANIC CHEMISTRY. B.A, Emory Univ, 57; Ph.D.(org. chem), Ga. Inst. Technol, 61. CHEMIST, REDSTONE RES. LABS, ROHM & HAAS CO, 60- Am. Chem. Soc; The Chem. Soc. Stereochemistry; high energy organic compounds. Address: Redstone Research Labs, Rohm and Haas Co, Huntsville, AL 35807.

ENGLE, JOHN FRANKLIN, b. Shoshone, Idaho, Aug. 15, 21; m. 44; c. 5. ELECTRICAL ENGINEERING. B.S, Oregon State, 47, M.S, 51. Instr. ELEC. ENG, ORE. STATE UNIV, 47-52, asst. prof, 52-58, assoc. prof, 58-69, PROF, 69- Consult, hydroelec. design br, N.Pac.Div, U.S. Army Crops Eng, 62- U.S.A.F, 42-46, 1st Lt. Asn. Comput. Mach; Am. Soc. Eng. Educ; Inst. Elec. & Electronics Eng. Electric power systems; digital simulation; component modeling; on-line digital control. Address: Dept. of Electrical Engineering, Oregon State University, Corvallis, OR 97331.

ENGLE, MARY ALLEN (ENGLISH), b. Madill, Okla, Jan. 26, 22; m. 45; c. 2. PEDIATRICS, CARDIOLOGY. A.B, Baylor, 42; M.D, Hopkins, 45. Intern pediat, univ. hosp, Hopkins, 45-46, asst. dir, outpatient dept, 46-47, asst. physician, cardiac clin, 47-48, instr, sch. med, 46-48; asst. pediat, MED. COL, CORNELL UNIV, 48-49, fel, pediat. & asst. pharmacol, 49-50, instr. PEDIAT, 50-51, 52-54, asst. prof, 54-59, assoc. prof, 59-69, PROF, 69-; DIR. PEDIAT. CARDIOL. & ATTEND. PEDIATRICIAN, N.Y. HOSP, 62-, asst. res. & sr. asst. res, 48-49, asst. attend. pediatrician, 52-59, assoc. attend. pediatrician, 59-62. Asst. res, Sydenham Hosp, Md, 46; med. dir, Inst. Care of Premature Infants, 52-55; mem. exec. comt, adv. comt. & chmn. study sect. congenital heart disease, Inter-Soc. Comn. Heart Disease Resources, 69-71. Dept, Am. Bd. Pediat, cert, cardiol. Spence-Chapin

Award, 58. Am. Acad. Pediat; Am. Heart Asn; Soc. Pediat. Res; Am. Col. Chest Physicians; Am. Pediat. Soc; Asn. Europ. Pediat. Cardiol; Am. Col. Cardiol. Pediatric cardiology, especially congenital malformations of heart and great vessels. Address: New York Hospital, 525 E. 68th St, New York, NY 10021.

ENGLE, PAUL R(ANDAL), b. Newton, Iowa, Oct. 16, 19; m. 45; c. 1. ASTRONOMY, PHYSICS. B.A, Pan Am. Col, 58; Nat. Sci. Found. summer insts, Yale, 59, Arizona, 61 & Georgetown, 62; summers, State Univ. N.Y. Col. Oswego, 69, Mich. State Univ, 70, 71. Jr. engr. & instr. astron, phys. sci. lab, New Mexico State, 48-51; flight instr. & asst. to dir, Calif. East. Aviation, Tex, 51-58; DIR. OBSERV, PAN AM. UNIV, 56-, GEOD. SATELLITE PROG, 66- Prin. investr, Nat. Sci. Found. grants, 62-65; dir, NASA-Goddard Minitrack Optical Tracking Sta, 66- U.S.A.A.F.R. Asn. Lunar & Planetary Observers; Am. Astronaut. Soc; Am. Asn. Physics Teachers; Am. Astron. Soc; Brit. Astron. Asn; Pan Am. Soc. Astrophys. Res.(pres, 61-). Astronomical instrumentation; development of course programs in astro-science and astronomy for college and high school levels. Address: Observatory & Astro-Science Center, Pan American University, Edinburg, TX 78539.

ENGLE, RALPH L(ANDIS), JR, b. Phila, Pa, June 11, 20; m. 45; c. 2. MEDICINE, HEMATOLOGY. B.S, Florida, 42; M.D, Hopkins, 45. Intern path, NEW YORK HOSP, 45-46, med, 48-49, asst. res, 49-51, res. hematol, 50-51, asst. attend. physician, 54-57, assoc. attend. physician, 57-69, ATTEND. PHYSICIAN, 69-; PROF. MED, MED. COL, CORNELL UNIV, 69-, asst, 49-51, res. fel, 50, asst. prof. med, 52-57, assoc. prof, 57-69. Am. Cancer Soc. fel, Washington (St. Louis), 51-52; Markle scholar, 52-57; chief hemat. div. dept. med, New York Hosp, 61-67; consult, Vet. Admin. Hosp, New York, 64-; chief div. med. systs. & comput. sci, dept. med, New York Hosp-Cornell Univ, 67-; dir. dept. med. systs. & comput. serv, New York Hosp, 68-; mem, cancer clin. invest. rev. comt, Nat. Cancer Inst, 68-; comt. sci. & tech. commun, Nat. Acad. Sci-Nat. Acad. Eng, 67-70. Dipl, Am. Bd. Internal Med. Med.C, 46-48, Capt. AAAS; Am. Soc. Hemat; Am. Physiol. Soc; Am. Fedn. Clin. Res; Am. Med. Asn; Soc. Exp. Biol. & Med; Asn. Comput. Mach; Am. Soc. Info. Sci. Hematology; pathology; computer applications to medicine. Address: New York Hospital, 525 E. 68th St, New York, NY 10021.

ENGLE, ROBERT B, b. Decatur, Ill, Apr. 10, 31; m. 53; c. 4. APPLIED MECHANICS. B.S, Purdue, 53, M.S, 58; Ph.D.(appl. mech), Mich. State, 67. Instr. appl. mech, Mich. State, 58-66; MECH. ENGR, LAWRENCE RADIATION LAB, 66- Ord.C, U.S.A, 53, Res, 57-, Maj. Acoustic emission-research dealing with basic mechanisms and application of techniques to material evaluation; creep behavior of composite materials-development of test techniques and equipment. Address: 1024 Via Madrid, Livermore, CA 94550.

ENGLE, R(OBERT) F(RY), JR, b. Phila, Pa, Jan. 6, 10; m. 40; c. 3. CHEMISTRY. B.S, Haverford Col, 32; Ph.D.(phys. chem), Cornell, 37. Asst. chem, Cornell, 33-37; res. chemist, Solvay Process Co, N.Y, 37-43; Anthracite Inst, Pa, 43-46; TEXTILE FIBERS DEPT, E.I. DU PONT DE NEMOURS & CO, INC, 46-63, PATENT ASSOC, 63- Am. Chem. Soc. Phase rule studies; electrochemistry; corrosion; process development; combustion of solid fuels; synthetic fiber research and development; patent liaison. Address: Textile Fibers Dept, E.I. du Pont de Nemours & Co, Inc, Wilmington, DE 19898.

ENGLE, ROBERT R(UFUS), b. Sullivan Co, Ind, Jan. 29, 30; m. 54; c. 6. ORGANIC CHEMISTRY. B.A, DePauw, 51; Am. Platinum Works fel, Wayne State, 52-53, M.S, 53, fels, 55-58, Ph.D.(chem), 58. Asst, Wayne State, 51-52, 55; sr. res. chemist, Riker Labs, Inc, 58-65; HEAD, CHEM. & DRUG PROCUREMENT SECT, CANCER CHEMOTHER. NAT. SERV. CTR, NAT. CANCER INST, 65- Chem.C, 53-55. Am. Chem. Soc; Am. Asn. Cancer Res. Synthesis; chemistry of natural products; structure determination; pharmaceuticals; cancer chemotherapy. Address: 8305 Tuckerman Lane, Potomac, MD 20854.

ENGLEHART, RICHARD W(ILSON), b. Sept. 2, 38; m. 64; c. 2. NUCLEAR ENGINEERING. B.S, Carnegie-Mellon Univ, 60; Nat. Sci. Found. coop. fels, Pa. State Univ, 62 & 63, M.S, 63, Atomic Energy Comn. traineeship, 67, Ph.D.(nuclear eng), 69. Mech. engr, Atlantic Res. Corp, summer 60; proj. engr, U.S. Army reactors group, Atomic Energy Comn, 64-66; ASST. PROF. NUCLEAR ENG, UNIV. FLA, 68- Reactor supvr, Univ. Fla, 69-71; sr. nuclear engr, Fla. Power Corp, summer 71; Am. Soc. Eng. Educ-Ford Found. resident fel. prog, consult. engr, Gilbert Assocs, Inc, 71-72. C.Eng, U.S.A, 64-66, Capt. Am. Nuclear Soc; Am. Soc. Eng. Educ. Nuclear reactor power calibrations; neutron diffraction from vibrating crystals; thermal and hydraulic analysis; radionuclide transport through the environment; environmental aspects of electric power plants; teaching methods. Address: 202 Nuclear Sciences Bldg, University of Florida, Gainesville, FL 32601.

ENGLEHART, EDWIN T(HOMAS), JR, b. Johnstown, Pa, Aug. 7, 21; m. 51; c. 1. CHEMISTRY. B.S, Pa. State, 43. Res. engr, corrosion, res. labs, Aluminum Co. of Am, 43-59, SECT. HEAD CHEM. METALL. DIV, ALCOA RES. LABS, 59- Fel. Am. Inst. Chem; Sci. Res. Soc. Am. Solution of fundamental and practical corrosion problems dealing with aluminum, its alloys and other metals. Address: 450 Dakota Dr, New Kensington, PA 15068.

ENGLEMAN, CHRISTIAN L, b. Vancouver, Wash, Apr. 3, 06; m; c. 5. PHYSICS. B.S, U.S. Naval Acad, 30; M.S, Harvard, 39. Mem. mat. surv. anal. group, hqs, U.S. Navy, Australia & Japan, 45, mem. staff, electronics coord. off, Bikini Atomic Tests, 46, dir. Bikini sci. resurvey, 47, commun. & electronics test off, Eniwetok Atomic Tests, 48, res. & develop. bd, Off. Secy. Defense, 49, dir. electronics design & develop, U.S. Navy Bur. Ships, 50; sci. consult, 53; pres, Engleman & Co, Inc, 56-61; v.pres, C-E-I-R, Inc, 61-62; exec. v.pres, Wachtel & Co, D.C, 63-65; v.pres, Nat. Health Fedn, 65-69; CONSULT, 69- Pres, Davohn Corp, 57-64; treas, Data Dynamics, 63-64, mem. bd. dirs, 63-65. Financial & mgt. consult, 64- Trustee & treas, Found. Nutrit. & Stress Res, 65-66. Fel. Inst. Elec. & Electronics Eng. Address: Kanati Falls Ranch, Route 2, P.O. Box 504, Washougal, WA 98671.

ENGLEMAN, EPHRAIM P(HILIP), b. San Jose, Calif, March 24, 11; m. 41; c. 3. MEDICINE. A.B, Stanford, 33; M.D, Columbia, 37. Asst. clin. prof. MED, SCH. MED, UNIV. CALIF, SAN FRANCISCO, 48-57, assoc. clin. prof, 57-64, PROF, 64-, CHIEF RHEUMATIC DISEASE GROUP, MED. CTR, 58- Consult, regional off, U.S. Vet. Admin, San Francisco, 50-; San Francisco Army Hosp, 60-; secy-gen, Int. League Against Rheumatism, 61- Med.C, 42-47, Maj. Am. Rheumatism Asn.(pres, 62-63); Am. Col. Physicians; Am. Fedn. Clin. Res. Rheumatic diseases. Address: 359 N. San Mateo Dr, San Mateo, CA 94401.

ENGLEMAN, ROLF, JR, b. Norman, Okla, Mar. 16, 34; m. 56; c. 3. PHYSICAL CHEMISTRY. B.S, Oklahoma, 55; Ph.D.(chem), Calif. Inst. Tech, 59. STAFF MEM. CHEMIST, LOS ALAMOS SCI. LAB, 59- AAAS; Am. Chem. Soc; Am. Phys. Soc. Spectroscopy and kinetics of free radicals studied by flash photolysis and high resolution optical spectroscopy. Address: Los Alamos Scientific Lab, GMX2, P.O. Box 1663, Los Alamos, NM 87544.

ENGLEMAN, VICTOR SOLOMON, b. Brooklyn, N.Y, Dec. 31, 40; m. 65; c. 2. CHEMICAL ENGINEERING. B.S, Calif. Inst. Technol, 62; Nat. Sci. Found. fel, Univ. Calif, 63-64, M.S, 64, NASA trainee, 65-67, Ph.D.(chem. eng), 67. Proj. engr, Air Force Rocket Propulsion Lab, 67-70; RES. ENGR, ESSO RES. & ENG. CO, 70- Lectr, Golden Gate Col, 69-70. U.S.A.F, 67-70, Capt. Am. Chem. Soc; Am. Inst. Chem. Eng; Combustion Inst; Air Pollution Control Asn. Combustion; chemical kinetics; air pollution. Address: Esso Research & Engineering Co, P.O. Box 8, Linden, NJ 07036.

ENGLER, ARNOLD, b. Czernovitz, Romania, July 19, 27; m. 61. PHYSICS. Hebrew Univ, Israel, 46-47 & 49; Ph.D.(physics), Berne, 53. Res. assoc. PHYSICS, Berne, 53-54; Bristol, 54-56; Rochester, 56-58; sr. res. off, Oxford, 58-60; res. assoc. & assoc. prof, Duke, 60-61; assoc. prof, Northwestern, 61-62; Carnegie Inst. Technol, 62-66, PROF, CARNEGIE-MELLON UNIV, 66- Summer vis. assoc. physicist, Brookhaven Nat. Lab, 63; fel, St. Cross Col, Oxford, Eng, 66-67. Israeli Forces, 48-49, Sgt. Fel. Am. Phys. Soc; Italian Phys. Soc. Elementary particle physics; cosmic ray physics. Address: Dept. of Physics, Carnegie-Mellon University, Pittsburgh, PA 15213.

ENGLER, HAROLD S, b. Augusta, Ga, Jan. 10, 23; m. 50; c. 5. MEDICINE, SURGERY. M.D, Med. Col. Ga, 50. Instr. SURG, MED. COL. GA, 50-58, asst. prof, 58-61, assoc. prof, 61-66, PROF, 66- Dipl, Am. Bd. Surg, 58. U.S.A.F, 42-46, 1st Lt. Am. Col. Surg; James Ewing Soc. Cancer and surgical research. Address: Dept. of Surgery, Medical College of Georgia, Augusta, GA 30902.

ENGLER, RETO A(RNOLD), b. Zurich, Switz, Nov. 20, 31; U.S. citizen; m; c. 1. ORGANIC CHEMISTRY. Dipl. chem. eng, Swiss. Fed. Inst. Tech, 54; Ph.D.(chem), Tübingen, 58. Asst. virol, Max Planck Inst. Virus Res, 58-60; lectr. pediat, med. ctr, Univ. Kans, 60-61, asst. prof, 61-66, biochem, 66-68; virologist, div. microbiol, Fed. Food & Drug Admin, 68, res. chemist, 68-71; TOXICOLOGIST & CHEMIST, PESTICIDES TOLERANCES DIV, ENVIRON. PROTECTION AGENCY, 71- Lectr, Univ. Mo-Kansas City, 63-67. AAAS; N.Y. Acad. Sci; Am. Soc. Microbiol. Biosynthesis of viruses in plants and animals, especially the synthesis of viral nucleic acid; health hazard of viruses in food; virology; microbiological control of pests. Address: Pesticides Tolerances Division, Environmental Protection Agency, South Agricultural Bldg, 12th & C St. S.W, Washington, DC 20250.

ENGLERT, DU WAYNE C(LEVELAND), b. WaKeeney, Kans, Dec. 1, 32; m. 53; c. 2. POPULATION GENETICS. B.S, Kansas, 54; M.S, Purdue, 61, Ph.D.(genetics), 64. Asst. prof. ZOOL, SOUTH. ILL. UNIV, 63-69, ASSOC. PROF, 69- Vis. prof, dept. animal sci, Purdue Univ, 68-69. U.S.A, 54-56, Res, 56-62. Am. Genetics Asn; Genetics Soc. Am; Biomet. Soc; Genetics Soc. Can. Genotype by environment interactions in Drosophila and Tribolium; effects of environmental stress on sex ratio; selection and interrelationship of growth traits; genetic differences in growth curves; and genetic recombination in Tribolium castaneum. Address: Dept. of Zoology, Southern Illinois University, Carbondale, IL 62901.

ENGLERT, MARY ELIZABETH, b. New Orleans, La, July 11, 01. CHEMISTRY. A.B, Loyola (La), 23, M.A, 25; M.S, Wisconsin, 28, Ph.D.(org. chem), 33. Instr. CHEM, ST. MARY'S DOMINICAN COL, 24-28, PROF, 28- Assoc. res. mem, Inst. Divi Thomae, 40- AAAS; Am. Chem. Soc; Am. Inst. Chem. Local anesthetics; nucleoproteins; growth promoting substances; pyrazolones derived from carbethoxypiperidones. Address: 7214 St. Charles Ave, New Orleans, LA 70118.

ENGLERT, R(OBERT) D, b. Portland, Ore, Feb. 11, 20; m. 54. RESEARCH ADMINISTRATION. B.S, Univ. Portland, 42; B.S. & M.S, Ore. State Univ, 44; fel, Univ. Colo, 46-49, Ph.D.(org. chem), 49. Asst, Ore. State Univ, 43; biochemist, Naval Med. Res. Inst, 46; sr. org. chemist, Stanford Res. Inst, 49-55, mgr. phys. sci. res, South. Calif. Labs, 55-59, chmn, 59-62, dir, 62-68, exec. dir, 68-70; V.PRES. & GEN. MGR, ENVIRON. TECHNOL. DIV, DRESSER INDUST, INC, 70- U.S.N.R, 44-46. AAAS; Am. Chem. Soc; Am. Oil Chemists' Soc; Sci. Res. Soc. Am; Air Pollution Control Asn; Am. Inst. Chem. Fats and oils; chemistry of boron and antimony; herbicides and insecticides. Address: Environmental Technology Division, Dresser Industries, Inc, 1702 McGaw, Santa Ana, CA 92705.

ENGLES, EARL F(RANKLIN), JR, b. Henryetta, Okla, Aug. 7, 22; m. 45; c. 3. ORGANIC CHEMISTRY. B.S, Southeast. State Col, 43; M.S, Oklahoma, 48, Ph.D, 51. Group leader res, DOW CHEM. CO, 52-62, econ. eval. engr, 62-65, STAFF ASST. RES, 65-69, DOW INTERDISCIPLINE GROUP, 69- U.S.N.R, 43-46, Lt.(jg). Am. Chem. Soc. Preparation of alkyl-alkyl ketimines. Address: Dow Chemical Co, Dow Interdiscipline Group, 566 Bldg, Midland, MI 48640.

ENGLESBERG, ELLIS, b. N.Y, Oct. 19, 21; m. 42; c. 3. MICROBIOLOGY. B.A, Brooklyn Col, 45; M.A, California, 48, Ph.D.(bact), 50. Teaching asst. bact, California, 46-49, res. asst, 49-50, asst. res. bacteriologist, Hooper Found. Med. Res, 50-54; microbiologist, biol. lab, L.I. Biol. Asn, 54-58; PROF. bact, Pittsburgh, 58-65; MICROBIOL, UNIV. CALIF, SANTA BARBARA, 65-, chmn. dept, 66-69. Guggenheim fel, 71-72. Mem. adv. panel for genetic biol, Nat. Sci. Found, 62-65. U.S.A, 42-46, 2nd Lt. AAAS; Am. Soc. Microbiol; Genetics Soc. Am; Brit. Soc. Gen. Microbiol. Microbial physiology and genetics. Address: Dept. of Biological Sciences, University of California, Santa Barbara, CA 93106.

ENGLEY, FRANK B, JR, b. Wallingford, Conn, Oct. 26, 19; m. 48; c. 4. MICROBIOLOGY. B.S, Connecticut, 41; M.S, Pennsylvania, 44, Ph.D.(bact), 49. Technician, Atwater Lab, Conn. Agr. Exp. Sta, 38-41; asst. instr. bact, sch. med, Pennsylvania, 41-44; bacteriologist, Chem. Corps, U.S. Dept. Army, Camp Detrick, 46-50; assoc. prof. bact. & parasitol. & consult. bacteriologist, med. br. hosps, Texas, 50-55; PROF. MICROBIOL. & CHMN. DEPT, SCH. MED, UNIV. MO, 55-, asst. dean, 56-60, prof. prev. med. & chmn. dept, 60-61. Consult. bacteriologist, Vet. Admin. Hosp, 54-56. Sanit.C, U.S.A, 44-46. Dipl, Am. Bd. Microbiol. Fel. AAAS; Am. Soc. Microbiol; Soc. Exp. Biol. & Med; Sci. Res. Soc. Am; fel. Am. Pub. Health Asn; Asn. Am. Med. Cols; fel. Am. Acad. Microbiol; assoc. Am. Med. Asn; N.Y. Acad. Sci; Royal Soc. Health. Bacterial toxins; antiseptics and disinfectants; plastics in microbiology; ethylene oxide sterilization; survival of microorganisms. Address: Dept. of Microbiology, University of Missouri School of Medicine, Columbia, MO 65201.

ENGLISH, ALAN TAYLOUR, b. Los Angeles, Calif, Mar. 14, 34; m. 55; c. 4. METALLURGY. B.S, Stanford, 56; M.S, Mass. Inst. Tech, 60, Gen. Elec. Co. fel, 61-62, Ph.D.(metall), 63. MEM. TECH. STAFF, METALL. LAB, BELL TEL. LABS, MURRAY HILL, 63- U.S.N, 56-59, Lt.(jg). Am. Inst. Mining, Metall. & Petrol. Eng; Am. Soc. Metals. Metal processing; brittle fracture; hot working of metals; crystallographic and mechanical textures in metals; structure-dependant magnetic properties; recrystallization; phase transformations; solid phase welding; thin-film materials. Address: 4 Drum Hill Dr, Summit, NJ 07901.

ENGLISH, ALBERT CHARLES, b. York, Eng, Feb. 24, 19; nat; m. 50; c. 2. PHYSICAL CHEMISTRY. B.Sc, Durham, 40, M.Sc, 47; fel, Northwestern, 48-49, Ph.D, 49. Jr. sci. off, Ministry of Aircraft Prod, Eng, 40-42; sci. off, Atomic Energy Cmn. Proj, Can, 43-46; res. assoc, Northwestern, 46-48; asst. prof. chem, Kentucky, 49-51; res. engr, Gen. Elec. Co, 51-56; ASSOC. PROF. ELEC. ENG, UNIV. CALIF, BERKELEY, 56- AAAS; Am. Phys. Soc; Inst. Elec. & Electronics Eng. Inorganic analysis; microchemistry; radiochemistry; semiconductors; solid state physics; rectifiers. Address: Dept. of Electrical Engineering, University of California, Berkeley, CA 94720.

ENGLISH, ARTHUR R(OBERT), b. Kankakee, Ill, Feb. 29, 20; m. 52; c. 2. BACTERIOLOGY. B.S, Illinois, 42; M.S, Wisconsin, 46, Ph.D.(bact. & biochem), 50. RES. BACTERIOLOGIST, PFIZER INC, 50- U.S.N.R, 42-46, Lt. AAAS; Am. Soc. Microbiol; Soc. Indust. Microbiol; Soc. Exp. Biol. & Med; Am. Acad. Microbiol. Resistance to antibiotics; chemotherapeutic evaluation of new antibiotics. Address: Pfizer Inc, Bldg. 69, Groton, CT 06340.

ENGLISH, BRUCE V(AUGHAN), b. Richmond, Va, Aug. 6, 21; m. 49; PHYSICS. B.S, Randolph-Macon Col, 42; M.S, Indiana, 43; Danforth fel, Virginia, 56-57, Du Pont fel, 57-58, Ph.D.(physics), 58. Asst. physics, Indiana, 42-43; assoc. prof, Randolph-Macon Col, 43-44; physicist, U.S. Naval Res. Lab, Wash, D.C, 44-45, N.J, 45-46, Fla, 46-48; assoc. prof. physics, Randolph-Macon Col, 48-58, prof, 58-64, acting head dept, 52-58, head dept, 58-64; consult. physicist, 64-67; pres, Pollution Control Assocs, 67-71; PHYSICIST & CONSULT, 71- Ford fel, Pa. State Col, 51-52. With Manhattan Dist, Engrs, 42-43. AAAS; Am. Phys. Soc; Am. Asn. Physics Teachers; Acoust. Soc. Am; Brit. Soc. Clean Air. Ultracentrifuge; gravity; clean air; pollution control. Address: P.O. Box 267, Ashland, VA 23005.

ENGLISH, DARREL S(TARR), b. Newton, Kans, Sept. 6, 36; m. 60; c. 2. GENETICS. B.A, Southwestern Col, 59; M.S, La. State, Baton Rouge, 61; Nat. Sci. Found. Summer Insts, Purdue, 62 & Iowa State, 63, Ph.D.(genetics), Iowa State, 68. Asst. zool, La. State, 59-61; instr. biol, Millsaps Col, 61-64; asst. GENETICS, Iowa State, 64-65, instr, 65-67; asst. prof, NORTH. ARIZ. UNIV, 67-71, ASSOC. PROF, 71- Nat. Sci. Found. lectr. histochem, Vanderbilt Univ, 71. Am. Genetic Asn; Genetics Soc. Am. Developmental genetics of hemoglobin synthesis in Chironomus tentans; Drosophila mutagenesis. Address: Dept. of Biology, Northern Arizona University, Flagstaff, AZ 86001.

ENGLISH, FLOYD L, b. East Nicolaus, Calif, June 10, 34; m. 55; c. 2. SOLID STATE PHYSICS. A.B, Chico State Col, 59; M.S, Arizona State, 62, Ph.D.(physics), 65. Staff mem. tech, SANDIA LAB, 65-69, DIV. SUPVR. MICROELECTRONICS, 69- U.S.A, 54-57, Capt. Am. Phys. Soc; Inst. Elec. & Electronics Eng. Electrical characteristics of rectifying junctions; surface effects on ferroelectric and piezoelectric materials. Address: Division 1433, Sandia Corp, Albuquerque, NM 87115.

ENGLISH, JACKSON P(OLLARD), b. Richmond, Va, Jan. 25, 15; m. 39; c. 2. ORGANIC CHEMISTRY. B.S, Va. Mil. Inst, 35; Ph.D.(chem), Hopkins, 40. Chemist, Am. Cyanamid Co, 39-42, sr. group leader, chemother. div, 42-54, asst. to dir, 54-55, unit leader, org. chem. sect, Pearl River Labs, 55-56, asst. dir. exp. therapeut. sect, Lederle Labs, 56-60, dir. chem. res. & develop, agr. div, 60-69; DIR, RES. ADMIN, POLAROID CORP, 69- Fel. AAAS; Am. Chem. Soc; fel. N.Y. Acad. Sci; The Chem. Soc. Synthesis of chemotherapeutic agents; natural products; experimental therapeutics; pesticides; agricultural chemicals. Address: Polaroid Corp, 730 Main St, Cambridge, MA 02139.

ENGLISH, JAMES, JR, b. New Haven, Conn, Mar. 17, 12; m. 36; c. 2. ORGANIC CHEMISTRY. B.A, Yale, 33, Loomis fel, 35-36, Ph.D.(chem), 36. Lalor fel, Calif. Inst. Tech, 36-39; instr. chem, YALE, 39-43, asst. prof, 43-49, ASSOC. PROF. CHEM. & FEL, SAYBROOK COL, 49- Civilian with Atomic Energy Comn; Off. Sci. Res. & Develop. AAAS; Am. Chem. Soc. Organic synthesis; natural products; carbohydrates; synthesis of local anesthetics; isolation of plant hormones. Address: Dept. of Chemistry, Yale University, New Haven, CT 06520.

ENGLISH, JAMES A(NDREW), b. Harrison Valley, Pa, May 14, 10; m. 34, 60; c. 2. DENTISTRY. B.S, Pa. State Col, 32; D.D.S, Pennsylvania, 36, M.S, 48; Ph.D, Hopkins, 55. Intern, hosp, Pennsylvania, 35-36; head dent. br, Off. Naval Res. & Res. Div, Bur. Med. Surg, 52-53, res. assoc, dent. dept, Naval Med. Res. Inst, 52-58, head dent. br, 52-55, liaison off, Off. Naval Res, Eng, 56-57, head med. & dent. br, 58-60; PROF. ORAL BIOL, SCH. DENT, STATE UNIV. N.Y. BUFFALO, 60-, dean sch, 60-70. Chmn. comn. res, Int. Dent. Fedn; mem. nat. adv. dent. res. coun, Nat. Insts. Health. U.S.N, 36-60, Capt. AAAS; Am. Dent. Asn; fel. Am. Col. Dent; fel. Int. Col. Dent. Pathology; biochemistry; specific emphasis on dental problems. Address: Dept. of Oral Biology, School of Dentistry, State University of New York at Buffalo, 4510 Main St, Buffalo, NY 14226.

ENGLISH, J(OHN) MORLEY, b. Vancouver, B.C, Oct. 17, 15; m. 38; c. 2. ENGINEERING. B.A.Sc, British Columbia, 38; M.S, Southern California, 49; Ph.D, California, Los Angeles, 52. With Can. Dept. Mines & Resources, 35-38; Boeing Airplane Co, 38-40; resident tech. officer at Lockheed Aircraft Corp, British Air Cmn, 40-43, sect. supvr, spare parts eng. & mem. mgt. control staff, 43-45; res. staff mem, rocket ballistics test group, Calif. Inst. Tech, Edwards A.F. Base, 45; with Quinton Engrs, 46; lectr, Southern California, 47-49; assoc. prof, UNIV. CALIF, LOS ANGELES, 49-58, PROF, 58-, dir. eng. res, 59-62, head design, mgt. & planning div, 66-68. Mem. staff, Boeing Airplane Co, summer 54; mgr. aluminum struct. div, Harvey Aluminum Co, 56; Fulbright scholar, Robert Col, Istanbul, 57, Yugoslavia, 68; mgr. eng. design, Space Tech. Labs, Inc, Thomas-Ramo-Wooldridge, Inc, 62-63. Consult Harvey Aluminum Co, 51-56; ord. test sta, U.S. Navy, China Lake, 55; Northrop Aviation, 58-59; PI Steel, 57-60; Stanford Res. Inst, 58-59; TRW Inc, 63-; U.S. Agency Int. Develop, 65-; Bur. Yards & Docks, U.S. Navy, 65- Am. Soc. Civil Eng; Am. Soc. Eng. Educ.(Eugene L. Grant Award, 66); Inst. Mgt. Sci; assoc. fel. Am. Inst. Aeronaut. & Astronaut. Engineering economics; engineering management; operations research; structures. Address: 1140 Chantilly Rd, Los Angeles, CA 90024.

ENGLISH, JULIUS C, b. Plant City, Fla, Nov. 25, 21; m. 44; c. 6. MATHEMATICS. Ph.D.(math), Florida, 52. Math. physicist, Savannah River Lab, E.I. du Pont de Nemours & Co, 52-64; sr. scientist, Kaman Aircraft Co, 64-67; prin. scientist, B-K Dynamics, Inc, 67-69; MEM. TECH. STAFF, EAST. TECHNOL. CTR, XEROX DATA SYSTS, 70- U.S.A.A.F, 43-46. Elasticity; numerical computation analysis; operations research. Address: Eastern Technology Center, Xerox Data Systems, 1701 Research Blvd, Rockville, MD 20850.

ENGLISH, O(LIVER) SPURGEON, b. Presque Isle, Me, Sept. 27, 01. PSYCHIATRY. M.D, Jefferson Med. Col, 24. Intern, Jefferson Col. Hosp, 24-27; res. physician, Boston Psychopathic Hosp, 27-28; res. neurol. div, Montefiore Hosp. Chronic Disease, N.Y, 28-29; Commonwealth fel. PSYCHIAT, Harvard, 29-32; clin. prof, sch. med, TEMPLE UNIV, 33-38, prof, 38-70, EMER. PROF, 70-, head dept, 38-64. Psychiatrist, Charité Hosp, Ger, 29-30; Phila. Gen. Hosp, 33-47. Fel. Am. Med. Asn; fel. Am. Psychiat. Asn; Am. Psychoanal. Asn; fel. Am. Col. Physicians. Psycodynamics of psychosomatic disease; language of psychiatry; psychotherapy and public education. Address: 449 Righters Mill Rd, Narbeth, PA 19072.

ENGLISH, S(POFFORD) G(RADY), b. Mt. Pleasant, Tenn, Nov. 16, 15; m; c. 3. CHEMISTRY. B.S, Oklahoma, 38, M.S, 40; Ph.D.(chem), California, Berkeley, 43. Chemist, Okla. Geol. Surv, 36-40; asst. chem, California, 40-42; res. assoc, metall. lab, Chicago, 42-43; sect. chief, chem. div, Clinton Labs, Oak Ridge, 43-46; asst. prof. chem, California, Berkeley, 46-47; chief chem. br, div. res, U.S. ATOMIC ENERGY COMN, 47-60, spec. asst. to gen. mgr. for disarmament, 59-61, dep. dir, div. res, 60-61, ASST. GEN. MGR. FOR RES. & DEVELOP, 61-, CHMN. PLOWSHARE ADV. COMT, 59- U.S. del, UN Disarmament Conf, Eng, 55, Conf. on Statute of Int. Atomic Energy Agency, 56, Conf. on Discontinuance of Nuclear Weapons Tests, Switz, 59. Outstanding service award, Atomic Energy Comn, 56. Physical and nuclear chemistry; chemical kinetics; research and development of radiation detection instruments; administration of research. Address: United States Atomic Energy Commission, Washington, DC 20545.

ENGLISH, THOMAS DUNSTAN PATRICK, b. Pittsburgh, Pa, Nov. 21, 36; m. 58; c. 2. ELECTRICAL ENGINEERING, PHYSICS. B.S, Carnegie Inst. Tech, 58, Koppers Co. fel, 61, Ford Found. fel, 61-63, M.S, 62, Ph.D.(elec. eng), 63. Res. physicist, glass res. center, Pittsburgh Plate Glass Co, 58-60; staff engr. device metall, Int. Bus. Mach. Corp, 63-64, mem. staff comput. memories, Thomas J. Watson Res. Ctr, 64-68; GROUP ENGR, GEN. DYNAMICS CORP, 68- Am. Phys. Soc; Inst. Elec. & Electronics Eng. Resistive intermediate state of superconductive films of tin; solid state device metallurgy; computer memory research. Address: Microelectronics Dept, General Dynamics Corp, Ft. Worth, TX 76101.

ENGLISH, T(HOMAS) SAUNDERS, b. Wash, D.C, Aug. 6, 28; m. 67; c. 2. BIOLOGICAL OCEANOGRAPHY. B.S, Iowa State, 50, M.S, 51; Nat. Sci. Found. fel, Washington (Seattle), 52-53, Ph.D.(fisheries), 61; Fulbright fels, Oslo, 54 & Bergen, 54-55. Hatchery worker, Va. Comn. Game & Inland Fisheries, 47; asst, Iowa Co-op. Wildlife Res. Univ, 48, 49; res. assoc, Fisheries Res. Inst, Washington (Seattle), 51; lectr. fisheries, Alaska, 56-57; sr. oceanogr, Arctic Inst. N.Am, 57-58; instr. fisheries, Alaska, 58-59; asst. prof. OCEANOG, UNIV. WASH, 59-65, ASSOC. PROF, 65- U.S.A.F, 56-57, Capt. Am. Soc. Limnol. & Oceanog; Am. Fisheries Soc; Am. Inst. Fishery Res. Biol; Ecol. Soc. Am; Am. Soc. Ichthyol. & Herpet; Marine Biol. Asn. U.K; Plankton Soc. Japan. Fisheries biology; plankton sampling; arctic oceanography. Address: Dept. of Oceanography, University of Washington, Seattle, WA 98195.

ENGLISH, W(ILLIAM) DAVID, b. Toronto, Ont, Can, July 11, 25; nat; m. 46; c. 2. CHEMISTRY. B.Sc, Manitoba, 46; M.Sc, McGill, 50; Ph.D.(chem), Pa. State, 55. Sci. off, Defence Res. Chem. Labs, Can, 50-52; res. chemist, M.W. Kellogg Co, 55-57; U.S. Borax Res. Corp, Calif, 57-62; sr. res. scientist, McDONNELL DOUGLAS ASTRONAUT. CO, 62-67, SECT. CHIEF, 67- AAAS; Am. Chem. Soc; Sci. Res. Soc. Am; fel. Am. Inst. Chem; Soc. Aerospace Mat. & Process Eng; Cryogenic Soc. Am.(ed, Cryogenic Tech); Chem. Inst. Can; The Chem. Soc; Mex. Chem. Soc. Organometallic chemistry of silicon, boron, phosphorous; fluorine chemistry; inorganic and organic chemistry; materials science; cryogenics. Address: McDonnell Douglas Astronautics Co, 23800 Santa Ana Canyon Rd, Anaheim, CA 92806.

ENGLISH, W(ILLIAM) HARLEY, b. Lacrosse, Wash, Apr. 12, 11; m. 36; c. 3. PLANT PATHOLOGY. B.S, State Col. Wash, 35, Ph.D.(plant path), 40. Asst. plant path, State Col. Wash, 35-37, instr, 37-39; jr. pathologist, U.S. Dept. Agr, 39-43, asst. pathologist, 43-46; assoc. prof. PLANT PATH, Ore. State Col, 46-47; asst. prof, UNIV. CALIF, DAVIS, 47-50, assoc. prof, 50-56, PROF, 56- AAAS; Am. Phytopath. Soc. Bacterial and fungus diseases of deciduous fruit trees; mycology. Address: Dept. of Plant Pathology, University of California, Davis, CA 95616.

ENGLUND, BRUCE E(MERSON), b. Minneapolis, Minn, June 16, 24; m. 45; c. 2. ORGANIC CHEMISTRY. A.B, Carleton Col, 47; M.S, Illinois, 48, Atomic Energy Comn. fel, 49-50, Ph.D.(org. chem), 50. Res. chemist, chem. dept, E.I. du Pont de Nemours & Co, 50-55, res. supvr, film dept, 55-59, tech. supt, du Pont cellophane, 59-63, mgr. Indust. Films Customer Serv, 63-69; DIR. RES, Am. Process Equip. Corp, Fla, 69-70; KINETICS CORP, 70- U.S.N.R, Lt.(jg), 43-46. Am. Chem. Soc. Development of novel oil spill recovery equipment; non-polluting, external combustion Rankine cycle automotive engine systems, utilizing fluorocarbon working fluids; automotive emission measurement and control. Address: 8635 Midnight Pass Rd, Apt. C 206, Sarasota, FL 33581.

ENGLUND, CHARLES R, b. Oak Park, Ill, Feb. 20, 36; m. 56; c. 3. ORGANIC CHEMISTRY. B.S, Wheaton Col.(Ill), 58; M.A, Southern Illinois, 63, fel, 67-68, Ph.D.(chem), 68. Teacher, high sch, 58-60; asst. CHEM, Southern Illinois, 60-62; instr, Concordia Teachers Col.(Ill), 62-64, asst. prof, 64-65; instr, Southern Illinois, 65-67; ASSOC. PROF, BETHANY COL. (KANS), 68- Am. Chem. Soc. Preparation and structure determination of steroidal derivatives. Address: Dept. of Chemistry, Bethany College, Lindsborg, KS 67456.

ENGLUND, JOHN A(RTHUR), b. Omaha, Nebr, June 4, 26; m. 52; c. 5. MATHEMATICS. B.S, Creighton, 49; fel, Mass. Inst. Technol, 49-51, S.M, 51. Instr. math, Creighton, 51-54, asst. prof, 54-56; opers. analyst, Hq, Strategic Air Command, 56-62; mil. systs. analyst, U.S. Arms Control & Disarmament Agency, 62-63; mathematician, ANAL. SERV. INC, 63-64, chief, strategic br, 64-70, MGR. STRATEGIC DIV, 70- U.S.A.A.F, 44-46. Am. Math. Soc. Algebraic and analytic number theory; military systems analysis and operations research. Address: Strategic Division, Analytic Services Inc, 5613 Leesburg Pike, Falls Church, VA 22041.

ENGLUND, JOHN E(MIL), b. Canton, Ohio, July 5, 09; m. 42; c. 3. MECHANICAL ENGINEERING. Sc.B, Brown, 34. With Brown & Sharpe Mfg. Co, 34-40; Landis Tool Co, 40-41; assoc. MECH. ENG, COLUMBIA UNIV, 42-46, asst. prof, 46-47, assoc. prof, 47-56, PROF, 56-, dept. chmn, 55-58. Consult, mach. design & metalworking. AAAS; Am. Soc. Mech. Eng; Am. Soc. Eng. Educ; Soc. Hist. Technol. Research in gear tooth durability and metal cutting. Address: Dept. of Mechanical Engineering, School of Engineering & Applied Science, Columbia University, New York, NY 10027.

ENGLUND, PAUL THEODORE, b. Worcester, Mass, Mar. 25, 38; m. 61; c. 2. BIOCHEMISTRY. B.A, Hamilton Col, 60; Ph.D.(biochem), Rockefeller Univ, 66. Fel, sch. med, Stanford, 66-68; ASST. PROF. PHYSIOL. CHEM, SCH. MED, JOHNS HOPKINS UNIV, 68- Am. Chem. Soc. Protein chemistry; enzymology of nucleic acids. Address: Dept. of Physiological Chemistry, Johns Hopkins University School of Medicine, 725 N. Wolfe St, Baltimore, MD 21205.

ENGQUIST, ELMER H(OWARD), b. Chicago, Ill, Feb. 16, 21; m. 47; c. 5. CHEMICAL & NUCLEAR ENGINEERING. B.S, Illinois, 43; M.S, Northwestern, 47; M.S, Michigan, 58. Res. assoc, Chem. Warfare Serv. Develop. Lab, Mass. Inst. Tech, 43-45; chem. & electronic engr, Tech. Command, Army Chem. Center, 45-46; res. assoc. chem, Northwestern, 46-47; asst. chief radiological div, chem. & radiological labs, ARMY CHEM. CTR, 47-56, exec. asst. to chief scientist, chem. warfare labs, 56-58, dep. dir. res, CHEM. RES. & DEVELOP. LABS, EDGEWOOD ARSENAL, 58-62, dir. defensive systs, 62-65, CHIEF, DISSEMINATION RES. DEPT, 66- Am. Chem. Soc; Sci. Res. Soc. Am. Radiological defense; properties of aerosols; development of aerosol sampling equipment; efficiency of aerosol filtration equipment; chemical warfare; defensive equipment. Address: 624 S. Main St, P.O. Box 608, Bel Air, MD 21014.

ENGSTROM, E(LMER) W(ILLIAM), b. Minneapolis, Minn, Aug. 25, 01; m. 26; c. 1. ELECTRICAL ENGINEERING. B.S, Univ. Minn, 23; hon. D.Sc, N.Y. Univ, 49, Franklin & Marshall Col, 63, Rutgers, 63, Monmouth Col, 66; hon. LL.D, Findlay Col, 60, Rider Col, 61, W.Va. Univ, 62, Thiel Col, 63, N.Park Col, 64, Lycoming Col, 66, Houghton Col, 67; hon. Eng.D, Drexel Inst. Technol, 63, Lafayette Col, 66, Polytech. Inst. Brooklyn, 66; hon. D.F.A, Bethany Col, 66; hon. LH.D, Taylor Univ, 68. Radio engr, Gen. Electric Co, N.Y, 23-30; div. engr, in charge photophone, mfg. co, RCA CORP, N.J, 30-42, dir. gen. res, 42, dir. res, labs. div, 43, v.pres. in charge res, 45-51, v.pres. in charge, 51-54, exec. v.pres. res. & eng, 54-55, sr. exec. v.pres, 55-61, pres. & dir, 61-66, chief exec. off, 66-68, CHMN. EXEC. COMT, 66- Mem. Scand. res. & industs. tour, Norway, Sweden & Denmark, 46; adv. comt, res. div, col. eng, N.Y. Univ, 49-; defense sci. bd, U.S. Dept. Defense, 57; vis. comt, Nat. Bur. Standards; exec. tech. develop. bd, Polytech. Inst. Brooklyn; Nat. TV Syst. Comt; Radio Tech. Planning Bd; res. & develop. comt, Nat. Security Indust. Asn; chmn, vis. comt, Naval Res. Lab; mem. adv. coun, dept. elec. eng, Princeton; bd. trustees, Am-Scand. Found; Westmont Col, Calif; Univ. Minn. Found; bd. dirs, RCA Corp; Nat. Broadcasting Co; RCA Commun, Inc; Random House, Inc; Prudential Ins. Co. Am; bd. overseers, Found. Adv. Grad. Study Eng. Chmn. res. & eng. adv. panel electronics, Off. Asst. Secy. Defense, 54; v.chmn, Nat. Comn. Coop. Educ; chmn. Hoover Medal Bd. Award, 62; U.S. Indust. Payroll Savings Comt, 65. Trustee, Princeton Hosp; v.pres. & mem. bd. gov, Am. Swedish Hist. Found. Outstanding achievement award, Univ. Minn, 50; John Ericsson Medal, Am. Soc. Swedish Eng, 56; Christopher Columbus Int. prize, 59, Comdr, Order of Merit, Italy, 60; Order of Vasa, Sweden, 63 & Comndr, 65; award of merit, Aerospace Elec. Soc, 63; William Proctor Prize, Sci. Res. Soc. Am, 66. Nat. Acad. Eng.(Charles P. Steinmetz Centennial Medal, 65); fel. Inst. Elec. & Electronics Eng.(founders award, 66); Am. Soc. Metals (medal adv. res, 60); Electronic Industs. Asn.(medal of honor, 62); Aerospace Elec. Soc. (award of merit, 63); Indust. Res. Inst.(pres, 48; medal, 58); for. mem. Royal Swedish Acad. Eng. Sci.(silver plaquette, 49); hon. mem. Soc. Motion Picture & TV Eng.(progress medal, 55). High-power radio transmitters; broadcast-type receivers; sound motion pictures; radio tubes; black-and-white and color television. Address: RCA Corp, 30 Rockefeller Plaza, New York, NY 10020.

ENGSTROM, GEORGE WESLEY, b. Brookings, S.Dak, Oct. 24, 26; m. 61; c. 3. BIOCHEMISTRY, ORGANIC CHEMISTRY. B.S, S.Dak. State, 48, M.S, 53; Ph.D.(biochem), Wisconsin, 60. Teacher, high sch, S.Dak, 48-51; jr. chem. engr, Goodyear Tire & Rubber Co, Ohio, 53-56; fel. biochem, Wisconsin, 60-63; BIOCHEMIST, Mayo Clin, 63-65; NAT. ANIMAL DISEASE LAB, 65- Consult, gastroenterol. res. unit, St. Mary's Hosp, 63- Am. Chem. Soc. Mineral metabolism; vitamins; nutrition; intermediate metabolism; protein; toxicology. Address: National Animal Disease Lab, P.O. Box 70, Ames, IA 50010.

ENGSTROM, LEE EDWARD, b. Rock Island, Ill, Sept. 30, 41; div; c. 1. DEVELOPMENTAL GENETICS. B.S, Iowa Wesleyan Col, 65; M.S, Univ. Ill, Urbana, 67, Ph.D.(develop), 71. ASST. PROF. BIOL, BALL STATE UNIV, 70- Genetics Soc. Am; Soc. Develop. Biol; Am. Soc. Zool. Genetic controls and developmental relationships of gonad development in Drosophila melanogaster. Address: Dept. of Biology, Ball State University, Muncie, IN 47306.

ENGSTROM, RALPH W(ARREN), b. Grinnell, Iowa, Oct. 24, 14; m. 37; c. 2. PHYSICS. B.A, St. Olaf Col, 35; M.S, Northwestern, 37, univ. fel, 38-39, Ph.D.(physics), 39. Lab. asst. physics, St. Olaf Col, 34-35; asst, Northwestern, 35-38; instr. physics & math, St. Cloud State Teachers Col, Minn, 39-41; res. physicist, Nat. Defense Res. Comt, 41; RCA Mfg. Co, N.J, 41-43, TECH. ADV. ELECTRO-OPTICS PROD, RCA CORP, 43- Fel. Am. Phys. Soc. Multiplier phototubes; television camera tubes; photoconductors; image converter tubes. Address: 62 Orchard Rd, Blossom Hill, Lancaster, PA 17601.

ENGSTROM, RUBY M(ARIA), b. Duluth, Minn, July 21, 10; m. 49; c. 3. ANATOMY, PATHOLOGY. B.S, Northwestern, 36; M.S, Minnesota, 46, M.B, 48, M.D, 49. Dir. nursing, Swedish Covenant Hosp, Ill, 37-43; teaching asst. anat, Minnesota, 43-46; intern, Wayne County Gen. Hosp, Mich, 48-49, res. int. med, 49-50, path, 50-54, chief res, 54-55; pathologist, People's Community, Beyer, Annapolis & Outer Dr. Hosp, 59-61; PATHOLOGIST, CYTOL. & PATH. LAB, 56- Asst. Wayne County Hosp, 59-68. Borden award, 48. Am. Soc. Cytol; fel. Am. Soc. Clin. Path; fel. Col. Am. Path; Int. Acad. Path. Effect of urethane on mouse myelogenous leukemia; effect of urethane, x-rays, potassium arsenite and benzol in survival time in transplanted mouse leukemia; cytology of rabbit thymus; acute cor pulmonale in meconium embolism and fibrin embolism; fibrination and defibrination. Address: 22148 Michigan Ave, Dearborn, MI 48124.

ENGSTROM, WILLIAM WEBORG, b. Milaca, Minn, June 29, 15; m. 43; c. 3. MEDICINE. B.S, Minnesota, 37, M.D, 40, M.S, 45. Fel. & 1st asst. MED, Mayo Found, Rochester, 41-44; instr, sch. med, Yale, 46-48, asst. prof, 48-50; assoc. prof, MED. COL. WIS, 50-58, PROF. & CHMN. DEPT, 58-; MED. DIR, MILWAUKEE COUNTY HOSP, 58- Outstanding achievement award, Minnesota, 64. U.S.A, 44-46. AAAS; Am. Soc. Clin. Invest; Am. Col. Physicians; Am. Diabetes Asn; Am. Med. Asn; Asn. Am. Physicians. Disorders of metabolism; medical biochemistry; internal medicine. Address: Medical College of Wisconsin, Milwaukee County Hospital, Milwaukee, WI 53226.

ENIG, JULIUS W(ILLIAM), b. Brooklyn, N.Y, Apr. 29, 31; m. 58; c. 3. PHYSICS, MATHEMATICS. B.S, City Col. New York, 52; M.A, Maryland, 60. Res. physicist, chem. res. dept, U.S. NAVAL ORD. LAB, 52-64, sr. scientist, 64-69, CHIEF MATH. ANAL. DIV, 69- Vis. staff mem, dept. math, Imp. Col, London, 62-63. Meritorious civilian serv. award, U.S. Navy, 60. Combustion Inst; Am. Math. Soc; London Math. Soc; Edinburgh Math. Soc. Detonation and combustion theory of condensed explosives and propellants; explosives initiation phenomena; numerical solutions of compressible flow; high pressure equations of state of solids and liquids; thermal explosions; heat conduction. Address: Mathematical Analysis Division, U.S. Naval Ordnance Lab, Silver Spring, MD 20910.

ENKE, CHRISTIE GEORGE, b. Minneapolis, Minn, July 8, 33; m. 56; c. 3. ELECTROCHEMISTRY, ANALYTICAL CHEMISTRY. B.S, Principia Col, 55; M.S, Illinois, 57, Ph.D.(chem), 59. Instr. CHEM, Princeton, 59-61, asst. prof, 61-66; ASSOC. PROF, MICH. STATE UNIV, 66- Alfred P. Sloan res. fel, 64-67. AAAS; Am. Chem. Soc; Electrochem. Soc; Inst. Elec. & Electronics Eng. Electrochemistry, adsorption phenomena and the kinetics of fast charge-transfer reactions; chemical instrumentation, the application of laboratory computers to data acquisition and chemical measurement control systems. Address: Dept. of Chemistry, Michigan State University, East Lansing, MI 48823.

ENKE, GLENN L, b. Oakland, Calif, Jan. 8, 09; m. 34; c. 4. CIVIL ENGINEERING. B.S, California, Berkeley, 28. Detailer, Am. Bridge Co, Ind, 28-29; designer, indust. plant, Giffels & Vallet, Inc, Mich, 29-31; engr. design, Calif. Bridge Dept, 31-41; struct. engr, D.R. Warren Co, 41-42; asst. chief engr, Utah-Pomeroy-Morrison, 42-43; dist. engr, Morrison-Knudsen, Inc, Idaho, 43-47; struct. engr, Caldwell, Richards & Sorensen, Utah, 47-48; dist. engr, Utah Construct. Co, 48-52; prof. civil & mech. eng. & chmn. dept, Brigham Young, 52-53; chief engr, Church Jesus Christ Latter Day Saints, 53-55; gen. supvr. design eng, U.S. Steel Corp, 55-62; PROF. CIVIL ENG. SCI, BRIGHAM YOUNG UNIV, 62- Consult. struct. engr, 36-; partner, Enke & Long, Consult. Engrs, Calif, 54-; v.pres, Van Sickle Assocs, Consult, engrs, Colo, 56-; dir. west. zone, Nat. Coun. State Bd. Eng. Exam, 60-62. Lincoln Arc Welding Found. Award, 37, 42, 47, 59. U.S.N. Civil Eng.C.Res, 36-40, Lt. Fel. Am. Soc. Civil Eng; Nat. Soc. Prof. Eng; Am. Soc. Eng. Educ. Structural analysis methods for indeterminate structures; arc welding design; dynamics of long-span suspension systems; seismic force effects on multi-story buildings; engineering economics and law. Address: 1675 N. Oak Lane, Provo, UT 85601.

ENKEBOLL, WILLIAM, b. San Francisco, Calif, Feb. 2, 13; m. 47; c. 2. CIVIL ENGINEERING. B.S, Washington (Seattle), 35; scholar, Mass. Inst. Tech, 39-41, fel, 41-42, Sc.D.(civil eng), 47. Struct. draftsman, City Bridge Dept, Seattle, 35; asst. civil eng, Washington (Seattle), 36; engr, Pac. Car & Foundry Co, 36-37; instr. gen. eng, Washington (Seattle), 37-39; asst. civil eng, Mass. Inst. Tech, 39-41; struct. engr, Chance Vought Aircraft Co, Conn, 42-45; engr. in charge Pac. N.W. Off, DAMES & MOORE, 47-51, PARTNER, 51- Am. Soc. Civil Eng; Soc. Am. Mil. Eng. Consolidation of clay for foundation engineering. Address: Partner, Dames & Moore, 340 Market St, San Francisco, CA 94904.

ENLOE, LOUIS HENRY, b. Eldorado Springs, Mo, Mar. 4, 33; m. 56; c. 3. ELECTRICAL ENGINEERING, COMMUNICATIONS. B.S, Arizona, 55, M.S, 56, Ph.D.(elec. eng), 59. Instr. elec. eng, Arizona, 56-59; mem. tech. staff commun. res, BELL TEL. LABS, 59-66, head visual systs. res. dept, COMMUN. SYSTS. DIV, 66-67, HEAD OPTO-ELECTRONICS RES. DEPT, 67- Summer asst. electronics, Hughes Aircraft Corp, 56. Inst. Elec. & Electronics Eng. Noise and modulation theory, particularly problems associated with space communications; visual systems research. Address: Opto-Electronics Research Dept, Communications Systems Division, Bell Telephone Labs, Holmdell, NJ 07733.

ENLOW, DONALD H(UGH), b. Mosquero, N.Mex, Jan. 22, 27; m. 45; c. 1. ANATOMY. B.S, Houston, 49, M.S, 50; Ph.D, Agr. & Mech. Col, Texas, 55. Instr. zool, Houston, 49-52; asst, Agr. & Mech. Col, Texas, 52-53, curator natural hist. & anthrop, Witte Mus, 54-55; asst. prof. biol, West Texas State Col, 55-56; instr. ANAT, med. col, Univ. S.C, 56-57; SCH. MED, UNIV. MICH, 57-58, asst. prof, 58-62, assoc. prof, 62-67, PROF, 67-, DIR. PHYS. GROWTH PROG, CTR. HUMAN GROWTH & DEVELOP, 68- U.S.C.G.R, 45-46. Am. Asn. Anat; Soc. Vert. Paleont; Royal Soc. Med; Int. Asn. Dent. Res. Histology; embryology; gross and comparative anatomy; comparative histology of bone tissue; bone remodeling; facial growth. Address: Dept. of Anatomy, School of Medicine, University of Michigan, Ann Arbor, MI 48104.

ENLOWS, HAROLD E(UGENE), b. Mason City, Ill, June 11, 11; m. 40. PETROGRAPHY. B.S, Tulsa, 35; M.S, Chicago, 36; Ph.D.(econ. geol), Arizona, 39; cert, U.S. Naval Acad, 44; summers, Colorado, 39, Wisconsin, 46. Instr. GEOL, Tulsa, 38-43, prof, 46-64; assoc. prof, ORE. STATE UNIV, 64-70, PROF, 70- U.S.N.R, 43, Lt. Comdr. Mineral. Soc. Am; Soc. Econ. Paleont. & Mineral; Am. Asn. Petrol. Geol; Soc. Econ. Geol; Geol. Soc. Am. Stratigraphy of Great Basin; volcanics of Chiricahua Mountains; sedimentary petrography; volcanic sediments; volcanics of central Oregon. Address: Dept. of Geology, Oregon State University, Corvallis, OR 97331.

ENNEKING, EUGENE A, b. Idaho Co, Idaho, Jan. 17, 40; m. 65. MATHEMATICS, MATHEMATICAL STATISTICS. B.S, St. Martins Col, 62; M.A, Washington State, 64, Ph.D.(math), 66. Asst. MATH, Washington State, 62-66; ASST. PROF, St. Louis Univ, 66-69; PORTLAND STATE UNIV, 69- Am. Math. Soc; Inst. Math. Statist. Combinatorial theory; probability theory. Address: Dept. of Mathematics, Portland State University, Portland, OR 97207.

ENNEKING, MARJORIE, b. Eugene, Ore, June 21, 41; m. 65; c. 1. MATHEMATICS. B.A, Willamette, 62; M.A, Washington State, 64, Ph.D.(math), 66. Teaching asst. MATH, Wash. State Univ, 62-66; ASST. PROF, Univ. Mo-St. Louis, 66-68; PORTLAND STATE UNIV, 68- Am. Math. Soc; Math. Asn. Am. Address: Dept. of Mathematics, Portland State University, Portland, OR 97207.

ENNEKING, WILLIAM FISHER, b. Madison, Wis, May 9, 26; m. 47; c. 7. MEDICINE. B.S, Wisconsin, 45, M.D, 49; Chicago, 52-56. Intern, med. center, Colorado, 49-50; prof. orthop. surg. & dir. div, med. ctr, Mississippi, 56-59; assoc. prof. & dir. div, UNIV. FLA, 59-62, PROF. SURG. & PATH. & CHIEF DIV. ORTHOP. SURG, COL. MED, 62- Kappa Delta award, 58. U.S.N, 44-46, 50-52, Lt. Orthop. Res. Soc; Am. Med. Asn; N.Y. Acad. Sci. Clinical orthopedic pathology; immunological aspects of bone transplantation. Address: University of Florida Medical Center, Gainesville, FL 32601.

ENNEVER, JOHN J(OSEPH), b. Ossining, N.Y, June 7, 20; m. 46; c. 2. DENTISTRY, MICROBIOLOGY. Park Col, 39-42; D.D.S, Washington (St. Louis), 47; Procter & Gamble fel, Ohio State, 47-50, M.Sc, 50. Res. assoc, Ohio State, 47-50; asst. prof. periodont, Univ. Kansas City, 50-56; mem. res. staff, Procter & Gamble Co, 56-68; PROF. DENT, DENT. SCI. INST, UNIV. TEX, HOUSTON, 68- Sci. Res. Soc. Am; Int. Asn. Dent. Res. Oral microbiology; dental and oral diseases. Address: Dental Science Institute, University of Texas, P.O. Box 20068, Houston, TX 77025.

ENNIS, A(LFRED) G, b. Phila, Pa, Dec. 28, 06; m. 29; ELECTRICAL ENGINEERING. B.S, Pennsylvania, 28, E.E, 34; M.S, Mass. Inst. Technol, 30, D.E, Hopkins, 41. Assoc. prof. elec. eng, George Washington, 31-41; asst. supvr. degaussing res, U.S. Navy Dept, 41-43; asst. to v.pres, Submarine Signal Co, 43-46; PROJ. ENGR, APPL. PHYSICS LAB, JOHNS HOPKINS UNIV, 46- Inst. Elec. & Electronics Eng. Design and integration of weapon systems. Address: 1451 Dewberry Ct, McLean, VA 22101.

ENNIS, ELLA GRAY W(ILSON), b. Sampson Co, N.C, May 2, 25; m. 62. PHYSIOLOGY. A.B, North Carolina, Greensboro, 45, M.A, Chapel Hill, 48, Ph.D.(physiol), 64. Teacher, high sch, N.C, 45-47; dir. health & phys. ed, St. Mary's Jr. Col.(Md), 48-49; asst. prof, Furman, 49-56; res. assoc. pharmacol, SCH. MED, UNIV. N.C, CHAPEL HILL, 65, instr. PHYSIOL, 65-67, ASST. PROF, 67-, ASST. PROF. & CO-DIR. NURSING RES. DEVELOP. GRANT, SCH. NURSING, 69- Effect of various enzymes on in vitro blood coagulation tests; factor V and thrombin in the intrinsic and extrinsic clotting systems; colloidal aspects of blood clotting; nursing research with physiological implications. Address: Dept. of Physiology, School of Medicine, University of North Carolina, Chapel Hill, NC 27514.

ENNIS, HERBERT LEO, b. Brooklyn, N.Y, Jan. 6, 32; m. 60; c. 2. MICROBIOLOGY. B.S, Brooklyn Col, 53; Nat. Sci. Found. fel, Northwestern, 54-56, M.S, 54, Ph.D, 57. U.S. Pub. Health Serv. fel, Northwestern, 57-58; res. fel. bact. & immunol. & U.S. Pub. Health Serv. fel, Harvard, 58-59; fel, Brandeis, 59-60; instr. pharmacol, Harvard Med. Sch, 60-64; asst. prof. biochem, St. Jude Hosp. & col. med, Univ. Tenn, 64-66, assoc. prof, 66-69; ASSOC. MEM, ROCHE INST. MOLECULAR BIOL, 69- AAAS; Am. Soc. Microbiol; Brit. Soc. Gen. Microbiol; Am. Soc. Biol. Chem; N.Y. Acad. Sci. Microbial physiology; genetics; antibiotics. Address: Roche Institute of Molecular Biology, Nutley, NJ 07110.

ENNIS, WILLIAM BRICE, JR, b. Martin, Tenn, Feb. 26, 17; m. 47; c. 3. AGRONOMY. B.S, Tennessee, 39; fel. Maine, 39-41, M.S, 41; Ph.D.(bot. agron), Wisconsin, 48. Asst. agron, Wisconsin, 41-42; agronomist, U.S. Army, Camp Detrick, 46, 47-50; head dept, plant path. & physiol, Miss. Agr. Exp. Sta, 50-54; regional coordinator weed invests. sect, AGR. RESEARCH SERV, U.S. DEPT. AGR, Miss, 54-56, head, BELTSVILLE, MD, 56-57, CHIEF CROPS PROTECTION RES. BR, 57- Superior serv. award, U.S. Dept. Agr. U.S.N, 42-46, Lt. Comdr. Am. Soc. Agron; Am. Soc. Plant Physiol; hon. fel. Weed Sci. Soc. Am.(pres, 56-58). Experimental cytology and histology; plant growth regulators; herbicidal compositions; weed control; crops protection research; research administration. Address: Plant Industry Station, Agricultural Research Service, U.S. Dept. of Agriculture, Beltsville, MD 20705.

ENNOR, KENNETH STAFFORD, b. Wadebridge, Eng, May 15, 33; m. 65; c. 2. ORGANIC CHEMISTRY. B.Sc, Univ. London, 54, Dept. Sci. & Indust. Res. grant, 54-57, Ph.D.(org. chem), 57. Fels, Ohio State Univ, 57-58, Boston Univ, 58-59; tech. off. plastics res, plastics div, Imp. Chem. Industs. Ltd, Eng, 59-62; scientist appln. res. resins, Esso Res. Ltd, Eng, 62-65; sr. scientist appln. res. tall oil prod, Brit. Oxygen Chem. Ltd, Eng, 65-68; SR. APPLN. CHEMIST, CHEM. DIV, UNION CAMP CORP, 68- Assoc. Royal Inst. Chem; Brit. Oil & Colour Chem. Asn; Am. Chem. Soc; Fedn. Socs. Paint Technol. Carbohydrate chemistry; resins for surface coatings and printing inks; tall oil products; dimer acids; polyamide resins. Address: Chemical Division, Union Camp Corp, P.O. Box 570, Savannah, GA 31402.

ENNS, HENRY, b. Sask, Can, Apr. 8, 32; m. 61; c. 3. PLANT BREEDING, GENETICS. B.Sc, Manitoba, 57, M.Sc, 59; Nat. Res. Coun. asst. & Ph.D. (plant breeding, genetics), Saskatchewan, 62. Res. assoc. agron, Washington State, 61-63; plant breeder, plant breeding sta, Njoro, Govt. of Kenya, 64-65, Pyrethrum Res. Sta, Molo, 65-66; RES. OFF, RES. STA, CAN. DEPT. AGR, 66- Genetics Soc. Am; Genetics Soc. Can. Somatic instability in relation to wheat pericarp; polyploidy in Pyrethrum cinerariaefolium. Address: Canada Dept. of Agriculture, Research Station, Morden, Man, Can.

ENNS, J(OHN) H(ERMANN), b. Schonau, Russia, July 18, 07; nat. 32; m. 38; c. 3. PHYSICS. B.S, Kans. State Col, 32; A.M, Michigan, 35, Ph.D.(physics), 41. Instr. physics, Detroit Inst. Tech, 36-39; res. physicist, Diamond Chain & Mfg. Co, Indianapolis, 41-42; asst. prof. physics, Mich. State Col, 42-44; res. physicist, UNIV. MICH, 44-58, assoc. prof. ENG. MECH, 58-61, PROF, 61- Am. Phys. Soc; Optical Soc. Am. Sound and vibrations; emission spectroscopy; air interrupter type stabilized control gap for spark and alternating current arc source spectroscopy; solid state studies of photographic latent image formation; lattice dynamics and micromechanics of solids. Address: 2780 Heather Way, Ann Arbor, MI 48108.

ENNS, RICHARD HARVEY, b. Winnipeg, Man, Nov. 5, 38; m. 67; c. 2. THEORETICAL PHYSICS. B.Sc, Alberta, 60, Prov. Alta. scholar, 60-62, Nat. Res. Coun. Can. scholar, 62-63, Ph.D.(theoret. physics), 64. Asst. prof. PHYSICS, SIMON FRASER UNIV, 65-70, ASSOC. PROF, 70- Nat. Res. Coun. Can. fel, Liverpool, 64-65, res. grant, 65-71. Can. Asn. Physicists. Transport theory in solids; absorption and dispersion of sound in gases, nonlinear optics. Address: Dept. of Physics, Simon Fraser University, Burnaby, B.C, Can.

ENNS, THEODORE, b. Alexanderkrone, Russia, Jan. 10, 16; nat; m. 43; c. 3. PHYSICS. B.E, Saskatchewan, 37; Ph.D.(physics), Rochester, 40. Asst. physics, Rochester, 37-40; Washington (St. Louis), 40-41; res. fel. radiol, sch. med. & dent, Rochester, 41-42, res. assoc, dept. radio, 42-43, assoc, Manhattan dept, 43-46; chief physicist, Biochem. Res. Found, 46-48; asst. prof. med, Hopkins, 48-64, assoc. prof. physiol. chem, 57-64; RES. PHYSIOLOGIST, SCRIPPS INST. OCEANOG, UNIV. CALIF, SAN DIEGO, 62- Mem, Off. Sci. Res. & Develop, 44; Fulbright grant & Guggenheim fel, Univ. Oslo, 56-57; With Manhattan Proj. Am. Phys. Soc; Am. Physiol. Soc. Nuclear physics; cyclotrons; mass spectrometry; radioactive and stable tracers; respiration and renal physiology; biological transport. Address: Scripps Institution of Oceanography, University of California, San Diego, La Jolla, CA 92037.

ENNS, WILBUR R(ONALD), b. Henderson, Nebr, Feb. 26, 13; m. 46; c. 1. ENTOMOLOGY. B.S, Missouri, 41, A.M, 46; Ph.D.(entom), Kansas, 55. Asst. ENTOM, UNIV. MO-COLUMBIA, 42, instr, 48-52, asst. prof, 52-57, assoc. prof, 57-61, PROF, 61-, DIR. ENTOM. MUS, 52- U.S.A, 43-45. Entom. Soc. Am; Soc. Syst. Zool; Am. Entom. Soc; Am. Inst. Biol. Sci; Entom. Soc. Can. Insect taxonomy; control of fruit and vegetable insects; taxonomy of Acarina; biological control of insects and mites. Address: Dept. of Entomology, 1-79 Agriculture Bldg, University of Missouri-Columbia, Columbia, MO 65201.

ENNULAT, REINHARD D, b. Insterburg, Ger, July 9, 27; U.S. citizen; m. 56; c. 3. PHYSICS, MATHEMATICS. Vordiplom, Frankfurt, 50, hauptdiplom, 52, Dr. phil. nat.(physics), 58. Physicist, Hartmann & Braun AG, Germany, 53-58; U.S. Army Eng. Res. & Develop. Labs, Va, 58-59, supvry. physicist, 59-66, NIGHT VISION LAB, U.S. ARMY ELECTRONICS COMMAND, 66-70, DIR. FAR INFRARED TECH. AREA, 70- Mem, Comt. Int. Liquid Crystal Confs, 68, 70, 72. Am. Phys. Soc; Sci. Res. Soc. Am. Solid state physics; liquid crystal physics; physical optics; thermal imaging and infrared technology. Address: 8901 Camden St, Alexandria, VA 22308.

ENO, CHARLES F(RANKLIN), b. Atwater, Ohio, May 21, 20; m. 48; c. 2. SOIL TECHNOLOGY. B.S, Ohio State, 42, M.S, 48; Ph.D.(soil microbiol), Purdue, 51. Soil microbiologist, UNIV. FLA, 50-65, CHMN. SOILS DEPT, 65- U.S.A, 42-46, 51-52, Lt. Col. Am. Soc. Agron. Soil microbiology and related research in soil fertility. Address: 600 N.W. 36th Terr, Gainsville, FL 32601.

ENOCH, JACOB, b. Berlin, Ger, Feb. 17, 27; nat; m. 55; c. 3. THEORETICAL PHYSICS. B.S, Brooklyn Col, 52; M.S, Wisconsin, 54, Ph.D.(physics), 56. Asst. physics, Wisconsin, 52-56; mem. staff, Midwest. Univs. Res. Asn, 56-57; Los Alamos Sci. Lab, California, 57-60; space sci. lab, Gen. Elec. Co, 60-62, asst. prof. PHYSICS, UNIV. KANS, 62-64, ASSOC. PROF, 64- Am. Phys. Soc. Plasma physics; statistical mechanics; kinetic theory. Address: 801 Louisiana St, Lawrence, KS 66044.

ENOCH, JAY M(ARTIN), b. New York, N.Y, Apr. 20, 29; m. 51; c. 3. PHYSIOLOGICAL OPTICS. B.S, Columbia, 50; Rochester, 52-53; Ph.D.(physiol. optics), Ohio State, 56. Asst. dept. ophthal. res, Columbia, 48-50; asst. sect. head contact lenses, Army Med. Res. Lab, Ft. Knox, Ky, 51-52; asst. physiol. optics, Ohio State, 53-55, fel, 55-56, asst. prof, 57-58; res. instr. physiol. optics & ophthal, MED. SCH, WASH. UNIV, 58-59, res. asst. prof, 59-64, res. assoc. prof, 65-70, RES. PROF. OPHTHAL. & PSYCHOL, 70-, assoc. prof. psychol, 67-70. Res. assoc, mapping & charting res. lab, Ohio State, 56-57, assoc. supvr, 57-58; vis. fel, Nat. Phys. Lab, Eng, 59-60; career develop. award, U.S. Pub. Health Serv, 63-73; fel, Barnes Hosp, St. Louis, 59-, consult. ophthal, 70- Mem. comt. vision, Nat. Acad. Sci-Nat. Res. Coun, 59-; exec. secy, subcmt. vision & its disorders, Nat. Inst. Neurol. Diseases & Blindness, 65-69; mem. comt. safe uses of lasers, Am. Nat. Standard Inst, comt. ophthalmic lenses & chmn. subcomt. contact lens standards; Am. Comt. on Optics & Visual Physiol. U.S.A, 51-52, 2nd Lt. AAAS; fel. Optical Soc. Am; Am. Asn. Res. Vision & Ophthal; fel. Am. Acad. Optom; Ophthal; fel. Acad. Optom; Biophys. Soc; Brit. Contact Lens Soc. Retinal receptor optics and function; visual search; experimental perimetry; contact lenses. Address: 12608 Villa Hill Lane, Creve Coeur, MO 63141.

ENOCHS, EDGAR EARLE, b. McComb, Miss, Sept. 13, 32; m. 58; c. 6. MATHEMATICS. B.S, La. State, 58; Ph.D.(math), Notre Dame, 58. Instr. MATH, Chicago, 58-60; asst. prof, South Carolina, 60-63, assoc. prof, 63-67, PROF, UNIV. KY, 67- Nat. Sci. Found. res. grant, 63-64. Abelian group theory; modules over integral domains; general topology. Address: 215 N. Mill St, Lexington, KY 40508.

ENOCHS, N(ETTIE) JEAN, b. Jackson, Tenn, Dec. 13, 39. DEVELOPMENTAL BIOLOGY, BOTANY. B.S, David Lipscomb Col, 61; M.S, Purdue, 64, Ph.D.(biol), 67. Staff biologist, comn. undergrad. ed. biol. sci, Nat. Sci. Found, 66-67; ASST. PROF. BIOL, MICH. STATE UNIV, 67- AAAS; Bot. Soc. Am; Am. Inst. Biol. Sci; Nat. Asn. Biol. Teachers; Nat. Sci. Teachers Asn. Effects of gibberellic acid on plant growth; histological study of disease resistant reaction of plants; autoradiographic study of ribonucleic acid in plant cell; plant physiology and development. Address: Science & Mathematics Teaching Center, Michigan State University, East Lansing, MI 48823.

ENOS, HENRY F, JR, b. Malden, Mass, July 27, 27; m. 50; c. 4. BIOCHEMISTRY. B.S, New Hampshire, 51, M.S, 53; Ph.D.(biochem), Pa. State, 66. Chief chemist, Commercial Solvents Corp, 53-56; instr. pesticide residue anal, Pa. State, 56-60; RES. CHEMIST, U.S. Army Natick Labs, 60-66; PERRINE PRIMATE LAB, U.S. DEPT. HEALTH, EDUC. & WELFARE, 66- U.S.A, 45-46. AAAS; Am. Chem. Soc; Sci. Res. Soc. Am. Pesticide residue analysis; biochemistry and toxicology of pesticides and analytical problems associated with these areas. Address: Perrine Primate Lab, P.O. Box 490, Perrine, FL 33157.

ENOS, HERMAN I(SAAC), JR, b. Alhambra, Calif, Apr. 30, 20; m. 48; c. 3. ORGANIC CHEMISTRY. A.B, Southern California, 42, M.S, 43; Lilly fel, Illinois, 42-45, Ph.D.(org. chem), 46. Lilly fel, Columbia, 46; instr. org. chem, Swarthmore Col, 46-47, asst. prof, 47-48; res. chemist, RES. CTR, Hercules Powder Co, 48-54, res. supvr, 54-65, RES. ASSOC, 65-67, HERCULES INC, 67- With Off. Sci. Res. & Develop, 44. Am. Oil Chemists' Soc; Am. Chem. Soc; The Chem. Soc. Synthetic organic chemistry; rosin and terpenes; hydrocarbon alkylation and oxidation; hydroperoxides and peroxides; unsaturated fatty acids. Address: Pine & Paper Chemicals Research Division, Research Center, Hercules Inc, Wilmington, DE 19899.

ENOS, PAUL (PORTENIER), b. Topeka, Kans, July 25, 34; m. 58; c. 4. GEOLOGY. B.Sc, Kansas, 56; Fulbright scholar, Tübingen, 56-57; Nat. Sci. Found. fel, Stanford, 59-61, M.Sc, 61; Nat. Sci. Found. fel, Yale, 61-62, Ph.D.(geol), 65. Asst. instr. geol, Yale, 62-64; geologist, Shell Develop. Co, 64-65, res. geologist, 65-70; ASSOC. PROF. GEOL, STATE UNIV. N.Y. BINGHAMTON, 70- C.Eng, 57-59, 1st Lt. Soc. Econ. Paleont. & Mineral. Stratigraphy and sedimentology of flysch deposits; recent carbonates, Florida and Bahamas; cretaceous carbonates, Mexico. Address: Dept. of Geology, State University of New York at Binghamton, Binghamton, NY 13901.

ENQUIST, IRVING F(RITIOF), b. Superior, Wis, June 25, 20; m. 44; c. 3. SURGERY. B.S, Minnesota, 42, M.D, 44, M.S, 51. Instr. SURG, STATE UNIV. N.Y. DOWNSTATE MED. CTR, 52-53, asst. prof, 53-55, assoc. prof, 55-60, PROF, 60-; DIR. SURG, METHODIST HOSP. BROOKLYN, 65- Consult. surg, U.S. Vet. Hosp, Brooklyn; St. John's Episcopal Hosp, Brooklyn. U.S.A, 44-46, Capt. AAAS; Am. Col. Surg; Am. Surg. Asn; Soc. Surg. Alimentary Tract; James Ewing Soc; Int. Soc. Surg. Wound healing; gastrointestinal physiology. Address: Methodist Hospital of Brooklyn, 506 Sixth St, Brooklyn, NY 11215.

ENRIETTO, JOSEPH FRANCIS, b. Spring Valley, Ill, May 7, 31; m. 52; c. 4. METALLURGY. B.S, Illinois, 56, M.S, 57, Inland Steel fel, 57-60, Ph.D. (metall), 60. Sr. res. engr, res. lab, Jones & Laughlin Steel Corp, 60-63, supvr. physics of metals group, 63-66, asst, dir. phys. metall, 66-71; MGR. MAT. ENG, WESTINGHOUSE ELEC. CORP, 71- U.S.N, 51-53. Am. Inst. Mining, Metall. & Petrol. Eng. Internal friction in ferrous alloys; strain ageing; precipitation in ferrous base alloys; deep drawing; fatigue; nuclear pressure vessel materials. Address: Westinghouse Electric Corp, Monroeville Nuclear Center, Box 355, Pittsburgh, PA 15230.

ENRIGHT, J(AMES) T(HOMAS), b. Baker, Ore, Nov. 23, 32; m. 54; c. 3. ZOOLOGY. A.B, California, Los Angeles, 57, M.A, 59, Nat. Sci. Found. fel, 59-61, Ph.D.(zool), 61. Nat. Sci. Found. fel, Max-Planck-Inst. Physiol. of Behavior, Germany, 61-63; asst. prof. zool, UNIV. CALIF, Los Angeles, 63-66, OCEANOG, SAN DIEGO, 66-68, ASSOC. PROF, 68- U.S.A, 54-56. AAAS. Marine ecology; biological rhythms; photoperiodism; orientation. Address: Dept. of Oceanography, University of California at San Diego, La Jolla, CA 92037.

ENRIQUEZ, NITZA M, b. San German, P.R, Mar. 8, 37; m. 68; c. 1. MICROBIOLOGY. B.A, Col. New Rochelle, 58; M.S, Catholic Univ, 63. Instr. biol, Inter-Am. Univ. P.R, 59-61; res. asst. path, N.Y. Univ. Med. Center, 63-64; res. assoc. med. sci, P.R. Nuclear Center, 64-66; ASSOC. PROF. BIOL, INTER-AM. UNIV. P.R, 66- N.Y. Acad. Sci; Am. Soc. Microbiol. Address: Dept. of Biology, Inter-American University, San German, PR 00753.

ENROTH-CUGELL, CHRISTINA, b. Helsingfors, Finland, Aug. 27, 19; U.S. citizen; m. 55. VISION, NEUROPHYSIOLOGY. Med. lic, Karolinska Inst, Sweden, 48, fel, 50-53, Med. dr.(neurophysiol. of vision), 52, Ophthal. Specialist Cert, 57. Resident ophthal, Sabbatsberg Hosp, Stockholm, Sweden, 48-49; Karolinska Hosp, 53; Nat. Insts. Health res. fel. biol, Harvard, 53-54; resident ophthal, Karolinska Hosp, 54-56; Nat. Insts. Health spec. trainee, MED. SCH, NORTHWEST. UNIV, 58-61, asst. prof. PHYSIOL, 62-68, ASSOC. PROF, 68-, PHYSIOL. & BIOL. SCI. UNIV, 69- Nat. Insts. Health career develop. award, Northwest. Univ, 62- Am. Physiol. Soc; Int. Soc. Clin. Electroretinography. Visual physiology, particularly retinal neurophysiology. Address: Bio-Medical Engineering Center, Technological Institute, Northwestern University, 2145 Sheridan Rd, Evanston, IL 60201.

ENSBERG, EARL S, b. Grand Forks, N.Dak, June 11, 29; m. 63. PHYSICS. B.A, St. Olaf Col, 51; Ph.D.(physics), Washington(Seattle), 62. RES. ASSOC. PHYSICS, YALE, 62- U.S.A.F, 52-53, 1st Lt. Am. Phys. Soc. Magnetic resonance in optically oriented atoms. Address: Dept. of Physics, Yale University, New Haven, CT 06511.

ENSIGN, C(HESTER) O(SCAR), JR, b. Statesville, N.C, Oct. 23, 24; m. 50; c. 2. ECONOMIC GEOLOGY. B.S, North Carolina, 48, B.S, 50. From lab. instr. to asst, North Carolina, 49-51; explor. supvr. & asst. supvr. mines planning, Davison Chem. Co, 51-55; sr. explor. geologist, Am. Metal Climax, Inc, 55-61; chief geologist, COPPER RANGE CO, 61-68, v.pres. explor, 68-69, exec. v.pres, 69-70, pres, 70-71, CHIEF EXEC. OFF, 71- U.S.N.R, 43-46, Ens. Am. Inst. Mining, Metall. & Petrol. Eng; Geol. Soc. Am; Soc. Econ. Geol; Soc. Explor. Geophys; Can. Inst. Mining & Metall. Geological environments with which economic concentrations of metallic and certain non-metallic minerals are associated. Address: Copper Range Co, 630 Fifth Ave, New York, NY 10020.

ENSIGN, JERALD C, b. Salt Lake City, Utah, June 25, 32; m. 58; c. 2. BACTERIOLOGY. B.A, Brigham Young, 55; M.S, Southern California, 60, Nat. Insts. Health fel, 61-62, Ph.D.(bact. physiol), 62. Lectr, Southern California, 61-62; Nat. Insts. Health fel. microbiol, Illinois, 62-64; asst. prof. BACT, UNIV. WIS, MADISON, 64-69, ASSOC. PROF, 69- Nat. Insts. Health sr. fel, Univ. Göttingen, 71. Am. Soc. Microbiol; Brit. Soc. Gen. Microbiol. Physiology of starving bacteria; ecology of photosynthetic bacteria; bacterial cell wall lytic enzymes; morphogenesis and cell wall synthesis. Address: Dept. of Bacteriology, University of Wisconsin, Madison, WI 53706.

ENSIGN, PAUL R(OSELLE), b. Shantung, China, Aug. 27, 06; U.S. citizen; m. 39; c. 1. PUBLIC HEALTH, PEDIATRICS. B.A, Kansas, 27; M.D, Northwestern, 36; M.P.H, Hopkins, 42. Pediat. consult, State Health Dept, Ga, 43-45; div. dir. maternal & child health, State Bd. Health, Kans, 45-50, dep. state health officer, 50-51; div. dir. maternal & child health, State Health Dept, Mont, 51-55, dep. state health officer, 55-57; health officer, City-County Health Dept, Great Falls, 57-62; dir. div. ment. health, State Health Dept, Utah, 62-64; field consult, Ford Found, 64-69; DIR. PREV. DISEASE & ENVIRON. HEALTH, ACTING STATE DIR. HEALTH & DIR. CHILD HEALTH, UTAH STATE DIV. HEALTH, 69- Assoc. prof. prev. med. & instr. pediat, Kansas, 46-51; Nat. Insts. Ment. Health grant for community ment. health, Great Falls, Mont, 60-65; assoc. prof. prev. med, Utah, 62-64. Consult, health & family planning, Govt. of India, 64- Pres, Asn. State Maternal & Child Health Dirs, 54. Am. Pub. Health Asn. Maternal and child health, particularly nutrition, prevention of otitis media in Indian children; mental health and hospital nursery infections. Address: 4725 Bron Breck St, Salt Lake City, UT 84117.

ENSIGN, RONALD D, b. Cameron, Mo, Apr. 10, 22; m. 47; c. 2. PLANT BREEDING. B.S, Northwest. Mo. State Col, 47; M.S, Colo. State Univ, 49; Ph.D.(plant breeding), Cornell Univ, 52. Asst. agron, Colo. State Univ, 47-49; plant breeding, Cornell Univ, 49-52; supt, UNIV. IDAHO, 52-55, assoc. dir, AGR. EXP. STA, 55-70, DIR. & RES. PROF. AGRON, 70- U.S.N.R, 42-46. Am. Soc. Agron. Forage crops; corn; wheat. Address: Agricultural Experiment Station, University of Idaho, Moscow, ID 83843.

ENSIGN, STEWART ELLERY, b. Waterloo, Iowa, Nov. 25, 25; m. 46; c. 3. GENETICS. B.A, Bob Jones, 50; M.S, Wyoming, 54; Ph.D.(genetics), Nebraska, 59. Instr. biol, Bob Jones, 52-55; res. fel, Yale, 59-61; California, San Diego, 61-63; asst. prof. BIOL, WESTMONT COL, 63-70, PROF, 70- U.S.N.R, 43-46. AAAS; Am. Sci. Affiliation; Genetics Soc. Am; Asn. Am. Med. Cols. Reproductive isolation in the Affinis Subgroup of the genus Drosophila; gene-enzyme relationships in the tryptophan synthetase system of Neurospora crassa; production of ovarian proteins in Blattella germanica. Address: Dept. of Biology, Westmont College, 955 La Paz Rd, Santa Barbara, CA 93103.

ENSIGN, THOMAS CHARLES, b. Minneapolis, Minn, Mar. 6, 41; m. 62; c. 3. SOLID STATE PHYSICS. B.A, Macalester Col, 63; M.S, Wyoming, 65, Nat. Sci. Found. fel, 66, NASA fel, 66-68, Ph.D.(physics), 68. Lab. asst. physics, Macalester Col, 60-63; teaching asst, Wyoming, 63-64, res. asst, 64-65, teaching asst, 65-66, instr, summers 66, 67; Nat. Res. Coun. res. assoc, Nat. Bur. Standards, 68-69; RES. SCIENTIST, RES. INST. ADV. STUDIES, MARTIN MARIETTA CORP, 69- Am. Phys. Soc. Infrared detectors including coordinated electron paramagnetic resonance and optical studies of rare earth ion dopants in various host crystals for the purpose of investigating the fundamental factors governing the operation of infrared quantum counters. Address: Research Institute for Advanced Studies, Martin Marietta Corp, 1450 S. Rolling Rd, Baltimore, MD 21227.

ENSINCK, J(OHN) W(ILLIAM), b. Montreal, Can, Feb. 19, 31; m. 60; c. 1. ENDOCRINOLOGY. B.Sc, McGill, 52, M.D, 56. Res. med, Royal Victoria Hosp, 56-58; res. assoc. & asst. physician, Rockefeller Inst, 58-60; asst. med, sch. med, Washington (Seattle), 60-61, instr. & asst. dir, clin. res. center, univ. hosp, 61-62; vis. lectr, dept. med, Newcastle, 62-64; asst. prof. MED, SCH. MED, UNIV. WASH, 64-68, ASSOC. PROF, 68-, ASST. DIR. CLIN. RES. CTR, 64-, PROG. DIR, 70- R.C.A.F.R, 48-54. AAAS; Am. Diabetes Asn; Brit. Diabetic Asn; Am. Fedn. Clin. Res; Am. Soc. Clin. Invest; Endocrine Soc; Geront. Soc; N.Y. Acad. Sci; Soc. Exp. Biol. & Med. Endocrinological investigation with application of protein chemistry in relationship of insulin to carbohydrate metabolism. Address: Clinical Research Center, University of Washington Hospital, Seattle, WA 98105.

ENSMINGER, DALE, b. Mt. Perry, Ohio, Sept. 26, 23; m. 48; c. 6. ELECTRICAL & MECHANICAL ENGINEERING. B.M.E, Ohio State, 50, B.E.E, 50. Res. engr. ULTRASONICS, BATTELLE MEM. INST, 50-70, SR. ELEC. ENGR, 70- U.S.A, 43-46. Acoustical Soc. Am; Soc. Nondestructive Test. Low and high intensity applications of ultrasonics. Address: Dept. of Engineering Systems, Battelle Memorial Institute, 505 King Ave, Columbus, OH 43201.

ENSMINGER, L(EONARD) E(LROY), b. Stover, Mo, Sept. 25, 12; m. 41; c. 1. AGRONOMY. B.S, Missouri, 35; Rutgers, 35-36; Ph.D.(soil chem), Illinois, 40. Asst. prof. agr. chem, Idaho, 39-42; soil chemist, exp. sta, Florida, 42-44; assoc. prof. AGRON, AUBURN UNIV, 44-53, PROF, 53-, HEAD DEPT. AGRON. & SOILS, 66- Am. Soc. Agron. Factors affecting the availability to plants of native and added phosphorus in soils; identification of clay minerals in soils; sulfur in relation to soil fertility. Address: Dept. of Agronomy & Soils, Auburn University, Auburn, AL 36830.

ENSMINGER, RICHARD REESE, b. East Greenville, Pa, Oct. 13, 34; m. 61; c. 4. AEROSPACE ENGINEERING, ENGINEERING MECHANICS. B.S, St. Louis, 60; M.S, Washington (Seattle), 61, Ph.D, 65. Res. engr, Boeing Co, Wash, summer 62; ASST. PROF. AEROSPACE ENG, UNIV. TEX, AUSTIN, 65- U.S.A, 55-58, Sgt. Am. Inst. Aeronaut. & Astronaut; Am. Soc. Eng. Educ. Study of high pressure physics; intense stress waves in solids; explosive loading techniques; thermodynamic response of shock loading in solids. Address: Dept. of Aerospace Engineering, University of Texas at Austin, Austin, TX 78712.

ENSOR, CHARLES R(EGINALD), b. Scarborough, Eng, Apr. 22, 08; nat; m. 38; c. 2. PHARMACODYNAMICS. B.S, Emory, 34, M.S, 38; Chicago, 41. Lab. asst, med. sch, Emory, 34-38, instr. physiol, 38-46; jr. pharmacologist, PARKE-DAVIS & CO, 46-52, assoc. pharmacologist, 52-62, PHARMACOLOGIST, 62- Nutrition and metabolism; pharmacodynamics of central nerve system; cardiovascular and hemodynamics. Address: Research Dept, Parke-Davis & Co, Ann Arbor, MI 48106.

ENSOR, ELWOOD H(ENDERSON), b. Baltimore, Md, Feb. 1, 18; m. 41; c. 6. ORGANIC CHEMISTRY. B.S, Northwestern, 38, Ph.D.(org. chem), 42; fel. & M.S, Boston, 39; Illinois, 39-40. Res. chemist, develop. lab, U.S. Indust. Chem. Co, Baltimore, 41; asst. chem, Northwestern, 40-42, men's tutor, 40-41; res. chemist, exp. sta, Hercules Powder Co, Del, 42-46; V.PRES. G.D. SEARLE & CO, 46-, SR. V.PRES, G.D. SEARLE INT. CO, 68-, PRES, SEARLE CHEM, INC, 64- Lectr, Northwest. Univ, 47-51; DePaul Univ, 48-49; pres, G.D. Searle Far East; G.D. Searle of Can; Searle of Mex; Searle of Thailand; Ajax Chem. Co, Australia. Am. Chem. Soc. Therapeutics. Address: P.O. Box 5110, Chicago, IL 60680.

ENSTROM, RONALD EDWARD, b. N.Y.C, Mar. 22, 35; m. 58; c. 2. PHYSICAL METALLURGY, SOLID STATE PHYSICS. S.B, Mass. Inst. Tech, 57, S.M, 62, Sc.D, 63. Asst. metall, metals res. lab, Union Carbide Corp, 57-58; mat. engr, Nuclear Metals, Inc. Div, Textron, Inc, 58-60; asst. METALL, Mass. Inst. Tech, 60-63; MEM. TECH. STAFF, DAVID SARNOFF RES. CTR, RCA CORP, 63- Mem, U.S. Army Res. & Develop. Group, 63- David Sarnoff award. U.S.A, 58, Capt. Electrochem. Soc; Am. Phys. Soc; Am. Inst. Mining, Metall. & Petrol. Eng. Preparation and properties of superconducting materials; vapor phase synthesis and characterization of III-V compounds for microwave, rectifier and photo cathode applications; preparation and properties of refractory metal and nuclear alloys. Address: RCA Corp, David Sarnoff Research Center, Princeton, NJ 08540.

ENTENMAN, CECIL, b. Longville, La, Jan. 6, 12; m. 58; c. 4. PHYSIOLOGY, BIOCHEMISTRY. B.S, State Col. Wash, 35; Ph.D.(physiol), California, Berkeley, 40. Res. assoc. physiol, California, Berkeley, 41-42, physiologist, 42-44, instr, 44-48, asst. prof, 48-49; br. head biochem, U.S. Naval Radiol. Defense Lab, Calif, 49-62; DIR, INST. LIPID RES, 62- Lectr. pub. health nutrit, California, Berkeley, 62-, nutrit, 63-, res. biochemist dermat, sch. med, San Francisco, 62- Mem, Int. Conf. Biochem. Lipids. AAAS; Am. Chem. Soc; Am. Physiol. Soc; Soc. Exp. Biol. & Med; Am. Oil Chem. Soc; Am. Soc. Clin. Res; Am. Heart Asn; Am. Pub. Health Asn; N.Y. Acad. Sci. Pancreatic anti-fatty liver factors; endocrines and diet on lipid metabolism; transport; synthesis; skin lipid metabolism; influence of nutrition on obesity, blood and tissue lipids; biological effects of ionizing radiations. Address: Institute for Lipid Research, 2127 Bonar St, Berkeley, CA 94702.

ENTEMANN, C(HARLES) E, b. New York, N.Y, Feb. 6, 06; m. 35; c. 2. ORGANIC CHEMISTRY. A.B, Cornell, 29, Ph.D.(org. chem), 33. Instr. chem, Essex County Jr. Col, N.J, 33-35; chemist, Ekroth Labs, N.Y, 35-36; res. chemist, Pyridium Corp, N.Y, 36; Zonite Prods. Corp, N.J, 36-41; Laurel Hill res. lab, Gen. Chem. Co, N.Y, 41-44; asst. chief chemist, Lucidol Div, Novadel-Agene Corp, Buffalo, N.Y, 44-46, chief chemist, 46-51; res. chemist, Diamond Alkali Co, 51-56, group leader process develop. org. chem, 56-66; RES. MGR, AZTEC CHEM. DIV, DART INDUSTS, INC, 67- AAAS; Am. Chem. Soc. Organic peroxides; organic synthesis; agricultural pesticides; xylene chemicals; chlorination. Address: Aztec Chemicals, Division of Dart Industries Inc, Chemical Group, P.O. Box 249, 555 Garden St, Elyria, OH 44035.

ENTERLINE, H(ORATIO) T(HEODORE), b. Ashland, Pa, Oct. 16, 19; m. 41; c. 3. PATHOLOGY. B.S, Michigan, 41; M.D, Pennsylvania, 44. Assoc. surg. path, SCH. MED, UNIV. PA, 52-54, asst. prof, 54-55; assoc. prof. PATH, 55-64, PROF, 64- Consult, Children's Hosp. Phila; U.S. Naval Hosp, Phila; Vet. Admin. Hosp, Phila. Med.C, 45-47, Capt. Am. Soc. Clin. Path; Col. Am. Path; Am. Soc. Cytol; N.Y. Acad. Sci; Int. Acad. Path. Neoplasm motility of neoplastic cells; histologic and clinical aspects of various neoplasms; surgical pathology. Address: Dept. of Pathology, Division of Pathologic Anatomy, University of Pennsylvania Hospital, 3400 Spruce St, Philadelphia, PA 19104.

ENTIN, MARTIN A, b. Simferopole, Crimea, Oct. 19, 12; Can. citizen; m; c. 3. PLASTIC, RECONSTRUCTIVE & HAND SURGERY. B.A, Temple, 41; M.Sc, McGill, 42, M.D, C.M, 45. Res. surg, Montreal Gen. Hosp, 46-49; Nat. Res. Coun. Can. res. fel. surg. of hand, univ. hosp, Stanford, 49-50; clin. asst. plastic surg, Royal Victoria Hosp, 50-55; asst. lectr, McGill, 57-62; asst. surgeon ROYAL VICTORIA HOSP, 63-70, acting surgeon-in-chief, SUB-DEPT. PLASTIC SURG, 70-71, SURGEON-IN-CHARGE, 71-; ASST. PROF. SURG, McGILL UNIV, 64-, Nat. Res. Coun. Can, fel, 46-47, Med. Res. Coun. Exp. Work & Nat. Res. Coun. grants, 58-65. Res, Royal Victoria & Montreal Children's Hosps, 46-49; Defense Res. Bd. Can. grants, 51-54; found. award, Am. Soc. Plastic Surgery, 55; chmn, Plastic Surg. Res. Coun, 59. R.C.A.M.C, 43-45. Am. Soc. Plastic & Reconstruct. Surg. (assoc. ed, jour, 69-); fel. Am. Col. Surg; Am. Soc. Surg. Hand (v.pres, 71); Can. Med. Asn; Can. Soc. Plastic Surg; Brit. Asn. Plastic Surg; fel. Royal Soc. Med. Experimental and clinical investigation and reconstruction of congenital anomalies of upper extremities; experimental production of rheumatoid arthritis; wound healing evolve toward pathogenesis of thermal injury; investigation of feasibility of autogenous whole joint transplantation. Address: 1538 Sherbrooke St. W, Montreal, Can.

ENTNER, NATHAN, b. Phila, Pa, Oct. 1, 20; m. 47; c. 2. BIOCHEMISTRY. B.A, California, Los Angeles, 46, M.A, 48; Ph.D, California, 52. Res. assoc. pharmacol, sch. med, California, 52-54; sch. med, La. State, 54-55; asst. prof. PREV. MED, SCH. MED, N.Y. UNIV, 56-60, ASSOC. PROF, 60- U.S.A, 42-43. Am. Soc. Microbiol; Am. Soc. Biol. Chem. Biochemical bases of life processes. Address: Dept. of Preventive Medicine, New York University School of Medicine, 550 First Ave, New York, NY 10016.

ENTREKIN, DURWARD N(EAL), b. Ga, Nov. 25, 26; m. 54. PHARMACY. B.S, Georgia, 50; M.S, Florida, 51, Ph.D.(pharm), 53. Res. assoc. PHARM, E.R. Squibb & Sons, 53-57; asst. prof, SCH. PHARM, UNIV. GA, 57-59, assoc. prof, 59-65, PROF, 65-, ASSOC. DEAN, 68- U.S.N.R, 44-46. Am. Pharmaceut. Asn. Use of imitation flavors for masking distasteful drugs. Address: 250 Greencrest Dr, Athens, GA 30601.

ENTRINGER, R(OGER) C(HARLES), b. Iowa City, Iowa, May 17, 31; m. 55; c. 4. MATHEMATICS, NUMBER THEORY. B.S, Iowa, 52; M.S, New Mexico, 57, Ph.D.(math), 63; Univ. Calif, Los Angeles, 57-58. Instr. MATH, UNIV. N.MEX, 58-63, asst. prof, 63-69, ASSOC. PROF, 69- U.S.N, 53-55, Lt.(jg). Am. Math. Soc; Math. Asn. Am. Graph and combinatorial theory. Address: Dept. of Mathematics, University of New Mexico, Albuquerque, NM 87106.

ENY, D(ESIRE) MARC, b. Algiers, France, Feb. 8, 15; nat; m. 44; c. 2. ENVIRONMENT, PUBLIC WORKS. B.S, Univ. Algiers, 35; M.S.E, Breguet Inst, Paris, 38; Smith fel, Cornell Univ, 46, Dennison fel, 47-48, Ph.D.(chem, physiol), 48; Army War Col, 53; IBM Mgt. Ctr, 63. Mgr. electrochem. dept, Precision Metal Prod. Co, 40-43; res. assoc, Univ. Calif, 44-46; prof, Univ. Fla, 48-49; bio-engr, Firestone Tire & Rubber Co, 49-51; coord. for Latin Am, U.S. Dept. Agr, 51-53; chief biol. warfare br, U.S. Army Chem. Ctr, Md, 53-54, chem, biol. & nuclear protection div, 54-57, dir. chem, biol. & nuclear protection directorate, 57-62; dir. planning, U.S. Naval Exp. Sta, 62-63; mgr. eng. & prod. div, chem. group, Glidden Co, 63-66; environ. opers. div, Spindletop Ctr, Ky, 66-67; PRES, D. MARC ENY ASSOCS, 67- Consult, Army Res. Off. & Off. Civil Defense & Mobilization, 56-63; States of Ky. & Md; U.S. Econ. Develop. Admin, 66-68; City of Baltimore, 68-71; U.S. Small Bus. Admin, 68- Mem, State of Ky. Sci. Comn, 66-68; tech. adv, Baltimore Harbor Pollution Comt, 68-; chmn, Harford County Environ. Comt, 71- Commendation, U.S. Small Bus. Admin, 70; Wisdom Award, 70. U.S.A, 43-44. Fel. Am. Inst. Chem; Am. Soc. Civil Eng; Am. Inst. Chem. Eng; Inst. Elec. & Electronics Eng; Am. Pub. Works Asn; Am. Water Works Asn; Water Pollution Control Fedn; Nat. Soc. Prof. Eng; Inst. Munic. Eng; Am. Chem. Soc; Opers. Res. Soc. Am; Am. Pub. Health Asn. Environmental engineering; water; waste-water; air; solid waste studies; design; masterplans. Address: D. Marc Eny Associates, 1030 Hollingsworth Rd, Joppa, MD 21085.

ENYEART, CHARLES RICHARD, b. Saxton, Pa, July 21, 17; m. 43; c. 3. ORGANIC CHEMISTRY. B.S, Pa. State Col, 39, M.S, 40, Ph.D.(org. chem), 42. Res. chemist, GAF CORP, Easton, Pa, 43-54, process res. & develop. chemist, Linden, N.J, 54-56, CHIEF AREA CHEMIST, SURFACTANT PROD, 56- Am. Chem. Soc. Surfactants; textile auxiliaries; intermediates; chelates. Address: 55 Mountain Ave, Warren, NJ 07060.

ENZ, W(ALTER) W(ILLIAM) F(RED), b. Ft. Wayne, Ind, Apr. 29, 05; m. 31; c. 3. PLANT CHEMISTRY. B.S, Purdue, 27; M.S, Florida, 29; Fritzche Bros. fel, Wisconsin, 29-31, Ph.D, 31. Instr. pharmacy, Florida, 27-29; asst. prof. pharmaceut chem, Purdue, 31-32; with Upjohn Co, 32-42, 45-70; RETIRED. U.S.A, 42-45, Col. Am. Chem. Soc; Am. Pharmaceut. Asn. Solution of arsenous and mercuric iodide; chemistry of Brazil nut oil; thymoquinone and its oxidation products. Address: 2815 W. Michigan Ave, Kalamazoo, MI 94007.

ENZER, NORBERT BEVERLEY, b. Milwaukee, Wis, Nov. 26, 30; m. 56; c. 3. CHILD PSYCHIATRY, PEDIATRICS. B.A, Yale, 52; M.D, McGill Univ, 56. Intern pediat, med. ctr, Duke Univ, 56-57, resident, 57-58, 60-61, psychiat, 61-64, fel. child psychiat, 63-65, asst. prof. psychiat. & assoc. pediat, 65-68, assoc. prof. PSYCHIAT. & PEDIAT, SCH. MED, LA. STATE UNIV, 68-71, PROF, 71-, HEAD, DEPT. PSYCHIAT. & BIOBEHAV. SCI, 71- Med.C, 58-60, Capt. Am. Acad. Pediat; Am. Med. Asn; Am. Psychiat. Asn; Am. Acad. Child Psychiat; Soc. Res. Child Develop. Child psychiatry and development. Address: Dept. of Psychiatry & Biobehavioral Sciences, Louisiana State University School of Medicine, 1542 Tulane Ave, New Orleans, LA 70112.

ENZIAN, GEORGE H(ENRY), b. Forty Fort, Pa, May 4, 15; m. 37; c. 2. METALLURGY. B.S, Lehigh, 35, Met.E, 42; Carnegie Inst. Tech, 37-41. Metall. inspector, JONES & LAUGHLIN STEEL CORP, 35-37, metallographer, res. lab, 37-42, res. engr, 42-49, asst. mgr, metall. res. div, 49-53, mgr, 53-55, asst. dir. TECH. SERV, 55-69, DIR, 69- Instr, Pa. State Col, 41-45. Am. Soc. Metals; Am. Inst. Mining, Metall. & Petrol. Eng; Am. Iron & Steel Inst; Am. Soc. Test. & Mat; Soc. Automotive Eng; Brit. Iron & Steel Inst. Physical metallurgy of iron and steel; mechanical metallurgy; metallography; iron and steel raw materials and production. Address: Technical Services Division, Jones & Laughlin Steel Corp, 3 Gateway Center, Pittsburgh, PA 15230.

ENZIE, FRANK D(ORR), b. Dansville, N.Y, Feb. 8, 17; m. 41. VETERINARY MEDICINE. D.V.M, Ohio State, 40. Jr. veterinarian, tuberc. div, bur. animal indust, U.S. DEPT. AGR, 40-42, zool. div, 42-44, asst. veterinarian, 44-45, assoc. veterinarian, 45-48, parasitologist, 48-52, NAT. ANIMAL PARASITE LAB, 52-57, prin. parasitologist, 57-60, res. parasitologist, 60-63, res. vet, 63-71, DIR, 71- AAAS; Am. Vet. Med. Asn; Am. Soc. Parasitol; Am. Asn. Vet. Parasitol.(v.pres, 56-58); World Asn. Advan. Vet. Parasitol; Am. Inst. Biol. Sci; Animal Health Asn; Conf. Res. Workers Animal Diseases. Antiparasitics for domestic animals and poultry. Address: National Animal Parasite Lab, Veterinary Sciences Research Division, Agricultural Research Center, U.S. Dept. of Agriculture, Beltsville, MD 20705.

ENZIE, J(OSEPH) V(INCENT), b. Dansville, N.Y, Nov. 9, 10; m. 37; c. 2. HORTICULTURE. B.S, Oregon State, 33; Am. Cyanamid Co. fel, Ohio State, 35-36, M.S, 36; Texas A&M, 53-54, Ph,D, 55. Instr. hort, N.MEX. STATE UNIV, 36-37, asst. prof, 37-39, assoc. prof, 39-45, prof. & head dept, 45-63, asst. dean, col. agr. & home econ, 60-69, assoc. dean, 69-71, PROF. HORT, 71- Plant growth regulators; plant breeding; vegetable seed production. Address: 1134 N. Reymond St, Las Cruces, NM 88001.

ENZINGER, FRANZ M(ICHAEL), b. Rohrbach, Austria, Feb. 17, 23; U.S. citizen; m. 62; c. 1. PATHOLOGY. M.D, Innsbruck, 50. Asst. anat. & histol, Innsbruck, 50-51, forensic med, 53-54; intern, Westchester Hosp, Mt. Kisco, N.Y, 51-52; res. & instr. path, Iowa, 52-53, 54-57; assoc. pathologist, U.S. ARMED FORCES INST. PATH, 57-59, SR. PATHOLOGIST & CHIEF SOFT TISSUE BR, 60- Chief, Int. Center Soft Tissue Tumors, WHO. Am. Col. Path; Am. Soc. Clin. Path; Int. Acad. Path. Neoplastic diseases, especially soft tissue tumors; diagnostic pathology. Address: U.S. Armed Forces Institute of Pathology, 6825 16th St, Washington, DC 20305.

ENZMANN, ROBERT D, b. Peking, China, Nov. 5, 30; U.S. citizen; m. 58; c. 4. ELECTRICAL ENGINEERING, GEOLOGY. A.B, Harvard, 49; B.S. & M.S, Witwatersrand, 53; Nat. Sci. Found. scholar. & grant, Uppsala, 54-56; Ph.D, Mass. Inst. Technol, 56. Consult. geol. & geophys, mining co, Africa, Mediterranean Basin & Greenland, 50-57; Radio Corp. Am, 58-59, convair rep. & design specialist, 59-60, sr. engr, Alaska & Greenland, 60-62; CO. PLANS & PROJECTS, AVCO CORP, 62- Asst, Mass. Inst. Technol, 54-55; res. asst. prof, radiation lab, Michigan, 62; asst. prof, Northeastern, 63-; asst. prof, Univ. Boston. U.S.N, 43-46. Am. Geophys. Union; Am. Inst. Aeronaut. & Astronaut; Geol. Soc. S.Africa; Swedish Geol. Soc; Ger. Geol. Soc. Field geology; weapons systems design; space mission planning and planetology; use of instruments and engineering values in planetary orbital space, electrospheres, atmospheres, hydrospheres, lithospheres and endospheres. Address: 29 Adams St, Lexington, MA 02173.

EOFF, HERBERT JULIAN, b. Shirley, Ark, Apr. 3, 30; m. 58; c. 2. NUTRITION, BIOCHEMISTRY. B.S, Arkansas, 57, M.S, 58; Ph.D.(poultry sci), Texas A&M, 61. Dir. nutrit. res, WHITMOYER LABS, INC, ROHM AND HAAS CO, MYERSTOWN, 61-63, nutrit. dept, 63-65, DEVELOP. & TECH. SERV, 65-71, TECH. DIR, 71- U.S.A.F, 50-55, 1st Lt. Address: 33 Jay Ann Dr, Lebanon, PA 17042.

EOFF, KAY M, b. Refugio, Tex, Sept. 20, 32; m. 65. PHYSICS. B.S, Tex. Col. Arts & Sci, 53, M.S, 55; Ph.D.(physics), Univ. Fla, 63. Nuclear engr, Convair Div, Gen. Dynamics Corp, 54-55; ASST. PROF. PHYSICS & ASTRON, UNIV. FLA, 56- Am. Phys. Soc. Address: Rt. 2, Box 382-A, Gainesville, FL 32601.

EPAND, RICHARD M(AYER), b. N.Y.C, Dec. 31, 37; m. 65; c. 2. BIOPHYSICAL CHEMISTRY. A.B, Johns Hopkins Univ, 59; Nat. Insts. Health fel & Ph.D.(biochem), Columbia Univ, 64. Fel. biophys. chem, Cornell Univ, 65-68; vis. scientist, Inst. Biochem. Res, Buenos Aires, Arg, 68-69; ASST. PROF. CHEM, UNIV. GUELPH, 69- Am. Chem. Soc; Can. Biochem. Soc. The relationship between macromolecular structure and biological function, attained in part by the application of physical methods to the study of the conformation of biopolymers. Address: Dept. of Chemistry, Wellington College, University of Guelph, Guelph, Ont, Can.

EPEL, DAVID, b. Detroit, Mich, Mar. 26, 37; m. 60; c. 3. DEVELOPMENTAL & CELL BIOLOGY. A.B, Wayne State, 58; Nat. Insts. Health fel, Nat. Sci. Found. fel. & Ph.D.(zool), California, Berkeley, 63. Asst. prof. biol, Hopkins Marine Sta, Stanford Univ, 65-70; ASSOC. PROF. MARINE BIOL, UNIV. CALIF, SAN DIEGO, 70- Johnson Res. Found. fel, sch. med, Univ. Pa, 63-65. AAAS; Am. Soc. Cell Biol; Soc. Develop. Biol; Am. Soc. Zool; Am. Soc. Study Reproduction. Biochemistry of fertilization and early development; comparative embryology; heterotrophy in marine embryos. Address: Scripps Institute of Oceanography, University of California at San Diego, La Jolla, CA 92037.

EPEL, JOSEPH N(ORMAN), b. Mich, Jan. 27, 21; m. 48; c. 5. CHEMISTRY. B.S, Wayne, 43, Res. Corp. of Am. fel. & Ph.D.(phys. chem), 51. Rubber chemist, U.S. Rubber Co, 41-45; chem. consult. & v.pres, Hefco Labs, 45-49; PRES, DURALASTIC PRODS. CO. & LAMP PROD. CO, 52- Chem. consult, Detroit Test. Labs, 51- U.S.N.R, 45-46. Am. Chem. Soc; Soc. Plastics Eng. Molecular weight determination by light scattering measurements; reinforced plastics. Address: Duralastic Products Co, 5353 Concord, Detroit, MI 48211.

EPIS, R(UDY) C(HARLES), b. Bingham Canyon, Utah, Apr. 25, 30; m. 57; c. 1. GEOLOGY. A.B, Univ. Calif, Berkeley, 52, fel, 55-56, Ph.D.(geol), 56. Instr. GEOL, COLO. SCH. MINES, 56-57, from asst. prof. to assoc. prof, 57-69, PROF, 69- Geologist, U.S. Geol. Surv, 65- AAAS; Geol. Soc. Am; Am. Asn. Petrol. Geol. Structural and stratigraphic problems of southeastern Arizona; geological sciences; field geology; petrology; volcanology. Address: Dept. of Geology, Colorado School of Mines, Golden, CO 80401.

EPLER, JAMES L, b. Lancaster, Pa, Aug. 10, 37; m. 59; c. 4. GENETICS, BIOCHEMISTRY. B.S, Millersville State Col, 59; Nat. Sci. Found. fel, Fla. State, 61-64, M.S, 62, Ph.D.(zool), 63. Instr. radiation biol, Fla. State, 64; U.S. Pub. Health Serv. fel, BIOL. DIV, OAK RIDGE NAT. LAB, 64-66, BIOCHEMIST, 66-; LECTR. ZOOL. ENTOM, UNIV. TENN, 69- Genetics Soc. Am. Human genetics; chemical mutagenesis; nucleic acids. Address: Biology Division, Oak Ridge National Lab, Oak Ridge, TN 37830.

EPLEY, DONALD L, b. Edelstein, Ill, Dec. 21, 34; m. 63. ELECTRICAL ENGINEERING. B.S, Illinois, 56, M.S, 57, Ph.D.(elec. eng), 60. Asst. prof. ELEC. ENG, Stanford, 60-63; assoc. prof, UNIV. IOWA, 63-69, PROF, 69-, head dept, 64-69. Consult, Collins Radio Co, 64. Inst. Elec. & Electronics Eng; Soc. Indust. & Appl. Math; Asn. Comput. Mach. Switching theory and logical design; computer system analysis and design. Address: Dept. of Electrical Engineering, University of Iowa, Iowa City, IA 52240.

EPLEY, PAUL J, b. Los Angeles, Calif, Dec. 4, 41; m. 67. ECOLOGY, PHYSIOLOGY. B.A, Univ. South. Calif, 64, Ph.D.(biol), 71. Mat. testing engr, City of Los Angeles, 70-71; BIOLOGIST, U.S. NAVAL CIVIL ENG. LAB, PORT HUENEME, 71- Vis. asst. prof, Calif. State Col, Dominguez Hills, 70- AAAS; Am. Soc. Zool. Environmental engineering. Address: 6435 Corbin Ave, Woodland Hills, CA 91364.

EPLEY, RICHARD JESS, b. Pana, Ill, Aug. 31, 42. MEAT & FOOD SCIENCE. B.S, Univ. Ill, Urbana, 65; M.S, Univ. Mo-Columbia, 67, Ph.D.(animal husb), 70. Instr. food sci, Univ. Mo-Columbia, 69-70; ASST. PROF. ANIMAL SCI, UNIV. MINN, ST. PAUL, 70- AAAS; Am. Soc. Animal Sci; Am. Meat Sci. Asn. Applied studies in meat, animal and food sciences. Address: Dept. of Animal Science, University of Minnesota, St. Paul, MN 55101.

EPLING, GLENWOOD P(ERSHING), b. Butte, Mont, Dec. 15, 18; m. 42; c. 2. MICROSCOPIC ANATOMY. D.V.M, Colo. Agr. & Mech. Col, 42; M.S, 53. Jr. veterinarian, bur. animal indust, U.S. Dept. Agr, 43; asst. prof, COLO. STATE UNIV, 46-48, assoc. prof, 48-59, PROF. ANAT, 59-, CHMN. DEPT, 70- Nat. Insts. Health fel, California, Los Angeles, 61-62. Fel. AAAS; Electron Micros. Soc. Am; Am. Asn. Anat; Am. Asn. Vet. Anat; Am. Vet. Med. Asn; fel. Royal Micros. Soc. Analgesia; histology of skin; histology ovine hoof; verminous aneurysms; ultrastructural cytology; bovine lung and heart. Address: Dept. of Anatomy, Colorado State University, Ft. Collins, CO 80521.

EPNER, MARTIN, b. New York, N.Y, Dec. 14, 30; m. 54; c. 4. METALLURGY. B.S, N.Y. Univ, 54, M.S, 56. Res. engr, Sintercast Corp. Am, 54-56, res. assoc, 56-57, chief metallurgist, 57-60; tech. dir. protective coatings, Chromalloy Corp, 60-66, gen. mgr. TURBINE SUPPORT DIV, CHROMALLOY AM. CORP, N.Y, 66-67, TEX, 67-68, PRES, 68-, V.PRES, CORP, 69-, V.PRES. & GROUP EXEC, METALL. GROUP, 70- Am. Soc. Metals; Am. Soc. Test. & Mat. Powder metallurgy; diffusion coatings; surface diffusion associated phenomena. Address: Turbine Support Division, Chromalloy American Corp, 4430 Director Dr, San Antonio, TX 78219.

EPP, CHIROLD D(ELAIN), b. Fairview, Okla, Mar. 31, 39; m. 61; c. 3. NUCLEAR PHYSICS. B.S, Northwest. State Col.(Okla), 61; Atomic Energy Comn. fel, Univ. Okla, 61-62, M.S, 65; Atomic Energy Comn. fel, Univ. Tex, Austin, 68-69, Ph.D.(physics), 69. Instr. PHYSICS, Northwest. State Col. (Okla), 63-65; ASST. PROF, MIDWEST. UNIV, 69- Am. Phys. Soc; Am. Asn. Physics Teachers. High pressure research on pressure, volume, and temperature properties of argon to 10 kilobars; high energy nuclear physics with emphasis on quasi-free electron scattering from nuclei; physics teaching. Address: Dept. of Physics, Midwestern University, 3400 Taft Blvd, Wichita Falls, TX 76308.

EPP, EDWARD R(UDOLPH), b. Saskatoon, Sask, July 21, 29; m. 57. MEDICAL & RADIATION PHYSICS. B.A, Univ. Sask, 50, Can. Cancer Soc. scholar, 51-52, M.A, 52; Nat. Cancer Inst. Can. fel, McGill Univ, 53-55, Ph.D.(physics), 55. Res. asst. physics, Univ. Sask, summers 49, 50; asst. physics, Nat. Res. Coun. Can, 52-53; physicist radiation physics, dept. radiol, Montreal Gen. Hosp, 55-57; asst. BIOPHYS, SLOAN-KETTERING DIV, MED. COL, CORNELL UNIV, 57-58, assoc, 58-60, asst. prof, 60-66, assoc. prof, 66-70, PROF, 70-, CHMN. DEPT, 66-, MEM. & CHIEF, DIV. PHYS. BIOL, SLOAN-KETTERING INST. CANCER RES, 68-, assoc. mem, 64-68, assoc, 60-64, asst, 57-60. Consult, Reddy Mem. Hosp, 55-57; Montreal Children's Hosp, 56-57; mem. task group, Int. Comn. Radiol. Units & Measurements, 65-70; assoc. attend. physicist, dept. med. physics, Mem. Hosp. for Cancer & Allied Diseases, 67-; mem. radiation study sect, Nat. Insts. Health, 71- Dipl, Am. Bd. Health Physics, 61. AAAS; Can. Asn. Physicists; Am. Phys. Soc; Health Physics Soc; Radiation Res. Soc; Am. Asn. Physicists in Med. Radiobiology, especially cellular radiobiology; biophysics; health physics; effects of ionizing radiation of ultra-high intensity on living cells. Address: Division of Physical Biology, Sloan-Kettering Institute for Cancer Research, 410 E. 68th St, New York, NY 10021.

EPP, J(OHN) G(EORGE), b. Milwaukee, Wis, Jan. 17, 15; m. 42; c. 4. ANALYTICAL CHEMISTRY. B.S, Chicago, 37. Chemist, Dow Chem. Co, Mich, 37-42; chief chemist, Dow Magnesium Corp, 42-44; group leader, DOW CHEM. CO, Mich, 44-51, asst. lab. dir, Rocky Flats Plant, 51-54, asst. tech. dir, 54-58, mgr, qual. control & anal. labs, 58-62, tech. serv, 62-64, mfg, 64-69, div. serv, 69-70, QUAL. MFR, 70- Am. Chem. Soc. Address: 1676 Sunset Blvd, Boulder, CO 80302.

EPP, LEONARD G, b. Neptune, N.J, Aug. 14, 44; m. 69. DEVELOPMENTAL BIOLOGY. B.A, Gettysburg Col, 66; M.S, Pa. State Univ, 68, Ph.D.(zool), 70. ASST. PROF. BIOL, MT. UNION COL, 70- Partic, col. teacher res. participation prog, Ill. Inst. Technol, summer 71. AAAS; Am. Inst. Biol. Sci; Soc. Develop. Biol. Biology of hydra; development of pigmentation in amphibia. Address: Dept. of Biology, Mt. Union College, Alliance, OH 44601.

EPPELSHEIMER, DANIEL S(NELL). INDUSTRIAL ENGINEERING. B.S, Harvard, 32, Sc.D, 35. Asst. metal, Harvard, 34-35; res. metallurgist, res. lab, Union Carbide & Carbon Co, 35-38; res. assoc. prof. indust. eng, New Hampshire, 38-39, res. prof, 39-47, acting dir, Eng. exp. sta, 40-47; PROF. METALL. & NUCLEAR ENG, UNIV. MO-ROLLA, 47- Am. Inst. Mining, Metall. & Petrol. Eng; Am. Soc. Eng. Educ; Am. Soc. Test. & Mat; Am. Soc. Metals; Brit. Iron & Steel Inst; Ger. Foundrymen Asn; Am. Chem. Soc. General industrial research. Address: Dept. of Metallurgy, University of Missouri-Rolla, Rolla, MO 65401.

EPPENSTEIN, WALTER, b. Berlin, Germany, Dec. 14, 20; nat; m. 44; c. 3. PHYSICS. B.S, Robert Col. Istanbul, 42; M.S, Rensselaer Polytech, 52. Instr. PHYSICS, Robert Col. Istanbul, 42-46; RENSSELAER POLYTECH. INST, 46-53, asst. prof, 53-62, ASSOC. PROF, 62- Hon. res. assoc, Harvard, 64-65. Am. Soc. Eng. Educ; Am. Asn. Physics Teachers. Nuclear physics; vacuum technology; general physics and development of new demonstration and laboratory experiments. Address: Dept. of Physics, Rensselaer Polytechnic Institute, Troy, NY 12181.

EPPERSON, EDWARD R(OY), b. Burnsville, Miss, Oct. 14, 32; m. 60; c. 2. INORGANIC CHEMISTRY. B.S, Millsaps Col, 54; M.A, North Carolina, 57; Ph.D, Univ. of the Pacific, 65. Asst, North Carolina, 54-57; asst. prof. chem, Elon Col, 57-62, assoc. prof, 62-65, prof, 65-66; PROF. CHEM. & HEAD DEPT. PHYS. SCI, HIGH POINT COL, 66- Nat. Sci. Found. faculty fel, 64-65. Am. Chem. Soc. Synthesis of the anhydrous metal halides; lower oxidation states of molybdenum and tungsten. Address: 1115 Delk Dr, High Point, NC 27262.

EPPERSON, ERNEST REGINALD, b. Sedalia, Mo, Nov. 16, 06; m; c. 1. CHEMICAL ENGINEERING. B.S, Mo. Sch. Mines, 31, M.S, 32. Mat. engr, State Hwy. Dept, Mo, 32-42; res. instr, War Prod. Bd. contract, MICH. TECHNOL. UNIV, 42-44, asst. res. prof. CHEM. ENG, 44-59, ASSOC. PROF, 59- Summers, resident res. assoc, Argonne Nat. Lab, 58, 60, 61. Am. Chem. Soc; Am. Soc. Eng. Educ; Am. Inst. Chem. Eng. Unit operations in chemical engineering. Address: Dept. of Chemical Engineering, Michigan Technological University, Houghton, MI 49931.

EPPINK, RICHARD THEODORE, b. Cleveland, Ohio, May 7, 31. STRUCTURAL ENGINEERING, APPLIED MECHANICS. B.S, Case Inst. Technol, 53; M.S, Univ. Ill, 56, Ph.D.(civil eng), 60. Struct. engr, Glenn L. Martin Co, 53; instr, Univ. Ill, 59-60; mem. tech. staff, Nat. Eng. Sci. Co, 60-62; ASSOC. PROF. CIVIL ENG, UNIV. VA, 62- Summer fels, Am. Soc. Eng. Educ-NASA, 65, 66; struct. engr, Naval Ship Res. & Develop. Ctr, summers 67-71. U.S.A, 53-55. Am. Inst. Aeronaut. & Astronaut; Am. Soc. Civil Eng. Vibrations; blast effects of nuclear weapons; application and accuracy of finite element methods in structural analysis; numerical methods of structural analysis. Address: Dept. of Civil Engineering, School of Engineering & Applied Science, University of Virginia, Charlottesville, VA 22901.

EPPLE, AUGUST WILHELM, b. Wiesbaden, Ger, Sept. 26, 32; m. 66. COMPARATIVE ENDOCRINOLOGY. Ph.D.(zool), Frankfurt, 60. Res. assoc. zool, Frankfurt, 61-66; sr. res. assoc, Washington (Seattle), 66-67; ASSOC. PROF. ANAT, DANIEL BAUGH INST. ANAT, THOMAS JEFFERSON UNIV, 67- Fel. zool, Univ. Frankfurt, 62-63; vis. scientist, Zoophysiol. Lab, Copenhagen Univ, 64-65; Zool. Inst, Tokyo Univ, summer 67. Am. Diabetes Asn; Am. Asn. Anat; Am. Ornith. Union; European Asn. Study Diabetes; Ger. Zool. Soc; Ger. Soc. Mammal; Ger. Ornith. Soc; Senckenbergian Natural Sci. Soc. Comparative histophysiology of pancreatic islets; correlation of annual cycles of metabolism and endocrines in vertebrates; experimental diabetes. Address: Daniel Baugh Institute of Anatomy, Thomas Jefferson University, Philadelphia, PA 19107.

EPPLE, ROBERT (PAUL), b. Cleveland, Ohio, Aug. 1, 16; m. 44, 65; c. 2. CHEMISTRY. B.S, Juniata Col, 38; Wisconsin, 38; fel, Mass. Inst. Tech, 41-44, Ph.D.(chem), 47. Instr. Juniata Col, 38-41; tech. asst, Manhattan Proj, Mass. Inst. Tech, 44-46; instr. chem, Brown, 46-49, asst. prof. chem, 49-51; head inorg. chem. div, Tracerlab Inc, 51-56; chemist, Arthur D. Little, Inc, 56-62; mem, U.S. ATOMIC ENERGY COMN, 62-68, CHIEF NUCLEAR, STRUCT. & INORG. CHEM. BR, OFF. CHEM. PROGS, DIV. RES, 68- AAAS; Am. Chem. Soc. Polarography; polarographic studies of compounds of rhenium; reaction rates of ionic systems; industrial applications of fission product; radiation chemistry of gases. Address: Office of Chemistry Programs, Division of Research, U.S. Atomic Energy Commission, Washington, DC 20545.

EPPLER, RICHARD A(NDREW), b. Lynn, Mass, Apr. 30, 34; m. 59; c. 5. CERAMICS, MATERIALS SCIENCE. B.S, Carnegie Inst. Tech, 56; M.S, Illinois, 58, Ph.D.(chem. eng), 60. Res. scientist, Corning Glass Works, 59-65; SR. SCIENTIST, CERAMICS GROUP, GLIDDEN-DURKEE DIV, SCM CORP, 65- Lectr. math, Elmira Col, 64-65. Sig.C, U.S.A, 60, 1st Lt. Fel. Am. Inst. Chem; fel. Am. Ceramic Soc; Am. Chem. Soc; Electrochem. Soc; Nat. Soc. Prof. Eng. Crystallization phenomena, particularly from vitreous media; glass, glass-ceramic, glaze and enamel compositions and properties; solid state chemistry; reaction kinetics; high pressure research on solid materials; luminescent and photochromic materials. Address: Pemco Ceramics Group, SCM Corp, 5601 Eastern Ave, Baltimore, MD 21224.

EPPLEY, RICHARD W(AYNE), b. Puyallup, Wash, Oct. 12, 31; m. 53; c. 2. BIOLOGY. B.S, State Col. Wash, 53; Nat. Sci. Found. fel, Stanford, 53-54, U.S. Pub. Health Serv. fel, 55-57, Ph.D.(biol), 57. Instr. biol, Southern California, 57-59, asst. prof, 59-60, adj. assoc. prof, 61-63; plant physiologist, Northrop Corp, 60-63; assoc. res. biologist, UNIV. CALIF, SAN DIEGO, 63-70, LECTR. BIOL. & RES. BIOLOGIST, 70- Fel. AAAS; Am. Soc. Plant Physiol; Phycol. Soc. Am; Soc. Gen. Physiol. Algal physiology; biochemistry; ion transport; marine phytoplankton. Address: Institute of Marine Resources, University of California, San Diego, P.O. Box 109, La Jolla, CA 92037.

EPPLING, FREDERIC J(OHN), b. Sheboygan, Wis, Mar. 16, 20; m. 47; c. 4. NUCLEAR PHYSICS. Ph.B. & Ph.M, Wisconsin, 42, Atomic Energy Cmn. fel, 50-51, Ph.D.(physics), 53. Mem. res. staff nuclear physics, LAB. NUCLEAR SCI, MASS. INST. TECHNOL, 53-58, RES. PHYSICIST & LECTR, 58-, ASSOC. DIR, 64-, exec. officer, 62-64. U.S.N.R, 42-46, Res, 46-, Capt. Am. Phys. Soc. Study of energy levels of light nuclei; construction of electrostatic generators for nuclear research; mass spectroscopy. Address: R.F.D. Sunnyside Lane, Lincoln, MA 01773.

EPPRIGHT, ERCEL S(HERMAN), b. Isabel, Ill, May 4, 01; m. 24; c. 2. FOODS, NUTRITION. B.S, Missouri, 23; M.S, Texas, 30; Ph.D.(physiol. chem), Yale, 36. Teacher, schs, Mo, 20-22, 24; Kans, 23-24; instr. foods & nutrit, Texas, 29-31; prof. home econ. & head dept, Texas State Col. Women, 35-45; prof. foods & nutrit. & head dept, IOWA STATE UNIV, 45-61, asst. dean, col. home econ. & asst. dir, agr. & home econ. exp. sta, 61-66, prof. NUTRIT, 66-71; EMER. PROF, 71- Home economist, Food & Agr. Orgn, Iraq, 57-58; consult, Ford Found, Univ. Baroda, 66-67; Rockefeller Found, Univ. Minas Gerais, Brazil, 69. Am. Home Econ. Asn; Am. Dietetic Asn; Am. Inst. Nutrit. Dietary studies; food acceptance; nutritional status of school children; significance of certain salts and groups of salts in the nutrition of the albino rat. Address: 7709 Meadow Park Dr, Dallas, TX 75230.

EPPRIGHT, MARGARET A(NNE), b. Manor, Tex, Apr. 21, 13. BIOCHEMISTRY, NUTRITION. B.A, Texas, 33, M.A, 35, Fleischmann fel, 42-44, Ph.D. (chem), 45. Instr, pub. sch, Tex, 36-40; asst, Texas, 41, 44; assoc. prof. chem, Sam Houston State Col, 45-46; assoc. prof. nutrit. & res. assoc, Iowa State, 46-48; prof. chem. & head dept, Sam Houston State Col, 48-49; assoc. prof. HOME ECON, UNIV. TEX, AUSTIN, 49-54, PROF, 54-, head nutrit. div, 54-64, chmn. dept, 61-71. With Bur. Home Econ, U.S. Dept. Agr, 44. AAAS; Am. Pub. Health Asn; Am. Dietetic Asn; Am. Chem. Soc; fel. Am. Inst. Chem; Am. Home Econ. Asn. Synthesis of hydantoins; vitamin assay methods; nutritional status of population groups; mineral nutrition of microorganisms; metabolic patterns in health and disease. Address: Dept. of Home Economics, University of Texas at Austin, Austin, TX 78712.

EPPS, HARLAND WARREN, b. Hawthorne, Calif, July 29, 36. ASTRONOMY. B.A, Pomona Col, 59; M.S, Wisconsin, 61, Ph.D.(astron), 64. Prof. ASTRON, San Diego State Col, 64-65; asst. prof, UNIV. CALIF, LOS ANGELES, 65-70, ASSOC. PROF, 70- Am. Astron. Soc. Spectroscopy of peculiar stars and astronomical instrumentation. Address: Dept. of Astronomy, University of California, Los Angeles, CA 90024.

EPPS, WILLIAM M(ONROE), b. Latta, S.C, Oct. 31, 16; m. 42; c. 2. PLANT PATHOLOGY. B.S, Clemson, 37; Ph.D.(plant path), Cornell, 42. Asst, N.Y. State Col. Agr, Cornell, 38-42; assoc. plant pathologist, exp. sta, CLEMSON UNIV, 45-56; HEAD DEPT. bot. & bact, 56-69, PLANT PATH. & PHYSIOL, 69- U.S.A, 42-45, Res, 45-, Lt. Col. Am. Phytopath. Soc; Am. Hort. Soc. Vegetable diseases and breeding. Address: Dept. of Plant Pathology & Physiology, Clemson University, Clemson, SC 29631.

EPPSTEIN, S(AMUEL) H(ILLEL), b. Peoria, Ill, Mar. 2, 07; m. 46; c. 5. BIOCHEMISTRY. A.B, Chicago, 29; Ph.D.(biochem), Illinois, 36. Special res. assoc. biochem, Illinois, 36-37; instr, col. med, Nebraska, 38-40; RES. ASSOC, UPJOHN CO, 41- AAAS; Am. Chem. Soc. Protein chemistry, hormones and synthesis; immunology. Address: Dept. 7244, Upjohn Co, Kalamazoo, MI 49001.

EPREMIAN, E(DWARD), b. Schenectady, N.Y, Sept. 3, 21; m. 48; c. 2. METALLURGY. B.S, Mass. Inst. Tech, 43; M.S, Rensselaer Polytech, 47; D.Sc.(metall), Carnegie Inst. Tech, 51. Res. assoc. metall, res. lab, Gen. Elec. Co, 43-46; metals res. lab, Carnegie Inst. Tech, 50-51; sci. liaison officer, Off. Naval Res, London Br, 51-52, asst. sci. dir, 52-53, dept. sci. dir, 53-54; chief metals & mat. br, res. div, Atomic Energy Comn, 54-57; sr. metallurgist, res. lab, metals div, UNION CARBIDE CORP, 57-59, tech. coordinator, tech. dept, 60-61, mgr, new prod. mkt, 61-63, asst. dir. res, carbon prod. div, 63-65, gen. mgr, aerospace mat. dept, 65-68, gen. mgr, advan. mat. dept, 68-70, MGR. TANTALUM & COLUMBIUM PROD, MINING & METALS DIV, 70- Am. Soc. Metals; Am. Inst. Mining, Metall. & Petrol. Eng. Fatigue of metals; refractory metals; nuclear and high temperature metallurgy; physical chemistry; graphite technology. Address: Mining & Metals Division, Union Carbide Corp, 270 Park Ave, New York, NY 10017.

EPSTEIN, ALAN N(EIL), b. N.Y.C, July 29, 32; m. 57; c. 3. ANIMAL BEHAVIOR, NEUROPHYSIOLOGY. B.A. & M.A, Johns Hopkins Univ, 54, M.D, 58. Nat. Found. fel, inst. neurol. sci, sch. med, UNIV. PA, 58-61, asst. prof. zool, 61-64, assoc. prof. BIOL, 64-69, PROF, 69-, ASSOC. DIR, INST. NEUROL. SCI, 70- Consult. ed, J. Comp. & Physiol. Psychol; mem. neuropsychol. res. review comt, Nat. Inst. Ment. Health, 69- AAAS; Am. Soc. Zool; Am. Physiol. Soc; Soc. Neurosci; Soc. Animal Behav. Neurological basis of behavior; feeding and drinking and the specific hungers; behavioral thermoregulation. Address: Leidy Lab, Dept. of Biology, University of Pennsylvania, Philadelphia, PA 19104.

EPSTEIN, ARNOLD S, b. Can, July 31, 23; nat; m. 55; c. 1. SOLID STATE PHYSICS. B.S, Lehigh, 44; Radio Corp. Am. fel, Pennsylvania, 47-48, M.S, 49; Ph.D.(physics), Purdue, 54. Electronics engr, Radio Corp. Am, 44-47; asst. physics, Purdue, 50-54; res. physicist, Honeywell Res. Ctr, Minneapolis-Honeywell Regulator Co, 54-55; proj. engr, Int. Tel. & Tel. Co, 55-58; sr. res. physicist, res. & eng. div, MONSANTO CO, 58-62, res. specialist, 62-64, sr. res. specialist, cent. res. dept, 64-67, scientist, 67-70, SCI. FEL, 70- Am. Phys. Soc. Solid state, device, chemical and atomic physics; physical electronics. Address: 12127 Lake Como Dr, St. Louis, MO 63141.

EPSTEIN, ARTHUR W(ILLIAM), b. New York, N.Y, May 15, 23; m. 55; c. 4. PSYCHIATRY, NEUROLOGY. A.B, Columbia, 44, M.D, 47. Intern, Mount Sinai Hosp, N.Y, 47-48, res. neurol, 49-50; clin. asst. psychiat, State Hosp, Norristown, Pa, 48; asst, SCH. MED, TULANE UNIV, 50-52, instr. psychiat. & neurol, 52-54, asst. prof. neurol, 54-58, assoc. prof. PSYCHIAT. & NEUROL, 58-64, PROF, 64- AAAS; Am. Acad. Neurol; Soc. Biol. Psychiat; Am. Psychiat. Asn; Acad. Psychoanal. Brain behavior relationships, epileptic and dream mechanisms. Address: Dept. of Psychiatry & Neurology, Tulane University School of Medicine, 1430 Tulane Ave, New Orleans, LA 70112.

EPSTEIN, AUBREY, b. Detroit, Mich, June 4, 23; m. 50; c. 2. AUDIOLOGY, SPEECH PATHOLOGY. B.A, Indiana, 46; M.A, Western Reserve, 47; Ph.D. (speech path, audiol), Iowa, 53. Asst. prof. SPEECH PATH. & AUDIOL, Pittsburgh, 53-59, ASSOC. PROF, 59-63; IND. UNIV, BLOOMINGTON, 63- Consult, Vet. Admin, 55- Inf, 42-46. Fel. Am. Speech & Hearing Asn; Acoust. Soc. Am; assoc. fel. Am. Acad. Ophthal. & Otolaryngol. Auditory phenomena relative to aural pathology. Address: 2938 Ramble Rd. E, Bloomington, IN 47401.

EPSTEIN, BARRY D, b. New York, N.Y, Mar. 30, 42; m. 66; c. 1. ELECTROCHEMISTRY, ANALYTICAL CHEMISTRY. B.S, City Col. New York, 62; Nat. Inst. Gen. Med. Sci. fel, California, Riverside, 63-66, Ph.D.(anal. chem), 66. Res. fel. CHEM, Calif. Inst. Technol, 66-67; staff assoc, GULF GEN. ATOMIC, INC, 67-71, STAFF MEM, 71- Samuel Goldman award, 62. Am. Chem. Soc; Electrochem. Soc. Instrumentation; pollution analysis; batteries; biomaterials. Address: 6604 Edmonton Ave, San Diego, CA 92122.

EPSTEIN, BENJAMIN, b. Boston, Mass, Mar. 5, 18; m. 40; c. 3. STATISTICS, MATHEMATICS. B.S, Mass. Inst. Tech, 37, M.S, 38; Ph.D.(math), Illinois, 41; summers, Brown, 41, California, 47, 48. Asst. math, Illinois, 39-41, instr, 41-42; physicist & mathematician, Frankford Arsenal, 42-44; mem. staff, Westinghouse Elec. Corp, 44-45; coal res. lab, Carnegie Inst. Tech, 45-48, lectr. math, 45-48; assoc. prof, Wayne State, 48-55, prof, 55-60; statist. consult, 60-68; vis. prof, STATIST, ISRAEL INST. TECHNOL, 68-70, PROF, 70- Vis. prof, Stanford Univ, 55-56, 57-60; Nat. Sci. Found. lectr, prog. vis. lectr. statist, 63-65; summers, lectr, Univ. Calif, Berkeley, 50; Los Angeles, 59-62; N.Y. Univ, 59-65; Israel Inst. Technol, 64. Fel. AAAS; fel. Inst. Math. Statist; fel. Am. Statist. Asn; fel. Am. Soc. Qual. Control; Am. Math. Soc; Math. Asn. Am; Soc. Indust. & Appl. Math; Opers. Res. Soc. Am; Int. Asn. Statist. in Phys. Sci; Opers. Res. Soc. Israel. Mathematical statistics and theory of probability, particularly as applied to science and engineering; stochastic processes; theory of extreme values; life testing; reliability theory; order statistics; operations research. Address: Faculty of Industrial & Management Engineering, Israel Institute of Technology, Haifa, Israel.

EPSTEIN, BERNARD, b. Harrison, N.J, Aug. 10, 20; m. 47; c. 6. MATHEMATICS. B.A, N.Y. Univ, 40, M.S, 42; George Washington, 41-43; Ph.D. (appl. math), Brown, 47. Jr. physicist, Nat. Bur. Standards, D.C, 41-43; from asst. physicist to assoc. physicist, Manhattan Proj, 43-45; asst, div. appl. math. & instr. eng, Brown, 45-46; res. assoc. aeronaut. eng, grad. sch, Harvard, 46-47; instr. MATH, Pennsylvania, 47-49, asst. prof, 49-55, assoc. prof, 55-60; PROF, Yeshiva, 60-63; UNIV. N.MEX, 63- Vis. res. assoc, inst. math. sci, N.Y. Univ, 53; vis. assoc. prof, Stanford, 57-58; liaison scientist, U.S. Off. Naval Res, London, Eng, 64-66; vis. prof. math, Israel Inst. Technol, 71-72. With Off. Sci. Res. & Develop; U.S. Navy; Nat. Adv. Comt. Aeronaut, 44. Am. Math. Soc. Study of motion of compressible fluid by hodograph method; conformal mapping; boundary value problems of potential theory; extremal problems relating to analytic functions. Address: Dept. of Mathematics, University of New Mexico, Albuquerque, NM 87106.

EPSTEIN, CHARLES J(OSEPH), b. Phila, Pa, Sept. 3, 33; m. 56; c. 3. GENETICS, BIOCHEMISTRY. A.B, Harvard, 55, M.D, 59. Intern med, Peter Bent Brigham Hosp, Boston, Mass, 59-60, asst. resident, 60-61; res. assoc, Nat. Heart Inst, Nat. Insts. Health, 61-63, med. officer, Nat. Inst. Arthritis & Metab. Diseases, 63-66, chief sect. genetics & develop, lab. chem. biol, 66-67; ASSOC. PROF. PEDIAT, SCH. MED, UNIV. CALIF, SAN FRANCISCO, 67-, BIOCHEM, 70- Asst. med. & res. fel. med. genetics, sch. med, Washington (Seattle), 63-64; prof. lectr. inherited metab. diseases, sch. med, George Wash. Univ. & asst. med, Johns Hopkins Univ, 65-67. U.S.P.H.S, 61-63, Sr. Asst. Surg. Am. Fedn. Clin. Res; Am. Soc. Human Genetics; Am. Soc. Biol. Chem; Am. Soc. Clin. Invest; Soc. Pediatric Res; Am. Soc. Cell Biol; Soc. Develop. Biol. Medical genetics; hereditary diseases; biochemistry of early mammalian development; chromosome structure. Address: Dept. of Pediatrics, University of California School of Medicine, San Francisco, CA 94122.

EPSTEIN, DAVID W(ILLIAM), b. Russia, Jan. 11, 08, nat. 20; m. 30; c. 4. ELECTRICAL ENGINEERING. B.S, Lehigh, 30; M.Sc, Pennsylvania, 34, D.Sc.(elec. eng), 37. Student engr, Radio Corp. of Am. Victor Co, 30-31; jr. res. engr, Radio Corp. of Am. Mfg. Co, 31-33, res. engr, 33-42, sr. res. engr, in charge c-r tube and optics sect, RCA CORP, 42-53, assoc. lab. dir, 53-58, MGR. conversion tube oper, RCA Electronic Components & Devices, 58-69, TECH. PLANNING, RCA ELECTRONIC COMPONENTS, 69- With U.S.A; U.S.A.F; U.S.N, 44. AAAS; Am. Phys. Soc; fel. Inst. Elec. & Electronics Eng; Optical Soc. Am. Electron optics; high voltage cathode-ray tubes; high aperture reflective optical systems; electron guns; pulse-echo position indicators; color television; camera tubes; storage tubes; photo devices. Address: RCA Corp, RCA Electronic Components, Technical Planning, New Holland Pike, Lancaster, PA 17604.

EPSTEIN, EDWARD S(ELIG), b. New York, N.Y, Apr. 29, 31; m. 54; c. 4. METEOROLOGY. A.B, Harvard, 51; M.B.A, Columbia, 53; M.S, Pa. State, 54, Air Force fel, 58-59, Ph.D.(meteorol), 60. Res. assoc. & lectr. meteorol, Michigan, 59-61, asst. prof, 61-63; consult. to asst. secy. commerce for sci. & tech, U.S. Dept. Commerce, 63-64; assoc. prof. METEOROL, UNIV. MICH, 63-68, PROF, 68-, CHMN. DEPT. METEOROL. & OCEANOG, 71-, acting chmn, 69-70. Nat. Sci. Found. grants, 61-64, 65-68, 70-72; vis. prof, Int. Meteorol. Inst, Stockholm, 68-69. Mem, Nat. Sci. Found. adv. panel Atmos. Sci, 71-; Univ. Corp. Atmos. Res, rep, 69-, mem. goal & eval. comt, 69-71; ed, Jour. Appl. Meteorol, 71- U.S.A.F, 53-57, 1st Lt. Fel. Am. Meteorol. Soc; Am. Geophys. Union; Am. Statist. Asn; Royal Meteorol. Soc. Probability and statistics in meteorology; stochastic dynamic prediction. Address: Dept. of Meteorology & Oceanography, 4072 E. Engineering Bldg, University of Michigan, Ann Arbor, MI 48104.

EPSTEIN, ELIOT, b. Boston, Mass, Jan. 8, 29; m. 50; c. 3. SOIL PHYSICS. B.S, Syracuse, 51; M.S, Massachusetts, 53; fel, Purdue, 53, Ph.D, 55. Res. agronomist, Olin Mathieson Co, Conn, 55-56; Borden Co, N.Y, 56; SOIL SCIENTIST & PROJ. ADMINSTR, SOIL & WATER CONSERV, AGR. RES. SERV, U.S. DEPT. AGR, 56- Soil Sci. Soc. Am. Soil structure, moisture and temperature; physical chemistry; gaseous diffusion; plant physiology. Address: 325 Garland St, Bangor, ME 04401.

EPSTEIN, EMANUEL, b. Ger, Nov. 5, 16; nat; m. 43; c. 1. PLANT PHYSIOLOGY. B.S, California, 40, M.S, 41, Ph.D.(plant physiol), 50. Asst. bot, California, 43, plant nutrit, 46-49; assoc. plant physiologist, U.S. Dept. Agr, 49-51, plant physiologist, 51-58; lectr. PLANT NUTRIT. & assoc. plant physiologist, UNIV. CALIF, DAVIS, 58-65, PROF. & PLANT PHYSIOLOGIST, 65- Guest investr, biophys. lab, Carnegie Inst, 50; Guggenheim fel, Calif. Inst. Technol, 58; Fulbright res. grant, Australia, 65-66. Partic, Nat. Acad. Sci-Nat. Res. Coun. Desalination Res. Conf, Mass, 61. Adv, U.S. Del, Conf. Peaceful Uses Atomic Energy, 55. Cherubim Gold Medal, Univ. Pisa, 62. U.S.A, 43-46. AAAS; Am. Soc. Plant Physiol; Am. Inst. Biol. Sci; Scandinavian Soc. Plant Physiol; Japanese Soc. Plant Physiol. Mechanisms of ion transport in plants; salt relations of plants; genetic and ecological aspects of mineral plant nutrition. Address: 825 Oak Ave, Davis, CA 95616.

EPSTEIN, EMANUEL, b. Detroit, Mich, July 1, 22; m. 50; c. 3. BIOCHEMISTRY, CLINICAL CHEMISTRY. B.S, Wayne State, 45, M.S, 53, Ph.D.(biochem), 57. Chemist, Frederick Stearns & Co, 45-46; Fund Crippling Diseases, 46-47; univ. asst, Wayne State, 48-50, res. assoc, 50-57; res. chemist, St. Joseph Mercy Hosp, 57-68; CLIN. CHEMIST, WILLIAM BEAUMONT HOSP, 68- Asst. prof, Wayne State Univ, 63- Am. Asn. Clin. Chem; Endocrine Soc; Am. Chem. Soc. Steroid hormone analysis; spectrophotometry; chromatography; automation. Address: William Beaumont Hospital, 3601 W. 13 Mile Rd, Royal Oak, MI 48072.

EPSTEIN, ERVIN (HAROLD), b. Vallejo, Calif, May 17, 09; m. 36; c. 2. DERMATOLOGY. A.B, Univ. Calif, 31, M.D, 35. ASSOC. CLIN. PROF. DERMAT. MED, sch. med, Stanford Univ, 50-64; SCH. MED, UNIV. CALIF, SAN FRANCISCO, 62- Consult, hosps, Calif. U.S.A, 42-45, Capt. Am. Dermat. Asn; Soc. Invest. Dermat; Am. Acad. Dermat. Disease of the skin; skin surgery; regional dermatologic diagnosis; radio-dermatitis. Address: 400 30th St, Oakland, CA 94609.

EPSTEIN, EUGENE E(THAN), b. Los Angeles, Calif, Aug. 8, 34. ASTRONOMY. B.S, Calif. Inst. Technol, 56; M.S, Harvard, 59, Ph.D.(astron), 62. MEM. TECH. STAFF RADIO ASTRON, AEROSPACE CORP, 62- Am. Astron. Soc; Int. Astron. Union. Millimeter wavelength studies of the thermophysical characteristics of planetary surfaces; intensity and time variability of the millimeter emission of galactic objects, quasars and Seyfert galaxies. Address: Aerospace Corp, Box 95085, Los Angeles, CA 90045.

EPSTEIN, FRANKLIN HAROLD, b. Brooklyn, N.Y, May 5, 24; m. 51; c. 4. INTERNAL MEDICINE, PHYSIOLOGY. B.A, Brooklyn Col, 44; M.D, Yale, 47. House officer, Yale Med. Center, 47-49; res. fel, sch. med, Boston, 49-50; res. assoc. physiol, Walter Reed Army Med. Center, 50-52; asst. prof. MED, SCH. MED, YALE, 54-59, assoc. prof, 59-66, PROF, 66-, CHIEF, METAB. DIV, 65- Estab. investr, Am. Heart Asn, 56-61; career investr, U.S. Pub. Health Serv, 64-; consult. Off. Surgeon Gen, U.S. Army, 64-69; chmn, nephrol. test comt, Am. Bd. Internal Med, 70-; trustee, Mt. Desert Island Biol. Lab, 70- Med.C, 49-53, Res, 53-54, Capt. Am. Soc. Clin. Invest.(v.pres, 69-70); Am. Physiol. Soc; Asn. Am. Physicians. Renal physiology and disease. Address: Dept. of Internal Medicine, Yale University School of Medicine, 333 Cedar St, New Haven, CT 06510.

EPSTEIN, FREDERICK H(ERMON), b. Frankfurt am Main, Germany, July 24, 16; nat; m. 43; c. 2. MEDICINE. B.A, Cambridge, 40; M.A, M.B, B.Ch, 44, M.D, 56. Res. fel, Goldwater Mem. Hosp, N.Y. Univ, 49-51, asst. attend. physician, 51-56; asst. med, N.Y. Univ-Bellevue Med. Center, 52-56, clin. instr, col. med, 53-56; physician in charge res. dept, Sidney Hillman Health Center, 51-56; res. assoc. & lectr. EPIDEMIOL, SCH. PUB. HEALTH, UNIV. MICH, 56-59, assoc. prof, 59-63, PROF, 63-, DIR. CTR. RES. DISEASES HEART, 69- Res. fel, Nat. Heart Inst, U.S. Pub. Health Serv, 56-57, spec. res. fel, 56-59, res. career award, 62- Consult, cardiovasc. disease sect, WHO, 61, 68, 69, 70. Mem, coun. arteriosclerosis, Am. Heart Asn, comt. epidemiol. studies, 60-64, res. study comt, 62-64, chmn. comt. criteria & methods, Coun. Epidemiol, 61-, mem. exec. comt, 64-, chmn, 68-69; heart spec. proj. comt, Nat. Heart Inst, 63-66; comt. epidemiol, Nat. Acad. Sci-Nat. Res. Coun, 65-; comt. diet & heart disease, National Heart Inst, 67, 68, task force cardiac replacement, 68-69; epidemiol. & disease control study sect, Nat. Insts. Health, 70-; Surgeon Gen. adv. comt. smoking & heart disease, 67-70; coun. epidemiol. & prevention, Int. Soc. Cardiol, exec. comt, 70- AAAS; Geront. Soc; Am. Heart Asn; Am. Pub. Health Asn; Am. Fedn. Clin. Res; Am. Epidemiol. Soc; Soc. Exp. Biol. & Med; Harvey Soc; Royal Col. Physicians; Royal Col. Surgeons; Int. Epidemiol. Asn. Epidemiology of chronic diseases, especially atherosclerosis and heart disease. Address: Dept. of Epidemiology, School of Public Health, University of Michigan, Ann Arbor, MI 48104.

EPSTEIN, GABRIEL LEO, b. Manhattan, N.Y, Apr. 8, 41; m. 70. ATOMIC PHYSICS, SPECTROSCOPY. B.Ch.E, City Col. New York, 62; Ph.D.(physics), Univ. Calif, Berkeley, 69. Teaching asst. elementary physics, Univ. Calif, Berkeley, 63-65, res. asst. atomic physics & spectros, 65-69; Nat. Acad. Sci-Nat. Res. Coun. Res. assoc, Nat. Bur. Standards, Dept. Commerce, 69-70; STAFF SCIENTIST OPTICAL SYSTS, NASA GODDARD SPACE FLIGHT CTR, 70- AAAS; Optical Soc. Am. Fabry-Perot interferometry; optical isotope shifts and nuclear sizes; production and analysis of the spectra of moderately ionized atoms; construction of solar telescopes and photoelectric spectrometers. Address: NASA Goddard Space Flight Center, Code 683, Greenbelt, MD 20771.

EPSTEIN, GARY MARTIN, b. Los Angeles, Calif, June 9, 42; m. 65; c. 1. PARTICLE PHYSICS. B.A, Univ. Calif, Riverside, 64, Ph.D.(physics), 69. ASST. PROF. MATH, CALIF. STATE POLYTECH. COL, SAN LUIS OBISPO, 69- Am. Phys. Soc. Construction of dispersion relations for Regge parameters in high energy scattering theory; building of biomathematical models with the aid of interactive computer graphics. Address: Dept. of Mathematics, California State Polytechnic College, San Luis Obispo, San Luis Obispo, CA 93402.

EPSTEIN, GEORGE, b. Boston, Mass, Nov. 9, 26; m. 51; c. 2. PHYSICAL CHEMISTRY. B.S, Massachusetts, 48; M.S, Mass. Inst. Tech, 51. Asst, adhesives lab, Mass. Inst. Tech, 50-52; res. engr, N.Am. Aviation, Inc, 52-55; prin. engr. & dept. head, struct. mat. div, Aerojet-Gen. Corp. Div, Gen. Tire & Rubber Co, 55-61; prin. engr. & staff scientist, aeronutronic div, Ford Motor Co, 61-63; proj. scientist, Aerospace Res. Assocs, Inc, 63-66; STAFF ENGR, MAT. SCI. LAB, AEROSPACE CORP, 66- Instr, Univ. Calif, Los Angeles, 54- Mem. Fed. Steering Comt. Adhesives Technol, 71- West. Plastics distinguished serv. award, 63. U.S.N, 45-46. Am. Chem. Soc; Am. Soc. Test. & Mat; Soc. Plastics Eng; Soc. Plastics Indust; Soc. Aerospace Mat. & Process Eng.(meritorious serv. award, 63; v.pres, 63-64). Nonmetallic materials, plastics, resins, adhesives, sealants and coatings for high-performance applications; energy absorbing materials; advanced test and inspection methods; major applications to rockets, missiles and space vehicles. Address: 300 N. Orange Dr, Los Angeles, CA 90036.

EPSTEIN, GEORGE, b. Bayonne, N.J, July 4, 34; m. 56; c. 3. MATHEMATICS, COMPUTER SCIENCE. B.S, Calif. Inst. Technol, 55; M.S, Univ. Ill, 57; Ph.D.(math), Univ. Calif, Los Angeles, 59. Mem. tech. staff, comput. sci, Hughes Aircraft, Calif, 57-59; SR. STAFF SCIENTIST MATH. & COMPUT. SCI, ITT GILFILLAN, INC, VAN NUYS, 59- Am. Math. Soc; Math. Asn. Am; Asn. Symbolic Logic; Asn. Comput. Mach; Inst. Elec. & Electronics Eng; Int. Soc. Gen. Semantics. Cybernetics; philosophy; psychology; literature; electrical circuits and systems; linguistics and education; decision algebras. Address: 3726 Seahorn Dr, Malibu, CA 90265.

EPSTEIN, HAROLD M, b. Denver, Colo, Dec. 1, 28; m. 53; c. 3. NUCLEAR PHYSICS. B.S, Colorado, 50; Ph.D.(physics), Ohio State, 62. Trainee eng. physics, Allis-Chalmers Mfg. Co, 50-51; prin. physicist, Battelle Mem. Inst, 53-58, proj. leader physics, 58-60, asst. chief, 60-70; ADJ. ASSOC. PROF. MECH. ENG, OHIO STATE UNIV, 70- Chem.C, U.S.A, 51-53. Reactor engineering and analysis; heat transfer; fluid flow; stress analysis; nuclear weapons effects; plasma physics. Address: Dept. of Mechanical Engineering, Ohio State University, Columbus, OH 43210.

EPSTEIN, HERMAN, b. N.Y.C, June 1, 26; m. 49; c. 5. APPLIED PHYSICS, ELECTRICAL ENGINEERING. B.E.E, City Col. New York, 45; M.S, Columbia, 48; Ph.D.(elec. eng), Yale, 50. Instr. elec. eng, City Col. New York, 47-48; Yale, 48-50; dept. mgr. & proj. engr, Burroughs Corp, 50-58; v.pres. eng, Teledynamics, Inc, 59-60; pres, Omnitronics, Inc, Phila, 60-66; GEN. MGR. printer-reader bus. sect, Gen. Elec. Co, 66-68; SINGER CO, 68- Instr, Temple Univ, 50-56. U.S.A.A.F, 46-47. Sr. mem. Inst. Elec. & Electronics Eng; Am. Phys. Soc; Asn. Comput. Mach; Sci. Res. Soc. Am; Soc. Indust. & Appl. Math. Data handling systems; input-output devices for such systems; digital storage devices; circuit theory; electronics; feedback systems; applied physics; telemetry. Address: Singer Co, 915 Pembroke St, Bridgeport, CT 06608.

EPSTEIN, HERMAN T(HEODORE), b. Portland, Maine, Apr. 13, 20; m. 47; c. 4. BIOPHYSICS. B.A, Univ. Mich, 41, M.A, 43; Ph.D.(physics), 49. Physicist, supersonic aerodyn, Nat. Adv. Comt. Aeronaut, 44-46; asst. prof. biophys. & physics, Univ. Pittsburgh, 49-53; physics, BRANDEIS UNIV, 53-55, assoc. prof. BIOPHYS, 55-61, PROF, 61-, CHMN. DEPT. BIOL, 71- Nat. Sci. Found. sr. fel, 59-60; Guggenheim fel, 69-70; vis. prof, Tel Aviv Univ, 70-71. U.S.A.A.F, 44-47. Am. Phys. Soc; Am. Soc. Microbiol; Biophys. Soc. Biological and biophysical properties of viruses; effects of radiation on biological systems. Address: 36 Baskin Rd, Lexington, MA 02173.

EPSTEIN, IRVING J(ACOB), b. New York, N.Y, Aug. 24, 19; m. 48; c. 3. MATHEMATICS. B.S, City Col. New York, 41; Ph.D.(math), N.Y. Univ, 56. RES. MATHEMATICIAN, U.S. ARMY ELECTRONICS COMMAND, FT. MONMOUTH, 49-; ADJ. PROF. MATH, UNIV. COL, RUTGERS UNIV, 69-, lectr, 61-66, assoc. prof, 66-69. U.S.A, 41-45, Sgt. Am. Math. Soc; Math. Asn. Am. Mathematical physics with emphasis on algebraic and topological aspects of periodic solutions of systems of differential equations. Address: Dept. of Mathematics, University College, Rutgers, The State University, New Brunswick NJ 08903.

EPSTEIN, ISADORE, b. Tallinn, Estonia, Oct. 23, 19; nat; m. 64. ASTRONOMY, ASTROPHYSICS. A.B, Cincinnati, 41, M.S, 47; A.M, Princeton, 50, Ph.D.(astron), 50. Assoc. ASTRON, COLUMBIA UNIV, 50-53, asst. prof, 53-57, assoc. prof, 57-71, PROF, 71- Observer, Yale-Columbia South. Sta, Australia, 57-58; vis. astronomer, Nat. Observ, Cordoba, Arg, 58, 61, 62. U.S.A, 42-46. Am. Astron. Soc. Astronomical photometry. Address: Dept. of Astronomy, Columbia University, New York, NY 10027.

EPSTEIN, JACK, Psycholinguistics, see 6th ed, Dir. Am. Scholars, Vol. III.

EPSTEIN, JACK B(URTON), b. N.Y.C, Dec. 27, 35; m. 58; c. 1. GEOLOGY. B.S, Brooklyn Col, 56; M.A, Wyoming, 58; Ph.D, Ohio State, 70. Field asst. geol, U.S. GEOL. SURV, 56, GEOLOGIST, 57, 58-60, 64- Instr, Ohio State, 64. Geol. Soc. Am; Am. Asn. Petrol. Geol; Soc. Econ. Paleont. & Mineral. Areal geology of Western United States and Eastern Pennsylvania; groundwater investigations in Louisiana. Address: Agricultural Research Center, U.S. Geological Survey, Beltsville, MD 20705.

EPSTEIN, JEANNE A(LICE), b. N.J, Jan. 19, 23; m. 60; c. 1. MEDICINE. B.S, Rutgers, 42; M.D, Woman's Med. Col. Pa, 53. Res. technician rheumatic fever, Rockefeller Inst. Med. Res, 44-49; intern, Beth Israel Hosp, 53-54; asst. med, col. physicians & surgeons, Columbia, 54-55; fel. therapeut. & endocrinol, Bellevue Med. Ctr, N.Y. UNIV, 55-58, ASST. PROF. CLIN. MED, 58-; ASST. MED. DIR, MARGARET SANGER RES. BUR, 64-, endocrinologist, 56-64. Res, Columbia Div, Goldwater Hosp, 54-55; asst. adj, Beth Israel Hosp, 55-64; asst. attend, Knickerbocker Hosp, 57-64; asst. physician, hosp, N.Y. Univ, 57-; asst. vis, Bellevue Hosp, 58-; res. assoc, Irvington House, 59-62. Am. Soc. Microbiol; Endocrine Soc; Am. Fertil. Soc; Am. Med. Asn; Am. Fedn. Clin. Res. Rheumatic fever; etiology and prophylaxis; endocrinology of the gonads; infertility; clinical investigation in general endocrinology. Address: Margaret Sanger Research Bureau, 17 W. 16th St, New York, NY 10016.

EPSTEIN, JESS, b. Cincinnati, Ohio, Dec. 18, 07; m. 39; c. 3. PHYSICS. E.E, Cincinnati, 32, Baldwin fel, 32-34, M.S, 34. Co-operative engr, Crosley Radio Corp, Ohio, 26-31; instr. physics, Cincinnati Col. Pharm, 34-35; res. engr, Radio Corp. of Am. Mfg. Co, N.J, 35-42; David Sarnoff Res. Labs, RCA CORP, 42-62, tech. adminstr, missile & surface radar div, 62-67, CORP. STAFF ENGR, 67-, corp. staff, patents & licensing, 69. Inst. Elec. & Electronics Eng. Electromagnetic propagation problems; antennas; transmission lines. Address: Seven Little Brook Rd, Princeton, NJ 08540.

EPSTEIN, J(OSEPH), b. Phila, Pa, June 30, 18; m. 45; c. 4. PHYSICAL & ORGANIC CHEMISTRY. A.B, Temple, 38; M.S, Pennsylvania, 40; Ph.D, Univ. Del, 66. Plant chemist, trouble shooter, Chem. Corps. Med. Labs, Army Chem. Ctr, 40-44, res. assoc, toxicol, 44-45, chief, anal. sect, gassing br, 45-47, sanit. chem. br, 47-58, protection res. br, 58-62, CHIEF, defense res. div, chem. res. & develop. labs, 62-66; defense res. dept, res. labs, ARMY EDGEWOOD ARSENAL, 66-71, DEFENSE RES. BR, CHEM. LAB, 71- Consult, U.S. Pub. Health Serv, 54. AAAS; Sci. Res. Soc. Am; Am. Chem. Soc; Am. Ord. Asn; N.Y. Acad. Sci. Protection against and decontamination, detection and identification of chemical warfare agents; properties of chemical warfare materials in aqueous and non-aqueous media; reaction mechanisms and kinetics of reactions; development of analytical methods, especially micro methods. Address: Army Edgewood Arsenal, Chemical Lab, Defense Research Branch, Edgewood Arsenal, MD 21010.

EPSTEIN, LAWRENCE M(ELVIN), b. Brooklyn, N.Y, Apr. 23, 23; m. 46; c. 4. PHYSICAL CHEMISTRY. B.Ch.E, Cooper Union, 43; M.S, Polytech. Inst. Brooklyn, 52, Ph.D.(phys. chem), 55. Chemist, Am. Aniline Prods, 46-47; instr. anal. chem, New York Community Col, 47-55; fel. polymer properties, Mellon Inst, 55-56; sr. scientist radiation res, Westinghouse Res. Labs, 56-63, supvry. scientist, 63-67; ASSOC. PROF. CHEM, UNIV. PITTSBURGH, 67- U.S.N, 43-46. Am. Chem. Soc. Radiation chemistry and processing; radiation damage to materials; Mössbauer effect; chemical kinetics; polymer properties. Address: Dept. of Chemistry, University of Pittsburgh, Pittsburgh, PA 15213.

EPSTEIN, LEO F(RANCIS), b. N.Y.C, Dec. 9, 13; m. 42; c. 2. PHYSICAL CHEMISTRY. B.S, Mass. Inst. Tech, 35, Ph.D.(phys. chem), 39. Asst. photochem, solar energy res. comt, Mass. Inst. Tech, 39-41; asst. chemist, nat. defense res. comt, high explosives res. div, U.S. Bur. Mines, 41-42; res. engr, Crystal Res. Labs, Inc, Conn, 45-47; res. assoc, Knolls Atomic Power Lab, Gen. Elec. Co, 47-57, phys. chemist, Vallecitos Atomic Lab, 57-68; SR. CHEMIST, LIQUID METAL FAST BREEDER REACTOR OFF, ARGONNE NAT. LAB, 68- Sci. adv, U.S. delegation, Geneva Conf. on Peaceful Uses of Atomic Energy, 55. Ord. Dept, 42-46, Res, 46-63, Col. AAAS; Am. Chem. Soc; Math. Asn. Am; Am. Phys. Soc. Physical chemistry of solutions such as non-aqueous, electrolytes and liquid metals; dyestuff solutions; high explosives; mathematical analysis; ultrasonics; applications of physical chemistry to materials problems in nuclear systems. Address: Liquid Metal Fast Breeder Reactor Office, Argonne National Lab, Argonne, IL 60439.

EPSTEIN, LEON J, b. Jersey City, N.J, June 7, 17; c. 2. PSYCHIATRY. A.B, Vanderbilt, 37, M.A, 38; Ph.D, George Peabody Col, 41; M.D, Tennessee, 49. Staff psychiatrist, St. Elizabeths Hosp, Wash, D.C, 54-56; dep. dir. res, Calif. State Dept. Ment. Hyg, 56-61; asst. prof. PSYCHIAT, SCH. MED, UNIV. CALIF, SAN FRANCISCO, 61-64, assoc. prof, 64-68, PROF, 68-, V.CHMN. DEPT, 69-; ASSOC. MED. DIR, LANGLEY PORTER NEUROPSYCHIAT. INST, 61- Hon. staff specialist, Travis Air Force Base, Calif, 61-; mem. cmt. clin. drug eval, Psychopharmacol. Serv. Ctr, Nat. Inst. Ment. Health, 64- U.S.N.R, 41-46, Lt. Comdr. AAAS; Am. Psychiat. Asn; Am. Col. Neuropsychopharmacol. Psychopharmacology; emotional disorders in the elderly. Address: University of California Medical Center, San Francisco, CA 94122.

EPSTEIN, L(UDWIG) IVAN, b. Germany, Nov. 25, 18; nat; m. 55. THEORETICAL PHYSICS. B.S, Calif. Inst. Tech, 40, M.S, 41; Ph.D.(physics), Ohio State, 67. Mem. res. staff, U.S. Navy rocket proj, Calif. Inst. Tech, 43-46; optical engr, Bausch & Lomb Optical Co, N.Y, 47-54; mathematician & sr. engr, Martin Co, Md, 54-58; asst. prof. physics & math, Lowell Tech. Inst, 58-63; ASSOC. PROF. physics, Marietta Col, 63-64; BIOPHYS, HEALTH SCI. DIV, VA. COMMONWEALTH UNIV, 67- Am. Asn. Physics Teachers; Optical Soc. Am. Geometrical and physical optics; rockets; nomography; theory of molecular spectra; quantum mechanics; thermodynamics; statistical mechanics. Address; Dept. of Biophysics, Medical College of Virginia, P.O. Box 877, Virginia Commonwealth University, Richmond, VA 23219.

EPSTEIN, MARK R(OBERT), b. Forest Hills, N.Y, Feb. 7, 43; m. 65. ELECTRICAL ENGINEERING. S.B, Mass. Inst. Tech, 63, S.M, 64; Ph.D.(elec. eng), Stanford, 68. Res. asst, res. lab. electronics, Mass. Inst. Tech, 64; radiosci. lab, Stanford, 64-67, res. assoc, 67-68; staff engr, PAGE COMMUN. ENGRS, INC, 68-69, RES. & DEVELOP. MGR, 69- Assoc. mem. Int. Sci. Radio Union; Inst. Elec. & Electronics Eng. Radio wave propagation; communications systems; high frequency radio communications techniques; radio techniques; radio navigation techniques; satellite communications. Address: Page Communications Engineers, Inc, 3300 Whitehaven St. N.W, Washington, DC 20007.

EPSTEIN, MARTIN E(DEN), b. N.Y.C, Jan. 28, 26; m. 49; c. 5. ORGANIC CHEMISTRY. Le Clair fel, City Col, 47, B.S, 48; univ. fel, Syracuse, 50, Ph.D.(chem), 51. Res. chemist, Pa. Indust. Chem. Corp, 51-58, group leader, 59-60; res. assoc, CELANESE CORP, 60-65, sect. head, N.J, 65, proj. mgr, Celanese Fibers Co, N.C, 65-69, DIR. FIBERS, PLASTICS & COATING RES, CELANESE RES. CO, N.J, 69- U.S.A, 44-46. AAAS; Am. Chem. Soc; fel. Am. Inst. Chem. Diolefin and terpene polymers; free radical addition reactions; polymerization mechanisms; selective solvent extraction; wet, dry, melt spinning; elastomers; high melting polyamides; cigaret filtration; smoking materials. Address: Celanese Research Co, Box 1000, Summit, NJ 07901.

EPSTEIN, MARVIN P(HELPS), b. N.Y.C, Sept. 28, 20; m. 64; c. 1. MATHEMATICS. A.B, California, 47, A.M, 48; Atomic Energy Comn. fel, Columbia, 51-53, Ph.D.(math), 53. Asst. math, California, 47-48; lectr, Columbia, 49-51; instr, California, 53-55; asst. prof, Hopkins, 55-56; SUPVR, MATH. ANAL. & CONSULT. GROUP, BELL TEL. LABS, 56- Mem. staff, Stevens Inst. Tech, 58-60; Fairleigh Dickinson, 58-67, Drew Univ, 67-; Seton Hall Univ, 70- U.S.A, 42-46. Math. Asn. Am; Soc. Indust. & Appl. Math; Am. Asn. Comput. Mach. Differential algebra; analysis; numerical analysis; numerical linear algebra. Address: Bell Telephone Labs, Whippany, NJ 07981.

EPSTEIN, MAX, b. Lodz, Poland, Feb. 5, 25; U.S. citizen; m. 63; c. 3. ELECTRICAL ENGINEERING, SOLID STATE PHYSICS. B.S, Israel Inst. Technol, 52; M.S, Ill. Inst. Technol, 55, Ph.D.(elec. eng), 63. Instr. ELEC. ENG, Ill. Inst. Technol, 54-58, res. engr, IIT Res. Inst, 58-64, sr. res. engr, 64-67; ASSOC. PROF, NORTHWEST. UNIV, 67- Consult, IIT Res. Inst. Israel Defense Army, 48-49. AAAS; Am. Phys. Soc; Inst. Elec. & Electronics Eng. Magnetic devices; microacoustics. Address: Dept. of Electrical Engineering, Northwestern University, Evanston, IL 60201.

EPSTEIN, MELVIN, b. N.Y.C, July 17, 30; m. 51; c. 2. FLUID MECHANICS, PHYSICS. B.A.E, N.Y. Univ, 51; M.S, Mass. Inst. Tech, 53; Calif. Inst. Tech, 55-56; Ph.D.(appl. mech), Polytech. Inst. Brooklyn, 59. Aeronaut. engr, Douglas Aircraft Co, 54-55; sr. aerodynamicist, Repub. Aviation Corp, 56-57; sr. scientist, Gen. Appl. Sci. Labs, 57-59; res. scientist, eng. center, Southern California, 59-61; head theoret. gas dynamics sect, AEROSPACE CORP, 61-67, SR. STAFF SCIENTIST, AERODYN. & PROPULSION RES. LAB, 67- Lectr, Southern California, 61-; summer aeronaut. engr, Cornell Aeronaut. Lab, 51. Consult, Lockheed Aircraft Corp, 59-61. U.S.A.F, 53-54, 1st Lt. Am. Inst. Aeronaut. & Astronaut. Plasma physics. Address: Aerodynamics & Propulsion Research Lab, Aerospace Corp, Box 95085, Los Angeles, CA 90045.

EPSTEIN, MICHAEL, b. Brooklyn, N.Y, Jan. 5, 41; m. 68; c. 2. MECHANICAL ENGINEERING, MATHEMATICS. B.S, Polytech. Inst. Brooklyn, 63, fel, 63-69, M.S, 65, Ph.D.(mech. eng), 69. Res. scientist, Aerochem. Res. Labs, Inc, 68-70; sr. engr, Douglas United Nuclear, Inc, 70-71; ASST. MECH. ENGR, ARGONNE NAT. LAB, 71- Assoc. mem. Am. Inst. Aeronaut. & Astronaut. Theoretical work pertaining to fog formation phenomena in boundary layer flows, bubble growth and dissolution, vapor phase condensation, and solidification in melts. Address: Reactor Analysis and Safety Division, Bldg. 206, Argonne National Laboratory, 9700 South Cass Ave, Argonne, IL 60439.

EPSTEIN, MORTON B(ATLAN), b. New York, N.Y, June 8, 17; m. 42; c. 2. CHEMISTRY. B.S, N.Y. Univ, 37; Ph.D.(chem), Illinois, 42. Asst, Illinois, 41-42; chemist, Picatinny Arsenal, N.J, 42-45; Am. Petrol. Inst. & res. assoc, Nat. Bur. Standards, 46-49; res. assoc, Colgate Palmolive Co, 49-54; Onyx Oil & Chem. Co, 54-57; Colgate Palmolive Co, 57-63; div. adult health & aging, Chicago Bd. Health, 63-69; CLIN. CHEMIST, CHRIST COMMUNITY HOSP, 69- Assoc. clin. path, Chicago Med. Sch, 70-; consult, cardiovasc. res. prog, Chicago Health Res. Found; mem. adult screening comt, Chicago Heart Asn. With Off. Sci. Res. & Develop, U.S.A, 44. Am. Chem. Soc; Am. Oil Chem. Soc. Physical and thermodynamic properties of hydrocarbons; thermochemistry of propellants; physical chemistry of high explosives; analysis of petroleum; physical chemistry of detergents and foams; clinical biochemistry. Address: 5039 S. Ellis Ave, Chicago, IL 60615.

EPSTEIN, N(ATHAN) B(ERNIC), b. New Waterford, N.S, Mar, 3, 24; m. 51; c. 3. PSYCHIATRY. M.D, C.M, Dalhousie, 48; dipl. psychiat, McGill, 52; cert. psychoanal, Columbia, 55. Sr. intern & asst. resident psychiat, Allan Mem. Inst. & Royal Victoria Hosp, Montreal, 48-50; psychiat, resident & jr. physician, Boston State Hosp, Mass, 50-51; vol. clin. asst. child psychiat, outpatient dept, Mt. Sinai Hosp, New York, 51-53; acting dir, Ment. Health Center, Paterson, N.J, 53-54; mem. staff psychiat, JEWISH GEN. HOSP, 55-58, head sub-dept. child & family psychiat, 58-59, asst. psychiatrist, 59-60, PSYCHIATRIST-IN-CHIEF, 60-; PROF. PSYCHIAT. & CHMN. DEPT, McMASTER UNIV, 67- Res. assoc, McGill Univ, 55-58, lectr. & res. asst, 58-61, assoc. prof, 61-67, co-dir. human develop. study, 58, training analyst cmt. psychoanal, 59. Mem, Royal Col. Physicians & Surg. Can. Dipl, Am. Bd. Psychiat. & Neurol, 53. Fel. Acad. Psychoanal; fel. Am. Psychiat. Asn; Can. Psychiat. Asn; Can. Med. Asn; Can. Psychoanal. Soc. Family structure, organization and transaction dynamics and application to family therapy groups. Address: Dept. of Psychiatry, McMaster University, Hamilton, Ont, Can.

EPSTEIN, NATHAN I(SADOR), b. Yanova, Russia, Oct. 13, 01; nat; m. 39; c. 2. BIOCHEMISTRY. B.S, Mass. Inst. Tech, 22; Ph.D.(biochem), Columbia, 28; Paris, 29-30; Berlin, 30; Freiburg, 30-31; Vienna, 31-32; M.D, Munich, 34. Asst. chem, Mass. Agr. Col, 22-23; biochem, Columbia, 25-28; res. chemist, New Rochelle Res. Lab, N.Y, 28-29; Charlton fel. pediat, med. sch, Tufts Col, Boston Floating Hosp, 35-38; asst. instr, med. col, Tufts Col, 38-39; asst. pediatrician and res. fel, N.Y. Hosp. & CORNELL MED. CTR, 40-43, 46-52, asst. prof. clin. pediat, 52-61, ASSOC. CLIN. PROF. PEDIAT, 61- Private practice, 49- Asst. physician, Boston Dispensary, 38-39; pediatrician, N.Y. Sch. for Nursery Years, 47- Fel, Am. Bd. Pediat, 41- Med.C, U.S.A, 43-46. Am. Med. Asn; Am. Heart Asn; Rheumatic Asn; N.Y. Acad. Sci. Chemistry of sulfur dioxide, rickets and rheumatic fever; clinical aspects of rheumatic fever; morphology and chemistry of the uric acid infarct in the kidney of infants; biochemical studies of normal and abnormal muscles. Address: 175 King St, Chappaqua, NY 10514.

EPSTEIN, NORMAN, b. Montreal, Can, Dec. 6, 23; m. 47; c. 3. CHEMICAL ENGINEERING. B.E, McGill, 45, M.E, 46; E.Sc.D, N.Y. Univ, 53. Lectr. CHEM. ENG, McGill, 46-48; instr, N.Y. Univ, 49-51; UNIV. B.C, 51-54, asst. prof, 54-58, assoc. prof, 58-65, PROF, 65- Summers, res. eng, Nat. Res. Coun. Can, 54; Cominco, 55; technologist, Shell Oil Can, 56; engr, Can. Indust. Ltd, 58; supvr, summer practice sch, Du Pont Can, Ltd, 64; consult, Heat Transfer Res. Inc, 71- Am. Chem. Soc.(hon. scroll, 53); Am. Inst. Chem. Eng; fel. Chem. Inst. Can; Can. Soc. Chem. Eng. Momentum; heat; mass transfer; fouling of heat exchangers. Address: Dept. of Chemical Engineering, University of British Columbia, Vancouver 8, B.C, Can.

EPSTEIN, PETER FRANCIS, b. Vienna, Austria, June 21, 29; U.S. citizen; m. 52; c. 4. ORGANIC CHEMISTRY. B.Sc, Leeds, 50, Ph.D.(org. chem), 53. Res. chemist, Styrene Prod, Ltd, Eng, 56; McLaughlin Gormley King Co, Minn, 57-58; sr. chemist, Stauffer Chem. Co, Calif, 58-67; Chemagro Corp, Mo, 67-71; SR. RES. CHEMIST, VERONA CORP, 71- Mem. Zero Population Growth. Brit. Army, 54-56, Sgt. Am. Chem. Soc; Royal Inst. Chem. Synthesis of organic chemicals; investigation of processes in the dyestuff industry. Address: Verona Corp, P.O. Box 10288, Charleston, SC 29411.

EPSTEIN, ROBERT B(ERNARD), b. Chicago, Ill, June 9, 34; m. 57; c. 3. HEMATOLOGY. B.S, Univ. Ill, Urbana, 55, M.D, Univ. Ill, Chicago, 59. Intern, Univ. Ill. Res. & Educ. Hosp, Chicago, Ill, 59-60; resident med, Vet. Admin. West Side Hosp, 60-63; res. fel. hemat, Univ. Wash, 63-65, instr. MED, sch. med, 65-67, asst. prof, 67-70; Boerhaave prof, Univ. Leiden, 70-71; ASSOC. PROF, ABRAHAM LINCOLN SCH. MED, UNIV. ILL. COL. MED, 71-, CLIN. INVESTR, VET. ADMIN. WEST SIDE HOSP, 71- Asst. chief med, U.S. Pub. Health Serv. Hosp, Seattle, Wash, 66-70; consult, Children's Orthop. Hosp. & Med. Ctr, 68-70. U.S.P.H.S, 66-70, Sr. Surgeon. Am. Fedn. Clin. Res; Am. Med. Asn; Am. Soc. Hemat; N.Y. Acad. Sci; Transplantation Soc. Transplantation immunology, especially the relevance of histocompatibility to the transplantation of hemopoietic tissue in canines and man. Address: Veterans Administration West Side Hospital, 820 S. Damen Ave, Chicago, IL 60612.

EPSTEIN, ROBERT L, b. Brooklyn, N.Y, Apr. 1, 43; m. 66; c. 1. ANALYTICAL & PHYSICAL CHEMISTRY. B.S, City Col. New York, 63; Univ. Vt, 63-64; M.S, Polytech. Inst. Brooklyn, 69, Ph.D.(anal. chem), 71. Chemist, State Univ. N.Y. Downstate Med. Ctr, 64-66; Hoffmann-La Roche, Inc, N.J, 66-67; sr. chemist, Clairol Inc, Conn, 67-70; proj. leader anal. chem, Cybertek, Inc, N.Y, 70-71; GROUP LEADER HAIR PROD, REVLON INC, BRONX, 71- Am. Chem. Soc; Soc. Cosmetic Chem. Mathematical models to explain pH and reduction oxidation reactions; physical and analytical methods of evaluating properties of products such as lotions, gels and creams. Address: 4349 Bedford Ave, Brooklyn, NY 11229.

EPSTEIN, ROBERT M(ARVIN), b. N.Y.C, Mar. 10, 28; m. 50; c. 3. ANESTHESIOLOGY. B.S, Univ. Mich, 47, M.D, 51. Intern, Univ. hosp, Univ. Mich, 51-52; asst. resident ANESTHESIOL, Presby. Hosp, N.Y, 52-53, 55-56; instr, COL. PHYSICIANS & SURGEONS, COLUMBIA UNIV, 56-58, assoc, 58-59, asst. prof, 59-65, assoc. prof, 65-70, PROF, 70-; ATTEND. ANESTHESIOLOGIST, PRESBY. HOSP, 70-, asst. anesthesiol, 56-58, asst. attend. anesthesiologist, 58-65, assoc. attend. anesthesiologist, 65-70. John Simon Guggenheim Mem. Found. fel. & vis. scientist, dept. pharmacol, Oxford, 66-67; mem. anesthesiol. training comt, Nat. Inst. Gen. Med. Sci, 66-69; comt. anesthesia, Nat. Res. Coun, 70-71. Med.C, 53-55, Res, 55-61, Capt. AAAS; Am. Soc. Anesthesiol; Asn. Univ. Anesthetists (secy, 69-72); Am. Soc. Pharmacol. & Exp. Therapeut; Am. Physiol. Soc; N.Y. Acad. Med. Circulatory physiology; liver function; effects of carbon dioxide and of anesthetics; pharmacokinetics of anesthetics. Address: Presbyterian Hospital, 622 W. 168th St, New York, NY 10032.

EPSTEIN, SAMUEL, b. Poland, Dec. 9, 19; U.S. citizen; m. 46; c. 2. GEOCHEMISTRY. B.Sc, Manitoba, 41, M.Sc, 42; Ph.D.(phys. chem), McGill, 44. Res. chemist, Nat. Res. Coun. Can, 44-47; res. assoc, Inst. Nuclear Studies, Chicago, 49-52; res. fel, CALIF. INST. TECHNOL, 52-53, sr. res. fel, 53-54, assoc. prof. GEOCHEM, 54-59, PROF, 59- Stable isotope geochemistry. Address: Division of Geological & Planetary Sciences, California Institute of Technology, Pasadena, CA 91109.

EPSTEIN, SAMUEL I(SAAC), b. Boston, Mass, Sept. 30, 29; m. 53; c. 4. PHYSICAL CHEMISTRY. A.B, Harvard, 50, Ph.D.(chem), 54. Fel. chem, Yale, 54-56; instr, Tufts, 56-59, asst. prof, 59-63; sr. res. assoc, RES. & DEVELOP. CTR, LEVER BROS. CO, 63-70, RES. SCIENTIST, 70- Am. Chem. Soc. Proteins; detergents. Address: Research & Development Center, Lever Brothers Co, 45 River Rd, Edgewater, NJ 07020.

EPSTEIN, SAMUEL S(IDNEY), b. Russia, July 14, 06; nat; m. 35; c. 1. BACTERIOLOGY. B.S, R.I. State Col, 29; M.S, Iowa State, 32, Ph.D.(sanit. bact), 34. Fel. bact, Iowa State, 31-34; bacteriologist, Schwarz Labs, 34-37; dir. bact. res, Camel Lead, Color & Chem. Prod. Mfg. Corp, N.Y, 37-38; bacteriologist, Climax Rubber Co, 38-39; consult. bacteriologist, Foster D. Snell, Inc, 39-42; chief chemist, Kirsch's Beverages, Inc, 39-71, v.pres, 42-71; chief chemist & v.pres, No. Cal. Corp, 55-71; RETIRED. Chesterman Award, 51. AAAS; Soc. Soft Drink Technol; Am. Soc. Microbiol; Am. Pub. Health Asn; Inst. Food Technol; Am. Chem. Soc. New food products; flavor compounds; dietetic food products. Address: 1075 Miami Gardens Dr, 605, North Miami Beach, FL 33162.

EPSTEIN, SAMUEL STANLEY, b. Middlesborough, Eng, Apr. 13, 26; U.S. citizen; m. 59; c. 3. PATHOLOGY, ENVIRONMENTAL SCIENCES. B.Sc, Univ. London, 47, B.Med. & B.Surg, 50, dipl. trop. med. & surg, 52, dipl. path, 54, M.D, 58, dipl. microbiol. & pub. health, 63. Demonstr. morbid anat, Guy's Hosp, Univ. London, 50; house physician med, St. John's Hosp, Eng, 51; lectr. path. & bact, Inst. Laryngol. & Otol, Eng, 55-58; Brit. Empire Cancer Campaign fel. & tumor pathologist, Hosp. Sick Children & Chester Beatty Cancer Res. Inst, Eng, 58-60; consult. path, Mem. Hosp. Peterborough, Eng, 60; chief labs. environ. toxicol. & carcinogenesis, Children's Cancer Res. Found, Inc, Boston, Mass, 61-71; PROF. PHARMACOL. & SWETLAND PROF. ENVIRON. HEALTH & HUMAN ECOL, MED. SCH, CASE WEST. RESERVE UNIV, 71- Res. assoc. path, Harvard Med. Sch, 62-71. Consult, U.S. Senate Comt. Pub. Works, 70-; ctr. studies narcotic & drug abuse, Nat. Inst. Ment. Health, 70-; Environ. Health Progs, Inc, 70-; panel on polycyclic org. matter, Nat. Acad. Sci, 70-; pesticide bd, Commonwealth of Mass, 70-; U.S. Senate Subcomt. Exec. Reorgn. & Govt. Res, 71. Dipl, Am. Bd. Microbiol, 63. Montefiore Gold Medal Trop. Med, Royal Army Med. Corps, 53, Montefiore Prize Trop. Hyg, 53, Ranald Martin Prize Mil. Surg, 53. R.A.M.C, 52-55, Maj. AAAS; fel. Royal Soc. Health; Environ. Mutagen Soc.(secy, 69); Air Pollution Control Asn; Soc. Protozool; Am. Asn. Cancer Res; Soc. Toxicol.(achievement award, 69); Am. Asn. Path. & Bact. Toxicology; carcinogenesis; mutagenesis; preventive medicine; bacteriology and protozoology; biological hazards, including carcinogenesis, mutagenesis, due to chemical pollution of the environment, including food additives, pesticides, fertilizers, industrial chemicals and drugs; ecological effects of chemical pollutants. Address: Dept. of Pharmacology, Case Western Reserve University Medical School, 2119 Abington Rd, Cleveland, OH 44106.

EPSTEIN, SAUL T(HEODORE), b. Southampton, N.Y, June 14, 24; m. 48; c. 3. THEORETICAL PHYSICS. S.B, Mass. Inst. Tech, 44, Ph.D.(physics), 48. With Inst. Adv. Study, 47-48; instr. PHYSICS, Columbia, 48-51; Boston, 52-53; asst. prof, Nebraska, 54-56, assoc. prof, 57-60, prof, 60-63; PROF. & MEM. THEORET. CHEM. INST, UNIV. WIS, MADISON, 63- Am. Phys. Soc; Am. Asn. Physics Teachers. Basic quantum theory; atomic and molecular structure. Address: Dept. of Physics, University of Wisconsin, Madison, WI 53706.

EPSTEIN, SEYMOUR, b. N.Y.C, Mar. 19, 21; m. 55; c. 4. PHYSICS, ENGINEERING. B.M.E, City Col. New York, 43; M.S, Polytech. Inst. Brooklyn, 51, Ph.D.(physics), 61. Instr. physics & math, Univ. Akron, 43-44; physics, Assoc. Cols. Upper N.Y, 46-47; descriptive geometry, Brooklyn Col, 47-50; eng. writer consult, CBS-Columbia, Inc, 50-51; RES. PHYSICIST, ELECTRONIC DEVICES & TECHNOL. LAB, U.S. ARMY ELECTRONICS COMMAND, FT. MONMOUTH, 52- Tool engr, Goodyear Aircraft Corp, 43-44. U.S.N, 44-46. AAAS; Am. Phys. Soc. Solid state and crystal physics; semiconductors; semimetals; x-ray crystallography; lasers; elastic wave propagation. Address: U.S. Army Electronics Command, TL-QG, Ft. Monmouth, NJ 07703.

EPSTEIN, W(ALLACE) V(ICTOR), b. N.Y.C, Dec. 10, 26; m. 49; c. 3. INTERNAL MEDICINE. B.S, City Col, 48; M.D, Columbia, 52. Res. fel. internal med, Columbia, 55-56; UNIV. CALIF, SAN FRANCISCO, 56-58, asst. prof. MED, 58-64, ASSOC. PROF, 64- Am. Med. Asn; Am. Rheumatism Asn. Arthritis; clinical and experimental immunology. Address: University of California Medical Center, 671 Health Science East, San Francisco, CA 94122.

EPSTEIN, WILLIAM L, b. Cleveland, Ohio, Sept. 6, 25; m. 54; c. 2. MEDICINE, DERMATOLOGY. A.B, Univ. Calif, Berkeley, 49, M.D, San Francisco, 52. Instr. DERMAT, Univ. Pa, 56-57; asst. prof, UNIV. CALIF, SAN FRANCISCO, 57-63, assoc. prof, 63-69, PROF, 69-, DIR. DERMAT. RES, 57-, ACTING CHMN. DEPT, 70-, acting chmn. div, 66-67, chmn. div, 67-70. Consult. dermatologist, 57- U.S.A, 44-46. AAAS; Am. Med. Asn; Am. Acad. Dermat; Soc. Invest. Dermat; Am. Dermat. Asn; Am. Fedn. Clin. Res; N.Y. Acad. Sci. Immunology, especially delayed hypersensitivity and viral and cancer immunology; skin anatomy and epidermal cell turnover. Address: Dept. of Dermatology, University of California, San Francisco Medical Center, 1096 HSE, San Francisco, CA 94122.

EPSTEIN, W(ILLIAM) W(ARREN), b. Kremmling, Colo, Sept. 10, 31; m. 53; c. 3. ORGANIC CHEMISTRY. B.S, Denver, 53; U.S. Rubber Co. fel, California, 57-58, Ph.D.(chem), 59. Res. scientist, Weyerhaeuser Co, 58-60; asst. prof. CHEM, UNIV. UTAH, 61-67, ASSOC. PROF, 67- Fel. Univ. Ill, 60-61. Am. Chem. Soc. Natural products; photochemistry. Address: Dept. of Chemistry, University of Utah, Salt Lake City, UT 84112.

ERATH, EDWARD H(YDE), b. Chicago, Ill, Dec. 23, 29; m. 47; c. 1. CHEMICAL PHYSICS. B.S, Northwestern, 54; Hughes fels, California, Los Angeles, 55-57, 58-61, M.S, 57, Ph.D.(physics), 61. Physicist, Savannah River Proj, E.I. du Pont de Nemours & Co, 54-55; mem. tech. staff atomic physics, res. lab, Hughes Aircraft Co, 55-61; dir. res, Electronics Invest. Mgt. Corp, 61-62; mem, sr. staff phys. space sci, Hughes Aircraft Co, 62-64; asst. to dir. corp. planning, Douglas Aircraft Co, 64-66; PRES. & TRUSTEE, LOS ANGELES TECH. SERV. CORP, 67- Sci. consult, Electronics Invest. Mgt. Corp, 62-64. High polymer structure; crystalline field theory; atomic spectroscopy. Address: Los Angeles Technical Services Corp, 3600 Wilshire Blvd, Los Angeles, CA 90010.

ERB, DAVID KINSEY, b. Downie Twp, Ont, Sept. 24, 22; m. 49; c. 2. GEOLOGY, GEOGRAPHY. B.Sc, Western Ontario, 49; M.A, Toronto, 50; Ph.D. (geog), McGill, 63. Geologist, Imp. Oil Co, Alta. & Sask, 52-53; Hudson Bay Oil & Gas Co, Alta, 53-54; Can. Well Serv, Ltd, 54-55; Photog. Surv. Corp, Ltd, Ont, 55-56; Hunting Tech. & Explor. Serv, 56-59; chief photogeologist, Hunting Surv. Corp, Ltd, 59-61; asst. prof. geol, geomorphol. & air photo interpretation, Waterloo Lutheran, 61-62; sr. tech. assoc, Geotech. & Resources, Inc, N.Y, 62-63; assoc. prof. GEOG. & PLANNING, UNIV. WATERLOO, 63-67, PROF, 67- Can. External Aid vis. prof, Univ. West Indies, 67-68. R.C.N.V.R, 41-45. Asn. Am. Geog; Am. Soc. Photogram; Can. Asn. Geog; Geol. Asn. Can. Tropical geomorphology; application of aerial photography interpretation in the study of geomorphology, photogeology, engineering soils, and water resources; resource inventory with some emphasis on the humid tropics. Address: Dept. of Geography, Division of Environmental Studies, University of Waterloo, Waterloo, Ont, Can.

ERB, DONALD E, b. Taneytown, Md, Jan. 31, 28; m. 65. NUCLEAR ENGINEERING. B.A, West. Md. Col, 54; B.E.S, Hopkins, 56; Int. Sch. Nuclear Sci. & Eng, Argonne Nat. Lab, 56-57. Reactor engr, U.S. Atomic Energy Cmn, 57-67, chief water reactors br, 67-68; DIR. NUCLEAR UTILITIES TECH. ASSISTANCE PLAN, COLUMBUS LABS, BATTELLE MEM. INST, 68- Mem, Atomic Indust. Forum, 68- Am. Nuclear Soc. Design, development, construction and operation of civilian power reactors; power reactor fuel design and development. Address: 5473 River Forest Rd, Dublin, OH 43017.

ERB, J(OHN) HOFFMAN, b. Harrisburg, Pa, Nov. 7, 05; m. 33; c. 5. DAIRY TECHNOLOGY. B.S, Pa. State, 27; M.Sc, Ohio State, 28; Chicago, 32; Wisconsin, 36. Asst. supt. prod, Reid Ice Cream Co, 28-29; instr. dairy tech, Ohio State, 29-34, asst. prof, 34-43; lab. dir, Borden Co, 43-44, dir. prod, Midwest Div, 44-53, v.pres. in charge, 53-69, v.pres. res. & develop, 69-70; CONSULT, 70- Chmn, res. & develop. comt, Borden Fluid Milk & Ice Cream Div, 63-; mem. Ohio Environ. Health Planning Comt, Ohio Dept. Health. Am. Dairy Sci. Asn. Effect of pasteurization of nutritive value of milk; ingredients for ice cream; effect of light on vitamins and flavor of milk; condensed and dry milk; dairy products manufacturing. Address: 1697 Berkshire Rd, Columbus, OH 43221.

ERB, KENNETH LANDIS, b. Souderton, Pa, Apr. 28, 39; m. 64. MICROBIOLOGY. B.A, Goshen Col, 61; M.S, W.Va. Univ, 64, Ph.D.(agr. microbiol), 66. Lectr. BIOL, Vassar Col, 66-67, ASST. PROF, 67-69, HOFSTRA UNIV, 69- Mycol. Soc. Am; Phycol. Soc. Am; Int. Phycol. Soc. Microalgae parasitized by aquatic fungi. Address: Dept. of Biology, Hofstra University, Hempstead, NY 11550.

ERB, R(ALPH) E(UGENE), b. Dow, Ill, May 28, 17; m. 41; c. 1. ANIMAL PHYSIOLOGY. B.S, Illinois, 40; M.S, Purdue, 42, Ph.D.(physiol), 47. Asst. instr. dairy husb, Purdue, 40-43, instr, 46-47; asst. prof, State Col. Wash, 47-48, assoc. prof, 48-53, prof, 50-62; ASST. HEAD ANIMAL SCI. DEPT, PURDUE UNIV, 62- U.S.N, 43-46. Am. Dairy Sci. Asn; Am. Soc. Animal Sci; Endocrine Soc. Endocrine physiology; reproductive physiology; milk secretion. Address: Dept. of Animal Sciences, Purdue University, Lafayette, IN 47907.

ERB, RICHARD BRYAN, b. Calgary, Alta, Apr. 12, 31; m. 55; c. 2. AEROTHERMODYNAMICS, THERMAL CONTROL. B.Sc, Alberta, 52, M.Sc, 55; Athlone fel. & D.C.Ac, Col. Aeronaut, Cranfield, Eng, 54; Sloan fel. & M.S, Mass. Inst. Tech, 68. Sessional demonstrator civil eng, Alberta, 54-55; aerodynamicist, Avro Aircraft, Ont, 55-59; aerospace technologist, NASA MANNED SPACECRAFT CTR, HOUSTON, 59-62, head thermal anal. sect, 62-63, chief thermostructures br, aerothermodyn. thermal control, 63-65, asst. chief structures div, 65-68, asst. chief lunar & earth sci, 69, MGR. lunar lab, 69-70, EARTH OBSERVATIONS APPLNS, 70-, dep. mgr. lunar lab, 68-69. Am. Inst. Aeronaut. & Astronaut. Boundary layer analysis of interactions with body conduction; mobile boundary fluid mechanics of sediment transport; aerothermodynamics of entry vehicles; thermal protection and control systems; interpersonal perception and communication. Address: 426 Terrace Dr, Seabrook, TX 77586.

ERB, ROBERT ALLAN, b. Ridley Park, Pa, Jan. 30, 32; m. 53; c. 3. PHYSICAL CHEMISTRY. B.S, Pennsylvania, 53; M.S, Drexel Inst, 59; Ph.D.(phys. chem), Temple, 65. Chemist, Gates Eng. Co, Del, 53-54; res. asst, RES. LABS, FRANKLIN INST, 54-56, res. engr, 56-61, sr. res. chemist, 61-65, sr. staff chemist, 65-68; PRIN. SCIENTIST, 68- AAAS; Am. Chem. Soc; Soc. Rheol; Sci. Res. Soc. Am; Soc. Plastics Eng; Water Pollution Control. Fedn. Physical chemistry of surfaces; technology of polymeric and colloidal materials; adhesion; rheology; heterogeneous nucleation; desalination; medical applications of physical science; environmental science; waste management. Address: Research Labs, Franklin Institute, 20th & Parkway, Philadelphia, PA 19103.

ERB, WILLIAM H, b. New Berlinville, Pa, Apr. 23, 07; m; c. 3. SURGERY. A.B, Pennsylvania, 27, M.D, 30. Asst. instr. physiol, UNIV. PA, 32-33, res, Dr. Frazier's, thyroid & physiol, 32-33; Dr. Eliason fel, 33-36, instr. surg, 37-40, assoc. surg, 40-46, asst. prof, grad. sch. med, 46-50, assoc. prof. CLIN. SURG, SCH. MED, 50-53, PROF, 53- Acting surgeon, Phila. Gen. Hosp, 42-46, surgeon, 46-, chmn. dept. surg, 59-, pres. med. staff, 65-67; chief surg, Taylor Hosp, Ridley Park, 42-; surgeon, Presby. Hosp, 55-; chief surg, Riddle Hosp, 62-66, assoc. surg, 66-; asst. surgeon, hosp, Univ. Pa. Clin. prof, Woman's Med. Col. Pa, 46-49, assoc. prof, 49-50. Dipl, Am. Bd. Surg, 39. Am. Med. Asn; fel. Am. Col. Surg. Gastrocystostomy in pancreatic cysts; importance of scout plate in acute surgical abdomen. Address: 3910 Powelton Ave, Suite 301, Philadelphia, PA 19104.

ERBAR, JOHN HAROLD, b. El Reno, Okla, Nov. 23, 31; m. 59. CHEMICAL ENGINEERING. B.S, Okla. State, 54, M.S, 59, Ph.D.(chem. eng), 60. Res. engr, Calif. Res. Corp, 60-61; plant foreman, Standard Oil Co. Calif, 61-62; asst. prof. CHEM. ENG, OKLA. STATE UNIV, 62-65, assoc. prof, 65-69, PROF, 69- Summers, engr-in-training, Magnolia Petrol. Co, 56, jr. engr, Black, Sivalls & Bryson, Inc, 57, res. engr, Calif. Res. Corp, 63; Ford Found. Engr. Res, Monsanto Co, 66-67. Ord.C, 54-56, 1st Lt. Am. Inst. Chem. Eng; Am. Chem. Soc; Nat. Soc. Prof. Eng. Transport properties of liquid mixtures; distillation; reaction kinetics. Address: 1 Fox Ledge Lane, R.R. 4, Stillwater, OK 74074.

ERBE, LAWRENCE WAYNE, b. Ancon, C.Z, June 30, 24; m. 55; c. 5. BOTANY. B.S, Vermont, 53, M.S, 55; Ph.D.(bot), Texas, 60. Asst. prof. BIOL, UNIV. SOUTHWEST. LA, 60-66, ASSOC. PROF, 66- U.S.A, 46-48. Bot. Soc. Am. Hybridization of Lotus tenuis and Lotus corniculatus; biosystematics of annual phloxes. Address: Dept. of Biology, University of Southwestern Louisiana, Lafayette, LA 70501.

ERBER, THOMAS, b. Vienna, Austria, Dec. 6, 30; nat; m. 57. PHYSICS. B.Sc, Mass. Inst. Tech, 51; M.S, Chicago, 53, Ph.D.(physics), 57. Asst. prof. PHYSICS, ILL. INST. TECHNOL, 57-62, assoc. prof, 62-69, PROF, 69-, faculty fel, 58-59. Res. fel, Brussels, 63-64; vis. scientist, Stanford Linear Accelerator Ctr, 70; vis. prof, Graz Univ, 71. Hon. prof, Graz Univ. Fel. Am. Phys. Soc; Am. Math. Soc; Austrian Physics Soc; Europ. Phys. Soc. Classical and quantum electrodynamics; ultra high magnetic fields; cooperative systems. Address: Dept. of Physics, Illinois Institute of Technology, Chicago, IL 60616.

ERBISCH, FREDERIC H, b. Sebewaing, Mich, June 24, 37; m. 57; c. 2. BOTANY, CYTOLOGY. B.S, Mich. State Univ, 59; M.S, Univ. Mich, 61, Ph.D. (bot), 66. PROF. BOT, MICH. TECHNOL. UNIV, 63- AAAS; Am. Bryol. & Lichenological Soc; Mycol. Soc. Am. Cytodevelopment of lichen asci and ascospores; effects of gamma irradiation on lichens and lichen-forming fungi and algae. Address: Dept. of Biological Sciences, Michigan Technological University, Houghton, MI 49931.

ERBY, WILLIAM A(RTHUR), b. Lebanon, Pa, Apr. 4, 33; m. 57; c. 2. ORGANIC CHEMISTRY. B.S, Lebanon Valley Col, 55; M.S, Bucknell, 57; Ph.D. (chem), State Univ. N.Y. Col. Forestry, 61. Chemist, Kimberly Clark Corp, 60-63, Air Prod. & Chem. Inc, 63-64, group leader, 64-68; mgr. res, DAUBERT CHEM. CO, 68-70, V.PRES, 70- Am. Chem. Soc. Wood, polymer, and textile chemistry. Address: Daubert Chemical Co, 4700 Central Ave, Chicago, IL 60638.

ERCEGOVICH, CHARLES D(RAGO), b. Gilbert, Minn, Oct. 12, 25; m. 57. BIOCHEMISTRY. B.S, Iowa State, 50; M.S, Pa. State, 55, Ph.D. & M.R.S, 57. Proj. leader, agr. chem, Tenn. Corp. Res. Lab, 57-60; staff biochemist, Geigy Agr. Chem. Co, 60-65; ASSOC. PROF, PA. STATE UNIV, 65- U.S.A.A.F, 43-46, U.S.A.F.R, 46-, Maj. AAAS; Am. Chem. Soc; Weed Sci. Soc. Am; Entom. Soc. Am. Agricultural chemistry; pesticides mode of action, fate and metabolism. Address: Dept. of Entomology, Pennsylvania State University, University Park, PA 16802.

ERCHAK, MICHAEL, JR, b. Shadyside, Ohio, Mar. 9, 14; m. 42; c. 3. POLYMER CHEMISTRY. B.Sc, Ohio State, 40; Ph.D.(chem), Polytech. Inst. Brooklyn, 45. Res. chemist, Merck & Co, 41-43; group leader res, Allied Chem. Corp, 45-50, sr. proj. leader, 50-55, tech. dir, Semet Solvoy Petrochem. Div, 56-60; V.PRES. res. & develop, CHEM. GROUP, DART INDUSTS. INC, 60-68, TECH. OPPORTUNITIES, 68- AAAS; Am. Chem. Soc; Soc. Plastics Eng; Am. Inst. Chem. Research and manufacture of polymers and chemicals; high pressure and high temperature technology; polymer processing and fabrication technology. Address: 289 Brookmere Ct, Ridgewood, NJ 07450.

ERCOLI, NICOLO, b. Italy, Nov. 20, 05; nat; m. 33; c. 2. PHARMACOLOGY, CHEMOTHERAPY. Ph.D.(chem, colloids), Modena, 30; M.D, Padua, 37. Asst. prof. pharmacol, Padua, 33-38; fel. from Padua, Inst. Fournier, Paris, 38; pharmacologist, res. lab, Hoffmann-La Roche, N.J, 39-46; dir. dept. pharmacol. & chemother, Warner Inst. Therapeut. Res, N.Y, 46-49; sci. dir, Instituto Sieroterapico Milanese, Milan, 49-52; dir. dept. pharmacol. & chemother, Armour Labs, 52-59; head dept. exp. therapeut, Venezuelan Inst. Sci. Res, 59-64; prof. pharmacol. & chmn. dept, Jose Vargas Sch. Med, Venezuela, 64-68; PROF. PHARMACOL. & HEAD PARASITOL. RES, FACULTY SCI, CENT. UNIV. VENEZUELA, 68- AAAS; Am. Soc. Trop. Med. & Hyg; Am. Soc. Pharmacol. & Exp. Therapeut; Soc. Exp. Biol. & Med. Pharmacology of chemotherapeutics, analgesics, antispasmodics and enzymes; bacterial, viral and antiparasitic chemotherapy. Address: Faculty of Sciences, Central University of Venezuela, Apartado 51163, Caracas, Venezuela.

ERDAL, BRUCE ROBERT, b. Albuquerque, N.Mex, June 15, 39; m. 70. NUCLEAR CHEMISTRY, RADIOCHEMISTRY. B.S, New Mexico, 61; Shell fel, Washington (St. Louis), 62, Nat. Sci. Found. & univ. fels. & Ph.D.(nuclear chem), 66. Asst. chem. Washington (St. Louis), 61-63, nuclear chem, 63-66, res. assoc, 66-67; Brookhaven Nat. Lab, N.Y, 67-69; Nat. Sci. Found. fel, EUROP. ORGN. NUCLEAR RES, 69-70, VIS. SCIENTIST, NUCLEAR PHYSICS DIV, 70- AAAS; Am. Chem. Soc. Nuclear structure, fission and reactions; radiochemistry; electromagnetic isotope separation. Address: Nuclear Physics Division, European Organization for Nuclear Research, 1211 Geneva 23, Switz.

ERDELYI, EDWARD, b. Hlohovec, Czech, July 13, 08; U.S. citizen; m. 58. ELECTRICAL ENGINEERING, APPLIED MATHEMATICS. Dipl. Ing, Brno Tech, 29; dipl. math, Masaryk Univ, Brno, 29; Ph.D.(elec. eng), Michigan, 55. Asst. elec. eng, Royal Aircraft Estab, Eng, 41-47; lectr, Newark Col. Eng. & City Col. New York, 47-49; asst. prof, Mo. Sch. Mines, 49-50; Washington (St. Louis), 50-51; prof, Detroit, 51-52; Syracuse, 52-56; sr. anal. engr. res. & develop, Gen. Elec. Co, Pa, 56-59; Sharp Prof. ELEC. ENG, Delaware, 59-64; PROF, UNIV. COLO, BOULDER, 64- R.A.F, 42-46, Flight Lt. AAAS; fel. Inst. Elec. & Electronics Eng; Am. Soc. Mech. Eng; Brit. Inst. Elec. Eng. Noise phenomena in rotating electrical machines; solution of nonlinear partial differential equations of electric machines; analysis and design of aerospace electrical equipment; optimization of electrical apparatus. Address: 325 20th, Boulder, CO 80302.

ERDELYI, IVAN NICHOLAS, b. Timisoara, Romania, Apr. 14, 26; U.S. citizen; m. 50. MATHEMATICS. Grad, Cluj, 51; Docent, Rome, 68. Asst. prof. physics & math, Polytech. Inst. Timisoara, 51-59; math. analyst, Olivetti Gen. Elec, Italy, 62-67; ASSOC. PROF. comput. sci, Kansas State, 67-69; MATH, TEMPLE UNIV, 69- Am. Math. Soc; N.Y. Acad. Sci. Abstract and functional analysis. Address: Dept. of Mathematics, Temple University, Philadelphia, PA 19122.

ERDEY, MICHAEL ROLAND ALEXANDER, b. Mezöberény, Hungary, Oct. 2, 27; m. 56; c. 3. MATHEMATICS, PHYSICS. M.Sc, Szeged, 52; Ph.D.(elec. eng), Leeds, 59. Observer & evaluator seismical measurements, Eötvös Loránd Geophys. Inst, Hungary, 51-53; head field group, Sci. Water Res. Inst, 53-54; res. asst, dept. elec. eng, Leeds, 56-60; asst. prof. network & systs, Mich. State, 60-63; PROF. & HEAD DEPT. ELEC. ENG, TUSKEGEE INST, 63- Am. Soc. Eng. Educ; sr. mem. Inst. Elec. & Electronics Eng. Graphical network theory; unification of network and field theories. Address: Dept. of Electrical Engineering, P.O. Box 357, Tuskegee Institute, Tuskegee, AL 36088.

ERDLE, PHILIP J, b. Bethlehem, Pa, Sept. 17, 30; m. 52; c. 5. MECHANICS. B.S, U.S. Mil. Acad, 52; M.S, Michigan, 60; Ph.D, Colorado, 64. U.S. AIR FORCE, 52-, asst. prof. mech, U.S. AIR FORCE ACAD, 60-62, asst. dean res, 63-64, prof. mech. & asst. dean eng. & basic sci, 64-65, PROF. ENG. MECH. & HEAD DEPT, 65- Pres, Int. Sci. & Eng. Exchange Inc. U.S.A.F, 52-, Col. Am. Soc. Eng. Educ; Soc. Exp. Stress Anal. Vibrations and photoelastic research involving uses of epoxy resins to simulate reinforced structures in interferometer investigations. Address: DFEM, U.S. Air Force Academy, CO 80840.

ERDLEY, HAROLD F(REDERICK), b. Los Angeles, Calif, Nov. 27, 25; m. 52; c. 5. ELECTRONIC ENGINEERING. B.S, California, 48, M.S, 50. Systs. engr, N.Am. Aviation, Inc, 50-54; electromech. sect. head, Litton Industs, 54-57, mgr. guid. & control dept, 57-59, div. guid. systs. lab, 59-60, v.pres. & dir. eng, Litton Systs, Inc, 60-61, electromech. eng, 61-63, instrument res, 63-68; dir. NAVIG. SYSTS. PROGS, TELEDYNE SYSTS. CO, 68-70, V.PRES, 70- U.S.N, 44-46. Inst. Elec. & Electronics Eng; Am. Inst. Aeronaut. & Astronaut. Inertial navigation systems and associated devices. Address: Teledyne Systems Co, 19601 Nordhoff St, Northridge, CA 91324.

ERDMAN, ANNE MARIE, b. Voorburg, Netherlands, June 10, 16; nat. FOOD, NUTRITION. B.S, Col. Home Econ, Netherlands, 39, Dipl, 42; M.S, Fla. State, 53, Ph.D, 56. Instr. foods & nutrit, Col. Home Econ, Netherlands, 42-52; res. assoc, Inst. Rural Home Econ. Res, 56-57; assoc. prof. FOOD & NUTRIT, FLA. STATE UNIV, 57-71, PROF, 71- Govt. dietitian, Pub. Health Serv, Indonesia. AAAS; Am. Home Econ. Asn; Am. Dietetic Asn; Inst. Food Tech. Food consumption patterns, factors affecting them. Address: Dept. of Food & Nutrition, Florida State University, Tallahassee, FL 32306.

ERDMAN, DONALD E, b. Baltimore, Md, Aug. 4, 25; m. 49; c. 2. ORGANIC CHEMISTRY. B.A, Clark Col, 51; M.S, Union Col, 70. Appln. engr, chem. mat. dept, Gen. Elec. Co, 51-52, prod. engr, 51-56, insulating mat. dept, 57-62, develop. chemist, 62-68, specialist fabricating insulation, 68-71; OWNER, ERDMAN TIRE CO, 71- U.S.A, 44-46. Am. Chem. Soc. Manufacturing and administration. Address: Erdman Tire Co, 605 Fallsway, Baltimore, MD 21202.

ERDMAN, HOWARD E, b. Hazleton, Pa, May 18, 30; m. 59; c. 2. GENETICS. B.S, Muhlenberg Col, 53; M.S, Lehigh Univ, 55; Ph.D.(genetics), N.C. State Col, 59. Scientist ecol, Gen. Elec. Co, 59-65, sr. res. scientist, Battelle Northwest Labs, 65-70; ASSOC. PROF, DEPT. BIOL, TEX. WOMAN'S COL, 71- Prog. off, Int. Atomic Energy Agency, Vienna, Austria, 66-69. AAAS; Ecol. Soc. Am; Entom. Soc. Am; Entom. Soc. Can. Genetics, morphology, cytology, and histopathology of radiation effects; population ecology. Address: Dept. of Biology, Texas Woman's University, Denton, TX 76204.

ERDMAN, JAMES ALLEN, b. Milwaukee, Wis, Dec. 20, 35; m. 59; c. 2. PLANT ECOLOGY, GEOCHEMISTRY. B.A, N.Cent. Col.(Ill), 58; M.A, Univ. Colo, Boulder, 62, Ph.D.(bot), 69. Plant ecologist, Wetherill Mesa Proj, Mesa Verde Nat. Park, 62-64; instr. bot, Ft. Lewis Col, 66-67; BOTANIST, U.S. GEOL. SURV, 67- Am. Inst. Biol. Sci; Ecol. Soc. Am. Environmental geochemistry, especially establishing baselines for the elemental composition of plant and surficial materials in order that observed anomalies may be placed in perspective; sampling designs for regional geochemical studies. Address: Branch of Regional Geochemistry, U.S. Geological Survey, Denver, CO 80225.

ERDMAN, J(OHN) GORDON, b. Baltimore, Md, Apr. 12, 19; m. 48. GEOCHEMISTRY. A.B, Hopkins, 40, Alumni scholar, 40-42; Ph.D.(org. chem), 43. Jr. instr. org. chem, Hopkins, 42-43; res. chemist, Nat. Defense Res. Cmt, 43-45; Off. Sci. Res. & Develop. & fel, Mellon Inst, 45-56, sr. fel, 56-65; MGR. GEOCHEM. BR, PHILLIPS PETROL. CO, 65- AAAS; Am. Chem. Soc; Geol. Soc. Am; Am. Inst. Chem; Geochem. Soc; Am. Geophys. Union. Biochemistry of proteins; chemical structure and synthesis of pyrrole pigments, hemins and chlorophylls; chemical, thermal and radiation stability of porphyrin metallo complexes; porphyrin and non-porphyrin metallo complexes in crude oil; organic chemistry of aquatic sediments as related to crude oil; chemical structure of natural bitumens; geological and geochemical methods for discovery of minerals and petroleum. Address: Research & Development Dept, Phillips Petroleum Co, Bartlesville, OK 74004.

ERDMAN, JOHN PAUL, b. Oak Park, Ill, Oct. 2, 42; m. 65; c. 1. ORGANIC CHEMISTRY. B.S, Univ. Miami, 64; Ph.D.(org. chem), Univ. Md, 71. RES. CHEMIST, ELASTOMER CHEM. DEPT, EXP. STA, E.I. DU PONT DE NEMOURS & CO, INC, 69- Am. Chem. Soc; Sci. Res. Soc. Am. Thermodynamics of cyclic dienes; olefinic carbanions; organic fluorine chemistry. Address: Elastomer Chemicals Dept, E.I. du Pont de Nemours & Co, Inc, Experimental Station, Wilmington, DE 19898.

ERDMAN, KIMBALL S, b. Salt Lake City, Utah, June 13, 37; m. 67; c. 3. BOTANY. B.A, Brigham Young, 59, M.S, 61; Ph.D.(bot), Iowa State, 64. Asst. prof. bot, Weber State Col, 64-67; assoc. prof. BIOL, SLIPPERY ROCK STATE COL, 67-71, PROF, 71- Am. Soc. Plant Taxon. Distribution of the native trees of Utah; monograph of the genus Spenopholis; natural areas of western Pennsylvania. Address: Dept. of Biology, Slippery Rock State College, Slippery Rock, PA 16057.

ERDMAN, OSCAR ALVIN, b. Barons, Alta, May 5, 15; m. 50; c. 3. GEOLOGY. B.Sc, Alberta, 39, M.Sc, 41; Ph.D.(geol), Chicago, 46. Geologist, Geol. Surv. Can, Ont, 43-46; Can. Gulf Oil Co, Alta, 46-50, chief geologist, 50-56; Brit. Am. Oil Co. Ltd, 56-66, mgr. explor, 66-69; MEM. TECH. STAFF, GULF OIL CAN, LTD, 69- Am. Asn. Petrol. Geol; Soc. Explor. Geophys; Can. Inst. Mining & Metall; Geol. Asn. Can. Exploration for gas and oil. Address: Gulf Oil Canada, Ltd, Box 130, Calgary, Alta, Can.

ERDMAN, WILLIAM JAMES, II, b. Phila, Pa, Apr. 8, 21. MEDICINE. B.A, Swarthmore Col, 43; M.D, Univ. Pa, 50, M.Sc, 52. Asst. instr. PHYS. MED. & REHAB, sch. med, UNIV. PA, 51-53, instr, 53-54, asst. prof, 54-56, assoc. prof, SCH. MED. & GRAD. SCH. MED, 56-60, PROF, 60-, CHMN. DEPT, 56-, ASST. DEAN, 68-, DIR. DEPT. PHYS. MED. & REHAB, UNIV. HOSP, 56-, MED. DIR, 68-, ASST. DEAN SCH. MED, 68-, assoc, grad.sch. med, 54-55, acting chmn. dept, 54-55, asst. prof, 55-56. Mem. spec. med. adv. group, Vet. Admin; chief, Phila. Gen. Hosp; attend. physician & consult, Vet. Admin. Hosp, Phila, consult, Lebanon & Wilmington; Valley Forge Army Hosp. Dipl, Am. Bd. Phys. Med. & Rehab. U.S.A, 43-46. AAAS; fel. Am. Col. Physicians; Am. Cong. Rehab. Med.(pres, 64-65, treas, 70, Gold Key Award, 66); Int. Rehab. Med. Asn.(treas, 70-). Neuromuscular disorders. Address: Dept. of Physical Medicine & Rehabilitation, University of Pennsylvania Hospital, Philadelphia, PA 19104.

ERDMANN, DAVID E, b. St. Charles, Minn, July 15, 39; m. 69. ANALYTICAL & INORGANIC CHEMISTRY. B.S, Winona State Col, 60; M.S, Univ. Nebr, Lincoln, 66, NASA fel, 66-68, Ph.D.(chem), 68. Chemist, WATER RESOURCES DIV, U.S. GEOL. SURV, 68-71, RES. CHEMIST, 71- Am. Chem. Soc. Investigation of spectroscopic properties of some copper II beta-ketoamine chelates; improvement and development of analytical methods for water analysis; automation of water analysis methods. Address: Water Resources Division, U.S. Geological Survey, Bldg. 25, Denver Federal Center, Denver, CO 80225.

ERDMANN, JOACHIM C(HRISTIAN), b. Danzig, Danzig, June 5, 28; m. 57; c. 3. PHYSICS. Vordiplom, Brunswick Tech, 52, dipl, 55, Dr.rer. nat. (physics), 58. Physicist, Osram Studiengesellschaft, Germany, 54-60; RES. SPECIALIST SOLID STATE PHYSICS, BOEING CO, 60- Am. Phys. Soc; Am. Inst. Mining, Metall. & Petrol. Eng; Soc. Nondestructive Test; Soc. Photog. Sci. & Eng; German Phys. Soc. Transport properties of metals and semiconductors; low temperature experimental physics; mechanical properties of metals; coherent light optics. Address: Boeing Scientific Research Labs, P.O. Box 3981, Seattle, WA 98124.

ERDOGAN, FAZIL, b. Kars, Turkey, Feb. 5, 25; m. 61; c. 2. APPLIED MECHANICS. M.S, Tech. Univ. Istanbul, 48; Ph.D.(mech. eng), Lehigh, 55. Instr. eng, Tech. Univ. Istanbul, 48-52; asst, LEHIGH UNIV, 52-55, asst. prof. mech. eng, 57-60, assoc. prof, 60-63, PROF. MECH, 63- Turkish Army, 55-57. Am. Soc. Mech. Eng; Soc. Eng. Sci; Soc. Indust. & Appl. Math; Am. Math. Soc; Turkish Soc. Pure & Appl. Math. Mechanics of nonhomogeneous media; thermoelasticity; viscoelasticity; brittle fracture; metal fatigue; integral equations. Address: Dept. of Mechanical Engineering & Mechanics, Lehigh University, Bethlehem, PA 18015.

ERDÖS, E(RVIN) G(EORGE), b. Budapest, Hungary, Oct. 16, 22; U.S. citizen; m. 52; c. 3. PHARMACOLOGY. Szigorlo orvos, Eotvos Lorand, Hungary, 45-50; M.D, Munich, 50. Asst, inst. pathophysiol, Budapest, 47-50; res. assoc. biochem, res. lab, Surg. Clinic, Munich, 52-54; res. fel, sch. med, Pittsburgh, 54-55; res. assoc. anesthesia, Mercy Hosp, Pa, 55-58; fel. biochem, Mellon Inst, 58-63; clin. asst. prof. PHARMACOL, Pittsburgh, 58-61, clin. assoc. prof, 61-63; prof, SCH. MED, UNIV. OKLA, 63-70, GEORGE LYNN CROSS RES. PROF, 70- AAAS; Am. Soc. Pharmacol. & Exp. Therapeut; European Soc. Biochem, Pharmacol. Biochemical pharmacology. Address: Dept. of Pharmacology, University of Oklahoma School of Medicine, 800 N.E. 13th, Oklahoma City, OK 73104.

ERDOSS, B(ELA) K(ALMAN), b. Stari-Becej, Jugoslavia, July 3, 03; nat; m. 36; c. 1. MECHANICAL ENGINEERING, APPLIED MECHANICS. Dipl.M.E, Royal Joseph Univ. Eng, Budapest, 33; Byllesby fel, Lehigh, 42-44, M.S, 43, Ph.D.(mech. eng), 44; hon. Eng.M, Stevens Inst. Tech, 54. Consult. engr, Hungary, Jugoslavia & Gt. Britain, 27-40; chief engr. & dir, Fabric Hand Printers, Brooklyn, 40-41; chief engr, managing dir. & v.pres, Phillipsburg Mills, Inc, N.J, 41-43; asst. civil eng, Lehigh, 43-44, instr. mech. eng, 44-45, asst. prof, 45-46, assoc. prof, 46-49, dir. U.S. Air Force res. & develop. contract, inst. res, 46-49; prof. fluid dynamics, Stevens Inst. Tech, 47-56, chmn. dept, 49-52; PRES, KORFUND DYNAMICS CORP, 56- Consult. engr, 27-56; adv, coop. curricula, fluid dynamics, N.Y. Univ. & Webb Inst. Naval Archit. With U.S.A.A.F; U.S.N, 44. Am. Soc. Mech. Eng; Am. Phys. Soc; Am. Soc. Eng. Educ; Am. Inst. Aeronaut. & Astronaut; Soc. Exp. Stress Anal; Instrument Soc. Am; Soc. Naval Archit. & Marine Eng; N.Y. Acad. Sci; Asn. Maritime & Aeronaut. France. Flow visualization techniques; pressure-velocity relations in gas dynamics; supersonic aerodynamics; hydrodynamics of ship design; control and measurement of shock, vibration and noise. Address: Stoneleigh, Alger Ct, Bronxville, NY 10708.

ERDTMANN, BERND DIETRICH, b. Breslau, Ger, Aug. 17, 39. PALEONTOLOGY, PALEOECOLOGY. M.S, Univ. Hamburg, 62; fel, Univ. Oslo, 62-64, Ph.D.(geol), 65. Fel. GEOL, Laval Univ, 66; Can. Nat. Res. Coun. fel, Carleton Univ, 66-68; ASST. PROF, IND. UNIV, FT. WAYNE 68- Attend, Int. Conf. Continental Drift, Newf, 67; Consult, Can. Geol. Surv, 68-71. Ger. Geol. Soc; Norweg. Geol. Soc; Swedish Geol. Soc; Geol. Soc. Am; Soc. Econ. Paleont. & Mineral. Paleontology, biostratigraphy, and numerical taxonomy of Ordovician graptolites; taphonomy and fossilization of Recent invertebrate marine biota; paleoichnology (trace fossils). Address: Dept. of Geology, Indiana University at Fort Wayne, Fort Wayne, IN 46805.

ÉRDY, NICHOLAS Z(OLTAN), b. Zomba, Hungary, June 2, 31; U.S. citizen. POLYMER & PHYSICAL CHEMISTRY. Dipl, Veszprem Tech, 53; fel, Polytech. Inst. Brooklyn, 60-64, Ph.D.(chem), 64. Jr. res. engr, petrochem, Hungarian Oil & Gas Res. Inst, 53-55, res. engr, 55-56, petrol. chem, Esso Res. & Eng. Co, Standard Oil Co, N.J, 57-60; SR. RES. CHEMIST, cent. res. dept, FMC Corp, 64-68; STAUFFER CHEM. CO, 68- Am. Chem. Soc. Polymer division; urea-hydro-carbon complexes; extractive crystallization of heavy oil fractions; lubricant and gasoline additives; light scattering of macromolecular solutions; rheology of plastics; block copolymers; gels. Address: 430 W. 34th St, Apt. 12D, New York, NY 10001.

EREKSON, ARTHUR BEAU, b. Murray, Utah, June 25, 06; m. 39; c. 3. DAIRY BACTERIOLOGY. B.A, Utah, 28; B.S, Utah State Agr. Col, 31; M.S, Wisconsin, 32, 34-35. Teacher, high sch, Utah, 28-30; fieldman, Kohli Cheese Factory, Wis, 30; asst. dairy bact, Wisconsin, 30-33, res. fel. & asst, 34-35; res. dir, Lakeshire Marty Co. Div, BORDEN FOODS CO, Plymouth, Wis, 35-54, prod. process cheese, dough develop. & package, N.Y, 54-56, dir, res, 56-58, V.PRES. res, 58-61, prod. 61-65, prod. coord, 65-67, SPEC. RES. & ENG, 68-, Pac. cheese div, 54-55. Mem, Nat. Cheese Inst, 40-, chmn, 48. Am. Dairy Sci. Asn. Flavor development in cheddar cheese; packaging of natural cheese. Address: 41 Church Lane, Scarsdale, NY 10583.

ERF, ROBERT K, b. Cleveland, Ohio, Oct. 29, 31; m. 54; c. 4. ENGINEERING PHYSICS, ACOUSTICS. B.S.E.E, Michigan, 53; M.S, Harvard, 54. Res. engr, UNITED AIRCRAFT CORP. RES. LABS, 54-61, supvr. gen. instrumentation, 61-68, CHIEF, OPTICS & ACOUST, 68- Optical Soc. Am; Acoust. Soc. Am. Absorption photometry; optical scattering phenomena; interferometry; holography; ultrasonics; spectroscopy and applications of lasers to optical instruments; holographic technology for flow visualization; nondestructive testing; strain measurement and vibration analysis. Address: United Aircraft Corp. Research Labs, Silver Lane, East Hartford, CT 06108.

ERGUN, SABRI, b. Gerede, Turkey, Oct. 19, 19; nat; m. 49; c. 3. PHYSICAL CHEMISTRY. B.S. & M.S, Columbia, 44. Fel, Carnegie Inst. Tech, 46-47; Sc.D.(phys. chem), Vienna Tech, 56. Mem. staff, coal res. lab, Carnegie Inst. Tech, 48-54; supvry. phys. chemist, U.S. BUR. MINES, 54-56, chief, spec. coal res. sect, 56-60, PROJ. COORDINATOR, SOLID STATE PHYSICS, 61- Turkish A.A.F, 39-42, Res, 42-48, Capt. Am. Chem. Soc; Am. Phys. Soc. Heterogeneous kinetics; fluid dynamics; diffusion; x-ray scattering by noncrystalline matter; optical properties of solids; carbon; coals. Address: U.S. Bureau of Mines, 4800 Forbes St, Pittsburgh, PA 15213.

ERHAN, SEMIH, b. Bursa, Turkey, Oct. 14, 29; m. 58; c. 2. BIOCHEMISTRY, CHEMICAL ENGINEERING. M.S, Univ. Ankara, 53; Ph.D.(biochem), Okla. State Univ, 65. Res. chemist, Mineral, Explor. Inst, Turkey, Ankara, 56-57; eng. consult, Union of Chambers of Commerce & Indust, Turkey, 57-59; mgr. raw mat, Cement Indust. Corp, 59-60; res. chemist, Lurgi Gesellschaft für Mineralöl-Technik, Ger, 61-62; Damon Runyon Fund cancer res. fel, 65-66; res. investr. BIOCHEM, UNIV. PA, 66-68, SCH. VET. MED, 68-70, ASST. PROF, 70- Ord.C, Turkish Naval Res, 54-56, Ens. Union. Chem. & Chem. Eng. Turkey; Am. Chem. Soc. Control of nucleic acid syntheses and cell cycle and their involvement in oncogenesis; protein synthesis; development of new enzyme purification methods. Address: Lippincott Bldg, 25th & Locust St, Philadelphia, PA 19103.

ERHARDT, PETER F(RANKLIN), b. Grand Rapids, Mich, June 26, 33; m. 58; c. 4. POLYMER PHYSICS. B.S, Aquinas Col, 55; M.S, Michigan, 57; Ph.D. (phys. chem), Massachusetts, 68. Instr. chem, Aquinas Col, 57-60; res. trainee polymer physics, Gen. Elec. Res. Lab, N.Y, 60-63; res. asst, Polymer Res. Inst, Massachusetts, Amherst, 63-66; res. chemist, Gen. Elec. Co, 66-67; scientist, XEROX CORP, 67-70, SR. SCIENTIST, 70- AAAS; Am. Chem. Soc. Rheology; rheo-optics and optical properties of synthetic polymers; mechanical, thermal property measurements on polymers and structure-property correlations. Address: 26 Maryvale Dr; Webster, NY 14580.

ERHART, RAINER R, b. Monstab, Ger, June 25, 35; U.S. citizen; m. 61; c. 2. PHYSICAL GEOGRAPHY. B.A, Eastern Michigan, 59; M.A, Illinois, 61, Ph.D.(geog), 67. Asst. prof. GEOG, WEST. MICH. UNIV, 65-68, ASSOC. PROF, 68- AAAS; Asn. Am. Geog; Am. Geog. Soc; Nat. Coun. Geog. Educ; Am. Soc. Photogram. New media development in geography; remote sensing; agricultural geography. Address: Dept. of Geography, Western Michigan University, Kalamazoo, MI 49001.

ERIC, JOHN H(OWARD), b. N.Y.C, Apr. 25, 14; m. 42; c. 2. GEOLOGY. S.B, Harvard, 37, A.M, 40, fel, 41-42; Ph.D.(struct. geol), 42. Instr, Williams Col, 42; geologist, U.S. GEOL. SURV, 42-60, ASST. CHIEF, PUB. DIV, 61- AAAS; Geol. Soc. Am. Geology of eastern Vermont, foothill copper belt of California and Mother Lode of California; structural geology; economic geology; geology of Uranium. Address: U.S. Geological Survey, Washington, DC 20242.

ERICH, JOHN B, b. Chicago, Ill, Jan. 14, 07; m. 32. PLASTIC SURGERY. B.S, Illinois, 29, M.D, 32, D.D.S, 33, M.S, 34. HEAD DEPT. PLASTIC SURG. MAYO CLIN, 38-; PROF, MAYO GRAD. SCH. MED, UNIV. MINN, 57-, assoc. prof, 46-57. Dipl, Am. Bd. Plastic Surg, 42; Am. Bd. Otolaryngol, 49. U.S.N.R, 42-48. Am. Med. Asn; Am. Col. Surg; Am. Asn. Plastic Surg; Am. Soc. Plastic & Reconstruct. Surg; Am. Acad. Ophthal. & Otolaryngol; Am. Laryngol, Rhinol. & Otol. Soc; Am. Laryngol. Asn. Maxillofacial surgery. Address: Mayo Clinic, Rochester, MN 55901.

ERICH, L(ESTER) C(HARLES), b. Bethlehem, Pa, Dec. 7, 16; m. 40; c. 1. PHYSICS. B.S, Lehigh, 40, M.S, 50, Ph.D, 61. Physicist, Socony Vacuum Labs, 40-47; instr. PHYSICS, LAFAYETTE COL, 47-56, asst. prof, 56-61, ASSOC. PROF, 61- Am. Phys. Soc; Am. Asn. Physics Teachers. Nuclear physics; x-ray scattering and diffraction; nuclear quadrupole resonance; electron paramagnetic resonance; optical pumping. Address: Dept. of Physics, Lafayette College, Easton, PA 18042.

ERICHSEN, ALVIN W, b. Altamont, S.Dak; m. 55; c. 2. PLANT CYTOLOGY & GENETICS. B.S, S.Dak. State, 59, Ph.D.(plant breeding), 62. Res. assoc. genetics & cytogenetics, Illinois, 62-63; PLANT BREEDER, GREAT WEST. SUGAR CO, 63- U.S.N, 51-55. Am. Soc. Agron; Am. Soc. Sugar Beet Technol. Sugar beet varietal improvement. Address: Great Western Sugar Co, P.O. Box 539, Longmont, CO 80501.

ERICKSEN, GEORGE E(DWARD), b. Butte, Mont, Mar. 17, 20; m. 48. ECONOMIC GEOLOGY. B.A, Montana State, 46; M.A, Indiana, 49; Nat. Sci. Found. fel. & Ph.D.(geol), Columbia, 54. GEOLOGIST, U.S. Geol. Surv, 42-45, 46; Ind. Geol. Surv, 47; U.S. GEOL. SURV, 48- Instr, Indiana, 47-49. AAAS; Geol. Soc. Am; Soc. Econ. Geol; Am. Mineral. Soc; Geochem. Soc; Seismol. Soc. Am; Am. Inst. Min, Metall. & Petrol. Eng; Inst. Min. Eng. Chile; Peruvian Geol. Soc; Geol. Soc. Chile. Study of metalliferous and saline deposits of the Andes; geology and mineralogy of Chilean nitrate deposits; engineering geology related to earthquakes; reserves and distribution of carbonate rocks of the United States. Address: U.S. Geological Survey, Washington, DC 20242.

ERICKSEN, JERALD LaVERNE, b. Portland, Ore, Dec. 20, 24; m. 46; c. 2. B.S, Washington (Seattle), 47; fel, Oregon State, 47-49, M.A, 49; Ph.D. (math), Indiana, 51. Asst, Washington (Seattle), 46-47; res. & asst, Indiana, 49-51; mathematician, Naval Res. Lab, 51-52, 53-57; assoc. prof. THEORET. MECH, JOHNS HOPKINS UNIV, 57-60, PROF, 60- Res. assoc, Indiana, 52-53; lectr, Maryland, 51-52, 53-57. U.S.N.R, 43-45, Lt.(jg). Math. Asn. Am; Soc. Natural Philos.(treas, 63-64); Soc. Rheol. Nonlinear continuum theories. Address: Dept. of Mechanics, Johns Hopkins University, Baltimore, MD 21218.

ERICKSEN, WILHELM S(KJELSTAD), b. Green Bay, Wis, May 3, 12; m. 39; c. 3. MATHEMATICS. B.A, St. Olaf Col, 36; M.A, Wisconsin, 38, Ph.D. (math), 43. Asst. prof. math, St. Olaf Col, 42-43; prof, N.Dak. State Teachers Col, Minot, 43-44; fel. mech, Brown, 44; aerodynamicist, Bell Aircraft Corp, Buffalo, 45-46; mathematician, Forest Prod. Lab, U.S. Forest Serv, 46-53; PROF. MATH, AIR FORCE INST. TECHNOL, 53- Am. Math. Soc; Math. Asn. Am. Sandwich construction for aircraft; stresses in wood structural members. Address: Air Force Institute of Technology, Wright-Patterson Air Force Base, Dayton, OH 45432.

ERICKSON, ALAN E(RIC), b. Boston, Mass, Feb. 6, 28; m. 51; c. 4. EMBRYOLOGY. A.B, Middlebury Col, 49; M.A, Boston, 55, Ph.D.(biol), 60; M.L.S, Simmons Col, 68. Asst. inst. biol, Boston, 54-55, instr, 55-60; scientist embryol, Worcester Found. Exp. Biol, 60-66; SCI. SPECIALIST, WIDENER LIBR, HARVARD, 66-, ACTING ASSOC. LIBRN. FOR ADMIN, HARVARD UNIV. LIBR, 70- U.S.A.F, 51-54, Res, 54-, Maj. AAAS; Teratology Soc; Am. Soc. Info. Sci. Hormones in development of the embryonic reproductive system. Address: Widener Library, Harvard University, Cambridge, MA 02138.

ERICKSON, ALBERT W, b. Chicago, Ill, June 23, 29; m. 54; c. 3. WILDLIFE ECOLOGY, MAMMALOGY. B.S, Mich. State, 54, M.S, 55, Ph.D.(fisheries, wildlife), 64. Instr. wildlife mgt, Mich. State, 55-56; res. game biologist, Mich. Dept. Conserv, 56-58; reg. game supvr, Alaska Dept. Fish & Game, 58-64; Nat. Insts. Health fel. anat, med. sch, Wisconsin, 64-65; assoc. prof. fisheries & wildlife & curator mammals, Mus. Natural Hist, Univ. Minn, Minneapolis, 65-70; PROF. ECOL. & DIR. WILDERNESS RES. CTR, UNIV. IDAHO, 70- Res. grants, World Wildlife Fund, 65-67; N.Y. Zool. Soc. & U.S. Pub. Health Serv, 66-67; sci. adv, Norsk Polar Inst, Oslo, Norway, 66-68; Nat. Sci. Found, Off. Polar Prog. res. grant, 67-70; consult, natural sci. adv. comt, Nat. Park Serv. 69. Wildlife Soc; Am. Soc. Mammal; Ecol. Soc. Am; Animal Behav. Soc. Ecology; management and physiology of bears and seals; wilderness management. Address: Wilderness Research Center, College of Forestry, University of Idaho, Moscow, ID 83843.

ERICKSON, A(NTON) EARL, b. Chicago, Ill, June 5, 19; m. 43; c. 3. SOIL SCIENCE. B.S, Illinois, 41, Ph.D.(agron), 48. Asst. soil surv, Illinois, 41-48; asst. prof. SOIL SCI, MICH. STATE UNIV, 48-54, assoc. prof, 54-59, PROF, 59- Fel. AAAS; Am. Soc. Agron; Soil Sci. Soc. Am. Soil physics; x-ray diffraction; clay mineralogy; radioactive tracers. Address: Dept. of Soil Science, Michigan State University, East Lansing, MI 48823.

ERICKSON, BERT H(AZEN), b. Richmond, Utah, May 9, 31; m. 62; c. 5. ANIMAL BREEDING, EMBRYOLOGY. B.S, Utah State, 56; M.S, Kansas State, 57, Ph.D.(animal breeding), 61. ASSOC. PROF. REPROD. PHYSIOL, AGR. RES. LAB, ATOMIC ENERGY COMN, UNIV. TENN, 60- U.S.A, 51-53, Sgt. AAAS; Am. Soc. Animal Sci; Brit. Soc. Study Fertil. Steroid determinations in tissues and fluids; effects of ionizing radiation on germ cells of domestic animals. Address: Agricultural Research Lab, University of Tennessee, Atomic Energy Commission, 1299 Bethel Valley Rd, Oak Ridge, TN 37830.

ERICKSON, BRUCE WAYNE, b. New Haven, Conn, Oct. 19, 42; m. 69. ORGANIC CHEMISTRY & BIOCHEMISTRY. B.S, Ohio State Univ, 63; Nat. Sci. Found. fels, Harvard, 63-64 & 65-68, A.M, 65, Ph.D.(org.chem), 70. RES. ASSOC. ORG. CHEM, ROCKEFELLER UNIV, 69- AAAS; Am. Chem. Soc; The Chem. Soc. Solid-phase synthesis of peptides and proteins; organometallic reagents for the chemical synthesis of complex organic molecules. Address: Rockefeller University, New York, NY 10021.

ERICKSON, CARL J, Psychol, Animal Behav, see Suppl. I to 11th ed, Soc. & Behav. Vols.

ERICKSON, CARL O, b. Ames, Iowa, May 21, 24. METEOROLOGY. A.B, Guilford Col, 49; M.S, Chicago, 55. Meteorologist, U.S. Weather Bur, 49-53, 55-60, RES. METEOROLOGIST, 60-65, NAT. ENVIRON. SATELLITE SERV, NAT. OCEANIC & ATMOSPHERIC ADMIN, 65- U.S.A, 42-45, T/Sgt. Am. Geophys. Union; Am. Meteorol. Soc. Synoptic meteorology; applications of meteorological satellite data to synoptic weather analysis and interpretation. Address: National Environmental Satellite Service, National Oceanic & Atmospheric Administration, Suitland, MD 20233.

ERICKSON, CARLTON KUEHL, b. Manistee, Mich, Apr. 6, 39; m. 65; c. 1. PHARMACOLOGY. B.S, Ferris State Col, 61; M.S, Purdue, 63, Nat. Insts. Health fel, 63-65, Ph.D.(pharmacol), 65. Asst. prof. PHARMACOL, COL. PHARM, UNIV. KANS, 65-69, ASSOC. PROF, 69- Consult, Alza Corp. AAAS; Am. Pharmaceut. Asn; Soc. Neurosci. Cholinergic involvement in learned behavior; neurophysiology of learning and memory; alcohol addiction in laboratory animals. Address: Dept. of Pharmacology, School of Pharmacy, University of Kansas, Lawrence, KS 66044.

ERICKSON, C(HARLES) E(DWARD), b. Racine, Wis, Jan. 10, 20. INORGANIC CHEMISTRY. B.S, Michigan, 42, M.S, 43; Standard Oil Co. fel, Cornell, 50-51, Ph.D.(chem), 53. Chemist, Linde Air Prods. Res. Lab, 43-49; res. asst, Cornell, 49-50, asst, 51-52; instr, RUTGERS UNIV, 52-53, asst. prof. INORG. CHEM, 53-58, assoc. prof, 58-65, PROF, 65- Am. Chem. Soc. Organic and non-organic compounds of boron; concepts of inorganic chemistry. Address: 585 Sutton Lane, Piscataway, NJ 08854.

ERICKSON, CLIFFORD WAYNE, b. Duluth, Minn, Jan. 9, 37; m. 61; c. 3. PLASMA PHYSICS, PHYSICAL ELECTRONICS. B.A, Harvard, 58, M.A, 60; Stockholm, 58-59; Ph.D.(physics), Wisconsin, 67. Staff mem. physics, Sandia Lab, N.Mex, 61-62; vis. scientist, Inst. Plasma Physics, Munich, Ger, 67-68; PRIN. RES. SCIENTIST, HONEYWELL RES. CTR, 68- Rotary Int. fel, 58-59. AAAS; Am. Phys. Soc. Toroidal confinement of plasmas; electrical discharges in gases. Address: Honeywell Research Center, 500 Washington Ave. S, M.S. 1330, Hopkins, MN 55343.

ERICKSON, CYRUS C(ONRAD), b. Alexandria, Minn, Aug. 18, 09; m. 37; c. 3. PATHOLOGY. B.S, Univ. Minn, 30, B.M, 32, M.D, 33. Fel. pediat, Univ. Minn, 34-35; asst. res. & res. assoc. path, med. sch, Univ. Rochester, 35-37; instr, sch. med, Duke Univ, 37-39, assoc, 39-46, assoc. prof, 46-50, assoc. pathologist, univ. hosp, 39-42, 46-50; PROF. PATH, MED. SCH, UNIV. TENN, 50-, acting chmn. dept, 68-71. Consult, U.S. Vet. Admin. Bur, 55-; hosps. Dipl, Am. Bd. Path. M.C, 42-46, Lt. Col. Am. Med. Asn; Am. Soc. Exp. Path.(secy, 53-56, v.pres, 58-59, pres, 59-60); Am. Soc. Clin. Path; Am. Soc. Cytol.(v.pres, 57-59, pres, 60-61, award, 65); fel. Col. Am. Path; Am. Asn. Path. & Bact; Am. Cancer Soc.(distinguished serv. award, 69); Int. Acad. Path; Int. Acad. Cytol. Choline deficiency and tumor incidence in rats; histogenesis and incidence of intraepithelial carcinoma of cervix in humans; factors influencing development of carcinoma of cervix in mice with prolonged sex steroid administration; investigations on uterine cancer by epidemiological study following genital cytology population screening. Address: Dept. of Pathology, University of Tennessee, Memphis, TN 38103.

ERICKSON, DAVID E(DWARD), b. Grand Island, Nebr, July 15, 31; m. 56; c. 3. PHYSICAL CHEMISTRY. B.S, S.Dak. Sch. Mines & Technol, 52; Ph.D.(chem), Ohio State, 56. Res. chemist, E.I. du Pont de Nemours & Co, 56-64; sr. res. chemist, res. div, GEN. TIRE CO, 64-66, group leader, RES. & DEVELOP. CTR, 66-69, DEVELOP. ASSOC, CHEM-PLASTICS DIV, 69- Am. Chem. Soc. Physical and polymer chemistry; colloids; adhesion; rheology. Address: Chemical-Plastics Division, Research & Development Center, General Tire Co, Akron, OH 44309.

ERICKSON, DAVID R, b. Portland, Ore, Oct. 26, 29; m. 51; c. 3. AGRICULTURAL CHEMISTRY. B.S, Oregon State, 57, M.S, 58; Ph.D.(agr. chem), California, Davis, 63. Res. lipid chemist, SWIFT & CO, 63-67, head, edible fats & margarine res. div, 67-70, GEN. MGR. INDUST. PRODS. RES, 70- U.S.A, 50-53, Sgt. Am. Dairy Sci. Asn; Inst. Food Tech; Am. Oil Chem. Soc. Oxidation of milk and antioxidants in milk and milk products; chemistry of processing edible fats and oils. Address: 4730 Main St, Downers Grove, IL 60515.

ERICKSON, DONALD J(OHAN), b. Denver, Colo, Oct. 21, 14; m. 41; c. 2. MEDICINE. B.A, Denver, 36; M.D, Colorado, 40; M.S, Minnesota, 48. Intern, Wis. Gen. Hosp, 40-41; fel. PHYS. MED. & REHAB, Mayo Grad. Sch. Med, UNIV. MINN, 41-44, instr. med, univ, 46-48, MAYO GRAD. SCH. MED, 49-56, ASST. PROF, 56- Private practice, Minn, 46-48; consult, Mayo Clin, 48- U.S.N.R, 43-46. Am. Cong. Rehab. Med.(pres, 62); Am. Med. Asn; Am. Acad. Phys. Med. & Rehab; Am. Col. Physicians. Physical medicine; rehabilitation. Address: Mayo Graduate School of Medicine, University of Minnesota, Rochester, MN 55901.

ERICKSON, DUANE G(ORDON), b. Vinton, Iowa, Jan. 30, 31; m. 52; c. 1. PARASITOLOGY. B.A, Minnesota, 53, Nat. Sci. Found. fel, 53-54, M.S, 57, Ph.D, 64. U.S. ARMY, 57-, parasitologist, Sixth Army Med. Lab, Calif, 56, asst. gen. zool. & histol, Minnesota, 56-57, parasitologist, Second Army Med. Lab, Md, 57-58, chief helminthol. dept, Army Trop. Res. Med. Lab, P.R, 59-61, asst. chief, dept. med. zool, Walter Reed Army Inst. Res, 64-65, consult. parasitol, U.S. Army & chief parasitol. br, Ninth Med. Lab, Viet Nam, 66-67, coord. schistosomiasis res. & chief schistosomiasis unit, dept. med, Walter Reed Army Inst. Res, 67-71, CHIEF DEPT. MED. ZOOL, 406TH MED. LAB, JAPAN, 71- U.S.A, 54-56, 57-, Lt. Col; Bronze Star Medal, 67. Am. Soc. Parasitol; Am. Soc. Trop. Med. & Hyg. Schistosomatoidea; immunity and pathology of parasitic infections; medical entomology; electron microscopy; immunity and pathology of schistosomiasis; chemotherapy of schistosomiasis; ultrastructural pathology. Address: Dept. of Medical Zoology, 406th Medical Laboratory, USAMCJ, APO San Francisco 96343.

ERICKSON, DUANE OTTO, b. Fargo, N.Dak, Mar. 26, 30; m. 54; c. 3. ANIMAL SCIENCE, BIOLOGICAL CHEMISTRY. B.S, N.Dak. State, 57, M.S, 60, Ph.D.(animal sci, biochem), 65. Instr. & asst. ANIMAL SCI, N.DAK. STATE UNIV, 59-65, asst. prof, 65-67, ASSOC. PROF, 67- Ord.C, U.S.A, 51-53. AAAS; Am. Soc. Animal Sci. Development of methods for forage evaluation; metabolism within the rumen of a ruminant. Address: Dept. of Animal Science, North Dakota State University, Fargo, ND 58102.

ERICKSON, EDWARD A(XEL), b. Brooklyn, N.Y, June 4, 08; m. 31; c. 2. ENGINEERING. M.E, Polytech. Inst. Brooklyn, 37. Test engr, Williamsburgh Power Plant Corp, N.Y, 29-41; asst. mech. engr, bur. ships, U.S. Navy, N.Y, 41-45; res. engr, Battelle Mem. Inst, 45-48; sr. combustion engr, mat. testing & develop. lab, Sears, Roebuck & Co, 48-53; PROJ. ENGR, HEATING, AIR CONDITIONING & REFRIG. DEPT, UNDERWRITERS LABS, INC, 53- Am. Soc. Mech. Eng; Am. Soc. Metals; Am. Soc. Heat, Refrig. & Air-Conditioning Eng. Smokeless and hand-fired bituminous coal burning heat equipment covering space heaters, ranges, furnaces, water heaters and boilers; merchandise testing and development of coal-burning space heaters, ranges and water heaters, oil-burning equipment; safety controls; limit controls, boilers, furnaces and water heaters. Address: Heating, Air Conditioning & Refrigeration Dept, Underwriters Labs, Inc, P.O. Box 247, Northbrook, IL 60062.

ERICKSON, EDWARD HERBERT, b. Oakland, Calif, Feb. 16, 44; m. 66; c. 1. MEDICINAL CHEMISTRY. B.A, Univ. Calif, Santa Barbara, 65, Ph.D.(org. chem), 68. RES. CHEMIST, RIKER LABS, INC, 3M CO, NORTHRIDGE, CALIF, 68- AAAS; Am. Chem. Soc. Enzyme inhibition and rational drug design; preparation of antiinflammatory and antiallergic drugs. Address: Bldg. 218-1, 3M Center, St. Paul, MN 55101.

ERICKSON, EDWIN BACAUE, b. Phila, Pa, May 18, 38; m. 64; c. 1. BIOCHEMISTRY, MICROBIOLOGY. B.S, Albright Col, 60; Ph.D.(biochem. & microbiol), Bryn Mawr Col, 69. Disease control investr, U.S. Pub. Health Serv, 62; instr. biol, Drexel Inst, 62-66; assoc. prof. physiol, East Stroudsburg State Col, 68-69; ASST. PROF. BIOCHEM, HAMILTON COL, 69- AAAS; Soc. Protozool; Am. Soc. Zool. Transport mechanisms of ions in protozoa. Address: Dept. of Biochemistry, Hamilton College, Clinton, NY 13323.

ERICKSON, EDWIN R(ICHARD), b. Biggsville, Ill, Nov. 3, 00; m. 26; c. 1. CHEMISTRY. B.A, Carthage Col, 31; M.A, Buffalo, 33; Ph.D, 37. Instr. inorg. chem, Carthage Col, 33-34, assoc. prof. chem, 34-35, prof, 37-40; res. chemist synthetic rubber, Mathieson Alkali Works, 41-45; supvr. plastics res, Armour Res. Found, 45-46; chmn. dept. CHEM, AUGUSTANA COL.(ILL), 46-49, div. sci, 53-69, EMER. PROF, 69- Assoc.dir, Augustana Res. Found, 46-69, dir, 69- Am. Chem. Soc. Teaching of chemistry; academic and industrial research; administration of science. Address: 2424 Fourth St, Moline, IL 61265.

ERICKSON, EDWIN S(YLVESTER), JR, b. Brooklyn, N.Y, July 9, 28; m. 53; c. 4. MINERALOGY, GEOCHEMISTRY. B.S, City Col. New York, 51; Columbia, 51-52; Ph.D.(mineral), Pa. State, 63. Geologist, U.S. Geol. Surv, 52-53; res. asst. geochem. & mineral, Pa. State, 53-58; RES. ENGR, BETHLEHEM STEEL CORP, 58- Assoc, dept. geol, Lehigh Univ, 66- Metall. Soc; Mineral. Soc. Am. Mineralogical investigation of raw materials and refractories for iron and steelmaking; agglomerated iron and manganese ores; mineralogy of refractory clays and bentonites. Address: Homer Research Labs, Bethlehem Steel Co, Bethlehem, PA 18016.

ERICKSON, ETHEL ELMA, b. Chisholm, Minn, July 24, 14; m. 46; c. 2. PATHOLOGY. B.S, Minnesota, 37, M.D, 46. Resident PATH, Lenox Hill Hosp, New York, 46; intern & resident, Ill. Res. & Ed. Hosp. Chicago, Ill. 47-50; CLIN. ASSOC. PROF, BAYLOR COL. MED, 50-; ASST. MED. EXAMINER, HARRIS COUNTY, 69- Pathologist & asst. chief. Vet. Admin. Hosp, 50-65; chief pathologist, Sharpstown Gen. Hosp, 64-69. Am. Med. Asn; Col. Am. Path; Am. Soc. Clin. Path; Am. Asn. Path. & Bact; Am. Med. Women's Asn; Int. Acad. Path. Forensic pathology; neoplasia; neuropathology; skin. Address: Medical Examiners Office, 1502 Ben Taub Loop, Houston, TX 77025.

ERICKSON, EUGENE E, b. Fargo, N.Dak, Sept. 15, 23; m. 46; c. 5. CHEMICAL ENGINEERING. B.Ch.E, Minnesota, 44; Ph.D.(chem. eng), N.C. State Col, 57. Res. chem. engr, Russell-Miller Milling Co, Minn, 44-50; Minn. Mining & Mfg. Co, 50-52; N.C. State Col, 52-57; atomic energy div, Phillips Petrol. Co, 57-60, group leader, 60-62, staff engr. reactor safety, 62-63; sr. chem. engr, N. STAR RES. & DEVELOP. INST, 63-64, assoc. dir. phys. sci. & eng. div, 64-66, dir. div, 66-70, TECH. DIR, INST, 70- Am. Chem. Soc; Am. Inst. Chem. Eng. Liquid-liquid extraction; fermentation; nuclear fuels processing; chemical economics; research administration; environmental systems. Address: North Star Research & Development Institute, 3100 38th Ave. S, Minneapolis, MN 55406.

ERICKSON, GLEN W(ALTER), b. St. Paul, Minn, Aug. 1, 34; m. 55; c. 3. THEORETICAL PHYSICS. B.S, Minnesota, 55, Nat. Sci. Found. fels, 57-59, Ph.D.(physics), 60. Res. assoc, inst. field physics, North Carolina, 60-62, vis. asst. prof. PHYSICS, 61-62; adj. asst. prof, N.Y. Univ, 62-64; ASSOC. PROF, UNIV. CALIF, DAVIS, 64- Assoc. physicist Oak Ridge Nat. Labs, Union Carbide Nuclear Corp, summer, 62; sr. res. fel, Sci. Res. Coun. Eng, 70-71; mem. comt. fundamental constants, Nat. Res. Coun-Nat. Acad. Sci, 69-71. Am. Phys. Soc. Quantum field theory, especially quantum electrodynamics. Address: Dept. of Physics, University of California, Davis, CA 95616.

ERICKSON, HAROLD P(AUL), b. Chattanooga, Tenn, Jan. 16, 40; m. 65; c. 1. BIOPHYSICS, ELECTRON MICROSCOPY. B.S, Carnegie-Mellon Univ, 62; Nat. Insts. Health grant, Johns Hopkins Univ, 62-65 & fel, 65-68, Ph.D.(biophys), 68. Res. assoc. biophys, Johns Hopkins Univ, 68; Nat. Insts. Health res. fel, Med. Res. Coun. Lab. Molecular Biol, Cambridge, Eng, 68-70; ASST. PROF. ANAT, MED. CTR, DUKE UNIV, 70- Molecular biology; high resolution electron microscopy of nucleic acids and protein structures; theory of image formation and computer processing in electron microscopy. Address: Dept. of Anatomy, Duke University Medical Center, Durham, NC 27710.

ERICKSON, HARVEY D, b. Belgrade, Minn, Apr. 12, 12; m. 54; c. 1. WOOD SCIENCE & TECHNOLOGY. B.S, Minnesota, 34, Am. Creosoting Co. fel, 34-37; M.S, 36, Ph.D.(wood tech, biochem), 37. Asst. prof. forest util, West. Virginia, 37-40, assoc. prof, 40-47, prof, 47; assoc. prof. FOREST PROD, UNIV. WASH, 47-59, PROF, 59- AAAS; Am. Chem. Soc; Soc. Wood Sci. & Technol; Soc. Am. Foresters; Tech. Asn. Pulp & Paper Indust; Forest Prod. Res. Soc. Permeability of wood; effect of chemicals on strength of woods; wood shrinkage; wood-moisture relations; wood quality and growth factors affecting quality; chemical analysis of wood; wood preservation; freeze drying effects on wood. Address: College of Forest Resources, University of Washington, Seattle, WA 98105.

ERICKSON, HOMER T(HEODORE), b. Pulaski, Wis, Mar. 8, 25; m. 55; c. 4. HORTICULTURE. B.S, Wisconsin, 51, M.S, 53, Ph.D.(hort, genetics), 54. Asst. prof. HORT, Maine, 54-56; PURDUE UNIV, 56-64, PROF, 64-, HEAD DEPT, 67- With Purdue training team, Agr. Univ, Minas Gerais, 59-63, hon. prof, 63. U.S.A, 46-47. AAAS; Wilson Ornith. Soc; Am. Soc. Hort. Sci; Am. Genetic Asn. Physiology and genetics of the more important commercial vegetables; tropical horticulture in general. Address: 1409 N. Salisbury St, West Lafayette, IN 47906.

ERICKSON, HOWARD H(UGH), b. Wahoo, Nebr, Mar. 16, 36; m. 59; c. 2. PHYSIOLOGY, BIOMEDICAL ENGINEERING. B.S. & D.V.M, Kansas State, 59; Cambridge, 60; Oxford, 62; Ph.D.(physiol. biomed. eng), Iowa State, 66. VET. CORPS, U.S. AIR FORCE, 60-, area vet, 59th Vet. Inspection Flight, U.K, 60-63, res. vet. officer, biodynamics br, U.S. AIR FORCE SCH. AEROSPACE MED, 66-68, VET. PHYSIOLOGIST, 68-70, VET. SCIENTIST, APPL. PHYSIOL. BR, 70- Vis. mem. grad. faculty, Tex. A&M Univ, 68-; spec. mem. grad. faculty, Colo. State Univ, 70- AAAS; Am. Vet. Med. Asn; Am. Pub. Health Asn; Asn. Advan. Med. Instrumentation; Soc. Vet. Physiol. & Pharmacol; Inst. Elec. & Electronics Eng; Aerospace Med. Asn; Am. Physiol. Soc; Int. Fedn. Med. & Biol. Eng; Acad. Vet. Cardiol; Instrument Soc. Am; Biomed. Eng. Soc; N.Y. Acad. Sci. Artificial heart control; fiber optics; reflection oximetry; weightlessness; acceleration; cardiopulmonary physiology, instrumentation and control. Address: Applied Physiology Branch, U.S. Air Force School of Aerospace Medicine, Brooks Air Force Base, TX 78235.

ERICKSON, HOWARD RALPH, b. Indiana, Pa, Nov. 23, 19; m. 55; c. 3. VERTEBRATE ZOOLOGY. B.S, Indiana Univ. Pa, 52; M.S, Pa. State, 56; Ph.D. (vert. zool), Cornell, 59. Res. asst. zool, Pa. State, 54-56; vert. zool, Cornell, 56-59; instr. biol. & zool, TOWSON STATE COL, 59-62, assoc. prof. vert. zool, 62-66, PROF. VERT. ZOOL & CHMN. DEPT. BIOL. SCI, 66-, annual res. grant, 66-68. Summer lectr, Maryland, 60-66. U.S.A, 52-54, 1st Lt. AAAS; Am. Soc. Mammal; Ecol. Soc. Am; Wildlife Soc. Environmental conservation; vertebrate ecology; muskrat growth; reproduction; population dynamics; movements; control methods and procedures; ecology of fresh water piscine species. Address: Dept. of Biological Sciences, Towson State College, Baltimore, MD 21204.

ERICKSON, JAMES C, III, b. Phila, Pa, Oct. 7, 27; m. 56; c. 1. ANESTHESIOLOGY. B.A, Pennsylvania, 49; M.D, Temple, 53, M.Sc, 58. Instr. ANESTHESIOL, med. sch, Temple, 57-58; assoc, Guthrie Clin, 58-61; med. sch, Temple, 61-64, asst. prof, 64-67; PROF, Woman's Med. Col. Pa, 67-69; JEFFERSON MED. COL, THOMAS JEFFERSON UNIV, 69- Dipl, Am. Bd. Anesthesiol, 60. U.S.A, 46-47. Am. Col. Anesthesiol; Am. Med. Asn; Am. Soc. Anesthesiol; Int. Anesthesia Res. Soc. Vasopressor effect of indigo carmine; clinical evaluation of local anesthetic drugs; pain control and diagnostic evaluation; evaluation of neurolytic agents. Address: Thomas Jefferson University Hospital, Philadelphia, PA 19107.

ERICKSON, JAMES G(EORGE), b. Sioux City, Iowa, May 18, 29; m. 50; c. 3. ZOOLOGY. B.A, Doane Col, 50; Iowa Conserv. Cmn. fel. & M.S, Iowa State, 51; Nat. Defense Ed. Act. fel. & Ph.D.(zool. & physiol), Wyoming, 64. Fisheries biologist, div. wildlife, Ohio Dept. Nat. Resources, 53-56; Wyo. Game & Fish Cmn, 56-61; asst. prof. BIOL, FT. LEWIS COL, 64-67, ASSOC. PROF, 67- U.S.A, 51-53. Am. Soc. Zool. Behavior and endocrinology of fishes. Address: Dept. of Biology, Ft. Lewis College, Durango, CO 81301.

ERICKSON, JAY WILLIAM, b. Fredonia, N.Y, Aug. 6, 34; m. 55; c. 3. SCIENCE EDUCATION, INORGANIC CHEMISTRY. B.S, State Univ. N.Y. Col. Fredonia, 59; N.Y. State regents fel, Teachers Col, Columbia, 59-61, Sci. Manpower fel, 59-63, M.A, 60, Ph.D.(sci. ed), 63. Instr. sci. ed, Teachers Col, Columbia, 62-63; asst. prof. ed, Univ. South, 63-64; ASSOC. PROF. NATURAL SCI, UNIV. COLUMBIA, 64-, SCI. ADV. CHEM, FACULTY OF EDUC, KABUL, AFGHANISTAN, 66- Consult, develop. sr. level sec. sch. course in space sci, & jr. high sch. space sci. curriculum, NASA, 65-66; Pelham New York Tryout Ctr. Elem. Sci. Mat, Am. Asn. Adv. Sci, 65-66. AAAS; Nat. Sci. Teachers Asn; Nat. Asn. Res. Sci. Teaching. Curriculum development in science. Address: Dept. of Natural Sciences, Teachers College, Columbia University, New York, NY 10027.

ERICKSON, JOHN (ELMER), b. Sioux City, Iowa, June 17, 23; m. 46; c. 3. GENETICS. B.A, Omaha, 48; M.A, Indiana, 50; Danforth fel, Oregon, 62, Nat. Insts. Health fel, 63, Ph.D.(genetics), 64. Instr. biol, McCook Jr. Col, 54-59; Oregon, 59-62; asst. prof. BIOL, WEST. WASH. STATE COL, 64-66, ASSOC. PROF, 66- U.S.A.A.F, 43-46. Genetics Soc. Am. Cytogenetics of meiotic drive in Drosophila males; fragmentation of Y chromosome; mating, insemination and fertility problems. Address: Dept. of Biology, Western Washington State College, Bellingham, WA 98225.

ERICKSON, JOHN G(ERHARD), b. Northfield, Minn, July 14, 17; m. 54; c. 4. ORGANIC CHEMISTRY. B.A, St. Olaf Col, 38; M.S, N.Dak. State Col, 40; Ph.D.(org. chem), Minnesota, 44. Asst, N.Dak. State Col, 38-40; instr, St. Olaf Col, 40-41; chemist, Minn. Valley Canning Co, 41; res. asst. soils, Minnesota, 41, asst, 42-44; res. chemist, Am. Cyanamid Co, 44-50; sr. res. chemist, Gen. Mills, Inc, 51-56; MINN. MINING & MFG. CO, 56-59, supvr, 59-64, mgr. synthesis res, 64-66, DIR. SCI. & TECH. COMMUN, 66- Dir. & treas, Avochem, Inc, 53-61, pres, 59-61. Am. Chem. Soc; The Chem. Soc. Organic nitrogen compounds; heterocycles; sugar derivatives; acrylic derivatives; hydrogen cyanide; orthoformic esters; glycidyl esters; polymers; fluorine chemistry; textile agents; greases; rocket propellants; birds of the Labrador coast; flight behavior of the Procellariiformes. Address: Minnesota Mining & Manufacturing Co, 3M Center, 220-11E, St. Paul, MN 55101.

ERICKSON, JOHN M, b. Curtiss, Wis, Apr. 28, 18; m. 48; c. 4. PHYSICAL CHEMISTRY. B.S, Wisconsin, 40; M.S, S.Dak. State, 53; Ph.D.(phys. chem), Iowa State, 56. From prod. dept. foreman to cost control engr, Procter & Gamble Mfg. Co, Ill, 40-43; instr. chem. & math, S.Dak. State, 47-51; asst, Iowa State, 51-56; assoc. prof. phys. chem, S.Dak. State, 56-60; CHEM, ST. CLOUD STATE COL, 60-66, PROF, 66- U.S.N.R, 43-46, Res, 46-52. Am. Chem. Soc. Complex ions in mixed solvents; ion-exchange equilibria; water pollution. Address: Dept. of Chemistry, St. Cloud State College, St. Cloud, MN 56301.

ERICKSON, J(OHN) MARK, b. Orange, N.J, Dec. 21, 43. INVERTEBRATE PALEONTOLOGY. B.S, Tufts Univ, 65; M.S, Univ. N.Dak, 68, Ph.D, 71. ASST. PROF. INVERT. PALEONT, ST. LAWRENCE UNIV, 71- Fel. AAAS; Geol. Soc. Am; Paleont. Soc; Am. Soc. Limnol. & Oceanog; Brit. Palaeont. Asn; Paleont. Res. Inst; Soc. Econ. Paleont. & Mineral. Upper Cretaceous gastropod taxonomy, paleoecology and zoogeography; molluscan paleontology and paleoecology; sedimentation, paleolimnology and post-Pleistocene history of temperate lakes; paleosynecological relationships of invertebrates. Address: Dept. of Geology, St. Lawrence University, Canton, NY 13617.

ERICKSON, JOHN O(TTO), b. Minn, May 12, 15; m. 52; c. 3. ELECTRON MICROSCOPY. B.S, Minnesota, 39; Ph.D.(biochem), Duke, 44. Res. assoc. serum proteins, Duke, 44-45; res. biochemist, radioisotopes & immunol, Am. Cyanamid Co, 45-48; immunol, Rochester, 48-49, biophysicist, radioisotope unit, VET. ADMIN, 49-61, biophysicist assoc. dir, WEST. RES. SUPPORT CENTER, 61-65, BIOPHYSICIST, 65- AAAS; N.Y. Acad. Sci; Am. Chem. Soc; Electron Micros. Soc. Am; Am. Asn. Immunol. Electron microscopy; ultrastructural pathology. Address: Lab. Service, Veterans Administration Hospital 113, 5901 E. Seventh St, Long Beach, CA 90801.

ERICKSON, JOHN R(OBERT), b. Flaxton, N.Dak, Sept. 4, 39. PLANT GENETICS. B.S, Washington State, 63; Nat. Defense Ed. Act. fel, N.Dak. State, 63, Ph.D.(agron), 67. Res. geneticist, crops res. div, U.S. Dept. Agr, 67-69; ASST. PROF. AGRON, N.DAK. STATE UNIV, 69- U.S.A, 58-60. Am. Soc. Agron. Genetics and biochemistry of economic plant characteristics, especially respiratory enzymes; winter wheat breeding. Address: Dept. of Agronomy, North Dakota State University, Fargo, ND 58102.

ERICKSON, JOHN W(ILLIAM), b. Chicago, Ill, June 13, 25; m. 47; c. 8. GEOLOGY. A.B, Augustana Col, 50; Iowa, 50. Jr. computer geophysics, Atlantic Ref. Co, 51-52; stratigrapher geol, Chem. & Geol. Labs, 52-54; geologist, GULF OIL CORP, 54-58, rep, DENVER DIV, GULF RES. & DEVELOP. CO, 58-60, SR. GEOLOGIST, 60- U.S.N.R, 43-46, 50-51. Am. Asn. Petrol. Geol; Geol. Soc. Am. Stratigraphy; subsurface and petroleum geology; geological data processing techniques. Address: 2822 N.W. 19th St, Oklahoma City, OK 73107.

ERICKSON, JON DAVID, b. Manchester, Iowa, Oct. 13, 37; m. 63; c. 3. PHYSICS, NUCLEAR ENGINEERING. B.S.E, Michigan, 59, M.S.E, 62, Ph.D.(nuclear eng), 66. Site dir. & res. engr, Mt. Haleakala Observ, UNIV. MICH, Hawaii, 66-69, DIR. RES. & ANAL, INST. SCI. & TECH, 69- Mem. lidar safety comt, ad hoc lidar probing of atmosphere group, Nat. Center Atmospheric Res, 68-70; Atomic Energy Comn. fel. nuclear sci. & eng; Alfred P. Sloan nat. scholar. AAAS; Am. Phys. Soc; Am. Nuclear Soc. Multispectral remote sensing of environment; pattern recognition; lidar probing of the atmosphere; study of gases, liquids and solids by slow-neutron inelastic scattering; infrared and optical tracking of space objects. Address: 1753 McIntyre, Ann Arbor, MI 48105.

ERICKSON, KAREN LOUISE, b. Covington, Mich, Aug. 4, 39. ORGANIC CHEMISTRY. B.S, Siena Heights Col, 60; Gulf Oil Co. fel, 63-64; Ph.D. (org. chem), Purdue, 65. Nat. Insts. Health fel. ORG. CHEM, Cornell, 64-65; asst. prof, CLARK UNIV, 65-69, ASSOC. PROF, 69- Am. Chem. Soc. Structure and synthesis in natural products; rearrangement reactions. Address: Dept. of Chemistry, Clark University, Worcester, MA 01610.

ERICKSON, KENNETH A, Geog, see Suppl. I to 11th ed, Soc. & Behav. Vols.

ERICKSON, KENNETH N(EIL), b. Minneapolis, Minn, Oct. 1, 40; m. 65; c. 2. ELEMENTARY PARTICLE & SPACE PHYSICS. B.A, Augsburg Col, 62; M.S, Mich. State Univ, 64; NASA trainee, Colo. State Univ, 66-69, Ph.D. (physics), 70. Instr. PHYSICS, AUGSBURG COL, 64-65, ASSOC. PROF, 70- Assoc. prof, Univ. Minn, Minneapolis, 70- Am. Phys. Soc; Am. Geophys. Union. Cosmic rays; magnetospheric physics, particularly the behavior of 50-1000 kiloelectron volt electronics trapped in outer radiation belts of the earth. Address: Dept. of Physics, Augsburg College, Eighth St. at 21st Ave. S, Minneapolis, MN 55404.

ERICKSON, KENNETH W(ARNE), b. Dallas, Tex, Mar. 10, 15; m. 43. PHYSICS. B.A, Texas, 39, Ph.D.(physics), 50. Assoc. physicist, weapon res, degaussing, mines & torpedoes, Naval Ord. Lab, 41-46; staff mem. fel, Los Alamos Sci. Lab, 48-50; dept. mgr. weapons syst. anal. dept, Sandia Corp, 50-57; gen. mgr, Kaman Nuclear Div, Kaman Aircraft Corp, 57-68, PRES, KAMAN SCI. CORP, 68- Address: Kaman Sciences Corp, 1700 Garden of the Gods Rd, Colorado Springs, CO 80907.

ERICKSON, LAMBERT C(ORNELIUS), b. Goodridge, Minn, May 30, 10; m. 40; c. 1. WEED SCIENCE, AGRONOMY. B.S, Minnesota, 40, Ph.D.(agron), 59; M.S, Wyoming, 43. Asst. state seed analyst, Minn, 40-41; state seed analyst, Wyo, 41-45; assoc. agronomist, UNIV. IDAHO, 45-63, AGRONOMIST & PROF. AGRON, 63- Tech. adv, state dept. agr, Wyo, 42-45; mem, Columbia Basin Interagency Comt, 49-52; Fulbright fel, div. weed control, Norweg. Plant Protection Inst, 69-70. Am. Soc. Agron; Weed Sci. Soc. Am. Herbicide residues in soils and crops; herbicides and our environment. Address: Dept. of Plant Science, University of Idaho, Moscow, ID 83843.

ERICKSON, LARRY EUGENE, b. Wahoo, Nebr, Oct. 8, 38; m. 62. CHEMICAL ENGINEERING. B.S, Kansas State, 60, Nat. Defense Ed. Act fel, 60-63, Nat. Sci. Found. fel, 63-64, Ph.D.(chem. eng), 64. Instr. CHEM. ENG, KANS. STATE UNIV, 64-65, asst. prof, 65-68, ASSOC. PROF, 68- U.S. Pub. Health Serv. spec. res. fel, 67-68, career develop. award, 70- Assoc. Am. Inst. Chem. Eng; Am. Chem. Soc. Optimum process design; desalination; biochemical engineering; transport theory. Address: Dept. of Chemical Engineering, Kansas State University, Manhattan, KS 66502.

ERICKSON, LOUIS C(ARL), b. Wilmington, Calif, Feb. 13, 14; m. 41; c. 2. PLANT PHYSIOLOGY. A.B, Univ. Calif, Los Angeles, 37, M.A, 39; Ph.D. (bot), Univ. Calif, Berkeley, 46. Asst. plant physiologist, bur. plant indust, U.S. Dept. Agr, 43-45; plant physiologist, Thompson Hort. Chem. Corp, 46-48; asst. plant physiologist, citrus res. ctr. & agr. exp. sta, UNIV. CALIF, RIVERSIDE, 48-54, assoc. plant physiologist, 54-60, plant physiologist, 60-67, PROF. BOT, UNIV, 67- AAAS; Am. Soc. Hort. Sci; Am. Soc. Plant Physiol; Bot. Soc. Am; Japanese Soc. Plant Physiol. Citrus and avocado fruit development. Address: Dept. of Biochemistry, University of California, Riverside, CA 92502.

ERICKSON, LUTHER E, b. Pulaski, Wis, June 30, 33; m. 57; c. 2. PHYSICAL CHEMISTRY. B.A, St. Olaf Col, 55; Ph.D.(phys. chem), Wisconsin, 59. Asst. prof. CHEM, Dickinson Col, 59-62; GRINNELL COL, 62-63, assoc. prof, 64-69, PROF, 69- Petrol. Res. Fund faculty award, summers 61 & 62; Nat. Sci. Found. sci. faculty fel, Univ. N.C, 68-69. AAAS; Am. Chem. Soc. Nuclear magnetic resonance spectroscopy; complex ions and co-ordination compounds; conformational analysis of metal chelates. Address: Dept. of Chemistry, Grinnell College, Grinnell, IA 50112.

ERICKSON, LYNDEN E(DWIN), b. Ft. William, Ont, June 6, 38; m. 65; c. 2. PHYSICS. B.Sc, Queen's (Ont), 59; S.M, Chicago, 61, Ph.D.(physics), 66. RES. OFFICER PHYSICS, NAT. RES. COUN, 65- Am. Phys. Soc. Electron paramagnetic resonance absorption of lanthanides, actinides, organic molecules in null magnetic field; laser Q-switching theory and experiment; fluorescence of dyes in solution. Address: Radio & Electrical Engineering Division, National Research Council, Ottawa, Ont. K1A 0R8, Can.

ERICKSON, MARY M(ARILLA), b. Ripon, Wis, Sept. 2, 05. ZOOLOGY. A.B, Willamette, 27; M.A, California, 29, Ph.D.(zool), 35. Teacher, high sch, Oregon, 27-28; teaching fel. zool, California, 29-33, asst. mus. vert. zool, 34-35, res. assoc, 35-36; prof. biol, Willamette, 36-38; instr. sci, UNIV. CALIF, SANTA BARBARA, 39-43, asst. prof. ZOOL, 43-47, assoc. prof, 47-55, PROF, 55-, acting chmn. dept. biol. sci, 52-53, chmn, 54-59. AAAS; Am. Inst. Biol. Sci; N.Y. Acad. Sci; Cooper Ornith. Soc; Wilson Ornith. Soc; Ecol. Soc. Am; Am. Ornith. Union. Ornithology; life history studies; annual testis cycle of Zonotrichias; behavior. Address: 2270 Biological Sciences Unit 1, University of California, Santa Barbara, CA 93106.

ERICKSON, MAX P(ERRY), b. Salt Lake City, Utah, Aug. 18, 16; m. 38; c. 8. GEOLOGY, MINERALOGY. B.S, Utah, 38, M.S, 40; Stanford, 40-41, 45-46. Geologist, U.S. Geol. Surv, 41-45; asst. prof. MINERAL, UNIV. UTAH, 47-61, ASSOC. PROF, 61-, MINERALOGIST, ENG. STA, 46- Petrology of the Thomas Range, Utah; petrology; structural geology. Address: Dept. of Mineralogy, University of Utah, Salt Lake City, UT 84112.

ERICKSON, PORTER W, b. Minn, Jan. 22, 09; m. 44. ORGANIC CHEMISTRY. A.B, Concordia Col.(Moorhead, Minn), 47; Ph.D.(chem), Maryland, 52. CHEMIST & PROJ. ENGR. STRUCT. PLASTICS, U.S. NAVAL ORD. LAB, 51- U.S.N.R, 42-46, Res, 46. Am. Chem. Soc; Soc. Plastics Eng. Mechanism of etherification for carbinols; development of high strength plastic reinforcements through use of chemical finishes. Address: U.S. Naval Ordnance Lab, White Oak, Silver Spring, MD 20910.

ERICKSON, RALPH LEROY, b. Egan, S.Dak, May 17, 23; m. 47, 70; c. 4. GEOLOGY. B.A, Miami (Ohio), 47; M.S, Mich. State, 48; Ph.D.(geol), Minnesota, 51. Geologist, U.S. Geol. Surv, 51-55; v.pres. & chief geologist, Uranium Res. & Develop. Co, 55-58; Geologist, U.S. GEOL. SURV, 58-66, chief br. explor. res, 66-70, GEOLOGIST, 70- Meritorious serv. award, U.S. Geol. Surv, 70. U.S.A, 43-46, S/Sgt. Asn. Explor. Geochem; Soc. Econ. Geol; Geol. Soc. Am; Am. Inst. Mining, Metall. & Petrol. Eng. Geochemical methods, both field and laboratory, that will aid in the search for concealed ore deposits; geochemistry and petrology of alkalic igneous rocks. Address: U.S. Geological Survey, Bldg. 25, Federal Center, Denver, CO 80225.

ERICKSON, RALPH O, b. Duluth, Minn, Oct. 27, 14; m. 45; c. 2. BOTANY. B.A, Gustavus Adolphus Col, 35; summers, Michigan, 36, Minnesota, 37-38; M.S, Washington (St. Louis), 41, Ph.D.(bot), 44. Instr. biol, Gustavus Adolphus Col, 35-39; asst. bot, Washington (St. Louis), 40-41; asst. chemist, West. Cartridge Co, Ill, 42-44; instr. BOT, Rochester, 44-47; res. assoc, UNIV. PA, 47-49, assoc. prof, 49-54, PROF, 54-, CHMN. BIOL. GRAD. GROUP, 68-, acting chmn. dept. bot, 61-63. Guggenheim fel, 54-55. Bot. Soc. Am; Soc. Develop. Biol.(secy, 57-58, pres, 59); Am. Soc. Nat. Cell growth and differentiation in plants; natural variation in plants. Address: Dept. of Biology, University of Pennsylvania, Philadelphia, PA 19104.

ERICKSON, RANDALL L, b. Harris, Minn, Apr. 24, 39; m. 61; c. 1. PHYSICAL & POLYMER CHEMISTRY. B.A, Concordia Col.(Moorhead, Minn), 61; Ph.D.(phys. chem), N.Dak. State, 65. Res. chemist, textile fibers dept, E.I. du Pont de Nemours & Co, Va, 65-67; sr. res. chemist, adhesives, coatings & sealers div, 3M CO, 67-68, SUPVR. BLDG. SERV. & CLEANING PROD. DIV, 68- Am. Chem. Soc. Solvation of extracted metal complexes by organic solvents; physical chemistry of polymers-structure property relationships. Address: Bldg. Service & Cleaning Products Division, 3M Co, St. Paul, MN 55101.

ERICKSON, RAY C(HARLES), b. St. Peter, Minn, Jan. 30, 18; m. 53; c. 3. BIOLOGY, WILDLIFE ECOLOGY. A.B, Gustavus Adolphus Col, 41; M.S, Iowa State Col, 42, Ph.D.(econ. zool), 48. Collaborator, U.S. FISH & WILDLIFE SERV, 39-41, jr. biologist, Patuxent Res. Refuge, Md, 41, asst, Malheur Nat. Wildlife Refuge, 42, 46-47, refuge mgr, 48, wildlife mgt. biologist, 48-55, head, habitat improv. sect, wildlife refuges br, 55-58, res. staff specialist, wildlife res. div, 58-65, ASST. DIR. IN CHARGE ENDANGERED WILDLIFE RES. PROG, BUR. SPORT FISHERIES & WILDLIFE, PATUXENT WILDLIFE RES. CTR, 65- Distinguished serv. award, U.S. Dept. Interior, 68. U.S.N, 42-46, Lt(jg). Am. Ornith. Union; assoc. Wildlife Soc; Ecol. Soc. Am. Waterfowl and waterfowl habitat ecology and management studies; preservation of rare and endangered wildlife species; endangered wildlife research supervision. Address: Bureau of Sport Fisheries & Wildlife, Patuxent Wildlife Research Center, Laurel, MD 20810.

ERICKSON, RAYMOND C, b. Ironwood, Mich, Apr. 28, 29; m. 64; c. 2. MICROBIOLOGY. B.S, Mich. State, 51; M.S, Wisconsin, 57, Ph.D.(bact), 60. Sr. res. microbiologist, SQUIBB INST. MED. RES, 60-70, RES. FEL, 70- U.S.A, 52-54, Res, 54-62, 1st Lt. Am. Soc. Microbiol; Brit. Soc. Gen. Microbiol. Microbial fermentations and transformations; antibiotics; enzymology. Address: Squibb Institute for Medical Research, New Brunswick, NJ 08903.

ERICKSON, RAYMOND L(EROY), b. Fargo, N.Dak, Dec. 9, 23; m. 52; c. 3. ORGANIC CHEMISTRY. B.S, Mont. State Col, 47; M.S, Maryland, 50. Chemist, Merck & Co, Inc, 49-56; prod. & market develop, market res, KAY-FRIES CHEM. INC, 56-67, TECH. DIR, 67- U.S.N.R, 44-46. Am. Chem. Soc; fel. Am. Inst. Chem. Steroids; vitamins. Address: Kay-Fries Chemicals Inc, Stony Point, NY 10980.

ERICKSON, RICHARD A(MES), b. Bryant, S.Dak, Sept. 12, 23; m. 43; c. 4. PHYSICS. B.S, S.Dak. Sch. Mines & Tech, 44; fel, Oak Ridge Inst. Nuclear Studies, 49-51; Ph.D.(physics), Agr. & Mech. Col, Tex, 52. Asst. prof. PHYSICS, Tennessee, 51-53; OHIO STATE UNIV, 54-61, ASSOC. PROF, 61- U.S.N.R, 44-46. Neutron diffraction; low temperature physics. Address: Dept. of Physics, Ohio State University, 174 W. 18th Ave, Columbus, OH 43210.

ERICKSON, ROBERT E, b. Everett, Mass, June 14, 26; m. 51; c. 3. ORGANIC CHEMISTRY, BIOCHEMISTRY. B.S, Mass. Inst. Tech, 50, Ph.D. (chem), 56. Res. chemist, Merck & Co, Inc, 50-52, 56-66; sr. res. assoc, GIVAUDAN CORP, 66-70, ASSOC. DIR. RES, 70- U.S.N, 44-46. AAAS; Am. Chem. Soc. Chemistry of natural products; terpenes alkaloids from plants; molecular rearrangements. Address: Givaudan Corp, 125 Delawanna Ave, Clifton, NJ 07014.

ERICKSON, ROBERT JOSEPH, b. Chicago, Ill, Sept. 20, 41; m. 64; c. 2. MICROBIAL GENETICS. B.A, Wabash Col, 63; M.A, Wesleyan Univ, 65; U.S. Pub. Health Serv. grant & Ph.D.(microbial genetics), Rutgers Univ, 68. Fel. biol. & med. res, Argonne Nat. Lab, 68-70; RES. SCIENTIST GENETICS, MOLECULAR BIOL. LAB, MILES LABS, INC, 70- Fel. microbiol, Univ. Notre Dame, 70. AAAS; Genetics Soc. Am; Am. Soc. Microbiol. Mechanisms by which living cells react to the exposure to foreign DNA and how the cells can regulate the transcription of the foreign genetic information after uptake; somatic cell genetics. Address: 1116 Woodward Ave, Elkhart, IN 46514.

ERICKSON, R(OBERT) P(ORTER), b. South Bend, Ind, Feb. 13, 30; m. 58; c. 2. PHYSIOLOGICAL PSYCHOLOGY. B.S, Northwestern, 51; M.Sc, Brown, 56, Corrinna Borden Keen fel, 57-58, Ph.D.(psychol), 58. Res. assoc. psychol, Brown, 58-59, instr, 59; fel. physiol. & biophys, Univ. Wash, 59-61; asst. prof. PSYCHOL, DUKE UNIV, 61-65, ASSOC. PROF, 65- U.S.N, 51-54, Res, 54-59, Lt.(jg). Am. Physiol. Soc; Psychonomic Soc; Am. Psychol. Asn. Sensory systems and behavior processes. Address: Dept. of Psychology, Duke University, Durham, NC 27706.

ERICKSON, ROBERT W, b. McIntosh, Minn, Jan. 31, 29; m. 56; c. 8. FOREST PRODUCTS. B.S, Univ. Minn, St. Paul, 58, M.S, 63, Ph.D.(forest prod. eng), 66. Lab. technician wood drying, forest prod. lab, Univ. Calif, 58-61; asst. forest prod, COL. FORESTRY, UNIV. MINN, ST. PAUL, 61-62, instr. wood seasoning, 62-66, asst. prof. WOOD-FLUID RELS, 66-70, ASSOC. PROF, 70- Vis. wood scientist, Soc. Wood Sci. & Technol, N.C, 71; vis. seminarist, Can. Forest Prod. Labs, B.C, 70. U.S.A.F, 48-52, S/Sgt. Effect of surface tension upon the permeability of wood to distilled water; effects of pre-freezing upon the subsequent accelerated drying behavior of redwood and other collapse susceptible species; factors that influence the flexural creep behavior of wood during dehydration from the green condition. Address: 2215 Doswell Ave, St. Paul, MN 55108.

ERICKSON, ROLAND IRVIN, b. Benson, Minn, Nov. 8, 07; m. 63; c. 2. MINING ENGINEERING, GEOLOGY. E.M, Minnesota, Minneapolis, 30; M.S, North Dakota, 54. Engr, Chile, 30-32; asst. gen. supt. mining, Bolivian Tin & Tungston Corp, 36-38; geologist, U.S. Corps Army Engrs, Ark, 38-39; gen. mgr, supt. & chief engr, Cia Minera Unificada, Bolivia, 39-47; supt. mining, Cleveland Cliffs Iron Co, Minn, 48-51; chief engr, Reserve Mining Co, 51; prof. mining, North Dakota, 51-54; MINING CONSULT, 54-; PROF. MINING, UNIV. ORIENTE, VENEZUELA, 66-67 & 71- Consult, Liberia Mining Co, Butler Ore Co, Tex. Gulf Sulphur Co. & others, 51-; E.J. Longyear Co, Minn, 55-60; Pan. Am. Commodities, Peru, 56-63; West. Nuclear Corp, Colo, 58-61; consult, Big Horn Mining, Utah, 67-; prof. Univ. Alaska, 68-70. Nat. Soc. Prof. Eng; Am. Inst. Mining, Metall. & Petrol. Eng; Soc. Am. Mil. Eng. Mine planning and layout, including ore reserves, equipment selection, manpower, operating and capital cost. Address: Dept. of Mining Engineering, University of Oriente, Ciudad Bolívar, Venezuela.

ERICKSON, RONALD E, b. Peoria, Ill, Apr. 20, 33; m. 58; c. 2. ORGANIC CHEMISTRY. B.S, Bradley, 55; Ph.D.(org. chem), Iowa, 59. Welch fel, Texas, 58-59, Rosalie B. Hite fel, 61; NATO fel, Karlsruhe Tech, 60-61; asst. prof. CHEM, Canisius Col, 61-65; assoc. prof, UNIV. MONT, 65-70, PROF, 70- Am. Chem. Soc; The Chem. Soc; Soc. Ger. Chem. Organic mechanisms; organic chemistry of ozone; environmental education. Address: Dept. of Chemistry, University of Montana, Missoula, MT 59801.

ERICKSON, STANTON JOHN, b. Rockford, Ill, Jan. 14, 25; m. 49; c. 3. MICROBIOLOGY. B.S, Southern Methodist, 52, M.S, 53; Texas, 59-60. RES. BIOLOGIST, marine lab, Fla. Bd. Conserv, 63-65; NAT. MARINE WATER QUAL. LAB, Water Qual. Off, Environ. Protection Agency, 66- Med.C, U.S.A, 43-46, Sgt. Phycol. Soc. Am; Am. Soc. Limnol. & Oceanog; Int. Phycol. Soc; Marine Biol. Asn. U.K. Marine algal culture, nutrition and isolation; biological assays. Address: National Marine Water Quality Lab, P.O. Box 277, West Kingston, RI 02892.

ERICKSON, THEODORE C(HARLES), b. Alexandria, Minn, Sept. 23, 06; m. 46; c. 4. NEUROSURGERY, NEUROPHYSIOLOGY. B.S, Minnesota, 28, fel, 28-29, M.A, 29, M.D, 31; fel, McGill, 33-34, M.Sc, 34, Ph.D.(neurosurg), 39. Univ. Hosp, Pennsylvania, 31-33; res. surgeon, Montreal Neurol. Inst, McGill, 34-35, lectr. neurosurg, Univ, 39-41; assoc. prof. SURG, MED. SCH, UNIV. WIS, MADISON, 41-50, PROF, 50-, CHIEF NEUROSURG, UNIV. HOSPS, 50- AAAS; Soc. Neurol. Surg; Am. Neurol. Asn; Am. Acad. Neurol. Surg.(secy-treas, 42-47); Am. Med. Asn; Am. Asn. Neurol. Surg. Epilepsy; brain tumors; hypertension; cerebral localization. Address: Dept. of Surgery, University of Wisconsin School of Medicine, Madison, WI 53706.

ERICKSON, WALLACE A(LFRED), b. Chicago, Ill, Aug. 4, 11; m. 35; c. 5. CHEMISTRY. B.S, Chicago, 32, Ph.D.(chem), 36. Res. chemist, Jackson lab, E.I. du Pont de Nemours & Co, N.J, 35-39; PRES, WALLACE A. ERICKSON & CO, 40- Am. Chem. Soc; Am. Sci. Affiliation. Organic synthesis; high polymers; Diazo compounds; science-scripture correlation; cancer chemotherapeutic agents; carcinogens. Address: Wallace A. Erickson & Co, 842 N. Wells St, Chicago, IL 60610.

ERICKSON, WAYNE DOUGLAS, b. Lansing, Mich, Feb. 19, 32; m. 59; c. 1. CHEMICAL ENGINEERING. B.S, Mich. State, 54, M.S, 55; S.M, Mass. Inst. Tech, 58, Sc.D.(chem. eng), 62. Res. engr, LANGLEY RES. CTR, NASA, 58-59, head, thermal proj. sect, 59-64, res. engr, 64-65, head aerothermochem. br, 65-70, HEAD LIFE SUPPORT BR, 70- Mem. res. staff, phys. chem. dept, Cambridge, 70-71. U.S.A.F, 55-57, Res, 57-66, Capt. Combustion Inst. Chemical kinetics of high temperature systems; combustion research; thermodynamics; aerothermochemistry; chemical process systems; molecular computations. Address: 303 Hamrick Dr, Hampton, VA 23366.

ERICKSON, WILLIAM CLARENCE, b. Chicago, Ill, Nov. 21, 30; m. 52; c. 4. ASTRONOMY. B.A, Minnesota, 51, Nat. Sci. Found. fel, 53-55, M.A, 55, Ph.D.(physics), 56. Lectr. physics, Minnesota, 55-56; fel, Carnegie Inst, 56-57; sr. staff scientist, Convair Sci. Res. Lab. Div, Gen. Dynamic Corp, 57-62; Benelux Cross Antenna Proj, 62-63; assoc. prof. ASTRON, UNIV. MD, 63-68, PROF, 68- Mem, Int. Sci. Radio Union; Int. Astron. Union. Am. Astron. Soc; Royal Astron. Soc. Theory and observations in radio astronomy. Address: Dept. of Physics & Astronomy, University of Maryland, College Park, MD 20740.

ERICKSON, WILLIAM HARRY, b. McKeesport, Pa, Apr. 4, 16; m. 41; c. 2. ELECTRICAL ENGINEERING. B.S, Pittsburgh, 38; M.S, Carnegie Inst. Tech, 46. Jr. engr, Duquesne Light Co, Pa, 38-42; instr. ELEC. ENG, Naval Training Prog, CORNELL UNIV, 42-45, asst. prof, 45-47, assoc. prof, 47-53, PROF, 53-, ASSOC. DEAN COL. ENG, 65-, asst. dir. elec. eng, 59-65. Fel. Inst. Elec. & Electronics Eng. Address: Dept. of Electrical Engineering, Cornell University, Ithaca, NY 14850.

ERICKSON, W(ILLIAM) H(ENRY), b. Sault Ste. Marie, Ont, July 31, 33; m. 56; c. 2. PHYSICAL METALLURGY. B.Sc, Michigan Tech, 56, M.Sc, 60; Ph.D. (metall), Durham, 63. Phys. metallurgist, Can. Armament Res. & Develop. Estab, 56-58; instr. eng. mech, Michigan Tech, 59-60; res. assoc. metall, Durham, 60-63; res. off, reactor mat. br, chem. & metall. div, Atomic Energy Can, Ltd, 63-66; head mat. lab, Can. Armament Res. & Develop. Estab, 66-69, SECT. LEADER, mat. & mech. sect, 69-71, ORD. SECT, DEFENCE RES. ESTAB. VALCARTIER, 71- Cumulative damage in fatigue; ductile and brittle fracture; hydrogen solubility in metals; heavy metal technology; terminal ballistics. Address: Defence Research Establishment Valcartier, P.O. Box 880, Courcelette, Que, Can.

ERICSON, ALFRED (THEODORE), b. Quincy, Kans, Oct. 8, 28; m. 48; c. 2. BIOCHEMISTRY. B.S.Ed, Kans. State Teachers Col, 50; M.S, Kansas State, 53, Ph.D.(chem), 56. asst. instr. chem, Kansas State, 53-56; asst. prof. CHEM, KANS. STATE TEACHERS COL, 56-59, assoc. prof, 59-63, PROF, 63- AAAS; Am. Chem. Soc. Chemical education; tracer techniques; protein chemistry. Address: Dept. of Chemistry, Kansas State Teachers College, Emporia, KS 66801.

ERICSON, COREY WILLIAM, b. Bronx, N.Y, Oct. 14, 39; m. 62; c. 3. THEORETICAL & PHYSICAL CHEMISTRY. A.B, Franklin & Marshal Col, 61;

Ph.D.(chem), Delaware, 65. Res. chemist, TEXTILE FIBERS DEPT, SPUNBONDED TECH. DIV, E.I. DU PONT DE NEMOURS & CO, INC, 65-68, sr. res. chemist, 68-69, RES. SUPVR, 69-71, FIBER SURFACE RES. SECT, 71- Am. Chem. Soc. Statistical mechanics; polymer physics; fiber structure; nonwoven fabric structure and properties. Address: 304 King George Rd, Greenville, NC 27834.

ERICSON, DAVID B(ARNARD), b. New York, N.Y, July 19, 04. GEOLOGY. B.S, Mass. Inst. Tech, 31; M.S, Calif. Inst. Tech, 33. Engr, Metrop. Water Dist. South. Calif, 34-35; geologist, Barnsdall Oil Co, 36-37; Petrol. Grubu, Turkey, 38-40; instr. Ohio State, 42-43; asst. state geologist, Geol. Surv, Fla, 43-45; MARINE GEOLOGIST, Woods Hole Oceanog. Inst, 45-47; LAMONT-DOHERTY GEOL. OBSERV, 47- AAAS; Am. Geophys. Union; Glaciol. Soc. Marine sedimentation; turbidity currents; submarine canyons; planktonic Foraminifera; Pleistocene climates. Address: Lamont-Doherty Geological Observatory, Palisades, NY 10964.

ERICSON, DAVID M(ARTIN), JR, b. Dubois, Pa, Sept. 15, 32; m. 53; c. 3. NUCLEAR ENGINEERING. B.S, Pa. State, 55; M.S, Air Force Inst. Tech, 59; Ph.D.(nuclear eng), Michigan, 69. U.S. AIR FORCE, 55-, proj. engr. guided missiles, Hq. Tactical Air Command, 55-57, shift supvr, reactor oper, Nuclear Eng. Test Facility, 59-61, exec. off. res. & develop, aeronautical systs. div, Directorate Eng. Test, 61, proj. off. nuclear weapon effects, Spec. Weapons Ctr, 61-62, proj. engr. nuclear blast effects, Weapons Lab, 65-67, group leader x-ray effects, 67-69, ASST. PROF. NUCLEAR ENG, AIR FORCE INST. TECHNOL, 69-, DEP. HEAD DEPT. PHYSICS, 71- U.S.A.F, 55-, Lt. Col. Am. Nuclear Soc; Am. Soc. Eng. Educ. Scale effects in cavitating flows; shock wave generation and propagation in solids; material response. Address: Dept. of Physics, Air Force Institute of Technology, Wright Patterson Air Force Base, OH 45433.

ERICSON, HARTLEY C, b. Chicago, Ill, June 16, 27; m. 54; c. 2. ORGANIC CHEMISTRY. B.S, Illinois, 49; M.S, Northwestern, 53. Asst, Northwestern, 49-53; instr. chem, eve. sch, N.Park Col, 53-61; develop. chemist, ABBOTT LABS, 53-61, sci. rels, 61-62, mgr. govt. registration dept, 62-68, DIR. CORP. REGULATORY OPERS, 68- Researcher, Marine Biol. Labs, Mass, 52. Sci. Achievement award, Abbott Labs, 65. Am. Chem. Soc. Study of phosphagens in annelids; use of fluotitanates in dental impression materials. Address: Abbott Labs, North Chicago, IL 60064.

ERICSON, JOHN E(DWARD), b. Glenwood Springs, Colo, Apr. 1, 34; m. 54; c. 5. GENETICS, BOTANY. B.S, Colorado State, 56; Nat. Defense Ed. Act fel, Montana State, 63-66, Ph.D.(genetics), 68. ASSOC. PROF. BIOL, ANGELO STATE UNIV, 66- AAAS; Am. Genetic Asn. Biosystematics of the genus Agropyron; taxonomy of stone pines. Address: Dept. of Biology, Angelo State University, San Angelo, TX 76901.

ERICSON, ROBERT PAUL, b. Kearny, N.J, Oct. 25, 20; m. 44; c. 2. CHEMISTRY. B.S, Union Col, 42; Iowa State Col, 44-46; M.S, Stevens Inst. Tech, 50. Chemist, Pittsburgh Plate Glass Co, 41-42; instr. physics, Carnegie Inst. Tech, 43-44; chemist, Pittsburgh Plate Glass Co, 46-59, Springdale Res. & Develop. Ctr, 59-71, DIR. MKT. SERV, CHEM. DIV, PPG INDUSTS, 71- Civilian with Manhattan Proj, 44, U.S.A, 44-46. Am. Chem. Soc. Methods of producing pure, lesser known metals; rare earth metals; paint vehicles. Address: Marketing Service, Chemical Division, PPG Industries, 1 Gateway Center, Pittsburgh, PA 15222.

ERICSON, WILLIAM, b. N.Y.C, Dec. 30, 24; m. 52; c. 1. PHYSICS. B.S, Colorado, 49; M.S, N.Y. Univ, 52, Ph.D.(physics), 58. Instr. physics, City Col. New York, 52-53; asst. prof, State Univ. N.Y. Maritime Col, 53-57; res. scientist, RES. DEPT, GRUMMAN AIRCRAFT ENG. CORP, 57-63, STAFF SCIENTIST & GROUP HEAD, 63- Lectr, Adelphi, 62- U.S.A, 43-46. Am. Phys. Soc. Magnetohydrodynamics; plasma physics. Address: 25 Winding Lane, Levittown, NY 11756.

ERICSSON, RONALD J, b. Belle Fourche, S.Dak, July 17, 35; m. 56; c. 2. REPRODUCTIVE PHYSIOLOGY, ENDOCRINOLOGY. B.S, Colorado State, 57; M.S, Kentucky, 61; Ph.D.(reprod. physiol), 64. Res. asst. reprod. physiol, Kentucky, 60-63; trainee endocrinol, Wisconsin, 63-64; SR. RES. SCIENTIST MALE REPROD, UPJOHN CO, 64- Lectr, West. Mich. Univ, 64-66, adj. assoc. prof, 68- Qm.C, 58, Res, 58-65, Capt. AAAS; Asn. Study Animal Behav; Endocrine Soc; Int. Soc. Res. Reproduction; Soc. Exp. Biol. & Med; Brit. Soc. Study Fertil; Soc. Study Reproduction. Human male contraception; chemosterilants for pest control; spermatogenesis and sperm fertility; separation of x and y sperm. Address: Fertility Research, Upjohn Co, 301 Henrietta St, Kalamazoo, MI 49001.

ERIKS, KLAAS, b. Alkmaar, Netherlands, June 16, 22; nat; m. 49; c. 3. PHYSICAL CHEMISTRY. Chem. Cand, Amsterdam, 43, Chem. Drs, 48, fel. & Ph.D.(chem), 52. Res. assoc. physics, Pa. State, 52-53; fel. CHEM, Minnesota, 53-54; asst. prof, BOSTON UNIV, 54-58, assoc. prof, 58-65, PROF, 65- Fulbright res. scholar, Copenhagen, 63-64; mem. dent. training comt, Nat. Inst. Dent. Res, 65-69; vis. res. scholar, Netherlands Reactor Ctr, Petten, 71-72; mem, Nat. Comt. on Crystallog. Am. Chem. Soc; Am. Crystallog. Asn; Royal Netherlands Chem. Soc. X-ray structure determination in fields of heteropoly salts; carbonium ions; transition metal ion complexes, especially with amino acids; organic and inorganic sulphates, phosphates and fluorides. Address: Dept. of Chemistry, Boston University, Boston, MA 02215.

ERIKSEN, CLYDE H(EDMAN), b. Santa Barbara, Calif, May 1, 33; m. 58; c. 2. PHYSIOLOGICAL ECOLOGY, LIMNOLOGY. B.A, California, Santa Barbara, 55; fel, Illinois, 55-57, M.S, 56; fel, Michigan, 57-60, Ph.D.(zool), 61. Instr. biol, exten. serv, California, 54-55, teaching fel, 57; field res. asst. limnol, Great Lakes Res. Inst, 57; field specialist, Nat. Sanit. Found, 58-59; asst. prof. zool, Los Angeles State Col, 60-63, Nat. Sci. Found. Inst. Biol. Sci, 61; asst. prof. ZOOL, Univ. Toronto, 63-66, ASSOC. PROF, 66-67; CLAREMONT COLS, 67-, CHMN. JOINT SCI. DEPT, 69- Consult, Allen Hancock Found, Univ. South. Calif, 61-63. Outstanding Educators Am. Award, 70. Entom. Soc. Am; Ecol. Soc. Am; Am. Soc. Limnol. & Oceanog; Int. Asn. Theoret. & Appl. Limnol; Can. Soc. Zool. Physiological ecology of aquatic invertebrates; western limnology. Address: Joint Science Dept, Baxter Science Lab, Claremont Colleges, Claremont, CA 91711.

ERIKSEN, L(EONARD) H(ENRY), b. Jersey City, N.J, Nov. 27, 13; m. 45; c. 1. ORGANIC CHEMISTRY. A.B, Gettysburg Col, 36, M.A, 37. Chemist, PICATINNY ARSENAL, DOVER, 42-57, DIR. explosives & propellants lab, 57-63, RES. LABS, 63- Am. Chem. Soc. Chemistry and physics of military explosives and rocket propellants. Address: 15 Hanover Rd, Mountain Lakes, NJ 07046.

ERIKSEN, NILS, b. Seattle, Wash, Sept. 11, 15; m. 47; c. 2. BIOCHEMISTRY. B.S, Washington (Seattle), 39, Ph.D.(chem), 44. Asst. toxicol, sch. med. & dent, Rochester, 44-45; mycol, Johns Hopkins Hosp, 46-47; Scripps Metab. Clin, 47-48; biochemist, field serv, Nat. Cancer Inst, 48-52; asst. prof. PATH, SCH. MED, UNIV. WASH, 52-57, CHEMIST, 57- AAAS; Am. Chem. Soc. Toxicology of fluorine and hydrogen fluoride; immunochemistry of pathogenic fungi; evaluation of cancer diagnostic tests; analysis of human serum proteins; chemistry of biological amines; characterization of abnormal tissue proteins. Address: Dept. of Pathology, University of Washington School of Medicine, Seattle, WA 98195.

ERIKSEN, STUART P, b. San Francisco, Calif, Nov. 13, 30; m. 55; c. 3. PHARMACEUTICAL CHEMISTRY. B.Sc, California, 52, M.Sc, 54, Ph.D. (pharmaceut. chem), 56. Sr. res. pharmacist, Smith, Kline & French Labs, 55-60; assoc. prof. pharm, Univ. Wis, Madison, 60-65; dir. med. res, ALLERGAN PHARMACEUT, 65-70, DIR. RES. OPERS, 70- Instr, Hahnemann Med. Col, 58-60; vis. lectr, sch. pharm, Temple Univ, 59-60. Med.C, U.S.A.R, Capt. AAAS; Am. Chem. Soc; Am. Pharmaceut. Asn. Physical pharmacy; drug molecules in solution; rheology; drug degradation; lipid chemistry. Address: Pharmaceutical Development Lab, Allergan Pharmaceuticals, 18600 Von Karman Ave, Irvine, CA 92664.

ERIKSEN, WARREN T(HORLEIF), b. Newport News, Va, Aug. 12, 23; m. 50. PHYSICAL CHEMISTRY. B.S, Florida, 48, Ph.D.(chem), 52. Asst, Florida, 50-52; res. chemist, Carbide & Carbon Chem. Co, 52-54; mem. res. staff, Raytheon Co, 55-59, mgr. adv. eng, Raytheon Semiconductor Div, 59-62; tech. dir, Hoffman Semiconductor Div, 62-63, v.pres. & gen. mgr, 64-65, chief engr, gen. prod. dept, Tex. Instruments Inc, 65-67, dept. mgr, 67-70, PLANT MGR, TEX. INSTRUMENTS LTD, 70- U.S.A, 43-46. Am. Chem. Soc; Electrochem. Soc; Am. Inst. Physics; sr. mem. Inst. Elec. & Electronics Eng; Am. Phys. Soc. Thermodynamic measurements; high polymer physics; solution properties; semiconductor surface physics; electroluminescence; semiconductor device development. Address: Texas Instruments Ltd, Manton Lane, Bedford, Eng.

ERIKSON, G(EORGE) E(MIL), b. Palmer, Mass, May 3, 20; m. 50; c. 4. ANATOMY. B.S, Mass. State Col, 41; Sheldon traveling fel, 46; M.A, Harvard, 46, Wyman scholar, 46-47, Ph.D.(biol), 48. Teaching fel. biol, Harvard, 42-46, reader hist. sci. & learning, 43-45, asst. prof. gen. ed. biol, 49-52, teaching fel. anat, Harvard Med. Sch, 45-47, instr, 47-49, res. fel, 49-52, assoc, 52-55, asst. prof, 55-65, assoc. curator, Warren Anat. Mus, 61-65; PROF. MED. SCI, BROWN UNIV, 65- Austin teaching fel, 44-45; Guggenheim fel, 49; consult. med. & pub. health, Rockefeller Found, 59; state dept. specialist, Brazil, 62; anatomist, dept. surg, R.I. Hosp, 65- AAAS; Am. Soc. Zool; Am. Asn. Anat; Am. Asn. Hist. Med; Am. Soc. Mammal; Hist. Sci. Soc; Am. Asn. Phys. Anthrop. Comparative biology of new world primates. Address: Division of Biological & Medical Sciences, Morphology Section, Brown University, Box G, Providence, RI 02912.

ERIKSON, J. ALDEN, b. Milwaukee, Wis, Mar. 3, 26; m. 55; c. 3. ORGANIC CHEMISTRY. B.S, Wisconsin, 50; Ph.D.(chem), Mass. Inst. Technol, 53. Chemist, paint & brush div, Pittsburgh Plate Glass Co, 53-59, sr. res. chemist, coatings & resins div, 59-68, PROJ. LEADER, PPG INDUSTS, INC, 68- U.S.A, 44-46, T/Sgt. Am. Chem. Soc. Alkyds; melamine and urea formaldehyde resins; thermosetting free radically polymerised copolymers; oil free polyesters; polyurethanes; silicone modified resins. Address: 4212 E. Ewalt Rd, Gibsonia, PA 15044.

ERIKSON, JAY ARTHUR, b. Seattle, Wash, May 2, 22; m. 55; c. 3. PHYSICAL CHEMISTRY. B.S, Univ. Wash, 48, M.S, 49, Procter & Gamble fel, 50, Ph.D.(phys. chem), 54. Instr. petrol. ref. eng, Colo. Sch. Mines, 54-55; chemist, agr. div, Shell Develop. Co, 55-61; Santa Barbara Res. Ctr, 61-63; U.S. Polymeric Div, HITCO, 64-67, MAT. & PROCESS ENGR, AUTONETICS, N.AM. ROCKWELL CORP, 67- U.S.A, 43-45. Am. Chem. Soc; Soc. Aerospace Mat. & Process Eng. Reaction kinetics of pesticide decompositions and lead sulfide film depositions; surface treatments of carbon fibers and powders. Address: 13501 Flint Dr, Santa Ana, CA 92705.

ERIKSON, JOHN MARTIN, b. Ypsilanti, Mich, Nov. 30, 39; m. 62; c. 2. ORGANIC CHEMISTRY. B.A, Oberlin Col, 61; Ph.D.(org. chem), Stanford, 65; Wisconsin, 65-66. ASST. PROF. CHEM, WABASH COL, 66- Am. Chem. Soc. Structure elucidation of furan oxidation products; metallation of furan compounds. Address: Dept. of Chemistry, Wabash College, Crawfordsville, IN 47933.

ERIKSON, LLOYD B(ERNHARDT), b. Chicago, Ill, Jan. 12, 26; m. 53; c. 2. ANATOMY. B.A, Rochester, 49; B.A, Oxford, 52, M.A, 56; Ph.D.(anat), Illinois, 59. Asst. anat, Illinois, 56-58; instr, British Columbia, 58-60; asst. prof, faculty med, UNIV. ALTA, 60-67, ASSOC. RES, SURG-MED. RES. UNIT, 67- U.S.N, 44-46. Am. Asn. Anat. Primate reproductive physiology. Address: Surgical-Medical Rescarch Unit, University of Alberta, Edmonton, Alta, Can.

ERIKSON, R(AYMOND) L(EO), b. Eagle, Wis, Jan. 24, 36; m. 58. MOLECULAR BIOLOGY. B.S, Wisconsin, 58, M.S, 61, Ph.D.(molecular biol), 63. U.S. Pub. Health Serv. fel, SCH. MED, UNIV. COLO, DENVER, 63-65, asst. prof. PATH, 65-69, ASSOC. PROF, 69- U.S.A.R, 57-63. Nucleic acids. Address: Dept. of Pathology, University of Colorado School of Medicine, 4200 E. Ninth Ave, Denver, CO 80220.

ERINGEN, A(HMED) CEMAL, b. Kayseri, Turkey, Feb. 15, 21; m. 49; c. 4. APPLIED MECHANICS. M.S, Adv. Eng. Sch. Istanbul, 43; fel, Polytech. Inst. Brooklyn, 47-48, Ph.D.(appl. mech), 48. Res. engr, Turkish Aircraft Co, 43-44; int. trainee, Glenn L. Martin Co, 44-45; group head fuselage sect. & head struct. sect, Turkish Air League Co, 45-47; res. asst. prof. mech, Ill. Inst. Tech, 48-50, res. assoc. prof, 50-53; assoc. prof. eng. mech, Purdue, 53-55, prof. eng. sci, 55-66; PROF. AEROSPACE & MECH. SCI. & CHMN. SOLID MECH. PROG, PRINCETON, 66- Consult, Armour Res. Found, 48-50; Gen. Motors; Picatinny Arsenal; Gen. Tech. Corp. Am. Math. Soc; Soc. Eng. Sci.(pres. & ed-in-chief, Int. J. Eng. Sci, 63-). Elasticity; plate and shell theory; theory of nonlinear oscillations; stress waves; molecular theory of gases and liquids; continuum physics; nonlinear theory of electromagnetic elastic solids; microelasticity; microfluids; theory of chemically reacting media; liquid crystals; micromagnetism. Address: Dept. of Aerospace & Mechanical Sciences, D-329 Engineering Quadrangle, Princeton University, Princeton, NJ 08540.

ERK, FRANK C(HRIS), b. Evansville, Ind, Dec. 17, 24; m. 48; c. 3. GENETICS. A.B, Evansville Col, 48; Bruce fel, Hopkins, 51-52, Ph.D.(genetics), 52. Jr. instr. biol, Hopkins, 48-51; assoc. prof. & head dept, Washington Col, 52-57; prof. natural sci, STATE UNIV. N.Y. STONY BROOK, 57-61, PROF. BIOL. SCI, 62-, chmn. dept, 62-67, dept. biol, 58-61, div. sci. & math, 59-60. Vis. assoc. prof, Univ. Chicago, 54-55; vis. investr, poultry res. centre, Agr. Res. Coun, Scotland, 64-65; Genetics Inst, Milan, 65; Masonic Med. Res. Lab, 68-71; Univ. Sussex, 71-72. Consult, Biol. Sci. Curriculum Study, 60-70; examiner advan. placement biol, Col. Entrance Exam. Bd, 67-71. U.S.A.A.F, 43-46, 1st Lt. AAAS; Genetics Soc. Am; Am. Genetic Asn; Soc. Study Evolution; Nat. Asn. Biol. Teachers; Genetics Soc. Can. Developmental genetics; melanotic tumors, chromosomal aberrations; population genetics of Drosophila; nutrition; aging. Address: Division of Biological Sciences, State University of New York at Stony Brook, Stony Brook, NY 11790.

ERKILETIAN, D(ICKRAN) H(AGOP), JR, b. Mayfield, Ky, Sept. 22, 13; m. 40; c. 3. MATHEMATICS. A.B, West. Ky. State Col, 36; A.M, Illinois, 38. Asst. MATH, Illinois, 40-41; instr, Fenn Col, 41-42; UNIV. MO-ROLLA, 42-46, asst. prof, 46-54, assoc. prof, 54-59, PROF, 59-, prof-in-charge freshman-sophomore math, 65-67, acting chmn. dept, 62-63, chmn, 63-64. Asst, Kansas, 46-47. Am. Math. Soc; Am. Soc. Eng. Educ; Math. Asn. Am. Differential equations. Address: 8 Summit Dr, Rolla, MO 65401.

ERKKILA, A(RMAS) VICTOR, b. Fitchburg, Mass, July 24, 13; m. 38; c. 6. ORGANIC & PHYSICAL CHEMISTRY. B.S, Middlebury Col, 34; fel. & D.Sc.(chem), Stuttgart Tech, 35. Chemist, res. & develop. dept, Nat. Aniline Div, Allied Chem. Corp, 35-54, supvr. patents & library div, 55-66, dir. patent & library serv, indust. chem. div, 66-68, mgr. patents & licensing, specialty chem. div, 68-70; PATENT ADV, PICATINNY ARSENAL, U.S. GOVT, 70- Am. Chem. Soc. Colloids, colloidal electrolytes: patent liaison and prosecution service; scientific information service. Address: 20 Butterworth Dr, Morristown, NJ 07960.

ERKKILA, LEO F, b. Butte, Mont, Apr. 4, 10; m. 42; c. 2. FISHERIES BIOLOGY. B.S, Washington (Seattle), 34. Biol. aid, U.S. Bur. Fisheries, 34, fishery researcher, Calif. Div. Fish & Game, 35-36; Steinhart Aquarium, Calif. Acad. Sci, 37-38; jr. aquatic biologist, U.S. Bur. Reclamation, Dept. Interior, 39-40; U.S. Corps Engrs, 40-41; asst. aquatic biologist, U.S. FISH & WILDLIFE SERV, 41-42, fishery res. biologist, 45-61, ASST. LAB. DIR, U.S. BUR. COMMERCIAL FISHERIES, 62- U.S.N.R, 42-45, Lt. Comdr. Am. Fisheries Soc; Am. Inst. Fishery Res. Biol. Great Lakes fisheries; sea lamprey control; effects of water use projects on migratory fish. Address: Bureau of Commercial Fisheries, U.S. Fish & Wildlife Service, P.O. Box 640, Ann Arbor, MI 48106.

ERKMAN, JOHN O(RIN), b. Enfield, Ill, Feb. 26, 22; m. 44; c. 2. PHYSICS. B.S, Southern Illinois, 46; M.S, Illinois, 47. Physicist, Gen. Elec. Co, 50-54; Stanford Res. Inst, 54-67; SUPVRY. RES. PHYSICIST, U.S. NAVAL ORD. LAB, 67- Sig.C, U.S.A, 43-45. Am. Phys. Soc. Sensitivity and detonability of explosives and propellants; measurement of reaction time in detonations and detonation parameters; propagation and attenuation of shock waves in solids. Address: U.S. Naval Ordnance Lab, Silver Spring, MD 20910.

ERLANDER, STIG R(OBERT), b. Minneapolis, Minn, May 24, 28; m. 52; c. 3. BIOPHYSICAL CHEMISTRY. B.A, Minnesota, 51; Drexel Inst, 51-52; Ph.D. (biochem), Iowa State, 56; Purdue, 57-59. Asst, Iowa State, 53-56; chemist, north. regional lab, north. utilization res. & develop. div, U.S. Dept. Agr, 59-61, prin. chemist, 61-66; prof. chem. & nutrit, AMBASSADOR COL, 66-69, PROF. CHEM. & BIOL. SCI. & HEAD DEPT. CHEM, 69- Nat. Insts. Health res. fel, Purdue, 57-59. U.S.N, 46-48, 51-52. AAAS; Am. Chem. Soc; Am. Inst. Chem; Am. Asn. Cereal Chem. Formation of atherosclerosis and diabetes mellitus; physical properties of proteins and starch; mechanisms by which starch is synthesized; ultracentrifuge theory; helical structure of DNA and RNA—in opposition to the Watson-Crick model. Address: Dept. of Chemistry, Ambassador College, 300 W. Green St, Pasadena, CA 91105.

ERLANDSEN, STANLEY L, b. Chicago, Ill, May 21, 41; m. 62; c. 3. ANATOMY, ELECTRON MICROSCOPY. B.S, Dana Col, 63; Ph.D.(anat), Univ. Minn, Minneapolis, 67. U.S. Pub. Health Serv. sr. fel. electron micros, Univ. Wash, 67-69; ASST. PROF. ANAT, UNIV. IOWA, 69- Am. Asn. Anat; Am. Soc. Cell Biol. Ultrastructure of intestinal microorganisms and their interaction with intestinal mucosa; fine structure and function of the Paneth cell; organ culture of fetal rat pancreas. Address: Dept. of Anatomy, University of Iowa, Iowa City, IA 52240.

ERLANDSON, ARVID L(EONARD), b. Norway, Mich, Sept. 26, 29; m. 55; c. 4. BACTERIOLOGY. B.S, Michigan, 51, M.S, 52, Ph.D, 54. City bacteriologist, Ann Arbor Health Dept, 51-53; asst. bact, Michigan, 53-54; res. bacteriologist, U.S. Naval Med. Res. Inst, 54-58; Parke, Davis & Co, 58-64; asst. prof. microbiol. & immunol, sch. med, Marquette Univ, 64-71; DIR. MICROBIOL. RES, BRONSON METHODIST HOSP, KALAMAZOO, MICH, 71- Med.Serv.C, 54-58, Lt. Am. Soc. Microbiol. Bacterial physiology; bacillary dysentery; experimental pyelonephritis; pathogenesis of experimental infections; host resistance mechanisms. Address: Bronson Methodist Hospital, 252 E. Lovell St, Kalamazoo, MI 49006.

ERLANDSON, PAUL M(cKILLOP), b. Washington, D.C, Oct. 27, 20; m. 41; c. 5. ENGINEERING PHYSICS. B.S, Mass. Inst. Tech, 41; M.A, Texas, 49, Ph.D.(physics), 50. Test design engr. radio mfg, Crosley Corp, 37-39; cost control engr, electronics mfg, Radio Corp. Am, 41-42; res. physicist, defense res. lab, Texas, 46-50; chmn. dept. physics, Southwest Res. Inst, 50-56, asst. v.pres, 55-56; DIR. res. physics, Continental Can Co, Inc, 56-59; res, Schlumberger Well Surv. Corp, 59-61; eng. res, CONTINENTAL CAN CO, INC, 61-67, CORP. RES, 67- U.S.N.R, 42-46. Lt. Am. Phys. Soc; Sci. Res. Soc. Am; Acoustical Soc. Am; Instrument Soc. Am; Inst. Elec. & Electronics Eng; Am. Soc. Mech. Eng. Information systems; high energy rate metalworking; energy conversion devices; instrumentation and physical measurements; industrial inspection systems; welding methods; research management; packaging systems. Address: 12345 S. 88th Ave, Palos Park, IL 60464.

ERLANGER, BERNARD F(ERDINAND), b. N.Y.C, July 13, 23; m. 46; c. 3. BIOCHEMISTRY. B.S, City Col. New York, 43; M.S, N.Y. Univ, 49; Ph.D. (biochem), Columbia Univ, 51. Assoc. biochem, COLUMBIA UNIV, 51-52, assoc. MICROBIOL, 52-55, asst. prof, 55-59, assoc. prof, 59-66, PROF, 66-Vis. scientist, Istituto Superiore di Sanita, Rome, 61-62; mem. comt. Fulbright-Hays Acts Awards, Nat. Acad. Sci, 66-72; Fulbright scholar, Univ. Repub, Uruguay, 67; Guggenheim fel, Inst. Biophys. & Biochem, Paris, 69-70. U.S.A, 44-46. AAAS; Am. Chem. Soc; Am. Soc. Biol. Chem. Protein chemistry; peptide synthesis and enzymology; immunochemistry of nucleic acids. Address: Dept. of Microbiology, Columbia University, 630 W. 168th St, New York, NY 10032.

ERLBACH, ERICH, b. Wuerzburg, Germany, Dec. 17, 33; U.S. citizen; m. 57; c. 3. PHYSICS. A.B, Columbia, 55, A.M, 57, Ph.D.(physics), 60. Asst. physics, Columbia Col, 55-57; Watson Lab, Int. Bus. Mach, 57-60, physicist, res. center, 60-62; asst. prof. PHYSICS, CITY COL. NEW YORK, 62-66, ASSOC. PROF, 66- Mem. staff, Nevis Cyclotron Labs, summer 55; Bettis Plant, Westinghouse Elec. Corp, summer 56; lectr, City Col. New York, 57-59; Nat. Sci. Found. res. partic, Univ. Md, 68-69. AAAS; Am. Phys. Soc. Cryogenics, especially superconductivity; solid state physics, particularly semiconductors and metals. Address: Dept. of Physics, City College of New York, 139th St. & Convent Ave, New York, NY 10031.

ERLEBACH, WOODLAND (EUSTACE), b. Vancouver, B.C, Feb. 23, 22; m. 45; c. 1. ENVIRONMENTAL SCIENCES. B.A.Sc, British Columbia, 51, M.A.Sc, 53; Athlone fel. & Ph.D.(radiation chem), Cambridge, 57. Asst. res. off. radioactive waste disposal, Atomic Energy Can, Ltd, 55-59, chemist IV radioisotope develop, commercial prod, 59-64; sr. res. scientist neutron activation studies, Isotopes, Inc, 64-65, asst. tech. dir, N.J, 65-66; dir. develop. & prod. dept, Hazleton Nuclear Sci. Corp, Calif, 66-67; sr. sci. adv, Isotopes, Inc, N.J, 67-68; mgr. sci. serv. & environ. sci. isotopes, Teledyne Co, 68-71; INTERAGENCY TECH. COORD, WATER QUAL. SERV, ONT. WATER RESOURCES COMN, 71- Can. Army, 39-45. Am. Soc. Test. & Mat. Environmental radioactivity, water and air quality. Address: 39 La Rush Dr, Weston, Ont, Can.

ERLENMEYER-KIMLING, L, b. Princeton, N.J, Apr. 18, 32; m. 51. PSYCHOLOGY. B.S, Columbia, 57, scholar, 57-58, Ph.D.(psychol), 61. Asst. behavior genetics & lectr. psychol, Columbia, 58-60; res. scientist MED. GENETICS, N.Y. STATE PSYCHIAT. INST, 60-62; sr. res. scientist, 62-69, ASSOC. RES. SCIENTIST, 69- Asst, col. physicians & surgeons, Columbia Univ, 62-66, res. assoc, 66-69, asst. prof, 69-; Genetics Soc. Am. travel grant, Int. Cong. Genetics, Netherlands, 63. AAAS; Am. Psychol. Asn; Am. Eugenics Soc; Am. Soc. Human Genetics; Am. Psychopath. Asn; Animal Behav. Soc; Genetics Soc. Am; Soc. Neurosci; Am. Soc. Nat; Am. Inst. Biol. Sci. Experimental behavior genetics; medical and psychiatric genetics; population-genetic and demographic aspects of schizophrenia. Address: Dept. of Medical Genetics, New York State Psychiatric Institute, 722 W. 168th St, New York, NY 10032.

ERLICH, V(ICTOR) L(EOPOLD), b. Vienna, Austria, March 24, 88; nat; m. 23. PHYSICAL CHEMISTRY. Chem.E, Inst. Tech, Austria, 10, D.Tech. Sci, 11. Chief chemist, Nitrogen Works, Inc, Austria & Jugoslavia, 11-28; tech. mgr, Soc. Fould Springer, France, 30-38; Soc. Vernis de Bonneuil, 38-40; DIR. RES. & V.PRES, Reeves Plastics, Inc, 50-, REEVES BROS, INC, 58- Consult. N.Y, 42- Am. Chem. Soc; Soc. Plastics Eng; Am. Asn. Textile Technol; Am. Asn. Textile Chem. & Colorists; N.Y. Acad. Sci; Fiber Soc. Polymer chemistry, natural and synthetics; polyolefins and their processing to fibers; synthetic nitrogen compounds, cyanamid; proteolytic and amylolytic enzyme reactions on agricultural products. Address: 890 Park Ave, New York, NY 10021.

ERLICHSON, HERMAN, b. Brooklyn, N.Y, Mar. 22, 31; m; c. 3. PHYSICS. B.S, City Col. New York, 53; A.M, Harvard, 54; M.A, Columbia, 61, Ph.D. (philos), 68. Res. & develop. engr, Bell Aircraft Corp, 53; res, develop. & sales engr, Gen. Elec. Co, 54-56; res. & develop. engr, Kollsman Instrument Corp, 56-60; from asst. prof. to PROF. PHYSICS, STATEN ISLAND COMMUNITY COL, 60- Philos. Sci. Asn; Am. Asn. Physics Teachers. Quantum mechanics; philosophy of physics. Address: Dept. of Physics & Geology, Staten Island Community College, 715 Ocean Terr, Staten Island, NY 10301.

ERMAN, DON C(OUTRE), b. Richmond, Ind, Mar. 7, 40; m. 65. AQUATIC ECOLOGY, FISHERIES. A.B, DePauw Univ, 62; Univ. Durham, 62-63; M.S, Purdue Univ, 65; Ph.D.(fisheries, aquatic ecol), Utah State Univ, 69. ASST. PROF. FISHERIES & AQUATIC ECOL, UNIV. CALIF, BERKELEY, 69-Am. Fisheries Soc; Ecol. Soc. Am; Am. Inst. Biol. Sci. Freshwater benthic invertebrate communities; community ordination; secondary production; bog production. Address: School of Forestry & Conservation, University of California, Berkeley, CA 94720.

ERMAN, JAMES E(DWIN), b. Lodi, Calif, Dec. 16, 40; m. 71. PHYSICAL BIOCHEMISTRY. B.S, Univ. Calif, Berkeley, 62; Ph.D.(phys. chem), Mass. Inst. Technol, 66. Res. chemist, Chevron Res. Co, 66-68; fel, Johnson Res.

Found, Univ. Pa, 68-70; ASST. PROF. CHEM, NORTH. ILL. UNIV, 70-Am. Chem. Soc. Enzyme catalyzed oxidation-reduction reactions; rapid reaction techniques. Address: Dept. of Chemistry, Northern Illinois University, DeKalb, IL 60115.

ERMAN, WILLIAM F, b. Butler, Mo, May 22, 31; m. 60; c. 4. ORGANIC CHEMISTRY. B.S, Univ. Notre Dame, 53; Union Carbide Corp. fel, Mass. Inst. Technol, 55-56, Ph.D.(org. chem), 57. Res. chemist & group leader natural prod. chem, PROCTER & GAMBLE CO, 57-66, SECT. HEAD NATURAL PROD. CHEM, 66- Lectr, Xavier Univ.(Ohio), 63. AAAS; Am. Chem. Soc; Am. Inst. Chem. Natural products chemistry, particularly isolation, structure determination, reactions and synthesis of mono- and sesquiterpenes; organic photochemical transformations; medicinal chemistry; pesticide chemistry; perfume chemistry. Address: Miami Valley Labs, Procter & Gamble Co, Cincinnati, OH 45239.

ERMENC, EUGENE D, b. Milwaukee, Wis, Mar. 29, 19; m. 43; c. 1. CHEMICAL ENGINEERING. B.S, Wisconsin, 40; M.S, Ga. Inst. Tech, 42. Jr. engr, Monsanto Chem. Co, 42-46, sr. engr, 46-50, plant engr, 50; proj. engr, plaskon div, Libbey-Owens-Ford, 50-51; dir. eng, Wis. Alumni Res. Found, 51-55; staff engr, Food Mach. & Chem. Corp, 55-56, co-ordinator pilot opers, 56-58, mgr. process eng, 59-61; dir. res, Philip Cary Mfg. Co, 61-69; DIR. AIR POLLUTION CONTROL, CITY OF CINCINNATI, 69- Am. Inst. Chem. Eng. Engineering economics; process evaluation; oxides of nitrogen; simplification of complex engineering calculations. Address: 555 Abilene Trail, Cincinnati, OH 45215.

ERMENC, JOSEPH JOHN, b. Milwaukee, Wis, Nov. 11, 12; m. 51; c. 3. ENGINEERING. B.S, Wisconsin, 34; M.S, Michigan, 40; hon. M.A, Dartmouth Col, 45. Cadet gas engr, Milwaukee Gas Light Co, 34-36; engr-draftsman, Badger Meter Mfg. Co, Milwaukee, 36-37; instr. practical mech, Purdue, 37-38; MECH. ENG, Rensselaer Polytech. Inst, 38-42; asst. prof. THAYER SCH. ENG, DARTMOUTH COL, 42-45, PROF, 45- Nat. Sci. Found. sci. faculty fel, 62-63; hon. res. assoc, Univ. Col, London, 62-63. Mem. adv. comt. to Selective Serv. Dir, N.H, 55-62. Am. Soc. Mech. Eng; Am. Soc. Eng. Educ; Newcomen Soc. History of technology; heat-power engineering. Address: Thayer School of Engineering, Dartmouth College, Hanover, NH 03755.

ERMUTLU, ILHAN M, b. Istanbul, Turkey, June 24, 27; U.S. citizen; m. 56; c. 2. PSYCHIATRY. M.D, Ankara, 52. Intern, Knickerbocker Hosp, N.Y, 54-55; res. psychiat, Bellevue Hosp, 55-56; Hillside Hosp, 56-58; neurol, Goldwater Mem. Hosp, 58-59; chief of serv. psychiat, East. State Hosp, Va, 59-61; dir, Tidewater Ment. Health Clin, 61-63; private practice, Richmond, Va, 63-64; asst. to dir. DIV. MENT. HEALTH, GA. DEPT. PUB. HEALTH, 64-65, dir. community serv. br, 65-70, SUPT. GA. REGIONAL HOSP, SAVANNAH, 70- Assoc. in psychiat, sch. med, Emory, 64- Med.C, Turkish Army, 53-54. Fel. Am. Psychiat. Asn; fel. Am. Pub. Health Asn; Am. Med. Asn. Mental health. Address: P.O. Box 13607, Savannah, GA 31406.

ERN, ERNEST HENRY, b. Irvington, N.J, Apr. 27, 33; m. 56; c. 3. PETROLOGY, GEOLOGY. B.S, Bates Col, 55; M.S, Lehigh, 57, Ph.D.(geol), 59. Asst. geol, Lehigh, 55-59; asst. prof, Marshall, 59-62; UNIV. VA, 62-68, ASSOC. PROF. ENVIRON. SCI, 68-, DEAN ADMISSIONS, 67-, asst. dean col. arts & sci, 66-67. Summers, eng. geologist, U.S. Army Corps Eng, Huntington Dist, 60, 61, 62, Nat. Sci. Found. grant, Int. Field Inst, Italy, 64. Consult, Vt. Geol. Surv, 56-59; Va. Div. Mineral Resources, 62- AAAS; Geol. Soc. Am; Nat. Asn. Geol. Teachers. Metamorphic petrology; geotechnics; metamorphism and structural evolution of the Appalachian Piedmont; foundation investigation studies for engineering structures. Address: Dept. of Environmental Sciences, University of Virginia, Charlottesville, VA 22903.

ERN, VLADIMIRO, b. Belgrad, Yugoslavia, June 8, 30; m. 56. SOLID STATE PHYSICS. Licenciado, La Plata, 53, Ph.D.(physics), 55, Elec-Mech. Eng, 58. Asst. physics, La Plata, 55-56; prof, Southern Univ, Argentina, 57-58; Nat. Res. Coun. Argentina fel, Sterling Chem. Lab, Yale, 59-60; mem. staff, lab. insulation res, Mass. Inst. Tech, 61; assoc. prof. physics, Buenos Aires, 62-63; mem. staff, lab. insulation res, Mass. Inst. Tech, 63-64; RES. PHYSICIST, CENT. RES. DEPT, E.I. DU PONT DE NEMOURS & CO, 64- Vis. scientist, phys. solids group, Ecole Normale Supérieure, Univ. Paris, 71. Am. Phys. Soc. Molecular crystals; electronic properties of solids. Address: Experimental Station, E.I. du Pont de Nemours & Co, Wilmington, DE 19898.

ERNER, WILLIAM E(DWARD), b. Dubuque, Iowa, June 13, 24; m. 56; c. 4. ORGANIC CHEMISTRY. B.S, Loras Col, 46; Off. Naval Res. fel, 47-49, Ph.D.(chem), Notre Dame, 49. Res. chemist, acrylic polymers, Wallace A. Erickson & Co, 49-50; catalysis & petrochems, Houdry Process Corp, 51-59, proj. dir, 59-63; supvr, Carwin Div, Upjohn Co, 64-65; assoc. dir. res. & develop, Air Prods. & Chem, Inc, 65-71; PRES, MARBIL PROD. & DEVELOP, INC, 71- AAAS; Am. Chem. Soc. Alkylation; copolymerization; petroleum catalytic processes; petrochemicals; isocyanates and urethane chemicals; agricultural chemicals. Address: Brookhaven, R.D. 2, Allentown, PA 18103.

ERNEST, JOHN ARTHUR, b. N.Y, Dec. 12, 35. MATHEMATICS. B.A, Drew, 57; M.S, Illinois, 58, Ph.D.(math), 60. Lectr. MATH, Franklin & Marshall Col, 60; mem, Inst. Adv. Study, 60-62; asst. prof, Univ. Rochester, 62-66; vis. assoc. prof, Tulane Univ, 66-67; assoc. prof, UNIV. CALIF, SANTA BARBARA, 67-70, PROF, 70- Nat. Sci. Found. fel, 60-62; vis. asst. prof, Univ. Calif, Berkeley, 65-66. Am. Math. Soc; Fedn. Am. Sci; Math. Asn. Am; Soc. Social Responsibility in Sci. Functional analysis; infinite dimensional representations of topological groups; operator theory. Address: Dept. of Mathematics, University of California, Santa Barbara, CA 93106.

ERNEST, J(OHN) TERRY, b. Sycamore, Ill, June 26, 35; m. 65; c. 1. OPHTHALMOLOGY. B.A, Northwestern, 57; M.D, Chicago, 61, U.S. Pub. Health Serv. fel, 62-65, Ph.D.(visual sci), 67. Instr. ophthal, Chicago, 65-67; investr. visual sci, Walter Reed Army Inst. Res, D.C, 67-70; ASST. PROF. OPHTHAL, UNIV. CHICAGO, 70- Heed Ophthalmic Found. fel, 66-67. Dipl, Am. Bd. Ophthal. Med.C, U.S.A, 67-70, Lt. Col. AAAS; fel. Am. Acad.

Ophthal. & Otolaryngol; Asn. Res. Vision & Ophthal. Visual science; visual physiology, especially pathology of the optic nerve. Address: Dept. of Ophthalmology, University of Chicago, 950 E. 59th St, Chicago, IL 60637.

ERNEST, LELAND C, b. Burlington, Colo, July 20, 36; m. 58; c. 2. PLANT PHYSIOLOGY. A.B, Northwest Nazarene Col, 58; M.S, Brown, 62; Ph.D.(bot), Iowa, 65. Asst. prof. BIOL, EAST. NAZARENE COL, 65-70, ASSOC. PROF, 70- Summers, res. assoc, Wayne State Univ, 66, Herbert H. Lehman Col, 69 & 70. U.S.A, 58-60. Am. Soc. Plant Physiol; Scand. Soc. Plant Physiol. Environmental and physiological factors involved in the growth of higher plants. Address: Dept. of Biology, Eastern Nazarene College, 23 E. Elm Ave, Quincy, MA 02170.

ERNEST, TERRY E(UGENE), b. Los Angeles, Calif, 1941; m; c. 2. CHEMICAL ENGINEERING, RESEARCH ADMINISTRATION. B.S, Calif. Inst. Technol, 63, M.S, 65; Ph.D.(chem. eng), Univ. South. Calif, 69. RES. ENGR, UNION OIL CO. CALIF, BREA, 67- Am. Inst. Chem. Eng; Am. Chem. Soc. Research planning as to methods of planning, evaluating and controlling research projects. Address: 3027 N. Pinewood, Orange, CA 92667.

ERNSBERGER, F(RED) M(ARTIN), b. Ada, Ohio, Sept. 20, 19; m; c. 4. PHYSICAL CHEMISTRY. A.B, Ohio Northern, 41; Master Builders Co. fel, Ohio State, 41-46, Ph.D.(phys. chem), 46. Grad. asst. quantitative anal, Ohio State, 41-44, asst, univ. res. found, 45-46; lab. shift foreman, Tenn. Eastman Corp, Oak Ridge, 44-45; RES. CHEMIST, U.S. Naval Ord. Test Sta, 47-54; Southwest Res. Inst, 54-56; Mellon Inst. of Indust. Res, 57; GLASS RES. CTR, PPG INDUSTS, INC, 58- Am. Chem. Soc; fel. Am. Ceramic Soc. (Frank Forrest Award, 64, Toledo Glass & Ceramic Award, 70). Glass-ceramics; glass; surface structure and strength of glass. Address: Glass Research Center, PPG Industries, Inc, Box 11472, Pittsburgh, PA 15238.

ERNSBERGER, M(AURICE) L(EON), b. Toledo, Ohio, Aug. 14, 11; m. 36; c. 3. B.S, Toledo, 33; A.M, Ohio State, 34, Ph.D.(org. chem), 36. Asst. chem, Ohio State, 32-36; res. chemist, Chem. Dept, Exp. Sta, E. I. DU PONT DE NEMOURS & CO, 36-41, res. supvr, 41, dir. lab, pioneering res. div, textile fibers dept, 50-52, asst. tech. dir. ORG. CHEM. DEPT, 52-56, DIR. RES, 56- AAAS; Am. Chem. Soc; Soc. Indust. Chem; Am. Inst. Chem. Synthetic organic chemistry; absorption spectroscopy of metallo-organic compounds; cellulose chemistry; polymer chemistry. Address: Organic Chemicals Dept, E.I. du Pont de Nemours & Co, Wilmington, DE 19898.

ERNSDORFF, BEDE (PAUL), O.S.B, b. Yakima, Wash, Jan. 7, 09. CHEMISTRY. B.S, St. Benedict's Col, 34; M.S, Michigan, 36; Switzer fel, Stanford, 43-44, du Pont fel, 44-45, Ph.D.(chem), 46. Instr. chem, St. Martin's Col, 38-42; lab. asst, Stanford, 44; PROF. CHEM, ST. MARTIN'S COL, 45-, dean, 49-58. Summers, vis. scholar, Utah, 59, 60; Oak Ridge Inst. Nuclear Studies, 64. Assoc, Off. Sci. Res. & Develop, 44. AAAS; Am. Chem. Soc; fel. Am. Inst. Chem. Heterocyclic organic synthesis; new combinations of pyridine quinoline as possible antimalarial drugs. Address: St. Martin's College, Olympia, WA 98503.

ERNSDORFF, LOUIS EDWARD, b. Dubuque, Iowa, Apr. 4, 11. MATHEMATICS. A.B, Loras Col, 32; M.S, Notre Dame, 40. Assoc. prof. MATH, LORAS COL, 40-65, PROF, 65- Math. Asn. Am. Address: Dept. of Mathematics, Loras College, Dubuque, IA 52001.

ERNST, ADRIAN JOHN, b. Minneapolis, Minn, Mar. 31, 14; m. 37; c. 3. CHEMISTRY. B.A, Carleton Col, 35. Jr. biol. aid, bur. animal indust, U.S. DEPT. AGR, 41-42, jr. chemist, agr. res. admin, 42-43, agr. res. chemist, NORTH. UTILIZATION RES. & DEVELOP. DIV, 43-47, paper technologist, 47-57, assoc. chemist, 57-64, RES. CHEMIST, 64- Am. Chem. Soc; Tech. Asn. Pulp & Paper Indust. Application of modified starches, flours and cereal products for new industrial applications in paper and board products such as wet end additives, sizing materials and coating adhesives. Address: Northern Utilization Research & Development Division, Peoria, IL 61614.

ERNST, CARL HENRY, b. Lancaster, Pa, Sept. 28, 38; m. 69. HERPETOLOGY, MAMMALOGY. B.S, Millersville State Col, 60; M.Ed, West Chester State Col, 63; fel, Kentucky, 68-69, Ph.D.(biol), 69. Asst. prof. biol, Elizabethtown Col, 66-67; curator vert, Kentucky, 67-69; ASST. PROF. BIOL, SOUTHWEST MINN. STATE COL, 69- Ky. Res. Found. summer res. grant, 68 & 69; Sigma Xi res. grant-in-aid, 69; Minn. State Col. grants, 70, 71. Am. Soc. Ichthyol. & Herpet; Soc. Study Amphibians & Reptiles; Am. Soc. Mammal. Ethology, ecology and taxonomy of turtles. Address: Dept. of Biology, Southwest Minnesota State College, Marshall, MN 56258.

ERNST, EDWARD W, b. Great Falls, Mont, Aug. 28, 24; m. 50; c. 2. ELECTRICAL ENGINEERING. B.S, Illinois, 49, M.S, 50, Ph.D.(elec. eng), 55. Res. assoc. elec. eng, Illinois, 46-55; res. engr, Gen. Elec. Co, N.Y, 55; Stewart-Warner Electronics Corp, 55-58; assoc. prof. ELEC. ENG, UNIV. ILL, URBANA, 58-68, PROF, 68-, ASSOC. HEAD DEPT, 71- Pres, Nat. Electronics Conf, 64. AAAS; Inst. Elec. & Electronics Eng. Radiolocation; electronic systems; digital systems; experimentation. Address: Dept. of Electrical Engineering, University of Illinois, Urbana, IL 61801.

ERNST, G(EORGE) C(AMPBELL), b. Des Moines, Iowa, Oct. 15, 05; m. 34; c. 3. STRUCTURAL ENGINEERING. B.S.C.E, Michigan, 29, C.E, 58; M.S, Iowa State Col, 32. Instr. & jr. mat. engr, Iowa State Col, 30-36; instr. civil eng, Maryland, 36-37, asst. prof, 37-41; dir. mat. lab. & asst. prof. civil eng, L.C. Smith Col. Appl. Sci, Syracuse, 41-42; sr. engr, forest prod. lab, U.S. Forest Serv, 42-45; assoc. prof. CIVIL ENG. & acting chmn. dept, UNIV. NEBR, LINCOLN, 45-48, PROF, 48-, chmn. dept, 48-55, dir. eng. exp. sta, 55-70. Am. Concrete Inst; Am. Soc. Civil Eng. Structural analysis; reinforced concrete; timber and plywoods; stresses in framed structures. Address: 2045 Euclid Ave, Lincoln, NE 68502.

ERNST, GEORGE W, b. St. Marys, Pa, May 25, 39; m; c. 1. COMPUTER SCIENCE. B.S, Carnegie Inst. Tech, 61, Rand fels, 61-66, M.S, 62, Ph.D.(elec. eng), 66. Asst. prof. eng, CASE WEST. RESERVE UNIV, 66-70, ASSOC. PROF. COMPUT. & INFO. SCI, 70- Asn. Comput. Mach. Artificial intelligence. Address: Dept. of Computing & Information Sciences, Crawford Hall, Case Western Reserve University, University Circle, Cleveland, OH 44106.

ERNST, JOHN L, b. Hancock, Md, July 2, 20; m. 45; c. 2. ORGANIC CHEMISTRY. B.A, Delaware, 42. Prod. supvr. nitro cellulose, Hercules Powder Co, 42-45; res. chemist, cationic polymerization, Esso Res. Labs, La, 45-54; sect. head polymer appln. res, ENJAY CHEM. CO. Div, Humble Oil & Ref. Co, 54-60, dist. mgr, 60-63, MGR, chem. raw mat. dept, 63-66, SYNTHETIC RUBBER DIV, 66- U.S.A, 45-46, Sgt. Am. Chem. Soc; Am. Soc. Test. & Mat. Cationic polymerization; polymer structure; elastomer compounding and applications. Address: Synthetic Rubber Division, Enjay Chemical Co, 60 W. 49th St, New York, NY 10020.

ERNST, JOHN VERLON, b. Glencoe, Okla, Mar. 2, 35; m. 58; c. 4. PARASITOLOGY, PROTOZOOLOGY. B.S, Portland State Col, 62; Nat. Defense Ed. Act fel, Utah State, 62-65, Nat. Insts. Health fel, 65-67, M.S, 67, Ph.D.(zool), 68. Nat. Insts. Health trainee, Massachusetts, 67-68; MICROBIOLOGIST, REGIONAL PARASITE RES. LAB, ANIMAL DISEASE & PARASITE RES. DIV, U.S. DEPT. AGR, 68- U.S.A, 54-57. Am. Soc. Parasitol; Soc. Protozool; Wildlife Disease Asn. Mammalian coccidiosis. Address: Regional Lab, Animal Disease & Parasite Research Division, U.S. Dept. of Agriculture, P.O. Drawer 952, Auburn, AL 36830.

ERNST, MARTIN L, b. New York, N.Y, Mar. 28, 20; m. 53; c. 2. PHYSICS. B.S, Mass. Inst. Tech, 41. Physicist, Naval Ord. Lab, 41; Bur. Ord, 42; opers. analyst, U.S. Air Force, 43-46, electronics engr, Cambridge Res. Ctr, 46-48; opers. analyst, opers. eval. group, Off. Chief Naval Opers, 48-53, assoc. dir, 53-59; SR. STAFF MEM, V.PRES. OPERS. RES. SECT. & MGT. SCI. DIV, ARTHUR D. LITTLE, INC, 59- Opers. Res. Soc. Am. Address: Management Sciences Division, Arthur D. Little, Inc, 35 Acorn St, Cambridge, MA 02140.

ERNST, RALPH AMBROSE, b. Saline, Mich, July 5, 38; m. 67; c. 1. POULTRY SCIENCE, PHYSIOLOGY. B.S, Mich. State Univ, 59, M.S, 63, Ph.D.(avian physiol), 66. Teacher, Milan area schs, Mich, 59-60; Carson City schs, Mich, 60-61; EXTEN. POULTRY SPECIALIST, UNIV. CALIF, DAVIS, 66- Poultry Sci. Asn; World Poultry Sci. Asn. Poultry physiology with emphasis on production. Address: Dept. of Avian Sciences, University of California, Davis, CA 95616.

ERNST, RICHARD EDWARD, b. Elgin, Ill, July 2, 42; m. 67. PHYSICAL CHEMISTRY. B.A, Grinnell Col, 64; Nat. Insts. Health fel. & Ph.D.(phys. chem), Univ. Wis, Madison, 68. RES. CHEMIST, E.I. DU PONT DE NEMOURS & CO, WILMINGTON, 68- Am. Chem. Soc; Res. Soc. Am. Stereochemistry of transition metal complexes by nuclear magnetic resonance; radiation chemistry of polymers; pollution control. Address: R.D. 1, Kennett Square, PA 19348.

ERNST, ROBERT R, b. Pottsville, Pa, Mar. 20, 16; m. 42; c. 7. MICROBIOLOGY, ANALTYICAL CHEMISTRY. B.S, Pa. State, 56, M.S, 59. Engr, U.S. Merchant Marine, 37-43; private bus, 43-53; res. assoc. microbiol, Pa. State, 56-59; scientist, CASTLE CO, SYBRON CORP, 59-63, res. dir, 63-69, SR. STAFF SCIENTIST, 69- AAAS; Am. Soc. Microbiol; Am. Chem. Soc; Am. Inst. Biol. Sci; Am. Asn. Contamination Control. Sterilization technologies; water and waste microbiological treatment and control; contamination and infections control; monitoring for microbial contamination in air, water, food and surfaces. Address: 858 Landing Rd. N, Rochester, NY 14625.

ERNST, RUNYON G(ILES), b. Perth Amboy, N.Y, Mar. 12, 12; m. 37; c. 1. CHEMICAL ENGINEERING. Ch.E, Rensselaer Polytech, 32; M.Sc, Rutgers, 33. Res. chemist & spectroscopist, U.S. METALS REF. CO. DIV, AM. METAL CLIMAX, INC, 33-55, res. engr. & supvr. res. & develop. div, 56-70, MGR. CHEM. RES, AMAX BASE METALS TECH. DEPT, CARTERET, 70- Am. Chem. Soc; Am. Inst. Mining, Metall. & Petrol. Eng; Am. Soc. Test. & Mat. Extractive metallurgy; high purity metals and semiconductors; instrumental methods of analytical chemistry. Address: 596 Barron Ave, Woodbridge, NJ 07095.

ERNST, STEPHEN ARNOLD, b. St. Louis, Mo, Mar. 31, 40; m. 71. CELL BIOLOGY. A.B, Brown, 62, U.S. Pub. Health Serv. traineeship, 64-68, Ph.D.(cell biol), 68; M.S, Syracuse, 64. Fel. cell biol, Brown, 68; res. assoc, Rice, 68-71; ASST. PROF. ANAT, SCH. MED, TEMPLE UNIV, 71- Nat. Found. Cystic Fibrosis res. fel, 68-71; Moody Found. res. grant, 70-71. Histochem. Soc; Electron Micros. Soc. Am; Am. Asn. Anat; Am. Soc. Cell Biol. Electron microscopy; cytochemistry and biochemistry of electrolyte transporting tissues; histochemistry of the cell surface. Address: Dept. of Anatomy, Temple University School of Medicine, Philadelphia, PA 19140.

ERNST, W(ALLACE) G(ARY), b. St. Louis, Mo, Dec. 14, 31; m. 56; c. 4. PETROLOGY, GEOCHEMISTRY. B.A, Carleton Col, 53; M.S, Univ. Minn, 55; univ. fels, Johns Hopkins Univ, 55-56, 57-58; Nat. Sci. Found. fel, 56-57, Ph.D.(geol), 59. Geologist, petrol. br, U.S. Geol. Surv, 55-56; fel, geophys. lab, Johns Hopkins Univ, 58-60; asst. prof. GEOL. & GEOPHYS, UNIV. CALIF, LOS ANGELES, 60-64, assoc. prof, 64-68, PROF, 68- AAAS; fel. Mineral. Soc. Am.(award, 69); Mineral. Soc. Gt. Brit. & Ireland; Am. Geophys. Union; fel. Geol. Soc. Am; Geochem. Soc. Geochemistry; igneous and metamorphic petrology; application of theoretical and experimental phase equilibria to geologic problems; plate tectonics. Address: Dept. of Geology, University of California, Los Angeles, CA 90024.

ERNST, WALLACE R(OY), b. Los Angeles, Calif, May 2, 28. TAXONOMIC BOTANY. A.B, California, Los Angeles, 50, M.A, 53; fel, Stanford, 59, Ph.D.(biol. sci), 62. Herbarium botanist, California, Berkeley, 60-61; botanist, Gray Herbarium & Arnold Arboretum, Harvard, 61-63; assoc. curator, DIV. PHANEROGAMS, SMITHSONIAN INST, 63-70, CURATOR, 70- Prof. in absentia, Univ. Kans, 65- Cooley award, Am. Inst. Biol. Sci, 61, 63. Med.Serv.C, U.S.A, 53-55, Res, 55-62. AAAS; Am. Soc. Plant Taxon; Bot. Soc. Am; Int. Asn. Plant Taxon. Taxonomy, morphology and cytology of flowering plants, especially Papaveracae, Fumariaceae and Loasaceae. Address: Dept. of Botany, Smithsonian Institution, Washington, DC 20560.

ERNST, WALTER, b. Berlin, Germany, Jan. 12, 01; nat; m. 33; c. 4. MECHANICAL ENGINEERING. Dipl, Tech. Hochsch, Germany, 23. Apprentice mechanic, Mesta Mach. Co, 23-24; draftsman & designer, Homestead Valve Mfg. Co, 24-26; develop. engr, Hydraul. Press Mfg. Co, 26-32, chief engr, 32-38, dir. eng, 38-44; v.pres. & dir, Commonwealth Eng. Co, Ohio, 45-64, pres, 64-65; SR. PARTNER, ERNST & ASSOCS, 65- Nat. Fluid Power Asn. Award, 63. Am. Soc. Mech. Eng. Industrial hydraulics; fluid mechanics and power circuits; hydraulic, machine tool and press controls; hydraulic component and special machine design; automation through hydraulics. Address: Ernst & Associates, 225 W. Hillcrest Ave, Dayton, OH 45405.

ERNST-FONBERG, MARYLOU, b. Harrisburg, Pa, Jan. 18, 37; m. 69. BIOCHEMISTRY. B.A, Susquehanna Univ, 58; M.D, Temple Univ, 62; Ph.D.(biochem), Yale, 67. Vis. scientist, dept. chem. immunol, Weizmann Inst. Sci, 66-67; res. fel. chem, Harvard, 68-69; ASST. PROF. BIOL, YALE, 69- Biochemical characterization of the enzymes of lipid biosynthesis and investigation of alterations in this enzymology in conjunction with the development of organelles. Address: Kline Biology Tower, Yale University, New Haven, CT 06520.

ERNSTENE, MARSHALL P(AUL), b. Boston, Mass, Mar. 24, 30; m. 60; c. 2. PHYSICS, ELECTRICAL ENGINEERING. B.A, Harvard, 52; Nat. Sci. Found. fel, Calif. Inst. Technol, 52-55, Ph.D.(physics, elec. eng), 59. Sr. scientist, PLASMA SYSTS. DIV, ELECTRO-OPTICAL SYSTS, INC, XEROX CORP, 59-61, ASSOC. MGR, 61- AAAS; Am. Inst. Aeronaut. & Astronaut; Am. Phys. Soc; Am. Vacuum Soc; Inst. Elec. & Electronics Eng. Ion propulsion; plasma physics; high energy nuclear physics; vacuum technology. Address: Electro-Optical Systems, Inc, 300 N. Halstead St, Pasadena, CA 91107.

ERNSTER, ARTHUR F, b. Chicago, Ill, Nov. 4, 15; m. 45; c. 2. ANALYTICAL CHEMISTRY. B.S, Lewis Inst, 37; M.S, Wisconsin, 40. Instr. chem, Lewis Inst, 35 39; Wisconsin, 40-41; asst. chief chemist, aircraft div, Buick Motor Co, Gen. Motors Corp, 41-45; res. chemist, Glidden Co, 45-46; asst. to chief chemist, D.A. Stuart Oil Co, 46-50; supvr. chem. & spectros. labs, aircraft eng. div, Ford Motor Co, 50-59; chem. lab, QUAL. ASSURANCE, LOCKHEED MISSILE & SPACE CO, 59, mgr. mat. & process control labs, 59-71, MGR. OPERS. ENG, 71- AAAS; Soc. Aerospace Mat. & Process Eng; Am. Soc. Qual. Control; Am. Chem. Soc; Am. Soc. Metals; Am. Soc. Test. & Mat. Analytical chemistry; instrumental analysis. Address: 5615 Walbrook Dr, San Jose, CA 95129.

ERNSTROM, CARL ANTHON, b. Draper, Utah, Mar. 28, 22; m. 49; c. 4. FOOD SCIENCE. B.S, Utah State, 49, M.S, 51; Ph.D.(dairy indust), Wisconsin, 56. Exten. specialist, dairy indust, State of Wis, 53-55; research assoc, Chris Hansen's Lab, 55-56; assoc. prof. dairy & food indust, Wisconsin, 60-65; prof. dairy sci, UTAH STATE UNIV, 65-67, HEAD DEPT. FOOD SCI. & INDUSTS, 67- U.S.M.C.R, 43-52, Capt. AAAS; Am. Dairy Sci. Asn. Milk coagulating enzymes and chemistry of milk clotting. Address: Dept. of Food Science & Industries, Utah State University, Logan, UT 84321.

ERPENBECK, JEROME J(OHN), b. Ft. Thomas, Ky, Aug. 22, 33; m. 56; c. 8. THEORETICAL CHEMISTRY. B.S, Villa Madonna Col, 53; M.S, Louisville, 55; Visking Corp. fel, Illinois, 56-57, Ph.D.(chem), 57. Asst. Sterling chem. lab, Yale, 57-59; STAFF MEM, LOS ALAMOS SCI. LAB, 59- Transport and detonation theories; reactive hydrodynamics; statistical mechanics of fluids. Address: 3 Kiowa Lane, White Rock, Los Alamos, NM 87544.

ERPINO, MICHAEL J(AMES), b. Schenectady, N.Y, May 30, 39; m. 61; c. 3. ENDOCRINOLOGY, HISTOLOGY. B.S, Pa. State, 62; M.S, Wyoming, 64, Ph.D.(physiol), 67. Nat. Insts. Health fel. endocrinol, Cornell, 67-68; ASST. PROF. ZOOL, CHICO STATE COL, 68- AAAS; Am. Soc. Zool; Am. Ornith. Union; Am. Soc. Mammal. Seasonal endocrine changes in amniotes with emphasis on ovary and pituitary; hormones and behavior; histology of vertebrate endocrines. Address: Dept. of Biological Sciences, Chico State College, Chico, CA 95926.

ERREDE, LOUIS A(NTHONY), b. New Britain, Conn, May 26, 23; m. 46; c. 4. ORGANIC CHEMISTRY. B.S, Michigan, 47; Abbott fel, 49-50, Ph.D.(chem), Minnesota, 51. Res. supvr, M.W. Kellogg Co, 51-57; MINN. MINING & MFG. CO, 57-63, mgr. phys. chem. sect, Cent. Res. Lab, 63-68, DIR, ORG. & EXPLOR. RES, MINN. 3M RES. LTD, HARLOW, 68- Instr, Newark Col. Eng, 52-55. U.S.A, 44-46. Sci. Res. Soc. Am; Am. Chem. Soc. Synthesis of antimalarials; aromatic amines; fluorocarbons and hydrocarbons; kinetics; radioactive tracer studies; pyrolysis; photochemistry; chemistry of free radicals; surface, photographic and heterocyclic chemistry. Address: 'Springhead' Stortford Rd, Hatfield Heath near Bishop's Stortford, Hertfordshire, England.

ERRERA, SAMUEL J(OSEPH), b. Hammonton, N.J, Jan. 7, 26; m. 49; c. 2. STRUCTURAL ENGINEERING. B.S, Rutgers, 49; M.S, Illinois, 51; Ph.D. (struct), Cornell, 65. Engr. of tests, Fritz Eng. Lab, Lehigh, 51-62, instr, 51-55, asst. prof, 55-60, assoc. prof, 60-62; mgr. struct. lab, Cornell, 62-65, mgr, struct. res, 65-70, assoc. prof. civil eng, 68-70; SR. ENGR, BETHLEHEM STEEL CORP, 70- Lectr, Am. Iron & Steel Inst, W.Va. Univ, summers, 66-68; consult, Allegheny-Ludlum Steel Corp. & R.C. Mahon Co, 66-70; methods engr, adv. composites group, Grumman Aircraft Co, 68-69. U.S.A, 44-46, Sgt. Am. Soc. Civil Eng; Am. Soc. Eng. Educ. Research management; light gauge steel structures; diaphram bracing; structural materials; composite design; advanced structural composites. Address: Engineering Dept, Bethlehem Steel Corp, Bethlehem, PA 18016.

ERRETT, D(ARYL) D(ALE), b. Gridley, Kans, Dec. 2, 22; m. 53; c. 1. PHYSICS. B.A. & Iden scholar, Kans. State Teachers Col, 44; M.S, Purdue, 48, Ph.D.(physics), 51. Teaching asst, Kans. State Teachers Col, 41-44; res. asst, Purdue, 46-51; res. specialist, electro mech. dept, N.AM. ROCKWELL CORP, 51-54, res. physicist, SANTA BARBARA RES. CTR, GOLETA, CALIF, 54-67, SR. STAFF PHYSICIST, 67- Asst, Purdue Res. Found, 46-51. Sig.C, U.S.A, 44-46. Am. Phys. Soc. Electrical discharge through gases; electronic accelerators; inertial guidance systems; infrared detection systems; infrared optical design; computer programs for optical design and analysis; evaporated thermopile detectors. Address: 345 Conejo Rd, Santa Barabara, CA 93103.

ERRINGTON, ROY F(RANKLIN), b. Ont, Mar. 7, 15; m. 40; c. 2. PHYSICS, MATHEMATICS. B.A, Toronto, 39, M.A, 40. Res. assoc, Toronto, 40-41; mgr. qual. control dept, Res. Enterprises, Ltd, 42-46; sales mgr, Eldorado Mining & Ref, Ltd, 46-52; V.PRES. COMMERCIAL PROD, ATOMIC ENERGY CAN, LTD, 52- Am. Nuclear Soc; Can. Asn. Physicists; Can. Nuclear Asn. Economics; administration; nuclear science; geophysics. Address: Commercial Products, Atomic Energy of Canada, Ltd, P.O. Box 6300, Postal Station J, Ottawa, Ont, Can K2A 3W3.

ERSHOFF, B(ENJAMIN) H, b. Phila, Pa, Jan. 31, 14; m. 41; c. 2. NUTRITION. A.B, California, Los Angeles, 37; Abbott Labs. fel, California, 40-41, Ph.D.(animal nutrit), 42. Dir. res, Emory W. Thurston Labs, 42-50, sci. dir, 50-53; dir, West. Biol. Labs, 54-62; Inst. Biol. Res, 62-65; SCI. DIR, INST. ARTERIOSCLEROSIS RES, 65-; RES. PROF. BIOCHEM, SCH. MED, LOMA LINDA UNIV, 66- Res. assoc, Univ. South. Calif, 48-52, vis. assoc. prof, 52-56, vis. prof, 56-69, adj. prof, 59- AAAS; Inst. Food Technol; Am. Chem. Soc; Soc. Exp. Biol. & Med; Am. Inst. Nutrit; N.Y. Acad. Sci. Nutrition and stress; vitamin-endocrine interrelationships; unidentified nutrients. Address: Institute for Arteriosclerosis Research, 9331 Venice Blvd, Culver City, CA 90230.

ERSKINE, ANTHONY J, b. Whinfield, Eng, June 25, 31; Can. citizen; m. 55; c. 3. WILDLIFE BIOLOGY. B.Sc, Acadia, 52; M.A, Queen's (Ont), 55, Ph.D.(org. chem), 57; M.A, British Columbia, 60. Tech. off. animal chem, sci. serv, Can. Dept. Agr, 52-53; Nat. Res. Coun. Can. fel, Atlantic Regional Lab, 56-57; BIOLOGIST, CAN. WILDLIFE SERV, DEPT. ENVIRON, 60- Am. Ornith. Union; Can. Soc. Wildlife & Fishery Biol; Brit. Ornith. Union; Ger. Ornith. Soc. Structures of plant polysaccharides; biology of waterfowl, especially bufflehead and common merganser, breeding biology, populations and migration. Address: Dept. of the Environment, Canadian Wildlife Service, 400 Laurier Ave. W, Ottawa 4, Ont, Can.

ERSKINE, CHRISTOPHER F(ORBES), b. Worcester, Mass, Apr. 30, 27; m. 52; c. 3. GEOLOGY. A.B, Harvard, 49; Colo. Sch. Mines, 49-50. Geologist, eng. geol. br, U.S. Geol. Surv, 50-57; consult. eng. geologist, E.B. Waggoner, 57-60; proj. geologist, Woodward-Clyde-Sherard & Assocs, 60-62; water geologist, Kennecott Copper Corp, Utah, 62-70, GROUNDWATER GEOLOGIST, AMAX EXPLOR, INC, 70- U.S.A, 45-46. Geol. Soc. Am; Am. Inst. Mining, Metall. & Petrol. Eng; Asn. Eng. Geol; Am. Inst. Prof. Geol; Am. Water Resources Asn. Engineering geology; groundwater geology. Address: 365 Rangeview Dr, Littleton, CO 80120.

ERSKINE, DONALD B, b. Utica, N.Y, Jan. 18, 23; m. 53; c. 2. CHEMICAL ENGINEERING. B.Chem.E, Cornell, 48. Prod. engr, Calumet & Hecla Copper Co, 48-49, res. engr, 49-50; develop. engr, Chem. Construct. Corp, 50-53; proj. engr, Titanium Metals Corp, 53-59; Pittsburgh Chem. Co, 59-61; Fluor Corp, 61-63; systs. engr, CALGON CORP, 63-64, DIR. ENG, 64- U.S.A.A.F, 43-46, 1st Lt. Am. Chem. Soc; Am. Inst. Chem. Eng. Hydrometallurgy of copper; application of activated carbon. Address: 110 Lang Dr, Coraopolis, PA 15108.

ERSKINE, GORDON JOHN, b. Vancouver, B.C, Sept. 19, 39; m. 69; c. 1. INORGANIC & ORGANOMETALLIC CHEMISTRY. B.Sc, Toronto, 61; Ph.D. (inorg. chem), London, 64. Hooker Chem. res. fel, CHEM, Univ. Col, London, 64-65; Salters' Inst. Indust. Chem. res. fel, Cambridge, 65-66; asst. prof, Queen's (Ont), 66-69; ASSOC. PROF, SILLIMAN UNIV, PHILIPPINES, 69- Chem. Inst. Can; The Chem. Soc. Preparative inorganic chemistry; reactions of coordinated ligands of the transition metals; organometallic transition metal chemistry. Address: 62 Valleyview Ave, Kingston, Ont, Can.

ERSKINE, HELEN, Psychol, see Suppl. I to 11th ed, Soc. & Behav. Vols.

ERSKINE, JAMES CHRISTIAN, JR, b. Port Arthur, Tex, Sept. 24, 37. SOLID STATE PHYSICS. A.B, Washington & Jefferson Col, 59; M.S, Western Reserve, 63, NASA fel. & Ph.D.(physics), 66. Instr. physics, Western Reserve, 65-66; fel, Brandeis Univ, 66-68, instr, 68-69; PHYSICIST, ZENITH RADIO CORP, 69- AAAS; Am. Phys. Soc. Positron annihilation techniques used to study electron momentum distribution in solids; physics of thin films. Address: Zenith Radio Corp, 6001 W. Dickens Ave, Chicago, IL 60639.

ERSKINE, JOHN R(OBERT), b. Milwaukee, Wis, Mar. 18, 31; m. 56; c. 6. PHYSICS. B.S, Rochester, 53; Ph.D.(physics), Notre Dame, 60. Res. assoc. nuclear physics, Mass. Inst. Tech, 60-61, instr. physics, 61-62; res. assoc, ARGONNE NAT. LAB, 62-63, asst. physicist, 63-65, ASSOC. PHYSICIST, 65- Vis. assoc. prof, Univ. Minn, 71-72. U.S.N, 53-56, Lt.(jg). Am. Phys. Soc; Fedn. Am. Sci. Experimental nuclear physics; nuclear spectroscopy with charged particle reactions. Address: Argonne National Lab, Argonne, IL 60440.

ERSKINE, WILLIAM H(ENRY), b. Akita, Japan, Dec. 6, 08; m. 40; c. 3. MATHEMATICS. A.B, Bethany Col. (W.Va), 31; Ph.D, Hopkins, 35. Asst. prof. math, Bethany Col.(W.Va), 35-39; instr, Wright Jr. Col, Ill, 39-42; supvry. mathematician, Nat. Security Agency, Defense Dept, 42-61; ASSOC. PROF. MATH, CATH. UNIV. AM, 61- Lectr, George Washington, 42-50. Applied mathematics; algebra; numerical analysis. Address: Dept. of Mathematics, Catholic University of America, Washington, DC 20017.

ERSLEV, ALLAN JACOB, b. Copenhagen, Denmark, April 20, 19; nat; m. 47; c. 4. MEDICINE. M.D, Copenhagen, Denmark, 45. Rosenstock Mem. fel, Sloan Kettering Inst, 46-47; asst. res. med, sch. med, Yale, 48-50, Runyon res. fel, 50-51, instr. med, 51-53; assoc, Harvard Med. Sch, 55-58, asst. prof, 58-59; assoc. prof, JEFFERSON MED. COL, 59-63, CARDEZA RES. PROF. MED. & DIR. CARDEZA FOUND. HEMAT. RES, 63- Res. assoc, Thorndike Mem. Lab, Mass, 55-59. Consult, U.S. Army, 55- Med.C, 53-55, Capt. Am. Soc. Clin. Invest; Am. Fedn. Clin. Res; Asn. Am. Physicians; Am. Soc. Hemat; Int. Soc. Hemat. Hematology. Address: Dept. of Medicine, Jefferson Medical College, Philadelphia, PA 19107.

ERSPAMER, J(ACK) L(AVERNE), b. Chehalis, Wash, Apr. 9, 18; m. 45; c. 1. PLANT MORPHOLOGY & ANATOMY. B.S, Washington (Seattle), 41; Ph.D. (bot), California, 53. Teaching asst, California, 48-51, research asst. plant path, citrus exp. sta, 53-56; PROF. BIOL, CALIF. STATE POLYTECH. COL,

KELLOGG-VOORHIS, 56- C.Eng, 41-45, 1st Lt. Bot. Soc. Am. Morphology and anatomy of gymnosperms. Address: Dept. of Biological Sciences, California State Polytechnic College, Kellogg-Voorhis, Pomona, CA 93402.

ERTEL, ROBERT J(AMES), b. Buffalo, Minn, May 8, 32; m. 58; c. 4. PHARMACOLOGY, ENDOCRINOLOGY. B.S, Col. St. Thomas, 54; Ph.D. (pharmacol), Univ. Minn, Minneapolis, 65. Jr. scientist, med. sch, Univ. Minn, 58-65, res. fel. biochem, 65-66; res. assoc, Nat. Heart Inst, Md, 66-68; asst. prof. PHARMACOL, SCH. PHARM, UNIV. PITTSBURGH, 68-71, ASSOC. PROF, 71- Endocrine Soc; Am. Asn. Cols. Pharm. Actions of drugs on the spontaneous activity of heart cells grown in tissue culture; effect of chronic administration of drugs on periferal autonomic function; endocrine physiology in chronic stress; neuroendocrinology and protein biosynthesis. Address: Dept. of Pharmacology, 1106 Salk Hall, University of Pittsburgh, Pittsburgh, PA 15213.

ERTELT, H(ENRY), ROBINSON, b. New Haven, Conn, Apr. 29, 24; m. 48; c. 3. ORGANIC CHEMISTRY. B.S, Yale, 49, Socony-Vacuum Oil Co. fel, 51-52, Ph.D.(org. chem), 52; J.D, N.Y. Univ, 70. Res. chemist, Esso Res. & Eng. Co, 52-66; PATENT ATTORNEY, FMC CORP, 66- Sig.C, U.S.A, 43-46, Res, 46-68, Maj. AAAS; Am. Chem. Soc. Organic synthesis; additives for petroleum products; rocket propellants; agricultural pesticides; patent law. Address: FMC Corp, 633 Third Ave, New York, NY 10017.

ERTEZA, AHMED, b. Rajbari, East Pakistan, Aug. 1, 24; nat; m. 57; c. 2. ELECTRICAL ENGINEERING. B.Sc, Calcutta, 45, M.S, 47; M.S, Stanford, 51, E.E, 52; Ph.D.(elec. eng), Carnegie Inst. Tech, 54. Engr, Dacca Broadcasting Sta, Radio Pakistan, 47-48; sr. lectr. electronics & radio eng, Dacca, 48-50; elec. engr, nuclear instrumentation, Nuclear Res. Ctr, Pa, 53-54; asst. prof. ELEC. ENG, Ahsanullah Eng. Col, East Pakistan, 55-58; Bradley, 58; assoc. prof, UNIV. N.MEX, 58-63, PROF, 63- Am. Soc. Eng. Educ; Inst. Elec. & Electronics Eng; assoc. mem. Inst. Eng. Pakistan. Electromagnetics and microwave; magnetohydrodynamics; nuclear instrumentation; analog and digital computation; energy conversion; controls. Address: Dept. of Electrical Engineering & Computer Science, University of New Mexico, Albuquerque, NM 87106.

ERTINGSHAUSEN, GERHARD, b. Grossbodungen, Ger, Feb. 8, 37; m. 68. ORGANIC & PHYSICAL ORGANIC CHEMISTRY. B.S, Tech. Univ, Berlin, 60, M.S, 64, Ph.D.(phys. org. chem), 66; fel, Paris, 60-61. Fel, exp. sta. chem. labs, Univ. Mo, 66-67; sect. head anal. tech, Technicon Corp, N.Y, 67-69; MGR. CHEM. RES, UNION CARBIDE RES. INST, TARRYTOWN, 69- Am. Chem. Soc. Synthesis of naturally occurring polyacetylenic compounds; kinetics of gamma ray induced chemical reaction; gas and liquid chromatography of amino acids and carbohydrates; automated chemical analysis. Address: 2500 Johnson Ave, Apt. 17B, Riverdale, NY 10463.

ERULKAR, SOLOMON D(AVID), b. Calcutta, India, Aug. 18, 24; m. 50; c. 2. NEUROPHYSIOLOGY. B.A, Toronto, 48, M.A, 49; fel, Hopkins, 52, Ph.D. (physiol), 52; D.Phil, Oxford, 57. Fel, U.S. Pub. Health Serv, Hopkins, 52-54; British Med. Res. Coun. grant, Oxford, 55-58; asst. prof. otol. & physiol. & dir. dept, Temple, 59-60, dir. res. otol, 59-60; dept. demonstr. physiol, Oxford, 55-58; asst. prof. PHARMACOL, UNIV. PA, 60-62, assoc. prof, 62-67, PROF, 67- Hon. res. assoc, Univ. Col, London, 67-68. Patterns of discharge of single units in central nervous system with respect to auditory pathways; mechanisms of central synaptic transmission. Address: Dept. of Pharmacology, University of Pennsylvania Medical School, Philadelphia, PA 19104.

ERVIN, BURL H, b. Ardmore, Okla, July 22, 24; m. 46; c. 3. AEROSPACE ENGINEERING. B.S, Agr. & Mech. Col. Tex, 45, Humble Oil Col fel, 47-48, M.S, 48. Instr. mech. eng, Agr. & Mech. Col. Tex, 46-49, asst. prof, 49-50; res. assoc. theoret. mech, Illinois, 50-51; specialist, N.Am. Aviation, Inc, 51-53; asst. chief tech. planning, defense group, Rheem Mfg. Co, Calif, 53; chief engr, Nortronics Div, NORTHROP CORP, 58-61, syst. support dept. tech. dir, 61-64, dir. planning, 64-67, MGR. TACTICAL SYSTS. PROGS, ELECTRO-MECH. DIV, 67- Consult, U.S. Navl Ord. Lab, Md, 49; U.S. Army Combat Surveillance Agency, 58. U.S.N, 45-46. Assoc. fel. Am. Inst. Aeronaut. & Astronaut. Aerospace systems; operations analysis as related to defense and weapons effectiveness. Address: 18085 Darmel Pl, Santa Ana, CA 92705.

ERVIN, FRANK (RAYMOND), b. Little Rock, Ark, Nov. 3, 26; m. 47; c. 5. PSYCHIATRY. M.D, Tulane, 51, fel, 52-55. Asst. psychiat. & neurol, med. sch, Tulane, 52-57; instr. PSYCHIAT, MED. SCH, HARVARD, 57-62, asst. prof, 62-68, assoc. clin. prof, 68-69, ASSOC. PROF, 69-; DIR. STANLEY COBB LABS. PSYCHOL. RES, MASS. GEN. HOSP, 69- Nat. Inst. Ment. Health career res. fel, 62- Dir. Monroe Area Guidance Center, La, 53-57; consult. psychiatrist, State Training Inst, La, 53-57; asst, Mass. Gen. Hosp, 57-63, psychiatrist, 63-; adj. prof, Hampshire Col. Dipl, Am Bd. Psychiat. & Neurol. U.S.N, 46-48. Neurophysiologic aspects of behavior. Address: Box 70, Massachusetts General Hospital, Boston, MA 02114.

ERVIN, GUY, JR, b. Washington, D.C, Nov. 14, 15; m. 39; c. 4. PHYSICAL CHEMISTRY. B.S, George Washington, 37; M.S, Maryland, 41; fel, Pa. State Col, 46-49, Ph.D.(ceramics), 49. Jr. chemist, Bur. Mines & Md, 37-41, assoc. phys. chemist, 41-44; res. chemist, Westvaco Chem. Co, 44-46; res. engr, ceramic & abrasive prods, Norton Co, 49-57, res. assoc, exploratory res. sect, 57-59; sr. tech. specialist, ATOMICS INT. DIV, N.AM. ROCKWELL CORP, 59-63, SUPVR. SOLID STATE CHEM, 63- AAAS; Am. Chem. Soc; Am. Ceramic Soc. Inorganic phase equilibria, high pressure mineral synthesis; alumina and its hydrates; extractive metallurgy of titanium and zirconium; high temperature chemistry; metal oxidation kinetics; beryllium, uranium carbide and other reactor materials. Address: 8451 Amestoy Ave, Northridge, CA 91324.

ERVIN, ROBERT F(RANCIS), b. Jackson, Ohio, Dec. 28, 13; m. 40; c. 6. BACTERIOLOGY. B.S, Notre Dame, 36, fel, 37-38, M.S, 38. Asst, labs. bact, Notre Dame, 36-38, instr, 39-43, asst. res. prof, 43-49, assoc. res. prof, 49-57, asst. dir. Lobund Inst. 49-57; mgr. res. admin, PARKE, DAVIS & CO, 57-64, staff dir. clin. invest, 64-69, MGR. RES. ADMIN. SERV, 69- Civilian with U.S.A; U.S.N, 44. Am. Soc. Microbiol. Bacteriological, photographic and germfree life; research administration. Address: Parke, Davis & Co, Ann Arbor, MI 48106.

ERWAY, LAWRENCE C(LIFTON), JR, b. Lawrenceville, Pa, Apr. 27, 38; m. 60; c. 4. DEVELOPMENTAL GENETICS. B.A, Barrington Col, 60; M.A, Brown, 63; Ph.D.(genetics), California, Davis, 68. Instr. biol, Barrington Col, 61-64; trainee genetics, California, Davis, 64-66, res. technician, 66-68; ASST. PROF. BIOL, UNIV. CINCINNATI, 68- Genetics Soc. Am. Effects of trace elements and genes on birth defects, including pigmentary and neurological defects in mice and man, with particular emphasis on prevention of certain hereditary disorders, specifically otolith defects. Address: Dept. of Biological Sciences, University of Cincinnati, Cincinnati, OH 45221.

ERWIN, ALBERT R, b. Charlotte, N.C, May 1, 31; m. 54; c. 1. PHYSICS. B.S, Duke, 53; M.A, Harvard, 57, Ph.D.(physics), 59. Jr. res. assoc, Brookhaven Nat. Lab, 57-58; instr. PHYSICS, UNIV. WIS, MADISON, 58-59, asst. prof, 59-62, assoc. prof, 62-65, PROF, 65- High energy particle physics. Address: Dept. of Physics, Sterling Hall University of Wisconsin, Madison, WI 53706.

ERWIN, CHESLEY P(ARA), b. Oklahoma, June 5, 20; m. 49; c. 2. MEDICINE, PATHOLOGY. B.A, Oklahoma, 42, M.D, 51. Res. PATH, Milwaukee County Hosp, 52-55; Milwaukee Hosp, 55-56; instr, SCH. MED, MARQUETTE UNIV, 56-57, asst. prof, 57-64, ASSOC. PROF, 64- Dipl, Am. Bd. Path, 56. U.S.A, 42-46, Res, 46-51, Capt. Am. Soc. Clin. Path; Am. Med. Asn; Col. Am. Path. Study of animal tumors; oncogenic and oncolytic factors; Rickettsiae; viruses. Address: 561 N. 15th St, Milwaukee, WI 53233.

ERWIN, DAVID B(ISHOP), SR, b. Flushing, N.Y, May 30, 24; m. 45; c. 5. ELECTRICAL ENGINEERING. B.S, Purdue, 48. Engr. test set develop, Hawthorne Works, WEST. ELEC. CO, 48-53, St. Paul Shops, 53-55, dept. chief electronic switching systs. develop, Hawthorne Works, 55-60, Columbus Works, 60-62, asst. supt. develop. eng, 62-66, MGR. ELECTRONIC SWITCHING SYSTS. ENG, LISLE PLANT, 66- U.S.A, 43-46, 1st Lt. Sr. mem. Inst. Elec. & Electronics Eng. Manufacturing techniques for production of electronic switching system. Address: 1428 Clyde Dr, Naperville, IL 60540.

ERWIN, D(ONALD) C, b. Concord, Nebr, Nov. 24, 20; m. 48; c. 2. PLANT PATHOLOGY. B.S, Nebraska, 49, M.A, 50; Ph.D.(plant path), California, 53. Asst. plant path, Nebraska, 49-50; Univ. Calif, Davis, 50-53; jr. plant pathologist, UNIV. CALIF, RIVERSIDE, 53-54, asst. plant pathologist, 54-60, ASSOC. PLANT PATHOLOGIST, 60-, PROF. PLANT PATH, 66-, assoc. prof, 61-66. Guggenheim res. fel, 59. Med.C, U.S.A, 42-46. AAAS; Am. Phytopath. Soc; Mycol. Soc. Am. Diseases of agronomic crops; biology of Phytophthora; systemic fungicides. Address: 3376 Sunnyside Dr, Riverside, CA 92506.

ERWIN, JAMES V, b. Horton, Kans, Sept. 28, 25; m. 44; c. 4. CHEMICAL ENGINEERING. B.Sc, Univ. Nebr, Lincoln, 50. Res. & develop. engr, MINN. MINNING & MFG. CO, 50-54, proj. leader reflective prod, 54-56, supvr. res. & develop. thermal & reflective prod, 56-59, mgr. thermal, reflective & decorative prod, 59-61, tech. mgr, reflective & decorative prod, 61-64, tech. mgr. decorative prod. dept, 64-67, TECH. DIR. VISUAL PROD. DIV, 67- U.S.A.A.F, 43-46. Am. Inst. Chem. Eng. Radiation physics; surface chemistry and physics; imaging chemistry; surface coatings technology; environmental technology; optics; adhesion physics. Address: Visual Products Division, 3 M Center, Minnesota Mining & Manufacturing Co, Bldg. 235-N-209-A, St. Paul, MN 55101.

ERWIN, ROBERT B(RUCE), b. Burlington, Vt, Mar. 19, 28; m. 56; c. 4. GEOLOGY. B.A, Vermont, 52; Sc.M, Brown, 55; Ph.D, Cornell, 59. Geologist, Vt. Geol. Surv, 55; Texaco, Inc, 59-61; asst. prof. geol, St. Lawrence, 61-64; geologist, W.VA. GEOL. & ECON. SURV, 64-65, dir. res, 65-66, asst. state geologist, 66-69, DIR. & STATE GEOLOGIST, 69- U.S.N, 46-48, Res, 48-54. AAAS; Am. Asn. Petrol. Geol; Soc. Econ. Paleont. & Mineral; Geol. Soc. Am; Am. Inst. Prof. Geol. Paleontology and stratigraphy of lower Paleozoic rocks; Gulf Coast Stratigraphy and structure; lower Paleozoic time-stratigraphic relationships; paleontology of West Virginia. Address: West Virginia Geological & Economic Survey, Box 879, Morgantown, WV 26505.

ERWIN, VIRGIL GENE, b. Cahone, Colo, Nov. 1, 37; m. 59; c. 3. PHARMACOLOGY, BIOCHEMISTRY. B.S, Colorado, 60, M.S, 62, Ph.D.(pharmacol. & biochem), 65. Fel, sch. med, Hopkins, 65-67; asst. prof. PHARM, SCH. PHARM, UNIV. COLO, BOULDER, 67-71, ASSOC. PROF, 71- Am. Soc. Neurochem; Am. Soc. Pharmacol. & Exp. Therapeut. Biochemical pharmacology; mechanism of action of therapeutic agents on various cellular processes. Address: University of Colorado School of Pharmacy, Boulder, CO 80302.

ERWIN, W(ILLIAM) G(RADY), b. Boonshill, Tenn, Jan. 12, 08; m. 28; c. 1. GENETICS, ORNITHOLOGY. B.S, Peabody Col, 31, M.A, 33; Ph.D.(zool), Mich. State Univ, 40. Prin. & teacher, high schs, Miss, 26-36; instr. biol, Henderson State Teachers Univ, 36-37; asst. zool, Mich. State Col, 37-40; instr, 40-42; prof. BIOL. & head dept, Henderson State Teachers Col, 42-45; PROF, NORTHWEST. STATE UNIV, 45-, HEAD DEPT, 51- AAAS; Am. Inst. Biol. Sci; Nat. Asn. Biol. Teachers; Am. Genetic Asn; Am. Soc. Human Genetics. Genetics of the rat; human genetics. Address: Dept. of Biological Sciences, Northwestern State University, Natchitoches, LA 71457.

ERYASA, YILMAZ, b. Istanbul, Turkey, Dec. 28, 28; m. 60; c. 3. ANESTHESIOLOGY. B.A, Istanbul, 46, M.D, 52. Instr. ANESTHESIOL, VANDERBILT UNIV, 61-63, asst. prof, 63-67, ASSOC. PROF, 67- Turkish Army, 53-54, Lt. Int. Anesthesia Res. Soc. Muscle relaxants; catecholamines. Address: Dept. of Anesthesiology, Vanderbilt University Nashville, TN 37203.

ERZURUMLU, HACIK, b. Istanbul, Turkey, Mar. 7, 34; m. 63. STRUCTURAL ENGINEERING, APPLIED MECHANICS. Prof. degree civil eng, Tech. Univ. Istanbul, 57; M.S, Univ. Tex, Austin, 62, univ. fel, Ford Found. fel. & Ph.D. (civil eng), 70. Instr. eng, PORTLAND STATE UNIV, 62-65, asst. prof. STRUCT. ENG, 65-68, ASSOC. PROF, 68- Consult. & qualified instr, Off. Civil Defense, 66- Prof. Soc. Nuclear Defense; Am. Soc. Civil Eng; Am. Concrete Inst; Am. Soc. Eng. Educ. Ultimate strength considerations of hybrid beams and girders; static and fatigue investigations of orthotropic plate bridge decks and of tubular joints. Address: Dept. of Applied Science & Engineering, Portland State University, Portland, OR 97207.

ESAKI, LEO, b. Osaka, Japan, Mar. 12, 25; m. 59; c. 2. SOLID STATE PHYSICS. B.S, Tokyo, 47, Ph.D.(physics), 59. Res. mem. solid state physics, Kobe Kogyo Corp, 47-56; chief physicist, Sony Corp, 56-60; IBM FEL, THOMAS J. WATSON RES. CTR, IBM CORP, 60- Nishina Found. Mem. Award, Japan, 59; Asahi Award, 60; Toyo Rayon Found. Prom. Sci. & Tech. Award, 61; Stuart Ballentine Medal, Franklin Inst, Pa, 61; Japan Acad. Award, 65. Am. Phys. Soc; fel. Inst. Elec. & Electronics Eng.(Mem. Prize Award, Inst. Radio Eng, 61); Phys. Soc. Japan; Inst. Elec. Commun. Eng. Japan. Solid state physics and electronics of semiconductors and semimetals, particularly tunneling in the p-n junction of semiconductors. Address: Thomas J. Watson Research Center, IBM Corp, P.O. Box 218, Yorktown Heights, NY 10598.

ESARY, JAMES D(ANIEL), b. Seattle, Wash, Apr. 8, 26; m. 47; c. 2. MATHEMATICAL STATISTICS. A.B, Whitman Col, 48, Chicago, 48-49; M.A, California, 51, Ph.D.(statist), 57. Asst. statist, California, 50-51, 53-57; math. statistician, Boeing Airplane Co, 57-58, Boeing Sci. Res. Labs, 59-70; ASSOC. PROF. OPER. RES, NAVAL POSTGRAD. SCH, 70- Vis. lectr, Soc. Indust. & Appl. Math. Prog, 63-64 & 67-69; Univ. Calif, Berkeley, 67; vis. lectr. prog. statist, 68-71. U.S.A.R, 44-45, 51-52, Res, 52-59, Capt. Am. Math. Soc; Soc. Indust. & Appl. Math; Am. Statist. Asn; Math. Asn. Am; Inst. Math. Statist. Reliability theory; probability; industrial applications. Address: Dept. of Operations Research & Administrative Sciences, Naval Postgraduate School, Monterey, CA 93940.

ESAU, KATHERINE, b. Ekaterinoslav, Russia, Apr. 3, 98; nat. BOTANY. Agr. Col, Germany, 22; Ph.D, Univ. Calif, 31, LL.D, 66; hon. D.Sc, Mills Col, 62. Instr. bot. & jr. botanist, UNIV. CALIF, Davis, 31-37, asst. prof. & asst. botanist, 37-43, assoc. prof. & assoc. botanist, 43-49, prof. & botanist, 49-63, prof, SANTA BARBARA, 63-65, EMER. PROF, BOT, 65- Guggenheim fel, 40; Prather lectr, Harvard, 60. Nat. Acad. Sci; AAAS; Am. Acad. Arts & Sci; Am. Philos. Soc; Bot. Soc. Am.(pres, 51); Int. Soc. Plant Morphol; Royal Swedish Acad. Sci. Anatomy of healthy and virus diseased seed plants. Address: Dept. of Biological Sciences, University of California, Santa Barbara, CA 93106.

ESAYIAN, MANUEL, b. Cleveland, Ohio, Dec. 12, 28; m. 54; c. 2. ORGANIC CHEMISTRY. B.S, Western Reserve, 53, M.S, 57, Du Pont fel, 58-59, Ph.D. (org. chem), 60; Temple, 63-64. Chemist, veg. res. lab, Sherwin Williams Paint Co, 53; cryogenics engr, H.L. Johnston Inc, 53-54; chemist electronics, Victoreen Instrument Co, 54-55; adhesives, B.F. Goodrich Co, 55-56; res. chemist, exp. sta, E.I. DU PONT DE NEMOURS & CO, INC, 60-67, tech. rep, mkt. sect, FLUOROCARBONS DIV, 67-68, MKT. REP, PLASTICS DEPT, 68- U.S.M.C, 46-48, 50-51, Sgt. Am. Chem. Soc; Sci. Res. Soc. Am. Chain initiation and transfer in free radical polymerization; polymer characterization; stabilization, coloring and weatherability of plastics; adhesives, gas liquifaction; preparation of electronic components. Address: 2011 Ferndale Dr, Westwood Manor, Wilmington, DE 19810.

ESBER, DR. HENRY JEMIL, b. El-Mina, Lebanon, Aug. 28, 38; U.S. citizen; m; c. 1. IMMUNOLOGY, MICROBIOLOGY. B.S, Col. William & Mary, 61; M.S, North Carolina, 63; Ph.D.(microbiol), West Virginia, 67. Bacteriologist-in-charge, Portsmouth Gen. Hosp, 63-64; RES. IMMUNOLOGIST, MASON RES. INST, 67- Fel. diagnostic virol, Los Angeles County Health Dept, 67; instr. immunol, Clark, 69-; clin. lab. consult, Hahnemann Hosp, Worcester, 69- AAAS; Am. Soc. Microbiol; Am. Pub. Health Asn. Lung antibodies and autoimmunity; silicosis and environmental health; immunosuppressive activity of inhalents; immune enhancement by bacterial fractions; tumor immunology; inflammation; radioimmunoassays of protein hormones and steroids; competitive protein binding of steroids. Address: Dept. of Immunology, Mason Research Institute, Harvard St, Worcester, MA 01608.

ESBITT, ALAN S, b. Jersey City, N.J, Sept. 29, 35; m. 66; c. 2. PHYSICAL CHEMISTRY, SOLID STATE PHYSICS. B.S, Mass. Inst. Technol, 57; M.A, Harvard, 58, Ph.D.(phys. chem), 61. Staff mem, Lincoln Lab, Mass. Inst. Technol, 58-59; physicist, Gen. Tel. & Electronics Labs, 61-62; physical chemist, GEN. INSTRUMENT CORP, 63-65, dir. res, 65-68, DIR. ENG, 69- Sig.C, 62-63, 1st Lt. Electrochem. Soc; Inst. Elec. & Electronics Eng. Semiconductor physics and devices; thin films; photoconductivity; microwave spectroscopy. Address: 583 Caledonia Rd, Dix Hills, NY 11746.

ESCALANTE, EDWARD, b. El Paso, Tex, Nov. 5, 36; m. 63; c. 4. METALLURGY, CORROSION. B.S, Univ. Tex, El Paso, 60; M.S, Univ. Md, 66. METALLURGIST, NAT. BUR. STANDARDS, 60- Nat. Asn. Corrosion Eng. Mechanical properties of anodic films on metals in aqueous environments; stress corrosion of pure copper; corrosion of metals underground. Address: National Bureau of Standards, Washington, DC 20234.

ESCH, GERALD WISLER, b. Wichita, Kans, June 22, 36; m. 58; c. 2. ZOOLOGY, PARASITOLOGY. B.S, Colo. Col, 58; M.S, Oklahoma, 61, Nat. Insts. Health fel, 61-63, Ph.D.(zool), 63. Nat. Insts. Health trainee, North Carolina, 63-65; ASST. PROF. biol, Wake Forest Col, 65-68; MICROBIOL. & PUB. HEALTH, COL. HUMAN MED, MICH. STATE UNIV, 68-, vis. prof, biol. sta, summers 65 & 66. AAAS; Am. Soc. Parasitol. Classification, taxonomy and physiology of taenioid cestodes; histopathology and electron microscopy of adult and larval cestodes. Address: Dept. of Microbiology & Public Health, College of Human Medicine, Michigan State University, East Lansing, MI 48823.

ESCH, HARALD ERICH, b. Düsseldorf, Ger, Dec. 22, 31; m. 55; c. 3. BIOLOGY, ZOOLOGY. Dr.rer.nat.(zool), Wurzburg, 60. Res. scientist, Ger. Res. Asn, 60-62; sci. asst. radiation res, Univ. Munich, 62-64; res. scientist, UNIV. NOTRE DAME, 64-65, asst. prof. BIOL, 65-67, assoc. prof, 67-69, PROF, 69- Vis. prof. bee commun, Univ. São Paulo, 64; mem. comt. African Honey Bee, Nat. Res. Coun. AAAS; Radiation Res. Soc; Ger. Zool. Soc. Communication in bees; electrophysiology; radiation effects on cellular level. Address: Dept. of Biology, University of Notre Dame, Notre Dame, IN 46556.

ESCH, LOUIS JAMES, b. Grand Rapids, Mich, Apr. 11, 32; m. 52; c. 6. PHYSICS. B.S, Aquinas Col, 59; M.S, Rensselaer Polytech. Inst, 62, Ph.D. (nuclear eng. & sci), 71. PHYSICIST, KNOLLS ATOMIC POWER LAB, GEN. ELEC. CO, 59- U.S.N, 51-55. Am. Nuclear Soc. Integral and differential measurements of cross sections of fissile and nonfissile nuclides to neutrons of low and intermediate energies. Address: 3 Woodcrest Dr, Scotia, NY 12302.

ESCH, ROBIN ERNEST, b. Md, Feb. 25, 30; m. 66; c. 3. APPLIED MATHEMATICS. B.A, Harvard, 51, A.M, 53, Ph.D.(appl. math), 57. Asst. prof. appl. math, Harvard, 58-62; head appl. mech. dept, Sperry Rand Res. Ctr, Sudbury, 62-66; PROF. MATH, BOSTON UNIV, 66-, CHMN. DEPT, 68- Math. Asn. Am; Am. Math. Soc; Soc. Indust. & Appl. Math. Numerical analysis. Address: 371 Plainfield Rd, Concord, MA 01742.

ESCHENBACH, ARTHUR E(DWIN), b. New York, N.Y, Jan. 31, 18; m. 44; c. 2. PSYCHOLOGY. A.B, Cornell, 47; M.A, Florida, 49, fel, 50-51, Ph.D.(psychol), 55. Res. psychologist, U.S. Air Force, 51-66; ASSOC. PROF. PSYCHOL, Univ. of the Pac, 66-67, JACKSONVILLE UNIV, 67- U.S.A.A.F, 42-45. Am. Psychol. Asn. Clinical psychology; physiology; bioastronautics, human factors engineering; occupational health, safety, life support systems in aerospace vehicles and missle systems. Address: 11440 Starboard Dr, Jacksonville, FL 32225.

ESCHENBACH, R(ICHARD) C(OREY), b. Williamsport, Pa, Apr. 9, 27; m. 66; c. 3. MECHANICAL ENGINEERING. B.S, Carnegie Inst. Technol, 48, M.S, 49; Westinghouse & Pa. State scholar, Shell Co. & Gen. Motors Corp. fel, Purdue Univ, 55-57, Ph.D.(mech. eng), 57. Res. engr, supvr. res, div. head, DEVELOP. ASSOC, LINDE DIV, UNION CARBIDE CORP, 48-55, 57- AAAS; Am. Inst. Min, Metall. & Petrol. Eng; Combustion Inst. Combustion; pyrometallurgy; arc radiation; arc gas heaters; high flux heat transfer. Address: Linde Division, Union Carbide Corp, Tarrytown Technical Center, Tarrytown, NY 10591.

ESCHENBERG, KATHRYN (MARCELLA), b. St. Louis, Mo, Dec. 12, 23. ZOOLOGY, EMBRYOLOGY. B.A, Miami (Ohio), 46; M.A, Colorado, 50; Ph.D.(zool), Washington (Seattle), 57. Asst. biol. & vert. physiol, Colorado, 48-49, instr, 49-51; asst. zool, embryol. & cell physiol, Washington (Seattle), 51-56; Nat. Cancer Inst. res. fel, Princeton, 57; asst. prof. zool, cell biol. & embryol, MT. HOLYOKE COL, 58-64, assoc. prof. BIOL. SCI, 64-70, PROF. & CHMN. DEPT, 70- AAAS; Am. Inst. Biol. Sci; Am. Soc. Zool; Soc. Develop. Biol. Developmental biology; cytology; oogenesis. Address: Dept. of Biological Sciences, Mount Holyoke College, South Hadley, MA 01075.

ESCHENBRENNER, ALLEN (BERNARD), b. St. Louis, Mo, Apr. 10, 11; m. 40; c. 3. MEDICINE. M.D, Washington (St. Louis), 35. Curator path. mus, sch. med, Washington (St. Louis), 34-35, res. & asst. path, Barnes Hosp, 35-36, asst. med, 36-38; med. surgeon, marine hosps, U.S. Pub. Health Serv, 38-42, mem. staff, Nat. Cancer Inst, 42-53, communicable disease ctr, virus & rickettsia sect, 53-56, hemat. & biochem. sect, 56-60; ASSOC. PROF. APPL. BIOL, GA. INST. TECHNOL, 60- U.S.P.H.S, 38-60, Med. Dir. Am. Soc. Exp. Biol. & Med; Tissue Cult. Asn; N.Y. Acad. Sci. Histopathology; radiobiology; histochemistry; clinical and fundamental laboratory research facilities; virology; tissue culture. Address: Engineering Experiment Station, Georgia Institute of Technology, Atlanta, GA 30332.

ESCHENFELDER, ANDREW H(ERBERT), b. Newark, N.J, June 13, 25; m. 49; c. 2. PHYSICS. B.S, Rutgers, 49, fel, 51-52, Ph.D.(physics), 52. Ultrasonic res, Aberdeen Proving Ground, 50; physicist, IBM Res. Ctr, IBM CORP, 52-55, mgr. magnetics dept, 57-60, dir. solid state sci, 60-63, components, 63-66, consult. to dir. res, res. div, SAN JOSE RES. LAB, 66-67, DIR. LAB, 67-, SR. PHYSICIST, 56- U.S.N. Civil Eng, 43-46. Am. Phys. Soc; Inst. Elec. & Electronics Eng. Magnetism; cryogenics; paramagnetic resonance; solid state. Address: San Jose Research Lab, IBM Corp, Monterey & Cottle Rd, San Jose, CA 95114.

ESCHENROEDER, ALAN Q, b. St. Louis, Mo, Feb. 22, 33; m. 56; c. 2. MECHANICAL ENGINEERING, AERODYNAMICS. B.M.E, Cornell, 55, Ph.D.(mech. eng), 59. Res. engr, Ballistic Res. Labs, 55-57; aerodyn, Cornell Aeronaut. Lab, 59-62; head aerophys. Sect, Defense Res. Labs, Gen. Motors Corp, 62-67; staff scientist, GEN. RES. CORP, 67-70, ASSOC. DIR. SOCIAL SYSTS. DEPT, 70- City councilman, City of Santa Barbara, 69-73. Ord.C, 55-57, 1st Lt. Air Pollution Control Asn. Air pollution control analyses; combustion; nonequilibrium gasdynamics; turbulence. Address: Social Systems Dept, General Research Corp, P.O. Box 3587, Santa Barbara, CA 93105.

ESCHER, DORIS J(ANE) W(OLF), b. N.Y.C, July 1, 17; m. 38; c. 2. CARDIOLOGY. B.A, Barnard Col, Columbia Univ, 38; M.D, N.Y. Univ, 42. Resident med, Jewish Hosp. of Brooklyn, 43-44; asst. physician, cardiac clin, Bellevue Hosp, 45-48; asst, med. div, MONTEFIORE HOSP, & MED. CTR, 48-49, HEAD, CARDIAC CATHETERIZATION UNIT, 50-, ASSOC. ATTEND. RADIOL, 57-; ATTEND. PHYSICIAN, MED, 67-; ASSOC. PROF. MED, ALBERT EINSTEIN COL. MED, 70-, asst. prof, 66-70. Fel, col. med, N.Y. Univ, 45-46; clin. asst, Mt. Sinai Hosp, 46-48; fel, med. div, Montefiore Hosp, 46; Rosenstock Mem. Found. fel, 47-48, adj, 51-57, assoc, 57-67; lectr, Columbia Univ, 57-64. AAAS; Am. Heart Asn; Am. Fedn. Clin. Res; N.Y. Acad. Sci; Int. Cardiovasc. Soc; Asn. Advan. Med. Instrumentation; fel. Am. Col. Cardiol; Am. Soc. Artificial Internal Organs. Diagnosis and clinical research in cardiovascular disease; artificial cardiac pacing; methods, material, physiology; artificial organs. Address: Cardiac Catheterization Lab, Montefiore Hospital & Medical Center, 111 E. 210th St, Bronx, NY 10467.

ESCHINASI, EMILE H(AVIV), b. Cairo, Egypt, Jan. 18, 14; U.S. citizen; m. 47; c. 2. ORGANIC CHEMISTRY. M.Sc, Hebrew Univ, Israel, 41, Ph.D. (chem), 43. Res. chemist, Cent. Citrus Prods. Res. Lab, Israel, 43-49; D. Sief Res. Inst, 49-53; res. assoc, Northwestern, 53-55; res. chemist, GIVAUDAN CORP, 56-70, GROUP LEADER RES, 70- Am. Chem. Soc;

Chem. Soc. France. Organic and terpene chemistry; synthesis of aromatics and pharmaceuticals; catalysis. Address: 625 Pleasant Valley Way, West Orange, NJ 07052.

ESCHLE, JAMES L(EE), b. Groom, Tex, Jan. 20, 37; m. 58; c. 2. ENTOMOLOGY. B.S, Tex. Tech. Col, 60; M.S, Wisconsin, 62, Ph.D.(entom), 64. Asst. entom, Wisconsin, 60-64; ENTOMOLOGIST, ENTOM. RES. DIV, U.S. DEPT. AGR, 64- Entom. Soc. Am. Biology and control of flies affecting livestock. Address: P.O. Box 232, Kerrville, TX 78028.

ESCHMAN, DONALD F(RAZIER), b. Granville, Ohio, Oct. 22, 23; m. 46; c. 4. GEOMORPHOLOGY. A.B, Denison, 47; M.A, Harvard, 50, Ph.D.(geol), 53. Fel. geol, Harvard, 47-51; instr, Tufts Col, 51-53, acting head dept, 52-53; instr. GEOMORPHOL, UNIV. MICH, 53-56, asst. prof, 56-59, assoc. prof, 59-64, PROF, 64-, chmn. dept. geol. & mineral, 61-66, chmn. faculty counsr, col. lit, sci. & arts, 58-59. Geologist, U.S. Geol. Surv, 48- U.S.N.R, 43-46, Lt. Geol. Soc. Am; Nat. Asn. Geol. Teachers; Arctic Inst. N.Am. Pleistocene geology of southwestern Alberta and southeastern Michigan; glacial geology: Michigan River Basin, North Park, Colorado; erosional history of North Park; engineering geology; surficial and bedrock geology of Athol Quadrangle, Massachusetts igneous and metamorphic geology, and glacial geology; formation of river terraces; geomorphology of Huerfano Park, Colorado and of southern Rocky Mountains; glacial history of southern Michigan; Glacial Grand Valley. Address: Dept. of Geology & Mineralogy, University of Michigan, Ann Arbor, MI 48104.

ESCHMEYER, PAUL H(ENRY), b. New Bremen, Ohio, June 7, 16. BIOLOGY. B.S.F, Michigan, 38, M.S, 39, Ph.D.(zool), 49. Fish mgt. agent, State Div. Conserv. & Nat. Resources, Ohio, 39-40; dist. fisheries biologist, Inst. Fisheries Res, Mich, 41-42, asst. fisheries biologist, 47-49; aquatic biologist, State Conserv. Cmn, Mo, 49-50; fishery res. biologist, U.S. Fish & Wildlife Serv, 50-56; asst. dir, Inst. Fisheries Res, Mich, 56-61; Great Lakes Biol. Lab, U.S. Bur. Commercial Fisheries, 61-64, biol. ed, div. biol. res, 65-70; FISHERY BIOLOGIST, GREAT LAKES FISHERY LAB, U.S. BUR. SPORT FISHERIES & WILDLIFE, 70- U.S.N, 42-45. Fel. Am. Inst. Fishery Res. Biol; Am. Fisheries Soc; Am. Soc. Ichthyol. & Herpet; Am. Soc. Limnol. & Oceanog; Wildlife Soc; Am. Soc. Zool. Fishery biology; natural history of freshwater fishes. Address: Great Lakes Fishery Lab, U.S. Bureau of Sport Fisheries and Wildlife, P.O. Box 640, Ann Arbor, MI 48107.

ESCHMEYER, WILLIAM N(EIL), b. Knoxville, Tenn, Feb. 11, 39; m. 67; c. 1. ICHTHYOLOGY, MARINE BIOLOGY. B.S, Michigan, 62; Ohio State, summer 61; M.S, Miami (Fla), 64, Bur. Commercial Fisheries fel, 64-65, Ph.D. (marine biol), 67. Res. asst. ICHTHYOL, Inst. Marine Sci, Miami, 66-67; asst. curator, CALIF. ACAD. SCI, 67-69, CHMN. & ASSOC. CURATOR, 69- Supv. ichthyologist, Vanderbilt Proj, Calif. Acad. Sci, 67-69; prin. investr, Nat. Sci. Found. grants, study of Indo-Pac. scorpionfishes & transfer of Stanford Univ. fish collection to Calif. Acad. Sci. Am. Soc. Ichthyol. & Herpet; Am. Fisheries Soc. Systematics, zoogeography and biology of fishes. Address: Dept. of Ichthyology, California Academy of Sciences Golden Gate Park, San Francisco, CA 94118.

ESCHNER, ALBERT, JR, b. Los Angeles, Calif, Oct 6, 27; m. 51; c. 4. ELECTRICAL ENGINEERING. B.S, Calif. Inst. Technol, 50; M.S, Univ. South. Calif, 53. Design & res. engr, radar div, Hughes Aircraft Co, 51-57, circuits sect. head, comput. div, 58-62, mgr. advan. tech. dept. 62-63, mgr. syst. tech. dept, radar div, 64-67; asst. chief engr. & chief scientist, AVIONICS & SENSORS DIV, N.AM. ROCKWELL CORP, 67-71, MGR. RADAR SONAR ENG, 71- U.S.N, 45-46. Sr. mem. Inst. Elec. & Electronics Eng. Technical management of research and development programs for advanced avionics and sensor systems; radar, sonar, electro-optics, microelectronics, displays; analog and digital signal processing. Address: 1011 Grandview Ave, Fullerton, CA 92632.

ESCHNER, ARTHUR R(ICHARD), b. Buffalo, N.Y, Sept. 29, 25; m. 51; c. 3. FORESTRY, HYDROLOGY. B.S, State Univ. N.Y. Col. Forestry, Syracuse, 50, Ph.D.(silvicult), 65; M.S, Iowa State Col, 52. Res. forester, cent. states forest exp. sta, U.S. Forest Serv, 53-54, northeast. forest exp. sta, Pa, 54-58, W.Va, 59-61, res. forester & proj. leader, N.Y, 61-64; asst. prof. FOREST INFLUENCES, STATE UNIV. N.Y. COL. FORESTRY, SYRACUSE UNIV, 64-65, assoc. prof, 65-70, PROF, 70- U.S.N.R, 43-46. AAAS; Soc. Am. Foresters; Soil Sci. Soc. Am; Am. Geophys. Union. Effect of forest conditions on the disposition of precipitation and energy; watershed management, especially soil moisture, evaporation, transpiration and snow accumulation and dissipation. Address: State University of New York College of Forestry at Syracuse University, Syracuse, NY 13210.

ESCHNER, EDWARD G(EORGE), b. N.Y, June 3, 13; m. 36; c. 5. RADIOLOGY. M.D, Buffalo, 36. Res. orthop, Buffalo Gen. Hosp, 37-38, radiol, 38-40, assoc, 40-42; private practice, 46-47; DIR. RADIOL, E.J. MEYER MEM. HOSP, 47-; CLIN. PROF. RADIOL, SCH. MED, STATE UNIV, N.Y. BUFFALO, 54-, ACTING HEAD DEPT, 66- U.S.A, 42-45, Lt. Col. Radiol. Soc. N.Am; Am. Col. Radiol; Am. Med. Asn; Pan-Am. Med. Asn. Address: 1275 Delaware Ave, Buffalo, NY 14209.

ESCOBAL, PEDRO RAMON, b. Logroño, Spain, June 1, 36; U.S. citizen; m. 67. SPACE SCIENCE, ASTRODYNAMICS. B.A, N.Y. Univ, 57, B.A.E, 59; M.S, California, Los Angeles, 64. Res. engr, Rocketdyne Div, N.Am. Aviation, Inc, 59-61; mem. tech. staff, Aerospace Corp, 61-62; sr. scientist, Lockheed-Calif. Co, 62-64; sect. head space mech, TRW Systs, 64-66, asst. mgr. mission design dept, 66-69; ASST. PROJ. MGR, SYSTS. ANAL. LAB, HUGHES AIRCRAFT CO, 69- Chance-Vought Mem. Prize for airplane design, 59. Am. Inst. Aeronaut. & Astronaut; Am. Astronaut. Soc. Mathematics; celestial mechanics; computer systems and program development; management and research oriented scientific activities. Address: Systems Analysis Lab, Hughes Aircraft Co, 1950 E. Imperial Blvd, El Segundo, CA 90009.

ESCOBAR, MARIO R, b. Lima, Peru, Jan. 31, 31; U.S. citizen; m. 59; c. 2. MICROBIOLOGY, BIOCHEMISTRY. B.A, Louisville, 54; M.S, Georgetown, 60; Ph.D.(bact, biochem), Indiana, 63. Med. technologist, clin. path. lab, St. Mary & Elizabeth Hosp, Louisville, Ky, 52-54; supvr, Miller Clin, Morgantown, 54-55; res. asst. hemat, Walter Reed Army Inst. Res, 55-57; serologist & supvr, path. & serol. clin. labs, Children's Hosp, Wash, D.C, 57-61; asst. bact. & med. microbiol, Indiana, 61-63; Nat. Acad. Sci-Nat. Res. Coun. res. assoc. enteric bact, commun. disease ctr, U.S. Pub. Health Serv, Ga, 63-64, dir. clin. path, clin. pub. health labs, Ohio, 64-65; Nat. Cancer Inst. fel. cancer & virol, Univ. Miami, 65-67; asst. prof. virol, faculty mem, dept. path. & head diag. & res. virus labs, Med. Col. Va, 67-69; ASST. PROF. CLIN. PATH, VA. COMMONWEALTH UNIV, 69- Med.Serv.C, U.S.A, 55-57. AAAS; Am. Soc. Microbiol; Am. Inst. Biol. Sci; Tissue Cult. Asn; Sci. Res. Soc. Am; Brit. Soc. Gen. Microbiol. Serology of Histoplasma capsulatum; immunology of pneumococcus; serology of Serratia; bacteriophages and immunogenetics of Salmonella; preservation of human erythrocytes; laboratory diagnosis of viral diseases; virus purification; oncogenic viruses; role of lymphocyte in cancer immunity. Address: Dept. of Clinical Pathology, Virginia Commonwealth University, Richmond, VA 23219.

ESCOFFERY, CHARLES A(LEXANDER), b. Managua, Nicaragua, Feb. 25, 17; nat; m. 42; c. 2. PHYSICAL CHEMISTRY. B.S, Acadia Univ, 37; McGill Univ, 37-39; Ph.D.(phys. chem), Mass. Inst. Technol, 44; hon. D.Sc, Acadia Univ, 71. Lab. asst, Acadia, 34-37; demonstr, McGill, 37-39; asst, Mass. Inst. Tech, 41-42; res. eng, Fed. Tel. & Radio Corp, N.J, 42-45, dir. res. & develop. dept, selenium div, 45-47, res. eng, Fed. Telecommunications Labs, 47-48, Fed. Tel. & Radio Corp, 48-50; sr. chemist, Int. Rectifier Corp, 50-54, chief chemist, 54-58, mgr. mil. res, 58-59, mil. prod, 59-60, tech. asst. to pres, 60-62; staff engr. mat. tech. dept, HUGHES AIRCRAFT CO, 62-67, asst. mgr. mat. & process eng, ELECTRODYNAMICS DIV, 67-70, SR. STAFF ENGR, 70- R.E. Templin Award, Am. Soc. Test. & Mat, 69. Am. Phys. Soc; Inst. Elec. & Electronics Eng; Electrochem. Soc; Sci. Res. Soc. Am; fel. Am. Inst. Chem; Am. Ceramic Soc; Soc. Aerospace Mat. & Process Eng. Materials and processes for vacuum tubes, ceramics, metallizing, oxide cathodes, potting and encapsulation, microwave absorbers. Address: Hughes Aircraft Co, P.O. Box 2999, Torrance, CA 90509.

ESCUDIER, M(ARCEL) P(AUL), b. Cambridge, Eng, July 17, 42; m. 66. FLUID MECHANICS. B.Sc, Univ. London, 63, dipl, Imp. Col, 64, Beit fel, 65, Ph.D.(mech. eng), 67. Res. assoc. MECH. ENG, Mass. Inst. Technol, 67-69; ASST. PROF, UNIV. SOUTH. CALIF, 69- Consult. liquid propulsion sect, Jet Propulsion Lab, 70-; dir, Univ. Consult, Inc, 71- Am. Inst. Aeronaut. & Astronaut. Turbulent shear-flow studies, especially convective heat transfer; numerical calculation of boundary-layer development; plume motion in stratified atmosphere; large-scale structure of a plane jet; chemically-reacting plume motion. Address: Dept. of Mechanical Engineering, University of Southern California, Los Angeles, CA 90007.

ESCUE, R(ICHARD) B(YRD), JR, b. Denton, Tex, Apr. 24, 19; m. 45; c. 3. CHEMISTRY. B.A, North Texas State, 39, M.A, 40; fel, Calif. Inst. Tech, 40-43, Ph.D.(chem, physics), 44; Oak Ridge Inst. Nuclear Studies, 51. Lab. asst. chem, North Texas State, 40; physicist, Neches Butane Prod. Co, Tex, 43-45; asst. prof. chem, N.TEX. STATE UNIV, 45-47, assoc. prof. chem. & phys, 47-53, PROF. CHEM, 53- Res. grants-in-aid, Res. Corp, N.Y, 45-48; Robert A. Welch Found, Tex, 55-64; Am. Acad. Arts & Sci, 56; Nat. Insts. Health, 57-58; counsr, Oak Ridge Inst. Nuclear Studies, 58- AAAS; Am. Chem. Soc. Molten salts; radiochemistry; phase systems; microscopy. Address: Dept. of Chemistry, North Texas State University, Denton, TX 76203.

ESENTHER, GLENN R, b. Chicago, Ill, June 23, 26; m. 55; c. 10. ENTOMOLOGY. B.S, St. Ambrose Col, 51; M.S, Marquette, 53; Ph.D.(entom), Wisconsin, 61. Instr. zool, Marquette, 53-54; biol, Xavier (Ohio), 54-55; ENTOMOLOGIST, FOREST PROD. LAB, U.S. FOREST SERV, 60- U.S.A, 44-46. Entom. Soc. Am; Forest Prod. Res. Soc. Biology, particularly ecology and control of termites and other wood products insects. Address: U.S. Forest Products Lab, Madison, WI 53705.

ESHBACH, JOHN R(OBERT), b. Bethlehem, Pa, Oct. 7, 22; m. 44; c. 4. SOLID STATE PHYSICS. B.S, Northwestern, 44, B.S, 46, M.S, 47; Ph.D. (physics), Mass. Inst. Tech, 51. Res. assoc. photoconductive cells, Northwestern, 46-47; res. asst. microwave spectros, Mass. Inst. Tech, 48-50; res. assoc, GEN. ELEC. RES. LAB, 51-62, mgr. light prod. studies, 62-68, MGR. MICROWAVE BR, 68- U.S.N.R, 44-45, 53, Lt.(jg), Am. Phys. Soc; Inst. Elec. & Electronics Eng. Microwave spectroscopy; magnetism; ferrite devices; luminescence; microwave devices. Address: 2755 Rosendale Rd, Schenectady, NY 12309.

ESHBAUGH, WILLIAM HARDY, b. Glen Ridge, N.J, May 1, 36; m. 58; c. 3. BIOSYSTEMATICS, ETHNOBOTANY. A.B, Cornell, 59; M.A, Indiana, 61, Nat. Sci. Found. summer fel, 63, Ph.D.(bot), 64. Lectr. bot, Indiana, 62; ASST. PROF. BOT. & CURATOR HERBARIUM, Southern Illinois, 65-67; MIAMI UNIV, 67- Chem.C, 64-65, Res, 65-; Capt; Army commendation medal, 65. AAAS; Am. Soc. Plant Taxon; Bot. Soc; Am; Soc. Study Evolution. Biosystematic and phytogeographic studies in the Empetraceae and the genus Capsicum and allied genera. Address: Dept. of Botany, Miami University, Oxford, OH 45056.

ESHGHY, SIAVASH, b. Ahvaz, Iran, Feb. 12, 35; m. 59; c. 3. HEAT TRANSFER, FLUID MECHANICS. B.S.E, Univ. Tehran, 57; M.S.E, Univ. Mich, Ann Arbor, 60, Ph.D.(mech. eng), 63. Asst. prof. mech. eng, Carnegie Inst. Technol, 63-68, assoc. prof, Carnegie-Mellon Univ, 68-70; SR. RES. SCIENTIST & GROUP LEADER, ROCKWELL MFG. CO, 70- Consult, space-defense div, Am. Optical Co, 65-68; vis. res. analyst, Rockwell Mfg. Co, 69-70; sr. lectr, Carnegie-Mellon Univ, 70- Am. Soc. Mech. Eng; Soc. Automotive Eng. Gas-film lubrication, flow measurement and control. Address: Central Research, Rockwell Mfg. Co, 400 N. Lexington Ave, Pittsburgh, PA 15208.

ESHLEMAN, RONALD L, b. Shellsville, Pa, Aug. 24, 33; m. 59. MECHANICAL & AEROSPACE ENGINEERING. B.S.M.E, Lafayette Col, 59; M.S, Lehigh, 61; Ph.D.(mech. & aerospace eng), Ill. Inst. Tech, 67. Teaching asst. mech. eng, Lehigh, 59-61; instr, Ill. Inst. Tech, 61-64; asst. res.

engr, IIT RES. INST, 64-66, assoc. res. engr, 66-67, res. engr, 67-69, SR. RES. ENGR, 69- Consult, Am. Nat. Standards Inst, 68-, chmn. comt. S2-55; tech. ed, Shock & Vibration Digest, 69- U.S.N, 53-55. Nat. Soc. Prof. Eng; N.Y. Acad. Sci; Am. Soc. Mech. Eng. Engineering analysis; rotor dynamics; Shock and vibration isolation; dynamics of machines; digital simulation of machines; tape dynamics. Address: 333 Ridge Ave, Clarendon Hills, IL 60514.

ESHLEMAN, VON R(USSEL), b. Darke Co, Ohio, Sept. 17, 24; m. 47; c. 4. ELECTRICAL ENGINEERING. B.E.E, George Washington, 49; M.S, Stanford, 50, Atomic Energy Comn. fel, 51-52, Ph.D.(elec. eng), 52. Res. assoc, radio propagation lab, STANFORD UNIV, 52-56, instr. elec. eng, 56-57, asst. prof, 57-59, assoc. prof, 59-61, PROF. ELEC. ENG, & CO-DIR. CTR. RADAR ASTRON, 61- Mem. exec. comt. comn, Int. Sci. Radio Union, 63-66; consult, Nat. Acad. Sci; Nat. Bur. Standards; Inst. Defense Anal; Stanford Res. Inst; N.Am. Aviation, Inc; mem, Int. Astronaut. Cong; Int. Astron. Union. U.S.N.R, 43-46. Fel. AAAS; fel. Inst. Elec. & Electronics Eng; Am. Astron. Soc; Am. Geophys. Union; fel. Royal Astron. Soc. Radar astronomy; ionospheric and plasma physics; radio wave propagation; astronautics. Address: Center for Radar Astronomy, Stanford University, Stanford, CA 94305.

ESKELSON, CLEAMOND D, b. American Fork, Utah, Sept. 27, 27; m. 46; c. 1. BIOCHEMISTRY, ORGANIC CHEMISTRY. B.S, Utah, 50; M.S, Louisville, 57; Ph.D.(biochem), Nebraska, Omaha, 67. Analyst, Am. Smelting & Ref. Agr. Lab, Utah, summer 50; res. technician, dept. internal med, Univ. Utah, 50-51; analyst, Geneva Steel Co, 51-52; biochemist, Army Med. Res. Lab, Ft. Knox, Ky, 52-55; clin. chemist, Vet. Admin. Hosp, Omaha, Nebr, 57-59, biochemist, Vet. Admin. Radioisotope Lab, 59-67; CHEMIST, VET. ADMIN. HOSP, TUCSON, ARIZ, 67- Consult, Creighton, 58-59; instr, col. med, Nebraska, 67-68; Licensed Beverage Indust. res. grant, 68-69. U.S.N, 45-46. AAAS; N.Y. Acad. Sci; Am. Chem. Soc; Soc. Nuclear Med; Asn. Clin. Med. Thyroid physiology; effects of x-irradiation on biological systems; mechanisms for controlling cholesterolgenesis; vitaminology; development of radiometric procedures for diagnosing cancer. Address: Veterans Administartion Hospital, Tucson, AZ 87513.

ESKELUND, KENNETH H, b. Waterville, Maine, Feb. 13, 24; m. 50; c. 3. VETERINARY MEDICINE. D.V.M, Mich. State, 51. Diagnostician, S.Jersey Diag. Lab, 51-52; veterinarian-in-charge poultry, State of Ind, 52-53; veterinarian mgr, Ft. Halifax Poultry Co, 53-57; PRES. & DIR, Maine Biol. Labs, Inc, 57-66, GEN. MGR, MAINE BIOL. LAB, DIV, MORTON-NORWICH PROD. INC, 66- Pres, Maine Poultry Serv, 58-; Maine Poultry Consults, 59- U.S.A.F, 43-46, Sgt. Am. Vet. Med. Asn; Am. Asn. Avian Path; Poultry Sci. Asn; U.S. Animal Health Asn; N.Y. Acad. Sci. Development of inactivated avian vaccines. Address: Maine Biological Labs, P.O. Box 255, Waterville, ME 04901.

ESKER, DONALD WILLIAM, b. Harvey, Ill, Jan. 23, 33; m. 62. PLASMA PHYSICS. B.S, Eastern Illinois, 60; M.S, Purdue, 62. Res. assoc. plasma physics, RES. DIV, McDONNELL AIRCRAFT CORP, 62-64, res. scientist, 64-67, assoc. scientist, 67-71, SR. GROUP ENGR, PROPULSION SYSTS, 71- U.S.N, 52-56. Am. Asn. Physics Teachers. Arc-jet thrusters for electric propulsion space systems. Address: Dept. 243, Bldg. 32, McDonnell Aircraft Corp, P.O. Box 516, St. Louis, MO 63166.

ESKEW, CLETIS T(HEODORE), b. Cloud Chief, Okla, July 10, 04; m. 36; c. 1. BIOLOGY. B.S, Southwest. State Col.(Okla), 31; Wyoming, 35; M.S, Oklahoma, 37; Ed.D, North Texas State, 60. Prof. biol, Mangum Jr. Col, 37-39; Southwest. State Col.(Okla), 39-42; Midwest. Univ, 42-69, dir. div. sci. & math, 61-68, assoc. dean instruction, 61-69, dean div. grad. stud, 68-69, dean, 48-49, liberal arts, 59-61; RETIRED. Distinguished serv. award, Midwest. Univ, 69. Taxonomy and ecology; plant physiology; vegetation of Oklahoma and Texas. Address: 2718 Chase Dr, Wichita Falls, TX 76308.

ESKIN, NEASON AKIVA MICHAEL, b. Birmingham, Eng, May 4, 41; m. 70. FOOD CHEMISTRY, BIOCHEMISTRY. B.Sc, Univ. Birmingham, 63, Ph.D. (physiol. chem), 66. Lectr. biochem, Borough Polytech, Eng, 66-68; ASST. PROF. FOOD CHEM, UNIV. MAN, 69- Can. Inst. Food Technol; Brit. Inst. Food Sci. & Technol; Inst. Food Technol. Nonenzymic browning reactions; fatty acid composition of beef, especially intramuscular and extramuscular and fat; rancidity in fish products; texture of vegetables. Address: Dept. of Foods & Nutrition, Faculty of Home Economics, University of Manitoba, Winnipeg 19, Man, Can.

ESKINAZI, SALAMON, b. Izmir, Turkey, Nov. 25, 22; nat; m. 51; c. 2. MECHANICS. B.S, Robert Col, Turkey, 46; M.S, Wyoming, 48; D.Eng, Hopkins, 54. Res. assoc, Hopkins, 50-53, instr. MECH. ENG, 53-55; assoc. prof, SYRACUSE UNIV, 55-61, PROF, 61-, CHMN. DEPT. MECH. & AEROSPACE ENG, 66- Fulbright scholar, France & assoc. prof, Poitiers, 63-64; lectr, Cambridge & Oxford, 63-64. Consult, Fairchild Aircraft & Carrier Corp, 59-; Howard, Needles, Tammer & Bergendoff, 67; Tenn. Technol. Univ, 68-69; Gen. Elec. Corp, 70. Am. Soc. Mech. Eng; Am. Soc. Eng. Educ; Am. Inst. Aeronaut. & Astronaut. Fluid and statistical mechanics; heat transfer; thermodynamics; general mechanics of continuum; magnetohydrodynamics; fluid mechanics and thermodynamics of the environment. Address: Dept. of Mechanical & Aerospace Engineering, Syracuse University, Syracuse, NY 13210.

ESKRIDGE, CHARLES D(eWITT), III, b. Walterboro, S.C, Aug. 21, 37; m. 57; c. 3. ENGINEERING MECHANICS. B.S, Va. Polytech, 59, M.S, 63, Ph.D. (eng. mech), 64. Instr. eng. mech, Va. Polytech, 59-64; RES. ENGR. DYNAMICS, DOUGLAS AIRCRAFT CO, INC, 64- Spinning bodies with variable mass; solid mechanics of plates. Address: 1004 Lepley Rd, Hanahan, SC 29406.

ESLICK, ROBERT FREEMAN, b. Walla Walla, Wash, Dec. 24, 16; m. 39; c. 1. PLANT BREEDING, AGRONOMY. B.S, Washington State, 39; M.S, Wyoming, 42; Wisconsin, 48; Oregon State, 56. Instr. AGRON. & asst. agronomist, Wyoming, 39-42; asst. prof. & asst. agronomist, Colorado State, 42-43, 46; assoc. prof. & assoc. agronomist, MONT. STATE UNIV, 46-58, PROF. & AGRONOMIST, 58- Med.C, U.S.A, 44-45. Fel. AAAS; fel. Am. Soc. Agron.

Cultural and plant breeding studies with forage grasses and legumes, oil crops, oats and barley; barley genetics. Address: Dept. of Plant & Soil Science, Montana State University, Bozeman, MT 59715.

ESLYN, WALLACE E(UGENE), b. Lawrenceville, Ill, Nov. 13, 24; m. 47; c. 5. PLANT PATHOLOGY. B.S, Montana State, 50, M.S, 53; Ph.D.(plant path), Iowa State Col, 56. Plant pathologist, forest prod. lab, U.S. FOREST SERV, 57, forest insect. & disease lab, N.Mex, 57-60, FOREST PROD. LAB, 60-69, SUPV. RES. PLANT PATHOLOGIST, BIODEGRADATION & CONTROL PROJ, SOLID WOOD PROD. RES.DIV, 69- U.S.M.C, 43-45, 50-51, S/Sgt. Soc. Am. Foresters; Am. Phytopath. Soc; Mycol. Soc. Am. Forest products pathology and mycology. Address: Solid Wood Research, Forest Products Lab, U.S. Forest Service, Madison, WI 53705.

ESMAY, DONALD L(EVERN), b. Murdo, S.Dak, Nov. 1, 17; m. 45; c. 6. ORGANIC CHEMISTRY. B.A, Dakota Wesleyan, 46; Ph.D.(chem), Iowa State, 51. Res. chemist, Standard Oil Co.(Ind), 52-55; tech. dir. org. prod. div, Lithium Corp. Am, 56-60; RES. SPECIALIST, MINN. MINING & MFG. CO, 61- U.S.A, 40-45. Am. Chem. Soc. Organometallic and fluorine compounds; heterocycles; hydrocarbon conversions; petroleum, lithium, propellant and fluorine chemistry; polymers; organic syntheses; propellants; market research; research and chemical company management; rocket propellants; polyurethanes; foams. Address: 1237 98th Lane N.W, Coon Rapids, MN 55433.

ESMAY, MERLE L(INDEN), b. Greene Co, Iowa, Dec. 27, 20; m. 42; c. 2. AGRICULTURAL ENGINEERING. B.S.A.E, S.Dak. State Univ, 42; M.S.A.E, Iowa State Univ, 47; Ph.D.(agr. eng. & struct. eng), 51. Exten. agr. engr, S.Dak. State Univ, 46; asst. prof. teaching & res, Iowa State Univ, 47-51; PROF, Univ. Mo, 51-55; AGR. ENG, MICH. STATE UNIV, 55-, chief party, univ. contract adv. team Taiwan, 62-64. Partic, Int. Cong, Australia, 62, Philippines, 63, Switz, 64, Eng, 65, Ger, 69, Spain & Belgium, 70, Philippines & Italy, 71. C.Eng, 42-46, Capt. Am. Soc. Agr. Eng.(Metal Bldg. Mfrs. Asn. Award, 66; engr. of the year, Mich. Sect, 66); Am. Soc. Eng. Educ. Environmental requirements of livestock shelters; rice drying, storage and handling; mechanization in developing countries. Address: Dept. of Agricultural Engineering, Michigan State University, East Lansing, MI 48823.

ESPANA, CARLOS, b. Mexico City, Mex, Mar. 1, 19; m. 49. VIROLOGY, IMMUNOLOGY. Pharmacist, Univ. Guanajuato, 37; M.S, Nat. Polytech. Inst, Mex, 43; Latin Am. fel, Univ. Calif, Berkeley, 44-45, univ. fel, 45-46, Nat. Found. Infantile Paralysis fel, 46-49, Ph.D, 49. Head sect. virol, E.R. Squibb & Sons, 49-51, res. assoc. microbiol, Squibb Inst. Med. Res, 51-52, head dept. chemother, 52-54; res. assoc. vet. med, Univ. Pa, 54-57, res. asst. prof, 57-63; specialist, NAT. CTR. PRIMATE BIOL, UNIV. CALIF, DAVIS, 64-68, RES. ASSOC. VIROL, 68- Prin. investr. grants, E.R. Squibb & Sons of Mex. Div, Mathieson Corp, 54-60 & Nat. Inst. Allergy & Infectious Diseases, 60-63; rep, Nat. Anaplasmosis Conf, 57 & 62; mem. ad hoc comt. of consult. on simian viruses, diag. virol. sect, viral carcinogenesis br, Nat. Cancer Inst, 65-67; partic, Workshops on Virus Diseases of Non-Human Primates, 68 & 71; Int. Conf. Exp. Med. & Surg. in Primates, 69. Am. Soc. Microbiol; fel. N.Y. Acad. Sci; fel. Am. Acad. Microbiol; Mex. Asn. Microbiol; Mex. Asn. Chem. Bact. Studies on isolation, epidemiology and immunologic properties of arboviruses; development of viral vaccines; experimental chemotherapy of viral diseases; studies on the nature and immunologic properties of Anaplasma marginale; simian viruses—zoonoses. Address: National Center for Primate Biology, University of California, Davis, CA 95616.

ESPELIE, M(ARY) SOLVEIG, b. New London, Conn, Dec. 24, 40. MATHEMATICS, ALGEBRA. B.A, Luther Col, 62; M.A, Univ. Md, College Park, 64, Nat. Sci. Found. grants, 64 & 68, Ph.D.(Banach algebras), 68. Asst, Univ. Md, College Park, 62-68; ASST. PROF. MATH, Univ. Cincinnati, 68-69; HOWARD UNIV, 69- Am. Math. Soc; Math. Asn. Am. Investigation of multiplicative and extreme operators between Banach*-algebras, with identity or approximate identity, and their integral representations; topological properties of the space of multiplicative operators of norm one. Address: Dept. of Mathematics, Howard University, Washington, DC 20001.

ESPENSCHEID, WILTON F, b. Sodus, N.Y, Nov. 26, 34; m. 56; c. 4. PHYSICAL CHEMISTRY. B.S, Clarkson Tech, 56, M.S, 57, Ph.D.(chem), 65. SR. RES. CHEMIST, MOBIL OIL CORP, 58- U.S.A.R, 56-62, 2nd Lt. Colloid chemistry; aerosols; light scattering; aqueous and nonaqueous soap systems; fluids. Address: 3 Taylor Rd, R.D. 4, Princeton, NJ 08540.

ESPENSHADE, G(ILBERT) H(OWRY), b. State College, Pa, Nov. 28, 12; m. 38; c. 3. GEOLOGY. B.S, Pa. State, 33; A.M, Princeton, 35, Ph.D. (econ. geol), 37. Mine geologist, Cerro de Pasco Copper Corp, 37-39; from recorder to assoc. geologist, U.S. GEOL. SURV, 40-50, GEOLOGIST, 50- AAAS; Geol. Soc. Am; Soc. Econ. Geol; Mineral. Soc. Am. Geology and ore deposits of the Appalachians; mineral deposits; metamorphic rocks; structural geology. Address: U.S. Geological Survey, Washington, DC 20242.

ESPENSON, JAMES H(ENRY), b. Los Angeles, Calif, Apr. 1, 37; m. 60; c. 1. INORGANIC CHEMISTRY. B.S, Calif. Inst. Technol, 58; Ph.D.(inorg. chem), Wisconsin, 62. Res. assoc, Stanford, 62-63; instr. CHEM, IOWA STATE UNIV, 63-65, asst. prof, 65-67, assoc. prof, 68-71, PROF, 71- Fel, Alfred P. Sloan Found, 68-70. AAAS; Am. Chem. Soc; The Chem. Soc. Inorganic and bio-inorganic reaction mechanisms; kinetics of reactions of metal complexes; vitamin B_{12} and metalloporphyrin chemistry; electron transfer and substitution reactions. Address: Dept. of Chemistry, Iowa State University, Ames, IA 50010.

ESPERSEN, G(EORGE) A(NDREW), b. Jersey City, N.J, May 17, 06; m. 35; c. 2. PHYSICS. B.S, N.Y. Univ, 31; Carnegie grant, Inst. Theoret. Physics, Denmark. Tube develop. engr, Hygrade Sylvania Corp, 32-39; Nat. Union Radio Corp, 39-40; proj. engr, klystron tubes, Sperry Gyroscope Co, 40-42; chief transmitting tube develop. engr, N.AM. PHILIPS CO. & PHILIPS LABS, 42-62, res. physicist & sect. chief in charge microwave tube sect, 45-62, STAFF ASST, 62- Am. Phys. Soc; Inst. Elec. & Electronics Eng. Physics, design of electronic and gaseous tubes; design development and production of radar tubes. Address: 65 Bellewood Ave, Dobbs Ferry, NY 10522.

ESPERTI, ROBERT V(INCENT), b. Detroit, Mich, Jan. 10, 27; m. 51; c. 1. MATHEMATICS. A.B, Wayne, 49; M.S, Purdue, 51. Asst. Purdue, 49-51; mathematician, U.S. Naval Avionics Facility, 51-58; sr. mathematician, Allison Div, GEN. MOTORS CORP, 58-60, sr. res. mathematician, Gen. Motors Defense Res. Labs, 60-70, DEVELOP. ENGR, GEN. MOTORS ELEC. RES. LABS, 70- U.S.N, 45-46, Res, 46- Math. Asn. Am. Applied mathematics; celestial mechanics. Address: 3610 Capri Dr, Santa Barbara, CA 93105.

ESPEY, LAWRENCE LEE, b. Mercedes, Tex, Sept. 5, 35; m. 59; c. 3. REPRODUCTIVE PHYSIOLOGY. B.A, Texas, 58, M.A, 61; Ph.D.(physiol), Fla. State, 64. Res. technologist PHYSIOL, dent. br, Texas, 59-60; Nat. Insts. Health fel. & res. assoc, Univ. Mich. 64-66; asst. prof, TRINITY UNIV, 66-70, ASSOC. PROF, 70- Instr, Fla. State Univ, summer, 64; grants, Nat. Inst. Child Health & Human Develop, 67-69, 69-70, 70-71; Morrison Trust grant, 67-68. AAAS; Am. Physiol. Soc; Soc. Study Reproduction. Physical and chemical mechanisms of mammalian ovulation. Address: Dept. of Biology, Trinity University, San Antonio, TX 78284.

ESPEY, WILLIAM H, JR, b. Raleigh, N.C, Sept. 4, 37; m. 60; c. 2. CIVIL ENGINEERING, WATER RESOURCES. B.S, Univ. Tex, 60, M.S, 63; U.S. Pub. Health Serv, fel, 63-64, Ph.D.(civil eng), 65. Instr. civil eng, Texas, 60-61, res. assoc, 64-65; hydraulic engr, U.S. Geol. Surv, 61-63; PROG. MGR. OCEAN SCI. & WATER RESOURCES, TRACOR, INC, 65- Am. Geophys. Union; Am. Soc. Civil Eng; Water Pollution Control Fedn; Marine Technol. Soc. Development and application of mathematical models and computer simulation techniques to the solution of water resources and oceanographic problems. Address: Ocean Sciences & Water Resources, Tracor, Inc, 6500 Tracor Lane, Austin, TX 78721.

ESPINO, RAMON LUIS, b. Santiago, Cuba, Aug. 18, 41; U.S. citizen; CHEMICAL ENGINEERING. B.S, La. State Univ, 64; M.S, Mass. Inst. Technol, 66, D.Sc.(chem. eng), 68. Asst. dir. chem. eng, Mass. Inst. Technol, 66-67; MGR. PROCESS DEVELOP, CHEM SYSTS. INC, HACKENSACK, N.J, 68- Am. Chem. Soc; Am. Inst. Chem. Eng. Chemical kinetics and reaction engineering; heterogeneous catalysis; cryogenic engineering. Address: 151 E. 80th St, Apt. 8D, New York, NY 10021.

ESPINOSA, ROBERT J, b. Portland, Ore, May 30, 31; m. 51; c. 4. ELECTRONIC ENGINEERING. B.S, Seattle, 60; M.S, Stanford, 63. Sr. engr, Varian Assocs, 60-67; HEAD HIGH POWER RES. & DEVELOP, ELECTRON DEVICES DEPT, WATKINS-JOHNSON CO, 67- Inst. Elec. & Electronics Eng. Medium and high power traveling wave tubes; high power pulsed TWT's for radar and broadband continuous wave amplifier; TWT's for countermeasures and communications transmitters; microwave electronics. Address: Electron Devices Dept, Watkins-Johnson Co, 3333 Hillview Ave, Palo Alto, CA 94303.

ESPLIN, DON W(YNN), b. Cedar City, Utah, Apr. 2, 27; m. 46; c. 4. PHARMACOLOGY. B.S, Utah, 50, fel, M.S, 52, Nat. Sci. Found. fel, Ph.D.(pharmacol), 55. Asst. bact. Utah, 49-52, asst. pharmacol, 52-55, instr, 55-58, asst. res. prof. PHARMACOL, 58-63, assoc. prof. 63-67, PROF, 67-68; McGILL UNIV, 68- Nat. Inst. Health travel fel, Belgium, 57, Sr. Fel, 58-63. Spec. lectr, London, 62; assoc, Med. Res. Coun, 69. Abel award, 61; Golden Plate award, Acad. Achievement, 62. AAAS; Am. Soc. Pharmacol. Pharmacology of central nervous system; neurohumoral transmitters; neurotoxins; convulsive disorders; physiological instrumentation; microbiology. Address: Dept. of Pharmacology & Therapeutics, McIntyre Medical Center, McGill University, Montreal, 2, Que, Can.

ESPOSITO, JOHN NICHOLAS, b. Youngstown, Ohio, July 23, 38; m. 63; c. 2. INORGANIC CHEMISTRY. B.S, Youngstown, 60; Ph.D.(chem), Case, 66. SR. RES. SCIENTIST, RES. LABS, WESTINGHOUSE ELEC. CORP, 66- Chem.C, 61-62, 1st Lt. AAAS; Am. Chem. Soc. Combustion of metals; inorganic chemistry of hexacoordinated silicon and germanium; surface chemistry; high temperature chemistry. Address: Westinghouse Electric Corp, Research & Development Center, Pittsburgh, PA 15235.

ESPOSITO, MICHAEL SALVATORE, b. Brooklyn, N.Y, Nov. 30, 40; c. 1. GENETICS, BIOCHEMISTRY. B.S, Brooklyn Col, 61; Nat. Insts. Health fel. & Ph.D.(genetics), Univ. Wash, 67. Nat. Insts. Health fel, lab. molecular biol, Univ. Wis, Madison, 67-69; ASST. PROF. BIOL, UNIV. CHICAGO, 69- Nat. Sci. Found. grants, 69-70, 71- AAAS; Genetics Soc. Am; Am. Soc. Microbiol. Yeast genetics and physiology; biochemical and genetic regulation of recombination, meiosis and sporulation. Address: Dept. of Biology, University of Chicago, 1103 E. 57th St, Chicago, IL 60637.

ESPOSITO, RAFFAELE, b. Rome, Italy, Aug. 11, 32; m. 62; c. 1. COMMUNICATIONS. Dr.Ing.(elec. eng), Rome, 56. Asst. prof. elec. eng, Rome, 57-59; Fulbright asst. prof, Arkansas, 59-60; res. scientist COMMUN. THEORY, Raytheon Res. Div, 60-61; sr. staff mem, Selenia S.p.A, Italy, 61-63; sr. res. scientist, RAYTHEON RES. DIV, 63- 66, PRIN. RES. SCIENTIST, 66- Italian Air Force, 57-59, 2nd Lt. Inst. Elec. & Electronics Eng; Am. Soc. Eng. Ed; Soc. Indust. & Appl. Math. Communication theory, applications to several fields in electrical engineering. Address: Raytheon Research Division, 28 Seyon St, Waltham, MA 02154.

ESPOSITO, RAYMOND G(ABRIEL), b. Garfield, N.J, Aug. 29, 27; m. 52; c. 1. MICROBIAL PHYSIOLOGY. B.Sc, Illinois, 50; M.Sc, Wisconsin, 55, Ph.D. (bact), 57. Res. biologist, Lederle Labs, 50-53, RES. MICROBIOLOGIST, 57-59; Nutrilite Prod. Inc, 59-64; AM. CYANAMID CO, 64- U.S.N.R, 45-46. Biological nitrogen fixation; intrinsic factor isolation; growth factors; amine acid biosynthesis; fermentations. Address: American Cyanamid Co, Box 383, Princeton, NJ 08540.

ESPOSITO, ROBERT JOHN, b. Philadelphia, Pa, Jan. 12, 37; m. 71. PHYSICS. B.A, Temple, 58, Ph.D.(physics), 68; M.S, Pennsylvania, 60. RES. PHYSICIST, PITMAN DUNN RES. LAB, FRANKFORD ARSENAL, 59- Am. Phys. Soc. Solid state physics; theoretical physics; thin films; optical properties of solids; applied research on munition systems. Address: Frankford Arsenal Pitman Dunn Research Lab, Philadelphia, PA 19137.

ESPOSITO, ROCHELLE E, b. Brooklyn, N.Y, June 28, 41; m. 64; c. 1. GENETICS. B.S, Brooklyn Col, 62; Ph.D.(genetics), Washington (Seattle), 67. ASST. PROF. BIOL, UNIV. CHICAGO, 69- Genetics Soc. Am; Am. Soc. Microbiol. Genetic recombination; genetic and biochemical control of meiosis. Address: Dept. of Biology, University of Chicago, Chicago, IL 60637.

ESPOSITO, VITO MICHAEL, b. Logan, W.Va, Sept. 11, 40; m. 60; c. 1. IMMUNOLOGY, MICROBIOLOGY. B.S, Marshall, 62; M.S, West Virginia, 65, Ph.D.(biochem. genetics), 66. Res. asst. biochem. genetics, West Virginia, 62-66; scientist, commissioned corp, U.S. Pub. Health Serv, Nat. Insts. Health, Md, 67-69, sr. staff fel. & immunologist, lab. blood prod, div. biologics standards, 69-71; DIR. BIOL. RES. & DEVELOP, DADE DIV. AM. HOSP. SUPPLY CORP, 71- U.S.P.H.S, 67-69, Scientist. AAAS; Genetics Soc. Am; Am. Soc. Microbiol; N.Y. Acad. Sci. Genetic basis of antibody synthesis; biochemistry of host-pathogen relationship; biochemistry of development and aging, especially enzymes and subcellular organelles; mechanisms of immunity; diagnostic reagents; genetics. Address: Biological Research & Development Dept, Dade Division American Hospital Supply Corp, 1851 Delaware Pkwy, Miami, FL 33152.

ESPOY, HENRY M(ARTI), b. San Francisco, Calif, Oct. 22, 17; m. 45; c. 2. ANALYTICAL CHEMISTRY. B.S, Loyola (Calif), 39; A.M, California, Los Angeles, 42; Southern California, 48. Res. chemist, Van Camp Labs, 41-49; chemist, Barnett Labs, 49-50, chief chemist, 50-57; LAB. DIR, Terminal Testing Labs, Inc, 57-59; DAYLIN LABS INC, 69- Am. Chem. Soc; Am. Oil Chem. Soc; Inst. Food Technol. Pesticide residues; fats and oils; food and agricultural chemistry. Address: Daylin Labs Inc, 2800 Jewell Ave, Los Angeles, CA 90058.

ESPY, HERBERT H(ASTINGS), b. Rochester, N.Y, June 4, 31; m. 53; c. 2. PHYSICAL ORGANIC CHEMISTRY. A.B, Harvard, 52; Union Carbide & Carbon fel, Wisconsin, 55-56, Ph.D.(phys. org. chem), 56. Res. chemist, HERCULES, INC, 56-70, SR. RES. CHEMIST, 71- Am. Chem. Soc. Vinyl and condensation polymers; aromatic substitution; kinetics of nucleophilic reactions; paper chemicals; polyelectrolyte interactions. Address: Research Center, Hercules, Inc, Wilmington, DE 19899.

ESQUIVEL, AGERICO LIWAG, b. Manila, Philippines, June 5, 32. PHYSICS. A.B, Berchmans Col, Philippines, 55, M.A, 56; Ph.D.(physics), St. Louis, 63. Res. physicist, Res. Inst. Adv. Studies, Md, 63-64; mats. res. lab, Martin Co, 64-66; RES. SCIENTIST, BOEING CO, 66- Summer, Nat. Sci. Found. res. grant, Mass. Inst. Technol, 63 & travel grant, Int. Union Crystallog, Italy, 63. Am. Phys. Soc; Am. Crystallog. Asn; Am. Soc. Metals; Am. Inst. Mining, Metall. & Petrol. Eng. Metal physics; x-ray and electron diffraction; transmission electron microscopy. Address: 2019 Dayton Dr. S.E, Renton, WA 98055.

ESRIG, MELVIN I, b. Brooklyn, N.Y, Mar. 15, 30; m. 54; c. 3. CIVIL ENGINEERING, SOIL MECHANICS. B.B.A, City Col. New York, 51; B.C.E, Polytech. Inst. Brooklyn, 54; M.S, Illinois, 59, Ph.D.(civil eng), 61. Trainee, Corps Engrs, U.S. Army, 54; civil engr, Lockwood, Kessler & Bartlett, Inc, 54-56; H.G. Holzmacher & Assocs, 56-57; soils engr, Warzyn Eng, 61-62; asst. prof. civil eng, Cornell, 62-66, assoc. prof, 66-70; ASSOC, WOODWARD-MOORHOUSE & ASSOC, INC, CLIFTON, 70- Mem, Hwy. Res. Bd, Nat. Acad. Sci-Nat. Res. Coun. AAAS; N.Y. Acad. Sci; Am. Soc. Civil Eng. Foundation engineering. Address: 43 Royden Rd, Tenafly, NJ 07670.

ESSARY, ESKEL O(REN), b. Clarkrange, Tenn, June 2, 17; m. 39; c. 1. POULTRY SCIENCE. B.S, Okla. State, 47, M.S, 49; Ph.D, Mich. State, 61. Asst. prof. poultry husb, Tennessee, 49-52; chemist, Swift Res. Labs, Swift & Co, 52-55; PROF. FOOD SCI. & TECHNOL, VA. POLYTECH. INST. & STATE UNIV, 55- U.S.A.A.F, 43-46. AAAS; Poultry Sci. Asn; Inst. Food Technol; World Poultry Sci. Asn. Poultry specialty items; shelf-life and quality of poultry products; influence of rations on quality and yields of poultry; cooking methods on nutritive value of poultry; influence of feed additives in lyaer rations on quality and functional properties of eggs. Address: Dept. of Food Science, Virginia Polytechnic Institute & State University, Blacksburg, VA 24061.

ESSE, ROBERT C(ARLYLE), b. Walnut Grove, Minn, May 17, 32; m. 54; c. 2. ORGANIC CHEMISTRY. B.A, St. Olaf Col, 54; Ph.D.(org. chem), Oregon State, 59. GROUP LEADER ANTIBIOTICS, PHARMACEUT. PROD. DEVELOP. SECT, LEDERLE LABS. DIV, AM. CYANAMID CO, 59- Am. Chem. Soc. Synthesis of coumarins and furocoumarins; synthetic modification of tetracycline antibiotics. Address: Pharmaceutical Products Development Section, Lederle Labs. Division, American Cyanamid Co, Pearl River, NY 10965.

ESSELEN, WILLIAM B, b. Boston, Mass, July 31, 12; m. 47; c. 1. FOOD TECHNOLOGY. B.S, Mass. State Col, 34, fel, 34-35, M.S, 35, Ph.D.(food tech), 38. Asst. nutrit, Mass. State Col, 36-38; food technologist, Owens-Ill. Glass Co, 39-41; asst. res. prof. FOOD TECH, UNIV. MASS, AMHERST, 41-47, assoc. res. prof, 47-51, res. prof, 51-57, HEAD DEPT, 57- Vis. prof, Hokkaido, 60-61; Univ. West Indies, Trinidad, 71-72. Consult, war food admin, U.S. Dept. Agr, 42-45; food technician, Qm. Corps, U.S. Dept. Army, 45. Am. Soc. Microbiol; Am. Chem. Soc; fel. Am. Pub. Health Asn; Inst. Food Technol. Nutritive fruits; effect of canning, freezing and dehydration on nutrition of foods; determination of process times for canned foods; use of glass containers for foods; apple products. Address: Dept. of Food Science & Technology, University of Massachusetts, Amherst, MA 01002.

ESSELMAN, W(ALTER) H(ENRY), b. Hoboken, N.J, March 19, 17; m. 43; c. 4. ELECTRICAL ENGINEERING. B.S, Newark Col. Eng, 38; M.S, Stevens Inst. Tech, 44; Dr.E.(elec. eng), Polytech. Inst. Brooklyn, 53. Elec. engr, regulating & control systs, Westinghouse Elec. Corp, 38-40, servo & comput. systs. Navy fire control equip, 40-45, develop. engr, control & servosysts, 45-50, mgr. power plant syst, Bettis Atomic Power Div, 50-52, syst. subdiv. atomic power div, 52-53, tech. asst. to mgr, test & develop. nuclear power plants, submarine thermal control test facility, 53-58, mgr. adv. develop. & planning, Bettis Atomic Power Div, 58-59, sr. dept. mgr, astronuclear lab, 59-61, mgr. eng. develop, Nerva Proj, 61-64, dep. mgr, Pa, 64-68, proj. mgr, 68-69, exec. asst. to gen. mgr, 69-70; DIR. HANFORD ENG. DEVELOP. LAB, 70- Instr, Polytech. Inst. Brooklyn, 48. Fel. Am. Nuclear Soc; fel. Inst. Elec. & Electronics Eng; Am. Inst. Aeronaut. & Astronaut. Control and servomechanism systems; magnetic amplifiers; control systems for nuclear power plants; overall characteristics of nuclear plants. Address: Hanford Engineering Development Lab, P.O. Box 1970, Richland, WA 99352.

ESSENBURG, F(RANKLIN), b. Holland, Mich, Aug. 2, 24; m. 46; c. 2. MECHANICS. B.S.E, Michigan, 45, LL.B, 48, M.S, 49, M.S.E, 50, Ph.D.(mech), 56. Patent attorney, Bell Tel. Labs, 50-51; private construct. bus, 51-53; instr. MECH, Michigan, 53-56, asst. prof, 56-58; assoc. prof, Ill. Inst. Technol, 58-61, prof, 61-62; PROF, UNIV. COLO. BOULDER, 62-, chmn. dept. mech. eng, 62-70. U.S.N, 43-45. Am. Soc. Mech. Eng; Am. Soc. Eng. Educ: Soc. Eng. Sci. Continuum mechanics; plate and shell theory; dynamics and vibration. Address: 2165 Vassar Dr, Boulder, CO 80303.

ESSENE, ERIC J, b. Berkeley, Calif, Apr. 26, 39; m. 63; c. 2. GEOLOGY. B.S, Mass. Inst. Technol, 61; Nat. Sci. Found. fel. & Ph.D.(geol), California, Berkeley, 67. Nat. Sci. Found. fel, GEOL, Cambridge, 66-68; ASST. PROF, UNIV. MICH, 68- Univ. res. fel. & co-investr. returned lunar samples, Australian Nat. Univ, 68-70. Petrology and high pressure temperature experimentation on lower crust and upper mantle; thermodynamics and analytical mineralogy; experimentation bearing on the origin of the moon; hydrothermal experiments applicable to metamorphic rocks. Address: Dept. of Geology & Mineralogy, University of Michigan, Ann Arbor, MI 48104.

ESSENWANGER, OSKAR M, b. Munich, W.Ger, Aug. 25, 20; U.S. citizen; m. 47. ATMOSPHERIC PHYSICS. Dipl, Vienna, 43; Dr.rer.nat.(physics), Würzburg, 50. Instr. meteorol, German Air Force, 44-45; res. meteorologist, German Weather Serv, 46-57; Nat. Weather Records Center, 57-61; chief aerophys. br, U.S. ARMY MISSILE COMMAND, 61-71, GROUP LEADER, AEROPHYS, 71- Proj. assoc, Univ. Wis, 56-57; Ger. rep, comt. statist. methods, World Meteorol. Org, 57; affiliated prof, dept. atmospheric physics, Colo. State Univ, 68; adj. prof, Univ. Ala, Huntsville, 71. Am. Meteorol. Soc; Am. Statist. Asn; Am. Soc. Qual. Control; Am. Geophys. Union; Ger. Meteorol. Soc. Physical structure of the atmosphere, especially mathematical analysis and statistical representation of atmospheric parameters for missile design and trajectory analysis; development of statistical methods in climatology. Address: 610 Mountain Gap Dr, Huntsville, AL 35803.

ESSER, ARISTIDE HENRI, b. Padalarang, Indonesia, May 11, 30; U.S. citizen; m. 56; c. 2. PSYCHIATRY, HUMAN ECOLOGY. M.D, Univ. Amsterdam, 55. Intern, Amsterdam Univ. Hosp, 55-56; res. psychiat, Wolfheze Ment. Hosp, Netherlands, 56-57; staff res, Endegeest Psychiat. Clin, 58-61; Lederle Int. res. fel, Yale, 61-62; med. dir. res. ward, Rockland State Hosp, 62-68, dir. psychiat. res, Letchworth Village, 69-71; DEP. DIR, CENT. BERGEN COMMUNITY MENT. HEALTH CTR, 71- City of Leyden travel grant to Ger, Austria & Switz, 60; supvr. psychiatrist, Endegeest Psychiat. Clin, 64; subj. adv, Encyclop. Int, Grolier, Inc, 67-; consult, Jewish Child Care Asn, N.Y, 68-; assoc. prof. div. man-environ. rels, Pa. State Univ, 69-; dir. social biol. labs, Rockland State Hosp, 69-; vis. lectr, sch. archit, Va. Polytech. Inst & State Univ; attend. psychiatrist, col. physicians & surgeons, Columbia Univ, 70- Royal Netherlands Army, 52-54, Sgt. AAAS; Int. Soc. Gen. Semantics; Am. Psychiat. Asn; Animal Behav. Soc; Drug Info. Asn; Soc. Psychophysiol. Res; Soc. Biol. Psychiat; Am. Asn. Ment. Deficiency; Am. Acad. Ment. Retardation; Am. Therapeut. Soc; Am. Med. Asn; N.Y. Acad. Sci; Royal Netherlands Asn. Advan. Med; Netherland Asn. Psychiat. & Neurol. Methodology for clinical and behavioral evaluations in psychiatry, mental retardation and animal studies, especially with the use of on-line computers; ethology and psychopharmacology in man-environment relations; social pollution. Address: Research Center, Rockland State Hospital, Orangeburg, NY 10962.

ESSER, MARTINUS HENDRICUS MAC, b. Berlin, Ger, 18; nat; m. 57; c. 2. MATHEMATICS. Ph.D.(math), Northwestern, 47; Paris, 48. Asst. biophys, Chicago, 45-46; instr. MATH, Ill. Inst. Technol, 46-52; Georgia Inst. Tech, 52-55; instr, Maryland, 55-58; asst. prof, UNIV. DAYTON, 58-61, ASSOC. PROF, 61- Am. Math. Soc; Math. Asn. Am. Hilbert space. Address: 221 Claranna Ave, Dayton, OH 45419.

ESSER, ROBERT E(MMET), b. Milwaukee, Wis, July 14, 16; m. 41; c. 5. BIOLOGY. B.S, Marquette, 38, M.S, 40, Ph.D.(cytol), 42. Asst, Marquette, 38-42, instr. zool, 42-45; owner-technician, Michaelis-Esser, Inc, Wis, 45-46; asst. prof. BOT. & ZOOL, UNIV. WIS-PARKSIDE, 46-71, ASSOC. PROF, 71- Cytology of ferns; invertebrate zoology; microscopic biological technique. Address: Dept. of Botany & Zoology, University of Wisconsin-Parkside, Wood Rd, Kenosha, WI 53140.

ESSERY, JOHN M, b. Plymouth, Eng, June 15, 36; m. 62; c. 2. ORGANIC & MEDICINAL CHEMISTRY. B.Sc, Exeter, 57, Ph.D.(chem), 60. Fel, Nat. Res. Coun. Can, 60-62; SR. RES. SCIENTIST, BRISTOL LABS, SYRACUSE UNIV, 62- Am. Chem. Soc; The Chem. Soc. Chemistry of betalactam antibiotics; chemistry of heterocyclic compounds; biosynthesis of natural products. Address: 416 Churchill Lane, Fayetteville, NY 13066.

ESSEX, HIRAM E(LI), b. Glasford, Ill, Jan. 28, 93; m. 26; c. 3. PHYSIOLOGY. B.S, Knox Col, 19; M.S, Illinois, 24, Ph.D.(zool), 27. Asst. zool, Illinois, 23-27, instr. 27-28; asst. prof. PHYSIOL, MAYO GRAD. SCH. MED. UNIV. MINN, 28-37, assoc. prof, 37-44, prof, 44-58, EMER. PROF. 58- Mayo Lectr, 53; mem. cardiovasc. study sect, U.S. Pub. Health Serv, 49-54; Hatfield Lectr, 58; dir. undergrad. res, St. Mary's Col.(Minn), 58-71. Alumni Achievement award, Knox Col, 58. With Off. Sci. Res. & Develop, 44. U.S.A, 17-19, Lt. AAAS; Nat. Soc. Med. Res.(pres, 61-65); Am. Micros.

Soc; Am. Soc. Zool; Soc. Exp. Biol. & Med; Am. Soc. Pharmacol. & Exp. Therapeut; Am. Physiol. Soc.(pres, 54). Life histories of cestodes; experimental surgery and pathology; toxicology; immunity; circulation; neurology; endocrinology. Address: 711 Seventh St. S.W, Rochester, MN 55901.

ESSIG, CARL FOHL, b. Canton, Ohio, July 31, 19; m. 45; c. 3. MEDICINE, NEUROLOGY. B.S, Kent State, 42; M.D, Western Reserve, 47. Asst. chem, Rutgers, 42-43; intern, Watts Hosp, N.C, 47-48; med. physiologist neuropharmacol, Army Chem. Center, Md, 48-49; neurophysiologist, Nat. Inst. Mental Health, 49-52; clin. fel. neurol, Mass. General Hosp, 52-54; neuropharmacologist & neurologist, addiction res. ctr, Nat. Inst. Mental Health, U.S. Pub. Health Serv. Hosp, 54-69, chief neurol. sect, clin. res. ctr, 69-70, chief res. sects, 70-71; RETIRED. U.S.P.H.S, 49-71, Med. Dir. Am. Acad. Neurol; Am. Physiol. Soc. Experimental neurology; neuropharmacology; electroencephalography. Address: 1455 Forbes Rd, Lexington, KY 40505.

ESSIG, FREDERICK C(HARLES), b. Los Angeles, Calif, Feb. 20, 24; m. 45; c. 4. EXPERIMENTAL PHYSICS. B.S, Calif. Inst. Tech, 46; M.S, Southern California, 53. Elec. engr, Douglas Aircraft Co, 47; Range Instrument Dept, U.S. Naval Air Missile Test Center, 48-50; res. asst, physics, Southern California, 50-51; physicist & elec. sci. fuze dept, U.S. Naval Ord. Lab, Corona, 52-55, supvr. physicist magnetism br, 55-57, physicist, sci. staff, 57-61, head electronics div, res. dept, 61-70, HEAD APPL. PHYSICS DIV, RES. DEPT, NAVAL WEAPONS CTR, 70- U.S.N.R, 43-46. Am. Phys. Soc. Solid state physics; electromagnetic propagation; scientific program planning and administration. Address: 509 Ticonderoga, China Lake, CA 93555.

ESSIG, G(USTAVE) A(LFRED), b. Phila, Pa, June 11, 15; m. 42; c. 2. PHYSICS. B.A, Washington & Lee, 42. Asst. radio engr. Sig.C, U.S. Army, 42, officer in charge radar training, 42-46; asst. physicist, nucleonics, Monsanto Chem. Co, 46-48, supvr. phys. chem. processes & radiog, MOUND LAB, MONSANTO RES. CORP, 48-55, gen. supvr. radiochem. & appl. nuclear & phys. chem, 55-62, asst. to v.pres. & plant mgr, 62-63, mgr. planning & reporting, 63-65, asst. to v.pres. & plant mgr, 65-69, SPEC. ASSIGNMENT, LAB. TECHNOL. RELATED TO FINANCE, 69- Sig.C, 42-46, Res, 53-54, Capt. Am. Phys. Soc; Am. Asn. Physics Teachers. Research and development through pilot plant to production; radiochemistry; radiography; nuclear physics; physical chemistry; vacuum techniques; electronics; instrumentation. Address: 1215 Meadowview Dr, Miamisburg, OH 45342.

ESSIG, HENRY J, b. Eppstein, Ger, Apr. 26, 26; U.S. citizen; m. 49; c. 4. ORGANIC CHEMISTRY. B.S, Western Reserve, 51, M.S, 52, Ph.D.(org. chem), 60. Chemist, Grant Photo Prods, 51-52; B.F GOODRICH CHEM. CO, 52-60, assoc. develop. scientist, 60-63, develop. scientist, 63-68, SR. DEVELOP. SCIENTIST, 68- U.S. Merchant Marine, 44-46; U.S.A, 46-48. Am. Chem. Soc. Kinetic studies of heterogeneous catalysis; monomer synthesis and polymerization. Address: 31480 Detroit Rd, Westlake, OH 44145.

ESSIG, HENRY WERNER, b. Paragould, Ark, Dec. 9, 30; m. 53; c. 2. ANIMAL NUTRITION. B.S.A, Arkansas, 53, M.S, 56; Ph.D.(nutrit), 59. Assoc. prof. NUTRIT, MISS. STATE UNIV, 59-70, PROF, 70- U.S.A, 53-55, 1st Lt. Am. Soc. Animal Sci; Am. Dairy Sci. Asn. Ruminant nutrition; studies of cattle and sheep. Address: Dept. of Animal Science, Mississippi State University, Box 5228, State College, MS 39762.

ESSIGMANN, MARTIN W(HITE), b. Bethel, Vt, Jan. 14, 17; m. 43; c. 3. ELECTRICAL ENGINEERING. B.S, Tufts Col, 38; S.M, Mass. Inst. Tech, 47. Instr. ELEC. ENG, Northeastern, 38-44; vis. instr, Mass. Inst. Tech, 44-47; asst. prof. NORTHEAST. UNIV, 47-50, prof. & coordinator electronics res, 50-61, head dept. elec. eng, 54-61, DEAN RES, 61- Vis. asst. prof, Mass. Inst. Tech, 47-48. Civilian with U.S.A.F; Off. Sci. Res. & Develop, 44. AAAS; Am. Soc. Eng. Educ; Inst. Elec. & Electronics Eng. Digital computers; nonlinear devices; speech analysis; principles of radar; information theory. Address: 10 Roland St, Medford, MA 02155.

ESSINGTON, EDWARD HERBERT, b. Santa Barbara, Calif, Feb. 19, 37; m. 57; c. 2. SOIL SCIENCE. B.S, Calif. State Polytech. Col, 58; M.S, California, Los Angeles, 64. Lab. technician, dept. nuclear med. & radiation biol, Univ. Calif, Los Angeles, 57-65; sr. assoc. soil scientist, Hazleton-Nuclear Sci. Corp. Div, Isotopes Inc, 65-66; Palo Alto Labs, TELEDYNE ISOTOPES, Calif, 66-67, SOIL SCIENTIST, 67-71, NEV, 71- AAAS; Health Physics Soc. Soil-plant relations; radionuclide uptake by plants; radionuclide and pollutant migration and chemistry in soils and groundwater systems; groundwater tracing; health physics. Address: Teledyne Isotopes, 2765 S. Highland Dr, Las Vegas, NV 89102.

ESSLER, WARREN O(RVEL), b. Davenport, Iowa, Apr. 22, 24; m. 44; c. 3. ELECTRICAL ENGINEERING. B.S, Iowa, 53, M.S, 55, Nat. Sci. faculty fel, 58-59, Nat. Pub. Health fel, 59-60, Ph.D.(elec. eng, physiol), 60. Res. assoc. audiol, Iowa, 53-54; ELEC. ENG, Collins Radio Corp, 54-55; instr, S.Dak. State Col, 55-57; asst. prof, 57-61; PROF. & DEAN, COL. TECHNOL, UNIV. VT, 61- U.S.A, 42-45. Am. Soc. Eng. Educ; Nat. Soc. Prof. Eng; Inst. Elec. & Electronics Eng. Medical electronics. Address: College of Technology, University of Vermont, Burlington, VT 05401.

ESSLINGER, JACK H(OUSTON), b. Ponca City, Okla, July 19, 31; m. 55; c. 3. PARASITOLOGY. B.S, Oklahoma, 53; Nat. Sci. Found. fel, Rice Inst, 54-56, M.A, 55, Ph.D.(biol), 58. Instr. PARASITOL, sch. med, TULANE UNIV, 62, asst. prof, 62-67, ASSOC. PROF, SCH. PUB. HEALTH & TROP. MED, 67- Vis. prof, Valle, Colombia & assoc, Int. Ctr. Med. Res. & Training, 63. Am. Soc. Parasitol; Am. Soc. Trop. Med. & Hyg; Soc. Syst. Zool. Medical entomology; filariasis of mammals. Address: Dept. of Parasitology, School of Public Health & Tropical Medicine, Tulane University, 1430 Tulane Ave, New Orleans, LA 70112.

ESSLINGER, WILLIAM GLENN, b. Huntsville, Ala, Oct. 21, 37; m. 58; c. 3. ORGANIC CHEMISTRY. B.S, Alabama, 62, NASA grant, 62-63 & fel, 64-66, M.S, 64, Ph.D.(org. chem), 66. Asst. prof. CHEM, Union Univ.(Tenn), 66-68; W.GA. COL. 68-71, ASSOC. PROF, 71- Nat. Sci. Found. grant dir, Ga.

Sci. Teacher Proj, 69- Am. Chem. Soc. Conformational effects on reactions at exocyclic positions of cycloalkylcarbinyl derivatives; thermal decomposition of esters. Address: Dept. of Chemistry, West Georgia College, Carrollton, GA 30117.

ESSMAN, WALTER B(ERNARD), b. New York, N.Y, Dec. 25, 33; m. 62; c. 1. PHYSIOLOGICAL PSYCHOLOGY. B.A, N.Y. Univ, 54; M.A, North Dakota, 55, Ph.D.(psychol), 57. Asst. psychol, North Dakota, 54-55, 56-57; Nebraska, 55-56; fel. neurophysiol, Albert Einstein Col. Med, 59-61, res. assoc. physiol, 61-62; asst. prof. PSYCHOL, QUEENS COL.(N.Y), 62-64, assoc. prof, 65-67, PROF, 67- Fel. neurochem, Mt. Sinai Hosp, 64- Med.Serv.C, 57-59, Capt. AAAS; Fedn. Am. Socs. Exp. Biol; Am. Psychol. Asn; N.Y. Acad. Sci. Psychophysiology; neural and chemical basis of learning and memory; physiological stress. Address: Dept. of Psychology, Queens College, Flushing, NY 11367.

ESSNER, EDWARD S(TANLEY), b. N.Y.C, Mar. 31, 27; m. 58; c. 2. CYTOLOGY, ELECTRON MICROSCOPY. B.S, Long Island, 47; Ph.D.(zool), Pennsylvania, 51. Sr. asst. scientist, lab. chem. pharm, Nat. Cancer Inst, 52-56; Nat. Cancer Inst. spec. fel. path, Albert Einstein Col. Med, 56-58, res. asst. prof, 58-64; ASSOC. MEM, DIV. CYTOL, SLOAN-KETTERING INST. CANCER RES, 64- Am. Soc. Cell Biol; Electron Micros. Soc. Am; Int. Soc. Cell Biol; Am. Asn. Cancer Res; Histochem. Soc. Biochemical cytology; cancer; enzyme localization; cell organelles. Address: Sloan-Kettering Institute for Cancer Research, 410 E. 68th St, New York, NY 10021.

ESTABROOK, F(RANK) B(EHLE), b. Nampa, Idaho, June 22, 22; m. 50; c. 1. PHYSICS. B.A, Miami (Ohio), 43; M.S, Calif. Inst. Tech, 47, Ph.D.(physics), 50. Asst. prof. physics, Miami (Ohio), 50-51, assoc. prof, 51-52; sr. engr. reactor physics, N.Am. Aviation, 52-55; physicist, U.S. Army Off. Ord. Res, 55-60; MEM. TECH. STAFF, JET PROPULSION LAB, CALIF. INST. TECHNOL, 60-, LECTR. APPL. MATH, 71-, physics, 62-65. U.S.N.R, 44-46, Lt. AAAS; Am. Phys. Soc. Neutron and reactor physics; geophysics; relativity and gravitation; applied mathematics. Address: 853 Lyndon St, South Pasadena, CA 91030.

ESTABROOK, GAYLORD B(EALE), b. Logansport, Ind, Oct. 9, 99; m. 26. PHYSICS. B.S, Purdue, 21; M.S, Ohio State, 22; Hopkins, 28-30; Ph.D.(physics), Pittsburgh, 32. Asst. chem, Ohio State, 21-22; instr. physics, Ga. Tech, 22-24, asst. prof, 24-28; asst, Pittsburgh, 30-32; Md. Acad. Sci, 33-36; instr, Univ. Md, 37-39, asst. prof, 39-47, assoc. prof, 47-50, prof, 50-70; RETIRED. U.S.A, 18. AAAS; Am. Phys. Soc; Am. Asn. Physics Teachers. Electrolytic cells; small thermocouples; vaporization of platinum and molybdenum in high electrostatic fields. Address: 1 University Pkwy. E, Baltimore, MD 21218.

ESTABROOK, RONALD (WINFIELD), b. Albany, N.Y, Jan. 3, 26; m. 47; c. 4. BIOCHEMISTRY. B.S, Rensselaer Polytech, 50; U.S. Pub. Health Serv. fel. & Ph.D.(biochem), Rochester, 54. Fel, Johnson Found. Med. Physics, Univ. Pa, 54-57, res. assoc, 57-58, asst. prof. phys. biochem, 59-61, assoc. prof, 61-65, prof, 65-68; VIRGINIA LAZENBY O'HARA PROF. BIOCHEM & CHMN. DEPT, UNIV. TEX. SOUTHWEST. MED. SCH, DALLAS, 68- Fel, Am. Heart Asn, 57-58; U.S. Pub. Health Serv, 58- U.S.N.R, 44-58, Lt.(jg). Am. Chem. Soc; Fedn. Am. Socs. Exp. Biol; Am. Soc. Biol. Chem. Application of physical methods to study of intracellular biochemical processes. Address: Dept. of Biochemistry, University of Texas (Southwestern) Medical School, Dallas, TX 75235.

ESTEE, CHARLES REMINGTON, b. Hecla, S.Dak, Oct. 7, 21; m. 43; c. 3. CHEMISTRY. B.S, Jamestown Col, 42; M.S, Iowa, 44, du Pont fel, 45-46, Ph.D.(phys. chem), 47. Asst. chem, Iowa, 42, asst, 43, instr, 43-44; jr. chemist, Tenn. Eastman Corp, Oak Ridge, 44-45; instr, Iowa, 46-47; acting prof, UNIV. S.DAK, 47-48, PROF. CHEM, 48-, HEAD DEPT, 52- AAAS; Am. Chem. Soc; Nat. Sci. Teachers Asn. Electrical properties of colloids; science education. Address: Dept. of Chemistry, University of South Dakota, Vermillion, SD 57069.

ESTEP, HERSCHEL LEONARD, b. Dunbar, Va, Nov. 29, 29; m. 52; c. 6. MEDICINE, ENDOCRINOLOGY. A.B, King Col, 52; M.D, Hopkins, 56. Fel. endocrinol, Vanderbilt, 61-62; DIR. ENDOCRINE RES. LAB. & ASSOC. PROF. MED, HEALTH SCI. DIV, VA. COMMONWEALTH UNIV, 62- U.S. Pub. Health Serv. res. grant, 62-65; Am. Cancer Soc. grant, 68-70; consult, McGuire Vet. Admin. Hosp, 68-71. Endocrine Soc; Am. Fedn. Clin. Res. Neuroendocrine regulation of adrenocorticotropic and gonadotropic hormones; mechanisms of control of parathyroid hormone secretion. Address: Dept. of Medicine, Health Sciences Division, Virginia Commonwealth University, Richmond, VA 23219.

ESTERER, A(RNULF) K(ARL), b. Tsingtao, China, Aug. 17, 05; nat; m. 31; c. 3. WOOD CHEMISTRY. Ph.D.(chem), Munich Univ, 30. Res. chemist, Benzol-Verband, Germany, 32-34; group leader, fundamental res, Can. Int. Paper Co, 34-40; res. assoc, Michigan, 42-44; chief sect. applied chem. & tech. planning, Weyerhaeuser Co, 44-55, prof. specialist, wood chem, cent. res. & develop, 55-70; RETIRED. AAAS; Am. Chem. Soc; Forest Prod. Res. Soc. Utilization of wood; characterization of cellulose in solution; oxidation of hydrocarbons; hydraulic brake fluids. Address: 2357 Cascade Way, Longview, WA 98632.

ESTERGREEN, V(ICTOR) LINÉ, b. Lynden, Wash, Dec. 15, 25; m. 50; c. 1. ANIMAL PHYSIOLOGY, ENDOCRINOLOGY. B.S, Washington State, 50, M.S, 56; Ph.D.(dairy sci), Illinois, 60. Asst. herdsman, Washington State, 50-51; instr, high schs, Wash, 52-54; trainee biol. chem, steroid training inst, Univ. Utah, 60-61; res. assoc. animal physiol, WASH. STATE UNIV, 61-62, asst. prof. DAIRY SCI, 62-67, ASSOC. PROF, 67- U.S.N.R, 44-47. Am. Dairy Sci. Asn; Endocrine Soc; Am. Soc. Animal Sci. Bovine reproduction and corticosteroid hormones; endocrinology of reproduction in farm animals. Address: Dept. of Animal Sciences, Washington State University, Pullman, WA 99163.

ESTERLING, DONALD M, b. Chicago, Ill, Nov. 18, 42; m. 64; c. 2. THEORETICAL & SOLID STATE PHYSICS. B.S, Notre Dame, 64; NASA fel, Brandeis, 64-67, M.A, 66, Ph.D.(physics), 68. ASST. PROF. PHYSICS, IND. UNIV, BLOOMINGTON, 68- Application of many-body techniques to solid state physics; magnetic transitions; insulator-metal transitions; electronic properties of disordered systems. Address: Dept. of Physics, Indiana University, Bloomington, IN 47401.

ESTERLING, ROBERT JOHN, b. Chicago, Ill, Aug. 13, 38; m. 60; c. 2. ELEMENTARY PARTICLE PHYSICS. S.B, Mass. Inst. Tech, 60; Ph.D.(physics), California, Berkeley, 64. Res. Assoc. PHYSICS, Chicago, 64-68; asst. prof, Rutgers Univ, 68-71; RES. ASSOC, RUTHERFORD LAB, 71- Fermi fel, Univ. Chicago, 64-66. Am. Phys. Soc. Address: Rutherford Lab, Chilton, Didcot, Berkshire, Eng.

ESTERLUND, R(OBERT) A(LAN), b. Chicago, Ill, May 11, 36; m. 63. NUCLEAR CHEMISTRY. B.S, Illinois, 58; Ph.D.(chem), Washington (St. Louis), 63. Res. assoc. chem, Washington (St. Louis), 63-64; Brookhaven Nat. Lab, 64-66; asst. prof, North. Ill. Univ, 66-71; MEM. STAFF, INST. NUCLEAR CHEM, UNIV. MARBURG, 71- Am. Phys. Soc. Measurement of nuclear reaction cross-sections; calculations via the compound-statistical model; scattering measurements of energy spectra and angular distributions; spectroscopy of delayed-proton emitters. Address: Institute for Nuclear Chemistry, University of Marburg, Biegenstrasse 12, 355 Marburg, Germany.

ESTERLY, JOHN ROOSEVELT, b. Friedensburg, Pa, Mar. 13, 33; m. 57; c. 4. PEDIATRIC & PULMONARY PATHOLOGY. B.S, Yale, 55; M.D, Hopkins, 59. U.S. Pub. Health Serv. fels, Hammersmith Hosp, Royal Postgrad. Med. Sch, Univ. London, 63-64 & Johns Hopkins Hosp. & Med. Sch, 64-66; asst. prof. PATH, OBSTET. & GYNEC, UNIV. CHICAGO, 68-70, ASSOC. PROF, 70- Nat. Insts. Health res. career develop. award, 71- U.S.A.R, 66-68, Capt. Am. Thoracic Soc; Am. Asn. Path. & Bact; Am. Soc. Exp. Path; Reticuloendothelial Soc; Histochem. Soc. Histochemistry of hydrolytic enzymes; pulmonary reactions to injury; pathology of neonatal adaptation; cystic fibrosis. Address: Dept. of Pathology, University of Chicago, Chicago, IL 60637.

ESTERLY, NANCY BURTON, b. N.Y.C, Apr. 14, 35; m. 57; c. 4. PEDIATRICS, DERMATOLOGY. B.S, Smith Col, 56; M.D, Hopkins, 60. U.S. Pub. Health Serv. fel. dermat, sch. med, Hopkins, 64-67, instr. pediat, 67-68; Univ. Chicago, 68-69, ASST. PROF, 69-70; DERMAT, COL. MED, UNIV. ILL, CHICAGO CIRCLE, 70- Attend. physician, Hines Vet. Admin. Hosp; consult, Chicago State Tuberc. Sanitarium. Dipl, Am. Bd. Pediat, 66; Am. Bd. Dermat, 70. Soc. Invest. Dermat. Ichthyosis; human hair defects; neonatal skin reactivity. Address: Dept. of Dermatology, University of Illinois at the Medical Center, 808 S. Wood St, Chicago, IL 60612.

ESTERMANN, EVA F(RANCES), b. San Francisco, Calif, Feb. 26, 32. PLANT PHYSIOLOGY. B.S, California, 53, Ph.D.(plant nutrit. soils), 58. Jr. res. biochemist, California, Berkeley, 58-60; asst. prof. BIOL, SAN FRANCISCO STATE COL, 60-64, assoc. prof, 64-69, PROF, 69- Am. Soc. Plant Physiol. Bacterial nutrition at surfaces; physiological ecology; spore metabolism. Address: 141 Walnut Ave, Mill Valley, CA 94941.

ESTERMANN, I(MMANUEL), b. Berlin, Germany, Mar. 31, 00; nat; m. 23; c. 2. PHYSICS. D.Sc.(phys. chem), Hamburg, 21. Asst. physics, Rostock Univ, 21-22; instr. phys. chem, Hamburg, 22-28, privat-docent physics, 28-33; assoc. prof, Carnegie Inst. Tech, 33-45, prof, 45-52; dir. mat. sci. div, Off. Naval Res, 51-58, dep. sci. dir, 55-58, res. coordinator, 58-59, sci. dir, London, 59-64; VIS. PROF. PHYSICS, ISRAEL INST. TECHNOL, 64- Rockefeller fel, California, 31-32; emer. prof, Hamburg, 58- Consult, Manhattan Dist, 43-45; with Off. Sci. Res. & Develop; Off. Naval Res; Nat. Bur. Standards, 45-46. Ed, Methods Exp. Physics; Advances Atomic & Molecular Physics. Pittsburgh Physics award, 55; Silver medal, City of Paris, 62; U.S. Navy Distinguished Civilian Serv. award, 65. AAAS; Faraday Soc; fel. Am. Phys. Soc; Am. Asn. Physics Teachers; Sci. Res. Soc. Am. Molecular beams; low temperature, chemical, atomic and nuclear physics; solid state; semiconductors. Address: Dept. of Physics, Israel Institute of Technology, Haifa, Israel.

ESTERSON, GERALD L(EE), b. Baltimore, Md, June 29, 27; m. 52; c. 2. CHEMICAL ENGINEERING. B.Eng, Hopkins, 51, D.Eng.(elec. eng), 56. Res. assoc. oceanog. instrumentation, inst. co-op. res, Hopkins, 54-56; sr. engr. air arm div, Westinghouse Elec. Co, 56-58; asst. prof. chem. eng, WASH. UNIV, 58-61, assoc. prof. appl. math, 61-65, ENG, 65-71, PROF, 71-, dir. inst. continuing educ, 65-71. Consult, Compumatix, Inc, 59; Monsanto Co, 59-61, 64-; McGraw-Hill Book Co, Inc, 62-63. U.S. Merchant Marine, 45-47. Inst. Elec. & Electronics Eng; Am. Inst. Chem. Eng; Soc. Indust. & Appl. Math; Instrument Soc; Soc. Eng. Sci.(treas). General systems theory; simulation and modeling of industrial and environmental systems; automatic control. Address: Dept. of Chemical Engineering, School of Engineering & Applied Science, Washington University, St. Louis, MO 63130.

ESTES, EDNA E, b. Jasper, Ala, Nov. 23, 21. BOTANY, BIOLOGY. B.S, Alabama, 48, M.S, 49, univ. fel, 54-56, South. fund fel, 56-57, Ph.D.(bot), 57. Asst. prof. biol, Flora Macdonald Col, 49-53; instr, mobile ctr, Alabama, 53-54, Univ, summers 55-56; instr. sci. & head biol. dept, St. Mary's Sem-Jr. Col, 57-59; asst. prof. BIOL, Del Mar Col, 59-60; assoc. prof, SALISBURY STATE COL, 60-65, PROF, 65- W.A.C, 43-45. AAAS; Bot. Soc. Am. Plant physiology, particularly relation of phosphorus nutrition to photosynthesis; correlating the uptake and distribution of phosphorus-32 in higher plants with certain photosynthetic factors, particularly chlorophyll pattern, light, and carbon dioxide supply. Address: Dept. of Biology, Salisbury State College, Salisbury, MD 21801.

ESTES, E(DWARD) HARVEY, JR, b. Gay, Ga, May 1, 25; m. 48; c. 5. MEDICINE. B.S, Emory, 44, M.D, 47. Intern med, Grady Mem. Hosp, Atlanta, 47-48, asst. res, 49-50; fel. physiol, Emory, 48-49, cardiovasc. physiol, 50; sr. asst. res. med, hosp, Duke, 52-53, fel, med. sch, 53-54; chief, cardiovasc. sect, Vet. Admin. Hosp, 54-55; cardiol. dept, Duke Hosp, 55-58; chief med. serv, Vet. Admin. Hosp, Durham, N.C, 58-63; PROF. MED, MED. CTR, DUKE UNIV, 63-, CHMN. DEPT. COMMUNITY HEALTH SCI, 66-

U.S.N, 50-52. Cardiovascular physiology; electrocardiography. Address: Dept. of Community Health Sciences, Duke University Medical Center, Durham, NC 27710.

ESTES, FRANCES L(ORRAINE), b. Mendon, Mich, Dec. 25, 15. BIOCHEMISTRY. A.B, Kalamazoo Col, 40; M.S, Chicago, 48; Ph.D, Rutgers, 53. Control chemist, Johnson & Johnson Surg. Supplies, 41-42; asst. catalysis, inst. gas. tech, Ill. Inst. Tech, 43-47; instr, Douglass Col, Rutgers, 48-53, asst. prof, 53-56; res. assoc. biochem, col. med, Baylor, 56-61; res. asst. prof, Med. Br, Univ. Tex, 61-67; BIOCHEMIST, Vet. Admin. Hosp, Houston, Tex, 67-69; GULF SOUTH RES. INST, 69- AAAS; Am. Chem. Soc; N.Y. Acad. Sci; fel. Am. Inst. Chem. Gas phase reactions and biological interactions. Address: 4847 McDermed, Houston, TX 77035.

ESTES, HOWARD M, JR, b. Tulare, Calif, Jan. 30, 28; m. 54; c. 4. SYSTEMS ENGINEERING. B.S, U.S. Naval Acad, 50; M.S.(aeronaut. eng) & M.S.(instrumentation eng), Michigan, 58, Ph.D.(instrumentation eng), 61; Armed Forces Staff Col, 64-65; Indust. Col. Armed Forces, 68-69. U.S. AIR FORCE, 50-, assoc. prof. mech, U.S. Air Force Acad, 60-64, proj. engr, Off. Dep. Chief Staff, Res. & Develop, Hq. Air Force, Wash, D.C, 65-69, Comdr, Air Force Rocket Propulsion Lab, Edwards AFB, Calif, 69-71, DEP. DIR. LABS, HQ. AIR FORCE SYSTS. COMMAND, 71- U.S.A.F, 50-, Col. Inst. Elec. & Electronics Eng. Optimal and adaptive control; aerospace mechanics; national space policy. Address: Air Force Systems Command (DL), Andrews Air Force Base, Washington, DC 20331.

ESTES, JAMES RUSSELL, b. Burkburnett, Tex, Aug. 28, 37; m. 62; c. 2. SYSTEMATIC BOTANY. B.S, Midwestern, 59; Nat. Sci. Found. fel, Oregon State, 65-67, Ph.D.(bot), 67. Asst. prof. bot. & microbiol. UNIV. OKLA, 67-71, ASSOC. PROF. BOT. & ASST. CURATOR HERBARIUM, 71- U.S.A, 60-62, Capt. Am. Soc. Plant Taxon. Systematic study of the Artemisia ludoviciana polyploid complex; autopolyploidy as an evolutionary process. Address: Room 135, Dept. of Botany & Microbiology, University of Oklahoma, 770 S. Oval, Norman, OK 73069.

ESTES, JOHN E(ARLE), JR, b. Chicago, Ill, Sept. 5, 18; m. 40; c. 3. MEDICINE. B.S, Illinois, 42, M.D, 43; M.S, Minnesota, 47. Consult. med, Mayo Clin, 48-60, head vascular diseases, 58-60; asst. prof. med, Mayo Found, Minnesota, 54-60; DIR, ARIZ. RADIOISOTOPE LAB, 64-; SOUTHWEST FOUND. MED. RES. & EDUC, 65-; DIR. DEPT. NUCLEAR MED, GOOD SAMARITAN HOSP, 71- Private practice, internal med, 60- Mem, Coun. Arteriosclerosis, Am. Heart Asn. Dipl, Am. Bd. Internal Med, 50. Med.C, U.S.A, 52-54, Capt. Fel. Am. Med. Asn; fel. Am. Col. Physicians; Am. Heart Asn; Int. Col. Angiol; Soc. Nuclear Med. Peripheral vascular diseases. Address: Park Central-North Medical Bldg, 555 W. Catalina Dr, Phoenix, AZ 85013.

ESTES, JOHN H, b. Youngstown, Ohio, Jan. 10, 16; m. 46; c. 3. ORGANIC CHEMISTRY, METALLURGY. B.S, Youngstown, 40; M.S, Washington State, 48, Ph.D.(org. chem), 52. Metallurgist, Carnegie Ill. Steel Co, 40; Mullins Mfg. Corp, 40-42; RES. CHEMIST, TEXACO RES. CTR, 52- Med.C, 42-46, S/Sgt. Am. Chem. Soc. Zeolite synthesis; commercial process; catalysis in reforming field; gasoline additive studies. Address: Cedar Hill Rd, Route 6, Wappingers Falls, NY 12590.

ESTES, LELAND L(LOYD), b. Danville, Va, Nov. 6, 20; m. 46; c. 2. ORGANIC CHEMISTRY. B.S, Va. Mil. Inst, 43; Ph.D.(org. chem), Mass. Inst. Tech, 49. Res. chemist, E.I. DU PONT DE NEMOURS & CO, 49-55, supvr, 55-65, SR. SUPVR, 65- U.S.A, 43-46, Res, 46-53, Capt. Am. Chem. Soc. Synthetic chemistry; textile finishes; synthetic polymers and polymerization; cellulose acetate rayon; nylon; Dacron; nonwoven fabrics. Address: 502 Cunniff Pkwy, Goodlettsville, TN 37072.

ESTES, NELSON N, b. Oct. 15, 15; m. 44; c. 3. PHYSICS. B.S, Texas. Group leader mine & depth charge div, Naval ord. lab, Md, 41-47, chief sub-div, mine div, 47-51, div. chief underwater acoustics, 51-57; tech. dir, Tex. Res. Assocs. Corp, 57-62, dir. tech. planning, Tracor, Inc, 62-65; INDEPENDENT CONSULT, 65- Air and underwater acoustics; influence control mechanisms; automation; systems analysis; theoretical physics. Address: 4605 Edgemont Dr, Austin, TX 78731.

ESTES, REEDUS RAY, b. Winfield, Ala, Nov. 10, 14; m. 46; c. 1. CHEMISTRY. B.S, Berry Col, 36; M.S, Emory, 38; Ph.D.(chem), Texas, 44. Res. chemist, Armour Labs, 44-46; asst. prof. chem, Kentucky, 46-53; res. chemist, Emery Industs, Inc, 53-58; SR. RES. CHEMIST, A.E. Staley Mfg. Co, 58-71; WM. WRIGLEY JR. CO, 71- Organic and polymer chemistry; synthetic polymers; carbohydrates; analytical methods and instrumentation. Address: Wm. Wrigley Jr. Co, 3535 S. Ashland Ave, Chicago, IL 60609.

ESTES, RICHARD, b. San Rafael, Calif, May 9, 32; m. 55; c. 1. VERTEBRATE PALEONTOLOGY, HERPETOLOGY. B.A, Univ. Calif, Berkeley, 55, M.A, 57, grant, 59, Ph.D.(paleont), 60. Mus. preparator vert. paleont, Univ. Calif, Berkeley, 57-58, 59-60, asst. 58-59, vert. zool, 60; asst. prof. BIOL, BOSTON UNIV, 60-65, assoc. prof, 65-68, PROF, 68- Assoc. vert. paleont, mus. comp. zool, Harvard, 60-; Nat. Sci. Found. res. grants, 61-67, 68-70; Am. Philos. Soc. res. grant, 64-65; Sigma Xi res. grant, 65; Nat. Acad. Sci, Marsh Fund res. grant, 70. AAAS; Am. Soc. Ichthyol. & Herpet; Am. Soc. Zool; Soc. Vert. Paleont; Soc. Study Evolution. Paleoecological and evolutionary phenomena in fossil lower vertebrate faunas; anatomy and relationships of fossil and recent Amphibia and Reptilia. Address: Dept. of Biology, Boston University, 2 Cummington St, Boston, MA 02215.

ESTES, TIMOTHY KING, b. Kalamazoo, Mich, Oct. 1, 40; m. 61; c. 2. PAPER & ORGANIC CHEMISTRY. B.S, Western Michigan, 62; M.S, Lawrence, 64, Ph.D.(paper chem), 67. SR. RES. SPECIALIST PAPERBOARD, PACKAGING CORP. AM, 66- Am. Chem. Soc; Tech. Asn. Pulp & Paper Indust. Bark and wood chemistry; kraft pulping; air pollution; paperboard physics. Address: Technical Development Group, Packaging Corp. of America, 470 Market St. S.W, Grand Rapids, MI 49502.

ESTES, WILLIAM K(AYE), b. Minneapolis, Minn, June 17, 19; m. 42; c. 2. PSYCHOLOGY. B.A, Minnesota, 40, Ph.D.(psychol), 43. Res. specialist, Gen. Mills, Inc, 43; instr. PSYCHOL, Indiana, 46-47, from asst. prof. to PROF, 47-61; Stanford Univ, 62-68; ROCKEFELLER UNIV, 68- Faculty res. fel, Soc. Sci. Res. Coun, 52-55; fel, Ctr. Adv. Study Behav. Sci, 55-56. Ed, J. Comp. Physiol. Psychol, 62-68. U.S.A, 43-46, 1st Lt. Nat. Acad. Sci; AAAS; Am. Psychol. Asn.(award, 63); Soc. Exp. Psychol.(Warren medal, 63); Inst. Math. Statist. Human and animal learning; behavior theory; quantitative methods. Address: Dept. of Psychology, Rockefeller University, New York, NY 10021.

ESTEVE, RAMON M, JR, b. Barcelona, Spain, May 3, 23, U.S. citizen; m. 53; c. 6. PHYSICAL ORGANIC CHEMISTRY. B.A, Southern Methodist, 48; M.S. & Ph.D.(chem), Mass. Inst. Tech, 51. Res. assoc. & res. dir. Qm. textile proj, Rhode Island, 51-54; prof. textile res. Tex. Woman's Univ, 55-67; PRES. ESTEVE, S.A, 67- Tech. aide, Nat. Res. Coun. 55-67; mem. adv. cmt. flame & thermal protection combat clothing, Nat. Res. Coun, 55- U.S.N.R, 43-46, Lt.(jg). Am. Chem. Soc; Am. Asn. Textile Chem. & Colorists. Textile and cellulose chemistry; polymers. Address: Esteve, S.A, Place de la Gare 10, Lausanne, Switz. CH 1001.

ESTEY, R(ALPH) H(OWARD), b. Millville, N.B, Dec. 9, 16; m. 44; c. 2. PLANT PATHOLOGY. B.Sc, McGill Univ, 51, Ph.D.(plant path), 56; M.S, Maine, 54; B.Ed, New Brunswick, 60. Instr, pub. sch, N.B, Can, 45-53; PLANT PATH, Connecticut, 56-57; asst. prof, MACDONALD COL, McGILL UNIV, 57-61, ASSOC. PROF, 61-, CHMN. DEPT, 70- Dipl, Imp. Col, London, 65. Can. Army, 41-45. Soc. Nematol; Mycol. Soc. Am; Agr. Inst. Can; Brit. Mycol. Soc; Can. Phytopath. Soc; Can. Hort. Soc. Plant root diseases, especially those incited by nematodes and fungi. Address: Dept. of Plant Pathology, Macdonald College of McGill University, Saint Anne de Bellevue, Que, Can.

ESTILL, WESLEY B(OYD), b. Enid, Okla, Mar. 24, 24; m. 48; c. 7. INORGANIC CHEMISTRY. B.S, Coe Col, 49; M.S, Okla. State, 51. Mem. staff, res. lab, Armour & Co, 51-52; res. lab, Ozark-Mahoning Co, 52-54; emission spectroscopist, Oak Ridge Nat. Lab, 54-57; ELECTRON MICROSCOPIST, SANDIA CORP, 57- U.S.N, 43-46. Electron Micros. Soc. Am; Electron Probe Anal. Soc. Am. Complex ions; distillation of fluoride and ruthenium; adhesion of thin films; shock loaded metals; microanalysis; electron microprobe; electron diffraction; electron scanning; electron microscopy. Address: Division 8311, Sandia Lab, Sandia Corp, Livermore, CA 94550.

ESTIN, ROBERT W(ILLIAM), b. Paterson, N.J, Nov. 17, 31; m. 64; c. 1. PHYSICS. B.S, Ill. Inst. Tech, 53, M.S, 55, Ph.D.(physics), 63. Teacher, high sch, Ill, 55-56; instr. physics, Ill. Inst. Tech, 56-62, asst. prof, 63-65; assoc. prof, Roosevelt Univ, 65-68, prof, 68-71, chmn. dept, 67-71; STAFF SCIENTIST, PHYS. SCI. GROUP, NEWTON COL. SACRED HEART, 71- Lectr, Univ. Ill, 63; mem. phys. sci. study comt, Ed. Servs, Inc, 65-66. Am. Phys. Soc; Am. Asn. Physics Teachers; Fedn. Am. Sci. Physics education at secondary, elementary and intermediate college levels; new curricular developments, including teacher training. Address: Physical Science Group, Newton College of the Sacred Heart, 885 Centre St, Newton, MA 02159.

ESTLE, THOMAS L(EO), b. Columbus Junction, Iowa, Jan. 8, 31; m. 53; c. 4. SOLID STATE PHYSICS. B.A, Rice Inst, 53; M.S, Illinois, 54, Ph.D. (physics), 57. Fulbright scholar, 57-58; mem. tech. staff, Tex. Instruments, Inc, 58-62, head defect physics sect, 62-66, sr. res. physicist, 66-67; PROF. PHYSICS, RICE UNIV, 67- AAAS; Am. Phys. Soc. Magnetic resonance; point imperfections in nonmetals. Address: Dept. of Physics, Rice University, Houston, TX 77001.

ESTLOW, W(ILLIS) L(UTHER), b. Merino, Colo, Apr. 9, 16; m. 37; c. 4. PHYSICAL GEOGRAPHY, BIOLOGY. A.B, Denver, 44; M.S, Wisconsin, 48; Washburn, 54-56; Kans. State Col, 57; Nat. Sci. Found. fels, Miami (Fla), summer 58, California, Santa Barbara, summer 59 & Hawaii, 59-61; Ed.D. (sci. ed), Colorado, 60. Instr. geog, Denver, 43-44; writer, Zool. Soc. Phila, 45-46; instr. geog, Wisconsin, 46-47; exten. ed. adminstr, Colorado, 47-49; tech. asst. to supt. high altitude observ, Harvard & Colorado, 49-50; field rep, Colo. United, 50-52; admissions counsr, Stephens Col, 53-54; dir. eve. col, Washburn, 54-56; chmn. biol. prog, Kansas State, 56-66; prof. natural sci, chmn. dept. biol. & chmn. dept. earth sci, Lea Col, 67-69. Asst. Chamberlin Observ, Denver, 45; vis. prof, Hilo Campus, Hawaii, 61; Kans. Wesleyan, 64; prof. natural sci. & geog. & chmn. div. gen. ed. sci, State Univ. N.Y. Col. New Paltz, 65-67. Summers, asst, Wisconsin, 47, vis. lectr, Colorado, 57, vis. prof, Springfield Col, 63, Moorehead State Col, 65. U.S. Merchant Marine, 44. AAAS; Asn. Am. Geog; Nat. Coun. Geog. Educ; Nat. Asn. Geol. Teachers. Teaching and text presentation of science materials to college level nonmajors, especially in earth and life sciences. Address: 1102 Maplehill Dr, Albert Lea, MN 56007.

ESTOQUE, MARIANO A, b. Manila, Philippines, Dec. 31, 21; m. 51; c. 4. METEOROLOGY. B.S, Philippines, 47; M.S, N.Y. Univ, 49, Ph.D.(meteorol), 50. Res. assoc. meteorol, Hopkins, 52-53; Chicago, 53-56; McGill, 56-57; atmospheric physicist, Geophys. Res. Directorate, U.S. Air Force, 57-60; PROF. METEOROL, Univ. Hawaii, 60-66; INST. ATMOSPHERIC SCI, UNIV. MIAMI, 66- Am. Meteorol. Soc; Am. Geophys. Union; Royal Meteorol. Soc. Numerical weather prediction; tropical meteorology; atmospheric boundary layer phenomena; convection; hurricane dynamics. Address: Institute of Atmospheric Science, University of Miami, Coral Gables, FL 33124.

ESTRIN, GERALD, b. New York, N.Y, Sept. 9, 21; m. 41; c. 3. COMPUTER SCIENCE. B.S, Wisconsin, 48, Alumni res. found. fel, 48-49, M.S, 49, Radio Corp. Am. fel, 49-50, Ph.D.(elec. eng), 50. Res. engr, Inst. Adv. Study, Princeton, 50-53, 55-56; dir. electronic computer proj, Lipsky fel, Weizmann Inst. Sci, Israel, 53-55; assoc. prof. ENG, UNIV. CALIF, LOS ANGELES, 56-58, PROF, 58- Lipsky fel, 54; consult, Nat. Cash Register Co, 57; Telemeter Magnetics, Inc, 58-61; Ampex Corp, 61-63; Guggenheim fel, 63, 67; mem. adv. bd, appl. math. div, Argonne Nat. Lab, 66-68; int. prog. comt, Int. Fedn. Info. Processing Cong, 68; int. prog. chmn, Jerusalem Conf. Info. Technol, 71; mem. bd. gov, Weizmann Inst. Sci, Israel, 71; Asn. Comput. Mach. lectr; Inst. Elec. & Electronics Eng. distinguished speaker; mem. math. & comput. sci. res. adv. comt, Atomic Energy Comn. Sig.C, 42-43; U.S.A.A.F, 43-45. Fel. Inst. Elec. & Electronics Eng; Asn. Comput. Mach; Am. Soc. Eng. Educ; N.Y. Acad. Sci. Digital computer systems. Address: Computer Science Dept, 3732 Boelter Hall, University of California, Los Angeles, CA 90024.

ESTRIN, NORMAN FREDERICK, b. Brooklyn, N.Y, Apr. 1, 39; m. 61; c. 3. ORGANIC CHEMISTRY. B.S, Brooklyn Col, 59; M.S, N.Y. Univ, 62; Ph.D. (org. chem), Fla. State Univ, 68. Teaching asst. chem, N.Y. Univ, 60-61; teacher, Norris High Sch, N.Y, 61-62; Jane Addams Voc. High Sch, 62; chemist, Clairol Res. Labs, Conn, 62-64; res. asst, Fla. State Univ, 64-68; DIR. SCI, COSMETIC, TOILETRY & FRAGRANCE ASN. INC, D.C, 68- AAAS; Am. Chem. Soc; Am. Inst. Chem; Soc. Cosmetic Chem; N.Y. Acad. Sci. Synthesis of sequence peptide polymers and study of their structure and possible utility as models for active sites of certain enzymes. Address: 14109 Flint Rock Rd, Rockville, MD 20853.

ESTRUP, FAIZA FAWAZ, b. Joun, Lebanon, Apr. 15, 33; U.S. citizen; m. 60. BIOPHYSICS, MOLECULAR BIOLOGY. A.B, Boston Univ, 53; Am. Univ. Beirut, 55-56; M.S, Yale, 60, Ph.D.(biophys), 61. Res. asst. spectros, Huntington Res. Labs, Harvard, 53-55; mem. tech. staff biophys, Bell Tel. Labs, Inc, 62-63; faculty mem. chem, Haverford Col, 64-65, res. assoc. biol, 65-68; RES. ASSOC. BIOL. & MED. SCI, BROWN UNIV, 68- Res. fel, Inst. Biophys, Geneva, Switz, 61-62. AAAS; Biophys. Soc. Research on ribosomal proteins using immunochemical techniques; research on host-induced modification of phage deoxyribonucleic acid. Address: 15 Adelphi Ave, Providence, RI 02906.

ESTRUP, P(EDER) J(AN) Z, b. Copenhagen, Denmark, July 15, 31; m. 60. PHYSICAL CHEMISTRY. M.Sc, Royal Polytech. Inst, Denmark, 54; Ph.D. (phys. chem), Yale, 59. Res. assoc. nuclear chem, European Ctr. Nuclear Res, Switz, 59-61; res. scientist phys. chem, Bell Tel. Labs, N.J, 61-64; Bartol Res. Found, Franklin Inst, 64-67; assoc. prof. PHYSICS & CHEM, BROWN UNIV, 67-70, PROF, 70- Danish Army, 54-56, Lt. Am. Phys. Soc; Am. Chem. Soc; Am. Vacuum Soc; Catalysis Soc. Physics and chemistry of solid surfaces; low energy electron diffraction; photoelectron spectroscopy; adsorption phenomena. Address: Dept. of Physics, Brown University, Providence, RI 02912.

ESVAL, ORLAND E, b. Brooklyn, N.Y, Nov. 21, 31; m. 57; c. 4. INORGANIC CHEMISTRY. B.A, North Carolina, 60, Oak Ridge Inst. Nuclear Studies fel, 61-62, Ph.D.(inorg. chem), 63. Res. chemist textile fibers, E.I. du Pont de Nemours & Co, 62-66; TECH. DIR, WRIGHT CHEM. CORP, 66- V.pres. & dir, Triangle Chem. Lab, 64- U.S.A.F, 52-58, Res, 58-, Capt. Physical properties of synthetic fibers as related to fabric properties; mechanism and structure of polymeric cations and anions in aqueous media. Address: P.O. Box 241, Wrightsville Beach, NC 28480.

ETCHELLS, JOHN L(INCOLN), b. Bristol, Pa, Feb. 12, 09; m. 40; c. 2. BACTERIOLOGY. B.S, Mich. State Col, 31, M.S, 32, fel, 34-35, Ph.D. (bact), 41. Asst. bact, Mich. State Col, 31-32; N.Y. State Psychiat. Inst. & Hosp, 33-34; asst. bacteriologist, bur. chem. & soils, U.S. DEPT. AGR, 35-41, assoc. bacteriologist, bur. agr. & indust. chem, 41, bacteriologist, 41-65, RES. MICROBIOLOGIST, 65-, IN CHARGE FOOD FERMENTATIONS LAB, AGR. RES. SERV, 39- Guest scholar, Kansas State, 58; Puerto Rico, 59; prof, N.C. State, 53- Mem. admin. bd, grad. sch, N.C. State, 56, 59; grad. exec. cmt, Univ. N.C, 56-59; Gov. Sci. Adv. Cmt, N.C, 61-; adv. comt. inst. agr. & indust. microbiol, Univ. Mass, 62- Silver Medal & superior serv. citation, U.S. Dept. Agr, 51. Fel. Am. Acad. Microbiol; fel. Am. Pub. Health Asn; Inst. Food Technol; fel. Royal Soc. Health. Microbiology of brine fermentations. Address: 122 Faircloth St, Raleigh, NC 27607.

ETEMAD, GALEN A(LBERT), b. Mashad, Iran, Nov. 1, 22; U.S. citizen; m. 51; c. 3. GAS DYNAMICS, AEROTHERMODYNAMICS. B.S, Univ. Tehran, 45; M.S, Harvard, 48; Ph.D.(mech. eng), Univ. Calif, Berkeley, 53. Supt. tech. installation, Univ. Tehran, 45-47; teaching assoc. mech. eng, Univ. Calif, Berkeley, 48-51, lectr, 51-53; assoc. prof, State Univ. N.Y. Buffalo, 53-56; res. specialist thermodyn, N.Am. Aviation, Inc, 56-58; mgr. thermodyn. dept, Lockheed Missiles & Space Co, 58-63; mgr. aerothermodyn, propulsion & ord. dept, Martin Marietta Corp, 63-65; mgr. aeromech, SPACE DIV, N.AM. ROCKWELL CORP, 65-66, head gas dynamics, 66-71, ASST. TO MGR, SPACE SHUTTLE TECHNOL, 71- Res. grant, Res. Corp. Am, 55. Lectr, Univ. Calif, Los Angeles, 56-58; Univ. South. Calif, 57-58; Univ. Calif, Berkeley, 58-59; Univ. Santa Clara, 60-63; Stanford Univ, 63; vis. prof, Ayra-Mehr Indust. Univ, 69-70. Medal of Coronation, Nat. Iranian TV, 69. Assoc. fel. Am. Inst. Aeronaut. & Astronaut; Am. Soc. Mech. Eng. Reentry heating; rocket exhaust flow characteristics and base heating; flow around rotating bodies; thermal protection system; gaseous radiation; radiation properties; radiation heat transfer. Address: 12012 Penford Dr, LaMirada, CA 90638.

ETESON, DONALD CALVERT, b. Worcester, Mass, May 22, 27; m. 48; c. 2. ELECTRICAL ENGINEERING. B.S, Worcester Polytech, 48, M.S, 56, Ph.D. (elec. eng), 66. Instr. ELEC. ENG, Worcester Jr. Col, 48-56, assoc. prof, 56-62; instr, WORCESTER POLYTECH INST, 62-66, asst. prof, 66-69, ASSOC. PROF, 69- Inst. Elec. & Electronics Eng. Radio noise in electrical transmission networks; digital transmission networks; hybrid computation. Address: Dept. of Electrical Engineering, Worcester Polytechnic Institute, Worcester, MA 01609.

ETGEN, GARRET J(AY), b. Hackensack, N.J, Aug. 20, 37; m. 60; c. 2. MATHEMATICS. B.S, Col. William & Mary, 59; Woodrow Wilson fel, Wisconsin, 59-60, M.S, 61; univ. fel, North Carolina, 61-62, Ph.D.(math), 64. Asst. chief appl. math. br, hq, NASA, 64-67; asst. prof. MATH, UNIV. HOUSTON, 67-69, ASSOC. PROF, 69- Asst. prof. lectr, George Washington, 65-67. U.S.A, 64-66, Capt. AAAS; Am. Math. Soc; Math. Asn. Am. Differential equations; matrix theory. Address: Dept. of Mathematics, University of Houston, Houston, TX 77004.

ETGEN, WILLIAM M, b. Toledo, Ohio, May 7, 29; m. 50; c. 6. DAIRY & ANIMAL SCIENCE. B.S, Ohio State, 51, M.Sc, 55, Ph.D.(dairy sci), 58. Res. assoc. dairy sci, Ohio State, 54-55; dairy husbandman, U.S. Dept. Agr, 55-58; asst. prof. dairy sci, Univ. R.I, 59-63, assoc. prof, 63-64, animal sci, 64-68, chmn. dept, 67-68; PROF. DAIRY SCI, VA. POLYTECH. INST. & STATE UNIV, 68- Am. Dairy Sci. Asn. Physiology of reproduction and of lactation; animal nutrition; dairy management and production. Address: Dept. of Dairy Science, Virginia Polytechnic Institute & State University, Blacksburg, VA 24061.

ETGES, FRANK J(OSEPH), b. Chicago, Ill, June 18, 24; m. 47; c. 5. PARASITOLOGY, MALACOLOGY. A.B, Illinois, 48, M.S, 49; fel. & Ph.D.(invert. zool), N.Y. Univ, 53. Asst. biol, N.Y. Univ, 49-53; asst. prof. ZOOL, Arkansas, 53-54; asst. prof, UNIV. CINCINNATI, 54-62, assoc. prof, 62-65, PROF, 65-, DIR. GRAD. STUD. BIOL, 67-, fel. grad. sch, 71. Interam. res. fel, 62-63; Nat. Insts. Health fel, London Sch. Hyg. & Trop. Med, 71-72. Sigma Xi Distinguished Res. Award, 66. U.S.A, 43-46. Am. Soc. Trop. Med. & Hyg; Am. Soc. Parasitol; Soc. Protozool; Am. Micros. Soc; Royal Soc. Trop. Med. & Hyg. Orientation, behavior, growth and reproduction of schistosome vector snails; morphology, life history, taxonomy and physiology of animal parasites. Address: Dept. of Biological Sciences, University of Cincinnati, Cincinnati, OH 45221.

ETHERIDGE, ALBERT L(OUIS), b. Wilmar, Ark, Aug. 9, 40; m. 62. ZOOLOGY, DEVELOPMENTAL BIOLOGY. B.S, Ark. Agr. & Mech. Col, 64; M.S, Mississippi, 65; Ph.D.(zool), Texas, Austin, 68. Asst. prof. zool. La. State Univ, Baton Rouge, 68-71; ASSOC. PROF. BIOL, UNIV. ARK, MONTICELLO, 71- AAAS; Am. Soc. Zool; Soc. Develop. Biol. Experimental embryology; embryonic induction of the mesonephric kidney in amphibians. Address: Dept. of Biology, University of Arkansas at Monticello, College Heights, AR 71655.

ETHERIDGE, DAVID E(LLIOTT), b. Montreal, Que, July 1, 18; m. 47; c. 4. FOREST PATHOLOGY. B.Sc, Univ. N.B, 50; M.Sc, McGill Univ, 53; Ph.D. (plant path) & D.I.C, Univ. London, 56. Asst. forest pathologist, forest entom. & path. br, Can. Dept. of Forestry, NB, 50-52, forest pathologist, Alta, 52-58, Que, 58-67, RES. SCIENTIST, PAC. FOREST RES. CENTRE, CAN. DEPT. OF ENVIRON, CAN. FORESTRY SERV, 67- Forest pathologist, Food & Agr. Orgn, U.N, Govt. Tanganyika, 63-64; sr. res. fel, Forest Res. Inst, Rotorua, N.Z, 66-67; consult. trop. forest path, U.N. Develop. Prog. Forestry Proj, Dominican Republic, 69-70. Can. Army, 39-45. Can. Phytopath. Soc; Can. Inst. Forestry; Commonwealth Forestry Asn; Prof. Inst. Pub. Serv. Can; Int. Soc. Trop. Foresters. Physiology and ecology of wood destroying fungi; tropical forest pathology; biological control of decay. Address: Pacific Forest Research Centre, Canada Dept. of the Environment, 506 W. Burnside Rd, Victoria, B.C, Can.

ETHERIDGE, RICHARD EMMETT, b. Houston, Tex, Sept. 16, 29. HERPETOLOGY, PALEONTOLOGY. B.S, Tulane, 51; M.S, Michigan, 52, Ph.D. (zool), 59. Lectr. ZOOL, Southern California, 59-61; asst. prof, SAN DIEGO STATE COL, 61-66, assoc. prof, 66-70, PROF, 70-, CHMN. DEPT, 69- Nat. Sci. Found. fel, 60-61; curator herpet. San Diego Natural Hist. Mus. & Res. assoc, Los Angeles County Mus, 61- U.S.N, 52-56. AAAS; Am. Soc. Ichthyol. & Herpet; Soc. Vert. Paleont; Soc. Study Evolution. Comparative osteology; systematics and evolution of lizards; especially the family Iguanidae; late Cenozoic lizard fossils of North America and the West Indies. Address: Dept. of Zoology, San Diego State College, San Diego, CA 92115.

ETHERINGTON, HAROLD, b. London, Eng, Jan. 7, 00; nat; m. 28; c. 1. NUCLEAR ENGINEERING. B.Sc, London, 21; assoc, Royal Sch. Mines, 21. Supt. steel plant, Lena Goldfields, Ltd, 26-30; res. engr, A.O. Smith Corp, 30-32; lectr, Milwaukee Voc. Sch, 32-36; asst. engr, Allis-Chalmers Mfg. Co, 37-42, mech. engr, eng. develop. div, 42-46; sect. leader, Oak Ridge Nat. Lab, 46-47, dir. power pile div, 47-48; from dir. naval reactor div. to dir. reactor eng. div, Argonne Nat. Lab, 48-53; asst. to v.pres. mfg, ACF Industs, Inc, 53-56, v.pres. nuclear prod, Erco Div, 56-59; mgr. atomic energy dept, Allis-Chalmers Mfg. Co, 59-61, gen. mgr. atomic energy div, 61-63; ATOMIC ENERGY CONSULT, 63- Ed, Nuclear Eng. Handbook; mem. adv. comt. reactor safeguards, U.S. Atomic Energy Comn, 63- Am. Nuclear Soc; Am. Soc. Mech. Eng. Modern furnace technology. Address: 84 Lighthouse Dr, Jupiter, FL 33458.

ETHERINGTON, ROBERT W(ILLIAM), JR, b. Valley Falls, R.I, Jan. 11, 24; m. 52; c. 4. ORGANIC CHEMISTRY. B.S, Providence Col, 46; M.S, Case, 51, Ph.D.(org. chem), 53. Asst. chem, Case, 51-52; RES. CHEMIST, petrol. chem. res. & develop. div, Celanese Corp. Am, 52-55; Petro-Tex Chem. Corp, 55-66; group leader, CENT. RES. & DEVELOP. LABS, MOBIL CHEM. CO, EDISON, 66-71, RES. ASSOC, 71- U.S.A, 46-47. AAAS; Am. Chem. Soc. Catalysis by ion exchange resins; aliphatic organic chemistry; petrochemicals; heterogeneous catalysis; hydrocarbon oxidation. Address: 403 S. Main St, Pennington, NJ 08534.

ETHERINGTON, THEODORE L(AYTON), b. Indianapolis, Ind, Mar. 1, 19; m. 41; c. 2. CHEMICAL ENGINEERING. B.S.Ch.E, Purdue, 43. Anal. chemist, Allison Div, Gen. Motors Corp, 40-42; design engr, Reilly Tar & Chem. Corp, 46-47; res. engr, P.R. Mallory, Inc, 47-48; assoc. res. lab, GEN. ELEC. CO, 48-61, mgr. adv. eng, outdoor lighting dept, 61-66; MGR. ENG, LIGHTING SYSTS. BUS. DEPT, 66- Instr, Purdue, 45-48. U.S.A, 42-46, Res, 46-52, 1st Lt. Am. Chem. Soc. Advanced development; lighting technologies; chemical process. Address: Lighting Systems Business Dept, General Electric Co, Hendersonville, NC 28739.

ETHERTON, BUD, b. Wardner, Idaho, Nov. 16, 30; m. 57; c. 2. BOTANY. B.S, Washington State, 56, Ph.D.(bot), 62; Harvard, 57-58. Res. assoc. bot, Washington State, 61-62; Nat. Sci. Found. fel. biophys, Edinburgh, 62-63; lectr. plant sci, Vassar Col, 63-64, asst. prof. biol, 64-67; vis. scientist, biol. & med. res, Argonne Nat. Lab, 67-68; ASSOC. PROF. BOT, UNIV. VT, 68- AAAS; Am. Soc. Plant Physiol. Electrical potentials and ion uptake in plant cells. Address: 42 Elsom Parkway, South Burlington, VT 05401.

ETHINGTON, ROBERT LOREN, b. State Center, Iowa, Feb. 13, 32; m. 54; c. 2. WOOD SCIENCE & TECHNOLOGY, ENGINEERING MECHANICS. B.S, Iowa State, 57, M.S, 59, Ph.D.(wood tech), 63. Instr, Iowa State, 59-63; technologist, U.S. FOREST PROD. LAB, 63-64, PROJ. LEADER FUNDA-

MENTAL PROPERTIES, 64- U.S.A, 52-54. Forest Prod. Res. Soc; Soc. Wood Sci. & Tech; Am. Soc. Test. & Mat.(award of merit, 70). Fundamental physical and mechanical properties of wood; stress grading; development of allowable stresses for wood; sampling methods for wood property evaluation. Address: U.S. Forest Products Lab, Madison, WI 53705.

ETHINTON, RAYMOND L(INDSAY), b. State Center, Iowa, Aug. 28, 29; m. 55; c. 2. GEOLOGY, PALEONTOLOGY. B.S, Iowa State Col, 51, M.S, 55; Ph.D.(geol), Univ. Iowa, 58. Asst. prof. GEOL, Ariz. State Univ, 58-62; UNIV. MO-COLUMBIA, 62-65, assoc. prof, 65-68, PROF, 68- Co-ed, J. Paleontol, 69- U.S.A, 51-53, Res, 53-58. Paleont. Soc; Geol. Soc. Am; Soc. Econ. Paleont. & Mineral; Am. Asn. Petrol. Geol; Brit. Asn. Paleont; Int. Palaeont. Union. Conodonts of North America. Address: Dept. of Geology, University of Missouri-Columbia, Columbia, MO 65201.

ETHRIDGE, NOEL H(AROLD), b. Plains, Ga, Aug. 7, 27; m. 49; c. 3. PHYSICS. B.S, Ga. Inst. Tech, 48. Physicist, Ballistic Res. Labs, Aberdeen Proving Ground, Md, 50-58; Oak Ridge Nat. Lab, 58-60; SUPVR. PHYSICIST, BALLISTIC RES. LABS, ABERDEEN PROVING GROUND, 60- U.S. Army tech. mem, shielding panel, Defense Atomic Support Agency, 61-63, U.S. rep, Tripartite Tech. Corp. Prog, 62-65. U.S.A, 46-47. Am. Phys. Soc. Nuclear and high explosive blast effects on military equipment; blast drag forces; measurement of blast parameters; large-scale HE blast phenomena. Address: 503 E. Lee Way, Bel Air, MD 21014.

ETKIN, BERNARD, b. Toronto, Ont, May 17, 18; m. 42; c. 2. AEROSPACE ENGINEERING. B.A.Sc, Toronto, 41, M.A.Sc, 47; hon. D.Eng, Carleton Univ.(Ont), 71. Lectr. AEROSPACE ENG, UNIV. TORONTO, 42-48, asst. prof, 48-53, assoc. prof, 54-57, PROF, 57-, CHMN. DIV. ENG. SCI, INST. AEROSPACE STUDIES, 67- Indust. consult, 40-; aerodynamicist, Nat. Res. Coun. Can, 45; mem. aerodyn. dept, Royal Aircraft Estab, Eng, 58-59. Mem. aerodyn. subcomt, adv. comt. aeronaut. res, Nat. Res. Coun. Can, 44-49, assoc. comt. aerodyn, 61-, chmn, 62. Fel. Am. Inst. Aeronaut. & Astronaut; fel. Can. Aeronaut. & Space Inst.(Centennial Medal, 67, McCurdy Award, 69); fel. Royal Soc. Can. Subsonic aerodynamics; wing theory; turbulence; dynamics of atmospheric flight; architectural aerodynamics; university government. Address: Institute for Aerospace Studies, University of Toronto, Toronto 181, Ont, Can.

ETKIN, WILLIAM, b. New York, Dec. 10, 06; m. 32; c. 2. ZOOLOGY. B.S, City Col. New York, 28, fel, 28-29; M.A, Cornell, 30; Ph.D.(zool), Chicago, 34. From tutor to prof. BIOL, City Col. New York, 34-67; PROF, YESHIVA COL, 67- Lectr, Columbia Univ, 51-52; prof, Albert Einstein Col. Med, 55- Am. Soc. Zool; Am. Asn. Anat; Soc. Exp. Biol. & Med; Soc. Develop. Biol; Ecol. Soc. Am; Endocrine Soc. Hormones in development; social behavior of animals; amphibian metamorphosis; experimental morphology; endocrinology; animal behavior. Address: Dept. of Biology, Yeshiva College, Washington Heights, New York, NY 10033.

ETKIND, IRVING J, b. New Haven, Conn, May 29, 16; m. 44; c. 2. ELECTRONICS. B.S, Maryland, 39; Yale. Elec. engr, U.S. Dept. Navy, Pa, 40-45; elec. designer, Stone & Webster Eng. Co, Boston, 46-47; elec. engr, Raytheon Mfg. Co, 48-50; elec. proj. engr, Workshop Assocs, 50-51; electronics engr, U.S. Navy, 51-56; electronic scientist, Air Force Cambridge Labs, 56-63, ELECTRONICS ENGR, electronics syst. div, U.S. Air Force, 63-64; microwave radiation lab, electronics res. center, NASA, 64-66; ELECTRONICS SYST. DIV, U.S. AIR FORCE, L.G. HANSOM FIELD, 66- Inst. Elec. & Electronics Eng. Physical electronics; communications; propagation; microwave electronics. Address: 54 Copeland St, Waltham, MA 02154.

ETNIER, DAVID ALLEN, b. St. Cloud, Minn, Dec. 2, 38; m. 64; c. 2. ICHTHYOLOGY. B.S, Minnesota, 61, Ph.D.(zool), 66. ASST. PROF. ZOOL, UNIV. TENN, KNOXVILLE, 66-, grad. sch. res. award, summer 68. Am. Soc. Ichthyol. & Herpet; Am. Fisheries Soc. Taxonomy and ecology of freshwater fishes of eastern United States; biology of aquatic insects, especially Trichoptera taxonomy. Address: Dept. of Zoology, University of Tennessee, Knoxville, TN 37916.

ETSTEN, BENJAMIN E, b. Lawrence, Mass, May 24, 08; m. 38; c. 3. ANESTHESIOLOGY. B.S, Tufts, 32; M.D, St. Andrew's Med. Sch, Scotland, 36. Instr. anesthesiol, Albany Med. Col, Union (N.Y), 40-41, asst. prof. ANESTHESIA, 42-48; MED. SCH, TUFTS UNIV, 49-50, assoc. prof, 50-52, PROF, 52-; ANESTHETIST-IN-CHIEF, NEW ENG. MED. CTR. HOSPS, 54- Dir. anesthesia, Albany Hosp, 42-48; New England Center Hosp, 48-53; consult, Vet. Admin. Hosp, Mass, 52-; Lemuel Shattuck & New England Hosps, 55-; Cape Cod & St. Margaret's Hosps, 58. AAAS; Am. Soc. Anesthesiol; Am. Col. Anesthesiol; Am. Soc. Pharmacol. & Exp. Therapeut; Am. Med. Asn. Cardiocirculatory physiology and pharmacology as applied to anesthesia. Address: Dept. of Anesthesia, New England Medical Center Hospitals, 171 Harrison Ave, Boston, MA 02111.

ETTELDORF, JAMES N, b. Lennox, S.Dak, Aug. 25, 09; m. 36; c. 2. PEDIATRICS. B.S, S.Dak. State, 32; fel, Tennessee, 32-34, M.S, 36, M.D, 42. Instr. med. pharmacol, Tennessee, 34-40, intern, 42-43; asst. res. PEDIAT, Tennessee & Washington (St. Louis), 43-45; assoc. prof, MED. UNITS, COL. MED, UNIV. TENN, MEMPHIS, 48-55, prof, 55-70, GOODMAN PROF, 70- Mem. exec. comt, J. Pediat. Educ. Found, 59-63; off. exam, Am. Bd. Pediat, 59-, secy. & mem. exec. comt, 64-69, Am. Med. Asn. rep, 64-70, mem. written exam. comt, 64-70, chmn, 68-70. AAAS; Am. Med. Asn; Soc. Pediat. Res; Am. Pediat. Soc; Am. Acad. Pediat; Am. Soc. Nephrology; Am. Soc. Pediat. Nephrology. Fluids and electrolytes; renal disease; endocrine and metabolic disorders. Address: Dept. of Pediatrics, Medical Units, University of Tennessee, 800 Madison Ave, Memphis, TN 38103.

ETTENBERG, M(ORRIS), b. Canton, Ohio, May 22, 16; m. 40; c. 1. ELECTRICAL ENGINEERING. B.A, City Col. New York, 35, M.S, 36; Ph.D.(physics), N.Y. Univ, 49; B.J.P, Jewish Theol. Sem, 38. Radar engr, U.S. Navy Yard, N.Y, 42-45; proj. engr, Sperry Gyroscope Co, 45-47, 49-51, proj. engr, 51-54, eng. dept. head, 54-58; res. prof. electrophys, Polytech. Inst. Brooklyn, 58-63; PROF. ELEC. ENG, CITY COL. NEW YORK, 63- Fulbright lectr, Israel Inst. Tech, 61-62. AAAS; Am. Phys. Soc; Inst. Elec. & Electronics Eng. Microwaves; microwave electronic tubes; klystrons; traveling wave tubes. Address: Dept. of Electrical Engineering, City College of New York, New York, NY 10031.

ETTER, ALFRED G(ORDON), b. St. Louis, Mo, Sept. 7, 19; m. 44; c. 2. ECOLOGY. A.B, Washington (St. Louis), 41, Ph.D.(bot), 50; Wisconsin, 46-47. Instr. biol, New Mexico Mil. Inst, 51; fel, Ford Found. Fund Adv. Ed, 51-52; res. assoc, sch. med, Washington (St. Louis), 52-57; asst. prof. fisheries & wildlife, Mich. State, 57-63; wildlife photographer & lectr, Nat. Audubon Soc, 63-64; field rep, Defenders Wildlife, 64-70; NATURALIST, MORTON ARBORETUM, 70- Summer mem. teaching staff, Inst. Field Biol, Aspen, Colo, 64-66. Am. Inst. Biol. Sci; Am. Soc. Mammal. Ecological effects of poisons; variation of plants with environment; environmental improvement with minimum maintenance. Address: Morton Arboretum, Lisle, IL 60532.

ETTER, CHARLES G, JR, b. Phila, Pa, July 15, 21; m. 47; c. 1. STRUCTURAL ENGINEERING. B.S, Drexel Inst. Tech, 43; M.S, Pennsylvania, 50; Sc.D.(civil eng), Mass. Inst. Tech, 53. Asst. prof. CIVIL ENG, Florida, 53; assoc. prof, Drexel Inst. Tech, 54-61; PROF, VILLANOVA UNIV, 61- Consult. civil engr, 54- C.Eng, 44-46, Capt. Am. Soc. Civil Eng; Am. Soc. Eng. Educ. Practical procedures for the analysis of shell structures and the evaluation of strucural stability and dynamic problems; more reliable methods for predicting shear and settlement failures in foundations. Address: Dept. of Civil Engineering, Villanova University, Villanova, PA 19085.

ETTER, DANIEL O, JR, b. Ft. Worth, Tex, Aug. 3, 29; m. 55; c. 2. OPERATIONS RESEARCH, MATHEMATICS. B.A, Texas Christian, 50, M.A, 52; Nat. Sci. Found. fel, Tulane, 52-55; Ph.D.(math), California, Los Angeles, 62. Eng. specialist, N.Am. Aviation Inc, Calif, 56-63; MEM. TECH. STAFF, INST. DEFENSE ANAL, 63- Am. Math. Soc; Opers. Res. Soc. Am; Soc. Indust. & Appl. Math; Inst. Mgt. Sci. Functional analysis; competition and attrition processes; optimal resource exploitation. Address: 2402 Nordok Place, Alexandria, VA 22306.

ETTER, L(EWIS) E(LMER), b. Pittsburgh, Pa, Jan. 17, 01; m. 27; c. 2. RADIOLOGY, ROENTGENOLOGY. B.S, Pittsburgh, 24, M.D, 27. Teaching fel. RADIOL, UNIV. PITTSBURGH, 46-47, instr, 47-50, asst. prof, 50-55; assoc. prof, 55-57, PROF, 57-, CONSULT. CLIN, 47- Consult, U.S. Vet. Admin, 47-53; West. Psychiat. Inst, 47-; Pittsburgh Tuberc. Hosp, 55-; chief radiol. serv, Vet. Admin. Hosp, Leech Farm Rd, 53-57; consult. roentgenologist, Warrendale Clin, 47- Chief radiol. serv. Falk Clin, Pittsburgh 57- Ed, Am. Lect. in Roentgen Diag, 58- Dipl, Am. Bd. Radiol, 46. Med.C, 41-46, Lt. Col. Fel. Am. Col. Radiol; Radiol. Soc. N.Am; Am. Roentgen Ray Soc.(cert. merit, 46, 49, Bronze medal, 62); Am. Soc. Neuroradiol. Magnification roentgenologic studies of the middle ear and mastoid process; historical data concerning discovery of roentgen rays; roentgen anatomical studies of the skull; high kilovoltage roentgenography in dentistry; combined copper and aluminum filtration in radiography. Address: School of Medicine, University of Pittsburgh, Pittsburgh, PA 15213.

ETTER, R(AYMOND) LEWIS, JR, b. Sherman, Tex, Aug. 10, 31; m. 57; c. 2. ORGANIC CHEMISTRY. B.S, Texas, 52, Ph.D.(org. chem), 57. Asst. org. chem, Texas, 52-56; res. chemist, TEX. EASTMAN CO, 56-62, SR. CHEMIST, 62- Am. Chem. Soc. Low molecular weight polymers; heterocyclic nitrogen compounds; polyolefins; synthetic resins; chlorinated polyolefins; paints; high pressure polymerization. Address: 1205 Azalea Dr, Longview, TX 75601.

ETTER, ROBERT MILLER, b. Chambersburg, Pa, July 13, 32; m. 57; c. 3. ORGANIC CHEMISTRY. A.B, Gettysburg Col, 54; Allied Chem. & Dye Corp. fel, Pa. State, 57-58; Ph.D.(org. chem), 59. Res. chemist dyes, Am Cyanamid Co, N.J, 58-62; explosives, Pa, 62-63; sr. res. chemist ORG. SYNTHESIS, S.C. JOHNSON & SON, INC, 63-65, res. supvr, 65-71, PROD. RES. MGR, 71- AAAS; Am. Chem. Soc; Am. Oil Chemists' Soc. Carbenes; reaction mechanisms; dyes; fiber finishes; explosives; insecticides; insect repellents; plant biochemistry. Address: 4511 Knollwood Dr, Racine, WI 53403.

ETTER, WILLIAM P(AUL), b. Thorntown, Ind, Dec. 3, 20; m. 44; c. 4. PHYSICS. B.S, U.S. Naval Acad, 43; B.S, U.S. Naval Postgrad. Sch, 50; M.S, California, Los Angeles, 51; Catholic Univ, 64-68. Eng. duty officer, Naval Ships Systs. Command, U.S. Navy, 43-65; prog. mgr, TRACOR, INC, 65-69, DIR. SAN DIEGO LAB, 69- U.S.N, 43-65, Comdr. Acoust. Soc. Am; Am. Soc. Naval Eng; Inst. Elec. & Electronics Eng. Underwater acoustics; military oceanography; physical acoustics. Address: Tracor Inc, 2923 Canon St, San Diego, CA 92106.

ETTINGER, ANNA MARIE CONWAY, b. Janesville, Wis, Nov. 4, 25; m. 69. ANATOMY. B.S, Univ. Wis, 46, M.S, 50, fel, 55-57; univ. fel, Univ. Ill, 63-65, Nat. Sci. Found. fel, 65-66, Ph.D.(anat), 67. Teacher, Barrington Sch. Syst, Ill, 46-49; Joliet Sch. Syst, 50-55; instr, ANAT, St. Louis Univ, 57-63; Univ. Ill, 66-67; asst. prof, SCH. DENT, UNIV. DETROIT, 67-69, ASSOC. PROF, 69-, CHMN. DEPT. ANAT. SCI, 71- Gen. res. support grants, 67 & 68; univ. res. grant, 68-69; Nat. Insts. Health res. grant, 69- Am. Asn. Anat; N.Y. Acad. Sci. Studies on the ontogeny of immune response in the chick. Address: Dept. of Anatomical Sciences, University of Detroit School of Dentistry, Detroit, MI 48207.

ETTINGER, G(EORGE) HAROLD, b. Kingston, Ont, May 9, 96; m. 20; c. 1. PHYSIOLOGY. B.A, Queen's(Ont), 16, M.D, 20, LL.D, 67; Edinburgh, 28-29; hon. D.Sc, Western Ontario, 58; hon. M.D, Ottawa(Can), 63. Lectr. physiol, Queen's Univ.(Ont), 20-28, asst. prof, 29-33, assoc. prof, 33-37, prof, 37-62, dean faculty med, 49-62; RETIRED. Res. assoc, Univ. Toronto, 31-35; mem. assoc. comt. med. res, Nat. Res. Coun. Can, 38, hon. secy, 42, asst. dir. div. med. res, 46-58; dir. med. planning, Alcoholism & Drug Addiction Res. Found, 62-70. Mem. Order of Brit. Empire. AAAS; Am. Asn. Anat; Am. Physiol. Soc; fel. Royal Soc. Can; Can. Physiol. Soc.(secy, 36-40, pres, 47). Cardiovascular physiology; alcohol and drug addiction. Address: Cartwright Point, Kingston, Ont, Can.

ETTLINGER, H(YMAN) J(OSEPH), b. St. Louis, Mo, Sept. 1, 89. MATHEMATICS. A.B, Washington (St. Louis), 10; A.M, Harvard, 11, Ph.D, 20; Chicago, 17. Prof. MATH, UNIV. TEX, AUSTIN, 13-69, EMER. PROF, 69- AAAS; Am. Math. Soc; Math. Asn. Am. Pure and applied mathematics; boundary values; definite integrals; differential and integral equations. Address: 3110 Harris Park Ave, Austin, TX 78705.

ETTLINGER, MARTIN G(ROSSMAN), b. Austin, Tex, Oct. 5, 25; m. 66. CHEMISTRY. B.A, Univ. Tex, 42, M.A, 43; Ph.D.(chem), Harvard, 46. Jr. fel, Harvard, 46-50, res. fel, 50-51; asst. prof. chem, Rice Inst, 51-56, assoc. prof, 56-65; vis. lectr. chem, Copenhagen Univ, 67-68, vis. prof. chem, Aarhus Univ, 68; Nat. Acad. Sci-Nat. Res. Coun. sr. vis. res. assoc, U.S. Army Natick Labs, 69-70; VIS. PROF. CHEM, COPENHAGEN UNIV, 70- Jewett fel, Calif. Inst. Technol, 46-47; hon. res. assoc, Gray Herbarium, Harvard, 69-71. Civilian with Off. Sci. Res. & Develop, 43-46. Am. Chem. Soc. Glucosinolates and cyanogenetic glycosides; comparative phytochemistry; vitamin C; mechanism of Michael additions. Address: Chemical Lab. II, H.C. Oersted Institute, Universitetsparken 5, 2100 Copenhagen Ø, Denmark.

ETTRE, KITTY, b. Budapest, Hungary, Aug. 19, 30; U.S. citizen; m. 53; c. 1. PHYSICAL CHEMISTRY. M.S, Budapest Inst. Technol, 52. Res. chemist, Res. Inst. Heavy Chem. Industs, Budapest, 52-54; Res. Inst. Telecommun, Budapest, 54-56; Max Planck Inst. Biophys, 57-58; develop. engr, Machlett Labs, Conn, 58-63; PRES, VITTA CORP, WILTON, 63- Am. Chem. Soc; Am. Ceramic Soc; Am. Soc. Test. & Mat; Nat. Inst. Ceramic Eng; Int. Soc. Hybrid Microelectronics. Thin-film coating; physico-chemical methods; special metallic and nonmetallic tapes, coatings and films used in the electronic industries. Address: 157 Grumman Ave, Norwalk, CT 06851.

ETTRE, LESLIE S(TEPHEN), b. Szombathely, Hungary, Sept. 16, 22; U.S. citizen; m. 53; c. 1. ANALYTICAL CHEMISTRY, INSTRUMENTATION. M.S, Budapest Tech, 45. Process chemist, G. Richter Pharmaceut. Co, Hungary, 46-49; res. assoc, Hungarian Res. Inst-Heavy Chem. Industs, 49-51, head tech. off, 51-53; mgr. indust. dept, Hungarian Plastics Indust. Res. Inst, 53-56; chemist, Lurgi Labs, Germany, 57-58; appln. chemist, Perkin-Elmer Corp, 58-62, chief appln. chemist, 62-68; EXEC. ED, ENCYCL. INDUST. CHEM. ANAL, JOHN WILEY & SONS, PUBL, 68- Regional ed, J. Chromatographia, 71- Am. Chem. Soc; Instrument Soc. Am; Air Pollution Control Asn; N.Y. Acad. Sci; Am. Soc. Test. & Mat; Brit. Soc. Anal. Chem; fel. Am. Inst. Chem. Theory, practice and application of gas chromatography; analytical instrumentation; scientific editing. Address: 157 Grumman Ave, Norwalk, CT 06851.

ETZEL, HOWARD W(ESLEY), b. Brooklyn, N.Y, Aug. 5, 22; m. 44; c. 2. SOLID STATE PHYSICS. B.S, Carnegie Inst. Tech, 44, M.S. & D.Sc. (physics), 49. Res. physicist, NAVAL RES. LAB, 50-56, head radiation effects sect, 56-62; assoc. prog. dir. physics, NAT. SCI. FOUND, 62-63, prog. dir. solid state & low temperature physics, WASH, D.C, 63-71, DEP. DIR, DIV. NAT. RES, 71- Fulbright res. scholar, France, 49-50; mem. solid state sci. panel, Nat. Acad. Sci-Nat. Res. Coun. Sig.C, 44-46, 1st Lt. Fel. Am. Phys. Soc; Sci. Res. Soc. Am. Electronic and optical properties of solids, lasers. Address: 7304 River Hill Rd, Oxon Hill, MD 20021.

ETZLER, D(ORR) H(OMER), b. Westboro, Wis, Apr. 30, 15; m. 38; c. 2. CHEMISTRY. B.S, Wisconsin, 35; fel, California, 35-38, Ph.D.(chem), 38. Res. chemist, STANDARD OIL CO. CALIF, 38-42, Calif. Res. Corp, 45-46, admin. asst, 46-50, asst. to gen. mgr, 50-55, MGR. gen. serv, 55-63, admin. & lab. serv, CHEVRON RES. CO, 63-67, orgn. planning, 67-70, RES. SERV. DEPT, 70- Chem.C.Res, 42-45, Lt. Col. AAAS; Am. Chem. Soc. Photochemistry of acetyl halides; compounded lubricating oils; research administration. Address: Research Services Dept, Chevron Research Co, 576 Standard Ave, Richmond, CA 94802.

ETZLER, MARILYNN EDITH, b. Detroit, Mich, Oct. 30, 40. IMMUNOCHEMISTRY, BIOCHEMISTRY. B.S.(biol) & B.A.(chem), Otterbein Col, 62; Nat. Insts. Health trainee, Wash. Univ, 62-65 & fel, 65-66, Ph.D.(biol), 67. Res. assoc. develop. biol, Wash. Univ, 66-67; Nat. Insts. Health fel. immunochem, dept. microbiol, col. physicians & surgeons, Columbia Univ, 67-69; ASST. PROF. BIOCHEM, UNIV. CALIF, DAVIS, 69- Nat. Insts. Health grant, 71-74. Am. Soc. Cell Biol. Development of cell surface components; structure and specificity of plant agglutinins. Address: Dept. of Biochemistry & Biophysics, University of California, Davis, CA 95616.

ETZWEILER, GEORGE ARTHUR, b. Lewistown, Pa, Mar. 14, 20; m. 42; c. 3. ELECTRICAL ENGINEERING. B.S, Pa. State, 49, Ord. Res. Lab. fel, 49-50, M.S, 50, Am. Oil Found. fel, 60-61, Ph.D.(elec. eng), 64. Develop. engr, Ahrendt Instrument Co, Litton Industs, Inc, 50-55, chief develop. engr, 55-57; instr. ELEC. ENG, PA. STATE UNIV, 57-64, asst. prof, 64-67, ASSOC. PROF, 67- Lectr, Univ. Md, 56-57; consult, Bausch & Lomb, Inc, N.Y; P.R. Hoffman Co, Pa; Carborundum Co, Pa; chmn. tech. comt. components, Am. Automatic Control Coun; mem. tech. comt. components, Int. Fedn. Automatic Control, U.S. paper selection comt, Fifth Cong. U.S.N.R, 42-45. Sr. mem. Inst. Elec. & Electronics Eng; Am. Soc. Eng. Educ. Stability and performance of feedback control systems and control system components. Address: Dept. of Electrical Engineering, Pennsylvania State University, University Park, PA 16802.

ETZOLD, HELLMUTH, b. Leipzig, Ger, Apr. 30, 09; U.S. citizen; m. 35; c. 3. ACOUSTICS, ELECTROACOUSTICS. Leipzig, 28-30; Ph.D.(phys. chem), Freiburg, 34; venia legendi, Tech. Univ, Berlin, 51. ASSOC. PROF. ELEC. ENG, UNIV. R.I, 63- Tech. adv, subcomt. 29B, U.S. Nat. Comt, Int. Electrotech. Comn, 67-, secy. working group 7, 69-, mem. acoust. tech. adv. bd, 70- Inst. Elec. & Electronics Eng; Acoust. Soc. Am; Soc. Motion Pictures & TV Eng. Address: 81½ Central St, Narragansett, RI 02882.

EU, BYUNG CHAN, b. Seoul, Korea, July 7, 35; m. 64; c. 1. THEORETICAL CHEMISTRY. B.S, Seoul, 59; Ph.D.(chem), Brown, 66. Res. assoc. CHEM, Brown, 65-66; res. fel, Harvard, 66-67; ASST. PROF, McGILL UNIV, 67- Am. Phys. Soc. Theoretical study of molecular collisions of chemically reactive systems and chemical kinetics in gas phase. Address: Dept. of Chemistry, McGill University, Montreal, Que, Can.

EUBANK, HAROLD P(ORTER), b. Baltimore, Md, Oct. 23, 24; m. 48; c. 3. PHYSICS. B.S, Col. of William & Mary, 48; M.S, Syracuse, 50; Ph.D.(physics), Brown, 53. Asst. physics, Syracuse, 48-50; Brown, 50-52, res. assoc, 52-54, asst. prof, 54-59; MEM. RES. STAFF, PLASMA PHYSICS LAB, PRINCETON, 59- U.S.A, 43-46. Am. Phys. Soc. Experimental nuclear and plasma physics. Address: Plasma Physics Lab, Princeton University, Princeton, NJ 08540.

EUBANK, LOWELL D, b. Pratt Co, Kans, Apr. 5, 14; m. 40; c. 3. PHYSICAL CHEMISTRY. A.B, Kansas State, 36; fel, Illinois, 36-39, Ph.D, 39. Res. chemist, indust. & biochem. dept, E.I. DU PONT DE NEMOURS & CO, 39-41, sr. res. chemist, 42-43, area supvr, explosives dept, Hanford Plant, 44-45, res. supvr, indust. & biochem. dept, 46; sales develop. rep, 47-49, indust. marketing analyst, 50-53, asst. mgr. marketing res. div, develop. dept, 54-66, mgr. mkt. res. develop. dept, 66-69, ASSOC. MGR. ADVERT. DEPT, 70- Chem. Mkt. Res. Asn; Am. Mkt. Asn; Am. Chem. Soc. Galvanizing fluxes; hot dip metal coatings; marketing. Address: Advertising Dept, E.I. du Pont de Nemours & Co, Wilmington, DE 19898.

EUBANK, PHILIP TOBY, b. Greenup, Ill, May 12, 36; m. 60. CHEMICAL ENGINEERING. B.S, Rose Polytech. Inst, 58; Ph.D.(chem. eng), Northwest. Univ, 61. Asst. prof. CHEM. ENG, TEX. A&M UNIV, 61-64, assoc. prof, 64-68, PROF, 68- Nat. Sci. Found. grant, 63-70. Am. Inst. Chem. Eng; Am. Chem. Soc; Am. Soc. Eng. Educ. Volumetric and thermodynamic properties of polar fluids and of hydrocarbon fluids. Address: Dept. of Chemical Engineering, Texas A&M University, College Station, TX 77843.

EUBANK, WILLIAM R(ODERICK), b. Cynthiana, Ky, Jan. 21, 19; m. 45; c. 2. PHYSICAL CHEMISTRY. B.S, Kentucky, 40, M.S, 41; Pa. State, 41-42; Ph.D.(phys. chem), Hopkins, 47. Asst. phys. chem, Kentucky, 40-41; asst. ceramic lab, Pa. State, 41-42; res. phys. chemist, Keasbey & Mattison, Pa, 42-43; res. assoc, Nat. Bur. Standards, 44-48; consult, U.S. Naval Ord. Test. Sta, Calif, 48-51; res. chemist, Edgar Bros. Co, Ga, 51-52; gen. mgr, Ind. Hone Mfg. Co, Mich, 52-53; sr. res. chemist, cent. res. lab, MINN. MINING & MFG. CO, 53-61, proj. supvr, magnetic prod. lab, 61-64, mgr. mat. res, Revere-Mincom Div, 64-68, MGR. ANAL. RES. SERV, MAGNETIC PROD. DIV, 68- Fel, Mellon Inst, 43-44; Portland Cement Asn. fel, 44-48. AAAS; Am. Chem. Soc; Am. Inst. Chem; Am. Ceramic Soc; Electrochem. Soc; Electron Micros. Soc. Am. Phase equilibrium; temperature control; microscopy; refractories; enamels; cements; calcination; flame photometry; explosives; electrical ceramics; paint extenders; abrasive honing stones; low-melting glasses; metalloids and intermetallic compounds; ferrites; magnetic metals; electron microscopy; semiconductors; analytical chemistry. Address: Magnetic Products Division, Minnesota Mining & Manufacturing Co, 3M Center, St. Paul, MN 55101.

EUBANKS, I(SAAC) DWAINE, b. San Angelo, Tex, Sept. 22, 38; m. 59; c. 3. INORGANIC CHEMISTRY. B.S, Univ. Tex, 60, Dow Chem. Co. fel, 62, Ph.D. (inorg. chem), 63. Chemist, Savannah River Lab, E.I. du Pont de Nemours & Co, Inc, 63-67; asst. prof. CHEM, OKLA. STATE UNIV, 67-71, ASSOC. PROF, 71- Am. Chem. Soc; The Chem. Soc. Coordination chemistry of the lanthanides in nonaqueous solvents. Address: Dept. of Chemistry, Oklahoma State University, Stillwater, OK 74074.

EUBANKS, L(LOYD) STANLEY, b. San Antonio, Tex, Sept. 24, 31; m. 51; c. 3. CHEMICAL ENGINEERING. B.A, Rice, 52, B.S, 53, Ph.D.(chem. eng), 57. Res. engr, MONSANTO CO, 57-59, sr. res. engr, 59-61, sr. chem. engr, 61-64, PROCESS SPECIALIST, 64- Am. Inst. Chem. Eng. Phase equilibria. Address: Monsanto Co, P.O. Box 1311, Texas City, TX 77591.

EUBANKS, ROBERT ALONZO, b. Chicago, Ill, June 3, 26. THEORETICAL & APPLIED MECHANICS, CIVIL ENGINEERING. B.S, Ill. Inst. Tech, 50, M.S, 51, Ph.D, 53. Instr. mech, Ill. Inst. Tech, 50-52, asst. prof, 53-54; sr. engr, Bulova Res. Lab, N.Y, 54-55; res. engr, Am. Mach. & Foundry Co, Ill, 55-56; scientist, Borg Warner Res. Center, 56-60; sr scientist, Armour Res. Found, 60-62, mgr. vibrations, 62-64; sci. adv. mech. & struct. eng, IIT Res. Inst, 64-65; PROF. CIVIL ENG, UNIV. ILL, URBANA, 65-, George A. Miller vis. prof, 64-65. Adj. prof, Ill. Inst. Tech, 62-65, consult, IIT Res. Inst, 65-; Booz-Allen Appl. Res. Inc, 65- Mem. cmt. vibration & shock, Int. Standards Orgn, 63- U.S.A, 42-46. Am. Soc. Mech; Am. Math. Soc; Soc. Indust. & Appl. Math; Am. Soc. Civil Eng. Mathematical theory of elasticity; rotor stability; elastic wave propagation; protective construction; vibrations and shock; terminal ballistics. Address: 3106 Civil Engineering Bldg, University of Illinois, Urbana, IL 61801.

EUBANKS, WILLIAM HUNTER, b. Columbus, Miss, Dec. 13, 21; m. 44; c. 3. ENGINEERING GRAPHICS. B.S, Miss. State, 47, M.S, 53. Draftsman, Mobile Dist. Corp. Eng. Design & Construct, Columbus Air Force Base, 41, 42; from instr. to PROF. ENG. GRAPHICS, MISS. STATE UNIV, 47-, HEAD DEPT, 60- Estimator, U.S. Steel Corp, Graphics, summers 53, 55. C.Eng, U.S.A, 43-47. Am. Soc. Eng. Educ; Nat. Soc. Prof. Eng. Interpretation and graphical analysis of research data; use of photography in presenting graphical research data and as an aid in comparing graphical and analytical interpretation of research data; methods of graphic presentation; graphic analysis; creative design projects for freshman engineering students. Address: Dept. of Engineering Graphics, Mississippi State University, State College, MS 39762.

EUDY, WILLIAM W(AYNE), b. Oakboro, N.C, Sept. 1, 39; m. 61; c. 1. MICROBIOLOGY, BIOCHEMISTRY. B.S, Wake Forest, 61, fel. & M.A, 69; Nat. Defense Ed. Act fel. & Ph.D.(microbiol), N.C. State, 69. SR. RES. MICROBIOLOGIST, Norwich Pharmacal Co, 68-71; INT. PAPER CO, 71- U.S.A.R, 62-68, 1st Lt. AAAS; Am. Chem. Soc; Am. Soc. Microbiol. Biochemical characterization of our small animal pyelonephritis model infection; developmental biology; enzymology; infection; molecular biology. Address: International Paper Co, Corporate Research Center, Tuxedo Park, NY 10987.

EUGERE, EDWARD J(OSEPH), b. New Orleans, La, May 26, 30; m. 54; c. 4. PHARMACY, PHARMACOLOGY. B.S, Xavier, 51; M.S, Wayne State, 53; Fesler fel, Connecticut, 54-56, Ph.D.(pharmacol), 56. Asst. prof. PHARMACOL, Detroit Inst. Technol, 56-58; PROF, TEX. SOUTH. UNIV, 58-, dean, sch. pharm, 58-70. Summers, lectr, Highland Park Jr. Col, 56-57, Detroit Inst. Technol, 57-58. Mem. pharm. review comt, pub. adv. group, Nat. Insts. Health, 69- Am. Pharmaceut. Asn; Am. Asn. Cols. Pharm. Chemotherapy of trichomoniasis; medicinal applications of ion exchange substances. Address: School of Pharmacy, Texas Southern University, 3201 Wheeler, Houston, TX 77004.

EUGSTER, H(ANS) P(ETER), b. Landquart, Switz, Nov. 19, 25; nat; m. 53; c. 3. GEOCHEMISTRY. Dipl. Ing. Geol, Swiss Fed. Inst. Tech, 48, fel, 50, Dr.Sc.Nat, 51. Crystallographer, Swiss Inst. Study Snow & Avalanches, 48; vis. investr, geophys. lab, Carnegie Inst, 52-53, geochemist, 53-58; assoc. prof. GEOL, JOHNS HOPKINS UNIV, 58-60, PROF, 60- With U.S. Geol. Surv, 58. Swiss Army, 45-51. Fel. Geol. Soc. Am; Geochem. Soc; fel. Am. Geophys. Union. Petrology, geochemistry and physical chemistry of silicates, oxydes and carbonates; synthesis and phase relations of minerals; redox reactions and salt deposits. Address: Dept. of Geology, Johns Hopkins University, Baltimore, MD 21218.

EUKEL, WARREN W(ENZL), b. Plummer, Minn, Mar. 4, 21; m. 46; c. 3. ENGINEERING PHYSICS. B.S, California, 50. Physicist, radiation lab, California, 50-53; Chromatic TV, Calif, 53-54; Appl. Radiation Corp, 54-64; mem. staff, W.M. BROBECK & ASSOCS, BERKELEY, 64-66, opers. mgr, 66-67, V.PRES, 67- Mem. cmt. high level dosimetry, Nat. Acad. Sci; adv. bd, qm. res. & develop, Nat. Res. Coun. U.S.A.A.F, 43-46. AAAS; Inst. Elec. & Electronics Eng; Am. Nuclear Soc. Ion sources and gaseous discharge; electron linear accelerators; peaceful uses of radiation. Address: 950 Gilman St, Berkeley, CA 94710.

EULER, FERDINAND K(ARL), b. Ingelheim, Germany, Feb. 25, 27; U.S. citizen; m. 60; c. 2. PHYSICS, CRYSTALLOGRAPHY. Darmstadt Tech, 46-49; dipl, Munich Tech, 52. RES. PHYSICIST, AIR FORCE CAMBRIDGE RES. LABS, 53- German Air Force, 43-45. AAAS; Am. Phys. Soc; Sci. Res. Soc. Am. Ion implantation; radiation effects; semiconductors; magnetism; x-ray crystallography. Address: Air Force Cambridge Research Labs, Laurence Hanscom Field, Bedford, MA 01730.

EULER, KENNETH L. b. Natrona Heights, Pa, July 25, 37. PHARMACOGNOSY. B.S, Pittsburgh, 59, M.S, 62; Am. Found. Pharmaceut. Ed. fel, Washington (Seattle), 62-64, Ph.D.(pharmacog), 65. Asst. prof. PHARMACOG, Univ. Md, 65-67; UNIV. HOUSTON, 67-68, ASSOC. PROF, 68- Am. Pharmaceut. Asn; Am. Acad. Pharmaceut. Sci; Am. Soc. Pharmacog; Soc. Econ. Biol. Plant chemistry and biochemistry; isolation and identification of plant constituents having physiological activity and study of their biosynthetic pathways. Address: College of Pharmacy, University of Houston, Houston, TX 77004.

EULER, ROBERT DONALD, b. Bellevue, Ohio, Nov. 30, 23; m. 51; c. 2. PHYSICAL CHEMISTRY. B.A, Oberlin Col, 47; M.S, Michigan, 49, E.I. du Pont de Nemours & Co. fel, 53-54, Ph.D, 54. Res. chemist, TEXTILE FIBERS DEPT, E.I. DU PONT DE NEMOURS & CO, INC, 54-60, res. supvr, 60-70, PROCESS SUPVR, 70- U.S.N.R, 43-47, Lt.(jg). Am. Chem. Soc. Low temperature calorimetry of inorganic fluorides; synthetic textile and industrial fiber research and development. Address: E.I. du Pont de Nemours & Co, Inc, Waynesboro, VA 22980.

EURE, SPURGEON B, b. Columbia, Miss, Nov. 18, 22. OPTOMETRY. B.S, Southern Mississippi, 48; O.D, South. Col. Optom, 54; M.A, Memphis, 65. Asst. prof. biol, Southern Mississippi, 55-61, asst. dir. reading clin, 59-61; dean, SOUTH. COL. OPTOM, 61-65, PRES, 65- Mem, Am. Optom. Found, 54-, chmn. adv. res. coun, 56; chmn. bd, Miss. Optom. Found, 59. George J. Haus award, 54; alumni award, Univ. Southern Mississippi, 55. U.S.A.A.F, 42-45, T/Sgt. Am. Optom. Asn; Am. Acad. Optom. Optometry and administrative research. Address: 1246 Union Ave, Memphis, TN 38104.

EUSTICE, ALBERT L, b. Kenosha, Wis, June 30, 29; m. 52; c. 2. METALLURGY. B.S, Wisconsin, 51; Ph.D.(metall), Iowa State, 60. Chemist, Fansteel Metall. Corp, Ill, 51-53; res. asst. metall, Iowa State, 55-60; SR. RES. METALLURGIST MAT. SCI, ENG. DEPT, E.I. DU PONT DE NEMOURS & CO, INC, 60- U.S.A, 53-55. Am. Soc. Metals; Am. Inst. Mining, Metall. & Petrol. Eng. Properties of existing engineering materials and development of improved materials. Address: Engineering Materials Lab, Experimental Station, E.I. du Pont de Nemours & Co, Inc, Wilmington, DE 19898.

EUSTIS, ROBERT H(ENRY), b. Minneapolis, Minn, Apr. 18, 20; m. 43; c. 2. MECHANICAL ENGINEERING. B.Mech. Eng, Minnesota, 42, M.S, 44; Sc.D.(mech. eng), Mass. Inst. Tech, 53. Instr. mech. eng, Minnesota, 43-44; aeronaut. res. scientist, Nat. Adv. Cmt. Aeronaut, 44-47; instr. mech. eng, Mass. Inst. Tech, 48, asst. prof, 49-51; chief engr. & asst. to pres, Thermal Res. & Eng. Corp, 51-53; sr. mech. engr, Stanford Res. Inst, 53-56; assoc. prof. MECH. ENG, STANFORD UNIV, 56-62, PROF, 62-, DIR. HIGH TEMPERATURE GASODYNAMICS LAB, 71- Am. Soc. Mech. Eng; Am. Soc. Eng. Educ; Combustion Inst; Am. Phys. Soc. Magnetohydrodynamics; heat transfer; fluid mechanics. Address: Dept. of Mechanical Engineering, Stanford University, Stanford, CA 94305.

EUSTIS, WILLIAM H(ENRY), b. Coeur D'Alene, Idaho, Dec. 26, 21; m. 49; c. 1. POLYMER CHEMISTRY. Ph.D.(chem), California, 51. Technologist, Shell Oil Co, 51-60, sr. engr, Shell Chem. Co. Div, 60-65; INSTR, YAKIMA VALLEY COL, 65- Ord. Dept, 43-46, Maj. Am. Chem. Soc. Analytical petroleum; organic reaction mechanisms. Address: Yakima Valley College, Yakima, WA 98902.

EUSTON, CHARLES B, b. Richmond, Va, June 30, 24; m. 46; c. 4. PHYSICAL CHEMISTRY. Ph.D.(chem), Connecticut, 54. Asst. instr. chem, Connecticut, 50-54; chemist, U.S. Naval Ord. Test Sta, 51; E.I. du Pont de Nemours & Co, 54-60; sr. res. chemist, F & M Sci. Corp, Pa, 60-61, dir. res. & eng, 61-64, managing dir, F & M Sci. Europa, 64-67; SECT. MGR. RES. & DEVELOP, HEWLETT-PACKARD, 67- C.Eng, U.S.A, 43-46. Gas chromatography; instrumental analysis. Address: R. D. 2, Box 206, Hockessin, DE 19707.

EUVERARD, MAYNARD R(AY), b. Highland Co, Ohio, Apr. 7, 17; m. 41; c. 1. PHYSICS. A.B, Miami (Ohio), 38; fel, scholar & M.S, Cincinnati, 40. Physicist, Interchem. Corp, 39-41, dir. standards & phys. evaluation dept, 46-48, physicist, finishes div, 48-49, asst. chief corp. eng, 50-53; mgr. eng, commercial develop. div, Am. Mach. & Foundry Co, 53-57, asst. to pres, Union Mach. Div, 58-63, mgr. bus. develop, Bakery Mach. Div, 63-71; MGR. VELTEN & PULVER, INC, 71- Advan. mgt. prog, 24th session, Harvard, 53. U.S.M.C, 41-46. AAAS; Am. Soc. Test. & Mat; Am. Soc. Bakery Eng. Machinery and processes for the bakery trade. Address: Velten & Pulver, Inc, 103rd & Ridgeland Ave, Chicago Ridge, IL 60415.

EVALDSON, RUNE L, b. Okelbo, Sweden, Nov. 21, 18; nat; m. 42; c. 5. ENGINEERING MECHANICS. B.S, Illinois, 41; Ph.D.(eng. mech), Stanford, 50. Sr. anal. engr, Hamilton Standard Propellers, United Aircraft Corp, 41-47; asst. dynamics, elasticity, Stanford, 47-50; consult, Booz-Allen & Hamilton, 50-53; assoc. prof. MECH. ENG, UNIV. MICH, 53-56, PROF, 56-, assoc. dir. inst. sci. & technol, 58-70, managing dir, Willow Run Labs, 65-67, dir, 67-70. Dynamics; elasticity; fatigue of metals; operations research; research administration. Address: Dept. of Mechanical Engineering, College of Engineering, University of Michigan, Ann Arbor, MI 48104.

EVANEGA, GEORGE R, b. Cementon, Pa, Feb. 6, 36; m. 63; c. 2. ORGANIC CHEMISTRY. B.S, Lehigh, 57; M.S, Yale, 58, Ph.D.(org. chem), 60. Nat. Inst. Health fel, Freiburg, 60-61; res. chemist, Union Carbide Res. Inst, N.Y, 62-69, mgr. biomed. instrumentation, 69; res. chemist, MED. RES. LABS, PFIZER INC, 69-70, proj. leader diabetes, 70, MGR. DIAG. RES, 71- Am. Chem. Soc; The Chem. Soc. Photochemistry; medicinal chemistry. Address: Pfizer Inc, Medical Research Labs, Groton, CT 06340.

EVANS, A(DELBERT) S(IEGFRIED), b. Okeene, Okla, May 16, 17; m. 39, 55; c. 2. IMMUNOCHEMISTRY. B.S, Am. Univ, 60; M.S, Rutgers, 64. Instr. med. entom. & parasitol, Naval Med. Sch, 36-39, parasitologist, Naval Med. Res. Inst, Nat. Naval Med. Ctr, 39-64; BIOCHEMIST, ARMED FORCES RADIOBIOL. RES. INST, DEFENSE NUCLEAR AGENCY, 65- Consult, immunochem, sch. trop. med, P.R, 63. Except. Serv. Medal, Defense Atomic Support Agency, 68. U.S.N, 36-56. Am. Chem. Soc; Am. Soc. Biol. Chem; Radiation Res. Soc. Am; N.Y. Acad. Sci. Chemistry of immune reactions; physicochemical characterization of metabolic responses to radiation stimuli in synthesis of circulating macromolecules. Address: Armed Forces Radiobiological Research Institute, Defense Nuclear Agency, Bethesda, MD 20014.

EVANS, ALBERT E(DWIN), JR, b. Tarrytown, N.Y, Apr. 21, 30; m. 56; c. 2. PHYSICS. B.S, Yale, 52; M.S, Ohio State, 53; Ph.D.(physics), Maryland, 65. Engr, nuclear div, Martin-Marietta Co, 57-58, sr. engr, 58; physicist, radiation physics div, U.S. Naval Ord. Lab, 58-67; STAFF PHYSICIST, NUCLEAR ASSAY RES. GROUP, LOS ALAMOS SCI. LAB, UNIV. CALIF, 67- U.S.A.F, 52-56, Res, 56-59, 62-, Maj. Am. Phys. Soc; Am. Nuclear Soc. Gamma ray spectroscopy of nuclear reactions; low-energy particle accelerators, construction and renovation; measurement of flux and power distributions in nuclear reactors; nondestructive assay of fissionable materials, physics of delayed neutrons. Address: Nuclear Assay Research Group, University of California, Los Alamos Scientific Lab, P.O. Box 1663, Los Alamos, NM 87544.

EVANS, A(LFRED) S(PRING), b. Buffalo, N.Y, Aug. 21, 17; m. 50; c. 3. INTERNAL MEDICINE. A.B, Univ. Mich, 39, M.P.H, 60; M.D, Buffalo, 43; hon. M.A, Yale, 66. Asst. prof. prev. med, Yale, 46-52; assoc. prof. prev. med. & med. microbiol, Univ. Wis, 52-59, prof. prev. med. & chmn. dept, 59-66; PROF. EPIDEMIOL. & DIR. DIV. INT. EPIDEMIOL. & WHO SERUM REFERENCE BANK, DEPT. EPIDEMIOL. & PUB. HEALTH, YALE SCH. MED, 66- Ed, Yale J. Biol. & Med. Dipl, Am. Bd. Internal Med, 51. U.S.A, 44-46, 50-52. Am. Pub. Health Asn; Am. Med. Asn. Infectious mononucleosis; viral hepatitis; respiratory viruses. Address: Yale University School of Medicine, 333 Cedar St, New Haven, CT 06520.

EVANS, ALLAN ROBERT, b. Paxton, Ill, Aug. 10, 43; m. 69. SOLID STATE PHYSICS, SPECTROSCOPY. B.S, & Gen. Motors scholar, Univ. Ill, Urbana, 65; Woodrow Wilson fel, A.D. White fel, Hughes fel. & Ph.D.(physics), Cornell Univ, 70. Mem. tech. staff, Hughes Res. Labs, Calif, 68-70; ASST. PROF. PHYSICS, UNIV. CALIF, IRVINE, 70- Honeywell Award in Eng, Col. eng, Univ. Ill, Urbana, 65. AAAS; Am. Phys. Soc; Am. Asn. Physics Teachers; Optical Soc. Am. Laser raman spectroscopy of solids; properties of defects in crystals; laser physics; optical spectroscopy. Address: Dept. of Physics, University of California, Irvine, CA 92664.

EVANS, ALLISON B(ICKLE), b. Erie, Pa, Aug. 29, 10. CHEMISTRY. B.S.E, Michigan, 32, M.S, 33, A.M, 50; Firestone fel, Akron, 33-34. Chemist, Firestone Tire & Rubber Co, Akron, 34-36; Erie Lab, Pa, 36-39; U.S. Rubber Reclaiming Co, Buffalo, 39; Erie Forge Co, Pa, 40-42; chem. engr, Bliley Elec. Co, 42-45; chemist, Griffin Mfg. Co, 45-46; res. chemist, eng. res. inst, Michigan, 47-48; field mfg. engr, assembly & overhaul dept, aircraft gas turbine div, Gen. Elec. Co, 51-56; tech. ed, Redstone Div, Thiokol Chem. Corp, 57-62; specifications chemist, Lockhead Propulsion Co, 62-66; pub. analyst, Gordon M. Genge Indust, 66-68; CHEMIST, PROD. DEPT, INDUST. DIV, STAUFFER CHEM. CO, 68- Anal. chemist, Quartermaster Food & Container Inst, 50-51. Am. Chem. Soc; Am. Soc. Metals; Am. Inst. Chem. Eng. Analytical chemistry; elastomers; electrodeposition; manufacturing; jet propulsion; technical editing. Address: 228 Alvord St, Ridgecrest, CA 93555.

EVANS, ARTHUR, JR, b. Pittsburgh, Pa, Feb. 23, 33; m. 55; c. 3. COMPUTER SCIENCE. B.S, Carnegie Inst. Technol, 57, M.S, 59, Ph.D, 65. Mgr. prog. develop, comput. ctr, Carnegie Inst. Technol, 64-65; assoc. prof. comput. sci, MASS. INST. TECHNOL, 65-71, MEM. RES. STAFF, LINCOLN LAB, 71- U.S.A, 54-56. Asn. Comput. Mach. Theory of computer programming languages. Address: Lincoln Lab, P.O. Box 73, Lexington, MA 02173.

EVANS, ARTHUR T, b. Huron, S.Dak, Nov. 26, 19; m. 42; c. 4. UROLOGIC SURGERY. A.B, Miami (Ohio), 41; M.D, Chicago, 44. PROF. UROL, MED. CTR, UNIV. CINCINNATI, 69-, DIR, 61-; CHRISTIAN R. HOLMES HOSP,

69- Mem. staff, div. urol, Cincinnati Gen. Hosp, 61-; Cincinnati Children's Hosp. Med.C, U.S.A.F, 46-48, Capt. Am. Med. Asn; Am. Col. Surg; Am. Urol. Asn; Int. Col. Surg. Translumbar arteriography as presently used in renal angiography and in studying renal circulation. Address: 250 William H. Taft. Rd, Cincinnati, OH 45219.

EVANS, ARWEL, b. Port Talbot, S.Wales, Aug. 26, 30. MATHEMATICS. B.Sc, Wales, 50, studentship, 50-52, M.Sc, 51; Univ. Wales fel, Cambridge, 52-54, Ph.D.(pure math), 59. Instr. & lectr. pure math, Western Ontario, 54-59; instr, Yale, 59-60; ASSOC. PROF. MATH, McGILL UNIV, 60- Am. Math. Soc. Nonabsolute integration and measure theory; summability and classical analysis; abstract measure theory. Address: Dept. of Mathematics, McGill University, Montreal, Que, Can.

EVANS, AUDREY ELIZABETH, b. York, Eng, Mar. 6, 25; U.S. citizen. PEDIATRICS, BIOCHEMISTRY. L.R.C.P, S.E, Edinburgh, 50; Brandeis, 63-65. Res. med. & surg, Royal Infirmary, Edinburgh, 51-52; clin. fel. pediat, Children's Med. Center, Boston, 53-54, res. tumor ther, 57-58, asst. physician, 58-62, assoc. med, 62-65; res. PEDIAT, Johns Hopkins Hosp, 54-56; instr, Harvard Med. Sch, 61-65; asst. prof, Univ. Chicago, 65-69; ASSOC. PROF, UNIV. PA, 69- Fulbright scholar. & U.S. Pub. Health Serv. spec. fel, 63-65. Dipl, Am. Bd. Pediat, 57. AAAS; Am. Acad. Pediat; Am. Asn. Cancer Res; Am. Pediat. Soc; Royal Soc. Med. Pediatric hematology and oncology; biochemistry and enzymology of leukemia. Address: Children's Hospital of Philadelphia, 1840 Bainbridge St, Philadelphia, PA 19146.

EVANS, A(USTIN) MURRAY, b. New York, N.Y, June 15, 32; m; c. 3. BOTANY. A.B, Oberlin Col, 56, A.M, 60; Yale, summer, 56; Ph.D.(bot), Michigan, 64. Instr. eng, Tunghai Univ, 56-58; asst. prof. BOT, UNIV. TENN, KNOXVILLE, 64-69, ASSOC. PROF, 69-, DIR. HERBARIUM, 70- Nat. Sci. Found. res. grant, 65-69; vis. prof, Univ. Va, summers, 66, 70; vis. scientist, Orgn. Trop. Studies, Calif, 67. U.S.N.R, 52-54. Bot. Soc. Am; Asn. Trop. Biol; Am. Fern Soc; Am. Soc. Plant Taxon; Am. Inst. Biol. Sci; Int. Asn. Plant Taxon; Brit. Pteridol. Soc. Address: Dept. of Botany, University of Tennessee, Knoxville, TN 37916.

EVANS, BERNARD W(ILLIAM), b. London, Eng, July 16, 34; m. 62. GEOLOGY. B.Sc, London, 55; D.Phil(geol), Oxford, 59. Asst. geol, Glasgow, 58-59; demonstr. mineral, Oxford, 59-61; asst. res. geologist, Univ. Calif, Berkeley, 61-66, assoc. prof. GEOL, 66-69; PROF, UNIV. WASH, 69- AAAS; Mineral. Soc. Am.(award, 70); Am. Geophys. Union; Geol. Soc. Am; Brit. Geol. Soc; Mineral. Soc. Gt. Brit. & Ireland, Petrology and mineralogy of metamorphic and igneous rocks; utilizing the optical emission spectrograph and the electron probe microanalyzer. Address: Dept. of Geological Sciences, University of Washington, Seattle, WA 98105.

EVANS, BURTON R(OBERT), b. Harvey, Ill, Sept. 26, 29; m. 59; c. 3. MEDICAL ENTOMOLOGY. B.A, Millikin, 51; M.Ed, Maryland, 55, Ph.D.(med. entom), 58; M.P.H, Tulane, 65. Sta. entomologist, for. quarantine div, U.S. Pub. Health Serv, 58-67; Aedes Aegyptic Eradication Proj, Communicable Disease Ctr, 67-69; PROJ. OFF, PESTICIDES PROG, DIV. PESTICIDE COMMUNITY STUDIES, ENVIRON. PROTECTION AGENCY, 69- U.S.N.R, 51-53; U.S.P.H.S, 58-, Comdr. Am. Mosquito Control Asn; Am. Entom. Soc. Transmission of filariae by mosquitoes; evaluation of insecticides for mosquito control; surveys for the presence of various insects of medical importance. Address: Environmental Protection Agency, Division of Pesticide Community Studies, 4770 Buford Highway, Chamblee, GA 30341.

EVANS, CHARLES A(LBERT), b. Minneapolis, Minn, Feb. 18, 12; m. 39; c. 4. MICROBIOLOGY. B.S, Minnesota, 35, M.B, 36, M.D, 37, Ph.D.(bact), 43. Teaching asst. bact, Univ. Minn, 37-38; agent diseases fur animals & wildlife, bur. biol. surv, U.S. Dept. Agr, 38-41; asst. scientist & later assoc. scientist, Minnesota, 38-41; Nat. Res. Council fel, Rochester, 41-42; biol. res. supvr, State Dept. Conserv, Minn, 42-43; asst. prof. bact, Univ. Minn, 42-44, assoc. prof, 44-46; PROF. MICROBIOL, UNIV. WASH, 46-, chmn. dept, 46-70, spec. asst. to pres. Univ. & dir, off. spec. student progs, 68-70. Mem. microbiol. panel, Off. Naval Res, 48-51; microbiol. study sect, Nat. Insts. Health, 51-56, 57-58; Nat. Adv. Cancer Coun, 58-60, 64-67. AAAS; Am. Soc. Microbiol.(v.pres, Soc. Bact, 59, pres, 59-60); Soc. Exp. Biol. & Med; Am. Acad. Microbiol. Pathogenesis of and immunity to viral infections; normal flora of human skin. Address: Dept. of Microbiology, University of Washington, Seattle, WA 98105.

EVANS, CHARLES P, b. New York, N.Y, May 8, 30; m. 57; c. 3. ORGANIC CHEMISTRY. B.A, Bridgeport, 59; N.Y. Univ, 59. Anal. chemist, Olin Mathieson Chem. Corp, 57-59, res. chemist; 59-62; Escambia Chem. Corp, 62-68; v.pres. res. & opers, VITEK RES. CORP, STAMFORD, 68-70, PRES, 70- U.S.A, 47-50. Am. Chem. Soc; Sci. Res. Soc. Am. Suspension and emulsion polymerization reaction. Address: 12 Glenbrook Rd, Trumbull, CT 06611.

EVANS, CHESTER EVAN, b. Malad, Idaho, Jan. 11, 19; m. 44; c. 3. SOIL SCIENCE, CONSERVATION. B.S, Idaho, 40; M.S, Tennessee, 42; Ph.D.(soils), Wisconsin, 47. Develop. chemist, Hercules Powder Co, 42-45; agronomist, bur. plant indust. soils & agr. eng, U.S. DEPT. AGR, 47-48, assoc. agronomist, Ohio Agr. Exp. Sta, 48-50, soil scientist, SOIL & WATER CONSERV. RES. DIV, AGR. RES. SERV, 50-53, supvry. soil scientist, West. States, 53-54, work, proj. leader & asst. head sect. integration of practices, 54-57, acting head sect. soil & water mgt. res. 54-55, asst. br. chief, Pac. Southwest States, 57-61, CHIEF NORTH. PLAINS BR, 61- Chmn, Nat. Soil Res. Comt, 55; leader, U.S. res. scientists tour res. progs, Agency Int. Develop, U.S. Dept. State, India, 67. Soil Sci. Soc. Am; fel. Am. Soc. Agron; Soil Conserv. Soc. Am; Int. Soc. Soil Sci. Soil and water management; watershed engineering; development of permanently productive agricultural systems. Address: Soil & Water Conservation Research Division, U.S. Dept. of Agriculture, P.O. Box E, Ft. Collins, CO 80521.

EVANS, CLYDE EDSEL, b. Arley, Ala, Dec. 29, 27; m. 51; c. 3. SOIL SCIENCE. B.S, Abilene Christian Col, 55; M.S, Auburn, 57; Ph.D.(soil sci), N.C. State, 68. ASSOC. PROF. SOIL SCI, AUBURN UNIV, 57- U.S.M.C, 51-53. Am. Soc. Agron. Soil fertility research with phosphorus and potassium, particulary soil testing for fertilizer requirements; fertility requirements for certain vegetable crops. Address: Dept. of Agronomy, Auburn University, Auburn, AL 36830.

EVANS, CYRIL D(AVID), b. Anaconda, Mont, May 18, 09; m. 33; c. 2. OIL & PROTEIN CHEMISTRY. B.S, Mont. State Col, 31, M.S, 33; Ph.D.(biochem), Minnesota, 38. Asst. chem, exp. sta, Mont. State Col, 31-35; asst. chem, Minnesota, 35-38, instr, 38-39; res. chemist, Armour Res. Found, 39-41; assoc. chemist, NORTH. REGIONAL RES. LAB, BUR. AGR. & INDUST. CHEM, 41-42, CHEMIST, 42- AAAS; Am. Chem. Soc. Industrial protein utilization; protein fiber production; extraction and production of proteins; refining and processing of edible oils and fats; psychometric evaluation of fats and fatty foods; stabilization of fats. Address: Northern Regional Research Lab, Bureau of Agriculture & Industrial Chemistry, 1815 University Ave, Peoria, IL 61604.

EVANS, D(ANIEL) D(ONALD), b. Oak Hill, Ohio, Aug. 13, 20; m. 46; c. 4. SOIL PHYSICS. B.S, Ohio State, 47; M.S, Iowa State, 50, Ph.D.(soil physics), 52. Assoc. soil physics, Iowa State, 50-52, asst. prof, 52-53; from assoc. prof. to prof. soils, Ore. State Univ, 53-63; PROF. HYDROL. & WATER RESOURCES, UNIV. ARIZ, 63-, AGR. CHEM. & SOILS, 71-, HEAD DEPT. HYDROL. & WATER RESOURCES, 63- Adv. to Kenya Ministry Agr, 60-62. U.S.A, 42-45. AAAS; Soil Sci. Soc. Am; Am. Soc. Agron; Am. Geophys. Union; Am. Water Resources Asn. Soil physics and hydrology. Address: Dept. of Hydrology & Water Resources, University of Arizona, Tucson, AZ 85721.

EVANS, DAVID ALBERT, b. Washington, D.C, Jan. 11, 41; m. 62. ORGANIC CHEMISTRY. A.B, Oberlin Col, 63; Dow Chem. Co. fel, Calif. Inst. Tech, 64-65, Nat. Insts. Health, 65-67, Ph.D.(synthetic org. chem), 67. ASST. PROF. ORG. CHEM, UNIV. CALIF, LOS ANGELES, 67- Am. Chem. Soc. Petrol. Res. Fund grant, 67-68. Am. Chem. Soc; Brit. Chem. Soc. Organoboron chemistry; chemistry and synthesis of naturally-occurring substances; thermal rearrangements. Address: Dept. of Chemistry, University of California, Los Angeles, CA 90024.

EVANS, DAVID ARNOLD, b. San Mateo, Calif, Sept. 24, 38; m. 63; c. 2. ENTOMOLOGY. B.A, Carleton Col, 60; M.S, Wisconsin, 62, Ph.D.(entom), 65. Res. asst. entom, Wisconsin, 60-64, instr, 64-65; ASST. PROF. BIOL, KALAMAZOO COL, 65- AAAS; Entom. Soc. Am. Migratory behavior of the corn leaf aphid; taxonomy and bionomics of the velvet ants; aquatic entomology. Address: Dept. of Biology, Kalamazoo College, Kalamazoo, MI 49001.

EVANS, DAVID ARTHUR, b. Gloucester, Eng, Aug. 5, 39; m. 62; c. 2. PARTICLE PHYSICS. B.A, Cambridge, 60, M.A, 64; Ph.D.(particle physics), Oxford, 64. Dept. Sci. & Indust. Res. fel. PARTICLE PHYSICS, nuclear physics lab, Oxford, 63-64, dept. res. asst, 64-65; res. assoc, Univ. Calif, Riverside, 65-67; ASST. PROF, STATE UNIV. N.Y. BUFFALO, 67- Res. assoc, Rutherford High Energy Lab, Eng, 71. Heavy hyperfragment production; K+ meson decay spectrum; partial wave analysis of K-P interactions; statistical techniques in particle physics data analysis; design of on-line measuring systems. Address: Dept. of Physics, State University of New York at Buffalo, Buffalo, NY 14214.

EVANS, DAVID C(ANNON), b. Salt Lake City, Utah, Feb. 24, 24; m. 47; c. 7. ELECTRICAL ENGINEERING. B.S, Utah, 49, Ph.D.(physics), 53. Dir. eng, comput. div, Bendix Corp, 53-62; prof. elec. eng. & assoc. dir. comput. center, California, Berkeley, 62-65; PROF. ELEC. ENG. & DIR. COMPUT. SCI, UNIV. UTAH, 66- Mem. comn. on educ, Nat. Acad. Eng. Am. Phys. Soc; Asn. Comput. Mach; Inst. Elec. & Electronics Eng. Computing and information processing systems. Address: Computer Science-MEB 3160, University of Utah, Salt Lake City, UT 84112.

EVANS, DAVID HUDSON, b. Chicago, Ill, June 9, 40; m. 62; c. 2. COMPARATIVE PHYSIOLOGY, ICTHYOLOGY. B.A, DePauw, 62; Ph.D.(biol), Stanford, 67. Nat. Insts. Health fel, Lancaster, 67-69; ASST. PROF. BIOL, UNIV. MIAMI, 69- Am. Soc. Zool; Soc. Exp. Biol. & Med. Ion and water balance of teleost fish and decapod Crustacea. Address: Dept. of Biology, University of Miami, Coral Gables, FL 33124.

EVANS, DAVID H(UNDEN), b. Philadelphia, Pa, Apr. 16, 24; m. 50; c. 2. APPLIED MATHEMATICS. B.S, Lehigh, 48; Ph.D.(appl. math), Brown, 53. Mem. tech. staff, Bell Tel. Labs, 53-61; sr. res. mathematician. res. labs, Gen. Motors Corp, 61-68; lectr. & res. engr, Univ. Mich, 68-69; vis. prof. ENG, OAKLAND UNIV, 69-71, PROF, 71- U.S.A, 43-45. Opers. Res. Soc. Am; Am. Soc. Qual. Control; Inst. Mgt. Sci. Vehicular and telephone traffic theory; statistics applied to tolerancing. Address: School of Engineering, Oakland University, Rochester, MI 48063.

EVANS, DAVID LeCOUNT, b. San Francisco, Calif, Mar. 15, 06; m. 37; c. 2. GEOLOGY. A.B, Stanford, 27, M.A, 28. Asst. geologist, Cananea Copper Co. Div, Anaconda Co, 28-32; chief engr, Compania Unificada, Bolivia, 33-35; chief geologist, Climax Molybdenum Co, Am. Metal Climax, Inc, Colo, 36-40, shift boss, 43-45; field geologist, Freeport Sulphur Co, Nev, 40-42; mineral specialist, Bd. Econ. Warfare, Wash, 42-43; field geologist, Ohio Oil Co, 45-48, geophysicist, 48-51; CONSULT. GEOLOGIST, KANS. & NEV, 51- Assoc, Behre Dolbear & Co; mem, Nev. Oil & Gas Comn. Am. Inst. Mining, Metall. & Petrol. Eng; Am. Asn. Petrol. Geol; Soc. Econ. Geol; Geol. Soc. Am. Economic geology. Address: 1700 Royal Dr, Reno, NV 89503.

EVANS, DAVID S(TANLEY), b. Cardiff, Wales, Jan. 28, 16; m. 49; c. 2. MATHEMATICS. B.A, Cambridge, 37, M.A. & Ph.D.(astron), 41, Sc.D, 71. Res. asst. ASTRON, Univ. Observ, Oxford, 38-46; second asst, Radcliffe Observ, Pretoria, S.Africa, 46-51; chief asst, Royal Observ, Cape, S.Africa, 51-68; PROF, UNIV. TEX, AUSTIN, 68- Nat. Sci. Found. sr. vis. scientist, Univ. Texas, 65-66. Fel. Royal Astron. Soc; fel. Royal Soc. S.Africa; Astron. Soc. South. Africa (past pres. & v.pres); fel. Brit. Inst. Physics & Phys. Soc; Int. Astron. Union; Am. Astron. Soc. Observational astronomy; history of astronomy. Address: Dept. of Astronomy, University of Texas at Austin, Austin, TX 78712.

EVANS, DAVID W, b. Erie, Pa, Oct. 6, 33; m. 63; c. 2. AGRONOMY, PLANT PHYSIOLOGY. B.S, Yale, 55; univ. fel, Cornell Univ, 55-56, Nat. Sci. Found. fels, 57-60, M.S, 58, univ. assistantship, 60-61, Ph.D.(agron), 62. Res. assoc, Univ. Mich, Ann Arbor, 61-63; ASST. AGRONOMIST, IRRIGATED AGR. RES. & EXTEN. CTR, WASH. STATE UNIV, 63- Am. Inst. Biol. Sci; Am. Soc. Agron; Crop Sci. Soc. Am; Am. Soc. Plant Physiol. Plant root-oxygen relationships; plant-water relationships; forage crop production and management; grass seed production and physiology; alfalfa physiology and forage quality; alfalfa-stem nematode relationships. Address: Irrigated Agricultural Research & Extension Center, Washington State University, Prosser, WA 99350.

EVANS, DENNIS HYDE, b. Grinnell, Iowa, Mar. 28, 39; m. 58; c. 3. ANALYTICAL CHEMISTRY, ELECTROCHEMISTRY. B.S, Ottawa Univ, 60; Woodrow Wilson fel, Harvard, 60-61, Danforth fel, 60-64, A.M, 61, Nat. Insts. Health fel, 61-64, Ph.D.(chem), 64. Instr. CHEM, Harvard, 64-66; asst. prof, UNIV. WIS, MADISON, 66-70, ASSOC. PROF, 70- Am. Chem. Soc. Characterization and analytical application of electrode reactions; organic electrochemistry. Address: Dept. of Chemistry, University of Wisconsin, 1101 University Ave, Madison, WI 53706.

EVANS, DONALD B, b. Cleveland, Ohio, Oct. 11, 33. METALLURGICAL ENGINEERING. B.S, Mass. Inst. Tech, 55; M.S, Michigan, 59, Ph.D.(metall. eng), 63. Develop. engr, Mallinckrodt Chem. Works, 58; sr. engr, Martin Marietta Corp, 63-69; STAFF ENGR, TRW SYSTS. GROUP, 69- C.Eng, 55-57, 1st Lt. Am. Inst. Mining, Metall. & Petrol. Eng; Am. Soc. Metals. New thermoelectric power generation materials and devices; thermodynamics of chemical reactions involved in steel making. Address: TRW Systems Group, One Space Park, Redondo Beach, CA 90503.

EVANS, DONOVAN LEE, b. Verona, Ohio, Mar. 14, 39; m. 60; c. 3. MECHANICAL ENGINEERING. B.S.M.E, Cincinnati, 62; Nat. Defense Ed. Act fel. & Ph.D.(mech. eng), Northwestern, 67. Res. asst. MECH. ENG, Northwestern, 65-66; asst. prof, to ASSOC. PROF, ARIZ. STATE UNIV, 66- Summer lab. engr, Delco Prod. Div, Gen. Motors Corp, 62. Thermosciences; high temperature gas dynamics; radiation from gasses. Address: Dept. of Mechanical Engineering, Arizona State University, Tempe, AZ 85281.

EVANS, DORIS L, b. Weehawken, N.J, July 2, 23. CRYSTALLOGRAPHY, PHYSICS. B.A, Hunter Col, 43; M.A, N.Y. Univ, 45; Nat. Insts. Health fel, Birkbeck Col, 66-68; Ph.D.(crystallog), Univ. London, 69. Tech. asst, Bell Tel. Labs, 42-45; asst. proj. engr, Sperry Gyroscope Co, 46-49; physicist, Mt. Sinai Hosp, 49-51; assoc. res. specialist, Rutgers Univ, 51-59; SR. RES. PHYSICIST, CORNING GLASS WORKS, 59- Am. Crystallog. Asn; Am. Inst. Physics. Relationship between structure and properties of inorganic materials; phase transitions; atomic clustering in metals and alloys; structural definition of amorphous solids and liquids. Address: Corning Glass Works, Research & Development Labs, Sullivan Park, Corning, NY 14830.

EVANS, D(OUGLAS) FENNELL, b. Carlsbad, N.Mex, Mar. 16, 37; m. 63; c. 1. PHYSICAL & BIOPHYSICAL CHEMISTRY. B.A, Pomona Col, 59; Nat. Insts. Health fel, Mass. Inst. Technol, 60-63, Ph.D.(chem), 63. Fel, Mellon Inst, 63-66; asst. prof. CHEM, CASE WEST. RESERVE UNIV, 66-69, ASSOC. PROF, 70- Summer fel, Brown Univ, 63. Am. Chem. Soc. Electrolyte solutions; physical properties of bile; membrane transport. Address: Dept. of Chemistry, Millis Science Center, Case Western Reserve University, Cleveland, OH 44106.

EVANS, DOYLE JOSEPH, JR, b. New Orleans, La, Nov. 15, 38; m. 64. MICROBIOLOGY, BIOCHEMISTRY. B.S, Southwestern Louisiana, 60, M.S, 62; Ph.D.(microbiol), Wake Forest, 68. Resident res. assoc. microbiol, dept. dent. res, Naval Med. Res. Inst, Nat. Naval Med. Ctr, 68-70; CHIEF BACTERIOLOGIST, PAKISTAN-SEATO CHOLERA RES. LAB, DACCA, 70- AAAS; Am. Soc. Microbiol. Oral bacteria-yeast interrelationships; production and characterization of virulence factors of Asiatic cholera; characterization of cell membrane enzymes of bacteria, their structure and function. Address: Pakistan-SEATO Cholera Research Lab, G.P.O. Box 128, Dacca 2, East Pakistan.

EVANS, E. ROBERT, b. Buffalo, N.Y, Apr. 5, 34; m. 56; c. 3. ORGANIC CHEMISTRY. B.A, Buffalo, 54; M.S, Canisius Col, 61; Ph.D.(phys. org. chem), 65. Anal. chemist, Hooker Chem. Corp, 54-55; res. chemist, plastics div, Allied Chem. Corp, 58-60; polymer chemist, Ludicol Div, Wallace & Tiernan Inc, 60-61; res. chemist, elastomers dept, E.I. du Pont de Nemours & Co, Inc, 64-71; SR. RES. CHEMIST, PENNWALT CORP, 71- U.S.A, 55-57, Res, 57-, Capt. Am. Chem. Soc. Actively synthesizing new elastomeric type polymers and development of curing accelerators and antiozonants for these polymers; thermoplastic fluoropolymers. Address: 2406 Landon Dr, Chalfonte, Wilmington, DE 19810.

EVANS, E(ARL) A(LISON), JR, b. Baltimore, Md, Mar. 11, 10. BIOCHEMISTRY. B.Sc, Hopkins, 31; fel, Columbia, 34-37, Ph.D.(biochem), 36. Asst. pharmacol, sch. med, Hopkins, 31-32, asst. endocrine res, 32-34; instr. BIOCHEM, CHICAGO, 37-39, asst. prof, 39-41, assoc. prof. & acting chmn. dept, 41-42, PROF. & CHMN. DEPT, 42- Int. Ed. Bd, fel, Sheffield, 39-40; Orgn. Am. States lectr, 61. Chief sci. officer, U.S. State Dept, London, 47-48; spec. consult, U.S. Pub. Health Serv, 47-51; consult, Secy. State, 51-53; adv. Am. Found. Continuing Ed, 62- Mem. bd. sci. counsr, Nat. Inst. Arthritis & Metab. Diseases, 60-63; div. med. sci, Nat. Res. Coun, 62-64, divisional comt. biol. & med, Nat. Sci. Found, 62-66, chmn. comt. postdoct. fels, Nat. Acad. Sci-Nat. Res. Coun, 63-65; Nat. Acad. Sci-Nat. Res. Coun, mem. postdoctoral res. fel. bd, for Air Force Off. Sci. Res, 66-68. With Off. Sci. Res. & Develop. AAAS; Am. Soc. Biol. Chem.(treas, 47-51); Am. Chem. Soc; Soc. Exp. Biol. & Med; Am. Soc. Microbiol; assoc. mem. Am. Med. Asn; cor. mem. Argentina Chem. Asn; Brit. Biochem. Soc. Chemistry of insulin and toad poisons; etiology of tetanus poisoning; metabolism of malaria parasite; carbon dioxide fixation in mammalian tissues; carbohydrate and protein metabolism; radioactive isotopes; mechanism of virus reproduction. Address: Dept. of Biochemistry, University of Chicago, 947 E. 58th St, Chicago, IL 60637.

EVANS, EDWARD B(ENJAMIN), b. Cleveland, Ohio, Oct. 5, 22; m. 52; c. 1. PHYSICAL METALLURGY. B.S, Case, 49, M.S, 53, Ph.D.(metall), 58. Asst. metallurgist, Nat. Acme Mfg. Co, 41-43; Armour Res. Found, 49-50; res. assoc. METALL, Case, 50-57, asst. prof, 57-61; sr. res. metallurgist, Thompson-Ramo-Wooldridge, Inc, 61-66; PROF, FLA. STATE UNIV, 66- U.S.A.A.F, 43-45. Am. Soc. Metals; Nat. Asn. Corrosion Eng; Am. Ord. Asn. High temperature oxidation; heat treatment; x-ray diffraction; fuel cells. Address: School of Engineering Sciences, Florida State University, Tallahassee, FL 32306.

EVANS, EDWARD STANLEY, JR, b. Portland, Ore, July 30, 26; m. 57; c. 1. ANATOMY. A.B, California, 51, Ph.D.(endocrinol), 56. Asst. ANAT, UNIV. CALIF, BERKELEY, 53-56, instr, 56-58, asst. prof, 58-64, ASSOC. PROF, 64- U.S.A, 44-46. AAAS; Am. Asn. Anat; Soc. Exp. Biol. & Med; N.Y. Acad. Sci. Hormonal factors influencing the interrelation between growth calorigenesis and erythropoiesis in the mammal. Address: Dept. of Physiology-Anatomy, University of California, Berkeley, CA 94720.

EVANS, EDWARD WILLIAM, b. Frackville, Pa, Sept. 1, 32; m. 54; c. 4. MATHEMATICS. B.S, Kutztown State Col, 54; M.Ed, Temple, 58; M.A, Michigan, 61, Ph.D.(math, math. ed), 64. Teacher, high sch, Pa, 55-61; Nat. Sci. Found. fel, Michigan, 61-63, univ. & teaching fels, 64; PROF. MATH, KUTZTOWN STATE COL, 64-, CHMN. DEPT, 65- Nat. Defense Ed. Act vis. lectr, high schs, 65- Consult, high schs. math. progs, 64- U.S.A.F, 54-55. Math. Asn. Am; Am. Math. Soc. Teaching and learning of mathematics; abstract algebra; foundations of geometry. Address: 3225 Stoudt-Ferry Rd, Riverview Park, Reading, PA 19605.

EVANS, E(DWIN) V(ICTOR), b. Toronto, Ont, Mar. 30, 14; m. 40; c. 2. NUTRITION. B.A, Western Ontario, 36: M.A, 37; Ont. Res. Found. fel, Toronto, 37-41. Asst. prof. animal nutrit, Ont, Agr. Col, 41-46, assoc. prof, 46-48; biochem. dir, W.R. Drynan Nutrit. Lab, Ont, 48-50; assoc. prof. NUTRIT, COL. BIOL. SCI, UNIV. GUELPH, 51-68, 71-, prof. & head dept. biochem, nutrit. & food sci, 68-71. Assoc. prof. & acting head dept. biochem, nutrit. & food sci, Univ. Ghana, 65-66. AAAS; Animal Nutrit. Res. Coun; N.Y. Acad. Soc; Am. Soc. Animal Sci; Brit. Nutrit. Soc; Can. Physiol. Soc; Can. Biochem. Soc; Nutrit. Soc. Can.(secy, 60-65). Chemical and biological vitamin assays and investigations animal and human nutrition. Address: Dept. of Nutrition, University of Guelph, Guelph, Ont, Can.

EVANS, EMERSON M, b. Horton, Ala, Jan. 24, 21; m. 45; c. 6. AGRONOMY. B.S, Ala. Polytech, 43; M.S, Cornell, 49; Purdue, 51-53. Asst. agronomist, AUBURN UNIV, 49-53, assoc. agronomist, 53-62, ASSOC. PROF. AGRON, 62- U.S.A, 43-46, Res, 46-60, Capt. Am. Soc. Agron; Soil Sci. Soc. Am. Forage crops physiology; soil fertility; forage production and management. Address: Dept. of Agronomy & Soils, Auburn University, 368 Bowden Dr, Auburn, AL 36830.

EVANS, ERNEST C(OLSTON), b. New York, N.Y, July 19, 20; m. 42; c. 3. ENGINEERING PHYSICS. B.S, Tennessee, 54, M.S, 57. Develop. engr, UNION CARBIDE CORP, 46-54, sect. head barrier testing, 54-56, dept. head phys. measurements, 56-60, separations systs. & biomed. eng, 60-67, SUPT. SEPARATIONS SYST. DIV, 67- U.S.A.A.F, 42-46, S/Sgt. Instrument Soc. Am; Sci. Res. Soc. Am; N.Y. Acad. Sci. Biomedical engineering; sterile containment; centrifuges; isotope separation systems; mass spectrometry; gas flow measurement; analytical instruments; pilot plant design. Address: Separations System Division, Union Carbide Corp, Nuclear Division, P.O. Box P, Oak Ridge, TN 37830.

EVANS, E(RNEST) EDWARD, (JR), b. Parkersburg, W.Va, Dec. 14, 22; m. 47. MICROBIOLOGY, IMMUNOLOGY. A.B, Ohio, 45; M.S, Ohio State, 47; Ph.D. (microbiol), Southern California, 50. Asst. bact, Ohio State, 45-47; asst. & lectr, Southern California, 47-50; instr, Michigan, 50-51, asst. prof, 51-55; assoc. prof. MICROBIOL, MED. CTR, UNIV. ALA, BIRMINGHAM, 55-61, PROF, 61-, chmn. dept, 61-69. Mem. comt. bact. techniques, 54-58; vis. investr, Lerner Marine Lab, Am. Mus. Nat. Hist, 66- vis. res. biologist, Univ. Calif, Santa Barbara, 70; sr. res. microbiologist, Mote Marine Lab, 70- Fel. AAAS; Am. Soc. Microbiol; Soc. Exp. Biol. & Med; Am. Asn. Immunol; fel. Am. Acad. Microbiol; Soc. Invert. Path; Int. Soc. Human & Animal Mycol. Molecular and cellular aspects of the evolution of immunity; immunoglobulin structure; complement; pathology, immunology, and microbiology of marine vertebrates and invertebrates. Address: Medical Center, University of Alabama, Birmingham, AL 35233.

EVANS, ERSEL A(RTHUR), b. Trenton, Nebr, July 17, 22; m. 45; c. 2. INORGANIC CHEMISTRY. B.A, Reed Col, 47; Res. Corp. fel, Oregon State, 49-50, du Pont fel, 50-51, Ph.D.(chem), 52. Engr, fuel tech, Gen. Elec. Co, 51-56, supvr. ceramic fuel develop, Hanford Atomic Prods. Oper, 56-62, MGR. ceramic res. & develop, 62-64; plutonium fuels develop, Vallescitos Atomic Lab, 64-67; mat. dept, Pac. Northwest Labs, Battelle Mem. Inst, 67-68, fuels & mat. dept, 68-69, fuels dept, fast flux test facility proj, 69-70; fuels & mat. dept, WADCO, WESTINGHOUSE ELECTRIC CORP, 70-71, MAT. TECHNOL, 71- U.S. del, Int. Conf. Peaceful Uses Atomic Energy, Geneva, 64 & 71. U.S.N, 43-45. Am. Soc. Metals; fel. Am. Nuclear Soc; fel. Am. Inst. Chem; N.Y. Acad. Sci. Metallic, ceramic and cermet reactor fuels; high temperature structural and ceramic materials; plutonium compounds; sodium technology, chemistry and chemical engineering. Address: 2224 Benton St, Richland, WA 99352.

EVANS, EVAN C(YFEILIOG), III, b. San Francisco, Calif, Nov. 19, 22; m. 45; c. 3. PHYSICS, BIOPHYSICS. A.B, Univ. Calif, Berkeley, 48, Ph.D.(biophys), 63. Head, weapon capabilities br, U.S. Naval Radiol. Defense Lab, 64-66, weapon effects br, 66-69; SR. SCIENTIST, BIOSYSTS. DIV, NAVAL UNDERSEA RES. & DEVELOP. CTR, HAWAII LAB, 69- Naval Radiol. Defense Lab. fel, 61; lectr, Univ. Calif, Berkeley, 64-65; affiliate grad. faculty, Univ. Hawaii, 71- U.S.N, 42-46, Res, 46-59, Lt. AAAS; Am. Phys. Soc; N.Y. Acad. Sci; Am. Soc. Plant Physiol; Marine Technol. Soc. Absorption and translocation of radionuclides in higher plants; effects of ionizing radiation on plants; atomic physics; micromeritics; radioecology of Pacific Ocean basin; underwater acoustics; bioacoustics of marine mammals. Address: 44-702 Nanamoana Pl, Kaneohe, HI 96744.

EVANS, EVAN FRANKLIN, b. Kenesaw, Nebr, Mar. 17, 18; m. 44; c. 5. ORGANIC CHEMISTRY. B.A, Nebraska, 39, M.A, 40; Ph.D.(chem), Ohio State, 43. Res. chemist, Hercules Powder Co, 44-50; E.I. DU PONT DE NEMOURS & CO, INC, 51-52, res. supvr, 52-59, res. mgr, 59-71, RES. ASSOC, 71- AAAS; Am. Chem. Soc. Synthesis acyclic sugar derivatives; fundamental and applied research on cellulose and cellulose derivatives; polymers; synthetic fibers; textiles. Address: 1702 Cambridge Dr, Kinston, NC 28501.

EVANS, (GEORGE) FOSTER, b. Salt Lake City, Utah, Jan. 16, 15; m. 45; c. 1. PHYSICS. B.S, Brigham Young, 36; Ph.D.(physics), Chicago, 41. Asst. physics, Brigham Young, 35-36; instr. optics, North. Ill. Col. Optom, 40; acting instr. physics, Wisconsin, 41; instr, Colorado, 41-43, asst. prof, 43-46; STAFF MEM, LOS ALAMOS SCI. LAB, 46- Res. fel, radiation lab, California, 42. With Office Sci. Res. & Develop, 44. AAAS; Am. Phys. Soc; Am. Asn. Physics Teachers. Cosmic rays; hydrodynamics; nuclear physics; transport theory in plasmas. Address: Los Alamos Scientific Lab, Box 1663, Los Alamos, NM 87544.

EVANS, FRANCIS C(OPE), b. Germantown, Pa, Dec. 2, 14; m. 42; c. 4. ECOLOGY. B.S, Haverford Col, 36; Rhodes scholar, Oxford, 36-39, Ph.D. (animal ecol), 40; Claypole Mem. fel, California, 39-40. Asst, Hooper Found, California, 39-41, jr. zoologist, exp. sta. & col. agr, 42-43; instr. biol, Haverford Col, 43-46, asst. prof, 46-58, acting dean, 45; asst. prof. ZOÖL, UNIV. MICH, 48-52, assoc. prof, 52-59, PROF, 59-, DIR. LAB. VERT. BIOL, 56-, asst. biologist, 48-52. Mem. Oxford Univ. expeds, Faeroe Islands, 37, Iceland, 39; lectr, Bryn Mawr Col, 48; dir, E.S. George Reserve, 59-; Guggenheim fel, 62. Fel. AAAS; Am. Soc. Mammal; Ecol. Soc. Am.(ed, Ecol. Monogr, 56-62); Brit. Ecol. Soc. Ecology of natural communities; dynamics of vertebrate populations; patterns of spatial distribution; animal epidemiology. Address: Dept. of Zoology, University of Michigan, Ann Arbor, MI 48104.

EVANS, FRANCIS EUGENE, b. Olney, Ill, June 18, 28; m. 50; c. 4. ORGANIC & ANALYTICAL CHEMISTRY. A.B, DePauw Univ, 50; Ph.D.(org. chem), Mich. State Univ, 55. Res. chemist, National Aniline Div, ALLIED CHEM. CORP, 55-65, sr. scientist, Indust. Chem. Div, 65-70, TECH. SUPVR, SPECIALTY CHEM. DIV, 70- Am. Chem. Soc. Organo metallics; surfactants; anhydrides; Friedel-Crafts reactions; catalytic chemistry. Address: 37 Woodside Dr, Hamburg, NY 14075.

EVANS, F(RANCIS) (GAYNOR), b. LeMars, Iowa, Dec. 7, 07; m. 38. ANATOMY, ZOOLOGY. B.A, Coe Col, 31; Roberts fel, Columbia, 31-38, M.A, 32, Ph.D.(comp. anat), 39. Instr. biol, City Col. New York, 35-36; lectr. zool, Columbia, 36; instr, New Hampshire, 38-41; Duke, 41-43; asst. prof. human gross anat, sch. med, Maryland, 43-45; asst. prof, col. med, Wayne State, 45-50, assoc. prof, 50-58, PROF, 58-59, ANAT, UNIV. MICH, 59- Fulbright res. scholar, Italy, 56-57; vis. prof, Gothenburg Univ, 62-63 & Kyoto Prefectural Univ. Med, 68. Morrison Prize, N.Y. Acad. Sci, 38. Fel. AAAS; Am. Asn. Anat; Am. Physiol. Soc; Am. Asn. Phys. Anthrop; Orthop. Res. Soc; Am. Asn. Automotive Med; French Asn. Anat. Comparative osteology; biomechanics of the human skeleton; stress and strain in bones; mechanical properties and structure of bone. Address: Dept. of Anatomy, 4812 Medical Science Bldg. II, University of Michigan, Ann Arbor, MI 48104.

EVANS, FRANCIS J(OHN), b. Jersey City, N.J, Sept. 19, 38. ORGANIC CHEMISTRY. B.S, St. Peter's Col.(N.J), 59; Nat. Insts. Health fel. & Ph.D. (org. chem), New Hampshire, 63. Sr. chemist, EASTMAN KODAK CO, 62-70; RES. ASSOC, 70- Am. Chem. Soc; Soc. Photog. Sci. & Engrs. Photographic emulsions; color photographic chemistry. Address: Eastman Kodak Co, Research Labs. Bldg, 59, Kodak Park, Rochester, NY 14650.

EVANS, F(RANKLIN) JAMES, JR, b. Hazelton, Pa, June 1, 21; m. 47; c. 2. ORGANIC CHEMISTRY. B.S, Lafayette Col, 42; M.S, Pa. State Col, 49; Ph.D.(chem), Ohio State, 52. Engr. prod. explosives, E.I. DU PONT DE NEMOURS & CO, 42-45, rayon res, 45-47, res. chemist TEXTILE FIBERS, 53-59, sr. res. chemist, 59-66, RES. ASSOC, 66- Am. Chem. Soc; Am. Inst. Chem. Eng. Textile fibers; organo silicones; steric hindrance. Address: 406 Garland Rd, Northwood, Wilmington, DE 19803.

EVANS, FREDERICK R(EAD), b. Salt Lake City, Utah, Sept. 9, 13; m. 36; c. 4. PROTOZOOLOGY. B.A, Utah, 34, M.A, 36; Ph.D.(protozool), Stanford, 41. Instr. BIOL, Stanford, 40-45; asst. prof, UNIV. UTAH, 45-53, assoc. prof, 53-60, PROF, 60- Am. Inst. Biol. Sci. fel. Am. Micros. Soc; fel. Soc. Protozool. Nutrition of free-living protozoa; cystment in protozoa; protozoan populations; nuclear reorganization in the ciliates; uptake by protozoa of radioactive substances; parasitic protozoa; morphogenesis of ciliates. Address: Dept. of Biology, University of Utah, Salt Lake City, UT 84112.

EVANS, GEOFFREY, b. Mountain Ash, Wales, Jan. 25, 35; m. 59; c. 3. CARDIOVASCULAR SURGERY. M.B, B.S, London, 58; M.R.C.S, Royal Col. Surgeons, 58. House surgeon, St. Mary's Hosp, London, 58, casualty surgeon, 59, tutor anat. & physiol, 59-60, lectr. surg, 62-66, sr. registr, 64-67; house physician, Paddington Gen. Hosp, 58-59, surg. registr, 63-64; sr. house officer, Royal Nat. Orthop. Hosp, 60; surg. registr, Southlands Hosp, Sussex, 61-62; Can. Heart Found fel. path, McMASTER UNIV, 67-69, ASSOC. PROF. SURG, 68- Consult, Hamilton Civic, St. Joseph's, Chedoke & Joseph Brant Hosps, 69. Fel, Royal Col. Surgeons Eng, 62; mem, Am. Heart Found. Asn. Acad. Surg; Am. Heart Asn; Soc. Univ. Surg. Importance of platelet interaction with surfaces in determining the duration of arterial prosthetic replacements and with formed complexes such as antigen antibody complexes in the etiology of disseminated intravascular thrombosis. Address: Dept. of Surgery, McMaster University, Hamilton, Ont, Can.

EVANS, GEORGE EDWARD, b. Great Falls, Mont, Aug. 31, 32; m. 55; c. 2. ORNAMENTAL HORTICULTURE, PLANT PROPAGATION. B.S, Montana State, 57; M.S, Mich. State, 58; Ph.D.(ornamental hort), 69. Instr. HORT, MONTANA STATE UNIV, 62-65, asst. prof, 65-70, ASSOC. PROF, 70- U.S.A, 53-55. Am. Hort. Soc; Int. Plant Propagators Soc. Graft compatibility studies in intergeneric grafts of members of the rose family and in the genus Juniperus with major emphasis on anatomical aspects; ornamental plant hardiness and adaptability; turfgrass investigations. Address: Dept. of Plant & Soil Science, Montana State University, Bozeman, MT 59715.

EVANS, G(EORGE) HARLOWE, b. Dallas, Texas, Dec. 12, 03; m. 27; c. 2. PHYSICAL CHEMISTRY. B.S, Michigan, 25, M.S, 26, Ph.D.(chem), 35; summers, Iowa, 28-30. Res. chemist, Newport Co, Carrollville, Wis, 26-28; prof. math. & physics, John Fletcher Col, 28-32; chem, Taylor, 33-41; Huntingdon Col, 41-45; Ill. Wesleyan, 45-46; PROF. CHEM, ILL. STATE UNIV, 46- Vis. prof, Southern Illinois, 52; summers, res. assoc, Argonne Nat. Lab, 54, 55, 58, 62. AAAS; Am. Chem. Soc. Nat. Sci. Teachers Asn. Anthraquinone dyes; dielectric constants; viscosity of viscous oils; electrochromatography of metal ions. Address: 1609 N. Fell Ave, Bloomington, IL 61701.

EVANS, GEORGE L(EONARD), b. Wilkes-Barre, Pa, Aug. 3, 31; m. 58; c. 3. MICROBIOLOGY. B.S, King's Col.(Pa), 54; M.S, Fordham, 57; Nat. Insts. Health fel, Temple, 59-61, Ph.D.(microbiol), 62. Sr. scientist, Warner Lambert Res. Inst, 62-64, univ. labs, 64-65; Hoffman-La Roche, 65-69; DIR. DIAG. RES, SCHERING CORP, 69- Am. Soc. Microbiol; Am. Asn. Clin. Chem; N.Y. Acad. Sci. Host defense mechanisms; diagnostic aids; medical microbiology; immunology; clinical chemistry. Address: Diagnostic Research Dept, Schering Corp, 86 Orange St, Bloomfield, NJ 07003.

EVANS, GEORGE LYMAN, b. San Francisco, Calif, Aug. 13, 20; m. 46; c. 3. ORGANIC & ANALYTICAL CHEMISTRY. B.A, Stanford, 42; M.Sc, Ohio State, 44, Ph.D.(org. chem), 47. Res. chemist, chem. dept, E.I. DU PONT DE NEMOURS & CO, 47-51, FABRICS & FINISHES DEPT, 51-62, staff chemist, 62-68, RES. ASSOC, 68- Am. Chem. Soc. Analytical development; analysis of organic systems; gas chromatography. Address: Fabrics & Finishes Dept, E.I. du Pont de Nemours & Co, 3500 Gray's Ferry Ave, Philadelphia, PA 19146.

EVANS, GEORGE W(ILLIAM), b. Chicago, Ill, May 21, 26; m. 53; c. 5. MEAT SCIENCE. B.A, Univ. Wis, Madison, 55. Lab. technician, RES. DEPT, OSCAR MAYER & CO, 47-51, proj. engr, 51-58, proj. leader, 58-61, res. technologist, 61-67, RES. ANALYST, 67- U.S.N.R, 44-47. AAAS; Am. Soc. Qual. Control; Inst. Food Technol; Am. Statist. Asn. Edible rendering; evaluation of cattle, swine; sensory evaluation of meats; stability and sanitation of meat products; food protein sources; irradiation. Address: 5507 Monona Pass, Monona, WI 53716.

EVANS, GEORGE W(ILLIAM), II, b. Houston, Tex, June 8, 20; m. 43; c. 2. APPLIED MATHEMATICS. A.B, California, 42, A.M, 43; Ph.D.(math), N.Y. Univ, 51. Instr. math, Wash. Sq, Col, N.Y. Univ, 46-50; mathematician, Argonne Nat. Lab, 50-53; radiation Lab, California, Livermore, 53-54; res. mathematician, Stanford Res. Inst, 54-62, mgr. math. sci. dept, 62-66, sr. res. mathematician, 66-68; ASSOC. PROF. MATH, UNIV. SANTA CLARA, 66- U.S.N.R, 43-45, Res, 46-53, Lt. Am. Math. Soc. Heat conduction; high speed computors; time series analysis; gaming and simulation. Address: 14511 DeBell Dr, Los Altos Hills, CA 94022.

EVANS, GORDON G(OODWIN), b. Brooklyn, N.Y, Feb. 13, 21; m. 44; c. 6. ORGANIC CHEMISTRY. A.B, Princeton, 42; Ph.D.(chem), Harvard, 50. Mem. staff, Merck & Co, 41; rayon dept, pioneering res. sect, E.I. du Pont de Nemours & Co, 42-43; res. scientist, Carbide & Carbon Chem. Co, 46; instr. CHEM, TUFTS UNIV, 49-52, asst. prof, 52-65, ASSOC. PROF, 65-, chmn. dept, 66-68. Petrol. Res. Fund faculty award, 62-63. U.S.A, 43-46. AAAS; Am. Chem. Soc. Synthesis and structure of heterocyclic compounds. Address: Dept. of Chemistry, Tufts University, Medford, MA 02155.

EVANS, GRIFFITH C(ONRAD), b. Boston, Mass, May 11, 87; m. 17; c. 3. MATHEMATICS. A.B, Harvard, 07, A.M, 08, Ph.D.(math), 10; hon. LL.D, California, 56. Instr. math, Harvard, 06-07, 09-10, Sheldon traveling fel, Rome, 10-12; asst. prof. math, Rice Inst, 12-16, prof, 16-34; MATH. SCI, UNIV. CALIF, BERKELEY, 34-54, chmn. dept, 34-49, EMER. PROF, 54-, Ed, Am. J. Math, 27-35. Mem, Nat. Res. Coun, 27-30, 40-43, 50-53. Sig.C, Air Branch, 18-19, Capt. Tech. consult. & sci. expert, Army Ord, 43-47. Nat. Acad. Sci; AAAS (v.pres, K, 31, A, 36); Am. Math. Soc.(v.pres, 24-26, pres, 38-40); Math. Asn. Am.(v.pres, 32); fel. Economet. Soc; Am. Philos. Soc; Am. Acad. Arts & Sci. Integral equations; potential theory; complex variable; theoretical economics. Address: Dept. of Mathematical Sciences, University of California, Berkeley, CA 94720.

EVANS, HAROLD J, b. Woodburn, Ky, Feb. 19, 21; m. 46; c. 2. PLANT NUTRITION & BIOCHEMISTRY. B.S, Kentucky, 46, fel, 46-48, M.S, 48; fel, Rutgers, 48-50, Ph.D.(soil chem, plant physiol), 50. Asst. prof. bot, N.C. State Col, 50-51; fel, Hopkins, 51-52; assoc. prof. bot, N.C. State Col, 52-57, PROF, 57-61; PLANT PHYSIOL, ORE. STATE UNIV, 61- Consult, Nat. Sci. Found, 64; Rockefeller Found. vis. prof, Univ. Sussex, 69. Hoblitzelle Nat. Award, 65. Med.C, U.S.A, 43-46. Am. Soc. Plant Physiol.(pres-elect, 70); Am. Soc. Biol. Chem; Brit. Biochem. Soc. Role of cobalt in metabolism of symbionts and Rhizobium; biochemical role of univalent cations; mechanism of nitrogen fixation. Address: Dept. of Botany & Plant Pathology, Oregon State University, Corvallis, OR 97331.

EVANS, HARRISON SILAS, b. Monroe, Iowa, Aug. 4, 11; m. 34; c. 2. MEDICINE, PSYCHIATRY. Union Col.(Nebr), 29-31; M.D, Col. Med. Evangelists, 36. Res. psychiat, Harding Hosp, Worthington, Ohio, 36-39, staff psychiatrist, 39-42, co-dir, 46-62; PROF. PSYCHIAT. & CHMN. DEPT, SCH. MED, LOMA LINDA UNIV, 62- Clin. assoc. prof, Ohio State, 46-62, asst. prof, sch. soc. admin, 58-62. Dipl, Am. Bd. Psychiat. & Neurol, 46. U.S.A, 42-46, Lt. Col. Fel. Am. Psychiat. Asn; Am. Acad. Neurol. Medical student education in psychiatry and psychotherapy; community mental health. Address: Dept. of Psychiatry, Loma Linda University School of Medicine, Loma Linda, CA 92354.

EVANS, HARRY D(EAN), b. Arcola, Mo, July 10, 15; m. 41; c. 1. CHEMICAL ENGINEERING. B.S, Illinois, 37; Am. Petrol. Inst. fel, Calif. Inst. Tech, 37-38, M.S, 38. Jr. res. engr, SHELL DEVELOP. CO, 38-42, engr,

46-53, develop. supvr, 53, engr, Shell Lab, Amsterdam, 53-54, sr. technologist, N.Y, 55-56, develop. supvr. oil processing, 56-65, DEPT. HEAD, licensing & design eng. dept, 65-68, PROCESS ENG, CHEM. DEPT, 68-. U.S.A, 42-45, Lt. Col. Am. Inst. Chem. Eng. Thermodynamic properties of hydrocarbons; high pressure phase equilibria; mass transfer; fluid flow; petroleum process and equipment design and development; chemical process design. Address: Shell Development Co, Emeryville, CA 94608.

EVANS, HELEN HARRINGTON, b. Cleveland, Ohio, May 11, 24; m. 66; c. 1. BIOCHEMISTRY. B.S, Purdue Univ, 46; Ph.D.(biochem), West. Reserve Univ, 53. Sr. instr. biochem, CASE WEST. RESERVE UNIV, 56-58, asst. prof, 58-64, ASSOC. PROF. BIOCHEM. & RADIOL, 64- Vis. scientist, Scripps Clin. & Res. Found, Calif, 65-66. Am. Chem. Soc; Radiation Res. Soc; Am. Soc. Biol. Chem; Am. Soc. Microbiol. Effect of ionizing radiation on desoxyribonucleic acid; control of macromolecular synthesis and the mitotic cycle. Address: Division of Radiation Biology, Case Western Reserve University, 2065 Adelbert Rd, Cleveland, OH 44106.

EVANS, H(ENRY) L(EWIS), b. Cwmgwrach, Wales, Mar. 26, 25; m. 63. MATHEMATICAL PHYSICS, FLUID MECHANICS. B.Sc, Wales, 49, M.Sc, 51; Commonwealth Sci. & Indust. Res. Orgn. studentship, London, 57-59, Ph.D.(pure sci) & dipl, Imp. Col, 60. Res. off, div. food preservation, Commonwealth Sci. & Indust. Res. Orgn, Sydney, Australia, 52-59, prin. res. off, in charge physics sect, 60-62; lectr. MECH. ENG, Imp. Col, London, 62-65; ASSOC. PROF, WATERLOO UNIV, 65-67, PROF, 67-, vis. prof, 64. Summer vis. res. assoc, Brown, 63. Fel. Brit. Inst. Physics & Phys. Soc. Development of methods for estimating heat, mass and momentum transfer for incompressible laminar flow. Address: Dept. of Mechanical Engineering, University of Waterloo, Waterloo, Ont, Can.

EVANS, H(ILTON) B(ERNARD), b. Moab, Utah, Jan. 7, 29; m. 48; c. 3. PHYSICS, GEOPHYSICS. B.A, Utah, 54, fel, 58-59, Ph.D.(geophys), 59. Physicist, U.S. Geol. Surv, Utah, 55-57, res. physicist, 57-58, nuclear physicist, 58-59; res. physicist, MARATHON OIL CO, 59-62, adv. res. physicist, 62-66, SR. RES. PHYSICIST, 66- Teacher, Utah, 53-59, asst, 55-58; mem. budget comt, City of Littleton, 62, water comt, 63-; logging & coring adv. comt. deep sea core test prog, Joint Oceanog. Insts. Deep Earth Sampling, 67- U.S.A.A.F, 46-49, Sgt. Soc. Prof. Well Log Analysts; Marine Technol. Soc; Soc. Explor. Geophys. Well logging methods and interpretation; natural radioactivity of the atmosphere; radioactive methods of prospecting; computer evaluation applied to logging and geophysics problems; radiation physics; physical measurements on geologic materials; marine minerals exploration. Address: Marathon Oil Co, Research Center, P.O. Box 269, Littleton, CO 80120.

EVANS, HIRAM J(OHN), b. Granville, N.Y, May 13, 16; m. 44; c. 4. BIOLOGY. B.A, Hamilton Col, 37; M.A, Williams Col, 39; fel, Harvard, 39-42, A.M, 41, Ph.D.(biol), 42. Asst, Williams Col, 37-39; res. assoc. zool, Swarthmore Col, 46; asst. prof, Syracuse, 47-53, assoc. prof, 53-64; prof. BIOL, New Col, 64-65; PROF. & DEAN, CURRY COL, 65- V.chmn. dept. zool, Syracuse, 47-54, 59-64; secy. bd. trustees, Biol. Abstracts, 50-65. U.S.A.A.F, 42-46, Maj. Am. Soc. Zool; Soc. Develop. Biol. Development and innervation of the chick ear; analysis of microquantities of respiratory gases; adrenal steroids and embryonic development. Address: Curry College, 848 Brush Hill Rd, Milton, MA 02186.

EVANS, HOWARD E(DWARD), b. New York, N.Y, Sept. 22, 22; m. 49; c. 2. VERTEBRATE ANATOMY. B.S, Cornell, 44, Ph.D.(zool), 50. Asst. herpetol, Mus. Natural Hist, 38-40; technician zool, CORNELL UNIV, 40-42, asst, 46-50, asst. prof. ANAT, N.Y. STATE VET. COL, 50-52, assoc. prof, 52-60, PROF, 60-, SECY. VET. COL, 67- Nat. Sci. Found. fel. & vis. prof, California, 57; vis. prof, Phipps Inst, med. sch, Pennsylvania, 64. U.S.A, 43-46, 1st Lt. Hon. mem, Am. Vet. Med. Asn; Am. Asn. Anat; Am. Soc. Zool; Am. Asn. Vet. Anat; Am. Soc. Mammal; Am. Soc. Ichthyol. & Herpet. Tooth succession in vertebrates; fetal growth anatomy of dogs; cyclopia in sheep. Address: Dept. of Anatomy, N.Y. State Veterinary College, Cornell University, Ithaca, NY 14850.

EVANS, HOWARD ENSIGN, b. East Hartford, Conn, Feb. 23, 19; m. 54; c. 3. ENTOMOLOGY. B.A, Connecticut, 40; M.S, Cornell, 41, Ph.D.(entom), 49. Asst. entom, Cornell, 47-49; asst. prof, Kans. State Col, 49-52; insect taxon, Cornell, 52-54, assoc. prof, 54-60; assoc. curator MUS. COMP. ZOOL, HARVARD, 60-64, curator insects, 64-69, ALEXANDER AGASSIZ PROF. ZOOL, 69- Guggenheim fel, Nat. Univ. Mex, 59 & Commonwealth Sci. & Indust. Res. Orgn, Canberra, Australia, 69. U.S.A, 42-45, 2nd Lt. Entom. Soc. Am; Soc. Study Evolution. Taxonomy of Pompilidae and Bethylidae; comparative ethology of solitary wasps. Address: 17 Frances Rd, Lexington, MA 02173.

EVANS, HOWARD TASKER, JR, b. Ancon, C.Z, Sept. 9, 19; m. 42, 66; c. 2. INORGANIC CHEMISTRY. S.B, Mass. Inst. Tech, 42, fels, 42, 44-45, Ph.D. (inorg. chem), 48. Mem. res. staff, div. indust. co-op, Mass. Inst. Tech, 43-44, 47-49, instr. sect. graphics, 45-48; res. physicist, Philips Labs, Inc, 49-52; PHYSICIST, U.S. GEOL. SURV, 52- Guggenheim Found. vis. res. scientist, Royal Inst. Tech, Sweden, 60-61. Civilian with Off. Sci. Res. & Develop, 44. Mineral. Soc. Am; Am. Crystallog. Asn.(secy, 50-51, v.pres, 63, pres, 64). Am. Chem. Soc. Crystal chemistry; x-ray crystallography of inorganic compounds and minerals; x-ray diffraction and crystal structure determination; crystal growth and morphology; optical crystallography. Address: U.S. Geological Survey, Washington, DC 20242.

EVANS, HUGH E, b. N.Y.C, July 6, 34; m. 60; c. 2. PEDIATRICS, INFECTIOUS DISEASE. B.A, Columbia Univ, 54; M.D, State Univ. N.Y. Downstate Med. Ctr, 58. Intern pediat, Johns Hopkins Hosp, 58-59, asst. resident, 59-60; clin. assoc. infectious diseases, Nat. Insts. Health, 60-62; sr. asst. resident, Johns Hopkins Hosp, 62, chief resident pediat, 62-63; private practice, Ohio, 63-65; res. assoc, Mt. Sinai Hosp, 65-66; asst. prof. CLIN. PEDIAT, COLUMBIA UNIV, 66-68, ASSOC. PROF, 68-; ATTENDING PEDIATRICIAN, HARLEM HOSP, 69-, ASSOC. DIR. PEDIAT, 67-, asst. attending pediatrician, 66-69. Dipl, Am. Bd. Pediat, 63. U.S.P.H.S, 60-62, Res, 62-, Sr. Asst. Surg. Soc. Pediat. Res; Am. Thoracic Soc; Am. Acad. Pediat; Am. Fedn. Clin. Res; Am. Soc. Microbiol. Infection in the neonatal period;

bacterial flora of newborns; enzyme inhibitor levels in the respiratory distress syndrome; clinical and laboratory aspects of new respiratory viruses. Address: Dept. of Pediatrics, Harlem Hospital Center, New York, NY 10037.

EVANS, J. B, b. Deniliquin, Australia, July 14, 26; m. 55; c. 2. MINERAL ENGINEERING. B.Min.E, Univ. Melbourne, 51, B.S, 58. Laborer, N. Broken Hill Ltd, Australia, 52-53, jr. engr, 53-54; Howe Sound Mining Co, Can, 54-55; Can. Explor. Ltd, Placer Develop. Ltd, 55-56, field engr, 56-67, eval. engr, 57-61, chief engr, Craigmont Mines Ltd, 61-62; gen. mgr, Molybdenum Corp. Am, 62-63, v.pres, 63-64; managing dir, Mineral Engrs. Proprietary Ltd, 64-69; PROF. MINERAL ENG. & HEAD DEPT. UNIV. B.C, 69- Managing dir, Austiminex Proprietary Ltd, 64-69; vis. prof, Univ. Ibadan, 70; mem, Nat. Adv. Comt. Mining & Metal. Res, Can, 71-; councillor, B.C. & Yukon Chamber Mines, 71- Royal Australian Navy, 44-46. Australian Inst. Mining & Metal; Can. Inst. Mining & Metal. Mine property evaluation; mine effluent discharges. Address: Dept. of Mineral Engineering, University of British Columbia, Vancouver 8, B.C, Can.

EVANS, JACQUELINE P, b. Philadelphia, Pa, Jan. 12, 23. MATHEMATICS. B.A, Vassar Col, 44, fel, 44-45; M.A, Radcliffe Col, Ph.D.(math), 54. Teacher, private sch, Pa, 45-46; instr. MATH, Wilson Col, 46-49; Wellesley Col, 51-52, 53-54; Smith Col, 54-56; asst. prof, WELLESLEY COL, 56-62, assoc. prof, 62-68, PROF, 68- Am. Math. Soc. Math. Asn. Am. Approximation and interpolation by functions analytic and bounded in regions of the complex plane. Address: Dept. of Mathematics, Wellesley College, Wellesley, MA 02181.

EVANS, JAMES B(OWEN), b. Algonquin, Ill, June 24, 30. RADIOCHEMISTRY. B.S, Northwestern, 52; M.S, Wisconsin, 54, Du Pont fel, 54-55, Ph.D.(chem), 58. Asst. prof. chem, Colorado, 57-64; consult. scientist, 64-67; ASSOC. PROF. CHEM, TEMPLE BUELL COL, 67- Am. Chem. Soc. Radioisotope applications; radiological physics; instrumentation. Address: Dept. of Chemistry, Temple Buell College, 1800 Pontiac St, Denver, CO 80220.

EVANS, JAMES B(RAINERD), b. Gainesville, N.Y, Jan. 25, 21; m. 46; c. 3. BACTERIOLOGY. B.S, Houghton Col, 41; Ph.D.(bact), Cornell, 48. Asst. prof. bact, Cornell, 48; bacteriologist, Am. Meat Inst. Found, 48-57, chief div. bact, 57-59; PROF. BACT. N.C. STATE UNIV, 60-, HEAD DEPT. MICROBIOL, 65- Res. assoc, Chicago, 54-59. U.S.N.R, 44-46. Am. Acad. Microbiol; Am. Soc. Microbiol; Am. Inst. Biol. Sci; Am. Pub. Health Asn; Brit. Soc. Gen. Microbiol. Physiology and taxonomy of staphylococci, micrococci and lactic bacteria. Address: Dept. of Microbiology, North Carolina State University, Raleigh, NC 27607.

EVANS, JAMES ERIC LLOYD, b. Miniota, Man, May 25, 14; m. 40; c. 2. ECONOMIC GEOLOGY. B.Sc, Manitoba, 36; M.A, Queen's (Ont), 42; Royal Soc. Can. fel. & Ph.D, Columbia, 44. Res. geologist, Falconbridge Nickel Mines, Ltd, 42-45; field geologist, Frobisher, Ltd, 45-50; mgr, Amco Explor, Inc, 50-54; field mgr, Tech. Mines Consult, Ltd, 54-56; chief geologist, Rio Tinto Can. Explor, Ltd, 56-70; DIR. EXPLOR, DENISON MINES LTD, 70- Dir, Can. Geol. Found; mem, Nat. Adv. Comt. on Res. in Geol. Sci. Can. Centennial Medal. Geol. Soc. Am; Soc. Econ. Geol; Geol. Asn. Can.(secy, 63-65, pres, 67-68); Can. Inst. Mining & Metall. Petrography and petrology of the mine; identification and metallurgy of various mine, mill and smelter products; mineral exploration in Canada, United States, Chile, Brazil and Costa Rica. Address: 1375 Stavebank Rd, Mississauga, Ont, Can.

EVANS, JAMES FORREST, Agr. Commun, see 12th ed, Soc. & Behav. Vols.

EVANS, JAMES ORNETTE, b. Roanoke, Tex, July 27, 20; m. 59; c. 1. AGRICULTURAL ENGINEERING, SOIL SCIENCE. B.S, Wisconsin, 47, M.S, 52; Colo. Agr. & Mech. Col, 51. Assembler, Int. Harvester Co, 47-48; land classification specialist, Bur. Reclamation, U.S. Dept. Interior, 48-53; conservationist, div. lands & soil, Ohio Dept. Natural Resources, 53-56 & 57-64; soil scientist, Kuljian Corp. Phila, opers. in Iraq, 56-57; proj. soil scientist, U.S. Dept. Health, Ed. & Welfare, 64-67; res. soil scientist, Cincinnati Water Res. Lab, Fed. Water Pollution Control Admin, U.S. Dept. Interior, 67-68; RES. HYDROLOGIST, DIV. FOREST ENVIRON. RES, FOREST SERV, U.S. DEPT. AGR, 68- U.S.A, 43-46. Am. Soc. Agron; Soil Conserv. Soc. Am; Int. Soc. Soil Sci; Am. Geophys. Union. Soil and water relationships-infiltration, hydraulic conductivity, drainage; irrigation, salinity; oxidation and assimilation of organic and inorganic sludges and effluents; soil fertility and conditioning; erosion, sedimentation and pollution abatement; water yields; recycling wastes. Address: Forest Service, U.S. Dept. of Agriculture, Washington, DC 20250.

EVANS, JAMES R, b. Whittier, Calif, June 8, 31; m. 54; c. 7. ECONOMIC GEOLOGY. B.A, Whittier Col, 56; M.S, Southern California, 58; California, Los Angeles, 59-60, Davis, 64-68. GEOLOGIST ECON. GEOL, STATE DIV. MINES & GEOL, CALIF, 58- Geologist, Cerr Mineral Explor. Co, 70. U.S.N, 50-53, Res, 53- Geol. Soc. Am; Mineral. Soc. Am; Soc. Econ. Geol. Geologic field mapping and application of techniques of metamorphic petrology to study of metallic and nonmetallic mineral deposits to determine their origin, distribution, and economic potential. Address: California Division of Mines & Geology, Rm. 1065, 107 S. Broadway, Los Angeles, CA 90012.

EVANS, JAMES SPURGEON, b. Big Sandy, Tenn, Aug. 19, 31; m. 56; c. 2. ANATOMY. B.S, Univ. Tenn, 58; M.S, La. State Univ, 60; Ph.D.(reprod. physiol), Univ. Ky, 64. Nat. Insts. Health fel. ANAT, med. sch, Univ. Ky, 64-65; instr, MED. UNITS, UNIV. TENN, 65-69, ASST. PROF, 69- AAAS; Neuroendocrinology; general endocrinology and reproductive physiology. Address: Dept. of Anatomy, University of Tennessee Medical Units, Memphis, TN 38103.

EVANS, JAMES S(TUART), b. Bridgton, Maine, Jan. 16, 41. PHYSICAL & INORGANIC CHEMISTRY. B.S, Bates Col, 62; Nat. Sci. Found. fel, Princeton, 63-65 & summer, 63, M.A, 64, Ph.D.(chem), 66. Res. assoc. CHEM, Princeton, 66; ASST. PROF. LAWRENCE UNIV. 66-. chmn. dept, 68-71. AAAS; Am. Chem. Soc; Am. Phys. Soc; N.Y. Acad. Sci. Inorganic chemistry, especially coordination compounds and noble metals; physical chemistry; nuclear chemistry. Address: Dept. of Chemistry, Lawrence University, Appleton, WI 54911.

EVANS, J(AMES) WARREN, b. Edna, Tex, Oct. 31, 38; m. 59; c. 1. PHYSIOLOGY, BIOCHEMISTRY. B.S, Colorado State, 64; Texas A&M, 57-58; Nat. Insts. Health trainee, California, Davis, 64-66, Nat. Insts. Health fel, 66-68, Ph.D.(physiol), 68. ASST. PROF. ANIMAL SCI. & PHYSIOL. & ASST. PHYSIOLOGIST, EXTEN. SERV, UNIV. CALIF, DAVIS, 68- U.S.A, 61-67. Effects of gravity on metabolism; physiology of reproduction in the mare; equine nutrition. Address: Dept. of Animal Science, University of California, Davis, Calif. 95616.

EVANS, JAMES W(ILLIAM), b. Chilhowee, Mo, Sept. 21, 08; m. 30; c. 1. AGRICULTURAL BIOCHEMISTRY. B.S, Cent. Mo. State Teachers Col, 28; Missouri, 29; Ph.D.(agr. biochem), Minnesota, 40. Spec. analyst, Union Starch & Ref. Co, 30-32, res. chemist, 32-37; asst. biochem, Minnesota, 38-39, instr, 39-40; res. chemist, Union Starch & Ref. Co, 40-43; from res. chemist to sect. leader, Gen. Mills, Inc, Minn, 43-50; DIR. RES, AM. MAIZE PROD. CO, 50-59, v.pres. res. & develop, 59-64, PRES. & CHIEF EXEC. OFF, 64- Am. Chem. Soc; Am. Asn. Cereal Chem; Am. Asn. Textile Chem. & Colorists; Inst. Food Tech. Corn and wheat starches; corn syrups and sugars; caramel coloring; moisture methods for syrups and sugars; composition of starch hydrolysates; development of packaged foods as soups, cake, pie crust and biscuit mixes, breakfast cereals and instant puddings. Address: American Maize Products Co, 250 Park Ave, New York, NY 10017.

EVANS, JAMES W(ILLIAM), b. Yorkshire, Eng, Aug. 22, 43; m. 67; c. 1. CHEMICAL ENGINEERING. B.Sc, Univ. London, 64; Nat. Sci. Found. fel, State Univ. N.Y. Buffalo, 68, C.C. Furnas fel, 69-70, Ph.D.(chem. eng), 70. Tech. adv, Int. Comput. Ltd, Eng, 64-65; chemist, Cyanamid of Canada Ltd, 65-67; PROCESS DEVELOP. ENGR, ETHYL CORP, 70- Am. Inst. Mining, Metall. & Petrol. Eng. Process metallurgy, particularly gas-solid reactions and their optimization, radiant heat transfer, continuous casting, vapometallurgical refining, fluidized beds, arc furnaces. Address: Dept. of Research & Development, Ethyl Corp, P.O. Box 341, Baton Rouge, LA 70821.

EVANS, JOHN C, b. Oklahoma City, Okla, Jan. 21, 38; m. 59; c. 3. ASTROPHYSICS. B.S, Oklahoma, 60; M.S, Rensselaer Polytech, 62; M.S, Michigan, 64, fel. & Ph.D.(astron), 66. ASST. PROF. PHYSICS, KANS. STATE UNIV, 66- Am. Astron. Soc. Stellar structure, specifically stellar atmospheres, thermal and dynamic structures of stellar atmospheres, line formation, chemical abundances, stellar and solar magnetic fields. Address: Dept. of Physics, College of Arts & Sciences, Kansas State University, Manhattan, KS 66502.

EVANS, JOHN CATHCART, b. Grand Rapids, Mich, Oct. 19, 24; m. 47; c. 2. RADIOTHERAPY. M.D, Michigan, 48. Assoc. prof. RADIOL, Albert Einstein Col. Med, 55-67; PROF, SCH. MED, DUKE UNIV, 67- Vis. staff, Bronx Munic. Hosp. Center, 55- U.S.N.R, 49-55, Lt. Radiol. Soc. N.Am; Am. Radium Soc; Radiation Res. Soc; Am. Col. Radiol. Radiotherapeutic and chemotherapeutic treatment of malignant disease; radiobiology. Address: Dept. of Radiology, Duke University Medical School, Durham, NC 27706.

EVANS, JOHN C(YRIL), b. New Quay, Wales, Nov. 8, 29; U.S. citizen; m. 53; c. 2. PHYSICAL CHEMISTRY. B.Sc, Wales, 50, Ph.D.(molecular spectros) 53, D.Sc.(molecular spectros), 64. Nat. Res. Coun. Can. fel, 53-55; phys. chemist, PHYS. RES. LAB, DOW CHEM. CO, 55-62, assoc. scientist, 62-68, RES. SCIENTIST, 68- AAAS; Am. Chem. Soc; Optical Soc. Am; Coblentz Soc. Raman, infrared, ultraviolet and visible absorption spectroscopy; fluorescence spectroscopy and nuclear quadrupole resonance spectroscopy in the study of molecular structure. Address: Physical Research Lab, Dow Chemical Co, Midland, MI 48640.

EVANS, JOHN E(DWARD), b. Sisseton, S.Dak, July 14, 25; m. 50; c. 3. MEDICAL BACTERIOLOGY. B.A, Luther Col.(Iowa), 49; M.A, South Dakota, 51; Rotary Found. fel, London, 54-55, Med. Res. Coun. fel, 55-58, Ph.D.(bact), 58. Asst, Wisconsin, 51-52; rheumatic fever res. inst, Northwestern, 52-54; vis. asst. prof. MICROBIOL, UNIV. HOUSTON, 58-59, asst. prof, 59-62, assoc. prof, 62-68, PROF, 68- U.S.N, 43-46. AAAS; Genetics Soc. Am; Biophys. Soc; Am. Soc. Microbiol; Soc. Indust. Microbiol; Am. Sci. Affiliation. Regulation of growth and cell division in microorganisms. Address: Dept. of Biology, University of Houston, Houston, TX 77004.

EVANS, JOHN E(LLIS), b. Oak Hill, Ohio, Oct. 2, 14; m. 48. PHYSICS. B.Sc, & B.A, Ohio State, 36, M.A, 37, 41-42; fel, Rice Inst, 45-47, Ph.D.(physics), 47. Tutor math, Ohio State, 36-37; teacher, high sch, Ohio, 37-38; prof. physics & math, civilian pilot traning prog, Rio Grande Col, 38-41; asst. physics, Ohio State, 41-42; staff mem, radiation lab, Mass. Inst. Tech, 42-45; fel. physics, Rice Inst, 47-48; staff mem, Los Alamos Sci. Lab, 48-52; group leader, atomic energy div, Phillips Petrol. Co, 52-54, sect. head, 54-56, dir. nuclear physics res, 56-61; SR. CONSULT. SCIENTIST, PHYS. SCI. LAB, LOCKHEED MISSILES & SPACE CO, 61- Civilian with U.S.N; Off. Sci. Res. & Develop. AAAS; fel. Am. Phys. Soc; Am. Geophys. Union; Am. Nuclear Soc. Am. Asn. Physics Teachers. Auroral and nuclear physics; homogeneous reactor development; neutron crystal spectrometry. Address: Lockheed Palo Alto Research Labs, Dept. 52-14, Bldg. 202, 3251 Hanover St, Palo Alto, CA 94304.

EVANS, JOHN JOSEPH, b. Cleveland, Ohio, Aug. 2, 38; m. 59; c. 4. BIOCHEMISTRY. B.A, Case Western Reserve, 60, M.A, 64, Ph.D.(biol), 66. Fel. biol, Case Western Reserve, 66-67; Nat. Res. Coun-Nat. Acad. Sci-Nat. Acad. Eng. res. assoc, AGR. RES. SERV, U.S. DEPT. AGR, 67-69, BIOCHEMIST, WEST. MKT. & NUTRIT. DIV, 69- AAAS; Am. Asn. Cereal Chem. Plant enzymes, especially peroxidase isoenzymes. Address: Richard B. Russell Agricultural Research Center, Agricultural Research Service, U.S. Dept. of Agriculture, P.O. Box 5677, Athens, GA 30604.

EVANS, JOHN M(cCALLUM), b. Hamburg, N.Y, July 19, 13; m. 41; c. 1. MEDICINE. B.A, Denison, 35; M.D, Buffalo, 39. Instr. MED, sch. med, Buffalo, 41; asst, Harvard Med. Sch, 46-48, fel, 46-47; asst. clin. prof, SCH. MED, GEORGE WASHINGTON UNIV, 48-52, assoc. clin. prof, 52-54, assoc. prof. med, 54-60, PROF, 60-, ASSOC. HOSP. & DIR. CARDIOVASC. RES. LAB, 48-, CARDIAC CLINS, 51- Lectr, Catholic Univ, 58- Private practice; vis. physician, Walter Reed Gen. Hosp, 48-; consult, U.S. Soldiers Home Hosp, 48-; Newton D. Baker Vet. Admin. Hosp, 50-, Alto Vet. Hosp, 58-; Wash. Hosp. Ctr, 64- Med.C, U.S.A, 41-48. AAAS; Am. Heart Asn; Am. Fedn. Clin. Res. Cardiovascular diseases. Address: 1250 Connecticut Ave, Washington, DC 20036.

EVANS, JOHN R(OBERT), b. Toronto, Ont, Oct. 1, 29; m. 54; c. 6. MEDICINE. M.D, Univ. Toronto, 52; D.Phil, Oxford, 55. Assoc. med, Univ. Toronto, 60-65, asst. prof, 65-67; prof, dean faculty med. & prin. col. health sci, McMASTER UNIV, 65-67, V.PRES. HEALTH SCI, 67- Markle scholar acad. med, 60-65. Fel, Royal Col. Physicians & Surgeons, Can, 58. Am. Physiol. Soc; Cardiac Muscle Soc; Can. Physiol. Soc; Can. Soc. Clin. Invest; Can. Cardiovasc. Soc. Natural history of congenital and acquired heart disease, myocardial metabolism, particularly myocardial lipid metabolism. Address: Health Sciences Center, McMaster University, Hamilton 16, Ont, Can.

EVANS, JOHN STANTON, b. Camilla, Ga, Oct. 12, 21; m. 48; c. 3. PHYSICS. B.S.I.A, Berry Col, 42; M.S, Emory Univ, 48; Ph.D., Univ. Tenn, 59. Instr. physics, Martin Br, Univ. Tenn, 52; AERONAUT. RES. ENG, NASA, 52- U.S.A, 43-46. Am. Phys. Soc. Gas dynamics; plasma physics; radio propagation; chemical kinetics. Address: 243 E. Queens Dr, Williamsburg, VA 23185.

EVANS, JOHN S(TONE), b. Sterling, Ill, Sept. 14, 10; m. 35; c. 3. ENDOCRINOLOGY. B.S, Western Michigan, 33; Ph.D.(biochem), Chicago, 39. Res. chemist, Upjohn Co, 34-36; asst. chem, Chicago, 37-38, res. assoc, 38-39; res. chemist, UPJOHN CO, 40-43, head prod. dept, 43-46, res. chemist, 46-50, head dept. microbiol, 50-56, RES. CHEMIST, 56- With Off. Sci. Res. & Develop, 44. AAAS; Am. Chem. Soc; Endocrine Soc; Soc. Exp. Biol. & Med; N.Y. Acad. Sci. Antibiotic fermentation; extraction of antibiotics; cancer chemotherapy; cancer immunology. Address: Hypersensitivity Diseases Research, Upjohn Co, Kalamazoo, MI 49001.

EVANS, JOHN V, b. Manchester, Eng, July 5, 33; m. 58; c. 3. RADIO PHYSICS. B.Sc, Manchester, 54, Ph.D.(physics), 57. Leverhulme res. fel. radio astron, Jodrell Bank Exp. Sta, Manchester, 57-60; staff mem, Lincoln Lab, Mass. Inst. Tech, 60-66; George A. Miller vis. prof. elec. eng, Illinois, 66-67; staff mem, LINCOLN LAB, MASS. INST. TECHNOL, 67-70, ASSOC. GROUP LEADER, 70- Mem, Int. Union Radio Sci, 63-, nat. comt, 68-70, secy, 70- AAAS; fel. Inst. Elec. & Electronics Eng; Am. Astron. Soc; Int. Astron. Union. Radar studies of the moon, Venus, meteors and the ionosphere. Address: Lincoln Lab, Massachusetts Institute of Technology, Lexington, MA 02173.

EVANS, JOHN W, b. Mt. Vernon, N.Y, Jan. 20, 35; div; c. 2. MATHEMATICAL BIOLOGY. M.D, Cornell Univ, 58; Ph.D.(math), Univ. Calif, Los Angeles, 66. Sr. surgeon, math. res. branch, Nat. Inst. Arthritis & Metab. Disease, 66-68; ASSOC. PROF. MATH, UNIV. CALIF, SAN DIEGO, 68- Am. Math. Soc. Mathematical models of nerve impulse conduction; pulmonary gas wash-out studies. Address: Dept. of Mathematics, University of California, San Diego, P.O. Box 109, La Jolla, CA 92037.

EVANS, JOHN W(AINWRIGHT, JR), b. New York, N.Y, May 14, 09; m. 32; c. 3. ASTRONOMY, GEOPHYSICS. A.B, Swarthmore Col, 32; Pennsylvania, 32-34; A.M, Harvard, 36, Ph.D.(astron), 38; hon. Sc.D, Univ. N.Mex, 67 & Swarthmore Col, 70. Instr. astron, Minnesota, 37-38; astron. & math, Mills Col, 38-41, asst. prof, 41-42; optical res. worker, Nat. Defense Res. Comt, Rochester, 42-46, asst. prof. optics, 45-46; astronomer, High Altitude Observ. Harvard-Colorado, 46-52; DIR, SACRAMENTO PEAK OBSERV. & MEM. STAFF, CAMBRIDGE RES. LABS, U.S. AIR FORCE, 52- Distinguished civilian serv. award, Dept. Defense, 65-; Rockefeller Pub. Serv. Award Sci, Technol. & Eng, 69. Civilian with U.S.A.F. AAAS (Cleveland prize, 57); Am. Astron. Soc; fel. Am. Acad. Arts & Sci; Int. Astron. Union. Solar physics; solar terrestrial effects; optical design. Address: Sacramento Peak Observatory, Sacramento Peak, Sunspot, NM 88349.

EVANS, JOHN WILLIAM, b. Montreal, Que, Apr. 10, 34. ZOOLOGY. B.Sc, McGill, 57, M.Sc, 59; Ph.D.(ecol), Oregon, 66. Asst. prof. BIOL, MEM. UNIV. NEWF, 66-71, ASSOC. PROF, 71- Can. Soc. Zool. Marine invertebrate zoology; ecology of rock and shell borers; distribution of teredo in Newfoundland waters; faunal and microecological study of epifauna living on sea scallop shells; long-term photogrammetric studies of beach-rock erosion on coast of Barbados, W.I. Address: Dept. of Biology, Memorial University of Newfoundland, St. John's, Newf, Can.

EVANS, J(OSEPH) A(NDREW), b. Lawrence, Mass, Oct. 1, 04; m. 37; c. 3. ENTOMOLOGY, PLANT PATHOLOGY. B.S, Massachusetts, 28; Ph.D, Cornell, 42. Asst. county agr. agent, Cornell, 29-36, exten. entomologist, 37-44; mgr. tech. serv, E.I. du Pont de Nemours & Co, Inc, 44-60, prod. mgr, 60-69; RETIRED. Entom. Soc. Am. Horticulture. Address: 114 Blue Rock Rd, Wilmington, DE 19809.

EVANS, JOSEPH LISTON, b. Lebanon, Ky, June 27, 30; m. 55; c. 2. NUTRITION. B.S, Univ. Ky, 52, M.S, 55; Ph.D.(nutrit, biochem), Univ. Fla, 59. Asst. animal sci, Univ. Ky, 54-55; NUTRIT, Univ. Fla, 55-59; asst. prof, RUTGERS UNIV, 59-64, assoc. prof, 64-69, PROF, 69- U.S.A, 52-54. Am. Soc. Animal Sci; Am. Inst. Nutrit; Am. Chem. Soc; Am. Dairy Sci. Asn. Nutritional biochemical mechanisms involving utilization of minerals in rats, man and cattle and nitrogen utilization in cattle. Address: Dept. of Animal Sciences & Nutrition, Rutgers University, New Brunswick, NJ 08903.

EVANS, JOSEPH P(ATRICK), b. La Crosse, Wis, Nov. 29, 04; m. 29; c. 8. NEUROSURGERY. A.B, Harvard, 25, M.D, 29; fel, McGill, 29-30, M.Sc, 30, Ph.D, 37; hon. D.Sc, Loyola (Ill), 64. Intern gen. surg, Chicago, 30-31; neurosurg. training, McGill, 31-34; Cambridge, 34-35; clin. clerk, Nat. Hosp, Queen Square, Eng; neuropath, London Hosp, 35-36; res. fel. & asst. neurosurgeon, Montreal Neurol. Inst, 36-37; from instr. to assoc. prof.

surg, & dir. neurosurg. div, col. med, Univ. Cincinnati, 37-54; prof. NEUROL. SURG, HOSPS. & CLINS, UNIV. CHICAGO, 54-70, EMER. PROF, 70- Rockefeller fel, 35-36; clin. clerk, Neurol. Forschungs Inst, Breslau, 35-36; neurosurg. rep, Unitarian Serv, Comt. & WHO, Austria, 47; asst. prof, Yale, 48. Am. Acad. Neurol. Surg.(pres, 40); fel. Am. Col. Surg; fel. Am. Med. Asn; Asn. Res. Nerv. & Ment. Diseases; Am. Asn. Neurol. Surg; Soc. Neurol. Surg; hon. mem, Austrian Soc. Surg. Neurosurgery and allied fields; cerebral cicatrix; trauma. Address: Dept. of Neurological Surgery, University of Chicago Hospitals & Clinics, Chicago, IL 60637.

EVANS, KENNETH J(ACK), b. Chickasha, Okla, July 8, 29; m. 55; c. 4. VERTEBRATE ZOOLOGY, ECOLOGY. B.S, Oklahoma, 57, M.S, 58, South. Fel. Found. fel, California, Berkeley, 58-60, Ph.D.(zool), Riverside, 64. Instr. zool, Redlands, 60-61; assoc. BIOL, California, Riverside, 63-64; from asst. prof. to ASSOC. PROF, CHICO STATE COL, 64- U.S.A.F, 47-54, T/Sgt. Am. Soc. Mammal; Am. Soc. Zool. Ecology of amphibians and reptiles. Address: Dept. of Biological Sciences, Chico State College, First & Normal Sts, Chico, CA 95926.

EVANS, LANCE SAYLOR, b. Phila, Pa, Sept. 29, 44; m. 65; c. 3. PLANT PHYSIOLOGY, HISTOCHEMISTRY. B.S, Calif. State Polytech. Col, Kellogg-Voorhis, 67; Nat. Sci. Found. traineeship, Univ. Calif, Riverside, 68-70, Ph.D.(plant sci. & physiol), 70. Nat. Inst. Environ. Health Sci. res. fel. plant sci, UNIV. CALIF, RIVERSIDE, 70-71, RES. BIOLOGIST, 71- AAAS; Am. Soc. Plant Physiol; Bot. Soc. Am; Am. Inst. Biol. Sci; Int. Soc. Plant Morphol. Botanical histochemistry; air and water pollution; plant morphogenesis and anatomy. Address: Dept. of Biology, University of California, Riverside, CA 92502.

EVANS, LATIMER R(ICHARD), b. Washington, D.C, Nov. 4, 18; m. 42; c. 4. CHEMISTRY. B.S, American Univ, 41; fel, Purdue, 42-44, Ph.D.(org. chem), 45. Asst. chem, Purdue, 41-42, Manhattan Proj. fel, 45; res. chemist, E.I. du Pont de Nemours & Co, 46-50; asst. prof. CHEM, N.MEX. STATE UNIV, 50-54, assoc. prof, 54-61, PROF, 61- Am. Inst. Chem. Medal, 41. With Off. Sci. Res. & Develop; U.S.A; Nat. Bur. Standards, 44. Am. Chem. Soc. Chlorination; fluorination of chloro compounds; azeotrope distillation as separation method; fluorination with antimony pentafluoride; chlorination of ethers; kinetics; mechanisms. Address: Dept. of Chemistry, New Mexico State University, University Park, NM 88001.

EVANS, LAURIE E(DWARD), b. Unity, Sask, Oct. 14, 33; m. 60; c. 3. CYTOGENETICS, PLANT BREEDING. B.S.A, Saskatchewan, 54; M.Sc, Manitoba, 56, Ph.D.(plant sci, cytogenetics), 59. Res. asst. PLANT SCI, UNIV. MANITOBA, 59-61, res. assoc, 61-63, asst. prof. to ASSOC. PROF, 63- Genetics Soc. Can. Cytogenetics of wheat and related species and triticale improvement. Address: Dept. of Plant Science, College of Agriculture, University of Manitoba, Winnipeg, Man, Can.

EVANS, LAWRENCE B(OYD), b. Ft. Sumner, N.Mex, Oct. 27, 34; m. 63; c. 2. CHEMICAL ENGINEERING. B.S, Univ. Okla, 56; M.S.E, Univ. Mich, 57, Ph.D.(chem. eng), 62. Asst. prof. CHEM. ENG, MASS. INST. TECHNOL, 62-68, ASSOC. PROF, 68- Am. Inst. Chem. Eng; Am. Chem. Soc; Am. Soc. Mech. Eng; Asn. Comput. Mach. Computer aided chemical process analysis; process dynamics and control; applied mathematics; natural convection; radiative, heat and mass transfer. Address: 29 Coolidge Hill Rd, Cambridge, MA 02138.

EVANS, LAWRENCE E(UGENE), b. San Antonio, Tex, Sept. 18, 32; m. 56; c. 2. PHYSICS. B.S, Birmingham-South. Col, 53; Ph.D.(physics), Hopkins, 60. Res. assoc. PHYSICS, Wisconsin, 60-62, instr, 62-63; asst. prof. to ASSOC. PROF, DUKE UNIV, 63- Am. Phys. Soc. Quantum field theory; quantum electrodynamics; theory of elementary particles. Address: Dept. of Physics, Duke University, Durham, NC 27706.

EVANS, L(EE) E, b. Newton, Miss, May 27, 22; m. 48; c. 3. ANIMAL HUSBANDRY. B.S, Alcorn Agr. & Mech. Col, 43; M.S, Iowa State, 47; Ph.D. (animal sci), Illinois, 56. Teacher voc. agr, Newton Voc. Sch, 47-51; dir. dept. agr, Alcorn Agr. & Mech. Col, 51-53; asst, Illinois, 53-55; head dept. ANIMAL HUSB, FLA. A&M UNIV, 55-68, PROF, 68- Organizer & dir, course livestock prods. & improv, Colombia, S.Am, summer, 71. U.S.A.R, 42-48. Am. Soc. Animal Sci; Genetics Soc. Am. Improvement of farm livestock through better methods and techniques of breeding; experimenting with cattle fed crops fertilized with sewage as part of recycling of human waste. Address: Dept. of Animal Science, Florida A&M University, Box 170, Tallahassee, FL 32307.

EVANS, LEONARD, b. London, U.K, Feb. 21, 39; m. 66; c. 2. OPERATIONS RESEARCH, HUMAN FACTORS. B.Sc, Queen's Univ.(Belfast), 60; D.Phil. (physics), Oxford, 65. Fel. physics, div. pure physics, Nat. Res. Coun. Can, 65-67; ASSOC. SR. RES. PHYSICIST, THEORETICAL PHYSICS DEPT, GEN. MOTORS RES. LABS, 67- Opers. Res. Soc. Am. Mathematical modelling; vehicular traffic; driver-vehicle studies; human factors and psychophysics; atomic physics; operations research. Address: Theoretical Physics Dept, General Motors Research Labs, 12 Mile & Mound Rds, Warren, MI 48090.

EVANS, LESTER J, b. Valley Falls, Kans, Mar. 9, 97; m. 21; c. 2. MEDICINE. M.D, Washington (St. Louis), 21; hon. LL.D, Case West. Reserve Univ, 60; hon. D.M.Sc, Mich. State Univ, 71. Med. dir, Child Health Demonstration, N.Dak, 23-27; Commonwealth Fund, 28-59; with Center Rehab. Serv, N.Y. Univ, 59-62; N.Y. State Comn. Med. Ed, 62-64; consult, Illinois, 64-66; Mich. State, 65-69; RETIRED. Expert comt. tech. & prof. ed, WHO, 52-67. AAAS; Am. Pub. Health Asn; Asn. Am. Med. Cols. Medical education and administration. Address: Salisbury, CT 06068.

EVANS, L(LEWELLYN) THOMAS, b. Elizabeth, Colo, Sept. 15, 04; m. 47. ZOOLOGY. A.B, Denver, 25, A.M, 31; Austin fel, Harvard, 34-35, Ph.D. (endocrinol), Harvard, 36. Teacher, pub. sch, Colo, 25-27; asst. prof. & head dept. biol, Robert Col, Istanbul, 27-33; asst. zool, Harvard, 35-36; Nat. Res. Coun. fel, 36-37; asst. prof, Montana, 37-39; Missouri, 39-41; res. assoc, Denver, 41-47; asst. prof. anat, L.I. Col. Med, 48-50; biol. lab, Cold Springs Harbor, L.I, 54; Albert Einstein Col. Med, Yeshiva, 55-59; DIR. RES. LAB, MONADNOCK RES. INST, 59- Curator, Mus. Natural Hist, Denver, 44-47; res. assoc, Am. Mus. Natural Hist, 49-52; Macy Found, 54-55; lectr, Tex. Univ. Centennial, 58; prof. comp. psychol, Keene State Col, 60-65; prof, Franklin Pierce Col, 66- Dir, Exped. to Cent. & West. Mex, 42-44; chmn. ethol. sect, lizard ecol. symp, Missouri, 65. Am. Asn. Anat; Am. Soc. Zool; Am. Soc. Ichthyol. & Herpet. Developmental mechanics; morphology of vertebrates; comparative neurology; evolution of sense organs; evolution of social behavior; endocrine relationships and comparative psychology; anatomy and physiology of vertebrates. Address: Monadnock Research Institute, P.O. Box 453, Jaffrey Center, NH 03454.

EVANS, LLOYD ROBERTS, b. Columbus, Ohio, Nov. 22, 11; m. 40; c. 2. INTERNAL MEDICINE. A.B, Ohio State, 33; M.D, Harvard, 40. Asst. internal med, Peter Bent Brigham Hosp, Boston, Mass, 40-41, house officer, 41-42; instr, Ohio State & res, univ. hosp, 45-47; U.S. Pub. Health Serv. fel, Mass. Gen. Hosp, 47-48; lectr, Univ. Wyo, 52-62; assoc. prof, col. med, Ohio State Univ, 63-68, prof, 68-71, asst. dean, col. med, 63-69, v.provost curriculum, 69-71; private practice. Med.C, 42-45, Maj. Fel. Am. Col. Physicians. Internal medicine; medical education. Address: 208 Garfield, Laramie, WY 82070.

EVANS, LOUIS PETER, b. Marlboro, Mass, Nov. 3, 08; m. 41; c. 2. CHEMICAL ENGINEERING. B.Sc, Mass. Inst. Tech, 31. Chem. engr, Beacon Res. Labs, Texas Co, N.Y, 32-37; RES. DEPT, MOBIL OIL CORP, 38-64, MGR. TECH. TRAINING, 64- Tech. consult, Petrol. Admin. War, 45. AAAS; Am. Soc. Eng. Educ; Am. Inst. Chem. Eng. Petroleum refining; catalytic cracking and reforming; synthetic fuels; shale oil processing; technical training and continuing education. Address: 545 King St, Woodbury, NJ 08096.

EVANS, MARJORIE W(OODARD), b. Denver, Colo, Mar. 15, 21; m. 43; c. 2. PHYSICAL CHEMISTRY. B.A, Colorado, 42; Ph.D.(phys. chem), California, Berkeley, 45. Teaching asst, California, 42-45; res. chemist, Calif. Res. Corp, 45-46; res. assoc, Proj. Squid, N.Y. Univ, 46-49; consult, Princeton, 50-51; res. assoc, Armour Res. Found, 51-53; sr. res. physicist & group head, Stanford Res. Inst, 54-63, dir, Poulter Labs, 64-68, exec. dir. phys. sciences div, 68-69; PARTNER, EVANS ASSOC, 69- Am. Chem. Soc; Am. Phys. Soc; Am. Inst. Aeronaut. & Astronaut; Combustion Inst.(dir, 68-); French Soc. Phys. Chem. Fire, combustion, explosion. Address: 14511 De Bell Dr, Los Altos Hills, CA 94022.

EVANS, MARSHALL P(IERSON), b. Middle River, Minn, July 4, 17; m. 40; c. 2. CROP BREEDING. B.S, Minnesota, 42; M.S, Iowa State Col, 44. Res. assoc. forage crops & instr. crop prod, Iowa State Col, 42-45; plant breeder, Minn. Valley Canning Co, 45-50; mgr. agr. res, GREEN GIANT CO, 50-66, mgr. agron, 66-68, ASST. DIR. AGR. RES. & SEED PROD, 68- Pres, Nat. Sweet Corn Breeders Association, 62-63. Variety development and evaluation; plant pathology and physiology; vegetable crops. Address: Green Giant Co, Le Sueur, MN 56058.

EVANS, MARY JO, b. Maysville, Mo, Nov. 28, 35; m. 68; c. 1. MICROBIOLOGY. B.A, William Jewell Col, 57; M.S, Missouri, 65; Ph.D.(microbiol), Tennessee, 68. Res. asst. virol, Missouri, 57-58, res. fel, 64-65; teaching fel. microbiol, Tennessee, 65-66; trainee virol, St. Jude Children's Res. Hosp, 66-68; cancer res. scientist, ROSWELL PARK MEM. INST, 68-69, SR. CANCER RES. SCIENTIST, 69- Am. Soc. Microbiol. Molecular biology of myxoviruses; neoantigens of cells transformed by deoxyribonucleic acid viruses. Address: Viral Oncology Section, Roswell Park Memorial Institute, 666 Elm St, Buffalo, NY 14203.

EVANS, MICHAEL LEIGH, b. Detroit, Mich, July 26, 41; m. 62; c. 3. BIOLOGY. B.A, Michigan, 63, M.S, 65; California, Berkeley, 66; Ph.D.(biol), California, Santa Cruz, 67. Teaching asst. biol, California Santa Cruz, 65-67; ASST. PROF. Kalamazoo Col, 67-70; BOT, OHIO STATE UNIV, 70- Am. Soc. Plant Physiol; Bot. Soc. Am. Plant growth hormones, especially short-term effects. Address: Dept. of Botany, Ohio State University, Columbus, OH 43210.

EVANS, NOEL DEE, b. Deming, N.Mex, Apr. 9, 40; m. 66. MATHEMATICS. B.A, Texas, Austin, 62, fels, 62-64, Ph.D.(math), 68. ASST. PROF. MATH, ANGELO STATE UNIV, 68- Am. Math. Soc. Functors in categories of banach spaces. Address: Dept. of Mathematics, Angelo State University, San Angelo, TX 76901.

EVANS, NORMAN A(LLEN), b. S.Dak, Dec. 3, 22; m. 44; c. 4. ENGINEERING. B.S, S.Dak. State Col, 44; M.S, Utah State, 47; Ph.D, Colorado State, 63. Asst, col. eng, Utah State, 46-47; asst. prof. agr. eng, N.Dak. Agr. Col, 47-51; asst. civil eng, COLO. STATE UNIV, 51-52, asst. prof, 52-54, assoc. prof, 54-57, AGR. ENG, 57-59, PROF, 59-, DIR. ENVIRON RESOURCES CTR, 67-, ASSOC. DIR. AGR. EXP. STA, 69-, DIR. OFF. GEN. UNIV. RES, 70-, head dept. agr. eng, 57-69. V.chmn, Colo. Water Pollution Control Comn, 70-74; mem. bd. dirs, Engr. Coun. Prof. Develop, 70-72. U.S.A, 44-46, 1st Lt. Fel. AAAS; Am. Soc. Agr. Eng.(v.pres, 68-70); Am. Soc. Eng. Educ; Soil Sci. Soc. Am; Am. Soc. Civil Eng. Fluid mechanics of porous media; drainage; irrigation practices. Address: Colorado State University, Ft. Collins, CO 80521.

EVANS, NORMAN A(RTHUR), b. Crayford, Eng, Dec. 1, 33; m. 57; c. 2. AERONAUTICAL & MECHANICAL ENGINEERING. B.Sc. & A.C.G.I, Univ. London, 57; M.A. & Ph.D.(aeronaut. eng), Princeton, 63. Sr. sci. off, Royal Aircraft Estab, Eng, 63-65; prin. scientist, SPACE SCI. LAB, GEN. ELEC. CO, 65-69, CONSULT, 69-; ASSOC. PROF. MECH. ENG, TOWNE SCH. CIVIL & MECH. ENG, UNIV. PA, 69- Nat. Sci. Found. res. grant, 71-73. R.A.F, 52-54. Am. Inst. Aeronaut. & Astronaut; Am. Soc. Eng. Educ. Ramjet aerodynamics; engine-airframe integration; supersonic boundary layer control; nonequilibrium magnetohydrodynamic power generation; unsteady boundary layers; bluff body vortex shedding; constricted duct flows; laser scattering in random media. Address: Towne School of Civil & Mechanical Engineering, University of Pennsylvania, Philadelphia, PA 19104.

EVANS, RAEFORD G, b. Coleman, Tex, Aug. 20, 19; m. 42; c. 3. AGRONOMY, GENETICS. B.S, Tex. A&M Univ, 41; M.S, Univ. Wyo, 63, Ph.D. (agron), 69. Agronomist, Tex. A&M Univ, 41-44; farm mgr, TARLETON STATE COL, 55-58, instr. AGRON, 59-63, asst. prof, 63-69, ASSOC. PROF, 69- Asst, Univ. Wyo, 66-67. Am. Soc. Agron; Crop Sci. Soc. Am; Am. Genetic Asn; Soil Conserv. Soc. Am. Plant breeding; crop production; weed and range science. Address: 1010 Cleveland, Stephenville, TX 76401.

EVANS, RALPH A(IKEN), b. Oak Park, Ill, Feb. 2, 24. PHYSICS. B.S, Lehigh, 44; Ph.D.(physics), California, 54. Radio engr, centimeter wave sect, Naval Res. Lab, 44-46; physicist, inst. eng. res, California, 47-54; res. physicist, power transmission & mat. handling, Linkbelt Res. Lab, 54-59, dir. res. lab, 59-61; SR. PHYSICIST, RES. TRIANGLE INST, 61- U.S.N.R, 44-45. Am. Phys. Soc; Am. Asn. Physics Teachers; Am. Soc. Metals; Am. Soc. Test. & Mat; sr. mem. Am. Soc. Qual. Control; sr. mem. Inst. Elec. & Electronics Eng.(ed, Trans. on Reliability). Electronics instrumentation; mechanical testing; fatigue; solid state physics; reliability; electronics instrumentation. Address: Research Triangle Institute, P.O. Box 12194, Research Triangle Park, NC 27709.

EVANS, RALPH M(ERRILL), b. Haverhill, Mass, May 30, 05; m. 29; c. 3. PHYSICS. B.S, Mass. Inst. Tech, 29. Mem. staff, Twentieth Century-Fox Film Corp, 29-33; DeLuxe Labs, Inc, 33-35; Eastman Kodak Co, 35-45, supt, color control dept, 45-53, dir. photog. tech. div, 53-70; RETIRED. Life fel. Soc. Motion Picture & TV Eng.(Warner Medal, 49, Progress Medal, 57, H.T. Kalmus Medal, 61); life fel. Optical Soc. Am; hon. mem. Inter-Soc. Color Coun.(secy, 51-70, Godlove Award, 59, spec. citation, 70). Visual psychology of color and of color photography. Address: 431 Thomas Ave, Rochester, NY 14617.

EVANS, RAND B(OYD), b. Baytown, Tex, Feb. 20, 42; m. 63; c. 3. PSYCHOLOGY. B.A, Texas, 63, M.A, 64, John W. Dallenbach fel. & Ph.D.(exp. psychol), 67. Asst. prof. PSYCHOL, WRIGHT STATE UNIV, 67-70, ASSOC. PROF, 70- Res. grant, Wilhelm Wundt Arch, Leipzig, Ger, 68-69. AAAS; Int. Soc. Hist. Behav. & Social Sci; Hist. Sci. Soc; Am. Psychol. Asn; Acoustical Soc. Am. Psychophysics of sensory systems; methodology in psychological research; ageing and motor processes; history of psychology; psychoacoustics. Address: Dept. of Psychology, Wright State University, Dayton, OH 45431.

EVANS, RAYMOND A(RTHUR), b. Albuquerque, N.Mex, Mar. 31, 25; m. 50; c. 1. PLANT ECOLOGY. A.B, Univ. Redlands, 50; Ph.D, Univ. Calif, 56. Asst. specialist rangeland soils & plants, Univ. Calif, 54-58; RANGE SCIENTIST WEED INVESTS. ON GRAZING LANDS, PLANT SCI. RES. DIV, AGR. RES. SERV, U.S. DEPT. AGR, 58- U.S.A, 43-45. AAAS; Ecol. Soc. Am; Soc. Range Mgt; Weed Sci. Soc. Am. Range weed control and revegetation; competition studies involving range weeds and forage species emphasizing factors of soil moisture, temperature and nutrients; utilization of field, greenhouse and laboratory techniques; employment of microenvironmental monitoring. Address: Renewable Resources Center, University of Nevada, 920 Valley Rd, Reno, NV 89502.

EVANS, RICHARD C(ASTLEMAN), b. Salisbury, Md, Nov. 8, 16; m. 47; c. 3. CHEMISTRY. B.S, George Washington, 38, A.M, 40; Ph.D.(org. chem), Hopkins, 43. Lab. asst, George Washington, 38-39; jr. instr, Hopkins, 39-42, res. chemist, Nat. Defense Res. Comt. contract, 42-46; chemist, Ballistic Res. Lab, Md, 46-47; res. chemist, Catalyst Res. Corp, 47-52; asst. res. & develop. mgr, elec. div, Olin Mathieson Chem. Corp, Conn, 52-56, mgr. electrochem. res. dept, 56-61; SR. CHEMIST, APPL. PHYSICS LAB, JOHNS HOPKINS UNIV, 61- N.Y. Acad. Sci; Am. Chem. Soc; Electrochem. Soc. Synthesis of organic nitrogen compounds; synthesis and reactions of metallic carbonyls; reactions of gases under high pressure; the pyridazine series; ultraviolet absorption spectrum of pyridazine; electrochemistry of fused salts; thermal batteries; evaporation of metals; pyrotechnics; thermal, dry and space batteries; thermoelectricity. Address: 14514 Manor Park Dr, Rockville, MD 20853.

EVANS, RICHARD T(ODD), b. Evanston, Ill, Oct. 2, 32; m. 69; c. 2. MICROBIOLOGY, IMMUNOLOGY. A.B, Cent. Methodist Col, 54; M.S, Missouri, 59, Ph.D.(microbiol), 63. Asst. microbiol, Missouri, 57-59, asst. instr, 59-62, U.S. Pub. Health Serv. fel, 62-63; Am. Dent. Asn. res. assoc, Nat. Insts. Health, 63-66; ASST. PROF. ORAL BIOL, SCH. DENT, STATE UNIV. N.Y. BUFFALO, 66-, DIR. GRAD. STUDIES ORAL BIOL, 70- Med.C, U.S.A, 55-57. AAAS; Am. Soc. Microbiol; N.Y. Acad. Sci. Immunochemistry of bacterial antigens; host-parasite relationships of periodontal disease; enzyme-antienzyme interactions; microbiology of dental caries. Address: Dept. of Oral Biology, School of Dentistry, State University of New York at Buffalo, 4510 Main St, Buffalo, NY 14226.

EVANS, ROBERT B, III, b. New Orleans, La, Sept. 24, 23; m. 42; c. 3. PHYSICAL CHEMISTRY. B.S, Agr. & Mech. Col, Tex, 49, M.S, 50, Ph.D. (chem), 55. Assoc. technologist, Tex. Petrol. Res. Comt, Tex, 51-54; res. engr. well completion prod. probs, Pan Am. Petrol. Corp, 54-57; CHEMIST, UNION CARBIDE CORP, 57- U.S.A.A.F, 42-45, Capt. Am. Chem. Soc; Am. Inst. Min, Metall. & Petrol. Eng. Corrosion; fused salts; gaseous state; fluid flow; diffusion; structure and properties of gases. Address: Reactor Chemistry Division, Oak Ridge National Lab, P.O. Box 10, Oak Ridge, TN 37831.

EVANS, ROBERT JOHN, b. Logan, Utah, Mar. 18, 09; m. 41; c. 2. BIOCHEMISTRY. B.S, Utah State, 34, M.S, 36; Ph.D.(biochem), Wisconsin, 39. Instr. chem. & physics, Carbon Col, 39-40; asst. poultryman, exp. sta, Wash. State, 40-42, asst. chemist, 42-44, assoc. chemist, 44-47; PROF. agr. chem, MICH. STATE UNIV: 47-61, BIOCHEM, 61- Res. proj, Cambridge, 63-64; Univ. Col. London, Univ. Edinburgh, Rowett Res. Inst. & Univ. Cambridge, 71. Res. achievement award, Poultry & Egg Nat. Bd, 58. AAAS; Am. Chem. Soc. Am. Inst. Nutrit; Poultry Sci. Asn. Biochemistry of eggs; chemistry of proteins and amino acids; mineral metabolism; sulfur amino acids in biochemistry and nutrition; influence of hen's diet on composition of eggs; egg yolk lipo-proteins; seed proteins; fatty acid metabolism of laying hens. Address: Dept. of Biochemistry, Michigan State University, East Lansing, MI 48823.

EVANS, ROBERT J(OHN), b. Osage City, Kans, Mar. 18, 28; m. 51; c. 2. ORGANIC CHEMISTRY. B.Sc, Nebraska, 51; Rutgers; Nat. Sci. Found. fel, Washington, 58-59, Ph.D.(chem), 59. Org. chemist, Merck & Co, N.J, 51-54; hydrocarbons div, Monsanto Co, 59-66, asst. prof. CHEM, ILL. COL, 66-68, ASSOC. PROF, 68- Med.C, U.S.A, 54-56. Am. Chem. Soc; Brit. Chem. Soc. Oxidation of organic compounds. Address: Dept. of Chemistry, Illinois College, Jacksonville, IL 62650.

EVANS, ROBERT L, b. Phila, Pa, Apr. 30, 25; m. 46; c. 2. INTERNAL MEDICINE, MEDICAL EDUCATION. M.D, Jefferson Med. Col, 52. Instr. med, Jefferson Med. Col, 56-60; dir. med. educ, York Hosp, York, Pa, 60-65; assoc. prof. med, col. med, Univ. Md, 65-70, asst. dean med, 67-70; PROF. MED. & DEAN ROCKFORD SCH. MED, UNIV. ILL. COL. MED, 71- V.pres. med. affairs, York Hosp, York, Pa, 65-70; mem, Pres. Comn. Health Manpower, 66-68; consult, adminrs. med. panel, Fed. Aviation Agency, 68-; mem. bd. trustees, Educ. Coun. Foreign Med. Grads, 69-; Thomas Jefferson Univ, 71- U.S.A, 43-46, T/Sgt. AAAS; Am. Med. Asn; N.Y. Acad. Sci; Asn. Hosp. Med. Educ.(secy-treas, v.pres, pres, 66-68); Soc. Teachers Family Med. Medical care delivery, especially quality of care evaluation and its relationship to continuing education; impact of graduate and under graduate education on medical care delivery systems and costs. Address: 1601 Parkview Ave, Rockford, IL 61101.

EVANS, ROBERT L(EONARD), b. Duluth, Minn, May 30, 17; m. 41, 57; c. 3. MATHEMATICAL BIOLOGY. B.Ch, Minnesota, 38, M.S, 39, Ph.D.(math, phys. chem), 51. Assoc. metallurgist, hydrometal, U.S. Bur. Mines, 40-44; res. assoc. internal ballistics, Allegany Ballistics Lab, 44-45; instr. math. & mech, UNIV. MINN, MINNEAPOLIS, 45-54, asst. prof. PHYSIOL, 54-63, LECTR, 63-, asst. prof, biostatistics, 63-68, assoc. prof. biometry, 68-71. AAAS; Am. Math. Soc; Am. Chem. Soc. Quantitative biology; red cell survival and sludging; kinetics of ion diffusion: reaction and transport; pulsatile liquid flow; tissue mechanics and indicator dilution. Address: Dept. of Physiology, University of Minnesota, Minneapolis, MN 55455.

EVANS, ROBERT MELVIN, b. New Lexington, Ohio, Jan. 27, 14; m. 41; c. 2. METALLURGY. B.S, Ohio State, 43. From jr. asst. to technician, bur. agr. eng. & soil conserv. serv, U.S. Dept. Agr, 37-39; res. engr, BATTELLE MEM. INST, 43-64, SR. ENGR, 64-, METALS JOINING DIV, 53- Special alloy development; special lubricants for metal fabrication; information analysis; metals joining. Address: Battelle Memorial Institute, 505 King Ave, Columbus, OH 43210.

EVANS, ROBERT MORTON, b. Cleveland, Ohio, Oct. 28, 17; m. 42, 65; c. 4. POLYMER CHEMISTRY. B.S, Antioch Col, 41; Ph.D.(chem), Case West. Reserve Univ, 59. V.PRES. RES. & ENG, MAMECO INT, 45-; PRES. & FOUNDER, ISONETICS INC, 70- Res. assoc, Case Inst. Technol, 60-61; pres, Prog. Design, Inc, 67-70; mem. res. adv. comt, Fedn. Socs. Paint Technol. Roon Award, 64. Am. Soc. Test. & Mat; Fedn. Socs. Paint Technol; N.Y. Acad. Sci; fel. Am. Inst. Chem. Specialty coatings and adhesives; sealants and flooring materials; all polymeric and some organic-inorganic alloys. Address: Research & Engineering, Mameco International, 4475 E. 175th St, Cleveland, OH 44128.

EVANS, ROBERT RALPH, b. Denver, Colo, Mar. 25, 39; m. 62; c. 2. VERTEBRATE ZOOLOGY. B.S, Univ. Colo, Boulder, 62; A.M, Boston Univ, 65, Nat. Sci. Found. fel, 67-69, Ph.D.(biol), 69. Instr. biol, COMMUNITY COL. DENVER, 69-70, DIR. DIV. SCI. & MATH, 70- AAAS; Am. Soc. Zool; Am. Soc. Ichthyol. & Herpet; Nat. Asn. Biol. Teachers. Sound producing mechanisms in marine fishes. Address: 2520 Albion, Denver, CO 80207.

EVANS, ROBERT S(HERMAN), b. Seattle, Wash, May 29, 12; m. 41; c. 3. MEDICAL SCIENCES. B.S, Washington (Seattle), 34; M.D, Harvard, 38. Intern med, Boston City Hosp, 38-39, asst. res, 40-41; Thorndike Mem. Lab, Harvard, 40-41; hosps, Stanford, 41-42, instr. MED, sch. med, 42-46, asst. prof, 46-48, assoc. prof, 48-51; SCH. MED, UNIV. WASH, 51-59, PROF, 59-; CHIEF, VET. ADMIN. HOSP, 51- Am. Fedn. Clin. Res; Am. Soc. Clin. Invest; Asn. Am. Physicians. Hematological disorders. Address: Veterans Administration Hospital, 4435 Beacon Ave, Seattle, WA 98108.

EVANS, ROBERT W, b. Columbia Co, Wis, Aug. 21, 19; m. 49; c. 4. PHYSICAL CHEMISTRY, PHYSICS. B.S, Wisconsin, 41, M.S, 49, Ph.D.(phys. chem), 51. Asst. chem, Wisconsin, 46-51; instr, Colo. Sch. Mines, 51-52; res. chemist, mech. div, Denver Res. Inst, Denver, 52-63, sr. res. chemist, 64-69; MEM. STAFF, ORD. DIV, ATLANTIC RES. CORP, 69- U.S.A.F, 42-46, Res, 46-, Lt. Col. AAAS; Am. Chem. Soc; Am. Astronaut. Soc; Am. Ord. Asn. High energy chemical reactions; explosives; pyrotechnics; kinetics; photochemistry; thermodynamics; infrared; damage mechanisms; photosynthesis. Address: Ordnance Division, Atlantic Research Corp, 7511 Wellington Rd, Gainesville, VA 22314.

EVANS, ROBLEY D(UNGLISON), b. University Place, Nebr, May 18, 07; m. 28; c. 3. PHYSICS. B.S, Calif. Inst. Technol, 28, M.S, 29, Ph.D.(physics), 32. Asst. eng, Calif. Inst. Technol, 28, hist, 27-30, 31-32, teaching fel. physics, 29-32; Nat. Res. Coun. fel, Univ. Calif, 32-34; asst. prof, MASS. INST. TECHNOL, 34-38, assoc. prof, 38-45, PROF. PHYSICS & DIR. RADIOACTIVITY CTR, 45- Dir. res. lab, C.F. Braun Co, Calif, 29-31; mem. comt. radiation protection, Mass. Inst. Technol, 55-, comt. radioisotope utilization & adv. med. dept, 59-, clin. res. ctr. policy comt, 64-; vis. prof, Ariz. State Univ, 66-67. Consult, Off. Sci. Res. & Develop, 44-46; Peter Bent Brigham Hosp, 45-, mem. isotopes comt, 64-; consult, U.S. Dept. State, 46-47; U.S. Dept. Army, 47-49, Surgeon Gen, 62-69; Brookhaven Nat. Lab, 47-55, mem. vis. comn. med. dept, 65-68; consult, Los Alamos Sci. Lab, 48-64; Mass. Gen. Hosp, 48-, mem. comt. isotopes, 50-; consult, U.S. Secy. Defense, 49-54; Walter Reed Army Med. Ctr, 49-56;

Atomic Energy Comn, 50-, mem. adv. comt. isotope distribution, 48-53, chmn, 52-53; consult, U.S. Naval Radiol. Defense Lab, 52-69; U.S. Pub. Health Serv, 61-; adv, Univ. Chicago & mem. res. comt, radiol. physics div, Argonne Nat. Lab, 64-68, chmn, 67-68; coun. mem, Nat. Comt. Radiation Protection & Measurements, 65-71; consult, Fed. Radiation Coun, 65-69; Roger Williams Hosp, 65-; Fed. Aviation Agency, 67, chmn. standing comt. radiation biol. aspects of supersonic transport, 67. Chmn. comt. standards radioactivity, Nat. Res. Coun, 38-46, subcomt. shipment radioactive substances & v.chmn. comt. nuclear sci, 46-; chmn, Int. Conf. Appl. Nuclear Physics, 40; mem. adv. comt. safe handling radioactive luminous compounds, Nat. Bur. Standards, 41, consult, 60, mem. adv. panel on radiation physics, 63-66, chmn, 64; mem. mixed comn. radiobiol, Int. Union Pure & Appl. Physics, 47-53; joint comn. standards, units & constants radioactivity, Int. Coun. Sci. Unions, 48-51, joint comn. radioactivity, 51-55; Aircraft Nuclear Propulsion Med. Adv. Group, 53-55; adv. comt. rules & regulations radiation protection, Mass. Dept. Labor & Industs, 57-; subcomt. rel. hazard factors, Nat. Comt. Radiation Protection & Measurements, 57-; subcomt. symbols, units & nomenclature, comt. nuclear sci, Nat. Acad. Sci-Nat. Res. Coun, 62-67, panel adv. to Nat. Bur. Standards, 63, chmn, 64; mem. ad hoc adv. comt. radiation path, Armed Forces Inst. Path, 62-64; sci. adv. bd, cancer res. inst, New Eng. Deaconess Hosp, 63-69; chmn. task group high energy & space radiation dosimetry, Int. Comn. Radiol. Units & Measurements, 64-67; sr. U.S. del, Int. Asn. Radiation Res, 66; mem. comt. radioactive waste mgt, Nat. Acad. Sci, 68-70; v.chmn. adv. comt, U.S. Transuranium Registry, 68-; mem. tech. adv. comt, Ariz. Atomic Energy Comn, 71- Presidential Cert. Merit, 48; dipl, Am. Bd. Health Physics, 61; Hull Gold Medal, Am. Med. Asn, 63; Silvanus Thompson Award & Medal, Brit. Inst. Radiol, 66. Fel. AAAS (Theobald Smith Medal, 37); fel. Am. Phys. Soc; fel. Am. Acad. Arts & Sci; Am. Asn. Physics Teachers; Am. Nuclear Soc; Am. Asn. Physicists in Med; Am. Indust. Hyg. Asn; Health Physics Soc.(pres-elect, 71); Radiation Res. Soc. (ed, Radiation Res, 59-, v.pres, 65-66, pres, 66-67); assoc. Am. Roentgen Ray Soc; fel. N.Y. Acad. Sci; hon. for. mem. Swedish Royal Soc. Arts & Sci. Radioactivity; radioactive tracers in engineering and biology; geological age measurement by radioactivity; instrumentation; biological effects of radiation; pure and applied nuclear physics. Address: Room 6-209, Massachusetts Institute of Technology, 77 Massachusetts Ave, Cambridge, MA 02139.

EVANS, ROGER JAMES, b. Oxford, Eng. STRUCTURAL ENGINEERING, SOLID MECHANICS. B.Sc, Birmingham, 55; Sc.M, Brown, 59; Ph.D.(struct. eng), California, Berkeley, 65. Lectr. civil eng, Birmingham, 59-61; preceptor, civil eng. dept, Columbia Univ, 65-66; ASST. PROF. CIVIL ENG, UNIV. WASH, 66- R.A.F, 55-57, Flying Officer. Theory of elasticity; elastic wave propagation; geophysical problems including rheological behavior of ice and seismic phenomena. Address: Dept. of Civil Engineering, University of Washington, Seattle, WA 98105.

EVANS, ROGER L(YNWOOD), b. Ipswich, Eng, June 25, 28; m. 54; c. 3. INORGANIC CHEMISTRY. B.A, Oxford, 52, M.A, 55, D.Phil.(natural sci), 58; M.S, Minnesota, 55. SR. CHEMIST, cent. res. labs, MINN. MINING & MFG. CO, 58-67, NUCLEAR PROD. LAB, 3M CTR, 67- Brit. Army, 46-49, 2nd Lt. Am. Chem. Soc; Soc. Nuclear Med. Elements of periodic groups III and IV; polymer chemistry; radiopharmaceuticals. Address: Nuclear Products Lab, 3M Center, Minnesota Mining & Manufacturing Co, St. Paul, MN 55101.

EVANS, ROGER MALCOLM, b. Coronation, Alta, May 27, 35. ZOOLOGY. B.Sc, Alberta, 60, M.Sc, 61; Ph.D.(behavior of gulls), Wisconsin, 66. ASST. PROF. ZOOL, UNIV. MANITOBA, 66- Am. Ornith. Union; Animal Behavior Soc. Development of behavior and communication in Precocial birds; behavioral aspects of population control. Address: Dept. of Zoology, University of Manitoba, Winnipeg, Man, Can.

EVANS, RONALD DALE, b. Lanagan, Mo, Aug. 15, 33; m. 52; c. 4. MECHANICAL ENGINEERING, APPLIED PHYSICS. B.S, E.Cent. State Col, 56; Nat. Sci. Found. Summer Insts, Oklahoma Baptist, 59 & West Texas State, 60; Nat. Sci. Found. fels, Arizona State, 60-61, 65-68, M.N.S, 62, M.S, 67, Ph.D.(mech. eng, math, physics), 68. Teacher, high sch, Tex, 58-61; Ariz, 61-62; physicist, Motorola, Inc, summer 62; field engr, Schlumberger Well Surv. Corp, Okla, 62-63; systs. engr, Sperry Syroscope Co, N.Y, 63-64; analyst, RCA Serv. Co, Fla. 64-65; asst. prof. eng, FLA. TECHNOL. UNIV, 68-69, ASSOC. PROF. MECH. ENG. & AEROSPACE SCI. & CHMN. DEPT, 69- AAAS; Am. Soc. Mech. Eng; Inst. Elec. & Electronics Eng; Am. Inst. Aeronaut. & Astronaut. Radiation gas dynamics; inertial navigation and guidance systems; magneto fluid dynamics; Laser-Doppler techniques in turbulent flow; applied mathematics; bio-fluid mechanics. Address: Dept. of Mechanical Engineering & Aerospace Science, Florida Technological University, P.O. Box 25000, Orlando, FL 32816.

EVANS, R(USSELL) STUART, b. Saskatoon, Sask, Nov. 18, 23; m. 45; c. 3. WOOD CHEMISTRY. B.A, British Columbia, 49, Powell River Pulp & Paper fel, 49-51, M.A, 51; Ph.D.(org. chem), Saskatchewan, 56. Res. chemist plant residue chem, Prairie Regional Lab, Nat. Res. Coun. Can, 51-56; wood chem. & tech, Rayonier Can. Ltd, 56-59, group leader, 59-61, sect. leader, east. res. div, Rayonier Inc, 61-65; MGR. CELLULOSE RES. DEPT, COLUMBIA CELLULOSE CO, LTD, 65- R.C.N, 41-45. Am. Chem. Soc. Wood and fiber chemistry and technology; plant and microbiological chemistry; industrial chemistry of cellulose, lignin and wood extractives. Address: Columbia Cellulose Co, Ltd, Technical Centre, 1111 W. Hastings St, Vancouver 1, B.C, Can.

EVANS, SHELDON, b. Brooklyn, N.Y, June 24, 31; m. 60. PHYSICAL CHEMISTRY. B.S, Queens Col.(N.Y), 53; M.S, N.Y, Univ, 55, Ph.D.(phys. chem), 59. Asst, N.Y. Univ, 53-55; instr. gen. chem, Brooklyn Col, 58-59; res. metallurgist electrochem, cent. res. & eng, Continental Can Co, 59-61; res. specialist electrochem, Rocketdyne Div, N.Am. Rockwell Corp, Calif, 61-70; SUPVR. ION EXCHANGE LAB, NEGEV INST. ARID ZONE RES, ISRAEL, 70- Israel Chem. Soc; Electrochem. Soc. Electrochemistry; corrosion. Address: Negev Institute for Arid Zone Research, P.O. Box 1025, Beersheba, Israel.

EVANS, S(ILAS) M(cAFEE), b. Madison, Wis, Aug. 4, 10; m. 36; c. 4. EXPERIMENTAL MEDICINE. B.A, Ripon Col, 30; M.D, Wisconsin, 36. Asst. dir. extramural educ. med, Wisconsin, 45-47; jr. consult, Vet. Admin. Hosp, Milwaukee, 46-48; ASST. CLIN. PROF. MED, MARQUETTE UNIV, 69-; CHIEF MED. SERV, MILWAUKEE HOSP, 53- Mem. med. staff, Columbia & Milwaukee Children's Hosps; coun. arteriosclerosis, Am. Heart Asn. Med.C, U.S.A, 43-45. Am. Thoracic Soc; Am. Fedn. Clin. Res; Am. Med. Asn. Arteriosclerosis and fibrotic reactions. Address: 811 E. Wisconsin Ave, Milwaukee, WI 53202.

EVANS, SLAYTON ALVIN, JR, b. Chicago, Ill, May 17, 43; m. 67. ORGANIC CHEMISTRY. B.S, Tougaloo Col, 65; Ill. Inst. Technol, 65-66; Nat. Sci. Found. summer traineeship, Case West. Reserve Univ, 67, M.S, 68, Ph.D. (chem), 70. Res. chemist, Abbott Labs, summers 64 & 65; asst. instr. & fel. CHEM, Univ. Tex, Arlington, 69-70; TEACHING FEL, UNIV. NOTRE DAME, 70- AAAS; Am. Chem. Soc. Stereochemical and conformational investigations of sulfur containing heterocycles with nuclear magnetic resonance, infrared and ultraviolet spectroscopy; synthesis and mechanistic investigations of cyclic heterocycles. Address: Dept. of Chemistry, University of Notre Dame, Notre Dame, IN 46556.

EVANS, STANFORD KENT, b. Salt Lake City, Utah, June 30, 39; m. 62; c. 1. CERAMIC ENGINEERING, SOLID STATE PHYSICS. B.A, Utah, 61, fel, 64-65, Ph.D.(ceramic eng), 66. Ceramist, plutonium fuels develop, NUCLEONICS LAB, GEN. ELEC. CO, 65-70, TECH. SPECIALIST, PLUTONIUM RES. LAB, 70- Ord.C, 61-62, Res, 62-, 1st Lt. Am. Ceramic Soc; Am. Nuclear Soc. Thermodynamic and physical properties of uranium and plutonium oxides; transient irradiations of nuclear fuels; fuel-fission product-cladding interactions and fuel-coolant interactions in fast breeder reactors. Address: Nucleonics Lab, General Electric Co, P.O. Box 846, Pleasanton, CA 94566.

EVANS, T(AYLOR) H(ERBERT), b. Edmonton, Alta, Mar. 22, 18; m. 43; c. 4. ORGANIC CHEMISTRY. B.Sc, Alberta, 37, M.Sc, 38, Nat. Res. Coun. Can. bursar & student, 38-39, 39-40; Can. Pulp & Paper Asn. Scholar, McGill, 40-41, Ph.D.(chem), 41. Sessional lectr. chem, McGill, 41-43; res. chemist, res. labs, Dominion Rubber Co, Ltd, 43-59, mgr. mkt. res, Naugatuck Chem. Div, 59-62, econ. develop. dept, 62-64, develop. dept, 64-68, TECH. SPECIALIST, GUELPH RES. LABS, UNIROYAL LTD, 68- Fel. Chem. Inst. Can. Dextran; lignin; vapor phase dehydration reactions; liquid phase oxidation reactions; organic phosphorus compounds; pharmaceuticals; industrial organic chemicals. Address: 38 Suffolk St. W, Guelph, Ont, Can.

EVANS, TED RAYMOND, b. Klamath Falls, Ore, Apr. 30, 39; m. 64; c. 2. PHYSICAL ORGANIC CHEMISTRY. B.S, Oregon, 62; Ph.D.(chem), Rochester, 66. Fel. chem, Wesleyan, 66-69; SR. CHEMIST, EASTMAN KODAK CO, 69- Am. Chem. Soc. Photochemistry; free radical and sulfur chemistry; organometallics. Address: Research Labs, Eastman Kodak Co, Bldg. 82, Rochester, NY 14650.

EVANS, THOMAS E(DWARD), b. Springfield, Vt, July 22, 39; m. 66; c. 1. MOLECULAR BIOLOGY. B.A, DePauw, 61; Ph.D.(biol), Case Western Reserve, 67. ASST. PROF. RADIOL. & MICROBIOL, CASE WEST. RESERVE UNIV, 67- AAAS; Am. Soc. Microbiol. Nucleic acid metabolism in eukaryotes, especially as related to nuclear division cycles; nonnuclear DNA metabolism. Address: Division of Radiation Biology, Wearn Bldg, Case Western Reserve University, Cleveland, OH 44106.

EVANS, THOMAS F(REDERICK), b. New York, N.Y, Oct. 18, 24; m. 59. CHEMICAL ENGINEERING. B.S, Washington (Seattle), 45; Ph.D.(chem. eng), Princeton, 50. Res. engr, Textile Res. Inst, 50-53; develop. engr, Gen. Elec. Co, 53-63; assoc. prof, Colombia, 63-64; Fulbright lectr, Univ. Seville, 64-65; asst. prof. chem. eng, Pa. State Univ, 65-71; CHEM. DESIGN ENGR, NIAGARA MOHAWK POWER CORP, 71- Am. Nuclear Soc; Am. Chem. Soc; Am. Inst. Chem. Eng. Nuclear energy; power generation; environmental control. Address: 4 Seminary St, Cazenovia, NY 13035.

EVANS, THOMAS G(EORGE), b. Taylor, Pa, Feb. 16, 34. MATHEMATICS, COMPUTER SCIENCE. B.A, Princeton, 55; Ph.D.(math), Mass. Inst. Technol, 63. RES. MATHEMATICIAN, U.S. AIR FORCE CAMBRIDGE RES. LABS, 62- Asn. Comput. Mach; Am. Math. Soc; Math. Asn. Am. Heuristic programming approach to artificial intelligence, emphasizing description and processing of complex patterns; development of facilities for convenient conversational use of computers, especially for program debugging. Address: U.S. Air Force Cambridge Research Labs, L.G. Hanscom Field, Bedford, MA 01730.

EVANS, T(HOMAS) H(AYHURST), b. Los Angeles, Calif, Apr. 8, 06; m. 45; c. 3. CIVIL ENGINEERING. B.S, Calif. Inst. Tech, 29, M.S, 30; summer, Carnegie Inst. Tech, 32, Michigan, 35-38. Instr. eng. mech, eng. sch, Yale, 30-35; asst. prof. civil eng. & mech, Virginia, 35-38, assoc. prof, 38-42, dir, eng. sci, mgt. & war training, 40-42; prof. civil eng. & dir, SCH. ENG, Ga. Tech, 45-49; DEAN, Colorado State, 49-63; FRESNO STATE COL, 63- First dean, Asian Inst. Technol, Bangkok, Thailand, 59-61. Eng.C, 42-45, Col. Am. Soc. Civil Eng; Am. Soc. Eng. Educ; Nat. Soc. Prof. Eng; Am. Soc. Mech. Eng; Inst. Elec. & Electronics Eng. Mechanics of plates; structural stresses; city planning; administration of engineering education and research. Address: Engineering School, Fresno State College, Fresno CA 93710.

EVANS, THOMAS P(ASSMORE), b. West Grove, Pa, Aug. 19, 21; m. 47; c. 4. ELECTRICAL ENGINEERING. B.S, Swarthmore Col, 42; M.Eng, Yale, 48. Engr, atomic power div, Westinghouse Elec. Corp, Pa, 48-51; chief systs. engr. res. & develop, Am. Mach. & Foundry Co, N.Y, 51-54, dept. dir, 54-56, dir, 56-60; res, O.M. Scott & Sons Co, Ohio, 60-62; res. & develop, W.A. Sheaffer Pen Co, 62-65, v.pres. res. & develop, 65-67; DIR. RES, MICH. TECHNOL. UNIV, 67- U.S.N, 43-46, Lt. Inst. Elec. & Electronics Eng; Soc. Plastics Eng; Am. Phys. Soc; Am. Forestry Asn; Am. Ord. Asn. Management of research and development, nuclear power plants and reactor shielding; solar energy; water conversion; servomechanisms; electrical power generation. Address: Michigan Technological University, Houghton, MI 49931.

EVANS, THOMAS REESE, b. Scranton, Pa, Dec. 10, 31; m. 57; c. 4. RADIO ENGINEERING. B.S, Maryland, 54, M.S, 62. Electronic engr, Naval Air Test Center, 54-55; assoc. engr, Ord. Eng. Corp, 55-56; intermediate engr, Develop. Eng. Corp, 56-57; engr, Jansky & Bailey, Inc, 57-61; sr. engr, propagations systs. study, White Electromagnetics, Inc, 61-62, staff scientist, 62; sr. engr, Booz Allen Appl. Res, Inc, 62-63, proj. engr, 63-64, res. dir, 64-69; MEM. SR. STAFF, APPL. PHYSICS LAB, JOHNS HOPKINS UNIV, 69- Lectr, Maryland, 60-61. Development of specialized antennas for aviation and communication usage; radio wave propagation; radio systems engineering; system analysis and operations research in military communications. Address: The Applied Physics Lab, Johns Hopkins University, 8621 Georgia Ave, Silver Spring, MD 20910.

EVANS, THOMAS RICHARD, b. Cleveland, Ohio, May 5, 41; m. 68. PHYSIOLOGICAL PSYCHOLOGY. B.S.S, John Carroll, 63; Ph.D.(psychol), Texas, Austin, 67. Engr-scientist & psychologist, Tracor, Inc, 65-67, group dir, sensory info. res. lab, 67-69, head dept. PSYCHOL, 69-70; CHMN. DEPT, JOHN CARROLL UNIV, 70- Spec. instr, St. Edward's Univ. & Univ. Tex, Austin, 67-68; consult. physiol. psychol, med. instruments div, Tracor, Inc, 67-69. U.S.M.C, 59-65. AAAS; Am. Psychol. Asn. Neurophysiological correlates of emotional behavior; psychopharmacology; sensory processing by the human nervous system; behavior modification. Address: 1544 Clubside Rd, Cleveland, OH 44124.

EVANS, THOMAS W(ALTER), b. Tioga, N.Dak, May 27, 23; m. 45; c. 2. PHYSICAL CHEMISTRY. B.S, N.Dak. State, 47; Du Pont Co. Grant-in-aid, Wisconsin, 50-52, Ph.D.(phys. chem), 52. Metallurgist, Hanford Works, Gen. Elec. Co, 52-56, sr. engr, Hanford Atomic Prods. Oper, 56-67; res. assoc, Pac. Northwest Labs, Battelle Mem. Inst, 67-68, prog. consult, 68, assoc. dept. mgr, fast flux test facility div, 68-70; STAFF CONSULT, WADCO CORP, WESTINGHOUSE ELEC. CORP, 70- U.S.A.F, 43-45, Res, 45-53, 2nd Lt. AAAS; Am. Soc. Metals; Am. Nuclear Soc. X-ray crystallography; physical metallurgy of uranium; irradiation damage; volcanology; design, development and testing of thermal and fast reactor fuel elements. Address: Wadco Corp, P.O. Box 1970, Richland, WA 99352.

EVANS, TITUS C(ARR), b. Lorena, Tex, Dec. 9, 07; m; c. 3. RADIATION BIOLOGY. B.A, Baylor, 29; M.S, Iowa, 31, Ph.D.(zool), 34. Asst. zool, Iowa, 29-34, res. assoc, 34-36; asst. prof, Texas A&M, 36-38; res. asst. prof. radiol, Univ. Iowa, 38-43; asst. prof, Columbia Univ, 43-48; res. prof. radiol. & radiobiol, COL. MED, UNIV. IOWA, 48-69, PROF. RADIATION RES. & RADIOL, 69-, HEAD RADIATION RES. LAB, 48- AAAS; Soc. Nuclear Med.(pres, 60-61, ed, J. Nuclear Med); Am. Soc. Zool; Soc. Exp. Biol. & Med; Am. Asn. Cancer Res; Am. Roentgen Ray Soc; Radiation Res. Soc. (ed, Radiation Res); Soc. Gen. Physiol; N.Y. Acad. Sci; Fedn. Am. Socs. Exp. Biol. Effect of x-rays on embryonic development and cell division; modification of radiosensitivity; application of radioisotopes to biological and medical studies; relative biological effectiveness of fast neutrons. Address: Radiation Research Lab, College of Medicine, University of Iowa, IA 52241.

EVANS, TOMMY N(ICHOLAS), b. Batesville, Ark, Apr. 12, 22; m. 45; c. 1. MEDICINE. A.B, Baylor, 42; M.D, Vanderbilt, 45. Instr. OBSTET. & GYNECOL, Michigan, 49-53, asst. prof, 53-56, assoc. prof, 56-60, prof, 60-65; PROF. & CHMN. DEPT, SCH. MED, WAYNE STATE UNIV, 65-, ACTING DEAN, 70- Consult, Vet. Admin. Hosp, 56- Dipl, Am. Bd. Obstet. & Gynec. Med.C, 46-48, Lt.(jg). Am. Med. Asn; Am. Col. Surg; Am. Col. Obstet. & Gynec; Am. Asn. Obstet. & Gynec; Am. Gynec. Soc. Human reproduction; gynecologic endocrinology; obstetrics and gynecology. Address: Dept. of Gynecology & Obstetrics, Hutzel Hospital, 432 E. Hancock St, Detroit, MI 48201.

EVANS, TREVOR, b. Wolverhampton, Eng, Dec. 22, 25; m. 53; c. 4. MATHEMATICS. B.A, Jesus Col, Oxford, 46, M.A, 50; M.Sc, Manchester Univ, 48; D.Sc, Oxford, 60. Asst. lectr. pure math, Manchester Univ, 46-50; instr. MATH, Wisconsin, 50-51; mem. Inst. Adv. Study, 52-53; res. assoc, Chicago, 53-54; from asst. prof. to PROF. & HEAD DEPT, EMORY UNIV, 54- Vis. prof, Univ. Nebr, 59-60; mem. comt. exam, math. achievement test, Col. Entrance Exam. Bd, 64-69, chmn, 69-; vis. prof, Calif. Inst. Technol, 68. Am. Math. Soc; Math. Asn. Am; Asn. Symbolic Logic; London Math. Soc. Structure of non-associative systems; decision problems in algebraic systems. Address: Dept. of Mathematics, Emory University, Atlanta, GA 30322.

EVANS, VIRGINIA J(OHN), b. Baltimore, Md, Mar. 19, 13. CELL BIOLOGY, CANCER. A.B, Goucher Col, 35; M.Sc, Hopkins, 40, scholar, 41-43, Sc.D. (biochem), 43. Chem. technician, blood chem. lab, Hopkins, 38-39; asst. tissue culturist, tissue culture lab, dept. surg, Hopkins Hosp, 40-41; asst. to dermatologist, med. sch, Hopkins, 41-42, instr. biochem, sch. hyg. & nurses sch, 43-44; fel. NAT. CANCER INST, NAT. INSTS. HEALTH, 44-46, biologist, 46-64, HEAD, TISSUE CULTURE SECT, LAB. BIOL, 64- Mem. bd. gov. & chmn. exec. comt, W. Alton Jones Cell Sci. Ctr, 70. Soc. Develop. Biol; Tissue Culture Asn.(v.pres, 68-70, 70-72); Am. Asn. Cancer Res; Am. Soc. Exp. Path; Am. Soc. Cell Biol; Soc. Cryobiol; Int. Soc. Cell Biol; Am. Inst. Biol. Sci; N.Y. Acad. Sci. Nutritional dermatoses of rats; cell physiology with special reference to tissue culture in cancer; nutrition and endocrinology of tissue cultures; carcinogenesis studies in mammalian tissue culture. Address: Tissue Culture Section, National Cancer Institute, National Institutes of Health, Bethesda, MD 20014.

EVANS, WARREN W(ILLIAM), b. Wis, Nov. 23, 21. PHYSICAL CHEMISTRY. B.S, Wisconsin, 43, Ph.D.(chem), 52. Chemist, res. & develop, Carbide & Carbon Co, 47-49; sr. res. chemist, PHOTOG, E.I. DU PONT DE NEMOURS & CO, INC, 52-70, RES. ASSOC, 70- U.S.A, 43-46, 1st Lt. Sr. mem. Am. Chem. Soc. Photographic chemistry; mechanical properties of polymers. Address: E.I. du Pont de Nemours & Co, Inc, Photo Products Dept, Parlin, NJ 08859.

EVANS, WAYNE R(USSELL), b. Utica, N.Y, July 2, 21; m. 46; c. 2. PHYSICS. B.A, Cornell, 43, M.S, 47. Engr, Eastman Kodak Co, 46; asst. physics, Cornell, 47; systs. develop. engr, EASTMAN KODAK CO, 47-58, sr. proj. engr. develop, 59-60, sr. supv. eng, 61-62, asst. prog. mgr. eng, 63-64, staff asst. to gen. mgr, 64-65, asst. mgr, commercial & prof. prod. develop. & eng, 66-68, MGR. ENG, COMMERCIAL & PROF. PROD, APPARATUS DIV, 68- U.S.M.C.R, 43-46, Capt. Optical Soc. Am; Soc. Photog. Sci. & Eng. Electronics; applied mathematics; infrared optics; photographic systems. Address: Apparatus Division, Eastman Kodak Co, 901 Elmgrove Rd, Rochester, NY 14650.

EVANS, W(ILLIAM) BUELL, b. Monticello, Miss, June 5, 18; m. 45; c. 3. MATHEMATICS, METEOROLOGY. B.S, Southern Mississippi, 39; M.S, La. State, 41; M.S, Mass. Inst. Tech, 44; Ph.D.(math), Illinois, 50. Assoc. prof. math, Ga. Inst. Tech, 50-60; assoc. prof. eng, California, Los Angeles & with Eng. Gadjah Mada Proj, Indonesia, 60-64; assoc. prof. MATH. & BIOMET, EMORY UNIV, 65-68, PROF, 68-, DIR. COMPUTING CTR, 65- Summers, vis. prof. math, Vermont, 57; Nat. Sci. Found. Summer Inst. for Math. & Sci. Teachers, 58-60. Mem. adv. bd, South. Land Timber & Pulp Corp, 59-62. U.S.A.F, 42-46, 51-53, Res, 53-, Lt.Col. Am. Math. Soc; Math. Asn. Am; Soc. Indust. & Appl. Math; Biomet. Soc. Numerical analysis; general methods of approximation; infinite exponentials. Address: Computing Center, Emory University, Atlanta, GA 30322.

EVANS, W(ILLIAM) D(YFED), b. Trochu, Alta, June 16, 20; m. 43; c. 3. CYTOGENETICS, HORTICULTURE. B.Sc, Alberta, 49, M.Sc, 54; Ph.D.(cytogenetics), Reading, 64. Asst. fruit crops, Govt. of Can, 49-57; ASSOC. PROF. PLANT BREEDING, ONT. AGR. COL, UNIV. GUELPH, 57- Can. Army, 39-45, Sgt. Can. Soc. Hort. Sci.(pres, 58-59); Am. Soc. Hort. Sci; Genetics Soc. Can. Interspecific hybridization of Fragaria and Rubus; breeding of raspberries and strawberries. Address: Ontario Agricultural College, University of Guelph, Guelph, Ont, Can.

EVANS, WILLIAM EUGENE, b. Elkhart, Ind, Oct. 11, 30; m. 53; c. 2. MARINE ZOOLOGY, BIOACOUSTICS. B.S, Bowling Green State, 53; M.A, Ohio State, 54; Southern California, 58-62; California, Los Angeles, 63-67. Res. asst, Ohio State Res. Found, 53-54; lab. res. analyst, Douglas Aircraft Co, Calif, 56-59; sr. scientist, Lockheed Aircraft Corp, 60-64; res. zoologist, Naval Missile Center, Calif, 64; biologist, Off. Naval Res. Ships Opportunity Prog, 64; res. zoologist, Naval Ord. Test Sta, 64-68; staff scientist, res. eng. dept, Naval Undersea Warfare Ctr, 68-69, sr. res. zoologist, ocean sci. dept, NAVAL UNDERSEA RES. & DEVELOP. CTR, 69-71, SR. RES. ZOOLOGIST & ASST. HEAD, MARINE BIO-SCI. DIV, 71- Prin. investr, Off. Naval Res. Prog. Marine acoustics, 62-64; co-prin. investr. bio-acoustics, Nat. Insts. Health grant, 64-66; hon. res. assoc. Los Angeles County Mus, 65-67; lectr, California, Irvine, 66- Alternate mem. ad. hoc comt. marine mammals, int. biol. prog, Nat. Res. Coun, 68-, mem. marine mammals coun. U.S.A, 54-56, 64-66. AAAS; Acoustical Soc. Am; Animal Behav. Soc; Am. Soc. Mammal. Animal behavior; social communication and development of radio-telemetric devices for studying animal behavior in the field. Address: Marine Bio-Sciences Division, Code 502, Naval Undersea Research & Development Center, San Diego, CA 92132.

EVANS, WILLIAM G(EORGE), Swansea, Wales, Aug. 11, 23; nat; m. 56; c. 2. INSECT ECOLOGY. B.S, Cornell, 52, M.S, 54, Ph.D.(entom), 56. Asst. prof. ENTOM, Va. Polytech. Inst, 56-58; UNIV. ALTA, 59-61, assoc. prof, 61-69, PROF, 69- U.S.A, 43-46. Entom. Soc. Am; Ecol. Soc. Am; Entom. Soc. Can; Am. Ornith. Union. Insect ecology; insect behavior; mechanisms of orientation; rhythmic activities; marine insects; insects attracted to forest fires. Address: Dept. of Entomology, University of Alberta, Edmonton, Alta, Can.

EVANS, W(ILLIA)M H(ARRINGTON), b. Salem, Ore, Feb. 26, 21; m. 65. PHYSICAL CHEMISTRY. B.A, Willamette, 42; fel, Iowa State Col, 42-44; Ph.D.(phys. chem), Ore. State Col, 47. Tech. coord. & mat. expeditor, Naval Ord. Lab, Wash, D.C, 44-45; asst, Ore. State Col, 45-47; CHEMIST, THERMOCHEM. SECT, NAT. BUR. STANDARDS, 47- Lectr, Cath. Univ, 50-54. Am. Chem. Soc. Equilibria in solutions; thermochemistry and thermodynamics. Address: Thermochemistry Section, National Bureau of Standards, Washington, DC 20234.

EVANS, WILLIAM J(OHN), b. El Dorado, Ark, June 30, 24; m. 55; c. 3. PHYSICAL CHEMISTRY. B.S, Tulane, 49, M.S, 51, Ph.D.(chem), 54. Asst. chem, Tulane, 51-54; res. chemist, Chemstrand Corp, 54; CHEMIST, SOUTH. REGIONAL RES. LAB, 54- Tech. aid, Manhattan Eng. Dist. Proj, 43-46; vis. scientist, Regina Elena Inst. Tumor Res. & Inst. Molecular Biol, Rome, Italy, 67-68. Am. Chem. Soc; Sci. Res. Soc. Am. Physical chemistry of proteins; molecular weight; calorimetric studies of enzymes. Address: Southern Regional Research Lab, P.O. Box 19687, New Orleans, LA 70179.

EVANS, W(ILLIAM) L, b. Calvert, Tex, Aug. 28, 24; m. 48; c. 3. CYTOLOGY. B.A, Univ. Tex, 49, M.A, 50, Ph.D.(zool), 55. Instr. ZOOL, UNIV. ARK, FAYETTEVILLE, 55-58, asst. prof, 58-62, assoc. prof, 62-68, PROF, 68- U.S.A, 42-46; U.S.A.F.R, 46-52. Am. Genetic Asn. Environmental effects on the cell and evolutionary cytology; electron microscopy. Address: Dept. of Zoology, University of Arkansas, Fayetteville, AR 72701.

EVANS, WILLIAM L(EWIS), b. Wilkes-Barre, Pa, June 11, 26; m. 56. PHYSICAL & ORGANIC CHEMISTRY. B.S, Wilkes Col, 51; Ph.D.(chem), Pa. State, 57. Jr. chemist, Gen. Aniline & Film Co, 51-52, chemist, ozalid div, 52-53; asst, Pa. State, 53-57; sr. chemist, ozalid div, Gen. Aniline & Film Co, 57-60; RES. CHEMIST, explosives dept, East. lab, E.I. DU PONT DE NEMOURS & CO, INC, Gibbstown, 60-69; ORG. CHEM. DEPT, CHAMBERS WORKS, 69- U.S.A, 44-46. Am. Chem. Soc. Organic synthesis; correlation of structure and reactivity; mechanisms; infra-red; catalysts; explosives; dye development. Address: 601 Whitman Dr, Blackwood, NJ 08012.

EVANS, WILLIAM P(AUL), b. Peoria, Ill, July 19, 22; m. 49; c. 3. PHYSICS. B.S. & M.S, Illinois, 47. INSTR. MATH, BRADLEY UNIV, 47-; STAFF

PHYSICIST, RES. DEPT, CATERPILLAR TRACTOR CO, 48- U.S.N.R, 43-46, Lt.(jg). Am. Phys. Soc; Soc. Automotive Eng; Am. Soc. Metals. Fatigue, crack propagation; fracture mechanics; residual stress; radioisotope techniques. Address: Technical Center, Research Dept, Caterpillar Tractor Co, Peoria, IL 61602.

EVANS, W(INIFRED) DOYLE, b. Logansport, La, Sept. 10, 34; m. 56; c. 2. PHYSICS. B.S, La. Polytech. Inst, 56; M.S, Univ. Calif, Los Angeles, 58; Ph.D.(physics), Univ. N.Mex, 67. Asst. prof. physics, La. Polytech. Inst, 58-60; STAFF MEM, solid state physics dept, Langley Res. Ctr, NASA, 60-61; PHYSICS DIV, LOS ALAMOS SCI. LAB, 61- Am. Geophys. Union; Am. Astron. Soc. X-ray emission from the solar corona; stellar x-ray sources; ultra-soft x-ray spectroscopy. Address: Los Alamos Scientific Lab, Box 1663, Los Alamos, NM 87544.

EVANSON, ROBERT V(ERNE), b. Hammond, Ind, Nov. 3, 20; m. 47; c. 2. PHARMACY. B.S, Purdue, 47, M.S, 49, Ph.D.(pharm. admin), 53; Indiana, summers, 50, 51. Retail sales clerk, E.C. Minas Co, 40-41; apprentice pharmacist, Physician's Supply Co, 46; asst. instr. pharm, PURDUE UNIV, 47-48, instr. pharm. admin, 48-53, asst. prof, 53-57, assoc. prof, 57-63, PROF, 63-, HEAD DEPT. PHARM. ADMIN, 66- Fel, Am. Found. Pharmaceut. Educ. U.S.A, 43-46. Fel. Acad. Pharmaceut. Sci; Am. Pharmaceut. Asn. Disintegration of compressed tablets; economic study of drug store operation. Address: 400 Lindberg Ave, West Lafayette, IN 47906.

EVARD, RENE, b. Geneva, Switzerland, Oct. 25, 27; nat; m. 52; c. 1. BIOCHEMISTRY. B.A, Emmanuel Col, 52; M.S, Mich. State, 55, Ph.D.(chem), 59. ASST. PROF. CHEM, UNION COL.(NEBR), 58- Am. Chem. Soc. Mechanism of enzyme action; isolation; purification and characterization of bacteroid pyrophosphatase. Address: Dept. of Chemistry, Union College, Lincoln, NE 68506.

EVARTS, EDWARD V(AUGHAN), b. N.Y.C, Mar. 28, 26; m. 50; c. 3. PSYCHIATRY, NEUROPHYSIOLOGY. M.D, Harvard, 48. Med. house officer, Peter Bent Brigham Hosp, 48-49; asst, Yerkes Labs. Primate Biol, 49-50; Moseley travelling fel. neurol, Nat. Hosp, London, 50-51; asst. res. psychiatrist, Payne Whitney Clinic, 51-53; CHIEF physiol. sect, lab. clin. sci, NAT. INST. MENT. HEALTH, 53-71, LAB. NEUROPHYSIOL, 71- Am. Physiol. Soc; Am. Psychiat. Asn; Soc. Neurosci. Neurophysiological correlates of behavior. Address: Lab. of Neurophysiology, National Institutes of Mental Health, Bldg. 36, Room 2D-12, Bethesda, MD 20014.

EVATT, NATHAN SPENCE, b. Albany, Tex, July 8, 26; m. 51; c. 1. AGRONOMY. B.S, Tex. A&M Univ, 48, M.S, 51. Asst. agronomist, Tex. A&M Univ, 48-49; supvr, Farmers Home Admin, U.S. Dept. Agr, 51-52, soil scientist, off. exp. stas, 52-54; ASSOC. PROF. AGRON, TEX. A&M UNIV, 54- U.S. adv, Int. Rice Comn, Food & Agr. Orgn. UN, Ceylon, 59 & La, 66; speaker, Int. Rice Res. Inst, Philippines, 64; part-time consult, 64-70. U.S.N, 44-46. Am. Soc. Agron; Soil Sci. Soc. Am; Crop Sci. Soc. Am; Am. Soc. Agr. Eng; Weed Sci. Soc. Am. Applied soil fertility investigations with rice—rates and ratios, sources, methods, timings, variety-fertilizer, irrigation, ratoon studies. Address: 5770 Pickwick Lane, Beaumont, TX 77706.

EVCES, CHARLES RICHARD, b. East Liverpool, Ohio, Dec. 31, 38; m. 62; c. 2. ENGINEERING MECHANICS, MECHANICAL ENGINEERING. B.S.M.E, Notre Dame, 60, M.S.M.E, 63; NASA fel, West Virginia, 65-67, Ph.D.(eng), 67. ASST. PROF. MECH. ENG, UNIV. ALA, TUSCALOOSA, 67- Am. Soc. Mech. Eng. Dynamics and vibrations; vehicle systems. Address: Dept. of Aerospace Engineering, Mechanical Engineering & Engineering Mechanics, University of Alabama in Tuscaloosa, University, AL 35486.

EVELAND, H(ARMON) E(DWIN), b. Urbana, Ill, Feb. 9, 24; m. 44; c. 4. GEOLOGY. B.S, Illinois, 47, M.S, 48, Ph.D.(geol), 50. Asst. prof. GEOL, Tennessee, 50-51; PROF. & HEAD DEPT, LAMAR UNIV, 51- U.S.A.A.F, 43-45, 1st Lt. Geol. Soc. Am; Soc. Econ. Paleont. & Mineral. Pleistocene stratigraphy; geomorphology; physiography. Address: Dept. of Geology, Lamar University, Box 10031 Lamar Station, Beaumont, TX 77710.

EVELAND, WARREN C, b. Watsonville, Calif, Aug. 24, 04; m. 40; c. 2. BACTERIOLOGY. A.B, California, 30; M.S.P.H, Michigan, 39; Ph.D, Maryland, 52. Lab. technician, Nev. State Hyg. Lab, 30-35; dir. pub. health labs, Alaska Territorial Dept. Health, 37-41; chief lab. serv, U.S. Army Hosp, 41-45; bact. & serol. sect, U.S. Army Labs, 45-53; bact. div, Med. Gen. Lab, Japan, 53-56; bact. & immunol. br, Armed Forces Inst. Path, 56-59; assoc. prof. EPIDEMIOL, SCH. PUB. HEALTH, UNIV. MICH, 59-67, PROF, 67- Chmn. standards & exam. comt. microbiol, Am. Bd. Med. Microbiol. Dipl, Am. Bd. Med. Microbiol. U.S.A, 35-59, Col. Am. Soc. Microbiol; Asn. Mil. Surg, U.S; Am. Pub. Health Asn; N.Y. Acad. Sci; fel. Am. Acad. Microbiol; Am. Inst. Biol. Sci; Soc. Exp. Biol. & Med; Brit. Soc. Gen. Microbiol; Can. Soc. Microbiol; Wildlife Disease Asn. Medical and public health bacteriology; fluorescent antibody techniques in diagnosis. Address: Dept. of Epidemiology, University of Michigan School of Public Health, Ann Arbor, MI 48104.

EVELEIGH, DOUGLAS E(DWARD), b. Croydon, Eng, Dec. 6, 33; m. 62; c. 2. MICROBIOLOGY. B.Sc, London, 56; Ph.D.(mycol), Exeter, 59. Fel, Nat. Res. Coun, Halifax, 59-61; Nat. Acad. Sci-Nat. Res. Coun. vis. scientist, U.S. Dept. Army, Natick, Mass, 61-63; res. assoc. BACT, Wisconsin, 63-65; asst. res. off, Nat. Res. Coun, Saskatoon, 65-70; ASSOC. PROF. DEPT. BIOCHEM. & MICROBIOL, RUTGERS UNIV, 70- Am. Soc. Microbiol; Brit. Biochem. Soc; Brit. Soc. Gen. Microbiol. Fungal ecology; microbial polysaccharides. Address: Dept. of Biochemistry & Microbiology, College of Agriculture, Rutgers University, New Brunswick, NJ 08903.

EVELEIGH, VIRGIL W(ILLIAM), b. Dexter, N.Y, Aug. 20, 31; m. 56; c. 3. ELECTRICAL ENGINEERING. B.S, Purdue, 57, M.S, 58, Ph.D.(elec. eng), 61. Technician commun. systs, Gen. Elec. Co, N.Y, 53-54, field serv. engr.

radar systs, 54, engr. control systs, 61-64; ASSOC. PROF. ELEC. ENG, SYRACUSE,UNIV, 64- Consult, Gen. Elec. Co, 64- U.S.A.F, 49-52, S/Sgt. Inst. Elec. & Electronics Eng; Am. Inst. Aeronaut. & Astronaut. Control systems; computational methods for optimizing nonlinear and time varying systems; adaptive control methods and practice. Address: 271 Link Hall, Syracuse University, Syracuse, NY 13210.

EVELETH, DONALD F(RANCIS), b. Salt Lake City, Utah, Nov. 3, 05; m. 28; c. 3; m. 52. VETERINARY SCIENCE. B.S, California, 28, M.A, 30; Ph.D. (biochem), Western Reserve, 32; D.V.M, Iowa State, 34. Asst. biochem, Western Reserve, 30-32; Iowa State, 32-34, asst. prof. vet. res, 34-35; fel, California, 35; assoc. prof. vet. res, 35-39; prof, Arkansas, 39-43; N.Dak. Agr. Col, 43-64; CONSULT, ANIMAL HEALTH DIV, WIS. STATE DEPT. AGR, 64- Am. Vet. Med. Asn; Am. Soc. Biol. Chem; U.S. Animal Health Asn; Fedn. Am. Socs. Exp. Biol. Blood chemistry of domestic animals; parasitism of animals and birds; vitamin A requirements of sheep; dwarfism of cattle. Address: Animal Health Division, Wisconsin State Dept. of Agriculture, Madison, WI 53711.

EVELYN, KENNETH A(USTIN), b. Jamaica, B.W.I, June 19, 11; Can. citizen; m. 39; c. 2. MEDICINE. B.Sc, McGill, 32, M.D, 38. Res. fel. exp. med, univ. Clin, McGill & Royal Victoria Hosp, 34-40; physics, univ, 45-46, path, 46-47, assoc. prof. med. & dir. inst. biophys, 48-54, assoc. physician, hosp, 48-54; res. prof. med. & dir. med. res. inst, UNIV. B.C, 54-58, PROF. MED, 59-, DIR. G.F. STRONG LAB. MED. RES, 59- Fel, Royal Col. Physicians & Surgeons of Can. R.C.A.F, 40-45. Am. Soc. Clin. Invest; fel. Am. Col. Physicians; Can. Physiol. Soc; Can. Med. Asn; Can. Fedn. Biol. Soc. Photoelectric colorimetry; aviation medicine; decompression sickness; color and night vision; cardiovascular disease; hypertension; radioactive isotopes. Address: G.F. Strong Lab. for Medical Research, Tenth Ave. & Heather St, Vancouver, B.C, Can.

EVENDEN, FRED G(EORGE), b. Woodburn, Ore, Apr. 11, 21; m. 49; c. 2. ECOLOGY. Ph.D.(zool), Ore. State Col, 49. Wildlife res. biologist, U.S. Fish & Wildlife Serv, 48-53; exec. dir. Calif. Jr. Mus, 53-56, conservationist, 56-63; exec. secy, WILDLIFE SOC, 63-68, EXEC. DIR, 68- U.S.A.A.F, 43-46. Fel. AAAS; Am. Fisheries Soc; Nat. Audubon Soc; Cooper Ornith. Soc; Am. Ornith. Union; Wilson Ornith. Soc; Am. Forestry Asn; Wilderness Soc; Wildlife Soc; Can. Soc. Wildlife & Fisheries Biol. Conservation; bird ecology; natural history distribution. Address: 7805 English Way, Bethesda, MD 20034.

EVENS, F(LOYD) MONTE, b. Herculaneum, Mo, Jan. 21, 32; m. 52; c. 5. ANALYTICAL CHEMISTRY, SPECTROSCOPY. B.S, Southeast Mo. State Col, 55; M.S, Iowa State, 59, Ph.D.(anal. chem), 62. Chem. technician, Mallinckrodt Chem. Co, 53; jr. res. assoc, Ames Lab, Atomic Energy Cmn, Iowa State, 54-62; res. chemist, Procter & Gamble Co, 62-63; res. scientist, CONTINENTAL OIL CO, 63-68, RES. GROUP LEADER, 68- Am. Chem. Soc; Soc. Appl. Spectros. Instrumental methods of chemical analysis; atomic and molecular spectroscopy; gas chromatography; chemical separations. Address: 2716 Larchmont, Ponca City, OK 74601.

EVENS, LEONARD, b. Brooklyn, N.Y, June 28, 33; m. 58; c. 3. MATHEMATICS. A.B, Cornell, 55; A.M, Harvard, 56, Nat. Sci. Found. fel, 56-59, Ph.D.(math), 60. Instr. MATH, Chicago, 60-61; asst. prof, California, Berkeley, 61-64; assoc. prof, NORTHWEST. UNIV, 64-69, PROF, 69- Am. Math. Soc. Homological algebra; group theory. Address: Dept. of Mathematics, Northwestern University, Evanston, IL 60201.

EVENSEN, THOMAS JAMES, b. Menominee, Mich, Jan. 21, 33; m. 55; c. 2. ORGANIC CHEMISTRY. A.B, Augustana Col.(Ill), 55; Monsanto fel, Minnesota, Minneapolis, 58, Ph.D.(org. chem), 59. Teaching asst. org. chem, Minnesota, Minneapolis, 55-57; sr. chemist, MINN. MINING & MFG. CO, 59-67, res. specialist, 68-70, RES. SUPVR, 70- Am. Chem. Soc. New product designs; imaging systems. Address: Minnesota Mining & Manufacturing Co, 3M Center, St. Paul, MN 55101.

EVENSON, CATHERINE N(ANCY) DOBBIN, b. Enterprise, Ore, Apr. 18, 09; m. 42; c. 2. ZOOLOGY. B.Sc.Ed, Washington (Seattle), 32, M.S, 33; Ph.D. (zool), Cornell, 39. Teacher, pub. sch, Ore, 33-37; instr. zool, Smith Col, 39-43; curriculum dept, pub. sch, Calif, 43-44; substitute teacher, Ore, 53-63; ASST. PROF. BIOL, LEWIS & CLARK COL, 63- Grants, Nat. Sci. Found. Insts. summers 65 & 66. AAAS; Am. Nature Study Soc. Freshwater Ostracoda; fish air-bladders; nature study. Address: Dept. of Biology, Box 97, Lewis & Clark College, Portland, OR 97219.

EVENSON, KENNETH M(ELVIN), b. Waukesha, Wis, June 5, 32; m. 55; c. 4. ATOMIC & MOLECULAR PHYSICS. B.S, Mont. State Col, 55; Fulbright fel, Tübingen, 55-56; Purdue, 56-57; M.S, Oregon State, 60, Ph.D.(physics), 64. PHYSICIST, NAT. BUR. STANDARDS, 63- Am. Phys. Soc. Quantum electronics; atomic and molecular structure; chemical kinetics; electron paramagnetic resonance; microwave and optical spectroscopy. Address: Salina Star Route, Boulder, CO 80302.

EVENSON, WILLIAM E(DWIN), b. Martinez, Calif, Oct. 12, 41; m. 64; c. 3. SOLID STATE PHYSICS. B.S, Brigham Young Univ, 65; Woodrow Wilson & Nat. Sci. Found. fels, Iowa State Univ, 65-66, Danforth Found. fel, 65-68, Ph.D.(physics), 68. Res. assoc. PHYSICS, Univ. Pa, 68-70; ASST. PROF, BRIGHAM YOUNG UNIV, 70- Nat. Sci. Found. fel, 68-69. Am. Phys. Soc; Am. Asn. Physics Teachers. Theory of magnetism in the rare earth metals; theory of magnetism in transition metals; theory of dilute magnetic alloys; theory of melting; theory of ferroelectrics. Address: Dept. of Physics, Brigham Young University, Provo, UT 84601.

EVERARD, NOEL JAMES, b. New Orleans, La, Dec. 24, 23; m. 50; c. 2. CIVIL ENGINEERING, MECHANICS. B.S, La. State, 48, M.S, 57; Nat. Safety Coun. fel, Texas A&M, 58-59, Ph.D.(civil eng), 62. Instr. civil eng, La.

State, 48-49, asst. prof, 56-60; design engr, David W. Godat & Assocs, Consult. Engrs, La, 49-53, chief engr, 53-56; assoc. prof. ENG. MECH, UNIV. TEX, ARLINGTON, 60-62, PROF, 62- Consult, William Dawson, civil engr, La, 56-60; J. Weldon Hunnicut, consult. engr, Tex, 60-; Freese, Nichols & Endress, 63- C.Eng, U.S.A, 42-46, Capt. Am. Soc. Civil Eng; Am. Concrete Inst; Int. Asn. Bridge & Struct. Eng. Theoretical and applied mechanics; column design and torsion in beams of reinforced concrete. Address: Dept. of Engineering Mechanics, University of Texas at Arlington, Arlington, TX 76010.

EVEREST, F(REDERICK) ALTON, b. Gaston, Oregon, Nov. 22, 09; m. 34; c. 3. ELECTRICAL ENGINEERING. B.S, Oregon State Col, 32; E.E, Stanford, 36; California, Los Angeles, 46-47; hon. D.Sc, Wheaton, 59. Television engr, Don Lee Broadcasting Co, 36; asst. prof. elec. eng, Oregon State Col, 36-41; engr. & sect. chief, California div. war res, U.S. Navy Radio & Sound Lab, San Diego, 41-45; assoc. dir, Moody Inst. Sci, Los Angeles, 45-53, dir, 53-70; SR. LECTR. & HEAD DIV. CINEMATOG, DEPT. COMMUN, HONG KONG BAPTIST COL, 70- AAAS; Acoust. Soc. Am; sr. mem. Inst. Elec. & Electronics Eng; fel. Am. Sci. Affiliation; fel. Soc. Motion Picture & TV Eng. Television video amplifiers; high efficiency radiotelephone transmitters; electric fence controllers; directional broadcast antennae; propagation of underwater sound; underwater sounds of biological origin; cardiac pulse duplicator; scientific films. Address: c/o Hong Kong Baptist College, 224 Waterloo Rd, Kowloon, Hong Kong, China.

EVERETT, ALLEN E(DWARD), b. Kansas City, Mo, July 8, 33; m. 66. THEORETICAL PHYSICS. A.B, Princeton, 55; Nat. Sci. Found. fel, Harvard, 55-56, A.M, 56, Int. Bus. Mach. Corp. fel, 59-60, Ph.D.(physics), 61. Asst. prof. PHYSICS, TUFTS UNIV, 60-65, ASSOC. PROF, 65- Am. Phys. Soc. Theory of elementary particles. Address: Dept. of Physics, Tufts University, Medford, MA 02155.

EVERETT, ARDELL GORDON, b. Cambridge, Mass, July 27, 37; m. 60; c. 3. GEOLOGY, INORGANIC CHEMISTRY. A.B, Cornell Univ, 59; M.S, Univ. Okla, 62; fels, Univ. Tex, Austin, 63-66, Ph.D.(geol), 68. Jr. geologist, Shell Oil Co, Colo, 60; teaching asst. geol. & geophys, Univ. Okla, 61-62; jr geologist, Texaco, Inc, Utah, summer 62; instr. geol, Ohio State Univ, 67-68, asst. prof, 68-69; staff asst, water qual. & res, Dept. Interior, Wash, D.C, 69-70, acting dep. asst. secy. appl. sci. & eng, 70, dep. asst. secy, 70, DIR, OFF. TECH. ANAL, ENVIRON. PROTECTION AGENCY, 70- Consult, Susquehanna-West, Inc, summer 67; adv, Chaco Canyon Nat. Monument, Nat. Park Serv, N.Mex, summer 68. Franklin Gilliam Prize, Univ. Tex. Libr, 67. Transportation C, U.S.A.R, 59-64, C.Eng, 64-67, 1st Lt. AAAS; fel. Geol. Soc. Am; Am. Geophys. Union; Geochem. Soc; Int. Asn. Geochem. & Cosmochem; Soc. Econ. Paleont. & Mineral; Soc. Min. Eng. Environmental geology and resources management; environmental and archaeo-environmental problems; sedimentology; trace element geochemistry; economic geology. Address: Environmental Protection Agency, Washington, DC 20460.

EVERETT, C(ORNELIUS) J(OSEPH), b. New Orleans, La, Sept. 19, 14; m. 40; c. 2. MATHEMATICS. B.S, Tulane, 35; fel, Wisconsin, 37-39, M.A, 38, Ph.D.(math), 40. Sterling res. fel. math, Yale, 40-41; instr, Michigan, 41-42; Wisconsin, 42-44; asst. prof, 44-47; res. mathematician, LOS ALAMOS SCI. LAB, UNIV. CALIF, 47-50, MEM. STAFF, 50- AAAS; Am. Math. Soc. Abstract algebra; lattice theory; probability; ring structure; vector spaces over rings. Address: Los Alamos Scientific Lab, University of California, Los Alamos, NM 87544.

EVERETT, GEORGE A(LBERT), b. Lewiston, Maine, Sept. 22, 24. BIOCHEMISTRY. A.B, Oberlin Col, 47; Purdue, 49-50; M.S, Cornell, 59. Chemist pharmaceut. res, Norwich Pharmacal Co, 47-49, biochemist, 50-53; jr. anal. chemist, Purdue, 49-50; asst. med. res, Yale, 53-54; biochemist, Dept. Army, Ft. Detrick, 54-55, Walter Reed Army Med. Ctr, 55-56; BIOCHEMIST, AGR. RES. SERV, U.S. DEPT. AGR, 56- Structural studies of nucleic acids. Address: U.S. Plant, Soil & Nutrition Lab, Tower Rd, Ithaca, NY 14850.

EVERETT, GLEN E(XNER), b. St. George, Utah, Oct. 3, 34; m. 58; c. 3. SOLID STATE PHYSICS. B.A, Utah, 56; M.S, Chicago, 57, Ph.D.(physics), 61. Acting asst. prof. PHYSICS, UNIV. CALIF, RIVERSIDE, 60-62, asst. prof, 62-68, ASSOC. PROF, 68- Consult, U.S. Naval Weapons Ctr, Calif, 63- Am. Phys. Soc. Cyclotron resonance in metals; ferro and antiferromagnetic resonance in binary rare earth compounds. Address: Dept. of Physics, University of California, Riverside, CA 92502.

EVERETT, G(ROVER) W(OODROW), b. Newton, Miss, Sept. 11, 12; m. 37; c. 2. ANALYTICAL CHEMISTRY. B.S, Virginia, 35; M.A, George Washington, 40; Ph.D, North Carolina, 55. Teacher pub. sch, Va, 36-42; asst. to assoc. prof. CHEM, Lynchburg Col, 47-55; PROF, E. CAROLINA UNIV, 55-, chmn. dept, 60-66. U.S.N, 42-46, Comdr. AAAS; Am. Chem. Soc. Coulometric titrations; chronopotentiometry. Address: Dept. of Chemistry, East Carolina University, Gree ille, NC 27834.

EVERETT, H(ARRY) S(CHEIDY), b. Scheidys, Pa, Jan. 25, 91; m. 14; c. 3. MATHEMATICS. A.B, Bucknell, 12, A.M, 13, Sc.M, 14; fel, Chicago, 21-22, Ph.D.(math), 22. Teacher, pub. sch, Pa, 08-15; instr. math, Bucknell, 15-18, asst. prof. math. & astron, 18-22, prof. appl. math. & astron, 22-27; lectr, Adler Planetarium, 33-56; vis. prof, Pa. State, 56-60; prof. MATH, EAST STROUDSBURG STATE COL, 60-66, EMER. EXTEN. PROF, 66- Exten. prof. math. & secy. dept, Chicago, 27-64, dean, cols, 28-31, prof, dept. home study, 22-27. Algebra; expression of forms as determinants whose elements are forms. Address: 147 Analomink St, East Stroudsburg, PA 18301.

EVERETT, HERBERT L(YMAN), b. New Haven, Conn, Aug. 9, 22; m. 44; c. 2. PLANT BREEDING, GENETICS. B.A, Yale, 44, M.S, 47, Ph.D.(genetics), 49. Res. asst, dept. PLANT BREEDING, Conn. Agr. Exp. Sta, New Haven, 49-52; asst. prof, CORNELL UNIV, 52-53, assoc. prof, 53-64, PROF, 64-, DIR. RESIDENT INSTR, COL. AGR, 66- Proj. leader & vis. prof, Cornell Univ. grad. Educ. Prog, col. agr, Univ. Philippines, 64-65. U.S.A.A.F, 43-45, 1st Lt. AAAS; Genetics Soc. Am; Am. Soc. Agron; Am. Soc. Hort. Sci. Plant breeding research and genetics research in corn. Address: Office of Resident Instruction, College of Agriculture, Cornell University, Ithaca, NY 14850.

EVERETT, HUGH, III, b. Wash. D.C, Nov. 11, 30; m. 56; c. 2. MATHEMATICAL PHYSICS. B.Ch.E, Cath. Univ, 53; Nat. Sci. Found. fel, Princeton, 53-56, Ph.D.(theoret. phys), 57. Head math. sect, weapons systs. eval. group, Inst. Defense Anal, 56-64; dir. Lambda Div, Defense Res. Corp, 64-65; PRES, LAMBDA CORP, 65- Am. Phys. Soc; Opers. Res. Soc. Am. Foundations of quantum mechanics; general relativity; theory of games; applications of electronic computers; operations research. Address: Lambda Corp, 1501 Wilson Ave, Arlington, VA 22305.

EVERETT, JAMES PEEK, JR, b. Rockmart, Ga, Dec. 9, 30; m; c. 1. ANIMAL NUTRITION. B.S, Auburn, 52; M.S, Kentucky, 57; Ph.D.(animal nutrit), Mich. State, 62. Asst. prof. dairy nutrit, N.C. State Col, 60-63; MGR. DAIRY RES, RALSTON PURINA CO, 63- U.S.N, 52-54, Lt.(jg). Am. Dairy Sci. Asn; Am. Soc. Animal Sci. Nutrient requirements and physiological factors affecting voluntary feed intake of ruminants. Address: Ralston Purina Co, 835 S. Eighth St, St. Louis, MO 63188.

EVERETT, JOHN E(DWARD), b. Weldon, N.C, Sept. 14, 13; m. 41; c. 1. ORGANIC CHEMISTRY. B.S. & A.B, Carson Newman Col, 34; Am. Scandinavian Found. fel, Stockholm, 37-38; Ph.D.(chem), North Carolina, 39. Res. chemist, E.I. DU PONT DE NEMOURS & CO, 39-61, SR CHEMIST, 61- Am. Chem. Soc. Chlorinated solvents; organic sulfur compounds. Address: 2000 Forest Dr, Waynesboro, VA 22980.

EVERETT, JOHN W(ENDELL), b. Ovid, Mich, Mar. 5, 06; m. 32; c. 2. ANATOMY. A.B, Olivet Col, 28; Ph.D.(zool), Yale, 32. Instr. biol, Goucher Col, 30-31; ANAT, DUKE UNIV, 32-35, assoc, 35-39, asst. prof, 39-46, assoc. prof, 46-50, PROF, 50- Vis. prof, California, Los Angeles, 52; Tennessee, 54. Mem. neuroendocrinol. panel, Int. Brain Res. Orgn. AAAS; Am. Asn. Anat; Am. Physiol. Soc; Endocrine Soc; Soc. Exp. Biol. & Med; Biol. Stain Comn; fel. N.Y. Acad. Sci; Soc. Study Reproduction (Carl G. Hartman Lect. award, 71); Int. Soc. Res. Reproduction. Physiology of reproduction; endocrinology of the ovary and hypophysis; hypothalamic control of hypophysis. Address: Dept. of Anatomy, Duke University Medical Center, Box 2917, Durham, NC 27710.

EVERETT, KAYE, b. Corning, N.Y, Jan. 8, 34; m. 56; c. 2. GEOLOGY. B.A, Buffalo, 55; M.S, Utah, 58; Ph.D.(geol), Ohio State, 63. Res. assoc. geomorphol, inst. polar studies, Ohio State Univ, 61-64; polar & mt. geologist, U.S. Army Natick Labs, 64-67; asst. prof. AGRON, COL. AGR. & HOME ECON, OHIO STATE UNIV, 67-70, ASSOC. PROF, 70- AAAS; Am. Geophys. Union; Arctic Inst. N.Am; Geol. Soc. Am; Am. Polar Soc. Geomorphology and pedology; genesis, classification and distribution of polar and mountain soils, primarily Alaska, Canadian Arctic and Greenland; slope morphology, mass wasting, permafrost and patterned ground development. Address: Dept. of Agronomy, College of Agriculture & Home Economics, Ohio State University, Columbus, OH 43210.

EVERETT, KENNETH GARY, b. Vicksburg, Miss, Nov. 25, 42. INORGANIC CHEMISTRY. B.S, Washington & Lee, 64; Ph.D.(chem), Stanford, 68. ASST. PROF. CHEM, Northeast La. State Col, 68-69; STETSON UNIV, 69- Consult, Columbian Carbon Co, La, 69- Am. Chem. Soc. Chemical kinetics and mechanisms of inorganic reactions. Address: Dept. of Chemistry, Stetson University, DeLand, FL 32720.

EVERETT, MARK ALLEN, b. Oklahoma City, Okla, May 30, 28. MEDICINE, DERMATOLOGY. B.A, Oklahoma, 47, M.D, 51; Tulane, 52. Intern pediat, Michigan, 51-52, resident DERMAT, 54-56, instr, 56-57; MED. SCH, UNIV. OKLA, 57-59, asst. prof, 59-63, assoc. prof, 63-68, PROF, 68-, HEAD DEPT, 70-, DERMATOLOGIST-IN-CHIEF, UNIV. HOSP, 70-, dir. res. labs, 59, dir. resident training & res, 63-64, chmn. dept. dermat, 64-70. Consult, Vet. Admin. Hosp, Okla. City, Okla; St. Anthony Hosp, Okla. City, Okla. Dipl, Am. Bd. Dermat, 58. U.S.A.F, 52-54, Capt. Am. Med. Asn; Am. Acad. Dermat; Am. Dermat. Asn; Soc. Invest. Dermat; Radiation Res. Soc; N.Y. Acad. Sci; Int. Soc. Trop. Dermat; World Med. Asn. Cutaneous photobiology; ultraviolet erythema; clinical dermatology; dermatopathology; medical education and organization. Address: Dept. of Dermatology, University of Oklahoma Medical School, Oklahoma City, OK 73104.

EVERETT, MARK R(EUBEN), b. Slatington, Pa, Nov. 2, 99; m. 24; c. 2. BIOCHEMISTRY. B.Sc, Bucknell, 20, hon. D.Sc, 48; Austin fel, Harvard, 20-21, Ph.D.(biochem), 24. Teaching fel, Harvard Med. Sch, 20-24; prof. biochem. & pharmacol, dean SCH. MED, UNIV. OKLA, 24-35, biochem, 35-64, dean, 47-64, supt. univ. hosps, 47-57, dir. med. center, 57-64, EMER. DEAN & REGENTS PROF. MED. SCI, 64- Mem. bd. dir, Okla. Med. Res. Found; Okla. Comt. Crippled Children. U.S.A, 18. AAAS; Am. Chem. Soc; Am. Asn. Cancer Res; Am. Soc. Biol. Chem; Soc. Exp. Biol. & Med; fel. Am. Inst. Chem. Analytical chemistry, metabolism and oxidation of carbohydrates. Address: University of Oklahoma School of Medicine, 801 N.E. 13th St, Oklahoma City, OK 73104.

EVERETT, NEWTON B, b. Dundee, Tex, May 12, 16; m. 40; c. 2. ANATOMY. B.S, North Texas State, 37, M.S, 38; Ph.D.(zool), Michigan, 42. Asst. zool, Michigan, 38-40, teaching fel, 40-42; instr. ANAT, HISTOL. & EMBRYOL, Michigan, 42-46; asst. prof, UNIV. WASH, 46-48, assoc. prof, 48-55, admin. officer, 55-57, PROF, 57-, CHMN. DEPT, 61- Instr, N.Tex. State Univ, 39. Am. Soc. Hemat; Am. Soc. Cell Biol; Am. Physiol. Soc; Am. Asn. Anat; Reticuloendothelial Soc; Int. Soc. Hemat; Int. Soc. Cell Biol; affiliate Royal Soc. Med; cor. fel. Brazilian Col. Anat. Lymphocyte kinetics and function; hemopoiesis; fetal circulation; radiobiology; neuroanatomy. Address: Dept. of Biological Structure, University of Washington, Seattle, WA 98105.

EVERETT, PAUL H(ARRISON), b. Lake City, Fla, Nov. 5, 27; m. 51; c. 6. SOIL SCIENCE. B.S.A, Univ. Fla, 50, M.S.A, 55; Ph.D.(soil microbiol),

Purdue Univ, 58. Asst. prof, UNIV. FLA, 58-64, assoc. prof, 64-68, PROF. SOIL SCI, 68- U.S.A, 46-47, 50-51, M/Sgt. Am. Soc. Agron; Am. Soc. Hort. Sci. Soil fertility and plant nutrition, involving macronutrients and micronutrients as related to yield and quality of vegetables. Address: Agricultural Research Center, University of Florida, Rt. 1, Box 2G, Immokalee, FL 33934.

EVERETT, PAUL M(ARVIN), b. Toledo, Ohio, Mar. 15, 40; m. 68; c. 1. SOLID STATE PHYSICS. B.S, Case Inst. Technol, 62; NASA trainee, Case West. Reserve Univ, 65-67, univ. fel, 67-68, Ph.D.(solid state physics), 68. RES. ASSOC. PHYSICS, LA. STATE UNIV, BATON ROUGE, 68- Am. Phys. Soc; Am. Asn. Physics Teachers. Properties of electrons in metals; study of fermi surfaces via the de Haas-van Alphen and galvanomagnetic effects. Address: Dept. of Physics & Astronomy, Louisiana State University, Baton Rouge, LA 70803.

EVERETT, ROBERT LINE, b. Duquesne, Pa, June 19, 28; m. 52; c. 2. MECHANICAL ENGINEERING. B.S, Pittsburgh, 51 & 57. Res. engr, GEN. MOTORS CORP, 57-63, assoc. sr. res. engr, 63-67, SR. RES. ENGR, 67- U.S.A.F, 51-53, 2nd Lt. Soc. Automotive Eng. Engine, fuel relationships, emissions; durability; driveability; abnormal combustion. Address: General Motors Research Labs, 12 Mile & Mound Rds, Warren, MI 48090.

EVERETT, ROBERT R(IVERS), b. Yonkers, N.Y, June 26, 21; m. 44; c. 5. ELECTRICAL ENGINEERING. B.S, Duke, 42; M.S, Mass. Inst. Tech, 43. Res. & develop. engr, servomechanism lab, Mass. Inst. Tech, 42-51, assoc. dir, digital comput. lab. & assoc. head, digital comput. div, Lincoln Lab, 51-56, head, digital comput. div, 56-58; tech. dir. command & control systs, MITRE CORP, 58-59, v.pres. tech. opers, 59-69, exec. v.pres, 69, PRES, 69- Consult, air defense panel, President's Sci. Adv. Comt, 59-60; comdr, Air Force Systs. Command, U.S. Air Force Range Tech. Adv. Group, 62; mem. air traffic control adv. comt, U.S. Dept. Transportation, 68-69; mem, Off. Dir. Defense Res. & Eng, systs. eng. mgt. panel, 68-69; mem. sci. adv. bd, U.S. Air Force, 69- AAAS; fel. Inst. Elec. & Electronics Eng; Asn. Comput. Mach. Computer technology; military command control, surveillance and communications systems. Address: The Mitre Corp, P.O. Box 208, Bedford, MA 01730.

EVERETT, ROBERT W, JR, b. New Orleans, La, June 13, 21; m. 52; c. 1. GEOLOGY. B.S, Tulane, 42. Seismic computor, Ark. Fuel Oil, 42-43; micropaleontologist, TEXACO, INC, 46-53, res. geologist, 53-58, micropaleontologist in charge of lab, 59-67, MICROPALEONTOLOGIST, 67- U.S.A.A.F, 43-46. Am. Asn. Petrol. Geol. Foraminifera as used in economic work in oil industry; salt dome research; Gulf Coast geology and paleontology; nannofossil research in the Tertiary of Gulf Coast and especially South Louisiana; subsurface deltaic research. Address: 6511 General Diaz, New Orleans, LA 70124.

EVERETT, TRAVIS REX, b. Post, Tex, Feb. 18, 28; m. 51; c. 1. ENTOMOLOGY. B.A, Texas Tech. Col, 50, fel, 50-51, M.S, 51; New Mexico, 53-55; Ph.D.(entom), Iowa State, 59. Teacher, pub. sch, 50-53; asst. biol, New Mexico, 53-55; entom, Iowa State, 55-56; res. entomologist, entom. res. div, U.S. Dept. of Agr, 56-65; assoc. prof. ENTOM, La. State Univ, Baton Rouge, 65-66; CONSULT, FORD FOUND, 66- U.S.N, 46-47. Entom. Soc. Am. Insect biology and ecology. Address: Ford Foundation, 32 Ferozshah Rd, New Delhi-1, India.

EVERETT, WILBUR W(AYNE), b. Benton, Ark, Mar. 4, 32; m. 54; c. 2. BIOPHYSICAL CHEMISTRY. B.S, Ouachita Baptist Col, 54; Nat. Sci. Found. fel, Purdue, 57-59, Ph.D.(chem), 59. Instr. chem, Purdue, 55-56; asst. scientist, gerontol. br, Nat. Heart Inst, Nat. Insts. Health, 59-61; PROF. CHEM, OUACHITA BAPTIST UNIV, 61-, CHMN. DEPT, 66- U.S.P.H.S, Res, Sr. Asst. Scientist. Fel. Am. Inst. chem; Am. Chem. Soc; Physical chemistry; structure of proteins and carbohydrate high polymers; application of thermodynamics and hydrodynamics to solutions of macromolecules. Address: Dept. of Chemistry, Ouachita Baptist University, Arkadelphia, AR 71923.

EVERETT, WILLIS L(YNN), b. Birmingham, Mich, June 8, 23; m. 49; c. 2. NUCLEAR ENGINEERING. B.S, Michigan, 55, M.S, 57, Ph.D.(nuclear eng), 62. Asst, radiation lab, Michigan, 59-60; proj. engr, Bendix Systs. Div, 61-62; asst. prof. physics, Wyoming, 62-64, ASSOC. PROF. eng, 64-65; NUCLEAR ENG, UNIV. N.MEX, 65- U.S.A.A.F, 43-46, Sgt. Am. Nuclear Soc; Am. Soc. Eng. Educ; Am. Phys. Soc. Plasma systems; thermonuclear devices. Address: College of Engineering, University of New Mexico, Albuquerque, NM 87106.

EVERHARD, MARTIN E(DWARD), b. Pittsburgh, Pa, Jan. 28, 33; m. 68; c. 5. PHYSICAL CHEMISTRY, SURGERY. B.S, Col. William & Mary, 53; Du Pont fel, Virginia, 57-59, Ph.D.(phys. chem), 59; M.D, N.Y. Univ, 67. Sr. res. scientist phys. chem, Squibb Inst. Med. Res, Olin Mathieson Chem. Corp, 59-63; Rubin scholar. med, sch. med, N.Y. Univ, 63-64, merit scholar, 64-67; mem. surg. house staff, St. Vincent's Hosp, Bridgeport, Conn, 67-68; surg. resident, MONTEFIORE HOSP. & MED. CTR, 68-71, CHIEF RESIDENT SURG, 71- Squibb Inst. grant, 63-65. U.S.N, 53-57, Lt. Am. Chem. Soc; N.Y. Acad. Sci; Am. Med. Asn. Aqueous solution theory; kinetics of color reactions; differential thermal analysis; medical applications of transport through lipid-like membranes; vitamin B_{12} like compounds; clinical and vascular surgery; intestinal blood flow. Address: Dept. of Surgery, Montefiore Hospital & Medical Center, 111 E. 210th St, Bronx, NY 10467.

EVERHART, DONALD LEE, b. Erie, Pa, Jan. 27, 32; m. 55. IMMUNOCHEMISTRY. B.S, Grove City Col, 54; A.M, Boston, 58, fels, 59-61, Ph.D. (immunochem, biochem), 61. Res. assoc, Mem. Res. Center & Hosp, Tennessee, 61-63; assoc. biochemist, res. inst, Ill. Inst. Tech, 63-64, res. immunochemist, 64-66; ASST. PROF. MICROBIOL, MED. COL. VA, 66- U.S.A, 55-56, Res, 56-63. AAAS; Am. Chem. Soc. Chemical nature of the antigen. Address: 1810 Briardale Lane, Richmond, VA 23229.

EVERHART, DONALD L(OUGH), b. Troy, Ohio, July 18, 17; m. 42; c. 4. GEOLOGY. A.B, Denison, 39; Austin scholar, Harvard, 39, Sheldon traveling fel, 40, A.M, 42, Ph.D.(geol), 53. Asst. geol, Denison, 37-39; fel. mineral, Harvard, 40-42; geologist, U.S. Geol. Surv, 42-48; geologist & chief, geol. br, U.S. Atomic Energy Cmn, 49-54, geol. adv. div, raw materials, 54-59; chief geologist, INT. MINERALS & CHEM. CORP, 59-70, DIV. VICE PRES, MINING & EXPLOR, 70- Fel. Geol. Soc. Am; Soc. Econ. Geol. Petrology and geology of batholithic igneous rocks; geology of the Franciscan group of California; geology of quicksilver and uranium ore deposits; genesis and economic geology of uranium deposits; economic geology of phosphate and potash deposits. Address: International Minerals & Chemical Corp, 5401 Old Orchard Rd, Skokie, IL 60076.

EVERHART, EDGAR, b. Akron, Ohio, June 20, 20; m. 43; c. 2. ASTRONOMY, PHYSICS. A.B, Oberlin Col, 42; Ph.D.(physics), Mass. Inst. Tech, 48. Staff mem, radiation lab, Mass. Inst. Tech, 42-45, res. assoc, 45-48; instr. PHYSICS, Dartmouth Col, 48-50; asst. prof, Univ. Conn, 50-56, assoc. prof, 56-60, PROF, 60-69; UNIV. DENVER, 69- Civilian with Off. Sci. Res. & Develop; U.S.A.A.F; U.S.N, 44. Am. Phys. Soc; Am. Astron. Soc; Int. Astron. Union. Atomic and ionic collision studies; astronomical optics; comets; celestial mechanics. Address: Dept. of Physics & Astronomy, University of Denver, Denver, CO 80210.

EVERHART, J(OHN) O(TIS), b. Mechanicsburg, Ohio, Oct. 23, 05; m. 29; c. 2. CERAMIC ENGINEERING. B.Cer.E, Ohio State, 28, Cer.E, 34, M.Sc, 35, Ph.D.(ceramic eng), 37. Res. engr, eng. exp. sta, Ohio State, 28-37, asst. prof, 34-37, mgr. clay prod. exp. plant, 30-33; ceramic engr, Ky. Fire Brick Co, 38-40, asst. to gen. supt. & v.pres, 41-44; res. dir, Nat. Clay Pipe Res. Corp, 44-54; res. prof. eng. exp. sta, OHIO STATE UNIV, 54-56, acting chmn. dept. ceramic eng, 57-58, dir. ceramic res, 58-70, PROF. CERAMIC ENG, 70-, CHMN. DEPT, 58- Trustee, Edward Orton, Jr, Ceramic Found, 61-; dir, Massic Tile Co, 63-68. Fel. Am. Ceramic Soc; Nat. Inst. Ceramic Eng; Can. Ceramic Soc. Refractories; stress strain relations in ceramic materials; mechanized drying; petrography of ceramic materials; glaze improvement; de-airing; pipe joints; continuous drying and firing. Address: Dept. of Ceramic Engineering, Ohio State University, 2041 N. College Rd, Columbus, OH 43210.

EVERHART, THOMAS E(UGENE), b. Kansas City, Mo, Feb. 15, 32; m. 53; c. 4. ELECTRICAL ENGINEERING. William Scott Garrish scholar & A.B, Harvard, 53; M.Sc, California, Los Angeles, 55; Marshall scholar & Ph.D. (eng), Cambridge, 58. Mem. tech. staff, Hughes Res. Labs, 53-55; asst. prof. ELEC. ENG, UNIV. CALIF, BERKELEY, 58-62, assoc. prof, 62-67, PROF, 67-, Miller res. prof, 69-70. Fel. scientist, Westinghouse Res. Labs, 62-63; Nat. Sci. Found. sr. fel. & guest prof, Univ. Tübingen, 66-67; consult, Ampex Corp; Hughes Res. Labs. AAAS; fel. Inst. Elec. & Electronics Eng; Electron Micros. Soc. Am. Scanning electron microscopy; electron physics; electron beam recording; semiconductor electronics. Address: Dept. of Electrical Engineering & Computer Sciences, University of California, Berkeley, CA 94720.

EVERHART, W(ATSON) HARRY, b. Connellsville, Pa, June 5, 18; m. 39; c. 3. BIOLOGY. B.S, Westminster Col.(Pa), 40; M.S, Pittsburgh, 42; Ph.D.(fishery biol), Cornell, 48. Asst. embryol. & anat, Pittsburgh, 40-42; fishery biol, Cornell, 45, biol, 47-48; state fishery biologist, Conn, 47; asst. prof. fishery biol. & ichthyol, Univ. Maine, 48-53, assoc. prof. zool, 53-59, prof, 59-67; fishery biologist, Maine Inland Fisheries & Game, 48-50, chief fishery res. & mgr, 50-67; PROF. BIOL. & CHMN. FISHERY MAJOR, COLO. STATE UNIV, 67- Mem. Atlantic Sea Run Salmon Comn, 53-67; consult, Colo. Game, Fish & Parks Dept, 67- U.S.A.A.F, 42-45. Am. Fisheries Soc; Am. Soc. Ichthyol. & Herpet; Am. Soc. Limnol. & Oceanog; Wildlife Soc. Fishery biology. Address: Dept. of Fishery & Wildlife Biology, Colorado State University, Fort Collins, CO 80521.

EVERING, FREDERICK CHRISTIAN, JR, b. Baltimore, Md, Mar. 20, 36; m. 65. ELECTRICAL ENGINEERING. B.E.S, Hopkins, 58, M.S.E, 60, Ph.D. (elec. eng), 65. Electronic engr, U.S. Dept. Defense, 60-62; instr. ELEC. ENG, Johns Hopkins Univ, 62-65; asst. prof, UNIV. VT, 65-69, ASSOC. PROF, 69- Inst. Elec. & Electronics Eng; Am. Soc. Eng. Educ. Microwave diffraction; low noise systems; special purpose computers; bioengineering; psychological and neurological instrumentation. Address: Dept. of Electrical Engineering, University of Vermont, Burlington, VT 05401.

EVERINGHAM, JOHN W(HEELER), b. Santa Monica, Calif, July 22, 32; m. 55; c. 3. ZOOLOGY, ANATOMY. B.A, California, Los Angeles, 54; Nat. Sci. Found. fel, Washington (Seattle), 59-60, M.S, 61, U.S. Pub. Health Serv. fel, 62-64, Ph.D.(biol. struct), 64. Instr. anat, med. sch, Northwest. Univ, 64-68, asst. prof, 68-71; ASSOC. PROF. HISTOL, DENT. COL, UNIV. ILL, CHICAGO, 71- Res. grant, Northwest. Univ, 65- U.S.A, 55-57. Am. Asn. Anat; Am. Soc. Cell Biol; Soc. Develop. Biol. Invertebrate embryology; fine structure and cytochemistry of tunicate eggs and embryos; neurulation in chordate embryos. Address: Dept. of Histology, University of Illinois College of Dentistry, 808 S. Wood St, Chicago, IL 60680.

EVERITT, C. W. FRANCIS, b. Sevenoaks, Eng, Mar. 8, 34. PHYSICS, HISTORY OF SCIENCE. B.Sc, London, 55, Ph.D.(physics), 59, A.R.C.S, Royal Col, Sci, 55, dipl, Imp. Col, 58. Vis. res. fel, PHYSICS, Nat. Phys-Tech. Inst, 55; res. assoc, Imp. Col, London, 58-60; Pennsylvania, 60-61; STANFORD, 62-66, res. physicist, 66-67, SR. RES. PHYSICIST, 67- Instr. physics, Univ. Pennsylvania, 61-63; mem. space relativity cmt, Int. Acad. Astronaut, 65- Am. Phys. Soc. Electron optics; paleomagnetism; liquid helium; low temperature and space physics; history of physics. Address: Dept. of Physics, Stanford University, Stanford, CA 94305.

EVERITT, W(ILLIAM) L(ITTELL), b. Baltimore, Md, Apr. 14, 00; m. 23; c. 3. ELECTRICAL ENGINEERING. E.E, Cornell Univ, 22; M.S, Univ. Mich, 26, hon. D.Eng, 67; Ph.D.(physics), Ohio State Univ, 33, hon. D.Sc, 66; hon. D.Eng, Bradley Univ, 59, Tri-State Col, 64, Mich. Technol. Univ, 67; hon. D.Sc, Monmouth Col.(Ill), 64, Univ. Ill, 69; hon. D.Ing, Univ. of the Andes, Colombia, 66; hon. LL.D, Univ. Denver, 68. Instr. elec. eng, Cornell Univ, 20-22; engr, North Elec. Mfg. Co, Ohio, 22-24; instr. elec. eng, Univ. Mich, 24-26; asst. prof, Ohio State Univ, 26-29, assoc. prof, 29-34, prof, 34-44; prof. & head dept, UNIV. ILL, URBANA, 44-49, dean, COL. ENG, 49-68, EMER. DEAN, 68- Mem, Nat. Defense Res. Comt, 40-42; dir. oper. res. off. chief signal off, U.S. War Dept, 42-46; mem. electronics comt, res. & develop. bd, Nat. Mil. Estab, 47-53; Senate Adv. Comt. Color TV, 49-50; President's Commun. Policy Bd, 50-51; Comt. Eval. Functions, U.S. Bur. Standards, 53; tech. adv. panel electronics, Off. Asst. Secy. Defense Res. & Develop, 54-57, gen. sci, 57-60; President's Comt. Scientists & Eng, 56-57; chmn. bd. vis, U.S. Army Signal Corps Sch, 57-60; bd. dirs, Assoc. Midwest Univs, 58-65, pres, 61-62; mem. adv. comt, Pac. Missile Range, U.S. Navy, 58-62; pres, Eng. Coun. Prof. Develop, 58-61; mem. sci. adv. panel, U.S. Army, 59-63; chmn, Comn. Eng. Educ, 64-66; telecommun. comt, Nat. Acad. Eng, 68- U.S.M.C, 18-19. Am. Acad. Eng; fel. Inst. Elec. & Electronics Eng.(pres, Inst. Radio Eng, 45; medal of honor, 54, elec. eng. educ. medal, 57, Kelly medal, 63); Acoust. Soc. Am; Am. Soc. Eng. Educ. (v.pres, 53-55, pres, 56-57; Lamme Medal, 57); Nat. Soc. Prof. Eng.(award, 69). Radio circuits and antennas; vacuum tube detectors and amplifiers; impedance matching networks; high frequency transmission lines; speech compression. Address: 106 Engineering Hall, College of Engineering, University of Illinois, Urbana, IL 61801.

EVERLING, FRIEDRICH GUSTAV, b. Berlin, Ger, July 2, 27; U.S. citizen; m; c. 2. PHYSICS. Dipl. physics, Mainz, 52, Ph.D.(mass spectros), 55. Asst, Max Planck Inst. Chem, Mainz, Ger, 52-55, res. assoc, Otto Hahn Inst, 55-59; prof. assoc, nuclear data group, Nat. Acad. Sci, D.C, 59-61; res. assoc, Ames Lab, Atomic Energy Comn. & dept. physics, Iowa State Univ, 61-64; sr. sci. assoc, inst. nuclear physics, Tech. Univ, Berlin, 64-66; ASSOC. PROF PHYSICS, N.C. STATE UNIV. & TRIANGLE UNIVS NUCLEAR LAB, DUKE UNIV, 66- Am. Phys. Soc; German Phys. Soc. Mass spectroscopy; atomic masses; nuclear systematics and spectroscopy; nuclear reactions with accelerators. Address: Dept. of Physics, North Carolina State University, Raleigh, NC 27607.

EVERLY, CHARLES RAY, b. Oklahoma City, Okla, Oct. 13, 44; m. 65; c. 1. ORGANIC CHEMISTRY. B.A, Phillips, 66; Nat. Sci. Found. fel. & Atomic Energy Comn. Funds, Arkansas, 66-69, Ph.D.(org. chem), 70. ASST. PROF. CHEM, PHILLIPS UNIV, 69- Am. Chem. Soc. Organic reaction mechanics. Address: Dept. of Chemistry, Phillips University, Enid, OK 73701.

EVERNDEN, JACK F(OORD), b. Okeechobee, Fla, Mar. 12, 22; m. 65. SEISMOLOGY, GEOPHYSICS. Ph.D.(geophys), Univ. Calif, 51. Asst. prof. geol. & geophys, Univ. Calif, Berkeley, 53-57, assoc. prof, 57-62, prof, 62-65; res. assoc, Vela Seismol. Ctr, Va, 65-67; res. assoc. to tech. dir, Air Force Tech. Appl. Ctr, U.S. Dept. Defense, 67-69, res. assoc. & prog. monitor, Advan. Res. Projs. Agency, 69-71; RES. ASSOC, ARMS CONTROL & DISARMAMENT AGENCY, U.S. DEPT. STATE, 71- Newcombe-Cleveland Prize, AAAS, 62; outstanding civilian serv. medal, U.S. Air Force, 68. U.S.A.A.F, 42-46, Lt. Geol. Soc. Am; Seismol. Soc. Am; Am. Asn. Petrol. Geol. Earthquake seismology; field geology; geochronometry. Address: 108 Gibbon St, Alexandria, VA 22314.

EVEROTE, WARREN PETER, b. Farmington, Minn, Oct. 12, 13; m. 40; c. 1. CHEMISTRY. A.B, California, Los Angeles, 35, A.M, 36; Ph.D.(sci. ed), Columbia, 43. Instr. sch, Los Angeles, 38-42; res. assoc, bur. ed. res. sci, Teachers Col, Columbia, 42-43, instr. sci, Lincoln Sch, 42-43; mem. motion picture rev. bd, personnel bur, U.S. Naval Reserve, D.C, 44; officer in charge still photog. & combat motion pictures, Ord. Bur, 44-45; assoc. res. & prod, Encycl. Britannica Films, 45-49, assoc. producer, 49-52, exec. producer, 52-53, dir, 53-55, v.pres, 55-62, pres, 62-64, Encycl. Britannica Press, 64-65, managing dir, Encycl. Britannica Ltd, England, 65-66, pres, develop. div, Ill, 66-67, Encycl. Britannica Educ. Crop, 67-70; RETIRED. V.pres, Encycl. Britannica Educ. Corp, 70- AAAS; N.Y. Acad. Sci; Nat. Asn. Res. Sci. Teaching. Science education, particularly pertaining to agriculture and chemistry; techniques in motion picture production; isolation and synthesis of amino acids; science motion pictures. Address: 4265 Cresta Ave, Santa Barbara, CA 93110.

EVERS, CARL GUSTAV, b. Lake Benton, Minn, July 30, 34; m. 60; c. 3. MEDICINE, PATHOLOGY. B.A, Mankato State Col, 55; M.D, Minnesota, 59. Intern, MED. CTR, UNIV. MISS, 59-60, resident PATH, 60-64, instr, 64-66, asst. prof, 66-68, ASSOC. PROF, 68- U.S. Pub. Health Serv. trainee anat. & exp. path, 63-64, proj. dir, training prog. cytotech. grant, 66- Dipl, Am. Bd. Path, 65. Med.C, U.S.A, 60-62; Nat. Guard, 60-, Maj. AAAS; Int. Acad. Path. Pathogenesis of human immune disorders, particularly renal diseases, by experiments dealing with animal models. Address: Dept. of Pathology, University of Mississippi Medical Center, Jackson, MS 39216.

EVERS, GERALD WAYNE, b. Fredericksburg, Tex, Jan. 17, 43; m. 66; c. 1. AGRONOMY, PLANT PHYSIOLOGY. B.S, Tex, A&M Univ, 66, M.S, 68, Ph.D.(agron), 70. ASST. PROF. AGRON, TEX. AGR. EXP. STA, 71- Nat. Guard, 61. Am. Agron. Soc; Crop Sci. Soc. Am. Seed production in buffelgrass; proper management of kleingrass; tropical grass and legume research. Address: Rt. 5, Box 366, Beaumont, TX 77706.

EVERS, PATRICIA W(EBER), b. Hamilton, Ohio, Dec. 29, 27; m. 59. PHARMACOLOGY, INFORMATION SCIENCE. A.B, Col. Mt. St. Joseph, 49; M.S, St. Louis, 51; Pennsylvania, 53-56. Res. asst, col. med, Cincinnati, 51-52; instr. biol, Rosemont Col, 52-53; lit. scientist, SMITH, KLINE & FRENCH LABS, 55-57, SR. INFO. SCIENTIST, 57- AAAS; N.Y. Acad. Sci; Am. Soc. Info. Sci; Drug Info. Asn. Drug development dealing with communications to Food and Drug Administration; creative analysis of information and identification of new technologies for drug research programs, especially in gastroenterology. Address: Smith, Kline & French Labs, 1500 Spring Garden St, Philadelphia, PA 19101.

EVERS, ROBERT A(UGUST), b. Quincy, Ill, Jan. 17, 12; m. 34; c. 2. BOTANY. B.S, Kans. State Col, 33; M.S, Illinois, 41, Ph.D.(bot), 52. Instr, Quincy Bd. Educ, Ill, 35-46; asst. botanist, STATE NATURAL HIST. SURV, ILL, 46-56, assoc. botanist, 56-65, BOTANIST, 65- Consult, Ill Nature Preserves Comn; res. assoc, West. Ill. Univ. Bot. Soc. Am; Ecol. Soc. Am; Am. Soc. Plant Taxon. Flora and vegetation of Illinois; ecology; taxonomy; paleobotany. Address: Illinois State Natural History Survey, Natural Resources Bldg, Urbana, IL 61801.

EVERS, ROBERT C, b. St. Henry, Ohio, Nov. 10, 39; m. 62; c. 4. ORGANIC & POLYMER CHEMISTRY. B.S, Dayton, 61; U.S. Rubber fel, Notre Dame, 62, NASA fel, 63, Ph.D.(org. chem), 65. RES. CHEMIST, AIR FORCE MAT. LAB, WRIGHT-PATTERSON AFB, 64- AAAS; Am. Chem. Soc. Anionic polymerization of vinyl monomers; synthesis of aromatic and heterocyclic monomers and polymers; fluorocarbon chemistry. Address: 839 Silverleaf Dr, Dayton, OH 45431.

EVERS, WILLIAM JOHN, b. Long Branch, N.J, Sept. 3, 32. ORGANIC CHEMISTRY. B.S, Monmouth Col,(N.J), 60; Nat. Defense Educ. Act fel, Univ. Maine, 60-63, M.S, 62, Ph.D.(org. chem), 65. Chemist, chem. res. ctr, Edgewood Arsenal, Dept. of Army, 65-66; PROJ. LEADER NATURAL PROD. & ORG. SYNTHESIS, INT. FLAVORS & FRAGRANCES, INC, 66- U.S.N, 52-56, Lt. AAAS; Am. Chem. Soc. Heterocyclic and organosulfur chemistry; natural product chemistry of flavors and fragrances. Address: Apt. 7C, 10 Ocean Blvd, Atlantic Highlands, NJ 07716.

EVERS, WILLIAM L, b. Pittsburgh, Pa, Aug. 13, 06; m. 64; c. 1. ORGANIC CHEMISTRY. B.S, Akron, 28; Parke Davis fel, Northwestern, 29, M.S, 29; fel. Pa. State, 29-31, Ph.D.(org. chem), 32. Res. chemist, Socony Mobil Co, Inc, 31-35; res. mgr, Rohm and Haas Co, 35-52; res. mgr, Celanese Corp, 52-64, dir. univ. sci. rels, 64-68; EXEC. DIR. CAMILLE & HENRY DREYFUS FOUND, 68- Mem. vis. comt. biol, Harvard. Am. Chem. Soc; Asn. Res. Dirs; Commercial Chem. Develop. Asn. Polymer chemistry; organophosphorus chemicals; ion exchange resins; organoarsenicals; molecular rearrangements. Address: 445 Park Ave, New York, NY 10022.

EVERSMEYER, HAROLD EDWIN, b. Randolph, Kans, July 7, 27; m. 44; c. 4. PLANT PATHOLOGY, BOTANY. B.S, Kansas State, 51, Nat. Defense Ed. Act fel, 60-64, Ph.D.(plant path), 65. County 4-H Club agent, exten. serv, Kansas State, Olathe, 51-54, Emporia, 56-60; assoc. prof, BIOL. SCI, MURRAY STATE UNIV, 64-70, PROF, 70- U.S.A, 54-56. Am. Phytopath. Soc; Soc. Nematol; Am. Inst. Biol. Sci. Phytonematology—occurrence and damage by plant parasitic nematodes. Address: Dept. of Biological Sciences, Murray State University, Murray, KY 42071.

EVERSOLE, RUSSELL A(NSON), b. Oak Park, Ill, Oct. 18, 26; m. 52; c. 4. BIOCHEMISTRY. B.S, Illinois, 48; U.S. Pub. Health Serv. fel, Stanford, 54-55, Ph.D, 55. Instr. microbiol, Connecticut, 48-50; asst, Stanford, 50-55; Stoner-Mudge sr. res. fel, Pittsburgh, 55-57; tech. dir, Vitamins, Inc, 57-59; mgr. cent. res. labs, Cargill, Inc, 59-65; dir. res, Technicon Instrument Co, 65-66; head biol. sci. & pioneering res. div, Nat. Biscuit Co, 66-67; asst. to pres, Schwarz Serv. Int. Ltd, 67-68; tech. dir, York Res. Corp, 68-70; DIR. ENVIRON. SCI, EBASCO SERV, INC, 70- U.S.N.R, 44-46. Am. Chem. Soc; Am. Soc. Microbiol; N.Y. Acad. Sci; Am. Inst. Chem; Air Pollution Control Asn; Water Pollution Control Fedn. Foods and drugs; chemical research and new product development; air, water and solid waste management and pollution control; patent prosecution; government regulations and liaison. Address: Ebasco Services, Inc, Grant Rd, Purdy Station, New York, NY 10578.

EVERSOLE, WILBURN JOHN, b. Jackson, Ky, Oct. 29, 15; m. 41; c. 2. ENDOCRINOLOGY. A.B, Berea Col, 36; M.Sc, N.Y. Univ, 38, Ph.D.(vert. zool, endocrinol), 40. Asst, N.Y. Univ, 40-42; res. assoc, Princeton, 42-43; instr, Rice Univ, 43-46; from asst. prof. to assoc. prof, Syracuse Univ, 46-51; PROF, Univ. N.Mex, 51-59; LIFE SCI, IND. STATE UNIV, 60- Damon Runyon grant, 51-53; consult, Atomic Energy Comn, 51-59; Nat. Insts. Health grants, 53-58; Am. Cancer Soc. grants, 55-57; consult, Vet. Admin. Hosp, 57-59; Guggenheim fel, 58. Fel. AAAS; Am. Inst. Biol. Sci; Am. Physiol. Soc; Am. Soc. Zool. Endocrine physiology of the adrenals and gonads with emphasis on the regulation of reproduction, kidney function, and water and electrolyte metabolism. Address: Dept. of Life Sciences, Indiana State University, Terre Haute, IN 47809.

EVERSOLE, W(ILLIAM) G(EORGE), b. Caledonia, Mo, June 9, 98; m; c. 3. PHYSICAL CHEMISTRY. A.B, Westminster Col.(Mo), 20; M.S, Iowa, 22, Ph.D.(phys. chem), 24. Instr. chem, sch. med, St. Louis, 24-28; asst. prof, Iowa, 28-35, assoc. prof, 35-43; res. chemist, Linde Co, 43-63; prof. chem, Ark. Polytech. Col, 63-70; RETIRED. With Atomic Energy Comn, 44. Am. Chem. Soc. Electrokinetics; interfacial tension; diffusion; synthetic crystals; high temperature reactions; high pressure chemistry. Address: Farmington, MO 63640.

EVERSON, DALE O, b. Geneva Lake, Wis, Feb. 1, 30; m. 54; c. 2. ANIMAL BREEDING, STATISTICS. B.S, Idaho, 52, M.S, 56; Ph.D.(animal breeding), Iowa State, 60. Biometrician, agr. res. serv, U.S. Dept. Agr, 60-62; assoc. exp. sta. statistician, UNIV. IDAHO, 62-66, PROF. & EXP. STA. STATISTICIAN, 66- Qm.C, 52-54, Sgt. Am. Dairy Sci. Asn; Am. Soc. Animal Sci. Animal breeding and statistic methodology. Address: Experiment Station, College of Agriculture, University of Idaho, Moscow, ID 83843.

EVERSON, EVERETT H(ENRY), b. Whitehall, Wis, Oct. 8, 23; m. 47; c. 2. GENETICS, PLANT BREEDING. B.S, Wisconsin, 49; Ph.D.(genetics), California, 52. Res. agronomist, agronomy, Pillsbury Mills, Inc, 49; asst. California, 49-52; asst. prof. weed control & plant breeding, Arizona, 52-54; res. agronomist genetics & plant breeding, U.S. Dept. Agr, Washington State, 54-56; assoc. prof. CROP SCI, GENETICS & PLANT BREEDING, MICH. STATE UNIV, 56-63, PROF, 64- U.S.A.A.F, 43-46. Am. Soc. Agron; Am. Genetic Asn; Crop Sci. Soc. Am. Genetics and plant breeding; major organism; wheat; genus Triticum. Address: Dept. of Crop & Soil Sciences, Michigan State University, East Lansing, MI 48823.

EVERSON, H(OWARD) E, b. Milan, Ohio, Feb. 26, 18; m. 47; c. 3. INORGANIC & PHYSICAL CHEMISTRY. B.A, Western Reserve, 40, M.S, 47, Ph.D.(chem), 48. Res. chemist, Wyandotte Chems. Corp, 40-42; asst. prof. chem, Cincinnati, 48-51; res. chemist & group leader, Diamond Alkali Co, 51-55; asst. to res. dir, 55-56, chief staff engr, 56-58, asst. dir. res, 58-61, dir. res, 61-67, TECH. DIR, RES. CTR, DIAMOND SHAMROCK CORP, 67- U.S.M.C, 42-46, Capt. Hydrotropic solvents; effect of salts on the aqueous solubility of non-electrolytes. Address: Research Center, Diamond Shamrock Corp, P.O. Box 348, Painesville, OH 44077.

EVERSON, L(EROY) E(VERETT), b. Westboro, Wis, Apr. 2, 14; m. 41; c. 4. AGRONOMY. B.S, Minnesota, 39, M.S, 48, Ph.D.(agron), 50. Asst. SEED

TECHNOL, Cornell, 39-42; asst. prof, IOWA STATE UNIV, 48-51, assoc. prof, 51-58, PROF, 58- U.S.N.R, 42-46, Res, 46-, Lt. Comdr. Hon. mem. Soc. Commercial Seed Technol; Am. Soc. Agron; Asn. Off. Seed Anal. (v.pres, 57-58, pres, 58-59); Int. Seed Test. Soc. Seed technology; extension and administration. Address: Seed Lab, Iowa State University, Ames, IA 50010.

EVERSON, RONALD W(ARD), b. Dodgeville, Wis, Sept. 14, 31. OPTOMETRY, PHYSIOLOGICAL OPTICS. B.S, Chicago Col. Optom, 53, O.D, 54; Am. Optical Co. fel, Indiana, 58-60, M.S, 59. Lectr. optom, Indiana, 61-64; assoc. prof. OPTOM. & dir. grad. prog. physiol. optics, Pacific Univ, 64-67; ASST. PROF, IND. UNIV, BLOOMINGTON, 68- U.S.A, 55-57, 1st Lt. AAAS; Optical Soc, Am; Am. Optom. Asn; fel. Am. Acad. Optom. Human color vision; illumination principles; visual acuity; binocular vision and strabismus. Address: Division of Optometry, Indiana University, Bloomington, IN 47401.

EVERT, CARL F, JR, b. Springfield, Ohio, Dec. 31, 23; m. 50; c. 3. ELECTRICAL ENGINEERING, COMPUTER SCIENCE. B.S.E.E, Purdue, 49, M.S.E.E, 50; Gen. Elec. Co, fel, Wisconsin, 57-58, Ph.D.(elec. eng), 59. Instr. ELEC. ENG, UNIV. CINCINNATI, 50-54, asst. prof, 54-59, assoc. prof, 59-62, PROF, 62-, PROF. IN CHARGE, COMPUT. SCI. LAB, 67-, dir. univ. comput. ctr, 61-67. Nat. Sci. Found. consult, India Eng. Prog, summers 67, 68, 69. U.S.N, 42-46. Inst. Elec. & Electronics Eng; Asn. Comput. Mach. Analog and digital computers applied to engineering, biomedical and scientific problems. Address: University of Cincinnati College of Engineering, Cincinnati, OH 45221.

EVERT, HENRY E(ARL), b. Sherwood, Mich, Mar. 2, 15; m. 46. ORGANIC CHEMISTRY. B.S, Mich. State Col, 37, M.S, 38; Ph.D.(sanit. chem), Iowa, 41; Hopkins, 46-47. Asst. org. chem, Mich. State Col, 37-38; inorg. chem, Iowa, 38-39, sanit. chem, 39-40, storeroom asst, 40-41; res. chemist, Masonite Corp, 41-43; U.S. Pub. Health Serv. consult. chemist, eng. dept, Hopkins, 46-47; asst. prof. chem, George Washington, 47-48; prof. physiol. chem, Scranton, 48-49; asst. pharmacol, Virginia, 49-52; asst. prof. biochem, sch. med, State Univ. N.Y, 52-62; PROF. CHEM. & CHMN. DEPT, NASSAU COMMUNITY COL, 62- U.S.N, 43-46, Lt. Fel. AAAS; fel. Am. Inst. Chem; Am. Chem. Soc. Carbohydrates; catalysis; wood chemistry; enzymology; chemical oceanography. Address: 353 Harmon Ave, P.O. Box 326, Garden City, NY 11530.

EVERT, RAY FRANKLIN, b. Mt. Carmel, Pa, Feb. 20, 31; m. 60; c. 2. BOTANY. B.S, Pa. State, 52, M.S, 54; Ph.D.(bot), California, Davis, 58. Instr. BOT, Mont. State Col, 58-59, asst. prof, 59-60; UNIV. WIS, MADISON, 60-63, assoc. prof, 63-66, PROF, 66- Nat. Sci. Found. Res. grants, 59-60, 61-62, 63-66, 67-68, 69-70, 71-73; mem. cell biol. fel. rev. panel, Nat. Insts. Health, 64-68; Guggenheim Found. fel, 65-66; vis. prof, Univ. Natal, spring 71; forstbotanisches inst, Univ. Göttingen, summer 71. AAAS; Bot. Soc. Am; Am. Inst. Biol. Sci. Light and electron microscopic investigations of the ontogeny, structure and seasonal development of the phloem. Address: Dept. of Botany, University of Wisconsin, Madison, WI 53706.

EVERTSBUSCH, VALESKA, b. Pateros, Wash, Mar. 4, 15. PHARMACOLOGY. B.Sc, Washington State, 50; Ph.D.(pharmacol), Chicago, 54. Assoc. pharmacol, Chicago, 54-55; ed, div. biol. & med. res, Argonne Nat. Lab, 55-63; BIOCHEMIST & ED, BIOMED. RES. DIV, LAWRENCE RADIATION LAB, UNIV. CALIF, 64- Radiation biology; semantic and editorial problems in scientific communication. Address: 1333 Juniper, Livermore, CA 94550.

EVERY, RICHARD L, b. Kingfisher, Okla, Aug. 9, 27; m. 48; c. 4. PHYSICAL CHEMISTRY. B.S, Okla. State, 57; Nat. Sci. Found. fel. & Ph.D.(phys. chem), Texas, 60. Group supvr. phys. chem, CONTINENTAL OIL CO, 60-67, mat. sci. group leader, 67, SECT. HEAD CHEM. DEVELOP, 67- Am. Chem. Soc. Surface chemistry; combustion and fuels; slurry handling; liquid fertilizers; transition metal oxides; solid electrodes; cryogenic chemistry. Address: 1407 De Soto, Ponca City, OK 74601.

EVES, HOWARD (WHITLEY), b. Paterson, N.J, Jan. 10, 11; m. 40; c. 5. MATHEMATICS. B.S, Virginia, 34; M.A, Harvard, 35; Princeton, 36-37; Syracuse, 42-43; Ph.D.(math), Ore. State Col, 48. Asst. calculus, Harvard & Radcliffe Col, 35-36; land surveyor, Gen. Housing Corp, N.J, 40-41; instr. math, Allen Acad, Texas, 41-42; mathematician, Tenn. Valley Auth, 42; asst. prof. MATH, Syracuse, 42-45; chmn. dept, Col. Puget Sound, 45-46; asst. prof, Ore. State Col, 46-48, assoc. prof, 48-51; PROF, State Univ. N.Y, 51-54; UNIV. MAINE, ORONO, 54- Am. Math. Soc; Math. Asn. Am; Math. Soc. France. Differential and algebraic geometry; theory of dissections; history of mathematics. Address: Dept. of Mathematics, University of Maine at Orono, Orono, ME 04473.

EVESLAGE, SYLVESTER L(EE), b. Ripley, Ohio, Apr. 25, 23; m. 55; c. 4. ORGANIC CHEMISTRY. B.S, Notre Dame, 44, M.S, 45, Du Pont fel, 46-48, Ph.D.(org. chem), 53. Instr. CHEM, UNIV. DAYTON, 48-51, asst. prof, 51-56, assoc. prof, 56-66, PROF, 66- AAAS; Am. Chem. Soc. Ion exchange chromatography; synthesis of chemotherapeutic compounds. Address: Dept. of Chemistry, University of Dayton, Dayton, OH 45409.

EVETT, ARTHUR A, b. Pasco, Wash, Apr. 12, 25; m. 46; c. 2. PHYSICS. B.S, Washington State, 48, Pepsi Cola fel, 48-51, Ph.D.(physics), 51. Adv. sci. warfare, weapons systs. eval. group, U.S. Dept. Defense, D.C, 51-52; instr. PHYSICS, Yale, 52-55; asst. prof, Washington State, 56-58; assoc. prof, Univ. Ariz, 58-61, PROF, 61-68; CALIF. STATE COL, DOMINGUEZ HILLS, 68- U.S.A.A.F, 43-45. Am. Phys. Soc. Relativity theory; intermolecular forces; surface physics. Address: Dept. of Physics, California State College at Dominguez Hills, Dominguez Hills, CA 90246.

EVETT, JACK B(URNIE), b. York, Pa, May 26, 42; m. 69; c. 1. CIVIL ENGINEERING. B.S, South Carolina, 64, M.S, 65; Ph.D.(civil eng), Texas A&M, 68. ASST. PROF. CIVIL ENG, UNIV. N.C, CHARLOTTE, 67- Am. Soc. Civil Eng; Am. Soc. Eng. Educ. Waste dispersion patterns in an estuarine system; water resources planning and development. Address: College of Engineering, University of North Carolina at Charlotte, UNCC Station, Charlotte, NC 28213.

EVETT, JAY FREDRICK, b. Lewiston, Idaho, Nov. 5, 31; m. 57; c. 1. PHYSICS, BIOPHYSICS. B.S, Wash. State Univ, 53, B.S, 57; M.S, Northwest. Univ, 58; Nat. Sci. Found. fel, Ore. State Univ, 66, Ph.D.(biophys), 68. Nuclear engr, U.S. Atomic Energy Comn, 60-61; asst. prof. PHYSICS, Moorhead State Col, 61-65, ASSOC. PROF, 65-66; ORE. COL. EDUC, 68- U.S.A, 54-56. AAAS; Am. Phys. Soc; Am. Asn. Physics Teachers. Polarization of fluorescence studies of macromolecules. Address: Dept. of Natural Sciences, Oregon College of Education, Monmouth, OR 97361.

EVINS, CHARLES VICTOR, b. Frankfort, Ky, Feb. 16, 41; m. 63; c. 3. ANALYTICAL CHEMISTRY. B.S, Mass. Inst. Tech, 63; Ph.D.(anal. chem), Purdue, 67. Res. chemist, Celanese Res. Co, Summit, 66-69; GROUP LEADER, ANAL. CHEM, FIBER INDUSTS, INC, 69- Am. Chem. Soc. Electroanalytical chemistry; x-ray fluorescence and diffraction spectroscopy; atomic absorption spectrophotometry; electron paramagnetic resonance and emission spectroscopy; gel permeation chromatography. Address: Fiber Industries, Inc, Archdale Dr, Charlotte, NC 28210.

EVITT, W(ILLIAM) R(OBERT), b. Baltimore, Md, Dec. 9, 23; m. 50; c. 3. GEOLOGY. A.B, Hopkins, 42, Ph.D.(geol), 50. Asst, Hopkins, 46-48; instr. geol, Rochester, 48-51, asst. prof, 51-55, assoc. prof, 55-56; sr. res. geologist, Jersey Prod. Res. Co, 56-59, res. assoc, 59-62; PROF. GEOL, STANFORD UNIV, 62- U.S.A.A.F, 42-46, Capt. Paleont. Soc.(ed, jour, 53-56, v.pres, 58); Bot. Soc. Am; Geol. Soc. Am; Am. Asn. Stratig. Palynologists; Int. Asn. Plant Taxon. Palynology; dinoflagellate morphology; invertebrate paleontology. Address: Dept. of Geology, Stanford University, Stanford, CA 94305.

EVLETH, EARL M(ANSFIELD), b. Evanston, Ill, Dec. 7, 31; m. 55; c. 1. THEORETICAL & ORGANIC CHEMISTRY. B.S, Calif. Inst. Tech, 54; Ph.D. (chem), Southern California, 63. Chemist, Shell Oil Co, 54-55; res. chemist, Am. Potash & Chem. Co, 55-57, 60-61; Int. Bus. Mach. Corp, 62-69; ASST. PROF. NATURAL SCI, UNIV. CALIF, SANTA CRUZ, 69- Am. Phys. Soc; Am. Chem. Soc; The Chem. Soc. Synthetic organic and inorganic chemistry; computer simulation; photochemistry and energy transfer mechanisms; spectra-structure correlations; semi-empirical molecular orbital calculations. Address: Division of Natural Sciences, University of California, Santa Cruz, CA 95060.

EVNIN, ANTHONY B, b. N.Y.C, Mar. 10, 41; m. 62; c. 2. ORGANIC & ORGANOMETALLIC CHEMISTRY. B.A, Princeton, 62; Nat. Insts. Health fel, Mass. Inst. Technol, 63-66, Ph.D.(org. chem), 66. Scientist RES. INST, UNION CARBIDE CORP, TARRYTOWN, 66-70, GROUP LEADER, 70- Am. Chem. Soc; Sci. Res. Soc. Am. Heterogeneous and homogeneous catalysis, especially metal-catalyzed oxidations; main group organometallic chemistry emphasizing unsaturated stannanes and lithium compounds; cycloaddition reactions of azadienes and dienophiles; fluorine chemistry. Address: 16 Hamilton Dr, Chappaqua, NY 10514.

EVONUK, EUGENE, b. Springfield, Ore, Oct. 11, 21; m. 46. PHYSIOLOGY. B.S, Oregon, 52, M.S, 53; Am. Heart Asn. fel, Iowa, 59, Ph.D.(physiol), 60. Instr. health educ, Oregon, 53-55, asst. prof, 55-58; res. physiologist, Arctic Aeromed. Lab, U.S. Dept. Air Force, 60-63, chief, physiol. br, 63-67; PROF. & DIR. CTR. RES. HUMAN PERFORMANCE, UNIV. ORE, 67- U.S.A.A.F, 42-45. Fel. AAAS; Am. Physiol. Soc; Aerospace Med. Asn; Am. Polar Soc; Undersea Med. Soc; Am. Soc. Zool; fel. Arctic Inst. N.Am. Cardiovascular effects of mild and profound cooling; thermal and metabolic responses to cooling; physiology of work and altitude. Address: Center for Research on Human Performance, University of Oregon, Eugene, OR 97403.

EVOY, WILLIAM (HARRINGTON), b. Phila, Pa, July 1, 38; m. 64; c. 2. NEUROPHYSIOLOGY. B.A, Reed Col, 60; M.A, Oregon, 62, U.S. Pub. Health Serv. trainee, 61-64, Ph.D.(biol), 64. Res. assoc. comp. neurophysiol, Stanford Univ, 64-66; asst. prof. BIOL, UNIV. MIAMI, 66-69, ASSOC. PROF, 69- Grass Found. summer fel, Marine Biol. Lab, Woods Hole, 64. Am. Soc. Zool. Comparative physiology of crustacean nervous and neuromuscular systems, particularly the organization and detailed function of central nervous systems in behavior. Address: Lab. for Quantitative Biology, Dept. of Biology, University of Miami, P.O. Box 8074, Coral Gables, FL 33124.

EVRARD, THOMAS O, b. Allentown, Pa, June 2, 30; m. 49; c. 4. PLANT PHYSIOLOGY. B.S, Pa. State Univ, 56; M.S, Rutgers Univ, 58; Ph.D.(plant physiol), Va. Polytech. Inst, 67. Researcher sugarcane, United Fruit Sugar Co, 58-60; tech. serv. rep, Diamond Shamrock Corp, 60-63; instr. plant physiol, Va. Polytech. Inst, 63-67; mgr. tech. serv. & advertising, CIBA AGROCHEM. CO, 67-69, ASST. DIR. RES. & DEVELOP, 69- U.S.A, 48-52, S/Sgt. Plant growth regulators; aquatic plant control; pesticides and other agricultural chemicals; effects of pesticides on the environment; pesticides regulations. Address: 1046 22nd Ave, Vero Beach, FL 32960.

EVTUHOV, VIKTOR, b. Poland, May 24, 35; U.S. citizen; m. 57; c. 2. ELECTRICAL ENGINEERING, PHYSICS. B.S, California, Los Angeles, 56; M.S, Calif. Inst. Tech, 57, Ph.D.(elec. eng), 61. Mem. tech. staff, HUGHES RES. LAB, 56, 60-65, sr. staff physicist, 65-70, HEAD QUANTUM ELECTRONICS SECT, LASER DEPT, 70- Res. fel. & instr. elec. eng, Calif. Inst. Technol, 60-61, sr. res. fel, 70- AAAS; Am. Phys. Soc; Inst. Elec. & Electronics Eng. Physical electronics; secondary emission; theory of semiconductors; band structure; quantum electronics; lasers. Address: Laser Dept, Hughes Research Lab, 3011 Malibu Canyon Rd, Malibu, CA 90265.

EVVARD, JOHN C(OOPER), b. Ames, Iowa, Dec. 9, 15; m. 41; c. 6. AERODYNAMICS. B.S, Calif. Inst. Tech, 39, fel, 39-42, M.S, 40, Ph.D.(physics), 43. Res. physicist, Nat. Adv. Cmt. Aeronaut, 42, head small scale engines sect, 42-45, chief special projs. panel, 45-49, mem, internal flow sub-cmt, 48-58, fluid mech. sub-cmt, 48-58, asst. dir. res, LEWIS RES. CENTER, NASA, 58-61, dep. assoc. dir. res, 61-68, assoc. dir, 68-70, DIR. ADVAN. RES. & MEM. OFF. ADVAN. RES. & TECHNOL. RES. COUN, 70- Instr, Case West. Reserve Univ, 43-45, spec. lectr, 48-; Jerome Clarke Hunsaker prof. aeronaut, Mass. Inst. Technol, 67-68. Exceptional Sci. Achievement Award, NASA, 68, Am. Phys. Soc; Am. Inst. Aeronaut. & Astronaut. Mass spectroscopy; anti-knock aviation gasoline; power plant for supersonic flight; supersonic aerodynamics; nuclear physics; materials and structures; space flight sciences; research administration. Address: Lewis Research Center, NASA, 21000 Brookpark Rd, Cleveland, OH 44135.

EWALD, ARNO W(ILFORD), b. Fond du Lac, Wis, May 14, 18; m. 43; c. 4. PHYSICS. B.S, Wis. State Col, 41; M.S, Michigan, 42, Ph.D.(physics), 48. Fel. PHYSICS, Univ. Mich, 41-44, res. assoc, 44-48; instr, NORTHWEST. UNIV.(ILL), 48-51, asst. prof, 51-56, assoc. prof, 56-61, PROF, 61- Res. assoc, Nat. Defense Res. Comt, 44-45. Fel. Am. Phys. Soc. Semiconductors; photoconductivity; energy band structure determinations; infrared phenomena; crystal physics. Address: Dept. of Physics, Northwestern University, Evanston, IL 60201.

EWALD, FRED PETERSON, JR, b. Saginaw, Mich, Mar. 25, 32. ANALYTICAL CHEMISTRY, PHYSICS. B.S, Aquinas Col, 54; Ph.D.(anal. chem), Kansas, 62. Technician anal. chem, Haviland Prod, 52-54; asst. chem, Kansas, 54-59; SUPVR. ANAL. CHEM, CHEM. DIV, PPG INDUSTS, INC, 60- Summers, jr. chemist, Continental Oil Co, 56, chemist, Argonne Nat. Lab, 57. Am. Chem. Soc. Nonaqueous electrochemistry; gas chromatography; mass spectrometry; air and water pollution analysis; infrared spectroscopy, emission and absorption spectroscopy; herbicide residue analysis. Address: 1598 Wooster Rd. W, Barberton, OH 44203.

EWALD, P(AUL) P(ETER), b. Berlin, Ger, Jan. 23, 88. PHYSICS, CRYSTALLOGRAPHY. M.A, Queens (Ireland), 46; Ph.D.(physics), Munich, Ger, 12, hon. Dr, Stuttgart Tech. Univ, Ger, Univ. Paris, Munich Univ. & Adelphi Univ. Privat-docent, Munich, Ger, 18-21; prof. theoret. physics, Stuttgart Tech. Univ, 21-37; fel, Cambridge, 37-39; lectr. & prof. math. physics, Queens (Ireland), 36-49; head dept, POLYTECH. INST. BROOKLYN, 49-57, prof, 57-59; EMER. PROF, 59- Mem, Int. Union Crystallog, ed, Acta Crystallog, 48-59, mem. exec. comt, 48-66, pres, 60-63; emer. prof, Univ. Stuttgart. Fel. Am. Acad. Arts & Sci; fel. Royal Soc; cor. mem. Göttingen Acad. Sci; cor. mem. Bavarian Acad. Sci; hon. mem, Fr. Soc. Mineral & Crystallog; hon. mem. Ger. Mineral Soc; Leopoldine Ger. Acad. Res. Nat. Sci. X-ray and light optics; crystal structure analysis; solid state physics. Address: 108 Sheldon Rd, Ithaca, NY 14850.

EWALD, WILLIAM PHILIP, b. Whitestone, N.Y, Mar. 27, 22; m. 44; c. 4. OPTICS. B.S, Univ. Rochester, 45. Sr. proj. engr, EASTMAN KODAK CO, 45-66, SR. SUPV. DEVELOP. ENGR, 66- U.S.N, 43-45. Optical Soc. Am; Soc. Motion Picture & TV Eng. Design and development of original optical systems; photography. Address: Apparatus Division, Eastman Kodak Co, Elmgrove Plant, Rochester, NY 14650.

EWALT, JACK R, b. Medicine Lodge, Kans, Jan. 27, 10; m. 31; c. 2. PSYCHIATRY. Stoiber scholar, Colorado, M.D, 33. Commonwealth Fund fellow psychiat, psychopath. hosp, Colorado, 34-37, asst. prof, univ, 37-41; prof, Texas, 41-51, dir. psychopath. hosp, 45-50, administr. med. br, hosps, 48-50, dean, postgrad. sch. med, 50-51; comnr, State Dept. Mental Health, Mass, 51-58; SUPT, MASS. MENT. HEALTH CTR, 58-; BULLARD PROF. PSYCHIAT, HARVARD MED. SCH, 62-, clin. prof, 52-58, prof, 58-62. Consult, surgeon gen, U.S. Dept. Air Force, 51-54. Am. Acad. Arts & Sci; fel. Am. Psychiat. Asn.(treas; pres, 63-64); fel. Am. Med. Asn. Neuropyphilis; schizophrenia; amputations; tissue culture. Address: Massachusetts Mental Health Center, 74 Fenwood Rd, Boston, MA 02115.

EWAN, GEORGE T, b. Edinburgh, Scotland, May 6, 27; m. 52; c. 2. PHYSICS. B.Sc, Edinburgh, 48, Ph.D.(physics), 52. Asst. lectr. PHYSICS, Edinburgh, 50-52; res. assoc, McGill, 52-55; asst. res. officer, Atomic Energy Can. Ltd, 55-58, assoc. res. off, 58-62, sr. res. off, 62-70; PROF, QUEEN'S UNIV, 70- Nat. Res. Coun. Can. fel, 54-55; Ford Found. fel, Niels Bohr Inst, Copenhagen, 61-62; vis. scientist, Lawrence Radiation Lab, 66. Radiation Indust. Award, Am. Nuclear Soc, 67. Nuclear physics; high resolution β- and γ-ray spectroscopy; semiconductor detectors; applications of nuclear techniques. Address: Dept. of Physics, Queen's University, Kingston, Ont, Can.

EWAN, JOSEPH (ANDORFER), b. Phila, Pa, Oct. 24, 09; m. 35; c. 3. BOTANY. A.B, California, 34, 34-37. Asst. phanerogamic bot, California, 33-37; instr. biol, Colorado, 37-44; botanist, For. Econ. Admin, Colombia, 44-45; asst. curator div. plants, Smithsonian Inst, 45-46; assoc. botanist, bur. plant indust, U.S. Dept. Agr. Md, 46-47; asst. prof. BOT, TULANE UNIV. LA, 47-52, assoc. prof, 52-57, PROF, 57- Am. Philos. Soc. grant, 49-52, 54, 58, 64; Guggenheim fel, 54; Nat. Sci. Found. fel, 59-61; lectr, Univ. Hawaii, summer, 67; ed, Classica Bot. Am, 66- Off. del, int. conf, Nat. Sci. Res. Center, France, 56; panelist, Lilly Conf. Res. Opportunities Am. Cultural Hist, Mo, 59. Mem. Wash. Acad. Sci. bot. explor, S.Am. AAAS; Am. Fern Soc.(v.pres, 41-47, pres, 58-59); Am. Soc. Plant Taxon; Cooper Ornith. Soc; Torrey Bot. Club; Hist. Sci. Soc; Bot. Soc. Am; Brit. Soc. Bibliog. Nat. Hist. Taxonomy of Delphinium, Vismia and American Gentinacaea; biography and bibliography of naturalists; phytogeography and flora of Louisiana. Address: Dept. of Biology, Tulane University of Louisiana, New Orleans, LA 70118.

EWAN, MAURICE A(LBERTSON), b. Morocco, Ind, July 3, 13; m. 37; c. 3. CHEMISTRY. B.S, Purdue, 36. Anal. chemist, Swift & Co, Ill, 36-39, prod. supvr, 39-42; asst. chemist, Purdue, 42-46; group leader anal. res. div, res. labs, Cent. Soya Co, Inc, Ind, 46-49; res. supvr. CLINTON CORN PROCESSING CO. DIV, STANDARD BRANDS, INC, 49-63, MGR. FEED SECT, TECH. SERV. DEPT, 63- With Off. Sci. Res. & Develop, 44. Am. Chem. Soc; Am. Oil Chemists' Soc. Fertilizer analysis methods; isolation and characterization of soybean phosphatides; development of analytical methods for controlling soybean processing; corn wet milling. Address: Clinton Corn Processing Co, Clinton, IA 52732.

EWAN, RICHARD C(OLIN), b. Cuba, Ill, Sept. 10, 34; m. 56; c. 4. ANIMAL SCIENCE, BIOCHEMISTRY. B.S, Illinois, 56, M.S, 57; Ph.D.(animal sci, & biochem), Wisconsin, 66. ASSOC. PROF. ANIMAL SCI, IOWA STATE UNIV, 66- U.S.A.F, 57-62, 1st Lt. Am. Soc. Animal Sci. Vitamin and mineral interactions in nutrition. Address: Dept. of Animal Science, Iowa State University, Ames, IA 50010.

EWART, HUGH WALLACE, JR, b. Decatur, Ill, Oct. 18, 39; m. 63; c. 2. ORGANIC CHEMISTRY. B.S, Trinity Col.(Conn), 61; M.S, Yale, 63, Nat. Insts. Health fel. & Ph.D.(org. chem), 67; Sci. Res. Coun. Eng. fel, Southampton, 66-67. RES. CHEMIST, OLYMPIC RES. DIV, ITT RAYONIER INC, 68- Am. Chem. Soc; The Chem. Soc. Synthetic chemistry of small ring systems via cycloaddition reactions; separation and identification of natural products and derivatives; photochemistry of organic compounds. Address: Olympic Research Division, ITT Rayonier, Inc, Shelton, WA 98584.

EWART, MERVYN H, b. Can, Dec. 23, 20; m. 57; c. 2. BIOCHEMISTRY. B.S.A, Ont. Agr. Col, 44; M.Sc, McGill, 46; Ph.D.(agr. biochem), Minnesota, 51. Res. chemist, Can. Dept. Health & Welfare, 51-54; asst. prof. CHEM, ALBANY COL. PHARM, UNION UNIV.(N.Y), 54-59, assoc. prof, 59-65, PROF. & CHMN. DEPT, 65- Vis. prof, State Univ. Col. Ed, Albany, 59; consult, Christian Hansen Labs, 56. Am. Chem. Soc. Enzymes; metabolism; chemical analysis. Address: Albany College of Pharmacy, Union University, 106 New Scotland Ave, Albany, NY 12208.

EWART, R(ALPH) BRADLEY, b. Mt. Pleasant, Iowa, Mar. 4, 32; m. 64. BOTANY. B.A, Univ. Iowa, 56; Nat. Sci. Found. fel, Wash. Univ, 59-60, M.A, 62, Nat. Sci. Found. trainee, summer 68, hon. jr. fel. & Nat. Defense Educ. Act, 68-69, Ph.D.(bot), 69. Instr, high sch, Ill, 56-59, 60-63, 64-66; Guatemala, Cent.Am, 63-64; teaching asst. biol, Wash. Univ, 66-68; ASST. PROF. BIOL. & BOT, NORTHWEST MO. STATE COL, 69- U.S.A, 53-55. AAAS; Phycol. Soc. Am; Am. Inst. Biol. Sci. Anatomical studies of the fossil genus Scolecopteris; developmental studies of cell wall synthesis in the zoospore of Vaucheria sessilis; photography of algae, fungi, and lower vascular plants. Address: Dept. of Biology, Northwest Missouri State College, Maryville, MO 64468.

EWART, ROSWELL H(ORR), b. N. Plainfield, N.J, Apr. 17, 03; m. 40; c. 1. PHYSICAL CHEMISTRY. Ch.E, Lehigh, 25; Ph.D.(phys. chem), Illinois, 33. Asst. chem. engr, Bur. Chem, Wash, D.C, 25-26; control chemist, Calco Chem. Co, N.J, 26-27; chief chemist, Hercules Powder Co, Mo, 27-29; asst. chem, Illinois, 29-33; res. chemist, gen. labs, U.S. Rubber Co, 33-35, Naugatuck chem. div, 35-39, gen. labs, 39-57, mgr. synthetic fiber & radiation res. dept, 57-64, polymer physics dept, 64-65, mgr. indust. rels. & salary admin, 65-68; ASST. PROF. SCI, MONTCLAIR STATE COL, 68- Mem, Oper. Comt. Indust. Reactor Labs. Am. Chem. Soc. Molecular structures of high polymers; emulsion and stereospecific polymerization; viscosity and light scattering of high polymer solutions; polymer rheology; radiation chemistry; nuclear reactors; adhesion; colloids; inorganic polymers; underwater technology. Address: Dept. of Chemistry, Montclair State College, Upper Montclair, NJ 07043.

EWART, TERRY E, b. Seattle, Wash, July 6, 34; m. 54; c. 4. PHYSICS. B.S, Washington (Seattle), 59, Ph.D.(physics), 65. Sr. physicist, APPL. PHYSICS LAB, UNIV. WASH, 59-68, HEAD OCEAN PHYSICS GROUP, 68-, SR. RES. ASSOC, DEPT. OCEANOG, 70- Consult, State Bur. Fisheries, 62-65. AAAS; Marine Technol. Soc; Am. Phys. Soc. High energy particle physics; underwater acoustics. Address: Applied Physics Lab, University of Washington, 1013 E. 40th St, Seattle, WA 98105.

EWART, W(ILLIAM) H(OWARD), b. Radersburgh, Mont, Mar. 8, 13; m. 34; c. 3. ECONOMIC ENTOMOLOGY. B.A, Ohio State, 36, M.Sc, 37; Ph.D. (econ. entom), 41. Asst. econ. entom, Cornell, 37-41; entomologist, Tex. Agr. Exp. Sta, Winter Haven, 41-45; asst. entomologist, UNIV. CALIF, RIVERSIDE, 45-50, assoc. entomologist, 50-58, ENTOMOLOGIST, 58- AAAS; assoc. Am. Entom. Soc. Biology and control of various citrus and avocado insect pests. Address: Dept. of Entomology, University of California, Riverside, CA 92502.

EWBANK, WALTER JAMES, b. Lawrenceburg, Ind, Aug. 1, 14; m. 39; c. 5. MECHANICAL ENGINEERING. B.S, Purdue, 36; M.S, Va. Polytech, 38. Dir. res, Briggs Filtration Co, 38-48; asst. prof. MECH. ENG, UNIV. OKLA, 48-53, assoc. prof, 53-59, PROF, 59- Consult, Cato Oil & Grease Co, Okla, 50-70; Jesco Lubricants Co, Mo, 56-58; res. inst, Univ. Okla, 58-; vis. prof, Univ. Calif, Los Angeles, 63-64. Am. Soc. Mech. Eng; Soc. Automotive Eng; Am. Soc. Lubrication Eng. Thermodynamics; fuels and combustion; lubrication engineering; design of pollution control systems. Address: School of Aerospace, Mechanical & Nuclear Engineering, University of Oklahoma, Norman, OK 73069.

EWBANK, W(ESLEY) BRUCE, b. Olivet, Kans, Sept. 21, 32; m. 57; c. 2. NUCLEAR & ATOMIC PHYSICS. B.S, Kansas, 54, Ph.D.(physics), California, Berkeley, 60. Asst, California, Berkeley, 54-59, RES. ASSOC. NUCLEAR PHYSICS, Lawrence Radiation Lab, 59-62; NUCLEAR DATA PROJ, Nat. Acad. Sci-Nat. Res. Coun, 62-63; OAK RIDGE NAT. LAB, 64- Lectr, California, Berkeley, 61-62; summers, res. asst, Los Alamos Sci. Lab, 55, 56. Am. Phys. Soc. Measurement of nuclear moments by atomic-beam spectroscopy; collection and synthesis of experimental results in nuclear-structure physics for publication of nuclear data sheets. Address: Nuclear Data Project, Oak Ridge National Lab, P.O. Box X, Oak Ridge, TN 37830.

EWELL, RAYMOND (HENRY), b. Brockton, Mass, June 18, 08; m. 45; c. 2. CHEMISTRY, ECONOMICS. B.S, Toledo, 28; M.S, Purdue, 30; M.A, George Washington, 35; Ph.D.(phys. chem), Princeton, 37. Jr. chemist.& petrographer, mineral prods. div, Bur. Standards, 30-35; instr, Purdue, 37-39, asst. prof, 39-41; tech. aide, Nat. Defense Res. Cmt, 41-45; sr. chem. economist, Shell Chem. Corp, 45-48; chmn. dept. chem. & chem. eng, Stanford Res. Inst, 48-50, mgr. chem. econ. serv, 50-53; asst. dir, Nat. Sci. Found, 53-56; consult. indust. res, Govt. Philippines, 55-57; V.PRES. RES, STATE UNIV. N.Y. BUFFALO, 57- Adv. indust. develop, Govt. India, 56-; consult, UN, 63-; U.S. Agency Int. Develop, 64-; sr indust. develop. off, UN Indust. Develop. Orgn, 71-72. Medal of Merit, 48. Am. Chem. Soc; Am. Inst. Chem. Eng. Fertilizer; chemical economics; economics of research; thermodynamics; viscosity. Address: 56 Highgate Ave, Buffalo, NY 14214.

EWELL, R(OBERT) BARTLETT, b. Brockton, Mass, Mar. 16, 12; m. 34; c. 3. CHEMICAL ENGINEERING. B.A, Ohio State, 34; Ph.D.(phys. chem), Wisconsin, 39. Asst. chem, Wisconsin, 34-38; res. chemist, Universal Oil

Prod. Co, Ill, 38-40; technologist, Wilmington Ref, SHELL OIL CO, Calif, 40-44, Head Off, San Francisco, 44-48, spec. duty, The Hague, Holland, 48-51, Wilmington Ref, 51-60, Wood River Ref, 60-66, STAFF ENGR, HEAD OFF, HOUSTON, 66- Theoretical study of intermolecular energy; velocity of sound in hydrocarbons; thermal and catalytic cracking, pilot and commercial scale; refinery economics; operations research; data processing; computer control. Address: 1431 Davon Lane, Houston, TX 77058.

EWEN, ALWYN B(RADLEY), b. Saskatoon, Sask, Oct. 24, 32; m. 54; c. 2. INSECT PHYSIOLOGY. B.A, Saskatchewan, 55, M.A, 57; Ph.D.(insect physiol), Alberta, 61. RES. OFFICER, CAN. DEPT. AGR, 57- AAAS; Am. Soc. Zool; Can. Soc. Zool; fel. Royal Entom. Soc. London. Physiology of insect reproduction; insect hormones and their use in control; grasshopper embryology; cancer in insects. Address: Research Station, Canada Dept. of Agriculture, University Campus, Saskatoon, Sask, Can.

EWEN, EDWARD F(RANCIS), b. Woodriver, Ill, Jan. 11, 23; m. 54; c. 2. ANALYTICAL CHEMISTRY. Fel, St. Louis, 46-51, Ph.D.(chem), 52. Mkt. dir, E.H. Sargent & Co, 51-69, V.PRES, SARGENT-WELCH SCI. CO, 69- U.S.N.R, 44-46. Am. Chem. Soc. Analytical instrumentation in chemistry. Address: 1050 Woodbine Lane, Northbrook, IL 60062.

EWEN, HAROLD IRVING, b. Chicopee, Mass, Mar. 5, 22; m. 56; c. 6. ASTRONOMY, PHYSICS. B.A, Amherst Col, 43; Nat. Res. Coun. fel, Harvard, 46, M.A, 48, Ph.D.(physics), 51. RES. ASSOC. ASTRON, HARVARD, 52-; PRES, EWEN KNIGHT CORP, 52-; EWEN DAE CORP, 58- Mem. Cmn. V, Int. Sci. Radio Union, 52- U.S.N.R, 43-46, Lt. Fel. AAAS; Am. Acad. Arts & Sci; sr. mem. Inst. Elec. & Electronics Eng; Int. Astron. Union. Microwave detection and analysis of interstellar gases; radio telescope and microwave radiometric receiver techniques. Address: Ewen Knight Corp, Oak & Pine St, Natick, MA 01760.

EWEN, LILLIAN M(ARY), b. Petty, Scotland, Aug. 3, 34; m. 64; c. 2. BIOCHEMISTRY. CLINICAL CHEMISTRY. B.S, Aberdeen Univ, 56; M.S.A, Univ. Toronto, 63; Reserve Bank Australia scholar, Univ. New South Wales, 64-67, Ph.D.(biochem), 68. Res. biologist, Huntingdon Res. Ctr, Eng, 56-59; res. scientist, Ont. Agr. Col, Univ. Guelph, 60-64; CLIN. BIOCHEMIST, VANCOUVER GEN. HOSP, 68- AAAS; Nutrit. Soc. Can; Can. Soc. Clin. Chem; Am. Asn. Clin. Chem. Vitamin A metabolism and nutritional muscular dystrophy in chicks; biochemical aspects of some Australian bull dog ant venoms; gamma-glutamyl transpeptidase, especially some clinical implications of elevated serum levels. Address: Dept. of Pathology, Vancouver General Hospital, Vancouver, B.C, Can.

EWERT, ADAM, b. Mt. Lake, Minn, Dec. 1, 27; m. 60; c. 1. PARASITOLOGY, MEDICAL ENTOMOLOGY. B.A, Tabor Col, 51; Notre Dame, 57-58; M.A, Texas, 60; Ph.D.(parasitol), Tulane, 63. Asst. prof. parasitol. & lectr, faculty med, Univ. Singapore, 64-67; ASST. PROF. MICROBIOL, UNIV. TEX. MED. BR. GALVESTON, 67- Am. Soc. Trop. Med. & Hyg; Am. Soc. Parasitol; Royal Soc. Trop. Med. & Hyg. Immunological tolerance; host-parasite interactions involving microfilaria and mosquitoes. Address: Dept. of Microbiology, University of Texas Medical Branch, Galveston, TX 77550.

EWING, BEN B, b. Donna, Tex, Apr. 4, 24; m. 47; c. 3. SANITARY ENGINEERING. B.S.C.E, Texas, 44, M.S, 49; Ph.D.(sanit. eng), California, 59. Instr. civil eng, Texas, 47-51, asst. prof, 51-52; civil engr, Hqs. Fourth Army, Ft. Sam Houston, 52-53; asst. prof. civil eng, Texas, 53-55; assoc, California, 55-56, asst. res. engr, 56-58; asst. prof. civil eng, Texas, 58; assoc. prof. sanit. eng, UNIV. ILL, URBANA, 58-61, PROF, 61-, SANIT. ENG. & NUCLEAR ENG, 67-, DIR. WATER RESOURCES CTR, 66- U.S.N.R, 43-46, Lt.(jg). Water Pollution Control Fedn; Am. Soc. Civil Eng; Am. Soc. Eng. Educ; Am. Water Works Asn; Am. Geophys. Union; Am. Asn. Prof. Sanit. Eng. Water quality and pollution; reactions between organic compounds and clay minerals; radioactive waste disposal; ground water pollution recharge of ground water supplies. Address: Dept. of Civil Engineering, University of Illinois at Urbana, Urbana, IL 61801.

EWING, CHANNING LESTER, b. Jefferson City, Mo, May 28, 27; m. 56; c. 2. BIOENGINEERING, AEROSPACE MEDICINE. M.D, Med. Col. Va, 52; M.P.H, Johns Hopkins Univ, 63. U.S. NAVY, 52-, intern, U.S. Naval Hosp, Portsmouth, Va, 52-53; flight surgeon, USS Wright & USS Ticonderoga, 53-58, resident, prev. med, aerospace crew equipment lab, Naval Air Eng. Ctr, Phila, 58-60, sr. med. off, USS Essex, 60-62, resident, aerospace crew equipment lab, Naval Air Eng. Ctr, 63-64, asst. dir. training, Naval Aerospace Med. Inst, 64-67, chief, bioeng. sci. div, res. dept, 67-69, dist. med. off, 17th Naval Dist, Kodiak, Alaska, 69-70, chief bioeng. sci. div, NAVAL AEROSPACE MED. INST, 70-71, OFF-IN-CHARGE, NAVAL AEROSPACE MED. RES. LAB. DETACHMENT, 71- Partic, NASA Gemini 5 proj, 65, Gemini 9 proj, 66. Dipl, Am. Bd. Prev. Med, 64. Med.C, U.S.N, 52-, Capt. Fel. Am. Col. Prev. Med; Aerospace Med. Asn; Am. Inst. Aeronaut. & Astronaut; Am. Med. Asn; Am. Asn. Automotive Med; Am. Nat. Standards Inst. Biomechanics; physiological basis of protective equipment design, especially dynamic response of living human head and neck to impact acceleration, mechanism of ejection vertebral fracture and head protection against crash injury. Address: Naval Aerospace Medical Research Lab, Box 29407 Michoud Station, New Orleans, LA 70129.

EWING, CLAIR E(UGENE), b. Blue Rapids, Kans, Sept. 20, 15; m. 42; c. 5. GEODESY. B.S, Kansas State, 41; M.S, Colorado, 50; Ph.D.(geod), Ohio State, 55. U.S. Air Force, 41-69, dir. range develop, Atlantic Missile Range, Patrick Air Force Base, Fla, 55-58, comdr, Air Tech. Intel. Ctr, Tex, 59-60, dep. comdr, Air Force Pac. Missile Range, 60-67, v.comdr, Air Force West. Test Range, 67-69; CHIEF SCIENTIST, FED. ELEC. CORP, 69- U.S.A.F, 41-69, Col.(Ret). Sci. Res. Soc. Am; Am. Geophys. Union. Missile and space range instrumentation; electronic surveying; geodetic computations. Address: Western Test Range Division, Federal Electric Corp, P.O. Box 1965, Vandenberg AFB, CA 93437.

EWING, DEAN EDGAR, b. Ft. Wayne, Ind, Aug. 15, 32; m. 69. VETERINARY MEDICINE, RADIOBIOLOGY. B.S, Mich. State Univ, 54, D.V.M, 56; M.S, Univ. Rochester, 62. Vet, Bur. Poultry Inspection, Dept. Agr, State of Calif, 56-58; U.S. AIR FORCE, 58-, chief vet. serv, 3605th Air Force Hosp, El-

lington AFB, Tex, 58-59, 821st Med. Group, Ellsworth AFB, S.Dak, 59-61, res. vet, 6570th Aerospace Med. Res. Lab, Wright-Patterson AFB, Ohio, 62-63, chief bioastronaut. group, Air Force Weapons Lab, Kirtland AFB, N.Mex, 63-68, vet. civic action, 606th Spec. Opers. Squadron, Nakhon Phanom Royal Thai AFB, Thailand, 68-69, bioenviron. br, AIR FORCE WEAPONS LAB, 69, CHIEF BIOMED. BR, 69- Speaker, Space Cong, 66; Cong. Int. Astronaut. Fedn, 66; Nat. Biomed. Sci. Instrumentation Symp, 67; Nat. Symp. Natural & Man-made Radiation in Space, 71. U.S.A.F, 58-, Maj; Commendation Medal, 66. Am. Vet. Med. Asn. Research management in areas ranging from basic biology to radiation effects in both natural and man-made environments; laboratory animal medicine and other aspects of veterinary medicine; conservation-ecology. Address: 633 Monroe, Apt. 3, Albuquerque, NM 87110.

EWING, DONALD J(AMES), JR, b. Toledo, Ohio, Jan. 7, 31; m. 57; c. 2. ELECTRICAL ENGINEERING. B.S, Univ. Toledo, 52; M.S, Mass. Inst. Technol, 54; Ph.D.(elec. eng), Univ. Wis, 71. Asst. ELEC. ENG, Mass. Inst. Technol, 52-54; instr, UNIV. TOLEDO, 54-56, asst. prof, 56-58, ASSOC. PROF, 58- Summers, Nat. Sci. Found. & Atomic Energy Comn. grants, 56, 58, Hughes Aircraft Co, 59, Bell Telephone Labs, 60; Nat. Sci. Found. faculty fel, 62-63. Inst. Elec. & Electronics Eng; Soc. Indust. & Appl. Math; Int. Asn. Analog Comput; Simulation Coun. Feed back control systems and computers. Address: Dept. of Electrical Engineering, University of Toledo, Toledo, OH 43606.

EWING, DOUGLAS H(ANCOCK), b. Mitchell, Ind, June 24, 15; m. 38; c. 3. PHYSICS. A.B, Butler, 35; M.S, Rochester, 37, Ph.D.(physics), 39. Assoc. prof. physics, Smith Col, 39-41; tech. staff asst. to dir. & chmn. overseas off, radiation lab, Mass. Inst. Tech, 41-45; mgr. adv. develop. sect, Victor Div, Radio Corp. of Am, 45-49; dir. develop, air navigation develop. bd, Civil Aeronaut. Admin, 49-51; dir. res. serv, labs. div, Radio Corp. of Am, 51-53, phys. & chem. res. lab, 53-54, admin. dir, 54-55, v.pres, 55-57, v.pres, res. & eng, 57-64, staff v.pres, 64-68; LECTR. ELECTRONICS, UNIV. PA, 69- Tech. dir, labs. div, RCA Corp, 61-64, chmn. ed. comt, 62-68. With U.S.A: Off. Sci. Res. & Develop, 44. Fel. Am. Phys. Soc; fel. Inst. Elec. & Electronics Eng. Air navigation and traffic control; solid state physics. Address: P.O. Box 65, Lumberville, PA 18933.

EWING, ELMER ELLIS, b. Normal, Ill, Sept. 16, 31; m. 55; c. 5. VEGETABLE CROPS. B.S, Illinois, 53, M.S, 54; Ph.D.(veg. crops), Cornell, 59. Sci. aide, agr. prog. for Latin Am, Rockefeller Found, 56-57; instr. VEG. CROPS, CORNELL UNIV, 58-59, asst. prof, 59-65, ASSOC. PROF, 65- Nat. Sci. Found. fel. hort, Purdue Univ, 65-66. Am. Soc. Hort. Sci; Potato Asn. Am; Am. Soc. Plant Physiol; Europ. Asn. Potato Res. Physiological problems of potato. Address: Dept. of Vegetable Crops, Cornell University, Ithaca, NY 14850.

EWING, GALEN W(OOD), b. Boston, Mass, Mar. 14, 14; m. 42; c. 3. PHYSICAL ANALYTICAL CHEMISTRY. B.S, Col. William & Mary, 36; Ph.D. (phys. chem), Chicago, 39. Prof. chem. & physics, Blackburn Col, 39-42; res. phys. chemist, Sterling Winthrop Res. Inst, 42-46; asst. prof. CHEM, Union Col.(N.Y), 46-52, assoc. prof, 52-57; prof, New Mexico Highlands, 57-64. Chmn. dept, 59-61; PROF, SETON HALL UNIV, 64-, CHMN. DEPT, 69- AAAS; Soc. Appl. Spectros; Am. Chem. Soc. Instrumental analysis; absorption spectrophotometry. Address: Dept. of Chemistry, Seton Hall University, South Orange, NJ 07079.

EWING, GEORGE E(DWARD), b. Charlotte, N.C, Nov. 28, 33; div; c. 1. PHYSICAL CHEMISTRY. B.S, Yale, 56; Ph.D.(chem), California, Berkeley, 60. Sr. scientist, Jet Propulsion Lab, 60-63; instr. CHEM, IND. UNIV, BLOOMINGTON, 63-64, asst. prof, 64-68, assoc. prof, 68-71, PROF, 71- Mem. tech. staff, Bell Tel. Labs, N.J, 69-70. Am. Chem. Soc; Am. Phys. Soc. Molecular spectroscopy; low temperature chemistry. Address: Dept. of Chemistry, Indiana University, Bloomington, IN 47401.

EWING, GEORGE M(cNAUGHT), b. Lexington, Mo, Sept. 30, 07; m. 37; c. 3. MATHEMATICS. A.B, Missouri, 29, A.M, 30, Ph.D.(math), 35. Instr. math, Missouri, 30-39, asst. prof, 39-44, assoc. prof, 44-50, prof, 50-58; res. assoc, Okla. Res. Inst, combat develop. dept, U.S. Army Artillery & Missile Sch, 57-60; prof. MATH, UNIV. OKLA, 60-63, GEORGE L. CROSS RES. PROF, 63- Instr, Princeton, 40-41; mem, Inst. Advan. Study, 40-41; mathematician, Naval Ord. Lab, 44-45; Sandia Corp, 51-52, summer 53; Ramo-Wooldridge Corp, 54. Am. Math. Soc; Soc. Indust. & Appl. Math; Math. Asn. Am. Calculus of variations; optimal control theory; ordinary differential equations. Address: Dept. of Mathematics, University of Oklahoma, Norman, OK 73069.

EWING, GERALD DEAN, b. Alliance, Nebr, Jan. 6, 32; m. 52; c. 3. ELECTRONICS, INSTRUMENTATION. B.S.E.E, California, Berkeley, 57, M.S.E.E, 59; Collins Radio Co. scholar, Oregon State, 61, E.E, 62, Found. Instrumentation Ed. & Res. scholar, 62, 63, Ph.D.(elec. eng), 64. Elec. engr, Lawrence Radiation Lab, California, 56-58; electronics engr, electronics defense lab, Sylvania Elec. Prod, Inc, Gen. Tel. & Electronics Corp, 58-60; semiconductor appln. engr, Rheem Semiconductor Corp, 60-61; supvr. appln. eng, Shockley Transistor, Clevelite Corp, 61; instr. ELEC. ENG, Oregon State, 61-63; ASSOC. PROF, NAVAL POSTGRAD. SCH, 63- Lectr, Foothill Col, 58-61; consult, Lind Instrument Corp, Calif, 60-61; Sylvania Elec. Prod, Inc, Gen. Tel. & Electronics Corp, 63; lectr, Hartnel Col, 64-; summers, electronics engr, Shockley Transistor, Clevelite Corp, 62, Am. Soc. Eng. Educ. fel, NASA, Stanford Univ, 64; mem. part-time staff, Behav. Sci. Inst, Calif, 66- U.S.N, 51-53. Inst. Elec. & Electronics Eng. Solid state devices; oceanography. Address: Code 52 EW, Naval Postgraduate School, Monterey, CA 93940.

EWING, GIFFORD C(OCHRAN), b. Yonkers, N.Y, Nov. 1, 04; m. 65; c. 4. OCEANOGRAPHY. A.B, Yale, 26; M.S, California, 48, Ph.D.(oceanog), 50. Lab. instr, zool, Yale, 27-28, oceanogr, Bingham Oceanog. Lab, 29-30, oceanog. expeds, 31-32; oceanog. observ, Oper. Crossroads, Bikini, 46; asst. res. oceanogr, Scripps Inst, California, 50-58, assoc, 58-63, chmn. div. oceanic res, 62-64, res. oceanogr, 63-64; assoc. phys. oceanog, WOODS HOLE OCEANOG. INST, 64-67, SR. SCIENTIST THEORET. OCEANOG, 67- Chmn. antisubmarine warfare infrared comt, U.S. Navy, 61-65; vis. scientist, Mass. Inst. Technol, 64-65. Medaille Albert 1er, Prince de Monaco, Inst. Oceanog, France. U.S.N.R, 40-45, Capt. AAAS; Am. Meteorol. Soc; Am. Geophys. Union. Oceanographic reconnaissance from aircraft and spacecraft; remote sensing of the ocean; internal waves; physics of sea surface; oceanographic exploration of the Gulf of California; oceanic diffusion; oceanic thermal gradients; hydrology of coastal lagoons; natural history of the California gray whale. Address: Dept. of Theoretical Oceanography, Woods Hole Oceanographic Institute, Woods Hole, MA 02543.

EWING, GORDON J, b. Smithfield, Utah, Nov. 1, 31; m. 68; c. 11. PHYSICAL CHEMISTRY. B.S, Utah State Univ, 54, M.S, 57; Ph.D.(thermodyn), Pa. State Univ, 60. Asst. prof. CHEM, N.MEX. STATE UNIV, 62-68, ASSOC. PROF, 68- U.S.A, 1st Lt. AAAS; Am. Chem. Soc. Interactions of gases with respiratory pigments; thermometric titrations; solution thermodynamics. Address: Box 4411, University Park Station, Las Cruces, NM 88001.

EWING, JOHN A(LEXANDER), b. Largo, Scotland, Mar. 17, 23; U.S. citizen; m. 46; c. 2. PSYCHIATRY. M.B, Ch.B, Edinburgh, 46, M.D, 54; Dipl. Psychol. Med, London, 50. Res. psychiat, Cherry Knowle Hosp, Eng, 47-51; sr. physician, John Umstead Hosp, Butner, N.C, 51-54; instr. PSYCHIAT, SCH. MED, UNIV. NC, CHAPEL HILL, 54-56, asst. prof, 56-59, assoc. prof, 59-63, PROF, 63-, DIR. CTR. ALCOHOL STUDIES, 71-, chmn. dept. psychiat, 65-70. Asst. physician, psychiat. clin, Sunderland Royal Infirmary, Eng, 49-51; S.Shields Gen. Hosp, 49-51; psychiatrist, N.C. Alcoholic Rehab. Ctr, 51-54; clin. instr, North Carolina, 53-54; dir, psychiat. in-patient serv, N.C. Mem. Hosp, 57-64; consult. psychiatrist, Watts Hosp, Durham, N.C, 57- Am. Med. Asn; fel. Am. Psychiat. Asn; Am. Psychosom. Soc; Brit. Med. Asn; Royal Medico-Psychol. Asn; fel. Am. Col. Psychiat. Alcoholism and drug dependency; application of psychiatric principles in medical practice; psychoanalysis. Address: Dept. of Psychiatry, School of Medicine, University of North Carolina at Chapel Hill, Box 1020, Chapel Hill, NC 27515.

EWING, JOHN ARTHUR, b. Euchee, Tenn, June 24, 12; m. 39; c. 3. AGRONOMY, ANIMAL HUSBANDRY. B.S.A, Tennessee, 33, M.S, 46; D.P.A, Harvard, 56. Teacher, high sch, Tenn, 34-35; asst. county agent, demonstration prog, Tenn. Valley Authority, agr. exten. serv, UNIV. TENN, 35-44, asst. supt. Middle Tenn. Exp. Sta, 44-46, supt, 46-49, asst. dir, agr. exp. sta, 49-55, sr. v.dean col. agr, 55-57, dir, AGR. EXP. STA, 57-68, DEAN, 68- Admin. adv, Water Resource Res. South, 53-, exp. sta. rep, Soybean Res, South, 54-; prog. leader, agr. res. lab, Atomic Energy Cmn, Tennessee, 55-, exp. sta. rep, Seed & Plant Irradiation South, 56-, admin. adv. Grain Mkt. South, 60-; chmn, South. Agr. Exp. Sta. Dirs, 61-62; exp. sta. sect, Lang Grant Col. Asn, 62-63; mem, Nat. Tobacco Adv. Cmt, 62-64; Nat. Cotton Seed Policy Comt, 65-; agr. adv. comt, South. Regional Educ. Bd; adminr. adv, South. Land Econ. Res. Comt. Am. Soc. Agron. Irrigation of pastures; effects of fluorine effluents on cattle and crops; atomic energy in agricultural research. Address: Agricultural Experiment Station, University of Tennessee, Knoxville, TN 37916.

EWING, JOHN FREDERICK, b. East Lansing, Mich, July 12, 22; m. 42; c. 6. METALLURGICAL ENGINEERING. B.S.E, Univ. Mich, 46, M.S.E, 48, fel, 48-49, Ph.D.(metall. eng), 53. Asst. to metallurgist, U.S. Naval Res. Lab, 41-43; chemist, Fed. Mogul Res. Lab, 47-48; res. asst, Eng. Res. Inst. Univ. Mich, 49-50, res. assoc, 50-52, res. engr, 52-53; res. metallurgist, BABCOCK & WILCOX CO, 53-56, metallurgist supvr, res, 56-58, mgr. qual. control, NAVAL NUCLEAR FUEL DIV, 58-68, MGR, OPERS, 68- U.S.A.A.F, 43-45. Am. Soc. Metals; Am. Mgt. Asn. Study of metals at elevated temperatures; development of alloys for high temperature service. Address: 1515 Savoy Place, Lynchburg, VA 24503.

EWING, JOHN I, b. Lockney, Tex, July 5, 24; m. 48; c. 3. GEOPHYSICS. B.S, Harvard, 50. Res. assoc. GEOPHYSICS, LAMONT GEOL. OBSERV, 50-58, sr. res. scientist, 58-64, SR. RES. ASSOC, 64- U.S.A.A.F, 43-45. Seismol. Soc. Am; Am. Geophys. Union. Structure and constitution of the earth; underwater sound propagation. Address: Lamont Geological Observatory, Palisades, NY 10964.

EWING, LARRY L, b. Valley, Nebr, July 10, 36; m. 54; c. 4. PHYSIOLOGY. B.S, Univ. Nebr, 58; M.S, Univ. Ill, 60, Ph.D.(agr), 62. Assoc. prof. PHYSIOL, OKLA. STATE UNIV, 62-70, PROF, 70- Trainee steroid biochem, Univ. Utah, 64-65; Nat. Insts. Health spec. fel, med. sch, Johns Hopkins Univ, 68-69; vis. scientist, Ore. Regional Primate Res. Ctr, summer 71. Soc. Study Reproduction; Am. Physiol. Soc; Am. Soc. Zool; Brit. Soc. Study Fertil. Reproductive physiology. Address: Dept. of Physiological Sciences, Oklahoma State University, Stillwater, OK 74074.

EWING, MARGARET STEFFENS, b. New York, N.Y, Apr. 4, 40; m. 63; c. 3. ZOOLOGY, LIMNOLOGY. B.A, Oberlin Col, 62; U.S. Pub. Health Serv. fel, Okla. State, 63-66, M.S, 64, Ph.D.(zool), 66. Asst. prof. ZOOL, Miss. State Univ, 67-68; instr, OKLA. STATE UNIV, 69-70, ASST. PROF, 70- AAAS; Am. Soc. Limnol. & Oceanog. Community ecology. Address: Dept. of Zoology, Oklahoma State University, Stillwater, OK 74074.

EWING, (WILLIAM) MAURICE, b. Lockney, Tex, May 12, 06; m. 28, 44, 65; c. 5. GEOPHYSICS. B.A, Rice Inst, 26, fel, 26-29, M.A, 27, Ph.D.(physics), 31; hon. D.Sc, Wash. & Lee Univ, 49, Univ. Denver, 53, Lehigh Univ. & Univ. Utrecht, 57, Univ. R.I, 60, Univ. Durham, 63, Univ. Del, 68, L.I. Univ. & Nat. Univ. Colombia, 69, Cent. Col. Ky, 71; hon. LL.D, Dalhousie Univ, 60. Instr. physics, Univ. Pittsburgh, 29-30; Lehigh Univ, 30-36, asst. prof, 36-40, assoc. prof. GEOL, 40-44; COLUMBIA UNIV, 44-47, prof, 47-59, HIGGINS PROF, 59-, DIR. LAMONT-DOHERTY GEOL. OBSERV, 49- Guggenheim fels, 38-40, 53-55; res. assoc, Woods Hole Oceanog. Inst, 40-44; dir, Off. Sci. Res. & Develop. projs, 40-44; Joseph Henry lectr, 49; distinguished lectr, Am. Asn. Petrol. Geol, 47-53; Westbrook lectr, 51; Sir Harold Jeffrey lectr. & St. Edmund's Acad. lectr, 64; holiday sci. lectr, AAAS, 65; David Rivett lectr, Commonwealth Sci. & Indust. Res. Orgn, Australia, 67; assoc. ed, Deep Sea Res, 53-; Quaternaria, 54-57; mem. panel for seismol, Res. & Develop. Bd, 50-54; U.S. Nat. Comt, Int. Geophys. Year, 55-60, ex-officio mem, panel on seismol. & gravity & panel on oceanog, 57-60; comt. on oceanog, Nat. Acad. Sci, 57-64; space sci. working group on lunar explor, NASA, 59-61, lunal subcomt. consult, space sci. steering comt, 60-61; adv. comt, Geophys. Inst, Univ. Alaska, 63-71; U.S-Japan Comt. Sci. Coop, 67-70; bd. gov, Rice Univ, 69-; Oceanog. Adv. Comt, 70-; leader, marine geophys. exped, 35- U.S. Navy distinguished serv. award, 55; Order of Naval Merit, Argentine Repub, 57; Fleming Medal, Am. Inst. Geonomy & Natural Resources & Vetlesen Prize, Columbia Univ, 60; Priestley Award, Dickinson Col, 61; medal of honor, Rice Univ, 62; gold medal, Royal Astron. Soc, 64; sesquicentennial medal, St. Louis Univ, 69. Nat. Acad. Sci.(Agassiz Medal, 55, Carty Medal & Award, 63); AAAS; fel. Am. Phys. Soc; fel. Am. Math. Soc; fel. Geol. Soc. Am.(Day Medal, 49); hon. mem. Soc. Explor. Geophys; Am. Geog. Soc.(Cullum Geog. Medal, 61); Seismol. Soc. Am.(v.pres, 52-55, pres, 55-57); Am. Philos. Soc; Am. Geophys. Union (assoc. ed, J. Geophys. Res, 49-53, v.pres, 53-56, pres, 56-59, Bowie Medal, 57); Am. Acad. Arts & Sci; hon. mem. Am. Asn. Petrol. Geol.(Sidney Powers Mem. Medal, 68); hon. mem. Royal Soc. N.Z; Royal Netherlands Acad. Sci; Swedish Soc. Anthrop. & Geog; for. mem. Geol. Soc. London (Wollaston Medal, 69); cor. mem. Argentine Nat. Acad. Exact, Phys. & Natural Sci; hon. mem. Colombian Soc. Geol; hon. fel. Indian Geophys. Union. Earthquake seismology; submarine geology; gravity surveys; ocean bottom photography; submarine acoustics; seismic refraction and reflection surveys; magnetic surveys; oceanography; climatology; geothermal measurements. Address: Lamont-Doherty Geological Observatory, Columbia University, Palisades, NY 10964.

EWING, RICHARD D(WIGHT), b. Lansing, Mich, Jan. 17, 30; m. 54; c. 3. PHYSICS. B.A, Univ. Chicago, 50; M.S, Mich. State Univ, 54, Ph.D.(physics), 58. Asst. prof. PHYSICS, UNIV. DEL, 58-67, ASSOC. PROF, 67-, res. found. grant, 59-60. Am. Phys. Soc. Electron spin and nuclear magnetic resonance. Address: Dept. of Physics, University of Delaware, Newark, DE 19711.

EWING, RICHARD E(VERETT), b. Webster City, Iowa, Dec. 28, 19; m. 43; c. 3. PHYSICAL CHEMISTRY. B.S, Iowa State Col, 48; M.S, Idaho, 52; Ph.D.(chem), Washington State, 58. Chemist, Gen. Elec. Co, 48-52, 55-60; sr. scientist, Shockley Lab, Clevite Transistor Prod. Div, Calif, 60-62; supvr. semiconductor process res, H.P. Assocs, 62-65; PROJ. LEADER, H.P. LABS, HEWLETT PACKARD CO, PALO ALTO, 65- Am. Chem. Soc; Electrochem. Soc. Surface, inorganic and solid state chemistry. Address: 122 Lockhart Lane, Los Altos, CA 94022.

EWING, R(OBERT) A(RNO), b. Washington, D.C, June 20, 15; m. 47; c. 3. CHEMICAL ENGINEERING. B.Sc, Ohio State, 36, M.Sc, 37. Res. engr, Monsanto Chem. Co, 37-41; Eagle-Picher Co, 41-44, plant mgr, 44-47; res. engr, BATTELLE MEM. INST, 47-49, asst. div. chief, 49-60, res. assoc, 61-65, fel, 65- Am. Chem. Soc; Am. Nuclear Soc. Manufacture of elemental phosphorus and phosphates; manufacture of mineral wool insulation; recovery of uranium and thorium from ores; solvent extraction refining of uranium and thorium; radiotracer applications; neutron activation analysis; nuclear fuel reprocessing; radioactive waste disposal; nuclear safeguards. Address: Battelle Memorial Institute, 505 King Ave, Columbus, OH 43201.

EWING, RONALD I(RA), b. Dallas, Tex, July 13, 35; m. 57; c. 4. PHYSICS. B.A, Rice Inst, 56, M.A, 57, M.D. Anderson Tumor Inst. fel, 57-59, Ph.D. (physics), 59. STAFF MEM. PHYS. SCI. RES, SANDIA CORP, 59- Am. Phys. Soc; Am. Vacuum Soc. Nuclear and surface physics; secondary emission; ultra high vacuum. Address: Sandia Corp, Albuquerque, NM 87115.

EWING, SCOTT PRESTON, SR, b. Smithfield, Utah, May 20, 98; m. 27; c. 3. ELECTROCHEMISTRY. B.S, Utah State, 20; Ph.D.(physics), California, 25. Jr. asst. physicist, Nat. Bur. Standards, 26-29; res. assoc, Am. Gas Asn, 29-40; electrolysis engr, Panama Canal, 40-41; sr. metallurgist, Bur. Ships, U.S. Dept. Navy, 41-46; res. engr, Carter Oil Co, 46-63, consult. corrosion, Jersey Prod. Res. Co, 63-66; part-time consult, Esso Prod. Res. Co, Houston & adv. on corrosion, Oil & Gas Consult-Int, Tulsa, 66-70; RETIRED. Nat. Asn. Corrosion Eng.(Speller Award, 53). Corrosion prevention, especially buried and submerged steel structures such as pipe lines, tank bottoms, ships and lock gates. Address: 5508 E. 35th St, Tulsa, OK 74135.

EWING, SIDNEY A(LTON), b. Emory University, Ga, Dec. 1, 34; m. 63. VETERINARY PARASITOLOGY. B.S.A. & D.V.M, Georgia, 58; M.S, Wisconsin, 60; Ph.D.(vet. parasitol), Okla. State, 64. Asst. vet. sci, Wisconsin, 58-60, instr, summer, 60; vet. parasitol, Okla. State, 60-61, asst. prof, 61-64, assoc. prof. vet. parasitol & pub. health, 64-65; vet. path, parasitol. & pub. health, Kans. State Univ, 65-67; prof. vet. sci. & head dept, Miss. State Univ, 67-68; PROF. VET. PARASITOL. & PUB. HEALTH & HEAD DEPT, OKLA. STATE UNIV, 68- Co-investr, res. grant, 63-64; mem. adv. bd, Morris Animal Found, 67-69, consult, 69-; mem. comt. animal health, Nat. Res. Coun-Nat. Acad. Sci, 71- Am. Vet. Med. Asn; Am. Soc. Vet. Parasitol; Am. Soc. Parasitol. Swine lungworms; canine babesiosis; canine rickettsiosis. Address: Dept. of Veterinary Parasitology & Public Health, Oklahoma State University, Stillwater, OK 74074.

EWING, SOLON A(LEXANDER), b. Headrick, Okla, July 21, 30; m. 52; c. 2. ANIMAL NUTRITION. B.S, Okla. State, 52, M.S, 56, Ph.D.(animal nutrit), 58. Instr. animal sci, Okla. State, 56-58; asst. prof, Iowa State, 58-61, assoc. prof, 61-64; prof, Okla. State Univ, 64-68; ASST. DIR, IOWA AGR. & HOME ECON. EXP. STA, IOWA STATE UNIV, 68- U.S.A.F, 54-56, 1st Lt. Am. Soc. Animal Sci. Ruminant nutrition studies. Address: 104 Curtiss Hall, Iowa State University, Ames, IA 50010.

EWING, WILLIAM H(OWELL), b. Carnegie, Pa, Oct. 4, 14; m. 42; c. 2. BACTERIOLOGY. A.B, Washington & Jefferson Col, 37, M.A, 39; Michigan, 39-41; Ph.D.(bact), Cornell, 48. Instr. biol, Washington & Jefferson Col, 37-39; asst. bact, Michigan, 39-41; assoc. prof, N.Y. State Vet. Col, Cornell, 46-47, instr, 47, asst. prof, 48; bacteriologist & asst. in charge ENTERIC BACT. UNIT, CTR. DISEASE CONTROL, U.S. PUB. HEALTH SERV, 48-62, IN CHARGE INT. SHIGELLA CTR, 50-, CONSULT. & RES. MICROBIOLOGIST, 69-, chief enteric bact. unit, 62-69. Mem, Int. Subcomt. Enterobacteriaceae, 50-, past secy; consult, WHO, 55, adv, 58, expert adv. panel enteric diseases, 64-; assoc. prof, sch. pub. health, Univ. N.C, 62-; Linton fel. from Wash. & Jefferson Col, Marine Biol. Lab, Woods Hole. Kimble Methodology Res. Award, 56; U.S. Pub. Health Serv. Meritorious Serv. Award, 63. U.S.A, 41-46; U.S.P.H.S, 48-, Sci. Dir. Am. Soc. Microbiol; Am. Acad. Microbiol; Can. Soc. Microbiol; Brit. Soc. Gen. Microbiol. Antigenic analyses; antigens of enterobacteriaceae, especially Shigella, Escherichia, Salmonella; relationship of these bacteria to disease in man; biochemical characteristics and differentiation; classification & nomenclature. Address: Center for Disease Control, U.S. Public Health Service, 1600 Clifton Rd, Atlanta, GA 30333.

EWING, W(ILLIAM) McDANIEL, b. Smith's Grove, Ky, June 21, 10; m. 35; c. 1. MEDICINE. A.B, Vanderbilt, 31; M.D, Louisville, 35. Intern, N.Y. State Reconstruct. Hosp, 35-37; fel, Willis C. Campbell Clin. Tenn, 37-38; asst. prof. ORTHOP. SURG, SCH. MED, UNIV. LOUISVILLE, 38-64, ASSOC. PROF, 64- Pres. med. staff, Kosair Crippled Children's Hosp, 50, 63. Consult, U.S. Army, 47-; Vet. Admin, 48-; Ky. Baptist Hosp, 59. U.S.A, 42-46, Maj. Orthopedic surgery. Address: 452 Medical Towers, S, 234 E. Gray St, Louisville, KY 40202.

EXNER, BEATRICE B(ARBARA), b. Denham Springs, La, May 7, 14. MYCOLOGY. B.A, La. State, 35, M.S, 38, Ph.D, 47. Instr. biol. sci, Ward-Belmont Col, 42-43; asst. prof, Stephen F. Austin State Col, 47-48; Francis T. Nicholls Jr. Col, 48-52, assoc. prof, 52-59; from asst. prof. to ASSOC. PROF. BOT, LA. STATE UNIV, BATON ROUGE, 59- Bot. Soc. Am; Am. Phytopath. Soc. Life cycles and genetics of rhizoctonias. Address: Dept. of Botany, Louisiana State University, Baton Rouge, LA 70803.

EXTERMANN, RICHARD C, b. Menton, France, Jan. 24, 11; m. 38; c. 3. PHYSICS. Lic. ès Sci, Geneva, 33, D. ès Sci, 38; hon. Dr, Dijon, 57. Asst. prof. theoret. physics, Geneva, 38-40; res. fel. PHYSICS, Swiss Fed. Inst. Tech, 40-45; assoc. prof, Geneva, 46-47, PROF. & HEAD DEPT, 48-63; COOPER UNION, 63- Dir. res, French Nat. Cmt, Sci. Res, 48-63; Swiss del, Int. Atomic Energy Conf, UN, 55 & 58; mem, Swiss Atomic Energy Cmn, 55-63; head sci. secretariat, UNESCO Radioisotopes Conf, Paris, 57-58; vis. scientist, Europ. Orgn. Nuclear Res, Geneva, 60-61; consult, sci. directorate, Orgn. Econ. Coop. & Develop, Paris, 61-63; hon. prof, Univ. Geneva, 63; mem, Mayor's Task Force on Noise Control, N.Y, 66- Am. Phys. Soc; Am. Asn. Physics Teachers. Diffraction of light by ultrasonic waves; particle accelerators, neutron physics and low energy nuclear physics; nuclear moments and nuclear magnetic resonance high energy physics; astrophysics. Address: Dept. of Physics, Cooper Union, 51 Astor Pl, New York, NY 10003.

EXTON, JOHN H(OWARD), b. Auckland, N.Z, Aug. 29, 33; m. 57; c. 4. BIOCHEMISTRY. B.Med.Sc, New Zealand, 55; M.B, Ch.B, Otago, N.Z, 58, fel, 60-61, Ph.D.(biochem), 63. Asst. lectr. biochem, Otago, N.Z, 61-63; instr. PHYSIOL, SCH. MED, VANDERBILT UNIV, 63-66, asst. prof, 66-68, assoc. prof, 68-70, PROF, 70- Univ. Nat. scholar, 52-58; Med. Res. Coun. teaching fel, 54-55, fel, 60-61; U.K. Commonwealth scholar, 63; Bank N.Z. traveling fel, 63; investr, Howard Hughes Med. Inst, 68- Am. Soc. Biol. Chem; Biochem. Soc. Control of metabolism; mechanisms of hormone action; gluconeogenesis and ketogenesis; effects of insulin on liver. Address: Dept. of Physiology, Vanderbilt University School of Medicine, Nashville, TN 37203.

EYDE, RICHARD H(USTED), b. Lancaster, Pa, Dec. 23, 28; m. 57; c. 2. PLANT ANATOMY, PALEOBOTANY. B.S, Franklin & Marshall Col, 56; M.Sc, Ohio State, 57; Nat. Sci. Found. fel, Harvard, 58-60, Ph.D.(biol), 62; Fulbright scholar, Birbal Sahni Inst. Palaeobot, India, 60-61. Asst. BOT, SMITHSONIAN INST, 61-62, assoc. curator, 62-69, CURATOR, 69- Mem. Int. Orgn. Paleobot. Bot. Soc. Am; Torrey Bot. Club; Am. Soc. Plant Taxon; Int. Soc. Plant Morphol. Tertiary paleobotany; comparative anatomy and phylogeny of angiosperms, especially anatomy of flowers, fruits of Cornaceae and allied groups, including fossils. Address: Dept. of Botany, Smithsonian Institution, Washington, DC 20560.

EYE, JOHN DAVID, b. Franklin, W.Va, June 22, 23; m. 46; c. 4. SANITARY ENGINEERING, ENVIRONMENTAL HEALTH. B.S, Va. Polytech, 48, M.S, 49; Sc.D.(indust. health), Cincinnati, 66. Instr. civil eng, Southern California, 49-51; asst. prof. sanit. eng, Va. Polytech, 51-54, assoc. prof, 54-56; sanit. eng, UNIV. CINCINNATI, 56-66, PROF. ENVIRON. HEALTH, 66- Consult, Nat. Lead Co. Ohio, 60-65; Tanners Coun. Am, 65-; Naval Ord. Syst, 65- Nat. Soc. Prof. Eng; Am. Soc. Civil Eng; Am. Soc. Eng. Educ; Am. Pub. Health Asn; Am. Water Works Asn. Water quality management; industrial waste treatment. Address: Dept. of Civil Engineering, Location 71, University of Cincinnati, Cincinnati, OH 45221.

EYER, JAMES A(RTHUR), b. Rochester, N.Y, Dec. 18, 29; m. 60; c. 1. OPTICS, PHOTOGRAPHY. B.S, Mass. Inst. Tech, 51; Ph.D.(optics, physics), Rochester, 57. Res. assoc. optics, inst. optics, Univ. Rochester, 57-61, asst. prof, 61-63, asst. dir, 63-65; private consult, N.Y, 65-67; assoc. prof. OPTICAL SCI, UNIV. ARIZ, 67-69, PROF, 69-, ASSOC. DIR. OPTICAL SCI. CTR, 67- Optical Soc. Am; Soc. Photog. Sci. & Eng. Optical image evaluation; photographic image structure; photographic theory; applications of information theory to optical systems; photointerpretation techniques. Address: Optical Sciences Center, University of Arizona, Tucson, AZ 85721.

EYER, LESTER EMERY, b. Ithaca, Mich, Apr. 9, 12; m. 40; c. 3. BIOLOGY, ZOOLOGY. B.S, Alma Col.(Mich), 36; M.S, Michigan, 42; Ph.D.(zool), Mich. State, 54. Teacher, pub. sch, Mich, 36-43; instr. BIOL, ALMA COL. (MICH), 46-48, asst. prof, 48-50, PROF, 51-, head dept, 51-71. U.S.A.A.F, 43-46, 1st Lt. AAAS; Am. Ornith. Union; Wilson Ornith. Soc. Ecology of birds. Address: 5355 Blue Heron Dr, Alma, MI 48801.

EYERLY, GEORGE B(ROWN), b. Canton, Ill, Mar. 20, 17; m. 47. CERAMIC ENGINEERING. B.S, Illinois, 40; M.S, Washington (Seattle), 41. U.S. Bur. Mines fel, Northwest. Exp. Sta, 40-41; chief ceramist, Refractories Corp, Calif, 41-42; chief metall. sect, Manhattan Proj. & U.S. Atomic Energy Cmn, Oak Ridge, 46-47; asst. prof. ceramic eng, Washington (Seattle), 47-48; assoc. ceramist, Argonne Nat. Lab, 48-52; ceramic engr, Allen Bradley Co, 52-55; secy. & chief engr, Malvern Brick & Tile Co, 55-67; SR. ENGR, D.M. STEWARD MFG. CO, 67- Consult, U.S. Atomic Energy Comn, 59-62; mem, Ark. State Geol. Comn, 67; Gov. Tech. Adv. Comt, 67. U.S.A, 42-47. AAAS; Am. Ceramic Soc; Am. Soc. Metals; Am. Chem. Soc. High temperature materials; materials for reactor applications; ferromagnetic and nonmetallic ferroelectric materials; structural clay products. Address: D.M. Steward Manufacturing Co, P.O. Box 510, Chattanooga, TN 37401.

EYESTONE, SHIRLEY FREDERICK, b. Newton, Kans, Nov. 23, 19; m. 41; c. 1. ELECTRICAL ENGINEERING. B.S, Kansas State, 41; E.E, California, Los Angeles, 56. Test engr, Gen. Elec. Co, 41; res. engr, N.Am. Aviation, Inc, 46-48, supvr, precision instruments unit, 48-50, leader, autonavigator syst. eng. group, 50-51, proj. engr, maj. missile syst, 51-53, chief, guidance eng. sect, 53-56, mgr, 56-59, v.pres. & gen. mgr. inertial navig, Autonetics Div, 59-62, exec. v.pres-opers, 62-64, exec. v.pres-admin, 64-66, exec. v.pres, 66-67, pres, 67-70; V.PRES. INT. GROUP, VARIAN ASSOCS, 70- Distinguished serv. award, Kansas State, 61. U.S.A, 41-46, 1st Lt. Am. Inst. Navig; Am. Ord. Asn; Am. Inst. Aeronaut. & Astronaut. Inertial guidance, including key responsibility in the specialized field of precision instruments; management areas of development, design, fabrication and sale of military and commercial electronic equipment. Address: 2420 Sharon Oaks Dr, Menlo Park, CA 94025.

EYESTONE, WILLARD H(ALSEY), b. Mulberry, Kans, Jan. 7, 18; m. 52; c. 4. PATHOLOGY. B.S, Kans. State Col, 39, D.V.M, 41; M.P.H, Harvard, 47; Ph.D.(path), Wisconsin, 49. Instr. vet. sci, Wisconsin, 41; res. assoc. vet. path, Illinois, 42; Wisconsin, 47-49; head comparative path. lab, Nat. Cancer Inst, NAT. INSTS. HEALTH, 49-55, vet. & chief lab. aids br, 55-59, chief regional primate res. centers br, Nat. Heart Inst, 59-62, animal resources br, div. res. facilities & resources, 62-71, CHIEF OPTOM, PHARM, PODIATRY & VET. MED. EDUC. BR, DIV. PHYSICIAN & HEALTH PROFESSIONS EDUC, BUR. HEALTH MANPOWER EDUC, 71- Spec. cancer fel, Univ. Wis, 47-49; pathologist, Nat. Zool. Park, D.C, 50-59; lab. consult, Pan-Am. Sanit. Bur, Ecuador, 52; mem. comt. vet. med. res. & educ, Nat. Res. Coun, 68- Meritorious serv. medal, U.S. Pub. Health Serv, 70. Am. Vet. Med. Asn; Am. Col. Vet. Path.(pres, 61-62); Am. Asn. Path. & Bact; Am. Asn. Lab. Animal Sci.(Charles A. Griffin Award, 70); Int. Acad. Path. Cancer; pathogenesis of tumors; comparative pathology; research administration. Address: Bureau of Health Manpower Education, National Institutes of Health, Bethesda, MD 20014.

EYGES, LEONARD JAMES, b. Chelsea, Mass, Oct. 30, 20; m. 43; c. 1. THEORETICAL PHYSICS. B.S, Michigan, 42; M.S, Brown, 43; Ph.D, Cornell, 48. Staff mem, radiation lab, Mass. Inst. Tech, 43-46; Atomic Energy Cmn. fel, 48-49; res. physicist, radiation lab, California, 49-52; sci. attaché, State Dept. Paris, 52-53; instr. physics, Mass. Inst. Technol, 53-55, staff mem, Lincoln Lab, 55-56, 57-63; Nat. Sci. Found. sr. fel, 56-57; SR. PHYSICIST, AIR FORCE CAMBRIDGE RES. LABS, 63- Am. Phys. Soc. Solid state physics; many-body problem. Address: Air Force Cambridge Research Labs, L.G. Hanscom Field, Bedford, MA 01730.

EYKAMP, R. WILLIAM, b. Akron, Ohio, Nov. 23, 36; m. 65; c. 2. CHEMICAL ENGINEERING. B.S, Purdue, 58; Ph.D.(chem. eng), Mass. Inst. Tech, 65. Res. engr, Dewey & Almy Chem. Div, W. R. Grace & Co, 58-63, sr. res. engr, res. div, 66-68; prog. mgr, ABCOR INC, 69-71, MGR. RES. DEVELOP, INDUST. SEPARATION DIV, 71- AAAS; Am. Chem. Soc. High polymers; emulsion polymerization; transport properties of polymers; surface chemistry; membrane separation processes. Address: Abcor, Inc, 341 Vassar St, Cambridge, MA 02139.

EYLAR, EDWIN HAROLD, b. Bozeman, Mont, Sept. 4, 31. BIOCHEMISTRY. B.S, Mont. State Col, 53, M.S, 55; Ph.D.(biochem), Harvard, 58. Helen Hay Whitney fel, Mass. Gen. Hosp, 58-61; res. fel. biochem, sch. med, Ind. Univ, 61-62; Hastings asst. prof, sch. med, Univ. South. Calif, 62-67; DIR. DEPT. EXP. BIOL, MERCK INST. THERAPEUTIC RES, 71- Res. grants, U.S. Pub. Health Serv, 63-70; Am. Cancer Soc, 63-; Markle scholar, 63-68. Autoimmune disease; identification of disease inducing proteins; suppression of autoimmune disease; biosynthesis of glycoproteins; chemical basis for fertilization; arthritis; experimental allergic encaphalomyelitis and multiple sclerosis. Address: Dept. of Experimental Biology, Merck Institute for Therapeutic Research, Rahway, NJ 07065.

EYLER, ROBERT W(ILSON), b. Monmouth, Ill, Nov. 15, 18; m. 43; c. 4. ANALYTICAL CHEMISTRY. B.Sc, Monmouth Col, 40; Ph.D.(anal. chem), Illinois, 44. Asst. chem, Illinois, 40-44; res. chemist, exp. sta, HERCULES INC, 44-62, plant mgr, 62-66, asst. dir. opers, 66-68, DIR. OPERS, 68- Res. chemist, Mallinckrodt Chem. Works, Mo, 42. Am. Chem. Soc. X-ray diffraction and metallography; analytical and instrumental methods development; cellulose and inorganic chemicals research, development and production; solid propellant rocket research. Address: Hercules Inc, Wilmington, DE 19899.

EYMAN, DARRELL PAUL, b. Mason Co, Ill, Dec. 18, 37; m. 59; c. 3. INORGANIC CHEMISTRY. B.S, Eureka Col, 59; Bradley, summer, 59; Ph.D.(inorg. chem), Illinois, 64. Asst. prof. CHEM, UNIV. IOWA, 64-69, ASSOC. PROF, 69- Am. Chem. Soc. Structure and reactivity of organo-aluminum compounds. Address: Dept. of Chemistry, University of Iowa, Iowa City, IA 52240.

EYMAN, EARL DUANE, b. Canton, Ill, Sept. 24, 25; m. 51; c. 2. ENGINEERING, MATHEMATICS. B.S, Illinois, 49, M.S, 50; Ph.D.(elec. eng), Colorado, 66. Scientist, atomic power div, Westinghouse Elec. Corp, 50-51; res. engr, Caterpillar Tractor Co, 51-61, proj. engr. control, 61-66; assoc. prof. elec. & mech. eng, UNIV. IOWA, 66-69, PROF. ELEC. ENG. & HEAD DEPT, 69- U.S.N, 44-46. Sr. mem. Inst. Elec. & Electronics Eng; sr. mem. Instrument Soc. Am. Fluid mechanics; computers; electronics; mathematics; classical and modern control systems; remote control. Address: Dept. of Electrical Engineering, University of Iowa, Iowa City, IA 52240.

EYMAN, RICHARD KENNETH, Psychol. Measurement, Clin. Psychol, see 12th ed, Soc. & Behav. Vols.

EYRE, LAWRENCE A, Geog, Environ. Sci, see Suppl. I to 11th ed, Soc. & Behav. Vols.

EYRE, PETER, b. Glossop, Eng, Oct. 23, 36; m. 63; c. 2. PHARMACOLOGY, IMMUNOLOGY. B.V.M, Univ. Edinburgh, 60, fel, 60-62, B.Sc, 62, Ph.D. (pharmacol), 65; M.R.C.V.S, Royal Col. Vet. Surg, 60. Asst. lectr. PHARMACOL, Univ. Edinburgh, 62-64, lectr, 64-68; ASSOC. PROF, UNIV. GUELPH, 68- Brit. Pharmacol. Soc; Can. Physiol. Soc; Am. Soc. Vet. Physiol. & Pharmacol. Chemotherapy of parasitic diseases; pharmacologic actions of anti-parasitic drugs; pharmacologic mechanisms in allergy and anaphylaxis in domesticated herbivores. Address: Dept. of Biomedical Sciences, University of Guelph, Guelph, Ont, Can.

EYRING, EDWARD J, b. Oakland, Calif, Dec. 25, 34; m. 59; c. 5. ORTHOPEDICS, PHYSIOLOGICAL CHEMISTRY. B.A, Princeton, 55; M.D, Harvard, 59; Ph.D.(biochem), California, San Francisco, 67. Nat. Insts. Health trainee, sch. med, California, San Francisco, 64, Nat. Inst. Arthritis & Metab. Diseases spec. fel, grad. div, 65-67; ASST. PROF. ORTHOP. & PHYSIOL. CHEM, OHIO STATE UNIV, 67- Am. Rheumatism Asn; Orthop. Res. Soc; Am. Acad. Orthop. Surg; Am. Med. Asn; Am. Acad. Pediat; N.Y. Acad. Sci; Am. Inst. Chem. Chondromucoproteins; anti-inflammatory drug metabolism; surgical implants; pediatric orthopedics; arthritis. Address: 973 E. Broad St, Columbus, OH 43205.

EYRING, EDWARD M(ARCUS), b. Oakland, Calif, Jan. 7, 31; m. 54; c. 4. PHYSICAL CHEMISTRY. B.A, Utah, 55, M.S, 56, Nat. Sci. Found. fel, 59-60, Ph.D.(phys. chem), 60. Nat. Sci. Found. fel. fast reaction kinetics, Göttingen, 60-61; asst. prof. CHEM, UNIV. UTAH, 61-65, assoc. prof, 65-68, PROF, 68- U.S.A.F, 55-57, Capt. AAAS; Am. Chem. Soc. Kinetics of fast chemical reactions in solutions; acid dissociation constants; pulsed lasers. Address: Dept. of Chemistry, University of Utah, Salt Lake City, UT 84112.

EYRING, HENRY, b. Colonia Juarez, Chihuahua, Mex, Feb. 20, 01; U.S. citizen; m. 28; c. 3. PHYSICAL CHEMISTRY. B.S, Arizona, 23, Ariz. Bur. Mines fel, 23-24, M.S, 24; Ph.D.(chem), California, 27; hon. Sc.D, Utah, 52, Northwestern, 53, Princeton, 56, Seoul, 63, Brigham Young, 65, Case West. Reserve Univ; hon. LL.D, Ind. Cent. Col, 64, Univ. Calif, Davis. Instr. chem, Arizona, 24-25; teaching fel, California, 25-27; instr, Wisconsin, 27-28, res. assoc, 28-29; nat. res. fel, Berlin, 29-30; lectr, California, 30-31; res. assoc, Princeton, 31-36, assoc. prof. 36-38, prof, 38-46; prof. CHEM. & dean grad. sch, UNIV. UTAH, 46-67, DISTINGUISHED PROF, 67- Assoc. ed, Textile Res. J, Textile Res. Inst; ed, Annual Rev. Phys. Chem, Phi Kappa Phi, 56. Dir, Textile Found, 44-46; mem. sci. adv. comt, Welsh Found, 54-; mem, Nat. Sci. Found, 63-68. Alumni achievement award, Arizona, 47; Talmage award, Brigham Young, 59. With Off. Sci. Res. & Develop; U.S.A; U.S.N, 44. Nat. Acad. Sci.(mem, Nat. Sci. Bd, 62-68); AAAS (award, 33; v.pres, 46, mem. bd. dirs, 61-, pres, 63, pres. elect, 64); Am. Chem. Soc.(Nichols Medal, 51, Lewis Award, 63, Debye Award, 64, pres, 65-); Am. Philos. Soc. Radioactivity; application of quantum mechanics to chemistry; theory of reaction rates; theory of liquids. Address: Dept. of Chemistry, University of Utah, Salt Lake City, UT 84112.

EYRING, LeROY, b. Pima, Ariz, Dec. 26, 19; m. 41; c. 4. PHYSICAL CHEMISTRY. B.S, Arizona, 43; Ph.D.(chem), California, Berkeley, 49. Asst, California, Berkeley, 43-44, chemist, radiation lab, 46-49; asst. prof. CHEM, Iowa, 49-55, assoc. prof, 55-61; PROF, ARIZ. STATE UNIV, 61- Sr. fel, Nat. Sci. Found, 58-59; Guggenheim fel, 59-60; Fulbright award, 59-60. U.S.N.R, 44-46. Am. Chem. Soc. Solid state chemistry, especially thermodynamic, kinetic and high temperature studies of reactions involving oxide systems of the actinide, lanthanide and transition elements. Address: 6995 E. Jackrabbit Rd, Scottsdale, AZ 85251.

EYSTER, EUGENE H(ENDERSON), b. Wheaton, Minn, Mar. 21, 14; m. 42; c. 5. PHYSICAL CHEMISTRY. B.Chem, Minnesota, 35; Ph.D.(phys. chem), Calif. Inst. Tech, 38. Nat. Res. fel. molecular spectra, dept. physics, Michigan, 39-40; Hale fel, Calif. Inst. Tech, 41, group leader explosives res. lab, Nat. Defense Res. Cmt. & Office Sci. Res. & Develop, 42-45; subdiv. chief explosives div, U.S. Naval Ord. Lab, 46-48; alternate div. leader, LOS ALAMOS SCI. LAB, UNIV. CALIF, 49-70, DIV. LEADER, 70- AAAS; Am. Chem. Soc. Molecular spectra and structure; physical chemistry of explosives and detonation. Address: 1437 41st St, Los Alamos, NM 87544.

EYSTER, H(ENRY) CLYDE, b. Dornsife, Pa, July 10, 10; m. 38; c. 1. PLANT PHYSIOLOGY, PHYCOLOGY. A.B, Bucknell Univ, 32; A.M, Univ. Ill, 34, fel. 35-36, Ph.D.(bot), 36. Asst, Univ. Ill, 32-35; instr. bot, N.C. State Col, 36-37; asst. prof. bot, Univ. S.Dak, 37-44, assoc. prof, 44-46, head dept, 37-46; res. plant physiologist, Charles F. Kettering Found, 46-62; sr. res. biologist, Monsanto Res. Corp, 62-66; PROF. BIOL, MOBILE COL, 66-, CHMN. DIV. NATURAL SCI, 70- Assoc. prof. biol, Antioch Col, 46-51, prof, 51-62. Am. Phycol. Soc; Bot. Soc. Am; Am. Soc. Plant Physiol. Phytosynthesis; auxins; plant enzymes; hybrid vigor; plant genetics; Hill reaction; photophosphorylation; mineral and trace element nutrition of algae and duckweeds; nitrogen fixation; water pollution and eutrophication; aquaculture and mariculture. Address: Dept. of Biology, Mobile College, P.O. Box 13220, Mobile, AL 36613.

EYSTER, MARSHALL B(LACKWELL), b. Toledo, Ohio, Sept. 25, 23; m. 47; c. 3. ORNITHOLOGY. B.S, Chicago, 45; M.S, Illinois, 50, Ph.D.(zool), 52. Asst. zool, Illinois, 46-50; asst. prof. BIOL, UNIV. SOUTHWEST. LA, 50-54, assoc. prof, 54-66, PROF, 66- U.S.A, 42-46. Am. Ornith. Union; Wildlife Soc; Wilson Ornith. Soc; Cooper Ornith. Soc. Daily rhythm and nocturnal unrest in birds; ecological distribution of mammals. Address: Dept. of Biology, University of Southwestern Louisiana, Lafayette, LA 70501.

EYZAGUIRRE, CARLOS, b. Santiago, Chile, Apr. 28, 23; m. 47; c. 2. NEUROPHYSIOLOGY. M.D, Chile, 47. Fel. med, Hopkins Hosp, 47-50; asst. prof. neurophysiol. & pharmacol, Cath. Univ. Chile, 50-51, assoc. prof, 51-57; asst. res. prof. PHYSIOL, COL. MED, UNIV. UTAH, 57-62, PROF, 62-, HEAD DEPT, 65- Guggenheim fel, Hopkins, 53-55. Am. Physiol. Soc. Physiology of sensory receptors; efferent control of muscle spindles; physiology of chemoreceptors. Address: 2217 Laird Way, Salt Lake City, UT 84108.

EZEKIEL, DAVID H(IRSCH), b. Bryan, Tex, Sept. 26, 28; m. 52; c. 3. MICROBIOLOGY. B.S, Maryland, 48; Nat. Sci. Found. fel, Illinois, 53-55, Ph.D.(bact), Illinois, 59; Hite fel, M.D. Anderson Hosp. & Tumor Inst, 57-59. Asst. biologist, M.D. Anderson Hosp. & Tumor Inst, 59-61; asst. mem. res. labs, ALBERT EINSTEIN MED. CTR, 61-67, ASSOC. MEM. RES. LABS, 67- Res. asst. prof. microbiol, sch. med, Temple Univ, 63-66. U.S.A, 51-53. Am. Soc. Microbiol. Biosynthetic control mechanisms; biosynthesis of RNA. Address: Albert Einstein Medical Center, Philadelphia, PA 19141.

EZEKIEL, HERBERT M, b. Minneapolis, Minn, Feb. 23, 27; m. 48; c. 3. POLYMER CHEMISTRY. B.S, Maryland, 46. Chemist, Reed Res, Inc, 50; res. biochemist, U.S. Army Grad. Sch, 50-53; chemist, U.S. Geol. Surv, 53-55; jr. res. chemist, Nat. Cash Register Co, 55-57, sr. res. chemist, 57-65; MAT. RES. ENGR, AIR FORCE MAT. LAB, WRIGHT PATTERSON AIR FORCE BASE, 65- AAAS; fel. Am. Inst. Chem; Am. Chem. Soc. Reinforcing fibers, especially high strength, high modulus graphite fibers; high temperature organic and inorganic fibers; addition and condensation interfacial polymerizations; microencapsulation; water-vapor permeability of polymers. Address: 1201 Latchwood Ave, Dayton, OH 45405.

EZEKIEL, WALTER N(APHTALI), b. Richmond, Va, Apr. 26, 01; m. 26; c. 5. INDUSTRIAL MICROBIOLOGY. B.S, Maryland, 20, M.S, 21, Ph.D. (bot), 24. Asst. plant pathologist, exp. sta, Maryland, 20-25; Nat. Res. Coun. fel, Minnesota, 25-27; agent, bur. plant indust, U.S. Dept. Agr, 27-28; plant pathologist, exp. sta. & mem. grad. faculty, Agr. & Mech. Col, Texas, 28-44; prin. mycologist, Naval Ord. Lab, U.S. Dept. Navy, 44-46; head mycologist, Bur. Ord, 46-53, Bur. Yards & Docks, 53-54; tech. reports officer, Bur. Mines, U.S. Dept. Interior, 55-56, technologist, 56-64, microbiologist, res. ctr, 64-69, res. microbiologist, health div, 69-71; CONSULT, 71- AAAS; Am. Phytopath. Soc; Mycol. Soc. Am; hon. mem. Soc. Indust. Microbiol; Am. Inst. Biol. Sci; Am. Soc. Microbiol. Fruit rotting Sclerotinias; basis of physiologic resistance to Puccinia graminis tritici; Phymatotrichum omnivorum root rot; basis of immunity of monocots; soil fungicides; prevention deterioration electrical and electronic equipment; fungnertness of materials; technical writing and editing; industrial microbiology; coal-workers' pneumoconiosis; plant pathology. Address: 3105 34th St. N.W, Washington, DC 20008.

EZELL, JAMES BEN, JR, b. Gorgas, Ala, June 9, 28; m. 48; c. 2. ANALYTICAL CHEMISTRY. B.S, Florence State Teachers Col, 51. Lab. asst. anal. chem, extractive metall. div, REYNOLDS METALS CO, Ala, 51-52, lab. supvr, 52-54, asst. lab. supvr, ALUMINA RES. DIV, ARK, 56-62, lab. supvr, 62-66, ANAL. DIR, 66- Mem. task comt. 47 & working group 8, Int. Standards Orgn, 65-67, task group 129, 70- U.S.A, 54-56. Am. Chem. Soc; Am. Soc. Test. & Mat. Supervision of analytical section, including atomic absorption, emission spectroscopy, x-ray diffraction, x-ray fluorescence, flame photometry, electron microscopy and conventional wet and colorimetric analytical methods. Address: 1915 Southshore Dr, Benton, AR 72015.

EZELL, WAYLAND LEE, b. Stockton, Calif, Dec. 31, 37; m. 61; c. 3. SYSTEMATIC BOTANY, EVOLUTIONARY BIOLOGY. B.A, Univ. of the Pac, 59, M.A, 63; Sigma Xi grants, Ore. State Univ, 68 & 69, Ph.D.(syst. bot), 70. Instr. biol. & bot, Ventura Col, 62-66; res. asst. bot, Ore. State Univ, 67-68; ASST. PROF. BIOL, ST. CLOUD STATE COL, 70- Del, Int. Bot. Cong, Seattle, Wash, 69; fel, dept. bot, Univ. N.C, Chapel Hill, summer 71; lectr, Sigma Xi regional lect. exchange prog, 71. Bot. Soc. Am; Am. Soc. Plant Taxon; Int. Asn. Plant Taxon. Genetics, evolution and taxonomy of angiosperms, especially genus Mimulus of sections Eunanus and Eumimulus, using field herbarium, hybridization, cytological and biochemical methods. Address: Dept. of Biology, Saint Cloud State College, Saint Cloud, MN 56301.

EZEMENARI, F(IDEL) REX CHUKWUEMEKA, b. Uga, Nigeria, Dec. 18, 30; Can. citizen; m. 59; c. 3. ATMOSPHERIC & RADIATION PHYSICS. B.Sc, Univ. Col, Dublin, 56; Asn. Brit. Commonwealth Univs. U.K. Commonwealth fel, Queen's Univ, Belfast, 60-63, Hons, 63; Ph.D.(physics), Univ. Calgary, 67. Educ. off. chem. & math, Govt. Col, Umuahia, Nigeria, 58-60; teaching asst. physics, Univ. Calgary, 63-67; lectr, fall 67; res. meteorologist, CAN. METEOROL. SERV, 68-70, RES. SCIENTIST, 70- Brit. Inst. Physics & Phys. Soc. Low-level detection of radioactive substances; tracer studies of atmospheric circulation; upper atmospheric densities and their variabilities; sensors and tracking systems and techniques of acquiring meteorological data. Address: Atmospheric Environment Service, 4905 Dufferin St, Downsview, Ont, Can.

EZRA, ARTHUR ABRAHAM, b. Calcutta, India, July 9, 25; U.S. citizen; m. 56; c. 5. ENGINEERING MECHANICS. B.E, Calcutta, 46; M.S.E, Michigan, 48; Ph.D.(eng. mech), Stanford, 58. Engr, Int. Eng. Co, 48-49; struct. & hydraul. engr, U.S. Corps Engrs, 49-51; sr. struct. engr, San Francisco Harbor, 51-56; staff engr, Martin Co, 57-60, chief tech. develop, 60-62, mgr. aeromech. & mat. res, 62-66; HEAD MECH. DIV, DENVER RES. INST. & PROF. MECH. ENG, UNIV. DENVER, 66-, CHMN. DEPT. MECH. SCI. & ENVIRON. ENG, 68- Am. Inst. Aeronaut. & Astronaut; Am. Soc. Eng. Educ; Am. Soc. Mech. Eng. Technology transfer; explosive forming and welding of metals; energy absorbing devices and systems; ultra low cost housing. Address: 6124 Cherrywood Circle, Littleton, CO 80121.

EZRIN, CALVIN, b. Toronto, Ont, Oct. 1, 26; m. 46; c. 6. ENDOCRINOLOGY, INTERNAL MEDICINE. M.D, Univ. Toronto, 49. Res. assoc. path, div. neuropath, UNIV. TORONTO, 53-65, asst. prof, 65-68, PATH. & MED, 68-70, ASSOC. PROF, 70-, ASSOC. MED, DEPT. MED, 59- Stengel res. fel, Am. Col. Physicians, 53-54. Physician, Toronto Gen. Hosp, 54-; consult, dept. vet. affairs, Sunnybrook Hosp, Toronto, 54-; mem. Int. Comt. Nomenclature of Adenohypophysis, 63- Fel. Royal Col. Physicians, Can, 54- Endocrine Soc; Am. Diabetes Asn; Am. Thyroid Asn. Anterior pituitary cytology; insulin resistance; metabolic effects of glucagon; obesity; serum binding and kinetics of thyroid hormones; biology of trans-sexualism. Address: 4 Ava Crescent, Toronto 10, Ont, Can.

EZRIN, MYER, b. Boston, Mass, June 23, 26; m. 46; c. 3. ORGANIC CHEMISTRY. B.S, Tufts Col, 48; Clark fel, Yale, 52-53, Ph.D.(chem), 54. Asst, org. chem. lab, Yale, 50-52; chemist, coated fabric appln. of chlorosulfonated polyethylene, E.I. du Pont de Nemours & Co, Inc, 48-50; plastics div, Monsanto Co, 53-65; proj. leader anal. & phys. chem, DeBELL & RICHARDSON, INC, 65-69, MGR. ANAL. & TESTING DIV, 69- U.S.N.R, 44-46. Am. Chem. Soc. Electron exchange polymers; thermosetting resins; polymer characterization; molecular weight; thermal analysis. Address: 173 Academy Dr, Longmeadow, MA 01106.

EZZELL, BOBBY RAE, b. Goldsboro, N.C, June 20, 42; m. 69; ORGANIC CHEMISTRY. B.S, N.C. State Univ, 64, M.S, 66, Ph.D.(org. chem), 69. Chemist R.J. Reynolds Industs, 69-70; SR. RES. CHEMIST, DOW CHEM. CO, FREEPORT, 70- Am. Chem. Soc. Organophosphorus chemistry—chiefly heterocyclic including both synthesis and mechanism work; amine synthesis including amine containing polymers; structure relationships to biological activity and in general any useful property. Address: 12627 Monarch St, Houston, TX 77047.

F

FAAS, RICHARD WILLIAM, b. Appleton, Wis, Nov. 8, 31; m. 55; c. 3. GEOLOGY, PALEONTOLOGY. B.A, Lawrence Col, 53; M.S, Iowa State, 62, Ph.D.(geol, ecol), 64. Asst. prof. GEOL, LAFAYETTE COL, 64-68, ASSOC. PROF, 68-, HEAD DEPT, 70- U.S.C.G, 53-57. Geol. Soc. Am; Soc. Econ. Paleont. & Mineral; Arctic Inst. N.Am; Marine Technol. Soc. Triassic stratigraphy; estuarine and near-shore marine sedimentation; organic-inorganic interrelationships; paleoecology. Address: Dept. of Geology, Lafayette College, Easton, PA 18042.

FABENS, AUGUSTUS J(EROME), b. Boston, Mass, Jan. 4, 32. MATHEMATICS. A.B, Harvard, 53; Ph.D.(math), Stanford, 59. John Wesley Young Res. instr. MATH, Dartmouth Col, 59-61; lectr, Australian Nat. Univ, 61-63; asst. prof, Rhode Island, 63-64; BOSTON COL, 64-67, ASSOC. PROF, 67- U.S.A, 53-55. Am. Math. Soc. Probability; queuing and inventory theory. Address: Dept. of Mathematics, Boston College, Chestnut Hill, MA 02167.

FABER, DANIEL J, b. Milwaukee, Wis, Aug. 5, 32; m. 54; c. 1. OCEANOGRAPHY, FISHERIES BIOLOGY. B.S, Univ. Wis, 54, Ph.D.(zool), 63; M.Sc, Univ. R.I, 59. RES. SCIENTIST, Ont. Dept. Lands & Forests, 63-67, CAN. OCEANOG. IDENTIFICATION CENTRE, MUS. NATURAL SCI, 67- Am. Inst. Biol. Sci; Am. Soc. Limnol. & Oceanog; Ecol. Soc. Am; Plankton Soc. Japan. Biological oceanography and planktonology; developmental stages of coastal copepods; biological studies concerned with freshwater and marine larval fish. Address: Canadian Oceanographic Identification Centre, National Museum of Natural Sciences, Ottawa, Ont. K1A 0H8, Can.

FABER, J(AN) JOB, b. The Hague, Netherlands, June 16, 34; m. 57; c. 2. PHYSIOLOGY, BIOPHYSICS. Drs, Univ. Amsterdam, 57, M.B, 60; Ph.D. (biophys), Univ. West. Ont, 63. Res. asst. biophys, Univ. West. Ont, 60-62, res. assoc, 62-63; instr. phys. med, Univ. Wash, 63-65, asst. prof, 65-66; PHYSIOL, MED. SCH, UNIV. ORE, PORTLAND, 66-69, ASSOC. PROF, 69- Estab. investr, Am. Heart Asn, 68- Am. Physiol. Soc; Biophys. Soc; Soc. Exp. Biol. & Med; Am. Heart Asn. Cardiovascular sound; prenatal physiology; physiology of joints; muscle. Address: Dept. of Physiology, University of Oregon Medical School, Portland, OR 97201.

FABER, JOHN E(DGAR), JR, b. Highspire, Pa, Jan. 13, 03; m. 29. BACTERIOLOGY. B.S, Maryland, 26, M.S, 27, Ph.D.(bact), 37. Instr. bact, UNIV. MD, 27-37, asst. prof, 37-45, assoc. prof, 45-46, prof. & head dept, 46-68, EMER. PROF. MICROBIOL. & LECTR, 68- U.S.A, 42-46, Maj. AAAS; Am. Soc. Microbiol; Am. Acad. Microbiol; Am. Pub. Health Asn. Dental caries; complement fixation; oral pathogenic microorganisms; quaternary ammonium compounds; measurement; production and preservation of hemolytic activity of guinea pig complement; pleuropneumonia-like organisms. Address: 6900 Wake Forest Dr, College Park, MD 20740.

FABER, JOHN HENRY, b. Elkview, W.Va, May 8, 26; m. 47; c. 4. CHEMICAL ENGINEERING. B.S.Ch.E, West Virginia, 47. Asst. engr, W.Va. State Water Comn, 47-53; power engr, E.I. du Pont de Nemours & Co, 53-56; chem. engr, U.S. Bur. Mines, 56-63, proj. coordinator res, 63-68; EXEC. V.PRES. TRADE ASSOC, NAT. ASH ASN, INC, 68- Am. Asn. Cost Eng; Am. Soc. Test. & Mat; Am. Inst. Mining, Metall. & Petrol. Eng; Am. Concrete Inst; Am. Rd. Builders Asn. Chemicals from coal; coal gasification; electrostatic precipitation; fly ash utilization; coal mine refuse utilization. Address: National Ash Association, Inc, 1819 H St. N.W, Washington, DC 20006.

FABER, RICHARD LEON, b. Winthrop, Mass, May 7, 40; m. 64; c. 1. MATHEMATICS. B.S, Mass. Inst. Tech, 60; M.A, Brandeis, 62, Nat. Defense Ed. Act fel, 60-63, Nat. Sci. Found. summer fel, 64, Ph.D.(category theory), 65. Instr. MATH, Regis Col.(Mass), 64-65; instr, Pennsylvania, 65-67; asst. prof, Univ. Calif, San Diego, 67-68; BOSTON COL, 68-71, ASSOC. PROF, 71- Am. Math. Soc; Math. Asn. Am. Symmetric spaces; non-Euclidean and differential geometry. Address: 48 Chinian Path, Newton Center, MA 02159.

FABER, ROGER J(ACK), b. Grand Rapids, Mich, Oct. 4, 31; m. 56; c. 3. CHEMICAL PHYSICS. A.B, Calvin Col, 53; Union Carbide fel, Mich. State, 56-57, Ph.D.(chem), 58. Res. instr. chem, Mich. State, 57-58; PHYSICS, Calvin Col, 58-60, asst. prof, 60-62, assoc. prof, 62-64; Nat. Sci. Found. faculty fel. chem, Columbia, 64-65; asst. prof, LAKE FOREST COL, 65-68, ASSOC. PROF, 68- Asst. prof, Mich. State Univ, summer 59. AAAS; Am. Phys. Soc; Am. Asn. Physics Teachers; Am. Chem. Soc. Electron spin resonance; atomic collision processes. Address: Dept. of Physics, Lake Forest College, Lake Forest, IL 60045.

FABER, SHEPARD M(AZOR), b. Brooklyn, N.Y, Aug. 8, 28; m. 53; c. 4. SCIENCE EDUCATION. B.A, Emory, 49; M.A, Columbia, 50; Ed.D.(sci. ed), Florida, 60. Instr. sci. ed, Florida, 55; assoc. prof. sci, E.Carolina Col, 59-62; PHYS. SCI, UNIV. MIAMI, 62-70, PROF, 70- U.S.A.F, 51-53, 2nd Lt. Fel. AAAS; Nat. Asn. Res. Sci. Teaching. Science curriculum and instruction. Address: Dept. of Physical Science, University of Miami, Coral Gables, FL 33146.

FABERGÉ, A(LEXANDER) C(YRIL), b. Moscow, Russia, Feb. 26, 12; nat. GENETICS. B.Sc, Reading, 33, Ph.D.(genetics), London, 36, D.Sc.(genetics), 45. Res. worker, John Innes Inst, London, 33-37; asst. lectr, univ. col, London, 37-45; res. assoc. genetics, bot. dept, Wisconsin, 45-47; assoc. prof, Missouri, 47-55; scientist, biol. div, Oak Ridge Nat. Lab, 56-57; RES. SCIENTIST, GENETICS FOUND. & LECTR. ZOOL, UNIV. TEX, AUSTIN, 57- Res. worker, Rothamsted Exp. Sta, England, 41-42; exp. officer, Army Operational Res. Group, British Ministry of Supply, 42-45. Royal Armoured Corps, 40-41. Electron Micros. Soc. Am; Brit. Genetical Soc. Spontaneous and induced mutations and chromosome aberrations; nuclear structure; electron microscopy. Address: Dept. of Zoology, University of Texas, Austin, TX 78712.

FABES, EUGENE BARRY, b. Detroit, Mich, Feb. 6, 37; m. 59; c. 2. MATHEMATICS. A.B, Harvard, 59; M.S, Chicago, 62, Ph.D.(math), 65. Summer fel, MATH, Rice Univ, 65, asst. prof, 65-66; INST. TECHNOL, UNIV. MINN, MINNEAPOLIS, 66-68, ASSOC. PROF, 68- Singular integrals and partial differential equations. Address: School of Mathematics, Institute of Technology, University of Minnesota, Minneapolis, MN 55445.

FABIAN, LEONARD W(ILLIAM), b. North Little Rock, Ark, Nov. 12, 23; m. 47; c. 3. ANESTHESIOLOGY. B.S, Arkansas, 47, M.D, 51. Intern, Arkansas, 51-52, resident anesthesiol, 52-54; fel, Phila. Childrens Hosp, 54; instr. ANESTHESIOL, SCH. MED, Arkansas, 54-55; asst. prof, Duke, 55-58; PROF, Mississippi, 58-71, WASH. UNIV, 71- Dipl, Am. Bd. Anesthesiol. Hosp.C, U.S.N, 42-46. Am. Soc. Anesthesiol; fel. Am. Col. Anesthesiol; Am. Med. Asn. Chemistry and pharmacology of anesthetic drugs. Address: Washington University School of Medicine, St. Louis, MO 63110.

FABIAN, MICHAEL WILLIAM, b. Mercer, Pa, Sept. 27, 31; m. 52; c. 1. VERTEBRATE ZOOLOGY, EMBRYOLOGY. B.S, Grove City Col, 52; M.S, Mich. State, 54; Nat. Sci. Found. fel, Ohio State, 60-61, Ph.D.(zool), 64. Asst, Mich. State, 52-54; teacher, pub. schs, Ohio, 54-56; instr. gen. biol, Arizona State, 56-57; asst. prof. biol, Geneva Col, 57-61; assoc. prof. physiol, Westminster Col, 61-64; assoc. prof. physiol. & zool, GROVE CITY COL, 64-67, PROF. ECOL, 67-, CHMN. DEPT. BIOL, 64- Summers, res. investr, div. natural resources, State of Ohio, 59, res. participant, Nat. Sci. Found. Inst, 65. AAAS; Ecol. Soc. Am. Predatory or carnivorous activity of Crustacea on vertebrates. Address: Dept. of Biology, Grove City College, Grove City, PA 16127.

FABIAN, ROBERT JOHN, b. Cleveland, Ohio, Mar. 21, 39; m. 62. MATHEMATICAL LOGIC. B.S, Case, 61, M.S, 63, Ph.D.(math). 65. Asst. prof. math, Smith Col, 64-70; ASSOC. PROF. COMPUT. SCI, YORK UNIV.(ONT), 70- Vis. asst. prof, dept. appl. anal. & comput. sci, Univ. Waterloo, 68-69. Am. Math. Soc; Asn. Comput. Mach; Can. Comput. Sci. Asn. Theory of automata. Address: Dept. of Computer Science, York University, 4700 Keele St, Downsview 463, Ont, Can.

FABIANEK, JOHN, b. Perbeta, Slovakia, Dec. 3, 22; nat, 68. BIOCHEMISTRY, PHYSIOLOGY. D.Sc.(agron, biol. sci), Bratislava, 46; J.D, Paris, 55, Ph.D. (biochem, physiol), Sorbonne, 57. Res. assoc. physiol, Nat. Ctr. Sci. Res-Ministry Ed. France, 47-50, asst. prof. biochem, 50-57, assoc. prof, 57-60; asst. prof, N.Y. Med. Col, 61-65, assoc. prof, 65-67; assoc. prof. CHEM, N.Y. INST. TECHNOL, 67-68, PROF, 68-, DEP. CHMN. DEPT. LIFE SCI, 67- Del. French Govt, UN Atomic Energy Comn, Geneva, Switz, 59; mem, Inst. Res. Danube Basin Probs, Vienna. Fel. AAAS; Am. Chem. Soc; Am. Inst. Nutrit; Am. Rheumatism Asn; Geront. Soc; Harvey Soc; Am. Physiol. Soc; Soc. Exp. Biol. & Med; Asn. Am. Med. Cols; fel. N.Y. Acad. Sci; fel. Am. Inst. Chem; Biophys. Soc; Int. Asn. Dent. Res; Fr. Soc. Physiol; Fr. Soc. Biol. Chem; Chem. Soc. France; Brit. Biochem. Soc. Nutrition; ascorbic acid; niacin; mineral metabolism; bioflavonoids; mucopolysaccharides; collagen; capillary resistance and permeability; connective tissue permeability; skin biochemistry and physiology; glycoproteins; rheumatoid arthritis; endocrinology. Address: Dept. of Life Sciences, New York Institute of Technology, 888 Seventh Ave, New York, NY 10019.

FABIYI, AKINYELE, b. Lagos, Nigeria, Oct. 2, 24; m. 57; c. 2. VIROLOGY, IMMUNOCHEMISTRY. B.Sc, Syracuse, 52; M.Sc, Washington (Seattle), 54; univ. scholar, Pennsylvania, 56, Harrison scholar, 57, Ph.D.(med. microbiol), 58. Res. fel, grad. sch. pub. health, Pittsburgh, 58; vis. fel, Rockfeller Found, 58-59 & virus labs, Brazil & Trinidad, 59; sci. off. virol, W.African Coun. Med. Res, 59-61; res. assoc. pediat, sch. med, Kansas, 61-62, instr, 62-64, assoc. dir. arborvirus proj, 64; vis. scientist, Nat. Inst. Neurol. Diseases & Blindness, Nat. Insts. Health, 64-65, res. microbiologist & head, unit on vaccine & immunol. studies, 65-68; ASST. PROF. NEUROL. & CO-HEAD LAB. NEUROVIROL, MT. SINAI SCH. MED, 68- Summer asst. prof, sch. med, Univ. Kans, 64; asst. prof. pediat, sch. med, Georgetown Univ, 65-68. Teratology Soc; Am. Asn. Immunol; Royal Soc. Trop. Med. & Hyg. Antigenic analysis of influenza type A; epidemiological survey of arborvirus; yellow fever; antigenic analysis and immunogenic studies of enteroviruses; teratogenic viruses. Address: Dept. of Neurology, Mt. Sinai School of Medicine, 100th St. & Fifth Ave, New York, NY 10029.

FABRE, LOUIS FERNAND, JR, b. Akron, Ohio, Sept. 13, 41; m. 62; c. 2. PSYCHIATRY, PHYSIOLOGY. B.S, Univ. Akron, 63; Ph.D.(physiol), West. Reserve Univ, 66; M.D, Baylor Univ, 69. Res. specialist, TEX. RES. INST. MENT. SCI, 65-67, acting chief neuroendocrinol, 67-68, chief, 68-70, assoc. head DIV. MENT. RETARDATION, 70-71, HEAD, 71-; ASST. PROF. MENT. SCI, UNIV. TEX. GRAD. SCH. BIOMED. SCI, 69- Nat. Sci. Found. res. grants, 67-71; intern, Methodist Hosp, Houston, Tex, 69-70; Kelsey Leary Found. grant, 69-71; Nat. Inst. Ment. Health grant, 70-71; resident, Baylor Univ, 70- Endocrine Soc. Role of renal, anterior pituitary and posterior diencephalic mechanisms in the control of aldosterone secretion; endocrine function in alcoholism. Address: Texas Research Institute of Mental Sciences, Texas Medical Center, 1300 Moursund Rd, Houston, TX 77025.

FABREGA, DR. HORACIO, JR, Psychiat, Anthrop, see Suppl. I to 11th ed, Soc. & Behav. Vols.

FABREY, JAMES D(OUGLAS), b. N.Y.C, Oct. 29, 43; m. 67. MATHEMATICAL PHYSICS, MATHEMATICS. A.B, Cornell Univ, 65; hon. Woodrow Wilson & Nat. Sci. Found. fels. & Ph.D.(math), Mass. Inst. Technol, 69. ASST. PROF. MATH, UNIV. N.C, CHAPEL HILL, 69- Am. Math. Soc.

Functional analysis; operator algebras; differential equations. Address: Dept. of Mathematics, University of North Carolina at Chapel Hill, Chapel Hill, NC 27514.

FABRICAND, BURTON P(AUL), b. N.Y.C, Nov. 22, 23; m. 52; c. 2. PHYSICS. A.B, Columbia, 47, A.M, 49, Ph.D.(physics), 53. Proj. engr, Philco Corp, 52-54; lectr. & res. assoc. PHYSICS, Pennsylvania, 54-56; sr. res. scientist, Hudson Lab, Columbia, 57-69; CHMN. DEPT, PRATT INST, 69- Consult, Moore Sch. Elec. Eng, Pennsylvania, 54-60; Indust. Electronic Hardware Corp, 60-64. U.S.A, 43-46. Am. Phys. Soc. Nuclear magnetic resonance; atomic absorption spectroscopy; internal reflection spectroscopy; dosimetry; semiconductors; molecular beams; photonuclear reactions. Address: Dept. of Physics, Pratt Insitute, Brooklyn, NY 11205.

FABRICANT, JULIUS, b. Philadelphia, Pa, Mar. 30, 19; m. 45; c. 2. POULTRY PATHOLOGY. V.M.D, Pennsylvania, 42; B.S, Pa. State Col, 45; M.S, Cornell, 47, Ph.D.(poultry path), 49. Asst. animal path, Pa. State, 44-45; POULTRY DISEASES, STATE UNIV. N.Y. VET. COL, CORNELL UNIV, 46-49, asst. prof, 49-52, assoc. prof, 52-60, PROF, 60- Nat. Insts. Health fel, inst. gen. path, Aarhus, 64-65. AAAS; Am. Vet. Med. Asn; Poultry Sci. Asn. Poultry diseases, especially Newcastle, infectious bronchitis, chronic respiratory disease and infectious hepatitis of ducks; mycoplasma. Address: State University of New York Veterinary College, Cornell University, Ithaca, NY 14850.

FABRIKANT, IRENE B(ERGER), b. Krakow, Poland, Jan. 19, 33; U.S. citizen; m. 56. MICROBIOLOGY. B.Sc, McGill Univ, 54, M.Sc, 56; U.S. Pub. Health Serv. fels, Univ. Md, 58-61, 65-66, Ph.D.(microbiol), 66; Johns Hopkins Univ, 59-60. U.S. Pub. Health Serv. fel. microbiol, sch. med, Univ. Md, 66-67, instr, 67-71; ASST. PROF. MED, SCH. MED, UNIV. CONN, 71- Consult. typhus, WHO, 69, Pan-Am. Health Orgn, 71; assoc. mem. comn. rickettsial diseases, Armed Forces Epidemiol. Bd, 70- Fel. Royal Soc. Trop. Med. & Hyg; Am. Soc. Microbiol. Medical microbiology; rickettsiology; immunology; epidemiology; epidemic typhus; vaccines; chemotherapy; vector control; field studies; antigenic analysis; bioassay of vaccines and antigen fractions. Address: Dept. of Medicine, University of Connecticut School of Medicine, Farmington, CT 06032.

FABRIKANT, JACOB I, b. New York, N.Y, Feb. 9, 28; m. 56. RADIOLOGY, RADIATION BIOLOGY. B.Sc, McGill, 52, M.D, C.M, 56; Ph.D.(biophys), London, 64. Intern surg, med. center, Duke, 56-57, asst. path, sch. med, 57, fel. surg, 57-58; resident radiol, hosp. & fel, sch. med, Hopkins, 58-61; Nat. Acad. Sci-Nat. Res. Coun. James Picker Found. adv. fel. radiol, Univ. London, 61-64; sch. med. & sch. hyg. & pub. health, Johns Hopkins Univ, 64-65, asst. prof. radiol, sch. med, 64-68, assoc. prof, 68-70, asst. prof. radiol. sci, sch. hyg. & pub. health, 65-68, assoc. prof, 69-70, radiologist, univ. hosp, 64-70; PROF. RADIOL. & HEAD DEPT, UNIV. CONN, 70- Vis. prof, Bowman Gray Sch. Med, 68; clin. cancer prog, Georgetown Univ. Sch. Med. & Hosp, 69; col. med, Univ. Vt, 70; vis. radiation biologist, Am. Inst. Biol. Sci, 69-; William O'Brien Prof. radiation sci, sch. med. & univ. hosps, Univ. Minn, 70. Mem. comt. radiol, div. med. sci, Nat. Acad. Sci-Nat. Res. Coun, 67-, subcomt. radiobiol, 69-70, adv. comt. biol. effects ionizing radiations, 70-, subcomt. effects on growth & develop, 70-; neurol. study sect, Nat. Insts. Health, 69-; x-ray image prod. & related facilities adv. comt, Dept. Health, Educ. & Welfare, U.S. Pub. Health Serv, 68-69, med. radiation adv. comt, environ. control admin, 69-, long-term radiation effects adv. comt, 69-, radiol. health sci. educ. proj, 71- AAAS; Asn. Univ. Radiol; Brit. Inst. Radiol; Radiation Res. Soc; Brit. Asn. Radiation Res; Am. Inst. Biol. Sci. Clinical radiology; cellular and mammalian radiation biology; radiation effects on cell renewal and related systems. Address: Dept. of Radiology, University of Connecticut Hospital, Hartford, CT 06112.

FABRIS, HUBERT J, b. Vienna, Austria, Sept. 16, 26; m. 57; c. 1. ORGANIC CHEMISTRY. Ph.D, Univ. Vienna, 56. Chemist food res, Fed. Inst. Food Inspection, Austria, 56-57; sr. res. chemist, GEN. TIRE & RUBBER CO, 58-67, HEAD, POLYMER & CHEM. SYNTHESES, 67- Condensation polymers, especially isocyanate chemistry. Address: General Tire & Rubber Co, Akron, OH 44309.

FABRIZIO, ANGELINA M(ARIA), b. Montenero Valcocchiaro, Italy; U.S. citizen. MEDICAL MICROBIOLOGY. B.S, Villa Maria Col, 44; fel. & M.S, Kentucky, 47; Nat. Tuberc. Asn. fel, Pennsylvania, 48-51; Ph.D.(med. micorbiol), 52; cert, Hahnemann Med. Col. & Hosp, 55. Asst. bact, Kentucky, 45-46, instr, Italian, 46-47; res. bacteriologist, antibiotics, col. med, Univ. Cincinnati & Cincinnati Gen. Hosp, 47-48; res. assoc. exp. cancer & tissue cult, JEFFERSON MED. COL, 65-67, ASST. PROF. PATH, 67- Instr, sch. med, Univ. Pa, 60; res. consult, Vet. Admin. Hosp, Coatesville, Pa, 68- Fel. AAAS; Am. Soc. Microbiol; Tissue Cult. Asn; N.Y. Acad. Sci. Acetylmethylcarbinol production by coliforms; sensitivities of bacteria to antibiotics; tuberculin sensitivity; tissue culture; experimental tumors. Address: 2045 Spruce St, Philadelphia, PA 19103.

FABRO, SERGIO, b. Trieste, Italy, Sept. 3, 31; m. 58. PHARMACOLOGY, MEDICINE. M.D, Milan, 56; Brit. Coun. fel, Rome, 64-65, Ph.D.(biol. chem), 66 & Ph.D.(pharmacol), 68; Ph.D.(biochem), London, 67. Intern med, Univ. Milan, 56-57; asst. prof. path, Modena, 58-60, biochem, 61-62; res. asst, St. Mary's Hosp. Med. Sch, Univ. London, 62-67; RES. PROF. PHARMACOL, SCH. MED, GEORGE WASH. UNIV, 67- Biochem. award, Nat. Acad. Lincei, 65. Biochemistry of development; teratology. Address: Dept. of Pharmacology, George Washington University, 1339 H St. N.W, Washington, DC 20005.

FABRY, ANDRAS, b. Budapest, Hungary, Jan. 10, 37; m. 62; c. 1. TOXICOLOGY, VETERINARY SCIENCE. B.V.Sc, Liverpool, 62; Glasgow, 62-63. Assoc. vet, gen. practice, 63-65; vet, meat inspection div, Can. Dept. Agr, 65-67; asst. toxicologist, Mason Res. Inst, 67-68; SUPV. TOXICOLOGIST, SCHERING CORP, 68- Am. Vet. Med. Asn; Brit. Vet. Asn. Clinical aspects of new anesthetics; toxicological studies of cancer chemotherapeutic agents and new pharmaceuticals. Address: 16 Cedar Tree Lane, Sparta, NJ 07871.

FABRY, T(HOMAS) L(ESTER), b. Budapest, Hungary, May 30, 37; m. 59; c. 3. PHYSICAL & BIOPHYSICAL CHEMISTRY. B.Sc, St. Andrews, 61; Du Pont fel, Yale, 62-63, M.S. & Ph.D.(phys. chem), 63. Res. staff chemist, Yale, 63-65; MEM. RES. STAFF BIOPHYS. CHEM, Int. Bus. Mach. Corp, 65-70; ALBERT EINSTEIN COL. MED, 70- Lectr, Yale, 64-65; adj. asst. prof, Rockefeller Univ, 70- Irvine medal, 61. Bioenergetics; photosynthesis and electrontransport chain model systems; polymer and protein chemistry; electrolytic conductance. Address: Albert Einstein College of Medicine, 1300 Morris Park Ave, Bronx, NY 10461.

FABRYCKY, WOLTER J, b. Springfield, N.Y, Dec. 6, 32; m. 54; c. 2. INDUSTRIAL ENGINEERING. B.S.I.E, Wichita State, 57; M.S.I.E, Arkansas, 58; Ethyl Corp. fel, Okla. State, 60-62, Ph.D.(eng), 62. Jr. design engr, Cessna Aircraft Co, 54-57; instr. indust. eng, Arkansas, 57-60; asst. prof. indust. eng, Okla. State Univ, 62-64, assoc. prof, 64-65; PROF. INDUST. ENG. & OPERS. RES, VA. POLYTECH. INST. & STATE UNIV, 65-, ASSOC. DEAN ENG, 70- Prin. engr, Brown Eng. Co, Ala, 62-65; summers, opers. res. analyst, U.S. Air Force, 60, design engr, Ling-Temco-Vought, Tex, 58, 59. Am. Inst. Indust. Eng; Am. Soc. Eng. Educ; Opers. Res. Soc. Am. Systems engineering; engineering economy; operations research. Address: College of Engineering, Virginia Polytechnic Institute & State University, Blacksburg, VA 24061.

FABULA, A(NDREW) G(EORGE), b. Bayonne, N.J, May 30, 26; m. 53; c. 3. FLUID MECHANICS. B.S, Princeton, 49; M.S, Calif. Inst. Technol, 50, Aeronaut. Engr, 58; Ph.D, Pa. State Univ, 66. Aeronaut. res. engr, U.S. Naval Ord. Test Sta, 51-55, Off. Naval Res, 55-59, U.S. Naval Ord. Test Sta, 59-67, physicist, Naval Undersea Warfare Ctr, 67-68, staff scientist, NAVAL UNDERSEA RES. & DEVELOP. CTR, 68-70, HEAD FLUID MECH. BR, 70- U.S.A.A.F, 44-46. Soc. Rheol; Acoust. Soc. Am. Fluid mechanics; hydrodynamics and acoustohydrodynamics; boundary layer research; non-Newtonian fluids; radiated and self-noise of marine vehicles. Address: Code 6005, Naval Undersea Research & Development Center, San Diego, CA 92132.

FABUSS, BELA M, b. Piestany, Czech, July 24, 24; m. 50; c. 2. CHEMICAL ENGINEERING, ENVIRONMENTAL POLLUTION. Dipl, Budapest Tech, 46, Dr. Tech. Sci, 50. Asst. prof. inorg. chem, Budapest Tech, 50-52; assoc. prof. phys. chem, Veszprem Tech, 52-56; scientist, Nat. Coal Bd, Coal Res. Estab, Stoke Orchard, Eng, 57; res. group leader, Dom. Tar & Chem. Ltd, Montreal, Can, 57-60; sr. res. group leader, Monsanto Res. Corp, Mass, 60-68; TECH. DIR. ENVIRON. POLLUTION DIV, LOWELL TECHNOL. INST. RES. FOUND, 68- Am. Chem. Soc. Hydrocarbon and petroleum chemistry; reaction kinetics; unit operations; waste water treatment; water and air pollution control process development. Address: Environmental Pollution Division, Lowell Technological Institute Research Foundation, 450 Aiken St, Lowell, MA 01854.

FACEY, VERA L, b. Halifax, N.S, June 6, 09; nat. PLANT ECOLOGY, BOTANY. B.Sc, Dalhousie Univ, 36; M.A, Univ. Toronto, 40, Ph.D.(bot), 46. Teacher, pub. schs, N.S, 28-32 & 36-38; asst, Univ. Toronto, 38-40 & 43-45; lectr. bot, Dalhousie Univ, 40-41 & 42-43; N.S. Agr. Col, 45-47; asst. prof. biol, UNIV. N.DAK, 47-54, assoc. prof, 54-62, PROF. BIOL. & CURATOR HERBARIUM, 62- Fel. AAAS; Am. Soc. Plant Taxon; Int. Asn. Plant Taxon; Bot. Soc. Am; Ecol. Soc. Am; Torrey Bot. Club. Grassland ecology; aquatic vascular plants. Address: Dept. of Biology, University of North Dakota, Grand Forks, ND 58201.

FACKENTHAL, EDWARD, b. Pequest, N.J, Sept. 23, 03; m. 29; c. 3. PHYSICAL CHEMISTRY. B.S, Temple, 36; M.S, Pennsylvania, 38, Ph.D.(phys. chem), 53. Assoc. prof. physics & chem, SCH. PHARM, TEMPLE UNIV, 31-70, PROF. PHYSICS, 70- Theories of solutions. Address: Dept. of Physics, School of Pharmacy, Temple University, Philadelphia, PA 19122.

FACKLER, JOHN PAUL, JR, b. Toledo, Ohio, July 31, 34; m. 56; c. 4. INORGANIC CHEMISTRY. B.A, Valparaiso Univ, 56; Nat. Sci. Found. summer fel, Mass. Inst. Technol, 59, Allied Chem. & Dye Corp. fel, 59-60, Ph.D. (chem), 60. Asst. prof. CHEM, Univ. Calif, Berkeley, 60-62; CASE WEST. RESERVE UNIV, 62-64, assoc. prof, 64-70, PROF, 70- Nat Sci. Found. travel grant, Int. Coord. Conf, 64; Nat. Sci. Found. consult, Cent. State Univ, 67-69; lectr-consult, Fulbright Comt, Colombia, S.Am, 69; vis. assoc. prof, Univ. Calif, Santa Barbara, 69; mem, Int. Conf. Educ, Aspen, Colo, 70. AAAS; Am. Chem. Soc; The Chem. Soc; Am. Phys. Soc; Am. Crystallog. Asn. Transition-metal coordination chemistry; structural inorganic chemistry; spectroscopy of coordination compounds; chemistry of sulfur containing complexes; metal-metal bonding in nickel triad compounds; Jahn-Teller effects; bioinorganic chemistry. Address: Dept. of Chemistry, Case Western Reserve University, Cleveland, OH 44106.

FACKLER, WALTER V(ALENTINE), JR, b. Oak Park, Ill, Mar. 19, 20; m. 47; c. 3. PHYSICAL CHEMISTRY. Ph.D.(phys. chem), Iowa State Col, 53. Res. chemist, Bauer & Black, 53-56; res. supvr, Toni Co, 56-61; adv. scientist, Continental Can Co, 61-66; chemist, Van Straaten Chem. Co, 66-70; SR. RES. PROFESSIONAL, ARMOUR-DIAL, INC, 70- U.S.N.R, 41-46, Res, 46-55, Lt. Comdr. AAAS; Am. Chem. Soc. Detergents; polymers; plastic films; adhesives. Address: 1011 Gables Blvd, Wheaton, IL 60187.

FACTOR, ARNOLD, b. Boston, Mass, Apr. 1, 36; m. 61; c. 2. PHYSICAL ORGANIC CHEMISTRY. B.A, Brandeis, 58; E.I. du Pont de Nemours fel, Harvard, 59-60, M.A, 60, Procter & Gamble fel, 60-61, Nat. Insts. Health fel, 61-62, Ph.D.(chem), 63. Nat. Insts. Health fel, California, San Diego, 63-64; RES. CHEMIST, RES. & DEVELOP. CTR, GEN. ELEC. CO, 64- Am. Chem. Soc. Award of excellence, Gen. Elec. Co. Plastic Dept, 70. Electrophilic additions; autoxidation; free radical chemistry; phenol oxidations; polymer stabilization; Redox polymers. Address: General Electric Research & Development Center, P.O. Box 8, Schenectady, NY 12301.

FADDICK, ROBERT RAYMOND, b. Sudbury, Ont, May 18, 38; m. 65; c. 4. FLUID MECHANICS, HYDRAULIC ENGINEERING. B.Ap.S, Queen's Univ. (Ont), 61, M.Ap.S, 63; Ph.D.(civil eng), Mont. State Univ, 70. Res. asst. hydraul. eng, Queen's Univ.(Ont), 61-63; hydraul. engr, Alden Hydraul. Lab, Worcester Polytech. Inst, 63-66; res. asst. CIVIL ENG, Mont. State Univ,

66-69; ASST. PROF, COLO. SCH. MINES, 69- Hon. mem. Soc. Am. Mil. Eng; assoc. Am. Soc. Civil Eng. Transportation of solids in pipelines; rheology of mineral solids; compilation of a slurry pipeline computer data bank; pipeline and rheological aspects of coal-water slurries; hydraulic aspects of thermal pollution. Address: Dept. of Basic Engineering, Colorado School of Mines, Golden, CO 80401.

FADDOUL, EDWARD M(ICHAEL), JR, b. Sistersville, W.Va, Aug. 5, 36. BIOCHEMISTRY, PHYSICAL CHEMISTRY. B.S, Marietta Col, 58; M.S, Iowa State, 61, Ph.D.(biochem), 67. Sr. res. biochemist, Ross Labs. Div, Abbott Labs, 64-68; sr. res. scientist, Warren-Teed Pharmaceut, Inc, 68-70; RES. ASSOC. NEUROSURG, OHIO STATE UNIV. HOSP, 70- Am. Chem. Soc. Kinetics of Newcastle disease virus hemolysin; physical biochemistry of fat globule membranes of food emulsions; metabolism of compounds of interest in drug research; biochemical changes involved in brain edema. Address: Division of Neurosurgery, Room N-911, Ohio State University Hospital, 410 W. 10th Ave, Columbus, OH 43210.

FADDOUL, GEORGE PETER, b. Boothbay Center, Maine, July 11, 22; m. 53; c. 6. VETERINARY MEDICINE, PUBLIC HEALTH. D.V.M, Middlesex, 44; fel, Va. Polytech, 45; M.S, New Hampshire, 48. Instr. avian path, New Hampshire, 47-48, asst. prof, 48-50; PROF. AVIAN MED, UNIV. MASS, 50- Participant, Northeast. Conf. Lab. Workers, 50; Nat. Salmonella Surveillance Unit, 62- U.S.A, 45-46, Sgt. Am. Vet. Med. Asn; Am. Asn. Avian Path. Nature, behavior and effects of pesticides on ecological relationships in urban environments. Address: Waltham Field Station, University of Massachusetts, Waltham, MA 02154.

FADELL, ALBERT G(EORGE), b. Niagara Falls, N.Y, Jan. 5, 28; m. 71. MATHEMATICS. A.B, Univ. Buffalo, 49, M.A, 51; Ph.D, Ohio State Univ, 54. Asst. prof. MATH, STATE UNIV. N.Y. BUFFALO, 54-61, ASSOC. PROF, 61- v.chmn. dept, 69-70, assoc. provost faculty natural sci. math, 70-71. Am. Math. Soc; Math. Asn. Am. Real variables; measure theory. Address: 407 Countryside Lane, Williamsville, NY 14221.

FADELL, E(DWARD) R(ICHARD), b. Niagara Falls, N.Y, March 8, 26; m. 53; c. 2. MATHEMATICS. B.A, Buffalo, 48; fel, Ohio State, 48-52, M.A, 50, Ph.D.(math), 52. Peirce instr. MATH, Harvard, 52-55; instr, UNIV. WIS, MADISON, 55-56, asst. prof, 56-59, assoc. prof, 59-62, PROF, 62- Am. Math. Soc; Math. Asn. Am. Algebraic topology; fixed point theory; fiber spaces. Address: 3813 Hillcrest Dr, Madison, WI 53705.

FADER, WALTER JOHN, b. Boston, Mass, Jan. 12, 23; m. 52; c. 1. THEORETICAL PHYSICS. A.B, Harvard, 49; Ph.D.(physics), Mass. Inst. Tech, 55. PHYSICIST, Pratt & Whitney Div, UNITED AIRCRAFT CORP, 55-65, RES. LABS, 65- Am. Phys. Soc; Am. Nuclear Soc. Fast reactor criticality studies; theory of laser-produced plasmas and of their interaction with applied magnetic fields. Address: United Aircraft Corp. Research Labs, East Hartford, CT 06108.

FADNER, THOMAS ALAN, b. Milwaukee, Wis, Aug. 19, 29; m. 49; c. 2. POLYMER CHEMISTRY. B.S, Wis. State Col, Oshkosh, 51; S.C. Johnson & Son, Inc, & Atomic Energy Comn. grants, Polytech. Inst. Brooklyn, 57-60, Ph.D.(polymer chem), 61. Asst. chemist, S.C. Johnson & Son, Inc, 51-53, chemist, 53-57, sr. chemist, 60-62; lab. head paper specialties, Oxford Paper Co, 62-63, asst. dir, tech. specialties dept, 63-65, dir, 65-70; MGR. PROD. DEVELOP. DEPT, FIBER PRODS. RES. & DEVELOP, KENDALL CO, 70- Am. Chem. Soc; Tech. Asn. Pulp & Paper Indust. Application of physical properties of polymeric materials to commercial specialty products; paper/plastic, solid-state polymerization; colloidal phenomena; coating development; non-woven fabrics design. Address: Kendall Co, Walpole, MA 02081.

FADUM, RALPH E(IGIL), b. Pittsburgh, Pa, July 19, 12; m. 39; c. 1. SOILS. B.S, Univ. Ill, 35; M.S, Harvard, 37, Sc.D.(soil mech), 41; hon. D.E, Purdue Univ, 63. Asst. civil eng, Harvard, 35-37, instr, 37-41, faculty instr, 41-43; asst. prof. soil mech, Purdue Univ, 43-45, assoc. prof, 45-47, PROF, 47-49; CIVIL ENG, N.C. STATE UNIV, 49-, DEAN SCH. ENG, 62-, head dept. civil eng, 49-62. Chmn. bd. dirs, Water Resources Inst, 64- Chmn. panel soil mech, comt. geophys. & geog, Res. & Develop. Bd, Dept. Defense, 52-54, mem. adv. panel gen. sci, Asst. Secy. Defense, 54-58; adv. panel eng. sci, Nat. Sci. Found, 54-57; mem. army sci. adv. panel, Off. Chief Res. & Develop, Dept. Army, 59-, adv. group to commanding gen, Army Mobility Command, 63-, bd. consult, mobility & environ. div, U.S. Corps Engrs, 54-, Snow, Ice & Permafrost Res. Estab, 54-63, vehicular mobility studies, 55-, spec. consult. bd, Off. Chief Engrs, 55-, bd. consult, dynamic testing found, 60-; consult. soil mech. & found, Directorate Civil Eng, Dept. Air Force Hq, 55-70; mem. adv. comt, Am. Asn. State Hwy. Off. Rd. Test, Hwy. Res. Bd, Nat. Acad. Sci-Nat. Res. Coun, 56-62; Gov. Sci. Adv. Comt, N.C, 61-64; adv. comt. mobility eval. res, Res. Anal. Corp, 62-; adv. screening comt. eng, Assoc. Res. Coun, 62-70, chmn, 64; mem. res. adv. comt, Off. Fed. Hwy. Adminr, Bur. Pub. Rd, 62-70; adv. comt, Ford Found, 63-69; U.S. Nat. Coun. Soil Mech. & Found. Eng; U.S. rep, Int. Comt. Nomenclature; v.chmn, Army Sci. Adv. Panel, 66-70, chmn. adv. group, Commanding Gen. Army Tank & Automotive Command, 67-69; mem. adv. comt, Air Force Inst. Technol, 67-69; v.chmn. adv. group, Dept. Army & Air Force Intratheater Transportation Requirements Study, 67-69. Am. Soc. Civil Eng; Nat. Soc. Prof. Eng; Am. Soc. Eng. Educ. Soil mechanics; foundation engineering. Address: North Carolina State University, P.O. Box 5518, Raleigh, NC 27607.

FAESSINGER, R(OBERT) W(ILLIAM), b. Union City, N.J, Mar. 25, 16; m. 56. ORGANIC CHEMISTRY. B.S, St. Peters Col, 48; M.S, Fordham, 50, U.S. Pub. Health Serv. grant, 50-52; Ph.D.(chem), Rutgers, 55. Chemist, S.B. Penick & Co, N.Y, 53; res. group leader, SCOTT PAPER CO, 55-60, org. synthesis res. sect. head, 60-65; sci. assoc, 65-68, RES. MGR. ORG. SYNTHESIS, 68- U.S.A, 41-45, M/Sgt. Am. Chem. Soc. Natural and synthetic high polymers; synthesis of natural products; chemistry of nitrogen compounds. Address: Scott Paper Co, Scott Plaza, Philadelphia, PA 19113.

FAETH, GERARD MICHAEL, b. New York, N.Y, July 5, 36; m. 59; c. 3. MECHANICAL ENGINEERING. B.M.E, Union Col, 58; M.S, Pa. State, 61, Ph.D.(mech. eng), 64. Res. asst. MECH. ENG, PA. STATE UNIV, 58-64, asst. prof, 64-68, ASSOC. PROF, 68- Consult, ord. res. lab, Pa, 64-68, ASSOC. PROF, 68- Consult, ord. res. lab, Pa, 64- AAAS; Am. Soc. Mech. Eng; Am. Inst. Aeronaut. & Astronaut; Combustion Inst. Explosion hazards; heat and mass transfer to particles; ignition and combustion of bipropellant and monopropellant droplets; metal combustion. Address: 203 Mechanical Engineering Bldg, Pennsylvania State University, University Park, PA 16802.

FAETH, PAUL ALFRED, b. Pittsburgh, Pa, June 23, 28; m. 51; c. 3. PHYSICAL CHEMISTRY, CHEMICAL PHYSICS. B.A, Hiram Col, 50; M.S, Pittsburgh, 56; U.S. Air Force fel, Purdue, 57-61, Ph.D.(phys. chem), 61. Res. assoc. phys. chem, Mellon Inst. Indust. Res, 51-55; res. scientist chem. physics, Lewis Res. Ctr, NASA, 62-67; sr. scientist, Int. Tel. & Tel. Indust. Labs, 67-69, mgr. basic phosphors res, electron tube div, 69-71; ENVIRON. CONTROL PLANNER, THREE RIVERS COORD. COUN, ALLEN COUNTY, 71- U.S. Air Force fel, Purdue Univ, 61; Inst. Sci. & Technol. fel, Univ. Mich, 61-62. Chem.C, U.S.A, 55-57. Am. Chem. Soc; fel. Am. Inst. Chem. Physical chemistry of rare earth oxide systems; adsorption; solid state; surface chemistry; solar power; phosphors; environmental control. Address: 1152 Park Ave, New Haven, IN 46774.

FAFARMAN, A(LFRED), b. N.Y.C, Nov. 29, 17; m. 42; c. 2. PHYSICS. B.A, Brooklyn Col, 39; Ph.D.(physics), N.Y. Univ, 55. Phys. sci. aide, engr. bd, U.S. War Dept, 41-43; res. adminstr, Off. Naval Res, 46-49; res. assoc, physics dept, N.Y. Univ, 49-55; mem. tech. staff, Hughes Res. Labs, 55-65; CONSULT, HUGHES RES. & DEVELOP. LABS, CULVER CITY, 66- Lectr, Univ. Calif, Los Angeles, 56-67; NATO Adv. Study Inst, 66, 67, 70. Sig.C, U.S.A, 43-46, Res, 46-51, 1st Lt. Am. Phys. Soc; Sci. Res. Soc. Am. Liquid dielectrics; solid state physics; radiation effects; plasma physics; charged particle dynamics; traveling wave tube research; cosmic ray and nuclear physics. Address: 8016 Regis Way, Los Angeles, CA 90045.

FAFLICK, CARL E(DWARD), b. Cleveland, Ohio, Mar. 10, 22; m. 53; c. 3. ELECTRONICS. B.A, Oberlin Col, 43; M.A, Harvard, 48, Sheldon traveling fel, 50-51, Ph.D.(appl. sci), 53. Instr. & res. assoc, New Mexico State, 47; dir, adv. syst. planning, Sylvania Electronic Systs, GEN. TEL. & ELECTRONICS INC, 55-69, GEN. TEL. & ELECTRONICS INT. SYSTS. CORP, 69- Sig.C, 42-46, 1st Lt. Inst. Elec. & Electronics Eng. Antenna; propagation; microwave; space communications; data communications. Address: General Telephone & Electronics International Systems Corp, 40 Sylvan Rd, Waltham, MA 02154.

FAGAN, E(RNEST) BRAD, b. Joplin, Mo, Jan. 2, 43; m. 61; c. 2. ENTOMOLOGY. B.S, Missouri, 65, M.S, 67; Ph.D.(entom), Florida, 69. RES. ENTOMOLOGIST, AM. CYANAMID CO, 69- Entom. Soc. Am. Biology and control of spittlebugs; biology of aquatic midges; economic entomology. Address: American Cyanamid Co, P.O. Box 400, Princeton, NJ 08540.

FAGAN, JOHN J, b. N.Y.C, Jan. 19, 32. GEOLOGY. B.S, City Col. New York, 57; Nat. Sci. Found. fels, Columbia, 57-60, Ph.D.(geol), 60. Instr. GEOL, CITY COL. NEW YORK, 60-64, asst. prof, 65-69, ASSOC. PROF, 69- U.S.A, 52-54. Geol. Soc. Am; Nat. Asn. Geol. Teachers; Soc. Econ. Paleont. & Mineral. Stratigraphy and sedimentary petrology of eugeosynclinal rocks, especially bedded cherts and turbidites; studies in northern Nevada and New York. Address: Dept. of Earth & Planetary Science, City College of New York, Convent Ave. at 138th St, New York, NY 10031.

FAGAN, J(OHN) R(OBERT), b. Omaha, Nebr, Sept. 17, 35; m. 58; c. 5. CHEMICAL & NUCLEAR ENGINEERING. B.S, Nebraska, 57; M.S, Kansas State, 62; Ph.D.(nuclear eng), Purdue, 68. Jr. chem. engr, Argonne Nat. Lab, Ill, 57-59; instr, Kansas State, 59-62, asst. prof, 62-63; sr. res. engr, DETROIT DIESEL ALLISON DIV, GEN. MOTORS CORP, 63-66, res. scientist, 66-67, sect. chief, 67-68, MGR. THEORET. RES, 68- Ord.C, U.S.A, 1st Lt, discharged. Am. Inst. Aeronaut. & Astronaut; Am. Nuclear Soc. Internal aerodynamics of turbomachinery; nuclear reactor core physics and shielding. Address: Detroit Diesel Allison Division, General Motors Corp, Research Dept. 9887, P.O. Box 894, Indianapolis, IN 46206.

FAGAN, PAUL V, b. Newark, N.J, May 22, 27; m. 53; c. 4. BIOCHEMISTRY, ORGANIC CHEMISTRY. B.S, Seton Hall, 49; M.S, Fordham, 54. Chemist, Sterone Corp, 51-53; jr. scientist, Ethicon Inc, JOHNSON & JOHNSON, 53-55, asst. scientist, 55-59, assoc. scientist, DEVRO DIV, 59-66, SR. SCIENTIST, 66- U.S.N.R, 44-45. AAAS; Am. Chem. Soc; fel. Am. Inst. Chem. Process development, synthesis of parmaceuticals and fine chemicals; fiber forming polymer synthesis; chemical modification of natural fibers, edible film and casing; extrusion and processing of collagen; tanning processes of proteins. Address: 997 Shadow Oak Lane, Bridgewater Township, Somerville, NJ 08876.

FAGAN, RAYMOND, b. Brooklyn, N.Y, Dec. 27, 14; m. 36; c. 3. EPIDEMIOLOGY, ENVIRONMENTAL SCIENCES. B.A, N.Y. Univ, 35; D.V.M, Cornell Univ, 39; M.P.H, Harvard, 49. Jr. veterinarian, meat inspection, U.S. Dept. Agr, 39-41; milk sanitation, U.S. Pub. Health Serv, 42, vet. off. & epidemiologist, 46-54; assoc. prof. prev. med. & hyg. & chmn. dept, sch. vet. med, Univ. Pa, 54-56; sr. investr, virol, Wyeth Inst. Med. Res, 56-67; PRIN. SCIENTIST, BIOL, PHILIP MORRIS RES. CTR, 67- Adj. prof, Drexel Univ, 64-67; consult, WHO, 63-; Nat. Inst. Environ. Health Sci, 70- Vet.C, U.S.A, 42-46, U.S. Pub. Health Serv, 46-54. AAAS; Am. Soc. Microbiol; Am. Pub. Health Asn; Am. Vet. Med. Asn; Sci. Res. Soc. Am; Environ. Mutagen Soc; U.S. Animal Health Asn; N.Y. Acad. Sci. Environmental sciences; host-parasite relationships; epidemiology; virology; education. Address: Philip Morris Research Center, P.O. Box 26583, Richmond, VA 23261.

FAGEL, J(OHN) E(DWARD), b. Schenectady, N.Y, May 23, 24; m. 63; c. 1. PHYSICAL & ANALYTICAL CHEMISTRY. B.S, Union (N.Y), 50, M.S, 51. Asst. anal. chem, res. lab, GEN. ELEC. CO, N.Y, 51-56, supvr. inst. anal. unit, refractory metals lab, lamp div, 56-64, SR. CHEMIST, INDUST. & POWER CAPACITOR PROD. DEPT, 64- U.S.A.A.F, 43-45. AAAS; Am. Chem. Soc. Instrumental methods of analysis; vacuum fusion gas analysis; x-ray and infrared spectrography; polymer crystallinity; particle analysis; gas and liquid chromatography; dielectrics measurements. Address: Industrial & Power Capacitor Dept, General Electric Co, Hudson Falls, NY 12839.

FAGEN, EDWARD A(LLEN), b. Chicago, Ill, May 15, 31; m. 56, 67; c. 1. SOLID STATE PHYSICS. A.B, Harvard Col, 52; M.S, Purdue, 54; Ph.D. (physics), Pittsburgh, 67. Assoc. physicist, Armour Res. Found, 57-61; instr. physics, Pittsburgh, 67; SR. PHYSICIST, ENERGY CONVERSION DEVICES, INC, 67- Sig.C, U.S.A, 54-56. Am. Phys. Soc; Fedn. Am. Sci. Transport properties of superconductors and semiconductors. Address: Energy Conversion Devices, Inc, 1675 W. Maple Rd, Troy, MI 48084.

FAGEN, ROBERT E(RNEST), b. Minneapolis, Minn, Aug. 23, 29; m. 53; c. 3. MATHEMATICS. B.A, Minnesota, 49, M.A, 50, Ph.D.(math), 53. Asst. math, Minnesota, 49-53; mem. tech. staff, Bell Tel. Labs, 53-55; mathematician, Nat. Security Agency, 55-58; sr. staff consult, Hughes Aircraft Co, 58-60; dir, info. sci, Am. Systs, Inc, 60-61; gen. mgr, syst. sci. div, Control Data Corp, 62-66; PRES. & CHMN, COMPUT. COMMUN, INC, 66- Instr, Macalester Col. (St. Paul), 53; lectr, George Washington, 56-57. U.S.N.R, 55-58, Lt.(jg). Am. Math. Soc. Theory of probability; stochastic processes; theory of congestion and waiting lines; combinatorial analysis; information theory; computer applications to information processing. Address: Computer Communications, Inc, 5933 W. Slauson Ave, Culver City, CA 90230.

FAGER, E(DWARD) W(ILLIAM), b. Monterrey Park, Calif, April 2, 17; m. 48; c. 1. ECOLOGY. B.A, Yale, 39, Ph.D.(org. chem), 42; D.Phil.(zool), Oxford, 55. Instr. chem, Yale, 41-45; sect. leader res. on fluorocarbons, Manhattan Dist. proj, s.a.m. labs, Columbia, 45-46; Frank B. Jewett fel, Chicago, 46-47, asst. prof, Fels fund, 47-53; Merck sr. fel, Oxford, 53-55; fel. marine biol, SCRIPPS INST. OCEANOG, UNIV. CALIF, 56-57, assoc. prof. biol, 57-64, PROF. MARINE ECOL, 64-, vis. lectr, 57. AAAS; Ecol. Soc. Am; Am. Soc. Limnol. & Oceanog; Brit. Ecol. Soc. Population dynamics; community ecology of marine benthic invertebrates. Address: Scripps Institution of Oceanography, La Jolla, CA 92037.

FAGERSON, I(RVING) S(EYMOUR), b. Lawrence, Mass, June 7, 20; m. 53. FOOD SCIENCE. S.B, Mass. Inst. Tech, 42; Indust. Res. fel, Massachusetts, 47-49, M.S, 48, Ph.D.(food tech), 50. Asst. food tech, Mass. Inst. Tech, 42; mkt. specialist, U.S. Dept. Agr, 42-43; asst. prof. FOOD CHEM, UNIV. MASS, AMHERST, 49-54, assoc. prof, 54-58, PROF, 58- U.S.N, 43-46; U.S.A.R, 49-59, Capt. AAAS; Am. Chem. Soc; Inst. Food Technol; fel. Am. Inst. Chem; Soc. Appl. Spectros; N.Y. Acad. Sci. Mechanism of heat transfer in thermal processing; nutritive value of foods; chemistry of flavor; analysis instrumentation; gas chromatography. Address: Chenoweth Lab, University of Massachusetts, Amherst, MA 01002.

FAGERSTEN, E(RIK) G(ORAN), b. Uddevalla, Sweden, Sept. 22, 30; U.S. citizen. MICROBIOLOGY. B.Sc, Uppsala, Sweden, 53; Ph.D.(microbiol), Washington (Seattle), 56. Chemist, Dow Chem. Co, 56-60, lab. dir, indust. serv, 60-61, mgr. missile br, 61-64, tech. specialist, 64-65; v.pres. & dir. res. & develop, Dielec. Systs, Inc, 65-71; PRES, CUSTOM CIRCUITS CORP, 71- Address: Custom Circuits Corp, 1560 Orangethorpe Way, Anaheim, CA 92801.

FAGERSTROM, J(OHN) ALFRED, b. Ypsilanti, Mich, Jan. 4, 30; m. 53; c. 3. INVERTEBRATE PALEONTOLOGY. A.B, Oberlin Col, 52; M.S, Tennessee, 53; Ph.D.(geol), Michigan, 59. Instr. GEOL, UNIV. NEBR, LINCOLN, 58-60, asst. prof, 60-64, assoc. prof, 64-68, PROF, 68-, CHMN. DEPT, 70- U.S.A, 54-56. Int. Paleont. Union; Geol. Soc. Am; Paleont. Soc; Brit. Palaeont. Asn. Biostratigraphy of the Devonian rocks of the Great Lakes region; Pennsylvanian paleoecology of the mid-continent region; biometrical aspects of variation and ontogeny. Address: 420 Morrill Hall, Dept. of Geology, University of Nebraska, Lincoln, NE 68508.

FAGET, MAXIME A(LLAN), b. Stann Creek, British Honduras, Cent. Am, Aug. 26, 21; U.S. citizen; m. 47; c. 4. AERONAUTICAL ENGINEERING. B.S, La. State Univ, 43; Hon.D.Eng, Univ. Pittsburgh, 66. Aeronaut. res. scientist, Nat. Adv. Comt. Aeronaut, 46-58; chief, flight systs. div, Nat. Aeronaut. & Space Admin, 58-62; asst. dir. ENG. & DEVELOP, MANNED SPACECRAFT CTR, NASA, 62-66, DIR, 66- Fleming award, 60; NASA Medal outstanding leadership, 62. U.S.N, 43-46, Lt. Comdr. Cor. mem, Int. Acad. Astronaut; assoc. Am. Inst. Aeronaut. & Astronaut. Manned space flight; re-entry aerodynamics; propulsion; space power systems; guidance and control; life support systems. Address: Engineering & Development, Manned Spacecraft Center, NASA, Houston, TX 77058.

FAGG, LAWRENCE W(ELLBURN), b. N.J, Oct. 10, 23; m. 50, 58. NUCLEAR PHYSICS. B.S, U.S. Mil. Acad, 45; M.S, Maryland, 47; M.A, Illinois, 48; Ph.D.(physics), Hopkins, 53. PHYSICIST, Naval Res. Lab, 53-58; plasma physics, Atlantic Res. Corp, 58-63; ELECTRON SCATTERING, U.S. NAVAL RES. LAB, WASH, D.C, 63- U.S.A, 42-45. Am. Phys. Soc. Assignment of nuclear energy levels; plasma ion density studies; electron scattering. Address: Apt. A-1705, 1600 S. Joyce St, Arlington, VA 22202.

FAGGAN, JOSEPH E(DWARD), b. Philadelphia, Pa, Nov. 15, 21; m. 46; c. 2. ORGANIC CHEMISTRY. B.S, Notre Dame, 42, M.S, 44; Ph.D.(org. chem), Missouri, 49. Res. chemist, ETHYL CORP, 49-51, patent agent, 51-55, mgr. patent sect, 55-64, prog. mgr. res. & develop, 64-65, DIR, PETROL. CHEM. RES, 65- U.S.A, 44-46, 1st Lt. Fuel and lube additives; industrial chemicals. Address: 20232 Old Coach Rd, Birmingham, MI 48010.

FAGLEY, T(HOMAS) F(ISHER), b. Mt. Carmel, Pa, Sept. 7, 13. PHYSICAL CHEMISTRY. B.S, Bucknell, 35, M.S, 37; Lindsay Light Co. fel, Chicago, 46-47, Ph.D.(chem), 49. Instr. chem, Bucknell, 38-40, 42-46; instr, univ. col, Chicago, 47, teaching fel, 48-49; asst. prof. CHEM, TULANE UNIV, 49-54, assoc. prof, 54-61, PROF, 61- AAAS; Am. Chem. Soc. Microcalorimetry; heats of combustion; kinetics; thermodynamics of solutions. Address: Dept. of Chemistry, Tulane University, New Orleans, LA 70118.

FAGOT, HACKER JOSEPH, S.J, b. New Orleans, La, Mar. 19, 28. PHYSIOLOGICAL PSYCHOLOGY, PHYSICAL CHEMISTRY. B.S, Spring Hill Col, 51; M.S, Fordham, 54; S.T.L, Faculty St. Louis Gonzague, France, 58; Nat. Sci. Found. fels, Loyola (Ill), 60-62, Ph.D.(psychol), 62. Instr. PSYCHOL, Spring Hill Col, 62-64, asst. prof, 64-69; ASSOC. PROF, LOYOLA UNIV. (LA), 69- Kinetics of thione-thiol tautomerism; functions of the hippocampal system of the brain. Address: Dept. of Psychology, Loyola University, 6363 St. Charles Ave, New Orleans, LA 70118.

FAGOT, WILFRED CLARK, b. New Orleans, La, Dec. 5, 24. APPLIED MATHEMATICS, MATHEMATICAL PHYSICS. B.S, Texas, 45; M.S, Tulane, 47; M.S, Chicago, 52; Duke, 54-56. Physicist, Enrico Fermi Inst. Nuclear Studies, Chicago, 52-53, Chicago Midway Labs, 53-54; sr. systs. physicist, Norden Div, United Aircraft Corp, 56-61; sr. staff scientist, Kearfott Div, Gen. Precision Aerospace Div, 61-63; prin. scientist, Bedford Labs, missile systs. div, Raytheon Co, 63-65; asst. prof. MATH, JUNIATA COL, 65-66, ASSOC. PROF, 66-, CHMN. DEPT, 71- Nat. Sci. Found. sci. faculty fel, Pa. State Univ, 70-71. U.S.N, 42-46. Am. Math. Soc; Math. Asn. Am; Soc. Indust. & Appl. Math; Am. Phys. Soc; sr. mem. Inst. Elec. & Electronics Eng. Stochastic processes, electromagnetic theory, antennas, propagation, scattering, noise and radar clutter; perturbation theory; cosmic rays; radar and inertial systems analysis. Address: Dept. of Mathematics, Juniata College, Huntingdon, PA 16652.

FAHERTY, KEITH F, b. Platteville, Wis, Dec. 7, 31; m. 51; c. 5. CIVIL ENGINEERING. B.S, Wis. State, Platteville, 54; M.S, Illinois, Urbana, 62; Nat. Sci. Found. summer inst. fels, Notre Dame, 62, Colorado, 63, Okla. State, 64 & Stanford, 67; Nat. Sci. Found. fel, Iowa, summer 68 & 68-69. Trainee, U.S. Gypsum Co, 54-55, authorities engr, 55, construct. foreman, 55-57; instr. CIVIL ENG, WIS. STATE UNIV, PLATTEVILLE, 57-62, asst. prof, 62-65, ASSOC. PROF, 65-, HEAD DEPT, 66- Am. Soc. Civil Eng; Nat. Soc. Prof. Eng; Am. Soc. Eng. Educ; Am. Concrete Inst. Making mathematical models of structures. Address: 990 Mound View Dr, Platteville, WI 53818.

FAHEY, CHARLOTTE W(IEGHARD), b. St. Louis, Mo, Oct. 3, 09; m. 41; c. 1. ORGANIC CHEMISTRY. A.B, Washington (St. Louis), 30, M.S, 31; scholar, Yale, 36-37, Ph.D.(chem), 37; Chicago, 40. Asst. applied biochem, sch. med, Washington (St. Louis), 31-34; Henry Strong Denison Med. Found, 34-37; asst. prof. chem, SKIDMORE COL, 37-39, assoc. prof. CHEM. & MATH, 39-50, PROF, 50-, CHMN. DEPT. CHEM. & PHYSICS, 64-, physics, 59-64, Willett teaching award, 60. AAAS; Am. Chem. Soc; Am. Phys. Soc; N.Y. Acad. Sci. Anthraquinones; napthaquinones; bacterial polysaccharides; immunochemistry; lipids of the tubercle bacillus; lipids of mitochondria; photosynthetic enzymes. Address: Skidmore College, Saratoga Springs, NY 12866.

FAHEY, DARRYL RICHARD, b. Grand Forks, N.Dak, July 13, 42; m. 66; c. 1. ORGANIC CHEMISTRY. B.S, Univ. N.Dak, 64, Nat. Defense Educ. Act. fel, 65-68, alumni fel, 67-68, Ph.D.(org. chem), 69. RES. CHEMIST, PHILLIPS PETROL. CO, 68- Am. Chem. Soc; The Chem. Soc. Organometallic chemistry of transition metals; homogeneous catalysis; transition metals in organic synthesis. Address: Research & Development Dept, Phillips Petroleum Co, Bartlesville, OK 74004.

FAHEY, DENNIS M(ARTIN), b. Walla Walla, Wash, Feb. 17, 31; m. 53; c. 2. ORGANIC CHEMISTRY. A.B, Whitman Col, 53; Nat. Sci. Found. fel, Washington State, 54-56, Ph.D.(org. chem), 57. Res. chemist, E.I. du Pont de Nemours & Co, 57-59; Glidden Co, 59-60; fiber sect. leader, east. res. div, Rayonier, Inc, 60-65; mgr. org. res, Gustin-Bacon Mfg. Co, 65-67; Certain-Teed Saint Gobain Insulation Corp, 67-68; RES. ASSOC, FIBER GLASS DIV, PPG INDUSTS, 68- AAAS; Am. Chem. Soc; Tech. Asn. Pulp & Paper Indust. Fiber glass tire cord. Address: Glass Research Center, PPG Industries, P.O. Box 11472, Pittsburgh, PA 15238.

FAHEY, JACK E(DWARD), b. Enumclaw, Wash, Oct. 23, 04; m. 30; c. 2. CHEMISTRY. B.S, Oregon State, 28. Chemist, pesticide chems. res, Agr. Res. Serv, U.S. Dept. Agr, Wash, 29-34, in charge field sta, 34-64, anal. res. sect, pesticide chem, res. br, 64-66; Purdue residue res. lab, dept. ENTOM, PURDUE UNIV, 66-70; EMER. PROF, 70- Entom. Soc. Am; Am. Chem. Soc. Insecticides; analytical study of insecticide residues in food, forage and fiber; methods development; monitoring of insecticides in the environment of man. Address: 1720 S. 14th St, Lafayette, IN 47905.

FAHEY, JOHN JAMES, b. Freemansburg, W.Va, Sept. 8, 06; m. 43; c. 7. ORTHOPEDIC SURGERY. M.D, Ohio State, 31. Intern, St. Francis Hosp, Evanston, Ill. & Chicago Lying-in-Hosp, 31-33; res. surgeon, Mercy Hosp, Baltimore, 33-34; univ. clinics, Chicago, 34-36; prof. anat, Mississippi, 36; CHIEF ORTHOP. DEPT, ST. FRANCIS HOSP, EVANSTON, ILL, 38- From instr. to assoc. prof. orthop. surg, sch. med, Illinois, 43-49; assoc. prof, med. sch, Northwestern, 55-71. Dipl, Am. Bd. Orthop. Surg, 41. Clin. Orthop. Soc; Am. Orthop. Asn; fel. Am. Acad. Orthop. Surg; fel. Am. Col. Surg; Int. Soc. Orthop. Surg. & Traumatol. Circulation of the femoral head; pathology of dislocations of the shoulder; healing of tendon and fascia to bone; fractures; congenital deformities; acute slipped femoral epiphysis; congenital sarcoma; snapping thumb and fingers in children and adults. Address: 1791 W. Howard St, Chicago, IL 60626.

FAHEY, JOHN L(ESLIE), b. Cleveland, Ohio, Sept. 8, 24; m. 54; c. 3. IMMUNOLOGY. M.S, Wayne State, 49; M.D, Harvard, 51. Intern med, Presby. Hosp, N.Y, 51-52, asst. res, 52-53; clin. assoc, Nat. Cancer Inst, Nat. Insts. Health, 53-54, sr. investr, metab, 54-63, chief, immunol. br, 64-71; PROF. MED. MICROBIOL. & IMMUNOL. & CHMN. DEPT, SCH. MED, UNIV. CALIF, LOS ANGELES, 71- U.S.A, 43-46; U.S. Pub. Health Serv, 52-71, Med. Dir. Am. Physiol. Soc; Soc. Exp. Biol. & Med; Am. Asn. Cancer Res; Am. Fedn. Clin. Res; Am. Soc. Clin. Invest; Am. Asn. Immunol. Immunology; clinical oncology. Address: Dept. of Medical Microbiology & Immunology, School of Medicine, University of California at Los Angeles, Los Angeles, CA 90024.

FAHEY, MICHAEL D(UNCAN), b. Walla Walla, Wash, Jan. 28, 29; m. 51; c. 2. ORGANIC CHEMISTRY. B.A, Whitman Col, 50; M.A, Ore. State Col, 54, fel. & Ph.D.(chem), 57. Res. chemist, Olympic Res. Div, Rayonier, Inc, 56-60, sect. leader pioneering, cent. res. div, 60-62; group leader pulping & papermaking, res. & develop. div, Union Bag-Camp Paper Corp, N.J, 62-64; sr. res. chemist, cent. res. div, CROWN ZELLERBACH CORP, Wash, 64-66, group leader dissolving pulps, Columbia Cellulose Ltd, Can, 66-68, SR. RES. CHEMIST, CENT. RES. DIV, 68- U.S.M.C, 51-52, Res, 52-59. AAAS; Am. Chem. Soc. Organic chemistry of forest products; cellulose lignin and other chemical constituents derived from wood or bark. Address: Central Research Division, Crown Zellerbach Corp, Camas, WA 98607.

FAHEY, PAUL F(ARRELL), JR, b. Lock Haven, Pa, July 2, 42; m. 65; c. 2. PHYSICS. B.S, Scranton, 64; NASA traineeship, Virginia, 64-67, M.S, 66, Ph.D.(physics), 68. ASST. PROF. PHYSICS, UNIV. SCRANTON, 68- Am. Phys. Soc. Physical properties of biopolymers; pressure-volume-temperature relations of liquids. Address: Dept. of Physics, University of Scranton, Scranton, PA 18510.

FAHEY, ROBERT C, b. Sacramento, Calif, Feb. 8, 36; m. 60; c. 1. ORGANIC CHEMISTRY. B.S, California, Berkeley, 57; Ph.D.(org. chem), Chicago, 63. Asst. prof. CHEM, UNIV. CALIF, SAN DIEGO, 63-70, ASSOC. PROF, 70- Alfred P. Sloan Found. fel, 66-68; John Simon Guggenheim Found. fel, 70-71. U.S.A.F, 58-60, 1st Lt. AAAS; Am. Chem. Soc; Brit. Chem. Soc. Mechanisms of organic reactions; structure and properties of enyzmes; nuclear magnetic resonance spectroscopy. Address: Dept. of Chemistry, University of California at San Diego, P.O. Box 109, La Jolla, CA 92037.

FAHEY, WALTER JOHN, b. Winnipeg, Man, Can, Apr. 10, 27; U.S. citizen; m. 49; c. 4. ELECTRICAL ENGINEERING. B.S, Case, 57, fels, 57-59, 62-63, M.S, 59, Ph.D.(elec. eng), 63. Instr. ELEC. ENG, Case, 59-62; asst. prof, Ohio Univ, 63-65, assoc. prof, 65-67, prof, 67-69, chmn. dept, 66-67, dean col. eng. & technol, 67-68; PROF. & DEAN COL. ENG, UNIV. ARIZ, 69- Instr. adult div, Cleveland Pub. Schs, 59-62; Am. Coun. Educ. fel, 67-68. Summers, appln. engr, Ohio Bell Tel, 56; staff mem, appl. physics res, Sandia Corp, N.Mex, 60; mem, Ohio Crime Comn, 67-68; Ariz. State Bd. Tech. Registr, 69-70; dir, Aviation Res. & Educ. Found, Ariz, 70- U.S.N, 45-48, 50-52. Inst. Elec. & Electronics Eng; Am. Soc. Eng. Educ. Electrical properties of materials; theoretical electromagnetics; plasma dynamics and gaseous electronics; methods of engineering education. Address: College of Engineering, University of Arizona, Tucson, AZ 85721.

FAHIDY, THOMAS Z(OLTAN), b. Budapest, Hungary, June 17, 34; Can. citizen; m. 62; c. 1. CHEMICAL ENGINEERING, APPLIED MATHEMATICS. B.Sc, Queen's (Ont), 59, M.Sc, 61; Ph.D.(chem. eng), Illinois, Urbana, 65. Asst. prof. CHEM. ENG, UNIV. WATERLOO, 64-67, assoc. prof, 67-71, PROF, 71- Hon. res. assoc. & Shell vis. fel, Univ. Col, London, 68-69. Am. Inst. Chem. Eng; Can. Soc. Chem. Eng; Simulation Coun; N.Y. Acad. Sci. Mathematical modelling of complex chemical processes; digital simulation; theory of process dynamics and control. Address: Dept. of Chemical Engineering, University of Waterloo, Waterloo, Ont, Can.

FAHIEN, LEONARD A, b. St. Louis, Mo, July 26, 34; m. 58; c. 3. PHARMACOLOGY, BIOCHEMISTRY. A.B, Wash. Univ, 56, M.D, 60. Intern med, Univ. Wis, 60-61; Nat. Insts. Health fel. biochem, Wash. Univ, 61-62; physiol. chem, Univ. Wis, 62-64; asst. prof. PHARMACOL, UNIV. WIS, MADISON, 66-70, ASSOC. PROF, 70- Nat. Insts. Health res. grant, 66- & career res. develop. award, 68-73. U.S.P.H.S, 64-66, Surg. AAAS. Regulation of enzyme activity; studies of enzyme complexes; effects of drugs on enzyme catalyzed reaction. Address: Dept. of Pharmacology, University of Wisconsin, 426 N. Charter St, Madison, WI 53706.

FAHIEN, RAY W, b. St. Louis, Mo, Dec. 26, 23. CHEMICAL ENGINEERING. B.S.Ch.E, Washington (St. Louis), 47; M.S.Ch.E, Mo. Sch. Mines, 50; Ph.D, Purdue, 54. Instr. chem. eng, Mo. Sch. Mines, 47-50; chem. engr, Ethyl Corp, 53-54; asst. prof. CHEM. ENG, Iowa State, 54-57, assoc. prof, 57-59, prof, 59-64; PROF, UNIV. FLA, 64-, chmn. dept, 64-69. Sr. engr, Ames Lab, U.S. Atomic Energy Cmn, 54-64; vis. prof, Wisconsin, 59-60; Fulbright lectr, Brazil, 64. AAAS; Am. Inst. Chem. Eng; Am. Chem. Soc; Am; Soc. Eng. Educ.(ed, Chem. Eng. Educ. J, 67-). Transport of heat; mass and momentum; turbulent diffusion; applied mathematics. Address: Dept. of Chemical Engineering, University of Florida, Gainesville, FL 32601.

FAHIM, MOSTAFA SAFWAT, b. Cairo, Egypt, Oct. 7, 31; c. 1. REPRODUCTIVE BIOLOGY. B.S, Cairo Univ, 53; Egyptian Govt. fel, 56-59; M.S, Univ. Mo-Columbia, 58, foreign stud. fel, 57-60, Ph.D.(reproductive biol), 61. Asst. dir. animal sci. dept, Ministry of Land Reform, Egypt, 61-63; dir. animal reproduction dept, Off. of the Pres, Algeria, 63-66; res. assoc. OBSTET. & GYNEC, SCH. MED, UNIV. MO-COLUMBIA, 66-68, asst. prof, 68-71, ASSOC. PROF, 71- Prof, Univ. Ain Shams, Cairo, 61-63; consult, Inst. de Serotherapie de Toulouse, France & N.Africa Div, Russel Pharmaceut. Co, 63-66. AAAS; N.Y. Acad. Sci; Soc. Study Reproduction; Am. Fertil. Soc. Human reproduction biology; effects of drugs and environmental chemicals on the fetus and newborn. Address: Dept. of Obstetrics & Gynecology, University of Missouri-Columbia, Columbia, MO 65201.

FAHIMI, HOSSEIN DARIUSH, b. Teheran, Iran, May 7, 33; m. 63; c. 2. PATHOLOGY, ELECTRON MICROSCOPY. M.D, Univ. Heidelberg, 58. Assoc. PATH, HARVARD MED. SCH, 66-69, asst. prof, 69-71, ASSOC. PROF, 71- Assoc. vis. physician, Mallory Inst. Path, 66-; Nat. Insts. Health career res. develop award, 71. AAAS; Am. Soc. Cell Biol; Histochem. Soc; Am. Soc. Exp. Path; Am. Asn. Path. & Bact; Am. Fedn. Clin. Res. Experimental cell research; histochemistry; cytochemistry. Address: Harvard Pathology Unit, Mallory Institute of Pathology, 784 Massachusetts Ave, Boston, MA 02118.

FAHL, R(OY) J(ACKSON), JR, b. Richmond, Va, Oct. 8, 25; m. 53; c. 2. ORGANIC CHEMISTRY. B.S, Washington & Lee, 48; fel, North Carolina, 51-52, Ph.D.(chem), 53. Asst, North Carolina, 48-51; res. chemist metallo-org. compounds, E.I. DU PONT DE NEMOURS & CO, INC, 52-56, supvr, pigments lab, 56-62, mgr, 63, tech. mgr. white pigments, 63-69, ASST. DIR. TECH. SERV. LAB, 69- U.S.A.A.F, 43-46. Am. Chem. Soc. Pigments. Address: Technical Service Lab, E.I. du Pont de Nemours & Co, Inc, Wilmington, DE 19898.

FAHLBERG, WILLSON J(OEL), b. Madison, Wis, July 20, 18; m; c. 4. IMMUNOLOGY. Ph.B, Wisconsin, 48, M.S, 49, Ph.D, 51. Asst. MICROBIOL, Wisconsin, 48-50; instr, COL. MED, BAYLOR UNIV, 51-53, asst. prof, 53-60, ASSOC. PROF, 60-; DIR. MED. AFFAIRS, MEM. BAPTIST HOSP. SYST, 69- Consult. microbiologist, Methodist Hosp, 53-; Vet. Admin. Lab, 54-; Mem. Hosp; Univ. Texas M.D. Anderson Hosp. & Tumor Inst; Houston State Psychiatric Inst; Jefferson Davis Hosp. Houston; St. Joseph's Hosp; Tex. Inst. Rehab. & Res. Dipl, Am. Bd. Microbiol. Med.C, U.S.A, 44-45. AAAS; Am. Soc. Microbiol; N.Y. Acad. Sci; fel. Am. Acad. Microbiol; fel. Am. Pub. Health Asn; Am. Asn. Lab. Animal Sci; Soc. Exp. Biol. & Med; Am. Asn. Cancer Res; fel. Royal Soc. Health. Allergy; infectious diseases. Address: Memorial Baptist Hospital System, 1100 Louisiana, Houston, TX 77002.

FAHLEN, THEODORE S(TAUFFER), b. San Francisco, Calif, Sept. 5, 41; m. 63; c. 2. PHYSICS, MATHEMATICS. B.S, Stanford, 63; M.S, New Mexico, 64, Ph.D.(physics), 67. Res. asst. physics, New Mexico, 64-67; SR. ENGR, AEROJET-GEN. CORP, 67- Optical Soc. Am. Single particle minimum ignition energy scattering; laser applications; carbon dioxide laser development. Address: 355 N. Garsden, Covina, CA 91722.

FAHLQUIST, DAVIS A, b. Providence, R.I, July 16, 26; wid; c. 5. GEOPHYSICS. B.S, Brown Univ, 50; Ph.D.(geophys), Mass. Inst. Technol, 63. Engr, Owens Corning Fiberglas Corp, 51-53; res. asst. geophys, Woods Hole Oceanog. Inst, 58-63, res. assoc, 63; asst. prof, TEX. A&M UNIV, 63-67, ASSOC. PROF. GEOPHYS, 67-, OCEANOG, 69- U.S.N.R, 44-46. AAAS; Am. Geophys. Union; Seismol. Soc. Am; Soc. Explor. Geophys. Marine geophysics; seismic refraction studies in deep water areas; continuous seismic reflection profiling in ocean areas. Address: Dept. of Oceanography, Texas A&M University, College Station, TX 77843.

FAHMY, ABDEL AZIZ, b. Giza, Egypt, Apr. 24, 25; m. 53; c. 2. METALLURGY, NUCLEAR ENGINEERING. B.Eng, Cairo, 47; Ph.D.(metall), Sheffield, 53. Demonstr. metall, Cairo, 47-53, lectr, 53-60, assoc. prof, 60-65, chair prof, 65-68; vis. prof. METALL. ENG, N.C. STATE UNIV, 68-69, PROF, 69- Vis. researcher, for. student summer proj, Mass. Inst. Tech, 55; participant int. sch. nuclear sci. & eng, Atoms for Peace Prog, N.C. State & Argonne Nat. Lab, 56-57; spec. lectr, N.C. State, 57-59; vis. prof. nat. comn. nuclear energy, Brazil, summer 59; resident res. assoc, Argonne Nat. Lab, 63-64; prof, American Univ. Cairo, 66-68; mem. state awards comt. eng. sci, Egypt, 67-68. Consult, Argonne Nat. Lab, 68-70; IBM Corp, 68- Formation of austenite; structure of cement; effect of irradiation on properties of materials; neutron radiography and microradiography; interphase stresses in multiphase materials; thermal expansion of multiphase and composite materials; x-ray stress measurement. Address: Dept. of Materials Engineering, North Carolina State University, Raleigh, NC 27607.

FAHMY, ALY, b. Cairo, Egypt; U.S. citizen. PATHOLOGY. M.D, Fouad Univ, Egypt, 49; Ph.D.(med), Univ. London, 56. Instr. PATH, faculty med, Fouad Univ, Egypt, 56-57, asst. prof, 57-61; Alexander von Humboldt Found. res. fel, sch. med, Univ. Düsseldorf, 61-62; asst. prof, sch. med, Emory Univ, 62-63; sr. pathologist, sch. med, Univ. Düsseldorf, 63-64; asst. prof, Meharry Med. Col, 64-65, assoc. prof, 65-70; PROF, SCH. MED, UNIV. SHERBROOKE, 70- Vis. prof, Int. Tech. Coop. Prog, Paris, 61; from asst. prof. to assoc. prof, sch. med, Vanderbilt Univ, 65-70; asst. chief lab. serv, Vet. Admin. Hosp, Nashville, Tenn, 65-70; consult, bone & joint panel, Can. Tumor Reference Ctr. Fel. Col. Am. Path; Am. Soc. Clin. Path; Int. Acad. Path; Electron Micros. Soc. Am; Am. Med. Asn; hon. mem. Egyptian Orthop. Asn. Pathology of tumors; bone and joint pathology; application of electron microscopy to surgical pathology; bone growth problems; hormonal and genetic skeletal disturbances. Address: Dept. of Pathology, University of Sherbrooke School of Medicine, Sherbrooke, Que, Can.

FAHMY, M(OHAMED) H(AMED), b. Ismailia, Egypt, Dec. 14, 40; m. 67; c. 2. GENETICS, ANIMAL HUSBANDRY. B.Sc, Ain Shams, Cairo, 60, M.Sc, 64, Ph.D.(animal breeding), 67. Researcher ANIMAL BREEDING, Desert Inst, Egypt, 61-67; RES. SCIENTIST, CAN. DEPT. AGR, 68- Am. Soc. Animal Sci; Can. Soc. Animal Prod. Swine, beef cattle, dairy cattle and sheep breeding. Address: Research Station, Canada Dept. of Agriculture, Lennoxville, Que, Can.

FAHNESTOCK, GEORGE R(EEDER), b. Cincinnati, Ohio, June 25, 14; m. 46; c. 5. FORESTRY. A.B, Cincinnati, 36; M.F, Yale, 38. Field asst, forest mgt, North. Rocky Mt. Forest & Range Exp. Sta, 38-39; with Coeur D'Alene Nat. Forest, 39, foreman & jr. forester, 39-41, asst. ranger, nat. forest admin, 46; res. forester forest mgt, Allegheny Forest Exp. Sta, 41-42; dist. ranger, Gallatin Nat. Forest, 46-50; Flathead Nat. Forest, 50-51; res. forester, forest fire, North. Rocky Mt. & Inter-Mt. Forest & Range Exp. Sta, 51-57; res. forester & asst. div. chief. South. Forest Exp. Sta, 57-60, div. chief, 60-64, proj. leader, 64-65; Pac. Northwest Forest & Range Exp. Sta, 65-71; CONSULT. FOREST FIRE & ENVIRON. PROBS, 71- U.S.N.R, 42-54, Lt. Comdr. AAAS; Soc. Am. Foresters. Physical properties of forest fuels; forest fire behavior; fire danger measurement; fire control planning; fire prevention. Address: 16310 Ashworth Ave. N, Seattle, WA 98133.

FAHNESTOCK, ROBERT K(ENDALL), b. Urbana, Ill, Mar. 22, 32; m. 54; c. 2. GEOLOGY. B.S, Illinois, 54; Ph.D.(geol), Cornell, 60. Geologist, U.S. Geol. Surv, 60-63; asst. prof. GEOL, Univ. Tex, 63-67; ASSOC. PROF, STATE UNIV. N.Y. COL. FREDONIA, 67- C.Eng, 54-56, 1st Lt. AAAS; Geol. Soc. Am; Am. Asn. Petrol. Geol; Soc. Econ. Paleont. & Mineral; Glaciol. Soc; Asn. Eng. Geol. Geomorphology; fluvial morphology and processes; sediment transport and sedimentary structures. Address: Dept. of Geology, State University of New York College at Fredonia, Fredonia, NY 14063.

FAHNING, M(ELVYN) L(UVERNE), b. St. Peter, Minn, Apr. 28, 36; m. 56; c. 3. REPRODUCTIVE PHYSIOLOGY. B.S, Univ. Minn, 58, M.S, 60, D.V.M. & Ph.D, 64. ASST. PROF. dairy husb, UNIV. MINN, ST. PAUL, 64-65, dairy husb. & vet. anat, 65-66, VET. OBSTET. & GYNEC, 66- Am. Dairy Sci. Asn; Am. Soc. Animal Sci; Am. Vet. Med. Asn; Soc. Study Reproduction; Brit. Soc. Study Fertil. Ovum transplantation; superovulation; synchronization of estrus of cattle and swine; insemination of swine; collection and chemical analysis of female reproductive tract fluids. Address: Dept. of Obstetrics & Gynecology, University of Minnesota, St. Paul, MN 55101.

FAHNOE, FREDERICK, b. Pittsburgh, Pa, Aug. 16, 19; m. 42; c. 4. CHEMICAL ENGINEERING. B.Chem, Cornell, 40, scholar. & Ch.E, 41. Chem. engr, Dow Chem. Co, Mich, 41-43; cent. res. lab, Gen. Aniline & Film Corp, 46-49; group leader res. & develop, Vitro Corp. of Am, 49-54; proj. mgr, M.W. Kellogg Co, 54-58; tech. supvr, Reactive Metals, Inc, 58-61, opers. mgr, 62-65; plant mgr, USI Europe N.V, Antwerp, Belg, 65-69; CORP. PLANNER, NAT. DISTILLERS & CHEM. CORP, 69- U.S.N, 43-45, Lt. Am. Chem. Soc; Electrochem. Soc; Am. Soc. Test. & Mat; Am. Inst. Chem. Eng. Process engineering on fluorocarbon polymers; high density polyethylene; process development and engineering on titanium and zirconium sponge production; high pressure polyethylene. Address: 99 Park Ave, New York, NY 10017.

FAHRENBACH, MARVIN J(AY), b. Buena Vista, Va, Apr. 11, 18; m. 49; c. 3. ORGANIC CHEMISTRY. B.S, Yale, 39, Ph.D.(org. chem), 42. Org. chemist, Calco Chem. Div, AM. CYANAMID CO, 42-51, physiol. chemist, dept. nutrition & physiol, LEDERLE LABS. DIV, PEARL RIVER, 51-59, GROUP LEADER, biochem. res. dept, 59-66, pharmacol. & exp. therapeut. res. dept, 66-70, CARDIOVASC-RENAL PHARMACOL. RES. DEPT, 70- AAAS; Am. Chem. Soc; Am. Inst. Chem; N.Y. Acad. Sci. Pharmaceuticals; sulfonamides; vitamins; hormones; antiseptics of the quaternary ammonium salt type; anticoagulants; lipide metabolism; atherosclerosis. Address: Buckberg Rd, Tomkins Cove, NY 10986.

FAHRENBACH, WOLF H(ENRICH), b. Berlin, Ger, Apr. 21, 32; U.S. citizen; m. 55. HISTOLOGY, CYTOLOGY. B.A, California, Berkeley, 54; Nat. Insts. Health fel, Washington (Seattle), 60-61, Ph.D.(invert. zool), 61. Asst. zool, Washington (Seattle), 57-60; Nat. Sci. Found. fel. anat, Harvard Med. Sch, 61-63; ASSOC. PROF. EXP. BIOL, MED. SCH, UNIV. ORE, 63-; SCIENTIST ELECTRON MICROS. & CHMN. DEPT, ORE. REGIONAL PRIMATE RES. CTR, 67-, assoc. scientist, 63-67. U.S.A, 54-56. AAAS; Am. Asn. Anat; Am. Soc. Cell Biol; Electron Micros. Soc. Am. Vertebrate and invertebrate histology and cytology; electron microscopy of invertebrate visual systems. Address: Dept. of Electron Microscopy, Oregon Regional Primate Research Center, Beaverton, OR 97005.

FAHRENTHOLD, PAUL DAVID, b. Houston, Tex, Oct. 26, 37; m. 60; c. 3. INORGANIC CHEMISTRY, CHEMICAL ENGINEERING. B.S, Univ. Tex, 60; M.S, Rice Univ, 62; NASA fel, Univ. Houston, 65, Ph.D.(chem), 66; Fla. State Univ, 66. Process engr, Union Carbide Int. Co, 61-63; res. chemist, Tex. Eastman Co, 66-68; TECH. ASST. TO PRES, CALUMET INDUSTS, INC, 68-, V.PRES, CALUMET PETROCHEM, INC, 69- Studies of heterogenous acid catalysis of vapor phase reactions; liquid phase acid catalysis and engineering aspects of commercial development. Address: Calumet Petrochemicals, Inc, P.O. Box 751, Natchez, MS 39120.

FAHRENHOLTZ, KENNETH E(ARL), b. Peoria, Ill, Aug. 9, 34; m. 59. ORGANIC CHEMISTRY. B.S, Bradley, 56; Nat. Sci. Found. fel, Rochester, 56-57, Ph.D.(org. chem), 60. Sr. chemist, Strasenburgh Labs, 60-62; RES. DIV, HOFFMAN-LA ROCHE, INC, 62-71, RES. FEL, 71- Am. Chem. Soc; Brit. Chem. Soc. Organic synthesis; heterocyclic compounds; steroids; medicinal chemistry. Address: 28 Winding Lane, Bloomfield, NJ 07003.

FAHRNEY, DAVID (EMORY), b. Stapleton, Nebr, Feb. 1, 34; m. 69. BIOCHEMISTRY. B.A, Reed Col, 59; Nat. Sci. Found. fel, Columbia, 59-63, Ph.D.(biochem), 63. Nat. Insts. Health fel, biophys. chem, California, San Diego, 63-64, asst. prof. chem, Los Angeles, 64-69; ASSOC. PROF. BIOCHEM, COLO. STATE UNIV, 69- U.S.A, 56-58. Am. Chem. Soc; Am. Soc. Biol. Chem. Structure and function of enzymes; identification of functional groups in active sites of enzymes and proteins. Address: Dept. of Biochemistry, Colorado State University, Ft. Collins, CO 80521.

FAHSEL, MICHAEL JOHN, b. Carthage, N.Y, June 7, 39; m. 59; c. 3. ANALYTICAL CHEMISTRY. B.S, Rochester Inst. Tech, 61; Ph.D.(anal. chem), Iowa State Univ, 65. Anal. chemist, E.I. DU PONT DE NEMOURS & CO, INC, 65-69, supvr. anal. group, PETROL. LAB, 69-71, SUPVR. LUBRICANTS GROUP, 71- Am. Chem. Soc; Am. Soc. Test. & Mat. Chromatography; electroanalytical chemistry; spectrophotometry. Address: Petroleum Lab, E.I. du Pont de Nemours & Co, Inc, Wilmington, DE 19898.

FAHSELT, DIANNE, b. Cabri, Sask, May 12, 41. BOTANY. B.A, Univ. Sask, 63, Hons, 64; Ph.D.(bot), Wash. State Univ, 67. ASST. PROF. BOT, UNIV. WEST. ONT, 67- Nat. Res. Coun. Can. grant, 67-71; dept. univ. affairs grant, 69. AAAS; Bot. Soc. Am; Am. Soc. Plant Taxon; Can. Bot. Asn; Int. Asn. Plant Taxon. Chemical taxonomy; comparative flavonoid studies in genus Dicentra; genetics and evolution. Address: Dept. of Plant Sciences, University of Western Ontario, London, Ont, Can.

FAHY, W(ILLIAM) E(ARL), b. Rochester, N.Y, Aug. 6, 19; m. 42; c. 3. VERTEBRATE ZOOLOGY, ICHTHYOLOGY. B.Sc, Cornell, 46, Ph.D.(biol), Rochester, 51. Asst, Rochester, 47-50; acting instr, 48; res. biologist, MARINE BIOL, INST. MARINE SCIS, UNIV. N.C, 51-52, asst. prof, 52-55, assoc. prof, 55-63, PROF, 63- U.S.A.A.F, 44-45. Am. Soc. Ichthyol. & Herpet; Soc. Syst. Zool; Am. Soc. Zool. Influence of environmental factors on meristic structures in fishes; taxonomy; ecology; life histories of eastern North American fresh and salt water fishes; growth, setting and life history of marine mollusks. Address: Institute of Marine Sciences, University of North Carolina, Morehead City, NC 28557.

FAIER, HARRY, b. Poland, Oct. 11, 34; Can. citizen; m. 62; c. 4. THEORETICAL PHYSICS. B.Sc, Sir George Williams Univ, 59; Ph.D.(physics), Northwest. Univ, 65. Res. physicist, Carnegie Inst. Technol, 65-67; ASST. PROF. PHYSICS, ST. JOHN'S UNIV.(N.Y), 67- Am. Phys. Soc. Theory of meson decay, weak and electromagnetic modes; cosmology and foundations of field theory. Address: Dept. of Physics, St. John's University, Jamaica, NY 11432.

FAIGENBAUM, MARK A(LAN), b. Troy, N.Y, June 22, 42. PHYSICAL & POLYMER CHEMISTRY. B.S, Rensselaer Polytech. Inst, 64, Ph.D.(phys. chem), 67. STAFF CHEMIST, IBM CORP, 67- Sci. Res. Soc. Am; Am. Chem. Soc. Polymer coatings. Address: IBM Corp, D/C 30, Bldg. 904, P.O. Box 390, Poughkeepsie, NY 12602.

FAILEY, C(RAWFORD) F(AIRBANKS), b. Terre Haute, Ind, Jan. 30, 00. CHEMISTRY. Ph.B, Yale, 21; Ph.D, California, 26. Instr. pharmacol, sch. med, Hopkins, 29-30; asst. prof. biochem, Columbia, 30-37; res. assoc. pharmacol, Chicago, 42-45, assoc. prof. biochem, 45-47, prof, 47-49; private res, 50-62; VIS. PROF. BIOCHEM, UNIV. CHICAGO, 62- Am. Soc. Biol. Chem; Am. Chem. Soc. Thermodynamics of aqueous solutions; chemical senses. Address: Apt. 930 S, 1450 E. 55th Place, Chicago, IL 60637.

FAILL, RODGER T(ANNER), b. Niagara Falls, N.Y, May 1, 36; m. 63; c. 4. STRUCTURAL GEOLOGY. B.S, Columbia, 61, M.A, 64, Ph.D.(geol), 66. GEOLOGIST, PA. GEOL. SURV, 65- Geol. Soc. Am; Am. Geophys. Union. Experimental rock deformation. Address: Pennsylvania Geological Survey, Harrisburg, PA 17120.

FAILLA, PATRICIA McCLEMENT, b. New York, N.Y, Dec. 22, 25; wid. BIOPHYSICS. A.B, Barnard Col, Columbia, 46, Atomic Energy Cmn. fel, Columbia, 48-50, Ph.D.(biophys), 58. Asst. physicist, physics lab, Dept. Hosps, New York, 46-48; res. scientist, radio. res. lab, col. physicians & surgeons, Columbia, 50-60; ASSOC. BIOPHYSICIST, RADIOL. PHYSICS DIV, ARGONNE NAT. LAB, 60- Mem. corp, Marine Biol. Lab, Woods Hole. AAAS; Radiation Res. Soc; Biophys. Soc; N.Y. Acad. Sci; Am. Asn. Physicists in Med. Dosimetry of ionizing radiations and the effects of radiation of biological systems. Address: Radiological Physics Division, Argonne National Lab, Argonne, IL 60439.

FAILLACE, LOUIS A, b. Brooklyn, N.Y, June 7, 32; m. 63; c. 3. PSYCHIATRY. M.D, Marquette Univ, 57. Intern med, Boston City Hosp, 57-58; asst. resident psychiat. & neurol, Bellevue Hosp, N.Y.C, 58-59; res. fel. neurochem, Mass. Ment. Health Ctr, 59-61; asst. resident psychiat, Johns Hopkins Hosp, 61-63, resident psychiatrist, 63-64; clin. assoc. psychopharmacol, clin. neuropharmacol. res. ctr, Nat. Insts. Ment. Health, St. Elizabeth's Hosp, 64-66; assoc. physician, psychosom. clin, Johns Hopkins Univ, 66-67; chief psychiatry, Baltimore City Hosps, 67-71; PROF. PSYCHIAT. & DIR. PROG, UNIV. TEX. MED. SCH. HOUSTON, TEX. MED. CTR, 71- Res. fels, Harvard & Nat. Insts. Health, 60-61; assoc. prof, Johns Hopkins Univ, 68-71; consult. psychiatrist, Good Samaritan Hosp, 68-71. Dipl, Am. Bd. Psychiat. & Neurol, 70. U.S.P.H.S, 64-66, Sr. Surg. Am. Psychiat. Asn; assoc. Am. Geriat. Soc; Am. Psychosom. Soc; N.Y. Acad. Sci. Clinical effects of psychoactive drugs; psychological, behavioral and metabolic factors in alcoholism. Address: Program in Psychiatry, 102 Jesse Jones Library Bldg, University of Texas Medical School at Houston, Texas Medical Center, Houston, TX 77025.

FAIMAN, CHARLES, b. Winnipeg, Man, Dec. 6, 39; m. 63; c. 3. ENDOCRINOLOGY, PHYSIOLOGY. B.Sc. & M.D, Univ. Man, 62, M.Sc, 66. Res. fel. physiol, Univ. Man, 64-65; res. asst. med, Univ. Ill, 65-67; res. assoc. endocrinol, Mayo Found, 67-68; ASST. PROF. PHYSIOL, UNIV. MAN, 68- Med. Res. Coun. Can. fel, 64-68, scholar, 68-; dir. clin. invest. unit, Winnipeg Gen. Hosp, 71- Prowse Prize, Univ. Man, 66. Endocrine Soc; Can. Soc. Clin. Invest; Am. Fedn. Clin. Res; Soc. Exp. Biol. & Med. Reproductive endocrinology, especially gonadotropin regulation in humans in health and in disease, gonadotropin secretion in chimpanzees and human fetal gonadal steroid production. Address: G4-Winnipeg General Hospital, 700 William Ave, Winnipeg 3, Man, Can.

FAIMAN, MICHAEL, b. London, Eng, Mar. 27, 35; m. 65; c. 2. COMPUTER SCIENCE. B.A, Cambridge, 56; M.S, Univ. Ill, Urbana-Champaign, 64, Ph.D, 66. Engr, Elliott Automation, Eng, 56-60; asst. prof. COMPUT. SCI, UNIV. ILL, URBANA-CHAMPAIGN, 66-70, ASSOC. PROF, 70- Computer logic and hardware; digital-analog systems; optical information processing. Address: Dept. of Computer Science, University of Illinois at Urbana-Champaign, Urbana, IL 61801.

FAIMAN, MORRIS DAVID, b. Winnipeg, Man, June 24, 32; m. 62; c. 2. PHARMACOLOGY, TOXICOLOGY. B.S, Univ. Man, 55; M.S, Univ. Minn, 61, Ph.D, 65. Asst. prof. pharm, UNIV. KANS, 65-69, ASSOC. PROF. PHARMACOL. & TOXICOL, 69- AAAS; Am. Pharmaceut. Asn; Soc. Toxicol; Aerospace Med. Asn. Biopharmaceutics; pharmacokinetics; oxygen toxicity; biogenic amines. Address: School of Pharmacy, Dept. of Pharmacology & Toxicology, University of Kansas, Lawrence, KS 66044.

FAIMAN, ROBERT N(EIL), b. Excelsior, Minn, June 25, 23; m. 44; c. 2. ELECTRICAL ENGINEERING. B.S.E.E, N.Dak. State Col, 47; M.S.E.E, Washington (Seattle), 48; Ph.D, Purdue, 56. Assoc. elec. eng, Washington (Seattle), 47-48; from asst. prof. to prof. & chmn. dept, N.Dak. State Col, 48-58; dean col. technol, UNIV. N.H, 59-67, V.PRES. RES, 67- Engr, eng. sci. prog, Nat. Sci. Found, 57-59; mem, N.H. Bd. Registr. Prof. Engrs. U.S.A.A.F, 43-46, Res, 46-, Maj. Am. Soc. Eng. Educ; sr. mem. Inst. Elec. & Electronics Eng. Circuit analysis and synthesis; control systems. Address: Thompson Hall, University of New Hampshire, Durham, NH 03824.

FAIN, J(ACOB) MITCHELL, b. Brooklyn, N.Y, Sept. 15, 01; m. 29. CHEMICAL ENGINEERING. A.B, Columbia, 21, Ch.E, 23, Ph.D.(chem. eng), 32. Chemist, Paramount Prods. Co, Long Island City, 23-24; asst. supt. storage battery mfg, Neidich Elec. Mfg. Co, Brooklyn, 24-26; chem. engr, Flintkote Co, N.J, 26-31; consult. chemist & engr, Foster D. Snell, Inc, 33-42, res. dir, 46-64; INDEPENDENT RES. CHEM. ENGR, 64- U.S.A.A.F, 42-46, Col. Am. Chem. Soc. Rubber; plastics; flameproofing of textiles; bituminous compositions. Address: 10250 W. Bay Harbor Dr, Bay Harbor Islands, Miami Beach, FL 33154.

FAIN, JANICE B(LOOM), b. Hot Springs, Ark, Jan. 8, 27; m. 48; c. 1. PHYSICS. B.A, Texas, 48, M.A, 51, Ph.D.(physics), 56; Paris, 56-57. Eng. specialist, Chance Vought Aircraft, Tex, 56, 57-59; mem. tech. staff, Pac. Missile Range, Land-Air, Inc, Point Mugu, 59-61; scientist, Supreme Hq. Allied Powers Europe Tech. Ctr, Holland, 61-63; exec. adv, Douglas Aircraft Co, Calif, 63-66; mem. prof. staff, Ctr. Naval Anal, Va, 66-69; SR. ASSOC, CACI, 69- Soroptomist Int. fel, Univ. Paris, 56-57. Am. Phys. Soc; Inst. Mgt. Sci. Simulation; military operations analysis; quantitative techniques in international relations. Address: CACI, 1815 Ft. Myer Dr, Arlington, VA 22209.

FAIN, JOHN NICHOLAS, b. Jefferson City, Tenn, Aug. 18, 34; m. 58; c. 3. BIOCHEMISTRY. B.S, Carson-Newman Col, 56; Commonwealth fel, Emory, 56-57, U.S. Pub. Health Serv. fel, 58-59, Sr. Tull Honor fel, 59-60, Ph.D. (biochem), 60. Res. assoc. biochem, Emory, 60-61; Nat. Sci. Found. fel, 61-62; U.S. Pub. Health Serv. fel, 62-63; chemist, Nat. Inst. Arthritis & Metab. Diseases, Nat. Insts. Health, 63-65; asst. prof. MED. SCI, BROWN UNIV, 65-68, assoc. prof, 68-71, PROF, 71- AAAS; Am. Soc. Biol. Chem; Endocrine Soc. Mechanism of hormone action. Address: Division of Biological & Medical Science, Brown University, Providence, RI 02912.

FAIN, ROBERT C, b. Santa Rosa, Tex, Oct. 19, 36; m. 58; c. 2. ORGANIC & ORGANOMETALLIC CHEMISTRY. B.S, Southwest Tex. State, 58, M.A, 59; Ph.D.(chem), Texas, 65. Instr. chem, Southwest Tex. State, 59-61; res. chemist, Celanese Corp, N.J, 65-66; assoc. prof. chem, TARLETON STATE COL, 66-68, PROF. PHYS. SCI. & HEAD DEPT, 68-, DEAN SCH. ARTS & SCI, 70- Am. Chem. Soc. Pi complexes of transition metals. Address: Dept. of Chemistry, Tarleton State College, Stephenville, TX 76402.

FAIN, SAMUEL C(LARK), JR, b. Jefferson City, Tenn, Aug. 13, 42; m. 66. SOLID STATE PHYSICS. B.A, Reed Col, 65; Nat. Sci. Found. trainee, Univ. Ill, Urbana-Champaign, 65-69, M.S, 66, Ph.D.(physics), 69. NATO fel. PHYSICS, Natuurkundig Lab, Univ. Amsterdam, 69-70; ASST. PROF, UNIV. WASH, 70- Alfred P. Sloan res. fel, 71-73. Am. Phys. Soc. Properties of solid helium; electronic properties of metals and alloys; surface physics. Address: Dept. of Physics, University of Washington, Seattle, WA 98195.

FAIN, WILLIAM W(HARTON), b. Augusta, Ga, Apr. 23, 27; m. 48; c. 1. OPERATIONS RESEARCH. B.A, Texas, 50, M.A, 51, Ph.D.(physics), 55; Paris, 56-57. Res. scientist, Electro-Mechanics Co, Texas, 53-56; eng. specialist, Chance-Vought Aircraft, 56, 57-59; mem. tech. staff, Pacific Missile Range, Land-Air Inc, Point Mugu, 60-61; scientist, Supreme Hq. Allied Powers Europe Tech. Ctr, Holland, 61-63; exec. adv, Douglas Aircraft Co, Calif, 63-66; mem. prof. staff, Ctr. Naval Anal, Va, 66-69; mgr. opers. res. dept, CACI, ARLINGTON, VA, 69-71, EXEC. V.PRES, 71- Inst. Defense Anal. fel. opers. anal, 61-63; consult, steering comt, Spring Joint Comput. Conf, 71, Can. Dept. Nat. Defence, United Aircraft Co, U.S. Army War Col, Indust. Col. Armed Forces & Univ. South. Calif. U.S.A, 45-46, Sgt. AAAS; Opers. Res. Soc. Am; Int. Studies Asn. Simulation and gaming; military operations research; quantitative techniques in international studies; applications of game theory; computer applications. Address: 5547 29th St. N.W, Washington, DC 20015.

FAINBERG, ARNOLD H(AROLD), b. Brooklyn, N.Y, Apr. 9, 22. PHYSICAL-ORGANIC CHEMISTRY. B.A, Cornell, 42, fel, 49-51, Ph.D.(chem), 50. Asst, Cornell, 42-44; res. chemist, Manhattan proj, Monsanto Chem. Co, 44-46; asst, Cornell, 46-49; mem. staff dept. chem, California, Los Angeles, 51-56; sr. res. chemist, Whitemarsh Res. Lab, Pennsalt Chem. Corp, PA, 56-62, proj. leader, tech. ctr, 62-67, SR. RES. SCIENTIST, PENNWALT CORP, 67- Am. Chem. Soc. Organic fluorine chemistry; mechanism of solvolytic reactions; radiochemistry; gas chromatography; phase equilibria; infrared spectroscopy. Address: 311 Murray Dr, Apt. D, King of Prussia, PA 19406.

FAINBERG, JOSEPH, b. Passaic, N.J, Oct. 18, 30; m. 56; c. 3. RADIO ASTRONOMY. A.B, Chicago, 50, B.S, 51, M.S, 53; Ph.D.(elec. eng), Hopkins, 65. Res. asst. cosmic rays, Chicago, 50-53, meson physics, 53-57; res. scientist, Hopkins, 57-66; PHYSICIST, GODDARD SPACE FLIGHT CTR, NASA, 66- Instr, Roosevelt, 53-54. AAAS; Am. Astron Soc; Am. Phys. Soc; Inst. Elec. & Electronics Eng. Cosmic rays; meson physics; scattering and diffraction of electromagnetic waves; space physics. Address: Lab. of Extraterrestrial Physics, NASA Goddard Space Flight Center, Greenbelt, MD 20771.

FAINSTAT, THEODORE, b. Montreal, Que, July 14, 29. OBSTETRICS, GYNECOLOGY. B.Sc, McGill, 50, M.Sc, 51, M.D, 55; Ph.D, Univ. Cambridge, 70. Instr. genetics, McGill, 50-51; intern, Montreal, 55-56; fel. OBSTET. & GYNEC, sch. med, Harvard, 56-63, asst, 64-66; assoc. prof, MED. SCH, NORTHWEST. UNIV, 67-68, PROF, 68-, KELLOGG FACULTY FEL, CTR. TEACHING PROF, 70- Asst. res. med, Boston, 56-57; res. fel. endocrinol, Harvard Biol. Labs, 57-60; asst. res. surg, Boston, 60; Josiah Macy Jr. Found. fel. obstet. & gynec, sch. med, Harvard, 57-63; sr. investr, Nat. Insts. Health grant, 58-63; res, Boston Lying-In Hosp. & Free Hosp. for Women, Boston & Brookline, Mass, 61-63; asst. obstetrician & gynecologist, Boston City Hosp. & Boston Lying-In Hosp, 64-66; Am. Cancer Soc. scholar, Strangeways Res. Lab, Eng, 64-66. Sr. attend, Chicago Wesley Mem. Hosp, 69- Soc. Study Reproduction; Am. Col. Obstet. & Gynec.(pres. award, 68); Soc. Gynec. Invest; Endocrine Soc; Teratology Soc; Fertil. Soc; Brit. Soc. Study Fertil; Int. Soc. Res. Biol. Reproduction; N.Y. Acad. Sci. Biology of reproduction. Address: Dept. of Obstetrics & Gynecology, Northwestern Medical School, 303 E. Chicago Ave, Chicago, IL 60611.

FAIR, FRANK V(ERNON), b. Ford City, Pa, Oct. 24, 25; m. 49; c. 3. ANALYTICAL CHEMISTRY. B.S, Pa. State Col, 49; M.S, Illinois, 51, Ph.D. (chem), 53. Chemist, res. & develop. div, Pittsburgh Consolidation Coal Co, 53-57; res. mgr, res. lab, Speer Carbon Co, Pa, 57-66; tech. dir, O. Hommel Co, Pa, 66-67; DIR. BASIC DEVELOP, RES. & DEVELOP. LAB, AIRCO SPEER DIV, AIR REDUCTION CO, INC, 67- U.S.N.R, 44-46. Am. Chem. Soc. Polarography and infrared; carbon and graphite products; high temperature physical measurements. Address: 802 Pasadena Ave, Niagara Falls, NY 14302.

FAIR, HARRY D(AVID), JR, b. Indiana, Pa, Dec. 2, 36; m. 64; c. 1. SOLID STATE PHYSICS. B.S, Indiana Univ. Pa, 58; fel, Delaware, 59-60, M.S, 60, Dept. Army fel, 62-65, Ph.D.(solid state physics), 67. Teaching asst. physics, Delaware, 58-59; res. physicist, Picatinny Arsenal, 60-62; vis. scientist, Delaware, 62-65; solid state physicist, explosives lab, PICATINNY ARSENAL, 65-69, chief point defect & electron energy level sect, 69-71, CHIEF, SOLID STATE BR, 71- Ord.C, U.S.A.R, 60-62, 1st Lt. Am. Phys. Soc; Am. Asn. Physics Teachers; Sci. Res. Soc. Am. Impurity levels in crystals using electron spin resonance; optical absorption; photoconductivity of II-VI compound semiconductors and explosive crystals. Address: Solid State Branch, Picatinny Arsenal, Dover, NJ 07801.

FAIR, JAMES R(UTHERFORD), JR, b. Charleston, Mo, Oct. 14, 20; m. 50; c. 3. CHEMICAL ENGINEERING. B.S, Ga. Inst. Tech, 42; M.S, Michigan, 49; Gulf Oil fel, Texas, 52-53, Humble Oil fel, 54, Ph.D.(chem. eng), 54. Chemist & res. engr, Monsanto Co, Marshall, Texas, 42-43, res. & design engr, 43-45, develop. assoc, Mo, 45-47, proj. leader, engr, Texas City, 47-52; process design engr, Shell Develop. Co, Calif, 54-56; res. group leader & sect. leader, MONSANTO CO, 56-61, eng. mgr, 61-69, ENG. DIR, 69- Affiliate prof, Washington, 64- Am. Chem. Soc; Am. Inst. Chem. Eng. Physical separation methods; heat transfer equipment; chemical reactor design; hydrocarbon pyrolysis operations. Address: Central Engineering Dept, Monsanto Co, 800 N. Lindbergh Blvd, St. Louis, MO 63166.

FAIR, JERRELL FRANKLIN, b. Petersburg, Ind, June 3, 37; m. 59. MICROBIOLOGY. Nat. Defense Ed. Act fel. & B.S, Colorado State, 59, U.S. Pub. Health Serv. fel. & M.S, 63; Ph.D.(microbiol), 65. Instr. microbiol, Colorado State, 65-66; asst. prof. biol, Drake, 66-68; Univ. Houston, 68-69; MEM. STAFF, HOUSTON RES. INST, 69- Am. Soc. Microbiol. Aquatic bacteriology; microbial ecology; Enterobacteriaceae; water pollution. Address: 7575 Bellaire Blvd, Houston, TX 77036.

FAIRALL, NORMAN, b. Frazeysburg, Ohio, March 26, 06. MATHEMATICS. B.S, Muskingum Col, 31; M.A, Ohio State, 37; Columbia, 49. Teacher MATH, Ohio (Athens) at Zanesville, 46-58; asst. prof, UNIV. TOLEDO, 58-71, EMER. PROF, 71- Teacher, pub. sch, Ohio, 37-58. Sig.C, U.S.A, 42-45. Properties of a point associated with a triangle by means of circular coordinates. Address: 983 Grafton Rd, Apt. 3, Newark, OH 43055.

FAIRBAIRN, ALASTAIR ROBERT, b. Upminster, Eng, Mar. 4, 31; U.S. citizen; m. 58. PHYSICAL CHEMISTRY. B.Sc. & A.R.C.S, Univ. London, 53, Ph.D.(phys. chem), 57. Sci. off. fluid flow, Royal Aircraft Estab, Farnborough, Eng, 56-58; Gen. Motors fel. combustion studies, Imp. Col, Univ. London, 58-62; prin. res. scientist reaction kinetics, Avco Everet Res. Lab, Mass. 62-68; RES. PHYSICIST SOLAR RADIATION PROCESSES, AIR FORCE CAMBRIDGE RES. LABS, 68- High temperature gas dynamics; reaction processes and kinetics; optical radiation phenomena. Address: 33 Bartley St, Wakefield, MA 01880.

FAIRBAIRN, D(ONALD), b. Ottawa, Ont, Feb. 4, 16; m. 44; c. 3. BIOCHEMISTRY. B.A, Queen's (Can), 38; Ph.D.(biochem), Rochester, 42. Sr. fel. chem, Pittsburgh, 42-43; res. fel, Queen's (Can), 45-46; asst. prof. parasitol, McGill, 46-50, assoc. prof, 50-62; COMMONWEALTH PROF. ZOOL, UNIV. MASS, AMHERST, 62-, head dept, 62-70. Vis. prof, Univ. Sydney, 69. Can. C.W.S, 43-45. AAAS; Am. Soc. Biol. Chem; Am. Chem. Soc; Am. Soc. Parasitol; Brit. Biochem. Soc. Lipids; enzymology; biochemistry of parasites. Address: Dept. of Zoology, University of Massachusetts, Amherst, MA 01002.

FAIRBAIRN, HAROLD WILLIAMS, b. Ottawa, Ont, Can, July 10, 06; nat; m. 39; c. 4. PETROLOGY. B.Sc, Queen's (Can), 29; Wisconsin, 29-30; A.M, Harvard, 31, Ph.D.(mineral, geol), 32. Field asst, Geol. Surv. Can, 26-32; Royal Soc. Can. traveling fel, Innsbruck, Göttingen & Berlin, 32-34; instr. mineral, Queen's (Can), 34-37; asst. prof. PETROL, MASS. INST. TECHNOL, 37-43, assoc. prof, 43-55, PROF, 55-, petrographer, Manhattan Dist. proj, 44. Surv. chief, Ont. Dept. Mines, Can, 35-39; Que. Dept. Mines, 40; Geol. Surv, Can, 42. AAAS; Geochem. Soc; fel. Geol. Soc. Am; fel. Mineral. Soc. Am; Am. Geophys. Union; Am. Acad. Arts & Sci; Geol. Asn. Can. Structural petrology; optical crystallography; metamorphism; geochronology. Address: Dept. of Earth & Planetary Science, Massachusetts Institute of Technology, Cambridge, MA 02139.

FAIRBAIRN, JOHN F, II, b. Buffalo, N.Y, Nov. 2, 22; m. 60; c. 2. MEDICINE. M.D, Buffalo, 45. Private practice, Buffalo, N.Y, 52-53, 54, 55-56; Nat. Heart Inst. trainee, MAYO CLIN, 54-55, CONSULT. INTERNAL MED, 56-, HEAD SECT. PERIPHERAL VASCULAR DISEASES, 60- Instr. med, Mayo Grad. Sch. Med, Minnesota, 59-63, asst. prof, 63-66, assoc. prof. clin. med, 66- Attend. physician & consult, St. Mary's & Methodist Hosps, Rochester, 56-; mem. coun. arteriosclerosis, Am. Heart Asn, 63, adv. bd. coun. circulation, 64. Am. Fedn. Clin. Res; Am. Heart Asn; fel. Am. Col. Physicians. Atherosclerosis, hypertension and vascular diseases in general. Address: Mayo Clinic, 200 First St. S.W, Rochester, MN 55901.

FAIRBANK, HENRY A(LAN), b. Lewistown, Mont, Nov. 9, 18; m. 43; c. 3. PHYSICS. A.B, Whitman Col, 40; Ph.D.(physics), Yale, 44; M.A, Oxford, 53; hon. D.Sc, Whitman Col, 71. Staff mem, Los Alamos Lab, N.Mex, 44-45; instr. PHYSICS, Yale, 42-44, 45-48, asst. prof, 48-54, assoc. prof, 54-62; PROF. & CHMN. DEPT, DUKE UNIV, 62- Guggenheim fel, Oxford, 53-54; consult, Los Alamos Sci. Lab, 57- Fel. Am. Phys. Soc; Am. Asn. Physics Teachers. Low temperature physics; liquefier design; properties of liquid and solid He^3 and He^4; electrical and thermal conductivities. Address: Dept. of Physics, Duke University, Durham, NC 27706.

FAIRBANK, WILLIAM M(ARTIN), b. Minneapolis, Minn, Feb. 24, 17; m. 41; c. 3. PHYSICS. A.B, Whitman Col, 39, hon. D.Sc, 65; fel, Washington (Seattle), 40-42; Sheffield fel, Yale, 45-46, Ph.D.(physics), 48. Staff mem, radiation lab, Mass. Inst. Tech, 42-45; asst. prof. PHYSICS, Amherst Col, 47-52; assoc. prof, Duke, 52-58, PROF, 58-59; STANFORD UNIV, 59- Scientist of year, Calif. Mus. Sci. & Indust, 61; Res. Corp. award, 65. Nat. Acad. Sci; fel. Am. Phys. Soc.(Oliver E. Buckley prize, 63). Microwave radar systems and microwave propagation; cryogenics; superconductivity; properties of helium II and III; separation of helium isotopes. Address: Dept. of Physics, Stanford University, Stanford, CA 94305.

FAIRBANKS, DANIEL F(URTH), b. San Mateo, Calif, Mar. 6, 25; m. 53; c. 4. CHEMICAL ENGINEERING. B.A.S, California, 45, M.S, 49; Sc.D.(chem. eng), Mass. Inst. Tech, 52. Dir. practice sch, Mass. Inst. Tech, 52-53, asst. prof. chem. eng, 53-62; sr. chem. engr, Nat. Res. Corp, Norton Co, 62-67, dir. res. & develop, Supercon Div, 67-68; MGR. CHEM. RES. DIV, DENNISON MFG. CO, 68- AAAS; Am. Inst. Chem. Eng; Am. Chem. Soc. Heat transfer; reprographics; adhesion. Address: Research Division, Dennison Manufacturing Co, Framingham, MA 01701.

FAIRBANKS, GILBERT WAYNE, b. Hartford, Conn, July 26, 37; m. 69. PHYSIOLOGY. B.S, Trinity Col.(Conn), 59; M.A, Wesleyan, 61; Nat. Defense Ed. Act fel. & Ph.D, South Carolina, 64. ASSOC. PROF. BIOL, FURMAN UNIV, 64- Ed, S.C. Acad. Sci. Bull; S.C. Biologist Newsletter. AAAS. Effect of hyperthermic conditions on lipids in animal tissues; membrane lipids of protozoans. Address: Dept. of Biology, Furman University, Greenville, SC 29613.

FAIRBANKS, HAROLD V, b. Des Plaines, Ill, Dec. 7, 15; m. 51. METALLURGY. B.S, Mich. State Col, 37, M.S, 39; Mass. Inst. Tech. Instr. gen. chem, Mich. State Col, 37-39; chem. eng, Louisville, 40-42; asst. prof, Rose Polytech, 42-47; METALL, UNIV. W.VA, 47-49, assoc. prof, 49-55, PROF, 55- Adv, Purdue team Int. Coop. Admin, Chen Kung Univ, Tainan, Taiwan, 57-59; co-dir. grad. studies mat. sci. eng, Univ. W.Va, 63. AAAS; Am. Soc. Metals; Am. Inst. Min, Metall. & Petrol. Eng; Am. Soc. Test. & Mat; Nat. Asn. Corrosion Eng; Am. Soc. Eng. Educ; Nat. Soc. Prof. Eng; Int. Metallog. Soc. Application of high intensity sonics to various processes. Address: 909 Riverview Dr, Morgantown, WV 26505.

FAIRBANKS, LAURENCE D(EE), b. Wilson Co, Kans, May 23, 26; m. 53; c. 3. INVERTEBRATE ZOOLOGY. A.B, Kansas, 49, M.A, 56; Nat. Insts. Health fel, Tulane, 58-63, Ph.D.(zool), 59. Instr. zool, SCH. MED, TULANE UNIV, LA, 58-66, asst. prof. MED, 66-70, ASSOC. PROF. & INSTR, DEPT. PHYS. EDUC, 70- U.S.A, 50-51. AAAS; Am. Soc. Limnol. & Oceanog; Am. Soc. Zool; Entom. Soc. Am. Physiology and ecology of invertebrates, Mollusca and Insecta; general biology of aging. Address: Dept. of Medicine, School of Medicine, Tulane University, 1430 Tulane Ave, New Orleans, LA 70112.

FAIRBANKS, MICHAEL B(RUCE), b. Rogers City, Mich, Aug. 31, 44; m. 62; c. 2. COMPARATIVE PHYSIOLOGY. B.S, Mich. State Univ. 66, M.S. & Nat. Insts. Health trainee, 68, Ph.D.(physiol), 70. ASST. PROF. ANAT. & PHYSIOL, OHIO STATE UNIV, 70- AAAS; Am. Soc. Zool. Ocular oxygen concentration in teleosts; pollutants and aquatic pathology; retinal oxygen toxicity. Address: Dept. of Zoology, Ohio State University, Columbus, OH 43210.

FAIRBANKS, THEODORE H, b. Waterville, Maine, Oct. 6, 25; m. 64; c. 7. ORGANIC CHEMISTRY. B.A, Middlebury Col, 49; Ph.D.(chem), Delaware, 54. Res. chemist, Am. Viscose Corp, 53-58, sr. res. chemist, 58-63, group leader explor. res. AM. VISCOSE DIV, FMC CORP, 63-66, RES. ASSOC, 66- U.S.N.R, 44-46. Organic reaction mechanisms; polymer chemistry and extrusion; cellular materials; adhesion. Address: Research & Development, American Viscose Division, FMC Corp, Marcus Hook, PA 19061.

FAIRBANKS, VIRGIL, b. Ann Arbor, Mich, June 7, 30; m. 55; c. 3. INTERNAL MEDICINE, HEMATOLOGY. B.A, Utah, 51; M.D, Michigan, 54. Intern internal med, Bellevue Hosp, New York, N.Y, 54-55; resident, col. med, Utah, 57-59; fel. hemat, Scripps Clin, La Jolla, Calif, 59-60; asst. physician, City of Hope Med. Ctr, Duarte, 60-61, assoc. physician, 61-63; asst. prof. internal med, Calif. Col. Med, 63-64; MEM. RES. & TEACHING STAFF, MAYO CLIN, 65- Sr. attend. physician, Los Angeles County Hosp. & consult, Vet. Admin. Hosp, Long Beach, 63-64. U.S.N, 55-57, Lt. Comdr. AAAS; Am. Soc. Hemat; Am. Fedn. Clin. Res; Am. Col. Physicians; Int. Soc. Hemat. Pharmacology of veratrum alkaloids; glycolytic functions of human erythrocyte; iron metabolism; human genetics. Address: Dept. of Laboratory Medicine, Mayo Clinic, Rochester, MN 55901.

FAIRBRIDGE, RHODES W(HITMORE), b. Pinjarra, Australia, May 21, 14; m. 43; c. 1. GEOLOGY. B.A, Queen's Univ, 36; B.S, Oxford, 40; D.Sc, Univ. Western Australia, 44. Field geologist, Iraq Petroleum Co, 38-41; lectr. geol, Univ. Western Australia, 46-53; assoc. prof, Illinois, 53-54; prof, Columbia Univ, 55-68; GEOCHEMIST, GEOSCI. INSTRUMENTS CORP, 68- Leader, Nile Exped, Columbia Univ, 61; vis. prof, Sorbonne, 62. Consult, Hydro-Elec. Comn. Tasmania, 47; Richfield Oil Co, 48; Australian Bur. Mineral Resources, 50; Snowy Mts. Hydro-Elec. Authority, 51; Pure Oil Co, 55-56; Life Magazine, 56-; Office Naval Res, 56-; Nat. Acad. Sci, 58-59. Ed, Geol. Series, Van. Nostrand Co, 58-; Encyclopedia Earth Sci, 63- Royal Australian A.F, 42-46. Fel. Geol. Soc. Am; Soc. Econ. Paleont. & Mineral; fel. Am. Geog. Soc; Nat. Asn. Geol. Teachers; Am. Asn. Petrol. Geol; Am. Geophys. Union; N.Y. Acad. Sci. Gravitational processes in sedimentation and tectonics; littoral sedimentation; coral reefs; eustatic changes of sea-level; paleoclimatology; geomorphology; geosynclines; world geotectonics. Address: Geoscience Instruments Corp, 435 E. Third St, Mt. Vernon, NY 10553.

FAIRBROTHERS, DAVID E(ARL), b. Absecon, N.J, Sept. 24, 25; m. 49; c. 2. BOTANY. B.S, Syracuse, 50; M.S, Cornell, 52, Ph.D.(bot), 54. Asst. BOT, Cornell, 50-54, instr, 54; RUTGERS UNIV, 54-57, asst. prof, 57-60, assoc. prof, 60-65, PROF, 65- Rockefeller Res. Found. grant, 52; Nat. Sci. Found. grant, 57, 60, 63, 65, 67 & 69. U.S.A, 43-46. AAAS; Bot. Soc. Am; Am. Soc. Plant Taxon; Soc. Study Evolution; Torrey Bot. Club; Int. Soc. Plant Taxon; Am. Inst. Biol. Sci. Chemosystematics; experimental taxonomy; scanning electron microscope. Address: Dept. of Botany, Rutgers, The State University, New Brunswick, NJ 08903.

FAIRCHILD, C(LIFFORD) E(UGENE), b. Philip, S.Dak, Sept. 19, 34; m. 60; c. 2. ATOMIC & MOLECULAR PHYSICS. B.A, Fresno State, 56; Nat. Sci. Found. fel, Washington (Seattle), 59, Ph.D.(physics), 62. Asst. prof. PHYSICS, ORE. STATE UNIV, 62-66, ASSOC. PROF, 66- Am. Phys. Soc. Natural lifetimes of excited states; electron impact excitation; velocity distributions of dissociation products; upper atmospheric physics; auroral physics. Address: Dept. of Physics, Oregon State University, Corvallis, OR 97331.

FAIRCHILD, EDWARD J(OSEPH), II, b. Gallup, N.Mex, Feb. 5, 23; m. 44; c. 3. PHARMACOLOGY, PHYSIOLOGY. Fel, La. State, 50-54, Ph.D.(biol, biochem), 54. Biologist, fisheries sect, fish & game div, State Wild Life & Fisheries Cmn, La, 54-56; toxicologist, div. occup. health, U.S. Pub. Health Serv, 56-61, res. pharmacologist, occup. health res. & training facility, 61-66; assoc. dir, toxic hazards res. unit, Aerojet-Gen. Corp, Wright Patterson AFB, 66-67, lab. dir, 67; staff scientist, air qual. criteria & standards develop. prog, Nat. Ctr. Air Pollution Control, Pub. Health Serv, 67-68, chief res. injury control prog, Nat. Ctr. Urban & Indust. Health, 68; acting dir. div. safety serv, off. prod. safety, bur. med, Food & Drug Admin, 68-69; dep. dir. div. criteria & standards develop, Bur. Occup. Safety & Health, 69-70, acting dir, 70-71, ACTING ASSOC. DIR. CINCINNATI OPER, NAT. INST. OCCUP. SAFETY & HEALTH, 71- Silver Medal superior serv, Dept. Health, Educ. & Welfare, 64. U.S.A, 42-43, Res, 43-46, 1st Lt. AAAS; Soc. Toxicol; Am. Conf. Govt. Indust. Hygienists; Soc. Exp. Biol. & Med. Neurohumoral mechanisms in pathophysiology and toxicology of respiratory irritant gases; protective mechanisms against toxic pulmonary edema; pharmacodynamics in toxicology and experimental pathology. Address: National Institute for Occupational Safety & Health, 1014 Broadway, Cincinnati, OH 45202.

FAIRCHILD, GLEN A, b. Perryville, Mo, Mar. 29, 34; m. 60; c. 3. EPIDEMIOLOGY, VIROLOGY. B.S, Missouri, 56, D.V.M, 58; M.P.H, Minnesota, 63. Vet. officer & tech. adv, air pollution control prog, U.S. PUB. HEALTH SERV, D.C, 59-60, vet. epidemiologist, Ohio Dept. Health, 60-64, SR. VET. OFF, div. air pollution, sch. vet. med, Pennsylvania, 64-67, NAT. AIR POLLUTION CONTROL ADMIN, DEPT. PREV. MED, SCH. MED, UNIV. WASH, 67- U.S.P.H.S, 59-, Sr. Vet. Off. Am. Pub. Health Asn; Am. Vet. Med. Asn; N.Y. Acad. Sci. Veterinary epidemiology; environmental effects on respiratory infection in lower animals from a microbiological point of view. Address: Dept. of Environmental Health, School of Public Health & Community Medicine, University of Washington, Seattle, WA 98105.

FAIRCHILD, (ALEXANDER) G(RAHAM) B(ELL), b. Washington, D.C, Aug. 17, 06; m. 38; c. 2. ENTOMOLOGY. B.S, Harvard, 32, M.S, 34, Ph.D, 42. Asst. entomologist, exp. sta, Florida, 34-35; entomologist, yellow fever serv, int. health div, Rockefeller Found, 35-37; jr. med. entomologist & later entomologist, Gorgas Mem. Lab, 38-71, asst. dir, 58-71; COURTESY PROF. ENTOM, UNIV. FLA, 71- Asst. prof, Minnesota, 49-50; Douglas Lake Biol. Sta, Michigan, 56-57; mem. trop. med. & parasitol. sect, Nat. Inst. Allergy & Infectious Diseases, 61-65; res. assoc, Mus. Comparative Zool, Harvard, 65-; Fla. State Collection Arthropods, 70- Sanit.C, 43-46, Capt. AAAS; Am. Soc. Trop. Med. & Hyg; Entom. Soc. Am.(founders mem. award, 68); Soc. Syst. Zool. Taxonomy of arthropods of medical importance; insects affecting man and animals, especially Tabanidae, Simuliidae, Psychodidae and Ixodidae. Address: Dept. of Entomology, University of Florida, Gainesville, FL 32601.

FAIRCHILD, H(OMER) E(ATON), b. Sioux Rapids, Iowa, Oct. 1, 21; m. 49; c. 3. MEDICAL ENTOMOLOGY. B.S, S.Dak. State Col, 44; Iowa State Col; Agr. & Mech. Col. Tex; Ph.D.(entom), Kans. State Col, 53. Asst. state entomologist nursery inspection, State Dept. Agr, Iowa, 44; res. assoc. & instr. wildlife res, Iowa State Col, 44-45; farm supvr. farm security admin, U.S. Dept. Agr, 45-46, agent vet. entom, bur. entom. & plant quarantine, 46-49; entomologist, indust. & biochem. dept, E.I. du Pont de Nemours & Co, 52-60; prod. supvr, agr. chem. div, Geigy Chem. Corp, 60-61, tech. serv. mgr, 61-63, staff res. specialist, 63-66; prod. specialist, agr. prod, Union Carbide Corp, 66-67, coord, prod. develop, 67-68, tech. mgr. commercial agr. prods, 68-70, mkt. mgr, 70-71; ENTOMOLOGIST, OFF. PESTICIDE PROGS, ENVIRON. PROTECTION AGENCY, 71- AAAS; Entom. Soc. Am. Control of insects affecting livestock; insect and mammalian toxicology; insecticidal residues in animal tissues and products. Address: Office of Pesticide Programs, Environmental Protection Agency, Water Side Mall, Washington, DC 20024.

FAIRCHILD, JACK, b. Houston, Tex, Oct. 25, 28; m. 51; c. 6. AEROSPACE ENGINEERING. B.S, Texas, 53; M.S, Southern California, 59; Nat. Sci. Found. fel, Oklahoma, 62-63, 64, Ford Found. fel, 63-64, Ph.D.(eng. sci), 64. Aerodynamicist, Bell Helicopter Corp, 53-54; sr. aerodynamicist, Chance Vought Aircraft Corp, 54-56; lectr. AEROSPACE ENG, aviation safety div, Southern California, 56-60; instr. & res. engr, Oklahoma, 60-62; assoc. prof, UNIV. TEX, ARLINGTON, 64-70, PROF, 70- Adv, U.S. Army Bd. Aircraft Accident Invest, 57-59; consult, aircraft div, Hughes Tool Co, 58-59. U.S.N, 46-51, Lt.(jg). Am. Inst. Aeronaut. & Astronaut; Am. Soc. Eng. Educ; Nat. Soc. Prof. Eng. Flight mechanics, vibration and aeroelasticity. Address: Dept. of Aerospace Engineering, University of Texas at Arlington, Arlington, TX 76010.

FAIRCHILD, MAHLON DAVID, b. Reno, Nev, May 7, 23. PHARMACOLOGY, NEUROPHYSIOLOGY. B.S, Nevada, 48; M.S, Southern California, 54; Ph.D. (pharmacol), California, Los Angeles, 63. RES. PHARMACOLOGIST, lab. neurol. res, Loma Linda Univ, 55-58; California, Los Angeles, 58-63; VET. ADMIN. HOSP, LONG BEACH, 63-; ASSOC. PROF. PHARMACOL, SCH. MED, UNIV. CALIF, LOS ANGELES, 71-, asst. prof, 63-71. U.S.M.C. & U.S.N.A.F, 42-45. Am. Soc. Pharmacol. & Exp. Therapeut. Research in neuropharmacological properties of centrally active drugs with electrographic and behavioral correlates of activity and application of electronic computer technology to quantification of the results. Address: Veterans Administration Hospital, 5901 E. Seventh St, Long Beach, CA 90801.

FAIRCHILD, MAHLON L(OWELL), b. Spencer, Iowa, Oct. 13, 30; m. 54; c. 3. ENTOMOLOGY. B.S, Iowa State, 52, M.S, 53, Ph.D.(entomol), 59. Asst. entom, Iowa State, 52-53, 55-56; entomologist, European corn borer res. lab, agr. res. serv, U.S. Dept. Agr, 57-59; asst. prof. ENTOM, UNIV. MO-COLUMBIA, 59-64, assoc. prof, 64-67, PROF, 67-, CHMN. DEPT, 69- Med.C, U.S.A, 53-55. Am. Entom. Soc. Insecticidal control of the European corn borer; biology and control of corn insects. Address: Dept. of Entomology, University of Missouri-Columbia, Columbia, MO 65201.

FAIRCHILD, RALPH GRANDISON, b. Trenton, N.J, Sept. 24, 35; m. 58; c. 4. RADIOLOGICAL PHYSICS. B.S, St. Lawrence, 58; M.S, Cornell, 61. PHYSICIST, BROOKHAVEN NAT. LAB, 61- Am. Asn. Physicist in Med; Health Physics Soc. Mixed field dosimetry; use of neutrons in diagnosis and therapy. Address: Medical Physics Division, Brookhaven National Lab, Upton, NY 11973.

FAIRCHILD, WILLIAM WARREN, b. Rutland, Vt, July 30, 38. MATHEMATICS. B.A, Swarthmore Col, 60; M.A, Pennsylvania, 63; Ph.D.(math), Illinois, 67. Physicist, Bartol Res. Found, Franklin Inst, 60-62; asst. prof. MATH, Northwest. Univ, 67-70; ASSOC. PROF, UNION COL.(N.Y), 70- Am. Math.

Soc. Functional analysis, particularly convolution algebras. Address: Dept. of Mathematics, Union College, Schenectady, NY 12308.

FAIRCLOTH, WAYNE R(EYNOLDS), b. Whigham, Ga, Jan. 15, 32; m. 66; c. 2. BOTANY, SYSTEMATIC BOTANY. B.S, Valdosta State Col, 55; M.Ed, North Carolina, 59; Ph.D.(bot), Georgia, 71. Teacher, high sch, Ga, 51-61; asst. prof. biol, VALDOSTA STATE COL, 61-67, assoc. prof, 67-71, PROF. BIOL. & CURATOR HERBARIUM, 71- AAAS; Bot. Soc. Am; Am. Fern Soc. Ecology and systematics of vascular flora of the Atlantic and Gulf Coastal plains, particularly phytogeography. Address: Dept. of Biology, Valdosta State College, Valdosta, GA 31601.

FAIRHALL, A(RTHUR) W(ILLIAM), b. Hamilton, Ont, Mar. 2, 25; nat; m. 53; c. 3. CHEMISTRY. B.Sc, Queen's Univ.(Ont), 46; Ph.D.(chem), Mass. Inst. Technol, 52. Res. chemist, Eldorado Mining & Ref. Co, Ltd, 46-48; res. assoc. CHEM, Mass. Inst. Technol, 52-54; asst. prof, UNIV. WASH, 54-58, assoc. prof, 58-63, PROF, 63- Guggenheim fel, 63-64. Am. Chem. Soc; Am. Phys. Soc. Nuclear reactions; nuclear fission; radiocarbon dating. Address: Dept. of Chemistry, University of Washington, Seattle, WA 98195.

FAIRHURST, CARL W(AYNE), b. St. Joseph, Mo, Dec. 13, 26; m. 56; c. 3. DENTAL MATERIALS. M.S, Marquette Univ, 59; Ph.D, Northwest. Univ, 66. Asst. instr. dent. mat, sch. dent, Marquette Univ, 47-49, asst, 52, asst. instr, 52-55, instr, 55-59, asst. prof, 59-66, assoc. prof, 66-67, chmn. dept, 64-67; dir. dent. mat. res, S.S. White Co, 67-69, GEN. MGR. RES. & DEVELOP, S.S. WHITE DIV, PENNWALT CORP, 69- U.S.A, 45-46. Am. Dent. Asn; Am. Crystallog. Asn; Int. Asn. Dent. Res. Physics, chemistry and metallurgy of the materials employed in dentistry. Address: S.S. White Division, Pennwalt Corp, 900 First Ave, King of Prussia, PA 19406.

FAIRHURST, C(HARLES), b. Widnes, Eng, Aug. 5, 29; m. 57; c. 7. MINING ENGINEERING. B.Eng, Sheffield, 52, Ph.D.(mining), 55. Mining engr, northwest div, Nat. Coal Bd, 55-56; res. fel. mineral & metall. eng, UNIV. MINN, MINNEAPOLIS, 56-57, asst. prof, 57-60, assoc. prof, 60-65, PROF, 65-70, CIVIL & MINERAL ENG, 70-, assoc. head dept. mineral & metall. eng, 65-68, head, 68-70. Int. Soc. Rock Mech; Am. Inst. Mining, Metall. & Petrol. Eng; Soc. Exp. Stress Anal. Rock mechanics. Address: Dept. of Civil & Mineral Engineering, University of Minnesota, Minneapolis, MN 55455.

FAIRLESS, BILLY J, b. Vienna, Ill, Sept. 27, 39; m. 62; c. 1. BIOPHYSICS, PHYSICAL CHEMISTRY. B.A, South. Ill. Univ, 63; M.S, Univ. Houston, 67, Ph.D.(biophys), 68. Anal. chemist, Girdler Catalyst, 61-63; res. assoc, Princeton, 67-68; asst. prof. CHEM, IND. STATE UNIV, EVANSVILLE, 68-71, ASSOC. PROF, 71- Chemist, Environ. Pollution Control, 71- Am. Chem. Soc. Instrumental methods of organic and biological molecule structure determination; analytical methods for measuring organic pollutants in micro quantities. Address: Dept. of Chemistry, Indiana State University, Highway 62, Evansville, IN 47712.

FAIRLEY, ARTHUR S(AMUEL), b. Roseland, N.J, Oct. 29, 01; m. 27; c. 1. ASTRONOMY. A.B, Amherst Col, 23, A.M, 25; Thaw fel, Princeton, 26-27, Ph.D.(astrophys), 27; Maine, 37-38. Instr. physics, Amherst Col, 23-24; prof. astron, Cent. Col, 27-28; instr, Yerkes Observ, Chicago, 28-32; taecher, pub. sch, N.Y, 32-36; prin, Maine, 36-41; head physics dept, Maine Maritime Acad, 45-59; assoc. prof. physics, Colby Col, 59-66, prof, 66-67; acting dean instr, Maine Maritime Acad, 67-68, acad. dean, 68-70; RETIRED. U.S.N, 41-45, Comdr. AAAS; Am. Phys. Soc; Am. Astron. Soc. Astronomical photometry and spectroscopy. Address: Castine, ME 04421.

FAIRLEY, HENRY BARRIE FLEMING, b. London, Eng, Apr. 24, 27; Can. citizen; m. 50; c. 3. ANESTHESIA. M.B, B.S, London, 49. Clin. asst. anesthesia, Univ. Toronto, 55-56, clin. teacher, 56-61, assoc, 61-64, assoc. prof, 64-67, PROF, 67-69; ANESTHESIOL, UNIV. CALIF, SAN FRANCISCO, 69- Anesthetist, Toronto Gen. Hosp, 55-60, sr. anesthetist, 60-69. Dipl. anesthesia, Royal Col. Surgeons, Eng, 51, fel, faculty anesthetists, 54; dipl. anesthesiol, Royal Col. Physicians & Surgeons, Can, 56. R.A.F, 51-54, Squadron Leader. Asn. Univ. Anesthetists; Can. Anaesthetists Soc; Asn. Anaesthetists Gt. Brit. & North. Ireland; hon. mem. Australian & N.Z. Socs. Anaesthetists. Respiratory physiology as applied to anesthesia and the management of respiratory failure. Address: Dept. of Anesthesiology, University of California, San Francisco, CA 94122.

FAIRLEY, JAMES L(AFAYETTE), (JR), b. Orland, Calif, Oct. 15, 20; m. 48. BIOLOGICAL CHEMISTRY. A.B, San Jose State Col, 42; cert, California, Los Angeles, 43; Ph.D.(chem), Stanford, 50. Instr. meteorol, California, Los Angeles, 43-44; physics & chem, San Jose State Col, 46-47; asst. biochem, Stanford, 47-49, res. assoc, 49-51; res. biochemist, radiation lab, California, 51-52; asst. prof. CHEM, MICH. STATE UNIV, 52-58, assoc. prof, 58-62, PROF. BIOCHEM, 62- U.S.A.A.F, 42-46, Capt. AAAS; Am. Chem. Soc; Am. Soc. Biol. Chem; Am. Soc. Plant Physiol. Deoxyribonucleases; pyrimidine biosynthesis. Address: Dept. of Biochemistry, Michigan State University, East Lansing, MI 98823.

FAIRLEY, WILLIAM M(ERLE), b. Millinocket, Maine, Oct. 13, 28; m. 60. GEOLOGY. A.B, Colby Col, 49; M.S, Maine, 51; Ph.D, Hopkins, 62. Geologist, Ga. Marble Co, 57-58; asst. prof. GEOL, UNIV. NOTRE DAME, 58-65, ASSOC. PROF, 65- U.S.M.C, 51-53. Geol. Soc. Am; Soc. Econ. Paleont. & Mineral. Petrology and structure of metamorphic rocks, especially marble and soapstone. Address: Dept. of Geology, University of Notre Dame, Notre Dame, IN 46556.

FAIRMAN, FREDERICK WALKER, b. Montreal, Que, May 29, 35; m. 57; c. 2. ELECTRICAL ENGINEERING, APPLIED MATHEMATICS. B.E, McGill Univ, 59; M.S.E.E, Univ. Pa, 62, Ph.D.(elec. eng), 68. Engr, Honeywell, Inc, 60-62; Instr. ELEC. ENG, Drexel Univ, 62-67; lectr, Univ. Del, 67-69; ASST. PROF, QUEEN'S UNIV.(ONT), 69- Inst. Elec. & Electronics Eng; Soc. Indust. & Appl. Math. Use and properties of signal processing by Poisson filtering with application to parameter identification of certain classes of time varying nonlinear and distributed systems. Address: Dept. of Electrical Engineering, Queen's University, Kingston, Ont, Can.

FAIRMAN, WILLIAM D(UANE), b. Paducah, Ky, June 7, 29; m. 57; c. 5. ANALYTICAL & PHYSICAL CHEMISTRY. B.S, Marquette, 50, M.S, 58; Ill. Inst. Technol, 63-64. Asst. chemist, ARGONNE NAT. LAB, 58-70, ASSOC. CHEMIST, 70- Abstractor, Chem. Abstracts, 65- U.S.A, 53-56. Am. Chem. Soc; Sci. Res. Soc. Am; fel. Am. Inst. Chem; Health Physics Soc. Separation and measurement of radionuclides in humans and the environment; analytical tracer chemistry; radiation spectroscopy; computer applications in radiation measurements; liquid scintillation counting techniques; whole body counting. Address: Argonne National Lab, Bioassay Dept, Bldg. 19, 9700 S. Cass Ave, Argonne, IL 60439.

FAIRWEATHER, GRAEME, b. Dundee, Scotland, Apr. 18, 42; m. 65; c. 2. NUMERICAL ANALYSIS. B.Sc, Univ. St. Andrews, 63, Carnegie Trust scholar, 63-65, Ph.D.(appl. math), 66. Lectr. appl. math, Univ. St. Andrews, 65-66; vis. lectr. math, Rice Univ, 66-67; lectr. appl. math, Univ. St. Andrews, 67-69; asst. prof. MATH, Rice Univ, 69-71; ASSOC. PROF, UNIV. KY, 71- Vacation assoc, U.K. Atomic Energy Auth, 68; vis. sr. res. off, numerical anal. div, Nat. Res. Inst. Math. Sci, S.Africa, 71. Am. Math. Soc; Soc. Indust. & Appl. Math; Math. Asn. Am. Numerical solution of elliptic and parabolic partial differential equations by the method of finite differences and by Galerkin's method. Address: Dept. of Mathematics, University of Kentucky, Lexington, KY 40506.

FAIRWEATHER, IAN L(AWSON), b. Clitheroe, Eng, Mar. 20, 33; m. 62; c. 2. NUCLEAR PHYSICS. B.Sc, Edinburgh, 56, Ph.D.(physics), 58. Nat. Res. Coun. fel, Manitoba, 59-60, asst. prof. PHYSICS, 60-61; UNIV. OTTAWA, 61-67, ASSOC. PROF, 67- Am. Asn. Physics Teachers; Can. Asn. Physicists. Low energy nuclear physics; gamma ray spectroscopy and nuclear reactions studies. Address: Dept. of Physics, University of Ottawa, Ottawa 2, Ont, Can.

FAISSLER, WILLIAM L, b. Hammond, Ind, Nov. 23, 38; m. 66. PHYSICS. B.A, Oberlin Col, 61; M.A, Harvard, 62, Ph.D.(physics), 67. Res. assoc. PHYSICS, NORTHEAST. UNIV, 67-70, ASST. PROF, 70- Am. Phys. Soc; Am. Forestry Asn. Address: Dept. of Physics, Northeastern University, Boston, MA 02115.

FAITH, CARL (CLIFTON), b. Covington, Ky, Apr. 28, 27; m. 51; c. 2. MATHEMATICS. B.S, Kentucky, 51; M.S, Purdue, 53, Ph.D.(math), 56. Asst. MATH, Purdue, 51-55; instr, Mich. State, 55-56, asst. prof, 56-57; Pa. State, 57-62; PROF, RUTGERS UNIV, 62- NATO fel, Univ. Heidelberg, 59-60; Nat. Sci. Found. fel, Inst. Advan. Study, 60-61, mem, 61-62, vis, summers 63, 65 & 71; consult, Inst. Defense Anal, 64; Rutgers faculty fel, Univ. Calif, Berkeley, 65-66; Nat. Sci. Found-U.S. Agency Int. Develop. consult, Delhi, Bombay, Madras & Calcutta, India, summer 68; Rutgers faculty fel, 69-70; Ford Found. vis. prof, Tulane Univ, fall 70; mem. screening comt. ing. exchange of persons, Sr. Fulbright Awards, 70-73. U.S.N, 45-46. Am. Math. Soc; Math. Asn. Am. Normal bases; Galois theory; structure theory and generations of fields and rings; commutativity theorems; structure of injective and projective modules and quotient, semiprime noetherian and quasi-frobenius rings; uniserial rings; module theory. Address: Dept. of Mathematics, Rutgers University, New Brunswick, NJ 08903.

FAITH, W(ILLIAM) L(AWRENCE), b. Hancock, Md, May 12, 07; m. 32; c. 3. CHEMICAL ENGINEERING. B.S, Maryland, 28; M.S, Illinois, 29, Ph.D. (chem. eng), 32. Chemist, U.S. Indust. Chem. Co, Md, 26-27; asst, Illinois, 28-31, spec. asst. chem. eng, eng. exp. sta, 31-32; res. chemist, Nat. Aluminate Corp, Ill, 33; asst. prof. chem. eng, Kans. State Col, 33-36, prof, 36-42, head dept, 39-42; prof. & head dept, Iowa, 42-44; vis. lectr. chem. eng, Catholic Univ, 44-45; dir. develop. eng, Chem. Div, Corn Prods. Ref. Co, 45-48, dir. eng, 48-54; chief engr, Air Pollution Found, 54-57, managing dir, 57-61; CONSULT. CHEM. ENGR, 61- Consult, chem. indust. br, off. prod. res. & develop, War Prod. Bd, Wash, 42-43, asst. dir, 44, dep. dir, 44-45. Mem. emergency action comt, Los Angeles County Air Pollution Control Bd, 56-63; sanit. eng. & occup. health study sect, U.S. Pub. Health Serv, 58-62; adv. comt. reactor safeguards, U.S. Atomic Energy Comn, 66-69. Trustee, Am. Sanit Eng. Intersoc. Bd, 57-64. Bronze medal, Univ. Mo, 69. AAAS; Am. Chem. Soc; Air Pollution Control Asn.(pres, 61-62); Am. Acad. Environ. Eng; Am. Inst. Chem. Eng; Am. Soc. Mech. Eng. Catalytic oxidation of organic compounds: chemical economics; air pollution and auto exhaust control. Address: 2540 Huntington Dr, San Marino, CA 91108.

FAIZI, SALIH, b. Kazan, U.S.S.R, Mar. 3, 10; U.S. citizen; m. 56; c. 2. MINERALOGY, GEOLOGY. B.S, Polytech. Inst. Novochevkassk, 32; Ph.D.(natural sci, math), Freiburg, 49. Geologist, res. orgns, U.S.S.R, 32-36; sr. scientist geol. res, Sci. Res. Inst. Gold, 37-41; mineralogist, Freiburg, 50-51; script writer, U.S. Info. Agency, 51-53; geologist, Nat. Lead Co, N.Y, 54-57; Am. Geol. Inst, 57-59; asst. ed. crystallog, McGraw-Hill Book Co, 59-60; prof. geol, Curry Col, 60-61; GEOLOGIST, BR. MIL. GEOL, U.S. GEOL. SURV, 61- Consult, mining orgns, W.Ger, 50-51. Soviet Army, 41-42, Capt. Geol. Soc. Am. Environmental factors affecting vulnerability of foundations to destruction by seismic waves, natural or artificial; mineralogy, crystallography, geology, physical and chemical properties and behavior of geologic subjects; early history of man and his environment, physical and geographic. Address: Branch of Military Geology, U.S. Geological Survey, Crystal Plaza Bldg, Washington, DC 20242.

FAJANS, EDGAR W, b. Manchester, Eng, Feb. 24, 11; nat; m. 36; c. 2. PHYSICAL & INORGANIC CHEMISTRY. Ph.D.(chem), Frankfurt, 34. Fel, photochem. res, Univ. Col, London, 35; mem. staff, colloid chem, agr. res. sta, Univ. Bristol, 36-37; res. chemist, Imp. Chem. Industs, 37-44; controller res. dept, BORON CHEM, Borax Consol, Ltd, London, 44-51; assoc. dir. chem. res, U.S. BORAX RES. CORP, 51-59, spce. asst. to v.pres, 59-63, MGR. CHEM. ECONS, 63- Am. Chem. Soc. Physical, inorganic and boron chemistry; chemical economics. Address: U.S. Borax Research Corp, 412 Crescent Way, Anaheim, CA 92801.

FAJANS, JACK, b. U.S.A, Nov. 17, 22; m. 44; c. 2. PHYSICS. B.Ch.E, City Col, 44; Ph.D.(physics), Mass. Inst. Tech, 50. Sr. engr, Sylvania Elec. Co, 50-53; ASSOC. PROF. PHYSICS, STEVENS INST. TECHNOL, 53- Consult, Huyck Indust. Controls, 56- U.S.A, 44-45. Optical Soc. Am; Am. Asn.

Physics Teachers. Low-temperature physics; superfluid helium; optical systems; instrumentation. Address: Dept. of Physics, Stevens Institute of Technology, Hoboken, NJ 07030.

FAJANS, STEFAN S(TANISLAUS), b. Munich, Germany, Mar. 15, 18; nat; m. 47; c. 2. INTERNAL MEDICINE. B.S, Michigan, 38, M.D, 42. Asst. prof. INTERNAL MED, SCH. MED, UNIV. MICH, 51-55, assoc. prof, 55-61, PROF, 61- Am. Col. Physicians res. fel, 49-50; Life Ins. Med. Res. fel, 50-52; consult. to Surgeon Gen, U.S. Pub. Health Serv, 58-62, 66-70; Banting Mem. Lect, Brit. Diabetic Asn, 68. Med.C, U.S.A, 43-46. Am. Soc. Clin. Invest; Endocrine Soc; Am. Diabetes Asn.(pres, 71-72); Am. Fedn. Clin. Res; Am. Col. Physicians. Endocrinology and metabolism; carbohydrate metabolism; diabetes; hypoglycemia; pituitary adrenal function. Address: University Hospital, Ann Arbor, MI 48104.

FAJER, ABRAM BENCJAN, b. Piaski, Poland, Sept. 12, 26; m. 56; c. 3. PHYSIOLOGY, ENDOCRINOLOGY. M.D, Sao Paulo, 51. Asst. prof. physiol, sch. med, Sao Paulo, 51-59, head lab. exp. endocrinol, 59-63; scientist, Worcester Found. Exp. Biol, 63-64; asst. prof. PHYSIOL, SCH. MED, UNIV. MD, BALTIMORE, 64-66, ASSOC. PROF, 66- Res. fel, Inst. Biol. & Exp. Med, Argentina, 54, pharmacol. lab, Edinburgh, 56-58. Adrenal cortex, ovarian and steroid physiology. Address: Dept. of Physiology, School of Medicine, University of Maryland, Baltimore, MD 21201.

FAJER, JACK, b. Brussels, Belg, June 22, 36; U.S. citizen; m. 59; c. 3. PHYSICAL CHEMISTRY. B.S, City Col. N.Y, 57; Ph.D.(phys. chem), Brandeis Univ, 63. Res. assoc, BROOKHAVEN NAT. LAB, 62-64, asst. chemist, 64-68, assoc. chemist, 68-69, CHEMIST, 69- Am. Chem. Soc; Brit. Chem. Soc. Electron spin resonance; electronic spectroscopy of complexes and metalloporphyrins in nonaqueous systems; photochemistry. Address: Brookhaven National Lab, Upton, NY 11973.

FALB, PETER L, b. N.Y.C, July 26, 36. APPLIED MATHEMATICS. A.B, Harvard, 56, M.A, 57, Ph.D.(math), 61. Mem. staff, Lincoln Lab, Mass. Inst. Technol, 60-65; assoc. prof. INFO. & CONTROL, Univ. Mich, 65-67; BROWN UNIV, 67-69, PROF, 69- Summer vis. assoc. prof. Stanford Univ, 65; consult, Electronics Res. Ctr, NASA, 65; Bolt Beranek & Newman, Inc, 66; chmn. & treas, Barberry Corp, 68-; dir. Data Ledger, Inc, 70- Am. Math. Soc; Inst. Elec. & Electronics Eng; Soc. Indust. & Appl. Math. Control theory; control system design; algebraic geometry; human factors. Address: Dept. of Applied Mathematics, Brown University, Providence, RI 02912.

FALB, RICHARD D, b. Ft. Wayne, Ind, July 29, 36; m. 58; c. 5. PHYSICAL ORGANIC CHEMISTRY, PHYSICAL BIOCHEMISTRY. B.S, Wheaton Col, 58; Ph.D.(phys. org. chem), Ohio State, 63. Sr. res. chemist, BATTELLE MEM. INST, 63-66, proj. leader DIV. BIOCHEM. & BIOMED. ENG, 66-68, assoc. chief, 68-69, CHIEF, 69- Sem. assoc, Columbia Univ, 67- Am. Chem. Soc; Am. Soc. Artificial Internal Organs. Biomaterials; blood coagulation chemistry; insolubilized enzymes. Address: Dept. of Biology, Environment & Chemistry, Battelle Memorial Institute, 505 King Ave, Columbus, OH 43201.

FALCK, FRANK JAMES, b. N.Y.C, Oct. 27, 25; m. 50; c. 1. AUDIOLOGY, SPEECH PATHOLOGY. A.B, Univ. Ky, 50, M.A, 51; Ph.D.(speech path), Pa. State Univ, 55. Asst. prof. & dir. speech path, sch. med, Vanderbilt Univ, 55-57; assoc. prof. & dir. speech & hearing, col. med, Univ. Vt, 57-69; PROF. SPEECH PATH. & AUDIOL, UNIV. HOUSTON, 69- State consult, Vt. Dept. Health, 57- U.S.A, 42-45. Am. Speech & Hearing Asn; Am. Psychol. Asn. Localization of auditory lesions; stuttering; audile-visile modability. Address: Dept. of Speech Pathology & Audiology, University of Houston, Houston, TX 77004.

FALCO, ELVIRA A(LLEGRA), (MRS. BASS), b. Brooklyn, N.Y, Dec. 13, 18; m. 46, 67; c. 1. ORGANIC CHEMISTRY. B.S, Cornell, 39, M.S, 40. Clin. chemist, Maryland, 40-41; analyst, Davison Chem. Co, 41-43; sr. biochemist, Burroughs Wellcome Co, 42-56; exec. asst, chem. files, SLOAN-KETTERING INST, 59-68, RES. ASSOC, 68- Am. Chem. Soc; N.Y. Acad. Sci. Chemistry of purine and pyrimidine antagonists; synthesis of the antimalarial, Daraprim, antibacterial, Trimethoprim, and uricosuric agent, Allopurinol. Address: Sloan-Kettering Institute, Rye, NY 10580.

FALCON, CARROLL JAMES, b. Rayne, La, Mar. 15, 41; m. 68. REPRODUCTIVE PHYSIOLOGY, ANIMAL SCIENCE. B.S, Southwestern Louisiana, 63; M.S, Kentucky, 65, Ph.D.(genetics), 67. Res. asst. ANIMAL SCI, Kentucky, 63-67; asst. prof, NICHOLLS STATE UNIV, 67-70, ASSOC. PROF, 70- AAAS; Am. Inst. Biol. Sci; Am. Soc. Animal Sci; Am. Soc. Study Reproduction; Am. Dairy Sci. Asn. Role of the uterus in hormone metabolism; sexual behavior of animals; growth stimulants; environmental influences on fertility; nutrition of ruminants. Address: Dept. of Agriculture, Nicholls State University, Thibodaux, LA 70301.

FALCON, LOUIS A, b. Tarrytown, N.Y, Sept. 6, 32; m. 59; c. 4. ENTOMOLOGY. B.S, California, Berkeley, 59, Ph.D.(entom), 64. Asst. entom, UNIV. CALIF, BERKELEY, 59-63, asst. invert. pathologist, 63-68, LECTR. ENTOM, 68-, ASSOC. INSECT PATHOLOGIST, 70-, asst. insect pathologist, 68-70. Consult, Food & Agr. Orgn, UN, Nicargua, 70-; Cotton Inc. grant. U.S.A, 54-56, Res, 56-59. AAAS; Entom. Soc. Am; Entom. Soc. Can. Agricultural entomology of plant pests, application techniques of insect pathogens Bacillus thuringiensis and viruses, microbial control and integrated control; population dynamics, sampling; insect flight, dispersal; developing countries in Latin America. Address: 1220 Navellier St, El Cerrito, CA 94530.

FALCONE, ALFONSO BENJAMIN, b. Bryn Mawr, Pa, July 24, 23; m. 55; c. 2. INTERNAL MEDICINE, BIOCHEMISTRY. A.B, Temple, 44, M.D, 47; Nat. Inst. Health fel, Minnesota, 51-53, Ph.D.(biochem), 54. Intern, Phila. Gen. Hosp, 47-48, asst. res. internal med, 48-49; res, Univ. Hosps, Minn, 49-51; asst. clin. prof, med, sch. med, Univ. Wis, Madison, 56-59, assoc. clin. prof, 59-63, asst. prof, Inst. Enzyme Res, 63-66, vis. prof, Inst, 66-67; INDEPENDENT CONSULT. METAB. & CARDIOVASC. DISEASES & LAB. MED, 67- U.S.A, 44-46; Med.C.Res, 54-56, Lt. Comdr. Am. Soc. Biol. Chem; Am. Chem. Soc; Am. Fedn. Clin. Res; fel. Am. Col. Physicians. Oxidative phosphorylation; mechanism of metabolic control; mechanism of enzyme action; mechanism of action of hormones and drugs; biological energy transduction; cell membrane function; transport across membranes. Address: 2240 E. Illinois Ave, Fresno, CA 93701.

FALCONER, DAVID G, b. Flint, Mich, Dec. 8, 39; m. 66. OPTICAL & PARTICLE PHYSICS. B.S, Univ. Mich, 62, M.S, 65, Ph.D.(physics), 69. Res. asst. physics, inst. sci. & technol, Univ. Mich, 62-65; res. assoc, Conductron Corp, Mich, 65-67; res. asst, Univ. Mich, 67-69; RES. PHYSICIST, STANFORD RES. INST, 69- AAAS; Am. Phys. Soc; Optical Soc. Am; Am. Asn. Physics Teachers; Am. Physicists Asn. Holography; laser optics; light scattering; proton structure; boson resonance; Regge-pole theory; Kalman-filter theory. Address: Stanford Research Institute, Menlo Park, CA 94025.

FALCONER, DAVID ROSS, b. Ayr, Scotland, Mar. 20, 38; U.S. citizen; m. 65; c. 1. COMPUTER SCIENCE. B.A, Texas, 59, Ph.D.(math), 66; M.S, Trinity (Tex), 62. Digital comput. programmer, fed. systs. div, Int. Bus. Mach. Corp, 60-61; numerical analyst, Southwest Res. Inst, 61-63; asst. res. scientist, labs. electronics & related sci. res, Texas, 64-65, asst. prof. math, Arlington, 65-67; comput. sci, Univ. Houston, 67-69; ASSOC. PROF. MATH. SCI. & ASSOC. DIR. INFO. SYSTS, FLA. TECHNOL. UNIV, 69- Consult, comput. ctr, Ling-Temco-Vought, Inc, 66-68; Naval Training Device Ctr, 70- Asn. Comput. Mach; Math. Asn. Am. Numerical analysis; data structures. Address: Dept. of Mathematical Sciences, Florida Technological University, P.O. Box 25000, Orlando, FL 32816.

FALCONER, DONALD W(ILLIAM), b. Wellsville, Ohio, May 7, 14; m. 42. MATHEMATICS, APPLIED PHYSICS. B.A, Col. of Wooster, 35. With Mackintosh-Hemphill Co, Pa, 36-41; proj. engr, U.S. ARMY CHEM. CORPS BIOL. LABS, FT. DETRICK, 46-49, chief appl. mech. sect, munition develop. div, 50-52, proj. eng. br, 53-55, asst. chief, div, 56-57, chief, 57-67, DIR. COMMODITY DEVELOP. & ENG. LAB, 67- Chem.C, U.S.A, 42-46, Res, 46-, Lt. Col; Commendation Ribbon, 46. Sci. Res. Soc. Am. Formation of aerosols with explosives and cold gases; dispersion of rotating bodies by aerodynamic forces; hermetic seals for containers; military systems analysis. Address: 1201 Pinewood Dr, Frederick, MD 21701.

FALCONER, WARREN E(DGAR), b. Brandon, Man, Can, Apr. 13, 36; m. 57; c. 2. PHYSICAL CHEMISTRY. B.Sc, Manitoba, 57, M.Sc, 58; Ph.D, Edinburgh, 61. Res. officer kinetics & catalysis, Nat. Res. Coun. Can, 61-63; mem. tech. staff, BELL TEL. LABS, INC, 63-69, HEAD, PHYS. CHEM. RES. & DEVELOP. DEPT, 69- NATO sci. fel, Louvain, 61. Combustion Inst; Am. Chem. Soc; Chem. Inst. Can. Photochemistry; chemical kinetics; free and trapped radicals; combustion chemistry; noble gas chemistry; flouride chemistry; ion molecule reactions. Address: Bell Telephone Labs, Inc, Murray Hill, NJ 07974.

FALEK, ARTHUR, b. N.Y.C, Mar. 23, 24; m. 49; c. 2. HUMAN GENETICS. B.S, Queen's Col.(N.Y), 48; M.A, N.Y. Univ, 49; Ph.D.(human genetics), Columbia, 57. Res. worker med. genetics, N.Y. State Psychiat. Inst, 49-50, psychol. asst, 50-51, res. scientist, N.Y. State Dept. Ment. Hyg, 51-57, sr. res. scientist, 58-65; asst. prof. PSYCHIAT, EMORY UNIV, 65-67, ASSOC. PROF, 67-, CHIEF DIV. HUMAN GENETICS, GA. MENT. HEALTH INST, 65- Asst, Columbia Univ, 50-53, assoc, 53-65. Consult, Ct. Dept. Health, 61-; mem, Inst. Study Human Variation; mem. comt. Huntington's chorea, WHO. U.S.A.A.F, 44-46. AAAS; Am. Soc. Human Genetics; Am. Eugenics Soc; fel. Gerontol. Soc; Soc. Biol. Psychiat; N.Y. Acad. Sci. Medical genetics; cytogenetics, psychogenetics and related fields. Address: Division of Human Genetics & Dept. of Psychiatry, Georgia Mental Health Institute, Emory University, Atlanta, GA 30306.

FALER, K(ENNETH) T(URNER), b. Rock Springs, Wyo, Mar. 13, 31. NUCLEAR CHEMISTRY. B.S, Idahc State, 53; Ph.D.(chem), California, Berkeley, 59. Jr. chemist, Am. Cyanamid Co. & Phillips Petrol. Co. Chem. Processing Plant, Idaho, 53-54, res. chemist, mat. testing reactor, atomic energy div, Phillips Petrol. Co, 59-61, group leader, nuclear chem. group, 61-67; mem. staff, Idaho Nuclear Corp, 67-69; ASSOC. PROF. CHEM, IDAHO STATE UNIV, 69-, affiliate asst. prof, 67-69. U.S.A, 54-56. Am. Chem. Soc. Nuclear fission and decay schemes; fuel waste disposal; fuel chemical processing, neutron cross sections; biological use of radioisotopes; biological fluid and electrolyte balance. Address: Dept. of Chemistry, Idaho State University, P.O. Box 232, Pocatello, ID 83201.

FALES, FRANK W(ECK), b. Missoula, Mont, Sept. 24, 14. BIOCHEMISTRY. B.S, Ore. State Col, 39; M.A, Stanford, 41, Ph.D.(physiol), 51. Asst. prof. BIOCHEM, EMORY UNIV, 51-65, ASSOC. PROF, 65-, dir. clin. biochem. lab, 51-61, biochemist, clin. res. facility, 61-71. Sanit.C, 42-46, Res, 46-52, 1st Lt. AAAS; Am. Fedn. Socs. Exp. Biol; Am. Inst. Chem; Am. Soc. Biol. Chem; Am. Asn. Clin. Chem. Carbohydrate metabolism; clinical chemistry. Address: Division of Basic Health Sciences, Emory University, Atlanta, GA 30322.

FALES, HENRY M(ARSHALL), b. New York, N.Y, Feb. 12, 27; m. 47; c. 3. ORGANIC CHEMISTRY. B.Sc, Rutgers, 48, Ph.D, 52. Assoc. res. specialist, Army ord. proj, Rutgers, 52-53; CHIEF LAB. CHEM, NAT. HEART & LUNG INST, NAT. INSTS. HEALTH, 53- U.S.N.R, 44-46. Am. Chem. Soc. Structural investigations of amaryllidaceae and other alkaloids; biosynthesis of alkaloids; structure of biological intermediates; infrared; chemical ionization mass spectroscopy; gas chromatography. Address: Bldg. 10, National Institutes of Health, Bethesda, MD 20014.

FALETTI, DUANE W, b. Spring Valley, Ill, Apr. 3, 34; m. 59; c. 2. CHEMICAL ENGINEERING. B.S, Illinois, 56; Procter & Gamble fel, Washington (Seattle), 58-59, Ph.D.(chem. eng), 59. Res. engr, Boeing Airplane Co, Wash, 59-60; chem. engr, APPL. PHYSICS LAB, UNIV. WASH, 60-62, SR. CHEM. ENGR, 62- Am. Inst. Chem. Eng. Underwater ordnance and thermal propulsion; electrochemistry; two-phase critical flow; radiation heat transfer. Address: Applied Physics Lab, University of Washington, 1013 N.E. 40th St, Seattle, WA 98105.

FALICOV, LEOPOLDO M(AXIMO), b. Buenos Aires, Argentina, June 24, 33; U.S. citizen; m. 59; c. 2. THEORETICAL & SOLID STATE PHYSICS. Lic. en cie, Buenos Aires, 57; Ph.D.(physics), Balseiro Inst. Physics, Argentina, 58; Univ. Buenos Aires fel, Cambridge, 58-60, Ph.D.(physics), 61. Res. assoc. PHYSICS, inst. study metals, Univ. Chicago, 60-61, instr, 61-62, asst. prof, 62-65, assoc. prof, 65-68, PROF, 68-69; UNIV. CALIF, BERKELEY, 69- Vis. staff mem, Bell Tel. Labs, 61; Sloan res. fel, 64-; vis. mem, Cavendish lab, Cambridge Univ. & vis. fel, Fitzwilliam Col, 66; vis. prof, La. State Univ, fall, 67; vis. staff mem, N.Am. Rockwell, summer 68; Fulbright fel, Colombia, 69; Orgn. Am. States vis. prof, Argentina, summer 70. Argentine Army, 54. Am. Phys. Soc. Electronic band structure of solids; superconductivity; many-body physics; theoretical chemistry. Address: Dept. of Physics, University of California, Berkeley, CA 94720.

FALK, ABRAHAM, b. N.Y.C, May 27, 05; m. 48; c. 2. CLINICAL MEDICINE. B.S, State Univ. N.Y. Teachers Col, Albany, 30; M.D, Albany Med. Col, 36. Instr. MED, UNIV. MINN, MINNEAPOLIS, 48-50, asst. prof, 50-70, ASSOC. PROF, 70- Chief staff, Vet. Admin. Hosp, 62- Med.C, 43-46, Maj. AAAS; Am. Thoracic Soc; Am. Col. Physicians. Chemotherapy of tuberculosis; pulmonary disease and physiology. Address: Veterans Administration Hospital, Minneapolis, MN 55417.

FALK, CATHERINE T, b. Louisville, Ky, Aug. 9, 39; m. 63. GENETICS, BIOSTATISTICS. B.A, Pomona Col, 61; Ph.D.(human genetics), Pittsburgh, 68. Res. fel. GENETICS, NEW YORK BLOOD CTR, 68-70, RES. ASSOC, 70- Vis. investr, Rockefeller Univ, 69- Genetics Soc. Am; Biomet. Soc. Study of mathematical models of genetic populations; analysis and computer simulation; analysis of human genetics data to estimate linkage between known genetic markers. Address: 893 Alpine Dr, Teaneck, NJ 07666.

FALK, CHARLES DAVID, b. Chicago, Ill; July 18, 39; m. 65. INORGANIC & PHYSICAL CHEMISTRY. B.S, Chicago, 61, NASA fel, 62-65, Ph.D.(chem), 66. U.S. Pub. Health Serv. fel. coord. chem, Sussex, 66-67; chemist, explosives dept, exp. sta, E.I. du Pont de Nemours & Co, 67-70; MGR. & ADMINR, CLIFFORD CHEM. CORP, CLIFFWOOD, 70- Am. Chem. Soc; The Chem. Soc; Am. Inst. Chem. Kinetics and mechanisms of coordination complexes; ligand exchange reactions; hydride transfer; oxidation reactions with metal complexes. Address: 113 Freneau Ave, Matawan, NJ 07747.

FALK, CHARLES E(UGENE), b. Hamm, Germany, Oct. 20, 23; nat; m. 48; c. 3. PHYSICS. B.A, N.Y. Univ, 44, M.S, 46; Atomic Energy Cmn. fel, Carnegie Inst. Tech, 48-49, D.Sc.(physics), 50. Instr. physics, Carnegie Inst. Tech, 49-50; assoc. physicist, Brookhaven Nat. Lab, 50-53, admin. scientist, 53-56, div. res, U.S. Atomic Energy Cmn, 56-58, asst. to dir, lab, 58-61, asst. dir, 61-62, assoc. dir, 62-66; planning dir, NAT. SCI. FOUND. 66-70, DIR. DIV. SCI. RESOURCES & POLICY STUDIES, 70- U.S.A, 44-46. AAAS; Am. Phys. Soc. High energy physics; particle accelerators; neutron scattering; deuteron stripping; research administration; science manpower and policy. Address: 8116 Lilly Stone Dr, Bethesda, MD 20034.

FALK, DORIS F(INGER), b. Corning, Calif, May 7, 11; m. 36. BIOLOGY. A.B, Univ. Calif, 31, M.A, 32, Ph.D.(ed. psychol, sci. ed), 56. Teacher, pub. sch, Wash, D.C, 42-44; chief chemist, Joseph E. Seagram & Sons, Inc, Ky, 44-46; asst. prof. chem, FRESNO STATE COL, 46-55, assoc. prof. BIOL, 55-59, PROF, 59-, supvr. secondary credential prog. life sci, 55-59, summers, instr, Nat. Sci. Found. Inst, 59, dir, 63. Dir, Cent. Valleys Sci. Fair, 57-59; mem. Calif. State Sci. Adv. Comt, 65-70. AAAS; Am. Inst. Biol. Sci. Science education. Address: 4551 N. College, Fresno, CA 93704.

FALK, EDWARD D, b. Tonopah, Nev, Mar. 13, 25; m. 52; c. 1. PHYSICS. A.B, California, Berkeley, 52; M.S, Ore. State Col, 56. Physicist, Gen. Elec. Co, Wash, 52-54; sr. scientist, Lockheed Aircraft Corp, Calif, 55-56; res. engr, atomics int. div, N.Am. Aviation, Inc, Calif, 56-57, sr. res. engr, 57, eng. supvr, 57-64, exec. adv. tech. planning, 64-65, eng. supvr. irradiation testing, 65-68; ASST. DIR. INSTRUMENTATION SYSTS. CTR, UNIV. WIS, MADISON, 68- Sig.C, 43-46, T/Sgt. Am. Nuclear Soc; Sci. Res. Sci. Am; sr. mem. Inst. Elec. & Electronics Eng; sr. mem. Instrument Soc. Am. Reactor instrumentation; in-pile fully instrumented capsule irradiations of fuels and fuel materials; design and development of instruments and instrumentation systems used in interdisciplinary research. Address: 1622 Gateway St, Middleton, WI 53562.

FALK, GERTRUDE, b. N.Y.C, Aug. 24, 25. BIOPHYSICS. B.S, Antioch Col, 47; fel, Rochester, 48-52, Ph.D.(physiol), 52. Fel. physiol, Chicago, 52, instr. natural scis, 53-54; Porter fel. psychiat, med. sch, Illinois, 52-53; instr. pharmacol, Washington (Seattle), 54-57, asst. prof, 57-61; HON. RES. ASST. BIOPHYS, UNIV. COL, LONDON, 61- Nat. Inst. Neurol. Diseases & Blindness spec. fel, 61-63; Guggenheim fel, 63-64. Am. Physiol. Soc; Brit. Biophys. Soc; Brit. Photobiol. Soc; Brit. Physiol. Soc. Excitation and contraction of muscle; visual excitation. Address: Dept. of Biophysics, University College, University of London, London, England.

FALK, HANS L(UDWIG), b. Breslau, Germany, Sept. 15, 19; nat; m. 50; c. 3. BIOCHEMISTRY. B.Sc, McGill, 44, Ph.D, 47. Instr. biochem, dept. path. & res. assoc. cancer, Chicago, 47-52; vis. asst. prof. biochem. & nutrit, Southern California, 52-56, adj. assoc. prof. path, 56-62; head, chem. sect, carcinogenesis studies br, Nat. Cancer Inst, 62-63, chief, 63-66, assoc. sci. dir. carcinogenesis & etiology, 66-68; ASSOC. DIR. LAB. RES, NAT. INST. ENVIRON. HEALTH SCIS, NAT. INSTS. HEALTH, 68- U.S. Pub. Health Serv. award, 68. AAAS; Am. Asn. Cancer Res; N.Y. Acad. Sci; Am. Soc. Cell Biol; Am. Soc. Exp. Path; Soc. Toxicol; Am. Inst. Chem; Royal Soc. Health. Carcinogenesis; metabolism of carcinogenic agents; spectroscopic analyses; tobacco and health research; toxicology of pesticides; teratogenicity of environmental chemicals. Address: National Institute of Environmental Health Sciences, National Institutes of Health, P.O. Box 12233, Research Triangle Park, NC 27709.

FALK, HAROLD, b. Sioux City, Iowa, Nov. 5, 33; m. 63. PHYSICS. B.S, Iowa State, 56; M.S, Arizona, 57; Ph.D.(physics), Washington (Seattle), 62. Res. asst. THEORET. PHYSICS, Washington (Seattle), 60-62; res. assoc, Pittsburg, 64-66; ASSOC. PROF, CITY COL. N.Y, 66- Summers, physicist, Air

Missile Text Ctr, U.S. Navy, 56, 57; mem. tech. staff, Bell Tel. Labs, Inc, 60. Sig.C, 62-64, 1st Lt. Am. Phys. Soc. Statistical mechanics of model systems. Address: Dept. of Physics, City College of New York, New York, NY 10031.

FALK, HAROLD CHARLES, b. Mitchell, S.Dak, May 9, 34; m. 56; c. 2. ELECTRICAL ENGINEERING. B.S, S.Dak. State, 56, M.S, 58; Ph.D.(elec. eng), Okla. State, 66. Instr. elec. eng, S.Dak. State, 58-59; U.S. AIR FORCE, 59-, electronics engr, aeronaut. systs. div, Wright-Patterson AFB, 59-63, instr. ELEC. ENG, U.S. Air Force Acad, 66-67, assist. prof, 67-69, ASSOC. PROF, 69-71; PAKISTAN COL. AERONAUT. ENG, 71- U.S.A.F, 59-, Maj. Inst. Elec. & Electronics Eng; Am. Soc. Eng. Educ. Internal circuits systems design, system analysis. Address: Dept. of State (Karachi), Washington, DC 20521.

FALK, I(SIDORE) S(YDNEY), b. Brooklyn, N.Y, Sept. 30, 99; m. 25; c. 2. PUBLIC HEALTH. Ph.B, Yale, 20, Ph.D.(pub. health), 23. Asst. pub. health, Yale, 15-20, instr, 20-23; asst. prof. hyg. & bact, Chicago, 23-26, assoc. prof, 26-29, prof, 29; assoc. dir. study, Comt. Costs Med. Care, D.C, 29-33; res. assoc, Milbank Mem. Fund, N.Y, 33-36, chief health studies, soc. security admin, 36-38, asst. dir, 38-40, dir. div. res. & statist, 40-54; consult, 54-61, prof. PUB. HEALTH, SCH. MED, YALE, 61-68, EMER. PROF, 68- Asst. dir. div. maternal & child welfare & dir. surv, City Health Dept, Chicago, Ill, 26-28; staff mem, President's Comt. Econ. Security, D.C, 34-35; adj. staff mem, health sect, League of Nations, 35; soc. security adv, Govt. Haiti, 50-53; adv. soc. serv, Int. Bank, Malaya, 54-55; exec. dir. & v.chmn. bd. dirs, Community Health Care Ctr. Plan, New Haven. Consult, pub. health & soc. security, Panama, 55-57; health & med. care, Canal Zone, 57-58; health serv, United Steelworkers, 58- Officer, Haiti Nat. Order of Merit, 53; Knight, Panamanian Order Vasco Nunez de Balboa, 56. Fel. AAAS; fel. Am. Pub. Health Asn; Am. Pub. Welfare Asn; Am. Hosp. Asn; Am. Econ. Asn; Am. Statist. Asn. Social and economic statistics; social security; economics of medical care and public health; vital statistics. Address: Community Health Center, 150 Sargent Dr, New Haven, CT 06511.

FALK, JOHN CARL, b. Algonac, Mich, May 28, 38. ORGANIC CHEMISTRY. B.A, Kalamazoo Col, 60; M.S, Michigan, 62, Ph.D.(org. chem), 64. Fel. phys. biochem, Northwestern, 64-65; res. chemist, Dow Chem. Co, 65-67; sr. res. chemist, BORG WARNER RES. CTR, 67-70, GROUP LEADER POLYMER SYNTHESIS, 70- AAAS; Am. Chem. Soc; Sci. Res. Soc. Am. Organic reaction mechanisms; physical biochemistry; polymer synthesis. Address: Borg Warner Research Center, Des Plaines, IL 60018.

FALK, JOHN L(IONEL), b. Toronto, Ont, Can, Dec. 27; 27; nat. PHYSIOLOGICAL PSYCHOLOGY. B.A, McGill, 50, M.A, 52; U.S. Pub. Health Serv. fel, Illinois, 55-56, Ph.D.(psychol), 56. Asst. psychol, McGill, 51-52; Illinois, 52-55; res. assoc, Yerkes Labs. Primate Biol, 56-57; res. fel. pharmacol, U.S. Pub. Health Serv, med. sch, Harvard, 57-58, res. fel. nutrit, sch. pub. health, 58-59, res. assoc. nutrit, 59-61, lectr. psychol, univ, 59-60; asst. prof. PSYCHOL, Univ. Colo, 61-62; Univ. Mich, 62-67; assoc. prof, Ariz. State Univ, 67-69; PROF, RUTGERS UNIV, 69- AAAS; Ecol. Soc. Am; Am. Psychol. Asn. Application of behavioral techniques to problems of water-electrolyte balance; central nervous system function. Address: Dept. of Psychology, Rutgers, The State University, New Brunswick, NJ 08903.

FALK, LESLIE A, Community Health, see 12th ed, Soc. & Behav. Vols.

FALK, LLOYD L(EOPOLD), b. Ocean Grove, N.J, Nov. 6, 19; m. 45; c. 3. SANITATION. B.Sc, Rutgers, 41, Ph.D.(sanit), 49. Res. assoc. Rutgers, 45-49; consult, ENG. DEPT, E.I. DU PONT DE NEMOURS & CO, 49-67, SR. CONSULT, 67- U.S.A.F, 42-45, 1st Lt. Am. Chem. Soc; Nat. Shellfisheries Asn; Water Pollution Control Fedn. Air pollution; waste and sewage treatment; industrial climatology and meteorology; water pollution control. Address: 123 Bette Rd, Wilmington, DE 19803.

FALK, MICHAEL, b. Warsaw, Poland, Sept. 22, 31; Can. citizen; m. 59; c. 2. PHYSICAL CHEMISTRY. B.Sc, McGill, 52; D.Sc.(chem), Laval, 58. Res. chemist, Can. Copper Refiners, Montreal E, 52-54; fel. SPECTROS. Nat. Res. Coun. Can, Ottawa, 58-60; res. assoc, Mass. Inst. Tech, 60-62; ASSOC. RES. OFF, ATLANTIC REGIONAL LAB, NAT. RES. COUN. CAN, HALIFAX, 62- Chem. Inst. Can. Molecular structure; infrared spectroscopy; hydration of biopolymers; hydrogen bonding; water. Address: Atlantic Regional Lab, National Research Council of Canada, Halifax, N.S, Can.

FALK, RICHARD H, b. Peru, Ill, Oct. 12, 38; m. 58; c. 4. BOTANY, CYTOLOGY. B.S, Illinois, Urbana, 64, M.S, 65, Nat. Insts. Health fel, & Ph.D.(bot), 68. Nat. Insts. Health fel, Harvard, 68-69; ASST. PROF. BOT, UNIV. CALIF, DAVIS, 69- U.S.N, 55-59. AAAS; Bot. Soc. Am; Am. Soc. Cell Biol; Am. Soc. Plant Physiol. Biological ultrastructure, particularly plastid ultrastructure and the relating of function with ultrastructure; scanning electron microscopy. Address: Dept. of Botany, University of California, Davis, CA 95616.

FALK, ROBERT A(LLAN), b. Brooklyn, N.Y, May 20, 30; m. 55; c. 2. ORGANIC & POLYMER CHEMISTRY. B.S, Polytech. Inst. Brooklyn, 52, M.S, 54, Ph.D.(iodonium salts), 61. Chemist, Colgate-Palmolive Co, 49-57; sr. chemist, Sperry Gyroscope Co, 57-65; sr. res. chemist, Thiokol Chem. Corp, 65-68; RES. CHEMIST, Allied Chem. Corp, 68-69; CIBA-GEIGY LTD, 69- Am. Chem. Soc; fel. The Chem. Soc. Fluorine chemistry; synthesis and characterization of new compounds and monomers; polymerizations; fluoroaromatics and fluoroheterocyclics; textiles; surfactants; fluorochemical stain repellents. Address: 35 Glenside Dr, New City, NY 10956.

FALK, THEODORE J(OHN), b. Meriden, Conn, Oct. 9, 31; m. 55; c. 3. AERODYNAMICS. AERONAUTICAL ENGINEERING. B.Aero. Eng, Rensselaer Polytech, 53; univ. fel, Cornell, 54-55, M.Aero.Eng, 56, Nat. Sci. Found. fel, 59-60, Ph.D.(aero. eng), 63. Res. engr, res. dept, United Aircraft Corp, 53-54; sr. aerodyn. engr, Gen. Dynamics/Convair, 56-59; PRIN. AERODYNAMICIST, CORNELL AERONAUT. LAB, BUFFALO, 63- Am. Inst. Aeronaut. & Astronaut. Shock tubes, chemical lasers and chemical transfer lasers; current layer diffusion in magnetic pinch; metallic evaporation and condensation. Address: 10880 Boyd Dr, Clarence, NY 14031.

FALK, WILLIE ROBERT, b. Dundurn, Sask, Mar. 12, 37; m. 60; c. 2. NUCLEAR PHYSICS. B.Sc, Saskatchewan, 59, M.Sc, 62; Ph.D.(physics), British Columbia, 65. Nat. Res. Coun. Can. overseas fel. NUCLEAR PHYSICS, Swiss Fed. Inst. Technol, 65-67; ASSOC. PROF, UNIV. MANITOBA, 67- Am. Phys. Soc; Can. Asn. Physicists. Annihilation of positrons in gases; nuclear reaction studies. Address: Dept. of Physics, University of Manitoba, Winnipeg, Man, Can.

FALKEHAG, S. INGEMAR, b. Falkenberg, Sweden, May 28, 30; m. 55; c. 2. ORGANIC & SURFACE CHEMISTRY. M.S, Chalmers Tech, Sweden, 59, Ph.D.(org. chem), 62. Res. chemist, res. dept, W.Va. Pulp & Paper Co, 62-64, GROUP LEADER LIGNIN & PULPING, 64-69, RES. CTR, WESTVACO, INC, 69- AAAS; Am. Chem. Soc; Philos. Sci. Asn; Tech. Asn. Pulp & Paper Indust; Brit. Chem. Soc; Swedish Chem. Soc; World Future Soc. Structure and reactions of lignin and other wood components; technical utilization of lignin; solution properties of macromolecules; research management and technology transfer; normative forecasting. Address: Westvaco, Inc, Research Center, North Charleston, SC 29406.

FALKENBACH, GEORGE J(OSEPH), b. Columbus, Ohio, July 24, 27; m. 53; c. 4. ELECTRICAL ENGINEERING. B.E.E, Dayton, 48; M.S.E.E, Illinois, 50. Asst. instr. elec. eng, Illinois, 48-50; electronics engr, Bell Aircraft Corp, N.Y, 50-55; res. assoc, Lee Labs, Pa, 55; prin. elec. engr, BATTELLE, COLUMBUS LABS, 55-59, sr. elec. engr, 59-66, ASSOC. CHIEF, ELECTROMAGNETIC DIV, 66- Inst. Elec. & Electronics Eng. Microwave components; antennas and radomes; radar systems; dielectric and magnetic materials; ferromagnetism; electromagnetic theory; ionospheric radar techniques, systems and equipment. Address: Battelle, Columbus Labs, 505 King Ave, Columbus, OH 43201.

FALKENBERG, PHILIPPE R(OY), Exp. Psychol, see Suppl. I to 11th ed, Soc. & Behav. Vols.

FALKENSTEIN, GARY LEE, b. Bottineau, N.Dak, Oct. 8, 37; m. 69; c. 1. CHEMICAL ENGINEERING, PHYSICAL CHEMISTRY. S.B, Mass. Inst. Tech, 59, S.M, 61, Ph.D.(chem. eng), 64. Asst. dir. sch. chem. eng. practice, Mass. Inst. Technol, 60-61, sr. res. engr, res. dept, ROCKETDYNE DIV, N.AM. ROCKWELL CORP, 63-66, prin. scientist, 66-67, MGR, ADVAN. PROGS, CANOGA PARK, 67- Am. Inst. Chem. Eng; Am. Inst. Aeronaut. & Astronaut. Combustion, heat transfer, oxygen-hydrogen catalysis and gas dynamics as related to liquid rocket propulsion; surface chemistry, reactions and properties of polyelectrolyte materials. Address: 22812 Carsamba Dr, Calabasas, CA 91302.

FALKIE, THOMAS VICTOR, b. Butler Twp, Pa, Sept. 5, 34; m. 57; c. 5. MINING ENGINEERING, MANAGEMENT SCIENCE. B.S, Pa. State Univ, 56, M.S, 58, fel, 58-61, Ph.D.(mining eng), 61. Res. asst. mining, Pa. State Univ, 56-58; opers. res. consult, Int. Minerals & Chem. Corp, Ill, 61-62, opers. res. engr, Fla, 63-64, chief. minerals planning, 64-65, asst. mgr. spec. projs, 65-66, minerals planning & prod. control mgr, 66-68, prod. supt, 68-69; ASSOC. PROF. MINERAL ENG. & HEAD. DEPT. & CHMN. MINERAL ENG. MGT. PROG, COL. EARTH & MINERAL SCI, PA. STATE UNIV, 69- Mem, indust. adv. comt, col. eng, Univ. S.Fla, 65-69, adj. prof, 66; consult, Fla. State Bd. Regents, 66-67; U.S. del, Conf. on Tunnelling, Orgn. Econ. Coop. & Develop, 70; invited partic, Panel on Mineral Sci. & Technol. Educ. Policy, Nat. Acad. Eng. & U.S. Bur. Mines, 71; consult, UN, 71. Am. Inst. Min, Metall. & Petrol. Eng; Am. Inst. Indust. Eng; Opers. Res. Soc. Am; Coal Min. Inst. Am. Operations research; mine systems engineering; land reclamation and other phases of mine environmental control; industrial engineering; economic analysis; mineral resource management; surface and underground mining. Address: Dept. of Mineral Engineering, Pennsylvania State University, 118 Mineral Industries Bldg, University Park, PA 16802.

FALKIEWICZ, MICHAEL J(OSEPH), b. Brooklyn, N.Y, Oct. 8, 42; m. 66; c. 1. PHYSICAL CHEMISTRY. B.S, City Col. New York, 65; Atomic Energy Comn. grant, Syracuse Univ, 66-68, Ph.D.(phys. chem), 70. RES. CHEMIST, COLGATE-PALMOLIVE CO, PISCATAWAY, 70- Am. Chem. Soc; The Chem. Soc. Absolute viscosities of molten metals and alloys by an oscillating closed cup method; surface chemistry of glass surface in contact with liquid phase. Address: Greenwood Pl, R.D. 3, Flemington, NJ 08822.

FALKINHAM, JOSEPH OLIVER, III, b. Oakland, Calif, May 3, 42; m. 67; c. 1. MICROBIOLOGY, MICROBIAL GENETICS. A.B, California, Berkeley, 64, Ph.D.(microbiol), 69. Teaching asst. bacteriol, California, Berkeley, 66-67; DIR. CLIN. LAB, DAVID GRANT MED. CTR, U.S. AIR FORCE, 69- Am. Soc. Microbiol; Genetics Soc. Am. Physiology, genetics and regulation of microbes, especially Esherichia coli; genetic linkage relationships in male strains of Escherichia coli; desoxyribonculeic acid replication in bacteria and its regulation. Address: 101 Kenwere Circle, Travis Air Force Base, CA 94535.

FALKNER, FRANK (TARDREW), b. Hale, Eng, Oct. 27, 18; nat; m. 47; c. 2. PEDIATRICS. B.A, Cambridge, 45; L.R.C.P. & M.R.C.S, London, 45, M.R.C.P, 62. Chief res, London Hosp, 45-48; res. physician, Childrens Hosp. & Res. Found, Cincinnati, Ohio, 48-49; res. scholar pediat, Liverpool, 49-51; res. med. officer, inst. child health, London, 51-53, lectr. child health, 53-56; asst. prof, sch. med, Univ. Louisville, 56-59, assoc. prof, 59-63, prof. PEDIAT. & chmn. dept, 63-68; assoc. dir, Nat. Inst. Child Health, 68-71; DIR, FELS RES. INST, YELLOW SPRINGS, 71-; FELS PROF, COL. MED, UNIV. CINCINNATI, 71- Asst. consult, Hosp. des enfants Malades, France, 53; dir. growth study sect, Cent. Int. de l'Enfrance, Paris, 53, coord. off, 54; asst, Hosp. Sick Children, London, 54-56; Markle scholar, 57-61; consult, Nat. Inst. Child Health; Nat. Inst. Neurol. Disease & Stroke; maternal & child health servs, Dept. Health, Educ. & Welfare. Chmn. comt. comn. human develop, Int. Union Nutrit. Scis; series ed, Monogr. Pediat; co-ed, Mod. Probs. Pediat. Brit. Home Guard, 34-45. Soc. Pediat. Res; Soc. Res. Child Develop; Am. Asn. Phys. Anthrop; fel. Royal Statist. Soc; fel. Royal Soc. Med; hon. fel. French Soc. Biotypol; Am. Pediat. Soc; fel. Am. Acad. Pediat. Prenatal biology; normal-abnormal growth. Address: Fels Division, Pediatric Research, Cincinnati General Hospital, Cincinnati, OH 45229.

FALKOW, STANLEY, b. Albany, N.Y, Jan. 24, 34; m. 58; c. 2. MICROBIOLOGY. B.S, Maine, 55; Nat. Cancer Inst. fel. & M.S, Brown, 59, Nat. Cancer Inst. fel. & Ph.D.(biol), 60. Chief, dept. bact, Newport Hosp, R.I, 56-58; res. microbiologist, Walter Reed Army Inst. Res, 60-66; assoc. prof. MICROBIOL, SCHS. MED. & DENT, GEORGETOWN UNIV, 66-70, PROF, 70- Soc. Am. Bact. president's fel, 60-61; mem. comn. enteric infections, Armed Forces Epidemiol. Bd. AAAS; Am. Soc. Microbiol; Genetics Soc. Am; Am. Inst. Biol. Sci; affiliate Royal Soc. Med. Microbial genetics; molecular biology. Address: Dept. of Microbiology, Georgetown University School of Medicine, 3900 Reservoir Rd. N.W, Washington, DC 20007.

FALL, HARRY H, b. Lucenec, Czech, Dec. 8, 20; nat; m. 47; c. 3. PHYSICAL ORGANIC CHEMISTRY. B.S, Pa. State Col, 42, Am. Petrol. Inst. fel, 48-50, Ph.D.(chem), 50. Res. chemist, Sylvania Indust. Corp, 42-44; SR. RES. CHEMIST, Upjohn Co, 51-56; Mobay Chem. Co, 56-57; Gen. Tire & Rubber Co, 57-64; GOODYEAR TIRE & RUBBER CO, 64- U.S.A, 44-46, 1st Lt. AAAS; Am. Chem. Soc; fel. Am. Inst. Chem; N.Y. Acad. Sci. Cellulose ethers; cellophane coatings; origin of petroleum; pterine chemistry; chemotherapy of experimental neoplastic diseases; kinetics of polyether glycol formation and polymerization; synthesis of novel epoxides; block and graft polymers. Address: 3959 Cardinal Rd, Akron, OH 44313.

FALLDING, MARGARET HURLSTONE HARDY, Biol, Histol, see HARDY FALLDING, MARGARET HURLSTONE.

FALLER, ALAN J(UDSON), b. Boston, Mass, Mar. 4, 29; m. 51; c. 4. METEOROLOGY. S.B, Mass. Inst. Tech, 51, M.S, 53, Sc.D.(meteorol), 57. Asst, Mass. Inst. Tech, 51-54; res. assoc, Oceanog. Inst, Woods Hole, 54-57; Chicago, 57-58; Oceanog. Inst, Woods Hole, 58-63; res. assoc. prof, INST. FLUID DYNAMICS & APPL. MATH, UNIV. MD, COLLEGE PARK, 63-66, RES. PROF, 66- Guggenheim fel, 60-61. AAAS; Am. Meteorol. Soc; Am. Geophys. Union; Am. Phys. Soc; Am. Soc. Oceanog. Hydrodynamic model experiments applied to the circulations of the oceans and the atmosphere. Address: Institute for Fluid Dynamics & Applied Mathematics, University of Maryland, College Park, MD 20782.

FALLER, JAMES E, b. Mishawaka, Ind, Jan. 17, 34; m. 59; c. 2. PHYSICS, ASTROPHYSICS. A.B, Indiana, 55; M.A, Princeton, 57, Ph.D.(physics), 63. Instr. physics, Princeton, 59-62; Nat. Res. Coun. fel, joint inst. for lab. astrophys, Nat. Bur. Standards, 63-64, physicist, 64-66; asst. prof. PHYSICS, WESLEYAN UNIV, 66-68, assoc. prof, 68-71, PROF, 71- Mem. comt. on fundamental constants, Nat. Acad. Sci-Nat. Res. Coun, 71- Arnold O. Beckman Award, Instrument Soc. Am, 70. AAAS; Am. Phys. Soc; Optical Soc. Am; Am. Asn. Physics Teachers; Am. Geophys. Union. Precision experiments; atomic physics; physical optics; gravitation; fundamental constants and invariants; geophysics; experimental relativity. Address: Dept. of Physics, Wesleyan University, Middletown, CT 06457.

FALLER, JOHN WILLIAM, b. Louisville, Ky, Jan. 7, 42. INORGANIC & ORGANOMETALLIC CHEMISTRY. B.S, Louisville, 63, M.S, 64; Ph.D. (inorg. & phys. chem), Mass. Inst. Tech, 67. Asst. prof. CHEM, YALE, 67-71, ASSOC. PROF, 71- Petrol. Res. Fund grant, 67-69; A.P. Sloan fel, 70-72. Am. Chem. Soc; Brit. Chem. Soc. Synthesis and elucidation of structure and bonding of inorganic and organometallic compounds; stereospecific synthesis using transition metal complexes; mechanisms of catalysis; intramolecular rearrangement mechanisms of organometallics. Address: Dept. of Chemistry, Yale University, New Haven, CT 06520.

FALLER, LARRY D(EAN), b. Mishawaka, Ind, Oct. 20, 36; m. 64; c. 1. BIOPHYSICAL CHEMISTRY. A.B, Wabash Col, 58; M.S, Yale, 59, Woodrow Wilson, Danforth & Nat. Insts. Health fels, 63, Ph.D.(phys. chem), 64. Nat. Insts. Health fel. phys. chem, Max Planck Inst. Phys. Chem, 64-66; ASST. PROF. CHEM, WESLEYAN UNIV, 66- AAAS; Am. Chem. Soc. Kinetics of enzyme action, particularly the application of relaxation methods to the study of fast steps in enzyme catalyses; application of relaxation and stopped-flow methods. Address: 029 Hall-Atwater Lab, Wesleyan University, Middletown CT 06457.

FALLGATTER, MICHAEL, b. Chicago, Ill, Jan. 6, 36. PHYSICAL CHEMISTRY. B.S, Lawrence, 57; Nat. Sci. Found. fel. & Ph.D.(chem), Northwestern, 63. Asst. prof. CHEM, Dana Col, 60-62; res. assoc, Florida, 63-65; ASST. PROF, CARROLL COL.(WIS), 65- Am. Chem. Soc. Radiation chemistry of polymers and organic solutions; mass spectrometry. Address: Dept. of Chemistry, Carroll College, Waukesha, WI 53186.

FALLIERS, CONSTANTINE J, b. Athens, Greece, Dec. 10, 24; nat; m. 53; c. 4. ALLERGY, PEDIATRICS. M.D, Nat. Univ. Athens, 51. Intern, Evangelismos Hosp, Athens, Greece, 51; Fulbright fel. basic med. sci. & clin. pediat, med. center, Colorado, 51-53, res, 52-53; pediat, Calif. Babies & Children's Hosp, Los Angeles, 53-54; Kaiser Found. Hosp, Oakland, 54-55; mem. Permanente Med. Group, Walnut Creek, Calif, 55-57; fel. pediat. allergy & clin. res, Jewish Nat. Home Asthmatic Children & CHILDREN'S ASTHEMA RES. INST. & HOSP, 57-59, dir. clin. serv, 59-63, med. dir, 63-69, HEAD CLIN. RES, 69- ASST. CLIN. PROF. PEDIAT, MED. CTR, UNIV. COLO, DENVER, 64-, instr, 61-64. Co-investr, U.S. Pub. Health Serv. grants, 62-68, res. support grant, 64; co-investr, Fleischman Found. grant, 64-65. Mem. courtesy staff, Children's Hosp, Denver, Colo, 63- Dipl, Am. Bd. Pediat, 58, cert. pediat. allergy, 65. Am. Med. Asn; Am. Acad. Pediat; Am. Acad. Allergy; Am. Col. Allergists; Am. Psychosom. Soc; Soc. Biol. Rhythm; Soc. Exp. Biol. & Med; N.Y. Acad. Sci. Longitudinal study of asthma; growth and development, especially in relation to allergy and immunology; metabolic and endocrine aspects of allergic disease and therapy; clinical pharmacology; cybernetics and information theory as applied to biology and medicine. Address: Children's Asthma Research Institute, 3401 W. 19th Ave, Denver, CO 80204.

FALLIS, ALBERT MURRAY, b. Wellington Co, Ont, Jan. 2, 07; m. 38; c. 3. PARASITOLOGY. B.A, Toronto, 32, Ph.D.(parasitol), 37, F.R.S.C, 58. Asst. biol, UNIV. TORONTO, 31-32, demonstr. PARASITOL, sch. hyg, 37-43, lectr, 42-45, assoc. prof, 45-48, PROF, 48-, HEAD DEPT, 66-, assoc. dean, sch. grad. studies, 67-70; CONSULT, ONT. RES. FOUND, 66-, dir. parasitol, 47-66, res. fel, 32-47. Chmn. adv. comn. entom. res, Defense

Res. Bd, 69-70. Am. Soc. Parasitol. (v.pres, 69-70); Entom. Soc. Am; Entom. Soc. Can; Royal Can. Inst. (hon. ed, 49-54, pres, 55-56); Can. Soc. Zool; Soc. Protozool; Am. Soc. Trop. Med. & Hyg. Animal parasites; protozoa; helminths; insects. Address: Dept. of Parasitology, School of Hygiene, University of Toronto, Toronto 181, Ont, Can.

FALLIS, A(LEXANDER) G(RAHAM), b. Toronto, Ont, Aug. 20, 40; m. 67; c. 2. ORGANIC CHEMISTRY. B.Sc, Univ. Toronto, 63, Prov. Ont. fel, 63-67, M.A, 64, Ph.D. (org. chem), 67. Nat. Res. Coun. Can. fel, Oxford, 67-69; ASST. PROF. ORG. CHEM, MEM. UNIV. NEWF, 69- Nat. Res. Coun. Can. res. grants, 69- Am. Chem. Soc; Chem. Inst. Can; The Chem. Soc. Structural and synthetic organic chemistry with emphasis on photochemistry; insect attractants; reactions of bridged ring carbonyl compounds. Address: Dept. of Chemistry, Memorial University of Newfoundland, St. Johns, Newf, Can.

FALLON, DANIEL, b. Cartagena, Colombia, Aug. 24, 38; U.S. citizen; m. 64; c. 1. EXPERIMENTAL PSYCHOLOGY. A.B, Antioch Col, 61; Nat. Defense Ed. Act fel, Virginia, 61-64, M.A, 63, Du Pont fel, 64-65, Ph.D. (exp. psychol), 65. ASST. PROF. PSYCHOL, STATE UNIV. N.Y. BINGHAMTON, 65-, ASST. DEAN, HARPUR COL, 69- Nat. Inst. Ment. Health grant, 66-67; Nat. Inst. Child Health Human Develop. grant, 67-70. AAAS; Am. Psychol. Asn; Psychonomic Soc. Motivation; punishment; reinforcement theory. Address: Dept. of Psychology, State University of New York at Binghamton, Binghamton, NY 13901.

FALLON, HAROLD JOSEPH, b. N.Y.C, Aug. 13, 31; m. 55; c. 4. PHARMACOLOGY. B.A, Yale, 53, M.D, 57. Instr. internal med, North Carolina, 61-62; fel. liver disease, Yale, 62-63; Nat. Insts. Health spec. fel. biochem, Duke, 63-64; asst. prof. internal med, UNIV. N.C, CHAPEL HILL, 64-67, assoc. prof, 67-70, PROF. MED. & PHARMACOL, 70- Consult, metabolism study sect, U.S. Pub. Health Serv. Sinsheimer Fund award, 65-70; Burroughs-Wellcome Scholar, 70. Dipl, Am. Bd. Internal Med, 65. U.S.P.H.S, 59-61, Surgeon. AAAS; Am. Fedn. Clin. Res; Am. Med. Asn; Am. Soc. Clin. Invest; Am. Soc. Pharmacol. & Exp. Therapeut; Am. Oil Chem. Soc; Asn. Am. Physicians. Pyrimidine metabolism in man; regulation of metabolic pathways; lipid biosynthesis; serine metabolism; alcohol metabolism; gastroenterology. Address: Dept. of Medicine, School of Medicine, University of North Carolina, Chapel Hill, NC 27514.

FALLON, LESLIE D(ODDS), b. Plattekill, N.Y, Feb. 1, 16; m. 42; c. 4. PHYSICAL CHEMISTRY. B.S, Geneva Col, 36; Ph.D. (phys. chem), Yale, 39; Pittsburgh, 44-46. Asst. prof. chem, Geneva Col, 39-42, prof, 42-44; indust. fel, Mellon Inst, 44-46; prof. PHYSICS, Geneva Col, 46-61; ASSOC. PROF, N.MEX. INST. MINING & TECHNOL, 61- AAAS; Am. Asn. Physics Teachers. Electrolytes of solution; adhesives; ionization of water; water-dioxane mixtures; atomic physics. Address: 726 Bagley St, Socorro, NM 87801.

FALLON, JOSEPH G(REENLEAF), b. Los Angeles, Calif, Oct. 2, 11; m. 34; c. 3. PUBLIC HEALTH. B.A, Pacific Union Col, 38; M.P.H, Mass. Inst. Technol, 44. Asst. prof. biol, PACIFIC UNION COL, 38-42, ASSOC. PROF, biol. & health, 44-45, biol, nursing & health, 47-55, biol, 55-57, BIOL. & HEALTH, 57-, vis. prof, exten, Honolulu, 50. Instr, sch. med, Loma Linda Univ. Regional sanit. engr. UN Relief & Rehab. Admin, China, 46. AAAS; Am. Soc. Microbiol; Am. Soc. Parasitol; fel. Am. Pub. Health Asn; fel. Royal Soc. Health; fel. Royal Soc. Trop. Med. & Hyg; fel. Am. Sch. Health Asn; Int. Union Health Educ; Int. Cong. Trop. Med. & Malaria. Pollution studies on rivers; health surveys. Address: Dept. of Biology, Pacific Union College, Angwin, CA 94508.

FALLON, ROBERT J(OSEPH), b. Brooklyn, N.Y, Apr. 11, 32; m. 61; c. 3. PHYSICAL CHEMISTRY. B.A, Catholic Univ, 53, M.S, 55, Ph.D, 59. Res. assoc, Maryland, 58-60, asst. prof. phys. chem, 60-62; sr. scientist, Melpar, Inc, 62-68; mem. consult. staff, ADVAN. MAT. CONCEPTS AGENCY, U.S. ARMY, 68-70, CHIEF, APPL. SCI. DIV, 70- Lectr, Cath. Univ, summer, 55; chemist, Nat. Bur. Standards, 56-57. Am. Chem. Soc; Am. Phys. Soc. Chemical kinetics and molecular spectroscopy. Address: U.S. Army Advanced Materiel Concepts Agency, 2461 Eisenhower Ave, Alexandria, VA 22314.

FALLS, EUGENE K(ELTY), b. Columbus, Ohio, July 20, 09; m. 41; c. 3. MECHANICAL ENGINEERING. M.E, Akron, 32; M.Sc, Ohio State, 38, fel, 40-41, Ph.D. (mech. eng), 41. Engr, Goodyear Tire & Rubber Co, Ohio, 28-36; mech. engr, Aluminum Co. Am, 36-37; test engr, Nat. Bd. Boiler & Pressure Vessel Inspectors, 38-41; instr. & asst. prof, mech. eng, Clarkson Tech, 41-44; asst. prof, Rochester, 44-46; sr. res. thermodynamicist, Cornell Aeronaut. Lab, N.Y, 46-47; assoc. prof, mech. eng, Ill. Inst. Tech, 47-49; assoc. mech. engr, Argonne Nat. Lab, Ill, 48-53; tech. supvr. & res. assoc, Mueller Brass Co, 53-55; CONSULT. ENGR, PRESSURE RELIEF SYSTEMS & COMPONENTS, 55- Lab. asst, Ohio State, 38-40. Consult. & develop. engr, Manning, Maxwell & Moore, Inc, Conn, 41-52. Am. Soc. Mech. Eng; Am. Soc. Eng. Educ; Sci. Res. Soc. Am; Nat. Soc. Prof. Eng. Fluid flow in safety valves; design of maximum capacity safety valves; capacities of water relief valves; development of flow theory and design of blowdown type wind tunnel; nuclear fission engineering calculations. Address: 4445 N. River Rd, Port Huron, MI 48060.

FALLS, HAROLD F(RANCIS), b. Winchester, Ind, Nov. 26, 09; m. 42; c. 3. OPHTHALMOLOGY, GENETICS. M.D, Univ. Mich, 36, M.S, 39. Assoc. prof. OPHTHAL, UNIV. MICH, 47-60, PROF, 60-, ASSOC. GENETICIST, INST. HUMAN BIOL, UNIV, 46- Am. Ophthal. Soc; Am. Soc. Human Genetics; Genetics Soc. Am; Am. Acad. Ophthal. & Otolaryngol; Am. Asn. Ophthal; Pan-Am. Asn. Ophthal. Human genetics. Address: 1525 Harding Rd, Ann Arbor, MI 48104.

FALLS, J(AMES) BRUCE, b. Toronto, Ont, Dec. 18, 23; m. 52; c. 3. ECOLOGY. B.A, Toronto, 48, Ph.D. (zool), 53. Lectr. zool, Toronto, 52-53; Nat. Res. Coun. Can. Overseas fel, 53-54; lectr, ZOOL, UNIV. TORONTO, 54-58, asst. prof, 58-61; assoc. prof, 61-66, PROF, 66- Royal Soc. & Nuffield Found. Commonwealth bursary, 64. R.C.A.F, 43-45. Am. Ornith. Union; Am. Soc. Mammal; Ecol. Soc. Am; Wilson Ornith. Soc; Can. Soc. Fishery & Wildlife Biol; Can. Soc. Zool. Bioacoustics, bird song and territorial behavior, populations distribution, behavior and activity of mammals. Address: Dept. of Zoology, University of Toronto, Toronto 5, Ont, Can.

FALLS, WILLIAM RANDOLPH, SR, b. Ironton, Ohio, Sept. 15, 29; m. 56; c. 3. SCIENCE EDUCATION, PHYSICS. B.S, Rio Grande Col, 53; Nat. Sci. Found. fel. & M.A, Marshall Univ, 59; Nat. Sci. Found. fel, Univ. Okla, 61, Oak Ridge Inst. Nuclear Studies, 62; Ed.D. (sci. educ), Ind. Univ, Bloomington, 70. ASSOC. PROF. PHYSICS & HEAD DEPT. SCI. EDUC, MOREHEAD STATE UNIV, 61- Atomic Energy Comn. res. grant & resident physicist, 65- U.S.A, 53-55, Sgt. AAAS; Nat. Sci. Teachers Asn; Am. Asn. Physics Teachers. Trace elements present in post oak trees as revealed through activation analysis; intense gamma field's effects on metals. Address: Dept. of Science Education, Lappin Hall, Morehead State University, Morehead, KY 40351.

FALLSCHEER, HERMAN O, b. Ogden, Utah, Apr. 16, 11; m. 42; c. 2. AGRICULTURAL & FOOD CHEMISTRY. B.S, State Col. Wash, 33, M.S, 35. Chemist, Yakima Indust. Lab, 35-36; exp. sta, State Col. Wash, 36-37, tree fruit br. exp. sta, 38-42; asst. state chemist, State of Wash, 37-38; chemist, U.S. FOOD & DRUG ADMIN, 42-59, SUPVRY. CHEMIST, 59- Am. Chem. Soc. Methods of development and studies on pesticide residues. Address: 7441 Henefer, Los Angeles, CA 90045.

FALLWELL, ERNEST L(YNWOOD), b. Farmville, Va, Mar. 13, 24; m. 52; c. 2. CHEMICAL ENGINEERING. B.Ch.E, N.C. State Col, 48. Engr, ammonia & polychem. dept, E.I. DU PONT DE NEMOURS & CO, INC, 48-59, res. engr, film dept, 59-60, staff engr, 60-63, SR. RES. ENGR, TEXTILE FIBERS DEPT, 63- U.S.A.A.F, 43-46, S/Sgt. Am. Inst. Chem. Eng. Process development of nylon intermediates; polyolefin resins and films; nylon fibers. Address: P.O. Box 71, Chattanooga, TN 37401.

FALLWELL, W(ILLIAM) FRANKLIN, JR, b. Farmville, Va, Aug. 7, 13; m. 39; c. 4. ORGANIC CHEMISTRY. B.S, Hamden-Sydney Col, 34; fel, Mass. Inst. Tech, 36-37, Ph.D. (org. chem), 38. RES. CHEMIST, Simplex Wire & Cable Co, 38-45; Dewey & Almy Chem. Co, 45-60; MONSANTO CO, 60- Am. Chem. Soc. Emulsion and mass copolymerization; ester and polyester synthesis and production; plasticizers; synthetic resin and rubber development for electrical insulation; organic synthesis of chemicals and resins; condensation by sodium. Address: Monsanto Co, 800 N. Lindbergh Blvd, St. Louis, MO 63166.

FALOON, WILLIAM W(ASSELL), b. Pittsburgh, Pa, July 6, 20; m. 48; c. 3. GASTROENTEROLOGY. A.B, Allegheny Col, 41; M.D, Harvard, 44. Intern, Pa. Hosp, Phila, 44-45; asst. res. med, Albany Hosp, N.Y, 45-46, res, 46-47; res. fel, Thorndike Mem. Lab, Harvard Med. Sch. & Boston City Hosp, 47-48; asst. prof. oncol. & instr. med, Albany Med. Col, 48-50; instr. MED. State Univ. N.Y. Upstate Med. Ctr, 50-51, assoc. prof, 56-64, prof, 64-68; physician-in-chief, Cottage & Gen. Hosp, Santa Barbara, Calif, 68-69; PROF. SCH. MED. & DENT, UNIV. ROCHESTER, 69-; CHIEF OF MED, HIGHLAND HOSP, N.Y, 70- Consult, adv. comt, Surgeon Gen. Dipl, Am. Bd. Internal Med. AAAS; fel. Am. Col. Physicians; Am. Gastroenterol. Asn; Endocrine Soc; Am. Fedn. Clin. Res; Am. Asn. Study Liver Disease; Am. Soc. Clin. Nutrit; Int. Soc. Study Liver Disease. Gastroenterology; nutrition; metabolic disease. Address: Highland Hospital, South Ave. at Bellevue, Rochester, NY 14620.

FALSONE, JACK J(OSEPH), b. Queens, N.Y, Nov. 6, 23; m. 45; c. 2. MEDICINE. A.B, Columbia Col. (N.Y), 44; M.D, L.I. Col. Med, 47. Instr. med, sch. med, Yale, 55-61, asst. clin. prof, 61-69; private practice, 53- Asst. attend. physician, Norwalk Hosp, 54-61, attend. physician, 61-; out-patient dept, Yale-New Haven Community Hosp, 55-69. U.S.A, 43-46, Med.C, 51-53, Capt. Am. Med. Asn; Am. Col. Physicians. Diseases of the chest. Address: 147 East Ave, Norwalk, CT 06851.

FALTER, JOHN MAX, b. West Bend, Wis, Dec. 13, 30; m. 59; c. 3. ENTOMOLOGY. B.S, Wisconsin, 52, M.S, 59, Ph.D. (entom), 64. Instr. ENTOM, Wisconsin, 61-64; asst. prof, N.C. STATE UNIV, 64-67, ASSOC. PROF, 67- U.S.N, 52-55, Lt. (jg). Entom. Soc. Am. Economic entomology; biology and control of economic pests. Address: Dept. of Entomology, North Carolina State University, Gardner Hall, Raleigh, NC 27607.

FALUDI, GEORGINA, b. Budapest, Hungary, Mar. 2, 27; nat; m. 57; c. 2. MEDICINE, ENDOCRINOLOGY. M.D, Budapest, 51. Instr. physiol, sch. med, Budapest, 47-50, med, 52-55, asst. prof, 56-57; res. fel. nutrit, Inst. Nutrit. Sci, 50-51; trainee, Nat. Inst. Arthritis & Metab. Diseases, 59-60; res. instr, HAHNEMANN MED. COL. & HOSP, 60-62, ASSOC. MED, 62-, ATTEND, 60-, DIR. DIABETIC & OBESITY CLINS, 61-, ASST. PROF, 66- Rockefeller Found. grant, sch. med, Vienna, 57. Am. Med. Asn; Am. Col. Physicians; Am. Diabetes Asn; Am. Fedn. Clin. Res; N.Y. Acad. Sci. Etiology, pathogenesis and therapy of diabetes mellitus and obesity; connections between obesity and diabetes; mechanism of action of oral hypoglycemic agents; side effects of steroids; functional hypoglycemia; early latent diabetes and prediabetes. Address: Dept. of Medicine, Hahnemann Medical College, 230 N. Broad St, Philadelphia, PA 19102.

FALVEY, FRANCES E(LIZABETH), b. Longview, Tex, Apr. 30, 14. MATHEMATICS. B.A. & B.M, Southern Methodist, 36, M.A, 37; Ed.D, Columbia, 49. Asst. instr. math, Southern Methodist, 36-37; head dept, Ward-Belmont Jr. Col, 38-44; freshman dean & instr. ed, Hollins Col, 44-46; asst. prof. math, Millikin, 48-49, assoc. prof, 49-59, dean of women, 48-59, dir. student affairs, 51-59; dean, Milwaukee-Downer Col, 59-64; HEADMISTRESS, SEVEN HILLS SCH, 65- AAAS; Am. Math. Soc; Math. Asn. Am. Statistics; finance; personnel. Address: Seven Hills School, Lynchburg, VA 24503.

FALXA, MARTIN LOUIS, b. Buffalo, Wyo, Aug. 4, 39; m. 65. POLYMER CHEMISTRY. B.S. & Thom fel, Mass. Inst. Tech, 61, Am. Cyanamid fel. & M.S, 62; univ. fel. & Ph.D. (polymer chem), Polytech. Inst. Brooklyn, 65. Nat. Insts. Health res. fel. path, Harvard Med. Sch, 66-69; group leader biomed. polymers, Theodore Clark Lab, Kendall Co, 69-70; PROJ. MGR. INSTANT COLOR FILM, POLAROID CORP, 70- AAAS; Am. Chem. Soc; N.Y. Acad. Sci. Improvement of photographic, chemical, physical and coating properties of new Polacolor films; development of dyes, silvers and polymers for instant color photographic products. Address: Polaroid Corp, Bldg. 4, 1265 Main St, Waltham, MA 02154.

FAMILANT, HAROLD M(ELVIN), b. Suffolk, Va, Apr. 26, 41; m. 69; c. 1. PHYSICS. B.S, Univ. Va, 62, M.S, 64, Ph.D.(physics), 66. Polymer scientist, E.I. du Pont de Nemours & Co, Inc, 66-68; fiber physicist, Dow Badische Co, 68-69; RES. SPECIALIST, MONSANTO CO, 69- Am. Chem. Soc. Physical, rheological, and structural property characterization of man-made polymeric fibers; fundamental investigations of commercial fiber processing systems. Address: Monsanto Co, Bldg. 750, P.O. Box 1507, Room P 257, Pensacola, FL 32502.

FAMULARO, KENDALL (FERRIS), b. Pasadena, Calif, June 8, 28. NUCLEAR PHYSICS. B.S, Calif. Inst. Tech, 49; Ph.D.(physics), Rice Inst, 53. RES. ASSOC. PHYSICS, Minnesota, 52-57; LOS ALAMOS SCI. LAB, 57- Am. Phys. Soc. Nuclear reactions. Address: P.O. Box 1663, Los Alamos, NM 87544.

FAN, CHANG-YUN, b. China, Jan. 7, 18; U.S. citizen; m. 50; c. 3. NUCLEAR PHYSICS. B.S, Cent. Univ, China, 41; M.S, Chicago, 50, Ph.D.(physics), 52. Asst. nuclear physics, Chicago, 48-51, res. assoc. astrophysics, 52-57; asst. prof. physics, Arkansas, 57-58; sr. physicist, appl. scis. labs, Univ. Chicago, 58-67, assoc, Enrico Fermi Inst. Nuclear Studies, 58-67; PROF. PHYSICS, UNIV. ARIZ, 67- Atomic and nuclear reactions related to astronomical phenomena; origin of cosmic radiations. Address: Dept. of Physics, University of Arizona, Tucson, AZ 85721.

FAN, CHIEN, b. Kiang-Su, China, Apr. 1, 30; m. 58; c. 3. ENGINEERING SCIENCE, MECHANICAL ENGINEERING. B.S, Taiwan, 54; M.S, Illinois, 58, Ph.D.(mech. eng), 64. Asst. prof. eng. sci, Fla. State Univ, 61-65; RES. SPECIALIST, LOCKHEED MISSILES & SPACE CO, ALA, 65- Am. Inst. Aeronaut. & Astronaut. Gas dynamics; heat transfer. Address: Lockheed Missiles & Space Co, Huntsville, AL 35807.

FAN, DAVID P, b. Hong Kong, Jan. 18, 42; U.S. citizen; m. 69; c. 2. BIOLOGY. B.S, Purdue Univ, 61; Ph.D.(biol), Mass. Inst. Technol, 65. Fels, Med. Res. Coun. Lab. Molecular Biol, Eng, 65-67, Univ. Geneva, 67-69; ASST. PROF. GENETICS & CELL BIOL, UNIV. MINN, ST. PAUL, 69- Am. Soc. Microbiol. Bacterial cell envelope growth as related to growth and division. Address: Dept. of Genetics & Cell Biology, University of Minnesota, St. Paul, MN 55101.

FAN, DER-FONG, b. Taiwan, Feb. 27, 40; m. 65; c. 3. PLANT BIOCHEMISTRY, SOIL SCIENCE. B.S, Taiwan, 62; Ph.D.(bot), McGill, 67. Res. asst. biochem, Dept. Agr. Chem, Taiwan, 63-64; RES. ASSOC. MICROBIOL, UNIV. PITTSBURGH, 68- Am. Soc. Plant Physiol. Plant hormone; sugar nucleotide metabolism; enzymology; protein and carbohydrate chemistry. Address: Dept. of Microbiology, University of Pittsburgh, Pittsburgh, PA 15213.

FAN, HSING Y(UN), b. Changsha, Hunan, China, Apr. 27, 14; m. 47; c. 1. AGRICULTURAL BIOCHEMISTRY. B.S, Nat. Tsing Hua, 35; Ph.D.(agr. biochem), Minnesota, 45. Asst, Nat. Tsing Hua, 35-40; Chinese Found. res. fel. insect physiol, Minnesota, 45-46, res. assoc, 48; res. chemist, Julius Hyman & Co, 48-52; SR. RES. CHEMIST, SHELL DEVELOP. CO, 53- With Office Sci. Res. & Develop; U.S.A, 44. Am. Chem. Soc. Organic analysis; vitamins; pesticides; permeability of insect cuticle. Address: 1933 La Villa Rose Ct, Modesto, CA 95350.

FAN, JOYCE W(ANG), b. China, Oct. 2, 19; nat; m. 43; c. 2. ORGANIC CHEMISTRY. B.S, Wheaton Col, 42; M.S, Iowa, 44, Ph.D.(chem), 46. Fel, Northwestern, 46-47; lectr. CHEM, Southern California, 47-48; asst. prof, Houston, 50-56, assoc. prof, 56-64; PROF, HOUSTON BAPTIST COL, 64-, HEAD DEPT, 67- Am. Chem. Soc; fel. Am. Inst. Chem. Polarography as applied to organic compounds. Address: Dept. of Chemistry, Houston Baptist College, 7502 Fondren, Houston, TX 77036.

FAN, H(SU) Y(UN), b. Shanghai, China, June 4, 12; nat; m. 41; c. 4. PHYSICS. M.S, Mass. Inst. Technol, 34, Sc.D, 37. Assoc. prof, Nat. Tsing Hua Univ, China, 37-39, prof, 39-47; mem. staff, Electron. Res. Lab, Mass. Inst. Tech, 48; vis. prof. PHYSICS, PURDUE UNIV, 48-49, assoc. prof, 49-51, prof, 51-63, DUNCAN DISTINGUISHED PROF, 63- Past mem. various comts. & panels, Nat. Acad. Sci-Nat. Sci. Found; cor. mem, semiconductor comn, Int. Union Pure & Appl. Physics. Am. Phys. Soc. Solid state physics; semiconductors. Address: Dept. of Physics, Purdue University, Lafayette, IN 47907.

FAN, KY, b. Hangchow, China, Sept. 19, 14; nat; m. 36. MATHEMATICS. B.S, Peking, 36; D.Sc.(math), Paris, 41. French Nat. Sci. fel, Paris & Inst. Henri Poincare, 42-45; mem, Inst. Adv. Study, 45-47; asst. prof. MATH, Notre Dame, 47-49, assoc. prof, 49-52, PROF, 52-60; Wayne State, 60-61; Northwest. Univ, 61-65; UNIV. CALIF, SANTA BARBARA, 65- Am. Math. Soc; Math. Asn. Am. Functional analysis; topology. Address: Dept. of Mathematics, University of California, Santa Barbara, CA 93106.

FAN, LIANG-TSENG, b. Taiwan, China, Aug. 7, 29; nat; m. 58; c. 2. CHEMICAL ENGINEERING, MATHEMATICS. B.S, Taiwan, 51; M.S, Kansas State, 54; Ph.D.(chem. eng), West Virginia, 57, M.S.(math), 58. Jr. chem. engr, Taiwan Agr. Chem. Works, 51-52; asst. CHEM. ENG, Kansas State, 52-54; West Virginia, 54-58; instr, KANS. STATE UNIV, 58-59, asst. prof, 59-61, assoc. prof, 61-63, prof, 63-67, KANS. POWER & LIGHT DISTINGUISHED PROF, 67-, DIR. INST. SYSTS. DESIGN & OPTIMIZATION, 67-, HEAD DEPT. CHEM. ENG, 68- Phys. chemist, U.S. Bur. Mines, 56-58, chem. engr, 58-59; consult, Nat. Air Pollution Control Admin, 69- AAAS; Am. Chem. Soc; Am. Inst. Chem. Eng; Soc. Eng. Sci; Japanese Soc. Chem. Eng. Mass and heat transfer; fluidization; chemical process design; applied mathematics; optimization; chemical process dynamics; mathematical optimization technique; air and water pollution control; desalination. Address: Dept. of Chemical Engineering, Kansas State University, Manhattan, KS 66502.

FAN, PAUL H(SIU-TSU), b. Tsingtao, China, May 20, 17; m. 43; c. 2. GEOLOGY. B.S, Wheaton Col, 42; M.S, Iowa, 45, Ph.D.(geol), 47. Chemist, Atlas Powder Co, Mo, 42-43; asst, Iowa, 44-47; asst. prof. GEOL, UNIV. HOUSTON, 48-50, assoc. prof, 50-54, PROF, 54-, acting chmn. dept, 53-54, chmn, 54-61. Am. Asn. Petrol. Geol; Soc. Econ. Paleont. & Mineral; Geochem. Soc. Sedimentation; stratigraphy; geomorphology. Address: Dept. of Geology, University of Houston, Houston, TX 77035.

FAN, POW-FOONG, b. Palembang, Indonesia, Sept. 4, 33; m. 65. GEOLOGY. B.S, Wheaton Col.(Ill), 55; M.A, California, Los Angeles, 63, Ph.D.(geol), 65. Asst. geophysicist, INST. GEOPHYS, UNIV. HAWAII, 65-70, asst. prof, 66-70, ASSOC. GEOPHYSICIST, 70-, ASSOC. PROF. DEPT. GEOL. & GEOPHYS, 70-, asst. prof, 66-70. Geol. Soc. Am; Soc. Econ. Paleont. & Mineral. Mineralogy of sediments; sedimentation processes; marine geology, relation of gravity anomalies to geology of Asia; geology of Asia. Address: Institute of Geophysics, University of Hawaii, 2525 Correa Rd, Honolulu, HI 96822.

FAN, STEPHEN S(HU-TU), b. Shanghai, China, Jan. 2, 34; m. 59; c. 4. CHEMICAL ENGINEERING. B.S, Stanford, 57, M.S, 60, Am. Chem. Soc. Petrol. Res. Fund. fel. & Ph.D.(chem. eng), 62. Summer res. fel, Stanford, 62; asst. prof. CHEM. ENG, UNIV. N.H, 62-66, ASSOC. PROF, 66-, CHMN. DEPT, 71-, acting chmn. dept, 70-71. Am. Inst. Chem. Eng; Am. Soc. Eng. Educ. Properties and heat transfer in chemically reacting systems; adsorption of gases; flow through porous media; applied kinetics. Address: Dept. of Chemical Engineering, University of New Hampshire, Durham, NH 03824.

FANALE, DANTE THEODORE, b. Quecreek, Pa, Mar. 4, 18; m. 46; c. 3. ANALYTICAL CHEMISTRY. B.S, Pa. State, 40. Chemist, GULF RES. & DEVELOP. CO, 40-57, sect. supvr, 57-63, SR. PROJ. CHEMIST, 63- Am. Chem. Soc. Analytical research in petroleum industry. Address: Gulf Research & Development Co, P.O. Drawer 2038, Pittsburgh, PA 15230.

FANALE, FRASER P, b. Providence, R.I, May 27, 36. PLANETOLOGY. B.S, Upsala Col, 57; M.A, Columbia, 61, Ph.D.(geol), 64. Res. assoc. chem, Brookhaven Nat. Lab, 63-65; physics & geophys, CALIF. INST. TECHNOL, 65-66, SR. SCIENTIST, LUNAR & PLANETARY SCI, JET PROPULSION LAB, 66- Absolute dating of fossils; planetology; origin and evolution of planetary atmospheres, especially that of Mars. Address: Jet Propulsion Lab, California Institute of Technology, 4800 Oak Grove Dr, Pasadena, CA 91109.

FANALE, LOUISA P, b. Fall River, Mass; m; c. 2. ZOOLOGY, IMMUNOLOGY. Ph.B, Brown, 50; M.S, Rutgers, 59, Nat. Sci. Found. fel, 60-61, Ph.D, 67. Instr. BIOL, Fairleigh Dickinson Univ, 50-52; UPSALA COL, 52-59, asst. prof, 59-67, ASSOC. PROF, 67- Am. Soc. Microbiol; Am. Genetic Asn; Genetics Soc. Am. Relation of tyrosinase to melanotic masses in Drosophilia; erythrocyte receptor sites for influenza A virus; immunological comparison of the endotoxins of various gram negative bacteria. Address: Dept. of Biology, Upsala College, East Orange, NJ 07019.

FANCHER, LLEWELLYN (W), b. Merced, Calif, Mar. 30, 17; m. 42; c. 1. ORGANIC & AGRICULTURAL CHEMISTRY. A.B, California, Berkeley, 41. Observer, U.S. Steel Corp, 41-42; raw mat. inspector, 42-44; res. chemist, Ragooland-Broy Labs, 44-45; Multiphase, Inc, 45-52; group leader, STAUFFER CHEM. CO, 52-59, sect. leader, 59-64, res. assoc, 64-70, SR. RES. ASSOC, 70- AAAS; Am. Chem. Soc; fel. Am. Inst. Chem; N.Y. Acad. Sci. Industrial products and processes; new agricultural compounds such as pesticides, herbicides, fungicides and bactericides. Address: Stauffer Chemical Co, 1200 S. 47th St, Richmond, CA 94804.

FANCHER, OTIS E(ARL), b. McCool, Miss, Jan. 17, 16; m. 46. CHEMISTRY. B.S, Miss. State Col, 38; Ph.D.(org. chem), Northwestern, 42. Res. assoc, Nat. Defense Res. Cmt. contract, Northwestern, 42-45; res. chemist, G.D. Searle & Co, Ill, 45-46; asst. prof. chem, Miss. State Col, 46-47; head org. sect, Miles-Ames Res. Lab, 47-59, dir. chem. therapeut. res. lab, Miles Labs, Inc, 59-63, therapeut. res. labs, 63-66; V.PRES. & SCI. DIR, INDUST. BIOTEST. LABS, INC, 66- AAAS; Am. Chem. Soc; Am. Inst. Chem; N.Y. Acad. Sci; Soc. Toxicol. Synthesis of pharmacologically active organic compounds; toxicological studies. Address: Industrial Biotest Labs, Inc, 1810 Frontage Rd, Northbrook, IL 60062.

FANCHER, PAUL S(TRIMPLE), b. San Antonio, Tex, Jan. 5, 32; m. 54; c. 4. INSTRUMENTATION & ENGINEERING. B.S.E, Michigan, 53, M.S.E, 59, Instm.E, 64. Asst, UNIV. MICH, 57-59, res. assoc, 59-61, assoc. res. engr, 61-70, RES. ENGR, 70- Mem, Simulation Coun, Inc, 64- U.S.A, 53-56. Simulation of gas turbine engines and dynamical systems; optimal control theory; highway vehicle dynamics. Address: Highway Safety Research Institute, University of Michigan, Huron Parkway & Baxter Rd, Ann Arbor, MI 48105.

FAND, IRWIN, b. Paterson, N.J, Mar. 13, 28. BIOLOGY. A.B, Cornell, 49; M.S, N.Y. Univ, 52, Ph.D, 56. Instr. BIOL, ADELPHI UNIV, 56-58, asst. prof, 58-62, assoc. prof, 62-68, PROF, 68-; ASSOC. RES. SCIENTIST CYTOPHYSIOL, CREEDMOOR INST. PSYCHOBIOL. STUDIES, 56- Tissue Culture Asn; N.Y. Acad. Sci. Analysis of the behavior of mammalian somatic cells in vitro with special reference to the nervous system; neuropharmacology; cytoendocrinology; cytotoxicity. Address: Dept. of Biology, Adelphi University, Garden City, NY 11530.

FAND, RICHARD M, b. Poland, Aug. 13, 23; U.S. citizen. MECHANICAL ENGINEERING. B.S, Rensselaer Polytech, 46; M.S, Columbia, 49; Ph.D. (mech. eng), Cornell, 59. Mech. engr, U.S. Govt. 46-48; res. engr, Bendix Aviation Corp, 51; engr, Canadair, Ltd, 52; instr. mech. eng, Cornell, 52-55; res. engr, Mass. Inst. Technol, 55-61; sr. eng, scientist, Bolt Beranek & Newman, Inc, 61-66; PROF. MECH. ENG, UNIV. HAWAII, 66- U.S.N, 43-46, Lt.(jg). Am. Soc. Mech. Eng; Am. Soc. Eng. Educ. Influence of mechanical and acoustical vibrations on heat and mass transfer; boundary layer flow in gases and liquids; heat transfer; thermoelectric cooling. Address: Dept. of Mechanical Engineering, University of Hawaii, Honolulu, HI 96822.

FAND, SALLY B(OGOLUB), b. Chicago, Ill, Feb. 9, 27; m. 52; c. 2. MEDICINE, ENDOCRINOLOGY. A.B, Illinois, 46; M.S, Chicago, 48; M.D, 52. Intern, Billings Hosp, 52-53; Am. Cancer Soc. fel, Chicago, 53-55; med. off, Nat. Insts. Health, 55-58; sr. asst. res. med, N.C. Mem. Hosp, 58-59; instr. anat. & internal med, southwest. med. sch, Texas, 59-60; Am. Cancer Soc. exchange fel, Sweden & Eng, 60-61; clin. investr, Vet. Admin. Hosp, Dallas, Tex, 61-62; asst. prof. med. sch. med, State Univ. N.Y. Buffalo & chief spec. histochem, Vet. Admin. Hosp, Buffalo, 62-67; ASSOC. PROF. PATH, SCH. MED, WAYNE STATE UNIV. & CHIEF SECT. SPEC. HISTOCHEM, VET. ADMIN. HOSP, MICH, 67- Histochem. Soc; Endocrine Soc. Histochemistry; oncology, especially human pituitary glands. Address: Lab. Service, Veterans Administration Hospital, Allen Park, MI 48101.

FAND, THEODORE IRA, b. Brooklyn, N.Y, Dec. 1, 15; m. 41; c. 3. ORGANIC & PHARMACEUTICAL CHEMISTRY. B.S, Brooklyn Col, 35; M.S, Michigan, 36; Ph.D.(chem), Polytech. Inst. Brooklyn, 54. Jr. chemist, anal, Veterans Admin, 36-38; asst. chemist, Bd. Transportation, N.Y, 38-42; asst. dir, develop. & eng, Nepera Chem. Co, Inc, 42-57; DIR. prod. develop, WARNER LAMBERT RES. INST, 57-62, PHARMACEUT. RES. & DEVELOP, 62- AAAS; Am. Chem. Soc; Am. Pharmaceut. Asn; Soc. Cosmetic Chem; N.Y. Acad. Sci. Pharmaceutical research and development; new dosage forms; drug absorption; pharmaceutical technology; pyridine chemistry; heterocycles and vitamins. Address: Warner Lambert Research Institute, 170 Tabor Rd, Morris Plains, NJ 07950.

FANELLI, GEORGE M(ARION), JR, b. Pelham, N.Y, Oct. 5, 26; m. 49; c. 4. PHARMACOLOGY. B.S, George Washington, 50; M.S, N.Y. Univ, 57, Ph.D. (biol), 62. Biologist, Hazleton Labs, Inc, 51-52; pharmacologist, Chas. Pfizer & Co, Inc, 52-58; res. scientist, Lederle Labs. Div, Am. Cyanamid Co, 58-63; U.S. Pub. Health Serv. res. fel. physiol, Harvard Med. Sch, 63-65; RES. FEL. PHARMACOL, MERCK SHARP & DOHME RES. LABS, 65- Summer fel, Mt. Desert Island Biol. Lab, 63. U.S.A.A.F, 44-46. Int. Primatol. Soc; Brit. Primate Soc. Comparative renal physiology; mechanisms of excretion of nitrogeneous products; effects of drugs on renal transport processes; organic acid transport in nonhuman primates; chimpanzee renal function; pharmacology of diuretics. Address: Merck Sharp & Dohme Research Labs, West Point, PA 19486.

FANESTIL, DARRELL D(EAN), b. Great Bend, Kans, Oct. 31, 33; m. 55; c. 4. INTERNAL MEDICINE, PHYSIOLOGY. B.A, Kansas, 55, M.D, 58. Intern internal med, Los Angeles County Gen. Hosp, 58-59; res, Lahey Clin, 59-60; trainee cardiol, Scripps Clin. & Res. Found, 60-61, U.S. Pub. Health Serv. res. fel. biochem, 61-62; Am. Heart Asn. adv. res. fel. nephrology, Univ. California Med. Center, San Francisco, 64-66; asst. prof. INTERNAL MED, SCH. MED, Univ. Kans, 66-68, ASSOC. PROF, 68-70; UNIV. CALIF, SAN DIEGO, 70- Am. Heart Asn. estab. investr, 66-71; Markle scholar acad. med, 66-71. U.S.P.H.S, 62-64, Lt. Comdr. AAAS; Am. Fedn. Clin. Res; Am. Physiol. Soc; Am. Soc. Nephrology; N.Y. Acad. Sci. Mechanism of action of aldosterone and hypertension; effects of carbon dioxide on ion transport; relationships between metabolism and ion transport. Address: Dept. of Internal Medicine, School of Medicine, University of California at San Diego, La Jolla, CA 92037.

FANG, CHENG-SHEN, b. Taipei, Taiwan, Mar. 29, 36. SPECTROSCOPY, HEAT TRANSFER. B.S, Nat. Taiwan Univ, 58; M.S. Univ. Houston, 65, Ph.D.(chem. eng), 68. Shift supvr, ammonia plant, factory 6, Taiwan Fertilizer Co, Ltd, 60-62; teaching asst. CHEM. ENG, Univ. Houston, 64-67, fel, 68-69; ASST. PROF, UNIV. SOUTHWEST. LA, 69- Taiwan Mil. Serv, 58-60, 2nd Lt. Am. Inst. Chem. Eng. High pressure infrared spectroscopy; infrared emission for remote sensing of gas species; radiative heat transfer. Address: Dept. of Chemical Engineering, University of Southwestern Louisiana, P.O. Box 4568, USL Station, Lafayette, LA 70501.

FANG, FABIAN T(IEN-HWA), b. Nanking, China, Oct. 14, 29; nat; m. 55; c. 1. ORGANIC CHEMISTRY. B.S, Nat. Cent. Univ, China, 49; M.S, Illinois, 52, Ph.D.(chem), 54. Res. assoc. chem, Notre Dame, 54-55; Iowa State, 55-57; sr. res. chemist, Rohm & Haas Co, 57-64; asst. prof. CHEM, Univ. Wis, Milwaukee, 64-69; vis. assoc, Calif. Inst. Technol, 70; ASSOC. PROF. & CHMN. DEPT, CALIF. STATE COL, BAKERSFIELD, 70- Am. Chem. Soc; Am. Inst. Chem; Catalysis Soc; Brit. Chem. Soc. Organic chemistry; macromolecular chemistry; heterogeneous catalysis. Address: Dept. of Chemistry, California State College, Bakersfield, CA 93309.

FANG, FRANK F, b. Peiping, China, Sept. 11, 30; m. 57; c. 3. ELECTRONICS. B.S, Taiwan, 52; M.S, Notre Dame, 54; Ph.D.(elec. eng), Illinois, 59. Assoc. phys. electronics, Illinois, 57-59; res. engr, Boeing Airplane Co, 59-60; RES. STAFF MEM, IBM CORP, 60- Inst. Elec. & Electronics Eng; Sci. Res. Soc. Am. Solid state science; semiconductor physics; solid state electronics. Address: Thomas J. Watson Research Center, IBM Corp, P.O. Box 218, Yorktown Heights, NY 10598.

FANG, GAUTIER TIEN-NI, b. Nanking, China, Feb. 2, 32; m. 62; c. 2. ELECTRICAL ENGINEERING, ELECTROPHYSICS. B.S, Nat. Taiwan Univ, 55; M.S, Univ. Minn, Minneapolis, 62, fel, 62-65, Ph.D.(elec. eng, physics), 66. Electronic engr, Chinese Civil Aeronaut. Admin, 55-59; instr. elec. eng, Univ. Minn, Minneapolis, 62-65, res. & faculty assoc, Air Force res. grant plasma electronics, 66-67; faculty assoc, Nat. Sci. Found. res. grant & asst. prof. ELECTRONICS, UNIV. HAWAII, 67-70, ASSOC. PROF, 70- Mem, Int. Cong. Acoust, 68 & 71; consult, Hawaii Lab, Naval Undersea Res. & Develop. Ctr, 69-70; prin. investr, Hawaii Elec. Co. res. grant, 70; prin. investr, Nat. Sci. Found. res. grant, 71- Am. Phys. Soc. Propagation of waves in random media with imperfect boundaries; coupling of energy and information among atmospheric-oceanic layers; conduction of charges in amorphous substances and applications; ultrasonics in medical diagnostics. Address: 65 Kaneohe Bay Dr, Kailua, Oahu, HI 96734.

FANG, JAMES C, b. Oct. 26, 22; U.S. citizen; m. 58; c. 3. ORGANIC CHEMISTRY. B.A, Nat. Cent. Univ, China, 42; Ph.D.(org. chem), Yale, 49. Res. chemist, E.I. DU PONT DE NEMOURS & CO, INC, 48-63, RES. ASSOC, 63- AAAS; Am. Chem. Soc. Polymer science; coating technology. Address: E.I. du Pont de Nemours & Co, Inc, 3500 Grays Ferry Ave, Philadelphia, PA 19146.

FANG, JEN-HO, b. Tainan, Formosa, Oct. 21, 29; m. 61; c. 2. MINERALOGY. B.S, Taiwan, 53; Li Found. fel, Minnesota, 55-57, M.S, 57; Ph.D. (geochem), Pa. State, 61. Res. assoc. chem, Boston, 61-62; mem. div. sponsored res, Mass. Inst. Technol, 62-64; asst. prof. GEOL. & TECHNOL, SOUTH. ILL. UNIV, 64-67, assoc. prof, 67-71, PROF, 71- Am. Crystallog. Ans; fel. Mineral. Soc. Am; Am. Geochem. Soc. X-ray crystallography; x-ray and neutron diffraction; physics of minerals; single-crystal growth of gemstones. Address: Dept. of Geology, Southern Illinois University, Carbondale, IL 62901.

FANG, JOONG, b. Piongyang, Korea, Mar. 30, 23; U.S. citizen; m. 56; c. 1. MATHEMATICS, PHILOSOPHY. M.A, Yale, 50; Dr.Phil, Mainz, 57. Asst. prof. math, Jinhae Col. & Pusan, Korea, 45-48; Defiance Col, 57-58; Valparaiso, 58-59; St. John's (Minn), 59-62; assoc. prof, Northern Illinois, 62-67; philos. & math, Memphis State Univ, 67-68, prof, 68-71; VIS. PROF. MATH, UNIV. MUNSTER, 71- Ed, Philosophia Mathematica, Asn. Philos. Math, 64- Math. Asn. Am; Am. Math. Soc; Asn. Symbolic Logic. Foundation and philosophy of mathematics; philosophy of science. Address: 7543 Calmbach, West Germany.

FANG, S(HENG) C(HUNG), b. Foochow, Fukien, China, June 27, 16; nat; m. 48. AGRICULTURAL CHEMISTRY. B.S, Fukien Christian Univ, 37; M.S, Ore. State Col, 44, Ph.D.(biochem), 48. Instr. AGR. CHEM, ORE. STATE UNIV, 48-53, asst. prof. & asst. chemist, 53-57, assoc. prof. & assoc. chemist, 57-71, PROF, 71- Weed Sci. Soc. Am; Am. Soc. Plant Physiol; Am. Chem. Soc; Am. Soc. Biol. Chem. Radioactive tracer studies in agricultural and biological chemistry; herbicides; plant growth regulators. Address: Dept. of Agricultural Chemistry, Oregon State University, Corvallis, OR 97331.

FANG, SO-FEI, b. Chung-King Szechuan, China, Mar. 2, 40; m. 69; c. 1. MATHEMATICS. B.S, Nat. Taiwan Univ, 62; M.A, Univ. Pa, 66, Ph.D. (math), 67. ASST. PROF. MATH, Univ. Wis-Milwaukee, 67-68; UNIV. MASS, BOSTON, 68- Am. Math. Soc. Classical groups over valuation rings. Address: Dept. of Mathematics, University of Massachusetts, 100 Arlington St, Boston, MA 02116.

FANG, T(SUN) C(HUN), b. Wuyuan, China, Mar. 11, 14; U.S. citizen; m. 39; c. 1. FLIGHT & APPLIED MECHANICS. B.S, Tsinghua Univ, Peking, 36; M.S, Polytech. Inst. Brooklyn, 47, Ph.D.(appl. mech), 69. Res. engr, Chinese Air Force, Repub. of China, 36-47, chief engr, 47-56; design engr, Norma Hoffmann Bearings Corp, 57-59; sr. engr, struct. dept, Repub. Aviation Corp, 59-61, prin. engr, res. dept, 61-64, spec. mathematician, 64-65; res. engr, RES. DEPT, GRUMMAN AEROSPACE CORP, 65-69, RES. SCIENTIST, 69- Guidance and control; potential theory; perturbation methods; optimization technique; plates and shells; sandwich structure; wave mechanics. Address: 26 Lois Lane, Old Bethpage, NY 11804.

FANGER, CARLETON G(EORGE), b. Wolsey, S.D, Mar. 22, 24; m. 45; c. 3. APPLIED & ENGINEERING MECHANICS. B.S, Ore. State Univ, 47, M.S, 48. Mech. eng. trainee, Consol. Vultee Aircraft Corp, summer 48; asst. prof. eng, Vanport Exten. Ctr, 48-52; Portland State Exten. Ctr, 52-55; assoc. prof, PORTLAND STATE UNIV, 55-60, APPL. SCI, 60-69, PROF, 69- Summers, mech. engr, U.S. Army Corps Engrs, 51, 52, 56, 59, 61, 62; qual. instr. nuclear defense, Off. Civil Defense, 66- U.S.N.R, 44-46. Am. Soc. Mech. Eng; Nat. Soc. Prof. Eng. Development and publication of textual materials. Address: Dept. of Applied Science, Portland State University, Portland, OR 97207.

FANGER, HERBERT, b. Millis, Mass, Sept. 15, 14; m. 42; c. 2. PATHOLOGY. A.B, Harvard, 36; M.D, N.Y. Med. Col, 40. Instr. PATH, sch. med, Boston, 43-44, 46-47, 49-52; Harvard Med. Sch, 47-49; asst. prof, SCH. MED, BOSTON UNIV, 52-57, ASSOC. PROF, 57-; PATHOLOGIST-DIR, INST. PATH, R.I. HOSP, 49-, assoc. pathologist & acting dir, 49; PROF, BROWN UNIV, 65- Assoc. pathologist, Peter Bent Brigham Hosp, Boston, Mass, 47-49. Consult, Veterans Admin. Hosp, R.I; Morton Hosp, Taunton, Mass. Med.C, U.S.A, 44-46. Soc. Clin. Path; Am. Med. Asn; Am. Asn. Path. & Bact; Col. Am. Path. Histochemistry in neoplastic diseases; biology of neoplasms; malignant melanomas; thrombocythemia; uterine and breast cancer. Address: Dept. of Pathology, Rhode Island Hospital, Providence, RI 20902.

FANGER, MICHAEL W(ALTER), b. Ft. Wayne, Ind, July 3, 40; m. 62; c. 1. IMMUNOLOGY, BIOCHEMISTRY. B.A, Wabash Col, 62; U.S. Pub. Health Serv. fel, Yale, 63-67, Ph.D.(biochem), 67. Nat. Insts. Health fel, Nat. Inst. Med. Res, London, Eng, 67-68; fel, med. sch, Univ. Ill, 68-69, Nat. Insts. Health fel, 69-70; ASST. PROF. MICROBIOL, CASE WEST. RESERVE UNIV, 70- Initiation of the immune response by the mechanism of transformation of the small lymphocyte. Address: Dept. of Microbiology, School of Medicine, Case Western Reserve University, Cleveland, OH 44106.

FANGMEIER, DELMAR DEAN, b. Hubbell, Nebr, Oct. 27, 32; m. 69. AGRICULTURAL ENGINEERING, HYDRAULICS. B.Sc, Nebraska, 54 & 60, M.Sc, 61; Nat. Defense Ed. Act & Nat. Sci. Found. fels. & Ph.D.(eng), California, Davis, 67. Agr. engr, Agr. Res. Serv, U.S. Dept. Agr, 61; asst. prof. civil eng, Wyoming, 66-68; ASSOC. PROF. AGR. ENG, UNIV. ARIZ, 68- U.S.A, 54-56, 1st Lt. Am. Soc. Agr. Eng; Am. Soc. Civil Eng; Am. Soc. Eng. Educ. Steady and unsteady potential flow with free surfaces and gravity; hydraulics of surface irrigation; water utilization by agriculture. Address: Dept. of Agricultural Engineering, University of Arizona, Tucson, AZ 85721.

FANGUY, ROY CHARLES, b. New Orleans, La, Nov. 23, 29; m. 51; c. 2. GENETICS, IMMUNOGENETICS. B.S, Miss. State, 51; M.S, Auburn, 53; Ph.D.(poultry breeding), Texas A&M, 58. Asst. prof. IMMUNOGENETICS, TEX. A&M UNIV, 58-64, ASSOC. PROF, 64- U.S. Pub. Health Serv. grant, 58- Sig.C, 53-55, 1st Lt. Poultry Sci. Asn. Poultry breeding; physiology. Address: Dept. of Poultry Science, Texas A&M University, College Station, TX 77843.

FANKHAUSER, G(ERHARD), b. Burgdorf, Switz, Mar. 11, 01; nat. 39; m. 31; c. 3. ZOOLOGY. Geneva, 20; Zurich, 21; Ph.D.(zool), Bern, 24. Asst.

zool, Bern, 25-29; Rockefeller Found. fel, Chicago, 29-30; Yale, 30-31; asst. prof. BIOL, PRINCETON, 31-39, assoc. prof, 39-46, prof, 46-56, Edwin Grant Conklin prof, 56-69, EMER. PROF, 69- AAAS; Am. Soc. Nat; Am. Soc. Zool; Am. Asn. Anat; Genetics Soc. Am; Am. Genetic Asn; Soc. Develop. Biol.(pres, 56-57); Swiss Zool. Soc; Swiss Nature Soc; Int. Soc. Cell Biol; Int. Soc. Develop. Biol. Heteroploidy; fertilization and polyspermy in salamanders; experimental embryology, cytology and developmental genetics of amphibians. Address: Dept. of Biology, Princeton University, Princeton, NJ 08540.

FANKHAUSER, JAMES C(HRISTIAN), b. U.S. citizen, June 2, 30; m. 57; c. 2. METEOROLOGY. A.B, Nebr. Wesleyan, 51; Pa. State, 57; Chicago, 58-61. Synoptic meteorologist, U.S. Weather Bur, 56-59, pub. serv. meteorologist, 59-62, RES. METEOROLOGIST, 62-67, LAB. ATMOSPHERIC SCI, NAT. CTR. ATMOSPHERIC RES, 67-, superior performance award, 62-63. U.S.A.F, 51-55, S/Sgt. Am. Meteorol. Soc. Kinematics and dynamics of severe convective storms. Address: National Center for Atmospheric Research, Boulder, CO 80302.

FANN, HUOO-LONG, b. Formosa, China, Mar. 29, 31; m. 62. NUCLEAR PHYSICS. B.S, Taiwan Norm. Univ, 56; Ph.D.(physics), Maryland, 64. Asst. prof. PHYSICS, MERRIMACK COL, 64-68, ASSOC. PROF, 68- Summer res. assoc, Maryland, 64. Am. Phys. Soc. Experimental nuclear physics concerning reaction theories for light nuclei. Address: 65 Franklin St, Lawrence, MA 01840.

FANNELÖP, TORSTEIN KJELL, b. Alesund, Norway, Oct. 15, 31; U.S. citizen; m. 57; c. 2. FLUID MECHANICS, HEAT TRANSFER. Mech. Engr, Norweg. Inst. Technol, 55, Dr. Techn.(fluid mech), 70; M.Sc, Univ. Wash, 57; Ph.D.(aeronaut, astronaut), Stanford Univ, 65. Aerodynamicist, Saab Aircraft Co, Sweden, 56, res. engr, 58-60; aerodynamicist, Boeing Co, Wash, 57-58, 60-61; sr. staff scientist, res. & adv. develop. div, Avco Corp, 64-66, sect. chief flight mech, Avco Systs Div, 66-71; CHIEF SCIENTIST, AERONAUT. RES. INST. SWEDEN, 71- Royal Norweg. Air Force, Sgt. Am. Inst. Aeronaut. & Astronaut. Boundary layer theory; hypersonic flow fields; numerical methods in fluid mechanics. Address: Aeronautical Research Institute of Sweden, S-161 11, Bromma 11, Sweden.

FANNIN, BOB M(EREDITH), b. Midland, Texas, June 9, 22; m. 47; c. 3. ELECTRICAL ENGINEERING. B.S, Texas, 44, M.S, 47, Ph.D.(elec. eng), 56. Instr. math, Arlington State Col, 47-48; res. assoc. sch. elec. eng, Cornell, 48-51; res. engr, elec. eng. res. lab, Texas, 51-56; ASSOC. PROF. ELEC. ENG, New Mexico, 56-58; UNIV. TEX, 58- Mem. comn. II, U.S. Nat. Comt. of Int. Sci. Radio Union. U.S.N.R, 44-46, Lt.(jg). Sr. mem. Inst. Elec. & Electronics Eng. Tropospheric radio wave program. Address: 4709 Crestway, Austin, TX 78731.

FANNING, DELVIN S(EYMOUR), b. Copenhagen, N.Y, July 13, 31; m. 58; c. 3. SOIL SCIENCE. B.S, Cornell, 54, M.S, 59; Ph.D.(soil sci), Wisconsin, 64. Soil scientist, soil conserv. serv, U.S. Dept. Agr, 53-63; asst. prof. SOIL MINERAL. & CLASSIFICATION, UNIV. MD, COLLEGE PARK, 64-69, ASSOC. PROF, 69- U.S.A, 54-56. AAAS; Am. Soc. Agron; Soil Sci. Soc. Am; Mineral. Soc. Am; Clay Minerals Soc; Soil Conserv. Soc. Am; Nat. Speleol. Soc; Soc. Appl. Spectros; Am. Quaternary Asn. Speleology; mineralogy of soils in relation to their genesis; clay mineral identification by combinations of chemical and x-ray diffraction procedures. Address: Dept. of Agronomy, University of Maryland, College Park, MD 20742.

FANNING, JAMES COLLIER, b. Atlanta, Ga, Nov. 8, 31; m. 57; c. 3. INORGANIC CHEMISTRY. B.S, The Citadel, 53; M.S, Ga. Inst. Technol, 56, Ph.D.(chem), 60. Instr. CHEM, Ga. Inst. Technol, 57-59; fel, Tulane, 60-61; asst. prof, CLEMSON UNIV, 61-65, assoc. prof, 65-71, PROF, 71- Vis. lectr, Univ. Ill, 66-67. Chem.C, 60, Res, 53-61, Capt. Am. Chem. Soc. Solution theory and chemistry of transition metals. Address: Dept. of Chemistry, Clemson University, Clemson, SC 29631.

FANNING, ROBERT J(OSEPH), b. Cleora, Okla, Oct. 23, 25; m. 49; c. 2. CHEMICAL & ELECTRICAL ENGINEERING. B.S, Oklahoma, 45, Rapp fel, 55-56, Dow Chem. fel, 56, Nat. Sci. Found. grant, 56-57, Ph.D.(chem. eng), 58; Du Pont fel, Missouri, 46-47, M.S, 47. Chem. engr, elastomers, Phillips Petrol. Co, 47-49, polyolefins, 49-51; process engr, styrene-butadiene rubber plant, Phillips Chem. Co, 51-55; systems engr. & head automation group, Continental Oil Co, 57-64; SR. CHEM. ENG. ASSOC, ETHYL CORP, 64- Guest lectr, La. State Univ. U.S.N.R, 45-56, Lt.(jg). Am. Inst. Chem. Eng; Am. Chem. Soc. Process computer, digital and analog; process dynamic analysis; systems engineering; synthetic fatty chemicals development organo-metallic synthesis; non-ferrous metals research. Address: Research & Development Dept, Ethyl Corp, P.O. Box 341, Baton Rouge, LA 70821.

FANO, ROBERT M(ARIO), b. Torino, Italy, Nov. 11, 17; nat; m. 49; c. 3. ELECTRICAL ENGINEERING. S.B, Mass. Inst. Tech, 41, Sc.D.(elec. eng), 47. Asst. elec. eng, MASS. INST. TECHNOL, 41-43, instr, 43-44, radiation lab, 44-46, res. assoc, electronics res. lab, 46-47, asst. prof. elec. commun, 47-51, assoc. prof, 51-56, prof, 56-62, FORD PROF. ENG, 62-, ASSOC. HEAD ELEC. ENG. DEPT, FOR COMPUT. SCI. & ENG, 71-, dir. Proj. MAC, 63-68, group leader, Lincoln Lab, 51-53. Fel. Inst. Elec. & Electronics Eng; Am. Acad. Arts & Sci; Asn. Comput. Mach. Microwave circuit components; network synthesis; transmission of information; computer sciences; theoretical limitations on the broad band matching of arbitrary impedances. Address: Dept. of Electrical Engineering, 545 Technology Square, Rm. 514, Massachusetts Institute of Technology, Cambridge, MA 02139.

FANO, U(GO), b. Torino, Italy, July 28, 12; nat; m. 39; c. 2. THEORETICAL PHYSICS. D.Sc.(math), Torino, 34. Italian Dept. Ed. Int. fel, Leipzig, 36-37; instr. physics, Rome, 38-39; res. assoc, Wash. Biophys. Inst, 39-40; res. fel. genetics, Carnegie Inst, 40-41, res. assoc, 42-43, physicist & mathematician, 43-45; consult. & ballistician, ballistics res. lab, Aberdeen Proving Ground, Md, 44-45; res. assoc, Carnegie Inst, 46; physicist, Nat. Bur. Standards, 46-66; PROF. PHYSICS, UNIV. CHICAGO, 66- Prof. lectr, George Washington, 46-47, 57-58; California, 58, 68; vis. prof, Catholic Univ, 63-64. Rockefeller Pub. Serv. award, 56-57. Am. Phys. Soc; Radiation Res. Soc. Intermediate energy atomic physics; theoretical spectroscopy and nuclear physics; genetics of Drosophila and bacteria; theory of diffraction and of propagation of radiations through matter and of their effects on matter. Address: Dept. of Physics, University of Chicago, Chicago, IL 60637.

FANSHAWE, JOHN R(ICHARDSON), II, b. Phila, Pa, Oct. 20, 06; m. 37; c. 3. PETROLEUM GEOLOGY. A.B, Princeton, 29, M.A, 31, Ph.D.(geol), 39; Dr.es.Sc, Lille, 30. Asst. geol, Princeton, 30-32; master physics & geol, Deerfield Acad, Mass, 33-35; instr. geol, Williams Col, 35-39; geologist, Ohio Oil Co, Ill, 40-42; dist. geologist & dist. dir. reserves, dist. IV, Petrol. Admin. War, Colo, 43-45; sr. geologist, Gen. Petrol. Corp, Wyo, 45-47; dist. mgr. & mgr. explor, Seaboard Oil Co. of Del, 47-51; consult. geologist, 51-62; v.pres. & res. mgr, Forest Cyprus Corp, 63-64; staff geologist, Mont. Power Co, 64-71; CONSULT. GEOLOGIST, 71- Geol. Soc. Am; Am. Asn. Petrol. Geol; Am. Inst. Prof. Geol. Structural theory and interpretation; regional stratigraphy; application of geophysics to petrol exploration; geology of mineral fuels. Address: 3116 E. MacDonald Dr, Billings, MT 59102.

FANSLOW, DON J, b. Yankton, S.Dak, Apr. 16, 36. ZOOLOGY, ENDOCRINOLOGY. B.A, Yankton Col, 58; M.A, South Dakota, 60; univ. fel, Indiana, 62, NASA trainee, 63-64, Ph.D.(zool), 65. ASSOC. PROF. BIOL, NORTHEAST. ILL. STATE UNIV, 65- AAAS; Am. Soc. Zool. Endocrinology. Address: Dept. of Biology, Northeastern Illinois State University, Bryn Mawr at St. Louis, Chicago, IL 60625.

FANSLOW, GLENN E, b. Minot, N.Dak, Sept. 5, 27; m. 60; c. 2. ELECTRICAL ENGINEERING, PHYSICS. B.S, N.Dak. Agr. Col, 53; M.S, Iowa State, 57, Ph.D.(elec. eng), 62. Elec. engr, Gen. Elec. Co, 53-55; instr. ELEC. ENG, IOWA STATE UNIV, 55-61, asst. prof, 62-69, ASSOC. PROF, 70- Nat. Sci. Found. grant, 64-65; NASA-Am. Soc. Eng. Educ. summer faculty fel, 67, 68. U.S.N, 45-48. AAAS; Inst. Elec. & Electronics Eng; Int. Microwave Power Inst. Applications of microwave power in the processing of materials; microwave generation, instrumentation and design. Address: Dept. of Electrical Engineering, Coover Hall, Iowa State University, Ames, IA 50010.

FANTA, GEORGE F(REDERICK), b. Chicago, Ill, Aug. 30, 34; m. 57; c. 3. ORGANIC CHEMISTRY. B.S, Purdue, 56; Ph.D.(org. chem), Univ. Ill, 60. ORG. CHEMIST, Ethyl Corp, 60-63; NORTH. MKT. & NUTRIT. DIV, U.S. DEPT. AGR, 63- Am. Chem. Soc. Chemistry of starch and starch derivatives. Address: Northern Marketing & Nutrition Division, U.S. Dept. of Agriculture, 1815 N. University St, Peoria, IL 61604.

FANTA, PAUL E(DWARD), b. Chicago, Ill, July 24, 21; m. 49; c. 2. ORGANIC CHEMISTRY. B.S, Illinois, 42; Ph.D.(chem), Rochester, 46. Asst. CHEM, Rochester, 42-44, Manhattan Proj, 44-46, fel, 46-47; instr, Harvard, 47-48; asst. prof, ILL. INST. TECHNOL, 48-53, assoc. prof, 53-61, PROF, 61- Nat. Sci. Found. fel, Imp. Col, London, 56-57; exchange scholar, Czech. Acad. Sci, Prague, 63-64; Acad. Sci. U.S.S.R, Moscow, 70-71. With Atomic Energy Comn, 44. Am. Chem. Soc; The Chem. Soc. Nitrogen heterocycles; stereochemistry. Address: Dept. of Chemistry, Illinois Institute of Technology, Chicago, IL 60616.

FANTAZIER, RICHARD MICHAEL, b. Wilkinsburg, Pa, Aug. 3, 40; m. 63; c. 4. ORGANIC CHEMISTRY. B.S, Carnegie-Mellon Univ, 62; Ph.D.(org. chem), Rochester, 67. Union Carbide fel, 66-67; RES. CHEMIST, ARMSTRONG CORK CO, 67- Am. Chem. Soc; Brit. Chem. Soc. Free radical chemistry; kinetics and mechanisms of peroxide decompositions; structure and reactivity of vinyl and propargyl radicals; amine photochemistry; Azo compounds. Address: Research & Development Center, Armstrong Cork Co, Lancaster, PA 17604.

FANTE, RONALD L(OUIS), b. Philadelphia, Pa, Oct. 27, 36; m. 61; c. 3. PLASMA PHYSICS. B.S, Pennsylvania, 58; Nat. Sci. Found. fel. & M.S, Mass. Inst. Tech, 60; fel. & Ph.D.(elec. eng), Princeton, 63. Sr. physicist, Space Sci. Inc, 63-64; staff scientist, res. & adv. develop. div, AVCO CORP, 64-70, SR. CONSULT. SCIENTIST, AVCO SYSTS. DIV, 70- Inst. Elec. & Electronics Eng. Radiation from and scattering by plasmas; microwave breakdown; kinetic theory of gases; stochastic processes. Address: 26 Sherwood Rd, Reading, MA 01867.

FANTI, ROY, b. Brooklyn, N.Y, Dec. 23, 25; m. 47; c. 2. AERODYNAMICS. B.S, Rensselaer Polytech, 47, M.S, 48. Instr. physics, Rensselaer Polytech, 47, asst. aerodyn, 47-48; res. engr, RES. LABS, UNITED AIRCRAFT CORP, 48-53, supvr. aeroelasticity & flutter, 53-58, sr. res. engr, 57-59, head mat. res. sect, 59-63, chief mat. sci. sect, 63-67, MGR. mat. sci. lab, 67-68, MAT. LAB, 68- Eve. instr, West. New Eng. Col, 54-59, 64- U.S.N, 44-46, Res, 46-47, Lt.(jg). Fundamental materials research; high-temperature technology; advanced materials engineering; structural dynamics; unsteady aerodynamics; stall flutter research; theory of thin airfoils, isolated and in cascade. Address: Research Labs, United Aircraft Corp, 400 Main St, East Hartford, CT 06108.

FANTINI, AMEDEO A(LEXANDER), b. N.Y.C, Feb. 11, 22; m. 54; c. 3. MICROBIAL GENETICS. B.A, N.Y. Univ, 52; M.A, Columbia, 59, Eli Lilly fel, 58-60, Ph.D.(genetics), 61. Virol, Chas. Pfizer & Co, 46-50; biologist cancer res, Lederle Labs. Div, Am. Cyanamid Co, 52-54, mycol, 54-56; asst, Columbia, 56-58; res. microbiologist, LEDERLE LABS. DIV, AM. CYANAMID CO, 60-65, SR. RES. MICROBIOLOGIST, 65- U.S.A, 42-46, Sgt. Genetics Soc. Am; Am. Soc. Microbiol; Soc. Indust. Microbiol. Genetics and physiology of fungi and streptomyces in relation to increased yields of antibiotics; microbial fermentations. Address: 2 The Glen, New City, NY 10956.

FANUCCI, JEROME B(EN), b. Glen Lyon, Pa, Oct. 7, 24; m. 52; c. 2. AERODYNAMICS. B.S, Pa. State, 44, M.S, 52, Ph.D.(aeronaut. eng), 56. Aeronaut. engr, East. Aircraft Corp, N.J, 44-45, Repub. Aviation Corp, N.Y, 47-50; instr. aeronaut. eng, Pa. State, 52-56, asst. prof, 56-57; res. eng. gas dynamics, missile & space vehicle div, Gen. Elec. Co, Pa, 57-59;

sr. res. scientist, plasma & space appl. physics, Radio Corp. Am, N.J, 59-64; PROF. AEROSPACE ENG. & CHMN. DEPT, UNIV. W.VA, 64- Consult, RCA Corp, N.J, 64- U.S.A.A.F, 46-47. Assoc. fel. Am. Inst. Aeronaut. & Astronaut; Am. Soc. Eng. Educ. Heat transfer; Laminar incompressible and compressible boundary layer theory; mass addition in boundary layer; boundary layer stability; ablation of reentry vehicles; blast wave theory of conducting fluids in magnetic fields; magnetohydrodynamic alternating current power generation. Address: 1313 Anderson Ave, Morgantown, WV 26505.

FARA, MARK, b. Tamroy, W.Va, Mar. 1, 24; m. 53; c. 3. GEOLOGY. B.S, Va. Polytech, 56, M.S, 57. Asst. prof. geol, Va. Polytech, 57-63; res. mgr, W.Va. State Rd. Cmn, 63-65; staff geologist, Lone Star Cement Corp, N.Y, 65-67, chief geologist, 67-70; MGR. MINERAL RESOURCES DEVELOP, PA. GLASS SAND CORP, W.VA, 70- U.S.N, 43-46. Correlation of Pennsylvanian coals in the subsurface of southwestern Virginia and southern West Virginia; beneficiation of Clinton ferruginous sandstone of southwestern Virginia; investigation of high-calcium limestone deposits. Address: Pennsylvania Glass Sand Corp, Berkeley Springs, WV 25411.

FARABEE, RAY L, b. Coal City, Ala, June 8, 00; m. 25; c. 3. METALLURGY. B.S, Alabama, 22, M.S, 24; Met.E, 27. Metallurgist, Repub. Steel Co, 22-24; sch. mines, Alabama, 24-26, prof. chem. & metall. eng, 26-40; v.pres, Cent. Foundry Co, 40-53; Delta Tank Co, 53-56; prof. METALL. ENG, UNIV. ALA, TUSCALOOSA, 56-70; EMER. PROF, 70- Prof, Purdue, 28-29, 38-39; dir, Gen. Gas Corp, 53-56. Consult, Union Carbide Nuclear Co. div, Union Carbide Corp; Cent. Foundry Co; Kilby Steel Co. U.S.A, 18. Am. Soc. Metals; Am. Foundrymen's Soc; Am. Ord. Asn; Brit. Inst. Metals. Materials of construction in atomic reactors; cold and hot extrusion of metals and alloys, especially the exotic metals; ductile iron; welding research. Address: Dept. of Metallurgical Engineering, University of Alabama at Tuscaloosa, University, AL 35486.

FARADAY, BRUCE (JOHN), b. N.Y.C, Dec. 9, 19; m. 50; c. 5. SOLID STATE PHYSICS. A.B, Fordham, 40, M.S, 47; Ph.D, Catholic Univ, 63. SOLID STATE SUPVRY. PHYSICIST, U.S. NAVAL RES. LAB, 48-, HEAD SEMICONDUCTOR SECT, 65- Instr, Prince George's Community Col, 60-, lectr, 65-; Univ. Md, 67- Sig.C, U.S.A, 43-46. Fel. Am. Phys. Soc; Acoustical Soc. Am; Sci. Res. Soc. Am. Radiation damage; color centers; luminescence; energy conversion. Address: Solid State Division, U.S. Naval Research Lab, Code 6465, Washington, DC 20390.

FARAGO, JOHN, b. Budapest, Hungary, Sept. 12, 17; nat; m. 45; c. 2. POLYMER CHEMISTRY, APPLIED PSYCHOLOGY. Dipl. Chem. Eng, Budapest Tech, 39, Dr.Tech.Sc, 47; M.S, Va. Commonwealth Univ, 68. Asst. to org. chair, Univ. of Sci, Budapest, 39-40, 44-45; res. supvr, Egger Pharmaceut, 40-43; res. engr, Grab Textile Factory, Gyor, Hungary, 44, asst. dir, Chem. Inst. City Budapest, 46-47; res. assoc, George Washington, 47-51, res. prof, 52; res. chemist, TEXTILE FIBERS DEPT, E.I. DU PONT DE NEMOURS & CO, INC, 52-56, sr. res. chemist, 56-60, res. assoc, 60; res. supvr, 61-70, RES. FEL, 70- Lectr, George Wash. Univ, 48-52. AAAS; Am. Chem. Soc; Am. Inst. Chem; Sci. Res. Soc. Am; Am. Psychol. Asn. Structure, application and analysis of polymers; learning; motivation. Address: 214 Hillwood Ave, Richmond, VA 23226.

FARAH, ALFRED E(MIL), b. Nazareth, Palestine, July 10, 14; m. 43. PHARMACOLOGY. B.A, American Univ. Beirut, 37, M.D, 40. Instr. pharmacol, American Univ. Beirut, 40-43, asst. prof, 43-45; vis. lectr. & res. fel, Harvard Med. Sch, 45-47; asst. prof. med. sch, Univ. Wash, 47-50; assoc. prof, State University of N.Y. Upstate Med. Ctr, 50-53, prof. & chmn. dept, 53-68; DIR. BIOL. DIV, STERLING-WINTHROP RES. INST, 68- Am. Soc. Pharmacol; Soc. Exp. Biol. & Med; Cardiac Muscle Soc. Cardiac and kidney pharmacology; cardiac glycosides; mercurial diuretics; secretory activity of kidney; pharmacology of enzyme inhibitors. Address: Sterling-Winthrop Research Institute, Rensselaer, NY 12144.

FARAH, BASIL, b. Bethlehem, Jordan, Sept. 5, 33; U.S. citizen; m; c. 4. ORGANIC CHEMISTRY. B.Sc, Mich. State, 55; M.Sc, Maine, 57, Ph.D. (org. chem), 60. Res. chemist, gen. chem. div, Allied Chem. Corp, N.J, 59-64; sr. res. chemist, cent. res. lab, Air Prod. & Chem. Corp, Pa, 64; sr. patent chemist, Nat. Aniline Div, Allied Chem. Corp, Buffalo, 64-66; SR. RES. CHEMIST, SPENCER KELLOG DIV, TEXTRON, BUFFALO, 66- Am. Chem. Soc. Organic sulfur and organic fluorine compounds; elemental and electrolytic fluorination; hydrophobic and oleophobic textile finishes; steroids; patent law; abstracting; information retrieval; coatings; polyurethanes; adhesives. Address: 11197 Clinton St, Elma, NY 14059.

FARAN, JAMES J(OHN), JR, b. Youngstown, Ohio, Apr. 1, 21; m. 49; c. 4. ELECTRONICS, ACOUSTICS. A.B, Washington & Jefferson Col, 43; Mass. Inst. Tech; M.A, Harvard, 47, Ph.D.(acoustics), 51. Res. assoc. elec. measurements, Underwater Sound Lab, Harvard, 43-45; electronic circuits; Systems Res. Lab, Hopkins, 46-47; fel. acoustics, Harvard, 51-52; engr. electronic circuits, GEN. RADIO CO, 52-71, GROUP LEADER ENG. PROG, 71- Fel. Acoustical Soc. Am; Inst. Elec. & Electronics Eng. Electrical impedance measurements; sound scattering; correlation techniques in acoustics; electronic circuit design; computer programming. Address: Tabor Hill Rd, Lincoln, MA 01773.

FARB, NORMAN EDWIN, b. Rockford, Ill, Apr. 2, 30; m. 55; c. 4. SOLID STATE PHYSICS, MATHEMATICS. B.S, Utah, 59, Nat. Defense Ed. Act. fel, 57-63, Ph.D.(physics), 63. Engr, Link Aviation, 54-57; res. specialist solid state physics, autonetics div, N.Am. Aviation, Inc, 63-69; LAB. MGR, MICROCERAMICS DIV, GULTON INDUSTS, INC, 69- U.S.A.F, 50-54, S/Sgt. Am. Phys. Soc. Dislocation, motion and diffusion in metal oxides; electronic properties of metal oxides; strain properties of tunnel diodes; ferroelectrics; photoconductors. Address: Microceramics Division, Gulton Industries, Inc, 212 Durham Ave, Metuchen, NJ 08840.

FARBAR, LEONARD, b. Vancouver, B.C, Can, Dec. 13, 11; U.S. citizen. MECHANICAL & CHEMICAL ENGINEERING. B.S, California, 36, fel, 36-38, M.S, 38. Process engr. chem. mech. eng, Tidewater Oil Co, Calif, 38-42; lectr. MECH. ENG, UNIV. CALIF, BERKELEY, 46-50, asst. prof, 50-52, assoc. prof, 52-66, PROF, 66-, head eng. exten, 64-67. Mem. staff, U.S. Naval Acad, 60-61. U.S.N, 42-46, Res, 46-, Comdr. Am. Soc. Mech. Eng. Thermodynamics, power and cryogenic refrigeration; heat transfer; fluid dynamics and heat transfer to Newtonian and non-Newtonian mixtures; gas-solids mixtures. Address: Dept. of Mechanical Engineering, University of California, Berkeley, CA 94720.

FARBER, ELLIOT, b. N.Y.C, May 7, 32. PHYSICS. B.S, Brooklyn Col, 54; A.M, Columbia, 56; Ph.D.(physics), Stevens Inst. Tech, 66. Jr. physicist, Naval Res. Lab, 53, physicist, 54; microwave engr, Sylvania Elec. Prods, Inc, 56; instr. PHYSICS, Pratt Inst, 57-62, asst. prof, 63-67; ASSOC. PROF, NEWARK COL. ENG, 67- Res. assoc, Stevens Inst. Technol, 65-67. Am. Asn. Physics Teachers. Plasma physics. Address: Dept. of Physics, Newark College of Engineering, Newark, NJ 07102.

FARBER, ELLIOTT, b. N.Y.C, Mar. 12, 28; m. 55; c. 3. POLYMER CHEMISTRY. B.A, N.Y. Univ, 50; M.S, Polytech. Inst. Brooklyn, 52, Ph.D.(polymer chem), 59. Asst. chem. consult, Prof. Kurt G. Stern, 52-55; res. chemist, cent. res. dept, Texaco, Inc, 59-61; polymer dept, cent. res. div, FMC Corp, 61-63; from supvr. to MGR. POLYMERIZATION RES, TENNECO PLASTICS DIV, TENNECO CHEM, INC, 63- U.S.A, 46-47. Am. Chem. Soc; Soc. Plastics Eng. Correlation of chemical and physical properties with molecular structure, polymer synthesis and evaluation; polymerization kinetics, suspension and emulsion polymerizations. Address: 16 Llanfair Lane, Trenton, NJ 08618.

FARBER, EMMANUEL, b. Toronto, Ont, Can, Oct. 19, 18; U.S. citizen; m. 42; c. 1. PATHOLOGY, BIOCHEMISTRY. M.D, Toronto, 42; Am. Cancer Soc. fel, California, Berkeley, 47-49, Ph.D.(biochem), 49. Am. Cancer Soc. fel. cancer res, Cook County Hosp, Ill, 49-50; instr. path, sch. med, Tulane, 50-51, asst. prof. path. & lectr. biochem, 51-55, assoc. prof. path. & biochem, 55-59, Am. Cancer Soc. res. prof, 59-61; prof. path. & chmn. dept, sch. med, Univ. Pittsburgh, 61-70; AM. CANCER SOC. RES. PROF. PATH. & BIOCHEM. & SR. INVESTR, FELS RES. INST, TEMPLE UNIV, 70- Vis. prof, Middlesex Hosp, med. sch, London, 68-69; mem. adv. comt. smoking & health, Surgeon Gen, 62; chmn. path. B study sect, Nat. Insts. Health, 62-66; consult, div. chronic diseases, Dept. Health, Educ. & Welfare; v.pres, Asn. Cancer Res, 71-72, bd. dirs, 70-73. Second Annual Parke-Davis award, 58; Fourth Annual Teplitz mem. award, 61. R.C.A.M.C, 43-46, Capt. Am. Gastroenterol. Asn; Am. Soc. Biol. Chem; Am. Chem. Soc; Am. Soc. Exp. Path; Am. Asn. Path. & Bact; Biochem. Soc; Histochem. Soc. (pres, 66-67); N.Y. Acad. Sci. Biochemical pathology; carcinogenesis, cytochemistry and histochemistry. Address: Fels Research Institute, School of Medicine, Temple University, Philadelphia, PA 19140.

FARBER, ERICH A(LEXANDER), b. Vienna, Austria, Sept. 7, 21; nat; m. 49; c. 2. MECHANICAL ENGINEERING. B.S, Missouri, 43, fel. & M.S, 46; fel, Iowa, 46-49, Ph.D.(mech. eng), 49. Mach. operator, Erving Paper Mills, Mass, 40-41; drafting & blueprinting, City of Columbia, Mo. & Univ. Mo, 41-43; instr. physics & math, Missouri, 43-46; MECH. ENG, Iowa, 46-49; asst. prof, Wisconsin, 49-54, assoc. prof, 54; PROF. & RES. PROF, UNIV. FLA, 54-, DIR. SOLAR ENERGY LAB, 65- Asst, Missouri, 42-43; consult, Standard Oil Co. (Ind), 46-49; Foster Wheeler Corp, 47-49; Bergstrom Mfg. Corp, 50-52; Cleaver Brooks Corp, 50-54; El. Kells Mfg. Corp, 50-54; U.S. Navy, 51-54; A.C. Spark Plugs Corp, 52-54; Perfex Corp, 53-54; E.I. du Pont de Nemours & Co, 55-; Union Carbide Corp, Oak Ridge Nat. Lab, Atomic Energy Comn, 56-; Sperry Electronic Tube Corp, 57-; off. saline water, U.S. Dept. Interior, 58-; Electro-Mech. Res. Corp, 62-; NASA, 63- Citation, Res. Directorate, Air Force Off. Sci. Res. U.S.A, 44-46; Silver Star Medal. Fel. Am. Soc. Mech. Eng.(Worcester Reed Warner Gold Medal); Am. Soc. Eng. Educ; Solar Energy Soc. Heat transfer; solar energy; fluid flow; thermodynamics; energy conversion. Address: 1218 N.E. Fifth St, Gainesville, FL 32601.

FARBER, EUGENE M, b. Buffalo, N.Y, July 24, 17; m. 44; c. 4. DERMATOLOGY. A.B, Oberlin Col, 39; M.D, Buffalo, 43; M.S, Minnesota, 46. Intern, Buffalo Gen. Hosp, N.Y, 43-44; fel. dermat. & syphilol, Mayo Clin, 44-48, asst, 47-48; instr. dermat, SCH. MED, STANFORD UNIV, 48, asst. prof. path, 49-50, assoc. prof, DERMAT, 50-54, clin. prof, 54-60, PROF, 60-, DIR. DIV, 50- Consult, Surg. Gen, U.S. Air Force, 57-64; Calif. State Dept. Pub. Health, 63- Mem. gen. clin. res. ctr. comt, Nat. Insts. Health, 65. Soc. Exp. Biol. & Med; Am. Soc. Clin. Invest; Soc. Invest. Dermat.(v.pres, 65); Am. Dermat. Asn; Am. Fedn. Clin. Res; Microcirc. Soc; Am. Acad. Dermat; Am. Asn. Prof. Dermat.(secy, 67, pres, 68); hon. mem. Dermat. Soc. India; Asn. Invest. Dermat. Venezuela; Czech. Med. Soc; Danish Dermat. Soc; Israeli Dermat. Soc; Austrian Dermat. Asn; Yugoslavian Soc. Dermat; Norway Soc. Dermat; Soc. Venezuelan Dermat. & Leprology; French Soc. Dermat; Brit. Asn. Dermat. Peripheral vascular diseases; cutaneous blood flow in various dermatoses and psoriasis. Address: Dept. of Dermatology, School of Medicine, Stanford University, Stanford, CA 94035.

FARBER, FLORENCE EILEEN, b. N.Y.C, Aug. 11, 39. MOLECULAR & CELL BIOLOGY. A.B, Mt. Holyoke Col, 61; U.S. Pub. Health Serv. trainee, Columbia Univ, 61-64, NASA fel, 64-66, Ph.D.(biochem), 66. Res. asst. chem, Mt. Holyoke Col, 60; Nat. Sci. Found. fel, Free Univ. Brussels, 66-68; lectr. cell physiol, Univ. Calif, Berkeley, 68-69; ASST. PROF. PHYSIOL. & BIOPHYS, COL. MED, UNIV. VT, 69- Am. Heart Asn. sr. fel, 69. Underlying mechanisms existing between RNA synthesis and protein synthesis during differentiation of higher cells; nature and control of cell differentiation; integration of nuclear and cytoplasmic genetic systems. Address: Dept. of Physiology & Biophysics, College of Medicine, University of Vermont, Burlington, VT 05401.

FARBER, HERMAN, b. N.Y.C, Dec. 3, 19; m. 43; c. 2. ELECTROPHYSICS. B.A, Brooklyn Col, 41; fel, Polytech. Inst. Brooklyn, 50-51, M.E.E, 52. Res. engr, Bristol Co, 46-49; from asst. to ASSOC. PROF. elec. eng, POLYTECH. INST. BROOKLYN, 54-60, ELECTROPHYSICS, 60- Res. chemist, Manhattan Proj, Tenn, 43-46. Am. Phys. Soc; Am. Asn. Physics Teachers; sr. mem. Inst. Elec. & Electronics Eng. Electromagnetic properties of materials, including the electric strength of solids and liquids at microwave frequencies; cryogenic engineering; plasma diagnostics; chemical synthesis using discharge and plasmas. Address: Polytechnic Institute of Brooklyn, Graduate Center, Farmingdale, NY 11735.

FARBER, HUGH ARTHUR, b. Muskegon, Mich, Oct. 6, 33; m. 54; c. 3. ORGANIC CHEMISTRY. B.S.Ch, Mich. State, 56; Allied Chem. fel, Northwestern, 58, Ph.D.(org. chem), 60. Res. org. chemist, DOW CHEM. CO, 59-66, proj. leader, 66-68, GROUP LEADER, RES. & DEVELOP, 68- Am. Chem. Soc; Sci. Res. Soc. Am. Preparation of monomer, polymer modification and agricultural chemicals; study of reaction mechanisms; rearrangement of epoxides; reactions of aziridines; chlorinated solvents; ecology of chlorinated solvents. Address: 2807 Highbrook Dr, Midland, MI 48640.

FARBER, JOSEPH, b. Newark, N.J, June 1, 24; m. 51; c. 2. PHYSICAL CHEMISTRY. B.S, City Col. New York, 45; Ph.D.(phys. chem), Wisconsin, 51. From res. engr. to sr. thermodyn. engr, Convair, Gen. Dynamics Corp, Calif, 51-55; mgr. real gas eng, Gen. Elec. Co, 55-56, aerophys. sect, space sci. lab, 56-64, adv. systs. eng, 64-67; chief engr, space & reentry systs. div, Philco-Ford Corp, 67-69, prog. mgr, mid-course surv. systs, 69-70; PRES. & GEN. MGR, KMS TECHNOL. CTR, DIV. KMS INDUSTS, INC, 70- Am. Chem. Soc; Am. Phys. Soc; Am. Inst. Aeronaut. & Astronaut; Solar Energy Soc. Systems engineering; operations analysis; space science nuclear power; aerophysics; plasma physics; magnetohydrodynamics. Address: KMS Technology Center, Division of KMS Industries, Inc, 7810 Burnet Ave, Van Nuys, CA 91405.

FARBER, LESLIE H(ILLEL), b. Carlsbad, N.Mex, July 11, 12; m. 36, 60; c. 4. PSYCHIATRY. A.B, Stanford, 34, M.D, 38. Res. psychiat, St. Elizabeth's Hosp, Wash, D.C, 39-40, asst. med. officer, 40-41; psychiatrist, Wash. Inst. Mental Hygiene, 41-42; dir, Norfolk Inst. Mental Hygiene, Va, 43-46; private practice, psychiat. & psychoanal, Calif, 46-53; Wash, D.C, 53-; chmn, faculty, Wash. Sch. Psychiat, 55-62; CHMN, ASN. EXISTENTIAL PSYCHOL. & PSYCHIAT, 63- Field fel, 41-42; psychiatrist, Chestnut Lodge Sanatorium, Md, 41-42; Armed Forces Induction Sta, Va, 42; mem. attend. staff, Mt. Zion Psychiat. Clinic, Calif, 47-53; teaching analyst, Wash. Psychoanal. Inst, 55-, training & supvry. analyst, 56-; v.pres, William Alanson White Psychiat. Found, 55- Consult, Ft. Miley Hosp. & regional off, Vet. Admin, San Francisco, Calif, 46-48; exten. counseling ctr, Univ. California, 48-50; Jewish Family Serv. Agency, 50-53; Vet. Admin. Hosp, Roanoke, Va, 54; Nat. Inst. Mental Health, Nat. Insts. Health, 54- Dipl, Am. Bd. Psychiat. & Neurol, 44. Dir, dept. psychiat, U.S. Marine Hosp, Va, 45-46, U.S. Pub. Health Serv. Res, 42-46, Surg. Fel. Am. Psychiat. Asn; Am. Psychoanal. Asn; fel. Am. Col. Physicians. Relation between psychiatry and the humanities and religion. Address: 129 W. 94th St, New York, NY 10025.

FARBER, L(IONEL), b. Chicago, Ill, Sept. 7, 08; m. 34; c. 2. BIOCHEMISTRY, FOOD TECHNOLOGY. A.B, Toronto, 30; M.A, 31, Ph.D.(biochem), 34; fel, N.Y. Univ, 31-32; hon. D.Sc, Calif. Col. Podiatry, 58. Asst. chem, Toronto, 30-31, Banting Res. Found. fel. biochem, 34-37; instr. agr. chem, exp. sta, Arkansas, 37; res. asst, HOOPER FOUND, MED. CTR, UNIV. CALIF, SAN FRANCISCO, 37-39, res. assoc, 39-46, res. biochemist in charge seafood res. lab, 46-69; EMER. RES. BIOCHEMIST, 69- Prof, Calif. Col. Podiatric Med, 69-70; consult, fisheries & fishery prods; vis, fishery res. insts. & labs. Fel. AAAS; Am. Chem. Soc; Am. Soc. Microbiol; Inst. Food Tech; Am. Fisheries Soc; fel. Am. Inst. Chem; sr. fel. Orgn. European Econ. Coop. Pancreatic proteinase; ascorbic acid and glutathione; biochemical changes in fish during spoilage; refrigeration of fish; canning technology of fish and other preservation methods; radiation preservation of fish; bacterial ecology of fishery products. Address: 75 Circle Ave, Mill Valley, CA 94941.

FARBER, MILTON, b. Los Angeles, Calif, Oct. 6, 16; m. 42; c. 3. PHYSICAL CHEMISTRY. B.S, California, 38; M.S, Minnesota, 39. Chief chem. engr, Colloidal Prods, Hawaii, 41-42; area supvr, Ky. Ord. Works, 42-43; sr. res. engr, Manhattan Proj, Tenn, 43-46; jet propulsion lab, Calif. Inst. Tech, 46-55; assoc. dir. res, Aerojet-Gen. Corp. Div, Gen. Tire & Rubber Co, 55-57, head propulsion lab, Hughes Tool Co, 57-59; v.pres, Maremont Corp, Rocket Power, Inc, 59-67; PRES, SPACE SCI, INC, 67- Am. Chem. Soc. Thermodynamics; separation of isotopes; thermal diffusion; mass spectroscopy; kinetics. Address: Space Sciences, Inc, 135 W. Maple Ave, Monrovia, CA 91016.

FARBER, MILTON, b. N.Y.C, Mar. 11, 23; m. 53; c. 3. POLYMER CHEMISTRY. B.S, City Univ. New York, 42; A.M, Columbia, 47, Ph.D.(chem), 49. Asst. chem, Columbia, 46-49; res. fel. biochem, med. col, Cornell, 49-51, res. assoc, 51-52; sr. chemist, Herstein Labs, 53-54; group leader, United Merchants Labs, 54-57; res. scientist, RES. CTR, UNIROYAL, INC, 57-64, SR. SCIENTIST, 64- Mil. Microanalyst, Chem.Corps, Edgewood Arsenal, 45-46. Am. Chem. Soc. Stabilization and degradation mechanisms of polymers; fiber reinforced plastics; synthesis and spinning of fibers. Address: 64 Gerdes Ave, Verona, NJ 07044.

FARBER, MORTON SHELDON, b. N.Y.C, Apr. 25, 44; m. 67. HIGH ENERGY PHYSICS. B.S, Queens Col.(N.Y.), 64; Ph.D.(high energy physics), Rochester, 69. RES. ASSOC. HIGH ENERGY PHYSICS, UNIV. NOTRE DAME, 69- Am. Phys. Soc. Experimental high energy physics. bubble chamber technique. Address: Dept. of Physics, University of Notre Dame, Notre Dame, IN 46556.

FARBER, PAUL A, b. Brooklyn, N.Y, Sept. 13, 38; m. 60; c. 2. MICROBIOLOGY. A.B, Michigan, 60, D.D.S, 62; Nat. Insts. Health fel, Rochester, 62-67, Ph.D.(microbiol), 67. ASST. PROF. MICROBIOL, SCH. DENT, TEMPLE UNIV, 67- Nat. Insts. Health spec. fel, Nat. Inst. Dent. Res, 70-71. Dent.C, U.S.A.R, Capt. AAAS; Am. Soc. Microbiol. Virus infection during pregnancy; immunology of the mouse. Address: Temple University School of Dentistry, 3223 N. Broad St, Philadelphia, PA 19140.

FARBER, PAUL L, Hist. of Sci, see 6th ed, Dir. Am. Scholars, Vol. I.

FARBER, PHILLIP ANDREW, b. Wilkes-Barre, Pa, Sept. 19, 34; m. 65; c. 2. CYTOLOGY, CYTOGENETICS. B.S, King's Col, 56; M.S, Boston Col, 58; Ph.D.(biol), Catholic Univ, 63. Asst. biol, Boston Col, 56-57; St. Louis, 58-59; Catholic Univ, 61-62; asst. instr, Georgetown, 62-63; res. biologist, lab. perinatal physiol, Nat. Insts. Health, 63-64; res. instr. phys. med. & rehab, med. ctr, N.Y. Univ, 64-66; PROF. BIOL, BLOOMSBURG STATE COL, 66- U.S. Pub. Health Serv. res. grant, 65; consult. cytogenetics, Geisinger Med. Ctr, 67- AAAS; Am. Soc. Human Genetics; Am. Soc. Cell Biol; Teratology Soc; Am. Inst. Biol. Sci; Tissue Cult. Asn. Human and mammalian cytogenetics. Address: Dept. of Biology, Bloomsburg State College, Bloomsburg, PA 17815.

FARBER, SAUL JOSEPH, b. New York, N.Y, Feb. 11, 18; m. 49; c. 2. MEDICINE. A.B, N.Y. Univ, 38, M.D, 42. Fel. MED, col. med, N.Y. UNIV, 48-49, instr, 49-53, asst. prof, 53-57, assoc. prof, 57-62, prof, 62-66, NATHAN FRIEDMAN PROF. & CHMN. DEPT, SCH. MED. & DIR. MED, UNIV. HOSP. & UNIV. MED. SERV, BELLEVUE HOSP, 66-, acting dean, schs. med, 63-66. Chmn, Asn. Career Scientists & Health Res. Coun, 62- Dipl, Am. Bd. Internal Med, 55. U.S.N.R, 42-46, Lt. Am. Soc. Clin. Invest.(secy-treas, 57-60); Asn. Am. Physicians; Am. Fedn. Clin. Res; Harvey Soc.(treas, 63-); Soc. Exp. Biol. & Med; Am. Physiol. Soc; N.Y. Acad. Med. Physiological and biochemical clinical investigation related to human disease. Address: Post-Graduate Medical School, New York University School of Medicine, 550 First Ave, New York, NY 10016.

FARBER, SERGIO JULIO, b. Argentina, Jan. 30, 38; m. 60; c. 2. ORGANIC CHEMISTRY. M.S. & Nat. Coun. Tech. & Sci. Res. fel, Buenos Aires, 62, Ph.D.(org. chem), 65. Teaching asst. org. chem, Buenos Aires, 62-64, instr, 64-66; res. chemist, California, Santa Barbara, 67-68; sr. res. chemist, Calbiochem, Inc, Calif, 68-70; LAB. DIR, NUCLEAR DYNAMICS, INC, EL MONTE, 70- Lectr, California, Santa Barbara, summer 68. Argentine Army, 61. Am. Chem. Soc; N.Y. Acad. Sci. Synthesis and mechanism of reaction of organic compounds; study of methods for the synthesis of labeled compounds. Address: 475 Ladera St, Monterey Park, CA 91754.

FARBER, SEYMOUR M(ORGAN), b. Buffalo, N.Y, June 3, 12; m. 40; c. 3. THORACIC DISEASES. B.A, Buffalo, 31; M.D, Harvard, 39. From instr. to CLIN. PROF. MED, SCH. MED, UNIV. CALIF, SAN FRANCISCO, 42-, DIR. CONTINUING ED. MED. & HEALTH SCI, 63-, from dean educ. serv. to DEAN CONTINUING EDUC. HEALTH SCIS, 63- Lectr, sch. pub. health, California, Berkeley, 48-, spec. asst. to pres, 64- In charge tuberc. & chest serv, San Francisco Gen. Hosp, 45-; spec. consult, Nat. Cancer Inst, 58-60; nat. consult. to Surgeon Gen, U.S. Air Force, 62- Mem. President's Cmt. Status of Women, 62-63. Am. Col. Chest Physicians (pres. elect, 59, pres, 59-60); Am. Col. Cardiol; Am. Med. Asn; Am. Fedn. Clin. Res; N.Y. Acad. Sci. Cancer of lung; pulmonary cytology; chemotherapy of lung cancer; chemotherapy of tuberculosis pulmonary pathophysiology; continuing education in medicine and the health sciences. Address: Medical Center, University of California, San Francisco, CA 94122.

FARBER, SIDNEY, b. Buffalo, N.Y, Sept. 30, 03; m. 27; c. 4. PATHOLOGY. B.S, Buffalo, 23; Freiburg & Heidelberg, 23-24; M.D, Harvard, 27; hon. D.Sc, Suffolk, 60, Boston, 61, Providence Col, 61; hon. M.D, Ghent, 62, Louvain, 65; hon. L.H.D, Brandeis, 63; hon. D.Sc, Albert Einstein Col. Med, 66; hon. M.D, Karolinska Inst, 69; hon. D.Sc, N.Y. Med. Col, 70. Asst. PATH, Harvard Med. Sch, 27-28; Munich, 28-29; instr, HARVARD MED. SCH, 29-34, assoc, 34-38, asst. prof, 38-48, prof, 48-67, S. Burt Wolbach prof, 67-70, EMER. PROF, 70-; CONSULT. PATH. & ONCOL, MED. CTR, CHILDREN'S HOSP, MASS, 70- Moseley traveling fel, Harvard, 35-36; pathologist, Children's Hosp, Mass, 29-47, pathologist in chief, 47-70, emer. pathologist, 70-, chmn. staff, med. ctr, 46-70, emer. chmn, 70-; dir. res, Children's Cancer Res. Found, 48-, pres, 70-; co-chmn. Senator Yarborough comn. consults. on conquest cancer, 70- Great medal, Univ. Ghent, 59; Albert Lasker award, 66; Boston medal, 67; Jurzykowski award, 70; Papanicolaou award, 71. Am. Cancer Soc.(pres, 70, award, 70); Am. Soc. Exp. Path; Soc. Pediat. Res; Am. Pediat. Soc; Am. Asn. Path. & Bact. Pathologic physiology of respiratory and cardiovascular systems; tumors; pathology of infancy and childhood. Address: Children's Cancer Research Foundation, 35 Binney St, Boston, MA 02115.

FARBMAN, ALBERT IRVING, b. Boston, Mass, Aug. 25, 34; m. 61; c. 3. HISTOLOGY, CYTOLOGY. A.B, Harvard, 55, D.M.D, 59; U.S. Pub. Health Serv. fel, N.Y. Univ, 59-61, M.S, 61, Ph.D.(basic med. sci), 64. Instr. ANAT, sch. med, N.Y. Univ, 62-64; asst. prof, NORTHWEST. UNIV, 64-67, ASSOC. PROF, 67- U.S. Pub. Health Serv. training res. grant, 61-64; res. career develop. award, Nat. Inst. Dent. Res, 66-71. AAAS; Am. Asn. Anat; Am. Soc. Cell Biol. Cytodifferentiation of taste buds; keratinization of oral epithelium and epidermis. Address: Dept. of Anatomy, Northwestern University, 303 E. Chicago Ave, Chicago, IL 60611.

FARDIG, OLIVER B, b. Chicago, Ill, Jan. 5, 18; m. 43; c. 4. BIOCHEMISTRY. B.A, Carleton Col, 40; M.S, Pa. State Col, 42, Nat. Canners Asn. fel, 44-46; Ph.D.(biochem), 47. Asst. chem, Pa. State Col, 42-44; RES. CHEMIST, BRISTOL LABS, BRISTOL-MYERS CO, 47- Am. Chem. Soc. Foods and nutrition; food processing and nutritive changes; vitamins in foods; penicillin chemistry; new antibiotic isolation. Address: Fermentation Development Labs, Bristol Labs, Bristol-Myers Co, Box 657, Syracuse, NY 13201.

FARE, LOUIS RICHARD, b. Chicago, Ill, Oct. 4, 31; m. 53; c. 4. MICROBIOLOGY, STEROID CHEMISTRY. B.S, Manhattan Col, 53; M.S, Massachusetts 57. Jr. analyst microbiol, SMITH KLINE & FRENCH LABS, 57-59, chem, 59-61, microbiologist, 61-65, SR. MICROBIOLOGIST, 66- Med.C, U.S.A, 53-55. Am. Soc. Microbiol; Am. Chem. Soc. Thermal inactivation of organisms, biological and biochemical analysis; steroid hydroxylation and degradation by microbes; transformation and isolation of organic compounds by microbes or enzymes. Address: Smith Kline & French Labs, 1500 Spring Garden St, Philadelphia, PA 19101.

FARELL, D(AVID) M(ENDEL), b. Newport News, Va, Aug. 23, 03; m. 29; c. 1. MEDICINE. A.B, Hopkins, 24; M.D, Jefferson Med. Col, 28. Assoc. prof. OBSTET. & GYNEC, JEFFERSON MED. COL, 52-63, prof, 63-71, HON. PROF, 71- Dipl, Am. Bd. Obstet. & Gynec. Fel. Am. Col. Surg; Am. Col. Obstet. & Gynec; Asn. Prof. Obstet. & Gynec. Fetal electrocardiography; pelvic malignancy; ectopic pregnancy; gynecology and obstetrics. Address: 1912 Spruce St, Philadelphia, PA 19103.

FARESE, ROBERT V, b. Newark, N.J, Jan. 23, 34; m. 58; c. 5. MEDICINE, ENDOCRINOLOGY. St. Peter's Col, 51-54; M.D, Georgetown, 58. U.S. Pub. Health Serv. res. fel, 61-62; asst. prof. med, State Univ. N.Y. Buffalo,

62-67, asst. res. prof. biochem, 66-67; sr. investr, Nat. Inst. Child Health & Human Develop, 67-70; ASSOC. PROF. MED, SCH. MED, ST. LOUIS UNIV, 70- Clin. assoc. physician, Buffalo Gen. Hosp, 62-; Nat. Insts. Health res. grant, 63-69; chief endocrinol, Buffalo Vet. Admin. Hosp, 66-67. Endocrine Soc; Am. Fedn. Clin. Res. Endocrinology, control of adrenal growth and function by adrenocorticotropic hormone. Address: 275 Blakmer Pl, Webster Groves, MO 63119.

FAREWELL, JOHN P, b. Worchester, Mass, May 29, 42; m. 68; c. 2. PHYSICAL & POLYMER CHEMISTRY. B.S.Ed, State Univ. N.Y. Col. Plattsburgh, 64; Ph.D.(chem), State Univ. N.Y. Buffalo, 69. RES. SCIENTIST, UNION CAMP CORP, 68- Am. Chem. Soc; Tech. Asn. Pulp & Paper Indust. Chlorophyl synthesis; physical chemistry of polymers and ion exchange; properties of paper. Address: Research & Development Division, Union Camp Corp, P.O. Box 412, Princeton, NJ 08540.

FARHA, FLOYD, b. Shattuck, Okla, Aug. 1, 33; m. 58; c. 4. INORGANIC CHEMISTRY. B.A, Wichita, 55, M.S, 57; Ph.D.(chem, math), Kansas, 65. RES. CHEMIST, Boeing Aircraft Co, 57-59, 60-61; PHILLIPS PETROL. CO, 65- U.S.A.F, 59-60, Res, 60-70, Capt. Am. Chem. Soc. Organometallic and nonaqueous solvent chemistry; homogeneous and heterogeneous catalysis. Address: Research & Development Dept, Phillips Petroleum Co, Bartlesville, OK 74003.

FARHI, LEON E(LIE), b. Cairo, Egypt, Oct. 9, 23; U.S. citizen; m. 49; c. 2. PHYSIOLOGY. B.Sc, Am. Univ. Beirut, 40; M.D, Univ. St. Joseph, Lebanon, 47. Resident, Hadassah Univ. Hosp, Israel, 50-52; res. fel, Trudeau Sanatorium, 53; res. fel. physiol, Univ. Rochester, 53-54; res. fel. & asst. physician, sch. med, Johns Hopkins Univ, 54-55; instr. physiol. & pulmonary diseases, Hebrew Univ, Israel, 56-58; asst. prof. PHYSIOL, STATE UNIV. N.Y. BUFFALO, 58-62, assoc. prof, 62-66, PROF, 66- Vis. prof, Univ. Fribourg, 65-66; Nat. Sci. Found. sr. fel, 65-66; consult, Erie County Health Dept; U.S. Pub. Health Serv. Am. Physiol. Soc; Aerospace Med. Asn; Underseas Med. Soc. Pulmonary physiology and physiopathology; environmental and cardio-respiratory physiology. Address: Dept. of Physiology, State University of New York at Buffalo, Buffalo, NY 14214.

FARIES, DILLARD WAYNE, b. Mooreland, Okla, Sept. 28, 41; m. 65; c. 2. PHYSICS. B.A, Rice Univ, 63; Nat. Sci. Found. fel, Univ. Calif, Berkeley, 63-65, Ph.D.(physics), 69. Summers, jr. engr, Radio Corp. Am, 62, geophys. trainee, Shell Oil Co, 63; res. asst. PHYSICS, Univ. Calif, Berkeley, 65-69; ASST. PROF, WHEATON COL. (ILL), 69- Am. Asn. Physics Teachers. Nonlinear interaction of electromagnetic fields with matter. Address: Dept. of Physics, Wheaton College, Wheaton, IL 60187.

FARINA, JOSEPH PETER, b. Queens, N.Y, May 11, 31; m. 55; c. 4. MICROBIOLOGY, PHYSIOLOGY. B.S, St. John's Col, 53; M.S, St. John's (N.Y), 58, M.S.E, 60, Ph.D.(microbiol), 67. Teacher, high sch, N.Y, 58-67; from assoc. prof. to PROF. BIOL, LOWELL STATE COL, 67-, DIR. MED. TECHNOL. MAJ, 70- Sr. lab. technician, Mercy Hosp, N.Y, 58-63, instr, 62-67, radiol. physics, 67-; Peninsular Gen. Hosp, N.Y, 65-66; Nat. Sci. Found. res. summer participant, 68. U.S.A, 54-56. AAAS; Am. Soc. Zool; N.Y. Acad. Sci; Soc. Protozool; Am. Inst. Biol. Sci; Am. Soc. Med. Tech. Axenic cultivation and nutritional requirements of Blepharisma, a pink ciliate. Address: Dept. of Biology, Lowell State College, Lowell, MA 01854.

FARINA, ROBERT DONALD, b. Schenectady, N.Y, Sept. 29, 34; m. 66; c. 2. INORGANIC & PHYSICAL CHEMISTRY. B.Ch.E, Rensselaer Polytech, 57; M.S, Union Col, 63; Ph.D.(chem), State Univ. N.Y. Buffalo, 68. Engr, Stauffer Chem. Co, 57-60; test engr, Knolls Atomic Power Lab, Gen. Elec. Co, 60-63; fels. CHEM, California, 67-69 & Utah, 69; ASSOC. PROF, W.KY. UNIV, 69- Sig.C, U.S.A, 58, 1st Lt. Am. Chem. Soc; Am. Inst. Chem. Eng. Kinetic studies of fast reactions in solution; coordination chemistry of transition metal complexes. Address: Dept. of Chemistry, Western Kentucky University, Bowling Green, KY 42101.

FARINHOLT, L(ARKIN) H(UNDLEY), b. Baltimore, Md, Sept. 24, 05; m. 47; c. 3. CHEMISTRY. B.S, Hopkins, 27; Rhodes scholar, Oxford, 28-31, Ph.D. (org. chem), 31. Res, Hynson, Westcott & Dunning, Inc, Md, 32-33; asst. prof. chem, Washington & Lee, 33-37, assoc. prof, 37-41; exec. officer, explosives res. lab, Off. Sci. Res. & Develop. & Nat. Defense Res. Cmt, 41-45; assoc. prof, chem, Columbia, 47-54, prof, 54-60, dir. chem. labs, 53-60; ADMINSTR. PROG. BASIC RES. PHYS. SCI, ALFRED P. SLOAN FOUND, 60-, v.pres. & trustee, 62-69. Sci. attache, U.S. Embassey, London, 51-52; dep. sci. adv, Dept. State, 58-60. Spec. asst. to chmn, Nat. Defense Res. Cmt, 45-46; mem, cmt. Int. Exchange Persons, 53-56. Presidential Cert. of Merit. AAAS; Am. Chem. Soc. Explosives; organic synthesis. Address: Alfred P. Sloan Foundation, 630 Fifth Ave, New York, NY 10020.

FARIS, BURT F(ROMENT), b. Ft. Worth, Texas, Aug. 28, 10; m. 44. CHEMISTRY. B.S, Texas Christian, 31; Ph.D.(org. chem), Virginia, 35. Mallinckrodt fel, alkaloid chem, Virginia, 35-36; chemist, E.I. du Pont de Nemours & Co, 36-43; Manhattan Proj, Chicago, Oak Ridge & Hanford, 43-46; rayon dept, E.I. DU PONT DE NEMOURS & CO, INC, 46-47, res. supvr, 47-52; MGR. DYEING & FINISHING, TECH. SERV. SECT, TEXTILE FIBERS DEPT, 52- With Office Sci. Res. & Develop, 44. Am. Chem. Soc; Am. Asn. Textile Chem. & Colorists. Dyeing and finishing of fabrics from synthetic fibers and from blends of synthetic and natural fibers. Address: E.I. du Pont de Nemours & Co, Inc, Centre Rd. Bldg, Wilmington, DE 19898.

FARIS, DONALD G(EORGE), b. Peking, China, July 5, 30; Can. citizen; m. 55; c. 3. GENETICS, PLANT PHYSIOLOGY. B.S.A, Univ. B.C, 54, M.S.A, 56; Ph.D.(genetics), Univ. Calif, Davis, 63. Spec. off, plant breeding, Ministry Agr, North. Nigeria, 55-59; res. off, CEREAL BREEDING, RES. BR, CAN. DEPT. AGR, 63-65, RES. SCIENTIST, 65- Mem, Can. Comt. Grain Breeding, 71-74. Agr. Inst. Can; Genetics Soc. Can, Can. Soc. Agron. Evolution of Vigna sinensis; effects of temperature, photoperiod and genotype on germination; development and yield in Hordeum vulgare. Address; Research Station, Canada Dept. of Agriculture, Box 29, Beaverlodge, Alta, Can.

FARIS, F(RANK) E(DGAR), b. Durango, Colo, Apr. 4, 19; m. 40; c. 3. PHYSICS. B.Eng, Southern California, 46; Ph.D.(physics), California, Los Angeles, 50. Supvr. template, preliminary prod. & modification dept, Lockheed Aircraft Corp, 40-45; asst. physics, California, Los Angeles, 46-49; res. engr, Atomics Int. Div, N.Am. Aviation, Inc, 49-52, group leader radiation effects, 52-55, reactor oper, 55-56, chief reactor develop. dept, 56-58; gen. tech. mgr, Interatom Int. Atomreaktorbau, Inc, Ger, 58-67; PRES, Faris, Jacobson & Assocs, Inc, Mass, 67-70; INTERDEVELOP, INC, 70- Consult, new bus. develop. Am. Phys. Soc; Am. Nuclear Soc. Reactor development. Address: Interdevelopment, Inc, 176 Second Ave, Waltham, MA 02154.

FARIS, JOHN J(AY), b. Grandview, Wash, Nov. 7, 21; m. 42; c. 4. PHYSICS. B.A, Reed Col, 43; Ph.D.(physics), Washington (Seattle), 51. Assoc. prof. PHYSICS, Pacific, 50-54; asst. prof, Colo. State Univ, 54-58, assoc. prof, 58-64, prof, 64-68; PROF. & CHMN. DEPT, STOUT STATE UNIV, 68- U.S.N.R, 45, Ens. Am. Phys. Soc; Am. Asn. Physics Teachers. Secondary emission of electrons; electroretinagram; microwaves; magnetism. Address: Dept. of Physics, Stout State University, Menomonie, WI 54751.

FARIS, S(AM) R(USSELL), b. Moore, Okla, Nov. 5, 17; m. 42; c. 5. PHYSICAL CHEMISTRY. B.S, Oklahoma, 42, M.S, 46, Ph.D.(chem), 49. Sr. res. technologist, FIELD RES. LAB, MOBIL RES. & DEVELOP. CORP, 49-54, RES. ASSOC, 54- Chem.C, 42-46, Lt. AAAS; Am. Chem. Soc. Electrochemistry; electrokinetics; analytical chemistry; fluid flow in porous media. Address: Mobil Research & Development Corp, Field Research Lab, P.O. Box 900, Dallas, TX 75221.

FARIS, WILLIAM GUIGNARD, b. Montreal, Que, Can, Nov. 22, 39; U.S. citizen. MATHEMATICAL PHYSICS. B.A, Washington (Seattle), 60; Ph.D. Princeton (math), 65. Asst. prof. math, Cornell Univ, 64-70; MATHEMATICIAN, ADVAN. STUDIES CTR, BATTELLE INST, SWITZ, 70- Am. Math. Soc. Applications of functional analysis to differential equations of quantum mechanics. Address: Battelle Institute Advanced Studies Center, Geneva, Switz.

FARISH, DONALD JAMES, b. Winnipeg, Man, Dec. 7, 42; m. 64; c. 1. ZOOLOGY, ENTOMOLOGY. B.Sc, British Columbia, 63; M.S, N.C. State, 65; Richmond fel, Harvard, 65-68, Ph.D.(biol), 69. Instr. zool. & entom, UNIV. MO-COLUMBIA, 68-69, ASST. PROF. BIOL. SCI. & ENTOM. & GROUP LEADER BEHAV. SCI, 70- Univ. Mo. Res. Coun. grant, 69, 70, 71. Animal Behav. Soc; Entom. Soc. Am. Animal behavior and evolution with special reference to land dwelling arthropods; genetic control of behavior; polymorphism; phoresy. Address: Division of Biological Sciences, University of Missouri-Columbia, Columbia, MO 65201.

FARISON, JAMES BLAIR, b. McClure, Ohio, May 26, 38; m. 61; c. 2. ENGINEERING & EDUCATION. B.S, Univ. Toledo, 60; Phi Kappa Phi fel, 60-61, Stanford Univ, M.S, 61, Nat. Sci. Found. fel, 61-64, Ph.D.(elec. eng), 64. Asst. prof. ELEC. ENG, UNIV. TOLEDO, 64-67, ASSOC. PROF, 67-, DEAN, 71-, acting dean, 70-71, asst. dean, graduate studies, 69-70. Sr. mem. Inst. Elec. & Electronics Eng; Am. Soc. Eng. Educ; sr. mem. Instrument Soc. Am; Nat. Soc. Prof. Eng. Systems analysis and design; theory of information; communication and control; random processes; discrete-time systems; system identification. College of Engineering, University of Toledo, Toledo, OH 43606.

FARKAS, DANIEL FREDERICK, b. Boston, Mass, June 20, 33; m. 59; c. 2. FOOD TECHNOLOGY. B.S, Mass. Inst. Tech, 54, univ. scholar. & M.S, 55, Gen. Foods fel, 58-59, Ph.D.(foods sci), 60. Staff food technologist, Arthur D. Little, Inc, Mass, 60-62; asst. prof. food processing, Cornell Univ, 62-67; RES. CHEM. ENGR, AGR. RES. SERV, WEST. REGIONAL RES. LABS, U.S. DEPT. AGR, 67-, ACTING HEAD UNIT OPERS. INVESTS, 70- Adj. assoc. prof, nutrit. sci. dept, Univ. Calif, Berkeley; mem. comt. on fruit & veg. prod, adv. bd. on mil. personnel supplies, Nat. Res. Coun, 71-73. Qm.C, 55-57, Res, 57-, Maj. AAAS; Am. Chem. Soc; Inst. Food Technol; Am. Inst. Chem. Eng; N.Y. Acad. Sci. Food processing; dehydration thermal processing; new process development for food industry. Address: U.S. Dept. of Agriculture, Agriculture Research Service, Western Regional Research Lab, Berkeley, CA 94710.

FARKAS, EUGENE, b. Melvindale, Mich, Dec. 11, 26; m. 56; c. 3. ORGANIC & MEDICINAL CHEMISTRY. B.S, Wayne State, 49, Ph.D.(org. chem), 52. Res. assoc, Mass. Inst. Technol, 52-53; Wayne State, 53-54; SR. SCIENTIST, LILLY RES. LABS, 54-70, ANAL. DEVELOP. METAB, 70- U.S.A, 44-47. Am. Chem. Soc; Brit. Chem. Soc; Swiss Chem. Soc. Steroids; alkaloids and natural products; organic synthesis. Address: Research Lab, Eli Lilly & Co, Indianapolis, IN 46205.

FARKAS, HERSHEL M, b. N.Y.C, Dec. 2, 39; m. 60; c. 2. MATHEMATICS. B.S, Yeshiva, 61, Nat. Defense Educ. Act fel, 61-64, M.S, 63, Ph.D.(math), 65. Res. assoc. MATH, Belfer Grad. Sch. Sci, Yeshiva, 65-66; asst. prof, Johns Hopkins Univ, 66-68; assoc. prof, STATE UNIV. N.Y. STONY BROOK, 68-71, PROF, 71- Sloan Found. fel, 70-72. Am. Math. Soc. Moduli of compact Riemann surfaces. Address: Dept. of Mathematics, State University of New York at Stony Brook, Stony Brook, NY 11790.

FARKAS, MARTIN S(TEVEN), b. Youngstown, Ohio, Nov. 22, 33; m. 62; c. 2. METALLURGICAL ENGINEERING. B.S, Ohio State Univ, 56, M.S, 62. Res. assoc. METALL, BATTELLE MEM. INST, 56-66, ASSOC. FEL, 66- Am. Soc. Metals; Am. Inst. Mining, Metall. & Petrol. Eng. Metals and minerals economics. Address: Dept. of Social & Management System, Battelle Memorial Institute, 505 King Ave, Columbus, OH 43201.

FARKAS, ROLAND ZOLTAN, b. New York, N.Y, June 25, 10; m. 46; c. 4. ORGANIC CHEMISTRY, MEDICINE. M.D, Eötvös Lóránd, 33. Res. chemist, New Eng. Res. Asn, 37-40; Morton Chem. Co, 40-46; tech. dir, Texize Chem. Inc, 46-59; TECH. DIR. & PRES, EDCO CHEM. CO, INC, 59- Consult, Deering Milliken Res. Corp, 59-66; Coastal Chem. Co, 64-; Sylvan Chem. Div, Magnolia Industs. Inc, 66- Am. Chem. Soc. Synthesis of textile chemical auxiliary products; organic surface active agents; emulsion and emulsion polymerization. Address: Edco Chemical Co, Inc, P.O. Box 5025, Columbia, SC 29205.

FARKAS, TIBOR G, b. Budapest, Hungary, Aug, 12, 27; U.S. citizen; m. 49, 71; c. 2. OPHTHALMOLOGY, BIOCHEMISTRY. A.B, Columbia, 49; univ. fels. Western Reserve, 54-58, 60-62, Nat. Coun. Combat Blindness fel, 58-60, M.D, 61, Ph.D.(anat), 62. Res. asst. biochem, N.Y. Univ, 50-52; res. fel. pharmacol, Western Reserve, 61-62; U.S. Pub. Health Serv. trainee OPHTHAL, UNIV. CHICAGO, 62-64, asst. prof, UNIV. CLINS, 62-70, ASSOC. PROF, 70- Chem.C, U.S.A, 52-54. AAAS; Am. Chem. Soc; Am. Col. Surg; Am. Diabetes Asn; Am. Med. Asn; Asn. Res. Vision & Ophthal. Intermediary metabolism of the crystalline lens; ophthalmic complications of diabetes; fatty acid synthesis; ophthalmic pathology; diseases of the pigment epithelium. Address: Dept. of Ophthalmology, University of Chicago Clinics, 950 E. 59th St, Chicago, IL 60637.

FARKAS, WALTER ROBERT, b. New York, N.Y, June 30, 33; m. 56; c. 2. BIOCHEMISTRY. B.S, City Col. New York, 55; scholar, Duke, 55-58, Ph.D. (biochem), 60. Res. asst. biochem, Duke, 55-60; res. assoc, sch. med, N.Y. Univ, 60-63; fel. hemat, col. physicians & surgeons, Columbia, 63-66; asst. prof. BIOCHEM, MEM. RES. CTR, UNIV. TENN, 66-70, ASSOC. PROF, 70- Life Ins. Med. Res. Fund grant, 67-70; Nat. Insts. Health grant, 68-71. Am. Chem. Soc; Am. Soc. Biol. Chem. Mammalian sulfur metabolism; biosynthesis of lysine; control mechanisms in hemoglobin biosynthesis; biological effects of metals; transfer RNA of erythroid cells. Address: Memorial Research Center, University of Tennessee, Knoxville, TN 37920.

FARKAS-HIMSLEY, HANNAH, b. Moscow, Russia, May 3, 18; Can. citizen; m. 40; c. 2. BACTERIOLOGY, MICROBIOLOGY. M.Sc, Hebrew Univ, Israel, 40, Ph.D.(bact), 46. Asst. bact, Hadassah Med. Sch, Hebrew Univ, 49-53, 55-57; attache sci, Israel Embassy, Eng, 53-55; fel. MICROBIOL, SCH. HYG, UNIV. TORONTO, 58-59, grant, 59, asst. prof, 59-62, ASSOC. PROF, 62- Res. grants, Nat. Res. Coun. Can, 60-61, Med. Res. Coun. Can, 61-70, Can. Nat. Health, 67-69, Toronto, summer 64. Am. Soc. Microbiol; N.Y. Acad. Sci; Can. Soc. Microbiol; Royal Inst. Gt. Brit. Drug resistance to streptomycin and penicillin; bacteriocin production by vibrio comma, mode of action, and the possible relation to virulence; halogen resistant bacteria in treated swimming pools; diagnosis of pseudomallei; survey of staphylococcus on Easter Island. Address: Dept. of Microbiology, School of Hygiene, University of Toronto, Toronto 5, Ont, Can.

FARKASS, IMRE, b. Budapest, Hungary, Sept. 26, 19; nat; m. 51. PHYSICS. Dipl, Budapest Tech, 42. Asst. prof. physics, Budapest Tech, 42-46, lectr, inst. physics, 47-49, assoc. head, vacuum res. lab, 50-56; head dept. math. & physics, Agr. Univ. Budapest, 54-56; sr. physicist, Nat. Res. Corp, Mass, 57-60; dir. appl. physics dept, Ilikon Corp, Mass, 61-65; MEM. TECH. STAFF, BELL TEL. LABS, 65- Invited lectr, Mass. Inst. Technol, 64; Northeastern, 65; Johns Hopkins, 69. Am. Phys. Soc. Applied physics; vacuum physics and technology; flexible printed circuits; interconnection technology. Address: Bell Telephone Labs, Whippany, NJ 07981.

FARLEY, B(ELMONT) G(REENLEE), b. Cape Girardeau, Mo, Dec. 29, 20; m. 53; c. 3. BIOPHYSICS. B.S, Maryland, 41; Yale, 45-48, M.S, 46, Sheffield-Loomis fel, 46-48, Ph.D.(physics), 48. Asst. math, Mass. Inst. Tech, 41-42, mem. staff, Radiation Lab, 42-45; instr. physics, Yale, 47-48; mem. tech. staff, Bell Tel. Labs, 48-53; mem. staff, Lincoln Labs, Mass. Inst. Tech, 53-64; ASSOC. PROF. biophys, Johnson Found, sch. med, Pennsylvania, 64-70; INFO. SCI, TEMPLE UNIV, 70- Civilian technician, Off. Sci. Res. & Develop, 43. Am. Math. Soc; Am. Physiol. Soc; Am. Phys. Soc; Inst. Elec. & Electronics Eng; Biophys. Soc; Fedn. Am. Soc. Exp. Biol. Theoretical and experimental neurophysiology. Address: Dept. of Information Science, Temple University, Philadelphia, PA 19122.

FARLEY, CHARLES P(ETER), b. St. Louis, MO, Dec. 20, 26; m. 52; c. 4. ORGANIC CHEMISTRY. B.S, St. Louis, 50; Ph.D.(chem), Notre Dame, 56. Res. chemist, Shell Oil Co, 55-60; MONSANTO CO, ST. LOUIS, 60-68, develop. proj. engr, 68-71, MKT. SUPVR, 71- Am. Chem. Soc; Soc. Plastics Eng; Internal additives for paper; impregnating chemicals for paper and paper coatings; plasticizers for polyvinyl chloride plastisols; flame retardant additives for plastic materials. Address: 1460 Nashua Dr, Florissant, MO 63033.

FARLEY, DONALD T, (JR), b. N.Y.C, Oct. 26, 33; m. 56; c. 3. IONOSPHERIC PHYSICS. B.Eng.Phys, Cornell, 56, H.C. Ford fel, 56-57, Nat. Sci. Found. fel, 58-59, Ph.D.(ionospheric physics), 60. NATO fel. ionospheric physics, Cambridge, 59-60; docent, Chalmers Tech. Sweden, 60-61; physicist, Jicamarca Radar Observ, Lima, Peru, U.S. Nat. Bur. Standards, 61-64, dir, 64-67; PROF. ELEC. ENG, CORNELL UNIV, 67- Mem. comn. III & IV, Int. Sci. Radio Union, exec. comt. comn. IV, 66-69. Nat. Bur. Standards award, 63; Environ. Sci. Serv. Admin. award, 64; U.S. Dept. Commerce gold medal, 67. Am. Geophys. Union. Ionospheric physics; scattering of radio waves from thermal fluctuations in a plasma; plasma instabilities in the ionosphere. Address: Dept. of Electrical Engineering, Cornell University, Ithaca, NY 14850.

FARLEY, EUGENE S(HEDDEN), JR, b. Upland Borough, Pa, Feb. 6, 27; m. 55; c. 4. MEDICINE, PUBLIC HEALTH. B.S, Swarthmore Col, 50; M.D, Univ. Rochester, 54; M.P.H, Johns Hopkins Univ, 67. Intern, Phila. Gen. Hosp, 54-55; resident gen. practice, med. ctr, Univ. Colo, 55-56; internal med, Univ. Vt. & De Goesbriand Hosp, 58-59; private practice, 59-66; resident fel, pub. health, Johns Hopkins Sch. Hyg. & Pub. Health, 66-67; ASSOC. PROF. MED, PREV. MED. & COMMUNITY HEALTH & PEDIAT. & DIR. FAMILY MED. PROG, SCH. MED, UNIV. ROCHESTER, 67- U.S.N.R, 45-46; U.S.P.H.S, 56-58, Sr. Asst. Surg. Am. Acad. Gen. Practice; Am. Med. Asn; Asn. Am. Med. Cols; Am. Pub. Health Asn; Asn. Teachers Prev. Med; Soc. Teachers Family Med. Development and implementation of systems of primary care; use of ancillaries who allow provision of more efficient and effective medical care to those needing it; built-in research potential in all primary care practices. Address: Family Medicine Program, University of Rochester School of Medicine & Dentistry, Mt. Vernon Ave, Rochester, NY 14620.

FARLEY, FRANCIS FREDERIC, b. Perrysburg, Ohio, Oct. 9, 12; m. 41; c. 3. CHEMISTRY. A.B, St. John's Col.(Ohio), 34; M.S, Detroit, 36; fel, Iowa State, Ph.D.(plant chem), 41. Asst. chemist, Nat. Biscuit Co, Ohio, 33-37; asst. plant chem, exp. sta, Iowa, 36-41; instr. chem, Detroit, 41-42; sr. res. chemist, Wood River Res. Labs, SHELL OIL CO, 42-43, group leader lubricants, 43-45, chief res. chemist, 45-53, Martinez Res. Lab, 53-61, res. dir, 61-64, dept. head, SHELL DEVELOP. CO, 64-70, REGIONAL REP, ENVIRON. CONSERV, 70- Am. Chem. Soc; Air Pollution Control Asn; Water Pollution Control Fedn; Am. Petrol. Inst. Petroleum product and process development; air and water conservation; environmental sciences. Address: Shell Development Co, Emeryville, CA 94608.

FARLEY, JAMES D, b. Olney, Ill, Sept. 28, 38; m. 65; c. 2. PLANT PATHOLOGY. B.S, Ill. Wesleyan, 61; M.S, Mich. State, 63, Ph.D.(plant path), 68. Asst. res. PLANT PATH, California, Berkeley, 68-69; ASST. PROF, OHIO AGR. RES. & DEVELOP. CTR, OHIO STATE UNIV, 69- Am. Phytopath. Soc. Soil borne diseases. Address: Ohio Agricultural Research & Development Center, Ohio State University, Wooster, OH 44691.

FARLEY, OTIS R(HANOR), b. Twin Falls, Idaho, May 15, 10; m. 33; c. 2. INTERNAL MEDICINE. B.A, California, Los Angeles, 33; M.D, Chicago, 40. Intern med. & surg, Dept. Health, Educ. & Welfare, St. Elizabeth's Hosp, 40-42, chief med. serv, 45-46, chief staff & dir. med. & surg. br, 56-70; assoc. clin. prof. med, sch. med, George Washington Univ, 60-70; RETIRED. Med.C, 42-46, Res, 46-50, Lt. Col. Am. Med. Asn. Psychiatry; management; hospital administration. Address: 245 Rustic Pl, Eugene, OR 97401.

FARLEY, ROGER DEAN, b. Jefferson, Iowa, Feb. 2, 35; m. 61; c. 1. COMPARATIVE PHYSIOLOGY. B.A, Univ. North. Iowa, 57; M.S, Iowa, 62; Ph.D.(insect neurophysiol), California, Santa Barbara, 66. Nat. Insts. Health fel, Tufts, 66-67; ASST. PROF. ZOOL, UNIV. CALIF, RIVERSIDE, 67- U.S.A, 57-59. Am. Soc. Zool. Neural control of respiratory and evasive behavior in arthropods; ultrastructure and physiology of arthropod sense organs. Address: Dept. of Biology, University of California, Riverside, CA 92502.

FARLEY, THOMAS ALBERT, b. Wash, D.C, Feb. 10, 33; m. 58; c. 2. GEOPHYSICS. B.S, George Washington, 54; Nat. Sci. Found. fel, Mass. Inst. Tech, 54-55, Ph.D.(physics), 59. Mem. tech. staff, space tech. labs, Thompson-Ramo-Wooldridge, Inc, 59-61; RES. GEOPHYSICIST, INST. GEOPHYS. & PLANETARY PHYSICS, UNIV. CALIF, LOS ANGELES, 61- Am. Phys. Soc; Am. Geophys. Union. Experimental measurements of fields and particles in space. Address: 12733 Woodley Ave, Granada Hills, CA 91344.

FARLEY, WILLIAM C, b. St. Paul, Minn, Feb. 4, 37; m. 60; c. 2. ORGANIC CHEMISTRY. B.S, Xavier, 59, M.S, 61; Ph.D.(org. chem), Ohio State, 67. Develop. chemist, EASTMAN KODAK CO, 61-63, SR. CHEMIST, 67- Am. Chem. Soc. Photographic developing agents; unsaturated heterocyclic systems; organic chemistry of chloramine. Address: Eastman Kodak Co, Research Labs, Kodak Park, Rochester, NY 14650.

FARLIN, STANLEY DEAN, b. Carns, Nebr, Sept. 16, 35; m. 54; c. 4. ANIMAL SCIENCE, ANIMAL NUTRITION. B.S, Nebraska, Lincoln, 61; M.S, Colorado State, 63; Ph.D.(animal nutrit), Illinois, Urbana, 67. Asst. prof. animal nutrit. & asst. animal scientist, Univ. Idaho, 67-70; ASSOC. PROF. ANIMAL SCI. & EXTEN. LIVESTOCK SPECIALIST, UNIV. NEBR, 70- Washburn lectr, Colo. State Univ, 68. AAAS; Am. Soc. Animal Sci. Ruminant nutrition; beef cattle nutrition and management. Address: Dept. of Animal Science, University of Nebraska, South Central Station, Clay Center, NE 68933.

FARLOW, STANLEY JEROME, b. Emmetsburg, Iowa, Mar. 7, 37; m. 67. APPLIED MATHEMATICS. B.S, Iowa State Univ, 59; M.S, Univ. Iowa, 62; U.S. Pub. Health Serv. fel, 64; Ph.D.(math), Ore. State Univ, 67. Mathematician, Nat. Insts. Health, 62-68; ASST. PROF. MATH, UNIV. MAINE, 68- U.S.P.H.S, 62-68, Lt. Comdr. Am. Math. Soc; Math. Asn. Am. Mathematical modeling of biological systems; partial differential equations; control theory; numerical analysis; computer systems. Address: Dept. of Mathematics, University of Maine, Orono, ME 04473.

FARMANFARMAIAN, ALLAHVERDI, b. Teheran, Iran, June 10, 29; m. 58; c. 2. PHYSIOLOGY, BIOLOGICAL SCIENCES. B.A, Reed Col, 52; Rockefeller Fund scholar, Stanford Univ, 54, M.A, 55, Eli Lilly scholar, 56, Curt Dietz scholar. & Ph.D.(physiol), 59. ASSOC. PROF. PHYSIOL, Pahlavi Univ, Iran, 61-66; Univ. Tehran, 66-67; RUTGERS UNIV, 67- Instr, marine biol. lab, Woods Hole, Mass, summers, 60-65, sr. investr, 66-71; mem, Marine Biol. Lab. Corp, 63; prin. investr, Nat. Sci. Found. grant, 66-69, coord, 68-69; coord, Nat. Insts. Health grant, 69-71. Fel. AAAS; Am. Physiol. Soc; Soc. Gen. Physiol; Am. Soc. Zool. Comparative approach to the mechanisms of membrane transport; nutrition and ecological physiology of marine animals. Address: Dept. of Physiology, Rutgers University, New Brunswick, NJ 08903.

FARMER, B(OBBY) J(OE), b. Aledo, Tex, Dec. 18, 32; m. 52; c. 2. NUCLEAR PHYSICS. B.A, Texas Christian, 54; fel, Rice Inst, 56-59, M.S, 57, Ph.D.(nuclear physics), 59. SR. SCIENTIST, LING-TEMCO-VOUGHT RES. CTR, 59- Summer jr. nuclear engr, Convair div, Gen. Dynamics Corp, Ft. Worth, 54. Am. Phys. Soc; Am. Nuclear Soc. Particle reactions induced by accelerated charged particles; heavy charged particle, neutron and beta spectroscopy; space radiation spectrometers; electron-bremsstrahlung; proto-alpha; cosmic ray; bremsstrahlung cross section; micrometeoroid detection. Address: Ling-Temco-Vought Research Center, Box 6144, Dallas, TX 75222.

FARMER, CHARLES HENRY, Statist, see Suppl. I to 11th ed. Soc. & Behav. Vols.

FARMER, D(ONALD) J(ACKSON), b. Morenci, Ariz, Apr. 7, 25; m. 49; c. 2. PHYSICS. B.S, Washington (Seattle), 50, Ph.D.(physics), 54. Res. assoc, Washington (Seattle), 54-55; mem. tech. staff, Ramo-Wooldridge Corp, 55-58; sr. staff, Space Tech. Labs, Inc, 58-60, assoc. dept. mgr, 59-60; mgr. quantum electronics, Gen. Tech. Corp, 60-63, v.pres, 63-64, pres, 64-69; v.pres, Tracor, Inc, 64-67, sr. v.pres, 67-71; CONSULT, 71- U.S.A.A.F,

44-46. Am. Phys. Soc. Atomic and nuclear physics; upper atmosphere physics; radio propagation; physical electronics. Address: 419 Surfview Dr, Pacific Palisades, CA 90272.

FARMER, DOUGLAS ALEXANDER, b. Winnipeg, Man, Can, Jan. 22, 16; nat; m. 43; c. 5. SURGERY. A.B, Michigan, 38; M.D, Harvard Med. Sch, 42. Intern, Mass. Gen. Hosp, 42-43; res, Mass. Mem. Hosp, 43-48, fel. SURG, 48-49; instr, sch. med, Boston Univ, 50-54, asst. prof, 54-59, assoc. prof, 59-67, asst, 46-58; ASSOC. CLIN. PROF, SCH. MED, YALE, 67-; CHMN. DEPT. SURG, HOSP. OF ST. RAPHAEL, NEW HAVEN, CONN, 67- Asst, Mass. Mem. Hosp, 48-51, asst. vis. surgeon, 51-54, assoc. vis. surgeon, 54-59, vis. surgeon, 59-; consult, Vet. Admin. Hosp, Providence, R.I, attend. surgeon, Boston, Mass. Med.C, 43-46, Capt. Am. Med. Asn; Am. Col. Surg. Investigation of gastric function with particular reference to ulcer and cancer. Address: 1450 Chapel St, New Haven, CT 06511.

FARMER, FLORENCE AMELIA, b. Ste. Anne de Bellevue, Que, May 10, 18. NUTRITION, PHYSIOLOGY. B.H.S, McGill Univ, 39, M.Sc, 44, Ph.D.(nutrit), 47. Asst. prof. nutrit, Macdonald Col, McGill Univ, 48-59; lectr. home sci, Women's Christian Col, Univ. Madras, 59-64; ASSOC. PROF. NUTRIT, MACDONALD COL, McGILL UNIV, 64- Can. Dietetic Asn; Can. Home Econ. Asn; Can. Inst. Food Technol; Nutrit. Soc. Can. Nutrient analysis of meat and fish from the Arctic; incorporation of fish protein concentrate in Canadian foods; flavor testing of irradiated chicken; flavor testing of paper mill effluent-treated fish. Address: School of Food Science, Box 276, Macdonald College, Que, Can.

FARMER, GEORGE T(HOMAS), JR, b. Pulaski, Va, May 26, 37; m. 68. GEOLOGY, PALEONTOLOGY. B.S, Virginia, 58, M.S, 60; Ph.D.(geol), Cincinnati, 68. Mus. specialist paleont, Smithsonian Inst, 63-64; lectr. GEOL, Howard, 64-65; asst. prof, MADISON COL.(VA), 65-68, ASSOC. PROF, 68- Geol. Consult, 68- AAAS; Paleont. Soc. Invertebrate paleontology; Paleozoic Bryozoa; stratigraphy and structure of the Appalachians west of the Blue Ridge. Address: Dept. of Geology, Madison College, Harrisonburg, VA 22801.

FARMER, GERALD I(RVINE), b. Manhattan, Kans, Mar. 1, 34; m. 60; c. 3. ATOMIC & CHEMICAL PHYSICS. B.S, Wyoming, 56; Heidelberg, 61-62; Pa. State, 62-63; M.S, Wisconsin, 64, Ph.D.(physics), 67. Chemist, Aerojet-Gen. Corp, Calif, 56-58; supvr. elec. test & checkout, missile div, Chrysler Corp, 58-61; MGR. ADVAN. LASER DEPT, IBM CORP, 67- Lectr, George Washington Univ, 70- U.S.A, 57, Res, 57-65, Capt. AAAS; Am. Phys. Soc; Optical Soc. Am. Time-resolved spectra of rare gas afterglows; laser and molecular physics; organic dye lasers; gas discharges; non-linear optics. Address: IBM Corp, 18100 Frederick Pike, Gaithersburg, MD 20760.

FARMER, JAMES, b. Guthrie, Okla, Sept. 12, 34. APPLIED MATHEMATICS. B.S, Univ. Okla, 56; S.M, Harvard, 61; M.B.A, Univ. Calif, Los Angeles, 62. Commun. engr, Rand Corp, 60-67; dir. instnl. studies & comput. ctr, San Fernando Valley State Col, 67-68; info. systs, CALIF. STATE COLS, 68-70, DIR. ANAL. STUDIES, 70- Asst. prof, San Fernando Valley State Col, 64-67; consult, Agency Int. Develop, U.S. State Dept, 64-67. U.S.A, 56-59, Res, 59-64, Capt. AAAS; N.Y. Acad. Sci. Systems analysis; communications systems; economic analysis. Address: P.O. Box 847, Guthrie, OK 73044.

FARMER, J(AMES) B(ERNARD), b. Liverpool, Eng, Dec. 13, 28. PHYSICAL CHEMISTRY. B.Sc, Liverpool, 50, Ph.D.(chem), 53. Fel. CHEM, Nat. Res. Coun. Can, 53-55; Laval, 55-56; UNIV. B.C, 56-57, asst. prof, 57-64, assoc. prof, 64- Am. Phys. Soc; Faraday Soc. Electron spin resonance spectrometry; stabilization of free radicals at low temperature. Address: Dept. of Chemistry, University of British Columbia, Vancouver, B.C, Can.

FARMER, JAMES LEE, b. South Gate, Calif, Aug. 8, 38; m. 67; c. 2. BIOCHEMICAL GENETICS. B.S, Calif. Inst. Tech, 60; Brigham Young, 60-61; U.S. Pub. Health Serv. traineeship & Ph.D.(biol), Brown, 66. Instr. biophys, med. center, Colorado, 66-68; ASST. PROF. ZOOL, BRIGHAM YOUNG UNIV, 69- Nat. Sci. Found. res. grant, 66-68. AAAS; Am. Soc. Microbiol. Biosynthesis of deoxynucleotides; genetic systems in eukaryotes. Address: Dept. of Zoology, Brigham Young University, Provo, UT 84601.

FARMER, JOHN JAMES, III, b. Newnan, Ga, Aug. 12, 43; m. 68. MICROBIOLOGY, ECOLOGY. B.S, Ga. Inst. Technol, 65; Nat. Sci. Found. fel, Univ. Ga, 66 & 67, Ph.D.(microbiol), 68. Sr. asst. scientist, Nat. Insts. Health, 68-70; ASST. PROF. MICROBIOL, UNIV. ALA, TUSCALOOSA, 70- Attending microbiologist, Druid City Hosp, 70-; mem, Int. Pseudomonas Typing Comt, 71- Bausch & Lomb Sci. Medal, 61; Chem. Rubber Co. Award, 66. U.S.P.H.S, 68-70, Sr. Asst. Scientist. AAAS; Am. Soc. Microbiol. Epidemiology of hospital-acquired infections; medical and clinical microbiology; microbial ecology of the hospital and other environments. Address: Dept. of Microbiology, University of Alabama, Box H, University, AL 35486.

FARMER, JOHN N(EVILLE), b. Simla, India, June 19, 29; nat; m. 52; c. 3. PARASITOLOGY. A.B, Col. of Wooster, 53; M.S, Iowa State, 58, Ph.D. (parasitol), 60. Asst, Iowa State, 53-54, 56-59, instr. ZOOL, 59-60; asst. prof, UNIV. MO-COLUMBIA, 60-65, assoc. prof, 65-70, PROF, 70- U.S.A, 54-56. Am. Soc. Parasitol. Parasitic protozoa; avian haemosporidian organisms; entomology; potential invertebrate hosts for the Haemosporidia. Address: Division of Biological Sciences, University of Missouri-Columbia, Columbia, MO 65201.

FARMER, LARRY B(ERT), b. Greenville, S.C, Jan. 5, 36; m. 60; c. 2. ORGANIC CHEMISTRY. B.S, Wofford Col, 58; Ph.D.(org. chem), Tennessee, 63. Res. chemist, DEERING MILLIKEN RES. CORP, 64-65, SR. RES. CHEMIST, chem. div, 65-70, RES. DIV, 70- Chem.C, U.S.A, 63-64, 1st Lt. Am. Chem. Soc. Organic syntheses; natural products; textile fibers. Address: Research Division, Deering Milliken Research Corp, Spartanburg, SC 29301.

FARMER, LOWELL J, b. Annandale, Minn, Jan. 13, 07; m. 29; c. 2. PLANT PATHOLOGY, FORESTRY. B.S, Idaho, 30, M.S, 31; Ph.D.(plant path), Utah, 65. Forester, U.S. Forest Serv, 34-65; plant pathologist, CALIF. DEPT. AGR, 66-69, CITRUS VIROLOGIST, PLANT INDUST, 69- Mem. West. Int. Forest Disease Work Conf. Soc. Am. Foresters; Am. Phytopath. Soc; Int. Orgn. Citrus Virol. Yeast fungi associated with bark beetles; epidemiology of tristeza virus in California. Address: California Dept. of Agriculture, 3239 Chicago Ave, Riverside, CA 92507.

FARMER, MELVIN LEE, b. Buhl, Idaho, Feb. 18, 38; m. 59; c. 4. ORGANIC CHEMISTRY. A.B, Harvard, 60; univ. fel, Illinois, 60-61; Standard Oil Calif. fel, 62-63, U.S. Pub. Health Serv. fel, 63-64, Ph.D.(org. chem), 64. Res. chemist, UNION CARBIDE CORP, 64-71, PROJ. SCIENTIST, 71- Am. Chem. Soc. Synthesis; use of olefinic compounds; textile chemicals; emulsion polymerization; coatings and paints. Address: Union Carbide Corp, Box 8361, South Charleston, WV 25303.

FARMER, PATRICK STEWART, b. Saskatoon, Sask, Jan. 27, 42; m. 67. MEDICINAL CHEMISTRY. B.S.P, Saskatchewan, 62, M.Sc, 64; Ph.D. (pharm. & chem), Portsmouth Col. Tech, Eng, 68. ASST. PROF. PHARMACEUT. CHEM, COL. PHARM, DALHOUSIE UNIV, 68- Chem. Inst. Can; Acad. Pharmaceut. Sci. Synthesis of fatty acids with smooth muscle stimulant activity; heterocyclic compounds with potential antimetabolite and radioprotective activity. Address: College of Pharmacy, Dalhousie University, Halifax, N.S, Can.

FARMER, ROBERT E, JR, b. Rehoboth Beach, Del, Dec. 3, 30; m. 60; c. 2. FORESTRY, PLANT PHYSIOLOGY. B.S.F, Michigan, 53, M.F, 57, Ph.D. (forestry), 61. Res. forester, south. hardwoods lab, U.S. Forest Serv, 61-67; PLANT PHYSIOLOGIST, TENN. VALLEY AUTH, 67- U.S.A, 53-55, 1st Lt. AAAS; Ecol. Soc. Am; Soc. Am. Foresters; Am. Soc. Plant Physiol. Physiological ecology of forest trees; forest tree breeding. Address: Division of Forestry, Fisheries & Wildlife Development, Tennessee Valley Authority, Norris, TN 37828.

FARMER, SUSAN WALKER, b. N.Y.C, Nov. 4, 43; m. 69. PHYSIOLOGY, ENDOCRINOLOGY. B.A, Trinity Col.(D.C), 65; U.S. Pub. Health Serv. grant & Ph.D.(physiol), Univ. Calif, Berkeley, 70. RES. PHYSIOLOGIST, UNIV. CALIF, SAN FRANCISCO, 70- Soc. Study Reprod. Male and female reproductive endocrinology; structure and function relationships of pituitary hormones. Address: Hormone Research Lab, University of California, San Francisco, CA 94122.

FARMER, T. ALBERT, JR, b. Smithfield, N.C, Jan. 28, 32; m. 56; c. 4. ENDOCRINOLOGY. B.S, North Carolina, 53, M.D, 57. Nat. Insts. Health fel. endocrinol, 59-60; asst. prof. med. & asst. dean, MED. COL, UNIV. ALA, BIRMINGHAM, 65-67, assoc. prof. MED, 67-69, PROF, 69-, EXEC. ASSOC. DEAN & DIR. UNDERGRAD. MED. EDUC, 68-, assoc. dean, 67-68. Ward physician, Walson Army Hosp, Ft. Dix, N.J, 61-63. Am. Fedn. Clin. Res; fel. Am. Col. Physicians; Endocrine Soc. Endocrinology of the adrenal gland; medical education; internal medicine. Address: Dept. of Medicine, University of Alabama School of Medicine, 1919 Seventh Ave. S, Birmingham, AL 35233.

FARMER, T(HOMAS) S(HELBY), b. New Orleans, La, Sept. 2, 31; m. 55; c. 3. CHEMICAL ENGINEERING. B.S, Tulane, 52; Standard Oil Co.(Ind). fel, Princeton, 52-53, M.S.E, 53. Jr. engr, res. & develop. div, Humble Oil & Ref. Co, 53, asst. res. chem. engr, 55-57, res. chem. engr, 57-59, sr. res. chem. engr, 59-61, sect. head, 61-64, dept. head, 64-65; mgr, Baytown Res. & Develop. Div, Esso Res. & Eng. Co, Tex, 65-67, strategy & new bus. planning div, corp. planning dept, Esso Chem. Co. Inc, N.Y, 67-68, v.pres, Esso Chem. S.A, Belg, 68-71; PRES. CHEM. & PLASTICS GROUP, BORG-WARNER CORP, 71- U.S.A, 53-55. AAAS; Am. Chem. Soc; Am. Inst. Chem. Eng. Administration of research and development in the field of petroleum refining. Address: Borg-Warner Corp, 200 S. Michigan Ave, Chicago, IL 60604.

FARMER, THOMAS W(OHLSEN), b. Lancaster, Pa, Sept. 18, 14; m. 41; c. 2. NEUROLOGY. A.B, Harvard, 35; M.A, Duke, 37; M.D, Harvard, 41. Asst. prof. neurol, Southwest. Med. Sch, Texas, 48-49, assoc. prof, 49-50, prof, 50-52, prof. med. & acting chmn. dept, 51-52; PROF. NEUROL. MED, SCH. MED, UNIV. N.C, CHAPEL HILL, 52- Nat. Insts. of Health spec. fel, Inst. of Neurophysiol, Denmark, 57-58. U.S.N.R, 44-46. Am. Med. Asn; Am. Col. Physicians; Am. Neurol. Asn; Am. Acad. Neurol.(secy, 55-57); Am. Epilepsy Soc; Asn. Res. Nerv. & Ment. Disease. Virus infections of the nervous system, including lymphocytic choriomeningitis and Coxsackie viruses; neurosyphilis; radioactive iodine in brain tumor localizations; electrophysiology of muscle. Address: Division of Neurology, Dept. of Medicine, University of North Carolina School of Medicine, Chapel Hill, NC 27514.

FARMER, WALTER J(OSEPH), b. Anderson, Ind, Nov. 1, 38; m. 62; c. 2. SOIL CHEMISTRY. B.S, Indiana, 61; M.S, Purdue, 64, Ph.D.(soil chem), 66. Asst. chemist, UNIV. CALIF, RIVERSIDE, 66-70, ASST. PROF. SOIL SCI, 70- Am. Soc. Agron; Soil Sci. Soc. Am; Am. Chem. Soc. Chemistry of organic matter reactions in soils; fate of pesticides in soils. Address: Dept. of Soil Science & Agricultural Engineering, University of California, Riverside, CA 92502.

FARMER, WILLIAM S(ILAS), JR, b. Waterville, Maine, Apr. 16, 22; m. 47; c. 4. CHEMICAL ENGINEERING. B.S, Tufts, 44; M.S, Tennessee, 50, du Pont fel, 56. Chem. engr, Texas Co, 44; tech. supvr, Fercleve Corp, 45; develop. engr, Oak Ridge Nat. Lab, 46-49, sr. develop. engr, 50-53; proj. engr, adv. design sect, Pratt & Whitney Aircraft Co, 54-55, aircraft nuclear propulsion, 56-57; sr. nuclear engr. & sect. head, ACF Industs, Inc, 58; proj. mgr. Elk river nuclear power reactor, Allis-Chalmers Mfg. Co, 59, mgr. planning dept, 60-62, tech. dir, 62-70; MEM. STAFF, ATOMIC ENERGY COMN, 70- Am. Chem. Soc; Am. Nuclear Soc; Am. Inst. Chem. Eng. Nuclear engineering; heat transfer and fluid mechanics; chemical engineering. Address: 10115 Green Forest Dr, Silver Spring, MD 20903.

FARMILO, CHARLES G, b. Edmonton, Alta, Nov. 28, 17; m. 44; c. 3. ORGANIC CHEMISTRY, PSYCHOPHARMACOLOGY. B.Sc, Univ. Alta, 42, M.Sc, 43; Nat. Res. Coun. Can. fel, McGill Univ, 46, Ph.D.(chem), 48. Teacher, pub. sch, Alta, 36-39; asst. chem, C.M. & S. Co. Ltd, B.C, 42; Nat. Res. Labs, Ont, 42-44; sect. head org. chem. & narcotics, Food &

Drug Directorate, 48-65; adv. from External Aid Off. Can, dir. Cent. Chem. Lab, Ghana, 65-68, consult, secretariat on drug abuse, ment. health div, DEPT. NAT. HEALTH & WELFARE, 68-69, RES. ASSOC, DRUG INQUIRY COMN, 69- Can. Govt. appointee, UN Progs. Res. on opium & cannabis, 48-; mem. rev. comt, crime detection labs, Royal Can. Mounted Police, 52-53; spec. comt, UN Experts on Opium, 57-58. Can. Soc. Forensic Sci. (pres, 57-59); Prof. Inst. Pub. Serv. Can; fel. Chem. Inst. Can. Development of methods for assay, characterization, composition and origin of opium, heroin and cannabis; identification, isolation and assay of narcotics, barbiturates, amphetamines and tranquilizers; psychomimetics; international narcotics law and administration; analysis of street drugs; metabolism of Δ 9-THC; studies of motivation and cause of non-medical use of drugs. Address: Drug Inquiry Commission, Dept. of National Health & Welfare, 75 Albert St, Ottawa, Ont, Can.

FARN, CHARLES LUH-SUN, b. Checkiang, China, Sept. 19, 34; m. 62; c. 2. FLUID MECHANICS. B.S, Taiwan, 58; M.S, N.C. State Col, 62; Ph.D.(mech. eng), Michigan, 65. Asst. prof. fluid mech, Carnegie-Mellon Univ, 65-68; SR. ENGR, WESTINGHOUSE RES. & DEVELOP. CTR, 68- Am. Soc. Mech. Eng. Boundary layers; magnetohydrodynamic generators; wave propagations; electrokinetics; turbulence; aerodynamics of turbomachines. Address: Westinghouse Research & Development Center, Pittsburgh, PA 15235.

FARNELL, ALBERT B(ENNETT), b. Shreveport, La, July 18, 17; m. 41; c. 3. MATHEMATICS. A.B, Centenary Col, 38; M.S, La. State, 40; Ph.D.(math), California, 44. Asst. prof. math, Colorado, 46-48, 49-51; lectr, Princeton, 48-49; sr. res. engr, N.Am. Aviation, 53-56; sr. staff scientist, Convair Sci. Res. Lab. Div, Gen. Dynamics Corp, 56-63, 65-66; PROF. MATH, COLO. STATE UNIV, 63-65, 66- U.S.A, 42-46, 51-53. Am. Math. Soc; Soc. Indust. & Appl. Math; Math. Asn. Am. Matrix algebra; nonlinear differential equations; characteristic roots of matrix polynomials and infinite matrices; digital computation. Address: Dept. of Mathematics, Colorado State University, Ft. Collins, CO 80521.

FARNELL, DANIEL R(EESE), b. Mobile, Ala, Feb. 7, 32; m. 54; c. 3. VETERINARY MEDICINE. Spring Hill Col, 49-50; D.V.M, Auburn Univ, 57, M.S, 62; Ph.D, Mich. State Univ, 69. Res. scientist, South. Res. Inst, 57-61; Nat. Insts. Health res. fel, Auburn Univ, 61-62, assoc. prof. animal disease res, 62-67; Nat. Insts. Health spec. fel, Mich. State Univ, 67-69; PROF. VET. SCI. & HEAD DEPT, MISS. STATE UNIV, 69- Dipl, Am. Col. Lab. Animal Med, 66. U.S.A, 51-52. AAAS; Am. Vet. Med. Asn; Conf. Res. Workers Animal Diseases; Am. Asn. Lab. Animal Sci. Pathology; nutrition; toxicology; endocrinology. Address: Dept. of Veterinary Science, Mississippi State University, State College, MS 39762.

FARNELL, G(ERALD) W(ILLIAM), b. Toronto, Ont, Aug. 31, 25; m. 48; c. 2. ELECTRICAL ENGINEERING, PHYSICS. B.A.Sc, Toronto, 48; S.M, Mass. Inst. Technol, 50; Ph.D, McGill, 57. Asst, res. lab. electronics, Mass. Inst. Technol, 48-50; lectr. elec. eng, McGILL UNIV, 50-54, asst. prof. elec. eng. & physics, 54-57, assoc. prof, 57-61, PROF. ENG. PHYSICS, 61-, CHMN. DEPT, 67- Nuffield fel, Clarendon Lab, Oxford, 60-61; Royal Can. Army, 43-45, Lt. Fel. Inst. Elec. & Electronics Eng. Solid state electronics; ultrasonics and elastic surface waves. Address: Dept. of Electrical Engineering, McGill University, Montreal 110, Que, Can.

FARNER, DONALD S(ANKEY), b. Waumandee, Wis, May 2, 15; m. 40; c. 2. PHYSIOLOGY, ZOOLOGY. B.S, Hamline Univ, 37, hon. D.Sc, 62; M.A, Univ. Wis, 39, Ph.D.(zool), 41. Asst. biol, Hamline Univ, 35-37; zool, Univ. Wis, 37-41, instr, 41-43; asst. prof. & asst. curator birds, Univ. Kans, 46-47; assoc. prof. ZOOPHYSIOL, Wash. State Univ, 47-52, PROF, 52-65, dean grad. sch, 60-64; UNIV. WASH, 65-, CHMN. DEPT. ZOOL, 66- Fulbright res. scholar & hon. lectr, Otago, N.Z, 53-54; Guggenheim fel, West. Australia, 58-59. U.S.N.R, 43-46, Med.Serv.C.Res, 46-, Capt. AAAS; Soc. Exp. Biol. & Med; Ecol. Soc. Am; Am. Soc. Zool; Am. Physiol. Soc; Am. Chem. Soc; Int. Union Biol. Sci.(secy-gen, 64-67, pres, 67-); Cooper Ornith. Soc; Am. Ornith. Union; Soc. Syst. Zool; Am. Soc. Nat. Avian and comparative physiology; zoophysiology. Address: Dept. of Zoology, University of Washington, Seattle, WA 98105.

FARNES, PATRICIA, b. Portland, Ore, May 16, 31. HEMATOLOGY. B.A, Willamette, 53; M.S, Oregon, 56, M.D, 56. Intern med, Presby. Hosp, Chicago, Ill, 56-57, res. internal med, 57-58, fel. hemat, 58-60; res. internal med, R.I. HOSP, PROVIDENCE, 60-61, res. assoc. path, 61-68, CHIEF EXP. CELL BIOL. SECT, DEPT. PATH. & ASST. PROF. MED.(RES), BROWN UNIV, 68- Nat. Heart Inst. fel, Presby-St. Luke's Hosp, Chicago, Ill, 59-60; Nat. Insts. Health res. grants, 60-; U.S. Pub. Health Serv, 61-65; Am. Cancer Soc, 66-68. Internist, Civil Hosp. of Beni Messous, Algiers, 62. Mem. med. adv. bd, Hemophilia Guild, 65. AAAS; Tissue Culture Asn; Am. Soc. Cell Biol; Am. Fedn. Clin. Res; Reticuloendothelial Soc; Am. Hemat. Soc. Tissue culture; Haemic cell culture, especially in vitro differentiation of granulocytes and in vitro modulations of lymphocytes; phytomitogens and modes of action; histochemistry of in vitro cells. Address: 66 Bowden Ave, Barrington, RI 02806.

FARNHAM, A(LFORD) G(AILEY), b. Traer, Iowa, Apr. 17, 15; m. 41; c. 3. ORGANIC CHEMISTRY. B.S, Monmouth Col, 37; M.S, Iowa, 39, Ph.D.(chem), 41. RES. CHEMIST, BAKELITE CORP, UNION CARBIDE PLASTICS CO. DIV, UNION CARBIDE CORP, 41- With Nat. Defense Res. Comt, 44. Am. Chem. Soc. Reactions of monochloroamine with organomagnesium compounds; azoyl derivatives of sugars and separation by chromatographic adsorption; synthetic resins. Address: Research Dept, Bakelite Corp, Union Carbide Plastics Co, One River Rd, Bound Brook, NJ 08805.

FARNHAM, PAUL REX, b. St. Louis, Mo, Nov. 2, 31; m. 55. STRUCTURAL GEOLOGY, GEOPHYSICS. B.S, West. Md. Col, 53; M.S, Va. Polytech, 60; Ph.D.(structural geol), Minnesota, Minneapolis, 67. Assoc. engr, Martin Co, Md, 56-57; teaching asst. phys. geol. & mineral, Va. Polytech, 58-59, instr, 59-61; teaching assoc. phys. geol, Minnesota, Minneapolis, 61-66; res. geophysicist, seismic data lab, Earth Sci. Co, Teledyne, Inc, 67-69; dir. tech. educ, Bison Instruments, 69-70; ASST. PROF. GEOL, COL. ST. THOMAS, 70- U.S.A.R, 53-61, Lt. Instrumentation and data processing in earthquake seismology and synthesis of geophysical and geological data to establish structural geologic relationships. Address: Dept. of Geology, College of St. Thomas, St. Paul, MN 55101.

FARNHAM, ROUSE S(MITH), b. Evergreen, Ala, Jan. 29, 18; m. 51; c. 2. SOIL SCIENCE. B.S, Ala. Polytech, 41; Ph.D.(agron), Ohio State, 51. Soil surveyor, agr. exp. sta, Ala. Polytech, 41-42, 46; asst. prof. SOILS, UNIV. MINN, MINNEAPOLIS, 58-69, PROF, 69-, SOIL SCIENTIST, SOIL CONSERV. SURV, 50- U.S.A.A.F, 42-46. Soil genesis and classification. Address: Dept. of Soil Science, University of Minnesota, Minneapolis, MN 55455.

FARNSWORTH, CARL L(EON), b. Lincoln, Nebr, Aug. 5, 30. ORGANIC CHEMISTRY. B.S, Texas, 55, Jefferson Chem. Co. & Humble Oil Co, fels. & M.A, 58, Ph.D.(chem), 61. Res. chemist, Spruance Film Res. & Develop. Lab, film dept, E.I. du Pont de Nemours & Co, Inc, 60-66; chemist, W.H. Brady Co, 66-67; ASST. PROF. CHEM, WIS. STATE UNIV, STEVENS POINT, 67- U.S.A, 51-53. Am. Chem. Soc. Polymerization and process development; film coatings. Address: Dept. of Chemistry, Wisconsin State University, Stevens Point, WI 54481.

FARNSWORTH, C(LINTON) EUGENE, b. Cresco, Iowa, May 24, 04; m. 30; c. 2. FORESTRY. B.S.F, Iowa State Col, 26; M.F, Yale, 28; Minnesota, 35; Ph.D.(forest ecol), Michigan, 45. Jr. forester, U.S. Forest Serv, Idaho, 26-30; sr. instr, N.Y. State Ranger Sch, 30-31, asst. prof, 31-36, assoc. prof, 36-47; SILVICULT, N.Y. STATE COL. FORESTRY, SYRACUSE UNIV, 47-49, PROF, 49-, CHMN. DEPT, 59- Teacher, Syracuse, 43-44; vis. prof, col. forestry, Philippines, 57-59. AAAS; fel. Soc. Am. Foresters; Am. Inst. Biol. Sci. Forest ecology; silviculture; elongation of tree species of northern New York. Address: New York State College of Forestry, Syracuse University, Syracuse, NY 13210.

FARNSWORTH, DANA L(YDA), b. Troy, W.Va, Apr. 7, 05; m. 31. MEDICINE. A.B, Univ. W.Va, 27, B.S, 31; M.D, Harvard, 33; hon. S.D, Salem Col.(W.Va), 59, Williams Col, 61, Univ. W.Va, 65, Fairfield Univ, 69; hon. L.H.D, Lesley Col, 62, Roosevelt Univ, 70; hon. LL.D, Univ. Notre Dame, 64, Harvard, 71. Instr, pub. sch, W.Va, 27-29; intern, Mass. Gen. Hosp, 33-35; asst. res, Boston City Hosp, 35; asst. dir. health, Williams Col, 35-45, dir, 45-46; prof. & med. dir, Mass. Inst. Technol, 46-54, acting dean students, 50-51; Oliver prof. hyg. & dir. Univ. Health Serv, HARVARD, 54-71, EMER. OLIVER PROF. HYG. & CONSULT. PSYCHIAT, SCH. PUB. HEALTH, 71- From asst. physician to physician, Mass. Gen. Hosp, 46-66, mem. bd. consultation, 66-; Lowell lectr, 56; Salmon lectr, 64; v.chmn, Nat. Comn. Marijuana & Drug Abuse, 71. Chmn, 4th Nat. Conf. Health in Cols; 1st Int. Conf. Student Ment. Health, 57; 2nd Nat. Cong. Ment. Illness & Health, Am. Med. Asn, 64. Dipl, Am. Bd. Psychiat. & Neurol; Menninger Award, Am. Col. Physicians, 70; distinguished serv. award, Soc. Adolescent Psychiat, 71; Pax Christi award, St. John's Univ, 71. U.S.N.R, 41-45, Comdr. Fel. Am. Psychiat. Asn.(distinguished serv. award, 71); fel. Am. Acad. Arts & Sci; Am. Col. Health Asn.(pres, 53); Group Advan. Psychiat.(pres, 57-59). Applications of psychiatry to education; reactions of college students to social systems; effects of stress; community mental health programs. Address: 55 Shattuck St, Boston, MA 02115.

FARNSWORTH, HARRISON EDWARD, b. Ripon, Wis, Mar. 24, 96; m. 60; c. 1. A.B, Ripon Col, 18; M.A, Wisconsin, 21, Ph.D.(physics), 22; hon.D.Sc, Fairfield Univ, 71. Res. physicist, West. Elec. Co, 18; instr. PHYSICS, Pittsburgh, 18-19; nat. res. fel, Wisconsin, 22-24; assoc. prof, Maine, 24-26; asst. prof, BROWN UNIV, 26-29, assoc. prof, 29-46, prof, 46-60, res. prof, 60-70, EMER. RES. PROF, 70-, Annette L.R. Barstow prof, 63-70, chmn. dept, 42-43. Res. physicist, radiation lab, Mass. Inst. Technol, 41; Nat. Defense Res. Comt. off. investr, Brown, 42-43. Consult, Boonton Radio Corp, N.J, 44-45; Philips Labs, Inc, N.Y, 47-48; Brookhaven Nat. Lab, 47-48; Lawrence Radiation Lab, California, 62-65; dir, Barus Lab. Surface Physics, 46-70. Co-op. expert, Int. Critical Tables; exec. secy, panel electron tubes, Res. & Develop. Bd. & dir, coord. Group Electron Tube Reliability, City of New York, 52-53; mem. phys. sci. coun, Brown, 53-63, exec. comt, 54-56; vis. res. prof, Wash. State Univ, summer 70; consult, Nat. Phys. Res. Lab, S.Africa, 70-71. Alumni citation, Ripon Col, 47. Mem. Off. Naval Res, U.S. Dept. Navy, 46-47. AAAS; fel. Am. Phys. Soc; Am. Chem. Soc; fel. Am. Acad. Arts & Sci; Inst. Elec. & Electronics Eng; Royal Soc. Arts. Surface physics and chemistry with metal and semiconductor single crystals; secondary electron emission from metals; gas adsorption and surface catalysis on crystals; thermionic and photoelectric emission; electron diffraction. Address: Dept. of Physics, Brown University, Providence, RI 02912.

FARNSWORTH, MARIE, b. Holden, Mo, July 19, 96. CHEMISTRY. B.S, Chicago, 18, Ph.D.(chem), 22. Instr. chem, Iowa State, 22-23; res. chemist, U.S. Bur. Mines, 23-26; instr. chem, N.Y. Univ, 26-35; res, Munich & London, 35-36; res. chemist, Fogg Art Mus, Harvard, 36-37; chemist, Agora Excavations, Greece, 38-40; res. supvr, res. & develop. lab, M & T Corp, 40-61; Ford Found. fel, 61-64; RES. ASSOC, DEPT. HIST. & ARCHAEOL, COLUMBIA UNIV, 64- Vis. prof, Univ. Mo-Columbia, 70- Am. Chem. Soc; Archaeol. Inst. Am. Analytical chemistry; technical problems of archaeology. Address: 276 W. 11th St, New York, NY 10014.

FARNSWORTH, MARJORIE W(HYTE), b. Detroit, Mich, Nov. 18, 21; m. 45; c. 2. ZOOLOGY. B.A, Mt. Holyoke Col, 44; M.S, Cornell, 46; Atomic Energy Comn. fel, Missouri, 49-50, Ph.D.(zool), 51. Asst. entom, Cornell, 44-46; instr. zool, Missouri, 46-49, 50-51, res. fel, 49-50, asst. prof, 51-52; cytologist, Roswell Park Mem. Inst, 52-53; lectr. & res. assoc. BIOL, STATE UNIV. N.Y. BUFFALO, 53-64, ASSOC. PROF, 65- Fel. AAAS; Genetics Soc. Am; Am. Soc. Zool. Biochemical genetics of Drosophila. Address: Dept. of Biology, State University of New York at Buffalo, Buffalo, NY 14214.

FARNSWORTH, NORMAN R, b. Lynn, Mass, Mar. 23, 30; m. 53. PHARMACOGNOSY, PHYTOCHEMISTRY. B.S, Mass. Col. Pharm, 53, M.S, 55; Ph.D. (pharm), Pittsburgh, 59. Instr. biol. sci, Pittsburgh, 55-59, asst. prof. pharmacog, 59-61, assoc. prof, 61-63, chmn. dept, 64-70, prof, 63-70; PROF. PHARMACOG. & HEAD DEPT. PHARMACOG. & PHARMACOL, COL. PHARM, UNIV. ILL. MED. CTR, 70- Consult, Schering AG, Berlin; Amazon Natural Drug Co; Gillette; A.D. Little. Med.Serv.C, U.S.A, 48-49, 50-51. Am. Soc. Pharmacog.(v.pres, 59-61, pres, 61-62); Soc. Econ. Bot; Am. Pharmaceut. Asn; Am. Chem. Soc; Marine Technol. Soc. Evaluation of medicinal folklore; design and evaluation of phytochemical screening procedures; isolation, identification and structure elucidation of Catharanthus alkaloids; investigation of plants for biologically active substances. Address: 2800 N. Lake Shore Dr, Chicago, IL 60657.

FARNSWORTH, PATRICIA NORDSTROM, b. Sioux City, Iowa, Aug. 18, 30; m. 52; c. 4. PHYSIOLOGY, BIOCHEMISTRY. B.A, Morningside Col, 51; Roberts fel. & M.S, Columbia, 52, Roberts fel. & Ph.D.(physiol), 60. Instr. zool, Hofstra Col, 52-54; genetics & zool, Marymount Col, 56-57; asst. physiol, Columbia, 58-59, instr. occup. & phys. ther, 59-60, fel. med, col. physicians & surgeons, 62-63; ASST. PROF. genetics & physiol, Fairleigh Dickinson, 63-67; physiol, BARNARD COL, COLUMBIA UNIV, 67-69, BIOL, 69- Consult, Dept. Health, Englewood, N.J, 66-; vis. lectr, Harvard, 70-; consult, Arthur D. Little, Inc, 71; Nat. Inst. Health sr. res. fel, 71. AAAS; N.Y. Acad. Sci; Am. Inst. Biol. Sci; Am. Zool. Soc. Circulation; cell membrane chemistry; lipid metabolism; marine physiology. Address: Dept. of Biology, Barnard College, Columbia University, New York, NY 10027.

FARNSWORTH, PHILLIP L, b. Panguitch, Utah, July 5, 36; m. 55; c. 5. MATERIALS SCIENCE, CERAMICS. B.S, Utah, 58; Sc.D.(ceramics), Mass. Inst. Technol, 64. Engr, Gen. Elec. Co, Wash, 58-61; sr. scientist, PAC. NORTHWEST LABS, BATTELLE MEM. INST, 65-66, mgr. ceramics res, 66-69, spec. asst. to pres, 69-70, MGR. CERAMICS & GRAPHITE SECT, 70- Am. Ceramic Soc. High temperature mechanical properties of ceramic materials. Address: 2128 Hudson, Richland, WA 99352.

FARNSWORTH, RAYMOND B(ARTLETT), b. Enterprise, Utah, May 21, 15; m. 43; c. 4. AGRONOMY. B.S, Brigham Young, 37; fel, Mass. State Col, M.S, 38; fel, Ohio State, Ph.D.(soil physics), 41; Harvard, 44; California, 48. Asst. bact, Brigham Young, 35-37; asst, Ohio State, 38-40; sugar beet technologist, Ohio Exp. Sta, 41-43; agronomist, Paulding Sugar Co, 40; asst. prof. AGRON, BRIGHAM YOUNG UNIV, 46-47, assoc. prof, 48-52, PROF, 52-, acting dean col. appl. sci, 52, chmn. dept. agron, 52-55, acting dean col. biol. & agr. sci, 55-58. Vis. soil scientist, Ore. State Col, 58-59; adv, U.S. Opers. Mission, Karadj Agr. Col, Iran, 59-61; assoc. dir. grad. fel. prog, Nat. Sci. Found, 65-66. U.S.N, 44-46. Am. Soc. Agron. Soil aeration and drainage; nitrogen-fixation by algae; use of potassium in quality of crops; Follier analysis of plants, an indicator of nutrient needs; effect of soil structure on sugar beet growth; calcium-magnesium-potassium ratio in relation to energy of exchange. Address: Dept. of Agronomy, Brigham Young University, Provo, UT 84601.

FARNSWORTH, ROY LOTHROP, b. Shirley, Mass, Mar. 4, 28; m. 57; c. 3. GEOLOGY. A.B, Boston, 49, A.M, 56, Ph.D.(geol), 61; spring, Massachusetts, 53. Teacher, pub. schs, Mass, 53-55, 60-61; instr. GEOL, Trinity Col.(Conn), 57-59; asst. prof, Mass. State Col. Lowell, spring 60; BATES COL, 61-68, ASSOC. PROF, 68- C.Eng, U.S.A, 50-52. AAAS; Geol. Soc. Am; Nat. Asn. Geol. Teachers; Am. Quaternary Asn. Structural geology, genesis analysis of land forms; development of earth science curriculum for secondary schools. Address: Dept. of Geology, Bates College, Lewiston, ME 04240.

FARNSWORTH, WELLS E(UGENE), b. Hartford, Conn, July 10, 21; m. 45; c. 2. BIOCHEMISTRY. B.S, Trinity Col.(Conn), 46; M.A, Missouri, 49, Ph.D.(endocrine physiol, chem), 51. Endocrinologist, Wm. S. Merrell Co, Ohio, 51-52; res. biochemist, U.S. VET. ADMIN. HOSP, 52-61, DIR. BIOCHEM. RES, 61-; ASSOC. PROF. BIOCHEM, STATE UNIV. N.Y. BUFFALO, 67-, asst. prof, 64-67. Consult, Edward J. Meyer Hosp, 57-58. Med.C, U.S.A, 43-46. Endocrine Soc; Brit. Biochem. Soc; Soc. Study Reproduction; fel. Am. Inst. Chem; Am. Chem. Soc. Steroid metabolism; influence of steroid on prostate metabolism and protein synthesis in vitro. Address: U.S. Veterans Administration Hospital, 3495 Bailey Ave, Buffalo, NY 14215.

FARNUM, BRUCE W(AYNE), b. Fargo, N.Dak, Apr. 5, 35; m. 59; c. 1. ORGANIC CHEMISTRY. B.S, N.Dak. State, 57, M.S, 59; Ph.D.(org. chem), Delaware, 69. Instr. CHEM, Moorhead State Col, 59; assoc. prof, MINOT STATE COL, 64-69, PROF, 69- Dir, Nat. Sci. Found. Col. Sci. Improv. Proj. for two year col. chem. dept. in N.Dak, 69-70. U.S.N.R, 53-55; U.S.A.R, 55-68, Capt. Am. Chem. Soc. Mechanism of chromic acid oxidation of alcohols; chromic acid oxidation of cyclic ketones to lactones. Address: Dept. of Chemistry, Minot State College, Minot, ND 58701.

FARNUM, DONALD G, b. Oakland, Calif, Apr. 3, 34; m. 53; c. 4. ORGANIC CHEMISTRY. A.B, Harvard, 56, Ph.D.(org. chem), 59. Chemist, Arthur D. Little, Inc, 53-59; instr. CHEM, Cornell Univ, 59-62, asst. prof, 62-66; ASSOC. PROF, MICH. STATE UNIV, 66- Sloan Found. fel, 62. Am. Chem. Soc. Organic synthesis; stable carbonium ions; structures which test current concepts; bridged polycyclic olefins; novel aromatic and pseudoaromatic systems; reactive intermediates; heterocycles; photochemical synthesis. Address: Dept. of Chemistry, Michigan State University, East Lansing, MI 48823.

FARONA, MICHAEL F, b. Cleveland, Ohio, Jan. 30, 35; m. 60; c. 1. INORGANIC CHEMISTRY. B.S, Western Reserve, 56; M.S, Ohio State, 62, Ph.D.(chem), 64. Asst. prof. CHEM, UNIV. AKRON, 64-68, ASSOC. PROF, 68- Med.C, U.S.A.R, 57-63. Am. Chem. Soc; The Chem. Soc. Transition metal chemistry, including homogeneous catalysis, metal carbonyls, organometallics, coordination compounds, and low-frequency infrared spectroscopy. Address: Dept. of Chemistry, The University of Akron, Akron, OH 44304.

FARONE, WILLIAM ANTHONY, b. Cortland, N.Y, Feb. 1, 40; m. 62; c. 1. PHYSICAL CHEMISTRY. B.S, Clarkson Tech, 61, Nat. Defense Ed. Act fel, 63-65, M.S, 63, Ph.D.(chem), 65. Res. physicist, U.S. Army Electronics Res. & Develop. Activity, White Sands Missile Range, N.Mex, 64-65; assoc. prof. phys. chem, Va. State Col, 65-67; sr. res. assoc, LEVER BROS. CO, 67-69, SECT. CHIEF, new prod. group, RES. & DEVELOP. DIV, 69-70, DETERGENTS EVAL. SECT, 70- Prin. investr, Res. Corp. res. grant, 65-67; co-prin. investr, Nat. Sci. Found. res. grant, 66-67. AAAS; Optical Soc. Am; Am. Chem. Soc. Colloid science, particularly use of electromagnetic scattering to determine particle properties and interactions. Address: Detergents Evaluation Section, Research & Development Division, Lever Brothers Co, 45 River Rd, Edgewater, NJ 07020.

FARQUHAR, GALE B(URTON), b. Oakland, Calif, Jan. 5, 27; m. 51; c. 3. ORGANIC CHEMISTRY. A.B, Occidental Col, 50, M.A, 51. Res. & develop. engr, SUPERIOR OIL CO, 51-60, STAFF CORROSION ENGR, 60- Med.C, U.S.A, 45-46. Am. Chem. Soc; Am. Inst. Chem; Nat. Asn. Corrosion Eng. Waterflood and bacterial corrosion. Address: 5814 Portal Dr, Houston, TX 77035.

FARQUHAR, JOHN W(ILLIAM), b. Winnipeg, Man, June 13, 27; nat. MEDICINE, PREVENTIVE MEDICINE. A.B, California, 49, M.D, 52. Fel. med, Minnesota, 54-56; California, 56-57, instr. & chief resident, 57-58; res. assoc. & asst. physician, hosp, Rockefeller Inst, 58-62; asst. prof. MED, SCH. MED, STANFORD UNIV, 62-66, ASSOC. PROF, 66- U.S.A, 44-45. Harvey Soc; Am. Soc. Clin. Invest; Am. Heart Asn. Epidemiology of cardiovascular disease, human nutrition and atherosclerosis; behavior and communication in respect to human health. Address: Dept. of Medicine, Stanford University School of Medicine, Medical Center, Stanford, CA 94305.

FARQUHAR, MARILYN G(IST), b. Tulare, Calif, July 11, 28; m. 51; c. 2. EXPERIMENTAL PATHOLOGY. M.A, California, 53, Ph.D.(exp. path), 55; fel, Minnesota, 54-55. Jr. res. pathologist, California, 53-54, asst. res. pathologist, 55-58; guest investr, Rockefeller Inst, 58-59, res. assoc, 59-62; assoc. res. pathologist, UNIV. CALIF, SAN FRANCISCO, 62-64, assoc. prof. PATH, 64-69, PROF. IN RESIDENCE, 69- Vis. prof, Rockefeller Univ, 69. Am. Soc. Cell Biol; Am. Soc. Exp. Path; Am. Asn. Anat; Electron Micros. Soc. Am; Microcirculatory Soc; Int. Soc. Cell Biol; Int. Acad. Path. Electron microscopy of anterior pituitary gland, kidney and brain; glomerular pathology; capillary and cellular permeability; cell secretion. Address: Dept. of Pathology, University of California School of Medicine, San Francisco, CA 94122.

FARQUHAR, O(SWALD) C(ORNELL), b. Gt. Britain, Sept. 26, 21; m. 53; c. 3. ECONOMIC GEOLOGY. B.A, Oxford, 40, M.A, 47; Ph.D.(geol), Aberdeen, Scotland, 51. Lectr. geol. & mineral, Aberdeen, Scotland, 48-53; asst. prof. GEOL, Kansas, 54-57; assoc. prof, UNIV. MASS, AMHERST, 57-61, PROF, 61- Sr. res. fel, Dept. Sci. & Indust. Res, Wellington, N.Z, 63-64. R.A.F, 40-46. Soc. Econ. Geol; Geochem. Soc; Geol. Soc. Am; Am. Asn. Petrol. Geol; Brit. Geol. Soc; Brit. Geol. Asn. Engineering geology; mineral deposits; petrology. Address: Dept. of Geology, University of Massachusetts, Amherst, MA 01002.

FARQUHAR, R(ONALD) M(cCUNN), b. Montreal, Que, Nov. 25, 29; m. 55; c. 3. GEOPHYSICS. B.A, Toronto, 51, M.A, 52, Ph.D.(physics), 54. Fel. PHYSICS, McMaster, 54-55, lectr, UNIV. TORONTO, 55-56, asst. prof, 56-62, ASSOC. PROF, 62- Royal Soc. Can. traveling fel, 64. Fel. Royal Soc. Can; Am. Geophys. Union; Can. Asn. Physicists. Geological age determinations; mass spectrometry; natural isotopic variations. Address: Dept. of Physics, University of Toronto, Toronto, Ont, Can.

FARR, JOHN B, b. Santa Monica, Calif, Oct. 9, 29; m. 52; c. 2. GEOPHYSICS, GEOLOGY. A.B, Univ. Calif, Berkeley, 51, M.A, 52, Ph.D.(geophys), 54; J.D, Univ. Tulsa, 71. Geophysicist, AMOCO PROD. CO, 55-56, sr. geophysicist, 56-58, party geophysicist, 58-61, dist. geophysicist, 61-63, sr. staff geologist, 63-64, geophys. supvr, 64-65, res. assoc, GEOPHYS, 65, spec. res. assoc, 65-71, MGR. RES. SECT, 71- Seismol. Soc. Am; Am. Asn. Petrol. Geol; Soc. Explor. Geophys.(best presentation award); Am. Geophys. Union. Oceanography; seismology; optics; law. Address: P.O. Box 591, Tulsa, OK 74102.

FARR, KENNETH E(DWARD), b. Philadelphia, Pa, May 6, 17; m. 68. ELECTRONIC ENGINEERING. B.S.E.E, Bucknell, 59; Nat. Sci. Found. fel, Pennsylvania; M.S.E.E, Drexel Inst, 63. Field serv. engr, Philco Corp, 40-41; inspector, radio mat, U.S. Army Sig. Corps, 42; sr. engr. licensee lab, adv. develop, field serv. engr. & engr. in charge field serv. sch, Hazeltine Corp, 42-48; eng. sect. mgr, adv. develop, Westinghouse Elec. Co, 48-57; sr. eng. specialist underwater systs. eng, Philco Corp, 60-61; mgr. indust. prod. eng, Jerrold Electronics Corp, 61-63; ENG. SECT. MGR. STORAGE SYSTS. RES, WESTINGHOUSE ELEC. CO, 63- Sr. mem. Inst. Elec. & Electronics Eng. Color, slow-scan and educational television; band-width compression; magnetic video recording. Address: 732 Garden City Dr, Monroeville, PA 15146.

FARR, LEE E(DWARD), b. Albuquerque, N.Mex, Oct. 13, 07; m. 36; c. 3. MEDICINE. B.S, Yale, 29, M.D, 33. Intern pediat, New Haven Hosp, 32-33; asst. pediatrician, sch. med, Yale, 33-34; asst. & assoc. hosps, Rockefeller Inst. Med. Res, 34-40; dir. res. & physician-in-chief, Alfred I. du Pont Inst, Del, 40-49; med. dir. & chmn. med. res. ctr. & physician-in-chief lab. hosp, Brookhaven Nat. Lab, 48-62; prof. nuclear & environ. med, grad. sch. biomed. sci. & chief sect. nuclear med, Univ. Tex. M.D. Anderson Hosp. & Tumor Inst, 62-67, prof. environ. health & chmn. dept, Univ. Tex. Sch. Pub. Health, Houston, 67-68; CHIEF, emergency health serv. unit, CALIF. STATE DEPT. PUB. HEALTH, 68-70, BUR. EMERGENCY MED. SERV, 70- Vis. assoc. prof, sch. med, Univ. Pa, 40-49; Sigma Xi-Sci. Res. Soc. Am. nat. lectr, 52-53; Gordon Wilson lectr, 56; Sommers Mem. Lectr, Univ. Ore, 60. Mem. adv. comt, Naval Med. Res, Nat. Res. Coun, 53-69, adv. comt, Atomic Bomb Casualty Comn, 55-68, chmn, 57-69, Am. Acad. Pediat. liaison rep, 57; mem. adv. comt. med. uses radioisotopes, Atomic Energy Comn, 64- Mead Johnson Award, 40; Gold Cross, Order of Phoenix, Greece, 60; Order Merit, W.Ger, 63. U.S.N, 42-46, Med.C.Res, 46-67, Capt.(Ret). Fel. AAAS; fel. Am. Med. Asn; fel. Am. Acad. Pediat; Am. Pediat. Soc; Soc. Pediat. Res; Am. Soc. Clin. Invest; Radiation Res. Soc; Soc. Nuclear Med; Am. Soc. Exp. Path; Soc. Exp. Biol. & Med; Am. Pub. Health Asn; Harvey Soc; fel. N.Y. Acad. Sci; fel. Royal Soc. Arts. Organization of emergency medical service systems; non-industrial noise as a health hazard; interaction between man and environment; neutron capture therapy; reactors and isotopes in medicine; protein metabolism renal physiology. Address: State Dept. of Public Health, 2151 Berkeley Way, Berkeley, CA 94704.

FARR, MARIE L(EONORE), b. Vienna, Austria, Sept. 6, 27; nat; div. MYCOLOGY. B.Sc, Mich. State, 48, M.S, 50; Washington State, 50-51; Ph.D.(mycol), Iowa, 57. Asst. botanist, sci. mus, Inst. Jamaica, W.I, 54-55; Mycologist, Inst. Mycol, Recife, Brazil, 58; assoc. mycologist, NAT. FUNGUS COLLECTIONS, 58-60, MYCOLOGIST, PLANT INDUST. STA, 60- Bot. Soc. Am; Am. Soc. Plant Taxon; Asn. Trop. Biol; Int. Asn. Plant Taxon. Taxonomy of Mycomycetes; taxonomy of tropical leaf inhabiting Pyrenomycetes, especially Perisporiales and black mildews. Address: Plant Industry Station, National Fungus Collections, U.S. Dept. of Agriculture, Beltsville, MD 20705.

FARR, MARION M(ARGARET), b. Chautauqua, N.Y, Apr. 18, 03. PARASITOLOGY. B.A, Syracuse, 25, M.A, 29. Lab. aide, Vassar Col, 25-27; Syracuse, 27-29; teacher, high sch, N.Y, 29-30; lab. aide, Nat. Insts. Health, U.S. Pub. Health Serv, 31-34; sci. aide, bur. animal indust, U.S. Dept. Agr, 34-38, from jr. parasitologist to sr. parasitologist, 38-65, animal disease & parasite res. div, 54-65; RES. ASSOC. ZOOL, UNIV. MD, 65- Fel. AAAS; Am. Soc. Parasitol; Soc. Protozool; Conf. Res. Workers Animal Diseases; Wildlife Disease Asn. Avian coccidosis; life histories, pathology and control of coccidia of poultry and related birds. Address: 515 Thayer Ave, Silver Spring, MD 20910.

FARR, RICHARD S(TUDLEY), b. Detroit, Mich, Oct. 30, 22; m. 44; c. 2. MEDICINE, ALLERGY. B.S, Chicago, 45, M.D, 46. Intern, U.S. Navy Hosp, Annapolis, 46-47, hematologist, Naval Med. Res. Inst, 47-48, 50-53; res. assoc. anat, Chicago, 48-50, instr. med, 54-55, asst. prof, 55-56; sr. res. fel. chem. & immunochem, Calif. Inst. Technol, 53-54; assoc. res. prof. anat, Pittsburgh, 56-57, asst. prof. med. & head sect. clin. immunol, 57-62, head div. allergy, immunol. & rheumatology, Scripps Clin. & Res. Found, 62-69, chmn. dept. clin. biol, 66-69; CHIEF DEPT. ALLERGY & CLIN. IMMUNOL, NAT. JEWISH HOSP. & RES. CTR, DENVER, 69-; PROF. MED, SCH. MED, UNIV. COLO, 69- Borden Award, Chicago, 46. Med.C, 43-54, Lt. AAAS; Am. Soc. Clin. Invest; Am. Acad. Allergy (pres, 70); Am. Soc. Exp. Path; Am. Med. Asn; Am. Asn. Anat; Am. Asn. Immunol. Morphogenesis of blood cells; irradiation illness; body temperature regulating mechanisms; immunochemistry; clinical immunology. Address: Dept. of Allergy & Clinical Immunology, National Jewish Hospital & Research Center, 3800 E. Colfax Ave, Denver, CO 80206.

FARR, THOMAS H(OWARD), b. Cannonsburg, Mich, Nov. 27, 19. ENTOMOLOGY. B.A, Western Michigan, 42; M.S, Mich. State, 48; Ph.D, Massachusetts, 53. Instr. entomol, Massachusetts, 51-53; ENTOMOLOGIST, SCI. MUS, INST. JAMAICA, 54- U.S.N.R, 42-46. Entom. Soc. Am. Biology of insects; taxonomy of Diptera. Address: Science Museum, Institute of Jamaica, 12-16 East St, Kingston, Jamaica, W.I.

FARR, WILLIAM CHARLES, b. Bayonne, N.J, Jan. 17, 41. PHYSIOLOGY, PHARMACOLOGY. B.S, Cincinnati, 62, Ph.D.(pharmacol), 67, M.D, 69. ASST. PROF. PHYSIOL. & INTERNAL MED, UNIV. CINCINNATI, 69- Cardiovascular physiology and pharmacology; autonomic effects on the cardiovascular system; pharmacology of angiotension; cardiac innervation. Address: Cardiac Research Lab, University of Cincinnati, Cincinnati, OH 45229.

FARR, WILLIAM MORRIS, b. Kansas City, Mo, Oct. 20, 38; m. 60; c. 2. PLASMA & REACTOR PHYSICS. B.A, Rice Univ, 60; Atomic Energy Comn. fel, Univ. Mich, 60-62 & 64-65, M.S, 62, Babcock & Wilcox fel, 65-66, Ph.D.(nuclear sci), 66. Physicist, Pac. Missile Range, U.S. Navy, summer 60; engr, Oak Ridge Nat. Lab, summer 62; res. engr, Atomics Int, 62-63 & summer 64; physicist, Oak Ridge Nat. Lab, 66-69; ASST. PROF. NUCLEAR ENG, UNIV. ARIZ, 69- Physicist, Culham Lab, U.K. Atomic Energy Auth, summer 70. Am. Phys. Soc; Am. Nuclear Soc. Theoretical study of microinstabilities in plasma with emphasis on those instabilities of importance to controlled fusion. Address: Dept. of Nuclear Engineering, University of Arizona, Tucson, AZ 85721.

FARRAH, GEORGE H(ENRY), b. Vancouver, Wash, July 30, 15; m. 40; c. 3. ANALYTICAL CHEMISTRY. B.S, Washington State, 38, Am. Dry Milk Inst. fel, 38-40, M.S, 40. Anal. chemist, Aluminum Co. Am, 40-51, tech. supv. lab, 51-56, res. chemist, Alcoa Res. Labs, 56-59, HEAD. ALCOA ENVIRON. HEALTH LAB, 59- Dipl, Am. Bd. Indust. Hyg. Am. Chem. Soc; fel. Am. Inst. Chem. Air pollution and trace analysis of plant and animal tissue; nonferrous metallurgy. Address: Environmental Health Lab, Alcoa Technical Center, P.O. Box 2970, Pittsburgh, PA 15230.

FARRALL, ARTHUR WILLIAM, b. Harvard, Nebr, Feb. 23, 99; m. 23; c. 2. AGRICULTURAL ENGINEERING. B.S, Nebraska, 21, M.S, 22, hon. D.Eng, 55; California, 26-27. Jr. agr. engr, California, 22-28, asst. prof, 28-29; dir. res. lab, Douthitt Eng. Co, Ill, 29-32; res. engr, Creamery Package Mfg. Co, 33-37, sr. res. engr, 37-42, dir. res, 42-45; prof. agr. eng, MICH. STATE UNIV, 45-68, head dept, 45-64, chmn. food technol. comt, 59-68, EMER. PROF. AGR. ENG, 68- Consult, Univ. Ill, 64; U.S. Dept. Agr, 64-65; Punjab Univ, 68; Inst. Food Technol, Campinas, Brazil, 70. Mem. res. adv. comt, res. lab, Nat. Restaurant Asn. U.S. del, Int. Dairy Cong, Stockholm, 49; partic, Int. Farm Mach, France, 61; Int. Dairy Cong, Copenhagen, 62; Int. Cong. Agr. Eng, Switz, 64. U.S.A, 17-18. Fel. Am. Soc. Agr. Eng. (pres, 62-63, Massey Ferguson Award, 71); Am. Dairy Sci. Asn; Am. Soc. Eng. Educ; Inst. Food Tech. Food machinery; ice cream freezers; continuous butter manufacturing machine; infrared radiant frost preventive machine; agricultural machinery; dairy and food engineering; inertial propulsion systems; food engineering; genealogy research. Address: 1858 Cahill Drive, East Lansing, MI 48823.

FARRALL, GEORGE A, b. Arlington, Mass, June 7, 30; m. 53; c. 3. PHYSICS. B.S, Tufts, 53, M.S, 55. PHYSICIST, GEN. ELEC. CO, 55-57, res. lab, 57-71, RES. & DEVELOP. CTR, 71- Am. Phys. Soc; Inst. Elec. & Electronics Eng. Gas and electrical discharges. Address: Research & Development Center, General Electric Co, P.O. Box 1088, Schenectady, NY 12301.

FARRAN, CHARLES FREDERICK, b. Cleveland, Ohio, July 26, 40; m. 62. PHYSICAL CHEMISTRY. A.B, Ohio Wesleyan, 62; du Pont summer fel, Michigan, 63, M.S, 64, Ph.D.(phys. chem), 66. Asst. gen. & phys. chem, Michigan, 62-64, phys. chem, 64-66; SR. RES. CHEMIST, EASTMAN KODAK CO, 66- Am. Inst. Chemists medal award, 62. AAAS; Am. Chem. Soc.(merit award, 62). Molecular spectroscopy; calculation and interpretation of potential constants; bonding and structure in nitrogen-phosphorous compounds; electrochemistry with noble metal electrodes; adsorption to metal surfaces; thin film studies using ellipsometry. Address: Research Labs, Kodak Park Bldg. 59, Eastman Kodak Co, 343 State St, Rochester, NY 14650.

FARRAND, W(ESTON) B(ROWNLOW), b. Miles City, Mont, Feb. 9, 26; m. 52. ENGINEERING PHYSICS. B.S, Mont. State Col, 49, M.S, 51. Physicist, Hanford Works, Gen. Elec. Co, 51-56; instrument group head, Poulter Lab, Stanford Res. Inst, 56-64; mgr. elec. eng, Link Ord. Div, Gen. Precision, Inc, 64-68, ord. eng, Singer-Link Ord. Prod, 68-70; MGR. ENG, SUNNYVALE DIV, SPACE ORD. SYSTS, INC, 70- U.S. Merchant Marines, 44-45. Am. Phys. Soc; Inst. Elec. & Electronics Eng; Am. Asn. Physics Teachers. Nuetron physics; electronic measurements and instruments; explosives and interior ballistics of rockets; high pressure phenomena; shock waves; physical electronics. Address: 3380 Cork Oak Way, Palo Alto, CA 94303.

FARRAND, WILLIAM R(ICHARD), b. Columbus, Ohio, Apr. 27, 31; m. 62; c. 2. GEOLOGY. B.Sc, Ohio State, 55, Bownocker scholar, 55-56, M.Sc, 56; Nat. Sci. Found. fel, Michigan, 56-60, Ph.D.(Pleistocene geol), 60. Res. assoc. Pleistocene geol, Lamont Geol. Observ, Columbia, 60-61, asst. prof, dept. geol, 61-64; vis. prof, inst. geol, Strasbourg, 64-65; asst. prof. PLEISTOCENE GEOL, UNIV. MICH, 65-67, ASSOC. PROF, 67- Nat. Acad. Sci. res. fel, Strasbourg, 63-64; vis. prof, Hebrew Univ, 71-72. Nat. Guard, 48-54, Sgt. AAAS; Geol. Soc. Am; Glaciol. Soc. Pleistocene geology; history of the Great Lakes and glacio-isostatic rebound; quaternary paleoclimate; chronology and paleoecology of prehistoric men and their environment. Address: Dept. of Geology & Mineralogy, University of Michigan, Ann Arbor, MI 48104.

FARRAR, DAVID T(URNER), b. Nashville, Tenn, Feb. 4, 41; m. 64. PHYSICAL CHEMISTRY. B.A, Vanderbilt, 63; Nat. Defense Ed. Act fel, South Carolina, 64-67, Ph.D.(phys. inorg. chem), 68. ASST. PROF. CHEM, TENN. TECHNOL. UNIV, 68- Nat. Sci. Found. res. participation col, teachers, 69-71. Am. Chem. Soc. Kinetics of rapid reactions; bomb calorimetry; solution calorimetry; coordination chemistry. Address: Dept. of Chemistry, Box 5055, Tennessee Technological University, Cookeville, TN 38501.

FARRAR, GEORGE E(LBERT), JR, b. Winter Park, Fla, Mar. 12, 06; m. 33; c. 2. INTERNAL MEDICINE. B.S, Wesleyan, 27; M.D, Hopkins, 31. Asst. pharmacol, Hopkins, 28-31; intern, univ. hosp, Michigan, 31-32, asst. res. med, 32-33, instr, univ. & T.H. Simpson Mem. Inst, 33-35; assoc. pharmacologist, food & drug admin, U.S. Dept. Agr, 35-36; asst. prof. MED, SCH. MED, TEMPLE UNIV, 36-44, from assoc. prof. to CLIN. PROF, 44-; DIR. MED. SERV, WYETH LABS, INC, 49-, consult. pharmaceut. advert, 40-49. Assoc. physician, Episcopal Hosp, Phila, 44-46, chief med. serv, 46-49; mem. revision comt, U.S. Pharmacopoeia, 50-60. AAAS; Am. Soc. Pharmacol. & Exp. Therapeut; fel. Am. Med. Asn; Am. Rheumatism Asn; fel. Am. Col. Physicians; Fedn. Am. Socs. Exp. Biol. Metabolism of iron; nutritional anemia; osteoporosis in adults; hyaluronidase in rheumatic diseases. Address: Medical Services, Wyeth Labs, Box 8299, Philadelphia, PA 19101.

FARRAR, GROVER L(OUIS), b. Lynchburg, Va, May 22, 36; m. 63; c. 2. ORGANIC CHEMISTRY. B.S, Randolph-Macon Col, 56; Ph.D.(org. chem), Calif. Inst. Tech, 61. Res. chemist, nitrogen div, Allied Chem. Corp, Va, 60-64; Denver Res. Ctr, Marathon Oil Co, 64-67; sr. res. chemist, CELANESE PLASTICS CO, 67-70, GROUP LEADER, 70- Am. Chem. Soc. Chemistry of organic nitrogen compounds; reagent additions to olefins; chlorination of aralkyl compounds; naphthalene dicarboxylates; polyester film. Address: Celanese Plastics Co, Box 828, Greer, SC 29651.

FARRAR, HARRY, IV, b. London, Eng, Dec. 31, 35; U.S. citizen; m. 62; c. 2. NUCLEAR PHYSICS. B.A, Toronto, 58; M.S, McMaster, 59, Ph.D.(physics), 62. Fel. nuclear physics, McMaster, 62; sr. physicist, ATOMICS INT. DIV, N.AM. ROCKWELL CORP, 62-67, res. specialist, 67-68, MEM. TECH. STAFF, 68- Can. Asn. Physicist. Mass spectrometric study of short-lived high activity fission products; charge distribution and fission yields of U^{233}, U^{235}, Pu^{241}; effects of space radiation on materials; fast reactor Doppler coefficient measurements; applying mass spectrometry to study integral cross sections by measurement of helium in metals after reactor irradiations; studying effects of helium on void formation in reactor materials. Address: Atomics International Division, North American Rockwell Corp, Canoga Park, CA 91304.

FARRAR, JOHN, b. Manchester, Eng, Mar. 30, 27; U.S. citizen; m. 55; c. 3. PHYSICAL CHEMISTRY. B.Sc, Manchester, 48, Ph.D.(chem), 51. Chemist, E.I. du Pont de Nemours & Co, 52-53; Shell Develop. Co, 53-56; Technicolor Corp, 56-59; prin. scientist, Rocketdyne Div, N.AM. ROCKWELL CORP, 59-67, MGR. AUTONETICS DIV, 67- Am. Chem. Soc; Electrochem. Soc. Electrochemistry and microelectronics; process development; desalination; batteries; photographic materials; crystal growth. Address: 10181 La Sierra Place, Santa Ana, CA 92705.

FARRAR, J(OHN) L(AIRD), b. Hamilton, Ont, Dec. 31, 13; m. 46. FORESTRY. B.Sc.F, Toronto, 36; M.F, Yale, 39, Ph.D, 55. Forester, Can. Int. Paper Co, 36-37; forest ecol, Can. Forestry Br, 37-41, 45-56; PROF. FORESTRY, UNIV. TORONTO, 56- Ed, Can. J. Forest Res. R.C.A.F, 41-45. Fel. AAAS; Ecol. Soc. Am; Can. Soc. Plant Physiol; Can. Inst. Forestry; Can. Bot. Asn; Tech. Asn. Pulp & Paper Indust. Forest ecology and tree physiology. Address: Faculty of Forestry, Toronto 5, Ont, Can.

FARRAR, JOHN THRUSTON, b. St. Louis, Mo, June 26, 20; m. 47; c. 2. INTERNAL MEDICINE, GASTROENTEROLOGY. A.B, Princeton, 42; M.D, Washington (St. Louis), 45. Asst. res. path, Boston City Hosp, 48-49; intern med, Mass. Mem. Hosp, Boston, Mass, 49-50, asst. res, 50-51, res. assoc, 51-54; chief gastroenterol. sect, med. serv, Vet. Admin. Hosp, New York, N.Y, 55-63, asst. dir. prof. serv. res, 56-63; assoc. prof. MED, MED. COL,

VA, 63-65, PROF, 65-, CHIEF GASTROENTEROL. SECT, 63- Asst, sch. med, Boston, 50-54, instr, 54-55. Ed, Am. Jour. Digestive Diseases, 68- Dipl, Am. Bd. Internal Med, 54, Am. Bd. Gastroenterol, 62. U.S.A, 46-48, Capt. Am. Med. Asn; Am. Gastroenterol. Asn; Am. Fedn. Clin. Res; Inst. Elec. & Electronics Eng. Gastroinestinal physiology, particularly absorption and motility; pancreatic exocrine physiology; medical electronics. Address: Gastroenterology Division, Medical College of Virginia, Richmond, VA 23219.

FARRAR, MARTIN W(ILBUR), b. Hazlehurst, Miss, Dec. 25, 22; m. 44; c. 2. ORGANIC CHEMISTRY. B.S, Miss. Col, 43, Ph.D.(org. chem), Pittsburgh, 50. Res. chemist, Monsanto Chem. Co, 50-54; proj. leader, Ethyl Corp, 54-55; res. group leader, Monsanto Chem. Co, 55-60, asst. res. dir, 60-62, MGR. RES, MONSANTO CO, 63- U.S.N.R, 43-46, Res, 46-48, Lt.(jg). Am. Chem. Soc. Organic synthesis; polymer chemistry. Address: Monsanto Co, 1700 S. 2nd St, St. Louis, MO 63177.

FARRAR, RALPH C(OLEMAN), b. Cabool, Mo, Sept. 22, 30; m. 53; c. 2. ORGANIC CHEMISTRY. B.S, Wichita, 53; Synthetic Rubber fel, Illinois, 53-54, Ph.D.(org. chem), 56. Chemist, rubber res. prog, Illinois, 54-56; RES. CHEMIST, SYNTHETIC RUBBER, PHILLIPS PETROL. CO, 56- Am. Chem. Soc; Am. Inst. Chem. New types of synthetic rubber. Address: 2352 London Lane, Bartlesville, OK 74003.

FARRAR, R(ICHARD) E(DWARD), b. Lynchburg, Va, Mar. 13, 17; m. 46; c. 1. CHEMICAL ENGINEERING. B.S, Va. Polytech, 38; M.E, Hopkins, 50, Dr. Eng, 51. Asst. chemist, control div, Mead Corp, 38-40; chief chemist, Columbia Paper Co, 40-41; prod. supvr, prod. div, U.S. Army Chem. Ctr, 41-43, area engr, develop. div, 45-48; mgr. res. & develop, Colgate-Palmolive Co, 51-60, res. coord, household prod. div, 60-62, dir. res. & develop, European Div.(London), Colgate-Palmolive Int, Inc, 62-67; dir. prod. develop, R.J. Reynolds Tobacco, N.D, 67-70; MEM. STAFF, DAIRY RES. INC, 70- U.S.A, 43-45. Am. Chem. Soc; Am. Inst. Chem. Eng. Administration of research and development. Address: Dairy Research Inc, 120 Eastman Bldg, Arlington Heights, IL 60004.

FARRAR, R(OBERT) LYNN, JR, b. Nashville, Tenn, Sept. 3, 21; m. 45; c. 3. PHYSICAL CHEMISTRY. A.B, Vanderbilt, 43; fel, Washington (Seattle), 47, M.S, 48; Ph.D.(chem), Tennessee, 53. Chemist, Carbide & Carbon Chem. Corp, 47-54, res. chemist, 54-58, head phys. chem. sect, OAK RIDGE GASEOUS DIFFUSION PLANT, UNION CARBIDE NUCLEAR CO, 58-61, special assignment, Y12 Plant, 61-62, DEVELOP. CONSULT. CHEM, 62- Instr, eve. sch, Tennessee, 57, vis. assoc. prof, Oak Ridge Grad. Prog, 58. U.S.N.R, 42-46, Lt. AAAS; Am. Chem. Soc; Sci. Res. Soc. Am; fel. Am. Inst. Chem. Fluorine and uranium chemistry; kinetics of solid-gas reactions; adsorption; corrosion; physical properties of inorganic fluorine compounds. Address: Oak Ridge Gaseous Diffusion Plant, Union Carbide Nuclear Co, P.O. Box P, Oak Ridge, TN 37830.

FARRAR, THOMAS C, b. Independence, Kans, Jan. 14, 33; m. 63; c. 2. PHYSICAL CHEMISTRY, MATHEMATICS. B.S, Wichita, 54; Ph.D.(phys. chem), Illinois, 59. Nat. Sci. Found. fel, Cambridge, 59-61; asst. prof. chem, Univ. Ore, 61-63; chemist, Nat. Bur. Standards, 63-67, inorg. chem. sect, 67-69, head magnetism group, 69-71; DIR. RES. & DEVELOP, JEOL, INC, 71- Silver medal, U.S. Dept. Commerce. Fel. Am. Inst. Chem; Am. Phys. Soc; Am. Chem. Soc; N.Y. Acad. Sci; Am. Soc. Test. & Mat. Experimental and theoretical nuclear magnetic resonance spectroscopy; theoretical chemistry. Address: Jeol Inc, 235 Birchwood Ave, Cranford, NJ 07016.

FARRAR, WILLIAM EDMUND, JR, b. Macon, Ga, May 28, 33; m. 57; c. 2. INFECTIOUS DISEASE, MICROBIOLOGY. B.S, Mercer Univ, 55; M.D, Med. Col. Ga, 58. Intern med, Talmadge Mem. Hosp, Augusta, 58-59, asst. resident, 59-60; sr. asst. resident, Grady Mem. Hosp, Atlanta, 60-61; U.S. Pub. Health Serv. fel, sch. med, Emory Univ, 61-62, asst. prof. prev. med, 65-68, assoc. med, 65-67, asst. prof. med, 67-70, assoc. prof. prev. med, 68-71, med, 70-71, dir. div. infectious diseases, dept. med, 69-71; PROF. MED. & HEAD SECT. INFECTIOUS DISEASES, DEPT. MED, MED. UNIV. S.C, 72- Vis. mem. staff, Grady Mem. Hosp, 65-; partic, int. conf. molecular biol. of Gram-negative bacteria, N.Y. Acad. Sci, 65; consult, Emory Univ. Clin, 65-71; consult. malaria res. prog, Nat. Insts. Health, Atlanta Fed. Prison, 67-; partic, int. conf. biol. effects of Gram-negative bacteria, Nat. Ctr. Sci. Res, France, 68. Med.C, 62-65, Capt. AAAS; Am. Fedn. Clin. Res; Am. Med. Asn; Am. Soc. Microbiol; fel. Am. Col. Physicians; Infectious Diseases Soc. Am. Resistance of bacteria to antibiotics; bacterial flora of gastrointestinal tract; bacterial endotoxins; infections due to Gram-negative bacteria. Address: Dept. of Medicine, Medical University of South Carolina, 80 Barre St, Charleston, SC 29401.

FARRAR, WINSTON C(ALVIN), b. Athens, Ala, Apr. 26, 34. PHYSICAL CHEMISTRY. B.A, Fisk, 55; M.S, Marquette, 57; Ph.D.(phys. chem), Syracuse, 61. Res. assoc, Yale, 61-63; prof. CHEM. & head dept, Tenn. State Univ, 63-69; PROF, ALA. A&M UNIV, 70- Vis. scientist, Nat. Bur. Standards, Wash, D.C, 71- Am. Chem. Soc. Address: Dept. of Chemistry, Alabama A&M University, Normal, AL 35762.

FARRAUTO, ROBERT J(OSEPH), b. N.Y.C, Nov. 22, 41; m. 64; c. 2. PHYSICAL & INORGANIC CHEMISTRY. B.S, Manhattan Col, 64; Ph.D.(chem), Rensselaer Polytech. Inst, 68. RES. CHEMIST, CORNING GLASS WORKS, 68- Spec. lectr, Elmira Col, 71. Am. Chem Soc. Electrode kinetics; silicate chemistry; gas adsorption; catalysis. Address: 7 Birch Circle, Painted Post, NY 14870.

FARRELL, CHARLES E(RNEST), b. Saltsburg, Pa, May 12, 09; m. 38; c. 2. ZOOLOGY. A.B, Waynesburg Col, 31; M.A, Michigan, 34; Ph.D.(zool), Duke, 51. Teacher, pub. sch, Pa, 31-43; instr, Waynesburg Col, 46-47, 50-51; asst, Duke, 47-50; asst. prof. zool, VANDERBILT UNIV, 51-56, ASSOC. PROF. BIOL, 56- U.S. Merchant Marine, 43-46. AAAS; Soc. Syst. Zool. Taxonomy and ecology of chiggers and vertebrates; biophysics of bird flight. Address: Dept. of Biology, Vanderbilt University, Nashville, TN 37203.

FARRELL, DAVID E, b. May 9, 39; Brit. citizen. PHYSICS. B.Sc, London, 60, Ph.D.(physics), 64. Res. asst. PHYSICS, London, 64; fel, Western Reserve, 64-66, instr, 66-67; ASST. PROF, CASE WEST. RESERVE UNIV, 67- Am. Phys. Soc. Low temperature physics; superconductivity. Address: Dept. of Physics, Case Western Reserve University, University Circle, Cleveland, OH 44106.

FARRELL, DESMOND L(AWRENCE), b. Cleveland, Ohio, Sept. 23, 21; m. 42; c. 4. CHEMICAL ENGINEERING. B.Ch.E, Cleveland State Univ, 46; Case Inst. Technol, 50-51. Asst. foreman, aluminum sulphate dept, gen. chem. div, Allied Chem. Co, 47; res. engr, Indust. Rayon Corp, 48, semiworks supvr. res, 53, prod. supt. nylon, 54-57; tech. supt. rayon, 57-58, plant mgr, 58-60; HERCULES, INC, 61-63, ASST. GEN. MGR, fibers dept, 64-66, fibers & film dept, 66-71, POLYMERS DEPT, 71- Sig.C, U.S.A, 45-46. AAAS; fel. Am. Inst. Chem. Eng; Am. Inst. Chem. Synthetic fibers; polyolefin polymer, fibers and film. Address: Polymers Dept, Hercules, Inc, Ninth & Market Sts, Wilmington, DE 19899.

FARRELL, E(DWARD) J(OSEPH), b. San Francisco, Calif, Mar. 28, 17; m. 54; c. 2. MATHEMATICS. B.Sc, Univ. San Francisco, 39; M.A, Stanford Univ, 42, Nat. Sci. Found. faculty fel, 57-58. Assoc. prof. MATH, UNIV. SAN FRANCISCO, 41-68, PROF, 68-, DIR. MATH. INST, 60- Nat. Sci. Found. dir. inst. progs, 60-, confs. geom, summers 67, 68, 70; consult, Calif. State Dept. Educ, 71- U.S.A, 44-46. AAAS; Am. Inst. Phys; Math. Asn. Am. Differential equations. Address: Dept. of Mathematics, University of San Francisco, San Francisco, CA 94117.

FARRELL, EUGENE PATRICK, b. Wamego, Kans, July 3, 11; m. 35; c. 5. ENGINEERING. B.S, Kansas State, 35, M.S, 53. Trainee, Gen. Mills, Inc, Minn, 35-38, miller, N.Y, 38-42, plant supt, Ky, 42-43, Iowa, 43-45, div. supt, Minn, 45-47; prod. mgr, Maney Milling Co, Nebr, 47-49; milling technologist, KANS. STATE UNIV, 49-53, assoc. prof. flour & feed milling indust, 53-67, PROF. GRAIN SCI. & INDUST, 67- Consult, 51- Flour milling; flow diagrams; equipment layout and operation; wheat quality evaluation and conditioning; feed grain grinding; corn and sorghum milling. Address: Dept. of Grain Science & Industries, Kansas State University, Manhattan, KS 66502.

FARRELL, GORDON L(EE) b, Helena, Mont, Apr. 16, 25. PHYSIOLOGY, INTERNAL MEDICINE. M.D, St. Louis, 48. Intern, U.S. Pub. Health Hosp, La, 48-49; instr. pharmacol, Utah, 51-52; res. fel. physiol, Western Reserve, 52-54, instr, 54-55, sr. instr, 55-56, asst. prof, 56-60, assoc. prof, 60-65; biochem. & psychiat, col. med, Baylor, 65-70; PROF. MENT. SCI, UNIV. TEX. GRAD. SCH. BIOMED. SCI, HOUSTON, 66- Clin. prof, Univ. Houston, 68-; asst. dir, Tex. Res. Inst. Ment. Sci; private practice, internal med, Ctr. Pavilion Hosp. & Hermann Hosp, 70- Estab. investr, Am. Heart Asn, 57-62; sr. visitant, Vet. Admin. Hosp, Cleveland. Ciba award, 59. U.S.N, 44-48; U.S.P.H.S, 48-52, Surgeon. Fel. AAAS; Am. Physiol. Soc; Endocrine Soc; Am. Heart Asn; assoc. Royal Soc. Med; hon. mem. Endocrine Soc. Chile. Physiology of endocrines; metabolic diseases and mental retardation. Address: 801 Center Pavilion Hospital, Houston, TX 77025.

FARRELL, HAROLD M(ARON), JR, b. Pottsville, Pa, Sept. 5, 40; m. 63; c. 2. BIOCHEMISTRY. B.S, Mt. St. Mary's Col.(Md), 62; M.S, Pa. State, 65, Ph.D.(biochem), 68. Asst. biochem, Pa. State, 63-66, res. asst, 66-67; RES. ASSOC. PROTEIN CHEM, EAST. REGIONAL LAB, U.S. DEPT. AGR, 67- AAAS; Am. Chem. Soc. Protein chemistry, especially the relation of protein structure to biological function. Address: Eastern Regional Lab, U.S. Dept. of Agriculture, 600 E. Mermaid Lane, Philadelphia, PA 19118.

FARRELL, JAMES H(ENRY), b. New Bedford, Mass, Nov. 10, 19; m. 50; c. 3. STRUCTURAL ENGINEERING. A.B, Brown, 48, M.S, 49. Sr. draftsman, Jackson & Moreland, 49-50; jr. civil engr, State Hwy. Dept, Mass, 50-51; struct. designer, Charles T. Main, Inc, 51-53; develop. engr, Arthur D. Little, Inc, 53-57; sr. mech. engr, Tech. Opers, Inc, 57-59; partner & sr. mech. engr, Conesco Consults, 59-61, v.pres. & gen. mgr, Conesco Div, Flow Corp, 61-69; V.PRES, JBF SCI. CORP, 69- Am. Soc. Civil Eng. Applied mechanics; acoustics; nuclear shielding; electronic instrumentation; environmental sciences; pollution. Address: JBF Scientific Corp, 2 Ray Ave, Burlington, MA 01803.

FARRELL, JAMES I, b. Butte, Mont, Nov. 15, 00; m. 34; c. 2. PHYSIOLOGY, UROLOGY. B.S, Chicago, 24, M.S, 25, M.D, Rush, 28; Ph.D.(physiol), Northwestern, 27. Instr. physiol, Chicago, 24-25; Northwestern, 25-28; Belcher fel. surg. & urol, Cleveland Clin, 28-31; res. urologist, N.Y. Post-Grad. Med. Sch, Columbia, 31-32; assoc. UROL, NORTHWEST. UNIV, 32-34, ASST. PROF, 34- Med.C, 43-46, Comdr. Am. Physiol. Soc; Am. Col. Surg. Physiology of urinary tract, stomach, pancreas and prostate; vocal cord paralysis. Address: 636 Church St, Evanston, IL 60201.

FARRELL, JAMES K(ENNETH), b. Fremont, Ohio, Apr. 26, 08; m. 30; c. 2. ORGANIC CHEMISTRY. A.B, Ohio State, 30, M.S, 32, Ph.D.(org. chem), 34. Res. chemist IV, rayon div, E.I. du Pont de Nemours & Co, Buffalo, N.Y, 35-40; sr. scientist, Solvay Process Div, Allied Chem. Corp, 40-67; PROF. CHEM, ONONDAGA COMMUNITY COL, 67- Am. Chem. Soc; Am. Inst. Aeronaut. & Astronaut; Electrochem. Soc. Viscose rayon research; physical testing; hydrogen peroxide high temperature reactions; electro-organic chemistry. Address: 116 Meadowbrook Dr, Syracuse, NY 13210.

FARRELL, JOHN A, b. Ft. Worth, Tex, Dec. 25, 35; m. 58; c. 1. NUCLEAR PHYSICS. B.A, Texas Christian, 59; Ph.D.(physics), Duke, 64. Res. assoc. physics, Duke Univ, 64-66; STAFF MEM. GROUP W-8, LOS ALAMOS SCI. LAB, UNIV. CALIF, 66- Am. Phys. Soc. Neutron total cross sections in the kilovolt energy region. Address: Group W-8, Los Alamos Scientific Lab, University of California, P.O. Box 1663, Los Alamos, NM 87544.

FARRELL, JOHN H(AROLD), b. Syracuse, N.Y, Sept. 21, 20; m. 46; c. 2. FOREST ECONOMICS, PUBLIC ADMINISTRATION. B.S, Syracuse, 42, fel, 47-50, M.F, 48, Ph.D.(pub. admin), 52. Asst. eng. aide, U.S. Army Eng. Corp, 42-43; eng. aide, Syracuse City Eng. Dept, 46-47; instr. & fel, N.Y. State Col. Forestry, Syracuse, 47-50; supv. forest appraiser, N.Y. State Bd. Equalization & Assessment, 50-51, 53-57; forest economist, proj. leader, U.S. Forest Serv, 57-60, chief. br. admin. & tech. serv, U.S. Forest Prod. Lab, 60-62, staff asst. progs. & legislation, 62-66; STAFF ASST. PROG. ANAL, OFF. SECY, U.S. DEPT. INTERIOR, 66- U.S.A.A.F, 43-46, U.S.A.F,

51-53, Res, 53-, Lt. Col; Bronze Star Medal, 53. AAAS; Soc. Am. Foresters; Am. Soc. Pub. Admin; Am. Forestry Asn. Forest economics; public administration in natural resources field; management; silviculture. Address: Office of the Secretary, U.S. Dept. of the Interior, Room 7244 Interior Bldg, Washington, DC 20240.

FARRELL, JOHN J(OSEPH), b. Seneca, Wis, Sept. 6, 17; m. 43; c. 2. SURGERY. A.B, Loras Col, 38; M.D, Wisconsin, 40; M.D, Harvard Med. Sch, 42. Instr. surg. & physiol, Albany Med. Col, 47-52, fel, Dazian Found, 48-49, dir. exp. surg, 51-54, asst. prof. SURG, 53; PROF. & CHMN. DEPT, SCH. MED, UNIV. MIAMI, 54-61, CLIN. PROF, 62-; CHIEF SURG, LAKE WORTH MED. CTR, 65- Surgeon-in-chief, Jackson Mem. Hosp, 54-; dir. surg, Biltmore Vet. Admin. Hosp, 57-; Dade County Hosp, 58-63; consult, Variety Children's Hosp, Coral Gables, 58-; Mt. Sinai Hosp, Miami Beach, 58- Dipl, Am. Bd. Surg, 53. U.S.A, 43-46, Capt. AAAS; Am. Med. Asn; fel. Am. Col. Surg; N.Y. Acad. Sci; dipl. mem. Pan-Am. Med. Asn. Gastrointestinal physiology and surgery; endocrine physiology and surgery. Address: Lake Worth Medical Center, 508 N. Federal Hwy, Lake Worth, FL 33460.

FARRELL, J(OSEPH) B(RENDAN), b. New York, N.Y, May 3, 23; m. 51; c. 7. CHEMICAL ENGINEERING. B.S, Notre Dame, 43; M.S, Mass. Inst. Tech, 47; Ph.D.(chem. eng), Cornell, 54. Chem. engr, Kellex Corp, 44-45; instr. chem. eng, Notre Dame, 47-49; res. chem. engr, M.W. Kellogg Co, 51-55; res. assoc, Am. Mach. & Foundry Co, 56-61; assoc. prof. chem. eng, Manhattan Col, 61-67; CHEM. ENGR, R.A, TAFT WATER RES. CTR, U.S. DEPT. INTERIOR, FED. WATER POLLUTION CONTROL ADMIN, 67- Indust. consult. Am. Chem. Soc; Am. Inst. Chem. Eng; Am. Soc. Eng. Educ. Flow of non-Newtonian liquids; film casting; drying; electrodialysis; wet oxidation of graphite; ultimate disposal of solid and liquid wastes from conventional and advanced methods for treatment of wastewater to eliminate pollution. Address: R.A. Taft Water Research Center, U.S. Dept. of Interior, Federal Water Pollution Control Administration, 4676 Columbia Pkwy, Cincinnati, OH 45226.

FARRELL, KENNETH THOMAS, b. Brookline, Mass, Mar. 21, 14; m. 39; c. 2. FOOD TECHNOLOGY. B.S, Mass. State Col, 38, fel, 38-40, Ph.D. (food tech), 40. Lab. asst. physiol, Mass. State Col, 37-40; res. food technologist, Beech-Nut Packing Corp, 40; chief chemist, Sardik Food Prod. Corp, N.Y, 40-41; jr. mkt. specialist, agr. mkt. admin, U.S. Dept. Agr, 41-42, asst. mkt. specialist, 42, assoc. mkt. specialist, 42-43, prin. purchasing off, 43-44; sr. indust. specialist, 44; plant mgr, Sardik Food Prod. Corp, N.Y, 44-48, from gen. mgr. to treas, Calif, 48-49, chief, gen. prod. div, Qm. Food & Container Inst, 49-57; prod. develop. dept, Corn Prod. Co, 57-60, prod. mgr, mkt. planning & long range planning dept, 60-64, dir. ingredient planning, Food Technol. Inst, 64-69; TECH. DIR, UNITED FRUIT CO, BOSTON, 69- Assoc. ed, Quick Frozen Foods Mag, Inst. Food Technol. Processing factors affecting vitamin content of foods; development of new dehydrated foods; development of complete rations; dry vinegar; syrups; food additives. Address: 40 Windsor Rd, Dover, MA 02030.

FARRELL, M(ICHAEL) A(NTHONY), b. New York, N.Y, Jan. 14, 04; m. 29; c. 4. BACTERIOLOGY. B.S, Pa. State, 28; M.S, Lehigh, 30; Ph.D.(bact), Yale, 34. Asst. bact, Lehigh, 28-30, instr, 30-32; asst, Pa. State Univ, 34, instr, 34-36, assoc. prof. & head div, 36-40, prof. & head dept, 40-47, asst. dir. exp. sta, 47-52, dir, 52-69, v.pres. res, 57-69; RETIRED. Trustee, Centre County Hosp. With Off. Sci. Res. & Develop, 44. AAAS; Am. Soc. Microbiol; fel. Am. Pub. Health Asn; Inst. Food Technol; N.Y. Acad. Med. Metabolism and respiratory mechanism of the streptococci, coliform bacteria in water and milk; living bacteria in coal, ancient rocks and meteorites, synthetic media for penicillin production; calf scours and calf pneumonia. Address: 420 Adams Ave, State College, PA 16801.

FARRELL, ROBERT L(AWRENCE), b. Zanesville, Ohio, Oct. 6, 25; m. 45; c. 4. VETERINARY PATHOLOGY. D.V.M, Ohio State, 50, M.Sc, 51, Ph.D. (vet. path), 54. Instr. VET. PATH, OHIO STATE UNIV, 51-54, asst. prof. 54-57, assoc. prof, 57-60, PROF, 60- U.S.A, 43-45. AAAS; Am. Col. Vet. Path; Am. Vet. Med. Asn; Conf. Res. Workers Animal Diseases; Int. Acad. Path. Animal mycoses; effect of air pollution on animals; viral and chemical oncogenesis in animals. Address: Dept. of Veterinary Pathology, Ohio State University, Columbus, OH 43210.

FARRELL, ROGER HAMLIN, b. Greensboro, N.C, July 23, 29. MATHEMATICS, MATHEMATICAL STATISTICS. Ph.B, Chicago, 47, M.S, 51; Ph.D.(math), Illinois, 59. Instr. MATH, CORNELL UNIV, 59-61, asst. prof, 61-63, assoc. prof, 63-67, PROF, 67- U.S.A.R, 54-56. Am. Math. Soc; Inst. Math. Statist; Am. Statist. Asn. Measure theory; probability theory; mathematical statistics. Address: Dept. of Mathematics, Cornell University, Ithaca, NY 14850.

FARRELL, R(OY) KEITH, b. Bend, Oregon, April 10, 26; m. 50; c. 1. VIROLOGY. B.S, Oregon State Col, 51; D.V.M, Washington State, 55. Co-op agent, U.S. DEPT. AGR, 55-58, VIROLOGIST, AGR. RES. SERV, animal disease res. sta, COL. VET. MED, WASH. STATE UNIV, 58-66, ENDOPARASITE VECTOR PIONEERING RES. LAB, 66-, LECTR. VET. PHYSIOL. & PHARMACOL, UNIV, 58- U.S.N.R, 44-46. Wildlife Disease Asn; Am. Vet. Med. Asn; Am. Col. Vet. Toxicol. Veterinary virology; role of endoparasites as vectors and reservoirs of viral and rickettsial disease. Address: Endoparasite Vector Pioneering Research Lab, College of Veterinary Medicine, Washington State University, Pullman, WA 99163.

FARREN, ANN L(OUISE), b. Portage, Pa, Dec. 5, 26. BIOCHEMISTRY, INFORMATION SCIENCE. A.B, Pennsylvania, 48. Biochemist, Valley Forge U.S. Army Hosp, Pa, 49-50; Jefferson Med. Col, 50-52; org. chemist, Smith Kline & French Labs, 52-53; anal. chemist, Rohm & Haas Co, 53-56; with info. off. pub. rels, news serv, Am. Chem. Soc, N.Y, 56-59; asst. to dir, Biol. Abstracts, Inc, 59-61, acting head, lit. acquisition dept, 61-62, PROF. RELS. OFF, BIOSCI. INFO. SERV, 62- Mem. Nat. Fedn. Sci. Abstracting & Indexing Serv. Fel. AAAS; Am. Chem. Soc; Nat. Asn. Sci. Writers; Am. Inst. Biol. Sci; Drug Info. Asn. Hepatic and metabolic diseases; organic syntheses; colchicine derivatives; ion exchange resins; abstracting, indexing, information retrieval. Address: Professional Services & Education Dept, BioSciences Information Service, 2100 Arch St, Philadelphia, PA 19103.

FARRIER, MAURICE H(UGH), b. Washington Co, Iowa, Sept. 18, 26; m. 56; c. 1. ENTOMOLOGY. B.S, Iowa State, 48, M.S, 50; Ph.D.(entom), N.C. State Col, 55. Asst. to state entomologist, State of Iowa, 50-52; asst. ENTOM, N.C. STATE UNIV, 54-55, asst. res. prof, 55-60, ASSOC. PROF, 60- Outstanding contrib. award, South. Insect Work Conf, 70. Entom. Soc. Am; Soc. Syst. Zool; Int. Soc. Soil Sci. Taxonomy of Veigaiidae and other gamasid mites in forest soils; forest entomology and bibliographic documentation in entomology and acarology. Address: Dept. of Entomology, Box 5215, North Carolina State University, Raleigh, NC 27607.

FARRIER, NOEL JOHN, b. Pittsburgh, Pa, Dec. 9, 37; div. INORGANIC CHEMISTRY. B.S, Carnegie Inst. Technol, 60; M.S, Univ. Pittsburgh, 64; U.S. Pub. Health Serv. fel, Ohio State Univ, 66-67, Cent. Ohio Heart Asn. grant & Ph.D.(inorg. coord. chem), 69. Lab. technician chem, Mellon Inst, 61; trainee metalloenzyme chem, clin. study ctr, Children's Hosp, Columbus, Ohio, 64; asst. prof. chem, Wittenberg Univ, 68-69; vis. res. assoc. physiol. chem, col. med, Ohio State Univ, 69-70; ASST. PROF. CHEM, RAYMOND WALTERS GEN. & TECH. COL, UNIV. CINCINNATI, 70- Am. Chem. Soc. Coordination compounds of cobalt III, copper II and copper I containing unusual monodentate ligands; kinetics; optical activity; infrared studies. Address: Raymond Walters General & Technical College, University of Cincinnati, 9555 Plainfield Rd, Cincinnati, OH 45236.

FARRINGER, L(ELAND) DWIGHT, b. Lena, Ill, May 28, 27; m. 50; c. 3. PHYSICS. B.A, Manchester Col, 49; B.D, Bethany Biblical Sem, 52; M.A, Ohio State, 55, Ph.D.(physics), 58. Asst. PHYSICS, Ohio State, 52-58, assoc. prof, MANCHESTER COL, 58-69, PROF, 69-, HEAD DEPT, 58- Am. Phys. Soc; Am. Asn. Physics Teachers. Nuclear magnetic resonance; physical electronics; electronic circuitry; scintillation spectrometry of gamma rays. Address: Dept. of Physics, Manchester College, North Manchester, IN 46962.

FARRINGTON, PAUL S(TEPHEN), b. Indianapolis, Ind, May 9, 19; m. 46; c. 5. ANALYTICAL CHEMISTRY. B.S, Calif. Inst. Tech, 41, Socony Vacuum fel. & M.S, 47, Ch.E, 48, Merck fel, 49-50, Ph.D.(chem), 50. Control & res. chemist, Kelco Co, 41-42; asst. chem, Calif. Inst. Tech, 42-45, 48-49; instr. CHEM, UNIV. CALIF, LOS ANGELES, 50, asst. prof, 51-56, assoc. prof, 56-62, PROF, 62-, ASSOC. DEAN COL. LETTERS & SCI, 62- Guggenheim Mem. Found. fel, Ger, 58-59. Am. Chem. Soc. Coulometric and other instrumental methods of analysis, inorganic complexes. Address: Dept. of Chemistry, University of California, Los Angeles, CA 90024.

FARRINGTON, WILLIAM B(ENFORD), b. New York, N.Y, March 10, 21; div; c. 3. STRUCTURAL GEOLOGY. B.C.E, Cornell, 47, M.S, 49; Ph.D.(geol), Mass. Inst. Tech, 53. Radio engr, radar design, Naval Res. Labs, 42-43; plant engr, Hope's Windows, Inc, 50-51; instr. geol, Massachusetts, 53-54; res. geophysicist, Humble Oil & Ref. Co, 54-56; investment analyst, Continental Res. Corp, 56-61; v.pres, Empire Resources Corp, Empire Trust Co, 61-64; sci. dir, U.S. Congress House Select Comt. Govt. Res, 64-65; PARTNER, FARRINGTON & LIGHT ASSOCS, 67- Eve. lectr, Univ. Houston, 55-56; pres, Farrington Eng. Corp, 58-67; eve. lectr, Univ. Calif, Los Angeles, 68- U.S.N, 43-46. Fel. AAAS; Geol. Soc. Am; Am. Inst. Aeronaut. & Astronaut; Soc. Explor. Geophys; Am. Petrol. Inst; Seismol. Soc. Am; Am. Astron. Soc; Am. Inst. Mining, Metall. & Petrol. Eng; Am. Asn. Petrol. Geol; Am. Geophys. Union. Theory and measurement of stress distribution in rocks. Address: Farrington & Light Associates, 64 Summit Ave, Redlands, CA 92373.

FARRIOR, WILLIAM L(AURIE), JR, b. Birmingham, Ala, July 31, 27; m. 56; c. 2. BIOCHEMISTRY. B.S, Alabama, 50, M.S, 55. Chemist, nutrit. div, Food & Drug Admin, 55-56; food anal, agr. res. ctr, U.S. Dept. Agr, 56-59; biochemist, tech. develop. labs, communicable disease ctr, U.S. Pub. Health Serv, 59-62; RES. CHEMIST, MORGANTOWN RES. CTR, BUR. OF MINES, 62- U.S.N, 45-46; U.S.A, 51-53, Lt. Am. Chem. Soc; Asn. Off. Anal. Chem. Analysis by gamma rays from neutron inelastic scatter and thermal neutron capture. Address: U.S. Dept. of the Interior, Bureau of Mines, Box 880, Morgantown, WV 26504.

FARRIS, DAVID A(LLEN), b. Bloomington, Ind, Mar. 26, 28; m. 56; c. 2. MARINE BIOLOGY. A.B, Indiana, 50; Eli Lilly Co. & Univ. fels & Ph.D. (biol), Stanford, 58. Field asst. fisheries, Ind. Lake & Stream Surv, 43-50; asst. biol, Stanford, 53-54; res. fisheries biologist, Bur. Commercial Fisheries, 55-60; asst. prof. BIOL, SAN DIEGO STATE COL, 60-63, assoc. prof, 63-66, PROF, 66- Proj. mgr, Nat. Sci. Found. grant, Calif. Spiny Lobster Proj. AAAS; Am. Soc. Limnol. & Oceanog; Am. Soc. Ichthyol. & Herpet; Am. Inst. Fishery Res. Biol. Population dynamics of egg and larval fish populations; the intrinsic and extrinsic factors which govern growth and death of fish larvae; factors which govern changes in the biochemistry of fishes. Address: Dept. of Biology, San Diego State College, San Diego, CA 92115.

FARRIS, HANSFORD WHITE, b. Blackford, Ky, Oct. 7, 19; m. 42; c. 2. ELECTRONICS, COMMUNICATIONS. B.S, East. Ky. State Teachers Col, 41, M.A, 42; M.S, Illinois, 48; Ph.D.(elec. eng), Michigan, 58. Asst. electronics, Illinois, 47-48, 51-53; asst. prof. elec. eng, Kentucky, 48-51; res. assoc, eng. res. inst, UNIV. MICH, 53-58; asst. prof. ELEC. ENG, 58-59, assoc. prof, 59-61, PROF, 61-, ASSOC. DEAN, COL. ENG, 68-, chmn. dept. elec. eng, 65-68, dir. electronics res. lab, 58-62, assoc. dir. inst. sci. & tech. & dir. indust. develop. div, 63-65. Secy, Nat. Electronics Conf, 64, v.pres, 65, pres, 66, bd. chmn, 69-70. Sig.C, 42-46, Capt. Inst. Elec. & Electronics Eng. Engineering concepts; communications techniques; energy demands. Address: College of Engineering, University of Michigan, Ann Arbor, MI 48104.

FARRIS, RUSSELL EUGENE, JR, b. San Francisco, Calif, Aug. 5, 37; m. 59; c. 2. ORGANIC CHEMISTRY. B.S, Pennsylvania, 59; Ph.D.(chem), Delaware, 64. RES. CHEMIST, DYESTUFF SECT, GAF CORP, 66- Lectr, Jacksonville Col, 64-66. Chem.C, U.S.A, 1st Lt. AAAS; Am. Chem. Soc; Am. Asn. Textile Chem. & Colorists. Purines and pyrimidines as tumor inhibitors; diazonium compounds as synthetic fiber dyes. Address: 5 Nina Ct, Elnora, NY 12065.

FARRISSEY, WILLIAM J(OSEPH), JR, b. Fall River, Mass, Nov. 19, 31; m. 57; c. 4. ORGANIC CHEMISTRY. B.S, Yale, 53, M.S, 55, DuPont fel,

55-56, Ph.D, 57. Fel, Rice, 56-57; instr. chem, Rutgers, 57-58; res. chemist, Humble Oil & Ref. Co, 58-61, sr. res. chemist, 61-63; group leader, CARWIN RES. LABS, UPJOHN CO, 63-64, head new prod, 64-66, mgr. process res, 66-69, MGR. POLYMER RES, 69- Am. Chem. Soc. High temperature polymers; polyimides; isocyanate polymers. Address: Maltby Lane, Northford, CT 06472.

FARROW, JOSEPH H(ELMS), b. Rocky Mount, Va, June 10, 04; m. 39. MEDICINE. B.S, Virginia, 26, M.D, 30. Intern, St. Elizabeth's Hosp, Richmond, Va, 30-31; res. surg, Watt's Hosp, Durham, N.C, 31-33; spec. fel. surg. & path, Presby. Hosp, New York, 33, jr. fel. surg, 33-34; intern, MEM. HOSP, 34, fel, 34-37, clin. asst, 37-41, asst. surgeon, 42-46, assoc. attend. surgeon, 47-60, attend. surgeon & chief breast serv, 60-69, EMER. CHIEF BREAST SERV, 69-; ASSOC. PROF. CLIN. SURG, MED. SCH, CORNELL & CLINICIAN, SLOAN-KETTERING INST, 60- Asst. dir. tumor clin. & attend. radiologist, St. Agnes Hosp, White Plains, 38-42; assoc. vis. surg, breast serv, James Ewing Hosp, 50-60, vis. surgeon, 60-70; consult. surgeon, Harlem Valley State Hosp, Wingdale, N.Y, 39-42; consult, tumor serv, Vassar Bros. Hosp, Poughkeepsie, N.Y, 39-; U.S. Naval Hosp, St. Albans, 48-; Yonkers Gen. Hosp, 52-; Fitkin Mem. & Stamford Hosps, 63-; Strang Cancer Prev. Clin, 53-62. Dipl, Am. Bd. Radiol. Med.C, 42-46, Comdr. AAAS; Am. Med. Asn; Am. Col. Surg; Am. Radium Soc.(treas, 62-63, pres, 65); Am. Asn. Cancer Res; James Ewing Soc.(pres, 57); Am. Col. Radiol; fel. N.Y. Acad. Med; Pan-Am. Med. Asn. Breast cancer. Address: 112 E. 74th St, New York, NY 10021.

FARROW, RICHARD P(AUL), b. Indianapolis, Ind, Dec. 4, 22; m. 46; c. 2. CHEMISTRY. A.B, Catholic Univ, 50; George Washington. Chemist, NAT. CANNERS ASN, 48-56, head chem. sect, WASH. LAB, 56-69, RES. MGR, 69- Chem.C, U.S.A, 43-46. AAAS; Am. Chem. Soc; Inst. Food Tech. Food analysis; analytical methods for pesticide residues; vitamin retention in canned foods; various problems in food technology; internal can corrosion; heavy metals in foods; food standards. Address: National Canners Association, 1133 20th St, N.W, Washington, DC 20036.

FARROW, W(ENDALL) M(OORE), b. Winchester, Mass, June 20, 22; m. 49; c. 2. MICROBIOLOGY. B.A, Iowa, 49, M.S, 51, Ph.D.(bot, mycol), 53. Asst, Iowa, 49-53; microbiologist, Commercial Solvents Corp, 53-56; Hoffmann-La Roche, Inc, 56-63; marine lab, Fla. Bd. Conserv, 63-65; Germfree Prod, Inc, 65-68; RES. ASSOC, LIFE SCI, INC, 68- U.S.A.A.F, 42-46. Mycol. Soc. Am; Am. Soc. Microbiol. Microbial fermentations; fungicides; carotenoids of microorganisms; soil fungi; marine bacteria and phytoplankton; animal breeding and development; gnotobiology. Address: Life Sciences, Inc, 2900 72nd St. N, St. Petersburg, FL 33710.

FARTHING, B(ARTON) R(OBY), b. Watauga Co, N.C, Feb. 20, 16; m. 38; c. 3. ANIMAL BREEDING. B.S, Wake Forest Col, 38; M.S, N.C. State Col, 54, Ph.D.(animal breeding), 58. Res. instr, N.C. State Col, 54-58, asst. prof, 58-59; exp. sta. statistician, LA. STATE UNIV, BATON ROUGE, 59-64, HEAD DEPT. EXP. STATIST, 64- U.S.A, 44-46. Biomet. Soc; Am. Soc. Animal Sci; Am. Dairy Sci. Asn. Design and analysis of experiments; methods of improving performance in farm animals. Address: Dept. of Experimental Statistics, Louisiana State University, Baton Rouge, LA 70803.

FARVOLDEN, R(OBERT) N(ORMAN), b. Forestburg, Alta, May 22, 28; m. 54; c. 2. HYDROGEOLOGY. B.Sc, Alberta, 51, Shell Oil fel, 55-56, M.Sc, 58; Ph.D, Illinois, 63. Head, groundwater div, Res. Coun. Alberta, 56-60; res. assoc, desert res. inst, Nevada, 62-64; asst. prof. GEOL, Univ. Ill, Urbana, 64-65, ASSOC. PROF, 65-67; Univ. West. Ont, 67-70; UNIV. WATERLOO, 70-, CHMN. DEPT. EARTH SCI, 70- Secy, Cmn. Groundwater, Int. Asn. Sci. Hydrol, 63-66. Can. Army, 50-54. Fel. Geol. Soc. Am; Am. Geophys. Union; fel. Geol. Asn. Can. Engineering geology; water resources development; solid-waste disposal. Address: Dept. of Earth Sciences, University of Waterloo, Waterloo, Ont, Can.

FARWELL, GEORGE W(ELLS), b. Oakland, Calif, Feb. 15, 20; m. 45; c. 4. PHYSICS. B.S, Harvard, 41; California, 41-42; fel, Chicago, 46-47, Ph.D. (physics), 48. Asst. physics, radiation lab, California, 42-43, physicist, Los Alamos Lab, N.Mex, 43-46; asst. prof. PHYSICS, UNIV. WASH, 48-55, assoc. prof, 55-59, PROF, 59-, V.PRES. RES, 67-, assoc. dean grad. sch, 59-65, asst. v.pres, 65-67. Sr. fel, Nat. Sci. Found, 60-61. Fel. Am. Phys. Soc. Nuclear physics. Address: Dept. of Physics, University of Washington, Seattle, WA 98105.

FARWELL, ROBERT W(ILLIAM), b. Providence, R.I, May 11, 27; m. 56; c. 2. PHYSICS. B.S, Yale, 50; Ohio State, 50; M.S, Pa. State, 55, Ph.D. (physics), 60. Res. asst. physics, ord. res. lab, PA. STATE UNIV, 51, res. assoc, 51-58, asst, dept. physics, 58-59, asst. prof. ENG. RES, ORD. RES. LAB, 60-65, ASSOC. PROF, 65- Nat. Sci. Found. teaching fel, summer, 59; mem. Int. Oceanog. Found. U.S.N, 45-46. Acoust. Soc. Am. Underwater sound transmission; reverberation; sound scattering; transducer calibrations; acoustic torpedoes; sonar; effect of sound on tissues; enzyme kinetics; ultraviolet and visible spectrophotometers. Address: Ordnance Research Lab, Pennsylvania State University, P.O. Box 30, State College, PA 16801.

FARY, ISTVAN, b. Gyula, Hungary, June 30, 22; m. 57; c. 1. MATHEMATICS. M.A, Eötvös Lórand, Budapest, 44; Ph.D, Szeged, 48; D.Sc, Sorbonne, 55. Asst. math, Nat. Sci. Res. Center, France, 48-52, in charge res, 52-55; res. fel, Nat. Res. Coun. Can, 55-56; assoc. prof. MATH, Montreal, 56-57; from assoc. prof. to PROF, UNIV. CALIF, BERKELEY, 57- Am. Math. Soc; Math. Asn. Am; Math. Soc. France. Algebraic topology; geometry. Address: Dept. of Mathematics, University of California, Berkeley, CA 94720.

FARY, RAYMOND W, JR, b. Long Branch, N.J, Apr. 14, 18; m. 41; c. 6. GEOLOGY. A.B, Washington (St. Louis), 47, M.A, 48. Explor. geologist, Pure Oil Co, Inc, 48-60; geologist, subsurface sect, Ohio Geol. Surv, 60-61; strategic studies sect, mil. geol. br, U.S. GEOL. SURV, 61-62, res. supvr, 62-64, chief east. area unit, geol. group, 64-66, CHIEF REMOTE SENSING EVAL. & COORD, STAFF, 66- U.S.A, 41-45. AAAS; Am. Soc. Photogram. Geological exploration for new oil reserves; application of geologic knowledge to engineering problems; availability and use of earth materials for construction; effect of geologic conditions on engineering projects; applications of airborne and spaceborne remote sensing systems to earth's resources exploration and inventory; land use analyses and planning; observation of environmental changes. Address: Remote Sensing Evaluation & Coordination Staff, U.S. Geological Survey, Washington, DC 20242.

FASANELLA, EDWIN L(ANE), b. Princeton, N.J, Aug. 6, 43; m. 61; c. 2. PHYSICS. B.S, N.C. State, 65; Nat. Sci. Found. trainee & Ph.D.(physics), Duke, 69. ASST. PROF. PHYSICS, STETSON UNIV, 69- Am. Asn. Physics Teachers. Electron spin resonance studies of radiation damage to various organic crystals. Address: Dept. of Physics, Stetson University, DeLand, FL 32720.

FASANELLA, R(OCKO) M(ICHAEL), b. Trenton, N.J, Aug. 4, 16; m. 44; c. 3. MEDICINE. B.A, Yale, 39, M.D, 43; Univ. Pa, 47-48. Intern, Grace-New Haven Community Hosp, 43-44, asst. resident ophthal, 48-49, instr, 50-51; intern, Mercer Hosp, 46-47; chief sect. OPHTHAL, YALE, 51-61, ASSOC. CLIN. PROF, 61- Consult, West Haven Vet. Admin. Hosp, Conn, 51-65; St. Raphaels Hosp, New Haven, 52-; Waterbury Hosp, 60-; Nat. Asn. Standard Med. Vocabulary, 61; coun. drugs, Am. Med. Asn, 61-; color comt, Regional Ctr. for Retarded, 63-; Atlanta Med. Res. Found, 69-; Windham Community Mem. Hosp, 71-; Yale-New Haven Hosp. Adv, nat. glaucoma prob, U.S. Pub. Health Serv, 54; co-chmn. selection comt, fel. prog, Guild of Opticians, N.E. Seabd, 56-62. Dipl, Am. Bd. Ophthal, 51, assoc. exam, 54- Med.C, 44-46, Capt. Dipl. mem. Pan-Am. Asn. Ophthal; dipl. mem. Pan-Am. Med. Asn; fel. Am. Acad. Ophthal. & Otolaryngol; fel. Am. Med. Asn; affiliate mem. Royal Soc. Surg. Eng; affiliate mem. Royal Soc. Med; Asn. Res. Vision & Ophthal; Peruvian Eye, Ear, Nose & Throat Soc; hon mem. Inst. Barraquer, Spain; French Soc. Ophthal; Am. Soc. Ophthal. & Optom, Colombia; Pan-Pac. Surg. Asn. Glaucoma and glaucoma surgery; complications in eye surgery and cataract surgery; retinal detachment surgery; ptosis surgery; corneal transplant surgery; experimental work in chemical zonulolysis. Address: 842 Howard Ave, New Haven, CT 06519.

FASBENDER, M. VERONICA, b. Hendricks, Minn, Feb. 14, 32. INVERTEBRATE ZOOLOGY, PALYNOLOGY. B.A, Mt. Marty Col, 54; M.A, South Dakota, 56; summer, Michigan, 56; Ph.D.(biol), St. Louis, 59. Sci. instr, high sch, S.Dak, 55-56; from instr. to PROF. BIOL, MT. MARTY COL, 59- Socony Mobil Oil Co. res. grant, 61-62; summer radiobiol. grant, St. Augustine's Col, 64; dir. Nat. Sci. Found. summer inst, Mt. Marty Col, 71. Bot. Soc. Am. Pollen morphological studies on tribes of the tropical Caesalpiniaceae, including the Amherstieae, Cynometreae, Sclerolobieae and Eucaesalpinieae. Address: Dept. of Biology, Mount Marty College, Yankton, SD 57078.

FASCE, CHARLES FRANCIS, JR, b. Pittsfield, Mass, May 18, 36; m. 61; c. 4. CLINICAL CHEMISTRY. B.S, Michigan, 58, M.S, Albany Med. Col, 63, Ph.D.(biochem), 66. Sr. clin. chemist, DIV. LABS. & RES, N.Y. STATE DEPT. HEALTH, 65-66, ASSOC. CLIN. CHEMIST, 66- Mitochondrial sulfur amino acid metabolism; liver protein metabolism in polyarthritis; methodology of clinical chemistry. Address: Division of Labs. & Research, New York State Dept. of Health, Albany, NY 12201.

FASCHING, JAMES L(E ROY), b. Dickinson, N.D, Mar. 15, 42; m. 69. NUCLEAR & ANALYTICAL CHEMISTRY. B.S, N.D. State Univ, 64; scholar, Mass. Inst. Technol, 64-66, S.M, 67, Ph.D.(chem), 70. Res. asst. CHEM, N.Dak. State Univ, 62-63, instr, 63; asst, Mass. Inst. Technol, 64-70; instr. UNIV. R.I, 69-70, ASST. PROF, 70- Chemist, Lawrence Radiation Lab, Univ. Calif, Livermore, summer 65. AAAS; Am. Phys. Soc; Am. Chem. Soc. Neutron activation analysis of biological samples; effects of trace elements on aging; freezing as a concentration method; development of piezoelectric sorption devices and radiation detectors. Address: Dept. of Chemistry, University of Rhode Island, Kingston, RI 02881.

FASENMYER, MARY CELINE, b. Crown, Pa, Oct. 4, 06. MATHEMATICS. A.B, Mercyhurst Col, 33; M.A, Pittsburgh, 39; Ph.D.(math), Michigan, 46. Teacher, parochial high schs, Pa, 26-42; asst. prof. MATH, MERCYHURST COL, 45-55, PROF, 55- Math. Asn. Am. Analysis; modern algebra. Address: Mercyhurst College, Erie, PA 16501.

FASICK, R(OSS) W(ADE), b. Harrisburg, Pa, Mar. 27, 33; m. 54; c. 1. ORGANIC CHEMISTRY. B.S, Lebanon Valley Col, 55; M.S, Delaware, 57, Ph.D, 60. RES. CHEMIST, ORG. CHEMS. DEPT, E.I. DU PONT DE NEMOURS & CO, INC, 59- Am. Chem. Soc. Synthetic organic; mechanism of rearrangements in hydrocarbon systems. Address: Organic Chemicals Dept, E.I. du Pont de Nemours & Co, Inc, Wilmington, DE 19898.

FASMAN, G(ERALD) D(AVID), b. Drumheller, Alta, May 28, 25; nat; m. 53; c. 3. BIOCHEMISTRY. B.Sc, Alberta, 48; Ph.D.(chem), Calif. Inst. Tech, 52. Royal Soc. Can. scholar, Cambridge, 51-53; Merck fel. natural sci, Eng. Tech. Inst, Zurich, 53-54; Weizmann fel, Weizmann Inst, 54-55; asst, Children's Res. Found, Boston, 55-56, res. assoc, 57-61, asst. head biophys. chem, 59-61; asst. prof. BIOCHEM, BRANDEIS UNIV, 61-63, assoc. prof, 63-67, PROF, 67- Asst, med. sch, Harvard, 57-58, res. assoc, 58-61, tutor, univ, 60-62. Estab. investr, Am. Heart Asn, 61-66. Fel. AAAS; fel. Am. Inst. Chem; Am. Chem. Soc; Am. Soc. Biol. Chem; N.Y. Acad. Sci; Biophys. Soc; The Chem. Soc. Enzymes, proteins, nucleic and polyamino acids; conformational studies of biopolymers. Address: Graduate Dept. of Biochemistry, Brandeis University, Waltham, MA 02154.

FASS, ARNOLD L(IONEL), b. New York, N.Y, Apr. 2, 22. MATHEMATICS. B.S. City Col. New York, 42; M.A, Columbia, 47, Ph.D.(math), 51. Lectr. MATH, Columbia, 48-51; tutor, QUEENS COL.(N.Y), 51, instr, 51-57, asst. prof, 58-62, ASSOC. PROF, 63- Lectr, Nat. Sci. Found. Inst. Teacher Training, 61-62. U.S.A.A.F, 43-45. AAAS; Am. Math. Soc; Math. Asn. Am. Homology and cohomology of linear algebras; topological methods in algebra; general linear algebra. Address: 41-25 Kissena Blvd, Flushing, NY 11355.

FASS, RICHARD A, b. Brooklyn, N.Y, June 13, 43; m. 64; c. 1. PHYSICAL CHEMISTRY. B.E, Cooper Union; Ph.D.(phys. chem), Wisconsin, 69. Res. assoc. photochem. kinetics & radiation chem, Wisconsin, 69; ASST. PROF. CHEM, POMONA COL, 69- Am. Chem. Soc. Reactions of hot and thermal hydrogen atoms produced by photolysis of hydrogen halides; reactions of hot free radicals in the gas phase; gas kinetics. Address: Dept. of Chemistry, Pomona College, Claremont, CA 91711.

FASS, STEPHEN M, b. N.Y.C, Aug. 22, 38; m. 66; c. 1. CHEMICAL ENGINEERING. B.Ch.E, Cooper Union, 60; M.S, Univ. Colo, 64, Ph.D.(chem. eng), 67. Engr, FMC Corp, Md, 60-61, res. engr, N.J, 61-62; sr. res. engr. U.S. Steel Corp, Pa, 66-68; RES. ENGR, GULF RES. & DEVELOP. CO, 68- Am. Chem. Soc; Am. Inst. Chem. Eng. Reaction kinetics; reactor design and process research in steel, petroleum and organic chemicals industries. Address: Process Sciences Dept, Gulf Research & Development Co, P.O. Drawer 2038, Pittsburgh, PA 15230.

FASSEL, VELMER A(RTHUR), b. Frohna, Mo, Apr. 26, 19; m. 43. PHYSICAL & ANALYTICAL CHEMISTRY. B.A, S.E. Mo. State Col, 41; fel, Iowa State Col, 41-42, Ph.D.(phys. chem), 47. Asst. spectros, Nat. Defense Res. Cmt. contract, IOWA STATE UNIV, 42-43, jr. chemist, Manhattan proj, 43-46, assoc. chemist, inst. atomic res, 46-47, asst. prof. CHEM, 47-51, assoc. prof, 51-54, PROF, 54-, DEP. DIR, INST. ATOMIC RES. & AMES LAB, ATOMIC ENERGY COMN, 69-, sect. chief, Ames Lab, 65-69. Lectr. tour, Sci. Coun. Japan, 62; U.S. ed, Spectrochimica Acta. Pittsburgh Spectros. Award, 69; Maurice F. Hasler Award, 71; Anachem Award, 71. Fel. AAAS; Am. Chem. Soc; fel. Optical Soc. Am; Coblentz Soc; Soc. Appl. Spectros.(medal award, 64). Emission spectroscopy; spectrographic analysis; infrared spectra and molecular structure correlations; fluorescence spectroscopy; analytical chemistry; determination of gases in metals. Address: Institute for Atomic Research, Iowa State University, Ames, IA 50010.

FASSELL, W(AYNE) MARTIN, JR, b. Salt Lake City, Utah, Oct. 20, 20; m. 43; c. 4. METALLURGY. B.S, Utah, 42, M.S, 47, Ph.D.(metall), 49. Assoc. prof. metall, Utah, 49-55; dir. res, Howe Sound Co, 55-58; staff scientist, res. lab, U.S. Steel Corp, 58-59; mgr. mat. & processes lab, aeronutronic div, Philco-Ford Corp, 59-71; V.PRES. & GEN. MGR, RESOURCES RECOVERY SYSTS. DIV, BARBER-COLMAN CO, 71- Consult, Howe Sound Co, 53-55. U.S.N, 43-46, Lt. Am. Chem. Soc; Am. Soc. Metals; Am. Inst. Mining, Metall. & Petrol. Eng.(gold medal, 57). Wet oxidation processes for ores, concentrates, sewage and garbage; automated photographic equipment and film processing systems. Address: 1882 McGaw Ave, Irvine Industrial Complex, Santa Ana, CA 92705.

FASSETT, DAVID W(ALTER), b. Broadalbin, N.Y, Nov. 13, 08; m. 34; c. 3. MEDICINE. A.B, Columbia, 33, 33-35; M.D, N.Y. Univ, 40. Biochemist, dept. exp. surg, N.Y. Univ, 35-36; pharmacologist, Wellcome Res. Lab, 36-38; Wellcome fel. therapeut, N.Y. Univ, 41, asst, col. med, 42-45; cardiologist, James M. Jackson Mem. Hosp, Fla, 45-48; DIR. LAB. INDUST. MED, EASTMAN KODAK CO, 48- Acting chief div. pharmacol, food & drug admin, Fed. Security Agency, D.C, 42-44; clin. assoc. prof. prev. med, Univ. Rochester, 65-; vis. lectr. occup. med, sch. pub. health, Harvard, 65- AAAS; Am. Soc. Pharmacol; Soc. Exp. Biol. & Med; Am. Indust. Hyg. Asn. (pres, 69-70); Soc. Toxicol. Pharmacology; industrial toxicology; industrial hygiene. Address: Lab. of Industrial Medicine, Eastman Kodak Co, 1669 Lake Ave, Rochester, NY 14650.

FASSETT, J. R, b. Minneapolis, Minn, Oct. 15, 33; m. 55; c. 2. ELECTRICAL ENGINEERING. B.E.E, Minnesota, 56, M.S, 58, Ph.D.(elec. eng), 62. Staff engr, COLLINS RADIO CO, 62-63, group head micro electronics, Iowa, 63-69, DEPT. HEAD SOLID STATE DEVICES & EQUIPMENT DIV, SOLID STATE DEVICES LAB, 69- Silicon active and passive devices; thin film microelectronics. Address: Solid State Devices & Equipment Division, Solid State Devices Lab, Collins Radio Co, 19700 Jamboree Blvd, Newport Beach, CA 92663.

FASSNACHT, J(OHN) H(ARTWELL), b. Wenonah, N.J, Oct. 22, 33; m. 60; c. 2. ORGANIC CHEMISTRY. A.B, Middlebury Col, 55; Nat. Sci. Found. fel. & Ph.D.(org. chem), Mass. Inst. Technol, 59. Res. chemist, ORG. CHEM. DEPT, Jackson Lab, E.I. DU PONT DE NEMOURS & CO, INC, 59-62, FREON PROD. DIV, 62-67, proj. leader, 67-68, TECH. ASST, 68- Am. Chem. Soc; The Chem. Soc. Synthetic organic chemistry; solvolysis of 1, 4-dihydrobenzyl-p-toluenesulfonates; aerosol food formulation. Address: Dept. of Organic Chemistry, Freon Products Division, E.I. du Pont de Nemours & Co, Inc, Wilmington, DE 19898.

FAST, C(LARENCE) R(OBERT), b. Tulsa, Okla, Feb. 12, 21; m. 44; c. 4. PETROLEUM ENGINEERING. B.S, Tulsa, 43. Liaison engr, Douglas Aircraft Co, 43; from apprentice engr. to RES. GROUP SUPVR, AMOCO PROD. CO, STANDARD OIL CO.(IND), 43- Chmn. nat. subcomt. perforating, Am. Petrol. Inst, exec. comt. prod. practices; Soc. Petrol. Eng. distinguished lectr, 70-71. Soc. Petrol. Eng.(Uren award); Am. Petrol. Inst. Direct research on drilling, well completion, stimulation, well operation and production practice. Address: Research Center, Amoco Production Co, Box 591, Tulsa, OK 74102.

FAST, HENRYK, b. Bochnia, Poland, Oct. 4, 25; nat; m. 68; c. 1. MATHEMATICS. Saratov, 45-46; Ph.M, Wroclaw, 50; Ph.D.(math), Polish Acad. Sci, 58. Asst. MATH, Wroclaw, 50-51, adjunct, 56-60; sr. asst, Polish Acad. Sci, 51-55; asst. prof, Univ. Notre Dame, 62-66; ASSOC. PROF, WAYNE STATE UNIV, 66- Am. Math. Soc; Math. Asn. Am. General measure and integration, especially geometrical measure theory; functions of real variables; convex sets and set theoretical geometry; integral geometry. Address: Dept. of Mathematics, Wayne State University, Detroit, MI 48202.

FAST, PAUL G(ERHARDT), b. Kitchener, Ont, Sept. 2, 31; m. 56; c. 3. ENTOMOLOGY. B.Sc, Bethel Col.(Kans), 55; Wichita, 55-56; M.S, Oklahoma, 57; Ph.D.(insect physiol), Western Ontario, 61. Sanitarian, dept. health, Wichita-Sedgwick Co, 55-56; entomologist, WHO Malaria Proj, Liberia, 58-59; RES. OFFICER INSECT PHYSIOL, INSECT PATH. RES. INST, CAN. DEPT. FORESTRY, 61- Entom. Soc. Am; Entom. Soc. Can. Chemistry and metabolism of lipids in insects; mode of action of insect toxins. Address: P.O. Box 490, Sault Ste, Marie, Ont, Can.

FAST, RONALD W(ALTER), b. Toledo, Ohio, Apr. 2, 34; m. 59; c. 2. PHYSICS. B.S, Washington & Lee, 56; M.S, Virginia, 58, Ph.D.(physics), 60. Physicist, U.S. Army Nuclear Defense Lab, 60-62; Midwest. Univs. Res. Asn, 62-67; assoc. scientist, phys. sci. lab, Univ. Wis, 67-70; MEM. STAFF, NAT. ACCELERATOR LAB, 70- U.S.A, 60-62, 1st Lt. Low temperature physics, especially on superconductivity and its technical applications. Address: National Accelerator Lab, Box 500, Batavia, IL 60510.

FAST, THOMAS N(ORMAND), b. Selma, Calif. Sept. 10, 22; m. 52; c. 2. MARINE BIOLOGY. B.S, Santa Clara, 49; Leslie Salt Co. fel, Stanford, 50, Ph.D, 60. Oceanog. technician, Stanford Univ, 52-56; instr. BIOL, UNIV. SANTA CLARA, 57-67, ASSOC. PROF, 67- ASEE-NASA summer faculty fel, Ames Res. Ctr, 67 & 68, 69 & 70. U.S.N.R, 42-46. AAAS; Am. Soc. Ichthyol. & Herpet. Ecology of bathypelagic fishes; cardiovascular dynamics in stress. Address: Dept. of Biology, University of Santa Clara, Santa Clara, CA 95053.

FATELEY, WILLIAM G(ENE), b. Franklin, Ind, May 17, 29; m. 53; c. 5. CHEMICAL PHYSICS. A.B, Franklin Col, 51, hon.D.Sc, 65; Northwestern, 51-53; Ph.D.(chem), Kansas State, 56. Asst. chem, Northwestern, 51-53; Kansas State, 53-55; res. assoc, Maryland, 56; res. fel, Minnesota, 56-57; res. chemist & head spectros. lab, James River Div, Dow Chem. Co, 57-60; fel. chem, CARNEGIE-MELLON UNIV, 60-62, head sci. rels, 62-63, asst. to pres, 63-67, sr. fel, 65-67, assoc. prof. CHEM, 67-70, PROF, 70-, ASST. TO V.PRES. RES, 67- Coblentz Award, 65. Am. Chem. Soc. Infrared and Raman Spectroscopy; structure of matter. Address: Dept. of Chemistry, Carnegie-Mellon University, Pittsburgh, PA 15213.

FATH, JOSEPH, b. Frankfurt, Germany, Aug. 31, 25; m. 45; c. 4. ORGANIC CHEMISTRY. B.Chem, Cornell, 44. Res. chemist, Montrose Chem. Co, 46-50; group leader, org. sect, Nuodex Prods. Co, 50-55; dir. res, Thompson Chem. Co, 55-65, v.pres, 65-69; v.pres. bus. develop. & planning, Nuodex Div, Tenneco Chem, Inc, 69-71, V.PRES. RES. & DEVELOP, INTERMEDIATES DIV, TENNECO CHEM. CO, PISCATAWAY, 71- U.S.A, 44-45. Am. Chem. Soc. Vinyl plasticizers and resins; organic intermediates; metalloorganics. Address: 18 Campbelton Circle, Princeton, NJ 08540.

FATIADI, ALEXANDER J(OHANN), b. Kharkov, Ukraine, Oct. 22, 23; U.S. citizen; m. 52; c. 4. ORGANIC CHEMISTRY. Johannes Guttenberg Univ, Mainz, 46-50; Dr.Nat.Sc, Tech. Husbandry Inst, Ger, 50; B.S. George Wash. Univ, 57, M.S, 59. Res. asst. chemist, George Wash. Univ, 56-59; org. chemist, NAT. BUR. STANDARDS, 59-67, RES. CHEMIST & PROJ. LEADER, 68- Cert, Nat. Bur. Standards, 65, 66, 68; Community Leaders Am, 70. Am. Chem. Soc; N.Y. Acad. Sci; The Chem. Soc; Ger. Chem. Soc. New periodic acid oxidations; clinical standards and chemistry; cyclic ketones; aromatization of cyclitols; polyhydroxy phenols; phenylhydrazine osazones and osotriazoles; oxidation of polycyclic aromatic hydrocarbons; stable free radicals; oxidation mechanisms; active manganese dioxide. Address: 7516 Carroll Ave, Takoma Park, MD 20012.

FATORA, FRANK C(HARLES), JR, b. Derry, Pa, Mar. 31, 24; m. 52; c. 6. ORGANIC CHEMISTRY. B.S, St. Vincent Col, 48; Ph.D.(chem), Notre Dame, 51. CHEMIST nat. prods, Miner Labs, 50-51; dyestuff intermediates, Sherwin-Williams Co, 51-54; AM. CYANAMID CO, 54- Sig.C, U.S.A, 44-46. Am. Chem. Soc; Am. Asn. Textile Chem. & Colorists; Am. Inst. Chem. Intermediates for textile and rubber chemicals. Address: 341 West End Ave, North Plainfield, NJ 07060.

FATT, IRVING, b. Chicago, Ill, Sept. 16, 20; m. 42; c. 1. PHYSICAL CHEMISTRY. B.S, California, Los Angeles, 47, M.S, 48; Ph.D, Southern California, 55. Instr. commun, Yale, 44-45; sr. res. chemist, Calif. Res. Corp, 48-57; PROF. PHYSIOL. OPTICS, SCH. OPTOM, UNIV. CALIF, BERKELEY, 57-, ENG. SCI, COL. ENG, 67- U.S.A.A.F, 45-46, 1st Lt. Am. Chem. Soc. Fluid flow through porous media; structure of porous media; bioengineering. Address: Hearst Mining Bldg, College of Engineering, University of California, Berkeley, CA 94720.

FATTEH, ABDULLAH V(ALIMOHAMMED), b. Gadha, India, Oct. 9, 32; m; c. 3. FORENSIC MEDICINE, LAW. Bai Kanoobai merit scholar, M.B, B.S. & M.C.P.S, Univ. Bombay, 60; D.M.J.(clin), Univ. London, 64, D.M.J.(path), 65; Ph.D.(forensic med), Queen's Univ. Belfast, 65. Rotating intern, J.J. Hosp, Bombay, India, 59-60; house physician, Kingston Gen. Hosp, Hull, Eng, 60; house surgeon, East Riding Gen. Hosp, Driffield, 61; registrar path, Whipps Cross Hosp, London, 62; asst. lectr. forensic med, Queen's Univ. Belfast, 62-66; fel. legal med, Med. Col. Va, 66-68; asst. pathologist, Armed Forces Inst. Pathol, 68-69; asst. prof. legal med, Med. Col. Va, 59-70; ASSOC. PROF. PATH, SCH. MED, UNIV. N.C, 70-; ASSOC. CHIEF MED. EXAM, STATE N.C, 70- Med. exam, City Richmond, Counties Henrico & Chesterfield, Va, 59-70; dir. path. lab, St. Elizabeth's Hosp, Richmond, Tidewater Mem. Hosp, Tappahannock & Richmond Nursing Home, 59-70; vis. path. consult. & staff physician, Piedmont State Hosp, Burkeville, 59-70; dir. Physicians Path. Lab, Richmond, 59-70. Am. Med. Asn; Brit. Med. Asn; Brit. Acad. Forensic Sci; Forensic Soc. Eng. Enzyme histochemistry and wound healing; artifacts and radiology in forensic pathology. Address: 805 Churchill Dr, Chapel Hill, NC 27514.

FATTIG, W. DONALD, b. DeKalb Co, Ga, Feb. 22, 36; m. 58; c. 1. GENETICS. A.B, Emory, 59, M.S, 60, Ph.D.(genetics), 63. Fel. microbiol, sch. med, Emory, 63-64; asst. prof. BIOL, Southwest. at Memphis, 64-68; ASSOC. PROF, UNIV. ALA, BIRMINGHAM, 68- Summer instr, Emory Univ, 61. Ord.C, U.S.A, 54-56. AAAS; Am. Genetic. Asn; Am. Inst. Biol. Sci; Am. Soc. Human Genetics; Genetics Soc. Am. Bacteriophage, human and drosophilia genetics; biological controls. Address: Dept. of Biology, University of Alabama, Birmingham, AL 35216.

FATTORINI, HECTOR O(SVALDO), b. Buenos Aires, Arg, Oct. 28, 38; m. 61; c. 3. MATHEMATICS. Lic. en Mat, Univ. Buenos Aires, 60; Org. Am.

States & Ford Found. fels. & Ph.D.(math), N.Y. Univ, 65. Res. assoc. MATH, Nat. Sci. & Tech. Res. Coun, Arg. & assoc. prof, sch. exact & natural sci, Univ. Buenos Aires, 65-66; res. assoc, Brown Univ, 67; asst. prof, UNIV. CALIF, LOS ANGELES, 67-70, ASSOC. PROF, 70-; PROF, SCH. EXACT & NATURAL SCI, UNIV. BUENOS AIRES, 70- U.S. Air Force Off. Sci. Res. & Off. Aerospace Res. grant, 67; NASA grant, 67; Off. Naval Res. contract, 67-68; Nat. Sci. Found. grant, 69- Am. Math. Soc; Soc. Industr. & Appl. Math; Arg. Math. Union. Control theory; differential equations in linear topological spaces; partial differential equations; control systems in infinite dimensional spaces; system theory. Address: Dept. of Mathematics, University of California, 405 Hilgard Ave, Los Angeles, CA 90024.

FATUR, LEO M, b. West Aliquippa, Pa, Feb. 1, 35; m. 64. EXPERIMENTAL PHYSICS. B.S, Carnegie Inst. Tech, 56, Ph.D.(physics), 63. PHYSICIST, SPERRY GYROSCOPE CO, 63- Am. Phys. Soc. Experimental research in laser technology. Address: Sperry Gyroscope Co, Great Neck, NY 11021.

FATZINGER, CARL W(ARREN), b. Albany, N.Y, June 9, 38; m. 67. INSECT ECOLOGY, ENTOMOLOGY. B.S, Univ. Mich, 60, M.S, 61; Ph.D.(entom), N.C. State Univ, 68. Entomologist, SOUTHEAST. FOREST EXP, STA, N.C, 62, Fla, 62-64, res. entomologist, 64, Res. Triangle Park, 64-68, FLA, 68-70, PRIN. INSECT ECOLOGIST, 70- Nat. Guard, S/Sgt. Soc. Am. Foresters; Entom. Soc. Am; Entom. Soc. Can. Behavior of insects affecting pine cones; effects of light and temperature on insect behavior; insect nutrition and internal morphology; radiography for detection of forest insects. Address: Southeastern Forest Experiment Station, Olustee, FL 32072.

FATZINGER, HARLEIGH E, b. Allentown, Pa, May 12, 19; m. 42; c. 1. PHYSICS. B.S, Muhlenberg Col, 41. Naval architect, design sect, Phila-Naval Base, 41-46; physicist, physics & ballistics sect, PITMAN-DUNN LABS, FRANKFORD ARSENAL, 46-53, CHIEF penetration mech. sect, 53-58, gen. physics sect, 58-65, HYPERDYNAMICS BR, 65- Sci. Res. Soc. Am; Am. Phys. Soc; Am. Ord. Asn. Solid state physics; physics of metals; penetration mechanics. Address: Physics Research Lab, Frankford Arsenal, Philadelphia, PA 19137.

FAUBION, BILLY DON, b. Breckenridge, Tex, May 24, 42; m. 63; c. 1. PHYSICAL CHEMISTRY. B.S, Texas A&M, 64, M.S, 65, Ph.D.(phys. chem), 68. Asst. prof. phys. chem, Adams State Col, 68-70; SCIENTIST, MASON & HANGER-SILAS MASON CO, INC, 70-, proj. scientist, summer 69. Am. Chem. Soc. Molecular and electronic structure of molecules; optical thermal analysis and polymorphic states of high explosives. Address: Mason & Hanger-Silas Mason Co, Inc, Box 647, Amarillo, TX 79105.

FAUBL, HERMANN, b. Hungary, Feb. 8, 42; U.S. citizen; m. 66; c. 2. ORGANIC CHEMISTRY. B.S, Loyola (Ill), 65; Nat. Sci. Found. traineeship, Northwestern, 65-66, Nat. Insts. Health fel, 66-69, Ph.D.(chem), 69. STAFF CHEMIST, PFIZER, INC, 69- Am. Chem. Soc. Synthetic organic chemistry; natural product synthesis; synthesis and properties of strained olefins; pharmaceutical chemistry; chemotherapy; antibiotics; antivirals. Address: Medical Research Labs, Pfizer, Inc, Groton, CT 06340.

FAUCETT, JAMES WALTER, b. Bloomington, Ind, Mar. 27, 06; m. 42; c. 2. ANALYTICAL CHEMISTRY, CHEMICAL ENGINEERING. A.B, Indiana, 32, A.M, 34, Ph.D.(chem), 42. Control & res. chemist, Lever Bros. Co, 34-36; prod. supt, Am. Maize Prods, 36-41; develop. engr, Nat. Starch & Chem. Corp, 42-46; plant mgr, D.C.A. Food Industs, 46-48; admin. asst. to gen. mgr, Farm Crops Corp, 48-49; gen. mgr, Trenton Chem. Co, 49-52; v.pres, Takamine Lab, Inc, 52-56, Takamine plant mgr, MILES LABS, INC, 56-69, MGR. SPEC. PROJS, MARSCHALL DIV, 69- Am. Chem. Soc; Am. Inst. Chem. Eng. Grain and food processing; fermentations; enzymes; plant and process design; applied microbiology; biotechnology & bioengineering; food marketing. Address: Marschall Division, Miles Labs, Inc, 193 Arlington Ave, Clifton, NJ 07015.

FAUCETT, ROBERT E, b. Dearborn, Mich, Nov. 21, 26; m. 46, 65; c. 3. ELECTRICAL ENGINEERING. B.S, Case West. Reserve Univ, 47, M.S, 51. Eng. asst, Cleveland Elec. Illum. Co, Ohio, 47-49, 50-51; mgr. photom. lab, tech. develop. & eval. ctr, Civil Aeronaut. Admin, Ind, 51-53; asst. mgr. photom. dept, Elec. Testing Labs, N.Y, 53-55; chief, eng. res. & develop. lab, U.S. Corps Engrs, Va, 55-56; SR. APPLN. ENGR, LIGHTING SYSTS. DEPT, GEN. ELEC. CO, 56- Gen. Elec. Co. managerial awards, 59 & 63. U.S.N.R, 44-46. Fel. Illum. Eng. Soc. Basic glare research; photometry; testing of lighting systems; design of outdoor floodlighting and roadway lighting systems; interior commercial and industrial lighting systems; computer application for solving complex lighting problems. Address: Lighting Systems Dept, General Electric Co, Hendersonville, NC 28739.

FAUCETT, T(HOMAS) R(ICHARD), b. Hatton, Mo, Aug. 22, 20; m. 42; c. 4. MECHANICAL ENGINEERING. B.S, Missouri, 42; M.S, Purdue, 49, Ph.D. (mech. eng), 52. Design analyst, Cleveland Diesel Engine Div, Gen. Motors Corp, 42-46; instr. MECH. ENG, Purdue, 46-52; assoc. prof, Rochester, 52-60; prof, sch. mines, Missouri, Rolla, 60-62; prof. & head dept, Iowa, 62-65; PROF. & CHMN. DEPT. MECH. & AEROSPACE ENG, UNIV. MO-ROLLA, 65- Am. Soc. Mech. Eng. Vibrations; dynamics; stress analysis. Address: Dept. of Mechanical & Aerospace Engineering, University of Missouri-Rolla, Rolla, MO 65401.

FAUCETT, WILLIAM M(UNROE), b. Union, S.C, Sept. 16, 16; m. 46; c. 1. MATHEMATICS. B.S, South Carolina, 42, M.S, 50; Ph.D.(math), Tulane, 54. Asst, Off. Naval Res. Contract, Tulane, 52-54; asst. prof. math, Kentucky, 54-55; sr. aerophysics engr, GEN. DYNAMICS/FT. WORTH, 55-58, sr. opers. analyst, 58-61, proj. opers. analyst, 61-63, DESIGN SPECIALIST, 63- Adj. prof, Texas Christian, 56- U.S.A, 42-45. Am. Math. Soc; Math. Asn. Am; Opers. Res. Soc. Am. Topology; topological semigroups; operations research. Address: 3500 Creston Ave, Ft. Worth, TX 76133.

FAUCETTE, JOHN ROBERTS, b. Asheville, N.C, May 31, 37; m. 59; c. 3. ANATOMY, NEUROANATOMY. B.S, North Carolina, 60, M.A, 66; Nat. Insts. Health fel, Alabama, 65-68, Ph.D.(neuroanat), 68. INSTR. MICROS. ANAT, MED. CTR, UNIV. ALA, BIRMINGHAM, 68- Vertebrate zoology; comparative neurology. Address: 2616 Lakeland Trail, Birmingham, AL 35243.

FAUCHALD, KRISTIAN, b. Oslo, Norway, July 1, 35; nat. SYSTEMATIC ZOOLOGY, MARINE BIOLOGY. Cand. Mag, Bergen, 59, Cand. Real, 61; Ph.D.(biol), Southern California, 69. Vitenskapelig assistent BIOL, Bergen, 59-64, amanuensis, 64-65; res. assoc, UNIV. SOUTH. CALIF, 67-69, ASST. PROF, 69- Sig.C, Norweg. Army, 55-57. Am. Soc. Zool. Systematics and biology of polychaetous annelids from world wide areas; benthic ecology. Address: Allan Hancock Found, University of Southern California, Los Angeles, CA 90007.

FAUDREE, RALPH JASPER, JR, b. Durant, Okla, Aug. 23, 39; m. 62; c. 2. MATHEMATICS. B.S, Oklahoma Baptist, 61; M.S, Purdue, 63; Ph.D.(math), 64. Instr. MATH, California, Berkeley, 64-66; asst. prof, Univ. Ill, Urbana, 66-70; ASSOC. PROF, MEMPHIS STATE UNIV, 70- Am. Math. Soc. Theory of groups. Address: Dept. of Mathematics, Memphis State University, Memphis, TN 38111.

FAUGHNAN, BRIAN WILFRED, b. Montreal, Que, Can, Aug. 5, 33; m. 67; c. 1. SOLID STATE PHYSICS. B.E, McGill, 55; M.S, Mass. Inst. Technol, 57, Ph.D.(physics), 59. MEM. TECH. STAFF, RCA CORP, N.J, 59-63, Japan, 63-64, DAVID SARNOFF RES. CTR, N.J, 64- Am. Phys. Soc. Electron spin resonance; radiation damage; semimetals; electron spin resonance and optical studies of photochronic and cathodochronic materials. Address: RCA Labs, David Sarnoff Research Center, Princeton, NJ 08540.

FAUGHT, DONALD THOMAS, C.S.B, b. North Bay, Ont, June 16, 15. MATHEMATICS. B.A, Univ. Toronto, 37; M.A, Univ. Mich, 44. Lectr. MATH, UNIV. WINDSOR, 54-55, asst. prof, 55-58, assoc. prof, 58-65, PROF, 65-, HEAD DEPT, 55- Pure mathematics; curricular revision of high school mathematics. Address: Dept. of Mathematics, University of Windsor, Windsor 11, Ont, Can.

FAUGHT, J(OHN) BRIAN, b. Toronto, Ont, Mar. 18, 42; m. 68. INORGANIC CHEMISTRY, X-RAY CRYSTALLOGRAPHY. B.Sc, Univ. Windsor, 65; M.S, Univ. Ill, Urbana, 67, Gulf Oil Corp. fel, 68-69, Ph.D.(inorg. chem), 69. Res. assoc, Univ. Fla, 69-70; ASST. PROF. CHEM, DALHOUSIE UNIV, 70- Am. Chem. Soc; Am. Crystallog. Asn. Synthesis and structural studies of phosphorus-nitrogen and arsenic-nitrogen compounds; structural analysis utilizing the techniques of x-ray crystallography, infra-red and Raman spectroscopy. Address: Dept. of Chemistry, Dalhousie University, Halifax, N.S, Can.

FAUL, HENRY. GEOPHYSICS. Ph.D.(geol, physics), Mass. Inst. Technol, 49. Prof. geophys, Southwest. Ctr. Advan. Stud, 63-66; PROF. & CHMN. DEPT. GEOL, UNIV. PA, 66- Nuclear geophysics. Address: Dept. of Geology, University of Pennsylvania, Philadelphia, PA 19104.

FAUL, WILLIAM H(ENRY), b. Evansville, Ind, May 25, 42. ORGANIC CHEMISTRY, PHOTOGRAPHIC SCIENCE. B.S, Univ. Cincinnati, 65; Nat. Insts. Health fel, Stanford Univ, 66-70, Ph.D.(org. chem), 70. Summer res. chemist, Eli Lilly & Co, Ind, 64; Dow Chem. Co. East. Res. Lab, Mass, 65; SR. RES. CHEMIST, COLOR PHOTOG. DIV, EASTMAN KODAK CO, 70- Mass spectroscopy and deuterium labeling of steroidal sapogenins; color photography and color photographic science. Address: Color Photography Division, Eastman Kodak Co. Research Labs, 343 State St, Rochester, NY 14650.

FAULCONER, ALBERT, JR, b. Arkansas City, Kans, Oct. 24, 11; m. ANESTHESIOLOGY. B.S, Kansas, 32, M.D, 36; Mayo Found. fel, Minnesota, 46, M.S, 47. Practicing physician, Mich, 38-41; anesthesiologist, Ft. Custer, Mich, 41-42; Finney Gen. Hosp, Ga, 43-45; PROF. ANESTHESIOL. & ASSOC. PROF. PHYSIOL, MAYO GRAD. SCH. MED, UNIV. MINN, 69-, CONSULT. & HEAD SECT. ANESTHESIOL, MAYO CLIN, 47- Mem. comt. anesthesia, Nat. Res. Coun, 50-61; dir, Am. Bd. Anesthesiol, pres, 63-64. U.S.A, 42-45, Fel. Am. Med. Asn; Am. Soc. Anesthesiol; fel. Am. Col. Anesthesiol. Methods for continuous gas analysis; respiratory and cardiovascular physiology during anesthesia; pathology of anoxia; investigation of blood and plasma substitutes. Address: Dept. of Anesthesiology & Physiology, Mayo Graduate School of Medicine, University of Minnesota, Rochester, MN 55902.

FAULCONER, ROBERT J(AMIESON), b. Sussex, Eng, July 11, 23; nat; m. 45; c. 4. PATHOLOGY. B.S, Col. of William & Mary, 43; M.D, Hopkins, 47. Fel. gynecol. path, Hopkins, 48-49; instr. path, Pennsylvania, 49-52; PATHOLOGIST, DePAUL HOSP, 54-, DIR. LABS, 66-; ASSOC. CLIN. PROF. PATH, MED. COL. VA, 70-, clin. assoc, 66-70. Consult. pathologist, U.S. Naval Hosp, Portsmouth; U.S. Pub. Health Hosp, Norfolk; consult, McDonald Army Hosp, Ft. Eustis, Va. Med.C, U.S.A, 52-54, Capt. AAAS; fel. Am. Soc. Clin. Path; Am. Med. Asn; Am. Asn. Anat; Am. Asn. Hist. Med; Col. Am. Path; Int. Acad. Path; Am. Cancer Soc. Pathologic anatomy; human embryology. Address: Dept. of Pathology, DePaul Hospital, Granby St. & Kingsley Lane, Norfolk, VA 23505.

FAULDERS, CHARLES R(AYMOND), b. Spokane, Wash, May 21, 27; m. 54; c. 5. MECHANICAL ENGINEERING. B.S, California, 48; Tau Beta Pi fel, Mass. Inst. Tech, 48-49, S.M, 50, M.E, 51, Sc.D.(mech. eng), 54. Asst. mech. eng, Mass. Inst. Tech, 49-54; aerodynamicist, aerophysics dept, N.Am. Aviation, Inc, 54-55, supvr. propulsion aerodyn, missile div, 55-57, res. specialist, eng. dept, 57-58, aerospace labs, 58-60; assoc. prof, Univ. Aix-Marseille, 60-62; MGR. flight technol, paraglider prog, N.Am. Aviation, Inc, 63-65, systs. eng, 65-66, FLIGHT SCIS, SPACE DIV, N.AM. ROCKWELL CORP, 66- U.S.N, 44-45. Am. Inst. Aeronaut. & Astronaut. Fluid mechanics; aerodynamics of compressors and turbines; space flight mechanics; optimization of powered space flight trajectories; magnetohydrodynamics; atmospheric flight dynamics of lifting vehicles. Address: Research, Engineering & Test Division, Space Division, Dept. 190/400, North American Rockwell Corp, 12214 Lakewood Blvd, Downey, CA 90241.

FAULK, DENNIS DERWIN, b. Searcy, Ark, Nov. 29, 36; m. 58; c. 2. ORGANIC CHEMISTRY. B.S, Ark. State Teachers Col, 58; Tex. Eastman Co. fel, Arkansas, 64-65, Ph.D.(org. chem), 66. Chemist, Gulf Oil Corp, 58-61; asst. chem, Arkansas, 61-66; res. chemist, Shell Oil Co, Deer Park, 66-67; asst. CHEM, CENT. MO. STATE COL, 67, asst. prof, 67-71, ASSOC. PROF, 71- Am. Chem. Soc. Heterogeneous catalysis; organic reaction mechanisms, acid-catalysed ketone rearrangements; spectroscopic identifications and correlations. Address: Dept. of Chemistry, Central Missouri State College, Warrensburg, MO 64093.

FAULK, M(URL) E(DMUND), JR, b. Columbus, Ohio, May 25, 22; m. 44; c. 2. NEUROPHYSIOLOGY. B.S, Va. Mil. Inst, 42; M.D, Western Reserve, 45. Asst. prof. neurol. & neurosurg, Tulane, 54-56; CONSULT, BEAUMONT NEUROL. CTR, 56- U.S.A, 46-49, Capt. Am. Acad. Neurol. Physiological correlates of psychic states; autonomic manifestations of epilepsy. Address: Beaumont Neurological Center, 3260 Fannin St, Beaumont, TX 77701.

FAULKIN, LESLIE J, JR, b. Peoria, Ill, July 4, 30; m. 50; c. 2. ANATOMY. B.A, California, Berkeley, 55, M.A, 57, Ph.D.(zool), 64. Asst. prof. ANAT, SCH. VET. MED, UNIV. CALIF, DAVIS, 64-69, ASSOC. PROF, 69- U.S.N, 52-54. AAAS; Am. Asn. Cancer Res; Am. Zool. Soc; Am. Asn. Anat. Experimental oncology; growth and development; growth regulation; endocrinology. Address: Dept. of Anatomy, School of Veterinary Medicine, University of California, Davis, CA 95616.

FAULKNER, D. JOHN, b. Bournemouth, Eng, June 10, 42; m. 66. ORGANIC CHEMISTRY. B.Sc, Imp. Col, London, 62; Ph.D.(org. chem), London, 65. Fel, Harvard, 65-67; Stanford, 67-68; ASST. PROF. OCEANOG, SCRIPPS INST, UNIV. CALIF, 68- Am. Chem. Soc; The Chem. Soc. Synthesis of complex molecules; studies of synthetic methods; isolation and identification of natural products. Address: Scripps Institution of Oceanography, La Jolla, CA 92037.

FAULKNER, DONALD N(EAL), b. Ravenna, Ky, Jan. 24, 31; m. 58; c. 1. BIOCHEMISTRY, PLANT PHYSIOLOGY. B.S, Lincoln Mem. Univ, 52; M.S, Oklahoma, 57. Res. asst. Atomic Energy Comn. proj, res. inst, Oklahoma, 52-55, 59-61, biol. surv, 55-56; biochemist AVIATION MED, CIVIL AEROMED. INST, 61-64, RES. BIOCHEMIST, 64- U.S.A, 56-58, Res, 58-62. Effects of auxins on plant metabolism; biochemical and biological effects of ionizing radiation; regulatory mechanisms in metabolism of amino acids and proteins; radiation-induced depression of acquired immunity. Address: Civil Aeromedical Institute, Federal Aviation Administration, P.O. Box 25082, Oklahoma City, OK 73125.

FAULKNER, FRANK D(AVID), b. Humansville, Mo, Apr. 6, 15; m. 41; c. 6. APPLIED MATHEMATICS. B.S, Kans. State Teachers Col, 40; M.S, Kans. State Col, 42; Ph.D.(appl. math), Univ. Mich, Ann Arbor, 69. Jr. physicist, appl. physics lab, Hopkins, 44-46; res. mathematician, eng. res. inst, Michigan, 46-50; assoc. prof. MATH, NAVAL POSTGRAD. SCH, 50-59, PROF, 59- Am. Math. Soc; Am. Astronaut. Soc; Math. Asn. Am; Soc. Indust. & Appl. Math. Numerical methods in optimization; mechanics; calculus of variations; applications in missile problems. Address: Dept. of Mathematics, Naval Postgraduate School, Monterey, CA 93940.

FAULKNER, GLENN E, b. Des Moines, Iowa, June 28, 25; m. 46; c. 5. METALLURGICAL ENGINEERING. B.Met.Eng, Minnesota, 50; M.Sc, Ohio State, 58. Res. engr, inst. atomic res, Iowa State Col, 50-51; asst. chief metals joining div, Battelle Mem. Inst, 51-63; res. eng. specialist, Aerojet Gen. Corp. Div, Gen. Tire & Rubber Co, 63-69; MEM. STAFF, IIT RES. INST, 69- U.S.N, 43-45. Am. Soc. Metals; Am. Welding Soc. Metals joining; welding and brazing ferrous and nonferrous alloys. Address: IIT Research Institute, 10 W. 35th St, Chicago, IL 60616.

FAULKNER, JAMES E(ARL), b. Delton, Mich, June 4, 26; m. 50; c. 1. PHYSICS. Ph.B, Chicago, 48, M.S, 50, Ph.D.(physics), 56. PHYSICIST APPLIED PHYSICS RES, Oak Ridge Nat. Lab, 53-54; Lawrence Radiation Lab, California, 54-64; Aerojet-Gen. Corp, 64-69; NUCLEAR DEFENSE RES. CORP, 69- U.S.A, 44-46. Am. Phys. Soc. Computation physics; numerical analysis; computer applications; applied mathematics. Address: Nuclear Defense Research Corp, Ste. 804, First National Bank Bldg. E, Albuquerque, NM 87108.

FAULKNER, J(AMES) EARL, b. Brigham City, Utah, Nov. 22, 28; m. 62; c. 7. STATISTICS. B.S, Utah State, 50; M.S, Kansas State, 52; Nat. Insts. Health fel. & Ph.D.(biostatist), Minnesota, 64. Instr. math, Utah State, 52-54; Minnesota, 56-62; asst. prof. STATIST, BRIGHAM YOUNG UNIV, 63-67, ASSOC. PROF, 67- Assoc. res. engr, aero div, Minneapolis-Honeywell Regulator Co, 57; consult, Toole Army Depot, 64-65; Hercules Inc, 66-68; technol. div, G.C.A. Corp, 68- Math. Asn. Am; Am. Statist. Asn; Biomet. Soc. Probability; mathematical statistics. Address: Dept. of Statistics, 214 MSCB, Brigham Young University, Provo, UT 84601.

FAULKNER, JOHN A, b. Kingston, Ont, Dec. 12, 23; m. 55; c. 2. PHYSIOLOGY. B.A, Queen's (Ont), 49, B.P.H.E, 50; cert, Ont. Col. Ed, Toronto, 51; M.S, Michigan, 56, Burke Aaron Hinsdale scholar, 61-62, Ph.D.(ed), 62. Teacher, high sch, Ont, 51-52; sci. & phys. ed, Glebe Collegiate Inst, Ont, 52-56; asst. prof. phys. ed, Western Ontario, 56-60; ed, UNIV. MICH, 60-66, assoc. prof. PHYSIOL, 66-71, PROF, 71- Mich. Heart Asn. grants, 63-67 & 69-; Nat. Insts. Health grants, 63-67, 71-; pres, Am. Col. Sports Med, 71-72. R.C.A.F, 42-45, Flying Officer. AAAS; Am. Physiol. Soc. Physiological adaptation of respiration, circulation, red blood cell intermediates and red-slow, red-fast and white-fast skeletal muscle cells to environmental stresses of exercise, hypoxia and temperature. Address: Dept. of Physiology, Medical Science Bldg, University of Michigan Medical School, Ann Arbor, MI 48104.

FAULKNER, JOHN E(DWARD), b. Plattsburg, Ohio, Oct. 5, 20; m. 46; c. 2. NUCLEAR PHYSICS. B.A, Oberlin Col, 42; Ph.D.(physics), Wisconsin, 50. Mem. staff, radiation lab, Mass. Inst. Tech, 42-46; physicist, Hanford Labs, Gen. Elec. Co, Wash, 50-52, supvr. exp. nuclear physics, 52-57, mgr. nuclear physics res, 57-63; consult. exp. physics, ASTRONUCLEAR LAB, WESTINGHOUSE ELEC. CO, 63-64, mgr, safeguards eng, 64-66, CONSULT. EXP. PHYSICS, 66- Consult, Secy. War, 45. Cert. of appreciation, U.S. War Dept. & U.S. Navy Dept, 47. Am. Phys. Soc; Am. Nuclear Soc. Low energy neutron physics; reactor physics; x-rays. Address: Astronuclear Lab, Westinghouse Electric Co, P.O. Box 10864, Pittsburgh, PA 15236.

FAULKNER, JOHN S(AMUEL), b. Memphis, Tenn, Sept. 30, 32; m. 57; c. 2. PHYSICS. B.S, Auburn, 54, M.S, 55; Du Pont fel, Ohio State, 58-59, Ph.D. (physics), 59. Asst. prof. physics, Florida, 59-62; MEM. STAFF, METALS & CERAMICS DIV, OAK RIDGE NAT. LAB, 62- Sr. Fulbright res. scholar, Univ. Sheffield, 68-69. Am. Phys. Soc. Theoretical solid state physics; electronic states in ordered and disordered systems. Address: Metals & Ceramics Division, Oak Ridge National Lab, P.O. Box X, Oak Ridge, TN 37830.

FAULKNER, KENNETH KEITH, b. Barbourville, Ky, April 28, 26; m. 55; c. 3. MEDICAL SCIENCES, ANATOMY. B.S, Lincoln Mem. Univ, 49; M.S, Oklahoma, 51, Nat. Insts. Health fel, 51-54, Ph.D.(med. sci), 55. Instr. ANAT, MED. CTR, UNIV. OKLA, 54-55, asst. prof, 55-65, assoc. prof, 65-70, PROF, 70- Summer, instr, Lincoln Mem. Univ, 49. A.U.S, 44-46. AAAS; Soc. Exp. Biol. & Med. Neurophysiology; neuroanatomy; effects of low temperatures on the intermediary metabolism of nervous tissue; physiology of vitamin C; audiovisual aids and methodology used in medical education. Address: Dept. of Anatomical Sciences, Medical Center, University of Oklahoma, Oklahoma City, OK 73105.

FAULKNER, LARRY R(AY), b. Shreveport, La, Nov. 26, 44; m. 65; c. 1. PHYSICAL & ANALYTICAL CHEMISTRY. B.S, South. Methodist Univ, 66; Nat. Sci. Found. fel, Univ. Tex, Austin, 66-69, Edward Weston fel. & Ph.D. (chem), 69. ASST. PROF. CHEM, HARVARD, 69- Phi Beta Kappa, Tex. Gamma Chap. res. award, 70. Am. Chem. Soc. Chemical reactions of excited states; chemiluminescent electron transfer processes; fluorescence and phosphorescence phenomena and techniques; electrochemistry and electroanalytical chemistry. Address: Dept. of Chemistry, Harvard University, Cambridge, MA 02138.

FAULKNER, LINDSEY R(ALPH), b. Colorado Springs, Colo, Sept. 15, 26; m. 58; c. 3. PLANT NEMATOLOGY. B.S.A, Colo. State Col, 52, M.S, 54; Ph.D.(plant path), Wisconsin, 59. Asst. plant pathologist, WASHINGTON STATE UNIV, 59-65, assoc. plant pathologist, 65-70, PROF. & PLANT PATHOLOGIST, 70- Am. Phytopath. Soc; Soc. Nematol. Plant diseases incited by nematodes; nematode and fungus interactions; nematode resistance in alfalfa and potato; nematode dissemination in irrigation water. Address: Irrigated Agriculture & Extension Center, Washington State University, Prosser, WA 99350.

FAULKNER, LLOYD (CLARENCE), b. Longmont, Colo, Oct. 24, 26; m. 54; c. 5. REPRODUCTIVE PHYSIOLOGY. D.V.M, Colorado State, 52; Ph.D. (animal physiol), Cornell, 63. Asst. prof. vet. clins. & surg, COLO. STATE UNIV, 55-59, assoc. prof, 59-63, vet. clins, surg, physiol. & endocrinol, 63-66, prof. vet. clins. & surg, 66-70, PROF. PHYSIOL. & BIOPHYS. & CHMN. DEPT, 70- U.S. Pub. Health Serv. fel, Nat. Inst. Arthritis & Metab. Diseases, 60-62. Dipl, Am. Col. Theriogenologists, 71. U.S.N, 44-46. Fel. AAAS; N.Y. Acad. Sci; Am. Vet. Med. Asn; Am. Dairy Sci. Asn; Am. Soc. Animal Sci. Testis-accessory sex gland relationships; estrogens in the bovine male; hypothalamo-hypophyseal relationships in the rat; fractionation of the bovine ejaculate; alterations in semen quality in bulls with lesions of the reproductive system. Address: Dept. of Physiology & Biophysics, Colorado State University, Ft. Collins, CO 80521.

FAULKNER, LYNN L, b. Fort Wayne, Ind, June 24, 41; m. 61; c. 2. MECHANICAL ENGINEERING, ACOUSTICS. B.S, Purdue Univ, 65, Nat. Defense Educ. Act fel, 65-68, M.S, 66, Ph.D.(mech. eng), 69. Apprentice draftsman eng, Gen. Elec. Co, Ind, 59-63; res. asst. MECH. ENG, Herrick Labs, Purdue Univ, 65-70; ASST. PROF, OHIO STATE UNIV, 70- Fel, Purdue Univ, 69-70. Am. Soc. Mech. Eng; Acoust. Soc. Am; Soc. Exp. Stress Anal; Am. Soc. Eng. Educ. Engineering acoustics; noise control; noise analysis of household appliances; vehicle noise; building acoustics; outdoor power equipment. Address: Dept. of Mechanical Engineering, Ohio State University, Columbus, OH 43210.

FAULKNER, MACON D, b. Paragould, Ark, Dec. 8, 28; m. 46; c. 2. AGRICULTURAL ENGINEERING. B.S, Arkansas State, 58; M.S, La. State, 59. Agr. engr, Rice Exp. Sta, La. State, Crowley, 59-61, extens. specialist, Baton Rouge, 61-62, La. State Univ-Ford Found. grant consult. agr. eng, Govt. of India, 63-64; agr. engr, RICE EXP. STA, LA. STATE UNIV, CROWLEY, 64-69, SUPT. & PROF. AGR. ENG, 70- Consult, Govt. India, 63-66; Govts. Pakistan, India, British Honduras, Japan, Guyana, and El Salvador, 67; mem. Rice Res. Task Force & Consult, Govt. Japan, 68; consult, Govts. India & Malaysia, 69; Govts. Indonesia & Nicaragua, 70. U.S.A, 52-53, Res, 53-61, 2nd Lt. Am. Soc. Agr. Eng. Rice processing. Address: Louisiana State University Rice Experiment Station, P.O. Box 1429, Crowley, LA 70526.

FAULKNER, PETER, b. Cardiff, Wales, July 8, 29; m. 50; c. 4. BIOCHEMISTRY. B.Sc, London, 50; Ph.D.(biochem), McGill, 54. Res. student, Montreal Gen. Hosp, 50-54; agr. res. off, lab. insect path, Can. Dept. Agr, 54-63; mem. sci. staff med. res. coun, virus res. unit, Carshalton Surv, Eng, 63-65; ASSOC, MED. RES. COUN. CAN, DEPT. MICROBIOL, QUEEN'S UNIV.(ONT), 65- Brit. Biochem. Soc. Insect and arbovirus-host relationships; genetic information transfer in RNA viruses. Address: Dept. of Microbiology, Queen's University, Kingston, Ont, Can.

FAULKNER, RUSSELL C(ONKLIN), JR, b. Barboursville, Ky, Jan. 31, 20; m. 54; c. 2. ZOOLOGY, EXPERIMENTAL MORPHOLOGY. B.S, Lincoln Mem. Univ, 48; M.S, Oklahoma, 52, Ph.D.(zool), 58. Asst. zool, Oklahoma, 48-55; asst. prof. BIOL, Oklahoma Baptist, 55-57; Texas Christian, 57-61, assoc. prof, 61-67; PROF. & HEAD DEPT, STEPHEN F. AUSTIN STATE UNIV, 67- Summers, asst. prof, Lincoln Mem. Univ, 48-52, res. participant, Oak Ridge Nat. Lab, 64. U.S.N, 41-45. Am. Inst. Biol. Sci; Am. Micros. Soc. Effects of radioisotopes on growth and development and use of histochemical methods in detecting effects; microtechnique; radioecological techniques. Address: Dept. of Biology, Stephen F. Austin State University, Box 3003, Nacogdoches, TX 75961.

FAULKNER, WILLARD R(ILEY), b. Jerry, Wash, Jan. 2, 15; m. 50. BIOCHEMISTRY. B.S, Idaho, 40; M.S, Denver, 50; Ph.D, Vanderbilt, 56. Asst. biochem, Vanderbilt, 52-56; clin. chemist, Cleveland Clin. Found, 56-68; ASSOC. PROF. BIOCHEM, SCH. MED. & DIR. CLIN. CHEM. LABS, MED. CTR, VANDERBILT UNIV, 68-, ACTING DIR. CLIN. LABS, 71- Med. bd. dirs, Nat. Registry Clin. Chem, 68-; chmn. licensure adv. comt, Tenn. Med. Lab. Act, 69-; co-ed, CRC, Critical Rev. Clin. Lab. Sci, 70- Bronze Award, Am. Soc. Clin. Path. & Col. Am. Path, 58; dipl, Am. Bd. Clin. Chem. U.S.A, 46-51. AAAS; Am. Microchem. Soc; Am. Chem. Soc; Am. Asn. Clin. Chem. Myoglobin; blood pH, urinary amino acids; blood ammonium; clinical microchemistry; normal clinical laboratory values; ionic calcium. Address: Clinical Chemistry Labs, Vanderbilt University Medical Center, Nashville, TN 37203.

FAUNCE, STUART F(RED), b. Medina, Ohio, Jan. 26, 22; m. 52; c. 3. MECHANICAL ENGINEERING. B.S, Ohio State, 48; M.S, Purdue, 49, Westinghouse Elec. Corp. fel. & Ph.D.(mech. eng), 51. Asst, Purdue, 48-51; sr. res. engr, Convair div, Gen. Dynamics Corp, 51-53; asst. prof. petrol. eng, Oklahoma, 53-55; res. engr, Armour Res. Found, Ill. Inst. Technol, 55-56; dir, new prod. develop, John Wood Co, 56-57, res, 57-58, v.pres. eng. & res, 58-64; MGR. ENG. & RES, ELECTRA MOTORS DIV, HEWITT-ROBINS, INC, 64- U.S.A, 42-45, Sgt. Am. Soc. Eng. Educ; Am. Soc. Mech. Eng. Heat transfer; thermodynamics; fluid mechanics of processes involving energy transformation. Address: Hewitt-Robins, Inc, Electra Motors Division, 1110 N. Lemon, Anaheim, CA 92803.

FAUPEL, JOSEPH H(ERMAN), b. Waukegan, Ill, Oct. 25, 16; m. 40; c. 9. ENGINEERING MECHANICS. B.S, Pa. State, 39, du Pont fel, 47-48, Ph.D. (eng. mech), 48; M.S, Pittsburgh, 42. Res. metallurgist, Aluminum Co. Am, 39-42; asst, Pa. State, 45-47; res. engr, E.I. DU PONT DE NEMOURS & CO, INC, 48-52, proj. engr, 52-55, res. assoc, 55-62, CONSULT, 62- Spec. lectr. mech. eng, Delaware, 49-51; mem, Pressure Vessel Res. Comt; Boiler & Pressure Vessel Comt; indust. & prof. adv. comt, Pa. State Univ. Chem.C, 42-45, Capt. Am. Soc. Metals; Am. Soc. Mech. Eng; Am. Soc. Test. & Mat. Mechanics of materials; stress analysis; pressure vessels; plasticity; elasticity; viscoelasticity; limit design; high temperature and high pressure mechanics. Address: E.I. du Pont de Nemours & Co, Inc, Wilmington, DE 19898.

FAURE, GUNTER, b. Tallinn, Estonia, May 11, 34; U.S. citizen; m. 59; c. 4. GEOCHEMISTRY, GEOCHRONOLOGY. B.Sc, Western Ontario, 57; Ph.D. (geol), Mass. Inst. Technol, 61. Res. assoc. geochronology, Mass. Inst. Technol, 61-62; asst. prof. GEOL, OHIO STATE UNIV, 62-65, assoc. prof, 65-68, PROF, 68- Nat. Sci. Found. res. grants, 64-71. AAAS; Geol. Soc. Am; Geochem. Soc; Am. Geophys. Union; Int. Asn. Geochem. & Cosmochem; German Geol. Asn. Origin of granitic rocks; age of the norite at Sudbury, Ontario; isotopic composition of strontium in volcanic rocks from Hawaii; isotopic composition of strontium in oceans and fresh water on continents; geochronology of the Transantarctic Mountains; isotope geochemistry of strontium in the base metal deposits of the Red Sea; chemical composition of water in the Great Lakes. Address: Dept. of Geology, Ohio State University, 125 S. Oval Dr, Columbus, OH 43210.

FAUROT, JAMES L(OVAAS), b. St. Croix Falls, Wis, Sept. 8, 23; m. 54; c. 1. FOREST ENGINEERING. B.S.F, Montana, 49; M.F, Washington (Seattle), 57. Instr. FOREST ENG, UNIV. MONT, 51-57, asst. prof, 57-69, ASSOC. PROF, 69- Consult, Mont. State Indust. Accident Bd, 54; U.S. Bur. Land Mgt, 54-55; Intermt. Forest. & Range Exp. Sta, U.S. Forest Serv, 60. U.S.A.A.F, 43-45. Production-cost analysis; mechanical properties of wood. Address: School of Forestry, University of Montana, Missoula, MT 59801.

FAUSCH, HOMER D(AVID), b. Buffalo Center, Iowa, April 5, 19; m. 43; c. 3. ANIMAL BREEDING. B.S, Minnesota, 47, M.S, 50, Ph.D.(animal breeding), 53. Assoc. prof. & animal husbandman, northwest exp. sta, Univ. Minn, 47-56; PROF. ANIMAL GENETICS, CALIF. STATE POLYTECH. COL, KELLOGG-VOORHIS, 56-, DIR. RES, 68- Lectr, Univ. Alta, 64-65. U.S.N.A.F, 42-45, Lt.(jg). AAAS; Am. Soc. Animal Sci. Effect of inbreeding on variability of economic traits in the Minnesota number one and number two breeds of swine; lipid metabolism in swine. Address: Dept. of Animal Science, California State Polytechnic College, Kellogg-Voorhis, 3801 W. Temple Ave, Pomona, CA 91768.

FAUST, CHARLES L(AWSON), b. St. Louis, Mo, Nov. 8, 06; m. 34; c. 3. CHEMICAL ENGINEERING. B.S, Washington (St. Louis), 30, indust. fel, 30-31, M.S, 31; Ph.D.(chem. eng), Minnesota, 34. Asst. chem, Minnesota, 31-34; res. engr, BATTELLE MEM. INST, 34-41, asst. supvr. electrochem. res, 41-44, supvr. electrochem. eng. res, 44-53, chief electrochem. eng. div, 53-69, assoc. mgr. chem. & chem. eng. dept, 69-71, SR. TECH. ADV, COLUMBUS LABS, 71- With War Metall. Subcomt, 44; mem, Int. Coun. Electrodeposition, 64-67; consult, Mining & Mat. Adv. Bd. Am. Chem. Soc.(ed, sect. 77, Chem. Abst); hon. mem, Electrochem. Soc.(v.pres, 48-50, pres, 50-51, Atcheson Medal, 62); Am. Electroplaters Soc.(Proctor Award, 42, gold medal, 51, Heusner Award, 55, sci. award, 61); Soc. Mfg. Engrs.(res. gold medal, 66); Brit. Inst. Metal Finishing (Hothersall Medal, 67). Electrodeposition of metals and alloys; electroforming; electropolishing; pickling; metal finishing; protection; alumina from clays; fuel cells; batteries; electrolysis; electrowinning; electrorefining; electrochemical machining. Address: 4354 Donington Rd, Columbus, OH 43220.

FAUST, CLAUDE MARIE, C.C.V.I, b. San Antonio, Tex, Nov. 18, 17. MATHEMATICS. B.A, Incarnate Word Col, 39; M.A, Catholic Univ; 54; M.S, Marquette, 55; South. Fels. Fund fel, Notre Dame, 57-59, Nat. Sci. Found. fel, 59-60, Ph.D.(math), 61. Instr. MATH, INCARNATE WORD COL, 46-56, asst. prof, 56-58, assoc. prof, 58-61, PROF, 61-, Minnie Stevens Piper prof, 67, dir. Nat. Sci. Found. In-Serv. Insts. High Sch. Teachers Math, 63-71. Vis. scientist, Nat. Sci. Found. Vis. Scientist Prog, Tex. Acad. Sci, 64-65; dir, Tex. Ctr. for Minn. Math. & Sci. Teaching Proj, Nat. Sci. Found, 63-68. Mat. Asn. Am; Am. Math. Soc. Complex analysis; boundary behavior of holomorphic functions in the unit disc. Address: Dept. of Mathematics, Incarnate Word College, 4301 Broadway, San Antonio, TX 78209.

FAUST, HOMER E(DWARD), b. Houghton,Co, Mich, Sept. 13, 08; m. 35; c. 4. DENTISTRY. D.D.S, Michigan, 33, M.S, 43. Clin. instr. crown & bridge ceramics, SCH. DENT, UNIV. MICH, ANN ARBOR, 37-39, instr. crown & bridge prosthodontics, 39-44, asst. prof. PROSTHODONTICS, 44-49, assoc. prof, 49-55, PROF, 55- Dir, Am. Acad. Crown & Bridge Prosthodontics, 55-56, secy. bd. censors. Am. Dent. Asn; Am. Acad. Restorative Dent. Restorative dentistry; crown and bridge prosthodontics. Address: 2458 Baseview Dr, Base Lake, Pinckney, MI 48169.

FAUST, JOHN A(NDREW), b. Kearsage, Mich, April 2, 19; m. 43; c. 1. MEDICINAL CHEMISTRY. B.S, Michigan, 41, M.S, 42, Ph.D, 49. Res. assoc, Michigan, 42-43; res. chemist, Bakelite Corp, 43-44; Frederick Stearns & Co, 44-47; SAHYUN LABS, Mich, 49, dir. org. res, CALIF, 49-65, V.PRES. RES, 65- Am. Chem. Soc. Antispasmodics; sympathomimetics; analgesics; anticonvulsants. Address: Sahyun Labs, 316 Castillo, Santa Barbara, CA 93101.

FAUST, J(OHN) PHILIP, b. New Orleans, La, Sept. 26, 24; m. 52; c. 3. INORGANIC CHEMISTRY. B.S, Loyola (La), 44; M.S, Illinois, 48; Atomic Energy Cmn. fel, Notre Dame, 48, Ph.D.(chem), 52. Chemist, Olin Mathieson Chem. Corp, 52-53, res. group leader, 53-54, chief inorg. res. sect, OLIN CORP, 54-57, proj. supvr, 58-62, MEM. STAFF, 63- U.S.N.R, 44-45. Am. Chem. Soc; Sci. Res. Soc. Am; fel. Am. Inst. Chem. Reactions of boron fluoride and boron chloride with phosgene; polarographic studies on inorganic coordination compounds; infrared studies of hydrogen bonding of ethylenediamine; infrared and ultraviolet studies of inorganic coordination compounds in the solid state; metal hydrides, boranes; catalysis high vacuum techniques; high energy fuels; high energy oxidizers; fluorine and pesticides; borazine polymers; hypochlorites; sanitizers; pollution control. Address: Olin Corp, 275 Winchester Ave, New Haven, CT 06504.

FAUST, J(OHN) W(ILLIAM), JR, b. Pittsburgh, Pa, July 25, 22; m. 47; c. 8. CRYSTAL GROWTH, SURFACE PHYSICS. B.S, Purdue, 44; M.A, Missouri, 49, Ph.D.(phys. chem), 51. Res. chemist, Westinghouse Elec. Corp, 51-59, supvry. engr, 59-63, sect. mgr, mat. characterization lab, 63-65, mgr. semiconductor crystals growth, 65-67; PROF. solid state sci, mat. res. labs, Pa. State Univ, 67-69; ENG, UNIV. S.C, 69- Co-chmn, int. comt. silicon carbide, Univ. S.C; mem, Electronics Mat. Comt; chmn, Third Int. Conf. Silicon Carbide; Conf. Chem. & Metall. of Semiconductors. Gordon Conf. Cert. Recognition. U.S.N, 42-46. AAAS; Electrochem. Soc; Am. Phys. Soc; Am. Inst. Mining, Metall. & Petrol. Eng; Am. Soc. Metals; fel. Am. Inst. Chem; Am. Chem. Soc. Etching and surface problems of semiconductors and metals; growth of metal and semiconductor crystals by numerous techniques; revealing dislocations; characterization of materials. Address: College of Engineering, University of South Carolina, Columbia, SC 29208.

FAUST, LEO G(EORGE), b. Fingal, N.Dak, Dec. 9, 29; m. 52; c. 1. PHYSICS, HEALTH PHYSICS. B.S, Humboldt State Col, 59. Engr. health physics, Gen. Elec. Co, 59-63, supvr. radiation monitoring, 63-64, sr. engr. radiation protection, 64-65; SR. RES. SCIENTIST RADIOL. PHYSICS, BATTELLE-NORTHWEST, 65- U.S.A.F, 50-54, T/Sgt. Am. Nuclear Soc; Health Physics Soc. Dosimetry of plutonium reactor fuels, their neutron and photon energy spectra, their changes with time and the effects of various shielding materials in reducing dose rates. Address: 40 Vienna Ctr, Richland, WA 99352.

FAUST, MIKLOS, b. Nagybereny, Hungary, Dec. 12, 27; m. 54; c. 1. POMOLOGY. B.S, Agr. Univ. Budapest, 52; M.S, Rutgers, 60; Ph.D.(pomol), 65. Mgr, Csaszartoltes State Farm, Hungary, 52-54, regional supvr, Ministry of State Farms, 55-57; res. assoc, Rutgers, 58-60; res. horticulturist, United Fruit Co, N.Y, 60-62; res. assoc, Cornell, 63-65; N.Y. State Agr. Exp. Sta, 65-66; AGR. RES. SERV, U.S. DEPT. AGR, 66-69, LEADER POME FRUIT INVESTS, 69- Am. Soc. Hort. Sci; Int. Soc. Hort. Sci. Postharvest physiology; biochemistry of fruits; metabolic changes in fruits exposed to different environmental conditions. Address: Agricultural Research Service, U.S. Dept. of Agriculture, Plant Industry Station, Beltsville, MD 20705.

FAUST, RICHARD A(HLVERS), b. Terre Haute, Ind, Sept. 6, 21; m. 43; c. 2. MICROBIOLOGY. B.S, Purdue, 48, M.S, 52, Ph.D.(bact), 58. Instr. bact, Purdue, 51-55; asst. prof. MICROBIOL, UNIV. MONT, 58-66, ASSOC. PROF, 66- U.S.A.A.F, 42-46. AAAS; Am. Soc. Microbiol. Physiology of Bordetella pertussis; microbial ecology of alpine soils. Address: Dept. of Microbiology, University of Montana, Missoula, MT 59801.

FAUST, R(ICHARD) E(DWARD), b. Greenfield, Mass, Oct. 26, 27; m. 53; c. 3. PHARMACEUTICAL CHEMISTRY. B.S, Mass. Col. Pharm, 51; Am. Found, Pharmaceut. Educ. fel, Purdue, 51-55, M.S, 53, Ph.D.(pharmaceut. chem), 55; M.B.A, Columbia Univ, 68. Res. assoc, Sterling-Winthrop Res. Inst, 54-55; asst. prof. pharm, Ferris State Col, 55-57; dir. res, Potter Drug & Chem. Corp, 57-61; mgr. new prod. creation, Merck & Co, 61-63; asst. dir. res. Johnson & Johnson Res. Ctr, 63-65, dir. prod. develop. & consult, 65-68; corp. planning mgr, HOFFMANN-LA ROCHE, INC, 68-69, DIR. RES. PLANNING, 69- Summer asst, Upjohn Co, 56; prof. lectr, Mass. Col. Pharm, 58-61. U.S.A, 46-48; U.S.P.H.S.R, Sr. Asst. Pharmacist. AAAS; Am. Pharmaceut. Asn; Soc. Cosmetic Chem; Soc. Invest. Dermat; Am. Chem. Soc. Cosmetic and dermatologic preparations; topical therapeutics; toiletries; soaps; research administration and planning. Address: Hoffmann-La Roche, Inc, Nutley, NJ 07110.

FAUST, ROBERT G(ILBERT), b. Brooklyn, N.Y, Nov. 9, 32; m. 56; c. 1. CELL PHYSIOLOGY, BIOPHYSICS. A.B, N.Y. Univ, 53; M.S, Southern California, 57; Sterry fel, Princeton, 58-60, Nat. Insts. Health fel, 59-60, Ph.D. (biol), 60. Asst. zool, Southern California, 55-57; biol, Princeton, 57-59; Nat. Insts. Health fel, Oxford, 60-62, Harvard Med. Sch, 62-63; asst. prof. PHYSIOL, SCH. MED, UNIV. N.C, CHAPEL HILL, 63-68, ASSOC. PROF, 68-, dir. space sci. prog, 68-72. Nat. Insts. Health grant, 64-72; NASA grant, 68-72; mem. physiol. study sect, Nat. Insts. Health, 70-74. U.S.A, 53-55. AAAS; Am. Physiol. Soc; Biophys. Soc; Brit. Biochem. Soc. Permeability of cells and tissues; mechanisms of active transport of electrolytes and non-electrolytes; use of model systems to interpret solute penetration into cells and tissues. Address: Dept. of Physiology, School of Medicine, University of North Carolina, Chapel Hill, NC 27514.

FAUST, SAMUEL DENTON, b. Shiloh, N.J, Aug. 11, 29; m. 60. ENVIRON-MENTAL SCIENCES. B.S, Gettysburg Col, 50; Ph.D.(environ. sci), 58. Chemist, W.A. Taylor & Co, Md, 50-54; res. fel, ENVIRON. SCI, RUTGERS UNIV, 54-58, asst. prof, 58-61, assoc. prof, 61-65, PROF, 65- Am. Chem. Soc; Am. Soc. Limnol. & Oceanog; Am. Water Works Asn; Am. Geophys. Union; Am. Soc. Test. & Mat. Water chemistry; water quality management; water resources. Address: Wikwames Yapewi, Change Water, NJ 07831.

FAUST, WALTER LUCK, b. Benton, Ark, Feb. 13, 34; m. 57; c. 3. PHYSICS. A.B, Columbia Col, 56; Radio Corp. Am. fel, 59-60; Ph.D.(Physics), Columbia Univ, 61. Mem. tech. staff, Bell Tel. Labs, Inc, 61-67; ASSOC. PROF. PHYSICS & ELEC. ENG, UNIV. SOUTH. CALIF, 67- Am. Phys. Soc. Gas lasers; infrared resonance. Address: Dept. of Physics & Electrical Engineering, 423 Seaver Science Center, University of Southern California, University Park, Los Angeles, CA 90007.

FAUST, WAYNE J(OHN), b. Madison, Wis, Dec. 19, 18; m. 43; c. 3. CHEMICAL ENGINEERING. B.S, Wisconsin, 40. Chem. engr, UNIVERSAL OIL PRODS. CO, 40-52, dir. automotive & aircraft div, 52-59, MGR. engine lab, 59-66, LAB. ENG. & OPERS, 66- U.S.A, 44-46. Soc. Automotive Eng; Am. Soc. Test & Mat; Coord. Res. Coun; Am. Petrol. Inst. Internal combustion engine and fuel relationships. Address: 1314 W. Clarendon, Arlington Heights, IL 60004.

FAUST, WILLIAM R(OSCOE), b. Shawnee, Okla, March 9, 18; m. 42; c. 3. NUCLEAR PHYSICS. B.S, Okla. Agr. & Mech. Col, 39; M.S, Ill. Inst. Tech, 41; Ph.D.(physics), Maryland, 49. Asst, Ill. Inst. Tech, 39-41; electronic scientist, NAVAL RES. LAB, 41-47, physicist nucleonics div, 47-51, PHYSICIST RADIATION DIV, 51-, assoc. supt, 54-64, SUPT, APPLN. RES. DIV, 64- Fel. Am. Phys. Soc. Multiple scattering; radiation shielding; plasma and ionospheric physics. Address: 6410 Walnut St. S.E, Washington, DC 20031.

FAUT, OWEN DONALD, b. Allentown, Pa, July 8, 36; m. 59; c. 4. INORGANIC CHEMISTRY. B.S, Muhlenburg Col, 58; Ph.D.(chem), Mass. Inst. Tech, 62. Asst. prof, CHEM, Hanover Col, 62-66, ASSOC. PROF, 66-67, WILKES COL, 67- Am. Chem. Soc. Electronic and molecular structures of first row transition metal compounds. Address: 22 Norton Ave, Dallas, PA 18612.

FAUTH, MAE I(RENE), b. Wrightsville, Pa, June 12, 13. INORGANIC CHEMISTRY. B.S, Lebanon Valley Col, 33; A.M, Columbia, 46; Ph.D.(chem), Pa. State, 55. Attend. nursing, Wernersville State Hosp, Pa, 35-43; asst. engr. elec. eng, West. Elec. Co, N.J, 43-45; head dept. sci, pub. sch, N.Y, 46-47; instr. chem, Hazleton Ctr, Pa. State Univ, 47-49, univ, 49-55; MGR. ANAL. BR, NAVAL ORD. STA, INDIAN HEAD, 55- Prof. lectr, Charles County Community Col, 59- Am. Chem. Soc; Am. Phys. Soc; fel. Am. Inst. Chem. Chemistry of rocket fuels; analysis and evaluation of solid propellants; automation; propellant reclamation; pollution abatement; environmental effects of chemicals. Address: 5192 Livingston Terr, Apt. 302, Oxon Hill, MD 20021.

FAUTIN, REED W(INGET), b. Monroe, Utah, Jan. 2, 08; m. 41; c. 3. ZOOLOGY. B.S, Brigham Young, 36; M.A, Illinois, 38, Ph.D.(zool), 41. Instr. ZOOL, Illinois, 45-46; asst. prof, UNIV. WYO, 46-49, assoc. prof, 49-53, PROF, 53-, DIR. WILDLIFE CONSERV. & MGT, 46- U.S.A, 42-45. Fel. AAAS; Am. Inst. Biol. Sci; Ecol. Soc. Am; Am. Soc. Mammal; Animal Behav. Soc; Wildlife Soc. Small mammal populations; wildlife management; biotic communities. Address: Dept. of Zoology, University of Wyoming, Laramie, WY 82070.

FAUVER, VERNON A(RTHUR), b. Hammond, Ind, Mar. 25, 28; m. 47; c. 2. CHEMICAL ENGINEERING. B.S, Purdue, 52, M.S, 53. Chem. engr, Eastman Kodak Co, N.Y, 53; styrene polymerization lab, DOW CHEM. CO, 54-58, process eng. dept, 58-59, C.J. Strosacker Res. & Develop. Lab, 59-61, res. engr, Edgar C. Britton Res. Lab, 61-66, PROCESS SPECIALIST, PROCESS ENG. DEPT, 66. U.S.N, 46-48. Am. Inst. Chem. Eng; Am. Chem. Soc. Bench-scale and pilot-plant process development; reaction engineering; separations processes. Address: Process Engineering Dept, 834 Bldg, Dow Chemical Co, Midland, MI 48640.

FAVALE, ANTHONY J(OHN), b. N.Y.C, Feb. 28, 35; wid; c. 3. NUCLEAR PHYSICS. B.S, Polytech. Inst. Brooklyn, 56; M.S, N.Y. Univ, 63. Res. physicist, GRUMMAN CORP, 56-57, 57-62, HEAD NUCLEAR SHIELDING & APPLNS. GROUP, 62- Guest scientist, reactor div, Brookhaven Nat. Lab, 61-64; lectr, C.W. Post Col, 64- U.S.A, 57, 1st Lt. Am. Phys. Soc. Ion beam physics and particle charging techniques for micrometeorite simulation; nuclear reaction cross-section measurements. Address: R.F.D. 1, Major Trescott Lane, Northport, NY 11768.

FAVATA, BENEDICT V(ICTOR), b. Dunkirk, N.Y, July 26, 09; m. 58. NEUROSURGERY. D.V.M, Cornell, 38; M.D, Rochester, 42. Lab. technician bact, Rochester Health Bur, N.Y, 40-42; intern, surg, obstet. & gynec, Strong Mem. Hosp, 42-43, res. surgeon, 43, 45-46, asst. res. surgeon, 44, asst. surgeon, 46-54, chief neurosurgeon, cerebral palsy clin, 50-56; CHIEF NEUROSURGEON, ROCHESTER VET. ADMIN. OUTPATIENT SERV, 48- Asst. surg, sch. med & dent, Rochester, 43-44, instr. neurol. surg, 45-46, surg, 46-54, cancer res. fel, sch. med, 46-54, assoc. path, 54. Pathologist, Manhattan Dist, 41-46, chief neurosurgeon, Monroe County Infirmary, 45-63; Genesee Hosp, 45-62. Wisdom award, 70; citations, Am. Legion; Disabled Am. Vets. AAAS; Am. Med. Asn; Tissue Cult. Asn; N.Y. Acad. Sci; fel. Int. Col. Surg; fel. Royal Soc. Health. Cancer; ecology; biophysics. Address: 64 Highland Ave, Rochester, NY 14620.

FAVERO, MARTIN, b. Butte, Mont, May 3, 37; m. 61; c. 2. MICROBIOLOGY. B.S, Gonzaga, 59; M.S, Washington State, 61, Ph.D.(bact), 64. Res. microbiologist planetary quarantine, CTR. DISEASE CONTROL, U.S. PUB. HEALTH SERV, 64- Superior serv. award, Health Serv. & Ment. Health Admin, 71. Am. Soc. Microbiol. Resistance of microorganisms to chlorine and iodine; microbial flora of chlorinated and iodinated swimming pools; environmental health; aerospace microbiology; microbial contamination of spacecraft; spacecraft sterilization; hospital acquired infections. Address: Center for Disease Control, U.S. Public Health Service, 4402 N. Seventh St, Phoenix, AZ 85014.

FAVIS, DIMITRIOS V(ASILIOS), b. Sparta, Greece, Sept. 10, 14; Can. citizen; m. 52; c. 2. PHYSICAL & INDUSTRIAL CHEMISTRY. B.Sc, Athens, 38 & 46; Pulp & Paper Inst. Can, 48-51; Ph.D.(phys. chem), McGill, 51. RES. CHEMIST, RES. DEPT, IMP. OIL ENTERPRISES LTD, 51- Greek Army, 39-41, 44-45, 2nd Lt. Sr. mem. Chem. Inst. Can; Am. Chem. Soc. Random fluctuations; heterogeneity of paper; petroleum refining; ozonization; Friedel-Crafts and Ziegler catalysis; oligomerization; synthetic lubricants; basic raw petrochemicals; additives. Address: Research Dept, Imperial Oil Enterprises Ltd, Sarnia, Ont, Can.

FAVORITE, FELIX, b. Quincy, Mass, Mar. 18, 25; m. 51; c. 4. OCEANOGRAPHY. B.S, Mass. Maritime Acad, 46; Boston Univ, 49-50; B.S, Univ. Wash, 55, M.S, 65; Ph.D, Ore. State Univ, 68. Asst. oceanog, Univ. Wash, 55-57; oceanogr, biol. lab, Bur. Commercial Fisheries, U.S. Fish & Wildlife Serv, 57-59, chief oceanog. invests, 59-70, PROG. DIR. OCEANOG, N.PAC. FISHERIES RES. CTR, NAT. MARINE FISHERIES SERV, NAT. OCEANIC & ATMOSPHERIC AGENCY, 70- Expert in oceanog, Int. North. Pac. Fisheries Comn, 59-; partic. U.S-Japan Coop. Sci. Prog, 64; mem, U.S-U.S.S.R. Oceanog. Exchange Prog, 64. U.S.N, 46-47, 50-53, Lt. Comdr. (Ret). N.Y. Acad. Sci; Oceanog. Soc. Japan. Oceanographic investigations in North Pacific and Bering Sea; physical, descriptive and fisheries oceanography. Address: North Pacific Fisheries Research Center, National Marine Fisheries Service, National Oceanic & Atmospheric Agency, 2725 Montlake Blvd, Seattle, WA 98102.

FAVORITE, FRANK G, JR, b. Baltimore, Md, Sept. 18, 22; m. 43; c. 1. MEDICAL ENTOMOLOGY. B.S, American Univ, 50; M.P.H, North Carolina, 55; Ph.D.(med. entom), Maryland, 60. Div. head med. entom, 3rd Med. Lab, U.S. Army, 50-52, 55-58, consult, Allied Forces, Korea, 52-54, div. head, Environ. Hyg. Agency, 59-62; prof. entom, George Wash. Univ, 64-65; STAFF SCIENTIST, space sci. bd, NAT. ACAD. SCI, 65-70, TOXICOL. CTR, 70- Mem, Armed Forces Pest Control Bd, 59-62, staff mem, 62-64. U.S.A.A.F, 40-46; U.S.A, 50-64, Lt. Col. AAAS; Am. Pub. Health Asn; Am. Inst. Biol. Sci. Bionomics of mosquito vectors of disease, particularly species involved in arbo-viruses transmissible to man; epidemiology of arthropodborne diseases; space life sciences; toxicology of environmental contaminants. Address: Toxicology Center, National Academy of Sciences, Washington, DC 20418.

FAVORITE, JOHN R, b. Muskegon, Mich, June 26, 16; m. 42; c. 2. CHEMICAL ENGINEERING. B.S, Purdue, 38. Engr, Goodyear Tire & Rubber Co, 38-49; Clopay Co, 49-50; supvr. Thermo-Fax prod. develop, MINN. MINING & MFG. CO, 50-55, tech. dir. duplicating prod. div, 55-64, group mkt. mgr. duplicating & microfilm prod, int. div, 64-67, PROJ. MGR. PHOTOG. PROD. DIV, 67- Am. Chem. Soc; Am. Inst. Chem. Eng. Product research and development. Address: 1292 Hillcrest Ave, St. Paul, MN 55116.

FAVOUR, CUTTING B(ROAD), b. Toreva, Ariz, July 19, 13; m. 41; c. 3. MEDICINE. A.B, Hendrix Col, 36; M.D, Hopkins, 40. Intern med, Osler wards, Hopkins Hosp, 40-41; asst. res, Peter Bent Brigham Hosp, Boston, Mass, 41-42, res, 42-43; instr. & asst, Harvard Med. Sch, 43-47, assoc, 47-54; asst. clin. prof, med. sch, Stanford, 55-60; prof. prev. med. & chmn. dept, sch. med, Georgetown, 60-62; chief dept. physiol, Nat. Jewish Hosp, Denver, Colo, 62-64; chief dept. exp. epidemiol, 64-66; dir. med. educ, St. Mary's Hosp, 66-70; MED. DIR, KAISER INDUSTS. CORP, 70- Res. fel. med, Harvard Med. Sch, 41-53; jr. assoc, Peter Bent Brigham Hosp, 43-45, assoc, 46-54, sr. assoc, 54; vis. investr, Rockefeller Inst. Med. Res, 46-47; lectr, Simmons Col, 47-54; consult, Channing Home for Tuberc, Boston, Mass, 48-54; attend, Rutland Vet. Hosp, 49-54; Robert Breck Brigham Hosp, 52-54; Vet. Admin. Hosp, West Roxbury, Mass, 53-54; consult, Boston Lying-In-Hosp, 54; Palo Alto Med. Clin, 54-60; head dept. immunol, Palo Alto Med. Res. Found, 54-60; asst. vis. physician, Stanford serv, City & County Hosp, San Francisco, 55-60; mem. staff, Palo Alto Hosp, 55-56; lectr. & consult, U.S. Navy Hosp, Oak Knoll, Calif, 56-60; chief, Georgetown Med. Serv, Wash. D.C. Gen. Hosp, 60-62; consult, Nat. Naval Med. Ctr, Bethesda, Md, 61-62; attend. staff, St. Mary's Hosp, San Francisco, 66-; lectr, sch. med, Univ. Calif, San Francisco, 67-; consult, Vet. Admin. Hosp, San Francisco & Livermore, 68-; Univ. Calif. Hosp, 69-; attend. staff, Highland Gen. Hosp, Oakland, 70-; San Francisco Gen. Hosp, 69-; St. Joseph's Hosp, 71- Dipl, Am. Bd. Internal Med, 54. AAAS; Soc. Exp. Biol. & Med; fel. Am. Col. Physicians; Am. Med. Asn; Am. Thoracic Soc; affiliate, Royal Soc. Med; Am. Rheumatism Asn; Am. Heart Asn; Am. Fedn. Clin. Res; N.Y. Acad. Sci. Immunology and microbiology applied to clinical medicine. Address: 300 Lakeside Dr, Oakland, CA 94604.

FAVRE, H(ENRI) A(LBERT), b. Payerne, Switzerland, Dec. 4, 26; m. 58; c. 3. ORGANIC CHEMISTRY. Ing. Chem. Dipl, Swiss Federal Inst. Tech, 48, Dr.Sc, 51. British Coun. student, Sheffield Univ, 51-52; asst. prof. ORG. CHEM, UNIV. MONTREAL, 52-57, assoc. prof, 57-60, dir. dept. chem, 59-63, PROF, 60- Chem. Inst. Can; The Chem. Soc. Stereochemistry. Address: Dept. of Chemistry, University of Montreal, P.O. Box 6128, Montreal, Que, Can.

FAVREAU, GERALD, b. Montreal, Que, Dec. 30, 33; m. 61; c. 3. PHARMACOGNOSY, PLANT CHEMISTRY. B.A, Univ. Montreal, 55, B.Sc, 59, D.Sc. (pharm), 64. ASSOC. PROF. PHARMACOG, LAVAL UNIV, 64- French-Can. Asn. Advan. Sci. Localization of drugs or related substances in plant organs and tissues. Address: School of Pharmacy, Laval University, Quebec 10, Que, Can.

FAVREAU, ROGER F, b. Montreal, Que, Apr. 22, 33; m. 58; c. 1. PHYSICS. B.Sc, McGill, 55, M.Sc, 57, Ph.D.(physics), 61. Res. physicist, explosives res. lab, Can. Indust, Ltd, 60-63; asst. prof. PHYSICS, ROYAL MIL. COL. (QUE), 63-65, assoc. prof, 65-69, PROF, 69- Can. Defence Res. Bd. res. grants, 64-67; consult, Explosive Res. Lab, 65- Am. Phys. Soc. Nuclear physics, especially neutron induced reactions in light nuclei; physics of explosives, especially application of explosives to mining; effects of shock waves on structures. Address: Dept. of Physics, College Militaire Royal de Saint-Jean, Saint-Jean, Que, Can.

FAVRET, A(NDREW) G(ILLIGAN), b. Cincinnati, Ohio, May 9, 25; m. 49; c. 11. ELECTRONICS. B.S, U.S. Mil. Acad, 45; M.S, Pennsylvania, 50; D.Eng.(elec. eng), Catholic Univ, 64. Staff mem, Lincoln Lab, Mass. Inst. Technol, 54-55; acting dir. planning, defense prod. group, Am. Mach. & Foundry Co, 55-56, mgr. syst. anal. dept, Alexandria Div, 56-59; sr. sci. adv. to asst. chief staff intel, U.S. Dept. Army, 59-63; assoc. prof. ELEC. ENG, CATH. UNIV. AM, 63-67, PROF, 67-, DIR. COMPUT. CTR, 68- U.S.A, 45-54, Capt. Sr. mem. Inst. Elec. & Electronics Eng; Asn. Comput. Mach. Digital computer applications; statistical decision theory; signal processing; digital computer systems; biomedical instrumentation; computer simulation. Address: 2105 Gatewood Pl, Silver Spring, MD 20903.

FAVRO, L(AWRENCE) D(ALE), b. Pittsburgh, Pa, Apr. 17, 32; m. 57; c. 2. THEORETICAL PHYSICS. A.B, Harvard, 54, A.M, 55, Ph.D.(physics), 59. Instr. PHYSICS, Columbia Univ, 59-62; asst. prof, WAYNE STATE UNIV, 62-66, ASSOC. PROF, 66- Am. Phys. Soc. Stochastic processes; statistical theory of energy levels; coherent processes in particle beams. Address: Dept. of Physics, Wayne State University, Detroit, MI 48202.

FAVSTRITSKY, NICOLAI A(LEXANDER), U.S. citizen; m. 70. ORGANIC & PHYSICAL CHEMISTRY. B.S, Univ. Calif, Berkeley, 63; M.S, Yale, 65; Ph.D.(phys. org. chem), Ore. State Univ, 69. RES. CHEMIST, CELANESE CHEM. CO, 69- Am. Chem. Soc. Organic sulfur mechanisms; hydrogenation of organic compounds; industrial organic processes; emulsion polymerizations. Address: Technical Center, Celanese Chemical Co, P.O. Box 9077, Corpus Christi, TX 78408.

FAW, RICHARD E, b. Adams Co, Ohio, June 22, 36; m. 61; c. 2. CHEMICAL & NUCLEAR ENGINEERING. B.S, Cincinnati, 59; Atomic Energy Cmn. fel, Minnesota, 60-61, Ph.D.(chem. eng), 62. Asst. prof. NUCLEAR ENG, KANS. STATE UNIV, 62-66, assoc. prof, 66-68, PROF, 68- U.S.A, 62-64, Res, 64-, Capt. Am. Nuclear Soc; Am. Chem. Soc; Am. Soc. Eng. Educ. Radiation transport theory; radiation shielding; radiation chemistry. Address: 1100 Thurston St, Manhattan, KS 66502.

FAW, WADE F(ARRIS), b. Eubank, Ky, Feb. 23, 42; m. 65; c. 1. AGRONOMY, PLANT PHYSIOLOGY. B.S, Berea Col, 65; Nat. Defense Educ. Act fel, W.Va. Univ, 65-68, univ. res. assistantship, 68-69, Ph.D.(agron), 69. Trainee farm planning, U.S. Soil Conserv. Serv, 63-65; ASST. PROF. AGRON, RICE BR. EXP. STA, UNIV. ARK, 69- Am. Soc. Agron; Crop Sci. Soc. Am. Response of plants to their environment; physiology of grain and forage crops. Address: Rice Branch Experiment Station, University of Arkansas, P.O. Box 351, Stuttgart, AR 72160.

FAWAZ, GEORGE, b. Deirmimas, Lebanon, Nov. 22, 13; nat; m. 46; c. 2. PHARMACOLOGY, BIOCHEMISTRY. A.B, American Univ, Beirut, 33, M.S, 35; Ph.D.(org. chem), Graz, Austria, 36; Göttingen, 37-38; M.D, Heidelberg, 55. Instr. biochem, AMERICAN UNIV. BEIRUT, 39-42, asst. prof, 42-49, assoc. prof. PHARMACOL, 49-53, PROF, 53- Rockefeller fel, Harvard, 46-47. Soc. Exp. Biol. & Med; Ger. Pharmacol. Soc. Organic phosphorus compounds of biological interest; cardiac and renal pharmacology and metabolism; synthetic antimalarials. Address: Dept. of Pharmacology, American University of Beirut, Beirut, Lebanon.

FAWAZ-ESTRUP, FAIZA, Biophys, Molecular Biol, see ESTRUP, FAIZA FAWAZ.

FAWCETT, COLVIN PETER, b. Blyth, Eng, Feb. 16, 35; m. 61; c. 2. BIOLOGICAL CHEMISTRY, ENDOCRINOLOGY. B.Sc, Univ. Durham, 56; Ph.D. (org. chem), Univ. Newcastle, 59. Fel, biochem, Brandeis Univ, 59-61; mem. sci. staff, Nat. Inst. Med. Res, Eng, 61-66; vis. asst. prof, neurochem, West. Reserve Univ, 66-67, ASST. PROF. PHYSIOL, SOUTHWEST. MED. SCH, UNIV. TEX, DALLAS, 67- Brit. Biochem. Soc; Endocrine Soc. Biochemistry of neurohypophysial function; control of hormonal secretion from anterior pituitary; isolation and characterization of hypophysiotrophic hormones from the hypothalamus particularly the gonadotropin releasing factors. Address: Dept. of Physiology, Southwestern Medical School, University of Texas, Dallas, TX 75235.

FAWCETT, DON WAYNE, b. Springdale, Iowa, Mar. 14, 17; m. 42; c. 4. ANATOMY, HISTOLOGY. A.B, Harvard, 38, M.D, 42. Surg. intern, Mass. Gen. Hosp, 42-43; res. fel. ANAT, Harvard Med. Sch, 46, instr, 46-47, assoc, 47-51, asst. prof, 51-55; prof. & head dept, med. col, Cornell, 55-59; HERSEY PROF. & HEAD DEPT, HARVARD MED. SCH, 59-, JAMES STILLMAN PROF. COMP. ANAT, 62-, curator, Warren Anat. Mus, 61-70. Markle scholar. med. sci, 49-54; Lederle med. faculty award, 54-56; consult, Nat. Insts. Health, 55-59, 64-; Ferris lectr, Yale, 57; Phillips lectr, Haverford Col, 58; Christiana Smith lectr, Mt. Holyoke Col, 66; Charnock Bradley lectr, Royal (Dick) Sch. Vet. Studies, Edinburgh, Sigmund Pollitzer lectr, N.Y. Univ. & Adam Miller lectr, State Univ. N.Y. Downstate Med. Ctr, 69; Robert Terry lectr, sch. med, Wash. Univ, Daniel Kempner lectr, Univ. Tex. Med. Br. Galveston, Harold Chaffer lectr, Univ. Otago, N.Z. & Sigma Xi nat. lectr, 70. Med.C, A.U.S, 43-45, Capt. Am. Soc. Zool; Histochem. Soc; Electron Micros. Soc. Am; Soc. Exp. Biol. & Med; Am. Soc. Mammal; Soc. Develop. Biol; Am. Asn. Anat.(1st v.pres, 59-60, pres, 65-66); Tissue Culture Asn.(v.pres, 54-55); fel. Am. Acad. Arts & Sci; Am. Soc. Cell Biol.(pres, 61-62) Int. Soc. Cell Biol; hon. fel. Royal Micros. Soc; hon. mem. Mex. Soc. Anat; hon. mem. Can. Asn. Anat; hon. assoc. mem. Anat. Soc. Gt. Brit. & Ireland; Soc. Study Reproduction. Electron microscopy; cytology; growth and differentiation; spermatogenesis; histophysiology of male reproductive tract; ultrastructure of cardiac muscle; ultrastructure liver. Address: Dept. of Anatomy, Harvard Medical School, Boston, MA 02115.

FAWCETT, EDWIN B(ABCOCK), b. Glen Ridge, N.J, July 9, 21; m. 57; c. 3. METEOROLOGY. A.B, Hamilton Col, 43; cert. meteorol, Chicago, 44. Meteorologist, seven day forecasting sect, U.S. WEATHER BUR, 46-50, supvr. meteorologist, Air Force Weather Center, 50-54, chief analyst, joint numerical weather prediction unit, 54-57, consult, hqs. air weather serv, 57-61, NAT. METEOROL. CENTER, 61-64, head forecast br, 64-69, dep. chief ANAL. & FORECAST DIV, 69-70, CHIEF, 70- U.S.A.A.F, 44-46, Lt. Col. Am. Meteorol. Soc. Seven day forecasting methods; synoptic meteorology; numerical prediction techniques. Address: 5511 Lorraine Dr, Camp Springs, MD 20031.

FAWCETT, ERIC, b. Blackburn, Eng, Aug. 23, 27; m. 54; c. 3. PHYSICS. M.A, Cambridge, 52, Ph.D.(physics), 54. Fel, div. low temperature & solid state physics, Nat. Res. Coun. Can, 54-56; sci. officer PHYSICS, Royal Radar Estab, Eng, 56-61; mem. tech. staff, Bell Tel. Labs, Inc, 61-70; PROF, UNIV. TORONTO, 70- R.N, Pilot Off. Am. Phys. Soc; Can. Asn. Physicists; fel. Brit. Inst. Physics & Phys. Soc. Experimental study of electronic structure of metals, including measurements of anomalous skin effect; cyclotron resonance; high-field galvanomagnetic effects especially in ferromagnetic metals; magnetostriction and thermal expansion in metals. Address: Dept. of Physics, University of Toronto, Toronto 12, Ont, Can.

FAWCETT, FRANK S(HUMATE), b. Greenville, S.C, Nov. 16, 19; m. 43; c. 2. ORGANIC CHEMISTRY. B.S, Furman, 40; M.S, Pennsylvania, 44; univ. fel, Mass. Inst. Tech, 46-47, Socony-Vacuum fel, 47, Du Pont fel, 47-48, Ph.D. (org. chem), 48. Jr. sci. aide, soil conserv. serv, U.S. Dept. Agr, S.C, 39-40; RES. CHEMIST, res. & develop. div, Socony-Vacuum Oil Co, N.J, 40-46; CENT. RES. DEPT, E.I. DU PONT DE NEMOURS & CO, INC, 48- Am. Chem. Soc; Sci. Res. Soc. Am. Side chain brominations; physical properties of thiophenes; synthesis of cyclic polyolefins; bridged-ring olefins; heterogeneous catalysis and hydrogenation; synthetic organic chemistry; fluorine chemistry. Address: Central Research Dept, Experimental Station, E.I. du Pont de Nemours & Co, Inc, Wilmington, DE 19898.

FAWCETT, JAMES JEFFREY, b. Blyth, Eng, July 6, 36; m. 60; c. 2. GEOLOGY. B.Sc, Manchester, 57, Ph.D.(geol), 61; Rotary Int. Found. fel, Pa. State, 59-60. Asst. geol, Manchester, 60-61; fel, Carnegie Inst. Geophys. Lab, 61-64; ASSOC. PROF. GEOL, UNIV. TORONTO, 64-, ASSOC. CHMN. DEPT, 70- Am. Geophys. Union; Mineral. Soc. Am; Mineral. Soc. Gt. Brit. & Ireland; Mineral. Asn. Can. Application of high temperature and pressure studies of rocks and minerals to problems of basalt petrogenesis; evolution of basaltic magmas and metamorphic rocks. Address: Dept. of Geology, University of Toronto, Toronto 5, Ont, Can.

FAWCETT, MARK S(TANLEY) b. Jamestown, N.Dak, Oct. 17, 32. ORGANIC CHEMISTRY. B.S, Northwestern, 54; Nat. Sci. Found. fel, Minnesota, 54-58, Ph.D.(org. chem), 58. Res. chemist, elastomers dept, E.I. DU PONT DE NEMOURS & CO, INC, 58-64, mkt. develop. asst, 64-70, MEM. STAFF MKT. RES, WILMINGTON, 70- Am. Chem. Soc. Structure of polyphenyl cyclopentadienes; elastomeric polymers. Address: R.D. 1, Box 426 E, Hockessin, DE 19707.

FAWCETT, ROBERT J(AMES), b. Walbridge, Ohio, June 9, 26; m. 50; c. 3. ORGANIC & POLYMER CHEMISTRY. B.S, Bowling Green State, 50; Ph.D. (org. chem), Mich. State, 57. Asst, Mich. State, 50-55; tech. chemist, org. chem, res. center, B.F. GOODRICH CO, 55-57, sr. tech. chemist, 57-60, proj. leader, 59-60, sect. leader polymer chem, 60-63, mgr, chem. res, RES. CTR, 63-68, DIR. MAT. RES, 68- Summers, asst, Wyeth, Inc, 52; eng. labs, Mich. State, 54. U.S.N, 44-46. Am. Chem. Soc. Elastomer and plastics research; polymers; monomers; organic chemistry mechanisms; polymer chemicals; new chemical processes; antioxidants; antizonants; rubber cure accelerators; curing agents; technological forecasting. Address: B.F. Goodrich Research Center, B.F. Goodrich Co, 9921 Brecksville Rd, Brecksville, OH 44141.

FAWCETT, S(HERWOOD) L(UTHER), b. Youngstown, Ohio, Dec. 25, 19; m. 53; c. 3. PHYSICS. B.S, Ohio State, 41; M.S, Case, 48, Atomic Energy Comn. fel. & Ph.D.(physics), 50. Instr. physics, Case, 46-48; physicist, BATTELLE MEM. INST, 50-52, asst. chief eng. mech. div, 52-54, chief, 54-57, asst. mgr. physics dept, 57-60, mgr, 60-62, metall. & physics dept, 62-64, dir. Pac. Northwest Lab, Wash, 65-67, exec. v.pres, inst, 67-68, PRES, 68- U.S.N, 41-46, Comdr. Am. Phys. Soc; Am. Nuclear Soc; Am. Soc. Metals; Am. Mgt. Asn. Reactor engineering; heat transfer; fluid flow; methods of electronic beam ejection from Betatrons; reactor irradiation experiments on reactor fuel elements. Address: Battelle Memorial Institute, 505 King Ave, Columbus, OH 43201.

FAX, D(AVID) H(IRSCH), b. Baltimore, Md, Oct. 4, 19; m. 42; c. 2. MECHANICAL ENGINEERING. B.E, Hopkins, 38. Engr, Allis-Chalmers Mfg. Co, Wis, 43-46; asst. prof. mech. eng, Hopkins, 46-54; adv. engr, atomic power dept, WESTINGHOUSE ELEC. CORP, 54-55, asst. to proj. mgr, 55-59, mgr. plant develop, 59, adv. develop, 59-61, consult. astronuclear Lab, 61-63, tech. asst. to v.pres. eng, 63-67, DIR. ENG. CONSULT, HQ. ENG, 67- Consult, Navy Eng. Exp. Sta, Md, 46-54; Atomic Energy Comn; Oak Ridge Nat. Lab. AAAS; Am. Soc. Mech. Eng; Am. Inst. Aeronaut. & Astronaut. Heat power, particularly area of atomic power and nuclear reactor systems. Address: Westinghouse Electric Corp, Westinghouse Bldg, Gateway Center, Pittsburgh, PA 15222.

FAXON, ROBERT, b. Ipswich, Mass, Apr. 4, 36; m. 57; c. 3. PHYSICAL INORGANIC CHEMISTRY. B.S. & A.B, East. Nazarene Col, 61; Ph.D.(chem), Syracuse, 66. MEM. TECH. STAFF RES. & DEVELOP, METALS & CONTROLS DIV, TEX. INSTRUMENTS INC, 65- U.S.N, 57-59. Ceramic materials. Address: 217 Pike Ave, Attleboro, MA 02703.

FAY, DOUGLAS P(AUL), b. Fayette, Iowa, Aug. 14, 43; m. 66; c. 1. INORGANIC CHEMISTRY. B.S, Upper Iowa Univ, 65; NASA fel, Okla. State Univ, 66-69, Ph.D.(inorg. chem), 69. Res. assoc. reaction kinetics, Brookhaven Nat. Lab, 69-71; V.PRES. RES. & DEVELOP, ALVA RES. CORP, 71- Am. Chem. Soc. Kinetics of electron-transfer and complex formation reactions; thermodynamics of complex formation of the lanthanide ions. Address: Alva Research Corp, P.O. Box 803, Alva, OK 73717.

FAY, EDWARD A(LLEN), b. Berkeley, Calif, Aug. 13, 18; m. 44; c. 3. MATHEMATICAL STATISTICS. A.B, California, 39; A.M, Harvard, 41; Ph.D.(math), Florida, 62. RES. MATH. STATISTICIAN, NAVAL UNDERWATER WEAPONS CTR, U.S. NAVAL ORD. TEST STA, 50- U.S.A, 43-46. Am. Math. Soc; Sci. Res. Soc. Am; Math. Asn. Am; Inst. Math. Statist. Combinatorial theory; stochastic processes; applications of statistical theory to industrial inspection. Address: 611 Saratoga Ave, China Lake, CA 93555.

FAY, FRANCIS H(OLLIS), b. Melrose, Mass, Nov. 18, 27; m. 52; c. 2. MAMMOLOGY, ORNITHOLOGY. B.S, New Hampshire, 50, fel, Massachusetts,

49-51, M.S, 52; fel, British Columbia, 51-55, Ph.D.(vert. zool), 55. Med. biologist, ARCTIC HEALTH RES. CTR, 55-67; RES. BIOLOGIST, U.S. PUB. HEALTH SERV, 67- Fel. AAAS; Am. Polar Soc; Am. Inst. Biol. Sci; Am. Soc. Mammal; Wildlife Soc; Ecol. Soc. Am; Am. Soc. Parasitol; Wildlife Disease Asn; fel. Arctic Inst. N.Am. Biology of pinnipeds; vertebrate populations; animal ecology. Address: Arctic Health Research Center, U.S. Public Health Service, College, AK 99701.

FAY, HOMER, b. Brooklyn, N.Y, Aug. 3, 28; m. 55; c. 2. MATERIALS SCIENCE. A.B, Bowdoin Col, 49; Ph.D.(chem), Mass. Inst. Tech, 53. Asst. anal. chem, Mass. Inst. Tech, 50-53; chemist, UNION CARBIDE CORP, 53-70, SR. SCIENTIST, RES. INST, TARRYTOWN, 70- Chemist, Ionics, Inc, 51. U.S.A, 46-48, Res, 48-51. AAAS; Am. Chem. Soc; Am. Phys. Soc. Solid state materials synthesis and properties; dielectrics and ferroelectrics; phase transitions and crystal structure. Address: R.F.D. 2, Box 200, Katonah, NY 10536.

FAY, JAMES A(LAN), b. Southold, N.Y, Nov. 1, 23; m. 46; c. 6. MECHANICAL ENGINEERING. B.S, Webb Inst. Naval Archit, 44; Soc. Naval Archit. scholar, Mass. Inst. Technol, 46-47, M.S, 47; Du Pont fel, Cornell, 49-50, Ph.D.(mech. eng), 51. Res. engr, Lima-Hamilton Corp, 47-49; asst. prof. eng. mech, Cornell, 51-55; PROF, MECH. ENG, MASS. INST. TECHNOL, 55- Consult, Am. Locomotive Co, 50-55; Avco Everett Res. Lab, 55-71; chmn, Boston Air Pollution Control Comn, 69- U.S.N.R, 43-46. Am. Soc. Mech. Eng; fel. Am. Phys. Soc; fel. Am. Inst. Aeronaut. & Astronaut; Air Pollution Control Asn; fel. Am. Acad. Arts & Sci. Gaseous detonations; hypersonic heat transfer; magnetohydrodynamics; plasma physics; high temperature gas dynamics; ionization phenomena; air and oil pollution. Address: Dept. of Mechanical Engineering, Massachusetts Institute of Technology, Cambridge, MA 02139.

FAY, MARCUS J, b. Adair, Iowa, July 5, 21; m. 44; c. 2. PLANT TAXONOMY. Ph.D.(bot), Iowa, 53. Asst, Iowa, 49-53, instr, 53; asst. prof. BIOL, WIS. STATE UNIV-EAU CLAIRE, 53-55, assoc. prof, 55-57, PROF, 57-, head dept, 57-70. U.S.A.A.F, 42-46, 1st Lt. Bot. Soc. Am; Am. Soc. Plant Taxon. Floristics and plant distribution studies. Address: Dept. of Biology, Wisconsin State University-Eau Claire, Eau Claire, WI 54701.

FAY, PHILIP S, b. Ballard, Wash, Jan. 24, 21; m. 42; c. 3. PETROLEUM. A.B, Cornell, 41; Standard Oil Co. fel, 41-42, 46-48, Ph.D.(chem), Western Reserve, 49. PROJ. LEADER, CHEM. & PHYS. RES. DIV, STANDARD OIL CO.(OHIO), 42-44, 49- U.S.N.R, 44-46. Am. Chem. Soc. Reaction of phosphorous pentasulfide with olefins; gasoline composition; combustion chamber deposits; reaction of hydrocarbons; organoboron chemistry; petrochemicals. Address: Standard Oil Co. of Ohio, 4440 Warrensville Rd, Cleveland, OH 44128.

FAY, RICHARD W(ILLIAM), b. Huron, S.Dak, Oct. 1, 12; m. 41; c. 3. ENTOMOLOGY. B.S, Iowa State Col, 34, fel, 34-35, M.S, 35; Ill. Natural Hist. Surv. fel, Illinois, 36-39, Ph.D.(entom), 40. Asst. econ. entom, Illinois, 35-38; entomologist, W.B. McCloud Co, 39-40; paint chemist, A. Pierce Gregg Co, Pa, 40-42; jr. entomologist, malaria control in war areas, U.S. Pub. Health Serv, 42-43, asst. sanitarian, Mo, 43-44, in charge lab. develop. of DDT, 44-45, asst. sanitarian in charge res. projs, tech. develop. div, 46-48, sanitarian in charge insecticide invest, 48-50, entomologist & asst. chief biol. sect, 53-59; biologist, environ. sanit. div, WHO, 59-61; asst. chief, TECH. DEVELOP. LAB, U.S. PUB. HEALTH SERV, 61-63, res. entomologist, 63-66, CHIEF BIOL. RES. UNIT, BIOL. SECT, CTR. DISEASE CONTROL, 66- Consult, WHO, Egypt, 54 & 57; Agency Int. Develop, Africa, 63, Cent. Am, 64. Entom. Soc. Am; Sci. Res. Soc. Am; Am. Mosquito Control Asn; Am. Soc. Trop. Med. & Hyg. Insecticides for insects of medical importance; insect physiology; insecticide resistance. Address: Biology Section, Technical Development Lab, Center for Disease Control, U.S. Public Health Service, P.O. Box 2167, Savannah, GA 31402.

FAY, RIMMON C, b. Santa Monica, Calif, July 22, 29; m. 58; c. 4. BIOCHEMISTRY, BACTERIOLOGY. B.A, California, Los Angeles, 53, Ph.D. (biochem), 61. Res. assoc. marine chem, Southern California, 61-64; consult. oceanog, County Sanit. Dist, Orange County, Calif, 64-66; OWNER & MGR, PAC. BIO-MARINE SUPPLY CO, 66- AAAS; Am. Soc. Limnol. & Oceanog; Am. Inst. Biol. Sci; Int. Asn. Water Pollution Res. Energy transfer mechanisms in organisms; natural history of marine organisms; methods of control of water pollution; biochemical processes in bacteria and marine organisms. Address: Pacific Bio-Marine Supply Co, P.O. Box 536, Venice, CA 90291.

FAY, ROBERT C(LINTON), b. Kenosha, Wis, Mar. 14, 36; m. 60. INORGANIC CHEMISTRY. A.B, Oberlin Col, 57; Wheaton Col.(Ill), 57-58; M.S, Illinois, 60, Dow Chem. Co. fel, 59-60, Nat. Sci. Found. fel, 60-62, Ph.D. (inorg. chem), 62. Asst. prof. CHEM, CORNELL UNIV, 62-68, ASSOC. PROF, 68- Nat. Sci. Found. faculty fel, Univ. E. Anglia & Univ. Sussex, 69-70. Am. Chem. Soc; The Chem. Soc; Am. Crystallog. Asn. Stereochemistry of metal complexes; applications of nuclear magnetic resonance spectroscopy to inorganic chemistry. Address: 318 Eastwood Ave, Ithaca, NY 14850.

FAY, ROBERT O(RAN), b. St. Louis, Mo, Mar. 4, 27; m. 66; c. 1. GEOLOGY. A.B, Washington (St. Louis), 49; Ph.D, Kansas, 61. GEOLOGIST, OKLA. GEOL. SURV, 56- Asst. prof, Oklahoma, 56-61. U.S.A, 45-46. AAAS. Tectonics; stratigraphy; paleontology; environmental geology. Address: Oklahoma Geological Survey, Norman, OK 73069.

FAY, WARREN H(ENRY), b. Scottsbluff, Nebr, Jan. 3, 29; m. 52; c. 1. SPEECH PATHOLOGY, AUDIOLOGY. B.A, Colo. State Col, 51; M.Ed, Oregon, 59; Purdue Res. Found. grant, Purdue, 62, Ph.D.(speech path, audiol), 63. Instr, high sch, Ore, 56-58; speech therapist, pub. schs, 58-60; instr. SPEECH PATH MED. SCH, UNIV. ORE, 62-67, ASSOC. PROF, 67- Mem. speech, lang. & hearing subcomt, Nat. Inst. Neurol. Disease & Blindness, 62-68. U.S.N, 51-55. AAAS; Am. Speech & Hearing Asn. Physiological aspects of language development and disorders, especially in the areas of echolalia and temporal coding of linguistic units. Address: University of Oregon Medical School, Portland, OR 97201.

FAYERWEATHER, B(RUCE) L(ELAND), b. Saginaw, Mich, Apr. 18, 09; m. 30; c. 4. ORGANIC & BIOLOGICAL CHEMISTRY. B.S, Mich. State, 31, M.S, 32. Res. org. chemist, Dow Chem. Co, 32-35, patent attorney, 35-57, asst. dir. patent dept, 57-63, mgr. inventions develop, 63-66, asst. dir. patent dept, 66-71; RETIRED. Am. Chem. Soc; fel. Am. Inst. Chem. Agricultural chemistry; biochemistry; bacteriology; patent law; exploitation technology. Address: 4309 James Dr, Midland, MI 48640.

FAYLE, HARLAN D(OWNING), b. Hibbing, Minn, July 24, 07; m. 36; c. 1. BIOCHEMISTRY, PHARMACOLOGY. B.A, Hamline, 31; M.S, Minnesota, 36, Ph.D.(biochem, pharmacol), 63. Instr. CHEM, Eveleth Jr. Col, 33-36; Hibbing Jr. Col, 36-46; Duluth Jr. Col, 46-48; Minnesota, Duluth, 48-54, asst. prof, 55-56, asst, Minneapolis, 54-55; assoc. prof. PURDUE UNIV, CALUMET CAMPUS, 56-65, PROF, 65-, CHMN. SECT, 56- Consult, Butler Mining Co, 40-42; Elliott Packing Co, 48-50; Mitchell Oil Co, 50-51. AAAS; Am. Chem. Soc; fel. Am. Inst. Chem; N.Y. Acad. Sci. Distribution and determination of cadmium in biological material; toxicology of cadmium. Address: Chemistry Section, Purdue University, Calumet Campus, 2233 171st St, Hammond, IN 46323.

FAYMON, KARL A(LOIS), b. St. Louis, Mo, Sept. 9, 27; m. 60; c. 2. SYSTEMS ANALYSIS. B.S, Michigan, 51, M.S, 52; Ph.D.(aerodyn), Case, 57. Instr, St. Louis, 52-53; instr. & asst, Case, 53-57; theoret. aerodynamicist, Convair Div, Gen. Dynamics Corp, 57-60; systs. analyst, Thompson-Ramo-Wooldridge, Inc, 60-63; CHIEF SYSTS. ANAL. OFF, LAUNCH VEHICLES DIV, LEWIS RES. CTR, NASA, CLEVELAND, 63- U.S.M.C, 45-46. Trajectory analysis; thermodynamics; applied mathematics; space launch vehicles systems analysis; structural and control dynamics. Address: 2066 Marshfield Rd, Mayfield Heights, OH 44124.

FAYON, A(BRAM) MIKO, b. Sofia, Bulgaria, Apr. 1, 20; U.S. citizen; m. 58; c. 3. CHEMICAL ENGINEERING. B.S, Istanbul, 47; M.S.E, Hopkins, 52; Texas Co. fel, N.Y. Univ, 54-56, Eng.Sc.D.(chem. eng), 59. Chemist, Baltimore Paint & Color Works, 48-51; chem. engr. res. & develop, U.S. Indust. Chem, 51-52; Chem. Construct. Corp, 52-54; asst. chem. eng, N.Y. Univ, 56-57, instr, 57-59, asst. prof, 59-60; res. chem. engr, Am. Cyanamid Co, Conn, 60-62, sr. res. chem. engr, 62-65; sr. process engr, Sci. Design Co, Inc, 65-66; assoc. engr, Mobil Oil Corp, 66-67, Mobil Res. & Develop. Corp, 67-70, OPERS. RES. COORD, MOBIL CHEM, CO, N.Y.C, 70- Consult, nuclear energy prods. div, Am. Car & Foundry, 56-57. Am. Inst. Chem. Eng; Am. Chem. Soc. Thermodynamics; heat transfer; fluid flow; combustion of solid propellants and evaluation of their ballistic properties and behavior in motors; high temperature reactions; process simulation of petroleum and petrochemical plants; development of computer methods related to process and process design problems. Address: 510 Siwanoy Pl, Pelham Manor, NY 10803.

FAYOS, JUAN VALLVEY, b. Camaguey, Cuba, Nov. 24, 29; U.S. citizen; m. 61; c. 4. RADIOLOGY. B.S, Inst. de Camaguey, 48; M.D, Havana, 55. Instr. RADIOL, UNIV. MICH, 61-63, asst. prof, 63-67, ASSOC. PROF, 67- Mem. staff, Wayne County Gen. Hosp, 66- Am. Med. Asn; Radiol. Soc. N.Am; Am. Soc. Therapeut. Radiol. Clinical radiation therapy. Address: 1805 Ivywood Dr, Ann Arbor, MI 48103.

FAZEKAS, GABRIEL ANDREW GEORGE, b. Kalocsa, Hungary, Mar. 16, 11; U.S. citizen; m. 42; c. 2. MECHANICAL ENGINEERING. Dipl. mech. eng, Swiss Fed. Inst. Tech, 34; Nat. Sci. Found. fel, Courant Inst. Math. Sci, N.Y. Univ, 62-63. Tech. sales engr, Ganz & Co. Ltd, Hungary, 34-38; asst. ed, Engrs. Digest, England, 38-39; design engr, Nat. Gas & Oil Co. Ltd, 39-42; sr. engr. develop, Rover Co. Ltd, 42-44; supvr. res, Lockheed Hydraulic Brake Co. Ltd, 44-47; asst. chief engr, Girlling Ltd, 47-51; PROF. MECH. ENG, Polytech. Inst. Brooklyn, 52-64; UNIV. HOUSTON, 64- Consult, B.F. Goodrich Co, Ohio, 55; mgr. mech. eng, Am. Mach. & Foundry Co, Conn, 57-59; consult, Bell Tel. Labs, N.J, 59; Airborne Industs, 61; Bostitch Inc, 62; Tungsol Inc, 63; guest lectr, Mass. Inst. Technol, 63; Fulbright fel, Cath. Univ. Rio de Janeiro, 64-65; consult, Mohasco Industs, 67; Dresser Instruments, 69. Am. Soc. Mech. Eng; Am. Soc. Eng. Educ; Brit. Inst. Mech. Eng. Tribomechanics and lubrication; mechanical design; patent matters. Address: Dept. of Mechanical Engineering, University of Houston, Cullen Blvd, Houston, TX 77004.

FAZIO, GIOVANNI G(ENE), b. San Antonio, Tex, May 26, 33; m. 59; c. 2. PHYSICS, ASTRONOMY. B.S. & B.A, St. Mary's, 54; Ph.D.(physics), Mass. Inst. Tech, 59. Res. assoc, Rochester, 59, instr. physics, 59-61, asst. prof, 61-62; PHYSICIST, SMITHSONIAN ASTROPHYS. OBSERV, 62-; LECTR. ASTRON, HARVARD, 62- Mem, Int. Astron. Union; summers, physicist, Naval Res. Lab, 55, 56. AAAS; Am. Astron. Soc; Am. Phys. Soc; fel. Royal Astron. Soc. Cosmic ray physics; gamma ray astronomy. Address: Smithsonian Astrophysical Observatory, 60 Garden St, Cambridge, MA 02138.

FAZIO, PAUL P(ALMERINO), b. Italy, Apr. 1, 39; Can. citizen; m. 66; c. 2. SOLID MECHANICS. B.A.Sc, Univ. Windsor, 63, M.A.Sc, 64, Ph.D.(struct), 68. Sessional instr, Univ. Windsor, 64-67; asst. prof. CIVIL ENG, SIR GEORGE WILLIAMS UNIV, 67-69, ASSOC. PROF, 70-, DIR, SYST. BLDG. CTR, 71- Jr. struct. eng, Can. Bridge Co, 63; struct. eng, Montreal Eng. Co, 68; mem. cent. comt, Can. Cong. Appl. Mech, 71-, chmn. papers comt, 71- Am. Soc. Civil Eng; Eng. Inst. Can.(Galbraith Prize, 67); Am. Concrete Inst; Am. Soc. Eng. Educ; Soc. Exp. Stress Anal; Int. Asn. Shell Struct; Am. Acad. Mech. Structures, especially structural analysis and design of folded plates, sandwich elements, panel connections and panelized building systems; development of wall panels; panel connections. Address: 118 Ashington Rd, Pointe Claire, Que, Can.

FAZIO, STEVE, b. Phoenix, Ariz, Sept. 2, 16; m. 40; c. 2. HORTICULTURE. B.S, Arizona, 40, M.S, 51. PROF. HORT, UNIV. ARIZ, 64-, HEAD DEPT, 65- Am. Soc. Hort. Sci; Int. Plant Propagators Soc. Propagation of woody and herbaceous plants in arid desert regions. Address: 3554 E. Calle Alarcon, Tucson, AZ 85716.

FEAD, JOHN WILLIAM NORMAN, b. Wetaskiwin, Alta, Can, Oct. 23, 23; m. 47; c. 3. CIVIL ENGINEERING. B.S, Alberta, 45, M.S, 49; Cabell fel,

Northwestern, 53-54, Ph.D, 57. Instr. civil eng, Alberta, 46-48; Saskatchewan, 48-49; S.Dak. State Col, 49-50, asst. prof, 50-51, assoc. prof, 55-57; lectr, Northwestern, 51-53; assoc. civil eng. & asst. res. engr, inst. transportation & traffic eng, California, 54-55; assoc. prof. CIVIL ENG, COLO. STATE UNIV, 57-61, PROF, 61-, HEAD DEPT, 65- Mem. city coun, Ft. Collins, Colo, 71- Am. Soc. Civil Eng; Am. Soc. Eng. Educ; Am. Concrete Inst. Structures and structural mechanics; soil mechanics and foundations. Address: Dept. of Civil Engineering, Colorado State University, Ft. Collins, CO 80521.

FEAGANS, WILLIAM MARION, b. Fortescue, Mo, Feb. 2, 27; m. 50; c. 3. ANATOMY. D.D.S, Missouri-Kansas City, 54; A.D. Williams fel, Med. Col. Va, 56-57, Nat. Insts. Health grant, 56-58, Ph.D.(anat), 60. Instr. clin. dent, sch. dent, Missouri-Kansas City, 54-55, asst. prof, 55-56; instr. anat, Med. Col. Va, 58-60, asst. prof, 60-63, assoc. prof, 63-66, curriculum coord. med. ed, 64-66; assoc. prof. anat, schs. med. & dent. med, Tufts, 66-70, asst. dean sch. dent. med, 66-69, assoc. dean, 69-70; PROF. ANAT, SCH. MED. & DEAN SCH. DENT, STATE UNIV. N.Y. BUFFALO, 70- Consult, surg. serv, U.S. Naval Hosp, Va, 58-66, dent. serv, 60-66. Histochem. Soc; Am. Asn. Anat; N.Y. Acad. Sci. Physiology of male reproduction; histochemistry and electron microscopy of oral tissues. Address: School of Dentistry, 143 Capen Hall, State University of New York at Buffalo, Buffalo, NY 14214.

FEAGIN, FRANK J, b. Kaufman, Texas, March 14, 14; m. 36; c. 3. GEOPHYSICS. B.S.E.E, Agr. & Mech. Col. Texas, 34. Asst. elec. eng, Agr. & Mech. Col. Texas, 34-35; attached helper, seismog. party, Humble Oil & Ref. Co, 35-37, seismog. operator, 37-41; asst. prof. elec. eng, Agr. & Mech. Col, Texas, 41-42; electronic develop. work, war contracts, Humble Oil & Ref. Co, 42-46, res. specialist, 46-54, sr. res. specialist, geophysics res. sect, 54-57, asst. chief geophysics res, 57-60, chief geophys. res. & eng. sect, 60-64; mgr. appl. geophys. div, ESSO PROD. RES. CO, 64-66, SR. RES. ASSOC, 66- Soc. Explor. Geophys; Inst. Elec. & Electronics Eng. Geophysical instruments; research management. Address: Esso Production Research Co, Box 2189, Houston, TX 77001.

FEAGIN, FREDERICK F, b. Pike Co, Ala, Nov. 22, 31; m; c. 2. DENTISTRY. B.S, Auburn Univ, 58; D.M.D, Univ. Ala, Birmingham, 64, Ph.D.(physiol, pharmacol), 69. Res. asst, SCH. DENT. UNIV. ALA. BIRMINGHAM, 60-64, res. assoc. & instr. CLIN. DENT, 65-69, ASST. PROF, 69-, INVESTR, INST. DENT. RES, 69-, ASST. PROF. PHYSIOL. & BIOPHYS, GRAD. FACULTY, UNIV, 69- Staff dentist & prin. investr, Vet. Admin. Hosp, Birmingham, Ala, 68-69, clin. investr, 69- Int. Asn. Dent. Res. Mechanisms of biological calcifications. Address: Dept. of Physiology & Biophysics, University of Alabama in Birmingham, 1919 Seventh Ave, South Birmingham, AL 35233.

FEAGIN, ROY C(HESTER), b. Andersonville, Ga, July 23, 14; m. 38; c. 2. CHEMICAL ENGINEERING. B.S, Ala. Polytech, 36, M.S, 37. Res. chemist, Gen. Elec. Co, N.Y, 37-39; Austenal Microcast Div, HOWMET CORP, 39-45, chief chemist, 45-56, mgr. chem. res, 56-67, assoc. res. dir, 67-68, MGR. INT. OPERS, SUPERALLOY GROUP, 68- Am. Chem. Soc; Am. Ceramic Soc; Int. Asn. Dent. Res; Am. Soc. Test. & Mat. Development of compositions and applications of plastics, cements, refractories to dental and high temperature alloy casting field. Address: Superalloy Group, Howmet Corp, 221 W. Webster Ave, Muskegon, MI 49440.

FEAIRHELLER, STEPHEN HENRY, b. Philadelphia, Pa, Nov. 4, 33; m. 59; c. 3. ORGANIC CHEMISTRY. B.S, Pa. State, 60; Nat. Sci. Found. fel, Mass. Inst. Tech, 62, Ph.D.(org. chem), 64. Res. chemist, East. Utilization Res. & Develop. Div, U.S. Dept. Agr, 64-69; asst. prof. chem, Ogontz Campus, Pa. State Univ, 69-70; RES. SCIENTIST, EAST. REGIONAL RES. LAB, U.S. DEPT. AGR, 70- U.S.A, 54-56. Am. Chem. Soc. Chemical modification of proteins. Address: Eastern Regional Research Lab, U.S. Dept. of Agriculture, 600 E. Mermaid Lane, Philadelphia, PA 19118.

FEAIRHELLER, WILLIAM RUSSELL, JR, b. Camden, N.J, Nov. 25, 31; m. 56; c. 5. PHYSICAL CHEMISTRY. B.A, Rutgers, 54; M.S, Maryland, 58; Delaware, 60-62. Anal. chemist, Am. Viscose Corp, 59-60; chemist, Avisun Corp, 60-63; sr. res. chemist, MONSANTO RES. CORP, 63-68, RES. GROUP LEADER, 68- Coblentz Soc; Soc. Appl. Spectros. Infrared and Raman spectroscopy; molecular structure; fine particle technology. Address: Monsanto Research Corp, Station B, Box 8, Dayton, OH 45407.

FEAKES, FRANK, b. York, Australia, Feb. 2, 23; m. 56; c. 4. CHEMICAL ENGINEERING. B.A, Western Australia, 48, M.Sc, 51, Gledden fel, 51-53, Fulbright fel, 51-52; Sc.D.(chem. eng), Mass. Inst. Technol, 56. Res. chemist, State Alunite Industs, West. Australia, 45-46, chief chemist, 46-48, plant supt, 48-51; res. officer chem. eng, dept. indust. develop, Govt. West. Australia, 57-59; res. assoc, Mass. Inst. Technol, 59-62; sr. chemist, NAT. RES. CORP, NORTON CO, 62-66, prog. dir. chem. eng, 66-68, Norton Res. Corp, 68-70, DIR. ADVAN. MAT. & COMPOSITES, 70- Am. Vacuum Soc; Am. Inst. Chem. Eng. Vacuum technology; production and measurement of low pressure; vapor deposition; thermal decomposition of solids; fluidization; physical adsorption; boron; hydrogen peroxide; composite materials. Address: National Research Corp, 70 Memorial Dr, Cambridge, MA 02142.

FEAR, FRANK A, b. Danville, Ky, Feb. 24, 22. VETERINARY MEDICINE. D.V.M, Texas A&M, 59. Asst. prof. path, col. vet. med, Texas A&M, 59-62; asst. pathologist, dept. animal sci. res, Merck Sharpe & Dohme Res. Labs, N.J, 62-65; CHIEF PATH. SECT, SOUTHWEST. FOUND. RES. & EDUC, 65- Am. Vet. Med. Asn. Address: 602 Prinz Dr, San Antonio, TX 78213.

FEAR, J(AMES) VAN DYCK, b. Morgantown, W.Va, Nov. 7, 25; m. 52; c. 3. CHEMICAL ENGINEERING. B.Ch.E, Louisville, 45, M.Ch.E, 47; advan. mgt. prog, Harvard, 70. Res. engr, SUN OIL CO, 48-60, sect. chief process develop, 60-66, mgr. process develop, 66-71, MGR. RES. & DEVELOP. SPEC. PROJS, 71- U.S.N.R, 42-59, Lt.(jg). Am. Inst. Chem. Eng; Am. Petrol. Inst; Am. Chem. Soc. Development of petroleum processes, especially in lubricating and waxes; hydrogenation and reforming; recovery of tar from Athabasca tar sands. Address: Research & Development Dept, Sun Oil Co, P.O. Box 426, Marcus Hook, PA 19061.

FEARING, HAROLD W, b. Nov. 9, 41. THEORETICAL PHYSICS. B.A, Kansas, 62; Nat. Sci. Found. fel, Stanford, 62-66, Ph.D, 67. Asst. Stanford, 62-64; resident student res. assoc, Argonne Nat. Labs, summer 64; vis. scientist, Europ. Orgn. Nuclear Res, 67-68; RES. ASSOC, STATE UNIV. N.Y. STONY BROOK, 68- Woodrow Wilson fel, 62-63; NATO fel, 67-68; Air Force Off. Sci. Res. fel, 68-69. Am. Phys. Soc. Address: State University of New York at Stony Brook, Stony Brook, NY 11790.

FEARING, OLIN S, b. Lawrence, Kans, Mar. 30, 28; m. 54; c. 2. BOTANY. A.B, Kansas, 50, M.A, 51; Ph.D, Texas, 59. Asst. prof. BIOL, TRINITY UNIV. (TEX), 59-66, ASSOC. PROF, 66- U.S.N.R, 52-60. AAAS; Am. Soc. Plant Taxon; Bot. Soc. Am. Cytotaxonomy of flowering plants; specifically the genus Cologania, Amphicarpaea and related genera; physiology and development of lichen symbionts. Address: Dept. of Biology, Trinity University, 715 Stadium Dr, San Antonio, TX 78212.

FEARING, RALPH B(URTON), b. Oak Park, Ill, Aug. 20, 18; m. 46; c. 2. ORGANIC CHEMISTRY. B.S, Chicago, 40, M.S, 43; Ph.D.(org. chem), Iowa State Col, 51. Res. assoc. war gases, Chicago, 43; anal. chem, Los Alamos Sci. Lab, 44-45; org. synthesis, Monsanto Chem. Co, 46-47; instr. chem, Iowa State Col, 47-51; asst. prof. org. chem, Utica Col, 51-56; res. chemist, Victor Div, STAUFFER CHEM. CO, 57-67, SR. CHEMIST, EAST. RES. LABS, DOBBS FERRY, 67- Organic synthesis; organic phosphorus chemistry; textile finishing chemistry. Address: 80 Barry Lane, Bardonia, NY 10954.

FEARN, JAMES ERNEST, b. Chattanooga, Tenn, Nov. 21, 20; m. 40; c. 3. PHYSICAL ORGANIC & POLYMER CHEMISTRY. B.S, Howard, 49, M.S, 50; U.S. Pub. Health fel, Catholic Univ, 52-54, Ph.D.(chem, physics), 54. Org. chemist, Nat. Cancer Inst, 50-52; RES. CHEMIST, Patuxent Res. Refuge, U.S. Dept. Interior, 55-57; POLYMER CHEM. SECT, NAT. BUR. STANDARDS, 57- U.S.A.F, 42-45, Res, 45-48. AAAS; Am. Chem. Soc; Faraday Soc; fel. Am. Inst. Chem. Synthesis of fluorocarbons and high thermostable polymers; kinetic studies; mechanism studies, free radical polymerization; high pressure reactions; abrasion of rubber. Address: 4446 Alabama Ave, S.E, Washington, DC 20019.

FEARN, RICHARD L(EE), b. Mobile, Ala, Mar. 24, 37; m. 69; c. 2. AERODYNAMICS. B.S. & M.S, Auburn Univ, 60; Ph.D.(physics), Univ. Fla, 65. ASST. PROF. AEROSPACE ENG, UNIV. FLA, 65- Engr, Arnold Eng. Develop. Ctr, summer 68; NASA-Am; Soc. Eng. Educ. summer faculty fel, 69 & 70. Am. Inst. Aeronaut. & Astronaut; Am. Soc. Eng. Educ. Jet in a cross flow; lifting surface theory. Address: Dept. of Aerospace Engineering, University of Florida, Gainesville, FL 32601.

FEARNLEY, LAWRENCE, b. Bradford, England, July 18, 32; m. 56. TOPOLOGY. B.Sc, London, 53; Nottingham, England, 54; Ph.D.(math, topology), Utah, 59. Asst. MATH, Utah, 54-57; from asst. prof. to assoc. prof, BRIGHAM YOUNG UNIV, 57-70, PROF, 70- Am. Math. Soc; Math. Asn. Am. Topology; topology of manifolds, limit spaces, continua. Address: Dept. of Mathematics, Brigham Young University, Provo, UT 84601.

FEARNS, EDWARD C(RANSHAW), b. Maynard, Mass, Sept. 14, 10; m. 44; c. 1. CHEMISTRY. B.S, Tufts, 32. Lab. asst. anal, Lever Bros. Co, Mass, 32-37, jr. chemist, 37-42, sr. res. chemist, 46-49; anal. lab. supvr, van Ameringen-Haebler, Inc, 49-57, anal. dept. mgr, 57-59; INT. FLAVORS & FRAGRANCES (U.S), 59-69, MGR. ANAL. SERVS, 69- Mem. specifications adv. comt. for Food Chem. Codex, Nat. Res. Coun. C.W.S, 42-46, 1st Lt. Am. Chem. Soc; fel. Am. Inst. Chem. Chemical and instrumental analysis of perfumes and flavors. Address: International Flavors & Fragrances, (U.S), 800 Rose Lane, Union Beach, NJ 07735.

FEARON, ROBERT EARL, b. Spokane, Wash, Nov. 17, 12; m. 38; c. 5. PHYSICS. B.S, Pittsburgh, 33, M.S, 34. Field engr, Schlumberger Well Surv, Tex, 36-38; res. engr, Eng. Lab, Inc, Okla, 38-39; Well Survs, Inc, 39-40, dir. res, 44-52; res. engr, Stanolind Oil & Gas Co, 40-44; DIR. RES, electrochem. labs, 52-71, ELECTROCHEM. DISCOVERIES, 71- Instr, Tulsa, 54- U.S.A, 44. Am. Chem. Soc. Problems of low level nuclear radiation measurement; radiochemistry; microradiochemistry; electrical measurements. Address: 530 S. Lewis, Tulsa, OK 74104.

FEARS, FULTON KELLER, b. Caney, Okla, Aug. 1, 20. CIVIL ENGINEERING. B.S, Oklahoma, 43; M.S, Purdue, 50, Ph.D.(civil eng), 57. Asst. prof. CIVIL ENG, UNIV. OKLA, 46-57, ASSOC. PROF, 57- Structural analysis; effect of air entrainment on durability of concrete. Address: Dept. of Civil Engineering, University of Oklahoma College of Engineering, Norman, OK 73069.

FEARY, THOMAS W, b. Springfield, Mass, July 22, 30; m; c. 4. MICROBIOLOGY. B.A, Univ. N.H, 56; Ph.D.(microbiol), Tulane Univ, 63; Univ. Tex, 63-64. Asst. prof. MICROBIOL, MED. CTR, UNIV. ALA, BIRMINGHAM, 64-69, ASSOC. PROF, 69-, BIOL, COL. GEN. STUDIES, 69-, DIR. GRAD. PROG. MICROBIOL, 70- Am. Soc. Microbiol. pres. fel, Cold Springs Harbor Biol. Labs, 59; Nat. Inst. Dent. Res. grant, 70-73. AAAS; Am. Soc. Microbiol; Soc. Gen. Microbiol; Soc. Indust. Microbiol. Microbial genetics; bacteriophage replication; infectious drug resistance; microbial parameters as indicators of water pollution. Address: Dept. of Microbiology, University of Alabama Medical Center, Birmingham, AL 35233.

FEASLEY, C(HARLES) F(REDERICK), b. Lexington, Ill, Jan. 21, 15; m. 40; c. 4. ORGANIC CHEMISTRY. A.B, Hanover Col, 37; M.S, Purdue, 40, Ph.D.(org. chem), 42. Asst. chem, Purdue, 37-41; res. chemist, res. dept, MOBIL OIL CORP, 41-44, sr. chemist, 45-57, supv. technologist, 57-62, asst. to mgr. toxicol. & pollution, 63-68, TOXICOL. ADV, 68-70, MED. DEPT, 70- AAAS; Am. Indust. Hyg. Asn; Soc. Toxicol; Am. Chem. Soc. Antiseptics; utilization of nitroalkanes; chemicals from petroleum; synthetic fuels from natural gas and coal; condensation of aryl diazonium salts and hydroxides with secondary nitroalkanes; development of laboratory tests for petroleum products; air and water pollution; toxicology of chemicals and petroleum products; food packaging materials; labeling of products; safety. Address: 37 N. Columbia St, Woodbury, NJ 08096.

FEASTER, CARL V(ANCE), b. Monon, Ind, Aug. 11, 21; m. 39; c. 3. PLANT BREEDING. B.S, Purdue, 44; M.A, Missouri, 47, Ph.D.(field crops), 50. AGRONOMIST, soybean res, bur. plant indust, soils & agr. eng, U.S. DEPT. AGR, 44-50, field crops res. br, PLANT INDUST. STA, AGR. RES. SERV, 50-56, COTTON BREEDING, COTTON & CORDAGE FIBERS BR, 56- Genetics; fiber plants. Address: Cotton Research Center, 4207 E. Broadway, Phoenix, AZ 85040.

FEASTER, GENE R(ICHARD), b. Winfield, Kans, Sept. 19, 18; m. 51. PHYSICS. B.S, Univ. Kans, 40, Ph.D.(physics), 53. Physicist, thermionic tubes, RCA Corp, N.J, 42-47; instr. physics, Univ. Kans, 47-52; adv. engr. thermionic tubes, Westinghouse Elec. Corp, 53-66, image intensifier & thermionic tubes, 66-67; ENG. ASSOC, CORNING GLASS WORKS, 67- Am. Soc. Test. & Mat; Am. Phys. Soc. Thermionic emission. Address: Optical Products Dept, Corning Glass Works, Corning, NY 14830.

FEASTER, JOHN P(IPKIN), b. St. Petersburg, Fla, Oct. 1, 20; m. 44; c. 3. BIOLOGICAL CHEMISTRY. B.A, Col. of William & Mary, 43; M.S, Emory, 48; Ph.D.(biochem), North Carolina, 51. Assoc. biochemist, agr. exp. sta, UNIV. FLA, 51-68, BIOCHEMIST & PROF, INST. FOOD & AGR. SCI, 68- Med. Dept, 43-46, Med.Serv.C. Res, 46-, Lt. Col. Am. Chem. Soc; Am. Soc. Animal Sci; Am. Inst. Nutrit. Mineral nutrition; placental transfer; lipid metabolism; pesticide toxicity. Address: 3021 S.W. 70th Lane, Gainesville, FL 32601.

FEATHER, A(LAN) L(EE), b. Mich, Aug. 31, 23; m. 50; c. 2. FOOD TECHNOLOGY. B.S, Mich. State Col, 47, M.S, 48. Asst. horticult, Mich. State Col, 47-48; canning technologist, CONTINENTAL CAN CO, INC, 48-49, customer res. rep, 49-52, dist. chief customer res, 52-67, prod. coord. beer prod, 67-70, MGR. CUSTOMER PACKAGING OPERS, PAC. METAL DIV, 70- U.S.A, 42-46, 51-52, 1st Lt. Inst. Food Technol; Master Brewers Asn. Am; Am. Soc. Brewing Chem; Soc. Soft Drink Technol. Packaging operations engineering; metal containers; new container development; canning methods and equipment; food spoilage and claims investigation. Address: Continental Can Co, Inc, 155 Bovet Rd, San Mateo, CA 94402.

FEATHER, BEN W(AYNE), b. Bowling Green, Mo, Apr. 4, 30; m. 53; c. 2. PSYCHIATRY, PSYCHOLOGY. A.B, Duke Univ, 52, Ph.D.(psychol), 65; M.D, George Wash. Univ, 56. Instr. & res. fel. psychiat, med. ctr, Duke Univ, 62-63, assoc, 63-64, asst. prof, 64-70, assoc. prof, 70-71, lectr. psychol, univ, 66-71; PROF. MED. SCI, BROWN UNIV. & MED. DIR, BUTLER HOSP, 71- Career develop. award, U.S. Pub. Health Serv, 63- U.S.P.H.S, 57-59, Sr. Asst. Surgeon. AAAS; Am. Med. Asn; Soc. Psychophysiol. Res; Am. Psychiat. Asn. Semantic conditioning and generalization in selected psychiatric disorders, especially schizophrenia; classical conditioning in human subjects. Address: Butler Hospital, 333 Grotto Ave, Providence, RI 02906.

FEATHER, MILTON S, b. Massillon, Ohio, Mar. 14, 36; m. 57; c. 1. BIOCHEMISTRY. B.S, Heidelberg Col, 58; M.S, Purdue, 61, Ph.D.(biochem), 63. Chemist, U.S. Forest Serv, 63-67; asst. prof. AGR. CHEM, UNIV. MO-COLUMBIA, 67-69, ASSOC. PROF, 69- U.S. Dept. Agr. trainee, Swedish Forest Prods. Res. Lab, Stockholm, 64-65. Am. Chem. Soc. Chemistry of nonenzymatic browning and dehydration reactions; structural studies on polysaccharides. Address: Dept. of Agricultural Chemistry, University of Missouri-Columbia, Columbia, MO 65201.

FEATHERS, WILLIAM D, b. Pittsburgh, Pa, Sept. 14, 27; m. 50; c. 6. CHEMICAL ENGINEERING. B.S, Pittsburgh, 50. Technician, Color Unlimited, Pa, 47-50; engr, Mellon Inst, 50; from engr. to SR. RES. ENGR, PHOTO PROD. DEPT, E.I. DU PONT DE NEMOURS & CO, Parlin, N.J, 51-69, WILMINGTON, 69- U.S.N, 46-47. Coating application methods and equipment development for photographic products. Address: 2307 Wynnwood Rd, Wilmington, DE 19810.

FEATHERSTON, FRANK H(UNTER), b. Washington, D.C, Mar. 9, 29; m. 51; c. 2. PHYSICS. B.S, U.S. Naval Acad, 50; M.S, U.S. Naval Postgrad. Sch, 57, Ph.D.(physics), 63; Armed Forces Staff Col, 65-66. U.S. NAVY, 50-, asst. nuclear physics, radiation lab, California, Berkeley, 56-57, opers. res. staff, Off. Comdr, Aircraft Early Warning Barrier, Pac, 57-58, SNAP reactor proj. officer, div. reactor develop, U.S. Atomic Energy Comn, 58-60, res. officer astronaut, U.S. Naval Missile Center, Calif, 63-65, Phoenix Proj. Mgr, hq, Naval Mat. Command, D.C, 66-68, dep. for avionics & armament, F-14/Phoenix Proj, Naval Air Systs. Command, 68-70, COMMANDING OFF, NAVAL TRAINING DEVICE CTR, 70- U.S.N, 50-, Capt. Am. Phys. Soc. K-meson research in nuclear emulsions; low temperature elastic constants of body-centered cubic transition metals; military science. Address: Naval Training Device Center, Orlando, FL 32813.

FEATHERSTON, WILLIAM ROY, b. Bentonville, Ark, Aug. 4, 35; m. 57; c. 3. NUTRITION, BIOCHEMISTRY. B.S.A, Arkansas, 57, M.S, 58; Ph.D. (biochem, poultry nutrit), Wisconsin, 62. Proj. assoc. biochem, Wisconsin, 61-62; asst. prof. NUTRIT, PURDUE UNIV, 62-65, assoc. prof, 65-68, PROF, 68- Med.Serv.C, 58, Capt. AAAS; Am. Inst. Nutrit; Soc. Exp. Biol. & Med; Poultry Sci. Asn. Biochemistry of nutrient utilization and interrelations in poultry and animals. Address: Dept. of Animal Science, Purdue University, Lafayette, IN 47907.

FEATHERSTONE, R(OBERT) M(ARION), b. Anderson, Ind, Dec. 24, 14; m. 40; c. 4. PHARMACOLOGY. B.A, Ball State Univ, 40, LL.D, 62; M.S, Iowa, 42, Ph.D.(biochem), 43. Instr. biochem, Med. Col, S.C, 43-44; assoc. pharmacol. & biochem, col. med, Iowa, 44-45, assoc. PHARMACOL, 45-46, asst. prof, 46-49, assoc. prof, 49-55, prof, 55-57; PROF. & CHMN. DEPT. SCH. MED, UNIV. CALIF, SAN FRANCISCO, 57- Res. grants, U.S. Dept. Health, Educ. & Welfare; Am. Cancer Soc; vis. prof, Middlesex Hosp. Med. Sch, London & Commonwealth fel, 65-66; lectr, Japanese Nat. Pharmacol. Soc, 67; Inst. Exp. Med, Leningrad, 68. Consult. to med. dept, Brookhaven Nat. Lab, Atomic Energy Comn, 50-57; Surg. Gen, Nat. Insts. Health; Linde Co, div. Union Carbide Corp. Mem. Int. Cong. Physiol. Sci, Buenos Aires, 59; Leiden, 62; European Cong. Anesthesia, Vienna, 62; Int. Pharmacol. Cong, Prague, 63, Basel, 69, San Francisco, 72, pres; mem. consult. panel, med. student res. training prog, Nat. Inst. Gen. Med. Sci, 61-63, mem. & chmn. study group pharmacol. training prog, 63-67; Nat. Inst. Neurol. Diseases & Stroke-U.S. del, U.S.S.R, 68; World Anesthesia Cong, London, 68; pharmacol-toxicol. rev. comt, 68-71. AAAS; Am. Chem. Soc; Am. Soc. Pharmacol. & Exp. Therapeut.(secy, 64-67, pres, 68-69); Am. Med. Asn; Soc. Exp. Biol. & Med; fel. Royal Soc. Med; Inst. Soc. Biochem. Pharmacol; Undersea Med. Soc.(v.pres, 69). Effects of drugs on cellular metabolism; general pharmacology; mechanisms of anesthesia. Address: School of Medicine, University of California, San Francisco Medical Center, San Francisco, CA 94122.

FEAY, DARRELL C(HARLES), b. Larchwood, Iowa, Mar. 13, 27; m. 52. INORGANIC CHEMISTRY, RADIOCHEMISTRY. B.S, Iowa, 50; Ph.D.(chem), California, 54. Asst. chem, California, 50-51, chemist, radiation lab, 51-54; res. chemist, DOW CHEM. CO, 54-64, PROJ. LEADER, 64- U.S.N.R, 45-46. Am. Inst. Chem. Application and development of polymerization catalysts; stereoselective catalysts; inorganic and polymer solvent extraction; spectroscopy; polymer chemistry. Address: Dow Chemical Co, 2800 Mitchell Dr, Walnut Creek, CA 94598.

FEAZEL, CHARLES E(LMO), JR, b. Crockett, Tex, Aug. 10, 21; m. 42; c. 2. ORGANIC CHEMISTRY. A.B, Harvard, 41; M.S, Maryland, 50, Ph.D.(chem), 53. Chemist, B.F. Goodrich Co, 41-46; appl. physics lab, Hopkins, 46-53; SR. CHEMIST, SOUTH. RES. INST, 53-, DIR. PHYS. SCI. RES, 56- Prof, Birmingham-South. Col, 54-55, 59-60. Fel. AAAS; Am. Chem. Soc; fel. Am. Inst. Chem. Organic synthesis; cellulose; plastics; polymer synthesis; alkaline degradation of carbohydrates. Address: Southern Research Institute, 2000 Ninth Ave. S, Birmingham, AL 35205.

FEAZEL, THOMAS A(NDERSON), b. Dallas, Tex, June 17, 23; m. 44; c. 1. CHEMICAL ENGINEERING. B.S, La. Polytech, 47; M.S, La. State, 49, Ph.D.(chem. eng), 51. Chem. engr, Phillips Petrol. Co, 47-48; asst. chem. eng, La. State, 48-51; DEVELOP. CHEM. ENGR, BUCKEYE CELLULOSE CORP, 51- Assoc. prof, Mississippi, 51-53. C.Eng, U.S.A, 44-46. Am. Inst. Chem. Eng; Tech. Asn. Pulp & Paper Indust. Fluid flow; pulping processes and equipment. Address: 4515 Princeton, Memphis, TN 38117.

FEBER, ROY CHESTER, JR, b. Lincoln, Nebr, Oct. 19, 20; m. 49; c. 5. CHEMISTRY. B.Sc, Nebraska, 42; Ill. Inst. Tech, 42-43; Ph.D.(chem), California, 48. Res. chemist, Manhattan Dist, California, 44-46, Knolls Atomic Power Lab, Gen. Elec. Co, 47-57; mem. staff, Los Alamos Sci. Lab, 57-60; sr. staff scientist, res. & adv. develop. div, Avco Corp, 60-62; STAFF MEM, LOS ALAMOS SCI. LAB, 62- Am. Chem. Soc. Solution chemistry; radiochemistry; high temperature chemistry. Address: Los Alamos Scientific Lab, Los Alamos, NM 87544.

FECHHEIMER, N(ATHAN) S, b. Cincinnati, Ohio, May 24, 25; m. 46; c. 2. ANIMAL GENETICS. B.S, Ohio State Univ, 49, M.Sc, 50; Ph.D.(dairy sci), 57. Asst. DAIRY SCI, OHIO STATE UNIV, 50-51, instr, 52-58, asst. prof, 58-60, assoc. prof, 60-65, PROF, 65- NATO fel, Univ. Edinburgh, 59-60, sr. vis. fel. genetics, 70-71; vis. investr, Jackson Lab, summer 62; mem. animal health comt, Nat. Res. Coun, 68-72. U.S.N, 43-46. Fel. AAAS; Genetics Soc. Am; Am. Soc. Animal Sci; Am. Genetic Asn; Am. Dairy Sci. Asn; Brit. Soc. Study Fertil; Soc. Study Reproduction. Mammalian genetics and cytogenetics; genetic influence on reproductive performance. Address: Dept. of Dairy Science, Ohio State University, 625 Stadium Dr, Columbus, OH 43210.

FECHNER, GILBERT H(ENRY), b. Northbrook, Ill, Dec. 20, 22; m. 48; c. 3. FOREST GENETICS. B.S, Colorado State, 47, M.S, 55; Ph.D, Minnesota, 64. Wood technologist, Hallack & Howard Lumber Co, 47-49; staff forester, Tenn. Valley Authority, 49-53; instr. forest mgt, COLO. STATE UNIV, 54-55, asst. prof, 55-63, assoc. prof, 63-67, PROF. FOREST GENETICS, 67- Charles A. Lory Award Outstanding Teaching, 69. Soc. Am. Foresters; Bot. Soc. Am. Morphology; silviculture; ecology. Address: Dept. of Forest & Wood Sciences, Colorado State University, Ft. Collins, CO 80521.

FEDDE, MARION ROGER, b. Ionia, Kans, Oct. 1, 35; m. 56; c. 3. PHYSIOLOGY. B.S, Kans. State Univ, 57; M.S, Univ. Minn, 59, Ph.D.(avian physiol), 63. Asst. prof. vet. anat, Univ. Minn, 63-64; asst. prof. PHYSIOL, KANS. STATE UNIV, 64-68, ASSOC. PROF, 68- Faculty res. award, col. vet. med, Kans. State Univ, 70. AAAS; Poultry Sci. Asn.(res. award, 64); World Poultry Sci. Asn; Am. Physiol. Soc; Int. Soc. Electromyog. & Kinesiology; Am. Soc. Vet. Physiol. & Pharmacol. Avian physiology, respiration; neurophysiology; myophysiology. Address: Dept. of Physiological Sciences, Kansas State University, Manhattan, KS 66502.

FEDDEMA, CHARLES, b. Whitinsville, Mass, Sept. 5, 20; m. 61; c. 1. BIOLOGY, BOTANY. A.B, Calvin Col, 51; M.S, Univ. Mich, 59, Ph.D.(bot), 66. Teacher, high sch, Mich, 54-57; teaching fel. bot, Univ. Mich, 59-64; PLANT TAXONOMIST, FOREST SERV, U.S. DEPT. AGR, 64- U.S. Merchant Marine, 43-47, Ens. Torrey Bot. Club; Am. Soc. Plant Taxon; Int. Asn. Plant Taxon. Botanical exploration in Mexico and Colombia; plant taxonomy of tropical and North America. Address: Forest Service Herbarium, 240 W. Prospect, Ft. Collins, CO 80521.

FEDDEMA, LEONARD W(ILLIAM), b. Whitinsville, Mass, Dec. 24, 23; m. 46. VEGETABLE CROPS. B.S, Massachusetts, 52; M.S, Delaware, 54; Ph.D. (veg. crops), Cornell, 59. Assoc. prof. veg. crops, Va. Polytech, 59-62; ASST. PROF. PERSONNEL ADMIN, CORNELL UNIV, 62-, VEG. CROPS, 70- U.S.A.A.F, 42-45. Am. Soc. Hort. Sci. Weed control chemicals in vegetable production and new techniques in vegetable production. Address: Office of Resident Instruction, College of Agriculture, 163 Roberts Hall, Cornell University, Ithaca, NY 14850.

FEDDER, RICHARD C(HARLES), b. East St. Louis, Ill, July 13, 31; m. 53; c. 3. PHYSICS. B.S, Illinois, 54; Ph.D.(physics), Washington (St. Louis), 63. Asst. physics, Washington (St. Louis), 56-63; staff physicist, Gen. Elec. Co, 63-67; ASSOC. PROF. PHYSICS, UNIV. CINCINNATI, 67- Summer faculty fel, NASA-Inst. Elec. & Electronics Eng, 70-71. Am. Phys. Soc. II-VI compounds; superconductivity; application of magnetic resonance to investigation of physical phenomena in solids including resonance phenomena. Address: Dept. of Physics, University of Cincinnati, Cincinnati, OH 45221.

FEDDERN, HENRY A, b. Poughkeepsie, N.Y, May 22, 38; m. 68. ICHTHYOL-OGY, MARINE ECOLOGY. B.S, Miami (Fla), 60, M.S, 63, Ph.D.(ichthyol), 68. Asst, inst. marine sci, Miami (Fla), 66-68; aquatic biologist, PRE-CISION VALVE CORP, 68-69, DIR. MARINE LAB, 69- Am. Soc. Ichthyol. & Herpet; Am. Littoral Soc. Tolerances of marine inshore fishes to in-secticides; factors influencing the survival and breeding of marine coral reef fishes. Address: Precision Valve Corp, 8737-A S.W. 132nd St, Miami, FL 33156.

FEDDERS, PETER ALAN, b. Minneapolis, Minn, Feb. 8, 39; m. 63; c. 2. PHYSICS. B.S, Yale, 61; M.A, Harvard, 62, Ph.D.(physics), 65. Res. assoc. PHYSICS, Princeton, 65-66, instr, 66-68; asst. prof, WASH. UNIV, 68-71, ASSOC. PROF, 71- Am. Phys. Soc. Solid state physics. Address: Dept. of Physics, Washington University, St. Louis, MO 63130.

FEDER, AARON, b. New York, N.Y, May 1, 15; m. 41; c. 2. MEDICINE. M.D, Maryland, 38. Instr. med, MED. COL, CORNELL UNIV, 42-50, asst. prof. clin. med, 50-59, assoc. prof, 59-65, CLIN. PROF. MED, 65- Mem. adv. bd, Hebrew Univ. Adj. attend. physician, Hosp, Joint Diseases, 40-53; attend. physician, New York Hosp; vis. physician & mem. med. bd, Bellevue Hosp; attend. physician & mem. med. bd, L.I. Jewish Hosp; cardiac consult, New York Dept. Health, 46-52; consult. physician, Booth Mem. Hosp; Long Beach Mem. Hosp; consult. med, N. Shore Mem. Hosp. Dipl, Am. Bd. In-ternal Med. Med.C, 42-46, Maj. AAAS; Am. Soc. Trop. Med. & Hyg; Am. Med. Asn; Asn. Am. Med. Cols; Asn. Mil. Surg; U,S; fel. Am. Col. Physi-cians; Am. Fedn. Clin. Res; fel. N.Y. Acad. Med. Vitamins in clinical med-icine; shock; atabrine toxicity. Address: 28 Meadow Woods Rd, Great Neck, NY 10020.

FEDER, BERNARD HERBERT, b. New York, N.Y, Feb. 11, 13; m. 41; c. 2. RADIOTHERAPY, RADIOLOGY. B.A, Southern California, 36, M.D, 40. Intern & resident, Los Angeles County Hosp, Calif, 39-41, resident, 46-49; head roentgenologist, Los Angeles County Harbor Gen. Hosp, Torrance, 49-52; chief radiother. sect, Vet. Admin. Hosp, Long Beach, 52-58, chief ra-diol. sect, 58-68, chief radiother. sect, 68-70; PROF. RADIOL, SCH. MED, UNIV. SOUTH. CALIF, 70-, ASSOC. RADIOTHERAPIST, LOS ANGELES COUNTY-UNIV. SOUTH. CALIF. MED. CTR, 70- From clin. instr. to clin. prof. radiol, sch. med, Univ. Calif, Los Angeles, 50-70; mem. attend. staff, Los Angeles Co. Harbor Gen. Hosp, Torrance, 52-; assoc. investr, Nat. Insts. Health grant, 60-66; prin. investr, Am. Cancer Soc. grant, 63-69; De-fense Atomic Support Agency grant, 67-70. Dipl, Am. Bd. Radiol, 49. Med.C, U.S.A, 41-46, Maj. Fel. Am. Col. Radiol; Am. Med. Asn; Am. Ra-dium Soc; Am. Soc. Therapeut. Radiol; Health Physics Soc; Radiation Res. Soc; Radiol. Soc. N.Am; Transplantation Soc. Radiation therapy; radiology; evaluation of preoperative irradiation utilizing a solid tumor model; detec-tion of minute doses of ionizing irradiation by mammals; autologous mar-row storage and reinfusion in management of human cancer; immunologic response in cancer irradiation. Address: Radiation Therapy Section, Out-patient Bldg, Room 1P-1, Los Angeles County-University of Southern Cal-ifornia Medical Center, 1200 N. State St, Los Angeles, CA 90033.

FEDER, DONALD P(ERRY), b. Rochester, N.Y, Feb. 2, 18; m. 48; c. 3. OPTICS. A.B, Rochester, 40. Physicist, geomet. optics, Rochester, 41-45; supt. optical design, Argus, Inc, 44-49; physicist in charge optical design, Nat. Bur. Standards, 49-56; OPTICAL DESIGNER, EASTMAN KODAK CO, 57- Application of computing machinery to optical design; numerical anal-ysis and programming digital computers. Address: 800 Thayer Rd, Fair-port, NY 14450.

FEDER, HARVEY HERMAN, b. N.Y.C, Mar. 28, 40; m. 61; c. 3. ANATOMY, REPRODUCTIVE PHYSIOLOGY. B.S, City Col. New York, 61; Univ. Kans, 61-63; Ph.D.(anat), Univ. Ore, 66. Asst. scientist, Ore. Regional Primate Res. Ctr, 63-70; ASSOC. PROF. PSYCHOL, INST. ANIMAL BEHAV, RUT-GERS UNIV, 70- U.S. Pub. Health Serv. res. fel, 65-67, at Oxford, 66-67; Nat. Insts. Health res. grant, 69-72; Nat. Inst. Ment. Health career develop. award, 70- AAAS; Brit. Soc. Endocrinol. Role of gonadal steroids in dif-ferentiation of sexual behavior of females; estimations of circulation go-nadal steroids. Address: Institute of Animal Behavior, Rutgers University, 101 Warren St, Newark, NJ 07102.

FEDER, HOWARD MITCHELL, b. N.Y.C, June 8, 22; m. 50; c. 4. MARINE BIOLOGY. A.B, California, Los Angeles, 48, M.A, 51; Univ. Honors fel, Stanford, 53-54, Eli Lilly & Co. fel, 54-55, Ph.D.(marine biol), 57. Asst. gen. zool, California, Los Angeles, 48, protozool & human anat, 50-51; ma-rine biol, Kerckhoff Marine Lab, Calif. Inst. Technol, 49; Arctic Res. Lab, Point Barrow, Alaska, 49-50; oceanographic technician, Hopkins Marine Sta, Stanford, 51-52, asst. marine invert. zool, 52, 54; instr. biol, Hartnell Col, 55-65, prof, 65-70; ASSOC. PROF. ZOOL. & MARINE SCI, UNIV. ALASKA, 70- Am. Acad. Arts & Sci. res. grants, 60-64; Nat. Sci. Found. res. grants, 62-67; Sea Grant res. grant, 70-71. Med.C, U.S.A.R, 42-46. Marine ecology; intertidal ecology; autecological study of the Pacific Coast ochre starfish, Pisaster ochraceus; fisheries biology, especially clams and oysters; ma-rine interstitial biology. Address: College of Biological Sciences & Insti-tute of Marine Science, University of Alaska, College, AK 99701.

FEDER, JOSEPH, b. St. Louis, Mo, Feb. 20, 32; m. 53; c. 4. BIOCHEMIS-TRY. B.S, Roosevelt, 53; M.S, Ill, Inst. Technol, 61, Ph.D.(biochem), 64; Nat. Insts. Health fel, Northwestern, 63-65. Res. biochemist, MONSANTO CO, 65-70, RES. GROUP LEADER, 70- Asst. prof, Univ. Mo-St. Louis, 66-70, assoc. prof, 70- AAAS; Am. Chem. Soc. Mechanism of action of en-zymes; kinetics of enzyme catalyzed reactions, primarily proteolytic en-zymes; protein structure and enzyme catalysis relationships. Address: New Enterprise Division, Monsanto Co, St. Louis, MO 63166.

FEDER, PAUL IRA, b. N.Y.C, Feb. 8, 43. STATISTICS. B.S, Polytech. Inst. Brooklyn, 63; M.S, Stanford, 64, Ph.D.(statist), 68. ASST. PROF. STATIST, YALE, 67- Inst. Math. Statist; Am. Statist. Asn. Nonlinear regression the-ory; sequential analysis; asymptotic distribution theory. Address: 581B Prospect St, New Haven, CT 06511.

FEDER, RAYMOND L, b. N.Y.C, Apr. 1, 20; m. 43; c. 2. CHEMICAL ENGI-NEERING. B.Che, Polytech. Inst. Brooklyn, 43, M.Ch.E, 47, D.Ch.E, 49.

Sr. engr. penicillin develop, Schenley Lab, 43-46; plant engr. indust. en-zymes, Takamine Lab, 48-51; supvr. process develop, PLASTICS DIV, ALLIED CHEM. CORP, 51-62, mgr. develop. lab, 62-63, nylon res. & develop, 63-65, mgr. polyolefins res. & develop, 65-67, TECH. MGR. FRANKFORD PLANT, 67- Instr, Drexel Inst. Technol, eve. div, 52-58, adj. prof, 58-62. Am. Chem. Soc; Am. Inst. Chem. Eng. Process development of organic chemicals; polyolefins and nylons; economic evaluation and process design; process improvement; quality control; process engineering for phenol from cumene, phthalic anhydride, from naphthalene; natural tar acids from carbolic oil. Address: Plastics Division, Allied Chemical Corp, Margaret & Bermuda Sts, Philadelphia, PA 19137.

FEDER, WALTER, b. New York, N.Y, May 11, 24; m. 52; c. 3. MEDICINE. A.B, N.Y. Univ, 44; M.D, State Univ. N.Y, 55. Instr. math, City Col, 46-51; intern, Univ. Clinics, Univ. Chicago, 55-56, resident, dept. med, 56-59, instr. MED, 59-61, ASST. PROF, 61-67; STATE UNIV. N.Y. DOWN-STATE MED. CTR, 67-; DIR. CARDIOL, MARIMONIDES MED. CTR, BROOKLYN, 67- Donner fel. of Nat. Acad. Sci-Nat. Res. Council, 58-59; Pub. Health Serv. res. fel, 59-61. Am. Math. Soc; Biophys. Soc; Am. Fedn. Clin. Res; Am. Heart Asn; Soc. Exp. Biol. & Med; fel. N.Y. Acad. Med. Cardiology; physiology and biophysics of the circulation; mathematical biology. Address: Marimonides Medical Center, 4802 10th Ave, Brooklyn, NY 11219.

FEDER, WILLIAM A(DOLPH), b. New York, N.Y, Oct. 15, 20; m. 45; c. 3. PLANT PATHOLOGY. A.B, Hopkins, 41; Ph.D.(plant path), California, 50. Asst. bot. & plant physiol, California, 48-49; storage disease pathologist, Indust. Res. Adv. Council, exp. sta, Hawaii, 50-51; asst. prof. plant path, N.Y. State Col. Agr, Cornell, 51-54, assoc. prof, 54; plant pathologist, crops res. div, Agr. Res. Serv, U.S. Dept. Agr, 54-66; PROF. PLANT PATH. & LEADER AIR POLLUTION RES. PROJS, UNIV. MASS, AMHERST, 66- Nat. Sci. Found. sr. fel, Eng, 58-59; Fulbright res. scholar, Israel, 64- U.S.N.R, 42-45, Lt. AAAS; Am. Phytopath. Soc; Bot. Soc. Am. Biological control of plant diseases, including nematodes; effects of air pollution on plant growth. Address: Suburban Experiment Station, University of Massa-chusetts, Waltham, 240 Beaver St, Waltham, MA 02154.

FEDERBUSH, PAUL GERARD, b. Newark, N.J, Mar. 23, 34; m. 56; c. 1. THEORETICAL PHYSICS. B.S, Mass. Inst. Technol, 55; Ph.D.(physics), Princeton, 58. Instr. physics, Mass. Inst. Technol, 58-60, asst. prof, 60-65; lectr. MATH, UNIV. MICH, ANN ARBOR, 65-67, assoc. prof, 67-71, PROF, 71- Am. Phys. Soc. Axiomatic field theory. Address: 1000 Cedar Bend Dr, Ann Arbor, MI 48105.

FEDERER, C. ANTHONY, b. N.Y.C, Jan. 19, 39; m. 60; c. 2. FORESTRY, METEOROLOGY. B.S, Massachusetts, 59; Nat. Sci. Found. fel, Wisconsin, 59-64, M.S, 62, Ph.D.(soils), 64. Assoc. Meteorologist, NORTHEAST. FOREST EXP. STA, U.S. FOREST SERV, 64-70, PRIN. METEOROLOGIST, 70- Am. Meteorol. Soc; Am. Geophys. Union; Am. Soc. Agron; Soil Sci. Soc. Am; Soc. Am. Foresters. Evapotranspiration from forests; energy balance of natural surfaces; radiation and light in and above vegetation; snowmelt; forest hydrology; soil water. Address: Northeastern Forest Experiment Station, P.O. Box 640, Durham, NH 03824.

FEDERER, HERBERT, b. Vienna, Austria, July 23, 20; nat; m. 49; c. 3. MATHEMATICS. A.B, Univ. Calif, 42, Ph.D.(math), 44. Instr. MATH, BROWN UNIV, 45-46, asst. prof, 46-48, assoc. prof, 48-51, prof, 51-66, FLORENCE PIRCE GRANT UNIV. PROF, 66- Sloan res. fel, 57-60; Nat. Sci. Found. fel, 64-65; mem, Nat. Res. Coun, 66-69. U.S.A, 44-45. Am. Math. Soc.(assoc. secy, 67-68); Am. Acad. Arts & Sci. Geometric measure theory. Address: Dept. of Mathematics, Brown University, Providence, RI 02912.

FEDERER, WALTER T(HEODORE), b. Cheyenne, Wyo, Aug. 23, 15; m. 45; c. 1. BIOSTATISTICS. B.S, Colo. State Col, 39; M.S, Kans. State Col, 41; Ph.D.(math. statist), Iowa State Col, 48. Asst. corn invests, U.S. Dept. Agr. & Kans. State Col, 39-41, Bur. Agr. Econ. & Iowa State Col, 41-42, geneti-cist, special Guayule res. proj, Bur. Plant Indust, 42-44, assoc. agr. statis-tician, Bur. Agr. Econ. & Iowa State Col, 44-48; PROF. BIOSTATIST, BIO-METRICS UNIT, CORNELL UNIV, 48- Head dept. exp. statist, Hawaiian Sugar Planters' Asn. & consult, Pineapple Res. Inst, 54-55; prof, univ. & U.S. Army Math. Res. Ctr, Univ. Wis, 62-63 & 69-70; chmn. & exec. secy, Comt. Pres. of Statist. Socs, 64-71. Fel. AAAS; Biomet. Soc.(secy, East. N.Am. Region, 50-53, pres. elect, 59, pres, 60); fel. Am. Statist. Asn; fel. Inst. Math. Statist; fel. Royal Statist. Soc; India Soc. Agr. Statist. Experi-mental design; statistical genetics and analyses. Address: Biometrics Unit, 337 Warren Hall, Cornell University, Ithaca, NY 14850.

FEDERICO, OLGA MARIA, b. New York, N.Y, Dec. 12, 23. ANIMAL PHYS-IOLOGY. B.A, Hunter Col, 46; M.S, Long Island, 60; Ph.D.(biol), N.Y. Univ, 68. Res. asst. rheumatologic disease, Hosp. Spec. Surg, 50-60; instr. biol, Long Island, 60-65; U.S. Pub. Health Serv. trainee hemat, N.Y. Univ, 65-68; instr. BIOL, Hunter Col, 66-67; Queens Col.(N.Y), 67-68; ASST. PROF, QUEENSBOROUGH COMMUNITY COL, 68- Hematology; medical laboratory science. Address: 376 Guyon Ave, Staten Island, NY 10306.

FEDERIGHI, ENRICO T(HOMAS), b. Norfolk, Va, Nov. 1, 27; m. 65; c. 1. ALGEBRA. A.B, Antioch Col, 50; M.A, Hopkins, 54; Ph.D, Indiana, 57. Jr. instr. math, Hopkins, 50-53; jr. engr, Bendix Radio, 53-55, asst. proj. engr, 56-57; SR. MATHEMATICIAN, APPL. PHYSICS LAB, JOHNS HOP-KINS UNIV, 58- Algebra and number theory; finite groups and algebraic number theory; statistics. Address: 5029 Round Tower Pl, Columbia, MD 21043.

FEDERIGHI, FRANCIS D, b. Xenia, Ohio, Oct. 19, 31; m. 55; c. 2. COM-PUTER SCIENCE. B.A, Oberlin Col, 53; M.A, Harvard, 55, Ph.D.(physics), 61. Theoret. physicist, Knolls Atomic Power Lab, Gen. Elec. Co, 59-66; ASSOC. PROF. COMPUT. SCI, STATE UNIV. N.Y. ALBANY, 66- Guest scientist, Swiss Fed. Inst. Reactor Res, 63-64. Mgt. award, Gen. Elec. Co, 60. AAAS; Asn. Comput. Mach; Math. Asn. Am; Soc. Indust. & Appl. Math. Nuclear reactor physics; programming languages; numerical methods. Address: Dept. of Computer Science, State University of New York at Albany, 1400 Washington Ave, Albany, NY 12203.

FEDERMAN, MICHELINE, b. Paris, France, Jan. 1, 39; U.S. citizen. CELL BIOLOGY, ELECTRON MICROSCOPY. B.S, Long Island, 61; Ph.D.(cell biol), Rutgers, 66. RES. ASSOC. CELL BIOL. & ELECTRON MICROS, Douglass Col, Rutgers, 66-67, Rutgers Med. Sch, 67-68; CANCER RES. INST, NEW ENG. DEACONESS HOSP, 68- AAAS; Electron Micros. Soc. Am; Am. Soc. Cell Biol. Ultrastructural aspects and function of organelles. Address: Cancer Research Institute, New England Deaconess Hospital, 194 Pilgrim Rd, Boston, MA 02215.

FEDEROWICZ, ROSE ANN, C.S.F.N, b. Orange, Conn, Sept. 5, 08. BIOLOGICAL SCIENCES. B.S, Cath. Univ. Am, 40, M.S, 50, Ph.D.(biol), 62. Teacher & prin, parochial schs, Mass, Pa. & N.Y, 26-54; instr. BIOL, HOLY FAMILY COL.(PA), 54-57, asst. prof, 57-62, assoc. prof, 62-68, PROF, 68-, CHMN. DEPT, 54- AAAS; Bot. Soc. Am; Nat. Asn. Biol. Teachers; Am. Soc. Plant Taxon. Plant taxonomy; parasitology. Address: Dept. of Biology, Holy Family College, Philadelphia, PA 19114.

FEDERSPIEL, CHARLES (FOSTER), b. Flint, Mich, May 3, 29; m. 57. BIOSTATISTICS. A.B, Michigan, 50, A.M, 52; Ph.D.(statist), N.C. State Col, 59. Statistician, communicable disease center, U.S. Pub. Health Serv, 52-54; ASSOC. PROF. BIOSTATIST, SCH. MED, VANDERBILT UNIV, 59- Biomet. Soc; Am. Statist. Asn; Am. Pub. Health Asn. Statistical methodology and its applications in biology and medicine. Address: Dept. of Preventive Medicine, Vanderbilt University School of Medicine, Nashville, TN 37203.

FEDINEC, ALEXANDER, b. Uzhorod, Czech, Jan. 29, 26; nat; m. 52; c. 2. ANATOMY. M.A, Kansas, 57, Ph.D.(anat), 58. Instr. ANAT, State Univ. N.Y. Downstate Med. Center, 58-60; asst. prof, Hahnemann Med. Col, 60-62; MED. UNITS, UNIV. TENN, MEMPHIS, 62-68, ASSOC. PROF, 68- Am. Asn. Anat; Am. Soc. Exp. Path. Mode of dispersal and action of neurotropic toxins; blood-brain barrier and placental permeability; teratology. Address: Dept. of Anatomy, University of Tennessee Medical Units, 875 Monroe Ave, Memphis, TN 38103.

FEDKIW, JOHN, Pub. Admin, see 12th ed, Soc. & Behav. Vols.

FEDOR, E(DWARD) J(OHN), b. Braddock, Pa, Feb. 15, 24. PHYSIOLOGY. B.S, Waynesburg Col, 47; M.S, West Virginia, 50; M.A. & Ph.D.(physiol), Princeton, 53. Instr. biol. & chem, Waynesburg Col, 47-58; physiol, West Virginia, 48-50; res. assoc. & instr. biol, Princeton, 50-53; instr. clin. physiol, sch. med, Tennessee, 53-54; res. assoc. exp. surg, sch. med, Pittsburgh, 54-57, asst. res. prof. surg, 57-61; sr. physiologist, Wallace Labs, N.J, 61-64; ABBOTT LABS, 64-69, head cardiovascular sect, 69-71, HEAD BLOOD PHYSIOL. SECT, 71- Proctor fel, Princeton, 53-54. U.S.N.R, 43-46. Am. Physiol. Soc; Soc. Exp. Biol. & Med; Soc. Nuclear Med; Am. Soc. Pharmacol. & Exp. Therapeut; Am. Heart Asn; Am. Chem. Soc. Cardiovascular physiology and fibrinolysis. Address: D-465, Abbott Labs, Abbott Park, North Chicago, IL 60064.

FEDOR, LEO RICHARD, b. Boston, Mass, Jan. 11, 34; m. 62; c. 2. ORGANIC CHEMISTRY. B.S, Mass. Col. Pharm, 55, M.S, 57; Ph.D.(org. chem), Indiana, 63. Instr. chem, E.Tex. State Col, 58-59; fel, Cornell, 63-64; California, Santa Barbara, 64-65; asst. prof. MED. CHEM, STATE UNIV. N.Y. BUFFALO, 65-69, ASSOC. PROF, 69- Am. Chem. Soc. Mechanisms of organic reactions related to enzymic reactions. Address: 38 Kaymar Dr, Tonawanda, NY 14150.

FEDOROFF, SERGEY, b. Daugavpils, Latvia, Feb. 20, 25; nat; m. 54; c. 4. EMBRYOLOGY, HISTOLOGY. B.A, Univ. Sask, 52, M.A, 55, Ph.D.(histol), 58. Demonstr. histol, UNIV. SASK, 53-55, instr. ANAT, 55-57, spec. lectr, 57-58, asst. prof, 58-62, assoc. prof, 62-64, PROF. & HEAD DEPT, 64-, ASST. DEAN COL. MED, 70-, admin. asst. to dean med, 60-62. Lederle med. faculty award, 57-60; mem. steering comt. study basic biol. res. Can, Sci. Secretariat, 66; mem, Med. Res. Coun. Assessment Group Anat. Res. Can, 67; mem. studentship comt, Med. Res. Coun. Can, 69-; Can. del, Pan-Am. Cong. Anat, Caracas, Venezuela, 69; mem. bd. gov, W. Alton Jones Cell Sci. Ctr, N.Y, 70. Can. Asn. Anat.(v.pres, 65-66, pres, 66-67); Am. Asn. Anat; Pan-Am. Asn. Anat; Am. Soc. Cell Biol; Can. Soc. Cell Biol; Int. Soc. Cell Biol; Tissue Cult. Asn.(v.pres, 64-68, pres, 68-); N.Y. Acad. Sci; Soc. Exp. Biol. & Med; Genetics Soc. Can; Am. Asn. Immunol; Can. Soc. Immunol; Transplantation Soc; cor. mem. Mex. Asn. Anat; hon. mem. Venezuelan Asn. Morphol. Cytogenetics; immunobiology; tissue culture; cell differentiation. Address: Dept. of Anatomy, University of Saskatchewan, Saskatoon, Sask, Can.

FEDRICK, JAMES L(OVE), b. Lordsburg, N.Mex, Apr. 17, 30; m. 64; c. 4. ORGANIC CHEMISTRY. B.S, Arizona, 53, M.S, 55; Ph.D.(chem), Illinois, 59. Org. chemist, org. chem. res. sect, Lederle Lab, AM. CYANAMID CO, 59-61, group leader, 61-63, tech. dir. fine chem. dept, PEARL RIVER, N.Y, 63-66, DIR. PROD. & PROCESS DEVELOP, MED. RES, LEDERLE LABS, CYANAMID INT, 66- Teacher, Bergen Col. Am. Chem. Soc; N.Y. Acad. Sci. Heterocyclic synthesis; medicinal chemistry; management of international research and development. Address: 10 Pembroke Trail, Upper Saddle River, NJ 07458.

FEDRO, ARTHUR JOHN, b. Chicago, Ill, July 7, 37; m. 60; c. 1. SOLID STATE PHYSICS. B.A, Northwestern, 59, Ph.D.(physics), 65. Asst. prof. PHYSICS, NORTH. ILL. UNIV, 65-69, ASSOC. PROF, 69- Consult, Argonne Nat. Lab, 66- Am. Phys. Soc. Solid state theory. Address: Dept. of Physics, Northern Illinois University, DeKalb, IL 60115.

FEDUCCIA, JOHN ALAN, b. Mobile, Ala, Apr. 25, 43; m. 69. ZOOLOGY, ORNITHOLOGY. B.S, La. State Univ, 65; M.A, Univ. Mich, Ph.D.(zool), 69. Lectr. zool, Univ. Mich, summer 69; ASST. PROF. biol, SOUTH. METHODIST UNIV, 69-71; ZOOL, UNIV. N.C, 71- Am. Ornith. Union; Cooper Ornith. Soc; Wilson Ornith. Soc; Soc. Study Evolution; Soc. Syst. Zool; Soc. Vert. Paleont. Avian systematics and evolution; avian paleontology. Address: Dept. of Zoology, University of North Carolina, Chapel Hill, NC 27514.

FEDUKOWICZ, HELENA, b. Ukraine, June 4, 00; nat; m. 21. OPHTHALMOLOGY. M.D, Med. Inst. Jekaterinoslav, Ukraine, 21; Ph.D, Med. Inst. Kiev, Ukraine, 35. Assoc. prof. OPHTHAL, Med. Inst, Kiev, 30-41; head dept, Int. Refugee Orgn. Hosp, Regensburg, West Germany, 45-49; from asst. to ADJ. ASSOC. PROF, SCH. MED, N.Y. UNIV, 50- External infections of the eye. Address: 85-24 110 St, Richmond Hill, New York, NY 11418.

FEE, GORDON GRAY, b. Sayre, Pa, Aug. 23, 34; m. 56; c. 2. NUCLEAR ENGINEERING, PHYSICS. B.S, Pa. State, 56; M.S, Tennessee, 62. Assoc. physicist, Oak Ridge Gaseous Diffusion Plan, UNION CARBIDE CORP, 56-57, sr. mech. engr, 57, staff engr, 57-59, sect. head res. compressor, 59-63, proj. supvr. nuclear thermionics, adv. develop. dept, Parma Res. Ctr, 63, sr. staff engr, develop. dept, 63-66, group leader systs. eng, electronics div, 66-69, prod. mgr, INSTRUMENT DEPT, 69-70, MKT. MGR, 71- Am. Inst. Aeronaut. & Astronaut; Marine Tech. Soc. Water and air pollution instrumentation; fuel cell systems engineering; compressor technology; process development gaseous diffusion technology. Address: Union Carbide Corp, Instrument Dept, Five New Street, White Plains, NY 10601.

FEE, JAMES ARTHUR, b. Nokomis, Sask, Aug. 30, 39; U.S. citizen; m. 60; c. 2. PHYSICAL BIOCHEMISTRY. B.A, Pasadena Col, 61; Ph.D.(biochem), Univ. South. Calif, 67. Nat. Sci. Found. fel. biochem, Gothenburg Univ, 67-69; Nat. Insts. Health trainee & res. assoc. biophysics, Univ. Mich, Ann Arbor, 69-70; ASST. PROF. CHEM, RENSSELAER POLYTECH. INST, 70- Am. Chem. Soc. Oxygen metabolism; role of metal ions in biological systems; mechanistic aspects of enzymatically catalyzed oxidation-reduction reactions. Address: Dept. of Chemistry, Rensselaer Polytechnic Institute, Troy, NY 12181.

FEEHS, R(ICHARD) H, b. Philadelphia, Pa, June 2, 33; m. 54; c. 4. CHEMICAL ENGINEERING. B.S, Drexel Inst, 55; M.Ch.E, Delaware, 59. Res. chem. engr, E.I. DU PONT DE NEMOURS & CO. INC, 55-62, res. supvr, 62-67, sr. supvr. mfg. div, 67-68, head div. res. & develop, 68-70, lab. mgr, 70-71, PROD. SUPT, 71- Am. Inst. Chem. Eng. Heat transfer; catalysis; economics; market evaluation. Address: Pigments Dept, E.I. du Pont de Nemours & Co. Inc, P.O. Box 310, Antioch, CA 94509.

FEELEY, EDWARD JOSEPH, b. N.Y.C, June 29, 26; m. 57; c. 7. MICROBIOLOGY. B.S, Manhattan Col, 51; M.S, Fordham Univ, 53, Ph.D.(cell biol), 55. Instr. biol, St. John's Univ.(N.Y), 55-57; Mundelein Col, 58-61; asst. prof. biol. sci, Loyola Univ.(La), 61-63, assoc. prof, 63-65; prof, Quinnipiac Col, 65-67; PROF. MICROBIOL. & MICROSCOPIC ANAT, N.Y. Col. Podiat, 67-71; CITY UNIV. N.Y, 71- Faculty res. fel, St. John's Univ. (N.Y), 56; Nat. Sci. Found. fels, Purdue Univ, 58 & 61; Asn. Cancer Res. grant-in-aid, Loyola Univ.(La), 61-62, 64-65; Schlierder Found. res. grant, 63-65; Fund for Podiat. Res. grant-in-aid, 67-70. A.U.S, 44-46. Am. Soc. Microbiol. Antiviral agents; chemotherapy and prophylaxis of animal and human viral diseases; mechanisms of action of antiviral agents. Address: 1258 Post Rd, Scarsdale, NY 10583.

FEELEY, JOHN C(ORNELIUS), b. Los Angeles, Calif, Mar. 7, 33; m. 57; c. 2. MICROBIOLOGY. A.B, California, Los Angeles, 55, Ph.D, 58. Asst. bact, California, Los Angeles, 55-58; sr. asst. scientist, DIV. BIOL. STANDARDS, NAT. INSTS. HEALTH, 58-62, scientist, 62-65, CHIEF SECT. BACT. VACCINES, 65-, MEM. CHOLERA ADV. COMT, 68- Mem. cholera panel, U.S-Japan Coop. Med. Sci. Prog, 65-; sr. scientist, U.S. Pub. Health Serv, 66-; mem, WHO Expert Panel Bact. Diseases, 67-; adj. assoc. prof. parasitol. & lab. practice, sch. pub. health, Univ. N.C, 68-; consult, U.S. Agency Int. Develop, 70- Dipl, Am. Bd. Microbiol, 64. AAAS; fel. Am. Acad. Microbiol; Soc. Exp. Biol. & Med; Am. Soc. Microbiol; Am. Pub. Health Asn. Hypersensitivity; bacteriophage; hemagglutination; serum bactericidal action; host-parasite relationships in brucellosis; standardization of biological products; bacteriology and immunology of cholera. Address: Bldg. 29, Room 432, National Institutes of Health, Bethesda, MD 20014.

FEELY, FRANK JOSEPH, JR, b. Chicago, Ill, Aug. 26, 18; m. 69; c. 7. MECHANICAL ENGINEERING. B.S, Michigan, 40. Engr, design div, Standard Oil Develop. Co, 40-48, group head, 48-51, asst. supv. engr, 51-55, asst. dir, 55-59, assoc. dir. planning eng. div, Esso Res. & Eng. Co, 59-61, dir. gen. eng. div, 61-64, asst. gen. mgr. gen. manager's off, 64-66, v.pres. & dir, 66-71; MGR. OPERS. COORD, LOGISTICS DEPT, STANDARD OIL CO. N.J, 71- Mem, Am. Petrol. Inst, 53-; v.pres. & mem. bd. dir. & exec. comt, Am. Nat. Standards Inst. Fel. Am. Soc. Mech. Eng. Mechanical engineering developments in catalytic cracking including stress analysis of piping expansion joints; brittle fracture in steel. Address: Standard Oil Co. New Jersey, 30 Rockefeller Plaza, New York, NY 10020.

FEELY, HERBERT WILLIAM, b. Brooklyn, N.Y, April 29, 28; m. 67; c. 4. GEOCHEMISTRY. B.S, City Col, 50; M.A, Columbia, 52, Ph.D.(geol), 56. Instr, Upsala Col, 55-57; sr. res. geochemist, Isotopes, Inc, 57-67; ASSOC. PROF. EARTH SCI, QUEENS COL.(N.Y), 67- Res. assoc, Columbia Univ, 56-57, sr. res. assoc, 67- Geochem. Soc; Am. Geophys. Union; Am. Meteorol. Soc. Geochemical age measurements; isotopic fractionation in geologic settings; radioactive fallout; atmospheric and marine geochemistry. Address: 31 Seneca Ave, Emerson, NJ 07630.

FEELY, WAYNE E(DMUND), b. Brooklyn, N.Y, May 24, 31; m. 55; c. 3. ORGANIC CHEMISTRY. B.S, Polytech. Inst. Brooklyn, 53; Union Carbide Corp. fel, Rochester, 55-56, Ph.D.(chem), 57. Asst, Rochester, 53-55; CHEMIST, ROHM & HAAS CO, 57- Chem.C, 57, 1st Lt. Am. Chem. Soc. Nitrogen heterocycles; synthetic lubricants; plasticizers; coating resins; general organic synthesis; plastics; urethane foams. Address: 1172 Lindsay Lane, Rydal, Jenkintown, PA 19046.

FEEMAN, GEORGE F(RANKLIN), b. Lebanon, Pa, Apr. 16, 30; m. 71; c. 4. MATHEMATICS. B.S, Muhlenberg Col, 51; M.S, Lehigh, 53, Danforth grant, 57, Ph.D.(math), 58. Instr. MATH, Muhlenberg Col, 54-57, asst. prof, 58-59; instr, Mass. Inst. Technol, 59-61; asst. prof, Williams Col, 61-66, assoc. prof, 66-69; PROF, OAKLAND UNIV, 69-, acting chmn. dept, 71-72. Nat. Sci. Found. sci. faculty fel, 65-66; math. coord, Detroit Teacher Intern Proj, 69-70; Urban Corps Proj, 69-70, 70-71; dir, Nat. Sci. Found. summer inst. for col. teachers, 70, inst. for jr. high sch. teachers, 71. Am. Math.

Soc; Math. Asn. Am. Differential geometry, especially geometry of Riemannian manifolds; problems in mathematics education, especially reading disabilities in mathematics. Address: Dept. of Mathematics, Oakland University, Rochester, MI 48063.

FEEMAN, JAMES FREDERIC, b. Lebanon, Pa, June 1, 22; m. 47; c. 4. ORGANIC CHEMISTRY. B.S, Muhlenberg Col, 45; M.S. Lehigh, 47, Ph.D.(chem), 49. Res. Found. fel, Ohio State, 49-50; res. chemist, ALTHOUSE DIV, CROMPTON & KNOWLES CORP, READING, 50-68, ASST. DIR. RES, 68- Sig.C, U.S.A, 42-46. Fel. AAAS; N.Y. Acad. Sci; fel. Am. Inst. Chem; Am. Chem. Soc; Am. Asn. Textile Chem. & Colorists. Textile dyes and auxiliaries; textile chemistry; dye intermediates; chemical information management; synthetic organic chemistry. Address: 1500 Garfield Ave, Wyomissing, PA 19610.

FEENBERG, EUGENE, b. Ft. Smith, Ark, Oct. 19, 06; m. 41; c. 2. PHYSICS. B.A. & M.A, Texas, 29; Parker traveling fel, Harvard, 31-33, Ph.D.(physics), 33. Instr. physics, Harvard, 33-35; lectr, Wisconsin, 35-36; temporary mem, Inst. Adv. Study, 36-38; asst. prof. physics, Wash. Sq. Col, N.Y. Univ, 38-42; mem. staff, Sperry Gyroscope Co, 42-45; asst. prof, PHYSICS, N.Y. Univ, 45-46; assoc. prof, WASHINGTON UNIV, 46-52, PROF, 52- Vis. prof. physics, State Univ. N.Y. Stony Brook, 68- Fel. Am. Phys. Soc. Theory of electron scattering; nuclear forces and structure; velocity modulation; perturbation methods in quantum theory; theory of quantum fluids. Address: Dept. of Physics, Washington University, St. Louis, MO 63130.

FEENEY, ROBERT E(ARL), b. Oak Park, Ill, Aug. 30, 13; m. 54; c. 2. BIOCHEMISTRY. B.S, Northwestern, 38; scholar, Wisconsin, 38-39, fel, 39-40, M.S, 40, Ph.D.(biochem), 42. Asst, Wisconsin, 40-42; res. assoc, Harvard Med. Sch, 42-43; chemist, west. regional res. lab, bur. agr. & indust. chem, U.S. Dept. Agr, 46-53; prof. biochem. & nutrit. & chmn. dept, Univ. Nebr, 53-60; PROF. FOOD SCI. & TECHNOL, UNIV. CALIF, DAVIS, 60- Chemist, exp. sta, Univ. Nebr, 53-60. U.S.A, 43-46, Capt. Am. Soc. Biol. Chem; Am. Chem. Soc; Am. Soc. Microbiol; Soc. Exp. Biol. & Med; Inst. Food Technol; Poultry Sci. Asn. Biochemistry of proteins; comparative and genetic biochemistry. Address: Dept. of Food Science & Technology, University of California, Davis, CA 95616.

FEENEY, ROBERT JAMES, b. Derby, Conn, Aug. 26, 25; m. 55; c. 5. ORGANIC CHEMISTRY. B.S, Yale, 47, Ph.D.(org. chem), 50. Lectr, Yale, 47-50; res. chemist, CHAS. PFIZER & CO, INC, 50-53, asst. mgr. new prod. develop, 53-55, res. proj. coordinator, 55-60, asst. to pres, 60-61, dir. commercial develop, 61-64, asst. to v.chmn. bd, 64-65, asst. to pres, 65-68, V.PRES, PFIZER INT, INC, 68- U.S.N.R, 44-46. AAAS; Am. Chem. Soc. Natural products, sterols and nucleosides; products of biological origins; antibiotics; vitamins, growth factors. Address: Pfizer International, Inc, 235 E. 42nd St, New York, NY 10017.

FEENSTRA, E(RNEST) S(TAR), b. Grand Rapids, Mich, Oct. 22, 17; m. 44; c. 3. ANIMAL PATHOLOGY. D.V.M, Mich. State, 42, M.S, 44, Ph.D.(animal path), 47. Asst. animal path, Mich. State, 42-47, asst, 44-47, asst. prof, 47-48; sect. head, res. div, UPJOHN CO, 48-56, MGR. PATH. & TOXICOL. RES, 56- Res. prof. path, Mich. State Univ, 70- Dipl, Am. Col. Lab. Animal Med. AAAS; Int. Acad. Path; Am. Sci. Affiliation; Am. Vet. Med. Asn; Am. Asn. Path. & Bact; Am. Col. Vet. Path; Am. Asn. Lab. Animal Sci. Experimental pathology and toxicology; diseases of laboratory animals. Address: The Upjohn Co, Kalamazoo, MI 49001.

FEENY, HAROLD F(RANCIS), b. Montreal, Que, Can, Oct. 15, 14; m. 40; c. 3. PHYSICS. B.Sc, McGill, 37, M.Sc, 40; Dr. es Sc.(physics), Laval, 42. Instr. PHYSICS, Laval, 39-42, asst. prof, 42-45; Manitoba, 45-46; assoc. prof, Delaware, 46-52, PROF, 52-64; NORTH. ILL. UNIV, 64- Am. Phys. Soc. Pressure broadening of microwave line widths. Address: Dept. of Physics, Northern Illinois University, De Kalb, IL 60115.

FEENY, PAUL P(ATRICK), b. Birmingham, Eng, Feb. 8, 40; m. 68; c. 1. ECOLOGY, ORGANIC CHEMISTRY. B.A, Oxford, 60 & 63, B.Sc, 61, M.A, 63, Ph.D.(zool), 66. ASST. PROF. ECOL, CORNELL UNIV, 67- Faculty trustee, Cornell Univ, 71-73. AAAS; Entom. Soc. Am; Ecol. Soc. Am; Am. Inst. Biol. Sci. Chemical ecology; ecological significance of secondary plant and animal chemical compounds, including attractants and repellants; biological control. Address: Dept. of Entomology, Comstock Hall, Cornell University, Ithaca, NY 14850.

FEERST, IRWIN, b. New York, N.Y, Nov. 18, 27; m. 50; c. 2. ELECTRONIC ENGINEERING. B.E.E, City Col. New York, 51; M.E.E, N.Y. Univ, 55. Private consult, 60-62; asst. prof. physics, Adelphi Univ, 62-69, PRIVATE CONSULT, 69- Nat. Sci. Found. grant, 64-66. Consult, Am. Mach. & Foundry Co, 62-64; Bucode Co, 69- U.S.N, 45-46. Inst. Elec. & Electronics Eng. Servomechanisms; tape transport design and development; cathode ray tube deflection systems; spectral analysis of signals; pulse and digital circuits and systems. Address: 368 Euclid Ave, Massapequa Park, NY 11762.

FEESE, BENNIE TAYLOR, b. Cane Valley, Ky, Dec. 21, 37; m. 60; c. 2. MOLECULAR BIOLOGY. A.B, Centre Col, 59; Woodrow Wilson fel, Washington (St. Louis), 60-61, Nat. Insts. Health trainee, 61-65, Ph.D.(molecular biol), 65. Asst. prof. BIOL, CENTRE COL. KY, 64-71, ASSOC. PROF, 71-, CHMN. MOLECULAR BIOL. PROG. COMT, 69-, chmn. life sci. prog, 67-69. AAAS. Contemporary evolution of enzyme systems in insects; control of protein synthesis in maturing avian erythrocytes. Address: Division of Science & Mathematics, Centre College, Danville, KY 40422.

FEESER, LARRY JAMES, b. Hanover, Pa, Feb. 23, 37; m. 61; c. 2. CIVIL ENGINEERING. B.S, Lehigh, 58; M.S, Colorado, 61; Ford Found. fel, Carnegie Inst. Tech, 61-63, Ph.D.(civil eng), 65. Instr. CIVIL ENG, UNIV. COLO, BOULDER, 58-61, asst. prof, 63-67, ASSOC. PROF, 67-, RES. ASSOC, COMPUT. CTR, 70- Mem, Nat. Coop. Hwy. Res. Prog; adv. comt. interactive comput. graphics, Nat. Sci. Found. faculty fel, Swiss Fed. Inst. Technol, 71-72. Am. Soc. Civil Eng; Am. Concrete Inst; Am. Soc. Eng. Educ; Asn. Comput. Mach; Int. Asn. Bridge & Struct. Eng; Int. Asn. Shell Struct. Dynamics and optimization of structures; computer applications; interactive computer graphics; highway computer graphics. Address: Dept. of Civil Engineering, University of Colorado, Boulder, CO 80302.

FEFER, MORTON, b. Milwaukee, Wis, Feb. 26, 28; m. 56. ORGANIC CHEMISTRY. B.S, Wisconsin, 50; Abbott fel, Northwestern, 54, Stauffer fel, 55, E.I. du Pont de Nemours & Co. summer fel, 56, Ph.D, 56. Res. org. chemist, Esso Res. & Eng. Co, 57-59; chemist market develop, Enjay Co, Inc, 59-70, PROD. SALES MGR, SPECIALTY ORG. ACIDS, ENJAY CHEM. CO, 70- U.S.N.R, 45-46, 51-53. AAAS; Am. Chem. Soc. Reaction mechanisms and kinetics. Address: Enjay Chemical Co, P.O. Box 3272, Houston, TX 77001.

FEFFER, JAMES J(OSEPH), b. N.Y.C, Nov. 3, 13; m. 41; c. 2. MEDICINE. A.B, Ind. Univ, 35, M.D, 38. Instr, sch. med, Georgetown Univ, 43-44; clin. instr. med, GEORGE WASHINGTON UNIV. MED. CTR, 44-47, assoc, 47-52, asst. clin. prof, 52-59, assoc. clin. prof, 59-64, clin. prof, 64-68, PROF. MED. & ASSOC. DEAN CLIN. AFFAIRS, 68- Consult, div. phys. manpower, bur. health manpower, U.S. Pub. Health Serv, 68- Dipl, Am. Bd. Internal Med. Fel. Am. Col. Physicians; fel. Am. Col. Chest Physicians; Am. Thoracic Soc; Am. Med. Asn; Asn. Am. Med. Cols; Pan-Am. Med. Asn; Am. Soc. Internal Med.(pres, 67-68); Am. Therapeut. Soc.(v.pres, 68-69); Am. Soc. Clin. Pharmacol. & Therapeut. Address: George Washington University Medical Center, Room 2500-North, 901 23rd St. N.W, Washington, DC 20037.

FEGEL, ARTHUR C(HRISTIAN), b. Perth, N.Y, Aug. 25, 10; m. 37; c. 2. MECHANICAL ENGINEERING. B.S, Syracuse, 33, M.S, 34, Ph.D.(forestry), 38. Tech. foreman, emergency conserv. work State Dept. Forestry & Waters, N.J, teaching fel, State Univ. N.Y. Col. Forestry, Syracuse, 33-34, 34-37; tech. foreman, U.S. Forest Serv, 34; engr, West. Elec. Co, 37-42, dept. chief, 42-44, div. chief, 44-47, asst. supt. mfg. eng, 47-52; v.pres, NASSAU SMELTING & REF. CO, 52-54, PRES, 54- AAAS; Am. Soc. Mech. Eng. Wood technology; manufacturing problems in production of communications equipment; a comparison of the mechanical and physical properties and the anatomical structure of root, stem and branch wood. Address: 1895 Lake Ave, Scotch Plains, NJ 07076.

FEGLEY, HARRY C, b. Sunbury, Pa, Dec. 29, 26; m. 57; c. 3. VETERINARY PATHOLOGY. V.M.D, Pennsylvania, 54. Supvr. animal care, Merck Sharp & Dohme Div, Merck, Inc, 57-61; assoc. vet. path, Pennsylvania, 61-65; VET. PATHOLOGIST, Affiliated Med. Enterprises, 65-68; AM. CYANAMID CO, 68- U.S.A.F, 54-56, Capt. Am. Vet. Med. Asn. Veterinary pathology; animal care; toxicology especially as related to research laboratory animals. Address: 325 W. County Line Rd, Hatboro, PA 19040.

FEGLEY, KENNETH A(LLEN), b. Mont Clare, Pa, Feb. 14, 23; m. 51; c. 3. ELECTRICAL ENGINEERING. B.S, Pennsylvania, 47, M.S, 50, Ph.D.(elec. eng), 55. Instr, MOORE SCH. ELEC. ENG, UNIV. PA, 47-53, assoc, 53-55, asst. prof. ELEC. ENG, 55-58, assoc. prof, 58-66, PROF, 66- U.S.N, 44-46. Am. Soc. Eng. Educ; Inst. Elec. & Electronics Eng. Navigation, control and optimization methods. Address: Moore School of Electrical Engineering, University of Pennsylvania, Philadelphia, PA 19104.

FEHDER, PAUL LEE, b. Portsmouth, Va, Sept. 30, 42; m. 71. INFORMATION SCIENCE, CHEMICAL PHYSICS. S.B, Mass. Inst. Technol, 64; Ph.D.(chem), Calif. Inst. Technol, 70. MEM. RES. STAFF INFO. SCI, RES. DIV, IBM CORP, 69- AAAS; Am. Chem. Soc; Asn. Comput. Mach. Development of automatic information processing-retrieval system; simulation studies of the microscopic properties of simple dense fluids. Address: Dept. K06, Bldg. 028, IBM Research Lab, Monterey & Cottle Rds, San Jose, CA 95114.

FEHER, GEORGE, b. Czech, May 29, 24; m. 49; c. 3. PHYSICS. B.S, California, 50, M.S, 51, Ph.D.(physics), 54. Res. physicist, Bell Tel. Labs, 54-60; PROF. SOLID STATE PHYSICS & BIOPHYS, UNIV. CALIF, SAN DIEGO, 60- Vis. assoc. prof, Columbia Univ, 59-60; vis. prof, Mass. Inst. Technol, 67-68; mem. bd. gov, Israel Inst. Technol, 68- Am. Phys. Soc. (prize, 60). Solid state physics; paramagnetic resonance; photosynthesis; biophysics. Address: Dept. of Physics, University of California, San Diego, La Jolla, CA 92037.

FEHLMANN, HERMAN ADAIR, b. Denver, Colo, Jan. 31, 17; m. 50; c. 2. MARINE BIOLOGY. B.A, Colorado, 48, M.A, 50; Ph.D, Stanford, 60. Asst. biol, Colorado, 48-50; curatorial asst, vert. collections, Stanford, 51-54, asst. biol, 54-55, arctic marine biol, 52-54, asst. curator marine biol, George Vanderbilt Found, 54-62; SUPVR, OCEANOG. SORTING CTR, SMITHSONIAN INST, 63- Field worker, Thailand & Viet Nam. U.S.A, 42-45. Soc. Syst. Zool; Am. Soc. Ichthyol. & Herpet. Marine ecology; systematic ichthyology; tropical herpetology; oceanology. Address: 7311 Wessex Dr, Camp Springs, MD 20031.

FEHLNER, FRANCIS P(AUL), b. Dolgeville, N.Y, Aug. 3, 34; m. 62; c. 3. PHYSICAL CHEMISTRY. B.S, Col. Holy Cross, 56; Nat. Sci. Found. fel. & Ph.D.(phys. chem), Rensselaer Polytech, 59. Res. chemist, RES. & DEVELOP. LAB, CORNING GLASS WORKS, 62-69, MGR, 69- U.S.A.F, 59-62, Res, 62-67, Capt. Am. Chem. Soc; Am. Vacuum Soc. Crystal growth; chemical kinetics; flame inhibition; vacuum-biology; field emission microscopy; ultra-high vacuum; gas adsorption on thin films; oxidation. Address: 83 E. Fourth St, Corning, NY 14830.

FEHLNER, THOMAS P(ATRICK), b. Dolgeville, N.Y, May 28, 37; m. 62; c. 4. PHYSICAL INORGANIC CHEMISTRY. B.S, St. Bernardine of Siena Col, 59; M.A, Hopkins, 61, Ph.D.(phys. chem), 63. Res. assoc, inst. coop. res, Hopkins, 63-64; asst. prof. CHEM, UNIV. NOTRE DAME, 64-67, ASSOC. PROF, 67- AAAS; Am. Chem. Soc. Characterization of unstable inorganic molecules and radicals by mass spectrometry; kinetics of the reactions of borane; ionization potential measurements. Address: Dept. of Chemistry, University of Notre Dame, Notre Dame, IN 46556.

FEHNEL, EDWARD A(DAM), b. Bethlehem, Pa, April 22, 22; m. 44; c. 2. ORGANIC CHEMISTRY. B.S, Lehigh, 43, fel, 43-44, 45-46, M.S, 44, Ph.D.(org. chem), 46. Instr, Moravian Prep. Sch, Pa, 43-44; res. chemist, cent.

res. lab, Allied Chem. & Dye Corp, N.J, 44-45; lectr. chem. & Am. Chem. Soc. fel, Pennsylvania, 46-48; asst. prof. CHEM, SWARTHMORE COL, 48-57, assoc. prof, 57-66, PROF, 66- Nat. Sci. Found. sci. faculty fel, Cambridge, 62; vis. prof. chem, Ind. Univ, summer 68. Am. Chem. Soc. Synthetic organic chemistry; preparation and properties of organic sulfur compounds; ultraviolet absorption spectroscopy; quinoline derivatives; arene oxides. Address: Dept. of Chemistry, Swarthmore College, Swarthmore, PA 19081.

FEHON, JACK HAROLD, b. Irvington, N.J, Dec. 14, 26; m. 50; c. 3. ZOOLOGY. B.S, Florida, 50, M.S, 52; Ph.D, Fla. State, 55. Instr. BIOL, Fla. State, 55-56; assoc. prof, QUEENS COL.(N.C), 56-59, prof, 59-62, DANA PROF, 62-, HEAD DEPT, 59- C.Eng, 44-47, 2nd Lt. AAAS. Uptake dissolved organic nutrients by marine invertebrates. Address: 2411 Vernon Dr, Charlotte, NC 28211.

FEHR, ROBERT O, b. Germany, Sept. 12, 11; nat; m. 41; c. 2. ACOUSTICS. Vordiplom, Inst. Tech, Berlin, 33; Dipl. Ing, Swiss Fed. Inst. Tech, 34; Dr. Tech. Sc, Zurich, 39. Test engr, Gen. Elec. Co, 37-38, develop. engr, gen. eng. lab, 39-46, sect. engr, 46-53, consult. engr, 53-56, mgr. mech. eng. lab, 56-61; prof. eng, Cornell, 61-64; v.pres. european opers, Branson Europa N.V, Branson Instruments, Inc, Netherlands, 64-66, v.pres. int. opers, Conn, 66-68; PRES, FEHR & FISKE, INC, 68- Mem. subcomt, Nat. Adv. Comt. Aeronaut. Acoust. Soc. Am; Inst. Elec. & Electronics Eng; Soc. Exp. Stress Anal; Aerospace Indust. Asn. Am. Acoustics; vibration; mechanical shock. Address: 37 Lake Ave. Extension, Danbury, CT 06810.

FEHRENBACHER, J(OE) B(ERNARD), b. Bogota, Ill, Nov. 5, 15; m. 41; c. 3. SOILS. M.S, Univ. Ill, 40; Ph.D, Purdue Univ, 64. Asst. soil physics, UNIV. ILL, URBANA, 38-42, 45-46, asst. prof, 46-60, assoc. prof, 60-66, PROF, PEDOLOGY, 66- Asst, Nat. Defense Res. Coun, Off. Sci. Res. & Develop, Northwestern, 42-45, res. assoc, Carnegie Inst. Tech, 45. Am. Forestry Asn; Soil Sci. Soc. Am; Soil Conserv. Soc. Am. Plant root development in relation to soil profile characteristics; soil classification and genesis. Address: N-405 Turner Hall, University of Illinois, Urbana, IL 61801.

FEHRLE, KURT G, b. Stuttgart, Ger, June 24, 28; U.S. citizen; m. 63; c. 1. ELECTRICAL ENGINEERING. D.Sc.(elec. eng), Stuttgart Tech, 58. Res. engr, Bausch & Lomb, N.Y, 58-61; asst. prof. elec. eng, Carnegie Inst. Technol, 62-66; ADVAN. SYSTS. ENGR, GEN. ELEC. CO, 66- Electrical power engineering. Address: Laboratory Operation, Room 10-750, General Electric Co, 6901 Elmwood Ave, Philadelphia, PA 19142.

FEHSENFELD, FRED C(HARLES), b. Kansas City, Mo, Oct. 10, 34; m. 56; c. 2. ATMOSPHERIC PHYSICS. B.A, Rice, 57; Tex. Thermonuclear Res. Found. summer fel, Texas, 60, Ph.D.(physics), 62. RES. SCIENTIST PHYSICS, NAT. BUR. STANDARDS, 62- Am. Phys. Soc; Sci. Res. Soc. Am. Thermal energy ion and neutral reaction rates. Address: Room 3522, Radio Bldg, National Bureau of Standards, Boulder, CO 80302.

FEIBELMAN, PETER J(ULIAN), b. N.Y.C, Nov. 12, 42. THEORETICAL PHYSICS. B.A, Columbia Univ, 63; Nat. Sci. Found. fel, Univ. Calif, San Diego, 63-67, Ph.D.(physics), 67. Nat. Sci. Found. fel. PHYSICS, Saclay Nuclear Res. Ctr, France, 68-69, Nat. Ctr. Sci. Res. researcher, 69; res. asst. prof, Univ. Ill, Urbana-Champaign, 69-71; ASST. PROF, STATE UNIV. N.Y. STONY BROOK, 71- Am. Phys. Soc. Many-particle problems; theory of solid surfaces; collective excitations at quantum fluid interfaces; theory of critical phenomena. Address: Dept. of Physics, State University of New York, Stony Brook, NY 11790.

FEIBELMAN, WALTER A, b. Berlin, Ger, Oct. 30, 25; U.S. citizen. PHYSICS, ASTRONOMY. B.S, Carnegie Inst. Tech, 56. Res. specialist, Westinghouse Res. Labs, 48-56, res. engr, 56-63; asst. res. prof. physics, Univ. Pittsburgh, 64-69, observer, Allegheny Observ, 55-69; PHYSICIST, ASTROPHYS. BR, GODDARD SPACE FLIGHT CTR, NASA, 69- Consult, Westinghouse Elec. Corp, 66- Am. Astron. Soc; fel. Meteoritical Soc; Royal Astron. Soc. Can. Microwave spectroscopy; thin films; infrared, visible and ultraviolet image converters; cold cathode electron emission; meteor spectroscopy; astrometry; interferometry; astronomical and upper-atmosphere instrumentation. Address: Astrophysics Branch, Code 673, Goddard Space Flight Center, NASA, Greenbelt, MD 20771.

FEIBES, WALTER, b. Aachen, Ger, Jan. 26, 28; U.S. citizen; m. 50; c. 3. STATISTICS, OPERATIONS RESEARCH. B.S, Union Col.(N.Y), 52; M.S, Western Reserve, 53; Ph.D.(opers. res), State Univ. N.Y. Buffalo, 68. Document analyst, Library Cong, 53-55; head librn, Appliance Park, Gen. Elec. Co, 55-62; ASSOC. PROF. MATH, WEST..KY. UNIV, 67- U.S.N, 46-48. Math. Asn. Am; Am. Statist. Asn; Inst. Mgt. Sci; Opers. Res. Soc. Am; Spec. Libraries Asn. Applied statistics; time series. Address: Dept. of Mathematics, Western Kentucky University, Bowling Green, KY 42101.

FEICHTMEIR, EDMUND FRANCIS, b. Ainsworth, Iowa, July 6, 15; m. 43; c. 4. AGRICULTURAL CHEMISTRY. A.B, California, 37, Ph.D.(agr. chem), 47. Agr. chemist, SHELL OIL CO, 47-50, prod. develop, Shell Chem. Co, 52-53, mgr. prod. appl. group, SHELL DEVELOP. CO, 53-71, DIR. AGR. CHEM, 71- U.S.N.R, 42-46, Lt. Effect of particle size and solubility of sulfur in carbon disulfide upon its toxicity to fungi. Address: Shell Development Co, Biological Science Research Center, P.O. Box 4248, Modesto, CA 95352.

FEICHTNER, JOHN DAVID, b. Erie, Pa, July 6, 30; m. 57. PHYSICS, QUANTUM ELECTRONICS. B.S, Stanford, 53; M.S, New Mexico State, 60; Ph.D. (physics), Colorado, 64. Physicist, Gen. Elec. Co, 55-57; res. asst. physics, Univ. Colo, 60-65; sr. res. scientist, WESTINGHOUSE RES. LABS, 65-71, FEL. SCIENTIST, 71- U.S.N.R, 57-60, Lt. Am. Phys. Soc; Inst. Elec. & Electronics Eng; Am. Asn. Physics Teachers. Atomic and molecular physics. Address: Westinghouse Research Labs, Churchill Borough, Pittsburgh, PA 15235.

FEIG, GERALD, b. Newark, N.J, July 29, 32; m. 56; c. 2. ORGANIC CHEMISTRY. B.A, Rutgers, 54, M.S, 57, Ph.D.(org. chem), 59. Sr. res. chemist,

Nat. Cash Register Co, 59-62; res. chemist, SUN CHEM. CORP, 62-63, res. group leader, 63-66, res. sect. head, 66-69, RES. DIR, CORP. RES. LAB, 69- Mem, Textile Res. Inst, 70- Indust. Res. Inst; Am. Chem. Soc; Soc. Photog. Sci. & Eng. Mechanisms of organic peroxide decompositions; photopolymerization systems and photoinitiators; photochromic compounds; thermography; electrostatic printing; polymer synthesis; textile chemical finishes; graphic arts. Address: 10 Eton Pl, Springfield, NJ 07081.

FEIGELSON, MURIEL, b. New York, N.Y, July 5, 26; m. 47; c. 2. BIOCHEMISTRY. B.S, Queens Col.(N.Y), 46; M.S, N.Y. Univ, 57, U.S. Pub. Health Serv. fel, 57-60, Ph.D.(cell physiol), 61. Trainee oncol. biochem, col. physicians & surgeons, Columbia, 60-62; U.S. Pub. Health Serv. fel, lab. exp. embryol, Col. France, 62-63; res. assoc. BIOCHEM, COL. PHYSICIANS & SURGEONS, COLUMBIA UNIV, 63-71, ASST. PROF, 71- AAAS; Am. Soc. Cell Biol; Harvey Soc; Endocrine Soc. Reproductive and developmental biochemistry and hormone action. Address: Dept. of Obstetrics & Gynecology, Harlem Hospital-Columbia University, 315 W. 125th St, New York, NY 10027.

FEIGELSON, PHILIP, b. New York, N.Y, Apr. 20, 25; m. 47; c. 2. BIOCHEMISTRY. B.S, Queens Col.(N.Y), 47; M.S, Syracuse, 48; Ph.D.(biochem), Wisconsin, 51. Asst. prof. BIOCHEM, Antioch Col, 51-54; res. assoc, Fels Res. Inst, 51-54; asst. prof, COL. PHYSICIANS & SURGEONS, COLUMBIA UNIV, 54-61, assoc. prof, 61-70, PROF, 70- Career investr, Health Res. Coun, N.Y, 59- N.Y. Acad. Sci; Am. Soc. Biol. Chem; Am. Chem. Soc; Am. Asn. Cancer Res; Harvey Soc. Mechanism of induced enzyme formation; mechanism of glucocorticoid action; enzyme catalysis. Address: Dept. of Biochemistry, College of Physicians & Surgeons, Columbia University, 99 Ft. Washington Ave, New York, NY 10032.

FEIGEN, GEORGE A(LEXANDER), b. Rostov-on-Don, Russia, Nov. 19, 16; nat; m. 48. PHYSIOLOGY, IMMUNOCHEMISTRY. A.B, California, 38; Ph.D.(immunol), Calif. Inst. Tech, 47. Asst. pharmacol, Calif. Inst. Tech, 39-42; fel. cardiovascular res, Cedars of Lebanon Hosp, Los Angeles, 42-43; physiologist, inst. med. physics, res. labs, California, 43, biochemist, dept. obstet. & gynecol, med. sch, 43; asst. chem, Calif. Inst. Tech, 43-47, teaching fel, 45-47, U.S. Pub. Health Serv. sr. res. fel, 47-48; res. assoc. pharmacol. & toxicol, sch. med, Southern California, 48-49; instr, SCH. MED, STANFORD UNIV, 49-52, asst. prof. PHYSIOL, 52-55, assoc. prof, 55-70, PROF, 70- Am. Heart Asn. traveling fel, Oxford, 56-57, Nat. Sci. Found. sr. fel, 63-64. Consult, sch. med, California, Los Angeles, 54; White Mt. High Altitude Res. Sta, California. With Atomic Energy Cmn; Off. Sci. Res. & Develop, 44. Am. Physiol. Soc; fel. N.Y. Acad. Sci. Hemorrhagic and burn shock; anaphylactic shock and blood substitutes; hemodynamics; myocardial failure; mechanism of erythrocyte sedimentation; spinal conduction; stimulants and depressants; immunology of tumors; cardiac anaphylaxis; physiology of mountain altitudes; chemistry of tetanus toxin; immunopharmacology of bacterial toxins and marine venoms. Address: Dept. of Physiology, Stanford University School of Medicine, Stanford, CA 94305.

FEIGENBAUM, ABRAHAM S(AMUEL), b. New York, N.Y, Mar. 11, 29; m. 52; c. 3. NUTRITION, BIOCHEMISTRY. B.S, Rutgers, 51, M.S, 59, Nat. Sci. Found. fel, 61, Ph.D.(nutrit), 62. Inspection chemist, E.R. Squibb & Sons Div, Olin Mathieson Chem. Corp, 54-56, assay methods anal. chemist, 56-57; res. asst. nutrit, poultry dept, Rutgers, 57-61; RES. SCIENTIST, N.J. BUR. RES. NEUROL. & PSYCHIAT, 61- Chem.C, 51-54, Res. 54-61, 1st Lt. AAAS; Am. Inst. Nutrit; Am. Chem. Soc; Soc. Exp. Biol. & Med; Am. Oil Chemists' Soc; Poultry Sci. Asn. Lipid metabolism in chickens, including fatty liver etiology and atherosclerosis; genetic variation in susceptibility to experimentally-induced atherosclerosis and spontaneous arteriosclerosis in rabbits. Address: Neuroendocrinology Section, New Jersey Bureau of Research in Neurology & Psychiatry, Box 1000, Princeton, NJ 08540.

FEIGENBAUM, EDWARD A(LBERT), b. Weehawken, N.J, Jan. 20, 36; m. 58; c. 2. COMPUTER SCIENCE, PSYCHOLOGY. B.S, Carnegie Inst. Tech, 56, univ. fel, Soc. Sci. Res. Coun. fel, Ford Found. fel. & Ph.D.(indust. admin), 60. Fulbright res. scholar, Gt. Brit, 59-60; asst. prof. bus. admin, California, Berkeley, 60-64; assoc. prof. COMPUT. SCI, STANFORD UNIV, 65-69, PROF, 69-, dir. comput. ctr, 65-69. Consult, indust. & govt, 57-; mem. comput. & biomath. sci. study sect, Nat. Insts. Health, 68-72. AAAS; Asn. Comput. Mach; Am. Psychol. Asn. Information processing models of cognitive processes; artificial intelligence; programming languages; verbal learning; models of human memory. Address: Dept. of Computer Science, Stanford University, Stanford, CA 94305.

FEIGENBAUM, HARVEY, b. East Chicago, Ind, Nov. 20, 33; m. 57; c. 3. MEDICINE. A.B, Indiana, 55, M.D, 58. Res. assoc, Krannert Inst. Cardiol, 62; instr. MED, MED. CTR, IND. UNIV, 62-64, asst. prof, 64-67, assoc. prof, 67-71, PROF, 71- Assoc. in med, Marion Co. Gen. Hosp, 65. Am. Fedn. Clin. Res; fel. Am. Col. Physicians; fel. Am. Col. Cardiol; Am. Inst. Ultrasonics in Med; Am. Soc. Clin. Invest. Clinical cardiology; electrophysiology; hemodynamics; echocardiography. Address: Indiana University Medical Center, Indianapolis, IN 46202.

FEIGENBAUM, WILLIAM M, b. New York, N.Y, May 3, 41; m. 68; c. 1. ORGANIC CHEMISTRY. B.A, N.Y. Univ, 62, M.S, 64, fel, 65, Ph.D.(pyrene chem), 67; law, Univ. N.Y. Buffalo, 70- Res. chemist, E.I. du Pont de Nemours & Co, 67-69. Am. Chem. Soc. Metal complexing in cyclic ethers; radical addition to pyrene and other polynuclear aromatic hydrocarbons; correlation of structure and reactivity in aromatics. Address: 30 Kenville Rd, Buffalo, NY 14215.

FEIGHAN, MARIA JOSITA, I.H.M, b. Phila, Pa, Aug. 29, 32. CHEMISTRY. A.B, Immaculata Col.(Pa), 64; M.Ed, Harvard, 67; Ph.D.(phys. chem), St. Louis Univ, 69. Teacher, high schs, Pa, 57-66; ASST. PROF. CHEM, IMMACULATA COL.(PA), 69- Am. Chem. Soc. Educational programs on pollution; spectroscopic studies of nitro compounds. Address: Dept. of Chemistry, Immaculata College, Immaculata, PA 19345.

FEIGHNER, GEORGE C(HRISTY), b. Chicago, Ill, Feb. 9, 26; m. 45; c. 3. ORGANIC CHEMISTRY. B.S, Michigan, 49, M.S, 50. Jr. res. chemist, PETROCHEM. RES, CONTINENTAL OIL CO, 50-51, assoc. res. chemist, 51-54, res. chemist, 54-57, sr. res. chemist, 57-58, res. group leader, 58-60, res. sect. supvr, 60-67, mgr. customer serv. lab, 67-69, PROJ. COORD, 69- U.S.N.R, 44-46. AAAS; Am. Oil Chemists' Soc; Am. Chem. Soc. Organic chemistry; petrochemicals; synthetic detergents; white mineral oils; lubricating oil additives; aluminum alkyls. Address: Continental Oil Co, Park 80 Plaza E, Saddle Brook, NJ 07662.

FEIGIN, IRWIN H(ARRIS), b. New York, N.Y, May 13, 15; m. 49; c. 2. NEUROPATHOLOGY. B.A, Columbia, 34; M.D, N.Y, Univ, 38. Res. neuropathologist, Vet. Admin. Hosp, Bronx, 47-51; asst. prof, col. physicians & surgeons, Columbia, 52-56; assoc. prof. NEUROPATH, COL. MED, N.Y. UNIV, 56-59, PROF, 59- Neuropathologist, Jewish Sanitarium & Hosp. Chronic Diseases, Brooklyn, 49-51; Bellevue Hosp, 59-; pathologist, Sydenham Hosp, New York, 50-51; assoc. pathologist, Mt. Sinai Hosp, 51-56. Med.C, U.S.A, 42-46. Histochem. Soc; Am. Asn. Neuropath; Asn. Res. Nerv. & Ment. Diseases; Am. Asn. Path. & Bact. Histochemistry. Address: Dept. of Pathology, New York University Medical Center, 550 First Ave, New York, NY 10016.

FEIGIN, RALPH DAVID, b. N.Y.C, Apr. 3, 38; m. 60; c. 3. PEDIATRICS, INFECTIOUS DISEASES. A.B, Columbia Univ, 58; M.D, Boston Univ, 62. Intern pediat, Boston City Hosp, 62-63, resident 63-64; children's serv, Mass. Gen. Hosp, 64-65, chief resident, 67-68; instr. PEDIAT, SCH. MED, WASH. UNIV, 68-69, ASST. PROF, 69- Fel. pediat, Harvard Med. Sch, 64-65 & 67-68; clin. asst, Mass. Gen. Hosp, Boston, 67-68; asst. pediatrician, St. Louis Children's, St. Louis Maternity & McMillan Hosps, 68; assoc. pediatrician, Mo. Crippled Children's Serv, 68; assoc. dir, clin. res. ctr, Wash. Univ, 68, mem. adv. comt, 68-, safety comt, joint med. adv. bd, 71-; med. records comt, St. Louis Children's Hosp, 70-71; Nat. Inst. Allergy & Infectious Diseases res. career develop. award, 70. Med.C, U.S.A, 65-67, Capt. AAAS; Am. Fedn. Clin. Res; Am. Soc. Microbiol; Soc. Pediat. Res; Infectious Diseases Soc. Am. Metabolic response of the host to infectious diseases, including the effect of time of infectious exposure upon the outcome of disease. Address: Dept. of Pediatrics, St. Louis Children's Hospital, St. Louis, MO 63110.

FEIGL, DOROTHY MARIE, b. Evanston, Ill, Feb. 25, 38. ORGANIC CHEMISTRY. B.S, Loyola (Ill), 61; Nat. Sci. Found. summer fel, Stanford, 62, univ. fel, 62-63; Du Pont summer fel, 63, Ph.D.(org. chem), 66. Res. assoc, Stanford, 65-66; asst. prof. ORG. CHEM, ST. MARY'S COL.(IND), 66-69, ASSOC. PROF, 69- Am. Chem. Soc; The Chem. Soc. Structure of the Grignard reagent; mechanism of the Grignard reduction reaction; steroid chemistry; polymer chemistry; strained ring systems. Address: Dept. of Chemistry, St. Mary's College, Notre Dame, IN 46556.

FEIGL, ERIC O, b. Iowa City, Iowa, June 5, 33; m. 57; c. 2. PHYSIOLOGY. B.A. & B.S, Minnesota, 54, M.D, 58. Intern, Phila. Gen. Hosp, 58-59; instr. physiol, sch. med, Pennsylvania, 59-61; vis. scientist, Gothenburg Univ, 61-62; instr. PHYSIOL, sch. med, George Washington, 62-64; asst. prof. sch. med, Pennsylvania, 64-69; ASSOC. PROF, SCH. MED, UNIV. WASH, 69- Nat. Insts. Health fel, 59-62 & res. career develop. award, 64-69, res. assoc, Nat. Heart Inst, 62-64. Mem. coun. basic sci, Am. Heart Asn. U.S.P.H.S, 62-64, Surg. AAAS; Am. Physiol. Soc; Cardiac Muscle Soc; Asn. Advan. Med. Instrumentation; N.Y. Acad. Sci. Neural control of the circulation; mechanical properties of the heart and blood vessels; hypertension; cardiovascular instrumentation. Address: Dept. of Physiology, University of Washington School of Medicine, Seattle, WA 98105.

FEIGL, FRANK JOSEPH, b. Chicago, Ill, Mar. 5, 36; m. 60; c. 3. SOLID STATE PHYSICS. A.B, Notre Dame, 58; Nat. Sci. Found. fels, Pittsburgh, 61-62 & 63-64, Mellon Found. fels, 62-63 & 64-65, Ph.D.(physics), 65. Res. assoc. metal physics, mat. res. lab, Univ. Ill, Urbana-Champaign, 65-67; asst. prof. PHYSICS, LEHIGH UNIV, 67-70, ASSOC. PROF, 70-, SR. STAFF MEM, MAT. RES. CTR, 67- Am. Phys. Soc. Magnetic resonance, optical processes, and transport in insulating solids. Address: Dept. of Physics, Lehigh University, Bethlehem, PA 18015.

FEIGL, POLLY CATHERINE, b. Minneapolis, Minn, July 30, 35; m. 57; c. 2. BIOSTATISTICS. B.A. & B.S, Chicago, 56; M.A, Minnesota, 57, Ph.D.(biostatist), 61. Statistician, Smith Kline & French Labs, 58-61; math. statistician, Nat. Cancer Inst, 62-64; res. assoc. med. statist, sch. med, Univ. Pa, 64-67, ASST. PROF, 67-69; BIOSTATIST, SCH. PUB. HEALTH & COMMUNITY MED, UNIV. WASH, 69- Am. Statist. Asn; Biomet. Soc. Statistical design and analysis of biomedical experiments. Address: Dept. of Biostatistics, School of Public Health & Community Medicine, University of Washington, Seattle, WA 98105.

FEIGN, DAVID, b. N.Y.C, Apr. 28, 23; m. 54; c. 4. COMPUTER SCIENCE. B.Mech.E, City Col. New York, 44; M.S, Univ. Buffalo, 53. Res. aerodynamicist, Nat. Adv. Comt. Aeronaut, 44-48; aeronaut. lab, Cornell Univ, 48-59, head digital comput. sect, 53-59; AUTONETICS DIV, N.AM. AVIATION, INC, 59-71, MEM. TECH. STAFF, 71-; SOFTWARE CONSULT, 67- Instr, Canisius Col, 58; teacher, Eldorado Sch. Gifted Child, 61-66; instr, Univ. Calif, Irvine, 66-69, res. engr, 69-71. Asn. Comput. Mach. Digital computers; artificial intelligence. Address: 1301 Landfair Circle, Tustin, CA 92705.

FEIKER, GEORGE E(DWARD), JR, b. Northampton, Mass, May 6, 18; m. 40; c. 3. ELECTRICAL ENGINEERING. B.S, Worcester Polytech, 39; M.S, Harvard, 40; Calif. Inst. Tech, 40-41. Asst. elec. eng, Calif. Inst. Tech, 40-41; engr, GEN. ELEC. CO, 41-48, MGR, microwave eng, 48-57, radio frequency & commun. eng, 57-64, electronic eng. lab, 64-65, electronic physics lab, 65-69, ELECTRONIC ENG. LAB, 69- Instr, Rensselaer Polytech, 46-48. Coffin Award, Gen. Elec. Co. Civilian with U.S.A; U.S.A.A.F; U.S.N, 44. AAAS; Inst. Elec. & Electronics Eng. Management of research and development in electrical power conversion and control; communications; microwave generation and radiation. Address: Electronic Engineering Lab, General Electric Co, Schenectady, NY 12309.

FEIKERT, GRANT STEPHEN, b. Days Creek, Ore, Mar. 20, 06; m. 27; c. 2. ELECTRICAL ENGINEERING. B.S, Ore. State Univ, 30, M.S, 32, E.E, 37. Radio engr, ORE. STATE UNIV, 29-39, asst. prof. ELEC. ENG, 39-47, assoc. prof, 47-57, PROF, 57- Dir. eng. Ed. TV Network, Ore, 57-64; asst. to dir. Ed. Media Div. Continuing Ed. Eng, Ore. State Syst. Higher Ed, 64- Civilian with Army Specialized Training Program. Sr. mem. Inst. Elec. & Electronics Eng. Radio wave propagation; radio broadcast engineering and industrial communication. Address: 321 N.W. 23rd St, Corvallis, OR 97330.

FEIL, PETER DELMAR, b. Buffalo, N.Y, Apr. 1, 43; m. 70. REPRODUCTIVE BIOLOGY, ORGANIC CHEMISTRY. B.S, Furman Univ, 66, Nat. Defense Educ. Act fel. & M.S, 67; U.S. Dept. Agr. assistantship & Ph.D.(org. chem), Univ. Tenn, Knoxville, 70. NAT. INSTS. HEALTH TRAINEE, DEPT. OBSTET-GYNEC, SCH. MED, VANDERBILT UNIV, 70- Am. Chem. Soc. Synthesis of glycoprotein model compounds; mechanisms of steroid hormone interactions with specific tissues; synthesis of steroid derivatives and their application to population control. Address: G-8 Berkley Hills Apts, Madison, TN 37115.

FEIL, VERNON J, b. Denhoff, N.Dak, Feb. 11, 33; m. 54; c. 2. ORGANIC CHEMISTRY. B.S, Jamestown Col, 54; M.S, N.Dak. State, 56. Res. asst. org. chem, William S. Merrell Co, Ohio, 56-63; asst. prof. chem, Jamestown Col, 63-66; RES. CHEMIST, METAB. & RADIATION RES. LAB, U.S. DEPT. AGR, 66- U.S.A, 57. Am. Chem. Soc. Organic synthesis; medicinal chemistry; metabolism studies. Address: 506 21st Ave. N, Fargo, ND 58102.

FEILD, FRANK J(OSEPH), b. Baltimore, Md, Nov. 30, 21; m. 45; c. 9. BIOCHEMISTRY. B.S, Loyola Col.(Md), 43. Asst. sr. chemist, CROWN CORK & SEAL CO, 50-51, sr. chemist, 51-54, group leader applied res, 54-55, chem. res, 55-57, supvr. customer res. servs, 57-58, div. mgr. tech. servs, 58-59, mgr. closure res, 59-62, mfg. res. serv, 62-67, MGR. CROWN & CLOSURE RES, 67- U.S.N, 44-50, Lt. Inst. Food Technol; Am. Soc. Brewing Chem; Soc. Soft Drink Technol.(2nd v.pres, 61-62, 1st v.pres, 62-63, pres, 63-64). Food and beverage technology. Address: Crown Cork & Seal Co, 4200 O'Donnell St, P.O. Box 1837, Baltimore, MD 21203.

FEILD, GEORGE BERNARD, b. Petersburg, Va, May 25, 08; m. CHEMISTRY. B.S, Va. Mil. Inst, 30; M.S, Vanderbilt, 33, Ph.D.(org. chem), 37. Mill chemist, Buckeye Cotton Oil Co, Ga, 30-32; instr. chem, Vanderbilt, 33-39; indust. fel, Mellon Inst, 39-44; res. chemist, Hercules Powder Co, 44-46, sales develop, 46-50, res. ctr, 50-53, res. supvr, 53-64, res. mgr, Del, 64-70; RETIRED. Am. Chem. Soc; Sci. Res. Soc. Am; Soc. Plastics Eng. Formulations of nitrocellulose lacquers; lubricating oil additives; explosive packaging; product development; resin emulsions; reconstituted wood products; plastics and elastomers. Address: P.O. Box 145, Stone Harbor, NJ 08247.

FEILD, R(OBERT) B(EVERLEY), b. Wilkes-Barre, Pa, May 18, 25; m. 51; c. 2. CHEMICAL ENGINEERING. B.Ch.E, Virginia, 48; M.S, Illinois, 50, Ph.D, 52. Res. sect. head, east. lab, E.I. DU PONT DE NEMOURS & CO, Gibbstown, 55-60, mgr. prod. develop, chem. prod. sales div, EXPLOSIVES DEPT, Carney's Point, 60-71, MGR. TECH. SERV, RES. & DEVELOP. DIV, EAST. LAB, GIBBSTOWN, 71- Am. Chem. Soc. Technical service; product development; market research. Address: 486 Westwood Dr, Woodbury, NJ 08096.

FEIN, A(LVIN) E(LI), b. Cleveland, Ohio, Jan. 29, 31; m. 56; c. 2. APPLIED MATHEMATICS. B.S, Case, 52; Ph.D.(physics), Mass. Inst. Tech, 58. Res. physicist, Westinghouse Res. & Develop. Ctr, 56-62, assoc. dir. appl. math, surface div, Westinghouse Defense & Space Ctr, 62-68; PRES, FEIN-MARQUART ASSOCS, INC, 68- Am. Phys. Soc; Am. Math. Soc; Inst. Elec. & Electronics Eng; Soc. Indust. & Appl. Math. Celestial mechanics; communication systems; control theory; numerical analysis; computer science; data processing. Address: Fein-Marquart Associates, Inc, 4000 N. Charles St, Baltimore MD 21218.

FEIN, HARRY D(AVID), b. New York, N.Y, Apr. 24, 12; m. 39; c. 2. INTERNAL MEDICINE, GASTROENTEROLOGY. B.S, Maryland, 32; M.D, N.Y. Univ, 36. Asst. prof. CLIN. MED, COL. MED, N.Y. UNIV, 50-69, ASSOC. PROF, 69- Attend. physician, Vet. Admin. Hosp, New York, 46-56; consult, Manhattan State Hosp, 58; attend. physician & chief gastroenterol, Lenox Hill Hosp, New York, 62; assoc. vis. physician, Bellevue & Univ. Hosps. Dipl, Am. Bd. Internal Med, 43; Am. Bd. Gastroenterol. Med.C, 43-46, Maj. Am. Med. Asn; fel. Am. Col. Physicians; fel. N.Y. Acad. Med; fel. Am. Col. Gastroenterol; Am. Gastroenterol. Asn; Pan-Am. Med. Asn. Address: 3 E. 71st St, New York, NY 10021.

FEIN, HARVEY L(ESTER), b. Washington, D.C, Mar. 4, 36. CHEMICAL ENGINEERING. B.Ch.E, Cornell, 59; S.M, Mass. Inst. Tech, 61, Sc.D. (chem. eng), 63. Res. engr, ATLANTIC RES. CORP, 63-66, head thermodyn. sect, 66-67, STAFF SCIENTIST, PROPULSION & ENG. RES. DEPT, 67- Am. Chem. Soc; Am. Inst. Aeronaut. & Astronaut; Combustion Inst. Combustion; gas dynamics; propulsion system analysis; solid propellants; thermodynamics; polymer physics; diffusion. Address: 2601 Woodley Pl. N.W, Washington, DC 20008.

FEIN, LOUIS, b. Brooklyn, N.Y, Oct. 1, 17; m. 42; c. 6. PHYSICS. B.S, Long Island, 38; M.S, Colorado, 41; scholar, Brown, 42, Ph.D.(physics), 47. Instr. physics & math, Earlham Col, 41-43; res. assoc, underwater sound lab, Harvard, 43-45; elec. engr, Submarine Sig. Co, 45-47; physicist, Martin-Hubbard Corp, 47-49; sect. head, comput. dept, Raytheon Mfg. Co, 49-52; pres, Comput. Control Co, Inc, 52-55; consult, 55-65; PRES, SYNNOETIC SYSTS, 65-69, COMPUT. CONSULT, 69- Lectr, Stanford, 56-64. Am. Phys. Soc; Asn. Comput. Mach; Inst. Elec. & Electronics Eng. Ultrasonic radiation and detection; electro-acoustic measurements and instrumentation; ultrasonic radiation from curved quartz crystals; design, operation, maintenance, application and evaluation of high speed digital computers; reliability of electronic equipment; artificial intelligence; information retrieval; simulation; social impact of automation; supradisciplinary education. Address: Synnoetic Systems, 431 Ferne Ave, Palo Alto, CA 94306.

FEIN, MARVIN MICHAEL, b. Brooklyn, N.Y, July 31, 23; m. 46; c. 2. ORGANIC CHEMISTRY. A.B, Brooklyn Col, 43; M.S, Purdue, 48, Westinghouse res. fel. & univ. res. found. fel, 48-49, Ph.D.(org. chem), 49. Res. chemist, Schenley Labs, 49-50; Nat. Aniline Div, Allied Chem. & Dye Corp, 50-55; sect. supvr. appl. chem. res, reaction motors div, Thiokol Chem. Corp, 56-64; mgr. indust. org. chem. & acetylenic chem. res. & develop, GAF Corp, 64-67, asst. mgr. res. develop. dept, 67, tech. dir. dyestuff & chem. prod, 67-70; V.PRES. RES. & DEVELOP, CHEM. SPECIALTIES, DART INDUSTS. INC, 70- U.S.A, 44-46. AAAS; Am. Inst. Chem; Am. Chem. Soc; Asn. Res. Dirs. Nitration; fluorination; organometallics; polymers; detergents; acetylenics; dyestuffs; pollution control; catalysts. Address: Chemical Group, Dart Industries, Inc, P.O. Box 37, Paramus, NJ 07652.

FEIN, R(ICHARD) S(AUL), b. Milwaukee, Wis, Apr. 25, 23; m. 48; c. 3. CHEMICAL ENGINEERING. B.S, Wisconsin, 47, Ph.D.(chem. eng), 49. Asst, Naval Res. Lab, Wisconsin, 46-49; chem. engr, TEXACO, INC, 49-57, group leader, 57-64, res. assoc, 64-68, FUNDAMENTAL RES. SUPVR, 68- U.S.N.R, 44-46. AAAS; Am. Chem. Soc; Sci. Res. Soc. Am; Am. Soc. Lubrication Eng.(Hunt award, 66); Am. Soc. Mech. Eng; Catalysis Soc. Laminar flame speeds and temperatures; fuel applications, primarily in engines and vehicles; engine lubrication; fundamentals of boundary lubrication; combustion chemistry. Address: 35 Sheldon Dr, Poughkeepsie, NY 12603.

FEINBERG, ALAN R(ICHARD), b. Chicago, Ill, Apr. 7, 23; m. 44; c. 5. MEDICINE. B.S, Northwestern, 43, B.M, 46, M.D, 47, M.S, 51. Asst, SCH. MED, NORTHWEST. UNIV, 50-51, instr. MED, 53-58, ASSOC, 58-, allergy res. lab, 50-64; MED. STAFF, DEPT. RES. & ED, EVANSTON HOSP, 64- Dipl, Am. Bd. Internal Med, 53; Am. Bd. Allergy, 54. U.S.A, 42-43, Med.C, 51-53, Capt. Am. Med. Asn; fel. Am. Col. Physicians; fel. Am. Acad. Allergy. Allergy and immunology; antihistamines; insect allergy; corticosteroids. Address: Allergy Research Lab, Evanston Hospital, 2650 Ridge Ave, Evanston, IL 60201.

FEINBERG, BARRY N(ORMAN), b. Chicago, Ill, Dec. 24, 38; m. 63. BIOMEDICAL ENGINEERING. B.S.E.Math. & B.S.E.E, Univ. Mich, 62; M.E.E, Univ. Louisville, 64; Ohio Thoracic Soc. grant, 68; Ph.D.(systs. eng), Case West. Reserve Univ, 69. Instr. math, Univ. Louisville, 62-64; lectr. control systs, Univ. Edinburgh, 68-69; ASST. PROF. ELEC. ENG, CLEVELAND STATE UNIV, 69- Res. grant, Cleveland State Univ, 70; consult, Vet. Admin. Hosp, Cleveland, Ohio, 71. AAAS. Application of systems theory and control theory to the biomedical area especially the use of mathematical models and optimization techniques for the detection and diagnosis of obstructive lung disease, asthma, bronchitis and emphysema. Address: Dept. of Electrical Engineering, Cleveland State University, 1983 E. 24th St, Cleveland, OH 44115.

FEINBERG, BERNARD, b. Pittsburgh, Pa, Aug. 26, 17; m. 43; c. 2. FOOD TECHNOLOGY. B.S, Pa. State, 43. Contract serv. officer, Qm. Procurement, U.S. Dept. Army, 46-56; tech. dir, Fairview Packing Co, 56-62; FOOD RES. CHEMIST, WEST. REGIONAL RES. LAB, U.S. DEPT. AGR, 62- UN food processing specialist, Dominican Repub, 71. Med.C, U.S.A, 43-46. Inst. Food Technol. Quality control; development of new products; investigation of stability of new potato products; legal and religious implications of imitation foods. Address: 1188 Keeler Ave, Berkeley, CA 94708.

FEINBERG, DONALD LESTER, b. Brooklyn, N.Y, Dec. 17, 25; m. 62. PEDIATRICS. B.A, Hamilton Col.(N.Y), 45; M.D, N.Y. Univ, 49. Intern, N.Y. Polyclinic Med. Sch. & Hosp, 49-50; Children's Med. Ctr, Harvard, 50-51; asst. res, Children's Hosp. of Mich, 51-52; jr. res, Sarah Morris Children's Hosp. of Michael Reese Hosp, Chicago, 52-53, sr. res, 53-54; asst. clin. prof. pediat, N.Y. Med. Col, 56-57, asst. prof, 57-69; FEL. PEDIAT. NEUROL, MT. SINAI SCH. MED, 70- Chief pediat. outpatient dept, Metropolitan Hosp, 56-57; pediat. consult. maternity, family planning & newborn bur, N.Y.C. Health Dept, 61-69; clin. prof, N.Y. Polyclin. Med. Sch. & Hosp, 60-64; dir. pediat, Knickerbocker Hosp, N.Y.C, 62-64. Dipl, Am. Bd. Pediat, 54. Med.C, U.S.A.F, 54-56, Capt. Fel. Am. Acad. Pediat. Address: Mount Sinai School of Medicine, 711 W. 190th St, New York, NY 10040.

FEINBERG, EDWIN H(AROLD), b. Boston, Mass, Dec. 20, 27; m. 54; c. 2. BIOLOGY, ANIMAL ECOLOGY. A.B, Boston, 50, A.M, 51; Ph.D.(animal ecol), Cornell, 62. Patent exam, Patent Off, D.C, 51-52; teacher, high sch, Ind, 52-54, N.Y, 54-58; Nat. Insts. Health co-trainee pop. biol, Stanford Univ, 62-64; asst. prof. biol, Wheeling Col, 64-66; Richmond Prof. Inst, 66-68; HEAD LIT. RESOURCES, BIOSCI. INFO. SERV. BIOL. ABSTRACTS, 68- U.S.A, 45-47. Animal population ecology; evolutionary selection experiments; mark-recapture analysis; limnology; insect life histories. Address: Literature Resources Dept, BioSciences Information Service of Biological Abstracts, 2100 Arch St, Philadelphia, PA 19103.

FEINBERG, G(ERALD), b. N.Y.C, May 27, 33; m. 68; c. 1. PHYSICS. B.A, Columbia, 53, Nat. Sci. Found. fel, 53-56, M.A, 54, Ph.D.(physics), 57. Mem, sch. math, inst. adv. study, Princeton, 56-57; res. assoc, Brookhaven Nat. Lab, 57-59; asst. prof. PHYSICS, COLUMBIA UNIV, 59-61, assoc. prof, 61-65, PROF, 65- Adj. asst. prof. & consult, physics dept, N.Y. Univ, 59; consult, Brookhaven Nat. Lab, 59-; overseas fel, Churchill Col, Cambridge, 63-64. Am. Phys. Soc. Elementary particles; field theory. Address: Dept. of Physics, Columbia University, New York, NY 10027.

FEINBERG, H(AROLD), b. Chicago, Ill, June 20, 22; m. 47; c. 2. PHARMACOLOGY. B.A, California, Los Angeles, 48, M.A, 50; Baxter fel, California, 51-52, Ph.D.(physiol), 52. Life Ins. med. res. fel, California, 52-53; chief biochemist, Children's Mem. Hosp. & instr. biochem, med. sch, Northwestern, 53-55; res. assoc, cardiovasc. dept, Med. Res. Inst, Michael Reese Hosp, 55-61; res. assoc. biochem, Univ. Birmingham, 61-63; assoc. prof. PHARMACOL, UNIV. ILL. COL. MED, 63-70, PROF, 70- Am. Heart Asn. res. fel, 56-58, adv. res. fel, 58-60, estab. investr, 60-65. U.S.A, 42-46. Am. Chem. Soc; Am. Physiol. Soc; Am. Soc. Pharmacol. & Exp. Therapeut. Cardiovascular physiology; metabolism of cardiac muscle. Address: 6949 Bennett, Chicago, IL 60649.

FEINBERG, I(RWIN), b. Brooklyn, N.Y, June 11, 28; m. 59. PSYCHIATRY. B.A, Brooklyn Col, 49; M.A, Swarthmore Col, 51; M.D, N.Y. Univ, 55. Asst. psychol, Swarthmore Col, 49-50; intern, Boston City Hosp, 55-56; resident psychiat, Boston Psychopathic Hosp, 56-57; res. psychiatrist, Nat. Inst. Ment. Health, 57-64; asst. prof. PSYCHIAT, State Univ. N.Y. Downstate Med. Ctr, 64-69; PROF, UNIV. CALIF, SAN FRANCISCO, 69-, V.CHMN. DEPT, 70-; CHIEF PSYCHIAT. SERV, FT. MILEY VET. ADMIN. HOSP, 69- Fel, Harvard Med. Sch, 56-57; Nat. Inst. Ment. Health trainee, Inst. Sci. Ed, Geneva, 60-61. U.S.P.H.S, 57-64, Res. Psychiatrist. AAAS. Clinical and experimental psychiatry; sleep disorder in mental illness. Address: Ft. Miley Veterans Administration Hospital, 42nd Ave. & Clement St, San Francisco, CA 94121.

FEINBERG, LEONARD J(AY), b. Long Branch, N.J, Sept. 7, 23; m. 48; c. 2. BIOCHEMISTRY. B.S, Rutgers, 47; M.S, George Washington, 50; Ph.D.(biochem), Pa. State, 52. Res. biochemist indust. waste develop, Barrett Div, Allied Chem. & Dye Corp, 52-56; CHIEF CARDIOL. RES. LABS, PHILA. GEN. HOSP, 56- U.S.A, 43-45. Am. Fedn. Clin. Res. Lipid metabolism as related to atherosclerosis; use of isotopes in determining defects in lipid metabolism in man. Address: Division of Cardiology, Philadelphia General Hospital, 34th & Civic Center Blvd, Philadelphia, PA 19104.

FEINBERG, MARTIN ROBERT, b. New York, N.Y, Apr. 2, 42; m. 65. CHEMICAL ENGINEERING. B.Ch.E, Cooper Union, 62; M.S, Purdue, 63; Ph.D. (chem. eng), Princeton, 68. ASST. PROF. CHEM. ENG, UNIV. ROCHESTER, 67- Am. Inst. Chem. Eng; Soc. Natural Philos; Soc. Rheol. Fluid and continuum mechanics; applied mathematics; thermodynamics; mathematics of complex chemical reaction systems. Address: Dept. of Chemical Engineering, University of Rochester, Rochester, NY 14627.

FEINBERG, MELVYN JOEL, b. New York, N.Y, Dec. 4, 38; m. 65; c. 1. CHEMICAL PHYSICS. A.B, Northwestern, 60; univ. fel, Michigan, 60-62, M.S, 62, Nat. Sci. Found. fel, 62-63, Ph.D.(phys. chem), 63. Nat. Sci. Found. fel. CHEM, Hopkins, 63-64 & Iowa State, 64-65, res. assoc, 65; ASST. PROF, TUFTS UNIV, 65- Am. Phys. Soc. Semi-empirical investigations on intermolecular forces; quantum mechanical calculations of the properties of small molecules; physical nature of the chemical bond. Address: Dept. of Chemistry, Tufts University, Medford, MA 02155.

FEINBERG, RICHARD, b. Rochester, N.Y, Apr. 7, 11; m. 36; c. 3. PSYCHOLOGY. B.S, Rochester, 33; Ph.D.(appl. psychol), Purdue, 47; hon. D.O.S, North. Ill. Col. Optom, 44. Optom. private practice, N.Y, 33-43; supvr. eye serv, Sperry Gyroscope Co, 43-45; res. assoc. psychol, Purdue, 45-47; prof. & dean col, Pac. Univ, 48-51; pres, North. Ill. Col. Optom, 52-56; dir. div. appl. visual sci, Titmus Optical Co, 56-60; indust. consult. human factors, 60-61; chief visual & auditory lab, Georgetown Clin. Res. Inst, Fed. Aviation Agency, Del, 61-66; PROF. ANALYST, NAT. INST. NEUROL. DISEASES & STROKE, 66- Res. assoc, univ. hosp, Georgetown Univ, 61-; res. ed, Eye, Ear, Nose & Throat J, 61-; J. Learning Disabilities. AAAS; Am. Psychol. Asn; Am. Acad. Optom; Am. Med. Writers Asn. Address: National Institute of Neurological Diseases & Stroke, Bethesda, MD 20014.

FEINBERG, RICHARD JUSTIN, b. Fall River, Mass, Dec. 27, 22; m. 53; c. 2. IMMUNOLOGY, ALLERGY. A.B, Wesleyan, 46; Sc.M, Brown, 48; M.D. & Ph.D.(microbiol), Pennsylvania, 57. Am. Diabetic Asn. intern & resident res. award, 57; ASST. PROF. MICROBIOL, SCH. MED, GEORGETOWN UNIV, 61- Nat. Insts. Health res. career develop. award, 62-65; consult, U.S. Naval Hosp, Bethesda, Md. Dipl, Am. Bd. Pediat. & cert, pediat. allergy, 66. U.S.N.R, 41-46, Lt.(jg). Am. Acad. Allergy; Am. Asn. Immunol. Physical, chemical and biological characterization of antibodies, particularly reagin antibody. Address: 5201 Connecticut Ave. N.W, Washington, DC 20015.

FEINBERG, ROBERT, b. Fall River, Mass, Dec. 27, 22; m. 53; c. 3. IMMUNOLOGY. A.B, Wesleyan, 45; Sc.M, Brown, 48; Chapin fel, 48-49, Rhode Island; Ph.D.(microbiol), Pennsylvania, 53. Instr. microbiol, Pennsylvania, 51-52; immunochemist, Walter Reed Army Inst. Res. 52-57; PRES. & ADMIN. DIR, SUBURBAN CLIN. LABS, INC, 57-, DIR, SUBURBAN SERUM LABS, 59- U.S.N.R, 43-46. Immunochemistry; antigen-antibody reactions with special reference to methods of detecting non precipitating antibodies in experimental animals and humans. Address: Suburban Clinical Labs, Inc, 10620 Georgia Ave, Silver Spring, MD 20902.

FEINBERG, ROBERT H(ERMAN), b. Chicago, Ill, Jan. 25, 27; m. 52; c. 2. BIOCHEMISTRY. B.S, Northwestern, 48; Ph.D.(physiol. chem), California, 58. Res. assoc. biochem, Palo Alto Med. Res. Found, 57-58; Okla. Med. Res. Inst. 58-60; ASST. PROF. BIOCHEM, Vanderbilt, 60-63; UNIV. TENN, KNOXVILLE, 63- Intermediary metabolism of amino acids and vitamins; enzymology; membrane transport. Address: Dept. of Biochemistry, University of Tennessee, Knoxville, TN 37916.

FEINBERG, ROBERT J, b. Chelsea, Mass, Apr. 6, 31; m. 64; c. 2. PHYSICS. B.S, Boston Col, 53, fel, 53-54, M.S, 54; Atomic Energy comn. fel, Rochester, 54-55; Atomic Energy Cmn. fel, Oak Ridge Sch. Reactor Tech, 55-56. Instr. physics, Boston Col, 53-54; physicist, Oak Ridge Nat. Lab, 54-55; radiol. physicist, KNOLLS ATOMIC POWER LAB, GEN. ELEC. CO, 56-58, supv. physicist, reactor safeguards & radiol. develop, 58-60, radiol. physics & eng, 60-62, proj. engr, 62-63, consult. nuclear & radiol. safety, 63-64, supvr, 64-66, MGR. HEALTH PHYSICS, 66- Summers, mem. staff, Picatiny Arsenal, 51, physicist, Nat. Bur. Standards, 52, mem. staff, Air Force Cambridge Res. Center, 53-54, health physicist, Brookhaven Nat. Lab, 55. Mem, Atomic Indust. Forum; Am. Inst. Physics. Dipl, Am. Bd. Health Physics, 61. Am. Nuclear Soc; Health Physics Soc. Atomic energy; nuclear engineering; reactor safeguards and hazards evaluation; radiological physics and engineering; radiation dosimetry and instrumentation, nuclear criticality analysis. Address: Knolls Atomic Power Lab, General Electric Co, Schenectady, NY 12301.

FEINBERG, ROBERT SAMUEL, b. Baltimore, Md, June 10, 40; m. 71. BIOORGANIC CHEMISTRY. B.A, Harvard, 61; Nat. Insts. Health fel, Oxford, 62-65, Ph.D.(org. chem), 65. RES. ASSOC, McCollum Pratt Inst, Johns

Hopkins Univ, 65-66, org. chem. dept, 66-69; ROCKEFELLER UNIV, 69- Am. Chem. Soc. Hemoglobin model compounds; solid-phase synthesis of peptides and proteins. Address: Rockefeller University, New York, NY 10021.

FEINDEL, WILLIAM H(OWARD), b. Bridgewater, N.S, July 12, 18; m; c. 6. NEUROSURGERY. Rhodes scholar. & B.A, Acadia, 39, hon. D.Sc, 63; M.Sc, Dalhousie, 42; M.D, C.M, McGill, 45; Med. Res. Coun. Gt. Brit. fel, Oxford, 48, Rockefeller Found. grant, 48-49, D.Phil.(neuroanat), 49. Med. res, exp. head injuries, Montreal Neurol. Inst, 42-44, Nat. Res. Coun. Can. fel. med, 49-50; lectr. NEUROSURG, McGill, 52-55; prof, Saskatchewan, 55-59; CONE PROF, McGILL UNIV, 59- Reford fel, Montreal Neurol. Inst, 53-55, neurosurgeon-in-chief, 63-; hon. asst. librarian, Osler Library, McGill, 64-; vis. lectr, Yale, 66; dir, fourth Can. Cong. Neurol. Sci, Montreal, 69; vis. prof, Univ. B.C, 70-71; vis. lectr, Univ. Calif, San Francisco, 71- Dipl, Am. Bd. Neurol. Surg, 55; fel, Royal Col. Physicians & Surgeons, Can, 55. R.C.A.M.C, 43-45. Am. Acad. Neurol; Am. Acad. Neurol. Surg; Soc. Neurol. Surg; Am. Asn. Neurol. Surg; Am. Neurol. Asn; Can. Neurosurg. Soc; Royal Soc. Med; Anat. Soc. Gt. Brit. & Ireland. Clinical neurosurgery; cerebral oedema; immersion foot; neurohistology of peripheral nervous system; anatomy of pain; temporal lobe function; radioisotopes in cerebral localization and circulation; 17th century medical history. Address: Montreal Neurological Institute, 3801 University St, Montreal 212, Que, Can.

FEINER, F(RANK), b. Hamburg, Germany, May 8, 28; nat; m. 52; c. 2. NUCLEAR PHYSICS. A.B, Princeton, 50; M.S, Carnegie Inst. Tech, 52, Ph.D. (physics), 55. Res. assoc, KNOLLS ATOMIC POWER LAB, GEN. ELEC. CO, 55-59, MGR. adv. exp. physics, 59-64, ADVAN. REACTOR PHYSICS, 64- Nat. Sci. Found. fel, 52-53; vis. prof, Cornell Univ, 67-68. Am. Phys. Soc; Am. Nuclear Soc. Experimental reactor physics; high energy particle physics. Address: Knolls Atomic Power Lab, General Electric Co, Box 1072, F Bldg, Schenectady, NY 12301.

FEINER, ROSE R(ESNICK), b. New York, N.Y, May 23, 14; m. 36; c. 2. BIOLOGY. B.A, Hunter Col, 34, Woods Hole scholar, 34; M.A, Columbia, 36, Ph.D.(bact), 41. Res. asst. bact, Columbia, 35-37, 40-42, 44-46, 49-52; instr. physiol, Hunter Col, 37-39; res. asst. bact, N.Y. Univ, 43-44; instr. BIOL, CITY COL. NEW YORK, 52-55, lectr, 55-59, instr, 59-61, asst. prof, 61-66, assoc. prof, 66-71, PROF, 71- AAAS; Am. Soc. Microbiol; Genetics Soc. Am. Microbiology. Address: Dept. of Biology, City College of New York, 139th St. & Convent Ave, New York, NY 10031.

FEINGOLD, ADOLPH, b. Poltava, U.S.S.R, Mar. 8, 20; m. 64; c. 2. MECHANICAL ENGINEERING. Ph.D, Genoa, 52. Assoc. prof. mech. eng. Univ. Mo-Rolla, 63-64, PROF, 64-66; CIVIL ENG, UNIV. OTTAWA, 66-, CHMN. DEPT. MECH. ENG, 67- Brit. Inst. Marine Eng; Israel Soc. Naval Archit. & Marine Eng.(pres, 61); Am. Soc. Mech. Eng; Eng. Inst. Can; Can. Soc. Mech. Eng; Am. Acad. Mech. Internal combustion engines; application of computors in design; heat transfer; arctic technology; low temperature environmental problems; marine engineering; ocean bed technology. Address: 330 Driveway, Apt. 801, Ottawa, Ont, Can.

FEINGOLD, ARNOLD M(OSES), b. Brooklyn, N.Y, Dec. 30, 20; m. 54; c. 2. NUCLEAR PHYSICS. A.B, Brooklyn Col, 41; Nat. Res. Coun. fel, Princeton, 46-49, M.S, 48, Ph.D.(physics), 52. Physicist, Langley Mem. Aeronaut. Lab, 41-46; instr. PHYSICS, Pennsylvania, 50-53, asst. prof, 53-55; Illinois, 55-57; assoc. prof, Utah, 57-60; PROF, STATE UNIV. N.Y. STONY BROOK, 60- AAAS; fel. Am. Phys. Soc; Am. Asn. Physics Teachers. Theoretical nuclear physics; tensor force effects in nuclei. Address: Dept. of Physics, State University of New York at Stony Brook, Stony Brook, NY 11790.

FEINGOLD, BEN F, b. Pittsburgh, Pa, June 15, 00. ALLERGY, IMMUNOLOGY. B.S, Pittsburgh, 21, M.D, 24. Instr. pediat, med. sch, Northwestern, 29-32; attend. pediatrician, Cedars of Lebanon Hosp, Los Angeles, Calif, 32-40, chief dept. pediat, 40-50; chief ALLERGY DEPT, PERMANENTE MED. GROUP, KAISER FOUND. HOSPS, 51-71, EMER. CHIEF, 71-, DIR. LAB. MED. ENTOM, RES. INST, 59- Attend. pediatrician, Chicago Lying-In Hosp, 29-32; Los Angeles County Hosp, 32-39; attend. pediatrician & assoc. allergy, Los Angeles Children's Hosp, 32-51. Fel. Am. Acad. Allergy; fel. Am. Col. Allergists; fel. Am. Acad. Pediat. Problems of clinical allergy; problems of immunology and immunochemistry, especially behavior of low molecular fractions and compounds in the antigen-antibody reaction. Address: 1050 Northpoint St, San Francisco, CA 94109.

FEINGOLD, DAVID S(IDNEY), b. Chelsea, Mass, Nov. 15, 22; m. 49; c. 3. BIOCHEMISTRY. B.S, Mass. Inst. Tech, 44; Ph.D.(biochem), Hebrew Univ, 56. Chemist, Lucidol Corp, 44; instr, Northeastern, 46-47; chemist, Hadassah Hosp, Jerusalem, 50-51; asst, med. sch, Hebrew Univ, 51-56; jr. res. biochemist, California, Berkeley, 56-58, asst. res. biochemist, 58-60; asst. prof. BIOL, FACULTY ARTS & SCI, UNIV. PITTSBURGH, 60-63, assoc. prof, 63-66, PROF, 66-, MICROBIOL, SCH. MED, 66- Nat. Insts. Health res. career develop. award, 65-75. State of Israel prize, 57. U.S.N, 44-46. Am. Chem. Soc; Am. Soc. Biol. Chem. Intermediary carbohydrate metabolism; enzymic transformations of carbohydrates; biosynthesis of poly- and oligosaccharides; transglycosylation; structure of polysaccharides; enzyme mechanism; dehydrogenases. Address: Dept. of Microbiology, School of Medicine, University of Pittsburgh, Pittsburgh, PA 15213.

FEINGOLD, EARL, b. Philadelphia, Pa, Dec. 4, 24; m. 47; c. 2. SOLID STATE PHYSICS. A.B, Temple, 50, fel, 50-51, A.M, 51, Ph.D.(physics), 59. Asst. instr. physics, Temple, 49-51; res. physicist, Brown Instrument Div, Minneapolis Honeywell Regulator Co, 51-52; res. center, Burroughs Corp, 52-54; solid state res. physicist, Atlantic Ref. Co, 54-59; SOLID STATE PHYSICIST, SPACE SCI. LAB, SPACE DIV, GEN. ELEC. CO, 59- U.S.A, 43-46. AAAS; Am. Phys. Soc; Sci. Res. Soc. Am; Int. Metallog. Soc. Physical and chemical characterization of matter; electron and optical microscopy; x-ray diffraction and spectroscopy; refractory-high-strength-special purpose materials; materials sciences; surface properties; thin films; physical metallurgy. Address: 708 Fox Hunt Lane, Warminster, PA 18974.

FEININGER, TOMAS, b. Stockholm, Sweden, Sept. 21, 35; U.S. citizen; m. 63; c. 2. GEOLOGY. B.A, Middlebury Col, 56; M.Sc, Brown Univ, 60, Ph.D. (geol), 64. Geologist, eng. geol. br, U.S. Geol. Surv, 56-59, br. regional geol, New Eng, 60-64, off. int. geol, 64-69; vis. res. assoc, Smithsonian Inst, 69-70; CHMN. DEPT. GEOL, MINING & PETROL, NAT. POLYTECH. SCH, QUITO, ECUADOR, 70- AAAS; Geol. Soc. Am; Ecuadorian Inst. Natural Sci. Igneous and metamorphic petrology. Address: Dept. of Geology, Mining & Petroleum, National Polytechnic School, Casilla 2759, Quito, Ecuador.

FEINLAND, RAYMOND, b. New York, N.Y, Oct. 12, 28; m. 59. PHYSICAL & ANALYTICAL CHEMISTRY. B.S, Brooklyn Col, 49; fel, Polytech. Inst. Brooklyn, 51-52, 55-56, M.S, 52, Ph.D.(chem), 57. Sr. res. chemist, Am. Cyanamid Co, Conn, 57-65; MGR. ANAL. RES, CLAIROL INC, 65- Chem.C, 52-54, Res, 54. Am. Chem. Soc. Gas-liquid chromatography; ion exchange resins; polymer solution theory; chromatography; spectrophotometry; general analytical techniques. Address: Research Lab, Clairol Inc, 90 Commerce Rd, Stamford, CT 06902.

FEINLEIB, JULIUS, b. Brooklyn, N.Y, Sept. 17, 36; m. 61. SOLID STATE PHYSICS. B.Eng.Phys, Cornell, 58; Wilson fel. & M.A, Harvard, 59, Nat. Sci. Found. fel. & Ph.D.(appl. & solid state physics), 63. Fel, Harvard, 63-64; staff physicist, Lincoln Lab, Mass. Inst. Technol, 64-69; mem. staff, Energy Conversion Devices, Inc, 69-71, MGR, PHYSICS LAB, ITEK CORP, 71- Am. Phys. Soc. High pressure physics of semiconductors; nuclear resonance in magnetic materials; optical properties of magnetic materials; amorphous semiconductors and optical computer memories. Address: 87 Wendell St, Cambridge, MA 02138.

FEINLEIB, MANNING, b. Brooklyn, N.Y, July 19, 35; m. 57; c. 3. EPIDEMIOLOGY, BIOSTATISTICS. A.B, Cornell, 56; M.D, State Univ. N.Y. Downstate Med. Ctr, 61; M.P.H, Harvard, 63, Dr.P.H, 66. Instr. statist, State Univ. N.Y, 58-59; fel. epidemiol, sch. pub. health, Harvard, 63-66; med. officer epidemiol, NAT. HEART & LUNG INST, 66-68, CHIEF FIELD EPIDEMIOL. RES. SECT, 68-, CHIEF EPIDEMIOL. BR, 70- Asst. med, Peter Bent Brigham Hosp, 62-66; assoc. registrar, Mass. Tumor Registry, 64-66; asst. prof, sch. pub. health, Harvard, 66-68. U.S.P.H.S, 66-68, Surg. AAAS; Am. Pub. Health Asn; Am. Statist. Asn; Biomet. Soc; Am. Epidemiol. Soc; Soc. Epidemiol. Res; Int. Epidemiol. Asn. Epidemiology of heart disease. Address: Epidemiology Branch, National Heart & Lung Institute, Bldg. 31, Room 1C17, Bethesda, MD 20014.

FEINLEIB, MARY ELLA (HARMAN), b. Italy, May 21, 38; U.S. citizen; m. 61. PLANT PHYSIOLOGY. A.B, Cornell, 59; Nat. Sci. Found. fel. & A.M, Radcliffe Col, 61; Nat. Insts. Health & Ph.D.(biol), Harvard, 66. Instr. BIOL, TUFTS UNIV, 65-66, ASST. PROF, 66- AAAS; Am. Soc. Plant Physiol; Scand. Soc. Plant Physiol. Phototaxis in algae, specifically in Chlamydomonas. Address: Dept. of Biology, Tufts University, Medford, MA 02155.

FEINLEIB, MORRIS, b. Berlin, Germany, July 16, 24; nat; m. 58; c. 2. CHEMICAL ENGINEERING, ELECTROCHEMISTRY. B.S, Columbia, 44, M.S, 45, Ph.D.(chem. eng), 48. Res. electrochemist, metals res. dept, Armour Res. Found, Ill, 48-52; res. electrochemist & group leader, reduction res. sect, Kaiser Aluminum & Chem. Corp, Wash. & Calif, 52-58; res. scientist, electrochem. sect, missiles & space div, Lockheed Aircraft Corp, 58-59; sr. res. engr, tube res. dept, VARIAN ASSOCS, 59-63, MGR. tube process develop, 63-67, chem. vapor deposition pilot facility, cent. res, 67-69, PHOTOCONDUCTOR PREP, ELECTROPHOTOG. UNIT, 69- C.Eng, U.S.A, 45-46. Electrochem. Soc; Am. Chem. Soc. High temperature materials and methods, including fused salts, chemical vapor deposition; batteries; electroplating; materials and chemical processes in electronics; special photoconductors. Address: Electrophotography Unit, Varian Associates, 611 Hansen Way, Palo Alto, CA 94303.

FEINLEIB, SIDNEY, b. Brooklyn, N.Y, Dec. 31, 38; m. 60. PHYSICAL CHEMISTRY. B.A, Columbia, 60, M.A, 61; Ph.D.(phys. chem), Minnesota, 65. Res. in PHYS. CHEM, Bell Tel. Labs, 65-68; CONSULT, ARTHUR D. LITTLE, INC, 68- AAAS; Am. Chem. Soc. Vacuum ultraviolet spectroscopy; vacuum ultraviolet spectroscopy; markets and technology in microfilm; reprography and video systems; Japanese business; technological forecasting; research evaluation. Address: Arthur D. Little, Inc, Acorn Park, Boston, MA 02140.

FEINMAN, J(EROME), b. Brooklyn, N.Y, Mar. 18, 28; m. 54; c. 3. CHEMICAL ENGINEERING. B.Ch.E, Polytech. Inst. Brooklyn, 49; M.S.Ch.E, Ill. Inst. Technol, 56; Ph.D.(chem. eng), Pittsburgh, 64. Chem. engr, Plicose Mfg. Co, 50; from proj. engr. to sr. proj. engr, APPL. RES. LAB, U.S. STEEL CORP, 52-60, sect. head, ore reduction tech. sect, 60-64, sr. process engr. process eng. div, 64-65, assoc. res. consult, 65-, SECT. SUPVR, 66, RAW MAT. PROCESSING DIV, 69- Chem.C, U.S.A, 50-52. Am. Chem. Soc; Am. Inst. Chem. Eng. Process research and development; fluidized reduction of iron ore; fluidization; heat transfer, process evaluation and engineering. Address: Applied Research Lab, U.S. Steel Corp, Monroeville, PA 15146.

FEINMAN, MAX L, b. N.Y.C, May 13, 05; m. 33; c. 2. SURGERY, ANATOMY. Columbia Univ, 22-24; M.D, State Univ. N.Y. Downstate Med. Ctr, 28. Fel. anat, L.I. Col. Hosp, 47-51, assoc. anat, 50-54; attend. surgeon, Wyckoff Heights Hosp, Brooklyn, N.Y, 58-64; DIR. MED. EDUC, DOCTORS HOSP, 64-; PROF. ANAT. & SURG, M.J. LEWI COL. PODIATRY, 65- Surgeon, Coney Island Hosp, 49-54; dir. surg, Lefferts Gen. Hosp, Brooklyn, N.Y, 58-63. General surgery; traumatic surgery. Address: 25 Sutton Pl. S, New York, NY 10022.

FEINROTH, MARTIN, b. New York, N.Y, Oct. 29, 41; m. 66. PHYSICS. A.B, Cornell, 62; Ph.D.(physics), Mass. Inst. Tech, 67. Res. assoc. PHYSICS, UNIV. MD, COLLEGE PARK, 67-69, ASST. PROF, 69- Am. Phys. Soc. Theoretical elementary particle physics. Address: Dept. of Physics, University of Maryland, College Park, MD 20742.

FEINS, IRVIN R, b. Boston, Mass, May 30, 41; m. 66; c. 1. INORGANIC CHEMISTRY. B.S, Boston Col, 62; Ph.D.(inorg. chem), Rensselaer Polytech, 66. RES. CHEMIST, AM CYANAMID CO, 66- Am. Chem. Soc. Transition metal complexes as applied to catalysis. Address: 1937 W. Main St, Stamford, CT 06905.

FEINSILVER, LEO, b. Cleveland, Ohio, Oct. 24, 13; m. 37; c. 3. BIOCHEMISTRY. B.S, Akron, 36; Western Reserve; Maryland. Chemist, Polson Rubber Co, 36-37; Miller Drug Co, 37; jr. chemist, Ord. Dept, U.S. Army, 41-42, asst. chemist, Qm. Corps, 42-46, gen. chemist & group leader, div. toxicol, directorate med. res, chem. warfare labs, 46-66, res. chemist, toxicol. dept, med. res. lab, Edgewood Arsenal, 66-71; RETIRED. AAAS; Am. Chem. Soc; Sci. Res. Soc. Am. Analytical biochemistry; chemistry of air pollution; toxicological mechanisms. Address: 1905 Hanson Rd, Edgewood, MD 21040.

FEINSTEIN, ALEJANDRO, b. La Plata, Argentina, May 30, 29; m. 59; c. 3. ASTROPHYSICS. Astronr, Univ. La Plata, 56, Dr. Astron, 60. Observer asst. astron, ASTRON. OBSERV, UNIV. LA PLATA, 48-56, instr, 52-56, tech. asst, 56-62, asst. prof, astrophys, 62-63, PROF. ASTRON, 63-, instr. math, faculty phys. sci. & math, 58-61. Nat. Coun. Sci. & Tech. Res, Argentina fel; Lick Observ, Calif, 61-62; Guggenheim Mem. Found. fel, Steward Observ, Univ. Ariz, 69-70. Argentine Astron. Asn; Royal Astron. Soc; Int. Astron. Union. Photoelectric photometry of stars at different wave lengths; distribution of stars in relation with galactic structure; open clusters. Address: Observatorio Astronómico, La Plata, Argentina.

FEINSTEIN, ALLEN IRWIN, b. Brooklyn, N.Y, Apr. 9, 40; m. 62; c. 3. ORGANIC CHEMISTRY. B.S, Brooklyn Col, 62; Shell Found. fel, Iowa State Univ, 65-66, Ph.D.(alkaloid biosynthesis), 67. Wax chemist, Austenal Co. Div, Howe Sound Corp, 62; RES. CHEMIST, AMOCO CHEM. CORP, 67- Instr, Aurora Col, 70- Am. Chem. Soc. Vapor phase oxidations of aliphatic and aromatic hydrocarbons; elevated temperature studies of free radical reactions. Address: Research & Development, Amoco Chemicals Corp, Box 400, Naperville, IL 60540.

FEINSTEIN, ALVAN R(ICHARD), b. Phila, Pa, Dec. 4, 25; m. 68; c. 1. INTERNAL MEDICINE. B.S, Chicago, 47, M.S, 48, M.D, 52. Asst. med, Rockefeller Inst, 54-56; clin. dir. rheumatic heart disease, Irvington House, 56-60, med. dir, 60-62; asst. prof. internal med, col. med, N.Y. Univ. Med. Ctr, 59-62; assoc. prof, SCH. MED, YALE, 64-69, PROF. MED. & EPIDEMIOL, 69-; CHIEF, EAST. RES. SUPPORT CTR, VET. ADMIN. HOSP, WEST HAVEN, 67-, clin. biostatist, 62-67. Consult, spec. serv. div, U.S. Pub. Health Serv, 60; Dept. Health, P.R, 60. U.S.A, 44-46, Sgt. Am. Soc. Clin. Invest; Am. Fedn. Clin. Res; Asn. Am. Physicians. Rheumatic fever; obesity; prognosis of cancer; clinical pharmacology and biostatistics. Address: Dept. of Medicine, Yale University School of Medicine, New Haven, CT 06510.

FEINSTEIN, HYMAN ISRAEL, b. Brooklyn, N.Y, Apr. 9, 11; m. 43; c. 1. ANALYTICAL & INORGANIC CHEMISTRY. A.B, Michigan, 30; M.A, Columbia, 32. Asst. instr, Long Island, 30-36; chemist, Customs Bur. Labs, 40-41; Nat. Bur. Standards, 36-40, 41-54; anal. chemist, U.S. Geol. Surv, 54-58; LECTR. CHEM. & ASSOC. PROF, GEORGE MASON COL, UNIV. VA, 58- Instr, Howard, 43-48; grad. sch, Nat. Bur. Standards, 50-53; lectr, Catholic Univ, 54. Chemist, Manhattan Proj, 43-47. AAAS; Am. Chem. Soc; Nat. Sci. Teachers Asn; Am. Inst. Chem. Rare elements; trace analysis; mineral and rock analysis; uranium; thorium; vanadium; coordination compounds of chromium; chemical literature and education; chemical microscopy; microchemistry. Address: Dept. of Chemistry, George Mason College of University of Virginia, Fairfax, VA 22030.

FEINSTEIN, IRWIN K, b. Chicago, Ill, Aug. 29, 14; m. 54; c. 2. MATHEMATICAL ANALYSIS. B.S, Ill. Inst. Tech, 36; M.A, Northwestern, 46, Ph.D. (math. ed), 52. Instr. math, UNIV. ILL, CHICAGO CIRCLE, 46-53, asst. prof, 53-60, assoc. prof. math. ed, 60-62, PROF, 62-66, MATH, 66- Vis. prof, R.I. Col, summer 61; Illinois, Urbana, summer 62; Northwestern, spring 63; Schwab Found. lectr, Mus. Sci. & Indust, Ill, 65-67. Chmn, Comn. Math. Preparation of Teachers of Elem. Sch. Math, 66; comt. strengthening teaching math, 70-71. U.S.C.G, 42-45, Lt. AAAS; Math. Asn. Am. Teacher education in mathematics. Address: Dept. of Mathematics, University of Illinois at Chicago Circle, Box 4348, Chicago, IL 60680.

FEINSTEIN, JOSEPH, b. New York, N.Y, July 8, 25; m. 52; c. 3. PHYSICS, ELECTRICAL ENGINEERING. B.E.E, Cooper Union, 44; M.A, Columbia, 47; Ph.D.(physics), N.Y. Univ, 51. Res. physicist, Nat. Bur. Standards, 49-54; mem. tech. staff, Bell Tel. Labs, 54-59; dir. res, S-F-D Labs, 59-64, V.PRES. RES, VARIAN ASSOCS, 64- AAAS; fel. Inst. Elec. & Electronics Eng. Electromagnetic theory; microwave electron tubes; power conversion; computers and peripherals. Address: 2398 Branner Dr, Menlo Park, CA 94026.

FEINSTEIN, LOUIS, b. Philadelphia, Pa, April 20, 12; m. 35; c. 2. BIOCHEMISTRY. A.B, Pennsylvania, 33, Raskob Found. scholar, 30-34, B.S, 34, M.S, 39; Ph.D.(chem), Georgetown, 46. Res. chemist, Barrett Co, 34-35; sch. med, Pennsylvania, 35-39; from jr. chemist to chemist, grain br, U.S. DEPT. AGR, 39-47, bur. entomol. & plant quarantine, 47-53, sr. res. biochemist, animal & poultry husbandry res, 53-56, supvry. chemist & prin. biochemist, biol. scis. br, 56-60, asst. chief, FIELD CROPS & ANIMAL PRODS. RES. BR, AGR. RES. SERV, 60-67, CHIEF, 67- AAAS; Am. Chem. Soc; Entom. Soc. Am; Asn. Off. Anal. Chem; fel. Am. Inst. Chem. Coal tar chemicals; liver and kidney metabolism; cereal chemistry; vitamins; plant alkaloids and insecticides; insect attractants and repellants; animal composition; quality evaluation of agricultural products. Address: Field Crops & Animal Products Research Branch, Agricultural Research Service, U.S. Dept. of Agriculture, Hyattsville, MD 20782.

FEINSTEIN, MAURICE B, b. New York, N.Y, Nov. 28, 29; m. 51; c. 3. PHARMACOLOGY. B.S, Columbia, 52, M.S, 54; Ph.D.(pharmacol), State Univ. N.Y, 60. Res. assoc. physiol, Inst. Muscle Disease, 60-62; instr. PHARMACOL, State Univ. N.Y. Downstate Med. Ctr, 62-64, asst. prof, 64-67, ASSOC. PROF, 67-69; McCOOK HOSP, SCHS. MED. & DENT. MED, UNIV. CONN, 69- U.S. Pub. Health Serv. grant, 63-65, 69-74. Med.Serv.C, U.S.A, 54-56. Am. Pharmacol. Soc; Harvey Soc. High energy phosphates and action of cardiac glycosides; calcium fluxes in muscle; mechanisms of rigor in muscle and local anesthetic action; membrane structure; fluorescent probes; ionophorous antibiotics; myelin structure. Address: Dept. of Pharmacology, McCook Hospital-University of Connecticut Health Center, 2 Holcomb St, Hartford, CT 06112.

FEINSTEIN, MYRON ELLIOT, b. New York, N.Y, Jan. 7, 43; m. 64; c. 1. SURFACE & PHYSICAL CHEMISTRY. B.S, City Col. New York, 63, M.A, 65; univ. scholar, teaching incentive award & Ph.D. (phys. chem), City Univ. New York, 67. Lectr. chem, City Col. New York, 64-67; res. chemist, Allied Chem. Corp, 67-68, sr. res. chemist, 68; established scientist, Unilever Res. Lab, Eng, 68-70, MGR. PROCESS DEVELOP. SOAPS & DETERGENTS, UNILEVER SCANDINAVIA, 70- E.I. du Pont de Nemours res. asst, 66. Am. Chem. Soc. Chemical process engineering; environmental engineering; wetting and detergency; colloidal surfactants; emulsions and foams; insoluble monolayers; surface potentials; fluorinated surfactants; eutrofication. Address: Östra Bergsgatan 17, Nyköping, Sweden S-611 00.

FEINSTEIN, ROBERT N(ORMAN), b. Milwaukee, Wis, Aug. 10, 15; m. 40; c. 2. BIOCHEMISTRY. B.S, Wisconsin, 37, M.S, 38, Ph.D.(physiol. chem), 40. Asst, McArdle Mem. Inst, Wisconsin, 38-39; res. assoc. dept. metabolism & endocrinol, Michael Reese Hosp, Chicago, 40-41; May Inst. Med. Res, Cincinnati, 46; instr. BIOCHEM, UNIV. CHICAGO, 47-48, asst. prof, 48-57, ASSOC. PROF, 57-, RES. ASSOC, 47-; SR. BIOCHEMIST, ARGONNE NAT. LAB, 59-, assoc. scientist, 54-59. Researcher, U.S.A.F. Radiation Lab, Univ. Chicago, 47-54; Guggenheim fel, Inst. of Radium, Paris, 59-60. U.S.A, 41-46. AAAS; Am. Chem. Soc; Am. Soc. Biol. Chem; Soc. Exp. Biol. & Med; Sci. Res. Soc. Am; Radiation Res. Soc. Radiation; enzymes; endocrines; cancer. Address: Division of Biological & Medical Research, Argonne National Lab, Argonne, IL 60439.

FEINSTONE, W(OLFFE) HARRY, b. Pultusk, Poland, Oct. 1, 13; nat; m. 38; c. 3. BACTERIOLOGY. B.S, Arkansas, 36; scholar, Hopkins, 36-39, Sc.D. (bact), 39. Asst. chemotherapy, Hopkins, 37-39; res. bacteriologist, Am. Cyanamid Co, 39-43; dir. biol. res, Pyridium Corp, 43-47; dir. res, Cent. Pharmacol. Co, 47-49; sci. dir, C.B. Kendall Co, 49-58; V.PRES, SCI. ADMIN, PLOUGH, INC, 58- Consult, 49-58. AAAS; Am. Chem. Soc; Soc. Exp. Biol. & Med; Am. Soc. Microbiol; Am. Inst. Chem. Chemotherapy; pharmaceutical development. Address: Plough, Inc, Box 377, Memphis, TN 38101.

FEIOCK, FRANK DONALD, b. Murray, Ky, June 22, 36; m. 54; c. 2. PHYSICS. A.B, Murray State Col, 58; Wilson fel, Kansas, 58-59, Nat. Sci. Found. fel, 59-61; Ph.D.(physics), Iowa, 64. Res. assoc. physics, Tufts, 64-65; assoc. res. scientist, Univ. Notre Dame, 65-69; STAFF PHYSICIST, KMS TECHNOL. CTR, KMS INDUSTS, INC, 69- Am. Phys. Soc. Atomic physics; materials response; statistical mechanics; numerical analysis. Address: 4271 Tacoma St, San Diego, CA 92117.

FEIR, DOROTHY JEAN, b. St. Louis, Mo, Jan. 29, 29. INSECT PHYSIOLOGY. B.S, Michigan, 50; M.S, Wyoming, 56; Ph.D.(entom), Wisconsin, 60. Instr. BIOL, Buffalo, 60-61; asst. prof, ST. LOUIS UNIV, 61-64, assoc. prof, 64-67, PROF, 67- AAAS; N.Y. Acad. Sci; Am. Physiol. Soc; Entom. Soc. Am; Am. Soc. Zool. Feeding behavior of insects; hematology and immunology of insects; action of hormones in insects. Address: Dept. of Biology, St. Louis University, St. Louis, MO 63104.

FEIRING, EMANUEL H(AROLD), b. New York, N.Y, Oct. 29, 13; m. 42. MEDICINE. B.S, City Col, 32; M.D, N.Y. Univ, 36. Assoc. prof. surg, ALBERT EINSTEIN COL. MED, YESHIVA UNIV, 54-70, CLIN. PROF. NEUROSURG, 70- Attend. surgeon, Bronx Munic. Hosp. Ctr, 54-; attend. neurosurgeon, Montefiore Hosp, 61; private practice. Med.C, U.S.A, 43-46. Asn. Res. Nerv. & Ment. Disease; Am. Asn. Neurol. Surg. Neurosurgery. Address: 40 E. 89th St, New York, NY 10028.

FEISEL, LYLE DEAN, b. Tama, Iowa, Oct. 16, 35; m. 57; c. 3. ELECTRICAL ENGINEERING. B.S, Iowa State, 61, Nat. Defense Ed. Act fel, 61-64, M.S, 63, Ph.D.(elec. eng), 64. Asst. prof. ELEC. ENG, S.DAK. SCH. MINES & TECHNOL, 64-68, ASSOC. PROF, 68- Nat. vis. prof, Cheng Kung Univ, Taiwan. U.S.N, 54-58. Inst. Elec. & Electronics Eng; Am. Vacuum Soc. Thin film circuitry and components, especially phenomena in thin insulating films with emphasis on active components. Address: Dept. of Electrical Engineering, South Dakota School of Mines & Technology, Rapid City, SD 57701.

FEIST, DALE DANIEL, b. Cincinnati, Ohio, Feb. 24, 38; m. 62; c. 2. ZOOLOGY, PHYSIOLOGY. A.B, Univ. Cincinnati, 60; Nat. Insts. Health fel, Univ. Calif, Berkeley, 66-69, Ph.D.(zool), 69. Nat. Insts. Health fel. physiol, Karolinska Inst, Sweden, 70-71; ASST. PROF. ZOOPHYSIOL, INST. ARCTIC BIOL, UNIV. ALASKA, 71- AAAS; Am. Soc. Zool; Am. Soc. Mammal; Ecol. Soc. Am. Adrenergic mechanisms in cold acclimation and hibernation; neuroendocrine aspects of acclimatization and adaptation to cold; role of catecholamines in thermogenesis; brown adipose tissue functions in cold adaptation. Address: Institute of Arctic Biology, University of Alaska, College, AK 99701.

FEIST, JOHN HANS, b. Frankfurt am Main, Ger, Apr. 5, 22; nat; m. 50; c. 2. MEDICINE, RADIOLOGY. B.Math, Lycee de Garcons, Epinal, France, 39; Columbia, 46; M.D, Temple, 50. Res. surg, Guthrie Clinic & Robert Packer Hosp, Sayre, Pa, 52-53, radiol, 54-56; instr. RADIOL, SCH. MED, UNIV. PITTSBURGH, 57-58, asst. prof, 58-60, assoc. prof, 60-71, CLIN. PROF, 71- Radiologist, Presby. & Woman's Hosps, Pittsburgh, Pa, 57-69; sr. attend, Allegheny Gen. Hosp, 70-; attend, Vet. Admin. Hosp. Med.C, 43-46, Sgt. AAAS; Soc. Nuclear Med; Radiol. Soc. N.Am; Am. Med. Asn; fel. Am. Col. Radiol; Am. Roentgen Ray Soc; fel. Am. Col. Chest Physicians. Study of bone metabolism by radiologic methods; physiologic interpretation of radiology; fluorographic methods; respiratory dynamics; enhancement of radiographic information and image quality. Address: Dept. of Radiology, Allegheny General Hospital, Pittsburgh, PA 15212.

FEIST, WILLIAM C(HARLES), b. St. Paul, Minn, Nov. 13, 34; m. 56; c. 2. ORGANIC & POLYMER CHEMISTRY. B.S, Hamline, 56; Ph.D.(org. chem), Colorado, 61. Res. chemist, Esso Res. & Eng. Co, Standard Oil Co. N.J,

60-64; ORG. CHEMIST FOREST PROD. LAB, U.S. FOREST SERV, 64- Am. Chem. Soc. Wood and water interactions; durability and dimensional stabilization of wood; biodegradation of wood; interaction of polymers with wood substance; molecular weight studies on polymeric materials. Address: 6809 Forest Glade Court, Middleton, WI 53562.

FEIST, WOLFGANG M(ARTIN), b. Oppeln, Ger, Mar. 12, 27; m. 57; c. 3. PHYSICS, MATHEMATICS. Dipl, Frankfurt, 54; Dr. rer. nat, Mainz, 57. Electronic scientist, Diamond Ord. Fuze Labs, D.C, 57-60; PRIN. SCIENTIST, RES. DIV, RAYTHEON CO, 60- German Army, 43-45. Inst. Elec. & Electronics Eng. Solid state physics; thin films; electronics. Address: Research Division, Raytheon Co, 28 Seyon St, Waltham, MA 02154.

FEIT, DAVID, b. N.Y.C, Sept. 17, 37; m. 59; c. 3. APPLIED MATHEMATICS, ENGINEERING MECHANICS. Daniel & Florence Guggenheim fel, Columbia, 59-61, M.S, 61, Sc.D.(eng. mech), 64. Res. engr, Davidson Lab, Stevens Inst. Tech, 59-60; res. scientist, TRG, Inc, N.Y, 60-61; SR. SCIENTIST, CAMBRIDGE ACOUST. ASSOCS, 64- N.Y. Acad. Sci; Am. Acad. Mech; Acoust. Soc. Am. Acoustics; mechanics; vibrations; mathematics. Address: 217 Follen Rd, Lexington, MA 02173.

FEIT, EUGENE DAVID, b. Chicago, Ill, Sept. 23, 35; m. 64; c. 3. PHYSICAL ORGANIC CHEMISTRY. M.S, Chicago, 64, Witco Chem. Co. fel, 64-65, NASA trainee, 65-68, Ph.D.(phys. org. chem), 68. CHEMIST, Am. Meat Inst. Found, 62-64; BELL TEL. LABS, 68- AAAS; N.Y. Acad. Sci; Am. Chem. Soc. Photopolymerization; organic photochemistry. Address: Bell Telephone Labs, Murray Hill, NJ 07974.

FEIT, IRA (NATHAN), b. Brooklyn, N.Y, Feb. 28, 40; m. 71. DEVELOPMENTAL BIOLOGY, MICROBIOLOGY. B.S, Brooklyn Col, 60; Woodrow Wilson fel, Princeton, 60-61, Nat. Insts. Health fel, 61-63, Nat. Sci. Found. fel, 63-64, M.A, 64, Ph.D.(biol), 65. Instr. BIOL, FRANKLIN & MARSHALL COL, 64-69, ASST. PROF, 69- Nat. Sci. Found. trainee, lab. quant. biol, Univ. Miami, 69-70. AAAS. Developmental control mechanisms in the cellular slime molds; changes in the polyribosome complement during cellular slime mold development. Address: Dept. of Biology, Franklin & Marshall College, Lancaster, PA 17604.

FEIT, IRVING N, b. Providence, R.I, Oct. 15, 42. ORGANIC CHEMISTRY. B.S, Univ. R.I, 64; Chas. Pfizer fel, Univ. Rochester, 68, Ph.D.(chem), 69. Fel, Univ. Calif, Santa Cruz, 69-70; ASST. PROF. CHEM, C.W. POST COL, L.I. UNIV, 70- Am. Chem. Soc. Base catalyzed and solvolytic elimination reactions; rearrangement and disproportionation of oligohalobenzenes. Address: Dept. of Chemistry, C.W. Post College, Long Island University. Greenvale, NY 11548.

FEIT, JULIUS, b. N.Y.C, Nov. 24, 19; m. 53; c. 2. ASTROPHYSICS. B.S, City Col. New York, 42; M.A, Columbia Univ, 59; M.S, Adelphi Univ, 63, Ph.D.(physics), 67. Lectr. PHYSICS, Adelphi Univ, 65-66; assoc. prof, QUEENSBOROUGH COMMUNITY COL, CITY UNIV. NEW YORK, 67-70, PROF, 70- U.S.A, 43-46, T/Sgt. Am. Geophys. Union; Am. Asn. Physics Teachers. Diffusion of solar flare cosmic rays through interplanetary space; effects of slow acceleration, external and internal boundaries and convection and energy loss in diffusion; modulation of galactic cosmic rays. Address: 101 Violet St, Massapequa Park, NY 11762.

FEIT, MICHAEL D(ENNIS), b. Easton, Pa, Nov. 15, 42; m. 67; c. 1. SOLID STATE PHYSICS. B.A, Lehigh Univ, 64; Ph.D.(physics), Rensselaer Polytech. Inst, 70. Res. asst. PHYSICS, Rensselaer Polytech. Inst, 66-69; RES. ASSOC, UNIV. ILL, URBANA, 69- AAAS; Am. Phys. Soc; Am. Asn. Physics Teachers. Theory of atomic migration in metals; diffusion, electromigration and thermomigration; electronic properties of point defects; transport properties. Address: Dept. of Physics, University of Illinois, Urbana, IL 61801.

FEIT, SIDNIE MARILYN, b. Hackensack, N.J, Nov. 29, 35; m. 57; c. 2. MATHEMATICS. B.A, Cornell Univ, 57, Nat. Sci. Found. fels, 57-58, 60-61, M.A, 63, Ph.D.(math), 68; univ. fel, Princeton-Cornell Univ, 58-59. Mathematician, Labs. Appl. Sci, Chicago, 60-61; lectr. math, Cornell Univ, 61-63; mathematician, Inst. Naval Studies, 63-64; ASST. PROF. MATH, Quinnipiac Col, 68-70; ALBERTUS MAGNUS COL, 70- Math. Asn. Am. Topology; geometry. Address: Dept. of Mathematics, Albertus Magnus College, New Haven, CT 06511.

FEIT, W(ALTER), b. Vienna, Austria, Oct. 26, 30; nat; m. 57; c. 2. MATHEMATICS. B.A, & M.S, Chicago, 51; Ph.D.(math), Michigan, 54. Instr. MATH, Cornell, 53-55, asst. prof, 56-60, assoc. prof, 60-64; PROF, YALE, 64- Nat. Sci. Found. fel, Inst. Adv. Study, 58-59. U.S.A, 55-56. Am. Math. Soc; Math. Asn. Am. Group theory and algebra. Address: Dept. of Mathematics, Yale University, New Haven, CT 06520.

FEITH, KENNETH E(DWIN), b. Chicago, Ill, May 14, 31; m. 51; c. 3. APPLIED PHYSICS, ACOUSTICS. B.Sc, Ill. Inst. Tech, 61. Tech. asst. physics & acoustics, IIT Res. Inst, 55-60, asst. physicist, 60-62, assoc. physicist, 62-65; sr. scientist, Tracor Inc, 65-69; V.PRES, INTERAND CORP, 69- Series of 20 lects. physics, design, & qual. assurance of magnetostriction transducers to res. & develop. div, indust. firm, 65; consult, indust. firms, 67- U.S.A.F, 51-55, S/Sgt. Acoust. Soc. Am. Electroacoustics; ultrasonics; noise pollution; architectural acoustics electronics; electronics; optics; electronic graphics. Address: 1393 Kersey Lane, Rockville, MD 20854.

FEJER, ANDREW AKOS, b. Budapest, Hungary, June 4, 13; nat; m. 38; c. 3. MECHANICAL ENGINEERING. M.E, Prague, 36; M.S, Calif. Inst. Tech, 39, fel, 39-41, Ph.D.(aeronaut), 45. Turbine engr, Skoda Works, Prague, 37-38; instr, Calif. Inst. Tech, 41-45; res. engr, Packard Motor Car Co, 45-49; prof. aeronaut. eng, Toledo, 49-58; prof. mech. eng. & dir. dept, ILL. INST. TECHNOL, 58-64, PROF. MECH. & AEROSPACE ENG, 64-, chmn. dept, 64-71. Vis. prof, Univ. Mich, 50-51; Univ. Nancy, 63; Univ. Lyons, 65 & 67; vis. scientist, Woods Hole Oceanog. Inst, summers, 57-65; lectr, Adv. Group Aerospace Res. & Develop, NATO, 62 & 68. Assoc. ed, Jour. Appl. Mech, 71-; mem. bd. dirs, Ill. Engrs. Coun, 63-67; grant, cult. exchange prog, U.S. Dept. State, 69. Consult, U.S. Air Force; Curtis Wright Co; Inst. Gas Technol, Chicago; Midland Ross Co, Toledo, Ohio; Ill. Inst. Technol. Res. Inst; World Book Encycl; Standard Educ. Soc, Chicago; Nat. Sci. Found; Nat. Acad. Sci. AAAS; assoc. fel. Am. Inst. Aeronaut. & Astronaut; Am. Soc. Mech. Eng; Am. Soc. Eng. Educ. Low speed aerodynamics; internal aerodynamics; fluid mechanics of rotating machinery; propulsion; swirling flows; nonsteady boundary layers; wind tunnels; wind effects on buildings. Address: 122 LeMoyne Pkwy, Oak Park, IL 60302.

FEJER, GEORGE, b. Debrecen, Hungary, May 30, 08; nat; m. 46; c. 2. MECHANICAL ENGINEERING. Grad, Swiss Fed. Inst. Tech, 31, Dr.sc.nat, 41. Res. engr, Color Metal A.G, Switz, 41-43; asst. physics, Berne, 43-45; res. engr, dist. heating & power plant, Swiss Fed. Inst. Tech, 45-47; Appl. Res. & Develop. Co, 47-48; consult, 48-51; res. engr, Armour Res. Found, Ill. Inst. Tech, 51-58; SR. ANAL. ENGR, BELL AEROSPACE CO, 58- AAAS; Am. Soc. Mech. Eng. Technical measurements; heat transfer; technical physics. Address: Bell Aerospace Co, P.O. Box 1, Buffalo, NY 14240.

FEJER, JULES A, b. Budapest, Hungary, Jan. 22, 14; m. 43; c. 1. ATMOSPHERIC & PLASMA PHYSICS. Dipl, Swiss Fed. Inst. Tech, 36; M.S.Eng, Witwatersrand, 49, D.Sc.(eng), 57. Res. engr, Hungarian Tungsten Lampworks, Ltd, 36-38; geophysicist, Oscar Weiss Consult. Geophysicists Ltd, S.Africa, 39-42; res. officer, Nat. Inst. Telecommun. Res, 46-58; defence sci. serv. officer, Defence Res. Telecommun. Estab, Can, 59-61; tech. specialist, Gen. Motors Defense Res. Labs, Calif, 61-62; prof. upper atmospheric & space sci, Southwest Ctr. Advan. Stud, 62-66; PROF. APPL. PHYSICS, UNIV. CALIF, SAN DIEGO, 66- Mem. Comn. IV, Int. Sci. Radio Union, 62- S.African Corp. Signals, 42-45, S/Sgt. Inst. Elec. & Electronics Eng; Am. Geophys. Union; Am. Inst. Physics. Wave propagation through irregular media; incoherent scattering of electromagnetic waves by plasmas; hydromagnetic propagation and stability; dynamo theory of geomagnetic variations; magnetic storm theory; ionospheric crossmodulation; radio-frequency plasma probes. Address: Dept. of Applied Physics & Information Science, University of California, San Diego, P.O. Box 109, La Jolla, CA 92037.

FEJER, STEPHEN OSCAR, b. Budapest, Hungary, Dec. 27, 16; Can. citizen; m. 50; c. 1. GENETICS. Dr. jur, Pazmany Peter Univ, Budapest, 39; fel, Int. Soc. Mediterranean & Alpine Geobot, France, 50; M. Agr. Sci, New Zealand, 52; fel, Calif. Inst. Tech, 58-59; Dr. Tech. Sc.(genetics), Swiss Fed. Inst. Tech, 67. Plant breeder grass genetics, grasslands div, Dept. Sci. & Indust. Res, N.Z, 50-61; GENETICIST, RES. STA, CAN. DEPT. AGR, 62- Genetics Soc. Am; Genetics Soc. Can; Can. Soc. Hort. Sci. Plant breeding for yield and its components; quantitative genetics and selection index; relations to environmental factors, adaptation and homeostasis; biochemical background of plant hormones; competition; frost resistance. Address: Research Station, Canada Dept. of Agriculture, Ottawa, Ont. K1H 0C6, Can.

FEKETE, FRANK, b. Everettsville, W.Va, Apr. 27, 24; m. 51; c. 2. ORGANIC CHEMISTRY. B.S, Pa. State, 49; Pittsburgh, 50-54; dipl, Buffalo, 57. Res. chemist, Dow Corning Corp, 49-50; jr. fel. organosilicon chem, Mellon Inst, 50-54; group leader unsaturated monomers & polymers, Pittsburgh Plate Glass Co, 54-55; silicones & phosphorus, Union Carbide Corp, 55-58; sr. fel. & head of fels, Mellon Inst, 58-63; proj. mgr, KOPPERS CO, INC, 64-67, mgr. polyester resin & reinforced plastics res. & develop, 67-70, MGR. MKT. DEVELOP. & REINFORCED PLASTIC RES. & DEVELOP. SECT, 70- U.S.A.A.F, 43-45. Am. Chem. Soc.(award, 58); Soc. Plastics Eng.(award, 69); Am. Soc. Test. & Mat; Nat. Asn. Corrosion Eng; Soc. Aerospace Mat. & Process Eng; Am. Inst. Aeronaut. & Astronaut. Organosilicon monomers, resins, polymers and elastomers; synthesis; unsaturated organic acrylics, vinyl and condensation monomers; plastics; polyesters; phosphorus, tin and boron chemistry; high temperature materials; acrylic interpolymers; ablative uses. Address: Reinforced Plastics, OMD, Koppers Co, Inc, Koppers Bldg, Pittsburgh, PA 15219.

FELBECK, DAVID K(NISELEY), b. Mt. Vernon, N.Y, Apr. 2, 26; div; c. 3. MECHANICAL ENGINEERING, MATERIALS SCIENCE. B.M.E, Cornell, 48; M.S, Mass. Inst. Tech, 49, Mech.E, 51, Sc.D.(mech. eng), 52. Fulbright lectr, Delft, 52-53; asst. prof. mech. eng, Mass. Inst. Tech, 53-55; exec. dir, Nat. Acad. Sci-Nat. Res. Coun, 55-61; assoc. prof. MECH. ENG, UNIV. MICH, ANN ARBOR, 61-65, PROF, 65- AAAS; Am. Soc. Mech. Eng; Am. Soc. Metals; Am. Inst. Mining, Metall. & Petrol. Eng. Fundamentals of mechanical behavior of solids; strengthening mechanisms; fracture analysis. Address: 2021 Woodside Rd, Ann Arbor, MI 48104.

FELBECK, GEORGE T(HEODORE), JR, b. Buffalo, N.Y, Sept. 18, 24; m. 50; c. 3. SOIL BIOCHEMISTRY. B.S, Mass. Inst. Tech, 49; M.S, Pa. State, 55, Nat. Sci. Found. fel, 55-56, Ph.D.(agron), 57. Asst. prof. agron, West Virginia, 56-57; lectr. biol, Yonsei Univ, Korea, 57-58; asst. prof. agron, Univ. Del, 58-64; assoc. prof. agr. chem, UNIV. R.I, 64-70, PROF. FOOD & RESOURCE CHEM, 70- U.S.A, 43-46. AAAS; Am. Soc. Agron; Soil Sci. Soc. Am. Chemistry of soil organic matter; organic geochemistry. Address: Dept. of Food & Resource Chemistry, University of Rhode Island, Kingston, RI 02881.

FELCH, RICHARD ELROY, b. Detroit, Mich, July 23, 40; m. 63. AGRONOMY. B.S, Rutgers Univ, 62; M.S, Univ. Nebr, Lincoln, 65; Utah State Univ, 66-67; Ph.D.(agr. climat), Iowa State Univ, 70. Res. scientist, Ont. Res. Found, Can, 64-66; extension agronomist, Iowa State Univ, 70-71; RES. METEOROLOGIST, ENVIRON. DATA SERV, DEPT. COMMERCE, 71- Am. Soc. Agron; Soil Sci. Soc. Am; Am. Meteorol. Soc. Agricultural climatology; meteorological indices for estimating crop maturity; soil-plant-water relations; water use by crops and moisture stress indices; weather and plant diseases, especially Southern corn leaf blight. Address: Agricultural Climatology Service Office, 4816-U.S. Dept. of Agriculture, South Bldg. Mail Unit, Washington, DC 20250.

FELD, BERNARD T(AUB), b. New York, N.Y, Dec. 21, 19; m. 47; c. 2. PHYSICS. B.S, City Col. N.Y, 39, fel, 39-40; Ph.D.(physics), Columbia, 45. Instr, evening session, City Col, N.Y, 40-41; res. assoc, Columbia, 41-42; physicist, metall. lab, Chicago, 42-44; Los Alamos lab, California, 44-46;

instr. PHYSICS, MASS. INST. TECHNOL, 46-47, asst. prof, 47-52, assoc. prof, 52-57, PROF, 57-, acting dir, lab. nuclear sci, 61-62. Guggenheim fel. & vis. prof, Rome, 53-54; vis. scientist & Ford fel, European Orgn. Nuclear Res, 60-61; vis. prof, Polytech. Sch, Paris, 66-67. Consult, Brookhaven Nat. Lab, 48-; asst. ed, Annals of Physics. Fel. Am. Acad. Arts & Sci; fel. Am. Phys. Soc; Fedn. Am. Sci. Neutron physics; atomic and molecular hyperfine structure and nuclear moments; meson physics and elementary particles, theory and experiment. Address: Dept. of Physics, Massachusetts Institute of Technology, Cambridge, MA 02139.

FELD, MICHAEL S, b. New York, N.Y, Nov. 11, 40; m. 63; c. 2. PHYSICS. S.B. & S.M, Mass. Inst. Tech, 63, Ph.D.(physics), 67. Fel. PHYSICS, MASS. INST. TECHNOL, 67-68, ASST. PROF, 68- AAAS; Am. Phys. Soc. Laser physics; non-linear optics; quantum electronics; laser-induced line narrowing effects in coupled Doppler-broadened systems. Address: 6-006, Massachusetts Institute of Technology, 77 Massachusetts Ave, Cambridge, MA 02139.

FELDBALLE, JEANETTE, O.P, b. Chicago, Ill, Jan. 6, 18. ZOOLOGY. B.S, Edgewood Col, 43; M.S, Wisconsin, 55, Ph.D, 60. Instr. zool, EDGEWOOD COL, 55-58, assoc. prof. BIOL, 57-65, PROF, 65-, CHMN. DIV. NATURAL SCI, 58- Nat. Sci. Found. faculty fel, 58-59. AAAS; Nat. Asn. Biol. Teachers. Endocrinology; physiology of reproduction. Address: Dept. of Biology, Edgewood College of the Sacred Heart, 855 Woodrow St, Madison, WI 53711.

FELDBERG, STEPHEN WILLIAM, b. New York, N.Y, July 22, 37. ELECTROCHEMISTRY. A.B, Princeton, 58, Ph.D.(chem), 61. Res. assoc, Brookhaven Nat. Lab, 61-63; vis. asst. prof, Kansas, 64; asst. chemist, BROOKHAVEN NAT. LAB, 64-66, assoc. chemist, 66-69, CHEMIST, 69- Studies of mechanism and kinetics of chemical reactions coupled with heterogeneous electron transfer; computer simulation techniques; studies of mass transport and membrane planning. Address: Brookhaven National Lab, 60 Rutherford Dr, Upton, NY 11973.

FELDER, DAVITT A, b. Providence, R.I, May 23, 16; m. 43; c. 4. MEDICINE. B.S, Rollins Col, 38; M.D, Yale, 42; Ph.D, Minnesota, 53. Clin. & res. fel, dept. surg, Harvard Med. Sch, Mass. Gen. Hosp, 48; res. fel, MED. SCH, UNIV. MINN, ST. PAUL, 50-51, clin. instr, 51-53, asst. prof. SURG, 53-57, CLIN. ASSOC. PROF, 57- Surg. supvr, St. Joseph's Hosp. Affiliation, St. Paul, 51- Med.C, 43-46, Lt. AAAS; Soc. Vascular Surg; fel. Am. Col. Surg; Am. Med. Asn; Asn. Am. Med. Cols; Int. Cardiovasc. Soc. Medical education; radiography of the blood vessels; autonomic nervous system; applied and experimental vascular surgery. Address: Central Medical Bldg, 393 N. Dunlap St, St. Paul, MN 55104.

FELDER, RICHARD MARK, b. New York, N.Y, July 21, 39; m. 63; c. 3. CHEMICAL ENGINEERING. B.Ch.E, City Col. New York, 62; Nat. Sci. Found. fel. & Ph.D.(chem. eng), Princeton, 66. NATO fel, theoret. physics div, Atomic Energy Res. Estab, Eng, 66-67; res. scientist, nuclear eng. dept, Brookhaven Nat. Lab, 67-69; ASST. PROF. CHEM. ENG, N.C. STATE UNIV, 69- Am. Inst. Chem. Eng. Chemical reaction engineering; process simulation and optimization; engineering applications of radioisotopes. Address: Dept. of Chemical Engineering, North Carolina State University, Raleigh, NC 27607.

FELDER, VIRGINIA I(SABELLE), b. Magnolia, Miss, Nov. 8, 05. MATHEMATICS. A.B, Miss. State Col. for Women, 27; M.S, Tulane, 31; summers, Duke, 38, La. State, 39, Chicago, 42, Northwestern, 50; Dr.Ed.(math), Columbia, 59. Teacher, pub. sch, Miss, 26-27; Copiah-Lincoln Jr. Col, 28-42; instr. radio mech, U.S. Air Force Prog, Conrad Hilton Hotel, Ill. & Truax Field, Wis, 42-43; instr. physics, cadet prog, Miss. State, 43-44; computer, Schlumberger Oil Co, Tex, 44; head math. dept, Sunflower Jr. Col, 44-46; head col. math, Odessa Col, 46-48; asst. prof. MATH, UNIV. SOUTH. MISS, 48-57, assoc. prof, 57-60, PROF, 60-, DIR. MATH. TEACHER EDUC. PROG, 48-, asst. dean women, 50-51. Prof, U.S. Armed Forces Inst, Japan, 51-53. Math. Asn. Am. Address: 706 Crestview Dr, Hattiesburg, MS 39401.

FELDHAUS, RICHARD J(OSEPH), b. Omaha, Nebr, May 6, 29; m. 53; c. 5. SURGERY. B.S, Creighton Univ, 53, M.S, 55, M.D, 59. Intern, St. Joseph Mem. Hosp, Omaha, Nebr, 59-60; resident surg, Creighton Univ. Affiliated Hosps, 60-62; Vet. Admin. Hosp, 62-64, staff surgeon, 64-65; chief surg, Vet. Admin. Hosp, Phoenix, Ariz, 67-71; DIR. SURG. EDUC, GOOD SAMARITAN HOSP, 71- Instr, sch. med, Creighton Univ, 62-67, asst. prof, 67. Fel. Am. Col. Surg. Perpheral vascular surgery; esophageal surgery. Address: Dept. of Surgery, Good Samaritan Hospital, Phoenix, AZ 85005.

FELDHERR, CARL M, b. N.Y.C, Jan. 3, 34; m. 59; c. 1. BIOLOGY. B.A, Hartwick,Col, 55; Ph.D.(physiol), Pennsylvania, 60. Damon Runyon fel, Pennsylvania, 60-62; asst. prof. physiol, Alberta, 62-65; ANAT. sch. med, Univ. Pa, 65-67; COL. MED, UNIV. FLA, 67-70, ASSOC. PROF, 70- AAAS; Am. Soc. Cell Biol. Permeability characteristics of the nuclear envelope. Address: Dept. of Anatomical Science, College of Medicine, University of Florida, Gainesville, FL 32601.

FELDKAMP, ROLLAND F(REDERICK), b. Ann Arbor, Mich, Aug. 6, 09; m. 36; c. 3. CHEMISTRY. B.S, Michigan, 34, M.S, 35, Ph.D.(pharmaceut. chem), 43. Res. chemist, Frederick Stearns Co, Mich, 35-47; sr. res. chemist, Sterling-Winthrop Res. Inst, N.Y, 47-51; dir. org. chem, Smith-Dorsey, Nebr, 51-53; pharmaceut. develop, Mead Johnson Res. Labs, 53-57, synthetic org. chem, 57-61, sr. res. fel, Mead Johnson Res. Center, 61-65; v.pres. & dir. res. & develop, Chem-Electro Corp, 65-68; INDEPENDENT CONSULT, 68- AAAS; Am. Chem. Soc. Insulin; autonomic drugs; air and water pollution. Address: 520 S. Pear St, Olympia, WA 98501.

FELDKIRCHNER, HARLAN LeROY, b. Chicago, Ill, June 15, 31; m. 64; c. 3. CHEMICAL ENGINEERING, FUEL TECHNOLOGY. B.S, Illinois, 54; M.S, Ill. Inst. Technol, 61. Chem. engr, INST. GAS TECHNOL, 54-69, SUPVR. COAL RES, 69- U.S.A, 54-56. Am. Chem. Soc; Am. Inst. Chem. Eng. Catalytic methanation; thermal cracking of petroleum; coal, oil shale and light distillate gasification. Address: Institute of Gas Technology, Process Research, 3424 S. State St, Chicago, IL 60616.

FELDMAHN, ALEXANDRA L, b. Sofia, Bulgaria, Sept. 21, 21; nat. MEDICINE. A.B. Brown, 42; M.D, Rochester, 50. Intern med, Strong Mem. Hosp, 50-51; res. fel. neurophysiol, U.S. Pub. Health Serv, UNIV. ROCHESTER, 51-53, fel. med, SCH. MED. & DENT, 51-54, instr. anat, med. & pediat, 55-58, asst. prof. med. neurol, 58-63, pediat. neurol, 58-64, CLIN. ASST. PROF. PEDIAT, 64- Asst. resident, Boston City Hosp, 54-55, resident, 57-58; teaching fel, Harvard, 57-58; assoc. physician & assoc. pediatrician, Strong Mem. Hosp, 58-65. Cerebral cortical control of autonomic functions. Address: 1501 East Ave, Rochester, NY 14610.

FELDMAN, ALAN S(IDNEY), b. New York, N.Y, Feb. 19, 27; m. 50; c. 2. AUDIOLOGY, SPEECH PATHOLOGY. A.B, Syracuse, 49, M.S, 51, Ph.D. (audiol, speech path), 56. Audiologist & speech pathologist, Mass. Eye & Ear Infirmary, 52-58; asst. prof. OTOLARYNGOL, STATE UNIV. N.Y. UPSTATE MED. CTR, 58-64, assoc. prof, 64-71, PROF, 71-, DIR. COMMUN. DISORDER UNIT, 64- Res. fel. lab. sensory commun, Syracuse, 58-, summers, vis. asst. prof, univ, 58-60. Consult, Syracuse Vet. Admin. Hosp, 58- U.S.N, 45-46. Acoust. Soc. Am; Int. Soc. Audiol; Am. Speech & Hearing Asn. Audition; problems in measurement and differential diagnosis of auditory disorders and speech communication. Address: 115 Hatherly Rd, Syracuse, NY 13224.

FELDMAN, A(LBERT) W(ILLIAM), b. Gardner, Ill, Aug. 6, 18; m; c. 2. PLANT PATHOLOGY. A.B, Illinois, 42; M.S, N.C. State Col, 44; Dorr fel, Minnesota, 44-45, Sherlin fel, 45-47, Ph.D.(plant path), 47. Asst. plant path, N.C. State Col, 42-43; agent, bur. plant indust, U.S. Dept. Agr, N.C, 43-44; res. assoc. PLANT PATH, Minnesota, 47; asst. res. prof, exp. sta, R.I. State Col, 47-51; sr. res. biologist & prod. develop. mgr, Naugatuck Chem. Div, U.S. Rubber Co, 51-58; plant pathologist, citrus exp. sta, UNIV. FLA, 58-70, PROF, AGR. RES. & EDUC. CTR, 70- Am. Phytopath. Soc; Am. Soc. Plant Physiol. Physiology of citrus diseases. Address: Agricultural Research & Education Center, University of Florida, Lake Alfred, FL 33850.

FELDMAN, ALFRED P(HILIP), b. Hamburg, Ger, Aug. 7, 23; U.S. citizen; m. 54; c. 2. ORGANIC CHEMISTRY. M.S, Univ. Chicago, 56. Asst. ed, Chem. Abstr. Serv, 56-60; chief coding sect, div. med. chem, WALTER REED ARMY INST. RES, 60-69, ASST. TO DIR, DIV. BIOMET. & MED. INFO. PROCESSING, 70- Tech. adv. to sci. & tech. info. div, U.S. Army Med. Res. & Develop. Command, Off. of Surg. Gen, 62-; U.S. Army liaison rep, comput. & biomath. sci. study sect, Nat. Insts. Health, 63-; mem. task group chem. info, Fed. Coun. Sci. & Technol, 71- U.S. Army Res. & Develop. Award, 70. AAAS; Am. Chem. Soc; Asn. Comput. Mach. Management of scientific information; man-machine interaction; chemical data processing. Address: Division of Biometrics & Medical Information Processing, Walter Reed Army Institute of Research, Washington, DC 20012.

FELDMAN, ALLAN M(URRY), b. Chicago, Ill, June 24, 30; m. 60; c. 4. ORGANIC CHEMISTRY. A.B, Chicago, 50, S.M, 53; Harvard, 53-57. Res. chemist, STAMFORD RES. LABS, AM. CYANAMID CO, 57-69, SR. RES. CHEMIST, 69- Am. Chem. Soc; Electrochem. Soc. Free radical reactions; synthesis of nitroxides; non-aqueous batteries; electro-organic synthesis. Address: Central Research Division, American Cyanamid Co, 1937 W. Main St, Stamford, CT 06904.

FELDMAN, ARNOLD, b. Allentown, Pa, Apr. 12, 24; m. 45; c. 1. RADIOLOGICAL PHYSICS. B.S, Pa. State Univ, 44; M.S, Calif. Inst. Technol, 48; Ph.D.(radiobiol), Univ. Colo, 60. Physics technician, Manhattan Dist. Proj, 44-46; Mayo Clin, 48-51; mem. faculty RADIOL. PHYSICS, sch. med, Univ. Colo, 51-64; consult, Mayo Clin, 64-68; MEM. FACULTY, SCH. MED, WASH. UNIV, 68- Nat. Cancer Inst. spec. fel, 62-63. U.S.A, 44-45. AAAS; Am. Asn. Physicists in Med; Radiol. Soc. N.Am; Radiation Res. Soc; Am. Phys. Soc; Am. Radium Soc; Am. Col. Radiol. Radiation dosimetry; radiobiology; cancer biology. Address: Dept. of Radiology, Washington University School of Medicine, 510 S. Kingshighway Blvd, St. Louis, MO 63110.

FELDMAN, ARTHUR, b. St. Louis, Mo, Apr. 6, 31; m. 53; c. 1. CIVIL ENGINEERING. B.S, Washington (St. Louis), 52; M.S, Illinois, 54, Ph.D.(civil eng), 60. Asst. civil eng, Illinois, 52-54, res. assoc, 54-59, asst. prof, 59-61; assoc. prof, Denver, 61-63; asst. res. scientist, MARTIN MARIETTA CORP, 63-66, SR. RES. SCIENTIST, 66- Instr, Off. Civil Defense, 62- Martin Author Award, 68, 69. Soc. Exp. Stress Anal; Am. Soc. Civil Eng. Composite pressure vessels; buckling and vibration of composite materials; reinforced concrete, blast and earthquake resistance; prestressed concrete; radiation protection. Address: Mail No. 1630, Martin Marietta Corp, P.O. Box 179, Denver, CO 80201.

FELDMAN, CHARLES, b. Baltimore, Md, March 20, 24; m. 46; c. 2. PHYSICS. A.B, Hopkins, 44, A.M, 49; Ph.D.(physics), Sorbonne, 52. Physicist, Aberdeen Proving Ground, 48; asst, inst. co-op. res, Hopkins, 49-50; physics master, grammar sch, Eng, 50-51; asst, Nat. Center Sci. Res, Paris, France, 51-53; physicist, crystal br, Naval Res. Lab, 53-60; sect. head, Melpar, Inc, 60-63, lab. mgr, 64-67; sr. staff mem, APPL. PHYSICS LAB, JOHNS HOPKINS UNIV, 67-69, PRIN. PROF. STAFF MEM, 69- Adj. prof, George Washington Univ, 69- U.S.A, 43-46. Am. Phys. Soc; Sci. Res. Soc. Am.(award, 58); Optical Soc. Am. Semiconducting properties of evaporated metal films; dielectric films; solid state physics, luminescence; thin-film electronics. Address: 2855 Davenport St. N.W, Washington, DC 20008.

FELDMAN, CHARLES F, b. Evansville, Ind, Jan. 29, 32; m. 53; c. 2. ORGANIC CHEMISTRY. A.B, Evansville Col, 53; M.S, Okla. State, 55, Ph.D. (org. chem), 57. Chemist, res. dept, plastics div, Monsanto Chem. Co, Tex, 56-59, sr. chemist, 59-60; sr. staff mem. polymer chem, res. & develop. div, Spencer Chem. Div, GULF OIL CORP, 60-62, group leader polymer synthesis, 62-63, applns. res, 63-66, new bus. analyst, chem. dept, 66-70, MGR. TRANSOCEAN CHEM. CO, 70- Am. Chem. Soc. Polyolefin polymerizations; solution properties; applications research in papercoating, textiles, glues, hot melt adhesives, papermaking; market development of emulsion and adhesive products; fermentation chemicals. Address: Transocean Chemical Co, Gulf Oil Corp, P.O. Box 2100, Houston, TX 77001.

FELDMAN, CHARLES LAWRENCE, b. Yonkers, N.Y, Dec. 18, 35; m. 56; c. 4. MECHANICAL ENGINEERING. Nat. Sci. Found. fel, Mass. Inst. Tech,

57-58, S.B. & S.M, 58, Mech.E, 60, Sc.D.(mech. eng), 62. Res. asst, Brookhaven Nat. Lab, 56; scientist commun. theory, Edgerton, Germeshausen & Grier, Inc, 58-59; asst, Mass. Inst. Tech, 59-60; sr. proj. engr, Joseph Kaye & Co, Inc, 61-62, dir. res, 62-65; asst. prof. MECH. ENG, WORCESTER POLYTECH INST, 65-67, assoc. prof, 67-71, PROF, 71- Instr, Lowell Inst, 58-59; lectr. indust. mgt, Northeastern, 62-63, eng, 63- Consult, Autonetics Div, N.Am. Aviation, Inc, 59-61; Joseph Kaye & Co, Inc, 60-61; res. assoc. biomath, med. sch, Harvard, 66-69, lectr, 69-; consult. math, dept. psychiat, Mass. Gen. Hosp, 67- Am. Phys. Soc; Inst. Elec. & Electronics Eng; Asn. Comput. Mach; Am. Soc. Mech. Eng. Application of statistical communication theory to computers and medicine; thermodynamics and fluid mechanics of multiphase flow. Address: 36 Canterbury Dr, Sudbury, MA 01776.

FELDMAN, CHESTER, b. South Bend, Ind, June 26, 20; m. 54; c. 1. MATHEMATICS. S.B, Chicago, 40, S.M, 41, Ph.D.(math), 50. Asst. prof, Antioch Col, 51-52; consult, Air-craft-Marine Prods, Inc, 52-53; instr. math, Purdue, 53-55; asst. prof, New Hampshire, 55-57; Connecticut, 57-63; assoc. prof, Kent State Univ, 63-68; ASSOC. ED, MATH. REV, UNIV. MICH, 68- Sig.C, U.S.A, 43-46. Fel. AAAS; Am. Math. Soc. Topological and Banach algebras. Address: "Math. Reviews," University of Michigan, 416 Fourth St, Ann Arbor, MI 48103.

FELDMAN, DANIEL J(ARED), b. New York, N.Y, Oct. 11, 13; m. 48; c. 3. REHABILITATION MEDICINE. A.B, Columbia, 34; M.D, N.Y. Univ, 38. Clin. asst. med, sch. med, N.Y. Univ, 47-49, clin. instr, 49-56, asst. prof. phys. med. & rehab, 56-58, assoc. prof, 58-60; assoc. prof. med, sch. med. & dir. rehab. serv, med. ctr, Stanford Univ, 60-68; clin. prof. med. & community med, Univ. Calif, San Diego, 69-71; DEP. DIR. ALCOHOLISM PROGS, ORANGE COUNTY DEPT. MENT. HEALTH, 71- Mem. vis. faculty, Univ. Utah, 56, 58, 59, 61-64; mem. staff, inst. phys. med. & rehab, med. ctr, N.Y. Univ, 56-60; vis. physician, Bellevue Hosp, N.Y, 58-60; vis. prof, grad. & postgrad. schs. med, Univ. Chile, 60; clin. dir, Casa Colina Hosp, Pomona, Calif, 68-71; vis. prof, Sch. Theol. Claremont, 70-; adj. prof, col. med, Univ. Calif, Irvine, 71- Dipl, Am. Bd. Internal Med, 49; Am. Bd. Phys. Med. & Rehab, 60. Med.C, 42-46, Maj. Fel. Am. Pub. Health Asn; fel. Am. Col. Physicians; fel. Am. Acad. Phys. Med. & Rehab; Chilean Rehab. Asn; Chilean Orthop. Asn; Mex. Rehab. Asn; fel. Royal Soc. Med. Chronic disease and disability. Address: 601 Mar Vista, Newport Beach, CA 92660.

FELDMAN, DANIEL S, b. Philadelphia, Pa, Feb. 26, 26; m. 57; c. 3. NEUROLOGY, NEUROPHYSIOLOGY. A.B, Pennsylvania, 45, M.D, 49. Fel, Nat. Inst. Neurol. Diseases & Blindness, 53-54; Abrahamson fel, Mt. Sinai Hosp, N.Y, 56; asst. prof. NEUROL, STATE UNIV. N.Y. DOWNSTATE MED. CTR, 61-66, ASSOC. PROF, 66- Dir. neurol, Maimonides Hosp, Brooklyn, 60-66; mem. med. adv. bd, Myasthenia Gravis Found, 62-; guest investr, dept. pharmacol, Univ. Lund, 64-65; career scientist, Health Res. Coun, City of New York, 66-; consult, Maimonides-Coney Island Med. Ctr, Brooklyn, 66-; vis. neurologist, Kings County Hosp, 66-; attending neurologist, State Univ. Hosp, 66- Med.C, 53-56, Lt. Am. Physiol. Soc; Am. Acad. Neurol; Am. Fedn. Clin. Res; Am. Med. Asn; Am. Psychiat. Asn; Am. Col. Physicians; Royal Soc. Med. Electrophysiological studies in vitro of parameters affecting chemical transmitter release and post-synaptic response in vertebrate, including human muscle; application of physiological systems and methods to study of human neuromuscular function in health and disease. Address: Dept. of Neurology, State University of New York Downstate Medical Center, Brooklyn, NY 11203.

FELDMAN, DAVID, b. Brooklyn, N.Y, June 16, 21; m. 46; c. 2. THEORETICAL PHYSICS. B.S, City Col. New York, 40; M.S, N.Y. Univ, 46; Thayer scholar, Harvard, 46-47, Parker fel, 47-48, Ph.D.(physics), 49. Atomic Energy Comn. fel, Inst. Adv. Study, 49-50; asst. prof. PHYSICS, Rochester, 50-56; assoc. prof, BROWN UNIV, 56-59, PROF, 59- Nat. Sci. Found. sr. fel, Paris, 62-63; mem. adv. panel for physics, Nat. Sci. Found, 68- Fel. Am. Phys. Soc; Ital. Phys. Soc. Quantum theory of fields; nuclear and high-energy physics. Address: Dept. of Physics, Brown University, Providence, RI 02912.

FELDMAN, DAVID, b. N.Y.C, Oct. 16, 27; m. 51; c. 3. ELECTRICAL ENGINEERING. B.S, Newark Col. Eng, 47, fel, 47-49, M.S, 49. Asst. prof. elec. eng, Cooper Union, 49-54; res. engr. non-linear magnetics, Polytech. Res. & Develop. Co, 54-56; DIR. COMPONENTS LAB, BELL TEL. LABS, INC, 56- Consult, Aerospace Industs. Asn, 62-66; Electronic Industs. Asn, 66-71. Inst. Elec. & Electronics Eng; Solar Energy Soc; Am. Vacuum Soc. Network design, thin film component development, electronic materials, feedback control. Address: Bell Telephone Labs, Inc, 555 Union Blvd, Allentown, PA 18103.

FELDMAN, DONALD W(ILLIAM), b. Memphis, Tenn, Oct. 5, 31; m. 55; c. 2. PHYSICS. B.S, Southwestern at Memphis, 52; M.S, Pa. State, 54; Westinghouse Elec. Co. fel, California, Berkeley, 57, Ph.D.(physics), 59. PHYSICIST, SOLID STATE SCI. DEPT, WESTINGHOUSE RES. LABS, 59- Am. Phys. Soc. Solid state physics; electron spin resonance; nuclear magnetic resonance; Raman spectroscopy. Address: Solid State Sciences Dept, Westinghouse Research Labs, Beulah Rd, Pittsburgh, PA 15235.

FELDMAN, EDWIN B(ARRY), b. Atlanta, Ga, Apr. 30, 25; m. 47; c. 3. INDUSTRIAL ENGINEERING. B.I.E, Ga. Inst. Tech, 50. Plant engr, Puritan Chem. Co, 49-52, plant mgr, 52-58, v.pres. & dir. eng, 58-60; PRES, SERV. ENG. ASSOCS, INC, 61- U.S.A, 43-46. Nat. Soc. Prof. Eng; Am. Inst. Indust. Eng; Am. Inst. Plant Eng; Inst. Sanit. Mgt; Am. Mgt. Asn. Application of engineering principles to industrial and institutional housekeeping and sanitation. Address: 1023 Burton Dr. N.E, Atlanta, GA 30329.

FELDMAN, ELAINE BOSSAK, b. New York, N.Y, Dec. 9, 26; m. 57; c. 3. MEDICINE. A.B, N.Y. Univ, 45, fel. & M.S, 48, M.D, 51. Intern, Mt. Sinai Hosp, N.Y, 51-52, res. path, 52, asst. res. med, 53, fel, 54-55, res. fel, N.Y. Heart Asn. & asst, 55-57; instr. MED, STATE UNIV. N.Y. DOWNSTATE MED. CTR, 57-59, asst. prof, 59-68, ASSOC. PROF, 68- Asst. vis. physician, Kings County Hosp, 57-66, assoc. vis. physician, 66-; U.S. Pub. Health Serv. spec. fel. physiol. chem, Univ. Lund, 64-65; attend. physician, State Univ. Hosp, 66- Endocrine Soc; Am. Heart Asn; Am. Fedn. Clin. Res. Endocrinology and metabolism, especially the effect of hormonal influences on serum lipids and proteins; newer steroid agents in the treatment of metastatic mammary carcinoma; control of cholesterol absorption and synthesis. Address: Dept. of Medicine, State University of New York Downstate Medical Center, Brooklyn, NY 11203.

FELDMAN, FREDRIC J, b. Brooklyn, N.Y, Feb. 9, 40; m. 62; c. 2. ANALYTICAL & INORGANIC CHEMISTRY. B.S, Brooklyn Col, 60; M.S, Maryland, 64, Ph.D.(anal. chem), 67. Prin. investr, Walter Reed Army Inst. Res, 64-68; pres, Chrisfeld Precision Instruments Corp, 64-70, dir. anal. lab, instrumentation lab, 68-70; PROG. MGR. BECKMAN INSTRUMENTS, 70- AAAS; Am. Chem. Soc; Am. Asn. Clin. Chem; Soc. Appl. Spectros. Research and development of atomic absorption and emission methods for the analysis of substances of clinical, biological and industrial importance; physiological mechanisms of chromium; coulometric and polarographic studies of biologically important substances. Address: 17381 Drey Lane, Huntington Beach, CA 92647.

FELDMAN, G(ERALD) L(EWIS), b. Buffalo, N.Y, Jan. 30, 31; m. 54; c. 3. BIOCHEMISTRY. B.S, Univ. Ga, 55; M.S, Tex. A&M Univ, 57, U.S. Pub. Health Serv. fel, 57-59, Ph.D.(biochem), 59. Clin. asst. prof. biochem, col. med, Baylor Univ, 59-62, asst. prof, 62-66, assoc. prof, 66-71, chief ophthalmic biochem, dept. ophthal, 62-71; V.PRES, HORNER-RAUSCH CONTACT LENS CO, 71- Res. biochemist, Methodist Hosp, 59-70; Nat. Inst. Neurol. Diseases & Blindness spec. fel, 64-66; dir. contact lenses, Med. Eye Assocs, 67-71; asst. ed, Contact Lens Med. Bull, 68- AAAS; fel. Am. Inst. Chem; Am. Med. Asn; Am. Acad. Ophthal. & Otolaryngol; Contact Lens Soc. Am.(ed, jour, 69-). Physiological aspects of contact lenses, especially related pathological problems and therapeutic approaches; development of new contact lens modalities, their cosmetic and therapeutic use; biochemistry of the eye; lipids of ocular tissues. Address: Horner-Rausch Contact Lens Co, 425 Mid-State Medical Center, Nashville, TN 37203.

FELDMAN, GORDON, b. Windsor, Ont, Dec. 6, 28. THEORETICAL PHYSICS. B.A, Toronto, 50, M.A, 51; Priestley fel. & Ph.D.(physics), Birmingham, 53. Asst. physics, Univ. Birmingham, 53-55; mem, Inst. Adv. Study, Princeton, 55-56; res. assoc. PHYSICS, Wisconsin, 56-57; asst. prof, JOHNS HOPKINS UNIV, 57-64, PROF, 65- Summer vis. assoc. prof, Univ. Wash, 56; Guggenheim fel, 62-63. High energy physics; elementary particles and field theory. Address: Dept. of Physics, Johns Hopkins University, Baltimore, MD 21218.

FELDMAN, HAROLD S(AMUEL), b. Boston, Mass, May 8, 17; m. 45; c. 3. PSYCHIATRY, PSYCHOPHARMACOLOGY. B.S, Mass. Col. Pharm, 39, Nat. Formulary fel, 39-42, M.S, 42; fel, Boston, 42-45, Ph.D.(pharmacol), 45, M.D, 49. Asst. pharmacol, sch. med, Boston, 42-45, assoc. prof. mat. med, sch. pharm, 45-49; DIR. MED. RES, MALTBIE LABS, NEWARK, 50-; DIR, DEPT. NEUROPSYCHOPHARMACOL, ESSEX CO, OVERBROOK HOSP, CEDAR GROVE, 63-; ASST. PROF. PSYCHIAT, N.J. COL. MED. & DENT, 67- Private practice. Clin. instr, N.Y. Med. Col; Seton Hall Col. Med. Staff psychiatrist & res. psychiat. training, Essex Co, Overbrook Hosp, 64-; dir. Quinn Rehab. Prog. Drug Addicts, Essex County, 67-; dir, Essex County Penitentiary Rehab. Prog. Narcotics Addicts, 68-71. Am. Druggist Award, 40. U.S.P.H.S, 49-52; U.S.C.G, 51-52. Fel. Am. Geriat. Soc; Am. Soc. Pharmacol. & Exp. Therapeut; Am. Med. Asn; assoc. Am. Pharmaceut. Asn; Am. Col. Cardiol; Am. Psychiat. Asn; fel. Am. Col. Clin. Pharmacol; fel. Acad. Psychosom. Med. Internal Medicine; clinical and experimental pharmacology; pharmacognosy; psychiatry. Address: Dept. of Psychiatry, New Jersey College of Medicine & Dentistry, 100 Bergen St, Newark, NJ 07103.

FELDMAN, HARRY A(LFRED), b. Newark, N.J, May 30, 14; m. 39; c. 4. MEDICINE. A.B, George Washington, 35, M.D, 39. Res. assoc. bact, George Washington, 36-39, asst. res. med, 40-41, fel. bact. infections, 41-42; intern, Gallinger Hosp, Wash, D.C, 39-40; fel. med, Harvard, 42; sr. fel. virus diseases, Nat. Res. Coun, 46-48; assoc. prof. med, STATE UNIV. N.Y. UPSTATE MED. CTR, 49-55, PROF. PREV. MED. & CHMN. DEPT, 55- Dir. res, Wieting-Johnson Hosp, 49-55; mem, Nat. Bd. Med. Exam, 65-70, chmn. prev. med. test comt, 67-69; mem. comn. acute respiratory diseases & chmn. comt. meningococcal infections, Armed Forces Epidemiol. Bd; mem. comn. toxoplasmosis, Int. Cong. Microbiol. U.S.A, 42-46, Lt. Col. AAAS; Am. Soc. Trop. Med. & Hyg; Soc. Pediat. Res; Am. Epidemiol. Soc; Am. Asn. Immunol; Am. Heart Asn; fel. Am. Pub. Health Asn; fel. Am. Acad. Microbiol; Asn. Teachers Prev. Med; Asn. Am. Physicians; Am. Soc. Microbiol; Am. Pediat. Soc. Evaluation of bacterial chemotherapeutic and sero-therapeutic agents; toxoplasmosis; epidemiology; respiratory diseases and meningitis. Address: State University of New York Upstate Medical Center, 750 E. Adams St, Syracuse, NY 13210.

FELDMAN, HENRY R(OBERT), b. N.Y.C, June 28, 32; m. 56; c. 1. ACOUSTICS. A.B, Harvard, 53; A.M, Columbia Univ, 58, Ph.D.(physics), 63. Res. asst. prof. physics, UNIV. WASH, 63-65, SR. PHYSICIST, APPL. PHYSICS LAB, 66- Chem.C, U.S.A, 53-55, Res, 55-61. AAAS; Acoust. Soc. Am; Am. Phys. Soc. Marine acoustics; atomic and molecular beams; optical pumping; trapping of charged particles; acoustic lenses. Address: Applied Physics Lab, University of Washington, 1013 N.E. 40th St, Seattle, WA 98105.

FELDMAN, HYMAN M(ORRIS), b. Pinsk, Poland, Dec. 5, 05; nat; m. 41; c. 3. MATHEMATICS. A.B, Washington (St. Louis), 30, M.S, 31, Ph.D.(math, physics), 33. Teacher pub. sch, Mo, 34-55; lectr. MATH, WASH. UNIV, 42-55, vis. assoc. prof, 55-56, asst. prof, 57-60, ASSOC. PROF, 60- Math. Asn. Am. General mathematics. Address: Dept. of Mathematics, Washington University, St. Louis, MO 63130.

FELDMAN, ISAAC, b. Wash, D.C, Mar. 6, 18; m. 56. CHEMISTRY, BIOPHYSICS. B.S, George Washington, 41; fel, Illinois, 47, Ph.D.(phys. chem), 47. Asst. chem, George Washington, 39-42, instr, 42-43; civilian instr, A.F. Scott Field, Ill, 42-43; asst. chem. Illinois, 44-47; assoc, ATOMIC ENERGY PROJ, ROCHESTER, 47-49, jr. scientist, 49-51, assoc. scientist, 51-53, SCIENTIST, 53-, PROF. BIOPHYS, SCH. MED. & DENT, 65-, instr, phys. chem, 47-53, asst. prof, 53-56, assoc. prof, 56-64. U.S. Pub. Health Serv. spec. res. fel. & hon. res. assoc, Univ. Col, London, 62-63. Am.

Chem. Soc; Radiation Res. Soc; Biophys. Soc. Chelate chemistry of toxic metals; luminescence of biological macromolecules; nuclear magnetic resonance. Address: Dept. of Radiation Biology & Biophysics, University of Rochester School of Medicine & Dentistry, Rochester, NY 14642.

FELDMAN, JACOB, b. Phila, Pa, Jan. 10, 28; div; c. 2. MATHEMATICS. B.A, Univ. Pa, 50; M.A, Univ. Ill, 51; Ph.D.(math), Univ. Chicago, 54. Vis. asst. prof, Columbia Univ, 56-57; asst. prof. MATH, UNIV. CALIF, BERKE-LEY, 57-64, PROF, 64- Res. mathematician, Bell Tel. Labs, summer 56; Nat. Sci. Found. fels, Inst. Adv. Study, 54-56 & 60-61; exchange visit, USSR, 67. Am. Math, Soc; Math. Asn. Am. Linear stochastic processes, especially Gaussian; continuous products of measurspaces and operator algebras; operator theory; operator algebras and their connection with physics; ergodic theory. Address: Dept. of Mathematics, University of California, Berkeley, CA 94704.

FELDMAN, JACOB RICHARD, b. Phila, Pa, Aug. 4, 12; m. 38; c. 2. CHEM-ISTRY. B.A, Temple, 34, M.A, 35; Ph.D.(org. chem), Pennsylvania, 41. Asst. instr, Temple, 34-35; asst, Pennsylvania, 35-36; biochemist, Phila. Inst. Med. Res, 36-38; chemist, U.S. Customs Lab, 38-44; group leader, res. center, GEN. FOODS CORP, 44-50, sect. head, 50-59, res. specialist, 59-62, sr. res. specialist, TECH. CTR, 62-68, MGR, BASIC RES, 68- AAAS; assoc. Am. Chem. Soc. Organic synthesis; spectroscopy of organic compounds; some reactions of methylene bis-amines as ammono aldehydes; isochorogenic acid isolation from coffee and structure studies; importance of nonvolitile compounds to the flavor of coffee. Address: Technical Center, General Foods Corp, 250 North St, White Plains, NY 10625.

FELDMAN, J(AMES) A(RTHUR), b. Canton, Minn, Aug. 31, 17; m. 46. CHEMICAL ENGINEERING. B.Sc, Iowa State, 39. Chemist, Glidden Co, Ill, 40; Phillips Petrol. Co, 41, group leader, 47-50, chief plant engr, 51-55, proj. engr, 56, pilot plant supvr, 57-61, proj. mgr. process optimiza-tion, 61-68; PROJ. MGR, APPLIED AUTOMATION, INC, 68- C.Eng, 42-44, Res, 44-51, Capt. Am. Inst. Chem. Eng. Operation of pilot plants and semicommercial plants in chemical and petrochemical branches; improve-ment of profit potential of processes and plants through coordinated study by multidiscipline teams. Address: Applied Automation, Inc, Pawhuska Rd, Bartlesville, OK 74003.

FELDMAN, JAMES MICHAEL, b. Pittsburgh, Pa, Sept. 29, 33; m. 55; c. 1. ELECTRICAL ENGINEERING, PHYSICS. B.S, Carnegie Inst. Tech, 57, M.S, 58, Ph.D.(elec. eng), 60. Asst. prof. ELEC. ENG, Carnegie Inst. Tech, 60-65; assoc. prof, NORTHEAST. UNIV, 65-71, PROF, 71- Res. engr. quantum electronics, Westinghouse Res. Labs, 61-64; vis. assoc. prof, Technion, Haifa, Israel, 71-72. Am. Phys. Soc; Inst. Elec. & Electronics Eng. High pressure electrical discharge phenomena; extremely intense light sources for optical pumping; optical maser materials; light propaga-tion and coherence in scattering media; semiconductor materials; optical properties of semiconductors. Address: Dept. of Electrical Engineering, Northeastern University, Boston, MA 02115.

FELDMAN, JEROME A, b. Pittsburgh, Pa, Dec. 5, 38; m. 61; c. 2. COM-PUTER SCIENCE, MATHEMATICS. B.A, Rochester, 60; M.A, Pittsburgh, 61; Ph.D.(comput. sci), Carnegie Inst. Tech, 64. Res. scientist comput. sci, Carnegie Inst. Tech, 63-64; staff mem. data systs, Lincoln Lab, Mass. Inst. Tech, 64-66; asst. prof. COMPUT. SCI, STANFORD UNIV, 66-69, ASSOC. PROF, 69- Fulbright lectr. & vis. prof. math. & comput. sci, Hebrew Univ, Jerusalem, 70-71. Asn. Comput. Mach. Programming languages; artificial intelligence. Address: Dept. of Computer Science, Stanford University, Stanford, CA 94305.

FELDMAN, JERRY F, b. Phila, Pa, May 11, 42; m. 69. GENETICS. Wood-row Wilson hon. fel. & B.A, Swarthmore Col, 63; Nat. Sci. Found. fel, C.E. Procter hon. fel. & M.A, Princeton, 65, Ph.D.(biol), 67. U.S. Pub. Health Serv. res. fel. BIOL, Calif. Inst. Technol, 67-69; ASST. PROF, STATE UNIV. N.Y. ALBANY, 69- Am. Soc. Microbiol; Genetics Soc. Am; Biophys. Soc. Biological clocks; genetic and biochemical approaches in micro-organisms; conidiation and sexual differentiation in Neurospora. Address: Dept. of Biology, State University of New York at Albany, 1400 Washington Ave, Albany, NY 12203.

FELDMAN, JOSE M, b. Entre Ríos, Argentina, Sept. 27, 27; m. 54, 68; c. 4. PLANT PATHOLOGY, VIROLOGY. Ing. Agron, Cuyo, 55. Asst. PLANT PATH, FACULTY AGRON, NAT. UNIV. CUYO, 56-57, instr, 57-67, ASSOC. PROF, 67-, ASSOC. PATHOLOGIST, 63- Nat. Coun. Sci. & Tech. Res. grants, Arg, 59, 62 & 63; fel, 62-63; lectr, 64-65, prin. researcher, 68. Arg. Soc. Plant Physiol; Latin Am. Phytopath. Asn. Plant virus diseases, especially vegetable crops and grapes; plant virus serology; inhibition of plant viruses; physiology of virus-diseased plants. Address: Dept. of Plant Pathology, Faculty Agricultural Science, National University of Cuyo, Chacras de Coria, Mendoza, Argentina.

FELDMAN, JOSEPH AARON, b. Fall River, Mass, Feb. 2, 25; m. 48; c. 3. PHARMACEUTICAL CHEMISTRY. B.S, R.I. Col. Pharm, 50; Found. Phar-maceut. Ed. fel, Wisconsin, 50-53, M.S, 52, Ph.D.(pharm), 56. Assoc. prof. PHARMACEUT. CHEM, DUQUESNE UNIV, 55-64, PROF, 64- Vis. anal. consult, Ciba-Geigy Co, Basel, Switz, 71. U.S.A, 43-46. Am. Chem. Soc; Am. Pharmaceut. Asn; Acad. Pharmaceut. Sci. Nonaqueous titration; analysis using chelometric methods; fluorimetry; pharmaceutical analysis; effects of solvent systems on drug stability. Address: School of Pharmacy, Duquesne University, Pittsburgh, PA 15219.

FELDMAN, JOSEPH D(AVID), b. Hartford, Conn, Dec. 13, 16; m. 49; c. 3. PATHOLOGY. B.A, Yale, 37; M.D, L.I. Col. Med, 41. Assoc. prof. path, sch. med, Pittsburgh, 54-56, prof, 56-61; MEM. STAFF, SCRIPPS CLIN. & RES. FOUND, UNIV. CALIF, SAN DIEGO, 61-, ADJ. PROF, PATH, UNIV, 68- U.S. Pub. Health Serv. fel, 48-50; lectr, Hadassah Med. Sch, Hebrew Univ. Jerusalem, 50-54; ed, Lab. Invest, J. Reticuloendothelial Soc, 66-; Am. Med. Asn. Archives Path, 66-; chmn, U.S. Pub. Health Serv. Path. B. Study Sect, 67-70, consult; ed-in-chief, J. Immunol, 71-; past ed, Lab. Invest. Proc. Soc. Exp. Biol. & Med; ed, Am. J. Path; J. Cellular Immunol. Dipl, Am. Bd. Path. Battalion Aid Surg, U.S.A, 42-46, Maj. Int. Acad. Path;

Histochem. Soc; Endocrine Soc; Electron Micros. Soc. Am; Am. Soc. Exp. Path; Am. Asn. Path. & Bact; Am. Asn. Immunol. Immunopathology; cy-tology. Address: Scripps Clinic & Research Foundation, University of Cali-fornia, San Diego, 476 Prospect St, La Jolla, CA 92037.

FELDMAN, JOSEPH LOUIS, b. N.Y.C, June 6, 38; m. 63; c. 2. SOLID STATE PHYSICS. B.S, Queens Col, 60; M.S, Rutgers, 62, Ph.D.(physics), 66. Res. fel. physics, Rensselaer Polytech, 65-68; RES. PHYSICIST, U.S. NAVAL RES. LAB, WASH, D.C, 68- Am. Phys. Soc. Lattice vibrations and thermal properties of solids; electronic properties of solids as a function of pres-sure. Address: 8111 Oaklake Ct, Alexandria, VA 22309.

FELDMAN, JULIAN, b. Brooklyn, N.Y, May 24, 15; m. 44; c. 3. ORGANIC CHEMISTRY. B.S, City Col, 35; A.M, Brooklyn Col, 40; Ph.D.(chem), Pitts-burgh, 50. Chief chemist, Pro-Medico Labs, 35-40; Gold-Leaf Pharmacal Co, 40-41; asst. chemist, bur. animal indust, U.S. Dept. Agr, 41; asst. plant mgr, Trubek Labs, 41-42; res. assoc, explosives res. lab, Nat. Defense Res. Cmn, 42-45; res. chemist, Bur. Mines, 45-53; group leader, NAT. DISTILLERS PRODS. & CHEM. CORP, 53-57, res. supvr, 57-59, SR. RES. ASSOC, 59- AAAS; Am. Chem. Soc. Separations and purifications; phase equilibria; distillation; kinetics; isomerization; catalysis; composition of fuels and carbonization products; molecular complexes; polynuclear com-pounds. Address: 7511 Sagamore Dr, Cincinnati, OH 45236.

FELDMAN, JULIUS, b. Chicago, Ill, Nov. 1, 13; m. 43; c. 3. ORGANIC CHEMISTRY. B.S, Chicago, 33, Ph.D.(org. chem), 37. Jr. chemist, Ill. State Geol. Surv, 34; asst. physiol, med. sch, Illinois, 37-40; asst. chem-ist, Ord. Dept, Ind, 41-42; res. chemist, Parker Pen Co, 43-58, dir, quality assurance lab, 58-60, plant process lab, 60-67; ASST. PROF. CHEM. & ASST. CHMN. DEPT, BOSTON UNIV, 67- Am. Chem. Soc. Writing inks. Address: Dept. of Chemistry, Boston University, 675 Commonwealth Ave, Boston, MA 02215.

FELDMAN, KARL THOMAS, JR, b. Independence, Kans, Feb. 20, 38; m. 60; c. 2. MECHANICAL ENGINEERING. B.S, Kansas, 61; M.S, Missouri, 62, Nat. Defense Ed. Act fel. & Ph.D.(thermoacoustics), 66. Asst. prof. MECH. ENG, UNIV. N.MEX, 64-68, ASSOC. PROF, 68-, DIR, ENG. COOP. EDUC. WITH INDUST, 70- Summer res. assoc, Univ. Mo, 64; consult, space iso-tope power dept, Sandia Lab, N.Mex, 66; Dikewood Corp, 66-67; dir, Nat. Sci. Found. instructional sci. equip. grant, 66-69, undergrad. res. partic. prog. grant, 68; dir. contract, Off. Naval Res, 67-68 & 70-; consult. & mem. bd. dir, Energy Conversion Systs, Inc, N.Mex, 68- Am. Soc. Mech. Eng; Am. Soc. Eng. Educ; Nat. Soc. Prof. Eng. Thermoacoustics, magnetohydro-dynamics and energy conversion. Address: Dept. of Mechanical Engineer-ing, University of New Mexico, Albuquerque, NM 87106.

FELDMAN, LARRY H(OWARD), b. Brooklyn, N.Y, Feb. 25, 42; m. 64; c. 2. PHYSICAL CHEMISTRY. B.S, Brooklyn Col, 62; Ph.D.(chem), Mich. State Univ, 66. Sr. res. chemist, res. labs, EASTMAN KODAK CO, 66-70, SR. DEVELOP. ENGR, KODAK PARK DIV, 70- Am. Chem. Soc; Soc. Photog. Sci. & Eng. Photographic science and technology of silver halide systems; electron attachment reactions in anhydrous ethylenediamine. Address: 315 Tioga Dr, Rochester, NY 14616.

FELDMAN, LAWRENCE, b. Havana, Cuba, Apr. 5, 22; U.S. citizen; m. 52. NUCLEAR PHYSICS. B.A, Brooklyn Col, 43; M.S, North Carolina, 44; Ph.D.(physics), Columbia, 50. Instr. physics, North Carolina, 43-44; physi-cist, Naval Ord. Lab, 44-46; asst. physics, Columbia, 46-48, res. assoc, 50-63, Higgins fel, 51-52; sr. res. assoc, Pennsylvania, 63-64; assoc. prof. PHYSICS, ST. JOHN'S UNIV.(N.Y), 64-69, PROF, 69- Lectr, City Col. New York, 52-64. Am. Phys. Soc. Beta Decay; weak interactions; nuclear re-actions; giant resonance phenomena; C-W cyclotron; high forbidden nuclear beta decay; calculations of atomic energy levels in helium. Address: Dept. of Physics, St. John's University, Jamaica, NY 11432.

FELDMAN, LAWRENCE A, b. Brooklyn, N.Y, Oct. 11, 38; m. 61; c. 1. MI-CROBIOLOGY, VIROLOGY. B.S, Univ. Wis, 60; M.A, Pa. State Univ, 62, Ph.D.(microbiol), 64. U.S. Pub. Health Serv. training fel. virol. & epide-miol, col. med, Baylor Univ, 64-66; instr. MICROBIOL, COL. MED. & DENT. N.J, NEWARK, 66-67, asst. prof, 67-71, ASSOC. PROF, 71- AAAS; Am. Soc. Microbiol; Brit. Soc. Gen. Microbiol. Viral diseases of the cen-tral nervous system; viral oncogenesis; abortive viral infections. Address: Dept. of Microbiology, College of Medicine & Dentistry of New Jersey, 100 Bergen St, Newark, NJ 07103.

FELDMAN, LEONARD, b. Jamaica, N.Y, Oct. 3, 23; m. 48; c. 2. MATHE-MATICS. B.S, Queen's Col.(N.Y), 48; M.A, Columbia, 50; Fund Adv. Ed. fel. Ford Found, 54-55; Ed.D.(counseling psychol), California, 57. Tech. writer, electron tube group, N.Y. Univ, 48-49; teacher, pub. schs, N.Y. & Calif, 49-57; asst. prof. MATH. & EDUC, SAN JOSE STATE COL, 57-62, assoc. prof, 62-70, PROF, 70- Dir, Nat. Sci. Found. Acad. Year Inst, 62-63, 66-68; Nat. Sci. Found. sci. faculty fel, 64-65; vis. assoc. prof, Colum-bia Univ. on assignment to Makerere Univ. Col, 68-70; mem, Int. Study Group Math. Learning. U.S.A, 43-46. AAAS; Math. Asn. Am. Evaluation of mathematics education; in-service education for teachers; learning theory; remedial mathematics. Address: Dept. of Mathematics, San Jose State College, San Jose, CA 95114.

FELDMAN, LOUIS A, b. Bay City, Mich, Nov. 26, 41. TOPOLOGY, GEOME-TRY. Nat. Sci. Found. & Woodrow Wilson fels. & B.S, Univ. Mich, 63; M.A, Univ. Calif, Berkeley, 65, Ph.D.(math), 69. Asst. MATH, Univ. Calif, Berkeley, 64-68; asst. prof, STANISLAUS STATE COL, 68-71, ASSOC. PROF, 71- Am. Math. Soc. Algebraic topology; the relationship between fibre bundles and topological transformation groups. Address: Dept. of Mathematics, Stanislaus State College, Turlock, CA 95380.

FELDMAN, LOUIS I(SRAEL), b. New York, N.Y, Dec. 6, 22; m. 45; c. 3. MI-CROBIOLOGY. B.S, Cornell, 46; M.S, Michigan, 48; Atomic Energy Comn. fel, Indiana, 49-50, Ph.D.(bact), 51. Asst. bact, Michigan, 46-48; res. bac-teriologist, Lederle Labs, Am. Cyanamid Co, 50-58, sr. res. biochemist, 58-64; HEAD MICROBIOL. RES. DEPT, WALLERSTEIN CO, 64- U.S.A.A.F, 43-45, 1st Lt. AAAS; Am. Soc. Microbiol; Am. Chem. Soc; N.Y. Acad. Sci.

Bacterial transaminases; physiology and metabolism of microorganisms; biosynthesis of antibiotics and steroids; enzyme synthesis. Address: Wallerstein Co, 125 Lake Ave, New York, NY 10303.

FELDMAN, MARCUS WILLIAM, b. Perth, Australia, Nov. 14, 42; m. 64; c. 1. MATHEMATICAL BIOLOGY. B.Sc, Western Australia, 64; M.Sc, Monash Univ, Australia, 66; Ph.D.(math. biol), Stanford, 69. Tutor math, Monash Univ, Australia, 64-65; res. asst, STANFORD UNIV, 65-69, ASST. PROF. BIOL, 69- Genetics Soc. Am. Mathematical models of genetical phenomena, primarily selection and recombination; population genetics and ecology of a theoretical nature. Address: Dept. of Biology, Stanford University, Stanford, CA 94305.

FELDMAN, MARTIN, b. N.Y.C, July 13, 35; m. 61; c. 1. PHYSICS. B.S, Rensselaer Polytech, 57; Ph.D.(physics), Cornell, 62. Res. assoc. physics, Cornell Univ, 62-63; asst. prof, Univ. Pa, 63-68; MEM. TECH. STAFF, BELL TEL. LABS, 68- Experimental high energy physics; electronics; Optics. Address: Bell Telephone Labs, Mountain Ave, Murray Hill, NJ 07974.

FELDMAN, MARTIN LOUIS, b. Brooklyn, N.Y, June 14, 41; m. 62; c. 2. ORGANIC CHEMISTRY. B.S, City Col. New York, 63; Ph.D.(org. chem), Pittsburgh, 66. CHEMIST, AM. CYANAMID CORP, BOUND BROOK, 66- Am. Chem. Soc. Organic synthesis; dyes; heterocycles. Address: 9 Fieldcrest Dr, East Brunswick, NJ 08816.

FELDMAN, MARTIN ROBERT, b. N.Y.C, Apr. 23, 38; m. 59; c. 2. ORGANIC CHEMISTRY. A.B, Columbia Univ, 58; Nat. Sci. Found fel, Univ. Calif, Los Angeles, 58-62, Ph.D.(phys. & org. chem), 63. Res. chemist, Univ. Calif, Berkeley, 62-63; asst. prof. CHEM, HOWARD UNIV, 63-68, assoc. prof, 68-71, PROF, 71- Nat. Sci. Found sci. faculty fel, Univ. Calif, Irvine, 69-70. Am. Chem. Soc; The Chem. Soc. Physical-organic chemistry. Address: Dept. of Chemistry, Howard University, Washington, DC 20001.

FELDMAN, MILTON H, b. N.Y.C, Mar. 17, 18; m. 46; c. 4. PHYSICAL CHEMISTRY. B.S, N.Y. Univ, 39, Ph.D.(phys. chem), 44. Scientist, Oak Ridge Nat. Lab, 46-69; res. engr, N.Am. Aviation Co, 49-53; adv. scientist, Bettis Atomic Power Lab, 53-59; dep. tech. dir, Defense Atomic Support Agency, 59-60; tech. dir. Winchester Environ. Lab, 60-61; chief radiation & radiochem. sect, Walter Reed Army Inst. Res, 61-66; CHIEF CHEM. & BIOL. OCEANOG, ENVIRON. PROTECTION AGENCY, 66- Fel. AAAS; fel. Am. Inst. Chem; fel. Royal Soc. Arts. Radiation effects; nuclear technology; environmental and planetary sciences; biophysics; chemical and biological oceanography. Address: Pacific Northwest Water Lab, 200 S.W. 35th St, Corvallis, OR 97330.

FELDMAN, NATHAN I, b. Brooklyn, N.Y, Mar. 31, 40. BIOCHEMISTRY. B.A, State Univ. N.Y, Buffalo, 61; U.S. Pub. Health Serv. fel, Tufts Univ, 62-65, Nat. Inst. Ment. Health & Blindness fel, 65-67, Ph.D.(biochem), 67. Nat. Multiple Sclerosis Soc. & Nat. Inst. Ment. Health & Blindness res. fels, N.Y. State Psychiat. Inst, 67-68; RES. ASSOC. BIOCHEM, ISAAC ALBERT RES. INST, 68- AAAS; Am. Chem. Soc; Am. Soc. Neurochem. Neurochemistry; lipid metabolism. Address: 1270 E. 19th St, Brooklyn, NY 11230.

FELDMAN, NATHANIEL E, b. New London, Conn, Oct. 7, 25; m. 46; c. 4. ELECTRONICS. B.S, California, Berkeley, 48, M.S, 50. Asst. elec. eng, California, Berkeley, 49-50, engr, Lawrence Radiation Lab, 51-54; instr. fire control radar, Hughes Aircraft Co, 55; leader adv. develop, defense electronic prod. div, Radio Corp. Am, 56-60; ENGR. SYSTS. ANAL, RAND CORP, 60- Consult, Adv. Res. Projs. Agency, U.S. Dept. Defense, 65-; chmn. tech. prog, third commun. satellite systs. conf, Am. Inst. Aeronaut; & Astronaut. U.S.A.A.F, 45-47. Sr. mem. Inst. Elec. & Electronics Eng; assoc. fel. Am. Inst. Aeronaut. & Astronaut. Satellite communications; components for microwave systems for radar electronic counter measures and aerospace communications; systems analysis and exploratory design. Address: Engineering Sciences Dept, Rand Corp, 1700 Main St, Santa Monica, CA 90406.

FELDMAN, NICHOLAS, b. Mukačevo, Czech, Sept. 25, 24; U.S. citizen; m. 58; c. 2. PETROLEUM & ANALYTICAL CHEMISTRY. M.S, Prague Tech. Univ, 49. Analytical chemist, Fiber Chem. Corp, N.J, 50-52, chief chemist, 52-57; res. chemist, ESSO RES. & ENG. CO, 57-63, sr. res. chemist, 63-68, RES. ASSOC, PROD. RES. DIV, 68- Am. Chem. Soc. Effect of fuel and lube additives on product quality; interaction of additives; mechanism of wax crystal modification; leather and textile specialties; analytical methods; compositional analysis. Address: Products Research Division, Esso Research & Engineering Co, P.O. Box 51, Linden, NJ 07036.

FELDMAN, PAUL D(ONALD), b. Brooklyn, N.Y, Nov. 4, 39; m. 65; c. 2. ATOMIC PHYSICS. A.B, Columbia, 60, Nat. Sci. Found. fel, 60-62, M.A, 62, Radio Corp. Am. fel, 62-63, Ph.D.(atomic physics), 64. Instr. PHYSICS, Columbia Univ, 64-65, res. assoc, Naval Res. Lab, 65-67; ASST. PROF, JOHNS HOPKINS UNIV, 67- Sloan Found. res. fel, 69- Am. Geophys. Union; Am. Astron. Soc; Am. Phys. Soc. Autoionization phenomena; collision processes; infrared astronomy; ionospheric physics. Address: Dept. of Physics, Johns Hopkins University, Baltimore, MD 21218.

FELDMAN, ROBERT SIMION, b. Utica, N.Y, March 6, 18; m; c. 3. PHYSIOLOGICAL PSYCHOLOGY. B.S, Michigan, 43, M.S, 44, Ph.D, 51. Instr. PSYCHOL, UNIV. MASS, AMHERST, 47-48, asst. prof, 48-52, assoc. prof, 52-56, PROF, 56- Res. psychologist, Northampton Vet. Admin. Hosp, 56-58. Am. Psychol. Asn. Neuropsychology; psychopharmacology. Address: Dept. of Psychology, University of Massachusetts, Amherst, MA 01002.

FELDMAN, S(AMUEL) M(ITCHELL), b. Phila, Pa, Sept. 26, 33; m. 54; c. 2. NEUROPHYSIOLOGY, PHYSIOLOGICAL PSYCHOLOGY. B.A, Univ. Pa, 54; M.A, Northwest. Univ, 55; Ph.D.(psychol), McGill Univ, 58. Fel. neurophysiol, Univ. Wash, 58-60, instr. physiol, 60-62; asst. prof, Albert Einstein Col. Med, 62-67, assoc. prof, 67-71; PROF. PSYCHOL, N.Y. UNIV, 71- Am. Psychol. Asn. Neurophysiology of emotion and motivation; central control of sensory stimulation. Address: Dept. of Psychology, 1053 Brown Bldg, New York University, New York, NY 10003.

FELDMAN, SANFORD EDWARD, b. San Francisco, Calif, Apr. 20, 14; m. 37; c. 3. SURGERY. A.B, Stanford Univ, 34, M.D, 38. SURGEON, MT. ZION HOSP, 46-; ATTEND. SURGEON, CHILDRENS HOSP, HAHNEMANN HOSP, 66-; ASSOC. RES. SURGEON, POULTRY DEPT, UNIV. CALIF, BERKELEY, 66-, San Francisco, 55-66. Lectr, med. ctr, Univ. Calif, San Francisco. U.S.A, 44-46. Central nervous system in nutrition. Address: 3633 California St, San Francisco, CA 94118.

FELDMAN, SAUL, b. Buenos Aires, Argentina, Apr. 22, 28; nat; m. 50; c. 3. ENGINEERING SCIENCE. B.S, California, Los Angeles, 52, M.S, 53; Ph.D. (mech. eng, Math), Calif. Inst. Tech, 55. Asst. eng, California, 52; res. engr, Marquardt Aircraft Co, 52-53; prin. res. scientist, Avco-Everett Res. Lab, 55-60; prin. scientist, Electro-Optical Systs, Inc, 60-62; founder, chmn. bd. dirs, chief exec. off. & tech. dir, Heliodyne Corp, Calif, 62-68, pres, Heliodyne div. KMS Industs, Inc, 68-69, new venture mgr, 69-70; PRIVATE CONSULT, 70- Guggenheim fel, Calif. Inst. Technol, 53-55; mem. penetration panel, U.S. Air Force, 62-64; indust. affiliate, aerospace & mech. eng. dept, Univ. Calif, San Diego, 67-69; mem, Ctr. Study Democratic Inst. Referee, Physics of Fluids, Am. Phys. Soc. & Jour. Fluid Mech, Gt. Brit, 58-62. Assoc. fel. Am. Inst. Aeronaut. & Astronaut; Am. Acad. Arts & Sci; World Future Soc. High temperature gas dynamics; hydrodynamic stability; gas dynamics phenomena resulting from atmospheric re-entry; gas dynamic lasers; thermonuclear fusion; futurology. Address: 2680 Charl Pl, Hollywood, CA 90046.

FELDMAN, STUART, b. Bronx, N.Y, Feb. 14, 41; m. 63; c. 2. PHARMACEUTICS, PHARMACEUTICAL CHEMISTRY. B.S, Columbia, 62, M.S, 66; Am. Fedn. Pharmaceut. Ed. fel, State Univ. N.Y. Buffalo, 68-69, Ph.D. (pharmaceut), 69. ASST. PROF. BIOPHARMACEUT. SCH. PHARM, TEMPLE UNIV, 69- AAAS; Am. Pharmaceut. Asn; Acad. Pharmaceut. Sci; N.Y. Acad. Sci. Effect of surface active agents on drug absorption; study of the biopharmaceutical factors influencing drug absorption, distribution and elimination. Address: School of Pharmacy, Temple University, Philadelphia, PA 19140.

FELDMAN, WILLIAM, b. New London, Conn, Sept. 15, 17; m. 49; c. 3. PHYSICS. B.S, Purdue, 39; fel, Pennsylvania, Ph.D.(physics), 42. Asst, Nat. Defense Res. Cmt. & Office Sci. Res. & Develop, Pennsylvania, 42; sr. physicist, radiation lab, California, 42-43; supt. pilot plant, Tenn. Eastman Corp, Oak Ridge, 43, asst. supt. prod. dept, 43-45; res. physicist, EASTMAN KODAK CO, 45-51, asst. supt. eng. & develop, guided missiles sect, naval ord. div, 51-56, asst. dir. res. & develop, apparatus & optical div, 56-64, proj. group mgr. RES. & ENG, 64-65, PROG. MGR, APPARATUS DIV, 65-, MGR. LUNAR ORBITER PROG, 66- NASA Pub. Serv. Award, 67; NASA Apollo Achievement Award, 70. AAAS; Am. Phys. Soc; Am. Inst. Physicis; N.Y. Acad. Sci. Electromagnetic isotope separation; nuclear physics; camera and shutter design; guided missiles; data processing; information storage and retrieval; professional motion picture and television equipment; space satellite projects; lunar orbiter. Address: Apparatus Division, Eastman Kodak Co, 901 Elmgrove Rd, Rochester, NY 14650.

FELDMAN, WILLIAM, b. Philadelphia, Pa, Feb. 9, 29; m. 51; c. 3. MICROBIOLOGY. B.A, Temple, 50; Ph.D.(microbiol), Pennsylvania, 55. Res. assoc. microbiol, Hahnemann Med. Col, 55-57; microbial metabolism, med. col, Cornell, 57-59; biochemist clin. biochem, Albert Einstein Med. Center, 59-64; res. biochemist, Episcopal Hosp, Phila, Pa, 64-67; biochemist, East State Sch. & Hosp, Trevose, Pa, 67-70; CLIN. CHEMIST, COOPER HOSP, 70- U.S.N, 50-52. AAAS; Am. Soc. Microbiol; Am. Asn. Clin. Chem. Microbial metabolism and biochemistry; respiratory enzymes, mucopolysaccharides and mucoproteins. Address: Cooper Hospital, Sixth & Stevens St, Camden, NJ 08103.

FELDMAN, WILLIAM H(UGH), b. Glasgow, Scotland, Nov. 30, 92; nat; m. 34; c. 2. EXPERIMENTAL PATHOLOGY. D.V.M, Colorado State, 17, M.S, 26, hon. D.Sc, 45; Michigan, 20. Asst. prof. vet. path, Colorado State & asst. vet. pathologist, exp. sta, 17-27; from instr. to prof. div, exp. med, MAYO GRAD. SCH. MED, UNIV. MINN, 27-57, EMER. PROF. PATH, 58- Chief lab. res. pulmonary diseases, dept. med. & surg, Vet. Admin, Wash, D.C, 57-67; Harben lectr, London, 46; Alvarenga prize lectr, Phila, 46. Chmn. med. adv. bd, Leonard Wood Mem, 56, 61 & 62; mem. sci. adv. bd, Armed Forces Inst. Path, 47-, emer. chmn. adv. comt, Registry Noteworthy Path, 67-; mem. comt. inst. res. grants, Am. Cancer Soc, 58-61; del, Int. Cong. Leprosy, Havana, 48, Brazil, 63. Gold medal, Am. Med. Asn, 44; Louis Pasteur medal, Pasteur Inst, 46; Dearholt medal, Miss. Valley Tuberc. Conf. & Miss. Valley Trudeau Soc, 53; award, Twelfth Int. Vet. Cong, 59; Karl F. Meyer Gold Headed Cane award & diploma, Am. Vet. Epidemiol. Soc, 70. Am. Soc. Exp. Path.(pres, 41 & 42); hon. mem. Am. Thoracic Soc.(Trudeau medal, 55); Am. Vet. Med. Asn; Am. Asn. Path. & Bact.(pres, 53); Conf. Res. Workers Animal Diseases (secy-treas, 38-48, pres, 52); Am. Col. Chest Physicians (serv. medal, 58); Am. Col. Vet. Path.(pres, 49, First Distinguished Mem, 70); hon. mem. Royal Soc. Med.(Varrier-Jones mem. medal, 58); hon. mem. Italian Soc. Vet. Sci; hon. mem. Peruvian Tuberc. Soc. Neoplasia of domesticated animals; experimental pathology and chemotherapy of tuberculosis and other mycobacterial diseases. Address: Emeritus Staff Office, Mayo Clinic, 200 First St. S.W, Rochester, MN 55901.

FELDMANN, EDWARD G(EORGE), b. Chicago, Ill, Oct. 13, 30; m. 52; c. 4. PHARMACEUTICAL CHEMISTRY. B.S, Loyola (Ill), 52; Am. Found. Pharmaceut. Ed. fel, Wisconsin, 53-55, M.S, 54, Ph.D.(pharmaceut. chem, biochem), 55. Lab. asst, Loyola (Ill), 51-52; Alumni Res. Found. asst, Wisconsin, 52-53; sr. chemist, chem. div, Am. Dental Asn, 55-58, dir, 58-59; chmn-elect, comt. nat. formulary & assoc. dir. revision, AM. PHARMACEUT. ASN, 59-60, chmn. comt. & dir. revision, 60-69, asst. exec. dir. sci. affairs, 69-70, ASSOC. EXEC. DIR, 70-, ED, J. PHARMACEUT. SCI, 60- Spec. lectr, George Washington Univ, 60-65; mem, Nat. Res. Coun, 71-; food codex panel, Nat. Acad. Sci-Nat. Res. Coun; expert panel pharmaceut, WHO. Am. Chem. Soc; Am. Pharmaceut. Asn; N.Y. Acad. Sci; assoc. mem. Am. Med. Asn; Int. Pharmaceut. Fedn. Analysis of pharmaceutical products; standards and specifications for drugs and dosage forms; chemistry of local anesthetics; chemical structure-therapeutic activity relationships; synthetic organic medicinal chemistry; federal drug law. Address: American Pharmaceutical Association, 2215 Constitution Ave, Washington, DC 20037.

FELDMANN, GEORGE WILFRED, b. Wilkes-Barre, Pa, Feb. 5, 15; m. CHEMICAL ENGINEERING. A.B, Columbia, 39, B.S, 40, Ch.E, 41. Res. chemist, Jackson Lab, E.I. DU PONT DE NEMOURS & CO, INC, 41, develop. engr, 41-45, indust. engr, eng. dept, 45-49, RES. CHEMIST, textile res. & rayon mfg, textile fibers dept, 49-54, pigments dept, 54-61, TRAFFIC RES. & DEVELOP, 61- Am. Inst. Chem. Eng. Rubber chemicals; flourine, titanium, T_1O_2 process development; cost reduction; financial analysis; marine engineering; movement of bulk dangerous products by barge and vessel. Address: Traffic Dept, E.I. du Pont de Nemours & Co, Inc, 4 Hoiland Dr, Wilmington, DE 19898.

FELDMANN, HERMAN FREDERICK, b. Chicago, Ill, July 17, 35; m. 65; c. 2. CHEMICAL ENGINEERING. B.S, Ill. Inst. Tech, 57, M.S, 63; Goethe Inst, W.Ger, 65. Proj. engr, Underwriter's Lab, Inc, 57-59; chem. engr, Hotpoint Co, 59-61; supvr. gasification res, Inst. Gas Tech, Ill. Inst. Tech, 61-65; SUPVRY. CHEM. RES. ENGR, PITTSBURGH COAL RES. CTR, U.S. BUR. MINES, 65- U.S.A, 59, Res, 59-67. Am. Inst. Chem. Eng. Conversion of solid fossil fuels to gaseous and liquid fuels and into the chemical aspects of magnetohydrodynamics; mathematical modeling of chemical processes. Address: U.S. Bureau of Mines, 4800 Forbes Ave, Pittsburgh, PA 15213.

FELDMANN, JAY WILLIAM, b. Chicago, Ill, Apr. 12, 35; m. 66; c. 2. APPLIED MECHANICS, MECHANICAL ENGINEERING. B.S.M.E, Northwestern, 60, Walter P. Murphy fel, 60-61, M.S.M.E, 62; NASA traineeship, Univ. Calif, San Diego, 65-68, Ph.D.(appl. mech), 68. Design engr, Indust. Filter & Pump Mfg. Co, Ill, 61-63; sr. res. engr, Narmco Res. & Develop. Div, Whittaker Corp, Calif, 63-64, proj. engr, 64-65; asst. prof. eng, San Diego State Col, 68-69; sr. engr, GULF GEN. ATOMIC INC, 69-70, STAFF ENGR, 71- Reviewer, Appl. Mech. Rev. Heating & air conditioning award & Wall St. J. student achievement award. Nuclear reactor technology; vibration of solids; earthquake effects; structures, basic and applied; matrix methods; theory of elasticity; finite difference techniques; finite element method; cryogenics; pressure vessels; pressure filtration. Address: 7322 Player Dr, San Diego, CA 92119.

FELDMANN, RODNEY M(ANSFIELD), b. Steele, N.Dak, Nov. 19, 39; m. 64; c. 1. INVERTEBRATE PALEONTOLOGY. B.S, North Dakota, 61, Nat. Defense Ed. Act fel, 61-64, M.S, 63, Ph.D.(paleont), 67. Teaching asst. GEOL, Univ. N.Dak, 62-65; instr, KENT STATE UNIV, 65-67, asst. prof, 67-71, ASSOC. PROF, 71-, asst. dean col. arts & sci, 66-67. Field geologist, N.Dak. State Geol. Surv, summers 61-65. Geol. Soc. Am; Paleont. Soc; Brit. Palaeont. Asn; Am. Asn. Petrol. Geol. Cretaceous stratigraphy and molluscan paleontology of the midcontinent; molluscan taxonomy and paleoecology; taxonomy of nephropid lobsters. Address: Dept. of Geology, Kent State University, Kent, OH 44242.

FELDMEIER, JOSEPH R(OBERT), b. Niles, Ohio, Feb. 17, 16; m. 42; c. 5. PHYSICS. B.S, Carnegie Inst. Tech, 38; M.S, Notre Dame, 40, Ph.D.(physics), 42. Asst, physics Notre Dame, 38-42; staff mem, radiation lab, Mass. Inst. Tech, 42-46; asst. prof. physics, Rutgers, 46-48; prof. & chmn. dept, Col. St. Thomas, 48-52; physics mgr, Bettis Atomic Power Lab, Westinghouse Elec. Corp, 52-60; assoc. dir. & dir. sci. lab, Philco Corp, 60-64; DIR, FRANKLIN INST. RES. LABS, 64-, V.PRES, FRANKLIN INST, 67- Tech. consult, Fed. Telecommun. Labs, N.J, 46-48; mem, Gov. Sci. Adv. Comt, 65-; adv. coun. sci, Univ. Notre Dame, 70- AAAS; Am. Nuclear Soc; fel. Am. Phys. Soc. Nuclear physics using Van der Graaf generator; design of radar transmitters; low temperature research using Collins liquefier; excitation of nuclei by x-ray; reactor physics; electronics. Address: Franklin Institute Research Labs, 20th & Parkway, Philadelphia, PA 19103.

FELDMESSER, JULIUS, b. N.Y.C, Oct. 23, 18; m. 44; c. 2. NEMATOLOGY, ZOOLOGY. A.B, Brooklyn Col, 40; George Washington, 41; M.S, N.Y. Univ. 51, Ph.D.(invert. zool, parasitol), 53. Asst. biol, N.Y. Univ, 48-49; jr. nematologist, AGR. RES. SERV, U.S. DEPT. AGR, 47-48, asst. nematologist, 48-52, assoc. nematologist, 52-54, nematologist, 54-58, sr. nematologist, 58-63, RESEARCH NEMATOLOGIST, 63- Consult, Spencer Chem. Co, 57, 58; Int. Mineral & Chem. Corp, 64. U.S.A.A.F, 45-46. Fel. AAAS; Soc. Nematol; Am. Soc. Zool; Am. Soc. Parasitol; Am. Phytopath. Soc. Parasitology; nematocide evaluation and development of evaluation techniques; host-parasite relationships; zoology and chemical control of plant-parasitic nematodes. Address: Nematology Investigations, Plant Industry Station, U.S. Dept. Agriculture, Beltsville, MD 20705.

FELDMETH, CARL ROBERT, b. Los Angeles, Calif, Mar. 16, 42; m. 64. ZOOLOGY, ENVIRONMENTAL PHYSIOLOGY. B.S, Calif. State Col. Los Angeles, 64; M.Sc, Toronto, 66, Ph.D.(zool), 68. Lectr. zool, Univ. Calif, LOS ANGELES, 68-71; ASST. PROF. BIOL, JOINT SCI. DEPT, CLAREMONT COLS, 71- Am. Soc. Limnol. & Oceanog; Can. Soc. Zool. Environmental physiology; marine crustacea; aquatic insects; respiratory and osmotic regulation; effect of thermal effluent on marine invertebrates and fish; comparative energy studies on swimming marine and freshwater fish; thermal tolerance of desert pupfish. Address: Joint Science Dept, Claremont Colleges, Claremont, CA 91711.

FELDSTEIN, AARON, b. Brooklyn, N.Y, May 24, 22. ORGANIC CHEMISTRY. B.A, Brooklyn Col, 44; Ph.D.(chem), Kansas, 52. Anal. chemist, pigments and dyes, Reichold Chems, Inc, 44-45; res. chemist, pharmaceut, Endo Prod, Inc, 45-47; asst. instr, Kansas, 47-51, fel. mech. org. reactions, 52-53; res. assoc. steroids, cancer res. lab, Tennessee, 53-55; SR. SCIENTIST, WORCESTER FOUND. EXP. BIOL, 55- AAAS; Am. Chem. Soc; N.Y. Acad. Sci; Am. Col. Neuropsychopharmacol. Psychopharmacology; neurochemistry; biochemistry. Address: Worcester Foundation for Experimental Biology, Shrewsbury, MA 01545.

FELDSTEIN, NATHAN, b. Haifa, Israel, Jan. 4, 37; U.S. citizen; m. 61; c. 1. PHYSICAL CHEMISTRY. B.Ch.E, City Col. New York, 60; M.S, N.Y. Univ, 64, Ph.D.(chem), 66. Engr, Corning Glass Works, 60; teaching fel. chem, N.Y. Univ, 62-64; lectr, Brooklyn Col, 64-66; RES. SCIENTIST, RCA LABS, 66- David sarnoff Achievement Award, 68. Chem.C, U.S.A, 60-61. Am. Chem. Soc; Electrochem. Soc. Adsorption effects in electrochemistry. Address: RCA Labs, David Sarnoff Research Center, Princeton, NJ 08540.

FELDZAMEN, ALVIN N(ORMAN), b. New York, N.Y, Feb. 10, 31. MATHEMATICS. B.S, Oklahoma, 50; M.A, Harvard, 52; Sheffield Sci. Sch. fel. Yale, 52-53, Jr. Sterling fel, 53-54, Ph.D, 59. Instr. math, Yale, 58-59; res. assoc, Univ. Chicago, 59-60; asst. prof, Univ. Wis, Madison, 59-67; dir. spec. projs. educ. commun, State Univ. N.Y, 67-69; dir. prod, ENCYCLOPAEDIA BRITANNICA EDUC. CORP, 69-70, V.PRES. & ED. DIR. FILMS & PUBL, 70- Exec. producer, comt. educ. media, Math. Asn. Am, 62- U.S.A, 54-56, Res, 56- Am. Math. Soc; Math. Asn. Am. Linear analysis; Hilbert and Banach spaces; new educational media; motion picture production. Address: Encyclopaedia Britannica Educational Corp-10, 425 N. Michigan Ave, Chicago, IL 60611.

FELEPPA, ALFRED E, JR, b. New Rochelle, N.Y, July 14, 41; m. 69; c. 1. MICROSCOPIC ANATOMY, HEMATOLOGY. B.A, Iona Col, 64; univ. scholar, Univ. Cincinnati, 66, Nat. Insts. Health fel, 67-70, Ph.D.(anat), 70. ASST. PROF. ANAT, MED. CTR, UNIV. NEBR, 70- Erythropoietin and erythropoiesis; tissues and organs in situ; tissue transplantation. Address: Dept. of Anatomy, University of Nebraska Medical Center, Omaha, NE 68105.

FELGER, CARL B(RYANT), b. Chicago, Ill, Dec. 12, 32; m. 56; c. 1. BIOCHEMISTRY. B.S, Monmouth Col.(Ill), 56; Ph.D.(biochem), St. Louis, 61. Res. supvr. BIOCHEM, Toni Co. Div, Gillette Co, 61-64, proj. supvr, GILLETTE RES. INST, INC, 64-68, GROUP LEADER, 68- AAAS; Am. Chem. Soc; N.Y. Acad. Sci; Int. Asn. Dent. Res; Soc. Cosmetic Chem. Biochemical research in dermatology, especially the sebaceous gland. Address: Gillette Research Institute, Inc, 1413 Research Blvd, Rockville, MD 20850.

FELGER, MAURICE M(ONROE), b. Fort Wayne, Ind, Feb. 5, 08; m. 33; c. 3. CHEMISTRY. A.B, Indiana, 30, A.M, 31, Ph.D.(chem), 33. Asst. chem, Indiana, 29-33, instr. exten. div, 33-39, asst. prof, Ft. Wayne ctr, 39-41; assoc. chemist, U.S. Nitrate Plant No. 2, Wilson Dam, 41-45; DEVELOP. CHEMIST, GEN. ELEC. CO, 45- Instr. eng. sci. & mgt. defense training, Alabama, 41-43. With Tenn. Valley Auth, 44. Am. Chem. Soc; Soc. Plastics Eng. Electrolytic deposition of metals; high pressure synthesis; synthetic resins as electrical insulation. Address: 315 Arcadia Ct, Fort Wayne, IN 46807.

FELICETTA, VINCENT F(RANK), b. Seattle, Wash, July 20, 19; m. 42; c. 2. ANALYTICAL CHEMISTRY. B.S, Washington (Seattle), 42; M.S, 51. Chemist, U.S. Rubber Co, Mich, 42-45; res. chemist, pulp mills res. proj, Washington (Seattle), 45-53, res. assoc, 53-57, res. asst. prof, 57-59; res. chemist, BELLINGHAM DIV, GA-PAC. CORP, 59-65, sr. chemist, 65-69, ADMIN. ASST, 69- Am. Chem. Soc. Spent sulfite liquor characterization and utilization. Address: 2958 Plymouth Dr, Bellingham, WA 98225.

FELICIANO, MANUEL, b. Mayaguez, P.R, Nov. 5, 28; m. 51; c. 8. MATHEMATICS. B.A, Polytech. Inst. P.R, 47; M.A, Columbia Univ, 51; Ph.D. (math), Univ. Tenn, 70. Instr. math, Cath. Univ. P.R, 51-53, asst. prof, 53-55, assoc. prof, 55-57; MATHEMATICIAN, OAK RIDGE NAT. LAB, 57-, PROG. CONSULT, 70-, prog. group leader, 62-70. Math. Asn. Am; Asn. Comput. Math. Programming languages, especially the algorithmic; special functions; ordinary differential equations. Address: Oak Ridge National Lab, P.O. Box X, Oak Ridge, TN 37831.

FELICIOTTI, ENIO, b. Southbridge, Mass, Oct. 9, 26; m. 50; c. 3. FOOD TECHNOLOGY. A.B, Boston, 49, A.M, 52; Ph.D.(food tech), Massachusetts, 56. Instr. food tech, Massachusetts, 53-55; mgr. customer res, Hazel Atlas Glass Div, Continental Can Co, Inc, 55-60; from mgr. prod. develop. to dir. res, THOMAS J. LIPTON, INC, 60-68, V.PRES. RES, 68- Tech. consult. For. Agr. Serv, U.S. Dept. Agr, 53-54. U.S.N.A.F, 43-46. AAAS; Am. Chem. Soc; Inst. Food Technol. Food research; administration. Address: Thomas J. Lipton, Inc, 800 Sylvan Ave, Englewood Cliffs, NJ 07631.

FELIG, PHILIP, b. New York, N.Y, Dec. 18, 36; m. 58; c. 3. INTERNAL MEDICINE, ENDOCRINOLOGY. A.B, Princeton, 57; M.D, Yale, 61. Intern, internal med, Yale-New Haven Hosp, Conn, 61-62, asst. res, 62-63 & 65-66, chief res, 66-67; U.S. Pub. Health Serv. spec. res. fel. metab-endocrinol, Joslin Res. Lab, Harvard Med. Sch. & Peter Bent Brigham Hosp, Boston, Mass, 67-69; ASST. PROF. INTERNAL MED, SCH. MED, YALE, 69- Am. Col. Physicians teaching & res. scholar, 69-72. U.S.A.F, 63-65, Capt; Commendation Medal, 67. Am. Fedn. Clin. Res; Am. Diabetes Asn. Regulation of gluconeogenesis; amino acid metabolism in the regulation of insulin secretion and gluconeogenesis; clinical diabetes mellitus. Address: Dept. of Internal Medicine, Yale University School of Medicine, New Haven, CT 06510.

FELIX, ARTHUR M, b. N.Y.C, June 15, 38; m. 67; c. 1. ORGANIC & PEPTIDE CHEMISTRY. B.A, N.Y. Univ, 59; Nat. Insts. Health fel, Polytech. Inst. Brooklyn, 63-64, Ph.D.(chem), 64. Nat. Insts. Health res. fel, Harvard, 64-66; SR. RES. CHEMIST, RES. DIV, HOFFMANN-LA ROCHE, INC, 66- Guest investr, Rockefeller Univ, 68-69; instr, Fairleigh Dickinson, 68- Am. Chem. Soc; The Chem. Soc; N.Y. Acad. Sci; Am. Inst. Chem. Classical and solid phase peptide synthesis; synthesis of new penicillin derivatives; synthesis and physical chemistry of polypeptides. Address: Hoffmann-La Roche, Inc, Research Division, Nutley, NJ 07110.

FELIX, C(HARLES) J(EFFREY), b. Lynch, Ky, July 2, 21; m. 57; c. 3. PALEOBOTANY. B.A, Tennessee, 49; M.A, Washington (St. Louis), 52, fel, 53-54, Ph.D.(paleobot), 54. Asst. bot, Washington (St. Louis), 50-53; paleobotanist, coal res. lab, U.S. Geol. Surv, Ohio State Univ, 54-56; SUN OIL CO, 56-64, SR. RES. GEOLOGIST, 64- U.S.M.C, 42-46. Am. Bryol. & Lichenological Soc; Bot. Soc. Am. Carboniferous plants of coal ball horizons; Paleozoic and Tertiary plant microfossils; palaeobotany and palynology of the Canadian Arctic. Address: Sun Oil Co, Key Areas Arctic, P.O. Box 2880, Dallas, TX 75221.

FELIX, ROBERT H(ANNA), b. Downs, Kans, May 29, 04; m. 33; c. 1. MENTAL HYGIENE. A.B, Colorado, 26, M.D, 30, hon. Sc.D, 53; M.P.H, Hopkins, 42; hon. Sc.D, Boston, 53; hon. LL.D, Univ. Chattanooga, 57; hon. LL.D, Ripon Col, 59; hon. Sc.D, Univ. Rochester, 64. Commonwealth Fund fel, Colo. Psychopath. Hosp, 31-33; staff psychiatrist, Hosp. for Fed. Prisoners,

Mo, 33-35, clin. dir, 35-36; chief psychiat. serv, U.S. Pub. Health Serv. Hosp, Ky, 36-38, dir. res, 38-40, exec. off, 40-41; psychiatrist, U.S. Coast Guard Acad, 42-43, sr. med. off, 43-44; asst. chief hosp, div, U.S. PUB. HEALTH SERV, 44, chief ment. hyg. div, 44-49, dir, Nat. Inst. Ment. Health, Nat. Insts. Health, 49-64; PROF. PSYCHIAT. & DEAN SCH. MED, ST. LOUIS UNIV, 64- Fel. Am. Med. Asn; fel. Am. Psychiat. Asn.(treas, 58-59, pres, 60-61); Am. Pub. Health Asn; fel. Am. Col. Physicians. Medical education; drug addiction; psychiatry; mental public health; mental hygiene and socio-environmental factors; medical school administration. Address: Office of the Dean, St. Louis University School of Medicine, 1402 S. Grand Blvd, St. Louis, MO 63104.

FELIX, W(ALTER) DALE, b. Sheridan, Wyo, May 25, 36; m. 58; c. 5. PHYSICAL CHEMISTRY. B.S, Utah, 58, Ph.D.(phys. chem), 62; Ohio State Univ, 66. Chemist RADIATION CHEM, Hanford Labs, Gen. Elec. Co, 62-64, sr. chemist, 64; SR. RES. SCIENTIST, PAC. NORTHWEST LABS. DIV, BATTELLE MEM. INST, 65- Am. Chem. Soc; Int. Microwave Power Inst. Liquid structure; radiation chemistry of aqueous systems; kinetics of rapid reactions; computer modeling of nuclear and chemical reactions. Address: 2213 Enterprise, Richland, WA 99352.

FELKNER, IRA CECIL, b. Alice, Tex, Jan. 3, 36; m. 69; c. 1. MICROBIAL GENETICS, MOLECULAR BIOLOGY. B.A, Univ. Tex, Austin, 58, M.A, 60, Nat. Insts. Health fel. & Ph.D.(microbiol), 66. Med. Res. Coun. Gt. Brit. fel, inst. animal genetics, Univ. Edinburgh, 65-66; res. scientist molecular biol, Southwest Ctr. Advan. Studies, 66-68; ASST. PROF. MICROBIOL, TEXAS TECH UNIV, 68- Asst. prof. genetics, Austin Col, 66-68; Brown Hazen Fund-Res. Corp. & Eli Lilly Co. grants, 69-71; del, Int. Cong. Microbiol, Mexico City, 70. Asn. U.S. Army, science award res. & develop, 62. Am. Soc. Microbiol. Nature of and regulation mechanisms controlling uptake and recombination in Bacillus subtilis; chemical and irradiation mutagenesis in bacteria; biochemical and physico-chemical aspects of microbial genetics. Address: Dept. of Biology, Texas Tech University, Lubbock, TX 79409.

FELL, CHARLES F(RANCIS), b. Toledo, Ohio, Sept. 17, 11; m. 35; c. 4. ELECTRICAL ENGINEERING. B.S, U.S. Mil. Acad, 34; M.Sc, Ohio State, 38. Exec. to chief signal officer, gen. hqs, U.S. Army, Far E, Manila & Tokyo, 45-48, mem. gen. staff logistics, Wash, D.C, 48-50, exec. to chief signal officer, Supreme Hqs, Allied Powers, Europe, NATO Hqs, Paris, France, 51-53, from chief, distrib. br. to dep. chief, signal supply hqs, Wash, D.C, 55-58; asst. prof. ELEC. ENG, Ohio State Univ, 57-60; assoc. prof, UNIV. NEV, RENO, 60-65, PROF, 65- U.S.A, 39-57, Col. Sr. mem. Inst. Elec. & Electronics Eng. Electronics; solid state. Address: Dept. of Electrical Engineering, University of Nevada, Reno, NV 89507.

FELL, COLIN, b. Flint, Mich, June 21, 30; m. 50; c. 4. PHYSIOLOGY. A.B, Antioch Col, 51; M.S, Wayne State, 53, Ph.D.(physiol), 57. Asst, Wayne State, 51-57; cardiovasc. res. trainee, med. col, Georgia, 57-58; Washington (Seattle), 58-60; instr. PHYSIOL, col. physicians & surgeons, Columbia Univ, 60-62; asst. prof, MED. COL, CORNELL UNIV, 62-71, ASSOC. PROF, 71- Am. Physiol. Soc; Harvey Soc. Cardiovascular physiology. Address: Dept. of Physiology, Medical College, Cornell University, 1300 York Ave, New York, NY 10021.

FELL, GEORGE B(RADY), b. Elgin, Ill, Sept. 27, 16; m. 48. ECOLOGY. B.S, Illinois, 38; M.S, Michigan, 40. Teacher, pub. sch, Ill, 40-41; bacteriologist & serologist, City Health Dept. Lab, Rockford, Ill, 46-48; soil conservationist, U.S. Soil Conserv. Serv, 48-49; exec. dir, Nature Conserv, 50-58; DIR, NATURAL LAND INST, 58- Mem, Ill. Nature Preserves Comn, 64-70, exec. secy, 70- Wildlife Soc; Ecol. Soc. Am. Methods of preserving and maintaining natural areas; analysis and management of natural vegetation. Address: 303 Penfield Pl, Rockford, IL 61108.

FELL, H(OWARD) BARRACLOUGH, b. Lewes, Eng, June 6, 17; m. 42; c. 3. INVERTEBRATE ZOOLOGY. B.Sc, New Zealand, 38, M.Sc, 39; Ph.D.(zool), Edinburgh, 41, D.Sc.(zool), 55; hon. A.M, Harvard, 65. Demonstr. zool, Edinburgh, 39-41; sr. lectr, Victoria, N.Z, 45-57, assoc. prof, 57-64; curator INVERT. ZOOL, MUS. COMP. ZOOL, HARVARD, 64-65, PROF, 65- R.E.M.E, 41-45, Maj. Fel. Am. Acad. Arts & Sci; fel. Royal Soc. N.Z. (Hector Medal & Prize, 59, Hutton Medal, 62); N.Z. Asn. Scientists (secy, 46, pres, 48). Evolution; general problems of marine biogeography; biology of deep-sea bottom faunas; systematics, morphology and paleontology of the Echinodermata. Address: Museum of Comparative Zoology, Harvard University, Cambridge, MA 02138.

FELL, J(AMES) M(ICHAEL) G(ARDNER), b. Vancouver, B.C, Can, Dec. 4, 23; m. 57; c. 2. MATHEMATICS. B.A, British Columbia, 43; M.A, California, 45, Ph.D.(math), 50. Jr. res. physicist, Nat. Res. Council, Can, 45-46; instr, Calif. Inst. Tech, 53-55; res. assoc, Chicago, 55-56; asst. prof. MATH, Univ. Wash, 56-64, PROF, 64-65; UNIV. PA, 65- Am. Math. Soc. Functional analysis; group representations. Address: Dept. of Mathematics, University of Pennsylvania, Philadelphia, PA 19104.

FELL, PAUL ERVEN, b. Richmond, Va, Oct. 4, 37; m. 71. DEVELOPMENTAL BIOLOGY. B.A, Hope Col, 60; Ph.D.(biol), Stanford, 68. Instr. biol, Stanford, 64-65; res. assoc, California, San Diego, 66-68; ASST. PROF. ZOOL, CONNACOL, 68- AAAS; Am. Soc. Zool; Soc. Develop. Biol. Tissue interactions during organogenesis in vertebrate embryos; cell interactions during oogenesis in sponges. Address: Dept. of Zoology, Box 1484, Connecticut College, New London, CT 06320.

FELL, RALPH VINCENT, b. Bearden, Ark, July 4, 24; m. 46; c. 3. NUTRITION, BIOCHEMISTRY. B.S, Arkansas, 52, M.S, 53; Ph.D.(nutrit), La. State, 59. Instr. AGR, South. State Col, 53-54, asst. prof, 54-57; PROF, NORTHWEST. STATE UNIV, 59-, head dept, 59-69. U.S.A, 43-45. Poultry Sci. Asn; Am. Dairy Sci. Asn; Am. Soc. Animal Sci. Amino acid utilization, particularly D amino acid by poultry. Address: Dept. of Agriculture, Northwestern State University, Natchitoches, LA 71457.

FELL, W(ILLIAM) F(RANCIS), b. Mont Clare, Pa, Mar. 9, 12; m. 38; c. 1. ELECTRICAL ENGINEERING. B.S.E.E, Mass. Inst. Tech, 34. Develop. & design engr. ELECTRONICS, RCA CORP, 34-46, eng. group leader, 46-

57, TECH. ADMINISTR, COMMUN. SYSTS. DIV, 57- Inst. Elec. & Electronics Eng. Communication equipment and system development, design and analysis. Address: Communications Systems Division, RCA Corp, Front & Cooper Sts, Camden, NJ 08102.

FELLER, DAVID D(OUGLAS), b. San Francisco, Calif, July 25, 22; m. 47; c. 3. PHYSIOLOGY. A.B, California, Los Angeles, 44, Nat. Cancer Inst. fel, Berkeley, 48-50, Ph.D.(physiol), 50. Instr. physiol, med. sch, Tufts, 50-52; prin. scientist & asst. chief radioisotope serv, Vet. Admin. Hosp, Seattle, Wash, 52-62; ASST. CHIEF ENVIRON. BIOL. DIV, AMES RES. CTR, NASA, 62- From instr. to res. assoc. prof, sch. med, Univ. Wash, 52-62; Am. Heart Asn. travel fel, World Cong. Cardiol, 58; Nat. Res. Coun. travel fel, World Cong. Physiol. Sci, 59. U.S.N.R, 44-46. Am. Physiol. Soc; Am. Soc. Exp. Biol. & Med; Can. Physiol. Soc. Thyroid iodine metabolism; biological effects of radioiodine; carbohydrate metabolism of normal and diabetic animals; lipid metabolism of adipose tissue; blood volume studies of obesity; cardiac output in animals and humans; effects of simulated space environments on metabolic processes; changes in pattern of hepatic regeneration with altered gravity. Address: Environmental Biology Division, NASA Ames Research Center, Moffett Field, CA 94035.

FELLER, M(ORRIS), b. Palmyra, Wis, Apr. 11, 19; m. 47; c. 3. PHYSICAL CHEMISTRY. A.B, California, Los Angeles, 40; M.S, Ill. Inst. Technol, 47. CHEMIST, Div. Lead Co, 40-43; Manhattan Proj, 43-45; Standard Oil Co. (Ind), 46-61; DYNA-CLEAN LABS, 62- Am. Chem. Soc. Smelting and refining of white metals; electrochemistry; refining of lubricating oils; analytical chemistry; distillation; ultrasonics; pollution control; recycling solvent wastes. Address: 458 W. Flower St, Phoenix, AZ 85013.

FELLER, RALPH P(AUL), b. Quincy, Mass, Aug. 31, 34; m. 59; c. 3. DENTISTRY, ORAL BIOLOGY. B.S, Tufts, 56, D.M.D. 64. Res. asst. biochem, Protein Found, 56-57; res. asst. dent. sch. dent. med, Tufts Univ, 60-64, res. assoc. biochem, 64-66, clin. instr. oral diag, 64-69; COORD, VET. ADMIN. DENT. RES. TRAINEE PROG. & CHIEF ORAL BIOL. RES. LAB, VET. ADMIN. OUTPATIENT CLIN, 69-; ASST. PROF. PROSTHETIC DENT, SCH. DENT. MED, HARVARD, 70- Sigma Xi res. grant-in-aid, 63-64; gen. practice, Mass, 64-69; res. dentist, Boston Vet. Admin. Hosp, 66-69. U.S.A.F, 57-60, Capt. AAAS; Am. Dent. Asn; Int. Asn. Dent. Res. Salivary gland physiology; olfaction and taste. Address: Veterans Administration Outpatient Clinic, 17 Court St, Boston, MA 02108.

FELLER, ROBERT L(IVINGSTON), b. Newark, N.J, Dec. 27, 19. PHYSICAL-ORGANIC CHEMISTRY. A.B, Dartmouth Col, 41; M.S, Rutgers, 43, Ph.D. (chem), 50. Instr. & lectr, Rutgers, 46-49; Nat. Gallery Art fel, MELLON INST. SCI, 50-63, SR. FEL, 63- Vis. scientist, Inst. Fine Arts, N.Y. Univ, 61. AAAS; Am. Chem. Soc; Am. Asn. Mus; Fedn. Socs. Paint Technol; Int. Inst. Conserv. Hist. & Artistic Works; Illum. Eng. Soc. Properties of methacrylate polymers; scientific examination of materials in the fine arts, particularly spirit varnishes; artists' pigments. Address: Mellon Institute of Science, 4400 Fifth Ave, Pittsburgh, PA 15213.

FELLER, WILLIAM, b. St. Paul, Minn, Nov. 2, 25; m. 64; c. 2. SURGERY. B.A, Minnesota, 48, B.S, 52, M.D, 54, Ph.D.(surg), 62. Instr. SURG, med. sch, Minnesota, 61-62; asst. prof, SCH. MED, GEORGETOWN UNIV, 64-69, ASSOC. PROF, 69- Vis. scientist, Nat. Cancer Inst, 62-64. AAAS; N.Y. Acad. Sci; Am. Asn. Cancer Res; Am. Col. Surg. Cancer virology; human breast cancer. Address: School of Medicine, Georgetown University, 3800 Reservoir Rd, N.W, Washington, DC 20007.

FELLERS, DAVID ANTHONY, b. Northampton, Mass, Jan. 3, 35; m. 61; c. 2. FOOD SCIENCE. B.S, Massachusetts, 57; Cornell, 58-59; M.S, Rutgers, 62, Ph.D.(food sci), 64. Res. food technologist, WEST. MKT. NUTRIT. RES. DIV, U.S. DEPT. AGR, 63-69, CHIEF CEREALS LAB, 69- U.S.A.R, 53-, Maj. Inst. Food Technol; Am. Asn. Cereal Chem; Am. Chem. Soc. Discoloration of beef by myoglobin auto-oxidation; development of protein concentrates and high protein foods from wheat and rice; lysine fortification of cereals; pregelatinized flours; stability of whole grain flours. Address: U.S. Dept. of Agriculture, 800 Buchanan St, Albany, CA 94710.

FELLERS, F(RANCIS) X(AVIER), b. Seattle, Wash, Feb. 6, 22. NEPHROLOGY, MEDICINE. B.A, Amherst Col, 44; M.D, Cornell, 46. Intern pediat, New York Hosp, 46-47; asst. res, Boston Floating Hosp, 53-56; res. fel, HARVARD MED. SCH, 56-58, asst, 58-60, assoc, 60-63, asst. prof. pediat, 63-69, ASSOC. PROF. CLIN. PEDIAT, 69- Asst, med. col, Tufts, 54-55; from asst. to sr. assoc. physician, Children's Med. Ctr, 56- U.S.A.A.F, 47-53. AAAS; N.Y. Acad. Sci. Metabolic disease in children. Address: Dept. of Clinical Pediatrics, Children's Medical Center, 300 Longwood Ave, Boston, MA 02115.

FELLERS, JOHN FRANCIS, b. Columbiana, Ohio, Mar. 17, 41; m. 62; c. 4. POLYMER CHEMISTRY. B.S, Bowling Green State, 63; Phillips Petrol. & Gen. Tire & Rubber Col fels. & Ph.D.(polymer chem), Akron, 67. Sr. res. scientist, Ford Motor Co, Mich, 66-71; ASST. PROF. CHEM. ENG, UNIV. TENN, KNOXVILLE, 71- Am. Chem. Soc. Kinetics of polymer reactions; organometallic initiated addition polymerizations and ionic condensation reactions; effect of chemical structure on mechanical strength and dynamic properties of polymers. Address: Dept. of Chemical & Metallurgical Engineering, University of Tennessee, Knoxville, TN 37916.

FELLERS, RUFUS GUSTAVUS, b. Columbia, S.C, Sept. 26, 20; m. 67; c. 3. ELECTRICAL ENGINEERING. B.S, South Carolina, 41; Ph.D.(elec. eng), Yale, 43. Asst. instr. elec. eng, Yale, 42-43, instr, 43-44; electronic scientist & sect. head, res. & develop. ultra-high frequencies, naval res. lab, 44-55; PROF. ELEC. ENG, UNIV. S.C, 55-, chmn. dept, 55-60, dean col. 60-69. Lectr, Univ. Md, 48-54; mem. nat. comt, Int. Sci. Radio Union, 68-71; mem. tech. staff, Bell Tel. Labs, 70-71. U.S.N, 44-45. Fel. Inst. Elec. & Electronics Eng; Int. Sci. Radio Union; Am. Soc. Eng. Educ. Millimeter waves; electromagnetic theory; microwave techniques. Address: College of Engineering, University of South Carolina, Columbia SC 29208.

FELLEY, DONALD L(OUIS), b. Memphis, Tenn, Feb. 7, 21; m. 49; c. 5. ORGANIC CHEMISTRY. B.S, Ark. State Col, 41; Ph.D.(org. chem), Illinois, 49. Mem. staff, tech. sales, ROHM & HAAS CO, 49-57, mgr. Société Minoc

Div, France, 57-64, asst. gen. mgr. for. opers. div, 64-68, v.pres. & prod. mgr. chem. div, 68-71, DIR, V.PRES. & GEN. MGR, FOR. OPERS. DIV, 71- Am. Chem. Soc. Synthesis of heterocyclic nitrogen compounds. Address: Rohm & Haas Co, Independence Mall W, Philadelphia, PA 19105.

FELLIG, JOSEF, b. Leipzig, Ger, June 16, 26; nat; m. 51; c. 1. BIOCHEMISTRY. Ph.D.(org. chem), Geneva, 51. Res. assoc. physiol, Tufts Col, 52-53; biochem. div, Mass. Inst. Tech, 53-56; group leader, res. dept, Union Carbide Chems. Co. Div, Union Carbide Corp, 56-60, Tonawanda Labs, Linde Co. Div, 60-62; SR. BIOCHEMIST, HOFFMANN-LA ROCHE, INC, 62- AAAS; Am. Chem. Soc. Biochemistry of nucleic acids and polysaccharides; cryobiology; drug metabolism. Address: Hoffmann-La Roche Inc, Nutley, NJ 07110.

FELLIN, DAVID GENE, b. Wallace, Idaho, Aug. 6, 29; m. 58; c. 3. FOREST ENTOMOLOGY. B.S, Idaho, 52; Montana State, 57-59; M.S, Oregon State, 60, Ph.D.(forest entom), 66. Forester, U.S. FOREST SERV, 54-55, entomologist, INTERMT. EXP. STA, 55-60, RES. ENTOMOLOGIST, 61- U.S.A, 52-54, S/Sgt. Entom. Soc. Am. Forest insects. Address: 2615 Sycamore, Missoula, MT 59801.

FELLING, WILLIAM E(DWARD), b. St. Louis, Mo, Nov, 26, 24; m. 48; c. 10. MATHEMATICS, STATISTICS. B.S.E.E, Iowa State, 45; M.S, St. Louis, 49, Ph.D.(math. statist), 59. Instr. math, St. Louis, 48-49, dir. math. dept, Parks Col. Aeronaut. Tech, 50-58; res. scientist, McDonnell Aircraft Corp, 58-61; dir. sci. liaison, Raytheon Co, 61-65; prog. assoc. sci. & eng, FORD FOUND, 65-66, PROG. OFF. RESOURCES & ENVIRON, 66- U.S.N, 42-46. AAAS; Am. Inst. Aeronaut. & Astronaut; Am. Astron. Soc; Inst. Elec. & Electronics Eng; Am. Soc. Eng. Educ. Environmental education, research and management; resource utilization. Address: Ford Foundation, Resources & Environment Program, 320 E. 43rd St, New York, NY 10017.

FELLINGER, L(OWELL) L(EE), b. Norris City, Ill, Sept. 7, 15; m. 41; c. 2. CHEMICAL ENGINEERING. B.S, Illinois, 37; Sc.D.(chem. eng), Mass. Inst. Tech, 41. Res. chem. engr, Monsanto Chem. Co, 42-43, group leader interim prod, 43-47, asst. dir. res, 47-51, asst. eng. mgr, 51-57, proj. sect. mgr, 57-60, asst. dir. eng, 60-62, eng. proj. mgr, 62-65, dir. process eng. dept, MONSANTO CO, 65-67, mgr. proj. sect, CENT. ENG. DEPT, 67-70, MGR. CHEM. ENG. SECT, 70- Am. Inst. Chem. Eng. Unit operations; process development; engineering project management. Address: Central Engineering Dept, Monsanto Co, 800 N. Lindbergh Blvd, St. Louis, MO 63166.

FELLINGER, ROBERT C(ECIL), b. Burlington, Iowa, Aug. 10, 22; m. 43; c. 2. MECHANICAL ENGINEERING. B.S, Iowa, 47; Westinghouse fel, Iowa State, 47-48, M.S, 48. Mech. engr, Manhattan Proj, Chicago, 44, res. MECH. ENG, Mass. Inst. Technol, 44-46; instr, IOWA STATE UNIV, 47-49, asst. prof, 49-55, assoc. prof, 55-60, PROF, 60- Consult, prod. liability, fires & explosions. Manhattan proj, C.Eng, 44-46. Am. Soc. Mech. Eng; Am. Soc. Eng. Educ. Thermodynamics; fuels and combustion; compressible flow. Address: Dept. of Mechanical Engineering, Iowa State University, Ames, IA 50010.

FELLMAN, J(ACOB) H(AROLD), b. N.Y.C, Apr. 25, 27; m. 50; c. 4. BIOCHEMISTRY. B.A, Univ. Kans, 48, M.A, 52, Ph.D, 54. Assoc. neurol, MED. SCH, UNIV. ORE, 56-58, asst. prof. biochem, 58-60, assoc. prof. biochem. & asst. prof. neurol, 60-66, assoc. prof. neurochem, 66-67, PROF. BIOCHEM, 67- Chemistry of neurohumoral substances. Address: University of Oregon Medical School, Portland, OR 97201.

FELLMANN, ROBERT P(AUL), b. Chicago, Ill, July 22, 24; m. 47. CHEMISTRY. A.B, Univ. Pa, 47. GROUP LEADER, RES. DEPT, ROHM & HAAS CO, 56- Am. Chem. Soc; Fedn. Am. Sci. Polymerization of acrylic monomers; monomer synthesis; polymer chemistry. Address: Research Dept. Rohm and Haas Co, P.O. Box 219, Bristol, PA 19007.

FELLNER, CARL H(EINZ), b. Vienna, Austria, Aug. 24, 17; m. 48; c. 2. PSYCHIATRY. M.D, Lausanne, Switz, 52. Intern & resident PSYCHIAT, Mapperley Hosp, Eng, 52-54; resident, Hadassah Univ. Hosp, Israel, 54-55; Albert Einstein Col. Med, 55-56, fel, 56; lectr, MED. SCH, UNIV. WIS, MADISON, 57, asst. prof, 58-62, assoc. prof, 62-69, PROF, 69- Brit. Army, 40-46. Am. Psychosom. Soc; Soc. Appl. Anthrop; Am. Med. Asn; Am. Psychiat. Asn; Asn. Adv. Psychother. Psychosomatic problems of adaptation; psychotherapeutic processes; hospital psychiatry. Address: Dept. of Psychiatry, University of Wisconsin Medical School, Madison, WI 53706.

FELLOWES, O(LIVER) N(ELSON), b. Steubenville, Ohio, July 23, 08; m. 38; c. 1. MICROBIOLOGY. B.S, Mt. Union Col, 30; M.S, Ohio State, 34, fel, 34-36, Ph.D.(virol), 38. Instr. bact, Ohio State,36-38; Iowa, 38-41; Tennessee, 41-42, dir. diag. lab, 41-42; res. assoc. virol, Sharp & Dohme, Inc, Pa, 42-44, head dept. virus vaccines, 44-48; chief virus br, Chem. Corps, Ft. Detrick, U.S. Dept. Army, 48-52, chief tech. opers, Ft. Terry, 52-54; prin. res. microbiologist, Plum Island Animal Disease Lab, U.S. Dept. Agr, 54-69; v.pres, Gray Industs, Fla, 69-71; consult, Pharmaceut. Res. Corp, 71; SCI. DIR, SANDERS MED. RES. FOUND, 71- Dipl, Am. Bd. Microbiol. AAAS; Am. Soc. Microbiol; Am. Acad. Microbiol; Soc. Cryobiol; Am. Asn. Immunol. Cultivation, adaptation, inactivation and immunology of human and animal viruses. Address: Sanders Medical Research Foundation, 3009 Spanish Trail, Delray Beach, FL 33444.

FELLOWS, GLENN, b. Rochester, N.Y, Apr. 8, 26; m. 52; c. 2. PHYSICS, ELECTRONICS. B.S, Rochester, 48; M.A, Harvard, 49, Ph.D.(applied physics), 55. Head electronics lab, phys. res. lab, Boston, 50-52; leader physics br, Melpar, Inc, 55-58, mgr, design dept, 58-59, asst. mgr, div. appl. sci, 59-60; dir. eng, Bay State Electronics, 60-63; TECH. DIR, SPEAR, INC, 64- U.S.N, 44-46. Noise theory; electro-optics; electronics; radio propagation; statistical communication theory; communication and surveillance systems. Address: 7 Spruce Hill Rd, Weston, MA 02193.

FELLOWS, JOHN A(LBERT), b. Greenfield, Mass, July 27, 06; m. 31; c. 3; m. 58. METALLURGY. A.B, Williams Col, 28; fel, Mass. Inst. Tech, 30-37, M.S, 32, Sc.D.(metall), 42. Asst. metallurgist, Am. Brake Shoe & Foundry Co, 37-39, foundry metallurgist, Am. Manganese Steel Div, 39-41, asst. chief metallurgist, co, 41-45; proj. engr, Manhattan Project Kellex Corp, 43-45; Carbide & Carbon Chems. Corp, 45-46; metallurgist, 46-47; asst. chief metallurgist, Am. Brake Shoe Co, 48-50, res. metallurgist, 51-53; chief staff metallurgist, Mallinckrodt Chem. Works, 53-55, mgr. metall. develop. dept, 56-58, asst. tech. dir, 59-66; dir. tech. prog, Am. Soc. Metals, 66-70; CONSULT, 70- Consult, Carbide & Carbon Chems. Corp, 48-57. Civilian with U.S.A, 44. Am. Inst. Mining, Metall. & Petrol. Eng; fel. Am. Soc. Metals (Howe Medal, 44, pres, 64-65); Am. Foundryman's Soc; Brit. Inst. Metals; Indian Inst. Metals; hon. mem. Iron & Steel Inst. Japan. Physical and process metallurgy of cast irons, highly alloyed steels, nonferrous metals; high temperature creep testing; metallurgy of uranium. Address: 15706 Chadbourne, Shaker Heights, OH 44120.

FELLOWS, LARRY D(EAN), b. Magnolia, Iowa, May 29, 34; m. 60; c. 3. STRATIGRAPHY, ENVIRONMENTAL GEOLOGY. B.S, Iowa State, 55; Nat. Sci. Found. fel, Michigan, 56-57, M.A, 57; Nat. Sci. Found. fel, Wisconsin, 61-62, Ph.D.(geol), 63. Geologist petrol. explor, Carter Oil Co, 57-59; asst. prof. geol, Southwest Mo. State Col, 62-65; GEOLOGIST, MO. GEOL. SURV. & WATER RESOURCES, 65-, ASST. STATE GEOLOGIST, 71-, chief stratig, 66-71. Geol. Soc. Am; Soc. Econ. Paleont. & Mineral. Stratigraphic and structural studies of Ouachita Province and Ozark uplift, with emphasis on the Mississippian System; basic and applied geology in karst areas. Address: Missouri Geological Survey & Water Resources, Box 250, Rolla, MO 65401.

FELLOWS, ROBERT E(LLIS), JR, b. Syracuse, N.Y, Aug. 4, 33; m. 57; c. 2. ENDOCRINOLOGY. A.B, Hamilton Col, 55; M.D, McGill, 59; Ph.D.(biochem), Duke, 69. Asst. prof. physiol. & med, SCH. MED, DUKE UNIV, 66-69, ASSOC. PROF. PHYSIOL. & ASST. PROF. MED, 70- U.S. Pub. Health Serv. fel, 64-66. AAAS; Endocrine Soc; Am. Chem. Soc; Brit. Biochem. Soc; N.Y. Acad. Sci. Chemistry and structure-function relationship of protein and peptide hormones. Address: MS I 328, Dept. of Physiology, Duke University Medical Center, Durham, NC 27710.

FELLOWS, ROBERT F(RANCIS), b. Cleveland, Ohio, July 27, 20; m. 43; c. 4. PHYSICAL CHEMISTRY. B.S, Baldwin-Wallace Col, 43; Williams Col.(Mass); Ph.D.(chem), Brown, 51. Test observer, Lubrizol Corp, 41-43; instr. chem, Williams Col.(Mass), 43-44; res. chemist, Dow Chem. Co, 51-53; head anal. sect, Sprague Elec. Co, 53-58; CHIEF PLANETARY ATMOSPHERES PROG, NASA, 59- U.S.N.R, 44-46, Lt.(jg). Am. Chem. Soc; Soc. Appl. Spectros; Am. Geophys. Union. Dielectrics and electrolytes; spectroscopy; instrumentation; x-ray diffraction; space sciences. Address: Office of Space Science & Applications, Code SL, NASA, Washington, DC 20546.

FELS, I(RVING) GORDON, b. N.Y.C, Dec. 24, 16; c. 3. BIOCHEMISTRY. B.A, Brooklyn Col, 40; M.A, Minnesota, 41; Swift & Co. fel, Oregon State Col, 47-49, Ph.D.(biochem), 49. Am. Scand. fel. chem. & Am. Cancer Soc. fel, 50-51; res. assoc, inst. exp. biol, California, 51-54; chief biochem. sect, radioisotope serv, Hines Vet. Admin. Hosp, 57-61; Old Dominion Found. res. fel, 61-64; sr. res. biochemist, VA. INST. SCI. RES, 61-67, HEAD DIV. BIOCHEM, 67- Horsley Res. Award, Va. Acad. Sci, 70. Sanit.C, U.S.A, 42-45. Am. Chem. Soc; The Chem. Soc; N.Y. Acad. Sci; Geront. Soc. Collagen aging. Address: Division of Biochemistry, Virginia Institute for Scientific Research, 6300 River Rd, Richmond, VA 23229.

FELS, MORTON, b. Montreal, Que, Sept. 26, 39; m. 61; c. 3. CHEMICAL & BIOMEDICAL ENGINEERING. B.Eng, McGill, 61, M.Eng, 65; Ph.D.(chem. eng), 68. Res. engr, Esso Res. & Eng. Co, 61-62; lectr. chem. eng, Univ. Waterloo, 66-67; RES. ENGR, BATTELLE MEM. INST, 68- Vis. fel. physiol, Ohio State, 69. Am. Chem. Soc. Fluid mechanics; mass transfer through polymers; biological problems in engineering; computer applications. Address: Battelle Memorial Institute, 505 King Ave, Columbus, OH 43201.

FELSEN, LEOPOLD B(ENNO), b. Munich, Ger, May 7, 24; nat; m. 44; c. 2. ELECTROPHYSICS. B.E.E, Polytech. Inst. Brooklyn, 48, jr. res. fel, 48-49, M.E.E, 49, D.E.E.(electrophysics), 52. Res. assoc, microwave res. inst, Polytech. Inst. Brooklyn, 49-53, res. asst. prof, 53-56, res. assoc. prof, 56-60; liaison scientist, Off. Naval Res, England, 60-61; PROF. ELECTROPHYS, POLYTECH. INST. BROOKLYN, 61- Mem. U.S. Comn. 6, Int. Sci. Radio Union, 70-73; vis. prof, Univ. Colo, summer 67; invited guest, Soviet Acad. Sci, Sept. 67. U.S.A, 43-46. Fel. Inst. Elec. & Electronics Eng. Propagation and diffraction of electromagnetic waves; microwave network theory and measurements; plasma research; propagation and diffraction of waves; plasmas; quasi-optics. Address: Graduate Center, Polytechnic Institute of Brooklyn, Route 110, Farmingdale, NY 11735.

FELSENFELD, AMBHAN D(ASANEYAVAJA), b. Dhonburi, Thailand, Oct. 8, 22; U.S. citizen; m. 61. VIROLOGY. M.D, Univ. Med. Sci, Bangkok, 50; M.P.H, Hopkins, 55. From instr. to asst. prof. path, Chulalongkorn Hosp. Med. Sch, 50-62; res. virologist, Armed Forces Inst. Path, 63-65; CHIEF DEPT. VIROL, DELTA PRIMATE RES. CTR, TULANE UNIV, 65- Fel, Communicable Disease Center, Ga, 53-54; Univ. Ill, Urbana, 54; res. fel, Rockefeller Found. Virus Lab, India, 57-58 & Virus Labs, New York, 60; fel, sch. pub. health, Pittsburgh, 59; lectr, sch. pub. health, Tulane, 65- AAAS; Med. Asn. Thailand; hon. mem. Asn. Mil. Surg. U.S. Arbo viruses; infectious hepatitis; tissue cultures. Address: Dept. of Virology, Tulane University Research Center, Covington, LA 70433.

FELSENFELD, GARY, b. New York, N.Y, Nov. 18, 29; m. 56; c. 3. BIOPHYSICS. A.B, Harvard, 51; Nat. Sci. Found. fel, 52-54; Ph.D.(chem), Calif. Inst. Tech, 55; Nat. Sci. Found. fel, Oxford, 54-55. Off, Nat. Insts. Health, U.S. Pub. Health Serv, 55-58; asst. prof. biophys, Pittsburgh, 58-61; CHIEF PHYS. CHEM, LAB. MOLECULAR BIOL, NAT. INST. ARTHRITIS & METAB. DISEASES, 61- Vis. prof, Harvard, 63. Am. Soc. Biol. Chem; Am. Chem. Soc; Biophys. Soc. Physical chemistry of nucleic acids and proteins; nucleoprotein complexes. Address: Lab. of Molecular Biology, National Institute of Arthritis & Metabolic Diseases, National Institutes of Health, Bethesda, MD 20014.

FELSENFELD, HERBERT WILLIAM, b. N.Y.C, May 25, 30; m. 61; c. 2. PHARMACOLOGY, BIOCHEMISTRY. B.S, Columbia, 52, M.S, 55; Am.

Pharmaceut. Asn. fel, Yale, 56-59, Ph.D.(biochem, pharmacol), 60, M.D, 67. Instr. PHARMACOL, sch. med, Yale, 67-68; ASST. PROF, SCH. MED, UNIV. CONN, 68- Am. Pharmaceut. Mfrs. Asn. award, 57-59. U.S.P.H.S, 60-62, scientist. Am. Soc. Pharmacol. & Exp. Therapeut. Antibiotic mechanisms; membranes and particulates of normal and neoplastic cells; neuraminic acid, sulfatide and ganglioside biochemistry; mast cell biochemistry. Address: Dept. of Pharmacology, University of Connecticut School of Medicine, Hartford, CT 06112.

FELSENFELD, OSCAR, b. Woellersdorf, Austria, May 21, 06; nat. MICROBIOLOGY. Ferran Inst. Barcelona fel, 30; M.D, Charles Univ, 30, M.S, 33; Scarritt Col, 40-41. Asst, Charles Univ, 30-33; bacteriologist, Czech. Army, 33-34; pub. health off, Czech, 34-40; assoc. clin. path, Meharry Med. Col, 40-41; supvry. bacteriologist, State Dept. Pub. Welfare, Ill, 42-43; from asst. prof. to assoc. prof. microbiol, Chicago Med. Sch, 44-49; prof. lectr, col. med, Illinois, 49-53; exec. dir, res. lab, Southeast Asia Treaty Orgn, 59-62; res. pathologist, Walter Reed Army Inst. Res, 62-65; PROF. MICROBIOL, MED. SCH, TULANE UNIV. & CHIEF, DIV. COMMUN. DISEASES, DELTA PRIMATE RES. CTR, 65-, PROF. TROP. MED, SCH. PUB. HEALTH & TROP. MED, 69- Chief bacteriologist, Mt. Sinai Hosp. & Res. Found, Chicago, Ill, 45-47; Schering fel, Sch. Trop. Med, P.R, 47-48; prof. lectr, sch. med, Loyola Univ, 48-49; dir. bact, Cook County Hosp. & Hektoen Inst. Med. Res, 48-53; dir. field servs, Trop. Res. Found, Chicago, 50-53; vis. prof, med. col, Univ. West Indies, 51-52; vis. prof. microbiol. & immunol, sch. med, Tulane Univ, 62-; secy. cholera panel, Int. Cong. Trop. Med. & Malaria, 63, chmn. cholera sect. & v.chmn. intestinal diseases, 68; panel mem, Int. Atomic Energy Agency, 68, 71; secy, Acad. Interdisciplinary Res, 69-70; panel mem, State Dept. Agency Int. Develop. Cholera Task Force, 70-71. Consult, WHO; inst. environ. health, Nat. Insts. Health, 68. Kitasato Medal, 66; Gamaleya Medal, 67. Med.C, U.S.A, 53-65, Res, 65-66, Col.(Ret). Soc. Exp. Biol. & Med; fel. Am. Pub. Health Asn; Col. Am. Path; fel. Am. Soc. Clin. Path; fel. Royal Soc. Health; Royal Soc. Trop. Med. & Hyg. Diseases transmitted from animals to man; food hygiene; water and highway sanitation; tropical diseases. Address: Delta Primate Research Center, Tulane University, Covington, LA 70433.

FELSENSTEIN, JOSEPH, b. Phila, Pa, May 9, 42. GENETICS, EVOLUTION. B.S, Univ. Wis, Madison, 64; Nat. Insts. Health fel, Univ. Chicago, 64, Ph.D. (zool), 68. Nat. Insts. Health fel, Inst. Animal Genetics, Scotland, 67-68; ASST. PROF. GENETICS, UNIV. WASH, 67- Genetics Soc. Am; Biomet. Soc; Soc. Syst. Zool. Theoretical population genetics, applied to evolution; statistical estimation of evolutionary trees. Address: Dept. of Genetics, University of Washington, Seattle, WA 98195.

FELSHER, MURRAY, b. N.Y.C, Oct. 8, 36; m. 61; c. 2. GEOLOGY, OCEANOGRAPHY. B.S. & Sigma Xi grant-in-aid, City Col, New York 59; Penrose grant, Univ. South. Calif, 62; univ scholar. & M.S, Univ. Mass, Amherst, 63; Shell Oil fel, 64; Owen-Coates fel, 65; Nat. Res. Coun. Can fel, McMaster Univ, 66-67; Ph.D.(geol. & oceanog), Univ. Tex, Austin, 71. Asst. prof. geol, Syracuse Univ, 67-69; assoc. dir. coun. educ. in geol. sci, Am. Geol. Inst, 69-71; SR. STAFF SCIENTIST, U.S. ENVIRON. PROTECTION AGENCY, 71- Consult. oceanog, Syracuse Univ. Res. Corp, 67-69. AAAS; Fine Particle Soc; Geol. Soc. Am; Int. Asn. Math. Geol; Int. Asn. Planetology; Int. Asn. Sedimentol; Marine Technol. Soc; Meteoritical Soc; Nat. Asn. Geol. Teachers; Soc. Econ. Paleont. & Mineral. Coastal morphology; marine geology; remote sensing; educational administration; sedimentology and sedimentary petrology; cosmology and planetary geology; mathematical geology. Address: 2731 Atlanta Dr, Wheaton, MD 20906.

FELSHER, ZACHARY, b. Russia, Nov. 21, 10; nat; m. 45; c. 1. DERMATOLOGY. B.S, Chicago, 31, M.D, Rush, 36. Asst. DERMAT, Clin, Chicago, 43-44, instr, 44-47; Illinois, 48-55; asst. prof, NORTHWEST. UNIV, 56-64, ASSOC. PROF, 64- Consult, U.S. Army Hqs, Chicago, 54-59; U.S. Pub. Health Serv. Hosp, 59- AAAS; Soc. Invest. Dermat; Am. Med. Asn; Am. Acad. Dermat; N.Y. Acad. Sci. Diseases of the skin; physiology and biochemistry of the skin, particularly fibrous proteins. Address: Dept. of Dermatology, Northwestern University Medical School, 303 E. Chicago Ave, Chicago, IL 60611.

FELSON, BENJAMIN, b. Newport, Ky, Oct. 21, 13; m. 36; c. 5. RADIOLOGY. B.S, Cincinnati, 31, M.D, 35. Intern, Cincinnati Gen. Hosp, 35-36; res. path, Cincinnati Gen. Hosp. & Univ. Cincinnati, 36-37, radiol, 37-40; fel. cancer therapy, Indianapolis City Hosp, 40-41; private practice, Tulsa, Okla, 41-42; asst. prof. RADIOL, UNIV. CINCINNATI, 45-48, assoc. prof, 48-51, PROF. & DIR, 51- Radiologist, Cincinnati Gen. Hosp, 45-48, assoc. dir, 48-51, dir. dept. radiol, 51-; radiologist, Drake Hosp, 51-; Children's Hosp, 51-; Dunham Hosp, 51-; Holmes Hosp, 59-; hon. fel. faculty radiologists, Royal Col. Surgeons, Ireland. Consult, Dayton Vet. Admin. Hosp; Cincinnati Vet. Admin. Hosp; U.S. Pub. Health Serv; Surgeon Gen, U.S. Air Force; Walter Reed Army Hosp; Armed Forces Inst. Path; cent. off, U.S. Vet. Admin; Surgeon Gen, U.S. Army; U.S. Navy Med. Dept. Chief radiol, Sta. Hosp, Ft. Harrison, Ind, 42-43, 28th Gen. Hosp, Europe, 43-45, Med.C, 42-45, Maj. Radiol. Soc. N.Am.(v.pres); fel. Am. Col. Radiol; fel. Am. Col. Chest Physicians; hon. mem. Can. Asn. Radiol; hon. mem. Colombian Radiol. Soc; hon. mem. Brazilian Radiol. Soc; Am. Roentgen Ray Soc.(1st v.pres, 71-). Radiology of diseases of the chest; fundamentals of chest roentgenology. Address: 3994 Rose Hill Ave, Cincinnati, OH 45229.

FELT, C(LARENCE) E(MANUAL), b. International Falls, Minn, Oct. 15, 10; m. 39; c. 3. CHEMICAL ENGINEERING. B.Ch.E, Minnesota, 33. Control chemist, GEN. MILLS, INC, 34-37, chemist, res. lab, 37-42, paper technologist, 42-50, sect. leader packaging res, 50-55, head phys. res, packaging dept, 55-63, ACTIVITY DIR. PROD. DEVELOP. SERV, 63- Tech. Asn. Pulp & Paper Indust. Flour and cereal; food packaging; puffing farina to render quick cooking. Address: Product Development Service, General Mills, Inc, 9200 Plymouth Ave. N, Minneapolis, MN 55427.

FELT, GAELEN L(EE), b. Honolulu, Hawaii, Oct. 15, 21; m. 46; c. 3; m. 57; c. 2. PHYSICS. A.B, Harvard, 43; Rutgers, 43-44; M.S, Calif. Inst. Tech, 48, Ph.D, 51. Jr. scientist, Manhattan Dist, Los Alamos Sci. Lab, California, 45-46, consult, 48-50, physicist, 50-51, group leader, 51-57, asst. div. leader, 57; mgr. systs. test dept, Titan-Intercontinental Ballistic Missile Prog. Off, Space Tech. Labs, Inc, Thompson-Ramo-Wooldridge, Inc, 58-59, sr. staff physicist, vehicle develop. lab, 59-60; mgr. opers, EG&G, INC, 60-63, v.pres. & gen. mgr, LAS VEGAS DIV, 63-67, GROUP V.PRES. TECH. SUPPORT, 67- U.S.A, 43-45. X-rays; optics. Address: EG&G, Inc, P.O. Box 1912, Las Vegas, NV 89101.

FELT, ROWLAND EARL, b. Idaho Falls, Idaho, Aug. 3, 36; m. 66; c. 2. CHEMICAL ENGINEERING. B.S, Idaho, 58, M.S, 59; Ph.D.(chem. eng), Iowa State, 64; Washington, 64- Instr. chem. eng, Idaho, 59-60; res. asst, Ames Lab, 60-64; STAFF ENGR, Gen. Elec. Co, Wash, 64-66; Isochem Inc, 66-67; OPERS. SUPPORT ENG. DEPT, ATLANTIC RICHFIELD HANFORD CO, 67- Am. Inst. Chem. Eng. Plutonium processing; development of processes to improve purity; plutonium scrap management studies. Address: Operations Support Engineering Dept, 234-5 Bldg, 200 W, Atlantic Richfield Hanford Co, Richland, WA 99352.

FELTEN, EDWARD J, b. Brooklyn, N.Y, Feb. 10, 23; m. 52; c. 3. PHYSICAL & INORGANIC CHEMISTRY. B.S, Mt. St. Mary's Col.(Md), 48; M.S, St. John's (N.Y), 52; Ph.D.(chem), Polytech. Inst. Brooklyn, 58. Anal. chemist, Port of N.Y. Authority, 48-50; phys. chemist, M.W. Kellogg Co, N.J, 50-52; Polytech. Inst. Brooklyn, 55-57; res. engr, aircraft nuclear propulsion dept, Gen. Elec. Co, Ohio, 57-58, 60-61, res. lab, N.Y, 58-60; SR. RES. ASSOC, PRATT & WHITNEY AIRCRAFT DIV, UNITED AIRCRAFT CORP, 61-67, FUEL CELL SECT, MAT. ENG. & RES. LAB, 67- U.S.A, 43-46, Sgt. Am. Chem. Soc; Am. Crystallog. Asn; Sci. Res. Soc. Am; Am. Ceramic Soc; Am. Soc. Metals. High temperature chemistry, including oxides, oxidation, sintering, diffusion, coatings, intermetallic compounds and x-ray crystallography; research and development of high temperature, solid state, fuel cell devices. Address: Fuel Cell Section, Materials Engineering & Research Lab, Pratt & Whitney Aircraft Division, United Aircraft Corp, P.O. Box 611, Middletown, CT 06458.

FELTEN, JAMES E(DGAR), b. Duluth, Minn, Sept. 8, 34. ASTROPHYSICS. B.A, Minnesota, Duluth, 56; Armstrong Cork fel, Cornell, 56-57, Du Pont scholar, 59-60, Ph.D.(astrophys), 65. Physicist, Aberdeen Proving Ground, summer 58; res. engr, Douglas Aircraft Co, summers 59-62; asst. res. physicist, California, San Diego, 65-68; vis. fel, Inst. Theoret. Astron, Cambridge, 68-70; Int. Astron. Union vis. fel, Tata Inst. Fundamental Res, Bombay, 70; vis. prof, Univs. Padua & Bologna, 70; VIS. ASSOC. PROF. & ASSOC. ASTRON, UNIV. ARIZ, 70- AAAS; Int. Astron. Union; Am. Astron. Soc; Am. Phys. Soc. High-energy astrophysics; x-ray and gamma-ray astronomy; cosmic rays; interstellar and intergalactic medium. Address: Steward Observatory, University of Arizona, Tucson, AZ 85721.

FELTHAM, L(EWELLYN) A(LLISTER) W(OODROW), b. Newf, Oct. 23, 26; m. 53; c. 3. BIOCHEMISTRY. B.Sc, Dalhousie Univ, 47; M.A, Univ. Toronto, 52, fels, 55-58, Ph.D.(path. chem), 60. Chemist, Pub. Health Labs, St. John's, Newf, 49-50, biochemist, 52-55, chief biochemist, 58-67; PROF. BIOCHEM. & HEAD DEPT, MEM. UNIV, 67- Consult. biochemist, Grace Hosp, St. John's, 58-66; St. Clare's Mercy Hosp, St. John's, 58-67; vis. lectr, dept. biol, Mem. Univ, 59-62, part-time assoc. prof, 62-67. AAAS; Can. Soc. Clin. Chem; Can. Biochem. Soc; The Biochem. Soc. Mechanism of action of hormones at the molecular level, particularly the effects of adrenocorticoid hormones on the kidney; properties of regulatory enzymes in marine animals. Address: Dept. of Biochemistry, Memorial University of Newfoundland, St. John's, Newf, Can.

FELTHAM, ROBERT D(EAN), b. Roswell, N.Mex, Nov. 18, 32; m. 54; c. 2. INORGANIC & PHYSICAL CHEMISTRY. B.Sc, Univ. N.Mex, 54; Ph.D. (chem), Univ. Calif, 57. Asst, Univ. N.Mex, 54; Univ. Calif, 54-57; res. fel, Mellon Inst, 58-64; asst. prof. CHEM, UNIV. ARIZ, 64-65, assoc. prof, 65-70, PROF, 71- Fulbright traveling fel, Denmark, 57-58; NATO fel, Univ. Col, London, 63-64. Am. Chem. Soc; Am. Phys. Soc; Brit. Chem. Soc. Bioinorganic chemistry; chemistry of metal coordination compounds, particularly metal organic compounds of the transition metal elements and the group V elements. Address: Dept. of Chemistry, University of Arizona, Tucson, AZ 85721.

FELTMAN, REUBEN, b. Newark, N.J, Nov. 3, 07; m. 30; c. 2. BIOCHEMISTRY. D.D.S, Pennsylvania, 30. Vis. attend, surgeon, dept. periodontia, Midtown Hosp, N.Y, 30-42; prin. investr, div. res. grants, U.S. Pub. Health Serv, 50-55; PRES, BD. HEALTH, CLIFTON, 55- Assoc. dent. surgeon, Passaic Gen. Hosp, 30-67, dir, dept. dent. & sr. oral surgeon, 67-, prin. investr, dent. res. lab; secy, med-dent. staff; dir, Power Conversion Inc, Calif, 67- Dipl, Am. Bd. Oral Med, 67; Int. Bd. Appl. Nutrit. Dent.C, 42-46, Maj. Fel. AAAS; fel. Am. Acad. Oral Med.(pres. elect, pres, 66-67); fel. Am. Inst. Chem; Am. Inst. Oral Biol; Am. Dent. Asn; N.Y. Acad. Sci. Determining effects of fluorides ingested during pregnancy and after birth; storage in placenta and transfer to fetus. Address: 211 Main Ave, Passaic, NJ 07055.

FELTNER, KURT C, b. Rock Springs, Wyo, May 23, 31; m. 51; c. 3. PLANT PHYSIOLOGY. B.S, Wyoming, 56, M.S, 59; Ph.D.(crop physiol), Arizona, 63. Mgr. seed cert. serv, Wyoming, 57-60, asst. prof. crop physiol, 62-64; assoc. prof. plant sci, Kans. State Univ, 65-70, prof, 70-71; HEAD DEPT. CROP & SOIL SCI, MONT. STATE UNIV, 71- U.S.A.F, 50-54, S/Sgt. Weed Sci. Soc. Am; Am. Soc. Agron; Int. Crop Improv. Asn. Physiology and ecology of higher economic plants, especially hardiness and competition; mode of action of phytotoxic chemicals. Address: Dept. of Crop & Soil Science, Montana State University, Bozeman, MT 59715.

FELTON, FRANCES G(RACE), b. Hydro, Okla, May 2, 18. MEDICAL MICROBIOLOGY. B.A, Okla. Col. for Women, 39; M.S, Oklahoma, 53, Ph.D. (microbiol), 58. Teacher, pub. sch, 39-40; technologist, St. Anthony Hosp, 41-44; serologist, U.S. War Dept, 44-46; chief technologist, VET. ADMIN. HOSP, 46-53, bacteriologist, 53-57, chief clin. lab, 57-63, CHIEF MICROBIOL. RES, 62-; PROF. MICROBIOL. & IMMUNOL. & LAB. MED, SCH. MED, UNIV. OKLA, 70-, DIR. CLIN. MICROBIOL, MED. CTR, 63-, asst. prof. microbiol, sch. med, 58-62, assoc. prof, 62-70, lab. med, 63-70. Am. Soc. Microbiol; Am. Thoracic Soc; Int. Union Against Tuberc. Mycology; tuberculosis; immunology. Address: Clinical Lab, Veterans Administration Hospital, 921 N.E. 13th St, Oklahoma City, OK 73104.

FELTON, GEORGE (EDWIN), Eldora, Iowa, May 22, 09; m. 37; c. 3. CHEMISTRY. B.S, Iowa State Col, 31, M.S, 33, Ph.D, 35. Res. chemist, Iowa State Agricultural Exp. Sta, 35-36; Gen. Foods Corp, 36-38; Am. Maize-Products, 38-43; Hawaiian Pineapple Co, 43-49, tech. dir, 49-64, v.pres, DOLE CO, 64-71, CHIEF SCI. ADV, 71- Carbohydrate chemistry; ion exchange; fruit growing, canning and freezing. Address: Dole Co, P.O. Drawer 3380, Honolulu, HI 96801.

FELTON, HERMAN R, b. Mount Vernon, N.Y, May 25, 18; m. 42; c. 2. PHYSICAL CHEMISTRY. B.S, Rensselaer Polytech, 39; M.S, Syracuse, 49, Ph.D. (chem), 51. Chemist, U.S. Chem. Warfare Serv, 41-45; purser, U.S. Maritime Serv, 45-46; asst, Syracuse, 46-51; res. chemist, E.I. du Pont de Nemours & Co, 51-70; mgr. instnl. develop, Waters Assocs, Inc, 70-71; V.PRES, CHROMATEC INC, 71- Am. Chem. Soc; Instrument Soc. Am. Physical methods in analysis; solubility of gases; combustion phenomena; instrumental analysis; gas and liquid chromatography. Address: 9 Barry Dr, Framingham, MA 01701.

FELTON, JEAN SPENCER, b. Oakland, Calif, Apr. 27, 11; m. 37; c. 3. MEDICINE. A.B, Stanford, 31, M.D, 35. Intern & res. surg, Mt. Zion & Dante Hosps, San Francisco, 35-38; practicing physician & surgeon, Calif, 36-40; med. dir, Oak Ridge Nat. Lab, 46-53; prof, dept. med. & dept. prev. med. & pub. health & dir, employees health serv, sch. med, Oklahoma, 53-58; prof. occupational health, dept. prev. med. & pub. health, sch. med, California, Los Angeles, 58-68; CLIN. PROF. COMMUN. MED. PUB. HEALTH, UNIV. SOUTH. CALIF, 68-; DIR. OCCUP. HEALTH SERV, DEPT. PERSONNEL, COUNTY OF LOS ANGELES, 68- Lectr, sociol. dept, Tennessee, 46-53. Consult, State Dept. Health, Okla, 53-58; Atlanta Area, U.S. Vet. Admin, 49-53, St. Louis Area, 53-58, Vet. Admin. Ctr, Los Angeles, 65-; occupational health admin, Calif. State Dept. Health, 58-, NASA, 64-; U.S. Pub. Health Serv, 65-; Oak Ridge Hosp. Ed, Indust. Med. & Surg, 50-51. Mem, President's Comt. on Employment of Handicapped; Nat. Safety Coun. Comt. Indust. Eye Protection, 47-51; Nat. Publicity Coun. Health & Welfare Servs, 47-49, dir, 49-54; chmn. adv. bd, Family Serv. Bur, Oak Ridge, 47-48, mem, 48-49; adv. comt. Social Security Admin, 55-62. Med.C, 40-46, Lt. Col. Fel. Am. Pub. Health Asn; Am. Indust. Hyg. Asn; fel. Indust. Med. Asn; fel. Am. Acad. Occup. Med; Nat. Rehabil. Asn. Occupational health methods and practices; health status of employee groups; mental health in industry; job performances of the physically impaired; communication in occupational health; history of occupational medicine; public speaking and medical writing. Address: Dept. of Personnel, B-50 Hall of Administration, County of Los Angeles, 222 N. Grand Ave, Los Angeles, CA 90012.

FELTON, KENNETH E(UGENE), b. Kenton, Ohio, Aug. 18, 20; m. 43; c. 1. AGRICULTURAL ENGINEERING. B.S, Maryland, 50 & 51; M.S, Pa. State, 62; summer, Colorado, 64. Engr, eng. div, Assoc. Factory Mutual Fire Ins. Cos, 51-52; sanit. engr, Interstate Cmn, Potomac River Basin, 52-54; agr. engr. irrig, South. States Co-op, 54; asst. prof. AGR. ENG, UNIV. MD, 54-63, ASSOC. PROF, 63- U.S.A, 42-46. Am. Soc. Agr. Eng. Structural components of farm and light industrial buildings; environmental requirements of poultry for maximum performance; proper design and arrangement of farm structures for optimum operation. Address: Dept. of Agriculture Engineering, College of Agriculture, University of Maryland, College Park, MD 20742.

FELTON, LEWIS P(ETER), b. Brooklyn, N.Y, Dec. 14, 38; m. 60; c. 2. STRUCTURAL & CIVIL ENGINEERING. B.C.E, Cooper Union, 59; M.S, Carnegie Inst. Tech, 61, Ph.D.(civil eng), 64. Mem. tech. staff, appl. mech. div, Aerospace Corp, 63-64; asst. prof. eng, UNIV. CALIF, LOS ANGELES, 64-71, ASSOC. PROF. MECH. & STRUCT, 71- Am. Soc. Civil Eng; Am. Inst. Aeronaut. & Astronaut; Am. Soc. Eng. Educ. Structural mechanics and design; experimental stress analysis. Address: Dept. of Mechanics & Structures, School of Engineering & Applied Science, University of California, Los Angeles, CA 90024.

FELTON, LLOYD C(ROSSER), b. Baltimore, Md, May 17, 20. ORGANIC CHEMISTRY. A.B, Princeton, 41, A.M, 42, Ph.D.(org. chem), 44. Asst. chem, Princeton, 41-43; RES. CHEMIST, Rohm & Haas, Phila, 44; HYNSON, WESTCOTT & DUNNING, 44- With Off. Sci. Res. & Develop, 44. Am. Chem. Soc. Synthetic organic chemistry in pharmaceuticals, particularly in fields of substituted phenols and sulfur compounds. Address: Chemical Research Lab, Hynson, Westcott & Dunning, Inc, 1030 N. Charles St, Baltimore, MD 21201.

FELTON, RONALD H, b. Washington, D.C, Jan. 12, 38. CHEMICAL PHYSICS. B.S, Mass. Inst. Technol, 58; Ph.D.(chem. physics), Harvard, 64. Fel. CHEM, Brandeis, 65-67; Nat. Sci. Found. fel, Mass. Inst. Tech, 67-68; ASST. PROF, GA. INST. TECHNOL, 68- Res. collab, Brookhaven Nat. Labs, 68- Am. Inst. Physics. Redox behavior of metalloporphyrins; electronic spectra of organic radicals; scattering theory. Address: Dept. of Chemistry, Georgia Institute of Technology, Atlanta, Ga. 30332.

FELTON, STALEY L(EE), b. Whaleyville, Va, Oct. 23, 20; m. 51; c. 4. ORGANIC CHEMISTRY. B.S, Va. Polytech, 50. Chemist, Va. Dept. Agr, 50-51; Tobacco Byprods. & Chem. Corp, 51-55; asst. mgr, res. & develop. dept, Diamond Black Leaf Co, 55-57; sr. chemist, Va-Carolina Chem. Corp, 57-64; PROD. MGR. PESTICIDES, INDUST. CHEM. DIV, MOBIL CHEM. CO, 64- U.S.N.R, 42-46. Am. Chem. Soc. Formulation of agricultural chemicals; field development of new agricultural chemicals such as insecticides, nematocides, herbicides, repellents and plant growth regulators. Address: 1704 Brentwood Rd, Richmond, VA 23222.

FELTON, STEPHEN M, b. Warsaw, Poland, June 14, 42; U.S. citizen; m. 66; c. 1. ORGANIC CHEMISTRY. B.S, Brooklyn Col, 63; Ph.D.(org. chem), Rutgers, 67. Asst. org. chem, Rutgers, 63-65, organo-phosphorus chem, 65-67; fel. bio-org. chem. with Prof. Thomas C. Bruice, California, Santa Barbara, 67-69; dir. res, FELTON INT. INC, BROOKLYN, 69-71, V.PRES. RES. & DEVELOP, 71- Am. Chem. Soc. Mechanism and synthesis in organo-phosphorus chemistry; mechanisms of bio-organic reactions by solution kinetics; model enzyme systems; organic synthetic methods; preservatives and bacteriacides in cosmetic products. Address: 60 E. Eighth St, Apt. 21P, New York, NY 10003.

FELTON, WARREN L(OCKER), II, b. Bartlesville, Okla, Oct. 25, 25; m. 49, 69; c. 5. SURGERY. B.S. & M.D, Washington (St. Louis), 49. Surg. intern, New Haven Hosp, Conn, 49-50, surg. asst. res. to chief res, 51-56; asst. thoracic surg, sch. med, Yale, 51-52, instr. surg, 54-56; chief gen. surg. serv, Valley Forge Army Hosp, Pa, 56-58; clin. asst. SURG, SCH. MED. UNIV. OKLA, 58-63, asst. prof, 63-67, ASSOC. CLIN. PROF, 67- Attend. physician, Vet. Admin. Hosp, 58-; consult, Cent. State Hosp, Norman, Okla, 60- U.S.N.R, 43-45; Med. C, U.S.A.R, 56-58, Capt. Am. Thoracic Soc; Soc. Thoracic Surg; Am. Col. Surgeons; Am. Med. Asn; Am. Asn. Thoracic Surg. Thoracic and cardiovascular surgery. Address: 1608 Dorchester Dr, Oklahoma City, OK 73120.

FELTS, JOHN HARVEY, b. Lumberton, N.C, Apr. 2, 24; m. 55; c. 2. INTERNAL MEDICINE. B.S, Wofford Col, 49; M.D, Med. Col. S.C, 49. Intern, Walter Reed Army Hosp, Wash, D.C, 49-50; N.C. Baptist Hosp, Winston-Salem, 50-51, asst. res. med, 51-52, res, 52-53; res. physician, West. N.C. Sanatorium Treatment Tuberculosis, Black Mountain, 53; instr. INTERNAL MED, BOWMAN GRAY SCH. MED, 55-59, asst. prof, 59-63, assoc. prof, 63-70, PROF, 70- Attending physician, cardiac & diabetic clin, regional off, Vet. Admin. Hosp, Winston-Salem 52-53; consult. physician, Vet. Admin. Hosp, Salisbury, 66- Dipl, Am. Bd. Internal Med, 57. U.S.A, 43-46, 53-55. Am. Fedn. Clin. Res; fel. Am. Col. Physicians; Am. Soc. Artificial Internal Organs. Renal disease and toxicology. Address: Bowman Gray School of Medicine, Wake Forest University, Winston-Salem, NC 27103.

FELTS, WAYNE M(OORE), b. Oakland, Calif, Aug. 5, 12; m. 42; c. 2. GEOLOGY. B.S, Oregon State Col, 34, M.S, 36; Ph.D.(geol), Cincinnati, 38. Mem. Columbia River Ethnol. Exped, Smithsonian Inst, 34-35; asst. geol, Cincinnati, 36-38, instr. geol, col. eng. & commerce, 38-41; assoc. geologist, Ohio River Div, Cincinnati Testing Lab, U.S. Eng. Corps, 42-43; mem. geol. dept, Phillips Petrol. Co, 43-47; geologist, Texas Co, 47-58, div. geologist, Los Angeles Div, TEXACO INC, 58-62, asst. to div. mgr, 62-66, MGR. HARD MINERALS, 66- Grant-in-aid, Ohio Acad. Sci, 37. AAAS; Am. Asn. Petrol. Geol; fel. Geol. Soc. Am; Am. Inst. Prof. Geol. Petrography; petrology; petroleum geology. Address: Texaco Inc, P.O. Box 2100, Denver, CO 80201.

FELTS, WILLIAM J(OSEPH) L(AWRENCE), b. Saginaw, Mich, Dec. 29, 24; m. 46; c. 3. ANATOMY. A.B, Michigan, 48, fel, 49-51, A.M, 51, Ph.D. (anat), 52. Instr. anat, Ind. Univ, 51-52; Tulane Univ, 52-55; asst. prof, Univ. Minn, Minneapolis, 55-60, assoc. prof, 60-66, prof, 66-68; PROF. ANAT. SCI. & CHMN. DEPT, MED. CTR, UNIV. OKLA, 68- Res. assoc, Eng. Res. Inst, Univ. Mich, 52. Am. Asn. Anat; Orthop. Res. Soc; Am. Asn. Phys. Anthrop; Am. Soc. Zool. Human growth and development; growth processes in bone and cartilage; connective tissue transplantation; mechanical organization of bone; skeletal aging; functional anatomy and adaptation in marine mammals; antarctic and arctic seals. Address: Dept. of Anatomical Sciences, University of Oklahoma, Medical Center, 800 N.E. 13th St, Oklahoma City, OK 73104.

FELTS, WILLIAM R(OBERT), b. Judsonia, Ark, Apr. 24, 23; m. 54; c. 4. INTERNAL MEDICINE. B.S, Arkansas, 45, M.D, 46. Intern, Garfield Mem. Hosp, Wash, D.C, 46-47; jr. res. med, Gallinger Munic. Hosp, Wash, D.C, 49-50, res, 50-51; sr. res, univ. hosp, George Washington, 51-52, chief res, 52-53; asst. chief arthritis res. unit, Vet. Admin. Hosp, Wash, D.C, 53-54; trainee rehabil. in med, univ. hosp, GEORGE WASH. UNIV, 55-57, instr. MED, SCH. MED, 58-59, asst. prof, 59-62, ASSOC. PROF, 62- Chief arthritis res. unit, Vet. Admin. Hosp, 58-62. Consult-lectr, U.S. Naval Hosp, Md, 57-70. U.S.A, 43-46, Med.C, 47-49, Capt. Am. Med. Asn; Am. Rheumatism Asn; Am. Soc. Internal Med; Am. Fedn. Clin. Res. Arthritis and rheumatic diseases; filariasis; mycoplasma; computers in medicine. Address: Dept. of Medicine, George Washington University School of Medicine, Washington, DC 20005.

FELTY, EVAN J, b. Columbus, Ohio, Dec. 22, 32; m. 58; c. 3. PHYSICAL CHEMISTRY. B.A, Bowling Green State, 54; Nat. Sci. Found. fel, Ohio State, 58, Allied Chem. Corp. fel, 59, Union Carbide Corp. fel, 60, Du Pont fel, 62, Ph.D.(phys. chem), 63. Sr. chemist mat. res, XEROX CORP, 63-64, scientist, 64-66, mgr. photoconductor systs. develop. br, 66-68, mgr. mat. sci. lab, 68-71, MGR. PHOTORECEPTOR TECHNOL. SECT, 71- Mem. panel on tellurium, comt. on tech. aspects of critical and strategic mat, Nat. Mat. Adv. Bd, Nat. Res. Coun-Nat. Acad. Sci, 69, comt. on fundamentals of amorphous mat, 70-71. U.S.A, 55-57, 1st Lt. AAAS; Am. Crystallog. Asn; fel. Am. Inst. Chem; Am. Chem. Soc. Electrical, optical and structural properties of inorganic glasses; structure of inorganic materials by x-ray diffraction techniques. Address: Research & Engineering Division, Business Products Group, Xerox Corp, Xerox Square, Rochester, NY 14644.

FELTZ, DONALD EVERETT, b. Sherman, Tex, Aug. 23, 33; m. 55; c. 2. NUCLEAR & MECHANICAL ENGINEERING. B.S, Texas A&M, 59, M.S, 63. Reactor supvr, NUCLEAR SCI. CTR, TEX. A&M UNIV, 61-63, chief facility opers, 63-65, ASST. DIR, 65- U.S.A, 53-55, Res, 55-, 1st Lt. Am. Soc. Mech. Eng; Am. Nuclear Soc. Investigations of neutron flux perturbations and the development on non-perturbing foils; reactor design, installation and operations; mechanical heat transfer systems; isotope production and applications; systems engineering. Address: Nuclear Science Center, Texas A&M University, College Station, TX 77843.

FELTZ, ELMER T, b. Buffalo, N.Y, Dec. 17, 27; m. 65; c. 3. VIROLOGY, BACTERIOLOGY. B.A, Buffalo, 51; M.S, N.Y. Univ, 52. Cancer res. scientist, Roswell Park Mem. Inst, 55-61; chief virol. lab, ARCTIC HEALTH RES. CTR, U.S. PUB. HEALTH SERV, 61-67, CHIEF VIROL. UNIT, 67- Adj. prof, Alaska Methodist, 63-65. Microbiologist, McMurdo Sta, fall 63; mem, N.Y. Zool. Exped. Antarctica-Deepfreeze 64, U.S. Antarctic Res. Prog. U.S.N, 46-47. Soc. Cryobiol; Am. Soc. Microbiol; N.Y. Acad. Sci. Tissue culture; serology. Address: Arctic Health Research Center, U.S. Pub. Health Service, University of Alaska, College, AK 99701.

FELTZIN, JOSEPH, b. New York, N.Y, Mar. 2, 21; m. 47; c. 1. ORGANIC CHEMISTRY. B.A, Brooklyn Col, 43, M.A, 50; fel, Polytech. Inst. Brooklyn, 51-53, Ph.D.(chem), 54. Asst. pharmaceut. chem, E.R. Squibb & Sons, 47-

51; res. chemist, flavors & perfumes Norda Chem. Co, 53-58; Aero-Jet Gen. Corp, Gen. Tire & Rubber Co, 58-64, group leader mat. res. & develop, struct. mat. div, 64-65; SUPVR. NEW PROD. DEVELOP, ATLAS CHEM. INDUST, 65- Med.C, U.S.A, 43-46. Am. Chem. Soc; N.Y. Acad. Sci. Epoxies; phenolics and related polymers; reinforced plastics applications; polyesters; urethane foams; elastomers; chemical additives to resins and plastics; thermoset and thermoplastic materials; polymer chemistry. Address: 102 E. Sutton Place, Wilmington, DE 19810.

FENBURR, HERBERT L(ESTER), b. New York, N.Y, Dec. 11, 13; m. 36; c. 1. CHEMICAL ENGINEERING. B.Ch.E, Ohio State, 34, M.S, 35, Ph.D.(chem. eng), 37. Asst. chem. eng, Ohio State, 34-35, instr, 35-37; CHEM. ENGR, INDUST. DIV, HANNA PAINT CO, 37- Pres, Fedn. Socs. Paint Technol, 67-68; Paint Res. Inst, 69- AAAS; Am. Chem. Soc; Am. Inst. Chem; Am. Inst. Chem. Eng; N.Y. Acad. Sci. Industrial finishes; wrinkles; synthetics; lacquers. Address: Industrial Division, Hanna Paint Co, 1313 Windsor Ave, Columbus, OH 43216.

FENCL, ROBERT (DANIEL), b. Chicago, Ill, April 22, 21; m. 50; c. 5. ORAL SURGERY. B.S.D. & D.D.S, Loyola (Ill), 46; M.Ph, Michigan, 53. ASST. PROF. ORAL SURG, UNIV. CLINICS & WALTER G. ZOLLER MEM. CLIN, UNIV. CHICAGO, 57- Mem, Bd. Educ, Cook County; bus. mgr, jour, Ill. Soc. Dent. for Children. U.S.A.F, 55-57, Maj. Am. Soc. Dent. for Children; Am. Dent. Asn; Am. Inst. Oral Biol; Am. Acad. Oral Path; fel. Am. Acad. Pedodont; Am. Acad. Oral Med. Bone study relative to normal versus abnormalities; sedimentation rates in oral pathosis. Address: 1933 S. Norfolk Ave, Westchester, IL 60153.

FEND, A(LVIN) V(INCENT), b. Chicago, Ill, Oct. 2, 22; m. 48; c. 2. MATHEMATICAL STATISTICS. B.S, Illinois, 49, M.S, 50, M.A, 51, Ph.D.(math. statist), 56. Asst. prof. math, Fla. State, 53-56; New Mexico State, 56-57; statistician, Tech. Opers, Inc, 57-58; SR. MATH. STATISTICIAN, STANFORD RES. INST, 58- U.S.N, 42-45. Am. Math. Soc; Inst. Math. Statist. Statistical decision theory. Address: Dept. of Mathematics, Stanford Research Institute, Menlo Park, CA 94025.

FENDALL, ROGER K, b. Newberg, Ore, Aug. 20, 35; m. 57; c. 4. AGRONOMY. B.S, Oregon State, 60; Nat. Defense Ed. Act fel, N.Dak. State, 60-64, Ph.D.(agron), 64. Asst. prof. agron, Wash. State Univ, 64-68; ORE. STATE UNIV, 68-70, ASSOC. PROF. AGRON, ASST. DEAN SCH. AGR. & HEAD ADV, 70- U.S.A, 54-56. Am. Soc. Agron. Physiology of seed germination; mechanisms of seed dormancy, inhibition and stimulation; physiology of flowering. Address: School of Agriculture, Oregon State University, Corvallis, OR 97331.

FENDER, DARWIN E(UGENE), b. Lawton, Okla, Sept. 4, 21; m. 43; c. 2. FORESTRY. B.S.F, Georgia, 42. Forester, INT. PAPER CO, 46-51, dist. forester, 53-57, tech. supvr. forestry, 56-65, dir. forest res, 65-70, CHIEF FORESTER, 70- U.S.A, 42-46, 51-53, Capt. Soc. Am. Foresters. Forest management. Address: Woodlands Dept, International Paper Co, P.O. Box 2328, Mobile, AL 36601.

FENDER, DEREK H(ENRY), b. Hethe, Eng, Dec. 4, 18; m. 44; c. 2. BIOLOGY, ELECTRICAL ENGINEERING. B.Sc, Univ. Reading, 39 & 47, Ph.D.(physics), 56. Sr. lectr. physics, Royal Mil. Col. Sci, Eng, 46-53; lectr, Univ. Reading, 53-61; assoc. prof. biol. & elec. eng, CALIF. INST. TECHNOL, 61-66, PROF. BIOL. & APPL. SCI, 66- Nat. Insts. Pub. Health grant, Univ. Reading, 56-61; Calif. Inst. Technol, 61-; mem. comt, Photobiol. Group, 58-61; rd. res. bd, Dept. Sci. & Indust. Res, Gt. Brit, 59-61; consult, Electronic Color Assocs, 63- Human Factors Soc; Optical Soc. Am; Brit. Biol. Eng. Soc. Interaction between the scanning motions of the human eye and the pattern recognition processes of which it is capable. Address: Computing Center, California Institute of Technology, 1201 E. California Ave, Pasadena, CA 91109.

FENDER, FRED G(EORGE), b. Phila, Pa, July 3, 08; m. 35; c. 1. APPLIED MATHEMATICS. B.S, Pennsylvania, 29, M.S, 30; Ph.D.(theoret. physics), 36. Instr. math, Rutgers, 37-42, asst. prof. physics, 42-44; develop. engr. & head electronics dept, develop. div, Curtiss Wright Corp, 44-45; group engr, pilotless plane div, Fairchild Engine & Airplane Corp, 45-46; PROF. MATH, RUTGERS UNIV, 46-, COMPUT. SCI, 67-, dir. ctr. info. processing, 58-67. Fel. AAAS; N.Y. Acad. Sci; Am. Math. Soc; Am. Phys. Soc; Math. Asn. Am; Asn. Comput. Mach. Numerical methods; computing machines. Address: Dept. of Computer Science, Rutgers University, New Brunswick, NJ 08903.

FENDERSON, CARLL NATHANIEL, b. Farmington, Maine, Sept. 30, 23; c. 1. BIOLOGY, ECOLOGY. B.S, Univ. Maine, Augusta, 50, M.S, 53; Ed.D.(biol), Columbia Univ, 69. Biologist, State of Maine, 54-58, dir. info. & educ, 58-64; exec. dir, Natural Resources Coun. Maine, 64-65; field rep, Nat. Wildlife Fedn, 65-69; assoc. prof. biol, UNIV. MAINE, AUGUSTA, 69-71, DEAN INSTR, 71- U.S.A.A.F, 42-46. AAAS; Am. Inst. Biol. Sci; Nat. Asn. Biol. Teachers; Am. Fisheries Soc. Fisheries biology; taxonomy of Salmonidae; general and educational problems of conservation. Address: Dept. of Biology, University of Maine, Augusta, ME 04330.

FENDLER, ELEANOR JOHNSON, b. Danville, Pa, June 27, 39; m. 65. ORGANIC & BIO-ORGANIC CHEMISTRY. B.A, Bucknell, 61; Nat. Sci. Found. summer fels, California, Santa Barbara, 64 & 65, univ. fel, 64-65, Ph.D. (phys. org. chem), 66. Res. assoc. statist, Upper Susquehanna Valley Prog. Coop. Res, Bucknell, 61-62; teacher, pub. schs, Pa, 62-63; part-time instr. CHEM, Univ. Calif, Santa Barbara, 63-64, res. assoc, 65-66; NASA fel, Univ. Pittsburgh, 66-68, res. asst. prof, 68-70; VIS. ASSOC. PROF, TEX. A&M UNIV, 70- Health Res. Serv. Found. grant, 68-70; Soc. Sigma Xi, grant-in-aid, 70-71; Nat. Insts. Health career develop. award, 70- Am. Chem. Soc; The Chem. Soc. Bio-organic and physical organic reaction mechanisms; kinetics of hydrolysis and solvolysis of esters; micelle catalysis; nucleophilic aromatic substitution. Address: Dept. of Chemistry, Texas A&M University, College Station, TX 77843.

FENDLER, JANOS HUGO, b. Budapest, Hungary, Aug. 12, 37; m. 65. PHYSICAL & ORGANIC CHEMISTRY. B.Sc, Leicester, 60; dipl. radiochem. Leicester Col. Tech, Eng, 62; v.chancellors & prin. of univs. of U.K. fel, London, 62-64, Ph.D.(phys-org. chem), 64. Nat. Sci. Found. fel. phys-org. chem, California, Santa Barbara, 64-66; fel. radiation chem, radiation res. labs, Mellon Inst. Sci, Carnegie-Mellon Univ, 66-70; ASSOC. PROF. CHEM, TEX. A&M UNIV, 70- Abstractor, Chem. Abstr, 65-70. AAAS; The Chem. Soc; Am. Chem. Soc; Faraday Soc. Elucidation of organic reaction mechanisms; micelle catalysis; nucleophilic aromatic substitutions; radiation induced reactions in dilute aqueous solution; radiation chemistry. Address: Dept. of Chemistry, Texas A&M University, College Station, TX 77843.

FENECH, EUGENE JOSEPH, b. San Francisco, Calif, Apr. 22, 31; m. 58; c. 3. CHEMICAL ENGINEERING, COMPUTER SCIENCE. B.S, Stanford, 53; M.S, California, Berkeley, 57, Ph.D.(chem. eng), 60. Asst. sr. engr, solid rocket opers, Aerojet Gen. Corp. Div, GEN. TIRE & RUBBER CO, 59-65, ENG. SUPVR, AEROJET NUCLEAR SYSTS CO. DIV, 65- Simulation Coun; Asn. Comput. Mach. Natural convection from horizontal surfaces; solid rocket performance prediction; hybrid computer simulation of nuclear engine for rocket vehicle application; nuclear rocket systems; computer center management; computer operations systems; systems analysis. Address: Aerojet Nuclear Systems Co, P.O. Box 13070, Sacramento, CA 95813.

FENECH, HENRI J, b. Alexandria, Egypt, Mar. 14, 25; U.S. citizen; m. 52; c. 2. NUCLEAR ENGINEERING, ENGINEERING SCIENCES. Dipl. Ecole Nationale d' Ingénieurs des Arts et Métiers, France, 46; S.M, Mass. Inst. Tech, 57, Sc.D.(nuclear eng), 59. Engr, Foster Wheeler, France, 52-55; staff mem, Gen. Atomic Div, Gen. Dynamics Corp, 59-60; asst. prof. NUCLEAR ENG, Mass. Inst. Tech, 60-63, assoc. prof, 63-69; PROF, UNIV. CALIF, SANTA BARBARA, 69-, V.CHMN. DEPT, 70- Atomic Energy Comn. res. grant, 57-62; NATO sr. sci. fel, 69; lectr, U.S.S.R, Acad. Sci, Moscow-Leningrad, 71. Am. Nuclear Soc; Am. Soc. Mech. Eng. Thermal contact resistance between surfaces; analysis of nuclear reactors; methods of optimization of power systems; nuclear power safety; nuclear cross-sections analysis. Address: Dept. of Chemical & Nuclear Engineering, University of California, Santa Barbara, CA 93106.

FENG, CHARLES CHAO YUAN, b. Macao, China, June 26, 24; U.S. citizen; m. 58; c. 2. METALLURGY, MECHANICAL ENGINEERING. B.M.E, Tsing Hua, China, 48; M.Sc, Rochester, 52; M.Sc, Stevens Inst. Tech, 55; Ph.D. (metall), Toronto, 57. Res. metallurgist, res. lab, Crucible Steel Co. Am, N.J, 52-55; instr. appl. physics, Toronto, 57-58; mem. res. staff, Ont. Res. Found, 58; assoc. staff, res. div, Raytheon Co, Mass, 58-61; scientist, Martin Marietta Corp, Md, 61-66; staff scientist, Lockheed Aircraft Corp, Ga, 66-70; RES. METALLURGIST, U.S. PICATINNY ARSENAL, 70- AAAS; Am. Inst. Mining, Metall. & Petrol. Eng; Am. Soc. Metals. Materials science, including crystallography; preferred orientation, texture and anisotropy defects in crystals, solidification, phase transformation, plastic deformation; mechanical twinning, strain aging and dislocation theory. Address: Metals Engineering Branch, Picatinny Arsenal, Dover, NJ 07801.

FENG, CHUAN C(HUNG) D(AVID), b. Shanghai, China, Sept. 15, 22; m; c. 3. STRUCTURAL & CIVIL ENGINEERING. B.S, Chiao Tung, 45; M.S, Missouri, 55, Ph.D.(civil eng), 59. Assoc. prof. CIVIL ENG, UNIV. COLO, BOULDER, 63-67, PROF, 67- Mem. staff, Calif. Inst. Tech; Stanford. Am. Soc. Civil Eng; Am. Concrete Inst; Am. Soc. Eng. Educ. Relaxation method for structural problems; optimization; flow graph analysis; systems engineering analysis. Address: College of Engineering, University of Colorado, Boulder, CO 80302.

FENG, CHUNG LIAO, b. Honan, China, June 1, 24; m. 57; c. 2. SYSTEMS ENGINEERING. B.S, Univ. Pa, 50, M.S, 54; M.A, Temple Univ, 57. Proj. engr, I-T-E Circuit Breaker Co, 51-54; res. engr, Brown Div, Honeywell Regulator Co, 54-58; group leader eng. anal, res. lab, Selas Corp. Am, 58-63; mgr. adv. develop. indust. controls, White Rodgers Co, 63-66; sr. engr, Conductron of Mo, 66-68; mgr. syst. & elec. eng, SELAS CORP. AM, 68-70, SECT. MGR. SYST. SCI, RES. LAB, 70- Chinese Army, 44-46, Capt. Am. Soc. Mech. Eng; Am. Phys. Soc; Instrument Soc. Am. Address: Research Lab, Selas Corp. of America, Dresher, PA 19025.

FENG, PAUL Y(EN-HSIUNG), b. Peking, China, Aug. 29, 26; nat; m. 47; c. 3. NUCLEAR & RADIATION CHEMISTRY. B.S, Catholic Univ, China, 47; Von Blarcom scholar & Ph.D.(chem), Washington (St. Louis), 54. Asst. chem, Washington (St. Louis), 50-51, res. chemist geochem, 51-54; chemist, Manu Mine Res. & Develop. Co, 54, chief chemist, 54-55, tech. dir, 55; assoc. physicist, IIT Res. Inst, 55-56, res. physicist, 56-57, group leader, 57-58, asst. supvr. nuclear physics, 58-59, supvr. chem. physics, 59-62, sci. adv, 62-67; assoc. prof. CHEM, MARQUETTE UNIV, 67-71, PROF, 71- Asst, Atomic Energy Comn. res. prog, Wash. Univ, 53-54; lectr, Ill. Inst. Technol, 56-58, adj. assoc. prof, 66-67; vis. prof, Tsinghus Univ. Inst. Nuclear Sci, Formosa, 58; tech. adv. U.S. Del, Int. Conf. Peaceful Uses Atomic Energy, Geneva, Switz, 58; Fulbright lectr, Taiwan, 65. AAAS; Faraday Soc; Am. Asn. Physics Teachers; Am. Chem. Soc; Radiation Res. Soc. Radiation effects; electric discharge and electron impact phenomena; high polymer physics; mass spectrometry; geochemistry and silicate chemistry; reactions at extreme temperatures. Address: Dept. of Chemistry, Marquette University, 535 N. 14th St, Milwaukee, WI 53233.

FENG, SUNG YEN, b. Shanghai, China, Oct. 1, 29; U.S. citizen; m. 63; c. 1. PHYSIOLOGICAL ECOLOGY. B.S, Taiwan, 54; M.A, Col. William & Mary, 58; Ph.D.(parasitol), Rutgers, 62. Res. asst, dept. zool. & N.J. Oyster Res. Lab, Rutgers, 60-62, res. assoc, N.J. Oyster Res. Lab, 62-66; asst. prof. systs. & environ. biol, MARINE RES. LAB, UNIV. CONN, 66-68, ASSOC. PROF. BIOL, 68- Am. Soc. Parasitol; Am. Soc. Protozool; Nat. Shellfisheries Asn; Soc. Invert. Path; Atlantic Estuarine Res. Soc; Am. Soc. Zool. Invertebrate pathobiology; diseases, pathology and defense mechanisms of marine molluscs; physiological ecology of marine molluscs; pathobiology of invertebrates; physiological ecology. Address: Marine Research Lab, University of Connecticut, Noank, CT 06340.

FENG, TSUAN H, b. Hangchow, China, Feb. 17, 18; nat; m. 51; c. 4. SANITARY ENGINEERING. B.S, Nat. Pei-Yang Univ, China, 40; M.S, Wisconsin, 46, Ph.D, 50. Engr, Eng. Servs, Mass, 50-51; instr. CIVIL ENG, UNIV. MASS, AMHERST, 51-52, asst. prof, 52-57, assoc. prof, 57-61, PROF, 61-, COORD. ENVIRON. ENG. PROG, 67- Summers, engr, Tighe & Bond Consult. Engrs, 51-55; Metcalf & Eddy Consult. Engrs, 55-58; sr. engr, div. sanit. eng, State of Mass, 59; sr. sanit. engr, U.S. Pub. Health Serv, 64; vis. prof, Nat. Taiwan Univ. & Nat. Sci. Coun, Repub. China, 71-72; consult, Morgenroth & Assocs, Mass; assoc, Gurnham & Assocs, Ill. Am. Soc. Civil Eng; Am. Soc. Eng. Educ; Water Pollution Control Fedn. Disinfection of water and sewage; biological treatment of sewage; filtration of water; sludge deposits in waters. Address: Dept. of Civil Engineering, University of Massachusetts School of Engineering, Amherst, MA 01002.

FENIAK, E(LIZABETH), b. Man, June 20; m. 45; c. 2. FOOD, NUTRITION. B.Sc, Univ. Man, 41; M.S, Univ. Minn, 43. Instr. foods, Univ. Minn, 43-46; lectr. & asst. prof, UNIV. MAN, 50-57, assoc. prof. FOODS & NUTRIT, 57-70, PROF, 70-, ASSOC. DEAN, FACULTY HOME ECON, 67- Address: Faculty of Home Economics, University of Manitoba, Winnipeg, Man, Can.

FENIAK, G(EORGE), b. Can, Jan. 28, 30; m. 62; c. 3. ORGANIC CHEMISTRY. B.Sc, Alberta, 50; Ph.D.(org. chem), Washington (Seattle), 55. Res. chemist, Eastman Kodak Co, 55-60; Nat. Res. Coun. Can. fel, Ottawa (Can), 60-62; RES. CHEMIST, Defence Res. Bd. Can, 62-65; POLYMER CORP, SARNIA, 65- Am. Chem. Soc; Chem. Inst. Can; Brit. Chem. Soc. Color photography; natural products; pharmacology; elastomers. Address: R.R. 1, Wyoming, Ont, Can.

FENICAL, WILLIAM HOWARD, b. Chicago, Ill, June 24, 41; m. 67. ORGANIC CHEMISTRY. B.S, Calif. State Polytech. Col, 63; M.S, San Jose State Col, 65; Ph.D.(chem), California, Riverside, 68. Teaching asst. org. chem, San Jose State Col, 64-65; California, Riverside, 65-68, Am. Cancer Soc. fel, 68-69; res. scientist, Shell Develop. Co, 69-70; MARINE ORG. CHEMIST, UNIV. CALIF, RIVERSIDE, 70- Am. Chem. Soc. Synthesis of polycyclic olefins and mechanisms of electrocyclic reactions; oxidation of hydrocarbons and mechanism of addition of excited molecular oxygen; extraction, structural elucidation and evaluation of new natural products from marine sources. Address: Dept. of Plant Pathology, University of California, Riverside, CA 92502.

FENICHEL, GERALD M, b. New York, N.Y, May 11, 35; m. 58; c. 3. NEUROLOGY. A.B, Hopkins, 55; M.D, Yale, 59. Fel. NEUROL, sch. med, Yale, 63-64; instr, SCH. MED, George Washington, 64-67, asst. prof, 67-69; PROF, SCH. MED, VANDERBILT UNIV, 69- U.S.P.H.S, 60-63, Res, 58-60, 63- Am. Acad. Neurol; Am. Neurol. Asn; Am. Med. Asn; Am. Acad. Cerebral Palsy. Muscle development; neuromuscular diseases of infancy and childhood. Address: Dept. of Neurology, Vanderbilt University School of Medicine, Nashville, TN 37203.

FENICHEL, HENRY, b. Hague, Netherlands, Apr. 13, 38; U.S. citizen; m. 61; c. 2. SOLID STATE PHYSICS, CRYOGENICS. B.S, Brooklyn Col, 60; M.S, Rutgers, 62, Ph.D.(physics), 65. Asst. prof. PHYSICS, UNIV. CINCINNATI, 65-69, ASSOC. PROF, 69- AAAS; Am. Phys. Soc; Am. Asn. Physics Teachers. Lattice dynamics; measurements of specific heats of inert gas solids; magnetic contribution to thermal properties of rare earths. Address: Dept. of Physics, University of Cincinnati, Cincinnati, OH 45221.

FENICHEL, RICHARD L(EE), b. New York, N.Y, July 23, 25; m. 51; c. 2. BIOCHEMISTRY, PHYSIOLOGY. A.B, N.Y. Univ, 47; Commonwealth fel, Polytech. Inst. Brooklyn, 48-50, M.S, 51; Ph.D.(physiol, biochem), Wayne State, 56. Biochemist, med. dept, Chrysler Corp, 51-54; asst, Wayne State, 54-56, res. assoc, 56-57; investr, Aviation Med. Accel Lab, 57-59; sr. res. scientist, Ortho Res. Found, 59-63; SR. SCIENTIST, WYETH LABS, 63- U.S.A, 43-45. AAAS; Am. Chem. Soc; N.Y. Acad. Sci. Protein isolation and characterization; blood coagulation; enzymatic studies; mechanisms of protein interactions; red blood cell studies; cardiovascular studies. Address: Wyeth Labs, Radnor, PA 19088.

FENICHEL, ROBERT ROSS, b. N.Y.C, Nov. 1, 41. COMPUTER SCIENCE. A.B, Harvard, 63, Ph.D.(appl. math), 67. Asst. prof. elec. eng, Mass. Inst. Technol, 66-71; RES. FEL, LAB. COMPUT. SCI, MASS. GEN. HOSP, 71- Consult, Gen. Elec. Medinet, 66-67; mem. planning group, Bd. on Comput. Sci. & Eng, Nat. Acad. Sci, 67. Asn. Comput. Mach. Analysis of computer-system capacity; supervisory-system design; education. Address: Lab. of Computer Science, Massachusetts General Hospital, Boston, MA 02114.

FENIMORE, DAVID CLARKE, b. Evansville, Ind, Jan. 27, 30; m. 65. ANALYTICAL CHEMISTRY, BIOCHEMISTRY. B.A, DePauw Univ, 52; Ph.D. (chem), Univ. Houston, 66. Chemist, Thomas & Skinner, Inc, 54-57; sect. leader instrumental anal, Baroid Div, Nat. Lead Co, 57-64; fel. chem. Univ. Houston, 66-67; sect. head anal. chem, TEX. RES. INST. MENT. SCI, 67-69, DIV. HEAD INSTRUMENTAL ANAL, 69- Instr, grad. sch. biomed. sci, Univ. Tex, 67-69, asst. prof, 69-; clin. asst. prof, dept. biophys, Univ. Houston, 70- U.S.A, 54-56. AAAS; Am. Chem. Soc; fel. Am. Inst. Chem; N.Y. Acad. Sci; Am. Soc. for Mass Spectrometry; Am. Soc. Test & Mat. Research in gas chromatographic instrumentation with emphasis on electron capture detector design and studies of electron capture processes; application of electron capture detection to ultramicro biochemical analysis. Address: Division of Instrumental Analysis, Texas Research Institute, 1300 Moursund, Houston, TX 77025.

FENJE, P(AUL), b. Novi Sad, Yugoslavia, June 14, 15; Can. citizen. VIROLOGY, MICROBIOLOGY. M.D, Univ. Zagreb, 40; dipl, pub. health, Fed. Inst. Hygiene, Belgrade, 49, specialist-microbiologist, 52. Microbiologist, Inst. Hygiene, Novi Sad, Yugoslavia, 45-54; Pasteur Inst, 55-57; MEM. RES. STAFF VIROL, CONNAUGHT MED. RES. LABS, 58-; ASST. PROF, SCH. HYGIENE, UNIV. TORONTO, 71- Consult, WHO, 67- AAAS; Can. Soc. Microbiol; Can. Asn. Med. Microbiol; Can. Pub. Health Asn. Bacteriology; rickettsiae; applied immunology; smallpox; rabies; epidemiology; anti-viral agents. Address: Connaught Medical Research Labs, 1755 Steeles Ave. W, Willowdale, Ont. Can.

FENLON, PAUL F(RANCIS), b. Cleveland, Ohio, Mar. 28, 23; m. 48; c. 3. OPTICS. B.S, Detroit, 48; Armour fel, Ill. Inst. Tech, 48-49, M.S, 51. RES. PHYSICIST OPTICS, Armour Res. Found, 48-60; R.C. Ingersoll Res. Ctr, Borg-Warner Corp, 60-64; ZENITH RADIO CORP, 64- U.S.A, 43-46. Optical Soc. Am; Sci. Res. Soc. Am; Am. Vacuum Soc. Optical properties of solids; thin film techniques; infrared spectroscopy and radiometry; response characteristics of infrared detectors. Address: Zenith Radio Corp, 1451 Arthur, Elk Grove, IL 60007.

FENN, H(OWARD) N(ATHAN), b. Milford, Conn, Nov. 11, 07; m. 48; c. 1. CHEMICAL ENGINEERING. B.S, Yale, 29. Chem. engr. org. chems, Dow Chem. Co, 29-37, develop. group engr. cellulose prods, 37-43, supt. silicone prod. mgr. silicone mfr, DOW CORNING CORP, 44-62, dir. mfg, 62-63, v.pres, mfg, 63-65, eng. & mfg, 65-71, V.PRES. & ASST. TO PRES, 71- Dir. Dow Corning Int, Ltd; Midland Silicones, Ltd. AAAS; Am. Inst. Chem. Eng; Am. Chem. Soc. Manufacture of silicones; development of silicone products; industrial management; industrial safety. Address: Dow Corning Corp, Midland, MI 48640.

FENN, JOHN B(ENNETT), b. New York, N.Y, June 15-17; m. 39; c. 3. CHEMISTRY. A.B, Berea Col, 37; Ph.D.(phys. chem), Yale, 40. Res. chemist, Monsanto Chem. Co, Ala, 40-42; Sharples Chems, Inc, Mich, 43-45; v.pres. & res. supvr, Exp, Inc, Va, 45-52; dir. proj. Squid, Forrestal Res. Ctr, Princeton, 52-62, lectr. aerospace & mech. sci, 59-60, PROF, 60-67; APPL. SCI. & CHEM, YALE, 67- AAAS; Am. Chem. Soc; Am. Inst. Aeronaut. & Astronaut; Combustion Inst; Am. Inst. Chem. Eng. Combustion; thermodynamics; propulsion; kinetics; molecular beams; rarefied gas dynamics. Address: School of Engineering & Applied Science, Mason Lab, Yale University, New Haven, CT 06520.

FENN, ROBERT M(ETCALFE), b. Battle Creek, Mich, Aug. 19, 13; m. 35. METEOROLOGY. A.B, Mercer Univ, 58; M.A, Univ. Okla, 68. Meteorologist, U.S. Weather Bur, 37-42, 54-59; Idlewild Int. Airport, 50; satellite res. meteorologist, Navy Weather Res. Facility, 59-63, sr. scientist meteorol, U.S. Naval Weapons Lab, 63-70; RETIRED. Observer, Joint Meteorol. Satellite Adv. Cmt, 60-64; assoc. mem. meteorol, working group, Range Comdr. Coun, 63-70. U.S.A.F, 48-50, U.S.N, 42-48, 50-54, Res, 54-68, Comdr. Am. Meteorol. Soc; Am. Ord. Asn. Ballistics, satellite and synoptic meteorology. Address: R. R. One, Box 135, King George, VA 22485.

FENN, ROBERT W, b. Nov. 19, 29; U.S. citizen; m. 58; c. 2. ATMOSPHERIC PHYSICS, OPTICS. M.S, Munich Tech, 55; Ph.D.(physics, meteorol), Munich, 63. Res. physicist, Agfa Camera Works, Germany, 55-57; U.S. Army Electronics Res. & Develop. Lab, Ft. Monmouth, N.J, 57-65; SUPVRY. PHYSICIST, AIR FORCE CAMBRIDGE RES. LABS, 65- Am. Meteorol. Soc; Optical Soc. Am. Optical physics. Address: Air Force Cambridge Research Labs, Laurence G. Hanscom Field, Bedford, MA 01730.

FENN, ROBERT WILLIAM, III, b. Phila, Pa, Feb. 1, 41; m. 64; c. 3. CHEMICAL ENGINEERING. B.E, Villanova Univ, 62; M.S, Carnegie-Mellon Univ, 65; Nat. Sci. Found. grant & Lever Bros. fel, Univ. Rochester, 65-67, Ph.D. (chem. eng), 68. SR. RES. ENGR, DIAMOND SHAMROCK CORP, 67- Am. Inst. Chem. Eng; Am. Chem. Soc; Water Pollution Control Fedn. Application of electrochemistry and electrochemical engineering principles to water and air pollution control as well as research and development on industrial electrochemical processes. Address: 6528 Mardon Dr, Painesville, OH 44077.

FENN, W(ILLARD) H(ENRY), b. Portland, Ore, Jan. 18, 16; m. 44; c. 1. ELECTRONIC ENGINEERING. B.S, California, 38, M.S, 39, Coffin Found. fel, 39-41. Assoc. head test equip. group, radiation lab, Mass. Inst. Tech, 41-45; from head commercial develop. to sales mgr, Polytech. Res. & Develop. Co, 46-51; head primary standards & instr. prod. group planning, Hughes Aircraft Co, 52-60, asst. to dir. physics lab, 58-60; v.pres. west coast div, FXR, Inc, 60-62; electronic consult, 62; southwest dist. mgr, Energy Systs, Inc, 63-64; dir. eng, Guide Industs, 64-65; SR. STAFF ENGR, TRW SYSTS. GROUP, REDONDO BEACH, 65- Electronic Industs. Asn; Inst. Elec. & Electronics Eng. Microwave tubes and instrumentation. Address: 14050A Marquesas Way, Marina Del Rey, CA 90291.

FENNELL, DOROTHY I(RENE), b. Middle Grove, Ill, Oct. 23, 16. MYCOLOGY. B.A, Illinois, 38. Under lab. helper, North. Regional Res. Lab, 42, jr. sci. aide, 42-43, jr. microbiologist, 43-45, microbiologist, 45, 47-55, coop agent, North. Regional Res. Lab. & Nat. Acad. Sci, 45-47; mycologist, Qm. Res. & Eng. Center, 55-62; res. assoc, dept. bact, Univ. Wis, 62-66; mycologist, Am. Type Cult. Collection, Md, 66-69; MICROBIOLOGIST, NORTH. UTILIZATION RES. & DEVELOP. DIV, AGR. RES. SERV. CULT. COLLECTION, 69- With Centraalbureau voor Schimmelcultures Baarn, Netherlands, 60-61. Superior serv. award, U.S. Dept. Agr, 50. AAAS; Am. Soc. Microbiol; Mycol. Soc. Am; Bot. Soc. Am; Soc. Indust. Microbiol. Taxonomy of the fungi; methods of culture maintenance; fermentative and degradative fungi. Address: Northern Utilization Research & Development Division, Agricultural Research Service Culture Collection, 1815 N. University, Peoria, IL 61604.

FENNELL, RICHARD A(DAMS), b. Decatur, Ala, April 19, 03; m. 37. ZOOLOGY. A.B, Birmingham-Southern Col, 27; Duke, 28-30; Ph.D.(cell physiol), Hopkins, 36. Technician, labs, State Bd. Health, Ala, 22-23; asst, Birmingham-Southern Col, 27-28; Duke, 28-30; instr. & asst. prof. biol, Birmingham-Southern Col, 30-33; asst, Hopkins, 33-36; instr. ZOOL, MICH. STATE UNIV, 36-41, asst. prof, 41-47, prof, 47-71, EMER. PROF, 71- Res. coop. agent, bur. animal indust, regional poultry lab, U.S. Dept. Agr, 44-46; Nat. Sci. Found. faculty fel, London Hosp. Med. Col. Eng, 59-60; consult, 70-71. Fel. AAAS; Am. Soc. Cell Biol; Am. Soc. Zool; Soc. Protozool. Ingestion and digestion in amoeba; social behavior in chickens; effects of biological extracts on ingestion by amoeba; reaction of vertebrate cells to protozoan extracts; avian hematology; histochemistry. Address: 4554 Cornell Rd, Okemos, MI 48864.

FENNELL, ROBERT E, b. Peoria, Ill, Apr. 21, 42; m. 69; c. 2. MATHEMATICS. B.A, Bradley, 64; M.S, Iowa, 66, Ph.D.(math), 69. Instr. MATH, Grinnell Col, 68-69; ASST. PROF, CLEMSON UNIV, 69- Am. Math. Soc; Soc. Indust. & Appl. Math; Math. Asn. Am. Differential equations. Address: Dept. of Mathematical Sciences, Clemson University, Clemson, SC 29631.

FENNELL, ROBERT H(ENRY), JR, b. Henrico Co, Va, June 12, 18; m. 44; c. 2. PATHOLOGY. B.S, Richmond, 40; M.D, Med. Col. Va, 43. Asst. prof. PATH, Tennessee, 50-51; instr, Harvard Med. Sch, 52-54; asst. prof, sch. med, Univ. Pittsburgh, 54-59, assoc. prof, 59-62, PROF, 62-71; MED. CTR, UNIV. COLO, DENVER, 71- Asst. pathologist, Mass. Gen. Hosp, Boston, 52-54; pathologist, Presby-Univ, Hosp, Pittsburgh, 58-71. Dipl, Am. Bd. Path, 51. Med.C, U.S.A, 44-46. Asn. Path. & Bact; Asn. Cancer Res; Soc. Cytol. Pathologic anatomy of cancer, particularly of early phases of the disease; immunohistologic techniques to evaluate role of immunity in cancer growth. Address: University of Colorado Medical Center, Denver, CO 80220.

FENNEL, WILLIAM E(DWARD), b. Moberly, Mo, Mar. 4, 23. ZOOLOGY. A.B, Missouri, 46, M.A, 49; fel, Michigan, 54-58, Ph.D.(zool), 59. Asst. zool, Missouri, 46-49; instr, East. Ill. State Col, 48; Missouri, 49-50; BIOL, Flint Jr. Col, Mich, 50-53; Brooklyn Col, 58-63, asst. prof, 63-67; assoc. prof, Pace Col, 67-69, PROF, 69-70; EAST. MICH. UNIV, 70- U.S.N, 43-46, Lt.(jg). Am. Micros. Soc; Soc. Syst. Zool; Ecol. Soc. Am; Am. Soc. Zool; Soc. Nematol. Aquatic free-living nematodes; natural history of invertebrates. Address: Dept. of Biology, Eastern Michigan University, Ypsilanti, MI 48197.

FENNEMA, OWEN RICHARD, b. Hinsdale, Ill, Jan. 23, 29; m. 48; c. 3. FOOD SCIENCE. B.S, Kansas State, 50; M.S, Wisconsin, 51, Ph.D.(food sci), 60. Proj. leader food process res, Pillsbury Co, Minn, 54-57; asst. prof. FOOD SCI, UNIV. WIS, MADISON, 60-64, assoc. prof, 64-69, PROF, 69- Ord.C, 51-53, 2nd Lt. Inst. Food Technol; Am. Chem. Soc; Soc. Cryobiol. Low temperature preservation; physical chemistry of food. Address: Dept. of Food Science, Babcock Hall, University of Wisconsin, Madison, WI 53706.

FENNER, G(UNTHER) E(RWIN), b. Frankfurt-am-Main, Germany, Aug. 8, 28; U.S. citizen. SOLID STATE PHYSICS, ELECTRICAL ENGINEERING. B.S, State Col. Eng, Frankfurt, Ger, 52; Polytech. Inst. Brooklyn, 55-56; Union Col.(N.Y), 56-57; Ph.D.(electrophysics), Rensselaer Polytech, 65. Develop. engr, Blonder Tongue Labs, 52-56; microwave engr, aircraft prod. dept, GEN. ELEC. CO, 56-58, electronic engr, gen. eng. lab, 58-60, PHYSICIST, RES. LAB, 60- Sig.C, U.S.A, 53-55. Transport and optical properties of semiconductors; parametric devices. Address: General Electric Research & Development Center, P.O. Box 8, Schenectady, NY 12301.

FENNER, HEINRICH, b. Arolsen, Ger, Sept. 23, 24; U.S. citizen; m. 56; c. 2. ANIMAL NUTRITION. Dipl, Hohenheim Agr. Univ, 51, D.Sc.(animal nutrit), 56; Fulbright scholar, Massachusetts, 51-52. Consult. ANIMAL NUTRIT, H. Fundel K.G, Ger, 55-56; res. instr, UNIV. MASS, AMHERST, 56-61, ASST. RES. PROF, 61- Ger. Air Force, 43-45. AAAS; Am. Dairy Sci. Asn; Am. Soc. Animal Sci; Am. Geog. Soc. Nutrient and energy metabolism in horses and ruminants; macro and minor elements in feed stuff and milk; improvement and development of analytical methods in nutritional research. Address: 188 West St, R.F.D. 5, Amherst, MA 01002.

FENNER, PETER, b. Zurich, Switz, Oct. 2, 37; U.S. citizen; m. 61; c. 2. GEOLOGY, MINERALOGY. B.S, City Col. New York, 59; Wilson P. Foss, Sr. fel, M.S, Illinois, 61, Ph.D.(sedimentology, clay mineral), 63. Instr. geol, Univ. Pa, 63-65, asst. prof, 65-67; from mem. to exec. dit, Coun. Educ. Geol. Sci, Am. Geol. Inst, 67-70; PROF. GEOL. & ASST. DEAN,COL. ENVIRON. & APPL. SCI, GOVERNORS STATE UNIV, 70- Lectr, City Col. New York, summer 60 & 62; chmn. instructional mat. prog. panel, Coun. Educ. Geol. Sci; adv. geol. ed, Appleton-Century-Crofts; scientist, Smithsonian Inst-Coast Guard oceanog. res. cruises; mem. bd. advs, Nat. Study Math. Requirements fo Scientists & Engrs. AAAS; Geol. Soc. Am; Soc. Econ. Paleont. & Mineral; Nat. Asn. Geol. Teachers; Int. Asn. Sedimentol; Clay Minerals Soc; Asn. Petrol. Geol; Fine Particle Soc. Application of quantititive methods to geology, particularly in clay mineral and trace element studies; environmental and earth-science education; oceanography. Address: College of Environmental & Applied Sciences, Governors State University, Park Forest South, IL 60466.

FENNESSY, JOHN JAMES, b. Clonmel, Ireland, Mar. 8, 33; m. 60; c. 5. RADIOLOGY. M.B, B.CH. & B.A.O, Nat. Univ. Ireland, 57. Instr. RADIOL, HOSPS. & CLINS, UNIV. CHICAGO, 63-65, asst. prof, 65-69, ASSOC. PROF, 69- Technique for the diagnosis of lung diseases and tumors; radiologic findings in ulcerative colitis. Address: Dept. of Radiology, University of Chicago Hospitals & Clinics, 950 E. 59th St, Chicago, IL 60637.

FENNEY, NICHOLAS W(ILLIAM), b. New Haven, Conn, July 18, 06; m. 30; c. 2. PHARMACY. Ph.G, Columbia Univ, 25; Ph.C, Univ. Conn, 30; M.P.H, Yale, 46. Instr. PHARM, COL. PHARM, UNIV. CONN, 25-38, assoc. prof, 39-50, prof, 50-68, EMER. PROF, 68- Vis. lectr, dept. pharmacol, sch. med, Yale, 35-42, dept. pub. health, 48-, cancer control sect, 48-49; mem. Conn. Adv. Comt. Foods & Drugs, 50-; Estab. Nicholas W. Fenney Scholar, Conn. Pharm. Asn, 65; Conn. Regional Med. Prog, 66-; Conn. Comprehensive Health Planning Coun, 68-70, 70-; pharmaceut. consult, Conn. Blue Cross, 68- Sydney Rome Achievement Award, 64; Bowl of Hygeia Award, 69; Nard-Lederle Nat. Interprof. Serv. Award, 69. Am. Pharmaceut. Asn; Am. Pub. Health Asn; fel. Am. Col. Apothecaries. Detoxication of toxic chemicals with vitamin C; bacteriology; sanitation; public health. Address: 62 Broadfield Rd, Hamden, CT 06517.

FENNEY, W(ILLIAM) N(ICHOLAS, JR), b. New Haven, Conn, July 12, 14; m. 43; c. 3. MECHANICAL ENGINEERING. B.E, Yale, 36, M.E, 38. Lab. asst, Yale, 36-38; proj. engr, Beacon lab, TEXACO INC, 36-39, staff engr, 39-41, asst. to chief technologist, 41-52, mgt. staff engr, RES. DIV, 52-68, dir. res. & technol. dept, 68-71, ASST. MGR. RES. & TECH. DEPT, 71- Civilian with U.S.A; U.S.A.A.F; U.S.N, 44. Combustion of liquid fuels; injection systems of compression ignition engines; fuel and lubricant performance. Address: Texaco, Inc, P.O. Box 509, Beacon, NY 12508.

FENNINGER, LEONARD DAVIS, b. Hampton, Va, Oct. 3, 17; m. 43; c. 2. MEDICINE. A.B, Princeton, 38; M.D, Univ. Rochester, 43. Instr. med, sch. med. & dent, Univ. Rochester, 47-54, asst. prof, 54-58, assoc. prof. & assoc. dean, 58-61, prof, 61-67; dir, bur. health manpower, U.S. Pub. Health Serv, Va, 67-69; ASSOC. DIR. HEALTH MANPOWER, NAT. INSTS. HEALTH, 69- Head clin. med. sect, Nat. Cancer Inst, Nat. Insts. Health, U.S. Pub. Health Serv, 52-54; med. dir, Strong Mem. Hosp, N.Y. 61-67. AAAS; N.Y. Acad. Sci. Protein and energy metabolism in cancer. Address: Room 111, Bldg. 1, National Institutes of Health, 9000 Rockville Pike, Bethesda, MD 20014.

FENOGLIO, RICHARD ANDREW, b. Joliet, Ill, Jan. 4, 41; m. 65; c. 2. ORGANIC CHEMISTRY. B.S, Illinois, 62; Ph.D.(org. chem), Yale, 67. RES. CHEMIST, E.I. DU PONT DE NEMOURS & CO, INC, 67- Am. Asn. Textile Chem. & Colorists; Am. Chem. Soc. Study of solvolyses and thermochemistry of small ring compounds; study of dye chemistry. Address: E.I. du Pont de Nemours & Co, Inc, P.O. Box 525, Wilmington, DE 19898.

FENRICK, HAROLD WILLIAM, b. Janesville, Wis, Mar. 31, 35; m. 63; c. 3. PHYSICAL CHEMISTRY. B.S, Beloit Col, 57; Danforth Found. fel, Univ. Wis, Madison, 61-65, Ph.D.(chem), 65. Instr. CHEM, Carleton Col, 65-66; asst. prof, Monmouth Col.(Ill), 66-68; ASSOC. PROF, WIS. STATE UNIV-PLATTEVILLE, 68- Res. assoc, P.R. Nuclear Ctr, summer 69. U.S.N, 57-61, Lt.(jg). Am. Chem. Soc. Radiation chemistry of solids; electron spin resonance studies of free radicals. Address: Dept. of Chemistry, Wisconsin State University-Platteville, Platteville, WI 53818.

FENSELAU, ALLAN H(ERMAN), b. Phila, Pa, May 17, 37; m. 62; c. 2. ORGANIC CHEMISTRY. B.S, Yale, 58; Nat. Sci. Found. fel, Stanford, 60-61, Ph.D.(org. chem), 64. Teacher, Univ. Sch, 58-60; fel. org. chem, inst. molecular biol, Syntex Res Center, Calif, 64-65; biochem, California, Berkeley, 65-67; ASST. PROF. PHYSIOL. CHEM, SCH. MED, JOHNS HOPKINS UNIV, 67- AAAS; Am. Chem. Soc; The Chem. Soc. Protein chemistry; enzymology, bioorganic chemistry. Address: Dept. of Physiological Chemistry, Johns Hopkins University School of Medicine, 725 N. Wolfe St, Baltimore, MD 21205.

FENSELAU, CATHERINE CLARKE, b. York, Nebr, Apr. 15, 39; m. 62; c. 2. ORGANIC CHEMISTRY. A.B, Bryn Mawr Col, 61; Ph.D.(org. chem), Stanford, 65. RES. ASSOC. MASS SPECTROMETRY, Univ. Calif, Berkeley, 65-66, res. chemist, space sci. lab, 66-67; ASST. PROF. PHARMACOL, SCH. MED, JOHNS HOPKINS UNIV, 69-, lectr, 67-69. Am. Asn. Univ. Women fel, 65-66. Am. Chem. Soc. Applications of mass spectrometry in biochemical and medical research; chemistry of gaseous ions. Address: Dept. of Pharmacology, Johns Hopkins University School of Medicine, 725 N. Wolfe St, Baltimore, MD 21205.

FENSHOLT, DOROTHY E(UNICE), b. Chicago, Ill, Oct. 23, 11. PHYCOLOGY. B.S, Northwestern, 33, M.S, 45, Ph.D.(bot), 51. Asst. introd. sci, Northwestern, 42-45, instr, 45-47; asst. prof. BIOL, ILL. STATE UNIV, 51-55, assoc. prof, 55-61, PROF, 61- AAAS; Am. Soc. Microbiol; Phycol. Soc. Am; Bot. Soc. Am. Morphology and taxonomy of the Cystoseiraceae and Sargassaceae, especially Cystoseira, Cystophyllum and Sargassum. Address: Dept. of Biology, Illinois State University, Normal, IL 61761.

FENSKE, PAUL RODERICK, b. Ellensberg, Wash, May 15, 25; m. 52; c. 4. GEOLOGY, HYDROGEOLOGY. B.S, S.Dak. Sch. Mines & Tech, 50; M.S, Michigan, 51; Ph.D.(geol), Colorado, 63. Geologist, Magnolia Petrol. Co, 51-56; Delfern Oil Co, 56-59; asst. prof. geol, Idaho State Univ, 63-65; mgr. earth sci. & eng, Teledyne Isotopes Palo Alto Labs, 65-71; RES. ASSOC, CTR. WATER RESOURCES RES, DESERT RES. INST, UNIV. NEV, RENO, 71- U.S.A, 43-46. Am. Geophys. Union; Am. Water Resources Asn. Origin of porosity in oil producing reefs; origin and significance of concretions; geochemistry of sedimentary rocks; hydrogeochemistry; hydrologic systems analysis; groundwater transport of contaminants. Address: Desert Research Institute, University of Nevada System, Center for Water Resources Research, Water Resources Bldg, Reno, NV 89507.

FENSOM, DAVID STRATHERN, b. Toronto, Ont, Apr. 10, 16; m. 44; c. 2. PLANT BIOPHYSICS & PHYSIOLOGY. B.A.Sc, Toronto, 38; Edinburgh, 60-61. Master sci. & head dept, Ridley Col.(Ont), 46-63; assoc. prof, BIOL, MT. ALLISON UNIV, 63-65, prof, 65-69, HEAD DEPT, 69- Mem. publicity cmt, Can. Soc. Plant Physiol, 67-68. Fel. Royal Inst. Chem; fel. Royal Soc. Arts; Can. Soc. Plant Physiol.(secy-treas, 69-71); Soc. Cryobiol; Brit. Soc. Exp. Biol. Electroosmosis, electrophysiology; long distance transport in plants; membrane phenomena. Address: Dept. of Biology, Mount Allison University, Sackville, N.B, Can.

FENSTER, ABRAHAM N, b. N.Y.C, Feb. 17, 42; m. 60; c. 4. ORGANIC & ORGANOMETALLIC CHEMISTRY. B.A, Hunter Col, 63; Nat. Sci. Found. fels, Polytech. Inst. Brooklyn, summer 64 & 64-65, M.S, 65; U.S.Army fel. & Ph.D.(org. chem), Univ. Mass, Boston, 68. Res. chemist, SPECIALTY CHEM. DIV, ALLIED CHEM. CORP, BUFFALO, 67-70, SR. RES. CHEMIST, 70- Part-time instr, Fairleigh Dickinson Univ, 69-70; mem, Info. Coun. Fabric Flammability. Am. Chem. Soc; The Chem. Soc. Synthesis and study of organoiodonium salts, organotin, organosilicon, organo-fluorine and phosphorous chemicals; fire extinguishing systems and fire retardants. Address: 187 Altair Dr, Getzville, NY 14068.

FENSTER, HENRY, b. Phila, Pa, Nov. 11, 24; m. 46; c. 2. MICROELECTRONICS. Ch.E, Pa. State Univ, 48. V.pres, Am. Leonic Mfg. Co, 55-59; sr. engr, Radio Corp. Am, 59-61; mgr. vector dept, Norden Div, United Aircraft Corp, 61-68; MGR. HYBRID CIRCUIT SUBSYSTS, RCA CORP, 65- Instr, Temple Univ, 56-60. U.S.A, 43-45. Am. Chem. Soc; Am. Electroplaters Soc; Int. Soc. Hybrid Microelectronics. Fabrication and processing of micro-miniature circuits. Address: 1104 Paper Mill Rd, Wyndmoor, Philadelphia, PA 19118.

FENSTER, PAUL, b. New York, N.Y, Sept. 17, 39; m. 61; c. 3. ELECTROPHYSICS. B.E.E, City Col. New York, 60; NASA traineeship, Polytech. Inst. Brooklyn, 61-67, M.S, 64, Ph.D.(electrophys), 67. Elec. engr, S-F-D Labs, Varian Assocs, 60-63; mem. tech. staff, Sperry Rand Res. Ctr, 67-68; vis. asst. prof. ELEC. ENG, CITY COL. NEW YORK, 68-69, ASST. PROF, 69- Tech. adv. Varian Assocs, Beverly, Mass, 68- Inst. Elec. & Electronics Eng; Optical Soc. Am. Solid state devices; short pulse technology; optics; microwave devices. Address: Dept. of Electrical Engineering, City College of New York, New York, NY 10031.

FENSTER, SAUL, b. New York, N.Y, Mar. 22, 33; m. 59; c. 3. MECHANICAL ENGINEERING. B.M.E, City Col. New York, 53; M.S, Columbia, 55; N.Y. Univ, 55-56; univ. fel, Michigan, 56-57, Shell Oil fel, 57-58, Ph.D.(heat transfer), 59. Tool designer, Tech. Facilities, Inc, 52; lectr. mech. eng, City Col. New York, 53-56; mech. engr, res. inst, Michigan, 58; res. engr. aerospace, Sperry Gyroscope Div, Sperry Rand Corp, 59-62; PROF. physics, FAIRLEIGH DICKINSON UNIV, 62-63, MECH. ENG, 63-, EXEC. ASST. TO PRES, 71-, chmn. dept. physics, 62-63, mech. eng, 63-70, grad. admin. asst. to dean col. sci. & eng, 65-70; assoc. dean col. sci. & eng, 70-71. Summers, mech. engr, East Design Co, 53 & 56, Babcock & Wilcox Co, 54, Wright Aero Div, Curtis-Wright Corp, 55, res. inst, Univ. Mich, 57; indust. consult, 62- Am. Soc. Mech. Eng; Am. Soc. Eng. Educ. Heat transfer; machine dynamics and design; structural analysis; cryogenic and societal engineering. Address: Fairleigh Dickinson University, Rutherford, NJ 07070.

FENSTER, WILLIAM E, b. Loganville, Wis, Aug. 5, 35; m. 63. SOIL CHEMISTRY, BACTERIOLOGY. B.S, Wisconsin, 58, M.S, 65, Ph.D.(soils), 67. Asst. prof. SOIL SCI, UNIV. MINN, ST. PAUL, 67-71, ASSOC. PROF, 71-, SOILS EXTEN. SPECIALIST, AGR. EXTEN. SERV, 69- U.S.A, 59-62. Am. Soc. Agron; Soil Sci. Soc. Am. Address: Dept. of Soil Science, University of Minnesota, St. Paul, MN 55071.

FENSTERMACHER, CHARLES ALVIN, b. Scranton, Pa, Mar. 31, 28. EXPERIMENTAL PHYSICS. B.S, Phila. Col. Pharm, 50; B.A, Swarthmore Col, 53; M.S, Yale, 55, Du Pont fel. & Ph.D.(physics), 57. Staff mem. weapons test div, LOS ALAMOS SCI. LAB, 57-59, GROUP LEADER, test div, Rover Prog, 59-69, RES. & DEVELOP. ELECTRICALLY EXCITED GAS LASERS, 69- Am. Phys. Soc. Gamma ray spectroscopy of neutron capture gamma rays from rare earths; weapons test measurements; Rover nuclear rocket reactor systems design and test. Address: 3215 Arizona, Los Alamos, NM 87544.

FENSTERMACHER, ROBERT LANE, b. Scranton, Pa, May 30, 41; m. 64; c. 1. ATMOSPHERIC PHYSICS, RADIO ASTRONOMY. B.A, Drew, 63; NASA fel. & Ph.D.(physics), Pa. State, 68. ASST. PROF. PHYSICS, DREW UNIV, 68- AAAS; Am. Asn. Physics Teachers; Am. Phys. Soc. Millimeter wave absorption in the Earth's atmosphere; interference holography. Address: Dept. of Physics, Drew University, Madison, NJ 07940.

FENTER, FELIX WEST, b. Paris, Tex, Sept. 16, 26; m. 51; c. 1. AERONAUTICAL ENGINEERING. B.S, Texas, 53, M.S, 54, Ph.D.(aeronaut. & space eng), 60. Asst. aeromech. div, Defense Res. Lab, Tex, 52-53, res. engr, 53-55, syst. develop. specialist, 55-58; eng. specialist, aerodyn. sect, CHANCE VOUGHT AIRCRAFT, INC, 58-60, sr. scientist, Vought Res. Center, 60-61, supvr, aerophysics group, Ling-Temco-Vought Res. Ctr, 61-62, asst. dir, 62-66, assoc. dir, LTV Res. Ctr, Ling-Temco-Vought, Inc, 66-71, V.PRES, ADVAN. TECHNOL. CTR, INC, 71- U.S.N, 45-49. AAAS; Am. Ord. Asn; Am. Inst. Aeronaut. & Astronaut. Supersonic and hypersonic aerodynamics; mechanics of viscous fluids. Address: Advanced Technology Center, Inc, P.O. Box 6144, Dallas, TX 75222.

FENTERS, JAMES DEAN, b. Attica, Ind, Sept. 23, 36. VIROLOGY, MICROBIOLOGY. B.S, Purdue, 58; Nat. Insts. Health fel. & M.S, Iowa, 61, Nat. Insts. Health fel. & Ph.D.(bact), 62. RES. VIROLOGIST, Abbott Labs, 62-67; RES. INST, ILL. INST. TECHNOL, 67- AAAS; Am. Soc. Microbiol. Tissue culture in relation to virus propagation; immune responses and serology; respiratory viruses; viral vaccines; viral reference reagents; antiviral chemotherapy. Address: Illinois Institute of Technology Research Institute, 10 W. 35th St, Chicago, IL 60616.

FENTIN, ARTHUR, b. Boston, Mass, July 22, 25; m. 48; c. 3. ORGANIC CHEMISTRY. A.B, Boston, 46, A.M, 47. Res. assoc. & flight photographer, optical res. labs, Boston, 46-49; res. supvr, Solvent Chem. Co, 49-52; prod. & anal. supvr, E.I. du Pont de Nemours & Co, 52-63; dir. res, Berkshire Color & Chem. Co, Pa, 64-65, plant mgr, Berkshire Color Div, Teneco Chem. Inc, 65-70; SR. PROD. SUPVR, E.I. DU PONT DE NEMOURS & CO, INC, PENNS GROVE, N.J, 70- U.S.A, 41-43. Am. Chem. Soc; Optical Soc. Am; Photog. Soc. Am. Analytical development; organic dyestuff and intermediate manufacture and analytical development; production supervision; photographic research. Address: 1507 Athens Rd, Green Acres, Wilmington, DE 19803.

FENTON, A(LBERT) J(AMES), b. Passaic, N.J, Apr. 12, 32; m. 53; c. 3. ANALYTICAL CHEMISTRY. A.B, Princeton, 54, Sayre fel, 54-55, McCay fel, 56-57, Ph.D.(chem), 59. Anal. researcher, Procter & Gamble Co, 57-61; dir. anal. res, Wallace Lab. Div, Carter Prod, Inc, 61-65; ANAL. RESEARCHER, IVORYDALE TECH. CTR, PROCTER & GAMBLE CO, 65- AAAS; Am. Chem. Soc; Am. Oil Chemists' Soc. Spectroscopy; electrochemistry and coulometry; analysis of detergents and cosmetics; pharmaceutical analysis. Address: Ivorydale Technical Center, Procter & Gamble Co, Cincinnati, OH 45217.

FENTON, DAVID GEORGE, b. London, Eng, June 8, 32; m; c. 2. PHYSICS. B.Sc, London, Eng, 55; Ph.D, Connecticut, 64. Asst, Purdue, 55-57; prod. engr, Taylor Instrument Co, 57-58; instr. PHYSICS, CONN. COL, 58-63, asst. prof, 63-68, ASSOC. PROF, 68- Summers, res. technician, Univ. Conn, 60, 63. Quantum mechanics of the electronic structure of molecules and of atomic collision processes. Address: Dept. of Physics, Connecticut College, New London, CT 06320.

FENTON, DONALD M(ASON), b. Los Angeles, Calif, May 23, 29; m. 53; c. 2. ORGANIC CHEMISTRY. B.S, California, Los Angeles, 52, Ph.D, 58. RES. CHEMIST, Rohm & Haas Co, 58-61; UNION OIL CO, 62- U.S.A, 53-55. Am. Chem. Soc. Mechanistic synthetic organic chemistry. Address: Union Oil Co, P.O. Box 76, Brea, CA 92621.

FENTON, JOHN WILLIAM, II, b. Salamanaca, N.Y, Feb. 4, 39; m. 65; c. 2. BIOCHEMISTRY, IMMUNOLOGY. B.S, Cornell Univ, 61; M.S, Univ. Wis, Madison, 64; U.S. Pub. Health Serv. fel, Univ. Calif, San Diego, 66-68, Ph.D.(biochem), 68. Fel. biochem, Univ. Calif, San Diego, spring 68; SR. RES. SCIENTIST, DIV. LABS. & RES, N.Y. STATE DEPT. HEALTH, 68- U.S. Pub. Health Serv. grant, 69-73; adj. asst. prof, dept. microbiol, Albany Med. Col, 70- AAAS; Am. Chem. Soc. Purification and characterization of human thrombin and other blood coagulation factors; production and purification of antibodies and diagnostic applications of immunochemistry; fluorescent antibody labeling of erythrocytes; affinity labeling of antibody active sites. Address: Division of Laboratories & Research, New York State Dept. of Health, New Scotland Ave, Albany, NY 12201.

FENTON, M. BROCK, b. Guyana, Oct. 20, 43; Can. citizen; m. 69. MAMMALOGY. B.Sc, Queen's (Ont), 65; M.Sc, Toronto, 66, Ph.D.(zool), 69. ASST. PROF. BIOL, CARLETON UNIV, 69- Biologist, Aguas Buenas field trip, Nat. Speleol. Soc, winter 68; res. assoc. mammal, Royal Ont. Mus; lectr, Queen's (Ont), summer 69. AAAS; Am. Soc. Mammal.(A.B. Howell award, 69); Can. Soc. Zool; Soc. Vert. Paleont; Nat. Speleol. Soc. Chiroptology; speleology; the ecology of bats with special references to their behavior; biology and paleontology of caves. Address: Dept. of Biology, Carleton University, Ottawa, Ont. K1S 5B6, Can.

FENTON, PAUL F(REDRIC), b. Stuttgart, Germany, Nov. 28, 15; nat. 33; m. 41; c. 2. BIOCHEMISTRY. B.S, Rochester, 38; M.S, Vermont, 40, Ph.D. (biochem), 44. Asst, Vermont, 38-40, instr. biochem, 40-45, asst. prof, 45; Nutrit. Found. fel, Yale, 45-46, asst. prof, nutrit, 46-49; assoc. prof. BIOL, BROWN UNIV, 49-54, PROF, 54- Guggenheim Mem. fel, 57-58; vis. prof, Emory, 57-58. Nutrit. panel, cmt. growth, Nat. Res. Coun, 49-52; mem. physiol. training cmt, Nat. Inst. Gen. Med. Sci, 61-65. Am. Inst. Nutrit; Am. Physiol. Soc; Soc. Exp. Biol. & Med. Nutritional biochemistry; physiology of digestive system; endocrinology and metabolism. Address: Division of Biological & Medical Sciences, Brown University, Providence, RI 02912.

FENTON, ROBERT E, b. Brooklyn, N.Y, Sept, 30, 33; m. 55; c. 2. ELECTRICAL ENGINEERING. B.E.E, Ohio State, 57, M.Sc, 60, Ph.D.(elec. eng), 65. Res. engr, N.Am. Aviation, Inc, 57; instr. elec. eng, OHIO STATE UNIV, 60-65, asst. prof. ELEC. ENG, 65-69, ASSOC. PROF, 69-, DIR. HWY. RES. GROUP, 70-, asst. supvr, commun. & controls syst. labs, 65-67, acting dir, 67-70. Mem, Hwy. Res. Bd. Comt. Hwy. Commun, 66-. U.S.A.F, 57-60, Capt. Inst. Elec. & Electronics Eng. Human factors engineering; automatic control and computer systems. Address: Dept. of Electrical Engineering, Ohio State University, 2015 Neil Ave, Columbus, OH 43210.

FENTON, ROBERT GEORGE, b. Budapest, Hungary, Apr. 3, 31; m. 57; c. 2. MECHANICAL ENGINEERING. Dipl. Ing, Univ. Budapest, 53; Ph.D.(mech. eng), Univ. New South Wales, 68. Sr. lectr. MECH. ENG, Univ. New South Wales, 62-68; ASSOC. PROF, UNIV. TORONTO, 68- Water Arbitration Prize, Inst. Mech. Engrs, 69. Experimental and analytical investigation of metal flow during machining and forming; yield criteria, thermal effects; machine tool vibration; wear analysis; tool life and machining economy; computerized design; reliability; simulation models; computer graphics. Address: Dept. of Mechanical Engineering, University of Toronto, Toronto, Ont, Can.

FENTON, STUART W(ILLIAM), b. London, Ont, Apr. 29, 22; m. 62. ORGANIC CHEMISTRY. B.Sc, Queen's (Ont), 45, M.Sc, 46; Ph.D.(chem), Mass. Inst. Tech, 50. Asst. prof. org. chem, UNIV. MINN, MINNEAPOLIS, 50-55, assoc. prof. CHEM. & assoc. chmn. dept, 55-61, PROF, 61-, chmn. dept, 61-68. AAAS; Am. Chem. Soc; The Chem. Soc. Organic synthesis and peroxides. Address: Dept. of Chemistry, University of Minnesota, Minneapolis, MN 55455.

FENTON, THOMAS E, b. Cabery, Ill, July 19, 33; m. 59; c. 4. SOIL GENESIS & CLASSIFICATION. B.S, Univ. Ill, Urbana, 59, M.S, 60; Ph.D.(soil genesis & classification), Iowa State Univ, 66. Instr, U.S. Army Europe Qm. Sch, 54-55; res. soil scientist, U.S. Dept. Agr, summers 61-64; res. assoc. agron, IOWA STATE UNIV, 64-66, asst. prof. SOIL GENESIS & CLASSIFICATION, 66-68, ASSOC. PROF, 68-, asst. prof, res. found, 68. Consult, Attorney Gen. Off, State of Iowa, 67-69. U.S.A, 53-55. AAAS; Clay Mineral Soc; Am. Soc. Agron; Soil Sci. Soc. Am; Soil Conserv. Soc. Am; Am. Chem. Soc. Soil genesis and classification combined with geomorphology. Address: Dept. of Agronomy, Iowa State University, Ames, IA 50010.

FENTON-MAY, ROUALEYN I(AIN), b. London, Eng, Mar. 25, 45. CHEMICAL ENGINEERING. B.Sc, Univ. Edinburgh, 67; univ. res. assistantship & M.S, Univ. Wis, Madison, 68, Ph.D.(chem. eng), 71. Asst. chem. eng, Univ. Wis, Madison, 67-71; SECT. TECH. HEAD NUTRIT. BEVERAGES DEPT, COCA-COLA EXPORT CORP, 71- Fulbright travel grant, U.S-U.K. Educ. Comn, London, 67. Brit. Inst. Chem. Eng; Inst. Food Technol; Am. Inst. Chem. Eng; Am. Chem. Soc. Applications of reverse osmosis and ultrafiltration in the food and dairy industries; cheese whey processing and utilization. Address: 444 E. 82nd St, Apt. 1A, New York, NY 10028.

FENTRESS, CARROLL D(EE), b. Canyon, Tex, Aug. 11, 11; m. 35; c. 3. CHEMICAL ENGINEERING. B.S, Mass. Inst. Tech, 34, M.S, 35. Chem. engr, Standard Oil Co.(Ind), 35-38, group leader, 38-46, dir. ref, oil & gas div, U.S. Dept. Interior, Wash. D.C, 46-50, asst. dir, 50-51, spec. asst. to dep. adminstr, exec. secy. & finance counsellor, petrol. admin. for defense, 51-54, asst. dir, off. oil & gas, 54-58; consult, 58-59; asst. to mgr, PHILLIPS PETROL. CO, WASH. D.C, 59-68, ASST. TO V.PRES, 68- U.S.A, 42-46, Maj. Am. Inst. Chem. Eng. Petroleum refining; sulfuric acid manufacture and recovery. Address: 10800 Fox Hunt Lane, Potomac, MD 20854.

FENVES, STEVEN J(OSEPH), b. Subotica, Yugoslavia, June 6, 31; U.S. citizen; m. 55; c. 4. CIVIL ENGINEERING. B.S, Illinois, 57, Tau Beta Pi fel, 56-57, M.S, 58, Ph.D.(eng), 61. Draftsman, Erik Floor & Assoc, Ill, 50-52; instr. civil eng, Illinois, 57-61, asst. prof, 61-62; vis. assoc. prof, Mass. Inst. Tech, 62-63; assoc. prof. civil eng, Univ. Ill, Urbana, 63-65, prof. civil eng. & res. prof, coord. sci. lab, 65-71; PROF. CIVIL ENG. & HEAD DEPT, CARNEGIE-MELLON UNIV, 72- Indust. & govt. consult, 57-; mem. comt. comput. eng. design, Comn. Eng. Educ, 62-; vis. prof. Cornell Univ, 70-71. C.Eng, U.S.A, 52-53. Am. Soc. Civil Eng; Am. Soc. Eng. Educ; Asn. Comput. Mach. Computer applications in civil engineering; structural dynamics, analysis and design; problem-oriented computer languages. Address: Dept. of Civil Engineering, Carnegie-Mellon University, Pittsburgh, PA 15213.

FENWICK, HARRY (SELWYN), b. Filer, Idaho, Sept. 24, 22; m. 46; c. 3. PLANT PATHOLOGY. B.S. Mont. State, 49, fel, 50-52, M.S, 52; fel, Nebraska, 52-53; Ore. State Col, 53-56, Ph.D.(plant path), 56. ASSOC. PROF. PLANT PATH, UNIV. IDAHO, 68-, EXTEN. PLANT PATHOLOGIST, 56- Am. Phytopath. Soc. Seedling diseases of sugarbeets; control of cereal rusts by chemotherapy; studies of dwarf bunt in cereals and grasses. Address: Dept. of Plant Pathology, University of Idaho, Moscow, ID 83843.

FENWICK, ROBERT B, b. Indianapolis, Ind, Apr. 13, 36; m. 60; c. 3. ELECTRICAL ENGINEERING. B.S, Purdue Univ, 58; univ. fel, Stanford Univ, 59-60, M.S, 59, Nat. Sci. Found. fels, 59-61, Ph.D.(elec. eng), 63. Res. assoc, radiosci. lab, Stanford Univ, 60-68; V.PRES, BARRY RES. CORP, 66-, SR. SCIENTIST, 68- Am. Geophys. Union; Inst. Elec. & Electronics Eng. Long distance high frequency radio wave propagation via the ionosphere; nature of horizontal gradients of electron density in the ionosphere; techniques of ionospheric measurement, especially ionospheric sounders. Address: Barry Research Corp, 1530 Page Mill Rd, Palo Alto, CA 94304.

FENYES, JOSEPH G(ABRIEL) E(GON), b. Paszto, Hungary, Mar. 19, 25; U.S. citizen; m. 57; c. 3. ORGANIC CHEMISTRY. B.Sc, Szeged, 48; Sorbonne, 50-51; Ph.D.(org. chem), McGill, 55. Lectr. org. chem, Royal Mil. Col.(Ont), 55-56; res. chemist, Shawinigan Chem. Ltd, Que, 56-58; res. group leader, Hyman Labs, Inc, Calif, 58-62; res. chemist, Ortho Div, Calif. Chem. Co, Richmond, 62, Chevron Chem. Co, Calif, 62-69; sr. res. chemist, BUCKMAN LABS, INC, 69-70, ORG. RES. CHEMIST, 70- Am. Chem. Soc. Synthesis of biologically active and agriculturally useful organic compounds; sulfenyl halides; halogen and sulfur containing fungicides; plant growth regulators; organophosphorous insecticides; B-substituted naphthalenes; heterocyclic chemicals; plastics additives; ultraviolet light absorbers; fire retardants. Address: 1827 Oak Hills Cove, Germantown, TN 38138.

FENYVES, E(RVIN) J, b. Budapest, Hungary, Aug. 29, 24; m. 51; c. 2. HIGH ENERGY & COSMIC RAY PHYSICS. M.S, Eötvös Lóránd Univ, Budapest, 46, Ph.D.(physics), 50; Cand. Phys. Sci, Hungarian Acad. Sci, 55, Dr. Phys. Sci, 60. Asst. prof. physics, Eötvös Lóránd Univ, Budapest, 46-51; res. fel, cent. res. inst. physics, Hungarian Acad. Sci, 51-59, head lab. cosmic rays, 59-65, dep. sci. dir, 65-69; res. fel. PHYSICS, Univ. Pa, 69-70; PROF, UNIV. TEX, DALLAS, 70- Part-time assoc. prof, Eötvös Lóránd Univ, Budapest, 60-64, part-time prof, 64-69; cor. mem. high energy nuclear physics comn, Int. Union Pure & Appl. Physics, 63-69, mem. cosmic ray comn, 66-70; v.dir, Joint Inst. Nuclear Res, Dubna, 64-66; head physics sect, Int. Atomic Energy Agency, Vienna, 68-69. Brodi-Schmidt Prize, Hungarian Phys. Soc, 52; Nat. Kossuth Prize, Hungarian Govt, 65; Prize for Books, Hungarian Acad. Sci, 67. Am. Phys. Soc. Nuclear radiation measurements. Address: Dept. of Physics, University of Texas at Dallas, P.O. Box 30365, Dallas, TX 75230.

FEORINO, PAUL M, b. N.Y.C, Feb. 28, 29; m. 51; c. 6. VIROLOGY. B.S, St. John, 52; M.S, Siena Col, 57; Ph.D.(microbiol), Emory, 65. Bacteriologist, N.Y. State Div. Labs. & Res, 52-53, virologist, 53-57; MICROBIOLOGIST, NAT. COMMUN. DISEASE CTR, U.S. PUB. HEALTH SERV, 57- U.S.A, 46-48. Tissue Cult. Asn; Sci. Res. Soc. Am; N.Y. Acad. Sci. Known oncogenic viruses and their relationships to cancer induction in humans; biological, chemical and physical characteristics of the enteroviruses. Address: Viral Oncology Lab, Communicable Disease Center, 1600 Clifton Rd, Atlanta, GA 30333.

FERADAY, MELVILLE ALBERT, b. Toronto, Ont, Jan. 13, 29; m. 58; c. 3. MECHANICAL ENGINEERING, MATERIALS SCIENCE. B.Sc, Queen's Univ. (Ont), 54; M.Sc, Univ. Waterloo, 70. Engr, Chalk River Nuclear Labs, ATOMIC ENERGY CAN, LTD, 56-58, commissioning engr, Colombo Plan, India, 58-60, FUEL DEVELOP. ENGR, CHALK RIVER NUCLEAR LABS, 60- Can. Army, 52-56, Lt. Design, development, metallurgy and irradiation of uranium based fuel elements, particularly metallic fuels and powder packed uranium dioxide fuels. Address: Chalk River Nuclear Labs, Chalk River, Ont, Can.

FERBEL, THOMAS, b. Radom, Poland, Dec. 12, 37; U.S. citizen; m. 63; c. 2. PHYSICS. B.S, Queens Col.(N.Y), 59; M.S, Yale, 60, Ph.D.(physics), 63. Res. staff physicist, Yale, 63-65; asst. prof. PHYSICS, UNIV. ROCHESTER, 65-69, ASSOC. PROF, 69- A.P. Sloan Found. res. fel, 70; J.S. Guggenheim Found. fel, 71. Am. Phys. Soc. Experimental elementary particle physics; strong interactions. Address: Dept. of Physics & Astronomy, University of Rochester, Rochester, NY 14627.

FERBER, HERBERT J(AMES), b. Chicago, Ill, Sept. 11, 06; m. 37; c. 2. GEOLOGY. B.S, Wisconsin, 38; Pittsburgh, 37-39; Carnegie Inst. Tech, 37-39; A.B, Fresno State Col, 43; M.A, East. N.Mex. Univ, 54. Asst. geophysicist, Gulf Res. Lab, Gulf Oil Corp, Pa, 37-39, geophysicist, Calif, 39-46, party chief, Gulf Res. & Develop. Co, 46-52, chief geophysicist, north. zones-Houston Div, 53-55, dist. geophysicist, 55-71; GEOPHYS. CONSULT, 71- Am. Asn. Petrol. Geol; Soc. Explor. Geophys. Geophysical prospecting; petroleum; natural gas; civil engineering. Address: 5456 Hartsdale Dr, Jackson, MS 39211.

FERBER, K(ELVIN) H(ALKET), b. Brooklyn, N.Y, Oct. 18, 10; m. 37; c. 2. ORGANIC CHEMISTRY. B.Chem, Cornell Univ, 32; M.B.A, State Univ. N.Y. Buffalo, 71. Supvr. anal. lab, SPECIALTY CHEM. DIV, ALLIED CHEM. CORP, 38-42, supt. quality control, 42-44, asst. to plant mgr, 45-49, supt. tests & inspections, 49-64, tech. mgr, 64-71, TECH. ASST. TO MGR, 71- Am. Chem. Soc; Am. Soc. Test. & Mat; fel. Am. Inst. Chem. Analytical research; absorption spectrophotometry; industrial toxicology; dyestuff application and testing; process and product development; environmental control. Address: Specialty Chemicals Division, Allied Chemical Corp, Box 1069, Buffalo, NY 14240.

FERBER, ROBERT R, b. Monongahela, Pa, June 11, 35; m. 64. ELECTRICAL ENGINEERING. B.S, Pittsburgh, 58; Buhl Found. fel, Carnegie Inst. Technol, 65, Nat. Defense Educ. Act fel. & M.S, 66; Ph.D.(elec. eng), Carnegie-Mellon Univ, 67. Audio engr, Radio Sta. WWSW, 52-56; head dept. eng, WRS Motion Picture Labs, 54-58; res. engr. radiation detection, Westing-

house Res. Labs, 58-66, ADV. ENGR, Westinghouse Astronuclear Labs, 67-71, POWER SYSTS. PLANNING, RES. & DEVELOP. SECT, WESTINGHOUSE ELEC. CORP, 71- Inst. Elec. & Electronics Eng; Nat. Soc. Prof. Eng. Advanced concepts in electric power generation; nuclear radiation effects; nuclear power; semiconductor physics. Address: Power Systems Planning, Research & Development Section, Westinghouse Electric Corp, 700 Braddock Ave, East Pittsburgh, PA 15112.

FERCHAU, HUGO A(LFRED), b. Mineola, N.Y, July 22, 29; m. 52; c. 4. BOTANY. B.S, Col. of William & Mary, 51; Ph.D.(bot), Duke, 59. Asst, Washington State, 52-53, acting jr. botanist, div. indust. res, 53-54; asst, Duke, 55-58; assoc. prof. BIOL, Wofford Col, 58-62; asst. prof, WEST. STATE COL. COLO, 62-66, assoc. prof, 66-69, PROF, 69- AAAS; Ecol. Soc. Am; Bot. Soc. Am. Ecology of mycorrhizae. Address: Dept. of Biology, Western State College of Colorado, Gunnison, CO 81230.

FERCHAUD, JOHN B(ARTHOLOMEW), b. New Orleans, La, June 14, 12; m. 47; c. 3. CHEMICAL ENGINEERING. B.S, La. State, 35. Process engr, Standard Oil Co. La, 35-36; plant chemist, Ark. Fuel Oil Co, 36-37; state chem. eng, Conserv. Dept, La, 37-42; supt. construct. & oper, Chem. Construct. Corp, N.Y, 42-51; tech. asst. to mfg. mgr, Lion Oil Co. Div, MONSANTO CO, 51-56, ENG. MGR, 56-61, AGR. div, 61-65, CENT. ENG. DEPT, 65- Am. Inst. Chem. Eng. Engineering and construction of manufacturing units. Address: 182 Meadow Lark Dr, St. Louis, MO 63141.

FEREBEE, SHIRLEY H(AWES), b. Huntington, Ind, Feb. 10, 13; m. 39, 71; c. 2. BIOSTATISTICS. A.B, Indiana, 33. Statistician, Ill. Emergency Relief Comn, 34-39; biostatistician, RES. SECT, TUBERC. PROG, U.S. PUB. HEALTH SERV, 45-48, asst. chief, 49-55, assoc. chief, 55-67, CHIEF, 67- Dept. Health, Ed. & Welfare superior serv. award, 56, distinguished serv. award, 63; pres, comn. prophylaxis, Int. Union Against Tuberculosis, 68-71. AAAS; Am. Statist. Asn; Am. Thoracic Soc. Large-scale controlled trials of therapeutic and prophylactic agents for tuberculosis in cooperation with hospitals and health departments throughout United States; methodology of clinical trials. Address: Research Section, Tuberculosis Branch, State & Community Services Division, Center for Disease Control, 5600 Fishers Lane, Room 13-06, Rockville, MD 20852.

FERENCE, MICHAEL, JR, b. Whiting, Ind, Nov. 6, 11; m. 37; c. 5. PHYSICS. B.S, Univ. Chicago, 33, M.A, 34, Ph.D.(physics), 37; D.Sc, Kenyon Col, 69. Instr. physics, Chicago, 37-40, asst. prof, 40-44, assoc. prof, 44-46; chief meteorol. br, Sig. Corps Eng. Labs, Evans Sig. Lab, 46-48, chief scientist, 48-51, tech. dir, 51-53; chief scientist, SCI. LAB, FORD MOTOR CO, 53-54, assoc. dir, 54-57, dir, 57-59, exec. dir, 59-62, V.PRES. RES, 62- Trustee, Rand Corp; mem. panel, Res. & Develop. Bd; tech. panel earth satellite program & comt. atmospheric sci, Nat. Acad. Sci; res. panel, Signal Corps Res. & Develop. Adv. Coun; adv. group on weather modification, Nat. Sci. Found; spec. adv. cmt. to Dept. Commerce; Rocket & Satellite Res. Panel; adv. comt, U.S. Weather Bur; President's Sci. Adv. Comt; bd. of trustees, Carnegie Inst; Dirs. Indust. Res; adv. comt, Puerto Rico Nuclear Ctr, Univ. P.R. Civilian with U.S.A.A.F, 44. Am. Phys. Soc; Am. Geophys. Soc; Am. Meteorol. Soc; Soc. Automotive Eng; fel. Inst. Elec. & Electronics Eng; Nat. Acad. Eng; Am. Inst. Phys; Sci. Res. Soc. Am. Physics of the upper atmosphere; experimental hydrodynamics; designs of radiosondes; radar; electronics; microwave propagation; x-ray spectroscopy. Address: Scientific Research Staff, Ford Motor Co, P.O. Box 2053, Dearborn, MI 48121.

FERENCZ, CHARLOTTE, b. Budapest, Hungary, Oct. 28, 21; U.S. citizen. PEDIATRIC CARDIOLOGY. B.Sc, McGill Univ, 44, M.D, C.M, 45; M.P.H, Johns Hopkins Univ, 70. Demonstr. pediat, McGill Univ, 52-54; asst. prof. PEDIAT, Johns Hopkins Univ, 54-59; med. col, Univ. Cincinnati, 59-60; SCH. MED, STATE UNIV. N.Y. BUFFALO, 60-66, ASSOC. PROF, 66-, CLIN. ASST. PROF. SOC. & PREV. MED, 71- Am. Acad. Pediat; N.Y. Acad. Sci; Am. Col. Cardiol; Am. Pub. Health Asn. Changes in the pulmonary vascular bed associated with congenital heart disease; normal growth of pulmonary vessels; epidemiology of heart disease and cardiac services in pediatric age group. Address: 219 Bryant St, Buffalo, NY 14222.

FERENCZ, NICHOLAS, b. Cleveland, Ohio, Apr. 22, 37; m; c. 2. CELL & RADIATION BIOLOGY. A.B, Hiram Col, 59; M.S, Cath. Univ. Am, 62, Ph.D. (cell biol), 67; dent, Case West. Reserve Univ, 71- Instr. radiol, Case West. Reserve Univ, 67-69, asst. prof. radiation biol, 69-71. Tissue Cult. Asn; Am. Dent. Asn. Tissue culture, radiobiology. Address: School of Dentistry, Case Western Reserve University, Cleveland, OH 44106.

FERENTZ, MELVIN, b. New York, N.Y, Oct. 14, 28; m. 48, 64; c. 3. PHYSICS. B.S, Brooklyn Col, 49; Harrison fel, Pennsylvania, 50-51, Tyndall fel, 51-52, Ph.D.(physics), 53. Asst. instr. physics, Pennsylvania, 48-50; assoc. physicist, Argonne Nat. Lab, 52-57; sr. mathematician analyst, Int. Bus. Machines Corp, 57-59; assoc. prof. physics, St. John's Univ.(N.Y), 59-65, prof. & chmn. dept, 65-66; PROF. PHYSICS, BROOKLYN COL, 66-, DEP. CHMN. GRAD. STUDIES, DEPT. PHYSICS, 67- Res. assoc, Columbia Univ, 64-66, vis. prof, 66; assoc. dir, City & State Univs. N.Y. Joint Inst. Learning & Instr, 67-; pres, Ferentz Assoc, Inc; consult, IBM Corp; Univac Div, Sperry Rand Corp; Grumman Aircraft Eng. Corp. Asn. Comput. Mach; Am. Phys. Soc. Theoretical physics; particle accelerator design; digital computers. Address: Dept. of Physics, Brooklyn College, Brooklyn, NY 11210.

FERENZI, GEORGE WILLIAM, b. Chicago, Ill, Jan. 17, 26; m. 50; c. 4. INTERNAL MEDICINE, HEMATOLOGY. M.D, Loyola Univ.(Ill), 52. ASST. CLIN. PROF. MED, STRITCH SCH. MED, LOYOLA UNIV. CHICAGO, 60- Sr. attend. physician & chmn. dept. med, Holy Cross Hosp, 62- U.S.A.A.F, 44-45, S/Sgt. Fel. Am. Col. Physicians; fel. Am. Soc. Hemat; Am. Med. Asn; fel. Int. Soc. Hemat; fel. Am. Soc. Clin. Oncol. Cancer and leukemia therapeutic research. Address: Stritch School of Medicine, Loyola University of Chicago, 8625 S. Cicero Ave, Chicago, IL 60652.

FERGIN, RICHARD KENNETH, b. Tacoma, Wash, Dec. 9, 33; m. 67. ENGINEERING, PHYSICAL CHEMISTRY. B.S, Wash. State Col, 55; M.S, New Mexico State, 61, Nat. Sci. Found. fel, 63-64, Sc.D.(mech. eng), 64. Tool engr, Boeing Airplane Co, 55-57; mech. engr, Ft. Belvoir, Va, 58-59; res. assoc, rocket sect, phys. sci. lab, New Mexico State, 59-60, asst. mech. eng, 60-61, instr, 61-63; assoc. prof. eng, San Diego State Col, 64-68; math, U.S. Int. Univ, 68; STAFF SCIENTIST, GEOSCI. LTD, 69- A.U.S, 57-59. Am. Soc. Heating, Refrig. & Air-Conditioning Eng; Am. Soc. Eng. Educ; Am. Soc. Mech. Eng; Soc. Automotive Eng; Nat. Soc. Prof. Eng. Binary liquid jet refrigeration using immiscible fluids; heat, mass, and momentum transfer with applications in heat removal and energy recovery; condensing mechanisms; micrometeorology; air and thermal pollution. Address: Geoscience Ltd, 410 S. Cedros Ave, Solana Beach, CA 92075.

FERGUS, CHARLES L(EONARD), b. Ottawa, Kans, Nov. 11, 17; m. 42; c. 3. MYCOLOGY. A.B, Ottawa (Kans), 40; M.A, Kansas, 42; Ph.D.(bot), Pa. State, 48. Lab. instr. biol, Ottawa (Kans), 38-40; bot. & med. mycol, Kansas, 40-41; instr. BOT, PA. STATE UNIV, 48-49, asst. prof, 49-53, assoc. prof, 53-60, PROF, 60- U.S.N.R, 42-45. Mycol. Soc. Am. Physiology and taxonomy of thermophilic molds and actinomycetes. Address: Dept. of Biology, 202 Buckhout Lab, Pennsylvania State University, University Park, PA 16802.

FERGUSON, A(LBERT) B(ARNETT), b. New York, N.Y, June 10, 19; m. 43; c. 3. ORTHOPEDIC SURGERY. B.A, Dartmouth Col, 41; M.D, Harvard, 43. Asst. ORTHOP. SURG, Harvard, 51-52; assoc. prof, SCH. MED, UNIV. PITTSBURGH, 53, prof, 54-58, SILVER PROF. & CHMN. DEPT, 58- U.S.N.R, 43-46, Lt.(jg). Am. Acad. Orthop. Surg; Am. Acad. Pediat. Physiology of muscles; growth. Address: Dept. of Orthopedic Surgery, University of Pittsburgh School of Medicine, Pittsburgh, PA 15213.

FERGUSON, A(LBERT) HAYDEN, b. Big Timber, Mont, Sept. 12, 28; m. 51; c. 2. SOIL PHYSICS. B.S, Mont. State Col, 50; M.S. Washington State, 56, Ph.D.(soils), 59. Soil scientist, U.S. Bur. Reclamation, 50-51; asst. SOILS, Washington State, 53-58; PROF, MONT. STATE UNIV, 58- Chem.C, U.S.A, 51-53. Am. Soc. Agron; Soil Sci. Soc. Am. Water movement in soils; soil-plant relationships. Address: Dept. of Plant & Soil Sciences, Montana State University, Bozeman, MT 59714.

FERGUSON, ALEX(ANDER) J(OHN), b. Ottawa, Ont, Mar. 15, 15; m. 46; c. 3. PHYSICS. B.Sc, McGill, 35, Nat. Res. Coun. Can. scholar, 37-39, Ph.D. (nuclear physics), 39. Demonstr. physics, McGill, 35-37; res. physicist, Nat. Res. Coun. Can, 39-40, RADAR RES, 40-46; CHALK RIVER NUCLEAR LABS, ATOMIC ENERGY CAN. LTD, 46- Am. Phys. Soc; Can. Asn. Physicists. Nuclear physics; electric networks; computer analysis. Address: Chalk River Nuclear Labs, Atomic Energy of Canada Ltd, Chalk River, Ont, Can.

FERGUSON, CARL E, b. Butterfield, Mo, Sept. 18, 16; m. 43; c. 1. AGRICULTURE. B.S, Univ. Mo-Columbia, 38, M.A, 39, Ph.D.(soil sci), 41. Soil surveyor, U.S. Dept. Agr, 41-42; agronomist, Econ. Coop. Admin, 49-50; from asst. prof. agron. to assoc. prof, Tex. A&M Univ, 46-51; soil scientist, U.S. Dept. Agr, 51-54; agron. adv, For. Opers. Admin, 54-56; agron. adv. res, Int. Coop. Admin, 56-59; soils & agr. res. adv, U.S. AGENCY INT. DEVELOP, 59-62, agr. off, 62-64, agr. specialist, 64-69, dep. food & agr. off, 69-70, FOOD & AGR. OFF, 70- U.S.A, 42-46, Capt. AAAS; Soil Sci. Soc. Am; Am. Soc. Agron. Soil fertility; crop production. Address: U.S. Agency for International Development, Box 85, FOP NY 09544.

FERGUSON, CHARLES WESLEY, b. Los Angeles, Calif, July 27, 22; m. 60. DENDROCHRONOLOGY. B.S, Mont. State Univ, 48; M.S, Univ. Ariz, 50, Ph.D.(range mgt), 60. Res. asst, LAB. TREE-RING RES, UNIV. ARIZ, 50-54, res. assoc, 61-63, asst. prof. DENDROCHRONOLOGY, 63-70, ASSOC. PROF, 70- AAAS; Tree Ring Soc.(secy-treas, 58-); Am. Soc. Range Mgt; Ecol. Soc. Am. Growth ring studies in big sagebrush and other nonconifers; development of a 8,200 year tree-ring chronology of bristlecone pine. Address: Lab. of Tree-Ring Research, University of Arizona, Tucson, AZ 85721.

FERGUSON, CLARENCE MEADD, b. Parkhill, Ont, June 21, 99; nat; m. 27; c. 2. POULTRY SCIENCE. B.S.A, Ont. Agr. Col, 21; Mich. State Col; Ohio State, 39. Instr. poultry husb, Ont. Agr. Col, 21; exten. poultryman, Mich. State Col, 22-23, asst. prof, 23-28; agr. technician, Ministry of Arg, Colombia, 28; exten. poultryman, Ohio State, 29-48, dir. agr. exten. serv, 49-52; administr. Fed. Exten. Serv, U.S. Dept. Agr, 53-60, asst. secy. agr, 60-61; prof. admin, Nat. Agr. Exten. Ctr. Advan. Study, Univ. Wis, 61-64; Dept. Adult Educ, N.C. STATE UNIV, 64-69, VIS. EMER. PROF. ADULT EDUC, 69- R.C.A.F, 18. Agriculture; home economics. Address: 740 Smallwood Dr, Raleigh, NC 27605.

FERGUSON, COLIN C, b. Winnipeg, Man, Oct. 3, 21; m. 49; c. 4. SURGERY. M.D, Manitoba, 45; dipl, McGill, 52; F.R.C.S, Royal Col. Surg, Can, 53. Demonstr. path, Manitoba, 44-45; Harrison fel. surg, Pennsylvania, 48-49; res. fel. pediat. surg, Boston Children's Hosp, 51-52; teaching fel. SURG, Harvard, 52-53; head dept, UNIV. MAN, 53-69, PROF, 53; SURGEON-IN-CHIEF, CHILDREN'S HOSP, 54- Consult. surgeon, Winnipeg Gen. Hosp, Man, 53-; guest lectr, Univ. Edinburgh, 56; mem. coun, Royal Col. Physicians & Surgeons Can, 62-70, chmn. comt. gen. surg, 68-; mem, Can. Coun. Hosp. Accreditation, 70-; consult, Shriners Crippled Children's Hosp, Winnipeg, Man. Can. Army, 42-45; R.C.N, 45-46, Surg. Lt. Comdr.(Ret). Am. Col. Surg; Am. Surg. Asn. Cardiac and pediatric surgery. Address: Dept. of Surgery, Children's Hospital, Winnipeg 3, Man, Can.

FERGUSON, DALE VERNON, b. Tulsa, Okla. Nov. 24, 43; m. 63; c. 2. MICROBIOLOGY. B.S, Okla. State Univ, 66, U.S. Pub. Health Serv. trainee & M.S, 67, Nat. Defense Educ. Act fel. & Ph.D.(microbiol), 70. Res. scientist virol, Armour-Baldwin Labs, 67-68; ASST. PROF. MICROBIOL, UNIV. ARK, LITTLE ROCK, 70- Am. Soc. Microbiol. Bacterial cell structure; antimicrobial action of antibiotics and chemotherapeutic agents; enzyme synthesis and control mechanisms. Address: Dept. of Biology, University of Arkansas at Little Rock, Little Rock, AR 72204.

FERGUSON, DAVID B, b. Conrad, Mont, May 19, 26; m. 50; c. 2. PLANT BREEDING. B.S, Mont. State Univ, 50; Ph.D.(plant genetics), Univ. Minn, 62. Asst. agron, Mont. State Univ, 54-57; plant genetics, Univ. Minn, 57-62; supt. PLANT BREEDING, Plains Br. Sta, N.Mex. State Univ, 62-66; RES. MGR, Lubbock, Tex. Br, NORTHRUP, KING & CO, 66-70, WOODLAND, CALIF. BR, 70- U.S.A.A.F, 44-46. AAAS; Am. Soc. Agron; Crop Sci. Soc. Am; Am. Genetic Asn. Corn breeding; wheat, sorghum and sudan breeding and administration. Address: Northrup, King & Co, Box 1406, Woodland, CA 95695.

FERGUSON, DAVID JOHN, b. Sandwich, Ill, May 24, 39; m. 60; c. 2. MATHEMATICS. B.S, Univ. Idaho, 64, Ph.D.(math), 71. ASST. PROF. MATH, BOISE STATE COL, 70- Am. Math. Soc; Math. Asn. Am. Structure of nonassociative nilalgebras. Address: 1224 Michigan, Boise, ID 83706.

FERGUSON, DENZEL E(DWARD), b. La Grande, Ore, Aug. 28, 29; m. 48; c. 2. BIOLOGY. B.S, Oregon State, 51, M.S, 52, fel, 54-56, Ph.D.(zool), 57. Asst. zool, Oregon State, 51-52; Kansas, 52-53; instr. biol, East. Ore. Col, 53-54; asst. prof. zool. & entom, Miss. State, 56-59, assoc. prof, 60-63, prof. zool, 64-69; PROF. BIOL. & COORD. ENVIRON. SCI, PORTLAND STATE UNIV, 69- AAAS; Am. Soc. Ichthyol. & Herpet; Am. Fisheries Soc; Am. Inst. Biol. Sci; Animal Behav. Soc. Anuran orientation; pesticide resistance in vertebrates; ecology. Address: Dept. of Biology, Portland State University, P.O. Box 751, Portland, OR 97207.

FERGUSON, DON ERNEST, b. Roswell, N.Mex, Oct, 12, 23; m. 44; c. 4. CHEMICAL ENGINEERING, PHYSICAL CHEMISTRY. B.S, Tennessee Tech, 44; M.A, Tennessee, 51. Chief chem. develop. sect, chem. tech. div, OAK RIDGE NAT. LAB, 55-63, asst. dir. CHEM. TECH. DIV, 63-64, DIR, 64- Mem. transplutonium prog. cmt, Atomic Energy Cmn, 64- U.S.N, 44-58, Lt. Comdr. Am. Nuclear Soc. Research and development in the fuel cycle for nuclear reactors and the production of transuranium elements. Address: Chemical Technology Division, Oak Ridge National Lab, Oak Ridge, TN 37830.

FERGUSON, DONALD J(OHN), b. Minneapolis, Minn, Nov. 19, 16; m. 43; c. 3. SURGERY. B.S, Yale, 39; M.D, Minnesota, 43, M.S. & Ph.D.(surg), 51. From asst. prof. to PROF. SURG, Univ. Minn, 52-60; UNIV. CHICAGO, 60- Med.C, 43-46, Capt. Am. col. Surg; Am. Surg. Asn; Soc. Univ. Surg. Surgical research. Address: 5629 S. Blackstone, Chicago, IL 60637.

FERGUSON, DONALD LEON, b. Logan, Utah, Nov. 23, 30; m. 61; c. 2. PARASITOLOGY, VETERINARY PARASITOLOGY. B.S, Utah State Univ, 56, M.S, 60; Ph.D.(parasitol), Univ. Nebr, Lincoln, 66. Parasitologist, Jensen-Salsbury Res. Labs, Mo, 60-62; ASSOC. PROF. VET. SCI. & PARASITOLOGIST, UNIV. NEBR, LINCOLN, 62- Consult, Am. Cyanamid Co, 71- U.S.A, 56-57, 1st Lt. Immunologic properties of parasites, in vitro cultivation of nematodes, x-irradiation of parasites and development and field evaluation of anthelmintic drugs and coccidiostats. Address: Dept. of Veterinary Science, University of Nebraska, Lincoln, NE 68503.

FERGUSON, DOUGLAS CAMPBELL, b. Halifax, N.S, Feb. 17, 26; U.S. citizen; m. 53; c. 2. INSECT TAXONOMY. B.Sc, Dalhousie, 50; M.S, Cornell, 56, Ph.D.(insect taxon), 67. Curatorial asst. entom, N.S. Mus. Can, 50-56, curator, 56-61, chief curator natural hist. & curator entom, 61-63; entomologist & curatorial assoc, Peabody Mus. Natural Hist, Yale, 63-67, lectr. biol. & res. staff biologist, univ, 67-69; RES. ENTOMOLOGIST, SYST. ENTOM. LAB, U.S. DEPT. AGR, 69- Ecol. Soc. Am; Soc. Syst. Zool; Entom. Soc. Can; Lepidop. Soc. Taxonomy of the superfamilies Pyraloidea, Geometroidea and Noctuoidea, especially of North America. Address: Systematic Entomology Lab, U.S. Dept. of Agriculture, c/o U.S. National Museum, Washington, DC 20560.

FERGUSON, EARL J, b. Dallas, Tex, June 30, 25; m. 46; c. 3. INDUSTRIAL ENGINEERING. B.S, Texas A&M, 49; M.S, Okla. State, 59, Ph.D.(indust. eng), 64. Time study engr, Montgomery Ward & Co, 49-51; mfg. engr, Gen. Dynamics Corp, 51-56; assoc. prof. indust. eng, OKLA. STATE UNIV, 56-69, PROF. INDUST. ENG. & MGT, 69- Summers, consult, Cities Serv. Oil Co, 58, Tinker Air Force Base & Charles Mach. Works, 59, Guy James, Inc, 61, Gulf Oil Corp, 62 & 63. U.S.N, Ens. Am. Inst. Indust. Eng; Nat. Soc. Prof. Eng. Management and management science; safety engineering; statistical quality control; industrial safety engineering. Address: School of Industrial Engineering & Management, Oklahoma State University, Stillwater, OK 74075.

FERGUSON, EDWARD C, III, b. Beaumont, Tex, Mar. 11, 26. OPHTHALMOLOGY. B.S, Northwestern, 46, B.M, 49, M.D, 50. Asst. prof. OPHTHAL, col. med, Iowa, 56-57; assoc. prof, UNIV. TEX. MED. BR. GALVESTON, 64-69, PROF, 69-, CHMN. DEPT, 64- Heed fel. ophthal, 57. Fel, Howe Lab. Ophthal, Mass. Eye & Ear Infirmary, 56-57. Dipl, Am. Bd. Ophthal, 57. U.S.N, 44-45; Med.C, U.S.A.F, 51-53, Capt. Am. Med. Asn; Asn. Res. Vision & Ophthal; Am. Acad. Ophthal. & Otolaryngol; Am. Col. Surg. Address: Dept. of Ophthalmology, University of Texas Medical Branch, Galveston, TX 77550.

FERGUSON, ELDON E(ARL), b. Rawlins, Wyo, Apr. 23, 26; m. 46; c. 2. PHYSICS. B.S, Oklahoma, 49, M.S, 50, Ph.D.(physics), 53. Physicist, Phillips Petrol. Co, 54-55; Naval Res. Lab, 55-57; asst. prof. physics, Texas, 57-60, assoc. prof, 60-62; CHIEF ATMOSPHERIC COLLISION PROCESSES SECT, AERONOMY LAB, NAT. OCEANIC & ATMOSPHERIC ADMIN. ENVIRON. RES. LABS, 63- Guggenheim fel, Max Planck Inst. Physics & Astrophys, 60-61; adjoint prof, Univ. Colo, Boulder, 66- Am. Phys. Soc; Am. Geophys. Union. Atomic physics; gaseous electronics; aeronomy; atomic and molecular spectroscopy. Address: Atmospheric Collision Processes Section, Aeronomy Lab, National Oceanic & Atmospheric Administration Environmental Research Labs, Boulder, CO 80302.

FERGUSON, FRANK C(URRIER), JR, b. New York, N.Y, Jan. 25, 20; m. 44; c. 5. PHARMACOLOGY. B.S, Bucknell, 40; M.D, Cornell, 43. Intern med, New Haven Hosp, 44; asst. res, Maine Gen. Hosp, 44-45; res. physician, Flower-Fifth Ave. Hosp, 45-46; res. fel, PHARMACOL, med. col, Cornell, 48-50, instr, 50-53, asst. prof, 53; PROF, ALBANY MED. COL, 53- Med.C, 46-48, Capt. Soc. Exp. Biol. & Med; Am. Soc. Pharmacol. & Exp. Therapeut. Folic acid antagonism; adrenergic blockade; pharmacology of colchicine. Address: Albany Medical College, 47 New Scotland Ave, Albany, NY 12208.

FERGUSON, FREDERICK F(ERDINAND), b. Knoxville, Tenn, July 7, 08; m. 40; c. 3. PARASITOLOGY. A.B, Tennessee, 32, M.S, 34; Ph.D.(biol), Virginia, 38. Du Pont scholar. biol, Virginia, 39; instr, Col. of William & Mary, 39-44; asst. prof. zool, Washington (Seattle), 46-49; chief, Puerto Rico Field Station, Communicable Disease Ctr, U.S. Pub. Health Serv, 49-66, trop. disease sect, 66-68, San Juan Labs, Ctr. Disease Control, 68-71. Hon. instr, Univ. Puerto Rico Sch. Med. Isaac Gonzalez Martinez Award, 62. U.S.P.H.S, Capt. Am. Micros. Soc; Am. Soc. Trop. Med. & Hyg. Taxonomy of Turbellaria; biology and control of schistosomiasis. Address: 1503 Condominium El Ferrol, Hato Rey, PR 00918.

FERGUSON, FREDERICK P(ALMER), b. Middletown, Conn, March 19, 16; m. 41; c. 5. PHYSIOLOGY. B.A, Wesleyan, 38, M.A, 39; C.P. Sigerfoos fel, Minnesota, 41, 42, Ph.D.(zool), 43. Asst. biol, Wesleyan, 38-39; zool, Minnesota, 39-43; instr. physiol, sch. med, La. State, 43-45; res. assoc, biochem. lab, Rutgers, 45-46, asst. prof, 46-47; biol, Wesleyan, 47-49; physiol, sch. med, Maryland, 49-51, assoc. prof, 51-55, prof, 55-60; CHIEF res. fel. sect, div. gen. med. sci, NAT. INSTS. HEALTH, 60-63, RES. FELS. BR, NAT. INST. GEN. MED. SCI, 63- Mem. corp, Marine Biol. Lab, Woods Hole, 49-; Mt. Desert Island Biol. Lab, 53- With U.S. Army; U.S. Navy, 43-45. Sustained high qual. performance award, U.S. Dept. Health, Educ. & Welfare, 70. Fel. AAAS; Am. Soc. Zool; Am. Physiol. Soc; Soc. Exp. Biol. & Med; fel. N.Y. Acad. Sci. Physiology of melanophores; electrocardiography; renal physiology; protein metabolism; hypoxia. Address: Research Fellowships Branch, National Institute of General Medical Sciences, National Institutes of Health, Bethesda, MD 20014.

FERGUSON, GARY GENE, b. East St. Louis, Ill, Jan. 2, 40; m. 63; c. 1. PHARMACOLOGY. B.S, Univ. Houston, 63; M.S, Baylor Univ, 65; Dunning Mem. fel, Univ. Colo, Boulder, 67-68, Ph.D.(pharmacol), 69. Instr. PHARMACOL, Univ. N.Mex, 65-69; ASST. PROF, NORTHEAST LA. UNIV, 69- Consult. pharmacol, Savage Labs, Inc, Tex, 70- U.S.A.R, 57-59. Cardiovascular pharmacology; psychopharmacology; drug screening. Address: Dept. of Pharmacology, Northeast Louisiana University College of Pharmacy, Monroe, LA 71201.

FERGUSON, GARY W(RIGHT), b. Cheyenne, Wyo, Apr. 15, 41; m. 63; c. 1. ANIMAL BEHAVIOR, HERPETOLOGY. B.S, Tulane Univ, 63; M.S, Tex. Tech. Univ, 65; Nat. Insts. Health fel, Univ. Mich, 66-69; Ph.D.(zool), 69. ASST. PROF. BIOL, KANS. STATE UNIV, 69- Lectr, Univ. Mich. & Univ. of the Pacific, 69; Soc. Sigma Xi res. grant, 69; res. grant, Kans. Agr. Exp. Sta, 70. AAAS; Am. Inst. Biol. Sci; Am. Soc. Ichthyol. & Herpet; Ecol. Soc. Am; Am. Soc. Syst. Zool. Reptilian social behavior and ecology; evolution of display differences; population regulation and behavior; early experience and fitness; hormonal control of reproductive colors; aggression. Address: Division of Biology, Kansas State University, Manhattan, KS 66502.

FERGUSON, GEORGE ALONZO, JR, b. Washington, D.C, May 25, 23; m. 45; c. 2. SOLID STATE PHYSICS. B.S, Howard, 47, M.S, 48; Atomic Energy Cmn. fels, Pennsylvania, 49-50; Ph.D.(physics), Catholic Univ, 65. Prof. physics, Clark Col, 50-53; RES. PHYSICIST, U.S. NAVAL RES. LAB, 54- Asst. prof. nuclear eng, Howard, 62-64, assoc. prof, 64-67, prof, 67- U.S.A, 42-46, 1st Sgt. AAAS; Am. Phys. Soc; Am. Inst. Physics Teachers; Sci. Res. Soc. Am. Nuclear physics and engineering. Address: U.S. Naval Research Lab, Code 6030, Washington, DC 20390.

FERGUSON, GEORGE E(RNEST), b. Stillwater, Minn, April 2, 06; m. 29; c. 1. HYDRAULIC ENGINEERING. B.C.E, Minnesota, 28. Hydraul. engr, U.S. GEOL. SURV, Texas, 28-31, Hawaii, 31-37, Wash, D.C, 37-40, dist. engr, Fla, 40-46, staff officer, water resources div, 46-48, chief prog. control br, 48-55, REGIONAL HYDROLOGIST, ATLANTIC COAST, 55- Am. Soc. Civil Eng; Am. Water Works Asn; Am. Geophys. Union. Hydrologic investigations. Address: U.S. Geological Survey, Room 317, Washington Bldg, Arlington Towers, Arlington, VA 22209.

FERGUSON, GEORGE R(AY), b. Bolivar, La, Jan. 8, 15; m. 56; c. 5. ENTOMOLOGY. B.S, Oregon State Col, 36, M.S, 39; California, 36-37; Ph.D. (entomol), Ohio State, 41. Asst, Oregon State Col, 37-39, asst. entomologist, 41-43; res. assoc, Crop Protection Inst, 43-45; chief entomologist, Geigy Chem. Corp, 45-47, tech. dir, 48-53, pres. agr. chem. div, 53-69, exec. v.pres, corp, 69-70, V.PRES, CIBA-GEIGY CORP, 70- Fel. AAAS; Entom. Soc. Am; Weed Sci. Soc. Am; Am. Chem. Soc. Insecticides; agriculture pest control. Address: Ciba-Geigy Corp, Saw Mill River Rd, Ardsley, NY 10502.

FERGUSON, HARRY, b. Dayton, Ohio, May 1, 14; m. 41. MATHEMATICS, MECHANICS. B.S, Boston, 39; A.M, Harvard, 49; Ph.D.(math), Pittsburgh, 58. Instr. math, Northeastern, 39-43, 47-48; Bowdoin Col, 43-44; Tufts, 44-47; Ohio, 48-50; mathematician, Wright-Patterson AFB, Ohio, 50-56, aeronaut. res. engr. fluid mech, 56-59; ASSOC. PROF. MATH, UNIV. CINCINNATI, 59- Mem, appl. math. br, Wright Air Develop. Ctr, 50-59. Am. Math. Soc; Math. Asn. Am; Am. Soc. Eng. Educ. Boundary value problems; turbulence; complex variables; Laplace transform; rigid body mechanics. Address: 3224 Fairway Dr, Dayton, OH 45409.

FERGUSON, H(ARRY) I(AN) S(YMONS), b. High Wycombe, Eng, June 25, 20; Can. citizen; m. 46; c. 3. PHYSICS. B.Sc, Western Ontario, 51, Nat. Res. Coun. Can. stud, 52-54, M.Sc, 53, Ph.D.(physics), 58. Res. assoc. physics, Western Ontario, 55-57; physicist, Ont. Cancer Treatment & Res. Found, London Clin, Victoria Hosp, 57-59; lectr. PHYSICS, UNIV. WEST. ONT, 59-60, asst. prof, 60-63, assoc. prof, 63-68, PROF, 68- R.A.F, 41-46. Can. Asn. Physicists. Molecular spectroscopy; optics and spectroscopy, particularly applied to laboratory astrophysics and molecular excitation. Address: Dept. of Physics, University of Western Ontario, London, Ont, Can.

FERGUSON, HELAMAN ROLFE PRATT, b. Salt Lake City, Utah, Aug. 11, 40; m. 63; c. 4. MATHEMATICS. A.B, Hamilton Col, 62; Univ. Wis, Madison, 62-63; M.S, Brigham Young Univ, 66; Nat. Sci. Found. fel, Bowdoin Col, 68; Nat. Sci. Found. fel, Univ. Montreal, 70; M.S. & Ph.D.(math), Univ. Wash, 71. Technician, control lab, Garlock Packing Corp, 58; mem. staff math, Hamilton Col, 60-61; writer, teaching mach, Hamilton Res. Assocs, 62; programmer & systs. analyst, data processing ctr, Church of Jesus Christ of Latter-day Saints, 63-64; asst. MATH, Brigham Young Univ, 65-66; asst. & instr, Univ. Wash, 66-71; ASST. PROF, BRIGHAM YOUNG UNIV, 71- Consult, urban data ctr, Univ. Wash, 70-71; Brigham Young Univ. Res. Div. grant, 71-72. Am. Math. Soc; Math. Asn. Am. Harmonic analysis; group representations; Lie groups and algebras; number theory; mathematical geography; mathematics of biological systems—the eye. Address: Dept. of Mathematics, 314 MSCB, Brigham Young University, Provo, UT 84601.

FERGUSON, HENRY (BRADFORD), b. Peggs, Okla, Mar. 25, 18; m. 42; c. 3. ELECTRICAL ENGINEERING. B.S, Okla. State, 42, M.S, 48, Ph.D.(elec. eng), 56. Test engr, Gen. Elec. Co, N.Y, 42-43, appln. engr, Minn, 43-44; instr. elec. eng, Okla. State, 46-47; Iowa State, 47-48; res. engr, Jersey Prod. Res. Co, 48-54, head, geophys. res. sect, 54-61; mgr, geophys. dept, Sperry Rand Res. Ctr, 61-62; DIR. EXPLOR. SCI. SECT, ATLANTIC REF. CO, 62- Tech. radar off, spec. devices div, Off. Res. & Invention, U.S.N, 44-46, Res, 46-54. Soc. Explor. Geophys; Inst. Elec. & Electronics Eng; Soc. Petrol. Eng. Information theory; network synthesis; elastic wave propagation; structure and characteristics of the earth's crust; meteorology; atmospheric electricity; electromagnetic wave propagation. Address: Atlantic Richfield Co, P.O. Box 2819-PRC R102, Dallas, TX 75221.

FERGUSON, HERMAN WHITE, b. Chapel Hill, Tenn, Dec. 28, 16; m. 43; c. 2. ECONOMIC GEOLOGY. B.A, Vanderbilt, 39, M.S, 40. Geol. aide to asst. geologist, div. geol, Tenn. Dept. Conserv, 40-46, asst. state geologist, 46-51, state geologist, 51-52; geologist, Tenn. Coal & Iron Div, U.S. STEEL CORP, 52-57, sr. geologist, Mich. Limestone Div, 57-64, mgr. geol. invests. stone & coal, 64-65, SR. GEOL. INT. DEPT, 65- U.S.N.R, 45-46. Inst. Mining Eng; Geol. Soc. Am; Soc. Econ. Geol. Structural and economic geology. Address: Room 2757, U.S. Steel Bldg, 600 Grant St, Pittsburgh, PA 15250.

FERGUSON, HUGH C(ARSON), b. Detroit, Mich, July 13, 21; m. 55; c. 2. PHARMACOLOGY. B.S, Wayne, 48; M.S, Purdue, 50, Ph.D, 52. Asst. prof. PHARMACOL, New Mexico, 52-58; assoc. prof, col. pharm, Ohio Northern, 58-61; head, pharmacol. lab, Distillation Prod. Indust. Div, Eastman Kodak Co, 61-66; group leader, RES. CTR, MEAD JOHNSON & CO, 66-69, sect. leader, 69-70, PRIN. INVESTR, 70- U.S.A, 42-44. Am. Pharmaceut. Asn; Am. Soc. Pharmacol. & Exp. Therapeut. Pharmacological investigation of plant products; cause of hypertension with relation to kidney function; new methods to evaluate drug action. Address: Dept. of Pharmacology, Research Center, Mead Johnson & Co, 2404 Pennsylvania, Evansville, IN 47712.

FERGUSON, J(AMES) HOMER, b. San Antonio, Tex, July 26, 36; m. 59; c. 1. PHYSIOLOGY, VERTEBRATE ZOOLOGY. B.S, Sul Ross State Col, 58; Ph.D.(zool), Arizona, 64. Asst. ZOOL, Arizona, 61-64; asst. prof, UNIV. IDAHO, 64-70, ASSOC. PROF, 70- Vis. asst. prof, Univ. Iowa, 69; Nat. Insts. Health spec. fel, 69. AAAS; Am. Soc. Ichthyol. & Herpet; Soc. Study Evolution; Am. Soc. Zool. Evolution; physiology of temperature adaptations in cold-blooded vertebrates; aquatic biology; mammalian and environmental physiology. Address: Dept. of Biological Science, University of Idaho, Moscow, ID 83843.

FERGUSON, JAMES J(OSEPH), JR, b. Glen Cove, N.Y, Feb. 1, 26; m. 52; c. 4. BIOCHEMISTRY, MEDICINE. B.A, Rochester, 46, M.D, 50. Intern, Mass. Gen. Hosp, 50-51, asst. res, 51-52, res, 55; res. fel. biochem, West. Reserve Univ, 56-58; assoc. BIOCHEM. & MED, UNIV. PA, 59-63, asst. prof, 63-66, assoc. prof, 66-71, PROF. & CHMN. DEPT, 71- Markle fel, 60-64. U.S.N.R, 52-55, Flight Surgeon. Am. Soc. Biol. Chem; Endocrine Soc. Metabolic regulation; enzyme engineering. Address: Dept. of Biochemistry, School of Medicine, University of Pennsylvania, Philadelphia, PA 19104.

FERGUSON, J(AMES) K(ENNETH) W(ALLACE), b. Tamsui, Formosa, Japan, Mar. 19, 07; m. 33; c. 4. PHARMACOLOGY. B.A, Toronto, 28, fel, 28-29, M.A, 29, M.D, 32. Nat. Res. Council fel, 33-34; instr. physiol, sch. med, Western Ontario, 34-35, asst. prof, 35-36; Ohio State, 36-38; pharmacol, Toronto, 38-41, prof. & head dept, 45-55; DIR, CONNAUGHT MED. RES. LABS, 55- R.C.A.F, M.C, 41-45. Am. Soc. Pharmacol. & Exp. Therapeut; Am. Physiol. Soc; Can. Physiol. Soc; fel. Royal Soc. Can. Anoxia and oxygen equipment; antithyroid drugs; carbon dioxide in tissues; uterine motility; anti-alcoholic drugs. Address: Connaught Medical Research Labs, Willowdale, Ont, Can.

FERGUSON, JAMES M(ALCOLM), b. Chicago, Ill, June 6, 31. NUCLEAR PHYSICS. B.S, Antioch Col, 53; Ph.D, Mass. Inst. Tech, 57. PHYSICIST, U.S. Naval Radiol. Defense Lab, 57-69; LAWRENCE RADIATION LAB, 69- Am. Phys. Soc. Gamma and beta-ray spectroscopy; neutron reactions; cross section measurements; nuclear level structure; nuclear fission. Address: Lawrence Radiation Lab, L-24, P.O. Box 808, Livermore, CA 94550.

FERGUSON, JAMES W(ILLIAMS), b. Camden, Ohio, Apr. 9, 08; m. 31, 63; c. 3. CHEMISTRY. A.B, Miami (Ohio), 29; A.M, Oberlin Col, 31; fel, Michigan, 31-34, Ph.D.(chem), 34. Asst, Oberlin Col, 29-31; chemist, res. & develop. dept, Nat. Aniline & Chem. Co, 34-36; instr. org. chem, Oregon State Col, 36-39, asst. prof, 39-42; chemist, Eli Lilly & Co, 42-48; assoc. prof. CHEM, Butler, 48-58; PROF, PORTLAND STATE UNIV, 58- Am. Chem. Soc.(secy-treas, 41); Sci. Res. Soc. Am. Organic molecular rearrangements; synthetic production of papaverine; distillation of malonic esters; preparation of alkyl cyanides. Address: Dept. of Chemistry, Portland State University, Portland, OR 97207.

FERGUSON, JOHN CARRUTHERS, b. Tuscaloosa, Ala, Mar. 2, 37; m. 61; c. 3. INVERTEBRATE ZOOLOGY, PHYSIOLOGY. B.A, Duke Univ, 58; M.A, Cornell Univ, 61, Nat. Sci. Found. fel, 62, Ph.D.(invert. zool), 63. Asst. prof. BIOL, FLA. PRESBY. COL, 63-66, ASSOC. PROF, 67- Nat. Sci. Found. grants, 64-; vis. investr, Marine Biol. Lab, Woods Hole, 66; proj. leader, Marine Biol. Prog, Jamaica, 68 & 69; vis. investr, Friday Harbor Labs, Wash, 70. U.S.N.R, 55-63. AAAS; Am. Soc. Zool; Am. Micros. Soc; Int. Oceanog. Found. Physiology and ecology of starfish nutrition. Address: Dept. of Biology, Florida Presbyterian College, St. Petersburg, FL 33733.

FERGUSON, JOHN H(OWARD), b. Edinburgh, Scotland, March 1, 02; nat; m. 27, 55; c. 6. PHYSIOLOGY. B.A, Cape Town, 21, Dr.Sc, 57; Rhodes scholar, Oxford, 23-26, B.A, 25, M.A, 31; M.D, Harvard, 28. Lectr. pharmacol, Cape Town, 23, asst. prof. bact, 28-31; asst. path, Harvard, 26-28; instr. physiol, sch. med, Yale, 31-34; asst. prof. physiol. & pharmacol, sch. med, Alabama, 34-35, assoc. prof, 35-37; asst. prof. pharmacol, Michigan, 37-43; acting head dept, MED. SCH, UNIV. N.C, CHAPEL HILL, 43-44, prof. PHYSIOL, 43-70, head dept, 43-67, EMER. PROF, 70- Res. grant, U.S. Pub. Health Serv. AAAS; fel. Am. Col. Physicians; Am. Physiol. Soc; Soc. Exp. Biol. & Med; Int. Soc. Hemat. Blood coagulation and related fields. Address: Dept. of Physiology, University of North Carolina School of Medicine, Chapel Hill, NC 27515.

FERGUSON, JOSEPH LUTHER, JR, b. Utica, Miss, May 22, 41. PLASMA PHYSICS. B.S, Miss. State, 63; Nat. Defense Ed. Act fel. & Ph.D.(plasma physics), Vanderbilt, 69. ASST. PROF. PHYSICS, MISS. STATE UNIV, 68- Res. physicist, Naval Res. Lab, Wash, D.C, summer 69. Am. Phys. Soc. Electromagnetic shock tube studies and laser-produced plasma studies. Address: Dept. of Physics, Mississippi State University, State College, MS 39762.

FERGUSON, LAING, b. Dunfermline, Scotland, Apr. 25, 35; m. 60; c. 3. GEOLOGY, PALEONTOLOGY. B.Sc, Univ. Edinburgh, 57, Ph.D.(paleont), 60. Nat. Res. Coun. Can. fel, Univ. Alta, 60-62; asst. prof. GEOL, MT. ALLISON UNIV, 62-68, ASSOC. PROF, 68- Fel, Univ. Edinburgh, 69-70. Paleont. Soc; Soc. Econ. Paleont. & Mineral; Asn. Petrol. Geol; fel. Geol. Soc. London; Brit. Paleont. Asn; Marine Biol. Asn. U.K; fel. Geol. Soc. Am. Upper Paleozoic paleoecology, especially brachiopods; effects of environmental factors on criteria used in brachiopod taxonomy; Permian faunas from the high Arctic; distortion of fossils by compaction; trace fossils; carboniferous ostracods. Address: Dept. of Geology, Mt. Allison University, Sackville, N.B, Can.

FERGUSON, LE BARON O, b. Oak Bluffs, Mass, Apr. 20, 39; m. 60; c. 3. MATHEMATICS. S.B, Mass. Inst. Tech, 61; M.A, Washington (Seattle), 63, Ph.D.(math), 65. Assoc. res. engr, Boeing Airplane Co, 61-62; asst. prof. MATH, UNIV. CALIF, RIVERSIDE, 65-70, ASSOC. PROF, 70- Vis. assoc. prof, Rensselaer Polytech. Inst, 70-71; Univ. Nancy, 71-72; Air Force Off. Sci. Res. grant, 71- Am. Math. Soc; Math. Asn. Am. Approximation theory. Address: Dept. of Mathematics, University of California, Riverside, CA 92502.

FERGUSON, LLOYD C, b. Lebanon, Ind, Sept. 10, 12; m. 35; c. 1. MICROBIOLOGY. D.V.M, Ohio State, 34; M.S, Wisconsin, 36, Ph.D.(immunogenetics), 40. Asst. vet. sci, Wisconsin, 34-36, instr. vet. sci. & genetics, 36-41; asst. prof. bact, Ohio State, 46-49, assoc. prof, 49-53; prof. vet. sci, agr. exp. sta, Ohio, 53-56; prof. microbiol. & pub. health, head dept. & dir. div. biol. sci, Mich. State, 56-59, dean col. sci. & arts, 59-63, prof. microbiol, 63-68; CHMN. DEPT. VET. SCI, OHIO AGR. RES. & DEVELOP. CTR, 68- Consult, off. state exp. sta, U.S. Dept. Agr, 58-62; mem. agr. bd, Nat. Acad. Sci-Nat. Res. Coun, 59-63; Am. Cancer Soc. scholar, 62-63; sci. adv, Univ. Nigeria, 65-67. U.S.A, 41-46, Maj. AAAS; Am. Soc. Microbiol; Am. Asn. Immunol; Am. Vet. Med. Asn. Immunology; autoimmunity. Address: Dept. of Veterinary Science, Ohio Agricultural Research & Development Center, Wooster, OH 44691.

FERGUSON, LLOYD N(OEL), b. Oakland, Calif, Feb. 9, 18; m. 44; c. 3. CHEMISTRY. B.S, California, 40, Ph.D.(chem), 43; hon. D.Sc, Howard Univ, 70. Asst. CHEM, Nat. Defense Res. Comt. Proj, California, 41-44; asst. prof, Agr. & Tech. Col, N.C, 44-45; Howard Univ, 45-48, assoc. prof, 48-55, prof, 55-65, head dept, 58-65; PROF, CALIF. STATE COL, LOS ANGELES, 65-, chmn. dept, 68-71. Guggenheim fel, Carlsberg Lab, Copenhagen, 53-54; vis. prof, Univ. Ore, summers 58, 60, 63; Nat. Sci. Found. faculty fel, Swiss Fed. Inst. Technol, 61-62; vis. prof, Univ. Nairobi, 71-72; consult, Col. Chem. Consult. Serv; vis. scientist, div. chem. educ, Am. Chem. Soc. Fel. AAAS; Am. Chem. Soc; fel. The Chem. Soc; fel. Am. Inst. Chem. Taste and molecular properties; electronic interactions between nonbonded groups; homoconjugation; chemistry of alicycles. Address: Dept. of Chemistry, California State College, Los Angeles, 5151 State College Dr, Los Angeles, CA 90032.

FERGUSON, M(ALCOLM) S(TUART), b. St. Thomas, Ont, Can, Apr. 1, 08; nat; m. 38. BIOLOGY. B.A, Western Ontario, 32, M.A, 34; fel, Illinois, 34-35, Ph.D.(invert. zool, parasitol), 37; Columbia, 42. Demonstr. zool, Western Ontario, 32-34; asst, Illinois, 34-36; res. investr, inst. parasitol, Macdonald Col, McGill, 38; Royal Soc. Can. fel, Rockefeller Inst, 38-39, fel, 39-40, asst, 40-43, 46-47; scientist dir, Communicable Disease Center, U.S. Pub. Health Serv, 47-61; chief, med. arts & photog. br, Nat. Insts. Health, 61-67; MULTI-MEDIA SPECIALIST, NAT. LIBR. MED, 67- Sanit.C, 43-46, Maj. Fel. AAAS; Am. Soc. Parasitol; Am. Soc. Trop. Med. & Hyg; fel. Royal Soc. Trop. Med. & Hyg. Life cycles of trematodes; sterile culture of helminths; migration and localization of parasites within the host; application of the motion picture camera as a tool in study of living organisms; production of technical motion pictures on medical and public health subjects; communication of scientific information through visual and verbal media. Address: National Library of Medicine, 8600 Rockville Pike, Bethesda, MD 20014.

FERGUSON, MARION LEE, b. Washington, Iowa, Nov. 27, 23; m. 46; c. 2. PHYSIOLOGY. B.A, Iowa, 49; Atomic Energy Comn. fel, Chicago, 49-50; M.S, Iowa State, 55, Ph.D.(physiol), 59; Nat. Insts. Health fel, Mass. Inst. Tech, 58. Instr. zool, Iowa State, 53-55, 57-60; head physiol. lab, life sci. res. dept, Goodyear Aerospace Corp, 60-65; assoc. prof. BIOL, KENT STATE UNIV, 65-69, PROF, 69-, DIR, CONSERV. LAB, 67- Vis. lectr, Univ. Colo, 61; dir. joint flight res. prog, U.S. Air Force-Goodyear Aerospace Corp, 62-63; partic, NASA Workshop Circadian Rhythms, D.C, 63, res. investr, NASA Biosatellite Prog, Ames. Res. Ctr, 63-65. U.S.A.F, 43-45. AAAS; Am. Inst. Biol. Sci; Am. Soc. Zool; N.Y. Acad. Sci. General and protozoan physiology; environmental biology. Address: Dept. of Biological Sciences, Kent State University, Kent, OH 44242.

FERGUSON, MARY HOBSON, b. Canton, Miss, Apr. 3, 27; m. 46, 69; c. 1. PHARMACY. B.S, Univ. Miss, 61, Ph.D.(pharm), 64. Sr. scientist, Alcon Labs, 64-67; LIT. SCIENTIST, SCI. DIV. & ASSOC. ED. J. PHARMACEUT. SCI, AM. PHARMACEUT. ASN, 67-, asst. ed, 67. Am. Pharmaceut. Asn; Am. Asn. Med. Writers Asn. Pharmaceutical product development; scientific technical writing and editing; scientific information computerized systems. Address: 522 S. Spring St, Falls Church, VA 22042.

FERGUSON, MAX B, b. Cedar, Iowa, Mar. 26, 16; m. 42; c. 3. ZOOLOGY, HUMAN PHYSIOLOGY. B.A, State Col. Iowa, 39; M.A, Iowa, 47; Ph.D.(zool), 50; Iowa State, 50. Teacher, pub. schs, Iowa, 35-37, 39-41; asst. ZOOL, Iowa, 47-49; instr, Iowa State, 49-50; asst. prof, EAST. ILL. UNIV, 50-52, assoc. prof, 52-62, PROF, 62- U.S.A.A.F, 42-46. Human taste; study of blood pressure and ear canal temperature changes in trackmen to develop theory for second wind. Address: Dept. of Zoology, Eastern Illinois University, Charleston, IL 61920.

FERGUSON, NOEL M(OORE), b. East St. Louis, Ill, Dec. 20, 07; m. 33; c. 2. PHARMACOGNOSY, BOTANY. Ph.G, St. Louis Col. Pharmacy, 30, Ph.C, 32, B.S, 33; A. B, Washington (St. Louis), 34, M.S, 35, Ph.D.(chem), 42. Asst. chem, St. Louis Col. Pharmacy, 30-32; instr. bot. & pharmacog, 32-33, asst. prof, 33-41, prof, 41-43; sr. res. chemist, Drs. Hess & Clark, Inc, 43-49; asst. prof. chem, Ashland Col, 43-49; DEAN COL. OF PHARM, UNIV. HOUSTON, 49- Consult. pharmaceut. chemist; spec. consult in connection with agency int. develop. prog, Fed. Univs, Brazil, 69-; adv, pharmaceut. drugs & res. in natural drugs, Brazil. Am. Chem. Soc; Am. Pharmaceut. Asn. Plant physiology; laxative drugs; anthelmintics; coccidiostatics; vitamine assay methods; study of natural drugs, quinine, and volatile oils of Indonesia. Address: Office of the Dean, College of Pharmacy, University of Houston, 3801 Cullen Blvd, Houston, TX 77004.

FERGUSON, PHILIP R(EX), b. Bloomington, Ind, July 27, 25; m. 48; c. 5. ORGANIC CHEMISTRY. B.A, Indiana, 47, M.A, 48; Ph.D.(org. chem), North Carolina, 57. Asst. prof. CHEM, West. Carolina Col, 57-60, assoc. prof, 60-61; asst. prof, FLA. PRESBY. COL, 61-67, ASSOC. PROF, 67- Mem. 10th Int. Cancer Cong. U.S.N.R, 43-46, Lt. Am. Chem. Soc; fel. Am. Inst. Chem. General organic syntheses in preparation of medicinals; synthesis and reactions of N-nitrosoamides and diazonium salts; structure and reactions of aromatic nitrogen heterocycles. Address: Division of Mathematics & Natural Sciences, Florida Presbyterian College, St. Petersburg, FL 33733.

FERGUSON, RAYMOND C(RAIG), b. Ft. Morgan, Colo, May 28, 22; m. 55; c. 2. PHYSICAL CHEMISTRY. B.S, Iowa State, 48, M.S, 50; Ph.D.(phys. chem), Harvard, 53. Jr. chemist, Ames Lab, Atomic Energy Comn, 48-50; teaching fel, Harvard, 50-53; chemist, E.I. DU PONT DE NEMOURS & CO, INC, 53-68, SUPVR, CENT. RES. DEPT, 68- AAAS; Am. Chem. Soc; Am. Phys. Soc; Soc. Appl. Spectros. Nuclear magnetic resonance infrared and microwave spectroscopy; polymer structure analysis; computer analysis of spectra. Address: Central Research Dept, E.I. du Pont de Nemours & Co, Inc, Wilmington, DE 19898.

FERGUSON, R(OBERT) B(URY), b. Galt, Ont, Feb. 5, 20; m. 48; c. 3. MINERALOGY. B.A, Toronto, 42, M.A, 43, Ph.D.(mineral), 48. Asst, Royal Ont. Mus. Mineral, 42-43; meteorologist, Can. Dept. Transport, 43-45; demonstr. geol. sci, Toronto, 45-47; asst. prof. MINERAL, UNIV. MAN, 47-50, assoc. prof, 51-59, PROF, 59- Nat. Res. Coun. Can. fel, crystallog. lab, Cambridge, 50-51. R.C.A.F, 45. Am. Crystallog. Asn; fel. Mineral. Soc. Am; Mineral. Asn. Can; fel. Royal Soc. Can. Crystallography of minerals. Address: Dept. of Earth Sciences, University of Manitoba, Winnipeg 19, Man, Can.

FERGUSON, ROBERT E(ARL), b. Seelyville, Ind, July 28, 23; m. 50; c. 5. PHYSICAL CHEMISTRY. B.A, Iowa, 48, Ph.D.(phys. chem), 52. Asst. isotopic compounds, Iowa, 49-50, rare earth oxides, 50-52; phys. chemist, NAT. BUR. STANDARDS, 52-61, chief elem. processes sect, 61-65, chief phys. chem. div, 65-68, ASST. TO DIR. PROG. PLANNING, 68- Am. Polit. Sci. Asn. fel. 64-65. U.S.A.A.F, 43-46. AAAS; Am. Chem. Soc; Combustion Inst. Solid gas equilibria; kinetics of hydrocarbon oxidation and carbon formation in flames; radical reactions at high temperatures; elementary ionization processes in gases. Address: 6307 Tone Dr, Washington, DC 20034.

FERGUSON, ROBERT GILMOUR, b. Anyox, B.C, Nov. 7, 22; m. 45; c. 4. ZOOLOGY, LIMNOLOGY. B.A, British Columbia, 49; Ph.D.(zool), Toronto, 59. Res. scientist fisheries, Ont. Dept. Lands & Forests, 53-68; assoc. prof. BIOL, Univ. Windsor, 68-69; ASST. PROF, WAYNE STATE UNIV, 69- Field sta. dir, Univ. Toronto, summers 69 & 70. Can. Army, 42-45, Lt. Am. Inst. Fishery Res. Biol; Am. Soc. Limnol. & Oceanog; Int. Asn. Gt. Lakes Res. Ecology; laboratory temperature and oxygen effects; river fauna and pollution; explosion effects on fish; life history of yellow perch and smelt; sonar surveys of fish; diel fish distribution; lake temperatures and fish distributions. Address: Dept. of Biology, Wayne State University, Detroit, MI 48202.

FERGUSON, ROBERT L(YNN), b. Mayfield, Ky, Apr. 1, 32; m. 54; c. 2. NUCLEAR CHEMISTRY. B.A, Murray State Col, 54; Du Pont fel, Washington (St. Louis), 56, Ph.D.(chem), 59. Chemist, OAK RIDGE NAT. LAB, 59-66, RES. STAFF MEM, 66- Summers, chemist, Mallinckrodt Chem. Works, 54-55; Savannah River Lab, E.I. du Pont de Nemours & Co, Inc, 56. AAAS; Am. Phys. Soc. Fission; nuclear properties and reactions; application of nuclear techniques to analytical chemistry. Address: P.O. Box X, Oak Ridge National Laboratory, Oak Ridge, TN 37830.

FERGUSON, ROGER K, b. Oklahoma City, Okla, May 21, 37; m. 63; c. 2. CLINICAL PHARMACOLOGY, PHARMACOLOGY. B.S, Univ. Nev, Reno, 61; Nat. Insts. Health fel, Univ. Utah, 63-64, M.D, 66; M.S, Univ. Iowa, 70. Fel. internal med, Univ. Iowa, 68-70, instr, 69-70; ASST. PROF. MED. & PHARMACOL, MICH. STATE UNIV, 70- AAAS; Am. Heart Asn; Am. Soc. Clin. Pharmacol. & Therapeut; Am. Fedn. Clin. Res. Analgesic drugs; antihypertensive drugs. Address: Dept. of Medicine, Michigan State University, East Lansing, MI 48823.

FERGUSON, SAMUEL A, b. Phila, Pa, Feb. 4, 32; m. 52; c. 3. PHARMACOLOGY, PHYSIOLOGY. B.A, Oakwood Col, 52; Ph.D.(gen. physiol), Pennsylvania, 61. Pharmacologist, Smith Kline & French Labs, 58-61; chief, pharmacol. br, Resources Res, Inc, 61-62; pharmacologist, Panoramic Res, Inc, 62; Stanford Res. Inst, 62-69; CHMN. DIV. LIFE SCI, COL. SAN MATEO, 69-; ASST. PROF. PHARMACOL, COL. DENT, UNIV. OF THE PAC, 69- Lectr, Univ. San Francisco, 62. Med.C, U.S.A, 53-55. Analgetics; psychopharmacology, depressants, anti-depressants, tranquilizers; cerebrospinal fluid electrolytes and behavior; narcotic addiction. Address: Division of Life Sciences, College of San Mateo, San Mateo, CA 94402.

FERGUSON, THOMAS, b. Union, S.C, June 30, 21. ZOOLOGY. B.A, Fisk, 43; M.S, Iowa, 48, Ph.D.(zool), 55. Instr-prof. BIOL, J.C. Smith Univ, 48-62; PROF, DEL. STATE COL, 62- U.S.A, 44-46. Am. Soc. Zool; Nat. Inst. Sci. Neuroembryology. Address: Dept. of Biology, Delaware State College, Dover, DE 19901.

FERGUSON, THOMAS M(ORGAN), b. Burnet, Tex, Nov. 8, 15; m. 38; c. 4. HISTOLOGY, NUTRITION. B.A, Southwestern (Texas), 36; Texas, 37; M.S, Texas A&M, 46, Ph.D.(zool. & biochem), 54. Teacher, high schs, Tex, 36-42; civilian instr. aircraft instruments, Army Air Force Tech. Training Command, 42-43; asst. prof. biol, TEX. A&M UNIV, 46-55, U.S. Pub. Health Serv. res. fel, 53-55, assoc. prof. POULTRY SCI, 55-65, PROF, 65- U.S.N.R, 43-46, Lt. AAAS; Fedn. Am. Socs. Exp. Biol; Am. Inst. Nutrit; Soc. Exp. Biol. & Med; Poultry Sci. Asn. Gross and microscopic abnormalities of vitamin B_{12}-deficient chick embryos and vitamin E deficient turkey embryos; avian physiology. Address: Dept. of Poultry Science, Texas A&M University, College Station, TX 77843.

FERGUSON, THOMAS S, b. Oakland, Calif, Dec. 14, 29; m. 58; c. 2. MATHEMATICAL STATISTICS. Ph.D.(statist), California, 56. PROF. MATH, UNIV. CALIF, LOS ANGELES, 56- Determination of distributions; decision theory. Address: Dept. of Mathematics, University of California, Los Angeles, CA 90024.

FERGUSON, WILFRED SAMUEL, b. Moosomin, Sask, July 3, 26; m. 53; c. 4. SOILS. B.S.A, Saskatchewan, 50, M.Sc, 52; Ph.D.(soils), Manitoba, 61. Res. off, RES. BR, CAN. DEPT. AGR, 52-70, RES. MGR, 70- Can. Soc. Soil Sci; Int. Soc. Soil Sci. Soil chemistry and fertility; phosphorus nutrition of plants as related to soil and climatic variables; agronomic practices on saline soils; effects of cultural practices on nitrogen in soil. Address: Central Experimental Farm, K.W. Neatby Bldg, Ottawa, Ont, Can. K1A 0C6.

FERGUSON, W(ILLIAM) A(LLEN), b. Roanoke, Mo, Mar. 6, 17; m. 42; c. 4. MATHEMATICS. B.A, Mo. Valley Col, 37; M.A, Illinois, 38, Ph.D.(math), 46. Asst. instr. MATH, UNIV. ILL, URBANA, 38-41, 45-46, instr, 46-48, asst. prof, 48-55, ASSOC. PROF, 55-, EXEC. SECY. DEPT, 68- U.S.A, 41-45, Lt. Col. Math. Asn. Am. Finite groups; algebra; classification of finite metabelian groups with six generators. Address: Dept. of Mathematics, 274 Altgeld Hall, University of Illinois, Urbana, IL 61801.

FERGUSON, WILLIAM E, b. Oakland, Calif, July 11, 21; m. 47; c. 2. ENTOMOLOGY. B.S, California, Berkeley, 46, M.S, 56, Ph.D.(entom), 61. Teacher, high sch, Calif, 47-48, teacher & counsr, 48-56; sr. lab. technician entom, California, Berkeley, 56-60, Nat. Insts. Health fel, 60-62; asst. prof. ENTOM, SAN JOSE STATE COL, 62-65, assoc. prof, 65-70, PROF, 70- Nat. Sci. Found. res. grant, 64-66; dir, Ctr. Res. & Adv. Studies, San Jose State Col, 66-68. Med.C, U.S.A, 43-45. Entom. Soc. Am; Soc. Syst. Zool. Systematic entomology; biology and systematics of the hymenopterous family Mutillidae; insect parasite-predator-pathogen complexes; insect postembryonic development, especially differentiation of environmental from genetic influences; insect photography. Address: Dept. of Biological Science, San Jose State College, San Jose, CA 95114.

FERGUSON, WILLIAM S(IDNEY), b. Chatfield, Minn, Nov. 15, 27; m. 48; c. 2. ANALYTICAL CHEMISTRY. B.S, Oregon State, 49, M.S, 53; Ph.D.(chem), Illinois, 56. Chemist, Gen. Elec. Co, 49-53; res. chemist, Ohio Oil Co, Colo, 56-59, adv. res. chemist, Marathon Oil Co, 59-65, sr. res. chemist, 65-70; DIR. ANAL. CHEM. FACILITY, COLO. STATE UNIV, 70- U.S.N.R, 45-46. AAAS; Am. Chem. Soc. Organic geochemistry; microanalytical and electroanalytical techniques; chromatography; fused salt electrochemistry. Address: Dept. of Chemistry, Colorado State University, Ft. Collins, CO 80521.

FERGUSSON, GORDON JOHN, b. Whangarei, N.Z, Aug. 2, 22; m. 47; c. 3. PHYSICS, GEOPHYSICS. B.Sc, Auckland, 41; M.Sc, Victoria, N.Z, 45, D.Sc, 64. Physicist, radio develop. lab, N.Z, 41-45; Chalk River Labs, Can, 45-46; sci. off, Atomic Energy Res. Estab, Eng, 46-48; physicist, Dom. Phys. Lab, N.Z, 49-53; sr. physicist, Inst. Nuclear Sci, N.Z, 54-59; sci. secy. nuclear radiation, UN, 59-60; assoc. prof. geophys, California, Los Angeles, 60-64; SR. PHYSICIST, Johnston Labs, Inc, 64-67, consult, 61-64; SCI. RES. INSTRUMENTS CORP, 67- Mechaelis Mem. award, 54; E.R. Cooper Mem. award, 59. AAAS; Am. Geophys. Union; fel. Royal Soc. N.Z. Carbon-14 and radioactive dating; nuclear instrumentation atmospheric radioactivity; low level radioactivity measurements. Address: 233 Ridgeley Rd, Lutherville, MD 21093.

FERGUSSON, WILLIAM B(LAKE), b. Boston, Mass, Apr. 24, 24; m. 48; c. 6. GEOLOGY. B.A, Boston, 51, M.A, 53; Ph.D.(geol), Arizona, 65. Geologist, Atomic Energy Cmn, 53-54; Silver Pick Mining Co, 54-56; instr. geol. Arizona, 56-59; geologist, Pa. R.R. Co, 59-67; asst. prof. CIVIL ENG, VILLANOVA UNIV, 67-69, ASSOC. PROF, 69- U.S.A, 42-45, Sgt. AAAS; fel. Geol. Soc. Am; Asn. Eng. Geol; Am. Inst. Mining, Metall. & Petrol. Eng. Physical stratigraphy; geology of non-metallic mineral deposits; engineering geology. Address: Dept. of Civil Engineering, Villanova University, Villanova, PA 19085.

FERIN, JURAJ, b. Topoľčany, Czech, Sept. 17, 25; m. 51; c. 2. RADIATION BIOLOGY & BIOPHYSICS. M.D, Slovak Univ, Bratislava, 50; Ph.D.(indust. med), Charles Univ, Prague, 55. Physician, Med. Sch. Bratislava, 50-51; fel. occup. med, Med. Sch. Prague, 51-54; res. scientist, Inst. Indust. Hyg. & Occup. Med, Bratislava, 54-59; sr. scientist, inst. exp. hyg, Slovak Acad. Sci, Bratislava, 59-68; PROF. RADIATION BIOL. & BIOPHYS, SCH. MED. & DENT, UNIV. ROCHESTER, 68- Dep. dir. inst. exp. med, Slovak Acad. Med, 61-65; assoc. prof, med. sch, Slovak Univ, Bratislava, 65-68; U.S. Pub. Health Serv. res. grant, 69-72. AAAS. Pathogenesis of pneumoconiosis; clearance of particles from the lung; environmental aspects of particle clearance from the lung; air pollutants and the response of the respiratory system, particularly clearance of particles; occupational and environmental health. Address: Dept. of Radiation Biology & Biophysics, University of Rochester School of Medicine & Dentistry, Rochester, NY 14620.

FERINGA, EARL R(OBERT), b. Grand Rapids, Mich, May 30, 32. NEUROLOGY. B.S, Calvin Col, 53; M.D, Northwestern, 57. Intern, Phila. Gen. Hosp, Pa, 57-58; clin. pharmacologist cancer chemotherapy, nat. serv. ctr, Nat. Insts. Health, 58, neuroanatomist, lab. neuroanat. sci, 59-62; col. physicians & surgeons, Columbia, 59; res. & assoc. neurol, Colo. Med. Ctr, 62-64; instr. NEUROL, med. ctr, UNIV. MICH, ANN ARBOR, 64-69, ASSOC. PROF, 69-; CHIEF NEUROL. SERV, ANN ARBOR VET. ADMIN. HOSP, 64- Consult, Wayne County Gen. Hosp, 66- U.S.P.H.S, 58-62, Res, 62-, Surg. Fel. Am. Acad. Neurol; Am. Med. Asn; Am. Col. Physicians; Soc. Clin. Neurol; Asn. Res. Nerv. & Ment. Disease; Soc. Neurosci. Neurology and neuroanatomy; regeneration of central nervous system, particularly the spinal cord. Address: Neurology Service (180), Ann Arbor Veterans Administration Hospital, Ann Arbor, MI 48105.

FERINGTON, THOMAS E(DWIN), b. Lockport, N.Y, Oct. 19, 26; m. 49; c. 2. PHYSICAL CHEMISTRY. B.A, Buffalo, 49; M.S, Calif. Inst. Tech, 52; Procter & Gamble fel, Princeton, 55-57, Ph.D.(chem), 57. Res. chemist, Chemstrand Corp, 51-54; instr. chem, Col. Wooster, 57-59, asst. prof, 59-61; res. chemist, W.R. GRACE & CO, 61-65, res. supvr, 65-69, RES. MGR, 69- U.S.N.R, 45-46. Am. Chem. Soc. Physical chemistry of high polymers; dilute solution properties; kinetics; chemistry of organic sulfur compounds; rheology; chemistry of metallorganic compounds. Address: Research Division, W. R. Grace & Co, Clarksville, MD 21029.

FERLING, JOHN A(LBRECHT), b. Koenigsberg, Ger, Sept. 16, 28; nat; m. 55; c. 2. MATHEMATICS. B.S, Upsala Col, 52; Ph.D.(math), Southern California, 59. Asst. MATH, Southern California, 52-55, lectr, 55-57; asst. prof, CLAREMONT MEN'S COL, 57-60, assoc. prof, 60-66, PROF, 66- Asst, Off. Naval Res, 55-57. Am. Math. Soc; Math. Asn. Am. Non-linear integral equations. Address: Dept. of Mathematics, Claremont Men's College, Claremont, CA 91712.

FERM, JOHN C(HARLES), b. East Liverpool, Ohio, March 21, 25; m. 49; c. 3. GEOLOGY. B.S, Pa. State, 46, M.S, 48, Gulf Oil Co. fel, 50-51, Ph.D.(mineral), 57. Instr. mineral, Pa. State, 51-52; geologist, U.S. Geol. Surv, 52-57; asst. prof. geol, La. State Univ, 57-64, assoc. prof, 64-67, prof, 67-69; PROF. & DIR. GEOL. GRAD. STUDIES, UNIV. S.C, 69- Lectr, Am. Geol. Inst. AAAS; Geol. Soc. Am; Soc. Econ. Paleont. & Mineral. Fluvial deltaic sedimentation; Carboniferous stratigraphy. Address: Dept. of Geology, University of South Carolina, Columbia, SC 29208.

FERM, RICHARD L, b. Kansas City, Mo, June 18, 24; m. 53; c. 3. CHEMICAL ENGINEERING. B.S, Kansas, 44, M.S, 45, Ph.D.(chem), 48. Instr. chem. eng, New Mexico, 48-51, asst. prof, 51-55; res. engr, Calif. Res. Corp, 55-61, sr. res. chemist, CHEVRON RES. CO, 61-69, SR. RES. ASSOC, 69- Am. Chem. Soc. Petroleum products; emulsions and surface chemistry; surfactants; adhesion; ecological uses of asphalt. Address: 3282 Theresa Lane, Lafayette, CA 94549.

FERM, ROBERT J(AMES), b. Kansas City, Mo, Dec. 22, 25. ORGANIC CHEMISTRY, CHEMICAL ENGINEERING. B.S, Univ. Kans, 46, M.S, 47; Ph.D.(chem), Univ. N.Mex, 50. SR. STAFF CHEMIST, AM. OIL CO, 50- Am. Chem. Soc; Sci. Res. Soc. Am; Inst. Chem. Eng. Petroleum chemistry; heterocyclic nitrogen compounds. Address: 1301 Maywood, Independence, MO 64502.

FERM, VERGIL H(ARKNESS), b. West Haven, Conn, Sept. 13, 24; m. 48; c. 4. BIOLOGY, EMBRYOLOGY. B.A, Col. Wooster, 46; M.D, Western Reserve, 48; M.S, Wisconsin, 50, Ph.D, 55. Intern, St. Luke's Hosp, Cleveland, Ohio, 48-49; asst. zool, Wisconsin, 49-51, 54-55; asst. prof. anat, Indiana, 55-57; assoc. prof, Florida, 57-61, U.S. Pub. Health Serv. sr. res. fel, 58-63; assoc. prof. path, DARTMOUTH MED. SCH, 61-66, PROF. & CHMN. DEPT. ANAT-CYTOL, 66- U.S.N.R, 43-45; Med.C, U.S.A, 52-53. Am. Asn. Anat; Am. Soc. Zool; Am. Soc. Human Genetics; Am. Soc. Exp. Path. Placental physiology; teratology; experimental embryology. Address: Dept. of Anatomy-Cytology, Dartmouth Medical School, Hanover, NH 03755.

FERMI, GIULIO, b. Rome, Italy, Feb. 16, 36; U.S. citizen; m. 60; c. 2. MOLECULAR BIOLOGY, SYSTEMS ANALYSIS. Oberlin Col, 52-55; M.A, Princeton, 57; Ph.D.(biophys), Univ. Calif, Berkeley, 62. Nat. Sci. Found. fel, Max Planck Inst. Biol, 61-62, Nat. Inst. Neurol. Diseases & Blindness fel, 62-63; staff mem, Inst. Defense Anal, 64-69; dir. systs. eval. group, Ctr. Naval Anal, 69; consult. systs. anal, Inst. Defense Anal, 70-71; TECH. OFF, LAB. MOLECULAR BIOL, MED. RES. COUN, 71- Mutation and replication mechanisms in bacteriophages; optomotor reaction of musca domestica; system evaluation techniques for military communications and antisubmarine warfare. Address: Medical Research Council Lab. of Molecular Biology, Hills Rd, Cambridge, England.

FERNALD, ARTHUR T(HOMAS), b. Nottingham, N.H, Dec. 13, 17; m. 55; c. 1. GEOLOGY. B.S, New Hampshire, 41; Mass. Inst. Tech, 41-42; fel, Harvard, 48-50, A.M, 51, Ph.D.(geomorphol), 56. Instr. geol, Colby Col, 46-47; GEOLOGIST, U.S. GEOL. SURV, 51- Vis. lectr, Michigan, 64. U.S.N.R, 42-46, Lt. AAAS; Geol. Soc. Am; Am. Meteorol. Soc; Am. Geophys. Union; Arctic Inst. N.Am; Glaciol. Soc. Geologic, geomorphic, and engineering studies in Alaska, Greenland, and Nevada. Address: U.S. Geological Survey, Denver, CO 80225.

FERNALD, HERBERT BYRON, b. Larchland, Ill, May 11, 12; m. 42; c. 3. CHEMISTRY. B.S, Monmouth Col, 35; Avery fel, Nebraska, 38-39, B.S, & Ph.D.(chem), 40. Res. chemist, E.I. du Pont de Nemours & Co, 39-43, plant chem. technologist, 43-47; res. chemist, Gen. Aniline & Film Corp, 47-52; GULF RES. & DEVELOP. CO, 52-68, RES. ASSOC 68- With Office Sci. Res.,

& Develop, 44. Am. Chem. Soc. Development of new compounds from old line heavy chemicals; acetylene and derivatives of acetylene; variation in the surface tension of solutions; petrochemicals; Ziegler chemistry; low molecular weight polymers; alpha olefins. Address: Gulf Research & Development Co, Drawer 2038, Pittsburgh, PA 15230.

FERNALD, ROBERT L(ESLIE), b. Larchland, Ill, Aug. 27, 14. EMBRYOLOGY. A.B, Monmouth Col, 37; fel. Univ. Calif, 37-41, Ph.D.(zool), 41. Instr. ZOOL, Coe Col, 41-42; UNIV. WASH, 46-47, asst. prof, 47-59, assoc. prof, 59-68, PROF, 68-, DIR. FRIDAY HARBOR LABS, 60-, acting dir, 58-60. U.S.N, 42-46. AAAS; Am. Soc. Zool. Experimental and comparative embryology of marine invertebrates. Address: Dept. of Zoology, Friday Harbor Labs, University of Washington, Seattle, WA 98195.

FERNANDES, JOHN HENRY, b. Tiverton, R.I, Aug. 21, 24; m. 47; c. 6. MECHANICAL ENGINEERING. B.S, R.I. State Col, 49; M.S, Lehigh, 53; Sc.D, Calvin Coolidge Col, 60. Serv. engr, Combustion Eng, Inc, 49-50; instr. mech. eng, Lafayette Col, 50-52, asst. prof, 52-55, assoc. prof, 55-60; prof. & head dept, Manhattan Col, 60-63; sr. proj. engr, new prod. div, COMBUSTION ENG, INC, 63-68, admin. asst. to v.pres, 68-70, COORD. POLLUTION CONTROL SYSTS, INDUST. GROUP, 70- Consult, McGinley Mills, N.J, 54-56; dir. eve. col, Lafayette Col, 57-60. U.S.A, 42-46, Res, 46-54, 2nd Lt. Am. Soc. Mech. Eng; Nat. Soc. Prof. Eng; Am. Soc. Eng. Educ; Instrument Soc. Am. Broad areas of thermodynamics and compressible flow; particularly steam power plants and gas turbines. Address: Industrial Group, Combustion Engineering, Inc, 1000 Prospect Hill Rd, Windsor, CT 06095.

FERNANDEZ, ALBERTO A(NTONIO), b. Buenos Aires, Arg, July 12, 25; m. 49; c. 1. BIOCHEMISTRY, CLINICAL CHEMISTRY. M.S, Buenos Aires, 54, Ph.D.(chem), 60. Chemist prod. control, Behring Inst, Arg, 52-55, chief control, 55-58; chief chem. res, Quimica Estrella, 58-61; res. chemist, Bio-Sci. Labs, 61-63, chief chem. res, 63-66; head res. & develop, Pfizer Int. Subsidiaries, Arg; DIR. RES, BIOCHEM. PROCEDURES, INC, NORTH HOLLYWOOD, 67- Am. Asn. Clin. Chem. Chemical methods of clinical analysis; industrial organic synthesis; basic biochemical research. Address: 6322 Ellenview Ave, Canoga Park, CA 91304.

FERNANDEZ, BERNAL, b. San Jose, Costa Rica, Jan. 27, 27; m. 46; c. 2. MICROBIAL PHYSIOLOGY. B.A, Texas, 51, Hite fel, 52-55, M.A, 53, Ph.D.(bact), 55. Asst. prof. immunol, UNIV. COSTA RICA, 55-56, res. scientist microbiol, 56-60, ASSOC. PROF. GEN. MICROBIOL, 60-, PROF. MED. MICROBIOL, 61-, chmn. dept. microbiol, 58-70, adv. for planning & construct. microbiol. bldg, 57-58. Am. Soc. Microbiol; Costa Rican Asn. Microbiol. Bacterial viruses; ciliate nutrition; sanitary bacteriology. Address: Dept. of Microbiology, University of Costa Rica, San Jose, Costa Rica.

FERNANDEZ, FERNANDO LAWRENCE, b. New York, N.Y, Dec. 31, 38; m. 63; c. 2. FLUID & APPLIED MECHANICS. B.S, Stevens Inst. Tech, 60, Dept. Health, Ed. & Welfare fel. & M.S, 61; Aerospace Corp. fel. & Ph.D. (aeronaut), Calif. Inst. Tech, 69. Thermodynamicist, Lockheed Missile & Space Co, 61-63; mem. tech. staff fluid mech, AEROSPACE CORP, 63-65, HEAD FLUID MECH. DEPT, 68- Am. Inst. Aeronaut. & Astronaut. Continuum mechanics with emphasis on high speed reacting viscous phenomena; application of singular perturbation techniques to fluid mechanic problems. Address: 350 Arrowview Dr, Redlands, CA 92373.

FERNANDEZ, JACK E(UGENE), b. Tampa, Fla, May 18, 30; m. 51; c. 3. ORGANIC CHEMISTRY. B.S.Ch, Florida, 51, M.S, 52, U.S. Army Office of Ord. Res. fel, 52-54, Ph.D.(chem), 54. Chemist, naval stores sta, U.S. Dept. Agr, 54; instr. & res. assoc, Duke Univ, 56-57; chemist, Tenn. Eastman Co, 57-60; asst. prof. CHEM, UNIV. S. FLA, 60-64, ASSOC. PROF, 64- U.S.A, 54-56. Am. Chem. Soc. Kinetics and mechanisms; infrared spectroscopy; polymers; history of chemistry; chemistry for the non-scientist. Address: Dept. of Chemistry, University of South Florida, Tampa, FL 33620.

FERNANDEZ, LeVERNE P(HELAN), b. Charlotte, N.C, July 9, 30; m. 54; c. 3. PHYSICAL CHEMISTRY. B.S, Col. of Charleston, 53; Clemson Col; Ph.D.(chem), Virginia, 58. Instr. chem, Clemson Col, 53-54; asst, Virginia, 54-58; RES. CHEMIST, Savannah River Lab, E.I. DU PONT DE NEMOURS & CO, INC, 58-66, SAVANNAH RIVER PLANT, 66- Vis. asst. res. prof, Med. Col. Ga, 64-65. Am. Chem. Soc. Entropy of ions in solution; complex ions; solution chemistry of the actinide elements; criticality safety of transportation, storage and reprocessing of nuclear fuels. Address: 922 Fairwood Ave, North Augusta, SC 29841.

FERNANDEZ, REMIGIO, b. Cuba, Aug. 23, 41; U.S. citizen; m. 63; c. 2. CHEMICAL ENGINEERING. B.Sc, Calif. Inst. Technol, 63; Ph.D.(chem. eng, math), Syracuse Univ, 68. CHEM. ENGR, RES. LABS, HALCON INT. INC, 67- Chemical reaction kinetics; homogeneous and heterogeneous gas phase reactions; heterogeneous liquid phase; heat and mass transfer in moving boundary systems; applied mathematics. Address: Halcon International Inc, 33 Industrial Ave, Little Ferry, NJ 07643.

FERNANDEZ-MORAN, HUMBERTO, b. Maracaibo, Venezuela, Feb. 18, 24; m. 53; c. 2. BIOPHYSICS. M.D, Munich, 44; Caracas, Venezuela, 45; fel, George Washington, 45-46; Nobel Inst. Physics, 47-49; Karolinska Inst, Sweden, 48-51; Ph.D.(biophys), Stockholm, 52. Asst, neurosurg. clin, Serafimerlasarettet, 46-48; prof. biophys, Caracas, 51, head dept, 54-58; asst. prof, Karolinska Inst, 52-54; dir, Venezuelan Inst. Neurol. & Brain Res, 54-58; res. assoc. neuropath, Harvard Med. Sch, 58-62; A.N. PRITZKER PROF. BIOPHYS, UNIV. CHICAGO, 62- Sci. & cult. attache to Legations of Venezuela in Sweden, Norway & Denmark, 47-54; vis. lectr, Mass. Inst. Technol, 58-62; assoc. biophysicist, neurosurg. serv, Mass. Gen. Hosp, 58-62; consult, 58-62; partic, Adv. Comt. Sci. Develop. in Latin Am, 58-; Minister of Educ, Venezuela, 58-; partic, U.S. Nat. Comn, UNESCO, 59- John Scott Award, 67. Am. Nuclear Soc; hon. mem. Am. Acad. Neurol; fel. Am. Acad. Arts & Sci. Biophysical research in the field of high resolution electron microscopy of molecular organization of cell constituents. Address: Dept. of Biophysics, University of Chicago, 5640 Ellis Ave, Chicago, IL 60637.

FERNANDEZ Y COSSIO, HECTOR R(AFAEL), b. Jaruco, Cuba, Feb. 18, 37. PHYSIOLOGY. B.Sc, Miami (Fla), 60, Heart Develop. Fund fel, 62-63, Cellular & Molecular Biol. Prog. fel, 63-64, Ph.D.(zool), 65; fel, Marine Biol. Lab, Woods Hole, summer 61. Teaching asst. zool, Miami (Fla), 60-65; Nat. Insts. Health fel, 65-67; staff res. biologist, Yale, 67-69; ASST. PROF. BIOL, UNIV. SOUTH CALIF, 69-, DIR, ARCTIC RES. PROJ, 71-, mem, Marine Lab. Faculty. Mem, Marine Biol. Lab, Woods Hole Oceanog. Inst, summers 65-67; investr, Naval Arctic Res. Lab, Pt. Barrow, Alaska & Fletcher's Ice Island. AAAS. Visual physiology, extraction and identification of crustacean visual pigments; electrophysiological studies of arthropod photoreceptors; plant physiology, study of electrical properties of plant cell membranes; physiology and ecology of marine arctic organisms. Address: Dept. of Biological Sciences, University of Southern California, Los Angeles, CA 90007.

FERNANDO, CONSTANTINE H(ERBERT), b. Colombo, Ceylon, Apr. 4, 29; m. 57; c. 3. FRESHWATER BIOLOGY, PARASITOLOGY. B.Sc, Ceylon, 52, scholar, 52-53; D.Phil.(entom), Oxford, 56. Asst. lectr. zool, Ceylon, 56-59; lectr, Singapore, 60-64; sr. res. officer, Dept. Fisheries, Ceylon, 64-65; assoc. prof. BIOL, UNIV. WATERLOO, 65-67, PROF, 67- Consult, Filariasis Res. Unit, WHO, Rangoon, Burma, 63. Royal Entom. Soc. London; Int. Soc. Limnol; Brit. Freshwater Biol. Asn; Brit. Ecol. Soc; Brit. Inst. Biol. Colonization of small freshwater habitats; helminth parasites of vertebrates; taxonomy and ecology of Potamonidae and aquatic Coleoptera and Hemiptera. Address: Dept. of Biology, University of Waterloo, Waterloo, Ont, Can.

FERNANDO, JOSEPH, b. Tuticorin, India, Mar. 22, 33; m. 66; c. 2. BIOCHEMISTRY, ORGANIC CHEMISTRY. B.Sc, Univ. Madras, 53, Hons, 55; Ph.D.(biochem), Duquesne Univ, 61. Lectr. chem, St. Philomena Col, Mysore, India, 55-56; V.O.C. Col, Tuticorin, 56-57; res. asst, Fisheries Technol. Labs, Tuticorin, 57-58; fel. biochem, Duquesne Univ, 61-62; res. assoc, West. Reserve Univ. at Metrop. Gen. Hosp, Cleveland, 62-66; fel, Albert Einstein Col. Med. at Univ. Farrara, Italy, 66-69, Albert Einstein Col. Med, N.Y, 69-70; RES. CHEMIST, CYBERTEK, INC, 70- Am. Chem. Soc. Thiols and disulfides in proteins; diagnosis of pancreatic lesions; fructose diphosphate in muscle—its role in gluconeogenesis; analytical methods for detection of steroids in biological fluids. Address: Cybertek, Inc, 200 Express St, Plainview, NY 11803.

FERNANDO, QUINTUS, b. Colombo, Ceylon, Nov. 23, 26; m. 50; c. 2. ANALYTICAL CHEMISTRY. B.S, Ceylon, 49; M.S, Louisville, 51, Ph.D. (chem), 53. Lectr. chem, Ceylon, 49, 54-57; asst. analyst, Govt. Ceylon, 53; res. assoc, Pittsburgh, 57-58, asst. prof, 58-61; assoc. prof, UNIV. ARIZ, 61-64, PROF, 64- Fel. Royal Inst. Chem. Interrelation of structure and stability of metal chelates; chromatography; polarography coulometry; kinetics of fast reactions. Address: Dept. of Chemistry, University of Arizona, Tucson, AZ 85721.

FERNBACH, DONALD J(OSEPH), b. Brooklyn, N.Y, Apr. 10, 25; m. 54; c. 4. PEDIATRICS, HEMATOLOGY. A.B, Tusculum Col, 48; M.D, George Washington, 52. Instr. zool, Tusculum Col, 47-48; Jesse Jones fel. pediat. hemat, Children's Med. Ctr, Boston, Mass, 56-57; instr. PEDIAT, BAYLOR COL. MED, 57-60, asst. prof, 60-65, assoc. prof, 65-71, PROF, 71- Summer fel. chemother, Children's Med. Ctr, 57. Consult, Wilford Hall Army Hosp, Lackland Air Force Base & Driscoll Found, Corpus Christi, Tex, 60- U.S.A, 43-46, Sgt. Am. Acad. Pediat; Am. Pediat. Soc; Am. Med. Asn; Am. Asn. Cancer Res; Am. Soc. Hemat. Cancer chemotherapy in children; possible viral etiology; clinical and epidemiological investigations of Pediatric neoplasia, especially childhood leukemia. Address: Texas Children's Hospital, 6621 Fannin St, Houston, TX 77025.

FERNBACH, SIDNEY, b. Phila, Pa, Aug. 4, 17; m. 55; c. 3. THEORETICAL PHYSICS. A.M, Temple, 40; Ph.D.(physics), California, 52. Physicist, Frankford Arsenal, 40-43; asst. instr, Pennsylvania, 43-44; asst, California, 46-48, physicist, Lawrence Radiation Lab, 48-51; mem. staff, Stanford, 51-52; head theoret. div, LAWRENCE RADIATION LAB, LIVERMORE, 58-68, HEAD, COMPUT. DEPT, 62- Mem, comput. sci. & eng. bd, Nat. Acad. Sci; adv. comt. to comput. activities, Nat. Sci. Found; mat. & comput. sci. res. adv. comt, U.S. Atomic Energy Comn. U.S.N.R, 44-46, Lt.(jg). Fel. Am. Phys. Soc; Asn. Comput. Mach; Soc. Indust. & Appl. Math; Math. Asn. Am. Neutron physics; cosmic ray shower theory; computation. Address: 4 Holiday Dr, Alamo, CA 94507.

FERNELIUS, A(LBERT) L(AWRENCE), b. Salt Lake City, Utah, Mar. 17, 21; m. 43; c. 2. MICROBIOLOGY. B.A, Utah, 48, fel, 48-50, M.A, 50; Ph.D.(vet. microbiol), Iowa State Univ, 67. Res. bacteriologist, Utah, 50-51; med. bacteriologist, Vet. Hosp, Albuquerque, 51-52; res. bacteriologist, biol. warfare labs, U.S. Chem. Corp, Ft. Detrick, 52-61; RES. MICROBIOLOGIST, NAT. ANIMAL DISEASE LAB, U.S. DEPT. AGR, 61- Chmn. N.Cent. region-37 comt. mucosal diseases cattle, U.S. Dept. Agr; mem. adv. comt, Am. type culture viruses & rickettsia; int. team small enveloped RNA viruses, WHO; orgn. prog. comparative virol, Food & Agr. Orgn. U.S.A.A.F, 42-45. AAAS; Am. Soc. Microbiol; Sci. Res. Soc. Am; Am. Inst. Biol. Sci; Conf. Res. Workers Animal Diseases; N.Y. Acad. Sci. Immunology and immunochemistry of Pasteurella tularensis; sporulation, germination, and virulence mechanisms of Bacillus anthracis; cytopathology, cytochemistry, immunofluorescence and electron microscopy of animal viruses. Address: 1310 Glendale Ave, Ames, IA 50010.

FERNELIUS, NILS C(ONARD), b. Columbus, Ohio, Nov. 10, 34. SOLID STATE PHYSICS. A.B, Harvard, 56; Oxford, 56-57; M.S, Univ. Ill, Urbana, 59, Nat. Sci. Found. fel, 59-62, Ph.D.(physics), 66; travel grant, NATO summer sch, Ghent, Belg, 61. Res. assoc, dept. physics, Univ. Ill, Urbana, 66-67; asst. physicist, mat. sci. div, Argonne Nat. Lab, 68-71; V.PRES, RES. CONSULTANTS, INC, 71- Am. Phys. Soc; Optical Soc. Am; Am. Asn. Physics Teachers. Studies of point defects using nuclear magnetic resonance and nuclear quadrupole resonance; laser applications, particularly scattering of laser light and holography; photoelectron spectroscopy. Address: Research Consultants, Inc, P.O. Box 456, Clearwater, FL 33517.

FERNELIUS, W(ILLIS) CONARD, b. Riverdale, Utah, Aug. 7, 05; m. 31; c. 2. CHEMISTRY. A.B, Stanford, 26, A.M, 27, fel, 27-28, Ph.D.(chem), 28; Munich, 30; hon. Sc.D, Franklin & Marshall Col, 59. Asst, Stanford, 26-27; instr. chem, Ohio State, 28-32, asst. prof, 32-36, assoc. prof, 36-40, prof, 40-42; Purdue, 42-47; chmn. dept, Syracuse, 47-49; prof. & head dept, Pa. State, 49-60; assoc. dir. res, Koppers Co, Inc, 60-70; DISTINGUISHED PROF, DEPT. CHEM, UNIV. S.FLA, 70- Asst. lab. dir, Manhattan Dist, 43-45, lab. dir, 45-46; Guggenheim fel, Oxford, 56-57; Fulbright fel, Cairo, 60. Asst. ed, Chem. Abstracts, 39-49. Mem. cmt. documentation & nomenclature, Nat. Res. Coun; comn. nomenclature inorg. compounds, Int. Union Pure & Appl. Chem, 63-71, chmn, 71- AAAS; Am. Chem. Soc; Mfg. Chem. Asn; fel. Am. Inst. Chem; fel. The Chem. Soc. Nitrogen systems of compounds; chemistry of liquid ammonia solutions; chemical and physical study of coordination compounds; radioactivity; less familiar elements; electron spectroscopy. Address: Dept. of Chemistry, University of South Florida, Tampa, FL 36620.

FERNIE, JOHN DONALD, b. Pretoria, S.Africa, Nov. 13, 33; Can. citizen; m. 55; c. 2. ASTRONOMY. B.Sc, Univ. Cape Town, 53, Hons, 54, M.Sc, 55; Ph.D.(astron), Ind. Univ, 58. Lectr. ASTRON, Univ. Cape Town, 58-61; asst. prof, UNIV. TORONTO, 61-64, assoc. prof, DAVID DUNLAP OBSERV, 64-67, PROF, 67- Mem. nat. comt. Can, Int. Astron. Union, 66-71. Am. Astron. Soc; fel. Royal Astron. Soc; Int. Astron. Union. History of modern astronomy; variable stars; galactic structure; photoelectric photometry. Address: David Dunlap Observatory, University of Toronto, Richmond Hill, Ont, Can.

FERNOW, LEONARD R(EYNOLDS), b. Ithaca, N.Y, Apr. 29, 30; m. 56; c. 4. GEOLOGY. A.B. & M.S, Cornell, 56, Ph.D.(paleont), 61. Instr. geol. & invert. paleont, Cornell, 60-61; geologist, Texaco, Inc, 61-64; asst. prof. GEOL, UNIV. MD, 64-68, ASSOC. PROF, 68- Am. Geol. Inst. mem, Int. Field Inst, Paris Basin, summer 65. U.S.A, 52-55, 2nd Lt. AAAS; Geol. Soc. Am; Am. Paleont. Soc; Ecol. Soc. Am; Int. Palaeont. Union. Middle Devonian paleoecology of New York; tertiary stratigraphy of the gulf coast. Address: Dept. of Agronomy, University of Maryland, College Park, MD 20740.

FERNSLER, GEORGE L(OUIS), b. St. Louis, Mo, Dec. 18, 08; m. 38; c. 3. PHYSICAL SCIENCES. B.S.E.E, Drexel Inst, 31. Res. engr, TV, Philco Corp, 31-33; sect. head, Farnsworth TV, 33-41; res. engr, Radio Corp. Am. Labs, 41-57; sr. tech. specialist, govt. & indust. res. div, Philco Corp, 57-60; MEM. STAFF, MITRE CORP, 60- Inst. Elec. & Electronics Eng. Television; FM radar; microwave test equipment; radio systems research. Address: 2 Smith Dr, Bedford, MA 01730.

FERONE, ROBERT, b. Mt. Vernon, N.Y, Nov. 8, 36; m. 60; c. 4. MICROBIOLOGY, BIOCHEMISTRY. B.A, N.Y. Univ, 58, M.S, 63. Res. microbiologist, WELLCOME RES. LABS, BURROUGHS WELLCOME & CO, 58-68, SR. RES. MICROBIOLOGIST, 68- AAAS; Am. Soc. Trop. Med. & Hyg. Chemotherapy; antifolate inhibitors; folate metabolism in malaria; antibacterial and antimalarial drugs. Address: Burroughs Wellcome & Co, Research Triangle Park, NC 27709.

FERRAND, EDWARD F(RANCIS), JR, b. N.Y.C, Aug. 26, 21; m. 45; c. 3. CHEMISTRY. B.S, St. John's (N.Y), 42; Ph.D.(phys. org. chem), Pa. State Univ, 65. Chemist, Am. Cyanamid Co, 42-44; from instr. to assoc. prof. chem, Cooper Union, 47-67; dir. bur. tech. serv, NEW YORK CITY DEPT. AIR RESOURCES, 67-71, ASST. COMNR. SCI. & TECHNOL, 71- Nat. Sci. Found. sci. faculty fel. U.S.N, 44-46. Am. Chem. Soc; Am. Soc. Eng. Educ; Air Pollution Control Asn; N.Y. Acad. Sci; Am. Soc. Test. & Mat. Sampling and analyses of the atmosphere; air monitoring instrumentation and data processing; air pollution and public health effects; pollution emissions inventory of industry, motor vehicle and residential use of fuels. Address: New York City Dept. of Air Resources, 51 Astor Pl, New York, NY 10003.

FERRANTE, FRANK L, b. Passaic, N.J, May 6, 37; m. 59; c. 2. PHYSIOLOGY. B.S, Fordham, 58; M.S, Rutgers, 64, Ph.D.(physiol, biochem), 65. Asst. prof. PHYSIOL, COL. MED. & DENT. N.J, N.J. MED. SCH, 65-71, ASSOC. PROF, 71- Environmental and cardiovascular physiology; adaptations of diving mammals to protracted apnea. Address: Dept. of Physiology, College of Medicine & Dentistry of New Jersey, New Jersey Medical School, 100 Bergen St, Newark, NJ 07103.

FERRANTE, W(ILLIAM) R(OBERT), b. Providence, R.I, March 9, 28; m. 68; c. 2. ENGINEERING MECHANICS. Sc.B, Rhode Island, 49; Sc.M, Brown, 55; Nat. Sci. Found. fel, Va. Polytech, 58-59, Ph.D.(eng. mech), 62. Instr. math, Rhode Island, 49-50; asst. prof. mech, Lafayette Col, 52-56; assoc. prof, mech. eng, UNIV. R.I, 56-68, PROF. MECH. ENG. & APPL. MECH, 68-, DEAN. GRAD. SCH, 69-, assoc. dean, 67-69. Mathematician, Boeing Airplane Co, summer 55; res. engr, Allis-Chalmers Mfg. Co, summer 56; Fulbright fel, Al-Hikma Univ. Baghdad, 63-64. U.S.A.R, 49-71, Maj, Ret. Asn. Higher Educ; Am. Soc. Mech. Eng; Am. Soc. Eng. Educ; Math. Asn. Am. Applied mechanics; elasticity; shell theory; applied mathematics. Address: Graduate School, University of Rhode Island, Kingston, RI 02881.

FERRAR, JOSEPH C, b. Lansing, Mich, Dec. 10, 39; m. 61; c. 4. MATHEMATICS. B.S, Mich. State Univ, 60; Nat. Sci. Found. fel, Yale, 61-65, Ph.D.(math), 66. ASSOC. PROF. MATH, OHIO STATE UNIV, 65- Vis. lectr, State Univ. Utrecht, 67-68; Nat. Sci. Found. res. grant, 67- U.S.A.R, 57-65. Am. Math. Soc. Classification of Lie algebras and the related algebraic structures. Address: Dept. of Mathematics, Ohio State University, Columbus, OH 43210.

FERRARA, J(OHN) M(ICHAEL), b. Chicago, Ill, May 8, 29; m. 51; c. 5. ORGANIC CHEMISTRY. B.S, Northern Illinois, 51, M.S, 53. Teacher, pub. sch, Ill, 52-53; asst. chief chemist, Kentile, Inc, 53-54; researcher, Witco Chem. Co, 54-56; chemist, NALCO CHEM. CO, 56-59, proj. leader, 59-61, group leader, 61-67, SECT. HEAD METAL INDUSTS. LAB, 67- Am. Chem. Soc. Petroleum refining, particularly processing with chemicals and additives for finished products. Address: Metal Industries Lab, Nalco Chemical Co, 9165 S. Harbor Ave, Chicago, IL 60617.

FERRARA, LOUIS W, b. Chicago, Ill, Aug. 27, 23; m. 53; c. 6. ANALYTICAL CHEMISTRY, BIOCHEMISTRY. B.S, Illinois, Chicago, 52. Sr. res. chemist, INT. MINERALS & CHEM. CORP, 52-65, supvr. anal. chem, 65-67, anal. serv. specialist, 67-68, MGR. ANAL. SERV, 68- U.S.A.A.F, 43-46, Sgt. Am. Chem. Soc; Inst. Food Technol; Soc. Appl. Spectros. Organic and inorganic chemistry; microbiology; plants and soils. Address: Growth Sciences Center, International Minerals & Chemicals Corp, P.O. Box 192, Libertyville, IL 60048.

FERRARI, ANGELO M, b. Gualeguaychú, Arg, Aug. 30, 34; m. 59; c. 3. NUCLEAR PHYSICS. Lic. fisica, Inst. Physics, Arg, 59; Rochester, 59-60; Oak Ridge Inst. Nuclear Studies, 60. From asst. lab. instr. electronics to prof. nuclear electronics, Inst. Physics, Arg, 58-64; design engr, Tennelec, Inc, 64-68, v.pres. in charge eng, 68-69, v.pres. & gen. mgr, 69-71; CONSULT, COMBUSTION ENG, INC, 71- Mem. design group, Bariloche Atomic Ctr, Arg, 59, work on electronic nuclear instrumentation, 62-63; asst. to Dr. D. Morken, atomic energy proj, Univ. Rochester, 59-60; asst. to Dr. A.P. Sanders, electronic radiation dosimetry proj, sch. med, Duke, 60; asst. to C.J. Borkowski, radiation detectors proj, Oak Ridge Nat. Lab, 60-61. Sci. Res. Soc. Am. Electronic instrumentation. Address: Combustion Engineering, Inc, Dept. 485, Prospect Hill Rd, Windsor, CT 06095.

FERRARI, HARRY M, b. Detroit, Mich, May 20, 32; m. 60; c. 1. METALLURGICAL ENGINEERING. B.S, Wayne State, 54; M.S, Michigan, 55, Ph.D.(metall. eng), 58. Asst. chief engr, aeronaut. div, Ryan Industs, 52-53; metallurgist, Pontiac Div, Gen. Motors Corp, 53-54; assoc. metallurgist, eng. res. inst, Michigan, 54-58; sr. engr. thermoelec. mat, ATOMIC POWER DIV, WESTINGHOUSE ELEC. CO, 58-60, tech. adv. nuclear mat, European Atomic Energy Comn, Brussels, Belgium, 60-61, sr. res. engr, 61-63, supvry. engr, 63-64, MGR. nuclear fuel tech, 64-69, FUEL ASSEMBLY DEVELOP, 69- Fel, Michigan, 58; lectr, Milan Polytech, 61-62. Fel. Am. Nuclear Soc; Am. Soc. Metals; Am. Inst. Mining, Metall. & Petrol. Eng. Studies on nuclear fuel materials, advanced fuel assembly designs and effects of irradiation on material properties. Address: Nuclear Fuel Division, Westinghouse Electric Corp, Box 355, Pittsburgh, PA 15230.

FERRARI, JOHN E, b. New York, N.Y, Dec. 22, 23; m. 50; c. 2. ORGANIC CHEMISTRY. B.S, Polytech. Inst. Brooklyn, 51, M.S, 64. Jr. chemist, Interchem. Corp, 50-52, chemist, 52-55, sr. chemist, 55-61, GROUP LEADER phys. chem, 61-63, org. chem, 63-69, bldg. indust. group, INMONT CORP, 69-70, COLOR SYSTS, 70- U.S.A, 42-46. AAAS; Am. Chem. Soc. Dyestuffs; pigments; organic intermediates; specialty resins; dispersions of pigments; dyes and resins; textile printing systems; organic market development. Address: Inmont Corp, 150 Wagaraw Rd, Hawthorne, NJ 07506.

FERRARI, JOHN LOUIS, b. Pavia, Italy, Dec. 29, 29; U.S. citizen. ORGANIC CHEMISTRY. B.S, City Col. New York, 52; M.S, Fordham, 57, Ph.D.(chem), 63. Instr. ORG. CHEM, Fordham, 59-60; res. fel, Ohio State, 60-61; Massachusetts, 61-64; SCIENTIST, RES. DIV, POLAROID CORP, 64- Chem.C, U.S.A, 52-54. AAAS; Am. Chem. Soc; The Chem. Soc; Soc. Photog. Sci. & Eng. Determination of aromatic structure; organic syntheses; heterocyclic chemistry; photographic chemistry. Address: Research Division, Polaroid Corp, Cambridge, MA 02139.

FERRARI, LAWRENCE A, b. Hackensack, N.J, Nov. 30, 37; m. 64; c. 1. PHYSICS. M.E, Stevens Inst. Tech, 58, M.S, 60, Ph.D.(physics), 65. Vis. res. assoc. PHYSICS, plasma physics lab, Princeton, 64-65; asst. prof, QUEENS COL.(N.Y), 65-69, PROF, 69-, CHMN. DEPT, 70- Am. Phys. Soc. Experimental plasma physics. Address: Dept. of Physics, Queens College, Flushing, NY 11367.

FERRARI, RICHARD ALAN, b. Minneapolis, Minn, June 13, 32; m. 58; c. 3. BIOCHEMISTRY. B.A, Cornell, 54, M.F.S, 55; Washington (St. Louis), 55-56; Ph.D.(biochem), Pa. State, 59. Assoc. res. biologist BIOCHEM, STERLING-WINTHROP RES. INST, 59-63, RES. BIOLOGIST, 63-, GROUP LEADER, 64- AAAS; Am. Chem. Soc. Photosynthesis of plant lipids; purification and kinetics of enzymes; central nervous system biochemistry; radiobiology; biochemical pharmacology. Address: Sterling-Winthrop Research Institute, Rensselaer, NY 12144.

FERRARO, CHARLES F(RANK), b. New York, N.Y, Sept. 14, 24; m. 59; c. 3. PHYSICAL CHEMISTRY. B.S, Polytech. Inst. Brooklyn, 44; M.A, Columbia, 46, Ph.D.(chem), 50. Instr. chem, Fordham, 49-51, asst. prof, 51-56; MGR. CENT. RES. DEPT, FMC CORP, 56- Physical, molecular and dielectric properties of polymers; polymer applications and new polymer product development. Address: 12 Millbrook Lane, Trenton, NJ 08638.

FERRARO, JOHN J, b. New York, N.Y, Apr. 20, 31; m. 54; c. 5. ORGANIC CHEMISTRY, BIOCHEMISTRY. B.S, Fordham, 52; Nat. Insts. Health fel, Polytech. Inst. Brooklyn, 57-61, Ph.D.(org. chem), 61. Res. assoc. peptide chem, med. col, Cornell, 62-63, instr. biochem, 63-64; asst. prof. biochem. & org. chem, St. John's Univ.(N.Y), 64-69; ASSOC. PROF. CHEM, L.I. UNIV, 69- U.S.A, 55-57. AAAS; Am. Chem. Soc; The Chem. Soc. Address: Dept. of Chemistry, Long Island University, Brooklyn Center, Brooklyn, NY 11201.

FERRARO, JOHN R(ALPH), b. Chicago, Ill, Jan. 27, 18; m. 47; c. 3. INORGANIC CHEMISTRY. B.S, Ill. Inst. Tech, 41, Ph.D.(chem), 54; M.S, Northwestern, 48. Supv. chemist, tetryl labs, Kankakee Arsenal, Ill, 41-43; lab. asst, Northwestern, 46-48; assoc. chemist, ARGONNE NAT. LAB, 48-68, SR. SCIENTIST, 68- U.S.A.A.F, 43-46. Am. Chem. Soc; Soc. Appl. Spectros.(pres, 65, ed, jour, 68-); Coblentz Soc. Infrared spectroscopy of inorganic complexes and coordination compounds; Raman spectra; vibrational spectroscopy at high pressures; molecular spectroscopy; nuclear magnetic resonance. Address: Chemistry Dept, Argonne National Lab, 9700 S. Cass Ave, Argonne, IL 60439.

FERRE, M(AURICE) (CAMILLE), b. Avallon, France, Apr. 25, 21; U.S. citizen; m. 45; c. 3. PHYSICS. Lic. es S, Paris Univ, 43, Agreg. Sc. Phys, 45. Engr, underwater sound, Naval Eng. Corps, French Navy, 45-48; head res. dept, well logging & geophys, Ridgefield Res. Lab, Schumberger Well Surv. Corp, 48-58, tech. adv. to v.pres, 58-63; gen. mgr, Ctr. Indust. Res. under

Contract, Villeubanne, France, 63-68; IN CHARGE MISSION, FRENCH NAT. AGENCY RES. DEVELOP, 68- Inst. Elec. & Electronics Eng. Electro-acoustics, underwater sound; electromagnetic and quasi-static fields; optical instruments. Address: French National Agency for Research Development, Tour Aurore, Paris-Defense, France 92.

FERREE, DAVID C, b. Lock Haven, Pa, Feb. 9, 43; m. 68. HORTICULTURE, POMOLOGY. B.S, Pa. State Univ, 65; M.S, Univ. Md, College Park, 68, Ph.D, 69. ASST. PROF. HORT, OHIO AGR. RES. & DEVELOP. CTR, 71- Chem.C, U.S.A.R, 69-71, Capt. Am. Soc. Hort. Sci. Integrating present knowledge and techniques of apple production management into efficient systems for high density orchards, with emphasis on light relations as affected by pruning and training systems. Address: Dept. of Horticulture, Ohio Agricultural Research & Development Center, Wooster, OH 44691.

FERREIRA, LAURENCE E, b. Livermore, Calif, Mar. 23, 28; m. 54; c. 3. CERAMIC ENGINEERING. B.S, California, Berkeley, 52, M.S, 55. Ceramic engr, West. Gold & Platinum Co, Calif, 53-56; dir. res, COORS PORCELAIN CO, 56-71; CONSULT. CERAMIST, 71. PACE award, Nat. Inst. Ceramic Eng, 65. U.S.A, 46-47. Fel. Am. Ceramic Soc; Am. Soc. Test. & Mat. Research management development of oxide ceramics for industrial use; ceramic processing method development. Address: 218 Lookout View Dr, Golden, CO 80401.

FERREIRA, RICARDO C(ARVALHO), b. Recife, Brazil, Jan. 16, 28; m. 52; c. 4. QUANTUM CHEMISTRY. B.Sc, Cath. Univ. Pernambuco, 52; D.Sc. (chem), Fed. Univ. Pernambuco, 57. Nat. Res. Coun. Brazil. fel, Brazilian Ctr. Phys. Res, 57-58, assoc. prof. theoret. chem, 61-62; asst. prof. inorg. chem, Fed. Univ. Pernambuco, 58-61, prof, 62-67; assoc. prof. chem, Earlham Col, 68-71; MEM. STAFF, CECINE, 71- Rockefeller Found. fel, Calif. Inst. Tech, 59-60; vis. assoc. prof, Indiana, 63-64; Columbia, 65. Brazilian Soc. Advan. Sci; Brazilian Acad. Sci; Am. Chem. Soc. Chemistry of complex compounds; chemical bonding; molecular structure. Address: CECINE, Caixa Postal 2047, Cidade Universitaria, Recife, Pernambuco, Brazil.

FERREL, ROBERT E(UGENE), b. Allerton, Iowa, July 16, 20; m. 47; c. 4. CHEMISTRY. A.B, Fresno State Col, 42. CHEMIST, west. regional res. lab, bur. agr, & indust. chem, U.S. Dept. Agr, 42-47; bioprod, Ore. Ltd, 48-50; Vet. Br, 6th Army Area Med. Lab, 51-54; NEW PROD. INVEST, CEREAL LAB, WEST. UTILIZATION RES. & DEVELOP. DIV, U.S. DEPT. AGR, 54- AAAS; Inst. Food Technol; Am. Asn. Cereal Chem. Cereal products development; chemical modification of proteins; protein hydrolysis products. Address: Cereal Lab, Western Utilization Research & Development Division, U.S. Dept. of Agriculture, 800 Buchanan St, Albany, CA 94710.

FERRELL, D(OCTOR) THOMAS, JR, b. Durham, N.C, Sept. 28, 22; m. 65; c. 1. PHYSICAL CHEMISTRY. B.S, Eastern Ky. State Col, 43; A.M, Duke, 48, Ph.D.(chem), 50. Chemist, Naval Ord. Lab, Md, 50-56; mgr. res. & develop, battery lab, Am. Machine & Foundry Co, 57-58, asst. lab. mgr, 58-59; asst. gen. mgr, missile battery div, Elec. Storage Battery Co, 59-60, assoc. dir. eng, exide indust. div, 60-62, asst. dir, 62-65, tech. coord, ESB INC, 65-69, MGR. LEAD ACID ENG, EXIDE POWER SYSTS. DIV, 69- U.S.A, 43-46, Res, 46-53, 1st Lt. Am. Chem. Soc; Electrochem. Soc; Am. Inst. Aeronaut. & Astronaut. Electrochemistry; electrode reactions; batteries. Address: ESB Inc, P.O. Box 5723, Philadelphia, PA 19120.

FERRELL, EDWARD F(RANCIS), b. Louisa, Ky, Apr. 19, 14; m. 45; c. 3. PHYSICAL METALLURGY. B.S, West. Ky. State Col, 39; M.S, Vanderbilt, 40, fel, 45-47, Ph.D, 50. Analyst, Electro Metall. Co, W.Va, 41-42; mem. staff, Battelle Mem. Inst, 47-55; instr. chem, Bowling Green State, 55-57; asst. prof, Colo. Sch. Mines, 57-64; PHYS. METALLURGIST, U.S. BUR. MINES, 64- U.S.A, 42-45. Am. Chem. Soc; Am. Soc. Eng. Educ; Metall. Soc; Am. Ceramic Soc. Properties of metallic carbides and silicides; cermets; refractory metals; powder metallurgy; vapor phase deposition; oxidation rare earth metals; metal-ceramic bonding; refractory metals; ceramics. Address: Reno Center, U.S. Bureau of Mines, 1605 Evans Ave, Reno, NV 89503.

FERRELL, HOWARD H, b. Shreveport, La, Apr. 11, 29; m. 54; c. 3. PETROLEUM ENGINEERING. B.S, Okla. State, 51, M.S, 57; Shell fel, Texas A&M, 58, Gulf fel, 59, Ph.D.(petrol. eng), 61. Eng. trainee, Stanolind Oil & Gas Co, 51-52; res. eng, CONTINENTAL OIL CO, 59-61, res. group supvr, 61-65, RES. GROUP LEADER, 65- U.S.N, 52-55, Res, 55-, Comdr. Soc. Petrol. Eng. Water-oil displacement in porous underground rock; application of the displacement mechanism for development of oil recovery processes; techniques to evaluate the characteristics of underground oil bearing strata. Address: Continental Oil Co, Box 1267, Ponca City, OK 74261.

FERRELL, RAY EDWARD, JR, b. New Orleans, La, Jan. 29, 41; m. 62; c. 1. MINERALOGY, GEOCHEMISTRY. B.S, Southwestern Louisiana, 62; M.S, Illinois, 65, Nat. Lead fel. & Ph.D.(geol), 66. ASST. PROF. GEOL, LA. STATE UNIV, 66- Mineral. Soc. Am; Clay Minerals Soc. Origin and geologic importance of clay minerals. Address: Dept. of Geology, Louisiana State University, Baton Rouge, LA 70803.

FERRELL, RICHARD A(LLAN), b. Santa Ana, Calif, April 28, 26; m. 52; c. 2. PHYSICS. B.S, Calif. Inst. Tech, 48, M.S, 49; Ph.D.(physics), Princeton, 52. Asst. prof. PHYSICS, UNIV. MD, 53-56, assoc. prof, 56-59, PROF, 59- Atomic energy fel, Max-Planck-Inst, Gottingen, 51-53; sr. fel, Nat. Sci. Found, European Orgn. Nuclear Res, Geneva, 59-60, Univ. Paris, 68-69. Consult, Rand Corp, 54-58; U.S. Naval Ord. Lab, 56-62. U.S.N, 44-46. Am. Phys. Soc; Am. Asn. Physics Teachers. Theoretical, nuclear and solid state physics. Address: Dept. of Physics, University of Maryland, College Park, MD 20742.

FERRELL, WILLIAM JAMES, b. Wheeling, W.Va, Apr. 7, 40; m. 60; c. 3. BIOCHEMISTRY, ORGANIC CHEMISTRY. B.S, W. Liberty State Col, 61; M.S, W.Va. Univ, 63; Ph.D.(biochem), Univ. Pittsburgh, 67. ASST. PROF. BIOCHEM, UNIV. DETROIT, 67- Grant-in-aid, Mich. Heart Asn, 68-69 & 71-72, Licensed Beverage Industs, 68-69 & 70-71; Nat. Insts. Health, 70-73. Am. Oil Chem. Soc. Isolation, characterization and biosynthesis of aldehydrogenic lipids and glycerol thioethers; biosynthesis and metabolism of free fatty aldehydes; effects of alcohol on liver and heart membrane lipids; enzymatic interconversion of fatty acids, alcohols and aldehydes. Address: Dept. of Chemistry, Biochemistry Division, University of Detroit, Detroit, MI 48221.

FERRELL, WILLIAM K(REITER), b. Barberton, Ohio, Oct. 18, 19; m. 49; c. 3. FORESTRY. B.S, Michigan, 41; Knight Found. scholar, Duke, 41-42, M.F, 46, Ph.D.(forest soils), 49. Asst. forest soils specialist, Idaho, 48-53, asst. prof. forestry, 53-56; FOREST MGT, ORE. STATE UNIV, 56-57, assoc. prof, 57-65; PROF, 65- Nat. Sci. Found. sci. faculty fel, Denmark, 64-65. U.S.A.A.F, 42-46, Capt. AAAS; Soc. Am. Foresters; Am. Soc. Plant Physiol; Ecol. Soc. Am. Photosynthesis, respiration, and drought resistance studies of tree seedlings; ecotypic variation. Address: School of Forestry, Oregon State University, Corvallis, OR 97331.

FERRELL, WILLIAM RUSSELL, b. Cleveland, Ohio, June 19, 32; m. 54; c. 2. SYSTEMS ENGINEERING, HUMAN FACTORS. B.A, Swarthmore Col, 54; S.B. & S.M, Mass. Inst. Technol, 61, M.E, 63, Ph.D.(mech. eng), 64. Res. asst. mech. eng, Mass. Inst. Technol, 61-62, instr, 62-64, asst. prof, 64-68, assoc. prof, 68-69; PROF. SYSTS. ENG, UNIV. ARIZ, 69- Ford fel, Mass. Inst. Technol, 64-66. Sig.C, U.S.A, 54-56. Human Factors Soc; Inst. Elec. & Electronics Eng.(ed, Trans. Man-Mach. Systs, 69-70, co-ed, Trans. Systs, Man & Cybernetics, 70-71). Human performance in engineering systems; remote manipulation; decision making; aids for the blind; manual control; engineering design. Address: Systems & Industrial Engineering Dept, University of Arizona, Tucson, AZ 85721.

FERREN, RICHARD A(NTHONY), b. New Brunswick, N.J, Jan. 19, 31; m. 56; c. 5. PHYSICAL ORGANIC CHEMISTRY. B.S, Villanova, 52; M.S, Pennsylvania, 54, Ph.D.(chem), 56. RES. CHEMIST, Pennsalt Chem. Co, 56-69, PENWALT CHEM. CO, 69- Am. Chem. Soc; Soc. Rheol. Polymer chemistry. Address: R.D. 1, Warren Rd, Ambler, PA 19406.

FERRER, JOSE M, b. N.Y.C, Nov. 25, 12; m. 39; c. 5. SURGERY. A.B, Princeton, 34; M.D, Columbia Univ, 38. DIR. SURG, first surg. div, Bellevue Hosp, 62-67; HARLEM HOSP. CTR, COL. PHYSICIANS & SURGEONS, COLUMBIA UNIV, 67-, PROF. SURG, UNIV, 67- Attend. surgeon, Presby. & Babies Hosps, Columbia-Presby. Med. Ctr, 64- Dipl, Am. Bd. Surg, 44. Med.C, U.S.A, 42-45, Maj. Fel. Am. Col. Surg; fel. Am. Med. Asn; Int. Soc. Surg. Address: 161 Ft. Washington Ave, New York, NY 10032.

FERRER-MONGE, JOSE A(NTONIO), b. Havana, Cuba, June 25, 23; nat; m. 46; c. 1. BIOLOGY. B.S.A, Col. Agr, P.R, 45; M.A, Missouri, 48; Ph.D. (genetics), La. State, 58. Asst. geneticist, Inst. Trop. Agr. P.R, 45-47; asst. prof. biol. & bot. genetics, UNIV. P.R, 48-58, PROF. BIOL, 64-; P.R. NUCLEAR CTR, 58- Radiation Res. Soc. Genetics; biological effects of radiation. Address: Puerto Rico Nuclear Center, College Station, Mayaguez, PR 00709.

FERRETTI, ALDO, b. Rome, Italy, Jan. 22, 29; U.S. citizen; m. 56; c. 2. ORGANIC CHEMISTRY. Ph.D.(chem), Rome, 53. Org. chemist, Nat. Hydrocarbon Corp, Italy, 53-57; Fulbright fel, Illinois, 57-59; res. chemist, Farmitalia Div, Montecatini S.A, 59-62; res. assoc, Vanderbilt, 62-63; res. chemist, U.S. Naval Propellant Plant, 63-64; sr. scientist, Tenco Div, Coca-Cola Co, N.J, 64-68; RES. CHEMIST, U.S. DEPT. AGR, 68- Am. Chem. Soc; Brit. Chem. Soc. Synthetic organic chemistry; organic sulfur chemistry; ergot alkaloids; chemistry of natural products; lysergic acid derivatives. Address: 8516 Howell Rd, Bethesda, MD 20034.

FERRETTI, JOSEPH JEROME, b. Chicago, Ill, Dec. 23, 37; m. 65; c. 2. BIOCHEMISTRY, MICROBIOLOGY. B.S, Loyola Univ. Chicago, 60; Northwest. Univ, 60-62; M.S, Univ. Minn, Minneapolis, 65, Ph.D.(biochem), 67. Res. asst. biochem, med. sch, Northwest. Univ, 60-62; U.S. Pub. Health Serv. fel, Johns Hopkins Univ, 67-69; ASST. PROF. MICROBIOL, MED. CTR, UNIV. OKLA, 69- AAAS; Am. Soc. Microbiol. Control of enzyme and nucleic acid synthesis in synchronous populations of bacteria; biochemical-genetic studies on histidine biosynthesis; genetic studies on group A Streptococci and their bacteriophage. Address: Dept. of Microbiology, University of Oklahoma Medical Center, Oklahoma City, OK 73108.

FERRI, ANTONIO, b. Norcia, Italy, Apr. 5, 12; nat; m; c. 3. AERODYNAMICS. Dr.(elec. eng), Rome, 34, Dr.(aeronaut. eng), 36. Aerodyn. res. scientist, Direzione Sup. Studi ed Esperienze, Italy, 35-37, head supersonic wind tunnel, Guidonia, 37-40, aerodyn. br, 40-43; Partisan Brigade Spartaco, 43-44; sr. scientist, NASA, 44-49, head gas dynamics br, 49-51; prof. aerodyn, Polytech. Inst. Brooklyn, 51-64; N.Y. UNIV, 64-67, ASTOR PROF. AEROSPACE SCI, 67-, DIR. AEROSPACE LABS, 64- Asst. prof, Univ. Rome, 36-40, assoc. prof, 40-43; dir. aerospace inst, Polytech. Inst. Brooklyn, 54-64, head dept. aero. eng, 57-64; pres, Gen. Appl. Sci. Labs, Inc, 56-67; consult, Dept. Army, Dept. Air Force, NASA, Adv. Group Aeronaut. Res. & Develop. Premio dell'Accademia d' Italia Award, 38; Libero Docente in Aerodinamica, 42; Sci. Achievement award, 54; Italian Hist. Soc. Award of America, 59; Dept. Air Force, Commendation for Meritorius Civilian Serv, 66, Outstanding Achievement Award, 70. Nat. Acad. Eng; fel. Am. Astronaut. Soc; fel. Am. Inst. Aeronaut. & Astronaut. (award, 71); Int. Acad. Astronaut. Aerodynamics; hypersonics; propulsion; astronautics; supersonic combustion; air-breathing engines; noise. Address: Aerospace Lab, New York University, 177th St. & Harlem River, Bronx, NY 10453.

FERRIANS, OSCAR J(OHN), JR, b. Touchet, Wash, Mar 9, 28; m. 53. GEOLOGY. B.S, State Col. Wash, 52, M.S, 58. GEOLOGIST, U.S. GEOL. SURV, 53- AAAS; Geol. Soc. Am; Arctic Inst. N.Am; Am. Quaternary Asn. Areal, surficial, glacial, economic, engineering and environmental geology; geomorphology; permafrost; earthquake effects; gold placer deposits; remote sensing. Address: U.S. Geological Survey, 345 Middlefield Rd, Menlo Park, CA 94025.

FERRIER, BARBARA M(AY), b. Edinburgh, Scotland, Aug. 7, 32; m. 63; c. 2. BIOCHEMISTRY. B.Sc, Univ. Edinburgh, 54, Ph.D.(chem), 58. Asst. chem,

Univ. Edinburgh, 54-58; res. fel, Hickrill Chem. Res. Found, N.Y, 58-59; asst. lectr, Bedford Col, Univ. London, 59-61; res. fel, Yale, 61-62; res. assoc. biochem, med. col, Cornell Univ, 62-63, instr, 63-66; res. assoc, obstet. physiol, Clin. Hosp, Montevideo, Uruguay, 66-68; ASSOC. PROF. BIOCHEM, McMASTER UNIV, 69- Am. Chem. Soc; Brit. Chem. Soc; Can. Biochem. Soc; Int. Soc. Res. Reproduction; Latin Am. Asn. Res. Human Reproduction. Metabolism of peptide and protein hormones in pregnancy. Address: 165 Chedoke Ave, Hamilton 12, Ont, Can.

FERRIGNO, PETER D, b. Washington, D.C, Aug. 26, 27; m. 52; c. 4. DENTISTRY. B.S, Georgetown, 50, D.D.S, 55; M.S, Catholic Univ, 52; fel, Ohio State, 56-57, M.S, 57. From instr. to assoc. prof. PERIODONT, SCH. DENT, GEORGETOWN UNIV, 59-68, PROF, 68-, CHMN. DEPT, 60- Consult, Vet. Admin, 63-; Montgomery Jr. Col, 61; U.S. Navy. Dipl, Am. Bd. Endodont, 65. U.S.A, 46-48, Sgt. Am. Dent. Asn; Am. Asn. Endodont; Am. Acad. Periodont; Int. Asn. Dent. Res. Fibrogenesis on periodontal ligament in rats by radioautolosis. Address: Dept. of Periodontics, Georgetown University School of Dentistry, 3900 Reservoir Rd, Washington, DC 20007.

FERRIGNO, THOMAS HOWARD, b. Newark, N.J, Dec. 3, 25; m. 47; c. 2. ORGANIC CHEMISTRY. B.S, Seton Hall, 51. Plant chemist, Pabco Prods, Inc, 50-55; res. supvr. minerals & chem, Philipp Corp, 55-63; asst. tech. dir, United Clay Mines Corp, 63-65; mgr. appl. res, United Sierra Div, Cypress Mines Corp, 65-67; group leader, Tenneco Plastics Div, 67-70; MINERAL INDUST. CONSULT, 70- Soc. Plastics Eng; Am. Chem. Soc. Application of minerals in paints, plastics, rubber and allied fields; surface treatment of minerals; product development and promotion. Address: 29 Clover Hill Circle, Trenton, NJ 08638.

FERRILL, MITCHELL, b. Cobden, Ill, Feb. 16, 34; m. 57; c. 3. FOREST ECOLOGY & MENSURATION. B.S.F, Missouri, 57; M.F, La. State, 58; D.F. (forest ecol), Duke, 63. Lectr. mensuration & wood tech, Southern Illinois, 60-61; asst. prof. ecol. & mensuration, UNIV. CONN, 63-68, ASSOC. PROF. FOREST ECOL, 68-, HEAD, NATURAL RESOURCE CONSERV. SECT, 70- C.Eng, 58-60, 1st Lt. Am. Soc. Photogram; Ecol. Soc. Am; Soc. Am. Foresters. Forest ecology and aerial photo interpretation; ecology of bottomland hardwoods; radioecological techniques for study of longleaf pine root extension. Address: Box U-87, University of Connecticut, Storrs, CT 06268.

FERRIS, B(ENJAMIN) G(REELEY), JR, b. U.S.A, Jan. 24, 19; m. 42; c. 5. PHYSIOLOGY. A.B, Harvard, 40, M.D, 43. House off. med, Children's Hosp, Boston, 43-44, asst. res, 44-45, 47-48; res. fel, SCH. PUB. HEALTH, HARVARD, 48-50, assoc. physiol, 50-53, asst. prof, 53-58, assoc. prof. ENVIRON. HEALTH & SAFETY, 58-71, PROF, 71-, DIR. ENVIRON. HEALTH & SAFETY, UNIV. HEALTH SERV, 58- Med.C, 45-47, Capt. AAAS; Am. Physiol. Soc; fel. Am. Col. Prev. Med; Am. Pub. Health Asn; Royal Soc. Med; Int. Epidemiol. Asn; Am. Epidemiol. Soc. Pulmonary physiology; occupational medicine. Address: Dept. of Physiology, Harvard School of Public Health, 665 Huntington Ave, Boston, MA 02115.

FERRIS, BERNARD J(OE), b. Denver, Colo, Nov. 16, 22; m; c. 2. PETROLEUM GEOLOGY, ORGANIC GEOCHEMISTRY. Geol.E, Colo. Sch. Mines, 47, Shell Oil Co. fel. & M.Geol.E, 48. Geologist, SHELL OIL CO, 48-53, dist. geologist, 53-54, div. explor. mgr, 54-56, sr. geologist, 56-60, mgr. geol. dept, Shell Develop. Co, 60-63, chief geologist, Shell Oil Co, 63-66, div. explor. mgr, 66-69, sr. res. assoc, SHELL DEVELOP. CO, 69-70, MGR. GEOL. DEPT, 70- C.Eng, U.S.A, 43-46, 1st Lt. Am. Asn. Petrol. Geol; Geol. Soc. Am. Use of fossil calcareous algae in biostratigraphy; geological and chemical investigations of the origin and migration of petroleum hydrocarbons in the subsurface. Address: Shell Development Co, P.O. Box 481, Houston, TX 77001.

FERRIS, CLIFFORD D, b. Phila, Pa, Nov. 19, 35. ELECTRICAL ENGINEERING. B.S, Pennsylvania, 57, M.S, 58; Am. Mach. & Foundry Co. grant & D.Sc.(math. physics), George Washington, 62. Engr, electronic instrument div, Burroughs Corp, Pa, 53, basic physics div, res. ctr, 55-56; res. asst, Pennsylvania, 56-57, res. assoc, electromed. res. lab. & consult, dept. pharmacol. & dept. therapeut. res, univ. hosp, 57-59, asst. instr. ELEC. ENG, 58-59; instr, George Wash. Univ, 59-60, asst. prof, 60-62, ASSOC. PROF, 62-63; Drexel Inst. Technol, 63-64; Univ. Md, 64-68; UNIV. WYO, 68- Systs. analyst, res. lab, Melpar, Inc, Va, 59; consult, instrument eng. & develop. br, Nat. Insts. Health, 60-62; vis. scientist, Armed Forces Inst. Path, Walter Reed Army Med. Ctr, D.C, 61-68. AAAS; Inst. Elec. & Electronics Eng; Am. Soc. Eng. Educ; N.Y. Acad. Sci. Cardiac resuscitation by electronic stimulation; interaction of electromagnetic fields with biological systems. Address: Dept. of Electrical Engineering, University of Wyoming, Laramie, WY 82070.

FERRIS, CLINTON S, JR, b. Chicago, Ill, Aug. 13, 33; m. 59; c. 3. ECONOMIC GEOLOGY, PETROLOGY. B.S, Colo. Col, 55; M.Sc, Univ. Sask, 61; Pan Am. Petrol. fel, Univ. Wyo, 61-62, Nat. Sci. Found. fel, 62-64, Ph.D. (geol), 65. Geologist, KERR-McGEE CORP, 64-67, sr. geologist, 68-69, EXPLOR. ADV, 70- U.S.C.G.R, 56-69, Res, 59-, Lt. Comdr. Geol. Soc. Am; Soc. Econ. Geol; Am. Inst. Min, Metall. & Petrol. Eng. Sandstone uranium genesis and ore controls; porphyry copper genesis and relation to rock alteration; structural geology. Address: 6158 Hoyt Ct, Arvada, CO 80002.

FERRIS, CRAIG, b. Los Angeles, Calif, Mar. 22, 13; m. 34; c. 2. GEOPHYSICS. A.B, Friends, 34; Oklahoma, 34-36. Geophysicist, Am. Seismograph Co, 36-38; Mott-Smith Corp, 38-43; PARTNER, E.V. McCOLLUM & CO, 43- V.pres, GeoSeis, Inc. & pres, SeisDrill, Inc, 49-; v.pres, Namco Int. Panama, Inc, 58-65. Lectr, geol. & geophys. socs, 65. Soc. Explor. Geophys. (secy-treas, 64). Exploration for petroleum and minerals. Address: 1243 E. 28th St, Tulsa, OK 74114.

FERRIS, DEAM H(UNTER), b. Mankato, Minn, July 8, 12; m. 35; c. 4. ZOOLOGY. A.B, Drake, 34, M.A, 38; Ph.D.(vet. sci, zool), Wisconsin, 53. Teacher, high schs, Iowa & Kans, 35-42; instr. audio-visual educ, Wisconsin, 46-48; prof. biol. & natural hist, Graceland Col, 48-57; ASSOC. PROF. VET. PATH. & HYGIENE, COL. VET. MED, UNIV. ILL, URBANA, 57- Proj. assoc, Wisconsin, summers 53-57; virologist, Near E. Animal Health Inst, Food & Agr. Orgn, UN, 64-66. Chem.C, 42-46, Res, 46-, Lt. Col. Fel. AAAS; Am. Soc. Microbiol; Am. Soc. Parasitol; Biol. Photog. Asn; Wildlife Disease Asn; Conf. Res. Workers Animal Diseases; Am. Vet. Med. Asn; Am. Soc. Trop. Med. & Hyg; fel. Royal Soc. Health. Epizootiology and epidemiology of infectious diseases; transmission of vesicular stomatitis virus; equine encephalomyelitis; leptospirosis; Coxiella burneti, arborviruses of Near East; transmissible swine gastroenteritis; avian malaria; abortive rabies in equidae; production of autotutorial single concept films on rabies, visceral and cutaneous larva migrans; development of autotutorial carrels for university instruction. Address: College of Veterinary Medicine, University of Illinois, Urbana, IL 61801.

FERRIS, D(ELACY) F(AATZ), b. Westmont, N.J, May 24, 15; m. 40; c. 2. MECHANICAL ENGINEERING. B.S, Drexel Inst, 38; M.S, Rutgers, 41. Instr. mech. eng, Rutgers, 38-41; proj. engr, Curtiss Propeller, 41-48; from proj. engr. to dir. opers, Reaction Motors Div, Thiokol Chem. Corp, N.J, 48-63; MGR. CONTROLS DESIGN, ROCKETDYNE DIV, N.AM. ROCKWELL, INC, 63- Packaged liquid propellant rocket powerplants; rocket engine for X-15 airplane; descent engine for lunar exploratory module; controls for space shuttle main engine. Address: 7743 Milwood Ave, Canoga Park, CA 91304.

FERRIS, D(EWARD) O(LMSTED), b. Niagara Falls, Ont, Can, Jan. 5, 07; nat; m. 38; c. 2. SURGERY. M.D, Queen's (Can), 31; fel, Mayo Found, 37-43, M.S, Minnesota, 41. Practicing physician, Can, 33-37; instr. SURG, MAYO GRAD. SCH. MED, UNIV. MINN, 45-47, asst. prof, 47-52, assoc. prof, 52-62, PROF. CLIN. SURG, 62-; HEAD SECT. GEN. SURG, MAYO CLIN, 45- Dipl, Am. Bd. Surg, 43. Fel. Am. Col. Surg; Am. Med. Asn; Int. Soc. Surg. Surgery of biliary tract and pancreas; gastro-intestinal surgery and functioning lesions of the adrenal gland; tumors of the testis. Address: Dept. of Surgery, Mayo Graduate School of Medicine, University of Minnesota, Rochester, MN 55901.

FERRIS, HORACE G(ARFIELD), b. Los Angeles, Calif, Aug. 3, 13; m. 45; c. 2. PHYSICS. B.A, Pomona Col, 36; M.A, California, Los Angeles, 39, Ph.D.(physics), 49. Asst. physics, California, Los Angeles, 39-40; instr, Long Beach Jr. Col, 41-42; physicist, U.S. Naval Ord. Test Sta, 45-46; lectr. physics, Southern California, 46-49; instr, San Diego State Col, 49-51; asst. res. physicist, Scripps Inst, California, 51-55; assoc. prof. PHYSICS, Chapman Col, 55-58; asst. prof, CALIF. STATE POLYTECH. COL, KELLOGG-VOORHIS, 58-61, assoc. prof, 51-65, PROF, 65- Civilian physicist, U.S. Navy, 42-43, instr, mil. training prog, Pomona Col, 43-44; res. assoc, Calif. Inst. Technol, 44-45; consult, Robert Shaw Fulton Controls Co, 56-57; U.S. Naval Radiol. Defense Lab, 56-59, Civil Eng. Lab, 59-60; Hughes Aircraft Co, 57-69; assoc. instr, Univ. Calif, Los Angeles, 64-66. AAAS; Acoust. Soc. Am; Am. Asn. Physics Teachers. Theoretical acoustics; spherical acoustic resonators; theory of electromagnetic waves; dipole antenna in a conducting half space; radial and axial heat flow in composite cylinders; geothermal gradient in ocean floor by probe methods; hydrodynamics of stratified fluids including the ocean; partial differential equations of physics; methods of mathematical physics; measurement of thermal conductivities at high temperatures by transient methods; underwater acoustics, including theory of sound transmission in the ocean. Address: 12533 Killion St, North Hollywood, CA 91607.

FERRIS, JAMES P(ETER), b. Nyack, N.Y, July 25, 32; m. 55; c. 2. BIOLOGICAL & ORGANIC CHEMISTRY. B.S, Univ. Pa, 54; Ph.D, Ind. Univ, 58. Lectr. chem, Ind. Univ, 58; res. assoc, Mass. Inst. Tech, 58-59; instr. org. chem, Fla. State Univ, 59-60, asst. prof, 61-64; res. assoc, Salk Inst. Biol. Studies, 64-67; ASSOC. PROF. CHEM, RENSSELAER POLYTECH. INST, 67- Summers, chemist, Kay-Fries Chems, Inc, N.Y, 54; mem. tech. staff, Bell Tel. Labs, N.J, 55; U.S. Pub. Health Serv. career award, 69-74. Am. Chem. Soc; Brit. Chem. Soc. Chemistry of the origins of life; photochemistry; chemistry of hydrocyanic acid and nitriles; solvated electron reductions; oxidase enzymes and cytochrome P-450. Address: Dept. of Chemistry, Rensselaer Polytechnic Institute, Troy, NY 12181.

FERRIS, JOHN GUY, b. Weatherly, Pa, June 15, 13; m. 35; c. 2. ENGINEERING. B.S, Lehigh, 34. Jr. engr, T.H. Moyer Co, 34-35, asst. engr. & estimator, 37-38; exp. engr, Mack Truck Co, 35-36; jr. engr, U.S. Eng. Corps, 36-37; from jr. to asst. engr, U.S. GEOL. SURV, N.Y, 38-43, asst. to assoc. engr, Ind, 43-45, dist. engr, Mich, 45-52, staff engr, mid-west, 52-57, hydraul. engr. res, D.C, 57-61, Ariz, 61-67, STAFF HYDROLOGIST, WATER RESOURCES DIV, GROUND WATER BR, 67- Lectr, Mich. State, 53-54; American Univ, 60-61; Arizona, 61- U.N. Tech. adv, Lebanon, 64-65. AAAS; Am. Soc. Petrol. Eng; Am. Inst. Mining, Metall. & Petrol. Eng; Am. Soc. Civil Eng; Am. Geophys. Union; Am. Water Works Asn. Groundwater hydrology and hydraulics. Address: Water Resources Division, Ground Water Branch, U.S. Geological Survey, 18th & F Sts. N.W, Washington, DC 20242.

FERRIS, JOHN M(ASON), b. Mount Vernon, N.Y, July 9, 27; m. 53; c. 2. NEMATOLOGY. B.S, Cornell, 51, Ph.D.(plant path), 56. Asst. plant path, Cornell, 51-56; asst. plant pathologist, State Natural Hist. Surv, Ill, 57-58; asst. prof. phytonematol, PURDUE UNIV, 58-62, ASSOC. PROF. NEMATOL, 62- U.S.A, 45-46. AAAS; Am. Phytopath. Soc; Soc. Nematol.(ed, Nematol. News Letter, 63-65); Soc. Europ. Nematol. Diseases caused by plant parasitic nematodes; physiology and ecology of nematodes. Address: Dept. of Entomology, Purdue University, Lafayette, IN 47907.

FERRIS, JOHN T, b. Chicago, Ill, May 15, 22; m. 50; c. 2. PHYSICS, PHOTOGRAPHY. B.A, Northland Col, 47; M.S, Houston, 51. Mgr. photog. prod. & instr. photog, Houston, 48-49, chmn. dept, 49-59; staff physicist, adv. develop. dept, RES. DIV, BAUSCH & LOMB, INC, 59-61, fiber optics dept, 61-63, sect. head, 63-65, DEPT. HEAD, INFO. SYSTS. DEPT, 65- Consult, M.D. Anderson Audio Visual Center, Texas, 55; Color Processing Co, 56; automation res. div, Southwest. Indust. Electronics Co. Div, Dresser Industs, Inc, 57-59. U.S.A.F, Sgt. Optical Soc. Am; Soc. Photog. Sci. & Eng. Applications of light and light sensitive materials to science and industry, including photography, fiber optics, cryptography, metrology and development of electro optical devices. Address: Bausch & Lomb, Inc, 635 St. Paul St, Rochester, NY 14602.

FERRIS, L(ESLIE) M(ANNIGEL), b. Fargo, N.Dak, Nov. 29, 31; m. 53; c. 3. PHYSICAL CHEMISTRY. B.S, N.Dak. Agr. Col, 53, M.S, 55. ASST. SECT. CHIEF, CHEM. TECHNOL. DIV, OAK RIDGE NAT. LAB, 55- Am. Chem. Soc. Processes for dissolution of nuclear reactor fuels; chemistry of the lanthanides, actinides and carbides; molten salt chemistry; chemistry of liquid alloys. Address: Chemical Technology Division, Oak Ridge National Lab, Oak Ridge, TN 37830.

FERRIS, PHILIP, b. N.Y.C, Mar. 17, 30; m. 53; c. 2. ONCOLOGY. B.S, City Col. New York, 52, M.S, 57; scholar, Hofstra Univ, 63-65, M.A, 65; Ph.D. (biol), N.Y. Univ, 70. Teacher, pub. schs, N.Y, 53-58; high sch, 58-59; res. asst. ONCOL, WALDEMAR MED. RES. FOUND, 60-69, RES. ASSOC, 69-; Nat. Sci. Found. res. grant, 65-71. N.Y. Acad. Sci. Cancer virology; immunology and cytokinetics of chloroleukemia; biomedical research. Address: 8 Cedar Drive S, Old Bethpage, NY 11804.

FERRIS, ROBERT C(LARKE), b. Vancouver, B.C, Can, Dec. 28, 19; nat; m. 41; c. 2. CHEMISTRY. B.S, Washington (Seattle), 44; fel, Northwestern, 46-47, M.S, 47; fel, Utah, 48-49, Ph.D.(chem), 49. Consult. chemist, A.J. Norton Labs, Wash, 44-45; develop. chemist, Aerojet Eng. Corp, 49-51; process res. supvr, Purex Corp, Ltd, 51-52, dir. res, 52-59; pres, Chem. Lab. Prods, Inc, 59-62; Circle Industs, Inc, 62-63; mgr. surfactant develop, Monsanto Co, 63-67; dir. res, STEPAN CHEM. CO, 67-70, DIR. COMMERCIAL DEVELOP, 70- U.S.N.R, 44-46, Lt.(jg). Am. Chem. Soc; Am. Soc. Test. & Mat; Am. Oil Chem. Soc. Pyrolysis and photolysis of organic compounds; synthesis of nitropolymers; synthetic detergents and bleaches. Address: Stepan Chemical Co, Edens & Winnetka, Northfield, IL 60093.

FERRIS, ROBERT MONSOUR, b. Omaha, Nebr, Sept. 1, 38; m. 61; c. 5. BIOCHEMISTRY, NEUROCHEMISTRY. B.S, Creighton Univ, 60; M.S, Univ. Nebr, 63, Ph.D.(biochem), 67. Nat. Insts. Health neurosci. res. fel, sch. med, Duke Univ, 67-70; SR. PHARMACOLOGIST, BURROUGHS WELLCOME & CO. U.S.A, INC, 70- AAAS; Am. Chem. Soc. Biochemical and pharmacological properties governing the uptake, storage, synthesis and release of neurotransmittens in peripheral and central nervous systems. Address: Dept. of Pharmacology, Neurochemistry Section, Burroughs Wellcome & Co. U.S.A, Inc, 3030 Cornwallis Rd, Research Triangle Park, NC 27709.

FERRIS, ROBERT T(HOMAS), b. Pittsfield, Mass, Apr. 14, 37; m. 63; c. 2. IMMUNOLOGY, PERIODONTOLOGY. D.D.S, Emory, 61; M.Sc, Ohio State, 64, Ph.D.(microbiol), 67. Lab. instr. biol, Spring Hill Col, 56-57; Nat. Inst. Dent. Res. trainee periodont, 64-65; teaching assoc. microbiol, Ohio State, 65-66, Nat. Inst. Dent. Res. fel, 66-67; asst. prof. periodont. & microbiol, CASE WEST. RESERVE UNIV, 67-68, ASSOC. PROF, 68-70, ORAL BIOL. & PERIODONT, 70-, CHMN. DIV. GRAD. PERIODONT, 70- Attend. dentist, Lakeside Hosp, Cleveland, 68-; consult. periodont, Vet. Admin. Hosp. & Highland View Hosp, Cleveland, 68-; Dent.C, U.S.N, 61-63, Lt. Am. Dent. Asn; Am. Acad. Periodont; Am. Soc. Microbiol; Int. Asn. Dent. Res. Antigenicity of gingival tissue components; immunologically competent cells of oral mucous membranes; immune response to oral bacteria; criteria for evaluation of periodontal therapeutic procedures. Address: Dept. of Periodontics, Case Western Reserve University School of Dentistry, Cleveland, OH 44106.

FERRIS, THOMAS FRANCIS, b. Boston, Mass, Dec. 27, 30; m. 57; c. 4. INTERNAL MEDICINE. A.B, Georgetown, 52; M.D, Yale, 56. Intern, Osler Serv, Johns Hopkins Hosp, Baltimore, Md, 56-57; U.S. Pub. Health Serv. Clin. fel. renal disease, New Haven Hosp, Conn, 59-60, res, 60-62, U.S. Pub. Health Serv. res. fel, 62-63; instr. MED, sch. med, Yale, 63-65, asst. prof, 65-67; assoc. prof. COL. MED, OHIO STATE UNIV, 67-71, PROF, 71-, DIR. RENAL DISEASE, UNIV. HOSP, 67- John & Mary R. Markle scholar acad. med, 64-69; vis. investr, Regius Dept. Med, Oxford, 66-67. Med.C, U.S.A.R, 57-59, Capt. Am. Fedn. Clin. Res; Am. Soc. Nephrology. Renal physiology; hypertension; diseases of the kidney. Address: College of Medicine, Ohio State University, 410 W. Tenth Ave, Columbus, Ohio 43210.

FERRIS, VIRGINIA ROGERS, b. Abilene, Kans, March 26, 27; m. 53; c. 2. NEMATOLOGY. B.A, Wellesley Col, 49; M.S, Cornell, 52, Horton-Hallowell fel. from Wellesley, 52-53, Nat. Sci. Found. fel, 53-54, Ph.D.(plant path), 54. Asst. plant path, Cornell, 49-52, asst. prof, 54-56; consult. plant pathologist, 56-65; asst. prof. ENTOM, PURDUE UNIV, 65-70, ASSOC. PROF, 70-, ASST. DEAN GRAD. SCH, 71- Soc. Nematol.(secy, 65-68, v.pres, 68-69, pres, 69-70); Am. Phytopath. Soc; Ecol. Soc. Am; Soc. Syst. Zool; Soc. Study Evolution; Soc. Europ. Nematol. Nematode systematics, bionomics and ecology; plant diseases caused by nematodes. Address: Dept. of Entomology, Purdue University, Lafayette, IN 47907.

FERRIS, W(ARREN) R(OBERT), b. Terre Haute, Ind, May 14, 04; m. 27; c. 3. ELECTRICAL ENGINEERING. B.S, Rose Polytech, 27; M.S, Union (N.Y), 32; N.Y. Univ, 41; Princeton, 44; D.E, Polytech. Inst. Brooklyn, 46. Student engr, Gen. Elec. Co, N.Y, 27-28, res. engr, 28-30; vacuum tube engr, Radiotron Co, Radio Corp. of Am, N.J, 30-33, res. engr, 33-42, labs, 42-46; physicist, Naval Res. Lab, Wash, D.C, 46-56; PROF. ELEC. ENG, UNIV. S.C, 56- Instr. vacuum tube theory & application, Maryland, 47-54. AAAS; Am. Soc. Eng. Educ; fel. Inst. Elec. & Electronics Eng; Sci. Res. Soc. Am. High frequency electronics; thermionic emission and vacuum tube research; low frequency characteristics; alternating current operation; high frequency effects; low-noise developments; fundamental emission study; network analysis and synthesis. Address: Dept. of Electrical Engineering, University of South Carolina, Columbia, SC 29208.

FERRIS, WAYNE R(OBERT), b. Lockman, Iowa, Mar. 21, 21; m. 49. CYTOLOGY. Ph.D.(zool), Chicago, 59. Asst. ZOOL, Chicago, 50-; instr, UNIV. ARIZ, 58-59, asst. prof, 59-62, assoc. prof, 62-66, PROF, 66- U.S.N.R, 41-42; U.S.M.C.R, 42-, Maj. Myogenesis of vertebrate striated muscle; cytochemistry and ultrastructural aspects of induction mechanisms; electron microscopy. Address: Dept. of Zoology, University of Arizona, Tucson, AZ 85721.

FERRIS-PRABHU, ALBERT V(ICTOR) M(ICHAEL), b. Meerut, Uttar Pradesh, India, Sept. 5, 32; m. 67; c. 1. SOLID STATE PHYSICS. B.M.E, Dayton, 57; M.S.E. & M.A, Princeton, 60; Knights Columbus fel, Catholic Univ, 60-63, Ph.D.(solid state physics), 63. Asst. physics & math, Dayton, 56-57; programmer math, Int. Bus. Mach. Res. Center, 57-58; asst. mech. eng, Princeton, 58-60; res. assoc. mat. theory group, Mass. Inst. Tech, 63-64; physicist, Goddard Space Flight Center, NASA, 64-66; assoc. prof. appl. sci, George Wash. Univ, 66-68; ADV. PHYSICIST, COMPONENTS DIV, IBM CORP, 68- Mech. engr, data systs. div, Int. Bus. Mach. Corp, summers 59 & 60; lectr, Cath. Univ. Am, 66; consult, Wolf Res. & Develop. Corp, 67-; Adaptronics, Inc, 68- Am. Phys. Soc. Diffusion in semiconductors; amorphous semiconductors; semiconductor memories. Address: Components Division, IBM Corp, P.O. Box A, Essex Junction, VT 05452.

FERRISS, DONALD P, b. Rutherford, N.J, Apr. 17, 24; m. 52; c. 3. PHYSICAL METALLURGY, CERAMICS. M.E, Stevens Inst. Technol, 50, M.S, 54; Sc.D.(metall), Mass. Inst. Technol, 61. Res. engr. powder metall, Stevens Inst. Technol, 50-57; instr. metall, Mass. Inst. Technol, 57-61; res. metallurgist, ENG. MAT. LAB, E.I. DU PONT DE NEMOURS & CO, 61-66, RES. ASSOC, 66- U.S.A, 43-45. Am. Soc. Metals; Am. Inst. Mining, Metall. & Petrol. Eng; Sci. Res. Soc. Am. Special processing of metal powders; deformation and fracture of metals; mechanical properties of ceramics; wear of materials. Address: Engineering Materials Lab, Experimental Station, E.I. du Pont de Nemours & Co, Wilmington, DE 19898.

FERRISS, GREGORY STARK, b. Summit, N.J, Aug. 2, 24; m. 57; c. 2. NEUROLOGY. A.B, Harvard, 46; M.D, Tulane, 51. Instr. NEUROL, SCH. MED, LA. STATE UNIV, 55-58, asst. prof, 58-62, assoc. prof, 62-67, PROF, 67- Vis. physician, Charity Hosp. La, New Orleans, 55-; South. Baptist Hosp, 63-; consult, La. Regional Ment. Health Ctr, 55-; East La. State Hosp, Jackson, 55-57; State Colony & Training Sch, Pineville, 57-; Vet. Admin. Hosp, Alexandria, 59-; Cent. La. State Hosp, Pineville, 60-; head neurol. sect, collaborative child develop. proj, Charity Hosp. La, 60- Am. Acad. Neurol; Am. Asn. Ment. Deficiency; Am. Electroencephalog. Soc; Am. Epilepsy Soc; Asn. Res. Nerv. & Ment. Disease. Clinical electroencephalography and neurophysiology. Address: Dept. of Neurology, Louisiana State University School of Medicine, 1542 Tulane Ave, New Orleans, LA 70112.

FERRO, B(ERNARD) J(OSEPH), b. Caibarien, Cuba, Dec. 19, 20; nat; m. 45; c. 4. MECHANICAL ENGINEERING. M.E, La. State, 41. From process engr. to mgr. process develop. group, Phillips Petrol. Co, Okla, 41-53; asst. v.pres, & gas & petrol. sales mgr, Air Prods, Inc, 53-60, mgr. west. dist, 60-62; mkt. mgr, CRYOGENIC DIV, U.S. PHILIPS CORP, 62-63, GEN. MGR, 63- Am. Inst. Chem. Eng. Low-temperature processing techniques of natural gas and light hydrocarbons; extraction and purification of helium; nitrogen removal; deep extraction of heavier components from natural gas by low-temperature means; petrochemical plant design, economics and operation; cryogenic systems and hardware design and sales; closed cycle cryogenic refrigeration systems for industrial and defense applications. Address: U.S. Philips Corp, Cryogenic Division, P.O. Box 2200, Ashton, RI 02864.

FERRON, JOHN R(OYAL), b. Anoka, Minn, Oct. 29, 26; m. 51; c. 4. CHEMICAL ENGINEERING. B.Ch.E, Minnesota, 48, M.S, 50; Ph.D.(chem. eng), Univ. Wis, 58. Instr. chem, Macalester Col, 48-49; asst. chem. eng, Minnesota, 49-50; engr, E.I. du Pont de Nemours & Co, 50-54; instr. CHEM. ENG, Univ. Wis, 54-57; asst. prof, Univ. Del, 58-63, assoc. prof, 63-67, prof, 67-69; PROF. & CHMN. DEPT, UNIV. ROCHESTER, 69- Nat. Sci. Found. sci. faculty fel, Univ. Naples, 66-67. Am. Chem. Soc; Am. Inst. Chem. Eng; N.Y. Acad. Sci; Soc. Indust. & Appl. Math; Soc. Natural Philos. High temperature reactions and transport phenomena; fluidization; optimization; applied mathematics. Address: Dept. of Chemical Engineering, University of Rochester, Rochester, NY 14627.

FERRY, ANDREW P, b. N.Y.C, June 15, 29; m. 64. OPHTHALMOLOGY, PATHOLOGY. B.S, Manhattan Col, 50; M.D, Georgetown Univ, 54. Intern med, hosp, Duke Univ, 54-55; asst. resident, hosp, Univ. Mich, Ann Arbor, 57-58; resident ophthal, New York Hosp-Cornell Med. Ctr, 58-61; Nat. Inst. Neurol. Diseases & Blindness spec. fel, Armed Forces Inst. Path, 61-64; dir. Jordan Eye Bank, St. John Ophthalmic Hosp, Jerusalem, Jordan, 64-65; ASSOC. PROF. OPHTHAL. & ASST. PROF. PATH, MT. SINAI SCH. MED, 65- Instr, col. med, Cornell Univ, 60-61; consult, Manhattan Eye, Ear & Throat Hosp, New York, 66-; Beth Israel Med. Ctr, 67-; Am. Acad. Ophthal. & Otolaryngol, 69- Kober Medal & Gold Medal Prev. Med, sch. med, Georgetown Univ, 54; appointed by Queen Elizabeth II to position of Off. in Grand Priory in British Realm of Most Venerable Order of Hosp. of St. John of Jerusalem, 68. U.S.A.F, 55-57, Capt. Fel. Am. Col. Surg; Asn. Res. Vision & Ophthal; Am. Med. Asn.(Billings Bronze Medal, 65). Ophthalmic pathology, especially pathology of ocular tumors. Address: Dept. of Ophthalmology, Mt. Sinai School of Medicine, Fifth Ave. at 100th St, New York, NY 10029.

FERRY, C(LAYTON) W(ALTON), b. Pingree, N.Dak, June 9, 08; m. 34; c. 2. ORGANIC CHEMISTRY. B.S, North Dakota, 31; Hancock fel, Hopkins, 31-35, Ph.D.(chem), 35. Instr. org. chem, Hopkins, 34-35; res. chemist, Burroughs-Wellcome & Co, Inc, 35-38, develop. chemist, 38-41, chief develop. chemist, 41-46, dir. qual. control, 46-70; RETIRED. Mem, comt. revision, U.S. Pharmacopeia, 60-70. Am. Chem. Soc; Am. Pharmaceut. Asn; N.Y. Acad. Sci. Synthesis of substituted primary amines, ureas and guanidines; substituted mercapto compounds; sulfones; isolation of digitalis glycosides. Address: Old Litchfield Rd, Washington, CT 06793.

FERRY, DAVID K, b. San Antonio, Tex, Oct. 25, 40; m. 62. ELECTRICAL ENGINEERING, SOLID STATE PHYSICS. B.S, Tex. Tech. Col, 62, M.S, 63; Ph.D.(elec. eng), Texas, Austin, 66. Instr. elec. eng, Texas, Austin, summer 66; Nat. Sci. Found. fel. physics, Vienna, 66-67; asst. prof. ELEC. ENG, TEX. TECH UNIV, 66-70, ASSOC. PROF, 70- AAAS; Am. Phys. Soc; Inst. Elec. & Electronics Eng. High field transport in semiconductors, including hot electron effects, impact ionization, solid state plasmas and superconducting thin films; acoustics surface waves. Address: Dept. of Electrical Engineering, Texas Tech University, Lubbock, TX 79409.

FERRY, JAMES A, b. Mazomanie, Wis, Sept. 9, 37; m. 64; c. 2. NUCLEAR PHYSICS. B.S, Wisconsin, 59, M.S, 62, Ph.D.(physics), 65. Res. assoc. physics, Wisconsin, 65-66; mgr. accelerator div. & v.pres, NAT. ELECTROSTATICS CORP, 66-70, V.PRES. PROD, 70- Am. Phys. Soc. Low energy nuclear physics particle accelerator design and construction; ultra high vacuum technology. Address: National Electrostatics Corp, Box 117, Middleton, WI 53562.

FERRY, JOHN D(OUGLASS), b. Dawson, Yukon Territory, Can, May 4, 12, U.S. citizen; m. 44; c. 2. PHYSICAL CHEMISTRY. A.B, Stanford, 32, Ph.D.(chem), 35. Attached worker, Nat. Inst. Med. Res, London, 32-34; private asst, Hopkins Marine Sta, Stanford, 35-36; instr. & tutor biochem. scis, Harvard, 36-38, jr. fel, soc. fels, 38-41; assoc. chemist, Oceanog. Inst, Woods Hole, 41-45; res. assoc, Harvard, 42-45; asst. prof. CHEM, UNIV. WIS, MADISON, 46, assoc. prof, 46-47, PROF, 47-, chmn. dept, 59-67. Nat. Sci. Found. fel, Brussels, 59, Strasbourg & Kyoto, 68; vis. lectr, Kyoto, 68; chmn, Int. Comt. Rheology, 63-68. Nat. Acad. Sci; fel. Am. Acad. Arts & Sci; Am. Chem Soc.(Lilly award, 46, Kendall award, 60); fel. Am. Phys. Soc.(high polymer physics prize, 66); Am. Soc. Biol. Chem; Soc. Rheol. (Bingham medal, 53, v.pres, 59-61, pres, 61-63). Ultrafiltration; polymers of high molecular weight; proteins; mechanical properties of viscoelastic materials. Address: Dept. of Chemistry, University of Wisconsin, Madison, WI 53706.

FERSHT, A. EDWARD, b. London, Eng, Mar. 24, 37; m. 66; c. 1. PHYSICAL CHEMISTRY. B.S, London, 58, Ph.D.(appl. phys. chem), 61. Nat. Res. Coun. Can. fel, 61-63; res. chemist, E.I. DU PONT DE NEMOURS & CO, INC, 63-69, STAFF SCIENTIST, 69- Am. Chem. Soc. Relationship of structure to polymer properties; applications and properties of polymeric films, especially for electrical insulation. Address: E.I. du Pont de Nemours & Co, Inc, Film Dept, P.O. Box 89, Circleville, OH 43113.

FERSTANDIG, LOUIS L(LOYD), b. Brooklyn, N.Y, Apr. 26, 24; m. 46; c. 3. ORGANIC CHEMISTRY. B.S, Illinois, 44; Nat. Res. Coun. fel, Cornell, 46-49, Ph.D.(chem), 49. Res. assoc, Minnesota, 49-50; res. chemist, Calif. Res. Corp, 50-56, group supvr, 56-60, res. assoc, 60-64; RES. DIR, HALOCARBON PROD. CORP, 64- U.S.A.A.F, 44-46. Am. Chem. Soc. Chemicals for use in plastics, fiber and surface coating; stereospecific polymers; isocyanates; molecular complexes; allophanates; hydrogen bonding; organic halogen compounds. Address: Halocarbon Products Corp, 82 Burlews Ct, Hackensack, NJ 07601.

FERSTER, CHARLES B(OHRIS), b. Freehold, N.J, Nov. 1, 22; m. 63; c. 4. EXPERIMENTAL PSYCHOLOGY. B.S, Rutgers, 47; M.A, Columbia, 48; Ph.D.(psychol), 50. Res. fel, Harvard, 50-55; res. assoc, Yerkes Labs. Primate Biol, Fla, 55-57; asst. prof. psychol, Inst. Psychiat. Res. Indiana, 57-60; assoc. prof, 61-62; Maryland, 62; assoc. dir, Inst. Behavioral Res, 62-65, res. assoc, 65-67; PROF. PSYCHOL, Georgetown Univ, 67-69; AM. UNIV, 69-, CHMN. DEPT, 70- Mem, Int. Brain Res. Orgn. U.S.A.A.F, 43-46. Soc. Exp. Anal. Behavior (ed, Jour, 58-61); Am. Psychol. Asn; Soc. Biol. Psychiat. Experimental analysis of human and animal behavior. Address: Dept. of Psychology, American University, Washington, DC 20016.

FERTIG, JOHN W(ILLIAM), b. Lebanon, Pa, Oct. 13, 11; m. 39; c. 2. BIOSTATISTICS. B.A, Ursinus Col, 31; Ph.D.(biometry), Minnesota, 35; hon. M.D, Uruguay, 53. Teaching asst. biometry & bot, Minnesota, 31-35; assoc. biometrician, Mem. Found. Neuro-Endocrine Res, Mass, 35-37; res. assoc. BIOSTATIST, sch. hyg. & pub. health, Hopkins, 37-40; PROF, SCH. PUB. HEALTH & ADMIN. MED, COL. PHYSICIANS & SURG, COLUMBIA UNIV, 40- Vis. lectr, Univ. Ky, 38-40; vis. prof, N.Y. Univ, 43-45; Univ. P.R, 48-53; vis. lectr, Yale, 49; Univ. Minn, 49; consult, Pan Am. Sanit. Bur, Latin Am, 53-71; hon. prof, Univ. Chile, 59. With Off. Sci. Res. & Develop, 44. AAAS; Biomet. Soc; fel. Am. Pub. Health Asn; Pop. Asn. Am. Inst. Math. Statist; fel. Am. Statist. Asn. Tests of statistical hypotheses; bio-assay; analysis of follow-up data; calibration curves; analysis of public health and medical data; analysis of dental research. Address: Dept. of Biostatistics, School of Public Health & Administrative Medicine, Columbia University, 600 W. 168th St, New York, NY 10032.

FERTIG, JOSEPH, b. Berlin, Ger, Jan. 6, 31; m. 58; c. 3. ORGANIC & POLYMER CHEMISTRY. B.Sc, London, 54, Ph.D.(org. chem), 57. Asst, North. Polytech, London, 54-56; sr. master chem, Hasmonean Grammer Sch. Boys, London, Eng, 56-57; res. chemist, Nat. Starch & Chem. Corp, N.J, 58-60, supvr, 60-65, res. assoc, 65-67, sect. leader org. chem. res, 67; sr. group leader, Merck & Co, Inc, 67-70; SR. SCIENTIST, HYDROPHILICS LTD, 70- Lectr, North. Polytech, London, 55-57. AAAS; Am. Chem. Soc. Synthesis of polymerizable monomers; organic chemical modification of high polymers. Address: 25 Harofe St, Haifa, Israel.

FERTIG, STANFORD N(EWTON), b. Marlinton, W.Va, July 10, 19; m. 49; c. 1. AGRONOMY. B.S, West Virginia, 46, M.S, 47; Ph.D, Cornell, 50. Asst. prof. agron, Cornell, 50-52, assoc. prof, 52-57, prof, 57-66; DIR. RES. & DEVELOP. AGR. CHEM, AMCHEM. PROD, INC, 66- Vis. assoc. prof, Philippines, 54-56. Mem, weeds sub-comt, Nat. Acad. Sci, 64- U.S.N, 42-46, Lt.(jg). P.I. Asn. Adv. Res. Weed control. Address: AmChem Products, Inc, Brookside Ave, Ambler, PA 19002.

FERTIS, DEMETER G(EORGE), b. Athens, Greece, July 25, 26; nat; m. 53; c. 2. STRUCTURAL DYNAMICS. B.S, Mich. State, 52, scholar, 50-55, M.S, 55; Michigan, 56-57; D.E, Athens Tech, 64. Bridge design engr, Mich. State Hwy. Dept, 52-55, phys. res. engr, 56-57; asst. prof. eng. mech, Wayne State, 57-63; assoc. prof. CIVIL ENG, Univ. Iowa, 64-66; PROF, UNIV. AKRON, 66- Consult, Atomic Power Develop. Assocs, 57-; Power Reactor Develop. Co, 57-; Ford Motor Res. Ctr, 61-; Gen. Motors Proving Grounds, 62- Greek Army, 48-50. Am. Soc. Civil Eng; Am. Concrete Inst; Indust. Math. Soc; N.Y. Acad. Sci; Am. Soc. Eng. Educ. Structures; vibrations; urban planning; theoretical mechanics; acoustic stochastic method and approach to determine concrete material properties; developer of the method of the equivalent systems and the concept of the dynamic hinge. Address: Dept. of Civil Engineering, University of Akron, Akron, OH 44304.

FERTL, WALTER HANS, b. Vienna, Austria, Mar. 16, 40; m. 65; c. 2. GEOPHYSICS. Dipl. Ing, Mining & Metall. Col, Austria, 63, Dr. mont, 71; M.S, Univ. Tex, Austin, 66, Ph.D.(petrol. eng), 68. Asst. mgr, well serv. & workover dept, Austrian State Oil Co, Vienna, 63-65; RES. SCIENTIST, PROD. RES. DIV, CONTINENTAL OIL CO, 68- Lectr, Univ. Zulia, Venezuela, 67; eng. found. sem,Univ. Tex; guest lectr, Mining & Metall. Col, Austria, 71; Tech. Univ. Istanbul, 71. Soc. Prof. Well Log Analysts; Soc. Petrol. Eng; Can. Well Logging Soc; Soc. Explor. Geophys; Austrian Soc. Petrol. & Mining Eng. Geophysical well logging research and tool responses; development and improvement of interpretation methods; laboratory and field investigations of physical and chemical rock properties with special emphasis on abnormally pressured formations. Address: Continental Oil Co, Production Research Division, Research & Development Dept, Room 122, Ponca City, OK 74601.

FERTZIGER, ALLEN PHILIP, b. N.Y.C, June 27, 41; m. 70. NEUROPHYSIOLOGY, NEUROBIOLOGY. B.S, City Col. New York, 63; Nat. Insts. Health fel. & Ph.D.(physiol), Univ. Mich, 68. Fel. anat, Albert Einstein Col. Med, 68-70; ASST. PROF. PHYSIOL, MED. SCH, UNIV. MD, BALTIMORE, 70- Am. Physiol. Soc; Electroencephalog. Soc; Soc. Neurosci; Am. Inst. Biol. Sci. Electrophysiology of epilepsy; mechanism of action of anticonvulsant drugs; developmental neurobiology. Address: 5991 Western Run Dr, Baltimore, MD 21209.

FERY, RICHARD L(EE), b. Salem, Ore, Dec. 4, 43; m. 70. GENETICS, PLANT BREEDING. B.S, Ore. State Univ, 66; Nat. Defense Educ. Act fel, Purdue Univ, 66-69, univ. assistantship, 69-70, Ph.D.(plant genetics & breeding), 70. RES. HORTICULTURIST, U.S. VEGETABLE BREEDING LAB, AGR. RES. SERV, 70- U.S.A, 70, Res, 70-, 1st Lt. Am. Soc. Hort. Sci.(Marian W. Meadows Award, 71). Host plant resistance to insects. Address: U.S. Vegetable Breeding Lab, Agricultural Research Service, P.O. Box 3348, Charleston, SC 29407.

FERZIGER, JOEL H(ENRY), b. Brooklyn, N.Y, Mar. 24, 37; m. 61; c. 3. NUCLEAR ENGINEERING. B.Ch.E, Cooper Union, 57; Nat. Sci. Found. fel, Michigan, 57-60, M.S.E, 59, Ph.D.(nuclear eng), 62. Asst. prof. NUCLEAR ENG, STANFORD UNIV, 61-65, ASSOC. PROF, 65- Fulbright res. fel, Netherlands, 67-68. Consult, Gen. Elec. Co. & Encyclop. Britannica Films, 61-67. Am. Phys. Soc; Am. Nuclear Soc. Transport theory; reactor physics; kinetic theory of fluids; radiative transfer. Address: School of Engineering, Stanford University, Stanford, CA 94305.

FESHBACH, HERMAN, b. New York, N.Y, Feb. 2, 17; m. 40; c. 3. NUCLEAR PHYSICS. B.S, City Col, 37; Ph.D.(physics), Mass. Inst. Tech, 42. Tutor PHYSICS, City Col, 37-38; MASS. INST. TECHNOL, 41-45, asst. prof, 45-47, assoc. prof, 47-54, PROF, 54- Guggenheim fel, 54-55, Ford Found. fel, 62-63. With Atomic Energy Comn; Off. Sci. Res. & Develop, 44. Nat. Acad. Sci; fel. Am. Phys. Soc; Am. Acad. Arts & Sci. Theoretical physics with particular reference to nuclear physics. Address: Dept. of Physics, Massachusetts Institute of Technology, Cambridge, MA 02139.

FESSENDEN, PETER, b. Newton, Mass, Sept. 5, 37; m. 59; c. 2. NUCLEAR PHYSICS. A.B, Williams Col, 59; Sc.M, Brown, 63, Ph.D.(physics), 65. Appointee exp. nuclear physics, Los Alamos Sci. Lab, 65-66; ASST. PROF. PHYSICS, ORE. STATE UNIV, 67- Am. Asn. Physics Teachers; Am. Phys. Soc. Low energy experimental nuclear physics using nuclear particle accelerators. Address: Dept. of Physics, Oregon State University, Corvallis, OR 97331.

FESSENDEN, RALPH JAMES, b. Chicago, Ill, Oct. 25, 32; m. 55; c. 1. CHEMISTRY. B.S, Illinois, 55; Ph.D.(chem), California, 58. Asst. prof. CHEM, San Jose State Col, 58-64, assoc. prof, 64-67; PROF. & CHMN. DEPT, UNIV. MONT, 67- Alfred P. Sloan fel, 65-67. Am. Chem. Soc. Organo-metallic chemistry; organo-silicon chemistry. Address: Dept. of Chemistry, University of Montana, Missoula, MT 59801.

FESSENDEN, RICHARD W(ARREN), b. Northampton, Mass, Jan. 22, 34; m. 57; c. 2. PHYSICAL CHEMISTRY. B.S, Massachusetts, 55; Nat. Sci. Found. fel, Mass. Inst. Tech, 56-58, Ph.D.(phys. chem), 58. Nat. Sci. Found. fel, Calif. Inst. Technol, 58-59; fel, RADIATION RES. LABS, MELLON INST, 59-62, SR. FEL, 62-, PROF. CHEM, CARNEGIE-MELLON UNIV, 67- AAAS; Am. Chem. Soc; Am. Phys. Soc. Electron spin resonance; radiation chemistry. Address: Radiation Research Labs, Carnegie-Mellon University, 4400 Fifth Ave, Pittsburgh, PA 15213.

FESSENDEN-RADEN, JUNE M(ARION), b. Whitinsville, Mass, Sept. 2, 37; div; c. 1. BIOCHEMISTRY. A.B, Brown, 59; Nat. Insts. Health fel. & Ph.D. (biochem), Tufts, 63. Nat. Sci. Found. fel. BIOCHEM, Pub. Health Res. Inst. of City of New York, Inc, 63-65 & Am. Cancer Soc. fel, 65-66; consult, Am. Pub. Health Serv, 66; ASST. PROF, CORNELL, 66- AAAS; Am. Soc. Biol. Chem; Am. Chem. Soc. Analysis of complex multi-enzyme systems such as protein synthesis and oxidative phosphorylation, isolation and reconstitution of these systems, using antibodies in defining these systems. Address: Dept. of Biochemistry & Molecular Biology, Wing Hall, Cornell University, Ithaca, NY 14850.

FESSLER, JOHN H(ANS), b. Vienna, Austria, June 15, 28; m. 58; c. 2. BIOCHEMISTRY, BIOPHYSICS. B.A, Oxford, 49, B.Sc, 51, B.A. & M.A, 52, Ph.D.(biochem), 56. Res. fel. biochem. & med, Mass. Gen. Hosp. & Harvard Med. Sch, 56-58; sci. off, biochem, unit for body temperature res, Med. Res. Coun, Eng, 58-61; sr. res. fel. biophys. & molecular biol, Calif. Inst. Technol, 61-66; assoc. prof. MOLECULAR BIOL. & ZOOL, UNIV. CALIF, LOS ANGELES, 66-70, PROF, 70- Arthritis & Rheumatism Found. fel. & Fulbright grant, 56-58; Wellcome fel, Royal Soc. Med, 59-60. Biophys. Soc; Brit. Biophys. Soc; Brit. Biochem. Soc; Soc. Develop. Biol. Macromolecules of connective tissue; physical chemistry of proteins; ultracentrifugal analysis. Address: Molecular Biology Institute, Dept. of Zoology, University of California, Los Angeles, CA 90024.

FESSLER, ROBERT GLENN, b. Omaha, Nebr, Apr. 25, 29; m. 53; c. 3. PHYSICAL & INORGANIC CHEMISTRY. B.S, Univ. Ill, Urbana-Champaign, 50, M.S, 51; Ph.D.(phys. chem), Duke Univ, 58. Res. chemist, AM. CYANAMID CO, BOUND BROOK, 58-69, GROUP LEADER NEW PROD. RES, 69- Ord.C, U.S.A, 52-55, 1st Lt. Am. Chem. Soc. Effect of variations in solid state properties on physical characteristics such as magnetic properties, colloidal stability and visible spectra; interrelation of crystal structure, particle size and shape, defect structure, polymorphic form and surface characteristics with physical and chemical behavior of solids. Address: 15 E. Brook Rd, Martinsville, NJ 08836.

FESSLER, WILLIAM ANDREW, b. Richmond, Ind, Apr. 14, 40; m. 67; c. 2. ORGANIC & POLYMER CHEMISTRY. Ph.D.(org. chem), Univ. Notre Dame, 66. CHEMIST, RES. & DEVELOP. CTR, GEN. ELEC. CO, 66- Am. Chem. Soc. High temperature polymer synthesis; poly imides; organosilicon block copolymers; reaction of organosiloxane with anionic species; poly amides; organometallic compounds of group I A and II A metals. Address: Bldg. K 1, Box 8, General Electric Research & Development Center, Schenectady, NY 12301.

FESTER, DALE A(RTHUR), b. Sterling, Colo, Nov. 7, 32; m. 53; c. 4. CHEMICAL ENGINEERING. B.S, Denver, 53, M.S, 61. Engr, Phillips Petrol. Co, 53; proj. assoc, G.O.B. Löf, Consult. Chem. Eng, 56-61; sr. engr, DENVER DIV, MARTIN MARIETTA CORP, 61-62, design specialist, 62-67, staff engr, 67-70, SR. RES. SCIENTIST, 70- Proj. asst. solar energy, Univ. Wis, 56-61. U.S.A, 53-55. AAAS; Am. Inst. Chem. Eng; Am. Inst. Aeronaut. & Astronaut. Low gravity fluid behavior, high energy liquid propellants; pressurization systems; fluid mechanics; heat transfer; mass transfer; pressurized gas absorption; material compatibility; solar energy utilization. Address: 2916 S. Fenton, Denver, CO 80227.

FESTER, KEITH EDWARD, b. Glendale, Calif, Nov. 16, 42; m. 67; c. 2. ELECTROCHEMISTRY. B.S, Loyola (Calif), 64; M.S, Creighton, 66; Nat. Sci. Found. fel, Univ. of the Pacific, 67-68, Ph.D.(phys. chem), 68. ELECTROCHEMIST, MEDTRONIC, INC, 69- Am. Chem. Soc; Electrochem. Soc; N.Y. Acad. Sci. Complex ion polarography; applied research in the design and use of chemical cells as implantable power sources. Address: Medtronic, Inc, Applied Research Lab, 3055 Old Highway Eight, Minneapolis, MN 55418.

FETCHER, E(DWIN) S(TANTON), b. Winnetka, Ill, Aug. 9, 09; m. 53; c. 4. PHYSICAL & ENVIRONMENTAL SCIENCES. B.S, Harvard, 31; Ph.D.(phys. chem), Chicago, 34. Res. chemist, Universal Oil Prod. Co, 35-36; Rockefeller Inst. Med. Res, 37; instr. physiol, Chicago, 37-40; Minnesota, 40-43; res. physiologist, environ. physiol. & equip. develop, Air Mat. Comd, U.S. Air Force, 43-49; rancher & stockman, Fetcher Ranch, 49-62; res. assoc, lab. physiol. hyg, sch. pub. health, Univ. Minn, Minneapolis, 62-70; CURATOR ENVIRON. SCI, SCI. MUS. OF MINN, 70- AAAS. Membrane chemistry and physiology; water balance of marine mammals; emergency drinking water on the oceans; special protective flight clothing; livestock production; agribusiness; epidemiology of coronary heart disease. Address: Science Museum of Minnesota, 30 E. Tenth St, St. Paul, MN 55101.

FETCHIN, JOHN A, b. Sewickley, Pa, Feb. 22, 42; m. 66; c. 2. INORGANIC CHEMISTRY. B.S, Pittsburgh, 65; Ph.D.(inorg. chem), Case-West. Reserve Univ, 69. RES. CHEMIST, AM. CYANAMID CO, 69- AAAS; Am. Chem. Soc. Inorganic, organometallic and coordination chemistry; synthetic and preparative techniques; reaction of coordinated ligands; homo and heterogeneous catalysis; activation of small molecules; redox mechanisms; paper, pulp, and lignin chemistry; bleaching. Address: American Cyanamid Co, 1937 W. Main St, Stamfort, CT 06904.

FETH, GEORGE C(LARENCE), b. Pittsburgh, Pa, Aug. 17, 31; m. 57; c. 3. ELECTRICAL ENGINEERING. B.S, Carnegie Inst. Technol, 53, M.S, 54, Coffin fel, 55-56, Ph.D.(elec. eng), 56. Engr, Gen. Elec. Co, 56-61; mgr. magnetic film devices res, THOMAS J. WATSON RES. CTR, IBM CORP, 61-62, exploratory memory res, 62-64, integrated circuits & systs. res, 64-65, res. tech. planning staff, 65-67, res. staff mem. memory & storage res, 67-69, MGR. ENG. & SYST. ANAL, 69- Sr. mem. Inst. Elec. & Electronics Eng. Magnetic amplifiers; electrical controls; solid state devices and circuits; magnetic memories; tunnel-diode memories; integrated circuits and systems; computer power supplies, memory and storage devices and systems. Address: Thomas J. Watson Research Center, IBM Corp, P.O. Box 218, Yorktown Heights, NY 10598.

FETH, JOHN H(ENRY), b. Bronxville, N.Y, June 1, 13; m. 43; c. 2. GEOLOGY. B.A, Dartmouth Col, 34; M.A, Columbia, 35; New Mexico, 43-44; Ph.D.(geol), Arizona, 47. Teaching fel. geol, Arizona, 44-46, instr, 46-49; geologist, U.S. GEOL. SURV, 49-65, HYDROLOGIST, 65- Geol. Soc. Am; Geochem. Soc; Am. Asn. Petrol. Geol; Am. Inst. Prof. Geol. Geohydrology in Western United States; saline ground water resources; Pleistocene deposits; geochemistry of ground water; effects urbanization on hydrology. Address: U.S. Geological Survey, 345 Middlefield Rd, Menlo Park, CA 94025.

FETHERSTON, T(HEODORE) R(AYMOND), b. Chicago, Ill, Oct. 6, 11; m. 37; c. 1. FOOD CHEMISTRY. B.S, Illinois, 34. Chemist & bacteriologist, Beatrice Creamery, 34-35; chemist, Griffith Labs, Inc, 35-59; tech. dir. Knickerbocker Mills Co, 60-66; tech. prod. mgr, Archibald & Kendall, Inc, N.Y, 66-67; chemist, Griffith Labs, N.J, 67-70; ANAL. CHEMIST, APOLLO CHEM. CORP, CLIFTON, 70- Am. Chem. Soc; Am. Inst. Chem; Cinnamon and sweet aromatic spices; food flavors and seasoning; protein hydrolysates; fireside deposit analysis. Address: 48 E. Dr, Livingston, NJ 07034.

FETKOVICH, JOHN G(ABRIEL), b. Aliquippa, Pa, June 9, 31; m. 58; c. 2. HIGH ENERGY PHYSICS. B.S, Carnegie Inst. Technol, 53, M.S, 55, Ph.D.(physics), 59. Res. physicist, CARNEGIE-MELLON UNIV, 59-61, asst. prof. PHYSICS, 61-64, assoc. prof, 64-68, PROF, 68- Consult, Argonne Nat. Lab, 60-70, Argonne Univs. Asn. appointee, 70-71; Rutherford High Energy Lab, England, 71-72. Sig.C, 60-61, 1st Lt. AAAS; Am. Phys. Soc; Am. Asn. Physics Teachers. Physics of elementary particles. Address: Dept. of Physics, Carnegie-Mellon University, Pittsburgh, PA 15213.

FETNER, EUGENE MACELEE, b. Winter Garden, Fla, Feb. 2, 29; m. 51; c. 2. ELECTRONIC ENGINEERING. B.E.E, Florida, 51, M.S.E, 58; Fla. State, 51-52. Engr, radio-frequency propagation, MISSILE TEST PROJ, Radio Corp. Am, PATRICK AFB, 56-61, leader spec. eng, 61-64, telemetry, 64-68, MGR. ANTENNA SYSTS, RCA CORP, 68- Instr, Brevard Eng. Col, 60-, head dept, 61-63, asst. dean, 63- U.S.A.F, 51-55, Res, 55-58, Capt. Inst. Elec. & Electronics Eng. Antennas; radiofrequency propagation; telemetry; meteorology. Address: 656 Forest Dr, Melbourne, FL 32901.

FETNER, R(OBERT) H(ENRY), b. Savannah, Ga, Feb. 22, 22; m. 44; c. 2. BIOLOGY. B.S, Miami (Fla), 50, M.S, 52; Ph.D.(biol), Emory, 55. Res. asst. prof. APPL. BIOL, eng. exp. sta, GA. INST. TECHNOL, 55-58, res. assoc. prof, 59-64, RES. PROF, NUCLEAR RES. CTR, 64-, DIR. SCH. BIOL, 65- Radiation biology; cellular physiology; cytogenetics. Address: School of Biology, Georgia Institute of Technology, Atlanta, GA 30332.

FETSCHER, CHARLES A(RTHUR), b. N.Y.C, Dec. 7, 13; m. 42; c. 3. ORGANIC CHEMISTRY. B.S, Col. of Holy Cross, 34, M.S, 35; Ph.D.(org. chem), Columbia, 38. Res. chemist, Cuban Mining Co, Cuba, 38-40; Shawinigan Resins Corp, Mass, 41-45; asst. dir. res, Cluett Peabody & Co, N.Y, 45-55; dir. cent. res. labs, Nopco Chem. Co, 55-65; GROUP MGR. RES, HYSOL DIV, DEXTER CORP, 65- Fel. AAAS; Fiber Soc; Am. Chem. Soc. Resins, plastics and additives. Address: 1306 Buchanan Ave, Olean, NY 14760.

FETSKO, JACQUELINE MARIE, b. Allentown, Pa, Jan. 14, 26. PHYSICAL CHEMISTRY. B.A, Pennsylvania, 46; M.S, Lehigh, 53. Tech. asst, NAT. PRINTING INK RES. INST, LEHIGH UNIV, 49-55, res. supvr, 55-61, asst. res. dir, 61-66, asst. to dir, ctr. for surface & coating res, 66-69, ED, 69- Asst. ed, Encyclop. Org. Coatings, 56-58; consult, Scott Paper Co, 56-58; Handy & Harman, 59-60. Tech. Asn. Pulp & Paper Indust. Printing ink-paper relationships; transfer; surface strength; optical properties. Address: National Printing Ink Research Institute, Lehigh University, Bethlehem, PA 18015.

FETT, E. REINOLD, b. Grand Haven, Mich, Sept. 18, 27; m. 51; c. 2. ANALYTICAL CHEMISTRY. A.B, Hope Col, 51; M.S, Illinois, 53, Ph.D.(chem), 55. Asst. res. chemist, UNION OIL CO. CALIF, 55-56, res. chemist, 57-61, sr. res. scientist, 62-70, RES. ASSOC, 71- U.S.A, 46-48. Am. Chem. Soc. Development and application of instrumentation as applied to analytical chemistry. Address: Union Research Center, Box 76, Brea, CA 92621.

FETT, GILBERT H(OWARD), b. Chicago, Ill, June 19, 09; m. 36; c. 4. ELECTRICAL ENGINEERING. B.S, Illinois, 31, Ph.D.(elec. eng), 40; M.S, Iowa State Col, 32. Asst. elec. eng, Iowa State Col, 31-32; res. engr, Littlefuse Labs, Ill, 33-35; instr. ELEC. ENG, UNIV. ILL, URBANA-CHAMPAIGN, 35-41, assoc, 41-43, asst. prof, 43-45, assoc. prof, 45-47, PROF, 47-, asst, 35-37. Jr. engr, Fed. Power Comn, Ill, 37; guest prof. & U.S. Agency Int. Develop. group leader, Indian Inst. Tech, Kharagpur, 62-64; summers, res. assoc, Argonne Nat. Lab, 56- Consult, 56- Dir, Nat. Electronics Conf, 45, v.pres, 47, exec. v.pres, 48, pres, 49. Fel. Am. Phys. Soc; fel. Inst. Elec. & Electronics Eng. Arc welding; arc discharges; electric circuit theory; oscillators; servomechanisms; nonlinear systems. Address: Dept. of Electrical Engineering, University of Illinois, Urbana-Champaign, Urbana, IL 61801.

FETT, JOHN D, b. New York, N.Y, Mar. 2, 33; m. 56; c. 3. GEOLOGY, GEOPHYSICS. B.S, Redlands, 54; Calif. Inst. Tech, 54-56; California, Los Angeles, 57-59, M.S, Riverside, 67. Chemist, Naval Ord. Test Sta, Calif, 54-55; gravity observer, Lamont Geol. Observ, Columbia, 56-57; res. asst. Inst. Geophys, California, Los Angeles, 57-59; geologist, Beylik Drilling Co, 59-60; consult, John D. Fett & Assocs, 60-69; PRIN. CONSULT, EARTH SCIS. ASSOCS, 69- Dir, East. Munic. Water Dist. Geol. Soc. Am; Soc. Explor. Geophys; Seismol. Soc. Am; Am. Geophys. Union; Am. Inst. Mining, Metall. & Petrol. Eng; sr. mem. Instrument Soc. Am; Am. Water Works Asn; Am. Soc. Test. & Mat; Soc. Econ. Paleont. & Mineral; European Asn. Explor. Geophys; Asn. Eng. Geol. New techniques for the application of geophysics to problems in engineering geology and ground water studies. Address: 26745 Meridian St, Hemet, CA 92343.

FETT, ROBERT W, b. Rhinelander, Wis, Aug. 3, 28; m. 54; c. 5. METEOROLOGY. Res. satellite meteorologist, Nat. Weather Satellite Ctr, Wash, D.C, 61-66, meteorologist-weather reconnaissance pilot, U.S. Air Force, Mariana Islands, 66-68, STAFF METEOROLOGIST, Hq. Air Weather Serv, Scott AFB, Ill, 68-71; NAT. ENVIRON. SATELLITE SERV, WASH, D.C, 71- U.S.A.F, 52-71, Lt. Col. Am. Meteorol. Soc. Applications of satellite data to field of tropical meteorology; nature and structure of tropical cyclones as revealed by satellite observations. Address: 3131 Port Way, Annapolis, MD 21403.

FETTE, C(LARENCE) WILLIAM, b. Wheeling, W.Va, Mar. 22, 31; m. 60; c. 3. NUCLEAR & MATHEMATICAL PHYSICS. B.S.(math), Carnegie Inst. Technol, 53, B.S.(physics) & M.S, 58. Mathematician, anal. sect. proof & develop. servs, Aberdeen Proving Ground, 53-54; asst. prof. physics & chmn. dept, Wheeling Col, 58-61; res. physicist, Graham Res. Lab, Jones & Laughlin Steel Corp, 61-62; U.S. Bur. Mines, 62-64; asst. res. physicist, Carnegie Inst. Technol, 64-66; instr. PHYSICS, Univ. Pittsburgh, 66-70; ASST. PROF, PA. STATE UNIV, 70- Nat. Sci. Found. ultrasonics res. grant, 60, instr, sec. teachers res. prog. physics, 64-65. U.S.A, 54-55, Res, 55- Am. Phys. Soc; Am. Asn. Physics Teachers; Instrument Soc. Am. General relativity research primarily concerned with gravitational radiation problems; elementary particle physics; ultraviolet spectroanalysis of coal structures; high temperature research and instrumentation in basic oxygen steel making. Address: 6012 Irishtown Rd, Bethel Park, PA 15102.

FETTER, ALEXANDER L(EES), b. Phila, Pa, May 16, 37; m. 62; c. 2. PHYSICS. A.B, Williams Col, 58; Rhodes Scholar, 58-60, B.A, Oxford, 60, M.A, 64; Ph.D.(physics), Harvard, 63. Miller res. fel, PHYSICS, California, Berkeley, 63-65; asst. prof, STANFORD UNIV, 65-68, ASSOC. PROF, 68- Alfred P. Sloan res. fel, 68-70. Am. Phys. Soc. Low-temperature behavior of quantum fluids, especially superfluid helium and type-II superconductors; general theory of many-particle systems; quantum hydrodynamics. Address: Dept. of Physics, Stanford University, Stanford, CA 94305.

FETTER, BERNARD FRANK, b. Baltimore, Md, Jan. 21, 21; m. 45; c. 4. PATHOLOGY. A.B, Hopkins, 41; M.D, Duke, 44. Instr. PATH, MED. CTR, DUKE UNIV, 51-53, assoc, 53-55, asst. prof, 55-59, assoc. prof, 59-67,

PROF, 67- Med.C, 45-47, Capt. Am. Med. Asn; Am. Asn. Path. & Bact; Col. Am. Path. Surgical pathology. Address: Medical Center, Duke University, Box 3220, Durham, NC 27706.

FETTER, EDWARD J, b. N.Y.C, May 17, 33; m. 58; c. 6. ORGANIC & POLYMER CHEMISTRY. B.A, La Salle Col, 55; M.S, Univ. Md, 58, Goodyear fel, 58-60, Nat. Insts. Health fel, 60-61, Ph.D.(org. chem), 61. Polymer res. chemist, AM. CYANAMID CO, 61-69, GROUP LEADER, 69- Am. Chem. Soc. Ester pyrolysis as a route to exocyclic dienes and Diels-Alder reactions; dielectric polymers for use in electroluminescence and capacitors; water soluble polymers; film orientation studies; new surfactants for emulsion polymerizations; specialty monomers; polyesters. Address: Industrial Chemicals & Plastics Division, American Cyanamid Co, 1937 W. Main St, Stamford, CT 06904.

FETTER, NEIL ROSS, b. Dayton, Ohio, Dec. 7, 29. ANALYTICAL CHEMISTRY. B.S, Antioch Col, 52; M.S, Univ. Ore, 54, fel, 54-55, Ph.D.(chem), 57. Inorg. chemist, U.S. Naval Ord. Test Sta, 56-59, organometallic chemist, U.S. Naval Ord. Lab, 59-70; ANAL. CHEMIST, DEPT. GEOL. SCI, UNIV. CALIF, RIVERSIDE, 70- AAAS. Chemical analysis of geological materials. Address: Dept. of Geological Sciences, Room 1224, University of California, Riverside, CA 92502.

FETTERLY, LLOYD C(OCHRAN), b. Victoria, B.C, Jan. 7, 19; U.S. citizen; m. 42; c. 3. ORGANIC CHEMISTRY, CHEMICAL ENGINEERING. B.S, Washington (Seattle), 40, M.S, 41, Ph.D.(chem. eng), 50. From technologist to group leader res, Shell Oil Co, Calif, 41-47; instr. chem. eng, Washington (Seattle), 47-48; res. chemist, SHELL DEVELOP. CO. DIV, SHELL OIL CO, 50-54, RES. SUPVR, 54- Am. Chem. Soc; Am. Inst. Chem. Eng; fel. Am. Inst. Chem. Heterogeneous catalysis; free radical and cationic mechanisms; oxidation; alkylation; polymerization; phenols; aromatics; olefins; acrolein; radiation resistant fluid; petroleum refining; urea-thiourea extractive crystallization; liquid-liquid extraction; extractive distillation; heat transfer of heterogeneous fluids. Address: Shell Development Co, Emeryville, CA 94608.

FETTERMAN, D(AVID) S, b. Cleveland, Ohio, July 31, 31; m. 53; c. 2. CHEMICAL ENGINEERING. B.S, Lehigh, 53. Chem. engr, Atomic Energy Cmn, 53-55; proj. leader, Callery Chem. Co, 57-60; process engr, Pennsalt Chem. Corp, 60-66; sr. develop. engr, Atlantic Richfield Corp, ARCO CHEM. CO, 66-71, MGR. PLANNING & EVAL, 71- Group leader, Chem. Warfare Lab, U.S.A, 55-57. Am. Chem. Soc; Am. Inst. Chem. Eng. Development of research results into practical economical processes for commercial production of chemicals. Address: Supply & Transportation Dept, Arco Chemical Co, 260 S. Broad St, Philadelphia, PA 19101.

FETTERMAN, JAMES W(ILLIAM), b. Shamokin, Pa, Feb. 4, 34; m. 62; c. 3. MINERAL & MINING ENGINEERING. B.S, Pa. State, 56, M.S, 58, Ph.D. (mineral prep. eng), 61. Res. asst. mineral prep. eng, Pa. State, 56-58; res. investr. chem, N.J. ZINC CO, 61-69, res. supvr. RES. DEPT, 69-70, SUPVR. APPLN. RES, 70- Am. Inst. Mining, Metall. & Petrol. Eng; Am. Chem. Soc. Mineral preparation engineering hydrometallurgy; colloid and surface chemistry of inorganic pigments; polymer applications; reprography and paper technology. Address: Research Dept, New Jersey Zinc Co, 211 Franklin Ave, Bldg, Palmerton, PA 18071.

FETTERS, KARL L(EROY), b. Alliance, Ohio, Nov. 28, 09; m. 32, 68; c. 5. METALLURGICAL ENGINEERING. B.S, Carnegie Inst. Tech, 31; hon. fel. & Am. Inst. Min. & Metall. Eng. fel, Mass. Inst. Tech, 39-40, D.Sc.(metall. eng), 40. Asst. metallurgist, Nat. Tube Co, 33-36; open hearth metallurgist, Youngstown Sheet & Tube Co, Ohio, 36-38, asst, 38-39, metallurigst, 40-41; asst. prof. metall. & staff mem. metals res. lab, Carnegie Inst. Tech, 41-43; special metal. engr, YOUNGSTOWN SHEET & TUBE CO, 43-50, asst. to v.pres. in charge opers, 50-59, V.PRES. res. & develop, 59-70, TECH. SERV, 70- With Off. Sci. Res. & Develop, 44. Am. Soc; Metals; Am. Inst. Mining, Metall. & Petrol. Eng.(pres, 64-65); Am. Iron & Steel Inst; Nat. Acad. Eng; Brit. Iron & Steel Inst. Slag metal reactions as applied to steelmaking; basic open hearth research; ingot structures; corrosion studies; electrolytic tin plate. Address: Two Oak Dr, Poland, OH 44514.

FETTERS, LEWIS, b. Toledo, Ohio, Mar. 29, 36. PHYSICAL & POLYMER CHEMISTRY. A.B, Col, Wooster, 58; Ph.D.(chem), Akron, 62. Nat. Sci. Found. fel, POLYMER CHEM, Akron, 62-63; Nat. Acad. Sci-Nat. Res. Coun. Coun. fel, Nat. Bur. Standards, 63-65; PROF, INST. POLYMER SCI, UNIV. AKRON, 67- Ionic polymerization kinetics; polymer rheology and synthesis; solution properties of polymers; radiation polymerization. Address: Institute of Polymer Science, University of Akron, Akron, OH 44304.

FETTES, E(DWARD) M(ACKAY), b. Brooklyn, N.Y, Jan. 10, 18; m. 41, 53; c. 6. POLYMER CHEMISTRY. S.B, Mass. Inst. Technol, 40; Ph.D.(chem), Polytech. Inst. Brooklyn, 57. Develop. chemist, U.S. Rubber Co, R.I, 40-41; res. chemist, Kendall Co, Mass, 41-42; Thiokol Chem. Corp, N.J, 42-44, group leader, 44-45, asst. develop. mgr, 45-46, mgr. develop. dept, 46-50, res. & develop. dept, 51-58, dir. res. & develop, 58-60; mgr. plastics res, Koppers Co, Inc, 60-70; TECH. DIR. POLYMERS, NORTH. PETROCHEM. CO, 70- AAAS; Asn. Res. Dirs; Am. Chem. Soc; Commercial Develop. Asn; Am. Inst. Chem; Faraday Soc; Soc. Plastics Eng; Brit. Plastics Inst. Elastomers; plastics; resins. Address: Polymer Technical Center, Northern Petrochemical Co, Morris, IL 60450.

FETTES, JAMES JOSEPH, b. Ottawa, Ont, Can, Oct. 30, 14; m. 45; c. 3. FOREST ENTOMOLOGY. B.Sc, New Brunswick, 45; Ph.D.(forest entom), Toronto, 51. Res. officer, forest biol. div, Can. Dept. Agr, 45-50; head chem. control. sect, CAN. DEPT. FORESTRY, 51-64, DIR. CHEM. CONTROL. RES. INST, 64- Mem. interdepartmental cmt. forest spraying opers, 58-66; entom. panel subcmt, Defence Res. Bd, 62-66; Fed. Interdepartmental Cmt. Pesticides, 63-66; dir. Int. Agr. Aviation Centre, The Hague, Netherlands, 64-; mem. assoc. cmt. agr. & forestry aviation, Nat. Res. Coun. Can, 65-66. Emtom. Soc. Can; Can. Inst. Forestry. Direct control of forest pests; airplane spraying and forestry aviation; forest insect toxicology; research and development of aircraft spraying equipment. Address: Chemical Control Research Institute, Dept. of the Environment, 25 Pickering Pl, Ottawa, Ont. K1A 0H3, Can.

FETZER, HOMER D, b. San Antonio, Tex, Oct. 19, 32; m. 54; c. 5. ATOMIC & NUCLEAR PHYSICS. B.S, St. Mary's (Tex), 54; M.A, Texas, 59, Nat. Sci. Found. summer fel, 59, Ph.D.(electron scattering), 65. Instr. PHYSICS, ST. MARY'S UNIV. (TEX), 59-62, asst. prof, 62-65, assoc. prof. & chmn. dept, 65-69, PROF. & GRAD. ADV, 70- Nat. Sci. Found. sci. faculty fel, 63-65; summer sr. res. physicist, earth sci. applns. sect, Southwest. Res. Inst, 66- U.S.A, 54-57, 1st Lt. Am. Asn. Physics Teachers; Sci. Res. Soc. Am. Neutron activation; low energy nuclear physics; use of low energy accelerator for education and research; x-ray fluorescent analysis of trace elements in air sedimentation samples. Address: Dept. of Physics, St. Mary's University, San Antonio, TX 78284.

FETZER, M(AURICE) C(HARLES), b. Minneapolis, Minn, Mar. 16, 07; m. 33; c. 4. PHYSICAL METALLURGY. Met.E, Minnesota, 29; Purdue, 29-30; Jennings scholar, Harvard, 32-34; Sc.D.(metall), 34. Instr. metall, Purdue, 29-30; asst. metallurgist, Am. Steel & Wire Co, Mass, 32-34; asst. prof. metall, Wash. State Col, 36-37; Pa. State Col, 37-42; metallurgist in charge labs, Carpenter Steel Co, 42-48; SUPVR. RES. PHYS. METALL, CTR. FOR TECHNOL, KAISER ALUMINUM & CHEM. CORP, 49- Am. Soc. Metals (Howe medal, 46); Am. Inst. Mining, Metall. & Petrol. Eng. Investigation and development of aluminum alloys and ferrous alloys. Address: Center for Technology, Kaiser Aluminum & Chemical Corp, Pleasanton, CA 94566.

FETZER, WALLACE G(ORDON), b. Minneapolis, Minn, Feb. 11, 05; m. 32; c. 2. ECONOMIC GEOLOGY. E.M, Minnesota, 29, Ph.D.(geol. & phys. chem), 34. Mining engr. & geologist, Soc. Forestry & Mining, Belg. Congo, 29-31; tech. adv, geol. & petrol, Colombia, 35-43; Latin Am. rep, Butler Bros, 43-45; geologist, N.J. Zinc Co, 46-47; chief Colo. explor. br, U.S. Atomic Energy Comn, 47-50; chief geologist, west div, Vanadium Corp. Am, 51-52; dir. res. & develop, Oglebay Norton Co, 52-71; CONSULT. ECON. GEOL, 71- Fel. AAAS; Am. Inst. Prof. Geol; Am. Geophys. Union; Soc. Econ. Geol; fel. Geol. Soc. Am. Control and reduction of long range missiles, atmospheric impact and seismic effects produced by large-scale open cut blasts; geology of metallic and nonmetallic deposits, North America, South America and Africa; application of mathematical physics to the elimination or minimization of blasting hazards and to other engineering problems. Address: 4692 W. 227th St, Fairview Park, OH 44126.

FEUCHT, DONALD LEE, b. Akron, Ohio, Aug. 25, 33; m. 58; c. 2. ELECTRICAL ENGINEERING. B.S, Valparaiso, 55; M.S, Carnegie Inst. Tech, 56, Ph.D.(elec. eng), 61. Instr. ELEC. ENG, CARNEGIE-MELLON UNIV, 58-60, asst. prof, 60-65, assoc. prof, 65-69, PROF. & ASSOC. HEAD DEPT, 69- Summers, electronics engr, Gen. Dynamics/Convair, 56, res. assoc, Int. Bus. Mach. Corp, 61; consult, Technograph Printed Circuits, Inc, 61; Union Carbide Corp, 63; Power Components, 65-67; PPG Industs, 67-69; Aluminum Asn. Am, 67-69; Essex Int, 67- Am. Phys. Soc; Am. Soc. Eng. Educ; Inst. Elec. & Electronics Eng; Electrochem. Soc. Theoretical and experimental properties of semiconductor heterojunctions; fabrication, and electrical and optical properties of semiconductor devices; integrated circuits. Address: Dept. of Electrical Engineering, Carnegie-Mellon University, Pittsburgh, PA 15213.

FEUCHT, JAMES R(OGER), b. Denver, Colo, June 6, 33; m. 56; c. 3. HORTICULTURE, BOTANY. B.S, Colo. State Univ, 56; M.S, Mich. State Univ, 57, Ph.D.(hort), 60. Teaching asst. hort, Mich. State Univ, 56-60; asst. prof, West. Ill. Univ, 60; Rutgers Univ, 61-66; EXTEN. ASSOC. PROF. HORT. & EXTEN. HORTICULTURIST, COLO. STATE UNIV, 66- U.S.A, 60, 1st Lt. Am. Soc. Hort. Sci; Am. Hort. Soc. Landscape horticulture; air-layering of pine and spruce using several potential rooting hormones; effects of gibberellin A-3 on cell growth in Phaseolus vulgaris L, an anatomical study; various applied research in insect control on landscape plants. Address: 909 York St, Denver, CO 80206.

FEUCHTWANG, THOMAS EMANUEL, b. Budapest, Hungary, May 21, 30; m. 53; c. 4. THEORETICAL & SOLID STATE PHYSICS. B.E.E, Ga. Inst. Tech, 53; Francis J. Cole fel. & M.S, Calif. Inst. Tech, 54; Ph.D.(microwave theory), Stanford, 60. Res. asst, microwave lab, Stanford, 54-59; res. assoc. PHYSICS, Illinois, 60-62; asst. prof, Minnesota, Minneapolis, 62-65; assoc. prof, PA. STATE UNIV, 65-70, PROF, 70- Summers, vis. lab. atomic & solid state physics, Cornell & Vis. consult, Westinghouse Res. Labs, Pa, 63; vis. prof, dept. physics, Tel-Aviv Univ, Israel, 71-72. Sig.C, Israeli Army, 48-50. Am. Phys. Soc. Lattice dynamics; electronic structure of point defects in ionic crystals; theory of low energy electron scattering from single crystals; Mössbauer effect and localized lattice modes; tunneling through surfaces and junctions. Address: Dept. of Physics, Pennsylvania State University, University Park, PA 16802.

FEUER, G(EORGE), b. Szeged, Hungary, Mar. 12, 21; m. 49; c. 3. BIOCHEMICAL PHARMACOLOGY, PATHOLOGICAL CHEMISTRY. B.S, Univ. Szeged, 43, Ph.D.(phys. chem) & high sch. teaching dipl, 44; Cand.Med.Sci, Hungarian Acad. Sci, 52. Asst. lectr. org. chem, Univ. Szeged, 45-46, sr. lectr. biochem, 46-48; Univ. Budapest, 48-50; sr. res. assoc, Hungarian Acad. Sci, 50-53, head of muscular & neurochem, 53-56; biochem, Cancer Res. Inst, Budapest, 56; guest worker, Pasteur Inst, Paris, 57; sr. res. assoc. neurochem, inst. psychiat, Univ. London, 57-62; neuropsychiat, Med. Res. Coun, Carshalton, Eng, 62-63; head biochem, Brit. Indust. Biol. Res. Asn, Carshalton, 63-68; asst. prof. PATH. CHEM, UNIV. TORONTO, 68, ASSOC. PROF, 68- Prof. biochem, Eötvös Lórând Univ, 50-53; secy. biochem. comt, Hungarian Acad. Sci, 52-56; chmn. session, Fourth Int. Goitre Conf, London, Eng, 60; vis. prof, Warner-Lambert Res. Inst. Can, 69- Res. award, Budapest County Coun, 45; Order of Merit, 2nd Class, Hungarian People's Repub, 53. Fel. Royal Inst. Chem; Brit. Biochem. Soc; Can. Biochem. Soc; Can. Asn. Res. Toxicol; Can. Soc. Chemother. Mechanism of muscular contraction; neurochemistry; metabolism of thyroid and other hormones in connection with emotional behavior; biochemical organization of the liver function in relation to its response to drugs and toxic compounds. Address: Dept. of Pathological Chemistry, University of Toronto, Room 521, Banting Institute, 100 College St, Toronto 181, Ont, Can.

FEUER, HENRY, b. Stanislau, Poland, Apr. 4, 12; nat; m. 46. ORGANIC CHEMISTRY. M.S, Vienna, 34, Ph.D.(org. chem), 37. Fel, Sorbonne, 39; Purdue, 43-46; pharmacist, Toledo Hosp, Ohio, 41-43; instr. CHEM, univ. exten, Indiana, 46; asst. prof, PURDUE UNIV, 46-54, assoc. prof, 54-61, PROF, 61- Vis. prof, Hebrew Univ, Israel, 64- AAAS; Am. Chem. Soc. Organic nitrogen compounds; synthesis and reactions of nitro compounds and heterocyclic systems. Address: Dept. of Chemistry, Purdue University, Lafayette, IN 47907.

FEUER, IRVING, b. New York, N.Y, Oct. 19, 22; m. 58; c. 2. PHYSICAL CHEMISTRY. B.S, City Col, 43; M.S, Polytech. Inst. Brooklyn, 55. Phys. chemist, Can. Radium & Uranium Corp, 42-44, 45-47; phys. chemist & head balance res, Seederer-Kohlbusch, Inc, 47-49; physicist in charge isotope lab, Beth Israel Hosp, 50-59; phys. chemist, Cambridge Res. Ctr, U.S. Air Force, 59-60; DIR. APPL. RES. & DEVELOP, CANRAD PRECISION INDUSTS, INC, 60- Consult, N.Y. Univ-Bellevue Med. Ctr, 54-59. U.S.N, 44-45. AAAS; Am. Vacuum Soc; Am. Chem. Soc. Radioactivity; nuclear instrumentation; radio isotopes; radiation effects on surfaces; microbalance design; catalysis; electroluminescence; phosphors; radioactive light sources; tritium. Address: 27 Seaview Lane, Port Washington, NY 11050.

FEUER, MICHAEL, b. Rybushka, U.S.S.R, Aug. 28, 42; U.S. citizen; m. 65; c. 2. ELEMENTARY PARTICLE PHYSICS. A.B, Harvard, 64, Ph.D.(physics) & Nat. Sci. Found. fel, 69; Nat. Sci. Found. fel, California, Berkeley, 64-66. STAFF ENGR. IBM CORP, 68- Parity violation in nuclear processes; diffusion of impurities in silicon. Address: 18 Crescent Rd, Poughkeepsie, NY 12601.

FEUER, PAULA B(ERGER), b. New York, N.Y, Feb. 11, 22; m. 46. PHYSICS. B.A, Hunter Col, 41; M.S, Purdue, 46, Ph.D.(physics), 51. Instr. physics, PURDUE UNIV, 46-55, asst. prof. ENG. SCI, 55-57, assoc. prof, 57-65, PROF, 65- Vis. prof, Hebrew Univ, Israel, 64. Am. Phys. Soc; Soc. Eng. Sci.(treas, 64-69). Solid state physics; electronic properties solids; gas-surface interactions. Address: Dept. of Engineering Sciences, School of Aeronautics, Astronautics & Engineering Sciences, Purdue University, Lafayette, IN 47907.

FEUER, REESHON, b. Marlow, N.H, Jan. 11, 17; m. 41; c. 3. SOIL SCIENCE. B.S, New Hampshire, 40, M.S, 51; Ph.D, Cornell, 55. Asst. soil surv. & agron. & instr. agron, New Hampshire, 39-40; soil scientist, soil conserv. serv, U.S. Dept. Agr, 41-45; div. soil surv, 46; asst. prof. agron. & asst. soil surv, New Hampshire, 47-51; asst. soil sci, CORNELL UNIV, 51-55, asst. prof. AGRON, exten, 55-58, assoc. prof, 58-68, PROF, 68- Pedalogical consult, phys. res. labs, Boston Univ, 52-53; consult, Donald J. Belcher & Assocs, Inc, 54; Doane Agr. Serv, Inc, 55; Tippetts-Abbett-McCarthy-Stratton Co, 59; Rural Welfare Coun. Venezuela, 59-60; soils consult, Beasley & Beasley, Wash. D.C, 63-64; Australian soils consult, Planners Collaborative, N.Y, 64-; Ford Found. sponsored vis. prof. Cornell Univ. grad. educ. prog, col. agr, Univ. Philippines, 68-71. Soil Sci. Soc. Am; Am. Soc. Agron; Soil Conserv. Soc. Am; Int. Soc. Soil Sci. Classification and utilization of soils; soil association maps; soil and crop management; forest soils; exploratory investigation of soils and agricultural potential of soils of Brasilia, in the central plateau of Brazil. Address: Dept. of Agronomy, College of Agriculture & Home Economics, Cornell University, Ithaca, NY 14850.

FEUER, ROBERT C(HARLES), b. New York, N.Y, Feb. 23, 36, m. 69. ZOOLOGY. B.S, Cornell, 56; M.S, Tulane, 58; fel, Michigan, 59-60; Nat. Sci. Found. Co-op. fel, Utah, 62-63; Ph.D, 66. Asst, Tulane, 56-58; asst. prof. biol, Hartwick Col, 60-61; asst, Utah, 61-62; instr. BIOL. SCI, Purdue Univ. Calumet Campus, 63-64; PHILA. COL. PHARM, 64-66, ASST. PROF, 66- Asst. prof, Tulane Univ, summer 61. Am. Soc. Ichthyol. & Herpet; Soc. Syst. Zool; Brit. Herpet. Soc. Taxonomic herpetology, especially Chelydridae; ecology. Address: Dept. of Biological Sciences, Philadelphia College of Pharmacy & Science, 43rd St, Kingsessing & Woodland Aves, Philadelphia, PA 19104.

FEUERSANGER, ALFRED E(RNST), b. Ragnit, Germany, July 29, 27; U.S. citizen; m. 55; c. 5. PHYSICS. B.S, Tech. Univ. Aachen, 51; M.S, Polytech. Inst. Brooklyn, 57. Res. asst. physics, Polytech. Inst. Brooklyn, 52-53, 55-57; sr. engr, res. labs, Sylvania Elec. Prod, Inc, GEN. TEL. & ELECTRONICS CORP, 57-60, res. engr, GEN. TEL. & ELECTRONICS LABS, INC, 60-63, adv. res. engr, 63-70, ENGR. SPECIALIST, 70- Chmn. thin films, Electronic Components Conf, D.C, 67; session chmn, Int. Vacuum Cong, Boston, Mass, 71. Sig.C, U.S.A, 53-55. Am. Phys. Soc; Am. Asn. Physics Teachers; Am. Vacuum Soc; N.Y. Acad. Sci. Crystal growth; diffusion; dielectric and conduction behavior of ice crystals; properties of semiconductor surfaces and devices; preparation and properties of highpermittivity dielectric films; thin film tunneling and switching; integrated circuits; interference microscopy. Address: General Telephone & Electronics Labs, 208-20 Willets Point Blvd, Bayside, NY 11360.

FEUERSTEIN, DONALD L(EE), b. San Bernardino, Calif, Mar. 26, 32; m. 62; c. 1. SANITARY ENGINEERING. B.S, Univ. Calif, Berkeley, 54, M.S, 59, Ph.D, 66, Los Angeles, 54-55. Assoc. engr, E.A. Pearson, consult. engr, 58; sr. engr, Eng-Sci, Inc, 60-61; asst. dir. sanit. eng. res. lab, Univ. Calif, Berkeley, 61-66, asst. prof. civil eng, Irvine, 66-67; sr. eng. specialist, Aerojet-Gen. Corp, div. Gen. Tire & Rubber Co, Calif, 67-71; DIR. RES. & DEVELOP. LAB, ENG-SCI, INC, 71- U.S.A.F, 54-58, Res, 58-, 1st Lt. Am. Soc. Civil Eng; Am. Meteorol. Soc; Air Pollution Control. Asn. Wastewater treatment and disposal; general air and water pollution; dispersion mechanisms and phenomena in water and air. Address: Research & Development Lab, Engineering-Science, Inc, 600 Bancroft Way, Berkeley, CA 94710.

FEUERSTEIN, ERWIN, b. Vienna, Austria, Apr. 12, 22; m. 51; c. 1. ELECTRICAL ENGINEERING. B.S, Ohio State, 47, M.Sc, 49. Engr, Melpar, Inc, 50-52; engr. theory group, Lab. Electronics, Inc, 52-57, mgr, 57-67; MEM. TECH. STAFF, RADAR TECHNOL. DEPT, MITRE CORP, 67- U.S.A, 43-46. Inst. Elec. & Electronics Eng. Fourier analysis; circuit theory; information theory; applied physics. Address: Radar Technology Dept, Mitre Corp, Box 208, Bedford, MA 01730.

FEUERSTEIN, IRWIN, b. N.Y.C, Sept. 18, 39. CHEMICAL ENGINEERING, FLUID MECHANICS. B.Ch.E, City Col. New York, 62; M.S.Ch.E, Newark Col. Eng, 65; Ph.D.(chem. eng), Univ. Mass, Amherst, 69. Process engr, Esso Res. & Eng. Co, 62-64; fel. exp. med, McGill Univ, 69-70; ASST. PROF. CHEM. ENG, McMASTER UNIV, 70- Am. Inst. Chem. Eng; Can. Soc. Chem. Eng. Coalescence phenomena, experimental and theoretical; biological fluid mechanics, especially model studies of flow in arterial shapes prone to artery disease; hemodynamics, especially motion of red cell suspensions. Address: Dept. of Chemical Engineering, McMaster University, Hamilton, Ont, Can.

FEUERSTEIN, SEYMOUR, b. New York, N.Y, Dec. 12, 31; m. 57; c. 3. METALLURGY. B.S, Arizona, 53; M.S. California, Berkeley, 58, Ph.D.(metall), 62. Metallurgist, Gen. Elec. Co, N.Y, 53; Goodyear Aircraft Co, Ariz, 56; res. engr, California, 56-61, Lawrence Radiation Lab, California, Berkeley, 60-61; mem. tech. staff, MAT. SCI. LAB, AEROSPACE CORP, CALIF, 61-67, HEAD SURFACE & LUBRICATION PHENOMENA SECT, 67- Lectr, eng. exten, California, Los Angeles, 64- U.S.A.F, 54-55, 1st Lt. Am. Vacuum Soc. Mechanical properties of materials; crystal and surface physics; crystal growth; vacuum and radiation effects on materials; lubrication phenomena. Address: 12961 Chandler Blvd, Van Nuys, CA 91401.

FEURT, SELDON D(ICK), b. Wichita, Kans, Oct. 21, 23; m. 42; c. 2. PHARMACOLOGY. B.S, Loyola, 49; M.S, Florida, 51, Ph.D.(pharmacol), 53. Asst, Florida, 49-50, instr. pharmacy, 50-53; assoc. prof. pharmacol. & pharmacog, Georgia, 53-58, prof, 58-59; DEAN COL. PHARM, UNIV. TENN, MEMPHIS, 59- U.S.N.R, 42-45. AAAS; Am. Pharmaceut. Asn. Phytopharmacological investigations; endocrines and central nervous system active compounds; projectile type automatic injecting hypodermic syringe. Address: College of Pharmacy, University of Tennessee, Memphis, TN 38103.

FEURZEIG, WALLACE, b. Chicago, Ill, June 10, 27; m. 56; c. 3. MATHEMATICS. Ph.B, Chicago, 45, B.S, 48; M.S, Ill. Inst. Tech, 53. Statistician, biol. div, Argonne Nat. Lab, 48-50, mathematician, physics div, 50-53; Inst. Air Weapons Res, Chicago, 53-61; group leader, Comput. Opers, 58-61; Comput. Assocs, Inc, 61-62; DEPT. HEAD, BOLT BERANEK & NEWMAN, INC, CAMBRIDGE, 62- U.S.A, 47-48. AAAS; Asn. Comput. Mach. Man-computer communication; artificial intelligence; educational technology; programming systems; mathematical simulation; heuristic programming. Address: 13 White Pine Lane, Lexington, MA 02173.

FEUSTEL, EDWARD ALVIN, b. Fort Wayne, Ind, June 18, 40. COMPUTER SCIENCE. B.S.E.E. & M.S.E.E, Mass. Inst. Technol, 64; Nat. Sci. Found. trainee, Princeton, 64-65, NASA trainee, 65-67, M.A, 66, Ph.D.(elec. eng), 67. Res. fel, Calif. Inst. Technol, 67; syst. programmer, commun. res. div, Inst. Defense Anal, N.J, 68; ASST. PROF. COMPUT. SCI, RICE UNIV, 68- Lectr. elec. eng, Princeton, 68; consult, Inst. Defense Anal, 68-; del, NATO advan. summer sch. info. syst, Copenhagen, 70, oper. syst, Munich, 71. AAAS; Inst. Math. Statist; Inst. Elec. & Electronics Eng; Asn. Comput. Mach; Nat. Soc. Prof. Eng. Nonparametric decision theory using rank statistics; language and operating system design for large scale digital computers; Heuristic programming; decision making and learning in complex systems. Address: Dept. of Electrical Engineering, Rice University, Houston, TX 77001.

FEVOLD, H(ARRY) L(EONARD), b. Badger, Iowa, Oct. 21, 02; m. 28; c. 3. CHEMISTRY. B.A, St. Olaf Col, 25; M.S, Wisconsin, 26; Ph.D.(chem), 28. Asst. chem, Wisconsin, 26-28, res. assoc, 28-35, asst. prof. biol. chem, Harvard, 35-41; sr. biochemist, west. regional res. lab, bur. agr. & indust. chem, U.S. Dept. Agr, Berkeley, 41-47; chief food res. div, QM Food & Container Inst, 47-51; dir. biochem. res, Baxter Labs, Inc, 51-53, res. dir, 53-55, dir. res. & develop, 55-57, res. coord, 57-68; RETIRED. AAAS; Am. Chem. Soc; Am. Soc. Biol. Chem; Soc. Exp. Biol. & Med; Inst. Food Tech. Osmosis; physiology and chemistry of hormones; proteins; lipoproteins; nutrition; antibiotics; vitamins; chemistry of food deterioration. Address: 128 Carriage Way Dr, Hinsdale, IL 60521.

FEVOLD, H(ARRY) RICHARD, b. Madison, Wis, Jan. 28, 35; m. 58; c. 3. BIOCHEMISTRY, ENDOCRINOLOGY. B.S, Montana, 56; Nat. Insts. Health fels, Utah, 56-61, Ph.D.(biochem), 61. Asst. biochem, Utah, 61; Nat. Insts. Health fel, biochem. inst, Uppsala, 61-63; asst. prof, Univ. Mont, 63-66; assoc prof, 66-70; proj. assoc, McArdle Labs, Univ Wis, Madison, 70-71; PROF. CHEM, UNIV. MONT, 71- Nat. Insts. Health res. grant, 64-, career develop. award, 65-; Nat. Sci. Found. res. grant, 64- AAAS; Am. Soc. Biol. Chem; Endocrine Soc; Am. Chem. Soc; N.Y. Acad. Sci; Am. Ornith. Union; Cooper Ornith. Soc. Biosynthesis of steroid hormones and their regulation; avian endocrinology. Address: Dept. of Chemistry, University of Montana, Missoula, MT 59801.

FEWER, DARRELL R(AYMOND), b. Perth, N.B, Can, Mar. 12, 23; m. 49; c. 1. PHYSICS, ELECTRONICS. B.Sc, New Brunswick, 50; Air Force Cambridge Res. Labs. fel, 51-52; M.Sc, Western Ontario, 52. Mem. tech. staff, Bell Tel. Labs, N.J, 52-57; sr. proj. engr, semiconductor components div, Tex. Instruments Inc, 57-58, br. mgr. semiconductor surface studies, res. & eng. dept, 58-60; v.pres. res. & eng. & mem. bd. dirs, Tex. Res. & Electronic Corp, 60-63; BR. MGR. reliability sci, semiconductor res. & develop. labs, TEX. INSTRUMENTS INC, 63-69, OPTOELECTRONICS DEPT, ADVAN. TECHNOL. & STRATEGIC PLANNING DIV, 69- R.C.A.F, 41-46, Flight Lt. Am. Phys. Soc; sr. mem. Inst. Elec. & Electronics Eng.(W.R.G. Baker Award, 57). Semiconductor device characterization and applications; semiconductor surface physics; electrochemical devices. Address: 6123 Desco Dr, Dallas, TX 75225.

FEY, RICHARD S(MOUSE), b. Cumberland, Md, April 11, 24; m. 53; c. 1. CHEMICAL ENGINEERING. B.S, South Carolina, 45, Maryland, 48, Ph.D. (chem. eng), 53. Engr. coal res, U.S. Bur. Mines, 49-51; assoc. proj. engr. plastics res, U.S. Naval Ord. Lab, 51-52; instr. chem. eng, Maryland, 52-53; res. assoc. rocket res, HERCULES INC, 53-57, group supvr. rocket develop, 57-58, asst. supt. dept, 58-59, supt. dept, 59-62, div. mgr, 62-64, mgr. adv. tech. studies, 64-66, mgr. adv. design dept, 66-67, mgr. adv. ord. studies, 67, mgr. progs, Bacchus Works, Utah, 68-70, MGR. PROPULSION MKT, 70- U.S.N.R, 43-46, Lt.(jg). Am. Chem. Soc; Am. Inst.

Chem. Eng; Am. Inst. Aeronaut. & Astronaut. Development of numerous successful military and civilian space agency high performance rockets. Address: Hercules Inc, 910 Market St, Wilmington, DE 19803.

FEYERHERM, HARVEY A(UGUST), b. West Point, Nebr, Apr. 27, 19; m. 44; c. 3. PHYSIOLOGY. A.B, Nebr. Wesleyan, 40; M.S, Iowa State, 43, Ph.D, 50. Instr. physiol, Iowa State, 42-43, asst. prof, 46-50; BIOL, NORTH. ILL. UNIV, 50-53, assoc. prof, 53-55, PROF, 55-, head dept, 64-69. Nat. Sci. Found. teaching fel, 59-60. Sanit.C, 43-46, Capt. AAAS; Am. Physiol. Soc; Am. Soc. Zool. Comparative invertebrate physiology. Address: Dept. of Biology, Northern Illinois University, DeKalb, IL 60115.

FEYERHERM, M(ARVIN) P(AUL), b. West Point, Nebr, Feb. 10, 17; m. 59; c. 3. PHYSICS. B.A, Nebr. Wesleyan, 39; M.S, Univ. Iowa, 42. Design engr, RCA CORP, 42-50, appl. engr, 50-55, engr, 55-60, adminr, 60-69, PROD. ASSURANCE ADMINR, 69- Inst. Elec. & Electronics Eng. Electronic circuits, systems and component parts; reliability analysis of electronic systems. Address: Astroelectronics Division, RCA Corp, Box 800, Princeton, NJ 08540.

FEYK, JOHN A(NTHONY), b. N.Y.C, Dec. 15, 27; m. 55; c. 1. MECHANICAL & AERONAUTICAL ENGINEERING. B.E, Yale, 48; M.S, Mass. Inst. Technol, 50. Mem. tech. staff, Hughes Aircraft Co, 50-56; prof. staff, Systs. Labs. Corp, 56-57; from consult. to mem. staff, Systs. Corp. Am, 58; assoc. prof. heat transfer & thermodyn, Univ. Ky. Assistance Prog, Bandung Inst. Tech, Indonesia, 58-61; mem. staff, Aerospace Corp, Calif, 62-63; assoc. prof, Univ. Calif, Los Angeles Assistance Prog, Gadjah Mada Univ, Jogjakarta, 63-65; MEM. STAFF, AEROSPACE CORP, LOS ANGELES, 65- Am. Inst. Aeronaut. & Astronaut; Combustion Inst. Fluid Mechanics; heat transfer; thermodynamics; solid rocket propulsion; aerodynamics; celestial mechanics. Address: 2727 San Ramon Dr, Miraleste, CA 90732.

FEYNMAN, RICHARD PHILLIPS, b. New York, N.Y, May 11, 18; m. 60; c. 2. THEORETICAL PHYSICS. B.S, Mass. Inst. Tech, 39; Procter fel, Princeton, 40-42; Ph.D.(theoret. physics), 42. Physicist, atomic energy proj, Princeton, 41-42; Los Alamos proj, N.Mex, 42-45; assoc. prof. PHYSICS, Cornell, 45-51; TOLMAN PROF, CALIF. INST. TECHNOL, 51- Einstein award, 54; Nobel prize in physics, 65. AAAS; Am. Phys. Soc; for. mem. Royal Soc. Quantum electrodynamics; principles of least action in quantum mechanics; liquid helium; beta-decay and weak interactions. Address: California Institute of Technology, Lauritsen Lab. of Physics, Pasadena, CA 91109.

FEZER, KARL D(IETRICH), b. Englewood, N.J, Mar. 2, 30; m. 52; c. 4. SCIENCE EDUCATION, PHILOSOPHY OF SCIENCE. B.S, Cornell, 51, fel, 55-56, Ph.D.(plant path), 57; fel, Haverford Col, 51-52, M.A, 53; fel, Minnesota, 56-57. Asst. plant path, Cornell Univ, 52-55; instr, Univ. Minn, St. Paul, 57-59, asst. prof, 59-62; div. sci. & math, Univ. Minn, Morris, 62-63; tutor, St. John's Col, 63-66; assoc. prof. BIOL, CONCORD COL, 66-67, PROF. & CHMN. DEPT, 67- Dir, workshop high sch. biol, Nat. Sci. Found, 71. AAAS; Am. Inst. Biol. Sci; Nat. Sci. Teachers Asn. Philosophy and history of science in relation to science education; lambda killing in paramecium; senescence in plants. Address: Dept. of Biology, Concord College, Athens, WV 24712.

FIALA, ALAN D(ALE), b. Beatrice, Nebr, Nov. 9, 42. ASTRONOMY. B.A, Carleton Col, 63; Woodrow Wilson fel, Yale, 63, M.S, 64, Ph.D.(astron), 68. Summers, phys. sci. aide, U.S. NAVAL OBSERV, 62, ASTRONR, 63-67 & 68- Instr, grad. sch, U.S. Dept. Agr, 69- AAAS; Am. Astron. Soc; Am. Inst. Navig; Am. Inst. Aeronaut. & Astronaut; N.Y. Acad. Sci. Celestial mechanics; mass of Jupiter; minor planet orbits; general and special perturbations; numerical analysis; computer applications; stellar dynamics; orbital mechanics; ephemerides; astrodynamics. Address: U.S. Naval Observatory, Washington, DC 20390.

FIALA, J(OSEPH) N(ORMAN), b. Dayton, Ohio, Jan. 25, 09; m. 33; c. 1. AEROSPACE ENGINEERING. Columbia, 32; RCA Inst, 58. From mem. staff to civilian asst. to dir. res. & develop. & hq. staff, Wash, U.S. Air Force, Ohio, 26-52; consult, 52-57; DIR, Gen. Res. Asn, 57-61; defense electronic ctr, 61-67, RES. ELECTRO-MAGNETIC SPECTRUM, 67- Assoc. Am. Inst. Aeronaut. & Astronaut. Space science; aeronautical field of military technical administration; wind direction indicator; electronics. Address: 875 S.W. Fourth Ct, Apt. 6A, Boca Raton, FL 33432.

FIALA, OLIVER JOHN, b. Chicago, Ill, Nov. 30, 10; m; c. 2. CHEMICAL ENGINEERING. B.S, Armour Inst. Tech, 31. Tech. dir, Durkee Famous Foods Div, Glidden Co, Ill, 31-39, Ky, 39-42, N.Y, 42-47, Ill, 47-51, dir. res, Ky, 51-59, tech. dir, 59-61, dir. res. & develop, 61-70, TECH. DIR, SOUTH. REGION, DURKEE FAMOUS FOODS, GLIDDEN-DURKEE DIV, SCM CORP, 70- AAAS; Am. Oil Chemist's Soc; Am. Asn. Cereal Chem; Inst. Food Technol; Am. Inst. Chem; Am. Soybean Asn. Vegetable fat and oil technology; organic, inorganic, and analytical chemistry; food technology. Address: Durkee Famous Foods, Glidden-Durkee Division, SCM Corp, 1303 S. Shelby St, Louisville, KY 40201.

FIALA, SILVIO (EMERICH) (IVAN), b. Prague, Czech, Jan. 1, 12; nat; m. 37; c. 2. PHYSIOLOGY, CANCER. M.D, Charles Univ, Prague, 37. Head dept. virus res, Nat. Inst. Health, Czech, 42-46; Rockefeller fel, Rockefeller Inst, 46-47; Nat. Cancer Inst. res. fel, Univ. Pa, 48-50; res. assoc. path, Columbia Univ, 53-62; mem. staff, cell physiol. lab, Vet. Admin. Hosp, San Fernando, Calif, 62-66, CHIEF CELL PHYSIOL. LAB, 66-71, VET. ADMIN. CTR, W.VA, 71- Adj. assoc. prof, Univ. South. Calif, 62-71. Cell physiology; cancer research. Address: Cell Physiology Lab, Veterans Administration Center, Martinsburg, WV 25401.

FIALER, PHILIP A, b. San Francisco, Calif, Nov. 6, 38; m. 67; c. 2. ELECTRICAL ENGINEERING. B.S, Stanford Univ, 60, M.S, 64, Ph.D.(elec. eng), 70. Sr. res. engr, ELECTRONICS, Lockheed Missiles & Space Co, Calif, 61-67; res. assoc, radiosci. lab, Stanford Univ, 67-70; RES. ENGR, IONOSPHERIC DYNAMICS LAB, 70- Consult, Barry Res. Corp, 68-69; west. develop. labs, Philco-Ford, 69-70. AAAS; Inst. Elec. & Electronics Eng. Ionospheric structure and physics; motions, waves and irregularities in the ionosphere; radio propagation through irregular media; ray tracing; computer methods of image processing. Address: Ionospheric Dynamics Lab, Stanford Research Institute, 333 Ravenwood Ave, Menlo Park, CA 94025.

FIALKOW, AARON D(AVID), b. N.Y.C, Aug. 9, 11; m. 40; c. 3. MATHEMATICS. B.S, & M.S, City Col. New York, 31; scholar, Columbia, 33-34, fel, 35-36, Ph.D.(math), 36. Teacher, high sch, N.Y, 32-33, 35; Nat. Res. fel, Inst. Adv. Study & Princeton, 36-37; instr, Brooklyn Col, 37-42; lectr, Columbia, 42-45; math. res. engr, Fed. Telecommun. Labs, 45-46; head math. sect, Control Instrument Co, 46-54; adj. prof. MATH, POLYTECH. INST. BROOKLYN, 46-47, assoc. prof, 47-51, PROF, 51- Am. Math. Soc. Differential geometry; electric network theory. Address: Polytechnic Institute of Brooklyn, 333 Jay St, Brooklyn, NY 11201.

FIALKOW, PHILIP JACK, b. New York, N.Y, Aug. 20, 34; m. 60; c. 2. INTERNAL MEDICINE, MEDICAL GENETICS. A.B, Pennsylvania, 56; M.D, Tufts, 60. Intern med, sch. med, California, San Francisco, 60-61, res, 61-62; univ. hosps, UNIV. WASH, 62-63, fel. MED. & GENETICS, SCH. MED, 63-65, instr, 65-66, asst. prof, 66-69, ASSOC. PROF, 69- Genetics Soc. Am; Am. Soc. Human Genetics; Am. Soc. Clin. Invest; fel. Am. Col. Physicians. Human genetics; etiology of chromosomal abnormalities; genetics of immunologic diseases. Address: Dept. of Medicine, University of Washington, Seattle, WA 98195.

FIBEL, LEWIS R(OBERT), b. N.Y.C, Oct. 30, 15; m. 46; c. 1. CHEMISTRY. A.B, Cornell Univ, 34; A.M, Univ. Kans, 36; Ph.D.(org. chem), Polytech. Inst. Brooklyn, 47. Asst, chem. dept, Mt. Sinai Hosp, N.Y.C, 36-37; res. chemist, Lawrence R. Bruce, Inc, Conn, 37-41; chemist, W.M. Grosvenor Lab, 42-49; head dept. chem. technol, New York City Community Col, 49-59, dean stud, 59-62; Flint Community Jr. Col, 62-64; collegiate technol. div, Dutchess Community Col, 64-66; specialist occup. educ, Am. Asn. Jr. Cols, Wash, D.C, 66-69; exec. dir, Md. State Bd. Community Cols, 69-71; PROF. EDUC, VA. POLYTECH. INST. & STATE UNIV, 71- U.S.N, 44-46, Ens. Fel. AAAS; Am. Chem. Soc; Am. Soc. Eng. Educ. Chemical education; organic synthesis; synthesis of pyridine and pyrazine derivatives; educational administration. Address: College of Education, Virginia Polytechnic Institute & State University, Blacksburg, VA 24061.

FICALORA, PETER, b. Brooklyn, N.Y, Apr. 9, 38; m. 61; c. 5. PHYSICAL & SOLID STATE CHEMISTRY. B.S, Manhattan Col, 60; Ph.D.(solid state tech), Pa. State, 65. Fel, Rice Univ, 65-68; asst. prof. metall, SYRACUSE UNIV, 68-70, ASSOC. PROF. MAT. SCI, 70- Nat. Sci. Found. res. grant & Petrol. Res. starter grant, 68- Am. Chem. Soc; Am. Inst. Mining, Metall. & Petrol. Eng. High temperature chemistry. Address: Dept. of Chemical Engineering & Materials Science, Link Hall, Syracuse University, Syracuse, NY 13210.

FICENEC, JOHN ROBERT, b. Rochester, Minn, Oct. 29, 38; m. 59; c. 3. ELEMENTARY PARTICLE PHYSICS. B.S, St. John's (Minn), 60; Atomic Energy Cmn. fel, Illinois, Urbana, 60-62, M.S, 61, univ. fel, 62-63, Ph.D. (physics), 66. ASST. PROF. PHYSICS, VA. POLYTECH. INST. & STATE UNIV, 68- Guest asst. physicist, Brookhaven Nat. Lab, 68-, asst. physicist, summers 68-71. Grants, Res. Corp, 69-70 & Petrol. Res. Fund, 69-72. U.S.A, 66-68, Capt. AAAS; Am. Phys. Soc. Bubble chamber physics; electron scattering from nickel, tin and zirconium isotopes at 300 MeV/c; preparation of counter-spark chamber experiment to study p-p interactions; magnetic monopole search. Address: Dept. of Physics, Virginia Polytechnic Institute & State University, Blacksburg, VA 24061.

FICH, SYLVAN, b. N.Y.C, Aug. 8, 10; m. 44. ELECTRICAL ENGINEERING. B.Sc, Cooper Union, 31; M.Sc, Rutgers, 32. Instr. math. & eng, Union Jr. Col, 33-39, dean eve. session, 40-42; instr. elec. eng, Rutgers, 42-44; mem. staff, wave propagation res, Columbia, 44-45; asst. prof. ELEC. ENG, RUTGERS UNIV, 45-48, assoc. prof, 48-55, PROF, 55-, DIR. GRAD. PROGS. ELEC. ENG, 68- Consult, Essex Electronics Co, 49-52; Plastron Co, 69-70. Inst. Elec. & Electronics Eng. Electromagnetic waves and radiation; biomedical engineering; writing textbooks in electrical engineering. Address: Dept. of Electrical Engineering, Murray Hall, Rutgers University, New Brunswick, NJ 08903.

FICHER, MIGUEL, b. Buenos Aires, Arg, July 24, 22; U.S. citizen; m. 50; c. 3. ENDOCRINOLOGY, CHEMISTRY. Lic. in Chem, Univ. Buenos Aires, 48, Ph.D, 50. Instr. biol. anal, chem. sch, Univ. Buenos Aires, 50; sub-dir. clin. lab, Moron County Hosp, Arg, 56-57; dir. clin. lab, Private Policlinic, Arg, 57-61; endocrine diag. lab, Jewish Hosp, St. Lewis, Mo, 61-65; RES. MEM. endocrinol, Univ. Buenos Aires, 65-66; STEROID CHEM, DEPT. ENDOCRINOL, ALBERT EINSTEIN MED. CTR, 66- Consult. chem. invest, St. Louis State Sch. & Hosp, 64-65. Am. Asn. Clin. Chem. Biosynthesis of steroid hormones by gonads, in humans and animals; study of pituitary-gonad axis; reproduction and spermatogenesis. Address: Dept. of Endocrinology, Albert Einstein Medical Center, York & Tabor Rds, Philadelphia, PA 19141.

FICHTEL, CARL EDWIN, b. St. Louis, Mo, July 13, 33. PHYSICS. B.S, Wash. Univ, 55, Ph.D.(physics), 60. Asst. physics, Wash. Univ, 56-59; scientist, GODDARD SPACE FLIGHT CTR, NASA, 59-60, head nuclear emulsion sect, 60-66, head gamma ray & nuclear emulsion sect, 66-70, HEAD GAMMA RAY & NUCLEAR EMULSION BR, 70- Del, Int. Cosmic Ray Conf, 61, 63, 65, 67; vis. lectr, Univ. Md, 63-; del, Int. Astron. Union, 70. John C. Lindsay Mem. Award, Goddard Space Flight Ctr, 68. Am. Phys. Soc; Am. Astron. Soc. High energy astrophysics; galactic cosmic rays; solar cosmic rays, especially solar particle composition and its relation to solar abundances; gamma ray astronomy; cosmic ray propagation and confinement; spark chambers. Address: Code 662, Goddard Space Flight Center, NASA, Greenbelt, MD 20771.

FICHTER, EDSON (HARVEY), b. Randolph, Iowa, July 3, 10; m. 35; c. 2. ANIMAL ECOLOGY, MAMMALOGY. B.S, Nebraska, 35, M.S, 37, Ph.D. (zool), 42. Lab. asst. zool, Nebraska, 35-39, mus. asst, state mus, 39-41, asst. curator, 41-42; biologist, State Game, Forestation & Parks Comn, 42-43, 45-52; from assoc. prof. to PROF. ZOOL, IDAHO STATE UNIV, 52-,

CURATOR MAMMAL, MUS, 68- Asst, Gorgas Mem. Lab, Panama. U.S.A, 43-45. Am. Soc. Mammal; Wildlife Soc; Wilson Ornith. Soc; Wilderness Soc. Animal behavior; terrestrial animal ecology; distribution of mammals; predation; populations; ornithology. Address: Dept. of Biology, Idaho State University, Pocatello, ID 83201.

FICK, BESSIE D(AVEY), b. Detroit, Mich, Nov. 8, 20; m. 64. NUTRITION. B.S, Wayne, 43; M.S, Oregon State Col, 45, exp. sta. fel, 48-49, Ph.D.(foods, nutrit), 49. Asst, Oregon State Col, 43-48; assoc. prof. home econ. & res. assoc, lab. human nutrit, Alabama, 49-53, prof. home econ. & head dept. food & nutrit, 53-61; prof. & head dept. N.Mex. State Univ, 61-66; instr. home econ, East. Ariz. Col, 66-70, head dept, 67; PROF. NUTRIT. & FOODS, AUBURN UNIV, 70- Am. Dietetic Asn; Am. Inst. Nutrit; Am. Home Econ. Asn. Human nutrition; ascorbic acid metabolism during adolescence; utilization of ascorbic acid. Address: Dept. of Nutrition & Foods, School of Home Economics, Auburn University, Auburn, AL 36830.

FICK, CLIFFORD GEORGE, b. Ida Grove, Iowa, Dec. 13, 04. RADIO ENGINEERING. B.S, Iowa State, 25. From radio engr. to asst. designing engr, transmitter div, Gen. Elec. Co, 25-44, chief engr, receiver div, 44-48, mgr, communications res. sect, res. lab, 48-54, res. liaison sect, 54-64, res. admin, 64-66, res. & develop. ctr, 66-69; RETIRED. Civilian with Nat. Defense Res. Comt. Fel. Inst. Elec. & Electronics Eng. Television; wide band antenna circuits for transmitters; frequency stabilization of transmitters; industrial research management. Address: 55 N. Brandywine Ave, Schenectady, NY 12307.

FICK, GARY WARREN, b. O'Neill, Nebr, July 10, 43; m. 69. AGRONOMY, PLANT PHYSIOLOGY. B.S, Univ. Nebr, Lincoln, 65; Fulbright-Hays fel, Massey Univ, N.Z, 66, Dipl. Agr. Sci, 67; Nat. Defense Educ. Act fel, Univ. Calif, Davis, 67, Ph.D.(plant physiol), 71. ASST. PROF. AGRON, CORNELL UNIV, 71- Soc. Range Mgt; Am. Soc. Plant Physiol; Am. Soc. Agron; Crop Sci. Soc. Am. Range management; sugar beet physiology; forage crop physiology. Address: Dept. of Agronomy, Cornell University, Ithaca, NY 14850.

FICK, GERHARDT N(ELSON), b. Pelican Rapids, Minn, Mar. 6, 42; m. 68; c. 1. PLANT BREEDING, GENETICS. B.S, Univ. Minn, St. Paul, 64, M.S, 66; Nat. Insts. Health fel, Univ. Calif, Davis, 71, Ph.D.(plant genetics), 71. Assoc. sci, Univ. Minn, St. Paul, 65-68; RES. GENETICIST, STATE EXP. STA, AGR. RES. SERV, U.S. DEPT. AGR, 71- U.S.A.R, 66- Am. Soc. Agron; Crop Sci. Soc. Am. Applied breeding for development of hybrid sunflowers; genetics of sunflowers involving studies on yield, disease and insect resistance, chemical composition, size and shape of seed, cytoplasmic-genetic systems of male sterility. Address: Dept. of Agronomy, North Dakota State University, Fargo, ND 58102.

FICK, HERBERT JOHN, b. Minn, Jan. 4, 37; m. 60; c. 2. ORGANIC CHEMISTRY, PHYSICS. B.A, St. Olaf Col, 59; M.S, Chicago, 60. Supvr. corp. chem. lab, G.T. SCHJELDAHL CO, 63-65, mgr. mat. eng, elec. prod. div, 65-66, eng. mgr. U.K. div, 66-69, chemist, 69, mgr. display devices mfg, 69-71, PROG. MGR, NEW PROCESS DEVELOP, 71- Am. Chem. Soc. Flexible printed wiring; adhesives; electroluminescent display. Address: 318 Summer, Northfield, MN 55057.

FICKE, ROBERT CARL, b. Davenport, Iowa, Feb. 21, 09; m. 43; c. 5. CHEMICAL ENGINEERING. B.S, Princeton, 33, Ch.E, 34. Jr. engr, E.I. du Pont de Nemours & Co, N.J, 34-35, chem. eng, Va, 36-37, Pa, 38, group supvr, N.J, 39-44, sect. supvr, 44-52, div. engr, 52-53, dir. consults, 54-56, personnel planning, 56, gen. dir. consults, 57-61, dir. systs. eng, 61-66, mgr. econ. eval. & opers. res, 66-71; RETIRED. Am. Inst. Chem. Eng. Development of chemical processing equipment. Address: 809 Augusta Rd, Wilmington, DE 19807.

FICKEN, FREDERICK A(RTHUR), b. Moore's Hill, Ind, Aug. 13, 10; m. 40; c. 1. MATHEMATICS. A.B, Oberlin Col, 31; A.M, Ohio State, 32; Rhodes scholar, Oxford, 32-35, B.A, 34; Ph.D.(math), Princeton, 38; Brown, 42. Asst. MATH, Ohio State, 31-32; Princeton, 35-37; instr, Lafayette Col, 37-38; Cornell Univ, 38-42; PROF, Univ. Tenn, 42-59; UNIV. HEIGHTS CTR, N.Y. UNIV, 59-, res. assoc, inst. math. sci, 49-51, chmn. math. dept, 59-67. Consult, opers. res, Off. Sci. Res. & Develop, U.S.N, 44-45; Res. & Develop. Bd, Nat. Mil. Estab, 48; Carbide & Carbon Chem. Corp, Tenn, 46-64. AAAS (secy. math. sect, 69-); Soc. Indust. & Appl. Math; Am. Math. Soc; Math. Asn. Am. (ed, Am. Math. Monthly, 62-66). Abstract linear spaces; differential equations. Address: Dept. of Mathematics, University Heights Center, New York University, Bronx, NY 10453.

FICKEN, MILLICENT SIGLER, b. Washington, D.C, July 27, 33; m. 55; c. 2. VERTEBRATE ZOOLOGY. B.S, Cornell Univ, 55, Ph.D.(zool), 60. Res. assoc. ZOOL, Univ. Md, 63-68; asst. prof, UNIV. WIS, MILWAUKEE, 68-70, ASSOC. PROF, 70, DIR. FIELD STAS, 68- Am. Ornith. Union; Soc. Study Evolution. Ornithology; animal communication; evolution of avian behavior. Address: Dept. of Zoology, University of Wisconsin-Milwaukee, Milwaukee, WI 53201.

FICKEN, ROBERT W, b. Brooklyn, N.Y, Feb. 26, 32; m. 55; c. 2. ANIMAL BEHAVIOR, ORNITHOLOGY. B.S, Cornell, 53, Ph.D.(vert. zool), 60. Res. assoc. animal behav, Cornell, 60-62; asst. prof. ZOOL, Maryland, 62-68; RES. ASSOC, UNIV. WIS-MILWAUKEE, 68- U.S.A, 53-55; Res, 55-64, Capt. AAAS; Am. Ornith. Union; Brit. Avicult. Soc; Brit. Ornith. Union. Comparative avian ethology; ecology; systematics; speciation; interspecific communication; evolution of signalling systems; species recognition; analysis of vocalizations; geographic variation. Address: Dept. of Zoology, University of Wisconsin, Milwaukee, WI 53211.

FICKESS, DOUGLAS R(ICARDO), b. Piedmont, Okla, Aug. 25, 31; m. 53; c. 2. ZOOLOGY, PHYSIOLOGY. B.S, Oklahoma, 54, M.S, 56; Ph.D.(zool), Missouri, 63. Asst. prof. BIOL, WESTMINSTER COL.(MO), 62-66, assoc. prof, 66-69, PROF, 69-, CHMN. DEPT, 66- U.S.A, 56-58, 1st Lt. Am. Soc. Mammal; Am. Soc. Zool. Effects of population density dependent factors on the histology and physiology of adrenal glands in mammals and reptiles. Address: Dept. of Biology, Westminster College, Fulton, MO 65251.

FICKETT, FREDERICK R(OLAND), b. Portland, Maine, Sept. 30, 37; m. 61; c. 2. PHYSICS. B.S, New Hampshire, 60; M.S, Arizona, 62; Nat. Sci. Found. fel, Oregon State, 64-66, U.S. Bur. Mines fel, 66-67, Ph.D.(physics), 67. Nat. Bur. Standards-Nat. Res. Coun. res. assoc, 67-69, MEM. STAFF, CRYOGENICS DIV, NAT. BUR. STANDARDS, 69- Am. Phys. Soc. Plasma physics; nuclear magnetic resonance; properties of metals and alloys at cryogenic temperatures, particularly electronic transport properties. Address: 1635 Norwood Ave, Boulder, CO 80302.

FICKETT, WILDON, b. Tucson, Ariz, Mar. 25, 27; m. 45; c. 5. PHYSICAL CHEMISTRY. B.S, Arizona, 48; Ph.D.(chem), Calif. Inst. Tech, 51. MEM. STAFF, LOS ALAMOS SCI. LAB, UNIV. CALIF, 51- U.S.N.R, 45-46. Am. Phys. Soc. Explosives. Address: 284 El Conejo, Los Alamos, NM 87544.

FICKINGER, WILLIAM (JOSEPH), b. N.Y.C, July 18, 34. HIGH ENERGY PHYSICS. B.S, Manhattan Col, 55; Ph.D.(physics), Yale, 61. Asst. prof. physics, Kentucky, 61-62; asst. physicist, Brookhaven Nat. Lab, 62-63, 64-65; assoc. physicist, Saclay Nuclear Res. Ctr, France, 63-64, 65-66; asst. prof. PHYSICS, Vanderbilt Univ, 66-67; ASSOC. PROF, CASE WEST. RESERVE UNIV, 67- Am. Phys. Soc. Pi meson production through resonance formation in hydrogen and deuterium bubble chamber experiments. Address: Dept. of Physics, Case Western Reserve University, Cleveland, OH 44106.

FICKLER, STUART I(RWIN), b. N.Y.C, July 24, 32; m. 52; c. 3. THEORETICAL PHYSICS. B.A, N.Y. Univ, 55; M.S, Syracuse, 58, Ph.D, 61. DEP. DIR. GEN. PHYSICS RES. LAB. & RES. PHYSICIST, AEROSPACE RES. LABS, WRIGHT-PATTERSON AIR FORCE BASE, 61- Nat. Acad. Sci. resident res. assoc, 61-62; adj. asst. prof, Cincinnati, 63, 64. Am. Phys. Soc. Quantization of the Yang-Mills Field and of general relativity; internal symmetries; thermodynamic applications to corporate behavior; physical models of behavior; decision theory. Address: Aerospace Research Labs, LG, Wright-Patterson Air Force Base, OH 45433.

FICSOR, GYULA, b. Kiskunhalas, Hungary, Apr. 11, 36; U.S. citizen; m. 65; c. 1. GENETICS. B.S, Colo. State Univ, 60; Ph.D.(genetics), Univ. Mo-Columbia, 65. Nat. Insts. Health fel, 65-66; res. assoc, Molecular Biol. Lab, Univ. Wis, 67; asst. prof. GENETICS, WEST. MICH. UNIV, 67-71, ASSOC. PROF, 72- U.S.A.R, 60-66. Genetics Soc. Am; Environ. Mutagen Soc. Development of tissue and organ specific test methods in mammals for the mutagenic testing of chemicals in the human environment; mutagenesis in bacteria and mammals; controlling element mediated genetic regulation. Address: Dept. of Biology, Western Michigan University, Kalamazoo, MI 49001.

FIDDLER, WALTER, b. Vienna, Austria, Feb. 5, 36; U.S. citizen. ORGANIC CHEMISTRY. A.B, Temple, 59, Ph.D.(org. chem), 65. RES. CHEMIST FLAVOR INVESTS, EAST. UTILIZATION RES. & DEVELOP. DIV, U.S. DEPT. AGR, 65- Am. Chem. Soc; Inst. Food Technol. Pyrimidine containing sulfonamides; retrieval of chemical information; smoke flavor investigations; determination of carcinogens in food products. Address: Eastern Regional Research Lab, U.S. Dept. of Agriculture, 600 E. Mermaid Lane, Philadelphia, PA 19118.

FIDELIS (REMSKI), MARIE, I.H.M, b. Maybee, Mich, Mar. 3, 03. BOTANY, CYTOLOGY. B.A, Michigan, 24, M.A, 36, Ph.D.(bot), 53. Teacher, St. Mary Acad, Mich, 24-38; parochial sch, 38-45; prin, 45-50; PROF. BIOL, Marygrove Col, 52-70; ST. JOSEPH COL. FLA, 70- AAAS; Bot. Soc. Am. Morphology; taxonomy; genetics. Address: St. Joseph College of Florida, Jensen Beach, FL 33457.

FIDEN, WILLIAM H, b. New York, N.Y, July 19, 24; m. 49; c. 3. PHYSICS, ELECTRONICS. B.S, Kansas State, 49; M.S, Columbia, 51. Instr. physics, Kansas State, 48-49; undergrad. & grad. lab. physics, Columbia, 50-51; sr. physicist, ERA Div, Remington Rand Group, Sperry Rand Corp, 51-54; res. physicist, Union Switch & Signal Co, 54-55; mem. sr. tech. staff, space tech. labs, Thompson-Ramo-Wooldridge, Inc, 55-60; Ryan Commun, Inc, 60-61; res. dir, Adv. Commun, Inc, 61-63, v.pres. res. & develop, 63-69; ASST. DEPT. MGR, MISSILE SYSTS. DIV, HUGHES AIRCRAFT CO, 69- Instr, George Washington, 52-53. U.S.N, 43-46. Inst. Elec. & Electronics Eng; Am. Phys. Soc. High frequency, very high frequency and ultra high frequency radio propagation; radio transmission through shock wave; signal modulation analysis; communication and electronic reconnaissance systems; high frequency radio navigation. Address: Missile Systems Division, Hughes Aircraft Co, Falbrook & Roscoe, Canoga Park, CA 91304.

FIDLAR, M(ARION) M(OORE), b. Vincennes, Ind, June 7, 09; m. 37. GEOLOGY. A.B, Indiana, 34, A.M, 36, Ph.D.(geol), 42; Rector scholar, DePauw. Asst. geol, Indiana, 34-36; asst. state geologist, Ind. Div. Geol, 36-38; dist. geologist, Ohio Oil Co, Ill, 38-43; sr. geologist, MT. FUEL SUPPLY CO, 43-45, chief geologist, 45-51, mgr. explor. div, 51-54, v.pres, 54-58, exec. v.pres, 58-62, PRES, 62-, DIR, 55- Distinguished Alumni Serv. award, Indiana, 64. AAAS; Soc. Explor. Geophys; fel. Geol. Soc. Am; Am. Asn. Petrol. Geol; Am. Inst. Mining, Metall. & Petrol. Eng. Pleistocene glaciation; physiography; paleozoic stratigraphy; Mesozoic stratigraphy; geologic surface and subsurface structure; oil and gas accumulation. Address: Mountain Fuel Supply Co, P.O. Box 11368, Salt Lake City, UT 84111.

FIDLER, HAROLD A(LVIN), b. Phila, Pa, Aug. 2, 10; m. 39; c. 3. CIVIL ENGINEERING. B.S, Drexel Inst, 32, hon. D.E, 63; S.M, Mass. Inst. Tech, 34, Savage fel, 34-35, Sc.D.(struct), 40. Asst. soil mech, Mass. Inst. Tech, 35-38, instr. civil eng, 38-40; asst. to engr. in charge found. invest. sect, U.S. Eng. Off. Binghamton Dist, 40-41, engr. in charge, 42, area engr, Manhattan Dist, Berkeley Area, 42-45, dept. dir. res. div, 45-46, asst. chief declassification & pub. br, 46-47; chief tech. info. br, U.S. Atomic Energy Comn, 47, chief declassification br, Wash, D.C, 47-49, mgr. Berkeley Area off, 49-52, dep. mgr. San Francisco opers. off, 52-54, mgr, 54-57; asst. dir, LAWRENCE BERKELEY LAB, UNIV. CALIF, 58-61, ASSOC. DIR, 61- C.Eng, U.S.A, 43-46. Assoc. Am. Soc. Civil Eng. Soil as an engineering material of construction. Address: Lawrence Berkeley Lab, University of California, Berkeley, CA 94720.

FIDLER, H(ERBERT) K(AUFFMAN), b. Winnipeg, Man, April 24, 10; m. 45; c. 3. MEDICINE. M.D, Manitoba, 34, B.Sc, 35. Asst. prof. path. & bacter, Alabama, 36-38; assoc. prof. path, Univ. B.C, 54-56, clin. prof, 56-71; dir. labs. & dept. path, Vancouver Gen. Hosp, 47-67, consult. surg. path, 67-71; sr. cytopathologist, cent. cytol. lab, B.C. Cancer Inst, 66-67, dir. lab, 67-71; RETIRED. R.A.M.C, 39-45, Maj. Can. Asn. Path.(pres, 53); Int. Acad. Cytol. Pathology; exfoliative cytology. Address: Central Cytology Lab, British Columbia Cancer Institute, 2656 Heather St, Vancouver 9, B.C, Can.

FIDLERIS, VILIUS, b. Düsseldorf, Ger, May 10, 28; m. 54; c. 2. PHYSICS, PHYSICAL METALLURGY. B.Sc, London, 53; B.S, Nottingham, 55, Ph.D. (rheol. suspensions), 58. Res. scientist, Coal Res. Estab, Nat. Coal Bd, Eng, 58-59; sr. sci. officer metall ceramic fuels, U.K. Atomic Energy Authority, 60-61; ASSOC. RES. OFF. IRRADIATION, ATOMIC ENERGY CAN, 61- Rheology of Newtonian suspensions; creep of zirconium and its alloys in and out of neutron flux. Address: Atomic Energy of Canada, Ltd, Chalk River, Ont, Can.

FIDONE, SALVATORE JOSEPH, b. N.Y.C, June 10, 39; m. 62; c. 2. PHYSIOLOGY, NEUROPHYSIOLOGY. B.S, Georgetown, 62; Ph.D.(physiol), State Univ. N.Y, 67. Nat. Insts. Health fel. neurophysiol, COL. MED, UNIV. UTAH, 67-69, instr, 69-70, ASST. PROF. PHYSIOL, 70- Soc. Neurosci; Am. Physiol. Soc. Neurochemistry of carotid body chemoreception; motor cortex—pyramidal control of fusimotor neurons. Address: Dept. of Physiology, University of Utah College of Medicine, Salt Lake City, UT 84112.

FIEDELMAN, HOWARD W(ILLIAM), b. Sheboygan, Wis, April 23, 16; m. 47; c. 2. CHEMICAL ENGINEERING. B.S, Wisconsin, 38. From chem. engr. to res. supvr, cent. res. lab, Morton Salt Co, 39-67, DIR. SALT RES, MORTON SALT DIV, MORTON-NORWICH PROD, INC, 67- U.S.A.A.F, 42-46, Capt. Am. Chem. Soc. Salt technology; purification of salt from brines; theoretical aspects of caking. Address: 812 Muriel St, Woodstock, IL 60098.

FIEDLER, GEORGE J(OSEPH), b. Bushton, Kans, Mar. 18, 04; m. 29. ELECTRICAL ENGINEERING. B.S, Kansas State, 26, E.E, 34; M.S, Kansas, 32; Michigan, 41-43. Student engr, Gen. Elec. Co, Schenectady, 26-28; radio engr, Radio Corp. Am, 28-31; asst. & instr. elec. eng, Kansas, 31-33; admin. asst. to dean, N.Y. State Col. for Teachers, 33-35; asst. prof. elec. eng, Union (N.Y), 35-39; assoc. prof, Mont. State Col, 39-43; assoc. prof, California, 43-45; head measurements & circuit design sect, radio div, U.S. Navy Electronics Lab, San Diego, 45-46; prin. engr. controls & instrumentation sect, Sverdrup & Parcel, Inc, 46-59, systs. eng. sect, 59-66, Sverdrup & Parcel & Assocs, Inc, 66-70; RETIRED. With Off. Sci. Res. & Develop, 44. Fel. AAAS; fel. Inst. Elec. & Electronics Eng; fel. Instrument. Soc. Am. Radio receivers, loudspeakers, test equipment; antennas; ultrahigh frequency techniques; supersonic instrumentation; automatic process controls and instrumentation. Address: St. Armands Towers, Apt. 72 N, 1 Benjamin Franklin Dr, Sarasota, FL 33577.

FIEDLER, H(OWARD) C(HARLES), b. Chicago, Ill, June 24, 24; m. 49; c. 5. PHYSICAL METALLURGY. B.S, Purdue, 49; M.S, Mass. Inst. Technol, 50, Sc.D.(metall), 53. Res. assoc, metal dept, res. lab, GEN. ELEC. CO, 53-59, METALLURGIST, 59-66, RES. & DEVELOP. CTR, 66- U.S.A, 43-46. Am. Soc. Metals; Am. Inst. Mining, Metall. & Petrol. Eng. Soft magnetic materials; recrystallization; surface alloying. Address: Research & Development Center, General Electric Co, Schenectady, NY 12309.

FIEHLER, HARLAN E(DWARD), b. Frohna, Mo, Oct. 10, 25; m. 58; c. 2. ANALYTICAL CHEMISTRY. B.S, Southeast Mo. State Col, 50; Ph.D.(chem), Univ. Mo, 59. Instr. CHEM, Ind. Univ, 58-61, ASST. PROF, 61-66; MIDDLETOWN BR, MIAMI UNIV, 66- U.S.N, 44-46. Am. Chem. Soc. Electrochemistry and optical absorption of transition metal salts in solution. Address: Dept. of Chemistry, Miami University, Middletown Branch, 4200 Manchester Rd, Middletown, OH 45042.

FIEKERS, BERNARD ALBERT, S.J, b. Cambridge, Mass, Jan. 19, 06. CHEMISTRY. A.B, Boston Col, 27, A.M, 33, fel, 33-34, M.S, 34; Ph.L, Weston Col, 33; Ignatius Col, Valkenburg, Netherlands, 35-39; fel, Clark, 41-42, Ph.D.(chem), 42. Lab. instr. physics, Boston Col, 26-27, asst. chem, 33-34, instr. anal. chem, 34-35; COL. HOLY CROSS, 40-42, PROF. CHEM, 42-, chmn. dept. & dir. grad. div, 42-62. Instr, Loyola (Calif), 57; summers, lab. instr, Boston Col, 27, instr, 46, consult, 52, 53, instr, Gonzaga, 61. AAAS; Am. Chem. Soc; Am. Asn. Jesuit Sci.(pres, 47, ed, Bul, 48-50, 56-60); fel. Am. Inst. Chem. Organic nitrogen compounds; education laboratory apparatus. Address: Dept. of Chemistry, College of the Holy Cross, Worcester, MA 01610.

FIEL, LARRY DEAN, b. Shattuck, Okla, June 18, 40; m. 62; c. 2. PHYSICS, ELECTROCHEMISTRY. B.S, Northwest. State Col.(Okla), 62; univ. fel, Texas, 62-63, Ph.D.(physics), 66. Engr. scientist, Tracor, Inc, 65-66; asst. prof. physics, Colo. State Col, 66-68; ADV. SCIENTIST, CONTINENTAL CAN CO, 68- Summer res. asst, Oak Ridge Nat. Lab, 61. Electrochem. Soc. Corrosion of metals in aqueous and non-aqueous systems. Address: 6518 S. Richmond Ave, Clarendon Hills, IL 60514.

FIELD, ARTHUR KIRK, b. North Adams, Mass, Jan. 6, 38; m. 60; c. 2. VIROLOGY, BIOCHEMISTRY. B.S, Cornell, 60, M.S, 61; Nat. Insts. Health fel, California, Berkeley, 62-65, Ph.D.(virol, biochem), 65. RES. FEL, MERCK INST. THERAPEUT. RES, WEST POINT, 65- Am. Soc. Microbiol; N.Y. Acad. Sci. Bacterial viruses; cytomegaloviruses; mode of action of interferon and means of interferon induction. Address: 376 Meadowbrook Rd, North Wales, M.R. 1, PA 19454.

FIELD, BYRON DUSTIN, b. Charlotte, Mich, June 2, 18; m. 41; c. 2. SPECTROSCOPY. B.S, Mich. State, 39, M.S, 42. Asst. spectroscopist, Wyandotte Chem. Corp, Mich, 41-43; spectroscopist, MALLINCKRODT CHEM. WORKS, 43-56, HEAD PHYS. METHODS LAB, 56- Am. Chem. Soc; Optical Soc. Am; Soc. Appl. Spectros; Spectros. Soc. Can. Spectrochemical analysis of chemical products; absorption spectra; infrared spectroscopy; x-ray diffraction and fluorescence spectroscopy; general instrumental analytical chemistry; atomic absorption spectroscopy; computer applications in analytical chemistry. Address: Dept. of Quality Control, Mallinckrodt Chemical Works, P.O. Box 5439, St. Louis, MO 63160.

FIELD, CHRIS, Cult. Geog, Environ. Sci, see 12th ed, Soc. & Behav. Vols.

FIELD, CROSBY, b. Jamestown, N.Y, Mar. 12, 89; m. 16; c. 3. B.S, N.Y, Univ, 09; M.E, Cornell, 12; M.S, Union (N.Y), 14; Polytech. Inst. Brooklyn, 30, 48. Engr, Gen. Elec. Co, 12-14; consult. engr, 14-15; chief engr, Standard Aniline Prods, Inc, 15-17; eng. mgr, Nat. Aniline & Chem. Co, 19-23; v.pres, dir. & secy, Brillo Mfg. Co, Inc, 23-45; pres, FLAKICE CORP, 23-68, V.PRES. ENG, 68- Pres, Chem. Mach. Corp, 23-37. U.S. Army Legion of Merit Ord. Dept, 17-19, 41-45, Col. AAAS; fel. Am. Soc. Mech. Eng. (medal, 53); fel. Inst. Elec. & Electronics Eng; fel. Am. Soc. Heat, Refrig. & Air-Conditioning Eng.(past pres); Am. Chem. Soc; Am. Inst. Chem. Eng; Soc. Mfg. Eng; Am. Ord. Asn; Soc. Exp. Stress Anal; Am. Crystallog. Asn; Processes and equipment for manufacture of metal wools, small pieces of ice, freezing of liquid foods and for utilizing mercury vapor as a heating and cooling medium; design and construction of automatic packaging equipment. Address: 8029 Harbor View Terrace, Brooklyn, NY 11209.

FIELD, CYRUS WEST, b. Duluth, Minn, May 5, 33; m. 58; c. 4. PETROLOGY. B.A, Dartmouth Col, 56; M.S, Yale, 57, Ph.D.(geol), 61. Res. asst. geol, Yale, 58-60; geologist, Bear Creek Mining Co, Kennecott Copper Corp, 60-63; asst. prof. GEOL, ORE. STATE UNIV, 63-68, ASSOC. PROF, 68- Soc. Econ. Geol; Geochem. Soc; Geol. Soc. Am; Am. Inst. Mining, Metall. & Petrol. Eng. Sulfur isotope abundances in minerals; geochemistry and mineralogy of ore deposits. Address: Dept. of Geology, Oregon State University, Corvallis, OR 97331.

FIELD, EDMUND, b. Chicago, Ill, Jan. 22, 11; m. 36; c. 2. PHYSICAL CHEMISTRY. B.S, Armour Inst. Tech, 32; univ. fel, Northwestern, 35-36, Ph.D.(phys. chem), 36. Res. chemist, ammonia dept, exp. sta, E.I. du Pont de Nemours & Co, 36-37; res. assoc. catalysis, AM. OIL CO. DIV, STANDARD OIL CO. (IND), 48-58, sr. res. assoc, 58-62; ASST. DIR. EXPLOR. RES, 62- AAAS; Am. Chem. Soc. Catalytic hydrogenation and oxidation; mechanism of catalysis; catalytic organic synthesis; polymerization; food technology. Address: American Oil Co, Box 431, Whiting, IN 46394.

FIELD, EDWARD C, JR, b. Brooklyn, N.Y, Oct. 1, 36; m. 60; c. 1. PLASMA PHYSICS. B.S, Lehigh, 58; M.S, California, Los Angeles, 60, Nat. Sci. Found. fel, 63, Ph.D.(theoret. physics), 64. Summer consult, RAND CORP, 60-64, PHYS. SCIENTIST, 64- Nuclear weapons effects, particularly geophysical aspects; theoretical plasma physics, especially kinetic theory of plasma. Address: Rand Corp, 1700 Main St, Santa Monica, CA 90406.

FIELD, FRANK H(ENRY), b. Keansburg, N.J, Feb. 27, 22; m. 44, 59; c. 2. PHYSICAL CHEMISTRY. B.S, Duke, 43, M.A, 44, Ph.D.(chem), 48. Instr. & asst. prof. chem, Texas, 47-52, res. chemist, Humble Oil & Ref. Co, 52-53, sr. res. chemist, 53-60, res. specialist, 60-62, res. assoc, 62-65, Esso Res. & Eng. Co, 65-68, sr. res. assoc, 68-70; PROF. CHEM, ROCKEFELLER UNIV, 70- Guggenheim fel, 63-64. Am. Chem. Soc; Am. Soc. Mass Spectrometry (v.pres, 70-72). Mass spectrometry, electron impact studies, energies and reactions of gaseous ions; radiation chemistry. Address: Dept. of Chemistry, Rockefeller University, New York, NY 10021.

FIELD, FRANKLYN, b. New York, N.Y, Mar. 30, 27; m. 47; c. 3. METEOROLOGY, OPTOMETRY. B.A, Brooklyn Col, 47; B.S, Columbia, 49; O.D, Mass. Col. Optom, 60. Meteorologist, U.S. Weather Bur, 47-48; gen. mgr, Weather Fotocast Corp, 50-56; pres, Int. Weather Corp, 56-60; dir. air pollution res, Med. Health & Res. Coun. N.Y, 60; res. fel. air pollution & health, Albert Einstein Col. Med, 61-66; v.pres. aerosol res, Spray-Technol. Corp, 63-66; sci. ed, WNBC, N.Y, 66-70; PRES, WEATHER SCI, INC, 70- Consult. meteorologist, Nat. Broadcasting Corp, 59-; New York Dept. Air Pollution Control, 60- U.S.A.A.F, 44-47, 1st Lt. Am. Meteorol. Soc; Am. Optom. Asn; Air Pollution Control Asn; Am. Pub. Health Asn. Air pollution, meteorology and effects upon health; bioclimatology. Address: 111 Fairwater Ave, Massapequa, NY 11758.

FIELD, GEORGE, B(ROOKS), b. Providence, R.I, Oct. 25, 29; m. 56; c. 2. ASTROPHYSICS. B.S, Mass. Inst. Technol, 51; Nat. Sci. Found. fel, Princeton, 54-55, Ph.D.(astron), 55. Physicist, Naval Ord. Lab, 51-52; res. asst, Princeton, 52-54; jr. fel. astron, Harvard Soc. Fels, 55-57; asst. prof. ASTRON, Princeton, 57-62, assoc. prof, 62-65; PROF, UNIV. CALIF, BERKELEY, 65-, CHMN. DEPT, 70- Guggenheim fel, 60-61; mem. planetology subcomt, space sci. steering comt, NASA, 64-66, astron. missions bd, 68-70; Phillips Visitor, Haverford Col, 65 & 71; partic. summer study on space sci, Nat. Acad. Sci-Nat. Res. Coun, 65, mem. panel on astron. adv. to Off. Naval Res, 65-66, physics surv. comt, 69-, astron. surv. comt, 69-, panel on radio astron, astron. surv, 69-, chmn. panel astrophys. & relativity, physics & astron. survs, 69-; Nat. Sci. Found. grants, astrophys, 65-; mem. astron. panel, Nat. Sci. Found, 66-67, chmn, 67-69; space sci. panel, President's Sci. Adv. Comt, 66-67; vis. comt, Nat. Radio Astron. Observ, 67-69; co-ed, Gordon & Breach series astrophys. & space sci, 68-; correspondent, Comments on Astrophys. & Space Physics, 68-; vis. prof, Cambridge, 69; trustee-at-large, Assoc. Univs, Inc, 69- AAAS; fel. Am. Phys. Soc; Am. Astron. Soc; Royal Astron. Soc; Int. Astron. Union. Dynamics of interstellar matter; including galaxy and star formation; instabilities in dilute gases; cosmology, including background radiation and intergalactic matter. Address: Dept. of Astronomy, University of California, Berkeley, CA 94720.

FIELD, GEORGE FRANCIS, b. Stockton, Calif, Dec. 26, 34; m. 62; c. 2. ORGANIC CHEMISTRY. A.B, Pomona Col, 56; Nat. Sci. Found. fel, Harvard, 56-58, Ph.D.(org. chem), 62. Fel, Hopkins, 60-62; sr. chemist, HOFFMANN-LA ROCHE, INC, 62-70, RES. FEL, 70- Am. Chem. Soc. Medicinal chemistry; heterocyclic synthesis. Address: Chemical Research Dept, Hoffmann-La Roche, Inc, Nutley, NJ 07110.

FIELD, GEORGE ROBERT, b. Vienna, Austria, Oct. 16, 19; U.S. citizen; m. 46; c. 3. ELECTRICAL ENGINEERING. B.S.E.E, Washington (St. Louis), 48; M.S, Drexel Univ, 60-& 71. Design & develop. engr, MISSILE & SURFACE RADAR DIV, RCA CORP, 48-55, design & develop. leader, 55-56, mgr. radar data conversion eng, 56-61, design support & integration, 61-62; eng. opers, 62-63, design & develop. eng, 63-64, mgr. tech. assurance, 64-69, MGR. TECH. OPERS, 69- U.S.A, 43-45, M/Sgt. Sr. mem. Inst. Elec. & Electronics Eng. Design and development of electronic equipment for missile range instrumentation; strategic and defensive systems and space exploration. Address: Missile & Surface Radar Division, RCA Corp, Marne Highway & Borton's Landing Rd, Moorestown, N.J. 08057.

FIELD, GEO(RGE) S(YDNEY), b. Wimbledon, Eng, Oct. 23, 05; m. 30; c. 3. PHYSICS. B.Sc, Alberta, 29, Nat. Res. Coun. Can. bursar, 29-30, M.Sc, 30, D.Sc.(ultrasonics), 37. Jr. res. physicist & physicist, Nat. Res. Coun. Can, 30-47; dir. sci. res. & develop, Royal Can. Navy, 47-48; deputy dir. gen, Can. Defence Res. Bd, 48-52, chief div. A. & sci. adv. to chief naval staff, 52-54, chief scientist, 54-64, v.chmn, 64-66; RETIRED. Order of the British Empire, 46. Fel. Acoust. Soc. Am; fel. Inst. Elec. & Electronics Eng; fel. Royal Soc. Can. Ultrashort radio waves; ultrasonics; acoustics. Address: 1833 Riverside Dr, Apt. 1020, Ottawa, Ont. K1G 0E8, Can.

FIELD, GORDON, b. West Barnstable, Mass, Aug. 19, 21; m. 42; c. 4. ENTOMOLOGY. B.S, Massachusetts, 43, M.S, 48, Ph.D.(entom), 57. Instr. entom, Massachusetts, 46-51; asst. chief entomologist, U.S. Army Surgeon Gen. Off, Wash, D.C, 51-52, instr. med. entom, med. field serv. sch, Fort Sam Houston, Tex, 52-53, commanding officer malaria control, med. sect, U.S. Army Hq, Canal Zone, 53-56, liaison officer insecticide resistance, U.S. Army Labs, Mass, 57-59, commanding officer med. entom, 37th Med. Co, 8th Army, Korea, 59-60, chief dept, 406th Med. Lab, Med. Command, Japan, 60-62, chief med. entom. div, U.S. Army Environ. Hyg. Agency, 63-66, Womack Army Hosp, Ft. Bragg, N.C, 66-67; adj. prof. entom, N.C. State, 67-68; asst. prof, UNIV. R.I, 68-69, chmn. dept. plant path. & entom, 69-71, EXTEN. & RES. ENTOMOLOGIST, 71- U.S.A, 43-46, Med.Serv.C, 51-67, Lt. Col.(ret). AAAS; Entom. Soc. Am; Am. Mosquito Control Asn. Medical and applied entomology; taxonomy of black flies. Address: Dept. of Plant Pathology & Entomology, University of Rhode Island, Kingston, RI 02881.

FIELD, HERBERT C(YRE), b. Cleveland, Ohio, Nov. 2, 30; m. 53; c. 4. PHYSICS. B.S, Case, 53; M.S, Purdue, 57. Physicist, exp. physics div, Lawrence Radiation Lab, Calif, 53-54; exp. shock hydrodyn. div, 54-55; exp. physics group, Atomics Int. Div, N.Am. Aviation, Inc, 57-59, sr. physicist, reactor physics group, 59-63; REACTOR SAFETY SPECIALIST, DIV. OPER. SAFETY, U.S. ATOMIC ENERGY COMN, 63- Consult, U.S. Navy, 70-71. AAAS; Am. Phys. Soc; Am. Nuclear Soc. Nuclear reactors, especially their safety evaluation; experimental neutron physics; administration of safety programs. Address: Division of Operational Safety, U.S. Atomic Energy Commission, Washington, DC 20545.

FIELD, JACK EVERETT, b. Gary, Ind, June 3, 27; m. 58; c. 2. INORGANIC CHEMISTRY. A.B, Harvard, 52; M.S, Tulane, 55, Ph.D.(inorg. chem), 57; Fulbright fel, Münster, 56-57. Chemist, E.I. du Pont de Nemours & Co, 57-63; res. chemist, Corning Glass Works, 64-66; prof. phys. sci, NICHOLLS STATE UNIV, 66-71, PROF. CHEM. & HEAD DEPT, 71- U.S.A.F, 45-48, T/Sgt. AAAS; Am. Chem. Soc. Inorganic chemistry of the solid state and surfaces, including crystal growth. Address: Dept. of Chemistry, Nicholls State University, Thibodaux, LA 70301.

FIELD, JAMES B(ERNARD), b. Ft. Wayne, Ind, May 28, 26; m. 54; c. 4. MEDICINE. M.D, Harvard, 51. Intern med, Mass. Gen. Hosp, 51-52, asst. res, 52-53, res, 53-54; sr. investr. clin. endocrinol. br, Nat. Insts. Health, 54-62; assoc. prof. MED, SCH. MED, UNIV. PITTSBURGH, 62-66, PROF, 66-, DIR. CLIN. RES. UNIT, 62- Consult. diabetes & arthritis prog, div. chronic diseases, U.S. Pub. Health Serv; mem. endocrinol. study sect, U.S. Pub. Health Serv, 65-67, chmn, 67-69; U.S. Pub. Health Serv. training grant, 70-74; ed, Metabolism, 70- Eli Lilly award, Am. Diabetes Asn, 58; Van. Meter prize, Am. Goiter Asn, 61. U.S.A, 44-45; U.S.P.H.S, 54-60, Sr. Surg. Am. Soc. Clin. Invest; Endocrine Soc; Am. Physiol. Soc; Am. Fedn. Clin. Res; Am. Diabetes Asn; Asn. Am. Physicians. Diabetes mellitus and endocrinology. Address: Dept. of Medicine, University of Pittsburgh School of Medicine, Pittsburgh, PA 15213.

FIELD, JOHN B(YRON), b. New York, N.Y, May 15, 19; m. 44; c. 2. MEDICINE. Ph.G. & Ph.C, St. John's (N.Y), 39, scholar & B.S, 40; M.S, Wisconsin, 41, scholar & Ph.D.(biochem), 44; M.D, Rochester, 48. Asst, St. John's (N.Y), 39-40; Wisconsin, 40-45; instr. biochem. Manhattan Proj, Rochester, 45-48, consult, Atomic Energy Proj, 48-50; res, New York Hosp. & med. col, Cornell, 48-50, mem. cancer ctr, 50-51; asst. clin. prof. med, sch. med, Southern California, 51-59; dir. cancer chemother. lab, Mt. Sinai Hosp, 60-61; sci. dir, West. Inst. Cancer & Leukemia Res, 61-66, DIR, WEST. FOUND. CANCER RES, 66- Assoc. clin. prof. & chief med. oncol, col. med, Univ. Calif, 63-64. With Off. Sci. Res. & Develop, 44. Am. Chem. Soc; Soc. Exp. Biol. & Med; Am. Soc. Biol. Chem; Am. Cancer Soc; Am. Asn. Cancer Res; Am. Fedn. Clin. Res; Am. Soc. Clin. Oncol. Blood coagulation on prothrombin and fibrinogen with vitamin K and dicumarol and liver agents; cancer chemotherapy in development and trial of new agents. Address: Western Foundation for Cancer Research, 465 N. Roxbury Dr, Beverly Hills, CA 90210.

FIELD, JOSEPH H(ERMAN), b. Pittsburgh, Pa, May 29, 20; m. 47; c. 2. CHEMICAL ENGINEERING. B.S, Carnegie Inst. Technol, 40; M.S, Pittsburgh, 44. From jr. engr. to supv. chem. engr, U.S. Bur. Mines, 41-58, acting chief, gas synthesis sect, 58-60, proj. coord. eng, 60-69; V.PRES. ENG, BENFIELD CORP, 69- U.S.N, 44-46. Am. Chem. Soc; Air Pollution Control Asn; Am. Inst. Chem. Eng; Brit. Inst. Fuel. Synthetic liquid and high-British thermal unit gas from coal; air pollution, SO_2 removal from flue gas; gas purification. Address: Benfield Corp, 666 Washington Rd, Pittsburgh, PA 15228.

FIELD, LAMAR, b. Montgomery, Ala, July 19, 22; m. 48; c. 2. ORGANIC CHEMISTRY. S.B, Mass. Inst. Tech, 44, fel, 46-47, Socony-Vacuum fel, 47-48, Ph.D.(chem), 49. Asst. chemist, res. lab, Merck & Co, Inc, 44-46; instr. ORG. CHEM, VANDERBILT UNIV, 49, asst. prof, 49-52, assoc. prof, 52-59, PROF, 59-, chmn. dept. chem, 61-67. Consult. to chem. indust, 55-; vis. assoc, Am. Chem. Soc, 63-, vis. scientist, 66-; consult, Nat. Insts. Health, 65-69; Coulter lectr, Univ. Miss, 68; lectr, int. meetings, Ireland, 69, Italy, 70; civilian with Off. Sci. Res. & Develop. William Barton Rogers Award, 44; L.C. Glenn Award, 52. Am. Chem. Soc; The Chem. Soc. Synthetic, structural, medicinal and biological aspects of organic chemistry, especially with reference to organic sulfur compounds. Address: Box 1507, Station B, Vanderbilt University, Nashville, TN 37203.

FIELD, LESTER M(ARSHALL), b. Chicago, Ill, Feb. 9, 18; m. 42; c. 2. ELECTRICAL ENGINEERING. B.S, Purdue, 39; Ph.D.(elec. eng), Stanford, 44; hon. Dr.Eng, Purdue, 68. Asst, Stanford, 39-41, instr, 41-42, acting asst. prof, 43-44; phys. res. staff, Bell Tel. Labs, 44-46; acting assoc. prof, elec. eng, Stanford, 46-47, acting prof, 47-50, prof, 50-52; vis. prof, Calif. Inst. Technol, 52-53, prof, 53-55; assoc. dir. res. labs, HUGHES AIRCRAFT CO, 55-59, mgr. microwave tube div, 59-61, v.pres. res, 61-66, V.PRES, 66-, CHIEF SCIENTIST, 69-, assoc. dir, Hughes Res. Labs, 66-69. Prof, Calif. Inst. Technol, 55-60. Nat. Acad. Eng; Am. Phys. Soc; fel. Inst. Elec. & Electronics Eng. Electron optics; interaction of electron streams and electromagnetic waves; microwaves; electromagnetic theory; plasma physics. Address: Hughes Aircraft Co, 3011 Malibu Canyon Rd, Malibu, CA 90265.

FIELD, MARVIN FREDERICK, b. Manistee, Mich, Oct. 3, 26; m. 51; c. 3. MICROBIOLOGY. A.B, Central Michigan, 48; M.S, Mich. State, 50; Ph.D. (microbiol), Minnesota, 57. Instr. microbiol, Rochester, 50-51; res. microbiologist, Chas. Pfizer & Co, N.Y, 51-53, microbiologist, Ind, 57-62; sr. virologist, Jensen Salsbery Labs. Div, Richardson-Merrell, Inc, 62-63; asst. prof. DENT, UNIV. MO-KANSAS CITY, 63-70, ASSOC. PROF, 70- Asst. prof. microbiol, med. ctr, Kansas, 63-69. AAAS; Am. Chem. Soc; Am. Soc. Microbiol. Electron microscopy; virology. Address: School of Dentistry, University of Missouri-Kansas City, 650 E. 25th St, Kansas City, MO 64108.

FIELD, MICHAEL, b. N.Y.C, Feb. 21, 14; m. 42; c. 2. PHYSICS. B.M.E, city Col. New York, 37; M.S, Columbia, 38; fel, Cincinnati, 44-46, Ph.D. (physics), 48. Res. engr, Cincinnati Milling Mach. Co, 38-45, res. physicist, 46-48; partner, METCUT RES. ASSOCS, INC, 48-58, PRES, 59- AAAS; Am. Soc. Metals; Soc. Automotive Eng; Soc. Exp. Stress Anal; Am. Inst. Aeronaut. & Astronaut; Am. Soc. Info. Sci; Soc. Mfg. Eng. Physics and mechanics of metal cutting; machinability; high temperature mechanical testing; machine tools; metallurgy. Address: 9060 Spooky Ridge Lane, Cincinnati, OH 45242.

FIELD, NATHAN D(AVID), b. New York, N.Y, Aug. 21, 25; m. 49; c. 3. POLYMER & ORGANIC CHEMISTRY. B.S, City Col. New York, 45; A.M, Columbia, 49; Ph.D, Polytech. Inst. Brooklyn, 56. Res. chemist, Glyco Prod, 45-48; Hart Prod, 49-52; asst, Polytech. Inst. Brooklyn, 52-56; res. chemist, textile fibers, E.I. du Pont de Nemours & Co, 56-62; res. supvr, Atlantic Ref. Co, 62-64; mgr. polymer res, Gen. Aniline & Film Corp, 64-67, mgr. cent. res. lab, GAF Corp, 67-70; DIR. RES. & DEVELOP, INT. PLAYTEX CORP, 70- U.S.A.A.F, 45-46. Am. Chem. Soc. Polymers; polymer microstructure; structure-property; kinetics of polymerization; surfactants. Address: 2736 Liberty St, Allentown, PA 18104.

FIELD, NORMAN J, b. New York, N.Y, Dec. 5, 22; m. 46; c. 4. PHYSICS. B.S, City Col.(New York), 42; M.S, Polytech. Inst. Brooklyn, 59. Electronic engr, Sig.C. Radar Lab, 42-44, chief optical micros, eng. labs, 46-53, external res, 53-54, asst. to dir. res, 54-58; asst. dir. inst. explor. res, U.S. Army Sig. Res. & Develop. Lab, 58-62, DEP. DIR. RES, U.S. ARMY ELECTRONICS LABS, 62- Adj. prof. Monmouth Col, 56- U.S.A, 44-46. Am. Phys. Soc; Optical Soc. Am; Am. Chem. Soc; Am. Asn. Physics Teachers. Crystal physics and chemistry; optical properties of solids; administration of research. Address: 726 Sycamore Ave, Shrewsbury, NJ 07701.

FIELD, PAUL E(UGENE), b. Easton, Pa, June 16, 34; m. 60; c. 3. PHYSICAL & INORGANIC CHEMISTRY. B.S, Moravian Col, 57; M.S, Pa. State, 61, Ph.D.(chem), 63. Asst. prof. CHEM, VA. POLYTECH. INST. & STATE UNIV, 63-68, ASSOC. PROF, 68- U.S.A, 57-59. AAAS; Am. Chem. Soc. Thermodynamic properties of molten salts; high temperature calorimetry and magnetic properties of inorganic compounds. Address: Dept. of Chemistry, Virginia Polytechnic Institute & State University, Blacksburg, VA 24061.

FIELD, RAY A, b. Ogden, Utah, Dec. 15, 33; m. 58; c. 4. ANIMAL SCIENCE. B.S, Brigham Young, 58; M.S, Kentucky, 60, Ph.D.(animal sci), 63. Meat specialist, Nat. Livestock & Meat Bd, 58; res. asst, Kentucky, 59-62; asst. prof. MEAT SCI, UNIV. WYO, 62-66, assoc. prof, 66-70, PROF, 70- Am. Meat Sci. Asn; Inst. Food Technol; Am. Soc. Animal Sci. Live animal and carcass evaluation; inheritance of quality in meat; consumer acceptance, and palatability characteristics of meat; postmortem biochemistry of collagen as related to tenderness. Address: Dept. of Animal Sciences, University of Wyoming, University Station Box 3354, Laramie, WY 82071.

FIELD, RICHARD A(LLAN), b. Chicago, Ill, Mar. 2, 22; m. 42, 55; c. 4. MEDICINE, BIOCHEMISTRY. A.B, Harvard, 43, M.D, 50. Nat. Cancer Inst. fel. biochem, sch. med, Wash. Univ, 54; teaching fel. med, Harvard Med. Sch, 55, instr, 57-58, assoc, 58-63, asst. prof, 63-66; assoc. prof. med. & dir. div. diabetes & metab. diseases, Jefferson Med. Col, 66-68, prof. med. & dir. div. endocrinol. & metab. diseases, 68-70; ASSOC. CLIN. PROF. MED, HARVARD MED. SCH, 70-; ASSOC, RETINA FOUND, 70- Asst, Mass. Gen. Hosp, 57-58, chief diabetes unit, 57-66, asst. physician, 58-66; assoc. physician, Beth Israel Hosp, Boston, 70-; consult, Mass. Eye & Ear Infirmary, 70- U.S.A, 42-46, Med.C. Res, 46-, Capt. Clinical and biochemical research in the field of carbohydrate metabolism and diabetes. Address: Retina Foundation, 20 Staniford St, Boston, MA 02114.

FIELD, RICHARD E(UGENE), b. Jackson, Mich, April 17, 19; m. 43; c. 5. ORGANIC CHEMISTRY. B.S, Michigan, 41, M.S, 43, Ph.D.(org. chem), 45. Res. chemist, Gen. Aniline & Film Co, 45-55; SR. RES. CHEMIST, Barrett div, Allied Chem. Corp, 55-58; Gen. Tire & Rubber Co, 58-69; RES. & DEVELOP. DIV, ASHLAND OIL, INC, 70- Am. Chem. Soc. Synthetic organic chemistry; acetylene derivatives; new product research and development; polymer intermediates. Address: Ashland Oil, Inc, P.O. Box 2458, Columbus, OH 43216.

FIELD, RICHARD J(EFFREY), b. Attleboro, Mass, Oct. 26, 41; m. 66. PHYSICAL CHEMISTRY. B.S, Univ. Mass, 63; M.S, Col. Holy Cross, 64; Ph.D.(phys. chem), Univ. R.I, 68. RES. ASSOC. PHYS. CHEM, UNIV. ORE, 68-, VIS. ASST. PROF, 70- Am. Chem. Soc. Gas phase kinetics, reactions of bromine atoms with small organic molecules and thermochemical quantities derived from these studies, addition of free radicals to olefins;

solution kinetics, application of photochemical space intermittency to the determination of diffusion coefficients, chemical reactions with oscillatory steady states. Address: Dept. of Chemistry, University of Oregon, Eugene, OR 97403.

FIELD, THEODORE E(STES), b. Auburn, Maine, Feb. 19, 08; m. 39; c. 2. PHYSICAL CHEMISTRY. B.S, Bates Col, 29; Maine fel, Hopkins, Ph.D. (phys. chem), 34. Res. chemist, CORHART REFRACTORIES CO, 35-38, dir. res, 38-45, tech. dir, 45-58, TECH. CONSULT, DEVELOP. DEPT, 58- Am. Chem. Soc; Am. Ceramic Soc; Electrochem. Soc; fel. Am. Inst. Chem; Brit. Ceramic Soc; Royal Netherlands Chem. Soc. Properties of systems of fused and crystallized oxides; effect of pressure upon the vapor pressure of a dissociating solid. Address: Development Dept, Corhart Refractories Co, 1600 W. Lee St, Louisville, KY 40210.

FIELDER, D(ANIEL) C(URTIS), b. North Kingstown, R.I, Oct. 9, 17; m. 44. ELECTRICAL ENGINEERING. B.S, Rhode Island, 40, E.E, 50; M.S, Ga. Inst. Technol, 48, Ph.D.(elec. eng), 57. Jr. design engr. transformers & switchgear, Westinghouse Elec. Corp, 40-41; design engr. degaussing & compass compensation, Bur. Ships, Wash, D.C, 41-46; asst. ELEC. ENG, Ga. Inst. Technol, 46-47; instr, Syracuse, 47-48; asst. prof, GA. INST. TECHNOL, 48-57, assoc. prof, 57-63, PROF, 63- Sr. mem. Inst. Elec. & Electronics Eng; Math. Asn. Am. Graph theory; combinatorics; electric circuit theory; digital computer theory. Address: School of Electrical Engineering, Georgia Institute of Technology, Atlanta, GA 30332.

FIELDER, DOUGLAS S(TRATTON), b. Wash, D.C, July 22, 40; m. 68. NUCLEAR PHYSICS. B.S, Va. Mil. Inst, 62; M.S, Univ. Va, 64, Ph.D.(physics), 67. From asst. prof. to ASSOC. PROF. PHYSICS & CHMN. DEPT, STATE UNIV. N.Y. COL. ONEONTA, 69- Eng.C, U.S.A, 67-69, Capt. Am. Phys. Soc; Am. Asn. Physics Teachers. Determination of absolute cross sections for several photoneutron reactions; photonuclear physics. Address: Dept. of Physics, State University of New York College at Oneonta, Oneonta, NY 13820.

FIELDER, WILLIAM, b. Bloomington, Ind, Feb. 19, 28; m. 58; c. 2. INORGANIC CHEMISTRY. B.S, Indiana, 51, M.S, 53; Ph.D.(inorg. chem), West. Reserve, 58. Plant asst, Mallinckrodt Chem. Works, 51-53; AERO RES. SCIENTIST, NASA LEWIS RES. CTR, 58- Am. Chem. Soc. Ionic transport in solids. Address: NASA Lewis Research Center, 21000 Brookpark Rd, Cleveland, OH 44135.

FIELDHOUSE, DONALD J(OHN), b. Dodgeville, Wis, Nov. 18, 25; m. 49; c. 4. HORTICULTURE. Ph.D.(hort), Wisconsin, 54. From asst. prof. HORT. to ASSOC. PROF, UNIV. DEL, 54- C.Eng, U.S.A, 43-46. Am. Soc. Hort. Sci. Irrigation of vegetable crops; vegetable physiology; agricultural climatology; soil, plant, and water relationships; air pollution; plant growth regulators; crop physiology; plant pathology. Address: Dept. of Plant Science, College of Agricultural Sciences, University of Delaware, Newark, DE 19711.

FIELDHOUSE, JOHN W, b. Rensselaer, Ind, Oct. 17, 41; m. 63; c. 1. ORGANIC CHEMISTRY. B.A, Hope Col, 63; Ph.D.(organo-sulfur chem), Purdue, 68. RES. CHEMIST, FIRESTONE TIRE & RUBBER CO, 68- Am. Chem. Soc. Olefin and rubber intermediates synthesis. Address: 114 E. Archwood, Akron, OH 44301.

FIELDING, CHRISTOPHER J, b. Cheadle, Eng, Jan. 26, 42; m. 68. METABOLISM, BIOCHEMISTRY. B.Sc, Univ. London, 62, Ph.D.(genetics), 65; hon. M.A, Oxford, 65. Res. fel. BIOCHEM, Oxford, 65-67, investr, 67-69; AM. HEART ASN. ESTAB. INVESTR, dept. med, Univ. Chicago, 70-71; SCH. MED, UNIV. CALIF, SAN FRANCISCO, 71- Fel. New Col, Oxford, 65-69; independent investr, Med. Res. Coun. Grant, 67-69; Am. Heart Asn. grant, 71-; U.S. Pub. Health Serv. grant, Nat. Heart & Lung Inst, 71- Brit. Biochem. Soc; fel. Am. Heart Asn. Lipid metabolism; metabolism and structure of plasma lipoproteins; enzymology of lipases and acyl transferases; hepatic uptake and output of lipoproteins. Address: School of Medicine, Cardiovascular Research Institute, University of California, San Francisco, CA 94122.

FIELDING, MAX J(AE), b. Orem,Utah, Jan. 17, 26; m. 48; c. 4. NEMATOLOGY. B.S, Brigham Young, 48; M.S, La. State, 56. Nematologist, U.S. Dept. Agr, 48-56; res. biologist, E.I. DU PONT DE NEMOURS & CO, 56-66, SR. RES. BIOLOGIST, 66- Nematode taxonomy physiology, ecology; control of parasitic nematodes by chemicals; control of soil fungi. Address: Experimental Station, E.I. du Pont de Nemours & Co, Wilmington, DE 19803.

FIELDING, PETER GOODWIN, b. Farnborough, Eng, Dec. 15, 19; m. 45; c. 2. AERONAUTICS. Aero. Eng, N.Gloucester Tech. Col, 43; A.F.R.Ae.S, Brit. Inst. Eng. Tech, 55. Sr. engr. struct, Gloster Aircraft Ltd, 39-45; De Havilland Aircraft Ltd, 45-47; proj. engr, Saunders-Roe Ltd, 47-49, tech. asst. to chief engr, 49-53, proj. coord, 53-55; proj. dir. aerospace systs, Lockheed Aircraft Corp, 55-59; res. dir. systs. anal, Booz Allen Appl. Res, Inc, Md, 59-67, v.pres, 67-71; CONSULT, 71- Consult, U.S. Army Transportation Corp, 59-63; Off. Naval Res, 60-63; U.S. Maritime Admin, 62-65; Bur. Pub Rds. & Dept. Commerce, 65-; Advan. Res. Proj. Agency, 70-; Naval Ships Res. & Develop. Ctr, 70- Assoc. fel. Am. Inst. Aeronaut. & Astronaut; Soc. Naval Archit. & Marine Eng; fel. Royal Aeronaut. Soc. Weapons and transportation system design; feasibility analysis; force structure analysis; cost-effectiveness analysis; systems analysis; transportation analysis; operations research; parametric cost analysis; economics of transportation systems; air cushion concepts; arctic research. Address: 8510 16th St, Silver Spring, MD 20910.

FIELDS, BERNARD NATHAN, b. Brooklyn, N.Y, Mar. 24, 38; m. 66; c. 4. MEDICINE, VIROLOGY. A.B, Brandeis, 58; M.D, N.Y. Univ, 62. U.S. Pub. Health Serv, res. fel. infectious disease, Mass. Gen. Hosp, Harvard Med. Sch, 64-65; med. virologist, commun. disease ctr, U.S. Pub. Health Serv, 65-67; res. fel, ALBERT EINSTEIN COL. MED, 67-70, asst. prof. CELL BIOL. & MED, 70-71, ASSOC. PROF, 71- Nat. Sci. Found. grant; Am. Cancer Soc. grant. U.S.P.H.S, 65-67, Res, 67-, Asst. Surg. Harvey Soc; Am. Soc. Microbiol. Paracolon bacteria, clinical, epidemiologic and bacteriologic; new arboviruses; characterization of isolates; tissue culture; antigen preparation; epidemiology of arboviruses; reovirus; genetics; biochemistry; animal virus genetics. Address: Dept. of Medicine, Albert Einstein College of Medicine, 1300 Morris Park Ave, Bronx, NY 10461.

FIELDS, CLARK L(EROY), b. Pipestone, Minn, Oct. 25, 37; m. 63; c. 1. INORGANIC CHEMISTRY. B.A, Pasadena Col, 59; M.S, Iowa, 62, Ph.D.(inorg. chem), 64. ASSOC. PROF. CHEM, UNIV. NORTH. COLO, 64- AAAS; Am. Chem. Soc. Chemistry of boron and transition metal hydrides. Address: Dept. of Chemistry, University of Northern Colorado, Greeley, CO 80631.

FIELDS, D(AVIS) S(TUART), JR, b. Lexington, Ky, Apr. 17, 29; m. 55; c. 3. PHYSICAL METALLURGY. B.S, Kentucky, 50, Gordon McKay fel, Harvard, 50-51; Aluminum Co. Am. fel, Mass. Inst. Technol, 53-57, M.S, 54, Sc.D. (metall), 57. Phys. metallurgist, Watertown Arsenal Labs, 51-52; res. metallurgist res. labs, Aluminum Co. Am, 57-60; asst. prof. metall, Kentucky, 60-62, assoc. prof, 62; staff metallurgist, IBM CORP, 62-64, adv. metallurgist, 64-67, SR. ENGR, 67- Lectr, Univ. Ky, 62-67. U.S.A.R, 50-62, Capt. Am. Soc. Metals; Am. Inst. Mining, Metall. & Petrol. Eng; Am. Soc. Test. & Mat; Sci. Res. Soc. Am. Mechanical metallurgy; strain hardening behavior of metals and alloys; relationship to working and forming operations; relationship to microstructural characteristics; practical applications of superplastic alloys. Address: 7330 Island Circle, Boulder, CO 80301.

FIELDS, DONALD L(EE), b. Louisville, Ky, May 16, 32; m. 53; c. 4. ORGANIC CHEMISTRY. B.S, East. Ky. State Col, 54; Ph.D.(chem), Ohio State, 58. Res. chemist, EASTMAN KODAK CO, 58-60, sr. res. chemist, 60-64, RES. ASSOC. CHEM, 64- U.S.A.R, 53-57, 2nd Lt. Am. Chem. Soc. Exploratory research in synthetic organic chemistry. Address: 40 Old Pond Rd, Rochester, NY 14625.

FIELDS, ELLIS KIRBY, b. Chicago, Ill, May 10, 17; m. 39; c. 3. CHEMISTRY. B.S, Chicago, 36, univ. fel, Ph.D.(org. chem), 38. Eli Lilly res. fel, Chicago, 38-41; dir. res, develop. lab, Chicago, 41-50; res. assoc, STANDARD OIL CO.(IND), 50-62, SR. RES. ASSOC, AMOCO CHEM. CORP. DIV, 62- Mem. staff, Kings Col, London, 62-; mem. petrol. res. fund adv. bd, Am. Petrol. Inst. AAAS; Am. Chem. Soc.(assoc. ed, Chem. Revs, Petrol. Preprints); Faraday Soc; The Chem. Soc; Soc. Chem. Indust. Petrochemicals; oxidation process; lube oils and additives; pesticides. Address: Davenport House, 559 Ashland Ave, River Forest, IL 60305.

FIELDS, HARRY, b. Brooklyn, N.Y, Aug. 5, 11; m. 37; c. 2. OBSTETRICS & GYNECOLOGY. B.S, Haverford, 32; M.D, Pennsylvania, 36. ASSOC. PROF. OBSTET. & GYNEC, SCH. MED, UNIV. PA, 56- Dipl, Am. Bd. Obstet. & Gynec, 44. Am. Col. Obstet. & Gynec; fel. Am. Col. Surg. Address: Dept. of Obstetrics & Gynecology, University of Pennsylvania School of Medicine, 133 S. 36th St, Philadelphia, PA 19104.

FIELDS, JERRY L, b. Green City, Mo, Aug. 5, 36. MATHEMATICS. A.B, Harvard, 58, A.M, 61, Ph.D.(math), 64. sr. mathematician, Midwest Res. Inst, 64-68; vis. assoc. prof, MATH, Tsing Hua Univ, Taiwan, 68-69, ASSOC. PROF, UNIV. ALTA, 69- Math. Asn. Am; Am. Math. Soc; Soc. Indust. & Appl. Math. Approximation theory, asymptotic analysis. Address: Dept. of Mathematics, University of Alberta, Edmonton, Alta, Can.

FIELDS, JOSEPH EDWARD, b. Crestline, Ohio, Jan. 17, 16; m. 46; c. 1. ORGANIC CHEMISTRY. B.S, Otterbein Col, 37; M.Sc, Ohio State, 39, Ph.D. (chem), 41. Asst. chem, Ohio State, 37-41; chemist, Texas Co, N.Y, 41-46; MONSANTO CO, 46-54, group leader, polymer res, 54-69, ADVAN. SCIENTIST, NEW ENTERPRISE DIV. & SR. RES. GROUP LEADER, LIFE SCI, 69- Am. Chem. Soc. Polyelectrolytes; desalination; membrane processes; liquid ammonia; lubricating oil additives; plastics; reinforced polymers; polymer physics. Address: Research Center, Monsanto Co, 800 N. Lindbergh Blvd, St. Louis, MO 63166.

FIELDS, MARION LEE, b. Plainfield, Ind, Dec. 15, 26; m. 46; c. 4. FOOD SCIENCE, MICROBIOLOGY. A.B, Indiana, 50; M.S, Purdue, 56, Ph.D.(food tech), 59. Sanitarian, Ind. State Bd. Health, 51-54; asst. hort, Purdue, 54-56, instr, 56-59, asst. prof, 59-60; UNIV. MO, COLUMBIA, 60-64, assoc. prof, 64-67, FOOD SCI. & NUTRIT, 67-69, PROF, 69- U.S.A, 45-46. Inst. Food Technol; Am. Soc. Microbiol. Microbial ecology; heat resistance of bacterial spores. Address: Dept. of Food Science & Nutrition, University of Missouri, Columbia, MO 65201.

FIELDS, MELVIN, b. Muncie, Ind, June 30, 20; m. 40. ORGANIC CHEMISTRY. B.S, Harvard, 42, M.S, 43, Ph.D.(org. chem), 44. Mem. staff, comt. med. res, antimalarial proj, Harvard, 44-45; res. chemist, Polaroid Corp, 45-48; dir. org. chem. div, Tracerlab, Inc, 48-52; group leader, ELECTROCHEM. DEPT, E.I. DU PONT DE NEMOURS & CO, INC, 52-55, res. supvr, 55-68, RES. MGR, 68- Am. Chem. Soc. Synthetic organic chemistry; polarography; ultraviolet and infrared spectra of organic compounds; radiochemistry and synthesis of isotopically labelled compounds; vinyl polymers. Address: 609 Berwick Rd, Edenridge, Wilmington, DE 19803.

FIELDS, RAYMOND I(RA), b. Carcassonne, Ky, March 15, 17; m. 39; c. 1. MATHEMATICAL STATISTICS. A.B, East. Ky. State Col, 38; M.A, Arizona, 46; Southern Fels. Fund fel, Va. Polytech, 57-58, Ph.D.(statist), 60. Teacher & prin, pub. schs, Ky, Ohio & Ariz, 35-45; instr. math, Kentucky, 46-47; asst. prof. eng. math, UNIV. LOUISVILLE, 48-57, assoc. prof, 58-63, prof. & acting head dept, 63-71, PROF. APPL. MATH. & COMPUT. SCI, 71- Vis. prof. biomet, Med. Ctr, La. State Univ, 62- Am. Statist. Asn; Math. Asn. Am. Design of experiments and statistical inference. Address: Speed Scientific School, University of Louisville, Louisville, KY 40208.

FIELDS, REUBEN E(LBERT), b. Society Hill, S.C, Sept. 30, 16; m. 45; c. 3. NUCLEAR PHYSICS. B.S, Ga. Inst. Tech, 40; M.S, Wisconsin, 51, Ph.D. (physics), 54. Assoc. engr, Rural Electrification Admin, 40-42; physicist, NUCLEAR PHYSICS, Argonne Nat. Lab, 44-46, 47-49; STAFF SCIENTIST,

FT. WORTH DIV, GEN. DYNAMICS CORP, 53- Lectr, South. Methodist Univ; adj. prof, Tex. Christian Univ. C.Eng, U.S.A, 42-46. Am. Phys. Soc; Am. Nuclear Soc. Photoneutron sources; neutron cross sections; nuclear forces; nuclear reactor hazards; environmental pollution analysis. Address: 4132 Clayton Rd. W, Fort Worth, TX 76116.

FIELDS, ROBERT W(ILLIAM), b. San Leandro, Calif, Sept. 17, 20; m. 45; c. 2. VERTEBRATE PALEONTOLOGY. B.A, California, 49, Alexander scholar, 51-52, Ph.D.(vert. paleont), 52. Asst. teacher vert. paleont, California, 49-51; geologist, Shell Oil Co, 52-55; asst. prof. GEOL, UNIV. MONT, assoc. prof, 58-64, PROF, 64-, chmn. dept, 64-70. Field leader exped, Colombia, S.Am, California. U.S.A.A.F, 42-46. Soc. Vert. Paleont; Geol. Soc. Am. Evolution and paleoecology of Tertiary intermontane basins of the Northern Rocky Mountain province; mammalian vertebrate paleontology; evolution of South American hystricomorph rodents; comparative anatomy and evolution of Tertiary mammals; stratigraphy. Address: Dept. of Geology, University of Montana, Missoula, MT 59801.

FIELDS, THEODORE, b. Chicago, Ill, Jan. 23, 22; m. 45; c. 3. MEDICAL PHYSICS. B.S, Chicago, 42; M.S, De Paul, 53. Physicist, Manhattan Proj, Chicago, 43-45; chief engr, Precision Radiation Instrument Co, 48-49; instr. radiation physics, med. sch, Northwest. Univ, 49-61; ASST. PROF. RADIOL, STRITCH SCH. MED, LOYOLA UNIV, CHICAGO, 61- Chief physics sect, Vet. Admin. Hines Hosp, 49-65; physicist, radiation ctr, Cook County Hosp, Chicago, 58-, radiation physicist, 66- Dipl, Am. Bd. Radiol, 50; Am. Bd. Health Physics, 60. U.S.A.F, 45-47. Am. Phys. Soc; Radiation Res. Soc; Soc. Nuclear Med; Health Physics Soc; Inst. Elec. & Electronics Eng; fel. Am. Col. Radiol; Am. Pub. Health Asn. Radiation safety in medicine, industry, and teaching; quality control evaluations of x-ray diagnostic procedures and nuclear medicine; neutron activation analysis; whole body counting. Address: 1141 Hohlfelder Rd, Glencoe, IL 60022.

FIELDS, THOMAS H(ENRY), b. Kearny, N.J, Oct. 23, 30. NUCLEAR PHYSICS. B.S. & M.S, Carnegie Inst. Technol, 51, Ph.D.(physics), 54. Asst. prof. physics, Carnegie Inst. Technol, 55-58, assoc. prof, 58-60; prof, Northwest. Univ, 60-69; DIR. HIGH ENERGY PHYSICS DIV, ARGONNE NAT. LAB, 64- Fel. Am. Phys. Soc. Experimental particle physics; bubble chambers. Address: High Energy Physics Division, Argonne National Lab, Argonne, IL 60439.

FIELDS, T(HOMAS) L(YNN), b. Baltimore, Md, Oct. 12, 25; m. 47; c. 2. B.S, Ala. Polytech, 52, M.S, 54. RES. CHEMIST, LEDERLE LABS, AM. CYANAMID CO, 54- Am. Chem. Soc. Chemistry of natural products; total synthesis and chemical modifications of tetracyclines. Address: Lederle Labs, American Cyanamid Co, Pearl River, NY 10965.

FIELDS, VICTOR HUGO, b. Milwaukee, Wis, July 11, 07; m. 41; div; c. 1. ORGANIC CHEMISTRY. B.A, Fisk, 31, M.A, 35; Ph.D.(chem), Marquette, 44. Instr. chem, Fisk, 35-37; prof. and head dept, Fla. Agr. & Mech. Col, 47-49; prof. & chmn. dept, HAMPTON INST, 49-56, PROF. NATURAL SCI. & MATH. & CHMN. DEPT, 56-, DIR. DIV. SCI. & MATH, 67- AAAS; Am. Chem. Soc; Nat. Inst. Sci.(ed, Transactions). Preparation and properties of substituted brom methyl fluoresceins. Address: 911 Victoria Blvd, Hampton, VA 23361.

FIELDS, W(ILLIAM) GORDON, b. Victoria, B.C, Mar. 29, 12; m. 50; c. 3. INVERTEBRATE ZOOLOGY. B.A, British Columbia, 37; A.M, Stanford, 49, Ph.D.(biol), 63. Teacher, pub. sch, B.C, 38-40; instr. biol. & zool, UNIV. VICTORIA (B.C), 40-46, asst. prof, 46-56, assoc. prof, 56-61, PROF. BIOL, 61-, head dept, 58-70. AAAS; Soc. Syst. Zool; Can. Soc. Zool. Marine biology; structure, development, food relations, reproduction, life histories and taxonomy of marine invertebrate animals, particularly cephalopods; biological oceanography. Address: Dept. of Biology, University of Victoria, Victoria, B.C, Can.

FIELDS, WILLIAM STRAUS, b. Baltimore, Md, Aug. 18, 13; m. 41; c. 2. NEUROLOGY. A.B, Harvard, 34, M.D, 38. Rockefeller fel, sch. med, Washington (St. Louis), 46-49; assoc. prof. NEUROL, Baylor Univ. Col. Med, 49-51, prof, 51-67, chmn. dept, 59-65; PROF, Univ. Tex. Med. Sch, Dallas, 67-69, Univ. Tex. Grad. Sch. Biomed. Sci, Houston, 69-70, MED. SCH, UNIV. TEX, HOUSTON, 70- Assoc. neurologist, St. Luke's Episcopal Hosp, Tex; Tex. Children's Hosp; Rosewood Gen. Hosp, Tex; chief neurol. serv, St. Anthony Ctr, Tex; mem. exec. comt. & study group chmn, Joint Comt. Stroke Facilities; adv. comt, psychiat, neurol. & psychol. serv, Vet. Admin; med. adv. bd, Myasthenia Gravis Found, Inc; consult, hearings & appeals bds, Social Security Admin, U.S. Dept. Health, Educ. & Welfare. Mem. Order of Brit. Empire, 46; dipl, Am. Bd. Psychiat. & Neurol, 50. R.C.N, 41-46, Surg. Lt. Comdr. Am. Acad. Neurol; Am. Asn. Neurol. Surg; Am. Cong. Rehab. Med; Am. Epilepsy Soc; Am. Med. Asn; Am. Neurol. Asn; Asn. Res. Nerv. & Ment. Disease. Epilepsy; cerebrovascular disease. Address: Section of Neurology, University of Texas Medical School, 6301 Almeda Rd, Houston, TX 77021.

FIELDSTEEL, A(RNOLD) HOWARD, b. New York, N.Y, May 14, 18; m. VIROLOGY. B.A, Hopkins, 39; Ph.D.(bact), Michigan, 50. Nat. Found. Infantile Paralysis fel. virol, Children's Hosp. Res. Found, Cincinnati, 50-53; virologist, Pitman-Moore, Co, 53-55; Cutter Labs, 55-57; dir. virus lab, Mont. State Bd. Health, 57-61; assoc. res. virologist, dept. path, med. center, California, San Francisco, 61-62; sr. virologist, STANFORD RES. INST, 62-69; MGR. VIROL. PROG, 69- Med.C, U.S.A, 41-45. AAAS; Soc. Exp. Biol. & Med; Am. Asn. Cancer Res; Am. Soc. Microbiol; Int. Leprosy Asn. Murine leukemias; viral carcinogenesis; in vivo and in vitro studies of virus transformed malignant cells; defective leukemia virus; tissue culture studies on Mycobacterium leprae; immunosuppression and susceptibility to disease. Address: Life Sciences Division, Stanford Research Institute, Menlo Park, CA 94025.

FIENBERG, STEPHEN ELLIOTT, Statist, Math. Biol, see Suppl. I to 11th ed, Soc. & Behav. Vols.

FIERING, MYRON B, b. New York, N.Y, Apr. 5, 34; m. 57; c. 2. CIVIL ENGINEERING, APPLIED MATHEMATICS. A.B, Harvard, 55, S.M, 58, Ph.D.(eng), 60. Soils engr, Tippetts, Abbott, McCarthy, Stratton, 55-57; asst. prof. eng, California, Los Angeles, 60-61; res. fel. environ. eng, HARVARD, 61-62, lectr. appl. math, 62-63, asst. prof. ENG. & APPL. MATH, 63-70, GORDON McKAY PROF, 70- Summer Fulbright lectr, Australia, 64. Consult, U.S. Pub. Health Serv, 63- U.S.N.R, 51-53. Am. Soc. Civil Eng; Am. Geophys. Union; Sci. Res. Soc. Am; Int. Asn. Sci. Hydrol. Water resources; statistics. Address: Pierce Hall 118, Harvard University, Cambridge, MA 02138.

FIERMAN, LOUIS BEN, b. Cleveland, Ohio, May 11, 22; m. 47; c. 2. PSYCHIATRY. B.S, Western Reserve, 44, M.D, 46. Rotating intern, Cleveland City Hosp, 46-47; res. internal med, Vet. Admin. Hosp, Newington, Conn, 49-50, neuropsychiat, 50-51; PSYCHIAT, SCH. MED, YALE, 51-53, instr. & chief resident, psychiat. inst, 52-53, clin. instr, 53-56, asst. clin. prof, 56-60, ASSOC. CLIN. PROF, 60-; HOSP. DIR, ELMCREST MANOR, 71- Chief resident, Grace New Haven Community Hosp, 52-53, attend. psychiatrist, 54-; staff psychiatrist, Vet. Admin. Hosp, West Haven, 53-60, chief psychiat. serv, 60-70. Med.C, 47-49, Capt. Am. Med. Asn; Am. Psychiat. Asn. Clinical psychiatry. Address: Elmcrest Manor, 25 Marlborough St, Portland, CT 06480.

FIERO, G(EORGE) WILLIAM, JR, b. Buffalo, N.Y, Jan. 16, 36; m. 59; c. 3. GEOLOGY, ENVIRONEMNTAL SCIENCES. B.A, Dartmouth Col, 57; M.S, Wyoming, 59; Ph.D.(geol), Wisconsin, 68. Explor. geologist, Texaco, Inc, 59-61, exploitation geologist, 61-63; teacher geol, Mt. Hermon Sch, 63-66; RES. ASSOC. & PROF. HYDROGEOL, DESERT RES. INST, UNIV. NEV, LAS VEGAS, 68- Stanley A. Tyler Award, Univ. Wis, 68. AAAS; Am. Asn. Petrol. Geol; Am. Geophys. Union; Am. Water Resources Asn; Geol. Soc. Am; Nat. Asn. Geol. Teachers; Soc. Econ. Paleont. & Mineral. Regional ground water flow systems; hydrogeochemical relationships of ground water flow; ground water effects on geothermal gradients; remote sensing in water resource studies; hydrogeological aspects of water pollution. Address: Desert Research Institute, University of Nevada, 4624 Maryland Pkwy. S, Las Vegas, NV 89109.

FIERSTINE, HARRY LEE, b. Long Beach, Calif, Aug. 14, 32; m. 58; c. 3. COMPARATIVE ANATOMY, ICHTHYOLOGY. B.S, Long Beach State Col, 57; M.A, California, Los Angeles, 61, Ph.D.(zool), 65. Instr. zool, Calif. State Col. Long Beach, 64-65, asst. prof, 65-66; CALIF. STATE POLYTECH. COL, SAN LUIS OBISPO, 66-69, ASSOC. PROF, 69- U.S.A, 53-55. Am. Soc. Zool; Am. Soc. Ichthyol. & Herpet; Soc. Vert. Paleont. Functional fish anatomy; tertiary fish paleontology. Address: Dept. of Biological Sciences, California State Polytechnic College, San Luis Obispo, CA 93401.

FIESENHEISER, E(LMER) I(RVING), b. South Bend, Ind, Aug. 4, 06; m; c. 1. STRUCTURAL ENGINEERING. B.S, Purdue, 30, C.E, 45; M.S, Ill. Inst. Tech, 46. Struct. engr, Am. Bridge Co, Pa, 30-35; Truscon Steel Co, Ohio, 35; asst. engr, U.S. Pub. Roads Admin, St. Paul, 35-41; designer, City Sanit. Dist, Chicago, 41-42; from instr. to prof. CIVIL ENG, ILL. INST. TECHNOL, 43-52, PROF, 54-, dir. dept, 54-70. Design squad leader, Arthur G. McKee, Ind, 42-44; Consult. struct. engr, 43-; chief struct. engr, Conrad & Yong, Inc, Chicago, 46-47. AAAS; Am. Concrete Inst; Am. Soc. Civil Eng; Am. Soc. Eng. Educ; Am. Rwy. Eng. Asn; Int. Asn. Bridge & Struct. Eng. Civil engineering. Address: Dept. of Civil Engineering, Illinois Institute of Technology, 3300 Federal St, Chicago, IL 60616.

FIESER, LOUIS F(REDERICK), b. Columbus, Ohio, April 7, 99; m. 32. ORGANIC CHEMISTRY. A.B, Williams Col, 20, hon. D.Sc, 39; Ph.D.(chem), Harvard, 24; hon. Pharm.D, Paris, 53. Sheldon fel, Frankfurt & Oxford, 24-25; assoc. & assoc. prof. chem, Bryn Mawr Col, 25-30; asst. prof, HARVARD, 30-34, assoc. prof, 34-37, prof. 37-39, Sheldon Emery prof. ORG. CHEM, 39-68, EMER. SHELDON EMERY PROF, 68- Consult, Merck & Co, 40-64; A.D. Little Co, 48-; past ed, Org. Syntheses; mem. planning bd, Weizmann Inst. Sci; Surgeon General's Adv. Comt. Smoking & Health, 63; prof. Smith Col, 67-68. Judd prize, 41; teaching award, Mfg. Chemists Asn. & Norris teaching award, 59; Nichols medal, Am. Chem. Soc, 63. Civilian with Off. Sci. Res. & Develop, 44; mem. Alsos Mission, European Theater Opers, U.S.A. Fel. Nat. Acad. Sci; fel. Am. Philos. Soc; fel. Am. Acad. Arts & Sci; hon. mem. Am. Asn. Cancer Res. Oxidation-reduction; quinones; aromatic chemistry; carcinogenic hydroquinones; vitamin K; steroids; resin acids; naphthoquinone antimalarials; chemotherapy; cortisone; pharmaceuticals. Address: Converse Memorial Lab, Harvard University, Cambridge, MA 02138.

FIESS, HAROLD ALVIN, b. Ringoes, N.J, April 28, 17; m. 43; c. 4. CHEMISTRY. B.S, Wheaton Col.(Ill), 39; M.S, Illinois, 42, Ph.D.(chem), 44. Chemist, Am. Cyanamid Co, N.J, 39-40; asst. CHEM, Illinois, 40-43; instr, WHEATON COL, 44-48, asst. prof, 48-52, assoc. prof, 52-58, PROF, 58- Res. assoc, Northwestern 49-50. Am. Chem. Soc. Analytical chemistry; food chemistry. Address: Dept. of Chemistry, Wheaton College, Wheaton, IL 60187.

FIESTER, CLARK GEORGE, b. Hazleton, Pa, Jan. 25, 34; m. 57; c. 2. ELECTRICAL ENGINEERING. B.S.E.E, Pa. State, 55; M.S.E.E, Stanford, 60. Mem. tech. staff systs. anal, Bell Tel. Labs, 55; SYST. LABS. MGR, SYLVANIA ELECTRONIC SYSTS-WEST. DIV, 57- U.S.A.F, 55-57, 1st Lt. Formulation of advanced system concepts for electronic warfare and reconnaisance systems. Address: 545 Ft. Laramie Dr, Sunnyvale, CA 94087.

FIETZ, WILLIAM ADOLF, b. Corinna, Maine, Sept. 20, 31; m. 60; c. 2. LOW TEMPERATURE PHYSICS. B.E.E, Cornell, 57, M.S, 63, Ph.D.(appl. physics), 67. Field engr, Fla. Power & Light Co, Miami, 57-60; res. physicist, Linde Div. Lab, Union Carbide Corp, N.Y, 66-71; STAFF SCIENTIST, INTERMAGNETICS GEN. CORP, 71- U.S.A, 58-64. AAAS; Am. Phys. Soc; Inst. Elec. & Electronics Eng. Superconductivity of high field-high current materials; properties of plasma-plated metal powders. Address: Intermagnetics General Corp, P.O. Box 711, Schenectady, NY 12305.

FIEVE, RONALD R(OBERT), b. Stevens Point, Wis, Mar. 5, 30; m. 63; c. 2. PSYCHIATRY. B.M.S, Wisconsin, 51; M.D, Harvard Med. Sch, 55. Intern, Columbia Med. Div, Bellevue Hosp, 55-56; asst. res. int. med, N.Y. Hosp, Cornell Univ, 56-57; res. psychiat, N.Y. State Psychiat. Inst, 57-60; instr, COL. PHYSICIANS & SURGEONS, COLUMBIA UNIV, 60-62, assoc, 64-67, asst. prof, 67-71, ASSOC. PROF. CLIN. PSYCHIAT, 71- Dir. personnel med. clin. & acute psychiat. serv, N.Y. State Psychiat. Inst, 60-; prin. res. scientist & chief psychiat. res, 62-, dir. metab. res. serv, 63-; prin. investr, Nat. Insts. Ment. Health res. grant psychopharmacol; Atomic Energy Comn. res. grant, summer.68. Mem, WHO, 60-; asst. exam, Am. Bd. Psychiat. & Neurol, 66- Dipl, Am. Bd. Psychiat. & Neurol, 62; Richard H. Hutchings Award. Am. Med. Asn; Am. Psychiat. Asn; Acad. Psychoanal; Am. Col. Neuropsychopharmacol; Am. Psychopath. Asn; Int. Col. Neuropsychopharmacol. Behavioral and biological psychiatry; lithium; manic depressive illness and psychopharmacology. Address: 722 W. 168th St, New York, NY 10032.

FIFE, EARL H(ANSON), JR, b. Elkton, Ky, April 14, 15; m. 41; c. 3. IMMUNOLOGY. B.S, Washington (Seattle), 48; M.S, Maryland, 51. Asst. chem, Swedish Hosp, Wash, 47-48; supvry. microbiologist, DEPT. SEROL, WALTER REED ARMY INST. RES, 48-65, CHIEF DEPT, 65- Spec. consult, Pan-Am. Health Orgn, 66- Registered, Nat. Registry Microbiol. Med. Dept, 42-47, Sgt. AAAS; fel. Am. Inst. Chem; Soc. Exp. Biol. & Med; Am. Soc. Trop. Med. & Hyg; N.Y. Acad. Sci; fel. Royal Soc. Trop. Med. & Hyg; Am. Soc. Microbiol. Development of serodiagnostic tests for parasitic diseases; mechanisms of immune hemolysis and complement fixation; application of fluorescent antibody technics in serodiagnosis; factors affecting immune response; immunochemistry; microbiology. Address: Dept. of Serology, Walter Reed Army Institute of Research, Walter Reed Army Medical Center, Washington, DC 20012.

FIFE, JAMES MILTON, b. Idaho Falls, Idaho, Nov. 8, 01; m. 23; c. 4. BIOCHEMISTRY. B.S, Utah State, 24, M.A, 25; fel, Iowa State, 25-27, Ph.D. (soil microbiol), 27. Nat. Res. Coun. fel. & res. assoc, California, Berkeley, 27-29; CHEMIST, SUGAR CROPS SECT, AGR. RES. SERV, U.S. DEPT. AGR, 29- AAAS; Am. Soc. Plant Physiol; Am. Soc. Sugar Beet Technol. Plant physiology; soil microbiology; thermodynamic factors involved in nitrogen fixation and assimilation by azotobacter; thermal induction requirements for flowering of sugar beets; properties of phloem exudate of sugar beets; identification of sugar beet plants resistant to beet yellows on the basis of the amino acid pattern in infected leaves. Address: 337 San Juan Dr, Salinas, CA 93901.

FIFE, PAUL CHASE, b. Cedar City, Utah, Feb. 14, 30; m. 59; c. 3. MATHEMATICS, CONTINUUM MECHANICS. B.A, Univ. Chicago, 51; B.A, Univ. Calif, Berkeley, 53; Ph.D.(math), N.Y. Univ, 59. From instr. to asst. prof. MATH, Stanford Univ, 59-63; from asst. prof. to assoc. prof, Univ. Minn, 63-68; PROF, UNIV. ARIZ, 69- Res. grants, Off. Naval Res, Air Force Off. Sci. Res. & Nat. Sci. Found, 59-; U.S. Dept. State Fulbright res. grant, Ger, 66-67; teaching grant, Peru, 71. Am. Math. Soc; Soc. Natural Philos. Various aspects of partial differential equations of elliptic and parabolic types; singular perturbations of partial differential equations; elastic plate theory; fluid dynamics. Address: Dept. of Mathematics, University of Arizona, Tucson, AZ 85721.

FIFE, WILLIAM PAUL, b. Plymouth, Ind, Nov, 23, 17; m. 47; c. 2. PHYSIOLOGY, ANATOMY. B.S, Oregon, 56; George Washington, 56-58; Ph.D. (physiol), Ohio State, 62. Asst. chief aerospace med. res. div, U.S. Air Force Sch. Aerospace Med, 62-67; ASST. DIR. INST. LIFE SCI, TEX. A&M UNIV, 67-, PROF. BIOL, 70-, acting head dept, 67-70. U.S.A.F, 39-67, Col. Am. Physiol. Soc; Aerospace Med. Asn. Cardiovascular and aerospace physiology, including environmental physiology. Address: Institute of Life Sciences, Texas A&M University, College Station, TX 77843.

FIFE, WILMER KRAFFT, b. Wellsville, Ohio, Oct. 19, 33; m. 59; c. 3. BIO-ORGANIC CHEMISTRY. B.Sc, Case, 55; Nat. Sci. Found. fel, Wisconsin, 55-56; Nat. Sci. Found. fel, Ohio State, 56, Sinclair Oil Co. fel, 58-59, Du Pont summer fel. & Ph.D.(org. chem), 60. Asst. prof. CHEM, Muskingum Col, 60-64, assoc. prof, 64-70, prof, 70-71, chmn. dept, 66-71; PROF. & CHMN. DEPT, IND. UNIV-PURDUE UNIV, INDIANAPOLIS, 71- Res. grants, Res. Corp, 60-61 & Nat. Sci. Found, 62-66; Nat. Insts. Health spec. fel, Harvard, 65-66, Chandler Lab, Columbia, 68-69; Nat. Sci. Found. res. grant, 71. AAAS; Am. Chem. Soc. Function of metal ions in enzymes; enzyme models; transformations of energy. Address: Dept. of Chemistry, Indiana University-Purdue University at Indianapolis, 1201 E. 38th St, Indianapolis, IN 46205.

FIFER, ROBERT A(LAN), b. Abington, Pa, Nov. 25, 43; m. 65; c. 1. PHYSICAL CHEMISTRY. B.S, Gordon Col, 65; Nat. Defense Educ. Act fel, Temple Univ, 67-69, Ph.D.(phys. chem), 69. Res. fel. CHEM, Cornell Univ, 69-71; SR. RES. ASSOC, BOSTON COL, 71- Am. Chem. Soc; Am. Phys. Soc. High temperature chemical kinetics behind shock waves; reactions of sulfur- and fluorine-containing compounds; low temperature vibrational spectroscopy. Address: Dept. of Chemistry, Boston College, Chestnut Hill, MA 02167.

FIFER, S(HIRLEY) ANNE, b. Harrisburg, Va, Sept. 20, 42. PHYSIOLOGICAL PSYCHOLOGY, NEUROCHEMISTRY. A.B, Bridgewater Col, 62; Nat. Defense Educ. Act fel, Univ. Ky, 63-64, M.Sc, 64; Ph.D.(physiol. psychol), Univ. Mont, 66. U.S. Pub. Health Serv. trainee, Brain Res. Inst, Univ. Calif, Los Angeles, 66-68; clin. res. psychologist, psychol. serv, Vet. Admin. Hosp, Knoxville, Iowa, 68-69; acting asst. prof. PSYCHOL, DRAKE UNIV, 69-70, ASST. PROF, 70- Behavioral effects of indolalkylamines and catechol amines, especially learning; chemical and electrophysiological effects of manipulation of endogeneous levels of biogenic amines. Address: Dept. of Psychology, Drake University, Des Moines, IA 50311.

FIFIELD, WILLARD M(ERWIN), b. Schenectady, N.Y, Jan. 17, 08; m. 35. AGRICULTURE. B.S.A, Florida, 30, M.S, 32; Summers, Cornell, 37, 39, 40. Asst, exp. sta, UNIV. FLA, 30-32, asst. horticulturist, subtrop. exp. sta, 32-38, horticulturist acting in charge, 39-40, asst. dir, agr. exp. sta, 41-50, dir, 50-55, provost, 55-62; EMER. PROVOST AGR, 62-; SECY-MGR, FLA. AGR. RES. INST, INC, 62- U.S.A.A.F, 42-46, Res, 46-, Lt. Col. Fel. AAAS; Am. Soc. Hort. Sci. Culture, varieties and handling of vegetable crops; winter grown potatoes and tomatoes; pesticides and fertilizers. Address: Florida Agricultural Research Institute, Inc, 519 N.E. First St, Gainesville, FL 32601.

FIGDOR, S(ANFORD) K(ERMIT), b. N.Y.C, Mar. 3, 26; m. 48; c. 2. ORGANIC CHEMISTRY. B.A, N.Y. Univ, 49; M.S, New Brunswick, 51, Ph.D.(chem), 53. Am. Heart Asn. fel, Wayne State, 53-54; res. chemist, RES. LABS, CHARLES PFIZER & CO, 54-68, HEAD RADIOCHEM, 68- U.S.N, 44-46. Am. Chem. Soc. Natural products; alkaloids; steroids; organic synthetic medicinals. Address: Medical Research Labs, Charles Pfizer & Co, Groton, CT 06340.

FIGGE, DAVID C, b. Twin Falls, Idaho, May 20, 25; m. 51; c. 2. OBSTETRICS, GYNECOLOGY. B.S. & M.D, Northwestern, 50. Res. fel. OBSTET. & GYNEC, SCH. MED, UNIV. WASH, 55-56, instr, 56-57, asst. prof, 57-61, assoc. prof, 61-69, PROF, 70-, DIR. GYNEC, UNIV. HOSP, 69-; OBSTETRICIAN-GYNECOLOGIST-IN-CHIEF, KING'S COUNTY HOSP, 63- Am. Cancer Soc. fel. gynec, 54-56. Investigation and management of gynecologic cancer; tissue culture investigations in uterine tissues. Address: Dept. of Obstetrics & Gynecology, University of Washington, BB 643 University Hospital, Seattle, WA 98105.

FIGGE, FRANK H(ENRY) J(OHN), b. Silver Cliff, Colo, Dec. 23, 04; m. 32; c. 2. ANATOMY. A.B, Colo. Col, 27; hon. Sc.D, 68; Colorado, 28-29; Ph.D. (anat), Maryland, 34. Asst. biol, Colo. Col, 25-26, head asst. biol. & comp. anat, 26-28, observer in charge meteorol. sta, 26-28; asst. anat, sch. med, Colorado, 28-29; SCH. MED, UNIV. MD, 29-30, instr, 30-34, assoc, 34-35, asst. prof, 35-36, assoc. prof, 36-47, PROF. exp. anat, 47-49, ANAT, 49-, CHMN. DEPT, 55- Rockefeller fel, sch. med, Yale, 40-41; vis. prof, Pennsylvania, 49. Mem. corp, Marine Biol. Lab, Woods Hole, 39-; trustee, Biol. Stain Comn, 47-, pres, 54-57. AAAS; Am. Soc. Nat; Am. Asn. Anat; Soc. Exp. Biol. & Med; Am. Asn. Cancer Res; Histochem. Soc; Am. Genetic Asn; Asn. Am. Med. Cols. Comparative experimental morphology; cytochemistry of melanin pigments; enzymology; sex hormones; porphyrin in metabolism; evaluation of jet injection therapeutic techniques; fluorescence phenomena; cosmic radiation and cancer; radio-biology. Address: Dept. of Anatomy, University of Maryland School of Medicine, Baltimore, MD 21201.

FIGHTMASTER, WALTER J(OHN), Indust. & Eng. Psychol, see 12th ed, Soc. & Behav. Vols.

FIGLEY, M(ELVIN) M(ORGAN), b. Toledo, Ohio, Dec. 5, 20; m. 46; c. 3. RADIOLOGY. M.D, Harvard, 44. Asst. prof. RADIOL, Michigan, 48-56, assoc. prof, 56-58; PROF. & CHMN. DEPT, UNIV. WASH, 58- Markle Found. scholar, 53-58. U.S.A, 46-48. Radiol. Soc. N.Am; Am. Roentgen Ray Soc; Am. Med. Asn; Am. Col. Radiol; Asn. Univ. Radiol. Cardiovascular radiology. Address: 7010 51st Ave. N.E, Seattle, WA 98115.

FIGUERAS, J(OHN), b. Rochester, N.Y, Oct. 28, 24; m. 49; c. 4. ORGANIC CHEMISTRY. B.S, Rochester, 49; M.S, Illinois, 50, Ph.D.(chem), 52. Instr. chem, Ill. Inst. Tech, 52-53; RES. CHEMIST, ORG. CHEM, EASTMAN KODAK CO, 53- U.S.A, 43-46. Am. Chem. Soc. Aminoketones; couplers for color photography; organic synthesis. Address: 436 Heritage Dr, Rochester, NY 14615.

FIGUERAS, PATRICIA A(NN) M(cVEIGH), b. Detroit, Mich, Jan. 23, 33; m. 70. ORGANIC CHEMISTRY. B.S, Univ, Mich, 53, fel, 54-56, fel. & M.A, 57, Ph.D.(chem), 58; M.S, Univ. Minn, 54. Asst. chem, Univ. Minn, 53-54; RES. ASSOC, EASTMAN KODAK CO, 58- Am. Chem. Soc. Organic free radical reactions; organic sulfur-containing compounds; photographic applications of chemistry; computer systems and software. Address: 436 Heritage Dr, Rochester, NY 14615.

FIGUEROA, WILLIAM G(UTIERREZ), b. El Paso, Tex, May 25, 21; m. 46; c. 4. INTERNAL MEDICINE. A.B, Tex. West. Col, 42; M.D, St. Louis, 46. Intern, Robert B. Green Hosp, San Antonio, Texas, 46; Los Angeles County Gen. Hosp, 46-47; res. internal med, Vet. Admin. Hosp, Los Angeles, 50-53; jr. res. metabolist, UNIV. CALIF, LOS ANGELES, 52-53, instr. MED, 53-55, asst. prof, 55-61, ASSOC. PROF, 61- Attend. physician, Vet. Admin. Hosp, Los Angeles, 53- Dipl, Am. Bd. Internal Med. U.S.A, 47-49. Am. Med. Asn. Diseases of metabolism; iron metabolism in various diseases states using radioactive iron; the nature and mechanism of anemia in various blood dyscrasias. Address: School of Medicine, University of California, Los Angeles, CA 90024.

FIGUEROLA, LUIS F, b. Chepen, Peru, Mar. 20, 38; m. 64; c. 3. PLANT SCIENCE, AGRONOMY. Agron. engr, Agrarian Univ, Peru, 61; M.S, E.Tex. State Univ, 66; Ph.D.(agron, plant physiol), Ore. State Univ, 69. Supvr. crop prod, Peruvian Ministry Agr, 61-62, assoc. mgr. eng. irrigation develop, 62-63, mgr, 63-65; RES. AGRONOMIST, AGR. RES. CTR, STAUFFER CHEM. CO, 69- Am. Soc. Agron; Am. Soc. Plant Physiol; Weed Sci. Soc. Am; Soil Sci. Soc. Am; Scand. Soc. Plant Physiol. Irrigation management and development; herbicide research, especially mode of action of herbicides and effect of environmental factors on the phytotoxicity of herbicides. Address: Agriculture Research Center, Stauffer Chemical Co, P.O. Box 760, Mountain View, CA 94040.

FIGWER, J(OZEF) JACEK, b. Mielec, Poland, Mar. 16, 28; U.S. citizen; m. 55; c. 2. ACOUSTICS, ELECTRICAL ENGINEERING. M.S, Silesian Polytech, 51; Dr. acoustics, Sci. Res. Inst. Cinematography, Moscow, 58. Develop. engr, Filmowe Biuro Techniczne, Poland, 51-55; res. asst. acoustics, Sci. Res. Inst. Cinematography, Moscow, 55-58; sr. engr, Exp. Ctr. Cinematography, Poland, 58-60; res. asst, Warsaw Tech, 58-60; develop. engr, Deutsche Grammophon, G.m.b.H, W.Ger, 60-62; CONSULT. ACOUSTICS, BOLT, BERANEK & NEWMAN, INC, 62- Acoust. Soc. Am; Soc. Motion Picture & TV Eng. Sound engineering; magnetic recording; architectural acoustics; noise control. Address: Bolt, Beranek & Newman, Inc, 50 Moulton St, Cambridge, MA 02138.

FIKE, H(AROLD) L(ESTER), b. Toledo, Ohio, Jan. 30, 26; m. 56; c. 4. BIOCHEMISTRY, ORGANIC CHEMISTRY. B.S, Toledo, 50; M.B.A, Northwestern, 63. Res. chemist, Int. Mineral & Chem. Corp, 52-56, sr. res. chemist, 56-59, asst. dir. res, 60-63, economist, 63-68; DIR. RES, SULPHUR INST, 68- U.S.N, 43-46. Am. Chem. Soc; Chem. Mkt. Res. Asn. Development of processes for the recovery of amino acids from natural sources and resolution of racemic mixtures of amino acids; mechanisms of sulfur reactions and development of new uses for sulfur. Address: 1725 K St. N.W, Room 508, Washington, DC 20006.

FIKE, WILLIAM T(HOMAS), JR, b. McKeesport, Pa, Nov. 22, 28; m. 52; c. 1. AGRONOMY. B.S, Pa. State Univ, 52, M.S, 56; Ph.D.(agron), Univ. Minn, 62. Asst. prof. CROP SCI, N.C. STATE UNIV, 59-68, ASSOC. PROF, 68-U.S.A, 52-54, 1st Lt. Am. Soc. Agron. Introduction, evaluation and improvement of new and established crops; oil, fiber, forage and feed for industrial and agricultural uses. Address: Dept. of Crop Science, North Carolina State University, Raleigh, NC 27607.

FIKE, WINSTON, b. Pittsfield, Mass, Feb. 15, 21; div; c. 4. ANALYTICAL CHEMISTRY. A.B, N.Y. State Col, Albany, 41; Ph.D.(chem), Rensselaer Polytech, 50. Analyst pharmaceut. control, Sterling-Winthrop Corp, 41-45; anal. chemist, Tenn. Eastman Corp, 45-46; asst. prof. org. chem, Thiel Col, 50-52; res. chemist, Ansco Div, Gen. Aniline & Film Corp, 52-55; asst. prof. anal. chem, Utica Col, Syracuse, 55-63; res. assoc. chromatog, County Coroner's Off, 63-65; CHEMIST, ANAL. METHODS DEVELOP, WM. S. MERRELL CO, 65- Nat. Insts. Health grant, 63-69; consult, sch. med, Case West. Reserve Univ, 63-69. Am. Chem. Soc. Chemistry of mercury; thin-layer and gas chromatography of blood volatiles; drugs and their metabolites. Address: Analytical Chemistry Dept, Wm. S. Merrell Co, Cincinnati, OH 45215.

FIKIORIS, JOHN G(EORGE), b. Sparta, Greece, Apr. 9, 31; U.S. citizen; m. 60; c. 1. MATHEMATICAL PHYSICS. Dipl, Athens Tech, 55; M.S, Rensselaer Polytech, 58; McKay fel, Harvard, 59-60; Bell Tel. Labs. fel, 60-61, M.A. & Ph.D.(appl. physics), 63. Elec. engr, power plant installations, Ammann & Whitney Co, Greece, 55-56; power systs, Boston Edison Co, Mass, 58-59; staff scientist scattering & diffraction, Avco Corp, Mass, 62-66; assoc. prof. ELEC. ENG, UNIV. TOLEDO, 66-71, PROF, 71- Electromagnetic theory; antennas in nonhomogeneous media; scattering and diffraction theory; differential and integral equations; potential theory. Address: 2360 Goddard Rd, Toledo, OH 43606.

FILACHIONE, EDWARD M(ARIO), b. Concord, N.H, Oct. 10, 09; m. 45; c. 4. CHEMISTRY. B.S, Illinois, 31; Ph.D.(org. chem), Northwestern, 35. Asst. chem, Northwestern, 31-35; instr, De Paul, 35-37; Maine, 37-38; du Pont fel, Cornell, 38-39; RES. CHEMIST, Columbia chem. div, Pittsburgh Plate Glass Co, Ohio, 39-41; EAST. REGIONAL RES. LAB, BUR. AGR. & INDUST. CHEM, U.S. DEPT. AGR, 41- AAAS; Am. Chem. Soc; Am. Leather Chem. Asn.(Alsop award, 60). Pyrolysis of triphenylmethyl ethers; organoboron chemistry; synthetic organic chemistry; lactic acid esters, amide and other derivatives; polymers; leather chemistry. Address: Eastern Regional Research Lab, U.S. Dept. of Agriculture, Chestnut Hill Station, Philadelphia, PA 19118.

FILANDRO, A(NTHONY) S(ALVATORE), b. N.Y.C, Oct. 10, 30; m. 58; c. 2. ORGANIC CHEMISTRY. B.S, Fordham, 50. Chemist, Florasynth Labs, 50-51; VA. DARE EXTRACT CO, 51-56, chief chemist, 56-64, TECH. DIR, 64- Mem. Food Chem. Codex Specifications Comt; med. res. comt. & bd. dirs, Flavor Extract Man Asn. Inst. Food. Technol; N.Y. Acad. Sci; Soc. Soft Drink Technol. Flavoring extracts; natural and synthetic flavoring compounds; analytical methods for flavors. Address: 603 Foxhurst Rd, Baldwin, NY 11510.

FILANO, ALBERT E(UGENE), b. Penfield, Pa, Aug. 17, 25; m. 50; c. 4. MATHEMATICS. B.S, Pennsylvania, 48, M.S, 49; Ph.D.(math. ed), Pa. State, 54. Instr. MATH, Hobart Col, 49-50; State Univ. N.Y. Col. Oswego, 50-52; Pa. State, 52-56; PROF, WEST CHESTER STATE COL, 56-, V.PRES. ACAD. AFFAIRS, 70-, chmn. dept. math, 58-69, dir. div. sci. & math, 67-69, interim dean faculty & acad. affairs, 69-70. Dir. & prof, math. insts, Nat. Sci. Found, 62-; summer mem. adv. panel eval. inst. grant proposals, 63- U.S.A.A.F, 43-45, S/Sgt; Distinguished Flying Cross; Air Medal & Oak Leaves. Math. Asn. Am. Mathematics education. Address: West Chester State College, West Chester, PA 19380.

FILAR, LEO J(OHN), b. Wilkes Barre, Pa, Feb. 8, 17; m. 54; c. 1. CHEMISTRY. B.S, Scranton, 39, Carnegie Inst. Tech, 41; fel, Purdue, 43-47, Ph.D.(org. chem), 48. Instr. chem, Alliance Col, 39-42; asst. tech. dept, Carnegie Library, Pittsburgh, 42-43; res. chemist, Hercules Powder Co, 47-64, RES. SUPVR, 64-69, HERCULES INC, 69- Am. Chem. Soc. Emulsion copolymerization; preparation of substituted styrenes; preparation of new types of synthetic rubber; organic peroxides; phenols; oxidation of alkylphenols. Address: Research Center, Hercules Inc, Wilmington, DE 19899.

FILATOVS, GEORGE J(URI), b. Vilani, Latvia, Mar. 29, 41. METALLURGICAL ENGINEERING. B.S, Wash. Univ, 63; U.S. Bur. Mines fel, Univ. Mo-Rolla, 66-69, Ph.D.(metall. eng), 69. Assoc. engr, McDonnell Aircraft Co, 63-65; asst, Univ. Mo-Rolla, 65-66; metallurgist, U.S. Bur. Mines, 66-69; ASST. PROF. METALL. & MAT. SCI, YOUNGSTOWN STATE UNIV, 69- Am. Soc. Mech. Eng. Physics of solids; mechanical properties of materials; dislocation theory; deformation of materials. Address: Dept. of Metallurgical Engineering, Youngstown State University, Youngstown, OH 44503.

FILBERT, AUGUSTUS M(YERS), b. Hazleton, Pa, Sept. 28, 33; m. 63; c. 2. PHYSICAL CHEMISTRY. B.S, Lehigh, 55; Ph.D.(phys. chem), Pennsylvania, 62. Lab. asst, Pennsylvania, 55-61; sr. chemist, CORNING GLASS WORKS, 61-62, res. chemist 63-70, SR. RES. CHEMIST, 70- U.S.A, 62-63, Res, 63-65, Capt. AAAS; Am. Chem. Soc; Am. Ceramic Soc; Am. Ord. Asn. Metalammonia solutions; solution chemistry; glass composition; chemistry and physics of glass; conductivity studies; surface chemistry of glass. Address: 210 W. Fourth St, Corning, NY 14830.

FILBERT, ROBERT B(ROBST), JR, b. Womelsdorf, Pa, Feb. 15, 21; m. 50; c. 2. CHEMICAL ENGINEERING. B.S, Pa. State Col, 41, M.S, 47. Control chemist, Hercules Powder Co, N.J, 40, design engr, Wilmington, 41-43; res. engr, BATTELLE MEM. INST, 47-51, asst. supvr. chem. eng. res, 51-53, chief, 53-60, asst. mgr, 60-63, assoc. mgr. chem. & chem. eng. dept, 63-69, dir. environ. progs, 69-70, resident adv, Repub. Chile, 70-71, ASST. TO V.PRES. ADMIN, CROPS PROPERTY MGT, 71- U.S.N, 42-46. Am. Chem. Soc; Am. Inst. Chem. Eng; Nat. Soc. Prof. Eng; fel. Am. Inst. Chem. Process design and development; inorganic and organic chemistry; fertilizer technology; hydrometallurgy; rocket propellants; nuclear fuels; computer applications; management of research. Address: Battelle Memorial Institute, Columbus Labs, 505 King Ave, Columbus, OH 43201.

FILBERT, WILLIAM F(REDERICK), b. Twin Brooks, S.Dak, Aug. 21, 07; m. 38; c. 2. ORGANIC CHEMISTRY. B.S, Dakota Wesleyan, 28; M.S, Minnesota, 33, Ph.D.(org. chem), 34. Asst. chem, Minnesota, 28-32; instr, Dakota Wesleyan, 32-33; res. chemist, East. Lab, E.I. DU PONT DE NEMOURS & CO, 35-47, Burnside lab, 47-52, res. supt, EAST. LAB, 52-57, res. coordinator, 57-61, tech. asst, 61-69, RES. STAFF CHEMIST, PATENTS-TECH. LIAISON, 69- Civilian with Nat. Defense Res. Comt; U.S.A; U.S.N, 44. Am. Chem. Soc. Explosives chemistry; initiating devices; cellulose products; industrial organic chemistry. Address: Explosives Dept, Eastern Lab, E.I. du Pont de Nemours & Co, Gibbstown, NJ 08027.

FILBEY, A(LLEN) H(OWARD), b. Wis, Jan. 14, 27; m. 49; c. 4. ORGANIC CHEMISTRY. B.S, Wisconsin, 48; M.S, Michigan, 49, Res. Corp. fel. & Ph.D.(chem), 53. Res. chemist, ETHYL CORP, 52-58, asst. res. supvr. chem. res, 58-60, res. supvr, 60-63, ASST. DIR. CHEM. RES. & DEVELOP, 63- U.S.N, 44-46. Am. Chem. Soc. Homogeneous catalysis; bromine chemicals; alkylated aromatics; antioxidants. Address: Ethyl Corp, 1600 W. Eight Mile Rd, Detroit, MI 48220.

FILBY, ROYSTON HERBERT, b. London, Eng, Feb. 16, 34; m. 65; c. 2. NUCLEAR CHEMISTRY, GEOCHEMISTRY. B.Sc, London, 55; M.Sc, McMaster, 57; Finnish Govt. fel, Helsinki, 60-61; Ph.D.(chem), Wash. State Univ, 71. Res. fel. geochem, Oslo, 61-64; head dept. chem, El Salvador, 64-67; chemist, WASH. STATE UNIV, 67-70, asst. prof. chem, 70-71, ASSOC. PROF. CHEM. & ASST. DIR. NUCLEAR RADIATION CTR, 71-, dir. trace element lab, 70-71. Orgn. European Econ. Coop. sr. vis. fel, European Atomic Energy Comn, Mol, Belgium, 62. Am. Chem. Soc; Geol. Soc. Finland; fel. Am. Inst. Chem. Geochemistry of meteorites, neutron activation analysis and petroleum geochemistry. Address: Nuclear Radiation Center, Washington State University, Pullman, WA 99163.

FILER, LLOYD JACKSON, JR, b. Grove City, Pa, Sept. 30, 19; m. 42; c. 3. PEDIATRICS, NUTRITION. B.S, Pittsburgh, 41, Ph.D.(biochem), 44; M.D, Rochester, 52. Sr. res. fel, Pittsburgh, 44-45; res. fel, Rochester, 45-52, intern, Strong Mem. Hosp, 52-53; med. dir, Ross Labs, 53-65; PROF. PEDIAT, COL. MED, UNIV. IOWA, 65- Instr. physiol, Rochester, 45-47, asst. clin. prof. pediat, sch. med, Ohio State, 53-65. Med.C, 56-58, Capt. Am. Pediat. Sco; Soc. Pediat. Res; Am. Soc. Clin. Nutrit; Am. Med. Asn; Am. Inst. Nutrit. Autoxidation of fats and oils; x-ray diffraction studies in glycerides; vitamin E in animal and human nutrition; nutritional studies on infants; studies on body composition; biochemistry. Address: University Hospitals, University of Iowa, Iowa City, IA 52240.

FILER, THEODORE H, JR, b. Galveston, Tex, Aug. 15, 28; m. 50; c. 2. PLANT PATHOLOGY, SOILS. B.S, Texas A&M, 50, M.S, 58; Ph.D.(plant path), Washington State, 64. Instr. forest & gen. path, Washington State, 62-63; PLANT PATHOLOGIST, U.S. FOREST SERV, 63- U.S.A, 52-54, Capt. Am. Phytopath. Soc; Mycol. Soc. Am; Am. Forestry Asn; Int. Soc. Plant Path. Factors concerned with development and control of root rot, decay and cankers of hardwood trees; fungi and significance of hardwood mycorrhizae; regeneration diseases in hardwood nurseries and plantations. Address: Southern Hardwoods Lab, P.O. Box 227, Stoneville, MS 38776.

FILGO, HOLLAND C(LEVELAND), b. Van Alstyne, Tex, Mar. 28, 26. MATHEMATICS. B.S, Baylor Univ, 48; M.A, Rice Univ, 51, Ph.D.(math), 53. Asst. MATH, Rice Univ, 51-53; asst. prof, Univ. Ala, 53-57, assoc. prof, 57-60; asst. prof, Univ. Ga, 60-61; assoc. prof, NORTHEAST. UNIV, 61-70, PROF, 70- U.S.N.R, 44-46. Am. Math. Soc; Math. Asn. Am. Complex analysis. Address: Dept. of Mathematics, Northeastern University, Boston, MA 02115.

FILICE, FRANCIS P, b. Hollister, Calif, Aug. 19, 22; m. 47; c. 6. ZOOLOGY. B.S, Univ. San Francisco, 43; M.A, Univ. Calif, 45, Ph.D.(zool), 49. Instr. BIOL, UNIV. SAN FRANCISCO, 47-49, asst. prof, 49-55, assoc. prof, 55-60, PROF, 60- Protozoan cytology; invertebrate ecology. Address: 2130 Fulton St, San Francisco, CA 94117.

FILINGER, GEORGE ALBERT, b. Cuba, Kans, Apr. 23, 97; m. 29. HORTICULTURE. B.S, Kans. State Col. Agr, 24, M.S, 25; Wisconsin, 25-26; Minnesota, 29-30; Ph.D.(biol), Ohio State, 31. Asst. Kans. State Col. Agr, 24-25; Wisconsin, 25-26; asst. entomologist, Ohio Exp. Sta, 26-31; asst. prof. pomol, KANS. STATE UNIV, 31-37, assoc. prof, 37-47, prof, 47-66, EMER. PROF. HORT, 66- Group leader, U.S. Agency Int. Develop, India, 56-58. Am. Soc. Hort. Sci. Fruit rootstocks; preserving fruits and vegetables by freezing. Address: Dept. of Horticulture, Kansas State University, Manhattan, KS 66504.

FILIPESCU, NICOLAE, b. Predeal, Rumania, July 30, 35; U.S. citizen; m. 63; c. 3. ORGANIC & PHYSICAL CHEMISTRY. Ph.D.(chem. eng), Bucharest Polytech, 57; Ph.D.(phys. & org. chem), George Washington, 64. Chem. engr, res. labs, Anticorrosion Plant, Rumania, 57-59; sr. chemist, Res. Inst. Construct. Mat, 59; chem. engr, U.S. Armed Forces, W.Germany, 59-60; sr. scientist, Melpar, Inc, 60-63; asst. prof. CHEM, GEORGE WASHINGTON UNIV, 63-66, assoc. prof, 66-71, PROF, 71- Res. grant & consult, Goddard Space Flight Ctr, NASA, 64-; consult, Lockheed Elec. Co, 66-70; res. grant, Atomic Energy Comn, 69-; consult, TAAG, Inc, 70-71. Am. Chem. Soc; The Chem. Soc. Photochemistry; intra- and intermolecular energy transfer; molecular spectroscopy; reaction mechanisms; free radicals. Address: Dept. of Chemistry, George Washington University, Washington, DC 20006.

FILIPOVICH, GEORGE, b. Priluki, Ukraine, Feb. 27, 18; U.S. citizen; m. 49; c. 2. SOLID STATE PHYSICS. B.S, Kharkov State Univ, 41; M.S, Univ. Minn, 59. SR. PHYSICIST, 3M CO, ST. PAUL, 53- Union Carbide Chem. Co-Am. Chem. Soc. Award, 58-59. Am. Phys. Soc. Properties of thin films; photoconductivity; nuclear magnetic resonance; electron paramagnetic resonance. Address: 2115 Franklin Ave. S.E, Minneapolis, MN 55414.

FILIPOWSKY, R(ICHARD) F(REDERICK) J(OSEPH), b. Vienna, Austria, July 7, 15; m. 39; c. 4. PHYSICS, ELECTRONIC ENGINEERING. Dipl, Tech. Univ, Vienna, 39, D.Sc, 55. Res. engr, Telefunken Inc, Germany, 39-42, sr. engr, 42-46; head & ed, Radio Tontechnik Elektromedizin, Austria, 46-48; chief lab. engr, Marconi Corp, Portugal, 48-50; prof. electronics & head dept, Madras Inst. Tech, India, 50-55; adv. engr. communications systems, Westinghouse Elec. Co, Md, 55-59; asst. dir. res. & develop. & head adv. develop, Collins Radio Co, Calif, 59-61; mgr. tech. develop, IBM Corp, Md, 61-65, chief adv. space systs. develop, 65-70; PROF. ENG. TELECOMMUNICATIONS, UNIV. S.FLA, 70- Lectr, Mich. State Univ, summer, 59. Fel. Inst. Elec. & Electronics Eng; Brit. Inst. Radio Eng.(Hertz Premium, 56); fel. Australian Inst. Radio Eng. Communication systems; data transmission systems; information theory; space electronics systems. Address: 1816 Bearss Ave, Tampa, FL 33612.

FILIPPENKO, VLADIMIR I, b. Belgrade, Yugoslavia, Aug. 23, 30; U.S. citizen; m. 52; c. 2. APPLIED MATHEMATICS, PHYSICS. B.A, California, Berkeley, 53, Ph.D.(appl. math), 64. Res. mathematician, inst. eng. res, California, Berkeley, 57-59, assoc. math, 59-62, res. asst, 62-64; sr. res. mathematician high velocity physics, Gen. Motors Corp, 64-68; asst. prof. MATH, SAN FERNANDO VALLEY STATE COL, 68-71, ASSOC. PROF, 71- Off. Naval Res. fel, 64; summer, res. mathematician, Gen. Elec. Lab, 59. Am. Math. Soc. Partial and ordinary differential equations; fluid mechanics. Address: 5903 Via Lemora, Golita, CA 93017.

FILIPPINI, FLORIDO A(LFRED), b. Bessemer, Mich, Feb. 12, 16; m. 45; c. 7. CHEMICAL ENGINEERING. B.S, Mich. State, 41. Prod. & process control engr, Gen. Chem. Co, N.Y, 41-44; chief control labs, R.P. Scherer Corp, Mich, 44-59; methods develop. & quality control supvr, MILES LABS, INC, Elkhart, 59-65; QUAL. & IDENTITY CONTROL SUPVR, AMES. PRODS, INC, 65- Am. Chem. Soc; Am. Pharmaceut. Asn. Pharmaceutical quality control and methods development. Address: Miles Labs, Inc, 1127 Myrtle, Elkhart, IN 46514.

FILKINS, JAMES P, b. Milwaukee, Wis, Apr. 10, 36; m. 59; c. 6. PHYSIOLOGY. B.S, Marquette, 57, M.S, 59, Ph.D.(physiol), 64. Instr. physiol, sch. med, Marquette, 64-65; asst. prof. physiol. & biophys, Univ. Tenn, 65-69, ASSOC. PROF, 69-71; PHYSIOL, STRITCH SCH. MED, LOYOLA UNIV. CHICAGO, 71- U.S. Pub. Health Serv. fel, 64-65. AAAS; Reticuloendothelial Soc; Am. Physiol. Soc. Physiopathology of the reticuloendothelial system; mechanism of hepatic phagocytosis; physiology of shock; lysosome function. Address: Stritch School of Medicine, Loyola University of Chicago, 2160 S. First Ave, Maywood, IL 60153.

FILLER, LEWIS, b. N.Y.C, Feb. 15, 28; m. 54; c. 3. APPLIED MECHANICS. B.Aero.Eng, N.Y. Univ, 51, M.Aero.Eng, 53, D.Eng.Sci, 58. Instr. aeronaut. eng, N.Y. Univ, 52-57; res. specialist, Boeing Airplane Co, 57-59; vis. asst. prof. aeronaut. eng, Washington (Seattle), 59; assoc. res. scientist, Denver Div, Martin Co, 59-62; assoc. prof. MECH. ENG, SEATTLE UNIV, 62-68, PROF, 68- Lectr, Univ. Colo, 60-62. AAAS; Am. Phys. Soc. Fluid mechanics; applied mathematics. Address: Route 6, Box 6854, Bainbridge Island, WA 98110.

FILLER, R(OBERT), b. Brooklyn, N.Y, Feb. 2, 23; m. 45, 59; c. 5. ORGANIC CHEMISTRY. B.S, City Col. New York, 43; M.S, Iowa, 47, Ph.D.(chem), 49. Asst. chemist, Off. Sci. Res. & Develop, Columbia, 43-44; asst, dept. pharmacol, col. med, Iowa, 47-49; asst. prof. chem, Albany Col. Pharm, 49-50; res. fel, Purdue, 50-51; res. chemist, Wright Air Develop. Center, U.S. Air Force, 51-53; instr. CHEM, Ohio Wesleyan, 53-54, asst. prof, ILL. INST. TECHNOL, 55-61, assoc. prof, 61-66, PROF, 66-, CHMN. DEPT, 68-, acting chmn. dept, 66-68. Nat. Insts. Health spec. fel, Cambridge, 62-63; summers, res. assoc, Ohio State, 54, Chicago, 56-57. Med.C, U.S.A, 44-46. AAAS; Am. Chem. Soc; The Chem. Soc. Organic fluorine chemistry; heterocyclic chemistry; amino acids; structure and reactivity relationships; brain chemistry. Address: Dept. of Chemistry, Illinois Institute of Technology, Chicago, IL 60616.

FILLEY, GILES F(RANKLIN), b. N.Y.C, Apr. 30, 15; m. 42; c. 4. PHYSIOLOGY. B.A, Williams Col, 37; M.D, Johns Hopkins Univ, 42. Assoc. physiologist, Edward L. Trudeau Found, 47-53; dir. dept. physiol, Trudeau-Saranac Inst, 53-55; asst. prof. MED, SCH. MED, UNIV. COLO, DENVER, 55-59, ASSOC. PROF, 59- Clinical physiologist, Webb-Waring Inst. Med. Res, 55- Am. Thoracic Soc; Am. Physiol. Soc; Am. Clin. & Climat. Asn; fel. Am. Col. Physicians. Respiratory physiology. Address: Dept. of Medicine, University of Colorado School of Medicine, Denver, CO 80220.

FILLEY, JOHN P(ATON), b. New Haven, Conn, Sept. 25, 22; m. 48; c. 4. PSYCHIATRY. B.S, Yale, 48, M.D, 52. Intern pediat, hosps, Univ. Minn, 52-53; res. psychiat, N.C. Mem. Hosp, 53-55, fel, child psychiat, 55-57, instr, 57-58; asst. prof. MENTAL HEALTH, SCH. PUB. HEALTH, UNIV. N.C, CHAPEL HILL, 58-60, ASSOC. PROF, 60-, CLIN. ASST. PROF. PSYCHIAT, SCH. MED, 70- U.S.N.R, 43-46. Am. Psychiat. Asn; Am. Pub. Health Asn. Personality development; preventive psychiatry; social psychiatry. Address: Dept. of Mental Health, University of North Carolina School of Public Health, Chapel Hill, NC 27514.

FILLIOS, LOUIS CHARLES, b. Boston, Mass, July 1, 23; m. 47; c. 3. BIOCHEMISTRY, NUTRITION. A.B, Harvard, 48, M.S, 53, U.S. Pub. Health Serv. fel, 54-56, Sc.D, 56. Asst. nutrit, Harvard, 53-54, res. fel, 56-57, res. assoc, 57-58, assoc. 58-60; res. assoc. biochem, Mass. Inst. Technol, 60-61, asst. prof. nutrit, 61-62, physiol. chem, 62-65, assoc. prof, 65-66; assoc. res. prof. biochem. & path, med. sch, BOSTON UNIV, 66-68, assoc. prof. biochem, sch. med. & assoc. prof. nutrit, grad. sch, dent, 68-69, PROF. BIOCHEM, SCH. MED. & SCH. GRAD. DENT, 69-, DIR. DIV. ORAL BIOL, 69-, co-chmn. div. med. & dent. sci. grad. sch, 70-71. Am. Heart Asn. estab. investr, 61-66. U.S.A.A.F, 43-45, 1st Lt; Distinguished Flying Cross. Fel. AAAS; Am. Inst. Nutrit; Brit. Biochem. Soc; N.Y. Acad. Sci. Endocrinology; experimental atherosclerosis; lipid, cholesterol, thyroid and nucleic acid metabolism; protein synthesis. Address: Boston University Medical Center, Boston, MA 02118.

FILLIPPONE, WALTER R, b. Newark, N.J, Mar. 17, 21; m. 43; c. 2. GEOLOGY, GEOPHYSICS. B.A, Marietta Col, 42; M.Sc, Calif. Inst. Tech, 44. Seismologist, United Geophys. Co, 43-45, party chief, 46-51, area mgr, Alaska, 52, Rocky Mts, 53-55; sr. geophysicist, UNION OIL CO. CALIF, 55-60, div. geologist, 61-65, SR. RES. ASSOC, 65- Soc. Explor. Geophys. Applied geophysics; exploration seismic interpretation and techniques. Address: Union Oil Co. of California, Research Center, Box 76, Brea, CA 92621.

FILLMORE, PETER A(RTHUR), b. Moncton, N.B, Oct. 28, 36; m. 60; c. 3. MATHEMATICS. B.Sc, Dalhousie, 57; M.A, Minnesota, Minneapolis, 60, Ph.D.(math), 62. Instr. MATH, Chicago, 62-64; asst. prof, IND. UNIV, 64-67, assoc. prof, 67-71, PROF, 71- Vis. assoc. prof, Univ. Toronto, 70-71. Am. Math. Soc; Math. Asn. Am. Foundations; functional analysis; rings of operators; operator theory. Address: Dept. of Mathematics, Indiana University, Bloomington, IN 47401.

FILLMORE, RICHARD H(AROLD), b. Springhill, N.S, Mar. 19, 12; m. 42; c. 1. HORTICULTURE. B.A, Acadia, 45; fel, Massachusetts, 45-56; M.S, Cornell, 47. Curator of grounds, Acadia, 39-45; propagator, Arnold Arboretum, Harvard, 47-52; mgr. propagation dept, Shenandoah Nurseries, Iowa, 52-55; asst. prof. hort, Ohio State, 56; horticulturist in charge, SARAH P. DUKE GARDENS, DUKE UNIV, 56-62, ASSOC. DIR, 62- Vis. prof, N.C. State Col, Univ. N.C, fall, 66-67. Am. Soc. Hort. Sci; Int. Plant Propagators Soc.(pres, 54-55); Int. Dendrol. Soc; fel. Royal Hort. Soc; Nat. Soc. Hort. France. Plant propagation and breeding; water relations of plants; plant growth substances; ornamental horticulture; landscape gardening. Address: Sarah P. Duke Gardens, Duke University, Durham, NC 27706.

FILMER, DAVID L(EE), b. Youngstown, Ohio, June 4, 32; m. 57; c. 3. BIOCHEMISTRY, BIOPHYSICS. A.B, Youngstown, 54; M.S, Wisconsin, 58, Ph.D.(biochem), 61. Res. assoc. enzyme mechanisms, Brookhaven Nat. Lab, 61-63, asst. biochemist, 63-65; asst. prof. BIOPHYS, PURDUE UNIV, 65-68, ASSOC. PROF, 68- Mem. analog comput. educ. users group, Simulation Coun, Inc. AAAS; Asn. Comput. Mach. Physical biochemistry; bio-medical applications of computers; fast reaction kinetics; enzyme mechanisms; bioinstrumentation. Address: Dept. of Biological Science, Purdue University, Lafayette, IN 47907.

FILMER, ROBERT WILLIAM, b. Binghamton, N.Y, June 2, 32; m. 57; c. 4. AGRICULTURAL & CIVIL ENGINEERING. B.S, Cornell, 56, B.Agr.Eng, 57; M.S, Colorado State, 64, Ph.D.(fluid mech), 66. Proj. engr, Miami Valley Labs, Procter & Gamble Co, 58-61; civil engr, Colorado State Univ, 65-66; ASST. PROF. CIVIL ENG, ORE. STATE UNIV, 66- Bausch & Lomb Photogram. Award, 58. C.Eng, U.S.A.R, 57-64, Capt. Transport and removal of virus-sized particles in porous media; experimental diffusion studies in turbulent flow fields; ocean engineering; applied marine hydrodynamics; progressive education; experiential learning through group processes. Address: Dept. of Civil Engineering, Oregon State University, Corvallis, OR 97331.

FILNER, BARBARA, b. Phila, Pa, Nov. 15, 41. PLANT PHYSIOLOGY. B.S, Queens Col.(N.Y), 62; Ph.D.(plant physiol), Brandeis Univ, 67. Res. assoc. plant physiol, Mich. State Univ, 67-69; Nat. Inst. Health fel, Inst. Cancer Res, 69-71; ASST. PROF. BIOL. SCI, COLUMBIA UNIV, 71- Am. Asn. Plant Physiol. Protein synthesis; plant virology; developmental biology. Address: Dept. of Biological Sciences, Columbia University, New York, NY 10027.

FILNER, PHILIP, b. Phila, Pa, July 12, 39; m. 67; c. 1. BIOCHEMISTRY. B.A, Hopkins, 60; Ph.D.(biochem), Calif. Inst. Tech, 65. Asst. prof. BIOCHEM, MSU/AEC PLANT RES. LAB, MICH. STATE UNIV, 65-69, ASSOC. PROF, 69- AAAS; Am. Soc. Biol. Chem; Am. Soc. Plant Physiol; Soc. Develop. Biol; Am. Soc. Microbiol. Plant biochemistry; mechanisms of enzyme regulation and role of enzymes in development; biochemistry of cultured plant cells; enyzmes of nitrate and sulfate assimilation; animoacyl tRNA synthetases; microtubule proetins. Address: MSU/AEC Plant Research Lab, Michigan State University, East Lansing, MI 48823.

FILSETH, STEPHEN V, b. Portland, Ore, Nov. 7, 36; m. 58; c. 3. PHYSICAL CHEMISTRY. B.S, Stanford Univ, 58; Ph.D.(phys. chem), Univ. Wis, 62. Asst. prof. CHEM, Harvey Mudd Col, 62-67, assoc. prof, 67-71; SR. ASSOC. PROF, YORK UNIV.(ONT), 71- Am. Phys. Soc. Kinetics of elementary, homogeneous gas phase reactions; chemical aeronomy; gas phase photochemistry and energy transfer. Address: Centre for Research in Experimental Space Science, York University, Toronto, Ont, Can.

FILSON, DON P, b. Chicago, Ill, Feb. 6, 31; m. 57; c. 5. PHYSICAL CHEMISTRY. A.B, Park Col, 52; Univ. Kans, 52-53; Nat. Sci. Found. fel, Univ. Ill, 56-58, M.S, 62, Ph.D, 67. Assoc. prof. CHEM, ILL. COL, 60-67, PROF, 67- U.S.A, 53-55, Sgt. AAAS; Am. Chem. Soc. Precipitation problems; hydrodynamic properties of macromolecules. Address: 710 W. Beecher, Jacksonville, IL 62650.

FILSON, MALCOLM HAROLD, b. Chattanooga, Tenn, Oct. 19, 07; m. 32; wid; c. 3; m. 60. CHEMISTRY. B.S, Kentucky, 29, M.S, 31; fel, Michigan, 31-34, Ph.D.(anal. chem), 36; Mich. State, 52, 53. Asst. anal. chem, Kentucky, 29-31, asst. res. chemist, exp. sta, 29; instr. inorg. chem, Ohio Northern, 34-35; prof. chem. & head dept. chem. & physics, Miss. Woman's Col, 35-36; mem. faculty, CENT. MICH. UNIV, 35-42, PROF. CHEM, 42-, chmn. dept. chem. & physics, 55-65, chmn. dept. chem, 55-71. Summer fel, Nat. Sci. Found, Wisconsin, 59, Cornell Col, 60, Ohio Wesleyan, 63, Florida, 64; consult, U.S.Army. Fel. AAAS; Am. Chem. Soc; Sci. Res. Soc. Am; Nat. Sci. Teachers Asn. Analytical chemistry; chromyl chloride; chromium plating baths; chromyl fluoride; periodates; perchloric acid in analytical chemistry; solubilities and viscosity as applied to silver, lead and mercury compounds. Address: Dept. of Chemistry, Central Michigan University, Mt. Pleasant, MI 48858.

FILTEAU, GABRIEL, b. Quebec, Que, Oct. 16, 18; m. 46; c. 2. ZOOLOGY. B.A, Laval, 39, B.Sc.A, 44, Ph.D.(biol), 51; Queen's (Can), 40-42. Asst. biologist, biol. sta, St. Laurent, Que, 44-46; lectr. ZOOL, LAVAL UNIV, 46-50, asst. prof, 50-55, PROF, 55-, HEAD DEPT. BIOL, 61-, ASST. DEAN, FACULTY OF SCI, 70- Asst. biologist, biol. sta, St. Laurent, Que, 46-50. Fel, Nuffield Found, Eng, 56. R.C.A.F, 58-, Wing Comdr. French-Can. Asn. Adv. Sci; Brit. Freshwater Biol. Asn. Freshwater biology, especially plankton; invertebrate zoology. Address: Faculty of Science, Laval University, Quebec, Que, Can.

FIMIAN, WALTER J(OSEPH), JR, b. New York, N.Y, May 22, 26; m. 50; c. 5. MORPHOLOGY, RADIOBIOLOGY. A.B, Vermont, 50; fel, Notre Dame, 51-52, 53-54, M.S, 52, Ph.D, 55. Instr. & res. investigator, Marquette, 54-55; asst. prof. ZOOL, BOSTON COL, 55-60, ASSOC. PROF, 60- U.S.N, 44-46.

AAAS; Radiation Res. Soc; Am. Soc. Zool. Tissue Culture studies; amphibian regeneration; melanin synthesis; experimental morphogenesis; radiation biology. Address: Dept. of Biology, Boston College, Chestnut Hill, MA 02167.

FINA, LOUIS R, b. Cleveland, Ohio, Dec. 13, 18; m. 46; c. 3. BACTERIOLOGY. A.B, Illinois, 42, M.S, 48, Ph.D.(bact, chem), 50. Asst. prof. BACT, Univ. Wyo, 50-52; Univ. Ark, 52-54; PROF. & MICROBIOLOGIST, KANS. STATE UNIV, 54- Vis. prof, Rowett Res. Inst, Scotland, 62. Med.C, U.S.N, 42-46. Am. Soc. Microbiol; Am. Dairy Sci. Asn. Methane fermentation; industrial problems; Rumen microbiology; disinfectants. Address: Division of Biology & Microbiology, Kansas State University, Manhattan, KS 66502.

FINAMORE, FRANK J(OSEPH), b. Paterson, N.J, Aug. 3, 26; m. 48; c. 3. BIOCHEMISTRY. B.A, Virginia, 49, M.S, 51; Ph.D.(physiol), Fla. State, 54. Asst. physiol, Fla. State, 51-54; instr. biochem, col. med, Illinois, 54, res. assoc, Inst. tuberc. res, 54-55; asst. prof. physiol. Southern Illinois, 55-59, assoc. prof, 59-62; BIOCHEMIST, OAK RIDGE NAT. LAB, 62-, PROF. BIOCHEM, UNIV. TENN-OAK RIDGE BIOMED. GRAD. SCH, 67- Res. partic, Oak Ridge Nat. Lab, 57-59. U.S.N, 45-46. Am. Soc. Biol. Chem; Soc. Develop. Biol; Am. Chem. Soc. Chemical embryology; nucleic acid chemistry and physiology. Address: Biology Division, Oak Ridge National Lab, Oak Ridge, TN 37830.

FINBERG, LAURENCE, b. Chicago, Ill, May 20, 23; m. 45; c. 3. PEDIATRICS, PHYSIOLOGY. B.S, Chicago, 44, M.D, 46. Instr. pediat, sch. med, Hopkins, 51-56, asst. prof, 56-63, pediatrician, hosp, 51-63; PROF. PEDIAT, ALBERT EINSTEIN COL. MED, 63-; CHMN. PEDIAT. DEPT, MONTEFIORE HOSP. & MED. CENTER, 63-; ATTEND. PEDIATRICIAN, BRONX MUNIC. HOSP, 63- Asst. chief pediatrician, Baltimore City Hosp, 51-61, assoc. chief pediatrician, 61-63. U.S.P.H.S, 47-49. AAAS; Am. Pediat. Soc; Soc. Pediat. Res; Am. Fedn. Clin. Res; Am. Acad. Pediat; Harvey Soc; N.Y. Acad. Sci; Am. Inst. Nutrit. Electrolyte physiology, especially relating to disturbances of sodium and water osmotic equilibrium; metabolic and infectious diseases. Address: Dept. of Pediatrics, Montefiore Hospital & Medical Center, 111 E. 210th St, Bronx, NY 10467.

FINBY, NATHANIEL, b. New York, N.Y, May 31, 17; m. 47. RADIOLOGY. A.B, Hopkins, 38, M.D, 42. Intern, Grasslands Hosp, N.Y, 42-43; private practice, 46-52; res. radiol, New York Hosp, 52-55, attend. radiologist, 55-61; DIR. DEPT. RADIOL, ST. LUKE'S HOSP, 61-; ASSOC. CLIN. PROF, COL. PHYSICIANS & SURGEONS, COLUMBIA UNIV, 61- Asst. prof, med. col, Cornell, 56-58, assoc. prof, 58-61; consult, Rockefeller Univ, 56-; Vet. Admin. Hosp, Northport, L.I, 57-; St. Barnabas Hosp. Chronic Diseases, N.Y; mem, Adv. Bd. Seminars & Symposia. U.S.A, 43-46, Capt. Radiol. Soc. N.Am; fel. Am. Col. Radiol; fel. Am. Med. Asn; N.Y. Acad. Med; Radiation Res. Soc. Diagnostic radiology. Address: Dept. of Radiology, St. Luke's Hospital, 421 W. 113th St, New York, NY 10025.

FINCH, C(HARLES) R(ICHARD), b. Memphis, Tenn, Nov. 30, 28; m. 56; c. 4. CHEMICAL ENGINEERING. B.S, Maryland, 50, Ph.D.(chem. eng), 55. Asst. chem. eng, Maryland, 51-53, instr, 53-54; proj. leader, DOW CHEM. CO, 56-60, GROUP LEADER, 60- U.S.A.F, 54-56, 1st Lt. Soc. Plastics Eng; Am. Inst. Chem. Eng. Plastics development. Address: 1280 E. Chippewa Rd, Rt. 6, Midland, MI 48640.

FINCH, CLEMENT ALFRED, b. Broadalbin, N.Y, July 4, 15. MEDICINE. B.A, Union Col, 36; fel, Rochester, 38-39, M.D, 41. Intern med, Peter Bent Brigham Hosp, Boston, 41-42, asst. res, 42-43, res, 44-46, instr, Harvard Med. Sch, 46-48, assoc, 48-49; assoc. prof, SCH. MED, UNIV. WASH, 49-55, PROF. HEMAT. & HEAD DIV, 55- Res. fel. hemat, Evans Mem. Hosp, 43-44; jr. assoc, Peter Bent Brigham Hosp, Boston, 46-48, assoc, 48-49; mem. cmt. blood & transfusion probs, Nat. Res. Coun, 49-; nat. adv. arthritis & metab. diseases coun, Nat. Insts. Health, 62-; comt. dietary allowances, Nat. Acad. Sci, 65. Am. Med. Asn; Am. Soc. Hemat. (pres. elect); Soc. Nuclear Med; Europ. Soc. Hemat; Int. Soc. Blood Transfusion. Hematology and iron metabolism; biophysics; clinical pathology. Address: Division of Hematology, University of Washington Medical School, Seattle, WA 98195.

FINCH, DAN M, b. San Francisco, Calif, June 4, 15; m. 38; c. 2. ELECTRICAL ENGINEERING. B.S, California, 37; fel, Harvard, 37-38. Asst, Technicolor Motion Pictures, 38-40; asst. chief engr, Paramount Motion Pictures, 40-41; equipment engr, Dept. Motor Vehicles, Calif, 41-45; asst. prof. ELEC. ENG. UNIV. CALIF, BERKELEY, 45-50, assoc. prof, 50-55, PROF, 55- Civilian with Office Sci. Res. & Develop; Naval Res. Comt, 44. Am. Inst. Elec. & Electronics Eng; Illum. Eng. Soc; Soc. Automotive Eng. Motor vehicle and aircraft visibility under normal and adverse weather; fog visibility and transmission; illumination and radiation instruments. Address: Division of Transportation, University of California, Berkeley, CA 94720.

FINCH, DONALD I(RA), b. Grand Rapids, Mich, July 20, 07; m. 69. METALLURGY. B.S, Michigan, 29, 29-30. Res. & develop. metallurgist, metall. sect, res. & develop. dept, LEEDS & NORTHRUP CO, 30-33, 35-44, acting div. chief, 44-45, chief, 45-57, head, 57-68, PRIN. SCIENTIST, CORP. RES. DEPT, 68- Mem, Franklin Inst. With Off. Sci. Res. & Develop; U.S. Naval Ord. Lab, 44. Am. Soc. Metals; Am. Inst. Mining, Metall. & Petrol. Eng; fel. Am. Soc. Test. & Mat; Nat. Soc. Prof. Eng; Brit. Iron & Steel Inst; Brit. Inst. Metals. Thermoelectric thermometry; fundamental temperature measurement; metals and alloys for thermoelectric thermometry; metallurgy of resistance alloys and of special solders; special contact materials; diffusion in metals and metal impregnation; thermal analysis of steels and cast iron for composition control; automatic measurement and control of industrial furnace atmospheres; design and development of gas generators and ammonia dissociators; gas carburizing furnaces. Address: Leeds & Northrup Co, Technical Center, Dickerson Rd, North Wales, PA 19454.

FINCH, G(AYLORD) K(IRKWOOD), b. Owosso, Mich, Nov. 16, 23; m. 45; c. 4. ORGANIC CHEMISTRY. B.S.Ch.E, Michigan, 45, fel, 46-50, M.S, 48, Ph.D. (chem), 54. Ord. engr, U.S. Govt, 46; sr. chemist, TENN. EASTMAN CO, 50-60, chief chemist, 60-64, supvr. acid develop. & control dept, 64-66, ASST. DIV. SUPT, acid div, 66-70, polymers div, 70-71, ORG. CHEM. DIV, 71- U.S.N.R, 44-46, Lt.(jg). Am. Chem. Soc; Am. Inst. Chem. Eng. Synthesis, development and process improvement of aliphatic and aromatic oxygenated compounds; statistical design and interpretation of experiments; polymer chemistry; manufacture of polyesters; synthesis of dyes and fine organic chemicals. Address: 717 Yadkin St, Kingsport, TN 37660.

FINCH, HAROLD L(eROY), Educ. Admin, see 4th ed, Leaders in Education.

FINCH, HARRY C, b. Ringsted, Iowa, Jan. 15, 17; m. 45; c. 2. PLANT PATHOLOGY. B.A, Iowa State, 46, M.S, 47, Ph.D.(plant path), 50. Asst. prof. plant path, N.C. State, 50-54; assoc. prof, Pa. State, 54-59; proj. leader fungicides-nematocides, Monsanto Chem. Co, 59-62; from asst. prof. BIOL. SCI. to PROF, CALIF. STATE POLYTECH. COL, SAN LUIS OBISPO, 62- Nat. Sci. Found. summer fel, Purdue Univ, 64, grant, 64-65; U.S. aid technologist, Guatemala, 70-71. U.S.A.A.F, 40-45, T/Sgt. AAAS; Am. Phytopath. Soc; Mycol. Soc. Am. Diseases of fruit trees; virus diseases of plants; fungicide-nematocides. Address: Dept. of Biological Science, California State Polytechnic College, San Luis Obispo, CA 93401.

FINCH, JACK N(ORMAN), b. Esbon, Kans, Sept. 26, 23; m. 47; c. 2. PHYSICAL CHEMISTRY. B.S, Ft. Hays Kans. State Col, 48, M.S, 49; Ph.D, Kansas State, 57. Instr. chem, North. Okla. Jr. Col, 49-53; asst. prof, Northeast. State Col, 53; instr, Kansas State, 55-56; RES. CHEMIST, PHILLIPS PETROL. CO, 56- U.S.A.A.F, 42-46. Molecular structure, spectroscopy and catalysis. Address: 4762 Dartmouth Dr, Bartlesville, OK 74003.

FINCH, JOHN V(ERNOR), b. Madison, Wis, Mar. 4, 17; m. 43; c. 2. MATHEMATICS. A.B, Oberlin Col, 38; M.A, Wisconsin, 40; Ph.D.(math), Chicago, 51. Asst. math, Wisconsin, 38-39; instr. meteorol, Chicago, 46, asst. MATH, Chicago, 47-49; acting instr, Wisconsin, 49-50; asst. prof, BELOIT COL, 50-55, assoc. prof, 55-59, PROF, 59- U.S.A.A.F, 41-46, Capt. AAAS; Am. Math. Soc; Math. Asn. Am. Banach spaces. Address: Dept. of Mathematics, Beloit College, Beloit, WI 53511.

FINCH, NEVILLE, b. Greenock, Scotland, Nov. 30, 34; U.S. citizen. ORGANIC CHEMISTRY. B.Sc, Bristol, 55, Ph.D.(org. chem), 58. Fel, Wayne State, 58-59; Stanford, 59-60; sr. res. chemist, Ciba Pharmaceut. Co, 60-68, mgr. chem. res, 68-69, dir, 69-71, EXEC. DIR. CHEM. DIV, CIBA-GEIGY PHARMACEUT, 71- Am. Chem. Soc; The Chem. Soc. Synthetic organic and medicinal chemistry. Address: Ciba-Geigy Pharmaceuticals, Summit, NJ 07901.

FINCH, ROBERT ALLEN, b. Cleveland, Ohio, Mar. 15, 41; m. 68. ANATOMY. A.B, Oberlin Col, 63; Nat. Inst. Health fel, Case Western Reserve, 63-68, Ph.D.(anat), 68. Nat. Insts. Health trainee biol, Brandeis Univ, 68-70; ASST. PROF. ANAT, BOWMAN GRAY SCH. MED, 70- Am. Asn. Anat; Soc. Develop. Biol; Am. Soc. Zool. Vertebrate limb regeneration; chick limb development and associated control mechanisms. Address: Dept. of Anatomy, Bowman Gray School of Medicine, Winston-Salem, NC 27103.

FINCH, ROBERT DAVID, b. Westcliff, Eng, Aug. 18, 38; m. 63; c. 2. ACOUSTICS, PHYSICS. B.Sc, Univ. London, 59, M.Sc, 60, Ph.D.(physics), 63. Res. fel. physics, Univ. Calif, Los Angeles, 63-65; ASSOC. PROF. MECH. ENG, UNIV. HOUSTON, 65- Pres, Appl. Acoust. Corp, 71- Acoust. Soc. Am; Am. Phys. Soc. Nucleation and effects of ultrasonic cavitation; acoustical horns and transmission lines; ultrasonic nondestructive testing; underwater sound propagation. Address: Dept. of Mechanical Engineering, University of Houston, Houston, TX 77004.

FINCH, ROGERS B(URTON), b. Broadalbin, N.Y, Apr. 16, 20; m. 42; c. 5. TEXTILE TECHNOLOGY. S.B, Mass. Inst. Tech, 41, S.M, 47, Sc.D, 50. Textile technologist, Broadalbin Knitting Co, Inc, N.Y, 41; res. assoc. mech. eng, textile div, Mass. Inst. Tech, 46-47, asst. prof. textile tech, 47-53; dir. U.S. Opers. Mission, Burma, 53-54; asst. dir. res. div, Rensselaer Polytech, 54-58, assoc. dean, sch. sci, 58-60, dir. res. div, 60-61; dir. univ. rels, Peace Corps, D.C, 61-63; assoc. dean, Hartford Grad. Ctr, RENSSELAER POLYTECH. INST, 63-66, dir. acad. planning, 66-70, V.PRES. PLANNING, 70- Trustee, Dudley Observ, 70- Dir. heavy textile res. & develop, Qm. Depot, Ind, 43-45, U.S.A, 41-46, Res, 46-, Brig. Gen. AAAS; Am. Soc. Mech. Eng; Am. Soc. Eng. Educ; Asn. Instnl. Res; Soc. Col. & Univ. Planning. Comprehensive long-range planning in higher education; institutional research. Address: Rensselaer Polytechnic Institute, Troy, NY 12181.

FINCH, STUART CECIL, b. Broadalbin, N.Y, Aug. 6, 21; m. 46; c. 4. INTERNAL MEDICINE. Dartmouth Col, 38-41; M D, Rochester, 44. Intern surg, Baltimore City Hosp, Md, 44-45, asst. resident path, 45-46; res. fel. MED, Harvard Med. Sch, 48-49; asst. resident, Peter Bent Brigham Hosp, Mass, 49-50; asst, sch. med, Boston, 50-52, instr, 52-53; asst. prof, SCH. MED, YALE, 53-59, assoc. prof, 59-67, PROF, 67- Asst. dept. hematol, Peter Bent Brigham Hosp, 48-49; res. assoc, Evans Mem-Mass. Mem. Hosps, 50-52, asst. mem, 52-53; assoc. physician, Grace-New Haven Community Hosp, 53-; consult, West Haven Veterans Admin. Hosp, Conn, 53-; Laurel Heights Hosp, Derby, 58-; Meriden Hosp, 58- Med.C, 46-48, Capt. Am. Soc. Hemat; Am. Soc. Clin. Invest; Am. Med. Asn; Asn. Am. Physicians; Am. Fedn. Clin. Res; Int. Soc. Hemat. Iron metabolism; leukemia; leucocyte kinetics and immunology. Address: 333 Cedar St, New Haven, CT 06510.

FINCH, S(TUART) M(cINTYRE), b. Salt Lake City, Utah, Aug. 16, 19; m. 41; c. 2. PSYCHIATRY. Utah, 36-39; M.D, Colorado, 43; Phila. Psychoanal. Inst, 47-53. Intern, Alameda County Hosp, Oakland, Calif, 43-44; res. PSYCHIAT, sch. med, Temple, 46-49, instr, 49-53, assoc. prof, 54-56; MED. SCH, UNIV. MICH, 56-60, PROF, 60-, DIR, CHILDREN'S PSYCHIAT. HOSP, 56- Dir. child psychiat, sch. med, Temple, 49-56; attend. psychiatrist, St. Christopher's Hosp. for Children, 53-56; consult, Vet. Admin. Hosp, Battle Creek, 56-58; Battle Creek Child Guid. Clin, 56-58; Kalamazoo State Hosp, 56-58; fresh air camp, Michigan, 57-; mem. comt. cert. child psychiat, Am. Bd. Psychiat. & Neurol; mem, Gov. Ment. Health Adv. Coun. Med.C, 44-46, Capt. Am. Psychosom. Soc; Am. Med. Asn; Am. Psychiat. Asn; Am. Psychoanal. Asn; Am. Orthopsychiat. Asn; Acad. Res. Ment. Deficiency; Am. Acad. Child Psychiat; Am. Col. Psychiat. Psychophysiologic illness. Address: 304 Juniper Lane, Ann Arbor, MI 48104.

FINCH, THOMAS L(ASSFOLK), b. Madison, Wis, Nov. 26, 26. PHYSICS. B.A, Wisconsin, 47, M.A, 49, Ph.D.(physics), 57. Asst. prof. PHYSICS, Union (N.Y), 55-57; ST. LAWRENCE UNIV, 57-60, ASSOC. PROF, 60- Vis. lectr, Univ. Col. N.Wales, 64-65. AAAS; Am. Phys. Soc; Am. Asn. Physics

Teachers. Low-temperature physics; intermediate state of super conductors. Address: Dept. of Physics, St. Lawrence University, Canton, NY 13617.

FINCH, TUDOR R, b. Colorado Springs, Colo, Dec. 26, 14; m. 40; c. 2. SOLID STATE ELECTRONICS. B.S, Colorado, 38, M.S, 39. Mem. tech. staff & tech. supvr. networks, Bell Tel. Labs, 39-56, dept. head electronic switching systs, 56-61; asst. gen. mgr, Motorola Semiconductor Prod, Inc, Ariz, 61; DEPT. HEAD DIGITAL DEVICE INTEGRATION, BELL TEL. LABS, 61- Secy, Solid State Circuits Conf, 59, chmn, 61. Fel. Inst. Elec. & Electronics Eng. Transmission networks; digital electronics, computers and memory systems; advanced techniques for topological design and physical realization. Address: Bell Telephone Labs, Room 2A-230, Mountain Ave, Murray Hill, NJ 07974.

FINCH, WARREN I(RVIN), b. Union Co, S.Dak, Oct. 27, 24; m. 51; c. 3. GEOLOGY. B.S, S.Dak. Sch. Mines & Tech, 48; M.S, California, 54; Colo. Sch. Mines, 58-59. GEOLOGIST, U.S. GEOL. SURV, 48- U.S.A, 44-46. Fel. Geol. Soc. Am; Soc. Econ. Geol. Exploration for uranium deposits of the Colorado Plateau and beryllium; geology of uranium deposits in sandstone formations of the United States; regional geology of Jackson Purchase Region, Kentucky. Address: U.S. Geological Survey, Federal Center Bldg. 25, Denver, CO 80225.

FINCHAM, CHRISTOPHER J(OSEPH) B(ARRY), b. Hornsea, Eng, Dec. 23, 27; U.S. citizen; m. 54. PHYSICAL CHEMISTRY. B.Sc, London, 48, Ph.D. (chem), 52. Sci. officer, chem. dept, British Iron & Steel Res. Asn, 48-52; res. assoc. metall, Columbia, 53-54; lectr, Toronto, 54-56; mgr. prod. develop, metals div, Nat. Res. Corp, 56-61, tech. dir, 61-64, asst. gen. mgr, 64-68, MGR. METALS DIV, NORTON CO, 68- Am. Chem. Soc; Electrochem. Soc; Am. Inst. Mining, Metall. & Petrol. Eng. Physical chemistry of process metallurgy; high temperature chemistry; tantalum and its anodic oxide films as capacitors. Address: Metals Division, Norton Co, 45 Industrial Pl, Newton, MA 02164.

FINCHER, EDWARD L(ESTER), b. Atlanta, Ga, Jan. 16, 21; m. 48; c. 2. MICROBIOLOGY. B.A, Mercer, 48; M.Sc, Emory, 49; Ph.D.(bact), Georgia, 62. Res. biologist, eng. exp. sta, Ga. Inst. Tech, 50-58, asst. res. scientist, 58-60, asst. res. prof. biol, 60-63; res. microbiologist, biophys. sect, tech. br, commun. disease ctr, U.S. Pub. Health Serv, 64-65; ASSOC. PROF. environ. sci. & eng, Univ. N.C, 65-68; BIOL, GA. INST. TECHNOL, 68-, ACTING DIR. DEPT, 70- U.S. Pub. Health Serv. trainee, 58-59, res. fel, 59-60. U.S.N, 41-45. AAAS; Am. Soc. Microbiol; Brit. Soc. Gen. Microbiol. Aerobiology; bacterial growth and cytology; infection, host-parasite relationships; microbiology of the hospital environment; bacterial degradation of synthetic molecules; effect of chemical and physical factors on bacterial cells; electron microscopy. Address: School of Biology, Georgia Institute of Technology, Atlanta, GA 30332.

FINCHER, JOHN ALBERT, b. Union, S.C, Sept. 8, 11; m. 39; c. 3. ZOOLOGY. B.S, South Carolina, 33, M.S, 35; Ph.D.(zool), North Carolina, 39. Prin, pub. sch, S.C, 33-34; instr. biol, South Carolina, 34-35; lab. asst. zool, North Carolina, 35-39; instr. biol, Cumberland Col, 39-40; asst. prof, Millsaps Col, 40-43, assoc. prof, 43-46; prof. & head dept, Howard Col, 45-57, asst. to the pres, 55-57, dean, 57-68; PRES, CARSON-NEWMAN COL, 68- Fel, Highlands Biol. Lab, 39; trustee, Gorgas Scholar. Found, State Sci. Talent Search, 52-68; East End Mem. Hosp, Birmingham, Ala, 57-68. Fel. AAAS; Am. Soc. Zool. Invertebrate zoology; cell behavior and gametogenesis in sponges; growth of sponges from gemmules. Address: Office of the President, Carson-Newman College, Jefferson City, TN 37760.

FINCHER, JULIAN H, b. Cross Keys, S.C, July 22, 35; m. 66; c. 3. PHYSICAL PHARMACY. B.S, South Carolina, 58; M.S, Georgia, 62; Am. Found. Pharmaceut. Ed. fel. & Ph.D.(pharm), Connecticut, 64. Instr. pharm, South Carolina, 58-59; Georgia, 59-61; asst. prof, Univ. Miss, 64-67, assoc. prof. PHARMACEUT, 67-72, chmn. dept, 70-72; PROF, UNIV. S.C, 72- Consult, H.A. Salzman & Co. AAAS; Am. Pharmaceut. Asn; Am. Chem. Soc; Am. Col. Apothecaries; Acad. Pharmaceut. Sci. Biopharmaceutics; physical and chemical properties affecting drug release and absorption from dosage forms. Address: School of Pharmacy, University of South Carolina, Columbia, SC 29208.

FINCHER, MYRON G(USTIN), b. Corfu, N.Y, Nov. 25, 98; m. 24; c. 3. VETERINARY MEDICINE. D.V.M, Cornell, 20, M.S, 25; hon. Ph.D, Univ. Thessaloniki, Greece, 58. Instr. vet. med, STATE UNIV. N.Y. VET. COL, CORNELL UNIV, 20-25, asst. prof, 25-38, prof, 38-65, head dept. med. & obstet. & dir. ambulatory clin, 42-65, acting dean col, 43-44, EMER. PROF, 65-; prof. & head dept. vet. med. & surg, Kans. State Univ-U.S. Agency Int. Develop. Prog, Ahmadu Bello Univ, Nigeria, 65-67; vet. med. consult, BUR. VET. MED, U.S. FOOD & DRUG ADMIN, 67-68, VET. MED. OFF, 68- Private practice, Ky, 26-27; acting prof, vet. col, Ohio State, 40; lectr, Agr. & Mech. Col, Texas, 40; dir, N.Y. State Mastitis Res. & Control Prog, 46-65; Fulbright lectr, U.S. Dept. State, Thessaloniki, 58-59. Int. Ed. Exchange Serv. specialist, U.S. Dept. State, Peru, Uruguay & Brazil, 60. Am. Fertil. Soc; Am. Vet. Med. Asn.(Borden Award, 54); Animal Health Asn; Int. Fertil. Asn; Conf. Res. Workers Animal Diseases. Diseases of genital organs of horses and cattle; bovine mastitis; acetonemia of cattle; fluorosis cattle and diseases of the newborn. Address: Crystal House, 2000 S. Eads St, Arlington, VA 22202.

FINCK, ALFRED, b. Atlantic City, N.J, Nov. 19, 26; m. 53; c. 2. PHYSIOLOGY, AUDIOLOGY. B.A, Syracuse, 53; Ph.D.(exp. psychol), Rochester, 59. Res. asst. exp. psychol, Rochester, 54-58; exp. physiol. psychol, Air Force Cambridge Res. Ctr, 59-61; Nat. Insts. Health spec. fel. neurophysiol. of hearing, sch. med, Hopkins, 61-63; asst. prof. physiol, SCH. MED, TEMPLE UNIV, 63-66, ASSOC. PROF. OTORHINOL-PHYSIOL, 66- U.S.N, 44. AAAS; Acoust. Soc. Am; Am. Psychol. Asn. Electrophysiology; motor skills; psycho-acoustics; auditory physiology. Address: Temple University School of Medicine, 3400 N. Broad St, Philadelphia, PA 19140.

FINCK, HENRY, b. N.Y.C, Oct. 12, 25; m. 56; c. 3. ANATOMY, CELL BIOLOGY. Ph.D.(anat), Chicago, 55. Instr. ANAT, Pennsylvania, 56-58, assoc, 58-60; asst. prof, SCH. MED, UNIV. PITTSBURGH, 60-65, ASSOC. PROF, 65- U.S.N, 42-44. Am. Asn. Anat. Electron microscopy; cytochemistry of proteins and nucleic acids; immunochemistry and immunofluorescence of muscle proteins. Address: Dept. of Anatomy, School of Medicine, University of Pittsburgh, Pittsburgh, PA 15213.

FINCK, J(OSEPH) LOUIS, b. Russia, Oct. 5, 93; nat; m. 25; c. 3. PHYSICS. B.S, Mass. Inst. Tech, 15; fel, Harvard, 20-21, A.M, 22; Ph.D.(physics), Hopkins, 23. Lab. asst, Nat. Bur. Standards, 16-19, asst. physicist, 22-23; dir. & owner, J.L. Finck Labs, 33-63, PRES, J.L.F. RES, INC, 63- AAAS; Am. Phys. Soc; N.Y. Acad. Sci. Thermodynamics; basic generalized theory; heat transfer. Address: 184-29 Aberdeen Rd, Jamaica, NY 11432.

FINCKE, JOHN K(IZLER), b. Kansas City, Kans, Sept. 18, 17; m. 41; c. 4. CHEMISTRY. B.A, Kansas, 39, M.A, 41. Chemist, Monsanto Chem. Co, Mo, 41-42, res. chemist, Ohio, 42-51, group leader, Santa Clara, 51-54, sect. leader, 54-59, asst. dir. res, 59-61, res. mgr, Monsanto Res. Corp, 64-68; MGR. COMPOSITE APPLNS, CHEMSTRAND RES. CTR, INC, 68- Am. Chem. Soc. Reaction of sulphur trioxide with organic compounds; synthetic detergents and high temperature polymers. Address: Chemstrand Research Center, Inc, Research Triangle Park, Durham, NC 27702.

FINCKE, MARGARET L(OUISE), b. Astoria, N.Y, Oct. 24, 00. NUTRITION. A.B, Mt. Holyoke Col, 21; A.M, Columbia, 32, Ph.D.(chem), 35. Asst. chem, Columbia, 28-35; assoc. prof. FOODS & NUTRIT, ORE. STATE UNIV, 35-44, prof, 44-69, head dept, 45-69, EMER. PROF, 69- Mem. food & nutrit. bd, Nat. Res. Council, 48-51; vis. prof. & dir, Sch. Home Econ, Hebrew Univ. Jerusalem, 69-71. AAAS; Am. Inst. Nutrit; Am. Home Econ. Asn; Am. Dietetic Asn. Availability of calcium; vitamins in foods; ascorbic acid and thiamine; riboflavin; metabolism of humans; nutritional status. Address: 124 N.W. 29th St, Corvallis, OR 97330.

FINCKE, NANCY C, b. Pittsburgh, Pa, Nov. 6, 38. GEOMETRY. B.S, Univ. Pittsburgh, 61, M.S, 62, Mellon fel, 64-66, Ph.D.(math), 66. Asst. prof. MATH, West. Ill. Univ, 66-68; ASSOC. PROF, Indiana Univ. Pa, 68-71; W.VA. STATE COL, 71- Am. Math. Soc; Math. Asn. Am. Projective planes. Address: Dept. of Mathematics, West Virginia State College, Institute, WV 25112.

FINCO, ARTHUR A, b. Ely, Minn, Mar. 1, 32; m. 60; c. 2. MATHEMATICS. B.S, St. Cloud State Col, 53; Gen. Elec. fel, Purdue, 57, Ph.D.(math. ed), 66; Nat. Sci. Inst, 58-59 & summers 58 & 59; M.A. Northern Iowa, 59. Instr, high sch, Minn, 56-58; math, Mankato State Col, 59-61; asst, PURDUE UNIV, FT. WAYNE, 61-65, asst. prof. MATH. & MATH. EDUC, 65-69, ASSOC. PROF, 69- U.S.A, 54-56. Math. Asn. Am; Am. Educ. Res. Asn. Mathematics education. Address: 4744 Innsbruck Dr, Ft. Wayne, IN 46815.

FINCO, DELMAR R, b. Roundup, Mont, Nov. 5, 36; m. 59; c. 4. VETERINARY MEDICINE. B.S, Minnesota, St. Paul, 57, D.V.M, 59, fel, 61-66, Ph.D.(canine leptospirosis), 66. Asst. prof. CLIN. VET. MED, Minnesota, St. Paul, 66-70; PROF, COL. VET. MED, UNIV. GA, 70- Am. Vet. Med. Asn; Am. Asn. Vet. Clinicians. Canine leptospirosis and studies of leptospira canicola; urogenital diseases of dog and cat. Address: Dept. of Medicine & Surgery, College of Veterinary Medicine, University of Georgia, Athens, GA 30601.

FINDEIS, A(RTHUR) F(REDERICK), JR, b. Columbus, Ohio, Oct. 27, 28; m. 55; c. 4. ANALYTICAL CHEMISTRY. B.S, Capital Univ, 52; M.S, Purdue, 55, Atomic Energy Comn. fel, 55-56, Ph.D.(chem), 57. Mem. tech. staff, Bell Tel. Lab, 56-57; sr. scientist, Radiochem. Inc, 57-58; lab. mgr, William H. Johnson Labs, Inc, 58-61; asst. prof. chem, Univ. Ala, 61-66, assoc. prof, 66-68, prof, 68; prog. dir. chem. instrumentation & anal, NAT. SCI. FOUND, 67-70, MEM. SCI. LIAISON STAFF, 70- Consult, U.S. Bur. Mines; Esso Res. & Eng; propulsion lab, U.S. Army Missile Command. U.S.N, 46-47. AAAS; Am. Chem. Soc; N.Am. Thermal Anal. Soc. Electrochemistry; radiochemical methods; thermal analysis; physiochemical methods of analysis; chemical instrumentation. Address: Science Liaison Staff, National Science Foundation, American Embassy, APO San Francisco CA 96503.

FINDER, JEROME G(ORDON), b. Chicago, Ill, Apr. 1, 06; m. 30; c. 3. ORTHOPEDIC SURGERY. B.A, Illinois, 26, B.S, 28; M.S. & M.D, 30. Intern, Cook County Hosp, Ill, 30-32, res, 32-33; hosp, Univ. Iowa, 33-36; asst. prof. ORTHOP. SURG, SCH. MED, NORTHWEST. UNIV.(ILL), 50-58, ASSOC. PROF, 58-; ATTEND. PHYSICIAN, MICHAEL REESE HOSP, 36-, chmn. dept. orthop. surg, 58-70. Assoc. attend. physician, Cook County Hosp, Chicago, Ill, 46-50, attend. physician, 50-52; attend. consult, Ill. Children's Hosp. Sch, 48-69. Dipl, Am. Bd. Orthop. Surg, 37. Med.C, U.S.A, 42-46, Maj. Am. Orthop. Asn; Pan-Am. Med. Asn; Clin. Orthop. Soc.(pres, 69); Am. Med. Asn; Am. Rheumatism Asn; Am. Acad. Orthop. Surg; Int. Soc. Orthop. Surg. & Traumatol. Address: 111 N. Wabash Ave, Chicago, IL 60602.

FINDLAY, DAVID CHRISTOPHER, b. Ottawa, Ont, Oct. 20, 32; m. 58; c. 4. PETROLOGY, ECONOMIC GEOLOGY. B.Sc, McGill, 55, M.Sc, 58; Ph.D. (geol), Queen's (Ont), 63. Field petrologist, Geol. Surv. Can, 63-66, resident geologist, 66-69, petrologist, 69-70; CONSULT. GEOLOGIST, 70- Secy, sub. cmt. deep drilling, Can. cmt, Int. Upper Mantle Proj. AAAS; Am. Mineral. Soc. Petrology of Canadian ultramafic rocks. Address: Box 220, Morrisburg, Ont, Can.

FINDLAY, GLEN MARSHALL, b. Shoal Lake, Man, July 15, 40; m. 58; c. 4. BIOLOGY, NUTRITIONAL BIOCHEMISTRY. B.S.A, Manitoba, 63, Nat. Res. Coun. Can. fel, 63-64, M.Sc, 64; Wright fel, Illinois, 66-67, Ph.D.(hydroperoxide metab), 69. Res. asst, Univ. Ill, 64-68; fel, div. biol, Nat. Res. Coun. Can, 68-70; ASST. PROF. PESTICIDE TOXICOL, UNIV. MANITOBA, 70- Can. Biochem. Soc. Investigation of mineral element and vitamin status of cattle; metabolism of methyl linoleate hydroperoxide in rabbits; dynamics of biocides in biological material; pesticide toxicology. Address: Dept. of Entomology, University of Manitoba, Winnipeg, Man, Can.

FINDLAY, JOHN A, b. Manchester, Eng, May 29, 36; Can. citizen; m. 63; c. 3. ORGANIC CHEMISTRY. B.Sc, New Brunswick, 58, Shell Oil fel. & Ph.D.(org. chem), 62. NATO-Dept. Indust. & Sci. Res. U.K. fel. ORG. CHEM, Cambridge, Eng, 62-63; lectr, UNIV. N.B, 63-65, asst. prof, 65-68,

ASSOC. PROF, 68- Chem. Inst. Can. Structural elucidation and synthesis of natural products, especially compounds of biological interest; organic reaction mechanisms. Address: Dept. of Chemistry, University of New Brunswick, Federicton, N.B, Can.

FINDLAY, JOHN W(ILSON), b. Kineton, Eng, Oct. 22, 15; nat; m. 53; c. 2. PHYSICS. B.A, Cambridge, 37, Ph.D.(physics), 50. Res, Cambridge, 37-39; univ. demonstr. & fel. & lectr. physics, Queens' Col, Cambridge, 45-53; mem. staff, Brit. Ministry Supply, 54-56; NAT. RADIO ASTRON. OBSERV, 57-65, 66, ASST. DIR, 66- Dir, Arecibo Ionospheric Observ, 65-66. Mem, Order of the Brit. Empire. R.A.F, 39-45. Fel. Inst. Elec. & Electronics Eng; fel. Brit. Inst. Physics & Phys. Soc. Physics of the ionosphere; radio astronomy. Address: National Radio Astronomy Observatory, Charlottesville, VA 22901.

FINDLAY, RAYMOND D(AVID), b. Toronto, Ont, Aug. 10, 38; m. 61; c. 3. ELECTRICAL ENGINEERING. B.A.Sc, Univ. Toronto, 63, M.A.Sc, 65, J. Edgar McAllister fel, 65-66, Nat. Res. Coun. Can. fel, 66-67, Ph.D.(elec. eng), 68; Nat. Sci. Found. bursary, Univ. Colo, Boulder, summer 66. Lectr. elec. eng, UNIV. N.B, 67-68, ASST. PROF. elec. eng. & comput. sci, 68-70, ELEC. ENG, 70- Nat. Res. Coun. Can. operating grant, 68-72. Am. Soc. Eng. Educ; Inst. Elec. & Electronics Eng. Electrical power and apparatus; analysis of induction heating systems, both magnetic and non magnetic, for temperature distributions, efficiency and electrical characteristics; current, loss and voltage distributions in low frequency, single-layer, air core solenoids; current and loss distributions in aluminum conductor steel-reinforced cable. Address: Dept. of Electrical Engineering, University of New Brunswick, Fredericton, N.B, Can.

FINDLAY, ROBERT A(RTEMAS), b. Vancouver, B.C, Jan. 27, 14; nat; m. 40; c. 3. PHYSICAL CHEMISTRY. Wesbrook scholar, British Columbia, 34, B.A, 34, M.A, 35; Nat. Res. Coun. Can. bursar & scholar, McGill, 35-36, Ph.D.(phys. chem), 37. Res. chemist, Imp. Oil Ltd, 37-39; chief chemist, Anglo-Can. Oils, Ltd, 39-40; res. chemist, Trinidad Leaseholds Ltd, 40-43; chem. engr, PHILLIPS PETROL. CO, 43-46, mgr, Bartlesville Pilot Plants, 46-53, asst. mgr, chem. eng. div, res. & develop. dept, 53-56, process develop. div, 56-64, DIR. chem. & automation develop, 64-65, eval. & mech. develop, 65-68, PETROL. PROCESSES RES. & DEVELOP, 68- Mem. comt. res.proj, Am. Petrol. Inst, 44-62, comt. res, data & info. serv, subcomt. tech. data. Distinguished Serv. Citation, Nat. Gas Processors Asn. Am. Chem. Soc; Am. Inst. Chem. Eng. Physical chemistry; petroleum chemistry, as pyrolysis of hydrocarbons; chemical engineering fundamentals, as liquid-liquid extraction, crystallization; plastics; polyethylene. Address: 1931 Polaris Dr, Bartlesville, OK 74003.

FINDLEN, HERBERT, b. Ft. Fairfield, Maine, Feb. 22, 20; m. 46; c. 1. HORTICULTURE. B.S, Maine, 42; Clinton DeWitt Smith fel, Cornell, 42, Ph.D.(veg. crops), 50. Asst. & agent, potato res, Cornell, 46-49; U.S. DEPT. AGR, 49-51, assoc. horticulturist, 51-52, horticulturist & field sta. leader, 52-63, RES. HORTICULTURIST, PLANT INDUSTRY STA, 63- U.S.A.A.F, 42-45. Am. Soc. Hort. Sci; Potato Asn. Am. Handling, transportation, storage and quality evaluation of horticultural crops. Address: 4620 Knox Rd, College Park, MD 20740.

FINDLER, NICHOLAS V(ICTOR), b. Budapest, Hungary, Nov. 24, 30; m. 55; c. 2. COMPUTER SCIENCE, APPLIED MATHEMATICS. B.E, Budapest Tech, 53, Ph.D.(math. physics), 56. Sr. lectr. theoret. physics, Budapest Tech, 56; vis. lectr, Vienna, 56-57; res. fel. theoret. physics & comput. sci, Sydney, 57-59; staff appl. mathematician, C.S.R. Co, Ltd, Australia, 59-63; res. assoc. comput. sci, Univ. Pittsburgh, 64; assoc. prof. COMPUT. SCI. & MATH, Kentucky, 64-66; PROF, STATE UNIV. N.Y. BUFFALO, 66- Participant, summer res. inst, Rand Corp, Calif, 63; adj. asst. prof. math, New South Wales, 62-63; res. scientist and Adv. Res. Proj. Agency fel, Carnegie Inst. Technol, 63-64; invited lectr, NATO Adv. Study Insts, 65-66 & 67-68; dir, NATO Advan. Study Inst, 70. Consult, various indust. firms, 64- AAAS; Asn. Comput. Mach; Am. Math. Soc; Soc. Indust. & Appl. Math; Int. Asn. Cybernet. Heuristic programming; special purpose computer languages; simulation of human cognitive behavior; man-machine relations; self-adaptive systems; computational linguistics; theoretical electrical engineering; mathematical physics; mathematical psychology; mathematical biophysics. Address: Dept. of Computer Science, State University of New York at Buffalo, 4226 Ridge Lea Rd, Amherst, NY 14226.

FINDLEY, DONALD E, b. Alfalfa Co, Okla, Nov. 3, 23; m. 45; c. 2. PHYSICS. B.S, Kansas State, 44, M.S, 47; Ph.D.(physics), Wisconsin, 52. Supvr. electronic systs, Autonetics Div, N.Am. Aviation, Inc, Downey, 51-55, sr. proj. engr, 55-62, mgr, radar systs, 62-64, chief engr, avionic systs, 64-66, asst. prog. dir, 66-67, asst. to v.pres, strike avionics syst. div, N.Am. Rockwell Corp, 67-70; DEP. ASST. SECY. SYSTS. ENG, DEPT. TRANSPORTATION, WASH, D.C, 70- U.S.N.R, 44-46, Lt.(jg). Am. Inst. Aeronaut. & Astronaut. Address: 6720 Towne Lane Ct, McLean, VA 22101.

FINDLEY, G(EORGE) B(ERNARD), b. Colliers, W.Va, Dec. 7, 12; m. 38; c. 2. MATHEMATICAL PHYSICS. B.S, Florida, 48, M.S, 50, Ph.D.(math), 52. Asst. math, Florida, 48-51, instr. physics & phys. sci, 51-52; head math. br, U.S. Navy Mine Defense Lab, 52-59; mathematician, Air Proving Ground Ctr, 59-67, RES. PHYSICIST, AIR FORCE ARMAMENT LAB, 67- U.S.A, 43-46. AAAS; Am. Math. Soc; Math. Asn. Am; Soc. Indust. & Appl. Math; Am. Inst. Aeronaut. & Astronaut; Am. Ord. Asn. Applied mathematics; aerodynamics; nonlinear differential equations. Address: Air Force Armament Lab, Eglin Air Force Base, FL 32542.

FINDLEY, JAMES S(MITH), b. Cleveland, Ohio, Dec. 28, 26; m. 49; c. 4. VERTEBRATE ZOOLOGY. A.B, Western Reserve, 50; Ph.D, Kansas, 55. Asst. instr, Kansas, 50-53, asst, Mus. Natural Hist, 53-54; instr. zool, South Dakota, 54-55; asst. prof. BIOL, UNIV. N.MEX, 55-61, assoc. prof, 61-70, PROF, 70- U.S.A, 45-46. AAAS; Am. Soc. Mammal; Ecol. Soc. Am; Cooper Ornith. Soc; Soc. Study Evolution. Taxonomic mammalogy; mammalian paleontology; ecology and zoogeography. Address: Dept. of Biology, University of New Mexico, Albuquerque, NM 87106.

FINDLEY, MARSHALL E(WING), b. Arkansas City, Kans, Oct. 13, 27; m. 55; c. 2. CHEMICAL ENGINEERING. B.S, Agr. & Mech. Col. Texas, 49; M.S, Inst. Paper Chem, 51; Ph.D.(chem. eng), Florida, 55. Chem. engr, Celotex Corp, La, 51-52; asst, Florida, 52-55; res. engr, E.I. du Pont de Nemours & Co, Tenn, 55-58; assoc. res. prof. CHEM. ENG, Auburn, 58-65; asst. pfo prof, UNIV. MO-ROLLA, 65-66, assoc. prof, 66-69, PROF, 69- Fulbright lectr, Alexandria, 62-63; eng. educ. adv, U.S. Aid Int. Develop, S.Vietnam, 69-71. Am. Chem. Soc; Am. Inst. Chem. Eng; Tech. Asn. Pulp & Paper Indust; Am. Soc. Eng. Educ. Pulp and paper; process control; water desalination. Address: Dept. of Chemical Engineering, University of Missouri-Rolla, Rolla, MO 65401.

FINDLEY, THOMAS, b. Chicago, Ill, Apr. 15, 01; m. 40; c. 2. MEDICINE. A.B, Princeton, 23; B.S, Minnesota, 25; M.D, Rush Med. Col, 28. Intern, univ. hosp, Philadelphia, 27-29; instr. med, Michigan, 29-32; res. fel. pharmacol, Pennsylvania, 32-35; asst. prof. med, Washington (St. Louis), 35-41; assoc. prof. clin. med, Tulane, 41-54; prof. MED, MED. COL. GA, 54-69, chmn. dept. med, 57-69, EMER. PROF, 69- Head dept. med, Ochsner Clin, 41-54; area coord. regional med. prog, Univ. Tenn, Knoxville, 69-71; private practice, Ga, 71- Am. Soc. Clin. Invest; Am. Med. Asn; Am. Clin. & Climat. Asn; Asn. Am. Physicians; fel. Am. Col. Physicians. Physiology of the kidney. Address: 206 Sheffield Bldg, 1938 Peachtree Rd. N.W, Atlanta, GA 30309.

FINDLEY, THOMAS WAGNER, b. New Orleans, La, Mar. 22, 21; m. 43; c. 3. ORGANIC CHEMISTRY. B.A, Swarthmore Col, 42; M.S, Ohio State, 48, Johnson & Son fel, 46-50, Ph.D.(physiol. chem), 50. Chemist, east. reg. res. lab, 42-44; asst. biochem, Mayo Clinic, 50-52; res. chemist, Swift & Co, 52-54, head tech. prods. res. div, 54-62, head, org. chem. res. div, 62-68; PROF. NATURAL SCI. & ENVIRON. STUDIES, FRIENDS WORLD COL, 68- U.S.A, 44-46. AAAS; Am. Chem. Soc; Am. Oil Chem. Soc. Electrophoresis; waxes; fats and oils; epoxidized oils. Address: Dept. of Natural Science & Environmental Studies, Friends World College, Mitchel Gardens, Westbury, NY 11590.

FINDLEY, WILLIAM N(ICHOLS), b. Mankato, Minn, Feb. 12, 14; m. 39; c. 1. MECHANICS, MATERIALS SCIENCE. A.B, Ill. Col, 36, hon. D.Sc, 70; B.S.E.(mech. eng) & B.S.E.(math), Michigan, 37; McMullen scholar, Cornell, 37-39, M.S, 39. Asst. eng. mech, Michigan, 36-37; instr. civil eng, George Washington, 38-39; theoret. & appl. mech, Illinois, 39-42, assoc, 42-43, asst. prof, 43-47, res. assoc. prof, 47-54; PROF. ENG, BROWN UNIV, 54-, dir. cent. facility mech. testing, 66-69. Consult, Lawrence Radiation Lab; mem. sci. adv. coun, Picatinny Arsenal, 51-62; orgn. comt, Joint Int. Conf. Creep, N.Y. & London, 63. Prize paper, Soc. Plastics Eng, 49, 50. Soc. Test. & Mat.(Dudley Medal, 45, Templin Award, 53 & 64); Soc. Exp. Stress Anal; Am. Soc. Eng. Educ; Soc. Rheol. Creep, fatigue and other strength properties of plastics at various temperatures; fatigue of metals in combined stress; photoelasticity; mechanics of creep; theories of fatigue; viscoelasticity. Address: Division of Engineering, Box D, Brown University, Providence, RI 02912.

FINDLEY, WILLIAM RAY, JR, b. Manhattan, Kans, June 26, 20; m. 43; c. 2. PLANT BREEDING. B.S, Kans. State Univ, 49, M.S, 50; Ph.D.(plant breeding), Univ. Md, 60. Asst. agronomist, div. cereal crops & diseases, U.S. DEPT. AGR, 50-53, assoc. agronomist, 53-56, RES. AGRONOMIST, CEREAL CROPS RES. BR, 56- U.S.A.A.F, 41-46, Capt. Am. Soc. Agron. Corn breeding and genetics, with emphasis on maize dwarf mosaic virus. Address: Dept. of Agronomy, Ohio Agricultural Research & Development Center, Wooster, OH 44691.

FINDLEY, WILLIAM R(OBERT), b. Detroit, Mich, Apr. 26, 35. INORGANIC CHEMISTRY. B.S, Denison Univ, 57; M.Sc, Ohio Univ, 61, Ph.D.(chem), 63. Chemist, DYE STUFFS & CHEM. DIV, CIBA-GEIGY INC, 63-64, prod. mgr. chelates, 64-66, TECH. DEVELOP. MGR. WHITENERS, 66- AAAS; Am. Chem. Soc; Am. Oil Chem. Soc. Chelates. Address: Ciba-Geigy Inc, Ardsley, NY 10502.

FINE, ALBERT S(AMUEL), b. Phila, Pa, Oct. 24, 23; m. 59; c. 1. BIOCHEMISTRY. B.A, Brooklyn Col, 50, M.A, 53; Ph.D, N.Y. Univ, 70. Asst. BIOCHEM. & ENZYM, col. med, N.Y. Univ, 50-52; biochemist, col. physicians & surgeons, Columbia, 52-56; spec. dent. res. prog, VET. ADMIN. HOSP, 56-66, spec. res. lab. oral tissue metab, 66-70, CHIEF DENT. RES. LAB, 70- U.S.A, 43-46. AAAS; Am. Chem. Soc; N.Y. Acad. Sci; Am. Inst. Biol. Sci; Int. Asn. Dent. Res. Intermediary metabolism of the oral tissues, cartilage and bone; comparative biochemistry of oxidative and electron transport enzymes associated with vertebrate and invertebrate tissues; oxidative metabolism during wound healing of epithelium. Address: Dental Research Lab, Veterans Administration Hospital, New York, NY 10010.

FINE, BEN S(ION), b. Peterborough, Ont, Can, Sept. 29, 28. OPHTHALMOLOGY. M.D, Toronto, 53. RES. ASSOC, ARMED FORCES INST. PATH, 58-; ASSOC. RES. PROF. OPHTHAL, GEORGE WASH. UNIV, 70-, assoc. prof, 64-70. Dipl, Am. Bd. Ophthal, 59. Electron Micros. Soc. Am. Ophthalmic pathology; investigations into the structure of the eye, both normal and abnormal. Address: Ophthalmic Pathology Branch, Armed Forces Institute of Pathology, Washington, DC 20305.

FINE, DONALD LEE, b. Nanticoke, Pa, Jan. 14, 43; m. 65; c. 2. MICROBIOLOGY. A.B, Wilkes Col, 64; Nat. Insts. Health fel. & M.S, Pa. State, 66, Nat. Insts. Health fel. & Ph.D.(microbiol), 68. Res. asst. limnol, Wilkes Col, 62-64; trainee MICROBIOL, Pa. State, 64-68, res. assoc, 68-69; proj. leader, virus & rickettsia div, U.S. Army Biol. Ctr, 69-71; CHIEF ONCOL, VIROL. & CELL BIOL, BIONETICS RES. LABS, INC, 71- U.S. Army outstanding achievement award. Sci. Res. Soc. Am; N.Y. Acad. Sci; Am. Soc. Microbiol. Limnology; ecology; cell physiology; virus biochemistry; virology and immunology with particular reference to arboviruses; viral oncology, with special interest in primates. Address: Bionetics Research Labs, Inc, 5510 Nicholson Lane, Kensington, MD 20795.

FINE, DWIGHT A(LBERT), b. Los Angeles, Calif, Sept. 17, 33. INORGANIC CHEMISTRY. B.S, California, Los Angeles, 56, Ph.D.(inorg. chem), Berkeley, 60. Asst. chem, California, Berkeley, 56-57, Lawrence Radiation Lab, 57-60; CHEMIST, NAVAL WEAPONS CTR, 60- Am. Chem. Soc. Coordination chemistry; solution chemistry of metals of Group VIII. Address: Code 6054, Michelson Lab, Naval Weapons Center, China Lake, CA 93555.

FINE, JACOB, b. Brockton, Mass, Feb. 10, 00; m; c. 2. SURGERY. A.B, Harvard, 20, M.D, 24. Moseley traveling fel, Royal Infirmary, Edinburgh,

35; asst. prof. SURG, HARVARD MED. SCH, 41-48, prof, 48-66, EMER. PROF, 66-, CONSULT, SEARS LAB, HARVARD SURG. UNIT, 66- Surgeon-in-chief, Beth Israel Hosp, 48- Mem. shock cmt, Nat. Res. Council. Civilian with Off. Sci. Res. & Develop; Off. Naval Res, 44. U.S.A, 17-19. AAAS; Am. Surg. Asn; Am. Acad. Arts & Sci; fel. N.Y. Acad. Sci; fel. Int. Soc. Surg. Defense mechanisms in massive tissue injury; gas absorption from tissues; traumatic shock; experimental physiology; care of surgical patients; antibacterial defense; bacterial endotoxins; peritoneal dialysis. Address: Sears Lab, Harvard Surgical Unit, Boston City Hospital, Boston, MA 02118.

FINE, LAWRENCE O(LIVER), b. Sheyenne, N.Dak, May 14, 17; m. 41; c. 3. SOIL CHEMISTRY. B.S, N.Dak. Agr. Col, 38; Ph.D.(soil chem), Univ. Wis, 41. Soil surveyor, U.S. Dept. Agr, 41-42; res. instr. agron, Univ. Ark, 42, asst. agronomist, 45-46; asst. prof. AGRON, S.DAK. STATE UNIV, 46-48, assoc. prof, 48-53, PROF, 53-, assoc. agronomist, 48-50, agronomist, exp. sta, 53-69, head dept. agron, univ, 58-69. Collab, soil & water div, agr. res. serv, U.S. Dept. Agr, 53- U.S.N.R, 42-45, Lt.(jg). Am. Soc. Agron; Soil Sci. Soc. Am; Am. Soc. Range Mgt. Salinity, phosphate supply and nutrition; general soil fertility; irrigation. Address: Dept. of Plant Science, South Dakota State University, Brookings, SD 57006.

FINE, LEONARD W, b. Bridgeport, Conn, Apr. 19, 35; m. 58; c. 2. ORGANIC CHEMISTRY. B.S, Marietta Col, 58; U.S. Pub. Health Serv. fel, Maryland, 60-62, Ph.D.(org. chem), 62. RES. CHEMIST, Harris Res. Lab, Gillette Co, 62-64; Ethyl Corp, Mich, 64-66; AM. CYANAMID CO, BRIDGEPORT, 66- Assoc. prof, Housatonic Community Col, 70. AAAS; Am. Chem. Soc; N.Y. Acad. Sci. Synthesis and reactions of pyrimidine heterocycles; peroxide oxidations of organic compounds; synthesis of alpha-amino acids; natural auxins and synthetic plant growth regulators; organometallics and organometallic catalysis; history of chemistry. Address: 15 Grey Hollow Rd, Norwalk, CT 06850.

FINE, MELVIN H(ERBERT), b. Newark, N.J, Feb. 1, 39; m. 61; c. 4. BOTANY. B.A, Delaware, 60; M.S, Yale, 62, Ph.D.(biol), 68. Instr. bot, Union Col, 65-68; res. assoc, Antioch Col. & Charles F. Kettering Res. Lab, 68-70; ASST. PROF. BIOL, CENT. STATE UNIV, 70- AAAS; Am. Inst. Biol. Sci; Am. Soc. Plant Physiol; Bot. Soc. Am; Int. Asn. Plant Tissue Cult; Scandinavian Soc. Plant Physiol. Plant morphogenesis; plant tissue culture; tracheary element differentiation; biology education. Address: Dept. of Biology, Central State University, Wilberforce, OH 45384.

FINE, MORRIS EUGENE, b. Jamestown, N.Dak, April 12, 18; m. 50; c. 2. METALLURGY. B.Met.E, Minnesota, 40, Superior Metal Prods. Co. fel, 40-42, M.S, 42, Ph.D.(phys. metall), 43. Instr. phys. metall, Minnesota, 42-44; assoc. metallurgist, Manhattan Proj, Chicago, 44-45; California, Los Alamos, N.Mex, 45; mem. tech. staff, Bell Tel. Labs, 46-54; prof. metall, tech. inst, NORTHWEST. UNIV, 54-64, WALTER P. MURPHY PROF. MAT. SCI, MAT. RES. CTR, 64-, chmn. dept. mat. sci, 54-60, res. ctr, 60-64. Mem. mat. adv. bd, Nat. Acad. Sci, 65-69; vis. prof, Stanford Univ, 67-68. AAAS; fel. Am. Soc. Metals; fel. Am. Phys. Soc; Am. Soc. Eng. Educ; Metall. Soc; Am. Ceramic Soc; Am. Inst. Mining, Metall. & Petrol. Eng. Phase transformations in solids; precipitation hardening; theory of the strength of metals and alloys; elasticity and internal friction of solids; magnetic properties of metals and ceramics; materials science. Address: Dept. of Materials Science, Northwestern University, Evanston, IL 60201.

FINE, MORRIS M(ILTON), b. St. Louis, Mo, Nov. 15, 14; m. 37; c. 1. EXTRACTIVE METALLURGY, METALLURGY. B.S, Wash. Univ, 35; Univ. Mo-Rolla, 42, 47. Chemist, U.S. BUR. MINES, Mo, 35-40, metallurgist, 41-55, sect. chief mineral dressing, 56-59, proj. coord. METALL, Minn, 59-70, RES. DIR, ROLLA METALL. RES. CTR, 71- Superior performance award, U.S. Bur. Mines, 64, meritorious serv. award, 69. Am. Inst. Mining, Metall. & Petrol. Eng; Soc. Sigma Xi(pres, 59). Agglomeration and reduction of iron ore raw materials; extractive metallurgy of iron and copper; iron and steel process metallurgy; beneficiation of complex ores. Address: Rolla Metallurgy Research Center, U.S. Bureau of Mines, P.O. Box 280, Rolla, MO 65401.

FINE, NATHAN J(ACOB), b. Phila, Pa, Oct. 22, 16; m. 43; c. 3. MATHEMATICS. B.S, Temple, 36; Univ. scholar, Pennsylvania, 38, 39, A.M, 39, scholar, 40, Ph.D.(math), 46. Teacher, pub. sch, Pa, 41; instr. math, Cornell, 42; Purdue, 42-44; res. mathematician, Naval Ord. Plant, Ind, 44-45; res. mathematician, Opers. Eval. Group, D.C, 46-47, consult, 47-48; asst. prof. MATH, Pennsylvania, 47-53, assoc. prof, 53-56, PROF, 56-63, PA. STATE UNIV, 63- Nat. Sci. Found. fel, 53-54; Guggenheim Mem. fel, 58-59; Earle Raymond Hedrick lectr, 66. Am. Math. Soc; Math. Asn. Am. Number theory; orthogonal series; harmonic analysis; combinatorics; group theory; basic hypergeometric series; probability; rings of continuous functions. Address: Dept. of Mathematics, McAllister Hall, Pennsylvania State University, University Park, PA 16802.

FINE, PAUL C(HARLES), b. Dallas, Texas, June 28, 15. PHYSICS. B.A, Oklahoma, 35; Coffin fel, Calif. Inst. Tech, 35-36, M.S, 36, Ph.D.(physics), 39. Asst, Calif. Inst. Tech, 36-38; instr. physics, Oregon, 39; Texas, 39-42; tech. aide, Nat. Defense Res. Comt, 42-45; fel, Calif. Inst. Tech, 45-46; sci. adv, U.S. delegation, U.N. Atomic Energy Comn, New York, 46-47; special asst, div. mil. application, U.S. ATOMIC ENERGY COMN, 48-55, asst. to comnr, 55-56, DIR. DIV. OPERS. ANAL. & FORECASTING, 56- Theoretical physics; normal modes of vibration of the atoms in crystal lattices; nuclear power. Address: Division of Operations Analysis & Forecasting, U.S. Atomic Energy Commission, Washington, DC 20545.

FINE, SAMUEL, b. Baranowiczach, Poland, Jan. 21, 25; Can. citizen. MEDICINE, BIOPHYSICS. B.A.Sc, Toronto, 46, M.D, 57, fel, 48-50; S.M, Mass. Inst. Tech, 53. Jr. engr, Can. Gen. Elec. Co, 47-48; staff mem, Res. Lab. of Electronics, Mass. Inst. Tech, 51-53; civil serv. appointment, Nat. Insts. Health, 58-59; res. assoc, med, Brookhaven Nat. Lab, 59-61; assoc. prof. elec. eng, NORTHEAST. UNIV, 61-64, PROF. BIO-MED. ENG, 64-, CHMN. DEPT, 70- Mem, adv. comt. optical masers to Surgeon Gen, U.S. Army, 64- Royal Canadian Electro-Mechanical Engrs, 45. Inst. Elec. & Electronics Eng; Soc. Nuclear Med. Electrical engineering; bio-medical engineering; nuclear medicine; biological effects of laser radiation. Address: Dept. of Biophysics & Biomedical Engineering, Northeastern University, 360 Huntington Ave, Boston, MA 02115.

FINE, STEPHEN ALAN, b. Boston, Mass, Oct. 11, 41; m. 67. ORGANIC CHEMISTRY. S.B, Mass. Inst. Tech, 63; M.A, Brandeis, 65; Ph.D.(chem), Northeastern, 68. Fel. CHEM, Lehigh, 68-69; ASST. PROF, LAFAYETTE COL, 69- Am. Chem. Soc. Mechanisms of organic reactions. Address: 2112 Pennsylvania Ave, Bethlehem, PA 18018.

FINE, TERRENCE LEON, b. New York, N.Y, Mar. 9, 39; m. 64. ELECTRICAL ENGINEERING. B.E.E, City Col. New York, 58; McKay fel, Harvard, 58, Nat. Sci. Found. fel. & S.M, 59, Ph.D.(appl. physics), 63. Res. fel, Harvard, 63-64; Miller Inst. fel, California, Berkeley, 64-66; asst. prof. ELEC. ENG, CORNELL UNIV, 66-70, ASSOC. PROF, 70- Consult, Dynamics Res. Corp, 62-64; Signatron, Inc, 62-66. Inst. Elec. & Electronics Eng; Inst. Math. Statist. Decision theory; foundations of probability and statistics. Address: School of Electrical Engineering, Cornell University College of Engineering, Ithaca, NY 14850.

FINEBERG, CHARLES, b. Phila, Pa, Jan. 1, 21; m. 46; c. 3. THORACIC SURGERY. B.S, Wake Forest Col, 40; M.D, Hahnemann Med. Col, 50. Intern med, Mt. Sinai Hosp, 50-51; res. SURG, THOMAS JEFFERSON UNIV, 51-55, asst, 55-56, instr, 56-58, assoc, 58-62, asst. prof, 63-67, ASSOC. PROF, 67-; CHMN. DEPT. SURG, DAROFF DIV, ALBERT EINSTEIN MED. CTR, 68- Res. fel, Thomas Jefferson Univ, 51-52; dir, clin. cancer training, tumor adv. group, 66-68; U.S. Pub. Health Serv. fel, Nat. Cancer Inst, 52-54. Dipl, Am. Bd. Surg, 56; Am. Bd. Thoracic Surg, 57. Fel. Am. Col. Surg; fel. Am. Asn. Thoracic Surg; Am. Med. Asn. U.S.C.G.R, 41-46, Lt. Comdr. Surgical correction of coronary artery disease and malabsorption syndromes; surgical uses of hyperbaric oxygenation; carcinoma of the breast. Address: Dept. of Surgery, Daroff Division, Albert Einstein Medical Center, 1429 S. Fifth St, Philadelphia, PA 19147.

FINEBERG, HERBERT, b. Portland, Maine, Jan. 16, 15; m. 41; c. 2. ORGANIC CHEMISTRY. B.S, Trinity, 35; Ph.D, Illinois, 41. Org. res. chemist, Eastman Kodak Co, 35-38; asst. instr. chem, Illinois, 38-41; chief chemist, Conn. Hard Rubber Co, 41-46; v.pres. res, Geral Chem. Co, 46-48; v.pres. res, Glyco Prods. Co, 48-62; mgr. proj. eval. sect, Archer-Daniels-Midland, 62-68; MGR. PROJ. ANAL, ASHLAND OIL CO, 68- AAAS; Am. Chem. Soc. Evaluation of all research projects, fields, polymers, fats and derivatives, foods and allied products, plasticizers. Address: Ashland Oil Co, P.O. Box 2219, Columbus, OH 43216.

FINEBERG, R(ICHARD) A(RNOLD), b. St. Paul, Minn, Mar. 8, 22; m. 43; c. 1. BIOCHEMISTRY. S.B, Chicago, 42, M.D, 45; U.S. Pub. Health Serv. fel, California, 51-53, Ph.D.(biochem), 54. Intern, Naval Hosps, Shoemaker & Oakland, Calif, 45-46; asst. prof. BIOCHEM, UNIV. CALIF, SAN FRANCISCO, 54-60, ASSOC. PROF, 60- Asst. resident, Kaiser Hosp, San Francisco, 60-61. U.S.N, 46-47. AAAS. Protein chemistry and biosynthesis. Address: Rm. S-960, University of California, San Francisco, CA 94122.

FINEGAN, JOEL (DEAN), b. Gary, Ind, Dec. 12, 31; m. 55. SOLID STATE PHYSICS. B.A, Wesleyan, 54; M.S, Case, 58, Nat. Sci. Found. summer fel, 60, Ph.D.(physics), 61. Res. physicist, MINN. MINING & MFG. CO, 61-64, RES. & DEVELOP. PHYSICIST, 65- Intrinsic stress in thin films and correlation with structure; sound reproduction acoustics and mechanics. Address: 152 Wildwood Ave, Birchwood, MN 55110.

FINEGOLD, HAROLD, b. Lawrence, Mass, Jan. 13, 29. PHYSICAL & ORGANIC CHEMISTRY. A.B, Boston, 51; A.M, Harvard, 53. Instr. chem, Boston, 52-53; PHYS. CHEMIST, Nat. Bur. Standards, 57-65; AGR. RES. SERV, U.S. DEPT. AGR, 65- Phys. chemist, Army Chem. Center, Md, U.S.A, 53-57. Am. Chem. Soc; The Chem. Soc. Nuclear resonance and other physical studies of organic-phosphorus and lipophilic materials. Address: Agricultural Research Service, U.S. Dept. of Agriculture, Beltsville, MD 20705.

FINEGOLD, LEONARD X, b. London, Eng, Feb. 15, 35; m. 65; c. 2. PHYSICS. B.Sc, London, 56, Dept. Sci. & Indust. Res. studentship, 56-59, Ph.D. (physics), 59. Res. fel, Div. Eng. & Appl. Physics, Harvard, 59-62; Lawrence Radiation Lab. & Univ. California, Berkeley, 62-65; asst. prof. PHYSICS, UNIV. COLO, BOULDER, 65-70, ASSOC. PROF, 70- Am. Cancer Soc. res. scholar. biol, Univ. Calif, San Diego, 71-72. Brit. Inst. Physics. Solid state at low temperature; phonons and electrons; one and two dimensional systems; physics of high polymers; biology. Address: Dept. of Physics, University of Colorado, Boulder, CO 80302.

FINEGOLD, SYDNEY M(ARTIN), b. New York, N.Y, Aug. 12, 21; m. 47; c. 3. INTERNAL MEDICINE. A.B, California, Los Angeles, 43; M.D. Texas, 49. Intern, U.S. Pub. Health Serv, U.S. Marine Hosp, 49-50; fel. MED, med. sch, Minnesota, 50-52; resident, Wadsworth Vet. Hosp, Los Angeles, 53-54; instr, MED. SCH, UNIV. CALIF, LOS ANGELES, 55-57, asst. clin. prof, 57-59, asst. prof, 59-62, assoc. prof, 62-68, PROF, 68-; SECT. CHIEF. GEN. MED. & INFECTIOUS DISEASES, WADSWORTH VET. HOSP, 61-, chest & infectious diseases, 57-61. Attend. physician, Minn. Gen. Hosp, 51-52; mem. cmt, infectious diseases res. prog, Vet. Admin; mem. subcomt, Int. Comn. on Nomenclature of Bacteria. Dipl, Am. Bd. Internal Med, 57. U.S.M.C.R, 43; U.S.N.R, 43-45; U.S.A.R, 52-53. Fel. AAAS; fel. Am. Acad. Microbiol; Am. Fedn. Clin. Res; fel. Am. Col. Physicians; Infectious Disease Soc. Am. Infectious diseases; antibiotics; intestinal flora; anaerobic bacteria and anaerobic infections; epidemiology of hospital infections. Address: Wadsworth Veterans Hospital, Los Angeles, CA 90073.

FINELLI, A(NTHONY) F(RANCIS), b. Newton, Mass, June 18, 22; m. 56; c. 3. ORGANIC CHEMISTRY. B.S, Boston Col, 43; M.S, Pennsylvania, 47, Du Pont fel, 49-50, Ph.D.(chem), 50. Org. res. chemist, GOODYEAR TIRE & RUBBER CO, 50-64, HEAD URETHANE ELASTOMERS RES, 64- U.S.N.R, 44-46. Am. Chem. Soc; Am. Inst. Chem.(Honor Scroll, 70); Am. Soc. Artificial Internal Organs. Artificial heart valves, ventricles and arterial grafts; morphine chemistry; vinyl chloride polymers. Address: 575 Castle Blvd, Akron, OH 44313.

FINEMAN, MANUEL N(ATHAN), b. Montreal, Que, Sept. 9, 20; nat; m. 45; c. 3. CHEMISTRY. B.Sc, McGill, 41, Nat. Res. Council Can. student, 41-44, Ph.D.(phys. chem), 44. Jr. chemist, Nat. Res. Council Can, 44-46; Bristol-Myers Co. fel, Stanford, 46-47; res. chemist, Rohm & Haas Co,

47-51, group leader, 52-56; tech. dir, Puritan Chem. Co, 56-69, v.pres. res, 69-70; DIR. RES. & DEVELOP, AVMOR LTD, 70- Judge & consult, Atlanta Sci. Cong, 61-70. Chem. Inst. Can; Am. Chem. Soc; Am. Oil Chem. Soc. Detergency of hard surfaces and role of substrate; foaming of nonionic surfactants; crushproofing in cotton; wet strength resins for paper; osmotic properties of colloidal electrolytes; kinetics of cure of resol resins; pore structure and adsorptive properties of charcoal; evaluation of low foaming detergents. Address: Avmor Ltd, 433 Rue Ste. Hélène, Montreal 125, Que, Can.

FINEMAN, MORTON A, b. Kearny, N.J, Aug. 9, 19; m. 49; c. 2. PHYSICAL CHEMISTRY. B.A, Indiana, 41; Ph.D.(chem), Pittsburgh, 48. Asst, Pittsburgh, 41-44; mem. res. staff, Sprague Elec. Co, 48-50; res. fel, Minnesota, 50-52; asst. prof. chem, Providence Col, 52-55, assoc. prof, 55-59, prof, 59-61; sr. res. staff mem, gen. atomic div, Gen. Dynamics Corp, 61-66; CHMN. DEPT. PHYSICS, LYCOMING COL, 66- Am. Chem. Soc; Am. Phys. Soc; Am. Asn. Physics Teachers. Thermodynamics of solid solutions; chemical kinetics; electron impact studies of gases; negative ions; chemical reactive cross sections via crossed beam techniques. Address: 2608 Blair St, R.D. 3, Montoursville, PA 17754.

FINERMAN, A(ARON), b. N.Y.C, Apr. 1, 25; m. 68; c. 4. COMPUTER SCIENCE. B.C.E, City Col. New York, 48; S.M, Mass. Inst. Tech, 51, Sc.D. (civil eng), 56. Instr, City Col. New York, 48-49, lectr, 51-54; engr, Thomas Worcester & Co, 49; proj. engr. struct. design, Voorhees, Walker, Foley & Smith, 51-54; res. engr, Mass. Inst. Tech, 54-55, instr. struct. eng, 55-56; mgr. digital comput. & data process, Repub. Aviation Corp, 56-61; prof. eng. & dir. comput. ctr, State Univ. N.Y. Stony Brook, 61-69, prof. comput. sci, 69-71; MGR. OFF. COMPUT. & INFO. SYSTS, JET PROPULSION LAB, 71- Pres, SHARE, 61-62; Nat. Acad. Sci. sabbatical leave award & sr. res. assoc, Jet Propulsion Lab, 68-69. U.S.A, 44-46. AAAS; Asn. Comput. Mach.(ed-in-chief, Comput. Rev, 63-67). Scientific and administrative computing applications; education in computing science; management of computing center. Address: 1001 El Vago St, La Canada, CA 91011.

FINERTY, JOHN C(HARLES), b. Chicago, Ill, Oct. 20, 14; m. 40; c. 2. ANATOMY. A.B, Kalamazoo Col, 37; M.S, Kans. State Col, 39; Ph.D.(zool), Wisconsin, 42; Michigan, 43-44. Asst. zool, Kansas State, 37-39; Wisconsin, 39-42; Rackham Found. fel, Michigan, 42-43, instr. physiol, 43, anat, 43-46; asst. prof. sch. med, Washington (St. Louis), 46-49, assoc. prof, 49; med. br, Texas, 49-52, prof, 52-56; anat, med. sch, Univ. Miami, 56-66, chmn. dept, 56-66, asst. dean, 56-62, assoc. dean, 62-66; PROF. ANAT, SCH. MED, LA. STATE UNIV, 66-, V.CHANCELLOR ACAD. AFFAIRS, 71-, dean, sch. med, 66-71. AAAS; Am. Asn. Anat; Am. Physiol. Soc; Soc. Exp. Biol. & Med; Endocrine Soc; Am. Soc. Zool; Radiation Res. Soc. Experimental endocrinology; pituitary cytophysiology; correlation of microscopic structure and function; neurohumoral control of respiration; gross human anatomy; parabiosis; protection from x-irradiation; effects of fat-deficiency. Address: Louisiana State University, 1542 Tulane Ave, New Orleans, LA 70112.

FINESTONE, ALBERT J(USTIN), b. Philadelphia, Pa, May 12, 21; m. 51; c. 3. MEDICINE. A.B, Temple, 42, M.D, 45, M.Sc, 51. Asst. prof. MED, SCH. MED, TEMPLE UNIV, 58-64, CLIN. PROF, 64-; HEAD DIABETIC SECT, EPISCOPAL HOSP, 64- Med.C, 46-48, Capt. Am. Med. Asn; Am. Diabetes Asn; Am. Col. Physicians; Am. Psychosom. Soc; Am. Fedn. Clin. Res. Metabolic diseases. Address: Dept. of Medicine, Temple University School of Medicine, Philadelphia, PA 19140.

FINESTONE, A(RNOLD) B(ARON), b. New York, N.Y, Dec. 19, 29; m. 54; c. 3. POLYMER CHEMISTRY. B.A, N.Y. Univ, 51; fel, Polytech. Inst. Brooklyn, 53-55, Ph.D.(polymer chem), 55. Res. chemist, res. lab, Westinghouse Elec. Corp, 55-56, group leader, 56-57; long range res, Foster Grant Co, Inc, 57-59, mgr. styrene polymer res, 59-62, co-dir. res. & develop, 62-64, dir. res. & develop. & mkt, 64-65, v.pres. & dir. res. & develop. & mkt, 65-68, planning & develop, 68-70; EXEC. V.PRES. DEVELOP. & ENG, CHEM. GROUP, DART INDUSTS. INC, 70- Am. Chem. Soc; Soc. Plastics Eng; Soc. Plastic Indust; The Chem. Soc. Polymerization and copolymerization; homogeneous and heterogeneous catalysis; utilization and synthesis of thermoset and thermoplastic resins; process and project engineering; plant engineering and construction. Address: 51 Indian Dr, Woodcliff Lake, NJ 07675.

FINFGELD, CHARLES R, b. Chicago, Ill, June 30, 36; m. 58; c. 2. PHYSICS. B.A, Oberlin Col, 58; M.S, Western Reserve, 60; Illinois, 59-61; Ph.D.(physics), Va. Polytech, 68. Res. assoc. physics, Coordinated Sci. Lab, Illinois, 61-62; res. & develop. engr, Electron Tube Div, Int. Tel. & Tel. Corp, 62-64; instr. PHYSICS, ROANOKE COL, 64-65, asst. prof, 65-70, ASSOC. PROF, 70- Prin. investr, U.S. Atomic Energy Comn. contract, 66- Am. Phys. Soc; Am. Asn. Physics Teachers; Am. Vacuum Soc. Surface physics. Address: Dept. of Physics, Roanoke College, Salem, VA 24153.

FINFROCK, DWIGHT CURTIS, b. Bement, Ill, July 31, 17; m. 45; c. 3. AGRONOMY. B.S, California, Davis, 50, M.S, 55. Specialist agron, California, Davis, 53-60; consult, Ford Found, 61-65; AGRONOMIST, Rockefeller Found, 65-69; FORD FOUND. & VIS. PROF. FACULTY OF AGR, UNIV. CHIENGMAI, 69- U.S.A.A.F, 42-45, S/Sgt. Am. Soc. Agron; Crop Sci. Soc. Am; Soil Sci. Soc. Am. General agronomic research of rice, corn and sorghum under tropical conditions. Address: The Ford Foundation, G.P.O. Box 1436, Bangkok, Thailand.

FINGER, FRANK W(HITNEY), b. Naples, N.Y, Apr. 16, 15; m. 58; c. 5. EXPERIMENTAL PSYCHOLOGY. A.B, Syracuse Univ, 36, M.A, 37; fel, Brown Univ, 39-40, Ph.D.(psychol), 40. Asst. PSYCHOL, Brown Univ, 37-39, instr, 40-42; acting asst. prof, UNIV. VA, 42-43, asst. prof, 44-48, assoc. prof, 48-55, PROF, 55- AAAS; fel. Am. Psychol. Asn. Physiological, comparative and abnormal psychology. Address: Dept. of Psychology, Gilmer Hall, University of Virginia, Charlottesville, VA 22901.

FINGER, F(REDERICK) G(EORGE), b. New York, N.Y, July 2, 24; m. 49. METEOROLOGY. B.A, N.Y. Univ, 57. Res. asst. meteorol, N.Y. Univ, 52-58; meteorologist, off. meteorol. res, U.S. Weather Bur, 58-60, res. meteorologist, 60-67, CHIEF, NAT. METEOROL. CTR. UPPER AIR BR, NAT. WEATHER SERV, NAT. OCEANOG. & ATMOSPHERIC ADMIN, 67- U.S.C.G, 43-45. Am. Meteorol. Soc; Am. Geophys. Union. Stratospheric meteorology; validity of high-level radiosonde measurements; application of rocketsonde data; atmospheric tides; computerized analysis systems for stratospheric data. Address: National Weather Service, National Oceanographic & Atmospheric Administration, Iverson Mall Office Bldg, Suite 301, 3737 Branch Ave, Hillcrest Heights, MD 20031.

FINGER, G(LENN) C(HARLES), b. Bloomington, Ill, May 3, 05; m. 56. ORGANIC CHEMISTRY. B.S, Illinois, 27, M.S, 28, Ph.D.(org. chem), 38; Lilly fel, Purdue, 29-30. Asst. chem, Purdue, 28-29; Illinois, 30-32; asst. chemist, ILL. GEOL. SURV, 33-39, assoc. chemist, 39-43, chemist, 43-45, chemist & head fluorine sect, 45-62, PRIN. CHEMIST & HEAD CHEM. GROUP, 62- With Nat. Defense Res. Cmt; Off. Naval Res, 44. Am. Chem. Soc; The Chem. Soc. Inorganic and organic chemistry of fluorine compounds; analytical chemistry; bacteriology; insecticides; pyrolytic reactions; industrial and chemical products from Illinois minerals. Address: Illinois State Geological Survey, Urbana, IL 61801.

FINGER, HAROLD B, b. New York, N.Y, Feb. 18, 24; m. 49; c. 3. AERONAUTICAL ENGINEERING, URBAN DEVELOPMENT. B.Mech.E, City Col. New York, 44; M.Aero.E, Case, 50. Aeronaut. res. scientist, Nat. Adv. Cmt. Aeronaut, 44-52, head axial flow compressor sect, Lewis Res. Center, 52-54, assoc. chief compressor res. br, 54-57, head nuclear radiation shield & nuclear rocket design group, 57-58, chief nuclear engine progs, NASA, 58-61, asst. dir. nuclear applns, 61, dir. nuclear systs. & space power, 61-67, assoc. adminr. orgn. & mgr, 67-69; ASST. SECY. RES. & TECHNOL, DEPT. HOUSING & URBAN DEVELOP, 69- Mgr. space nuclear propulsion off, Atomic Energy Comn. & NASA, 60-67, dir. space nuclear systs, Atomic Energy Comn, 65-67. U.S.A.A.F.R, 44-45. Am. Inst. Aeronaut. & Astronaut; Am. Soc. Pub. Admin. Nuclear engineering; aircraft superchargers, compressors and turbines for aircraft gas turbine engines; research and development and engineering management of work on nuclear propulsion and nuclear electric generating systems for space applications; urban growth and development; housing; local and state government. Address: 6908 Millwood Rd, Bethesda, MD 20034.

FINGER, IRVING, b. Peekskill, N.Y, Sept. 23, 24. GENETICS. B.A, Swarthmore Col, 50; Nat. Sci. Found. fel, Pennsylvania, 52-53, Phila. Brewers Found. fel, 53-54, Ph.D.(zool), 55. Am. Cancer Soc. fel, Columbia, 56-58; asst. prof. BIOL, HAVERFORD COL, 57-62, assoc. prof, 62-69, PROF, 69- U.S. Pub. Health Serv. spec. fel, California, San Diego, 63-64; summer instr, Pennsylvania, 56. U.S.A. 42-45. Genetics Soc. Am; Soc. Protozool; Am. Soc. Zool. Immunology; microbial genetics; protozoology; cellular differentiation. Address: Dept. of Biology, Haverford College, Haverford, PA 19041.

FINGER, KENNETH F, b. Antigo, Wis, Jan. 2, 29; m. 51; c. 1. BIOCHEMICAL PHARMACOLOGY. B.S, Wisconsin, 51, M.S, 53, Ph.D.(pharm, pharmacol), 55. Sr. investr. pharmaceut. chem, Chas. Pfizer & Co, 55-57, res. supvr, 59-61, res. mgr, 61-63; guest worker, Nat. Heart Inst, 57-59; assoc. prof. PHARMACOL, sch. pharm, Univ. Wis, Madison, 63-67, prof, 67-68; PROF. & DEAN COL. PHARM, UNIV. FLA, 68- Am. Soc. Pharmacol. & Exp. Therapeut; Am. Pharmaceut. Asn. Biochemical pharmacology; drug metabolism; biochemistry of function; drug-receptor interactions; catecholamines; anti-diabetic drugs and drugs affecting behavior. Address: College of Pharmacy, University of Florida, Gainesville, FL 32601.

FINGER, LARRY W, b. Terril, Iowa, May 22, 40; m. 62; c. 2. MINERALOGY, CRYSTALLOGRAPHY. B.Phys, Minnesota, 62, Ph.D.(crystal struct), 67. Fel, GEOPHYS. LAB, CARNEGIE INST, 67-69, STAFF MEM, 69- AAAS; Mineral Soc. Am; Am. Crystallog. Asn; Am. Geophys. Union. Crystallography and crystal structures of minerals in solid-solution series and the computations required in these studies. Address: Geophysical Laboratory, Carnegie Institution of Washington, 2801 Upton St. N.W, Washington, DC 20008.

FINGERMAN, MILTON, b. Boston, Mass, May 21, 28; m. 58; c. 2. COMPARATIVE ANIMAL PHYSIOLOGY. B.S, Boston Col, 48; M.S, Northwestern, 49, Ph.D.(biol), 52. Asst, Northwestern, 49-51; instr. ZOOL, TULANE UNIV. LA, 54-56, asst. prof, 56-60, assoc. prof, 60-63; PROF, 63-, chmn. dept. biol, 66-69. Mem. adv. panel regulatory biol, Nat. Sci. Found, 66-69; supply dept. comt, Marine Biol. Lab, Woods Hole, 70-, comt. chmn, 71- Chem.C, U.S.A, 52-54, Sgt. AAAS; Am. Inst. Biol. Sci; Am. Physiol. Soc; Am. Soc. Zool; Am. Soc. Nat; Soc. Biol. Rhythm. Comparative endocrinology; biological chronometry; animal color changes; crustacean physiology and endocrinology; chromatophores. Address: Dept. of Biology, Tulane University of Louisiana, New Orleans, LA 70118.

FINGL, E(DWARD) (GEORGE), b. Oak Park, Ill, Oct. 24, 23; m. 56. PHARMACOLOGY. B.S, Purdue, 43, M.S, 49; Fulbright fel, Edinburgh, 51-52; Ph.D.(pharmacol), Utah, 52. Asst. pharmaceut. chem, Purdue, 46-49; asst. PHARMACOL, COL. MED, UNIV. UTAH, 49-51, U.S. Pub. Health Serv. fel, 52-53, asst. res. prof, 53-54, asst. prof, 54-60, ASSOC. PROF, 60- U.S.A, 43-44; U.S.N.R, 44-46. AAAS; Am. Soc. Pharmacol. & Exp. Therapeut. Pharmacodynamics; renal function; neurohypophysis; drug tolerance. Address: Dept. of Pharmacology, University of Utah College of Medicine, Salt Lake City, UT 84112.

FINHOLT, ALBERT E(DWARD), b. Chicago, Ill, Jan. 28, 18; m. 41; c. 4. CHEMISTRY. A.B, Knox Col, 38; Purdue, 38-39; Ph.D.(chem), Chicago, 46. Res. chemist, Gen. Printing Ink Co, Ill, 39-42; res. assoc. on staff chem. dept. & assoc. dir. hydride proj, U.S.N, 45-47; chief chemist, Metal Hydrides, Inc, 47-49; assoc. prof. chem, ST. OLAF COL, 49-54, PROF, 54-64, 71-, chmn. dept. chem, 57-64, dean, 64-71, v.pres, 66-71. Civilian, Sig.C, U.S.N, 42-45. AAAS; Am. Chem. Soc. Inorganic and metal hydrides; preparation of aluminum hydrides and their use in inorganic and organic chemistry; organometallics. Address: Dept. of Chemistry, St. Olaf College, Northfield, MN 55057.

FINHOLT, JAMES E, b. Oak Park, Ill, Oct. 28, 33; m. 56; c. 1. PHYSICAL & INORGANIC CHEMISTRY. B.A, St. Olaf Col, 55; Nat. Sci. Found. fel, California, Berkeley, 55-56, Ph.D.(chem), 60. ASST. PROF. CHEM, Albion

Col, 59-60; CARLETON COL, 60- Petrol. Res. Found. grant, theoret. inorg. chem, Columbia Univ, 65-66. Am. Chem. Soc. Physical properties of coordination compounds in aqueous solution; chromium species. Address: Dept. of Chemistry, Carleton College, Northfield, MN 55057.

FINHOLT, R(OBERT) W(ILTON), b. Chicago, Ill, July 8, 21; m. 45; c. 2. CHEMISTRY. A.B, Knox Col, 42; fel, Purdue, 43-46, Ph.D.(org. chem), 47. Asst. chem, Purdue, 42-43; asst. prof, Union Col.(N.Y), 46-50; res. assoc, Gen. Elec. Co, Schenectady, 50-51, res. chemist, locomotive dept, Pa, 51-53, supvr, insulation lab, 53-56, mgr. chem. lab, major appliance div, 56-61, mkt, chem. develop, 61-63, polymer prods, 63-65, proj. mgr, corporate planning, 65-66; mgr. mfg. & eng, plating div, M&T Chemicals, 66-68; MGR. COMMERCIAL DEVELOP, PLASTICS DIV, AM. CYANAMID CO, 68- Civilian with Off. Rubber Reserve, 44. Am. Chem. Soc; Soc. Plastic Eng; Inst. Elec. & Electronics Eng; Soc. Indust. Chem. High polymers; wood preservatives; electrical insulation; plastics; organic chemicals; commercial development. Address: American Cyanamid Co, IC&P Division, 1937 W. Main St, Stamford, CT 06904.

FINIZIO, MICHAEL, b. Pozzuoli, Italy, Nov. 27, 38; m. 66; c. 2. ORGANIC & BIOLOGICAL CHEMISTRY. D.Sc.(org-biol. chem), Naples, 62. SCIENTIST, ENDO LABS, INC, GARDEN CITY, 63- Am. Chem. Soc. Medicinal chemistry and organic synthesis. Address: 85-14 163rd Ave, Howard Beach, NY 11414.

FINK, ANTHONY LAWRENCE, b. Hertford, Eng, Jan. 25, 43; m. 66. BIOLOGICAL ORGANIC CHEMISTRY. B.Sc, Queen's (Ont), 64, Nat. Res. Coun. Can. fels, 65-68, Ph.D.(org. chem), 68. Nat. Res. Coun. Can. fel. CHEM, Northwest. Univ, 67-69; ASST. PROF, UNIV. CALIF, SANTA CRUZ, 69- AAAS; Am. Chem. Soc; Chem. Inst. Can. Mechanisms of enzyme reactions; polyfunctional and intramolecular catalysis; biologically active carbohydrates; mechanisms of membrane transport. Address: Dept. of Chemistry, University of California, Santa Cruz, CA 95060.

FINK, ARLINGTON M, b. Armour, S.Dak, Dec. 15, 32. MATHEMATICS. B.A, Wartburg Col, 56; M.S, Iowa State, 58, Ph.D.(math), 60. Res. assoc. MATH, Mathematica, Princeton, N.J, 60; instr, Virginia, 60-62; asst. prof, Univ. Nebr, Lincoln, 62-67; ASSOC. PROF, IOWA STATE UNIV, 67- U.S.A, 52-54. Am. Math. Soc; Math. Asn. Am. Almost periodic functions; ordinary differential equations. Address: Dept. of Mathematics, Iowa State University, Ames, IA 50010.

FINK, AUSTIN I(RA), b. N.Y.C, Nov. 18, 20; m. 56; c. 3. OPHTHALMOLOGY. A.B, Michigan, 41; M.D, L.I. Col. Med, 44. Instr. OPHTHAL, med. col, Cornell, 50-57; asst. prof, COL. MED, STATE UNIV. N.Y. DOWNSTATE MED. CTR, 55-63, ASSOC. PROF, 63- Med.C, 46-48, Capt. Blood vessels of conjunctiva and retina in relation to disease; surgery of congenital cataracts; electron microscopy of Schlemms canal and surrounding structures. Address: Dept. of Ophthalmology, State University of New York Downstate Medical Center, Brooklyn, NY 11203.

FINK, B(ERNARD) RAYMOND, b. London, Eng, May 25, 14; nat; m. 44; c. 2. ANESTHESIOLOGY. B.Sc, London, 35, M.B.B.S, 38. Med. supt, Methodist Mission Hosp, S.Africa, 47-49; instr. anesthesiol, Columbia, 52-54, assoc, 54-56, asst. prof, 56-59, assoc. prof, 59-64; PROF. ANESTHESIOL. & ASST. CHMN. RES, SCH. MED, UNIV. WASH, 64- Fulbright lectr, Turku, 59; Commonwealth Fund fel, Monaco, 63. Assoc. attend. anesthesiologist, Presby. Hosp, New York, 55-64. S.African Med.C, 40-46, Capt. AAAS; Am. Physiol. Soc; Am. Soc. Pharmacol. & Exp. Therapeut; Soc. Toxicol; Soc. Exp. Biol. & Med; Asn. Advan. Med. Instrumentation; Am. Soc. Anesthesiol; Am. Med. Asn; Asn. Univ. Anesthetists. Cellular biology of anesthesia; rapid axoplasmic transport; mechanics of the human larynx. Address: Dept. of Anesthesiology RC-40, University of Washington School of Medicine, Seattle, WA 98195.

FINK, CARL K(EISTER), b. Export, Pa, Feb. 7, 09; m. 38; c. 2. PHYSICAL CHEMISTRY. B.S, Grove City Col, 31; Ph.D.(chem), Virginia, 35. Instr. chem, Virginia, 35-37; from asst. to assoc. prof, Grove City Col, 37-45; res. chemist, Carbide & Carbon Chem. Co, 45-46; indust. fel, Mellon Inst, 46-51, sr. fel, 51-59; asst. dir. res. & develop. dept, Union Carbide Chem. Div, 59-71, MGR. ENVIRON. IMPROV. SERV, CHEM. & PLASTICS, UNION CARBIDE CORP, 71- Am. Chem. Soc. Thermodynamic properties of thallium halides; solvents, plasticizers and resin intermediates with special emphasis on their use in surface coatings applications. Address: Chemicals & Plastics, Union Carbide Corp, 270 Park Ave, 22nd Floor, New York, NY 10017.

FINK, CHESTER W(ALTER), b. N.Y.C, May 6, 28; m. 55; c. 3. PEDIATRICS. B.A, Duke, 47, M.D, 51. Fel. PEDIAT, sch. med, Western Reserve, 56-57; instr, SOUTHWEST MED. SCH, UNIV. TEX, 57-59, asst. prof, 59-64, assoc. prof, 64-71, PROF, 71- Soc. Pediat. Res; Am. Rheumatism Asn. Med.C, 54-56, Capt. Rheumatoid arthritis and allied diseases; endocrinology. Address: Dept. of Pediatrics, Southwestern Medical School, University of Texas, Dallas, TX 75235.

FINK, C(OLLIN) E(THELBERT), b. Columbia, Pa, Aug. 21, 10; m. 48; c. 1. CHEMICAL ENGINEERING. B.S, Pa. State Col, 32; M.S, Mass. Inst. Tech, 33; Ph.D.(chem. eng), Columbia, 44. Prod. engr, cracking dept, Atlantic Ref. Co, 33-36; res. lubricating oils, Pa. State, 36-40; asst. chem. eng, Columbia, 40-44; pilot plant & develop, Am. Cyanamid Co, 44-45; res. & develop. floor coverings, Armstrong Cork Co, 45-46; develop. & prod. cathode ray tubes, Radio Corp. Am, 46-47; assoc. prof. chem. eng, Drexel Inst, 47-51, prof, 51-57; assoc. prof. CHEM, FRANKLIN & MARSHALL COL, 57-66, PROF, 66- AAAS; Am. Chem. Soc; Am. Soc. Eng. Educ; Am. Inst. Chem. Eng. Viscosity-density-pressure characteristics of lubrication oils; binders in activated carbons; pulsating flow of fluids; heart-lung machine for cardiac surgery. Address: Dept. of Chemistry, Franklin & Marshall College, Lancaster, PA 17604.

FINK, DAVID WARREN, b. Brooklyn, N.Y, Mar. 30, 44; m. 67; c. 1. ANALYTICAL CHEMISTRY. B.S, Brooklyn Col, 64; Du Pont fel, Lehigh Univ, 67, Ph.D.(anal. chem), 69. SR. RES. CHEMIST, res. ctr, Lever Bros. Co, Edgewater, 69-71; MERCK & CO, RAHWAY, 71- Am. Chem. Soc. Luminescence of metal chelates; properties of excited states; analytical applications of fluorescence spectroscopy. Address: 31 Ethan Allen Rd, Freehold, NJ 07728.

FINK, D(ELMAR) S(IMON), b. Chicago, Ill, Sept. 17, 07; m. 31; c. 2. AGRONOMY. B.S, Wisconsin, 30, M.S, 31, Ph.D.(soil chem), 34. Asst. biologist, exp. sta, Maine, 34-42; asst. agronomist, Cornell, 43-45; agriculturist, Am. Cyanamid Co, N.Y, 45-51; DIR. RES, WIS. FARMCO SERV. CO-OP, 51- AAAS; assoc. Am. Soc. Agron; assoc. Am. Chem. Soc. Agricultural chemicals in relation to soil fertility and to crop defoliation, top-killing and weed-killing. Address: Wisconsin Farmco Service Co-op, P.O. Box 1149, Madison, WI 53701.

FINK, DON R(OGER), b. Reading, Pa, Apr. 27, 31; m. 52; c. 5. GEOPHYSICS, ELECTRONICS. A.B, Harvard, 52; Sinclair fel, Washington (St. Louis), 53-54, A.M, 54. Asst, geophys. anal. group, Mass. Inst. Tech, 54-56; asst. geophysicist, Woods Hole Oceanog. Inst, 56-59; res. geophysicist, Humble Oil & Ref. Co, 59-63; res. scientist, Melpar, Inc, 63-64, sr. scientist, 64; sr. eng. specialist, Philco Corp, 64-65, proj. mgr, 65-67; sr. eng. specialist, GEN. ATRONICS CORP, 67-70, CHIEF GEOPHYSICIST, MAGNAVOX, 70- Soc. Explor. Geophys; Am. Geophys. Union; Seismol. Soc. Am; Inst. Elec. & Electronics Eng; Asn. Comput. Mach; Marine Tech. Soc. Elastic wave propagation; geomagnetism; oceanography and underwater systems; information theory; computer applications; communication systems; geophysical exploration. Address: General Atronics Corp, 1200 E. Mermaid Lane, Philadelphia, PA 19118.

FINK, DONALD G(LEN), b. Englewood, N.J, Nov. 8, 11; m. 48; c. 3. ELECTRICAL ENGINEERING, ELECTRONICS. B.Sc, Mass. Inst. Tech, 33; M.Sc, Columbia, 42. Asst, Mass. Inst. Tech, 33-34, staff mem, radiation lab, 41-43; asst. ed, McGraw-Hill Pub. Co, 34-37, managing ed, electronics, 37-41, exec. ed, 45-46, ed-in-chief, 46-52; expert consult, Off. Secy. War, 43-45; consult, bur. ships, U.S. Navy, 46; dir. res, PHILCO CORP, 52-61, v.pres, 61; GEN. MGR, INST. ELEC. & ELECTRONICS ENGRS, 62- Consult, TV standards, Belgian Govt, 52-; ed, Standard Handbook for Elec. Engrs, 68-; mem. & consult, Army Sci. Adv. Panel, 57- Medal of Freedom, 46; Presidential Cert. Merit, 48; Outstanding Civilian Serv. Medal, Dept. of the Army, 69. Civilian with U.S.A; U.S.A.A.F, 44. Fel. Inst. Elec. & Electronics Eng.(ed, Proceedings, Inst. Radio Eng, 56-57, pres, 58); fel. Brit. Inst. Elec. Eng; Nat. Acad. Eng. Computer systems; radio and radar navigation systems; pulsed transmitters; television, color systems and standards; semiconductor devices; stereophonic sound systems. Address: 45 Kitchel Rd, Mt. Kisco, NY 10549.

FINK, DONALD LLOYD, b. Chicago, Ill, Sept. 29, 32; m. 57; c. 3. PEDIATRICS. S.B. & A.B, Chicago, 52, M.D, 56. Intern, Moffitt Hosp, San Francisco, 56-57, fel. pediat. allergy, 61-62; res. pediat, Chicago, 57-59; private practice, 62-63; asst. prof. PEDIAT. & AMBULATORY & COMMUNITY MED, UNIV. CALIF, SAN FRANCISCO, 63-68, ASSOC. PROF, 68- Consult, Off. Econ. Opportunity, 65- U.S.N.R, 59-61, Lt. Am. Acad. Pediat; Asn. Am. Med. Cols; Am. Pub. Health Asn. Health services; medical education research and development; community medicine. Address: Dept. of Pediatrics, 694 Moffitt Hosp, University of California, San Francisco, CA 94122.

FINK, DWAYNE H(AROLD), b. Albert Lea, Minn, June 15, 32; m. 60; c. 3. SOIL & SURFACE CHEMISTRY. B.S, Univ. Minn, 60; M.S, Va. Polytech. Inst, 63, Ph.D.(agron), 65. Fel, Univ. Minn, 65-66; SOIL SCIENTIST, U.S. WATER CONSERV. LAB, AGR. RES. SERV, U.S. DEPT. AGR, 69- U.S.A, 52-54. Clay Minerals Soc; Int. Asn. Study Clays; Am. Soc. Agron. Surface chemistry of clay minerals, especially new method for determination of surface area and adsorption of pollutants; reduction of surface energy of natural soils to induce precipitation runoff. Address: U.S. Water Conservation Lab, Agriculture Research Service, U.S. Dept. of Agriculture, 4331 E. Broadway, Phoenix, AZ 85040.

FINK, FRANK HALL, b. Fairfax, Ala, Nov. 24, 30. INORGANIC CHEMISTRY. B.S, Auburn Univ, 53; Ph.D.(chem), Tulane Univ, 66. Asst. prof. CHEM, BIRMINGHAM-SOUTH. COL, 65-70, ASSOC. PROF, 70- U.S.A.F, 53-55, 1st Lt. Am. Chem. Soc. Synthesis of organometallic compounds of the lanthanide series; environmental assessment, especially water quality. Address: Dept. of Chemistry, Birmingham-Southern College, Birmingham, AL 35204.

FINK, FREDERICK C(HARLES), b. N.Y.C, May 22, 23; m. 48; c. 4. MICROBIOLOGY. B.S, Manhattan Col, 44; M.S, Syracuse, 48, fel, 48-51, Ph.D. (microbiol), 51. Instr. microbiol, Syracuse, 47-51; nursing microbiol, Syracuse Gen. Hosp, 48-49; coord, hosp. lab. adv. serv, Chas. Pfizer & Co, Inc, 51-64, mgr. clin. lab. invests, Pfizer Diagnostics Div, 64-67, mgr, new prod. develop. & invest. dept, 67-68, microbiol. serv, 68-71; ASST. PROF. MICROBIOL, INST. HEALTH SCI, HUNTER COL, 71- U.S.N.R, 42-46. Am. Soc. Microbiol; Am. Soc. Prof. Biol; Am. Soc. Med. Technol; Am. Pub. Health Asn; Am. Med. Writers' Asn. Nutrition and physiology of staphylococci; antibiotics, especially microbial susceptibility testing and assay of biological fluids. Address: Hunter College Institute of Health Sciences, 100-118 E. 107th St, New York, NY 10029.

FINK, FREDERICK WILLIAM, b. Newark, N.J, Mar. 27, 12; m. 38; c. 3. CORROSION ENGINEERING. E.E, Cornell, 35; M.Sc, Cambridge, 37. From res. engr. to fel. corrosion res, BATTELLE MEM. INST, 38-70, SR. SCIENTIST, PHYSICS & METALL. SECT, 70- Vis. lectr, Kjeller, Norway, 63; vis. prof, Tech. Univ. Denmark, 64; consult, ord. res. lab, Pa. State Univ, 67; co-chmn. tech. prog, 3rd Int. Conf. Marine Corrosion & Fouling, Wash, D.C, 72. Naval Ord. Award, 46. Am. Soc. Metals; Electrochem. Soc; Nat. Asn. Corrosion Eng.(Speller Award, 64); Am. Inst. Mining, Metall. & Petrol. Eng; fel. Am. Inst. Chem. Marine deterioration; boiler water and steam; sea and saline water; atmospheric corrosion. Address: Columbus Labs, Corrosion Division, Battelle Memorial Institute, Columbus, OH 43201.

FINK, GERALD RALPH, b. Brooklyn, N.Y, July 1, 40; m. 61; c. 2. GENETICS. B.A, Amherst Col, 62; M.S, Yale, 64, Ph.D.(biol), 65. Fel. biochem. genetics, Nat. Insts. Health, 65-67; asst. prof. GENETICS, STATE UNIV.

N.Y. COL. AGR, CORNELL UNIV, 67-71, ASSOC. PROF, 71- Mem. Nat. Sci. Found. adv. panel genetic biol, 70-; mem. summer faculty, Cold Spring Harbor Lab. Genetics Soc. Am.(assoc. ed, jour, 70-). Regulation of gene activity in eucaryotes; control of histidine biosynthesis in yeast. Address: 216 Bradford Hall, Cornell University, Ithaca, NY 14850.

FINK, GREGORY B(URNELL), b. Outlook, Mont, Aug. 3, 28; m. 57; c. 3. PHARMACOLOGY. B.S, Montana State, 50; Ph.D.(pharmacol), Utah, 60. Asst. prof. PHARMACOL, Washington State, 60-63; Kansas, 64; PROF, ORE. STATE UNIV, 64-, head dept, 64-70. Consult, Ore. State Drug. Adv. Coun. U.S.A, 51-52. Am. Pharmaceut. Asn; Am. Soc. Pharmacol. & Exp. Therapeut. Neuropharmacology; psychopharmacology. Address: Dept. of Pharmacology, Oregon State University School of Pharmacy, Corvallis, OR 97331.

FINK, H(ERMAN) J(OSEPH), b. Neutitschein, Czech, Aug. 16, 30; Can. citizen; m. 59; c. 3. SOLID STATE PHYSICS. B.A.Sc, British Columbia, 55, M.A.Sc, 56, Ph.D.(physics), 59. Nat. Res. Coun. Can. fel, Oxford, 59-61; mem. tech. staff parametric amplifiers & magnetic properties solids, Bell Tel. Labs, N.J, 61-63; res. specialist, electronic struct. solids, Atomics Int. Div, N.Am. Aviation, Inc, 63-69; acting prof. ELEC. ENG, UNIV. CALIF, DAVIS, 69-70, PROF, 70- Consult, Stanford Res. Inst, 70- Fel. Am. Phys. Soc. Properties of superconductors, semiconductors at low temperatures and microwave frequencies; resonance properties of magnetic materials. Address: Dept. of Electrical Engineering, University of California, Davis, CA 95616.

FINK, JAMES P(AUL), b. Calumet, Mich, Nov. 10, 40; m. 66; c. 1. MATHEMATICS, PHYSICS. B.S, Drexel Inst, 63; Nat. Sci. Found. fel, Stanford, 63-67, M.S, 65, Ph.D.(math), 67. Eng. technician, Clifton Precision Prod. Co, Inc, 59-62; instr. physics, Drexel Inst, 62-63; math, Stanford, 66-67; ASST. PROF. MATH. & PHYSICS, UNIV. PITTSBURGH, 67- Prof. employee, IBM Corp, summer, 64. Am. Math. Soc; Math. Asn. Am. Quantum field theory; differential equations; functional analysis. Address: Dept. of Mathematics, University of Pittsburgh, Pittsburgh, PA 15213.

FINK, JOEL H, b. New York, N.Y, July 17, 23; m..49; c. 2. PLASMA PHYSICS. B.E.E, Polytech. Inst. Brooklyn, 43; M.E.E, Cornell Univ, 63; Ph.D. (elec. eng), Carnegie-Mellon Univ, 69. ENGR, West. Elec. Co, Inc, 47-49; Sylvania Elec. Prods, Inc, 49-51; WESTINGHOUSE ELEC. CORP, 51- Lectr. elec. eng, Carnegie-Mellon Univ, 69- U.S.A, 43-46. Inst. Elec. & Electronics Eng. Particle beams; electron tubes; atmospheric electron beam welder; diffusion of ions and electrons across the lines of a magnetic field in a gas discharge. Address: 6744 Penn Ave, Pittsburgh, PA 15208.

FINK, JORDAN NORMAN, b. Milwaukee, Wis, Oct. 13, 34; m. 56; c. 3. ALLERGY, IMMUNOLOGY. B.S, Wisconsin, 56, M.D, 59. Asst. instr. sch. med, Marquette, 60-63; Nat. Insts. Health fel. allergy & immunol. & teaching assoc. med. sch, Northwestern, 63-65; instr. MED, MED. COL. WIS, 65-68, asst. prof, 68-70, ASSOC. PROF, 70- Clin. investr, Vet. Admin, 65-68. AAAS; Am. Asn. Immunol; fel. Am. Acad. Allergy. Basic mechanisms in human hypersensitivity, and their diagnosis and treatment. Address: 6550 N. Bethmaur, Milwaukee, WI 53209.

FINK, KATHRYN F(ERGUSON), b. State Center, Iowa, Feb. 13, 17; m. 41; c. 2. BIOCHEMISTRY. B.A, Iowa, 38; Nat. Res. Coun. fel, Rochester, 39-42; Ph.D.(biochem), 43. Res. technician, Mayo Inst. Exp. Med, Minn, 38-39; res. assoc, Manhattan Proj, Rochester, 43-46, Atomic Energy Proj, 46-47; assoc. clin. prof. biophys, sch. med, UNIV. CALIF, LOS ANGELES, 48-63, assoc. prof. res, biophys. & nuclear med, 64-66, prof, 66-67, RESIDENT PROF, DEPT. OF MED, MED. CTR, 67- Res. biochemist, Vet. Admin. Hosp, 47-61. Soc. Exp. Biol. & Med; Am. Soc. Biol. Chem. Intestinal secretion; traumatic shock; biological effects of radiation; thyroid chemistry; amino acids; pyrimidine and purine metabolism. Address: Dept. of Medicine, University of California Medical Center, Los Angeles, CA 90024.

FINK, KENNETH HOWARD, b. Omaha, Nebr, Dec. 11, 14; m. 40; c. 2. CHEMICAL ENGINEERING. B.S, Denver, 36. Analyst, Great West. Sugar Co, 38-39; Wilson & Co, 39-41; Joliet Ord. Works, Army Ord, 41-44, resident inspector, 44-45; res. engr, Podbielniak, Inc, 45-49; res. chemist, food res. div, ARMOUR & CO, 49-54, chief chemist, refinery, 54-56, asst. sect. head fats & oils, FOOD RES. DIV, 56-67, RES. ANALYST, 67- Am. Chem. Soc; Am. Oil Chemists' Soc. Technology of edible fats and oils; food analysis. Address: Food Chemistry Section, Armour & Co, 801 W. 22nd St, Oakbrook, IL 60521.

FINK, L(OYD) KENNETH, JR, b. Canton, Ill, Dec. 26, 36; m. 63; c. 1. MARINE GEOLOGY. B.S, Illinois, 61; Nat. Sci. Found. trainee, Miami (Fla), 66, Ph.D.(marine geol, geophys), 68. Fel. geophys, inst. marine sci, Miami (Fla), 68-69; ASST. PROF, IRA C. DARLING RES. CTR, UNIV. MAINE, 69- U.S.A, 57-59. Geol. Soc. Am; Am. Geophys. Union. Tectonics of seafloor; origin of island arcs. Address: Ira C. Darling Research Center, Walpole, ME 04573.

FINK, LYMAN R, b. Elk Point, S.Dak, Nov. 14, 12; m. 37; c. 3. ELECTRICAL ENGINEERING. B.S, California, Berkeley, 33, M.S, 34, E.E, 35, Ph.D.(elec. eng), 37. Mgr. electronics Lab, Gen. Elec. Co, 47-49, eng, radio & TV dept, 49-55, res. appln. dept, res. lab, 55-57, gen. mgr. x-ray dept, 57-59, atomic prod. div, 59-63, v.pres, 62-63, pres, Gen. Elec. X-ray of Can, 57-59; v.pres, Otis Elevator Co, 63-66, v.pres. & chief tech. off, Singer Co, 66-68, group v.pres, off. equip. group, 68-70; EXEC. V.PRES, CHURCH'S, INC, 70- Chmn. ad hoc comt. digital comput, Res. & Develop. Bd, 49-50; mem. comt. atomic energy, U.S. Chamber Commerce, 59-63; dir, Atomic Indust. Forum, 60-63, v.pres, 63. Fel. Inst. Elec. & Electronics Eng. Administration of engineering and research; television receivers; x-ray and medical electronics; commercial applications of atomic energy; atomic power plants; atomic fuel cycle. Address: 7500 Callaghan Rd, San Antonio, TX 78229.

FINK, MANFRED, b. Berlin, Ger, Aug. 16, 37; m. 64; c. 2. ATOMIC PHYSICS. Vordiplom, Karlsruhe, 58, Diplom, 61, Ph.D, 64. Fel. PHYSICS, Indiana, 65-66, res. assoc, 66-67; faculty assoc, UNIV. TEX, AUSTIN, 67-69, ASST. PROF, 69- Am. Phys. Soc; German Phys. Soc. Electron scattering from gases and numerical evaluation of the scattering theories; biophysics of viruses. Address: Dept. of Physics, University of Texas at Austin, Austin, TX 78712.

FINK, MARTIN RONALD, b. New York, N.Y, Apr. 27, 31; m. 52; c. 3. AERODYNAMICS. S.B, Mass. Inst. Tech, 52, S.M, 53. Engr, transonic aircraft control proj, Mass. Inst. Tech, 52-53; res. engr, RES. LABS, UNITED AIRCRAFT CORP, 53-59, supvr. missile aerodyn, 59-63, aerodyn, 63-68, SR. CONSULT. ENGR, 68- Am. Inst. Aeronaut. & Astronaut; Sci. Res. Soc. Am. Supersonic and hypersonic dynamic stability; hypersonic optimum configurations; supersonic cascades; compressor noise; transonic aerodynamics. Address: 55 Richmond Lane, West Hartford, CT 06117.

FINK, MARY A(LEXANDER), b. Camden, Tenn, Oct. 18, 19; m. 50. MICROBIOLOGY. B.S, Okla. Agr. & Mech. Col, 39; M.S, Michigan, 45; Ph.D.(bact), George Washington, 49. Immunologist, Camp Detrick, 46-49; res. assoc, R.B. Jackson Mem. Lab, 49-51; dept. microbiol, sch. med, Colorado, 51-58; immunologist, NAT. CANCER INST, 59-66, head immunol. sect, viral leukemia & lymphoma br, 66-70, chmn. test. & monitoring segment, spec. virus leukemia prog, 68, immunol-epidemiol. segment, 68-70, PROG. DIR. IMMUNOL, EXTRAMURAL AREA, 70- Am. Asn. Immunol; Soc. Exp. Biol. & Med; Am. Asn. Cancer Res; Brit. Soc. Immunol. Tularemia in humans; immunology and hypersensitivity particularly in mice; immune response to tumors; oncogenic viruses, especially leukemia. Address: 9414 Locust Hill Rd, Bethesda, MD 20014.

FINK, M(AXIMILIAN), b. Vienna, Austria, Jan. 16, 23; nat; m. 49; c. 3. NEUROPSYCHIATRY. B.A, N.Y. Univ, 42, M.D, 45. Supvry. psychiatrist, dept. exp. psychiat, Hillside Hosp, 53-54, dir, 54-62; res. prof. PSYCHIAT, sch. med, Wash. Univ, 62-66, PROF, N.Y. MED. COL, 66-, DIR. DIV. BIOL. PSYCHIAT, 67- Dir, Mo. Inst. Psychiat, 62-65, mem. comt. clin. drug eval, Nat. Inst. Ment. Health, 62-65; prof, Univ. Mo, 65-66. Award, Electroshock Res. Asn, 56. Med.C, Res, 46-47, Capt. Am. Electroencephalog. Soc; Soc. Biol. Psychiat.(Bennett Award, 58); fel. Am. Psychiat. Asn; Am. Psychopath. Asn; Am. Psychol. Asn; Asn. Res. Nerv. & Ment. Disease; Int. Col. Neuropsychopharmacol. Experimental alteration of human behavior by neurophysiologic agents; evaluation of psychiatric therapies; opiate dependence; cannabis research; convulsive therapy; electroencephalography. Address: Division of Biological Psychiatry, New York Medical College, 5 E. 102nd St, New York, NY 10029.

FINK, RICHARD D(AVID), b. New York, N.Y, July 14, 36; m. 61; c. 2. PHYSICAL & NUCLEAR CHEMISTRY. A.B, Harvard, 58; Nat. Sci. Found. & Eastman Kodak Co. fels, Mass. Inst. Tech, 60-61, Nat. Insts. Health fel, 61-62, Ph.D.(nuclear chem), 62; hon. M.A, Amherst Col, 71. Nat. Sci. Found. fel, CHEM, Yale, 62-63, Nat. Insts. Health fel, 63-64; asst. prof, AMHERST COL, 64-67, assoc. prof, 67-71, PROF, 71-, CHMN. DEPT, 70- Lectr, Yale, 62-64; Nat. Sci. Found. sci. faculty fel, King's Col, Univ. London, 68-69; Alfred P. Sloan res. fel, 70-74; Camille & Henry Dreyfus Teacher-Scholar Prize, 71-75. Am. Phys. Soc; Am. Chem. Soc. Physical and nuclear chemistry; chemistry of molecular beams; atomic and molecular interactions; nuclear reactions and fission. Address: Dept. of Chemistry, Amherst College, Amherst, MA 01002.

FINK, RICHARD W(ALTER), b. Detroit, Mich, Jan. 13, 28. NUCLEAR CHEMISTRY, PHYSICS. B.S, Michigan, 48; M.S, California, 49; Ph.D.(chem), Rochester, 53. Res. chemist, radiation lab, California, 48-49; Knolls Atomic Power Lab, 48-50; assoc. prof. chem, Arkansas, 53-61; PROF. physics, Marquette, 61-65; CHEM, GA. INST. TECHNOL, 65- Res. chemist, Los Alamos Sci. Lab, Univ. Calif, summer 51; consult, Phillips Petrol. Co, 57-; vis. prof, Werner Inst. Nuclear Chem, Univ. Uppsala, 59-60; mem staff, Argonne Nat. Lab, 63; vis. prof, Univ. Hamburg, 63-64; consult, Lawrence Radiation Lab, Univ. Calif, 63-; vis. exchange lectr, Yugoslavia, 71. Sigma Xi Award Outstanding Res. Publ, 71. Am. Phys. Soc. Nuclear reactions; fast neutron studies; x-ray fluorescence and Coster-Kronig yields; radioactivity studies and separations. Address: School of Chemistry, Georgia Institute of Technology, Atlanta, GA 30332.

FINK, ROBERT M(ORGAN), b. Greenville, Ill, Sept. 22, 15; m. 41; c. 2. BIOCHEMISTRY. A.B, Illinois, 37; fel, Lehigh, 37-38; fel, Rochester, 38-42, Ph.D.(biochem), 42. Res. assoc. radiol, Rochester, 42-46, sect. chief, Manhattan Dist. proj, 44-47, asst. prof. radiol. & biophys, 46-47; res. biochemist Vet. Admin. Hosp, Long Beach, Calif, 47-54; assoc. clin. prof. BIOL. CHEM, SCH. MED, UNIV. CALIF, LOS ANGELES, 47-54, assoc. prof, 54-63, PROF, 63- Am. Soc. Biol. Chem. Hormone chemistry and physiology; metabolism and health hazards of radioactive substances; thyroid chemistry; protein and nucleic acid metabolism. Address: Dept. of Biological Chemistry, University of California School of Medicine, Los Angeles, CA 90024.

FINK, RODNEY JAMES, b. Oregon, Mo, Apr. 10, 34; m. 58; c. 4. AGRONOMY, WEED SCIENCE. B.S, Missouri, 56, M.S, 61, Ph.D.(field crops), 66. Exten. agronomist, coop. exten. serv, Iowa State, 61-64; instr. field crops, Missouri, 64-66; assoc. prof. agr, Murray State Univ, 66-68, Univ. Found. grant, 66-67; ASSOC. PROF. AGR, WEST. ILL. UNIV, 68- Participant conf, cmt. ed. in agr. & natural resources, Nat. Res. Coun, 67; chmn. resident educ. sect, North Cent. Wood Control Conf. U.S.N, 56-60, Res, 60-, Comdr. AAAS; Weed Sci. Soc. Am; Soil Conserv. Soc. Am. Effectuating new, better and safer methods of controlling weeds in crop and non-crop areas; effects of herbicides on crop species; effects of fertilizer sources on nitrate pollution in soil; factors affecting soil persistence of herbicides. Address: Dept. of Agriculture, Western Illinois University, Macomb, IL 61455.

FINK, THOMAS EDWIN, b. Charleston, W.Va, Aug. 27, 41; m. 65; c. 2. ORGANIC CHEMISTRY. A.B, Cornell, 63; Smith Kline & French fel, Carnegie Inst. Tech, 63-67, Ph.D.(org. chem), 67. RES. CHEMIST, ESSO RES. LABS, 67-68, 70- Med.Serv.C, U.S.A, 68-70, Capt. Am. Chem. Soc. Petrochemicals and medicinal chemicals containing nitrogen and/or sulfur. Address: 12362 Mollylea Dr, Baton Rouge, LA 70815.

FINK, WILLIAM HENRY, b. Marshfield, Wis, Nov. 4, 41; m. 68. PHYSICAL CHEMISTRY. B.S, Wisconsin, 63; M.S, Princeton, 65, Ph.D.(phys. chem), 66. Res. assoc. chem, Princeton, 66-67; NATO res. fel. appl. math, Queen's (Belfast), 67-68; ASST. PROF. CHEM, UNIV. CALIF, DAVIS, 68- Am. Chem. Soc; Am. Phys. Soc. Application of quantum mechanical methods to problems of chemical interest; especially ab initio molecular structure calculations and electron-molecule collisions. Address: Dept. of Chemistry, University of California, Davis, CA 95616.

FINKBEINER, D(ANIEL) T(ALBOT), II, b. Aspinwall, Pa, Oct. 7, 19; m. 45; c. 4. MATHEMATICS. A.B, Washington & Jefferson Col, 41, M.A, 43; Ph.D.(math), Calif. Inst. Tech, 49. Instr. MATH, Washington & Jefferson Col, 41-43; asst, Calif. Inst. Tech, 46-49; instr, Yale, 49-51; assoc. prof, KENYON COL, 51-56, PROF, 56-, acting dean, 56-58. Nat. Sci. Found. fel, Princeton, 58-59; vis. prof, Western Australia, 64; Fulbright lectr, Australia, 69. U.S.N.R, 43-46, Lt. Am. Math. Soc; Math. Asn. Am. Lattice theory; convex sets in abstract linear spaces; linear algebra. Address: Dept. of Mathematics, Kenyon College, Gambier, OH 43022.

FINKBEINER, HERMAN L(AWRENCE), b. Syracuse, N.Y, July 20, 31; m. 54. PHYSICAL & ORGANIC CHEMISTRY. A.B, Park Col, 52; Britton fel, Michigan, 57-58, Int. Bus. Machines Corp. fel, 58-59, Ph.D.(chem), 60. Staff asst. org. chem, Spencer Chem. Co, 53-56; res. scientist, CORP. RES. & DEVELOP, GEN. ELEC. CO, 59-70, MGR. CHEM. SYNTHESIS & PROCESSING OPERS, 70- Am. Chem. Soc. Action of metal ions on organic reactions, especially biological reactions. Address: General Electric Co, P.O. Box 8, Schenectady, NY 12301.

FINKBEINER, JOHN A(RIS), b. Freeport, Pa, Sept. 3, 17; m; c. 2. MEDICINE. B.S, Pittsburgh, 39; M.D, Western Reserve, 42. Asst. med, Harrisburg Polyclin. Hosp, 46-51; ASST. PROF. CLIN. MED, COL. MED, CORNELL UNIV, 56-; CHIEF MED. NEOPLASIA SERV, LENOX HILL HOSP, 65-, ASSOC. PHYSICIAN, 66-, adj. physician, 64-66. Dir. tumor clin, Harrisburg Polyclin. Hosp, 49-51, consult, 53-; clin. asst, Mem. & James Ewing Hosps, 53-55, asst. attend. physician, 55-; assoc, Sloan-Kettering Inst. Cancer Res, 53-62, asst. clinician, 62-65. U.S.A, 44-46. AAAS; Am. Radium Soc; Am. Med. Asn; Am. Fedn. Clin. Res; fel. Am. Col. Physicians; Am. Soc. Cytol; James Ewing Soc; Am. Soc. Clin. Oncol; N.Y. Acad. Med; N.Y. Acad. Sci; Int. Soc. Internal Med. Internal medicine; oncology; Hodgkin's disease and other lymphomas; therapy of advanced breast cancer. Address: 34 E. 67th St, New York, NY 10021.

FINKE, GUENTHER BRUNO, b. Minden, Ger, May 31, 30; m. 57; c. 3. SOLID STATE PHYSICS, METALLURGY. Dipl, Brunswick Tech, 55, Dr. rer. Nat.(semiconductors), 57. Asst. tech. physics, Brunswick Tech, 55-57; magnetic mat, Widia-Factory-Krupp-Essen, Ger, 57-58, asst. dept. head, 58-60; DIR. RES. & DEVELOP, MAGNETIC METALS CO, 60- Inst. Elec. & Electronics Eng; Ger. Phys. Soc. Fuel cells; semiconductors; magnetic alloys. Address: Magnetic Metals Co, 1601 Hylton Rd, Pennsauken, NJ 08110.

FINKE, H(ERMAN) L(OUIS), b. Schenectady, N.Y, May 11, 18; m. 47; c. 3. PHYSICAL CHEMISTRY. B.S, Union Col, 39; M.S, Pa. State Col, 40, Ph.D. (chem), 45. Asst, Pa. State Col, 44-48; phys. chemist, U.S. Bur. Mines, 48-54; pres, World Chem. Co, 54-61; PROJ. LEADER, BARTLESVILLE PETROL. RES. CTR, U.S. DEPT. INTERIOR, 61- AAAS; Am. Chem. Soc. Thermodynamics; calorimetry of petroleum derivatives. Address: 1217 Grandview Rd, Bartlesville, OK 74003.

FINKE, R(EINALD) G(UY), b. San Francisco, Calif, June 10, 28; m. 51; c. 3. PHYSICS. A.B, California, Berkeley, 49, M.A, 51, Ph.D.(nuclear physics), 55. Physicist, linear accelerator, radiation lab, California, Berkeley, 50-54, sr. physicist, exp. hydrodyn. & fast photog, Lawrence Radiation Lab, 54-55, nuclear propulsion, 55-62; MEM. TECH. STAFF, INST. DEFENSE ANAL, 62- Am. Inst. Aeronaut. & Astronaut. Space technology; propulsion; flight mechanics; reactor physics; heat transfer. Address: Institute for Defense Analyses, 400 Army-Navy Dr, Arlington, VA 22202.

FINKEL, ASHER J(OSEPH), b. Chicago, Ill, June 5, 15; m. 43; c. 4. ZOOLOGY, MEDICINE. S.B, Univ. Chicago, 36, Ph.D.(zool), 47, M.D, 48. Asst. zool, Univ. Chicago, 36-42, intern univ. clins, 48-49, asst. med, 50-60, res. assoc, 60-70; DIR. DEPT. ENVIRON, PUB. & OCCUP. HEALTH, AM. MED. ASN, 70- Mem, Nat. Coun. Radiation Protection Sci. Comt. 34, 70-; assoc. biologist, Argonne Nat. Lab, Ill, 48, assoc. physician, 49-55, dir. health div, 55-70. U.S.A, 42-44. Ecol. Soc. Am; Am. Soc. Zool; Radiation Res. Soc; Soc. Exp. Biol. & Med; Soc. Nuclear Med; Am. Med. Asn; Indust. Med. Asn; Am. Acad. Occup. Med; Am. Pub. Health Asn. Radium metabolism; biological aspects of xenon compounds; lipids in mealworm larvae; experimental beryllium poisoning; experimental burns with NaK alloy; biological effects of deuterium; radium toxicity in man. Address: Dept. of Environmental, Public & Occupational Health, American Medical Association, 535 N. Dearborn St, Chicago, IL 60610.

FINKEL, HERMAN J(ACOB), b. Chicago, Ill, Mar. 9, 18; m. 41; c. 2. AGRICULTURAL ENGINEERING. B.S, Illinois, 40; Ph.D, Hebrew Univ, 57. Dairy farm inspector, Health Dept, St. Louis, Mo, 40-41; civil engr, Great Lakes div, Corps Eng, Ill, 41-43; agr. engr. & farm planner, Soil Conserv. Serv, N.Y, 43-46; consult. structural engr, Ill, 46-49; chief engr, soil conserv. serv, Israel Ministry Agr, 49-52; lectr. agr. eng, Israel Inst. Tech, 52-57; expert irrig. adv. to Govt. Peru, Food & Agr. Orgn, UN, 57-59; assoc. prof. agr. eng, ISRAEL INST. TECHNOL, 59-67, prof. & consult. engr, 67-70, V.PRES. ACAD. AFFAIRS, 70- Consult, water dept, Israel Ministry Agr, 56-57; U.N. Spec. Fund Peru, 60. Mem. agr. mission Haute Volta, W.Africa, 61; UNESCO teams ed. planning, Chile, Peru, Trinidad, Jamaica & Brit. Honduras, 64; agr. res, Brit. W.Indies, Thailand & Panama, 62-64; consult. engr, Iran, Uganda, Ivory Coast & Brazil, 70- Am. Soc. Agr. Eng; Soil Conserv. Soc. Am. Irrigation methods and efficiency; soil conservation, especially sand-dune control and economic water utilization; modernization of the traditional Arab village. Address: 42 Einstein St, Haifa, Israel.

FINKEL, LEONARD, b. Brooklyn, N.Y, Jan. 7, 31; m. 49; c. 2. ELECTRONICS. B.S, Rutgers, 52; Nat. Sci. Found. fel. & M.S, Harvard, 53. Test engr, Chelsea Fan & Blower Co, N.J, 51-52; develop. engr, Raymond Rosen Eng. Prod, Pa, 53-56, group supvr, 56-58; sect. mgr, Teledynamics, Inc, 58-60, asst. to chief engr, Tele Dynamics Div, Am. Bosch Arma Corp, Pa, 60-62, chief engr, 62-66, dir. tech. planning, 66-71; PROG. MGR. ADVAN. SYSTS. DEVELOP, RCA MISSILE & SURFACE RADAR DIV, RCA CORP, 71- Inst. Elec. & Electronics Eng. Radio telemetry; instrumentation; communications; air traffic control systems; instrumentation; communications; telemetry. Address: 14 Glen Lane, Cherry Hill, NJ 08034.

FINKEL, MAURICE, b. Philadelphia, Pa, Oct. 16, 20; m. 55; c. 3. BIOLOGY, SCIENCE EDUCATION. B.Sc, Phila. Col. Pharm, 47, M.Sc, 49; M.Ed, Denver, 51, Ed.D, 57. Instr. sci, Brown Mil. Acad, Calif, 51-52; asst. instr. chem, Rutgers, 52-55; prof. sci. ed, Northeast Mo. State Teachers Col, 55-62; prof. sci, Adams State Col, 62-64; asst. prof. natural sci, Mich. State Univ, 64-66; PROF. sci, Cumberland Co. Col, 66-67; BIOL, ADAMS STATE COL, 67- U.S.A, 43-46. AAAS; Science education at secondary level. Address: Dept. of Biology, Adams State College, Alamosa, CO 82804.

FINKEL, MIRIAM P(OSNER), b. Chicago, Ill, Jan. 22, 16; m. 43; c. 4. ONCOLOGY, RADIOBIOLOGY. S.B, Univ. Chicago, 38, Ph.D.(zool), 44. Assoc. biologist, metall. lab, Univ. Chicago, 44-46; ARGONNE NAT. LAB, 46-62, SR. BIOLOGIST, 62- Mem. subcomt, Nat. Coun. Radiation Protection & Measurements; subcomt. internal emitters, Nat. Acad. Sci-Nuclear Res. Coun. Health Physics Soc; Am. Soc. Zool; Soc. Exp. Biol. & Med; Radiation Res. Soc; Am. Soc. Exp. Path; Radiol. Soc. N.Am; Am. Asn. Cancer Res. Toxicity of radionuclides; radio-oncogenesis; viral oncogenesis; experimental pathology. Address: Experimental Radiation Pathology Group, Argonne National Lab, Argonne, IL 60439.

FINKELSTEIN, A(BRAHAM) B(ERNARD), b. New York, N.Y, Feb. 11, 23; m. 47; c. 3. APPLIED MATHEMATICS. B.S, City Col, 43; M.S, N.Y. Univ, 47, Ph.D.(math), 53. Asst. prof. math, Long Island, 48-53; sr. res. assoc. aero eng. & appl. mech, Polytech. Inst. Brooklyn, 53-57; PROF. eng. sci, PRATT INST, 57-64, MATH, 64-, CHMN. DEPT, 66- Consult, East. Res. Group, 55- U.S.A, 43-46. Am. Math. Soc; Math. Asn. Am. Water waves; underwater propulsion systems; transpiration cooling; differential equations. Address: School of Engineering & Science, Pratt Institute, Brooklyn, NY 11205.

FINKELSTEIN, BEATRICE, b. New York, N.Y, Sept. 19, 12. NUTRITION. B.A, Hunter Col, 33; M.Sc, Columbia, 36. Asst. animal nutrit, Columbia, 33-39; teaching fel. nutrit, State Col. Wash, 40-41; instr, Ala. Polytech, 41-46; asst. prof. nutrit. & physiol. chem, sch. nursing, Yale, 46-48; nutrit, Syracuse, 48-52; res. nutritionist, Aerospace Med. Labs, U.S. Air Force, Ohio, 52-62; sr. res. nutritionist, life support dept, Whirlpool Corp, 62-65; assoc. prof. nutrit, Univ. Utah, 65-67; PROF. FOODS & NUTRIT, KANS. STATE UNIV, 67- McLester Award, Asn. Mil. Surgeons, 60; except. civilian serv. award, U.S. Air Force, 61. Am. Dietetic Asn; Inst. Food Technol; fel. Am. Pub. Health Asn; Am. Home Econ. Asn. Development of feeding systems and foods that will fulfill the nutritional needs of astronauts before and during flight of varying duration. Address: College of Home Economics, Kansas State University, Manhattan, KS 66502.

FINKELSTEIN, DAVID, b. Phila, Pa, Apr. 27, 11; m. 39; c. 1. CARDIOLOGY. B.S, Temple Univ, 32, M.D, 35. ASST. CARDIOLOGIST, PHILA. GEN. HOSP, 37-; ASSOC. PROF. CARDIOL, GRAD. SCH. MED, UNIV. PA, 67-, instr, 50-51, assoc. med, 51-52, cardiol, 52-56, asst. prof, 56-67. Chief cardiac clin, St. Lukes & Childrens Hosps, Phila, 47-50; univ. grad. hosps, Univ. Pa, 64- Dipl, Am. Bd. Internal Med. Med.C, 43-46, Capt. Am. Med. Asn; Am. Heart Asn; Am. Col. Physicians; Am. Col. Cardiol. Clinical research in relationship to cardiovascular parameters. Address: Medical Graduate Bldg, Suite 104, 419 S. 19th St, Philadelphia, PA 19146.

FINKELSTEIN, DAVID, b. N.Y.C, July 19, 29; m. 48; c. 3. THEORETICAL PHYSICS. B.S, City Col. New York, 49; fel, Mass. Inst. Tech, 49-50, Ph.D. (physics), 53. Asst. PHYSICS, Mass. Inst. Technol, 50-53; instr, Stevens Inst. Tech, 53-54, asst. prof, 54-56, assoc. prof, 57-60; BELFER GRAD. SCH. SCI, YESHIVA UNIV, 60-64, PROF, 64- Res. assoc, N.Y. Univ, 54-; Ford fel, European Orgn. Nuclear Res, Geneva, 58-59. Consult, Brookhaven Nat. Lab, 57- Am. Phys. Soc; Am. Geophys. Union. Quantum mechanics; general relativity; geophysics. Address: 333 Liberty Rd, Teaneck, NJ 07666.

FINKELSTEIN, FRANCES, b. Jersey City, N.J; m; c. 3. BIOCHEMISTRY, MICROBIOLOGY. A.B, Hunter Col, 40; M.S, St. John's Univ.(N.Y), 63, N.Y. State Regents fel, 65-66, Nat. Insts. Health fel, 66-67, Ph.D.(microbial biochem), 70. Res. asst. biochem, North Shore Hosp, N.Y, 60-62, asst. biochemist, 62-64; res. asst, Nassau Hosp, N.Y, 64-65; ASST. DIR. BIOCHEM, NASSAU COUNTY MED. CTR, 71- AAAS; Am. Chem. Soc; Am. Soc. Microbiol. Microbial biochemistry and genetics. Address: 340 School St, Westbury, NY 11590.

FINKELSTEIN, JACOB, b. New York, N.Y, Oct. 27, 10; m. 45; c. 2. CHEMISTRY. B.S, City Col, 33; A.M, Columbia, 34, Ph.D.(chem), 39. RES. CHEMIST, Res. Corp, New York, 35; Merck & Co, N.J, 35-43; HOFFMANN-LA ROCHE, INC, 43- Mem. faculty, Fairleigh Dickinson Univ. AAAS; fel. Am. Inst. Chem; Am. Chem. Soc. Vitamins; sulfanilamides, antimalarials; contrast media; kidney clearance; synthetic organic chemicals; chemotherapeutics; antihistamines; antispasmodics; analgesics; curare, alkaloidal salts of organic acids for resolution and the use of quaternary hydroxides to resolve optically active substances; vasodilators; hypertension; blood sugar lowering and antiviral agents; tetracyclines; central nervous stimulants; tranquilizers; monamine oxidase inhibitors; anticholesterol drugs; unsaturated fatty and unsaturated amino fatty acids. Address: Chemical Research, Hoffmann-La Roche, Inc, Nutley, NJ 07110.

FINKELSTEIN, JAMES DAVID, b. New York, N.Y, Oct. 16, 33; m. 59; c. 2. INTERNAL MEDICINE, BIOCHEMISTRY. A.B, Harvard, 54; M.D, Columbia, 58. Intern med, Presby. Hosp, New York, 58, asst. res, 59-61; U.S. Pub. Health Serv. trainee gastroenterol, col. physicians & surgeons,

Columbia, 61-63; clin. assoc, Nat. Inst. Arthritis & Metab. Diseases, 63-65; asst. prof. MED, GEORGE WASH. UNIV, 66-69, ASSOC. PROF, 69-; CHIEF BIOCHEM. RES. LAB, VET. ADMIN. HOSP, 68-, GASTROENTEROL. & HEPATOLOGY, 70-, clin. investr, 65-68, med. investr, Vet. Admin, 70. Consult, Childrens Hosp, Wash, D.C, 67- Dipl, Am. Bd. Internal Med, 67; Arthur S. Flemming Award, 71. U.S.P.H.S, 63-65, Surg. AAAS; Am. Fedn. Clin. Res; Am. Gastroenterol. Asn; Am. Inst. Nutrit; Am. Soc. Clin. Nutrit. Sulfur amino acid metabolism; active transport across cell membranes; intestinal malabsorption. Address: Veterans Administration Hospital, 50 Irving St. N.W, Washington, DC 20422.

FINKELSTEIN, MANUEL, b. Scranton, Pa, Oct. 18, 28; m. 58; c. 2. ORGANIC CHEMISTRY. B.S, Scranton, 50; M.A, Williams Col, 52; Nat. Sci. Found. fel, Yale, 52-53, Eastman Kodak fel, 53-54, Sheffield fel, 54-55, Procter & Gamble summer fel, 54-55, Ph.D.(chem), 56; Fulbright scholar, Karlsruhe, Germany, 55-56. Asst. chem, Williams Col, 50-52; sr. engr. org. chem. res, SPRAGUE ELEC. CO, 56-62, SR. RES. SCIENTIST, 62- Vis. instr, Williams Col, 57-61, 68- Am. Chem. Soc; The Chem. Soc. Organic electrochemistry; organic synthesis; reaction mechanisms. Address: 4 Birchwood Terrace, North Adams, MA 01247.

FINKELSTEIN, MARK, b. New York, N.Y, Aug. 28, 39; m. 60; c. 2. MATHEMATICS. A.B, Cornell, 60; M.S, Stanford, 64, Ph.D.(math), 66. Mathematician, Nat. Security Agency, 60-62; Lawrence Radiation Lab, 62-63; sr. systs. analyst, Control Data Corp, 65; asst. prof. MATH, UNIV. CALIF, IRVINE, 66-70, ASSOC. PROF, 70- Sig.C, U.S.A, 57-58. Am. Math. Soc. Convex analytic functions; vector-valued functions; recursion theory. Address: 456 Cabrillo Terr, Corona Del Mar, CA 92625.

FINKELSTEIN, NISSON A(SCHER), b. Milton, Mass, June 11, 25; m. 50; c. 2. PHYSICAL OPTICS, SPECTROSCOPY. A.B, Harvard, 45; fel, Mass. Inst. Tech, 47-49, Ph.D.(physics), 49. Radar field engr, Navy Bur. Ships, 45; asst. elec. eng, Mass. Inst. Tech, 46-47, res. assoc, 49-50; res. physicist spectros, Bausch & Lomb Optical Co, 50-51, head spec. res. dept, 51-54, asst. dir. sci. bur, 54-59; asst. v.pres. & dir. res, Stromberg-Carlson Div, Gen. Dynamics/Electronics, 61-64; v.pres. & gen. mgr. govt. & indust. div, INT. LATEX CORP, 64-66, PRES. & MEM. BD. DIR, ILC INDUSTS, INC, & MEM. BD. DIR. CORP, 66- Lectr, inst. optics, Rochester, 55-; acting gen. mgr. Gen. Dynamics/Electronics, 62-63; v.pres. res. & develop, Glen Alden Corp, 68- AAAS; Acoust. Soc. Am; Inst. Elec. & Electronics Eng; Optical Soc. Am; Am. Phys. Soc; Opers. Res. Soc. Am; Am. Ord. Asn; Am. Asn. Physics Teachers. Scientific instrumentation; physical optics; application of digital computers to scientific and management calculation; electronics; administration of research and engineering; industrial general management. Address: ILC Industries, Inc, 1200 Philadelphia Pike, Wilmington, DE 19809.

FINKELSTEIN, PAUL, b. N.Y.C, Nov. 20, 22; m. 55; c. 2. BIOCHEMISTRY. B.A, Brooklyn Col, 43; Ph.D.(chem), Polytech. Inst. Brooklyn, 49. Fel, Chicago, 49-50; res. assoc, Ohio State, 50-51; res. biochemist, U.S. Naval Med. Res, 51-52; assoc. dir. res, Toni Co. Div, Gillette Co, 52-64, lab. dir, Gillette Med. Res. Inst, 64-68; DIR. CLIN. DERMAT, CARTER PROD. RES. DIV, CARTER-WALLACE, INC, 68- U.S.N.R, 43-46. Am. Chem. Soc; Soc. Cosmetic Chem; Soc. Invest. Dermat; Am. Soc. Clin. Pharmacol. & Therapeut. Photochemistry of proteins; biochemical effects of radiation; protein isolation and characterization; structure and functions of skin; clinical dermatological evaluations; pharmacology; toxicology. Address: 10 Springwood Dr, Princeton Junction, NJ 08550.

FINKELSTEIN, RICHARD A(LAN), b. New York, N.Y, Mar. 5, 30; m. 52; c. 3. MICROBIOLOGY. B.S, Oklahoma, 50; fel, Univ. Tex, 50-52, M.A, 52, Ph.D. (bact), 55. Res. scientist, Univ. Tex, 52-55, fel. microbiol, med. sch, Dallas, 55-58, instr, 58; chief bio-assay sect, div. commun. disease & immunol, Walter Reed Army Inst. Res, 58-67; ASSOC. PROF. MICROBIOL, SOUTHWEST. MED. COL, UNIV. TEX, 67- Dep. chief & chief dept. bact. & immunol, med. res. lab, SEATO, Thailand, 64-67; vis. assoc. prof, faculty grad. studies, Univ. Med. Sci, Bangkok, 64-67; mem, Nat. Comt. Cholera Res, Thailand, 64-67; consult, WHO; mem, Nat. Insts. Health Cholera Adv. Comt, 71- Cert. outstanding achievement, U.S. Army Sci. Conf, 64; dipl, Am. Bd. Med. Microbiol. Med.Serv.C.Res, 50-66, Maj. Am. Soc. Microbiol; Soc. Exp. Biol. & Med; Am. Asn. Immunol; N.Y. Acad. Sci. Pathogenesis and immunology of cholera; enteric diseases. Address: Dept. of Microbiology, University of Texas Medical School, 5323 Harry Hines Blvd, Dallas, TX 75235.

FINKELSTEIN, ROBERT JAY, b. Pittsfield, Mass, Mar. 26, 16. PHYSICS. B.A, Dartmouth Col, 37; Ph.D.(physics), Harvard, 41. Theoret. physicist, bur. ord, U.S. Navy Dept, 41-46; Argonne Nat. Lab, 46-47; fel, Inst. Adv. Study, 47-48; Calif. Inst. Tech, 48-49; asst. prof. PHYSICS, UNIV. CALIF, LOS ANGELES, 49-51, assoc. prof, 51-57, PROF, 57- Quantum theory; elementary particle theory. Address: Dept. of Physics, University of California, Los Angeles, CA 90024.

FINKENSTAEDT, JOHN T(URNER), b. Bay City, Mich, Apr. 16, 20; m. 43. MEDICINE, BIOCHEMISTRY. B.A, Williams Col.(Mass), 43; M.D, Harvard Med. Sch, 46; Ph.D.(biochem), Harvard, 50. Intern med, Mass. Gen. Hosp, Boston, Mass, 46-47, asst. resident, 47-48, resident, 49-50; res. fel, Harvard Med. Sch, 50-52, instr, 52-55; asst. prof. biochem. & med, Yale, 55-57; biochem, col. med. State Univ. N.Y. Downstate Med. Ctr, 57-60; assoc. prof. anat, med. col, Cornell, 60-67; ASSOC. DIR, LIFE EXTEN. INST, 67- Asst, Peter Bent Brigham Hosp, Boston, Mass, 50-53, jr. assoc, 53-55; investigator, Howard Hughes Med. Inst, 55-60; guest investr, Rockefeller Inst, 63-67. Dipl, Am. Bd. Internal Med, 55. U.S.A, 42-46, Res, 46-, 1st Lt. Am. Soc. Biol. Chem; Am. Soc. Clin. Invest; Harvey Soc; Am. Fedn. Clin. Res; N.Y. Acad. Sci. Structure and function of the intra-cellular proteolytic enzymes and certain specific inhibitors for these enzymes; subcellular structure, especially a correlation of structure and function. Address: 250 E. 32nd St, New York, NY 11226.

FINKLE, ALEX L, b. Paterson, N.J, May 31, 20; m. 53; c. 4. UROLOGY. A.B, Indiana, 41; M.A, California, 42, Ph.D.(physiol), 44, M.D, 46. Instr. UROL, Columbia, 53-54; asst. clin. prof, SCH. MED, UNIV. CALIF, 54-61, ASSOC. CLIN. PROF, 61- Med.C, 47-48, Lt.(jg). Mechanisms of renal failure; early detection and radical surgical treatment of prostatic cancer; renal physiology; sexual potency in men. Address: University of California School of Medicine, San Francisco, CA 94122.

FINKLE, BERNARD J(OSEPH), b. Chicago, Ill, Mar. 17, 21; m. 44; c. 2. PLANT BIOCHEMISTRY. B.S, Chicago, 42; Nat. Insts. Health fel, California, Los Angeles, 48-49, Ph.D.(plant biochem), 50. Chemist, Manhattan Proj, Univ. Chicago & Oak Ridge Nat. Lab, 43-46; Atomic Energy Comn. fel, Molteno Inst, Eng, 50; biochemist, California, 51-53; lab. dir, Atomic Res. Lab, 53-54; biochemist, Utah, 54-57; CHEMIST, FRUIT LAB, U.S. DEPT. AGR, 57- Fel, U.S-Japan Coop. Sci. Prog, Dept. Med. Chem, Kyoto, 66-67; adj. assoc. prof, dept. nutrit. sci, Univ. Calif, Berkeley, 71- Am. Soc. Biol. Chem; Phytochem. Soc. N.Am.(v.pres, 64-65, pres, 65-66); Am. Soc. Plant Physiol; Am. Chem. Soc. Biosynthesis and metabolism of phenolic acids, especially ascorbate and oxalate; factors in tissue freezing damage; thiol groups of papain; chlorophyll biogenesis; culture of green algae. Address: Fruit Lab, U.S. Dept. of Agriculture, Berkeley, CA 94710.

FINKLER, PAUL, b. Brooklyn, N.Y, Nov. 29, 36; m. 65; c. 1. PARTICLE & NUCLEAR PHYSICS. B.S, Brooklyn Col, 58; Nat. Sci. Found. fel, Purdue Univ, 61, Ph.D.(physics), 63. Res. appointee theoret. physics, Lawrence Radiation Lab, Univ. Calif, 63-65; ASST. PROF. PHYSICS, UNIV. NEBR, LINCOLN, 65- Am. Phys. Soc. High energy physics; dispersion relations; Regge pole theory; high energy phenomenology; electromagnetic interactions of particles. Address: Dept. of Physics, University of Nebraska, Lincoln, NE 68508.

FINKNER, A(LVA) L(EROY), Statist, see 12th ed, Soc. & Behav. Vols.

FINKNER, MORRIS D(ALE), b. Akron, Colo, Feb. 11, 21; m. 49; c. 2. BIOMETRY. B.S, Colo. Agr. & Mech. Col, 43; M.S, Kans. State Col, 47; Ph.D. (agron), N.C. State Col, 52. Asst. prof. forage crops, Miss. State Col, 47-49; asst. cotton breeding, N.C. State Col, 49-52; asst. prof. exp. statist, N.Mex. Agr. & Mech. Col, 52-55; biometrician, agr. res. serv, U.S. Dept. Agr, Md, 56-58, assoc. prof. EXP. STATIST, N.MEX. STATE UNIV, 58-64, PROF, 64-70, HEAD DEPT, 70-, DIR, UNIV. STATIST. CTR, 70- U.S.A, 43-46, Capt. Am. Soc. Agron; Biomet. Soc; Crop Sci. Soc. Am; Am. Statist. Asn. Design and analysis of experiments; data processing; climatology; plant breeding. Address: Dept. of Experimental Statistics, Box 3130, New Mexico State University, Las Cruces, NM 88001.

FINKNER, R(ALPH) E(UGENE), b. Akron, Colo, March 24, 25; m. 50; c. 3. PLANT BREEDING. B.S, Colorado State, 50; M.S, Iowa State Col, 52; Ph.D. (plant breeding, path), 53. Asst. agron, Iowa State Col, 50-53; plant breeder, Am. Crystal Sugar Co, 53-55, chief plant breeder, 55-56, res. sta. mgr, 56-66; SUPT. & PROF. AGRON, PLAINS BR. STA, N.MEX. STATE UNIV, 66- U.S. Agency Int. Develop. consult, Paraguay, 70, Turkey, 71. U.S.N, 45-46, Res, 46-50. Am. Soc. Sugar Beet Technol.(dir, 60-61, 66-67); Crop Sci. Soc. Am; Am. Soc. Agron. Development of improved beet varieties; development of high yielding, high protein grain sorghum hybrids. Address: Plains Branch Experiment Station, New Mexico State University, Star Rt, Clovis, NM 88101.

FINKNER, VERNE C(LIFFORD), b. Akron, Colo, Dec. 23, 22; m. 47; c. 3. BIOLOGY, PLANT BREEDING. B.S, Col. Agr. & Mech. Col, 47; M.S, Kansas State Col, 48; Ph.D.(plant breeding), Iowa State Col, 50. Asst. prof. PLANT BREEDING & CROP PROD, Ohio State, 50-54; assoc. prof, UNIV. KY, 54-63, PROF, 63- Assoc. prof, N.C. State Univ, 61-63. U.S.N.R, 42-46, Lt.(jg). Am. Soc. Agron. Small grain breeding. Address: Dept. of Agronomy, University of Kentucky, Lexington, KY 40506.

FINKS, A(BRAHAM) J(OSEPH), b. Providence, R.I, Oct. 13, 90; m. 21; c. 1. ANALYTICAL CHEMISTRY. B.S, George Washington, 17. Organic chemist, U.S. Dept. Agr, 16-22; asst. chemist, N.Y. Naval Shipyard, 31-43, assoc. chemist, 43-46, supvry. gen. chemist, 46-60; chemist, N.Y. Testing Labs, Inc, 60-66; RETIRED. Am. Chem. Soc. Fuels and lubricants; hydraulic fluids; organic protective coatings; industrial water utilization; vegetable protein. Address: 29-10 137th St, Flushing, NY 11354.

FINKS, ROBERT M(ELVIN), b. Portland, Maine, May 12, 27. INVERTEBRATE PALEONTOLOGY, GEOLOGY. B.S, Queens Col.(N.Y), 47; M.A, Columbia, 54, Ph.D.(geol), 59. Asst. zool, Columbia, 47-48, curatorial asst. paleontol, 48-49; lectr. GEOL, Hofstra Col, 49-50; asst. instr, Rutgers, 50-54; lectr, Brooklyn Col, 55-58, instr, 59-61; lectr, QUEENS COL.(N.Y), 61-62, asst. prof, 62-65, assoc. prof, 66-70, PROF, 71- Summer asst, Columbia Univ, 51; lectr, Hunter Col, 52-54; geologist, U.S. Geol. Surv, 52-54, 63-; mus. aide, Smithsonian Inst, 56-57; res. assoc, Am. Mus. Nat. Hist, 61-; vis. prof, Syracuse Univ, 62; Univ. Wyoming, 65; res. assoc. Smithsonian Inst, 68- Fel. AAAS; fel. Geol. Soc. Am; Brit. Palaeont. Asn; Brit. Palaeontograph. Soc; Paleont. Soc; Soc. Syst. Zool. Fossil sponges; paleoecology; biostratigraphy; evolution of ecosystems; Paleozoic corals. Address: 67 Remsen St, Brooklyn, NY 11201.

FINLAND, M(AXWELL), b. Russia, Mar. 15, 02; nat. INFECTIOUS DISEASE. B.S, Harvard, 22, M.D, 26; hon. D.Sc, Western Reserve, 64. Asst. res. physician, Boston Sanitarium, 26-27; med. house off, 2nd med. serv, Boston City Hosp, 27-28; Folsom fel, HARVARD MED. SCH, 28-29, asst, 29-32, Peabody fel, 32-37, instr, 35-37, assoc. med, 37-40, asst. prof, 40-46, assoc. prof, 46-62, prof, 62-63, George Richards Minot Prof, 63-68, EMER. PROF, 68- Res. physician, 2nd med. serv. & pneumonia patients, Boston City Hosp, 28-29, asst. physics, 28-38, jr. vis. physician, 38-54, chief, 4th med. serv, 39-63, dir. 2nd & 4th med. servs, 63-, asst. res. physician, Thorndike Mem. Lab, 29-32, asst. physician, 32-41, assoc. physician, 41-46, assoc. dir, 46-63, dir, 63-68, hon. physician & epidemiologist, 68-; vis. physician, Pondville Hosp, Wrentham, 33-57. Mem. subcmt. infectious diseases, Nat. Res. Coun, 46-58, drug res. bd, Nat. Acad. Sci, 64-71. Chapin Award, 65; Bristol Award, 66, Modern Medicine Award, 69; John Phillips Mem. Award, Oscar B. Hunter Award & Sheen Award, 71. AAAS; Am. Soc. Clin. Invest.(v.pres, 47); Am. Soc. Microbiol; Soc. Exp. Biol. & Med; Am. Epidemiol. Soc; fel. Am. Med. Asn; Am. Asn. Immunol; master Am. Col. Physicians;

Asn. Am. Physicians; fel. Am. Acad. Arts & Sci; N.Y. Acad. Sci; Infectious Diseases Soc. Am.(pres, 64). Clinical and laboratory investigations of infectious diseases, including chemotherapy and antibiotics. Address: Boston City Hospital, 818 Harrison Ave, Boston, MA 02118.

FINLAY, ALEX(ANDER), b. Marquette, Mich, May 29, 25; m. 46; c. 2. ELECTRICAL ENGINEERING. B.S.E.E, Michigan, 46; Pittsburgh. Develop. engr, Union Switch & Signal Co, 46-53; prin. elec. engr, Battelle Mem. Inst, 53-54, asst. div. chief, 54-57, div. chief elec. eng, 57-61; mem. staff, SANGAMO ELEC. CO, 61-63, asst. v.pres. & dir. electronic apparatus eng, 63-68, V.PRES. & DIR. ENG, 68- U.S.N, 43-46, Lt.(jg). Sonar and underwater acoustics; magnetic tape recording; instrumentation and control of industrial processes; new product development in electrical and electronic industries; fundamental research in materials and devices for electronic or electrical uses. Address: Sangamo Electric Co, 11th & Converse Sts, Springfield, IL 62705.

FINLAY, GORDON R(OY), b. Innisfail, Alta, Oct. 24, 13; m. 53. INORGANIC CHEMISTRY. B.Sc, Alberta, 38, Tegler fel, 38-39, M.Sc, 39; Ph.D.(inorg. chem), Cornell, 42. Asst. chem, Cornell, 39-42; res. chemist, Norton Co, 42-55, sect. head, 55-57, asst. dir. res, 57-66, res. assoc, 66-68; SR. DEMONSTR, DEPT. CHEM, BROCK UNIV, 68- AAAS; Am. Chem. Soc; Am. Ceramic Soc; Mineral. Soc. Am; Nat. Inst. Ceramic Eng; fel. Chem. Inst. Can. Boron compounds; high temperature materials; boron trifluoride complexes. Address: Dept. of Chemistry, Brock University, St. Catharines, Ont, Can.

FINLAY, J(OSEPH) B(URTON), b. Collins, Ohio, Sept. 15, 21; m. 42; c. 2. ORGANIC CHEMISTRY. B.A, Bowling Green State, 43; Kent State; Ph.D. (org. chem), North Carolina, 52. Instr. chem, Bowling Green State, 46-48; CHEMIST, E.I. DU PONT DE NEMOURS & CO, INC, 51- U.S.N.R, 44-46, Lt.(jg). AAAS; Am. Chem. Soc. Elastomeric materials. Address: 1229 Lakewood Dr, Wilmington, DE 19803.

FINLAY, PETER S(TEVENSON), b. Montclair, N.J, Oct. 12, 24; m. 56; c. 3. ZOOLOGY. B.A, Williams Col.(Mass), 49; M.S, Vermont, 53; Ph.D.(zool), Syracuse, 57. Assoc. prof. BIOL, ALFRED UNIV, 56-70, PROF, 70- U.S.N, 43-46, Res, 46- Soc. Protozool; Am. Soc. Parasitol; Am. Soc. Zool. Red cell parasites of amphibia. Address: Dept. of Biology, Alfred University, Alfred, NY 14802.

FINLAY, ROGER W, b. Pittsburgh, Pa, Oct. 22, 35; m. 56; c. 2. NUCLEAR PHYSICS. A.B, Hopkins, 57, Gilman fel, 57-60, Ph.D.(physics), 62. Asst, Hopkins, 60-62; asst. prof. PHYSICS, OHIO UNIV, 62-65, assoc. prof, 65-69, PROF, 69- Vis. scientist, Max Planck Inst. Nuclear Physics, Heidelberg, 68-69. Am. Phys. Soc. Nuclear structure and nuclear reaction mechanisms; nuclear radiation detectors. Address: Dept. of Physics, Ohio University, Athens, OH 45701.

FINLAY, WALTER L(EONARD), b. Brooklyn, N.Y, Mar. 20, 13; m. 37; c. 2. PHYSICAL METALLURGY. B.S, Lehigh, 36; M.Sc, Yale, 47, D.Eng, 48. Supvr. chem. & metall. res, Remington Arms Co, 39-51; res. mgr, Rem-Cru Titanium, Inc, 51-55, v.pres. res, 54-58; dir. res. Crucible Steel Co. Am, 58-62, asst. v.pres. adv. tech, 62-65; asst. v.pres. res, COPPER RANGE CO, 65-67, dir. res, 67-70, V.PRES. RES. & DEVELOP, 70- Chmn. mat. adv. bd, Nat. Acad. Sci. Am. Soc. Metals; Electrochem. Soc; Am. Inst. Mining, Metall. & Petrol. Eng; Brit. Inst. Metals; Brit. Iron & Steel Inst. Small arms ballistics; titanium; steels; refractory metals. Address: Copper Range Co, 630 Fifth Ave, New York, NY 10020.

FINLAYSON, BIRDWELL, b. Pocatello, Idaho, Oct. 28, 32; m. 55; c. 2. UROLOGY, BIOPHYSICS. Idaho State Col, 50-51; Utah, 51-53; M.D, Chicago, 57, U.S. Pub. Health Serv. fels, 61-67, Ph.D.(biophys), 67. Intern, Chicago, 57-58, res. UROL, 58-63; asst. prof, UNIV. FLA, 67-70, ASSOC. PROF, 70- Urolithiasis; rapid reaction kinetics of actomyosin. Address: Division of Urology, University of Florida School of Medicine, Gainesville, FL 32601.

FINLAYSON, BRUCE ALAN, b. Waterloo, Iowa, July 18, 39; m. 61; c. 3. CHEMICAL ENGINEERING. B.A, Rice, 61, M.S, 63; Nat. Sci. Found. fel, Minnesota, 62-65, Ph.D.(chem. eng), 65. Proj. officer appl. physics, Off. Naval Res, 65-67; ASST. PROF. CHEM. ENG, UNIV. WASH, 67- U.S.N.R, 65-67, Lt. AAAS; Am. Inst. Chem. Eng; Am. Phys. Soc; Am. Chem. Soc. Fluid mechanics; convective instability; approximate and variational methods of analysis; nucleate boiling. Address: Dept. of Chemical Engineering, University of Washington, Seattle, WA 98105.

FINLAYSON, D(OUGLAS) G(ORDON), b. Winnipeg, Man, Dec. 27, 18; m. 43; c. 3. ENTOMOLOGY. B.A, British Columbia, 48, M.A, 50; Nat. Res. Coun, Can. fel, Western Ontario, 51, 52; Ph.D, 65. Tech. off, RES. DIV. ENTOM, CAN. DEPT. AGR, 49-51, asst. entomologist, 51-56, assoc. entomologist, 56-60, ENTOMOLOGIST, 60- R.C.A.F, 40-45. Am. Entom. Soc; Brit. Asn. Appl. Biol; Entom. Soc. Can. Chemical control of field crop insects; effects of soil on longevity of insecticides. Address: Research Station, Canada Dept. of Agriculture, 6660 N.W. Marine Dr, Vancouver 8, B.C, Can.

FINLAYSON, FRANK S(TANLEY), b. Worcester, Mass, Nov. 6, 08; m. 35; c. 3. MECHANICAL ENGINEERING. B.S, Worcester Polytech, 31, M.S, 45. Instr. MECH. ENG, WORCESTER POLYTECH. INST, 37-43, asst. prof, 43-47, assoc. prof, 47-58, PROF, 58- Instr, Massachusetts, 40-41; Worcester Jr. Col, 41-44; res. engr, Alden Res. Labs, 46-51; CONSULT, 51- Am. Soc. Mech. Eng; Am. Soc. Eng. Educ. Machine design; fluid mechanics; hydraulic machinery. Address: 24 Juniper Rd, Worcester, MA 01602.

FINLAYSON, HENRY C, b. Vulcan, Alta, July 5, 30; m. 57; c. 3. MATHEMATICAL ANALYSIS. B.Sc, Alberta, 52, M.Sc, 54; Ph.D.(math), Minnesota, 64. Lectr. MATH, Alberta, 54-55; UNIV. MAN, 56-62, asst. prof, 62-69, ASSOC. PROF, 69- Math. Asn. Am; Am. Math. Soc. Integration in function space. Address: Faculty of Mathematics, University of Manitoba, Winnipeg, Man, Can.

FINLAYSON, JAMES B(RUCE), b. Montrose, Colo, July 3, 37; m. 70. ANALYTICAL CHEMISTRY, GEOCHEMISTRY. B.A, Univ. Ore, 59; M.S, La. State Univ, Baton Rouge, 62; Ph.D.(anal. chem), Univ. Hawaii, 67. Scientist, chem. div, Dept. Sci. & Indust. Res, N.Z. Govt, 67-70; ASST. PROF. CHEM, HILO COL, UNIV. HAWAII, 70- Am. Chem. Soc. Volcano chemistry; volcanic gases and volatiles; gas analysis by gas chromatography, geothermal chemistry; trace methods of analysis; water analysis, especially trace metals in natural waters. Address: Dept. of Chemistry, University of Hawaii, Hilo College, P.O. Box 1357, Hilo, HI 96720.

FINLAYSON, JOHN S(YLVESTER), b. Philadelphia, Pa, Sept. 19, 33; m. 57; c. 2. BIOCHEMISTRY. B.A, Marietta Col, 53; M.S, Wisconsin, 55, Nat. Cancer Inst. fel, 55-57, Ph.D.(biochem), 57. Wisconsin Alumni Res. Found. asst, 53-55; Nat. Cancer Inst. fel, Inst. Radiophysics, Stockholm, Sweden, 57-58; BIOCHEMIST, LAB. BLOOD & BLOOD PROD, DIV. BIOL. STANDARDS, NAT. INSTS. HEALTH, 58- Mem. adv. comt. gamma globulins, Comn. Plasma Fractionation. U.S.P.H.S, 58-61, Sr. Asst. Scientist. Soc. Exp. Biol. & Med; Int. Soc. Thrombosis & Haemostasis. Plasma and urine proteins; coagulation. Address: Lab. Blood & Blood Products, Division of Biologics Standards, National Institutes of Health, Bethesda, MD 20014.

FINLEY, A(RTHUR) M(ARION), b. La Monte, Mo, April 15, 18; m. 43; c. 6. PLANT PATHOLOGY. B.S, Missouri, 41, M.A, 48, Ph.D.(plant path), 50. Asst. plant pathologist, UNIV. IDAHO, 50-54, assoc. plant pathologist & assoc. prof. PLANT PATH, 54-55, PLANT PATHOLOGIST & PROF, 55-, HEAD DEPT. PLANT SCI, 63-, plant path, 55-63. Qm.C, U.S.A, 42-46. Am. Phytopath. Soc. Diseases of vegetable crops; soil borne pathogenic organisms. Address: Dept. of Plant Sciences, University of Idaho, Moscow, ID 83843.

FINLEY, DAVID EMANUEL, b. Springfield, Ill, July 23, 35; m. 60; c. 2. BIOLOGY, BOTANY. B.S, Western Illinois, 62, M.S, 64; Ph.D.(bot), Illinois, 67. Teaching asst. bot, Illinois, Urbana, 63-67; ASSOC. PROF. BIOL, LINCOLN UNIV.(MO), 67- U.S.A.F, 54-57. Mycol. Soc. Am; Bot. Soc. Am; Am. Inst. Biol. Sci. Taxonomy of the Stilbellaceae; fungal cytology. Address: Dept. of Biology, Lincoln University, Jefferson City, MO 65101.

FINLEY, EMMETT ATKINS, b. Dyersburg, Tenn, June 28, 16; m. 41; c. 2. GEOLOGY. Univ. Tennessee, 36-40. Jr. geologist, Tenn. Valley Authority, 39-43; geologist, Magnolia Petrol. Co, 43-46; Creole Petrol. Corp, 46-48; U.S. GEOL. SURV, 49-54, regional geologist, 54-63, CHIEF BR. MINERAL CLASSIFICATION, 63- Am. Asn. Petrol. Geol; fel. Geol. Soc. Am; Am. Inst. Prof. Geol. Geologic classification of federal lands, primarily for the mineral fuels and mineral fertilizers. Address: U.S. Geological Survey, 3232 General Services Bldg, Washington, DC 20242.

FINLEY, HAROLD E(UGENE), b. Palatka, Fla, Nov. 30, 05; m. 30; c. 2. PROTOZOOLOGY. B.S, Morehouse Col, 28; M.S, Wisconsin, 29, Ph.D.(zool), 42. From instr. to assoc. prof. ZOOL, W.Va. State Col, 29-38; prof. & head dept, Morehouse Col, 38-47; PROF, ATLANTA, 38-47; HOWARD UNIV, 47-, head dept, 47-69. Vis. prof, Univ. Wash, summers 68 & 70. AAAS; Am. Soc. Zool; Electron Micros. Soc. Am; Soc. Protozool.(v.pres, 63-64, pres, 66-67); Nat. Inst. Sci; N.Y. Acad. Sci; Am. Micros. Soc.(pres, 71). Cytology, physiology and taxonomy of ciliates; radiation biology and electron microscopy; ciliates. Address: Dept. of Zoology, Howard University, Washington, DC 20001.

FINLEY, HOWARD F(ARRAR), b. Winnfield, La, June 29, 29; m. 56; c. 4. PHYSICAL CHEMISTRY. B.S, Northwest. State Col.(La), 49; Ph.D.(phys. chem), Texas, 58. Res. chemist, Defense Res. Lab, 50-51 & 55-58; corrosion engr, Creole Petrol. Corp, 58-60, supvr. corrosion sect, 60-61, tech. serv, 61-63, gen. eng, 63-64, coordinator opers. anal, 64-67; PRES, HOWARD FINLEY CORP, 67- U.S.N.R, 51-54, Res, 47-51, 54-67, Lt. Comdr. Inst. Mgt. Sci; Nat. Asn. Corrosion Eng; Soc. Petrol. Eng; Am. Chem. Soc. Applied mathematics; optimization theory; reliability theory; corrosion; surface phenomena; adsorption. Address: Howard Finley Corp, 6400 Westpark Dr, Houston, TX 77027.

FINLEY, JAMES DANIEL, III, b. Louisville, Ky, Aug. 2, 41; m. 62. THEORETICAL & HIGH ENERGY PHYSICS. B.S. & B.A, Texas, Austin, 63; Leeds & Northrup fel, California, Berkeley, 63-66, Ph.D.(physics), 68. ASST. PROF. PHYSICS, UNIV. N.MEX, 68- General relativity; theoretical high energy physics; scattering theory. Address: Dept. of Physics & Astronomy, University of New Mexico, 800 Yale Blvd. N.E, Albuquerque, NM 87106.

FINLEY, JAMES J(ASON), b. Carterville, Ill, Apr. 4, 17; m. 40; c. 4. ELECTROCHEMICAL ENGINEERING. B.Ed, Southern Illinois, 39. Chemist, Westvaco Chlorine Prods, 40-43; assoc. res. chemist, UNION CARBIDE CORP, nuclear div, 45-55, develop. engr, metals div, 55-63, carbon prod. div, nuclear prod. dept, 63-68, PROD. ENGR, NUCLEAR DIV, 68- U.S.A.A.F, 43-45. Am. Chem. Soc; Electrochem. Soc. Electrochemical separation of radiochemicals; engineering of fluorine generation and handling; ion selective diaphragm electrolysis; fused salt electrolysis; nuclear fuel element syntheses and fabrication; extractive metallurgy; materials engineering. Address: Nuclear Division, Union Carbide Corp, P.O. Box Y, Oak Ridge, TN 37380.

FINLEY, J(OHN) BROWNING, b. Crowley, La, July 18, 19; m. 43; c. 4. CHEMICAL ENGINEERING. B.S, Southwestern Louisiana, 41, B.S.Ch.E, 42, M.S, 60; Ph.D.(chem. eng), Okla. State, 64. Petrol. chemist, Humble Oil & Ref. Co, 42-47; private consult, 47-50; mgr, Crowley Motor Co, Inc, 50-56; Am. Rice Milling Co, Inc, 56-58; PROF. CHEM. ENG, TEX. A&I UNIV, 63- Am. Inst. Chem. Eng; Am. Chem. Soc; Am. Soc. Eng. Educ; Nat. Soc. Prof. Eng. Diffusion in electrolytes and mass transfer studies; nuclear engineering and radioisotope applications in research. Address: Box 2139 Station 1, Kingsville, TX 78363.

FINLEY, K(AY) THOMAS, b. Elmira, N.Y, Aug. 29, 34; m. 56; c. 2. PHYSICAL ORGANIC CHEMISTRY. B.S, Rochester Inst. Tech, 59; Nat. Sci. Found. fel, Rochester, 60-61, Ph.D.(chem), 63. Asst. prof. chem, Rochester Inst. Technol, 62-66, assoc. prof, 66; sr. res. chemist, Eastman Kodak Co, 66-70; PROF. CHEM. & DEAN SCI. & MATH, STATE UNIV. N.Y. COL. BROCKPORT, 70- U.S.N, 52-55. AAAS; Am. Chem. Soc; The Chem. Soc. Michael condensation kinetic studies; acyloin condensation as a cyclization method; nucleophilic addition to quinonoid systems; chromatography; history of chemistry. Address: Dept. of Chemistry, State University of New York College at Brockport, Brockport, NY 14420.

FINLEY, MALCOLM H(EDGES), b. Santa Ana, Calif, Sept. 13, 00; m. 30; c. 3. PSYCHIATRY, PSYCHOLOGY. B.S, Mass. Inst. Tech, 24; M.A, Pomona Col, 26; M.D, Hopkins, 32. Asst. psychiatrist, Judge Baker Guid. Center, Boston, 36-37; psychiatrist, Child Guid. Clin, Portland, Maine, 37; pub. schs, Ill. & Calif, 37-45; STAFF PSYCHIATRIST, St. Lukes Hosp, 46-60; PAC. MED. CTR, 59- Instr, California, 45-47; clin. asst, med. sch. Stanford, 50-53, asst. clin. prof, 53-59; assoc. staff mem, Ross Gen. Hosp, Calif, 68- Consult, regional off, U.S. Vet. Admin, 59-60. Am. Med. Asn; Nat. Ment. Health Asn; Am. Orthopsychiat. Asn; Am. Psychiat. Asn. Parenthood; parent personality influence on child development; emotional tension in the formation and psychotherapy of neuroses and psychoses; blood pressure and its relation to emotional tension. Address: 280 Margarita Dr, San Rafael, CA 94901.

FINLEY, ROBERT B(YRON), JR, b. Pittsfield, Mass, Aug. 22, 17; m. 46; c. 3. VERTEBRATE ZOOLOGY. A.B, California, 41; fel, Kansas, 48-49, Ph.D.(zool), 56. Instr. zool. & asst. curator mus. natural hist, Kansas, 50-51; sci. intel. analyst, Off. Naval Intel, 55-59; mem. staff, DENVER WILDLIFE RES. CTR, U.S. FISH & WILDLIFE SERV, 59-65, CHIEF SECT. WILDLIFE ECOL. PUB. LANDS, 65- U.S.N.R, 41-45, 52-55, Lt. Comdr. Soc. Syst. Zool; Soc. Study Evolution; Wildlife Soc; Am. Soc. Mammal; Am. Soc. Ichthyol. & Herpet; Cooper Ornith. Soc. Biogeography; evolution of mammals and reptiles; paleobiology of Pleistocene; ecology; wildlife management; effects of chemicals on wildlife. Address: 745 Miller Ct, Lakewood, CO 80215.

FINLEY, SARA CREWS, b. Lineville, Ala, Feb. 26, 30; m. 52; c. 2. MEDICAL GENETICS, PEDIATRICS. B.S, Alabama, 51; M.D, Med. Col. Ala, 55. Nat. Insts. Health fel. pediat, UNIV. ALA. SCH. MED, 56-59, instr, 60-62, asst. prof. PEDIAT, 62-68, ASSOC. PROF, 68-, CO-DIR, LAB. MED. GENETICS, 62-, ASST. PROF. PHYSIOL. & BIOPHYS, 67- Nat. Insts. Health trainee, inst. med. genetics, Univ. Uppsala, 61-62; mem, White House Conf. Health, 65. Am. Soc. Human Genetics; Am. Fedn. Clin. Res; N.Y. Acad. Med. Cytogenetics; congenital malformations; human growth and development; genetic counseling. Address: 2725 Cherokee Rd, Birmingham, AL 35216.

FINLEY, THEODORE N, b. Seattle, Wash, Aug. 21, 27; m. 50; c. 4. INTERNAL MEDICINE. B.S, Washington (Seattle), 50; M.D, Hopkins, 54. Resident med, California, 54-57, instr, 58-61; physiol, Buffalo, 57-58; from asst. prof. to assoc. prof. physiol. & anesthesiol, Washington (Seattle), 61-64; assoc. prof. med, Univ. N.Mex, 64-68; ASSOC. CHIEF MED. & DIR. PULMONARY LAB, MT. ZION HOSP. & MED. CTR, 68-; ASSOC. CLIN. PROF, MED. SCH, UNIV. CALIF, SAN FRANCISCO, 70- Nat. Tuberc. Asn. fel, 58-61. U.S.N.R, 45-46. Am. Physiol. Soc. Physiology of the normal lung; diseases of the lung; alterations in physiology; biochemistry; anatomy; biophysics. Address: Pulmonary Lab, Mt. Zion Hospital & Medical Center, 1600 Divisadero St, San Francisco, CA 94115.

FINLEY, WAYNE H(OUSE), b. Goodwater, Ala, Apr. 7, 27; m. 52; c. 2. GENETICS, BIOCHEMISTRY. B.S, Jacksonville State Col, 47; M.A, Alabama, 50, M.S, 55, Ph.D.(biochem), 58, M.D, 60. Teacher, sr. high sch, Ala, 49-51; asst. prof. PEDIAT, SCH. MED, UNIV. ALA, BIRMINGHAM, 62-66, assoc. prof, 66-70, PROF, 70-, ASST. PROF. BIOCHEM, 65-, PHYSIOL. & BIOPHYSICS, 67-, DIR. LAB. MED. GENETICS, 66- Fel, inst. med. genetics, Univ. Uppsala, 61-62; prin. investr, U.S. Pub. Health Serv. res. grant, 62-68; co-prin. investr, U.S. Dept. Health, Educ. & Welfare training res. grant, 64- U.S.A, 45-46, Chem.C, 51-53, Res, 53-, Maj. AAAS; Am. Soc. Human Genetics; Am. Fedn. Clin. Res; Am. Chem. Soc; Am. Inst. Chem; Am. Ord. Asn. Medical genetics; organic syntheses of new alkylating agents and their screening against transplantable animal tumors; cell culture techniques and human cytogenetics including mitotic and meiotic studies. Address: Lab. of Medical Genetics, University of Alabama in Birmingham, Birmingham, AL 35233.

FINLON, FRANCIS P(AUL), b. Carbondale, Pa, Sept. 2, 24; m. 47; c. 2. ELECTRICAL ENGINEERING. B.S, Pa. State, 47, M.S, 48, assoc. prof. ENG. RES, PA. STATE, 47-64, PROF, 64- C.Eng, U.S.A, 44-46. Inst. Elec. & Electronics Eng. Underwater ordnance. Address: Ordnance Research Lab, Pennsylvania State University, University Park, PA 16801.

FINN, ALBERT CHRISTENSON, b. Boston, Mass, Mar. 31, 34. THEORETICAL PHYSICS. B.S, Mass. Inst. Technol, 55, Ph.D.(physics), 59. Res. assoc. theoret. physics, Stanford Univ, 62-64, linear accelerator ctr, 64-66; ASST. PROF. PHYSICS, SAN FRANCISCO STATE COL, 66- Sig.C, 59-62, 1st Lt. Am. Phys. Soc. Theoretical high energy and particle physics. Address: Dept. of Physics, San Francisco State College, 1600 Holloway Ave, San Francisco, CA 94132.

FINN, ARTHUR LEONARD, b. Boston, Mass, Mar. 24, 34; m. 56; c. 3. PHYSIOLOGY, BIOPHYSICS. A.B, Harvard, 54; M.D, Boston, 58. Intern med, Mass. Mem. Hosp, Boston, 58-59; res, Duke Hosp, Durham, N.C, 59-60 & 62-63; fel. metab, North Carolina, Chapel Hill, 60-62; adv. res. fel. membrane transport, Nat. Heart Inst, 63-65; asst. prof. physiol. & med, sch. med, Yale, 65-70; ASSOC. PROF. MED, SCH. MED, UNIV. N.C, 70- Med.C, U.S.A.R, 56-69, Capt. AAAS; Biophys. Soc; Am. Fedn. Clin. Res; Am. Soc. Nephrol; Am. Physiol. Soc; Soc. Gen. Physiol. Membrane biophysics; transport of ions and water in the isolated toad bladder. Address: Dept. of Medicine, University of North Carolina School of Medicine, Chapel Hill, NC 27514.

FINN, D(AVID) L(ESTER), b. Memphis, Tenn, Mar. 24, 24; m. 48; c. 3. ELECTRICAL ENGINEERING. B.S.E.E, Purdue, 48, M.S, 50, Ph.D.(elec. eng), 52. PROF. ELEC. ENG, GA. INST. TECHNOL, 52- U.S.A.A.F, 42-46. Inst. Elec. & Electronics Eng. Applied mathematics; random processes; sampling theory. Address: Dept. of Electrical Engineering, Georgia Institute of Technology, Atlanta, GA 30332.

FINN, EDWARD J, b. Ridgefield Park, N.J, July 24, 30; m. 54; c. 4. THEORETICAL PHYSICS. B.S, Col. Holy Cross, 51; M.S, Catholic Univ, 55; Ph.D.(physics), Georgetown, 62. Instr. physics, Georgetown, 52-54; St. Vincent Col, 54-55; physicist, Naval Res. Lab, 55-56; asst. prof. PHYSICS, GEORGETOWN UNIV, 56-64, ASSOC. PROF, 64- Physicist, Naval Res. Lab, 56-, summer, 54; lectr, Nat. Univ. Mex, 71. Am. Asn. Physics Teachers; Acoust. Soc. Am; Am. Phys. Soc. Sound velocity; long-range ray tracing; vibrational and rotational energies of diatomic molecules; molecular lasers; science curriculum development. Address: Dept. of Physics, Georgetown University, Washington, DC 20007.

FINN, FRANCES M, b. Pittsburgh, Pa, May 6, 37; m. 65. BIOCHEMISTRY. B.S, Pittsburgh, 59, M.S, 61, U.S. Pub. Health Serv. fel, 61-64, Ph.D.(biochem), 64. U.S. Pub. Health Serv. res. fel, Harvard, 64-65; res. assoc, UNIV. PITTSBURGH, 65-69, ASST. PROF. BIOCHEM, 69- Am. Chem. Soc. Structure-function studies with peptide hormones and enzymes. Address: Protein Research Lab, 1276-A Scaife Hall, University of Pittsburgh, Pittsburgh, PA 15213.

FINN, FRED NORMAN, b. Long Beach, Calif, Oct. 20, 23; m. 49; c. 2. CIVIL ENGINEERING. B.S, New Mexico, 44; M.S, California, Berkeley, 50. Jr. engr, South. Calif. Edison Co, 46-47; teaching asst. civil eng, California, 47-48, lectr, 48-54, jr. engr, 48-51, asst. engr, 53-54; dist. engr, Asphalt Inst, 54-56, spec. projs. engr, 56-60, chmn. road test bd. study & staff engr, 60-63, chief eng. anal. sect, 63; tech. dir. prod. eng. & mkt, Golden Bear Oil Co, 63-64; chief engr, Woodward, Clyde, Sherard & Assocs, 64-66; v.pres. eng, Mat. Res. & Develop, Inc, 66-68; div. staff engr, Asphalt Inst, 68-71; ENG. CONSULT, 71- Mem. Hwy. Res. Bd, Nat. Acad. Sci-Nat. Res. Coun. U.S.N, 45-46, 51-53, Lt. Asn. Asphalt Paving Technol.(1st v.pres, 66); Am. Soc. Civil Eng. Materials, design and construction of highway pavement systems, especially basic properties of materials as they relate to pavement performance. Address: 334 Clyde Dr, Walnut Creek, CA 94598.

FINN, JAMES BERNARD, b. Hollidaysburg, Pa, Mar. 14, 11; m. 38; c. 2. HISTOLOGY. B.S, Villanova Col, 32; Pa. State, 33-34; M.S, Pittsburgh, 37, Ph.D.(biol), 41. Asst. zool, Pittsburgh, 34-37; asst. prof, Mt. Mercy Col, 36-38, assoc. prof. biol, 38-46; ed. rep, W.B. Saunders Co, 46-50, asst. mgr. col. dept, 50-51, dent. ed, acting med. ed. & field dir. educ. dept, 52-56; secy, C.V. MOSBY CO, 57-61, ed, 57-70, MEM. BD. DIRS, 60-, SR. V.PRES. & ED-IN-CHIEF, 70-, ed, 57-70, v.pres, 61-70. Embryology: comparative size of cells in three species of salamanders. Address: C.V. Mosby Co, 11830 Westline Industrial Dr, St. Louis, MO 63141.

FINN, JAMES C(RAMPTON), JR, b. Detroit, Mich, Oct. 18, 24; m. 55; c. 2. PLANT PHYSIOLOGY. B.S, Mich. State, 52, M.S, 53; Ph.D.(bot), California, Los Angeles, 58. Plant physiologist cotton physiol, Delta Exp. Sta, U.S. Dept. Agr, Miss, 58; asst. prof. hort, Agr. & Mech. Col, Texas, 58-59; prin. scientist biol, aero-space labs, missile div, N.Am. Aviation, Inc, 59-62, asst. dir. life sci. dept, space & info. systs. div, 62-63, tech. dir. res. planning aerospace sci, 63-65, staff scientist, life sci. opers, 65-68, sci. adv, Autonetics Div, N.Am. Rockwell Corp, 68; SR. SCIENTIST, MICROBICS OPERS, BECKMAN INSTRUMENTS, INC, 68- U.S.A.A.F, 43-46. AAAS. Photoperiodism; plant growth regulators; biological rhythms; closed ecological systems; research administration. Address: Microbics Operations, Beckman Instruments, Inc, 2500 Harbor Blvd, Fullerton, CA 92634.

FINN, JOHN M(ARTIN), b. Philadelphia, Pa, Nov. 16, 19; m. 54; c. 3. ELECTROCHEMISTRY, PHYSICAL CHEMISTRY. A.B, Harvard, 48; M.S, Pennsylvania, 49, Ph.D.(chem), 53. Chemist, E.I. du Pont de Nemours & Co, Inc, 40-42, shift supvr, 42-43, area engr, 43-44; asst. instr, Pennsylvania, 48-51, asst, 51-52; proj. supvr. chem, Horizons, Inc, 52-55; res. chemist, UNION CARBIDE CORP, 55-70, SR. RES. SCIENTIST, 70- U.S.A, 44-46. Am. Chem. Soc; Electrochem. Soc. Liquid ammonia chemistry; phosphide chemistry; complex ions; boron chemistry; anode processes; fused salts and glasses; high temperature chemistry. Address: 7663 Alan Pkwy, Cleveland, OH 44130.

FINN, RAYMOND F(RANCIS), b. New Windsor, N.Y, Oct. 14, 09; m. 43; c. 1. FORESTRY. B.S, Minnesota, 38; M.S, Mich. State, 58, Ph.D, 66. Mem. staff tree physiol, Black Rock Forest, 33-38, asst. dir, 39-43, 46-49; MEM. STAFF FOREST MGT, CENT. & N.CENT. STATES FOREST EXP. STATIONS, U.S. FOREST SERV, 49-; ASSOC. PROF. FORESTRY, IOWA STATE UNIV, 66- U.S.A.A.F, 43-45. Soc. Am. Foresters; Soil Sci. Soc. Am; Am. Soc. Plant Physiol. Forest tree nutrition; silviculture; mycorrhizae. Address: Dept. of Forestry, Iowa State University, Ames, IA 50010.

FINN, R(OBERT) K(AUL), b. Waukesha, Wis, May 3, 20; m. 49; c. 5. CHEMICAL ENGINEERING. B.Ch, Cornell, 41, Ch.E, 42; Ph.D.(chem. eng), Minnesota, 49. Res. chem. engr, Merck & Co, Inc, 42-46; asst. prof. CHEM. ENG, Illinois, 49-55; from assoc. prof. to PROF, CORNELL UNIV, 55- Consult, Vio Bin Corp, Ill, 51-55; Commercial Solvents Corp, Ind, 53-55; vis. prof, Univ. Calif, Berkeley, 69. AAAS; Am. Chem. Soc; Am. Soc. Microbiol; Am. Inst. Chem. Eng. Bioengineering, application of chemical engineering principles to the recovery and purification of natural products; fermentation engineering. Address: 172 Olin Hall, Cornell University, Ithaca, NY 14850.

FINN, SIDNEY B(ERNARD), b. Freedom, Pa, Feb. 2, 08; m. 38; c. 2. DENTISTRY. B.A, Ohio State, 30; D.M.D, Harvard, 34; M.S, Rochester, 40. Sr. dentist, N.Y. State Dept. Health, 40-44, assoc. res. dentist, in charge Newburgh-Kingston Fluorine Study, 44-50; prof. dent. & chmn. dept. pedodontics, SCH. DENT, UNIV. ALA, 50-68, DIR. APPL. RES, INST. DENT. RES, 68- Consult, Children's Hosp; Vet. Admin. Hosp, Tuskegee; dir. dent. clins, Sch. Deaf & Blind. AAAS; Am. Dent. Asn; Am. Pub. Health Asn; Am. Soc. Dent. for Children (Award of Excellence, 68); Am. Acad. Pedodontics; Int. Dent. Fedn; Am. Col. Dent; Int. Asn. Dent. Res. Dental genetics and caries; clinical pedodontics; fluorine; phosphates and dental caries. Address: Institute of Dental Research, University of Alabama, 1919 Seventh Ave. S, Birmingham, AL 35233.

FINN, WILLIAM DANIEL LIAM, b. Cork, Ireland, Aug. 25, 33. SOIL MECHANICS. B.E, Nat. Univ. Ireland, 54; M.Sc, Washington (Seattle), 57,

Ph.D, 60. Instr, Washington (Seattle), 56-60; asst. prof. CIVIL ENG, British Columbia, 61; PROF, UNIV. B.C, 64-, DEAN APPL. SCI, 70-, head dept. civil eng, 64-70. Partner, Pan-Am. Eng. & Comput. Serv, Ltd. Am. Soc. Civil Eng; Am. Soc. Eng. Educ. Creep of soils; plasticity theory in soil mechanics; soil structure interaction during earthquakes; seismic response of earth dams; ocean engineering. Address: Faculty of Applied Science, University of British Columbia, Vancouver 8, B.C, Can.

FINNEGAN, CYRIL V(INCENT), b. Dover, N.H, July 17, 22; m. 47; c. 9. ZOOLOGY. B.S, Bates Col, 46; M.S, Notre Dame, 48, Ph.D.(zool), 51. Instr. gen. biol, Wabash Col, 49-50; res. fel, Stanford, 51-52; instr. embryol. & anat, St. Louis, 52-55, asst. prof, 55-56; Notre Dame, 56-58; DEVELOP. BIOL. & MORPHOGENESIS, UNIV. B.C, 58-60, assoc. prof, 60-64, PROF, 64-, CHMN. BIOL. PROG, 69- U.S.A, 42-45. Am. Soc. Zool; Soc. Develop. Biol; Int. Soc. Develop. Biol; Tissue Culture Asn; Can. Soc. Cell Biol; Can. Soc. Zool. Tissue interactions in induction in Amphibia; developmental biology. Address: Dept. of Zoology, University of British Columbia, Vancouver 8, B.C, Can.

FINNEGAN, JOSEPH V(INCENT), b. Los Angeles, Calif, Dec. 22, 15; m. 44; c. 3. INTERNAL MEDICINE. A.B, Creighton, 36; M.D, St. Louis, 42, M.Int. Med, 48. Instr. int. med, ST. LOUIS UNIV, 48-50, sr. instr, 50-52, asst. prof. INTERNAL MED, 52-56, ASSOC. CLIN. PROF. & DIR, STUDENT HEALTH SERV, 56- V.chmn. cancer control cmt, St. Louis Univ. Hosp, 48-51, chief med. out-patient serv. dept, 54-56, mem. int. med. dept. exec. cmt, 54-58. Ed, Missouri Medicine, 62. Autopsy pathologist, Fitzsimons Gen. Hosp, Med.C, U.S.A, 44-46. Am. Med. Asn; fel. Am. Col. Physicians. Infectious diseases. Address: 11153 Clarissa Dr, St. Louis, MO 63141.

FINNEGAN, R(AYMOND) J(OSEPH), b. Cochran, Ont, Mar. 2, 22; m. 49, 71; c. 2. FISHERIES, FORESTRY. B.Sc, Univ. N.B, 48, M.Sc, 50; Ph.D.(zool), Univ. B.C, 59. RES. SCIENTIST, Can. Dept. Agr, 48-60; Can. Dept. Forestry, 60-67; LAURENTIAN FOREST RES. CTR, CAN. DEPT. FISHERIES & FORESTRY, 67- Can. Army, 44-45. Entom. Soc. Am; Entom. Soc. Can; French Asn. Adv. Sci. Ecological study of nursery, plantation, and woodlot insects; vectors of Dutch elm disease; scolytid damaging maple regeneration; needle miner on pine; ants as limiting factor of insect pests; weevils attacking pines. Address: Laurentian Forest Research Center, Canadian Dept. of Fisheries & Forestry, 1080 du Vallon Rd, Que. 10, Que, Can.

FINNEGAN, R(ICHARD) A(LLEN), b. Minneapolis, Minn, Feb. 5, 32; m. 56; c. 3. ORGANIC CHEMISTRY. B.A, Minnesota, 53; Ph.D.(org. chem), Mass. Inst. Technol, 57. Res. fel, Chicago, 57-58; Wayne State Univ, 58-59; asst. prof. chem, Ohio State Univ, 59-63; assoc. prof. MED. CHEM, STATE UNIV. N.Y. BUFFALO, 63-66, PROF, 66- Am. Chem. Soc; N.Y. Acad. Sci; Am. Pharmaceut. Asn; The Chem. Soc. Natural products chemistry; photochemistry; organoalkali metal chemistry. Address: Dept. of Medicinal Chemistry, School of Pharmacy, State University of New York at Buffalo, Buffalo, NY 14214.

FINNEGAN, THOMAS (JOSEPH), b. Waterbury, Conn, June 11, 01; wid. CHEMICAL ENGINEERING. B.S.Ch.E, Polytech. Inst. Brooklyn, 39. Lab. asst, Scovill Mfg. Co, 18-24; chemist, New York Steam Corp, 24-29, chemist in charge, 29-38; res. assoc, Consol. Edison Co. New York, Inc, 38-42; chem. engr, Buffalo Niagara Elec. Corp, 42-50, Niagara Mohawk Power Corp, N.Y, 50-70; RETIRED. Chem. engr, affiliated co, Niagara-Hudson Syst, 42-50; part-time chem. eng. consult. Am. Nuclear Soc; Am. Chem. Soc; fel. Am. Soc. Mech. Eng; Nat. Soc. Prof. Eng; fel. Am. Inst. Chem. Corrosion of boilers and steam operated equipment; treatment of water for boilers; steam purity including methods of measuring it; combustion problems; power station design; fossil fuel and nuclear plants. Address: 66 Summer St, Buffalo, NY 14209.

FINNEGAN, WALTER DANIEL, b. Anaconda, Mont, Mar. 31, 23; m. 48; c. 2. METALLURGY. B.S, Mont. Col. Mineral Sci. & Tech, 48, M.S, 49. Engr. metall, U.S. Bur. Mines, 49-52; res. metallurgist, KAISER ALUMINUM & CHEM. CORP, 52-55, asst. supvr. joining br, dept. metall. res, Wash, 55-56, supvr, 56-70, SR. RES. ASSOC, CTR. TECHNOL, CALIF, 70- U.S.N.R, 43-46. Am. Welding Soc; Am. Soc. Metals. Metallurgy and joining of aluminum alloys. Address: Center for Technology, Kaiser Aluminum & Chemical Corp, P.O. Box 870, Pleasanton, CA 94566.

FINNEGAN, WILLIAM G(EORGE), b. Hancock, Mich, Dec. 19, 23; m. 52; c. 2. ATMOSPHERIC SCIENCES. B.S, California, 44; Ph.D.(chem), Ohio State, 49; Calif. Inst. Tech, 50. Res. chemist, Eastman Kodak Co, 44-45; asst, Ohio State, 45-48, res. asst, 48-49; chemist, U.S. Naval Ord. Test Sta, 50-69, SR. RES. SCIENTIST, NAVAL WEAPONS CTR, 69- L.T.E. Thompson Award, U.S. Naval Ord. Test Sta, 64. AAAS; Am. Chem. Soc; Am. Meteorol. Soc. Weather modification; cloud physics; pyrotechnic chemistry; guanidine, tetrazole and fluorocarbon chemistry. Address: 705 Ticonderoga, China Lake, CA 93555.

FINNEMORE, DOUGLAS K, b. Cuba, N.Y, Sept. 9, 34; m. 56; c. 2. SOLID STATE PHYSICS. B.S, Pa. State Univ, 56; M.S, Univ. Ill, 58, Ph.D.(superconductivity), 62. Res. assoc. PHYSICS, Univ. Ill, 62; Ames Lab, 62-63; asst. prof, IOWA STATE UNIV, 63-65, assoc. prof, 65-68, PROF, 68- Am. Phys. Soc. Superconductivity. Address: Dept. of Physics, Iowa State University, Ames, IA 50010.

FINNERTY, DEANE W(ARD), b. Audubon, Iowa, Mar. 17, 23; m. 44; c. 3. AGRONOMY. B.Sc, Colo. Agr. & Mech. Col, 48; M.S, Kans. State Col, 49; Ph.D.(agron), Nebraska, 53. Asst, Kans. State Col, 48-49; agron, Nebraska, 50-53; AGRONOMIST, INDUST. & BIOCHEM. DEPT, E.I. DU PONT DE NEMOURS & CO, INC, 53- U.S.A.A.F, 42-46. Weed control; plant ecology. Address: Industrial & Biochemicals Dept, E.I. du Pont de Nemours & Co, Inc, 40-47 St, Western Springs, IL 60558.

FINNERTY, F(RANK) A(MBROSE), JR, b. Montclair, N.J, Nov. 3, 23; m. 46; c. 6. CARDIOLOGY. A.B, Georgetown, 43, M.D, 47. Vis. physician, Georgetown med. div, Gen. Hosp, Wash, D.C, 52, dir. toxemia clin, 52, chief cardiovascular res, 52-71; CHIEF MED, COLUMBIA HOSP. WOMEN, 70-; from asst. prof. med. & pharmacol. to CLIN. PROF. MED. & OBSTET. & GYNEC, MED. SCH, GEORGETOWN UNIV, 55- Res. fel, Am. Heart Asn, 55, estab. investr, 57. Vis. physician, med. center, Georgetown, 52- U.S.A.R, 53-55, Capt. Am. Med. Asn; Am. Heart Asn; Am. Fedn. Clin. Res. Cardiovascular research; hypertension toxemias of pregnancy; postural hypotension. Address: 1726 I St. N.W, Washington, DC 20006.

FINNERTY, JAMES LAWRENCE, S.J, b. Sioux Falls, S.Dak, Mar. 9, 27. BIOCHEMISTRY. B.S, Marquette, 48; M.S, Illinois, 50; Ph.D.(chem), Loyola (Ill), 60. Instr. CHEM, St. Mary's Col.(Kans), 60-64; PROF, SOGANG UNIV, KOREA, 66- Fulbright lectr, Korea, 66- Am. Chem. Soc. Organic reaction mechanisms; syntheses; natural products. Address: Dept. of Chemistry, Sogang University, I.P.O. 1142, Seoul, Korea.

FINNERTY, WILLIAM R(OBERT), b. Keokuk, Iowa, May 2, 29; m. 53; c. 6. MICROBIAL PHYSIOLOGY, BIOCHEMISTRY. B.A, Iowa, 55, Am. Chem. Soc. fel. & Ph.D.(microbiol), 61. Teaching fel. microbiol, Iowa, 57-58, res. asst, 58-60, instr, 60, res. assoc, 60-61; U.S. Pub. Health Serv. fel. biochem. & enzym, Oak Ridge Nat. Labs, 61-62; asst. prof. MICROBIOL, sch. med, Ind. Univ, 62-65, ASSOC. PROF, 65-68; UNIV. GA, 68- U.S.A.F, 48-52, Sgt. AAAS; Am. Soc. Microbiol; Am. Soc. Biol. Chem; Am. Chem. Soc. Mechanism of oxidation of aliphatic hydrocarbons by microorganisms; control mechanisms; lipids; phospholipid biosynthesis; membranes. Address: Dept. of Microbiology, University of Georgia, Athens, GA 30601.

FINNEY, CLIFTON DONALD, b. Dubuque, Iowa, Apr. 7, 41; m. 68. PHYSICAL & RADIATION CHEMISTRY. B.A, Austin Col, 64; Phillips Petrol. fel, Kans. State Univ, 68-69, Ph.D.(phys. chem), 70. Fel. CHEM, Univ. Toronto, 69-71, lectr, 70-71; ASST. PROF, DRAKE UNIV, 71- Am. Chem. Soc; Am. Soc. Mass Spectrometry. Radiation chemistry of hydrocarbon gases; low energy electron impact; energetics of formation of gaseous positive ions as applied to structural problems; techniques in electron impact studies. Address: Dept. of Chemistry, Drake University, Des Moines, IA 50311.

FINNEY, ESSEX EUGENE, JR, b. Powhatan, Va, May 16, 37; m. 59; c. 2. AGRICULTURAL ENGINEERING. B.S, Va. Polytech, 59; M.S, Pa. State, 61; Ph.D.(eng), Mich. State, 63. RES. AGR. ENGR, MKT. QUAL. RES. DIV, AGR. RES. SERV, U.S. DEPT. AGR, BELTSVILLE, 65- Transportation C, U.S.A, 63-65, Capt. Am. Soc. Agr. Eng.(Paper award, 69); Inst. Food Technol. Instrumentation and techniques for measuring physical properties and characteristics associated with quality within agricultural and food products; Address: 3600 Jeff Rd, Landover, MD 20785.

FINNEY, JAMES W(ILLIAM), b. Jasper Co, Ill, Nov. 10, 31; m. 54; c. 2. MICROBIOLOGY, IMMUNOLOGY. B.A, Univ. Tex, 55, M.A, 57; Ph.D, Baylor Univ, 66. Res. scientist radiobiol, sch. aviation med, Texas, 52-57, clin. asst. microbiol, southwest. med. sch, 57-62; instr, col. dent, Baylor Univ, 62-66, asst. prof. microbiol. & physiol, grad. div, 66-67, ASSOC. PROF, 67-71; RADIOL, N.J. COL. MED. & DENT, 71- Chief res. microbiol, Vet. Admin. Hosp, McKinney, 57-58, Dallas, 58-; consult, Charles A. Sammons, Dept. Irradiation Therapy & Nuclear Med, Med. Ctr, Baylor Univ, 59-62, asst. chief cancer res, 62-63, dir. res. labs, C.A. Sammons Res. Div, 64-67, dir. div, 67-69, dir. inst. biomed. res, med. ctr, 69-71; clin. instr. radiation biol, southwest. med. sch, Univ. Tex, 68-71. U.S.A.F.R, 49-53. Radiobiology. Address: N.J. College of Medicine & Dentistry, Jersey City, NJ 07304.

FINNEY, JOSEPH J, b. New York, N.Y, Mar. 11, 27; m. 61; c. 2. GEOLOGY, MINERALOGY. B.S, U.S. Merchant Marine Acad, 50; univ. fel, New Mexico, 57-59, M.S, 59; univ. fel, Wisconsin, 59-61, Nat. Sci. Found. fel, 61-62, Ph.D.(struct. mineral), 62. ASSOC. PROF. GEOL. & MINERAL, COLO. SCH. MINES, 62- Res. grants, Colo. Sch. Mines Found, Inc, 62- & Res. Corp, 63. U.S.N, 53-55, Res, 55-, Lt. Mineral Soc. Am; Mineral. Asn. Can; Mineral. Soc. Gt. Brit. & Ireland; Am. Crystallog. Asn. Structural mineralogy; investigations in structure of minerals; crystal chemistry. Address: Dept. of Geology, Colorado School of Mines, Golden, CO 80401.

FINNEY, KARL F(REDERICK), b. Salina, Kans, July 25, 11; m. 35; c. 3. CHEMISTRY. A.B, Kans. Wesleyan, 35; B.S, Kansas State, 36, M.S, 37; Ohio State, 37. Assoc. chemist, hard winter wheat qual. lab, U.S. DEPT. AGR, Kansas State, 38-43, from assoc. chemist to chemist, soft wheat lab, Ohio Exp. Sta, 43-46; PROF. GRAIN SCI. & RES. CHEMIST IN CHARGE HARD WINTER WHEAT QUAL. LAB, KANS. STATE UNIV, 46- AAAS; Am. Chem. Soc; Am. Soc. Agron; Am. Asn. Cereal Chem. Wheat quality evaluation; micromilling and microbaking; flour fractionation and reconstitution; characterizing gluten proteins; foliar spraying the wheat plant with ureas; effects of environmental factors; baking techniques and ingredients; fats and lipids; amylases; proteases; varying stages of wheat maturity, and gamma irradiation on physical, chemical, and baking properties of wheat varieties. Address: Hard Winter Wheat Quality Lab, PSR, Dept. of Grain Science, Kansas State University, Manhattan, KS 66502.

FINNEY, ROSS L(EE), b. Springfield, Mass, May 31, 33; m. 63. MATHEMATICS. B.A, Michigan, 54, M.A, 55, Nat. Sci. Found. fel, 59-61, Ph.D.(math), 62; Fulbright fel, Paris, 56-57. Instr. MATH, Mass. Inst. Technol, 61-63; Princeton, 63-66; asst. prof, UNIV. ILL, URBANA-CHAMPAIGN, 66-68, ASSOC. PROF, 68- Lectr, Nairobi, Kenya, summer, 67; Bo, Sierra Leone, 68, 69; Addis Ababa, Ethiopia, 71. Chmn. curriculum comt, African Math. Prog, U.S. Agency Int. Develop, 62, secondary C writing group, 65-67. Am. Math. Soc; Math. Asn. Am. Combinatorial and general topology. Address: Dept. of Mathematics, University of Illinois, Urbana-Champaign, Altgeld Hall, Urbana, IL 61801.

FINNEY, WILLIAM J(ETTON), b. Shreveport, La, Nov. 2, 20; m. 45; c. 3. PHYSICS. S.B, Mass. Inst. Technol, 43, 45-46. With Bell Tel. Labs, 42; underwater sound lab, Mass. Inst. Technol, 43-45; proj. engr, sound div, Naval Res. Lab, 45; sect. head, SOUND DIV, NAVAL RES. LAB, 46-47, HEAD ELECTRONICS BR, 48- Mem. comt. on hearing & bioacoustics, Nat. Res. Coun; res. fel. appl. physics, Harvard, 66-67. Acoust. Soc. Am; Sci. Res. Soc. Am; Asn. Comput. Mach; Inst. Elec. & Electronics Eng. Theory of vibrating plates; communications theory and its application to psychoacoustical and psychooptical problems; high speed electronic computers for research applications; building acoustics; solid state physics. Address: Naval Research Lab, Washington, DC 20607.

FINNIE, I(AIN), b. Hong Kong, July 18, 28; nat. MECHANICAL ENGINEERING. B.Sc, Glasgow, 49; S.M, Mass. Inst. Technol, 50, M.E, 51, Sc.D.(mech. eng), 53. Instr. mech. eng, Mass. Inst. Tech, 52-53; engr, Shell Develop. Co, 53-61; assoc. prof. MECH. ENG, UNIV. CALIF, BERKELEY, 61-63, PROF, 63- Soc. Exp. Stress Anal; Am. Soc. Mech. Eng; Am. Soc. Test. Mat; Brit. Inst. Mech. Eng. Mechanical behavior of engineering materials, especially creep, erosion and fracture, stress and vibration analysis. Address: Dept. of Mechanical Engineering, University of California, Berkeley, CA 94720.

FINNIE, THOMAS CARROLL, b. Caseyville, Ky, Nov. 25, 18; m. 39; c. 2. CARTOGRAPHY, PHOTOGRAMMETRY. B.S, Univ. Ky, 40; M.S, George Washington Univ, 64; dipl, Indust. Col. Armed Forces, 64. Civil engr, Ky. & N.C, 37-42; instr. math. & eng, Univ. Ky, 42-44; sr. cartog. engr, U.S. Army engr. orgns, Philippines, 46-47; instr. math, Univ. Ky, 47-48; photogram. engr, U.S. AIR FORCE AERONAUT. CHART & INFO. CTR, 48-52, asst. chief prod. & distrib. plant, 52-54, chief, 54-62, TECH. DIR, 62- U.S. Air Force rep, Commonwealth Surv. Off. Conf, 67 & 71; Mil. Surv. & Mapping Conf, 67 & 71. Eng.C, U.S.A, 44-46, 1st Lt. Am. Soc. Photogram; Am. Cong. Surv. & Mapping (nat. dir, 63-64, 69-71); Am. Inst. Navig; Nat. Soc. Prof. Eng. Address: 1861 N. Signal Hill Dr, Kirkwood, MO 63122.

FINNIGAN, FREDERICK T(HOMAS), b. New Haven, Conn, Mar. 4, 17; m. 41; c. 2. MECHANICAL ENGINEERING. B.S, Tri-State Col, 40; Lake Forest Col, 46-47. Res. engr. petrol. prod, Res. Center, Pure Oil Co, 40-49, fleet supvr. prod. performance, 49-56, div. dir. engines & fuels, 56-67; SUPVR. PROD. EVAL, PROD. RES. DIV, UNION OIL CO. CALIF, 67- Mem. diesel emission task force, Automotive Mfrs. Assoc, 64- U.S.N.R, 42-46, Lt. Soc. Automotive Eng; Coord. Res. Coun. Applied research and development in improvement of gasoline, lubricants and distillate fuels; development and application of associated hardware. Address: Products Research Division, Union Oil Co. of California Research Center, P.O. Box 76, Brea, CA 92621.

FINNIGAN, J(EROME) W(OODRUFF), b. Oak Park, Ill, Feb. 9, 24; m. 49; c. 4. CHEMICAL ENGINEERING. B.S, Northwestern, 50; M.S, Idaho, 53; Ph.D.(chem. eng), Oregon State, 58. Reactor engr, Hanford Atomic Prod. Oper, Gen. Elec. Co, 50-56, supvr. reactor tech. develop. oper, 58-62; proj. mgr. & res. & develop. mgr, TRW Systs, 62-70; MGR. FUELS & MAT. DEPT, BATTELLE-NORTHWEST LABS, 70- U.S.N, 43-46. Am. Nuclear Soc; Am. Inst. Chem. Eng; Am. Ord. Asn. Nuclear reactor and systems engineering; materials development and technology applied to nuclear and non-nuclear projects for government and industry. Address: 2322 Enterprise Dr, Richland, WA 99352.

FINNIGAN, ROBERT EMMET, b. Buffalo, N.Y, May 27, 27; m. 50; c. 6. ELECTRICAL ENGINEERING. B.S, U.S. Naval Acad, 49; M.S, Illinois, 54, Ph.D.(elec. eng), 57. Officer navig, intel, U.S. Air Force, 49-52, asst. elec. eng, U.S. Air Force Inst. Tech, 55-57; head reactor controls group, propulsion div, Lawrence Radiation Lab, California, 57-62; sr. res. engr, eng. sci. div, Stanford Res. Inst, 62-63; dir. integrated controls dept, res. & comput. div, Electronic Assocs, Inc, 63-65, dir. sci. instruments div, 65-67; pres, Stanford Sci. Instruments, Inc, 67; PRES, FINNIGAN CORP, 67- U.S.N, 45-49; U.S.A.F.R, 59-, Capt. Sr. mem. Inst. Elec. & Electronics Eng. Electronics and automatic feedback control systems; scientific instrumentation; reactor control systems and other nonlinear systems. Address: Finnigan Corp, 595 N. Pastoria Ave, Sunnyvale, CA 94086.

FINSTEIN, MELVIN S, b. Cambridge, Mass, June 25, 31; m. 51; c. 3. MICROBIOLOGY. B.S, Cornell, 59, M.S, 61; Ph.D.(soil microbiol), California, Berkeley, 64. Asst. prof. ENVIRON. SCI, RUTGERS UNIV, 64-70, ASSOC. PROF, 70- U.S.A, 54-56. Am. Soc. Microbiol; Am. Soc. Limnol. & Oceanog. Physiology of autotrophic bacteria; microbiology of polluted waters; waste water treatment processes. Address: Dept. of Environmental Science, Rutgers, The State University, New Brunswick, NJ 08903.

FINSTER, M(IECZYSLAW), b. Lwow, Poland, Aug. 1, 24; U.S. citizen; m. 51; c. 2. PHYSIOLOGY, PHARMACOLOGY. M.D, Geneva, 57. Res. anesthesiol, Columbia-Presby. Med. Ctr, 58-60, Nat. Insts. Health res. fel. anat, COL. PHYSICIANS & SURGEONS, COLUMBIA UNIV, 60-61, instr. ANESTHESIA, 61-62, assoc, 62-64, asst. prof, 64-70, ASSOC. PROF, 70- Body temperature regulation in homeotherms, adults and newborns; transmission of drugs across the placenta; neonatal pharmacology. Address: 622 W. 168th St, New York, NY 10032.

FINSTON, H(ARMON) L(EO), b. Chicago, Ill, Feb. 16, 22; m. 50; c. 4. NUCLEAR CHEMISTRY. B.S.A.S, Ill. Inst. Tech, 43; Ph.D.(chem), Ohio State, 50. Curator chem, Lewis Inst. Br, Ill. Inst. Tech, 42-43; jr. chemist, Manhattan Dist, metall. lab, Chicago, 43-45; asst. cyclotron chem, Ohio State, 45-50; assoc. chemist, dept. chem, Brookhaven Nat. Lab, 50-51, assoc. chemist & supvr, radiochem. anal. sect, dept. nuclear eng, 51-58, chemist, 58-60, leader, radiochem. anal. group, 60-63; PROF. CHEM, BROOKLYN COL, CITY UNIV. NEW YORK, 63- Mem. subcmt. radiochem, Nat. Res. Coun, 57-60, subcmt. use radioactivity standards, 62; fel, Israel Atomic Energy Comn, 65; consult, U.S. Army Nuclear Defense Lab. Am. Chem. Soc; Am. Nuclear Soc. Nuclear, radio and analytical chemistry. Address: Dept. of Chemistry, Brooklyn College, City University of New York, Ave. H & Bedford Ave, Brooklyn, NY 11210.

FINSTON, MORTON, b. Chicago, Ill, Oct. 18, 19; m. 55; c. 2. AERONAUTICS. B.S, Northwestern, 41; Ph.D.(appl. math), Brown, 49. Asst. aero eng, Calif. Inst. Tech, 42-45; res. assoc. appl. math, Brown, 45-48; mem. staff, Naval supersonic lab, MASS. INST. TECHNOL, 48-51, asst. prof, aero eng. dept, 51-56, assoc. prof. DEPT. AERONAUT. & ASTRONAUT, 56-63, PROF, 63- Am. Inst. Aeronaut. & Astronaut; Am. Math. Soc. Applied mechanics; aerodynamics; heat transfer; fluid mechanics. Address: Dept. of Aeronautics & Astronautics, Massachusetts Institute of Technology, Cambridge, MA 02139.

FINSTON, ROLAND A, b. Chicago, Ill, Jan. 27, 37; m. 60; c. 2. HEALTH & RADIOLOGICAL PHYSICS. A.B. & S.B, Univ. Chicago, 57; Atomic Energy Comn. fel. & M.S, Vanderbilt Univ, 59; Nat. Cancer Inst. fel. & Ph.D.(biophys), Cornell Univ, 65. Assoc. prof. radiol. physics, Ore. State Univ, 65-66; SR. HEALTH PHYSICIST, STANFORD UNIV, 66-, LECTR. RADIOL, 70- Health Physics Soc; Soc. Nuclear Med; Am. Asn. Physicists in Med. Radiation dosimetry; radiation biology; radiological health; radiological physics; dosimetry in nuclear medicine. Address: Health Physics Office, 67 Encina Hall, Stanford, CA 94305.

FINZI, LEO ALDO, b. Padova, Italy, Dec. 16, 04; nat; m. 33. ELECTRICAL ENGINEERING. Elec. Eng, Naples, 26; Dr.Ing, Inst. Tech. Aachen, 32. Develop. engr, Hochspannungs-lab, Westinghouse Elec. Corp, East. Pittsburgh, 40-46; PROF. ELEC. ENG, CARNEGIE-MELLON UNIV, 46-, Buhl prof, 55. Carnegie Corp. award, 55. Fel. Inst. Elec. & Electronics Eng. Electric machines design and control; nonlinear devices. Address: 606 South Ave, Circleville, Irwin, PA 15642.

FIORE, ANTHONY WILLIAM, b. Youngstown, Ohio, Oct. 26, 20; m. 44. AERONAUTICAL & ASTRONAUTICAL ENGINEERING. B.S, Cincinnati, 48, M.S, 49; Ph.D.(aeronaut & astronaut. eng), Ohio State, 66. Instr, aeronaut. dept, col. eng, Cincinnati, 48-49; aeronaut. develop. engr, aircraft lab, Air Material Command, WRIGHT PATTERSON AIR FORCE BASE, 49-52, aeronaut. res. engr, aircraft lab, Wright Air Develop. Center, 52-54, aeronaut. res. lab, 54-65, ASST. FOR EXP. AERODYN. RES, HYPERSONIC RES. LAB, AEROSPACE RES. LAB, AIR FORCE SYST. COMMAND, 65- U.S.A, 43-46; U.S.A.F, 46-51, Capt. Assoc. fel. Am. Inst. Aeronaut. & Astronaut. Theoretical and experimental basic research in aerodynamics; subsonic, transonic, supersonic and hypersonic aerodynamic research. Address: 5463 Grantland Dr, Dayton, OH 45429.

FIORE, CARL, b. New Haven, Conn, Sept. 9, 28; m. 56. PHYSIOLOGY, ZOOLOGY. B.A, Yale, 50; M.S, Fordham, 56, Ph.D.(physiol), 59. Instr. physiol, col. pharm, Fordham, 56-58, res. assoc. biol, 58-61; asst. prof, Bronx Community Col, 61-63; fel, develop. biol. ctr, West. Reserve Univ, 63-66; assoc. prof. BIOL, CENT. CONN. STATE COL, 66-68, PROF, 68- U.S.A, 51-53. AAAS; Am. Soc. Zool; Entom. Soc. Am. Physiology and biochemistry of aging; effects of parental age; insect physiology; effects of temperature and humidity on life cycles; cytology; cell physiology. Address: Dept. of Biology, Central Connecticut State College, New Britain, CT 06050.

FIORE, JOSEPH V(INCENT), b. N.Y, Oct. 9, 20; m. 50; c. 3. BIOCHEMISTRY. B.S, Fordham, 43, M.S, 47, Ph.D.(chem), 50. Chief biochem. & clin. biochem, Rochester Gen. Hosp, 50-53; group leader, cereal chem, Fleischmann Labs. Div, Standards Brands, Inc, 53-60; mgr. tobacco res. group, AMF INC, 60-64, area mgr, chem. develop. lab, 64-66, MGR, food & tobacco lab, res. div, 66-70, TOBACCO & ANAL. LAB, 70- U.S.A, 43-46, 1st Lt. Am. Chem. Soc; Inst. Food Technol; N.Y. Acad. Sci; Water Pollution Control Fedn; Tech. Asn. Pulp & Paper Indust; Am. Water Works Asn. Enzymology; fermentation; clinical biochemistry; ecological sciences; analytical chemistry. Address: Chemistry & Physical Lab, AMF Technical Center, AMF Inc, 689 Hope St, Stamford, CT 06907.

FIORE, NICHOLAS F, b. Pittsburgh, Pa, Sept. 24, 39; m. 60; c. 4. PHYSICAL METALLURGY. B.S, Carnegie Inst. Technol, 60, Allegheny Ludlum fel. & M.S, 63, Ph.D.(metall), 64. Asst. prof. metall, UNIV. NOTRE DAME, 66-69, ASSOC. PROF. METALL. & CHMN. DEPT. METALL. ENG. & MAT. SCI, 69- Consult, E.I. du Pont de Nemours & Co, Inc, 68-; Shellite Div, Cabot Corp, 68-; Union Carbide Corp, 68-; mem. basic res. subcomt, Welding Res. Coun. Sig.C, 64-66, Res, 66-, Capt. Am. Soc. Metals; Am. Welding Soc; Am. Foundrymen's Soc; Am. Inst. Mining, Metall. & Petrol. Eng. Internal friction; phase transformations; casting; welding; nondestructive testing. Address: Dept. of Metallurgical Engineering & Materials Science, Box E, University of Notre Dame, IN 46556.

FIORI, BART J, b. Passaic, N.J, Dec. 7, 30; m. 56; c. 4. ENTOMOLOGY. B.S, Georgia, 54; Ph.D.(entom), Cornell, 63. Field res. specialist, Ortho Div, Calif. Chem. Co, 63-64; ENTOMOLOGIST, AGR. RES. SERV, U.S. DEPT. AGR, 64- Asst. prof, Cornell Univ, 69- U.S.A, 54-56, Sgt. Entom. Soc. Am. Petroleum oils as ovicides; evaluation of insecticides; physical, chemical and biological control of the European chafer Amphimallon majalis. Address: Agricultural Experiment Station, Agricultural Research Service, U.S. Dept. of Agriculture, Geneva, NY 14456.

FIORICA, VINCENT, b. Rochester, N.Y, Dec. 12, 31; m. 57; c. 2. PHYSIOLOGY. A.B, Rochester, 53; M.S, Illinois, 55, Ph.D.(physiol), 58. Asst. prof. physiol, Univ. Iowa, 59-61; res. physiologist, environ. physiol. br, Civil Aeromed. Res. Inst, Fed. Aviation Agency, 61-62, CHIEF METAB. RES, 62-63, metab. sect, 63-65, PHYSIOL LAB, CIVIL AEROMED. INST, FED. AVIATION ADMIN, 65- Soc. Exp. Biol. & Med; Am. Physiol. Soc. Catecholamine release during environmental stress; regulation of sympathicoadrenomedullary activity; circadian variations in electrolyte excretion; physiology of stress and sleep deprivation. Address: 2619 W. Trenton Rd, Norman, OK 73069.

FIOTO, GEORGE A(NTHONY), b. Brooklyn, N.Y, Nov. 22, 33; m. 56; c. 3. PHYSICAL CHEMISTRY, BIOCHEMISTRY. B.S, Manhattan Col, 55; Polytech. Inst. Brooklyn, 55-57. Res. chemist, Revlon Inc, 55-59, sr. res. chemist, 59-61, tech. staff asst. liaison, 61-63, dept. head, emulsion & colloid chem, 63-65, asst. dir. res, skin treatment, toiletries & make-up prod, 65-68; V.PRES. RES. & DEVELOP, NOXELL CORP, 68- U.S.C.G.R, 57-64. Soc. Cosmetic Chem.(secy, 64-66). Emulsion technology; colloid chemistry; rheological properties of dispersions; chemistry of surface active agents. Address: Noxell Corp, 11050 York. Rd, Baltimore, MD 21023.

FIRBY, JAMES R, b. Detroit, Mich, Nov. 28, 33; m. 56; c. 1. INVERTEBRATE PALEONTOLOGY, STRATIGRAPHY. B.A, San Francisco State Col, 60; M.A, California, Berkeley, 63, Ph.D.(paleont), 69. ASST. PROF. GEOL, MACKAY SCH. MINES, UNIV. NEV, RENO, 66- U.S.A, 56-58; U.S.N.R, 58-61. Cenozoic non-marine Mollusca, especially of Western North America. Address: Mackay School of Mines, University of Nevada, Reno, NV 89507.

FIRE, PHILIP, b. Paterson, N.J, Dec. 18, 25; m. 51; c. 2. ELECTRICAL ENGINEERING. B.S. & M.S, Mass. Inst. Tech, 52; engr, Stanford, 59, Ph.D. (elec. eng), 64. Staff engr, Lincoln Lab, Mass. Inst. Tech, 52-54; SR. SYSTS. ENGR, SYLVANIA ELECTRONIC SYSTS, GEN. TEL. & ELECTRONICS CORP, 55- Summer asst, Gen. Cable Corp, 51. U.S.N, 44-46. Sci. Res. Soc. Am; Inst. Elec. & Electronics Eng. Error-correcting codes for communication systems; analysis and synthesis of electronic systems. Address: Electronic Defense Lab, Sylvania Electronic Systems, P.O. Box 205, Mountain View, CA 94040.

FIREBAUGH, MORRIS W, b. Freeport, Ill, July 5, 37; m. 60; c. 2. PHYSICS. A.B, Manchester Col, 59; M.S, Illinois, 60, Ph.D.(physics), 66. Res. assoc. high-energy physics, Illinois, 66-67; instr. PHYSICS, Wisconsin, 67-69, ASST. PROF, UNIV. WIS-PARKSIDE, 69- Woodrow Wilson fel, 59-60. Am. Phys. Soc; Am. Asn. Physics Teachers. Investigations in meson and strange particle production in high energy interactions. Address: Dept. of Physics, University of Wisconsin-Parkside, Kenosha, WI 53140.

FIREHAMMER, B(URTON) D(EFOREST), b. Franklin, Mont, Apr. 29, 23; m. 64. VETERINARY BACTERIOLOGY. B.S, Mont. State Col, 48, M.S, 51. Asst. VET. RES, VET. RES. LAB, AGR. EXP. STA, MONT. STATE UNIV, 48-53, asst. prof, 53-60, assoc. prof, 60-66, PROF, 66- Med.C, U.S.A, 45-46. Am. Soc. Microbiol; U.S. Animal Health Asn; Conf. Res. Workers Animal Diseases. Mastitis of sheep; vibrionic absortion of sheep; bovine abortion due to Haemophilus; intestinal vibrios of sheep; bovine vibriosis vaccines; mycoplasma. Address: Veterinary Research Lab, Montana State University, Bozeman, MO 59715.

FIREMAN, EDWARD L(EONARD), b. Pittsburgh, Pa, March 23, 22; m. 47; c. 3. PHYSICS. B.S, Carnegie Inst. Tech, 42, M.S, 45; Ph.D.(physics), Princeton, 48. Asst. solid state physics, Carnegie Inst. Tech, 42-46; Atomic Energy Cmn. fel, Princeton, 48-50; assoc. scientist physics, Brookhaven Nat. Lab, 50-56; PHYSICIST, SMITHSONIAN ASTROPHYS. OBSERV, 56-; RES. ASSOC, HARVARD OBSERV, 56-, LECTR, 64- Guest scientist, Brookhaven Nat. Lab, 56- Pres, comn. meteorites, Int. Astron. Union Am. Phys. Soc; Am. Astron Soc; Am. Meteorol. Soc; Am. Geophys. Union; Fedn. Am. Sci. Meteorites; radioactive and stable isotopes in meteorites; age determinations; beta decay; cloud chambers; natural tritium; lunar materials; radioactive and stable isotopes in lunar material. Address: Smithsonian Astrophysical Observatory, Harvard College Observatory, Cambridge, MA 02138.

FIREMAN, MILTON, b. San Francisco, Calif, Oct. 4, 10; m. 37; c. 3. SOIL SCIENCE. B.S, Arizona, 33, M.S, 34; Ph.D.(soil sci), California, 43. Asst. soils, Arizona, 34-36; fel, California, 36-39, asst, 39-40; jr. soil surveyor, soil conserv. serv, U.S. Dept. Agr, 41, jr. soil scientist, U.S. regional salinity lab, bur. plant indust, 41-43, asst. soil scientist, 43-45, assoc. soil scientist, 45-48, soil scientist, 48-52, sr. soil scientist, 52-55, exten. soils & water specialist, agr. exten. serv, California, 55-65; mem. staff, Tipton & Kalmbach, Inc, Colo, 65-71; AGRICULTURIST, AGR. PROJS. DEPT, INT. BANK FOR RECONSTRUCTION & DEVELOP, 71- Consult, 55- Soil Sci. Soc. Am; Am. Soc. Agron; Am. Chem. Soc; Int. Soc. Soil Sci. Diagnosis and improvement of saline and alkali soils; soil analysis; moisture movement in soils; water resources and management. Address: Agriculture Projects Dept, International Bank for Reconstruction & Development, 1818 H St, Washington, DC 20433.

FIREMAN, PHILIP, b. Pittsburgh, Pa, Feb. 28, 32; m. 57; c. 5. PEDIATRICS, IMMUNOLOGY. B.S, Pittsburgh, 53; M.D, Chicago, 57. Mead-Johnson fel. pediat, 58-60; clin. assoc, Nat. Insts. Health, 60-62; U.S. Pub. Health Serv. res. fel, Harvard Med. Sch, 62-63; instr. SCH. MED, UNIV. PITTSBURGH, 63-64, asst. prof. PEDIAT, 64-69, ASSOC. PROF, SCH. MED, 69-; DIR. ALLERGY-IMMUNOL, CHILDREN'S HOSP. PITTSBURGH, 68- Res. collab, Brookhaven Nat. Lab, 64-69. Interstate Postgrad. Med. Asn. res. award, 64; U.S. Pub. Health Serv. res. career develop. award, 65. U.S.P.H.S, 60-62, Sr. Asst. Surg. Immediate and delayed hypersensitivity; protein metabolism. Address: Children's Hospital, 125 DeSoto St, Pittsburgh, PA 15213.

FIRESTONE, RAYMOND A, b. New York, N.Y, Jan. 20, 31; m. 52; c. 4. ORGANIC CHEMISTRY. A.B, Cornell, 51; Ph.D.(org. chem), Columbia, 54. SR. CHEMIST, MERCK & CO, RAHWAY, 56- Chem.C, U.S.A, 54-56. Synthesis and mechanism in organic chemistry. Address: 60 Hunter Ave, Fanwood, NJ 07023.

FIRESTONE, RICHARD F(RANCIS), b. Canton, Ohio, June 18, 26; m. 54; c. 3. PHYSICAL CHEMISTRY. A.B, Oberlin Col, 50; Ph.D, Wisconsin, 54. Asst. chem, Wisconsin, 50-51, radiochem, 51-54; resident res. assoc. chem. div, Argonne Nat. Lab, 54-55, instr, Int. Sch. Nuclear Sci. & Eng, 55-56; asst. prof. CHEM, Western Reserve, 56-60; assoc. prof, OHIO STATE UNIV, 61-67, PROF, 67- U.S.N.R, 44-46. AAAS; Am. Phys. Soc; Am. Chem. Soc. Radiation chemistry; kinetics of ionizing-radiation induced reactions; pulse radiolysis of liquids and gases. Address: Dept. of Chemistry, Ohio State University, 140 W. 18th Ave, Columbus, OH 43210.

FIRESTONE, WILLIAM L(OUIS), b. Chicago, Ill, June 20, 21; m. 53; c. 3. ELECTRICAL ENGINEERING. B.S, Colorado, 46; M.S, Ill. Inst. Tech, 49; Ph.D.(elec. eng), Northwestern, 52. Elec. tester, Seeburg Elec. Corp, 39-40; lab. technician, Motorola, Inc, 40-42; elec. engr, Manhattan Proj, California, 46; microwave engr, Motorola Radio, 46-49; lab. asst, Northwestern, 49-50; chief engr, res. dept, Motorola Inc, Ill, 51-60, dir. eng, commun. div, 60-62, asst. gen. mgr, Chicago Mil. Electronics Ctr, 62-64; v.pres, Hallecrafte Corp, 65-66; Whittaker Corp, Calif, 66-70, gen. mgr, tech. prod. div, 66-69, group exec, corp, 69-70; v.pres. & gen. mgr, F.W. Sickles Div, GEN. INSTRUMENTS CORP, 70-71, V.PRES. & GROUP EXEC. ENTERTAINMENT PROD, CHICOPEE, 71- Instr, U.S. Radio Mat. Sch, 42; Ill. Inst. Technol, 48-49 & 55-56; lectr, Northwest. Univ, 57. U.S.N, 42-46. Fel. Inst. Elec. & Electronics Eng. Communication engineering; communication theory and single sideband; engineering managements. Address: 400 Main St, Wilbraham, MA 01095.

FIREY, JOSEPH CARL, b. Roundup, Mont, Oct. 22, 18; m. 51; c. 3. MECHANICAL ENGINEERING. B.S, Univ. Wash, 40; M.S, Univ. Wis, 41. Instr. mech. eng, Univ. Wis, 41-42; res. engr, Calif. Res. Corp, 42-43, 46-54; asst. prof, MECH. ENG, UNIV. WASH, 54-56, assoc. prof, 56-59, PROF, 59- U.S.N.R, 43-59. Am. Soc. Mech. Eng; Soc. Automotive Eng; Am. Soc. Lubrication Eng. Combustion and lubrication problems in power generating equipment. Address: Dept. of Mechanical Engineering, University of Washington, Seattle, WA 98105.

FIREY, WILLIAM J(AMES), b. Roundup, Mont, Jan. 23, 23; m. 46; c. 2. MATHEMATICS. B.S, Washington (Seattle), 49; M.A, Toronto, 50; Ph.D. (math), Stanford, 54. Instr, MATH, Washington State, 53-57, asst. prof, 57-61; assoc. prof, ORE. STATE UNIV, 61-64, PROF, 64- Mathematician, Boeing Airplane Co, summers 57-59; mem. staff, Fulbright Res. Sch, Univ. Otago, N.Z, 67; vis. prof, Mich. State Univ, 69-70. U.S.A, 43-46. Am. Math. Soc; Math. Asn. Am; Can. Math. Cong. Theory of convex sets. Address: Dept. of Mathematics, Oregon State University, Corvallis, OR 97331.

FIRK, FRANK WILLIAM KENNETH, b. London, Eng, Nov. 2, 30; m. 52; c. 3. NUCLEAR PHYSICS. B.Sc, London, 56, M.Sc, 65, Ph.D.(physics), 67. Asst. exp. officer physics, Atomic Energy Res. Estab, Eng, 52-56, exp. officer, 56-59, sr. sci. officer, 59-62, prin. sci. officer, 62-65; sr. res. assoc. PHYSICS, YALE, 65-68, ASSOC. PROF, 68- Vis. scientist, Oak Ridge Nat. Lab, 60-61. R.A.F, 49-51. Am. Inst. Physics; Brit. Inst. Physics & Phys. Soc. Low energy neutron spectroscopy; nuclear photo-disintegration. Address: Dept. of Physics, Yale University, New Haven, CT 06520.

FIRKINS, JOHN F, b. Olympia, Wash, Jan. 31, 35; m. 63; c. 3. MATHEMATICS. B.A, St. Martin's Col, 57; M.S, Miami (Fla), 59; Washington (Seattle), 59-61; M.Ed, Gonzaga, 69. Instr. MATH, GONZAGA UNIV, 61-64, asst. prof, 64-70, ASSOC. PROF, 70-, CHMN. DEPT, 71- Consult, supt. of schs, State of Wash, 71- AAAS; Am. Math. Soc; Math. Asn. Am. Point set topology; mathematics attitudes of students and their relation to success in the classroom. Address: N. 5311 Maple, Spokane, WA 99208.

FIRKINS, JOHN L(IONEL), b. Victoria, B.C, Feb. 13, 42; m. 66; c. 1. PHYSICAL ORGANIC CHEMISTRY, BUSINESS ECONOMICS. B.Sc, Univ. Victoria (B.C.), 65; Ph.D.(chem, bus. econ), Calif. Inst. Technol, 70. SR. RES. & DEVELOP. CHEMIST, CELANESE FIBERS CO, 69- AAAS; Am. Chem. Soc; Chem. Inst. Can. Free radical reaction mechanisms; wood and cellulose chemistry; cellulose acetate and other textile fibers. Address: 5633 Alanhurst Pl, Charlotte, NC 28210.

FIRLE, TOMAS E(RASMUS), b. Berlin, Ger, July 4, 26; nat; m. 51; c. 3. ENERGY CONVERSION. B.S, California, Los Angeles, 52, Howard Hughes, fel, 53-55, M.S, 55. Res. physicist & head develop. group, semiconductor lab, Hughes Aircraft Co, 52-58; RES. PHYSICIST, GULF ENERGY & ENVIRON. SYSTS. INC, SAN DIEGO, 58- Lectr, California, Los Angeles, 57-58; California, San Diego, 59-61; discussion leader, Univ. Calif, San Diego & univ. exten, 62-; trustee, bd. educ, Del Mar Union Sch. Dist, 67; mem. ombudsman comt, Dept. Educ, 69; bd. dirs, Indust-Educ. Coun, 69; pres, Inter-Focus, Calif, 70- Sig.C, Ger. Army, 45. AAAS; Am. Phys. Soc; Sci. Res. Soc. Am; Inst. Elec. & Electronics Eng. Strength of materials; environmental effects; interpersonal human relationships; group and individual behaviorism; social and political psychology; human communications; effectiveness training; management consulting. Address: 327 Pine Needles Dr, Del Mar, CA 92014.

FIRMAGE, D(AVID) ALLAN, b. Nephi, Utah, Feb. 15, 18; m. 40; c. 6. CIVIL ENGINEERING. B.S, Utah, 40; M.S, Mass. Inst. Tech, 41. Stress analyst, E.G. Budd Mfg. Co, Pa, 41-42; res. engr. struct. eng, Res. & Develop. Labs, Ft. Belvoir, Va, 42-47; assoc. prof. civil eng, Florida, 47-52; asst, Mass. Inst. Tech, 52-53; asst. chief struct. engr, Patchen & Zimmerman, Engrs, Ga. 53-55; assoc. prof. civil eng, Brigham Young, 55-57; chief bridge design engr, Capitol Engrs, Saigon, Vietnam, 57-59; assoc. prof. CIVIL ENG, BRIGHAM YOUNG UNIV, 59-60, PROF, 60-, CHMN. DEPT, 69- Adv, Guindy Col. Eng, India, 63-64. Am. Soc. Eng. Educ; Am. Soc. Civil Eng; Int. Asn. Bridge & Struct. Eng. Structural design including mechanics and materials; design of highway bridges; textbooks. Address: Dept. of Civil Engineering, Brigham Young University, Provo, UT 84601

FIRMAN, DAVID, b. Cleveland, Ohio, July 25, 15; m. 47; c. 2. GEOGRAPHY. B.A, California, Los Angeles, 48, M.A, 49; Fulbright grant, India, 52-53; Ph.D, Maryland, 55. Asst. California, Los Angeles, 48; instr. GEOG, Maryland, 50-52, 53-55; PROF. & CHMN. DEPT, TOWSON STATE COL, 55- Fulbright prof, Peshawar, 58-59; lectr, Foreign Service Inst, D.C, 62- U.S.A.F, 41-46, Res, 46- AAAS; Asn. Am. Geog; fel. Am. Geog. Sci; Asn. Asian Studies; Asia Soc. Regional geography of Asia; economic and agricultural geography; water resources; interdisciplinary studies. Address: 113 Ardoon Rd, Lutherville, MD 21093.

FIRMAN, M(ELVIN) C(URTIS), b. Glenside, Pa, Jan. 11, 19; m. 45. BACTERIOLOGY. B.Sc, Phila. Col. Pharmacy, 40. Res. chemist, milk prods, Abbott's Dairies, 45-46; res. bacteriologist, solvents & vitamins, Publicker Alcohol Co, 46-48; antibiotics, Heyden Chem. Corp, 48-53; AM. CYANAMID CO, 53-55, tech. rep, FOOD INDUST, 55-56, field develop, 56-60, asst. tech. dir, fine chem. dept, 60-61, asst. to mgr. res. & develop, AGRODIV, 60-69, MGR. SALES COORD, 69- Vis. lectr, serv. training sch, U.S. Pub. Health Serv. Med.C, 41-45, 1st Lt. AAAS; Am. Chem. Soc; Inst. Food Tech. Anti-biotics; fermentation improvement; use in foods and new antibiotic research, including isolation of tetracycline; microbiological tests of antibiotics; antifungal agent; chemotherapeutic agents and antifungals; research administration; plant and animal products for health and nutrition. Address: 201 Varsity Ave, Princeton, NJ 08540.

FIRMINGER, HARLAN I(RWIN), b. Minneapolis, Minn, Dec. 31, 18; m. 42; c. 3. PATHOLOGY. A.B, Washington (St. Louis), 39, M.D, 43. Asst. path, sch. med, Washington (St. Louis), 43-44; sr. res, Mass. Gen. Hosp, 46-47; pathologist, Nat. Cancer Inst, 48-51; asst. prof. path. & oncol, med. sch, Kansas, 51-53, assoc. prof, 53-55, prof, 55-57; PROF. PATH, SCH. MED, UNIV MD, 57-, head dept, 57-67. Consult, Ft. Howard Vet. Hosp; mem. sci. adv. bd. consults, Armed Forces Inst. Path, 65-70, ed, Atlas of Tumor Path, 66-; mem. comt. path, Nat. Acad. Sci-Nat. Res. Coun, 65-71. Dipl, Am. Bd. Path, 49. Med.C, 44-46, Capt. Histochem. Soc; Am. Soc. Exp. Path;

Am. Asn. Cancer Res; Am. Asn. Path. & Bact; Soc. Exp. Biol. & Med; N.Y. Acad. Sci; Int. Acad. Path. Testicular tumors; induced tumors of the liver; endocrine pathology. Address: 660 W. Redwood St, Baltimore, MD 21201.

FIRNHABER, BERND E(RNST), b. Maracaibo, Venezuela, Aug. 20, 33. PHYSICAL & ORGANIC CHEMISTRY. Dipl, Karlsruhe Tech, 58, Dr.rer.nat. (chem), 61. Res. chemist, Engler-Bunte Inst, Karlsruhe Tech, 61-63; M.W. KELLOGG CO, New Market, 63-66, SUPVR. PROCESS RES, 66- Am. Chem. Soc; Sci. Res. Soc. Am; Soc. Ger. Chem; Ger. Soc. Mineral. & Coal Chem. Hydrocarbon chemistry; catalysis; free radical reactions. Address: 3 Stanford Dr, Somerville, NJ 08876.

FIRNKÄS, SEPP, b. Rinnberg, Ger, Nov. 16, 25; U.S. citizen; m. 55. CIVIL ENGINEERING. Dipl. Ing, Munich Tech, 53. Assoc. struct. eng, CETBA, Algeria, 54-56; proj. engr, Raymond Int. Inc, N.Y. & Venezuela, 56-59, chief engr, Northeast Concrete Prod, 59-61; PRES, SEPP FIRNKÄS ENG. INC, 61-; ASSOC. PROF. CIVIL ENG, NORTHEAST. UNIV, 62- Progressive Archit. struct. design award, 64; Prestressed Concrete Inst. struct. design award, 66. Am. Concrete Inst; Int. Asn. Shell Struct. Design and applications of reinforced and prestressed concrete; precast structural systems. Address: Dept. of Engineering, Northeastern University, Boston, MA 02115.

FIROR, JOHN WILLIAM, b. Athens, Ga, Oct. 18, 27; m. 50; c. 4. SOLAR PHYSICS, RADIO ASTRONOMY. B.S, Ga. Inst. Technol, 49; Ph.D.(physics), Univ. Chicago, 54. Staff mem, dept. terrestrial magnetism, Carnegie Inst, 53-61; assoc. dir, Nat. Ctr. Atmospheric Res. & dir, high altitude observ, 61-68, DIR, NAT. CTR. ATMOSPHERIC RES, 68- Mem. U.S. Nat. Comt, Int. Sci. Radio Union, 54-; Am. Astron. Soc. vis. prof, Nat. Ctr. Atmospheric Res, 60-61; adj. prof. astrophys, Univ. Colo, 62-68; vis. prof. Calif. Inst. Technol, spring 63; Sigma Xi-Sci. Res. Soc. Am. nat. lectr, fall 68. C. Eng, U.S.A, 45-46. Am. Astron. Soc; Am. Geophys. Union; Am. Meteorol. Soc; Int. Astron. Union. Physical conditions in solar atmosphere; solar-terrestrial relations; physics of earth's atmosphere. Address: National Center for Atmospheric Research, P.O. Box 1470, Boulder, CO 80302.

FIRRIOLO, DOMENIC, b. Brooklyn, N.Y, Sept. 4, 33; m. 59; c. 2. PHYSIOLOGY, ANATOMY. B.S, St. Francis Col.(N.Y), 54; M.S, St. John's (N.Y), 56, Ph.D.(physiol), 64. Instr. biol, L.I. UNIV, 56-60, asst. prof, 60-63, assoc. prof, 64-66, asst. dean col. lib. arts & sci, 66-70, PROF. BIOL, 70- Mem. bd. chiropractic exam, State of N.Y. Educ. Dept, 70- U.S.A.R, 57-63, Sgt. AAAS; N.Y. Acad. Sci. Comparative hematology; vertebrate erythropoiesis. Address: Dept. of Biology, Long Island University, Brooklyn Center, 385 Flatbush Ave. Extension, Brooklyn, NY 11201.

FIRSCHEIN, H(ILLIARD) E, b. Brooklyn, N.Y, April 7, 27. BIOCHEMISTRY. B.S, Ohio State, 48; M.S, Wisconsin, 50; Ph.D.(biochem), Rochester, 58. Asst, Wisconsin, 48-50; biochemist, Army Med. Res. Lab, Ft. Knox, Ky, 51-55; res. assoc, atomic energy proj, Rochester, 55-58, asst. scientist, 58-60, instr. biochem, Sch. Med. & Dent, 58-60, radiation biol, 59-60, biochem, sch. med, N.Y. Univ, 60-61, asst. prof, 61-64; asst. prof. biochem. orthop. surg, med. col, Cornell Univ, 64-69; ASSOC. RES. BIOCHEMIST, UNIV. CALIF, LOS ANGELES, 69- Sr. scientist, Hosp. for Spec. Surg, 64-69. U.S.A, 51-53. Am. Chem. Soc. Endocrinology; vitamins; metabolism. Address: Rehabilitation Center (A-329), University of California, 1000 Veteran Ave, Los Angeles, CA 90024.

FIRSCHING, F(ERDINAND) H(ENRY), b. Utica, N.Y, June 22, 23; m. 54; c. 6. ANALYTICAL CHEMISTRY. M.S, Syracuse, 51, Atomic Energy Cmn. assistantships, 53, 54, Ph.D.(chem), 55. Res. chemist, Skenandoa Rayon Corp, N.Y, 51-52; anal. chemist, Cowles Chem. Co, 52-53; sr. chemist explor. res, Diamond Alkali Co, Ohio, 55-58; asst. prof. ANAL. CHEM, Georgia, 58-63, assoc. prof, SCI. & TECH. DIV, SOUTH. ILL. UNIV, EDWARDSVILLE, 63-69, PROF, 69- U.S.A, 43-46. Am. Chem. Soc. Precipitation from homogeneous solution; development of analytical methods; use of radioactive tracers. Address: Science & Technology Division, Southern Illinois University, Edwardsville, IL 62025.

FIRSHEIN, W(ILLIAM), b. New York, N.Y, Aug. 28, 30; m. 54. MICROBIOLOGY. B.S, Brooklyn Col, 52; M.S, Rutgers, 53, Inst. Microbiol. fel, 55-58, Soc. Am. Bacteriologists fel, 57, Ph.D, 58. Microbiol physiologist, Camp Detrick, Md, 54-55; assoc. prof. BIOL, WESLEYAN UNIV, 58-70, PROF. & CHMN. DEPT, 70- U.S. Pub. Health Serv. career develop. award, 65-70. AAAS; Am. Soc. Microbiol. Microbial genetics; population changes and nucleic acid synthesis. Address: Shanklin Lab, Wesleyan University, Middletown, CN 06457.

FIRST, MELVIN W(ILLIAM), b. Boston, Mass, Dec. 23, 14; m. 38; c. 2. PUBLIC HEALTH. B.S, Mass. Inst. Technol, 36; M.S, Harvard, 47, U.S. Pub. Health Serv. fel, 47-50, Sc.D.(indust. hygiene eng), 50. Indust. hygiene engr, Dept. of Health, Detroit, Mich, 36-39; Mich. State Health Dept, 39-41; res. assoc, sch. pub. health, Harvard, 50-53; CONSULT. ENGR, 53-; PROF. ENVIRON. HEALTH ENG, SCH. PUB. HEALTH, HARVARD, 71-, assoc. prof. appl. indust. hyg, 62-71. Dipl, Environ. Eng. Intersoc. Bd; Am. Bd. Indust. Hyg. U.S.A, 41-46; C.Eng. Res, 46-, Lt. Col. Am. Chem. Soc; Nat. Soc. Prof. Eng; Am. Indust. Hyg. Asn; Air Pollution Control Asn. Air and gas purification equipment and techniques for control of industrial atmospheres and prevention of air pollution. Address: 295 Upland Ave, Newton Highlands, Boston, MA 02161.

FIRST, NEAL L, b. Ionia, Mich, Oct. 8, 30; m. 51; c. 4. REPRODUCTIVE PHYSIOLOGY. B.S, Mich. State, 52, M.S, 57, Ph.D.(animal physiol), 59. Instr. animal husb, Mich. State Univ, 59-60; asst. prof, UNIV. WIS, MADISON, 60-64, assoc. prof. MEAT & ANIMAL SCI, 64-69, PROF, 69- Sig.C, 52-54, Sgt. Am. Soc. Animal Sci; Am. Dairy Sci. Asn; Am. Genetic Asn; Am. Soc. Study Reproduction; Soc. Study Fertility. Reproductive physiology, especially of male livestock; artificial insemination. Address: Dept. of Meat & Animal Science, University of Wisconsin, Madison, WI 53706.

FIRST, R(OBERT) S(TANLEY), b. Mt. Vernon, N.Y, Sept. 19, 22; m. 55; c. 2. CHEMICAL ENGINEERING. B.S, Iowa, 43; M.B.A, Pennsylvania, 50. Chem. engr, Sharples Chems. Inc, 43-44; plant engr, Edcan Labs, 46-48; market res. analyst, Commercial Solvents Corp, 50-51; Food Machinery & Chem. Corp, 51-53; mgr. market res, plastics div, Celanese Corp. Am, 53-57; asst. to dir, market res. dept, Nat. Lead Co, 57-58; mgr. market res, Atlas Powder Co, 56-58; PRES, ROBERT S. FIRST, INC, 58- U.S.N, 44-46. Am. Chem. Soc; Commercial Develop. Asn; Am. Mgt. Asn; Inst. Chem. Eng; Soc. Plastics Indust; Soc. Indust. Chem. Expansion and diversification studies; joint ventures and acquisitions; market and economic research; foreign technical liaison; business administration. Address: Robert S. First, Inc, 405 Lexington Ave, New York, NY 10017.

FIRSTBROOK, JOHN B(RADSHAW), b. Toronto, Ont, Oct. 29, 19; m. 45; c. 3. PHYSIOLOGY, INTERNAL MEDICINE. M.D, Toronto, 45, Ph.D. (physiol), 51. Asst. physiol, Banting & Best Dept. Med. Res, Toronto, 48-51, res. assoc, 51-52; asst. prof, Queen's (Ont), 52-53; res. internal med, various hosps, 53-56; assoc. dir. field studies, sch. hyg, Toronto, 56-60, assoc. prof. physiol. hyg, 60-63, prof. appl. physiol, 63-64; assoc. dean faculty med, Queen's Univ.(Ont), 64-68; exec. secy, ASN. CAN. MED. COLS, 68-70, EXEC. DIR, 70- Cert. internal med, Royal Col. Physicians & Surgeons Can, 57. R.C.A.M.C, 43-46, Lt. Atherosclerosis; medical education. Address: 151 Slater St, Ottawa, Ont, Can. K1P 5H3.

FIRSTENBERGER, B(URNETT) G(EORGE), b. Seneca, Kans, July 18, 17; m. 43; c. 3. CHEMICAL ENGINEERING. B.S, Kansas, 39; fel, Iowa State Col, 39-42, Ph.D.(chem. eng), 42. Chemist, res. & develop, Nat. Aniline Div, ALLIED CHEM. CORP, 42-44, engr. & group leader eng. res, 45-48, asst. operating supvr. detergents div, 48-53, chief chemist, Moundsville Plant W.Va, 53-57, supt. quality control, 57-60, tech. asst. to plant mgr, 60-69, ENVIRON. ENGR, 69- Am. Inst. Chem. Eng. Utilization of agricultural wastes; synthetic organics; synthetic detergents; design, construction and operation of pilot plants; process design for pollution abatement. Address: Pheasant Hill Dr, Far Hills, NJ 07931.

FIRSTMAN, SIDNEY I(RVING), b. Chicago, Ill, Dec. 28, 31; m. 55; c. 5. OPERATIONS RESEARCH, ENGINEERING, B.S, California, Los Angeles, 54, M.S, 58; Ph.D.(eng, opers. res), Stanford, 64. Engr, Rand Corp, 56-63, group leader systs. anal, 63-65; asst. space & support opers, Planning Res. Corp, 65-66, mgr. space & support opers. sect, 66-67; mem. sr. staff systs. anal. of sociol-econ. systs, Rand Corp, 67-68; CORP. DIR. URBAN PROGS, PLANNING RES. CORP, 68- Sig.C, 54-56, 1st Lt. Opers. Res. Soc. Am; Am. Soc. Pub. Admin. Management of state and local government; city and regional development; system approaches to planning for local government. Address: Planning Research Corp, 1100 Glendon Ave, Los Angeles, CA 90024.

FIRTH, DAVID R(ICHARD), b. Bradford, Eng, Dec. 14, 32. PHYSICS, BIOPHYSICS. B.A, Cambridge, 54; M.A, Toronto, 55; Ph.D.(physics), McGill, 60. Instr. physics, Harvard, 60-63; Nat. Insts. Health fel. biophys, Washington (Seattle), 63-65; asst. prof. PHYSIOL, McGILL UNIV, 65-69, ASSOC. PROF, 69- High energy and low temperature physics; sensory mechanisms. Address: Dept. of Physiology, McIntyre Medical Sciences Center, McGill University, Montreal, Can.

FIRTH, FRANK EDWARD, b. Nashua, N.H, March 26, 05; m. 39; c. 3. BIOLOGY. B.S, Harvard, 36. Fisheries biologist, bur. fisheries, U.S. Dept. Commerce, 28-40, U.S. Fish & Wildlife Serv, 40-42, fisheries technologist & engr, 42-44; mgr. netting res. dept, Linen Thread Co, Inc, New York, 45-48; mgr. marine develop. sect. cuprinol. div, Darworth, Inc, 49-50; fisheries officer, sci. & tech. mission to Indonesia, For. Serv, U.S. Dept. State, Djakarta, 51-53; dir, Fisheries Eng, Inc, 54-66; ed. & writer, U.S. Army Natick Res. Labs, 66-68; MARINE RESOURCES WRITER, UNIV. R.I, 68- Hon. curator fishes, New Eng. Mus. Natural Hist, 34; fishing gear & methods consult, 54-55; surv. fisheries, Raytheon Int, Mex. & S.E. Asia, 55-; oceanic pollution studies consult, 71. Citation, U.S. Army Qm. Gen, 49; citation, secy. gen. agr, forestry & fisheries, Repub. Indonesia, 53. Liaison off, U.S. Fish & Wildlife Serv. & War Prod. Bd. Assoc. Am. Soc. Ichthyol. & Herpet; Am. Ord. Asn; fel. Am. Inst. Chem; fel. Am. Asn. Textile Chem. & Colorists; fel. N.Y. Acad. Sci; Mex. Natural Hist. Soc. Fisheries technology; engineering biology; netting and cordage fiber fungicides and improvements; marine protective finishes; economic development of natural resources; world fishing methods. Address: 1100 Randolph Ave, Milton, MA 02186.

FIRTH, WILLIAM C(HARLES), JR, b. Buffalo, N.Y, Apr. 9, 34; m. 61; c. 3. POLYMER CHEMISTRY. B.S, Rensselaer Polytech, 56; Shell Develop. Co. fel, univ. fel. & Ph.D.(org. chem), Colorado, 60. Asst. gen. chem, Colorado, 56-57; res. chemist, AM. CYANAMID CO, 60-64, SR. RES. CHEMIST, 64- Summers, jr. chemist, Am. Cyanamid Co, 55, chemist, 56; Eastman Kodak Co, 57. Am. Chem. Soc. Stereochemistry of reactions in a bridged polycyclic system; brominative decarboxylation reactions; fluorine chemistry; polymer synthesis. Address: Stamford Research Labs, American Cyanamid Co, 1937 W. Main St, Stamford, CN 06904.

FISCH, CHARLES, b. Poland, May 11, 21; nat; m. 43; c. 3. MEDICINE. A.B, Ind. Univ, 42, M.D, 44. Res. internal med, Vet. Admin. Hosp, Indianapolis, 48-50; fel. gastroenterol, Marion County Gen. Hosp, 50-51, cardiol, 51-53; PROF. MED. & DIR, CARDIOVASC. DIV, SCH. MED, IND. UNIV, 63-; DIR, KRANNERT HEART RES. INST, 53- Consult, La Rue Carter & St. Vincent's Hosps; fel, Coun. cardiol, Am. Heart Asn. Dipl, Am. Bd. Internal Med, 53, cardiovasc. med, 60. Am. Fedn. Clin Res; fel. Am. Col. Physicians; Am. Col. Cardiol; Am. Physiol. Soc. Electrolytes and drugs in cardiovascular disease. Address: Indiana University School of Medicine, 1100 W. Michigan, Indianapolis, IN 46202.

FISCH, FOREST N(ORLAND), b. Cope, Colo, July 6, 18; m. 43; c. 2. MATHEMATICS. A.B, Colo. State Col. Educ, 40, M.A, 47; George Peabody Col, 53-54. Asst. prof. MATH, UNIV. NORTH. COLO, 47-50, assoc. prof, 50-69, PROF, 69-, chmn. dept, 66-69. U.S.N.R, 42-45. Math. Asn. Am. General mathematics. Address: Dept. of Mathematics, University of Northern Colorado, Greeley, CO 80631.

FISCH, HERBERT A(LBERT), b. Cleveland, Ohio, Oct. 6, 23; m. 51; c. 3. CHEMICAL ENGINEERING. B.Sc, Case, 44; M.Sc, Ohio State, 48, Ph.D.

(chem. eng), 51. Asst. chem. eng, Ohio State, 47-48; chem. engr, Lubrizol Corp, Ohio 48-49; gaseous diffusion plant, Union Carbide Nuclear Co, Tenn, 51-53, phys. chemist, Oak Ridge Nat. Lab, 53-56; chem. engr, U.S. Atomic Energy Cmn, N.Y, 56-58; phys. chemist, Knolls Atomic Power Lab, Gen. Elec. Co, 58-62, res. metallurgist, lamp metals & components div, 62-67; PRIN. ENGR, TRW, INC, 67- U.S.A, 44-46, 2nd Lt. Am. Inst. Mining, Metall. & Petrol. Eng. Reactions between metals and gaseous or liquid environments; effects of nuclear radiation on corrosion; vacuum technology; high temperature oxidation/sulfidation resistant coatings; electrocoating. Address: TRW, Inc, 23555 Euclid Ave, Cleveland, OH 44117.

FISCH, MARCIA E(LIZABETH), b. Boston, Mass, Aug. 30, 43. ORGANIC CHEMISTRY. A.B, Mt. Holyoke Col, 65; M.A, Brandeis Univ, 67, Nat. Defense Educ. Act. fels, 67 & 70, Ph.D.(org. chem), 70. CHEMIST, POLAROID CORP, 71- Am. Chem. Soc. Organic synthesis. Address: 1684 Massachusetts Ave, Cambridge, MA 02138.

FISCH, MICHAEL H(AMILTON), b. Indianapolis, Ind, Oct. 2, 38; m. 64; c. 3. ORGANIC CHEMISTRY. A.B, Columbia Col, 60; Nat. Sci. Found. fel, Calif. Inst. Tech, 60-64, Ph.D.(chem), 65. NATO fel. org. chem, Inst. Chem, Strasbourg, France, 64-65; res. assoc, Mass. Inst. Tech, 65-66; ASST. PROF. CHEM, UNIV. CALIF, IRVINE, 66- Nat. Insts. Health fel, Mass. Inst. Tech, 66. Am. Chem. Soc; Brit. Chem. Soc; Chem. Soc. France. Organic photochemistry; transannular interactions; phytoalexins. Address: Dept. of Chemistry, University of California, Irvine, CA 92664.

FISCH, RICHARD S, b. N.Y.C, May 18, 32; m. 64; c. 1. PSYCHOPHYSICS. B.S, N.Y. Univ, 60; Columbia, 59-60. Mgr. color films, JERS Photo Serv, 55-56; supvr. color negative control, Technicolor Corp, 56-58, asst. mgr. qual. control, 58-60; supvr. photog. qual. control, MINN. MINING & MFG. CO, 60-64, asst. to photog. sci. mgr, 64-65, SUPVR. PHOTOG. COLOR TECH, 66- Guest instr, Columbia, 56-60. Photosci. observer, Perspective Quart. Photog. Sci, Eng, 64-; mem. ed. staff, Focal Press, N.Y. & Eng, 64- Sig.C, U.S.A, 53-55. Soc. Am. Photog. Sci. & Eng; Soc. Motion Picture & TV Eng; Royal Photog. Soc. Gt. Brit. Photographic science; photosensitive materials; manufacturing; testing. Address: 395 Woodlawn Ave, St. Paul, MN 55105.

FISCH, S(OLOMON), b. Havana, Cuba, May 30, 26; nat; m. 51; c. 4. INTERNAL MEDICINE, PHYSIOLOGY. B.S, Scranton, 45; fel, Rochester, 45-49, Ph.D, 49; M.D, N.Y. Univ, 53. Clin. instr. MED, N.Y. MED. COL, 59-64, clin. assoc, 64-65, ASST. CLIN. PROF, 65- Res. fel, cardiol, Vet. Hosp, New York, 58-60, dir. cardiac therapy res. unit, 60-70. Dipl, Am. Bd. Internal Med, 63. Chief med. servs, Hosp, Selfridge Air Force Base, Mich, U.S.A.F, 56-58, Res, 58-, Maj. Fel. Am. Col. Physicians; fel. Am. Col. Cardiol. Capillary hemodynamics; blood coagulation and anticoagulants; cardiovascular dynamics and therapy; clinical pharmacology and experimental therapeutics. Address: 1095 Park Ave, New York, NY 10028.

FISCHANG, WILLIAM J(OHN), b. Waterbury, Conn, Nov. 13, 32; m. 54; c. 2. ENTOMOLOGY. B.S, Cent. Conn. State Col, 54; Ph.D.(entom), Massachusetts, 63. Asst. prof. ENTOM, PURDUE UNIV, 63-66, assoc. prof, 66-70, PROF, 70- U.S.N.R, 54-57, Lt. Entom. Soc. Am; Am. Inst. Biol. Sci; Animal Behav. Soc. Insect response to light; pollination behavior of honey bees. Address: Dept. of Entomology, Purdue University, Lafayette, IN 47907.

FISCHBACH, D(AVID) B(IBB), b. Beckley, W.Va, Oct. 28, 26; m. 52; c. 2. SOLID STATE PHYSICS. B.A, Denison, 50, M.S, Yale, 51, du Pont fel, 52-53, Ph.D.(physics), 55. Res. engr, solid state physics, mats. sect, jet propulsion lab, Calif. Inst. Tech, 55-57, sr. res. engr, 57-61, res. specialist, 61-69; RES. ASSOC. PROF. & ACTING ASSOC. PROF. CERAMIC ENG, UNIV. WASH, 69- U.S.N, 44-46. Am. Phys. Soc; Metall. Soc. Behavior and properties of defects in solids; internal friction; ferromagnetic materials; properties and structure of carbons and graphite. Address: Ceramic Engineering Division, Roberts Hall, University of Washington, Seattle, WA 98105.

FISCHBACH, EUGENE, b. Meinerzhagen, Ger, June 18, 26; nat; m. 53; c. 2. MICROBIOLOGY. B.S, Champlain Col, 52. Lab. analyst, Borden Foods Co, 52-58, sanitarian, food processing plants, 58-60, supvr. food lab, 60-61; food technologist, D.C.A. Food Industs, Inc, 61-66; ITT CONTINENTAL BAKING CO, 66-67, RES. SUPVR, 67- U.S.N, 44-46. Am. Dairy Sci. Asn; Am. Soc. Microbiol; Am. Inst. Food Technol. Food protection, preservation, technology and poisoning. Address: Research Labs, ITT Continental Baking Co, P.O. Box 731, Rye, NY 10580.

FISCHBACH, FRITZ ALBERT, b. Kenosha, Wis, June 16, 37; m. 63; c. 2. BIOPHYSICS, BIOCHEMISTRY. B.S, Univ. Wis, 59, M.S, 61, Nat. Inst. Sci. fel, 61-65, Ph.D.(biophys), 65. Nat. Insts. Health fels. biophys, Univ. Sheffield, 65-66, 67-68 & Purdue Univ, 66-67; asst. prof, PHYSICS, UNIV. WISGREEN BAY, 68-70, ASSOC. PROF, 71- Summer res. awards, Wis. Alumnae Found, 69 & Nat. Sci. Found, 70. AAAS; Biophys. Soc. Structure of large biological molecules—viruses and iron storage molecules; mineral structure of biological iron crystals; natural atmospheric minerals and aerosols. Address: University of Wisconsin-Green Bay, 120 S. University Circle Dr, Green Bay, WI 54305.

FISCHBACH, HENRY, b. N.Y.C, May 2, 14; m. 45; c. 3. CHEMISTRY. A.B, Indiana, 35, A.M, 36, Ph.D.(inorg. chem), 38. Asst. chem, Indiana, 35-38; dir. ed. prog, Joseph E. Seagram & Sons, Inc, 39; food & drug inspector, FOOD & DRUG ADMIN, Dept. Health, Educ. & Welfare, 39-41, res. chemist, Wash, D.C, 41-45, in charge chem. res. antibiotics, med. div, 45-53, alkaloids div. pharmaceut. chem, 53-56, asst. to dir, bur. biol. & phys. scis, 56-59, DIR. div. food, 59-69, div. pesticides, bur. sci, 69-71, OFF. SCI, BUR. FOODS, 71- Secy. tech. cmt. lab. equip. & supplies, Fed. Specifications Bd, 48-54; panel mem, Bd. U.S. Civil Serv. Exam, 57-; mem. adv. panel & v.chmn. chem. cmt, food chemicals codex, food protection cmt, Nat. Acad. Sci-Nat. Res. Coun, 61-65, chmn, 65-; trace substances cmn, Int. Union Pure & Appl. Chem, 64-; mem. subcmt. reference mat, div. anal. chem, Nat. Acad. Sci-Nat. Res. Coun, 65-; chmn. joint Asn. Off. Anal. Chem-Am. Oil Chem. Soc-Am. Asn. Cereal Chem. mycotoxin comt, 65- Superior serv.

award, Dept. Health, Educ. & Welfare, 61, distinguished serv. award, 67. With Off. Sci. Res. & Develop; U.S.N, 44. AAAS; Am. Chem. Soc; Asn. Off. Anal. Chem; Inst. Food Tech. Antibiotics; food chemistry; chlorophyllins; continuous ascending chromatography; aflatoxins; pesticides; analytical research. Address: Bureau of Foods, Food & Drug Administration, Washington, DC 20204.

FISCHBACH, JOSEPH W(INSTON), b. N.Y.C, Nov. 12, 17; m. 45; c. 4. ENGINEERING. B.M.E, City Col, 38; M.M.E, N.Y. Univ, 44, M.A.E, 46, Dr.Eng.Sc, 52. Marine engr. submarines, Navy Yard, N.H, 39-41, mech. engr, Brooklyn Navy Yard, 41-44; ord. engr, rocket res, Ord. Ballistics Res. Labs, 45-46, chief rocket br, 46-49, mathematician, comput. lab, 49-52, chief anal. & comput. br, 52-54; asst. chief engr, U.S. Time Corp, 54-55; partner, Fischbach, Hamilton & Co, 55-56; mgt. consult, Booz, Allen & Hamilton, 56-59; PRES, FISCHBACH, McCOACH & ASSOC. INC, 59- Civilian with U.S.N, 39-44; U.S.A, 45-54. Am. Soc. Mech. Eng; Oper. Res. Soc. Am; Asn. Comput. Mach; Am. Inst. Aeronaut. & Astronaut; Inst. Mgt. Sci. Management and administration; mergers; organization studies; cost reductions; marketing; general surveys of operations systems and procedures; inventory, production, cost and management control; feasibility and application for electronic data processing; operations research; gradient methods for solution of differential equations; aerodynamics; rocket research; automatic processes and servo control; rockets and missiles. Address: 35 Beach Ave, Larchmont, NY 10538.

FISCHBACK, BRYANT C, b. Alhambra, Calif, Nov. 29, 26; m. 50; c. 3. ORGANIC CHEMISTRY. B.S, California, Los Angeles, 49. Chemist, RES. DEPT, DOW CHEM, U.S.A, 49-56, proj. leader, 56-68, TECH. RES. & DEVELOP. MGR, PROD. DEPTS-WEST, 68- U.S.A, 44-46. Am. Chem. Soc; Brit. Chem. Soc. Organic synthesis of new insecticides; herbicides; general agricultural chemicals; coccidiostats; animal health products; pharmaceuticals; mechanism of nitration reactions; synthesis of ore flotation agents; research and development of secondary oil recovery, mining and environmental control systems. Address: Product Depts-West, Dow Chemical, U.S.A, 2800 Mitchell Dr, Walnut Creek, CA 94598.

FISCHBARG, JORGE, b. Buenos Aires, Arg, Aug. 14, 35; m. 64; c. 2. PHYSIOLOGY, BIOPHYSICS. B.S, Univ. Buenos Aires, 53, M.D, 62, fel, 63-64; Ph.D.(physiol), Univ. Chicago, 71. Asst. biophys, sch. med, Univ. Buenos Aires, 62-64; trainee ophthal, eye res. lab, Univ. Louisville, 64-65; math. biol, Univ. Chicago 65-67, physiol, 67-70; ASST. PROF. OPHTHAL, COLUMBIA UNIV, 70- Res. grants, Fight for Sight, Inc, N.Y, 70- & Nat. Eye Inst, 71- Argentine army, 55-56. Biophys. Soc; Asn. Res. Vision & Ophthal. Ionic transport across biological membranes; electrophysiology of muscle. Address: Ophthalmology Research, Columbia University, 630 W. 168th St, New York, NY 10032.

FISCHBECK, HELMUT J, b. Tübingen, Ger, Oct. 19, 28; m. 55; c. 2. PHYSICS. M.A, Heidelberg, 55; Ph.D.(physics), Indiana, 60. Instr. PHYSICS, Univ. Mich, 60-61, asst. prof, 62-66; ASSOC. PROF. PHYSICS & RADIOL. SCIS, UNIV. OKLA, 66- Am. Phys. Soc. Nuclear spectroscopy. Address: Dept. of Physics, University of Oklahoma, Norman, OK 73069.

FISCHBECK, K(ENNETH) H(ENRY), b. Wallington, N.J, Mar. 30, 24; m. 47; c. 3. ENGINEERING. B S, Mass. Inst. Tech, 47; M.S, Wayne, 54; M.S, Pennsylvania, 58, Ph.D.(elec. eng), 61. Sr. engr, res. labs, Bendix Aviation Corp, 47-54; mem. tech. staff, defense elec. prod, Radio Corp. Am, 54-66, mgr. printing res, RCA Labs, 66-68, STAFF TECH. ADV, RCA CORP, 68- U.S.N.R, 43-47, Lt.(jg). AAAS; Am. Phys. Soc; Inst. Elec. & Electronics Eng. Automata and control; nuclear technology; energy conversion; electronic data processing; graphic arts. Address: RCA Corp, David Sarnoff Research Center, Princeton, NJ 08540.

FISCHBEIN, IRWIN W(ILLIAM), b. New York, N.Y, Dec. 6, 20; m. 42; c. 2. BIOPHYSICS. B.S, Syracuse, 43, M.S, 47; Ph.D.(biophys), California, 50. Res. technician, wood tech, Forest Prods. Lab, Texas Forest Serv, 46-47; tech. asst, sch. forestry, California, 47-50; res. physicist, electron micros, GILLETTE CO, 50-56, res, supvr, 56-57, sect. head, microphysics, 57-58, asst. dir. res, 58-71, DIR. CHEM. & MAT. RES. DIV, 71- Aircraft inspector, H.J. Heinz Co, 43; Hardman Peck & Co, 44. C.Eng, U.S.A, 44. AAAS; Am. Chem. Soc; Electron Micros. Soc. Am. Electron microscopy; metallurgy; corrosion; electron diffraction; surface phenomena; lubrication; polymer chemistry and fluorocarbons. Address: Chemical & Materials Research Division, Gillette Co, Gillette Park, Boston, MA 02106.

FISCHBEIN, WILLIAM L, b. N.Y.C, June 3, 41; m. 70. SPACE & ELEMENTARY PARTICLE PHYSICS. A.B, Columbia, 62; M.S, Wisconsin, Madison, 64, Ph.D.(physics), 67. Asst. prof. elem. particle physics, Carnegie-Mellon Univ, 66-67; RES. PHYSICIST, GRUMMAN AEROSPACE CORP, 67- AAAS; Am. Phys. Soc. Cosmic rays, cosmic ray measurements in space; high energy astrophysics; spark chambers; physics of light hyperfragments; neutral K meson phenomenology; accelerator beam design; bubble chambers. Address: Grumman Aerospace Corp, Research Dept. 583, Plant 26, Bethpage, NY 11714.

FISCHEL, DAVID, b. Du Bois, Pa, Sept. 12, 36; m. 60; c. 3. ASTROPHYSICS. Sc.B, Brown, 58; M.A, Indiana, 61, Ph.D.(astrophys), 63. RES. SCIENTIST astrophys, space sci. div, Ames Res. Ctr, NASA, 63-65; ASTROPHYS. LAB. SPACE SCI, ASTROPHYS. BR, GODDARD SPACE FLIGHT CTR, 65-, HEAD ANAL. SECT, LAB. OPTICAL ASTRON, 70- Asst, Los Alamos Sci. Lab, Univ. Calif, summers 59-61. Am. Astron. Soc; fel. Royal Astron. Soc; Int. Astron. Union. Theoretical model stellar atmospheres and interiors; quantum mechanics of atomic and molecular spectroscopy; numerical methods for electronic computers; plasma thermodynamics. Address: Code 670, Lab. for Optical Astronomy, Goddard Space Flight Center, NASA, Greenbelt, MD 20771.

FISCHEL, EDWARD E(LLIOT), b. N.Y, July 29, 20; m. 43; c. 2. INTERNAL MEDICINE. B.A, Columbia, 41, M.D, 44, Sc.D.(med), 48. Asst. physician, Presby. Hosp, 47-54; DIR. DEPT. MED, BRONX-LEBANON HOSP. CTR, 54-; ASSOC. CLIN. PROF. MED, COLUMBIA UNIV, 69-, assoc, dept. med, 50-55. Assoc. clin. prof, Albert Einstein Col. Med, 57-69; chmn. med.

admin. coun, Arthritis Found, 68-69; mem, med. & sci. adv. comt, Arthritis & Rheumatism Found; coun. rheumatic fever & congenital heart disease, Am. Heart Asn. AAAS; Am. Soc. Clin. Invest; Am. Soc. Exp. Biol. & Med; Am. Med. Asn; Am. Asn. Immunol; Am. Heart Asn; Am. Rheumatism Asn.(pres, 68-69); Asn. Am. Med. Cols; fel. Am. Col. Physicians; Am. Fedn. Clin. Res; Infectious Diseases Soc. Am. Immunochemistry; hypersensitivity reaction; rheumatic diseases; nephritis; inflamation; serum complement activity; immunosuppression by cortisone. Address: Bronx-Lebanon Hospital Center, 1276 Fulton Ave, Bronx, NY 10456.

FISCHELIS, ROBERT P(HILIPP), b. Phila, Pa, Aug. 16, 91; m. 19. PHARMACY, PHARMACEUTICAL CHEMISTRY. Ph.G, Medico-Chirurg. Col. Phila, 11, Ph.C, 12, Phar.D, 13; B.S, Temple, 12; Ph.M, Phila. Col. Pharm, 18, hon. Phar.D, 45; hon. Sc.D, Rutgers, 42. Instr. pharm. & org. chem, Medico-Chirurg. Col. Phila, 12-14; assoc. ed, Druggist Circular, 14-16; chemist & tech. exec, H.K. Mulfurd Co, 16-19; CONSULT. PHARMACIST & CHEMIST, 19-; EMER. DEAN COL. PHARM, OHIO NORTH. UNIV, 70- Ed, Pa. Pharmacist, 16-19; lectr, Phila. Col. Pharm, 16-45; pres, Drug Trade Bur. Pub. Info, 20-29, dir. & ed, 29-32; prof. & dean, N.J. Col. Pharm, 21-25; coop. state off, food & drug admin, Fed. Security Agency, 26-44; ed, N.J. Jour. Pharm, 27-29, 35-40; mem. res. staff, Comt. Costs Med. Care, 29-33; v.pres, Nat. Asn. Bds. Pharm, 31-34; Conf. Allied Med. Professions, 34; Nat. Health Conf, 38; revision comt, U.S. Pharmacopoeia, 40-; Am. Coun. Pharmaceut. Educ, 40-; dir. chem, drugs & health supplies div, off. civilian requirements, War Prod. Bd, 41-45; adv, Am. del. Int. Health Conf, 46-; prof. lectr, George Washington Univ, 46-; hon. consult, bur. med. & surg, U.S. Navy, 47-; mem. exec. comt, Nat. Health Assembly, 48-; dir. pharmacist, U.S. Pub. Health Serv: consult, Surgeon. Gen, Dept. Army; consult, Off. Civil Defense Planning; mem, Nat. Pharmaceut. Syllabus Comt; Pharmaceut. Recipe Book Comt; Res. Coun. Probs. of Alcohol; consult. to med. dir, Nat. Security Resources Bd. C.W.S, U.S.A, 18. AAAS; Am. Chem. Soc.(managing ed, J. Indust. & Eng. Chem, 22-27); Am. Pharmaceut. Asn.(secy, 23-25, v.pres, 33, pres, 34, exec. secy. & gen. mgr, 45-, ed. dir, Jour, 45-); Am. Asn. Cols. Pharm.(v.pres, 24); Am. Pub. Health Asn; Am. Med. Asn. Principles and practice of pharmacy; basic material for a pharmaceutical curriculum; industrial pharmacy; pharmaceutical education; pharmaceutical law enforcement; creosote; digitalis; costs of medicines; medical materials industry; ethylnitrite; drug control. Address: 1 University Pkwy, Ada, OH 45810.

FISCHELL, ROBERT E, b. New York, N.Y, Feb. 10, 29; m. 51; c. 3. SPACE PHYSICS. B.S.M.E, Duke, 51; M.S, Maryland, 53. Physicist, U.S. Naval Ord. Lab, Md, 51-56; prin. staff physicist, Emerson Res. Labs, 56-59; sr. staff physicist, APPL. PHYSICS LAB, JOHN HOPKINS UNIV, 59-60, proj. supvr, 60-64, GROUP SUPVR, 64-, PRIN. STAFF PHYSICIST, 63- Consult, U.S. Air Force, 59-61; mem. ad hoc comt, NASA Dept. Defense, 63; consult, French Space Agency, 65; prin. proj. scientist, Navy Navigation Satellites, 69-; consult, NASA Hq, 71; mem. space comt, Int. Fed. Auto. Control, 71- Nat. Capital Award, Wash. Acad. Sci, 64. Am. Inst. Aeronaut. & Astronaut; Am. Soc. Mech. Eng.(award, 63); Inst. Elec. & Electronics Eng. Attitude control systems for earth satellites; space electric power systems; cardiac pacemakers. Address: 1027 McCeney Ave, Silver Spring, MD 20901.

FISCHER, ALBERT G, b. Ilmenau, Ger, July 5, 28; U.S. citizen; m. 56; c. 3. SOLID STATE ELECTRONICS. Diplom-Physiker, Univ. Giessen, 55, Dr. phil. nat, 57. Scientist, lamp div, Gen. Elec. Co, 58-59; mem. tech. staff, RCA Labs, 59-71; ADV. SCIENTIST, RES. & DEVELOP. CTR, WESTINGHOUSE ELEC. CORP, 71- Electrochem. Soc; Inst. Elec. & Electronics Eng. Electro luminescence; materials science; single crystal growth; films; liquid crystals; thin-film transistors. Address: Research & Development Center, Westinghouse Electric Corp, Pittsburgh, PA 15235.

FISCHER, ÁLBERT K(ARL), b. Newark, N.J, Oct. 15, 31; m. 59; c. 3. INORGANIC CHEMISTRY. B.A, N.Y. Univ, 53; fel, Harvard, 53-57, M.A, 55, Ph.D.(chem), 58. Res. chemist, Union Carbide Metals Co. Div, Union Carbide Corp, 57-60, Union Carbide Chems. Co. Div, 60-62; ASSOC. CHEMIST, ARGONNE NAT. LAB, 62- AAAS; Am. Chem. Soc; Am. Inst. Chem; The Chem. Soc. Metal carbonyls; organometallics; fused salt and liquid metal chemistry. Address: Chemical Engineering Division, Argonne National Lab, Argonne, IL 60439.

FISCHER, ALFRED G(EORGE), b. Rothenburg, Ger, Dec. 10, 20; U.S. citizen; m. 39; c. 3. GEOLOGY. B.A, Wisconsin, 39, M.A, 40; Ph.D, Columbia, 50. Instr. geol, Va. Polytech, 41-43; geologist, Stanolind Oil & Gas Co, Kans, 43-44, Fla, 44-46; instr. geol, Rochester, 47-48; Kansas, 48-50, asst. prof, 50-51; sr. geologist, Int. Petrol. Co, Peru, 51-56; asst. prof. GEOL, PRINCETON, 56-57, assoc. prof, 57-63, PROF, 63- John Simon Guggenheim fel, 69-70. Geol. Soc. Am; Soc. Econ. Paleont. & Mineral; Paleont. Soc; Am. Asn. Petrol. Geol. Invertebrate paleontology; paleoecology; historical geology; carbonate sediments; sedimentation. Address: Dept. of Geology, Princeton University, Princeton, NJ 08540.

FISCHER, ANTHONY JOSEPH, b. Philadelphia, Pa, Jan. 8, 02; m. 29; c. 2. CHEMICAL ENGINEERING. B.S, Pennsylvania, 24; Dorr Sewage fel, Rutgers, 25-28, M.S, 26, Ph.D.(biol. chem), 28. Jr. chemist, sewage invests. lab, N.J. Exp. Sta, 24-25; sanit. develop. engineer, Dorr Co, N.Y, 28-50, asst. mgr. develop. dept, 50-56, dir. centrifugal tech. div, DORR-OLIVER, INC, 56-59, develop. dept, 59-63, EXEC. ENGR, GROWTH DEPT, 63- Field investr, For. Econ. Admin, 45. Allen award, N.Y. State Sewage Works Asn, 36; Agar award & hon. mem, Water Pollution Control Fedn, 50, Bedell award, 52. Am. Soc. Civil Eng; Am. Inst. Chem. Eng. Water, sewage and trade waste treatment; effect of various factors on digestion of raw sewage sludge; sewage disposal; chemical engineering processing. Address: 53 Stonehenge Rd, Manhasset, NY 11030.

FISCHER, ARTHUR H, b. Providence, R.I, May 15, 00; m. 38; c. 1. PHYSICAL CHEMISTRY. B.S, Mass. Inst. Technol, 22; Ph.D.(phys. chem), Berlin, 24. Res. chemist, Guggenheim Bros. Lab, 25-29, lab. mgr, 29-34; v.pres, MINEREC CORP, 34-49, PRES, 49- Instr, Wash. Sq. Col, N.Y. Univ, 25-26. AAAS; Am. Chem. Soc; Am. Inst. Mining, Metall. & Petrol. Eng. Surface chemistry; ore flotation. Address: Minerec Corp, Room 3546, 120 Broadway, New York, NY 10005.

FISCHER, BARBARA ANN, b. N.Y.C, Oct. 15, 38. PHYSIOLOGY. B,A, Missouri, 60; M.A, California, Berkeley, 62; NASA traineeship, St. Louis, 63-66, Ph.D.(physiol), 67. ASST. PROF. BIOL, UNIV. SOUTH. MISS, 67- Am. Soc. Ichthyol. & Herpet; Am. Soc. Zool. Comparative vertebrate physiology; environmental, space and human physiology; temperature regulation. Address: Dept. of Biology, University of Southern Mississippi, Hattiesburg, MS 39401.

FISCHER, C. RUTHERFORD, b. New York, N.Y, June 21, 34; m. 62; c. 1. MOLECULAR & SOLID STATE PHYSICS. B.S, City Col. New York, 54; M.S, Yale, 55, Ph.D.(physics), 60. Asst. prof. PHYSICS, New Mexico State, 59-61; Adelphi, 61-64; assoc. prof, QUEENS COL.(N.Y), 64-70, PROF, 70- Nat. Sci. Found. grant, Adelphi Univ, 62-64; consult, U.S. Army Res. Off, Durham, 70-71. Am. Phys. Soc. Nuclear scattering and binding; electron scattering by nuclei; scattering theory; molecular structure and spectra; point defects in ionic crystal; ionic interactions. Address: Dept. of Physics, Queens College, Flushing, NY 11367.

FISCHER, CARL C(ASTLE), b. Phila, Pa, Oct. 13, 02; m. 31; c. 3. PEDIATRICS. B.S, Princeton, 24; M.D, Hahnemann Med. Col, 28, hon. M.A, 38. Asst. PEDIAT, HAHNEMANN MED. COL, 30-33, from instr. to assoc. prof, 33-46, prof, 46-69, EMER. PROF, 69-, head dept, 46-67, dir. med. affairs, 67-69. Consult, Selective Serv. Fel. Am. Med. Asn; fel. Am. Col. Physicians; fel. Am. Acad. Pediat.(pres, 61-62). General pediatrics; problems of the newborn; nutrition; infant diseases; metabolic diseases. Address: Oak Hill, Apt. W-321, Narberth, PA 19072.

FISCHER, CHARLES CLAYTON, b. South Bend, Ind, Feb. 11, 28; m. 54; c. 1. FLORICULTURE, ORNAMENTAL HORTICULTURE. B.S, Mich. State, 55, M.S, 56. Asst. agr. agent, exten. serv, Colorado State, 56-57; 4-H agent, coop. exten. serv, Mich. State, 57-59; ASSOC. PROF. FLORICULT. & ORNAMENTAL HORT, CORNELL UNIV, 59- U.S.A, 46-48, Sgt. Am. Soc. Hort. Sci. Research interpretation for consumer application; conservatory plants; perennials; woody plants; landscaping. Address: 49C Plant Science Bldg, Cornell University, Ithaca, NY 14850.

FISCHER, CHARLOTTE FROESE, b. Ukraine, Russia, Sept. 21, 29; nat; m. 67; c. 1. APPLIED MATHEMATICS. B.A, Univ. B.C, 52, M.A, 54; Ph.D.(appl. math), Cambridge, 57. Asst. prof. math, Univ. B.C, 57-63, assoc. prof, 63-65, PROF, 65-67; APPL. ANALYSIS & COMPUT. SCI, UNIV. WATERLOO, 67- Programmer & numerical analyst, Pac. Oceanog. Group, B.C, 58; res. fel, Harvard, 63; Sloan fel, 64. Asn. Comput. Mach; Can. Math. Cong; Can. Info. Processing Soc; Soc. Indust. & Appl. Math. Atomic structure calculations; numerical analysis. Address: Dept. of Applied Analysis & Computer Science, University of Waterloo, Waterloo, Ont, Can.

FISCHER, CRAIG LELAND, b. Brooklyn, N.Y, Feb. 17, 37; m. 62; c. 2. ANATOMIC PATHOLOGY, LABORATORY MEDICINE. B.S, Kans. State Univ, 58; M.D, Univ. Kans, 62. Intern, anat. path, med. ctr, Univ. Kans, 63-64; res. med. off, Manned Spacecraft Ctr, NASA, 64-67; resident, clin. path, col. med, Baylor Univ, 67-68; pathologist & chief clin. labs, Manned Spacecraft Ctr, NASA, 68-71; DIR, PATH. LABS. OF HOUSTON, INC, 71- Res. fel. nuclear med, col. med, Baylor Univ, 65-66, adj. prof, Inst. Health Serv. Res, 70-; res. instr, dept. internal med, Univ. Tex. Med. Br, Galveston, 68-, clin. asst. prof, dept. path, 70- NASA sustained superior performance award, 69, superior achievement award, 69, Apollo Achievement Award, 70. Med.C, U.S.A, 65-67, Capt. AAAS; Aerospace Med. Asn; N.Y. Acad. Sci; Col. Am. Path; Under Sea Med. Soc; Am. Soc. Clin. Path; Am. Public Health Asn. Immunohematologic and clinical chemical alterations of man, incident to protracted space flight; laboratory data management; automation of the clinical laboratory. Address: 18614 Capetown Dr, Houston, TX 77058.

FISCHER, DAVID JOHN, b. Jefferson City, Mo, Apr. 30, 28; m. 54; c. 2. PHYSICAL CHEMISTRY. B.S, Missouri, 50, M.S, 52, E.I. du Pont de Nemours & Co. fel, 53-54, Ph.D.(phys. chem), 54. Proj. group leader, polymer res. lab, Dow Corning Corp, 56-59, dept. supvr, Hyper-Pure Silicon Div, 59-62; sr. chemist, Midwest Res. Inst, 62-65; mgr. microcircuits res. dept, CORNING GLASS WORKS, 65-68, mgr. spec. projs, adv. mkt. develop, 68-69, res. assoc, 69-70, MGR. BIO-ORGANIC DEVELOP, 70- U.S.A.F, 54-56, 1st Lt. Am. Chem. Soc; Electrochem. Soc. Inorganic polymers and elastomers; radiation effects in materials; preparation of solid state materials; energy conversion, thermoelectric and biological systems; fluorescent materials as simulants and tracers; stabilized and immobilized enzymes for industrial, clinical and medical applications. Address: Bio-Organic Development Dept, Corning Glass Works, Sullivan Park, Corning, NY 14830.

FISCHER, D(AVID) L(LOYD), b. Calif, June 7, 28; m. 56. NUCLEAR PHYSICS. B.S, California, 50, Ph.D.(physics), 56. PHYSICIST, ATOMIC POWER EQUIP. DEPT, GEN. ELEC. CO, 56- Am. Nuclear Soc. Reactor physics. Address: 6834 Hampton Dr, San Jose, CA 95120.

FISCHER, DAVID SEYMOUR, b. Brooklyn, N.Y, May 13, 30; m. 58; c. 3. INTERNAL MEDICINE, HEMATOLOGY. A.B, Williams Col, 51; M.D, Harvard, 55. Intern med, univ. serv, Kings County Hosp, Brooklyn, N.Y, 55-56; res, Univ. Utah Hosps, 56-57; Montefiore Hosp, New York, 57-58; clin. fel. hemat, Washington (Seattle), 58-59; Nat. Cancer Inst. res. fel, pharmacol, SCH. MED, YALE, 62-64, asst. prof. pharmacol. & med, 64-66, ASST. CLIN. PROF. MED, 66-, res. assoc. psychol, 66-67. Res. collab, Brookhaven Nat. Lab, 61-62. Med.C, U.S.A, 59-61, Capt. Dipl, Am. Bd. Internal Med. Am. Fedn. Clin. Res; fel. Am. Col. Physicians; Transplantation Soc; Am. Med. Asn; Am. Soc. Hemat; Am. Soc. Clin. Oncol. Chemotherapy of cancer; hematology. Address: 111 Park St, New Haven, CT 06511.

FISCHER, ED(MOND) H, b. Shanghai, China, Apr. 6, 20; m. 48; c. 2. BIOCHEMISTRY. Mat.Fed, State Col. Geneva, 39; Lic. es. Sc, Geneva, 43, dipl, 44, Ph.D.(chem), 47. Asst. org. chem. labs, Geneva, 46-48, Swiss Found. res. fel. chem, 48, privat-docent, 50, Rockefeller Found. res. fel, 50-53; asst. prof. BIOCHEM, SCH. MED, UNIV. WASH, 53-56, assoc. prof, 56-61, PROF, 61- Lederle med. faculty award, 55; Jaubert Prize, 68. Am. Chem. Soc; Am. Soc. Biol. Chem; Swiss Chem. Soc.(Warner medal, 52). Enzymology; carbohydrate metabolism; protein structure. Address: 3631 43rd, N.E, Seattle, WA 98105.

FISCHER, EDWARD G(EORGE), b. N.Y.C, March 31, 16; m. 44; c. 4. MECHANICS. B.S, Cooper Union, 36; M.S, 39, Ph.D.(math, eng), 46; Columbia. CONSULT. ENGR, RES. LAB, WESTINGHOUSE ELEC. CORP, 36- Instr, grad. sch, Pittsburgh, 46-59. Cert. appreciation, U.S. Army Corps Eng. Am. Soc. Mech. Eng; Soc. Exp. Stress Anal; Inst. Environ. Sci; Seismol. Soc. Am. Vibration; shock; noise; seismic design. Address: 5525 Third St, Verona, PA 15147.

FISCHER, ERNST, b. Breslau, Ger, Sept. 27, 96; nat. 40; m. 25; c. 2. MUSCULAR PHYSIOLOGY. M.D, Frankfurt, 24, Dr. habil (physiol), 28; Gottingen, 23. Instr. physiol, Frankfurt, 24-28, asst. prof, 28-34; vis. assoc, sch. med. & dent, Rochester, 34-35; assoc. physiol. & pharmacol, Med. Col. Va, 35-37, assoc. prof, physiol, 37-44, prof, 44-66, chief basic res. div, Baruch Ctr. Phys. Med, 44-49, chmn. dept. physiol, 63-66; vis. prof, Univ. Ankara Med. Ctr, 66-67; res. prof. phys. med. & rehab, Albany Med. Col, 68-71; RETIRED. Ger. Army, 14-18. AAAS; Soc. Exp. Biol. & Med; Am. Physiol. Soc; Soc. Gen. Physiol; fel. Am. Med. Asn. Nerve and muscle physiology; submicroscopical structure of muscle; enzyme system of muscles; prevention of muscular atrophy; physiology and pharmacology of muscle, heart, nerve and central nervous system. Address: 3110 Manor Dr, Richard, VA 23230.

FISCHER, EUGENE C(HARLES), b. New York, N.Y, Apr. 7, 40; m. 64; c. 3. MARINE MICROBIOLOGY, BIOLOGICAL OCEANOGRAPHY. B.S, Iona Col, 61; fel, St. John's (N.Y), 61-64, M.S, 63, Ph.D.(marine microbiol), 66. Staff scientist microbiol, U.S. Naval Appl. Sci. Lab, 64-65, res. oceanogr, 65-70, HEAD, OCEAN ENVIRON. BR, U.S. NAVAL SHIP RES. & DEVELOP. LAB, ANNAPOLIS, 70- Commanding Off. & Dir. Award, U.S. Naval Appl. Sci. Lab, 66. AAAS; Am. Soc. Microbiol; Sci. Res. Soc. Am; Int. Asn. Phys. Oceanog. Microbial physiology; deep ocean-high pressure microbial physiology; marine fouling; pollution abatement. Address: 107 Chautaugua Rd, Indian Hills, Arnold, MD 21012.

FISCHER, FERDINAND JOSEPH, b. Kansas City, Mo, June 13, 40; m. 62; c. 1. ENGINEERING MECHANICS, APPLIED MATHEMATICS. B.S, Kansas, 62; M.S, Rice, 64; Nat. Sci. Found. fel, Harvard, 64-66, M.A, 65, Ph.D.(appl. math), 68. Res. asst. eng. mech, Harvard, 66-68; mathematician, SHELL DEVELOP. CO, 67-70, RES. ENGR, 70- Lectr, Univ. Houston, 68- Am. Soc. Mech. Eng. Elastic shell theory; continuum mechanics; numerical analysis. Address: 13130 Rummel Creek, Houston, TX 77024.

FISCHER, FRANCIS (E), b. Waukegan, Ill, May 30, 21; m. 48; c. 3. ORGANIC CHEMISTRY. B.S, Univ. Ill, 45. Sr. res. chemist, ABBOTT LABS, 45-57, GROUP LEADER ORG. PREPARATIONS, 57- Am. Chem. Soc. Pharmaceuticals. Address: Dept. 482, Abbott Labs, North Chicago, IL 60064.

FISCHER, FRANZ, b. Nürnberg, Germany, Mar. 15, 08; nat; m. 40; c. 1. EXPERIMENTAL PHYSICS. B.A, Ohm Polytech, Germany, 29; Ph.D.(physics), Erlangen, 36. Develop. engr. acoustics, Siemens & Halske, Germany, 29-31, head dept. develop, 37-45; prof. physics, Ohm Polytech, 46-52; prin. engr. develop, Bulova Res. & Develop. Labs, 53-59; staff scientist, Consol. Diesel Elec. Corp, 59-61; dir. res. & develop. div, Mergenthaler Linotype Co, 61-71; RETIRED. Typesetting machinery; graphic arts and display systems; optical character recognition. Address: 27 Mohogan Lane, Port Chester, NY 10573.

FISCHER, FREDERIC PHILIP, b. N.Y.C, June 1, 08; m. 40; c. 3. ELECTRICAL ENGINEERING. B.Sc, Rutgers, 32; Byllesby fel, Lehigh, 33, M.Sc, 35; Mass. Inst. Technol; Maryland, 64. Asst. prof, Rutgers, 39-42; Lehigh, 42-44; assoc. prof, Connecticut, 44-50; PROF. ELEC. ENG. & CHMN. DEPT, STATE UNIV. N.Y. BUFFALO, 50- Summer lectr, radar sch, Mass. Inst. Tech, 43. Consult, Cornell Aeronaut. Lab; Pratt & Whitney Aircraft Corp; Allen D. Cardwell Mfg. Corp. Am. Soc. Eng. Educ; sr. mem. Inst. Elec. & Electronics Eng. Motional circuit theory; circuits with time-varying parameters; servocontrols; biomedical engineering with associated instrumentations. Address: Dept. of Electrical Engineering, State University of New York at Buffalo, Buffalo, NY 14214.

FISCHER, GASTON, b. La Chaux-de-Fonds, Switz, Sept. 28, 29; m. 61; c. 4. SOLID STATE PHYSICS. Dipl, Swiss Fed. Inst. Technol, 53; Ph.D.(physics), Univ. Neuchâtel, 59. Res. off, Nat. Res. Coun. Can, 56-62; mem. staff, RCA Cent. Lab, Princeton, 62-63, Zurich, 63-68; lectr, Univ. Neuchâtel, 63-66; PROF. PHYSICS, UNIV. MONTREAL, 68- Am. Phys. Soc; Am. Asn. Physics Teachers. Superconductivity. Address: Dept. of Physics, University of Montreal, P.O. Box 6128, Montreal 101, Que, Can.

FISCHER, GEORGE A, b. Cleveland, Ohio, Mar. 27, 39; m. 62; c. 2. BIOCHEMISTRY, CLINICAL CHEMISTRY. B.S, Univ. Detroit, 61, M.S, 64, Ph.D.(biochem), 67. CLINICAL CHEMIST, HARPER HOSP, 66- AAAS; Am. Chem. Soc; Am. Asn. Clin. Chem. Lipid metabolism; chemistry of snake venoms; hormone analysis; mechanisms and chemistry of hypertension. Address: Harper Hospital, 3825 Brush St, Detroit, MI 48201.

FISCHER, GEORGE J, b. Chicago, Ill, Aug. 6, 18; m. 48; c. 1. PHYSICS. B.S, Chicago, 46, M.S, 50; Ph.D.(physics), Iowa, 57. Instr. physics, Coe Col, 51-54; asst, Iowa, 55-56; asst. physicist, reactor eng. div, ARGONNE NAT. LAB, 56-58, assoc. physicist, 58-59, SR. PHYSICIST, 69-, HEAD ACCIDENT ANAL. & SAFETY EVAL. GROUP, REACTOR ANAL. & SAFETY DIV, 70- Am. Phys. Soc; Am. Nuclear Soc; Fedn. Am. Sci. Theoretical and experimental reactor physics. Address: 1048 Prairie Ave, Downers Grove, IL 60515.

FISCHER, GEORGE J, b. Bronx, N.Y, Mar. 30, 25; m. 48; c. 2. METALLURGICAL ENGINEERING. B.Met.E, Polytech. Inst. Brooklyn, 49, M.Met.E, 53. Instr. METALL, Polytech. Inst. Brooklyn, 48-50; plant metallurgist, West. Elec. Co, 50-53; dept. head, Sam Tour & Co, 53-55; asst. prof, POLYTECH. INST. BROOKLYN, 55-59, assoc. prof, 59-65, PROF, 65-, HEAD DEPT, 71-, admin. off, div. metall. eng, 61-71. Res. grants, Int. Nickel Co, 60-61, Curtiss-Wright Corp, 62-65; Nat. Sci. Found. res. grant, 63-65, summer inst. grants, 67-71. U.S.A, 44-65, S/Sgt. Am. Soc. Metals; Am. Inst. Mining, Metall. & Petrol. Eng; Am. Soc. Test. & Mat. Physical metallurgy; weldability criteria of metallic materials. Address: Division of Metallurgical Engineering, Polytechnic Institute of Brooklyn, 333 Jay St, Brooklyn, NY 11201.

FISCHER, GEORGE W(ILLIAM), b. Indianapolis, Ind, April 30, 06; m. 28; c. 2. PLANT PATHOLOGY. B.S, Butler, 28; M.S, Northwestern, 29; Cole fel, Michigan, 32-34, Ph.D.(mycol, plant path), 34. Asst. bot, Northwestern, 28-29; instr, Butler, 29-30; asst, Michigan, 30-32; instr. plant path, State Col. Wash, 34-36; agent, bur. plant indust, U.S. Dept. Agr, 36-37, assoc. pathologist, 37-44, pathologist, 44-45; prof. plant path. & chmn. dept, Wash. State Univ, 45-58, acting dean col. agr, 58-61, dean, 61-65, dir. resident instr, 65-67; exec. dir, Int. Bot. Cong, Seattle, Wash, 67-69; RETIRED. AAAS; Mycol. Soc. Am; Am. Phytopath. Soc.(v.pres, 55, pres, 57). Taxonomy and biology of smut fungi. Address: Star Route 2, Box 5-C, Union, WA 98592.

FISCHER, G(ERHARD) E(MIL), b. Berlin, Ger, Mar. 1, 28; nat; m. 51; c. 2. PARTICLE PHYSICS. B.A.Sc, Univ. Toronto, 49; Ph.D.(physics), Univ. Calif, 54. Instr. physics, Columbia Univ, 54-57, asst. prof, 57-59; res. fel, Harvard, 59-63, sr. res. assoc, 63-65; STAFF MEM. STANFORD LINEAR ACCELERATOR CTR, 65- Am. Phys. Soc. Nuclear reactions; pions; high energy physics. Address: Stanford Linear Accelerator Center, Box 4349, Stanford, CA 94305.

FISCHER, GLENN ALBERT, b. Pritchett, Colo, Nov. 18, 22; m. 46; c. 2. GENETICS, PHARMACOLOGY. B.S, Colorado, 49, M.S, Calif. Inst. Technol, 51, Ph.D.(genetics), 54. Res. assoc, Michigan, 54; asst. res. prof, sch. med, George Washington, 55; asst. prof. pharmacol, Puerto Rico, 55; sch. med, Yale, 58-63, assoc. prof, 63-69; PROF. BIOCHEM. PHARMACOL, BROWN UNIV, 69- Address: Dept. of Biological & Medical Sciences, Brown University, Providence, RI 02912.

FISCHER, G(LENN) A(LBERT), b. Lyons, Ill, May 27, 28; m. 58; c. 3. CHEMISTRY. A.B, Marion Col.(Ind), 55; M.A.T, Miami Univ, 65. Med. technician, Marion Gen. Hosp, Ind, 54-55; chief chemist, Midwest Aerosols, Inc, 55-62; teacher chem, Dwight D. Eisenhower High Sch, Blue Island, Ill, 62-63; Tinley Park High Sch, 63-67; teaching asst, Univ. Iowa, 67-69; CHEM. TEACHER, KIRKWOOD COMMUNITY COL, 69- Am. Chem. Soc. Research and development of aerosol products. Address: Dept. of Chemistry, Kirkwood Community College, Cedar Rapids, IA 52406.

FISCHER, GRACE M(AE), b. Weatherly, Pa, Nov. 25, 27. CARDIOVASCULAR RESEARCH, BIOMEDICAL ENGINEERING. B.S, Bucknell Univ, 49; M.D, Temple Univ, 53; M.S, Drexel Univ, 64. Res. fel. biomed. eng, Drexel Univ, 62-64; cardiovasc. res, BOCKUS RES. INST. & DEPT. PHYSIOL, SCH. MED, UNIV. PA, 64-66, res. assoc, 66-67, ASST. PROF. PHYSIOL, 67- Nat. Heart Inst. fel, 63-64, spec. fel, 65-66; Heart Asn. Southeast. Pa. res. grant, 70-71. AAAS. Arterial connective tissue, especially chemical and endocrine effects on arterial wall properties and collagen and elastin metabolism in arterial wall; regulation of cardiovascular processes. Address: Bockus Research Institute, University of Pennsylvania, 19th & Lombard St, Philadelphia, PA 19146.

FISCHER, HARRY W(ILLIAM), b. St. Louis, Mo, June 4, 21; m. 43; c. 5. RADIOLOGY. B.S, Chicago, 43, M.D, 45. Intern surg, Barnes Hosp, St. Louis, 45-46; res. & fel, Washington (St. Louis), 48-51; fel. pediat. surg, Children's Mem. Hosp, Chicago, 51-52; res. radiol, St. Louis City Hosp, 52-54; private practice, 54-56; mem. teaching staff, St. Louis City Hosp, 56; asst. prof. RADIOL, col. med, Univ. Iowa, 56-57, assoc. prof, 57-63, prof, 63-66; med. sch, Univ. Mich, 66-71; PROF. & CHMN. DEPT, SCH. MED, UNIV. ROCHESTER, 71-; RADIOLOGIST IN CHIEF, STRONG MEM. HOSP, 71- Dir. dept. radiol, Wayne County Gen. Hosp, 66-71. Med.C, 46-48, Lt.(jg). Am. Med. Asn; Radiol. Soc. N.Am; Am. Col. Radiol; Asn. Univ. Radiol; Soc. Exp. Biol. & Med; Reticuloendothelial Soc; Am. Roentgen Ray Soc; Int. Soc. Lymphology. Contrast visualization of liver, spleen and lymph nodes; toxicity of contrast media; excretion of contrast media by liver and kidney; adherence of contrast media to mucosal surfaces. Address: Dept. of Radiology, Strong Memorial Hospital, Rochester, NY 14642.

FISCHER, HERMAN, b. Phila, Pa, Apr. 26, 17; m. 51; c. 4. MEDICINE, PATHOLOGY. B.A, Pennsylvania, 39; M.D, Hahnemann Med. Col, 43. PROF. MED. TECH, SALEM COL. (W.VA), 51-; ASSOC. CLIN. PROF. PATH, SCH. MED, UNIV. W.VA, 64- Pathologist, St. Mary's Hosp, Clarksburg, W.Va, 49-; Clarksburg Vet. Admin. Hosp, 50-61; Union Protestant Hosp, 57-; Stonewall Jackson Mem. Hosp, Weston, 59-; consult. pathologist, Weston State Hosp, 66- U.S.A, 44-46, Maj. Col. Am. Path; Am. Soc. Clin. Path; Am. Med. Asn; Int. Acad. Path. Address: Dept. of Pathology, St. Mary's Hospital, Clarksburg, WV 26301.

FISCHER, HERMAN C, b. Holyoke, Mass, July 20, 19; m. 42; c. 3. INORGANIC CHEMISTRY. B.S, Rensselaer Polytech, 42; S.M, Mass. Inst. Technol, 50, Sc.D.(cementitious mat), 54. Jr. chemist anal. chem, Tenn. Valley Auth, Ala, 42-43; res. chemist, Warner Co, Pa, 46-48; asst. prof. mat, Mass. Inst. Technol, 48-55; asst. dir. res. polymers, Wasco Chem. Co, Maine, 55-56; res. chemist, N.J. Zinc Co, Pa, 56-57; sect. chief concrete admixtures, Johns-Manville res, N.J, 57-64, tech. serv. mgr, Johns-Manville Corp, N.Y, 64-66; cement & concrete chem. dept, Union Carbide Corp, N.Y, 66-69; DIR. RES. & QUAL. CONTROL, LOUISVILLE CEMENT CO, 69- Mem, Hwy. Res. Bd, Nat. Acad. Sci-Nat. Res. Coun. U.S.N, 43-46, Lt. Am. Chem. Soc. Am. Soc. Test. & Mat; Am. Concrete Inst. Inorganic cementitious materials, including portland cement concrete, cements, plaster, lime, mortars and chemicals for concrete. Address: Louisville Cement Co, Speed, IN 47172.

FISCHER, HUGO B, b. Lakehurst, N.J, Mar. 16, 37; m. 62; c. 1. CIVIL ENGINEERING. B.S, Calif. Inst. Technol, 58, M.S, 63, Ph.D.(civil eng), 66. Asst. prof. CIVIL ENG, UNIV. CALIF, BERKELEY, 66-70, ASSOC. PROF, 70- Res. hydraul. engr, U.S. Geol. Surv, 66-; NATO fel, Cambridge, 70-71. Lorenz G. Straub Award, 66. U.S.A.F, 58-62, 1st Lt. Am. Soc. Civil Eng. (J. James R. Croes Medal, 69, Hilgard Hydraul. Prize, 71); Am. Geophys. Union; Am. Acad. Polit. & Soc. Sci; Int. Asn. Hydraul. Res. Hydraulic aspects of pollutant dispersion in rivers, reservoirs, estuaries and coastal areas. Address: Dept. of Civil Engineering, University of California, Berkeley, CA 94720.

FISCHER, IMRE A, b. Budapest, Hungary, Apr. 12, 35; U.S. citizen; m. 61. BIOCHEMISTRY, MICROBIOLOGY. M.S, Louvain, 62, Ph.D.(microbial biochem), 65. Res. asst. microbial biochem, Louvain, 62-65; res. microbiologist, California, Davis, 65-67; res. biochemist, sch. med, California, Los Angeles, 67-69; Xerox/Med. Diag. Opers, 69-70; TECH. DIR, BIO-TECHNICS LABS, INC, 70- Res. assoc, Harbor Gen. Hosp, Torrance & sch. med, Univ. Calif, Los Angeles, 70. AAAS; Am. Chem. Soc; Am. Soc. Microbiol; Am. Soc. Qual. Control. Autotrophic microorganisms; phosphorus metabolism; enzyme isolation and kinetics; red blood cell aging; medical diagnostics; clinical and forensic chemistry and toxicology; microbial susceptibility and inhibition. Address: Bio-Technics Labs, Inc, 1133 Crenshaw Blvd, Los Angeles, CA 90019.

FISCHER, IRENE KAMINKA, b. Vienna, Austria, July 27, 07; U.S. citizen; m. 30; c. 2. GEODESY. M.A, Univ. Vienna, 31; Univ. Va, 49-50; U.S. Dept. Agr. Grad. Sch, 53-54; Georgetown Univ, 57. Mathematician, GEOID BR, U.S. ARMY TOPOG. COMMAND, 52-58, geodesist, 58-62, supvry. geodesist, 62-65, SUPVRY. RES. GEODESIST, 65-, BR. CHIEF, 62- Mem, Int. Union Geod. & Geophys, 54-; comt. S.Am. datum, Pan-Am. Inst. Geog. & Hist. Meritorious civilian performance award, Dept. of Army, 57, bronze leaf cluster, 66, res. & develop. achievement award, 66, decoration for except. civilian serv, 67; distinguished civilian serv. award, Dept. of Defense, 67. Int. Asn. Geod. Figure of the earth; shape of the geoid; parallax and distance of the moon; geodetic world datum; Fischer ellipsoid; mercury datum for Mercury, Gemini and Apollo projects; South American datum of 1969. Address: 301 Philadelphia Ave, Tacoma Park, MD 20012.

FISCHER, IRWIN, b. New York, N.Y, Nov. 23, 27; m. 54; c. 2. MATHEMATICS. B.S, City Col. New York, 48; A.M, Harvard, 49, Ph.D.(math), 53. Mathematician, Air Force Cambridge Res. Center, 52-54; instr. MATH, Minnesota, 54-55; Dartmouth Col, 55-57; from asst. prof. to assoc. prof, UNIV. COLO, BOULDER, 57-69, PROF, 69- Am. Math. Soc. Algebraic geometry. Address: Dept. of Mathematics, University of Colorado, Boulder, CO 80302.

FISCHER, JACK, b. N.Y.C, June 28, 20; m. 43; c. 2. PHYSICAL CHEMISTRY. B.S, City Col. New York, 45; Ph.D.(chem), New York, 50. Asst. prof. chem, Providence Col, 51-52; ASSOC. CHEMIST, ARGONNE NAT. LAB, 52- Inorganic phase rule, fluorine chemistry; uranium and plutonium fluorides, homogeneous and heterogeneous reactions with fluorine; fused salt high temperature studies; fluoride volatility processing of reactor fuels; fission product distribution in and physical properties of reactor materials at high temperature. Address: Chemical Engineering Division, Argonne National Lab, 9700 S. Cass Ave, Argonne, IL 60439.

FISCHER, JOHN EDWARD, b. Albany, N.Y, June 8, 39; m. 63; c. 3. SOLID STATE & NUCLEAR PHYSICS. B.M.E, Rensselaer Polytech. Inst, 61, Nat. Defense Educ. Act fel, 62-64, Atomic Energy Comn. fel, 64-65, Ph.D.(nuclear sci), 66; Atomic Energy Comn. fel, Calif. Inst. Technol, 61-62, M.S, 62. Res. assoc, Univ. Paris, 66-67; res. physicist, MICHELSON LAB, NAVAL WEAPONS CTR, 67-70, BR. HEAD, 70- Vis. assoc. prof, Univ. Pa, 71-72. Am. Phys. Soc; Am. Nuclear Soc. Defects in solids; radiation effects in semiconductors; energy band structure in semiconductors; modulation spectroscopy of solids; semiconductor detectors and detector materials; amorphous semiconductors; thin film processes, devices and materials. Address: Code 6019, Michelson Lab, Naval Weapons Center, China Lake, CA 93555.

FISCHER, JOHN E(UGENE), b. San Francisco, Calif, Sept. 19, 16. MATHEMATICS. M.A, Gonzaga Univ, 41; S.T.L, Alma Col.(Calif), 48; M.S, St. Louis Univ, 51, Ph.D.(math), 54. Lectr. MATH, Univ. Santa Clara, 41-44; asst. prof, UNIV. SAN FRANCISCO, 54-70; ASSOC. PROF, 70-, CHMN. DEPT, 54- Math. Asn. Am. Modern algebra and theory of numbers; applications in field of business administration; linear programming; operations research. Address: Dept. of Mathematics, University of San Francisco, San Francisco, CA 94117.

FISCHER, LAWRENCE J, b. Chicago, Ill, Sept. 2, 37; m. 63; c. 3. BIOCHEMICAL PHARMACOLOGY & TOXICOLOGY. B.S, Illinois, 59, M.S, 61; Nat. Sci. Found. fel, California, 62-63, Am. Found. Pharmaceut. Educ. fel, 64-65, Ph.D.(pharmaceut. chem), 65. Nat. Insts. Health fel. biochem, St. Mary's Hosp. Med. Sch, London, Eng, 65-66; sr. res. pharmacologist, Merck Inst. therapeut. res, 66-68; ASST. PROF. PHARMACOL, COL. MED, UNIV. IOWA, 68- AAAS; Am. Chem. Soc; Am. Pharmaceut. Asn; N.Y. Acad. Sci. Absorption; distribution; metabolism and excretion of drugs and chemicals. Address: Dept. of Pharmacology, School of Medicine, University of Iowa, Iowa City, IA 52240.

FISCHER, LEEWELLYN C, b. Litchfield, Minn, May 23, 37; m. 61; c. 1. PHYSICAL CHEMISTRY. B.S, Minnesota, 59; M.S, Carnegie Inst. Tech, 61, Ph.D.(phys. chem), 64. RES. CHEMIST, PHOTO PRODS. DEPT, E.I. DU PONT DE NEMOURS & CO, INC, 63- Am. Chem. Soc. Kinetics of fast reactions, specifically photolysis; photochemistry of liquids and thin films; free radical reactions in gas phase. Address: Two Timber Lane, Fairport, NY 14450.

FISCHER, LOUIS, b. Seattle, Wash, Aug. 18, 05; m. 29; c. 2. PHARMACEUTICAL CHEMISTRY. Ph.C. & B.S, Washington (Seattle), 26, M.S, 28, fel, 28-29, Ph.D.(pharmaceut. chem), 33. Pharm. stockman, Washington (Seattle), 26-28; asst. state chemist, Wash, 29-35; instr. pharm, UNIV. WASH, 35-37, asst. prof. pharmaceut. chem, 37-41, assoc. prof, 41-45, PROF. & CHMN. DEPT, 45-, ASSOC. DEAN, 60-, asst. to dean, 49-60. Chemist & bacteriologist, La Villa & Kristoferson Dairy, 25-29; med. rep, Consol. Dairy Prod, 40; official grader, U.S. Dept. Agr, 42-; res. chemist, Wash. Liquor Bd, 43-44. Summers, res. chemist, Nat. Canners Asn, 36-37, salmon examiner, 41; marketing specialist, food distribution agency, U.S. Dept. of Agr, 42; mem. U.S. Pharmacopoeia Revision Cmt, 50-70; adv. panel, Nat. Formulary, 61-70; fel. rev. panel, Nat. Insts. Health, 64-67; Nat. Prescription Surv. Bd. AAAS; Am. Pharmaceut. Asn; Inst. Food Tech. Phytochemistry; food chemistry. Address: Dept. of Pharmaceutical Chemistry, University of Washington, Seattle, WA 98105.

FISCHER, MARK S(AMUEL), b. Elmira, N.Y, Feb. 25, 43; m. 65; c. 1. PHYSICAL CHEMISTRY, BIOCHEMISTRY. A.B, Brandeis Univ, 65; E.C. Anthony Scholar. & Ph.D.(chem), Univ. Calif, Berkeley, 69. Acting instr. physics, Univ. Calif, Berkeley, 67; NAT. INSTS. HEALTH FEL. PHYSIOL. CHEM, MED. SCH, UNIV. WIS, MADISON, 70- AAAS; Am. Chem. Soc; Am. Crystallog. Asn. Biological growth and development; proteins of the cell nucleus; x-ray crystallography; porphyrins. Address: Dept. of Physiological Chemistry, University of Wisconsin Medical School, Madison, WI 53706.

FISCHER, PATRICK CARL, b. St. Louis, Mo, Dec. 3, 35; m. 67; c. 1. COMPUTER SCIENCE, MATHEMATICS. B.S, Michigan, 57, M.B.A, 58; Ph.D. (math), Mass. Inst. Technol, 62. Asst. prof. appl. math, Harvard, 62-65; assoc. prof. COMPUT. SCI, Cornell Univ, 65-68; vis. prof, UNIV. WATERLOO, 68-69, PROF, 69- Nat. Sci. Found. grants, 64-66, 66-68; Nat. Res. Coun. Can, 68-; vis. assoc. prof, Univ. B.C, 67-68. Asn. Comput. Mach; Am. Math. Soc; Math. Asn. Am; Asn. Symbolic Logic. Properties of measures of computational complexity; abstract program and machine structures; interactive information systems. Address: Dept. of Applied Analysis and Computer Science, University of Waterloo, Waterloo, Ontario, Can.

FISCHER, PAUL E(DGAR), b. Kansas City, Kans, Nov. 26, 19; m. 50; c. 2. PHYSICAL & ORGANIC CHEMISTRY. A.B, Cent. Mo. State Col, 41; Eli Lily fel, Chicago, 41-42, Nat. Res. Found. fel, 46-47, Ph.D.(chem), 47. Res. chemist, Nat. Defense Res. Comt. Prog, Chicago, 42-44, rubber reserve, 44-46; CHEVRON RES. CO, STANDARD OIL CO, CALIF, 47-70, SUPVR. TECH. INFO. SERV, 70- Am. Chem. Soc. Petroleum processes; hydrocarbon separations; polymerization; free radical reactions; hydrogenation; rubber chemistry. Address: Technical Information Center, Chevron Research Co, 576 Standard Ave, Richmond, CA 94802.

FISCHER, RICHARD B(ERNARD), b. Boston, Mass, Jan. 19, 19; m. 53; c. 3. BIOLOGY. B.S, Queens Col.(N.Y), 42; M.A, Columbia, 43; Ph.D.(zool), Cornell, 53. Asst. press serv, CORNELL UNIV, 51-52, biol, 52-53, PROF. NATURE & CONSERV. EDUC, 53- AAAS; Nat. Asn. Biol. Teachers; Conserv. Educ. Asn; Am. Nature Study Soc; Am. Ornith. Union; Wilson Ornith. Soc. Chimney swift; bird banding; ecology; natural history writing and photography; natural history. Address: College of Agriculture, Cornell University, Ithaca, NY 14850.

FISCHER, RICHARD P(HILIP), b. Marietta, Ohio, July 2, 10; m. 52; c. 3. ECONOMIC GEOLOGY. A.B, Ohio Wesleyan, 32; M.A, Princeton, 34, Ph.D. (geol), 36. Field geologist, Newfoundland Geol. Surv, St. John, 36; asst, Princeton, 36-37; GEOLOGIST, U.S. GEOL. SURV, 37- With Atomic Energy Comn; Off. Sci. Res. & Develop; U.S.A, 46. Fel. Geol. Soc. Am; Soc. Econ. Geol; Am. Asn. Petrol. Geol. Geology of uranium and vanadium deposits; mineral resources. Address: U.S. Geological Survey, Denver Federal Center, Denver, CO 80225.

FISCHER, ROBERT B(LANCHARD), b. Hartford, Conn, Oct. 24, 20; m. 46; c. 5. CHEMISTRY. B.S, Wheaton Col.(Ill), 42; Ph.D.(anal. chem), Illinois, 46. Radio broadcast engr, Chicago, 41; asst. anal. chem, Illinois, 42-44, instr, 46-48; res. chemist, metall. lab, Chicago, 44-46; asst. prof. CHEM, Indiana, 48-52, assoc. prof, 52-60, PROF, 60-63; CALIF. STATE COL, DOMINGUEZ HILLS, 63-, DEAN, SCH. NATURAL SCI. & MATH, 63- Vis. assoc, Calif. Inst. Technol, 59-60. Civilian with Manhattan proj, U.S.A, 44-46. AAAS; Am. Chem. Soc; Electron Micros. Soc. Am; Am. Soc. Oceanog; Am. Sci. Affiliation. Quantitative analysis; electron microscopy; instrumentation; science and society. Address: School of Natural Science & Mathematics, California State College at Dominguez Hills, 1000 E. Victoria St, Dominguez Hills, CA 90246.

FISCHER, ROBERT G(EORGE), b. St. Paul, Minn, Oct. 17, 20; m. 47; c. 3. MICROBIOLOGY. B.A, Univ. Minn, 42, M.S, 47, Ph.D, 48. Asst. bact, Univ. Minn, 45-48; asst. prof, UNIV. N.DAK, 48-51, assoc. prof, 51-55, prof, 55-62, PROF. MICROBIOL. & CHMN. DEPT, 62- Dipl, Am. Bd. Microbiol. U.S.A, 42-45, Capt. Am. Soc. Microbiol; Am. Acad. Microbiol. Viruses; experimental leukemia transmission; poliomyelitis; virus tumors. Address: 447 Campbell Dr, Grand Forks, ND 58201.

FISCHER, R(OBERT) L(EIGH), b. Chicago, Ill, July 29, 26; m. 54; c. 3. CLINICAL CHEMISTRY. B.S, North. Ill. State Teachers Col, 50; M.S, Illinois, 51, Ph.D.(biochem), 54. Asst, Illinois, 51-54; res. chemist, E.I. du Pont de Nemours & Co, 54-55; asst. prof. chem. med. sch. Tennessee, 55-61, res. assoc. pediat, 55-61; sr. res. chemist, Campbell Soup Co, 61-64, div. head proteins, 64-67; CHIEF CLIN. CHEMIST, PHILA. GEN. HOSP, 67- U.S.A, 45-46. AAAS; Am. Chem. Soc; Am. Asn. Clin. Chem. Clinical chemistry methods. Address: Philadelphia General Hospital, 34th & Civic Center Blvd, Philadelphia, PA 19104.

FISCHER, R(OLAND), b. Budapest, July 31, 15, U.S. citizen; m. 45. BIOCHEMISTRY. M.A. & Ph.D, Budapest, Basel, 45. Res. assoc. microbiol, Basel, 45-46; sci. dept, Geigy Co, Switzerland, 46-48; res. assoc. & asst, psychiat-biochem. lab, Basel, 49-51; head res. lab. psychiat. res, Pub. Health Serv, Sask, 52-57; asst. prof. psychiat. & physiol. chem, OHIO STATE UNIV, 57-62, assoc. prof, 63-67, PROF. EXP. PSYCHIAT, 67-, ASSOC. PROF. PHARMACOL, 69-, sr. res. biochemist, 57-67. Lectr, Saskatchewan, 55-57; consult, Battelle Mem. Inst; State Dept. Ment. Hyg, Ohio; bur. educ. res, Ohio State; res. psychopharmacologist, Drug Treatment & Res. Ctr, Vet. Admin. Hosp, Wash, D.C, 72-; lectr, sch. med, Johns Hopkins Univ, 72-; consult, Nat. Inst. Ment. Health, Md. Psychiat. Res. Ctr. & Student Asn. Study Hallucinogens, 72-; mem. int. sci. bd, Int. Soc. Art & Psychopathol. Mem. appl. biol. div, Nat. Res. Coun. Can, 51-52. Am. Chem. Soc; Soc. Biol. Psychiat; N.Y. Acad. Sci; Am. Soc. Human Genetics; Philos. Sci. Asn; Soc. Biol. Rhythm; Am. Soc. Pharmacol. & Exp. Therapeut; Brit. Soc. Philos. Sci; Asn. Psychophysiol. Study Sleep. Mechanisms of drug action; cytochemical demonstration of nervous activity; biochemistry and human behavior; biological model systems; gustatory pharmacology and pharmacogenetics; biological time; psychopharmacology. Address: Dept. of Pharmacology, College of Medicine, Ohio State University, Columbus, OH 43210.

FISCHER, R(OLAND) B(ARTON), b. Denver, Colo, Feb. 28, 20; m. 42; c. 2. PHYSICAL METALLURGY. Met.E, Colo. Sch. Mines, 42. Asst. metallurgist, Am. Smelting & Ref. Co, El Paso, Texas, 46; res. engr, Battelle Mem. Inst, 46-49, asst. supvr, 49-53, div. chief, 53-63; sr. develop. specialist, ROCKY FLATS PLANT, DOW CHEM. CO, 63-66, SR. RES. METALLURGIST, 66- Summer, asst. metallurgist, Card Iron Works, Colo, 41. C.Eng, 42-46, Res. 46-50, Lt. Am. Soc. Metals; Am. Inst. Mining, Metall. & Petrol. Eng. Non-ferrous metals, hard metals technology; tungsten carbide, powder metallurgy and others; high pressure research; nuclear materials; diamond technology. Address: 12035 Applewood Knolls Dr, Lakewood, CO 80215.

FISCHER, ROLAND L(EE), b. Detroit, Mich, Sept. 9, 24; m. 46; c. 3. ENTOMOLOGY. B.S, Michigan, 46; M.S, Mich. State Col, 48; Ph.D.(entomol), Kans. State Col, 52. Teacher, pub. schs, Mich, 46-47; asst. ENTOM, Mich. State Col, 47-48; Kans. State Col, 48-50, instr, 51; res. assoc, Kansas, 52; res. fel, Minnesota, 52-53; asst. prof, MICH. STATE UNIV, 53-59, assoc. prof, 59-64, PROF, 64-, curator entom, mus, 59-64. Mem, Am. Entom. Inst. AAAS; Entom. Soc. Am; Soc. Syst. Zool; Entom. Soc. Can; Int. Union Study Social Insects; fel. Royal Entom. Soc. London. Taxonomy of the Aculeate Hymenoptera, particularly the Apoidea; biological and phenological investigations in the Aculeate Hymenoptera; insect morphology; pollination of legume seed crops. Address: Dept. of Entomology, Michigan State University, East Lansing, MI 48823.

FISCHER, RUDOLPH F, b. Milwaukee, Wis, Feb. 27, 23; m. 44; c. 4. ORGANIC CHEMISTRY. B.S, Wisconsin, 48; fel, Illinois, 49-50, E.I. du Pont de Nemours & Co. fel, 50-51, Ph.D.(chem), 51. Tech. asst, Inst. Paper Chem, 48; chemist, Shell Develop. Co, 51-58, res. supvr, 58-60, tech. asst. to pres, 60-61, head org. chem. dept, 61-68, dir. res. & develop. plastics & resins, 68-70, MGR. PROD. DEVELOP. ELASTOMERS, SHELL CHEM. CO, 70- U.S.A, 43-46. Am. Chem. Soc. Applications of petrochemical products to paper, textile, surfactants, wood and mining fields; chemistry of natural products; products derived from petroleum. Address: Shell Chemical Co, One Shell Plaza, Houston, TX 77002.

FISCHER, SIGHART FRIEDRICH, b. Sept. 23, 38; Ger. citizen; m. 62; c. 2. PHYSICAL & THEORETICAL CHEMISTRY. Diplom, Univ. Göttingen, 63, Dr. rer. nat.(physics), 65. Asst. physics, Univ. Göttingen, 64-66; fel. chem, Northwest. Univ, 66-68; res. assoc. phys. chem, Univ. Chicago, 68; ASST. PROF. CHEM, NORTHWEST. UNIV, 68- Alfred P. Sloan Found. fel, 71-73. Transport properties in solids; hydrogen-bonded systems; theory of excitons; theory of non-radiative transitions; reaction kinetics. Address: Dept. of Chemistry, Northwestern University, Evanston, IL 60201.

FISCHER, THEODORE E, b. St. Louis, Mo, Mar. 10, 10; c. 2. DENTISTRY. B.S, Nat. Inst. Eng, 32; D.D.S, St. Louis Univ, 36. PROF. DENT. & CHMN. DEPT. DENT. MAT, SCH. DENT, UNIV. ALA, BIRMINGHAM, 63- Consult, U.S. Army, Ft. Benning; Vet. Admin, Tuskegee & Birmingham; mem. dent. health, res. & educ. comt, U.S. Pub. Health Serv; chmn. subcomt. zinc oxide, Int. Standards Orgn. U.S.A, 38-49; U.S.A.F, 49-63, Col. Fel. AAAS; fel. Am. Col. Dent; Am. Dent. Asn; Int. Asn. Dent. Res. Dental materials; silicate cements; acrylic resins; amalgam; alginates. Address: Dept. of Dental Materials, University of Alabama School of Dentistry, Birmingham, AL 35233.

FISCHER, THEODORE V(ERNON), b. Brillion, Wis, July 25, 39; m. 69; c. 1. ANATOMY. B.A, N.Cent. Col.(Ill), 61; Ph.D.(anat), Univ. Wis, 66. Fel. reproductive physiol, Univ. Wis, 66-67; ASST. PROF. ANAT, UNIV. MICH, 67- AAAS; Am. Asn. Anat; Soc. Study Reproduction; Am. Inst. Biol. Sci. Mammalian placentation; physiology of reproduction. Address: Dept. of Anatomy, University of Michigan, Ann Arbor, MI 48104.

FISCHER, TRAUGOTT E(RWIN), b. Aarau, Switz, Jan. 21, 32; m. 58; c. 3. SOLID STATE PHYSICS. Dipl, Swiss Fed. Inst. Tech, 56, Ph.D.(solid state physics), 63. Asst. solid state physics, Swiss Fed. Inst. Tech, 57-63; mem. tech. staff surface physics, Bell Tel. Labs, N.J, 63-66; ASSOC. PROF. ENG. & APPL. SCI, YALE, 66- Kern prize, Swiss Fed. Inst. Tech, 62. Swiss Army. Am. Vacuum Soc; fel. Am. Phys. Soc; Swiss Phys. Soc. Physical properties of surfaces; field emission; photoelectric emission; optical properties and energy-band structure of solids. Address: Becton Center, Yale University, New Haven, CT 06520.

FISCHER, VERA KISTIAKOWSKY, Nuclear Physics, see KISTIAKOWSKY, VERA FISCHER.

FISCHER, W(ERNER) H(ANS), b. Switzerland, Oct. 4, 09; nat; m. 36; c. 3. ORGANIC CHEMISTRY. D.Sc, Swiss Fed. Inst. Tech, 35. Res. steroid hormones, Prof. L. Ruzicka, 34-36; research & develop. chemist, Ciba Ltd, Switzerland, 36-40, mfg. chemist, CIBA PHARMACEUT. CO. DIV, CIBA-GEIGY CORP, 40-45, plant prod. chemist, 45-49, dir. prod, 49-50, V.PRES. IN CHARGE prod, 50-61, prod. & eng, 61-69, prod. & plant serv, 69-70, PROD. & ENG, 70- Am. Chem. Soc; Swiss Chem. Soc. Synthesis of monocyclic diterpene alcohol; steroid hormones. Address: 256 Oakridge Ave, Summit, NJ 07901.

FISCHER, WILLIAM A(LFRED), b. Chicago, Ill, April 15, 17; m. 45; c. 4. INVERTEBRATE PALEONTOLOGY. B.S, Beloit Col, 39, M.S, 41; Ph.D, Colorado, 53. Asst. geol, Beloit Col, 39-41; petrol. geologist, Carter Oil Co, 41-43; asst. prof. GEOL, COLO. COL, 49-55, assoc. prof, 55-58, PROF. & CHMN. DEPT, 58- Advan. of Educ. faculty fel, Ford Found, 54-55. U.S.N.R, 43-45, Ens. Micropaleontology. Address: 1217 N. Cedar St, Colorado Springs, CO 80903.

FISCHER-COLBRIE, ERWIN, b. Linz, Austria, June 5, 12; U.S. citizen; m. 46; c. 8. SOLID STATE & ELECTRONIC PHYSICS. Ph.D.(nuclear physics), Vienna, 36. Electron tube develop. engr, Tekade, Nuremberg, 39-43; sci. asst. nuclear physics & instrumentation, Vienna, 43-45; self employed electron devices, Austria, 45-50; electron tube develop. physicist, Siemens & Halske, 50-53; sr. physicist solid state & electron physics, electronics lab, General Elec. Co, 53-60, consult. physicist, cathode ray tube dept, 60-63; dir. mat. res, opto electronic devices, Sigma Instruments Co, 63-69; ASSOC. DIV. HEAD, LAWRENCE RADIATION LAB, 69- Am. Phys. Soc. Radiation-material interaction; device developments utilizing solid state effects. Address: 831 Arroyo Rd, Los Altos, CA 94022.

FISCHGRUND, WILLIAM SAMUEL, b. Franklin, N.J, June 21, 26; m. 49; c. 2. CHEMICAL ENGINEERING. B.S, Newark Col. Eng, 48, M.S, 52. Chemist, Volupté Inc, N.J, 48-51; spec. process engr, Wright Aeronaut. Div, Curtiss-Wright Corp, 51-54; finishing supt, Roto-Broil Corp, 54-55; plant supt, Gen. Magnaplate Corp, 54-56; mat. engr, reaction motors div, Thiokol Chem. Corp, 56-69; V.PRES, GEN. MAGNAPLATE CORP, 69- U.S.A, 45-46. Am. Chem. Soc. Material and process applications related to the aerospace industry. Address: 1480 Pleasant Valley Way, West Orange, NJ 07052.

FISCHL, F(RED) B, b. Czechoslovakia, Jan. 30, 21; nat; m. 47; c. 2. PETROLEUM CHEMISTRY. B.S, Pa. State Col, 43, M.S, 44, Ph.D.(org. chem), 46. Asst, Pa. State Col, 46-47; sales engr, Enjay labs, Esso Res. & Eng. Co, 47-58; mfg. coordinator, ENJAY CHEM. CO. DIV, HUMBLE OIL & REF. CO, 58-65, TECH. SALES ASSOC, 65- Am. Chem. Soc; Soc. Automotive Eng. Marketing of improvers for fuels and lubricants to international oil companies. Address: 54 Walnut St, Murray Hill, NJ 07974.

FISCHLER, MARTIN A(LVIN), b. New York, N.Y, Feb. 15, 32; m. 60; c. 2. ELECTRONICS, INFORMATION SCIENCE. B.E.E, City Col. New York, 54; M.S, Stanford, 58, Ph.D.(elec. eng), 62. Electronic engr, Nat. Bur. Standards, 56; scientist, LOCKHEED MISSILES & SPACE CO, 58-61, sr. scientist, 61-62, res. scientist, 62-71, STAFF SCIENTIST, 71- U.S.A, 54-56. Pattern Recognition Soc; Asn. Comput. Mach; Math. Asn. Am; Inst. Elec. & Electronics Eng. Artificial intelligence; switching theory; information theory; computer organization; information retrieval; operations research. Address: 966 Bonneville Way, Sunnyvale, CA 94087.

FISCHLSCHWEIGER, WERNER, b. Bremen, Ger, May 4, 32; m. 60; c. 2. HISTOLOGY, EMBRYOLOGY. Ph.D.(zool), Graz Univ, 57. Dir. tissue cult, Austrian Cancer Res. Inst, 58-62; asst. prof. HISTOL, med. sch, Graz Univ, 62-63; med. sch, St. Louis Univ, 63-65; ASSOC. PROF, dent. sch, Univ. Md, Baltimore, 65-69; COL. DENT, UNIV. FLA, 69- Int. Asn. Dent. Res; Ger. Zool. Soc. Electron microscopy of human tooth development; regeneration of Turbellaria. Address: Dept. of Basic Dental Sciences, College of Dentistry, University of Florida, Gainesville, FL 32601.

FISCHMAN, DONALD A, b. N.Y.C, Apr. 27, 36; m. 60; c. 3. MEDICINE. A.B, Kenyon Col, 57; M.D, Cornell, 61. Res. fel. anat, med. col, Cornell, 61-63, instr. anat, 64-65; fel. embryol, Strangeways Lab, Cambridge, Eng, 63-64; asst. prof. zool, Chicago, 65-66; asst. prof. BIOL. & ANAT, UNIV. CHICAGO, 68-71, ASSOC. PROF, 71-, ASSOC. DEAN CURRICULUM, DIV. BIOL. SCI, 70- N.Y. Heart Asn. res. fel, 61-63; U.S. Pub. Health Serv. fel, 63-64 & res. grant, 64-66, 71-; res. grants, Nat. Sci. Found, 68-; Chicago Heart Asn, 69-71. Med.C, 66-68, Capt. AAAS; Am. Asn. Anat; Am. Soc. Cell Biol; Soc. Develop. Biol; Biophys. Soc; Soc. Gen. Physiol. Anatomy; developmental biology; electron microscopy; development, growth and physiology of muscle; ultrastructure of bacterial cell walls and membranes. Address: 5401 S. Greenwood Ave, Chicago, IL 60615.

FISCHMAN, STUART L, b. Buffalo, N.Y, Nov. 29, 35; m. 60; c. 2. ORAL PATHOLOGY. Cornell Univ, 53-56; D.M.D, Harvard, 60. Intern dent, Boston Vet. Admin. Hosp, Mass, 60-61; clin. dent, SCH. DENT, STATE UNIV. N.Y. BUFFALO, 61-64, asst. prof. oral path, 64-67, ASSOC. PROF. ORAL MED, 67-, ASST. DEAN ACAD. DEVELOP. & FACILITIES PLANNING, 70- Res. assoc, Vet. Admin. Hosp, Buffalo, N.Y, 63-64; consult, U.S. Pub. Health Serv, 65-70; vis. prof, Nat. Univ. Asuncion, Paraguay, 69-; consult, WHO, 70- Dipl, Am. Bd. Oral Path, 69. AAAS; fel. Am. Acad. Oral Path; Am. Dent. Asn; Int. Asn. Dent. Res; Int. Dent. Fedn; Latin Am. Asn. Dent. Schs. Experimental oral pathology and periodontal diseases; clinical testing of therapeutic dentifrice; development of information retrieval system for oral pathology; oral diseases; tropical oral pathology. Address: Dept. of Oral Medicine, School of Dentistry, State University of New York at Buffalo, Buffalo, NY 14214.

FISCHTHAL, JACOB H(ENRY), b. Brooklyn, N.Y, April 18, 17; m. 42; c. 4. PARASITOLOGY. B.S, Long Island, 37; M.S, Iowa, 38; Ph.D.(zool); Michigan, 50, Aquatic biologist, N.Atlantic Fish. Invests, U.S. Fish & Wildlife Serv, 43; fish mgt. div, State Conserv. Dept, Wis, 43-48; instr. BIOL, Triple Cities Col, Syracuse, 48-50; asst. prof, STATE UNIV. N.Y. BINGHAMTON, 50-54, assoc. prof, 54-61, PROF, 61-, head dept, 56-59. Nat. Insts. Health res. grant, 53-55; Sigma Xi-Sci. Res. Soc. of Am. res. grant, 55; Office Naval Res, U.S. Navy res. grant, 58; Fulbright grants, Univ. Col. Cape Coast, Ghana, 65-66; Haile Sellassie I Univ, 68-69; State Univ. N.Y. faculty res. fels, 67, 68, 71. Consult, parasitol. dept, U.S. Naval Med. Res. Inst, 55-; law dept, div. water supply, City of New York, 56-65. Am. Soc. Parasitol. Ecology, taxonomy and zoogeography of trematodes of vertebrates. Address: Dept. of Biological Sciences, State University of New York at Binghamton, Binghamton, NY 13901.

FISCUS, ALVIN G, b. Newell, S.Dak, July 6, 30; m. 56; c. 3. VIROLOGY, MICROBIOLOGY. B.S, S.Dak. State, 56, M.S, 57; Ph.D.(microbiol), Arizona, 66. Dir. lab. clin. microbiol, Tucson Med. Center, Ariz, 66-67; ASSOC. PROF. MICROBIOL, MONTANA STATE UNIV, 67- Consult, Mont. Regional Med. Prog, 67- U.S.A, 52-54. Am. Soc. Microbiol. Clinical microbiology; viral and chemical oncology. Address: Dept. of Botany & Microbiology, Montana State University, Bozeman, MT 59715.

FISCUS, EDWIN L(AWSON), b. Ellwood City, Pa, Jan. 20, 42; m. 69. PLANT PHYSIOLOGY. B.S.Ed, Slippery Rock State Col, 64; M.S, Univ. Ariz, 66; Ph.D.(bot), Duke Univ, 69. RES. ASSOC. PLANT PHYSIOL, Auburn Univ, 69-70; DUKE UNIV, 70- AAAS; Am. Soc. Plant Physiol; Am. Inst. Biol. Sci; Am. Soc. Agron. Plant and soil water relations; root-oxygen relations; factors influencing salt and water uptake by roots and water movement through the plant. Address: Dept. of Botany, Duke University, Durham, NC 27706.

FISET, PAUL, b. Quebec, Que, Can, Nov. 7, 22; m. 53; c. 3. MICROBIOLOGY. B.A, Laval, 44, M.D, 49; Ph.D.(microbiol), Cambridge, 56. Asst. bacter, Laval, 55-57; asst. prof, sch. med. & dent, Rochester, 58-64, asst. med, 58-64; ASSOC. PROF. MICROBIOL, SCH. MED, UNIV. MD, BALTIMORE CITY, 64- Mem, comn. rickettsial diseases, Armed Forces Epidemiol. Bd; consult, Surgeon Gen, U.S. Army. AAAS; Am. Soc. Microbiol; N.Y. Acad. Sci; Am. Asn. Immunol. Address: Dept. of Microbiology, School of Medicine, University of Maryland, 660 W. Redwood St, Baltimore, MD 21201.

FISH, ARTHUR GEOFFREY, b. Pictou, N.S, Apr. 24, 33; m. 58; c. 2. PLANKTOLOGY, INVERTEBRATE ZOOLOGY. B.Sc, Carleton (Ont), 56; M.Sc, McGill, 58; Ph.D.(biol. oceanog), British Columbia, 68. Res. asst. biol. oceanog, Bellairs Res. Inst, McGill, 58-60; asst. prof. BIOL, UNIV. SOUTH. MISS, 64-69, ASSOC. PROF, 69- Summer lectr, Gulf Coast Res. Lab, Miss, 66-68; coop. col. sci. prog. earth sci, Nat. Sci. Found, 69; Benthonic study sea grant, Univs. Marine Ctr. Miss, NASA contract, Earth Resources Data & Technol. Studies, Miss, 70- Am. Inst. Biol. Sci. Nonparasitic marine zooplankton; zooplankton of the Mississippi Sound; interstitial faunal studies of marine and estuarine environments of the Mississippi Sound. Address: Dept. of Biology, University of Southern Mississippi, Box 445, Southern Station, Hattiesburg, MS 39401.

FISH, BARBARA, b. N.Y.C, July 31, 20; m. 53; c. 2. PSYCHIATRY. B.A, Columbia, 42; M.D, N.Y. Univ, 45; cert, William A. White Inst. Psychiat, 56. Intern & asst. res. med, Bellevue Hosp, 45-47; intern pediat, New York Hosp, 47-48; N.Y. Univ-Bellevue Med. Ctr, 48-49, psychiat, Bellevue Hosp, 49-52, clin. asst. psychiat, 51-55; instr. pediat. & psychiat, med. col, Cornell, 55-56, asst. prof, 56-60; assoc. prof. psychiat, SCH. MED, N.Y. UNIV, 60-70, PROF. CHILD PSYCHIAT, 70-; DIR. CHILD PSYCHIAT, BELLEVUE HOSP. CTR, 70-, psychiatrist in charge children's servs, psychiat. div, 60-70. Dipl. psychiat, Am. Bd. Psychiat. & Neurol, 55, child psychiat, 60, mem. comt. on certification in child psychiat, 69- Soc. Res. Child Develop; Am. Med. Asn; fel. Am. Psychiat. Asn; Am. Acad. Child Psychiat; Asn. Res. Nerv. & Ment. Diseases; Am. Orthopsychiat. Asn; fel. Am. Col. Neuropsychopharmacol. Child psychiatry, especially childhood schizophrenia and pharmacotherapy; infant development and early recognition of neuropsychiatric disorders. Address: Dept of Child Psychiatry, New York University School of Medicine, 550 First Ave, New York, NY 10016.

FISH, CHARLES J(OHN), b. Fall River, Mass, May 13, 99; m. 23; c. 1. BIO-OCEANOGRAPHY. Ph.B, Brown, 21, Sc.M, 22, Ph.D.(biol. of ocean popul), 23; hon. D.Sc, Univ. R.I, 66. Asst, U.S.S. Albatross, 22-24; marine invest, Bur. Fisheries, 24-27; dir, Buffalo Mus. Sci, 27-34; res. prof. ichthyol, Buffalo, 29-32; asst. prof. zool, UNIV. R.I, 34-35, assoc. prof. & acting in charge dept, 35-36, prof. in charge dept. & dir. marine lab, 36-46, consult. marine biol, 46-48, prof. marine biol. & dir. Narragansett Marine Lab, 48-62, prof. OCEANOG, GRAD. SCH. OCEANOG, 60-66, acting dean, 61-62, EMER. PROF, 66-, EMER. DIR, NARRAGANSETT MARINE LAB, 66- Assoc. marine biol, Oceanog. Inst, Woods Hole, 48-64, hon. staff mem, 64- Mem. corp, Bermuda Biol. Sta, 32-35; dir. coop. oceanog. invests, Gulf of Maine, 29-30; dir. coop. state & fed. invests, Narragansett Bay, 35-; Pres, Niagara Frontier Res. Coun, 30; exec. secy, Int. Passamaquoddy Fisheries Comn, 31-33; mem. Governor's Adv. Coun. Fish & Game, R.I, 39-48; chmn. comn. marine & commercial fisheries, R.I. Wildlife Fed, v.pres, 40-43; mem. U.S. comt. oceanog. of Pac, Nat. Res. Coun, 47-51; U.S. comt. explor. Atlantic shelf, 63- Expeds, plankton surv, L.I. Sound, 22-23, Vineyard Sound & Buzzards Bay, 23-24, Labrador Current, Newfoundland, 24, Continental Plateau of Gulf Stream, 24; oceanographer, Arcturus oceanog. exped, Bermuda, 29; int. oceanog. exped, Bahamas, 30; biol. surv, Coast of Maine & Mass. Bay, 24; oceanog. surv, Mass. Bay, 24-25, 26; dir. coop. surv, Lake Erie, 28-29; oceanog. invest, Gulf of Maine & Bay of Fundy, 30-33; weather sta. invest, cent. Atlantic & Labrador Sea, 52-54; mem, Trident expeds. cent. Atlantic, 63-64, cent. & S.Atlantic, 65. Charles J. Fish Oceanog. Lab, dedicated Rhode Island, 60. Off. d'acad, Republic France, 47-; Stamford Mus. award sci. achievement, 63. U.S.N, 18-19, 42-46, Res, 46-60, Capt. AAAS; Am. Soc. Limnol. & Oceanog; Am. Geophys. Union (ed, oceanog. sect, 45-47); Biology of marine plankton and fish populations of the North Atlantic. Address: 1291 Kingstowne Rd, Kingston, RI 02881.

FISH, DONALD C, b. N.Y.C, Apr. 19, 37; m. 58; c. 2. MICROBIOLOGY. B.S, Cornell, 58; M.S, Michigan, 61, Ph.D.(microbiol), 64. Asst. bact, Cornell, 57-58; lab. instr, Michigan, 58-61, asst, 61-64; microbiologist anthrax res, U.S. Army Biol. Labs, 64-71; DIR. MICROBIOL. DIV, WOODARD RES. CORP, 71- Summers, lab. technician, Brooklyn Hosp, N.Y, 58, instr. microbiol, sci. prog, Interlochen Arts Acad, Mich, 63. Chem.C, 64-66, Capt. Tissue Cult. Asn; Am. Soc. Microbiol; Am. Chem. Soc. Relationship of metabolic and genetic activities to virulence; characterization and genetics of tissue culture cells and virus. Address: 116 W. 14th St, Frederick, MD 21701.

FISH, FEROL F, JR, b. East Chicago, Ind, Jan. 15, 30; m. 56; c. 5. APPLIED PHYSICS. B.S, Ind. Univ, 55, A.M, 57; Nat. Sci. Found. fel, Pa. State Univ, 58-60, Ph.D.(geophys), 61. Geophys. investr, N.J. Zinc Co, 60-63; sr. res. scientist, Gen. Dynamics/Ft. Worth, 63-64; sr. scientist, Douglas Aircraft Co, 64-68; MGR. APPL. PHYSICS, ROY C. INGERSOLL RES. CTR, BORG-WARNER CORP, DES PLAINES, 68- U.S.A, 48-51. Am. Geophys. Union. Optics, acoustics and noise control; electrostatics; magnetism. Address: 1502 S. Fernandez, Arlington Heights, IL 60005.

FISH, F(LOYD) H(AMILTON), JR, b. Bryan, Tex, May 8, 23; m. 53; c. 5. MECHANICS. B.S, Va. Polytech, 43, M.S, 50. Asst. prof. fluid mech, Va. Polytech, 48-50; sr. res. engr, Textile fibers dept, E.I. DU PONT DE NEMOURS & CO, INC, 50-60, RES. SUPVR, TECH. DIV. FIBERS DEPT, 60- U.S.A, 43-46, Capt. Am. Soc. Mech. Eng; Soc. Automotive Eng. Mechanics of paper, fabrics and non-woven fabrics and cushioning structures, including manufacturing processes as well as products. Address: Christina Lab, E.I. du Pont de Nemours & Co, Inc, Wilmington, DE 19898.

FISH, FRANK H(AMILTON), b. Lethbridge, Alta, Can, May 6, 24; m. 45; c. 2. PHYSICS. B.Sc, Alberta, 49, M.Sc, 50. Res. officer, Ottawa Nat. Res. Council, 50-51; Defence Res. Bd. Can, 51-57; SR. RES. OFFICER, GILLETTE SAFETY RAZOR CO, 57- R.C.A.F, 42-45. Isotope applications; health physics; radiation dosimetry; corrosion and surface phenomena. Address: Research Dept, Gillette Co, Gillette Park, Boston, MA 02106.

FISH, FREDERIC F(ORWARD), b. Rochester, N.Y, July 25, 05; m. 30; c. 2. ZOOLOGY. B.S, Cornell, 28; D.Sc.(parasitic protozool), Hopkins, 31. Assoc. aquatic biologist, Bur. Fisheries, 31-34, dir, west coast path. lab, U.S. Fish & Wildlife Serv, 34-41, dir. west. fishculture invests, 41-49; biologist, U.S. Pub. Health Serv, 49-59; asst. chief, fish div, STATE WILDLIFE RESOURCES COMN, N.C, 59-71, ENVIRON. COORD, 71- Lectr, Washington (Seattle), 34-45; prof, Oregon State Col, 45-49. Human and avian malaria; fish parasites and diseases; public health and biological aspects of water pollution; environmental impact of development projects upon aquatic resources. Address: 3121 Eton Rd, Raleigh NC 27608.

FISH, HAROLD S(OMERS), b. Sidney, Maine, Mar. 5, 03; m. 37; c. 3. ANATOMY. A.B, Bowdoin Col, 25; Ph.D.(cytol), Harvard, 35. Instr. biol, Colby Col, 28-30; prof, Presby. Col.(S.C), 35-41; instr. ANAT, sch. med, Maryland, 41-42; med. sch, Hopkins, 42-45; asst. prof, sch. med, Louisville, 45-47; CHICAGO MED. SCH, 47-66, ASSOC. PROF, 66- Development of papillae on human tongue; papillae and nerve supply of rat tongue. Address: Dept. of Anatomy, Chicago Medical School, 2020 W. Ogden Ave, Chicago, IL 60612.

FISH, JAMES FRANKLIN, JR, b. Monongahela, Pa, Feb. 27, 41; m. 63; c. 1. BIOLOGICAL OCEANOGRAPHY, ANIMAL BEHAVIOR. B.S, Pa. State, 63; Nat. Defense Educ. Act fel, Rhode Island, 63-66, Ph.D.(oceanog), 69. Nat. Res. Coun. fel. bioacoustics, NAVAL UNDERSEA RES. & DEVELOP. CTR, 69-71, OCEANOGRAPHER, 71- AAAS; Animal Behav. Soc; Acoustical Soc. Am. Sound production and behavior of marine fishes and cetaceans; the effect of underwater sound on the vocalization and movement of marine animals. Address: Naval Undersea Research & Development Center, Code 5054, San Diego, CA 92132.

FISH, J(OACHIM) JOHN, b. Austria, Sept. 23, 04; nat; m. 32; c. 1. CHEMISTRY. Ph.D.(chem), Vienna, 27. Res. chemist & asst. to Prof. Frankel, Vienna, 27-28; res. chemist, Nordwark Works, Ger, 28-29; private lab. res, 29-40; chemist, res. & develop. cosmetics, V. Levy & Innis Speiden & Co, N.Y, 40-43; petrol. waxes, Warwick Wax Co, 43-59; V.PRES. RES. & DEVELOP, WEST. PETROCHEM. CORP, 59- Am. Chem. Soc; Am. Soc. Test. & Mat. Refining of petroleum waxes and their oxidation and polymerization. Address: Western Petrochemical Corp, Box 558, Chanute, KS 66720.

FISH, JOHN G, b. Chicago, Ill, Mar. 30, 38; m. 61; c. 4. ORGANIC CHEMISTRY. B.S, Western Michigan, 62; Houdry Process Co. fel. & Ph.D, Cincinnati, 68. MEM. TECH. STAFF, Mat. Group, TEX. INSTRUMENTS INC, DALLAS, 66-68, CENT. ANAL. & CHARACTERIZATION LAB, 68- Am. Chem. Soc; Am. Sci. Affiliation; The Chem. Soc. Analysis and characterization of polymers and plastics used in electronic processing, equipment and devices. Address: 1304 Cherokee Rd, Richardson, TX 75080.

FISH, LEONARD WILLIAM, Mkt. Res, Chem. Eng, see 12th ed, Soc. & Behav. Vols.

FISH, M(ARGARET) T(ROTTER), b. Medicine Hat, Alta, June 22, 27; m. 55; c. 3. MEDICINE. B.Sc, Alberta, 50, M.D, 55, M.Sc, 59. Assoc. prof. anat, Alberta, 56-64; asst. prof, Univ. Ottawa, 64-70; PHYSICIAN, HEALTH & COUNSELING SERV, CARLETON UNIV, 70- Res. assoc, Ont. Heart Found, 64-70. Can. Asn. Anat. Experimental embryology, production of cardiac anomalies in fetal rats by injection of trypan blue dye. Address: Health & Counseling Services, Carleton University, Ottawa, Ont, Can.

FISH, MARIE POLAND, b. Paterson, N.J, May 22, 02; m. 23; c. 1. MARINE BIOACOUSTICS, ICHTHYOLOGY. B.A, Smith Col, 21; R.I. State Col, 38; Sc.D, Univ. R.I, 66. Asst. cancer problems, div. med. res, Carnegie Institution, 21-22; instr, pub. sch, N.J, 22; hydrobiologist, Bur. Fisheries, 23-27; sr. ichthyologist, State Conserv. Dept, N.Y, 28-30; Int. Passamaquoddy Bay Invest, 31-33; res. assoc. ichthyol, Narragansett Marine Lab, R.I, 37-39, ichthyologist, 39-42; instr. zool, R.I. State Col, 41-43; asst. div. fishes, U.S. Nat. Mus, Smithsonian Institution, Wash, 43-46; ichthyologist, Oceanog. Inst, Woods Hole, 47-49; BIOL. OCEANOGRAPHER, NARRAGANSETT MARINE LAB, 49- Curator ichthyol, Buffalo Mus. Sci, 28-31, res. assoc, 31-; ichthyologist, Int. Co-op. Surv. of Lake Erie, 28-30; Gulf of Maine Co-op Surv, 29-30; sci. columnist, Providence Jour. Co, R.I, 37-39; dir. U.S. Navy Reference Library Underwater Sounds, 54-70, U.S. Navy Simultaneous Data Sta. Prog, 63-67; R-V Trident bioacoust. prog, 63-66. Consult, hydrobiol. adv. comt, Inst. Biol. Sci, Off. Naval Res, 55-; Int. Symposium on Perspectives in Marine Biol, 56; Inter-Island Marine Biol. Conf, P.R, 57. Chmn. adv. Kingfish Comt, U.S. Navy, 54- Asst, Arcturus oceanof. exped, 25; Bermuda oceanog. exped, 29; int. exped, 29-30; underwater sound proj, Bermuda, 51-52; Bimini, 52-53, 56-57; P.R, 55, 56; Virgin Islands, 56. Rep, Indo-Pac. Fisheries Coun. of UN, Thailand, 54; U.S. Navy rep, Ausschuss fur Funkortung int. conf, Ger, 56 & 61; Armes Navales conf, France, 56; Pac. Sci. Cong, Tokyo, 66. Stamford Mus. medal, 63; First Sophia Smith medal, Smith Col, 64; distinguished pub. serv. medal, U.S. Navy, 65; Nat. Fedn. Bus. & Prof. Woman's Club award, 66-67. Investigator, Office Naval Res, 44. Am. Soc. Ichthyol. & Herpet; Am. Soc. Limnol. & Oceanog; Soc. Woman Geog. Underwater sound of biological origin; life histories of marine and freshwater fishes; life history of the eel; ichthyology of the north and south Atlantic, Sargasso Sea, Caribbean Sea, north and south Pacific, Japanese and Indo-Pacific and Great Lakes areas. Address: 1291 Kingstowne Rd, Kingston, RI 02881.

FISH, MATHEWS B, b. Stockton, Calif, Jan. 26, 35; m. 57; c. 2. CLINICAL PATHOLOGY. A.B, California, Berkeley, 56, M.D, San Francisco, 59. Intern med, MED. CTR, SCH. MED, UNIV. CALIF, SAN FRANCISCO, 59-60, res. path, 60-64, asst. prof, 64-70, ASSOC. PROF. CLIN. PATH. & LAB. MED, 70-, ASSOC. DIR. CLIN. LABS, SAN FRANCISCO GEN. HOSP, 70-, asst. dir, 64-70. Intermediary metabolism in vitamin B_{12} and folic acid deficiency; intermediary metabolism, amino acids; hematology; clinical chemistry; radioisotopes and nuclear medicine. Address: Dept. of Clinical Pathology & Lab. Medicine, School of Medicine, University of California Medical Center, San Francisco, CA 94110.

FISH, RALPH C(OOPER), (JR), b. Beverly, N.J, Dec. 27, 13; m. 46. EPIZOOTIOLOGY. V.M.D, Pennsylvania, 39; M.P.H, Harvard, 51. Instr. vet. med, Pennsylvania, 39-40; vet, animal disease diagnosis & control, U.S. Dept. Agr, 40-50; lectr, Pan-Am. Foot & Mouth Disease Conf, Panama, 51, epizootiologist, 51-52; vet. epidemiologist, chem. corps, U.S. Dept. Army, 52-57; chief European mission res. animal diseases, AGR. RES. SERV, U.S. DEPT. AGR, 57-60, safety off, Plum Island Animal Disease Labs, 60-62, chief European mission res. animal diseases, 62-65, ASST. DIR. VET. SCI. RES. DIV, 65- Vet.C, U.S.A. Health Asn. Epizootiology, particularly foot and mouth disease. Address: Veterinary Sciences Research Division, Agricultural Research Service, U.S. Dept. of Agriculture, Beltsville, MD 20705.

FISH, RICHARD H(ERBERT), b. Providence, R.I, Sept. 7, 39; m. 61; c. 1. ORGANIC CHEMISTRY. B.S, Rhode Island, 61; Ph.D.(org. chem), New Hampshire, 65. Res. chemist org. herbicides, U.S. Borax Res. Corp, 65-67; fel, Univ. Calif, Irvine, 67-68; SR. RES. CHEMIST, ARCO CHEM. CO. RES. & DEVELOP. DIV, ATLANTIC RICHFIELD CO, 68- AAAS. Organotin and organogermanium hydride additions to dienes; synthesis of heterocycles; organoboron chemistry; organic photochemistry; free radical chemistry. Address: Arco Chemical Co. Research & Development Division, Atlantic Richfield Co, 1900 W. Crescent Ave, Anaheim, CA 92803.

FISH, RICHARD WAYNE, b. Gowrie, Iowa, Aug. 27, 34; m. 64; c. 1. ORGANIC GANIC CHEMISTRY. B.S, Iowa State, 56; Ph.D.(org. chem), Mich. State, 60. Res. chemist, Calif. Res. Corp, Standard Oil of Calif, 60-61; res. assoc. phys. org. chem, Brandeis, 61-63; Nat. Sci. Found. fel, California, Berkeley, 63-64; asst. prof. CHEM, SACRAMENTO STATE COL, 64-67, assoc. prof, 67-70, PROF, 70-, dir, Nat. Sci. Found. Undergrad. Res. Participation Prog, 65-71. Petrol. Res. Fund grant, 64-66; sr. res. fel, Brandeis Univ, 71-72. AAAS; Am. Chem. Soc. Physical organic chemistry; synthesis and reactions of aromatic, nonclassical aromatic and organometallic compounds; electrophilic reactions of metallocenes; stabilized carbonium on intermediates; benzyne intermediates and charge transfer studies. Address: Dept. of Chemistry, Sacramento State College, Sacremento, CA 95819.

FISH, STEWART A(LLISON), b. Benton, Ill, Nov. 4, 25; m. 57; c. 3. OBSTETRICS, GYNECOLOGY. Va. Polytech; M.D, Pennsylvania, 49. Asst. prof. OBSTET. & GYNECOL, southwest. med. sch, Texas, 54-58, clin. asst. prof, 58-62; private practice, 56-62; asst. prof, Univ. Ark, 62-66; PROF. & CHMN. DEPT, UNIV. TENN, MEMPHIS, 66- Mem. staff, City of Memphis Hosps, Baptist Mem. Hosp; consult, U.S. Naval Hosp; LeBonheur Children's Hosp; St. Joseph Hosp; Methodist Hosp. Dipl. Am. Bd. Obstet. & Gynecol, 58. U.S.N.R, 43-46, 51. Am. Col. Surg; Am. Med. Asn; Am. Col. Obstet. & Gynec; Asn. Profs. Gynec. & Obstet. Mammalian teratology; infectious diseases in pregnancy. Address: Dept. of Obstetrics & Gynecology, University of Tennessee College of Medicine, Memphis, TN 38103.

FISH, WAYNE WILLIAM, b. Helena, Okla, Apr. 21, 41; m. 62; c. 3. BIOCHEMISTRY. B.S, Okla. State, 63, Nat. Defense Ed. Act fel, 63-66, Nat. Insts. Health fel, 66-67, Ph.D.(biochem), 67. Res. assoc. BIOCHEM, med. ctr, Duke, 67-68, Nat. Insts. Health fel, 68-70; ASST. PROF, MED. UNIV. S.C, 70- AAAS; Am. Chem. Soc. Intrinsic physical and chemical properties of biological macromolecules, principally proteins; the subunit nature of proteins and the isolation and characterization of neuroproteins. Address: Dept. of Biochemistry, Medical University of South Carolina, Charleston, SC 29401.

FISH, WILLIAM A(RTHUR), b. Boston, Mass, Aug. 2, 21; m. 41; c. 7. ZOOLOGY. B.Sc, Notre Dame, 42; M.Sc, Ohio State, 46, Ph.D, 48. Asst. zool, Ohio State, 46, instr, 46-48; comp. anat, PROVIDENCE COL, 48-49, asst. prof. COMP. ANAT. & EMBRYOL, 49-52; assoc. prof, 52-55, PROF, 55- U.S.A, 42-46, Capt. AAAS; N.Y. Acad. Sci. Insect embryology; metabolism of thyroid in rats and of cholesterol in normal, neoplastic and embryonic tissue. Address: 168 Garden City Dr, Cranston, RI 02910.

FISH, WILLIAM MORGAN, b. Escanaba, Mich, Nov. 10, 18; m. 46; c. 3. CHEMICAL ENGINEERING. B.Ch.E, Marquette, 42. Chem. engr, Swenson Evaporator Co, 42-45, spec. proj. engr, C.K. Williams Co, 45-46; res. engr, ALUMINUM CO. OF AM, 46-49, sr. res. engr, Alcoa Res. Labs, 50-62, sr. scientist, 62-68, eng. adv, 68-71, MGR. PROCESS EQUIP. DEVELOP, ALUMINA & CHEM. DIV, 71- Sci. Res. Soc. Am; Instrument Soc. Am; Am. Inst. Chem. Eng. Fluidization; automation; consulting; alumina and fluoride processes. Address: 2273 Clairmont Dr, Pittsburgh, PA 15241.

FISH, WILLIAM R(ALPH), b. Hollidaysburg, Pa, Dec. 20, 15; m. 42; c. 2. CHEMISTRY. A.B, Lafayette Col, 38; fel, Brown, 38-39; fel, Yale, 39-41, M.S, 42; fel, Pa. State, 42-44, Ph.D.(biol. chem), 44. Res. chemist, Swift & Co, Chicago, 44-46; U.S. Naval Ord. Test Sta, 46-50, tech. dir. staff, 50-51, head, liquid propellant propulsion div, rocket develop. dept, 52-58; mgr. propellant res. & develop, liquid rocket opers, Aerojet-Gen. Corp, Div. of Gen. Tire & Rubber Co, 58-69; DIR. RES, NOBELL RES. LAB, 69- AAAS; Am. Chem. Soc; Cooper Ornith. Soc; Am. Ornith. Union. Liquid rocket propellants; chemistry and physiology of steroid hormones; ordnance chemistry; application of liquid-liquid extraction; biological acoustics. Address: 1863 Watt Ave, Apt. 24, Sacramento, CA 95825.

FISHBACK, W(ILLIAM) T(HOMPSON), b. Milwaukee, Wis, Jan. 28, 22; m. 60; c. 1. MATHEMATICS. A.B, Oberlin Col, 43; A.M, Harvard, 47, Ph.D. (math), 52. Mem. staff, radiation lab, Mass. Inst. Technol, 43-46; instr. MATH, Vermont, 50-51, asst. prof, 51-53; Ohio, 53-56, assoc. prof, 56-64, PROF, 64-66; EARLHAM COL, 66- Vis. prof, New Paltz State Teachers Col, 54; vis. lectr, Clark, 59, Harvard, 60, Denison, 64. Am. Math. Soc; Math. Asn. Am. Mathematical education; geometry. Address: Dept. of Mathematics, Earlham College, Richmond, IN 47374.

FISHBEIN, LAWRENCE, b. Brooklyn, N.Y, Oct. 27, 23; m. 48; c. 2. ORGANIC CHEMISTRY, BIOCHEMISTRY. B.S, Brooklyn Col, 48; M.S, Georgetown, 55, Ph.D.(org. chem), 58. Anal. chemist, U.S. Naval Propellant Plant, Md, 48-51, org. chemist, 51-56; lectr. chem, Georgetown, 56-58; sr. org. chemist, Tracer Lab, Inc, Mass, 58; E.R. Squibb & Sons, N.J, 58-60; Albright & Wilson, Ltd, Eng, 60-61; dir. prod. & develop, Chemed, Inc, Md, 61-63; staff scientist, Bionetics Res. Labs, Inc, Md, 63-67; CHIEF ORG. SYNTHESIS & ANAL. CHEM. BR, NAT. INST. ENVIRON. HEALTH SCI, 67- Adj. prof. entom. & toxicol, N.C. State Univ, 70- U.S.A, 43-46. AAAS; Am. Chem. Soc; Coblentz Soc; Soc. Chem. Indust; fel. Am. Inst. Chem; N.Y. Acad. Sci; The Chem. Soc; Royal Netherlands Chem. Soc. Paper, thin-layer and gas chromatography of carbamates, isomeric ureas and thioureas, synergistic agents; relationship of environmental agents in mutagenesis, carcinogenesis and teratogenesis; metabolism and photolysis of pesticides. Address: National Institute of Environmental Health Sciences, P.O. Box 12233, Research Triangle Park, NC 27709.

FISHBEIN, MORRIS, b. St. Louis, Mo, July 22, 89; m. 14; c. 3. MEDICINE. B.S, Univ. Chicago, 10, M.D, Rush Med. Col, 12; hon. D.Pharm, Rutgers Univ, 42; hon. LLD, Fla. South. Col, 57; hon. D.Sc, Chicago Med. Sch, 65. House physician, Durand Hosp, McCormick Inst. Infectious Diseases, 12-13; clin. assoc. MED, Rush Med. Col, UNIV. CHICAGO, 24-25, asst. clin. prof, 25-41, prof. lectr, SCH. MED, 42-57, EMER. PROF, 57-; UNIV. ILL. COL. MED, 57-, lectr. med. hist. & econ, 34-41, asst. prof. med, 41-45, clin. asst. prof, 45-57. Mem. bd. chief eds, Excerpta Medica, 48-71; contrib. ed, Postgrad. Med, 50-70; ed, World Wide Abstracts Gen. Med, 58-67; Med. World News, 60-; med. ed, Britannica Book of the Year, 45-; consult. ed, Family Health, 69-; consult. med. ed, Doubleday & Co. Mem. bd, Nat. Jewish Hosp, Denver, Colo; La Rabida Jackson Park Sanitarium, Chicago, Ill; Hektoen Inst. Med. Res; sci. adv. bd, City of Hope Med. Ctr, Calif; mem. gen. adv. comt, Nat. Found; mem. comt. prof. educ. & pub, v.pres. & mem. adv. comt, Int. Med. Cong; chmn, sci. adv. comt, Munic. Tuberc. Sanitarium, Chicago; pres, Inst. Adv. Learning Med. Sci, Calif; chmn. sci. adv. bd, Little City Found; consult, Nat. Libr. Med. Knight Comdr, Crown of Italy, 33; Order Carlos Finlay, Cuba, 42; Comdr. Civil Order of Health, Spain, 52; Presidential Cert. of Merit, 48; Officer's Cross, Order of Orange-Nassau, Netherlands, 54; med. alumni distinguished serv. award, Univ. Chicago, 56, alumni medal, 62, Rosenberger Medal, 68; Comdr. Cross Royal Order of Phoenix, Greece, 67. Mem. hist. adv. bd, hist. med. dept, U.S. Army, 42-45. AAAS; fel. Am. Geriat. Soc; Am. Med. Asn.(ed. jour, 24-50, Hygeia, 24-50); fel. Am. Pub. Health Asn; Med. Writers Asn. (award, 56, pres, 58-59); Inst. Med; Nat. Asn. Sci. Writers; fel. Royal Soc. Med; hon. mem. Med. Socs. Arg, Chile, & Guatemala. Isoagglutination; carbon monoxide poisoning and kidney function; medical research, economics and history; fads and quackery in medicine; foods; health superstitions; journalism. Address: 5454 S. Shore Dr, Chicago, IL 60615.

FISHBEIN, MORRIS, b. N.Y.C, Oct. 31, 16; m. 45; c. 3. MICROBIOLOGY. B.S, City Col. New York, 38; M.S, Kentucky, 41; Ph.D.(bact), Maryland, 52. Lab. asst, Kentucky, 41; bacteriologist in charge, Pensacola Lab, Fla. State Bd. Health, 41-42; chief biologist, Schwarz Labs, N.Y, 45; res. fel, U.S. Fish & Wildlife Serv, 45-47; RES. MICROBIOLOGIST, U.S. FOOD & DRUG ADMIN, 48- U.S.A.F, 43-45. AAAS; Am. Soc. Microbiol; Asn. Off. Anal. Chem. Effect of carcinogens on microorganisms; proteolysis of thermophylic microorganisms; physiology and metabolism of coliform group at elevated temperatures; shigella recovery methodology from foods; characterization of toxic factors from Vibrio parahaemolyticus. Address: 11512 Soward Dr, Silver Spring, MD 20902.

FISHBEIN, WILLIAM N(ICHOLS), b. Baltimore, Md, July 21, 33; m. 56; c. 3. BIOCHEMISTRY, MEDICINE. B.A, Johns Hopkins Univ, 53, M.D, 57; Ph.D. (biochem), Univ. Md, Baltimore City, 66. Intern med, Univ. Hosp, Baltimore, Md, 57-58, resident, 58-60, Nat. Insts. Health trainee neurochem, pediat. res. lab, 60-62; clin. assoc. med, Nat. Cancer Inst, 62-64; instr. biochem, med. sch, Univ. Md, Baltimore City, 64-65; CHIEF BIOCHEM. BR, BASIC SCI. DIV, ARMED FORCES INST. PATH, 65- Nat. Insts. Health spec. fel. neurochem, pediat. res. lab, Univ. Hosp, 64-65; res. grants cryobiol. & hepatic coma, U.S. Army Med. Res. & Develop. Command, Wash, D.C, 66-72, urease, Nat. Inst. Arthritis & Metab. Diseases, 67-74; scientist assoc, Univs. Assoc. Res. & Educ. in Path, Md, 67- U.S.P.H.S, 62-64, Comdr. Soc. Cryobiol; Am. Soc. Biol. Chem; Am. Soc. Exp. Path; Am. Soc. Cell Biol; N.Y. Acad. Sci.(A. Cressy Morrison Award, 68); Soc. Exp. Biol. & Med; Am. Fedn. Clin. Res. Enzyme structure and function; urease; cryobiology; hepatic coma; pathogenesis and treatment. Address: Biochemistry Branch, Basic Sciences Division, Armed Forces Institute of Pathology, Washington, DC 20305.

FISHBURNE, EDWARD STOKES, III, b. Charleston, S.C, Feb. 8, 36; m. 56; c. 2. MOLECULAR PHYSICS, AERONAUTICAL ENGINEERING. B.S, The Citadel, 57; Cincinnati, 57-58; Ph.D.(aeronaut. & astronaut. eng), Ohio State, 63. Scientist, Crosley Div, Avco Corp, Ohio, 57; Booz-Allen Appl. Res, Inc, 57-59; res. assoc. gas dynamics, rocket res. lab, Ohio State, 59-63, asst. supvr. rocket propulsion, 63-67; asst. prof. aeronaut. & astronaut. eng, univ, 63-67; res. scientist, GRUMMAN AEROSPACE CORP, 67-68, HEAD AERO-PHYS. SECT, RES. DEPT, 68-, consult, 66-67. Consult, Goodyear Aerospace Corp, 64-65; Indust. Nucleonics Corp, 65. AAAS; Am. Phys. Soc; Am. Inst. Aeronaut. & Astronaut; Combustion Inst. High temperature chemistry; energy exchange between molecules; spectroscopy; chemical physics. Address: Research Dept, Plant 35, Grumman Aerospace Corp, Bethpage, NY 11714.

FISHEL, CHARLES W(ESLEY), b. Dellroy, Ohio, Jan. 29, 19; m. 42; c. 2. MEDICAL MICROBIOLOGY. B.S, Montana State, 50, M.A, 52; Logan fel. & Ph.D, Chicago, 55. U.S. Pub. Health Serv. fel, Stanford, 55-56; instr. microbiol, sch. med, Colorado, 57-59, asst. prof, 59-64; PROF. & CHMN. DEPT, sch. med, Univ. Louisville, 64-70; MED. MICROBIOL, COL. MED, UNIV. S.FLA, 70- U.S.A, 44-46. Immunology; infectious diseases. Address: Dept. of Medical Microbiology, College of Medicine, University of South Florida, Tampa, FL 33620.

FISHEL, DERRY L(EE), b. Findlay, Ohio, July 15, 29; m. 67; c. 2. ORGANIC CHEMISTRY. B.A, Bowling Green State, 52; Ph.D.(org. chem), Ohio State, 59. Asst. prof. CHEM, South Dakota, 58-60; KENT STATE UNIV, 60-64, ASSOC. PROF, 64- The Chem. Soc; Am. Chem. Soc. Carbon-nitrogen rearrangement mechanisms; syntheses and properties of liquid crystals; mass spectrometry. Address: Dept. of Chemistry, Kent State University, Kent, OH 44242.

FISHEL, JOHN B, b. Hagerstown, Md, Sept. 24, 14; m. 45; c. 2. ORGANIC CHEMISTRY. B.S, Lehigh, 36; fel, Carnegie Inst. Tech, 36-38, Ohio State, 46-48, M.S, 48. Chemist, Neville Co, 38-39; Gulf Res. & Develop. Co, 39-42; prin. chemist, Battelle Mem. Inst, 48-56; org. res. chemist, res. lab, GEN. CIGAR CO, INC, 56-64, res. mgr, 64-69, MGR. RES. & DEVELOP. PROJS, 69- Chem.C, 42-46, Res, 46-, Col. Am. Chem. Soc; Am. Soc. Qual. Control. Alkylated phenols; tall oils; products of petroleum cracking; tobacco smoke. Address: General Cigar Co, Inc, Research & Development Center, 602 N. Charlotte St, Lancaster, PA 17604.

FISHER, A(LBERT) M(ADDEN), b. Toronto, Ont, May 27, 07; m. 45; c. 2. CHEMISTRY. B.A, Toronto, 31, M.A, 32, Ph.D, 34. Asst. chem, TORONTO, 31-32, asst, CONNAUGHT MED. RES. LABS, 32-39, res. assoc, 39-48, res. & admin. assoc, 48-50, asst. dir, 50-70, ASSOC. DIR, 70-, assoc. prof. PHYSIOL. HYG, SCH. HYG, 50-63, PROF, 63-, ACTING CHMN. ENVIRON. HEALTH, 69-, EXEC. SECY, INSULIN COMT, UNIV, 52-, secy, 44-52, assoc, sch. hyg, 45-48. Am. Soc. Biol. Chem; Am. Diabetes Asn; fel. Chem. Inst. Can; Can. Physiol. Soc. Chemistry of insulin; blood substitutes. Address: Connaught Medical Research Labs, University of Toronto, Toronto, Ont, Can.

FISHER, ANTHONY CLINTON, Econ, see Suppl. I to 11th ed, Soc. & Behav. Vols.

FISHER, AUSTIN W(ELLINGTON), JR, b. Newton, Mass, Jan. 25, 16; m. 39, 48; c. 4. ENGINEERING, MANAGEMENT SCIENCE. B.S, Massachusetts, 37; Sc.D.(chem. eng), Mass. Inst. Tech, 41. Asst, Mass. Inst. Tech, 39-41; process engr, Barrett div, Allied Chem. & Dye Corp, Pa, 41-44; proj. engr, Publicker Industs, Inc, 44-46; sr. chem. engr, Arthur D. Little, Inc, 46-51, head process eng. dept, 51-55, mgr, New England off, 55-57, tech. staff assoc, res. & develop. div, 58-59; v.pres. res. & develop, Ludlow Papers & Plastics Div, 59-60, exec. v.pres, 60-62, v.pres, res. & develop, Ludlow Corp, 62-64; consult. & lectr, 64-65; assoc. prof. ENG. MGT, NORTHEAST. UNIV, 65-67, PROF, 67- AAAS; Am. Chem. Soc; Soc. Chem. Indust; Am. Inst. Chem. Eng; Am. Soc. Eng. Educ. Management and interpersonal relations in technical organizations. Address: 780 Boylston St, Apt. 17C, Boston, MA 02199.

FISHER, BENJAMIN EDGAR, b. Detroit, Mich, Aug. 21, 21. CHEMISTRY. B.S, Lawrence Inst. Tech, 50; M.S, Bradley, 55; Iowa State, 56-57. Sci. aide, Detroit Tank Arsenal, Mich, 50-51; chemist, North. regional lab, U.S. Dept. Agr, 51-56; asst. chem, Iowa State, 56-57, Detroit Inst. Cancer Res, 57-58; CHEMIST, NORTH. REGIONAL RES. LAB, U.S. DEPT. AGR, 58- U.S.A, 43-46, S/Sgt. Am. Chem. Soc. Isolation and proof of structure of products from sugar-amine reactions; synthesis of furans, 4-pyrones and tetrazoles. Address: Northern Regional Research Lab, U.S. Dept. of Agriculture, 1815 N. University, Peoria, IL 61604.

FISHER, BERNARD, b. Pittsburgh, Pa, Aug. 23, 18; m. 48; c. 3. SURGERY. B.S, Pittsburgh, 40, M.D, 43. Rotating intern, Mercy Hosp, 43-44, res. & fel. surg, 44-50; teaching fel. path, UNIV. PITTSBURGH, 44-45, surg, 45-47, asst. instr. surg. & res. fel, exp. endocrinol, 47-50, instr. SURG, 50-53, asst. prof. & assoc. dir. Gibson Lab, 53-56, assoc. prof. & dir. LAB. SURG. RES, 56-59, PROF. & DIR, 59- Fel, Pennsylvania, 50-52; Markle Scholar, 53-58. Mem. staff, Pittsburgh Med. Ctr. Hosps. Consult, Oakland Vet. Admin. Hosp; mem. breast cancer task force, Nat. Cancer Inst, chmn. nat. surg. adjuvant breast proj. Dipl, Am. Bd. Surg, 52. AAAS; Soc. Exp. Biol. & Med; Soc. Univ. Surg; Am. Physiol. Soc; Am. Med. Asn; fel. Am. Col. Surg; Asn. Am. Med. Cols; Am. Surg. Asn; N.Y. Acad. Sci; Am. Asn. Cancer Res; Soc. Nuclear Med; Soc. Vascular Surg; Int. Cardiovasc. Soc; Int. Soc. Surg. Experimental surgery. Address: Dept. of Surgery, University of Pittsburgh Medical School, 3550 Terrace St, Pittsburgh, PA 16213.

FISHER, CALVIN L, b. Wilson, Va, May 24, 27; m. 60; c. 3. ORGANIC CHEMISTRY, TEXTILES. M.S, Richmond, 51. Res. chemist, E.I. DU PONT DE NEMOURS & CO, INC, 51-54, lab. supvr, 55-60, anal. res. supvr, 60-64, process supvr, 64-66, SR. PROCESS SUPVR, 66- U.S.N, 45-47. Am. Chem. Soc. Analytical research; polymer chemistry; textile processing; management. Address: 850 Hawthorne Lane, Waynesboro, VA 22980.

FISHER, CHARLES, b. Los Angeles, Calif, Mar. 26, 08; m. 30; c. 2. PSYCHIATRY, NEUROLOGY. Ph.B, Chicago, 29; fel, Northwestern, 32-34, Ph.D, 34, M.D, 39. Asst. neurol, med. sch, Northwestern, 34-36, instr, 36-39; jr. med. off, St. Elizabeths Hosp, 39-41; mem. staff, Chestnut Lodge Sanitarium, Md, 41-42; asst. surgeon, U.S. Pub. Health Serv, Marine Hosp, Ellis Island, 42-46; adj. psychiatrist, MT. SINAI HOSP, 46-54, res. assoc, 54-66, ATTEND. PSYCHIAT, 66- Lectr, Columbia Univ. & N.Y. Psychoanal. Inst, Marshall Field III res. grant, 41; Found. Fund res. grant psychiat, Yale, 54-60; res. grant, Nat. Inst. Ment. Health, Nat. Insts. Health, 60-; clin. prof. psychiat, Mt. Sinai Sch. Med, 66- Menninger award, 57. Am. Psychoanal. Asn; Am. Psychiat. Asn. Diabetes insipidus and the hypothalamico-hypophyseal control of water metabolism; relation of the hypothalamus to temperature regulation and fat metabolism; posterior pituitary physiology; nerve fiber size and sensation; dream psychology; dreams and perception; theory of perception; psychophysiology of sleep and dreams. Address: 141 E. 88th St, New York, NY 10028.

FISHER, C(HARLES) D(ONALD), b. Xenia, Ohio, June 15, 37; m. 65; c. 2. ORGANIC CHEMISTRY. A.B, Depauw Univ, 59; Ph.D.(chem), Univ. Wash, 63; M.B.A, Harvard, 69. Sr. scientist, Princeton Lab, Am. Can Co, 64-67; VENTURE MGR, CORP. RES, GEN. MILLS, INC, 69- Am. Chem. Soc; Inst. Food Technol. Research management; food science; synthetic organic chemistry; reaction mechanisms; x-ray crystallography. Address: General Mills, Inc, 9000 Plymouth Ave. N, Minneapolis, MN 55427.

FISHER, CHARLES E, b. Cuba, Kans, Apr. 18, 11; m. 35; c. 3. WEED SCIENCE. B.S, Kans. State Univ, 34; M.S, Tex. A&M Univ, 36. Asst. agronomist, TEX. A&M UNIV, 36-42, assoc. agronomist, 42-49, agronomist, 49-52, supt, 52-57, RES. & EXTEN. CTR, 57-68; PROF. IN CHARGE BRUSH CONTROL, 68- Consult, Int. Res. Inst, Brazil, 54-55; King Ranch Inc, Tex, Cuba, Brazil & Arg, 54-71; U.S. Agency Int. Develop, Arg, 62-63, Paraguay, 63-67; Dow Chem. Co, Panama, 67. Hoblitzelle Award, Renner Res. Found, 52. Am. Soc. Range Mgt; Am. Soc. Agron; Ecol. Soc. Am; Am. Soc. Soil Sci. Chemical and mechanical control of woody plants; range improvement; soil and water conservation. Address: Research & Extension Center, Texas A&M University, Lubbock, TX 79401.

FISHER, C(HARLES) HAROLD, b. Hiawatha, W.Va, Nov. 20, 06; m. 33, 68. ORGANIC CHEMISTRY. B.S, Roanoke Col, 28, hon. D.Sc, 63; M.S, Illinois, 29, Ph.D.(org. chem), 32; hon. D.Sc, Tulane, 53. Instr. org. chem, Harvard, 32-35; org. chemist, U.S. Bur. Mines, Pa, 35-40; head org. acids sect, east. regional res. lab, U.S. DEPT. AGR, 40-46, carbohydrate div, 46-50, DIR. SOUTH. MKT. & NUTRIT. RES. DIV, AGR. RES. SERV, 50- Mem. comt. chem. utilization of coal, Nat. Res. Coun, 39-41. South. chemists award, 56; Herty Award, 59. AAAS; Am. Chem. Soc; Am. Oil Chem. Soc; Am. Asn. Textile Chem. & Colorists; Am. Inst. Chem.(pres, 62-63, Chem. Pioneer Award, 66). Cotton textiles; cellulose; chemistry and utilization of farm crops. Address: Agricultural Research Service, U.S. Dept. of Agriculture, P.O. Box 19687, New Orleans, LA 70119.

FISHER, C(HARLES) P, b. Toronto, Ont, Apr. 13, 26; m. 56; c. 2. WATER RESOURCES. B.A.Sc, Toronto, 51, M.A.Sc, 58; Ph.D.(civil eng), Texas, 63. Surveyor, Ont. Dept. Hwys, 51-54; private consult, 54-59; prof. sanit. eng, Univ. Waterloo, 59-66; ACTING DIR. TECHNOL. DEVELOP. & SCI. SERV, ENVIRON. PROTECTION SERV, 66- R.C.A.F, 44-45, 49-57, Flight Lt. Water Pollution Control Fedn; Am. Water Works Asn; Int. Asn. Water Pollution Res. Biological waste treatment. Address: Environmental Protection Service, Ottawa, Ont, Can.

FISHER, C(HARLES) PAGE, JR, b. Richmond, Va, Sept. 24, 21; m. 44; c. 2. CIVIL ENGINEERING. B.S.C.E, Virginia, 49; S.M, Harvard, 50; Ph.D.(civil eng, physics), N.C. State, 62. Rodman, Va. Hwy. Dept, 39-41; in charge party land surv, W.W. La Prade & Bros, 45-46; engr, Metcalf & Eddy, 51; found. engr, Robertson & Assocs, 52-53; found. engr, H.S. Porter, 53-55; from instr. to assoc. prof. civil eng, N.C. State, 55-69; PRES, DEPCON GROUP, 69- Dir. & secy. corp, Troxler Electronic Labs, Inc, 62-; chmn. bd. & pres, Geotech. Eng. Co, 63-; prin, Gardner-Kline Assoc, 67- Mem. Spec. Comt, Hwy. Res. Bd, Nat. Sci. Found, 63- Troxler Electronic Labs, Inc, 58-; N.C. Hwy. Comn, 60-; Res. Triangle Inst, 64- U.S.N, 41-45. Am. Soc. Civil Eng; Am. Soc. Test. & Mat; Am. Soc. Eng. Educ; Consult. Eng. Coun. Measurement of the properties of earth materials in situ and in the laboratory; application of modern physics to civil engineering problems; quality control of engineering materials. Address: DEPCON Group, Box 10761, Raleigh, NC 27605.

FISHER, CHARLES R(AY), b. Carrollton, Mo, July 30, 40; m. 60; c. 2. MICROBIOLOGY, BIOCHEMICAL GENETICS. B.A, Central Methodist Col, 61; M.S, Purdue, 63; Nat. Sci. Found. summer fel, Illinois State, 66, Atomic Energy Comn. fel, 66-68, Ph.D.(biol), 68. Atomic Energy Comn. fel, OAK RIDGE NAT. LAB, 68-70, BIOLOGIST, 70-; ON LEAVE, RADIATION BIOLOGIST, LIFE SCI. DIV, INT. ATOMIC ENERGY AGENCY, VIENNA, AUSTRIA, 71- AAAS; Genetics Soc. Am. Microbial genetics; enzymology and control of purine biosynthesis; mechanism of action of antibiotics; bacterial flagellation; biochemistry of Neurospora; chemical and radiation mutagenesis. Address: Life Science Division, International Atomic Energy Agency, Kaerntnerring 11, P.O. Box 590, A-1011 Vienna, Austria.

FISHER, CLETUS G, b. Canton, Ohio, Sept. 22, 22; m. 46; c. 2. SPEECH PATHOLOGY, AUDIOLOGY. B.S, Kent State, 49; M.A, Iowa, 50; Ph.D. (audiol), Ohio State, 63. Instr. speech, Kans. State Col, 50-53; exec. dir, Hearing & Speech Center, Dayton, Ohio, 53-60; instr. speech, Ohio State, 62-63; asst. prof. speech path. & audiol, Univ. Iowa, 63-68; dir. speech & hearing div, dept. speech, NORTH. ILL. UNIV, 68-69, assoc. prof. SPEECH, 69-71, PROF, 71- U.S.A.A.F, 42-46. Am. Speech & Hearing Asn. Visual and aural perception of oral signals, including those with normal or with pathological hearing. Address: Dept. of Speech, Northern Illinois University, De Kalb, IL 60115.

FISHER, DALE J(OHN), b. Omro, Wis, June 4, 25; m. 57; c. 1. ANALYTICAL CHEMISTRY. B.S, Wis. State, Oshkosh, 47; Ph.D.(chem), Ind. Univ, 51. Chemist, ionic anal. group, OAK RIDGE NAT. LAB, 51-52, GROUP LEADER, ANAL. INSTRUMENTATION GROUP, ANAL. CHEM. DIV, 52- Mem. staff, Inst. Paper Chem, Wis, summer, 45; chemist, City of Oshkosh, summers, 47-49; all-univ. fel, 50-51; Am. Chem. Soc.(award, 69); Brit. Polarographic Soc. Analytical chemistry; design and new applications of instruments and methods for chemical analysis and research. Address: 22 Outer Dr, Oak Ridge, TN 37830.

FISHER, D(ANIEL) JEROME, b. Canton, N.Y, June 14, 96; m. 19; c. 3. MINERALOGY, CRYSTALLOGRAPHY. B.S, Chicago, 17, M.S, 20, Ph.D.(geol), 22; Michigan, 22; Berlin, 30-31. Instr. MINERAL, UNIV. CHICAGO, 21-26, asst. prof, 26-28, assoc. prof, 28-57, prof, 57-61, EMER. PROF, 61-; PROF, DEPT. GEOL, ARIZ. STATE UNIV, 70-, vis. prof, 68-70. Geologist, Ill. Geol. Surv, 21-34; jr. geologist, U.S. Geol. Surv, 24-25, asst. geologist, 25-36, sr. geologist, 43; geologist, S.Dak. Geol. Surv, 41-42; vis. prof, Northwestern, 65. Med. Dept, U.S.A, 17-19. Fel. AAAS; fel. Geol. Soc. Am; fel. Mineral. Soc. Am.(v.pres, 56, pres, 57); Mineral Soc. Gt. Brit. & Ireland; hon. mem. Mineral. Soc. India; Int. Mineral. Asn.(treas, 58-60, pres, 60-64). Crystallography; mineralogy; pegmatites; fuel geology; areal and stratigraphic geology; projection protractor to prepare gnomonic and stereographic projections; x-ray precession methods; microscopy; projections in structural studies; mineral phosphates; refractometry; goniometry. Address: 2101 E. Maryland Ave, Phoenix, AZ 85016.

FISHER, DAVID A(LEXANDER), b. Kitchener, Ont, Can, June 16, 07; U.S. citizen; m. 36; c. 2. MECHANICAL ENGINEERING. M.E, Cornell, 31, M.S, Columbia, 39. Instr. mech. eng, Cornell, 31-33; engr, Bronx Gas & Elec. Co, 35; instr. MECH. ENG, City Col. New York, 36-40; asst. prof, Tufts Col, 40-48; assoc. prof, UNIV. CONN, 48-58, PROF, 58- Mech. engr,

Jackson & Moreland, Mass, 45-48. Am. Soc. Mech. Eng; Am. Soc. Eng. Educ. Applied thermodynamics. Address: Dept. of Mechanical Engineering, University of Connecticut, Storrs, CT 06268.

FISHER, DAVID E, b. Phila, Pa, June 22, 32; m. 54; c. 3. NUCLEAR CHEMISTRY. B.S, Trinity Col, 54; Ph.D.(chem. physics), Florida, 58. Oak Ridge Inst. Nuclear Studies fel, Oak Ridge Nat. Lab, 57-58; res. assoc, Brookhaven Nat. Lab, 58-60; asst. prof. eng. physics, Cornell Univ, 60-66; assoc. prof. MARINE & ATMOSPHERIC SCI, INST. MARINE SCI, UNIV. MIAMI, 66-70, PROF, 70- AAAS; Meteoretical Soc; Am. Phys. Soc; Am. Chem. Soc; Am. Geophys. Union; Am. Geochem. Soc. Nuclear cosmochronology; cosmic-ray nuclear reactions in meteorites; activation analysis; isotopic abundances in meteorites and tektites; cosmic chemistry; marine geology and geochemistry; geochronology. Address: Institute of Marine Science, University of Miami, Miami, FL 33149.

FISHER, DAVID R(AYMOND), b. Los Angeles, Calif, Nov. 2, 39; m. 64. BIOLOGICAL STATISTICS. Occidental Col, 59-60; B.A, Univ. Calif, Los Angeles, 64; M.S, Univ. Ore, 66; Ph.D.(zool), Univ. Kans, 70. SCIENTIST ECOL, WHO, 70- Biomet. Soc; Am. Soc. Ichthyol. & Herpet; Soc. Study Evolution; Asn. Comput. Mach; Soc. Syst. Zool. Numerical taxonomy; theory of classification; systematics; ecology; statistical biology. Address: Ecology Unit/RECS, World Health Organization, Geneva, Switzerland.

FISHER, DELBERT A, b. Placerville, Calif, Aug. 12, 28; m. 51; c. 3. MEDICINE, PEDIATRICS. A.B, California, 50, M.D, 53. Instr. & res. assoc. pediat, endocrinol. & metab, sch. med, Oregon, 57-60; asst. prof. PEDIAT, sch. med, Univ. Ark, 60-63, assoc. prof, 63-68, asst. dir. clin. study ctr, 62-68; PROF, SCH. MED, UNIV. CALIF, LOS ANGELES, 68- Mem. reference panel, Am. Hosp. Form. Serv. U.S. Pub. Health Serv. career develop. award, 64- Dipl, Am. Bd. Pediat, 59, examiner, 70- U.S.A.F, 55-57. Soc. Pediat. Res; Endocrine Soc; Am. Acad. Pediat; Am. Pediat. Soc; Am. Thyroid. Asn; Am. Soc. Clin. Invest. Pediatric endocrinology and metabolism; thyroid disease; fluid and electrolyte metabolism. Address: Harbor General Hospital, 1000 W. Carson St, Torrance, CA 90509.

FISHER, DONALD B, b. Phila, Pa, Oct. 14, 35; m. 63. BOTANY. B.S, Washington (Seattle), 57; M.S, Wisconsin, 61; Nat. Insts. Health fel, Iowa State, 63-65, Ph.D.(biochem), 65. Asst. bot, Wisconsin, 59-61; biochem, Iowa State, 61-63; Nat. Insts. Health fel. bot, California, Berkeley, 65-67, res. botanist, 67-68; ASST. PROF. BOT, UNIV. GA, 68- Lectr. bot, summer 68. AAAS; Am. Soc. Plant Physiol; Am. Inst. Biol. Sci; Histochem. Soc. Transport of materials in plants; fertilization and embryo development in angiosperms. Address: Dept. of Botany, University of Georgia, Athens, Ga. 30601.

FISHER, DONALD D, b. Spokane, Wash, Dec. 20, 29; m. 51; c. 3. MATHEMATICS, COMPUTER SCIENCE. B.A, Washington State, 51, M.A, 53; Ph.D. (math), Stanford, 62. Asst. math, State Col. Wash, 51-53; mathematician, Douglas Aircraft Co, Inc, 53-54; asst. math, Stanford, 54-57, acting instr, 57-58; appl. sci. rep, Int. Bus. Mach. Corp, 58-60, mathematician, 60-62; res. assoc. comput. sci, Stanford, 62-65; dir. res. comput. ctr. & assoc. prof. prev. med. & math, Ind. Univ, 65-69; PROF. & HEAD, COMPUT. & INFO. SCI. DEPT, OKLA. STATE UNIV, 69- Asn. Comput. Mach; Soc. Indust. & Appl. Math. Numerical solutions of partial differential equations, particularly free boundary problems; computer applications in life sciences; computer based scheduling and simulation. Address: Computer & Information Science Dept, Mathematical Science Bldg, Oklahoma State University, Stillwater, OK 74074.

FISHER, D(ONALD) V(INCE), b. Kelowna, B.C, Feb. 3, 14; m. 51; c. 3. POMOLOGY. B.S.A, British Columbia, 33, M.S.A, 36; Ph.D.(plant physiol, hort), Iowa State, 41. Agr. asst, RES. STA, CAN. DEPT. AGR, 33-40, asst. supt, 41-43, pomologist-in-charge fruit harvesting & storage invests, 46-54, head POMOL. SECT, 55-71, DIR, 71- Can. Army, 43-46, Capt. Am. Pomol. Soc; fel. Am. Soc. Hort. Sci; Can. Soc. Hort. Sci; Agr. Inst. Can. Fruit maturity and cold storage; controlled atmosphere storage; air distribution and duct design under refrigerated forced air circulation systems; fruit thinning; fruit variety trials; use of hormones in pomology; high density orcharding. Address: Research Station, Canada Dept. of Agriculture, Summerland, B.C, Can.

FISHER, DONALD W(ILLIAM), b. Schenectady, N.Y, Sept. 8, 22; m. 55; c. 2. PALEONTOLOGY. A.B, Buffalo, 44, fel, 47-48, A.M, 48; Ph.D.(geol), Rochester, 52. Instr. geol, Union Col, 49-51, asst. prof, 52-53, sr. paleontologist & stratigrapher, N.Y. STATE MUS, STATE SCI. SERV, 53-55, STATE PALEONTOLOGIST, 55- Field geologist, State Geol. Surv, N.Y, 47-53. AAAS; fel. Geol. Soc. Am; Int. Paleont. Union; Paleont. Soc. Lower and Middle Ordovician and Silurian stratigraphy and paleontology of New York; Upper Cambrian stratigraphy of Adirondack border region; Taconic geology; tentaculitids; New York Pleistocene mammals. Address: 1 Lindenwald Court, Kinderhook, NY 12106.

FISHER, DOROTHY A, b. Hartford, Conn, Feb. 21, 11. ZOOLOGY. B.S, Keuka Col, 33; M.S, Cornell, 34, Ph.D, 42. Asst. biol, Keuka Col, 35-38; instr, Asheville Col, 42-46; asst. prof. ZOOL, MARSHALL UNIV, 46-53, assoc. prof, 54-57, PROF, 57- AAAS. Inheritance and causes of differences in learning ability of albino rats. Address: Dept. of Biological Sciences, Marshall University, Huntington, WV 25701.

FISHER, E(ARL) EUGENE, b. Monongahela, Pa, Dec. 18, 22; m. 44; c. 4. ORGANIC CHEMISTRY. B.S, Washington & Jefferson Col, 43; M.S, Ohio State, 44; Ph.D.(chem), Carnegie Inst. Tech, 48. Asst, Ohio State, 43-44; Carnegie Inst. Tech, 46-47, res. assoc, 47-48; res. chemist, org. chem, E.I. du Pont de Nemours & Co, 48-52, fabrics & finishes dept, 52-58; head explor. sect, chem. dept, A.E. Staley Mfg. Co, 58-61, dir. chem. res, 61-69, dir. food prod. res. & develop, 69-70; DIR. RES. & QUAL. CONTROL, WILLIAM WRIGLEY JR. CO, 70- U.S.N.R, 44-46, Lt.(jg). AAAS; Am. Chem. Soc; Sci. Res. Soc. Am; Inst. Food Technol; Am. Soc. Qual. Control; Am. Asn. Cereal Chem. Organic syntheses; carbohydrates; polymers; analytical methods. Address: 380 Carlisle Ave, Deerfield, IL 60015.

FISHER, EDWARD, b. Boston, Mass, Sept. 3, 13; m. 57. PHYSICS. B.S, Mass. Inst. Technol, 33; Ph.D.(theoret. physics), Cornell, 45. Instr. physics, Maryland, 42-43; Cornell, 43-45; asst. prof, Wyoming, 46-48; assoc. prof, Mo. Sch. Mines, 48-52; physicist, Gen. Precision Lab, 52-53; consult, 53-54; physicist, Atomic Power Develop. Assocs, 54-56; staff scientist, Lockheed Aircraft Corp, 57-59; prin. scientist, United Tech. Ctr, 59-63; PROF. PHYSICS, STATE UNIV. N.Y. COL. OSWEGO, 63- Am. Phys. Soc. Foundations of quantum mechanics; electrical rocket propulsion; nuclear reactor shielding; noise theory. Address: Dept. of Physics, State University of New York at Oswego, Oswego, NY 13126.

FISHER, EDWARD M(ORRIS), b. Boston, Mass, Dec. 11, 19; m. 45; c. 3. PHYSICAL SCIENCE. B.M.E, City Col. New York, 42. Army ord. indust. engr, 42-43; sr. res. assoc, Naval Ord. Lab, 46-61; PHYSICIST, Bur. Naval Weapons, 61-65; NAVAL AIR SYSTS. COMMAND, 65- U.S.N.R, 43-46, Lt. Inst. Elec & Electronics Eng. Research and technology in air launched ordnance. Address: 14100 Burning Bush Lane, Wheaton, MD 20906.

FISHER, EDWARD RICHARD, b. Detroit, Mich, Mar. 24, 38; m. 62; c. 2. CHEMICAL PHYSICS, ENGINEERING SCIENCE. B.Sc, California, Berkeley, 61; Ph.D.(chem. eng. sci), Hopkins, 65. Res. chemist, Lawrence Radiation Lab, 61, summers 62 & 64; asst. prof. chem, Copenhagen, 65-66; phys. chemist, space sci. lab, Gen. Elec. Co, Pa, 66-68; ASSOC. PROF. CHEM. ENG, WAYNE STATE UNIV, 68- Lectr, Copenhagen, 66; Gen. Elec. Grad. Prog, Rensselaer Polytech, 67. Am. Inst. Physics. Experimental and theoretical study of the details of energy transfer mechanisms in molecular collisions. Address: Dept. of Chemical Engineering, Wayne State University, Detroit, MI 48202.

FISHER, EDWARD S, b. Minneapolis, Minn, Apr. 23, 21; m. 53; c. 3. PHYSICAL METALLURGY. B.S, Minnesota, 48; M.S, Ill. Inst. Tech, 54. Asst. metallurgist, ARGONNE NAT. LAB, 48-55, ASSOC. METALLURGIST, 55- U.S.A, 43-46. Am. Inst. Min, Metall. & Petrol. Eng. Elastic constants in metal single crystals, particularly relation between elastic constant changes and phase changes. Address: Metallurgy Division, Argonne National Lab, Argonne, IL 60439.

FISHER, EDWIN R(ALPH), b. Pittsburgh, Pa, Sept. 2, 23; m. 53. PATHOLOGY. B.S, Pittsburgh, 45, M.D, 47. Assoc. pathologist, Cleveland Clinic, 52, 54; U.S. Pub. Health Serv, 52-54; assoc. prof. PATH, UNIV. PITTSBURGH, 54-58, PROF, 58-; DIR. LABS, SHADYSIDE HOSP, 70- Chief lab. serv, Vet. Admin. Hosp, 54-70. Parke-Davis award, 63. U.S.A, 43-46. AAAS; Am. Soc. Clin. Path; Am. Soc. Exp. Path; Am. Asn. Path. & Bact; Col. Am. Path; Am. Med. Asn; Int. Acad. Path. Histochemistry; pathology of gastrointestinal tract and thyroid. Address: Shadyside Hospital, 5230 Centre Ave, Pittsburgh, PA 15232.

FISHER, E(LLSWORTH) H(ENRY), b. Ottawa, Kans, Dec. 30, 11; m. 37; c. 2. ENTOMOLOGY. B.S, E.Cent. State Teachers Col, 34; M.S, Okla. Agr. & Mech. Col, 39; Ph.D.(entom), Univ. Wis, 48. Asst. prof. ENTOM, UNIV. WIS, MADISON, 45-48, assoc. prof, 48-61, PROF, 61-; COORD. PESTICIDE USE EDUC, 65- Am. Entom. Soc; Entom. Soc. Am. Insects of field crops, man, livestock and household; rats and mice; coordination of educational programs in the safe and economical uses of pesticides. Address: College of Agriculture, University of Wisconsin, Madison, WI 53706.

FISHER, ELTON, b. Parkfield, Calif, Mar. 7, 13; m. 40. B.S, Brigham Young Univ, 36, M.S, 37; fel, Iowa State Col, 37-42, Ph.D.(chem), 42; LL.B, Memphis State Univ, 60. Asst, Brigham Young Univ, 36-37; instr. chem, N.C. State Col, 42; fel, Koppers Co, Inc, Mellon Inst, 42-49; assoc. prof. chem, Memphis State Univ, 49-56; res. chemist, W.R. GRACE & CO, ARLINGTON, 56-59, sr. res. chemist, 59-62, MEM. STAFF, PATENT DEPT, 62- Am. Chem. Soc. Analytical chemistry; industrial chemistry. Address: 1505 Audmar Dr, McLean, VA 22101.

FISHER, (JAMES) ELWOOD, b. New Martinsville, W.Va, Apr. 12, 26; m. 56; c. 1. PARASITOLOGY, ECOLOGY. B.Sc, Fairmont State Col, 53; M.Sc, Miami (Ohio), 60; Ph.D.(biol), Va. Polytech, 67. Instr, high sch, Ohio, 53-59; asst. zool, Miami (Ohio), 59-60; asst. prof. BIOL, MADISON COL, 60-67, ASSOC. PROF, 67- U.S.N, 44-46. Am. Soc. Parasitol; Am. Soc. Limnol. & Oceanog. Parasites of wildlife, especially flukes and ectoparasites. Address: Dept. of Biology, Madison College, Harrisonburg, VA 22801.

FISHER, EMERSON K(INNEAR), b. Cleveland, Ohio, Aug. 25, 13; m. 47; c. 2. CHEMICAL ENGINEERING. B.S, Pa. State Col, 34. Asst, Pa. State Col, 34-37; asst. head chem. eng, GULF RES. & DEVELOP. CO, GULF OIL CORP, 37-41, process res. eng, 45-52, asst. chief develop. eng, 52-60, sect. supvr, 60-62, staff engr, 62-69, dir, econ. & comput. sci. div, 69-71, DIR, HAMARVILLE DIV, COMPUT. & COMMUN. SERV. DEPT, 71- U.S.N.R, 42-45, Lt. Comdr. Am. Chem. Soc; Am. Inst. Chem. Eng; Am. Asn. Cost Eng; Oper. Res. Soc. Am; Inst. Mgt. Sci. Computer programming; operations research; management sciences; economics; planning; data center management; general management. Address: Gulf Oil Corp, P.O. Drawer 2038, Pittsburgh, PA 15230.

FISHER, FARLEY, b. Cleveland, Ohio, Apr. 30, 38. ORGANIC & PHYSICAL CHEMISTRY. S.B, Mass. Inst. Tech, 60; Nat. Sci. Found. Coop. fel, Illinois, 61-64, Ph.D.(org. chem), 65. Res. fel. chem, Calif. Inst. Technol, 65-66; asst. prof, Tex. A&M Univ, 66-69; vis. lectr, Bucknell Univ, 69-70; ASSOC, CTR. SCI. IN PUB. INTEREST, 71- Assoc. chemist, Ames Lab, U.S. Atomic Energy Comn, 67. AAAS; Am. Chem. Soc; The Chem. Soc. Chemiluminescence; photochemistry; small-ring compounds; consumer products; environmental chemistry. Address: 1346 Connecticut Ave. N.W, Room 812, Washington, DC 20036.

FISHER, FLAKE LEROY, b. Springer, N.Mex, Aug. 7, 23; m. 48; c. 3. SOIL CHEMISTRY, PLANT NUTRITION. B.S, New Mexico State, 47; M.S, Texas A&M, 50, Ph.D.(soil chem), 59. Instr. agron, Texas A&M, 48-51; soil fertility, agr. exp. sta, 51-59, assoc. prof, 59-63; agronomist & dist. mgr, Best Fertilizers Co, 63-69; AGRONOMIST, OCCIDENTAL CHEM. TEX, 69- U.S.A.A.F, 42-45, 2nd Lt. Am. Soc. Agron; Soil Sci. Soc. Am. Soil fertility. Address: 1614 Armistead, College Station, TX 77840.

FISHER, FRANCENIA E(LEANORE), b. Green Cove Springs, Fla, Sept. 23, 24. PLANT PATHOLOGY. B.S, Fla. State, 45; Chicago, 45; M.S, Mich. State Col, 46. ASST. PROF. PLANT PATH. & ASST. PLANT PATHOLOGIST, CITRUS EXP. STA. UNIV. FLA, 46- AAAS; Soc. Econ. Bot; Am. Phytopath. Soc; Mycol. Soc. Am. Fungus diseases of citrus and their chemical control; fungus diseases of insects and mites attacking citrus and methods to increase efficacy of these diseases in coordination with artificial control measures; disease resistance. Address: Citrus Experiment Station, University of Florida, Lake Alfred, FL 33850.

FISHER, FRANCIS JOHN FULTON, b. Roxburgh, N.Z, Oct. 31, 26; Can. citizen; m. 49; c. 5. EVOLUTIONARY BIOLOGY, PLANT PHYSIOLOGY. B.Sc, Canterbury, 47, M.Sc, 49; univ. fel, New Zealand, 50 & 51, Nuffield Found. fel, 52 & 53, Ph.D.(exp. taxon), 54. Lectr. bot, Melbourne, 54-57; sr. lectr. Tasmania, 57-58; prin. sci. off, bot. div, N.Z. Dept. Sci. & Indust. Res, 58-65; assoc. prof. BIOL. SCI, SIMON FRASER UNIV, 65-67, PROF, 67- Nuffield Found. biol. res. grant, Australia, 54-55; Brit. Coun. travel grant, 55-56; Carnegie Corp. travel grant, 56; Carnegie Inst. Wash. res. fel, 56-57; dir, Tasmanian Bot. Gardens, 57-58; U.S. Pub. Health Serv. int. fel, 63-64, int. follow-up grant, 66-67; biol. consult, sch. soc. welfare, Calgary, 67-; Can. Environ. Sci. Ltd, 68-; Environ. Res. Consult, Ltd, 71- AAAS; Am. Inst. Biol. Sci; Can. Bot. Asn; Royal Soc. N.Z; Fr. Soc. Biogeog. Ecophysiology of New Zealand alpine screes; genecology of mountain ranunculus of New Zealand and North and South America; morphogenesis of leaves; adaptive change processes in living systems including human; biological basis of value systems. Address: Dept. of Biosciences, Simon Fraser University, Burnaby 2, B.C, Can.

FISHER, FRANK M, JR, b. Louisville, Ky, Oct. 16, 31; m. 56; c. 2. PARASITOLOGY, INVERTEBRATE PHYSIOLOGY. B.A, Hanover Col, 53; M.S, Purdue, 56, Ph.D.(invert. physiol), 61. Nat. Insts. Health fel, RICE UNIV, 61-63, asst. prof, BIOL, 63-69, ASSOC. PROF, 69- Instr. invert. zool, Marine Biol. Lab, Woods Hole, Mass, 64-; Nat. Insts. Health grant, 64-Med.C, U.S.A. Am. Soc. Zool; Am. Soc. Parasitol. Developmental physiology of animal parasites; membrane transport of carbohydrates; parasite biochemistry. Address: Dept. of Biology, Rice University, Houston, TX 77001.

FISHER, FRANK R(OBERT), b. Waterbury, Conn, Sept. 16, 21; m. 57; c. 2. ORGANIC CHEMISTRY. B.S, Michigan, 49; M.S, Pennsylvania, 50, Allied Chem. & Dye Corp. fel, 51-52, Ph.D.(chem), 53. Chemist, Am. Cyanamid Co, 52-54; res. assoc, Rhode Island, 54-55; EXEC. DIR. ADV. BD. MIL. PERSONNEL SUPPLIES, NAT. ACAD. SCI-NAT. RES. COUN, 55-U.S.A.A.F, 43-45. AAAS; Am. Chem. Soc. Coordination and administration. Address: 5706 Roosevelt St, Bethesda, MD 20034.

FISHER, FRANK ROYAL, b. Denver, Colo, Sept. 1, 18; m. 44; c. 3. PETROLEUM ENGINEERING. B.P.E, Colo. Sch. Mines, 40. Process engr, Sinclair Ref. Co, 40-42 & 45-47, admin. asst. to mgr, 47-51, mem. jr. bd. dirs, Sinclair Oil Corp, 52-53, corp. sect. Sinclair Res, Inc, 51-58, chmn. exec. prod. comt, Sinclair Ref. Co, 55-65; v.pres. opers, Sinclair Res, Inc, 58-65, v.pres. & dir. res, Sinclair Oil & Gas Co, 65-68, dir. prod. res, Sinclair Oil Corp, 68-69; ASST. DEPT. MGR. PROD. RES. ATLANTIC RICHFIELD CO, 69- U.S.N, 42-45, Lt, Silver Star; two Bronze Stars. Am. Inst. Chem. Eng; Am. Petrol. Inst. Petroleum refining; management and coordination of research. Address: Production Research Center, Atlantic Richfield Co, P.O. Box 2819, Dallas, TX 75221.

FISHER, FRANKLIN E(UGENE), b. Robinson, Ill, Mar. 8, 33; m. 59; c. 1. MECHANICAL ENGINEERING, ENGINEERING MECHANICS. B.S, Rose Polytech. Inst, 60; M.S, Univ. Md, College Park, 65, Ford Found. fel, 66-67, Kelly Tire fel, 68, Ph.D.(mech. eng), 69. Aerospace engr, aeronaut. systs. div, Wright-Patterson AFB, Ohio, 60-63; instr. MECH. ENG, Univ. Md, College Park, 64-69; ASST. PROF, LOYOLA UNIV. LOS ANGELES, 69-Res. mech. eng, Naval Res. Lab, Wash, D.C, 65-66. U.S.N, 51-55. Am. Soc. Mech. Eng; Am. Soc. Eng. Educ. Shock loading and vibration of structures as applied to mechanical engineering design. Address: Dept of Mechanical Engineering, Loyola University of Los Angeles, 7101 W. 80th St, Los Angeles, CA 90045.

FISHER, FRED DEAN, b. Lubbock, Tex, July 20, 34; m. 56; c. 4. CHEMICAL ENGINEERING, PHYSICAL CHEMISTRY. B.A, Linfield Col, 54; Tex. Tech. Col, 54-55; Dow fel, Oregon State, 58-59, Ph.D.(chem. eng), 60. Engr, Hanford Atomic Prods, Gen. Elec. Co, 59-64; engr, adv. mat. Ctr, Nuclear Mat. & Equip. Corp, 64-71; SR. ENGR, NUCLEAR FUELS DIV, WESTINGHOUSE ELEC. CORP, 71- Fel. Am. Inst. Chem; Am. Chem. Soc. Production technology of plutonium and plutonium materials. Address: 246 Main St, Leechburg, PA 15656.

FISHER, FREDERICK H(ENDRICK), b. Aberdeen, Wash, Dec. 30, 26; m. 55; c. 4. PHYSICS. B.S, Washington(Seattle), 49, univ. fels, 49-54, Ph.D. (physics), 57. Asst. physics, UNIV. CALIF, Los Angeles, 54-55, res. physicist, MARINE PHYS. LAB, SCRIPPS INST. OCEANOG, SAN DIEGO, 55-57, asst. res. physicist, 57-62, assoc. res. physicist, 62-68, RES. OCEANOGR. & LECTR, 68- Res. fel. acoust, Harvard, 57-58; dir. res, Havens Indust, 63-64; prof. & chmn. dept. physics, Univ. R.I, 70-71. Fel. Acoust. Soc. Am; sr. mem. Inst. Elec. & Electronics Eng; Am. Phys. Soc. Acoustics; physical chemistry; underwater sound; oceanography. Address: Marine Physical Lab, Scripps Institution of Oceanography, San Diego, CA 92152.

FISHER, FREDERICK STEPHEN, b. Highland Park, Mich, Aug. 5, 37; m. 61; c. 2. GEOLOGY, GEOCHEMISTRY. B.S, Wayne State, 61, M.S, 62; Ph.D. (geol), Wyoming, 66. GEOLOGIST, U.S. GEOL. SURV, 66- U.S.N.R, 55-63. Geol. Soc. Am. Geology and geochemistry of hydrothermal ore deposits. Address: U.S. Geological Survey, Bldg. 25, Federal Center, Denver, CO 80225.

FISHER, G. TOM, b. Jersey City, N.J, June 25, 29; m. 50; c. 4. ENTOMOLOGY. B.S, Iowa State, 50; Headlee fels, Rutgers, 52, 54, M.S, 52, Ph.D. (entom), 54. ASST. PROF. ENTOM. & EXTEN. ENTOMOLOGIST, UNIV. N.H, 69- Entom. Soc. Am. Extension teaching. Address: Dept. of Entomology, University of New Hampshire, Durham, NH 03824.

FISHER, G(ENE) J(ORDAN), b. Quitman, Miss, March 26, 31; m. 54; c. 2. ORGANIC CHEMISTRY. B.S, Texas, 52. Res. chemist, res. & develop. dept, CELANESE CHEM. CO, 52-57, sr. res. chemist, 57-59, group leader, 59-67, SECT. HEAD TECH. CTR, 67- Am. Chem. Soc. Reactions of ketene; reactions of formaldehyde; synthesis of monomers. Address: Celanese Chemical Co. Technical Center, P.O. Box 9077, Corpus Christi, TX 78408.

FISHER, GEORGE M. C, b. Anna, Ill, Nov. 30, 40; m. 65; c. 2. APPLIED MATHEMATICS, PHYSICS. B.S, Illinois, Champaign, 62; M.S, Brown, 64, Ph.D.(appl. math), 66. MEM. TECH. STAFF, BELL TEL. LABS, 65- AAAS. Continuum physics, particularly wave propagation and thermodynamics. Address: Bell Telephone Labs, 4G-526, Holmdel, NJ 07733.

FISHER, GEORGE PHILLIP, b. Quincy, Mass, May 10, 38; m. 64. ELEMENTARY PARTICLE PHYSICS. B.S, Mass. Inst. Technol, 59; M.S, Univ. Ill, 61, Ph.D.(physics), 65. Res. assoc. physics, Univ. Colo, Boulder, 64-65, asst. prof, 65-71; ASSOC. PHYSICIST, PHYSICS DEPT, BROOKHAVEN NAT. LAB, 71- Nat. Sci. Found. fel, Europ. Ctr. Nuclear Res, 67-68; U.S. Atomic Energy Comn. nuclear educ. & training appointment, Lawrence Radiation Lab, Berkeley, 69, Brookhaven Nat. Lab, 70; consult, Dow Chem. Co, 71. AAAS; Am. Phys. Soc; Am. Asn. Physics Teachers. Experimental high energy elementary particles research, using counters, spark chambers and bubble chambers; atomic physics. Address: Physics Dept, Brookhaven National Lab, Upton, NY 11973.

FISHER, GEORGE ROBERT, b. Long Prairie, Minn, Aug. 29, 28; m. 58; c. 4. REPRODUCTIVE PHYSIOLOGY, DAIRY HUSBANDRY. B.S, Univ. Minn, St. Paul, 51, Ph.D.(agr. invests. bovine semen), 66. Teacher, pub. sch, 52-53; salesman, E.G. Clinton Co, Minn, summer 55; teacher, pub. sch, 56-57, instr, 58-59; res. asst. dairy husb, Univ. Minn, St. Paul, 55-61; PROF. DAIRY HUSB, N.DAK. STATE UNIV. EXTEN, 61- U.S.A, 53-55, Sgt. Am. Soc. Animal Sci; Am. Dairy Sci. Asn. Investigations on bovine semen extenders and their application. Address: Dept. of Dairy Husbandry, North Dakota State University Station, Fargo, ND 58102.

FISHER, GEORGE WESCOTT, b. New Haven, Conn, May 16, 37; m. 59; c. 3. GEOLOGY. B.A, Dartmouth Col, 59; Woodrow Wilson Found. fel, Hopkins, 59-60, Nat. Sci. Found. fel, 60-63, M.A, 62, Ph.D.(geol), 63. Fel. petrol, Carnegie Inst. Geophys. Lab, 64-66; asst. prof. GEOL, JOHNS HOPKINS UNIV, 66-71, ASSOC. PROF, 71-; lectr, 65-66. U.S.A, 62-64, Res, 64-, Capt. AAAS; Mineral. Soc. Am; Geol. Soc. Am. Field and laboratory studies of the chemistry, structure and origin of metamorphic and igneous rocks. Address: Dept. of Earth & Planetary Sciences, Johns Hopkins University, Baltimore, MD 21218.

FISHER, GERALD THOMAS, b. Greenbrier, Tenn, July 5, 35; m. 60; c. 2. CHEMICAL ENGINEERING. B.S, Tennessee, 56, M.S, 59, Ph.D.(chem. eng), 60. Instr. CHEM. ENG, Tennessee, 56-60; asst. prof, VANDERBILT UNIV, 60-64, assoc. prof, 64-67, PROF, 67- Am. Inst. Chem. Eng; Am. Chem. Soc; Simulation Coun. Mass transfer; process dynamics and control; air and water pollution. Address: Box 1643 B, Vanderbilt University, Nashville, TN 37203.

FISHER, GORDON M(cCREA), b. St. Paul, Minn, Oct. 5, 25; m. 56; c. 2. MATHEMATICS, HISTORY & PHILOSOPHY OF SCIENCE. B.A, Miami (Fla), 51; Tulane, 53-55; fel, Michigan, 55-56; Ph.D.(math), La. State, 59. Instr. math, Miami (Fla), 53, 56-57; La. State, 57-59; Princeton, 59-62; lectr. math. & hon. lectr. hist. & philos. sci, Otago, N.Z, 62-64, sr. lectr. hist. & philos. sci. & hon. sr. lectr. math, 64-66; sr. lectr. math. & sr. lectr. hist. philos. sci, Univ. Waikato, 66-67; PROF. MATH, MADISON COL, 67- U.S.N, 43-45; U.S.A, 47-49. Am. Math. Soc; Math. Asn. Am. Analysis; history of mathematics. Address: Dept. of Mathematics, Madison College, Harrisonburg, VA 22801.

FISHER, GORDON P(AGE), b. Baltimore, Md, July 26, 22; m. 44; c. 4. CIVIL ENGINEERING. B.E, Hopkins, 42, D.Eng, 48. Engr. struct. res. div, NASA, 42-44; asst. prof. CIVIL ENG, CORNELL UNIV, 48-51, assoc. prof, 51-59, assoc. dean col. eng, 60-66, PROF, 59-, dir. water resources ctr, 62-64, head dept. environ. systs. eng, 66-71. Summer, mem. staff, eng. bridge div, Md. State Roads Comn, 48; sr. engr, Pittsburgh Des Moines Steel Co, Pa, 54-55, summer, 56, consult, 57; Power Reactor Develop. Co, Mich, 57-64; vis. prof, Chalmers Univ, 62-63; mem, Transportation Res. Forum; Hwy. Res. Bd, Nat. Acad. Sci-Nat. Res. Coun; expert mem, European Comt. Concrete. C.ENG, 44-46, 1st Lt. Am. Soc. Civil Eng.(Norman medal, 62); Am. Concrete Inst; Column Res. Coun; Opers. Res. Soc. Am. Buckling; foundation design; matrix formulation of structural theory; industrialization of building construction; water resources planning and management; analysis and design of transportation systems; traffic flow theory. Address: School of Civil & Environmental Engineering, Cornell University, Ithaca, NY 14850.

FISHER, GORDON S(TEWART), b. North Loup, Nebr, Dec. 9, 18; m. 49; c. 1. CHEMISTRY. B.S, Nebraska, 40, M.S, 41; Cornell, 41-42. Asst. chem, Nebraska, 40-41; Cornell, 41-42; chemist, south. regional res. lab, oilseed sect, bur. agr. & indust. chem, U.S. DEPT. AGR, 42-48, Naval Stores Res. Div, 48-58, HEAD TURPENTINE INVESTS, SOUTH. UTILIZATION RES. & DEVELOP. DIV, AGR. RES. SERV, OLUSTEE, 58- Vis. lectr, Florida, 59. Superior serv. award, U.S. Dept. Agr, 58. Am. Chem. Soc. Stabilization and analysis of vegetable oils; photochemistry of terpenes and resin acids; peroxide catalyzed additions to olefins; hydrogenation; oxidation and ozonization of vegetable oils and terpenes; preparation and reactions of terpene peroxides; analysis of pine gum; reactions of olefins with dienophiles. Address: 119 E. Monroe St, Lake City, FL 32055.

FISHER, HANS, b. Germany, Mar. 4, 28; nat; m. 51; c. 3. NUTRITIONAL BIOCHEMISTRY. B.S, Rutgers, 50; M.S, Connecticut, 52; Ralston Purina res. fel, Illinois, 53-54, Ph.D.(animal nutrit), 54. Asst. prof. NUTRIT, RUTGERS UNIV, 54-57, assoc. prof, 57-61, PROF, 61-, CHMN. DEPT, 66-, chmn. nutrit. coun, 61-63. Mem. bd. trustees, Rutgers Univ. Am. Feed Mfgs. award, 59. AAAS; Poultry Sci. Asn; Am. Inst. Nutrit; N.Y. Acad. Sci; Brit. Nutrit. Soc. Amino acid requirements; fatty acid metabolism. Address: Dept. of Nutrition, Rutgers University, New Brunswick, NJ 08903.

FISHER, H(AROLD) D(EAN), b. Kamloops, B.C, Apr. 8, 22; m. 47; c. 3. ZOOLOGY. B.A, British Columbia, 44, B.C. Sugar Ref. Co, Ltd. scholar, 46-47, M.A, 47; Ph.D, McGill, 54. Admin. asst. wildlife mgt, Can. Wildlife Serv, 47-48; assoc. biologist, Atlantic Biol. Sta, Fisheries Res. Bd. Can, N.B, 49-50, biologist, 50-55, sr. scientist, Arctic Unit, 56-58, prin. scientist & dir, 58-63; assoc. prof. ZOOL, UNIV. B.C, 63-66; PROF, 66- Seasonal field asst, Dom. Entomol. Lab, B.C, 40-43; sci. asst, Pac. Biol. Sta, Fisheries Res. Bd. Can, 44-46. Wildlife Soc; Am. Soc. Mammal; Can. Soc. Zool; Can. Soc. Wildlife & Fishery Biol. Mammalian life histories; reproduction, especially marine mammals; comparative vertebrate morphology. Address: Dept. of Zoology, University of British Columbia, Vancouver 8, B.C, Can.

FISHER, HAROLD M, b. Fayetteville, N.C, Feb. 19, 40; m. 63; c. 2. INORGANIC CHEMISTRY. B.S, Davidson Col, 62; M.S, Florida, 64, Ph.D.(inorg. chem), 66. Asst. gen. chem, Florida, 62-66; res. chemist, Atlantic-Richfield Co, 66; FIBER ENGR, FIBER INDUSTS, INC, 69- U.S.A, 66-69; Res, 69-70, Capt. Am. Chem. Soc. Inorganic chemistry, transition metal complexes, magnetically anomalous cobalt (II) spectra; propellant chemistry, burning rate modifiers, polybutadine, ferrocene derivatives; homogeneous catalysis, vaska-type complexes; fiber engineering, polyester, nylon. Address: 6500 Windyrush Rd, Charlotte, NC 28211.

FISHER, HAROLD WALLACE, b. Rutland, Vt, Oct. 27, 04; m. 30; c. 1. CHEMICAL ENGINEERING. B.S, Mass. Inst. Tech, 27; hon. D.Sc, Clarkson Tech, 60. Mem. staff, res. lab, Standard Oil Co. La, 27-29; Standard Oil Develop. Co, N.J, 29-30, hydro-eng. & chem, 30-32, Esso Labs, 32-33, asst. dir, 35-36, mgr. commercial dept, N.Y, 36-41, asst. mgr. sales eng, Standard Oil. Co, N.J, 33-35, mgr. chem. prod. dept, 41, dir, 45-47, mgr. chem. prod. dept. & v.pres, Stanco Distributors, Inc, 41-44, pres, Standard Alcohol Co, 44-47, Enjay Co, Inc, 47-48, dir. mfg. opers. E.Coast & mgr. chem. prod. dept, Esso Standard Oil Co, 48-49, dept. ref. coord, Standard Oil Co.(N.J), 49-50, ref. coord, 50-54, rep. in U.K, 54-57, managing dir, Iraq Petrol. Co, London, 57-59, dir. contact for Mid.E, ref. & transportation activities, Standard Oil Co.(N.J), 59-62, v.pres. & dir. chem. res. & ref, 62-69; RETIRED. Trustee, Sloan-Kettering Inst. Cancer Res, 64-70, chmn. bd, 70-; v.chmn. & chmn. exec. comt, Community Blood Coun. Greater New York, 69-71. Chem. Indust. Medal, 68. Nat. Acad. Eng; fel. AAAS; Am. Chem. Soc; Am. Inst. Chem. Eng; Soc. Automotive Eng; Brit. Soc. Chem. Indust. Address: P.O. Box 1792, Duxbury, MA 02332.

FISHER, HAROLD WILBUR, b. Galt, Ont, Can, Nov. 29, 28; U.S. citizen; m. 49; c. 2. BIOPHYSICS, MOLECULAR BIOLOGY. B.S, Michigan, 51, M.S, 53; Ph.D.(biophys), Colorado, 59. Res. assoc. biophys, Michigan, 50-53; chemist phys. chem, Eli Lilly Res. Labs, 53-55; instr. BIOPHYS, Colorado, 56-59, asst. prof, 60-63; assoc. prof, UNIV. R.I, 63-68, PROF, 68- Am. Cancer Soc. fel, 60-62. Biophys. Soc; Am. Soc. Cell Biol. Electron microscopy; bacteriophage; mammalian cell culture and genetics; cell fractionation and membranes; tumor viruses. Address: Dept. of Chemistry, University of Rhode Island, Kingston, RI 02881.

FISHER, H(ARRY) RUSSELL, b. Phila, Pa, May 4, 05; m; c. 3. PATHOLOGY, MEDICINE. B.S, Hahnemann Med. Col, 26, M.D, 28; award fel, Vienna, 38-39, dipl, 39. Prof. path. & oncol, Hahnemann Med. Col, 41-46; PATH, SCH. MED, UNIV. SOUTH. CALIF, 46-70, EMER. PROF, 70-; DIR. LABS, SANTA FE HOSP, LOS ANGELES, 56- Asst. pathologist, Hahnemann Hosp, 32-43; asst. physician, Coroner's Off, Phila, 39-43; pathologist, Moore-White Clinic, Los Angeles, 46-53; vis. pathologist, Los Angeles County Gen. Hosp, 47-; pathologist, Los Angeles Eye & Ear Hosp, 50-; dir. labs, Huntington Mem. Hosp, Pasadena, 53-56; pathologist, Good Hope Clinic, Los Angeles, 56-66; Col. Am. Path. del, Int. Cong. Clin. Pathologists, Madrid, 60, London, 63, Rome, 66, Montreal, 69; dir. Mem. Hosp. Glendale, 60-67, chief staff, 67-68; chmn. int. coun. socs. path, U.S. Comn. of Nat. Res. Coun, 70- Am. Soc. Clin. Path; Am. Med. Asn; Col. Am. Path.(v.pres, 64-65); Am. Col. Physicians; Int. Acad. Path. Natural history and pathogenesis of carcinoma in situ of the larynx; laryngeal pathology; phase microscopy; otosclerosis; hemtologic diagnosis. Address: 1920 Melwood Dr, Glendale, CA 91207.

FISHER, HARVEY F(RANKLIN), b. Cleveland, Ohio, June 12, 23; m. 64; c. 1. BIOCHEMISTRY. B.S, Western Reserve, 47; Atomic Energy Cmn. fel, Chicago, 51-52, Ph.D.(biochem), 52. Biochemist, col. physicians & surg, Columbia, 52-54; res. assoc. chem, Wisconsin, 54-56; instr, Massachusetts, 56-57; sr. assoc. biochem, Edsel B. Ford Inst, 57-63; assoc. prof. BIOCHEM, SCH. MED, UNIV. KANS, 63-65, PROF, 65-; DIR. MOLECULAR BIOCHEM. LAB, VET. ADMIN. HOSP, 63- C.Eng, U.S.A, 43-46. Am. Chem. Soc; Am. Soc. Biol. Chem. Mechanisms of enzymatic catalyses; protein structure. Address: Research Dept, Veterans Administration Hospital, 4801 Linwood Blvd, Kansas City, MO 64128.

FISHER, HARVEY I(RVIN), b. Edgar, Nebr, June 15, 16; m. 37; c. 3. VERTEBRATE MORPHOLOGY. B.S, Kans. State Col, 37; Ph.D.(comp. anat), Calif, 42. Asst. ZOOL, Calif, 37-41, vert. zool, mus. vert. zool, 41-42, tech. curator, 42-45; asst. prof, Hawaii, 45-48; Illinois, 48-50, assoc. prof, 50-55; PROF. & CHMN. DEPT, SOUTH. ILL. UNIV, 55- Exchange prof, Nevada, 47-48. AAAS; Soc. Study Evolution; Am. Soc. Zool; Am. Soc. Mammal; Am. Ornith. Union; Cooper Ornith. Soc; Wilson Ornith. Soc.(ed, The Auk); Indian Acad. Zool. Avian and functional anatomy; vertebrate natural history. Address: Dept. of Zoology, Southern Illinois University, Carbondale, IL 62901.

FISHER, HENRY B(ENEDICT), b. Geneseo, Ill, Mar. 6, 09; m. 41; c. 2. PHYSICAL CHEMISTRY. B.S, Antioch Col, 32; Ph.D.(phys. chem), Illinois, 37. Res. chemist, Darco Corp, Del, 36-41; res. supvr, Aluminum Co. Am, 41-46; from res. supvr. to SECT. MGR. SPEC. PROJ, PHILLIPS PETROL. CO, 46- Am. Chem. Soc; Am. Inst. Mining, Metall. & Petrol. Eng. Colloidal chemistry; adsorption; clays; inorganic chemistry; fused salt systems; drilling fluids; water chemistry; pollution; oil recovery; rheology. Address: 3420 Wildwood Ct, Bartlesville, OK 74003.

FISHER, H(ENRY) J(ULIAN), b. Montreal, Que, Mar. 1, 20; m. 47; c. 1. PHYSICAL METALLURGY. B.Sc, Queen's (Can), 42; M.Sc, Birmingham, 48; D.Eng, Yale, 53. Chemist, Crane Ltd, Can, 42-45; phys. metallurgist, Can. Dept. Mines & Tech. Survs, 45-54; res. phys. metallurgist, res. lab, Gen. Elec. Co, 54-60; mgr. alloy develop, Beryllium Corp, 60-63; dir. European opers, Martin Metals Co, 64-68; PROJ. DIR, CONTEMPORARY RES. INC, 68- AAAS; Am. Ord. Asn. Administration of technical sales; marketing metallurgical products; high temperature alloys; vacuum precision castings for gas turbines. Address: Contemporary Research Inc, 14 Tech Circle, Natick, MA 01760.

FISHER, IRVING S(ANBORN), b. Augusta, Maine, May 21, 20; m. 45; c. 3. GEOLOGY. A.B, Bates Col, 41; M.A, Harvard, 48, Ph.D.(geol), 52. Asst. instr. geol, Dartmouth Col, 41-42; field asst, U.S. Geol. Surv, 42; asst. prof. GEOL, UNIV. KY, 49-56, ASSOC. PROF, 56- U.S.N.R, 42-46, Lt. Fel. AAAS; Am. Asn. Petrol. Geol; Mineral. Soc. Am; Geol. Soc. Am; Soc. Econ. Paleont. & Mineral; Meteoritical Soc; Nat. Asn. Geol. Teachers. Petrology; mineralogy. Address: Dept. of Geology, University of Kentucky, Lexington, KY 40506.

FISHER, JACK BERNARD, b. N.Y.C, July 13, 43. BOTANY. B.S, Cornell Univ, 65, M.S, 66; Ph.D.(bot), Univ. Calif, Davis, 69. Cabot Found. res. fel, Harvard & Fairchild Trop. Garden, Miami, 69-71; ASST. PROF. BOT, OHIO UNIV, 71- Bot. Soc. Am; Asn. Trop. Biol; Int. Soc. Plant Morphol. Developmental anatomy and morphology, especially of monocotyledons; tropical botany and agriculture. Address: Dept. of Botany, Ohio University, Athens, OH 45701.

FISHER, JAMES F(REDERICK), b. Williamsport, Pa, Apr. 20, 25; m. 47; c. 3. BIOCHEMISTRY, ORGANIC CHEMISTRY. B.S, Pa. State, 50, Ph.D. (biochem), 60; M.S, Minnesota, 52. Res. chemist, Merck, Sharpe & Dohme Res. Labs, 52-57; Colgate Palmolive Co, 60-61; Wyeth Labs, Am. Home Prods. Corp, 61-63; proj. leader, citrus prods, U.S. Dept. Agr, 64-69; RES. CHEMIST, CITRUS EXP. STA, FLA. CITRUS COMN, LAKE ALFRED, 69- U.S.N, 42-45. AAAS; Am. Chem. Soc. Synthesis of steroids; structure elucidation; biosynthesis of plant phenolics. Address: 1032 Biltmore Dr. N.W, Winter Haven, FL 33880.

FISHER, JAMES H(AROLD), b. Mayfield, Ky, Nov. 8, 19; m. 43; c. 3. GEOLOGY. A.B, Illinois, 43, B.S, 47, M.S, 49, Shell Oil Co. fel, 51-52, Ph.D. (geol), 53. Asst, Illinois, 47-48; geologist, McCurtain Limestone Co, 48-49; Pure Oil Co, 49-51; asst. prof. GEOL, Illinois, 52-55; Nebraska, 55-57; MICH. STATE UNIV, 57-60, assoc. prof, 60-69, PROF, 70- Geol. Soc. Am; Am. Asn. Petrol. Geol. Petroleum geology; stratigraphy and structure of the Rocky Mountains and the Great Plains province; petroleum geology of the Michigan Basin. Address: Dept. of Geology, Michigan State University, East Lansing, MI 48823.

FISHER, JAMES LOUIS, b. Magrath, Alta, June 7, 43; m. 64; c. 2. ALGEBRA. B.S, Univ. Alta, 65; Ford Found. fel, Calif. Inst. Technol, 66, Ph.D. (math), 69. ASST. PROF. MATH, UNIV. ALTA, 69- Am. Math. Soc; Math. Asn. Am; Can. Math. Cong. Ring theory, especially structure of division rings. Address: Dept. of Mathematics, Faculty of Science, University of Alberta, Edmonton 7, Alta, Can.

FISHER, JAMES R(OBERT), b. El Paso, Texas, Sept. 18, 28; m. 49; c. 2. BIOCHEMISTRY. B.S, Texas West. Col, 50; M.A, Texas, 52, Ph.D.(chem), 54. Fel. CHEM, Texas, 54-55; instr, FLA. STATE UNIV, 55-57, asst. prof, 57-62, assoc. prof, 62-68, PROF, 68- U.S.A, 46-48. AAAS; Am. Soc. Zool; Am. Soc. Biol. Chem; Soc. Develop. Biol. Enzymes in embryonic development; mechanisms involved in controlling enzymatic activity; comparative biochemistry; enzyme mechanisms and kinetics. Address: Dept. of Chemistry, 103 IMB, Florida State University, Tallahassee, FL 32306.

FISHER, JAMES RUSSELL, b. New Castle, Pa, Sept. 24, 40. GEOCHEMISTRY, PHYSICAL INORGANIC CHEMISTRY. A.B, Harvard, 62; Ph.D.(geochem), Pa. State, 69. Nat. Acad. Sci. res. assoc. geochem, U.S. GEOL. SURV, 69-71, GEOLOGIST, 71- AAAS; Mineral. Soc. Am. Chemistry of aqueous solutions at elevated temperature and pressure; hydrothermal synthesis of crystalline materials; pressure-volume-temperature properties of gases and aqueous solutions. Address: U.S. Geological Survey, 1244 General Services Bldg, Washington, DC 20242.

FISHER, JAMES W, b. Startex, S.C, May 22, 25; m. 47; c. 6. PHARMACOLOGY. B.S, South Carolina, 47; George Washington, 48-50; U.S. Pub. Health fel, Louisville, 56-58, Ph.D, 58. Chemist org. synthesis, Abbott Pharmaceut. Labs, Ill, 48; pharmacologist, Armour Pharmaceut. Labs, 50-54; sr. pharmacologist, res. div, Lloyd Bros, Inc, Ohio, 54-56; instr. pharmacol, med. units, Univ. Tenn, Memphis, 58-60, asst. prof, 60-62, assoc. prof, 62-66, prof, 66-68; PROF. & CHMN. DEPT. PHARMACOL, SCH. MED, TULANE UNIV, 68- Guest investr, Argonne Cancer Res. Hosp, Chicago, summer, 61; guest lectr. & investr, Christie Hosp, Holt Radium Inst. & sch. med, Victoria Univ. Manchester, 63-64; mem. comt. erythropoietin, Nat. Heart & Lung Inst, 71-74. U.S.N.R, 44-46, Res, 46-57, Lt.(jg). AAAS; Am. Soc. Hemat; Am. Soc. Pharmacol. & Exp. Therapeut; Soc. Exp. Biol. & Med; Am. Soc. Nephrology. Hematopharmacology; erythropoietin, hormones and erythropoiesis; erythropoietic function of the kidney; adrenocortical steroids; anemia and kidney disease. Address: Dept. of Pharmacology, Tulane University School of Medicine, 1430 Tulane Ave, New Orleans, LA 70112.

FISHER, JAMES W(ALLWIN), b. Barrie, Ont, June 20, 11; m. 40; c. 1. EPIDEMIOLOGY, MICROBIOLOGY. B.A, Toronto, 39, M.A, 41, fels, 41-44, Ph.D.(epidemiol, biomet), 44; summers, Michigan, 38, 39, 41, North Carolina, 51, Ottawa (Can), 55. Demonstr. hyg. & prev. med, Toronto, 39-40; head sect. virol, hyg. lab, FED. DEPT. NAT. HEALTH & WELFARE, 44-50, consult, res. & statist, ment. health div, 50-60, res. develop. sect, 60-65, occupational health div, 65-69, SCI. ADV, DRUG ADV. BUR, FOOD & DRUG DIRECTORATE, 69- Dominion analyst, 44-50; guest lectr, Dalhousie Univ, 60-; dir. & sci. adv, Fisher & Wexler Ltd, Indust. & Pub. Affairs Consults, 69- Biomet. Soc. Virus infections; poliomyelitis; influenza; biological assay; design of experiments; medical-administration statistics. Address: Drug Advisory Bureau, Food & Drug Directorate, Federal Dept. of National Health & Welfare, Tunney's Pasture, Ottawa, Ont. K1A 0L2, Can.

FISHER, JOHN C(ROCKER), b. Ithaca, N.Y, Dec. 19, 19; m. 43; c. 3. PHYSICS. A.B, Ohio State, 41, Sc.D, Mass. Inst. Tech, 47. Res. engr, Battelle Mem. Inst, 41-42; asst. & later instr. mech, Mass. Inst. Tech, 42-47; res. assoc, GEN. ELEC. CO, 47-51, mgr. phys. metall. sect, 51-57, physicist, 57-63, MGR. liaison & transition, res. lab, 63-64, phys. sci. & info. disciplines, tech. mil. planning oper, Calif, 64-68, CONSULT. SCIENTIST, RE-ENTRY & ENVIRON. SYSTS. PRODS. DIV, PA, 69- Chief scientist, U.S. Air Force, Wash, D.C, 68-69; Campbell mem. lectr; Gillette mem. lectr. Alfred Noble Prize. AAAS; Am. Inst. Phys; Am. Phys. Soc; Am. Soc. Metals. Physical Sciences. Address: 425 Huston Rd, Radnor, PA 19087.

FISHER, J(OHN) E(DWIN), b. Toronto, Ont, Mar. 12, 23; m. 45; c. 2. PLANT PHYSIOLOGY. B.S.A, Toronto, 50; M.S, Iowa State Col, 52, Ph.D.(plant physiol), 53. Fel, Iowa State Col, 50-53; PLANT PHYSIOLOGIST, BOT. & PLANT PATH. DIV, sci. serv, CAN. DEPT. AGR, 53-59, NAT. PLANT RES. INST, 59- Governor-Gen. silver medal, 48. R.C.A.F, 42-46, Flight Lt; Distinguished Flying Cross, 44. Can. Soc. Plant Physiol. Photoperiodism and vernalization in plants; growth and differentiation in plants; chlorophyll synthesis. Address: Research Branch, National Plant Research Institute, Carling Ave, Ottawa, Ont, Can.

FISHER, JOHN F, b. East Liverpool, Ohio, July 23, 37; m. 59. ANALYTICAL & PHYSICAL CHEMISTRY. B.S, West Virginia, 59, M.S, 61, Ph.D.(chem), 63. Anal. chemist, res. & develop. dept, UNION CARBIDE CORP, 62-70, SR. ENG. SPECIALIST, ENG. DEPT, 70- Am. Chem. Soc. Gas chromatography; non-aqueous titrations; spectrophotometry; infrared spectroscopy; analytical instrumentation. Address: 313 Parkview Dr, St. Albans, WV 25177.

FISHER, JOHN G(ATEWOOD), b. McLaughlin, S.Dak, June 9, 24; m. 45; c. 5. ORGANIC CHEMISTRY. B.S, West.Ky. State Col, 47; Ph.D.(chem), Ohio State, 51. Asst. res. chemist, TENN. EASTMAN CO, 51-52, res. chemist, 52-55, sr. res. chemist, 55-67, RES. ASSOC, 67- U.S.A, 43-46. Am. Asn. Textile Chem. & Colorists; Am. Chem. Soc. Azo dyes and their intermediates; heterocyclic compounds; quarternary ammonium compounds; metal chelate compounds; general synthetic organic chemistry. Address: Research Labs, Tennessee Eastman Co, Kingsport, TN 37660.

FISHER, J(OHN) H(ENRY), b. Vancouver, B.C, Dec. 23, 14; m. 44; c. 3. ORGANIC CHEMISTRY, CHEMICAL ENGINEERING. B.S, British Columbia, 35, Carnegie fel. & M.A, 38; Nat. Res. Coun. Can. fel, McGill, 38-41, Ph.D.(chem), 41. Asst. res. dir, pulp & paper, Fraser Co, Ltd, 41-42; chemist chem. warfare, Allied War Supplies, Ltd, 43-44; res. engr, Ont. Paper Co, Ltd, 44-53; res. dir. pulp & paper & forest prod, MacMillan, Bloedel & Powell River, Ltd, 53-60, asst. res. dir. in charge pulp & paper res, 60-64; MGR. RES. & DEVELOP, B.C. FOREST PROD, LTD, 64- Tech. Asn. Pulp & Paper Indust; Am. Inst. Chem. Eng; Can. Pulp & Paper Asn. Kraft pulp; pollution control; chemical byproducts from pulping liquors and forest residues. Address: B.C. Forest Products, Ltd, 1190 Melville St, Vancouver, B.C, Can.

FISHER, JOHN H(ERBERT), b. Tipton, Mich, Dec. 19, 21; m. 47; c. 4. SURGERY. Michigan, 40-43; M.D, Harvard Med. Sch, 46; M.S, Tufts, 52. Surgeon, BOSTON FLOATING HOSP, 56-59, PEDIAT-SURGEON-IN-CHIEF, 60-; ASST. PROF. SURG, SCH. MED, TUFTS UNIV, 59- U.S.A, 47-49. Pediatric surgery. Address: 20 Ash St, Boston, MA 02111.

FISHER, JOHN JAMES, b. N.Y.C, Jan. 7, 07; m. 37; c. 3. PHYSIOLOGY. A.B, St. John's(N.Y), 32; M.A, Columbia Univ, 34, Ed.D, 49. Asst. Prof, Manhattan Col, 37-42, 46-51; PROF. BIOL. SCI. & ACAD. DEAN, LOWELL STATE COL, 51- U.S.A.A.F, 43-46, 1st Lt. Human physiology; science curriculum development. Address: Dept. of Biology, Lowell State College, Lowell, MA 01854.

FISHER, JOHN WILLIAM, b. Ancell, Mo, Feb. 15, 31; m. 52; c. 4. CIVIL ENGINEERING. B.S.C.E, Washington (St. Louis), 56; M.S, Lehigh, 58, Ph.D.(struct. joints), 64. Struct. res. asst, Lehigh, 56-58; asst. bridge res. engr, Hwy. Res. Bd, Nat. Acad. Sci-Nat. Res. Coun, 58-61; struct. res. instr, LEHIGH UNIV, 61-64, asst. prof. CIVIL ENG, 64-66, assoc. prof, 66-69, PROF, 69- Summer struct. analyst, McDonnell Aircraft Corp, 56. Struct. consult, Bethlehem Steel Corp, 64-65, 67-68, 71; Nelson Stud Welding Co, 65-; Am. Iron & Steel Inst, 66-67, 70-71; Air Prod. & Chem. Corp, 68; Del. River Port Auth, 68-69; Conn. Dept. Transportation, 70-71; Tex. Dept. Hwys, 71. Mem, Res. Coun. Riveted & Bolted Struct. Joints; Hwy. Res. Bd, Nat. Acad. Sci-Nat. Res. Coun. U.S.A, 51-53, 2nd Lt. Am. Soc. Civil Eng.(Walter L. Huber Res. Prize, 69); Nat. Soc. Prof. Eng; Int. Asn. Bridge & Struct. Eng. Behavior of welded connections; fatigue studies of bridge components; behavior of bridge structures; high strength bolts; bolted joints and composite beams. Address: Fritz Lab, Lehigh University, Bethlehem, PA 18015.

FISHER, JOSEPH E, b. N.Y.C, Nov. 21, 25; m; c. 3. MECHANICAL ENGINEERING. A.B, Columbia, 50, B.S.M.E, 52. Develop. engr, M.W. Kellogg Co. Div, Pullman Corp, N.Y, 51-54; proj. engr, Albuquerque Div, ACF Industs, Inc, 54-56, gen. supvr. develop. eng, 56-60, mgr. develop. & test, 60-63, mgr. mech. develop. & test eng, N.Mex, 63-67; mgr. prog. develop. & mgt, Gen. Elec. Aircraft Eng. Group, Mass, 67-69; MGR. ADVANCE PROCESS TECHNOL, PHILCO-FORD REFRIG. PROD. DIV, 69- U.S.A, 44-46. Soc. Exp. Stress Anal; Nat. Soc. Prof. Eng; Am. Welding Soc. Super pressure technology; experimental mechanics; product design and development; materials development. Address: Advance Process Technology, Philco-Ford Refrigeration Products Division, Connersville, IN 47331.

FISHER, KATHLEEN MARY, b. Long Branch, N.J, Aug. 4, 38; m. 59; c. 3. GENETICS. B.S, Rutgers, 60; Cincinnati, 61-62; Ph.D.(genetics), California, 69. Lab. technician malaria res, Christ Hosp. Inst. Med. Res, Cincinnati, Ohio, 60-63; res. specialist, Nat. Center Primate Biol, UNIV. CALIF, DAVIS, 63, lab. technician dept. genetics, 64-68; res. cytogeneticist, 69, ATOMIC ENERGY COMN. FEL, 69- AAAS; Genetics Soc. Am. Life cycle and drug response of Plasmodium cynomolgi; recombination and dominance in bacteriophage T4; chromosome ultrastructure. Address: Radiobiology Lab, University of California, Davis, CA 95616.

FISHER, KENNETH WALTER, b. Heston, Eng, Dec. 30, 31; m. 65; c. 5. BIOCHEMICAL GENETICS. B.Sc, London, 53, M.Sc, 54, Ph.D.(bact. genetics), 57. Res. worker, med. res. coun, microbial genetics res. unit, Hammersmith Hosp, London, Eng, 57-66; assoc. prof. BIOL, Kans. State Univ, 66-70; PROF, DOUGLASS COL, RUTGERS UNIV, 70- Vis. Worker, physiol. microbial serv, Pasteur Inst. Paris, 57-58; Rockefeller traveling fel. med, group biochem. studies, Princeton, 62-63; temporary assoc. prof, dept. physics, Kansas State, 64; Nat. Sci. Found. res. grant, 66-68, Eli Lilly grant in aid, 67-70. Genetics Soc. Am; Brit. Soc. Gen. Microbiol; Brit. Biochem. Soc; Brit. Genetical Soc; Royal Phys. Soc. Edinburgh; Royal Hort. Soc; Am. Soc. Microbiol. Bacterial genetics and chemistry; mechanism of conjunction in the bacterium, Escherichia coli. Address: Dept. of Biology, Douglass College of Rutgers, The State University, New Brunswick, NJ 08903.

FISHER, L(AWRENCE) E(LBERT), b. Sweetser, Ind, Mar. 31, 05; m. 30; c. 1; m. 51; c. 2. ELECTRICAL ENGINEERING. B.S, Michigan, 27. Test engr, mech. lab, Michigan, 27-28; design & lab. engr, Reynolds Spring Co, Mich, 28-29; design engr, Square D Co, Detroit, 29-33; Hudson Motor Car Co, 33-34; dir. res, Bulldog Elec. Prods. Co, 34-48; asst. chief engr, Howell Elec. Co, 48-49; prof. elec. eng. & head dept, Lawrence Inst. Tech, 49-51; application engr, distribution assemblies dept, Gen. Elec. Co, 51-57, syst. application engr, 57-70; OWNER, FISHER ENG. CO, 70- Consult, 49-51. Inst. Elec. & Electronics Eng; Nat. Soc. Prof. Eng. Technical specialization; busways and low voltage distribution systems. Address: 149 Sedgwick Rd, West Hartford, CT 06107.

FISHER, LEO JAMES, b. Shamokin, Pa, Feb. 28, 31; m. 56; c. 2. METEOROLOGY, OCEANOGRAPHY. B.S, Pa, State, 57. Meteorologist, United Aircraft Corp, 57; Trans World Airlines, 57-58; oceanogr, U.S. NAVAL OCEANOG. OFF, 58-60, prin. investr, diffusion studies, 60-65, prog. coordinator, 65-67, chief scientist, 67-69, BR. HEAD COASTAL OCEANOG, 69- U.S.A.F, 49-52, S/Sgt. Am. Meteorol. Soc; Marine Tech. Soc; Am. Geophys. Union. Coastal oceanographic processes; shallow water diffusion processes. Address: Ocean Science Dept, U.S. Naval Oceanographic Office, Washington, DC 20390.

FISHER, LEON H(AROLD), b. Montreal, Que, July 11, 18; nat; m. 41; c. 4. PHYSICS. B.S, California, 38, M.S, 40, univ. fel, 41-42, Ph.D.(physics), 43. Instr. pre-meteorol. physics, California, 43-44; physics, New Mexico, 44; assoc. scientist, Los Alamos Sci. Lab, California, 44-46; asst. prof. physics, N.Y. Univ, 46-50; assoc. prof, 50-57, prof, 57-61; mgr. plasma physics, Lockheed Missiles & Space Co, 61-62; head, plasma physics, Gen. Tel. & Electronics Labs, 62-63; sr. mem. & sr. consult. scientist, Lockheed Palo Alto Res. Lab, 63-70, asst. mgr, electronic sci. lab, 67-68; prof. elec. eng. & head dept. info. eng, Univ. Ill, Chicago Circle, 71; PROF. PHYSICS & DEAN SCH. SCI, CALIF. STATE COL, HAYWARD, 71- Vis. prof, Univ. South. Calif, summer, 48; chmn. Gaseous Electronics Conf, 48, 67, 68; vis. prof, Univ. Calif, Berkeley, summers 49, 51, 55; consult, Edgerton, Germeshausen & Grier, 54-55; Harry Diamond Labs, 58-61; Xerox Corp, 58-61; Army Res. Off. Durham, 58-63; Rome Air Develop. Ctr, 59-63; reentry physics panel, Nat. Acad. Sci, 65-66. AAAS; fel. Am. Phys. Soc; Am. Asn. Physics Teachers; Inst. Elec. & Electronics Eng. Ionization coefficients in gases; mechanism of electrical breakdown in gases; formation of negative ions; corona discharges; plasma physics. Address: Dept. of Physics, School of Science, California State College, Hayward, 25800 Hillary St, Hayward, CA 94542.

FISHER, LEONARD V, b. Elizabeth, N.J, May 22, 29; m. 63; c. 2. MEDICINE. B.Sc, Rutgers, 48; M.S, Yale, 50; M.D, Chicago, 54. Intern & res. med, Montefiore Hosp, N.Y, 54-57; vis. res. fel. MED, col. physicians & surgeons, Columbia, 57-60; asst. prof, Seton Hall Col. Med. & Dent, 60-61, clin. asst. prof, 61-64; asst. prof, N.Y. MED. COL, 64-70, ASSOC. PROF, 70-, CHIEF SECT. ENDOCRINOL. & METAB, B.S. COLER HOSP, 64- Nat. Found. fel, 57-59; spec. fel, Nat. Inst. Arthritis & Metab. Disease, Nat. Insts. Health, 59-60; dir. endocrinol. & biochem, St. Michael Hosp, Newark, N.J, 60-64; assoc. vis. physician, Metrop. Hosp, 64- AAAS; Am. Fedn. Clin. Res; N.Y. Acad. Sci; Soc. Nuclear Med; Am. Diabetes Asn. Neuroendocrine interrelationships; anterior pituitary influences in diabetes mellitus; geriatric endocrinology. Address: New York Medical College Center for Chronic Disease, B.S. Coler Hospital, Welfare Island, New York, NY 10017.

FISHER, LESLIE J(OHN), b. N.Y.C, Feb. 26, 40; m. 62. NEUROBIOLOGY. B.E.E, Rensselaer Polytech. Inst, 61; M.S, Tufts Univ, 66, NASA trainee, 66-69, Ph.D.(biol), 69. Nat. Insts. Health fel, SCH. MED, Johns Hopkins Univ, 69-71; VIS. ASST. PROF. PHYSIOL, UNIV. MD, 71- Partic. NATO Neurobiol. Advan. Study Inst, 71. U.S.A.F, 61-64, Capt. Am. Soc. Zool. Electrophysiological and electron microscopic studies of the development of neurons and neuron sets in the retina of the larval frog. Address: Dept. of Physiology, University of Maryland School of Medicine, Baltimore, MD 21201.

FISHER, LLOYD D, JR, b. Baltimore, Md, June 8, 39; m. 61; c. 2. STATISTICS & BIOSTATISTICS. S.B, Mass. Inst. Tech, 61; M.A, Dartmouth Col, 65, Ph.D.(math), 66. Sci. programmer, Lockheed Missiles & Space Co, 61-63; asst. prof. MATH, UNIV. WASH, 66-70, ASSOC. PROF, 70- Consult, Aerospace Corp, 66-67; Minneapolis-Honeywell Regulator Co, 68. AAAS; Am. Math. Soc; Biomet. Soc; Am. Statist. Asn; Royal Statist. Soc; Inst. Math. Statist. Address: Dept. of Mathematics, University of Washington, Seattle, WA 98105.

FISHER, LYMAN C(ARLYLE), b. Marion, Ind, June 30, 09; m. 34; c. 2. MECHANICAL ENGINEERING. B.S, Michigan, 32, M.S, 33. Mech. designer, Bulldog Elec. Prods. Co, Mich, 34-36; res. assoc, Michigan, 36-40; res. engr, Murray Corp. of Am, 40-41; mech. engr, NAVAL ORD. LAB, Wash, D.C, 41-46, assoc. chief mech. div, res. dept, WHITE OAK, MD, 46-50, chief, underwater ord. dept, 50-57, underwater mech. eng. dept, 57-68, UNDERWATER ORD. DIRECTORATE STAFF, 68- Distinguished Civilian Serv, U.S. Navy, 50. Am. Soc. Automotive Eng; Soc. Mech. Eng. Automotive and aeronautical engineering; ordnance research and development; management. Address: 1205 Schindler Dr, Silver Spring, MD 20903.

FISHER, LYMAN McA, b. Appin, Ont, Mar. 21, 23; m. 53; c. 4. CLINICAL PATHOLOGY, HEMATOLOGY. B.A, Western Ontario, 51; M.A, Saskatchewan, 54, Ph.D.(physiol), 57, M.D, 60. Lectr. physiol, Saskatchewan, 57-58; asst. prof. CLIN. PATH, MED. COL. VA, 60-64, assoc. prof, 64-70, PROF, 70- Dipl, Am. Bd. Clin. Path, 65. Can. Physiol. Soc; Am. Soc. Exp. Path; Am. Soc. Clin. Path. Effects of vitamins K, high fat diets and anticoagulants on blood coagulation. Address: Division of Clinical Pathology, Medical College of Virginia, Richmond, VA 23219.

FISHER, MICHAEL ELLIS, b. Fyzabad, Trinidad, Sept. 3, 31; m. 54; c. 4. MATHEMATICAL PHYSICS, CHEMISTRY. B.Sc, London, 51, fel, 53-55, Ph.D.(physics), 57. Lectr. math, Royal Air Force Tech. Col, 52-53; tutor physics, King's Col, London, 53-57, lectr. theoret. physics, 57-62, reader physics, 62-64, PROF, 65-66; CHEM. & MATH, CORNELL UNIV, 66- Dept. Sci. & Indust. Res. sr. res. fel, 56-58; guest investr, Rockefeller Inst, 63-64; John Simon Guggenheim mem. fel, 70-71; vis. prof, Stanford Univ, 70-71; Buhl lectr. theoret. physics, Carnegie-Mellon Univ, 71. Fel. Am. Phys. Soc.(Irving Langmuir Prize, 71); Brit. Inst. Physics & Phys. Soc; fel. Royal Soc; Soc. Indust. & Appl. Math; Math. Asn. Am. Theory and practice of electronic analog computing; statistical mechanics of phase transitions and critical phenomena; magnetism; polymer configurations; combinatorial mathematics; mathematical foundations of statistical mechanics. Address: Baker Lab, Cornell University, Ithaca, NY 14850.

FISHER, MYRON W, b. Marlboro, Mass, May 21, 18; m. 44; c. 3. BACTERIOLOGY. B.S, Mass. State Col, 39; M.S, Northwestern, 50, Ph.D.(microbiol), 51. Teaching & res. assoc. bact, Northwestern, 48-51; DIR, BACT. & IMMUNOL. RES, PARKE, DAVIS & CO, 51- Med.C, 42-48, Capt. AAAS; Am. Soc. Microbiol; N.Y. Acad. Sci. Mechanisms of action of antimicrobial agents; bacterial growth and nutrition; bacterial drug resistance; experimental chemotherapy and antibiotic therapy; evaluation of antibacterial agents; immunology of bacterial infections; relationships of therapy and immunology. Address: Research Labs, Parke, Davis & Co, Detroit, MI 48232.

FISHER, NEWMAN, b. San Francisco, Calif, Mar. 21, 28. MATHEMATICS. A.B, Calif, 50, M.A, 51; Stanford, 57-59; Ph.D.(math), Idaho, 62. Res. aeronaut. scientist, Ames Aeronaut. Lab, NASA, 52-55; instr. MATH, San Francisco State Col, 57-59; Idaho, 59-61; asst. prof, SAN FRANCISCO STATE COL, 61-68, assoc. prof, 68-71, PROF, 71-, CHMN. DEPT, 68- Vis. prof, Nat. Sci. Found. summer inst. for teachers, San Francisco, 61-63. Ord.C, U.S.A, 55-57. Am. Math. Soc; Soc. Indust. & Appl. Math; Math. Asn. Am. Transonic flow theory; stability theory of ordinary differential equations. Address: Dept. of Mathematics, San Francisco State College, San Francisco, CA 94132.

FISHER, NORMAN G(AIL), b. Akron, Ohio, May 28, 09; m. 32; c. 4. ORGANIC CHEMISTRY. B.S, Akron, 30; fel. & Ph.D.(org. chem), Wisconsin, 34. Res. chemist, exp. sta, E.I. DU PONT DE NEMOURS & CO, 34-38, asst. head, intel. div, CENT. RES. DEPT, 38-63, SUPVR, TECH. INFO. DIV, 64- Mem. Franklin Inst. AAAS; Faraday Soc; N.Y. Acad. Sci; Am. Chem. Soc; Swiss Chem. Soc. Chemical literature; scientific and technical information services. Address: Experiment Station, E.I. du Pont de Nemours & Co, Wilmington, DE 19898.

FISHER, PAUL J(OHN), b. Fayette, N.Y, Mar. 8, 15; m. 44; c. 3. BACTERIOLOGY, CHEMISTRY. A.B, Hobart Col, 39; Syracuse; Cornell. Bacteriologist, proj. bacter, Office Sci. Res. & Develop, 42-43; chemist, Evans Chemetics, Inc, 43-45; Clark-Cleveland, Inc, 45-64, CHIEF CHEMIST, 64-70, VICK MFG, 70- AAAS; Am. Soc. Microbiol; Am. Chem. Soc. Evaluation of germicides; water-soluble gums and paper chromatography; use of penicillin in gangrene infections. Address: 18 Ritchie Rd, Binghamton, NY 13901.

FISHER, PAUL L(EWIS), b. Wash, D.C, Oct. 6, 07; m. 33. BIOGEOGRAPHY. B.S, Maryland, 29, fel, 29-31, 32-34, M.S, 30, Ph.D.(physiol), 34; George Washington, 28; fel, Chicago, 31. Asst, Maryland, 29-34; jr. plant physiologist, div. forest path, U.S. Dept. Agr, Wash, 34-36; assoc. plant physiologist, Lake States Forest Exp. Sta, U.S. Forest Serv, 36-37; chmn. dept. plant sci, Riverside City Col, 37-41; farm prog. dir, Radio Sta. KPRO, Calif, 41-42; training specialist, U.S. Civil Serv. Comn, Wash, 42-43; technologist, U.S. Bur. Mines, 43-45; PROF. BIOL. & GEOG, FURMAN UNIV, 45- Farm prog. dir, radio sta. WFBC, 46-56. Seed germination; economic biology. Address: Dept. of Biology & Geography, Furman University, Greenville, SC 29613.

FISHER, PEARL D(AVIDOWITZ), b. N.Y.C, May 22, 20; m. 41; c. 2. BIOSTATISTICS. B.A, Brooklyn Col, 41; M.S, Columbia, 51; Ph.D.(prev. med, pub. health), Oklahoma, 58. Asst. parasitol. & epidemiol, sch. med, Oklahoma, 53-58, res. assoc. prev. med. & pub. health, 58-60, asst. prof, 60; life scientist advan. studies, Redstone Arsenal, NASA, 61-67; math. statistician & sr. analyst, off. biomet, Nat. Inst. Neurol. Diseases & Blindness, 67-71; ACTING CHIEF DIV. SERV. DELIVERY RES, NAT. CTR. FAMILY PLANNING SERV, HEALTH SERV; & MENT. HEALTH ADMIN, ROCKVILLE, 71- W.A.V.E.S, 43-46, Lt.(jg). Survival of man in space; radiation hazards; sterilization of spacecraft; duration of life studies on parasitic nematodes; survival evaluation of cancer patients; etiological factors of leukemia in children. Address: 13324 Sherwood Forest Dr, Silver Spring, MD 20904.

FISHER, PERRY WRIGHT, b. N.Y.C; m. 68. METEOROLOGY. B.Engr. Physics, Cornell Univ, 62; Nat. Defense Educ. Act fel, Univ. Mich, Ann Arbor, 66-69, M.S, 67, A.M, 68, Ph.D.(meteorol), 70. Res. asst. meteorologist, Univ. Mich, Ann Arbor, 66-70; ASST. PROF. GEOPHYS. & ENG, CASE WEST. RESERVE UNIV, 71- U.S.A, 62-65, 1st Lt. Am. Meteorol. Soc. Baroclinic instability of ultra-long waves; micrometeorology of ecosystems; air pollution potential and mixing height determination and prediction. Address: Dept. of Geology, Case Western Reserve University, Cleveland, OH 44106.

FISHER, P(ETER), b. Australia, Nov. 4, 30; m. 56; c. 2. SOLID STATE PHYSICS. B.Sc, Western Australia, 51 & 52, Imp. Chem. Industs. Australia & New Zealand fel. & Ph.D.(physics), 56. Asst. prof. PHYSICS, PURDUE UNIV, 56-63, assoc. prof, 63-68, PROF, 68- Soft x-ray spectroscopy of the solid state; infrared properties of semi-conductors. Address: Dept. of Physics, Purdue University, Lafayette, IN 47907.

FISHER, PHILIP C(HAPIN), b. Rochester, N.Y, Aug. 3, 26; m. 48; c. 1. PHYSICS. B.S, Rochester, 47; M.S, Illinois, 48, Ph.D.(physics), 53. Staff mem, Los Alamos Sci. Lab, California, 53-59; CONSULT. SCIENTIST, PHYS. SCI. LAB, LOCKHEED MISSILES & SPACE CO, 59- U.S.N.R, 44-46. Am. Phys. Soc; Am. Astron. Soc; Int. Astron. Union; Am. Geophys. Union. Bremsstrahlung; delayed gammas from fission; x-ray astronomy and instrumentation; space particle measurements. Address: Lockheed Missiles & Space Co, Dept. 52-14, Bldg. 202, 3251 Hanover St, Palo Alto, CA 94304.

FISHER, R(ALPH) W(ATHAN), b. Memphis, Tenn, Nov. 3, 26; m. 49; c. 3. CHEMICAL ENGINEERING. B.S, Illinois, 48. Tech. serv. engr, Gen. Mills, Inc, 48-49, asst. raw mat. supvr, 49-50, raw mat. supvr, 50-51, distillation supvr, 51, asst. plant supt, 51-54, plant supt, 54-56, dir. process develop, 56-59; prod. mgr, Foremost Chem. Prod. Co, 59-63, mgr, 63-65, gen. mgr, 65-69, PLANT MGR, ASHLAND CHEM. CO, 69- U.S.N, 44-46, Res, 46-61, Ens. Am. Chem. Soc; Am. Oil Chem. Soc. Fatty acid derivatives; organic chemicals. Address: Ashland Chemical Co, Box 9, Mapleton, IL 61547.

FISHER, RAY W, b. Anamosa, Iowa, Nov. 27, 21; m. 45; c. 4. MECHANICAL ENGINEERING, CHEMISTRY. B.S, Iowa State, 48. Asst. atomic res. & phys. chem, IOWA STATE UNIV, 43-48, res. assoc, AMES LAB, 49-57, assoc. engr, 57-62, engr, 62-64, head bldg. & eng. serv, 64-69, PLANT MGR, 69-, ASSOC. PROF. MECH. ENG, 63-, asst. prof, 61-63, admin. aide, 49-61. High temperature corrosion studies of components used in molten metal reactor concepts; design of research facilities; production of pure chemicals. Address: Research Bldg, Room 320, Iowa State University, Ames, IA 50010.

FISHER, RICHARD L(EROY), b. Lewistown, Pa, Sept. 20, 38; m. 62; c. 2. ANALYTICAL CHEMISTRY. B.S, Juniata Col, 61; M.S, Illinois, 64, Ph.D. (chem), 66. Res. chemist, E.I. DU PONT DE NEMOURS & CO, 66-70, SR. RES. CHEMIST, 70- Gas chromatography of inorganic fluorine compounds. Address: I & B Chemical Division, Experiment Station, E.I. du Pont de Nemours & Co, Wilmington, DE 19898.

FISHER, RICHARD R, b. Wichita, Kans, June 2, 41; m. 62; c. 1. ASTROPHYSICS, SOLAR ASTRONOMY. B.A, Grinnell Col, 61; fel, Colorado, 61-62, Ph.D.(astrophys), 65. Electronics technician, Beech Aircraft Co, Kans, summer 61; res. asst. solar astrophys. res, high altitude observ, Univ. Colorado, 62-65; asst. astrophysicist, Univ. Hawaii, 69, assoc. astrophysicist, 69-71, resident astronr, Mees Solar Observ. & asst. fiscal off, univ, 70-71; ASTROPHYSICIST, SACRAMENTO PEAK OBSERV, 71- Lectr, Dept. gen. sci, Maui Community Col, 70. Am. Astron. Soc; Optical Soc. Am; Int. Astron. Union. Solar research, including solar activity, coronal structure and chromospheric structure; instrument design and geometrical optics. Address: Sacramento Peak Observatory, Sunspot, NM 88349.

FISHER, RICHARD V(IRGIL), b. Whittier, Calif, Aug. 8, 28; m. 47; c. 4. GEOLOGY. B.A, Occidental Col, 52; Ph.D, Univ. Wash, 57. Acting instr. GEOL, UNIV. CALIF, SANTA BARBARA, 55-57, instr, 57-58, asst. prof, 58-63, lectr, 63-65, assoc. prof, 65-69, PROF. & CHMN. DEPT, 69- Nat. Sci. Found. grant, 61-67; vis. assoc. prof, Univ. Hawaii, 65-66; res. affiliate, Hawaii Inst. Geophys, 65-; NASA grant, 67-73; vis. lectr, Am. Geol. Inst, 70; prin. investr, NASA Apollo 12 lunar samples; mem. adv. comt, Archaeol. Res. Inc, Costa Mesa. U.S.A, 46-47. Fel. Geol. Soc. Am.(secy, Cordilleran Sect, 62-65); Int. Asn. Planetology. Emplacement processes, sedimentation and stratigraphy of volcaniclastic rocks; maar volcanoes; density currents and debris flows. Address: Dept. of Geological Sciences, University of California, Santa Barbara, CA 93106.

FISHER, ROBERT (WILLIAM), b. Bainsville, Ont, Apr. 18, 23; m. 48; c. 2. ENTOMOLOGY. B.S, McGill, 48, Ph.D.(entom), 51. ENTOMOLOGIST, Pesticide Res. Inst, CAN. DEPT. AGR, ONT, 51-58, RES. STA, 58- Bioassay; new methods of chemical control of fruit tree and vegetable pests; effects of environment, pest habit, and mode of application on efficiency of pesticides; droplet size and distribution of sprays; sprayer evaluation. Address: Research Station, Canada Dept. of Agriculture, Vineland Station, Ont, Can.

FISHER, ROBERT A(DOLPH), b. Spokane, Wash, June 9, 18; m. 50; c. 3. CHEMICAL ENGINEERING. B.S, Colorado, 40; Ph.D.(chem. eng), Purdue, 50. Asst. prof. chem. eng, Texas, 50-52; res. engr, res. inst, Denver, 52-54, assoc. prof, col. eng, 54-57, lectr, 57-58; chem. engr, Eaton Res. & Develop. Co, 57; assoc. prof. chem. eng, Denver, 58-63; RES. ENGR, DENVER RES. INST, 63- Res. participant, Oak Ridge Inst. Nuclear Studies, 52. Consult, Los Alamos Sci. Lab, 53; Martin Co, 58-59. Air Pollution Control Asn; Am. Inst. Chem. Eng. Heat and mass transfer; behavior of small-particle systems; engineering economics. Address: 8360 Moorecraft Ave, Canoga Park, CA 91304.

FISHER, ROBERT A(MOS), JR, b. Honey Grove, Pa, Mar. 25, 34; m. 58; c. 1. PHYSICAL CHEMISTRY. B.S, Juniata Col, 56; Ph.D.(phys. chem), Pa. State, 61. RES. CHEMIST, UNIV. CALIF, BERKELEY, 60- AAAS; Am. Phys. Soc. Photochemical reactions and rates; physical and chemical adsorption; low temperature, chemical and magneto thermodynamics; cryogenics; magnetism; single crystal growth. Address: Low Temperature Lab, University of California, Berkeley, CA 94720.

FISHER, ROBERT A(NDREWS), b. N.Y.C, Apr. 3, 19; m. 45; c. 2. BIOCHEMISTRY. A.B, Columbia, 41. Chemist & head yeast dept, Fleischmann Labs, Standard Brands, Inc, 41-50, asst. to tech. dir, 50-52; dir. res. & develop, Pacific Yeast Prods, Inc, 52-58; v.pres. mfg. & develop, Bioferm Corp, 58-61, dir. commercial develop, Bioferm Div, Int. Minerals & Chem. Corp, 61-64, prod. mgr, microbial insecticides, 64-67, tech. field specialist, 67-68; PRES, R.A. FORMULA CO, 61- Am. Chem. Soc. Vitamins and antibiotics and organic chemicals by fermentation; microbiol insecticides; nutrition for mountaineering. Address: R.A. Formula Co, 25 Miner St, Bakersfield, CA 93305.

FISHER, ROBERT C(HARLES), b. Shelbyville, Ind, July 30, 26; m. 46; c. 3. MATHEMATICS. Ph.D.(math), Univ. Kans, 52. Prof. math, Ohio State Univ, 52-71; CHMN. DEPT. MATH. & STATIST, FLA. INT. UNIV, 71- U.S.N.R, 44-46. Am. Math. Soc; Math. Asn. Am; Soc. Indust. & Appl. Math. Differential geometry; applied mathematics. Address: Dept. of Mathematics & Statistics, Florida International University, Miami, FL 33144.

FISHER, ROBERT EARL, b. Salt Lake City, Utah, Apr. 22, 39; m. 60; c. 4. CHEMICAL ENGINEERING. B.S, Utah, 61; Sc.D.(chem. eng), Mass. Inst. Tech, 66. Sr. process engr, Air Prod. & Chem, Inc, 66-67, staff engr, Pa, 67-70; RES. ENGR, AMOCO CHEM. CORP, 70- Lectr, Lehigh Univ, 66-68. Am. Chem. Soc; Am. Inst. Chem. Eng. Chemical process engineering and development. Address: 352 River Rd, Naperville, IL 60540.

FISHER, ROBERT GEORGE, b. Bound Brook, N.J, Jan 6, 17; m. 42; c. 3. NEUROSURGERY. B.S, Rutgers Univ, 38; M.D, Univ. Pa, 42; Ph.D. Univ. Minn, 51. Instr. neurosurg, Johns Hopkins Hosp, 49-51; Dartmouth Med. Sch, 51-55, asst. prof, 55-62, assoc. prof, 62-67, PROF, 67; SURG, & CHMN. DEPT. NEUROSURG, MED. SCH, UNIV. OKLA, 67- Chmn. dept. neurosurg, Hitchcock Clin, Dartmouth Med. Sch; consult, Vet. Hosp, White River Junction, Vt. Dipl. Am. Bd. Neurol. Surg, mem, 68- U.S.A, 43-46. Harvey Cushing Soc; Am. Med. Asn; Asn. Res. Nerv. & Ment. Disease; Am. Col. Surg; Cong. Neurol. Surg; Am. Acad. Neurol; Am. Acad. Neurol. Surg; Soc. Neurol. Surg. Cerebrovacsular hemodynamics; brain circulatory system research. Address: Dept. of Neurosurgery, University of Oklahoma School of Medicine, Oklahoma City, OK 73104.

FISHER, ROBERT JOHN, b. Milwaukee, Wis, July 20, 42; m. 64; c. 2. BACTERIAL PHYSIOLOGY. B.A, Drake Univ, 64; M.S, Univ. Wis, 67, Ph.D. (bact), 69. FEL. bioenergetics res, Retina Found, 69-70; DEPT. CELL PHYSIOL, BOSTON BIOMED. RES. INST, 70- Nat. Insts. Health fel, 71- Am. Soc. Microbiol. Oxidative phospharylation and nitrogen fixation. Address; Dept. of Cell Physiology, Boston Biomedical Research Institute, 20 Staniford St, Boston, MA 02114.

FISHER, ROBERT L, b. San Jose, Calif, June 31; m. 55; c. 3. ANIMAL ECOLOGY, MAMMALOGY. A.B, San Jose Col, 58; Ph.D.(vert. zool), Cornell, 68. ASSOC. PROF. BIOL, JUNIATA COL, 63- U.S.N, 51-54. Am. Inst. Biol. Sci; Am. Soc. Mammal; Ecol. Soc. Am; Nat. Speleol. Soc; Japanese Soc. Pop. Ecol. Ecology of microtine rodents. Address: Dept. of Biology, Juniata College, Huntingdon, PA 16652.

FISHER, ROBERT L(LOYD), b. Alhambra, Calif, Aug. 19, 25; div; c. 1. MARINE GEOLOGY. B.S, Calif. Inst. Tech, 49; Northwestern, 49-50; M.S, California, 52, Ph.D.(oceanog), 57. Jr. geologist, U.S. Geol. Surv, 49; RES. GEOLOGIST, SCRIPPS INST. OCEANOG, UNIV. CALIF, SAN DIEGO, 50- U.S.N.R, 44-46. Geol. Soc. Am; Seismol. Soc. Am; Am. Geophys. Union; Challenger Soc. Shipborne geophysical explorations of Pacific and Indian Ocean; deep-sea topography; crustal structure and composition in oceanic regions; oceanic trenches. Address: Scripps Institution of Oceanography, University of California, San Diego, La Jolla, CA 92037.

FISHER, ROGER K(ENDALL), b. Chicago, Ill, Apr. 19, 35; m. 63; c. 3. CHEMICAL ENGINEERING. B.Ch.E, Cornell, 57; Standard Oil Found. Ind. fel, Princeton, 58-59, Du Pont fel, 60-61, Ph.D.(chem. eng), 63. Instr. chem. eng, Princeton, 59-60; proj. chem. engr, Am. Oil Co, STANDARD OIL CO. IND, 61-64, AMOCO CHEM. CORP, 64-69, SR. RES. ENGR, 70- Fulbright res. fel, Osaka, 61-62. Am. Inst. Chem. Eng. Process design and economics; polymer processes. Address: Amoco Chemicals Corp, P.O. Box 400, Naperville, IL 60540.

FISHER, RONALD RICHARD, b. Peoria, Ill, Oct. 3, 41; m. 69. BIOCHEMISTRY. B.A, Ariz. State Univ, 64; U.S. Pub. Health Serv. fel, Cornell Univ, 66-70, Ph.D.(biochem), 70. Chemist, solid state diffusion, Motorola, Inc, 63-64; asst. chem, Ariz. State Univ, 64-66; fel. biochem, Univ. Calif, San Diego, 70-71; ASST. PROF. CHEM, UNIV. S.C, 71- AAAS; Am. Chem. Soc. Mitochondrial oxidative phosphorylation; bacterial photosynthesis; pyridine nucleotide enzymology; active ion transport. Address: Dept. of Chemistry, University of South Carolina, Columbia, SC 29208.

FISHER, RUSSELL (SYLVESTER), b. Bernie, Mo, Nov. 15, 16; m. 37; c. 2. PATHOLOGY. M.D, Med. Col. of Va, 42. Intern & resident med, Henry Ford Hosp, 42-44; res. fel. LEGAL MED, Harvard Med. Sch, 46-49; PROF. FORENSIC PATH, SCH. MED, UNIV. MD, 49- Chief med. exam, Md, 49-; lectr, sch. med, Hopkins, 50-, sch. hyg. & pub. health, 52- Consult, U.S. Army Chem. Center, 53-; Nat. Insts. Health Clin. Center, 57-; U.S. Armed Forces Inst. Path, 58-; Fed. Aviation Agency, 60- Dipl, Am. Bd. Path, path. anat, 50, forensic path, 59. U.S.N.R, 44-46. Am. Asn. Path. & Bact; Am. Soc. Clin. Path; Col. Am. Path; Am. Med. Asn; Am. Acad. Forensic Sci; Int. Acad. Path. Barbiturate poisoning and methods of determining barbiturates; effects of trauma on the central nervous system; causes of sudden death of infants; coronary artery disease; medicolegal pathology. Address: 111 Penn St, Baltimore, MD 21201.

FISHER, RUSSELL A(RDEN), b. Ludington, Mich, Sept. 11, 04; m. 29. PHYSICS. A.B, Michigan, 27, A.M, 29, Ph.D.(physics), 31. Instr. PHYSICS, Michigan, 27-31; NORTHWEST. UNIV, 31-32, asst. prof, 32-37, assoc. prof, 37-42, prof, 46-71, chmn. dept, 50-57, acting chmn, 60-61, EMER. PROF, 71- Order of the Brit. Empire. U.S.A, 42-46, Lt. Col; Bronze Star Medal. Am. Phys. Soc; Optical Soc. Am; Am. Asn. Physics Teachers. Atomic spectroscopy; nuclear moments; interferometry; nuclear spectroscopy. Address: 5548 Hamlet Lane, Ft. Myers, FL 33901.

FISHER, SALLIE A(NN), b. Green Bay, Wis, Sept. 10, 23. CHEMISTRY. B.S, Wisconsin, 45, M.S, 46, Ph.D.(anal. & inorg. chem), 49. Asst. quant. anal, Wisconsin, 44-48, asst, 48-49; instr, Mt. Holyoke Col, 49-50; asst. prof, Duluth br, Minnesota, 50-51; res. chemist, Rohm & Haas Co, 51-60; ASSOC. DIR. RES, ROBINETTE RES. LABS, INC, 60- Am. Chem. Soc; Am. Soc. Test. & Mat; Am. Water Works Asn; Electrochem. Soc. Ion exchange applications; textile finishes; surfactants; industrial waste treatment; metal recovery. Address: Robinette Research Labs, Inc, Central & Lancaster Ave, Berwyn, PA 19312.

FISHER, SAMUEL STURM, b. Pinconning, Mich, Feb. 25, 38; m. 59; c. 3. FLUID MECHANICS. M.E, Univ. Cincinnati, 61; Hughes fel. & M.S, Univ. Calif, Los Angeles, 63, NASA fel. & Ph.D.(eng), 67. Asst. prof. AEROSPACE ENG, UNIV. VA, 67-70, ASSOC. PROF, 70- Rarefied gas flows; molecular beams; gas-surface interactions; boundary layers; convective heat transfer; experimental methods. Address: School of Engineering & Applied Science, University of Virginia, Charlottesville, VA 22901.

FISHER, SAUL H(ARRISON), b. Brooklyn, N.Y, Feb. 20, 13; m. 45; c. 1. PSYCHIATRY. B.S, City Col. New York, 32; M.D, N.Y. Univ, 36. Asst. physiol, SCH. MED, N.Y. UNIV, 36-37, instr. med, 43-45, clin. asst. psychiat, 48-50, clin. instr, 50-54, asst. clin. prof, 54-57, asst. prof. CLIN. PSYCHIAT, 57-61, ASSOC. PROF, 61- Am. Med. Asn; Am. Psychiat. Asn; Am. Orthopsychiat. Asn; Acad. Psychoanal. Relationship of brain damage to personality; effect of severe stress on personality; biological studies in acute psychosis. Address: Dept. of Psychiatry, School of Medicine, New York University, New York, NY 10016.

FISHER, STANLEY P(ARKINS), b. Suffern, N.Y, Dec. 9, 19; m. 43; c. 2. PETROLEUM GEOLOGY. B.A, Virginia, 42; M.S, Oklahoma, 48; Ph.D. (geol), Cornell, 52. Instr. geol, Rutgers, 47-49; asst. prof. geol, North Dakota & asst. state geologist, N.Dak. Geol. Surv, 52-53; geologist oil explor, Nat. Petrol. Coun, Brazil, 53-54; regional explor. geologist, Mene Grande Oil Co. Div, Gulf Oil Corp, 54-60; asst. prof. GEOL, OHIO UNIV, 60-66, assoc. prof, 66-68, PROF, 68-, CHMN. DEPT, 70- U.S.N.R, 42-46, Lt. AAAS; Geol. Soc. Am; Am. Asn. Petrol. Geol. Sedimentology; structure and stratigraphy of Andes Mountains and Caribbean area; emphasis on stratigraphic and carbonate oil traps; landslides of central Ohio River Valley. Address: Dept. of Geology, Ohio University, Athens, OH 45701.

FISHER, STEPHEN D, b. Chicago, Ill, July 23, 41; m. 65. MATHEMATICS. B.S, Mass. Inst. Technol, 63; Nat. Sci. Found. fel, Univ. Wis, Madison, 65-67, Ph.D.(math), 67. Instr. MATH, Mass. Inst. Technol, 67-69; ASST. PROF, NORTHWEST. UNIV, 69- Am. Math. Soc. Complex analysis. Address: Dept. of Mathematics, Northwestern University, Evanston, IL 60201.

FISHER, STUART GORDON, b. Elmhurst, Ill, Mar. 1, 43; m. 65; c. 1. ECOLOGY, LIMNOLOGY. B.S, Wake Forest Col, 65, M.A, 67; Ph.D.(biol), Dartmouth Col, 71. ASST. PROF. BIOL, AMHERST COL, 70- AAAS; Am. Inst. Biol. Sci; Am. Soc. Limnol. & Oceanog. Ecosystem biology; metabolism of running water ecosystems; stream ecology. Address: Dept. of Biology, Amherst College, Amherst, MA 01002.

FISHER, T. RICHARD, b. Brownstown, Ill, Dec. 23, 21; m. 44; c. 4. BOTANY. B.S, Eastern Illinois, 47; Ph.D, Indiana, 54. Asst. prof, Appalachian State Teachers Col, 54-56; bot, Ohio State, 56-68; PROF. BIOL. & CHMN. DEPT, BOWLING GREEN STATE UNIV, 68- U.S.A, 41-46. Bot. Soc. Am; Am. Soc. Plant Taxon; Int. Asn. Plant Taxon. Biosystematic investigations of Silphium and other Compositae. Address: Dept. of Biology, Bowling Green State University, Bowling Green, OH 43402.

FISHER, THEODORE ROOSEVELT, b. Johnson Co, Mo, Jan. 7, 23; m. 46; c. 2. AGRICULTURE, SOIL CHEMISTRY. B.S, Missouri, 49, M.S, 50, Ph.D.(soils), 62. Fisheries biologist, Mo. Conserv. Cmn, 50-51; instr. soils, Missouri, 51-53; agronomist, U.S. Borax & Chem. Corp, 53-57; instr. SOILS, UNIV. MO-COLUMBIA, 57-62, asst. prof, 62-70, ASSOC. PROF, 70- U.S.A.A.F, 43-45, Maj. AAAS; Am. Soc. Agron; Soil Sci. Soc. Am. Soil fertility, testing and management; plant nutrition. Address: Dept. of Agronomy, 141 Mumford Hall, University of Missouri-Columbia, Columbia, MO 65201.

FISHER, T(HEODORE) W(ILLIAM), b. San Francisco, Calif, May 26, 21; m. 46; c. 1. ENTOMOLOGY. A.B, San Jose State Col, 43; Ph.D.(entom), Univ. Calif, Riverside, 52. Prin. lab. technician, citrus exp. sta, UNIV. CALIF, RIVERSIDE, 48-57, asst. entomologist, 57-64, assoc. specialist, 64-66, SPECIALIST ENTOM, DIV. BIOL. CONTROL, 66- U.S.A, 43-45, S/Sgt. Am. Entom. Soc. Biological control of pest mollusks; ecological pest management, especially administrative reorganization. Address: Dept. of Entomology, Division of Biological Control, College of Biological & Agricultural Sciences, University of California, Riverside, CA 92502.

FISHER, THOMAS HENRY, b. Fulton, Mo, Aug. 22, 38; m. 56; c. 3. ORGANIC & PHYSICAL CHEMISTRY. B.A, Westminster Col.(Mo), 60; Monsanto Chem. Co. fel, Illinois, Urbana, 61, Union Carbide fel. & M.S, 62, Allied Chem. Corp. fel, 63, Ph.D.(org. chem), 64. ASST. PROF. ORG. CHEM, MISS. STATE UNIV, 66- Chem.C, 64-66, Capt. Am. Chem. Soc. Organic reaction mechanisms; free radical decompositions; factors affecting free radical stability. Address: Box CH, Dept. of Chemistry, Mississippi State University, State College, MS 39762.

FISHER, THORNTON ROBERTS, b. Santa Monica, Calif, Feb. 16, 37. NUCLEAR PHYSICS. B.A, Wesleyan, 58; Ph.D.(physics), Calif. Inst. Technol, 63. Res. assoc. nuclear struct. physics, Calif. Inst. Technol, 63; Stanford Univ, 63-69; RES. SCIENTIST, LOCKHEED PALO ALTO RES. LAB, 69- Am. Phys. Soc. Nuclear structure physics; charged particle, gamma ray, and neutron producing reactions; semi-conductor detection systems; cryogenics. Address: Lockheed Palo Alto Research Lab, 3251 Hanover St, Palo Alto, CA 94304.

FISHER, VERNON J(ACOB), b. Sissonville, W.Va, Aug. 16, 21; m. 47; c. 3. HORTICULTURE. B.S, West Virginia, 43, M.S, 47; Ph.D.(hort), Mich. State, 50. Asst. hort, Mich. State, 47-49; assoc. prof. agr. & hort, Shepherd Col, 49-51; res. biologist, E.I. du Pont de Nemours & Co, Inc, 51-57; ASSOC. PROF. PLANT SCI, UNIV. DEL, 57- U.S.A, 43-46; Nat. Guard, 47-49, Capt. Am. Soc. Hort. Sci; Am. Pomol. Soc. Fruit root stocks; nutrition; varieties; weed control. Address: Dept. of Plant Science, University of Delaware, Newark, DE 19711.

FISHER, VICTOR A, b. New Westminister, B.C, Jan. 20, 38; m. 69; c. 1. SEDIMENTOLOGY, STRATIGRAPHY. B.A, Wash. State Univ, 61; M.A, Univ. Mont, 63; Ph.D.(geol), Fla. State Univ, 68. ASST. PROF. GEOL, West. Ill. Univ, 68-69; CALIF. STATE COL. CHICO, 69- Consult, Ayrshire Colleries Corp, 69-70; Lacanex Mining Co. Ltd, 70-71. AAAS; Soc. Econ.

Paleont. & Mineral; Geol. Soc. Am. Bottom sediments of the Antarctic Ocean; sediment distribution in reminant Pleistocene lakes. Address: Dept. of Geology, California State College at Chico, Chico, CA 95926.

FISHER, WALDO R(EYNOLDS), b. Phila, Pa, Sept. 10, 30; m. 60; c. 3. BIOCHEMISTRY, METABOLISM. B.A, Wesleyan Univ, 52; M.D, Univ. Pa, 56, Pa. Plan scholar, 61-64, Ph.D.(biochem), 64. Intern, Presby. Hosp, Phila, 56-57, asst. resident med, 57-58; fel. biochem, Univ. Pa, 58-63, instr, sch. med, 63-64; sr. resident, Peter Bent Brigham Hosp, Boston, 64-65; asst. prof. med, COL. MED, UNIV. FLA, 65-71, biochem, 68-71; ASSOC. PROF. MED. & BIOCHEM, 71- Nat. Insts. Health fel, 58-61, res. grants, 66-72 & res. career develop. award, 67-72; Am. Heart Asn. res. grant, 67-73; faculty develop. award, Univ. Fla, 70. Dipl, Am. Bd. Internal Med, 66. Am. Fedn. Clin. Res; Am. Soc. Biol. Chem. Biochemistry and physiology of human disease; altered structure and metabolism of plasma lipoproteins occurring in genetic hyperlipemic diseases; hydrophobic proteins important in membrane structure. Address: Depts. of Medicine & Biochemistry, University of Florida College of Medicine, Gainesville, FL 32601.

FISHER, WARNER D(OUGLASS), b. Sharon, Tenn, Aug. 17, 23; m. 48; c. 4. AGRONOMY. B.S, Purdue, 47; M.S, Utah State Agr. Col, 49; Ph.D.(plant breeding), Agr. & Mech. Col. Tex, 54. Instr. agron, Martin Br, Tennessee, 48-51; asst, Agr. & Mech. Col. Tex, 51-53; assoc. prof, Ala. Polytech, 53-54; PLANT BREEDER, COTTON RES. CTR, UNIV. ARIZ, 54- U.S.N, 43-46, Lt. Am. Soc. Agron. Cotton production and breeding. Address: Cotton Research Center, University of Arizona, 4201 E. Broadway, Phoenix, AZ 85040.

FISHER, WEBSTER E(VANS), b. Boston, Mass, Dec. 2, 07; m. 30; 50; c. 4. CHEMICAL ENGINEERING. A.B, Bowdoin Col, 28; M.S, Mass. Inst. Tech, 30. Chem. engr, Eastman Kodak Co, 30-41, 45-46, admin. supvr, 46-47, tech. assoc, 47-59, sr. tech. assoc, 59-71; RETIRED. Chem.C, 41-45, Maj. Am. Chem. Soc; Am. Inst. Chem. Eng. Development and design in fields of filtration, distillation, crystallization, drying, adsorption, electrochemistry, mixing, polymer manufacture, fluid dynamics and heat transfer. Address: 691 Oakridge Dr, Rochester, NY 14617.

FISHER, WILLIAM, b. N.Y.C, Mar. 31, 40; m. 66; c. 1. ORGANIC CHEMISTRY. B.S, City Col. New York, 61; summer fels, Univ. Ky, 65-67, Ph.D. (org. chem), 68. Teaching asst. chem, Univ. Ky, 61-68; ORG. CHEMIST, DEXTER CHEM. CORP, 68- AAAS; Am. Chem. Soc. Synthesis of azo compounds derived from nitrogen heterocycles; development of new surfactants for textile processes; development of new dyeing assistants for the dyebath. Address: 98 De Haven Dr, Yonkers, NY 10703.

FISHER, W(ILLIAM) D(AVID), b. Volens, Va, Mar. 18, 30; m. 56; c. 2. CELL PHYSIOLOGY. A.B, Duke, 50, Ph.D.(zool), 57. Instr. physiol, Fla. State, 57-58, asst. prof, 58-60; physiol. & radiol, State Univ, N.Y. Upstate Med. Ctr, 60-63; BIOLOGIST, BIOL. DIV, OAK RIDGE NAT. LAB, 63- Lectr, Oak Ridge Biomed. Grad. Sch, 69; molecular biologist, biol. div, U.S. Atomic Energy Comn, 69-70. AAAS; Am. Soc. Microbiol; Biophys. Soc; Am. Soc. Cell Biol; Radiation Res. Soc; Am. Soc. Zool; Soc. Gen. Physiol. Control of cell division in bacterial cells; biochemistry of anucleate cells, DNA-membrane association; cellular fractionations; radiation effects. Address: Biology Division, Oak Ridge National Lab, P.O. Box Y, Oak Ridge, TN 37830.

FISHER, W(ILLIAM) L(AWRENCE), b. Marion, Ill, Sept. 16, 32; m. 54; c. 3. GEOLOGY, PALEONTOLOGY. B.S, Southern Illinois, 54; M.S, Kansas, 58, Shell fel, 59-60, Nat. Sci. Found. summer fel, 59, 60, Ph.D.(geol), 61. Geologist, Aluminum Co. Am, 57; asst, Kans. Geol. Surv, 57-58; asst. geol, Univ. Kans, 58-60; res. assoc, BUR. ECON. GEOL, UNIV. TEX, AUSTIN, 60-64, res. scientist, 64-68, assoc. dir, 68-70, DIR, 70-, PROF. GEOL. SCI, 69-, spec. lectr, dept. geol. & assoc. mem, grad. faculty, 64-69; mem. grad. faculty, 69- U.S.A, 54-56. Geol. Soc. Am; Am. Asn. Petrol. Geol; Soc. Econ. Geol; Asn. Am. State Geol; Soc. Mining Eng; Soc. Econ. Paleont. & Mineral. Tertiary stratigraphy and paleontology of Gulf Coast; industrial rock and mineral deposits; environmental geology. Address: Bureau of Economic Geology, University of Texas at Austin, Box X, Austin, TX 78712.

FISHER, WILLIS A(LLAN), b. Saginaw, Mich, Oct. 5, 14; m. 40; c. 4. ORGANIC CHEMISTRY. B.S, Univ. Mich, 36, M.S, 37, du Pont fel, 38-39, Ph.D.(chem), 40. Res. chemist, Nat. Aniline Div, ALLIED CHEM. CORP, BUFFALO, N.Y, 39-55, group leader, 55-59, mgr. res. dyestuffs & pigments, 59-63, planning dyestuffs, 63-68, res. planning, SPECIALTY CHEM. DIV, 68-70, SR. SCIENTIST, 70- Am. Chem. Soc. Dyes and pigments; detergents; pharmaceuticals; research management. Address: P.O. Box 321, Brookside, NJ 07926.

FISHER, WILTON MONROE, b. Ryan, Okla, Aug. 4, 12; m. 39; c. 2. PUBLIC HEALTH, PREVENTIVE MEDICINE. B.A, Oklahoma, 32, M.S, 37; M.D, Baylor, 42; Ph.D.(parasitol), Rice Inst, 47. Instr. entomol, Okla. Biol. Surv, 32-33; asst. bact, col. med, Baylor, 33; teaching fel. biol, Rice Inst, 35-38; instr. entomol, Rocky Mt. Biol. Lab, 37-38; instr. bact, hyg. & prev. med, col. med, Baylor, 38-42, asst. prof. pub. health & prev. med, 42-45, assoc. prof, 45-48; lab. br, communicable disease center, U.S. Pub. Health Serv, 48-53, asst. chief & sr. surgeon, 49-53; chief res. & intern training div, cent. off, U.S. Vet. Admin, 53-55; air pollution med. prog, div. spec. health servs, U.S. Pub. Health Serv, 55-58, training br, div. personnel, 58-60, career develop. br, 60-64; asst. to chief, DIV. RES. GRANTS, NAT. INSTS. HEALTH, 62-63, EXEC. SECY. GEN, MED. STUDY SECT, 63- Dipl, Am. Bd. Prev. Med, 52- Fel. AAAS; Am. Soc. Microbiol; Am. Soc. Parasitol; Am. Soc. Trop. Med. & Hyg; Indust. Med. Asn; fel. Am. Pub. Health Asn; Am. Med. Asn. Relapsing fever; amebiasis; human malaria; bacteriology; science administration; gastroenterology; dermatology; rheumatic disease; nephrology. Address: 5220 Sangamore Rd, Washington, DC 20016.

FISHKIN, ARTHUR F(REDERIC), b. New York, N.Y, May 27, 30; m. 56; c. 4. BIOCHEMISTRY. A.B, Indiana, 51, A.M, 53; univ. fels, Iowa, 54-57, Ph.D. (biochem), 57. Instr. biochem, sch. med, La. State, 58-62, asst. prof, 62-64; CHEM, New Mexico State, 64-68; ASSOC. PROF, SCH. MED, CREIGHTON UNIV, 68- AAAS; Am. Chem. Soc; fel. Am. Inst. Chem. Glycoproteins of cardiovascular connective tissue; connective tissue biochemistry. Address: School of Medicine, Creighton University, 2500 California St, Omaha, NE 68131.

FISHLER, MAURICE CHARLES, b. Chicago, Ill, Nov. 9, 12; m. 34; c. 2. PHYSIOLOGY. A.B, California, Los Angeles, 36; Ph.D.(physiol), California, 43, Wilson scholar, 47, M.D, 47. Asst. physiol, California, 39-42, physiologist, Off. Sci. Res. & Develop, 42-43; asst. surgeon, U.S. Pub. Health Serv, Marine Hosp, San Francisco, 47-48; chief, biol. div, Naval Radiol. Defense Lab, 48-53, dept. med, Kaiser Found. Hosp, 50-59, staff physician, 59-65; INVESTR, KAISER FOUND. RES. INST, 66-, res. scientist, 59-65. Deputy mem, joint panel, res. & develop. bd, Dept. Defense, 51-53. U.S.A, 53-55. Metabolism of phospholipids with radioactive phosphorus; thoracic duct lymph; liverless animals; effects of radiation on living tissue. Address: Kaiser Foundation Research Institute, 14th & Cutting Blvd, Richmond, CA 94804.

FISHMAN, ALFRED P(AUL), b. New York, N.Y, Sept. 24, 18; m. 49; c. 2. PHYSIOLOGY. A.B, Michigan, 38, M.S, 39; M.D, Louisville, 43. Intern med, Jewish Hosp, Brooklyn, N.Y, 43-44; Dazian Found. fel. path, Mt. Sinai Hosp, New York. 46-47, asst. res. & res. med, 47-48; fel. cardiovascular physiol, Michael Reese Hosp, Chicago, Ill, 48-49; Am. Heart Asn. fels. physiol, Bellevue Hosp, New York, 49-50, Harvard, 50-51; Am. Heart Asn. estab. investigator, Columbia, 51-55, asst. prof. med, col. physicians & surg, 55-58, assoc. prof, 58-67; prof, Univ. Chicago, 67-69; PROF. MED. & ASSOC. DEAN, SCH. MED, UNIV. PA, 69-, DIR. CARDIOVASCULAR PULMONARY DIV. & CARDIOVASCULAR RES. CTR, 69- Dir. cardio-respiratory lab, Columbia-Presby. Med. Ctr, 55-66; trustee, Mt. Desert Island Biol. Lab, 55-; consult, Vet. Admin. Hosp, Bronx, N.Y, 61-67; Off. Sci. Tech, 62-; Commonwealth fel. physiol, Nuffield Inst. Med. Res, Oxford, Eng, 64-65; hon. consult. med, St. Mary's Hosp. Med. Sch, London, 64; Sir. Ernest Finch prof, Univ. Sheffield, 65; dir. cardiovasc. inst, Michael Reese Med. Ctr, Chicago, Ill, 67-69; mem. Nat. Adv. Heart Coun, 68- In charge med. & cardiovascular sects, Stark & Moor Gen. Hosps, Med.C, 44-46, Capt. AAAS; Asn. Am. Physicians; Am. Physiol. Soc; Am. Soc. Clin. Invest; Am. Soc. Exp. Biol. & Med; Harvey Soc; Am. Fedn. Clin. Res; fel. Am. Col. Physicians; Royal Soc. Med. Physiology of respiration and circulation; comparative physiology; internal medicine. Address: School of Medicine, University of Pennsylvania Hospital, 871 Maloney Bldg, 36th & Spruce St, Philadelphia, PA 19104.

FISHMAN, DAVID H, b. Brooklyn, N.Y, Aug. 21, 39; m. 62; c. 2. POLYMER SCIENCE. A.B, Columbia Col, 60; Am. Petrol. Inst. fel, Pa. State, 61-63, Am. Chem. Soc. fel, 63-64, Ph.D.(org. chem), 64. Res. chemist, org. chem. dept, E.I. du Pont de Nemours & Co, 64-66; CELANESE PLASTICS CO, 66-69, GROUP LEADER, PLASTIC MOLDING RESINS, 69- Am. Chem. Soc; Soc. Plastics Eng. Thermoplastic stabilization; polymerization and catalysis mechanisms; synthetic and physical organic chemistry; organometallics; biochemistry; photochemistry. Address: Celanese Plastics Co, Morris Ave, Summit, NJ 07901.

FISHMAN, ERWIN, b. Cleveland, Ohio, Nov. 7, 27; m. 50; c. 5. PHYSICAL CHEMISTRY. A.B, Oberlin Col, 50; Ph.D, Brown, 54. Res. assoc. CHEM, Illinois, 54-55; asst. prof, Syracuse Univ, 55-59, assoc. prof, 59-69; CHMN. DEPT, UNION COL.(N.Y), 69- U.S.A, 45-47. Am. Chem. Soc; Am. Phys. Soc. Infrared spectra of hydrogen bonded systems; hydrogen bonding and conformation. Address: Dept. of Chemistry, Union College, Schenectady, NY 12308.

FISHMAN, FRANK J, JR, b. Chicago, Ill, Jan. 18, 31; m. 54; c. 5. THEORETICAL PHYSICS, APPLIED MATHEMATICS. B.S, Illinois, 52; Nat. Sci. Found. fel. & A.M, Harvard, 53, Int. Bus. Mach. Corp. fel, 54, G.E. Sloan fel, 56, Nat. Sci. Found. fel. & Ph.D.(physics), 57. Prin. res. scientist, Avco-Everett Res. Lab, Avco Corp, 57-68; ASSOC. PROF. PHYSICS, ADRIAN COL, 68- Summer, scientist, Lincoln Labs, Mass. Inst. Tech, 55. AAAS; Am. Phys. Soc; Am. Asn. Physics Teachers; Am. Sci. Affiliation. Magnetohydrodynamics; generators, shock wave structure, kinetic models of gases and plasmas, dissipation in plasmas and magnetic annular shock tubes. Address: Dept. of Physics, Adrian College, Adrian, MI 49221.

FISHMAN, GERALD J(AY), b. St. Louis, Mo, Feb. 10, 43; m. 67; c. 1. ASTROPHYSICS, ASTRONOMY. B.S, Univ. Mo-Columbia, 65; Nat. Sci. Found. traineeship, Rice Univ, 65-68, M.S, 68, univ. fel, 68, Ph.D.(space sci), 69. Res. assoc. space sci, Rice Univ, 69; SR. PHYSICIST, TELEDYNE BROWN ENG. CO, 69- AAAS; Am. Astron. Soc; Am. Phys. Soc. Nuclear instrumentation; gamma-ray and x-ray astronomy; high energy and nuclear astrophysics; spacecraft experiment implementation. Address: 1018 Mira Vista Dr, Huntsville, AL 35802.

FISHMAN, HARVEY M, b. Lynn, Mass, Oct. 27, 37; m. 62; c. 2. BIOPHYSICS, PHYSICS. B.S, Mass. Inst. Technol, 58; Stanford Univ, 61-62; M.S, Univ. Calif, Berkeley, 64, Nat. Insts. Health fel, 65-68, Ph.D.(biophys), 68. Electronic design engr, res. & develop. lab, Hewlett-Packard Co, Calif, 59-63; develop. engr, space sci. lab, Univ. Calif, Berkeley, 64-66; staff fel, lab. biophys, Nat. Inst. Neurological Diseases & Stroke, Md, 68-70; ASST. PROF. BIOL. SCI, STATE UNIV. N.Y. ALBANY, 70- Asst. prof, dept. elec. eng, exten. div, San Jose State Col, 62; mem, Hewlett-Packard Co. honors coop. prog, Stanford Univ, 62; investr. & instr, Marine Biol. Lab, Mass, 68-71; faculty fel, res. found, State Univ. N.Y. Albany, 71; mem. corp, Marine Biol. Lab, Mass, 71- Ord.C, U.S.A.R, 58-68, Capt. AAAS; Biophys. Soc; Inst. Elec. & Electronics Eng; Soc. Neurosci; Soc. Gen. Physiol. Electrical noise and fluctuation phenomena in membranes and their relation to ion movements; conduction in squid axon membrane; advanced measurement techniques and instrumentation associated with membrane potential control systems. Address: Dept. of Biological Sciences, State University of New York at Albany, 1400 Washington Ave, Albany, NY 12203.

FISHMAN, IRVING Y(ALE), b. Ardmore, Okla, Sept. 12, 20; m. 42; c. 2. PHYSIOLOGY. B.S, Oklahoma, 42, M.S, 48; Ph.D.(physiol, biochem), Fla. State, 55. Special lectr. physiol, Fla. State, 51-54; instr. BIOL, GRINNELL COL, 54-55, asst. prof, 55-57, assoc. prof, 57-70, PROF, 71- Nat. Sci. Found, res. grants, 54- U.S.A, 42-46, Res, 46- AAAS; assoc. Am. Physiol. Soc; Am. Soc. Zool. Electrophysiological studies of chemoreception in mammals. Address: Dept. of Biology, Grinnell College, Grinnell, IA 50112.

FISHMAN, J(ACK), b. Poland, Sept. 27, 30; nat; m. 64; c. 3. ORGANIC CHEMISTRY. B.A, Yeshiva, 50; M.A, Columbia, 52; Ph.D, Wayne State, 55. Fel, Oxford, 55-56; res. assoc, Sloan-Kettering Inst. Cancer Res, 56-58, asst, 58-62; ASSOC, INST. STEROID RES, MONTEFIORE HOSP. & MED. CTR, 62-; PROF. BIOCHEM, ALBERT EINSTEIN COL. MED, YESHIVA UNIV, 70-, assoc. prof, 67-70. Endocrine Soc; Am. Chem. Soc; Am. Soc. Biol. Chem. Natural products, particularly steroids and alkaloids; metabolism of steroids. Address: Institute for Steroid Research, Montefiore Hospital & Medical Center, Bronx, NY 10467.

FISHMAN, JERRY H(ASKEL), b. Cracow, Poland, June 21, 23; U.S. citizen; m. 60; c. 1. PHYSICAL CHEMISTRY. B.S, Sir George Williams Col, 53; M.A, Brooklyn Col, 59; fel, Stevens Inst. Tech, 57-60, Ph.D.(phys. chem), 60. Chemist, Ciba Pharmaceut. Prod, Inc, N.J, 53-57; sect. head, LEESONA MOOS LABS, LEESONA CORP, 60-63, res. mgr, 63-68, TECH. MGR, 68- Fel. Am. Inst. Chem; Electrochem. Soc. Electro-organic synthesis; batteries; radiation effects on solids; refractory materials; sea water desalination; biophysics. Address: Dept. of Chemistry, Leesona Moos Labs, Lake Success Park, Community Dr, Great Neck, NY 11021.

FISHMAN, LOUIS, b. Brooklyn, N.Y, June 20, 22; m. 48; c. 3. BIOCHEMISTRY. A.B, N.Y. Univ, 49, M.S, 53, Ph.D.(biochem), 57. Res. assoc. COLLAGEN STRUCT, COL. DENT, N.Y. UNIV, 57-60, asst. res. prof, 60-66, ASSOC. PROF, 66- Consult, Manhattan Vet. Admin. Hosp. U.S.A, 43-45. AAAS; Am. Chem. Soc. Protein chemistry; protein structure; proteolytic and blood clotting enzymes; nerve growth factor. Address: New York University College of Dentistry, 342 E. 26th St, New York, NY 10010.

FISHMAN, MARSHALL L(EWIS), b. Phila, Pa, July 2, 37; m. 66; c. 2. PHYSICAL POLYMER CHEMISTRY. A.B, Temple, 59; Du Pont fel, Villanova, 59-60, univ. fel, 60-61, M.S, 61; univ. fels, Polytech. Inst. Brooklyn, 61-68, Ph.D.(chem), 68. Nat. Insts. Health res. fel. polymer chem, Polytech. Inst. Brooklyn, 68-69; Nat. Res. Coun. res. fel. phys. chem, east. region, U.S. DEPT. AGR, 69-71, RES. CHEMIST, RICHARD B. RUSSELL AGR. RES. CTR, 71- Am. Chem. Soc. Thermodynamics of polymerization; solution properties of polymers and detergents; interactions in solution between macromolecules, both synthetic and biological and cosolutes. Address: Richard B. Russell Agricultural Research Center, P.O. Box 5677, Athens, GA 30604.

FISHMAN, MARVIN, b. N.Y.C, Mar. 17, 28; m. 57; c. 2. IMMUNOLOGY. B.S, City Col, 49; M.S, Kentucky, 51; fel, Washington (St. Louis), 53, Ph.D.(microbiol), 54. Assoc. mem, Pub. Health Res. Inst, City of New York, Inc, 57-65, mem, 65-68; res. assoc. prof. PATH, POST-GRAD. MED. SCH, N.Y. UNIV, 68-70, RES. PROF, 70- Selman A. Waksman award, 66. Investr, Naval Radiation Defense Lab, 55-57, U.S.N.R, 55-, Lt. Am. Soc. Microbiol; Am. Asn. Immunol. Investigation in the mechanism of antibody formation and antibody action. Address: Dept. of Pathology, New York University Post-Graduate Medical School, 550 First Ave, New York, NY 10016.

FISHMAN, MARVIN JOSEPH, b. Denver, Colo, Apr. 15, 32; m. 57; c. 3. ANALYTICAL CHEMISTRY. B.A, Colorado, 54, M.S, 56. CHEMIST, U.S. GEOL. SURV. WATER RESOURCES, 56- U.S.A, 56. Am. Chem. Soc; Soc. Appl. Spectros. Water analysis; development of new or improved methods for determining inorganic constituents found in water development of atomic absorption methods for determining metals in water. Address: 3353 S. Niagara Way, Denver, CO 80222.

FISHMAN, MAX, b. Haverhill, Mass, Apr. 30, 21; m. 50; c. 4. ELECTRICAL ENGINEERING. B.Sc, Carnegie Inst. Tech, 42, M.Sc, 43, Buhl fel, 43-44, D.Sc.(elec. eng), 48. Instr, Carnegie Inst. Tech, 44; elec. engr, Radio Communication Eng. Co, 48-49; Transducer Corp, 50-52; sr. res. engr, Convair div, Gen. Dynamics Corp, 52-54; sr. engr, Ultrasonic Corp, 54-55; subsystem staff mgr. & staff scientist, Lockheed Aircraft Corp, 55-59; sr. res. engr, Stanford Res. Inst, 59-63, mem. tech. staff, Stanford Linear Accelerator Ctr, 63-71; ASSOC. PROF. ELEC. ENG, HOLON TECHNOL. UNIV, TEL-AVIV UNIV, 71-; SR. RES. ENGR, ISRAEL ELECTRO-OPTICAL INDUST. LTD, REHOVOT, 71- Consult, Corbin-Farnsworth Corp, 62-63; Mellonics S.D, Inc, 62-63. U.S.N.R, 44-46. Inst. Elec. & Electronics Eng. Instrumentation for high energy physics; control system design; control theory; opto-electronics; electronic circuit design. Address: 34 Jabotinsky St, Givatayim, Israel. 53 361.

FISHMAN, MORRIS, b. Montreal, Que, Mar. 2, 39; m. 67; c. 2. ORGANIC CHEMISTRY. B.Sc, McGill Univ, 60; Ph.D.(chem), Univ. N.B, 66. Lab. asst. chem, Ayerst, McKenna & Harrison, Que, 60-62; SR. RES. CHEMIST, FMC CORP, 66- Am. Chem. Soc; Chem. Inst. Can. Synthesizing organic compounds to be evaluated in medicinal or agricultural biological programs. Address: Central Research Dept, FMC Corp, P.O. Box 8, Princeton, NJ 08540.

FISHMAN, M(YER) M, b. Boston, Mass, Apr. 27, 18; m. 48; c. 2. BIOCHEMISTRY. B.S, City Col. New York, 38; M.S, Minnesota, 40, Ph.D, 42. Assoc. chemist, Sig. Corps, U.S. Army, 42-43; chemist, Stein, Hall & Co, 43-44; instr. CHEM, CITY COL. NEW YORK, 46-54, from asst. prof. to assoc. prof, 54-67, PROF, 67-, ASSOC. DEAN COL. LIB. ARTS & SCI, 69- U.S.A, 44-45. Am. Chem. Soc; N.Y. Acad. Sci. Physical biochemistry. Address: Dept. of Chemistry, City College of New York, New York, NY 10031.

FISHMAN, NORMAN, b. Petaluma, Calif, July 18, 24; m. 53; c. 2. CHEMICAL ENGINEERING. B.S, California, 48. Chem. engr, west. regional utilization lab, U.S. Dept. Agr, 49-53; proj. engr, Food Mach. & Chem. Corp, 53-54; sr. chem. engr, STANFORD RES. INST, 54-61, MGR. propellant eval,- 61-67, POLYMER TECHNOL, 67- U.S. Dept. Agr. Award, 54. U.S.N, 43-46, Res, 50-61, Lt. Am. Inst. Aeronaut. & Astronaut; Combustion Inst; Sci. Res. Soc. Am; Am. Chem. Soc. Applications of polymeric materials; new product development; characterization of polymer systems; combustion and ignition of polymers; fire retardance in polymers. Address: 2316 Blueridge Ave, Menlo Park, CA 94025.

FISHMAN, ROBERT A(LLEN), b. N.Y.C, May 30, 24; m. 56; c. 3. NEUROLOGY. A.B, Columbia, 44; M.D, Pennsylvania, 47. Intern & asst. resident med, New Haven Hosp, 47-49; resident neurol, Mass. Gen. Hosp, 49-50; asst. resident neurol, Neurol. Inst, 50-51; instr. NEUROL, col. physicians & surg, Columbia, 54-56, assoc, 56-57, asst. prof, 57-62, assoc. prof, 62-66; PROF. & CHMN. DEPT, SCH. MED, UNIV. CALIF, SAN FRANCISCO, 66- Markle scholar med. sci, 60-65; asst. med, Yale, 47-49; teaching fel, Harvard Med. Sch, 49-50; neurophysiologist, Army Med. Serv. Grad. Sch, D.C, 51-53; chief res, Neurol. Inst, 53-54, asst. attend. neurologist, 55-62, assoc. attend. neurologist, 62-66; co-dir, Neurol. Clin. Res. Ctr, 61-66; consult. neurologist, San Francisco Gen. Hosp; San Francisco Vet. Admin. Hosp; Letterman Gen. Hosp, San Francisco. Moses res. prize, Columbia Univ, 70. U.S.N, 43-45. AAAS; Am. Epilepsy Soc; N.Y. Acad. Sci; Int. Soc. Neurochem; Harvey Soc; Am. Neurol. Asn; Asn. Res. Nerv. & Ment. Diseases; Am. Fedn. Clin. Res; Am. Acad. Neurol.(v.pres, 71-72); Asn. Univ. Prof. Neurol.(pres, 71-72); Am. Med. Asn. Metabolic disorders of the nervous system; the blood brain barrier; cerebrospinal fluid. Address: Dept. of Neurology, Room 794M, University of California School of Medicine, San Francisco, CA 94122.

FISHMAN, ROBERT S(UMNER), b. Boston, Mass, May 17, 32; m. 57; c. 3. MATHEMATICS. B.S, Northeastern, 54; fel. & M.A, Vermont, 56; fel. & Ph.D.(math), Boston, 61. Assoc. prof. math, Emmanuel Col.(Mass), 61-63, prof, 63-65; Mass. State Col. Salem, 65-68; SR. MATHEMATICIAN, RAYTHEON CO, BEDFORD, 68- Lectr, Mass. Col. Pharm, 61-65. Soc. Indust. & Appl. Math; Am. Math. Soc; Math. Asn. Am; Asn. Symbolic Logic. The average of a function over a group of translations in a subinvariant measure space. Address: 20 Ruby Ave, Marblehead, MA 01945.

FISHMAN, SHEROLD, b. Winnipeg, Man, Jan. 24, 25; m. 54; c. 2. INTERNAL MEDICINE, ENDOCRINOLOGY. B.A, Univ. Sask, 45; Ph.D.(biochem), McGill Univ, 53; M.D, Univ. B.C, 59. Biochemist, Montreal Gen. Hosp, 51-54; life ins. med. res. fel, Univ. Pa, 54-55; res. fel, Univ. B.C, 55-59, clin. chemist, Univ. B.C, 60-62, partic. residency prog, internal med, 62-63; res. fel, Washington, 63-64; CONSULT, Royal Col. Physicians Can, 65; INTERNAL MED. & ENDOCRINOL, VANCOUVER GEN. HOSP, 65-; DIR, ISOTOPE LAB, SHAUGHNESSY HOSP, 65- Fel, Royal Col. Physicians Can. Can. Army, 42-45. Address: 7170 Hudson St, Vancouver, B.C, Can.

FISHMAN, WILLIAM HAROLD, b. Winnipeg, Man, Mar. 2, 14; nat; m. 39; c. 3. BIOCHEMISTRY, ONCOLOGY. B.S, Saskatchewan, 35; Ph.D.(biochem), Toronto, 39; Royal Soc. Can. fel, Edinburgh, 39; Cornell, 41. Instr. biochem, Bowman Gray Sch. Med, Wake Forest Col, 41-43, asst. prof, 43-45; res. assoc. biochem. & asst. prof. surg, Chicago, 45-48; res. prof. biochem. & nutrit, SCH. MED, TUFTS UNIV, 48-59, oncol, 59-70, PROF. PATH, 70-; DIR. CANCER RES, NEW ENG. CENTER HOSP, 59-, assoc. dir. & chief biochemist, cancer res. & cancer control unit, univ, 48-59. Fedn. fel, Int. Physiol. Cong, Oxford, England, 47; vis. prof, Nat. Sci. Found. travel award, Japan, 59; mem. tissue & cell biol. study sect, Vet. Admin. Gov. Gen. Medal, 31. Am. Soc. Biol. Chem; Am. Chem. Soc; Histochem. Soc; Soc. Exp. Biol. & Med; Endocrine Soc; Am. Asn. Cancer Res; Am. Fedn. Clin. Res; N.Y. Acad. Sci; Royal Soc. Med. Enzymes; beta-glucuronidase; prostatic acid phosphatase; steroids; renal beta-glucuronidase response to androgens; biochemistry; glucuronic acid metabolism; biochemical diagnostic tests; enzyme histochemistry; enzymorphology; experimental pathology. Address: Dept. of Pathology, Tufts University School of Medicine, 136 Harrison Ave, Boston, MA 02111.

FISK, CHARLES F(RANKLIN), b. Attleboro Falls, Mass, Sept. 6, 11; m. 41; c. 2. PHYSICAL CHEMISTRY. Sc.B, Brown, 33, fel, 35-37, Ph.D.(photochem), 37. Lab. asst. phys. chem, Brown, 33-35; res. chemist, gen. labs, U.S. RUBBER CO, N.J, 37-38, develop. chemist, R.I, 38-41, asst. chief qual. control, Des Moines ord, Iowa, 41-43, res. chemist, gen. labs, 43-47, sr. res. scientist, RES. CENTER, 57-64, RES. ASSOC, 65- Am. Chem. Soc. Photochemistry; fluorescence; liquid polyester resins; high polymers; correlation of composition, structure and physical properties; resin-rubber plastics; synthetic fibers. Address: 325 Monroe Ave, Wyckoff, NJ 07481.

FISK, DONALD, b. Sterling, Mich, Dec. 12, 37; m. 56; c. 3. MATHEMATICS. B.A, Mich. State, 59, Nat. Defense Ed. Act fel, 59-62, M.A, 60, Ph.D.(statist), 63. Asst. prof. MATH, Knox Col, 63-64; Kent State, 64-65; Northwest. Univ, 65-67; assoc. prof, Kent State Univ, 67-69; PROF, CENT. MICH. UNIV, 69- Am. Math Soc. Probability; decomposition of stochastic processes; stochastic integrals. Address: Dept. of Mathematics, Central Michigan University, Mt. Pleasant, MI 48858.

FISK, FRANK W(ILBUR), b. Logan, Utah, Apr. 15, 14; m. 44; c. 2. PHYSIOLOGY. B.S, Illinois, 36; M.S, Minnesota, 39, Ph.D.(entomol), 49. Jr. entomologist, U.S. Pub. Health Serv, 38-40, asst. entomologist, 41-43, sanitarian, 43-45, assoc. entomologist, 45-46; asst. prof. ZOOL. & ENTOMOL, OHIO STATE UNIV, 49-55, assoc. prof, 55-67, PROF, 67- U.S.P.H.S, Res, 57-, Scientist. Am. Entom. Soc. Digestive enzymes in insects; behavioral physiology. Address: Dept. of Entomology, Ohio State University, Columbus, OH 43210.

FISK, G(EORGE) RAYMOND, b. New Berlin, N.Y, May 24, 15; m. 55; c. 1. ANIMAL NUTRITION. Ph.D.(animal nutrit, biochem), Cornell, 55. Instr. chem, State Univ. N.Y. Albany, 38-40; Rhinebeck Cent. Sch, 40-43; SCI. & CHEM, STATE UNIV. N.Y. COL. CORTLAND, 46-49, asst. prof, 49-54, assoc. prof, 54-56, PROF, 56- Heusted fel, 53-54. U.S.N, 43-46, Lt. AAAS; Nat. Sci. Teachers Asn; Am. Chem. Soc; N.Y. Acad. Sci. Small animal nutrition; mineral metabolism. Address: Dept. of Science & Chemistry, State University of New York College at Cortland, Cortland, NY 13045.

FISK, GUY H(UBERT), b. Montreal, Que, Apr. 20, 08. MEDICINE. B.A, McGill, 39, M.D, C.M, 33. ASSOC. PROF. PHYS. & OCCUP. THER. & DIR. SCH, McGILL UNIV, 33- Dir, dept. phys. med, Montreal Gen. Hosp. Fel, Royal Col. Physicians & Surgeons, London, 37; fel, Royal College Physicians, Can. Can. Asn. Phys. Med. & Rehab; Int. Fedn. Phys. Med. Address: School of Physical & Occupational Therapy, McGill University, 3654 Drummond St, Montreal, Que, Can.

FISK, HENRY EUGENE, b. Chicago, Ill, June 29, 36; m. 62. HIGH ENERGY PHYSICS. B.S, Wyoming, 58; Ph.D.(physics), California, Los Angeles, 63. Instr. physics, California, Los Angeles, 62-63; asst. prof, Carnegie Inst. Technol, 63-68; scientific off, Rutherford High Energy Lab, Eng, 68-69; ASSOC. PROF. PHYSICS, CARNEGIE MELLON UNIV, 69- Am. Phys. Soc. Nuclear and particle physics. Address: Dept. of Physics, Carnegie Mellon University, Schenley Park, Pittsburgh, PA 15213.

FISK, HENRY G(RUNSKY), b. San Francisco, Calif, Apr. 26, 01; m. 34; c. 2. MINERALOGY. B.S, Occidental Col, 23; M.S, Illinois, 24; fel, Ohio State, 24-27, Ph.D.(mineral), 27. Ceramic engr, Gladding-McBean & Co, Calif, 27-28; petrographer, Universal Atlas Cement Co, Ind, 28-36; chem. engr. & in charge res. dept, Calaveras Cement Co, Calif, 36-38; supvr. ceramics & nonmetals res, Armour Res. Found, Ill, 38-43; dir, natural resources res. inst, Wyoming, 43-60; assoc. prof. GEOL, MONT. COL. MINERAL SCI. & TECHNOL, 60-70, EMER. PROF, 70- Trustee, Colo-Wyo. Acad. Res. Found, 50-53; mem. Phosphate Task Force, 52-53; consult. petrologist-petrographer, 70-; vice chmn, Columbia Basin inter-agency comt; mem, Mont. Coal Resources Res. Coun. Am. Mineral. Soc; Am. Inst. Prof. Geol. Refractories; phosphates; equilibrium studies in oxide systems; industrial minerals and fuel resources of the Mountain States. Address: Box 608, Conner, MT 59827.

FISK, J(AMES) B(ROWN), b. West Warwick, R.I, Aug. 30, 10; m. 38; c. 3. PHYSICS. S.B, Mass. Inst. Technol, 31, Ph.D.(theoret. physics), 35, fel, 34-36; hon. M.A, Harvard, 47, hon. D.Sc, 69; hon. Sc.D, Carnegie Inst. Technol, 56, Williams Col, 58, Newark Col. Eng, 59, Columbia Univ, 60, Colby Col, 62; hon. Dr.Eng, Univ. Mich, 63, Univ. Akron, 63; hon. Dr.Sci, N.Y. Univ, 63; hon. D.Sci, Rutgers Univ, 67; hon. LL.D, Lehigh Univ, 67, Ill. Inst. Technol, 68; hon. D.Litt, Newark State Col, 69. Asst. aeronaut. eng, Mass. Inst. Technol, 31-32; fel, Harvard, 36-38; assoc. prof, Univ. N.C, 38-39; electronics res. engr, Bell Tel. Labs, N.Y, 39-45, asst. dir. phys. res, 45-47; McKay prof. appl. physics, Harvard, 47-49; asst. dir. res, BELL TEL. LABS, 49-51, dir. res. phys. sci, 52-54, v.pres. res, 54-55, exec. v.pres, 55-59, PRES, 59- Dir. div. res, U.S. Atomic Energy Comn, Wash, D.C, 47-48, mem. gen. adv. comt, 52-58; mem. sci. adv. comt, Off. Defense Mobilization, 52-57; mem, President's Sci. Adv. Comt, 57-60, consult, 60-; life mem, Mass. Inst. Technol, 66-; trustee, Alfred P. Sloan Found. & John Guggenheim Mem. Found, 66- Presidential Certificate of Merit, 46; Indust. Res. Inst. Medal, 63. Nat. Acad. Sci; Nat. Acad. Eng; Am. Philos. Soc; fel. Am. Phys. Soc; fel. Am. Acad. Arts & Sci; fel. Inst. Elec. & Electronics Eng. Communications research and development. Address: Lee's Hill Rd, R.D, Basking Ridge, NJ 07920.

FISK, LEONARD O, b. Arvada, Colo, Oct. 21, 23; m. 48; c. 2. FISHERY BIOLOGY. B.S, Colorado State, 51, M.S, 53. Fish Technician, Colo. Fish & Game Dept, 51-53; aquatic biologist, Calif. Dept. Fish & Game, 53-55, fishery biologist, 55-60; recreation planner, river pollution surv, Calif. Dept. Water Resources, 60-61; FISHERY BIOLOGIST, CALIF. DEPT. FISH & GAME, 61- U.S.N, 42-46. Am. Fisheries Soc. Fishery management; production and utilization of natural and planted fisheries. Address: California Dept. of Fish & Game, Resources Bldg, Ninth & O Sts, Sacramento, CA 95814.

FISK, LeROY (HENRY), b. San Francisco, Calif, Nov. 11, 19; m. 51; c. 2. PARASITOLOGY. A.A, Modesto Jr. Col, 40; B.A, Col. of Pacific, 48, M.A, 49; Ph.D, Southern California, 49. Chief lab. technician, St. Joseph Hosp, Calif, 46-48; lab. asst. physiol, Southern California, 49-50; chief lab. technician, Figueroa Med. Labs, Calif, 50; lab. dir, Trinity Gen. Hosp, 52-54; asst. prof. PARASITOL, ORE. TECH. INST, 54-57, assoc. prof, 57-67, PROF, 67-, CHMN. DEPT. BIOL. SCI, 68-, CHMN. MED. ASSOCS. DIV, 57-Lab. Technician, U.S.N, 42-45, lab. dir, 51-52, Res, 45-51. Am. Soc. Parasitol; Am. Micros. Soc. Hematology; biochemistry. Address: Oregon Technical Institute, Box 2177, Klamath Falls, OR 97601.

FISKE, DAVID L(EWIS), b. Cambridge, Mass, June 19, 98; m. 25; c. 2. ENGINEERING. S.B, Mass. Inst. Tech, 20; M.S, Illinois, 24; Ph.D.(indust. eng), Columbia, 43. Draftsman & engr, Sinclair Co, Iowa, 20-22; asst. refrig. & ry. eng, Illinois, 22-27; ed, Refrig. Eng. & secy, Am. Soc. Refrig. Eng, N.Y, 27-47; consult. engr, 47-53; RES, ENGR, U.S. ARMY LABS, 53- Consult, meat lab, U.S. Dept. Agr; Dept. Army, 47-48; mem. adv. mission, Econ. Coop. Admin, Greece, 49; consult, Mass. U.S.A, 18-19, 41-45, Maj. Am. Soc. Heat, Refrig. & Air-conditioning Eng; Am. Soc. Mech. Eng. Refrigeration; humidity control; insulation; ultra low temperatures; vacuum technology; air-conditioning of space vehicles and space suits; portable heat power devices. Address: 18 Normandie Rd, Dover, MA 02030.

FISKE, MILAN DERBYSHIRE, b. Sharon, Wis, Nov. 15, 14; m. 36; c. 3. PHYSICS. B.S, Beloit Col, 37; fel, Wisconsin, 40-41, Ph.D.(physics), 41. Asst. physics, Wisconsin, 37-40; res. assoc, res. lab, GEN. ELEC. CO, 41-57, mgr. personnel & sci. rels, 57-59, res. personnel, 59-62, physicist, 62-66, MGR. personnel & admin, GEN. PHYSICS LAB, 66-68, progs. & admin, phys. sci. & eng, 68-69, PHYS. SCI. BR, 69- AAAS; fel. Am. Phys. Soc. Thermionics; gas discharges; T-R switches for radar; cryogenics; high-pressure effects at low temperature; radiation damage; superconductivity. Address: General Physics Lab, General Electric Research & Development Center, P.O. Box 8, Schenectady, NY 12301.

FISKE, RICHARD S(EWELL), b. Baltimore, Md, Sept. 5, 32; m. 59; c. 2. GEOLOGY. B.S.E, Princeton, 54, M.S.E, 55; Ohio Oil Co. fel, Johns Hopkins Univ, 58-60, Ph.D.(geol), 60. Geologist, Socony-Vacuum Oil Co, Venezuela, summer 54; Union Oil Co, Calif, 55-56; Am. Chem. Soc. Petrol. Res. Fund fel, Univ. Tokyo, 60-61; res. assoc, Johns Hopkins Univ, 61-63; GEOLOGIST, U.S. GEOL. SURV, 64- Geol. Soc. Am; Am. Geophys. Union. Petrology; volcanology; Cenozoic volcanic geology of the Pacific Northwest and Japan; volcanic sedimentation; applied geophysics; monitoring active Hawaiian volcanoes; Mesozoic volcanism of the Sierra Nevada. Address: U.S. Geological Survey, Washington, DC 20242.

FISKE, VIRGINIA M(AYO), b. Brooklyn, N.Y, Sept. 21, 10; m. 38; c. 3. ENDOCRINOLOGY. B.A, Mt. Holyoke Col, 32, M.A, 34; Ph.D.(endocrinol), Radcliffe Col, 39. Asst, Mt. Holyoke Col, 32-34; teacher & head sci. dept, Dana Hall Sch, Mass, 34-37; teacher sci, Winsor Sch, 37-38, 39-41, 42-43; asst, Harvard, 39-40; res. endocrinol, Pratt Diagnostic Clin, Boston, 42; instr. ZOOL. & PHYSIOL, WELLESLEY COL, 43-50, asst. prof, 50-56, lectr, 58-60, assoc. prof, 60-62, PROF, 62-, chmn. dept. biol. sci, 64-67. Res. assoc. & Nat. Sci. Found. sr. fel, Harvard, 56-57; U.S. Dept. Health, Educ. & Welfare res. grants, 56-; vis. scientist N.E. Regional Primate Res. Ctr, Harvard Med. Sch, 70-71. Endocrine Soc; Am. Physiol. Soc. Physiology of the pineal and pituitary glands; hypothalamus. Address: Dept. of Biological Sciences, Wellesley College, Wellesley, MA 02181.

FISKELL, J(OHN) G(ARTH) A(USTIN), b. Clearwater, Man, Can, May 8, 17; nat; m. 41; c. 7. SOIL CHEMISTRY. B.S.A, Toronto, 47, Can. Industs. Ltd. fel, 48-50; M.Sc, McGill, 49, Ph.D.(agr. chem), 51. Asst. assayer, Wright-Hargreaves Gold Mines, 38-41; asst. chemist, Welland Chem. Works, 41-44; asst. biochemist, SOILS, UNIV. FLA, 51-56, assoc. prof, 56-61, PROF. & BIOCHEMIST, 61- Can. Army, 44-45. Am. Chem. Soc. Soil mineralogy and chemistry; micronutrient relationships in plant nutrition; soil amendments; analytical methods; root absorption and desorption studies. Address: Dept. of Soils, Agricultural Experiment Station, University of Florida, Gainesville, FL 32601.

FISLER, GEORGE F(REDERICK), b. Saginaw, Mich, Nov. 29, 31. BIOLOGY, ZOOLOGY. B.S, Mich. State, 54, M.S, 56; Ph.D.(zool), Univ. Calif, Berkeley, 61. Res. zoologist, Hastings Natural Hist. Reservation, Univ. California, Carmel Valley, 60-61; jr. res. zoologist, 61-62; asst. prof. BIOL, Portland State Col, 62-64; SAN FERNANDO VALLEY STATE COL, 64-67, assoc. prof, 67-70, PROF, 70- Vis. scientist, Nat. Insts. Health & asst. prof, Univ. P.R, summer 63. Am. Soc. Mammal; Ecol. Soc. Am; Am. Ornith. Union; Cooper Ornith. Soc; Wilson Ornith. Soc; Brit. Ecol. Soc. Ecology, systematics, and behavior of mammals; behavior of birds. Address: Dept. of Biology, San Fernando Valley State College, Northridge, CA 91324.

FISSEL, GUY W(ILMER), b. Biglerville, Pa, June 4, 29; m. 53; c. 5. AGRICULTURAL & BIOLOGICAL CHEMISTRY. B.S, Pa. State, 52, M.S, 55. Biochemist, trop. res. lab, United Fruit Co, Honduras, 55-57; CHEMIST, CROPS RES. DIV, AGR. RES. SERV, U.S. DEPT. AGR, 58- Sig.C, U.S.A, 52-53. Asn. Off. Anal. Chem. Chemical analysis of forage crops including sugars and other carbohydrates, amino acids, vitamins, lignin and tannin. Address: 401 Sylvan Dr, State College, PA 16801.

FISSER, HERBERT GEORGE, b. Ames, Iowa, Mar. 9, 26; m. 52; c. 3. RANGE MANAGEMENT, ECOLOGY. B.S, Mont. State Col, 58, M.S, 61; Ph.D.(range mgt), Univ. Wyo, 62. RANGE MGT, UNIV. WYO, 59-61, asst. prof, 62-66, assoc. prof, 66-70, PROF, 70- Summer Inst. Radiation Ecol, Oak Ridge Inst. Nuclear Studies, 63. Ecol. Soc. Am; Am. Soc. Range Mgt. Game range improvement; plant pattern and distribution; grazing systems and wildlife interrelationships; plant phenology and seed production; range site productivity potential. Address: Plant Science Division, P.O. Box 3354, University Station, University of Wyoming, Laramie, WY 82070.

FISTEDIS, STANLEY H, b. Constantinople, Turkey, June 25, 25; U.S. citizen; m. 53; c. 2. STRUCTURAL ENGINEERING. B.S, Robert Col, Istanbul, 47; M.S, Montana State, 49; Ph.D.(eng. mech), Missouri, 53; M.B.A, Chicago, 65. Designer, Babcock & Wilcox Co, 48-49; instr. eng. mech, Missouri, 49-52; struct. engr, Western Knapp Eng. Co, 52-53; Johnson & Johnson Co, 53; Allen & Garcia Co, 53-54; spec. assignments engr, Girdler Co, 54-57; assoc. engr, ARGONNE NAT. LAB, 57-63, group head eng. mech, 63-66, mgr, 66-71, SR. ENGR, 71- Fel. Am. Soc. Civil Eng; Am. Nuclear Soc; Am. Concrete Inst; Nat. Soc. Prof. Eng. Structural mechanics; application of advances in mechanics of materials to industrial plant construction; prestressed and reinforced concrete; nuclear plant components; nuclear safety and containment. Address: 500 N. Parkwood, Park Ridge, IL 60068.

FISTER, EDWARD J(OHN), b. Mauch Chunk, Pa, Oct. 1, 11; m. 44; c. 3. ELECTRICAL ENGINEERING. B.S, Villanova, 37. Chief special projs. sect, Sig. Corps. Eng. Labs, 44-46, deputy chief radar br, 46-51, chief meteorol. br, 51-53, deputy dir, countermeasures div, 53-55, DIR, countermeasures div, 55-59, eng. sci. dept, 59-63, U.S. Army Electronics Labs, 63-71, RES. & DEVELOP. TECH. SUPPORT ACTIVITY, U.S. Army Electronics Command, 71- U.S. Army civilian meritorious serv. award, 45. Sr. mem. Inst. Elec. & Electronics Eng. Development and testing of communication gear and electronic weapons used by the army; standardization and reliability of equipment. Address: 1 Nicholson Pl, Oceanport, NJ 07757.

FITCH, ARTHUR H, b. Arkansas City, Kans, Sept. 24, 27; m. 51; c. 3. SOLID STATE PHYSICS. B.S, Kansas, 49, M.S, 52; Union Carbide fel, Hopkins, 54-55, Ph.D.(physics), 57. MEM. TECH. STAFF, BELL TEL. LABS, Murray Hill, 56-70, ATMOSPHERIC PHYSICS RES. DEPT, 70- U.S.N, 45-47. Inst. Elec. & Electronics Eng. Development of ultrasonic devices; superconductivity; ferroelectrics; infrared instrumentation; air pollution; atmospheric physics; optics. Address: Atmospheric Physics Research Dept, Room 3B-221, Bell Telephone Labs, Whippany, NJ 07981.

FITCH, COY D(EAN), b. Marthaville, La, Oct. 5, 34; m. 56; c. 2. MEDICINE, BIOCHEMISTRY. B.S, Arkansas, 56, M.S. & M.D, 58. Instr. biochem, sch. med, Univ. Ark, Little Rock, 59-62, asst. prof. med. & biochem, 62-66, ASSOC. PROF, 66-67; INTERNAL MED. & BIOCHEM, SCH. MED, ST. LOUIS UNIV, 67- Russell M. Wilder-Nat. Vitamin Found. fel, 59-62; Lederle med. faculty award, 66-67; mem. nutrit. study sect, Nat. Insts. Health, 67-71; dep. dir, div. biochem, Walter Reed Army Inst. Res, 69. Dipl, Am. Bd. Internal Med, 65. A.U.S, 67-69, Lt. Col. Am. Diabetes Asn; Am. Fedn. Clin. Res; Am. Inst. Nutrit; Am. Med. Asn; Soc. Exp. Biol. & Med. Metabolism and nutrition; membrane transport processes; role of vitamin E in hematopoiesis and muscle function; diseases of skeletal muscle; drug resistance in malaria. Address: Dept. of Internal Medicine, St. Louis University School of Medicine, St. Louis, MO 63104.

FITCH, ELLIOT BRYANT, b. Los Gatos, Calif, Apr. 30, 10; m. 38; c. 2. CHEMICAL ENGINEERING. B.S, Calif. Inst. Tech, 32; M.S, Connecticut, 64. Operator, Am. Potash & Chem. Corp, 33-34, shift boss, 34-35, chem. engr, 35-41, sr. res. chem. engr, 41-44; sales engr, Dorr Co, 44-46, res.

engr, 46-48, asst. to dir. res, 48-50, asst. dir. res, 50-53, dir. res, 53-57, Westport Labs, DORR-OLIVER, INC, 57-64, res. dir, 64-66, tech. adv, MURPHY DIV, 66-69, CHIEF SCIENTIST, 69- Am. Chem. Soc; Am. Inst. Chem. Eng; Am. Inst. Chem. Physical separation processes. Address: Murphy Division, Dorr-Oliver, Inc, 77 Havemeyer Lane, Stamford, CT 06904.

FITCH, ERNEST CHESTER, JR, b. Wichita, Kans, Nov. 30, 24; m. 48; c. 3. MECHANICAL ENGINEERING. B.S, Okla. State, 50, M.S, 51; South. Univs. Fund fel, Oklahoma, 59-60, Ph.D.(eng. sci), 64. Res. engr, Jersey Prod. Res. Corp, Okla, 51-53; PROF. MECH. ENG, OKLA. STATE UNIV, 53-, DIR. RES, FLUID POWER RES. CTR, 65- Summers, assoc. engr, B-47 hydraul. group, Boeing Co, Kans, 54, res. engr, John Deere Res. Div, Deere & Co, Iowa, 55, hydraul. engr, electro-hydraul. & gaging div, Cincinnati Milling Mach. Co, 56 & hydraul. adv, 57. Consult, indust. prod. div, Cessna Aircraft Co, Kans, 60-; fluid contamination consult, tractor div, Ford Motor Co, Mich, 65-; Allis-Chalmers Construct. Mach. Div, Ill, 66- Arch T. Colwell award, Soc. Automotive Eng, 70; annual achievement award, Fluid Power Soc, 70. Nat. Soc. Prof. Eng; Am. Inst. Min, Metall. & Petrol. Eng; Am. Soc. Test. & Mat. Fluid power and control systems areas, including fluid logic, servos and contamination, fluidics, filtration mechanics, conduit dynamics, control circuit synthesis, mathematical modeling and computer aided design. Address: 909 W. Osage Dr, Stillwater, OK 74074.

FITCH, FRANK W(ESLEY), b. Bushnell, Ill, May 30, 29; m. 51; c. 2. PATHOLOGY. M.D, Univ. Chicago, 53, M.S, 57, Ph.D.(path), 60. Intern, hosp, Univ. Mich, 53-54; fel. PATH, U.S. Pub. Health Serv, UNIV. CHICAGO, 54-57, instr, 57-60, asst. prof, 60-63, assoc. prof, 63-67, PROF, 67- Lederle Med. Faculty award, 58-61; Markle scholar acad. med, 61-66; vis. scientist, Inst. Biochem, Univ. Lausanne, 65-66. Med.C, 55-57, Capt. AAAS; Reticuloendothelial Soc; Radiation Res. Soc; Asn. Am. Med. Cols; Am. Soc. Exp. Path; Am. Asn. Path. & Bact; Am. Asn. Immunol. Experimental pathology; immunology. Address: Dept. of Pathology, University of Chicago, Chicago, IL 60637.

FITCH, HENRY SHELDON, b. Utica, N.Y, Dec. 25, 09; m. 46; c. 3. ECOLOGY. B.A, Oregon, 30; M.A, California, 33, fel, 34-36, Ph.D.(zool), 37. Wildlife technician, Hastings wildlife reserve, California, 37-38; biologist, U.S. Fish & Wildlife Serv, Wash, 38-47; instr. ZOOL, UNIV. KANS, 48-49, asst. prof, 49-52, assoc. prof, 52-59, PROF, 59-, SUPT, NATURAL HIST. RESERVATION, 48- U.S.A, 42-46. Am. Soc. Ichthyol. & Herpet; Am. Soc. Mammal; Cooper Ornith. Soc; Am. Ornith. Union. Systematics and natural history of North American and neotropical reptiles; economics and ecology of rodent populations; predator ecology. Address: Natural History Reservation, University of Kansas, R.R. 3, Box 142, Lawrence, KS 66044.

FITCH, HOWARD M(ONTGOMERY), b. Cobden, Ill, Sept. 25, 11; m. 37. CHEMISTRY. B.S, Texas Christian, 33; Ph.D.(org. chem), Virginia, 37. Res. chemist, E.I. du Pont de Nemours & Co, N.J, 37-44; res. assoc. org. med. chem, col. med, N.Y. Univ, 44-49; RES. CHEMIST, Campbell Pharmaceut. Co, 49-57; HANOVIA LIQUID GOLD DIV, ENGELHARD INDUST, INC, 57- Am. Chem. Soc; N.Y. Acad. Sci; The Chem. Soc. Synthesis of organic chemicals and their use as petroleum additives and medicinals, particularly alkaloids and related compounds; nuclear alkylated derivatives of morphine; phosphorus esters; metallo-organic compounds of precious metals. Address: 19 Colony Dr, Summit, NJ 07901.

FITCH, JAMES RICHARD, b. Brooklyn, N.Y, Oct. 21, 37; m. 60; c. 2. APPLIED MATHEMATICS. B.S, Union Col.(N.Y), 59, M.S, 63; Ph.D.(appl. math), Harvard, 67. Programmer, KNOLLS ATOMIC POWER LAB, GEN. ELEC. CO, 59-63, mathematician, 67-71, ENGR, 71- Res. fel. struct. mech, Harvard, 67. Soc. Indust. & Appl. Math. Address: 1920 Hexam Rd, Schenectady, NY 12309.

FITCH, JAMES S, b. Milwaukee, Wis, Mar. 20, 37. MATHEMATICS. B.S, Univ. Wis-Milwaukee, 59; M.S, Marquette Univ, 61; Ph.D.(math), Univ. Wis, Madison, 68. Mathematician, Allis-Chalmers, 64-67; LECTR. BUS. ADMIN, UNIV. WIS-MILWAUKEE, 68- Special functions; Jacobi polynomials. Address: Business School, University of Wisconsin-Milwaukee, Milwaukee, WI 53201.

FITCH, JOHN E(DGAR), b. San Diego, Calif, June 27, 18; m. 42; c. 3. ICHTHYOLOGY. A.B, San Diego State Col, 41; M.A, California, Los Angeles, 63. Biologist, State Dept. Fish & Game, Calif, 46-54; asst. dir, STATE FISHERIES LAB, TERMINAL ISLAND, 54-56, DIR, 56- Asst, Univ. Calif, Los Angeles 51; marine ed, Calif. Fish & Game, 52-62, ed-in-chief, 62-66; res. assoc, Los Angeles County Mus, 63-; mem. working group tuna taxon, UN Food & Agr. Org, 65-; res. assoc, Scripps Inst. Oceanog, Univ. Calif, San Diego, 66-; Santa Barbara Mus. Natural Hist, 67- Sig.C, U.S.A, 41-46. Am. Soc. Ichthyol. & Herpet; Am. Malacol. Union; Am. Inst. Fisheries Res. Biol; Am. Fisheries Soc. Comparative morphology of fish otoliths; fish biology, age composition, habit, habitats and systematics; importance and distribution of Pacific Coast bivalves. Address: 2657 Averill Ave, San Pedro, CA 90731.

FITCH, JOHN L(AWRENCE), b. Okla, Jan. 11, 23; m. 44; c. 2. GEOCHEMISTRY. B.S, Southern Methodist, 50, M.S, 51. Res. chemist, FIELD RES. LAB, Magnolia Petrol. Co, 51-56, sr. res. chemist, 56-60, res. assoc, Mobil Oil Corp, 60-64, res. sect. supvr, 64-70, RES. ASSOC, MOBIL RES. & DEVELOP. CORP, 70- U.S.A, 43; U.S.A.A.F, 43-46, 2nd Lt. AAAS; Am. Geophys. Union; Am. Chem. Soc; Geol. Soc. Am; Am. Inst. Mining, Metall. & Petrol. Eng. Inorganic analytical chemistry; rock magnetism; geochemistry of natural brines; physical properties of rocks; tectonophysics; oil well mechanics. Address: Field Research Lab, Mobil Research & Development Corp, P.O. Box 900, Dallas, TX 75221.

FITCH, JOHN WILLIAM, III, b. San Antonio, Tex, July 28, 38. ORGANOMETALLIC CHEMISTRY. B.S, Texas, Austin, 60, Ph.D.(chem), 65. Res. chemist, E.I. du Pont de Nemours & Co, 65-67; ASST. PROF. CHEM, SOUTHWEST TEX. STATE UNIV, 67- Robert A. Welch Found. grant, 69-71. Am. Chem. Soc. Organometallic synthesis; unusual olefin metal carbonyl complexes; bis-arenechromium chemistry. Address: Dept. of Chemistry, Southwest Texas State University, San Marcos, TX 78666.

FITCH, KENNETH L(EONARD), b. Genoa, Nebr, Mar. 8, 29; m. 50; c. 3. ANATOMY. B.S, Nebraska, 51; M.A, Kansas, 52; fel, Michigan, 52-55, Ph.D.(zool), 56. Asst. zool, Kansas, 51-52; instr, Ohio, 55-56; ANAT, Missouri, 56-58, asst. prof, 58-59; col. med, Univ. Nebr, 59-63; ASSOC. PROF, ILL. STATE UNIV, 63- AAAS; Am. Asn. Anat; Am. Soc. Zool. Amphibian embryology and reproduction; chemical embryology. Address: Dept. of Biology, Illinois State University, Normal, IL 61761.

FITCH, RICHARD ARNOLD, b. Bartlesville, Okla, July 17, 33; m. 59; c. 3. CHEMICAL ENGINEERING. B.S, Oklahoma, 56; M.S, Illinois, 57. Asst. develop. high pressure apparatus, Univ. Ill, 56-57; res. engr, petrol. reservoir res, Pan Am. Petrol. Corp, 57-68, SR. ENGR, AMOCO PROD. CO, 68- U.S.A.R, 58- Am. Inst. Mining, Metall. & Petrol. Eng. Development of better methods for oil recovery; reservoir engineering. Address: Amoco Production Co, P.O. Box 51921, Lafayette, LA 70501.

FITCH, ROBERT M(cLELLAN), b. Shanghai, China, Apr. 30, 28; U.S. citizen; m. 55; c. 3. POLYMER & COLLOID CHEMISTRY. A.B, Dartmouth Col, 49; fel, Michigan, 50-53, Ph.D.(chem), 54. Res. chemist, Marshall Lab, E.I. du Pont de Nemours & Co, Pa, 54-60, staff chemist, 60-62; asst. prof. CHEM, N.Dak. State, 62-65, assoc. prof, 65-67; ASSOC. PROF. & ASST. HEAD DEPT, UNIV. CONN, 67- Consult, S.C. Johnson & Son, Inc, Wis, 65- Fel. AAAS; Am. Chem. Soc. Macromolecular and colloid chemistry; mechanism of particle formation in polymer hydrosols; polymerization kinetics; structure-property relationships of polymers. Address: Dept. of Chemistry, University of Connecticut, Storrs, CT 06268.

FITCH, S(TEVEN) J(OSEPH), b. Chicago, Ill, Feb. 25, 30; m. 52, 67; c. 4. INORGANIC CHEMISTRY. B.S, Illinois, 52; Standard Oil Co.(Ohio) fel, Cornell, 56-57, Ph.D.(inorg. chem), 58. Sr. res. chemist, phosphorus chem, Monsanto Chem. Co, 57-64; dir, corporate res. dept, Glidden Co, 64-65, chem. res. dept, 65-66, MGR. pigments res. dept, inorg. res. ctr, 66-68, RES. DEPT, GLIDDEN-DURKEE DIV, SCM CORP, 68- Am. Chem. Soc; Am. Inst. Chem. Organophosphorus chemistry; metallic chlorides; boron hydrides; titanium dioxide chemistry technology and processes; colloids; plasma processes; pigments; inorganic and organic phosphorus chemistry; boron hydrides. Address: Research Dept, Glidden-Durkee Division, SCM Corp, 3901 Hawkins Point Rd, Baltimore, MD 21226.

FITCH, VAL L(OGSDON), b. Merriman, Nebr, Mar. 10, 23; m. 49; c. 2. PHYSICS. B.E, McGill, 48; Ph.D, Columbia, 54. Asst. scientist, Los Alamos Sci. Lab, 46-47; instr. PHYSICS, Columbia, 53-54; PRINCETON, 54-56, asst. prof, 56-59, assoc. prof, 59-60, PROF, 60- Sloan fel, 60-64; trustee, Assoc. Univs, Inc, 61-; Res. Corp. & E.O. Lawrence awards, 68; mem, President's Sci. Adv. Comt, 70-; consult, Dept. of Defense, Atomic Energy Comn. U.S.A, 43-46. Nat. Acad. Sci; Am. Acad. Arts & Sci; fel. Am. Phys. Soc. Meson physics. Address: 292 Hartley Ave, Princeton, NJ 08540.

FITCH, WALTER M, b. San Diego, Calif, May 21, 29; m. 51; c. 3. BIOCHEMISTRY. A.B, California, Berkeley, 53, Ph.D.(biochem), 58. Lab. technician, Calif. Res. Corp, 51-52; Pac. Guano Co, Calif, 53; res. physiologist, California, Berkeley, 57-58, Nat. Insts. Health fels. physiol, 58-59; pharmacol, sch. med, Stanford, 59-61; Fulbright fel. & lectr. biochem, Univ. Col, London, 61-62; asst. prof. PHYSIOL. CHEM, SCH. MED, UNIV. WIS, 62-67, ASSOC. PROF, 67- Nat. Inst. Neurol. Diseases & Blindness res. grant, 63-69; Nat. Sci. Found. res. grant, 65-; exam. physiol. chem, Wis. State Bd. Exam, 66-; mem. adv. bd, Biochem. Genetics, 66-; ed. bd, J. Molecular Evolution, 71- U.S.A, 54-56. AAAS; Am. Chem. Soc; Brit. Biochem. Soc; Am. Soc. Biol. Chem; Soc. Syst. Zool. Enzymology; kinetics; molecular genetics; evolution. Address: Dept. of Physiological Chemistry, 572 Medical Sciences Bldg, University of Wisconsin School of Medicine, Madison, WI 53706.

FITCH, WALTER S(TEWART), b. Oak Park, Ill, Mar. 6, 26; m. 47; c. 3. ASTRONOMY. A.B, Chicago, 48, Ph.D.(astron), 55. Instr. ASTRON, UNIV. ARIZ, 51-55, asst. prof, 55-60, assoc. prof, 60-63, PROF, 63- U.S.N.R, 43-46. Am. Astron. Soc; Int. Astron. Union. Astronomical photoelectric photometry; intrinsic variable stars. Address: Steward Observatory, University of Arizona, Tucson, AZ 85721.

FITCH, W(ILLIAM) CHESTER, b. Billings, Mont, Nov. 12, 16; m. 46; c. 1. INDUSTRIAL ENGINEERING. B.S, Mont. State Col, 38; M.S, Iowa State Col, 39, Ph.D.(eng. valuation), 40. Instr. eng. drawing, Iowa State Col, 39-41, mech. eng, 41-45; asst. prof. indust. eng, Mont. State Col, 45-46; lectr. mech. eng, California, 46-47; assoc. prof, Iowa State Col, 47-52; asst. dir. valuation div, Gannett, Fleming, Corddry & Carpenter, Inc, 52-58; prof. mech. eng. & head dept, Utah State, 58-59; asst. dir. valuation div, Gannett, Fleming, Corddry & Carpenter, Inc, 59-64; prof. mech. eng. & head dept, Mich. Technol. Univ, 64-68; PROF. ENG. & TECHNOL. & CHMN. DEPT, WEST. MICH. UNIV, 68- Consult. engr, 64- Civilian instr, electricians sch, U.S. Navy, 41-45. AAAS; Am. Soc. Eng. Educ; Am. Soc. Mech. Eng; Am. Inst. Indust. Eng; Nat. Soc. Prof. Eng. Statistical analyses of industrial property; depreciation and engineering economy. Address: Dept. of Engineering & Technology, Western Michigan University, Kalamazoo, MI 49001.

FITCHEN, FRANKLIN CHARLES, b. New Rochelle, N.Y, June 15, 28; m. 50; c. 3. ELECTRICAL ENGINEERING. B.S, Rhode Island, 50; M.S, Northeastern, 57; D.Eng, Yale, 64. Design engr, meter & instrument dept, Gen. Elec. Co, 50-56; assoc. prof. ELEC. ENG, Rhode Island, 56-65; PROF. & HEAD DEPT, S.DAK. STATE UNIV, 65- U.S.A, 54-55. Sr. mem. Inst. Elec. & Electronics Eng. Transistor and integrated circuits. Address: Dept. of Electrical Engineering, Harding Hall, South Dakota State University, Brookings, SD 57006.

FITCHETT, GILMER T(ROWER), b. Cape Charles, Va, June 16, 20; m. 53; c. 2. ORGANIC CHEMISTRY. B.S, Col. of William & Mary, 42; Ph.D. (chem), Virginia, 51. Anal. chemist, Norfolk Naval Shipyard, 42-43; develop. chemist, pharmaceut. dept, Am. Cyanamid Co, N.J, 51-66; Gane's Chem. Works, Inc, N.J, 66-68; SR. CHEMIST, CIBA-GEIGY LTD, SUMMIT,

68- U.S.N.R, 43-46, Lt.(jg). Phenylcyclopropyl amine derivatives and 5, 8-dimethoxyquinoline derivatives. Address: 13 Briar Circle, Greenbrook, NJ 08812.

FITE, GEORGE L, b. Austin, Tex, Feb. 20, 04; m. 36; c. 2. PATHOLOGY. A.B, Haverford Col, 24; M.S, Harvard, 28. Instr. path, med. sch, Hopkins, 29-32; asst, Rockefeller Inst, 32-34; res, Baltimore City Hosp, 35; instr. path, med. sch, Northwestern, 36; pathologist, leprosy invests, U.S. Pub. Health Serv, Honolulu, 37-41, Nat. Insts. Health, 41-45, U.S. Marine Hosp, La, 45-49, Nat. Inst. Arthritis & Metabolic Diseases, Nat. Insts. Health, 49-58, chief lab, Hosp, Carville, La, 58-64; MEM. ED. STAFF, J. AM. MED. ASN, 65- Leprosy; tuberculosis; encephalitis. Address: 535 N. Dearborn, Chicago, IL 60610.

FITE, LLOYD EMERY, b. Litchfield, Ill, Dec. 12, 30; m. 55. ELECTRICAL ENGINEERING. B.S, Agr. & Mech. Col. Tex, 60, M.S, 61, Ph.D.(elec. eng), Texas A&M, 68. Staff, ACTIVATION ANAL. RES. LAB, TEXAS A&M UNIV, 58-60, chief engr. & proj. engr, 60-62, ASSOC. HEAD, 62-, ASSOC. PROF. ELEC. ENG, 69- U.S.A.F, 52-56, S/Sgt. Inst. Elec. & Electronic Eng. Instrumentation and electronic data reduction equipment required to support and improve the technique of neutron activation analysis. Address: Activation Analysis Research Lab, Texas A&M University, College Station, TX 77843.

FITE, ROBERT C(ARL), b. Brinkman, Okla, July 26, 15, m. 40; c. 2. GEOGRAPHY. A.B, Cent. State Col.(Okla), 37; M.S, Okla. Agr. & Mech. Col, 47; Ph.D.(geol), Northwestern, 51. Asst. prof. geog. & meteorol, OKLA. STATE UNIV, 47-51, assoc. prof. GEOG, 51-56, PROF. & DIR. UNIV. EXTEN, 56- U.S.N, 42-45, Res, 45-, Lt. Comdr. AAAS; Am. Meteorol. Soc. Climatology; science education. Address: Oklahoma State University Extension, Stillwater, OK 74074.

FITE, WADE LANFORD, b. Apperson, Okla, Oct. 4, 25; m. 47; c. 4. PHYSICS. A.B, Kansas, 47; M.A, Harvard, 49, Ph.D.(physics), 51. Physicist, res. labs, Philco Corp, 51-52; instr. physics, Pennsylvania, 52-54; Nat. Sci. Found. hon. res. asst, Univ. Col, London, 54-55; mem. staff, Gen. Atomic Div, Gen. Dynamics Corp, 56-63; PROF. PHYSICS, UNIV. PITTSBURGH, 63- Consult, Nat. Bur. Standards, 53; Army Biol. Warfare Labs, 56-58; Gen. Atomic Div, Gen. Dynamics Corp, 63-; Inst. Defense Anal, 64-; bd. chmn, Extranuclear Labs, Inc, 67- U.S.A, 44-46, S/Sgt. AAAS; fel. Am. Phys. Soc; Am. Geophys. Union. Plasma, atomic and atomic collision physics; collision properties of atomic hydrogen; laboratory experimentation on upper atmosphere and astrophysics; chemical reactions; gas-surface phenomena; atomic beams. Address: Dept. of Physics, University of Pittsburgh, Pittsburgh, PA 15213.

FITELSON, JACOB, b. Boston, Mass, Feb. 8, 05; m. 28; c. 1. FOOD CHEMISTRY. B.S, Pennsylvania, 25; Ph.D.(phys. chem), N.Y. Univ, 37. Jr. chemist food anal, food & drug admin. U.S. Dept. Agr, 25-29, analyst, 29-34, chemist in charge food lab, 34-47, chief food chemist, 47-51; CONSULT. & ANAL. CHEMIST & DIR, FITELSON LABS, INC, 51- Fel. AAAS; Am. Chem. Soc; Am. Oil Chem. Soc; fel. Asn. Off. Anal. Chem. Methods of analysis in foods, chocolate products, oils; flavors. Address: Fitelson Labs, Inc, 254 W. 31st St, New York, NY 10001.

FITERRE, RAFAEL M, b. Guatanamo, Cuba, July 5, 00; m. MATHEMATICS. Ph.D.(math), Havana, 26, traveling scholar, 27-29, C.E, 34. Tutor math, Havana, 20-26, instr. physics, 26-27, asst. prof. math, 27-35, prof, 36-60, dean, sch. sci, 59-60; prof. math, Athens Col, 62-64; Univ. Ala, Huntsville, 64-71; ADJ. PROF. GEOMET, FLA. TECHNOL. UNIV, 71- Hon. dean, sch. eng, Oriente. Math. Asn. Am. Geometry, theoretics and applied mathematics. Address: 630 Magnolia Dr, Maitland, FL 32751.

FITKO, CHESTER W(ALTER), b. Chicago, Ill, July 18, 20; m. 50; c. 2. CHEMISTRY. B.S, DePaul, 42. Control chemist, Hills McCanna Co, 42-45; tech. dir. polymers, Acme Resin Corp, 45-57; group leader, Glidden Co, 57-58; sr. chemist, CONTINENTAL CAN CO, 58-69, ADV. SCIENTIST, 69- AAAS; Am. Chem. Soc. Synthesis of new polymers. Address: 1347 N. Lockwood Ave, Chicago, IL 60651.

FITT, PETER S(TANLEY), b. La Punta, Peru, Oct. 12, 31; Brit. citizen; m. 61; c. 2. BIOCHEMISTRY. B.Sc. & A.R.C.S, Univ. London, 53, Ph.D. (org. chem) & dipl, Imp. Col, 56. Sci. off, Royal Aircraft Estab, Eng, 56-57; res. assoc. biochem, med. col, Cornell, 57-58; tech. off, Imp. Chem. Industs, Ltd, Eng, 58-59; vis. res. fel, Sloan-Kettering Inst. Cancer Res, 59-62; vis. scientist, Inst. Physico-Chem. Biol, Paris, France, 62-64; asst. prof. BIOCHEM, UNIV. OTTAWA, 64-68, ASSOC. PROF, 68- AAAS; Can. Biochem. Soc; Brit. Biochem. Soc; The Chem. Soc; N.Y. Acad. Sci. Nucleic acid enzymology; molecular biology. Address: Dept. of Biochemistry, University of Ottawa, Ottawa, Ont. K1N 6N5, Can.

FITTERER, G(EORGE) R(AYMOND), b. Newark, Ohio, Apr. 10, 01; m. 25; c. 1. METALLURGY. B.S, Rose Polytech, 24; fel, Carnegie Inst. Tech, 25-27, M.S, 27; Ph.D.(metall), Pittsburgh, 30; hon. D.Sc, Rose Polytech, 61; D.Eng, Valparaiso Tech, Chile, 65; hon. Dr, Cath. Univ. Cordoba, 67. Metallurgist, Am. Chain Co, Ind, 24-25; metallographer, Stanley Works, Conn, 25-26; from asst. metallurgist to asst. dir. res, U.S. Bur. Mines, 27-31, head dept. metall, 31-33; pres, Fitterer Pyrometer Co, 34-38; chmn, metall. eng. dept, UNIV. PITTSBURGH, 38-51, dean schs. eng. & mines & dir. eng. res. div, 51-63, FIRST DISTINGUISHED PROF. METALL. ENG. & DIR. CTR. STUDY THERMODYN. PROPERTIES MAT, 63- Supvr. navy res. contracts, Nat. Defense Res. Comt, 42-; dir. res, Acid Open Hearth Res. Asn, 42-; eng. ed. contract, Int. Co-op. Admin, Chile. U.S. del, U.N, 1st Pan-Am. Metall. Conf, Bogota, Colombia, 2nd conf, São Paulo, Brazil. Am. Soc. Metals; Am. Inst. Mining, Metall. & Petrol. Eng; Brit. Iron & Steel Inst. Metallurgical thermodynamics; physical chemistry of steel making; high temperature measurement in liquid metals; liquid steel process metallurgy. Address: 409 Engineering Hall, University of Pittsburgh, Pittsburgh, PA 15213.

FITTS, CHARLES THOMAS, b. Jackson, Tenn, July 4, 32; m. 54; c. 4. SURGERY. B.A, Princeton, 53; M.D, Pennsylvania, 57. Chief trauma study br,

U.S. Army Surg. Res. Unit, Brooke Army Med. Ctr, Ft. Sam Houston, Tex, 63-65; asst. prof. SURG. MED. UNIV. S.C, 65-71, ASSOC. PROF, 71-, COORD. JR. TEACHING PROG. SURG, 65- Attend. surgeon, Med. Univ. S.C. Hosp. & Vet. Admin. Hosp, Charleston, 65-; chief of surg, Charleston County Hosp, 65-; consult. surg, U.S. Naval Hosp, Charleston, 65- Gold Medal, Southeast. Surg. Cong, 61. U.S.A, 63-65, Capt. Am. Asn. Surg. of Trauma; Am. Col. Surg; Asn. Acad. Surg; Asn. Am. Med. Cols; Am. Fedn. Clin. Res. General surgery; ceramic orthopedic implants; lymph dialysis, burn therapy, fluid replacement therapy in hemorrhagic shock. Address: Dept. of Surgery, Medical University of South Carolina, Charleston, SC 29401.

FITTS, DONALD D(ENNIS), b. Concord, N.H, Sept. 3, 32; m. 64; c. 2. CHEMISTRY. A.B, Harvard, 54; Nat. Sci. Found. fel, Yale, 54-57, Ph.D.(chem), 57. Nat. Sci. Found. fel, Amsterdam, Netherlands, 57-58; res. fel. CHEM, Yale, 58-59; asst. prof, UNIV. PA, 59-64, assoc. prof, 65-69, PROF, 69-, ASST. CHMN. DEPT, 65-, acting v.dean, col. lib. arts & sci, 63-64. NATO sr. sci. fel, Imp. Col, Univ. London, 71. Am. Chem. Soc; Am. Phys. Soc; Faraday Soc. Quantum-statistical mechanics; thermodynamics and statistical theory of irreversible processes; theory of liquids; theoretical chemistry. Address: Dept. of Chemistry, University of Pennsylvania, Philadelphia, PA 19104.

FITTS, JAMES WALTER, b. Ft. Riley, Kans, July 17, 13; m. 35; c. 3. AGRONOMY. B.Sc, Nebr. State Teachers Col, 35; M.S, Nebraska, 37; California, 47; Ph.D, Iowa State Col, 52. Instr. agron, Nebraska, 37-42, asst. prof. agron. & asst. exten. agronomist, 42-48; res. asst. prof. agron, exten. asst. prof. & in charge soil testing lab, Iowa State Col, 48-52; in charge soil testing div, dept. agr, N.C. STATE UNIV, 52-56, prof. soils & head dept, 56-64, DIR. INT. SOIL TESTING PROJ, 64- Chmn, Nat. Soil Test Work Group, 52-55. Soil Sci. Soc. Am.(v.pres, 59, pres, 60); fel. Am. Soc. Agron. Alkali soil; movement of water in soil during irrigation; soil fertility; commercial fertilizers; procedures and factors affecting soil testing; nitrogen availability. Address: Dept. of Soils, North Carolina State University, Raleigh, NC 27607.

FITTS, RICHARD EARL, b. Montpelier, Vt, Nov. 12, 31; m. 53; c. 7. ELECTRICAL ENGINEERING. B.E, Yale, 53; S.M, Mass. Inst. Tech, 55, Ph.D. (elec. eng), 66. U.S. AIR FORCE, 55-, proj. off, Rome Air Develop. Ctr, Griffiss Air Force Base, N.Y, 55-57 & 61-63, co-pilot, Pease Air Force Base, N.H, 58-61, forward air controller, Da Nang Air Base, Vietnam, 66-67, instr, U.S. AIR FORCE ACAD, 67-68, asst. prof, 68-70, ASSOC. PROF, 70- U.S.A.F, 51-, Maj. Inst. Elec. & Electronics Eng. Electromagnetic compatibility; nonlinear feedback control theory; electronic warfare. Address: Dept. of Electrical Engineering, U.S. Air Force Academy, CO 80840.

FITTS, WILLIAM T(HOMAS), JR, b. Jackson, Tenn, Oct. 6, 15; m. 42; c. 3. SURGERY. A.B, Union, 37; M.D, Pennsylvania, 40. Instr. SURG, SCH. MED, UNIV. PA, 45-48, assoc, 47-49, asst. prof, 49-52, assoc. prof, 52-56, PROF, 56-, ASSOC. CHIEF DEPT. GEN. SURG. & SPEC. ASSIGNMENT, SECT. TRAUMA SURG. SERV, UNIV. HOSP, 59-, CHIEF SURG. WARD DIV. B, 65-, div. II, 56-65, Morris prize, 40. Consult. ed, Jour. Trauma, 60-68, ed, 68- Med.C, 42-45, Capt. Am. Med. Asn; Soc. Univ. Surg; Am. Surg. Asn; Soc. Surg. Alimentary Tract; Am. Asn. Surg. Trauma (pres, 64-65). Healing of fractures; surgery of the adrenal gland; clinical studies on carcinoma of the breast. Address: Hospital of the University of Pennsylvania, 3400 Spruce St, Philadelphia, PA 19104.

FITZ, C(OLEMAN) DUDLEY, b. Fairmont, Minn, July 30, 21; m. 49; c. 4. PHYSICS, MECHANICAL ENGINEERING. B.M.E, Minnesota, 43, M.S, 46, Minneapolis-Honeywell Regulator Co. fel, 46-47, Ph.D, 54. Lectr. & res. assoc. physics & mech. eng, Minnesota, 46-57; dept. head physics & space sci, Vitro Corp. Am. Labs, 57-63; br. chief penetration aids, Ballistic Missile Defense Off, Adv. Res. Proj. Agency, Off. Secy. Defense, 63-65; v.pres. aerospace tech, Nat. Eng. Sci. Co, 65-66; advan. planning, MB Assocs, 67-71; CONSULT, BATTELLE MEM. INST, 71- Consult, Cargill, Inc, 53-54; Gen. Mills, Inc, 53-54, from sr. scientist to prin. scientist, 54-57; secy. & mem. bd. dir, Fairmont Rwy Motors, Inc, Treas. & mem. bd. dir. Fairmont Rwy. Motors, Ltd. Can, 60- U.S.A.A.F, 42-46, Maj. Am. Phys. Soc; Am. Soc. Mech. Eng; Am. Inst. Aeronaut. & Astronaut; Inst. Environ. Sci. Missile penetration systems; re-entry systems design; electronic countermeasures; nuclear effects; plasma physics and applications; advanced propulsion; space environment simulation; balloon technology; high altitude investigations; fine particle technology; impact and fracture phenomenon; friction and wear; biophysics. Address: 8455 Portland Place, McLean, VA 22101.

FITZ, H(AROLD) CARLTON, JR, b. Charleston, S.C, Aug. 30, 26; m. 49; c. 3. SPACE & ATMOSPHERIC PHYSICS. B.S, U.S. Mil. Acad, 49; M.S, Univ. Ala, 55; Ph.D.(solid state physics), Univ. Va, 62. Instr. physics, spec. weapons proj, U.S. Army, 55-57, syst. analyst, 57-59, satellite commun. agency, 61-64, asst. prof. physics, U.S. Mil. Acad, 64-65, assoc. prof, 65-67, test plans off, atmospheric effects div, Defense Atomic Support Agency, Wash, D.C, 67-70; staff scientist, Gen. Res. Corp, Va, 70; CHIEF ATMOSPHERIC EFFECTS DIV, Defense Atomic Support Agency, WASH, D.C, 70-71, DEFENSE NUCLEAR AGENCY, 71- U.S.A, 45-70, Lt. Col. U.S. Army, (Ret). Am. Phys. Soc; Am. Inst. Aeronaut. & Astronaut; Am. Geophys. Union. Design and effects of nuclear weapons; atmospheric and space environment; cosmic ray physics; satellite communications systems. Address: 6716 Fern Lane, Annandale, VA 22003.

FITZ, REGINALD HEBER, b. Boston, Mass, Oct. 28, 20; m. 46; c. 4. MEDICINE. A.B, Harvard, 42; M.D, Harvard Med. Sch, 45. Intern, Faulkner Hosp, Boston, Mass, 45-46; res. med. sch. med, Colorado, 48-50, instr, 50-53, asst. prof, 53-61, assoc. prof, 61, asst. dean, 57-59, assoc. dean, 59-61; prof. med, Univ. N.Mex, 61-71, dean sch. med, 61-68; SR. MED. ASSOC, COMMONWEALTH FUND, 71- Dir, N.Mex. Regional Med. Prog, 66-71. Dipl, Am. Bd. Int. Med, 53- Med.C, 46-48. AAAS; Am. Med. Asn; Am. Col. Physicians; Am. Fedn. Clin. Res; Am. Clin. & Climat. Asn. Medical education; internal medicine. Address: 1 E. 75th St, New York, NY 10021.

FITZ-JAMES, P(HILIP) C(HESTER), b. Vancouver, B.C, Nov. 25, 20; m. 48; c. 4. MICROBIOLOGY. B.S.A, British Columbia, 43; M.S.A, Toronto, 45; M.D, Western Ontario, 49, Ph.D.(bact, biochem), 53. Asst. penicillin prod, Banting Inst, Toronto, 43-44; assoc. prof. bact. & immunol, SCH. MED, UNIV. WEST. ONT, 53-67, PROF. BACT, IMMUNOL. & BIOCHEM, 67-, LECTR. BIOCHEM, 53-, summers, asst, 46-47. Res. assoc, Nat. Res. Coun. Can, 56-; Harrison award, Royal Soc. Can, 63. Brit. Biochem. Soc. Structure, composition and activities of bacteria, particularly the process of spore formation. Address: Dept. of Bacteriology & Immunology, Health Science Center, University of Western Ontario, London, Ont, Can.

FITZER, JACK, b. Joplin, Mo, Oct. 5, 26, m. 50; c. 3. ELECTRICAL ENGINEERING. B.S, Missouri, 51; M.S, Washington (St. Louis), 60, D.Sc,(elec. eng), 62. Design engr, Chance Vought Aircraft Co, 51-54; Emerson Elec. Mfg. Co, 54-59, consult, 59-62, sr. res. engr, 62-63; mem. res. & develop. staff, LTV Electrosysts, 63-67; asst. prof. ELEC. ENG, UNIV. TEX, ARLINGTON, 67-69, ASSOC. PROF, 69- U.S.N, 44-47. Inst. Elec. & Electronics Eng; Am. Inst. Aeronaut. & Astronaut. Automatic control, guidance; network theory. Address: Dept. of Electrical Engineering, University of Texas at Arlington, Arlington, TX 76010.

FITZGERALD, A(RTHUR) E(UGENE), b. Brooklyn, N.Y, Sept. 22, 09; m. 41; c. 3. ELECTRICAL ENGINEERING. E.E, Polytech. Inst. Brooklyn, 29; S.M, Mass. Inst. Tech, 31, Sc.D.(elec. eng), 37. Engr, Gen. Elec. Co, Mass. & N.Y, 29-31; from asst. to instr. elec. eng, Mass. Inst. Tech, 31-41, asst. prof, 41-44, assoc. prof, 44-52, prof, 52-54; proj. mgr. & chief elec. engr, Jackson & Moreland, Inc, Mass, 54-63; prof. elec. eng. & chmn. dept, NORTHEAST. UNIV, 63-66, DEAN FACULTY, 66-, V.PRES. ACAD. AFFAIRS, 67- Consult, Jackson & Moreland, Inc, 34-54, 63-; trustee, Southeast. Mass. Univ, 64- Fel. Inst. Elec. & Electronics Eng. Applications of electric power; analysis of power systems and of electric machinery. Address: Northeastern University, Boston, MA 02115.

FITZGERALD, CHARLES H, b. Conyers, Ga, Dec. 11, 21; m. 45; c. 1. FOREST PHYSIOLOGY & CHEMISTRY. B.S.F, Georgia, 42, M.S, 63, Ph.D.(chem), 66. Forest supt, Ga. Pac. Inc, Ala, 46-55; chief forester, Martin Timber Co, La, 55-61; res. asst. forest soils & plant chem, SCH. FOREST RESOURCES, UNIV. GA, 61-66, ASST. PROF. physiol. chem, 66-68, FOREST RESOURCES, 68- U.S.A, 42-45, Sgt. AAAS; Am. Chem. Soc; Am. Soc. Plant Physiol; Soc. Am. Foresters. Mode of action, degradation, species selectivity and practical application of herbicides; effects of pesticides on plants; variations of plant chemical content with age; chemical taxonomy; biochemistry of woody plants. Address: School of Forest Resources, University of Georgia, Athens, GA 30601.

FITZGERALD, C(ORNELIUS) G(ILBERT), b. N.Y.C, July 3, 17; m. 44; c. 1. ORGANIC CHEMISTRY. A.B, Columbia; Niagara, 42-43; Kentucky, 49-52; Ph.D.(chem), Nat. Bur. Standards Grad. Sch, 52. Res. worker biol, New York Bd. Health, 39-40; asst. eng, City Col, 40-41; chem, Nat. Oil Prods. Co, 41-42; res. chemist, Johnson & Johnson, 45-46; Wallace & Tiernan, 46-49; instr. chem, Kentucky, 49-51; res. chemist, Diamond Ord. Fuze Labs, Nat. Bur. Standards, 52-55; res. dir. plastics, Gar Wood Industs, 55-58; SR. RES. CHEMIST POLYMERS, SCOTT PAPER CO, 58- Instr, Nat. Bur. Standards Grad. Sch, 54-55; instr. eve. div, Pa. Mil. Col, 63-; res. dir, Hastings & Co, 66-; consult, Diamond Ord. Fuze Labs. C.W.S, U.S.A, 42-45. AAAS; Am. Chem. Soc; Am. Soc. Test. & Mat; Soc. Plastics Eng. Polymer chemistry; plastics technology and rheology; structural design of glass fiber reinforced plastic members; stress analysis; encapsulation of electronic components. Address: 204 W. Rose Valley Rd, Wallingford, PA 19086.

FITZGERALD, DONALD R(AY), b. Pomeroy, Wash, June 18, 23; m. 55; c. 2. PHYSICS. B.S, Chicago, 47, M.S, 49, Ph.D.(meteorol), 56. Asst, Chicago, 51-54, res. assoc, 54-61; RES. PHYSICIST, U.S. AIR FORCE CAMBRIDGE RES. LAB, 61- U.S.A.A.F, 43-46, Res, 46-, Lt. Col. Am. Meteorol. Soc; Am. Geophys. Union; Sci. Res. Soc. Am. Electrical structure of thunderstorms; general atmospheric electrostatic phenomena; instrumentation for cloud physics; research aircraft; atmospheric physics. Address: U.S. Air Force Cambridge Research Lab, L.G. Hanscom Field, Bedford, MA 01730.

FITZGERALD, DOROTHEA B(ABBITT), b. Boston, Mass, Mar. 3, 12; m. 45. BIOCHEMISTRY. B.S, Boston, 33. Asst. pharmacol, sch. med, Hopkins, 36-41; res. biochemist, Am. Cyanamid Co, 41-45; res. pharmacologist, sch. med, Duke, 46-48; pharmacologist, Nat. Cancer Inst, 49-53, biochemist, 53-63; consult, Nat. Inst. Dent. Res. Gnotobiotics, 64-65; biomed. consult, 65-67; biochemist, Nat. Inst. Dent. Res, 67-68; RES. SCIENTIST, INST. ORAL BIOL, MED. SCH, UNIV. MIAMI, 69- Guest investr, germ-free lab, Karolinska Inst, Sweden, 63. AAAS; Soc. Exp. Biol. & Med. Gnotobiotics. Address: Institute of Oral Biology, University of Miami Medical School, P.O. Box 875, Biscayne Annex, Miami, FL 33152.

FITZGERALD, DUANE GLENN, b. Jackson, Mich, Oct. 6, 31; m. 55; c. 4. NUCLEAR & ELECTRICAL ENGINEERING. B.S, Michigan, 57, M.S, 59; Ph.D.(elec. eng), Missouri, 66. Proj. engr, Bendix Corp, 59-62; reactor supvr, Missouri, 62-67; MGR. SYSTS. ANAL, ENG. DIV, NUS CORP, 67- U.S.N, 49-53. Am. Nuclear Soc; Inst. Elec. & Electronics Eng. Reliability analysis; protection system design and analysis; system kinetics analysis; direct digital control. Address: 5706 English Court, Bethesda, MD 20034.

FITZGERALD, EDWIN R(OGER), b. Oshkosh, Wis, July 14, 23; m. 46; c. 8. PHYSICS. B.S, Wisconsin, 44, M.S, 50, Ph.D.(physics), 51. Mem. tech. staff, B.F. Goodrich Co, 44-46; asst. physics & math, Wisconsin, 46-48, chem, 48-51, proj. assoc, 51-53; asst. prof. PHYSICS, Pa. State, 53-56, assoc. prof, 56-59, PROF, 59-61; JOHNS HOPKINS UNIV, 61- Am. Phys. Soc; Acoust. Soc. Am. Solid state physics; dynamic mechanical properties of solids; polymers, metals and long chain hydrocarbon compounds; dielectric properties of liquids and solids; wave mechanical explanations of deformation and other mechanical behavior. Address: Dept. of Mechanics, Johns Hopkins University, Baltimore, MD 21218.

FITZGERALD, EMERSON B(LANCHARD), b. Springfield, Mass, Oct. 11, 17; m. 56; c. 2. PHYSICAL CHEMISTRY. B.S, Am. Int. Col, 39; M.A, Boston, 41; Ph.D.(phys. chem), Yale, 50. Instr. chem, Am. Inst. Col, 39-40; chemist, E.I. du Pont de Nemours & Co, 41-42; B.B. Chem. Co, 42-43; Chicopee Mfg. Corp, 43-46; DeBell & Richardson, Inc, 46-47; asst, Princeton, 47-48; chemist, E.I. DU PONT DE NEMOURS & CO, 50-51, asst, 51-55, res. supvr, 55-68, RES. ASSOC, FABRICS & FINISHES DEPT, 68- Am. Chem. Soc. Physical chemistry and properties of polymers and plastics; polyelectrolytes; photo-oxidative degradation of organic surface coatings. Address: Fabrics & Finishes Dept, E.I. du Pont de Nemours & Co, Wilmington, DE 19898.

FITZGERALD, GEORGE P(ATRICK), b. Milwaukee, Wis, Sept. 22, 22; m. 43; c. 2. BOTANY. B.S, Univ. Wis, 48, M.S, 49, Ph.D.(bot), 50. Asst. BOT, UNIV. WIS, MADISON, 48-50, res. assoc, 50-68, SR. SCIENTIST, 68- U.S.A, 43-46. Phycol. Soc. Am. Mineral nutrition of algae; control of algae. Address: 2018 Dickson Pl, Madison, WI 53713.

FITZGERALD, GLENNA GIBBS, b. Westfield, Mass; m. BIOCHEMISTRY, PHARMACOLOGY. B.S. & M.S, Univ. Mass, Amherst; Ph.D.(pharmacol), Yale, 68. Res. assoc. pharmacol, Yale, 61-62; instr, George Washington Univ, 68-71; STAFF FEL, LAB. CEREBRAL METAB, SECT. DEVELOP. NEUROCHEM, NAT. INST. MENT. HEALTH, 71- Neurochemistry; biochemical basis of hormone actions; development and differentiation of the central nervous system. Address: Lab. of Cerebral Metabolism, National Institute of Mental Health, Bethesda, MD 20014.

FITZGERALD, JAMES EDWARD, b. Paris, Ill, Feb. 14, 31; m. 59; c. 3. VETERINARY PATHOLOGY, TOXICOLOGY. B.S, Univ. Ill, Urbana, 53, D.V.M, 55, M.S, 62, Ph.D.(vet. med), 64. Instr. vet. clin. med, Univ. Ill, Urbana, 55-56; vet, agr. res. ctr, Pfizer, Inc, 58-60; Nat. Insts. Health trainee vet. path. & hyg, col. vet. med, Univ. Ill, Urbana, 61-64; PATHOLOGIST, DEPT. TOXICOL, PARKE DAVIS & CO, 64- Vet.C, U.S.A.F, 56-58, Capt. Am. Vet. Med. Asn; Am. Col. Vet. Path; Soc. Toxicology. Experimental pathology and toxicology; animal neoplasia. Address: Dept. of Toxicology, Parke Davis & Co, 2800 Plymouth Rd, Ann Arbor, MI 48106.

FITZGERALD, JAMES ROBERT, b. Columbus, Ohio, Nov. 15, 10; m. 39; c. 3. OPHTHALMOLOGY. B.S.M, Loyola (Ill), 32, M.D, 34. Res. ophthal, Cook County Hosp, Ill, 35-39; SUPVRY. OPHTHALMOLOGIST, STATE OF ILL, 43-; PROF. OPHTHAL. & ACTING HEAD DEPT, STRITCH SCH. MED, LOYOLA UNIV. CHICAGO, 54- Sr. attend. ophthalmologist, St. Annes Hosp, 40-; Cook County Hosp, 43-69; chief ophthal. serv, Hines Vet. Hosp, 69- Clinical ophthalmology. Address: Stritch School of Medicine, Loyola University of Chicago, Chicago, IL 60612.

FITZGERALD, JAMES W(ILLIAM), b. Oshkosh, Wis, Dec. 2, 17; m. 47; c. 4. ACOUSTICS. B.S, Wisconsin, 40, 48-49; Case, 41-42; Maryland, 51-52. Res. physicist, B.F. Goodrich Co, 40-42; head propagation sect, Naval Res. Lab, 42-46; res. supvr, Eng. Res. Assocs, 46-48; res. instr. physics, Wisconsin, 48-49; head transducer design, Underwater Sound Lab, U.S. Navy Dept, 50; dir. electromech. div, Atlantic Res. Corp, 50-54; PRES. & chief scientist, Chesapeake Instrument Corp, 54-61; Geraldines Labs, 62-63; JAMES W. FITZGERALD & ASSOC, INC, 64- AAAS; Am. Phys. Soc; Acoustical Soc. Am; Marine Technol. Soc. Electrophysical acoustics; transducers; oceanography; anti-submarine warfare; ultrasonics; shock and vibration; instrumentation; viscoelastic properties of materials. Address: James W. Fitzgerald & Associate, Inc, P.O. Box 1510, Annapolis, MD 21404.

FITZGERALD, J(ERRY) M(ACK), b. Alliance, Nebr, Jan. 20, 37; m. 58; c. 2. ANALYTICAL CHEMISTRY. B.A, Colorado, 59; Woodrow Wilson fel, Princeton, 59-60, Procter & Gamble fel, 60-61, M.A, 61, Allied Chem. fel, 61-62, Ph.D.(anal. chem), 63. Res. assoc. CHEM, Purdue, 63-64; asst. prof, Seton Hall Univ, 64-68; UNIV. HOUSTON, 68-70, ASSOC. PROF, 70- Am. Chem. Soc; Soc. Appl. Spectros. Photochemical reactions for analytical determinations; electron spin resonance and fluorescence spectroscopy; continuous and automated analysis; spectral and electrochemical properties of mixed-liquid complexes. Address: Dept. of Chemistry, University of Houston, Houston, TX 77004.

FITZGERALD, J(OHN) EDMUND, b. Revere, Mass, Sept. 29, 23; m. 45; c. 4. APPLIED MECHANICS & PHYSICS. Tufts Col, 41-45; M.S, Harvard, 47; B.Sc.A.E. Univ. Col, Cork, 47, M.Sc, 70; Univ. Mich, summers 48, 49; D.Sc, (math, physics), Nat. Univ. Ireland, 71. Regional engr. struct, Liberty Mutual Ins. Co, 47; instr. eng. mech, Southern Methodist, 47-48; assoc. prof. civil eng, N.Dak. State Col, 48-51; supvr. struct, Armour Res. Found, 51-52; mgr. appl. mech, mech. res. labs, Am. Mach. & Foundry Co, 52-56; mgr. appl. physics, cent. res. lab, Borg-Warner Corp, 56-59; dir. res. & eng, Lockheed Propulsion Co, 59-66; PROF. CIVIL ENG. & CHMN. DEPT, UNIV. UTAH, 66- Consult, Math. Sci. Corp, 61-; chmn. struct. integrity comt, Interagency Chem. Rocket Propulsion Group, 63- U.S.N.R, 41-45. Am. Inst. Aeronaut. & Astronaut; Am. Phys. Soc; Soc. Eng. Sci; Soc. Exp. Stress Anal; Am. Soc. Civil Eng; Sci. Res. Soc. Am; Brit. Inst. Physics & Phys. Soc. Response of viscoelastic bodies to transient loads; dynamics of structures under transient loads; associated problems in rockets, structures and soils; nonlinear material behavior. Address: Dept. of Civil Engineering, University of Utah, Salt Lake City, UT 84112.

FITZGERALD, J(OHN) VINCENT, b. Charleroi, Pa, Aug. 31, 17; m. 46; c. 1. PHYSICAL CHEMISTRY. B.S, St. Vincent Col, 40; Ph.D.(phys. chem), Mass. Inst. Tech, 43; Cornell, 44-45. Lab. asst. phys. chem, St. Vincent Col, 36-40; res. investigator, Nat. Res. Corp, Mass, 41; heat res. lab, Nat. Defense Res. Comt, Mass. Inst. Tech, 42-43; res. labs, Corning Glass Works, N.Y, 43-44, prod. supt, Fall Brook plant, 44-46; res. investigator, Clinton Nat. Lab, Oak Ridge, 46-47, group leader, Power Pile Div, Oak Ridge Nat. Lab, 47-48; res. radioceramics, Pittsburgh Plate Glass Co, 48-52; DIR. TILE COUNCIL OF AM. RES. CTR, 53-; PRES, NAT. METAL REF. CO, 56- Res. prof, sch. ceramics, Rutgers, 53-57; v.pres, Queen's Labs, 59. Chmn. ad hoc comt. on mat. of the Nat. Acad. Sci-Nat. Res. Coun. Adv. Panel 10 to the Nat. Bur. Standards. Am. Chem. Soc; fel. Am. Ceramic Soc.(Forrest award, 49, Meyer award, 51); Am. Phys. Soc. Radioceramics; power nuclear reactor design; physical chemistry of glass and ceramics; radiation chemistry and physics; organic and inorganic adhesives; standards and specifications; industrial research management. Address: Tile Council of America Research Center, P.O. Box 326, Princeton, NJ 08540.

FITZGERALD, JOSEPH A(RTHUR), b. Cleveland, Ohio, Apr. 22, 25; m. 55; c. 7. MEDICINE, PSYCHIATRY. B.S, Case Western Reserve, 46; M.D, Loyola (Ill), 51. Intern gen. med, Milwaukee County Gen. Hosp, 51-52; res. PSYCHIAT, Cleveland Psychiat. Inst. & Hosp, 52-54; sr. res, MED. CTR, SCH. MED, IND. UNIV, INDIANAPOLIS, 57-58, instr, 58-62, asst. prof, 62-66, assoc. prof, 66-71, PROF, 71-; PSYCHIATRIST, LARUE D. CARTER HOSP, 58-, DIR. OUT-PATIENT CLIN, 62- Acting dir, Riley Child Guid. Clin, 58; lectr, post-grad. progs. gen. practitioners & non-psychiat. specialists, 60-; residency training cmt. psychiat, med. sch, Indiana, 60-, lectr. psychopath, sch. nursing, 67-; dir. diag. center, Marydale School for Girls, 61-68; mem. attend. staff, Tenth St. Vet. Admin. Hosp, 62-; consult, St. Mary's Child Center, 66- Dipl, Am. Bd. Psychiat. & Neurol, 59. Med.C, U.S.A.F, 54-57, Capt. Fel. Am. Psychiat. Asn. Anxiety; group process; primary prevention of mental disability through identifying high risk groups from perinatal and other preschool studies. Address: Larue D. Carter Hospital, 1315 W. Tenth, Indianapolis, IN 46202.

FITZGERALD, JOSEPH J(AMES), b. Boston, Mass, Mar. 3, 19; m. 46; c. 6. PHYSICS. B.S, Boston Col, 49, M.S, 50; Atomic Energy Cmn. fel, Rochester, 50-51. Supvr. radiol. physics, Knolls Atomic Power Lab, 51-57; asst. prof. physics, sch. pub. health, Harvard, 58-64; chmn. bd, Iso/Serve, Inc, 62-65, pres, 64-65, PRES. & CHMN. BD, CAMBRIDGE NUCLEAR CORP, 65- Consult, Mass. Gen. Hosp, 58-62; Peter Bent Brigham Hosp, 58-61; univ. health serv, Harvard, 58-61; Atomic Energy Cmn, Washington, D.C; Los Alamos Sci. Lab. Chmn. reactor safeguards cmt, Knolls Atomic Power Lab, 55-58, radioactive waste cmt, 56-58, consult, 57-58; adv. cmt, isotopes & radiation develop, Atomic Energy Cmn; comn, Atomic Energy in Mass, 59-64; pres, bd. dirs, Wood, Struthers & Winthrop, Mutual Funds; pres, Sanders Nuclear Corp. U.S.A, 42-45. Am. Nuclear Soc; Health Physics Soc.(news ed); Am. Indust. Hyg. Asn; Am. Col. Health Asn; Air Pollution Control Asn; Royal Soc. Health. Isotope production. Address: Cambridge Nuclear Corp, 575 Middlesex Turnpike, Billerica, MA 01821.

FITZGERALD, LAURENCE R(OCKWELL), b. Boston, Mass, Sept. 25, 16; m. 42; c. 3. PHYSIOLOGY. B.S, Tufts Col, 39; M.S, Iowa, 41, Ph.D.(zool), 49. Res. assoc. zool, Iowa, 48-49; instr. ANAT, MED. UNITS, UNIV. TENN, 49-52, asst. prof, 52-58, ASSOC. PROF, 58- Chmn. sect. anat. sci, Am. Asn. Dent. Schs, 71-72. U.S.A, 42-45. AAAS; Soc. Develop. Biol; Am. Soc. Zool; Am. Asn. Anat; Int. Asn. Dent. Res. Physiology of neonatal period. Address: Dept. of Anatomy, University of Tennessee Medical Units, Memphis, TN 38103.

FITZGERALD, MARIE A(NTON), b. Boston, Mass, Apr. 10, 22; m. 45; c. 3. PHYSIOLOGY. B.S, Columbia, 50; Ph.D.(physiol), Mass. Inst. Tech, 54. Asst. biol, Mass. Inst. Tech, 52-54, res. assoc, 54-55; fel. biophys, New Eng. Inst. Med. Res, 58-59; assoc, Inst. Biophys. Eng, 60-68; ASSOC. PROF. BIOL, HOLYOKE COMMUNITY COL, 68- Protein, physical chemistry; scientific illustration. Address: Dept. of Biology, Holyoke Community College, Holyoke, MA 01040.

FITZGERALD, MAURICE E, b. Holyoke, Mass, Dec. 16, 32; m. 60; c. 2. PHYSICAL & ANALYTICAL CHEMISTRY. B.A, St. Anselm's Col, 54; M.S, St. John's (N.Y), 56. Lab. asst. quant. anal, St. John's (N.Y), 54-56; develop. chemist, Borden Chem. Co, Pa, 56-57; jr. chemist, RES. & ENG, ARCO CHEM. CO. DIV, ATLANTIC RICHFIELD CO, PHILA, 57-64, res. chemist. & group leader, mass spectros. & comput. lab, 64-67, SR. CHEMIST & SUPVR, MASS. SPECTROS. & COMPUT. LAB, 67- Am. Chem. Soc; Soc. Appl. Spectros; Am. Soc. Test. & Mat.(ed, Annual Rev, 65-67). Application of mass spectrometry to quantitative analysis and structure determinations; application of time-shared computer for the automation of analytical instrumentation. Address: 517 Upland Rd, Havertown, PA 19083.

FITZGERALD, M(AURICE) PIM, b. Manchester, Eng, Aug. 14, 39; Can. citizen; m. 64; c. 1. ASTROPHYSICS. B.Sc, Univ. Toronto, 62, M.A, 63; Ph.D.(astron), Case West. Reserve Univ, 67. ASST. PROF. PHYSICS, UNIV. WATERLOO, 67- AAAS; Am. Astron. Soc; Royal Astron. Soc; Royal Astron. Soc. Can; Can. Asn. Physicists; Can. Astron. Soc. Galactic structure; interstellar dust; spectroscopic binary stars; photometry; space density studies; spectroscopy; radial velocities. Address: Dept. of Physics, University of Waterloo, Ont, Can.

FITZGERALD, PATRICK JAMES, b. Haverhill, Mass, Aug. 9, 13; m. 49; c. 1. PATHOLOGY. B.S, Massachusetts, 36; M.D, Tufts, 40. Intern med, Boston City Hosp, 40-41; res. & asst. pathologist, Mallory Inst. Path, 42-43, 46-47; fel, Nat. Cancer Inst, Mem. Center Cancer & Allied Diseases, 47-48; special res. fel. biophys. techs, Sloan-Kettering Inst, 48-49, asst. cellular res, 49-53; PROF. PATH. & CHMN. DEPT, COL. MED, STATE UNIV. N.Y. DOWNSTATE MED. CTR, 53- Sloan-Kettering Inst. fel, Nobel Med. Inst, Karolinska Inst, Stockholm, Sweden, 49-50; Sloan scholar, Sloan-Kettering Inst, 50-53; asst. prof, Sloan-Kettering div, med. col, Cornell, 52-53; vis. scientist, Oxford Univ, 59-60; State Univ. N.Y. distinguished res. fel, faculty sci, Inst. Biol. Chem, Marseille, France & vis. fel, St. Catherine's Col, Oxford Univ, 68. Asst. attend. pathologist, Mem. Center Cancer & Allied Diseases, 50-53; dir, inst. path, Kings County Hosp, 53- Consult, path. study sect, U.S. Pub. Health Serv, 58-62. Med.C, U.S.N, 43-46, Lt. Comdr. AAAS; Am. Soc. Clin. Path; Am. Soc. Exp. Path; Histochem. Soc; Electron Micros. Soc. Am; Am. Med. Asn; Am. Asn. Path. & Bact.(pres, 66-67); Col. Am. Path; Brit. Biochem. Soc; Royal Soc. Med. Nucleoprotein metabolism in growth and cancer. Address: Dept. of Pathology, State University of New York Downstate Medical Center, 450 Clarkson Ave, Brooklyn, NY 11203.

FITZGERALD, PAUL J(ACKSON), b. Nashville, Tenn, July 20, 24; m. 50; c. 3. PLANT BREEDING, PATHOLOGY. B.S, Tennessee, 50; M.S, Purdue, 52, Ph.D.(plant path, breeding & genetics), 54. Breeder, hard red winter wheat, intermountain area & res. agronomist, PLANT SCI. RES. DIV, AGR. RES. SERV, U.S. DEPT. AGR, 54-71, CHIEF CEREAL CROPS RES. BR, PLANT INDUST. STA, 71- Forage improv. leader, Rockefeller Found, Santiago, Chile, 60-62. U.S.N.R, 43-46. Am. Soc. Agron. Inheritance of resistance to insects and insect-transmitted disease in plants. Address: Cereal Crops Research Branch, Plant Science Research Division, Agricultural Research Service, Plant Industry Station, Beltsville, MD 20705.

FITZGERALD, PAUL R(AY), b. Elsinore, Utah, May 2, 20; m. 41; c. 4. ZOOLOGY, PARASITOLOGY. B.S, Utah State, 49, M.S, 50; fel. Illinois, 56-57, Ph.D, 61; Oak Ridge Inst. Nuclear Studies, 65. Instr. zool. & biol, Utah State Univ, 49-53; res. parasitologist, animal disease & parasite res. div, U.S. Dept. Agr, 53-66, coop. agent, 50-53; PROF. VET. PARASITOL, UNIV. ILL, URBANA-CHAMPAIGN, 66- Proj. dir. grants, Nat. Insts. Health, State of Ill. & commercial; Fulbright fel, Arg; La. State Univ. fel, 71; partic, Pac. Sci. Cong. U.S.N, 44-45. Am. Soc. Parasitol; Soc. Protozool; Am. Soc. Zool; Am. Inst. Biol. Sci. Parasitic protozoa, helminths; arthropods; domestic livestock; wild ruminants; physiology of parasites and effects upon hosts. Address: College of Veterinary Medicine, University of Illinois at Urbana, Urbana, IL 61801.

FITZGERALD, ROBERT J(AMES), b. New York, N.Y, Nov. 3, 18; m. 45. MICROBIOLOGY. B.S, Fordham, 39; M.S, Va. Polytech, 41; Ph.D.(pharmacol), Duke, 48. Res. bacteriologist, Am. Cyanamid Co, Conn, 41-45; jr. asst. sanitarian, U.S. Pub. Health Serv, Kans, 45-46, sr. asst. scientist, inst. dental res, Nat. Insts. Health, 48-50, scientist, 50-55, sr. scientist, 55-59, sci. dir, 59-69; PROF. ORAL BIOL, MED. SCH, UNIV. MIAMI, 69-; CHIEF, DENT. RES. UNIT, VET. ADMIN. HOSP, 69- Vis. scientist, Karolinska Inst, Sweden, 62. Sanit.C, U.S.P.H.S, 45-46, 2nd Lt. AAAS; Am. Soc. Microbiol; Am. Acad. Microbiol; Int. Asn. Dent. Res. Microbiology; germ free animals; oral biology chemotherapy. Address: Dental Research Unit 151, Veterans Administration Hospital, 1201 N.W. 16th St, Miami, FL 33125.

FITZGERALD, ROBERT WILLIAM, b. Canton, Ohio, May 30, 31; m. 54; c. 2. STRUCTURAL ENGINEERING, ENGINEERING MECHANICS. B.S, Worcester Polytech. Inst, 53, M.S, 60; Nat. Sci. Found. fel, Univ. Conn, 67-68, Ph.D.(civil eng), 69. Struct. engr, Harvey & Tracy Consult. Eng, Mass, 55-58; instr. mech, Worcester Jr. Col, 58-62; STRUCT. ENG. & MECH, Univ. Conn, 62-63; asst. prof, WORCESTER POLYTECH. INST, 63-69, ASSOC. PROF, 69- U.S.N, 53-55, Lt.(jg). Am. Soc. Civil Eng; Am. Concrete Inst; Soc. Plastics Eng; Am. Soc. Eng. Educ. Structural behavior of reinforced plastics laminates; low cost roofing systems utilizing vegetable fiber reinforced plastics; housing production studies. Address: Dept. of Civil Engineering, Worcester Polytechnic Institute, Worcester, MA 01609.

FITZGERALD, RONALD J(OHN), b. Hutchinson, Minn, Nov. 5, 41. INORGANIC CHEMISTRY. B.Chem, Univ. Minn, 64; Ph.D.(chem), Univ. Ill, Urbana, 68. ASST. PROF. CHEM, ILL. INST. TECHNOL, 68- Res. assoc, Univ. Col, Univ. London, summer 69. Am. Chem. Soc; The Chem. Soc. Magnetic resonance of paramagnetic complexes; organometallic chemistry of transition metal elements. Address: Dept. of Chemistry, Illinois Institute of Technology, Chicago, IL 60616.

FITZGERALD, THOMAS M(ICHAEL), b. Boston, Mass, Oct. 20, 36; m. 58; c. 3. PHYSICS. Sc.B, Boston Col, 58; Sc.M, Brown, 61, Ph.D.(physics), 63. Res. assoc. solid state physics, Brown Univ, 63-65; PHYSICIST, NASA Electronics Res. Ctr, 65-70; NAVAL UNDERWATER SYST. CTR, 70- Am. Phys. Soc. Phonon-phonon, electron-phonon interactions; elastic constants; effects of irradiation on ultrasonic properties of materials; defect studies; underwater acoustics; acousto-optics. Address: Naval Underwater Systems Center, TB2, Newport, RI 02840.

FITZGERALD, WARREN E(UGENE), b. Dallas, Tex, July 3, 31; m. 57; c. 5. PHYSICAL CHEMISTRY. B.S, St. Bernardine of Siena Col, 53; M.S, Rensselaer Polytech, 55, Ph.D.(chem), 57. Res. chemist, plastics div, MONSANTO CO, 57-62, Chemstrand Res. Ctr, Inc, 62-64, sr. res. chemist, 64-67, mgr. acrilan appln. res, 67-70, TECH. MKT. DIR, TEXTILES DIV, 70- Chemical physics; spectroscopy; thermodynamics; reaction kinetics; fiber spinning and characterization; solution and solid state properties of polymers; properties of textiles. Address: Monsanto Textiles Division, 350 Fifth Ave, New York, NY 10001.

FITZGIBBONS, JAMES P, b. Chicago, Ill, Mar. 16, 08; m. 50; c. 6. MEDICINE. B.S, & M.D, Loyola (Ill), 36. Asst. prof. OBSTET. & GYNECOL, UNIV. ILL. COL, MED, 36-60, CLIN. ASSOC. PROF, 60- Consult, Elgin State Hosp. & Boothe Mem. Hosp, Chicago, Ill; chmn. dept. obstet. & gynecol, Grant Hosp, Chicago, Ill. Med.C, 41-46, Capt. Am. Med. Asn; fel. Am. Col. Surg. fel. Am. Col. Obstet. & Gynec. Obstetrics and gynecology. Address: 4753 N. Broadway, Chicago, IL 60640.

FITZGIBBONS, J(OHN) D(AVID), b. Ithaca, N.Y, Apr. 18, 22; m. 46; c. 1. NUCLEAR ENGINEERING. B.S, N.C. State Col, 53; Oak Ridge Sch. Reactor Technol, 54-55. Indust. radiographer, Los Alamos Sci. Lab, 46-47; nuclear engr, BABCOCK & WILCOX CO, 53-58, proj. engr, res. reactors, 58-59, proj. mgr. & engr, 59-64, div. long range planning, 64-68, supvr. systs. data mgt, NAVAL NUCLEAR FUEL DIV, 68-69, SR. SYSTS. ANAL, 69- Med. Dept, U.S.A, 42-45. Research reactor design and development; planning and computer scheduling. Address: Naval Nuclear Fuel Division, Babcock & Wilcox Co, P.O. Box 785, Lynchburg, VA 24505.

FITZHUGH, ANDREW F(YFE), b. Phoenix, Ariz, Dec. 29, 12; m. 45; c. 4. CHEMISTRY. B.A, Stanford, 35; M.S, Arizona, 38. Asst, Arizona, 37-38; agr. & control chemist, Capital Fuel, Feed & Seed Co, Phoenix, 38-40; res. chemist, Shawinigan Resins Corp, 46-55, res. group leader, 55-65; RES. SPECIALIST, MONSANTO CO, 65- U.S.A, 40-46, Lt. Col. AAAS; Am. Chem. Soc. Physical and organic chemistry of polyvinyl acetals; wire enamel; magnet wire; safety glass. Address: Monsanto Co, Springfield, MA 01101.

FITZHUGH, HENRY ALLEN, JR, b. San Antonio, Tex, July 2, 39. ANIMAL BREEDING, GENETICS. B.S, Texas A&M, 61, M.S, 63, Ph.D.(animal breeding), 65. Spec. proj. leader animal sci, Exp. Biol. Sta. Llanos, Calabozo, Venezuela, 62; asst. genetics & genetics, Texas A&M, 63-65; NATO sci. fel, Animal Breeding Res. Orgn, Edinburgh, Scotland, 65-66; asst. prof.

ANIMAL SCI, TEX. A&M UNIV, 66-70, ASSOC. PROF, 70- Consult. Am. Soc. Animal Sci; Biomet. Soc; Am. Genetic Asn; Latin Am. Asn. Animal Prod. Quantitative genetics; biometrical study of genetic and environmental sources of variation in growth, production and efficiency of food utilization of animals. Address: Dept. of Animal Science, Texas A&M University, College Station, TX 77843.

FITZHUGH, HENRY ANTONIE, b. San Antonio, Tex, Sept. 9, 44. AERODYNAMICS, FLUID MECHANICS. S.B, Mass. Inst. Tech, 65; Ph.D.(aerodyn), London, 68. Staff mem. aerotransportation, div. sponsored res, Mass. Inst. Tech, 65; res. asst. aerodyn, Imp. Col, London, 65-68; res. scientist, McDonnell Res. Labs, McDonnel Douglas Corp, 68-70; SR. RES. FEL. HOVERCRAFT, NAT. PHYS. LAB, 70- Hypersonic boundary layer theory; transonics. Address: National Physical Lab, Teddington, Middlesex, England.

FITZHUGH, LOREN CHARLES, b. Kansas City, Mo, Oct. 16, 24. PSYCHOLOGY. B.A, Univ. Kansas City, 50, M.A, 52; Ph.D.(psychol), Purdue Univ, 58. Clin. psychologist, State Hosp, St. Joseph, Mo, 52-54; asst, Purdue Univ, 54-55; trainee, Vet. Admin. Hosp, Marion, Ind, 55-56; Indianapolis, 56-57, regional off, 57-58; dir. psychol. servs, New Castle State Hosp, Ind, 58-67; assoc. prof. psychol, Ind. Univ, Indianapolis, 67-68; DIR. PSYCHOL. SERVS, NEW CASTLE STATE HOSP, 67- U.S.A, 43-46. Assessment of the effects of brain damage; therapeutic planning. Address: Psychology Dept, New Castle State Hospital, New Castle, IN 47362.

FITZHUGH, O(SCAR) GARTH, b. Hood, Va, Aug. 26, 01; m. 29; c. 4. PHARMACOLOGY. B.S, Virginia, 27, M.S, 33, Ph.D.(physiol), 36; summers, Michigan, 32, 34. Instr. physiol. & pharmacol, Vermont, 34-36, asst. prof, 36-37; res. assoc. pharmacol, sch. med, Vanderbilt, 37-39; pharmacologist, Food & Drug Admin, 39-47, chief, chronic toxicity sect, div. pharmacol, 47-53, toxicity br, 53-64, dep. dir. div. toxicol. eval, 64-68, toxicol. dir, bur. sci, 68-70, assoc. dir. toxicol. res, off. pesticides, bur. foods & pesticides, 70-71; TOXICOL. ADV, OFF. PESTICIDE PROGS, ENVIRON. PROTECTION AGENCY, 71- With Off. Sci. Res. & Develop; U.S.A, 44. AAAS; Soc. Toxicol; Inst. Food Tech; Am. Soc. Pharmacol. & Exp. Therapeut; Soc. Exp. Biol. & Med. Adrenal cortex; anesthetics; chronic toxicology; coal tar colors; pesticides; food additives. Address: 4208 Dresden St, Kensington, MD 20795.

FITZHUGH, RICHARD, b. Concord, Mass, Mar. 30, 22; m. 63; c. 2. BIOPHYSICS. B.A, Colorado, 48; Pennsylvania; Ph.D.(biophys), Johns Hopkins, 53. Instr. physiol. optics, med. sch, Hopkins, 53-55; BIOPHYSICIST, NAT. INSTS. HEALTH, U.S. PUB. HEALTH SERV, 56- AAAS; Biophys. Soc. Physiology of the retina and nerve membrane; mathematical models of nerve cells and cell assemblies. Address: National Institutes of Health, Bldg. 36, 2A31, Bethesda, MD 20014.

FITZPATRICK, BEN, JR, b. Miami, Fla, Sept. 28, 32; m. 53; c. 3. MATHEMATICS. B.S, Ala. Polytech, 52, fel, 52-53; M.A. & Ph.D, Texas, 58. Asst. MATH, Texas, 55-56, special instr, 56-58, asst. prof, 58-59; AUBURN UNIV, 59-62, assoc. prof, 62-66, PROF, 66- Am. Math. Soc; Math. Asn. Am. Continua and point set theory; abstract spaces; theory of integration. Address: P.O. Box 855, Auburn, AL 36830.

FITZPATRICK, FRANCIS W(ILLIAM), b. New York, N.Y, Oct. 15, 14. ORGANIC & PHYSICAL CHEMISTRY. B.S, Fordham, 39, M.S, 50; fel, N.Y. Univ, 50-53, Ph.D.(phys. org. chem), 54. Asst. inorg. chem, Tex. Gulf Sulphur Co, N.Y, 40-42; chemist inorg. res. & develop, Stauffer Chem. Co, 46-48; instr. inorg. & org. chem, Manhattan Col, 54-56; chemist & group leader org. & natural prod, Fleischmann Labs. Div, Standard Brands, Inc, 56-60; asst. prof. CHEM, LEHMAN COL, 60-67, ASSOC. PROF, 67- U.S.A, 42-44. AAAS; Am. Chem. Soc. Organic synthesis; organic and physical aspects of organic chemistry; natural and synthetic high polymers. Address: Herbert H. Lehman College, Bedford Park Blvd. W, Bronx, NY 10468.

FITZPATRICK, F(REDERICK) L(INDER), b. Iowa City, Iowa, May 6, 00; m. 23; c. 1. ECONOMIC BIOLOGY. B.A, Iowa, 19, M.S, 21, Ph.D.(econ. zool-ecol), 24. Asst, Iowa, 20-23; asst. prof. biol, Colo. State Teachers Col, 23-24, assoc. prof, 24-25; prof. & head dept, zool, Coe Col, 25-31; assoc. prof. NATURAL SCI, TEACHERS COL, COLUMBIA UNIV, 31-38, prof, 38-65, EMER. PROF, 65-, head dept, 52-65. Ed, Naval Ord. & Gunnery; Damage Control; with Bikini Sci. Resurv; exec. off, Sci. Manpower Proj, Columbia Univ, 65- U.S.A, 18; U.S.N, 42-45, Comdr. AAAS; Nat. Asn. Res. Sci. Teaching; Nat. Sci. Teachers Asn. Economic mammalogy and entomology; science education; ecology and economic status of Citellus tridecemlineatus. Address: Teachers College, Columbia University, New York, NY 10027.

FITZPATRICK, HUGH M(ICHAEL), b. Pittsburgh, Pa, Apr. 22, 20; m. 44; c. 5. PHYSICS. B.S, George Washington, 44. Naval architect, David Taylor Model Basin, 42-48, PHYSICIST, 48-59; syst. eng. div, Cleveland, Pneumatic Indust. Inc, 59-63; OFF. NAVAL RES, 63- U.S.N, 44-45. Acoust. Soc. Am. Fluid mechanics; acoustics; hydromechanics; cavitation; hydrodynamic noise; propulsion; radio; astronomy. Address: Code 468, Office of Naval Research, Arlington, VA 22217.

FITZPATRICK, J. D, b. Kenova, W.Va, Oct. 27, 09; m. 36; c. 3. CHEMICAL ENGINEERING. Chem.E, Cincinnati, 35, M.S, 53, Ph.D, 56. Anal. chemist, Emery Indust, Inc, 34-37, res. chemist, 37-43, head dept. new prods. res, 43-51; res. fel, appl. sci. dept, Cincinnati, 51-56; mgr. basic res. sect, Emery Industs, Inc, 56-62; lectr, CHEM, Ohio Wesleyan Univ, 62-63, vis. assoc. prof, 63-65; RES. ASSOC, UNIV. ARIZ, 65- Am. Chem. Soc; Electrochem. Soc. Organic fatty acid research; development of fatty derivatives; oxidation of unsaturated fatty bodies; electrolytic cell for chromic acid regeneration; oils, fats, waxes; electrochemistry; mineralogy; general mathematics; textile products. Address: Dept. of Chemistry, University of Arizona, Tucson, AZ 85721.

FITZPATRICK, JIMMIE DOILE, b. Jonesboro, La, Aug. 6, 38; m. 59; c. 2. ORGANIC & ANALYTICAL CHEMISTRY. B.S, La. Polytech. Inst, 60; Shell Oil fel, Iowa State Univ, 62-63, M.S, 63; Nat. Insts. Health fel, Univ. Tex, Austin, 64-65, Ph.D.(org. chem), 66. Res. chemist, Phillips Petrol. Co, 65-66; res. assoc, Purdue Univ, 66-67; res. chemist, GAF Corp, 67-68; ASST. PROF. ORG. CHEM, UNIV. SOUTHWEST. LA, 68- Am. Chem. Soc. Organic synthesis; organometallic and polymer chemistry; homogenous and heterogenous catalysis; flavor chemistry. Address: 140 Orangewood Dr, Lafayette, LA 70501.

FITZPATRICK, JOHN McNEIL, b. San Francisco, Calif, Mar. 16, 19; m. 52; c. 6. METALLURGY. B.S, Mont. Sch. Mines, 42; S.M, Mass. Inst. Technol, 48. Eng. trainee metall, Wright Aeronaut. Corp, 42-44, engr, 46-47; res. asst. metall, Mass. Inst. Technol, 48-49, staff engr, 49-54; Nuclear Metals Inc, 54-56, asst. mgr. new develop. div, 56-60; mgr. res. & develop, metals div, Stauffer Chem. Co, 60-64; metall. develop, Fansteel Metall. Corp, 64-65; STAFF SCIENTIST, LOCKHEED MISSILES & SPACE CO, 65- U.S.A, 44-46, 1st Lt. Am. Inst. Mining, Metall. & Petrol. Eng; Am. Soc. Metals; Am. Soc. Test. & Mat. Metallurgy of nuclear metals, uranium, zirconium and their alloys; metallurgy of refractory metals and titanium; mechanical working of metals. Address: Dept. 52-30, Bldg. 204, Lockheed Palo Alto Research Lab, 3251 Hanover St, Palo Alto, CA 94304.

FITZPATRICK, J(OHN) T(HOMAS), b. Salt Lake City, Utah, Oct. 13, 18; m. 54; c. 2. CHEMISTRY. B.S, Harvard, 38; Ph.D.(org. chem), Illinois, 41. Res. chemist, Gen. Aniline Works, N.J, 41-42; CHEM. DIV, UNION CARBIDE CORP, 42-64, asst. dir. res. & develop, 64-69, RES. ASSOC, 69- Am. Chem. Soc. Catalysts for organic reactions; general organic synthesis; bioactive compounds. Address: 1621 Ridgeview Rd, Charleston, WV 25314.

FITZPATRICK, J(OSEPH) F(ERRIS), JR, b. New Orleans, La, Mar. 8, 32; m. 61; c. 3. INVERTEBRATE ZOÖLOGY. B.S, Tulane, 59, M.S, 61; P.F. du Pont fel, Virginia, 61-64, Marchant fel, 63-64, Ph.D.(biol), 64. Asst. zool, Tulane, 60, bot. & zool, 61; instr, dept. zool, Univ. Ky, 64; asst. prof. zool, Miss. State Univ, 64-69; ASSOC. PROF. BIOL, RANDOLPH-MACON WOMAN'S COL, 69- U.S.A, 52-54. Fel. AAAS; Am. Soc. Zool; Soc. Syst. Zool. Systematics of North American crawfishes. Address: Dept. of Biology, Randolph-Macon Woman's College, Lynchburg, VA 24504.

FITZPATRICK, LLOYD C(HARLES), b. Erie, Pa, May 12, 37; m. 59; c. 3. PHYSIOLOGICAL ECOLOGY. B.S, Mt. Union Col, 60; M.A, Kent State Univ, 66; NASA trainee, 66-69, Ph.D.(ecol), 70; Nat. Sci. Found. trainee, Argonne Nat. Labs, Chicago, 70. Instr, high sch, Fla, 60-61; Ohio, 61-66; BIOL. SCI, Kent State Univ, 68-70; ASST. PROF, N.TEX. STATE UNIV, 70- Nat. Sci. Found. fel, systs. ecol. inst, biol. sta, Univ. Okla, summer 71. AAAS; Ecol. Soc. Am; Am. Soc. Zool; Soc. Study Amphibians & Reptiles. Ecological energetics and physiology, especially ecological and geographical variations in thermal acclimation metabolism and isoenzyme patterns in salamanders; comparative bioenergetics of salamanders, lizards and small rodents. Address: Dept. of Biological Sciences, North Texas State University, Denton, TX 76203.

FITZPATRICK, MARJORIE H, b. Ensley Ala, Sept. 7, 29; m. 53; c. 3. MATHEMATICS. B.S, Jacksonville State Col, 51; M.S, Auburn, 60, Ph.D.(math), 64. Engr, Chance Vought Aircraft, 54-55; res. scientist, Mil. Physics Res. Lab, 56-57; instr. MATH, Auburn Univ, 63-64, ASST. PROF, 64-66; TUSKEGEE INST, 66- Am. Math. Soc. Matrix theory. Address: Dept. of Mathematics, Tuskegee Institute, AL 36088.

FITZPATRICK, MARTIN JAMES, b. Balboa, C.Z, Cent. Am, Aug. 5, 21; m. 46; c. 4. INTERNAL MEDICINE. B.S, Notre Dame, 42; M.D, Columbia, 45. Asst. prof. MED, sch. med, Kansas, 53-56, assoc. prof, 56-62, chief, sect. pulmonary disease, 53-62, dir, Lerrigo Mem. Lab, 57-62; assoc. prof, sch. med, N.Y. Univ, 62-69; PROF. MED, UNIV. OKLA; MED. CTR, 69- Dir, O'Donnell Mem. Res. Labs, 62-69; consult, Vet. Admin. Hosps, Oklahoma City, 69-, Kansas City, Mo. & Kans; Kans. State Tuberc. Sanatoria. Med.C, U.S.A, 46-48, 51-53. Am. Thoracic Soc; Am. Col. Physicians; Am. Fedn. Clin. Res. Biochemical properties of connective tissue. Address: Dept. of Medicine, University of Oklahoma Medical Center, 800 N.E. 13th St, Oklahoma City, OK 73104.

FITZPATRICK, M(ICHAEL) M(ORSON), b. N.Y.C, Aug. 8, 25; m. 46; c. 2. GEOPHYSICS. B.A, Toronto, 49, M.A, 50; Ph.D.(geophysics), Harvard, 60. Lectr. GEOPHYSICS, QUEEN'S UNIV.(ONT), 52-53, asst. prof, 53-64, ASSOC. PROF, 64- R.C.N, 43-45. Soc. Explor. Geophys; Geol. Asn. Can; Am. Geophys. Union. Earth's gravitational field. Address: Dept. of Geological Science, Queen's University, Kingston, Ont, Can.

FITZPATRICK, PHILIP M(ATTHEW), b. N.Y.C, Sept. 17, 15; m. 42; c. 2. PHYSICS. B.S, Oklahoma, 50, M.S, 51, fel, 51-53, Ph.D.(physics), 55. Asst. physics, Oklahoma, 53-55; physicist, U.S. Navy Mine Defense Lab, Fla, 55-59; Air Proving Ground Ctr, Eglin Air Force Base, 59-62; assoc. prof. MATH, AUBURN UNIV, 62-68, PROF, 68- Consult, U.S. Air Force, 62- U.S.A, 41; U.S.A.A.F, 41-45, Capt. AAAS; Am. Inst. Aeronaut. & Astronaut; Am. Phys. Soc; Am. Geophys. Union; Math. Asn. Am. Astrodynamics. Address: 107 Ryan St, Auburn, AL 36830.

FITZPATRICK, RANDAL E(VELYN), b. Barbados, B.W.I, June 27, 07; m. 36; c. 2. PHYTOPATHOLOGY. B.S.A, McGill, 29; Nat. Res. Council Can. bursar, Toronto, 30-31, Ph.D, 33. Asst. bot, Toronto, 33-35; asst. plant pathologist, plant path. lab, CAN. DEPT. AGR, Summerland, 36-46, officer-in-charge VANCOUVER, 46-57, DIR. AGR. RES. STA, 58- Hon. lectr, British Columbia. Agr. Inst. Can; Can. Phytopath. Soc. Diseases of fruit; plant viruses. Address: Canadian Agricultural Research Lab, Research Station, 6660 N.W. Marine Dr, Vancouver 8, B.C, Can.

FITZPATRICK, ROBERT C(HARLES), b. Port Huron, Mich, Jan. 18, 26; m; c. 2. GEOPHYSICS. B.S, Michigan, 48, M.S, 50. Packaging-material handling engr, Kaiser-Frazer Corp, 50-51; geophysicist, Air Force Cambridge Res. Center, 53-54, chief geodesy sect, 54-56; res. assoc, seismol. & acoustics, Willow Run Labs, Univ. Mich, 56-60, mem. staff, res. admin, 60-65, asst. dir, 65-67, assoc. dir, 67-69; mgr. mkt. res, Datamax Corp, 69-70; ASST. V.PRES. RES, STATE UNIV. N.Y. BUFFALO, 70- Geophysicist, Off. Naval Res, 51-53; mem, Nat. Coun. Univ. Res. Adminrs. U.S.N.R, 44-69, Lt. Comdr, Ret. Geol. Soc. Am; Soc. Explor. Geophys; Int. Asn. Gt. Lakes Res; Am. Geophys. Union. Physical oceanography; gravimetry; seismology. Address: 99 Parkledge Dr, Snyder, NY 14226.

FITZPATRICK, T(HOMAS) B(ERNARD), b. Madison, Wis, Dec. 19, 19; m. 44; c. 5. MEDICINE. A.B, Wisconsin, 41; M.D, Harvard, 45; Mayo Found. fel, Minnesota, 48-51, Ph.D, 52. Asst. prof. DERMAT, Michigan, 51-52; prof. & head div, med. sch, Oregon, 52-58; EDWARD WIGGLESWORTH PROF, HARVARD MED. SCH, 59-; CHIEF DERMAT. SERV, MASS. GEN. HOSP, 59- Chief dept. dermat, Multnomah & Children's Hosps, Portland, Ore, 52-58; Commonwealth fel. biochem, Radcliffe Infirmary, Oxford, Eng, 58-59; consult, Nat. Inst. Arthritis & Metab. Diseases, 60-; mem. dermat. training grants comt, U.S. Pub. Health Serv, 60-65; consult, Peter Bent Brigham Hosp, 62- Guest lectr, Univs. Tokyo, Tohoku & Kyoto, Japan, 56; Sigmund Pollitzer lect, N.Y. Univ, 62; Prosser White Oration, Royal Soc. Med, 64. Award, Mayo Found, 51; achievement award, Univ. Minnesota, 64; Myron Gordon award, Int. Union Against Cancer, 65. Dipl, Am. Bd. Dermat, 52. Med.C, 46-48, Capt. Am. Acad. Dermat; Am. Dermat. Asn; Am. Med. Asn; Am. Soc. Clin. Invest; Am. Soc. Exp. Path; Soc. Invest. Dermat.(pres, 59-60); Am. Acad. Arts & Sci; hon. mem. Brit. Asn. Dermat; fel. Royal Soc. Med; hon. mem. Dermat. Soc. Israel. Melanin biosynthesis; normal and abnormal reactions of man to light; molecular biology of melanin; origin of racial color; dermatology. Address: Harvard Medical School, Cambridge, MA 02138.

FITZPATRICK, THOMAS J(OSEPH), b. Phila, Pa, Sept. 6, 24. ORGANIC CHEMISTRY, FOOD SCIENCE & TECHNOLOGY. B.S, Pa. State, 50; M.S, Maryland, 52; Ph.D.(food tech), Massachusetts, 61. Under sci. aide ORG. CHEM, EAST. UTILIZATION RES. & DEVELOP. DIV, U.S. DEPT. AGR, 42-45, sci. aide, 45-50, res. asst, 50-55, res. assoc, 55-61, RES. CHEMIST, 61- U.S.A.A.F, 43-45, T/Sgt. Am. Chem. Soc; Potato Asn. Am. Polymerization of acrylic acid esters; synthetic elastomer lactoprene; amino acids of potatoes and their reactions with sugars, using chromatography. Address: Eastern Utilization Research & Development Division, U.S. Dept. of Agriculture, 600 E. Mermaid Lane, Philadelphia, PA 19118.

FITZPATRICK, WILLIAM HENRY, b. Newburyport, Mass, April 18, 16; m. 47; c. 4. BIOCHEMISTRY. B.S, Mass. State Col, 39, Glass Container Co. fel, 39-40, M.S, 40, Ph.D.(food tech), 44; Harvard, 45; Chicago, 47-48; Northwestern 48; Georgetown, 52-53; George Washington, 57; Rutgers, 58-59. Res. chemist plastics & rubber, Am. Steel & Wire Co, Mass, 41; asst. prof. food tech, Mass. State Col, 41-44; instr. med. sch, Chicago, 47-48; panel dir. med. scis, res. & develop. bd, Office Secy. Defense, 48-52; res. consult. biochem, U.S. Govt, 52-62, sci. info. exchange, Smithsonian Inst, 62-70, RES. CONSULT. BIOCHEM, U.S. GOVT, 70- Assoc. res. specialist, Rutgers Univ, 58-59. Consult, War Food Admin, U.S. Dept. Agr, 44. U.S.A, 44-48. N.Y. Acad. Sci. Nutritional biochemistry, especially the role of proteins and amino acids in nutrition; information storage and retrieval. Address: 6748 Bison St, Springfield, VA 22150.

FITZROY, NANCY DELOYE, b. Pittsfield, Mass, Oct. 5, 27; m. 51. ENGINEERING. B.Ch.E, Rensselaer Polytech. Inst, 49. Asst. engr, Knolls Atomic Power Lab, 50-52; develop. engr, Hermes Missile Proj, GEN. ELEC. CO, 52-53, gen. eng. lab, 53-63, heat transfer engr, advan. technol. labs, 63-65, CONSULT. HEAT TRANSFER, RES. & DEVELOP. CTR, 65- Lectr, advan. eng. course, Gen. Elec. Co, 62-67. Am. Soc. Mech. Eng; Am. Inst. Chem. Eng; Am. Helicopter Soc; affiliate mem. Nat. Soc. Prof. Eng. Heat transfer; thermal engineering; thermal properties of materials; high temperature radiation from nuclear source; cooling of integrated circuits; heat transfer in regenerator matrices; nuclear radiation shielding protection. Address: Corporate Research & Development, General Electric Co, P.O. Box 43, Schenectady, NY 12301.

FITZSIMMONS, DELBERT WAYNE, b. Bazine, Kans, Jan. 20, 32; m. 52; c. 4. AGRICULTURAL & IRRIGATION ENGINEERING. B.S, Univ. Idaho, 59, M.S, 62; Nat. Sci. Found. fel, Colo. State Univ, 64; Ph.D.(eng. sci), Wash. State Univ, 70. Instr. AGR. ENG, UNIV. IDAHO, 59-62, asst. prof, 62-68, assoc. prof, 68-71, PROF, 71-, ACTING CHMN. DEPT, 70- U.S.A.F, 51-55, S/Sgt. Am. Soc. Agr. Eng; Am. Soc. Eng. Educ; Nat. Soc. Prof. Eng. Unsteady flow into and through porous media; hydraulic characteristics of porous media; mathematical modeling of flow through soils; effects of irrigated agriculture on water quality. Address: Dept. of Agricultural Engineering, University of Idaho, Moscow, ID 83843.

FITZSIMMONS, JAMES G, Geog, Educ, see Suppl. I to 11th ed, Soc. & Behav. Vols.

FITZSIMMONS, J(OHN) PAUL, b. Hastings, Nebr, March 24, 15; m. 44; c. 2. GEOLOGY. B.S, Washington (Seattle), 40, fel, 41-43, 49, Ph.D.(geol), 49. Geologist, State Dept. Geol. & Mining Industs, Oregon, 43-44; U.S. Geol. Surv, 44-45; asst. prof. GEOL, UNIV. N.MEX, 49-57, assoc. prof, 57-64, PROF, 64- Geol. Soc. Am. Petrography and petrology; geophysics. Address: Dept. of Geology, University of New Mexico, Albuquerque, NM 87106.

FITZSIMMONS, VINCENT G(EORGE), b. Washington, D.C, Mar. 8, 12; m. 36; c. 4. LUBRICATION ENGINEERING. J.D, Cath. Univ. Am, 35. Technologist, lubrication br, chem. div, U.S. NAVAL RES. LAB, 42-57, consult, div, 57-63, head friction & wear sect, SURFACE CHEM. BR, 63-71, CONSULT, 71- Naval Res. Lab. Superior Accomplishment Award, 42; Navy Meritorious Civilian Serv. Award, 57; Naval Res. Lab. Spec. Achievement Award, 70. Am. Ord. Asn; Am. Soc. Lubrication Eng. Finding and developing novel synthetic fluid and dry film lubricating materials for military applications under extreme environmental conditions. Address: Surface Chemistry Branch, Code 6179, Chemistry Division, Naval Research Lab, Washington, DC 20390.

FITZWATER, DONALD (ROBERT), b. Kansas City, Mo, Oct. 5, 30; m. 51; c. 2. COMPUTER SCIENCE. B.A, William Jewell Col, 50; M.S, Iowa State Col, 52, Ph.D.(chem), 58. Asst. chem, Ames Lab, Atomic Energy Comn, Iowa State, 50-52, jr. chemist, 51-52, 55-58, assoc. chemist, 58-64, chemist, 64-67, asst. prof. chem, univ, 59-64, ASSOC. PROF, 64-67; COMPUTER SCI, UNIV. WIS, MADISON, 67- Chem.C, U.S.A, 53-55. Asn. Comput. Mach. Real time control; programming systems; information processing; system & language structures. Address: Dept. of Computer Science, University of Wisconsin, Madison, WI 53706.

FITZWATER, ROBERT N, b. Elkins, W.Va, Apr. 8, 24; m. 50; c. 1. CHEMISTRY. B.S, Rollins Col, 49; Gen. Motors Corp. fel, Florida, 55-58, Ph.D, 58. Asst, bur. entom. & plant quarantine, U.S. Dept. Agr, 51-53; Florida, 53-55; sr. chemist, res. labs, Gen. Motors Corp, 58-61; Martin Co, 62; asst. prof. chem, Rollins Col, 62-65; pharmacol, sch. med, Univ. Miami, 65-69; ASSOC. PROF. CHEM, GA. SOUTH. COL, 69- Address: Dept. of Chemistry, Georgia Southern College, Statesboro, GA 30458.

FITZWILLIAM, JAMES W(ILLIAM), b. Cleveland, Ohio, June 18, 18; m. 46, 70; c. 3. PHYSICS. B.S, Case, 40; fel, Mass. Inst. Tech, 41-42, 45-47; Ph.D.(physics), 47. Tech. aide, Nat. Defense Res. Comt, 42-43; physicist, Gulf Res. & Develop. Co, Pittsburgh, 43-45; Tex. Co, 47-53; tech. staff, BELL TEL. LABS, 53-58, dir. array radar lab, 62-65, dir. Sentinel Radar Lab, 65-68, EXEC. DIR. TEL. & PICTUREPHONE SYSTS. DIV, 68- Am. Phys. Soc; Am. Crystallog. Asn. X-ray diffraction; electron tube development; microwave radio and radar systems development; telephone apparatus development. Address: Division 33, Bell Telephone Labs, Holmdel, NJ 07733.

FIUMARA, NICHOLAS J, b. Boston, Mass, Oct. 31, 12; m. 44; c. 1. COMMUNICABLE & VENEREAL DISEASES. A.B, Boston Col, 34; M.D, Boston, 39; M.P.H, Harvard, 47. Assoc. clin. prof. DERMAT, SCH. MED, BOSTON UNIV, 51-69, CLIN. PROF, 69-; INSTR. EPIDEMIOL, SCH. PUB. HEALTH, HARVARD, 57- Lectr, sch. med, Tufts, 52-; instr. dermat, Harvard Med. Sch, 63-; vis. physician, Mass. Mem. Hosps, 57-; asst. clin. dermatologist, Mass. Gen. Hosp, 53-; assoc. vis. physician, Boston City Hosp, 58-; physician, dept. dermat. & syphil, Boston Dispensary, 59-; dir. div. commun. & venereal diseases, Boston. Consult, U.S. Pub. Health Serv; civilian consult, Armed Forces Disciplinary Control Bd; U.S. Navy, 43-46. Fel. Am. Med. Asn; fel. Am. Venereal Disease Asn; fel. Am. Col. Prev. Med; assoc. Am. Acad. Dermat. Common health; clinical and public health aspects of communicable and venereal diseases and dermatology. Address: 6 Gale Rd, Belmont, MA 02178.

FIVEL, DANIEL I, b. Baltimore, Md, Oct. 12, 32; m. 57; c. 1. THEORETICAL PHYSICS. Ph.D.(physics), Hopkins, 59. Res. assoc. PHYSICS, Pennsylvania, 59-61; Nat. Sci. Found. fel, Synchrotron Lab, Frascatti, Rome, Italy, 61-62; Mass. Inst. Technol, 62-63; asst. prof, UNIV. MD, COLLEGE PARK, 63-68, ASSOC. PROF, 68- Mem. exec. comt, Aspen Ctr. Physics, Colo. Am. Phys. Soc. Weak interactions; quantum field theory; dispersion relations; elementary particles; symmetry properties; potential theory. Address: Dept. of Physics, University of Maryland, College Park, MD 20742.

FIVES, WILLIAM PAUL, b. Honesdale, Pa, Apr. 17, 45; m. 68; ORGANIC CHEMISTRY. B.S, Mt. St. Mary's Col.(Md), 67; univ. assistantship, Lehigh Univ, 67-68, Nat. Sci. Found. traineeship, 68, Atlas Chem. Industs. res. grant, 68-71, Ph.D.(chem), 71. RES. CHEMIST, NASHUA CORP, 71- Am. Chem. Soc. Synthesis of organic compounds as potential medicinal agents; light sensitive and heat sensitive systems for use in copying processes. Address: Nashua Corp, 44 Franklin St, Nashua, NH 03060.

FIX, DELBERT D(ALE), b. Pierce, Nebr, Dec. 10, 26; m. 46; c. 2. ORGANIC CHEMISTRY. B.S, Nebraska, 48, M.S, 50; Ph.D.(chem), Colorado, 52. Asst, Nebraska, 48-49; Colorado, 49-52; res. chemist, EMULSION RES. DIV, RES. LAB, EASTMAN KODAK CO, 52-65, RES. ASSOC, 65- AAAS; Am. Chem. Soc. Organic synthesis; nitrogen heterocyclic chemistry; reaction mechanisms; photographic emulsions. Address: Eastman Kodak Co, Research Labs, 343 State St, Rochester, NY 14650.

FIX, JAMES D, b. Atlantic City, N.J, Jan. 24, 31; m. 54; c. 4. ANATOMY, PHYSICAL ANTHROPOLOGY. B.A, Delaware, 58; Dr.rer.nat.(anat. & phys. anthrop), Tübingen, 67. Instr. anat, sch. med, Louisville, 67-68, asst. prof, 68-70, ophthal, 70-71; ASSOC. PROF. PATH. & ANAT, SCH. MED, IND. UNIV, 71- Nat. Inst. Health spec. res. fel. ophthal, 70-71. N.Y. Acad. Sci. Cytoarchitecture of the central nervous system; retinal damage due to white light and laser exposure. Address: Dept. of Pathology, Indiana University Medical School, Indianapolis, IN 46204.

FIX, JAMES EDWARD, b. Dallas, Tex, June 19, 26; m. 51; c. 3. SEISMOLOGY, GEOPHYSICS. B.S, Tex. A&M Univ, 48; M.S.M.E, Purdue Univ, 49. V.pres, George J. Fix Co, 49-58; proj. engr, Tex. Instruments Inc, 58-59; Geotech. Corp, 59-67; SR. RES. GEOPHYSICIST, TELEDYNE GEOTECH, 67- C.Eng, U.S.A, 44-46. AAAS; Soc. Explor. Geophys; Am. Geophys. Union; Seismol. Soc. Am. Enhancement of earthquake phases with strain and inertial seismographs; earthquake source mechanisms; seismic wave transmission characteristics; earthquake hazard reduction; theoretical instrument noise. Address: Geophysical Research Dept, Teledyne Geotech, P.O. Box 28277, Dallas, TX 75228.

FIX, JOHN DEKLE, b. Melrose Park, Ill, Dec. 23, 41; m. 67; c. 1. ASTROPHYSICS. B.S, Purdue Univ, 63; M.A, Ind. Univ, Bloomington, 67, Ph.D. (astrophys), 69. ASST. PROF. ASTRON, UNIV IOWA, 69- Am. Geophys. Union vis. Scientist, 70- Am. Astron. Soc; Royal Astron. Soc. Particulate matter in stellar atmospheres and interstellar space; physical properties and observations of planetary surfaces. Address: Dept. of Physics & Astronomy, University of Iowa, Iowa City, IA 52240.

FIX, RICHARD C(ONRAD), b. Milwaukee, Wis, Dec. 26, 30; m. 58; c. 3. NUCLEAR CHEMISTRY. B.S, Wisconsin, 52; Ph.D.(chem), Mass. Inst. Tech, 56. Sr. Scientist, Tracerlab, Inc, 56-57; asst. tech. dir, Controls for Radiation, Inc, 57-63, v.pres. & dir. res. & develop, 63-65; sr. staff scientist, Tracerlab Div, Lab. for Electronics, Inc, 65-69; MGR. TECH. SERV. DEPT, ICN/TRACERLAB, WALTHAM, 69- Radiation Res. Soc; Am. Nuclear Soc; Health Physics Soc. Radiation physics; nuclear and medical instrumentation; dosimetry; environmental radioactivity; site surveys. Address: 484 Hosmer St, Marlboro, MA 01752.

FIXMAN, MARSHALL, b. St. Louis, Mo, Sept. 21, 30; m. 59; c. 3. PHYSICAL CHEMISTRY. Ph.D.(chem), Mass. Inst. Technol, 53. Jewett fel. phys. chem, Yale, 53-54; instr. CHEM, Harvard, 56-59; sr. fel, Mellon Inst, 59-61; PROF, Oregon, 61-65; YALE, 65- Arthur & Ruth Sloan vis. prof. chem,

Harvard, 65. U.S.A, 54-56. Am. Chem. Soc; Am. Phys. Soc. Theoretical chemistry; statistical mechanics. Address: Dept. of Chemistry, Yale University, New Haven, CT 06520.

FIXOTT, HENRY C(LINE), b. Portland, Ore, Aug. 28, 14; m. 40; c. 4. ROENTGENOLOGY. D.M.D, Univ. Ore, 38. Clin. instr. dent, sch. med, UNIV. ORE, 39-46, clin. assoc, SCH. DENT, 46-52, assoc. prof. ORAL ROENTGENOL, 52-57, PROF, 57-, HEAD DEPT, 52-, CLIN. ASSOC, SCH. MED, 46- Consult, Vet. Admin, Ore. & Barne's Hosps, 46-; consult. & chief dent. serv, Shriner's Hosp. for Crippled Children, 58-; consult, U.S. Army Madigan Gen. Hosp, 52-; Fulbright lectr, dept. of oral radiol, sch. dent, Univ. Tehran, 70-71. U.S.A, 41-45, Res, 38-41, 45-, Col. Am. Dent. Asn; fel. Am. Col. Dent; fel. Am. Acad. Dent. Radiol.(pres, 54); Am. Acad. Oral Path; Int. Acad. Maxillofacial Radiol. Radiation dosage; effects of radiation on color film; section roentgenology; oral roentgenology. Address: Dept. of Oral Roentgenology, University of Oregon Dental School, 611 S.W. Campus Dr, Portland, OR 97201.

FJARLIE, EARL J, b. Nanaimo, B.C, Apr. 10, 32; m. 59; c. 3. ATMOSPHERIC PHYSICS. B.A.Sc, British Columbia, 55, M.A.Sc, 58; Ph.D.(physics), Saskatchewan, 65. Defence serv. tech. off, Defence Res. Bd-Defence Res. Estab. Valcartier, 55, defence serv. sci. off, 57-59; MEM. SCI. STAFF, RCA LTD, 65- Part-time lectr. physics, Sir George Williams, 66- R.C.A.F, 50-57, Flying Off. Optical Soc. Am; Am. Asn. Physics Teachers; Can. Asn. Physicists; Eng. Inst. Can. Optoelectronic systems; infrared spectroscopy; radiometry. Address: 155 Braeside, Dollard Des Ormeaux 970, Que, Can.

FJELDBO, GUNNAR, b. Oslo, Norway, Mar. 24, 36; U.S. citizen; m. 62. ELECTRICAL ENGINEERING. Sivilingeniør, Norweg. Inst. Technol, 61; Ph.D.(elec. eng), Stanford Univ, 64. Res. assoc, Stanford Electronics Lab, 64-69; MEM. TECH. STAFF, JET PROPULSION LAB, 69- Partic, Mariner radio occultation exp, missions to Mars, 65, 69, Venus, 67. Am. Astron. Soc; Am. Geophys. Union; Inst. Elec. & Electronics Eng; Union Radio Sci. Int. Computer science; radio propagation and communication; radar astronomy; planetary atmospheres and surfaces. Address: Jet Propulsion Lab, 4800 Oak Grove Dr, Pasadena, CA 91103.

FJERDINGSTAD, E(JNAR) J(ULES), b. Copenhagen, Denmark, Jan. 28, 37; m. 63; c. 2. ZOOLOGY, NEUROCHEMISTRY. Mag. sci.(zool), Copenhagen, 62. Asst. prof. gen. zool, Copenhagen, 62-67; res. assoc. biochem, Duke, 67-68; anesthesiol, Baylor Col. Med, 68-69; ASST. PROF. BIOCHEM, UNIV. TENN, MEMPHIS, 69- Partic, inst. gen. biol, Copenhagen Univ, 71. AAAS; Scand. Soc. Cell Res; Biol. Soc. Copenhagen; Danish Soc. Natural Hist. Ultrastructural cytology of invertebrates; biochemical basis of learning and memory as studied through the phenomenon of chemical transfer of learned information. Address: Dept. of Biochemistry, University of Tennessee Medical Units, Memphis, TN 38103.

FLACCUS, EDWARD, b. Lansdowne, Pa, Feb. 4, 21; m. 47; c. 3. BOTANY, PLANT ECOLOGY. B.S, Haverford Col, 42; M.S, New Hampshire, 52; Nat. Sci. Found. fel, Duke, 57-58, Ph.D.(bot), 59. Teacher, private sch, 48-50, 51-55; asst. zool, New Hampshire, 50-51; asst. bot, Duke, 55-57, asst. prof, Univ. Minn, Duluth, 58-62, assoc. prof, 63-68; vis. prof, State Univ. N.Y. Stony Brook, 68-69; PROF. BIOL. SCI, BENNINGTON COL, 69- Vis. scientist, Brookhaven Nat. Lab, 68-69. Civilian Pub. Serv, 42-46. AAAS; Ecol. Soc. Am; Bot. Soc. Am; Am. Inst. Biol. Sci. Plant successions; forest ecology. Address: Science Division, Bennington College, Bennington, VT 05201.

FLACH, FREDERIC F(RANCIS), b. N.Y.C, Jan. 25, 27; m. 51; c. 4. PSYCHIATRY. B.A, St. Peters Col, 47; M.D, Cornell, 51. Intern, second med. div, Bellevue Hosp, 51-52, asst. res. psychiatrist, PAYNE WHITNEY CLIN, 53-56, res. psychiatrist, 56-58, asst. attend. psychiatrist, 58-61, assoc. attend. psychiatrist, 61-65, ATTEND. PSYCHIATRIST, 65-; ASSOC. PROF. CLIN. PSYCHIAT, MED. COL, CORNELL UNIV, 62-, asst. prof, 58-62. Asst. attend. psychiatrist, St. Vincent's Hosp, 58- U.S.N.R, 45-46, Lt.(jg). Am. Pub. Health Asn; fel. Am. Psychiat. Asn; Endocrin Soc; Am. Med. Asn. Direct activities of metabolic unit; electrolyte and endocrine metabolism in psychiatric disorders; integration of chemotherapy and analytic psychotherapy in clinical practice; development of programs in preventive psychiatry. Address: 420 E. 51st. St, New York, NY 10022.

FLACH, KLAUS W(ERNER), b. Kolbermoor, Bavaria, Ger, Mar. 24, 27; nat; m. 59; c. 2. SOIL SCIENCE. Dipl, Munich Tech, 50; M.S, Cornell, 54, Ph.D.(soils), 60. Asst. soils, Cornell, 53-58; SOIL SCIENTIST, SOIL SURV. LAB, SOIL CONSERV. SERV, U.S. DEPT. AGR, 58- Soil Sci. Soc. Am. Soil and soil mineralogy; thinsection techniques; clay mineralogy; soil classification and mapping. Address: Soil Survey Lab, Soil Conservation Service, P.O. Box 672, Riverside, CA 92502.

FLACK, J(OHN) E(RNEST), b. Ft. Collins, Colo, Jan. 28, 29; m. 51; c. 3. CIVIL ENGINEERING, WATER RESOURCES. B.Sc, Colo. State, 50; M.Sc, Iowa, 54; Ford Found. fel, Stanford, 64, Ph.D.(civil eng), 65. Asst. prof. civil eng, Univ. Colo, Boulder, 57-61, assoc. prof, 61-68; vis. prof. eng. & econ. planning, water resources ctr, Ga. Inst. Technol, 68-69; PROF. CIVIL ENG, UNIV. COLO, BOULDER, 69- Consult, Colo. Water Conserv. Bd, 57; City of Boulder, 60-62; Nat. Sci. Found. faculty fel, 62-63; dir, Ctr. Urban Eng. Studies, 69-; trustee, Rocky Mt. Hydraul. Lab; del, Univs. Coun. Water Resources. AAAS; Am. Soc. Eng. Educ; Am. Soc. Civil Eng; Am. Geophys. Union; Am. Water Resources Asn. Hydrology; fluid mechanics; water resources. Address: Dept. of Civil & Environmental Engineering, University of Colorado, Boulder, CO 80302.

FLACKE, WERNER E(RNET), b. Recke, Westfalen, Ger, July 14, 24; nat; m. 57; c. 3. PHARMACOLOGY. M.D, Dusseldorf, Ger, 50. Asst. pharmacol, Dusseldorf, Ger, 51-52; path, Koblenz, Rhein, 52-53; resident internal med, St. Elisabeth Hosp, Essen, Ruhr, 53-54; fel. PHARMACOL, Harvard Med. Sch, 54, instr, 55-57, assoc, 57-62, asst. prof, 62-69, assoc. prof, 69-70; PROF. & CHMN. DEPT, UNIV. ARK, LITTLE ROCK, 70- AAAS; Am. Soc. Pharmacol. & Exp. Therapeut; Asn. Advan. Med. Instrumentation; Biophys. Soc; Ger. Pharmacol. Soc. Pharmacology of excitable membranes; circulation; respiration; skeletal muscle. Address: Dept. of Pharmacology, University of Arkansas Medical Center, Little Rock, AR 72201.

FLADOS, NORMAN D, b. Nocona, Tex, Jan. 2, 23; m. 46; c. 3. PLANT PATHOLOGY. B.S, Texas, 51, M.Ed, 52; B.S, Agr. & Mech. Col, Texas, 54, Ph.D.(plant path), 58. Asst, Texas Agr. Exp. Sta, 54-58; assoc. prof. biol, Sam Houston State Teachers Col, 58-66; prof. & dir. dept, Midwestern Col, 66-71; CONSULT, GOV. COMT. COMPREHENSIVE HEALTH PLANNING, 71- U.S.N, 42-46, Lt. Am. Phytopath. Soc. Soil-borne plant diseases. Address: 1612 Redbud, McAllen, TX 78501.

FLAGG, JOHN F(ERARD), b. Wellsville, N.Y, Dec. 30, 14; m. 40; c. 2. ANALYTICAL CHEMISTRY. B.S, Rochester, 36; A.M, Princeton, 37, McCay fel, 38-39, Ph.D.(chem), 39. Instr. chem, Rochester, 39-43, asst. prof, 43-46; res. assoc, Gen. Elec. Co, 46-52, mgr. chem. & chem. eng, Knolls Atomic Power Lab, 52-56, proj. analyst, res. lab, 56-59, mgr. materials eng. lab, 59-61; dir. res, CENT. RES. DIV, AM. CYANAMID CO, 61-64, DIR. & GEN. MGR, 64- With Off. Sci. Res. & Develop, 44; Atomic Energy Comn. Am. Chem. Soc; Am. Nuclear Soc; The Chem. Soc. Application of radioactivity in inorganic and analytical chemistry; use of organic analytical reagents; processing of nuclear fuels; atomic power and tracer studies; analysis and evaluation of research trends; materials development. Address: Central Research Division, American Cyanamid Co, 1937 W. Main St, Stamford, CT 06902.

FLAGG, RAYMOND O(SBOURN), b. Martinsburg, W.Va, Jan. 31, 33; m. 56; c. 3. BIOLOGY. B.A, Shepherd Col, 57; Ph.D.(biol), Virginia, 61. Teacher, high sch, Md, 57; res. assoc. biol, Univ. Virginia, 61-62; HEAD BOT, CAROLINA BIOL. SUPPLY CO, 62- U.S.A, 52-55. AAAS; Bot. Soc. Am; Int. Asn. Plant Taxon. Plant cytogenetics and bisystematics; nutrition of Drosophila. Address: Carolina Biological Supply Co, Burlington; NC 27215.

FLAGLE, CHARLES D(ENHARD), b. Scottdale, Pa, Apr. 26, 19; m. 46, 65; c. 4. OPERATIONS RESEARCH. B.E, Hopkins, 40, M.Sc, 54, Dr.Eng, 55. Design engr. mech. eng, Westinghouse Elec. Corp, 40-46; res. assoc. fluid mech, inst. co-op. res, JOHNS HOPKINS UNIV, 50-53, mem. staff, opers. res. off, 53-55, consult, 55-62, DIR. OPERS. RES, HOSP, 56-, PROF, DEPT. OPERS. RES. & INDUST. ENG, SCH. ENG. SCI, 61-, PROF. PUB. HEALTH ADMIN, 63- Mem, Nat. Adv. Comt. Epidemiol. & Biometry, 63-66. Consult, U.S. Pub. Health Serv, 58-; New York Health Dept, 62-; Res. Anal. Corp, 62-; Calif. Dept. Pub. Health, 63-; Vet. Admin; Community Systs. Found. Opers. Res. Soc. Am; Inst. Mgt. Sci; Am. Pub. Health Asn. Operations research applied to health services, particularly applications of decision theory and stochastic processes. Address: Dept. of Public Health Administration, School of Hygiene & Public Health, Johns Hopkins University, Baltimore, MD 21218.

FLAHERTY, BERNARD EDWARD, b. Peru, Ind, Aug. 1, 17. PSYCHIATRY. A.B, Univ. Ind, 41, M.D, 44. Resident psychiatrist, Brentwood Hosp. Sawtelle, W. Los Angeles, U.S. Air Force, 47-49, Langley Porter Neuropsychiat. Inst, 56-57, chief. dept. psychiat, Sch. Aerospace Med, Brooks AFB, 57-60, chief prof. servs. & psychol. consult, Southeast Asia, Air Force Tachikawa, Japan, 60-62; chief aerospace med. & bioastronaut, Air Force Systs. Command, 62-65, chief prof. servs, 65-66, chief psychiat, Air Force Hosp, Andrews AFB, 66-67; private practice, adult psychiat, 67- Consult, Command & Staff Col, U.S. Air Force, 57-60; Fed. Aviation Admin, 68-; Civil Serv. Comn, 68-; Potomac Found, 69- Am. Med. Asn; Aerospace Med. Asn; Am. Col. Physicians. Criteria for psychophysiologic selection of aerospace crews; aspects of space flight. Address: 617 G St. S.W, Washington, DC 20024.

FLAHERTY, CHARLES FOSTER, JR, b. East Dennis, Mass, June 25, 37; m. 64; c. 2. PSYCHOLOGY. B.A, Northeastern, 64; M.A, Wisconsin, 67, Ph.D, 68. ASST. PROF. PSYCHOL, RUTGERS UNIV, 68- U.S.A.F, 55-59. Am. Psychol. Asn. Relationship between Pavlovian and instrumental learning; effects of context on conditioned incentive; problems of stimulus control; brain mechanisms involved in motivation and learning. Address: Dept. of Psychology, Rutgers University, New Brunswick, NJ 08903.

FLAHERTY, FRANCIS JOSEPH, b. Chicago, Ill, July 26, 35; m. 62; c. 2. GEOMETRY. B.A, Wisconsin, Madison, 56; M.S, Notre Dame, 59; Ph.D.(math), California, Berkeley, 65. Mathematician, Rand Corp, 56-57; asst. prof. MATH, San Francisco State Col, 59-65; Southern California, 65-67; ORE. STATE UNIV, 67-70, ASSOC. PROF, 70- Vis. prof, math. inst, Univ. Bonn, 71-72. Am. Math. Soc. Differential and integral geometry; differential topology. Address: Dept. of Mathematics, Oregon State University, Corvallis, OR 97331.

FLAHERTY, FRANKLIN TRIMBY, JR, b. Phila, Pa, Aug. 7, 34; m. 56; c. 2. MECHANICAL ENGINEERING, APPLIED MATHEMATICS. B.S, Mass. Inst. Technol, 56, M.S, 58; Eng.Sc.D, N.Y. Univ, 63. Res. asst, dynamic anal. & control labs, Mass. Inst. Technol, 56-58; mem. tech. staff, BELL TEL. LABS, 58-65, supvr. eng. mech. group, 65-69, HEAD POWER SYSTS. PHYS. DESIGN DEPT, 69- Dynamic behavior of discrete and continuous mechanical systems; communications equipment design. Address: Division 24, Bell Telephone Labs, Whippany Rd, Whippany, NJ 07981.

FLAIM, FRANCIS RICHARD, b. Sublet, Wyo, Nov. 2, 13; m. 44; c. 2. ZOOLOGY, BIOLOGY. B.A, Utah, 36, fel, 35-38, M.A, 38; Ph.D, Stanford, 56. Asst. zool, Utah, 34-35; instr, UNIV. SANTA CLARA, 38-44; asst. prof. ZOOL. & BIOL, 46-52, assoc. prof, 52-56, PROF, 56-, chmn. dept. biol, 60-66. Food technologist, Food Mach. Corp, Calif, 44-46. AAAS; Am. Soc. Mammal. Anatomy of muskrat; problems in comparative anatomy. Address: Dept. of Biology, University of Santa Clara, Santa Clara, CA 95053.

FLAJSMAN, FRANJO, b. Vidovec, Yugoslavia, Nov. 14, 28; m. 54. POLYMER CHEMISTRY. Dipl. chem, Zagreb, 52, Ph.D.(chem), 65. Res. asst. phys. chem, faculty sci, Univ. Zagreb, 54-56; res. assoc, Chem. Indust, 56-60; head phys. chem. dept, Org. Chem. Indust, 60-67; fel, Clarkson Tech, 67-68; RES. CHEMIST, TECH. CTR, AM. CEMENT CORP, 68- Stability of inorganic colloid suspensions; polymerization of caprolactam fractionation of polymers; characterization and mechanical testing of polymers; the effect of extrusion conditions on crystallinity; degradation of polymers in the atmosphere of air pollutants; polymer-cement composites. Address: Technical Center, American Cement Corp, 1550 Castellano Rd, Riverside, CA 92502.

FLAKE, J(OHN) C, b. Goliad, Texas, Mar. 13, 14; m. 42. DAIRY SCIENCE. B.S.A, Tennessee, 36; M.S, Purdue, 37; Ph.D.(dairy indust), Wisconsin, 40. Asst. dir. SANIT. STANDARDS, EVAPORATED MILK ASN, 40-55, DIR, 55- With U.S. Pub. Health Serv, 44-45. Am. Dairy Sci. Asn. Dairy bacteriology and chemistry; activated flavor in irradiated milk. Address: Evaporated Milk Association, 910 17th St. N.W, Washington, DC 20006.

FLAKS, JOEL G(EORGE), b. N.Y.C, Oct. 20, 27; m. 61; c. 2. BIOCHEMISTRY. B.A, Brooklyn Col, 50; fel, Mass. Inst. Technol, 53-55; Ph.D.(biochem), Univ. Pa, 57. Asst. instr. BIOCHEM, Univ. Pa, 51-53; instr, Mass. Inst. Technol, 55-57; SCH. MED, UNIV. PA, 58-59, assoc, 59-62, asst. prof, 62-66, ASSOC. PROF, 66- Damon Runyon Mem. Fund fel, 57-58; Nat. Found. summer fel, 58; Lalor Found. fel, summer, 60; U.S. Pub. Health Serv. career develop. award, 61-70; consult, microbial chem. study sect, Nat. Insts. Health, U.S. Pub. Health Serv, 69- U.S.N, 45-47. AAAS; Am. Chem. Soc; Am. Soc. Biol. Chem; Am. Soc. Microbiol.(ed, Antimicrobial Agents & Chemother, 71-); Genetics Soc. Am. Purine and pyrimidine biosynthesis and metabolism; microbial metabolism and alterations induced by bacteriophage infection; antimetabolite action; ribosome structure, function and genetics. Address: Dept. of Biochemistry, School of Medicine, University of Pennsylvania, Philadelphia, PA 19104.

FLAMBOE, EUGENE EARL, b. Davenport, Iowa, Dec. 1, 24; m. 53; c. 2. PHYSIOLOGY. B.S, Detroit, 51, M.S, 53; Ph.D.(physiol), Mich. State, 58. Assoc. pharmacologist, Eli Lilly & Co, 53-54; from instr. to assoc. prof. physiol, Colo. State Univ, 58-64; assoc. prof. biol, Univ. Detroit, 64-67, prof, 67-68, chmn. dept, 66-68; sr. staff physiologist, Nat. Hwy. Safety Bur, U.S. DEPT. TRANSPORTATION, 68, acting chief ACCIDENT INVEST. SYSTS. DESIGN DIV, 68-70, SR. STAFF, ACCIDENT INVEST. DIV, NAT. HWY. TRAFFIC SAFETY ADMIN, 70- Consult, Gen. Motors Styling Staff, Mich, 65-68. Leo E. Buss Mem. Award Prominence in Premed. & Dent. Educ, 66. Hosp.C, U.S.N, 43-46. Am. Physiol. Soc. Thyroid physiology; effects of stress on body; accident injury causation; human tolerance to deceleration; human factors in driving. Address: Room 5125F, Accident Investigation Division, National Highway Traffic Safety Administration, 400 Seventh St. S.W, Washington, DC 20590.

FLAMM, WILLIAM GARY, b. Cincinnati, Ohio, Dec. 7, 35; m. 58; c. 1. BIOLOGICAL CHEMISTRY. B.S, Cincinnati, 57, M.S, 59, Nat. Insts. Health fel, 59-62, Ph.D.(enzym), 62. Nat. Insts. Health res. fel. nucleic acid biosynthesis, div. biol, Calif. Inst. Tech, 62-64; res. chemist, carcinogenesis studies br, Nat. Cancer Inst, 64-68; RES. CHEMIST CELL BIOL, DIV. ENVIRON. HEALTH SCI, NAT. ENVIRON. HEALTH SCI. CTR, 68- Sr. res. fel, Univ. Edinburgh, 66-67. AAAS; Am. Chem. Soc; Biophys. Soc; Brit. Biochem. Soc. Structure and synthesis of nucleic acids and nucleoproteins. Address: Division of Environment Health Science, National Environmental Health Sciences Center, P.O. Box 12233, Research Triangle Park, NC 27709.

FLAMMER, CARSON, b. Kingston, Ont, Can, Oct. 30, 19; U.S. citizen; m. 45; c. 4. PHYSICS. B.S, Queen's (Ont), 41; M.S, Harvard, 46, Ph.D.(applied physics), 49. Design engr, Westinghouse Elec. & Mfg. Co, 41; asst, electron. res. lab, Harvard, 48-49; MGR. MATH. PHYSICS DEPT, STANFORD RES. INST, 49- Lectr, Stanford, 59. Can. Army, 42-45, Capt. Am. Phys. Soc; Am. Asn. Physics Teachers; Fedn. Am. Sci. Electromagnetic theory; theory of solid state; special functions in mathematical physics; plasma physics. Address: Stanford Research Institute, Menlo Park, CA 94025.

FLAMMER, GORDON H(ANS), b. St. Johns, Ariz, June 9, 26; m. 49; c. 6. CIVIL ENGINEERING. B.S, Utah State, 52, M.S, 53; Sigma Tau fel. & Ph.D.(civil eng), Minnesota, 58. Asst, Utah State, 52-53; Minnesota, 53-55, instr. CIVIL ENG, 55-58; asst. prof, UTAH STATE UNIV, 58-59, assoc. prof, 59-64, PROF, 64- Prof, Asian Inst. Technol, 66-67, acad. dean, 67-68; vis. prof, Stanford Univ, 70-71. U.S.N, 44-46. Am. Soc. Civil Eng; Am. Soc. Eng. Educ. Fluid mechanics; hydrodynamics; hydrology; hydraulic models; education research and methodology. Address: Dept. of Civil Engineering, Utah State University, Logan, UT 84321.

FLANAGAN, CARROLL EDWARD, b. Price Co, Wis, Dec. 18, 11; m. 39; c. 2. MATHEMATICS. Ed.B, Wis. State Univ, Oshkosh, 33; Ph.M, Wisconsin, 43, Ph.D.(math. ed, statist), 60. Prin, Waukau State Graded sch, Wis, 33-36, teacher, high sch, 36-42; MATH, Wis. State Univ, Superior, 42-44; WIS. STATE UNIV, WHITEWATER, 46-50, assoc. prof, 51-60, PROF, 60-, COORDINATOR SEC. ED, 63-, dir. lib. arts & sec. ed, 50-63. Consult, math. curriculum, 38-; modern math. elem. schs, 62-; tech. consult. math, North. Nigeria Teacher Educ. Proj, 65-68. AAAS; Am. Math. Soc; Math. Asn. Am. Mathematics curriculum; algebra. Address: Dept. of Mathematics, Wisconsin State University, Whitewater, WI 53190.

FLANAGAN, C(HARLES) LARKIN, b. Chicago, Ill, July 3, 26; m. 57; c. 1. INTERNAL MEDICINE. Ph.B, Chicago, 47, M.D, 51. Resident med, Chicago, 52-55; instr. MED, NORTHWEST. UNIV, 56-57, assoc, 57-59, asst. prof, 59-62, ASSOC. PROF, 62- Private practice, 62-; assoc. attend. physician, Chicago Wesley Mem. Hosp; dir. Army Med. res. proj, Ill, 54-56. Med. consult. to pres, Chicago Bd. Health, 62- U.S.N, 44-46. AAAS; Am. Fedn. Clin. Res. Renal tubular function. Address: 720 N. Michigan Ave, Chicago, IL 60611.

FLANAGAN, JAMES, O.F.M, b. Bloomfield, N.J, Mar. 15, 28. PHYSICAL CHEMISTRY. B.A, St. Bonaventure, 50; B.S, St. Bernardine of Siena Col, 56; Ph.D.(chem), Notre Dame, 64. Instr, Timon High Sch, 56-57; St. Joseph Sem, 57-59; asst. prof. CHEM, ST. BERNARDINE OF SIENA COL, 63-68, ASSOC. PROF, 68-, CHMN. SCI. DIV, 66-, asst. dean, 65-66. Am. Chem. Soc; Am. Phys. Soc. Microwave spectroscopy; phosphorescence decay; lifetimes of α-diketones. Address: St. Bernardine of Siena College, Loudonville, NY 12211.

FLANAGAN, JAMES L(OTON), b. Greenwood, Miss, Aug. 26, 25. ELECTRICAL ENGINEERING. B.S, Miss. State, 48; S.M, Mass. Inst. Tech, 50, Rockefeller Found. fel, 52-53, Sc.D.(elec. eng), 55. Res. engr, acoustics lab, Mass. Inst. Tech, 48-50, 53-54; asst. prof. elec. eng, Miss. State, 50-52; electronic scientist, U.S. Air Force Cambridge Res. Center, 54-57; mem. tech. staff, BELL TEL. LABS, 57-61, HEAD speech & auditory res. dept, 61-67, ACOUST. RES. DEPT, 67- U.S.A.F, 44-46, Res, 46-, 1st Lt. Fel. Acoust. Soc. Am; fel. Inst. Elec. & Electronics Eng. Digital communications; optimal coding of speech signals; acoustic theory of speech production; psychoacoustics of speech perception; digital filtering; computer simulation. Address: Acoustics Research Dept, Bell Telephone Labs, Murray Hill, NJ 07974.

FLANAGAN, JOHN C(LEMANS), Psychol, see 12th ed, Soc. & Behav. Vols.

FLANAGAN, JOHN V(ERNON), b. Miamisburg, Ohio, Dec. 28, 16; m. 40; c. 2. ORGANIC CHEMISTRY. B.S, Otterbein Col, 38; Ph.D.(org. chem), Ohio State, 43. Asst. chem, Ohio State, 39-43, res. chemist, Nat. Defense Res. Comt. contract, 43; metall. lab, Chicago, 43-45; Manhattan Proj, Monsanto Chem. Co, 45-46; E.I. DU PONT DE NEMOURS & CO, INC, N.Y, 46-49, res. supvr, 49-52, sr. process develop. supvr, 52-64, process supt, Kinston, N.C, 65-66; mfg. asst, for. Dacron plants, 66-69, STAFF ASST. TO DIR. DACRON MFG, 69- Am. Chem. Soc. Fluorination of organic compounds; effects of radiation on organic compounds; synthetic fibers; process development for Dacron polyester fiber. Address: E.I. du Pont de Nemours & Co, Inc, Wilmington, DE 19898.

FLANAGAN, JOSEPH E(DWARD), b. Chicago, Ill, Mar. 6, 28; m. 47; c. 2. MATHEMATICS. B.S, Univ. Ill, 49, M.S, 50, fel, 52-53, Ph.D.(math), 53. Asst. math, Univ. Ill, 49-52; asst. prof, Carnegie Inst. Technol, 53-55; appl. scientist, IBM CORP, 56-57, MGR. MATH, SYSTS. RES. INST, 58- U.S.N.R, 45. Am. Math. Soc; Inst. Math. Statist. Stochastic processes; communication theory; computers. Address: Dept. of Mathematics, Systems Research Institute, IBM Corp, 787 United Nations Plaza, New York, NY 10017.

FLANAGAN, PAT W(AYNE) K(EITH), b. Camargo, Ill, June 20, 31; m. 64; c. 2. PHYSICAL & ORGANIC CHEMISTRY. B.S, Miami (Ohio), 53; Nat. Sci. Found. fel, Ohio State, 53-56, Ph.D.(chem), 57. Res. chemist, CONTINENTAL OIL CO, 57-64, RES. ASSOC, 64- Am. Chem. Soc. Nuclear magnetic resonance, mass spectrometry and electron spin resonance of organic systems. Address: Rural Route 2, Fairway Lane, Ponca City, OK 74601.

FLANAGAN, R(ALPH) C(LARENCE, b. Campbellton, N.B, Nov. 22, 43; m. 65; c. 2. MECHANICAL ENGINEERING. B.Sc, Univ. N.B, 65, John Stephens Mem. prize, 65; H.R. McMillan fel, Univ. B.C, 66-69, Ph.D.(space dynamics), 69. Proj. engr, Can. Int. Paper Co, 65-66; lab. asst. MECH. ENG, Univ. B.C, 67-69; ASST. PROF, UNIV. TORONTO, 69- Can. Soc. Mech. Eng; Eng. Inst. Can. Passive stabilization and attitude control of spacecraft; space dynamics; classical mechanics; numerical and non-linear analysis; vibrations. Address: Dept. of Mechanical Engineering, University of Toronto, Toronto 5, Ont, Can.

FLANAGAN, ROBERT JOSEPH, b. Alexandria, Minn, Aug. 10, 24; m. 47; c. 3. MATHEMATICS. B.S, New Mexico, 49. Math. analyst, Sandia Corp, 48-49, supvr. data reduction, 49-52, staff mem. systs. anal. 52-57; res. engr, DIKEWOOD CORP, 57-59, sr. res. engr, 59-64, dir, 64-69, V.PRES, 69- U.S.A.A.F, 43-46, 1st Lt. Opers. Res. Soc. Am; Am. Geophys. Union. Cost effectiveness analyses of military and civil systems. Address: 1009 Bradbury Dr. S.E, Albuquerque, NM 87106.

FLANAGAN, TED B(ENJAMIN), b. Oakland, Calif, July 11, 29; m. 55; c. 3. PHYSICAL CHEMISTRY. B.S, California, Berkeley, 51; Ph.D.(phys. chem), Washington (Seattle), 55. Res. chemist, Picatinny Arsenal, N.J, 55-57; fel. phys. chem, Queen's (Belfast), 57-59; assoc. physicist, Brookhaven Nat. Lab, 59-61; asst. prof. PHYS. CHEM, UNIV. VT, 61-64, assoc. prof, 64-68, PROF, 68- Fulbright res. scholar, Munster, 67-68; petrol. Res. Found. int. faculty award, 67-68. U.S.A, 55-57. Am. Chem. Soc; Am. Phys. Soc; Faraday Soc. Heterogeneous catalysis; electrode reactions; hydrogen in Palladium and its alloys; kinetics of the thermal decomposition of solids; diffusion in solids. Address: Dept. of Chemistry, University of Vermont, Burlington, VT 05401.

FLANAGAN, TERRY MICHAEL, b. Waterloo, Iowa, Jan. 3, 38; m. 61; c. 1. SOLID STATE PHYSICS. B.S, Santa Clara, 60; M.S, Purdue, 63, Ph.D.(physics), 66. Res. asst. radiation effects physics, Purdue, 60-66; STAFF MEM, GULF ENERGY & ENVIRON. SYSTS. CO, 66- AAAS; Am. Phys. Soc. Radiation effects in semiconductors; ionization photoconductivity in insulators and semiconducting glasses. Address: 3176 Bunche Ave, San Diego, CA 92122.

FLANAGAN, T(HEODORE) R(OSS), b. New York, N.Y, May 9, 20; m. 43; c. 1. AGRONOMY. B.S, Rutgers, 48; M.S, Pa. State Col, 50, Ph.D, 51. Plant mgr. & field agronomist, Grange League Fedn, 51-52; ASST. PROF. PLANT & SOIL SCI. & ASST. AGRONOMIST, UNIV. VT, 53- U.S.A, 44-46. AAAS; Weed Sci. Soc. Am; Am. Soc. Agron. Cold resistance of Ladino clover; development and adaptation of birdsfoot trefoil; herbicides; weed control-extension; environmental pollution; ecology; natural resources. Address: Dept. of Plant & Soil Science, University of Vermont, Burlington, VT 05401.

FLANAGAN, THOMAS D(ONALD), b. Providence, R.I, Jan. 6, 35; m. 55; c. 4. VIROLOGY, IMMUNOLOGY. A.B, Rhode Island, 57, M.S, 62; Ph.D.(virol), State Univ. N.Y. Buffalo, 65. Chemist, U.S. Rubber Co, 56-60; res. asst, dept. animal pathol, Rhode Island, 60-62; fel, dept. bacteriol. & immunol, STATE UNIV. N.Y. BUFFALO, 65-66, instr. MICROBIOL, 66-68, ASST. PROF, 68- U.S.A.R, 54-56. Am. Soc. Microbiol; Tissue Culture Asn. Biology of myxoviruses; cellular response to virus infection. Address: Dept. of Microbiology, State University of New York at Buffalo Medical School, Buffalo, NY 14214.

FLANAGAN, THOMAS L(EO), b. Phila, Pa, Sept. 25, 16; m. 47; c. 9. CHEMICAL ENGINEERING. Dipl, Drexel, 43. Technician anal. chem, Rohm & Haas Co, 35-38, jr. chemist, 38-41, chemist anal. & textile chem, 41-47; jr. scientist, anal. chem, SMITH KLINE & FRENCH LABS, 48, biochemist, 48-50, sr. scientist, 50-56, group leader biochem. res, 56-62, asst. sect. head biochem. serv, 62-67, DRUG METABOLISM SECT, 63-66, sect. head, 66-67, ASSOC. DIR. BIOCHEM, 67- Am. Chem. Soc; N.Y. Acad. Sci. Drug metabolism, biochemical methods development; isotope tracer studies; instrumental methodology. Address: Drug Metabolism Section, Smith Kline & French Labs, 1500 Spring Garden St, Philadelphia, PA 19101.

FLANAGAN, WILLIAM F(RANCIS), b. Cambridge, Mass, Apr. 27, 27; m. 58; c. 5. PHYSICAL METALLURGY. S.B, Mass. Inst. Tech, 51, S.M, 53, Sc.D.(metall), 59. Asst, Mass. Inst. Tech, 51-53, 55-59, instr. phys. metall, 53-55; asst. prof. metall. eng, Univ. Wash, 59-66; sr. res. physicist, Gen. Motors Res. Lab, 66-68; ASSOC. PROF. MAT. SCI. & ENG, VANDERBILT UNIV, 68- U.S.N.R, 45-46. Am. Soc. Metals; Am. Inst. Mining, Metall. & Petrol. Eng. Materials engineering embracing solid state physics; deformation mechanisms; physics of solids. Address: Dept. of Materials Science & Engineering, Vanderbilt University, Nashville, TN 37203.

FLANDERS, C(LIFFORD) A(UTEN), b. Rutherford, N.J, May 3, 11; m. 38; c. 4. ANALYTICAL CHEMISTRY. B.S, Wagner Col, 33; M.A, Columbia, 34; Ph.D.(agr. biochem), West Virginia, 51. Asst. chem, Wagner Col, 31-33, asst. instr, 35-36; instr, N.C. State Col, 36-37, 38-40; Louisville, 40-45; asst. biochemist, exp. sta, West Virginia, 45-51; dir. chem. prods, Fisher Sci. Co, 51-54, chem. coordinator, 54-63, tech. dir, 63-66; ASSOC. PROF. CHEM, Pace Col, 66-69; WILLIAM PATERSON COL. N.J, 69- AAAS; Am. Chem. Soc; Am. Inst. Chem. Analytical chemistry. Address: 81 Beechwood Dr, Wayne, NJ 07470.

FLANDERS, HARLEY, b. Chicago, Ill, Sept. 13, 25; m. 46; c. 2. MATHEMATICS. B.S, Chicago, 46, M.S, 47, Ph.D.(math), 49; Univ. Col, London, 65-66. Bateman fel. MATH, Calif. Inst. Tech, 49-51; instr, California, 51-52, asst. prof, 53-58, assoc. prof, 58-60; PROF, Purdue Univ, 60-70; TEL-AVIV UNIV, 70- Nat. Sci. Found. fel, Cambridge, 57-58; ed-in-chief, Am. Math. Monthly, 68- Lester Ford Award, 69. AAAS; Am. Math. Soc; Math. Asn. Am.(v.pres, 59-61); London Math. Soc. Algebra; differential geometry. Address: Dept. of Mathematics, Tel-Aviv University, Ramat-Aviv, Israel.

FLANDERS, ROBERT B(ERNARD), b. Boston, Mass, Nov. 12, 15; m. 41; c. 2. NUCLEAR ENGINEERING. B.S, Tufts, 38; S.M, Mass. Inst. Technol, 58. Asst. qual. anal, Tufts, 36-38; asst. fire assayer, East. Smelting & Ref. Co, 38-39; asst. chem. engr, Whitlock Coil Pipe Co, 39-40; plant engr, Kelbar Powder Co, 40; asst. chem. engr, Nat. Fireworks Co, Am. Fireworks Co, 40-45; chem. engr, Process Eng. Co, 45-46; acting chief engr, M & C Nuclear, Inc. Div, Tex. Instruments, Inc, 57-60, res. staff proj. mgr, 60-67; NUCLEAR ENGR, STONE & WEBSTER ENG. CORP, 67- Am. Nuclear Soc; Am. Inst. Chem. Eng. Nuclear materials research and development; chemical engineering; metallurgy; ceramics; electrochemistry; radiochemistry; nuclear safety; nuclear power plant engineering; licensing; economic evaluation; engineered safeguards. Address: Stone & Webster Engineering Corp, 225 Franklin St, Boston, MA 02110.

FLANDRO, GARY A, b. Salt Lake City, Utah, Mar. 30, 34; m. 61; c. 1. MECHANICAL & AERONAUTICAL ENGINEERING. B.S, Utah, 57; M.S, Calif. Inst. Tech, 60, Ph.D.(aeronaut), 67. Sci. teacher, Liahona Col, Tonga, S.Pac, 59; res. engr, Jet Propulsion Lab, Calif. Inst. Tech, 60; sr. proj. engr, Sperry Utah Co, 60-61; instr. mech. eng, Utah, 61-63; teaching asst. aeronaut, Calif. Inst. Tech, 63-64, sr. res. engr, Jet Propulsion Lab, 64-66, mem. tech. staff, 66-67; ASSOC. PROF. MECH. ENG, UNIV. UTAH, 67- Am. Inst. Aeronaut. & Astronaut. Acoustic combustion instability and internal ballistics of rocket motors; astrodynamics; low thrust trajectory and mission analysis for interplanetary space missions. Address: Dept. of Mechanical Engineering, University of Utah, Salt Lake City, UT 84112.

FLANGAS, ARTHUR L(EONIDAS), b. Ely, Nev, June 20, 28. PLANT PATHOLOGY. B.S, Utah, 50; M.S, Wisconsin, 55, Ph.D.(plant path), 58. Asst, UNIV. WIS, MADISON, 54-57, proj. assoc, 58-64, MEM. STAFF, 64- Nat. Insts. Health for. travel fel, 62; vis. scientist, molecular anat. prog, Oak Ridge Nat. Lab, 67, 68. Del, Int. Bot. Cong, Montreal, 59, Edinburgh, 64. AAAS; Am. Phytopath. Soc; Am. Soc. Neurochem. Obligate parasitism; genetics of pathogenicity and specificity; fractionation of brain tissue by zonal centrifugation; neuron and glia separations; RNA and protein metabolism of brain. Address: Neuroscience Unit, Primate Research Center, University of Wisconsin, Madison, WI 53706.

FLANIGAN, ALAN E(VERETT), b. Hartford, Conn, Nov. 16, 11; m. 41; c. 3. PHYSICAL METALLURGY. A.B, Princeton, 34; M.S, California, 40, Ph.D.(metall), 47. Instr. mech. eng, Ill. Inst. Tech, 40-42; res. assoc, California, 42-46; asst. prof. ENG, UNIV. CALIF, LOS ANGELES, 46-49, assoc. prof, 49-54, PROF, 54- Am. Soc. Metals; Am. Welding Soc; Am. Inst. Mining, Metall. & Petrol. Eng; Brit. Iron & Steel Inst. Metallurgy of arc welding, various aspects; decomposition of austenite; hydrogen in steel; mechanical metallurgy. Address: Dept. of Engineering, University of California, Los Angeles, CA 90024.

FLANIGAN, FRANCIS J, b. Jersey City, N.J, May 7, 37. MATHEMATICS. B.S, St. Peter's Col.(N.J), 60; Ph.D.(math), California, Berkeley, 66. Instr. MATH, Pennsylvania, 66-68; ASST. PROF, UNIV. CALIF, SAN DIEGO, 68- Am. Math. Soc. Deformation of associative algebras; varieties of structure constants; diophantine equations. Address: Dept. of Mathematics, University of California, San Diego, P.O. Box 109, La Jolla, CA 92037.

FLANIGAN, FRANK McCHESNEY, b. Bluefield, W.Va, June 28, 15; m. 38. MECHANICAL ENGINEERING. B.S, West Virginia, 47; M.S, Florida, 51. Supvr. calibration room, Fischer & Porter Co, Pa, 43-45; res. fel, West Virginia, 45-47; assoc. prof. MECH. ENG, UNIV. FLA, 47-66, PROF, 66-, ASSOC. RES. PROF, ENG. & INDUST. EXP. STA, 54- Summer, mem. tech. adv. staff, Eglin Field, U.S. Air Force, 55. Am. Soc. Mech. Eng; Am. Soc. Heat, Refrig. & Air-Conditioning Eng. Heat transfer related to air conditioning and heating; solar energy applied to air conditioning; performance of heat pumps. Address: Dept. of Mechanical Engineering, University of Florida, Gainesville, FL 32601.

FLANIGAN, N(ORBERT) J(AMES), b. Green Bay, Wis, Aug. 12, 18; m. 46; c. 6. ANATOMY. A.B, St. Norbert Col, 40; M.S, Iowa, 53, Ph.D, 58. Instr. biol, St. Francis Col.(Pa), 46-47; Creighton, 48-52; zool, Iowa, 52-55; anat, sch. med, Southern California, 55-58, asst. prof. BIOL, 58-63; ST. NORBERT COL, 63-65, assoc. prof, 65-68, PROF, 68-, chmn. dept, 65-70. U.S.A, 41-46. AAAS; Am. Asn. Anat; Am. Soc. Zool. Comparative and functional neuroanatomy, especially Cetacea; Cetacean behavior. Address: Division of Natural Sciences, St. Norbert College, De Pere, WI 54115.

FLANIGAN, STEVENSON, b. Lebanon, Tenn, July 2, 26; m. 48; c. 3. MEDICINE. A.B, Washington (St. Louis), 49, M.D, 53. Asst. prof. NEUROSURG, sch. med, Yale, 61-64, assoc. prof, 64-67; PROF, MED. CTR, UNIV. ARK, LITTLE ROCK, 67- Consult, Vet. Admin. Hosp, West Haven, Conn, 61-; mem, Forum Univ. Neurosurgeons, 64- U.S.A, 44-46, Sgt. Am. Asn. Neurol. Surg; Cong. Neurol. Surg; Am. Col. Surg; Asn. Res. Nerv. & Ment. Disease. Biology of glial tumor cells; electrophysiology of basal nuclear groups and the urinary bladder; clinical neurosurgery. Address: Dept. of Neurosurgery, University of Arkansas Medical Center, 4301 W. Markham St, Little Rock, AR 72201.

FLANIGAN, WILLIAM J, b. Hot Springs, Ark, June 2, 30; c. 5. MEDICINE, PHYSIOLOGY. B.S, Arkansas, 53, M.D, 55. Med. house officer, Peter Bent Brigham Hosp, 55-56; asst. resident med, sch. med, Arkansas, 56; asst, Peter Bent Brigham Hosp, 59-63; asst. prof. MED, SCH. MED, UNIV. ARK, LITTLE ROCK, 63-67, ASSOC. PROF, 67-, HEAD RENAL SECT. & PROG. DIR. COORD. RES. COUN, 63- Res. fels, Harvard Med. Sch, 59, 60-61, Peter Bent Brigham Hosp, 61-63 & Nat. Sci. Found, 60-62; Am. Heart Asn. adv. res. fel, 62-63. Med.C, 56-60, Capt. Renal physiology and tissue transplantation. Address: School of Medicine, University of Arkansas Medical Center, 4301 W. Markham St, Little Rock, AR 72201.

FLANIGEN, EDITH M(ARIE), b. Buffalo, N.Y, Jan. 28, 29. INORGANIC & PHYSICAL CHEMISTRY. B.A, D'Youville Col, 50; fel, Syracuse, 51-52, M.S, 52. Asst, Syracuse, 50-51; res. chemist, Tonawanda Res. Lab, Linde Co, 52-60, sr. res. chemist, LINDE DIV. LABS, UNION CARBIDE CORP, 60-62, res. assoc, 62-67, sr. res. assoc, 67-69, SR. RES. SCIENTIST, 69- AAAS; Mineral Soc. Am; Am. Chem. Soc. Inorganic and physical chemistry research in crystalline zeolite adsorbents; hydrothermal synthesis of mineral phases, particularly silicates; crystal growth; organo-metallic compounds. Address: Linde Division Labs, Union Carbide Corp, Tarrytown Technical Center, Saw Mill River Rd. at Route 100C, Tarrytown, NY 10591.

FLANK, WILLIAM H, b. Akron, Ohio, Jan. 7, 32; m. 56; c. 2. PHYSICAL CHEMISTRY, CATALYSIS. A.B, Temple Univ, 58; Ph.D.(chem), Univ. Del, 65. RES. CHEMIST, Houdry Labs, Air Prod. & Chem. Inc, 58-71; MOLECULAR SIEVE DEPT, UNION CARBIDE CORP, 71- Lectr, Temple Univ, 67-70. AAAS; Am. Chem. Soc; Catalysis Soc; Int. Cong. Catalysis; Int. Confedn. Thermal Anal; Clay Minerals Soc. Heterogeneous catalysis; zeolite chemistry; preparation, characterization and application of zeolites and other catalytic materials; adsorption; catalytic theory; thermanalytical, chromatographic and porosimetry techniques. Address: Molecular Sieve Dept, Union Carbide Corp, Tarrytown Technical Center, Tarrytown, NY 10591.

FLANNAGAN, GORDON N(EEL), b. Clintwood, Va, Aug. 24, 19; m. 45; c. 2. PHYSICAL CHEMISTRY. B.A, Maryville Col.(Tenn), 40; M.S, Virginia, 42, Ph.D.(phys. chem), 44. Res. chemist, E.I. DU PONT DE NEMOURS & CO, INC, PARLIN, 44-51, SR. CHEMIST, 51- Chemical thermodynamics; high temperature calorimetry; high polymers; synthetic yarns; heat capacity of cadmium oxide at high temperatures; reactor technology; radiation shielding; nuclear instrumentation; moderator chemistry; radioactivity; x-rays; silver halides; photographic chemistry. Address: 144 Buena Vista Ave, Fair Haven, NJ 07701.

FLANNELLY, WILLIAM G, b. Scranton, Pa, May 15, 31; m. 55; c. 1. STRUCTURAL DYNAMICS. B.S, Rensselaer Polytech. Inst, 54. Mech. engr, Consol. Molded Prod. Corp, Pa, 54-55; Sylvania Elec. Prod. Co, Pa, 55-56; design engr, Hamilton Standard Div, United Aircraft Corp, 56-57; stress engr, KAMAN AIRCRAFT CORP, 57-58, dynamicist, 58-59, 60-63, test engr, 59-60, asst. chief vibrations res, 63-69, STAFF RES. ENGR, 69- Structural dynamics system identification; structural vibrations analyses; antiresonant theory; vibration control instruments; applied matrix algebra. Address: 108 Hilton Dr, South Windsor, CT 06074.

FLANNERY, ANTHONY FRANCIS, b. Shenandoah, Pa, May 24, 36; m. 62; c. 2. CHEMISTRY. B.S, Pa. State, 58; M.S, Villanova, 63; Ph.D.(chem), Pennsylvania, 66. Chemist, Kiwi Polish Co. Ltd, 58-61; res. chemist, Dacron Res. & Develop. Lab, E.I. du Pont de Nemours & Co, Inc, 66-71; HEAD RES. & DEVELOP, NAT. SPINNING CO. INC, 71- Sig.C, U.S.A, 59. Am. Chem. Soc. Applied research and production of textured textile yarns. Address: National Spinning Co. Inc, Box 545, Warsaw, NC 28398.

FLANNERY, JOHN B, JR, b. Providence, R.I, Mar. 15, 41; m. 68; c. 1. PHYSICAL CHEMISTRY. B.S, St. Vincent Col, 62; univ. assistantship, Rensselaer Polytech. Inst, 62, NASA traineeship, 63-65, Ph.D.(phys. chem), 65. Chemist, Texaco Exp. Inc, Va, summers 60-63 & phys. res. lab, Dow Chem. Co, Mich, 64; assoc. scientist, RES. LABS, XEROX CORP, ROCHESTER, 65-67, scientist, 67-71, sr. scientist, 71-, MGR, OPTICAL MAT. & DEVICES RES, 71- AAAS; Am. Chem. Soc. Photochemistry; thermochemistry; liquid crystals; spectroscopy; organic synthesis; dyes and pigments; electrooptics; optical data storage; photochromism; thermochromism. Address: 1258 Wildflower Dr, Webster, NY 14580.

FLANNERY, P(ATRICK) VINCENT, b. Killaloe, Ireland, Sept. 1, 13; nat; m. 49; c. 4. PHYSICS. B.S, St. Mary's Can, 39; M.S, Fordham, 41. Instr. pub. sch, N.Y. & Ill, 39-42; Wash, 42-47; instr. PHYSICS, PURDUE UNIV, 47-52, asst. prof, 52-60, ASSOC. PROF, 60- Summers, consult. to dir, Calumet Regional Sci. Fair, Reed Col, 60, Florida State, 59; Atomic Energy Cmn, Pa. State, Purdue & Argonne Nat. Lab, 58; Washington State, 64; Southern Methodist, 64. Am. Asn. Physics Teachers. Cosmic rays. Address: Dept. of Physics, Purdue University, Hammond, IN 46323.

FLANNERY, R(OBERT) J(AMES), b. Chicago, Ill, Sept. 10, 30; m. 54; c. 2. PHYSICAL CHEMISTRY. B.S, Loyola (Ill), 52; M.S, Wayne State, 54, Chas.

F. Kettering fel. & Ph.D.(chem), 58. Asst. proj. chemist, Standard Oil Co. (Ind), 58-60, proj. chemist, 60-62, proj. mgr, Am. Oil Co, 62-69, res. assoc, 69-70; COORD. CORP. RES. PLANNING, STANDARD OIL CO.(IND), 70- Am. Chem. Soc; Electrochem. Soc; Inst. Food Technol. Catalysis; electrochemistry; semiconductors; fuel cells; process computers; single cell protein. Address: Research Dept, Standard Oil Co.(Indiana), Standard Oil Research Center, P.O. Box 400, Naperville, IL 60540.

FLANNERY, WILLIAM L(OUIS), b. Jamestown, N.Dak, Dec. 22, 22; m. 48; c. 1. BACTERIOLOGY. B.A, North Dakota, 48; Ph.D.(bacter), Maryland, 53. Asst. bact, Maryland, 50-52, bacteriologist, U.S. Dept. Agr, 53; instr. microbiol, col. med, Baylor, 53-54, asst. prof, 54-56; prof, med. sch, El Salvador, 56-59; PROF. MICROBIOL. & HEAD DEPT, UNIV. SOUTHWEST. LA, 59- Med. ed. adv, Int. Co-op. Admin, San Salvador, 56-59. Med.C, U.S.A, 43-46. AAAS; Am. Soc. Microbiol; Brit. Soc. Gen. Microbiol. Nutrition, metabolism and physiology of bacteria; halophilic bacteria; thermophiles. Address: Dept. of Microbiology, University of Southwestern Louisiana, Lafayette, LA 70501.

FLASCHEN, S(TEWARD) S(AMUEL), b. Berwyn, Ill, May 28, 26; m. 49; c. 4. INORGANIC CHEMISTRY. B.S, Illinois, 47; M.A, Miami (Ohio), 48; Off. Naval Res. fel, Pa. State, 51-52, Ph.D.(geochem), 53. Instr. geol, Miami (Ohio), 47-48; mem. chem. res. staff, Bell Tel. Labs, 52-55, group supvr. chem. res. dept, 55-59; dir. res. & develop, semiconductor prods. div, Motorola, Inc, 59-64; components res. & develop, INT. TEL. & TEL. CORP, 64-66, dep. tech. dir, 66-69, V.PRES. & DEP. GEN. TECH. DIR, 69- U.S.N.R, 44-46. AAAS; Am. Chem. Soc; Am. Ceramic Soc; Inst. Elec. & Electronics Eng; Electrochem. Soc. Solid state materials; glasses; electronic ceramics; piezoelectrics; ferroelectrics; dielectrics; semiconductors. Address: International Telephone & Telegraph Corp, 320 Park Ave, New York, NY 10022.

FLASCHKA, HERMENEGILD A(RVED), b. Cilli, Yugoslavia, June 10, 15; U.S. citizen; m. 45; c. 2. ANALYTICAL CHEMISTRY. Dr.Phil, Graz, 38. Demonstr, Graz, 37-38, asst, 48-49, privat-docent, 53; sci. co-worker, Kaiser Wilhelm Inst, Ger, 45-46; chemist, Fa Schultz, 46-47; res. dir, Fa A. Zankl-Söhne, Austria, 49-53; lectr, Graz. Tech, 53-55; head anal. dept, Nat. Res. Ctr, Egypt, 55-57; guest prof, North Carolina, 57-58; assoc. prof. CHEM, GA. INST. TECHNOL, 58-62, prof, 62-65, REGENT'S PROF, 65- Consult, Grazer Glass Works, Austria, 50-55; J.T. Baker Chem. Co, N.J, 58- Ger. Army, 38-45. Am. Chem. Soc; Am. Microchem. Soc.(co-ed, Microchem. J); Austrian Chem. Soc.(Fritz Feigl award, 53). Ethylenediaminetetraacetic acid and related titrations; organic reagents; indicator theories; complexes in analytical chemistry; complementary tristimulus colorimetry; photometric titrations. Address: Dept. of Chemistry, Georgia Institute of Technology, Atlanta, GA 30332.

FLATH, ROBERT A(RTHUR), b. St. Louis, Mo, Mar. 14, 33; m. 55; c. 1. ORGANIC CHEMISTRY. B.S, Concordia Teachers Col.(Ill), 55; B.S, Long Beach State Col, 60; Dow Chem. Co. fel, California, Berkeley, 62-63, Ph.D. (org. chem), 64. RES. CHEMIST FRUIT COMPOSITION INVEST, WEST. UTILIZATION RES. & DEVELOP. DIV, U.S. DEPT. AGR, 64- AAAS; Am. Chem. Soc; The Chem. Soc. Solvolytic reaction mechanisms and rearrangements; terpenoid and flavor chemistry. Address: 207 Colgate, Kensington, CA 94708.

FLATHAU, WILLIAM J, b. Chicago, Ill, Apr. 16, 29; m; c. 1. CIVIL & STRUCTURAL ENGINEERING. B.S, Illinois, 51; cert. struct. dynamics, Mass. Inst. Technol, summer 55; M.S, Miss. State, 71. Civil engr. & supvr, Texaco Co, La, fall 55; hydraul. engr. & proj. off, U.S. ARMY ENGR. WATERWAYS EXP. STA, 56-58, civil engr. & proj. off, 58-64, res. civil engr, struct. dynamics sect, 63-65, RES. STRUCT. ENGR, PROTECTIVE STRUCT. BR, 64- Tech. mem. protective construct. panel, Dept. of Defense, 62- U.S.A, 53-55, Sgt. Am. Soc. Civil Eng; Soc. Am. Mil. Eng; Nat. Soc. Prfnl. Eng. Response of buried structures to dynamic loads and the development of simulation equipment for conducting dynamic tests in the laboratory of structural systems. Address: 2520 Cherry St, Vicksburg, MS 39180.

FLATO, JUD B, b. Brooklyn, N.Y, Feb. 21, 40; m. 63; c. 2. PHYSICAL CHEMISTRY. B.S, Polytech. Inst. Brooklyn, 61; M.S, N.Y. Univ, 63, Ph.D. (phys. chem), 68. Sr. res. chemist, Technicon, Inc, 66-67; PRINCETON APPL. RES. CORP, 67-71, MGR. CHEM. INSTRUMENT GROUP, 71- Am. Chem. Soc; Instrument Soc. Am; Soc. Appl. Spectros. Paramagnetic resonance and absorption spectroscopy in molten salts; design and development of scientific instrumentation in electrochemistry and spectroscopy; applications of electronics to chemistry. Address: 244 Glenn Ave, Trenton, NJ 08638.

FLATT, ADRIAN E(DE), b. Frinton, Eng, Aug. 26, 21; nat; m. 55; c. 1. SURGERY. B.A, Cambridge, 42, M.B, B.Ch. & M.A, 45, M.D, 51. Instr. anat, Cambridge, 50-51; Royal Col. Surgeons Eng, 51; from asst. to prof. surg, London Hosp, London Univ, 51-53, asst. orthop, 53-56; asst. prof. ORTHOP. SURG, UNIV. IOWA, 57-61, assoc. prof, 61-66, PROF, 66- Fulbright grant, 54-55. Civilian consult. hand surg, U.S. Air Force, Aerospace Med. Hosp, Wilford Hall, Tex. Fel, Royal Col. Surgeons, 53. R.A.F, 49-50, Maj. Am. Soc. Surg. of the Hand; Am. Soc. Plastic & Reconstruct. Surg; Am. Med. Asn; fel. Am. Col. Surg. Reconstructive surgery of the congenitally deformed, diseased or injured hand, especially the biomechanical influence of disease or injury on hand function. Address: Dept. of Orthopedic Surgery, University of Iowa, Iowa City, IA 52240.

FLATT, H(ORACE) P(ERRY), b. Wichita Falls, Tex, Aug. 28, 30; m. 57; c. 2. MATHEMATICS. B.A, Rice Inst, 51, M.A, 53, Ph.D.(math), 58. Physicist, Shell Oil Co, 53; asst. math, Rice Inst, 53-54, 56-58; mathematician, Thompson-Ramo-Wooldridge, Inc, 56; sr. res. engr, math. & supvr, programing unit, Atomics Int. Div, N.Am. Aviation, Inc, 58, group leader appl. math, 58-61; from spec. rep. west. regional off. to mgr. problem anal. dept, systs. res. & develop, ctr, IBM CORP, 61-66, mgr, Wash. Sci. Ctr, 66-69, MGR, PALO ALTO SCI. CTR, 69- U.S.A, 54-56. Am. Math. Soc; Soc. Indust. & Appl. Math. Numerical analysis in fields of ordinary and partial differential equations; nuclear code development. Address: Palo Alto Scientific Center, IBM Corp, 2670 Hanover St, Palo Alto, CA 94306.

FLATT, RONALD E(UGENE), b. Des Moines, Iowa, Dec. 10, 35; m. 58; c. 6. PATHOLOGY, LABORATORY ANIMAL MEDICINE. B.S, California, Davis, 60, D.V.M, 62, Nat. Insts. Health fel, 64-67, Ph.D.(comp. path), 67. Asst. prof. vet. path, Missouri-Columbia, 67-68, assoc. prof, 68-70; ASSOC. PROF. VET. PATH. & COORD. LAB. ANIMAL MED, VET. COL, IOWA STATE UNIV, 70- Consult, lab. animal med, Vet. Admin. Hosp, 68-69; chief morphol. path, Sinclair Comp. Med. Res. Farm, 67-70. Dipl, Am. Col. Vet. Path; Am. Col. Lab. Animal Med. Vet.C, U.S.A, 62-64, Capt. Am. Asn. Lab. Animal Sci; Am. Vet. Med. Asn. Spontaneous diseases of laboratory animals. Address: College of Veterinary Medicine, Iowa State University, Ames, IA 50010.

FLATT, WILLIAM P(ERRY), b. Newbern, Tenn, June 17, 31; m. 49; c. 2. ANIMAL NUTRITION. B.S, Tennessee, 52, Omicron Delta Kappa scholar, 52-53; Nat. Sci. Found. fel, Cornell, 53-55, Ph.D.(animal nutrit), 55. Res. resident, dept. animal husb, Cornell, 55; dairy cattle nutritionist & head energy metab. lab, nutrit. & physiol. sect, dairy cattle res. br, Agr. Res. Serv, U.S. Dept. Agr, 56-68, asst. dir. animal husbandry res. div, 68-69; prof. animal sci. & head dept, UNIV. GA, 69-70, DIR. AGR. EXP. STA, 70- Presidential citation, U.S. Dept. Agr, 65, superior serv. award, 68; Hoblitzelle Nat. Award Agr. Res, 68. AAAS; Am. Soc. Animal Sci; Am. Dairy Sci. Asn; Am. Inst. Nutrit. Biochemistry; physiology; energy metabolism of dairy cattle, especially the nutritive evaluation of forages and the energy requirements of cattle performing various functions; factors affecting rumen development. Address: 105 Conner Hall, University of Georgia, Athens, GA 30601.

FLATTO, LEOPOLD, b. Antwerp, Belg, Aug. 20, 29; U.S. citizen; m. 66; c. 2. MATHEMATICS. B.S, City Col. New York, 50; M.A, Johns Hopkins Univ, 51; Ph.D, Mass. Inst. Technol, 55. Mathematician, Reeves Instrument Corp, 55-57; prof. math, Brooklyn Polytech. Inst, 57-60; mathematician, IBM Res. Ctr. Yorktown Heights, 60-61; PROF. MATH, BELFER GRAD. SCH. SCI, YESHIVA UNIV, 61- Nat. Sci. Found. grant, 63-68; vis. prof, Hebrew Univ, 68-69. Am. Math. Soc. Mean value problems related to harmonic functions; finite reflection groups and their invariant theory; probability theory with emphasis on random walk problems. Address: Belfer Graduate School of Science, Yeshiva University, Amsterdam Ave. & 186th St, New York, NY 10033.

FLATTUM, ROGER FRANKLIN, b. Lanesboro, Minn, Apr. 18, 39; m. 62; c. 2. PHYSIOLOGY, PHARMACOLOGY. A.B, Winona State Col, 63; Ph.D.(insect physiol), Univ. Ill, Urbana, 68. Asst. prof. biol, Winona State Col, 67-68; U.S. Pub. Health Serv. fel, Purdue Univ, 68-69; ENTOMOLOGIST, SHELL DEVELOP. CO, 69- U.S.N, 61-63. Insect neurophysiology and neuropharmacology. Address: 2201 Codding Dr, Modesto, CA 95350.

FLAUGH, MICHAEL EDWARD, b. Findlay, Ohio, Nov. 14, 41; m. 66. ORGANIC CHEMISTRY. B.S, Dayton, 63; Ph.D.(chem), California, Berkeley, 68. Technician, Allison Div, Gen. Motors Corp, summers 62 & 63; SR. CHEMIST, ELI LILLY RES. LABS, 67- Am. Chem. Soc. Synthesis of organic structures, particularly heterocyclic compounds. Address: Eli Lilly Research Labs, Indianapolis, IN 46206.

FLAUTT, THOMAS JOSEPH, JR, b. Glendora, Miss, Feb. 8, 32; m. 55. PHYSICAL CHEMISTRY. B.S, St. Louis, 53; Ph.D.(chem), California, 57. Res. chemist, PROCTER & GAMBLE CO, 57-67, SECT. HEAD, 67- AAAS; Am. Chem. Soc. Nuclear magnetic resonance, mesomorphic phases; aqueous oxidation-reduction. Address: Miami Valley Lab, Procter & Gamble Co, Box 39175, Cincinnati, OH 45239.

FLAVIN, JOHN W(ILLIAM), S.J, b. Boston, Mass, July 16, 14. CYTOLOGY. A.B, Boston Col, 36, A.M, 41; M.S, Fordham, 43; Ph.D.(biol), Brown, 54. Instr, Cranwell Prep. Sch, 43-44; instr. BIOL, Col. of Holy Cross, 53-54; Boston Col, 54-58; asst. prof, COL. OF HOLY CROSS, 58-62, assoc. prof, 62-68, PROF, 68-, CHMN. DEPT, 62- AAAS; Am. Soc. Zool; Am. Asn. Jesuit Sci; N.Y. Acad. Sci. Cytophysiology of tumor cells in spontaneous hepatomas of C3H mice. Address: Dept. of Biology, College of the Holy Cross, Worcester, MA 01610.

FLAVIN, MARTIN, b. Chicago, Ill, May 18, 20. BIOCHEMISTRY. B.A, Stanford, 44; M.D, California, 47; Ph.D.(biochem), Columbia, 51. Sr. asst. surgeon, Nat. Heart Inst, 52-54; dept. biochem, N.Y. Univ, 54-56; Am. Heart Asn. estab. investr, dept. agr. biochem, California, 56-57; enzyme sect, NAT. HEART INST, 57-61, MED. DIR, 61- Med.C, U.S.A, 42-46; U.S.P.H.S.R, 46-, Med. Dir. Am. Soc. Biol. Chem. Enzymatic reaction mechanisms; chemical pathways of metabolism. Address: National Heart Institute, Bethesda, MD 20014.

FLAWN, PETER T(YRRELL), b. Miami, Fla, Feb. 17, 26; m. 46; c. 2. GEOLOGY. A.B, Oberlin Col, 47; M.S, Yale, 48, Ph.D.(geol), 51. Jr. geologist, U.S. Geol. Surv, 48-49; res. scientist & geologist, bur. econ. geol, UNIV. TEX, AUSTIN, 49-60, dir. bur. & prof. geol, 60-70, DIR. DIV. NATURAL RESOURCES & ENVIRON. & AD INTERIM V.PRES. ACAD. AFFAIRS, 70- U.S.A.A.F, 44-45. Fel. Geol. Soc. Am; Am. Asn. Petrol. Geol; Am. Inst. Mining, Metall. & Petrol. Eng. Economic and environmental geology; geology of Texas and Mexico. Address: Division of Natural Resources & Environment, University of Texas at Austin, Austin, TX 78712.

FLAX, ALEXANDER H(ENRY), b. New York, N.Y, Jan. 18, 21; m. 51; c. 1. AERONAUTICAL ENGINEERING. B.Ae.E, N.Y. Univ, 40; Ph.D.(physics), Buffalo, 58. Stress analyst, Curtiss-Wright Corp, N.Y, 40-44; chief aerodyn. & struct, Piasecki Helicopter Corp, Phila, 44-46, asst. head aeromech. dept, Cornell Aeronaut. Lab, 46-49, head aerodyn. res. dept, 49-55, asst. dir, 55-59; chief scientist, U.S. Dept. Air Force, 59-61; v.pres-tech. dir, Cornell Aeronaut. Labs, 61-63; asst. secy. res. & develop, U.S. Dept. Air Force, 64-69; PRES, INST. DEFENSE ANAL, 69-, v.pres. res, 69. Instr. eng. sci. & mgt. war training, Cornell Univ, 43, 48; exten. course, Pa. State Col, 45-46. Mem. comt. aerodyn, Nat. Adv. Comt. Aeronaut, 52-53, subcomt. high speed aerodyn, 54-58; res. adv. comt. aircraft aerodyn, NASA, 59-63; adv. comt, Defense Sci. Bd, Dept. Defense; 70-; Air Force Sci. Adv. Bd, 70-; Dept. of Transportation, 70-; Off. Sci. Technol, 70- Air Force Except. Civilian Serv. award, 61, 69; NASA Distinguished Serv.

Medal, 69. Nat. Acad. Eng; fel. Am. Inst. Aeronaut. & Astronaut.(Sperry Award, Inst. Aeronaut. Sci, 49). Aircraft flutter and vibration; aero-elastic effects on stability and control; helicopter dynamics and aerodynamics; supersonic aerodynamics; missile dynamics; lifting surface theory; high temperature gas dynamics. Address: Institute for Defense Analysis, 400 Army-Navy Dr, Arlington, VA 22202.

FLAX, MARTIN HOWARD, b. N.Y.C, Jan. 19, 28; m. 55; c. 3. PATHOLOGY. A.B, Cornell, 46; A.M, Columbia, 48, Nat. Cancer Inst, fel, 49-51, Ph.D, 53; M.D, Chicago, 55. Asst. zool, Columbia, 46-49; intern, Mt. Sinai Hosp, New York, 55-56; asst. path, med. sch, Chicago, 56-57; chief biophys. br, Armed Forces Inst. Path, 57-59; instr. PATH, Harvard Med. Sch, 61-63, assoc, 63-66, asst. prof, 66-70; PROF. & CHMN. DEPT, SCH. MED, TUFTS UNIV, 70-; PATHOLOGIST-IN-CHIEF, NEW ENG. MED. CTR. HOSPS, 70- Res. & clin. fel. path, Mass. Gen. Hosp, 59-61, asst, 61-70; Nat. Insts. Health career develop. award, 66-, consult, path. B study sect. Med.C, 57-59, Capt. Am. Soc. Exp. Path; Am. Asn. Path. & Bact; Int. Acad. Path. Immunopathology; electron microscopy. Address: Dept. of Pathology, Tufts University School of Medicine, 136 Harrison Ave, Boston, MA 02111.

FLEAGLE, ROBERT GUTHRIE, b. Baltimore, Md, Aug. 16, 18; m. 42; c. 2. METEOROLOGY. A.B, Hopkins, 40; M.S, N.Y. Univ, 44, Ph.D.(physics), 49. Teacher, high sch, Md, 40-41; asst, N.Y. Univ, 46-48; asst. prof. ATMOSPHERIC SCI, UNIV. WASH, 48-51, assoc. prof, 51-56, PROF, 56-, CHMN, DEPT, 67- Nat. Sci. Found. sr. fel, Imp. Col, Univ. London, 58-59; tech. asst, Off. Sci. & Technol, 63-64; chmn. comt. atmospheric sci, Nat. Acad. Sci, 69- U.S.A.A.F, 42-46. Am. Meteorol. Soc; Am. Geophys. Union; Royal Meteorol. Soc. Description and theory of large scale atmospheric motions; physics of air near the earth's surface. Address: Dept. of Atmospheric Sciences, University of Washington, Seattle, WA 98105.

FLECK, ARTHUR C, b. Chicago, Ill, Oct. 29, 36; m. 57; c. 2. COMPUTER SCIENCE. B.S, Western Michigan, 59; M.A, Mich. State, 60, Ph.D.(math), 64. Dir. prog. comput, Mich. State, 64-65; asst. prof. math. & comput, UNIV. IOWA, 65-67, ASSOC. PROF. COMPUT. SCI, 67- Am. Math. Soc; Asn. Comput. Mach. Automata theory. Address: Computer Center, Dept. of Mathematics, University of Iowa, Iowa City, IA 52240.

FLECK, ELMER E(LLSWORTH), b. Sterling, Ill, Dec. 24, 02; m. 34; c. 3. CHEMISTRY. A.B, Nebraska, 24, A.M, 25; Harvard fel, Princeton, Ph.D. (org. chem), 28. Asst. chem. pharmacol, Rockefeller Inst, 28-31, assoc, 31-34; chemist, E.I. du Pont de Nemours & Co, 35-36; assoc. chemist, naval stores res. div, bur. agr. chem. & eng, U.S. DEPT. AGR, 36-42, res. chemist, PESTICIDE CHEM. RES. BR, ENTOM. RES. DIV, 42-57, ASST. CHIEF, 57- AAAS; Am. Chem. Soc; Entom. Soc. Am. Structure of saponins; cardiac glycosides; triterpenes; dye stuff intermediates; chemistry of rosin and resin acids; chemistry of DDT; insecticides; repellents; attractants. Address: Pesticide Chemicals Research Branch, Entomological Research Division, U.S. Dept. of Agriculture, Beltsville, MD 20705.

FLECK, GEORGE M(ORRISON), b. Warren, Ind, May 13, 34; m. 59; c. 2. PHYSICAL CHEMISTRY. B.S, Yale, 56; Danforth fel, Wisconsin, 56-61, Du Pont fel, 59-60, Ph.D.(phys. chem), 61. Asst. prof. CHEM, SMITH COL, 61-67, ASSOC. PROF, 67- Summer instr, Univ. Wis, 61. Am. Chem. Soc. Systems chemistry; kinetics and mechanisms of chemical reactions in solution; multiple equilibria involving metal complexes in solution. Address: Dept. of Chemistry, Smith College, Northampton, MA 01060.

FLECK, JOSEPH A(MADEUS), JR, b. Kansas City, Mo, Mar. 10, 28; m. 61; c. 2. PHYSICS. A.B, Harvard, 48; M.A, Rice Inst, 50, Ph.D.(physics), 52. Assoc. physicist, Brookhaven Nat. Lab, 52-57; physicist, LAWRENCE RADIATION LAB, UNIV. CALIF, 57-69, GROUP LEADER THEORET. DIV, 69- Fulbright adv. res. fel, Norway, 57-58; consult, Atomic Energy Cmn, Halden proj, Norway, 58-59; Atomic Energy Res. Inst, Japan, 61; lectr, Univ. Calif, Davis, 67- Am. Phys. Soc. Reactor and nuclear weapons physics; Monte Carlo methods; radiative transfer; laser physics and quantum optics; numerical methods. Address: Theoretical Division, Lawrence Radiation Lab, University of California, Livermore, CA 94550.

FLECK, M(ARTIN) W(ILLIAM), b. Derry, Pa, Oct. 10, 04; m. 29, 52; c. 2. BIOLOGY. B.S, New Mexico, 38, M.S, 39; California, 40; Southern California, 45; Chicago, 46; Ph.D, Colorado, 54; Oak Ridge Inst. Nuclear Studies, 60. Med. technician, Bonnie Burn Sanitorium, N.J, 32-33; jr. biologist, soil conserv. serv, U.S. Dept. Agr, Albuquerque, 36; teacher, pub. sch, 39; assoc. prof. biol. & math. & chmn. sci. div, East. N.Mex. Col, 39-45; asst. prof. BIOL, UNIV. N.MEX, 45-50, assoc. prof, 50-61, prof, 61-70; EMER. PROF, 70- Summers, vis. prof. Hawaii, 62 & 63; Ford Found. fel, Nat. Univs. Nicaragua & Honduras, 63. Chmn, Governor's Tech. Radiation Adv. Coun, N.Mex, 61- Res. consult, Atomic Energy Comn, Los Alamos, 47-61. AAAS. Small mammal population of New Mexico; genetics of maize; agglutinable factors of blood of Pueblo Indians; permeability of erythrocytes. Address: Dept. of Biology, University of New Mexico, Albuquerque, NM 87106.

FLECK, RAYMOND A, b. Brooklyn, N.Y, Mar. 9, 27; m. 70; c. 1. ORGANIC CHEMISTRY. B.S, Univ. Notre Dame, 51, Ph.D.(phys. org. chem), 54; hon. L.H.D, Mt. Angel Col, 68. From instr. to prof. chem, St. Edward's Univ, 54-69, pres, 57-69; vis. scholar & res. assoc. environ. toxicol, UNIV. CALIF, DAVIS, 69-70, MEM. RES. STAFF FOOD PROTECTION & TOXICOL. CTR, 70-, Nat. Sci. Found. faculty fel, 69-70. U.S.N, 45-46. AAAS; Am. Chem. Soc. Environmental fate of chemicals; systems simulation; degradative paths of pesticides. Address: Food Protection & Toxicology Center, University of California, Davis, CA 95616.

FLECK, STEPHEN, b. Frankfurt-am-Main, Germany, Sept. 18, 12; nat; m. 45; c. 3. PSYCHIATRY. Goethe Univ, 31-33; Amsterdam, 33-35; M.D, Harvard, 40. Intern med, Beth Israel Hosp, Boston, 40-42; hosp, Hopkins, 46, res. psychiat, 46-48, asst, 48, instr. psychiat. & asst. med, 48-49; instr. psychiat, med. sch, Washington (Seattle), 49-50, asst. prof, 50-53; assoc. prof, SCH. MED, YALE, 53-54, PSYCHIAT. & PUB. HEALTH, 54-63; PROF, 63-, PSYCHIATRIST-IN-CHIEF, YALE PSYCHIAT. INST, 63-; CONN. MENT. HEALTH CTR, 69- Attend. staff, King County Hosp. & Vet. Admin. Hosp, Seattle, 51-53; consult, Vet. Admin. Hosp, West Haven, Conn, 53-; med. dir, Yale Psychiat. Inst, 54-63; lectr, State Hosp, Middletown Conn, 54- U.S.A, 42-43, Med.C, 43-46, Maj. AAAS; Am. Psychosom. Soc; Geront. Soc; Am. Med. Asn; Am. Psychiat. Asn; Am. Pub. Health Asn; Am. Fedn. Clin. Res. Schizophrenia, emotional aspects of motherhood outside marriage; conditioning and integration of the central nervous system; social structure of mental hospitals; family psychiatry. Address: Dept. of Psychiatry, Yale University School of Medicine, 333 Cedar St, New Haven, CT 06510.

FLECK, WILLIAM B(ROOKE), b. Phila, Pa, Dec. 3, 33; m. 68; c. 2. HYDROLOGY, GEOLOGY. B.A, Williams Col, 56; M.A, Boston Univ, 59. HYDROLOGIST, U.S. GEOL. SURV, 60- U.S.N, 56-57, Lt.(jg). Applied research in the delineation, analysis and modeling of Pleistocene aquifers. Address: U.S. Geological Survey, 700 Capitol Savings & Loan Bldg, Lansing, MI 48933.

FLECK, WILLIAM G(EORGE), b. Havertown, Pa, Nov. 17, 40; m. 67; c. 2. CIVIL ENGINEERING. B.C.E, Villanova, 62; M.S, Carnegie-Mellon Univ, 64, Ph.D.(civil eng), 68. ASSOC. PROF. CIVIL ENG, CLEVELAND STATE UNIV, 67- NASA summer faculty fel, Lewis-Case Western Reserve, 68 & 69. AAAS; Am. Soc. Eng. Educ. Fatigue crack propagation and fracture mechanics of materials. Address: Dept. of Civil Engineering, Cleveland State University, Cleveland, OH 44115.

FLECKENSTEIN, LEE J(OSEPH), b. Pittsburgh, Pa, Dec. 4, 30. ORGANIC CHEMISTRY. B.S, Carnegie Inst. Tech, 52; Moore fel, Mass. Inst. Tech, 56-57, Ph.D.(org. chem), 58. CHEMIST, RES. LABS, EASTMAN KODAK CO, 58- Sig.C, U.S.A, 53-55, Res, 52-53, 55- Am. Chem. Soc. Chemistry of medium-ring compounds; synthesis of organic dye-forming compounds. Address: Eastman Kodak Co, Research Labs, 343 State St, Rochester, NY 14650.

FLECKENSTEIN, WILLIAM OWEN, b. Scranton, Pa, Apr. 6, 25; m. 47; c. 2. ELECTRICAL ENGINEERING. B.S, Lehigh, 49; Commun. Develop. Training Prog, Bell Tel. Labs, Inc, 49-52. Mem. tech. staff, Bell Tel. Labs, 49-54, supvr. switching syst. design, 54-56, head dept. data commun. systs, 56-60, dir. data commun. develop, 60-66, dir. phys. design commun. equip, 66, exec. dir. data & PBX systs, 66-68; gen. mgr. res. & develop, West. Elec. Co, Inc, 68-70; EXEC. DIR. SWITCHING ENG. & LOCAL CROSSBAR DEVELOP. DIV, BELL TEL. LABS, 70- V.chmn. vis. comt, dept. elec. eng, Lehigh, 67-; mem. adv. coun, Polymer Mat. Prog, Princeton, 69- U.S.N, 43-46. Inst. Elec. & Electronics Eng. Switching system exploratory development and design; switching theory; digital systems, including data communication systems; manufacturing process technology; systems engineering. Address: Bell Telephone Labs, Inc, Holmdel, NJ 07733.

FLEDDERMANN, H(ARRY) T(AYLOR), b. New Orleans, La, Feb. 20, 10; m. 38; c. 4. MATHEMATICAL ANALYSIS. B.S, Spring Hill Col, 29; B.S, M.E, Detroit, 31; M.S, La. State, 37, Ph.D.(math), 40. Prof. math, Loyola, 31-63; PROF. MATH. & DIR. SCI. DIV, BISCAYNE COL, 63- Am. Math. Soc. Analysis and probability. Address: 2781 N.W. 151st St, Opa-Locka, FL 33054.

FLEDDERMANN, RICHARD G(RAYSON), b. Havana, Cuba, June 4, 22; U.S. citizen; m. 51; c. 3. AERONAUTICAL ENGINEERING. B.S, Loyola (La), 41; B.S.E. Michigan, 43, M.S.E, 47, Ph.D.(aeronaut. eng), 50. Aerodynamicist, El Segundo Div, Douglas Aircraft Co, 43; Higgins Industs, Inc, La, 43-44; res. assoc, eng. res. inst, Michigan, 45-60; assoc. prof. aeronaut. eng, Ga. Inst. Tech, 50-54; engr. aeronaut. res. & develop, Arnold Eng. Develop. Ctr, U.S. Air Force, 54-56; sr. staff scientist & chmn. theoret. aerodyn. group, Avco Mfg. Co, 56-59; sr. eng. scientist, Radio Corp. Am, 59-61; prin. staff engr, staff of v.pres. eng, Martin Co, 61-65, staff of dir. res. & eng, Denver Div, 65-66, mgr. space physics, 66-68; PROF. AERONAUT. SYSTS. & CHMN. DEPT, OMEGA COL, UNIV. W.FLA, 68- Consult, Arnold Eng. Develop. Ctr, U.S. Air Force, 51, 53-54. U.S.N, 44-46, Res, 46-, Lt. Comdr. Am. Inst. Aeronaut. & Astronaut. Hypersonic aerodynamics and heat transfer; ablation materials; properties of turbulent flow; fuel sprays. Address: Dept. of Aeronautical Systems, Omega College, University of West Florida, Pensacola, FL 32504.

FLEEK, JAMES B(URTON), b. Jamestown, N.Y, Sept. 19, 20; m. 42; c. 2. PHYSICAL CHEMISTRY. B.S, Allegheny Col, 42; A.M, Missouri, 47; Ed.D, Fla. State, 56. Instr. CHEM, Miami (Ohio), 47-48; Fla. State, 48-50; asst. prof, Jacksonville Jr. Col, 54-56; ASSOC. PROF, JACKSONVILLE UNIV, 56-, chmn. div. sci. & math, 56-58. Civilian Pub. Serv, 44-46. Science teachers training. Address: Dept. of Chemistry, Jacksonville University, Jacksonville, FL 32211.

FLEEKER, JAMES R, b. Emporia, Kans, Aug. 11, 37; m. 49; c. 4. BIOCHEMISTRY. B.A, Kans. State Teachers Col, 60; Nat. Insts. Health fel, Mich. State, 63-65, Ph.D.(biochem), 65. Res. assoc, Mich. State, 65-66; ASST. PROF. BIOCHEM, N.DAK. STATE UNIV, 66- AAAS. Metabolism of pesticides; plant metabolism. Address: Dept. of Biochemistry, North Dakota State University, Fargo, ND 58102.

FLEENOR, CHARLES R(EED), b. Bristol, Va, Nov. 1, 20; m. 40; c. 2. MATHEMATICS. A.B, Earlham Col, 50; Gen. Elec. Co. fel, Purdue, 54, M.S, 57. Head dept. MATH, pub. sch, Ind, 50-57; ASST. PROF, BURRIS LAB. SCH, BALL STATE UNIV, 57- Demonstration teacher & lectr, Nat. Sci. Found. Insts, Carleton Col, 60, 61; Michigan, 63, 64. U.S.N, 44-46. Nat. Coun. Teachers Math. Secondary mathematics curriculum; foundations of mathematics. Address: Dept. of Mathematics, Ball State University, Muncie, IN 47306.

FLEER, ALFRED W(ILLIAM), b. Quincy, Ill, July 19, 09; m. 47; c. 3. CHEMICAL ENGINEERING. B.S, Michigan, 32, fel, 32-33, M.S, 33, Mich. Gas Asn. fel, 33-35, Ph.D.(chem. eng), 35. Chem. engr. & petrol. technologist, Shell Petrol. Corp, 35-38; asst. prof. chem. eng, Virginia, 38-39; process engr, Gulf Oil Corp, 39-41; asst. to pres, Shell Develop. Co. div, Shell Oil Co, 41-49; mgr, mfg. develop. dept, Shell Chem. Corp, 49-51, eng, 51-52, operations, 52-53, res. develop. & eng, mfg. dept, 54-55, gen. mgr. tech.

mfg, 55-58, indust. chem. div, 59-64, admin. asst. to pres, 64-67, gen. mgr, 67-69, MGT. & ENG. CONSULT, 69- Distinguished alumni citation, col. eng, Michigan, 56; Pioneers of Progress in Chem. Indust, Putnam Pub. Co, 53. Ord.C.Res, 32-42. Am. Chem. Soc; Soc. Indust. Chem; Am. Inst. Chem. Eng. Combustion and catalytic gasification of fuels; petroleum refining; petroleum and organic chemicals. Address: P.O. Box 428, Ardsley-on-Hudson, NY 10503.

FLEESON, WILLIAM, b. Sterling, Kans, May 21, 15; m. 43; c. 5. MEDICINE, PSYCHIATRY. A.B, Kansas, 37; M.D, Yale, 42. Intern, Univ. hosps, Minnesota, 42-43; assoc. psychiatrist & dir. child guidance div, Minn. Psychiatric Inst, 46-55; asst. & assoc. prof. psychiat, col. med. sci, Minnesota, 56-63, asst. dean, col, 60-63; PROF. PSYCHIAT. & ASSOC. DEAN, SCH. MED, UNIV. CONN, 63- Fel, U.S. Pub. Health Serv, Judge Baker Guidance Center, Boston, Mass, 50-51; spec. fel, Nat. Inst. Health, Psychiat. & Rehabil, Minnesota, 55; mem. adv. mgt. prog, Harvard, 64; lectr. psychiat, sch. med, Yale, 65-; acting head dept. psychiat. & chief psychiat. serv, Univ. Conn-McCook Hosp, 67-68. Dipl, Am. Bd. Psychiat. & Neurol, 58. Med.C, U.S.A, 43-46. Fel. Am. Psychiat. Asn. Medical education and administration. Address: University of Connecticut School of Medicine, 1280 Asylum, Hartford, CT 06105.

FLEETWOOD, CHARLES WESLEY, b. Gent, Ind, Nov. 10, 04; m. 39; c. 1. CHEMISTRY. A.B, Hanover Col, 30; M.S, St. Louis, 32, Ph.D.(inorg. chem), 37. Asst. chem, St. Louis, 32-37; indust. res. chemist, U.S. Rubber Co, Indianapolis, 37-41; asst. supt. explosives dept, Des Moines Ord, 41-42; explosives supt, Eau Claire Ord. Plant, Wis, 42-44; indust. chemist, Gillette Plant, U.S. Rubber Co, 44-46; prof. chem, N.DAK. STATE UNIV, 46-47, ANAL. CHEM, 47-71, EMER. PROF, 71- Photoelectric colorimeter and its use in determining some elements of physiological importance found in deep well water; rubber; explosives; glass fabrication. Address: 1354 11th St. N, Fargo, ND 58102.

FLEGAL, CAL J, b. Kalamazoo, Mich, Feb. 25, 36; m. 58; c. 2. POULTRY NUTRITION. B.S, Mich. State, 58, M.S, 62, Ph.D.(poultry nutrit), 65. Asst, MICH. STATE UNIV, 60-63, nutrit. technician, dept. poultry sci, 63-65, EXTEN. SPECIALIST, POULTRY EXTEN, 65- U.S.A, 58-60, 1st Lt. Poultry Sci. Asn; World Poultry Sci. Asn. Vitamia A-Beta-Carotene relationships and activity; utilization of raw soybeans in poultry rations and the nutritional aspects of the fatty-liver syndrome in chickens. Address: 2391 E. Mount Hope, Okemos, MI 48864.

FLEGE, R(AYMOND) K(ENNETT), b. Williamstown, Ky, Mar. 17, 05. CHEMICAL ENGINEERING. A.B, Kentucky, 25, univ. fel, 26-27, M.S, 27; Mass. Inst. Tech, 32. Res. assoc. chem. eng, Mass. Inst. Tech, 27-32; res. engr, Bauer & Black Div, Kendall Co, 32-36, div. develop. & res, Kendall Mills Div, 36-44; plant mgr, North Star Woolen Mill Co, 44-48; asst. to pres, Stonecutter Mills Corp, 48-52; planning supvr, construct. div, E.I. du Pont de Nemours & Co, 52-53; Rust Eng. Corp, 53-54; prof. textile eng, Tex. Tech. Col, 54-61; Ga. Inst. Technol, 61-72; RETIRED. Am. Soc. Eng. Educ; Am. Soc. Mech. Eng; Am. Asn. Textile Chem. & Colorists. Address: 219 W. Paces Ferry Rd. N.W, Atlanta, GA 30305.

FLEGENHEIMER, HAROLD H(ANSLEO), b. Heilbronn, Ger, Feb. 18, 24; nat; m. 47; c. 2. CHEMICAL ENGINEERING. B.Ch.E, Cooper Union, 44; M.Ch.E, Polytech. Inst. Brooklyn, 47. Formulator org. coatings, Devoe & Raynolds Co, Inc, 47-54, tech. dir, Newark Plant, 54-66; East. tech. mgr, CELANESE COATINGS CO, 66-70, MGR. PROD. DEVELOP. PLANNING, 70- U.S.A, 44-46. Am. Chem. Soc; Nat. Asn. Corrosion Eng. Development of protective and decorative coatings; and related materials, especially polymers, resins: solvents and pigments. Address: Celanese Coatings Co, 9800 E. Bluegrass Pkwy, Jeffersontown, KY 40299.

FLEHARTY, EUGENE, b. Beaver Falls, Pa, Oct. 16, 34; m. 55; c. 2. ZOOLOGY. B.A, Hastings Col, 56; M.S, New Mexico, 58, Ph.D.(biol), 63. ASST. PROF. biol, Nebr. Wesleyan, 60-62; ZOOL, FT. HAYS KANS. STATE COL, 62- Am. Soc. Mammal; Ecol. Soc. Am. Mammalogy and herpetology distribution, taxonomy and ecology. Address: Dept. of Biology, Fort Hays Kansas State College, Hays, KS 67601.

FLEHINGER, B(ETTY) J(EANNE), b. Sandusky, Ohio, Apr. 4, 22; m. 70; c. 3. APPLIED MATHEMATICS. A.B, Barnard, 41; Rice fel, Cornell, 41-42, M.A, 42; Pfister fel, Columbia, 56-57, Ph.D.(appl. math), 60. Jr. physicist, Picatinny Arsenal, 42-43; jr. chemist, Guayule Emergency Rubber Proj, 43-44; chemist, Permanente Metals Corp, 44-45; asst, Columbia Univ, 52-57; MATHEMATICIAN, T.J. WATSON RES. CTR, IBM CORP, 57- Vis. assoc. prof, grad. sch. med. sci, Cornell Univ, 66-; vis. investr, Sloan Kettering Inst, 67- Inst. Math. Statist. Probability and statistics; reliability theory; medical statistics. Address: T.J. Watson Research Center, IBM Corp, P.O. Box 218, Yorktown Heights, NY 10598.

FLEIG, ALBERT J, JR, b. Rochester, N.Y, May 17, 37; m. 65; c. 1. SPACE SCIENCE, APPLIED PHYSICS. B.S, Purdue Univ, 58; Goddard fel, Catholic Univ, 62-68, Ph.D, 68. Design engr, Convair Astronaut, 58-60; systs. engr, Vitro Corp. Am, 60-62; systs. analyst, GODDARD SPACE FLIGHT CTR, NASA, 62-68, spec. asst. to dir. admin. & mgt, 68-70, HEAD, TECHNOL. APPLNS, 70- Lectr. aerospace eng, Univ. Md, 69-; mem, Simulation Coun, Inc. Asn. Advan. Med. Instrumentation. Applications of science and engineering to major problems of society, biomedical, environmental, public safety and transportation; attitude dynamics; computer simulation. Address: Code 730, Goddard Space Flight Center, NASA, Greenbelt, MD 20771.

FLEISCH, JEROME HERBERT, b. Bronx, N.Y, June 6, 41. PHARMACOLOGY. B.S, Columbia, 63; Ph.D.(pharmacol), Georgetown, 67. Res. fel. PHARMACOL, Harvard Med. Sch, 67-68; RES. ASSOC, NAT. HEART INST, 68- U.S.P.H.S, 68-, Sr. Asst. Scientist. AAAS; Am. Pharmaceut. Asn; N.Y. Acad. Sci. Autonomic, cardiovascular and receptor pharmacology. Address: National Heart Institute, Bldg. 3, Room 220, Bethesda, MD 20014.

FLEISCHAUER, PAUL D(ELL), b. Buffalo, N.Y, Sept. 23, 42; m. 65. PHYSICAL INORGANIC CHEMISTRY, PHOTOCHEMISTRY. B.A, Wesleyan, 64; Ph.D.(phys. chem), Southern California, 68. Nat. Sci. Found. exchange fel, Rome, 68-69; MEM. TECH. STAFF, AEROSPACE CORP, 69- Am. Chem. Soc. Photochemistry and studies of luminescence of transition metal coordination compounds and other inorganic molecules, reaction mechanisms and spectral characterization of these molecules. Address: Aerospace Corp, P.O. Box 95085, Los Angeles, CA 90045.

FLEISCHER, ALLAN A, b. Hartford, Conn, Feb. 6, 31; m. 56; c. 2. NUCLEAR PHYSICS. B.S, Yale, 52, M.S, 56, Ph.D.(physics), 59. Mem. tech. staff, Ramo-Wooldridge Corp, 59-60; dept. mgr, Edgerton, Germeshavsen & Grier, 60-63, tech. adv. to mgr, 63; dir. res, W.M. Brobeck & Assocs, 63-65; v.pres. res. & develop, Cyclotron Corp, Calif, 65-70; PRES. & CHIEF EXEC. OFF, MEDI-PHYSICS, INC, 70- Summer mem. tech. staff, Bell Tel. Labs, 56. U.S.N, 52-55, Lt.(jg). AAAS; Am. Phys. Soc; sr. mem. Inst. Elec. & Electronics Eng; Am. Nuclear Soc; Soc. Nuclear Med; N.Y. Acad. Sci. Radiopharmaceuticals; radioisotopes; nucleonics; accelerator development. Address: Medi-Physics, Inc, 5855 Christie Ave, Emeryville, CA 94608.

FLEISCHER, BECCA CATHERINE, b. Brooklyn, N.Y, Feb. 12, 30; m. 62. BIOCHEMISTRY. B.S, Brooklyn Col, 52; M.A, Indiana, 55, Nat. Insts. Health fel, 56-58, Ph.D.(biochem), 58. Proj. assoc, dept. genetics, Wisconsin, 58-62, trainee, enzyme inst, 62-64; RES. ASSOC. MOLECULAR BIOL, VANDERBILT UNIV, 64- AAAS; Am. Chem. Soc; Am. Soc. Biol. Chem. Comparative biochemistry of membranes; isolation and characterization of subcellular organelles of liver, particularly Golgi apparatus. Address: Dept. of Molecular Biology, Vanderbilt University, Nashville, TN 37203.

FLEISCHER, CLARA J(OEL), b. Poland, May 1, 12; U.S. citizen; m. 43; c. 2. MEDICINE. M.S, Prague, 32; M.D, Med. Col. Va, 42. Intern, Med. Col. Va, 42-43; indust. physician, E.I. du Pont de Nemours & Co, Va, 43-47; chief maternal & child health bur, Richmond Pub. Health Dept, 47-50; private practice, 50-53; asst. prof. PHYS. MED. & REHAB, col. med, Univ. Ill, 56-60; SCH. MED, UNIV. MD, 60-70, ASSOC. PROF, 70-; STAFF PHYSIATRIST, DEPT. REHAB. MED, SINAI HOSP. BALTIMORE, INC, 67- Consult, Va. State Dept. Welfare, 50-53; res, Med. Col. Va, 53-55; asst. chief dept. phys. med. & rehab, res. & educ, hosps, Univ. Ill, 56-60; consult, Perry Point Vet. Admin. Hosp, 61-67. Dipl, Am. Bd. Phys. Med. & Rehab. Am. Med. Asn; Am. Med. Women's Asn; Am. Cong. Rehab. Med; Am. Acad. Phys. Med. & Rehab; Am. Heart Asn; Am. Col. Physicians; Pan Am. Med. Asn. Physical medicine and rehabilitation. Address: Dept. of Rehabilitation Medicine, Sinai Hospital of Baltimore, Inc, Belvedere & Greenspring Ave, Baltimore, MD 21215.

FLEISCHER, EVERLY B, b. Salt Lake City, Utah, June 5, 36; m. 59; c. 2. CHEMISTRY. B.S, Yale, 58, M.S, 59, Ph.D.(chem), 61. Asst. prof. CHEM, Univ. Chicago, 61-68, assoc. prof, 68-71; PROF, UNIV. CALIF, IRVINE, 71- Am. Chem. Soc; The Chem. Soc. Physical inorganic chemistry; x-ray crystallography; porphyrin chemistry. Address: Dept. of Chemistry, University of California, Irvine, CA 92664.

FLEISCHER, GERALD A, b. St. Louis, Mo, Jan. 7, 33; m. 60; c. 2. INDUSTRIAL ENGINEERING. B.S, St. Louis, 54; M.S, California, Berkeley, 59; Ford Found. fel. & Ph.D.(indust. eng, eng-econ. planning), Stanford, 62. Instr. eng. ed, Heald Eng. Col, 58-59; opers. analyst, Consol. Freightways, Inc, 59-61; asst. prof. INDUST. ENG, Michigan, 63-64; assoc. prof, UNIV. SOUTH. CALIF, 64-71, PROF, 71- Statist. analyst, maritime cargo transportation conf. div, Nat. Acad. Sci-Nat. Res. Coun, 58; res. mgr, Hawaiian Marine Freightways, 60; acting asst. prof, Stanford, 60-62. Consult, U.S. Agency Int. Develop, 65-66; U.S. Navy, 66: Rand Corp, 66-; Nat. Coop. Hwy. Res. Prog, Nat. Acad. Sci, 70- U.S.N, 54-57, Res, 57-63, Lt. Am. Inst. Indust. Eng; Am. Soc. Eng. Educ. Engineering-economic planning and systems analysis, especially in public sector. Address: Dept. of Industrial & Systems Engineering, University of Southern California, Los Angeles, CA 90007.

FLEISCHER, HERBERT O(SWALD), b. Lake Geneva, Wis, June 22, 13; m. 40; c. 2. FORESTRY. B.A, Northwest. Col, 35; Wisconsin, 35-36; B.S, & M.F, Michigan, 38; Sheffield fel, Yale, 48-49, Ph.D, 52. Field asst, Lake States Forest & Range Exp. Sta, U.S. Forest Serv, 38, jr. forester, Nicolet Nat. Forest, Wis, 39; forester, Consol. Water Power & Paper Co, 39-40; forest prods. technologist, forest prods. lab, U.S. FOREST SERV, U.S. DEPT. AGR, 42-57, chief, div. timber processing, 57-64; DIR, forest prod. utilization & eng. res, 64-67, FOREST PROD. LAB, 67- Consult, For. Econ. Admin, 45. Civilian with U.S.A; U.S.A.A.F; U.S.N; Nat. Adv. Comt, 44. Soc. Am. Foresters; Forest Prod. Res. Soc.(pres, 64-65); Soc. Wood Sci. & Technol. Forest products utilization and engineering research. Address: Forest Products Lab, Forest Service, U.S. Dept. of Agriculture, Madison, WI 53705.

FLEISCHER, JOSEPH, b. Bridgeport, Conn, Dec. 27, 05; m. 39; c. 2. PHYSICAL CHEMISTRY. B.S, Yale, 27, Loomis fel, 27-29, Ph.D.(chem), 30. Res. chemist, Frigidaire Corp, 30-32, chem. consult, 32-34; chem. & patent consult, Olin Industs, Inc, 34-56; tech. adv. & patent mgr, Olin Mathieson Chem. Corp, 56-60, sr. patent assoc, 60-70; CHEM. & PATENT CONSULT, 71- Am. Chem. Soc; Sci. Res. Soc. Am. Phase rule; phenol-formaldehyde type polymers; drying oils; thermodynamic properties of chlorofluorides; liquid absorbents for refrigerant gases; congealing brines; cellulose; explosives; synthetic organic polymers; galvanic cells; non-ferrous metals; chemical patent literature. Address: 210 Yale Ave, New Haven, CT 06515.

FLEISCHER, MICHAEL, b. Bridgeport, Conn, Feb. 27, 08; m. 34; c. 2. GEOCHEMISTRY. B.S, Yale, 30, Ph.D.(chem), 33. Fel, Yale, 33-34; asst. to ed, Dana's Syst. Mineral, 35-36; asst. phys. chemist, geophys. lab, Carnegie Inst. Technol, 36-39; GEOCHEMIST, U.S. GEOL. SURV, 39- Asst. ed, Chem. Abstr, 40-; v.pres. comn. geochem, Int. Union Chem, 51-53, pres, 53-57; prof. lectr, George Wash. Univ, 57-65; chmn. comn. new minerals, Int. Mineral. Asn, 59-; mem, U.S. Nat. Comt. Geochem, 69- Am. Chem. Soc; fel. Mineral. Soc. Am.(v.pres, 51, pres, 52); fel. Geol. Soc. Am. (v.pres, 53); fel. Soc. Econ. Geol; Geochem. Soc.(v.pres, 63, pres, 64); Mineral. Asn. Can; Mineral. Soc. Gt. Brit. & Ireland; French Soc. Mineral. & Crystallog; Italian Mineral. Soc; Swiss Soc. Mineral. & Petrog; Soc. Environ. Geochem. & Health (v.pres, 71). Geochemical abundance and distribution of elements; chemical mineralogy. Address: U.S. Geological Survey, Washington, DC 20242.

FLEISCHER, ROBERT, b. Flushing, N.Y, Aug. 20, 18; m. 42; c. 3. ASTRONOMY. B.S, Harvard, 40, fel, 42, M.A, 47, Ph.D.(astron), 49; Steward Observ. fel, Arizona, 40-41. Asst, col. observ, Harvard, 41-42; instr. physics & astron, Rensselaer Polytech, 46-49, asst. prof, 49-55, assoc. prof, 55-58, prof. astron. & in charge observ, 58-62; prog. dir. solar-terrestrial res. & coord, int. years quiet sun, NAT. SCI. FOUND, 62-66, dep. head, off. int. sci. activities, 66-68, HEAD ASTRON. SECT, 68- Dir. res, Dudley Observ, 56-57; res. assoc, Nat. Radio Astron. Observ, 60; summer asst, Harvard, 48. Consult, Northrop Corp, 59-61; Gen. Elec. Co, 60-61. Mem, Int. Sci. Radio Union; Int. Astron. Union. Civilian Pub. Serv, 42-46. Fel. AAAS; Am. Astron. Soc; Am. Geophys. Union; Royal Astron. Soc. Can; Royal Astron. Soc. London. Optical and radio astronomy; geophysics; solar-terrestrial relations. Address: 1733 Church St. N.W, Washington, DC 20036.

FLEISCHER, ROBERT LOUIS, b. Columbus, Ohio, July 8, 30; m. 54; c. 2. PHYSICS. A.B, Harvard, 52, A.M, 53, fel, 55, Ph.D.(appl. physics), 57. Asst. prof. metall, Mass. Inst. Technol, 56-60; WITH RES. LAB, GEN. ELEC. CO, 60- Adj. prof, Rensselaer Polytech. Inst, 67-68; consult, U.S. Geol. Surv, 67-70; assoc. ed, Geochem. & Cosmochem. Acta, 70-71. Award, Am. Nuclear Soc, 64; Ernest O. Lawrence Award, 71; Inventor's award, Gen. Elec. Co, 71. AAAS; Am. Geophys. Union; fel. Am. Phys. Soc; Am. Astron. Soc; fel. Meteoritical Soc. Solid state physics; charged particle tracks in solids; superconductivity; crystal plasticity theory; dislocation theory; geochronology and application of geochronology to anthropology; applications of charged particle tracks in space sciences; nuclear physics and engineering. Address: Research Lab, General Electric Co, Schenectady, NY 12301.

FLEISCHER, SIDNEY, b. New York, N.Y, May 10, 30; m. 62. BIOCHEMISTRY. B.S, City Col. New York, 52; Nat. Cancer Inst. fel, Indiana, 56-57, Ph.D.(biochem), 57. Res. chemist, Heyden Chem. Corp, N.J, 52-54; asst, Indiana, 54-56, res. with Prof. Haurowitz, 57-58; res. fel, inst. enzyme res, Wisconsin, 58-60, asst. prof, 60-64, assoc. prof, DEPT. MOLECULAR BIOL, VANDERBILT UNIV, 64-68, PROF, 68- Estab. investr, Am. Heart Asn, 64-69; fel. coun. arteriosclerosis, 69- Am. Soc. Biol. Chem; Am. Chem. Soc; Am. Oil Chem. Soc; Brit. Biochem. Soc; Am. Soc. Cell Biol; N.Y. Acad. Sci; Biophys. Soc. Physiological role of lipids; electron transport and oxidative phosphorylation; structure and function of organelles and membranes; sub-cellular particles; enzymology. Address: Dept. of Molecular Biology, Vanderbilt University, Nashville, TN 37203.

FLEISCHER, THOMAS B, b. Oslo, Norway, Mar. 27, 29; m. 58; c. 3. PHYSICAL CHEMISTRY, PAPER TECHNOLOGY. B.S, Oslo, 50, 52 & 53, Ph.D. (phys. chem), 56. Res. chemist, W.Va Pulp & Paper Co, Md, 57-59; res. assoc. papermaking, Scott Paper Co, Pa, 59-61; res. group leader pulp-paper prod, A/B Borregaard, Sarpsborg, Norway, 61-66; mgr. res. & develop. phys. & chem. res, HUYCK RES. CTR, 66-68, mgr. felt & fabrics, 68-71, DIR. RES, 71- Royal Norweg. Guard, 51-52. Am. Tech. Asn. Pulp & Paper Industs. Structure of polymers; fillers and additives in paper; paper coating forming fabric development; dryer fabric development. Address: Huyck Research Center, Washington St, Rensselaer, NY 12144.

FLEISCHMAJER, RAUL, b. Buenos Aires, Arg, Dec. 17, 24; U.S. citizen; m. 57; c. 1. DERMATOLOGY, BIOCHEMISTRY. Dipl, N.Y. Univ, 62. Instr. dermat, N.Y. Univ, 60-62, asst. prof. dermat. & res. assoc. biochem, 62-63; assoc. prof. dermat, HAHNEMANN MED. COL, 63-, PROF. MED. & DIR. DERMAT, 69- Asst. vis. dermatologist, Bellevue Hosp, New York, 61-63; fel, Arthritis & Rheumatism Found, 62-64; asst. attend. physician, Phila. Gen. Hosp, 64-; consult, Vet. Admin. Hosps, Phila, 64-, Wilkes-Barre, 65- Henry Silver award, 63. AAAS; Am. Med. Asn; Soc. Invest. Dermat; Am. Acad. Dermat; N.Y. Acad. Sci. Disturbances of lipid metabolism; chemical structure of human connective tissue; role of connective tissue in experimental carcinogenesis; chemical structure of collagen in scleroderma. Address: Hahnemann Medical College of Philadelphia, 230 N. Broad St, Philadelphia, PA 19102.

FLEISCHMAN, ALAN ISADORE, b. Brooklyn, N.Y, Aug. 10, 28; m. 62; c. 2. BIOCHEMISTRY, MICROBIOLOGY. B.S, City Col. New York, 50; M.A, Brooklyn Col, 55; Ph.D.(biol), St. John's (N.Y), 60. Res. chemist fermentation, Liebmann Breweries, N.Y, 51-61; supv. biochemist, atherosclerosis res. group, St. Vincent's Hosp, Montclair, N.J, 61-66; RES. SCIENTIST, DIV. COMMUNITY HEALTH SERV, N.J. STATE DEPT. HEALTH, 66- Consult, Park-Hill Chem. Corp, N.Y, 51-52; Vegex Corp, 57; Squibb Inst. Med. Res, N.J, 59; res. assoc, health res. inst, Fairleigh Dickinson Univ, 63-; fel. Coun. Atherosclerosis & Epidemiol, Am. Heart Asn. Chem.C, U.S.A.R, 50-, Lt. Col. AAAS; Am. Chem. Soc; Am. Heart Asn; Am. Soc. Microbiol; Soc. Indust. Microbiol; fel. Am. Inst. Chem; Oil Chem. Soc; Brit. Soc. Gen. Microbiol. Human and animal lipid biochemistry and nutrition, including cation-lipid interactions; mycological biochemistry and enzymology. Address: 365 Lake Shore Dr, Parsippany, NJ 07057.

FLEISCHMAN, DARRELL EUGENE, b. Gooding, Idaho, Apr. 7, 34. BIOPHYSICS. B.S, Calif. Inst. Tech, 58; Arizona State, 62; Continental Oil fel, Arizona, 63-64, Ph.D.(chem), 65. Fel, CHARLES F. KETTERING RES. LAB, 64-65, staff scientist, 65-70, INVESTR, 70- U.S.A, 54-56. Biophys. Soc. Photosynthesis; vision. Address: Charles F. Kettering Research Lab, 150 E. South College St, Yellow Springs, OH 45387.

FLEISCHMAN, JULIAN B, b. Phila, Pa, Dec. 6, 33. MICROBIOLOGY. B.S, Yale, 55; Nat. Sci. Found. fel, Harvard, 55-56, Nat. Insts. Health fel, 56-59, Ph.D.(biochem), 60. Nat. Sci. Found. fel, Stanford, 59-61; Am. Cancer Soc. fel, St. Mary's Hosp, London & Pasteur Inst, Paris, 61-63; Weizmann Inst, Israel, 63-64; ASST. PROF. MICROBIOL, SCH. MED, WASH. UNIV, 64- AAAS; Am. Asn. Immunol. Structure and biosynthesis of immunoglobulins and antibodies. Address: Dept. of Microbiology, Washington University School of Medicine, St. Louis, MO 63110.

FLEISCHMAN, ROBERT WERDER, b. New York, N.Y, Feb. 13, 37; m. 63; c. 2. VETERINARY PATHOLOGY & MEDICINE. Columbia, 54-57; D.V.M, State Univ. N.Y. Vet. Col, Cornell, 61. Sr. asst. vet, lab. perinatal physiol, Nat. Inst. Neurol. Diseases & Blindness, 62-63; assoc. bacteriologist, Nat. Center Primate Biol, 64-65; fel. comp. path, sch. med, Hopkins, 66-69; PATHOLOGIST, MASON RES. INST, 69- Consult, Worcester Found. Exp. Biol, Mass. Dipl, Am. Col. Vet. Path, 70. U.S.P.H.S, 62-63, Lt. Am. Vet. Med. Asn; Am. Asn. Lab. Animal Sci; N.Y. Acad. Sci; Am. Col. Vet. Path. Primate care and pathology; laboratory animal medicine and pathology; zoo animal pathology; drug induced toxicology and pathology. Address: Mason Research Institute, 25 Harvard St, Worcester, MA 01608.

FLEISCHMANN, CHARLES WERNER, b. N.Y.C, Jan. 22, 36; m. 59; c. 3. INORGANIC CHEMISTRY, ELECTROCHEMISTRY. B.S, Queens Col.(N.Y), 57; Univ. Denver, 59-60; M.S, Polytech. Inst. Brooklyn, 65; NASA trainee, 66-69, Ph.D.(inorg. chem), 70. Jr. mkt. analyst, Allied Chem. & Dye Corp, N.Y, summer 55; jr. chemist, Jacques Loewe Res. Labs, 57-58; chemist, Leesona Moos Labs, 58-59 & 62-66; sr. engr, Mallory Battery Co, 69-70; SR. SCIENTIST, CENT. RES. LABS, NL INDUSTS, 70- Consult, Leesona Moos Labs, 66-67. U.S.A.F, 59-62, Res, 62-70, Capt. Am. Chem. Soc; Electrochem. Soc. Electrochemistry of molten salts; power sources; primary, secondary, fuel and radio-isotope cells; electrocrystallization; hydrogen in metal; magnetic anisotropy measurements of crystals; isolation of bio-active organics. Address: 9 Edwards Dr, Hightstown, NJ 08520.

FLEISCHMANN, G(EORGE), b. Budapest, Hungary, Oct. 31, 35; Can. citizen; m. 57; c. 3. PLANT PATHOLOGY. B.A, Toronto, 57, M.A, 59, Nat. Res. Coun. Can. fel, 60-62, Ph.D.(plant path), 62. PLANT PATHOLOGIST, CAN. DEPT. AGR. RES. STA, 62- Hon. prof, sch. grad. studies, Univ. Man, 64-; C.D. Howe Mem. fel, Hebrew Univ, Israel, 65-66. Am. Phytopath. Soc; Can. Phytopath. Soc; Genetics Soc. Can. Pathogenicity of oat crown rust, Puccinia coronata avenae; epidemiology of rust pathogen on oats. Address: Canada Dept. of Agriculture Research Station, 25 Dafoe Rd, Winnipeg 19, Man, Can.

FLEISCHMANN, HANS H, b. Munich, Ger, June 2, 33. PLASMA & ATOM PHYSICS. Dipl. physics, Munich Tech, 59, Dr. rer. nat, 62. Res. assoc. nuclear physics, Munich Tech, 62-63; staff mem, Gen. Atomic Div, Gen. Dynamic Corp, Calif, 63-67; ASSOC. PROF. APPL. PHYS, CORNELL UNIV, 67- Consult, Rohde & Schwarz, Munich, Ger, 59-63. Am. Phys. Soc; Inst. Elec. & Electronics Eng. Multiple scattering; nuclear resonance fluorescence; automatic control electronics; thermonuclear fusion; atomic collisions. Address: Dept. of Applied Physics, Clark Hall, Cornell University, Ithaca, NY 14850.

FLEISHER, DANIEL S, b. Philadelphia, Pa, Mar. 4, 27; m. 50; c. 3. PEDIATRICS. B.S, Villanova, 48; M.D, Hahnemann Med. Col, 53; M.Ed, Illinois, 67. ASSOC. PROF. PEDIAT, SCH. MED, TEMPLE UNIV. 63-, DIR. CONTINUING EDUC, CTR. HEALTH EDUC. STUDIES, HEALTH SCI. CTR, 67- Res. fel, Children's Hosp. of Phila, 56-58; Am. Heart Asn. res. fel, center for study med. ed, col. med, Illinois, 66-67. Dir. nephrology, St. Christopher's Hosp. for Children, Phila, 58- U.S.N.R, 45-46. AAAS; Soc. Pediat. Res; Am. Fedn. Clin. Res. Renal disease in children; education in the health sciences. Address: Center for Health Education Studies, Health Science Center, Temple University, Broad & Ontario Sts, Philadelphia, PA 19140.

FLEISHER, GERARD A(DALBERT), b. Dresden, Germany, Nov. 10, 11; nat; m. 37; c. 2. CHEMISTRY. Berlin, 30-34; Ph.D.(chem), Danzig Tech, 36. Res. chemist, Schering Corp, N.J, 37-42; res. assoc. chem, med. col, Cornell, 42-44; res. chemist, Gelatin Prods. Corp, Mich, 44-45; CONSULT, MAYO CLIN, 47-, PROF. BIOCHEM, MAYO GRAD. SCH. MED, UNIV. MINN, 64- Civilian with Off. Sci. Res. & Develop, 44. AAAS; Soc. Exp. Biol. & Med; Am. Chem. Soc; Am. Soc. Biol. Chem. Steroidal hormones; testosterone adrenal hormones; prolactin and gonadotrophic hormones; contributions to the chemistry of the progesterone group; steroids related to cortisone; kinetics of enzyme reactions; peptidases, transaminases and aldolase in human blood and tissues. Address: Dept. of Biochemistry, Mayo Graduate School of Medicine, University of Minnesota, Rochester, MN 55901.

FLEISHER, HAROLD, b. Kharkov, Russia, Oct. 12, 21; nat; m. 45; c. 3. PHYSICS, MATHEMATICS. B.A, Rochester, 42, M.S, 43; Turnbull fel, Case Inst. Tech, 48-50, Ph.D, 51. Res. assoc. physics, Rochester, 42-43; mem. staff radar circuitry, radiation lab, Mass. Inst. Tech, 43-45; sr. engr, video circuitry, Rauland Corp, 45-46; instr. physics, Case Inst. Tech, 46-50; mem. staff physics & comput, res. lab, Int. Bus. Mach. Corp, 50-61, sr. physicist, systs. develop. div, 61-65; mgr. adv. tech. develop, Poughkeepsie Systs. Develop. Div, 65-68, PROG. MGR, SYSTS. DEVELOP. DIV. LAB, IBM CORP, 68- Vis. prof, Vassar Col. Am. Phys. Soc; fel. Inst. Elec. & Electronics Eng; Sci. Res. Soc. Am. Semiconductors and cryogenic physics and devices; optics and quantum electronics; computer organization theory and design. Address: Dept. C-14, Systems Development Division Lab, IBM Corp, P.O. Box 390, Poughkeepsie, NY 12602.

FLEISHER, PENROD J(AY), b. Liberty, N.Y, Aug. 2, 37; m. 62; c. 2. GEOMORPHOLOGY, GLACIOLOGY. B.S, St. Lawrence Univ, 61; M.S, Univ. N.C, Chapel Hill, 63; Ph.D.(glacial geol), Wash. State Univ, 67. Geophysicist, Pan Am. Petrol. Corp, 63-64; ASSOC. PROF. GEOL, STATE UNIV. N.Y. COL. ONEONTA, 67- Geol. Soc. Am; Nat. Asn. Geol. Teachers. Glacial geology and periglacial geomorphology; model studies in glacier dynamics. Address: Dept. of Earth Science, State University of New York College at Oneonta, Oneonta, NY 13820.

FLEISHMAN, B(ERNARD) A(BRAHAM), b. N.Y.C, June 16, 25; m. 50; c. 3. APPLIED MATHEMATICS. B.A, City Col. New York, 44; M.S, N.Y. Univ, 48, Ph.D.(math), 52. Spec. instr. linguistics, U.S. Army Specialized Training Prog, Univ. Pa, 43-44; asst. physics, N.Y. Univ, 46-48, res. asst. & instr. math, 48-52; sr. staff mathematician, appl. physics lab, Johns Hopkins Univ, 52-55; asst. prof. MATH, RENSSELAER POLYTECH. INST, 55-57, assoc. prof, 57-61, PROF, 61- U.S.A, 44-46. Am. Math. Soc. Nonlinear vibrations; automatic controls; diffusion. Address: Colehamer Ave, Troy, NY 12180.

FLEISHMAN, MORTON R(OBERT), b. New York, N.Y, Jan. 21, 33; m. 61; c. 2. PHYSICS. B.S.E, Michigan, 54, Riggs fel. & M.S.E, 55; dipl, Oak Ridge Sch. Reactor Tech, 56; N.Y. Univ, 59. Asst. propulsion, aircraft propulsion lab, Michigan, 52-54; sr. scientist, NUCLEAR DEVELOP. CORP. AM, 56-63; NUCLEAR PHYSICIST, SPACE NUCLEAR SYSTS. OFF, 63- Summers, power plant engr, Glenn L. Martin Co, 54; proj. engr, eng. res. inst, Michigan, 55. Am. Nuclear Soc; Am. Inst. Aeronaut. & Astronaut. Theoretical and experimental reactor physics and shielding; unified field theory and quantum mechanics. Address: 5247 Evergreen Dr, North Olmstead, OH 44070.

FLEISIG, ROSS, b. Montreal, Can, Oct. 12, 21; nat; m. 43; c. 2. AERONAUTICAL ENGINEERING. B.Aero.Eng, Polytech. Inst. Brooklyn, 42, M.S, 55. From aerodynamicist to aerodyn. design engr, Chance Vought Aircraft, 42-50; flight control systems engr, Sperry Gyroscope Co, 50-54, eng. sect. head, missile systems, 54-58, astronaut. syst, 58-60; group head, guidance dynamics, GRUMMAN AIRCRAFT CORP, 60-62, head, lunar excursion module dynamics & performance anal, 62-65, lunar excursion module guid, navig. & control anal. & integration, 65-67, LM-5 space craft team mgr, 67-69, SPACE SYSTS. PROJ. MGR, 69- Mem. space rescue studies comt, Int. Acad. Astronaut. Fel. AAAS; fel. Am. Astronaut. Soc.(pres, 57-58, nat. dir, 59-67); assoc. fel, Am. Inst. Aeronaut. & Astronaut; fel. Brit. Interplanetary Soc. Aerodynamics; flight dynamics; flight control and guidance systems analyses and development; astronautics. Address: 58 Kilburn Rd, Garden City, NY 11530.

FLEITMAN, ALBERT HENRY, b. Kansas City, Mo, Mar. 19, 26; m. 52; c. 4. PHYSICAL METALLURGY. Met.E, Colo. Sch. Mines, 49; M.S, Ill. Inst. Tech, 56; M.B.A, Chicago, 59. Metallurgist, Inland Steel Co, 50-52; asst. supvr. phys. metall, Crane Co, 52-59; ASSOC. SCIENTIST, BROOKHAVEN NAT. LAB, 59-69, DEPT. APPL. SCI, 69- Asst. prof. physics, Suffolk Community Col, 63- U.S.N, 44-46. Am. Soc. Metals. High temperature alloy development; liquid metal corrosion; reactor metallurgy. Address: Dept. of Applied Science, Brookhaven National Lab, Upton, NY 11973.

FLEMAL, RONALD C(HARLES), b. Two Rivers, Wis, Feb. 17, 42; m. 64; c. 3. GEOLOGY. B.A, Northwest. Univ, 63; A.M, Princeton, 65, Ph.D.(geol), 67. ASST. PROF. GEOL, NORTH. ILL. UNIV, 67- Consult, U.S. Bur. Mines, 67- AAAS; Soc. Econ. Paleont. & Mineral; Geol. Soc. Am; Am. Quaternary Asn; Int. Asn. Math. Geol. Application of quantitative techniques in geology and geomorphology; quaternary geology. Address: Dept. of Geology, Northern Illinois University, DeKalb, IL 60015.

FLEMING, ALAN WAYNE, b. Kansas City, Mo, Dec. 2, 39; m. 61; c. 2. AERONAUTICS, ASTRONAUTICS. B.S, Univ. Kans, 61; M.S, Stanford Univ, 62, Ph.D.(aeronaut. & astronaut. sci), 66. Summers, stud. engr, Boeing Co, 60, asst. engr, 61, assoc. engr, Lockheed Missiles & Space Co, 62 & 63; RES. ENGR, STANFORD UNIV, 66- Am. Inst. Aeronaut. & Astronaut; Inst. Elec. & Electronics Eng. Modeling, simulation and control of systems, attitude and translation control of aerospace vehicles; satellite geodesy. Address: Dept. of Aeronautics & Astronautics, Stanford University, Stanford, CA 94305.

FLEMING, A(LLISTER) M(ELVILLE), b. Stellarton, N.S, Dec. 13, 20; m. 48; c. 2. MARINE BIOLOGY. B.Sc, Dalhousie, 47; M.A, Toronto, 52. MEM. SCI. STAFF, BIOL. STA, FISHERIES RES. BD. CAN, 47-, ASST. DIR, 55- Cod, groundfish statistics. Address: Fisheries Research Board of Canada, Biological Station, St. John', Newf, Can.

FLEMING, ARTHUR WILLIAM, b. Chicago, Ill, Sept. 29, 06; m; c. 3. PEDIATRICS. B.S, Notre Dame, 29; M.D, Rush Med. Col, 33; M.P.H, Univ. Mich, 68. Intern path, St. Luke Hosp, 34; Mercy Hosp, 34-35, res. pediat, Munic. Contagious Diseases Hosp, 35; Presby. Hosp, Chicago, Ill, 35-37; sr. pediatrician, Mercy Hosp, 40-66, attend. pediatrician & dir, cerebral palsy & children's rehab. clin, 47-55; ASSOC. DIR. INST. STUDY MENT. RETARDATION & RELATED DISABILITIES, CLIN. PROF. PEDIAT, SCH. MED. & ASSOC. PROF. MATERNAL & CHILD HEALTH, SCH. PUB. HEALTH, UNIV. MICH, ANN ARBOR, 69- Clin. prof, Stritch Sch. Med, Loyola Univ. Chicago, 38-66, secy. pediat. dept, 40-50, head pediat. dept, 61-67; med. dir, Martha Washington Home Crippled Children, 48-53; St. Joseph's Home Friendless, 49-65; Kiwanis Twin Lake Camp Crippled Children, 50-65; attend. pediatrician, Little Co. Mary Hosp, 50-, v.chmn. dept. pediat, 54-59, chmn, 59-66, dir. premature nursery, 55-65, pediat. consult, 68-; consult, St. Bernard's Hosp, Chicago, 62-68; mem. pediat. adv. comt, Chicago Bd. Health, 63-; pediat. consult, Mercy Hosp. & Cook County Hosp, 68- Am. Med. Asn; Am. Acad. Pediat; Am. Cong. Rehab. Med; Asn. Am. Med. Cols. Newborn and premature; mental and physically handicapped child; growth and development; general good pediatric care. Address: Institute for the Study of Mental Retardation & Related Disabilities, University of Michigan, 611 Church St, Fourth Floor, Ann Arbor, MI 48104.

FLEMING, A(TTIE) A(NDERSON), b. Russellville, Ala, Dec. 3, 21. PLANT GENETICS. B.S, Auburn, 43, M.S, 49; Ph.D.(plant genetics), Minnesota, 51. Asst. county agr. agent, Calhoun County, Ala, 43-45; asst. agron, Ala. Polytech, 47-49; agron. & plant genetics, Minnesota, 49-51; asst. prof. PLANT GENETICS, UNIV. GA, 51-55, assoc. prof, 55-61, PROF, 62- U.S.A, 46-47. AAAS; Am. Soc. Agron; Am. Genetic Asn; Genetics Soc. Can; Crop Sci. Soc. Am. Corn improvement; genetics of corn; disease and insect resistance of corn; field-plot technique. Address: Dept. of Agronomy, University of Georgia, Athens, GA 30601.

FLEMING, CHARLES L(E ROY), JR, b. Penns Grove, N.J, May 16, 14; m; c. 3. CHEMISTRY. A.B, Dartmouth Col, 35; A.M, Illinois, 36, Ph.D.(chem), 38. Assoc. dir. res. div, Standard Oil Develop. Co, 38-53, dir, 54-56, v.pres. & dir, res. div, Esso Res. & Eng. Co, 56-66, mgr. res. dept, Esso Europe, London, 66-71; PARTNER, CORP. DEVELOP. CONSULTS, 71- Am. Chem. Soc; Soc. Automotive Eng. Lubricating oils; petroleum additives; new synthesis of furans; chemicals. Address: Corporate Development Consultants, 71, Central Bldg, Southwark St, London SE1, England.

FLEMING, DAVID G(ORDON), b. N.Y.C, July 3, 26; m. 49; c. 1. PHYSIOLOGY. A.B, California, 48, Ph.D.(physiol), 52. Assoc. physiol, California, 52-53; asst. prof, Kansas, 53-58; physiologist, Gen. Elec. Co, 58-61; asst. prof. physiol, sch. med, CASE WEST. RESERVE UNIV, 61-70, ADJ. PROF. BIOMED. ENG, SCH. ENG, 70-, assoc. prof, 61-66, prof, 66-70. U.S.N.R, 44-46. AAAS; Biophys. Soc; Am. Physiol. Soc; Inst. Elec. & Electronics Eng; Am. Soc. Eng. Educ. Control and regulation in physiological systems; neurophysiology and bioengineering education. Address: Division of Biomedical Engineering, School of Engineering, Case Western Reserve University, Cleveland, OH 44106.

FLEMING, DONOVAN E(RNEST), b. Ogden, Utah, Aug. 16, 32; m. 55; c. 3. PHYSIOLOGICAL PSYCHOLOGY. B.S, Brigham Young, 56, M.S, 57; Ph.D. (physiol. psychol), Washington State, 62. Trainee, Vet. Admin. Hosp, Salt Lake City, Utah, 60-61; res. psychologist brain res, 61-64, dir. res. unit, Phoenix, Ariz, 64-71; PROF. PSYCHOL, BRIGHAM YOUNG UNIV, 71- Spec. instr. Brigham Young Univ, 60-64; res. instr, div. neurol, col. med. & lectr, dept. psychol, Univ. Utah, 62-64; res. asst. prof. psychol, Ariz. State Univ, 65-67, vis. assoc. prof, 67-71. U.S.N, 52-54. Am. Psychol. Asn; Am. Physiol. Soc. Physiological and psychological correlates in sensory systems. Address: Dept. of Psychology, Brigham Young University, Provo, UT 84601.

FLEMING, EDWARD H(OMER), JR, b. University City, Mo, Feb. 27, 25. NUCLEAR CHEMISTRY. A.B, Wabash Col, 49; Ph.D.(chem), California, 52. Chemist, Lawrence radiation lab, California, 49-52; res. chemist, Calif. Res. Corp, 52-55; ASST. HEAD DEPT. CHEM, LAWRENCE LIVERMORE LAB, UNIV. CALIF, 55- Tech. dir. Proj. Sulky & chmn. radioactivity working group, Atlantic-Pac. Interoceanic Canal Studies Comn, 67-70. U.S.N.R, 43-46. AAAS. Half-lives of uranium isotopes; gamma-ray scattering; oil soluble tracers; fallout from nuclear explosions; fission product decay chains; radiation doses from radionuclides. Address: Dept. of Chemistry, Lawrence Livermore Lab, University of California, Box 808, Livermore, CA 94550.

FLEMING, GORDON N, b. Pittsburgh, Pa, Apr. 14, 36; m. 58; c. 2. THEORETICAL PHYSICS. B.S, Pittsburgh, 58; Wilson fel, Pennsylvania, 58-59, Nat. Sci. Found. fel, 60-62, Ph.D.(physics), 64. Res. asst. prof. THEORET. PHYSICS, Washington (Seattle), 63-65; asst. prof, PA. STATE UNIV, 65-68, ASSOC. PROF, 68- Am. Phys. Soc. Relatavistic quantum theory; theory of elementary particles; foundations of quantum mechanics. Address: Dept. of Physics, Osmond Lab, Pennsylvania State University, University Park, PA 16802.

FLEMING, HAROLD W(ILLIAM), b. Ancon, Panama C.Z, April 21, 14; m. 42; c. 3. ORGANIC CHEMISTRY. B.A, Kenyon Col, 39; Sherwin-Williams fel. & Ph.D.(org. chem), Western Reserve, 43. Chemist, Sherwin-Williams Co, Ohio, 42-43; group leader, Phillips Petrol. Co, Okla, 43-51; dir. res. & develop, Girdler Corp, Ky, 51-57; v.pres. res. & develop, Catalysts & Chems, Inc, 57-65, v.pres. mfg, 65-69; PRES, CATALYST CONSULT. SERV, INC, 69- Am. Chem. Soc. Development of resins and drying oils; oxidation of hydrocarbons; hydrogenation of petroleum; development of synthetic fuels; new and improved commercial catalysts in petroleum, food, chemical and ammonia industries. Address: Catalyst Consulting Services, Inc, Mall Office Center, Suite 415, 400 Sherburn Lane, Louisville, KY 40207.

FLEMING, H(ENRY) CRESWELL, III, b. Laurens, S.C, Nov. 2, 44; m. 67. PHYSICAL CHEMISTRY. B.S, Colo. Col, 66; NASA fel, Univ. Colo, Boulder, 66-69, Ph.D.(phys. chem), 70. Staff mem, Sandia Corp, summer 66; CHEMIST, SHELL DEVELOP. CO, 70- Am. Chem. Soc. Electronic structure of molecular donor-acceptor complexes and magnetic resonance spectroscopy; all aspects of heterogeneous catalysis. Address: Shell Development Co, P.O. Box 24225, Oakland, CA 94623.

FLEMING, HENRY P(RIDGEN), b. New Haven, Conn, Aug. 9, 32; m. 54; c. 3. FOOD SCIENCE, MICROBIOLOGY. B.S, N.C. State, 54, M.S, 58; Ph.D.(food sci), Illinois, 63. Instr. animal sci, N.C. State, 58-60; microbiologist, Merck & Co, Inc, 63-64; FOOD TECHNOLOGIST FERMENTATION, DEPT. FOOD SCI, U.S. DEPT. AGR. & N.C. STATE UNIV, 64- U.S.A, 54-56, Capt. Inst. Food Technol; Am. Soc. Microbiol. Microbiology and chemistry of vegetable fermentations; lactic acid bacteria; spore forming bacteria; chemistry, microbiology, and quality of red meats. Address: 308 Westridge Dr, Raleigh, NC 27609.

FLEMING, HENRY STANTON, III, b. N.Y.C, June 5, 38; m. 58; c. 4. MARINE GEOLOGY, UNDERWATER ACOUSTICS. B.S, New Eng. Col, 60. Res. asst. oceanog, Lamont-Doherty Geol. Observ, 56-58; res. chemist, Lever Bros. Co, 60-65; res. asst. oceanog, Hudson Labs, Columbia, 65-67, assoc. res. scientist, 67-69; RES. OCEANOGR, NAVAL RES. LAB, 69- Mem, Int. Oceanog. Found. AAAS; Am. Geophys. Union. Submarine topography, geology, photography and acoustics; tectonics; seismicity; geological, geophysical and oceanographic exploration of the deep-sea; deep-sea research instruments; underwater sound propagation; magnetic surveys. Address: Naval Research Lab, Washington, DC 20390.

FLEMING, JAMES C(HARLES), b. Lancaster, Ohio, Aug. 25, 38; m. 68; c. 1. ORGANIC CHEMISTRY. B.S, Ohio, 60; Sinclair fel, Ohio State, 62-63, Lubrizol fel, 63-64, Ph.D.(diazooxides), 64. ORG. RES. CHEMIST, EASTMAN KODAK CO, 65- Am. Chem. Soc. Photographic and synthetic organic chemistry. Address: Eastman Kodak Co, Research Labs, Bldg. 59, Kodak Park, Rochester, NY 14601.

FLEMING, JAMES D(E WILEY), b. Bonita, Texas, Dec. 11, 13; m. 42. MECHANICAL ENGINEERING. B.S, Texas Tech. Col, 47; M.S, Wisconsin, 48, Ph.D.(mech. eng), 50. SR. RES. ENGR, RES. LAB, GEN. MOTORS CORP, 50- U.S.A, 41-45. Soc. Automotive Eng. Internal combustion engines; free piston engines; diesels. Address: Mechanical Research Dept, Research Lab, General Motors Corp, 12 Mile & Mound Rds, Warren, MI 48090.

FLEMING, JAMES J(OSEPH), b. Chicago, Ill, Feb. 26, 17; m. 50; c. 4. PHYSICS. B.S, Northwestern, 38. Physicist, Naval Res. Lab, 41-62, head opers. res. br, 45-62; assoc. supt. applns. res. div, 56-62; chief data systs.

div, GODDARD SPACE FLIGHT CTR, 62-67, dep. asst. dir, CTR. AUTOMATIC DATA PROCESSING, 67-70, ASST. DIR, 70- Navy meritorious civilian serv. award, 47, distinguished civilian serv. award, 60. AAAS; Am. Phys. Soc; Asn. Comput. Mach; Inst. Elec. & Electronics Eng; Am. Inst. Aeronaut. & Astronaut. Systems engineering; electronics; radar; digital computers; Address: NASA-Goddard Space Flight Center, Greenbelt, MD 20771.

FLEMING, JOHN F, b. Williamsport, Pa, Nov. 27, 21; m. 51; c. 1. SOIL SCIENCE. B.S, Pa. State, 47, M.S, 52. Soil scientist, Pa. Game Comn, 47-48; work unit conservationist, soil conserv. serv, U.S. DEPT. AGR, 48-56; soil scientist, 56-68, AGRICULTURIST, AGR. RES. SERV, 68- U.S.A, 43-46. Plant nutrition; clay minerals in soils; sulfur acid soils; cation exchange capacity of organic matter in soils. Address: 13006 Greenmount Ave, Beltsville, MD 20705.

FLEMING, JOHN F, b. Indiana, Pa, Dec. 15, 34; m. 57; c. 2. CIVIL ENGINEERING. B.S, Carnegie Inst. Tech, 57, M.S, 58, Ph.D.(civil eng), 60. Assoc. prof. civil eng, Northwestern, 60-65; proj. engr, Gen. Analytics, Inc, Pa, 65-69; ASSOC. PROF. CIVIL ENG, UNIV. PITTSBURGH, 69- Am. Soc. Civil Eng; Soc. Exp. Stress Anal. Structural dynamics; computer applications in structural design; structural model analysis. Address: Dept. of Civil Engineering, University of Pittsburgh, Pittsburgh, PA 15213.

FLEMING, LAWRENCE THOMAS, b. Tacoma, Wash, Sept. 26, 13; m. 37; c. 1. APPLIED PHYSICS. B.S, Calif. Inst. Technol, 37. Exam, U.S. Patent Off, D.C, 37-41; engr, U.S. Naval Ord. Lab, 41-46, sect. head, 46-50; head mech. group, electron tube lab, Nat. Bur. Standards, 50-53, group leader, 55-56; chief instrumentation sect, Diamond Ord. Fuze Labs, U.S. Army, 53-55; div. engr, res. dept, Southwest. Indust. Electronics Co, Tex, 56-59; prin. res. engr, res. ctr, Bell & Howell Co, 59-67; PRES, INNES INSTRUMENTS, 67- Fel. Acoust. Soc. Am. Instrumentation; mechanical measurements; vibration and shock; research administration; history, sociology and legal aspects of invention. Address: 625 S. Oak Knoll Ave, Pasadena, CA 91106.

FLEMING, PETER B, b. Trenton, N.J, Apr. 9, 41; m. 63; c. 3. INORGANIC CHEMISTRY. B.S, Union Col.(N.Y), 63; Ph.D.(inorg. chem), Iowa State Univ, 68. SR. CHEMIST, CENT. RES. LAB, 3M CO, 68- Metal-metal bonded complexes; niobium and tantalum clusters and complexes; copper chemistry; optical spectra and photochemistry of transition metal complexes. Address: 3M Co. Central Research Lab, Box 33221, St. Paul, MN 55133.

FLEMING, PHYLLIS JANE, b. Shelbyville, Ind, Oct. 9, 24. PHYSICS. B.A, Hanover Col, 46; M.S, Wisconsin, 48, Ph.D, 54. Instr. PHYSICS, Mt. Holyoke Col, 48-50; WELLESLEY COL, 53-55, asst. prof, 55-61, assoc. prof, 61-67, PROF, 67-, DEAN COL, 68- Am. Phys. Soc. Film flow of liquid helium II; photoconductivity of lead sulfide films. Address: Wellesley College, Wellesley, MA 02181.

FLEMING, RICHARD A(LLAN), b. Chicago, Ill, Sept. 16, 29; m. 53; c. 3. PHYSICAL CHEMISTRY. A.B, Knox Col, 51; M.S, Iowa State, 55, Ph.D. (chem), 57. Res. chemist, ELECTROCHEM. DEPT, E.I. DU PONT DE NEMOURS & CO, INC, 57-62, res. assoc, 62-64, staff scientist, 64, RES. SUPVR, 64- U.S.A, 51-53, 1st Lt. Sci. Res. Soc. Am; Am. Chem. Soc; Am. Soc. Metals. Physical chemistry of solids and liquids in the range of 500-1200 degrees centigrade; chemical processes. Address: 3202 Kammerer Dr, Wilmington, DE 19803.

FLEMING, RICHARD C(ORNWELL), b. Blue Island, Ill, Mar. 10, 32; m. 58; c. 5. ZOOLOGY, ENTOMOLOGY. A.B, Kalamazoo Col, 54; M.A, Kansas, 56; Western Mich, 57; summers, Nat. Sci. Found. sci. insts, Southern Illinois, Tulane, Oklahoma & Southwestern Louisiana, 59-62; Ph.D, Mich. State Univ, 68. Asst. instr. zool, Kansas, 54-56; teacher, high sch, Mich, 58-61; asst. prof. BIOL, OLIVET COL, 61-67, ASSOC. PROF, 67- Instr, Western Michigan, 59-60. Summers, biol. aide, Bear River Wildlife Res. Sta, U.S. Fish & Wildlife Serv, 55, 56, 57, Mich. State, 64-67, asst. prof, 69-71. Lepidop. Soc. Ornithology; entomology, especially distribution, behavior and morphology of Lepidoptera. Address: Dept. of Biology, Olivet College, Olivet, MI 49076.

FLEMING, RICHARD H(OWELL), b. Victoria, B.C, Can, Sept. 21, 09; nat; m. 33; c. 3. OCEANOGRAPHY. B.A, British Columbia, 29, M.A, 31; Ph.D. (oceanog), California, 35. Asst. chem, British Columbia, 29-31; oceanog, Scripps Inst, California, 31-35, res. assoc, 35-36, instr, 36-41, asst. prof, 41-46; chief, div. oceanog, Hydrographic Off, Dept. Navy, 46-50; PROF. OCEANOG. UNIV. WASH, 50-, CHMN. DEPT, 51-, exec. off. dept, 50-51. Sr. oceanogr, div. war res, Scripps Inst, California, 41-42, chief oceanog. sect, 42-44, admin. asst. & sr. oceanogr, 44-45, asst. dir, 45-46. Dep. mem, cmt. geophys. & geog, Res. & Develop. Bd; cmt. marine ecol, Pacific Sci. Bd, Nat. Res. Coun; chmn, cmt. Atlantic Weather Ships. Am. Geophys. Union. Chemical oceanography; biochemistry; naval applications of oceanography; oceanography of Central American Pacific. Address: Dept. of Oceanography, University of Washington, Seattle, WA 98105.

FLEMING, RICHARD JOSEPH, b. Stuart, Iowa, July 26, 38; m. 60; c. 3. MATHEMATICS. B.S, Northwest Mo. State Col, 60; M.S, Fla. State, 62, Ph.D.(math), 65. Instr. MATH, Fla. State, 62-63 & 64-65, asst. prof, 65; Missouri, 65-71; ASSOC. PROF, MEMPHIS STATE UNIV, 71- Summer res. fel, Missouri, 67, 68, 70. Am. Math. Soc. Theory of duality in locally convex topological vector spaces, particularly characterizations of reflexive Banach spaces and semi-reflexive locally convex spaces. Address: Dept. of Mathematics, Memphis State University, Memphis, TN 38111.

FLEMING, ROBERT LELAND, b. Ludington, Mich, Mar. 22, 05; m. 36; c. 2. BIOLOGY. B.A, Albion Col, 27; M.A, Drew, 28; Ph.D, Chicago, 47. Supvr, pub. sch, India, 47-53; area supt, United Mission to Nepal, 56-70; PRIVATE RES, 70- Fulbright grant, 64-65. Fel. Acad. Zool; Am. Ornith Union. Ornithology and pteridophytes of Nepal. Address: P.O. Box 229, Kathmandu, Nepal.

FLEMING, ROBERT W(ILLERTON), b. Bon Aire, Pa, May 28, 19; m. 43; c. 4. CHEMISTRY. B.S, Pittsburgh, 40; Tanners' Coun. fel, Cincinnati, 40-43, M.S, 41, Ph.D.(org. chem), 43. Chemists asst, Calgon, Inc, Pa, 37-42; chemist, Gen. Dyestuff Corp, N.Y, 43-44; asst, Manhattan Dist, Rochester, 44-46; res. chemist, Parke, Davis & Co, 46-63; HEAD DEPT. ORG. RES, WILLIAM S. MERRELL CO. DIV, RICHARDSON-MERRELL, INC, 63- AAAS; Am. Chem. Soc. Synthetic organic medicinals. Address: Dept. of Organic Research, William S. Merrell Co, Cincinnati, OH 45215.

FLEMING, SUZANNE M, I.H.M, b. Detroit, Mich, Feb. 4, 27. CHEMISTRY. B.S, Marygrove Col, 57; Mich. State scholar, Michigan, 58, M.S, 59, Rackham scholar, 60, univ. scholar, 61, Nat. Insts. Health fel, 62, Ph.D.(inorg. chem), 63. Teacher, St. Mary Convent, Mich, 48-58; asst. CHEM, Michigan, 61; instr, MARYGROVE COL, 62-64, asst. prof, 64-67, ASSOC. PROF, 67-, CHMN. NATURAL SCI. DIV, 70- Res. grants, Gulf Equip, 64, Sigma Xi, 64-65 & Nat. Insts. Health, 64-67; vis. lectr, Univ. Mich, 68-69. Am. Chem. Soc; fel. Am. Inst. Chem. Synthesis and study of bonding characteristics of transition metal complexes and Lewis acid-Lewis base complexes; boron hydride chemistry; spectroscopic studies of bonding. Address: Dept. of Chemistry, Marygrove College, 8425 W. McNichols Rd, Detroit, MI 48221.

FLEMING, SYDNEY W(INN), b. Thomasville, Ga, July 12, 24; m. 49; c. 4. PHYSICAL CHEMISTRY. B.A, Emory, 47, M.S, 48; Du Pont fel, Pennsylvania, 52-53, Ph.D.(chem), 54. Instr. chem, Emory, 48-49; res. phys. chemist, E.I. DU PONT DE NEMOURS & CO, 53-60, sr. res. phys. chemist, 60-61, res. supvr, 61-68, RES. ASSOC, 68- U.S.A, 44-46. Am. Chem. Soc; Optical Soc. Am; Sci. Res. Soc. Am. Polymer physical chemistry; optics; color. Address: Engineering Physics Lab, Experimental Station, E.I. du Pont de Nemours & Co, Wilmington, DE 19898.

FLEMING, THEODORE HARRIS, b. Detroit, Mich, Mar. 27, 42; m. 65; c. 1. ZOOLOGY, MAMMALIAN ECOLOGY. B.A, Albion Col, 64; univ. fel, Michigan, 64-65, Nat. Insts. Health fel, 67-69, M.S, 68, Ph.D.(zool), 69. Syst. zoologist, U.S. Nat. Mus, 66-67; ASST. PROF. BIOL, UNIV. MO-ST. LOUIS, 69- AAAS; Am. Soc. Mammal; Ecol. Soc. Am; Soc. Study Evolution. Evolution of mammalian reproductive rates; comparative demography of temperate and tropical rodent populations. Address: Dept. of Biology, University of Missouri-St. Louis, St. Louis, MO 63121.

FLEMING, THOMAS C(RAWLEY), b. Chicago, Ill, June 16, 21; m. 50; c. 5. MEDICINE. Calif. Inst. Technol; M.D, Columbia, 45. Intern med, St. Luke's Hosp, New York, 45-46; instr. physiol, col. physicians & surgeons, Columbia, 48-50; dept. clin. res, Hoffmann-La Roche, N.J, 50-55, dir. med. info, 55-56, prod. develop. mgr, 56-57; dir. clin. res, Mead Johnson & Co, 57-58, prod. develop, 58-59; med. dir, Warner-Chilcott Labs, N.J, 59-60; exec. v.pres. & med. dir, Robert E. Wilson, Inc, N.Y, 60-62; dir. med. ed. & chief chronic med, Bergen Pines County Hosp, Paramus, N.J, 62-64; med. dir, SUDLER & HENNESSEY, INC, 64-66, V.PRES. & MED. DIR, 66- Med.C, 46-48, Capt. AAAS; Am. Med. Asn; Sci. Res. Soc. Am; Am. Col. Angiol.(v.pres, 62-64); fel. Royal Soc. Health; N.Y. Acad. Sci. Clinical pharmacology; research administration. Address: Sudler & Hennessey, Inc, 130 E. 59th St, New York, NY 10022.

FLEMING, WALTER, b. Langham, Sask, May 20, 19; nat; m. 45; c. 1. MATHEMATICS. B.A, Saskatchewan, 42; M.A, Minnesota, 44, Ph.D.(math), 49. Asst. prof. MATH, New Brunswick, 45-46; lectr, Manitoba, 46-48; asst. prof, Ft. Hays Kans. State Col, 48-49; assoc. prof. & chmn. dept, Mankato State Col, 49-57; PROF. & CHMN. DEPT, HAMLINE UNIV, 57- Consult, St. Paul High Schs, 59- Math. Asn. Am; Am. Math. Soc. Integration in Wiener space. Address: Dept. of Mathematics, Hamline University, St. Paul, MN 55117.

FLEMING, WARREN R, b. Enterprise, Oregon, Nov. 30, 22; m. 58; c. 2. PHYSIOLOGY. B.S, Portland, 49, M.S, 52; Ph.D.(biol), Oregon, 55. Instr. biol, Oregon, 53-55; asst. prof. ZOOL, UNIV. MO-COLUMBIA, 55-59, assoc. prof, 59-63, PROF, 63- Am. Chem. Soc; Am. Soc. Zool; Soc. Gen. Physiol; Am. Physiol. Soc. General physiology; hormonal control of salt and water metabolism in fresh water teleosts. Address: Dept. of Zoology, University of Missouri-Columbia, Columbia, MO 65202.

FLEMING, WENDELL H(ELMS), b. Guthrie, Okla, Mar. 7, 28; m. 48; c. 3. MATHEMATICS. B.S, Purdue, 48, M.S, 49; Ph.D.(math), Wisconsin, 51. Mathematician, Rand Corp, 51-53, 54-55; res. proj. assoc, Wisconsin, 53-54; asst. prof. MATH, Purdue Univ, 55-58; BROWN UNIV, 58-60, assoc. prof, 60-63, PROF, 63-, chmn. dept, 65-68. Mem. staff, math. res. ctr, Univ. Wis, 62-63; Nat. Sci. Found. fel, 68-69. Fel. AAAS; Soc. Indust. & Appl. Math.(ed, SIAM Rev); Am. Math. Soc; Math. Asn. Am. Stochastic control; calculus of variations. Address: Dept. of Mathematics, Brown University, Providence, RI 02912.

FLEMING, WILLARD C(ORWIN), b. Sausalito, Calif, Oct. 11, 99; m. 24; c. 1. PERIODONTOLOGY, ORAL PATHOLOGY. D.D.S, California, 23; hon. D.Sc, Southern California, 46; LL.D, Univ. Toronto, 59, Univ. Calif, 69. Instr. oper. dent, UNIV. CALIF, SAN FRANCISCO, 23-29, asst. prof, 29-35, assoc. prof, 35-42, prof, 42-69, dean students, med. ctr, 39-66, v.provost, 59-64, v.chancellor, 64-65, chancellor, 66-69, EMER. PROF. OPER. DENT. & EMER. CHANCELLOR, MED. CTR, 69- Pres, Am. Asn. Dent. Schs, 46; dent. consult, Atomic Energy Comn, Los Alamos, 50-54; U.S. Dept. Navy, 54-57; consult, comt. fed. scholar. & loans, U.S. Pub. Health Serv, 64-66; Aid Int. Develop, 65- Mem. dent. res. adv. coun, Nat. Insts. Health, U.S. Pub. Health Serv, 58-64, rev. comt. dent. teaching facilities & construct, 64-66; comn. survey dent, Am. Coun. Educ, 58-61; mem. Governor's Comt. Dent. Educ. & Dent. Manpower Needs, Coord. Coun. Higher Educ, 64-65. U.S.A, 17-19. Am. Dent. Asn; Am. Col. Dent.(pres, 51-52); Int. Asn. Dent. Res. Bone, nutrition and calcium phosphorous studies; dental education; aptitude admission problems; curriculum studies; dental manpower studies; impact of changing social, political and economic philosophies on health science. Address: 5924 McAndrew Dr, Oakland, CA 94611.

FLEMING, W(ILLIAM) H(ERBERT), b. Galt, Ont, Sept. 3, 25; m. 45; c. 1. PHYSICS. B.Sc, McMaster Univ, 50, M.Sc, 51, Ph.D.(physics), 54. Fel, McMASTER UNIV, 54-58, reactor supt, 58-69, ASSOC. PROF. APPL. MATH, 66-, MGR. COMPUT. SYSTS. & PROG, 69- R.C.A.F, 43-46. Am.

Nuclear Soc; Can. Asn. Physicists. Nuclear reactor operation; digital computer programming systems. Address: Dept. of Applied Mathematics, McMaster University, Hamilton, Ont, Can.

FLEMING, WILLIAM LE(ROY), b. Morgantown, W.Va, Aug. 29, 05; m. 34; c. 4. PREVENTIVE MEDICINE. B.A, Vanderbilt, 25, M.S, 27, M.D, 32. Asst. bacter, sch. med, Vanderbilt, 25-28; intern & house physician, 2nd div, Bellevue Hosp, New York, 33-34; asst. res. & res. physician, med. serv, Vanderbilt Hosp, Nashville, 34-37; instr. med, Hopkins & Milbank fel, syphilis clinic, hosp, 37-39; mem. staff, internal health div, Rockefeller Found, 39; res. prof. syphilol, sch. pub. health, North Carolina, 39-45; assoc. prof. med, sch. med, Boston, 46-48, PROF. PREV. MED, 48-52; SCH. MED, UNIV. N.C, 52-, chmn. dept, 52-70, asst. dean, 57-70. Mem. staff, Evans Mem. Hosp, Boston, 46-52; vis. physician, Mass. Mem. Hosp, 46-52, chief, genito infectious disease clinic, 46-52; dir. gen. clinic, N.C. Mem. Hosp, 52-64; vis. prof. & consult. prev. med, Paulista Sch. Med, São Paulo, 62. Am. Soc. Clin. Invest; fel. Am. Med. Asn; Am. Pub. Health Asn; Am. Venereal Disease Asn.(pres, 54-55); Asn. Teachers Prev. Med.(pres, 59-60); Am. Col. Prev. Med; Int. Epidemiol. Asn. Research bacteriology; internal medicine; clinical experimental syphilology. Address: School of Medicine, University of North Carolina at Chapel Hill, Chapel Hill, NC 27514.

FLEMING, WILLIAM W(RIGHT), b. Wash, D.C, Jan. 30, 32; m. 52; c. 3. PHARMACOLOGY. A.B, Harvard, 54; univ. fel, Princeton, 54-55: Francis Hinton Maule fel, 55-56, M.A, 56, Proctor fel, 56-57, Ph.D.(biol), 57. Nat. Insts. Health res. fel. PHARMACOL, Harvard Med. Sch, 57-60; asst. prof, MED. SCH, W.VA. UNIV, 60-64, assoc. prof, 64-66, PROF. & HEAD DEPT, 66- AAAS; Soc. Exp. Biol. & Med; Am. Soc. Pharmacol. & Exp. Therapeut. (specific field ed, J. Autonomic Pharmacol). Autonomic and cardiovascular pharmacology. Address: Dept. of Pharmacology, West Virginia University Medical Center, Morgantown, WV 26506.

FLEMINGER, ABRAHAM, b. N.Y.C, Feb. 4, 25; m. 49; c. 1. INVERTEBRATE ZOOLOGY. B.S, Brooklyn Col, 50; fel, Harvard, 51-53, M.S, 52, Ph.D. (biol), 56; fel, Brandeis, 54-55. Biologist fishery res, U.S. Fish & Wildlife Serv, 56-60; res. biologist, SCRIPPS INST. OCEANOG, UNIV. CALIF, SAN DIEGO, 60-68, ASSOC. RES. BIOLOGIST, 68-, LECTR, 69- U.S.A.A.F, 43-45. AAAS; Am. Soc. Limnol. & Oceanog; Ecol. Soc. Am; Soc. Syst. Zool; Marine Biol. Asn. U.K. Ecology, distribution and systematics of marine zooplankton, especially the Copepoda; principles underlying spatial distribution of the oceans pelagic fauna. Address: 3785 Mt. Everest Blvd, San Diego, CA 92111.

FLEMINGS, MERTON CORSON, JR, b. Syracuse, N.Y, Sept. 20, 29; m. 56; c. 2. METALLURGY. S.B, Mass. Inst. Technol, 51, S.M, 52, Sc.D.(metall), 54. Metallurgist, Am. Brake Shoe Co, N.J, 54-56; asst. prof. metall, MASS. INST. TECHNOL, 56-61, assoc. prof, 61-69, ABEX CORP. PROF. METALL. & MAT. SCI, 69- Am. Inst. Mining, Metall. & Petrol. Eng.(Mathewson Gold Medal, 69); Am. Foundrymen's Soc.(Simpson Gold Medal, 61; Hoyt Mem. Lectr, 64). Education; foundry engineering and science; solidification of metals. Address: Dept. of Metallurgy, Room 8-407, Massachusetts Institute of Technology, Cambridge, MA 02139.

FLEMINGS, MILTON BAKER, b. Fulshear, Tex, Apr. 24, 17; m. 41; c. 3. ENTOMOLOGY, INSECT PHYSIOLOGY. B.S, Prairie View Agr. & Mech. Col, 39; M.S, Kansas State, 54; Ph.D.(biol), Fordham, 64. Teacher, high sch, Tex, 39-42; dir. entom. div, First U.S. Army Med. Lab, 57-64; assoc. prof. BIOL, C.W. POST COL, LONG ISLAND UNIV, 64-69, PROF, 69- Commanding officer prev. med. unit, U.S, Japan & Korea, U.S.A, 48-57. Entom. Soc. Am; Am. Mosquito Control Asn; Am. Inst. Biol. Sci. Ecology and control of insects; parasitology of medically important insects. Address: Dept. of Biology, C.W. Post College, Greenvale, NY 11548.

FLEMISTER, LAUNCE(LOT) J(OHNSON), b. Atlanta, Ga, Dec. 11, 13; m. 41. PHYSIOLOGY. A.B, Duke, 35, M.A, 39, Ph.D.(physiol), 41; Harvard, 35-37. Asst. physiol, Duke, 38-41; instr. pharmacol, sch. med, George Washington, 41-43; res. assoc, Sharp & Dohme, Phila, 46-47; asst. prof. ZOOL, SWARTHMORE COL, 47-51, assoc. prof, 51-66, PROF, 66- Fulbright fel, Peru, 59-60; consult, Nat. Sci. Found. Facilities Prog, 63-64. U.S.N.R, 42-46. Fel. AAAS; Am. Physiol. Soc; Am. Soc. Zool; Ecol. Soc. Am. Comparative aspects of water balance and metabolism; environmental adaptation. Address: Dept. of Biology, Swarthmore College, Swarthmore, PA 19081.

FLENGAS, S(PYRIDON) N, b. Athens, Greece, May 10, 25; Can. citizen; m. 50; c. 3. PHYSICAL CHEMISTRY. B.Sc, Nat. Univ. Athens, 51; Ph.D. (phys. chem), London, 55, D.Sc.(chem), 60, dipl, Imp. Col, 58. Res. fel, Nat. Res. Coun. Can, 56-58; sr. sci. officer, tech. surv, Dept. Mines, Ottawa, 58-60; asst. prof. METALL. & MAT. SCI, UNIV. TORONTO, 60-61, assoc. prof, 62-64, PROF, 65- Am. Chem. Soc; Electrochem. Soc; fel. Chem. Inst. Can; Brit. Chem. Soc; Faraday Soc. Electrochemical properties of molten salts; electro motive force measurements; electrical conductivities; high temperature calorimetry; phase relationships; solid state phenomena. Address: 36 Ealing Dr, Willowdale, Ont, Can.

FLESCH, ROBERT N(EIL), b. St. Paul, Minn, Nov. 12, 20; m. 49; c. 3. ORGANIC CHEMISTRY. B.S, St. Thomas Col, 42; Ph.D.(org. chem), Minnesota, 50. Sr. Chemist, MINN. MINING & MFG. CO, 50-53, new prod. mgr, printing prod, 53-62, appl. res. mgr, photo film div, 62-64, ELECTROCOLOR PROJ. MGR, 64- U.S.N.R, 44-46, Lt.(jg). Am. Chem. Soc; Soc. Photog. Sci. & Eng. Fluorenones; printing; diazos and zinc oxide photo systems. Address: Photo Production Lab, 20925 3M Co, 444 McKnight Rd, St. Paul, MN 55119.

FLESCHNER, C(HARLES) A(NTHONY), b. Little Rock, Ark, May 22, 11; m. 33; c. 2. ENTOMOLOGY. B.S, California, 42, Ph.D.(entomol), 48. Salesman, Stationers Corp, 28-38; asst. quarantine inspector, U.S. Dept. Agr, 41-43; prin. lab. asst, citrus exp. sta, UNIV. CALIF, RIVERSIDE, 43-45, lab. technician, 45-46, prin. lab. technician, 46-48, asst. entomologist, agr. exp. sta, 48-55, assoc. entomologist, 55-60, PROF. BIOL. CONTROL & ENTOMOLOGIST, CITRUS RES. CTR & AGR. EXP. STA, 60-, MEM, PLANT SCI. & ENTOM. RES. ADV. COMT, 64-, head dept. biol, 59-64. AAAS; Am. Entom. Soc. Biological control of insect pests. Address: Dept. of Entomology, Division of Biological Control, University of California, Riverside, CA 92502.

FLESH, EDWARD M(ANSFIELD), b. St. Louis, Mo, June 28, 07; m. 35; c. 2. ENGINEERING. B.S, Missouri, 29. Design engr, Curtiss-Wright Corp, 29-42, proj. engr. aircraft, 42-46; McDonnell Aircraft Corp, 46-59, eng. mgr. Proj. Mercury, 59-63, mgr. adv. design aircraft, 63-67, mgr. aircraft design eng, McDonnell Douglas Corp, 67-69, dir. design eng, aircraft div, 69-71; RETIRED. Nat. Soc. Aerospace Prof; Am. Inst. Aeronaut. & Astronaut; Soc. Automotive Eng. Address: 8330 Stanford, St. Louis, MO 63132.

FLESHER, GAIL TIMME, b. Oak Park, Ill, Mar. 19, 26; m. 63; c. 2. ELECTRICAL ENGINEERING. B.S, Ill. Inst. Tech, 48, M.S, 50, Armour Res. Found. fel, 50-51, Ph.D, 64. Instr. elec. eng, Ill. Inst. Tech, 52-55, asst. prof, 55-59: prin. engr, syst. div, Bendix Aviation Corp, 59-61; staff res. engr, defense res. lab, Gen. Motors Corp, 61-68; chief engr, IDEAS RES. CO, 68-69, PRES, 69- U.S.A, 44-46. Am. Phys. Soc; Inst. Elec. & Electronics Eng. Microwave electronics; field theory. Address: 5652 Cathedral Oaks Rd, Goleta, CA 93017.

FLESHER, JAMES W(ENDELL), b. Chicago, Ill, June 24, 25; m. 52; c. 3. PHARMACOLOGY. B.S, Northwestern, 49; Ph.D.(pharmacol), Loyola (Ill), 58. Control chemist edible fats & oils, Lever Bros. Co, 51-55; res. assoc, Ben May Lab. Cancer Res, Chicago, 58-62; asst. prof. PHARMACOL, UNIV. KY, 62-67, ASSOC. PROF, 67- Vis. prof, Inst. Cancer Res, Columbia Univ, 70-71. U.S.A.A.F, 43-46. AAAS; Am. Chem. Soc; Am. Soc. Pharmacol. & Exp. Therapeut; N.Y. Acad. Sci. Chemical carcinogenesis; steroid hormones; mechanism of drug action. Address: Dept. of Pharmacology, College of Medicine, University of Kentucky, Lexington, KY 40506.

FLESHLER, BERTRAM, b. New York, N.Y, May 1, 28; m. 56; c. 2. GASTROENTEROLOGY. A.B, Wisconsin, 48; M.D, Boston, 51. Intern med, Mass. Mem. Hosp, 51-52; asst. res, Georgetown Univ. Hosp, 52-53; Mt. Alto Vet. Admin. Hosp, 55-56; fel. gastroenterol, Mass. Mem. Hosp, 56-58; sr. instr. MED, SCH. MED, CASE WEST. RESERVE UNIV, 58-59, asst. prof, 59-67, ASSOC. PROF, 67- Assoc. vis. physician, Cleveland Metrop. Gen. Hosp, 58-59, dir. gastroenterol, 58-, vis. physician, 59-; consult, Vet. Admin. Hosp, 58-; Lutheran Hosp, 63-; Nat. Insts. Health res. career develop. award, 66-71; hon. sr. lectr. & consult, Kings Col. Hosp. Med. Sch, London, Eng, 68-69. U.S.A.F, 53-55, Capt. AAAS; Am. Fedn. Clin. Res; Am. Gastroenterol. Asn; fel. Am. Col. Physicians. Esophageal motility studies; amino acid absorption. Address: Dept. of Medicine, Cleveland Metropolitan General Hospital, 3395 Scranton Rd, Cleveland, OH 44109.

FLETCHALL, O(SCAR) HALE, b. Grant City, Mo, May 4, 20; m. 50. AGRONOMY. B.S, Missouri, 42, Ph.D.(field crops), 54. Asst. field crops, U.S. Dept. Agr. & Univ. Missouri, 38-42, asst. instr. & sci. aide field crops, 47-51, instr. field crops & agronomist, 52-54; asst. prof. FIELD CROPS, UNIV. MO-COLUMBIA, 54-57, assoc. prof, 57-61, PROF, 61- U.S.A, 42-46, 51-52, Capt. Am. Soc. Agron; Weed Sci. Soc. Am. Weed control in field crops and on non-crop land. Address: 212 Waters Hall, Dept. of Agronomy, University of Missouri-Columbia, Columbia, MO 65201.

FLETCHER, AARON N(ATHANIEL), b. Los Angeles, Calif, Dec. 24, 25; m. 51; c. 5. ANALYTICAL CHEMISTRY. B.S, Calif. Inst. Technol, 49; U.S. Naval Ord. Test Sta. Ed. fel, California, Los Angeles, 59-61, Ph.D. (anal. chem), 61. Lab. technician, South. Pac. Co, 49-50, chemist, 50-54; RES. CHEMIST, NAVAL WEAPONS CTR, CHINA LAKE, 54- U.S.A.A.F, 44-45. AAAS; Am. Chem. Soc; Sci. Res. Soc. Am. Chemiluminescence reaction mechanisms and quantum yields; effect of mixed electrolytes on equilibrium quotients; chemistry of titanium in solution; qualitative and quantitative infrared spectrophotometry; molecular structure of hydrogen bonded systems. Address: 303 Leyte Rd, China Lake, CA 93555.

FLETCHER, ALAN G(ORDON), b. Gibson's Landing, B.C, Jan. 2, 25; m. 49; c. 4. FLUID MECHANICS, WATER RESOURCES. B.A.Sc, Univ. B.C, 48; M.Sc, Calif. Inst. Technol, 52; Walter P. Murphy fel, Northwest. Univ, 62-64, Ph.D.(civil eng), 65. Engr-in-training, B.C, Elec. Co. Ltd, 48-51, hydraul. design engr, 52-56, supvr. hydro-planning, 56-59; asst. prof, civil eng, Univ. Idaho, 59-60, assoc. prof, 60-62; Univ. Utah, 64-69; DEAN COL. ENG, UNIV. N.DAK, 69- Danforth assoc, 65; mem, Hwy. Res. Bd, Nat. Acad. Sci-Nat. Res. Coun. Am. Soc. Civil Eng; Am. Soc. Eng. Educ; Eng. Inst. Can. Hydraulic engineering; flood waves in natural channels. Address: College of Engineering, University of North Dakota, Grand Forks, ND 58201.

FLETCHER, ANTHONY P(HILLIPS), b. Maidenhead, Eng, Feb. 25, 19; nat; m. 61. INTERNAL MEDICINE. M.B, B.S, London, 43, M.D, 49. Lectr. human physiol, St. Mary's Hosp. Med. Sch, London, 47-48; sr. med. registr, St. Mary's Hosp. & Wright-Fleming Inst. Microbiol, 50-53; Merck Int. fel. microbiol, col. med, N.Y. Univ, 53-54, res. assoc. med, 54-56; asst. prof. MED, SCH. MED, WASH. UNIV, 56-62, ASSOC. PROF, 62- Asst. attend. physician, Barnes Hosp. Group, 56- Mem. Royal Col. Physicians, 45- R.N.V.R, 44-47, Surgeon Lt. Am. Physiol. Soc; Am. Soc. Clin. Invest; Am. Fedn. Clin. Res. Physiological fibrinolysis and the development of enzymatic methods for the treatment of thrombo-embolic vascular disease; blood coagulation and plasma proteins. Address: Washington Univeristy School of Medicine, 600 S. Kingshighway, St. Louis, MO 63110.

FLETCHER, C(HARLES) H(OWARD), b. Cleveland, Ohio, Sept. 7, 17; m. 46; c. 1. PHYSICS, PHYSICAL CHEMISTRY. A.B, Western Reserve, 39, Standard Oil fel, 39-41, M.S, 42; M.A, Princeton, 44, Proctor fel, 45-46, Ph.D.(physics, phys. chem), 50. Asst. sta. div. 2, Nat. Defense Res. Comt, Princeton, 42-45, res. assoc, 48-50; instr. physics, Western Reserve, 46-48; res. asst. prof. aeronaut. eng, Illinois, 50-54; RES. STAFF SPECIALIST, INDEPENDENT RES. & DEVELOP, GENERAL DYNAMICS/FT. WORTH, 54-; ADJ. PROF. PHYSICS, TEX. CHRISTIAN UNIV, 56- AAAS; Am. Phys. Soc; Am. Asn. Physics Teachers; Inst. Elec. & Electronics Eng. Heterogeneous catalysis; kinematics of large molecule systems; interaction of shock waves; statistical mechanics; quantum mechanics; structure of matter; development of digital computer; missile and satellite dynamics; inertial guidance system design. Address: 3432 Pelham Rd, Ft. Worth, TX 76116.

FLETCHER, C(HARLES) L(EONARD), b. Columbus, Ohio, Sept. 30, 07; m. 30; c. 2. CHEMICAL ENGINEERING. B.Ch.E, Ohio State, 30, hon. Ch.E, 39. Chem. engr, cellulose esters develop, Eastman Kodak, N.Y, 30-33; cellulose esters develop. & quality control, TENN. EASTMAN CO, 33-36, asst. div. supt, 36-41, div. supt, 41-58, gen. supt, 58-63, ASST. WORKSMGR, 63- Am. Chem. Soc; Am. Inst. Chem. Eng; fel. Am. Inst. Chem; Nat. Soc. Prof. Eng. Plasticizers, photographic chemicals, dyes, inhibitors, antioxidants, antiozanants, aliphatic and aromatic chemicals and polyester resins production and development; production of cellulose esters, cellulose esters plastics and polyolefins plastics. Address: 1536 Fairidge Dr, Kingsport, TN 37664.

FLETCHER, DAVID A(DAMS), b. Minneapolis, Minn, Nov. 20, 06; m. 40; c. 2. CHEMISTRY. A.B, Minnesota, 29; Ph.D.(phys. chem), Cornell, 34. Asst. chem, Cornell, 29-33; res. chemist, Muralo Co, Staten Island, 34; Du Pont Viscoloid Co, N.J, 34-38, plastics dept, E.I. du Pont de Nemours & Co, 38-46; assoc. prof. chem, Pa. Col. Women, 46-49; Redlands, 49-54; sr. chemist, Grand Cent. Rocket Co, 54-56, head chem. res. dept, 56-59, dir. res, 59-60; v.pres. res, TALLEY INDUSTS, INC, 60-68, ASST. TO GEN. MGR, 68- Am. Inst. Aeronaut. & Astronaut; Am. Chem. Soc. Phase rule studies on polyiodides of calcium; synthetic resins and plastics; methyl methacrylate; styrene; cellulose acetate; polyvinyl butyral; organosilicon compounds; high temperature dielectrics. Address: 1058 W. Mountain View Dr, Mesa, AZ 85201.

FLETCHER, DEAN C(HARLES), b. Logan, Utah, June 14, 21; m. 44; c. 3. BIOCHEMISTRY, PHARMACOLOGY. B.S, Utah State Univ, 43, M.S, 48; Ph.D.(chem), Univ. Del, 51. Instr. physiol, Utah State Univ, 43, 48-49; res. assoc. biochem, res. found, Franklin Inst, 49-51; chemist, Stine Lab, E.I. du Pont de Nemours & Co, Inc, 51-57; DIR. DEPT. INVEST. MED, WASHOE MED. CTR, 57-; ALLIE M. LEE PROF. BIOCHEM, UNIV. NEV, RENO, 61-, ASSOC. DEAN SCH. MED. SCI, 71-, lectr. pharmacol, 57-60, chmn. dept. biochem, 62-71, dir. allied health sch. med. sci, 69-71. Lectr, Univ. Del, 52-57; asst. clin. prof. postgrad. med, col. med, Univ. Utah, 68-; dir. Reno Cancer Ctr; mem, Nev. Cancer Coord. Comt; consult, St. Mary's Hosp, Reno; Reno Vet. Admin. Hosp; Washoe Med. Ctr; Dade Chem. Co; Lamar Chem. Co, Calif. U.S.A, 43-46, 1st Lt. Am. Chem. Soc; Am. Asn. Clin. Chem; N.Y. Acad. Sci. Stress physiology; cancer chemotherapy; clinical investigations; toxicology. Address: School of Medical Sciences, University of Nevada, Reno, NV 89507.

FLETCHER, D(ELBERT) V(AN), b. Tampa, Fla, May 10, 18; m. 43; c. 3. CHEMICAL ENGINEERING. B.S, Ga. Inst. Tech, 40; M.Ch.E, Louisville, 41. Process engr, indust. & biochem. dept, E.I. DU PONT DE NEMOURS & CO, 41-46, tech. supt, Houston Works, 46-48, asst. process mgr, 48-50, process mgr, 50, asst. res. dir, 50-62, asst. planning mgr, 62-69, MGR, ACCOUNTING & PLANNING DIV, 69- Fel. Am. Inst. Chem; Am. Chem. Soc; Am. Inst. Chem. Eng. Process development. Address: Accounting & Planning Division, E.I. du Pont de Nemours & Co, 908 Farmers Bank Bldg, Wilmington, DE 19898.

FLETCHER, D(ONALD) W(ARREN), b. Phoenix, Ariz, June 8, 29; m. 63; c. 2. MICROBIOLOGY. B.S, Oregon State, 51, M.S, 53; Nat. Insts. Health fel, Washington State, 55, Ph.D.(bact), 56. Instr. bact, Washington State, 56-59; assoc. prof. BIOL, SAN FRANCISCO STATE COL, 59-67, PROF, 67-, ASSOC. DEAN SCH. NATURAL SCI, 70-, exec. dir, ctr. adv. med. tech, 68-69. Lectr. & consult, sch. med, Univ. Calif, San Francisco, 62-64; Fulbright lectr, Univ. Belgrade, 67-68; dean, col. arts & sci, Univ. Bridgeport, 69-70. AAAS; Am. Soc. Microbiol; Brit. Soc. Gen. Microbiol. Microbial physiology; bacterial ecology; rumen and soil microbiology; bacterial nutrition. Address: Division of Biology, San Francisco State College, San Francisco, CA 94132.

FLETCHER, EDWARD A(BRAHAM), b. Detroit, Mich, July 30, 24; m. 48; c. 3. CHEMISTRY, THERMODYNAMICS. B.S, Wayne State, 48; Du Pont & Atomic Energy Comn. fels. & Ph.D.(inorg. chem), Purdue, 52. Aeronaut. res. scientist, NASA, 52-56, head flame mech. sect, 56-57, propellant chem. sect, 57-59; assoc. prof, MECH. ENG, UNIV. MINN, MINNEAPOLIS, 59-60, PROF, 60-, DIR. GRAD. STUDIES, 71- Vis. exchange scientist, Byellorussian Acad. Sci, 64; vis. prof. Univ. Poitiers, 68. U.S.N, 42-46. Am. Chem. Soc; Combustion Inst; Combustion; propellant chemistry; ignition; fluorine chemistry; rocket and jet engine propulsion; chemical kinetics. Address: Dept. of Mechanical Engineering, University of Minnesota, Minneapolis, MN 55455.

FLETCHER, E(DWARD) ROYCE, b. Hays, Kans, May 20, 37. PHYSICS, ELECTRICAL ENGINEERING. B.S, New Mexico, 58, M.S, 60, Ph.D. (physics), 64. Electronic technician, LOVELACE FOUND. MED. EDUC. & RES, 56, math. analyst, 57-60, physicist, 61-63, head theoret. anal. sect, dept. physics, 64-70, HEAD DEPT. PHYSICS, 71- Inst. Elec. & Electronics Eng. Analysis of biological and physical systems in terms of the physical process and the development of mathematical models to simulate these systems. Address: Dept. of Physics, Lovelace Foundation, 5200 Gibson Blvd, S.E, Albuquerque, NM 87108.

FLETCHER, EWAN W(ATTS), b. Portland, Maine, Mar. 14, 16; m. 43; c. 3. APPLIED PHYSICS. Sc.B, Brown, 38; M.S, Harvard, 40, Ph.D.(appl. physics), 53. Instr. appl. mech, Brown, 40-42; electronics, Harvard, 42-45, res. assoc. microwaves, 45-51; electronics, Case, 51-53, assoc. prof. ELEC. ENG, 53-56; Mass. Inst. Tech, 56-61, res. assoc, 61-62; DIR. RES, LEDGEMONT LAB, KENNECOTT COPPER CORP, 61- AAAS; Am. Phys. Soc; Inst. Elec. & Electronics Eng; Am. Meteorol. Soc; N.Y. Acad. Sci; Am. Inst. Mining, Metall. & Petrol. Eng. Materials science; microwave spectroscopy; masers; instrumentation transducers. Address: Ledgemont Lab, Kennecott Copper Corp, 128 Spring St, Lexington, MA 02173.

FLETCHER, FRANK W(ILLIAM), b. Camden, N.J, Oct. 7, 37; m. 60; c. 3. GEOLOGY. B.A, Lafayette Col, 59; Ph.D.(geol), Rochester, 64. Eng. aide, soils div, N.J. State Hwy. Dept, 58-59; asst. geol, Rochester, 59-62; geologist, N.Y. State Mus. & Sci. Serv, 59-64; instr. GEOL, SUSQUEHANNA UNIV, 62-64, asst. prof, 64-68, ASSOC. PROF, 68-, DIR. INST. ENVIRON. STUDIES, 70- Cooperating geologist, Pa. Geol. Surv, 66- AAAS; Geol. Soc. Am; Soc. Econ. Paleont. & Mineral; Int. Asn. Sedimentol. Paleozoic stratigraphy; sedimentology; tectonics; environmental geology. Address: Institute for Environmental Studies, Susquehanna University, Selingsgrove, PA 17870.

FLETCHER, FRED W(ALKER), b. Marion, Ohio, Aug. 6, 04; m. 34; c. 3. ENTOMOLOGY. A.B, Miami (Ohio), 27; A.M, Ohio State, 29. Asst. zool, Ohio State, 27-28, asst. entomologist, 28-30, instr, 30-31; forest entomol, N.Y. State Col. Forestry, Syracuse, 31-37, asst. prof, 37; entomologist, Dow Chem. Co, 37-69; BIOCHEM. CONSULT, 69- Mem. cmt. plant & animal pests, Nat. Acad. Sci, 64- Entom. Soc. Am; Entom. Soc. Can. Development of insecticides, fungicides; fumigants and nematocides. Address: 1817 W. Sugnet Rd, Midland, MI 48640.

FLETCHER, GARTH L, b. Glasgow, Scotland, Apr. 15, 36; Can. citizen; m. 64. ANIMAL PHYSIOLOGY. B.Sc, Univ. B.C, 63; Ph.D.(biol), Univ. Calif, Santa Barbara, 67. RES. SCIENTIST, Halifax Lab, Fisheries Res. Bd. Can, 67-70, marine ecol. lab, Bedford Inst, 70-71; MARINE SCI. RES. LAB, MEM. UNIV. NEWF, 71- AAAS; Am. Soc. Zool. Water and electrolyte regulation in birds; steroid hormones in fish; toxicology of elemental phosphorus; mechanisms controlling heavy metal levels in fish. Address: Marine Sciences Research Lab, Memorial University of Newfoundland, St. John's, Newf, Can.

FLETCHER, GEORGE L(ELAND), b. Mahaffey, Pa, Nov. 4, 18; m. 40; c. 2. BIOCHEMISTRY. B.S, Pa. State, 40; M.S, Rochester, 47. Anal. chemist, H.H. Clapp Corp, 40-41; jr. res. chemist, Distillation Prod. Indust, 41-43; sr. res. chemist, Tenn. Eastman Co, 43-46, distillation prod. indust, EASTMAN KODAK CO, 46-67, RES. ASSOC, RES. LAB, 67- Asst, Rochester, 50-57. Am. Chem. Soc; Radiation Res. Soc. Process research and development of pharmaceutical compounds; radiation biochemistry; low energy interaction in biochemistry and organic reactions. Address: Eastman Kodak Co, Research Lab, 343 State St, Rochester, NY 14650.

FLETCHER, GILBERT H(UNGERFORD), b. Paris, France, Mar. 11, 11; nat; m. 44; c. 2. MEDICINE. B.A, Paris, 29; Louvain, Belgium, 32; M.S, Brussels, 35, M.D, 41. Instr. radiol, med. col, Cornell, 43-45; PROF. RADIOTHER. & HEAD DEPT. RADIOL, UNIV. TEX. M.D. ANDERSON HOSP. & TUMOR INST, 48- Jr. asst. radiologist, New York Hosp, 44-45; consult, Hermann Hosp, 50-; chmn. comt. radiation ther. studies, Nat. Cancer Inst, 63-71; consult, St. Joseph Hosp, Houston, Tex, 67-; nat. consult. to surgeon gen, U.S. Air Force, Wash, D.C, 68-; spec. prof, Univ. Tex. Grad. Sch. Biomed. Sci. Houston. Med.C, U.S.A, 45-47, Capt. Fel. Am. Col. Radiol; Am. Radium Soc.(treas, 59-61, pres, 62-63); Am. Roentgen Ray Soc; Radiol. Soc. N.Am; Soc. Nuclear Med; Inter-Am. Col. Radiol; N.Y. Acad. Sci. Radiotherapy. Address: Dept. of Radiotherapy, University of Texas M.D. Anderson Hospital & Tumor Institute, 6723 Bertner, Houston, TX 77025.

FLETCHER, HARRY FRANCIS, b. Victoria, B.C, Feb. 15, 23; m. 50; c. 6. SOIL CHEMISTRY. B.S.A, British Columbia, 49, M.S.A, 51; Ph.D.(soil chem), Illinois, 61. Soils res. chemist, exp. farm, Can. Dept. Agr, 60-66; sr. sci. off, CAN. DEPT. ENERGY, MINES & RESOURCES, 66-68, EXEC. SECY. NAT. ADV. COMT. WATER RESOURCES RES, 68- Mem, Can. Nat. Soil Fertil. Cmt, 56-58, 62- Can. Army, 42-43; R.C.A.F, 43-45, Sgt. Can. Soc. Soil Sci. Study and integration of the productivity factors of soil chemistry and physics, crop environment and variation, affecting crop yield. Address: Canada Dept. of Energy, Mines & Resources, Room E-248, No. 8 Temporary Bldg, Carling Ave, Ottawa, Ont, Can.

FLETCHER, HARRY H(UNTINGTON), b. Pittsburgh, Pa, Nov. 4, 07; m. 37; c. 3. CHEMISTRY. B.S, Yale, 29; Ph.D.(chem), Columbia, 39. Res. chemist, U.S. Rubber Co, 29-31; asst, Columbia, 31-35; res. chemist, res. ctr, U.S. Rubber Co, 36-63; teacher chem, Fairleigh Dickinson, 64-67; PATENT EXAM, U.S. PATENT OFF, WASH, D.C, 67- Am. Chem. Soc. Action of aqueous chlorine and hypochlorite on starches; adhesion of rubber to metal; antioxidants and accelerators for rubber; agricultural organic chemicals; transfer chemicals; chemical modification of cotton; patent liaison work; analytical-organic research; teaching. Address: 3308 Holloman Rd, Falls Church, VA 22042.

FLETCHER, HARVEY, b. Provo, Utah, Sept. 11, 84; m. 08; c. 6. PHYSICS. B.S, Brigham Young, 07, hon. Sc.D, 54; fel, Chicago, 10-11, Ph.D.(physics), 11; hon. Sc.D, Columbia, 35, Kenyon Col, 42, Stevens Inst. Tech, 42, Case, 42, Utah, 44. Instr. physics, Brigham Young, 07-08, prof, 11-16; instr, Chicago, 09-10; phys. res. dir, Bell Tel. Labs, 16-49; prof. elec. eng, Columbia, 49-52; DIR. RES, BRIGHAM YOUNG UNIV, 52-, dean col. phys. & eng. sci, 54-57. Mem. bd, Res. Council, Rutgers; nat. councilor, Ohio State Res. Founds; Nat. Res. Council, 33- Levy Gold Medal, Franklin Inst, 24; progress medal, Soc. Motion Picture & TV Eng, 49; gold medal, Audio Eng. Soc, 57. With Office Sci. Res. & Develop; U.S.A; U.S.N, 40-44. Nat. Acad. Sci; AAAS; fel. Am. Phys. Soc.(pres, 45); hon. mem. Am. Otol. Soc; fel. & hon. mem. Acoustical Soc. Am.(pres, 29-31, gold medal, 54); hon. mem. Am. Speech & Hearing Asn; fel. Inst. Elec. & Electronics Eng. Brownian movements; gaseous ionization; determination of elementary electrical charge and Avogadro's constant; Stokes' law of fall and of small particles; physical measurement of audition; loudness of complex sounds; physical nature of speech, music and noise; high quality transmission of speech and music; theory of hearing; audiometers and audiphones; transmission and music; theory of hearing; audiometers and audiphones; transmission and recording of sound in auditory perspective; speech; hearing. Address: 272 Eyring Science Center, Brigham Young University, Provo, UT 84601.

FLETCHER, HARVEY J(UNIOR), b. New York, N.Y, Apr. 9, 23; m. 53; c. 6. APPLIED MATHEMATICS. B.S, Mass. Inst. Tech, 44; M.S, Calif. Inst. Tech, 48; Ph.D.(math), Utah, 54. Instr, physics, Utah, 53; MATH, BRIGHAM YOUNG UNIV, 54, asst. prof, 54-57, assoc. prof, 57-61, PROF, 61-63, 64-, chmn. dept, 58-61, 62-63. Mem. tech. staff, Bell Tel. Labs, 61-62; Bellcom, 63-64; sr. tech. specialist, Hercules, Inc, 67-68; mem. tech. staff,

U.S. Air Force, Hill Field, 70- U.S.N.R, 44-46, Lt.(jg). Soc. Indust. & Appl. Math. Bending of plates; Fouier series; attitude of satellite; Apollo trajectories; diffusion theory; minuteman simulation; intercept trajectories. Address: 1175 Locust Circle, Provo, UT 84601.

FLETCHER, H(ERBERT) C(ALVIN), b. Logan, Utah, Nov. 25, 07; m. 37; c. 3. SOILS & WATERSHED RESEARCH. A.B, Utah State Univ, 32; M.S, Univ. Mo, 34; fel, Univ. Okla, 35-36; Georgetown Univ, 47-49. Soil scientist, soil conserv. serv, U.S. DEPT. AGR, 36-48, res. center leader forest soils, Rocky Mt. Forest & Range Exp. Sta, U.S. FOREST SERV, 48-55; area dir, west. soil & water mgt. res. br, Agr. Res. Serv, 55-60. Liaison officer to soil conserv. serv, 60-61, staff asst, resources prog. staff, Off. Secy. Interior, 61-63, chief div. watershed mgt. res, ROCKY MT. FOREST & RANGE EXP. STA, 63-65, ASST. DIR, 65- Adv, U.S. State Dept. & Libyan Govt, 61, Honduras Govt, 62; mem, White House Conf. Conserv, 62; West Wide Water Plan Comt, 70-; Forest Serv. adv. environ. & oil shale, 70- AAAS; Soil Sci. Soc. Am; Soil Conserv. Soc. Am; Am. Geophys. Union; Atmospheric Water Resources Res. Address: 1908 Sequoia Dr, Ft. Collins, CO 80521.

FLETCHER, H(ERBERT) J(AMES), b. St. Johns, Mich, July 3, 19; m. 42; c. 4. CHEMISTRY. B.S, Greenville Col, 40; M.S, N.Dak. State Col, 42. Res. chemist, Dow Chem. Co, 42-44; DOW CORNING CORP, 44-45, MGR, gen. pilot plant, 45-62, INT. DEPT, 64- Am. Chem. Soc; Am. Inst. Chem. Eng. Chemistry of silicon and its derivatives; development of processes for commercial preparation. Address: Dow Corning Corp, 3614 Cambridge St, Midland, MI 48640.

FLETCHER, HEWITT G(RENVILLE), JR, b. Boston, Mass, May 28, 17; m. 40; c. 3. ORGANIC CHEMISTRY. S.B, Mass. Inst. Technol, 39, Moore fel, 41-42, Ph.D.(org. chem), 42. Chemist, Atlantic Res. Assocs, 40-41; instr. chem, Mass. Inst. Technol, 42-47; res. assoc. & Chem. Found. fel, NAT. INSTS. HEALTH, U.S. PUB. HEALTH SERV, 45-48, CHEMIST, 49-, CHIEF SECT. CARBOHYDRATES, NAT. INST. ARTHRITIS & METAB. DISEASES, 51- Consult, Atlas Powder Co, Del, 44-45; chmn. subcomt. carbohydrates, comt. biol. chem, div. chem. & chem. technol, Nat. Res. Coun, 57-62; comt. pioneering res. adv. bd, U.S. Army Natick Labs, 58-69; mem. bd. dirs, Found. Advan. Educ. Sci, 59-70; v.chmn, Gordon Conf. Chem. Carbohydrates, 62, chmn, 64; bd. ed, J. Org. Chem, 63-66; ed. adv. bd, Carbohydrate Res, 65- Am. Chem. Soc.(Claude S. Hudson Award, div. carbohydrate chem, 68); The Chem. Soc. Chemistry of carbohydrates and related substances. Address: National Institute of Arthritis & Metabolic Diseases, National Institutes of Health, U.S. Public Health Service, Bethesda, MD 20014.

FLETCHER, JAMES C(HIPMAN), b. Millburn, N.J, June 5, 19; m. 46; c. 4. PHYSICS. A.B, Columbia, 40; univ. fel, Princeton, 42-43; fel, Calif. Inst. Technol, 45-48, Eastman Kodak Co. fel, 47-48, Ph.D.(physics), 48; hon. Sc.D, Univ. Utah, 71. Res. physicist, Bur. Ord. U.S. Navy, 40-41; spec. res. assoc, Cruft Lab, Harvard, 41-42; instr, Princeton, 42-45; teaching fel, Calif. Inst. Technol, 45-48; instr, Univ. Calif, Los Angeles, 48-50; dir. theory & anal. lab, Hughes Aircraft Co, 48-54; from assoc. dir. guided missile lab. to dir. electronics, guided missile res. div, space tech. labs, Ramo-Wooldridge Corp, 54-58; pres, Space Electronics Corp, 58-60; Space-Gen. Corp, 60-62, chmn. bd, 60-64, v.pres. systs, Aerojet-Gen. Corp, 62-64; pres, Univ. Utah, 64-71; ADMINR, NASA, 71- Mem. subcomt. stability & control, Nat. Adv. Comt. Aeronaut, 50-54; consult. then mem, President's Sci. Adv. Comt, 58-70, mem. strategic weapons panel, 59-61, command, control & intel. panel, 62-63, mil. aircraft panel, 64-67; chmn. ad hoc comt. rev. Skybolt Prog, 59; consult, Off. Secy. Defense, 59-64; Aerojet-Gen. & Space-Gen. Corps, 60-64; chmn. ad hoc comt. rev, Minuteman Command & Control Syst, 61; mem. command, control & intel. comt, U.S. Dept. Defense, 61-62; consult, Asst. Secy, U.S. Air Force, 61-64; mem. Woods Hole Summer Study Group Arms Control, 62; chmn. physics panel, rev. comt, Nat. Insts. Health, 62-64; consult, Arms Control & Disarmament Agency, 62-64; mem, Air Force Sci. Adv. Bd, 63. Civilian with Off. Sci. Res. & Develop, 44. Am. Phys. Soc; Am. Inst. Aeronaut. & Astronaut; Nat. Acad. Eng; Am. Mgt. Asn. Underwater acoustics; aerodynamics; shock waves; cosmic rays; magnetic survey of naval vessels; servomechanisms; radar; guided missiles and space electronics; guidance; instrumentation; administration of large scale research and development programs; communications and systems engineering. Address: NASA, Washington, DC 20546.

FLETCHER, JOEL E(UGENE), b. Logan, Utah, Jan. 7, 11; m. 34; c. 2. SOILS. B.S, Utah State Agr. Col, 34, M.S, 37; California, 41-42. Asst. soil surveyor, Utah State Agr. Col, 35; jr. soil expert, soil conserv. serv, U.S. Dept. Agr, Arizona, 36, jr. soil technologist, 36-38, asst. soil technologist, 38-41, col. agr, California, 41-43, Arizona, 43-44, soil scientist, 44-45, proj. supvr. soil conserv. exp. sta, 44-45, soil conservationist, 45-54, watershed tech. res. br, agr. res. serv, 54-59, soil scientist, Idaho, 59-63; PROF. HYDROL, UTAH STATE UNIV, 63- Soil Sci. Soc. Am; Am. Soc. Agron; Sci. Res. Soc. Am; Am. Geophys. Union. Erodibility of western soils; soil properties affecting infiltration; electrical methods for determining soil moisture; effect of tillage on soil structure and compaction; base exchange equilibria; freezing and moisture phenomena in frozen soils; rainfall-runoff relations; hydrologic instrumentation; weather modification. Address: Utah Water Research Lab, Utah State University, Box 1304, Logan, UT 84321.

FLETCHER, JOHN EDWARD, b. Banner Elk, N.C, June 12, 37; m. 64; c. 2. APPLIED MATHEMATICS. B.S, N.C. State, 59, M.S, 61; Maryland, 67- Res. asst. differential equations, N.C. State, 59-61; opers. res. sr. analyst, adv. concepts sect, adv. studies div, Lockeed-Ga. Co, 64-66; res. mathematician, LAB. APPL. STUDIES, DIV. COMPUT. RES. & TECH, NAT. INSTS. HEALTH, 66-69, HEAD APPL. MATH. SECT, 69- AAAS; Soc. Indust. & Appl. Math; N.Y. Acad. Sci. U.S.A.F, 61-64, Res, 64-69, Capt. Application of deterministic mathematical models to problems of biological sciences. Address: Division of Computer Research & Technology, National Institutes of Health, Bethesda, MD 20014.

FLETCHER, JOHN G, b. Manchester, Eng, Nov. 7, 25; Can. citizen; m. 55; c. 2. ERGONOMICS, BIOASTRONAUTICS. B.Sc, Victoria Univ. Manchester, 47, M.Sc, 49; Ph.D, Univ. London, 58. Demonstr. & lectr, Univ. Nottingham, 47-50, lectr, 51-53; sci. off, Colonial Med. Res. Comt, Nigeria, 50-51; Med. Res. Coun, Eng, 53-58; defence sci. serv. off, Defence Res. Med. Lab, Ont, 58-63; pres, Inter-Continental Sci. & Tech. Advice Bur, Ltd, Ont, 63-65; mem. faculty, indust. eng, State Univ. N.Y. Buffalo, 65-68; dir. res, Systs. Res. Labs, Inc, Tex, 68-70; V.PRES, ROTHE DEVELOP, INC, 70-; INSTR, ST. MARY'S UNIV. SAN ANTONIO, 71- Consult, Fitness & Amateur Sports Directorate, Ont, 63-64; sr. assoc, Webb Assocs, Inc, Ohio & Calif, 64-; expert, Int. Labour Orgn. & Govt. India, 64-65; consult, Int. Labour Orgn, Switz, 64-65. Can. Physiol. Soc; fel. Royal Inst. Chem; Brit. Ergonomics Res. Soc; Brit. Physiol. Soc. Biosciences, especially presentation of quantitative physiological information for design engineers; industrial physiology, especially applications towards improved productivity under difficult climatic conditions involving heavy physical work; environmental health science. Address: Rothe Development, Inc, 4614 Sinclair Rd, San Antonio, TX 78222.

FLETCHER, JOHN GEORGE, b. Aberdeen, S.Dak, Oct. 28, 34; m. 56; c. 3. COMPUTER SCIENCE. B.S, George Wash. Univ, 55; Nat. Sci. Found. fel, Princeton, 55-59, A.M, 57, Ph.D.(physics), 59. Mem. tech. staff, Bell Tel. Labs, 59; instr, Princeton, 59-60; PHYSICIST, LAWRENCE LIVERMORE LAB, UNIV. CALIF, 61- Consult, Grumman Aircraft Eng. Corp, 59-63; fel, Miller Inst, 60-62; consult, Ed. Serv, Inc, 61-63; lectr, Univ. Calif, Davis & Berkeley, 62-; comt. mem, Am. Nat. Standards Inst. Am. Phys. Soc; Asn. Comput. Mach. Computer languages and operating systems; symbol manipulation; relativity; automata. Address: L-61, Lawrence Livermore Lab, University of California, Box 808, Livermore, CA 94550.

FLETCHER, JOHN H(ARTLEY), b. Bronxville, N.Y, Oct. 3, 17; m. 47; c. 2. CHEMISTRY. Sc.B, Brown, 39; Sherman Clarke fel, Rochester, 41-42, Ph.D.(org. chem), 42. Asst, Rochester, 39-41; res. chemist, AM. CYANAMID CO, 42-50; group leader coding & indexing, 50-55, org. synthesis, 55-56, sect. mgr. basic res, 56-60, appl. res, 60-63, proj. supvr, mkt. develop, 64-70, MEM. STAFF, TECH. RECRUITMENT, 70- Sci. Res. Soc. Am; Am. Chem. Soc. Organic synthesis; parathion, malathion and other phosphorus compounds; sulfanilamide derivatives of the sulfilimine type; beta-hydroxy sulfonamide rearrangement; organic nonmenclature; indexing by molecular formula; water-soluble polymers; flame retardants; photochromic compounds; personal care products. Address: American Cyanamid Co, Wayne, NJ 07470.

FLETCHER, JOHN SAMUEL, b. Columbus, Nebr, Jan. 7, 38; m. 60; c. 2. PLANT PHYSIOLOGY, CELL BIOLOGY. B.S.E, Ohio State Univ, 60; M.N.S, Ariz. State Univ, 65; Ph.D.(plant physiol), Purdue Univ, 69. Asst. biol. & plant physiol, Purdue Univ, 65-68, plant physiol, 68-69; ASST. PROF. BOT, UNIV. OKLA, 69- Ord.C, U.S.A, 61-63, 1st Lt. Am. Soc. Plant Physiol; Am. Inst. Biol. Sci. Synthesis and utilization of amino acids in higher plant cells; growth and development of plant tissue cultures. Address: Dept. of Botany & Microbiology, University of Oklahoma, Norman, OK 73069.

FLETCHER, KENNETH STEELE, III, b. Springfield, Mass, May 4, 41; m. 63; c. 2. ANALYTICAL CHEMISTRY. B.S, Trinity Col.(Conn), 63; Ph.D. (chem), Univ. Mass, Amherst, 68. RES. CHEMIST, FOXBORO CO, 68- Am. Chem. Soc. Solid state ionic conductivity; ion selective electrode materials; refractory borides, nitrides, and carbides for voltametry and coulometry; voltametric hydrodynamics. Address: Research Center, Foxboro Co, Foxboro, MA 02035.

FLETCHER, LEROY S(TEVENSON), b. San Antonio, Tex, Oct. 10, 36; m. 66; c. 1. MECHANICAL ENGINEERING. B.S, Tex. A&M Univ, 58; M.S, Stanford Univ, 63, Engr, 64; Ph.D.(mech. eng), Ariz. State Univ, 68. Aeronaut. engr, Ames Aeronaut. Lab, Nat. Adv. Comt. Aeronaut, 58-61, aerospace engr, Ames Res. Ctr, NASA, 61-63; asst. heat transfer, dept. mech. eng, Stanford Univ, 62-63, thermodynamics, 63-64; mech. eng, Ariz. State Univ, 64-65, instr, 65-68; asst. prof. AEROSPACE ENG, RUTGERS UNIV, 68-71, ASSOC. PROF, 71- Aerospace engr, Ames Res. Ctr, summers, 65 & 66. Ralph R. Teeter award, Soc. Automotive Eng, 70. U.S.A.F, 58-61, Capt. Am. Soc. Mech. Eng; Am. Inst. Aeronaut. & Astronaut; Am. Soc. Eng. Educ. Heat transfer; conduction, convection, radiation; heat transfer at supersonic velocities; aerodynamics; fluid mechanics. Address: Dept. of Mechanical & Aerospace Engineering, Rutgers, The State University, New Brunswick, NJ 08903.

FLETCHER, LEWIS A(RROWOOD), b. McColl, S.C, Feb. 1, 01; m. 42. BIOCHEMISTRY. B.S, Clemson Col, 23; M.S, Oregon State Col, 26; Ph.D.(plant physiol), Maryland, 30. Pomologist, U.S. Dept. Agr, 30-35; farmer, 35-40; teacher, high sch, 41-42; personnel mgr, Imp. Gasket Co, 43-50; prof. CHEM, Brenau Col, 51-60; assoc. prof, UNIV. TENN, CHATTANOOGA, 60-63, prof, 63-71, EMER. PROF, 71- AAAS; Am. Chem. Soc; Am. Inst. Chem. Factors influencing red color on apples. Address: 644 Intermont Rd, Chattanooga, TN 37415.

FLETCHER, LOWELL W, b. Princeton, W.Va, Aug. 18, 20; m. 49; c. 4. ENTOMOLOGY. B.S, Concord Col, 47; M.S, West Virginia, 58; Trubek fel, Rutgers, 58-61, Ph.D.(entom), 61. Res. med. entomologist, U.S. DEPT. AGR, 61-69, res. entomologist, TOBACCO INSECT INVEST, 69-70, INSECT ECOLOGIST, 70- Med.Serv.C, 43-46, 49-55, Capt. Entom. Soc. Am. Insect attractants and pheromones. Address: Tobacco Insect Investigation, U.S. Dept. of Agriculture. P.O. Box 10125, Richmond, VA 23240.

FLETCHER, MARTIN J, b. N.Y.C, Aug. 24, 32; m. 60; c. 1. BIOCHEMISTRY. A.B, Columbia Col, 53; M.S, Purdue Univ, 58, Ph.D.(biochem), 59. Biochemist, Nat. Insts. Health, 59-62; chemist natural prods, Wallace Labs, Carter Prods, Inc, 62-68; DIR. BIOCHEM, AFFILIATED MED. ENTERPRISES, INC, 68- U.S.A, 53-55. AAAS; Am. Chem. Soc; Am. Soc. Pharmacog; N.Y. Acad. Sci. Biochemistry of energy metabolism; isolation, purification and identification of natural products. Address: Affiliated Medical Enterprises, Inc, P.O. Box 57, Princeton, NJ 08540.

FLETCHER, MARY ANN, b. Little Rock, Ark, July 23, 37; m. 60; div; c. 1. IMMUNOCHEMISTRY, MICROBIOLOGY. B.S, Tex. Tech. Col, 59; M.A, Texas, 61; Ph.D.(microbiol), Baylor, 66. Res. asst. microbiol, southwest.

med. sch, Texas, 59-61; res. assoc. immunochem, grad. res. inst, Baylor, 61-62 & 63-66; clin. bacteriologist, Spohn Hosp. & Driscoll Found. Children's Hosp, 62-63; res. assoc. immunochem, Evanston Hosp, 66-69; HEMAT, MICHAEL REESE HOSP, 69, ASST. DIR, 70- Bridegroom fund fel, 68; Leukemia Res. Found. Inc, grants, 70-; asst. prof, Ill. Inst. Technol, 70-; Nat. Insts. Health grant, 71- Am. Soc. Microbiol. Immunochemistry of erythrocyte antigens and antibodies. Address: Division of Hematology, Michael Reese Hospital, 2929 S. Ellis, Chicago, IL 60616.

FLETCHER, NEIL RUSSEL, b. Morenci, Mich, Oct. 17, 33; m. 58; c. 3. NUCLEAR PHYSICS. B.S, Mich. State, 55; Ph.D.(physics), Duke, 61. Res. assoc. PHYSICS, Duke Univ, 60-61; FLA. STATE UNIV, 61-63, asst. prof, 63-68, ASSOC. PROF, 68- Am. Phys. Soc. Low energy nuclear physics; direct reactions and reaction mechanisms; angular correlations; structure of light nuclei. Address: Dept. of Physics, Florida State University, Tallahassee, FL 32306.

FLETCHER, ORLIN K(ENYON), JR, b. Augusta, Ga, Nov. 25, 08; m. 34. BIOLOGY. B.S, Georgia, 42; M.P.H, North Carolina, 48. Biol. aide, div. sci. inquiry, U.S. Bur. Fisheries, 35-37; biol. technician, GA, 37-42, biol. aide, State Dept. Pub. Health, 42, biologist, 42-68, ASST. EPIDEMIOLOGIST, DEPT. HEALTH, 68- AAAS; Am. Soc. Trop. Med. & Hyg; Entom. Soc. Am; Am. Pub. Health Asn. Parasitology; medical entomology. Address: P.O. Box 1010, Albany, GA 31702.

FLETCHER, OSCAR JASPER, JR, b. Bennettsville, S.C, Oct. 18, 38; m. 63; c. 1. PATHOLOGY. B.S, Wofford Col, 60; D.V.M, Georgia, 64, M.S, 65; Ph.D.(vet. sci), Wisconsin, 68. Res. asst. PATH, Georgia, 64-65; trainee, Univ. Wisconsin, 65-68; ASST. PROF, UNIV. GA, 68- Dipl, Am. Col. Vet. Path. Am. Vet. Med. Asn. Rheumatoid; neoplastic diseases of domestic animals especially serum protein alterations; immunopathology. Address: Dept. of Pathology, University of Georgia School of Veterinary Medicine, Athens, GA 30601.

FLETCHER, PAUL C(HIPMAN), b. N.Y.C, Jan. 10, 26; m. 55; c. 4. SOLID STATE PHYSICS. B.S, Mass. Inst. Tech, 47; Ph.D, Columbia, 57. Res. physicist, res. labs, Hughes Aircraft Co, 57-61; mgr. quantum physics lab, Electro-Optical Systs, Inc, 61-66; chief space optics lab, NASA Electronic Res. Ctr, 66, optics lab, 66-70; HEAD ELECTROMAGNETICS TECHNOL. DEPT, NAVAL ELECTRONICS LAB. CTR, 70- U.S.N.R, 43-44. AAAS; Am. Phys. Soc; sr. mem. Inst. Elec. & Electronics Eng. Gaseous microwave spectroscopy; magnetism; lasers; electro-optics. Address: Naval Electronics Lab. Center, Code 2000, San Diego, CA 92152.

FLETCHER, PETER, b. N.Y.C, July 6, 39; m. 62. TOPOLOGY. B.S, Washington & Lee, 62; M.A, North Carolina, Chapel Hill, 64, Ph.D.(math), 66. ASSOC. PROF. MATH, VA. POLYTECH. INST. & STATE UNIV, 67- Am. Math. Soc; Math. Asn. Am. Quasi-uniform spaces; groups of homeomorphisms of topological spaces. Address: Dept. of Mathematics, Williams Hall, Virginia Polytechnic Institute & State University, Blacksburg, VA 24060.

FLETCHER, PETER C, b. Shrewsbury, Eng, Nov. 16, 35; m. 67. PHYSICAL CHEMISTRY, CERAMICS. B.Sc, Univ. Liverpool, 56, Imp. Chem. Industs. fel, 56-59, Ph.D.(surface chem), 59. Gulf Oil fel, State Univ. N.Y, 59-60; sr. scientist physics & surface chem, Owens-Ill. Co, Ohio, 60-70; MAT. ENGR, ELECTRONIC MAT. DIV, BELL & HOWELL CO, PASADENA, 70- Am. Chem. Soc; Am. Ceramic Soc; sr. mem. Am. Vacuum Soc. Surface physics and chemistry; heterogeneous catalysis; glass. Address: 890 Ridgeside Dr, Monrovia, CA 91016.

FLETCHER, PETER W(HITCOMB), b. Blacksburg, Va, Jan. 18, 13; m. 36; c. 1. FOREST SOILS. B.S, Pa. State, 33; M.F, Yale, 34; Ph.D, Missouri, 50. Jr. forestr, U.S. Forest Serv, 34-35, forest ranger, 35-38, fire control asst, 39, asst. silviculturist, 40-42, conservationist, 46-48; from instr. to prof, Univ. Mo, 48-59; dir. sch. forestry, PA. STATE UNIV, 59-66, PROF. FORESTRY, 66- U.S.N.R, 43-45, Lt. Soc. Am. Foresters; Ecol. Soc. Am; Am. Geophys. Union; Soil Sci. Soc. Am. Forest hydrology and watershed management; forest ecology. Address: School of Forest Resources, Pennsylvania State University, University Park, PA 16802.

FLETCHER, R(OBERT) C(HIPMAN), b. N.Y.C, May 27, 21; m. 45; c. 8. PHYSICS. B.S, Mass. Inst. Tech, 43, Nat. Res. fel, 45-49, Ph.D.(physics), 49. Mem. staff, radiation lab, Mass. Inst. Tech, 43-45, asst, insulation lab, 47-49; mem. tech. staff, Bell Tel. Labs, 49-58, dir. solid state device develop, 58-64; v.pres. res, Sandia Corp, 64-67; exec. dir. mil. systs. res. div. & ocean systs. div, BELL TEL. LABS, 67-71, EXEC. DIR. SOLID STATE COMPONENTS DIV, 71- Fel. Am. Phys. Soc; sr. mem. Inst. Elec. & Electronics Eng. Electron dynamics; magnetrons; traveling wave tubes; gas discharge; impulse breakdown of air; semiconductors; magnetic and ultrasonic devices; masers; solid state devices; optical devices. Address: Solid State Components Division, Bell Telephone Labs, Murray Hill, NJ 07974.

FLETCHER, ROBERT D(AWSON), b. Lampacitos, Mex, Feb. 11, 12; U.S. citizen; m. 35; c. 2. METEOROLOGY. B.S, Calif. Inst. Technol, 33, M.S, 34, 35; Sc.D.(meteorol), Mass. Inst. Technol, 41. Instr. mech. drawing, Calif. Inst. Technol, 33-34, asst. meteorol, 34-35; meteorologist, Am. Airlines, Inc, 35-39, lectr. & consult. meteorologist, 38-39; Bankhead-Jones agent, U.S. Weather Bur, 39-40, meteorologist & supv. forecaster, 40-46, chief hydrometeorol. sect, 46-50; consult, AIR WEATHER SERV, U.S. AIR FORCE, 50-62, dir. aerospace sci, 52-71, CHIEF SCIENTIST, SCOTT AFB, 71- Instr, Brown Univ, 39-40; asst, Mass. Inst. Technol, 39-40; instr, Univ. Calif, Los Angeles, 40-42; tech. consult, Off. Sci. Res. & Develop, 44; U.S. del, World Meteorol. Orgn, 52-; U.S. Air Force & Nat. Res. Coun. del, Pac. Sci. Cong, Manila, 53, Bangkok, 57; mem. panel meteorol, Int. Geophys. Year, 55-64; adv. group aeronaut. res. & develop, conf. polar meteorol, NATO, Norway, 56; Australian Conf. Trop. Storms, 56; comt. aircraft oper. probs, NASA, 59-63; U.S. del, Int. Union Geod. & Geophys, Finland, 60; liaison rep, comt. high altitude rocket & balloon res, Nat. Acad. Sci, 60-63, panel ed, 62-64. Decoration, U.S. Air Force, 62. U.S.A.A.F, 44-45. Fel. Am. Meteorol. Soc.(pres, 56-58, Charles Franklin Brooks Award, 70); assoc. fel. Am. Inst. Aeronaut. & Astronaut.(Robert M. Losey Award, 69); Am. Geophys. Union; Royal Meteorol. Soc. Aerospace meteorology; radar and tropical meteorology; weather forecasting; aviation and rocket meteorology; atmospheric pollution; hydrometeorology; high altitude meteorology. Address: 135 Roger Dr, Lebanon, IL 62254.

FLETCHER, ROBERT HOLTON, b. Lansing, Mich, June 19, 06; m. 33; c. 2. MECHANICAL ENGINEERING. B.S, Pa. State, 28. Exp. tester aeronaut. eng, Lycoming Mfg. Co, 28-31; owner, Adkins Ice Cream Co, 33-41; instr. ord. vehicles, U.S. Army, 41-43; res. engr. combat vehicles, Aberdeen Proving Grounds Md, 43-45; co-ordinator diversified occupations, Pub. Sch. System, Waco, Texas, 45-46; from instr. to ASSOC. PROF. MECH. ENG, TEX. A&M UNIV, 47- Consult, Boeing Airplane,Co, 51-52; Change Vought Aircraft, 53; Texas Power & Light Co, 54; Thompson-Ramo-Wooldridge, Inc, 54-58; Humble Oil & Ref. Co, 59-61; Pratt & Whitney Aircraft Co, 62-; Dallas Power & Light, 63-; Tex. Elec. Serv, 64-; Safety Brake Co; Mobile Oil Co, 69-70; results engr, Houston Lighting & Power Co, 65, 68, 70; proj. engr, Tex. Elec. Power Inst, 66-67. U.S.A.A.F, 31-32. Soc. Automotive Eng; Am. Soc. Eng. Educ. Automotive and aircraft engineering; reciprocating, gas turbine and high energy engines; plant efficiencies; oil string casing design. Address: Dept. of Mechanical Engineering, Texas A&M University, College Station, TX 77843.

FLETCHER, RONALD AUSTIN, b. Cape Comorin, India, July 1, 31; Can. citizen; m. 62; c. 2. PLANT PHYSIOLOGY. B.Sc, Delhi, 54; M.Sc, British Columbia, 61; Ph.D.(physiol), Alberta, 64. Sect. off. landscape hort, Govt. of India, 54-59; Nat. Res. Coun. Can-NATO overseas res. fel. sci, Eng, 64-65; asst. prof. BOT, UNIV. GUELPH, 65-68, ASSOC. PROF, 68- Can. Soc. Plant Physiol.(secy, 67-68); Am. Soc. Plant Physiol; Scand. Soc. Plant Physiol. Hormonal regulation of plant growth and development. Address: Dept. of Environmental Biology, University of Guelph, Guelph, Ont, Can.

FLETCHER, RONALD D, b. Foxboro, Mass, Jan. 18, 33; m; c. 3. VIROLOGY. B.S, Connecticut, 54, M.S, 59, Ph.D.(bact), 63; summers, Saskatchewan, 65 & Harvard Med. Sch, 66. Asst. bact, Connecticut, 58-59, instr. animal diseases, 59-63; Nat. Inst. Allergy & Infectious Diseases fel. microbiol, vet. bact. inst, Univ. Zurich, 63-64; res. virologist antimicrobial ther. dept, Lederle Labs, Am. Cyanamid Co, 64-67; ASSOC. PROF. MICROBIOL. & ASSOC. HEAD DEPT, SCH. DENT. MED, UNIV. PITTSBURGH, 67- Gen. res. support grant, Univ. Pittsburgh, 67-68; Am. Cancer Soc. instnl. res. grant, 68-69; Dept. Army life sci. div. grant, 69-71. Registered, Nat. Registry Microbiol. Med.Serv.C, U.S.A, 54-57, Res, 57-, Maj. Am. Soc. Microbiol; Tissue Cult. Asn; Int. Asn. Dent. Res; N.Y. Acad. Sci. The relationship between Mycoplasma species and selected respiratory viruses, in vitro and in vivo; the interaction of mycoplasma with organisms of the oral cavity. Address: Dept. of Microbiology, 645 Salk Hall, School of Dental Medicine, University of Pittsburgh, Pittsburgh, PA 15213.

FLETCHER, ROY JACKSON, b. Red Deer, Alta, Feb. 1, 35; m. 66; c. 3. CLIMATOLOGY. B.A, Alberta, 57; M.A, Minnesota, 59; Ph.D.(geog), Clark, 68. Lectr. GEOG, State Univ. N.Y. Buffalo, 61-68; ASSOC. PROF, UNIV. LETHBRIDGE, 68- Asn. Am. Geog; Am. Soc. Photogram; Arctic Inst. N.Am; Can. Asn. Geog. Synoptic and dynamic climatology; arctic, especially physical geography; transportation and human ecology; aerial photograph interpretation of arctic regions. Address: Dept. of Geography, University of Lethbridge, Lethbridge, Alta, Can.

FLETCHER, STEWART G(AILEY), b. Wilkinsburg, Pa, Jan. 20, 18; m. 42; c. 4. METALLURGY. B.S, Carnegie Inst. Tech, 38; Sc.D.(phys. metall), Mass. Inst. Tech, 43. Lab. instr. metall, Carnegie Inst. Tech, 37-39; asst, Mass. Inst. Tech, 39-42, res. assoc, 42-45; chief res. metallurgist, LATROBE STEEL CO, 45-47, chief metallurgist, 47-57, V.PRES. & TECH. DIR, 57- Lab. instr, Lowell Inst. Sch, 39-41, instr, 42-44. Summers, metall. asst, Aluminum Res. Labs, 35, 36, 37, mem. tech. staff, 38, 39, 40. Fel. AAAS; fel. Am. Soc. Metals(Howe Medal, 46-49; secy, 62-64, v.pres, 64-65, pres, 65-66); Am. Soc. Test. & Mat; Soc. Mfg. Eng; Soc. Automotive Eng; Am. Iron & Steel Inst; Am. Inst. Mining, Metall. & Petrol. Eng; Brit. Iron & Steel Inst. Metallography of steel; heat treatment of tool and die steels; alloying tool steels; electric steel making; vacuum melting of steels; superalloys; electroslag melting. Address: Latrobe Steel Co, 2626 S. Ligonier St, Latrobe, PA 15650.

FLETCHER, THOMAS F(RANCIS), b. N.Y.C, Mar. 26, 37; m. 60; c. 5. NEUROANATOMY, NEUROPHYSIOLOGY. D.V.M, Cornell, 61; Ph.D.(vet. anat), Minnesota, 65. U.S. Pub. Health Serv. fel, 61-64; asst. prof. VET. ANAT, COL. VET. MED, UNIV. MINN, ST. PAUL, 65-69, ASSOC. PROF, 69- U.S. Pub. Health Serv. grant, 65-66, 67- Am. Asn. Vet. Anat; World Asn. Vet. Anat. Neuroanatomy and neurophysiology of the spinal cord; anatomicophysiological basis of nervous disorders in domestic animals. Address: Dept. of Veterinary Anatomy, University of Minnesota, St. Paul, MN 55101.

FLETCHER, T(HOMAS) LLOYD, b. Boydton, Va, Jan. 4, 17; m. 41; c. 4. ORGANIC CHEMISTRY. A.B, Clark, 37, M.A, 38; Ph.D.(biochem, org. chem), Wisconsin, 49. Chemist, Lever Bros. Co, Mass, 39-42; Colonial-Beacon Oil Co, 42; teacher chem, Adm. Billard Acad, 42-43; chemist, Forest Prods. Lab, U.S. Forest Serv, 43-48; pulp mills res, UNIV. WASH, 48-51, res. chemist, DEPT. SURG, SCH. MED, 51-55, res. assoc. prof. SURG, 55-65, res. prof, 65-67, PROF, CHEM. RES. LAB, 67- Nat. Cancer Inst. res. career develop. award, 61-71. Fel. AAAS; Am. Chem. Soc; The Chem. Soc; Soc. Exp. Biol. & Med; N.Y. Acad. Sci. Chemistry of fluorene and other aryl polycyclics; carcinogenicity; cancer chemotherapy; gastrin; gastric physiology. Address: Dept. of Surgery, Chemistry Research Lab, University of Washington, Seattle, WA 98105.

FLETCHER, WILLIAM ELLIS, b. Colfax, La, Nov. 11, 36; m; c. 3. HORTICULTURE. B.S, Southwestern Louisiana, 58; M.S, Iowa State, 61, Ph.D, 64. Asst, Iowa State, 58-63, instr, 63-64; asst. prof. ornamental hort, Florida, 64-67; HORT, UNIV. SOUTHWEST. LA, 67-69, ASSOC. PROF, 69- Woody ornamentals; general nursery stock and foliage plants. Address: Dept. of Horticulture, College of Agriculture, University of Southwestern Louisiana, Lafayette, LA 70501.

FLETCHER, WILLIAM H(ENRY), b. Eureka, Kans, Apr. 25, 16; m. 49; c. 4. PHYSICAL CHEMISTRY. B.S, Col. of Idaho, 39; Wisconsin; Ph.D.(chem), Minnesota, 49. Res. chemist, Norwich Pharmacal Co, 40-42; Lubrizol Corp, 42-46; asst. prof. CHEM, UNIV. TENN, KNOXVILLE, 49-53, assoc. prof, 53-59, PROF, 59- Consult, Union Carbide Nuclear Co, 57. AAAS; Coblentz Soc; Soc. Appl. Spectros; Am. Chem. Soc; Am. Phys. Soc. Molecular spectroscopy; molecular force fields; laser Raman spectra. Address: 7132 Cheshire Dr, Knoxville, TN 37919.

FLETCHER, WILLIAM S(IGOURNEY), b. Arlington, Mass, May 7, 27; m. 49; c. 3. SURGERY. A.B, Dartmouth Col, 52; M.D, Harvard Med. Sch, 55. Am. Cancer Soc. clin. fel, Middlesex Hosp, London, Eng, 58-59; instr. SURG, MED. SCH, UNIV. ORE, 60-62, asst. prof, 62-65, assoc. prof, 65-70, PROF, 70- Am. Cancer Soc. adv. clin. fel, 60-63; Markle scholar. med. sci, 62-67. U.S.N. Am. Col. Surg; Am. Asn. Surg. of Trauma; James Ewing Soc; Am. Fedn. Clin. Res; Am. Med. Asn. Medical education; basic experimental and clinical cancer research; breeding a large standard laboratory dog. Address: Dept. of Surgery, University of Oregon Medical School, Portland, OR 97201.

FLETCHER, WILLIAM T(HOMAS), b. Durham, N.C, Aug. 19, 34. MATHEMATICS. B.S, N.C. Col. Durham, 56, M.S, 58; Ph.D.(math), Univ. Idaho, 66. Assoc. prof. MATH, LeMOYNE-OWEN COL, 57-71, PROF, 71- Summers, faculty assoc, U.S. Dept. Commerce, 67, U.S. Dept. Agr, 71, IBM faculty fel, Columbia Univ, 69, Nat. Urban League faculty fel, 70. U.S.A.R, 59. Math. Asn. Am; Am. Math. Soc. Lie algebras; abstract algebra; associative and non associative. Address: Dept. of Mathematics, LeMoyne-Owen College, Memphis, TN 38126.

FLETCHER, WORTH A(LBERT), b. Randolph Co, Ind, May 8, 00; m. 31; c. 1. CHEMISTRY. A.B, Indiana, 25, A.M, 26, Ph.D.(org. chem), 27. Assoc. prof. CHEM, UNIV. WICHITA, 27-31, prof, 31-70, registrar, 31-65, EMER. PROF, 70- Am. Chem. Soc. Use of nitro compounds as oxidizing agents; azo derivatives of guaiacol; diazo thio-ethers of thio-beta-naphthol. Address: 1166 N. Pinecrest, Wichita, KS 67208.

FLEURY, PAUL A, b. Baltimore, Md, July 20, 39; m. 64; c. 2. SOLID STATE PHYSICS, SPECTROSCOPY. B.S, John Carroll Univ, 60, M.S, 62; Nat. Sci. Found. fel, Mass. Inst. Technol, 62-65, Ph.D.(physics), 65. Mem. tech. staff, BELL TEL. LABS, 65-70, DEPT. HEAD PHYSICS, 70- Am. Phys. Soc. Nonlinear optical and inelastic laser light scattering studies of solids and simple fluids including semiconductors, ferroelectrics, magnets and their phase transitions. Address: Bell Telephone Labs, Room 1A161, Murray Hill, NJ 07974.

FLEXER, ABRAHAM SIDNEY, b. New Haven, Conn, Apr. 12, 35; m. 56; c. 2. MICROBIOLOGY, GENETICS. A.B, Clark, 59; Nat. Sci. Found. fel, Harvard, 59-60, A.B, 60, Maser fel, 60-61, Nat. Insts. Health fel, 62-63, Ph.D. (biol), 63. Instr. biol, Harvard, 63-66, asst. prof, 66-69; ASSOC. CHMN. DEPT. MOLECULAR, CELLULAR & DEVELOP. BIOL, UNIV. COLO, BOULDER, 69- U.S. Pub. Health Serv. res. grant, 63- Bot. Soc. Am. Microbial genetics; incompatibility in the fungi. Address: Dept. of Molecular, Cellular & Developmental Biology, University of Colorado, Boulder, CO 80302.

FLEXMAN, EDMUND A, JR, b. Harrisburg, Liberia, Aug. 13, 40; U.S. citizen; m. 64; c. 2. POLYMER SCIENCE, ORGANIC CHEMISTRY. B.A, Bradley Univ, 62; Ph.D.(org. chem), Ind. Univ, Bloomington, 67. Phys. sci. aid paper chem, north. regional lab, U.S. Dept. of Agr, 61-64; res. prog. fel, polymer chem, cent. res. div, 3M Co, summer 64; RES. CHEMIST, EXP. STA, DU PONT PLASTICS, 65- Am. Chem. Soc; Sci. Res. Soc. Am. Polymer chemistry and physics. Address: 10 Crestfield Rd, Crestfield, DE 19810.

FLEXNER, JOHN M, b. Louisville, Ky, Mar. 29, 26; m. 54; c. 4. INTERNAL MEDICINE, HEMATOLOGY. B.A, Yale, 50; M.D, Hopkins, 54. Intern, Vanderbilt Univ. Hosp, 54-55, asst. res. internal med, 55-56; Grace New Haven Hosp, Conn, 56-57; U.S. Pub. Health Serv. fel. hemat, SCH. MED, VANDERBILT UNIV, 57-59, instr. MED, 59-60, asst. prof, 61-71, ASSOC. PROF, 71- Asst. & vis. hematologist, Vanderbilt Univ. Hosp, 57-59, vis. hematologist & dir, hemat. labs & blood bank, 59- Consult, Thayer Vet. Admin. Hosp, Nashville, Tenn, 59-; Regional Blood Center Labs, 65- U.S.N, 44-46. AAAS; Am. Soc. Hemat. Effect of oral fat intake on blood coagulation; megaloblastic anemia due to anti-convulsants; paroxysmal nocturnal hemoglobinuria; myleran induced pulmonary pneumonitis and fibrosis. Address: 4213 Wallace Lane, Nashville, TN 37215.

FLEXNER, LOUIS B(ARKHOUSE), b. Louisville, Ky, Jan. 7, 02; m. 37. ANATOMY. B.S, Chicago, 22; M.D, Hopkins, 27. Loeb fel, Hopkins, 27-28; res. house officer, Clinics, Chicago, 28-29; instr. & assoc. anat, sch. med, Hopkins, 30-40; staff mem, DEPT. EMBRYOL, CARNEGIE INST, 40-51, RES. ASSOC, 51-; PROF. ANAT, SCH. MED, UNIV. PA, 51-, chmn. dept, 51-67, dir. inst. neurol. sci, 53-65. Mem, tech. aide comt. aviation med, Nat. Res. Coun, 42-45; mem, study sects, U.S. Pub. Health Serv, 51-; adv. bd, United Cerebral Palsy Asn, 56; Nat. Found, 59-64. Weinstein award, 57. With Off. Sci. Res. & Develop, 44. Nat. Acad. Sci; Am. Physiol. Soc; Brit. Biochem. Soc; Am. Acad. Arts & Sci; Am. Asn. Anat.(secy-treas, 56-64). Meninges and cerebrospinal fluid; learning and memory; fetal physiology. Address: Dept. of Anatomy, University of Pennsylvania School of Medicine, Philadelphia, PA 19104.

FLEXNER, WILLIAM W(ELCH), b. N.Y.C, Oct. 5, 04; m. 46. MATHEMATICS. B.S, Harvard, 26; A.M, Princeton, 27, Procter fel, 28-29, Ph.D.(math), 30. Res. assoc. math, Princeton, 29-30, instr, 30-31; lectr, Bryn Mawr Col, 31-32, assoc, 32-34; asst. prof, Cornell, 34-40, assoc. prof, 40-48; sr. statistician, statist. off, UN, 48-50, chief trade & transport statist. sect, 50-64, asst. dir. in charge Int. Trade Statist. Ctr, 64-66; statist. consult. & assoc. prof. MATH, sch. eng. & sci, COOPER UNION, 66-68, prof, 68-69; EMER. PROF, 69- Supplies off, UN Relief & Rehabil. Admin, 44-45; chief, tech. information div, European Cent. Inland Trans. Orgn, 45-47; tech. consult. on inland transport, Presidents Comt. on For. Aid, 47. Am. Math. Soc; Am. Geog. Soc; Am. Statist. Asn. Algebra; topology; cartography; economic statistics; large scale electronic data processing. Address: 431 E. 20th St, New York, NY 10010.

FLEXSER, LEO A(ARON), b. N.Y.C, June 20, 10; m. 39; c. 1. CHEMISTRY. A.B, Columbia, 31, A.M, 32, fel, 34-35, Ph.D.(chem), 35. Asst. chem, Columbia, 31-34; res. chemist, Montrose Chem. Co, N.J, 35-36, plant supt, 36-38; instr. chem, Brooklyn Col, 38; res. chemist, N.Y. Quinine & Chem. Co, 38-41; sr. chemist, HOFFMANN-LA ROCHE, INC, 41-45, group chief mfg. & develop. dept, 45-59, dir. chem. prod, 59-63, V.PRES, 63- Mem. bd. trustees, Jersey City State Col, N.J, 68- AAAS; Sci. Res. Soc. Am; Am. Chem. Soc; Soc. Chem. Indust; fel. Am. Inst. Chem; Am. Inst. Chem. Eng. Process research and development in synthesis and manufacture of vitamins and pharmaceutical chemicals; administration of fine chemical manufacturing and development. Address: Hoffmann-La Roche, Inc, Roche Park, Nutley, NJ 07110.

FLEYSHER, MAURICE H(ENRY), b. Phila, Pa, Jan. 1, 98; m. 39; c. 2. CHEMISTRY. B.S, Pennsylvania, 21, M.S, 22, Ph.D.(phys. chem), 24. Instr. physics & chem, Cent. High Sch, Phila, 24-25; res. chemist, Nat. Aniline Div, Allied Chem. Corp, 25-63; CANCER RES. SCIENTIST, ROSWELL PARK MEM. INST, 63- U.S.A, 18. Am. Chem. Soc; emer. fel. Am. Inst. Chem. Anthraquinone vat dyes; organic pigments; intermediates; sulfur dyes; nucleic acids; nucleosides; nucleotides; proteins; cancer antimetabolites; organic chemicals; activity coeffecients and transference numbers of hydrochloric acid in alcoholic solutions. Address: Roswell Park Memorial Institute, Buffalo, NY 14203.

FLICK, DONALD F(RANKLIN), b. Martinsburg, W.Va, Feb. 20, 22; m. 62; c. 2. BIOCHEMISTRY. A.B. & M.S, W.Va. Univ, 47; Ph.D.(biochem), George Wash. Univ, 58. Instr. pub. sch, W.Va, 47-48; with U.S. State Dept, Wash, D.C, 48-49; sanitarian, State Health Dept, W.Va, 49-50; biochemist, Vet. Admin, 50-53; instr, George Wash. Univ, 53-58; chief, nutrit. res. br, U.S. Army Med. Res. Lab, Ky, 58-59; toxicologist, U.S. FOOD & DRUG ADMIN, 59-69, HEALTH SCI. COORD, BUR. DRUGS, 69-; PROF. BIOCHEM, U.S. DEPT. AGR. GRAD. SCH, 63- Med. Dept, U.S.A, 42-46. Fel. AAAS; fel. Am. Inst. Chem; Am. Inst. Nutrit; Am. Inst. Biol. Sci; Soc. Exp. Biol. & Med; Am. Chem. Soc; Asn. Off. Anal. Chem; Soc. Res. Admin; Soc. Toxicol; fel. N.Y. Acad. Sci. Lipid and cholesterol metabolism; nutrition in the cold; obesity; anticoagulants; toxicity of cadmium, chlorinated hydrocarbon; bioassay for oral diuretics. Address: Division of Extramural & Clinical Research, Bureau of Drugs, Food & Drug Administration, Washington, DC 20204.

FLICK, GEORGE JOSEPH, b. New Orleans, La, May 30, 40; m. 67; c. 1. FOOD SCIENCE & TECHNOLOGY. B.A, La. State Univ, Baton Rouge, 63, M.S, 66; Ph.D.(food sci), 69; Florasynth fel, Inst. Food Technologists, 66; U.S. Pub. Health Serv. fel, 66-68; Bur. Commercial Fisheries scholar, 68-69. ASST. PROF. FOOD SCI. & TECHNOL, VA. POLYTECH. INST. & STATE UNIV, 69- Air Nat. Guard, 63-69. AAAS; Am. Chem. Soc; Inst. Food Technol. Separation and isolation of metabolic compounds in marine organisms; chemical and microbiological contaminents in processed seafood products that are of public health significance. Address: Dept. of Food Science & Technology, Virginia Polytechnic Institute & State University, Blacksburg, VA 24061.

FLICK, JOHN A, b. Camden, N.J, May 10, 17; m. 43; div; c. 5. MICROBIOLOGY. B.S, Haverford Col, 39; M.D, Harvard, 43. Instr. MED. MICROBIOL, SCH. MED, UNIV. PA, 44-53, ASSOC. PROF, 53-, CHMN. DEPT, DIV. GRAD. MED, 55- AAAS; Am. Asn. Immunol. Allergy; immunology. Address: Division of Graduate Medicine, University of Pennsylvania, Philadelphia, PA 19104.

FLICKER, HERBERT, b. Brooklyn, N.Y, Jan. 28, 30; m. 53; c. 2. PHYSICS. A.B, Cornell, 51; M.S, Pennsylvania, 53, Union Carbide Corp. fel, 57, Socony Vacuum fel, 58, Ph.D.(physics), 59. Mem. tech. staff, RCA Labs, 59-64; vis. assoc. prof. eng, Brown Univ, 64-65; mem. staff, TRW Systs. Group, 65-66; mgr. semiconductor dept, ELECTRO-OPTICAL SYSTS, XEROX CORP, 66-68, CHIEF SCIENTIST, ADVAN. SYSTS. & REQUIREMENTS, 68- U.S.A, 53-55. Am. Phys. Soc. Semiconductor physics; radiation damage in semiconductors; cryogenics; optical and electrical properties of semiconductors; infrared photodetectors, systems analysis. Address: Xerox Corp, 300 N. Halstead St, Pasadena, CA 91107.

FLICKINGER, DON, b. Erie, Pa, Nov. 26, 07. AVIATION MEDICINE. A.B, Stanford, 29, M.D, 33. Chief med. serv, U.S. Army Hosp, Ala, 34, sta. hosp, Calif, 33-37, March Field, 37-40, sr. flight surgeon, Wheeler Field, Hawaii, 40-41, command flight surgeon, 7th flighter interceptor squadron, 41-42, wing surgeon, hq. India-China Wing, 43-44, instr. aeromed, Air Force Sch. Appl. Tactics, Fla, 44-45, instr. reserv. off, training corps, Harvard Med. Sch. & Peter Bent Brigham Hosp, 45-46, dir. med. servs. & res, Sch. Aviation Med, Tex, 46-49, air surgeon, 8th air force, Carswell Air Force Base, 49-51, dir. human factors, res. & asst. dep. comdr. tech. opers, hq. Air Res. & Develop. Command, 51-55, comdr. Air Force Off. Sci. Res, 55-56, Europ. Off, Air Res. & Develop. Command, Belg, 56-57, surgeon, dir. life sci. & asst. bioastronaut, Air Force Systs. Command, D.C, 57-61; CONSULT. AEROSPACE MED, 61- Airpower Award, Air Force Asn, 59. Med.C, U.S.A.F, 34-61, Brig. Gen.(ret). Am. Astronaut. Soc; Am. Inst. Aeronaut. & Astronaut.(Jeffries Award, Inst. Aeronaut. Sci, 60); Am. Med. Asn; fel. Aerospace Med. Asn.(Lyster Award, Aero Med. Asn, 56); Asn. Mil. Surg; U.S. Pan-Am. Med. Asn; fel. Am. Col. Physicians. Stress and fatigue; vasomotor control mechanisms as affected by anoxia, hypoxia and temperature extremes; psychologic disorders of flying; bio-engineering problems in modern high-performance aircraft. Address: 2500 Que St. N.W, Washington, DC 20007.

FLICKINGER, GEORGE L(ATIMORE), JR, b. Hanover, Pa, May 21, 33; m. 58; c. 3. COMPARATIVE PATHOLOGY, REPRODUCTIVE PHYSIOLOGY. B.S, Pa. State, 54; V.M.D, Pennsylvania, 58, Ph.D.(path), 63. Assoc. dir. path, Penrose Res. Lab, 62-63; instr, UNIV. PA, 63-64, assoc, 64-66, OBSTET. & GYNEC, 64-66, ASST. PROF, 66- AAAS; Endocrine Soc. Hormone secretion by gonadal tissues; relationship of social behavior to reproductive performance. Address: Dept. of Obstetrics & Gynecology, Dulles Bldg, 5th Floor, University of Pennsylvania, Philadelphia, PA 19104.

FLICKINGER, LLOYD H(ENRY), b. Center Point, Iowa, Feb. 9, 04; m. 26; c. 2. CIVIL ENGINEERING. B.S.C.E, Iowa, 28. Jr. engr, Sanit. Dist. Chicago, Ill, 28-29; asst. engr, Mahoning Valley Sanit. Dist, Ohio, 29-32; draftsman, St. Paul Eng. Dist, Minn, 33-34; asst. engr, Minneapolis-St. Paul Sanit. Dist, 34-38; engr. examiner, Pub. Works Admin, 38-40; struct. designer, Panama Canal, 40-41; asst. area engr, Kansas Ord. Plant, 41-42; maintenance engr, U.S. Vet. Admin, 46-49; struct. engr, Garrison Dist, Corps Eng, 49-51, Omaha Dist, 51-52; planning engr, West. Air Defense Force, 52-53; prog. mgr, mil. construct, Pac. Div, Bur. Yards & Docks, U.S. Navy, 53-61, dir. contract div, Naval Facilities Eng. Command, 62-69; CONSULT. CIVIL ENGR, 69- C.Eng, 41-46, Res, 27-64, Lt. Col. Fel. Am. Soc. Civil Eng; Soc. Am. Mil. Eng. Contract administration and program management of large military construction projects in overseas areas. Address: 2037 Akaikai Loop, Pearl City, HI 96782.

FLICKINGER, REED ADAMS, b. Council Bluffs, Iowa, Apr. 5, 24; m. 49; c. 2. EMBRYOLOGY. B.A, Stanford, 46, Ph.D.(exp. embryol), 49. Instr. EMBRYOL, Pennsylvania, 49-52; asst. prof, California, Los Angeles, 52-58; assoc. prof, Iowa, 58-61; California, Davis, 61-64; PROF, STATE UNIV. N.Y. COL. BUFFALO, 64- Rockefeller res. fel, Brussels, Belgium, 50-51, Stockholm, Sweden, 51-52; U.S. Pub. Health Serv. spec. fel, Paris, 61. U.S.A, 43-45. Am. Soc. Zool; Soc. Develop. Biol; Am. Soc. Cell Biol; Int. Inst. Embryol. Experimental and chemical embryology; cancer research. Address: Dept. of Biology, State University of New York College at Buffalo, Buffalo, NY 14214.

FLICKINGER, STEPHEN ALBERT, b. Savanna, Ill, Feb. 12, 42; m. 66; c. 1. FISHERIES BIOLOGY. B.A, South. Ill. Univ, Carbondale, 64, M.A, 66; Ph.D. (fishery biol), Colo. State Univ, 69. ASST. PROF. FISHERY BIOL, COLO. STATE UNIV, 70- Am. Fisheries Soc. Culture of food, bait, and sport fishes. Address: Dept. of Fishery and Wildlife Biology, Colorado State University, Ft. Collins, CO 80521.

FLIEDER, DONALD (EMIL), b. Waterloo, Iowa, July 18, 24. DENTISTRY. B.A, Iowa State Teachers Col, 47; D.D.S, Iowa, 52, M.S, 54. Assoc. prof. dent, St. Louis, 56-62, prof. oral path, 62-70, dir. dept, 56-70; PROF. PATH, SCH. DENT, MARQUETTE UNIV, 70- Mem. adv. comt, White House Conf. Aging, 59. U.S.N, 43-44. Int. Asn. Dent. Res; Am. Dent. Asn. Address: Dept. of Pathology, Marquette University School of Dentistry, 604 N. 16th St, Milwaukee, WI 53233.

FLIEDNER, LEONARD JOHN, JR, b. Flushing, N.Y, Mar. 16, 37. ORGANIC CHEMISTRY. A.B, Princeton, 58; N.Y. State Regents fel, Fordham, 58-60, M.S, 60; Ph.D.(org. chem), Massachusetts, 65. Nat. Insts. Health res. asst. org. chem, Massachusetts, 62-65; SR. RES. CHEMIST, ENDO LABS, INC, GARDEN CITY, 65- Am. Chem. Soc. Synthetic organic chemistry; medicinal chemistry; synthesis of fibrinolytics and analgetics; heterocyclic chemistry, synthesis of mesoionic ring systems. Address: 33-67 157th St, Flushing, NY 11354.

FLIERL, DONALD W(ILLIAM), b. Buffalo, N.Y, Sept. 29, 18; m. 41; c. 2. PHYSICAL CHEMISTRY. A.B, Oberlin Col, 40. Chemist, Yerkes Res. Lab, E.I. DU PONT DE NEMOURS & CO, 46-53, lab. supvr, Circleville Plant, 53-55, res. chemist, 55-59, methods engr, 59-64, specialist, 64-69, GEN. SERV. SUPVR, CIRCLEVILLE RES. & DEVELOP. LAB, 69- U.S.A.A.F, 42-45, Res, 46-53, Capt. Fel. Am. Inst. Chem. Physical and electrical property measurements on thin films. Address: 350 E. Main St, Ashville, OH 43103.

FLIKKE, ARNOLD M(AURICE), b. Viroqua, Wis, July 8, 19; m. 42; c. 3. AGRICULTURAL ENGINEERING. B.S, Wisconsin, 41; M.S, Minnesota, 43, fel, 43-44. Instr. AGR. ENG. & RURAL ELECTRIFICATION, UNIV. MINN, MINNEAPOLIS, 46-49, asst. prof, 49-56, assoc. prof, 56-65, PROF, 65- U.S.N.R, 44-46, Lt.(jg). Am. Soc. Agr. Eng; Am. Soc. Eng. Educ. Application of electricity to agriculture; farm refrigeration; use of heat pump in agriculture; power and machinery design. Address: 3409 Downers Dr. N.E, Minneapolis, MN 55418.

FLINCHBAUGH, DAVID E(DWARD), b. Poughkeepsie, N.Y, Oct. 11, 34; m. 57; c. 4. PHYSICS. B.S, Union (N.Y), 57; Case, 57-59; M.S, Connecticut, 60, Ph.D.(physics), 63. Lab. asst, physics dept, Union (N.Y), 53-57; ed. asst, physics dept, Case, 57-59; Connecticut, 60-61, res. asst, 61-63; res. scientist, res. labs, United Aircraft Corp, 63-65; Andersen Labs, 65-66, mgr. res. & develop, 66-68; dir. res, Orlando Div, Control Laser Corp, 68-70, exec. v.pres, 70-71; PRES, AEROBEAM CORP, 71- Summers, physicist, Int. Bus. Mach. Res. & Develop. Labs, 56, 57, resident student assoc, physics sect, reactor eng. div, Argonne Nat. Lab, 58, res. engr, electromagnetics sect, United Aircraft Corp. Res. Labs, 59, 60 & 61; consult, Res. Corp, New York, 65- Am. Phys. Soc; Am. Inst. Physics; Optical Soc. Am; sr. mem. Inst. Elec. & Electronics Eng; Acoust. Soc. Am; Am. Mgt. Asn. High power gas ion lasers and acousto-optic beam deflectors and modulators. Address: Aerobeam Corp, P.O. Box 13416, Orlando, FL 32809.

FLING, MARGUERITE, b. New York, N.Y, Aug. 30, 18; m. 43. ORGANIC CHEMISTRY. A.B, Hunter Col, 41; Ph.D.(biol. & org. chem), Iowa State Col, 46. Res. fel, Calif. Inst. Technol, 46-68; RETIRED. Biochemical genetics in neurospora. Address: 4515 Cherryvale Ave, Soquel, CA 95073.

FLINK, EDMUND BERNEY, b. Isanti, Minn, Jan. 27, 14; m. 40; c. 4. MEDICINE. B.S. & M.B, Minnesota, 37, M.D, 38, Ph.D.(internal med), 45. Instr. internal med, sch. med, Minnesota, 42-43, asst. prof, 43-45, MED, 45-50, assoc. prof, 50-57, prof, 57-60; chief med. serv, Vet. Admin. Hosp, 52-60; PROF. & CHMN. DEPT. MED, MED. CTR, W.VA. UNIV, 60- Commonwealth Fund fel, Harvard, 48-49. Endocrine Soc; Am. Soc. Clin. Invest; fel. Am. Col. Physicians; Asn. Am. Physicians. Hemoglobin metabolism; clinical endocrinology; mineral metabolism. Address: Dept. of Medicine, West Virginia University Medical Center, Morgantown, WV 26506.

FLINN, DAVID R(OY), b. Jennings, Okla, Oct. 21, 37; m. 57; c. 3. PHYSICAL CHEMISTRY. B.S, East Texas State, 60, M.Ed, 61; Welch Found. fel. & Ph.D, North Texas State, 68. Instr. math. & chem, Ranger Jr. Col, 60-61 & 62-64; chem, East Texas State, 61-62; NAT. ACAD. SCI-NAT. RES. COUN. RES. FEL, U.S. NAVAL RES. LAB, 68- Am. Chem. Soc; Electrochem. Soc. Electrode mechanisms; double layer capacitance on platinum and mercury in aqueous solutions; development of new instrumental methods for fast rise-time studies of electrode double-layer charging; organic electrochemistry. Address: Code 6160, Naval Research Lab, Washington, DC 20390.

FLINN, EDWARD A(MBROSE), b. Oklahoma City, Okla, Aug. 27, 31; m. 62; c. 1. GEOPHYSICS. S.B, Mass. Inst. Tech, 53; Fulbright fel, Australian Nat. Univ, 58-60; Ph.D.(geophys), Calif. Inst. Tech, 60. Seismologist, Teledyne Systems Co, United Electrodynamics, Inc, 60-68, ASSOC. DIR, ALEXANDRIA LABS, TELEDYNE GEOTECH, 68- Vis. Assoc. prof. geophys, Brown Univ, 69. AAAS; Soc. Explor. Geophys; Am. Geophys. Union; Seismol. Soc. Am; Royal Astron. Soc. Theoretical seismology; structure of the earth's crust and upper mantle; large-scale seismological data processing; geophysical aspects of underground nuclear weapons test detection. Address: Teledyne Geotech, Box 334, Alexandria, VA 22313.

FLINN, EDWIN S(TANLEY), b. Boston, Mass, Sept. 11, 06; m. 31; c. 3. ORGANIC CHEMISTRY. B.Ch.E, Northeastern, 28; Zurich, 28; M.S, Pa. State Col, 35, Ph.D.(org. chem), 37. Chemist, A.C. Lawrence Leather Co, Mass, 28-29; chief chemist, Ashland Leather Co, Ky, 30-33; res. chemist & tech. rep, Rohm & Haas Co, 37-45; mgr. tannin extract div, Mead Corp, 46-52, asst. dir. res, 53-58; asst. to pres, Hurlbut Paper Co, 58-59, exec. v.pres, 59-64; gen. mgr. tech. papers div, Mead Corp, 64-68; RETIRED. Am. Chem. Soc; Am. Leather Chem. Asn.(pres, 54); Tech. Asn. Pulp & Paper Indust. Structure of fibrous protein and tannin molecule; high temperature catalytic depolymerization of tri-isobutylene; oxidation products of acenaphthene. Address: Trent's Ferry Rd, Route 4, Box 212 C, Lynchburg, VA 24503.

FLINN, JAMES EDWIN, b. Cincinnati, Ohio, Sept. 3, 34; m. 56; c. 3. CHEMICAL ENGINEERING. B.S, Purdue, 56; fel, Cincinnati, 62-63, NASA trainee, 63-65, Ph.D.(chem. eng), 65. Design engr, Dow Corning Corp, Mich, 56-57; develop. engr, Nat. Lead Co. Ohio, 60-62; sr. res. engr, Battelle Mem. Inst, 65-66, ASSOC. DIV. CHIEF, chem. process develop. div, 66-70, WASTE CONTROL & PROCESS TECHNOL. DIV, BATTELLE-COLUMBUS LABS, 70- U.S.A.F, 57-60, Res, 60-65, Capt. Am. Inst. Chem. Eng; Am. Chem. Soc. Process applications of electrical discharges; membrane technology; microencapsulation technology; water desalinization; biomedical engineering; advanced separation methods; coal desulfurization; air, water and solid waste pollution control technology. Address: Battelle-Columbus Labs, 505 King Ave, Columbus, OH 43201.

FLINN, PAUL A(NTHONY), b. New York, N.Y, Mar. 25, 26; m. 49; c. 5. PHYSICS, METALLURGY. A.B, Columbia Col.(Ill), 48; A.M, Columbia, 49; Sc.D, Mass. Inst. Tech, 52. Res. assoc. metall, Mass. Inst. Tech, 52; asst. prof. physics, Wayne, 53-54; mem. staff, res. labs, Westinghouse Elec. Corp, 54-63; PROF. PHYSICS & METALL. ENG, CARNEGIE-MELLON UNIV, 63- Vis. prof, Univ. Nancy, 67-68; Argonne Univs. Asn. distinguished appointment, 71. U.S.N.R, 44-45. AAAS; fel. Am. Phys. Soc; Am. Inst. Metall, Mining & Petrol. Eng. Structure of solids; Mössbauer effect. Address: Dept. of Physics, Carnegie-Mellon University, Pittsburgh, PA 15213.

FLINN, R(ICHARD) A(LFRED), b. Tarentum, Pa, Apr. 15, 29; m. 51; c. 4. PHYSICAL CHEMISTRY. B.S, Grove City Col, 50; fel, Pittsburgh, 50-54, Ph.D.(chem), 54. Res. chemist, Gulf Res. & Develop. Co, 54-56, group leader, 56-59, sr. group leader, 59-60, sect. mgr, 60-62; asst. dir. res. & develop, Air Prod. & Chem, Inc, Pa, 62-66; asst. mgr. chem. eng, Homer Res. Labs, BETHLEHEM STEEL CORP, Pa, 66-68, mem. planning staff, 68-70, V.PRES, MULTICON PROPERTIES, INC, 70- AAAS; Am. Chem. Soc; Am. Inst. Chem. Eng; Am. Soc. Metals. Chemical and petroleum process and product research; cryogenics; catalysis; thermodynamics; instrument development; contract research; corporate planning; industrialized housing. Address: Multicon Properties, Inc, 4645 Executive Dr, Columbus, OH 43215.

FLINN, RICHARD A(LOYSIUS), b. New York, N.Y, May 31, 16; m. 44; c. 5. METALLURGY. B.S, City Col, 36; M.S, Mass. Inst. Tech, 37, Sc.D.(phys. metall), 41. Res. metallurgist, Int. Nickel Co, N.J, 37-39; asst. phys. metall, Mass. Inst. Tech, 39-41; from metall. asst. to asst. chief metallurgist, Am. Brake Shoe Co, 41-52; PROF. METALL. ENG, UNIV. MICH, 52-, IN CHARGE, CAST METALS LAB, 52- With Atomic Energy Comn; Office Sci. Res. & Develop, 44. Am. Foundrymen's Soc.(Simpson Medal, 47); Am. Soc. Metals (Howe Medal, 44, 63); Am. Inst. Min, Metall. & Petrol. Eng; Brit. Inst. Metals. Physical and production metallurgy of cast metals; damping capacity of different metals; casting design and stress analysis; 100,000 psi tensile strength in gray cast iron; basic cupola melting; shell molding; basic oxygen steel making. Address: 140 Underdown Rd, Ann Arbor, MI 48105.

FLINNER, A(RTHUR) O(RAN), b. Leavenworth, Kans, Feb. 3, 07; m. 36; c. 2. MECHANICAL ENGINEERING. B.S, Kans. State Col, 29, M.S, 34; M.S, Mass. Inst. Tech, 37. Design draftsman, Stearman Aircraft Corp, Kans, 29; instr. MECH. ENG, KANS. STATE UNIV, 29-34, asst. prof, 34-40, assoc. prof, 45-48, PROF, 48- U.S.A, 40-45, Col. Am. Soc. Mech. Eng; Am. Soc. Eng. Educ; Am. Soc. Heat, Refrig. & Air Conditioning Eng. Thermal diffusivity of soils; conductivity of building materials; alcohol as engine fuel; performance of air washers. Address: Dept. of Mechanical Engineering, Kansas State University, Manhattan, KS 66502.

FLINNER, JACK L, b. Canton, Ohio, June 6, 31; m. 55; c. 3. NUCLEAR PHYSICS. A.B, Wittenberg, 53; M.S, Illinois, 55; Nat. Sci. Found. fel. & Ph.D.(physics), Ohio State, 65. ASSOC. PROF. PHYSICS, Wittenberg, 57-69; MANKATO STATE COL, 69- Am. Phys. Soc; Am. Asn. Physics Teachers. Low energy nuclear physics; gas scattering experiments; angular correlation. Address: Dept. of Physics, Mankato State College, Mankato, MN 56001.

FLINT, ARTHUR EMERSON, b. Owanka, S.Dak, Feb. 20, 13; m. 39; c. 2. ECONOMIC GEOLOGY, STRATIGRAPHY. B.S, Chicago, 48, M.S, 49, Ph.D.

(geol), 54. Geologist, U.S. Geol. Surv, 49-50, chief Iowa party, 50-53, Bull Canyon proj, 53-55; chief geologist, Radium King Mines, Inc, 55-59; consult. econ. geologist, 59-62; sr. geologist, Fed. Resources Corp, 63-64; PROF. GEOL. & CHMN. NATURAL SCI. DIV, CHAPMAN COL, 64- A.U.S, 42-46, U.S.A.R, 38-42, 46-53, Maj. AAAS; Geol. Soc. Am; Am. Inst. Min, Metall. & Petrol. Eng; Nat. Asn. Geol. Teachers. Research in the origin, occurrence and controls, particularly stratigraphic, of economic metalliferous deposits and in improved techniques for finding them. Address: 1219 E. Adams Ave, Orange, CA 92667.

FLINT, DELOS E(DWARD), b. Pasadena, Calif, Dec. 5, 18; m. 50; c. 5. ECONOMIC GEOLOGY. B.S. Calif. Inst. Tech, 39; M.S, Northwestern, 41. Asst, Northwestern, 40-41; jr. geologist, U.S. Geol. Surv, 41-42, geologist, 42-57; Freeport Sulphur Co, 57-64, CHIEF GEOLOGIST, 64-70, FREEPORT MINERALS CO, 70- U.S.A, 44-46. Am. Inst. Mining, Metall. & Petrol. Eng; Geochem. Soc; fel. Geol. Soc. Am; Soc. Econ. Geol. Areal, economic and military geology. Address: Route 1, Box 44, Covington, LA 70433.

FLINT, DONALD R(ICHARD), b. Kansas City, Mo, Sept. 2, 33; m. 57; c. 3. BIOCHEMISTRY. B.A, Rockhurst Col, 61; Ph.D.(biochem), Tulane, 67. Instr. biochem, sch. med, Tulane Univ, 61-66; sr. investr, Smith Kline & French Labs, 66-69; SR. RES. CHEMIST, CHEMAGRO CORP, 69- U.S.A.F, 52-56, Res, 56-60, S/Sgt. AAAS; Am. Chem. Soc; Am. Pharmaceut. Asn; Acad. Pharmaceut. Sci. Metabolism of drugs, pesticides and other xenobiotics; drug-metabolizing enzyme induction and inhibition; drug interactions; persistence and mobility of pesticides in soil and natural water; radiosynthetic and radiometric methodology. Address: Research & Development, Chemagro Corp, P.O. Box 4913, Hawthorne Rd, Kansas City, MO 64120.

FLINT, DUANE L(ESLIE), b. Cedaredge, Colo, Feb. 23, 30. CHEMICAL ENGINEERING. B.S, Wash. State Col, 52; M.S, Illinois, 56, Ph.D.(chem. eng), 58. Res. engr, UNION OIL CO. CALIF, 58-71, SR. RES. ENGR, 71- U.S.A.F, 52-54, Res, 54- Engineering services. Address: P.O. Box 76, Brea, CA 92621.

FLINT, E(INAR) P(HILIP), b. Wardner, Idaho, Aug. 10, 08; m. 37; c. 2. CHEMISTRY. B.S, Washington (Seattle), 30; A.M, George Washington, 32; Ph.D.(phys. chem), Maryland, 36. Jr. chemist, Bur. Standards, 30-36, assoc. chemist, 36-41, chemist, 41-44; supvr, inorg. chem. sect, Armour Res. Found, 44-46, mgr, ceramics & minerals dept, 46-54; dir. inorg. res, Mallinckrodt Chem. Works, 54-55; mgr. appl. inorg. res, Arthur D. Little, Inc, 55-62; asst. to pres, Ipsen Industs, Inc, 62-65; mgr. mat. dept, Alexandria Div, Am. Mach. & Foundry Co, 65-66; STAFF METALLURGIST, div. metall, U.S. BUR. MINES, 66-70, DIV. SOLID WASTES, 70- Fel. AAAS; Am. Chem. Soc; fel. Am. Ceramic Soc; Nat. Inst. Ceramic Eng; Am. Inst. Min, Metall. & Petrol. Eng; Am. Soc. Metals. Phase equilibria in oxide and silicate systems; hydrothermal synthesis; fine chemicals and pharmaceuticals; diamond, graphite and related materials; portland cement; ceramics; metallurgy; reclamation and utilization of solid wastes; professional writing. Address: 6229 Radcliff Rd, Alexandria, VA 22307.

FLINT, FRANKLIN F(ORD), b. Va, Aug. 4, 25; m. 48; c. 3. BIOLOGY. B.S, Lynchburg Col, 49; M.S, Univ. Va, 50, Ph.D.(biol), 55. Instr. biol, Randolph-Macon Woman's Col, 51-54, asst. prof, 54-58, assoc. prof, 58-66, prof, 66-68, chmn. dept, 62-68; staff biologist, comn. undergrad. educ. biol. sci, Nat. Sci. Found, Wash, D.C, 68-69; PROF. BIOL. & CHMN. DEPT, RANDOLPH-MACON WOMAN'S COL, 69- Res. grants, Am. Philos. Soc, 57; Am. Acad. Arts & Sci, 58; Fulbright res. scholar, Portugal, 64-65. U.S.N, 43-46, Res, 67-, Comdr. Bot. Soc. Am. Cell research; gametogenesis in the angiosperms. Address: Dept. of Biology, Randolph-Macon Woman's College, Lynchburg, VA 24504.

FLINT, GEORGE W(ESLEY), b. Bellflower, Ill, July 30, 05; m. 31; c. 1. CHEMISTRY. A.B, Illinois, 27; Chicago, 29-32. Anal. chemist, A.E. Staley Mfg. Co, Ill, 27-29; res. chemist, res. lab, Standard Oil Co, 29-50, sect. leader, 50-63, proj. mgr, 63-68; RETIRED. Am. Chem. Soc. Product development; emulsification; soluble oils; rust preventives; emulsified wax; polishes; industrial lubricants; insecticides; paraffin waxes; asphalts; fuels. Address: R.D. 1, Box 470, Homewood, IL 60430.

FLINT, HARRISON L(EIGH), b. Barre, Vt, Nov. 5, 29; m. 57; c. 4. ORNAMENTAL HORTICULTURE. B.S, Cornell, 51, Ph.D.(floricult), 58; M.S, Mich. State, 52. Asst, Mich. State, 51-52; Cornell, 53, 56-58; asst. prof. hort, Rhode Island, 58-62; assoc, Univ. Vt, 62-66; assoc. horticulturist, Arnold Arboretum, Harvard, 66-68; ASSOC. PROF. HORT, PURDUE UNIV, 68- U.S.A, 54-56. Am. Soc. Hort. Sci; Am. Asn. Bot. Gardens & Arboretums. Woody ornamental plant materials; adaptation and comparative physiology; cold resistance in plants. Address: Dept. of Horticulture, Purdue University, Lafayette, IN 47907.

FLINT, HOLLIS M(ITCHELL), b. Miami, Fla, May 28, 38; m. 60; c. 2. ENTOMOLOGY, RADIATION BIOLOGY. B.S, Stetson, 60; Ph.D.(entom), Florida, 64. RES. ENTOMOLOGIST, metab. & radiation res. lab, ENTOM. RES. DIV, AGR. RES. SERV, U.S. DEPT. AGR, N.Dak, 64-71, WEST. COTTON INSECTS LAB, 71- AAAS; Entom. Soc. Am. Effects of radiation on insect sterility, longevity, oviposition and mating behavior. Address: Western Cotton Insects Lab, Agricultural Research Service, 4135 E. Broadway, Phoenix, AZ 85040.

FLINT, JEAN C, b. Kansas City, Mo, Dec. 4, 99; m. 45; c. 2. ANIMAL PATHOLOGY. D.V.M, Colorado State, 32, M.S, 50; Ph.D.(path), Minnesota, 55. Asst. prof. vet. med, Colorado State, 32-34; gen. practice, Utah, 34-42, 45-48; instr. PATH, col. vet. med, Minnesota, 50-51; assoc. prof, COL. VET. MED, COLO. STATE UNIV, 55-58, prof, 58-69, EMER. PROF, 69- Mem. res. coun, Am. Vet. Med. Asn, 52-55, rev. res. manuscripts, 55-65. Vet.C, 42-45, Res, 45-47, Maj. Testicular degeneration; isosperm antibodies; chlortetracycline cattle feed; feline infectious anemia; necrobacillosis. Address: P.O. Box 1772, Estes Park, CO 80517.

FLINT, NORMAN K(EITH), b. North Newport, N.H, Oct. 16, 21; m. 46; c. 4. GEOLOGY. B.S, New Hampshire, 44; M.A, Ohio State, 46, Bownocker fel,

46-48, Ph.D.(geol), 48. Instr, GEOL, Ohio State, 48-49; asst. prof, UNIV. PITTSBURGH, 49-53, assoc. prof, 53-66, PROF, 66-, acting head dept, 57-60. Geologist, State Geol. Surv, Ohio, 48; U.S. Geol. Surv, 49; co-op. geologist, State Geol. Surv, Pa, 50-53, 56, 59-64; consult, 54-55, 57-58; prof. geol, Cent. Univ. Ecuador, 64-66. Geol. Soc. Am; Nat. Asn. Geol. Teachers; Am. Inst. Prof. Geol. Upper Paleozoic stratigraphy and areal geology; engineering geology; non-metallic economic geology; geology of Ecuador. Address: Dept. of Earth & Planetary Sciences, University of Pittsburgh, Pittsburgh, PA 15213.

FLINT, OLIVER S(IMEON), JR, b. Amherst, Mass, Oct. 10, 31; m. 54; c. 3. ENTOMOLOGY. B.S, Massachusetts, 53, M.S, 55; Nat. Sci. Found. fel, Cornell, 57-59, Ph.D.(entom), 60. ASSOC. CURATOR ENTOM, U.S. NAT. MUS, SMITHSONIAN INST, 60-, IN-CHARGE DIV. NEUROPTEROIDS, 63- Taxonomy and biology of caddis flies and dobson flies, especially those of the New World. Address: U.S. National Museum, Smithsonian Institution, Washington, DC 20560.

FLINT, RICHARD FOSTER, b. Chicago, Ill, Mar. 1, 02; m. 26; c. 1. GEOLOGY. B.S, Chicago, 22, Ph.D.(geol), 25; hon. M.A, Yale, 45; hon. D.Sc, Trinity Col.(Dublin), 63; hon. Sc.D, Wroclaw Univ, 66. From instr. to prof. geol, Yale, 25-70; RETIRED. Geologist, U.S. Geol. Surv, 46- Consult. Res. & Develop. Bd, 46-53; Off. Chief of Engrs, U.S. Army, 46-63. Co-ed, Radiocarbon, 59- Pres. Cong. Int. Asn. Quaternary Res, 65. Albrecht Penck Medal, Ger. Quaternary Asn, 66. U.S.A.R, 43-53; Lt. Col. AAAS; fel. Geol. Soc. Am; Am. Geophys. Union; Arctic Inst. N.Am; Am. Acad. Arts & Sci; Glaciol. Soc; hon. cor. mem. Geol. Socs. London, Edinburgh, Stockholm, Finland and Argentina. Pleistocene geology. Address: 2161 Yale Station, New Haven, CT 06520.

FLIPO, JEAN, b. St. Eustache, Que, Oct. 7, 24; m. 50; c. 3. VETERINARY MEDICINE. B.A, Montreal, 44, D.V.M, 49. PROF. SURG. ORTHOP, SCH. VET. MED. PROV. QUE, 50-, HEAD, SMALL ANIMALS CLIN, 58-, asst, 50-58. Gaines Vet. Award, Can, 70. Small animals surgery and orthopaedics. Address: School of Veterinary Medicine of the Province of Quebec, St. Hyacinthe, Que, Can.

FLIPPEN, R(ICHARD) B(ERNARD), b. Williamson, W.Va, Aug. 23, 30; m. 61; c. 2. SOLID STATE PHYSICS. A.B, West Virginia, 53, M.S, 54; Fulbright fel. Leiden, 54-55; Ph.D.(physics), Carnegie Inst. Tech, 60. PHYSICIST, CENT. RES. DEPT. E.I. DU PONT DE NEMOURS & CO, INC, 60- Sci. Res. Soc. Am; Am. Phys. Soc. Magnetic properties of materials; magnetic ordering transitions; superconductivity; low temperature thermal properties of materials; electrical transport properties of materials. Address: Experimental Station, E.I. du Pont de Nemours & Co, Wilmington, DE 19898.

FLIPSE, M(ARTIN) EUGENE, b. Monteville, N.J, Apr. 27, 19; m. 49; c. 6. PREVENTIVE MEDICINE. A.B, Hope Col, 40; M.D, Harvard Med. Sch, 43. Intern med, Boston City Hosp, Mass, 44, res. med. & contagious disease, 44-45; asst. res. path, Jackson Mem. Hosp, Miami, Fla, 48-49; fel. med, Mayo Found. & Clin, Minn, 49-51, staff asst, 52; res. pulmonary diseases, Nopening Sanatorium, 51; asst. prof. MED, SCH. MED, UNIV. MIAMI, 56-57, assoc. prof, 57-59, PROF, 59-, DIR. UNIV. HEALTH SERV, 57-, med. dir, Lahuis Clin. Labs, 64-69. Consult, Bahamian Ministry Health, 64-67, pres-elect, Nat. Comt. Clin. Lab. Standards. Dipl, Am. Bd. Internal Med. Head chest serv, Nat. Naval Med. Ctr, Md, U.S.N, 54-56, Res, 56-70, Comdr.(Ret). Am. Pub. Health Asn; fel. Am. Col. Physicians. Pulmonary disease; public health. Address: University of Miami Health Center, 5513 Merrick Dr, Coral Gables, FL 33146.

FLIPSE, R(OBERT) J(OSEPH), b. Topeka, Kans, July 18, 23; m. 44; c. 5. DAIRY SCIENCE. B.S, Kans. State Col, 47; M.S, Mich. State Col, 48; Ph.D. (animal nutrit), 50. Asst. DAIRY HUSB, Michigan State Col, 47-49; asst. prof, PA. STATE UNIV, 50-52, assoc. prof, 52-66, PROF, 66-, ASST. DIR. AGR. EXP. STA, 68- U.S.A, 43-46. Mem. sci. group chem. & physiol. of gametes, WHO, 65. Borden Award Res. in Dairy Sci, 69. Fel. AAAS; Am. Inst. Biol. Sci; Soc. Study Reproduction; Am. Soc. Animal Sci; Am. Dairy Sci. Asn. Cellular metabolism; nutrition and reproductive physiology; rumen physiology. Address: Agricultural Experiment Station, Pennsylvania State University, University Park, PA 16802.

FLISZAR, SANDOR, b. Lugano, Switz, May 11, 27; Can. citizen; m. 61; c. 3. PHYSICAL ORGANIC & QUANTUM CHEMISTRY. Ph.D.(chem), Univ. Geneva, 62. Res. chemist, Cyanamid European Res. Inst, Geneva, Switz, 62-64; asst. prof. PHYS. CHEM, UNIV. MONTREAL, 64-66, assoc. prof, 66-71, PROF, 71- Chem. Inst. Can. Ozone and Thallium chemistry; radiochemistry. Address: Dept. of Chemistry, University of Montreal, P.O. Box 6128, Montreal, Que, Can.

FLITCRAFT, R(ICHARD) K(IRBY), II, b. Woodstown, N.J, Sept. 5, 20; m. 42; c. 4. CHEMICAL ENGINEERING. B.S, Rutgers, 42; M.S, Washington (St. Louis), 48. Mem. tech. serv, org. chem. div, MONSANTO CO, 42-46, group leader, tech. serv, 46-48, supvr. prod. dept, 48-50, supt. tech. serv, 50-52, asst. dir. res, Meramec Div, 52-55, asst. dir. res, inorg. chem. div, 55-60, prod. bd. dir, 60, dir. res, 60-65, dir. mgt. info. & systs. dept, 65-67, asst. to pres, 67-68, group mgr, electronics enterprise, 68-69, gen. mgr, electronic prod. div, 69-71; DIR. MOUND LABS. & V.PRES, MONSANTO RES. CORP, 71- AAAS; Am. Chem. Soc; Am. Inst. Chem. Eng; Sci. Res. Soc. Am; Am. Mgt. Asn; Am. Inst. Chem; Inst. Elec. & Electronics Eng; Soc. Chem. Indust; N.Y. Acad. Sci. Surface active agents and detergents; phosphates; production and process development; management information systems; electronic data processing; electronic materials; light emitting devices. Address: Monsanto Research Corp, Mound Lab, P.O. Box 32, Miamisburg, OH 45342.

FLITTER, DAVID, b. Philadelphia, Pa, Aug. 1, 13; m. 42; c. 3. ORGANIC CHEMISTRY. Mayor's scholar, Pennsylvania, 30-34, B.S, 34; Am. Petrol. Inst. fel, Pa. State Col, 48-52, M.S, 50, Ph.D.(chem), 52. Chemist, R.T. French Co, 34-38; asst, Sun Oil Co, 38-41; jr. chemist, U.S. Govt, 41-42; chemist, Celanese Corp. Am, 42-45, supvr, 45-48; chemist, E.I. du Pont de Nemours & Co, 52-61; SR. CHEMIST, WYETH LABS, INC, 61- Am. Chem. Soc. Organic coatings; development of new drugs. Address: 270 Ellis Rd, Havertown, PA 19083.

FLITTNER, GLENN ARDEN, b. Los Angeles, Calif, Sept. 10, 28; m. 57; c. 2. MARINE ECOLOGY & METEOROLOGY. A.B, Univ. Calif, Berkeley, 51, M.A, 53; fel, Univ. Mich, 59, Ph.D.(fisheries), 64. Asst, Sagehen Creek Exp. Wildlife & Fisheries Proj, Univ. Calif, summers, 52-53, part-time lab. asst, 51-53; fishery res. biologist, biol. lab, Bur. Commercial Fisheries, U.S. Dept. Interior, Mich, 57-61, tuna resources lab, Calif, 61-70; PROF. BIOL. & DIR. BUR. MARINE SCI, SAN DIEGO STATE COL, 70- U.S.N.R, 53-57, Comdr. Am. Inst. Fishery Res. Biol; Am. Fisheries Soc; Marine Technol. Soc.(commendation, 68); Am. Meteorol. Soc; Ecol. Soc. Am; Am. Soc. Zool. Life history, ecology of marine fishery stocks; effects of physical characteristics of the environment on abundance, availability and distribution of stocks, special interest in forecasting availability and distribution of tuna stocks in relation to predicted changes in physical oceanographic parameters such as upper mixed layer temperature. Address: Bureau of Marine Sciences, San Diego State College, San Diego, CA 92115.

FLOCK, DONALD LOUIS, b. Calgary, Alta, Feb. 19, 30; m. 52; c. 4. PETROLEUM ENGINEERING. B.Sc, Oklahoma, 52, M.Sc, 53; Magnolia Petrol. Co. fel, Agr. & Mech. Col, Texas, 53-56, Ph.D, 56. Res. engr, Cities Serv. Res. & Develop. Co, Ltd, 56-57; assoc. prof. PETROL. ENG, UNIV. ALTA, 57-63, PROF, 63-, ASSOC. DEAN, FACULTY ENG, 69- Am. Inst. Mining, Metall. & Petrol. Eng. Petroleum production and reservoir engineering. Address: Faculty of Engineering, University of Alberta, Edmonton, Alta, Can.

FLOCK, EUNICE VERNA, b. Kellogg, Idaho, Aug. 20, 04. PHYSIOLOGICAL CHEMISTRY. B.S, Washington (Seattle), 26; M.S, Chicago, 30; Mayo Found. fel, Minnesota, 33-35, Ph.D.(physiol. chem), 35. Asst. physiol. chem, Mayo Clin, 30-33, instr, MAYO GRAD. SCH. MED, UNIV. MINN, ROCHESTER, 36-39, asst. prof, 39-45, assoc. prof, 45-57, prof. BIOCHEM, 57-69, EMER. PROF, 69- Vis. scientist, Phoenix Clin. Res. Sect, Phoenix Indian Med. Ctr, Nat. Inst. Arthritis & Metab. Diseases, 71- AAAS; Thyroid Asn. Am; N.Y. Acad. Sci; Am. Chem. Soc; Am. Soc. Biol. Chem. Fat metabolism; chemistry of lymph; amino acids; thyroxine; serotonin; epinephrine. Address: National Institute of Arthritis & Metabolic Diseases, Phoenix Clinical Research Section, Phoenix Indian Medical Center, 4212 N. 16th St, Room 541, Phoenix, AZ 85016.

FLOCK, WARREN L(INCOLN), b. Kellogg, Idaho, Oct. 26, 20; m. 57. ELECTRICAL ENGINEERING, GEOPHYSICS. B.S, Washington (Seattle), 42; M.S, California, Berkeley, 48, Ph.D.(eng), Los Angeles, 60. Staff mem, radiation lab, Mass. Inst. Tech, 42-45; partner, Radar Engrs, Wash, 45-46, lectr. & asst. engr, col. eng, California, Los Angeles, 50-56, lectr. assoc. engr, 56-60; assoc. prof. geophys, geophys. inst, Alaska, 60-62, PROF, 62-64; ELEC. ENG, UNIV. COLO, BOULDER, 64- U.S.A, 46-47. AAAS; Inst. Elec. & Electronics Eng; Am. Geophys. Union. Propagation of electromagnetic waves for study of the upper and lower atmosphere; radar ornithology; solar-terrestrial relations; natural resources and the environment. Address: Dept. of Electrical Engineering, University of Colorado, Boulder, CO 80302.

FLOCKEN, J(OHN) W, b. Sioux Falls, S.Dak, Sept. 2, 39; m. 64; c. 2. SOLID STATE PHYSICS. B.A, Augustana Col.(S.Dak), 61; Nuclear Sci. fel, Fla. State Univ, 61-62; M.S, Univ. Nebr, Lincoln, 64, Ph.D.(physics), 69. Scientist, Raven Industs, S.Dak, 64-65; physicist, Bendix Labs, Mich, 65-66; ASST. PROF. PHYSICS, UNIV. NEBR, OMAHA, 69- Air Nat. Guard, 57-63. Am. Phys. Soc. Lattice statics calculations; determination of atomic displacements about point defects in metals; formation and activation energies; interactions between pairs of defects in crystals. Address: Dept. of Physics, University of Nebraska at Omaha, Omaha, NE 68101.

FLOCKER, WILLIAM J(ACK), b. Clinton, Ind, Sept. 6, 17; m. 42; c. 4. SOIL PHYSICS. B.S, Univ. Ill, 40; Ph.D, Univ. Ariz, 51-55; dir. res, Turfgrass Farm, 55-56; assoc. olericulturist, UNIV. CALIF, DAVIS, 56-67, lectr, 56-66, assoc. prof. veg. crops, 66-67, PROF. VEG. CROPS & OLERICULTURIST, 67- U.S.A.A.F, 41-46, Res, 46-, Maj. Influence of compaction of physical properties of soil and ultimate effects on physiological responses in plants. Address: Dept. of Vegetable Crops, University of California, Davis, CA 95616.

FLOCKS, RUBIN H(ENRY), b. New York, N.Y, May 7, 06. UROLOGY. A.B, Hopkins, 26; M.D, 30. Res. house officer, Hopkins Hosp, 30-31; from asst. instr. UROL. to assoc. prof, UNIV. HOSPS, COL. MED, UNIV. IOWA, 31-46, PROF, 46-, HEAD DEPT, 49- Dipl, Am. Bd. Urol, 39, pres, 63- Clin. Soc. Genito-Urinary Surg; Am. Med. Asn; Am. Asn. Genito-Urinary Surg; Am. Urol. Asn.(prize, 37, 39, secy, 62-); fel. Am. Col. Surg. Calcium metabolism related particularly to renal stone; arterial distribution within prostate gland; urinary calcium excretion in patients with renal calculi; prostatic cancer. Address: University Hospital, University of Iowa, Iowa City, IA 52241.

FLODIN, N(ESTOR) W(INSTON), b. Chicago, Ill, Jan. 30, 15; m. 41; c. 2. CHEMISTRY. B.S, Chicago, 35, Ph.D.(inorg. chem), 38. Instr. chem, Cent. State Teachers Col, Stevens Point, 38-40; SR. CHEMIST, electrochem. dept, E.I. DU PONT DE NEMOURS & CO, INC, 40-61, planning div, indust. & biochem. dept, 61-66, PHARMACEUTICALS DIV, 66- Am. Chem. Soc; Am. Pub. Health Asn; Am. Inst. Nutrit. Organic boron compounds; acetylene chemistry; hydrogen cyanide; vinyl monomers and polymers; market research; amino acids in nutrition; food technology; pharmaceuticals marketing and research. Address; Pharmaceuticals Division, E.I. du Pont de Nemours & Co, Wilmington, DE 19898.

FLOE, CARL F(REDERICK), b. Dawson, Yukon, Can, Jan. 1, 08; nat; m. 35, 54; c. 4. METALLURGY. B.S, Washington State, 30, M.S, 32; Sc.D.(metall), Mass. Inst. Tech, 35. Instr. metall. & metallog, Washington State, 30-34, asst. prof, 35-36; METALL, Notre Dame, 36-39; asst. prof, MASS. INST. TECHNOL, 39-42, assoc. prof, 42-51, PROF, 51-, v.pres. res. admin, 59-69, exec. officer, dept. metall, 43-51, asst. provost, 52-57, v.chancellor, 57-59. Consult, Qm. Corps, U.S. Army, 44. Am. Chem. Soc; Am. Soc. Metals; Am. Inst. Mining, Metall. & Petrol. Eng; Brit. Inst. Metals. Surface hardening of metals; gases in metals; heat treatment of steel; failures in metals. Address: Dept. of Metallurgy & Materials Science, Massachusetts Institute of Technology, Cambridge, MA 02139.

FLOKSTRA, JOHN H(ILBERT), b. Chicago, Ill, Apr. 17, 25; m. 48; c. 3. CLINICAL CHEMISTRY. A.B, Calvin Col, 47; M.S, Mich. State Col, 50, Atomic Energy Cmn. fel, 51-52, Ph.D.(biochem), 52. Asst. biochem, Mich. State Col, 47-51; res. assoc. dept. biochem, UPJOHN CO, 52-59, HEAD CLIN. RES. LAB, 60- Am. Chem. Soc; Am. Asn. Clin. Chem; Am. Soc. Clin. Path. Clinical and biological chemistry. Address: Upjohn Co, Clinical Research Lab, 301 Henrietta St, Kalamazoo, MI 49001.

FLOM, DONALD G(ORDON), b. Kenyon, Minn, May 8, 24; m. 57; c. 3. PHYSICAL CHEMISTRY. B.A, St. Olaf Col, 44; M.S, Purdue, 49; Off. Naval Res. fel, Pa. State Col, 49-50, Du Pont Res. fel, 50-51, Ph.D.(chem), 52. Instr. chem, St. Olaf Col, 46-47; asst, Purdue, 47-49; res. assoc, res. lab, GEN. ELEC. CO, 51-59, phys. chemist, 59-61, mgr. chem. res, space sci. lab, Valley Forge Space Tech. Ctr, 61-71, MGR. CHEM. ENG. BR, RES. & DEVELOP. CTR, 71- U.S.N.R, 44-46, Lt.(jg). AAAS; Am. Chem. Soc; Faraday Soc; Am. Phys. Soc; Am. Soc. Lubrication Eng. Vapor liquid equilibria; chemical use of high frequency oscillators; surface chemistry; electrical contacts; friction and wear; polymer chemistry; reinforced composites; ablation. Address: Research & Development Center, General Electric Co, P.O. Box 8, Schenectady, NY 12301.

FLOM, MERTON C(LYDE), b. Pittsburgh, Pa, Aug. 19, 26; m. 48; c. 2. PHYSIOLOGICAL OPTICS. B.S, California, 50, M.Opt, 51, Am. Optom. Found, fel, 52-55, Ph.D.(physiol. optics), 57. Clin. instr, UNIV. CALIF, BERKELEY, 51-57, instr. PHYSIOL. OPTICS & OPTOM, 57-58, asst. prof, 58-62, assoc. prof, 62-67, PROF, 67-, ASST. DEAN SCH. OPTOM, 69-, v.chmn. dept, 62-63. Mem. optom. rev. comt, Dept. Health, Educ. & Welfare, 69-71. U.S.N.R, 44-46. AAAS; Am. Acad. Optom; Optical Soc. Am; Am. Optom. Asn. Physiological optics; binocular vision; motility; visual resolution. Address: School of Optometry, University of California, Berkeley, CA 94720.

FLOOD, CHARLES A(LBERT), b. Paterson, N.J, July 26, 04; m. 24; c. 3. GASTROENTEROLOGY. B.S, Columbia, 25, M.D, 28, Med.Sc.B, 32, Med.Sc.M, 33. Asst. med, COL. PHYSICIANS & SURG, COLUMBIA UNIV, 31-36, assoc, 37-48, asst. clin. prof, 48-53, assoc. prof. CLIN. MED, 54-63, prof, 63-70; EMER. PROF, 70- Dipl, Am. Bd. Internal Med; Am. Bd. Gastroenterol. Med.C, 42-46, Lt. Col. Am. Gastroenterol. Asn; Am. Col. Physicians; Am. Soc. Gastrointestinal Endoscopy. Internal medicine. Address: 464 Riverside Dr, New York, NY 10027.

FLOOD, E(DWARD) ALISON, b. St. John, N.B, Jan. 26, 04; m. 31; c. 1. SURFACE SCIENCE. B.Sc, Mt. Allison, 25; M.S, Brown, 27, Ph.D.(chem), 30. Instr. chem, Vermont, 27-28; Brown, 30-35; asst. res. chemist, Nat. Res. Lab, Can, 35-47, PRIN. SCI. OFF, NAT. RES. COUN. CAN, 47- Officer, Order of the Brit. Empire, 45. Can. Army, 40-47, Lt. Col; Legion of Merit, 50. AAAS; Am. Chem. Soc; fel. Royal Soc. Can. Structure of activated carbon; fluid flow mechanisms; adsorption. Address: 451 Roxborough Rd, Rockcliffe, Ottawa 2, Ont, Can.

FLOOD, JAMES E(LLIOTT), b. Stratford, Conn, Aug. 24, 09; m. 38; c. 1. CHEMICAL ENGINEERING. Ch.E, Pratt Inst, 31; Yale, 41-44. Chemist, Gen. Elec. Co, 31-37; chief chemist, Whitney Blake Co, 37-41; res. chemist, E.I. du Pont de Nemours & Co, 41-44; develop. engr, PLASTIC WIRE & CABLE CORP, 44-50, chief chemist, 50-55, TECH. DIR, 55-, V.PRES, 60- AAAS; Am. Chem. Soc. Administration of development laboratory; process engineering; quality control. Address: Plastic Wire & Cable Corp, E. Main St, Jewett City, CT 06351.

FLOOD, MERRILL M(EEKS), b. Seward, Nebr, Nov. 28, 08; m. 70; c. 6. MATHEMATICS, MANAGEMENT SCIENCE. A.B, Nebraska, 29, A.M, 30; Ph.D.(math), Princeton, 35. Instr. math, Nebraska, 29-31; asst. Princeton, 31-32, instr, 32-36, dir. statist. sect. surv, 36-40, res. assoc. math, 40-45, dir. appl. math. group, 44-45; owner, Merrill Flood & Assoc, 42-48; exec. dir, Am. Statist. Asn, 48; proj. off. logistics, Rand Corp, 49-52; prof. indust. eng. & dir. Columbia Inst. res. mgt. of indust. prod, Columbia Univ, 53-56; prof. indust. eng, Univ. Mich, Ann Arbor, 56-67, prof. math. biol, dept. psychiat. & sr. res. mathematician, ment. health res. inst, 60-67; prin. scientist, Syst. Develop. Corp, 67-69; PRES, MERRILL FLOOD & ASSOCS, 69- Indust. & govt. consult; pub. finance consult, Soc. Sci. Res. Coun, 36-37; tech. adv. to Governor, W.Va, 37-40; admin. consult, grad. sch. educ, Harvard, 40; tech. expert to ord. dept. & dir. Princeton Br, Frankford Arsenal, 43-44; expert consult. to Secy. War, 46; asst. dept. dir. res. & develop, gen. staff, U.S. Army, 47; assoc. dir. eng. res. inst, Univ. Mich, Ann Arbor, 56-58; vis. prof, univ. & vis. res. economist, space sci. lab, Univ. Calif, Berkeley, 63-64; vis. prof, Mass. Inst. Technol, 65-66; chmn, sci. info. coun, Nat. Sci. Found, 66-67. With Off. Sci. Res. & Develop, 44. AAAS; Opers. Res. Soc. Am.(pres, 61); Inst. Mgt. Sci.(pres, 55); Am. Inst. Indust. Eng.(v.pres, 62-65); Royal Econ. Soc; Asn. Comput. Mach. Algebra of matrices; system engineering. Address: Merrill Flood & Associates, Suite 219, 1505 Fourth St, Santa Monica, CA 90401.

FLOOD, WALTER A(LOYSIUS), b. N.Y.C, Apr. 27, 27; m. 54; c. 3. ELECTRICAL ENGINEERING. B.E.E, Cornell, 50, M.E.E, 52, McMullen fel, 52-53, Ph.D, 54. Asst. ionosphere lab, Cornell, 50-54, res. engr, aeronaut. lab, 54-59, head radio physics sect, 59-64, staff scientist, 64-67; PROF. ELEC. ENG, N.C. STATE UNIV, 67- Consult, Res. Triangle Inst; Stanford Res. Inst; Gen. Elec. Tempo Ctr. Advan. Study, Santa Barbara, Calif. U.S.A, 44-46. AAAS; Inst. Elec. & Electronics Eng; Am. Geophys. Union; Int. Sci. Radio Union. Upper atmospheric physics; ionospheric and tropospheric propagation; D-region backscatter; ionospheric drifts; rough surface backscatter; radio wave propagation; ionospheric scintillation and multipath phenomena. Address: Dept. of Electrical Engineering, North Carolina State University, Raleigh, NC 27606.

FLOOK, WILLIAM M(OWAT), JR, b. Briarcliff, N.Y, July 7, 21; m. 45; c. 5. PHYSICS. A.B, Harvard, 43; M.S, Brown, 49, Ph.D.(physics), 52. Asst. physics, Oceanog. Inst, Woods Hole, 46-47; res. supvr, E.I. DU PONT DE

NEMOURS & CO, 51-61, RES. ASSOC, 61-69, PELTRON LAB, 69- U.S.N.R, 43-46, Lt.(jg). AAAS; Optical Soc. Am; Sci. Res. Soc. Am; Am. Inst. Aeronaut. & Astronaut. Instrumentation; process control; optical and electronic measurements. Address: Peltron Lab, Box 3748, Greenville, DE 19807.

FLOOR, ERIK ROBERT, b. Rockford, Ill, Aug. 26, 41; m. 67. GENETICS. B.S, Wisconsin, Madison, 64; Nat. Insts. Health traineeship, California, Davis, 67-69, Ph.D.(genetics), 69. ASST. PROF. BIOL, BALL STATE UNIV, 69- Genetics Soc. Am; Am. Inst. Biol. Sci. Assembly of bacteriophage T4; growth of bacteria. Address: Dept. of Biology, Ball State University, Muncie, IN 47306.

FLOR, HAROLD H(ENRY), b. St. Paul, Minn, May 27, 00; m. 28; c. 2. PLANT PATHOLOGY. B.S, Univ. Minn, 22, M.S, 24, fel. 25-26, Ph.D. (plant path), 29; hon. D.Sc, N.Dak. State Univ, 62. Asst. plant pathologist, La. State, 26-29; assoc. pathologist, bur. plant indust, U.S. DEPT. AGR, State Col. Wash, 29-31, EXP. STA, N.DAK. STATE UNIV, 31-36, PATHOLOGIST, 36-, CROPS RES, AGR. RES. SERV, 53- Outstanding achievement award, Univ. Minn, 62; Elvin Charles Stakman Award, 67. U.S.A, 18. AAAS; Am. Soc. Agron; fel. Am. Phytopath. Soc.(Ruth Allen Award, 67; pres, 68); Am. Inst. Biol. Sci. Flax diseases; physiologic specialization; genetics and physiology of host-parasite interaction. Address: North Dakota State University, Fargo, ND 58102.

FLORA, CHARLES J(ERRY), b. Wabash, Ind, Nov. 16, 28; m. 50; c. 4. ECOLOGY. B.S, Purdue, 50; M.Ed, Florida, 55, fel, 56-57, Ed.D, 57. Teacher, pub. sch, Fla, 53-54; asst. prof. zool, WEST. WASH. STATE COL, 57-64, prof, 64-68, PRES, 68-, acad. dean, 65-67, interim pres, 67-68. U.S.A, 51-53. AAAS. Marine ecology; invertebrate zoology. Address: Western Washington State College, Bellingham, WA 98225.

FLORA, EDWARD B(ENJAMIN), b. Phillipsburg, Ohio, June 23, 29; m. 52; c. 3. MECHANICAL ENGINEERING. B.S, Carnegie Inst. Tech, 51, M.S, 53. Engr, nuclear res. center, Carnegie Inst. Tech, 51-52; proj. engr, Nevis Cyclotron Lab, Columbia, 53-58; sr. engr, Dalmo Victor Co, 58-63; V.PRES, ANAMET LABS, INC, 63- Am. Soc. Mech. Eng; Soc. Exp. Stress Anal; Am. Ceramic Soc. Analytical and experimental stress analysis; vibration. Address: Anamet Labs, Inc, 2827 Seventh St, Berkeley, CA 94710.

FLORA, HERBERT EDWARD, b. Mt. Jewett, Pa, June 27, 31; m. 54; c. 1. MECHANICAL & NUCLEAR ENGINEERING. B.S, Pa. State, 53; Virginia, 56-57. Student engr, boiler div, BABCOCK & WILCOX CO, 55-56, reactor engr, atomic energy div, 56-59, develop. engr. nuclear fuels plant, 59-60, safety engr, atomic energy div, 60-64, supvr. safety anal, 64-69, systs. design group, NUCLEAR POWER GENERATION DEPT, 69-70, MGR, PLANT PERFORMANCE SECT, 70- Consult. C.Eng, 53-55, 1st Lt. Analysis of nuclear reactor systems to ensure safety performance; development of design criteria. Address: Babcock & Wilcox Co, P.O. Box 1260, Lynchburg, VA 24505.

FLORA, JOHN W(ILLIAM), b. Missoula, Mont, June 16, 26; m. 52; c. 4. PHYSICS. B.S, Denver, 48. Asst. physics, Denver, 46-48; res. physicist, Gen. Elec. Co, 48-51; res. physicist & group leader, Calif. Res. & Develop. Co, 51-54; sr. res. engr, Atomics Int. Div, N.Am. Aviation, Inc, 54-56, supvr. reactor kinetics, 57, group leader, 58-62; reactor specialist, U.S. ATOMIC ENERGY CMN, 62-70, DIR. DIV. COMPLIANCE, 70- U.S.A.A.F, 44-45. AAAS; Am. Nuclear Soc. Criticality parameters of aqueous fissionable solutions; nuclear research reactor design and operation; neutron diffusion in homogeneous and heterogeneous media; experimental reactor kinetics. Address: 3076 S. High St, Denver, CO 80210.

FLORA, ROBERT MONTGOMERY, b. Richmond, Va, Oct. 1, 38; m. 65; c. 1. BIOCHEMISTRY. B.A, Bridgewater Col, 60; Western Reserve, 60-61; Nat. Sci. Found. fel, Va. Polytech. Inst, 63-64, Ph.D.(biochem), 65. Nat. Insts. Health trainee microbiol, Vanderbilt, 64-66; asst. prof. chem, Am. Univ, 66-68; SR. RES. BIOCHEMIST, WORTHINGTON BIOCHEM. CORP, 68- Mem. subcomt. enzymes, comt. specifications & criteria biochem. compounds, Nat. Res. Coun. AAAS; Am. Chem. Soc. Enzymology; enzyme applications; process development for commercial enzyme isolation; technical support for enzyme production and analytical services. Address: Worthington Biochemical Corp, Freehold, NJ 07728.

FLORA, ROGER E, b. Roanoke, Va, Feb. 5, 39; m. 63; c. 2. BIOSTATISTICS. B.A, Virginia, 60; M.S, Va. Polytech, 64, Ph.D.(statist), 66. ASST. PROF. statist, W.Va. Univ, 65-68; BIOMET, MED. COL. VA, VA. COMMONWEALTH UNIV, 68- Am. Statist. Asn; Biomet. Asn. Multivariate analysis with emphasis in classification and clustering techniques; statistical inference. Address: Medical College of Virginia, Virginia Commonwealth University, Box 923, MCV Station, Richmond, VA 23219.

FLORANCE, E(DWIN) T(RENT), b. Orange, N.J, Feb. 9, 33; m. 61. THEORETICAL PHYSICS. B.A, Amherst Col, 55; Nat. Sci. Found. fel, Harvard, 55-56, M.A, 56, univ. fel, 57-58, Ph.D.(physics), 61. Mgr. theoret. physics dept, Tech. Div, GCA Corp, 62-68; THEORETICAL PHYSICIST, SCI. DEPT, PASADENA BR. OFF, OFF. NAVAL RES, 68- AAAS; Am. Phys. Soc. Statistical mechanics, kinetic theory of gases; radiative transfer; plasma, atomic and mathematical physics; microwave propagation and radiometry; remote sensing of environment. Address: Scientific Dept, Office of Naval Research Branch Office, Pasadena, CA 91106.

FLOREA, HAROLD R(OBERT), b. New York, N.Y, July 24, 14; m. 47. ENGINEERING. M.E, Stevens Inst. Tech, 37. Dist. head, U.S. Navy Field Office, Ind, 41-45; Vt, 45-46; N.Y, 47-51; proj. engr, OFF. NAVAL RES, 51-57, HEAD, weapon syst, trainers flight br, 57-60, ADV. TECH. DEPT, 60- Am. Soc. Qual. Control; Am. Soc. Mech. Eng. Development and applications in training devices. Address: 2912 Ambergate Rd, Winter Park, FL 32789.

FLOREEN, STEPHEN, b. Chicago, Ill, July 19, 32; m. 61; c. 1. PHYSICAL METALLURGY. B.S, Mass. Inst. Technol, 54; M.S, Michigan, 55, Ph.D. (metall), 60. Res. asst, Michigan, 57-60; metallurgist STEELS & NICKEL ALLOYS, INT. NICKEL CO, 60-62, sect. head, 62-64, RES. ASSOC, 64- U.S.A.F, 55-57, 1st Lt. Am. Soc. Metals; Am. Inst. Mining, Metall. & Petrol Eng; Brit. Inst. Metals. High temperature metallurgy; surface effects; nickel alloys; high strength steels. Address: P.D. Merica Research Lab, International Nickel Co, Sterling Forest, Suffern, NY 10901.

FLORENTINE, F(RANK) P(AUL), JR, b. Phila, Pa, July 19, 19; m. 51; c. 2. ORGANIC CHEMISTRY. B.S, Pennsylvania, 40; M.S, Delaware, 50, Ph.D. (chem), 51. Chemist, Pa. Indust. Chem. Corp, 40-48; Rohm & Haas Co, 48-49; res. chemist, CHEM. DIV, GEN. ELEC. CO, 51-57, MGR. PHENOLICS RES. & DEVELOP, 57- Am. Chem. Soc. Effect of alicyclic rings on reactivity; polymers; ozonolysis; phenolic molding compounds and resins. Address: Chemical Materials Dept, General Electric Co, 1 Plastics Ave, Pittsfield, MA 01203.

FLORENTINE, GERARD JOSEPH, b. Brooklyn, N.Y, Mar. 13, 36; m. 59; c. 3. INSECT PHYSIOLOGY. B.S, Cornell, 59; Ph.D.(entom), Purdue, 65. ENTOMOLOGIST, U.S. ARMY NATICK LABS, 65- Entom. Soc. Am; Sci. Res. Soc. Am. Physiology; toxicology; biochemistry. Address: Pioneering Research Division, U.S. Army Natick Labs, Natick, MA 01760.

FLORES, GUSTAVO, b. San Luis Potosi, Mex, Mar. 16, 36; m. 63; c. 2. BIOCHEMISTRY, ANALYTICAL CHEMISTRY. B.S, Univ. San Luis Potosi, Mex, 58; Nat. Univ. Mex, 58-61; Univ. Wis, Madison, 61-63; M.S, Fla. State Univ, 69, Ph.D.(biochem), 71. Prof. biochem, Univ. San Luis Potosi, Mex, 63-66; FEL, ENVIRON. HEALTH SCI. CTR, ORE. STATE UNIV, 70- Influence of diet, toxics and hormones on urea and ammonium metabolism; developmental changes in amphibian metamorphosis; toxicology of hydrazines; interaction of chlorinated bisphenols at cellular level and their mechanism of toxicity. Address: 3417 S.E. Third St, Corvallis, OR 97330.

FLORES, IVAN, b. N.Y.C, Jan. 3, 23; m. 54; c. 2. COMPUTER SCIENCE, ELECTRICAL ENGINEERING. B.A, Brooklyn Col, 48; M.A, Columbia, 49; Ph.D.(ed), N.Y. Univ, 55. Sr. engr, Mergenthaler Linotype Co, 50-53; proj. engr, Balco Labs, 53-55; Nuclear Develop. Corp, 55-57; proj. supvr. comput. design, Remington Rand, 57-59; comput. consult, Dunlap & Assocs, 59-60; INDEPENDENT CONSULT. COMPUT. DESIGN, 60- Assoc. prof. elec. eng, Polytech. Inst. Brooklyn, 61-62; adj. prof, N.Y. Univ, 62-63; assoc. prof, Stevens Inst. Tech, 65-67; prof. statist, Baruch Col, City Univ. New York & consult, Army Sci. Adv. Panel, 69-70. AAAS; Inst. Elec. & Electronics Eng; Asn. Comput Mach.(ed, jour, 63-67); fel. Brit. Comput. Soc. Theory and design of general and special digital computers; programming computers; optical, magnetic character recognition; mathematical analysis, modeling; programming and software development. Address: 108 Eighth Ave, Brooklyn, NY 11215.

FLORES, ROMEO M, b. San Fernando, Philippines, Apr. 28, 39. SEDIMENTOLOGY, GEOLOGY. B.S, Philippines, 59; univ. fel, Tulsa, 60-62, M.S, 62; univ. fel, La. State, 62-66, Nat. Sci. Found. summer fel. & Ph.D.(geol), 66. Jr. geologist & micropaleontologist, Island Oil Co, Inc, Philippines, 59-60; proj. res. geologist, La. Div, Pan Am. Petrol. Corp, summer 64, res. scientist, res. center, Okla, summer 65; asst. prof. GEOL, SUL ROSS STATE UNIV, 66-67, assoc. prof, 67-69, PROF, 69-, CHMN. DEPT, 67- Fel, State Univ. N.Y. Col. Fredonia, summer 68. Int. Asn. Math. Geol; Am. Asn. Petrol. Geol; Soc. Econ. Paleont. & Mineral; Geol. Soc. Am. Sedimentology and statistical geology of the Pennsylvanian Allegheny formation of eastern Ohio; sedimentology of the Pennsylvanian Haymond formation, Marathon Basin, Texas; fluvial and lake sedimentation of Lake Erie, New York. Address: Dept. of Geology, Sul Ross State University, Alpine, TX 79830.

FLORES, SAMSON SOL, b. Luzon, Philippines, Jan. 6, 22; U.S. citizen; m. 51; c. 2. PROSTHODONTICS. Silliman, Philippines, 39-40; D.M.D, Centro Escolar Univ, Manila, 44; D.D.S, Illinois, 58. Asst. PROSTHODONTICS, COL. DENT, UNIV. ILL, 48-50, instr, 50-57, asst. prof, 57-64, assoc. prof, 64-68, PROF. & CLIN. DIR. DEPT, 68-, consult-chancellor. adv. coun, 69-71. Consult, mouth guard proj, U.S. Pub. Health Serv, 63; spec. patient geriatric proj, Ill. State Pub. Health, 63. A.U.S, 41-46, 1st Lt. Am. Col. Dent; Am. Dent. Asn; Am. Prosthodont. Soc; Acad. Gen. Dent. Oral surgical prosthesis after cancer patients are released; mouth protectors for use in general anesthesia. Address: Dept. of Prosthodontics, University of Illinois College of Dentistry, Chicago, IL 60612.

FLORES-GALLARDO, HECTOR, b. Naguabo, P.R, Nov. 28, 18; m. 44; c. 2. ORGANIC CHEMISTRY. B.S, Puerto Rico, 39; M.S, Florida, 42, Ph.D. (chem), 47. Dir. distillation dept, Butanol Plant, Arroyo P.R, 39-41, chief chemist, 47-49; res. chemist, Monsanto Chem. Co, Ala, 49-53; tech. dir, Am. Steroids, Inc, 53-55; v.pres. prod, Root Chems, Inc, 55-60; v.pres. prod. & develop, Productos Esteroides, S.A, 60-67, V.PRES. & MGR. CHEM. DIV, SEARLE DE MEX, S.A, 67- U.S.A, 44-46. AAAS; N.Y. Acad. Sci; Am. Chem. Soc. Organic isocyanates; detergents; antioxidants; steroids. Address: Searle de Mexico, S.A, P.O. Box 1848, Mexico D.F, Mex.

FLORESTANO, H(ERBERT) J(OSEPH), b. Annapolis, Md, July 23, 12; m. 42; c. 1. MICROBIOLOGY. A.B, St. John's Col. (Md), 34; Georgetown, 35-36; fel, Maryland, 37, 38, M.S, 37, Ph.D.(bact), 40. Res. bacteriologist, Maryland, 37, asst. bacteriologist, 38-40; res. bacteriologist chemother, Am. Cyanamid Co, 41-43; head microbiol. dept, Pitman-Moore Div, DOW CHEM. CO, 43-67, mgr. sci. serv, infectious diseases dept, human health res. & develop. labs, 67-71, MGR. SCI. SERV, MED. DEPT, 71- Res. assoc, Fla. Citrus Comn, 38-40. AAAS; Soc. Exp. Biol. & Med; Am. Soc. Microbiol; Am. Med. Writers Asn. Bacteriology of oral cavity and intestine; oral prophylaxis; dental caries; mastitis; dermatophytoses; germicides; sulfonamides; antibiotics; tuberculosis; chemotherapy. Address: Medical Dept, Dow Chemical Co, 1200 Madison Ave, Indianapolis, IN 46206.

FLOREY, K(LAUS), b. Dresden, Germany, July 4, 19; nat; m. 56; c. 2. ORGANIC CHEMISTRY. Dipl, Heidelberg, 47; fel, Pennsylvania, 47-49, Ph.D.(biochem), 54. Asst. org. chem, I.G. Farben, Germany, 44-45; res. chemist, Merck & Co, 49-50; res. asst, E.R. SQUIBB & SONS, 54-59; DIR. DEPT. ANAL. RES. & PHYS. CHEM, 59- AAAS; Am. Chem. Soc. Isolation, chemistry and development of natural products, steroids and medicinals; analytical research; chromatography; radiopharmaceuticals. Address: E.R. Squibb & Sons, New Brunswick, NJ 08903.

FLORIA, JOSEPH ANGELO, b. Washington, D.C, Nov. 29, 30; m. 55; c. 2. ORGANIC & ANALYTICAL CHEMISTRY. B.S, Mt. St. Mary's Col, 53; M.S, Fla. State, 56. Anal. chemist, Belle Works, E.I. DU PONT DE NEMOURS & CO, W.Va, 56-62, res. chemist, Jackson Lab, N.J, 62-64, FREON PROD. LAB, 64-70, TECH. ASSOC, 70- Am. Chem. Soc. Gas chromatography; microanalytical chemistry; wet chemical analyses. Address: Freon Products Lab, E.I. du Pont de Nemours & Co, P.O. Box 406, Wilmington, DE 19898.

FLORIAN, MICHAEL, b. Roumania, 39. OPERATIONS RESEARCH. B.Eng, McGill Univ, 62; M.Sc, Columbia Univ, 66, Dr.Eng.Sc, 69. Researcher, Can. Nat. R.R, 62-64; Can. Int. Paper, 65-69; ASST. PROF. COMPUT. SCI, UNIV. MONTREAL, 69- Inst. Mgt. Sci; Opers. Res. Soc. Am; Can. Opers. Res. Soc. Linear and nonlinear programming; networks. Address: Dept. of Computer Sciences, University of Montreal, Box 6128, Montreal 101, Que, Can.

FLORIAN, S(VATOPLUK) F(RED), b. Roudnice, Bohemia, Czech, Oct. 23, 15; Can. citizen; m. 54; c. 2. CYTOLOGY, GENETICS. Sci. Eng, Prague Tech, 39; B.S.A, British Columbia, 53, M.A, 55, Ph.D.(cytol), 58. Res. asst. cytol, Cancer Res. Inst. Sask, Can, 58-59; asst. prof. histol, sch. med, Ottawa (Can), 59-62; RES. SCIENTIST CYTOL, LAB. HYG, DEPT. NAT. HEALTH & WELFARE, 62- Nat. Cancer Inst. fel, 58-59. Am. Soc. Cell Biol; Electron. Micros. Soc. Am; Can. Asn. Anat. Cytogenetics of mammalian cells in tissue culture; cellular transformation. Address: Dept. National Health & Welfare, Lab. of Hygiene, Tunney's Pasture, Ottawa, Ont, Can.

FLORIDIS, THEMISTOCLES PHILOMILOS, b. Alexandroupolis, Greece, Nov. 5, 24; U.S. citizen; m. 53; c. 1. METALLURGY. Dipl, Athens Tech, 47; M.S, Mass. Inst. Tech, 54, Sc.D.(metall), 57. Chem. engr, Viamyl Ltd, Greece, 50-53; res. engr, foundry dept, Gen. Elec. Co, 57-59; sect. head phys. chem, appl. res. lab, U.S. Steel Corp, 59-64; assoc. prof. METALL. ENG, VA. POLYTECH. INST. & STATE UNIV, 64-68, PROF, 68- Royal Hellenic Navy, 47-50, Ens. Am. Inst. Mining, Metall. & Petrol. Eng; Am. Soc. Metals; Brit. Iron & Steel Inst. Physical chemistry of extraction and refining of metals; analysis of metallurgical processes. Address: P.O. Box 546, Blacksburg, VA 24060.

FLORIN, ROLAND E(RIC), b. Chicago, Ill, Jan. 18, 15; m. 49; c. 2. PHYSICAL CHEMISTRY. B.S, Illinois, 36, Ph.D.(phys. chem), 48; Chicago, 37-41. Abstractor, Standard Oil Co, Ill, 37-38, technologist, Ind, 38-41; asst, Illinois, 46-47; instr. phys. chem, Nebraska, 48-51; CHEMIST, NAT. BUR. STANDARDS, 51- Civilian with Rubber Reserve Corp, 44. AAAS; Am. Chem. Soc. Mechanism of polymerization; polymer degradation; deuterium compounds; fluorine compounds; copolymer composition. Address: Polymer Chemistry Section, National Bureau of Standards, Washington, DC 20234.

FLORINI, JAMES R(ALPH), b. Gillespie, Ill, Sept. 22, 31; m. 55; c. 2. BIOCHEMISTRY. B.A, Blackburn Col, 53; Ph.D.(biochem), Univ. Ill, 56. Asst. chem, Univ. Ill, 53-56; res. chemist, Lederle Labs, Am. Cyanamid Co, 56-60, group leader & sr. res. chemist, 60-66; assoc. prof. BIOCHEM, SYRACUSE UNIV, 66-70, PROF, 70- AAAS; Am. Chem. Soc; Am. Soc. Biol. Chem; Geront. Soc. Radioisotope tracers; RNA and protein synthesis in skeletal muscle; hormone action; muscular dystrophy; cardiac disease. Address: Dept. of Biology, College of Arts & Sciences, 116 Lyman, Syracuse University, Syracuse, NY 13210.

FLORIO, JOHN V(ICTOR), b. Italy, Oct. 25, 25; nat; m. 54; c. 4. PHYSICAL CHEMISTRY, PHYSICS. B.Ch.E, City Col, New York, 47; M.A, Columbia, 51; Ph.D.(chem), Iowa State Col, 52. Asst. phys. chem, Iowa State Col, 48-52; adv. sr. engr. non-linear mat. res, Gen. Tel. & Electronics Res. Labs, 52-67; RES. ASSOC. ENG. & APPL. SCI, BECTON CTR, YALE, 67- U.S.N.R, 44-46. Am. Chem. Soc; Sci. Res. Soc. Am; Am. Crystallog. Asn. Structure and chemistry of surfaces; adsorption; vacuum physics; thin films; x-ray crystallography; semi-conductors; insulators; thermionics. Address: Engineering & Applied Science Dept, Becton Center, Yale University, New Haven, CT 06520.

FLORIO, LLOYD JOSEPH, b. Batavia, N.Y, Mar. 9, 10; m. 37; c. 3. PUBLIC HEALTH. A.B, Cornell, 31; M.D, Rochester, 35; Dr.P.H, Harvard, 41; hon. D.Sc, Far East Univ, 66. Asst. dir, Calhoun County Health Dept, W.K. Kellogg Found, 37-41; assoc.prof. pub. health & lab. diagnosis, med. sch, Colorado, 41-46, prof, 46-47; prof. & head dept. pub. health & prev. med, 47-54; mgr. Dept. Health & Hosps, 52-59, chief, health div, U.S. AGENCY INT. DEVELOP, Manila, P.I, 59-69, PUB. HEALTH, 69-70, ASST. DIR, VIET NAM, 70- Trop. med. fel, Tulane & Costa Rica, 43; health off. city & county, Denver, 47-48; fel, WHO, 49; hon. prof, Univ. St. Thomas, Manila, 66-; consult, Am. Korean Found, 54. AAAS; Asn. Am. Med. Cols; Nat. Tuberc. Asn.(v.pres, 48); Soc. Exp. Biol. & Med; Am. Med. Asn; fel. Am. Pub. Health Asn; assoc. Am. Col. Physicians. Colorado tick fever; rheumatic fever; stillbirths and neonatal deaths in seven rural counties. Address: U.S.A.I.D./A.D.P.H, APO San Francisco, 96243.

FLORMAN, ALFRED L(EONARD), b. Jersey City, N.J, Oct. 11, 12; m. 44; c. 3. PEDIATRICS. A.B, Princeton, 34; M.D, Hopkins, 38. Intern, Hopkins Hosp, 38-40; Dazian fel, Harvard Med. Sch. 40-41; Welt fel, Rockefeller Inst. Hosp. & Mt. Sinai Hosp, 46-47; res, Mt. Sinai Hosp, 42, adj. pediatrician, 47-52, asst. attend. PEDIAT, 52-56, assoc. attend, 56-68; dir. pediat, N.Shore Hosp, 52-68; PROF, SCH. MED, N.Y. UNIV, 68- U.S.A, 43-45. Am. Pediat. Soc; Soc. Pediat. Res; fel. Am. Med. Asn; Am. Asn. Immunol; fel. Am. Acad. Pediat; N.Y. Acad. Med; Infectious Diseases Soc. Am. Tissue culture; virology with special attention to serology and hemagglutination; chick embryo and tissue culture techniques for virology; bacterial serology; non-specific enhancement of resistance to infection; intra-uterine infections. Address: Dept. of Pediatrics, School of Medicine, New York University, 550 First Ave, New York, NY 10016.

FLORMAN, EDWIN F(RANK), b. Venice, Ill, Feb. 16, 04; m. 47; c. 3. ELECTRONICS. M.S, Washington Univ, 34. Res. physicist, West. Cartridge Co, Ill, 34-41; radio engr, Nat. Bur. Standards, 41-44; Philco Radio Co, 44-46; Nat. Bur. Standards, D.C. & Colo, 46-65; RADIO TELECOMMUN. CONSULT, DEFENSE COMMUN. AGENCY, 65- Mem, Int. Radio Consult. Comt. Meri-

torious award, Dept. of Commerce, 56. AAAS; Sci. Res. Soc. Am; Inst. Elec. & Electronics Eng. Ballistic research; meteorological measurements; low frequency radio wave propagation studies; precise measurement of the velocity of propagation of radio waves; characteristics of atmospheric lightning discharges; tropospheric radio wave propagation; research and engineering of broadband telecommunication systems. Address: 10239 Brigade Dr, Fairfax, VA 22030.

FLORMAN, MONTE, b. N.Y.C, Nov. 19, 26; m; c. 3. ELECTRICAL & MECHANICAL ENGINEERING. B.E.E, N.Y. Univ, 46. Test engr. bur. standards, R.H. Macy & Co, 46-48; proj. engr, Consumers Union U.S, Inc, 48-52; engr, Am. Bosch Arma Corp, 52-53; proj. engr, CONSUMERS UNION U.S, INC, 53-57, head appliance div, 57-64, assoc. tech. dir, 64-70, ACTING TECH. DIR, 71- Adv. Underwriters' Labs, Consumer Adv. Coun. Inst. Elec. & Electronics Eng; Am. Soc. Mech. Eng; Am. Soc. Heat, Refrig. & Air Conditioning Eng; Soc. Automotive Eng. Development of test methods and standards for evaluation of electrical and mechanical consumer goods. Address: Consumers Union of the U.S, Inc, 256 Washington St, Mt. Vernon, NY 10550.

FLORSCHUETZ, LEON W(ALTER), b. Sublette, Ill, Aug. 11, 35; m. 57; c. 3. MECHANICAL ENGINEERING. B.S, Illinois, 58, M.S, 59, Atomic Energy Cmn. fel, 60-62, Ph.D.(eng), 64. Asst. MECH. ENG, Illinois, 62-63; asst. prof, ARIZ. STATE UNIV, 64-67, ASSOC. PROF, 67- Nat. Sci. Found. res. grant, 65-67; summers, asst. res. engr, adv. tech. labs, Am. Standard Corp, 59, asst, Illinois, 60, Am. Soc. Eng. Ed-Nat. Aeronaut. & Space Admin. faculty fel, 65 & Assoc. West. Univ. faculty partic, Los Alamos Sci. Labs, 70. Am. Soc. Eng. Educ; Am. Soc. Mech. Eng. Heat transfer; vapor bubble dynamics and boiling in single and binary component systems. Address: 1272 E. Manhatton Dr, Tempe, AZ 85281.

FLORSHEIM, WARNER H(ANNS), b. Hamburg, Germany, Dec. 11, 22; nat; m. 52; c. 2. BIOCHEMISTRY. B.A, Univ. Calif, Los Angeles, 43, M.A, 44, Ph.D.(chem), 48. Asst. chem, UNIV. CALIF, Los Angeles, 43-46, res. assoc. zool, 48-51, anat, med. sch, 51-53, asst. clin. prof. biol. chem, 55-71, ASSOC. CLIN. PROF. PHYSIOL, IRVINE, 71-; BIOCHEMIST, U.S. VET. ADMIN. HOSP, 53- U.S. Pub. Health Serv. fel. anat, Oxford, 63-64. Endocrine Soc; Soc. Exp. Biol. & Med; Am. Thyroid Asn; Am. Fedn. Clin. Res; Am. Physiol. Soc. Neuroendocrinology; thyroid function. Address: Veterans Administration Hospital, 5901 E. Seventh St, Long Beach, CA 90801.

FLORY, CURTIS M(cCAY), b. West Allis, Wis, Sept. 30, 13; m. 38; c. 2. PATHOLOGY. B.S, Chicago, 35, M.D, 38, Ph.D.(path), 40. Asst. path, Chicago, 38-41; instr. med. col, Cornell, 42-45, asst. prof, 45-48; PATHOLOGIST, HENRY W. PUTNAM MEM. HOSP, 48- Asst. pathologist, N.Y. Hosp, 42-48; asst. prof, col. med, Vermont, 64. AAAS; Am. Asn. Path. & Bact; fel. Col. Am. Path. Cancer research; effects of nervous stimuli on visceral disease; production of tumors by tobacco tars. Address: Henry W. Putnam Memorial Hospital, Bennington, VT 05201.

FLORY, LESLIE E(ARL), b. Sawyer, Kans, March 17, 07; m. 31; c. 2. ELECTRICAL ENGINEERING. B.S, Kansas, 30. Engr, RCA Corp, Camden, 30-42; res. engr, RCA Labs, 42-64, fel, 61, leader spec. systs. res, astroelectronics appl. res. lab, 64-67, CHIEF SCIENTIST, RCA med. electronics, 67-70; ROCHE MED. ELECTRONICS DIV, HOFFMANN-LA ROCHE, INC, 70- Secy-gen, Int. Fedn. Med. Electronics & Biol. Eng. Fel. Inst. Elec. & Electronics Eng. Television and television tubes; electronic computers; special electronic tubes and circuits; industrial television; transistor applications; medical electronics; astronomical and space television. Address: Roche Medical Electronics Division, Hoffmann-La Roche, Inc, Cranbury, NJ 08512.

FLORY, LESTER DELONG, b. Ashley, Pa, June 10, 99; m. 23; c. 1. RESEARCH ADMINISTRATION. B.S, U.S. Mil. Acad, 19; M.S, Mass. Inst. Technol, 30; Army War Col, 39-40. U.S. Army, 19-49, officer in charge, West Point Prep. Sch, Ft. Amador, C.Z, 21, instr. mech. drawing, U.S. Mil. Acad, 25-27, instr, Coast Artil. Sch, Ft. Monroe, Va, 30-33, communication & eng. officer, Hawaiian Separate Coast Artil. Brigade, 37-39, mem, U.S. Mil. Mission, Brazil, 40-41, U.S. War Dept. Gen. Staff, Wash, D.C, 42-43, C.G, 63rd A.A.A. Brigade, Texas, La, N.Y. & Ga, 43-44, asst. to deputy cmnr. & chief sect, U.S. Element Allied Cmn, Austria, 45-46, deputy pres. bd. no. four, Army field forces, 46-49; exec. dir, Opers. Res. Off, Hopkins, 49-61; exec. asst. to pres, Res. Anal. Corp, 61-63, CONSULT, 63- D.S. medal; Legion of Merit; Czechoslovakian Order of Merit, first class; Czechoslovakian War Cross, 39. U.S.A, 19-49, Brig. Gen.(Ret). Strategy and tactics; manpower research and planning; communications. Address: 7004 Beechwood Dr, Chevy Chase, MD 20015.

FLORY, PAUL J(OHN), b. Sterling, Ill, June 19, 10; m. 36; c. 3. PHYSICAL CHEMISTRY. B.Sc, Manchester Col, 31, hon. Sc.D, 50; M.S, Ohio State Univ, 31, Ph.D.(phys. chem), 34, hon. Sc.D, 70; hon. D.Sc, Polytech. Inst, Milano, Italy, 64; hon. D.Sc, Manchester Univ, 69. Res. chemist, exp. sta, E.I. du Pont de Nemours & Co, Del, 34-38; res. assoc. basic sci. lab, Cincinnati, 38-40; res. chemist, Esso Labs, Standard Oil Co.(N.J), 40-43; sect. head, res. lab, Goodyear Tire & Rubber Co, 43-48; prof. chem, Cornell, 48-56; exec. dir. res, Mellon Inst, 56-61; JACKSONWOOD PROF. CHEM. STANFORD UNIV, 62- Baker lectr, Cornell, 48. Chmn. cmt. macromolecular chem, Nat. Res. Coun, 55-59, mem-at-large, div. chem. & chem. tech, 59-62, Sullivant medal, Ohio State, 45; Colwyn medal, Inst. Rubber Chem.(Gt. Brit), 54; Chandler award, Columbia Univ, 70; Kirkwood Award, Yale, 71; Cresson Medal, Franklin Inst, Pa, 71. Nat. Acad. Sci; AAAS; Am. Phys. Soc.(prize, 62); Am. Chem. Soc.(Baekeland award, 47, DeByc Award, 69); Am. Acad. Arts & Sci; Soc. Plastics Eng.(25th Int. Award, 67). Polymerization mechanisms; constitution; configurational statistics; physical and thermodynamic properties of high polymers; theory of solutions; biopolymers. Address: Dept. of Chemistry, Stanford University, Stanford, CA 94305.

FLORY, W(ALTER) S, JR, b. Bridgewater, Va, Oct. 5, 07; m. 30; wid; c. 3. BOTANY, GENETICS. B.A, Bridgewater Col, 28, hon. Sc.D, 53; M.A, Virginia, 29, fel, 28-31, Ph.D.(plant genetics), 31. In charge tech. work,

Shaver Bros, Inc, Fla, 31-32; instr. math. & chem, Greenbrier Jr. Col, 32-34; prof. biol. & head dept, Bridgewater Col, 34-35; fel, Nat. Res. Coun, Bussey Inst. & Arnold Arboretum, Harvard, 35-36; horticulturist, exp. sta, Agr. & Mech. Col. Tex, 36-44; exp. sta, Va. Polytech, 44-47; prof. exp. hort, Virginia, 47-63; v.dir. & mgr, Blandy Exp. Farm, 47-63, curator, Orland E. White Arboretum, 55-63; BABCOCK PROF. BOT, WAKE FOREST UNIV, 63- Shelton Horsley Res. award, Va. Acad. Sci, 49; res. prize, Univ. Virginia, 50; pres. bd. trustees, Highlands Biol. Sta, 69-; I.F. Lewis Distinguished Serv. Award, Va. Acad. Sci, 69. AAAS; Genetics Soc. Am; Bot. Soc. Am; Am. Soc. Hort. Sci; Soc. Study Evolution; Torrey Bot. Club. Cytology and genetics of horticultural plants; cytotaxonomy of Amaryllidaceae; phylogeny, breeding, adaptability and cytology of woody ornamentals. Address: Wake Forest University, Box 7325, Reynolda Station, Winston-Salem, NC 27109.

FLOSS, HEINZ G, B. Berlin, Ger, Aug. 28, 34; m. 56; c. 4. BIOCHEMISTRY. B.S, Tech. Univ, Berlin, 56, M.S, 59; Ph.D.(org. chem), Munich Tech, 61. Sci. asst, Munich Tech, 61-64; fel. biochem, California, Davis, 64-65; sci. asst, Munich Tech, 65-66, dozent, 66; assoc. prof. MED. CHEM, PURDUE UNIV, 66-69, PROF, 69-, HEAD DEPT, 68- AAAS; Am. Chem. Soc; Am. Soc. Biol. Chem; Acad. Pharmaceut. Sci; Am. Soc. Pharmacog. Biosynthesis of secondary plant and mold metabolites; regulation of secondary metabolism; mechanisms of biosynthetic reactions. Address: Dept. of Medicinal Chemistry, School of Pharmacy and Pharmacal Sciences, Purdue University, Lafayette, IN 47907.

FLOTTE, C. THOMAS, b. Philadelphia, Pa, June 25, 22; m. 45; c. 3. MEDICINE, SURGERY. B.S, Franklin & Marshall Col, 43; M.D, Jefferson Med. Col, 46. Intern, hosp, Jefferson Med. Col, 46-47; res. surg, col. med, Michigan, 50-54, instr, 54-57, asst. prof. surg. & post-grad. med, 57-60; SURG, SCH. MED, UNIV. MD, 60-64, assoc. prof, 64-69, PROF. & HEAD DIV. TRANSPLANTATION SURG, 69- Consult, U.S. Pub. Health Serv. Hosp. & Nat. Insts. Health; ed, Md. State Med. Jour. U.S.N, 47-49, Lt. Am. Geriat. Soc; Am. Med. Asn; Asn. Am. Med. Cols; fel. Am. Col. Surg. Medical education; vascular and pediatric surgery. Address: University of Maryland School of Medicine, Baltimore, MD 21201.

FLOURET, GEORGE, b. Rosario, Santa Fe, Argentina, Jan. 5, 35; m. 63; c. 2. CHEMISTRY. B.S, Columbia Univ, 57, M.S, 59; Ph.D.(chem), Univ. Wis, 63. Asst. prof. org. med. chem, col. pharm, Univ. Wis, 62-63; res. assoc. biochem, med. col, Cornell Univ, 63-64, instr, 64-65; SR. RES. CHEMIST, ABBOTT RES. LABS, 65- Am. Chem. Soc. Synthesis of peptides; endocrinology. Address: Abbott Research Labs, North Chicago, IL 60064.

FLOURNOY, PHILIP ALEXANDER, b. Richmond, Va, Oct. 1, 34; m. 57; c. 2. NUCLEAR PHYSICS. B.S, Richmond, 56; M.S, Virginia, 58, Nat. Sci. Found. fel, 59-60, Ph.D.(nuclear physics), 60. Res. physicist, ENG. PHYSICS LAB, E.I. DU PONT DE NEMOURS & CO, 60-63, sr. res. physicist, 63-66, RES. MGR, 66- Summer asst, Texaco Exp. Inc, 56. Am. Phys. Soc. Photonuclear reactions; attenuated total reflectance spectroscopy; lasers; interferometry; physical optics. Address: Engineering Physics Lab, Experimental Station, E.I. du Pont de Nemours & Co, Wilmington, DE 19898.

FLOURNOY, ROBERT WILSON, b. Tulsa, Okla, Dec. 12, 36; m. 59; c. 4. PHYSIOLOGY. B.S, Tex. A&M Univ, 59, M.S, 61, Nat. Sci. Found. fel, 65-66, Ph.D.(physiol), 66. Instr. biol, Tex. A&M Univ, 61-65; asst. prof. ZOOL, LA. TECH UNIV, 66-69, ASSOC. PROF, 69- Res. fel, Inst. Biomed. Res, Tex, summer 69. AAAS. Effects of sympathomimetic amines and related compounds on the cardiovascular system of mammals; action of saponins on uterine motility in rodents; effects of environmental products on mammalian systems. Address: Dept. of Zoology, Louisiana Tech University, Box 5797, Tech Station, Ruston, LA 71270.

FLOURNOY, ROWLAND WILBURN, b. Kansas City, Kans, Aug. 28, 13; m. 36; c. 5. CHEMICAL ENGINEERING, METALLURGY. B.S, Kans. State Col, 35. Asst, Kans. State Col, 35-36; lab. supvr, Colgate-Palmolive-Peet Co, 36-42; tech. supt, Spencer Chem. Co, 42-45; sr. process engr, Corn Prods. Ref. Co, 45-56; chief chem. engr, eng. servs. dept, Reynolds Metals Co, 56-71; DIR. DIV. MONITORING, VA. STATE AIR POLLUTION CONTROL BD, 71- Am. Soc. Metals; Nat. Asn. Corrosion Eng; Am. Inst. Chem. Eng; Nat. Soc. Prof. Eng. Metallurgy of aluminum and stainless steel alloys; corrosion resistance; physical properties; cryogenics. Address: Box 352-4A, Manakin Sabot, VA 23103.

FLOUTZ, VAUGHN W(ILBUR), b. Battle Creek, Mich, Oct. 4, 04; m. 32, 44; c. 3. ORGANIC CHEMISTRY. A.B, Olivet Col, 26; M.A, Colorado, 29, Ph.D.(chem), 32. Asst. CHEM, Colorado, 26-27, instr, 27-29; asst. prof, Defiance Col, 29-31, head dept, 32-41; instr, UNIV. AKRON, 41-42, asst. prof, 42-47, assoc. prof, 47-65, prof, 65-70; EMER. PROF, 70- Am. Chem. Soc. Grignard reactions. Address: 327 Birchwood Ave, Cuyahoga Falls, OH 44221.

FLOWER, MICHAEL J(OE), b. Grants Pass, Ore, May 25, 42; m. 62; c. 2. DEVELOPMENTAL & MOLECULAR BIOLOGY. A.B, Stanford Univ, 64; NASA traineeship, Univ. Wis, Madison, 64-67, M.A, 67, Ph.D.(zool), 70. ASST. PROF. BIOL, SOUTH. ORE. COL, 69- Am. Soc. Zool; Soc. Develop. Biol. Cellular interactions in limb development; mechanisms of myogenesis and chondrogenesis; avian primordial germ cells; analytical and preparative cell separation techniques. Address: Dept. of Biology, Southern Oregon College, Ashland, OR 97520.

FLOWER, ROUSSEAU HAYNER, b. Center Brunswick, N.Y, March 21, 13; m. 50; c. 2. GEOLOGY, PALEONTOLOGY. A.B, Cornell, 34, A.M, 35; Indiana, 36-37; Ph.D.(paleont), Cincinnati, 39. Temporary paleontologist, N.Y. State Mus, 38; curator univ. mus, Cincinnati, 40-43; 44; lectr, Bryn Mawr Col, 43-44; temporary expert, N.Y. State Mus, 44-45, asst. state paleontologist, N.Y, 45-51; stratigraphic geologist, N.MEX. INST. MINING & TECHNOL, 51-66, SR. PALEONTOLOGIST, 66- AAAS; Soc. Syst. Zool; Paleont. Soc; fel. Geol. Soc. Am; Soc. Study Evolution; Geol. Soc. France. Paleozoic Nautiloidea, graptolites, cyathaspids; stratigraphy and faunas. Cambrian through Devonian; Ordovidian colonial corals. Address: New Mexico Institute of Mining & Technology, Socorro, NM 87801.

FLOWERDAY, A(LBERT) D(ALE), b. Nebr, June 14, 27; m. 51; c. 3. SOIL SCIENCE. B.S, Univ. Nebr, 50, M.S, 51, Ph.D.(agron), 58. From supt. Northeast. Nebr. Exp. Sta. to asst. prof. AGRON, UNIV. NEBR, LINCOLN, 57-66, ASSOC. PROF, 66-, mem. staff, mission to Nat. Univ. Colombia, 67-69, dir. exten, 67-70. Chem.C, U.S.A, 51-53. Am. Soc. Agron. Soil fertility. Address: Dept. of Agronomy, Keim Hall 241, College of Agriculture, University of Nebraska, Lincoln, NE 68503.

FLOWERDAY, THOMAS W(ILLIAM), b. San Francisco, Calif, Dec. 8, 32; m. 58; c. 4. ENVIRONMENTAL SCIENCES. B.S, California, Berkeley, 54; M.S, Stanford, 61. Engr. elec. eng, microwave tube lab, Sylvania Elec. Prod, Inc, 54-56, sr. engr, 58-59; sr. scientist space physics, Lockheed Missiles & Space Co, 59-63; res. scientist, Southwest Ctr. Advan. Studies, 63-69; PRIN. ENGR, ATLANTIC RES. CORP, 69- Sig.C, 56-58, 1st Lt. Am. Geophys. Union; Am. Vacuum Soc; Inst. Elec. & Electronics Eng. Study of air pollution including the development of instrumentation to monitor air quality and to locate sources of pollutants. Address: 17710 Oak St, Fountain Valley, CA 92708.

FLOWERS, ARCHIE I(NGRAM), b. Waelder, Tex, Dec. 26, 20; m. 43; c. 1. MICROBIOLOGY. B.S, Agr. & Mech. Col, Tex, 42, D.V.M, 50, M.S, 59. From assoc. prof. to prof. vet. microbiol, TEX. A&M UNIV, 55-65, PROF. VET. PUB. HEALTH & HEAD DEPT, 65- U.S.A.A.F, 43-50, Res, 50. Am. Vet. Med. Asn; Am. Asn. Avian Path. Veterinary microbiology; virology; bacteriology; poultry diseases. Address: Dept. of Veterinary Public Health, Texas A&M University, College Station, TX 77843.

FLOWERS, CHARLES E, JR, b. Zebulon, N.C, July 20, 20; wid; c. 2. OBSTETRICS, GYNECOLOGY. B.S, The Citadel, 41; M.D, Johns Hopkins Univ, 44. Asst. obstet. & gynec, Hopkins Hosp, 48-50; instr, col. med, State Univ. N.Y, 51-52, asst. prof, 52-53; assoc. prof, sch. med, Univ. N.C, 53-61, prof, 61-66; prof. obstet. & gynec. & chmn. dept, col. med, Baylor Univ, 66-69; obstetrician & gynecologist-in-chief, Ben Taub & Jefferson Davis Hosps, Houston, 66-69; PROF. OBSTET. & GYNEC. & CHMN. DEPT. MED. CTR, UNIV. ALA, BIRMINGHAM, 69- Med.C, U.S.A, 46-48. Fel. Am. Col. Surgeons; fel. Am. Col. Obstet. & Gynec; fel. Am. Gynec. Soc; fel. Am. Asn. Obstet. & Gynec. Obstetrical anesthesia and analgesia; metabolism in toxemia of pregnancy; studies of the endometrium and the menstrual cycle. Address: Dept. of Obstetrics & Gynecology, University of Alabama Medical Center, 1919 Seventh Ave. S, Birmingham, AL 35233.

FLOWERS, DANIEL F(ORT), b. N.Y.C, Jan. 21, 20; m. 58. MECHANICAL ENGINEERING. B.S, Va. Mil. Inst, 40; S.M, Mass. Inst. Tech, 42, Sc.D.(mech. eng), 49. Engr, DIFFERENTIAL CORP, 46-47, 49-56, V.PRES, 56- U.S.A.A.F, 42-46, Capt. Am. Soc. Mech. Eng; Am. Inst. Mining, Metall. & Petrol. Eng. Aircraft vibration and flutter; gas turbine control; railway vehicles; oil and gas production. Address: Differential Corp, Niels Esperson Bldg, 804 Travis, Houston, TX 77002.

FLOWERS, HAROLD L(EE), b. Hickory, N.C, June 25, 17; m. 41; c. 2. ELECTRONICS. B.S, Duke, 38; fel, Cincinnati, 38-41, M.S, 48. Asst, Proctor & Swartz, Inc, Pa, 38-41; asst. radio engr. radio & radar, Off. Chief Sig. Off, U.S. War Dept, Wash, D.C, 41-42; br. head missile command & report links, Naval Res. Lab, 42-50; dir. weapon syst, Goodyear Aircraft Corp, 50-61; gen. eng. mgr, Avco Electronics, Ohio, 61-63; eng. mgr, McDonnell Aircraft Corp, Mo, 63-66, chief engr. tactical missiles, Fla. Div, McDonnell Douglas Corp, 66-67, chief engr, Fla. Div, McDonnell Astronaut. Co, 67-71, DEP. PROG. MGR, McDONNELL DOUGLAS ASTRONAUT. CO, MO, 71- Mem. guided missile comt, res. & develop. bd, Dept. Defense, 49-53. U.S. Navy meritorious civil serv. award, 46. Assoc. fel. Am. Inst. Aeronaut. & Astronaut; fel. Inst. Elec. & Electronics Eng. Electronic guidance and missile systems; radar; weapon systems. Address: McDonnell Douglas Astronautics Co, P.O. Box 516, St. Louis, MO 63166.

FLOWERS, JOHN W(ILSON), b. Memphis, Tenn, Aug. 20, 10; m. 41; c. 1. PHYSICS. B.S, Southwestern (Tenn), 31; M.S, Virginia, 33, Ph.D.(physics), 35; Columbia Univ, 35-37. Mem. staff, Gen. Elec. Co, 37-47; assoc. prof. PHYSICS, UNIV. FLA, 47-53, PROF, 53- Sr. physicist, Aerojet Gen. Corp, 61; consult, Union Carbide Co, 52-; Gen. Dynamics/Ft. Worth, 59, 60; Sperry Rand, 61; Radiation Res. Corp, 64- AAAS; Am. Phys. Soc. Plasma, thermonuclear and space physics. Address: Williamson Hall, University of Florida, Gainesville, FL 32601.

FLOWERS, LEONARD C(OLERICK), b. Pittsburgh, Pa, Oct. 16, 04; m. 28; c. 3. PHYSICAL & ELECTROCHEMISTRY. B.S, Carnegie Inst. Tech, 27, M.S, 33; Cincinnati. Res. chemist edible oils, Procter & Gamble Co, 27-28; res. engr. insulating oil, Westinghouse Elec. Corp, 28-31, materials engr, elec. appliance div, 36-59, res. engr, insulation dept, 59-66, fel. engr. chem. sci. res. & develop, 66-67, adv. scientist, insulation & chem. technol, 67-69; CHEM. CONSULT, 69- Instr, Carnegie Inst. Technol, 31-33; Canal Zone Jr. Col, 33-36; West. New England Col, 40-59. Am. Chem. Soc; Am. Soc. Heat, Refrig. & Air Conditioning Eng. Chemistry of refrigerating systems; reverse osmosis desalinization. Address: 3371 MacArthur Dr, Murrysville, PA 15668.

FLOWERS, NANCY CAROLYN, b. McComb, Miss, Sept. 28, 28; m. 66; c. 3. CARDIOVASCULAR DISEASES. B.S, Miss. State Col. Women, 50; Med. Col. Va, 51-52; M.D, Univ. Tenn, Memphis, 58. Preceptorship under Dr. Ralph R. Braund, 58; intern, med, Roanoke Mem. Hosp, 58-59; preceptorship, int. med, Beckley Mem. Hosp, W.Va, 60, resident, 60-62; instr. med, col. med, Univ. Tenn, Memphis, 63-65, asst. prof, 65-67, physiol, 66-67; assoc. prof. MED, MED. COL. GA, 67-71, PROF, 71-; SECT. CHIEF CARDIOL, FOREST HILLS DIV, VET. ADMIN. HOSP, AUGUSTA, GA, 67- Nat. Insts. Health fel. & traineeship, col. med, Univ. Tenn, 62-65; res. physician cardiol, Kennedy Vet. Admin. Hosp, Memphis, Tenn, 63-67; dir. heart sta, John Gaston Hosp, 64-65; consult, William F. Bowld Hosp, 65-66; W.Tenn. Tuberculosis Hosp, 66-67; prin. investr, Am. Heart Asn. grant-in-aid, 69-72; co-investr, Nat. Insts. Health grant-in-aid, 67-74; dir. training prog, Vet. Admin. Hosp, Augusta, Ga, 70; fel. coun. clin. cardiol, Am. Heart Asn, 70. Dipl, Am. Bd. Int. Med, 66; Am. Bd. Cardiovasc. Disease, 70. Am. Med. Asn; Am. Fedn. Clin. Res; fel. Am. Col. Physicians; fel. Am. Col. Cardiol; fel. Am. Col. Chest Physicians. Distribution of electrocardiographic potential on the body surface with respect to the limits of the contained information, equivalent cardiac generator representation, clinical significance and A-V conduction system of the heart. Address: Forest Hills Division, Veterans Administration Hospital, Augusta, GA 30904.

FLOWERS, RALPH G(RANT), b. North Platte, Nebr, Apr. 11, 15; m. 40; c. 2. PHYSICAL CHEMISTRY. A.B, West Virginia, 38, fel, 38-39, M.S, 39; fel, N.Y. Univ, 39-41, Ph.D.(phys. chem), 42. Asst, Nat. Defense Res. Comt, Columbia, 41-42; res. chemist, GEN. ELEC. CO, 42-56, SR. CHEMIST, 56- Civilian with Off. Sci. Res. & Develop, 41-42. Am. Chem. Soc. Kinetics; polymers and resins; organic synthesis; oils; waxes; photolysis of azomethane in the presence of hydrogen; cellulose chemistry; solid insulation and wire enamels. Address: General Electric Co, 100 Woodlawn Ave, Pittsfield, MA 01201.

FLOYD, ACEY L, b. Galveston, Texas, Oct. 10, 23; m. 48; c. 4. PHYSICS. B.S, Ga. Inst. Tech, 47, M.S, 49; Ph.D.(physics), Calif. Inst. Tech, 54. Assoc. physicist, Phillips Petrol. Co, 47-48; res. assoc, State Eng. Exp. Sta, Ga. Inst. Tech, 48-49; physicist, U.S. Naval Civil Eng. Lab, 49-52; electron. scientist, Nat. Bur. Standards, 52-53; physicist, Lane-Wells Co, 53-57; dir. reliability, Hoffman Electronics Corp, 57-64; SR. SCIENTIFIC ADV, LOCKHEED AIRCRAFT CORP, 64- U.S.A.A.F, 42-45. Am. Phys. Soc. Molecular spectra; analogue computers; electronic reliability; navigation equipment; business and technology planning. Address: 2813 Magna Vista, Pasadena, CA 91107.

FLOYD, ALTON DAVID, b. Henderson, Ky, July 17, 41; m. 62; c. 2. ANATOMY. B.S, Kentucky, 63; Ph.D.(anat), Louisville, 68. Instr. ANAT, UNIV. MICH, ANN ARBOR, 67-70, ASST. PROF, 70- Cell nuclear differentiation and specialization; quantitative cytology. Address: 805 S. First St, Ann Arbor, MI 48103.

FLOYD, DENIS RAGAN, b. Los Angeles, Calif, Jan. 27, 38; m. 69. ALGEBRA. A.B, Reed Col, 60; Ph.D.(math), Univ. Wash, 66. Fel. MATH, N.Mex. State Univ, 66-67; asst. prof, Univ. Ariz, 67-70; ASSOC. PROF, ARYA MEHR UNIV. TECHNOL, 70- Partic, Nat. Sci. Found. Advan. Sci. Sem, Bowdoin Col, summers 65 & 67. AAAS; Am. Math. Soc. Ring theory, specifically, representation theory of finite dimensional associative algebra. Address: Dept. of Mathematics, Arya Mehr University of Technology, P.O. Box 3406, Eisenhower Blvd, Tehran, Iran.

FLOYD, DON E(DGAR), b. Iowa City, Iowa, Feb. 26, 18; m. 43; c. 1. ORGANIC CHEMISTRY. B.A, Iowa, 40, Ph.D.(org. chem), 43. Asst. chem, Iowa, 40-43; RES. CHEMIST, GEN. MILLS, INC, 43- Am. Chem. Soc; Am. Soc. Test. & Mat. Ester condensations; synthesis of amino acids; derivatives of fatty acids; resins and surface coatings; polyamide resins. Address: 2672 Parkview Ave, Robbinsdale, MN 55422.

FLOYD, E(DWIN) E(ARL), b. Eufaula, Ala, May 8, 24; m. 45; c. 3. MATHEMATICS. B.A, Alabama, 43; Ph.D.(math), Virginia, 48. Fine instr. MATH, Princeton, 48-49; asst. prof, UNIV. VA, 49-53, assoc. prof, 53-56, PROF, 56-, chmn. dept, 66-69. Mem, Inst. Advan. Study, 58-59, 63-64; Sloan res. fel, 60-64. Am. Math. Soc; Math. Asn. Am. Differential topology; cobordism; periodic maps; transformation groups. Address: Dept. of Mathematics, Faculty of Arts & Sciences, University of Virginia, Charlottesville, VA 22901.

FLOYD, ERNEST HAZEL, b. Aiken, S.C, Apr. 5, 14; m. 38; c. 1. ENTOMOLOGY. B.S, Clemson, 37; M.S, La. State, 39; Ohio State, 40. PROF. ENTOM, LA. STATE UNIV, BATON ROUGE, 41- Med.C, U.S.A, 43-46, T/Sgt. Entom. Soc. Am. Insects of stored corn, rice and grain sorghum. Address: 1962 Stuart Ave, Baton Rouge, LA 70808.

FLOYD, J.F. R(ABARDY), b. Pagosa Springs, Colo, May 22, 15; m. 44; c. 3. AERONAUTICAL ENGINEERING. B.S, Carnegie Inst. Tech, 37. Aerodynamicist, Glenn L. Martin Co, 37-43, chief aerodyn, 43-47; sr. engr. & mem. prin. prof. staff, APPL. PHYSICS LAB, JOHNS HOPKINS UNIV, 47-67, MISSILE SYST. PROJ. ENGR, 67- Am. Inst. Aeronaut. & Astronaut. Design and development of aircraft and guided missiles, particularly missile system design and launching techniques. Address: 9217 Crownwood Rd, Ellicott City, MD 21043.

FLOYD, JAMES WHITNEY, b. Bloomington, Idaho, May 11, 03; m; c. 4. FORESTRY. B.S, Utah State Agr. Col, 36; M.S, California, 42; Michigan, 57. Insect control, U.S. Forest Serv, Utah, 32-33, forest guard, Wyo, 33-34, recreational planner, Idaho, 34-35; instr. forestry, UTAH STATE UNIV, 35-36, asst. prof, 36-42, assoc. prof, 42-45, prof, 45-50, exten. forester, 35-45, head dept. forest mgt, 50-69, acting dean col. forestry, 59-61, dean, 61-69, EMER. PROF. FORESTRY, 69- Chief forester-firewarden, State Forest Prog, Utah, 42-61. Soc. Am. Foresters; Nat. Asn. State Foresters (pres, 58). Economics, markets and distribution of pinion pine-juniper type; forest fires. Address: Dept. of Forest Management, Utah State University, Logan, UT 84321.

FLOYD, JOHN (DeWITT), b. Arlington, Va, Sept. 22, 15; m. 49; c. 3. PHYSICAL CHEMISTRY. A.B, Bridgewater Col, 51; M.S, Virginia, 53, Ph.D, 55. Res. chemist, Hercules Powder Co, 55-66, res. supvr, Hercules, Inc, 66-67, indust. mgr. aquatrol div, 67-69, environ. serv. div, 69-71; MANAGING DIR, AWT SYSTS. INC, 71- U.S.N, 42-46. Am. Chem. Soc; Sci. Res. Soc. Am. Physical properties of aqueous polymer systems, both dispersed and solutions. Address: AWT Systems Inc, 910 Market St, Wilmington, DE 19899.

FLOYD, JOHN J(ULIUS), b. Atlanta, Ga, Dec. 30, 09; m. 39; c. 2. PHYSICS. A.B, Emory, 46; M.S, N.Y. Univ, 52. From jr. physicist to assoc. physicist, Oak Ridge Nat. Lab, Tenn, 45-47; res. coord, nuclear reactor, BROOKHAVEN NAT. LAB, 47-66, PHYSICIST, REACTOR DIV, 66- Civilian with Atomic Energy Comn, 46. U.S.A, 42-45. Am. Nuclear Soc. Photographic detection of nuclear particles; radioactivity of potassium. Address: Reactor Division, Brookhaven National Lab, Upton, NY 11973.

FLOYD, M(IDDLETON) BRAWNER, JR, b. Atlanta, Ga, Aug. 8, 38; m. 66. ORGANIC CHEMISTRY. B.A, Emory Univ, 60, M.S, 62; Ph.D.(chem), Yale, 66. U.S. Dept. Agr. res. assoc, Boston Univ, 65-67; CHEMIST, LEDERLE LABS, AM. CYANAMID CO, 67- AAAS; Am. Chem. Soc. Chemical synthesis of compounds for use as medicinal agents; study of autoxidation and photo-oxidation of heterocyclic compounds. Address: 5 Babbling Brook Lane, Suffern, NY 10901.

FLOYD, ROBERT A, b. Yosemite, Ky, Oct. 7, 40; m. 65. PLANT PHYSIOLOGY. B.S, Kentucky, 63, M.S, 65; Ph.D.(agron), Purdue, 69. Fel. agron, California, Davis, 68-69; Johnson Res. Found, Pennsylvania, 69-71; RES. ASSOC, CTR. BIOL. NATURAL SYSTS, WASH. UNIV, 71- AAAS; Am. Soc. Plant Physiol; Am. Soc. Agron. Bioenergetics; plant root-soil interface; photosynthesis; electron spin resonance biological systems. Address: Center for the Biology of Natural Systems, Washington University, St. Louis, MO 63130.

FLOYD, ROBERT W, b. New York, N.Y, June 8, 36; m. 57, 70; c. 3. COMPUTER SCIENCE. A.B, Chicago, 53, B.S, 58. Elec. engr, Westinghouse Elec. Corp, 55-56; analyst comput. appln, Armour Res. Found, 56-62; mathematician, Comput. Assocs, Inc, 62-65; assoc. prof. COMPUT. SCI, Carnegie-Mellon Univ, 65-68; STANFORD UNIV, 68-70, PROF, 70- AAAS; Asn. Comput. Mach. Syntax and semantics of computer programming languages; minimal algorithms; computer software; mechanical theorem proving. Address: Dept. of Computer Science, Stanford University, Stanford, CA 94305.

FLOYD, THOMAS M(ICHAEL), b. Birmingham, Ala, Aug. 4, 15; m. 42; c. 4. BACTERIOLOGY. B.S, Howard Col, 36; M.S, Chicago, 48; M.P.H, Hopkins, 55. HEAD, bact. div, Naval Med. Res. Unit, Guam, 46-48; bact. dept, Naval Med. Sch, Md, 48-51; Naval Med. Res. Unit, Egypt, 51-54; bact. div, naval med. res. inst, 55-62, bact. dept, prev. med. unit no. 6, 62-67, PREV. MED. UNIT 5, 67- Med.Serv.C, 41-, Capt. AAAS; Am. Soc. Microbiol; Am. Soc. Trop. Med. & Hyg. Epidemiology of diarrheal disease; pathogenesis of enteric organisms, particularly genus Shigella. Address: U.S. Navy Preventive Medicine Unit No. 5, Naval Station, San Diego, CA 92136.

FLOYD, WILLIAM B(ECKWITH), b. Atlanta, Ga, Dec. 27, 30; m. 53; c. 1. MATHEMATICS. A.B, Harvard, 52; M.S, Emory, 53. Sr. res. engr, appl. sci. div, Melpar, Inc, 56-59, head systs. res. lab, 59-60; sr. staff engr, info. sci. lab, Litton Systs, Inc, 60-66, tech. mgr, signal processing dept, data systs. div, 66-67; ASSOC. TECH. DIR, B-D SPEAR MED. SYSTS. DIV, BECTON, DICKINSON & CO, 67- U.S.A.F, 53-56, Res, 56-62, 1st Lt. AAAS; Math. Asn. Am; Inst. Elec. & Electronics Eng. Communication theory and dynamic programming to communications system design. Address: 59 Ash St, Weston, MA 02193.

FLOYD, WILLIS W(ALDO), b. Whitesboro, Tex, Aug. 2, 03; m. 32; c. 4. ORGANIC & PHYSICAL CHEMISTRY. A.B, N.Texas State Teachers Col, 25; A.M, Texas, 28; fel, Iowa, 30-31, Ph.D.(phys. chem), 31; Kansas, 33; Virginia, 34. Instr, pub. sch, Texas, 25-26; tutor chem, Texas, 26-29; asst, Iowa, 29-30; prof. chem, Ottawa, 31-36; prof. chem. & physics & head dept, SAM HOUSTON STATE UNIV, 36-47, PROF. CHEM, 48- Prof, Purdue, 47-48. Res, Oak Ridge Nat. Lab, 53. AAAS; Am. Chem. Soc. Petroleum nitrogen; sucrose inversion; chemical education; vitamin C, castor stalk; conductivity; reactor thorium; copper ores; oxinate solubilities; periodic group number eight congruency; 3'-uridylic acid yields; polyuridylic acid biosynthesis equation. Address: Dept. of Chemistry, Sam Houston State University, Huntsville, TX 77340.

FLUCK, EUGENE RICHARDS, b. Hazleton, Pa, Dec. 10, 34; m. 57; c. 2. BIOCHEMISTRY. B.S, Pa. State, 56, M.S, 60, Ph.D.(biochem), 62. METABOLIC CHEMIST, R.J. Reynolds Tobacco Co, 62-69; WYETH LABS. INC, 69- Am. Chem. Soc; N.Y. Acad. Sci. Drug metabolism and drug safety evaluations. Address: Metabolic Chemistry Section, Wyeth Labs, Inc, P.O. Box 8299, Philadelphia, PA 19101.

FLUCK, RICHARD CONARD, b. Clemmons, N.C, May 22, 38; m. 60; c. 3. AGRICULTURAL ENGINEERING. B.S, N.C. State, 60, M.S, 62, Ph.D.(agr. eng), 66. Asst. prof. agr. eng. & asst. agr. engr, UNIV. FLA, 65-69, ASSOC. PROF. AGR. ENG. & ASSOC. AGR. ENGR, 69- Am. Soc. Agr. Eng; Opers. Res. Soc. Am. Fruit and vegetable physical properties, harvesting and handling; operations research techniques applied to agricultural engineering problems; agricultural machinery management; agricultural engineering instrumentation. Address: Dept. of Agricultural Engineering, University of Florida, Gainesville, FL 32601.

FLUECK, JOHN A, b. Apr. 13, 33; U.S. citizen; c. 2. STATISTICS. B.S, Beloit Col, 55; M.B.A, Univ. Chicago, 58, Ph.D.(statist), 67. Lectr. statist, Univ. Chicago, 64-65, res. assoc. geophys, 65-69; ASSOC. PROF. STATIST, TEMPLE UNIV, 68- Vis. lectr, Univ. Ill, Chicago, 67-68; consult, panel weather & climate modification, Nat. Acad. Sci-Nat. Res. Coun, 68-70; Bur. of Budget, Wash, D.C, 70, vis. appointment, Off. Mgt. & Budget, Exec. Off. President, 70-71. U.S.A, 55-57. AAAS; Royal Statist. Soc; Am. Statist. Asn; Inst. Math. Statist; Biomet. Soc. Design and analysis of experiments in weather modification; data analysis; sample surveys; statistical decision theory. Address: Dept. of Statistics, Temple University, Philadelphia, PA 19122.

FLUEGEL, ROLF MANFRED, b. Joellenbeck, Ger, Feb. 10, 38; m. 61; c. 2. BIOCHEMISTRY. B.S, Univ. Göttingen, 62, M.S, 64, fel, 65-67, Ph.D.(org. chem), 67. RES. ASSOC. BIOCHEM, dept. chem, Max Planck Inst. Exp. Med, 68-69; med. ctr, Univ. Ky, 69-71; UNIV. WIS, MADISON, 71- Am. Chem. Soc. Nucleic acids. Address: Dept. of Biochemistry, University of Wisconsin, Madison, WI 53706.

FLÜGGE, WILHELM, b. Greiz, Germany, March 18, 04; nat; m. 38. ENGINEERING MECHANICS. Dipl.Ing, Tech. Hochsch. Dresden, Germany, 25, Dr.Ing, 27; Göttingen, 30-31. Asst, Dresden Tech, 25-27; struct. engr, Dyckerhoff & Widmann, 28-29; privat-docent, Göttingen, 32-37; chief structures res. div, German Inst. Res. Aeronaut, 38-45; res. group, Off. Nat. Studies Res. Aeronaut, France, 47-48; prof. ENG. MECH, STANFORD UNIV, 48-69, EMER. PROF, 69- Theodore Von Karman Medal, 70; Worcester Reed Warner Medal, 70. Fel. Am. Soc. Mech. Eng. Elasticity, plasticity and viscoelasticity; shells; plates; elastic stability; wave propagation. Address: Dept. of Applied Mechanics, Stanford University, Stanford, CA 94305.

FLÜGGE-LOTZ, IRMGARD, b. Hameln, Germany, July 16, 03; nat; m. 38. ENGINEERING MECHANICS. Dipl.Ing, Hannover Tech, 27, Dr.Ing, 29. From res. scientist to head dept. theoret. aerodyn, Aerodyn. Res. Inst, Germany, 29-38; consult. aerodyn. & dynamics of flight, German Inst. Res. Aeronaut, 38-45; chief res. group theoret. aerodyn, Off. Nat. Studies Res. Aeronaut, France, 46-48; lectr. eng. mech. & res. supvr, STANFORD UNIV, 49-60, prof. AERONAUT. ENG. & ENG. MECH, 60-68, EMER. PROF, 68- Achievement award, Soc. Women Engrs, 70. Fel. Am. Inst. Aeronaut. & Astronaut. Incompressible; compressible; viscous fluid flow; wing theory, boundary layer theory; nonlinear automatic controls; fluid mechanics; automatic control. Address: Dept. of Applied Mechanics, School of Engineering, Stanford University, Stanford, CA 94305.

FLUHARTY, ARVAN LAWRENCE, b. Haines, Ore, June 10, 34; m. 61; c. 3. BIOCHEMISTRY. B.S, Washington (Seattle), 56; Nat. Sci. Found. fel, California, Berkeley, 56-59, Ph.D.(biochem), 59. Asst. prof. biochem, Univ. South. Calif, 62-66, assoc. prof, 66-68; RES. SPECIALIST, PAC. STATE HOSP-CALIF. STATE DEPT. MENT. HYG, 68- Adj. assoc. prof. biochem, sch. med, Univ. South. Calif, 69- U.S.P.H.S, 59-62, Sr. Asst. Scientist. AAAS; Am. Chem. Soc; Am. Soc. Biol. Chem. Biochemistry of metabolic diseases; biochemistry of mental retardation; neurobiochemistry; metabolism of four carbon sugars; enzymatic dithiols; cellular energy transformations. Address: Research Dept, Pacific State Hospital, Pomona, CA 91768.

FLUHARTY, DEAN M(ILTON), b. Culdesac, Idaho, June 18, 16; m. 53; c. 5. VETERINARY PATHOLOGY. B.S, Idaho, 39; D.V.M, Mich. State, 42; Washington State, 56-57; M.S, Idaho, 62. Asst. bact, Mich. State, 39-42; supvry. veterinarian, Badger Breeders Co-op, Wis, 46-49; poultry disease diagnostician, Wash. State Dept. Agr, 49-52; ASSOC. PROF. VET. PATH, COL. VET. MED, WASH. STATE UNIV, 52- Private practice, 49. Vet.C, 43-46, Capt. Am. Vet. Med. Asn. Veterinary laboratory diagnostic methods; veterinary clinical pathology and meat hygiene; canine blood groups; hemolytic anemia of newborn puppies; bovine mastitis; staphylococcal diseases in animals and man. Address: College of Veterinary Medicine, Washington State University, Pullman, WA 99163.

FLUHARTY, REX G(ILBERT), b. Corvallis, Ore, Nov. 22, 18; m. 43; c. 2. NUCLEAR PHYSICS. B.S, Idaho, 39; fel, Washington (Seattle), 39-42; Ph.D. (physics), Mass. Inst. Tech, 49. Mem. staff, radiation lab, Mass. Inst. Tech, 42-45, res. assoc, 45-59; physicist, Oak Ridge Inst. Nuclear Studies, 49-52; physicist & mgr. nuclear technol. br, Phillips Petrol. Co, 52-66; mgr. nuclear technol. br, Idaho Nuclear Corp, 66-68; MEM. STAFF, LOS ALAMOS SCI. LAB, 68- Fel. Am. Phys. Soc; Am. Nuclear Soc. Radioactive and medical tracer research; low energy neutron cross sections; reactors as neutron sources. Address: 111 Los Pueblos, Los Alamos, NM 87544.

FLUHR, WALLACE EMORY, b. Louisville, Ky, Jan. 3, 32; m. 53; c. 5. STRUCTURAL DYNAMICS, NUCLEAR ENGINEERING. B.S, Kentucky, 54; M.S, Illinois, 59, Ph.D.(struct. dynamics), 60. U.S. AIR FORCE, 54-, base engr, Gunter AFB, Ala, 54-57, chief appl. res, ballistic syst. div, Calif, 60-63, assoc. prof. mech, U.S. AIR FORCE ACAD, 63-66, PROF. CIVIL ENG. & HEAD DEPT, 66- Chmn. dynamic forces adv. panel, U.S. Air Force, 60-; lectr, Univ. Calif, Los Angeles, 62- Am. Soc. Civil. Eng; Am. Soc. Eng. Educ; Am. Concrete Inst. Nuclear weapons effects and design of underground protective structures; structural dynamics. Address: Dept. of Civil Engineering; U.S. Air Force Academy, CO 80840.

FLUKE, DONALD J(OHN), b. Nankin, Ohio, Feb. 17, 23; m. 54; c. 2. BIOPHYSICS. B.A, Wooster Col, 47; M.S, Yale, 48, Ph.D.(physics), 50. Instr. physics, Yale, 50-52; biophysicist, Brookhaven Nat. Lab, 52-57; assoc. prof. ZOOL, DUKE UNIV, 58-65, PROF, 65-, CHMN. DEPT, 69-, chmn. acad. coun, 69-71. Lectr, California, 56-57, vis. assoc. prof, Donner lab, 58; vis. lectr, Am. Inst. Biol. Scientists, 61-63; vis. prof, inst. molecular biophysics, Fla. State, 64-65; tech. rep. biophys, div. biol. & med, U.S. Atomic Energy Comn, 68-69. U.S.A.A.F, 42-45. AAAS; Radiation Res. Soc; Biophys. Soc; Am. Asn. Physics Teachers. Ultraviolet action spectroscopy; biophysical application of accelerated ions on virus and enzyme; radiation biology. Address: Dept. of Zoology, Duke University, Durham, NC 27706.

FLUKER, SAM SPRUILL, b. Roane, Tex, Apr. 14, 31; m. 50; c. 2. ENTOMOLOGY. B.S, Tex. Tech Univ, 66; M.S, Univ. Hawaii, 67, Ph.D.(entom), 69. Entomologist, Mo. State Fruit Exp. Sta, 69; ASST. PROF. ENTOM. & ASST. ENTOMOLOGIST, INST. FOOD & AGR. SCI, AGR. RES. CTR, UNIV. FLA, 69- U.S.A.F, 48-60, Sgt. Entom. Soc. Am. Habits and behavior of Formicidae of Hawaii; biology and control of insects and mites attacking deciduous fruits and nuts. Address: Agricultural Research Center, University of Florida, Monticello, FL 32344.

FLUM, ROBERT S(AMUEL), SR, b. Indianapolis, Ind, July 3, 25; m. 47; c. 7. SYSTEMS ANALYSIS. B.S, Indiana, 49, Frederic Cottrell Res. Corp. fel, 50-51, M.S, 56. Asst. physics, Indiana, 49-50; discharge in gases, Maryland, 51-52; proj. engr. underwater acoust, U.S. Naval Ord. Lab, 52, physicist aero boundary layer, 52-54, ord. eng, 54-55, staff consult. aerodyn, 55-58, aerodevelop. eng, 58-61; mem. staff, Chicago, 61-63; physicist, U.S. NAVAL ORD. LAB, 63-65, SR. ANALYST, SYSTS. ANAL. OFF, ANTISUBMARINE WARFARE, SPEC. PROJ. OFF, 65- Superior accomplishment award, U.S. Navy, 61. U.S.A, 43-45. Opers. Res. Soc. Am; Am. Phys. Soc. Application of logic and common sense to the basic problems of optimization of the Naval antisubmarine warfare posture. Address: Systems Analysis Office, Code 880, U.S. Naval Ordnance Lab, White Oak, Silver Spring, MD 20910.

FLUMERFELT, RAYMOND W, b. Hobbs, N.Mex, Nov. 18, 39; m. 59; c. 1. CHEMICAL ENGINEERING. B.S, Lamar State Col, 61; M.S, Northwestern, 63, Ph.D.(chem. eng), 65. Asst. prof. eng. sci, Notre Dame, 65-67; fel, Univ. Wis, 67-68; asst. prof. CHEM. ENG, UNIV. HOUSTON, 68-70, ASSOC. PROF, 70- U.S.M.C.R, 56-62. Am. Inst. Chem. Eng; Soc. Rheol; Am. Chem. Soc. Rheology; biomedical engineering; applied mathematics. Address: Dept. of Chemical Engineering, University of Houston, Houston, TX 77004.

FLUNO, JOHN A(RTHUR), b. Appleton, Wis, July 21, 14; m. 42; c. 2. ENTOMOLOGY. B.S, Rollins Col, 37; M.S, Ohio State, 39. Field aide, bur. entomol. & plant quarantine, U.S. Dept. Agr, 37-38; asst, biol. surv, Ohio State, 38-40; instr. zool, Rollins Col, 41; jr. entomologist, U.S. Pub. Health Serv, 41-46; ENTOMOLOGIST, U.S. DEPT. AGR, 46-, ASST. TO CHIEF, INSECTS AFFECTING MAN & ANIMALS RES. BR, ENTOM. RES. DIV, 59- U.S.A, 43-46. Am. Mosquito Control Asn; Entom. Soc. Am. Ecology and control of mosquitoes; medical entomology. Address: Entomology Research Division, U.S. Dept. of Agriculture, Plant Industry Station, Beltsville, MD 20705.

FLURRY, ROBERT L(UTHER), JR, b. Hattiesburg, Miss, Nov. 15, 33; m. 57; c. 4. QUANTUM CHEMISTRY. A.B, Emory, 58, M.S, 59, univ. fel, Metrop. Found. fel. & Ph.D.(org. chem), 61. Nat. Insts. Health fel, 61-62; asst. prof. CHEM, LA. STATE UNIV, NEW ORLEANS, 62-66, assoc. prof, 66-70, PROF, 70- Vis. prof, Math. Inst, Eng, 68. Am. Chem. Soc; fel. Am. Inst. Chem; Faraday Soc. Applications of quantum chemistry to problems of chemical and biological interest. Address: Dept. of Chemistry, Louisiana State University in New Orleans, New Orleans, LA 70122.

FLURY, ALVIN G(ODFREY), b. Austin, Tex, Nov. 1, 20; m. 44; c. 4. VERTEBRATE ZOOLOGY. B.A, Texas, 48, M.A, 51. Aquatic biologist, freshwater fisheries, Tex. Game & Fish Cmn, 51-62; info-ed. officer, Tex. Parks & Wildlife Dept, 62-65; instr. BIOL, ANGELO STATE COL, 65-69, ASST. PROF, 69- U.S.N, 41-45. Am. Soc. Ichthyol. & Herpet; Soc. Study Evolution; Soc. Study Amphibians & Reptiles; Asn. Study Animal Behav; Ecol. Soc. Am. Reptiles; amphibians; fish; fish and wildlife conservation. Address: Dept. of Biology, Angelo State College, San Angelo, TX 76901.

FLUSSER, PETER R, b. Vienna, Austria, July 3, 30; U.S. citizen; m. 58; c. 4. MATHEMATICS. B.A, Ottawa Univ, 58; M.A, Univ. Kans, 60; Ed.D. (higher educ), Okla. State Univ, 71. Asst. prof. MATH, OTTAWA UNIV, 60-68, ASSOC. PROF, 68- Summers, asst. health physicist, Oak Ridge Nat. Lab, 58-63 & mathematician, Tech-Opers, 64 & 65. Am. Math. Soc; Math. Asn. Am. Probability theory; characterization theorems in probability, especially characterization theorems for random variables with values in topological groups. Address: Dept. of Mathematics, Ottawa University, Ottawa, KS 66067.

FLY, CLAUDE L(EE), b. Fulbright, Tex, June 23, 05; m. 27; c. 2. SOIL CHEMISTRY, PLANT PHYSIOLOGY. B.S, Okla. Agr. & Mech. Col, 27, fel, 27-28, M.S, 28; fel, Iowa State Col, 28-31, Ph.D.(soil chem), 31. Prof. chem. & head dept. sci, Panhandle Agr. & Mech. Col, 31-35; asst. soil surveyor, soil conserv. serv, U.S. Dept. Agr, 35, assoc. soil scientist, 35-39, soil scientist, Texas, 39-42, Nebr, 42-47, state soil scientist, Kans, 47-52; head land develop. dept, Int. Eng. Co. & Morrison-Knudsen-Afghanistan Co, 52-58; area dir. North. Great Plains, soil & water conserv, Agr. Res. Serv, U.S. Dept. Agr, 58-59, res. proj. leader, West. Br, 59-63; PRES, CLAUDE L. FLY & ASSOCS, 63- Soil scientist to Greece, Italy & Sicily, UN Relief & Rehab. Admin, 46-47; Kaiser Engrs, Ghana, W.Africa, Ivory Coast, 63-64; Int. Eng. Co-Peru, partner & dir, Agriconsult, 64-67; consult, Eng. Consult, Inc, Jamaica & Turkey, 66-67; Food & Agr. Orgn, UN, Jordan, Yugoslavia, Nigeria, Uruguay, Panama, 67-69; Int. Develop. Serv, Inc, Uruguay, 70-71. Mem. subcomt. South. Great Plains, President's Nat. Resources Bd, 28. Nat. Guard, 22-24. Hon. mem, Am. Soc. Agron; Soil Sci. Soc. Am; fel. Soil Conserv. Soc. Am; Am. Soc. Agr. Consult; Int. Soc. Soil Sci; Am. Soc. Agr. Eng; fel. Am. Inst. Chem. Soil-plant-climate interrelationships affecting land and water resource development and resource conservation; research, program planning and administration. Address: 1604 Prospect Lane, Ft. Collins, CO 80521.

FLY, LILLIAN BEAMAN, b. Waco, Tex, June 27, 15. IMMUNOLOGY, BACTERIOLOGY. B.A, Tex. Woman's Univ, 37; univ. fel, Univ. Miami, 47-48, M.S, 49; L.I. Biol. Labs, 52; Nat. Sci. Found. summer grant, Univ. N.C, 59. Asst. instr. bact, Univ. Miami, 48-49, instr, 49-52, asst. prof. bact. & bot, 52-66, chief archivist, 66-71; RETIRED. Chief investr, Charles Wrightsman grant, 52-53, E.L. Cotton grant, 54-58; invitational speaker, S.Am. Cong. Bot, 58; Nat. Res. Found. grant, 63-66. AAAS; Am. Soc. Microbiol; N.Y. Acad. Sci; Int. Oceanog. Found. Palynology of cores of fresh water lakes of Florida. Address: 4060 Battersea Rd, Miami, FL 33133.

FLYGARE, WILLIS H, b. Jackson, Minn, July 24, 36; m. 58; c. 4. CHEMICAL PHYSICS. B.A, St. Olaf Col, 58; Calif. Res. Corp. fel, California, Berkeley, 59, Shell Oil Co. fel, 60, Gen. Elec. fel, 61, Ph.D.(chem), 61. Asst. CHEM, Univ. Calif, Berkeley, 58-59; instr, UNIV. ILL, URBANA, 61-63, asst. prof; 63-65, assoc. prof, 65-66, PROF, 66- Sloan fel, 64-68; Guggenheim fel, 71. Fel. Am. Phys. Soc; Am. Chem. Soc; Faraday Soc. Theoretical molecular structure; small electric and magnetic interactions; microwave and infrared spectroscopy; light scattering; radio astronomy. Address: Noyes Chemistry Lab, Dept. of Chemistry, University of Illinois at Urbana, Urbana, IL 61801.

FLYGER, VAGN F(OLKMANN), b. Aalborg, Denmark, Jan. 14, 22; nat; m. 46; c. 2. ZOOLOGY. B.S, Cornell, 48; M.S, Pa. State, 52; Sc.D, Hopkins, 56. Game biologist, Md. Dept. Res. & Ed, 48-51; wildlife res, Md. Game & Inland Fish Dept, 54-55; sr. biologist, inland res. div, Md. Dept. Res. & Ed, 55-61; res. assoc. prof, NATURAL RESOURCES INST, UNIV. MD, 61-67, RES. PROF, 67-, CHMN. DEPT. FORESTRY, FISH & WILDLIFE, 71-, acting dir, 64-65. Med.C, 43-46, Sgt. AAAS; Am. Soc. Mammal; Wildlife Soc; Ecol. Soc. Am. Mammal behavior; factors influencing animal populations and especially biology of tree squirrels. Address: Natural Resources Institute, H.J. Patterson Hall, University of Maryland, College Park, MD 20740.

FLYNN, ARTHUR D(AVIS), b. Sulligent, Ala, Sept. 8, 30; m. 52; c. 2. ENTOMOLOGY. B.S, Auburn, 52, M.S, 56, Ph.D.(entom), 59. Asst. scientist, COMMUNICABLE DISEASE CTR, U.S. PUB. HEALTH SERV, 59-64, scientist, 64-66, SR. SCIENTIST, 66- U.S.N, 52-54, Lt.(jg). AAAS; Entom. Soc. Am; Am. Chem. Soc. Animal systemics; arthropods of medical importance; apiculture; insect toxicology. Address: Communicable Disease Center, U.S. Public Health Service, Savannah, GA 31402.

FLYNN, CARL M(UNRO), b. New Haven, Conn, Feb. 26, 07; m. 35; c. 4. ZOOLOGY. B.A, Maine, 30; M.A, Wesleyan, 32; M.A, Harvard, 39, Ph.D. (biol, zool), 40. Asst. zool, Maine, 29-30, instr, 33-36; asst. biol, Wesleyan, 30-32; Radcliffe Col, 37-39; instr, Suffolk, 39-40; ZOOL, UNIV. MAINE, ORONO, 40-45, asst. prof, 45-48, assoc. prof, 48-60, PROF, 60-, ASST. DEAN, COL. ARTS & SCI, 60- AAAS; assoc. Am. Soc. Zool.

Embryology; chick embryos; life history studies of potato aphids; insecticide control of potato aphids. Address: Dept. of Zoology, University of Maine at Orono, Orono, ME 04473.

FLYNN, C(HARLES) E(DWARD), b. Pittsfield, Mass, Apr. 23, 24; m. 46; c. 4. CHEMISTRY, FOOD TECHNOLOGY. B.S, Massachusetts, 49, M.S, 50. Assoc. technologist, cent. labs, Gen. Foods Corp, 50-54, proj. leader, 54-56, sect. head, Jell-o Res. Lab, 56-59, asst. to res. mgr, Jell-o div, 59-60, res. planning coord, Jell-o Div, 60-62, corp. res, 62-67, lab. mgr. develop, 62-67, tech. develop. assoc, GEN. FOODS INT, 67-69, TECH. DEVELOP. MGR, 69- U.S.A, 43-46. Am. Asn. Cereal Chem; Inst. Food Technol. Product development. Address: General Foods International, 250 North St, White Plains, NY 10602.

FLYNN, CHARLES MILTON, JR, b. Norwalk, Conn, Feb. 28, 40. INORGANIC & STRUCTURAL CHEMISTRY. B.S, Calif. Inst. Technol, 62; Nat. Sci. Found. fel, Univ. Ill, Urbana, 63-64, Ph.D.(inorg. chem), 67. Asst. prof. gen. chem, La Verne Col, 67-68; RES. ASSOC. INORG. CHEM, GEORGETOWN UNIV, 68- Am. Chem. Soc. Preparation and characterization of heteropoly complexes and other inorganic complexes; crystal structure determinations; lattice energies and solubilities of ionic compounds. Address: Dept. of Chemistry, Georgetown University, Washington, DC 20007.

FLYNN, COLIN PETER, b. Stockton-on-Tees, Eng, Aug. 18, 35; m. 61, 71; c. 1. SOLID STATE PHYSICS. B.Sc, Univ. Leeds, 57, Ph.D.(physics), 60; M.A, Cambridge, 66. Res. assoc. PHYSICS, UNIV. ILL, URBANA, 60-62, res. asst. prof, 62-64, asst. prof, 64-65, assoc. prof, 65-68, PROF, 68- Fel, Christ's Col, Cambridge, 66-67; consult, Atomic Energy Res. Estab, Eng, summer, 71. Fel. Am. Phys. Soc. Impurities and thermal defect structure in crystals; impurity magnetism and nuclear magnetic resonance in metals; diffusive hopping of ions and electrons in crystals; kinetics of defect equilibration. Address: Dept. of Physics & Materials Research Lab, University of Illinois, Urbana, IL 61801.

FLYNN, EDWARD ROBERT, b. Joliet, Ill, July 7, 34; m. 54; c. 6. PHYSICS. B.S, Illinois, 56; M.S, New Mexico, 64, Ph.D.(physics), 66. Accelerator engr, Illinois, 56-58; MEM. STAFF, LOS ALAMOS SCI. LAB, 58- NATO fel, Niels Bohr Inst, Copenhagen, 70-71. Am. Phys. Soc. Nuclear physics. Address: Los Alamos Scientific Lab, P.O. Box 1663, Los Alamos, NM 87544.

FLYNN, EDWIN H(AROLD), b. Dunlap, Iowa, Aug. 16, 20; m. 45; c. 3. BIO-ORGANIC CHEMISTRY. B.S, Nebraska, 44; fel, Illinois, 46-49, Ph.D.(biochem), 49. Asst. bact, Nebraska, 42-44; res. chemist, Merck & Co, 44-46; ELI LILLY & CO, 49-58, res. assoc, 58-66, RES. ADV, 66- Am. Chem. Soc; Am. Soc. Biol. Chem. Antibiotics; growth factors; bacterial polysaccharides; infectious disease processes; natural immunity. Address: 6512 Landborough Dr. S. Indianapolis, IN 46220.

FLYNN, GEORGE P(ATRICK), b. Fall River, Mass, Aug. 12, 36. PHYSICAL CHEMISTRY. B.S, Providence Col, 57; Ph.D.(phys. chem), Brown, 62. Res. asst. chem, Yale, 61-63; res. assoc, Brown Univ, 64-67; Mass. Inst. Technol, 67-70. Am. Chem. Soc. Viscosity of gases and other transport properties; statistical mechanics; science writing; textbook editing. Address: 27 Sowamsett Ave, Warren, RI 02885.

FLYNN, GEORGE WILLIAM, b. Hartford, Conn, July 11, 38; m. 70. CHEMICAL PHYSICS. B.S, Yale, 60; Nat. Sci. Found. fel, Harvard, 60-64, A.M. & Ph.D.(chem), 64. Fel. physics, Mass. Inst. Tech, 64-66; ASST. PROF. CHEM, COLUMBIA UNIV, 67- Nat. Sci. Found. fel, 64-65; Alfred P. Sloan fel, 68-71. Am. Phys. Soc; Am. Chem. Soc. Relaxation phenomena in molecular systems; development and uses of optical masers; laser temperature-jump kinetic studies. Address: Dept. of Chemistry, 315 Havemeyer Hall, Columbia University, New York, NY 10027.

FLYNN, GORDON LEONARD, b. Aug. 21, 36; U.S. citizen; m. 61; c. 3. PHYSICAL PHARMACY. B.S, Rutgers, 60; Ph.D.(phys. pharm), Wisconsin, 65. RES. ASSOC. PHARM. RES, UPJOHN CO, 65- Am. Chem. Soc; Am. Pharmaceut. Asn. Applications of physical chemistry to pharmaceutical systems; chemical kinetics, particularly solvolysis of organic phosphates; percutaneous absorption; membrane transport; physico-chemical basis for structure and biological activity profiles; diffusional models for drug availability. Address: The Upjohn Co, Dept. 7271, Kalamazoo, MI 49001.

FLYNN, GREGORY, JR, b. Newark, N.J, June 10, 18; m. 44; c. 3. MECHANICAL ENGINEERING. B.S, Gen. Motors Inst, 41. Jr. engr, RES. LAB, GEN. MOTORS CORP, 41-43, res. engr, 43-44, 46-50, sr. engr, 50-53, asst. dept. head, 53-57, head dept. mech. develop, 57-58, HEAD SPEC. PROJ. DEPT, 68- U.S.N.R, 44-46. N.Y. Acad. Sci; Soc. Automotive Eng. Diesel engines; internal combustion engines; stirling cycle engines; bearings; hydrodynamic lubrication; seals. Address: Research Lab, General Motors Corp, 12 Mile & Mound Rds, Warren, MI 48090.

FLYNN, HUGH G(UTHRIE), b. Lancaster, Ohio, Dec. 8, 12; m. 60; c. 3. PHYSICS. B.A, Ohio State, 39; M.S, Rensselaer Polytech, 46; M.A, Harvard, 50, Ph.D.(appl. physics), 56. Tech. aide cmt. undersea warfare, Nat. Res. Coun, 47-48; asst, Harvard, 50-56, res. fel. acoust, 56-60, dep. dir. acoust. res. lab, 58-60; assoc. prof. elec. eng, UNIV. ROCHESTER, 60-68, PROF. ELEC. ENG. & ASSOC. DEAN COL. ENG. & APPL. SCI, 68-, acting chmn. dept. elec. eng, 69-71. U.S.N.R, 42-47, Lt. Comdr. Am. Phys. Soc; fel. Acoust. Soc. Am. Applied physics; cavitation phenomena in liquids; ocean and atmospheric acoustics. Address: Dept. of Electrical Engineering, University of Rochester, Rochester, NY 14627.

FLYNN, JAMES P(ATRICK), b. Wilkes Barre, Pa, Aug. 1, 24; m. 54; c. 3. PHYSICAL & INORGANIC CHEMISTRY. B.S, Bucknell, 48; Atomic Energy Cmn. fel. & Ph.D.(chem), Iowa State, 53. Res. engr, Battelle Mem. Inst, 48-49; asst, Ames Lab, Atomic Energy Cmn, 49-53; res. & develop. engr, magnesium dept, DOW CHEM. CO, 53-58, res. chemist, sci. proj. lab, 58-67, PROJ. LEADER, PROD. DEPT. LABS, 67- Am. Chem. Soc; Sci. Res. Soc. Am; Am. Soc. Test. & Mat. Magnesium alloy and recovery of metals; propellant testing and compatibility; evaluation of chemical hazards; hazardous waste disposal. Address: Product Dept. Labs, The Dow Chemical Co, Midland, MI 48640.

FLYNN, JOHN BERNARD, b. Boston, Mass, Sept. 16, 27; m. 57; c. 3. PHYSICAL CHEMISTRY. B.S, Boston Col, 51, M.S, 52; Ph.D.(phys. chem), Mass. Inst. Tech, 56. Adv. develop. engr, Sylvania Elec. Prod, Inc. Div, Gen. Tel. & Electronics Corp, 56-61; prin. develop. engr, HONEYWELL RADIATION CTR, 61-66, res. supvr, 66-71, SR. PRIN. RES. SCIENTIST, 71- U.S.N.R, 45-46. Am. Chem. Soc; Electrochem. Soc. Solid state chemistry; semiconductor devices. Address: Honeywell Radiation Center, 2 Forbes Rd, Lexington, MA 02173.

FLYNN, J(OHN) E(DWARD), b. Springfield, Mass, Oct. 11, 22; m. 51; c. 5. ENTOMOLOGY. B.S, Massachusetts, 49; M.S, Cornell, 52; Ph.D, N.C. State Univ, 67. Asst. entomol, Cornell, 49-51; asst. entomologist, United Fruit Co, 51-54; instr. biol, N.Y. Mil. Acad, 54-56; asst. entomol, N.C. State Col, 56-59; asst. prof. BIOL, ALBANY COL. PHARM, UNION UNIV. (N.Y), 59-67, ASSOC. PROF, 67- U.S. Merchant Marine, 42-46. Address: Albany College of Pharmacy, Union University, New Scotland Ave, Albany, NY 12208.

FLYNN, JOHN JOSEPH, JR, b. Salida, Colo, Sept. 16, 31. ORGANIC CHEMISTRY. B.A, West. State Col. Colo, 53; M.S, Okla. State, 55; Ph.D.(chem), Purdue, 61. ASSOC. PROF. CHEM, PURDUE UNIV. FT. WAYNE, 58- Nat. Sci. Found. res. participation grant, Colorado, summers 65-66. Am. Chem. Soc. Organic sulfur chemistry; Diels-Alder reaction. Address: Dept. of Chemistry, Purdue University at Ft. Wayne, 2101 Coliseum Blvd. E, Ft. Wayne, IN 46805.

FLYNN, JOHN M(ATHEW), b. Cleveland, Ohio, Dec. 9, 29; m. 54; c. 7. CHEMICAL ENGINEERING. B.S.Ch.E, Case, 51, Heil fel, 52-53, M.S.Ch.E, 53, Ph.D, 56. Instr, Case, 51-52, asst, 52, res. assoc, 53-56; proj. leader, high pressure lab, DOW CHEM. CO, 56-60, lab. dir, 60-63, prod. supt, pelaspan, 63-66, sales mgr. chlorine based polymers, 66-67, bus. mgr, 67, MGR. RES. & DEVELOP, PLASTICS DEPT, 67- Am. Chem. Soc; Sci. Res. Soc. Am; Soc. Plastics Eng; Soc. Plastics Indust. Plastics technology; polyolefins and polystyrene. Address: Plastics Dept, Dow Chemical Co, 2040 Bldg, Dow Center, Midland, MI 48640.

FLYNN, JOSEPH H(ENRY), b. Washington, D.C, Oct. 28, 22; m. 52; c. 9. PHYSICAL CHEMISTRY. B.S, Georgetown, 43; Ph.D.(phys. chem), Catholic Univ, 54. Asst, Catholic Univ, 46-50; RES. CHEMIST, NAT. BUR. STANDARDS, 52- C.W.S, U.S.A, 43-46. AAAS; Am. Chem. Soc. Thermal analysis; polymer degradation; chemical kinetics; photochemistry and radiation chemistry of polymers. Address: 5309 Iroquois Rd, Washington, DC 20016.

FLYNN, KENNETH G, b. Hartford, Conn, Dec. 25, 33; m. 56; c. 3. ORGANIC CHEMISTRY. B.A, Univ. Conn, 55; M.S, Temple Univ, 59; Am-Scand. fel, Univ. Uppsala, 63-64; Phil. Lic.(org. chem), 65. Chemist, Houdry Process Corp, Pa, 58-59; res. chemist, cent. res, Am. Cyanamid Co, 59-65, asst. prod. mgr, pigments div, 65-66; prod. mgr, 66-69; dir. mkt. dyes & pigments, Am. Hoechst Corp, 69; V.PRES. PIGMENT MKT, SYNERGISTIC PIGMENTS CORP, BOUND BROOK, 69- AAAS; Am. Chem. Soc; Swed. Chem. Soc. Kinetics and mechanism of isocyanate-alcohol reaction; strong amine bases; organophosphines, reactions and preparation; organometallics; rearrangements of dihydroanthracenes; kinetics and mechanism. Address: 703 Donald Dr. S, Somerville, NJ 08876.

FLYNN, LAURA M(ARY), b. Postville, Iowa, Sept. 8, 97. AGRICULTURAL CHEMISTRY. B.S, Iowa State Col, 23, M.S, 27; Ph.D.(biochem), Washington (St. Louis), 50. Teacher, pub. sch, Iowa, 23-25; asst. chem, Iowa State Col, 25-28, 31-32; instr. sci. & foods, Frances Shimer Jr. Col, 28-31, 32-34; asst. home econ, Illinois, 34-35; instr. nutrit, Huntingdon Col, 35-36; dietetics & sci, Rochester Mech. Inst, 36-38; foods & nutrit, Stephens Col, 38-39; asst. biochem. div, Washington (St. Louis), 39-41; instr. foods & nutrit, Hood Col, 41-42; agr. chem, Univ. Mo-Columbia, 42-46, asst. prof. 46-54, assoc. prof, 54-68; RETIRED. AAAS; Am. Dietetic Asn; Am. Chem. Soc. Effect on environmental conditions on nutrients in foods and feeds; vitamin assay; bacterial nutrition and physiology; amino acid assay and amino acids in nutrition. Address: 611 Lee St, Columbia, MO 65201.

FLYNN, MARGARET ALBERI, b. Hurley, Wis, Nov. 22, 15; m. 38; c. 2. NUTRITION. B.S, Col. St. Catherine, 37; M.S, Iowa, 38; Ph.D.(nutrit), Missouri, Columbia, 66. Instr. nutrit, Col. St. Catherine, 38-39; res. asst. pediat, Iowa City Med. Center, 39-40; teaching dietitian, Levi Mem. Hosp, Hot Springs, Ark, 42-46 & Holy Name Hosp, Teaneck, N.J, 50-54; res. asst. pediat, UNIV. MO. MED. CTR, 61-63, ASSOC. PROF. NUTRIT, 66- Dipl, Am. Bd. Nutrit. Am. Dietetic Asn; Am. Inst. Nutrit; Am. Soc. Clin. Nutrit. Dietetics; body composition. Address: 1121 S. Glenwood Ave, Columbia, MO 65201.

FLYNN, MICHAEL J, b. N.Y.C, May 20, 34; m. 57; c. 4. COMPUTER SCIENCE, ELECTRICAL ENGINEERING. B.S, Manhattan Col, 55; M.S, Syracuse Univ, 60; Ph.D.(elec. eng), Purdue Univ, 61. Engr. & mgr, IBM Corp, 55-65; assoc. prof. systs. eng, Univ. Ill, Chicago Circle, 65-66; indust. & elec. eng, Northwest. Univ, 66-70; PROF. COMPUT. SCI, JOHNS HOPKINS UNIV, 70- Instr, Purdue Univ, 59-61; consult, IBM Corp, 65-68; Argonne Nat. Lab, 65-; pres, Recursive Sci, N.Y, 68-69; consult, U.S. Dept. Defense, 69-; Raytheon Co, 70-; lectr, prog. advan. study, Bolt, Beranek & Newman, 65-70; Univ. Mich, summer 70-; Inst. Res. Info. & Automation, Paris, summer 71; mem. adv. comt. data processing for antiballistic missile defense, Nat. Acad. Sci, 71- AAAS; Asn. Comput. Mach; Inst. Elec. & Electronics Eng. Organization of computer systems; models and analyses of programs and system arrangements; algorithms for optimal performance of arithmetic and storage operations; organization of microprogrammed systems. Address: Dept. of Computer Science, Johns Hopkins University, Baltimore, MD 21218.

FLYNN, P(AUL) D(AVID), b. Baltimore, Md, Oct. 23, 26. MECHANICS. B.E, Hopkins, 48, M.S.E, 50; Res. Corp. fel, Ill. Inst. Tech, 51-54, Ph.D.(mech), 54. Inst. mech. eng, Hopkins, 48-51; engr, Gen. Elec. Co, 54-59; assoc. prof. mech, Ill. Inst. Tech, 59-62; RES. PHYSICIST, FRANKFORD ARSENAL, 62-, consult, 60-62. Army Res. & Develop. Achievement Award, 65. U.S.N, 45-46. Am. Soc. Mech. Eng; Soc. Exp. Stress Anal; Soc. Photo Optical Instrument. Eng.(Fairbanks Mem. Award, 64); Soc. Motion Picture &

TV Eng; Sci. Res. Soc. Am. Photoelasticity; experimental stress analysis; high speed photography. Address: Frankford Arsenal, Pitman-Dunn Lab, Philadelphia, PA 19137.

FLYNN, ROBERT J(AMES), b. Chicago, Ill, Jan. 8, 23; m. 42; c. 6. VETERINARY MEDICINE. D.V.M, Mich. State Univ, 44. Supvr. animal facilities, ARGONNE NAT. LAB, 48-55, assoc. veterinarian, 48-66, ASST. DIR. DIV. BIOL. & MED RES, 62-, SR. VETERINARIAN, 66- Consult, Pan-Am. Health Orgn, 56-62; secy-treas, Am. Col. Lab. Animal Sci, 56-62, pres, 63; mem. adv. coun, Inst. Lab. Animal Resources, Nat. Acad. Sci-Nat. Res. Coun, 57-64; adv. bd. vet. specialties, Am. Vet. Med. Asn, 60-66, sci. prog. comt, 70-; consult, Nat. Insts. Health, 60-; biomed. res. found, Am. Med. Asn, 64-66; mem. coun. accreditation, Am. Asn. Accreditation Lab. Animal Care, 64-66, consult, 64-; Vet. Admin, 64-; mem, Nat. Res. Coun, 67-70, comt. vet. med. res. & educ, 68-71; Nat. Insts. Health Adult Develop. & Aging Res. & Training Comt, 70- Dipl, Am. Col. Lab. Animal Med, 57. A.U.S, 42-44. AAAS; Am. Asn. Lab. Animal Sci.(secy-treas, 53-62, pres, 64, Griffin Award, 68, Robert J. Flynn Award, 69); Radiation Res. Soc; Am. Vet. Med. Asn; Am. Asn. Zoo Vets; Am. Soc. Lab. Animal Practitioners; Asn. Gnotobiotics; Conf. Res. Workers Animal Diseases; Soc. Exp. Biol. & Med; U.S. Animal Health Asn; Wildlife Disease Asn; Ger. Soc. Lab. Animal Sci; Int. Asn. Aquatic Animal Med. Laboratory animal medicine; aging. Address: Division of Biological & Medical Research, Argonne National Lab, 9700 S. Cass Ave, Argonne, IL 60439.

FLYNN, ROBERT W, b. Brooklyn, N.Y, July 26, 34; m. 59; c. 3. PLASMA PHYSICS. B.S, U.S. Naval Acad, 58; U.S. Atomic Energy Comn. fel, Mass. Inst. Technol, 62-64, S.M, 65, Sc.D.(nuclear eng), 68. ASST. PROF. PHYSICS, UNIV. S.FLA, 68- U.S.N.R, Lt. Comdr. Am. Phys. Soc; Am. Asn. Physics Teachers. Large amplitude plasma waves; plasma mode coupling; plasma turbulence. Address: Dept. of Physics, University of South Florida, Tampa, FL 33620.

FLYNN, T(HOMAS) F(RANCIS), b. New Haven, Conn, Feb. 27, 27; m. 50; c. 6. ELECTRICAL ENGINEERING. B.E, Yale, 50, M.E, 51. Engr, PERKIN-ELMER CORP, 51-56, group leader, 56-60, chief engr, 60-69, DIR. ENG, INSTRUMENT DIV, 70- Lectr, Connecticut, 55-57. U.S.N, 45-46. Optical Soc. Am; Inst. Elec. & Electronics Eng. Scientific instrument development. Address: 38 Big Oak Circle, Stamford, CT 06903.

FLYNN, THOMAS GEOFFREY, b. Ystradgynlais, Wales, Feb. 20, 37; m. 61; c. 2. BIOCHEMISTRY. B.Sc, Univ. Wales, 60, M.Sc, 62, fel, 63-65, Ph.D. (biochem), 66. Res. asst. clin. chem, med. unit, Royal Infirmary, Cardiff, Wales, 60-62; fel. BIOCHEM, Univ. Col, Cardiff, 66-67; fel. & lectr, Queen's Univ.(Ont), 67-69; ASST. PROF, QUEEN'S UNIV.(ONT), 69- Del, NATO Conf. Protein Struct. & Function, Venice, Italy, 70. R.N.V.R, 56-57. Am. Chem. Soc; Brit. Biochem. Soc; Can. Biochem. Soc. Structure of enzymes in relation to their function, especially phosphoglyceromutase, glycerol dehydrogenase and glycerokinase. Address: Dept. of Biochemistry, Queen's University, Kingston, Ont, Can.

FLYNN, THOMAS M(URRAY), b. Huntsville, Tex, July 19, 33; m. 58; c. 3. CHEMICAL ENGINEERING. B.A, Rice Inst, 54, B.S, 55; M.S, Colorado, 56, Shell Oil fel, 57-58, Ph.D.(chem. eng), 58. Asst. explor. res, Magnolia Petrol. Co, 51-52; process engr. catalytic cracking, Shell Oil Co, 53-54; instr. chem. eng, Colorado, 55-58; proj. leader, cryogenic eng. labs, Nat. Bur. Standards, 56-61; mgr. cryogenic res. & develop, Bendix Corp, 61-63; chief cryogenic metrol. sect, NAT. BUR. STANDARDS, 63-66, sr. scientist for impact anal, inst. mat. res, 66-68, chief prog. coord. off, inst. basic standards, 68-70, COORD. PROG. PROMOTION, 70- Nat. Sci. Found. lectr, 64; lectr, Univ. Colo, 64- Am. Inst. Chem. Eng; Sci. Res. Soc. Am. Cryogenic engineering; physical equilibria of cryogenic fluids; cryogenic instrumentation. Address: Room 401A, National Bureau of Standards, Washington, DC 20234.

FLYNT, EDWARD R(EID), b. Powelton, Ga, April 19, 15; m. 53; c. 2. ELECTRICAL ENGINEERING. B.S, Ga. Inst. Tech, 39, M.S, 53. Engr, Ala. Power Co, 35-41, 45-48; res. engr, ENG. EXP. STA, GA. INST. TECHNOL, 48-53, spec. res. engr, 53-65, asst, 48-49, PRIN. RES. ENGR, 65- Sig.C.Res, 39-; U.S.A, 41-45, Lt. Col. Sr. mem. Inst. Elec. & Electronics Eng. Electronic instrumentation; radar reflection; radar systems. Address: 1475 N. Amanda Circle N.E, Atlanta, GA 30329.

FLYNT, WILLIAM E(DWARD), b. Ft. Worth, Tex, Oct. 28, 31; m. 56; c. 4. APPLIED PHYSICS. B.S, Texas, 54, M.A, 55, Ph.D.(physics), 58. Sr. engr, Autonetics Div, N.Am. Aviation, Inc, Calif, 58-60; RES. SCIENTIST, VARO, INC, 60- Optical Soc. Am. Applied research in electro-optical instruments; microwave plasma physics; thin-film microcircuits; applied research in image tubes. Address: 1722 Iroquois Dr, Garland, TX 75041.

FOA, J(OSEPH) V(ICTOR), b. Turin, Italy, July 10, 09; nat. 44; m. 42; c. 4. AERONAUTICAL ENGINEERING. Ph.D.(mech. eng), Turin, 31; Italian Air Ministry fel, Rome, 32-33, Ph.D.(aeronaut. eng), 33. From res. engr. to proj. engr, Piaggio Aircraft Co, Italy, 33-35, 37-39; chief engr, Studi Caproni, 35-37; proj. engr, Bellanca Aircraft Corp, Del, 39-50; instr. aeronaut. eng, Minnesota, 40-42; chief engr, Am. Aero-Marine Indust, Inc, Mass, 42-43; head design res, Curtiss-Wright Corp, N.Y, 42-45; head propulsion br, Cornell Aeronaut. Lab, 45-52; prof. aeronaut. eng, Rensselaer Polytech. Inst, 52-58, head dept, aeronaut. eng. & astronaut, 58-67; PROF. ENG. & APPL. SCI, GEORGE WASH. UNIV, 70- Fluid mechanics; propulsion; transportation. Address: Division of Engineering & Applied Science, George Washington University, Washington, DC 20006.

FOA, PIERO P(IO), b. Torino, Italy, Apr. 13, 11; nat; m. 41; c. 2. PHYSIOLOGY. M.D, Milan, 34, Ph.D.(chem), 38. Instr. biochem, Milan, 34-36; asst. prof. physiol, Pavia, 36-38; Mendelson fel. surg, Michigan, 39-42, fel. med, 42-43; asst. prof. PHYSIOL. & PHARMACOL, Chicago Med. Sch, 42-45, assoc. prof, 45-51, PROF, 51-61; COL. MED, WAYNE STATE UNIV, 61-; CHMN. DEPT. RES. & MEM. ATTEND. STAFF, SINAI HOSP. DETROIT, 61- AAAS; Am. Physiol. Soc; Soc. Exp. Biol. & Med; Endocrine Soc; Am. Diabetes Asn; Am. Fedn. Clin. Res. Arterial hypertension; metabolism of thiamine; choline deficiency; functional innervation of the bone marrow; metabolism of lactic and pyruvic acids; glucagon; insulin; prolactin; oral antidiabetic drugs. Address: Sinai Hospital of Detroit, 6767 W. Outer Dr, Detroit, MI 48235.

FOARD, DONALD E(DWARD), b. Alexandria, Va, Dec. 17, 29; m. 55; c. 3. BOTANY. B.A, Virginia, 52, M.A, 54; South. fels. fund fel, N.C. State Col, 56, Nat. Cancer Inst. fel, 58, Ph.D, 60. Asst. bot, Longwood Col, 54-56; asst. prof, Tennessee, 59-60; California, Los Angeles, 60-63; BIOLOGIST, OAK RIDGE NAT. LAB, 63- Am. Soc. Plant Physiol; Bot. Soc. Am. Morphogenesis; morphology; anatomy. Address: Biology Division, Oak Ridge National Lab, Oak Ridge, TN 37831.

FOBES, MELCHER P(RINCE), b. Portland, Maine, Sept. 18, 11; m. 42. MATHEMATICS. A.B, Bowdoin Col, 32; A.M, Harvard, 33, Ph.D.(math), 47; Chicago, 39-40. Instr. MATH, Harvard, 34-37; Bryn Mawr Col, 38-39; COL. OF WOOSTER, 40-43, asst. prof, 43-47, PROF, 47-, HEAD DEPT, 48- Math. Asn. Am. Topology; a conjectured inequality related to the product of Lipschitz Skeleton Cochains. Address: College of Wooster, Wooster, OH 44691.

FOCELLA, ANTONINO, b. Baucina, Italy, Dec. 11, 24; U.S. citizen; m. 55; c. 4. CHEMISTRY. Ph.D.(org. chem, biochem), Univ. Palermo, 55. Instr, Univ. Palermo, 52-55; anal. res. chemist, Pepsi Cola Co, 57-59; SR. ORG. RES. CHEMIST, HOFFMANN-LA ROCHE, INC, 60- Italian Army. Am. Chem. Soc. Food chemistry; pharmaceutical chemistry; natural products. Address: Chemical Research Dept, Hoffmann-La Roche, Inc, Bldg. 86, Lab. 918, Nutley, NJ 07110.

FOCHT, DENNIS D(OUGLASS), b. West Reading, Pa, Aug. 30, 41; m. 66. MICROBIOLOGY, SOIL SCIENCE. B.S, Rutgers Univ, 63; U.S. Pub. Health Serv. fel. & M.S, Iowa State Univ, 65, U.S. Pub. Health Serv. fel. & Ph.D. (bact), 68. Fel. microbiol, Cornell Univ, 68-70; ASST. PROF. SOIL MICROBIOL, UNIV. CALIF, RIVERSIDE, 70-, ASST. MICROBIOLOGIST, CITRUS RES. EXP. STA, 70- Proj. leader, West. Regional Res. Comt. on nitrogen in environ, 70- Am. Soc. Microbiol; Am. Soc. Agron. Microbial metabolism of environmental contaminants; microbial ecology; soil microbiology. Address: Dept. of Soil Science & Agricultural Engineering, University of California, Riverside, CA 92502.

FOCKE, ALFRED B(OSWORTH), b. Cleveland, Ohio, Sept. 30. 06; m. 28, 44; c. 6. PHYSICS. B.S, Case, 28; Ph.D.(physics), Calif. Inst. Tech, 32. Fel, Calif. Inst. Tech, 32-33; Nat. Res. fel, Yale, 33-34; instr. physics, Brown, 34-38, asst. prof, 38-45; head res. div, Navy Radio & Sound Lab, 45-46; sr. consult, Navy Electronics Lab, 46-52; head systems div, 52-53, assoc. tech. dir. res, 53; res. physicist & dir. marine phys. lab, Scripps Inst, California, 54-59; prof. PHYSICS, HARVEY MUDD COL, 59-71, SR. PROF, 71- Tech. dir, Pac. missile range, Naval Missile Ctr, 58-59; sci. dir, Off. Naval Res, London, 68-70; WIGWAM, U.S. Dept. Defense; mem. mine adv. cmt, Nat. Acad. Sci-Nat. Res. Coun. Meritorious civilian serv. Awards, 45, 53. Contract physicist, bur. ord, Navy Dept, 40-43, prin. physicist, 43-45. AAAS; fel. Am. Phys. Soc; fel. Acoust. Soc. Am; Am. Inst. Aeronaut. & Astronaut; Seismol. Soc. Am; Am. Geophys. Union; Inst. Elec. & Electronics Eng. Geophysics; properties of crystals; underwater ordnance; sound propagation; general electronics. Address: 550 W. 12th St, Claremont, CA 91711.

FOCKE, ARTHUR E(LDRIDGE), b. Cleveland, Ohio, June 17, 04; m. 29, 68. METALLURGY. B.Met.E, Ohio State, 25, M.S, 26, Ph.D.(metall), 28. Metallurgist, Cleveland Wire Div, Gen. Elec. Co, 27-29; chief engr, P.R. Mallory & Co, 29-30; res. metallurgist, Diamond Chain & Mfg. Co, 30-45, chief metallurgist, 45-51; mgr. mat. develop, aircraft nuclear power dept, Gen. Elec. Co, 51-61; assoc. prof. METALL. ENG, UNIV. CINCINNATI, 62-71, PROF, 71-; PRES, A.E. FOCKE CORP, 63- Bur. Standards fel. Am. Soc. Metals (pres, 50); Am. Soc. Test. & Mat; Am. Inst. Mining, Metall. & Petrol. Eng; Am. Nuclear Soc; Am. Soc. Eng. Educ; Brit. Iron & Steel Inst. Mechanical metallurgy; wear and fatigue; factors influencing the quality of tungsten incandescent lamp filaments; selection and development of materials for aircraft nuclear power plants. Address: 7799 E. Galbraith Rd, Cincinnati, OH 45243.

FODDEN, JOHN H(ENRY), b. Halifax, Eng, June 16, 18; m. 42; c. 6. PATHOLOGY. M.B. & Ch.B, Univ. Leeds, 41, M.D, 46; Royal Col. Physicians Can. fel, 56. Asst. path, Leeds, 41-44; asst. clin. pathologist, Royal Hosp, Sheffield, 45-46; asst. prof. path, Liverpool, 46-48; assoc. prof. Dalhousie, 48-52; med. sch, South Dakota, 52-57; assoc. dir. labs, Mt. Sinai Hosp, 57-60; DIR. LABS, MANITOWOC COUNTY HOSPS, 60- Registrar, Cancer Control Orgn, Radium Inst, 46-48; markle Found. Scholar, South Dakota, 51-56, Lederle Med. Faculty award scholar, 56-57. AAAS; Am. Soc. Exp. Path; Am. Soc. Clin. Path. Am. Asn. Path. & Bact; fel. Col. Am. Path. Etiologic and pathogenetic factors in peptic ulceration; hormonal factors in abnormal carbohydrate metabolism; clinical and experimental pathology. Address: Dept. of Pathology, Memorial Hospital, 333 Reed Ave, Manitowoc, WI 54220.

FODERARO, A(NTHONY) (HAROLDE), b. Scranton, Pa, Apr. 3, 26; m; c. 3. PHYSICS. B.S, Scranton, 50; Ph.D.(physics), Pittsburgh, 56. Asst. physics, Scranton, 48-49; Pittsburgh, 49-52; sr. scientist, atomic power div, Westinghouse Elec. Corp, 54, supvy. scientist radiation anal, 54-56; sr. nuclear physicist, res. labs, Gen. Motors Corp, 56-60; assoc. prof. NUCLEAR ENG, PA. STATE UNIV, 60-63, PROF, 63- Consult, Westinghouse Elec. Corp, 60-; Allison Div, Gen. Motors, 61-; HRB-Singer, Inc, & Nuclear Utility Serv, 62- U.S.A, 43-46. Am. Phys. Soc; Am. Nuclear Soc; Am. Asn. Physics Teachers. Reactor and upper atmosphere physics; radiation transport, effects and safety; nonlinear reactor kinetics; microscopic interaction theory. Address: Dept. of Nuclear Engineering, 231 Sackett Bldg, Pennsylvania State University, University Park, PA 16802.

FODOR, ANDREW R(OBERT), b. Hungary, Apr. 3, 10; nat; m. 57; c. 1. MICROBIOLOGY. B.A, N.Y. Univ, 36, M.S, 39, Ph.D.(microbiol), 54. Instr. microbiol, col. pharm, Columbia, 46-54; chief virol, med. labs, U.S. Army, Europe, Ger, 54-57; polio res, communicable disease ctr, U.S. PUB. HEALTH SERV, 57-59, virus diagnosis & methodol. unit, 59-62, dep. chief, lab. consultation & develop. sect, lab. br, CTR. DISEASE CONTROL, 62-66, chief biol. reagents sect, 66-69, CHIEF SCI. RESOURCES BR, 69-, sci. dir, U.S. Pub. Health. Chief microbiol, First Army Area Med. Lab, N.Y, 48-53, dir. clin. labs, 53-54. Dipl, Am. Bd. Microbiol, 62. U.S.A, 42-45, Res, 45-, Lt. Col. AAAS; Am. Soc. Microbiol; Sci. Res. Soc. Am.(secy-treas, 62-63); fel. Am. Acad. Microbiol; N.Y. Acad. Sci. Administration of national public health laboratory improvement program. Address: Center for Disease Control, Atlanta, GA 30333.

FODOR, GABOR, b. Budapest, Hungary, Dec. 5, 15; Can. citizen; m. 39, 64; c. 4. ORGANIC CHEMISTRY. State exam, Graz Tech, 34; Ph.D.(org. chem), Szeged, 37, Veniam Legendi, 45; D.Sc.(org. chem), Hungarian Acad. Sci, 52. Univ. demonstr. org. chem, Szeged, 35-38, assoc. prof, 45-49, prof, 49-57; res. assoc, Chinoin Pharmaceut. Ltd, Hungary 38-45; head lab. stereochem, Hungarian Acad. Sci, 58-65; prof. org. chem, Laval, 65-69; CENTENNIAL PROF. CHEM, W.VA. UNIV, 69- Overseas fel, Churchill Col, 61; vis. scientist, Nat. Res. Coun. Can, 64-65. Kossuth award, Hungary, 50 & 54; silver medalist, Univ. Helsinki, 58. Am. Chem. Soc; Can. Inst. Chem; Hungarian Acad. Sci; Swiss Chem. Soc; The Chem. Soc; Chem. Soc. France; Am. Inst. Chem. Constitutional and synthetic work in isoquinolines, ephedrines, adrenaline and its derivatives; elucidation of configuration, chloromycetine, the tropines, scopolamine, cocaines, sedridine and sphingosine; total synthesis of valeroidine and hyoscine; selective quaternization; mechanism of the Wallach rearrangement of chloral and of the von Braun cyanogen bromide and of the amide degradation reactions; nucleophilic dequaternization of azetidinium salts. Address: Dept. of Chemistry, West Virginia University, Morgantown, WV 26506.

FODOR, GEORGE EMERIC, b. Makó, Hungary, Feb. 13, 32; U.S. citizen; m; c. 2. ORGANIC CHEMISTRY. Dipl, Szeged, 55; univ. fel, Rice, 60-62, R.A. Welch fel, 62-65, Ph.D.(chem), 65. Chemist, Hungarian Oil Ref. Co, 55; mem. sci. staff, Hungarian Oil & Gas Res. Inst, 56; chemist, Pontiac Ref. Co, Tex, 57-60; asst. org. chem, Rice, 60-62; res. chemist, photo prod. dept, E.I. du Pont de Nemours & Co, N.J, 65-66; SR. RES. CHEMIST, SOUTHWEST RES. INST, 66- Am. Chem. Soc; Sci. Res. Soc. Am. Synthetic organic and petroleum chemistry. Address: Southwest Research Institute, P.O. Box 28510, San Antonio, TX 78284.

FODOR, L(AWRENCE) M(ARTIN), b. Cleveland, Ohio, Dec. 1, 37; m. 62; c. 3. INORGANIC & POLYMER CHEMISTRY. A.B, Western Reserve, 59; Sprague Elec. Co. fel, Cornell, 62-63, Ph.D.(inorg. chem), 63. RES. CHEMIST, PHILLIPS PETROL. CO, 63- Am. Chem. Soc; The Chem. Soc. Olefin polymerization; thermosetting plastics; organometallic compounds. Address: Phillips Petroleum Co, 341 RB1, Bartlesville, OK 74003.

FOECKE, HAROLD ANTHONY, b. Crofton, Nebr, Mar. 7, 26; m. 51; c. 7. ENGINEERING EDUCATION. B.S, Iowa State, 45, M.S, 48; Ph.D.(ed), Notre Dame, 62. Jr. res. fel, Iowa State, 46, instr. elec. eng, 46-48; sr. res. fel, Polytech. Inst. Brooklyn, 48-49, instr. elec. eng, 49-51, asst. prof, 51-52; Notre Dame, 54-58, 61-62; proj. dir. cmt. develop, eng. faculties, Am. Soc. Eng. Ed, 58-61; specialist eng. ed, U.S. Off. Ed, 62-65; dean eng, Gonzaga Univ, 65-68; DIR, DIV. SCI. TEACHING, UNESCO, PARIS, FRANCE, 68- U.S.N, 44-46, 52-54. AAAS; Am. Soc. Eng. Educ.(Arthur L. Williston Award, 68); Engineering education; science education; higher education. Address: U.S. Delegation, UNESCO, U.S. Embassy, APO New York 09777.

FOECKLER, FRANCIS H, JR, b. Wash, D.C, June 26, 26; m. 50; c. 1. PHYSIOLOGY, MICROBIOLOGY. A.B, St. Peter's Col.(N.J), 50; M.S, Catholic Univ, 52; Sc.D.(zool), Munich, 60. Asst. path, Sibley Mem. Hosp, D.C, 51-52; biol. technician, Ralph Parsons Co, Md, 53; chief bacteriologist & asst. pathologist, Hunter Mem. Labs, D.C, 53-54, dir. radioisotope lab, 61-64; res. assoc. biol, German Res. Asn. grant, Biol. Inst, Regensburg Philos-Theol. Col, 65-68; chief sci. info, Johann A. Wülfing Pharmaceut. Co, 68-70; SR. TOXICOLOGIST, CHEM. FABRIK VON HEYDEN, 70- U.S.A, 46-47. AAAS; Am. Soc. Microbiol; Am. Soc. Zool; Soc. Nuclear Med; N.Y. Acad. Sci. Toxicology; clinical pathology; side effects of drugs; hematology; clinical chemistry; nuclear medicine; role of intracellular symbionts in metabolism. Address: Chemische Fabrik von Heyden, Donaustauferstrasse 378, 84 Regensburg, West Germany.

FOEGE, WILLIAM HERBERT, b. Decorah, Iowa, Mar. 12, 36; m. 58; c. 3. MEDICINE, EPIDEMIOLOGY. B.A, Pacific Lutheran, 57; M.D, Washington (Seattle), 61; M.P.H, Harvard, 65. Intern, U.S. Pub. Health Serv. Hosp, Staten Island, N.Y, 61-62; epidemiologist, Epidemic Intel. Serv, Nat. Commun. Disease Ctr, 62-64; med. off, Emmanuel Med. Ctr, Lutheran Church-Mo. Synod, Nigeria Mission, 65-67; epidemiologist, SMALLPOX ERADICATION PROG, CTR. FOR DISEASE CONTROL, 67-69, DIR, 69- Consult, Smallpox Eradication Prog, Nigeria, 66-67. Dept. Health, Educ. & Welfare Superior Serv. Award. U.S.P.H.S, 61-64, Surg. Am. Pub. Health Asn; Royal Soc. Trop. Med. & Hyg. Epidemiology and control of communicable diseases in the tropics. Address: Center for Disease Control, 1600 Clifton Rd. N.E, Atlanta, GA 30333.

FOEHR, EDWARD G(OTTHARD), b. Phila, Pa, Sept. 22, 17; m. 41; c. 1. CHEMISTRY. B.S, Pa. State Col, 38, M.S, 41, Ph.D.(org. chem), 44. Asst. petrol. ref. lab, Pa. State Col, 38-44; RES. CHEMIST & SUPVR. RES, CHEVRON RES. CO, 44- With Off. Sci. Res. & Develop, 44. Am. Chem. Soc; Am. Soc. Lubrication Eng. Constant viscosity oils; type analysis of lubricating oils; industrial lubricants; hydraulic transmission fluids. Address: Chevron Research Co, 576 Standard Ave, Richmond, CA 94802.

FOELSCHE, HORST W(ILHELM) J(ULIUS), b. Darmstadt, Ger, Oct. 28, 37; m. 61; c. 2. PHYSICS. B.S, New Mexico, 59; M.S, Yale, 60, Ph.D.(physics), 63. Res. assoc. physics, Yale, 63-65; asst. physicist, ACCELLERATOR DEPT, BROOKHAVEN NAT. LAB, 65-67, assoc. physicist, 67-69, PHYSICIST, 69- High energy physics; experimental apparatus. Address: Accelerator Dept, Brookhaven National Lab, Upton, NY 11973.

FOELSCHE, TRUTZ, b. Thorn, Ger, Oct. 13, 06; U.S. citizen; m. 37; c. 4. PHYSICS, BIOPHYSICS. Dr. phil. nat.(physics, math, meteorol), Frankfurt, 36. Physicist & res. pilot, Flight Res. Ctr. D.F.S. Ernst Udet, Darmstadt-Braunschweig-Ainring, Ger, 37-38, chief electronic dept, 38-45; owner med. & commun. electronic lab, T. Foelsche, Bayrisch-Gmain, 45-49; asst, Max Planck Inst. Biophys, Frankfurt, 49-55; consult. & referee, Ger. Civil Defense Ctr, Bad Godesberg, 55-56; physicist, res. div. & off. of chief scientist, sci. & eng. staff, Air Force Missile Develop. Ctr, Holloman AFB, N.Mex, 56-59; div. physicist, LANGLEY RES. CTR, NASA, 59-61, STAFF SCIENTIST, 61- Langley Res. Ctr. liaison mem. particle & fields subcomt, space sci. steering comt, NASA, 60-65, mem. rev. comt. on radiation shielding, NASA-Off. Adv. Res. & Tech, 63-67, prin. investr. lunar orbiter radiation exp, 65-68 & supersonic transport radiation test. progs, Langley Res. Ctr, 65-; mem. neuropath. subcomt, comt. biol. effects of atomic radiation, Nat. Acad. Sci, 63-64. Group achievement award, NASA-Adminstr, exceptional sci. achievement award, Langley Res. Ctr, 67; Apollo achievement award, NASA-Adminstr, 69. AAAS; Am. Geophys. Union; Am. Astronaut. Soc; Aerospace Med. Asn; German Soc. Aeronaut. & Astronaut; Ger. Soc. Aviation & Space Med. Spectroscopy and nuclear spin; physics and biophysics of decimeter-ultrasonic-ionizing-radiation; tracking-guidance-medical applications; nuclear propulsion; space radiation and interaction with matter; dose analysis-radiobiology; space and planetary sciences. Address: 604 Old Landing Rd, Yorktown, VA 23490.

FOERING, LOUISE, b. Bethlehem, Pa, Nov. 27, 04. PHYSICAL CHEMISTRY. S.B, Simmons Col, 26; Ph.D.(phys. chem), Yale, 37. Technician, Rockefeller Inst, 28-34; lectr. phys. chem, Brooklyn Col, 40-41; instr. chem, Russell Sage Col, 41-45, asst. prof, 45-49; res. assoc, Stanford Univ, 49-61; Metronics Assoc, Inc, 61-66; RETIRED. Am. Chem. Soc. Theoretical electrochemistry; kinetics of homogeneous gas reactions. Address: 128 Escobar Rd, Portola Valley, CA 94025.

FOERNZLER, ERNEST C(ARL), b. Indianapolis, Ind, Apr. 12, 35; m. 64; c. 2. PHARMACEUTICAL CHEMISTRY. B.S, Purdue Univ, 57, M.S, 59, Am. Found. Pharmaceut. Educ. fel, 59-62, Ph.D.(phys. chem), 62. Instr. radiochem, Purdue Univ, 57-59; mem. opers. res. staff, Arthur D. Little, Inc, 62-65; MGR. COMPUT. SYSTS, HOFFMANN-LA ROCHE, INC, NUTLEY, 65- Summers, pharmaceut. chemist, Pitman-Moore Div, Dow Chem. Co, 56, 57, Smith Kline & French Labs, 59. Am. Pharmaceut. Asn; Asn. Comput. Mach; Opers. Res. Soc. Am; Am. Chem. Soc. Biomedical computer techniques; operations research; quantum biochemistry; computer systems and programming. Address: 32 Anona Dr, Saddle River, NJ 07458.

FOERSTER, DONALD R(AY), b. San Antonio, Tex, Apr. 9, 33; m. 58; c. 3. INORGANIC CHEMISTRY. B.S, Principia Col, 54; Jefferson Chem. Co. fel, Texas, 57-58, Ph.D.(chem), 58. Asst. prof. chem, Missouri, 58-61; asst. prof. & chmn. dept, Principia Col, 61-65; sr. res. chemist, Pittsburgh Plate Glass Co, 65-67, res. supvr. chem. div, 67-69; assoc. prof. chem, Principia Col, 69-71; CHEMIST, UNION SANIT. DIST, 71- Am. Chem. Soc; The Chem. Soc. Properties of inorganic compounds in non-aqueous solvents; coordination chemistry; electrodeposition in non-aqueous solvents. Address: Union Sanitary District, 8700 Thornton Ave, Newark, CA 94536.

FOERSTER, EDWARD L(eROY), SR, b. Chicago, Ill, Sept. 17, 19; m. 48; c. 3. CHEMICAL ENGINEERING. B.S, Illinois, 41; Chem.E, Virginia, 42. Asst. chem. engr, Merck & Co, Inc, 42-48, chem. eng, 48-52, sect. leader, 52-58, mgr. develop. & control, electronic chem. div, 58-59; consult, 59-60; INDUST. & COMMERCIAL CONSULT, 60- Am. Inst. Chem. Eng; Am. Chem. Soc; Water Pollution Control Fedn; Am. Inst. Chem; Nat. Soc. Prof. Eng. Waste disposal; by-product recovery; wood preserving; food processing; fermentation; ion exchange; organic chemical manufacturing; rendering. Address: Box 779, Harrisonburg, VA 22801.

FOERSTER, R(USSELL) E(ARLE), b. Neepawa, Man, May 29, 99; m. 25; c. 3. BIOLOGY. B.A, British Columbia, 21, Nat. Res. Coun. Can. bursar, 21-22, M.A, 22, Nat. Res. Coun. Can. stud, 22-23; Ph.D, Toronto, 24. Biol. Bd. Can, 24-31, chief biologist, 32-38; sr. scientist, Int. Pac. Salmon Fisheries Comn, 38-40; dir. Pac. Biol. Sta, Fisheries Res. Bd. Can, 40-50, prin. scientist, 50-62; RETIRED. Am. Soc. Limnol. & Oceanog; Am. Fisheries Soc; fel. Royal Soc. Can. Fisheries and fish culture; hydromedusa; life history, propagation and ecology of sockeye salmon. Address: Pacific Biological Station, Nanaimo, B.C, Can.

FOFONOFF, NICHOLAS PAUL, b. Queenstown, Alta, Aug. 18, 29; m. 51; c. 4. MECHANICS. B.A. & M.A, British Columbia, 51; Ph.D.(appl. math), Brown, 55. Asst. scientist, Pac. Oceanog. Group, Fisheries Res. Bd. Can, 54-55, assoc. scientist, 56-58, sr. scientist, 58-62; Woods Hole Oceanog. Inst, 62-69; GORDON McKAY PROF. PRACTICE OF PHYS. OCEANOG, HARVARD, 69- Nat. Res. Coun. Can. overseas fel, 55. Fluid mechanics; dynamics of ocean circulation; thermodynamics of sea water; measurement of ocean currents. Address: Dept. of Engineering & Applied Physics, Harvard University, Cambridge, MA 02138.

FOFT, JOHN WILLIAM, b. Los Angeles, Calif, May 13, 28; m. 57; c. 2. PATHOLOGY. B.S, Nebraska, 51, M.D, 54; Minnesota, 57-61. Pathologist, sch. aerospace med, U.S. Air Force, 61-63, chief dept. path, 63-64; asst. prof. path, Univ. Chicago, 64-68; assoc. prof, univ. hosps, UNIV. ALA, BIRMINGHAM, 68-70, PROF. CLIN. PATH. & CHMN. DEPT, SCH. MED, 70- U.S.A, 55-57; U.S.A.F, 61-64, Capt. AAAS; N.Y. Acad. Sci; Col. Am. Path; Am. Soc. Clin. Path; Am. Med. Asn; Am. Asn. Blood Banks; Am. Asn. Path. & Bact. Nucleic acid metabolism in developing immunocompetent cells, and in virus infected cells. Address: Dept. of Clinical Pathology, University of Alabama in Birmingham School of Medicine, Birmingham, AL 35233.

FOGARTY, CHARLES F(RANKLIN), b. Denver, Colo, May 27, 21; m. 43; c. 8. MINING ENGINEERING, GEOLOGY. E.M, Colo. Sch. Mines, 42, Dr.Sc.(geol), 52. Miner, Climax Molybdenum Co, 41; party chief geologist, Socony-Vacuum Oil Co, 46-50; geologist & mining engr, TEX. GULF SULPHUR CO, 52-53, asst. mgr. explor. dept, 53-54, mgr, 54-57, v.pres. & mgr, 58-61, sr. v.pres, 61, DIR, CO, 62-, PRES, 68-, exec. v.pres, 64-68. Distinguished achievement medal, Colo. Sch. Mines, 62. C.Eng, 42-46, Maj. Geol. Soc. Am; Soc. Econ. Geol; Am. Asn. Petrol. Geol; Am. Inst. Mining, Metall. & Petrol. Eng.(Hal Williams Hardinge Award, 69); Am. Petrol. Inst; Mining & Metall. Soc. Am.(pres, 67-68); Can. Inst. Mining & Metall; Soc. Explor. Geophys. Exploration in the fields of minerals, oil and gas; general mining and production problems. Address: Texas Gulf Sulphur Co, 200 Park Ave, New York, NY 10017.

FOGEL, BERNARD J, b. New York, N.Y, Nov. 30, 36; m. 58; c. 3. IMMUNOLOGY, PEDIATRICS. Emory, 54-56; M.D, Miami (Fla), 61. Intern pediat, Jackson Mem. Hosp, Miami, Fla, 61-62, res, 62-63; fel, sch. med, Hopkins, 63-64; asst. chief. pediat, Walter Reed Army Medical Ctr. & researcher immunol, Walter Reed Army Inst. Res, 64-66; ASSOC. PROF. PEDIAT, SCH. MED, UNIV. MIAMI, 66-, ASSOC. DEAN EDUC, 67- Chief res, Sinai Hosp, Baltimore, Md, 63-64; Am. Cancer Soc. fel, Jackson Mem. Hosp, 66-68. U.S.A, 64-66, Capt. Am. Fedn. Clin. Res. Complement system in human and animal diseases; osmotic fragility of erythrocytes; malaria; the human neonate. Address: Dept. of Pediatrics, University of Miami School of Medicine, Miami, FL 13136.

FOGEL, CHARLES M(ORTON), b. Syracuse, N.Y, June 21, 13; m. 47; c. 3. CIVIL ENGINEERING. B.A, Buffalo, 35, M.A, 38; Ohio State, Columbia. Teacher sci, pub. schs, Buffalo, N.Y, 37-41; instr. physics, Buffalo, 41-44; res. engr, Nat. Union Radio Corp, 44-46; asst. prof. ENG, STATE UNIV. N.Y, BUFFALO, 46-47, assoc. prof, 47-63, PROF, 63-, ASST. EXEC. V.PRES, 67-, asst. dean, 47-52, dir. div. gen. & tech. studies, 52-57, indust. liaison off, 52-58. Am. Soc. Eng. Educ. Tapered columns; general engineering. Address: School of Engineering, State University of New York at Buffalo, Hayes Hall, Buffalo, NY 14214.

FOGEL, L(AWRENCE) J, b. New York, N.Y, Mar. 2, 28; m. 63; c. 2. ELECTRICAL ENGINEERING, BIOTECHNOLOGY. B.E.E, N.Y. Univ, 48; M.S, Rutgers, 52; Polytech. Inst. Brooklyn, 52-56; Ph.D.(biotech), California, Los Angeles, 64. Tech. engr, Watson Lab, U.S. Air Force, Ft. Monmouth, N.J, 48-49; Armed Serv, Electro Standards Agency, 49-50; head airborne antenna group, Coles Signal Lab, Ft. Monmouth, 50-53; sr. tech. eng, Devenco, Inc, N.Y, 53; sr. staff engr, Stavid Eng. Inc, N.J, 53-56; head reliability anal. group, Gen. Dynamics/Convair, 56-60; spec. asst. to dir. res, Nat. Sci. Found, 60-61; sr. staff scientist, Gen. Dynamics/Astronaut, 61-65; PRES, DECISION SCI, INC, 65- Summer lectr, Univ. Calif, Los Angeles, 63; assoc. prof, San Diego State Col, 65-70, prof, 71; mem. creative sci. sem, N.Y. Univ, 66-; vis. prof, U.S. Int. Univ, 70. Am. Soc. Cybernet. (v.pres, 66, pres, 68 & 69); N.Y. Acad. Sci; Human Factors Soc; sr. mem. Inst. Elec. & Electronics Eng; sr. mem. Am. Inst. Aeronaut. & Astronaut; Am. Sociol. Asn. Logical analysis of decision making by individuals and larger scale social entities; design of man-machine systems including artificial intelligence; analysis of biophysical processes relating to decision making; artificial intelligence by means of simulating the evolution of finite-state mathematical machines; biotechnology, especially displays, controls and human decision making. Address: Decision Science, Inc, 4508 Mission Bay Dr, San Diego, CA 92109.

FOGEL, NORMAN, b. Chicago, Ill, May 20, 24; m. 60; c. 2. INORGANIC CHEMISTRY. B.S, Illinois, 50; M.S, Wisconsin, 51, Ph.D.(chem), 56. Instr. chem, exten. div, Wisconsin, 52-53, asst, 53-54, Wisconsin Alumni Res. Found. asst, 54-56; asst. prof. CHEM, OKLAHOMA, 56-63, assoc. prof, 63-68, PROF, 68- C.Eng, U.S.A, 43-46. Am. Chem. Soc. Inorganic complex ions in solution and in solid state; dissociation pressure, spectra and magnetism of transition metal halide hydrates. Address: Dept. of Chemistry, Room 116, 620 Parrington Oval, University of Oklahoma, Norman, OK 73069.

FOGEL, SEYMOUR, b. N.Y.C, Sept. 27, 19; m. 57; c. 2. GENETICS. B.S, Queen's Col, 41; Columbia, 41-42; Gregory scholar & fel. & Ph.D.(genetics), Missouri, 46. Asst. biol, Missouri, 42-43, instr. zool, 46; biol, Queen's Col, 46-50; from assoc. prof. to prof, Brooklyn Col, 50-69, exec. off. Ph.D. prog, 65-69; PROF. GENETICS & CHMN. DEPT, UNIV. CALIF, BERKELEY, 69- Sigma Xi grant in aid, Queen's Col. (N.Y), 47; U.S. Pub. Health training fel, 59, res. grant, 60; vis. assoc. prof, Stanford Univ; Guggenheim fel, Univ. Calif, 67-68. Genetics Soc. Am. Crossing over and mutation in yeast; radiation genetics. Address: Dept. of Genetics, 345 Mulford Hall, University of California, Berkeley, CA 94720.

FOGELBERG, JOHN M(ARSHALL), b. South Range, Wis, July 24, 06. CHEMISTRY. B.S, Wisconsin, 28, Ph.D.(phys. chem), 31. Res. chemist, R.T. French Co, 32-41, head tech. dept, 46-49, tech. dir, 49-71, v.pres, 61-71; RETIRED. C.W.S, U.S.A, 41-42; U.S.N.R, 42-46, Lt. Comdr. AAAS; Am. Chem. Soc; Inst. Food Technol. Spices, condiments and foods. Address: 8 Oak Manor Crescent, Pittsford, NY 14534.

FOGELBERG, SIDNEY OTTO, b. South Range, Wis, Aug. 15, 11; m. 44; c. 2. PLANT CYTOLOGY. B.A, Wisconsin, 35, M.A, 36, Ph.D.(bot), 38; Michigan, 43-44. Asst. bot, Wisconsin, 36-38, hort, 38, res. assoc, 54-55; head dept. bot, Carolina Biol. Supply Co, 46-51; dir, Mid-State Labs, 51-53; DIR. MICROS. SLIDE DEPT, GEN. BIOL. SUPPLY HOUSE, CHICAGO, 55- Teacher, Wis. State Col, 53-54. U.S.A, 42-45. AAAS; Am. Soc. Plant Taxon. Mitochrodria; preparation of microscope slides. Address: 216 Kentucky St, Park Forest, IL 60466.

FOGELSON, DAVID E(UGENE), b. St. Paul, Minn, Sept. 13, 26; m. 56; c. 1. GEOPHYSICS. B.A, Minnesota, 52, M.S, 56. Asst. seismol. oil explor, Shell Oil Co, 50-52; geologist, Minn. Dept. Hwys, 52-56; geophysicist, appl. physics lab, U.S. BUR. MINES, 57-61, res. geophysicist, TWIN CITIES MINING RES. CTR, 61-68, head explosive fragmentation lab, 61-70, SCI. RES. MGR, 70- Summer geophysicist, Scripps Inst, California, 56; prog. mgr, NASA Contract on Lunar Mining Studies, 70- U.S.N, 44-46. Seismol. Soc. Am. Engineering seismology; generation and propagation of explosive waves; damage to structure from blasting; rock mechanics; lunar mining studies. Address: Twin Cities Mining Research Center, U.S. Bureau of Mines, P.O. Box 1660, Twin Cities Airport Station, St. Paul, MN 55111.

FOGG, CHARLES P(HILLIP), b. Newburyport, Mass, Feb. 12, 23; m. 49; c. 1. PHYSIOLOGY. B.S, Boston, 52, Ed.M, 56, D.Ed, 63. Assoc. prof. SCI, BOSTON UNIV, 52-63, PROF, 63- U.S.A.A.F, 41-45. AAAS. Biological and physical science; science education. Address: Dept. of Science, College of Basic Studies, Boston University, Boston, MA 02215.

FOGG, DONALD ERNEST, b. Camden, N.J, Jan. 26, 22; m. 43; c. 3. VETERINARY SCIENCE. V.M.D, Pennsylvania, 45. Private practice, 45-49; with Bur. Animal Industry, U.S. Dept. Agr, 49; path, State of Delaware, 50; mgr. clin. res, Merck & Co, Inc, 51-60; tech. serv. dir, Del. Poultry Labs, Inc, 60-66; dir. vet. serv, Eshams Farms Corp, 66-71; VET. MED. OFF, CONSUMER & MKT. SERV, U.S. DEPT. AGR, 71- U.S.A, 43-44. Am. Vet. Med. Asn; Am. Asn. Avian Path; U.S. Animal Health Asn. Diseases of poultry. Address: Route 2, Box 76A, Dagsboro, DE 19939.

FOGG, EDWARD T(HOMPSON), b. Salem, N.J, Mar. 24, 27; m. 50. CHEMICAL ENGINEERING. B.Ch.E, Virginia, 49; M.S, fel, 51-53, Pennsylvania, 51, Ph.D.(chem. eng), 53. Asst. instr. chem. eng, Pennsylvania, 49-50, instr, 50-51; res. engr, Jackson Lab, E.I. DU PONT DE NEMOURS & CO, INC, 53-56, res. supvr, 56-60, div. head, 60-66, mgr. lab, 66-68, design supt, CHAMBERS WORKS, 68-70, WORKS ENGR, 70- U.S.A.A.F, 44-46. Am. Chem. Soc; Am. Inst. Chem. Eng. Address: Greenwich St, Alloway, NJ 08001.

FOGG, GEORGE G(ARRETT), b. Greensburg, Ind, Jan. 27, 38; m. 61. PLANT ECOLOGY, SYSTEMATIC BOTANY. A.B, Wabash Col, 60; M.S, Butler, 62; Washington (St. Louis), 63-64; Ph.D.(bot), Oklahoma, 66. Instr. bot, Hawaii, 62-63; asst. prof. biol, STATE UNIV. N.Y. STONY BROOK, 66-70, LECTR. BIOL. SCI. & ASST. TO EXEC. V.PRES, 70- Ecology, systematics and evolution in conifers with emphasis in the genus Pinus. Address: Office of the Executive Vice President, State University of New York at Stony Brook, Stony Brook, NY 11790.

FOGG, JOHN M(ILTON), JR, b. Phila, Pa, Nov. 8, 98; m; c. 2. BOTANY. B.S, Pennsylvania, 25; Ph.D.(bot), Harvard, 29; Sc.D, La Salle, 49. Jessup fel, Acad. Nat. Scis, Phila, 21-22; curator herbarium, UNIV. PA, 22-63, instr. BOT, 25-32; asst. prof, 32-41, assoc. prof. & dean col. arts & scis, 41-44, PROF, 44-, v.provost, 44-53, DIR, Morris Arboretum, 54-67; BARNES ARBORETUM, 67- AAAS; Bot. Soc. Am; Torrey Bot. Club. Systematic study of flowering plants; floristics; plant geography; flora of Pennsylvania. Address: Barnes Arboretum, Merion, PA 19066.

FOGG, PETER JOHN, b. Bristol, Eng, June 14, 31; m. 58; c. 3. WOOD TECHNOLOGY. B.Sc, Wales, 52; M.F, La. State, 61, Ph.D.(forestry), 68. Asst. conservator, Forest Dept, Govt. of Brit. Honduras, 55-58; instr. FORESTRY, LA. STATE UNIV, BATON ROUGE, 60-69, ASST. PROF, 69- Forest Prod. Res. Soc; Soc. Wood Sci. & Technol. Wood quality in relation to genetic and environmental factors; permeability of wood to liquids and gases; relation of wood properties to anatomical structure. Address: School of Forestry and Wildlife Management, Louisiana State University, Baton Rouge, LA 70803.

FOGGIO, RICHARD D(OMINIC), b. Newark, N.J, Feb. 16, 31; m. 53; c. 2. ORGANIC CHEMISTRY. A.B, Drew, 51; M.S, Virginia, 54, Ph.D.(chem), 56. Res. chemist, Colgate-Palmolive Co, N.J, 56-57; patent adminstr, SMITH KLINE & FRENCH LABS, 57-59, patent agent, 59-61, group leader chem. patents, 61-68, DIR. PHARMACEUT. PATENTS, 68- Am. Chem. Soc. Medicinal agents; sympathomimetic amines; adrenergic blockers. Address: Smith Kline & French Labs, 1500 Spring Garden St, Philadelphia, PA 19101.

FOGH, JØRGEN (ENGELL), b. Copenhagen, Denmark, Feb. 6, 23; m. 47; c. 2. MEDICINE. M.D, Copenhagen, 49. Asst. chief physician res, Danish Nat. Found. Infantile Paralysis, 51-53; asst. res. virologist, virus lab, California, 53-58; assoc. med. virologist, div. labs. & res, N.Y. State Dept. Health, 58-60; ASSOC. MEM, VIRUS CELL RES. SECT, SLOAN-KETTERING INST. CANCER RES, 60-; ASSOC. PROF. path, SLOAN-KETTERING DIV, MED. COL, CORNELL UNIV, 61-66, MICROBIOL, 66- Assoc, dept. microbiol, Albany Med. Col, 59-61; prin. cancer res. scientist, Roswell Park Mem. Inst, summer 60. Life-time career award, Nat. Cancer Inst, 64. AAAS; Am. Soc. Cell Biol; Tissue Cult. Asn; Electron Micros. Soc. Am; Am. Asn. Cancer Res; Am. Asn. Immunol; Am. Soc. Exp. Path; Int. Soc. Cell Biol; N.Y. Acad. Sci; Danish Med. Asn; Europ. Asn. Cancer Res; Europ. Tissue Cult. Soc; Nordic Genetics. Soc. Human viruses; tumor viruses; tissue culture; micromorphology of cells and viruses. Address: Sloan-Kettering Institute for Cancer Research, 145 Boston Post Rd, Rye, NY 10580.

FOGHT, JAMES L(OREN), b. Akron, Ohio, Apr. 6, 36; m. 61; c. 3. ORGANIC CHEMISTRY. B.S, Akron, 58; M.S, Illinois, 60, Ph.D.(chem), 63. Res. chemist, textile fibers dept, E.I. DU PONT DE NEMOURS & CO, INC, 63-65, sr. res. chemist, 65, supvr. textile res, 65-66, supvr. res, Dacron Res. Lab, 66-69, sr. supvr, Dacron Tech. Lab, 69-70, MGR. DACRON END USE RES, 70- AAAS; Am. Chem. Soc. Technology of textile fibers in relation to end uses; biosynthesis of antibiotics; polymer chemistry. Address: 706 Cardiff Rd, Wilmington, DE 19803.

FOGIEL, ADOLF W, PHYSICAL CHEMISTRY. Dipl, Karlsruhe Tech, 49; Sydney, 52-53; Ph.D.(phys. chem), Wayne State, 62. Chemist, By-Prod. & Chem, Australia, 50-52; res. chemist, Am. Agr. Chem. Co, Mich, 54-60, res. supvr, 60-62; RES. CHEMIST, E.I. DU PONT DE NEMOURS & CO, INC, 62- Am. Chem. Soc; Sci. Res. Soc. Am. Physical chemistry of polymers, especially elastomers. Address: 3309 N. Rockfield Dr, Wilmington, DE 19810.

FOGLE, BENSON TARRANT, b. Springfield, S.C, Sept. 8, 35; m. 62; c. 1. AERONOMY, METEOROLOGY. B.S, South Carolina, 56, M.S, 58; Ph.D.(geophys), Alaska, 66. Physicist, Boeing Sci. Res. Labs, 58-59; res. physicist, Stanford Res. Inst, 59-62; asst. geophysicist, geophys. inst, Univ. Alaska, 62-66, asst. prof. geophys, 66-67; fel, NAT. CTR ATMOSPHERIC RES, 67-68, STAFF SCIENTIST, 68- AAAS; Am. Meteorol. Soc. Noctilucent clouds; ionospheric current systems; effects of volcanic efflux on earth's atmosphere; upper atmosphere water vapor. Address: Advanced Study Program, National Center for Atmospheric Research, P.O. Box 1470, Boulder, CO 80302.

FOGLE, HAROLD W(ARMAN), b. Morgantown, W.Va, Apr. 23, 18; m. 47; c. 2. HORTICULTURE. B.S, West. Virginia, 40, M S, 41; Ph.D.(hort, plant genetics), Minnesota, 49. Asst. West Virginia, 38-41; asst. county supvr, Charlestown & Martinsburg, W.Va, 41-42; county supvr, Farm Security Admin, U.S. Dept. Agr, West Union, Morgantown & Buckhannon, 42-46; asst. Minnesota, 46-49; horticulturist, irrigation exp. sta, U.S. Dept. Agr. & Washington State, 49-63; STONE FRUIT INVEST. LEADER, PLANT SCI. RES. DIV, AGR. RES. SERV, PLANT INDUST. STA, U.S. DEPT. AGR, BELTSVILLE, 63- U.S.A.A.F, 43-46. Am. Soc. Hort. Sci; Am. Pomol. Soc.(v.pres); Genetics Soc. Am. Stone fruit breeding and varietal investigations; winter hardiness of tree fruits; inheritance studies with tomatoes and stone fruits; vegetative propagation of stone fruits. Address: 2014 Forest Dale Dr, Silver Spring, MD 20903.

FOGLE, MERLYN W(ILLIS), b. Royal, Iowa, Feb. 20, 18. ORGANIC CHEMISTRY. B.S, Iowa State Col, 40; M.S, Iowa, 46, Ph.D.(org. chem), 49. Asst,

Iowa, 45-49; CHEMIST, H.C. Moffat, 50; Bio-Process Co, 51; labs. div, Armour & Co, 51-54; Mich. State, 54-56; Dow Chem. Co, 56-58; Indust. Rayon Corp, 59-61; Elec. Autolite Corp, 61-62; CHRYSLER CORP, 62- Am. Chem. Soc. Bile acids; amino acids; cellulose; fuel cells; vehicle emissions; air pollution control. Address: 8401 18 Mile Rd, Apt. 15, Sterling Heights, MI 48078.

FOGLEMAN, MAX E, b. Morehead, Kans, Oct. 6, 31; m. 52; c. 4. HORTICULTURE, PLANT BREEDING. B.S, Kansas State, 58, M.S, 61; Ph.D. (hort), Iowa State Univ, 66. ASST. PROF. HORT, Kans. State Univ, 64-69; UNIV. KY, 69- U.S.A, 52-54. Am. Soc. Hort. Sci. Vegetable crop breeding. Address: Dept. of Horticulture, University of Kentucky, Lexington, KY 40506.

FOGLEMAN, RALPH WILLIAM, b. McDonald, Kans, Mar. 18, 26; m; c. 3. VETERINARY MEDICINE. D.V.M, Kansas State, 47. Asst. veterinarian, R.A. Self Animal Hosp, Tex, 47-48; veterinarian, R.W. Fogleman Small Animal Hosp, Nebr, 48-50; head agr. chem. dept, Hazleton Labs, Inc, Va, 53-57, mgr. west. div, 57-60; v.pres, Hazleton-Nuclear Sci. Corp, Calif, 60-61, sr. res. pharmacologist, Am. Cyanamid Co, 61-62; v.pres, AME Assocs, 62-65; pres, Biographics, Inc, 65; toxicologist & registrations supvr, CIBA Agrochem. Co, 65-69; DIR. TOXICOL, AFFILIATED MED. ENTERPRISES, INC, 69- Res. veterinarian, Chem. Ctr, Md, U.S.A.R, 50-53. Am. Vet. Med. Asn; Am. Col. Vet. Toxicol; Soc. Toxicol; Am. Acad. Clin. Toxicol. Research administration; applied biological sciences; toxicology of organic phosphate insecticides in man and animals; metabolism of pesticides in plants and animals; industrial hygiene. Address: Affiliated Medical Enterprises, Inc, Princeton Pike, P.O. Box 57, Princeton, NJ 08540.

FOGLEMAN, WAVELL WAINWRIGHT, b. Winston-Salem, N.C, July 17, 42. INORGANIC & THEORETICAL CHEMISTRY. B.S, Univ. N.C, Chapel Hill, 64; Ph.D.(chem), Tulane Univ. La, 68. Summer chemist, Columbian Carbon Co, 66; Esso Res. & Eng. Corp, 68; ASST. PROF. CHEM, OLD DOM. UNIV, 68- Am. Chem. Soc. Phosphine-transition metal complexes; molecular orbital calculations. Address: Alfriend Chemistry Labs, Old Dominion University, Norfolk, VA 23508.

FOGLER, HUGH SCOTT, b. Normal, Ill, Oct. 28, 39; m. 62; c. 1. CHEMICAL ENGINEERING. B.S, Illinois, 62; M.S, Colorado, 63, NASA fel, 63-65, Ph.D. (chem. eng), 65. Asst. prof, Michigan, 65; mem. res. staff, jet propulsion labs, U.S. Army, Pasadena, 66-68; ASST. PROF. CHEM. ENG, UNIV. MICH, ANN ARBOR, 68- Consult, Packaging Corp. Am, 66- U.S.A, 66-68, 1st Lt. Am. Inst. Chem. Eng; Acoust. Soc. Am. Applications of sonic and ultrasonic waves to transport phenomena and reaction kinetics. Address: 2028 E. Engineering Bldg, University of Michigan, Ann Arbor, MI 48104.

FOGLIA, V(IRGILIO) G(ERARDO), b. Buenos Aires, Argentina, Feb. 13, 05; m. 50; c. 3. PHYSIOLOGY, ENDOCRINOLOGY. M.D, Buenos Aires, 28. Fel. biochem, McGill, 37-38; assoc. prof. PHYSIOL, FACULTY MED, UNIV. BUENOS AIRES, 45-57, DIR. DEPT, 54- Spec. res. fel, Nat. Insts. Health, 49-50; hon. prof, faculty med, Cochabamba, 62. Mem, UNESCO Int. Sci. Cmn, Venezuela, 64; pres. VII cong, Int. Fedn. Diabetes, 70. Miguel Couto award, Acad. Med, Brazil, 44. Soc. Exp. Biol. & Med; Argentine Biol. Soc. (v.pres, 28); Argentine Soc. Endocrinol.(pres, 44-48); Argentine Soc. Diabetes (pres, 55-57); Mex. Soc. Nutrit. & Endocrinol; French Soc. Endocrinol; Int. Fedn. Diabetes (v.pres, 71, 72, 73); for. mem, Italian Med. Acad. Physiology of endocrine glands and diabetes. Address: Callao No. 1695, Piso 12, Dto. B, Buenos Aires, Argentina.

FOGLIO, MARIO E(USEBIO), b. Buenos Aires, Arg, Apr. 25, 31; m. 57; c. 3. SOLID STATE & THEORETICAL PHYSICS. Lic. en Química, Univ. Buenos Aires, 54, Dr. en Química, 58; Nat. Res. Coun. Arg. fel, Bristol Univ, 59-62, Ph.D.(physics), 62. Researcher, phys. chem, Arg. Atomic Energy Comn, 54-56, physics, 56-61; res. assoc, Bristol Univ, 61-62; researcher, Arg. Atomic Energy Comn, 62-68; res. assoc, Harvard, 68-69; ASSOC. PROF. PHYSICS, SOUTH. ILL. UNIV, 69- S.J. Guggenheim Mem. Found. fel, 68-69. Am. Phys. Soc. Spin lattice relaxation; electron spin resonance; magnetic impurities in dielectrics; ferrimagnetic relaxation in europium iron garnet. Address: Dept. of Physics, Southern Illinois University, Carbondale, IL 62901.

FOGWELL, JOSEPH WRAY, b. Topeka, Kans, Dec. 11, 15; m. 42; c. 2. MECHANICAL ENGINEERING. B.S, Kansas, 40, M.S, 45; Carnegie Inst. Tech, 41-42. Res. mech. engr, Aluminum Co. Am, 40-42; instr. mech. eng, Kansas, 42-44; mgr. indust. eng, Corning Glass Works, 44-45; prod. design engr, Cuno Eng. Corp, 45-47; chief engr, Stock Equip. Co, 47-51; sr. res. engr, Southwest Res. Inst, 51-56; private consult. engr, 56-57; from gen. mgr. to pres, Prestressing, Inc, 57-61; MGR, SOUTHWEST RES. INST, 61- Am. Soc. Mech. Eng; Am. Soc. Metals; Soc. Nondestructive Test. Electromechanical research and development. Address: Southwest Research Institute, P.O. Drawer 28510, San Antonio, TX 78228.

FOHLEN, GEORGE M(ARCEL), b. San Francisco, Calif, Jan. 3, 19; m. 46. ORGANIC & POLYMER CHEMISTRY. B.S, California, 40, Ph.D.(pharmaceut. chem), 44. Asst. pharm, California, 40-43; res. chemist, Oronite Chem. Co, Calif, 44-45; sr. res. chemist, Sterling-Winthrop Inst, N.Y, 45-47; res. & develop. dept, Barrett Div, Allied Chem. & Dye Corp, 47-55; Reichhold Chem, Inc, Calif, 55-60; mgr. anal. servs, Cutter Labs, Berkeley, 60-62; sr. res. chemist process develop, Kaiser Chem. Corp, Calif, 62-67; Appl. Space Prod, Inc, 67-70; RES. SCIENTIST CHEM. RES. PROJS, AMES RES. CTR, NASA, 70- NASA Award for develop. achievement, 69. Civilian with Off. Sci. Res. & Develop, 44. AAAS; Am. Chem. Soc. Analytical methods; spectroscopy; organic synthesis; dipole moments and structures of urea, thiourea and some sex hormones; industrial organic chemistry; plastics; high temperature polymers; intumescent coatings. Address: Chemical Research Projects Office, Ames Research Center, NASA, Moffett Field, CA 94035.

FOIL, ROBERT RODNEY, b. Bogalusa, La, Aug. 12, 34; m. 59; c. 2. FORESTRY. B.S, La. State Univ, Baton Rouge, 56, M.For, 60; D.For.(forest soils), Duke Univ, 65. Forester, Union Bag Corp, 56; instr. FORESTRY, La. State Univ, 59-62, asst. prof, 62-67; assoc. specialist, La. Exten. Serv, 67-68, specialist, 68-69; PROF. & HEAD DEPT, MISS. STATE UNIV, 69- U.S.A, 56-58. Soc. Am. Foresters; Am. Forestry Asn. Forest resource management and use, particularly efficient harvesting of timber crops without damaging soils or desirable vegetation. Address: Dept. of Forestry, Mississippi State University, State College, MS 39762.

FOILES, CARL L(UTHER), b. Hardin, Ill, Oct. 1, 35; m. 63; c. 1. PHYSICS. B.S, Arizona, 57, M.S, 60, Ph.D.(physics), 64. Res. & develop. engr, Hewlett Packard Co, summer 57; electronic engr, Naval Ord. Lab, Calif, summers 60, 61; Goodyear Aerospace Corp, Ohio, summer 63; res. assoc. PHYSICS, Mich. State, 64-66; Nat. Sci. Found. fel. Imp. Col. London, 66-67; ASST. PROF, MICH. STATE UNIV, 67- Am. Phys. Soc. Low temperature properties of metals and alloys; transport properties and magnetic properties. Address: Dept. of Physics, Michigan State University, East Lansing, MI 48823.

FOIN, OWEN F(RANCIS), JR, b. Fresno, Calif, Oct. 26, 08; m. 46; c. 4. PHYSICS, ELECTRICAL ENGINEERING. A.B, Fresno State Col, 36, 50-; Harvard, 43; Mass. Inst. Tech, 43-44. Asst. prof. physics, FRESNO STATE COL, 42-47, assoc. prof, 47-48, ELEC. ENG, 58-69, PROF, 69- Instr, Mass. Inst. Tech, 44-45; physicist & tech. consult, missile control div, U.S. Naval Res. Labs, 45-47. Consult, 51-; tech. consult, U.S. Naval Missile Ctr, Pac. Missile Range, Point Mugu, 57- U.S.N.R, 43-46, Res, 43-, Capt. Sr. mem. Inst. Elec. & Electronics Eng. Mathematics; physical electronics; electronics engineering, circuit and systems design; microwave techniques; solid state physics; communication; missile weapons systems, especially automatic stability and control, electronic countermeasures and electronic counter-counter-measures. Address: Dept. of Engineering, Fresno State College, Fresno, CA 93726.

FOISY, HECTOR B, b. Fort Covington, N.Y, Feb. 8, 36; m. 58; c. 5. MATHEMATICS. B.A, St. Michael's Col.(Vt), 58; Nat. Sci. Found. fel, Univ. Ill, Urbana, 61-62, M.A, 62; Nat. Sci. Found. fel, George Peabody Col, 66-67, Ph.D.(math), 71. Teacher & chmn. dept, high sch, N.Y, 58-61; ASSOC. PROF. MATH, STATE UNIV. N.Y. COL. POTSDAM, 62- Math. Asn. Am. Qualifications, duties and training of elementary school mathematics specialists. Address: Dept. of Mathematics, State University of New York College at Potsdam, Potsdam, NY 13676.

FOK, SAMUEL S(HIU) M(ING), b. Macao, China, Feb. 15, 26; U.S. citizen; m. 52; c. 3. CHEMICAL ENGINEERING. B.Ch.E, Ohio State, 49; M.S, Case, 51, Ph.D.(chem. eng), 55. Res. asst, Case, 50-54; res. engr, Indust. Rayon Corp, Ohio, 54-56; sr. staff engr, Shockley Transistor Corp, Calif, 56-60; mem. tech. staff, res. & develop. lab, Fairchild Semiconductor Corp, 60-70; microphotog. consult, 70-71; SR. STAFF ENGR, SILICONIX, INC, 71- Am. Chem. Soc; Electrochem. Soc; Soc. Photog. Sci. & Eng. Large scale integration, metal-oxide-silicon or LSI/MOS mask making; masking; photoresists; photofabrication; microphotography; semiconductor process development; plastic packaging; high polymers; chrome mask making; transparent mask; one to one projection system. Address: 820 Talisman Dr, Palo Alto, CA 94303.

FOK, SIU YUEN, b. Macau, China, Nov. 23, 37. CHEMICAL ENGINEERING. B.S, Taiwan, 60; M S, Cincinnati, 62; Ph.D.(chem. eng), Va. Polytech, 65. Fel. chem, Clarkson Tech, 65-66; sr. res. chemist, fibers & laminates div, Enjay Chem. Co, 66-69; PRIN. CHEMIST, DART INDUST, 69- Am. Chem. Soc; Am. Inst. Chem. Eng. Polymer physics and characterization; fiber spinning. Address: 325 S. Canfield Niles Rd, Youngstown, OH 44515.

FOK, THOMAS DSO YUN, b. Canton, China, July 1, 21; nat; m. 49. CIVIL ENGINEERING. B.Eng, Nat. Tung-Chi Univ, China, 45; M.S, Illinois, 48; M.B.A, N.Y. Univ, 50; Ph.D.(civil eng), Carnegie Inst, 56. Design engr, Richardson, Gordon & Assocs, Pa, 56-58; assoc. prof. civil eng, Youngstown Univ, 58-67, dir. comput. ctr, 63-67; PARTNER, MOSURE & FOK, CONSULT. ENGRS, 67- Consult, R.D. Werner Co, Inc, 58-; Automatic Sprinkler Corp, 59- Am. Soc. Eng. Educ; Am. Soc. Civil Eng; Am. Concrete Inst; Int. Asn. Bridge & Struct. Eng. Structural engineering; applied mechanics and programming for digital computers. Address: 325 S. Canfield-Niles Rd, Youngstown, OH 44515.

FOK, YU SI, b. China, Jan. 15, 32. WATER RESOURCES, HYDROLOGY. B.S, Nat. Taiwan Univ, 55; M.S, Utah State Univ, 59, Ph.D.(civil eng), 64. Res. asst. civil & irrig. eng, Utah State Univ, 57-63, asst. prof. agr. & irrig. eng. & asst. res. engr, Utah Water Res. Lab, 63-66; res. assoc, Univ. Ill, Urbana, 66-68; head, basin hydrol. sect, Tex. Water Rights Comn, Tex, 68-70; ASSOC. PROF. CIVIL ENG, WATER RESOURCES RES. CTR, UNIV. HAWAII, 70- Hydrologist, Ill. State Water Surv, Ill, 66-68; Am. Geophys. Union; Am. Water Resources Asn; Am. Soc. Civil Eng; Am. Soc. Agr. Eng. Soil physics—soil-water movement theory and practices and infiltration theory and application; stream system morphology—mechanics of stream morphological systems; hydrology—flood hydrology, water availability and streamflow forecasting; water resources systems analysis—optimization of water resources; irrigation and drainage science—hydraulics of irrigation water application. Address: Dept. of Civil Engineering, Water Resources Research Center, University of Hawaii, Honolulu, HI 96821.

FOLAND, NEAL EUGENE, b. Parnell, Mo, Dec. 9, 29; m. 56; c. 5. MATHEMATICS. B.S, Northeast Mo. State Teachers Col, 54; M.A, Missouri, 58, Ph.D.(math), 61. Asst. prof. MATH, Kansas State, 61-64, ASSOC. prof, 64-65; SOUTH. ILL. UNIV, 65-70, PROF, 70-, CHMN. DEPT, 71- U.S.N, 48-52. Am. Math. Soc; Math. Asn. Am. Topological dynamics. Address: Dept. of Mathematics, Southern Illinois University, Carbondale, IL 62901.

FOLAND, WILLIAM D(OUGLAS), b. Knoxville, Tenn, Jan. 15, 26; m. 55. PHYSICS. A.B, Tennessee, 51, M.S, 55, Ph.D.(physics), 58. Asst. PHYSICS, Univ. Tenn, 51-55, instr, 55-58; asst. prof, Univ. Mass, Amherst, 58-68; ASSOC. PROF, WASH. & JEFFERSON COL, 68- U.S.A, 44-46. Atomic collisions; theory. Address: Dept. of Physics, Washington & Jefferson College, Washington, PA 15301.

FOLCH-PI, J(ORDI), b. Barcelona, Spain, Mar. 25, 11; nat; m. 45; c. 3. BIOCHEMISTRY. B.S, Inst. Balmes, Barcelona, 27; M.D, Barcelona, 33; hon. M.A, Harvard, 51; hon. D.Sc, Univ. Montpellier, 67; hon. D.Sc, Univ. Chile, 69. Intern physiol, med. col, Barcelona, 31-33, asst. res. physician, 33-35; vol. worker biochem, Rockefeller Inst, 35-37, asst. chem, 37-42, assoc, 42-44; asst. prof. biol. chem, HARVARD MED. SCH, 44-51, assoc. prof, 51-56, PROF. NEUROCHEM, 56-, DIR. SCI. RES, McLEAN HOSP, 44- Rockefeller Found. fel, Rockefeller Inst, 36-37; special lectr, London, 59; special consult, Nat. Inst. Mental Health, Nat. Insts. Health, 51, 57-59, 60-, chmn. bd. sci, counsr, 60-64. Spanish Army, 34, Lt. Am. Soc. Biol. Chem; Harvey Soc; Asn. Res. Nerv. & Ment. Diseases; Am. Neurol. Asn; Am. Acad. Arts & Sci; Am. Acad. Neurol; Int. Soc. Neurochem.(secy, 67); Am. Soc. Neurochem.(secy, 69). Lipid, blood and brain chemistry; neurochemistry. Address: McLean Hospital, Belmont, MA 02178.

FOLCKEMER, FRANK B(ENJAMIN), b. Bowen, Ill, June 1, 14. CHEMISTRY. B.S, Illinois, 36, M.S, 38; Ph.D.(biophys. chem), Iowa State Col, 43. Res. chemist, Shell Oil Co, Inc, 43-49, asst. chief chemist, Shell Chem. Corp, 49-52, sr. chemist, N.J, 52-67, supvr. pesticide formulation, agr. res. div, Shell Develop. Co, 67-71; RETIRED. AAAS; Am. Chem. Soc. Formulations of insecticides, fungicides and herbicides; development of insecticide fertilizer mixtures. Address: 805 Tully Rd, Modesto, CA 95350.

FOLDEN, DEWEY BRAY, JR, b. Charleston, W.Va, Dec. 2, 23; m. 49. ANIMAL PHYSIOLOGY. B.S, Morris Harvey Col, 47, B.A, 48; M.S, West Virginia, 49; Maryland, 56. Instr. BIOL, Memphis State Col, 49-55; Dickinson Col, 55-57; MEMPHIS STATE UNIV, 57-59, asst. prof, 59-61, ASSOC. PROF, 61- Am. Physiol. Soc. summer grant, cardiovasc. res. prog, Med. Col. Ga, 58; Nat. Insts. Health res. grant, 59-60. U.S.N, 44-46. AAAS. Spectrophotometry of selected crab meat samples; renal blood flow in the decapsulated kidney. Address: Dept. of Biology, Memphis State University, Memphis, TN 38111.

FOLDES, FRANCIS F(ERENC), b. Budapest, Hungary, June 13, 10; nat; m. 38; c. 3. ANESTHESIOLOGY. M.D, Budapest, 34. Res. physician, Svabhegyi Sanatorium, Budapest, 35-39; private practice, 39-41; res. fel. anesthesia, Mass. Gen. Hosp. Boston, 41-42, res, 42-43, asst. anesthetist, 44-47; dir. dept. ANESTHESIOL, Mercy Hosp, Pittsburgh, Pa, 47-62; DIR. DEPT, MONTEFIORE HOSP. & MED. CTR, 62-; PROF, ALBERT EINSTEIN COL. MED, 64- Asst, Harvard Med. Sch, 43-47; assoc. prof, med. sch, Pittsburgh, 48-57, clin. prof, 57-62; mem. med. adv. bd, Myasthenia Gravis Found, 59-, v.chmn, 62-66, chmn, 66-68; v.pres, World Fedn. Socs. Anesthesiologists, 60-64, mem. sci. adv. & membership comts, 64-, pres, fedn, 68-72; mem. subcomt. anesthesiol, Comt. Revision U.S. Pharmacopeia, 60-; clin. prof, col. physicians & surgeons, Columbia Univ, 62-64; res. assoc, Mt. Sinai Hosp, N.Y. Dipl, Faculty Anaesthetists, Royal Australasian Col. Surgeons, 70; Royal Col. Surgeons Eng, 71; Semmelweis Award, Am. Hungarian Med. Asn, 66, George Wash. Award, 70. Am. Med. Asn; Am. Soc. Anesthesiol; fel. Am. Col. Anesthesiol; Am. Soc. Pharmacol. & Exp. Therapeut; Am. Chem. Soc; Soc. Exp. Biol. & Med; N.Y. Acad. Med; N.Y. Acad. Sci; Swiss Soc. Physiol. & Pharmacol; Royal Soc. Med; Int. Anesthesia Res. Soc. Neuropharmacology; enzymes; co-enzymes. Address: Dept. of Anethestiology, Montefiore Hospital & Medical Center, 111 E. 210th St, New York, NY 10467.

FOLDI, ANDREW PETER, b. Budapest, Hungary, Feb. 24, 31; U.S. citizen; m. 66. ORGANIC & POLYMER CHEMISTRY, CHEMICAL ENGINEERING. Dipl. Chem. Eng, Budapest Tech, 53; Ph.D.(org. chem), Delaware, 63. Design & prod. chem. engr, Chem. Complex, Hungary, 53-56; chem. engr, E.I. DU PONT DE NEMOURS & CO, 57-60, RES. CHEMIST, 62- Sci. Res. Soc. Am; Am. Chem. Soc. Industrial fibers; rubber technology; thermoplastics; organic intermediates; pharmaceutical and synthetic organic chemistry; fermentation technology; theoretical organic and industrial chemistry. Address: E.I. du Pont de Nemours & Co, Wilmington, DE 19898.

FOLDI, VERONIKA S(ZIRAKY), b. Pecs, Hungary, Dec. 18, 31; U.S. citizen; m. 59; c. 1. ORGANIC & POLYMER CHEMISTRY. B.S, Akron, 55; M.S, Illinois, 56. Chemist, PIONEERING RES. DIV, TEXTILE FIBERS DEPT, E.I. DU PONT DE NEMOURS & CO, INC, 56-64, RES. CHEMIST, 64- Am. Chem. Soc. Condensations and ring-opening polymerization; isolcyanate chemistry; fiber characterization; fabric development. Address: Pioneering Research Division, Textile Fibers Dept, E.I. du Pont de Nemours & Co, Inc, Wilmington, DE 19898.

FOLDS, JAMES DONALD, b. Augusta, Ga, Sept. 26, 40; m. 62; c. 2. MICROBIOLOGY, IMMUNOLOGY. B.S, Univ. Ga, 62; Ph.D.(microbiol). Med. Col. Ga, 67. U.S. Pub. Health Serv. fel. immunol, sch. med, Case West. Reserve Univ, 67-69; instr. BACT. & IMMUNOL, SCH. MED, UNIV. N.C, CHAPEL HILL, 69-70, ASST. PROF, 70- AAAS; Am. Soc. Microbiol. Antibody synthesis and secretion; control and regulation of antibody synthesis. Address: Dept. of Bacteriology & Immunology, School of Medicine, University of North Carolina at Chapel Hill, Chapel Hill, NC 27514.

FOLDVARI, TIBOR L, b. Budapest, Hungary, May 16, 36; U.S. citizen; m. 61; c. 2. BIOMEDICAL ENGINEERING, INSTRUMENTATION. S.B, Mass. Inst. Technol, 61, S.M, 63, Nat. Insts. Health fel. & Ph.D.(bioeng), 67. Staff mem. instrumentation, Mass. Inst. Technol, 61-63; consult, HARVARD APPARATUS CO, INC, MILLIS, 63-67, V.PRES. RES. & ENG, 67- Consult, Lion Res. Corp, Mass, 62-63; sect. ed, Biol. Abstr, 65-; adj. prof, biol. sci. ctr, Boston Univ, 68- Inst. Elec. & Electronics Eng; Am. Phys. Soc; sr. mem. Instrument Soc. Am; N.Y. Acad. Sci. Bioengineering; physiological measurements; scientific instrumentation; development of various biomedical instruments; physical methods of gas analysis; engineering and general management techniques. Address: 26 Parks Dr, Sherborn, MA 01770.

FOLDVARY, ELMER, b. Youngstown, Ohio, Mar. 9, 35; m. 65; c. 2. ORGANIC CHEMISTRY. B.S, Youngstown State Univ, 58; M.S, Tex. A&M Univ, 61, Ph.D.(chem), 64. Asst. prof. CHEM, YOUNGSTOWN STATE UNIV, 63-68, ASSOC. PROF, 68- Am. Chem. Soc; Sci. Res. Soc. Am. Linear free energy relationships; synthetics; polyester plastics; kinetics. Address: 34 Circle Dr, Poland, OH 44514.

FOLDY, LESLIE L(AWRANCE), b. Sabinov, Czech, Oct. 26, 19, U.S. citizen; m. 44; c. 2. THEORETICAL PHYSICS. B.S, Case Inst. Tech, 41; Ph.M, Wisconsin, 42; Nat. Res. Council fel, Inst. Adv. Study, 46-48; Ph.D.(physics), California, 48. Res. physicist, div. war res, Columbia, 42-45; radiation lab, California, 45-46; asst. prof. PHYSICS, CASE WEST. RESERVE UNIV, 48-50, assoc. prof, 50-53, prof, 53-66, INST. PROF, 66- Fulbright & Guggenheim fel, Inst. Theoret. Physics, Copenhagen, 53-54; Nat. Sci. Found. sr. fel, European Orgn. Nuclear Res, Geneva, 63-64. Fel. Am. Phys. Soc; fel. Acoust. Soc. Am; Fedn. Am. Sci. Acoustical theory; theoretical nuclear physics; quantum theory; quantum field theories; theory of high energy accelerators; elementary particle physics. Address: Dept. of Physics, Case Western Reserve University, Cleveland, OH 44106.

FOLEN, V(INCENT) J(AMES), b. Scranton, Pa, Jan. 17, 24; m. 54. PHYSICS. B.A, La Salle Col, 49; M.A, Pennsylvania, 54. Res. asst, Pennsylvania, 50-54; physicist, U.S. NAVAL RES. LAB, 54-59, HEAD FERRO MAGNETISM SECT, 59- Secy. adv. comt, Annual Conf. Magnetism & Magnetic Mat, 69 & 70. Publ. Award, Naval Res. Lab, 69 & 71. U.S.A.A.F, 43-46, S/Sgt. Fel. Am. Phys. Soc; Sci. Res. Soc. Am.(Pure Sci. Award, 71). Electron spin and ferromagnetic resonance; magnetoelectric effect; magnetocrystalline anisotropy; saturation magnetization; magnetic oxides; crystal synthesis; x-ray diffraction. Address: Code 6452, Ferro Magnetism Section, U.S. Naval Research Lab, Washington, DC 20390.

FOLEY, DEAN C(ARROLL), b. Pomeroy, Wash, Nov. 25, 25; m. 55. PLANT PATHOLOGY. B.S, Idaho, 49; M.S, West Virginia, 51; Ph.D.(plant path), Pa. State, 55. Asst. PLANT PATH, West Virginia, 49-51; Pa. State, 51-55; asst. prof, IOWA STATE UNIV, 55-61, ASSOC. PROF, 61- U.S.N.R, 43-45. AAAS; Am. Phytopath. Soc. Diseases resistance; diseases of cereals. Address: Dept. of Botany & Plant Pathology, Iowa State University, Ames, IA 50010.

FOLEY, DENNIS D(ONALD), b. Bainville, Mont, Mar. 17, 23; m. 47; c. 1. CHEMICAL ENGINEERING. B.Ch.Eng, Ohio State, 47, M.S, 49, Ph.D.(chem. eng), 54. Asst. engr, Tenn. Eastman Corp, Oak Ridge, 44-46; asst. physics, Ohio State, 47-50; Battelle Mem. Inst, 51-58; head mat. tech, nuclear power eng, Alco Prods, Inc, 58-61; mgr, nuclear prod. dept, Am. Standard Adv. Tech. Lab, 62-64; DIR. ENG, NEPTUNE METER CO, 65- U.S.A, 42-45. Am. Inst. Mining, Metall. & Petrol. Eng. Mass spectroscopy; beta ray spectroscopy; extraction and purification of thorium and uranium; distillation theory; nuclear power equipment; metering and measurement equipment and systems. Address: Neptune Meter Co, 845 N. Colony Rd, Wallingford, CT 06492.

FOLEY, EDWARD L(EO), b. Butte, Mont, Apr. 15, 30; m. 55; c. 6. PHYSICS. B.S, Mont. State Col, 54; M.S, Lehigh, 57, Ph.D.(physics), 62. Instr. PHYSICS, Lehigh Univ, 60-62; asst. prof, Univ. Vt, 62-66; ST. MICHAEL'S COL, 66-68, assoc. prof, 68-71, PROF, 71-, CHMN. DEPT, 67- Mem. advan. sci. sem, Denver Univ, 65; mem. summer conf. teaching physics in lib. arts cols, Middlebury Col, 69. U.S.N.R, 50-52. Am. Asn. Physics Teachers. Thermal diffusivities of metals; surface physics. Address: Dept. of Physics, St. Michael's College, Winooski, VT 05404.

FOLEY, FRANK C(LINGAN), b. Belleville, Ont, Aug. 8. 06; nat; m. 34; c. 1. GEOLOGY. B.A, Toronto, 29; Ph.D.(geol), Princeton, 38. Instr. geol, Dartmouth Col, 29-30; asst, Princeton, 30-33; from instr. to prof, North Dakota, 33-41; asst. geologist, U.S. Geol. Surv, 41-42, dist. geologist, 46-51; geologist, Ill. Geol. Surv, 51-54; PROF. GEOL, UNIV. KANS, 54- Acting state geologist, N.Dak, 35-36, asst. state geologist, 36-38, state geologist, 38-41; Kans. Geol. Surv, 54-70; mem, UN Mission, W.Africa, 68; UN Expert, Uganda, 71-72. C.Eng, 42-45, Maj. Geol. Soc. Am; Am. Soc. Econ. Geol; Am. Geophys. Union; Am. Inst. Prof. Geol. Groundwater geology. Address: Kansas Geological Survey, Lawrence, KS 66044.

FOLEY, G(EORGE) E(DWARD), b. Mechanicville, N.Y, Dec. 1, 12; m. 41; c. 1. MICROBIOLOGY. Sc.D.(microbiol), Amsterdam, 54. Asst, State Dept. Health, N.Y, 35-40; serologist, Roosevelt Hosp, N.Y, 40-41; assoc. epidemiol, Harvard Med. Sch. & sch. pub. health, 43-45; asst. bacteriologist, Mass. Gen. Hosp, 45-47; CHIEF MICROBIOL. LABS, CHILDREN'S CANCER RES. FOUND, 47-, ASSOC. DIR. LABS, 68-; RES. ASSOC. PATH. & BACTERIOLOGIST, CHILDREN'S HOSP. MED. CTR, 52-; LECTR. PATH, HARVARD MED. SCH, 64-, res. assoc, 52-64. Consult, Nat. Cancer Inst-Nat. Insts. Health, 56-, res. career award, 64-; mem. permanent sect. microbiol. standardization, Int. Asn. Microbiol. Dipl, Am. Bd. Med. Microbiol. Civilian with U.S.N, 41-45. Fel. AAAS; Am. Soc. Microbiol; Am. Soc. Pro. Biol; Am. Soc. Exp. Path; Am. Asn. Cancer Res; fel. Am. Pub. Health Asn; fel. Am. Acad. Microbiol; Royal Soc. Health. Medical bacteriology; epidemiology; experimental pathology; bacterial metabolism as related to chemotherapeutic agents; chemotherapeutic agents for infectious and neoplastic disease; cell culture; cell biology. Address: Children's Cancer Research Foundation, 35 Binney St, Boston, MA 02115.

FOLEY, GERARD M(OYLAN), b. Phila, Pa, Aug. 24, 16; m. 39; c. 2. INSTRUMENTATION. B.Sc, St. Andrews, 38. Res. engr, Battelle Mem. Inst, 38-46; res. technologist, LEEDS & NORTHRUP CO, 46-62, staff scientist, res. & develop. ctr, 62-70, CORP. SCIENTIST, 70- Lectr, Drexel Inst. Technol, 60-64. Sr. mem. Inst. Elec. & Electronics Eng; Health Physics Soc; Asn. Comput. Mach. Measurement and control; digital systems; temperature measurement; radiation safety. Address: Leeds & Northrup Technical Center, Dickerson Rd, North Wales, PA 19454.

FOLEY, H. THOMAS, b. Pittsburgh, Pa, Mar. 27, 33; m. 54; c. 2. INTERNAL MEDICINE, ONCOLOGY. B.S, Pittsburgh, 54; M.D, N.Y. Univ, 60. Intern & res, III & IV med. div, Bellevue Hosp, New York, 60-63; Liaison off. to east. solid tumor group, Nat. Cancer Inst, 63-65, sr. investr. radiation & med. br, 65-69, Baltimore Cancer Res. Ctr, 69-70; ASSOC. MED. OFF, GEORGETOWN MED. DIR, D.C. GEN. HOSP, 70- Asst. prof, Georgetown Univ. U.S.P.H.S, 63-67, Surg. Am. Fedn. Clin. Res. Clinical oncology; especially cancer chemotherapy and clinical pharmacology. Address: 3209 Crest Ave, Cheverly, MD 20785.

FOLEY, HENRY M(ICHAEL), b. Palmer, Mass, June 1, 17; m; c. 2. PHYSICS. B.S, Michigan, 38, M.A, 39, Coffin fel, 40-42, Ph.D.(physics), 42. Asst. physics, Michigan, 36-40, res. assoc, Off. Sci. Res. & Develop. proj, 42-44; res. physicst, appl. physics lab, Hopkins, 44-45; assoc. PHYSICS, COLUMBIA UNIV, 46-47, asst. prof, 48-50, assoc. prof, 50-54, PROF, 54-, CHMN. DEPT, 57-60, 71- Guggenheim fel, 54-55; Fulbright lectr, Utrecht,

55; liaison scientist, Off. Naval Res, London, 68-69. Am. Phys. Soc. Infrared spectroscopy; pressure broadening of spectral lines; atomic and molecular structure; atomic beams and magnetic moments; nuclear quadruple moments; radiation theory. Address: Dept. of Physics, Columbia University, New York, NY 10027.

FOLEY, H(OWARD) K(ENNETH), b. Youngstown, Ohio, Jan. 6, 20; m. 45; c. 2. POLYMER CHEMISTRY. B.S, Youngstown, 42; M.S, Akron, 56, Ph.D.(polymer chem), 64. Chem. operator, Plum Brook Ord. Works, Trojan Powder Co, Ohio, 42-44; qual. control.chemist, GOODYEAR TIRE & RUBBER CO, 44-46, res. chemist, 46-63, sr. res. chemist, 63-71, RES. SCIENTIST, 71- Am. Chem. Soc. Emulsion polymerization variables; shortstopping; popcorn polymer inhibition; analytical procedures pertaining to styrene-butadiene rubber and related polymers and the polymerization process; network properties of styrene-butadiene rubber, polymer-solvent interaction and stress versus strain; molecular weight distribution of styrene-butadiene rubbers. Address: Goodyear Tire & Rubber Co, Dept. 455B, 142 Goodyear Blvd, Akron, OH 44316.

FOLEY, JOHN F, b. Buffalo, N.Y, Feb. 1, 31; m. 55; c. 5. INTERNAL MEDICINE. M.D, Buffalo, 55; univ. fel, Yale, 55-56; univ. fel, Minnesota, 59-60, Ph.D.(internal med), 62. Res. specialist, Minnesota, 60-62, res. fel, internal med, 62-63; asst. prof, UNIV. NEBR, OMAHA, 63-68, PROF. MED, 68- U.S.P.H.S, 57-59. Am. Asn. Cancer Res; Am. Med. Asn; Tissue Cult. Asn; Am. Soc. Clin. Oncol; Am. Asn. Cancer Educ; fel. Am. Col. Physicians; Am. Fedn. Clin. Res. Tissue culture; cell interactions; chemical chemotherapy; preventive medicine; hormonal action on tissue culture cells. Address: Dept. of Internal Medicine, University of Nebraska, College of Medicine, 42nd St. & Dewey Ave, Omaha, NE 68105.

FOLEY, JOSEPH M(ICHAEL), b. Dorchester, Mass, Mar. 9, 16; m. 44. NEUROLOGY. A.B, Col. of Holy Cross, 37, hon. Sc.D, 62; M.D, Harvard, 41. Intern, Bellevue Hosp, N.Y, 41-43; asst. NEUROL, Harvard Med. Sch, 46-48, instr, 48-51, asst. prof, 51-59; PROF, Seton Hall Col. Med. & Dent, 59-61; SCH. MED, CASE WEST. RESERVE UNIV, 61-; DIR. DIV. NEUROL, UNIV. HOSPS. CLEVELAND, 66- Rockefeller asst, Boston City Hosp, 46-48; asst. prof, med. sch, Univ. Boston, 48-51; dir, dept. neurol, Jersey City Med. Ctr, 59-; consult, U.S. Air Force; mem. med. adv. bd. & res. rev. panel, Nat. Multiple Sclerosis Soc; coord, continuing med. educ, Case West. Reserve Univ; mem. bd. trustees, Col. Holy Cross. U.S.N, 43-46. Am. Neurol. Asn; Am. Asn. Neuropath; Asn. Res. Nerv. & Ment. Disease; Am. Acad. Neurol.(pres, 63-65); Am. Fedn. Clin. Res. Neurological medicine and pathology. Address: Division of Neurology, University Hospitals of Cleveland, Cleveland, OH 44106.

FOLEY, KENDALL FRANCIS, b. Pawtucket, R.I, Sept. 15, 41; m. 63; c. 2. ORGANIC CHEMISTRY. A.B, Brown, 63; Ph.D.(org. chem), Pa. State, 68. RES. CHEMIST, HERCULES, INC, 68- AAAS; Am. Chem. Soc. Synthesis and structural identification of alkaloids; polymer synthesis. Address: Hercules Research Center, Wilmington, DE 19899.

FOLEY, PATRICK J(OSEPH), b. Scotland, July 25, 26; Can. citizen; m. 64; c. 4. HUMAN FACTORS ENGINEERING. M.A, Glasgow Univ, 52. Sci. off, U.K. Ministry of Supply, 52-53; res. psychologist, Dept. Educ, Scotland, 53-54; sci. off, Defence Res. Bd. Can, 54-66; PROF. HUMAN FACTORS, FACULTY APPL. SCI. & ENG, UNIV. TORONTO, 66- Can. rep, human factors adv. group, NATO Sci. Comt; mem, Can. Nat. Comt, Int. Comn. Illum; Nat. Res. Coun. Asn. Comt. Exp. Psychol. Brit. Army, 43-48, Lt. Fel. Royal Soc. Arts; Human Factors Asn. Can. Engineering psychology, with particular reference to human performance theory; information processing and sensory-cognitive processes. Address: Dept. of Industrial Engineering, University of Toronto, Toronto 5, Ont, Can.

FOLEY, PATRICK JOSEPH, JR, b. Newark, N.J, May 26, 41; m. 62; c. 2. ORGANIC CHEMISTRY. B.S, St. Peter's Col, 63; M.A, Princeton, 65, Leroy-Wiley-McCay fel, 65-66, Ph.D.(org. chem), 66. Union Carbide Res. Inst. fel, 66-67; RES. CHEMIST, PLASTICS DEPT, E.I. DU PONT DE NEMOURS & CO, INC, 69- Ord.C, U.S.A, 67-69, Capt. Am. Chem. Soc. Plastics technology; flammability of plastics; plastics processing; glass, reinforced plastics. Address: 106 Crestwood Dr, Parkersburg, WV 26101.

FOLEY, RICHARD F, b. Worchester, Mass, May 2, 16; m. 54; c. 2. HORTICULTURE. B.S, Univ. NH, 48, M.S, 49; Ph.D, Cornell Univ, 55. Asst. horticulturist, U.S. Dept. Agr, 55-57; assoc. horticulturist, exp. sta, UNIV. IDAHO, 57-69, ASSOC. RES. PROF. HORT, 69- U.S.A, 39-43. Am. Soc. Hort. Sci. Plant physiology and breeding. Address: Branch Experiment Station, University of Idaho, Parma, ID 83660.

FOLEY, ROBERT T(HOMAS), b. Turners Falls, Mass, Dec. 21, 18; m. 45; c. 2. PHYSICAL CHEMISTRY. B.S, Massachusetts, 40; Hart fel. & M.S, Lafayette Col, 41; Pan-Am. fel. & Ph.D.(phys. chem), Texas, 48. Res. chemist, Am. Cyanamid Co, N.J, 41-45; instr. phys. chem, Texas, 45-48; res. chemist, Gen. Elec. Co, 48-52, supvr. gen. metall, 52-54, specialist surface chem, 54-61; supvr. electrochem, Melpar, Inc, Va, 61-64; RES. PROF. CHEM, AM. UNIV, 64- Consult, Union Carbide Corp; appl. physics lab, Johns Hopkins Univ; U.S. Army. AAAS; Am. Chem. Soc; Electrochem. Soc; Am. Electroplaters Asn; Nat. Asn. Corrosion Eng. Electrochemistry; energy conversion; fuel cells; batteries. Address: Dept. of Chemistry, American University, Washington, DC 20016.

FOLEY, ROY LEE, b. East St. Louis, Ill, July 18, 35; m. 60; c. 2. PHYSICAL CHEMISTRY, NUCLEAR MAGNETIC RESONANCE. B.S, Illinois State, 57; M.A, Southern Illinois, 59; Ph.D.(phys. chem), Mich. State, 64. Res. chemist, Celanese Res. Co, 64-68, sr. res. chemist, 68-69; analyst, Esso Chem. Co, Inc, 69-71; SR. PLANNING ANALYST, CORP. PLANNING, STANDARD OIL CO.(N.J), 71- Am. Phys. Soc; Am. Chem. Soc. Ultraviolet and Raman spectroscopy; high resolution, wide-line and carbon-13 nuclear magnetic resonance; electron spin resonance; gas adsorption studies. Address: Corporate Planning, Standard Oil Co.(N.J), 30 Rockefeller Plaza, New York, NY 10020.

FOLEY, WILLIAM M, b. Hoquiam, Wash, Mar. 12, 29; m. 53; c. 4. FLUID MECHANICS. B.S, Minnesota, 51; Hiller fel, Stanford, 55-57, M.S, 56, Ph.D.(aeronaut. & astronaut), 62. Supvr. gaseous physics group, res. labs, United Aircraft Corp, 58-65, chief aerophysics sect, 65-66, MGR. FLUID DYNAMICS LAB, UNITED AIRCRAFT RES. LABS, 67- Mem. res. adv. comt. aircraft aerodyn, NASA, 66-71. U.S.N, 52-55, Lt. Am. Phys. Soc; Am. Inst. Aeronaut. & Astronaut. Rarefied gas dynamics; fluid mechanics of gaseous core nuclear reactors; physics of gas-surface interactions. Address: 125 Farmstead Lane, Glastonbury, CT 06033.

FOLEY, WILLIAM T(HOMAS), b. New York, N.Y, Oct. 30, 11; m; c. 4. MEDICINE. A.B, Columbia, 33; M.D, Cornell, 37. Asst. prof. CLIN. MED, MED. COL, CORNELL UNIV, 51-59, ASSOC. PROF, 59- Chief vascular clinic, N.Y. Hosp. Consult, hosps. Mem, World Cardiac Cong, France, 50, D.C, 54, Belgium, 58; Pan-Am. Cardiac Cong, Buenos Aires, 52; Int. Conf. Thrombosis & Embolism, Basel, 54, Stockholm, 57, Belgium, 58, Mex, 62; conf. cerebral vascular disease, Josiah Macy, Jr. Found, 54, 58, 61, 64. Dipl, Am. Bd. Internal Med. Med.C, 38-46, Comdr; distinguished serv. medal. Sr. mem. Am. Soc. Clin. Invest; Harvey Soc; fel. Am. Med. Asn; Am. Heart Asn; fel. Am. Col. Physicians; Am. Col. Cardiol; hon. fel, Cardiol. Soc. Chile; hon. fel. Brazilian Cardiol. Soc; fel. N.Y. Acad. Med; hon. mem. Argentine Angiol. Soc; hon. mem. Argentine Cardiol. Soc. Clinical research in thromboembolism and vascular diseases; lymphedema; cerebrovascular disease. Address: 441 E. 68th St, New York, NY 10021.

FOLGER, DAVID W, b. Woburn, Mass, Nov. 21, 31; m. 56; c. 3. GEOLOGY. B.A, Dartmouth Col, 53; M.A, Columbia, 58, Ph.D.(submarine geol), 68. Petrol. geologist, Chevron Oil Co, 58-63; res. asst. submarine geol. & geophys, Lamont Geol. Observ, Columbia, 64-68; investr. submarine geol, Woods Hole Oceanog. Inst, 68-69; ASST. PROF. GEOL, MIDDLEBURY COL, 69-, ACTING CHMN. DEPT. GEOL. & GEOG, 70- U.S.N, 53-56, Res, 56-, Comdr. AAAS; Am. Geophys. Union; Soc. Econ. Paleont. & Mineral; Geol. Soc. Am. Submarine geology; processes of estuarine and deep sea sedimentation; composition of air and waterborne particulate matter; development of techniques for collection and evaluation of fine particulates; processes of lacustrine, estuarine, and deep sea sedimentation. Address: Dept. of Geology & Geography, Middlebury College, Middlebury, VT 05753.

FOLGER, ROBERT L(ANCASTER), b. Chicago, Ill, Jan. 27, 26; m. 48; c. 4. PHYSICAL CHEMISTRY. B.S, Illinois, 48; Ph.D.(chem), California, 51. Chemist, E.I. DU PONT DE NEMOURS & CO, 51-54, sr. supvr, 55-56, area supvr, 56-65, sr. res. supvr, 65-68, RES. MGR. ANAL. CHEM. DIV, 69- U.S.A, 44-46. Am. Chem. Soc. Nuclear and analytical chemistry; radiochemical separations; pyrometallurgical processes. Address: Savannah River Lab, E.I du Pont de Nemours & Co, Aiken, SC 29801.

FOLINAS, HELEN, R.S.M, b. Montpelier, Vt, June 5, 27. CELL PHYSIOLOGY. B.S, Trinity Col.(Vt), 52; M.S, St. Michael's Col.(Vt), 59; Nat. Sci. Found. fels, Fordham Univ, 61-62, 63-64, Ph.D.(physiol), 69. Instr. BIOL, TRINITY COL.(VT), 57-61, ASST. PROF. & CHMN. DEPT, 65- AAAS; Am. Soc. Cell Biol; Am. Soc. Zool; Am. Inst. Biol. Sci. Cell physiology with emphasis on the physiological and cellular aspects of development and inheritance. Address: Dept. of Biology, Trinity College, Colchester Ave, Burlington, VT 05401.

FOLINSBEE, R(OBERT) E(DWARD), b. Edmonton, Alta, Apr. 16, 17; m. 42; c. 4. GEOLOGY. B.Sc, Alberta, 38; M.S, Minnesota, 40, Ph.D.(petrol), 42. Asst. geologist, Geol. Surv. Can, 41-43; asst. prof. GEOL, UNIV. ALBERTA, 46-50, assoc. prof, 50-55, PROF, 55- Pres, 24th Int. Geol. Cong, Montreal, 72. R.C.A.F, 43-45. Geol. Soc. Am; Soc. Econ. Geol; Am. Geochem. Soc; Am. Asn. Petrol. Geol; Royal Soc. Can; Can. Inst. Mining & Metall; Geol. Asn. Can. Petrology; economic and structural geology; field geology; geochemistry. Address: Dept. of Geology, University of Alberta, Edmonton, Alta, Can.

FOLK, G(EORGE) E(DGAR), JR, b. Natick, Mass, Nov. 12, 14; m; c. 1. PHYSIOLOGY. A.B, Harvard, 37, Atkins traveling fel. & M.A, 40, Ph.D.(biol), 47. Instr. biol, St. Mark's Sch, 40-43; res. assoc, fatigue lab, Harvard, 43-47; asst. prof. biol, Bowdoin Col, 47-52, dir, Bowdoin Sci. Sta; assoc. prof. PHYSIOL, UNIV. IOWA, 52-65, PROF, 65- Physiologist, Climatic Res. Lab, 47; Univ. Iowa Col. Med. res. fel, Kings Col, Univ. London, 57-58; vis. res. prof, Arctic Aeromed. Lab, Ft. Wainwright, Alaska, 64-65; Fulbright fel, Netherlands, summer 69; Nat. Acad. Sci. cult. rep, Poland, summer 71; mem, Hibernation Info. Exchange, Off. Naval Res. Civilian with U.S.A; Off. Sci. Res. & Develop, 44. AAAS; Am. Physiol. Soc; Soc. Exp. Biol. & Med; Soc. Biol. Rhythm; Animal Behavior Soc; Arctic Inst. N.Am; Ecol. Soc. Am; Am. Soc. Mammal; Am. Soc. Zool; N.Y. Acad. Sci; Int. Soc. Biometeorol; Am. Polar Soc; Soc. Cryobiol; Am. Inst. Biol. Sci. Environmental physiology; factors influencing dissipation of heat by the human body and lower animals; mammalian physiology; biological rhythms. Address: Lab. of Environmental Physiology, Dept. of Physiology, University of Iowa, Iowa City, IA 52240.

FOLK, JOHN E(DWARD), b. Wash, D.C, Oct. 29, 25; m. 52; c. 1. BIOCHEMISTRY. B.S, Georgetown Univ, 48, M.S, 50, U.S. Pub. Health Serv. fel, 50-52, Ph.D.(biochem), 52. Am. Dent. Asn. fel, NAT. INSTS. HEALTH, 52-59, biochemist, 59-67, CHIEF, SECT. ENZYME CHEM, NAT. INST. DENT. RES, 67- U.S.N.R, 44-46. Am. Chem. Soc; Am. Soc. Biol. Chem. Enzyme mechanisms; relationships of enzyme structure and function. Address: 5701 Granby Rd, Derwood, MD 20855.

FOLK, ROBERT L(OUIS), b. Cleveland, Ohio, Sept. 30, 25; m. 46; c. 3. PETROLOGY. B.S, Pa. State Col, 46, M.S, 50, Ph.D.(mineral), 52. Asst. & instr. mineral, Pa. State Col, 46-50; res. geologist, Gulf Res. & Develop. Co, 51-52; asst. prof. GEOL, UNIV. TEX, AUSTIN, 52-56, assoc. prof, 56-61, PROF, 61- Petrography and genesis of limestones, dolomites, cherts, and sandstones; particle size distribution of recent sediments; geomorphology; sedimentary petrology; electron microscopy; texture of carbonate sands; natural history. Address: Dept. of Geology, University of Texas, Austin, TX 78704.

FOLK, R(OBERT) T(HOMAS), b. Reading, Pa, Oct. 17, 27; m. 58; c. 3. THEORETICAL PHYSICS. B.S, Lehigh, 53 & 54, Nat. Sci. Found. fel, 54-57, M.S, 55, Ph.D.(physics), 58. Instr. physics, Princeton, 57-59, 60-61; Nat.

Sci. Found. fel, Ger, 59-60; asst. prof. PHYSICS, LEHIGH UNIV, 61-63, assoc. prof, 63-66, PROF, 66- U.S.A.A.F, 46-49. Am. Phys. Soc. Theoretical nuclear physics. Address: Dept. of Physics, Lehigh University, Bethlehem, PA 18015.

FOLK, THEODORE LAMSON, b. Aurora, Ill, June 19, 40. ORGANIC CHEMISTRY, MASS SPECTROMETRY. B.A, Knox Col.(Ill), 62; M.S, Univ. Ariz, 65; Ph.D.(org. chem), Univ. Hawaii, 68; Univ. Akron, 69-70. Asst. chem, Univ. Ariz, 62-64; Univ. Hawaii, 65-68; SR. RES. CHEMIST, GOODYEAR TIRE & RUBBER CO, 68- Am. Chem. Soc; Am. Soc. Mass Spectrometry. Addition reactions of organolithium compounds on acetylenic systems; synthetic studies of polyhydroxynaphthoquinones; mass spectrometry of organic compounds. Address: Research Division, Goodyear Tire & Rubber Company, 142 Goodyear Blvd, Akron, OH 44316.

FOLKERS, KARL A(UGUST), b. Decatur, Ill, Sept. 1, 06; m. 32; c. 2. CHEMISTRY. B.S, Illinois, 28; Ph.D.(org. chem), Wisconsin, 31; hon. Sc.D, Phila. Col. Pharm, 62; hon. D.Pharm, Univ. Uppsala, 69; hon.Sc.D, Univ. Wis, 69. Squibb & Lilly fel, Yale, 31-34; lab. pure res, Merck & Co, Inc, 34-38, asst. dir. res, 38-45, dir. org. & biol. chem. res. div, 53-56, exec. dir. fundamental res, 56-62, v.pres. explor. res, 62-63; pres, Stanford Res. Inst, 63-68; PROF. CHEM. & DIR. INST. BIOMED. RES, UNIV. TEX, AUSTIN, 68- Mem. div. 9, Nat. Defense Res. Comt, 43-46; Harrison-Howe lectr, 49; Baker non-res. lectr, Cornell, 53; lectr. med. faculty, Lund, Stockholm, Uppsala Gothenborg Univs, Sweden, 54; Sturmer lectr, 57; chmn. adv. coun, dept. chem, Princeton, 58-64; guest lectr, Am-Swiss Found. Sci. Exchange, 61; Robert A. Welch Found. lectr, 63; courtesy prof, Stanford, 63-; courtesy lectr, California, Berkeley, 63-; Marchon vis. lectr, Newcastle, 64; F.F. Nord lectr, Fordham Univ, 71; mem. revision comt, U.S. Pharmacopoeia. Co-recipient, Mead Johnson & Co. Award, 40 & 49; Presidential Cert. of Merit, 48; Merck & Co, Inc. Award, 51; Spencer Award, 59; Perkin Medal, 60; co-recipient, Van Meter Prize, Am. Thyroid Asn, 69. Nat. Acad. Sci; AAAS; Am. Soc. Biol. Chem; Am. Inst. Chem; Am. Inst. Nutrit; Soc. Exp. Biol. & Med; N.Y. Acad. Sci; hon. mem. Italian Soc. Pharmaceut. Sci. Organic chemistry; catalytic hydrogenation; pyrimidine; alkaloids; vitamins; synthetic medicinals; antibiotics; hormones; coenzymes. Address: 6406 Mesa Dr, Austin, TX 78731.

FOLKERT, JAY E(RNEST), b. Holland, Mich, Dec. 16, 16; m. 46; c. 3. MATHEMATICS. A.B, Hope Col, 39; M.A, Michigan, 40; Ph.D.(math), Mich. State, 55. Teacher, pub. schs, 40-42, 46; from instr. MATH. to PROF, HOPE COL, 46-, chmn. dept, 57-71. U.S.A.A.F, 42-45, Capt. AAAS; Math. Asn. Am; Am. Math. Soc; Am. Sci. Affiliation. General mathematics; education. Address: Dept. of Mathematics, Hope College, Holland, MI 49423.

FOLKINS, HILLIS O(TTY), b. Millstream, N.B, Aug. 20, 11; nat; m. 39; c. 3. CHEMISTRY. B.Sc, Mt. Allison, 35; M.Sc, McGill, 37, Ph.D.(phys. chem), 39. Instr. chem, Mt. Allison, 35-36; McGill, 37-38; res. group leader, Pure Oil Co, 39-49, supvr. res. sect, 50-61, res. assoc, 61-65; SR. RES. ASSOC, RES. CTR, UNION OIL CO. CALIF, 65- Chemist, Imp. Oil Co, 36-38. Am. Chem. Soc. Reaction kinetics; free radicals in organic reactions; catalysis; hydrocarbon reactions; petrochemicals; thermodynamics; radiation chemistry. Address: Research Dept, Union Oil Co. of California, P.O. Box 76, Brea, CA 92621.

FOLKMAN, MOSES JUDAH, b. Cleveland, Ohio, Feb. 24, 33; m. 60; c. 1. SURGERY. B.A, Ohio State, 53; M.D, Harvard, 57. Intern SURG, Mass. Gen. Hosp, 57-58, asst. res, 58-60, sr. res. & chief res, 62-65; instr, HARVARD MED. SCH, 65-66, assoc, 66-67, PROF, 67-, JULIA DYCKMAN ANDRUS PROF. PEDIAT. SURG, 68-; SURGEON & CHIEF, CHILDREN'S HOSP. MED. CTR, 68- Nat. Cancer Inst. res. career develop. award, 65-70. Dipl, Am. Bd. Surg, 66, Am. Bd. Thoracic Surg, 68. Med.C, U.S.N.R, 60-62, Lt. N.Y. Acad. Sci. Tissue culture; diffusion of drugs and administration of anesthetics through silicone rubber; cancer research. Address: Children's Hospital Medical Center, 300 Longwood Ave, Boston, MA 02115.

FOLKS, HOMER C(LIFTON), b. Hydro, Okla, Aug. 6, 23; m. 50; c. 3. SOILS. B.S, Okla. State, 50; Ph.D.(soils), Iowa State, 54. Instr. soils, Iowa State, 53-54, exten. area agronomist, 54-55; asst. prof. soils, N.C. State Col, 55-58, assoc. prof, 58-59, asst. dir. instr, 59-63; PROF. AGRON. & ASSOC. DEAN COL. AGR, UNIV. MO-COLUMBIA, 63- U.S.A, 42-46, Sgt. Am. Soc. Agron. Soil genesis and morphology; mechanics of soil profile development. Address: Office of the Dean, College of Agriculture, 2-64 Agriculture Bldg, University of Missouri-Columbia, Columbia, MO 65201.

FOLKS, JOHN LEROY, b. Hydro, Okla, Oct. 12, 29; m. 56; c. 3. MATHEMATICAL STATISTICS. B.A, Okla. State, 53, M.S, 55; Alumni Asn. fel, Iowa State, 55-56, Nat. Sci. Found. fel, 56-57, Ph.D.(statist), 58. Statistician, opers. res, Tex. Instruments, 58-61; assoc. prof. math, OKLA. STATE UNIV, 61-66, PROF. MATH. & STATIST, 66-, CHMN. STATIST. UNIT, 70- Nat. Sci. Found. faculty fel, 66-67. U.S.A, 50-52. Am. Statist. Asn; Inst. Math. Statist; Am. Soc. Qual. Control; Biomet. Soc; Int. Statist. Inst. Experimental design; stochastic processes; reliability theory. Address: 22 University Circle, Stillwater, OK 74074.

FOLLAND, DONALD F(REEZE), b. Salt Lake City, Utah, Nov. 23, 10; m. 40; c. 5. ELECTRICAL ENGINEERING, ELECTRONICS. B.S, Utah, 33; M.S, Calif. Inst. Tech, 36. Asst. physics, Calif. Inst. Tech, 36-39; inventory asst, Utah Power & Light Co, 39-40; from asst. proj. engr. to sect. head, Sperry Gyroscope Co, 40-52; design specialist to sr. elec. group engr, astronaut. div, Gen. Dynamics/Convair, 52-59; head adv. projs. dept, eng. dept, Sperry-Utah Co, SPERRY-RAND CORP, 59-68, MGR. ADV. SYSTS. UNIVAC SALT LAKE CITY DEFENSE SYSTS. DIV, 68- Sr. mem. Inst. Elec. & Electronics Eng.(Community Serv. Award, 70); Guided missile radio tracking systems; radio guidance, range safety and missile guidance systems; fluidic control systems. Address: Univac Salt Lake City Defense Systems Division, Sperry Rand Corp, Salt Lake City, UT 84116.

FOLLAND, NATHAN ORLANDO, b. Greenbush, Minn, Jan. 12, 37; m. 60; c. 2. PHYSICS. B.A, Concordia Col, 59; Ph.D.(physics), Iowa State, 65. NATO fel, Messina, 65-66; ASST. PROF. PHYSICS, KANS. STATE UNIV, 66- Am. Phys. Soc. Band theory and optical properties of solids. Address: Dept. of Physics, Kansas State University, Manhattan, KS 66502.

FOLLETT, ROY H, b. Cowdrey, Colo, Feb. 27, 35; m. 59; c. 2. SOIL SCIENCE, AGRONOMY. B.S, Colo. State Univ, 57, M.S, 63, Ph.D.(soil sci), 69. Soil scientist, U.S. Geol. Surv, Kans, 57-58; Soil Conserv. Serv, Colo, 58-60; jr. agronomist, Colo. State Univ, 60-63; soil scientist, Soil Conserv. Serv, Colo, 63-64; jr. agronomist & ext. agronomist, Colo. State Univ, 64-70; EXT. AGRONOMIST, OHIO STATE UNIV, 70- U.S.A, 58, Res, 58-, Maj. Am. Soc. Agron; Soil Conserv. Soc. Am. Soil fertility; soil micronutrients; soil test correlations; saline soils. Address: Dept. of Agronomy, College of Agriculture, Ohio State University, 1885 Neil Ave, Columbus, OH 43210.

FOLLEY, KARL W(ILMOT), b. Elgin, Man, Can, Apr. 24, 05; nat; m. 34; c. 1. MATHEMATICS. B.Sc, Saskatchewan, 24, M.Sc, 25; M.A, Toronto, 26, fel, 26-28, Ph.D.(math), 28. Asst. prof. MATH, Trinity Col.(Conn), 28-29; instr, Col. City of Detroit, 29-30, asst. prof, 30-33; Wayne State Univ, 33-38, assoc. prof, 38-48, prof, 48-69, chmn. dept, 62-69; PROF. & CHMN. DEPT, UNIV. DETROIT, 69- Proj. supvr. training films, Jam Handy Corp, 42-46; vis. prof, U.S. Naval Postgrad. Sch, Calif, 56-57. Am. Math. Soc; Math. Asn. Am. Transfinite numbers; point set theory; simply ordered sets; generalized continuum hypothesis. Address: Dept. of Mathematics, University of Detroit, Detroit, MI 48221.

FOLLIN, JAMES W(IGHTMAN), JR, b. Phila, Pa, Oct. 20, 19; m. 52; c. 1. PHYSICS. B.S, Mass. Inst. Technol, 40; Chicago, 40-41; fel, Calif. Inst. Technol, 45-47, Ph.D.(physics), 47. Physicist, U.S. Navy underwater sound lab, div. war res, Columbia, 41-44; Off. Sci. Res. & Develop. rocket proj, Calif. Inst. Technol, 44-46; physicist, Naval Ord. Testing Sta, Calif, 47; instr. physics, Princeton, 47-48; PHYSICIST, APPLIED PHYSICS LAB, JOHNS HOPKINS UNIV, 48- Mem. staff, Inst. Advan. Study, 47-48. Am. Phys. Soc. Quantum mechanics; astro-physics; cosmic rays; underwater sound; ballistics; propagation of cosmic rays through interstellar space. Address: Applied Physics Lab, Johns Hopkins University, 8621 Georgia Ave, Silver Spring, MD 20910.

FOLLOWS, ALAN G(REAVES), b. Normanton, Eng, Dec. 20, 21; nat; m. 50; c. 3. CHEMISTRY, CHEMICAL ENGINEERING. B.Sc, Queen's (Can), 44, Niesh fel, 45, M.Sc, 45; Can. Industs, Ltd. fel, Toronto, 47, Ph.D.(elec), 48. Chem. res, Nat. Res. Council of Can, Queen's (Can), 44-45; lectr. phys. chem. Toronto, 47-48; res. chemist, solvay process div, ALLIED CHEM. CORP, 48-59, asst. dir. res, 59-69, MGR. TECHNOL, INDUST. CHEM. DIV, 69- AAAS; Am. Chem. Soc; Am. Inst. Chem. Electrochemistry; industrial research and management; titanium; alkalies. Address: Industrial Chemicals Division, Allied Chemical Corp, Solvay, NY 13209.

FOLLSTAD, MERLE N(ORMAN), b. Milwaukee, Wis, May 14, 31; m. 63; c. 1. BOTANY. B.S, Wisconsin, 55; M.S, Minnesota, 61, Ph.D.(plant path), 64. Res. asst, Inst. Paper Chem, Lawrence, 56-58; plant path, Minnesota, 58-64; res. plant pathologist, mkt. qual. res. div, U.S. Dept. Agr, 64-66; res. assoc, N.C. State Univ, 66-67; microbiologist, North. Regional Res. Lab, Ill, 67-68; ASST. PROF. BIOL, WIS. STATE UNIV, WHITEWATER, 68- AAAS; Botanical Soc. Am; Am. Phytopath. Soc; Am. Inst. Biol. Sci. Developmental anatomy of seed plants; plant histochemistry. Address: Dept. of Biology, Wisconsin State University, Whitewater, WI 53190.

FOLMER, O(RVILLE) F(REDERICK), JR, b. Charleroi, Pa, Sept. 16, 31; m. 52. ANALYTICAL & ORGANIC CHEMISTRY. B.S, West Virginia, 52, M.S, 54, Res. Corp. fel, 53-54, Nat. Sci. Found. fel, 55-57, Ph.D.(org. chem), 57. Appln. engr, Sci. Instruments Div, Beckman Instruments, Inc, 57-58; lab. supvr, Greenbrier Instruments, Inc, 58-59; res. chemist, anal. sect, res. serv. div, CONTINENTAL OIL CO, 59-68, SR. RES. SCIENTIST, 68- Am. Chem. Soc. Synthesis of organic boron compounds; nitro group and activated methylene group condensation reaction; gas chromatography. Address: Continental Oil Co, Drawer 1267, Ponca City, OK 74601.

FOLSE, DEAN S(YDNEY), b. Kansas City, Mo, Dec. 19, 21; m. 47. VETERINARY PATHOLOGY & PARASITOLOGY. B.S. & D.V.M, Agr. & Mech. Col, Texas, 45; M.S, Kansas State Col, 46; Ph.D, Univ. Tex, 70. Asst. prof. path, Ala. Polytech, 48-50, assoc. prof, 50-52; Kans. State Univ, 52-66; U.S. Atomic Energy Comn. histopathologist, inst. biol. & agr, Seibersdorf Reactor Ctr, Austria, 66-68; res. instr. PATH, UNIV. TEX. MED. BR. GALVESTON, 69-71, RES. ASST. PROF, 71- AAAS; Am. Soc. Parasitol; Am. Vet. Med. Asn. Address: Dept. of Pathology, University of Texas Medical Branch, Galveston, TX 77550.

FOLSOM, CLARENCE B(URTON), JR, b. Denver, Colo, June 14, 17; m. 41; c. 2. PETROLEUM ENGINEERING. M.Sc.(petrol. eng), Colo. Sch. Mines, 52. Petrol. engr, Phillips Petrol. Co, 41-46; head petrol. eng. dept, N.Mex. Sch. Mines, 47-53; CHIEF PETROL. ENGR, STATE GEOL. SURV, N.DAK, 53-; ASSOC. PROF. GEOL, UNIV. N.DAK, 70- C.Eng, 41-47, Capt. Oil and gas reserves; oil and gas conservation; secondary recovery of oil and gas. Address: Dept. of Geology, University of North Dakota, Grand Forks, ND 58201.

FOLSOM, L(UCAS) W(ENDELL), b. Langdon, Kans, Aug. 4, 14; m. 44; c. 1. GEOLOGY. A.B, West Virginia, 39, fel, 52-53, M.S, 53. Asst. field geologist, W.Va. Geol. Surv, 39, asst. geologist, 40-45; eng. aid, Equitable Gas Co, Pa, 39-40; geologist, Calif. Co, Ky, Wyo. & La, 45-50; Mt. Fuel Supply Co, 50-57, sr. geologist, 57-58, mgr. explor. div, Utah, 58-69; INSTR. NAT. SCI, GROVE CITY COL, 70- Consult. geologist, 69- Am. Inst. Prof. Geol. Geomorphology; structural geology; geology of oil and natural gas. Address: 415 Garden Ave, Grove City, PA 16127.

FOLSOM, MARY O'HEARN, b. Dubuque, Iowa, Jan. 4, 16; div; c. 2. MATHEMATICS. B.A, Univ. Iowa, 39, Ph.D.(math. educ), 58; M.Ed, Univ. Miami, 55. Res. analyst Japanese code, U.S. Govt. Mil. Intel, 43-45; asst. prof. EDUC, UNIV. MIAMI, 58-61, assoc. prof, 61-64, PROF, 64- Summers, res. asst, Univ. Ill, 61; assoc. prof, San Jose State Col, 63; Stanford Univ, 64, prof, 65; Mich. State Univ, 67. AAAS; Math. Asn. Am. Mathematics education. Address: University of Miami, Box 8065, Coral Gables, FL 33124.

FOLSOM, RICHARD G(ILMAN), b. Los Angeles, Calif, Feb. 3, 07; m. 29; c. 3. MECHANICAL ENGINEERING. B.S, Calif. Inst. Tech, 28, M.S, 29, fel, 28-32, Ph.D.(mech. eng), 32; hon. D.Sc, Northwestern, 62; hon. D.Sc, Union Col, 64; hon. D.Sc, Albany Med. Col, 71; hon. D.Eng, Rose Polytech. Inst, 71.

Engr, Pasadena, Calif, 32-33; instr. mech. eng, dept. eng, California, Berkeley, 33-37, asst. prof, 37-41, assoc. prof, 41-47, prof, 47-53, chmn. div. mech. eng, 48-53, prof. & dir. eng. res. inst, Michigan, 53-58; pres, Rensselaer Polytech. Inst, 58-71; private practice, 71- Staff engr, jet propulsion lab, Calif. Inst. Technol, 43-44. Nat. Acad. Eng; hon. mem. Am. Soc. Mech. Eng; hon. mem. Am. Soc. Eng. Educ; assoc. fel. Inst. Aeronaut. & Astronaut; Am. Inst. Chem. Eng. Pumps; fluid metering; fluid flow and heat transfer at low pressures; fundamental fluid mechanics; mechanical equipment. Address: 585 Oakville Crossroad, Napa, CA 94558.

FOLSOM, T(HEODORE) R(OBERT), b. San Diego, Calif, Mar, 20, 08; m. 35; c. 2. PHYSICS, OCEANOGRAPHY. B.S, Calif. Inst. Tech, 41, M.S, 32; Scripps Inst. Oceanog, 46-52; Ph.D.(phys. oceanog), 52. Asst. physicist, Soiland Clinic, 33; Lincoln Gen. Hosp, 33-36; assoc. physicist, Mem. Hosp, 37-42; physicist, Mass. Inst. Tech, 42-44; Food Mach. Corp, 44-45; private consult, 46-52; asst. res. oceanographer, SCRIPPS INST. OCEANOG, 52-59, sr. engr, 59-64, RES. OCEANOGRAPHER, 64- Consult, comt. effects of atomic radiation on oceanog. & fisheries, Nat. Acad. Sci-Nat. Res. Coun, 57, mem. subcomt. low-level contamination of mat. & reagents, 63-68; consult, Off. Naval Res, 64-; mem, Argonne Univs. Asn. rev. comt. radiol. physics div, Argonne Nat. Lab, 69-73, chmn, 70; mem, U.S. Senate Pub. Works Sub-Panel Ocean Dumping, 71. AAAS; Am. Phys. Soc; Am. Geophys. Union; Radiation Res. Soc; Am. Soc. Limnol. & Oceanog; N.Y. Acad. Sci. Techniques in oceanography and radiology, particularly measurements traces fallout radioactivity in marine environment, especially by gamma and alpha spectrometry. Address: Scripps Institution of Oceanography, University of California at San Diego, La Jolla, CA 92037.

FOLSOME, CLAIR E(DWIN), b. Ann Arbor, Mich, June 26, 35; m. 56; c. 4. MICROBIAL GENETICS. A.B, Harvard, 56, M.S, 59, Ph.D.(biol), 60. Res. asst. prof. genetics, grad. sch. med, Boston, 60-62; sr. lectr, Melbourne, 62-64; assoc. prof. MICROBIOL, UNIV. HAWAII, 64-67, PROF, 67- Nat. Res. Coun. sr. res. assoc, Ames Res. Ctr, NASA, 70-71. AAAS; Am. Soc. Microbiol; Am. Soc. Cell Biol; Genetics Soc. Am; Am. Soc. Zool; Am. Chem. Soc. Exobiology; analysis of extraterrestrial organic matter. Address: Dept. of Microbiology, University of Hawaii, Honolulu, HI 96822.

FOLT, V(ERNON) L(OUIS), b. Minneapolis, Minn, Aug. 2, 18; m. 46; c. 5. POLYMER SCIENCE. B.Ch.E, Univ. Minn, 41. Res. chemist, RES. CTR, B.F. GOODRICH CO, 41-60, SR. RES. ASSOC, 60- AAAS; Soc. Rheol; Am. Chem. Soc; Soc. Plastics Eng; Am. Inst. Chem. Rheology; structure and properties of polymers. Address: Research Center, B.F. Goodrich Co, Brecksville, OH 44101.

FOLTZ, CALVIN M(ARTIN), b. Akron, Pa, Nov. 29, 24; m. 53; c. 2. ORGANIC & MEDICINAL CHEMISTRY. B.Sc, Phila. Col. Pharm, 48, M.Sc, 49; Am. Found. Pharmaceut. Ed. fel, Purdue, 50-52, Ph.D.(med. chem), 54; Organon fel, Wayne State, 52-54. Res. fel, NAT. INST. ARTHRITIS & METAB. DISEASES, NAT. INSTS. HEALTH, U.S. PUB. HEALTH SERV, 55-56, RES. CHEMIST, LAB. CHEM, 56- U.S.N, 44-46. Am. Chem. Soc; The Chem. Soc. Synthesis of adrenergic blocking agents; stereochemistry; chemistry of amino acids, peptides and proteins; characterization of Factor 3, a source of selenium in deficiency diseases; heterocyclic chemistry; photochemistry. Address: Lab. of Chemistry, National Institute of Arthritis & Metabolic Diseases, National Insitutes of Health, U.S. Public Health Service, Bethesda, MD 20014.

FOLTZ, ELDON L(EROY), b. Ft. Collins, Colo, Mar. 28, 19; m. 43; c. 4. NEUROSURGERY. B.S, Mich. State Col, 41; M.D, Michigan, 43. Asst. res. surg, Michigan, 46-47; neurosurg. res, med. sch, Dartmouth, 47-49; clin. asst, Louisville, 49-50; Nat. Inst. Mental Health fel. & res. assoc. surg, Washington (Seattle), 50-51, instr. neurosurg, 51-53, asst. prof, 53-58, assoc. prof, 58-64, prof, 64-69; PROF. NEUROL. SURG. & CHMN. DIV, UNIV. CALIF, IRVINE, 69- Markle scholar, 54. Med.C, U.S.N.R, 44-46, Lt AAAS; Am. Asn. Neurol. Surg; Am. Electroencephalog. Soc; Neurosurg. Soc. Am; Am. Med. Asn; Am. Col. Surg; Am. Acad. Neurol; Am. Acad. Neurol. Surg. Cerebral concussion; consciousness; cerebral vascular disease; central factors of psychosomatic diseases; hydrocephalus. Address: Division of Neurological Surgery, University of California, Irvine, CA 92664.

FOLTZ, FLOYD M(ATHEW), b. Mitchell, S.Dak, Feb. 27, 27; m. 48; c. 2. ANATOMY. B.S, Dakota Wesleyan, 51; M.A, South Dakota, 54; Ph.D, Kansas, 58. Instr. ANAT, Kansas, 57-58; asst. prof, South Dakota, 58-65; ASSOC. PROF, SCH. MED, MED. CTR, UNIV. KANS, 65- U.S.N, 43-46. Am. Asn. Anat. Comparative neuroanatomy. Address: Dept. of Anatomy, School of Medicine, University of Kansas Medical Center, Kansas City, KS 66103.

FOLTZ, GEORGE E(DWARD), b. Pittsburgh, Pa, May 20, 24; m. 45, 55; c. 2. ORGANIC CHEMISTRY. B.S, Carnegie Inst. Technol, 47, M.S, 51, Ph.D. (chem), 52. Control chemist resins & solvents, Neville Co, 47-48; sr. res. chemist, exploratory org, Columbia-Southern Chem. Corp, 52-54; ASSOC. CHEMIST, NEVILLE CHEM. CO, 54- U.S.A, 44-46. Benzidine re-arrangement; polymer chemistry; indene chemistry. Address: 339 Goldsmith Rd, Pittsburgh, PA 15237.

FOLTZ, HARRY PARKER, b. Tacoma, Wash, Dec. 21, 22; m. 44; c. 3. METEOROLOGY. B.A, California, Los Angeles, 48; Chicago, 59; Ph.D.(atmospheric sci), Colorado State, 67. Analyst, U.S. WEATHER BUR, 44-46, forecaster, 46-60; meteorologist in charge, 60-65, CHIEF OPERS. SECT, 65- U.S.A.A.F, 43-44. Am. Meteorol. Soc. Predictive techniques for forecasting clear air turbulence. Address: U.S. Weather Bureau, Environmental Science Services Administration, Gramax Bldg, Silver Spring, MD 20910.

FOLTZ, NEVIN D, b. Akron, Pa, Feb. 12, 40; m. 65; c. 1. MOLECULAR PHYSICS. B.Sc, Pa. State, 62, M.Sc, 64, Ph.D.(physics), 68. Instr. PHYSICS, Pa. State, Commonwealth Campus, 64-66; ASST. PROF, MEM. UNIV. NEWF, 68- Optical Soc. Am; Am. Inst. Physics; Can. Asn. Physicists; Am. Phys. Soc. Nonlinear optics—stimulated light scattering from liquids and gases. Address: Dept. of Physics, Memorial University of Newfoundland, St. John's, Newf, Can.

FOLTZ, RODGER L, b. Milwaukee, Wis, Feb. 10, 34; m. 56; c. 2. ORGANIC CHEMISTRY. B.S, Mass. Inst. Technol, 56; Ph.D.(org. chem), Univ. Wis, 61. Res. chemist, Battelle Mem. Inst, 61-70, proj. leader, 70-71; ADJ. PROF, COL. PHARM, OHIO STATE UNIV, 71- Am. Chem. Soc; The Chem. Soc; Am. Soc. Mass Spectrometry. Organic mass spectrometry. Address: College of Pharmacy, Ohio State University, 1659 N. High, Columbus, OH 43210.

FOLTZ, THOMAS R(OBERTS), JR, b. Phila, Pa, July 8, 20; m. 45; c. 2. PROTEIN CHEMISTRY. B.S, Phila. Col. Pharm, 42; St. Joseph's Col.(Pa); A.M, Temple, 52; Boston Univ, 65; Cand. Phil, Northwest. Univ.(Ill), 70. Mem. staff, Gulf Ref. Co, 41; res. chemist, Phila. Quartz Co, 42-46; instr. textile chem, Phila. Textile Inst, 46-49, asst. prof, 49-54; chief chemist & dir. chem. res, Lockport Felt Co, 54-63; PROD. MGR, COLLAGEN & PROTEIN SPECIALTIES, ARMOUR FOOD CO, PHOENIX, 63- Am. Chem. Soc; fel. Am. Inst. Chem; Am. Mkt. Asn; Am. Leather Chem. Asn; Inst. Food Technol. Phase rule studies of system Na_2O, S_iO_2, H_2O; analytical methodology of textile chemistry; wool protein; denaturation; wool fabric finishing; leather chemistry; by-product utilization, meat or poultry; microwave, collagen and protein technology. Address: 6445 E. Calle Redonda, Scottsdale, AZ 85251.

FOLTZ, VIRGINIA C, b. Ashtabula, Ohio, Aug. 3, 11; m. 33; c. 2. RADIATION BIOLOGY, GENETICS. B.S, Baldwin-Wallace Col, 33; M.S, Houston, 67; Ph.D.(radiation biol), Texas Woman's Univ, 69. Instr. biol, Houston, 63-64; lectr. heredity, Texas Woman's Univ, spring 65; ASST. PROF. zool, La. Polytech, 69-70; BIOL, PAN AM. UNIV, 70- AAAS; Genetics Soc. Am. Radiation biology and genetic studies with Drosophila melanogaster subjected to radiation and some genetron and freon gases that may be found in polluted air. Address: Dept. of Biology, Pan American University, Edinburg, TX 78539.

FOLWEILER, ROBERT C(OOPER), b. Tallahassee, Fla, Aug. 2, 33; m. 61; c. 3. CRYSTAL GROWTH. B.A, Rice, 55, B.S, 56, M.S, 58. Res. asst. metall, Rice, 56-58; metallurgist ceramics, Gen. Elec. Res. Lab, 59-61; sr. scientist, res. & adv. develop. div, Avco Corp, 61; v.pres. & lab. dir, Lexington Labs, Inc, 61-68; ASST. MGR. APPL. PHYSICS DEPT, ELECTRO-OPTICS DIV, SANDERS ASSOCS, INC, 68- Vis. scientist, Mass. Inst. Technol, 69- Ord.C, 58-59, Res, 59-67, Capt. Am. Asn. Crystal Growth; Am. Ceramic Soc; Am. Inst. Mining, Metall. & Petrol. Eng. Crystal growth of dielectrics and semiconductors by vapor phase reaction and solution; development of process control for crystal growth; investigation of new laser hosts and active ions. Address: Electro-optics Division, Sanders Associates, Inc, 95 Canal St, Nashua, NH 03060.

FOLZ, SYLVESTER D, b. Marshfield, Wis, Feb. 26, 41; m. 62; c. 3. PARASITOLOGY, ZOOLOGY. B.S, Wisconsin, 64, M.S, 66, Ph.D.(parasitol), 68. Res. asst. PARASITOL, Wisconsin, 64-66, asst, 66-68; res. assoc, UPJOHN CO, 68-69, PROJ. LEADER, 69- Am. Soc. Parasitol; Am. Soc. Protozool; Wildlife Disease Asn. Helminthology; protozoology; coccidiosis; malaria; helminth studies in man and animals. Address: The Upjohn Co, Kalamazoo, MI 49001.

FOMON, JOHN J(OSEPH), b. Chicago, Ill, Feb. 10, 22; m; c. 5. SURGERY. B.S, Georgetown, 43, M.D, 46. Instr. SURG, sch. med. & dent, Rochester, 55; SCH. MED, UNIV. MIAMI, 55-56, asst. prof, 56-59, ASSOC. PROF, 59- Consult. surgeon, Vet. Admin. Hosp, Coral Gables, 55- Dipl, Nat. Bd. Med. Exam, 47; Am. Bd. Surg, 56; Am. Bd. Thoracic Surg, 61. Cardiovascular surgery; cancer. Address: Dept. of Surgery, Biscayne Annex, University of Miami, P.O. Box 875, Miami, FL 33152.

FOMON, SAMUEL JOSEPH, b. Chicago, Ill, Mar. 9, 23; m. 48; c. 5. PEDIATRICS, NUTRITION. A.B, Harvard, 45; M.D, Pennsylvania, 47. Res. pediat, Phila. Children's Hosp, 48-50; res. found. fel. biochem, Cincinnati Children's Hosp, 50-52; asst. prof. PEDIAT, UNIV. IOWA, 54-57, assoc. prof, 57-60, PROF, 60- Mem. comt. nutrit, Am. Acad. Pediat, 58-63, chmn, 60-63; consult. nutrit, maternal & child health serv, Health Serv. & Ment. Health Admin, 65-; chmn. sect. II, panel 2, White House Conf. on Food, Nutrit. & Health, 69. Career develop. award, U.S. Pub. Health Serv, 62-67. Med.Serv.C, 52-54, Capt. Am. Acad. Pediat.(Borden Award, 66); Am. Pub. Health Asn; Brit. Nutrit. Soc; Soc. Pediat. Res; Am. Pediat. Soc; Am. Inst. Nutrit; Am. Soc. Clin. Nutrit. Infant nutrition, growth, and body composition. Address: Dept. of Pediatrics, University Hospitals, University of Iowa, Iowa City, IA 52240.

FONASH, STEPHAN J(OSEPH), b. Phila, Pa, Oct. 28, 41; m. 68; c. 1. SOLID STATE PHYSICS, PHYSICAL ELECTRONICS. B.S, Pa. State Univ, 63; fel, Cornell Univ, 63-64; Nat. Sci. Found. fel, Univ. Pa, 64-66, univ. fel, 66-68, Ph.D.(eng), 68. Fel. surface physics, Univ. Pa, 68; ASST. PROF. ENG. SCI, PA. STATE UNIV, 68- NASA faculty fel, Jet Propulsion Lab, 70. Am. Phys. Soc; Am. Soc. Eng. Educ; Am. Soc. Test. & Mat. Interface and bulk phenomena exhibited by materials, especially field emission, field ionization, stress effects on junction characteristics, superconductivity, phonon and photon interaction with electrons, acoustic emission of materials under stress. Address: Dept. of Engineering Science, 231-B Sackett Bldg, Pennsylvania State University, University Park, PA 16802.

FONDA, LYMAN D, b. Coldwater, Mich, Apr. 13, 99; m. 33. PHARMACY. B.Sc, Purdue, 23; M.S, Florida, 27, M.A, N.Y. Univ, 38, Ph.D, 41. Instr. pharm, pharmacog. & pharmacol, Florida, 27-29; asst. prof. PHARM, Rutgers, 29-32; from asst. prof. to prof, Brooklyn Col. Pharm, 32-64; LECTR. & ADJ. PROF. PHARM, UNIV. N.C, 67- Researcher & dir. pilot plant oper, Bell Chem. Co. U.S.A, 18-19; Nat. Guard, 22-23, 1st Lt. Am. Pub. Health Asn; Am. Pharmaceut. Asn; Am. Asn. Cols. Pharm. Colormetric method for determination of pH in highly buffered liquids utilizing very small quantities of unknown; calculation of specific gravity of solutions; evaluation of Thixin in preparation of a series of new ointment bases; use of a colormetric test for the determination of hydrogen ion concentration of ophthalmic solutions. Address: 710 Overhill Terr, Durham, NC 27707.

FONDA, MARGARET L(EE), b. Cleveland, Ohio, July 13, 42. BIOCHEMISTRY. B.S, Univ. Del, 64; NASA traineeship, Univ. Tenn, Knoxville, 64-67,

Nat. Insts. Health fel, 67-68, Ph.D.(biochem), 68. Res. assoc. BIOCHEM, Iowa State Univ, 68-70; ASST. PROF, SCH. MED, UNIV. LOUISVILLE, 70- Nat. Insts. Health res. assoc, Iowa State Univ, 69-70. AAAS; Am. Chem. Soc. Mechanism of enzyme action; interaction of coenzymes and substrates with enzymes; control of enzyme action. Address: Dept. of Biochemistry, University of Louisville, School of Medicine, Louisville, KY 40201.

FONDA, RICHARD W(ESTON), b. Chicago, Ill, June 14, 40; m. 63; c. 2. PLANT ECOLOGY. B.A, Duke, 62; M.S, Illinois, 65, Ph.D.(bot), 67. ASST. PROF. biol, Western Illinois, 67-68; ECOL, WEST. WASH. STATE COL, 68-, BIOL. GRAD. PROG. ADV, 69- Field ecologist, intercampus sci. & ed. preserves comt, State of Wash. Cols. & Univs, summer 67; West. Illinois Univ. Res. Coun. grant, 68. AAAS; Ecol. Soc. Am; Torrey Bot. Club. Forest ecology in Olympic Mountains, Washington; alpine and subalpine environmental relationships; Illinois prairie and forest patterns; litter decomposition. Address: Dept. of Biology, Western Washington State College, Bellingham, WA 98225.

FONDAHL, JOHN W(ALKER), b. Wash, D.C, Nov. 4, 24; m. 46; c. 4. CIVIL ENGINEERING. B.S, Dartmouth Col, 47, M.S, 48. Struct. detailer, bridge div, Am. Bridge Co, 48; from instr. to asst. prof. civil eng, Hawaii, 48-51; engr. & estimator heavy construct, Winston Bros. Co, 51-52, off. engr, 52; proj. engr, Nimbus Dam & Powerhouse contract, with Al Johnson Construct. Co, 53-55; asst. prof. CIVIL ENG, STANFORD UNIV, 55-60, assoc. prof, 60-68, PROF, 68-; PRES, CONSTRUCT. DATA SYSTS. CORP, 69-, v.pres-treas, 68-69. Dir, Scott Co, Calif, 63-; dir, Proj. Mgt. Inst; consult, U.S. Atomic Energy Comn, Nev. Test Site, 65- U.S.M.C, 43-46. Am. Soc. Civil Eng; Am. Soc. Eng. Educ. Construction engineering; administration; planning and scheduling. Address: Dept. of Civil Engineering, Stanford University, Stanford, CA 94305.

FONDY, THOMAS PAUL, b. Pittsburgh, Pa, Dec. 24, 37; m. 63; c. 3. BIOCHEMISTRY. B.S, Duquesne Univ, 59, Nat. Sci. Found. fel, 59-61, Ph.D.(biochem), 61. Fel. BIOCHEM, Duquesne Univ, 61-62; Brandeis Univ, 62-65; asst. prof, SYRACUSE UNIV, 65-70, ASSOC. PROF, 70- Res. trainee, Nat. Inst. Neurol. Diseases & Blindness, 62-65. AAAS; Am. Chem. Soc; Fedn. Am. Sci; Brit. Biochem. Soc; Am. Soc. Biol. Chem. Comparative biochemistry of proteins in differentiation, disease, and evaluation, with specialization in Nictin-amide-Adenine Dinucleotide and Flavin-linked glycerol-3-phosphate dehydrogenases; Fluoro-analogs of glycolytic intermediates as anti-cancer agents. Address: Dept. of Biology, College of Arts & Sciences-109A Lyman, Syracuse University, Syracuse, NY 13210.

FONER, SAMUEL N(EWTON), b. N.Y.C, Mar. 21, 20. PHYSICS. B.S, Carnegie-Mellon Univ, 40, M.S, 41, D.Sc.(physics),,45. Asst. physics, Carnegie-Mellon Univ, 40-43, instr, 43-44, res. assoc, 44-45; PHYSICIST, APPL. PHYSICS LAB, JOHNS HOPKINS UNIV, 45- Mem. comt, Nat. Acad. Sci-Nat. Res. Coun; adv. Army Res. Off, 61-64. Phys. Sci. Award, Wash. Acad. Sci, 54. Civilian with Manhattan Proj, 44-45. AAAS; fel. Am. Phys. Soc. Mass spectrometry and reaction kinetics; electron spin resonance; free radicals; molecular beams; electronic physics; acoustics. Address: Applied Physics Lab, Johns Hopkins University, Silver Spring, MD 20910.

FONER, SIMON, b. Pittsburgh, Pa, Aug. 13, 25; m. 55; c. 2. PHYSICS. B.S, Carnegie Inst. Tech, 47, M.S, 48, D.Sc.(physics), 52. Asst. physics, Carnegie Inst. Tech, 47-52, res. physicist, 52-53; physicist, Lincoln Lab, MASS. INST. TECHNOL, 53-61, group leader, NAT. MAGNET LAB, 61-63, LEADER TRANSPORT & RESONANCE GROUP, 63-, proj. leader magnetism & superconductivity, 71. Mem. adv. comt. to Army Res. Off, Nat. Res. Coun, 67- U.S.N, 44-46. Fel. Am. Phys. Soc. Solid state physics; magnetism; high field superconductors; magnetic resonance; high magnetic fields; millimeter waves; hall effect; high speed photography; explosives. Address: National Magnet Lab, Massachusetts Institute of Technology, 170 Albany St, Cambridge, MA 02139.

FONG, CHING-YAO, b. Soochow, China, May 23, 35. SOLID STATE PHYSICS. B.S, Nat. Taiwan Univ, 58; M.S, Univ. Calif, Berkeley, 62, Ph.D.(physics), 68; Gordon McKay fel, Harvard, 62-63. Res. physicist, Lawrence Radiation Lab, Univ. Calif, Berkeley, 68; fel, UNIV. CALIF, DAVIS, summer 69, ASST. PROF. PHYSICS, 69- Asst. res. physicist, Univ. Calif, Berkeley, summer 70. Chinese Air Force, 58-60, 2nd Lt. Am. Phys. Soc. Optical properties of solids. Address: Dept. of Physics, University of California, Davis, CA 95616.

FONG, CONRAD T(UCK) O(NN), b. Honolulu, Hawaii, Sept. 16, 17; m. 43; c. 4. BIO-ORGANIC CHEMISTRY. B.S, Hawaii, 39; California, 40-43; Ph.D.(bio-org. chem), Calif. Inst. Tech, 46. Fel. radioactive lysine, Calif. Inst. Tech, 46-47; res. chemist, Lederle Labs. Div, Am. Cyanamid Co, 47-49; org. chemist, cancer control br, clin. trials unit, Nat. Cancer Inst, Nat. Insts. Health, U.S. Pub. Health Serv, 49-53; instr. dept. path, med. sch, Washington (Seattle), 54-56; assoc. scientist, Brookhaven Nat. Lab, 56-59, collab. med. res. center, 59-61; assoc. prof, Ore. State Univ, 61-65; SR. BIOCHEMIST, DEPT. NUCLEAR MED, L.I. JEWISH HOSP, QUEENS HOSP. CTR. AFFILIATION, 65- Res. assoc, sch. med, N.Y. Univ, 59-61. With U.S.Navy; Off. Res. & Inventions, 46. AAAS; Am. Chem. Soc; Brit. Chem. Soc; N.Y. Acad. Sci; Harvey Soc. Chemical aspects and mechanisms of hormone action. Dept. of Nuclear Medicine, Long Island Jewish Hospital, Queens Hospital Center Affiliation, 82-68 164th St, Jamaica, NY 11432.

FONG, DODD WING, b. Hong Kong, Aug. 4, 39; m. 70. PHYSICAL ORGANIC CHEMISTRY. B.S, Chung Chi Col, Hong Kong, 62; M.S, San Diego State Col, 64; Ph.D.(chem), Clarkson Col. Technol, 68. Fel. chem, Brandeis Univ, 67-68, res. assoc, 68-69; SR. CHEMIST, COMMERCIAL DEVELOP. DEPT, NALCO CHEM. CO, 69- Am. Chem. Soc. Kinetic and equilibrium studies; reaction mechanisms; polymer chemistry; synthesis and applications; adhesives. Address: Commercial Development Dept, Nalco Chemical Co, 6216 W. 66th Pl, Chicago, IL 60638.

FONG, FRANCIS K, b. Shanghai, China, Mar. 21, 38; m. 63; c. 2. SOLID STATE PHYSICS. A.B, Princeton, 59, Ph.D.(chem), 62. Res. assoc, Princeton, 62-63; mem. tech. staff, RCA Labs, 63-64; N.Am. Aviation Sci. Ctr, Calif, 64-68; assoc. prof. CHEM, PURDUE UNIV, 68-71, PROF, 71-

Am. Chem. Soc; Am. Phys. Soc. Zeeman and Stark spectroscopy; lifetimes of excited states; infrared quantum counter upconversion phenomena; multiphonon relaxation and energy transfer.in crystals and large molecules; quantum statistical mechanics of relaxation processes; solid state chemical physics. Address: Dept. of Chemistry, Purdue University, Lafayette, IN 47907.

FONG, HARRY H. S, b. Kwangtung, China, June 30, 35; U.S. citizen; m. 64; c. 2. PHARMACOGNOSY. B.S, Pittsburgh, 59, M.S, 62; Ph.D.(pharm), Ohio State, 65. Res. asst. prof. PHARMACOG, sch. pharm, Pittsburgh, 65-68, ASSOC. PROF, 68-70; COL. PHARM, UNIV. ILL, 70- AAAS; Am. Soc. Pharmacog; Am. Pharmaceut. Asn; Acad. Pharmaceut. Sci. Phytochemistry, isolation, characterization and/or identification of pharmacologically active principles from plants; biological and phytochemical screening of plants. Address: Dept. of Pharmacognosy & Pharmacology, College of Pharmacy, University of Illinois, 833 S. Wood St, Chicago, IL 60612.

FONG, JAMES T(SE-MING), b. Shanghai, China, Aug. 23, 27; nat; m. 64; c. 3. MECHANICAL ENGINEERING. S.B, Mass. Inst. Tech, 48; M.S, Columbia, 51. Develop. engr, Griscom-Russell Co, 48-50; mech. engr, Burns & Roe, Inc, 50-53; proj. engr, res. dept, Foster Wheeler Corp, 53-57; tech. staff of gen. mgr, BETTIS ATOMIC POWER LAB, WESTINGHOUSE ELEC. CORP, 57-66, supvr. irradiated components eng, 66-69, mgr. adv. cores-fuel syst. design & anal, 69-70, MGR. ADVAN. CORES, 70- Am. Nuclear Soc, Am. Soc. Mech. Eng. Nuclear reactor engineering; heat transfer; power plant design. Address: Bettis Atomic Power Lab, Westinghouse Electric Corp, Box 79, West Mifflin, PA 15122.

FONG, JEFFREY TSE-WEI, b. Shanghai, China, Nov. 24, 34; U.S. citizen; m. 56; c. 2. MATHEMATICAL PHYSICS, CONTINUUM MECHANICS. B.Sc, Hong Kong, 55; M.S, Columbia, 61; Ph.D.(mech), Stanford, 66. Eng. designer, Ebasco Serv. Inc, N.Y, 55-63; res. assoc. mech. & Nat. Acad. Sci-Nat. Res. Coun. resident math, NAT. BUR. STANDARDS, 66-68, PHYSICIST, 68- Summers, res. assoc. mech, Stanford, 66 & vis. res. fel. math, Hong Kong, 69. Am. Phys. Soc. Formulation and application of physical principles governing the motion of a deformable body; study of physical laws of a matter continuum in general. Address: National Bureau of Standards, Room 302, Bldg. 101, Washington, DC 20234.

FONG, JONES W, b. Sacramento, Calif, Sept. 7, 36; m. 64; c. 1. ORGANIC CHEMISTRY. B.S, California, Berkeley, 58; Eli Lilly fel, Rutgers, 60-62; Ph.D.(org. chem), 62. Chemist, Mat. & Process Labs, McClellan AFB, Calif, 57; teaching asst. chem, Rutgers, 58-60; res. chemist, fabrics & finishes dept, E.I. du Pont de Nemours & Co, 62-65; SR. RES. CHEMIST, TEXAS-U.S. CHEM. CO, 65- Am. Chem. Soc. Ziegler-Natta, emulsion and graft polymerization; organo-fluorine chemistry; chemistry of alkaloid and steroid. Address: Texas-U.S. Chemical Co. Research Center, Parisippany, NJ 07054.

FONG, PETER, b. Tungshang, China, Sept. 3, 24; m. 59; c. 3. THEORETICAL PHYSICS, MOLECULAR BIOLOGY. B.S, Chekiang, 45; M.S, Chicago, 50, Ph.D.(physics), 53. Physicist, inst. nuclear studies, Chicago, 54; asst. prof. PHYSICS, Utica Col, Syracuse Univ, 54-57, assoc. prof, 57-62, PROF, 62-66; EMORY UNIV, 66- Nat. Sci. Found. res. grants, 55-66; res. assoc, lab. nuclear sci, Mass. Inst. Technol, summers 56-57; res. fel, Kellogg Radiation Lab, Calif. Inst. Technol, 57; vis. prof, Cornell Univ, 63-64; Univ. Calif, Berkeley, 65-66. Am. Phys. Soc; fel. Biophys. Soc. Nuclear physics; astrophysics; quantum mechanics; thermodynamics; DNA functions; brain memory mechanism; philosophy of history. Address: Dept. of Physics, Emory University, Atlanta, GA 30322.

FONG-CHENG, CAROLINE K. Y, b. China, Aug. 24, 35; m. 68. VIROLOGY. B.Sc, Taiwan, 58; M.Sc, Saskatchewan, 63; Ph.D.(virol), Yale, 67. Asst. res. scientist, N.Y. Univ, 67; RES. ASSOC. VIROL, Yale, 68; inst. med. res, Putnam Mem. Hosp, 68-70; LAB. MED, YALE, 70- Am. Soc. Microbiol. Virus-cell interaction. Address: 152 Lamson St, West Haven, CT 06516.

FONGER, W(ILLIAM) H(AMILTON), b. Chicago, Ill, Sept. 19, 25; m. 53; c. 3. PHYSICS. S.B, Chicago, 48, S.M, 50, Ph.D.(physics), 53. MEM. TECH. STAFF, LABS, RCA CORP, 53- U.S.N.R, 43-46. Am. Phys. Soc. Solid state physics. Address: 174 Guyot Ave, Princeton, NJ 08540.

FONKALSRUD, ERIC W, b. Baltimore, Md, Aug. 31, 32; m. 59; c. 4. SURGERY. B.A, Washington (Seattle), 53; M.D, Hopkins, 57. Internship surg, Johns Hopkins Hosp, Baltimore, Md, 57-58, asst. res, 58-69; SCH. MED, UNIV. CALIF, LOS ANGELES, 59-62, chief res, 62-63, asst. prof. SURG, 63-68, assoc. prof, 68-71, PROF, 71-, CHIEF PEDIAT. SURG, 63-, Mead Johnson grad. training award surg, 63-65, Markle Scholar, 63-68. Instr, Ohio State & resident, Children's Hosp, Columbus, Ohio, 63-65; U.S. Pub. Health Serv. res. grants, 65-70; Calif. Inst. Cancer Res. & Los Angeles County Heart Asn. grants; James IV surg. traveller, Gt. Brit, 71; mem. surg. study sect, Nat. Insts. Health, 71-75. Dipl, Am. Bd. Surg, 64; Am. Bd. Thoracic Surg, 66. AAAS; fel. Am. Col. Surg; Am. Acad. Pediat; Soc. Univ. Surg; Am. Surg. Asn; Am. Pediat. Surg. Asn; N.Y. Acad. Sci; Am. Asn. Thoracic Surg; Transplantation Soc; Am. Med. Asn; Pan-Pac. Surg. Asn; Asn. Acad. Surg. Organ transplantation, experimental and clinical; pulmonary, hepatic and cardiac physiology; studies of neonatal physiology; development of new surgical techniques; use of computer assisted instruction in medical education. Address: Dept. of Surgery, University of California School of Medicine, Los Angeles, CA 90024.

FONKEN, DAVID W(ALTER), b. Denver, Colo, Oct. 9, 31; m. 53; c. 3. CIVIL ENGINEERING. B.S, Colo. State Univ, 53, M.C.E, 56. Hydraul. engr, U.S. Bur. Reclamation, 56-58; asst. prof. & asst. agr. engr, dept. agr. eng, Univ. Ariz, 58-61; hydrometeorologist, Harza Eng. Co, 61-68; RES. ASST. DEPT. AGR. ENG, UNIV. ARIZ, 68- U.S.A, 54-55, Res, 55-61. Am. Soc. Civil Eng; Am. Soc. Agr. Eng; Am. Geophys. Union; Am. Meteorol. Soc. Hydrologic studies in arid regions. Address: Dept. of Agricultural Engineering, University of Arizona, Tucson, AZ 85721.

FONKEN, GERHARD JOSEPH, b. Ger, Aug. 31, 28; nat; m. 52; c. 5. ORGANIC CHEMISTRY. B.S, California, 54, Ph.D.(chem), 57. Res. chemist, Procter & Gamble Co, 57-58; Stanford Res. Inst, 58-59; instr. CHEM, UNIV. TEX. AUSTIN, 59-65, ASSOC. PROF, 65-, outstanding teacher award, 63. U.S.A, 46-49, 50-51. Am. Chem. Soc. Natural products; structural determinations of organic compounds; organic photochemical transformations. Address: Dept. of Chemistry, University of Texas at Austin, Austin, TX 78712.

FONKEN, GUNTHER S(IEGFRIED), b. Krefeld, Ger, Jan. 29, 26; nat; m. 51; c. 4. ORGANIC CHEMISTRY. B.S, Mass. Inst. Technol, 46; Ph.D.(chem), Wisconsin, 51. Jr. chemist, res. dept, Merck & Co, Inc, 46-47; res. chemist, chem. dept, UPJOHN CO, 51-60, sect. head, biochem. dept, 60-68, RES. MGR, CANCER RES. DEPT, 68- Fel. AAAS; N.Y. Acad. Sci; Am. Soc. Microbiol; Am. Chem. Soc; Swiss Chem. Soc. Microbiological transformations; cancer research. Address: The Upjohn Co, 301 Henrietta St, Kalamazoo, MI 49001.

FONNESBECK, PAUL VANCE, b. Weston, Idaho, Aug. 4, 31; m. 53; c. 3. ANIMAL NUTRITION. B.S, Brigham Young, 53; M.S, Utah State, 59, Ph.D. (animal nutrit), 62. Asst. prof. NUTRIT, RUTGERS UNIV, 63-70, ASST. RES. PROF, 70- U.S.N, 53-56, Lt.(jg). Am. Soc. Animal Sci. Ruminant nutrition, especially digestion and metabolism and in vivo fermentation; horse nutrition, especially forage evaluation, Vitamin A requirements, macro-minerals, water metabolism and energy requirements for exercise. Address: Dept. of Animal Science, Rutgers, The State University, New Brunswick, N J 08903.

FONO, ANDREW, b. Budapest, Hungary, Apr. 24, 23; nat; m. 58; c. 2. ORGANIC CHEMISTRY. Ph.D.(chem), Pazmany Peter Univ, Hungary, 45. Asst, inst. org. chem. res, Stockholm, 46-47; res. fel. chem, Chicago, 47-51; head res. dept, Otto B. May Inc, 51-56; indust. res. assoc, inst. org. chem, Univ. Chicago, 57; sr. res. scientist, Firestone Tire & Rubber Co, Ohio, 58-59; RES. DIR, OTTO B. MAY, INC, NEWARK, 59- Am. Chem. Soc; fel. Am. Inst. Chem. Organic reaction mechanism; effect of metal ions and metallo-organic compounds on reactions in solution; polymer and dyestuff chemistry; colloid chemistry. Address: Otto B. May, Inc, 52 Amsterdam St, Newark, NJ 07105.

FONOROW, BENJAMIN H(IRSCH), b. New York, N.Y, June 21, 23; m. 49; c. 5. OCEANOGRAPHY. B.A, Connecticut, 48; Hopkins, 50-52; Maryland, 57-59. Mathematician, tides & currents, U.S. Coast & Geod. Surv, 48-50; oceanographer, Hydrographic Off, U.S. Dept. Navy, 50-55, ord. lab, Md, 55-60; mem. staff, Philco Corp, Pa, 60-65; owner & mgr, Precision Surv, Riverside, 63-65, chmn. bd. & v.pres, Precision Surv, Inc, Camden, 65-69; exec. v.pres, Ocean Dynamics Corp, 69-71; CONSULT. ENVIRON. RESOURCES, 71- Instr, Univ. Conn, 50; consult, Glen Assocs, 52; mem. oceanog. comt, Nat. Security Indust. Asn. U.S.A, 43-46; U.S.A.F.R, 48-, Maj. Am. Soc. Limnol. & Oceanog; Marine Technol. Soc; Instrument Soc. Am. Ocean engineering; marine systems; underwater communications and cable surveys; cable installation. Address: 22 Midfield Lane, Willingboro, NJ 08046.

FONSECA, ANTHONY G(UTIERRE), b. Chattanooga, Tenn, Mar. 31, 40; m. 65; c. 2. INORGANIC CHEMISTRY. A.B, Chattanooga, 62; M.S, Georgia, 66, Ph.D.(chem), 68. RES. SCIENTIST, CENT. RES. DIV, CONTINENTAL OIL CO, 68- Am. Chem. Soc. Transition metal coordination complexes with ammines and nitrogen heterocycles; inorganic sulfur and phosphorus chemistry. Address: Central Research Division, Continental Oil Co, Room 313A RB, Drawer 1267, Ponca City, OK 74601.

FONSWORTH, EMIL CHARLES, b. Houston, Tex, Sept. 3, 96; wid. PHYSICAL SCIENCE. A.B, Wiley Col, 18; M.A, Colo. State Col, 37; Ph.D.(sci. educ), Ohio State Univ, 57. Instr. natural sci, Huston Col, 19-23; teacher, high schs, 23-58, chmn. dept. chem. & physics, 26-58; PROF. phys. sci, Grambling Col, 58-63; physics & math, St. Augustine's Col.(N.C), 64-66; phys. sci, Miss. Valley State Col, 66-69; SCI. EDUC, BISHOP COL, 69- Sci. curriculum consult, South. Sch. Study, 39-42; summers, Phelps-Stokes Fund, 57, dir. Nat. Sci. Found. Stud. Insts, 62, 63; private consult. sci. educ, 67- AAAS; Am. Asn. Physics Teachers. Optical principles in fenestration and illumination for reading. Address: 3406 Prospect St, Houston, TX 77004.

FONTAINE, ARTHUR ROBERT, b. Lawrence, Mass, Aug. 1, 29; Can. citizen; m. 52; c. 2. ZOOLOGY. B.Sc, McGill, 52; Moyse travelling scholar. from McGill, London, 53-54; D.Phil.(zool), Oxford, 61. Researcher marine biol, Inst. Jamaica, Kingston, 52-53; instr. BIOL, Victoria Col, 56-58, asst. prof, 58-63; assoc. prof, UNIV. VICTORIA (B.C), 63-68, PROF, 68-, DEAN GRAD. STUDIES, 70-, assoc. dean, 69-70. Vis. prof, Friday Harbor Labs, Univ. Wash, 64, 65, 69; vis. zoologist, Dove Marine Lab, Newcastle-on-Tyne, 66-67. AAAS; Soc. Syst. Zool; Marine Biol. Asn. U.K; sci. fel. Zool. Soc. London. Functional morphology and experimental biology of echinoderms. Address: Dept. of Biology, University of Victoria, Victoria, B.C, Can.

FONTAINE, F(RANCIS) E(PHRAIM), b. Sheboygan, Wis, May 4, 16; m. 41; c. 2. BIOCHEMISTRY. B.S, Wisconsin, 38, M.S, 39, Ph.D.(biochem), 41. Asst, Wisconsin, 36-41; fermentation biochemist, Stauffer Chem. Co, 41-42; LEDERLE LABS. DIV, AM. CYANAMID CO, 42-54, mgr. prod, 54-57, dir. res, 57-63, PLANT MGR, 63- Am. Chem. Soc; Am. Inst. Chem. Eng. Pharmaceuticals and biologicals. Address: Lederle Labs. Division, American Cyanamid Co, Pearl River, NY 10965.

FONTAINE, JULIA CLARE, S.C.N, b. Chattanooga, Tenn, Dec. 11, 20. ANATOMY, BIOLOGY. B.S, Nazareth Col, 48; M.S, Catholic Univ, 56; Ph.D.(anat), Louisville, 69. Asst. prof. BIOL, SPALDING COL, 59-66, ASSOC. PROF. & CHMN. DEPT, 69- AAAS. Fluctuations in amounts of DNA in mammalian peripheral leukocytes; DNA changes in non-replicating cells; circadian rhythms in DNA content of specialized cells. Address: Dept. of Biology, Spalding College, 851 S. 4th St, Louisville, KY 40203.

FONTAINE, MARC F(RANCIS), b. Mexico City, Mex, Mar. 27, 26; nat; m. 49; c. 3. CHEMICAL ENGINEERING. B.S, La. State, 50, M.S, 51; Ph.D.(chem. eng), Okla. State, 54. Asst. chem. eng, Okla. State, 51-53, instr, 53, math, 53-54; res. chem. engr, res. center, TEXACO, INC, N.Y, 54-60, sr. engr-sci. liaison, Texaco U.K. Ltd, Eng, 60-62, res. chem. engr, BELLAIRE RES. LABS, TEX, 62-65, group leader, 65-68, sr. res. chem. engr. & proj. leader, 68-69, SUPVR, MECH. RES, 69- U.S.A.R, 54-64. AAAS; Am. Chem. Soc; Am. Inst. Chem. Eng; Am. Math. Soc; Am. Inst. Mining. Metall. & Petrol. Eng; Am. Statist. Asn; Brit. Chem. Soc; Brit. Inst. Chem. Eng; Brit. Inst. Petrol. Fuel technology; experimental design; production research, petroleum. Address: Bellaire Research Labs, Texaco, Inc, P.O. Box 425, Bellaire, TX 77401.

FONTAINE, RUSSELL EDGAR, b. Worcester, Mass, Oct. 9, 14; m. 45; c. 3. MEDICAL ENTOMOLOGY. B.S.A, Univ. Toronto, 39; M.P.H, Univ. Calif, 54; D.Sc, Tulane Univ, 69. Entomologist, U.S. Army, Korea, 46-47, Caribbean, 48-50; vector control specialist, Calif. State Dept. Pub. Health, 50-57; malaria adv, Agency For Int. Develop, Ethiopia, 58-60, regional malaria adv, Peru, 60-62, regional pub. health adv, Wash. D.C, 63-64; asst. chief Aedes aegypti eradication br, CTR. FOR DISEASE CONTROL, U.S. PUB. HEALTH SERV, 64-66, CHIEF OPERS. SECT, MALARIA ERADICATION BR; 67- Proj. dir, Anopheles Control Res. Unit, WHO, Nigeria, 69-71, Kenya, 71- Med.C, 42-46, Capt. AAAS; Am. Entom. Soc; Am. Mosquito Control Asn; Royal Soc. Trop. Med. & Hyg. Vector control; public health. Address: Center for Disease Control, U.S. Public Health Service, 1600 Clifton Rd, Atlanta, GA 30333.

FONTAINE, THOMAS D(AVIS), b. Utica, Miss, Apr. 12, 16; m. 41; c. 2. BIOCHEMISTRY. A.B, Miss. Col, 37; Ph.D.(biochem), Pittsburgh, 42. Asst. chem, Pittsburgh, 37-38; asst, Cotton Res. Found, Mellon Inst, 38-41; asst. chemist, oil, fat & protein div, south. regional res. lab, bur. agr. & indust. chem, U.S. Dept. Agr, 41-44, assoc. chemist, 44-45, biol, active compounds div, 45-46, chemist, 46-47, sr. biochemist, 47-48, prin. biochemist & head div, 48-52, prin. chemist & head biol. active chem. compounds div, east. utilization res. br, 52-55; admin. asst. to U.S. Senator John C. Stennis, 55-57; head fel. sect, sci. personnel & ed. div, Nat. Sci. Found, 57-65, dir, div. grad. educ. sci, 65-66, assoc. dir. sci. educ, 66-69, dep. asst. dir, 69-71; ASST. DIR, DIV. SPONSORED RES, UNIV. FLA, 71- Am. Chem. Soc. Am. Soc. Biol. Chem. Proteins; amino acids; enzymes; plant diseases; antibiotics from plants; plant growth modifiers; plant alkaloids; government. Address: Division of Sponsored Research, University of Florida, Gainesville, FL 32601.

FONTANA, B(EPPINO) J(OHN), b. San Francisco, Calif, Feb. 9, 16; m. 39; c. 1. PHYSICAL CHEMISTRY. B.S, California, 37, Ph.D.(chem), 40. Fel, radiation lab, California, 40-41, res. chemist, Nat. Defense Res. Cmt. proj, chem. dept, 42-47; assoc. res. chemist, Calif. Res. Corp, 47-50, res. chemist, 50-60, sr. res. chemist, 60-66; SR. RES. ASSOC, CHEVRON RES. CO, STANDARD OIL CO.(CALIF), 66- Res. guest, Nat. Bur. Standards, 57-58. Am. Chem. Soc. Thermodynamic properties; colloid and surface chemistry; petroleum products. Address: Chevron Research Co, Richmond, CA 94802.

FONTANA, C. MICHAEL, b. Lafferty, Ohio, May 16, 16; m. 41; c. 3. PHYSICAL CHEMISTRY. B.S, Ohio State, 37; M.S, Pa. State Col, 39, Ph.D. (chem), 42. Teacher, pub. schs, Ohio, 35-36; asst. chem, Pa. State Col, 37-41; instr, Tulane, 41-42; res. chemist, field res. dept, Magnolia Petrol. Co, 42-44, group leader, 44-46; sr. chemist, Socony-Vacuum Oil Co, 46-54; sr. chemist-res. assoc, Celanese Corp, 57-64; res. fel. explor. res, Marbon Chem. Div, Borg-Warner Corp, 65-71; CONSULT. CHEMIST, 71- AAAS; Am. Chem. Soc; Sci. Res. Soc. Am. Ionics; oxy-chlorination; catalysis; polymerization; kinetics; petroleum products; synthetic fibers; chemicals. Address: Route 2, Washington, WV 26181.

FONTANA, MARIO H, b. West Springfield, Mass, Mar. 30, 33; m. 58; c. 2. NUCLEAR SAFETY, HEAT TRANSFER. B.S, Univ. Mass, Amherst, 55; S.M, Mass. Inst. Technol, 57; Ph.D.(mech. eng), Purdue Univ, 68. Assoc. engr, Oak Ridge Nat. Lab, 57-61; sr. scientist, High Temperature Mat, Inc, Mass, 61-62; mem. sr. staff nuclear safety, Oak Ridge Nat. Lab, 62-63; sr. scientist plasma chem, Avco Res. & Advan. Develop, Mass, 63-64; instr. thermodyn, Purdue Univ, 64-65; ASST. DIR. NUCLEAR SAFETY PROGS, OAK RIDGE NAT. LAB, 65- AAAS; Am. Soc. Mech. Eng; Am. Nuclear Soc. Safety of nuclear reactors, both thermal and fast breeders; evaluation of potential reactor accidents and preventive safeguards; direction of safety research programs. Address: P.O. Box Y, Oak Ridge National Lab, Oak Ridge, TN 37830.

FONTANA, MARS G(UY), b. Iron Mountain, Mich, Apr. 6, 10; m. 37; c. 4. METALLURGY. B.S, Michigan, 31, M.S, 32, fel, 33, Ph.D.(metall. eng), 35. Asst. eng. res, Michigan, 29-34; metall. eng. & supvr, E.I. du Pont de Nemours & Co, 34-45; prof. METALL. RES. & METALL. ENG, OHIO STATE UNIV, 45-67, regents prof, 67-70, DURIRON PROF, 70-, CHMN. DEPT. METALL. ENG, 45- Consult. engr, Duriron Co, Ohio, 45- Fel. & hon. mem. Am. Soc. Metals; Electrochem. Soc; Nat. Asn. Corrosion Eng.(pres, 52; Speller Award, 56; ed, 'Corrosion,' 62-); Am. Inst. Chem. Eng; fel. Am. Inst. Mining, Metall. & Petrol. Eng; Fel. Metall. Soc; Nat. Acad. Eng. Corrosion; determination of oxygen and nitrogen in iron and steel by vacuum fusion and equilibrium in the system iron-oxygen-hydrogen at 1600 degrees centigrade. Address: Dept. of Metallurgical Engineering, Ohio State University, 116 W. 19th Ave, Columbus, OH 43210.

FONTANA, PETER R, b. Berne, Switz, Apr. 20, 35. THEORETICAL PHYSICS. Swiss Fed. Inst. Tech, 55-56; M.S, Miami (Ohio), 58; Ph.D.(physics), Yale, 60. Res. assoc. PHYSICS, Univ. Chicago, 60-62; asst. prof, Univ. Mich, Ann Arbor, 62-67; ASSOC. PROF, ORE. STATE UNIV, 67- Consult, Cornell Aeronaut. Lab, N.Y, 61-62. Am. Phys. Soc. Interatomic forces; scattering theory; calculation of atomic fine and hyperfine structure; atomic radiative decay processes. Address: Dept. of Physics, Oregon State University, Corvallis, OR 97330.

FONTANA, ROBERT E, b. Brooklyn, N.Y, Nov. 26, 15; m. 45; c. 3. ELECTRICAL ENGINEERING, ELECTRONICS. B.E.E, N.Y. Univ, 39; M.S, Univ. Ill, 47, Ph.D.(elec. eng), 49. Res. scientist, Sandia Corp, 49-54, asst. for nuclear develop. Hqs, D.C, 54-58, chief nuclear applns, Hq, air res. & develop. command, 58-61, dir, aerospace res. labs, 61-66; HEAD DEPT.

ELEC. ENG, AIR FORCE INST. TECHNOL, 66- Ed. joint newsletter, Inst. Elec. & Electronics Eng-Am. Soc. Eng. Educ, 70- U.S.A.F, 42-69, Col. (ret). Am. Soc. Eng. Educ; Inst. Elec. & Electronics Eng. Solid state electronics and control systems. Address: Air Force Institute of Technology, AFIT/ENE, Wright-Patterson Air Force Base, OH 45433.

FONTANA, VINCENT J, b. N.Y.C, Nov. 19, 23. IMMUNOLOGY, MEDICINE. M.D, L.I. Col. Med, 47. Assoc. prof. PEDIAT, SCH. MED, N.Y. UNIV, 57-69, PROF, 69- Fel, N.Y. Univ. Hosp, 51-52; consult, St. Alban's Naval Hosp, 55-; St. Mary's Hosp, New York, 60-; med. dir, New York Foundling Hosp, 62-; dir. pediat, St. Vincent's Hosp. & Med. Ctr, 62- U.S.N.R, 52-54, Lt. Fel. Am. Acad. Pediat; fel. Am. Acad. Allergy; Am. Med. Asn; Am. Fedn. Clin. Res; fel. N.Y. Acad. Med; Harvey Soc. Pediatric allergy and immunology. Address: 130 W. 12th St, New York, NY 10011.

FONTENELLE, LYDIA JULIA, b. New Orleans, La, May 28, 38. BIOCHEMISTRY. B.S, La. State Univ, Baton Rouge, 60; Nat. Insts. Health traineeship & Ph.D.(biochem), Tulane Univ, 67. Teacher, high schs, La, 60-61; lab. technician biochem, Tulane Univ, 61-63; Nat. Inst. Can. fel, McEachern Lab, Univ. Alta, 67-69; ASST. PROF. BIOCHEM. & PHARMACOL, COL. PHARM, IDAHO STATE UNIV, 69-, faculty grant, 70-71. Am. Chem. Soc; N.Y. Acad. Sci. Metabolism of drugs and the effects of drugs on control mechanisms of purine biosynthesis de novo. Address: College of Pharmacy, Idaho State University, Pocatello, ID 83201.

FONTENOT, J(OSEPH) P(AUL), b. Mamou, La, May 11, 27; m. 46; c. 6; ANIMAL NUTRITION. B.S, Southwestern Louisiana, 51; M.S, Okla. State, 53, Ph.D.(animal nutrit), 54. Instr. physiol. & pharmacol, Okla. State, 54-55; asst. prof. animal husb, Miss. State, 55-56; assoc. prof, ANIMAL SCI, BIOCHEM. & NUTRIT, VA. POLYTECH. INST. & STATE UNIV, 56-63, PROF, 63- Am. Feed Mfrs. Asn. Nutrit. Res. Award. U.S.N, 45-46. AAAS; Am. Soc. Animal Sci; Am. Inst. Nutrit; Animal Nutrit. Res. Coun. Ruminant nutrition; nitrogen requirement and metabolism; metabolic disturbances; administration of hormones and other drugs; forage utilization; cellulose digestion. Address: Dept. of Animal Science, Virginia Polytechnic Institute & State University, Blacksburg, VA 24061.

FONTHEIM, ERNEST G(UNTER), b. Berlin, Ger, Oct. 23, 22; U.S. citizen; m. 50; c. 2. PLASMA & SPACE PHYSICS. A.B. & B.S, Southwest Mo. State Col, 50; M.S, Lehigh, 52, Hood fel, 53-54, Ph.D.(physics), 60. Assoc. res. physicist, radiation lab, UNIV. MICH, ANN ARBOR, 60-62, SPACE PHYSICS RES. LAB, 62-64, RES. PHYSICIST, LAB. & LECTR. ELEC. ENG, UNIV, 64- Am. Phys. Soc; Am. Geophys. Union; Int. Union Radio Sci. Physics of the ionosphere, magnetosphere and upper atmosphere; theory of electrostatic probes; kinetic theory. Address: Space Physics Lab, University of Michigan, Ann Arbor, MI 48105.

FONTIJN, A(RTHUR), b. Amsterdam, Netherlands, Apr. 3, 28; nat; m. 57; c. 1. PHYSICAL CHEMISTRY. B.Sc, Amsterdam, 49, D.Sc.(phys. chem), 57. Nat. Res. Coun. Can. fel, Saskatchewan, 55-57; res. assoc. upper atmosphere chem. group, McGill, 57-60; phys. chemist, AEROCHEM. RES. LABS, INC, 60-68, HEAD REACTION KINETICS GROUP, 68- Am. Chem. Soc; Am. Phys. Soc; Combustion Inst; Am. Geophys. Union; Faraday Soc; N.Y. Acad. Sci; Air Pollution Control Asn. Gas kinetics; chemi-ionization and chemiluminescence; upper atmosphere and air pollution chemistry. Address: Aerochem Research Labs, Inc, P.O. Box 12, Princeton, NJ 08540.

FOODEN, JACK, b. Chicago, Ill, May 21, 27; m. 50; c. 2. ZOOLOGY. M.Ed, Chicago Teachers Col, 56; M.A, Chicago, 51, Nat. Sci. Found. fel, 57-60, Ph.D.(zool), 60. Teacher, Chicago Pub. Schs, 53-56; Nat. Insts. Health res. fel. primate taxon, Univ. Chicago & Chicago Natural Hist. Mus, 60-62; PROF. ZOOL, CHICAGO STATE UNIV, 62-;RES. ASSOC, DIV. MAMMALS, FIELD MUS. NAT. HIST, 64- U.S.A, 45-46. AAAS; Am. Soc. Mammal; Int. Primatol. Soc. Primatology; mammalogy. Address: Division of Mammals, Field Museum of Natural History, Chicago, IL 60605.

FOOHEY, WILLIAM L(OGAN), b. Fort Wayne, Ind, Jan. 1, 05; m. 32; c. 3. CHEMISTRY. B.S, Notre Dame, 26, Ph.D.(org. chem), 29. Res. chemist, Jackson lab, E.I. du Pont de Nemours & Co, Inc, 29-33, chief chemist, control & develop. lab, Chambers Works, 33-53, sr. res. chemist, 53-70; CONSULT, 70- Am. Chem. Soc. Catalysts; reactions of acetylene; organic intermediates; fungicides; azo colors. Address: 5149 Downwest Ride, Columbia, MD 21043.

FOOR, W. EUGENE, b. Wood, Pa, Feb. 7, 36; m. 58; c. 2. ZOOLOGY, PARASITOLOGY. B.S.E, Shippensburg State Col, 59; fel, Univ. Va, summers 59-62; fel, Columbia Univ, spring, 65; Ph.D.(zool); Univ. Mass, Amherst, 66. Teacher, high schs, Pa, 59-62; fel. parasitol, med. sch, Tulane Univ, 66-67, instr, sch. pub. health & trop. med, 67-68, asst. prof, 68-70; ASSOC. PROF. BIOL, WAYNE STATE UNIV, 70- Am. Soc. Parasitol. Ultrastructural studies of reproductive cells in parasitic nematodes; oogenesis, vitellogenesis and shell formation about newly fertilized eggs as well as the mechanism of oocyte penetration employed by spermatozoa. Address: Dept. of Biology, Wayne State University, Detroit, MI 48202.

FOORD, DELBERT C, b. Murray, Utah, Feb. 23, 13; m. 40; c. 2. BIOCHEMISTRY, BACTERIOLOGY. A.B, California, 35, M.A, 37. Med. asst, Arctic Exped, U.S. Pub. Health Serv, 37-38; asst. bact, Col. Agr, California, 38-39; res. bacteriologist, AM. CAN CO, Calif, 39-45, tech. asst. container mfg, 45-47, container develop, New York, 47-56, sr. asst. new prod, 56-62, mgr. tech. serv, milk container div, 62-65; tech. serv. rep. paper prod. res, 65-68, supvr. res. & develop, WIS, 68-70, SR. RES. ASSOC, TECH. SERV, 70- Fel. Am. Inst. Chem; Int. Asn. Milk, Food & Environ. Sanit. Public health aspects of milk containers and dairy equipment; fibre and plastic containers for the dairy industry. Address: 57 S. Meadows Dr, Appleton, WI 54911.

FOOS, BARBARA ANN, S.S.J, b. Rochester, N.Y, Mar. 25, 26. MATHEMATICS. B.S, Nazareth Col.(N.Y), 48; M.S, Notre Dame, 52, Ph.D.(math), 56. Instr. MATH, NAZARETH COL. ROCHESTER, 52-57, asst. prof, 57-62, assoc. prof, 62-66, PROF, 66-, CHMN. DEPT, 63- Summer instr, Nat. Sci. Found. Insts, Univ. Notre Dame, 57-63; vis. prof, Ithaca Col, 67-69,

acting chmn. dept, 68-69. Am. Math. Soc. Geometric function theory; curriculum development. Address: Dept. of Mathematics, Nazareth College of Rochester, 4245 East Ave, Rochester, NY 14610.

FOOS, RAYMOND A(NTHONY), b. Bowling Green, Ohio, Sept. 30, 28; m. 53; c. 10. PHYSICAL CHEMISTRY. B.S, Xavier (Ohio), 50, M.S, 53; Ph.D. (chem), Iowa State, 54. Res. chemist, Atomic Energy Cmn, 51-54; group leader, Union Carbide Metal Co, 54-57; supvr. metals & inorg. chem. U.S. Indust. Chems. Co, 57-59, polymer chem, 59-60; mgr. extraction & oxide, BRUSH BERYLLIUM CO, 60-66, metal oxide dept, 66-69, dir. corp. res. & develop, 69-70, V.PRES. RES. & DEVELOP, 70- Am. Chem. Soc; Am. Inst. Mining, Metall. & Petrol. Eng; Am. Ceramic Soc; Am. Ord. Asn. Extractive metallurgy of transition elements; sodium chemistry; electro chemistry; patents; liquid extraction; polymers; beryllium chemistry; manufacturing; ceramics; beryllium product metallurgy; powder technology; administration. Address: Brush Beryllium Co, 17876 St. Clair Ave, Cleveland, OH 44110.

FOOS, ROBERT YOUNG, b. Phila, Pa, Nov. 20, 22; m. 45; c. 4. OPHTHALMOLOGY, PATHOLOGY. B.S, California, Davis, 51, D.V.M, 53; M.D, California, Los Angeles, 63. Nat. Inst. Neurol. Diseases & Blindness spec. fel, 65-66; asst. prof. PATH, SCH. MED, UNIV. CALIF, LOS ANGELES, 66-70, ASSOC. PROF, 70-, DIR. OPHTHALMIC PATH. LABS, JULES STEIN EYE INSTITUTE, 67- U.S.A, 41-45, Capt. AAAS. Diseases of the retina; experimental ophthalmic pathology. Address: Dept. of Pathology, Jules Stein Eye Institute, University of California, Los Angeles, CA 90024.

FOOSE, RICHARD M(ARTIN), b. Lancaster, Pa, Oct. 9, 15; m. 43; c. 4. GEOLOGY. B.S, Franklin & Marshall Col, 37; M.S, Northwestern, 39; scholar, Hopkins, 41-42; Ph.D.(struct. & econ. geol), 42. Asst. instr. geol, Northwestern, 37-39; asst. geologist, State Topog. & Geol. Surv, Pa, 39-42, assoc. geologist, 42-43, sr. geologist, 43-46; prof. geol. & head dept, Franklin & Marshall Col, 46-57; chmn. dept. earth sci, Stanford Res. Inst, 57-63; PROF. GEOL. & CHMN. DEPT, AMHERST COL, 63- Ford fel, Stanford, 55-56; co-op. geologist, State Turnpike Cmn, Pa, 41; del, Int. Geol. Cong, 52, 56, 60, 68; mem, tech. work group 2, Nuclear Test Ban Discussions, Geneva, 59; Nat. Sci. Found. sr. fel, Swiss Fed. Inst. Tech, 62-63; vis. prof, Univ. Vienna, 68, Am. Univ. Beirut, 69; Nat. Acad. Sci. exchange fel, U.S.S.R, 69. Consult. geologist, 42- Fel. AAAS; fel. Geol. Soc. Am; Soc. Econ. Geol; Am. Geog. Soc; Am. Geophys. Union; Am. Inst. Mining, Metall. & Petrol. Eng. Identification of manganese oxides; origin and occurrence of hialumina clays; manganese minerals of Pennsylvania; ground water geology; tectonics of middle Rocky Mountains; catastrophic sinkhole development. Address: Dept. of Geology, Amherst College, Amherst, MA 01002.

FOOTE, BENJAMIN A(RCHER), b. Delaware, Ohio, Oct. 25, 28; m. 54; c. 4. ENTOMOLOGY. B.A, Ohio Wesleyan, 50; M.S, Ohio State, 52; Ph.D, Cornell, 61. Asst. entomol, Ohio State, 50-52; limnol, Cornell, 54-58; asst. entomologist, Idaho, 58-60; asst. prof. ENTOM, KENT STATE UNIV, 61-66, ASSOC. PROF, 66- Nat. Sci. Found. res. grant, 69-; Nat. Geog. Soc. grant, 71. U.S.A, 52-54. Entom. Soc. Am; Ecol. Soc. Am; Royal Entom. Soc. London. Ecology of acalyptrate Diptera; biological control of ragweeds. Address: Dept. of Biological Sciences, Kent State University, Kent, OH 44240.

FOOTE, C(ARLTON) DAN, b. State Center, Iowa, Jan. 16, 35; m. 59; c. 3. BIOCHEMISTRY, ORGANIC CHEMISTRY. B.A, Central Col, 57; Ph.D. (biochem), Illinois, 63. Nat. Insts. Health fel, 63-64; asst. prof. CHEM, Union Col.(KY), 64-65; EAST. ILL. UNIV, 65-70, ASSOC. PROF, 70- Am. Chem. Soc. Steroid biosynthesis; mechanisms of enzymes; cellular differentiation. Address: Dept. of Chemistry, Eastern Illinois University, Charleston, IL 61920.

FOOTE, CHRISTOPHER S, b. Hartford, Conn, June 5, 35; m. 60; c. 2. ORGANIC CHEMISTRY. B.S, Yale, 57; Fulbright fel, Göttingen, 57-58; A.M. & Ph.D. (org. chem), Harvard, 61. Instr. CHEM, UNIV. CALIF, LOS ANGELES, 61-62, asst. prof, 62-66, assoc. prof, 66-69, PROF, 69- Nat. Sci. Found. fel, 58-61; Alfred P. Sloan Found. fel, 65-67; J.S. Guggenheim Found. fel, 67-68; consult, Procter & Gamble; hon. mem. ed. bd, Photochem. & Photobiol. AAAS; Am. Chem. Soc; Brit. Chem. Soc. Organic photochemistry; chemical generation of molecules in excited states; reactions of singlet oxygen; photodynamic effect. Address: Dept. of Chemistry, University of California, Los Angeles, CA 90024.

FOOTE, FLORENCE M(ARTINDALE), b. Montague City, Mass, June 28, 11; wid. ANATOMY, EMBRYOLOGY. A.B, Mt. Holyoke Col, 32; A.M, 34; Ph.D.(embryol, endocrinol), Iowa, 40. Asst. zool, Mt. Holyoke Col, 32-34, instr, 35-38; Delaware, 40-41; biol, Wagner Col, 42-45, asst. prof, 46-47; zool, SOUTH. ILL. UNIV, 47-50, lectr, PHYSIOL, 50-62, assoc. prof, 63-68, PROF, 68- Guest investr, lab. exp. embryol, Col. France, 60-61. AAAS; Am. Asn. Anat; Soc. Develop. Biol; Int. Inst. Embryol. Vertebrate embryology. Address: Dept. of Physiology, Southern Illinois University, Carbondale, IL 62901.

FOOTE, FRANK G(ALE), b. Owosso, Mich, July 21, 06; m. 35; c. 1. PHYSICAL METALLURGY. A.B, Ohio Wesleyan, 28; M.A, Ohio State, 29; Ph.D. (metall), Columbia, 41. Asst. sch. mines, Columbia, 30-38; instr. metall, Cooper Union, 38-42, sr. metallurgist, metall. lab, Chicago, 42-46; assoc. prof, Columbia, 46-48; dir. metall. div, Argonne Nat. Lab, 48-65, sr. metallurgist, 65-68; RETIRED. Am. Phys. Soc; Am. Soc. Metals; Am. Nuclear Soc; Am. Crystallog. Asn; Am. Inst. Mining, Metall. & Petrol. Eng. Metallurgy of nuclear materials. Address: 4822 Northcott Ave, Downers Grove, IL 60515.

FOOTE, FREEMAN, b. Orange, N.J, Nov. 8, 08; m. 39; c. 1. GEOLOGY. A.B, Princeton, 31; Columbia, 31-37. Asst. geol, Columbia, 34-37; instr, WILLIAMS COL, 37-42, asst. prof, 42-48, assoc. prof, 48-56, prof, 56-68, EDWARD BRUST PROF. GEOL. & MINERAL, 68-, chmn. dept, 64-67. Summers, assoc. prof, Columbia, 52-53, Wesleyan, 55. Mem. sci. faculty fel. selection panel, Nat. Sci. Found, 64, 65, 68. U.S.N.R, 42-45, Res, 45-, Comdr. AAAS; fel. Geol. Soc. Am; Nat. Asn. Geol. Teachers.(secy, 57-60). Petrology; structural geology. Address: Dept. of Geology, Williams College, Williamstown, MA 01267.

FOOTE, GEORGE B(ROUGHTON), b. Port Henry, N.Y, Feb. 12, 09; m. 29; c. 2. DENTISTRY. Syracuse, 26-28; Alabama, 28-29; D.D.S, Atlanta-South. Dent. Col, 32; cert, Tufts, 51. Private practice, Ga, 32-39; PROF. PROSTHODONTICS, BAYLOR COL. DENT, 59- Consult, Ft. Hood, Tex; Vet. Admin. Hosp, Waco, Dallas. Dipl, Am. Bd. Prosthodontics, 52. Dent.C, 39-59, Res, 33-39, Col; Legion of Merit. Am. Dent. Asn; fel. Am. Col. Dent; Am. Prosthodontic Soc; Am. Col. Prosthodontics. All phases of dental and oral prosthesis. Address: Baylor College of Dentistry, Dallas, TX 75226.

FOOTE, GORDON L(EE), b. Evanston, Ill, Dec. 28, 16; m. 40; c. 4. ORGANIC CHEMISTRY. S.B, Mass. Inst. Tech, 38, Ph.D.(org. chem), 40. Chemist, chem. develop. & prods. res, PROCTER & GAMBLE CO, 40-41, 45-53, TECH. PERSONNEL, 53- C.W.S, U.S.A, 41-45. Am. Chem. Soc; Am. Inst. Chem. Eng. Organic process development; identification of sulfonic acids. Address: 1160 Beverly Hills Dr, Cincinnati, OH 45226.

FOOTE, JAMES H(ERBERT), b. Tacoma, Wash, Dec. 13, 29; m. 54; c. 2. PHYSICS. A.B, California, Berkeley, 53, Westinghouse fel, 55, Ph.D.(physics), 61. PHYSICIST, LAWRENCE LIVERMORE LAB, 60- Nat. Guard, 48-52. Am. Phys. Soc. Experimental research and computer analysis; controlled fusion and high temperature plasma physics; elementary particle scattering. Address: Lawrence Livermore Lab, Livermore, CA 94550.

FOOTE, JOE R(EEDER), b. Amarillo, Tex, Aug. 17, 19; m. 49; c. 4. APPLIED MATHEMATICS. B.S, Texas Tech. Col, 40; Ph.D.(math), Mass. Inst. Tech, 49. Instr. math, Texas, 40-41; Oklahoma, 45-46; Mass. Inst. Technol, 46-49; asst. prof, Iowa State Col, 49-51; mathematician, Wright-Patterson Air Force Base, 51-53; asst. prof. math, Oklahoma, 53-57; assoc. prof, div. eng. scis, Purdue, 57-58; prof. MATH. & dir, Holloman Grad. Ctr, N.Mex, 58-66; prof, Univ. Mo-Rolla, 66-70, chmn. dept, 67-70; PROF. & CHMN. DEPT, LA. STATE UNIV, NEW ORLEANS, 70- Mem. Inst. Math. Scis, N.Y. Univ, 56-57; consult, U.S. Air Force Missile Develop. Ctr, 56-65. U.S.A.A.F, 42-45. Math. Asn. Am; Am. Math. Soc; Soc. Indust. & Appl. Math. Flight dynamics; differential equations; optimization; calculus of variations; operations research for Inter-Continental Ballistic Missle defense. Address: Dept. of Mathematics, Louisiana State University of New Orleans, New Orleans, LA 70122.

FOOTE, J(OEL) LINDSLEY, b. Cleveland, Ohio, Jan. 11, 28; m. 51; c. 2. BIOCHEMISTRY. B.S, Miami (Ohio), 52; summer, Ohio State, 55; Nat. Sci. Found. fel, Case, 58-60, Ph.D.(org. chem), 60. Teacher, pub. schs, Ohio, 52-56; res. assoc. biochem, Michigan, 60-62, ASST. RES. BIOCHEMIST, ment. health res. inst, 64-65; DEPT. CHEM, WEST. MICH. UNIV, 65- Nat. Sci. Found. fel, 60-62; U.S. Pub. Health Serv. trainee, 62-64; part time instr, Michigan, 62-65. U.S.N, 46-48. Am. Chem. Soc. Metabolic role of biotin; lipid biochemistry; biochemistry of phenylketonuria; neurochemistry; glycosphingolipids; atherosclerosis. Address: Dept. of Chemistry, Western Michigan University, Kalamazoo, MI 49001.

FOOTE, JOHN K, b. Oakland, Calif, July 19, 24; m. 45; c. 3. PHYSICAL CHEMISTRY. B.S, California, Berkeley, 45, M.A, Santa Barbara, 62, Nat. Defense Ed. Act fel. & Ph.D.(phys. chem), Riverside, 66. Res. chemist, Calif. Res. Corp, Standard Oil Co. Calif, 46-61; asst. prof. CHEM, CALIF. STATE COL, DOMINGUEZ HILLS, 66-68, ASSOC. PROF, 68- U.S.N, 43-46, Lt.(jg). Am. Chem. Soc; Am. Phys. Soc. Photochemistry of aromatic compounds; solvent effects on spectra; organic reaction mechanisms. Address: Dept. of Chemistry, California State College, Dominguez Hills, 1000 E. Victoria, Dominguez Hills, CA 90247.

FOOTE, KENNETH G(ERALD), b. Cleveland, Ohio, Mar. 24, 35; m. 59; c. 3. BIOLOGY. A.B, Hiram Col, 58; M.S, Wisconsin, 62, Alumni Res. Found. fel, 62-63, Ph.D.(bot), 63. Asst. prof. BIOL, Sheboygan Ctr, Univ. Wis, 63-66; ASSOC. PROF, WIS. STATE UNIV, EAU CLAIRE, 66- Am. Bryol. & Lichenological Soc; Am. Inst. Biol. Sci; Ecol. Soc. Am. Ecology of saxicolous lichen and bryophyte communities. Address: Dept. of Biology, Wisconsin State University, Eau Claire, WI 54701.

FOOTE, MURRAY W(ILBUR), b. Charlotte, Vt, Mar. 22, 16; m. 40; c. 2. BIOCHEMISTRY. B.S, Vermont, 38, M.S, 50; Ph.D, Univ. Conn, 54. Asst. chemist, UNIV. VT, 40-51, asst. prof. biochem, 53-59, ASSOC. PROF, 59-69, MICROBIOL. & BIOCHEM, 69-, assoc. biochemist, 53-69. Am. Soc. Plant Physiol. Minor elements in plant metabolism; plant proteins and nitrogen metabolism in plants. Address: Dept. of Microbiology & Biochemistry, University of Vermont, Burlington, VT 05401.

FOOTE, RICHARD H(ERBERT), b. Bozeman, Mont, May 2, 18; m. 43, 64; c. 5. ENTOMOLOGY. B.S, Mont. State Col, 42; D.Sc.(parasitol), Hopkins, 52. Asst. entom, Minnesota, 42-43; entomologist, U.S. Pub. Health Serv, Ga, 47-49; Johns Hopkins Univ, 49-52, ENTOM. RES. DIV, AGR. RES. SERV, U.S. DEPT. AGR, 52-67, ASST. CHIEF INSECT IDENTIFICATION & PARASITE INTROD. RES. BR, 67- Mem. coun, Biol. Sci. Info; ed. bd, Abstracts Entom. Med.Serv.C, U.S.A, 43-45. Entom. Soc. Am; Soc. Syst. Zool; Am. Inst. Biol. Sci; Coun. Biol. Educ; Am. Soc. Info. Sci. Taxonomy of Tephritidae; philosophy of systematics; information storage and retrieval for biology. Address: Agricultural Research Service, U.S. Dept. Agriculture, North Bldg, Plant Industry Station, Beltsville, MD 20705.

FOOTE, R(OBERT) H(UTCHINSON), b. Gilead, Conn, Aug. 20, 22; m. 46; c. 2. ANIMAL PHYSIOLOGY. B.S, Connecticut, 43; M.S, Cornell, 47, Ph.D.(animal breeding), 50. Asst. ANIMAL BREEDING, CORNELL UNIV, 46-50, asst. prof, 50-55, assoc. prof, 55-63, PROF, 63- Fulbright scholar, Denmark, 58-59. Prof. merit, Cornell Univ, 68; N.Y. Farmers' award, 69. U.S.A, 43-45, Capt. AAAS; Am. Fertil. Soc; Am. Soc. Animal Sci.(award, 70); Am. Dairy Sci. Asn.(award, 70); Int. Fertil. Asn; Am. Inst. Biol. Sci; Soc. Study Reproduction. Superovulation; cellular preservation and cryogenic effects on sperm cells; embryo culture; fertility, embryonic mortality and congenital defects; aging and reproductive failure. Address: Dept. of Animal Science, 205 Morrison Hall, Cornell University, Ithaca, NY 14850.

FOOTE, ROBERT S, b. Decatur, Ill, June 6, 22; m. 53; c. 4. PHYSICS. B.S, Illinois, 48, M.S, 49. Mem. tech. staff, Nat. Bur. Standards, 49-55; sect. head, cent. res. lab, Tex. Instruments, Inc, 57-60, chief geonuclear opers, sci. serv. div, 61-68, PRES, GEOSENSORS INC, 69- C.Eng, 42-46, Res, 49-64. Am. Phys. Soc; sr. mem. Inst. Elec. & Electronics Eng. Gamma ray spectroscopy; advanced electronic technology; instrumentation. Address: Geosensors Inc, 9731 Denton Dr, Dallas, TX 75220.

FOOTE, WARREN C(HRISTOPHER), b. Orderville, Utah, Oct. 6, 27; m. 49; c. 6. ANIMAL PHYSIOLOGY. B.S, Utah State, 54; M.S, Wisconsin, 55, Ph.D, 58. Asst. prof. ANIMAL PHYSIOL, UTAH STATE UNIV, 58-63, assoc. prof, 63-69, PROF, 69- Consult, U.S. Aid Int. Develop, Bolivia; San Marcos Univ; Rockefeller Found. U.S. Merchant Marine, 45-46. Am. Soc. Animal Sci. Physiology and endocrinology of reproduction, animal behavior; mechanisms involved; influencing factors, their modification and control. Address: Dept. of Animal Science, Utah State University, Logan, UT 8421.

FOOTE, W(ILFORD) DARRELL, b. Kanab, Utah, Jan. 9, 31; m. 53; c. 3. ANIMAL PHYSIOLOGY. B.S, Utah State, 53; M.S, Wisconsin, 56, Ph.D, 59. Asst. genetics & ANIMAL HUSB, Wisconsin, 55-59; PROF. & PHYSIOLOGIST, UNIV. NEV, RENO, 59- U.S.A.F, 53-55, Res, 55-, 1st Lt. AAAS; Am. Soc. Animal Sci; Soc. Study Reproduction; Brit. Soc. Study Fertility. Physiology of reproduction. Address: Division of Animal Science, University of Nevada, Reno, NV 89507.

FOOTE, WILSON H(OOVER), b. Nephi, Utah, Jan. 30, 20; m. 52; c. 2. AGRONOMY, PLANT BREEDING. B.S, Utah State, 42; fel, Minnesota, 44-48, M.S, 46, Ph.D, 48. Field foreman, Nephi Dryland Exp. Sta, Utah State, 38-42; asst. agronomist, spec. guayule res. proj, bur. plant indust, soils & agr. eng, U.S. Dept. Agr, 43-44; from asst. prof. to assoc. prof. AGRON, ORE. STATE UNIV, 48-58, PROF. & AGRONOMIST, AGR. EXP. STA, 58-, ASSOC. DIR. STA, 70- Fel. Am. Soc. Agron. Plant breeding; cereal crop production; research administration. Address: Agricultural Experiment Station Ag. 127, Oregon State University, Corvallis, OR 97331.

FOOTT, WILLIAM HENRY, b. Winnipeg, Man, June 6, 21; m. 50; c. 3. ENTOMOLOGY. B.S.A, Manitoba, 51; M.S.A, Ont. Agr. Col, 53; Ph.D.(entom), Minnesota, 59. RES. SCIENTIST, RES. STA, CAN. DEPT. AGR, 53-R.C.A.F, 39-46. Entom. Soc. Can; Prof. Inst. Pub. Serv. Can. Ecology and control of insects attacking vegetables and field crops. Address: Research Station, Canada Dept. of Agriculture, Harrow, Ont, Can.

FOPEANO, JOHN V(INCENT), JR, b. Ann Arbor, Mich, Jan. 29, 28; m. 50; c. c. 4. BIOCHEMISTRY. B.A, Yale, 50; M.S, Michigan, 52, fel, 53-54, Ph.D. (biochem), 55. Instr. biochem, State Univ. N.Y. Buffalo, 54-57, from assoc. to asst. prof, 57-70, consult, dept. surg, 54-57; PROF. MED. TECHNOL. & CHMN. DEPT, CLIN. CTR, SCH. HEALTH & RELATED PROFESSIONS, STATE UNIV. N.Y, 70- Consult, Genesee Mem. Hosp, 58-; St. Jerome Hosp, Batavia, 58-; Mt. St. Mary's Hosp, Lewiston, N.Y. Am. Chem. Soc; Am. Asn. Clin. Chem. Amino acid and lipid metabolism. Address: Dept. of Medical Technology, Clinical Center, Bldg. AA, School of Health & Related Professions, State University of New York, 462 Grider St, New York, NY 14215.

FOPMA, ROBERT J, b. Arlene, Mich, July 10, 22; m. 48; c. 3. MATHEMATICS, STATISTICS. A.B, Hope Col, 42; Cincinnati, 46-50, 52-54. ASSOC. PROF. MATH, UNIV. CINCINNATI, 60-, ASST. PROVOST, 68-, asst. dean, col. eng, 67-68. Consult, Champion Paper Co. & Formica Corp, 55-68. U.S.N, 44-46, 50-52, Res, 52-, Comdr. Am. Soc. Eng. Educ; Am. Soc. Qual. Control; Math. Asn. Am; Am. Statist. Asn. Industrial statistics and quality control; design of experiments; dynamic control systems; mathematical and statistical models. Address: 119 McMicken Hall, University of Cincinnati, Cincinnati, OH 45221.

FORAL, RALPH FRANCIS, b. Omaha, Nebr, June 18, 34; c. 4. APPLIED MECHANICS. B.S, Nebraska, 56; M.S, Colorado, 58, Martin fel, 61-62, Ph.D, 63. Asst. res. scientist, Martin Co, Denver, 56-64; ASSOC. PROF. ENG. MECH, UNIV. NEBR, LINCOLN, 64- Consult, Brunswick Corp. Am. Acad. Mech; Soc. Exp. Stress Anal; Am. Soc. Test; & Mat; Am. Soc. Eng. Educ. Solid mechanics; composite materials; pressure vessels. Address: Dept. of Engineering Mechanics, University of Nebraska, Lincoln, NE 68508.

FORAN, M(ICHAEL) R(OY), b. Can, Nov. 21, 07; m. 35; c. 3. INDUSTRIAL CHEMISTRY. B.Sc, Saskatchewan, 33, M.Sc, 38; Ph.D.(chem), McGill, 44. Instr. chem, Regina Col, 38-42; asst. prof, Dalhousie, 44-48; PROF. CHEM. ENG, N.S. TECH. COL, 48-, DEAN GRAD. STUDIES, 67-, dir, 64-67. Mem. ed. bd, Can. Jour. Chem. Eng. Chem. Inst. Can. Utilization of blast furnace slag; utilization of diatomite in Nova Scotia; causes of moisture penetration through masonry; corrosion by industrial waters; atmospheric chlorides. Address: 1360 Barrington St, Halifax, N.S, Can.

FORBES, A(LBERT) R(ONALD), b. Victoria, B.C, Can, Oct. 16, 31. ENTOMOLOGY. B.A, British Columbia, 52; M.S, Oregon State, 55; Myers fel, California, 59-60, univ. fel, 60-61, Ph.D.(entom, zool), 63. Asst. entomologist, Field Crop Insect Lab, Victoria, B.C, 52-55; assoc. entomologist, RES. STA, CAN. DEPT. AGR, 56-67, RES. SCIENTIST, 67- Entom. Soc. Am; Entom. Soc. Can; Can. Soc. Zool. Economic entomology; systematics of aphididae; ultrastructure of insects. Address: Research Station, Canada Dept. of Agriculture, 6660 N.W. Marine Dr, Vancouver 8, B.C, Can.

FORBES, ALLAN L(OUIS), b. Richmond, Va, July 28, 28; m. 54; c. 3. INTERNAL MEDICINE. B.Sc, McGill, 49; M.D, Med. Col. Va, 53, M.S, 64; dipl, Nat. War Col, 68. Intern, Montreal Gen. Hosp, 53-54; from jr. asst. res. to sr. asst. res. internal med, Med. Col. Va, 54-56; assoc. med. & attend. physician, med. ctr, Colorado, 56-58, clin. investr. Vet. Admin. Hosp, Richmond, Va, 58-61; asst. dir. med. prog, interdept. cmt. nutrit. nat. defense, Nat. Insts. Health, 61-63; med. off, Dept. Army, 63-67, chief sci. anal. br, life sci. div, 68-70; DEP. DIR. DIV. NUTRIT, BUR. FOODS, FOOD & DRUG ADMIN, 71- Intern, King Edward VII Mem. Hosp, Bermuda, 53-54; Mead-Johnson scholar, Am. Col. Physicians, 55-56; lectr, Med. Col. Va, 58-Chief clin. physiol. br, physiol. div, U.S. Army Med. Res. & Nutrit. Lab, Med.C.Res, 56-67, Maj. AAAS; Am. Inst. Nutrit; Am. Soc. Clin. Nutrit; Am. Fedn. Clin. Res. Clinical nutrition and metabolic disease; international and environmental medicine. Address: Division of Nutrition, Bureau of Foods, Food & Drug Administration, 200 C St. S.W, Washington, DC 20204.

FORBES, (OLIVER) CLIFFORD, b. Eureka, Calif, May 25, 27. GENETICS. A.B, Humboldt State Col, 50; M.A, California, 52, Ph.D.(zool), 58. Instr. biol. sci, San Francisco State Col, 56-57; ZOOL, UNIV. IDAHO, 57-60, asst. prof, 60-68, ASSOC. PROF, 68- U.S.N, 45-46. Drosophila genetics; chromosome segregation; mutation; peromyscus genetics. Address: Dept. of Biological Sciences, University of Idaho, Moscow, ID 83843.

FORBES, GEORGE F(RANKLIN), b. Boston, Mass, June 26, 15; m. 43; c. 10. INDUSTRIAL MATHEMATICS. S.B, Northeastern, 39; St. Louis, 39-40; Harvard; New Hampshire; Mass. Inst. Tech. Asst. physics, New Hampshire, 41-42; math, Mass. Inst. Tech, 47-48; field engr, telemetering aerodyn, Raytheon Mfg. Co, 48-49; physicist, vibration testing, Naval Ord. Test Sta, Calif, 49-51; mathematician, flight test anal, Edwards Air Force Base, 51-52; math. analyst, comput, Lockheed Aircraft Corp, 52-56; ENG. SPECIALIST, COMPUT. APPLN, LITTON INDUSTS, 56- Mem, Simulation Coun. U.S.N, 42-47, Res, 47-68, Lt. Comdr. AAAS; Asn. Comput. Mach; assoc. fel. Am. Inst. Aeronaut. & Astronaut; fel. Brit. Interplanetary Soc. Space technology; applications of digital differential analyzers; trajectories of powered space rockets; extraterresterial life. Address: 15415 Lemarsh St, Mission Hills, CA 91340.

FORBES, GILBERT B(URNETT), b. Rochester, N.Y, Nov. 9, 15; m. 39; c. 2. PEDIATRICS. A.B, Rochester, 36, M.D, 40. Intern PEDIAT, Strong Mem. Hosp, Rochester, 40-41; instr, sch. med, Washington (St. Louis), 43-46, asst. prof, 47-50, assoc. prof, 50; prof. & chmn. dept, Southwest. Med. Sch, Texas, 50-53; assoc. prof, SCH. MED. & DENT, UNIV. ROCHESTER, 53-57, PROF, 57-, RADIATION BIOL. & BIOPHYS, 70- Res. physician, St. Louis Children's Hosp, 41-43, asst. pediatrician, 40-43; chief pediatrician, Los Alamos Hosp, 46-47; chief staff pediat, Parkland City-County Hosp. & med. dir, Children's Med. Center, Dallas, 50-53; assoc. pediatrician, Strong Mem. Hosp, 53-57, pediatrician, 57-; vis. res. fel, Oxford, 70-71; guest lectr; consult. hosps; mem. comt. infant nutrit, food & nutrit. bd, Nat. Res. Coun; sci. adv. comt, Nutrit. Found. AAAS; Am. Acad. Pediat.(Borden Award, 64); Am. Pediat. Soc; Soc. Pediat. Res.(pres, 60-61); Soc. Exp. Biol. & Med; Am. Med. Asn. Metabolism in infancy and childhood; diagnosis and therapy of clinical pediatrics; pediatric endocrinology; chemical growth; body fluid physiology; infant nutrition. Address: School of Medicine & Dentistry, University of Rochester, 260 Crittenden Blvd, Rochester, NY 14620.

FORBES, IAN, b. Pittsburgh, Pa, Jan. 16, 20; m. 44; c. 3. AGRONOMY. B.Sc, Maryland, 41, M.Sc, 49, Ph.D.(plant morphol), 54. Mem. res. staff, green sect, U.S. Golf Asn; plant indust. sta, U.S. DEPT. AGR, Beltsville, 41-42, 45-47, res. agronomist, plant indust. sta, 47-51, COASTAL PLAIN EXP. STA, GA, 51-63, SR. RES. AGRONOMIST, 63- Mem. Tenth Int. Grasslands Cong, Finland, 66. Sears Roebuck award, 60. U.S.A, 42-45, Capt. Am. Soc. Agron; Bot. Soc. Am; Am. Genetic Asn; Crop Sci. Soc. Am. Cytogenetics and breeding of forage legumes. Address: Plant Science Research Division, U.S. Dept. of Agriculture, Coastal Plain Experiment Station, University of Georgia, Tifton, GA 31794.

FORBES, I(RVIN) L, b. Deerford, La, Apr. 13, 02; m. 26; c. 1. BOTANY. B.A, La. State, 25, M.S, 28; Ph.D.(plant path), Minnesota, 35. Instr. bot, La. State, 25-29; plant path, Minnesota, 29-30, 31-32; asst. prof. bot, LA. STATE UNIV, BATON ROUGE, 30-31, 32-35, assoc. prof, 35-43, PROF, 43-56, PLANT PATH, 56-, plant pathologist & asst. dir, exp. sta, 43-56. Am. Phytopath. Soc. Plant pathology; diseases of crop plants, particularly cereals and sugar cane. Address: Dept. of Plant Pathology, Louisiana State University, Baton Rouge, LA 78802.

FORBES, JACK E(DWIN), b. Bloomington, Ill, Dec. 11, 28; m. 59. MATHEMATICS. B.S, Ill. Wesleyan, 49; M.S, Bradley, 52; Ph.D.(math), Purdue, 57. Instr. math, Bradley, 51-52; Purdue, 55-57, asst. prof, 57-60; dir. sec. math, Ed. Res. Coun, Cleveland, Ohio, 60-61; dir. res. math, Britannica Ctr. Studies Learning, Calif, 61-63; math. consult, Encyclop. Britannica Press, 63-64; PROF. MATH, CALUMET CAMPUS, PURDUE UNIV, 64- Vis. prof, Ball State Teachers Col, 58-60. U.S.N.R, 47-50. Am. Math. Soc; Math. Asn. Am; N.Y. Acad. Sci. Foundations; mathematics education; programmed instruction for teacher education. Address: Division of Mathematical Sciences, Calumet Campus, Purdue University, Hammond, IN 46323.

FORBES, JACK E(UGENE), b. St. Louis, Mo, July 10, 31. ASTROPHYSICS. A.B, Harvard Col, 53; Ph.D.(astron), California, Berkeley, 66. Res. assoc. astrophys, Ctr.Radiophys. & Space Res, Cornell, 64-67, instr, 66-67; ASST. PROF. ASTRON, WASHBURN OBSERV, UNIV. WIS, MADISON, 67- U.S.A, 54-57. Am. Phys. Soc; Am. Astron. Soc; Int. Astron. Union; fel. Royal Astron. Soc. Stellar structure and evolution; computational methods. Address: Dept. of Astronomy, Washburn Observatory, University of Wisconsin, Madison, WI 53706.

FORBES, JAMES, b. Yonkers, N.Y, July 9, 10; m. 37; c. 1. ENTOMOLOGY. B.S, Fordham, 32, fel, 32-36, M.S, 34, Ph.D.(entom), 36. Instr, BIOL, FORDHAM UNIV, 36-40, asst. prof, 40-53, assoc. prof, 53-66, PROF, 66- Sanit.C, U.S.A, 43-46. Entom. Soc. Am; Am. Soc. Zool. Anatomy and histology of the ants and the housefly; biology of mosquitoes; histology of primate skin. Address: Dept. of Biology, Fordham University, Bronx, NY 10458.

FORBES, JAMES FRANKLIN, b. Berwyn, Ill, Feb. 9, 41; m. 67; c. 2. ANALYTICAL & INORGANIC CHEMISTRY. B.S, Wheaton Col, 62; Ph.D.(inorg. chem), South. Ill. Univ, 68. Instr. chem, Drew Univ, 66-68, PROJ. CHEMIST, AMETEK TECH. PRODS, 68- Am. Chem. Soc. Complexing ability of octamethylpyrophosphoramide with transition metal ions; study of surface chemistry by evaporative rate analysis; study of organic coatings and residues by evaporative rate analysis. Address: 7631 El Lobo Circle, La Palma, CA 90620.

FORBES, MALCOLM H(OLLOWAY), b. New Haven, Conn, Aug. 20, 33; m. 63; c. 3. ORGANIC CHEMISTRY. B.S, Yale, 54; M.S, Trinity Col.(Conn), 58; Ph.D.(org. chem), Cambridge, 60. Res. assoc. antibiotics, Mass. Inst. Tech, 60-61, fel, 62-63; consult. chem, Ed. Serv, Inc, Mass, 63-64; acad. dean, Cazenovia Col, 65-70; DEAN COL. ARTS & SCI, MILLIKIN UNIV, 70- U.S.N, 54-56, 61-62, Res, 56-61, 62-, Comdr. Am. Asn. Higher Educ. AAAS; Am. Chem. Soc. College or university administration and improvement of academic programs; curriculum development and evaluation in the sciences. Address: College of Arts & Sciences, Millikin University, Decatur, IL 62522.

FORBES, MARTIN, b. Brussels, Belgium, July 25, 20; nat; m. 49; c. 2. MICROBIOLOGY. B.S, Moravian Col, 47; Harrison fel, Pennsylvania, 47, Abbott fel, 49, M.S, 49, Ph.D.(microbiol), 51. U.S. Army res. fel. microbiol, Univ. Hosp, Pennsylvania, 51-53, dir, animal res. proj. & res. assoc. dept. microbiol, sch. med, 53-58; asst. prof. microbiol, sch. med, Tempel, 58-59; group leader, dept. chemother, LEDERLE LABS, AM. CYANAMID CO, 59-65, head, dept. antimicrobial ther, 65-69, DIR. INFECTIOUS DISEASE THER. RES. SECT, 69- Res. assoc, Walter Reed Army Inst. Res, 53-58. U.S.A, 42-45. AAAS; Am. Inst. Nutrit; Am. Soc. Microbiol; N.Y. Acad. Sci. Antimicrobial agents and chemotherapy. Address: Infectious Disease Research Section, Lederle Labs, American Cyanamid Co, Pearl River, NY 10965.

FORBES, PAUL DONALD, b. Binghamton, N.Y, Mar. 3, 36; m. 60; c. 4. RADIATION BIOLOGY. B.S, Wheaton Col.(Ill), 57; Ph.D, Brown, 61. Instr. anat, sch. med, Temple, 61-64; ASSOC. PROF. biol, Barrington Col, 64-68; DERMAT, SCH. MED, TEMPLE UNIV, 68- U.S. Pub. Health Serv. traineeship cancer, sch. med, Temple, 61-64; radiobiologist, Roger Williams Gen. Hosp, Providence, R.I, 66-68. AAAS; Am. Inst. Biol. Sci; Am. Soc. Microbiol; Radiation Res. Soc; N.Y. Acad. Sci; Soc. Invest. Dermat. Experimental oncology; photobiology of the skin. Address: Skin & Cancer Hospital, Temple University Health Sciences Center School of Medicine, Philadelphia, PA 19140.

FORBES, RICHARD B(RAINARD), b. Ellington, N.Y, Aug. 29, 21; m. 50; c. 2. SOIL SCIENCE. B.S, Rollins Col, 43; M.S, Univ. Fla, 48; Ph.D.(agron, soils), Pa. State Univ, 56. Asst. soils chemist, exp. sta, Univ. Fla, 48-49, asst. prof. soils, Univ, 49-53; chemist, agent, U.S. Regional Pasture Res. Lab, Pa. State Univ, 53-56; asst. soils chemist, INST. FOOD & AGR. SCI, CENT. FLA. EXP. STA, UNIV. FLA, 56-67, ASSOC. SOILS CHEMIST, 67- U.S.A.A.F, 43-46, Capt. AAAS; Am. Soc. Agron; Soil Sci. Soc. Am. Soil fertility; vegetable crops; plant nutrients in farm drainage water. Address: Agricultural Research & Education Center, Box 909, University of Florida, Sanford, FL 32771.

FORBES, RICHARD BRYAN, b. Correctionville, Iowa, July 29, 36; m. 60; c. 2. VERTEBRATE ZOOLOGY, ECOLOGY. A.B, South Dakota, 58; Iowa State, 56-57; Iowa, summer 59; M.S, New Mexico, 61; Ph.D.(ecol), Minnesota, 64. Asst. prof. BIOL, PORTLAND STATE UNIV, 64-69, ASSOC. PROF, 69- AAAS; Am. Soc. Mammal; Ecol. Soc. Am. Ecology, physiology and intraspecific morphological variation of terrestrial vertebrates, particularly mammals. Address: Dept. of Biology, Portland State University, Portland, OR 97207.

FORBES, R(ICHARD) M(ATHER), b. Wooster, Ohio, Jan. 8, 16; m. 44; c. 3. NUTRITION. B.S, Pa. State Col, 38, M.S, 39; Ph.D.(nutrit), Cornell, 42. Instr. biochem, Wayne, 42; res. fel, Cornell, 42-43; asst. prof. animal husb, Kentucky, 46-49; assoc. prof. ANIMAL NUTRIT, UNIV. ILL, URBANA-CHAMPAIGN, 49-55, PROF, 55- Mem. comn. animal nutrit, Nat. Res. Coun, 61-70. U.S.A, 43-46. AAAS; Am. Soc. Animal Sci.(Gustav Bohstedt Award, 68); Am. Chem. Soc; Am. Inst. Nutrit. Nitrogen and mineral metabolism of animals. Address: Dept. of Animal Science, 124 Animal Sciences Lab, University of Illinois, Urbana-Champaign, Urbana, IL 61801.

FORBES, ROBERT B(RIEDWELL), b. Aberdeen, Wash, Mar. 14, 24; m. 53; c. 2. GEOLOGY. B.S, Washington (Seattle), 50, fel, 58-59, Ph.D.(geol), 59. Consult, res. & develop. div, Off. of Qm. Gen, Wash, D.C, 52-53, asst. chief, res. br, 53-56; res. assoc. GEOL, Washington (Seattle), 57-58; asst. prof, UNIV. ALASKA, 59-61, assoc. prof, 61-65, PROF, GEOPHYS. INST, 65-, chmn. dept, 65-70. Geologist, Juneau Ice Field res. proj, 49, 50; Nat. Sci. Found. sci. faculty fel, geol. inst, Tokyo, 63-64; with U.S. Geol. Surv, 69- U.S.A, 43-46. Fel. AAAS; fel. Arctic Inst. N.Am; Am. Asn. Petrol. Geol; Am. Polar Soc; fel. Geol. Soc. Am. Petrology and geochemistry of igneous and metamorphic rocks; volcanology and structural geology. Address: Geophysical Institute & Dept. of Geology, University of Alaska, College, AK 99701.

FORBES, STUART G(ORDON), b. Portland, Ore, Jan. 16, 19; m. 42; c. 3. PHYSICS. B.S, Ore. State Col, 41, M.S, 47, Ph.D.(physics), 51. Power engr, rotation test course, Westinghouse Elec. Co, 41-43, eng. & serv, 43-45; Off. Naval Res.Microwave Proj, physics, Ore. State Col, 46-48; asst, Los Alamos Sci. Lab, 48-51; res. engr, commun, Boeing Airplane Co, 51-52; group leader reactor physics, Phillips Petrol. Co, 52-54, chief physics sect, reactor proj. br, 54-57, dep. mgr, 57-60, mgr. Spert Proj, 59-60; staff mem, Space technol. labs, 60-64, mgr. elec. propulsion dept, Calif, 64-67; asst. mgr. technol, atomic energy div, Phillips Petrol. Co, Idaho, 67-69; SUB. PROJ. MGR, TRW SYSTS. GROUP, 69- Am. Nuclear Soc; Am. Inst. Aeronaut. & Astronaut. Space electric propulsion; ion engines; colloid engines; surface ionization; beam diagnostics; system optimization. Address: TRW Systems Group, P.O. Box 1310, San Bernardino, CA 92402.

FORBES, THOMAS R(OGERS), b. N.Y.C, Jan. 5, 11; m. 34; c. 2. ANATOMY. B.A, Rochester, 33, fel, 33-37, Ph.D.(anat), 37; hon. M.A, Yale, 62. Asst. anat, sch. med, Hopkins, 37-38, instr, 38-42; Guggenheim fel, 42; tech. aide, div. med. scis, Nat. Res. Coun. & cmt. med. res, Off. Sci. Res. & Develop, 42-45; instr. ANAT, SCH. MED, YALE, 45-46, asst. prof, 46-51, assoc. prof, 51-62, PROF, 62-, asst. dean sch, 48-60, assoc. dean, 60-70. Fel, Branford Col, Yale, 51-; mem. Faculty Hist. Pharm. & Med, Worshipful Soc. Apothecaries, London. AAAS; Endocrine Soc; Am. Soc. Zool; Soc. Exp. Biol. & Med; Am. Asn. Hist. Med; Am. Asn. Anat; Soc. Social Hist. Med; fel. Royal Soc. Med. Endocrinology and embryology of reptilian reproduction system; embryology of human reproductive system; physiology of sex hormones in mammals; history of biology and medicine. Address: Dept. of Anatomy, School of Medicine, Yale University, 333 Cedar St, New Haven, CT 06510.

FORBES, WARREN C, b. New York, N.Y, Nov. 25, 39; m. 61; c. 3. MINERALOGY. B.A, Hofstra, 61; Nat. Defense Ed. Act fel, Brown, 61-64, M.Sc, 63, univ. fel, 64-65, Ph.D.(mineral), 66. ASST. PROF. GEOL, Georgia, 65-66; UNIV. ILL, CHICAGO CIRCLE, 66- Am. Mineral Soc. Experimental determination of the stability relations of amphiboles and layer-lattice silicates; crystal chemistry. Address: Dept. of Geological Sciences, University of Illinois at Chicago Circle, Box 4348, Chicago, IL 60608.

FORBES, WILLIAM GARFIELD, b. Winnipeg, Man, July 15, 27; m. 52; c. 2. POLYMER CHEMISTRY. B.Sc, Univ. Man, 49, M.Sc, 50; Ph.D.(kinetics), Univ. Toronto, 53. Sr. res. chemist, POLYMER CORP. LTD, 53-61, res. assoc, 61-62, proj. supvr, 62-66, asst. mgr. res. & develop, 66-69, MGR. MKT. SERV, 69- Nat. Res. Coun. Can. fel, 51, 52. Chem. Inst. Can; Am. Chem. Soc. Gas phase kinetics; polymerization using free radicals or coordinate; catalysts; adhesion of high polymers; rheology of viscous solutions. Address: Polymer Corp. Ltd, Sarnia, Ont, Can.

FORBESS, DENNIS LYNN, b. Twin Falls, Idaho, Dec. 5, 38; m. 68; c. 2. ORGANIC & PHYSICAL ORGANIC CHEMISTRY. B.A, Univ. Ore, 61; Ph.D. (org. chem), Stanford Univ, 65. SR. RES. CHEMIST, CENT. RES. DIV, CROWN ZELLERBACH CORP, 65- Am. Chem. Soc; Soc. Photog. Sci. & Eng. Electrophotographic technology, theory and research and development; types of specially coated papers pertinent to the paper industry. Address: Central Research Division, Crown Zellerbach Corp, Camas, WA 98607.

FORBIS, ORIE LESTER, JR, b. Encinal, Tex, Dec. 25, 22; m. 46; c. 2. PEDIATRICS, PSYCHIATRY. B.A, Texas, 51, M.D, 53. Res. pediat, John Sealy Hosp, Tex, 54-57, psychiat. & neurol, 57-59; child psychiat, Hawthorn Ctr, Mich, 59-61; asst. prof. psychiat. & pediat. & dir. child guid. clin, med. ctr, Arkansas, 62-66; psychiatrist dir, Genesee County Ment. Health Serv. Bd, Mich, 66-67; dir. children's serv, Ment. Health-Ment. Retardation Ctr. Austin-Travis County, Austin, 67-69; CHIEF CHILD PSYCHIATRIST, NORTHWEST MENT. HEALTH CTR. & ASSOC. PROF. PEDIAT. & PSYCHIAT, MED. SCH, UNIV. TEX, SAN ANTONIO, 69- Summer dir. child guid. clin, Mott Found, Mich, 65. Consult, Northville State Hosp. & pub. schs, Mich; dir. ment. health planning, Ark. State Health Dept, 63-65. Hosp.C, 42-45, Med.C, 53-54, Lt.(jg). Am. Med. Asn; Am. Acad. Ment. Deficiency; Am. Psychiat. Asn. Child psychiatry; longitudinal studies of emotional development of children with special reference to socioeconomically-culturally deprived. Address: Community Guidance Center of Bexar County, 2135 Babcock Rd, San Antonio, TX 78229.

FORBRICH, CARL A, JR, b. San Antonio, Tex, Nov. 5, 39; m. 62; c. 2. AERONAUTICAL ENGINEERING. B.S, Univ. Tex, Austin, 61; M.S, Univ. Okla, 63; Ph.D.(aeronaut. eng), Stanford Univ, 67; Univ. Colo, Boulder, 69-71. Proj. engr, Boeing Aircraft Co, Wash, 61; U.S. AIR FORCE, 61-, aerodynamicist, Tinker Air Force Base, Okla, 61-64, instr. AERONAUT, U.S. AIR FORCE ACAD, 67-68, asst. prof, 68-70, assoc. prof, 70-71, RES. ASSOC, F.J. SEILER RES. LAB, 71- U.S.A.F, 61-, Capt. Am. Inst. Aeronaut. & Astronaut; Am. Soc. Eng. Educ. Experimental measurement of atomic oscillator strengths in high temperature gases; spectral line broadening. Address: F.J. Seiler Research Lab, U.S. Air Force Academy, Colorado Springs, CO 80840.

FORCE, CARLTON G(REGORY), b. Gouverneur, N.Y, Aug. 5, 26; m. 53; c. 4. PHYSICAL & ORGANIC CHEMISTRY. B.S, Clarkson Tech, 52, Ph.D.(phys. chem), 65; M.S, Illinois, 57. Chemist, Merck & Co, Inc, N.J, 52-56; res. chemist, Esso Res. & Eng. Co, 57-59; Latex Fiber Industs, Inc, N.Y, 59-61, sr. res. chemist, 63-67; res. chemist, WESTVACO CORP, 67-70, SR. RES. CHEMIST, 70- U.S.A, 45-47. Am. Chem. Soc; Am. Inst. Chem; Sci. Res. Soc. Am. Colloid chemistry particularly rubber latex systems and rosin and fatty acid emulsifiers; paper making chemistry. Address: 239 Hobcaw Dr, Mt. Pleasant, SC 29464.

FORCE, DON C(LEMENT), b. Clear Lake, S.Dak, July 5, 28; m. 53; c. 3. ENTOMOLOGY. B.A, Fresno State Col, 54; M.S, California, Davis, 58, Ph.D.(entom), Berkeley, 63. Entomologist, Stauffer Chem. Co, 56-58; lab. technologist biol. control, California, Berkeley, 58-62; entomologist, U.S. Dept. Agr, 62-65; asst. prof. entom, CALIF. STATE POLYTECH. COL, KELLOGG-VOORHIS, 65-68, ASSOC. PROF. BIOL SCI, 68- U.S.A, 47-50. AAAS; Entom. Soc. Am; Ecol. Soc. Am. Biological control of insects and weeds; bioclimatics of insect parasites. Address: Dept. of Biology Sciences, California State Polytechnic College, Kellogg-Voorhis, Pomona, CA 91768.

FORCHHEIMER, OTTO L(OUIS), b. Nurnberg, Bavaria, Sept. 18, 26; U.S. citizen; m. 57; c. 2. PHYSICAL & INORGANIC CHEMISTRY. B.Sc, McGill, 47; Ph.D.(chem), Brown, 51. Res. chemist, Chicago, 51-53; sr. res. chemist, Gen. Abrasive Co, 53-58, asst. dir. res, 58-59; mgr. chem. div, Trionics Corp, 59-62; DIR. RES, J.E. BAKER CO, 62-; V.PRES. & DIR, DOLOMITE BRICK CORP. AM, 67-, tech. dir, 62-67. Am. Chem. Soc; Am. Ceramic Soc; Am. Soc. Test. & Mat. Rates and mechanisms of inorganic reactions; chemistry of abrasives; refractories. Address: J.E. Baker Co, P.O. Box 1189, York, PA 17405.

FORCHIELLI, A(MERICO) LEWIS, b. Alpha, N.J, May 28, 22; m. 42; c. 1. CHEMISTRY. B.A, Lafayette Col, 47; Northeastern, 55-56. Chemist resins, Hercules Powder Co, 47-48; group leader, explosives, Picatinny Arsenal, 48-52; res. dir, waxes, Sure-Seal Corp, 52-53; res. chemist, cent. res. lab, Gen. Aniline & Film Corp, 53-54; Masury-Young Co, 54-56, dir. res. & mgr. lab, 56-66, res. dir, Masury-Columbia Co. Div, Alberto-Culver Co, 66-69; PROD. MGR, WAYLAND CHEM. DIV, PHILIP A. HUNT CHEM. CO, LINCOLN, 69- Am. Chem. Soc; fel. Am. Inst. Chem. Organic and polymer research; detergents; textile chemicals; lubricants; waxes and specialty products; chemical specialties field. Address: 17 Marywood Lane, Cumberland, RI 02864.

FORCHIELLI, ENRICO (HENRY), b. West Boylston, Mass, Jan. 26, 18; m. 47; c. 3. BIOCHEMISTRY. B.S, Mass. Col. Pharmacy, 40; A.B, Clark Univ, 51; M.A, Boston Univ, 53, Ph.D.(biochem), 56. Res. assoc. steroid metab, Worcester Found. Exp. Biol, 47-62; sr. scientist, 62-64; HEAD DEPT. STEROID METAB, SYNTEX RES. CTR, 64- U.S.A.A.F, 42-45. Am. Soc. Biol. Chem; Endocrine Soc. Steroid metabolism; biosynthesis enzymology. Address: Institute of Hormone Biology, Syntex Research Center, Stanford Industrial Park, Palo Alto, CA 94304.

FORCIER, GEORGE ARTHUR, b. Mapleville, R.I, Nov. 29, 38; m. 64; c. 2. ANALYTICAL CHEMISTRY. B.S, Providence Col, 60; M.S, Univ. Mass, 64, Ph.D.(anal. chem), 66. RES. CHEMIST, PFIZER INC, 66- Electroanalytical chemistry in acetonitrile; electroanalytical and other instrumental methods of analysis. Address: Pfizer Inc, Eastern Pt. Rd, Groton, CT 06340.

FORD, ARTHUR B, b. Seattle, Wash, Sept. 4, 32; m. 55; c. 2. GEOLOGY. B.S, Washington (Seattle), 54, M.S, 57, Ph.D.(geol), 59. Asst. prof. geol, San Diego State Col, 58-60; GEOLOGIST, U.S. GEOL. SURV, 60- Geol. Soc. Am. Geology of Antarctica and Alaska; metamorphic and igneous petrology. Address: Alaskan Geology Br, U.S. Geological Survey, 345 Middlefield Rd, Menlo Park, CA 94025.

FORD, BENNIE R, b. Wichita Falls, Tex, May 8, 36; m. 60; c. 2. ZOOLOGY. B.S, William Carey Col, 62; M.S, Oklahoma, 64, Ph.D.(biol), Oklahoma, 67. ASST. PROF. BIOL, Samford Univ, 68-71; LAWSON STATE JR. COL, 71- Samford Univ. Res. Fund grant, 68-69. C.Eng, U.S.A. Am. Soc. Parasitol; Am. Inst. Biol. Sci. Developmental physiology and life cycles of parasites. Address: Dept. of Biology, Lawson State Junior College, 3060 Wilson Rd. S.W, Birmingham, AL 35221.

FORD, C(LARENCE) E(DWARD), b. Chicago, Ill, May 13, 05; m. 35; c. 4. MECHANICAL ENGINEERING. B.S, Illinois, 31. Mem. staff, eng. design & develop, res. & develop. dept, Sinclair Res. Labs, Inc, 33-49, contractor liaison, ref. construct, 46-49, asst. dir. eng, res. & chem, 51-53, in charge mech. eng. prod. res, 53-63, ADMIN. MGR, TULSA RES. CTR, SINCLAIR OIL CORP, 63- Petroleum refining; petroleum production equipment design. Address: Tulsa Research Center, Sinclair Oil Corp, P.O. Box 7190, Tulsa, OK 74105.

FORD, C(LARENCE) QUENTIN, b. Glenwood, N.Mex, Aug. 6, 23; m. 50; c. 2. MECHANICAL ENGINEERING. B.S, Merchant Marine Acad, 44; B.S.M.E, New Mexico State, 49; M.S, Missouri, 50; Ph.D, Mich. State, 59. Instr. MECH. ENG, Missouri, 49-50; Washington State, 50-53, asst. prof, 53-56; instr, Mich. State Univ, 56-59; PROF, N.MEX. STATE UNIV, 59-, chmn. dept, 60-70. U.S.N, 42-46, Lt.(jg). AAAS; Am. Soc. Mech. Eng; Nat. Soc. Prof. Eng; Am. Soc. Eng. Educ. Combustion kinetics; rate of scale formation in boiling processes; heat transfer; thermodynamics. Address: Dept. of Mechanical Engineering, New Mexico State University, Las Cruces, NM 88001.

FORD, CLINTON B(ANKER), b. Ann Arbor, Mich, Mar. 1, 13; m. 40, 61. ASTRONOMY. A.B, Michigan, 35, M.S, 36. Asst. astron, Brown, 39-41; instr, Smith Col, 41-42; group leader pure sci, Ordwes Labs, Wesleyan, 46-50, asst. dir, 50-53; v.pres. & res. dir, NIKOR PRODS. CO, 53-61, TECH. CONSULT, 61- Trustee, Ithaca Col, 67- U.S.N, 42-46, Lt. AAAS; fel. Am. Astron. Soc; Optical Soc. Am; Am. Inst. Aeronaut. & Astronaut; Am. Asn. Variable Star Observers (secy, 48-, pres, 61-62); N.Y. Acad. Sci; Royal Astron. Soc. Can. Photometry of variable stars; celestial navigation; highspeed photography; spectroscopy; photo developing equipment. Address: Ten Canterbury Lane, Wilton, CT 06897.

FORD, DAVID A, b. Pasadena, Calif, Oct. 25, 35; m. 64; c. 2. MATHEMATICS. A.B, Occidental Col, 56; M.S, Utah, 58, Ph.D.(math), 62. Asst. prof. MATH, EMORY UNIV, 65-71, ASSOC. PROF, 71- Summer res. assoc, res. inst, Univ. Ala, 65. U.S.A.F, aerospace engr, George C. Marshall Space Flight Ctr, 62-65, 1st Lt. Am. Math. Soc; Math. Asn. Am. Functional analysis and ordinary differential equations; applications in the mathematical theory of optimal control. Address: Dept. of Mathematics, Emory University, Atlanta, GA 30322.

FORD, DENYS KENSINGTON, b. Newcastle, Eng, Aug. 8, 23; Can. citizen; m. 54; c. 3. MEDICINE, RHEUMATOLOGY. B.A, Cambridge, 44, M.B, 47, M.D, 53. Registr. MED, London Hosp. Med. Col, Eng, 51-53; fel, FACULTY MED, UNIV. B.C, 54-60, ASSOC. PROF, 60- Fel, Royal Col. Physicians & Surgeons Can. Am. Rheumatism Asn; N.Y. Acad. Sci; Can. Med. Asn; Can. Soc. Clin. Invest. Arthritis; tissue culture; virology; mycoplasmology; medical therapeutics. Address: Dept. of Medicine, Faculty of Medicine, University of British Columbia, Vancouver, B.C, Can.

FORD, DONALD H(ERBERT), b. Kansas City, Mo, Aug. 18, 21; m. 44; c. 1. ANATOMY, PHYSIOLOGY. B.A, Wesleyan, 47; fel, Kansas, 49-52, Ph.D. (anat), 52. Asst. physiol, Wesleyan, 47-49; asst. instr. ANAT, Kansas, 49-50; instr, STATE UNIV. N.Y. DOWNSTATE MED. CTR, 52-55, asst. prof, 55-59, assoc. prof, 59-68, PROF, 68- Consult, Veterans Admin. Hosp, Brooklyn, 59-; L.I. Col. Hosp. Med.C, U.S.A, 42-45. Endocrine Soc; Am. Asn. Anat; Am. Soc. Neurochem; Am. Physiol. Soc; Int. Soc. Neurochem; Int. Soc. Psychoneuroendocrinol.(past pres). Interrelationship between the nervous and endocrine system; thyroid-central nervous system interrelations; role of the neurosecretory system as an intermediary between the central nervous system and thyroid; neurochemistry, protein and ribonucleic acid metabolism. Address: Dept. of Anatomy, Downstate Medical Center, State University of New York, 450 Clarkson Ave, Brooklyn, NY 11203.

FORD, D(ONALD) H(OSKINS), b. Upland, Calif, July 28, 30; m. 53; c. 3. PLANT PATHOLOGY. B.A, Pomona Col, 52; M.A, Claremont Cols, 54; Ph.D.(plant path), Univ. Calif, 58. Asst. bot, Rancho Santa Ana Bot. Garden, 53-54; res. plant pathologist, forest serv, U.S. Dept. Agr, 54-55; asst. plant path, Univ. Calif, 55-58; plant pathologist, chem. plant disease control, ELI LILLY & CO, CALIF, 58-67, RES. SCIENTIST IN CHARGE PLANT PATH. INVEST, CALIF. RES. STA, 67- AAAS; Am. Phytopath. Soc; Am. Inst. Biol. Sci; Weed Sci. Soc. Am. Soil fungicides and nematocides; soil fungi in relation to plant roots; mycological interest in the order mucorales; herbicides; growth regulators. Address: Eli Lilly & Co, California Research Station, 7521 W. California, Fresno, CA 93706.

FORD, DWAIN. CHEMISTRY. B.A, Andrews, 49; Nat. Sci. Found. fels, Clark, summer 59 & 60-62, Ph.D.(chem), 62. Instr. sci. & math, Wis. Acad, 49-58; asst. prof. CHEM, ANDREWS UNIV, 62-63, assoc. prof, 63-67, PROF, 67-, chmn. dept, 63-71, ACAD. DEAN, 71- Am. Chem. Soc. Chemical carcinogenesis; fatty acid metabolism; organic reaction mechanisms. Address: Dept. of Chemistry, Andrews University, Berrien Springs, MI 49104.

FORD, E(RNEST) S(IDNEY), b. Springfield, Ark, Feb. 15, 04; m. 36; c. 3. BOTANY. A.B, Hendrix Col, 25; M.S, Univ. Chicago, 27, Ph.D, 42. Lab. asst, Libbey Glass Mfg. Co, 25-26; instr. biol, Doane Col, 27-29; BOT, Northwest. Univ, 30-38; Cornell Univ, 38-45; asst. prof, Univ. Tenn, 45-47; assoc. prof, UNIV. FLA, 47-49, prof, 49-71, EMER. PROF, 71- Consult, Corps Eng, U.S. Army, 51; U.S. Forest Serv, 57-58. AAAS; Bot. Soc. Am; Am. Soc. Plant Taxon. Plant morphology and ecology; morphology of citrus. Address: Dept. of Botany, College of Agriculture, University of Florida, Gainesville, FL 32601.

FORD, FLOYD MALLORY, b. Montgomery Co, Tenn, Feb. 21, 21; m. 45. ZOOLOGY. B.S, Tennessee, 49; M.A, George Peabody Col, 52; Carnegie Ford Found. fel. & Ph.D.(biol), Vanderbilt, 63. Instr. agr, instnl. on-the-farm training, 49-50; teacher, Jo Byrns High Sch, 50-51; instr. BIOL, AUSTIN PEAY STATE UNIV, 52-54, asst. prof, 55-57, assoc. prof, 58-62, PROF, 63- U.S.A, 42-45. AAAS; Am. Inst. Biol. Sci; Entom. Soc. Am; Nat. Audobon Soc. Taxonomy and ecology of collembola. Address: Dept. of Biology, Austin Peay State University, Clarksville, TN 37040.

FORD, FRANKLIN C, b. Chewelah, Wash, Jan. 28, 22; m. 48; c. 3. PHYSICS. B.S, California, Berkeley, 48, Ph.D.(physics), 52. Physicist, California, Berkeley, 51-52, Lawrence Radiation Lab, Livermore, 52-62; from dir. res. to v.pres. to GEN. MGR, PHYSICS INT. CO, SAN LEANDRO, 62- Dir, Terradynamics; consult, Aerospace Gen. Nucleonics, 58-62. U.S.N, Lt. Am. Phys. Soc; Am. Soc. Metals. Plasma physics; pulsed power systems; hydrodynamics. Address: 31 Golf Rd, Pleasanton, CA 94566.

FORD, FREDERICK EDDY, b. N.Y.C, Apr. 19, 37; m. 64; c. 3. CHEMICAL ENGINEERING, PHYSICAL CHEMISTRY. B.S, Carnegie Inst. Technol, 59; M.S, Univ. Ill, 61, Ph.D.(chem. eng), 63. Sr. res. chemist, EASTMAN KODAK CO, 63, RES. ASSOC, 69- Sig.C, U.S.A, 63-65. Am. Inst. Chem. Eng; Am. Chem. Soc; Soc. Motion Picture & TV Eng. Reaction kinetics; adsorption to silver halides; photographic film and developer formulation. Address: Eastman Kodak Research Lab, Bldg. 59, Kodak Park, Rochester, NY 14650.

FORD, GEORGE D(UDLEY), b. Morgantown, W.Va, Aug. 18, 40; m. 65; c. 2. PHYSIOLOGY, BIOPHYSICS. B.S. & RCA scholar, W.Va. Univ, 61, NASA fel. & Ph.D.(pharmacol), 67; M.S, Univ. Iowa, 64. Instr. pharmacol, W.Va. Univ, 67; fel. biophys, sch. med. & dent, Univ. Rochester, 67-70; ASST. PROF. PHYSIOL, HEALTH SCI. DIV, MED. COL. VA, VA. COMMONWEALTH UNIV, 70- Atomic Energy Comn. fel, atomic energy proj, sch. med. & dent, Univ. Rochester, 67-70. AAAS. Factors influencing water flow across membranes, particularly Nitella cells; mechanism of action of adrenergic agonists at membrane receptor sites; mathematical models of membrane transport and adrenergically mediated responses; bioinstrumentation. Address: Dept. of Physiology, Medical College of Virginia, Virginia Commonwealth University, Box 608, Richmond, VA 23219.

FORD, GEORGE P(RATT), b. Leesburg, Ga, Apr. 25, 19; m. 44; c. 2. CHEMISTRY. B.S, Ga. Tech, 40, 40-42; M.A, Columbia, 48, Ph.D.(chem), 49. RADIO CHEMIST, LOS ALAMOS SCI. LAB, UNIV. CALIF, 49- Sig.C, U.S.A, 42-46. Am. Chem. Soc; Am. Math. Soc; Am. Phys. Soc. Aerosols; radio chemistry; fission; statistical treatment of data. Address: Los Alamos Scientific Lab, University of California, Box 1663, Los Alamos, NM 87544.

FORD, GEORGE W(ILLARD), b. Detroit, Mich, Jan. 25, 27; m. 53; c. 3. THEORETICAL PHYSICS. A.B, Michigan, 49, M.S, 50, Nat. Sci. Found. fel, 52-54, Ph.D, 55. Asst. prof. PHYSICS, Notre Dame, 54-58; from asst. prof. to assoc. prof, UNIV. MICH, ANN ARBOR, 58-68, PROF, 68- Mem, Inst. Advan. Study, 55-56. U.S.N, 44-46. Am. Phys. Soc. Statistical mechanics; nuclear physics; graph theory. Address: Physics & Astronomy Bldg, Room 713, University of Michigan, Ann Arbor, MI 48104.

FORD, GILBERT C(LAYTON), b. Hill City, Kans, Mar. 31, 23; m. 46; c. 2. NUCLEAR PHYSICS. A.B, Colorado, 43; M.A, Harvard, 48, Atomic Energy Cmn. fel. & Ph.D.(nuclear physics), 51. Head dept. physics, NORTHWEST NAZARENE COL, 50-70, ACAD. V.PRES, 70- U.S.A, 44-46. Mass spectroscopy. Address: Dept. of Physics, Northwest Nazarene College, Nampa, ID 83651.

FORD, HARRY W, b. Maumee, Ohio, June 21, 22; m. 48; c. 2. HORTICULTURE. Ph.D.(hort), Ohio State, 50. Asst. horticulturist, CITRUS EXP. STA, FLORIDA, 50-56, assoc. horticulturist, 56-62, HORTICULTURIST, 62- U.S.A, 43-46. Am. Soc. Hort. Sci. Nematode resistant citrus rootstocks; anaerobic microbiological and chemical changes during water logging. Address: Agricultural Research & Education Center, Lake Alfred, FL 33850.

FORD, JAMES, b. Ryderwood, Wash, Sept. 30, 27; m. 51; c. 4. BIOLOGY, ZOOLOGY. B.A.(ed) & B.A.(biol), West. Wash. State Col, 51; M.S. Oregon State, 53, Nat. Sci. Found. fel. & Ph.D.(zool), 62. Instr. biol, high sch, Wash, 51-54; Skagit Valley Col, 54-56; Ore. Col. Ed, 56-57; chmn. dept, SKAGIT VALLEY COL, 57-66, chmn, div. natural sci, 64-66, DEAN INSTR, 66- Summer lectr, Nat. Sci. Found. Inst. Oceanog, 63-65. U.S.N, 45-46. AAAS. Chromosome study of pulmonate snails. Address: Skagit Valley College, Mt. Vernon, WA 98273.

FORD, JAMES, b. Chicago, Ill, Feb. 3, 34; m. 53; c. 6. METALLURGY. B.S.E, Michigan, 56, M.S.E, 57, Ph.D.(metall. eng), 62. Instr. metall. eng, Michigan, 58-61; res. scientist, res. labs, United Aircraft Corp, 61-63, sr. res. scientist, 63-64; group supvr, metals res. labs, Olin Mathieson Chem. Corp, 65-67, CHIEF, CHEM. METALL. SECT, OLIN CORP, NEW HAVEN, 67- Adj. asst. prof, Hartford Grad. Center, Rensselaer Polytech, 61-70; N.Am. ed, Corrosion Sci. Am. Soc. Metals; Am. Inst. Mining, Metall. & Petrol. Eng; Am. Soc. Mech. Eng; Am. Soc. Test. & Mat; Brit. Inst. Metals. Temper embrittlement of alloy steels; mechanism of solidification of eutectic alloys and resultant properties; physical metallurgy of copper and aluminum alloy development; oxidation and corrosion of copper and aluminum alloys. Address: 51 Pool Rd, North Haven, CT 06473.

FORD, JAMES L. C, JR, b. New York, N.Y, Jan. 24, 33; m. 59; c. 2. PHYSICS. B.A, Montana State, 55; M.S, Calif. Inst. Tech, 59, Ph.D.(physics), 62. PHYSICIST, OAK RIDGE NAT. LAB, 62- Am. Phys. Soc. Nuclear structure, particularly the medium weight nuclei; study of nuclear structure and nuclear reaction mechanisms by direct interactions and Coulomb excitation. Address: Physics Division, Oak Ridge National Lab, P.O. Box X, Oak Ridge, TN 37830.

FORD, J(AMES) W(ILLSON), b. Chicago, Ill, Nov. 26, 12; m. 34; c. 2. PHYSICS. A.B, Oberlin Col, 34; M.S, Case, 36; Ph.D, Pa. State Col, 40. Asst. physics, Case, 34-36; Pa. State Col, 36-40; asst. physicist, Spencer Lens Co, 40-44; head gen. physics sect, CORNELL AERONAUT. LAB, 44-50, atmospheric physics sect, 50-55, applied physics br, 55-57, asst. head APPLIED PHYSICS DEPT, 57-58, HEAD, 58- Optical Soc. Am; Am. Meteorol. Soc; Am. Ord. Asn. X-ray diffraction studies of preferred orientation in coldrolled metals; annealing of optical glass; telemetering for aircraft and missiles; aircraft navigational aids; nuclear instrumentation; atmospheric physics; electromagnetic propagation. Address: Cornell Aeronautical Lab, P.O. Box 235, Buffalo, NY 14221.

FORD, JARED H(EWES), b. Oberlin, Ohio, June 14, 11; m. 38; c. 2. CHEMISTRY. A.B, Oberlin Col, 31; Ph.D.(org. chem), Illinois, 35. Asst. chem, Illinois, 32-35; res. chemist, Kilgore Develop. Corp, 35-41; RES. ASSOC, UPJOHN CO, 41- AAAS; Am. Chem. Soc. Development of processes for the extraction and purification of organic compounds, including antibiotics, steroids and proteins; organic synthesis. Address: Upjohn Co, Kalamazoo, MI 49001.

FORD, JOHN A(LBERT), JR, b. Phoenixville, Pa, Jan. 28, 31; m. 55; c. 2. ORGANIC CHEMISTRY. B.S, Hobart Col, 53; M.S, Delaware, 56, Ph.D, 58. RES. CHEMIST, EASTMAN KODAK CO, 58- Organic synthesis of organophosphorus compounds, dyes and photographic chemicals. Address: Eastman Kodak Co, Bldg. 82, Kodak Park Works, Rochester, NY 14650.

FORD, J(OHN) HARLAN, b. Park River, N.Dak, Sept. 10, 28; m. 53; c. 2. AGRONOMY. B.S, N.Dak. State, 50; M.S, Minnesota, 59. RES. AGRONOMIST, CROPS RES. DIV, AGR. RES. SERV, U.S. DEPT. AGR, UNIV. MINN, ST. PAUL, 55- U.S.A, 51-53, Sgt. Flax investigations, including soil fertility, herbicides, yield components, influence of environment on boll and seed development, and oil content and quality. Address: Dept. of Agronomy, University of Minnesota, St. Paul, MN 55101.

FORD, JOHN P(HILIP), b. London, Eng, Mar. 2, 30; m. 58. STRATIGRAPHY, GEOLOGY. B.Sc, London, 59; Bownocker fel, Ohio State, 64-65, Ph.D.(geol), 65. Clerk, Brit. Mil. Admin, Libya, 47-49; Imp. Bank of Iran, Eng, 49-51; engr, A.V. Roe, Can, 51-56; assoc. dir. extramural studies, Antioch Col, 60-64; ASST. PROF. geol, DePauw, 65-66; EAST. ILL. UNIV, 66-68, GEOL. & GEOG, 68- Geol. Soc. Am; Am. Asn. Petrol. Geol; Nat. Asn. Geol. Teachers; Am. Geophys. Union. Ordovician stratigraphic geology, paleontology and sedimentation; continental interior of North America; field mapping and survey work; laboratory analysis of field data. Address: Dept. of Geology & Geography, Eastern Illinois University, Charleston, IL 61920.

FORD, JOSEPH, b. Asheville, N.C, Dec. 18, 27; m. 51; c. 3. THEORETICAL PHYSICS. B.S, Ga. Inst. Tech, 52; Ph.D.(physics), Hopkins, 56. Res. physicist, Electro Metall. Res. Labs, 56-58; asst. prof. PHYSICS, Miami (Fla), 58-60; vis. prof, Hopkins, 60-61; assoc. prof, GA. INST. TECHNOL, 61-66, PROF, 66- Consult, solid state div, Oak Ridge Nat. Lab, 64- U.S.N, 46-47. Fel. AAAS; Am. Phys. Soc. Statistical mechanics; solid state physics; nonlinear mechanics. Address: School of Physics, Georgia Institute of Technology, Atlanta, GA 30332.

FORD, KENNETH W(ILLIAM), b. West Palm Beach, Fla, May 1, 26; m. 53, 62; c. 6. THEORETICAL PHYSICS. B.A, Harvard, 48; Ph.D.(physics), Princeton, 53. Asst, Los Alamos Sci. Lab, 50-51, consult, 57-58; res. assoc, Indiana, 53-54, asst. prof. PHYSICS, 54-56, assoc. prof, 56-57; Brandeis, 58-61, PROF, 61-64; California, Irvine, 64-70; UNIV. MASS, BOSTON, 70- Fulbright fel, Göttingen, 55-56; Nat. Sci. Found. fel, Mass. Inst. Tech. & Imp. Col, London, 61-62; comnr. Col. Physics, 68-71. U.S.N, 44-46. Fel. Am. Phys. Soc; Am. Asn. Physics Teachers (pres-elect, 71, pres, 72). Nuclear theory; elementary particle theory; physics education. Address: Dept. of Physics, University of Massachusetts, Boston, MA 02116.

FORD, LEE, b. Auburn, Ind, June 16, 17. CYTOGENETICS. B.A, Wittenberg Col, 47; M.S, Minnesota, 49; Ph.D, Iowa State, 52. Assoc. prof, Anderson Col.(Ind), 52-55; vis. prof, Alberta, 55-56; assoc. prof. biol, Pacific Lutheran, 56-62; prof, Miss. State Col. Women, 62-64; chief cytogeneticist, Pac. Northwest Res. Found, Seattle, 64-66; prof. biol, head dept. & dir. mobility inst, Carson Col, 66-67; manpower economist, manpower, info. & res. sect, Nev. State Employ. Serv, 67-68; head cytogenetics lab, Inst. Basic Res. Ment. Retardation, 68-69; CONSULT, 69- Prof. biol. & spec. educ, Dominican Col.(N.Y), 68-69; adj. prof. cytogenetics, dept. biol, Wagner Col, 68-; nat. dir, Companion Collie Prog; dir, Canine Genetic Consult. Serv, Wash. Genetics Soc. Am; Am. Soc. Human Genetics; Am. Genetic Asn; Am. Soc. Zool. Cytogenetics of human pachytene chromosomes, canis familiaris mitotic and meiototic chromosomes and scleral estacia in collie dogs. Address: Box 230, Route 1, Butler, IN 46721.

FORD, LESTER R(ANDOLPH), JR, b. Houston, Tex, Sept. 23, 27; m. 50, 68; c. 9. MATHEMATICS. Ph.B, Chicago, 49, S.M, 50; Ph.D.(math), Illinois, 53. Asst, Illinois, 50-53; res. instr, Duke, 53-54; mathematician, Rand Corp, 54-57; dir. opers. res. Gen. Anal. Corp, 57-60; proj. mgr, C-E-I-R, Inc, 60-63; HEAD COMPUT. SCI. DEPT, GEN. RES. CORP, 63- U.S.A, 46-47. Am. Math. Soc; Math. Asn. Am; Opers. Res. Soc. Am. Point set topology; operations research; network flow theory; system simulation. Address: 520 Pintura Dr, Santa Barbara, CA 93111.

FORD, MILLER CLELL, JR, b. Lake Village, Ark, Mar. 24, 29; m. 61; c. 2. CIVIL ENGINEERING. B.S.C.E, Arkansas, 52, M.S.C.E, 60. Engr, Chance Vought Aircraft Co, 52-55; asst. prof. CIVIL ENG, COL. ENG, UNIV. ARK, FAYETTEVILLE, 59-67, ASSOC. PROF, 67- Nat. Sci. Found. summer inst, Notre Dame, 64; Civil Defense summer inst, Maine, 66. U.S.N, 55-58, Res, 58-, Lt. Comdr. Am. Soc. Civil Eng; Nat. Soc. Prof. Eng; Am. Soc. Eng. Educ; Am. Cong. Surv. & Mapping. Flexible pavement research on relationship of pavement and soil physical properties with pavement performance. Address: Engineering Bldg-328, College of Engineering, University of Arkansas, Fayetteville, AR 72701.

FORD, M(ILTON) D(AVID), b. Greene, N.Y, Oct. 14, 11; m. 32; c. 2. CHEMISTRY. B.S, Syracuse, 33, M.S, 34. Plastic res. chemist, ARMSTRONG CORK CO, 34-36, foreman, accotile dept, 36-38, gen. foreman, tile dept, 38-40, primary opers, 40-41, asst. plant mgr, Fla, 41-45, plant mgr, Ill, 45-53, Pa, 53-60, gen. mgr. tech. serv, 60-63, dir. mfg. & admin. serv, 63, V.PRES. TECH. SERV, 63- Am. Chem. Soc. General management. Address: Armstrong Cork Co, Lancaster, PA 17604.

FORD, NORMAN CORNELL, JR, b. Springfield, Mass, Feb. 9, 32; m. 55; c. 3. PHYSICS. B.S, Mass. Inst. Tech, 53; M.S, Syracuse, 60; Ph.D.(physics), California, Berkeley, 64. Mem. staff, PHYSICS, Mass. Inst. Tech, 64-65; asst. prof, UNIV. MASS, AMHERST, 65-68, ASSOC. PROF, 68- Am. Phys. Soc. Microwave resonance below 1 K; scattering of light from liquids near their critical point. Address: Dept. of Physics, University of Massachusetts, Amherst, MA 01002.

FORD, NORMAN L(EE), b. Osage City, Kans, Dec. 18, 34; m. 54; c. 2. ORNITHOLOGY, ECOLOGY. B.A, Kansas, 57; M.S, Michigan, 62, Ph.D.(zool), 67. Tech. asst. ornith, Univ. Mich. Mus. Zool, 57-67; asst. prof. BIOL, ST. JOHN'S UNIV.(MINN), 67-71, ASSOC. PROF, 71- Am. Ornith. Union; Wilson Ornith. Soc; Cooper Ornith. Soc. Distribution of North American birds; fossil raptors; anatomy and systematics of owls; winter ecology of birds and small mammals. Address: Dept. of Biology, St. John's University, Collegeville, MN 56321.

FORD, PATRICK L(ANG), b. Lake Charles, La, Sept. 23, 27; m. 50; c. 6. MATHEMATICS. B.S, La. State, 48, M.S, 49; Danforth grant, Missouri, 60-61, Ph.D, 61. Instr. MATH, Kemper Mil. Sch, 49-50; asst. prof, McNeese State Col, 50-55; instr, Missouri, 55-56; assoc. prof, McNEESE STATE UNIV, 56-65, PROF, 65-, HEAD DEPT, 62- Dir, Nat. Sci. Found. Inserv. Inst; consult. U.S.A, 48. Math. Asn. Am. Algebra; statistics. Address: Dept. of Mathematical Sciences, McNeese State University, Lake Charles, LA 70602.

FORD, PETER, b. Eng, Dec. 1, 15; m. 50; c. 2. EMBRYOLOGY, HISTOLOGY B.Sc, London, 38, McGregor scholar, 38-39, 45-46, Ph.D, 46. Asst. embryol, Univ. Col, London, 46-49; ASSOC. PROF. EMBRYOL, HISTOL. & HISTOCHEM, UNIV. B.C, 49- Fel. Zool. Soc. London; fel. Can. Soc. Zool; Asn. Brit. Zool; Can. Soc. Cell Biol. Histochemistry; descriptive experimental and histochemical embryology. Address: Dept. of Zoology, University of British Columbia, Vancouver, B.C, Can.

FORD, PETER C(AMPBELL), b. Salinas, Calif, July 10, 41; m. 63; c. 2. INORGANIC CHEMISTRY. B.S, Calif. Inst. Tech, 62; Nat. Insts. Health fel, Yale, 63-66, M.S, 63, Ph.D.(chem), 66. Nat. Sci. Found. fel, 66-67; ASST. PROF. CHEM, UNIV. CALIF, SANTA BARBARA, 67- Am. Chem. Soc; The Chem. Soc. Transition metal chemistry; reactions of coordinated ligands; oxidation mechanisms; photochemistry of metal complexes. Address: Dept. of Chemistry, University of California, Santa Barbara, CA 93106.

FORD, PETER W(ILBRAHAM), b. Hobart, Australia, Nov. 2, 29; m. 67. PHYSICS. B.Sc, Tasmania, 54, fel, 62-63, Ph.D.(physics), 63. Sr. physicist, Dept. External Affairs, Australia, 55-56; res. asst. physics, Univ. Tasmania, 56-59, acting dir. comput. installation, 63-64, res. physicist, 65; systs. analyst, Dept. Defense, Australia, 65-66; sr. physicist, ITEK CORP, 66-67, STAFF SCIENTIST, 67- Design and construction of electromechanical data recorders; computer application to theoretical optics; computer controlled mechanical and optical systems. Address: Itek Corp, 10 Maguire Rd, Lexington, MA 02173.

FORD, RICHARD ALAN, b. Ventura, Calif, June 14, 40; m. 65. PHYSICAL ORGANIC CHEMISTRY. B.S, Okla. State, 62; Ph.D.(org. chem) Wayne State, 67. Res. staff chemist, Yale, 67-68; ASST. PROF. CHEM, CATH. UNIV, AM, 68- Am. Chem. Soc. Nuclear magnetic resonance; stereochemistry. Address: Dept. of Chemistry, Catholic University of America, Washington, DC 20017.

FORD, RICHARD EARL, b. Des Moines, Iowa, May 25, 33; m. 54; c. 4; VIROLOGY, PLANT PATHOLOGY. B.S, Iowa State, 56; M.S, Cornell, 59, Ph.D.(plant path), 61. Res. technician plant path, Iowa State, 53-55, plant breeding, 55, asst. bot, 55-56, instr, 56; asst. plant path, Cornell, 56-59, plant virol, 59-61; asst. prof. plant virol, Oregon State & res. plant pathologist, U.S. Dept. Agr, 61-65; assoc. prof. PLANT VIROL, IOWA STATE UNIV, 65-69, PROF, 69- Mem, Int. Working Group Legume Viruses. Am. Phytopath. Soc. Plant virus; legume and corn viruses; serology; electron microscopy; interaction of viruses and other pathogens. Address: Dept. of Botany & Plant Pathology, Iowa State University, Ames, IA 50010.

FORD, RICHARD FISKE, b. Los Angeles, Calif, Mar. 7, 34; m. 57; c. 1. ECOLOGY, BIOLOGICAL OCEANOGRAPHY. B.A, Pomona Col, 56; Eli Lilly fel, Stanford Univ, 57-58, M.A, 59; U.S. Bur. Commercial Fisheries fel, Scripps Inst. Oceanog, Univ. Calif, 62-64, Ph.D.(oceanog), 65. Asst. prof. ECOL, SAN DIEGO STATE COL, 64-68, assoc. prof, 68-71, PROF, 71- Prin. investr, marine res. comt. grant, State of Calif, 65-67; prin. investr. & consult, San Diego Gas & Elec. Co. res. contracts, 68-, planning consult, Co, 70-; prin. investr, Nat. Sci. Found. grant, 68-70; consult, Gulf Gen. Atomic, Inc, San Diego, 68; Environ. Eng. Lab, Inc, 68-; Bissett-Berman, Inc, 70-; Ocean Sci. & Eng, Inc, Long Beach, 70-; prin. investr, Nat. Oceanic & Atmospheric Agency grant, 70-; lectr, Gulf Energy & Environ. Systs, Inc, San Diego, 70- AAAS; Am. Soc. Limnol. & Oceanog; Ecol. Soc. Am; Brit. Ecol. Soc; Marine Biol. Asn. U.K; Animal Behav. Soc; Am. Soc. Ichthyol. & Herpet. Population ecology, feeding relationships and related

behavior of benthic marine animals; ecological effects and beneficial uses of power station cooling water effluent; ecological effects of marine pollution. Address: Dept. of Biology, San Diego State College, San Diego, CA 92115.

FORD, R(ICHARD) W(ESTAWAY), b. London, Ont, Dec. 14, 30; m. 52; c. 2. PHYSICAL CHEMISTRY. B.Sc, Western Ontario, 52; M.A, Queen's (Ont), 54; Ph.D, McMaster, 57. Chemist, DOW CHEM. CO, 57-65, GROUP LEADER, POLYMER CHEM. SECT, RES. DEPT, 65- Chem. Inst. Can. Polymer chemistry. Address: 1371 Indian Rd, N, Sarnia, Ont, Can.

FORD, ROBERT SEDGWICK, b. Pascagoula, Miss, Aug. 8, 16; m. 37; c. 4. NUTRITION. B.S, Ga. Sch. Tech, 38. Jr. marine engr, Navy Civil Serv, 38-41; chief mech. engr, Ingalls Shipbldg. Corp, 41-48, 52-66; OWNER, ROBERT FORD ASSOCS, 48-; PRES, MAGNOLIA LAB, 61- AAAS; Am. Heart Asn; Int. Fedn. Food Technol. Nutritional pathology; relationship of nutrition to degenerative diseases; engineering research and development. Address: P.O. Box 1306, Pascagoula, MS 39567.

FORD, THOMAS A(VEN), b. Washington, D.C, Aug. 29, 17; m. 44; c. 4. CHEMISTRY. A.B, Wyoming, 37; fel, Yale, 39-40, Ph.D.(chem), 40. Asst. chem, Yale, 37-39; res. chemist, EXP. STA, E.I. DU PONT DE NEMOURS & CO, 40-64, supvr. pressure res. labs, 64-66, MGR. TECH. FACILITIES DIV, 66- AAAS; Am. Chem. Soc. Organic chemistry; fluorine chemistry; polymers. Address: Central Research Dept, Experimental Station, E.I. du Pont de Nemours & Co, Wilmington, DE 19898.

FORD, THOMAS M(ATTHEWS), b. Cambridge, Ohio, Sept. 11, 31; m. 59; c. 1. VETERINARY MEDICINE. B.S, Mich. State, 53, D.V.M, 57, M.S, 59. Asst, Mich. State, 57-58; res. dept, Kellogg Co, 58-60; instr. vet. hyg, Iowa State, 60-62; fel, Bowman Gray Sch. Med, 62-63; med. sch, Michigan, 63-64, dir, animal diag. lab, 64-67; VET, ABBOTT LABS, 67- U.S.A.F, 53-55. Am. Vet. Med. Asn; Am. Asn. Lab. Animal Sci. Nutrition, pathology and diseases of fur bearing animals; diseases of laboratory animals. Address: D-469, Abbott Labs, 1400 Sheridan Rd, North Chicago, IL 60064.

FORD, WARREN THOMAS, b. Kalamazoo, Mich, Mar. 22, 42; m. 67. ORGANIC CHEMISTRY. A.B, Wabash Col, 63; Ph.D.(org. chem), California, Los Angeles, 67. Nat. Sci. Found. res. fel. org. chem, Harvard, 67-68; ASST. PROF. CHEM, UNIV. ILL, URBANA, 68- AAAS; Am. Chem. Soc; The Chem. Soc. Mechanistic organic chemistry; solvent effects; carbanions; stereochemistry; kinetics. Address: Dept. of Chemistry, 261 E. Chemistry Bldg, University of Illinois, Urbana, IL 61801.

FORD, WILLIAM L(IVINGSTONE), b. Montreal, Que, Nov. 15, 13; m. 39; c. 2. CHEMISTRY, PHYSICS. B.A, British Columbia, 36, M.A, 37; Ph.D.(phys. chem), Northwestern, 40. Res. chemist, E.I. du Pont de Nemours & Co, Del, 40-44; oceanogr, Woods Hole Oceanog. Inst, Mass, 44-48; asst. supt, Naval Res. Estab, N.S, 49-50, head sect. underwater physics, 50-52; dir. sci. servs, Dept. Nat. Defence, Ont, 53-55; supt, Pacific Naval Lab, B.C, 55-59; sci. adv. to chief naval staff, Nat. Defence Hq, 59-63; chief personnel, Defence Res. Bd, 63-65; DIR. ATLANTIC OCEANOG. LAB, BEDFORD INST, CAN. DEPT. ENVIRON, 65- Am. Soc. Limnol. & Oceanog; Arctic Inst. N.Am. General management of program in chemical and physical oceanography; air-sea interaction; advanced instrumentation; hydrographic survey and support services including research fleet. Address: Atlantic Oceanographic Lab, Bedford Institute, Canada Dept. of Environment, Dartmouth, N.S, Can.

FORDHAM, CHRISTOPHER COLUMBUS, III, b. Greensboro, N.C, Nov. 28, 26; m. 47; c. 3. MEDICINE. M.D, Harvard, 51. Instr. med, sch. med, Univ. N.C, Chapel Hill, 58-60, asst. prof, 60-64, assoc. prof, 64-68, prof. med. & assoc. dean clin. sci, 68-69, asst. dean, 65-68; prof. med, v.pres. & dean sch. med, Med. Col. Ga, 69-71; PROF. MED. & DEAN SCH. MED, UNIV. N.C, CHAPEL HILL, 71- U.S.A.F, 55-57, Capt. AAAS; fel. Am. Col. Physicians; Am. Fedn. Clin. Res. Metabolism; renal physiology and disease; disease and disorders of water and electrolyte hemeostasis. Address: School of Medicine, University of North Carolina at Chapel Hill, Chapel Hill, NC 27514.

FORDHAM, J(AMES) L(YNN), b. Rodney, Ont, Mar. 27, 24; m. 46; c. 4. PHYSICAL CHEMISTRY. B.Sc, Univ. West. Ont, 46. Chemist, Uniroyal (Can) Ltd, 46-47; Polymer Corp, Ltd, 47-52; Monsanto Co, 52-55; sr. res. chemist, DIAMOND SHAMROCK CORP, 55-56, group leader, 57-59, mgr. polymer res. & develop, 59-65, asst. dir. res, 65-67, dir. res, 67-69, V.PRES. RES. & CORP. DEVELOP, 69- Am. Chem. Soc; N.Y. Acad. Sci; Soc. Plastics Eng. Synthesis, structure, properties and uses of chemicals, polymers and related products. Address: 9204 Creekwood Dr, Mentor, OH 44060.

FORDHAM, JOSEPH R(AYMOND), b. Hornell, N.Y, Sept. 1, 37; m. 62; c. 4. BIOCHEMISTRY, ORGANIC CHEMISTRY. B.S, Col. Holy Cross, 59; M.S, Purdue, 63, Ph.D.(biochem), 66. Asst. biochem, Purdue, 60-65; res. scientist, Joseph E. Seagram & Sons, 65-69; ASST. PROF. NUTRIT. & FOOD SCI, UNIV. KY, 69- AAAS; Am. Chem. Soc. Intermediary metabolism; rumen microbiology; short-chain fatty acid metabolism; proteolytic enzymes; flavor chemistry; terpene chemistry; effect of nutrition on lipogenesis; novel plant protein products; nutrition status. Address: 336 Queensway Dr, Lexington, KY 40502.

FORDHAM, WILLIAM DAVID, b. Marietta, Ohio, Apr. 24, 39; m. 64. BIOPHYSICAL & PHYSICAL CHEMISTRY. B.S, Marietta Col, 61; univ. fel, Yale, 61-62, M.S, 62, Nat. Insts. Health fel, 62-66, Ph.D.(biophys. chem), 67. RES. CHEMIST, org. chem. div, AM. CYANAMID CO, BOUND BROOK, 66-68, PIGMENTS DIV, 68- Am. Chem. Soc. Biological reaction mechanisms; organic phosphates; photochemistry; chemical kinetics; thermochemistry; nuclear magnetic resonance; pigments; surface chemistry. Address: 204 Helfreds Landing, Somerville, NJ 08876

FORDICE, MICHAEL W, b. St. Paul, Minn, Aug. 12, 40; m. 69. ORGANIC CHEMISTRY. B.A, Macalester Col, 62; Nat. Insts. Health fel, Mass. Inst. Tech, 63-66, Ph.D.(org. chem), 66. Sr. res. chemist, Merck Sharp & Dohme

Res. Labs, N.J, 66-70; CHIEF CHEM. SECT, LAB. SERV, VET. ADMIN. HOSP, EAST ORANGE, 70- Am. Chem. Soc; The Chem. Soc. Medicinal chemistry. Address: 118 Retford Ave, Cranford, NJ 07016.

FORDYCE, CLAUDE, JR, b. Washington, Ind, Oct. 12, 30; m. 50; c. 2. PLANT PATHOLOGY. B.S, Purdue, 58, M.S, 60, Ph.D.(plant path), 62. Asst. prof. plant path, Va. Polytech. Inst, 62-67; RES. PATHOLOGIST, U.S. DEPT. AGR, BELTSVILLE, MD, 67- U.S.A.F, 51-55, S/Sgt. Am. Phytopath. Soc. Research in diseases of ornamental plants especially soil borne microorganisms; diseases of the cultivated mushroom. Address: Dept. of Mushrooms & Microbiology, Vegetables & Ornamentals, Agricultural Research Service, U.S. Dept. of Agriculture, Beltsville, MD 20705.

FORDYCE, DAVID B(UCHANAN), b. Los Angeles, Calif, Oct. 15, 24; nat; m. 47; c. 3. PHYSICAL CHEMISTRY. B.A.Sc, British Columbia, 46; Carbide & Carbon, fel, Wisconsin, 49-50, Ph.D.(chem), 50. Asst. chem, Wisconsin, 47-48; res. chemist, ROHM & HAAS CO, 50-56, head lab, 56-63, RES. SUPVR, 63- Am. Chem. Soc. Application properties of ion exchange resins, water soluble polymers and surfactants; analytical chemistry. Address: 313 E. Central Ave, Moorestown, NJ 08057.

FORDYCE, JAMES S(TUART), b. London, Eng, Dec. 10, 31; nat; m. 54; c. 2. PHYSICAL CHEMISTRY. A.B, Dartmouth Col, 53; Ph.D.(phys. chem), Mass. Inst. Technol, 59. Asst, Mass. Inst. Technol, 53-59; res. chemist, Nat. Carbon Co. Div, Union Carbide Corp, 58-59, Union Carbide Consumer Prod. Co. Div, 59-63, develop. dept, 63-66; res. scientist, LEWIS RES. CTR, NASA, 66-68, sect. head, DIRECT ENERGY CONVERSION DIV, 68-71, CHIEF ENVIRON. RES. OFF, 71- AAAS; Am. Chem. Soc; fel. Am. Inst. Chem. Photochemistry; fast reaction kinetics; electronic and vibrational spectroscopy of molten salts and electrolyte solutions; electrochemistry; solid electrolytes; urban air pollution. Address: Lewis Research Center, NASA, 21000 Brookpark Rd, Cleveland, OH 44135.

FORDYCE, REID G(EORGE), b. Regina, Sask, Can, Apr. 14, 14; nat; m. 39; c. 4. PHYSICAL ORGANIC CHEMISTRY. B.A.Sc, British Columbia, 35, Carnegie scholar, 35, M.A. Sc, 36; Nat. Res. Coun. Can. bursar, McGill, 36, Ph.D.(org. chem), 39. Asst, McGill, 36; res. chemist, Thomas & Hochwalt labs, Monsanto Co, 39-44, group leader, 44-47, mgr. prod. develop. dept, 47-53, dir. tech. serv, 53-59; res. & develop, Fome-Cor Corp, 59-65, dir. commercial develop, Monsanto Res. Corp, 65-68, UNIV. RELS. & PROF. RECRUITING MGR, MONSANTO CO, 68- Fundamental exploratory research on vinyl copolymers; mechanism of emulsion copolymerization; structure versus physical and chemical properties of copolymers. Address: Monsanto Co, 800 N. Lindbergh Blvd, St. Louis, MO 63166.

FORE, HARRY W(AUGH), JR, b. Danville, Va, June 12, 24; m. 51; c. 2. DENTISTRY & EDUCATION. Univ. Richmond, 46-49; D.D.S, Med. Col. Va, 52. Private practice, 52-57; instr. oper. dent. & oral anat, SCH. DENT, MED. COL. VA, VA. COMMONWEALTH UNIV, 57-59, asst. prof, 59-63, assoc. prof. oper. dent, 63-67, PROF. RESTORATIVE DENT, 67-, DIR. DENT. AUXILIARY & DENT. AUXILIARY UTILIZATION PROGS, 68-, co-dir. dent. auxiliary utilization prog, 64-68. Partic, nat. & regional confs. & workshops in dent. auxiliary utilization & dent. assisting educ, 65, 67, 68 & 70; consult, Vet. Admin. Hosp, Salem, Va, 68- U.S.A.A.F, 43-46. Dental auxiliary utilization and education; curriculum design in dental hygiene and dental auxiliary utilization; expanded functions for dental auxiliaries; dental assisting and dental laboratory technology curriculum design and program planning. Address: Medical College of Virginia School of Dentistry, Virginia Commonwealth University, 521 N. 11th St, Richmond, VA 23219.

FORE, JULIAN M(ARK), b. Ft. Mitchell, Va, Feb. 12, 14; m. 37; c. 2. AGRICULTURAL ENGINEERING. B.Sc, Va. Polytech, 35; fel, Purdue, 35-37, M.Sc, 37. Res. instr. agr. eng, Purdue, 37-39; res. engr, Tenn. Valley Auth, 40-51; develop. engr. air handling, Aerovent Fan & Equip, Inc, 51-54; training engr. agr. equip, tractor & implement div, Ford Motor Co, 54-55; prof. AGR. ENG. & head dept, Massachusetts, 55-56; PROF, N.C. STATE UNIV, 56- Commandant, Army Res. Sch, 59-65. C.Eng, 42-46, Col. Am. Soc. Agr. Eng; Am. Soc. Eng. Educ. Development of electrical and mechanical devices to automate the agricultural industry; substitution of scientific sensing instruments for human judgment and choice. Address: Dept. of Agricultural Engineering, Box 5906, North Carolina State University, Raleigh, NC 27607.

FORE, R(OBERT) E(STES), b. Cameron, Mo, Nov. 3, 07; m. 36; c. 3. PLANT BREEDING, GENETICS. B.S, Iowa State Col, 29; M.S, Illinois, 31, Ph.D. (plant breeding), 35. Asst. agron, Illinois, 29-36; asst. prof. farm crops, Oregon State Agr. Col, 36-39, assoc. prof, ORE. STATE UNIV, 39-43, prof, 43-70, EMER. PROF. AGRON, 70- Vis. prof, Kasetsart Univ, Thailand, 58-60; plant sci. adv, Univ. Nigeria, 64-66. Am. Soc. Agron. Breeding of corn, hops and small grains; agronomic research with hops and corn. Address: Dept. of Agronomy, Oregon State University, Corvallis, OR 97331.

FOREE, EDWARD G(OLDEN), b. Sulphur, Ky, Feb. 24, 41; m. 62; c. 2. ENVIRONMENTAL & CIVIL ENGINEERING. B.S, Univ. Ky, 64; U.S. Pub. Health Serv. trainee, Stanford Univ, 64, M.S, 65, U.S. Pub. Health Serv. fel, 66, Ph.D.(civil eng), 68. ASST. PROF. CIVIL ENG, UNIV. KY, 68- Am. Soc. Limnol. & Oceanog; Am. Soc. Civil Eng; Water Pollution Control Fedn; Am. Water Works Asn; Am. Soc. Eng. Educ. Growth and decomposition of algae and related effects on water quality; plant nutrients and eutrophication; acid mine drainage; biological waste treatment. Address: Dept. of Civil Engineering, University of Kentucky, Lexington, KY 40506.

FORELLI, FRANK J(OHN), b. San Diego, Calif, Apr. 8, 32; m. 59; c. 1. MATHEMATICS. A.B, Univ. Calif, Berkeley, 54, M.A, 59, Ph.D.(math), 61. Instr. MATH, UNIV. WIS, MADISON, 61-63, asst. prof, 63-65, assoc. prof, 65-67, PROF, 67- U.S.N, 54-57, Lt.(jg). Am. Math. Soc. Mathematical analysis. Address: Dept. of Mathematics, University of Wisconsin, 213 Van Vleeck Hall, Madison, WI 53706.

FOREMAN, BRUCE M(ILBURN), JR, b. Arkadelphia, Ark, Nov. 10, 32; m. 64; c. 1. INFORMATION SCIENCE. B.S, Univ. Calif, Berkeley, 54, Ph.D.(nuclear chem), 58. Res. assoc, Brookhaven Nat. Lab, 58-60; res.

scientist chem, Columbia Univ, 60-64; asst. prof. physics, Univ. Tex, Austin, 64-68; SR. SCIENTIST, AM. INST. PHYSICS, 68- Am. Phys. Soc. Mechanisms of nuclear reactions. Address: Physics Information Division, American Institute of Physics, 335 E. 45th St, New York, NY 10017.

FOREMAN, (WILLIAM) CALVIN, b. Hannibal, Mo, Aug. 15, 10; m. 41; c. 3. MATHEMATICS. A.B, Westminster Col.(Mo), 32; M.A, Kansas, 41, fel, 49-50, Ph.D.(math), 52. Teacher, pub. schs, 35-40; asst. instr. MATH, Kansas, 40-41; instr, Omaha, 41-42; Kansas, 46-48, res. asst, 48-50; PROF, BAKER UNIV, 50-, CHMN. DIV. NATURAL SCI, 63-, CHMN. DEPT. MATH. & PRE-ENG, 50- Summers, co-dir, Nat. Sci. Found. summer inst. high sch. math. teachers, Ft. Hays Kans. State Col, 59-60, 62-64, mem. faculty, 65-69; Kans. State Teachers Col. 61. U.S.N.R, 42-46, Lt. Comdr. Am. Math. Soc; Math. Asn. Am. Differential geometry; vectors; matrices. Address: Dept. of Mathematics, Baker University, Baldwin City, KS 66006.

FOREMAN, C(HARLES) F(REDERICK), b. Blue Rapids, Kans, Nov. 9, 20; m. 46; c. 3. DAIRY SCIENCE. B.S, Kans. State Col, 48; M.S, 49; Ph.D, Missouri, 53. Asst. prof. dairy exten, Kans. State Col, 49-51; asst. instr, dairy husb, Missouri, 51-53; asst. prof, Minnesota, 53-54; IOWA STATE UNIV, 55-58, assoc. prof, 58-64, prof, 64-68, PROF. IN CHARGE DAIRY SCI, 68- U.S.A, 42-46, Res, 46-, Lt. Col. Am. Soc. Animal Sci; Am. Dairy Sci. Asn.(teaching award, 68). Animal nutrition and management. Address: Dept. of Animal Science, 123 Kildee Hall, Iowa State University, Ames, IA 50010.

FOREMAN, CHARLES WILLIAM, b. Lewis, Ind, Mar. 18, 23; m. 47; c. 1. ELECTRICAL ENGINEERING. B.S, Rose Polytech, 49. Test engr, Bell Aircraft Corp, 50-51; engr, Goodyear Aircraft Corp, 51-59; staff engr, Melpar, Inc, 59-61; engr, ANAL. SERV. INC, FALLS CHURCH, 61-65, asst. independent res, 61-70, MGR. RECONNAISSANCE DIV, 70- U.S.A, 43-46, T/Sgt. Inst. Elec. & Electronics Eng. Systems analysis of military problems. Address: 2525 Flint Hill Rd, Vienna, VA 22180.

FOREMAN, CHARLES W(ILLIAM), b. Norman Park, Ga, Nov. 2, 23; m. 51; c. 3. ZOOLOGY, PHYSIOLOGY. B.A, North Carolina, 49; M.A, Duke, 51, Ph.D.(physiol), 54. Asst. prof. biol, Wofford Col, 53-55; zool, Maryland, 55-56; assoc. prof. BIOL, Pfeiffer Col, 56-61, prof, 61-63; assoc. prof, UNIV. OF THE SOUTH, 63-66, PROF, 66- Res. partic, Oak Ridge Nat. Lab, Tenn, 60; trustee, Highlands Biol. Sta, N.C, 61- U.S.A, 43-46. Fel. AAAS; Am. Soc. Mammal; Genetics Soc. Am; N.Y. Acad. Sci. Taxonomic significance and genetic basis of hemoglobin structure. Address: Dept. of Biology, University of the South, Sewanee, TN 37375.

FOREMAN, DARHL L(OIS), b. Idaho Falls, Idaho, May 3, 24. ZOOLOGY, ENDOCRINOLOGY. B.S, George Wash. Univ, 46; M.A, Mt. Holyoke Col, 48; Ph.D.(zool), Univ. Chicago, 55. Instr. BIOL, CASE WEST. RESERVE UNIV, 54-56, asst. prof, 56-70, ASSOC. PROF, 70- Fel. AAAS; Am. Soc. Zool; Ecol. Soc. Am. Ovarian physiology; physiology of annual breeders; animal behavior and endocrine effects; endocrinology of sex and reproduction. Address: Dept. of Biology, Case Western Reserve University, Cleveland, OH 44106.

FOREMAN, DENNIS WALDEN, JR, b. Akron, Ohio, Dec. 27, 29; m. 53; c. 2. MINERALOGY, PHYSICAL CHEMISTRY. B.S, Mt. Union Col, 52; M.S, Ohio State, 60, Ph.D.(mineral), 66. Res. assoc. DENT, OHIO STATE UNIV, 66-68, asst. prof, 68-69, ASSOC. PROF, 69- U.S.A, 54-57, 1st Lt. AAAS; Am. Crystallog. Asn; Electron Micros. Soc. Am; Int. Asn. Dent. Res. Crystal structures of hydrogrossular, tin apatite; rates of phase changes in Ag_2HgI_4; mineralization in biological environments; bone and tooth structure; crystalline water in human enamel. Address: Room 407, Ohio State University College of Dentistry, 305 W. 12th Ave, Columbus, OH 43210.

FOREMAN, HARRY, b. Winnipeg, Man, Can, Mar. 5, 15; nat; m. 56; c. 2. POPULATION ECOLOGY, ENVIRONMENTAL STUDIES. B.Sc, Antioch Col, 38; Ph.D.(biochem), Ohio State, 42; M.D, California, 41. Fel, Atomic Energy Cmn, Nat. Res. Coun, Crocker Radiation Lab, California, 49-51; mem. staff, biomed. res. group, Los Alamos Sci. Lab, California, 51-62; assoc. prof. nuclear med, sch. pub. health, UNIV. MINN, MINNEAPOLIS, 62-66, assoc. dean, Off. Int. Progs, 66-69, DIR, CTR. POP. STUDIES, 69- U.S.A, 44-45. AAAS; fel. Soc. Exp. Biol. & Med; Radiation Res. Soc; Biophys. Soc. Toxicology of radioactive and heavy metals and chelating agents; renal pathology and physiology; clinical uses of radioactive isotopes. Address: Center of Population Studies, Mayo Memorial Bldg, University of Minnesota, Box 395, Minneapolis, MN 55455.

FOREMAN, HELEN PULVER, b. West New York, N.J, July 21, 23; m. 50. MICROPALEONTOLOGY. A.B, Berea Col, 46; M.A, Oberlin Col, 48. Geologist, U.S. Geol. Surv, 48-50; RES. ASSOC. GEOL, OBERLIN COL, 60- Mem, Paleont. Res. Inst. Radiolaria. Address: 131 S. Professor St, Oberlin, OH 44074.

FOREMAN, J(ESSE) WILLIAM, JR, b. Nashville, Tenn, Dec. 28, 32; m. 62. OPTICAL PHYSICS. B.S, Purdue, 54, Ph.D.(physics), 64; M.A, Columbia, 57. Physicist, missile & space div, Gen. Elec. Co, Pa, 62-64; sr. res. physicist, Brown Eng. Co, Ala, 64-66, prin. res. physicist, 66-67; eng. consult, space support div, Sperry Rand Corp, 67-70; PROF. PHYSICS & MATH, UNIV. MONTEVALLO, 70- Am. Phys. Soc; Optical Soc. Am; Am. Asn. Physics Teachers. Research and development of laser applications; design and analysis of optical and infrared systems. Address: Dept. of Physics & Mathematics, University of Montevallo, Montevallo, AL 35115.

FOREMAN, JOHN E(DWARD) K(ENDALL), b. Hamilton, Ont, Feb. 14, 22; m. 47; c. 4. MECHANICAL ENGINEERING. B.A.Sc, Toronto, 45; M.M.E, Cornell, 52. Special lectr, Toronto, 46-49; instr. & res. asst, Cornell, 49-52; res. engr, George Kent, Ltd, Eng, 52-54, head res. & develop, Can, 54-56; asst. prof. ENG. SCI, UNIV. WEST. ONT, 56-58, assoc. prof. 58-63, PROF, 63-, HEAD MECH. GROUP, 60- Can. Army, 44-45; R.C.A.F.R, 56-65, Wing Comdr. Am. Soc. Mech. Eng; Am. Soc. Eng. Educ; Eng. Inst. Can. Biomechanics; mechanical analysis; noise abatement. Address: Faculty of Engineering Science, University of Western Ontario, London 72, Ont, Can.

FOREMAN, KENNETH, b. New York, N.Y, July 30, 25; m. 54; c. 2. AERONAUTICAL ENGINEERING. B.Aero.Eng, N.Y. Univ, 50, M.Aero.Eng, 53; Polytech. Inst. Brooklyn. Res. engr, Bendix Aviation Corp, 51-52; proj. engr, Wright Aeronaut. Div, Curtiss-Wright Corp, N.J, 52-56; res. engr, engine div, Fairchild Engine & Airplane Corp, N.Y, 56-59; specialist & sci. res. engr, Repub. Aviation Corp, 59-65; chief proj. engr, Edo Corp, 65-66; RES. ENGR, GRUMMAN AEROSPACE CORP, BETHPAGE, 66- Abstractor, Fire Res. Abstr. & Revs, Nat. Acad. Sci. Am. Soc. Mech. Eng; Am. Inst. Aeronaut. & Astronaut. Propulsion; gas dynamics; chemical reactions resulting in heat addition; flow instrumentation; planetary atmospheres; space sciences; air and water pollution instrumentation systems; oceanographic instrumentation; systems engineering. Address: 32 Stratford Ct, North Bellmore, L.I, NY 11710.

FOREMAN, MELVIN (ORVIL), b. Oak Harbor, Ohio, Sept. 21, 03; m. 37; c. 1. ORGANIC CHEMISTRY. B.S, Capital Univ, 25; Lilly fel, Chicago, 26-27, 28-29, Maryland, 27-28; M.S. & Ph.D.(org. chem), Chicago, 29; Besancon, 46. Res. chemist, E.I. du Pont de Nemours & Co, Del, 29-32; mgr, Cole Mfg. Co, Ohio, 32-36; critic & supvr. teaching training phys. sci, Kent State, 36-43; PROF. CHEM, EAST. ILL. UNIV, 46- Consult, Hayward, Inc, Ohio, 37-43. U.S.A.A.F, 43-46, Capt. Am. Chem. Soc. Fungicides and insecticides; dehydration of foods; new product development. Address: Dept. of Chemistry, Eastern Illinois University, Charleston, IL 61920.

FOREMAN, R(OBERT) W(ALTER), b. Flint, Mich, Jan. 4, 23; m. 45; c. 2. ORGANIC CHEMISTRY. B.S, Michigan, 44, fel, 45-46, M.S, 46; Ph.D, Western Reserve, 55. Asst. chem, Manhattan Proj, 44; res. assoc. eng. res, Michigan, 44-45; res. chemist, Standard Oil Co, 46-66; DIR. RES. & DEVELOP, PARK CHEM. CO, 66-, MEM. BD. DIRS, 69- Am. Chem. Soc; Am. Soc. Metals. Metallurgy; organic chemistry; petroleum chemistry; molten salt chemistry; analytical chemistry; absorption spectroscopy. Address: Park Chemical Co, 8074 Military Ave, Detroit, MI 48204.

FOREMAN, RONALD LOUIS, b. Chicago, Ill, Oct. 26, 37; m. 59; c. 2. PHARMACOLOGY, TOXICOLOGY. B.S, Univ. Ill, Chicago, 60, M.S, 64, fel, summers 67 & 68, Ph.D.(pharm), 69. Nat. Insts. Health trainee PHARMACOL, UNIV. ILL. MED. CTR, 69-71, ASST. PROF, 71-; TOXICOLOGIST, CHICAGO BD. HEALTH LABS, 71- AAAS; Am. Chem. Soc; Am. Pharmaceut. Asn. Therapeutic and toxicological aspects of drug metabolism and distribution; epoxides as obligatory intermediates in the metabolism of olefins to glycols; public health aspects of drug use and toxicity. Address: Dept. of Medical Pharmacology, University of Illinois, P.O. Box 6998, Chicago, IL 60680.

FOREMAN, S. DALE, b. Amarillo, Tex, May 10, 23; m. 46; c. 1. CIVIL ENGINEERING, ENGINEERING MECHANICS. B.S, Tex. Tech. Col, 47; M.S, Colorado, 60, Nat. Sci. Found. fels, summers 62 & 63, Ph.D.(eng. mech), 66. Instr. civil eng, Tex. Tech. Col, 55-59, asst. prof, 60-63; ENG. MECH, COLO. SCH. MINES, 66-67, ASSOC. PROF, 67- Design engr, U.S. Bur. Reclamation, summer 61. U.S.A.A.F, 43-45, 1st Lt. Nat. Soc. Prof. Eng; Am. Soc. Eng. Educ. Stress analysis in shell structures; vibrations in unsymmetrical beams; finite element methods in rock mechanics. Address: Dept. of Engineering Mechanics, Colorado School of Mines, Golden, CO 80401.

FORER, ARTHUR H, b. Trenton, N.J, Dec. 17, 35; m. 64; c. 2. CELL BIOLOGY. B.S, Mass. Inst. Technol, 57; Univ. Rochester, 57-59; Univ. Wash, summer 59; Ph.D.(molecular biol), Dartmouth Med. Sch, 64. Am. Cancer Soc. fel, Carlsberg Found, Copenhagen, Denmark, 64-66; Helen Hay Whitney Found. fel, Cambridge & Duke Univ, 67-70; ASSOC. PROF. MOLECULAR BIOL, ODENSE UNIV, DENMARK, 70- Hargitt res. fel, Duke Univ, 69-70. AAAS; Am. Soc. Cell Biol; Brit. Soc. Exp. Biol; Norweg. Cell Biol. Soc. Chromosome motion in relation to general problems of cellular motility systems. Address: Molecular Biology Institute, Odense University, DK-5000, Odense, Denmark.

FOREST, BERTRAND, b. St. Pie-de-Guire, Que, May 31, 18; m. 45; c. 4. HORTICULTURE. B.A, Laval, 39, B.Sc, 43; M.Sc, McGill, 45; Ph.D.(agr), Cornell, 56. Agr. res. off, Can. Dept. Agr, 54-60; secy, Que. Agr. Res. Coun, 60-62, chmn, 62; CHIEF RES. SERV, QUE. DEPT. AGR, 62- Am. Soc. Hort. Sci; Am. Soc. Plant Physiol; Agr. Inst. Can; Can. Soc. Hort. Sci; Can. Soc. Plant Physiol; Genetics Soc. Can. Soils and plants research. Address: Research Service, Dept. of Agriculture, Parliament Bldg, Que 4e, Que, Can.

FOREST, EDWARD, b. New York, N.Y, Mar. 66, 33; m. 61; c. 2. PHYSICAL CHEMISTRY. B.S, Brooklyn Col, 55; U.S. Army Res. Off. grants, Durham, 60-61 & 62-63; Off. Naval Res. grant, 61-62; M.A, Princeton, 62, Ph.D. (phys. chem), 63. Instr. chem, Brooklyn Col, 58-59; asst, Princeton, 59-60; scientist, RES. DIV, XEROX CORP, WEBSTER, 63-69, MGR, 69- Med.C, U.S.A, 55-57. Am. Chem. Soc; Soc. Photog. Sci. & Eng. Microwave absorption and relaxation in liquid state; resistivities of liquid and solid state; charge transport in organic solid state; photo responsive systems. Address: 12 Panorama Trail, Rochester, NY 14625.

FOREST, HARVEY, b. Brooklyn, N.Y, Jan. 23, 37; m. 59; c. 2. PHYSICAL CHEMISTRY. B.S, Brooklyn,Col, 58; M.A, Columbia, 59, Ph.D.(chem), 64. Staff scientist, Gen. Precision Aerospace Res. Ctr, 64-66; SR. SCIENTIST, ZENITH RADIO CORP, 66- Luminescence of rare earth activated phosphors. Address: Zenith Radio Corp, 6001 W. Dickens Ave, Chicago, IL 60639.

FOREST, HERMAN S(ILVA), b. Chattanooga, Tenn, Feb. 18, 21; m. 63; c. 2. ENVIRONMENTAL MANAGEMENT, BIOLOGY. B.A, Tennessee, 42; M.S, Mich. State, 48, Atomic Energy Comn. fel, 49-51, Ph.D.(bot), 51. Asst. prof. biol, Col. William & Mary, 53-54; instr. bot, Tennessee, 54-55; bot. & biol, Oklahoma, 55-58; dir. students mus, Knoxville, 58-60; res. asst, med. ctr, Oklahoma, 60-61; res. assoc. BIOL, Univ. Rochester, 61-65; PROF, STATE UNIV. N.Y. COL. GENESEO, 65- Nat. Insts. Health fel, 61-62; Atomic Energy Comn. grant, 62-64; exchange scholar, Bot. Inst. U.S.S.R, Leningrad, 64; Nat. Sci. Found. grant, 65; dir. aquatic studies proj, State Univ. N.Y. Col. Geneseo, 68-71; Am. Inst. Biol. Sci. vis. biologist, 69-71; environ. consult, 71-; proj. dir, Environ. Resource Ctr, 71- AAAS; Am. Inst. Biol. Sci; Ecol. Soc. Am; Bot. Soc. Am; Am. Water Resources Asn; Phycol. Soc. Am. Water resources; philosophy of science; non-marine algae and rooted aquatics. Address: Dept. of Biology, State University of New York College at Geneseo, Geneseo, NY 14454.

FOREST, ROBERT D, b. Colorado Springs, Colo, May 14, 29; m; c. 2. PHYSICAL METALLURGY. Met.E, Colo. Sch. Mines, 52, M.S, 58, D.Sc.(metall), 61. Prof. scientist, DOW CHEM. CO, 52-53, 55-56, prof. design engr, 60-62, metall. res. supvr, 62-65, METALL. RES. DIR, 65- U.S.A, 53-55. Am. Soc. Metals; Am. Inst. Min, Metall. & Petrol. Eng; Sci. Res. Soc. Am. Physical metallurgy; solid state physics; ceramics; welding. Address: Dow Chemical Co, Box 888, Golden, CO 80401.

FORESTER, DONALD W(AYNE), b. Knoxville, Tenn, Apr. 7, 37; m. 59; c. 2. PHYSICS. B.A, Berea Col, 59; Woodrow Wilson fel, Tennessee, 59-60, M.S, 61, South. fel, 60-62, Nat. Sci. Found. fel, 62-63, Oak Ridge fel, 63-64, Ph.D.(physics), 64. Asst. prof. physics, Univ. Nebraska, Lincoln, 64-66; Res. Corp. grant & asst. prof. physics, Ga. Inst. Technol, 66-69; RES. PHYSICIST, MAGNETISM BR, SOLID STATE DIV, NAVAL RES. LAB, 69- Oak Ridge Inst. Nuclear Studies travel grant, 65-67; NASA res. grant, 66-69. Am. Phys. Soc. Mössbauer experiments; magnetic properties of solids; studies in electrical discharge; low temperature physics; optical properties of solids. Address: Magnetism Branch, Solid State Division, Naval Research Lab, Code 6451-F, Washington, DC 20390.

FORESTER, RALPH H, b. Chicago, Ill, Apr. 11, 28; m. 53; c. 2. POLYMER CHEMISTRY. B.A, Carleton Col, 50; Illinois, 50-51; Minnesota, 53. Chemist, G.H. Tennant Co, 55-66; RES. CHEMIST, N. STAR RES. & DEVELOP. INST, 66- U.S.A, 51-53. Fedn. Socs. Paint Technol. Biophysics, low-level bioelectric phenomena; epoxy ester and urethane coatings; metal fibers, reinforced plastics, abrasives and filters; ultrathin polymer membrane technology. Address: North Star Research & Development Institute, 3100 38th Ave. S, Minneapolis, MN 55406.

FORESTER, ROBERT D(ONALD), b. Los Angeles, Calif, July 27, 24; m. 49; c. 2. GEOPHYSICS. B.S, Calif. Inst. Tech, 49, M.S, 50, Hicks fel, 50-51, Ph.D, 53. Geophysicist & geologist, Standard Oil Co. Calif, 53-58; res. assoc, Pan-Am. Petrol. Corp, 59-65; v.pres. data processing & res, Petty Labs, Inc, Tex, 59-69; MEM. STAFF, INDUST. OPERS, TRW, INC, 69- U.S.N.R, 43-46. Soc. Explor. Geophys; Am. Asn. Petrol. Geol. Seismology. Address: TRW Industrial Operations, 9841 Airport Blvd, Los Angeles, CA 90045.

FORESTI, ROY J(OSEPH), JR, b. Baltimore, Md, Mar. 25, 25; m. 53; c. 2. CHEMICAL ENGINEERING. B.E, Hopkins, 47; M.S, Carnegie Inst. Tech, 48, fel, Pa. State Univ, 50-51, Ph.D.(fuel tech), 51. Asst, Pa. State Univ, 48-50; res. chem. engr, U.S. Bur. Mines, 51-54; res. chem. engr, Monsanto Chem. Co, 54-55, group leader, 55-59; lectr. chem. eng, Dayton & sr. res. scientist, res. inst, 59-61; assoc. prof. CHEM. ENG, Connecticut, 61-63; HEAD DEPT, CATHOLIC UNIV, 63- Sig.C, U.S.A, 45-46. Am. Chem. Soc; Am. Inst. Chem. Eng; Am. Soc. Eng. Educ; Soc. Rheol. Airborne solid dispersions; gasification of solids; oxidation of gases; nonideal liquids. Address: 301 Willington Dr, Silver Spring, MD 20904.

FORET, JAMES A, b. Lutcher, La, Sept. 3, 21; m. 46; c. 10. ORNAMENTAL HORTICULTURE, WEED SCIENCE. B.S, Univ. Southwest. La, 43; M.S, Iowa State Univ, 47, Ph.D.(plant physiol), 50. Instr. & res. asst. prof, Iowa State Univ, 46-50; assoc. prof. HORT, UNIV. SOUTHWEST. LA, 50-53, PROF, 53-, HEAD DEPT. PLANT INDUST. & GEN. AGR, 69-, head dept. gen. agr, 53-64. U.S.A, 43-45, Sgt. Weed Sci. Soc. Am; Am. Soc. Hort. Sci. Disposal of rice hulls; control of Elodea canadensis in lakes of Louisiana; control of alligatorweed in rice irrigation canals; herbicide residue studies in rice irrigation canals; aquatic week control. Address: Dept. of Plant Industry & General Agriculture, University of Southwestern Louisiana, Box 487, Lafayette, LA 70501.

FORET, JOHN E(MIL), b. N.Y.C, Nov. 19, 37; m. 60; c. 3. DEVELOPMENTAL BIOLOGY. B.A, Univ. N.H, 62, M.S, 63; A.M, Princeton, 65, Ph.D. (biol), 66. Nat. Insts. Health fel, 66-67; ASST. PROF. EMBRYOL, UNIV. N.H, 67- U.S.A, 56-58. Am. Soc. Zool; Soc. Develop. Biol. Cellular origins and control mechanisms in limb regeneration. Address: Dept. of Zoology, University of New Hampshire, Durham, NH 03824.

FORGACS, JOSEPH, b. Nokomis, Ill, Mar. 20, 17; m. 46; c. 5. MICROBIOLOGY. B.S, Illinois, 40, fel. & M.S, 42, Ph.D.(bact, hort), 44. Asst. hort, Illinois, 40-43, plant path, 43-44; bacteriologist & chief antibiotics & chemother, Camp Detrick, 46-54; mem. staff, res. div, Am. Cyanamid Co, 54-57, 60; dir. lab, Spring Valley Gen. Hosp, New York, 58-60; staff microbiologist & consult. mycotoxicologist, Good Samaritan Hosp, Suffern, N.Y, 60-69; CONSULT, GEN. FOODS CORP, 68-; DIR. MICROBIOL, AUTOMATED BIOCHEM. LABS, INC, 69- Consult. microbiologist, Tuxedo Mem. Hosp, New York, 60-64; consult. mycotoxicologist, agr. res. serv, U.S. Dept. Agr, 65- Sanit.C, 44-46, 2nd Lt. Am. Soc. Microbiol; Soc. Indust. Microbiol; N.Y. Acad. Sci; Int. Soc. Trop. Dermat. Food bacteriology and chemistry; antibiotics and chemotherapy; mycology; mycotoxicoses. Address: Microbiology Dept, Automated Biochemical Labs, Inc, Spring Valley, NY 10977.

FORGASH, ANDREW J(OHN), b. Dunellen, N.J, Nov. 21, 23; m. 44; c. 4. ENTOMOLOGY. B.S, Rutgers Univ, 49, Headlee fel, 48-52, M.S, 50, Ph.D. (entom), 52. Asst. res. specialist, chem, RUTGERS UNIV, 52-54, entom, 54-58, assoc. res. specialist, 58-61, from res. specialist to RES. PROF. ENTOM. & ECON. ZOOL, 61- U.S.A.A.F, 42-45. Entom. Soc. Am. Physiology; biochemistry; toxicology. Address: Dept. of Entomology & Economic Zoology, Rutgers University, New Brunswick, NJ 08903.

FORGENG, W(ILLIAM) D(ANIEL), b. Scranton, Pa, May 31, 09; m. 30; c. 2. METALLURGY. B.Chem, Cornell, 30, Ph.D.(micros), 34. Asst. chem, Cornell, 29-34; METALLURGIST, res. labs, UNION CARBIDE CORP, 34-53, MINING & METALS DIV, 53- With Atomic Energy Cmn; Off. Sci. Res. & Develop, 44. Am. Soc. Metals; Am. Soc. Test. & Mat. Metallurgy of ferro-alloys; effect of bismuth as an impurity on the structure and properties of tin. Address: Mining & Metals Division, Union Carbide Corp, Niagara Falls, NY 14302.

FORGENG, W(ILLIAM) D(ANIEL), JR, b. Niagara Falls, N.Y, July 26, 35; m. 58; c. 2. METALLURGY. B.Met.E, Cornell, 58; Gen. Elec. Co. fel, Purdue, 58-61, Ph.D.(metall. eng), 62. Sr. res. metallurgist, Rochester Prods. Div, Gen. Motors Corp, 62-64; ASSOC. RES. CONSULT, APPL. RES. LAB, U.S. STEEL CORP, 64- Am. Soc. Metals; Am. Soc. Test. & Mat. Physical metallurgy; metallurgical kinetics; metallography, particularly of carbon and low alloy steels. Address: Applied Research Lab, U.S. Steel Corp, Monroeville, PA 15146.

FORGOTSON, JAMES M(ORRIS), JR, b. Albuquerque, N.Mex, Mar. 17, 30; m. 58; c. 2. GEOLOGY, PETROLEUM ENGINEERING. A.B, Washington (St. Louis), 51; B.S, Texas, 52; M.S, Northwestern, 54, Ph.D.(geol), 56. Explor. geologist, 53-55; sr. res. engr, Pan Am. Petrol. Corp, 56-61, tech. group supvr, 61-62, res. group supvr, 62-68; V.PRES, PETROL. INFO. CORP, 68- Am. Asn. Petrol. Geol.(award, 64, secy-treas, 68-70); Soc. Econ. Paleont. & Mineral; Soc. Petrol. Eng; Am. Geophys. Union; Soc. Explor. Geophys. Regional stratigraphic studies applied to petroleum exploration; new methods of presenting quantitative geological data; use of electronic computers to process and statistically analyze geological data; well log analysis; interpretation of gravity and magnetic data. Address: Petroleum Information Corp, P.O. Box 2612, Denver, CO 80201.

FORGUE, STANLEY V(INCENT), b. Cleveland, Ohio, Oct. 6, 16; m. 42; c. 3. ELECTRONICS. B.S, Ohio State, 39, B.E.E. & M.S, 40, fel, 41-42; Princeton, 43-44. Asst. physics, Ohio State, 39-40, res. engr, eng. exp. sta, 40-41; SR. MEM. TECH. STAFF, RCA CORP. LABS, 42- Five awards for outstanding work in res, RCA Labs. AAAS; N.Y. Acad. Sci; Am. Phys. Soc; fel. Inst. Elec. & Electronics Eng. Pick-up tubes for television; development of first practical vidicon; photo-conductivity; thermionic emission; sonic properties of materials; electronic storage tubes; magnetostriction; color television pick-up and viewing tubes; infrared. Address: RCA Corp. Labs, Princeton, NJ 08540.

FORIST, ARLINGTON A(RDEANE), b. Lansing, Mich, Oct. 14, 22; m. 52; c. 5. BIOLOGICAL CHEMISTRY. B.S, Mich. State Col, 48, Ph.D.(biochem), 52. Asst, Qm. Food & Container Inst, Mich. State Col, 48-51; res. assoc, UPJOHN CO, 51-60, res. sect. head, 60-68, RES. MGR. PHYS. & ANAL. CHEM. RES, 68- U.S.A, 42-46. AAAS; Am. Chem. Soc; N.Y. Acad. Sci; Am. Soc. Clin. Pharmacol. & Therapeut; Acad. Pharmaceut. Sci; Am. Pharmaceut. Asn. Kinetics and mechanisms of organic reactions; organic and biochemical analyses; drug disposition. Address: Upjohn Co, Kalamazoo, MI 49001.

FORK, DAVID C(HARLES), b. Detroit, Mich, Mar. 4, 29; m. 58; c. 3. BOTANY. A.B, Univ. Calif, Berkeley, 51, Ph.D.(bot), 61. BIOI OGIST, DEPT. PLANT BIOL, CARNEGIE INST, 60-, fel, 60-61. Assoc. prof, Stanford Univ, 68- U.S.N, 52-56, Lt. AAAS; Am. Soc. Plant Physiol; Am. Inst. Biol. Sci. Study of the basic mechanisms of photosynthesis. Address: 111 Ramona Rd, Los Trancos Woods, Portola Valley, CA 94025.

FORK, R(ICHARD) L(YNN), b. Dearborn, Mich, Sept. 1, 35; m. 57; c. 2. ATOMIC PHYSICS, LASERS. B.S, Principia Col, 57; Ph.D.(physics), Mass. Inst. Technol, 62. MEM. TECH. STAFF, BELL TEL. LABS, 62- Fel. Am. Phys. Soc; Optical Soc. Am. Rare earth spectroscopy; magnetic resonance in gases; optical masers; nonlinear optical interactions in gases; photochromics; solid state dye lasers. Address: Bell Telephone Labs, Holmdel, NJ 07733.

FORKER, EDSON LEE, b. Pittsburgh, Pa, Aug. 28, 30; m. 55; c. 4. PHYSIOLOGY, INTERNAL MEDICINE. B.S, Haverford Col, 53; M.D, Pittsburgh, 57. Intern, Presby. Hosp, Denver, Colo, 57-58; res. internal med, univ. hosp, UNIV. IOWA, 60-63, Iowa Heart Asn. fel. physiol. & biophys, 63-65, asst. prof. med, COL. MED, 65-69; physiol. & biophys, 67-69, ASSOC. PROF. INTERNAL MED, PHYSIOL. & BIOPHYS, 69- Res. assoc, Vet. Admin. Hosp, Iowa City, Iowa, 65-67; Markle scholar. acad. med, 67; Nat. Insts. Health res. career develop. award, 68. Med.C, U.S.N.R, 58-60, Lt. AAAS; Am. Asn. Study Liver Diseases; Am. Fedn. Clin. Res; Soc. Exp. Biol. & Med; Am. Physiol. Soc; Am. Gastroenterol. Asn. Hepatic physiology; bile formation; membrane transport. Address: Dept. of Physiology & Biophysics, University of Iowa, Iowa City, IA 52240.

FORKER, ROBERT F(ENCIL), b. Pittsburgh, Pa, Mar. 5, 20; m. 43; c. 3. ORGANIC CHEMISTRY. B.A, Harvard, 42; M.S, Pa. State, 48, Ph.D.(org. chem), 49. Asst. in charge pilot plant res, Koppers United Co, Inc, 43-46; res. chemist, E.I. du Pont de Nemours & Co, 50-54; Brit. naphthalene sales agent, John N. Forker Coal Tar Chem, 54-63; develop. mgr. new eng. tar prod, Witco Chem. Co, Inc, 63-65, southwest. area mgr, Pioneer Prod. Div, 65-69; SR. INSTR. PROG, ACAD. COMPUT. TECHNOL, 69- AAAS; Am. Chem. Soc. Total synthesis of a quinine type alkaloid; steroids; organic chemical reaction mechanisms. Address: 11606 Windy Lane, Houston, TX 77024.

FORKEY, DAVID M(EDRICK), b. Minneapolis, Minn, Apr. 9, 40; m. 66. ORGANIC CHEMISTRY. B.A, St. Olaf Col, 62; Ph.D.(org. chem), Washington (Seattle), 67. Nat. Res. Coun. res. assoc. org. synthesis & mass spectrometry, Naval Weapons Ctr, Calif, 67-69; ASST. PROF. CHEM, SACRAMENTO STATE COL, 69- Am. Chem. Soc. Synthesis of theoretically interesting organic molecules and organic mass spectrometry. Address: Dept. of Chemistry, Sacramento State College, Sacramento, CA 95819.

FORKNER, CLAUDE E(LLIS), b. Stevensville, Mont, Aug. 14, 00; m. 27; c. 3. INTERNAL MEDICINE. B.A, Univ. Calif, Berkeley, 22, M.A, 23; fel, Harvard, 24-26, M.D, 26. Asst. anat, Univ. Calif, Berkeley, 22-23; intern, Hopkins Hosp, 26-27; asst. path. & bact, Rockefeller Inst. Med. Res, 27-29; Nat. Res. Coun. fel. path. & clin. invest, Univ. Freiburg, 29-30; Peabody fel. med, Harvard Med. Sch, 30-32; assoc. prof, Peking Union Med. Col, China, 32-36, hon. lectr, 36-37; asst. prof. clin. med, MED. COL, CORNELL UNIV, 37-43, assoc. prof, 43-53, prof. MED, 53-66, EMER. PROF, 66- Asst. physician, Thorndike Mem. Lab, Boston City Hosp, 30-32; mem. bd. dirs, China Aid Coun, 37-43, pres, 39-41; asst. attend. physician, New York Hosp, 37-45, assoc. attend. physician, 45-50, attend. physician, 50-66, consult, 66-; mem, Am. Comt. Chinese War Orphans, 38-41, pres, 39-41; mem. bd. dirs, Chinese Indust. Coop, 38-41; Am. Bur. Med. Aid to China, 38-43; United China Relief, 41-43; prof. & dir, China Med. Bd, 43-45; hon. prof, med. col, Cheeloo Univ, China, 43-45; Nat. Shanghai Med. Col, China, 43-45; attend. physician, Roosevelt Hosp, 46-51, consult, 51-69; mem. bd. dirs, C.T. Loo Chinese Educ. Fund, 47-69; mem. med. adv. coun, Iran Found, Inc, 51-65, bd. dirs, 54-62, pres, 55-58, chmn. bd, 58-61; consult, U.S. Naval Hosp, St. Albans, 52-53; consult, Bronx Vet. Admin. Hosp, 56-67; Hosp. Spec. Surg, 58-63; mem. bd. trustees, Teachers Col, Columbia Univ, 59-66; consult, New York Infirmary, 59-66; mem. med. adv. comt, Unitarian Serv. Comt, 61-67; nat. alumni chmn, prog. Harvard Med. Sch, 62-65; panel adv, N.Y. State Comt. Med. Educ, 62-; mem. bd. trustees, Med. Passport Found, Inc, 63-, exec. dir; consult. & med. dir, Fish Mem. Hosp, Deland, Fla, 69-70; mem. resources comt, Harvard Med. Sch, 71- Medal of Hon. Merit, Repub. China, 42; Companion Royal Order Homayun, Iran, 57. Dipl, Am. Bd. Internal Med, 37, mem. bd. dirs, 51-57. U.S.A, 18, Res, 22-27; Nat. Guard, 27-29; civilian consult, Surgeon Gen, U.S.A, 44-45, Col. AAAS; fel. Am. Med. Asn; Am. Soc. Clin. Invest; Asn. Am. Physicians; N.Y. Acad. Med. (v.pres, 54-55); Int. Soc. Hemat; Pan-Am. Med. Asn; fel, N.Y. Acad. Sci; Royal Soc. Health; Am. Clin. & Climat. Asn; Soc. Study Blood; fel. Am. Col. Physicians. Hematology; experimental tuberculosis; transmission of Kala-azar; medical education; medical records. Address: P.O. Box 820, DeLand, FL 32720.

FORKNER, CLAUDE ELLIS, JR, b. Boston, Mass, July 28, 28; m. 55; c. 3. INTERNAL MEDICINE. B.A, Harvard, 49; Virginia, 50; M.D, Cornell, 54. Intern med, second med. div, Bellevue Hosp, 54-55; clin. assoc, Nat. Cancer Inst, 55-57; jr. asst. res. med, Peter Bent Brigham Hosp, 57-58, asst, 58-60; asst. res, NEW YORK HOSP, 60-61, physician, OUTPATIENT DEPT, 61-69, ASST. ATTEND. PHYSICIAN, 69-; CLIN. ASST. PROF. MED, MED. COL, CORNELL UNIV, 69-, clin. instr, 61-69. Resident acute leukemia serv, Nat. Insts. Health Clin. Ctr, 56-57; Nat. Heart Inst. fel, Peter Bent Brigham Hosp, Boston, 58-60; res. fel. med, Boston Lying-In Hosp, Children's Med. Ctr. & Harvard Med. Sch, 58-60; asst. vis. physician, Bellevue Hosp. Ctr, 63-; asst. attend, outpatient dept, Roosevelt Hosp, 63- Dipl, Am. Bd. Internal Med. U.S.P.H.S.R, 55-57, Sr. Surgeon. AAAS; Am. Heart Asn; N.Y. Acad. Med; fel. Am. Col. Physicians; fel. Am. Col. Chest Physicians; Am. Fedn. Clin. Res; Royal Soc. Health. Chemotherapy of malignant diseases; skeletal and neurological manifestations of leukemia; Psuedomonas aeroginosa infections; pulmonary embolization; mechanisms of cyanosis; ammonia metabolism; vectorcardiography. Address: Mead Point, Greenwich, CT 06830.

FORLAND, MARVIN, b. Newark, N.J, Mar. 29, 33; m. 65; c. 1. INTERNAL MEDICINE. A.B, Colgate Univ, 54; M.D, Columbia Univ, 58. Intern & resident internal med, Univ. Chicago Hosps, 59-62, asst. prof. med, sch. med, Univ. Chicago, 64-68; ASSOC. PROF. MED. & CHIEF RENAL & ELECTROLYTE SECT, UNIV. TEX. MED. SCH, SAN ANTONIO, 68- Med.C, 62-64, Capt. Clinical nephrology and metabolism; renal physiology. Address: University of Texas Medical School, San Antonio, TX 78229.

FORLANO, ALBERT J(OSEPH), b. Brooklyn, N.Y, Aug. 18, 29; m. 57; c. 2. PHARMACEUTICAL CHEMISTRY. B.S, Long Island, 50; M.S, Columbia, 55; Ph.D.(pharmaceut. chem), Ohio State, 59. Chemist, pharmaceut. res. div, Chas. Pfizer & Co, 59-62; assoc. prof. pharmaceut. chem, SCH. PHARM, FERRIS STATE COL, 62-70, PROF. MED. CHEM, 70- Nat. Sci. Faculty res. grant, 63-65; Mead Johnson grant pharmaceut. res, 64-65. Med.C, U.S.A, 51-53. Am. Chem. Soc; Am. Pharmaceut. Asn. Chemical stability and biological behavior of new esters of vitamin A; amino acid derivatives of serotonin. Address: School of Pharmacy, Ferris State College, Big Rapids, MI 49307.

FORLANO, ROBERTO J(OSE), b. Buenos Aires, Arg, Nov. 5, 28; U.S. citizen; m. 69; c. 1. CERAMICS, METALLURGY. B.S, Univ. Buenos Aires, 53; M.S, Univ. Ill, 62, Ph.D.(ceramics eng), 65. CERAMIST, KNOLLS ATOMIC POWER LAB, GEN. ELEC. CO, 65- Am. Ceramic Soc; Am. Soc. Metals. Research in high temperature oxide and materials related with nuclear power applications. Address: Knolls Atomic Power Lab, General Electric Co, 1 River Rd, Schenectady, NY 12301.

FORMAINI, ROBERT LEWIS, b. Erie, Pa, Sept. 24, 22; m. 44; c. 2. ORGANIC & PHYSICAL CHEMISTRY. B.S, Gannon Col, 48; Cornell, 48-49; Richmond, 54-56. Res. chemist, res. lab, Colgate-Palmolive Co, N.J, 49-50; jr. res. chemist, nitrogen div, ALLIED CHEM. CORP, 52-56, res. chemist, 56-59, sr. res. chemist, 59-61, supvry. res. chemist, 61-63, mgr. appln. res, Va, 63-67, mgr. tech. servs, PLASTICS DIV, N.J. 67-69, MGR. PROD. DEVELOP, 69- Summer asst, Morse Chain Co. Div, Borg-Warner Corp, N.Y, 49. U.S.N, 42-46, 50-52, Res, 46-50, Lt. Am. Chem. Soc; Commercial Develop. Asn. Synthetic detergents, bleaches; synthesis and process development, organic industrial chemicals, coatings, wood adhesives, textile and laminating resins, polyesters, and paint vehicles. Address: Plastics Division, Allied Chemical Corp, Box 2365R, Morristown, NJ 07960.

FORMAL, SAMUEL B(ERNARD), b. Providence, R.I, Aug. 28, 23; m. 51; c. 3. MICROBIOLOGY. A.B, Brown, 45, Sc.M, 48; Ph.D.(microbiol), Boston, 52. Bacteriologist, Food & Drug Admin, 48-49; WALTER REED ARMY INST. RES, 52-56, CHIEF DEPT. APPL. IMMUNOL, 56- Mem. cmn. enteric infections, Armed Forces Epidemiol. Bd. Dipl, Am. Bd. Microbiol. U.S.N, 42-46, Lt.(jg). AAAS; Am. Soc. Microbiol; Am. Asn. Immunol; Am. Acad. Microbiol; Soc. Exp. Biol. & Med. Pathogenesis and immunity in enteric infections; non-specific immunity. Address: Dept. of Applied Immunology, Walter Reed Army Institute of Research, Washington, DC 20012.

FORMAN, ARTHUR, b. Cape Town, S.Africa, June 1, 36; m. 64; c. 1. PHYSICAL CHEMISTRY. B.Sc, Univ. Cape Town, 55; Crawford scholar. & B.A, Cambridge, 58, Kings Col. grant, S.African Coun. Sci. & Indust. Res. grant & Ph.D.(chem), 61. Res. assoc. chem, Enrico Fermi Inst. Nuclear Studies, 62-64; S.African Coun. Sci. & Indust. Res, 64-67; Harvard, 67-68; RES. ASSOC. CHEM. & ASST. SCIENTIST, MED. DEPT, BROOKHAVEN NAT. LAB, 68- Electron spin resonance studies of transition metal complexes;

aromatic free radicals; phosphorescent triplet states of organic molecules and porphyrin radicals. Address: Medical Dept, Brookhaven National Lab, Upton, NY 11973.

FORMAN, DONALD T, b. N.Y.C, Feb. 27, 32; m. 53; c. 3. BIOCHEMISTRY, ANALYTICAL CHEMISTRY. B.S, Brooklyn Col, 53; M.S, Wayne State Univ, 57, Am. Heart Asn. fel, 57-59, Ph.D.(biochem), 59. Chief biochemist, Hazleton Lab, 59-60; instr. BIOCHEM, MED. SCH, NORTHWEST. UNIV, 61-66, asst. prof, 66-69, ASSOC. PROF, 69-; DIR. CLIN. BIOCHEM, EVANSTON HOSP, 63- Dir. biochem, Mercy Hosp, 60-63; res. grants, Nat. Insts. Health, 63-64, 64-68; Am. Heart Asn, 63-64, 64-68. U.S.A, 53-55, Sgt. AAAS; Am. Chem. Soc; Am. Asn. Clin. Chem. Clinical biochemistry, development of better methods, more specific procedures for evaluating disease states; atherosclerosis. Address: Dept. of Clinical Biochemistry, Evanston Hospital, 2650 Ridge Ave, Evanston, IL 60201.

FORMAN, E(ARL) J(ULIAN), b. Hartford, Conn, June 22, 29; m. 53; c. 3. ANALYTICAL CHEMISTRY. B.A, Wesleyan, 53; Gen. Elec. Col. fel, Mass. Inst. Tech, 55-56, Ph.D.(anal. chem), 57. Res. chemist, Hercules Powder Co, 57-70; RES. GROUP LEADER, POLAROID CORP, 70- Am. Chem. Soc. Address: Chemical Development Dept, Polaroid Corp, 600 Main St, Cambridge, MA 02139.

FORMAN, G. LAWRENCE, b. Hartford, Conn, Nov. 13, 42; m. 69. MAMMALOGY, COMPARATIVE ANATOMY. B.A, Kansas, 64, M.A, 67, Ph.D. (mammal), 69. ASST. PROF. BIOL, ROCKFORD COL, 69-, CHMN. DEPT, 71- AAAS; Am. Soc. Mammal; Soc. Syst. Zool. Mammalian systematics; microanatomy of mammals; gastrointestinal morphology in relation to feeding habits; morphology of cellular types in mammals in relation to systematic arrangement; ecology of North American bats. Address: Dept. of Biology, Rockford College, Rockford, IL 61101.

FORMAN, GEORGE W, b. Salt Lake City, Utah, Dec. 9, 19; m. 41; c. 3. MECHANICAL ENGINEERING, ENGINEERING MECHANICS. B.S, Illinois, 41; M.S, Kansas, 58; Nat. Sci. Found. fel, Kansas State, 63-64. Design engr. & supvr. eng. training, Hamilton Standard Div, United Aircraft Corp, 41-46; mgr. mech. eng, Marley Co, 46-53; res. mgr, Butler Mfg. Co, 53-55; PROF. MECH. ENG, KANSAS, 55- Indust. consult, 55- Fel. Am. Soc. Mech. Eng. Machine design; composite materials research; structural response to impact loads. Address: Dept. of Mechanical Engineering, University of Kansas, Lawrence, KS 66044.

FORMAN, GUY, b. Dundee, Ky, Oct. 23, 06; m. 26. PHYSICS. B.S, West. Ky. State Col, 29; M.A, Indiana, 31; Ph.D, Kentucky, 50. Assoc. prof. physics, West. Ky. State Col, 29-43; Vanderbilt, 43-62; PROF. PHYSICS, UNIV. S.FLA, 62-, chmn. dept, 62-69. Am. Phys. Asn; Optical Soc. Am; Am. Asn. Physics Teachers. Action of light on selenium cells as a surface effect; coloration of quartz crystals by radiation with x-rays; x-ray excited phosphorescence of natural crystals; teaching elementary and intermediate physics. Address: Dept. of Physics, University of South Florida, Tampa, FL 33620.

FORMAN, IVIN ROSS, b. Rochester, N.Y, May 28, 20; m. 55; c. 3. INORGANIC CHEMISTRY. B.S, Rochester, 41. Photog. emulsion chemist, Haloid Co, 41-47, mgr. photog. prod. res, 47-55, asst. to works mgr, 55-57, supt. photog. prof. res, Haloid Xerox, Inc, 57-61, dir. sensitized mfg, XEROX CORP, 61-66, PHOTO PLANT MGR, 66- Am. Chem. Soc; Photog. Soc. Am. Photographic and xerographic sensitizing. Address: Xerox Corp, 282 Hollenbeck St, Rochester, NY 14621.

FORMAN, J(OSEPH) CHARLES, b. Chicago, Ill, Dec. 22, 31; m. 53; c. 3. CHEMICAL ENGINEERING. S.B, Mass. Inst. Technol, 53; fel, Northwestern, 56-57, M.S, 57, R.E. Cabell fel, 57-58; Ph.D.(chem. eng), 60. Mem. tech. proj. training prog, Dow Chem. Co, Mich, 53-54; chem. engr, develop. div, ABBOTT LABS, 56, sr. chem. engr, eng. develop. dept, 59-63, group leader, extreme conditions lab, 63-67, group leader fermentation eng, BIOL. DEVELOP. DEPT, 67-68, SECT. MGR, 68- U.S.A.F, 54-56, Res, 56-65, Capt. Am. Inst. Chem. Eng; Am. Chem. Soc. Biochemical engineering; industrial fermentations; environmental engineering, particularly water and air pollution control; advanced wastewater treatment; high pressure technology; catalysis; direction and evaluation of technical projects; technical management. Address: Dept. of Biological Development, Abbott Labs, Dept. 451, North Chicago, IL 60064.

FORMAN, LAWRENCE EDWARD, b. Virginia, Minn, Oct. 9, 10; m. 38; c. 6. ORGANIC CHEMISTRY. B.S.(chem), N.Dak. State Univ, 32, M.S, 33, B.S. (ed), 34; Ph.D.(chem), Kansas, 39. Asst. instr. chem, Kansas, 34-38; chemist, Cook Paint & Varnish Co, Mo, 38-42; sr. res. chemist, FIRESTONE TIRE & RUBBER CO, 46-61, RES. ASSOC, 61- U.S.A, 42-46, Chem.C.Res, 53-60, Lt. Col.(Ret). Am. Chem. Soc. Rubber chemistry; compounds of nitrogen and sulphur; phenol derivatives; polymer chemistry; synthetic isoprene and butadiene elastomers. Address: Central Research Labs, Firestone Tire & Rubber Co, Akron, OH 44317.

FORMAN, LOREN V(ERNE), b. Ames, Iowa, Oct. 24, 12; m. 39; c. 4. PAPER CHEMISTRY. B.S, Iowa State Col, 34; M.S, Lawrence Col, 36, Ph.D.(chem), 40; Am. Scand. Found. Nils R. Johaneson fel, Scandinavia, 39. Pulp & paper technologist, Munising Paper Co, Mich, 36-38; develop. engr, Mead Corp, Ohio, 40-42; group leader pulp & paper tech, Inst. Paper Chem, Lawrence Col, 42-45, coord. appl. res, 45-50; dir. pulp utilization, Scott Paper Co, 50-53, tech. dir, west coast div, 53-56, gen. mgr, Everett Plant, 56-57, west coast opers, 58-60, v.pres. res, develop. & eng, 60-69; PRES, PULP MFRS. RES. LEAGUE INC, 69- Tech. Asn. Pulp & Paper Indust. Bonding strength of adhesives; action of ultraviolet light on lignin. Address: Pulp Manufacturers Research League Inc, P.O. Box 436, Appleton, WI 54911.

FORMAN, RALPH, b. N.Y.C, Oct. 4, 21; m. 43; c. 3. PHYSICS. B.A, Brooklyn Col, 42; M.S, Maryland, 51, Ph.D, 54. PHYSICIST, Nat. Bur. Standards, 42-55; Union Carbide Corp, 55-64; LEWIS RES. CTR, NASA, 64- Am. Phys. Soc. Thermionic emission; properties of oxide cathodes; high vacuum technology; surface properties of germanium and silicon; space charge in high pressure inert gas filled thermionic diodes; studies of the electronic properties of irradiated gas plasma; high temperature heat pipes; high temperature thermal conductivity measurements. Address: Lewis Research Center, NASA, Cleveland, OH 44135.

FORMAN, RICHARD T. T, b. Richmond, Va, Nov. 10, 35; m. 63; c. 3. BOTANY. B.S, Haverford Col, 57; Ph.D.(bot), Univ. Pa, 61. Asst. instr. bot, Univ. Pa, 58-59, 60-61; Duke Univ, 59-60; mem. Am. Friend Serv. Comt. agr. exten. & community develop, Nat. Inst. Agr, Guatemala, 61-62; asst. prof. biol, Pan Am. Agr. Col, Honduras, 62-63; bot. & zool, Univ. Wis, 63-66; BOT, RUTGERS UNIV, 66-69, ASSOC. PROF, 69- Instr, Pigeon Lake Field Sta, Wis, summers 64 & 65; res. assoc, Mt. Wash. Observ, N.H, 68-; vis. scientist, Orgn. Trop. Studies, Costa Rica, 70; Fulbright grant, Bogota, Colombia, 70-71; on leave to dept. ecol. & systs, Cornell Univ, spring 71. Fel. AAAS; Ecol. Soc. Am; Am. Bryol. & Lichenological Soc; Bot. Soc. Am; Torrey Bot. Club; Asn. Trop. Biol. Ecosystems and communities; patterns of stress effects; tropical ecology; bryology. Address: Dept. of Botany, Rutgers, The State University, New Brunswick, NJ 08903.

FORMAN, STANLEY MAURICE, b. Brooklyn, N.Y, Mar. 5, 19; m. 48. PHYSICS. B.A, N.Y. Univ, 44, Ph.D.(physics), 55. Tutor physics, City Col. New York, 47-52; instr, Cooper Union, 52-53; sr. physicist, Winchester Div, Olin Mathieson Chem. Corp, 54-55; prin. engr, Repub. Aviation Corp, 55-56, sci. specialist, 56-59, assoc. scientist, 59-61, scientist, 61-63, chief theoret. physics, res. div, N.Y, 63-65; assoc. prof. PHYSICS, COOPER UNION, 65-70, PROF, 70- AAAS; Am. Phys. Soc; Am. Asn. Physics Teachers; N.Y. Acad. Sci. Retarded interactions charged particles; nuclear magnetic resonance; optical pumping; quantum and statistical mechanics. Address: Dept. of Physics, Cooper Union, Cooper Square, NY 10003.

FORMAN, S(YDNEY) A(LEXANDER), b. Toronto, Ont, May 11, 17; m. 41; c. 3. MINERALOGY, CRYSTALLOGRAPHY. B.A, Toronto, 41, M.A, 46. Mining engr, Lamaque Mining Co, 41-42; asst, Toronto, 46-49; crystal chemist, Can. Dept. Mines & Tech. Survs, 49-56; head, mineral. sect, mineral sci. div, Can. Dept. Mines & Tech. Surv, 56-64, sr. scientist, 64-66; SCI. ADV, sci. secretariat, Can, 66-71; MINISTRY OF STATE FOR SCIENCE & TECHNOL, CAN, 71- Can. rep, Int. Comt. Study Clays, 60. Fel. Mineral. Soc. Am; Am. Ceramic Soc; Am. Crystallog. Asn; Can. Soc. Soil Sci; Mineral. Asn. Can; Can. Asn. Appl. Spectros; Mineral. Soc. Gt. Brit. & Ireland. Effects of soil forming processes on soil minerals with particular emphasis on clay minerals and their paragenesis. Address: Ministry of State for Science & Technology, Ottawa, Ont. K1A 1A1, Can.

FORMAN, WILLIAM, b. N.Y.C, Oct. 16, 14; m. 38; c. 2. MATHEMATICS. B.S, Brooklyn Col, 36, M.A, 37; Ph.D, N.Y. Univ, 53. Lectr. MATH, BROOKLYN COL, 36-53, instr, 53-58, asst. prof, 58-62, assoc. prof, 62-71, PROF, 71- Asst, inst. math. & mech, N.Y. Univ, 51-52; consult, Systs. Res. Group, 59-62. U.S.A, 44-46. Am. Math. Soc; Math. Asn. Am. Theory of numbers; algebra. Address: Dept. of Mathematics, Brooklyn College, Brooklyn, NY 11210.

FORMANEK, EDWARD WILLIAM, b. Chicago, Ill, May 6, 42. ALGEBRA. B.S, Univ. Chicago, 63; M.S, DePaul Univ, 65; Ph.D.(math), Rice Univ, 70. Asst. prof. MATH, Univ. Mo-St. Louis, 70-71; FEL, CARLETON UNIV, Am. Math. Soc. Group theory. Address: Dept. of Mathematics, Carleton University, Ottawa, Ont, Can.

FORMANEK, R(OBERT) J(OSEPH), b. Schenectady, N.Y, Dec. 25, 22; m. 46; c. 2. CHEMICAL ENGINEERING. B.S.Ch.E, Purdue, 43. Trainee, B.F. Goodrich Co, 44-47, compounder, 47-51, textile engr, 51-54; mgr. textiles, DUNLOP TIRE & RUBBER CORP, 54-57, compounding & textiles, 57-61, tech. mgr, 61-64, asst. v.pres. tech, 64-69, V.PRES. TECH, 69- Am. Chem. Soc. Technical development of tires. Address: Dunlop Tire & Rubber Corp, Buffalo, NY 14240.

FORMICA, JOSEPH V(ICTOR), b. N.Y.C, July 3, 29; m. 56; c. 2. BIOCHEMISTRY. B.S, Syracuse Univ, 53, M.S, 54; George Wash. Univ, 56-59; Ph.D. (microbiol), Georgetown Univ, 67. Supvr. & bacteriologist, Ft. Detrick, Md, 54-58; assoc. neurochem, Nat. Insts. Health, 58-63; biochem, Georgetown Univ, 63-67, asst. prof. pediat. virol, 67-69; ASSOC. PROF. MICROBIOL, MED. COL. VA, 69- U.S.A, 46-48. Am. Chem. Soc; Am. Soc. Microbiol. Biochemical genetics; biosynthesis of antibiotics; biosynthetic pathway of actinomycin synthesis using specific auxotrophic streptomyces. Address: Dept. of Microbiology, Health Science Center, Medical College of Virginia, Box 847, Richmond, VA 23219.

FORMWALT, JOHN M(cCLELLAN), b. Florence, Ala, May 24, 15; m. 41, 64, 68; c. 2. PHYSICS. A.B, Carson-Newman Col, 37; A.M, Duke, 39; California; Rhode Island; Mass. Inst. Technol. Asst. physics, Duke, 37-39; instr. & asst. prof, Presby. Jr. Col, 39-40; physicist, U.S. Navy Bur. Ord, 40-41; 11th Naval Dist, 41-44; proj. engr. & head instrument sect, U.S.N. Torpedo Sta, 44-51; head instrumentation & measurements br, U.S. Navy Underwater Ord. Sta, 51-54, chief test div, 54-56, controls div, 56-57, adv. undersea weapons div, 57-58, HEAD adv. studies group, 58-66, shipborne equip. dept, 66-71, WEAPONS ANAL. DIV, NAVAL UNDERWATER WEAPONS CTR, 71-, EXEC. DIR. AZORES FIXED ACOUSTIC RANGE, 71- Physicist, U.S. Navy Bur. Ships instrumentation group, Opers. Crossroads, 46; Naval res. assoc, Inst. Naval Studies, Ctr. Naval Anal, 63-64. Am. Phys. Soc; sr. mem. Inst. Elec. & Electronics Eng. Apparatus for measuring chemical activity, particularly of catalysts; ferromagnetism; instrumentation; guidance and control; underwater sound; weapons systems; operations research. Address: Azores Fixed Acoustic Range Directorate Office, APO New York 09678.

FORNEFELD, EUGENE J(OSEPH), b. Sandusky, Ohio, May 4, 20; m. 44; c. 5. ORGANIC CHEMISTRY. B.S, Xavier (Ohio), 41; M.S, Detroit, 43; Ph.D.(org. chem), Michigan, 50. Res. assoc. pharmacol, Michigan, 50-51; RES. CHEMIST, ELI LILLY & CO, 51- U.S.A, 43-46. Am. Chem. Soc. Chemistry of 2-aryl-cyclohexanones; quantitative determination of morphine in biological media; structure, activity relationships in the case of acetylcholine; synthesis of natural products. Address: 7838 Forest Lane, Indianapolis, IN 46240.

FORNEY, ALBERT J, b. Vanport, Pa, July 8, 15; m. 42; c. 3. CHEMICAL ENGINEERING. B.S, Geneva Col, 47; B.S, Carnegie Inst. Technol, 57. Chemist, U.S. BUR. MINES, 47-50, chem. engr, 50-59, SUPVRY. CHEM. ENGR, 59- U.S.A.F, 43-46, 50-51, S/Sgt. Am. Chem. Soc; Am. Inst. Chem. Eng. Synthetic liquid and gaseous fuels and coal gasification; gas purification, fluidization, steam-iron process; sewage treatment; coal pretreatment; chemicals from coal. Address: U.S. Bureau of Mines, 4800 Forbes Ave, Pittsburgh, PA 15213.

FORNEY, DONALD M(ARTIN), JR, b. Ft. Huachuca, Ariz, Oct. 2, 29; m. 67; c. 2. ENGINEERING MECHANICS, MATERIALS SCIENCE. B.S, Texas A&M, 51; Columbia, 64-65. Lab. engr, Hughes Gun Co, 51-52, supvr. metall. testing, 52-53, sr. engr, spec. proj, 53-54; lab. proj. officer, U.S. Air Force Mat. Lab, 54-56; sr. test engr, Convair Div, Gen. Dynamics Corp, 56-57; sr. proj. engr, AIR FORCE MAT. LAB, 57-60, chief creep & dynamics sect, 60-63, tech. mgr. vibrations & fatigue, 63-68, mgr. adv. graphitic mat, 68-69, ASST. STRUCT. MAT, 69- U.S.A.F.R, Capt. Am. Soc. Test. & Mat; Inst. Environ. Sci. Fatigue-metals, structures; environmental effects; mechanical properties. Address: Air Force Materials Lab, Attn: LL, Wright-Patterson Air Force Base, OH 45433.

FORNEY, G. DAVID, JR, b. N.Y.C, Mar. 6, 40; m. 62; c. 3. INFORMATION SCIENCE. B.S.E, Princeton, 61; M.S, Mass. Inst. Technol, 63, Sc.D.(elec. eng), 65. Mem. tech. staff, CODEX CORP, 65-68, dir. res, 69-70, V.PRES. RES, 70- AAAS; Inst. Elec. & Electronics Eng. Information, communication and coding theory. Address: Codex Corp, 15 Riverdale Ave, Newton, MA 02195.

FORNEY, JOHN E(DGAR), b. Waterloo, Iowa, June 22, 17; m. 44; c. 3. MICROBIOLOGY. A.B, Manchester Col, 38; M.A, Stanford, 48, Ph.D. (bact), 49. Asst. prof. med. microbiol, Southern California, 49-55; asst. dir. labs, City Health Dept, Los Angeles, 55-63; asst. chief, lab. consult. & develop. sect, communicable disease ctr, U.S. PUB. HEALTH SERV, 63-68, CHIEF, LAB. LICENSURE SECT, CTR. DISEASE CONTROL, 68- Mem, Conf. State & Prov. Pub. Health Lab. Dirs. Med.Dept, 41-46, Res, 46-, Lt. Col. Am. Soc. Microbiol; Am. Pub. Health Asn; fel. Am. Acad. Microbiol; Sci. Res. Soc. Am. Public health microbiology. Address: 2060 Deborah Dr, Atlanta, GA 30345.

FORNEY, LeROY SNYDER, b. Lancaster, Pa, Aug. 11, 38; m. 64; c. 2. ORGANIC CHEMISTRY. B.S, Juniata Col, 60; Nat. Sci. Found. fel, 62-65 & Ph.D.(org. chem), State Univ. Col. Forestry & Ph.D.(chem), Syracuse, 65. Sr. res. chemist, EDISON TWP. LABS, MOBIL CHEM. CO, 65-69, PROJ. LEADER, CHEM. COATINGS, 69- AAAS; Am. Chem. Soc. Solvolytic reactions of substituted cyclopropanes; autoxidation of alkylaromatic substrates; electrophilic aromatic substitution mechanisms; chemical coatings technology. Address: Central Research Lab, Mobil Chemical Co, P.O. Box 240, Edison, NJ 08817.

FORNEY, ROBERT B(URNS), b. Ashley, Ind, July 9, 16; m. 41; c. 2. TOXICOLOGY. Ph.D, Ind. Univ, 48; hon. LL.D, Ind. Cent. Col, 64. Asst. prof. toxicol, SCH. MED, IND. UNIV-PURDUE UNIV, INDIANAPOLIS, 48-52, assoc. prof, 52-62, PROF. PHARMACOL. & TOXICOL, 62- Mem. traffic safety comt. & comt. alcohol & drugs, Nat. Safety Coun. Sanit.C, 43-46, Maj. Am. Soc. Pharmacol. & Exp. Therapeut; Soc. Toxicol; fel. Am. Acad. Forensic Sci; Am. Soc. Clin. Pharmacol. & Therapeut. Effects of alcohol, marihuana and other drugs on performance. Address: Dept. of Toxicology, School of Medicine, Indiana University-Purdue University of Indianapolis, Indianapolis, IN 46202.

FORNEY, R(OBERT) C(LYDE), b. Chicago, Ill, Mar. 13, 27; m. 48; c. 4. CHEMICAL ENGINEERING. B.S, Purdue, 47, M.S, 48, Ph.D.(chem. eng), 50. Res. engr, TEXTILE FIBERS DEPT, E.I. DU PONT DE NEMOURS & CO, INC, 50-52, group supvr, 52, plant res. supvr, 52-56, process supt, 56-59, asst. plant mgr, 59-63, tech. mgr, 63-64, prod. mgr, 64-66, dir. prod. mkt. div, 66-69, asst. gen. dir. mkt. div, 69-70, ASST. GEN. MGR, 70- Am. Chem. Soc; Am. Inst. Chem. Eng. Industrial relations; reaction kinetics. Address: Textile Fibers Dept, E.I. du Pont de Nemours & Co, Inc, 3410 Nemours Bldg, Wilmington, DE 19898.

FORNOFF, FRANK J(UNIOR), b. Mt. Carmel, Ill, March 29, 14. INORGANIC CHEMISTRY. A.B, Illinois, 36; M.S, Ohio State, 37, Procter & Gamble fel, 38-39, Ph.D.(inorg. chem), 39. Asst. chem, Ohio State, 36-37, asst, 37-38; Nat. Res. Coun. fel, California, 39-40; instr, Lehigh, 40-42, asst. prof, 42-44, 45-47, assoc. prof, 47-53; chem. engr, West. Elec. Co, N.Y, 44-45; assoc. prof, Kans. State Col, 53-56; CHMN. SCI. DEPT, TEST. DEVELOP. DIV, EDUC. TESTING SERV, 56- Lectr, Rutgers, 56- AAAS; Am. Chem. Soc. Separation of rare earth elements; preparation of hydrogen halides; science education. Address: Science Dept, Educational Testing Service, Princeton, NJ 08540.

FORNWALT, HOLMES J(OHN), b. Myerstown, Pa, Apr. 13, 08; m. 36. PHYSICAL CHEMISTRY. B.S, Lafayette Col, 29, du Pont fel, 29-30, M.S, 30; A.M, Harvard, 32, Emerson scholar, 33-34, Ph.D.(phys. chem), 35. Asst. chem, Harvard, 30-32, 34-35, private res. asst, 30-33, 35-36; res. chemist, Darco Corp, 36-46, sales dept, 46-50, sales rep, Darco dept, Atlas Powder Co, 50-55, indust. mgr, 55-58, prod. develop. supvr, 59-61, develop. mgr, 61-63, sr. develop. assoc, Atlas Chem. Industs, Inc, 64-66, consult, 66-68; RETIRED. Am. Chem. Soc. Fluidity and molecular association; adsorption of gases at high pressure; viscosity of solutions of electrolytes; testing, application and preparation of activated carbons. Address: 2201 Inglewood Rd, Fairfax, DE 19803.

FOROULIS, Z. ANDREW, b. Volos, Greece, Dec. 6, 26; U.S. citizen; m. 62. CHEMICAL & METALLURGICAL ENGINEERING. Dipl. chem, Nat. Univ. Athens, 54; M.S, Mass. Inst. Technol, 56, Weirton Steel fels, 58-60, Met.E, 60, Nat. Steel fel, 60-61, D.Sc.(metall. eng), 61. Chem. engr, Dewey & Almy Chem. Div, W.R. Grace & Co, 56-57; engr, ESSO RES. & ENG. CO, 61-62, sr. engr, 62-63, eng. assoc, 63-68, SR. ENG. ASSOC, 68- Adj. prof, N.Y. Univ, 68- Greek Army, 49-51. Am. Chem. Soc; Am. Phys. Soc; Electrochem. Soc; Am. Inst. Chem. Eng; Am. Inst. Min, Metall. & Petrol. Eng; Am. Soc. Metals; Faraday Soc; Am. Soc. Mech. Eng; Nat. Asn. Corrosion Eng; N.Y. Acad. Sci. Electrochemistry; research on environmental effects on materials, science and technology of water and treatment of water and waste water; thermodynamics and its application to process engineering. Address: Esso Research & Engineering Co, P.O. Box 101, Florham Park, NJ 07932.

FORRAY, MARVIN JULIAN, b. New York, N.Y, Apr. 18, 22; m. 45; c. 4. MATHEMATICS. B.A, N.Y. Univ, 43, M.S, 44, scholar, 44-45; Ph.D.(appl. mech), Columbia, 55. Instr. math, Polytech. Inst. Brooklyn, 44-53; sr. engr. struct, Repub. Aviation Corp, N.Y, 53-55, prin. engr. develop. & res, 55-58, design specialist, 58-61, develop. engr, 61-66, PROF. MATH, C.W. POST COL, 66- Lectr. & prof, Adelphi Col, 55-65. Math. Asn. Am; Am. Soc. Civil Eng. Applied mechanics; elasticity; thermoelasticity; plates and shells; instability of structures; vibrations; heat conduction; calculus of variations; differential equations; functions of a real and complex variable; transform theory. Address: 21 Edward St, Lynbrook, NY 11563.

FORRER, MAX P(AUL), b. St. Gallen, Switz, Oct. 15, 25; nat; m. 52; c. 2. ELECTRICAL ENGINEERING. Dipl. Ing, Swiss Fed. Inst. Tech, 50; Ph.D. (elec. eng), Stanford, 59. Develop. engr, commun. Standard Tel. & Radio Corp, Switz, 51-52; West. Elec. Co, N.J, 52-55; proj. engr. microwave electronics, microwave lab, Gen. Elec. Co, 55-61; proj. engr. & mgr. microwave component, Kane Eng. Lab, 61-63; head circuits develop. sect, CENTRE ELECTRONIQUE HORLOGER, 63-68, v.dir, 65-68, DIR, 68- Asst. Hansen Labs, Stanford Univ, 57-58. Victor Kullberg Medal, Urmakare Ambete, Stockholm, 70. Sr. mem. Inst. Elec. & Electronics Eng. Microwave components and tubes; high power klystrons; duplexer devices; microwave secondary emission devices. Address: Centre Electronique Horloger SA, Rue Breguet 2, Neuchatel, Switz.

FORREST, EDWARD J, b. Reynoldsville, Pa, Dec. 27, 17; m. 44; c. 3. ORTHODONTICS. B.S, Univ. Pittsburgh, 39, D.D.S, 41, M.S, 49, Ph.D. (philos), 53. Assoc. prof. orthod, Univ. Pittsburgh, 52-57, dir. grad. educ, 54-57; assoc. prof. orthod, Univ. Illinois, 57-59, asst. dean, 57-58; assoc. dean, 58-61, dir. postgrad. educ. & dent. asst. prog, 57-61, dir. grad. educ, 59-61; DEAN SCH. DENT. MED, UNIV. PITTSBURGH, 61- Chmn. dept. admissions, curriculum & postgrad. progs, Univ. Pittsburgh, 52-57; dean's comt, Vet. Admin, Oakland, 61-, med. adv. comt, Vet. Admin, Leech Farm, 61-, med. adv. comt, West. Psychiat. Inst. & Clin, 63-, Kane Hosp. Aged, Pittsburgh, 68- Columbia Award teaching dent, 63; special award, West. Pa. Soc. Dent. Children, 63. Dent.C, U.S.A, 42-46, Maj. Temporomandibular articulation in orthodontic treatment; dental teacher education. Address: Dean's Office, School of Dental Medicine, University of Pittsburgh, Pittsburgh, PA 15213.

FORREST, H(UGH) S(OMMERVILLE), b. Glasgow, Scotland, Apr. 28, 24; m. 54; c. 3. BIOCHEMISTRY. B.Sc, Glasgow, 44, Carnegie fel, 44-45; Ph.D.(chem), London, 48, D.Sc, 70; fel, Cambridge, 48-51, Ph.D.(chem), 51. Mem. sci. staff, Nat. Inst. Med. Res, Med. Res. Coun, Gt. Brit, 45-48; res. fel. biol, Calif. Inst. Tech, 51-54, sr. res. fel, 55-56; res. scientist, UNIV. TEX, AUSTIN, 56-57, assoc. prof. ZOOL, 57-63, PROF, 63- Am. Chem. Soc; The Chem. Soc; Am. Soc. Biol. Chem. Chemistry and biology of pteridines; chemistry of genetic systems and of developmental processes. Address: Dept. of Zoology, University of Texas at Austin, Austin, TX 78712.

FORREST, IRENE S(TEPHANIE), b. Charlottenburg, Ger, Aug. 20, 08; nat; m. 34; c. 1. BIOCHEMISTRY. Ph.D.(chem), Berlin, 32. Researcher, microbiol. & biochem, Pasteur Inst. Paris & Munic. Hosp.(Hotel Dieu), Paris, France, 32-34; asst. chemist, Istanbul, 35-36; researcher biochem, N.Y. Univ, 41-43; Moraine Prod. Div, Gen. Motors Corp, Ohio, 44; translator, U.S. War Dept, 45-47; nucleic acids res, N.Y. Univ, 48; endocrinol. res, St. Clare's Hosp, N.Y, 49-50, consult. chem, 51-52; biochem. res, Polytech. Inst. Brooklyn & N.Y. Med. Col, 53-56; CHIEF BIOCHEM. RES. LAB, VET. ADMIN. HOSP, Brockton, Mass, 57-61; PALO ALTO, CALIF, 61-; RES. ASSOC. PSYCHIAT, SCH. MED, STANFORD UNIV, 61- AAAS; Am. Chem. Soc; Soc. Exp. Biol. & Med; Am. Soc. Pharmacol. & Exp. Therapeut. General biochemistry; psychopharmacology; drug metabolism; phenothiazine drugs. Address: Biochemical Research Lab, Veterans Administration Hospital, Palo Alto, CA 94304.

FORREST, JAMES BENJAMIN, b. Newcastle, N.B, Oct. 8, 35; m. 60, 70; c. 2. CIVIL ENGINEERING. B.Sc, Univ. N.B, 59; Nat. Res. Coun. Can. assistantship, Univ. B.C, 61, M.A.Sc, 63; univ. assistantship & Ford Found. fel, Northwest. Univ, 63, Murphy Found. fel, 64, Ph.D.(civil eng), 66. Engr, Dept. Nat. Health & Welfare, Govt. Can, 59-60; design engr, Montreal Eng. Ltd, 60-61; site soils engr, G.E. Crippen & Assocs, summer 63; asst. prof. eng, Carleton Univ, 65-68; res. assoc. engr, civil eng. res. facility, Univ. N.Mex. 68-70; SR. PROJ. ENGR, NAVAL CIVIL ENG. LAB, 70- Founds. consult, P.A. McNeely & Assocs, Can, 65-68; vis. prof, div. bldg. res, Nat. Res. Coun. Can, summer 66. Am. Soc. Civil Eng; Int. Soc. Rock Mech. The consolidation and yielding of plastic clays subjected to steady state vibratory, quasi-static and impulsive loadings; response of organic soils to insitu loading; propagation of shock waves through jointed materials; the constitutive behavior of pavement component materials. Address: Naval Civil Engineering Lab, Code L53, Port Hueneme, CA 93043.

FORREST, JOHN CHARLES, b. Larned, Kans, July 30, 36; m. 64; c. 2. PHYSIOLOGY, BIOCHEMISTRY. B.S, Kansas State, 60, M.S, 62; Ph.D. (muscle physiol), Wisconsin, 66. Proj. asst. muscle chem. & physiol, Wisconsin, 65-66; asst. prof. ANIMAL SCI, Minnesota, 66-67; ASSOC. PROF, PURDUE UNIV, 67- Am. Soc. Animal Sci; Am. Meat Sci. Asn; Inst. Food Tech. Influence of ante-mortem physiology and stress on the post-mortem metabolism of skeletal and cardiac muscle. Address: Dept. of Animal Sciences, Purdue University, Lafayette, IN 47907.

FORREST, JOHN W(ILSON), b. Andes, N.Y, Nov. 23, 91; m. 22; c. 1. PHYSICS. B.S, Hamilton Col, 13, hon. M.S, 16; Harvard, 16. Instr. chem, Phillips Acad.(Andover), 13-14; physics, Worcester Acad, 14-17, head, sci. dept, 17-20; sr. design engr, Bausch & Lomb Optical Co, 20-42, supv. engr. & sect. head, 20-56, SPEC. CONSULT, BAUSCH & LOMB, INC, 64- U.S.A, 17-18. Optical Soc. Am; Am. Soc. Test. & Mat; Soc. Exp. Stress Anal. Design and development of apparatus of optical and electronic nature for the precise measurement of optical properties; optical systems for use in control and measuring instruments, refractometers and colorimeters. Address: 291 Landing Rd. S, Rochester, NY 14610.

FORREST, ROBERT BREWSTER, b. Minneapolis, Minn, Mar. 24, 34; m. 58; c. 1. PHOTOGRAMMETRY. B.A, Minnesota, 58; Ph.D.(geod. sci), Ohio State, 64. Geod. & photogrammetric res. asst, Ohio State Univ. Res. Found, 58-60, res. assoc, 60-63; photogrammetrist, Arecibo Ionospheric Observ, 63-65; SR. PRIN. PHOTOGRAMMETRIST, BENDIX RES. LABS, 65- U.S.A.F, 51-55, Res, 55-59, S/Sgt. Am. Soc. Photogram. Computer control applications to photogrammetric instrumentation; geometric modelling of image data; increased non-topographic application of photogrammetry. Address: Bendix Research Labs, Bendix Corp, 20800 10½ Mile Rd, Southfield, MI 48075.

FORREST, ROBERT J, b. Winnipeg, Man, Dec. 21, 28; m. 54; c. 3. BIOCHEMISTRY, ANIMAL NUTRITION. B.S.A, British Columbia, 54, M.S.A, 55; Ph.D.(biochem), Illinois, 59. RES. SCIENTIST BIOCHEM, CAN. DEPT. AGR, 59- Am. Chem. Soc; N.Y. Acad. Sci; Am. Soc. Animal Sci; Can. Soc. Animal Prod; Agr. Inst. Can. Acid soluble nucleotides of bovine mammary gland; beef production by dairy cattle; beef production; meats research; animal physiology and biochemistry. Address: Research Branch, Research Station, Canada Dept. of Agriculture, P.O. Box 1000, Agassiz, B.C, Can.

FORREST, ROBERT N(EAGLE), b. Pendleton, Ore, Nov. 25, 25; m. 51; c. 2. PHYSICS. B.S, Oregon, 50, M.S, 52 & 54, Ph.D.(physics), 59. Nuclear physicist, Lawrence Radiation Lab, California, 58-59; mem. staff geoastrophysics, sci. lab, Boeing Airplane Co, 59; asst. prof. surface physics, Oregon State, 59-63; physics, South. Ore. Col, 63-64; ASSOC. PROF. OPERS. ANAL, U.S. NAVAL POSTGRAD. SCH, 64- U.S.N, 44-46. AAAS; Am. Phys. Soc; Am. Asn. Physics Teachers; Am. Vacuum Soc. Gas sorption and sputtering. Address: Dept. of Operations Analysis, U.S. Naval Postgraduate School, Monterey, CA 93940.

FORREST, STEPHEN P(AUL), b. Reynoldsville, Pa, July 23, 12; m. 40; c. 3. DENTISTRY. B.S. & D.D.S, Pittsburgh, 36, M.S, 38. Prof. & chmn. dept. PROSTHETIC DENT, col. dent. & grad. sch, Baylor, 48-57; PROF. & CHMN. DEPT, SCH. DENT, ST. LOUIS UNIV, 56-, DEAN, 57-, assoc. dean, 56-57. Consult, U.S. Vet. Admin. Hosps, Tex. & Mo, 51-; crippled children's serv, Missouri, 57-; St. Mary's & Firmin Desloge Hosps, St. Louis, 57-; med. centre, Univ. Saigon, 68- Mem. nat. adv. dent. res. coun, dent. training comt. & chmn. prog. planning comt, Nat. Inst. Dent. Res, 60-64; mem. adv. bd, Orthod. Educ. & Res. Found. Dent.C, 43-46, Maj. Fel. AAAS; fel. Am. Col. Dent; Am. Dent. Asn; Am. Acad. Hist. Dent.(v.pres, 64-65); Int. Asn. Dent. Res; Asn. Mil. Surg. U.S; fel. Am. Pub. Health Asn; Geront. Soc. Oral health; prosthetic posterior teeth. Address: 1501 Windridge Dr, St. Louis, MO 63131.

FORREST, THOMAS PETER, b. Sydney Mines, N.S, July 7, 37; m. 64; c. 1. ORGANIC CHEMISTRY. B.Sc, Mt. Allison, 57; M.Sc, Dalhousie, 58; Ph.D. (chem), New Brunswick, 62. ASSOC. PROF. CHEM, DALHOUSIE UNIV, 63- NATO res. fel, 62-63. Natural products structural elucidation; heterocyclic chemistry. Address: Dept. of Chemistry, Dalhousie University, Halifax, N.S, Can.

FORRESTER, A(LVIN) THEODORE, b. Brooklyn, N.Y, Apr. 13, 18; m. 48; c. 5. PHYSICS. A.B, Cornell, 38, A.M, 39, Ph.D.(physics), 42. Res. assoc, Lawrence Radiation Lab, California, 42-45; physicist, RCA Labs, N.J, 45-46; asst. prof. physics, Southern California, 46-51, assoc. prof, 51-55; fel. engr, res. labs, Westinghouse Elec. Corp, 55-57, adv. physicist, 57-58; nuclear specialist, Atomic Int. Div, N.Am. Aviation, Inc, 58-59, propulsion specialist, Rocketdyne Div, 58-59; mgr. ion physics dept, Electro-Optical Systs, Inc, 59-65; PROF. physics, UNIV. CALIF, Irvine, 65-67; PHYSICS & ENG, LOS ANGELES, 67- Res. award, Am. Rocket Soc, 62. AAAS; fel. Am. Phys. Soc; assoc. fel. Am. Inst. Aeronaut. & Astronaut; fel. Inst. Elec. & Electronics Eng; Am. Asn. Physics Teachers; Optical Soc. Am. Plasma physics, electron and ion sources; coherence properties of radiation; photoelectric mixing; ion propulsion. Address: Room 7731, Boelter Hall, University of California, Los Angeles, CA 90024.

FORRESTER, DONALD JASON, b. Attleboro, Mass, Jan. 31, 37; m. 61; c. 3. ZOOLOGY, PARASITOLOGY. B.S, Massachusetts, Amherst, 58; M.S, Montana, 60; U.S. Pub. Health Serv. fel. & Ph.D.(zool), California, Davis, 67. Res. assoc. zool, Montana, 61-63; ASST. PROF, Clemson Univ, 67-69; parasitol, div. biol. sci, UNIV. FLA, 69-70, PARASITOL, DEPT. VET. SCI, 70- Am. Soc. Parasitol; Wildlife Disease Asn; Wildlife Soc. Parasites of wild animals; helminths of marine mammals; epizootiology and ecology of transmission of helminth parasites. Address: Dept. of Veterinary Science, University of Florida, Gainesville, FL 32601.

FORRESTER, FRANK R(OBERT), b. Rockaway, N.J, Oct. 9, 07; m. 36; c. 3. ANALYTICAL CHEMISTRY. B.S, Cooper Union, 30; A.M, Columbia, 40; Ph.D.(chem), N.Y. Univ, 52. Asst, Mass. Inst. Tech, 30-31; chemist, Koppers Co, 31-33; United Color & Pigment Co, 34; Barrett Co, 34-37; instr. chem, Cooper Union, 37-44; SR. CHEMIST, HOFFMANN-LA ROCHE INC, 44- Legion of Honor award, Essential Oil Asn, 61. Am. Chem. Soc; Sci. Res. Soc. Am; Soc. Appl. Spectros; Coblentz Soc; fel. Am. Inst. Chem. Physical chemistry; ultraviolet and infrared spectroscopy; chromatography. Address: 10 Sunset Dr. W, Nutley, NJ 07110.

FORRESTER, GLENN C(LIFFORD), b. Empire, Mich, m. 30; c. 2. CHEMISTRY. A.B, Michigan, 19, M.S, 20, Ph.D.(chem), 23. Res. chemist, Phosphorus Compounds Co, 23-24, mgr, 24-28; personnel mgr, rayon dept, E.I. du Pont de Nemours & Co, Inc, 28-31, res. rayon & cellophane depts, 31-32; private res, 32-40; mem. tech. dept, Roessler & Hasslacher chem. dept, E.I. du Pont de Nemours & Co, Inc, 40-46; owner, Intoximeter Asn, 46-47, CONSULT, INTOXIMETER INC, 67- Researcher, Niagara Alkali Co. U.S.N, 17-19. Am. Chem. Soc. Phosphorus sodium; geological history; chemistry tests for intoxication. Address: 135 Main St, Youngstown, NY 14174.

FORRESTER, J(AMES) DONALD, b. Salt Lake City, Utah, Apr. 6, 06; m. 29; c. 1. GEOLOGY. B.S, Utah, 28, Geol. Eng, 56; M.S, Cornell, 29, Long scholar, 33-34, Ph.D.(geol), 35. Asst. instr. metall, Utah, 27-28; asst. instr. geol, Cornell, 28-29, instr, 34-35; geologist, Anaconda Copper Mining Co, 29-32, 35-39; prof. geol. & head dept, Idaho, 39-44; prof. min. eng. & chmn. dept, Mo. Sch. Mines, 44-54; dean col. mines & dir. bur. mines & geol, Idaho, 54-56; dean COL. MINES, UNIV. ARIZ, 56-70, EMER. DEAN, 70-; DIR. DIV. ENVIRON. ENG. & RES, PHELPS DODGE CORP, 70-; EMER. DIR. ARIZ. BUR. MINES, 70-, dir, 56-70. Mem. adv. comt. eng, U.S. Civil Serv. Comn, 52-55; exec. reserve, U.S. Dept. Interior. Mining & Metall. Soc. Am; fel. Geol. Soc. Am; Soc. Econ. Geol; Am. Inst. Mining, Metall. & Petrol. Eng. Mechanization of mining operations; structural geology; geology of mineral deposits; use of explosives. Address: Division of Environmental Engineering & Research, Phelps Dodge Corp, P.O. Box 2265, Tucson, AZ 85702.

FORRESTER, JOHN S(TANLEY), b. Ger, Nov. 1, 26; nat; m. 54; c. 4. ANALYTICAL CHEMISTRY. B.S, City Col. New York, 50; M.A, Texas, 52, Atomic Energy Cmn. fel, 55, Ph.D, 56. Chemist, Shell Oil Co, Tex, 52-54; sr. chemist, res. labs, Humble Oil & Ref. Co, 56-60; v.pres. & tech. dir, MicroTek Instruments, Inc, 60-65; PRES, SCI. SYSTS. CORP, 65- Am. Chem. Soc; sr. mem. Instrument Soc. Am. Analytical chemistry of platinum metals; trace metals; ultraviolet and infrared spectroscopy; controlled environment and plant growth instrumentation. Address: 1024 Monterrey Blvd, Baton Rouge, LA 70815.

FORRESTER, SHERRI R(HODA), b. New York, N.Y, Aug. 8, 36. ORGANIC CHEMISTRY. B.S, Duke, 58; Ph.D.(org. chem), Northwestern, 62. ASST. PROF. CHEM, UNIV. N.C, GREENSBORO, 62- Am. Chem. Soc. Oxygen heterocyclics. Address: Dept. of Chemistry, University of North Carolina at Greensboro, Greensboro, NC 27412.

FORRETTE, JOHN ELMER, b. Chicago, Ill, Sept. 14, 22; m. 48; c. 1. ANALYTICAL CHEMISTRY. B.S, Loyola Univ.(Ill), 48; M.S, DePaul Univ, 55. Chemist, div. hwys, State of Ill, 48-56; res. chemist, Borg-Warner Corp, 57-61, sr. res. chemist, 61-63, group leader anal. chem, 63-67; group leader, VELSICOL CHEM. CO, 67-70, MGR. ANAL. RES, 70- U.S.A, 43-46. Sci. Res. Soc. Am; Am. Soc. Appl. Spectros; Am. Chem. Soc. Chemical spectroscopy; gas chromatography; general analytical chemistry. Address: 2848 Nordica, Chicago, IL 60634.

FORREY, ARDEN W, b. Nampa, Idaho, Dec. 19, 32; m. 61; c. 1. BIOCHEMISTRY. A.B, Washington, Seattle, 55, Ph.D.(biochem), 63. Trainee, dept. biochem, Washington, Seattle, 63-64; Nat. Inst. Arthritis and Metab. Diseases fel, Birmingham, 64-65; fel, Washington, Seattle, 65-66, lectr. biochem, 66-67, RES. ASSOC, DEPT. MED, CLIN. RES. CTR, HARBORVIEW HOSP. & UNIV. WASH, 67- Med.Serv.C, U.S.N.R, 55-57, Lt. AAAS; Am. Chem. Soc; Brit. Biochem. Soc; Am. Asn. Clin. Chem. Structure and active sites of proteins, particularly muscle phosphorylase and actin; clinical chemistry. Address: 4916 Purdue Ave, N.E, Seattle, WA 98105.

FORRO, F(REDERICK), JR, b. Woonsocket, R.I, May 17, 24; m. 44; c. 4. BIOPHYSICS. Brown fel, Yale, 47-48, M.D, 49. U.S. Pub. Health Serv. fel, Yale, 49-51; assoc. biophysicist, Brookhaven Nat. Lab, 51-55; asst. prof. biophys, Yale, 55-61, assoc. prof, 61-68; PROF. & CHMN. DEPT. GENETICS & CELL BIOL, UNIV. MINN, ST. PAUL, 68- Agent Europ. Atomic Energy Comn, dept. biol, Univ. Brussels, 66-67. U.S.A, 43-45. AAAS; Genetics Soc. Am; Biophys. Soc. Molecular biology, particularly self-duplication; radiation biology; origin of life. Address: Dept. of Genetics & Cell Biology, College of Biological Sciences, University of Minnesota, St. Paul, MN 55101.

FORS, ELTON W, b. Drake, N.Dak, Jan. 29, 34; m. 61. MATHEMATICS. B.S, North Dakota, 56, M.S, 59; Nat. Sci. Found. summer inst, Okla. State Univ, 62; Ph.D.(math. educ), Univ. Okla, 69. Assoc. prof. MATH, NORTH. STATE COL, 60-70, PROF, 70- Programmer, univac div, Remington Rand, summer 60. U.S.A, 57-58, Res, 58-65. Math. Asn. Am. Address; Box 674, Dept. of Mathematics, Northern State College, Aberdeen, SD 57401.

FORSBERG, JOHN HERBERT, b. Duluth, Minn, Apr. 24, 42; m. 66. INORGANIC CHEMISTRY. B.A, Minnesota, Duluth, 64; M.S, Illinois, 66, Ph.D. (chem), 68. ASSOC. PROF. CHEM, ST LOUIS UNIV, 68- Res. Corp. grant, 68- Am. Chem. Soc. Coordination chemistry in nonaqueous solvent; lanthanide chemistry Address: Dept. of Chemistry, St. Louis University, St. Louis, MO 63103.

FORSBERG, JUNIUS L(EONARD), b. Bertrand, Nebr, June 15, 07; m. 34; c. 1. PLANT PATHOLOGY. B.S, Colo. Agr. Col, 30; M.S, Mich. State Col, 32, Ph.D.(plant path), Illinois, 54. Asst. bot, Mich. State Col, 30-34; instr, Colo. Agr. & Mech. Col, 35, asst. prof, 35-44; res. pathologist, STATE NATURAL HIST. SURV, ILL, 44-47, assoc. plant pathologist, 47-55, PLANT PATHOLOGIST, 55-; PROF. PLANT PATH, UNIV. ILL, URBANA, 67- AAAS; Am. Phytopath. Soc. Gladiolus, pea and carnation diseases; diseases of miscellaneous ornamentals; fungicides. Address: 1002 W. Daniel St, Champaign, IL 61820.

FORSBERG, K(ENNETH) E(RIK), b. Sauk Centre, Minn, Mar. 5, 21; m. 49; c. 3. ELECTRICAL ENGINEERING. S.B, Mass. Inst. Tech, 51. Engr. radar & digital comput. design, Raytheon Mfg. Co, Mass, 49-50; eng. dept. head systs, Sperry Gyroscope Co, 51-67; ENG. STAFF SPECIALIST, GEN. DYNAMICS/CONVAIR, 67- U.S.A.A.F, 43-46, Res, 46-53, 1st Lt. Radar and weapon systems synthesis and application. Address: 8559 Prestwick Dr, La Jolla, CA 92037.

FORSBERG, KEVIN, b. Oakland, Calif, July 20, 34; m. 66; c. 3. APPLIED MECHANICS. S.B, Mass. Inst. Tech, 56; M.S, Stanford, 58, Ph.D.(eng. mech), 61. Scientist, LOCKHEED MISSILES & SPACE CO, 56-61, res. specialist shell dynamics, 62-64, MGR. SOLID MECH. LAB, 64-, SR. MEM. RES. LAB, 65- C.Eng, U.S.A, 61-62, Capt. Am. Soc. Mech. Eng; Am. Inst. Aeronaut. & Astronaut. Static and dynamic behavior of shell structures; application of computer technology and active computer graphics to engineering research and design problems. Address: Dept. 52-20, Bldg. 205, Lockheed Missiles & Space Co, 3251 Hanover St, Palo Alto, CA 94304.

FORSBERG, R(OBERT) A(RNOLD), b. Julesburg, Colo, Nov. 6, 30; m. 58; c. 3. AGRONOMY, PLANT GENETICS. B.S, Wisconsin, 52, M.S, 57, Ph.D.(agron, plant breeding), 61. Fel. statist. genetics N.C. State, 61-63; asst. prof. AGRON. & PLANT BREEDING, UNIV. WIS, MADISON, 63-69, ASSOC. PROF, 69- U.S.N, 52-56, Lt.(jg). Am. Soc. Agron; Crop Sci. Soc. Am. Interspecific hybridization in Avena; biometrical procedures as applied to quantitative inheritance and plant breeding. Address: Dept. of Agronomy, University of Wisconsin, Madison, WI 53706.

FORSBLAD, INGEMAR B(JORN), b. Gothenburg, Sweden, June 18, 27; m. 57; c. 2. ORGANIC CHEMISTRY, CHEMICAL ENGINEERING. M.S, Uppsala, 55, Ph.D.(org. chem), 58. Technician chem, Svenska Oljeslageri AB, Sweden, 45-46; Skanska Sttiksfabrik AB, 48; engr. org. chem, AB Bofors Nobelkrut, 50-51, Österteichische Stickstoffwerke, Austria, 55; fel, Fla. State, 58-59; RES. ASSOC, UPJOHN CO, 59-66, HEAD FINE CHEM, 66- Swedish Army, 49-50. Am. Chem. Soc; Swedish Chem. Soc. Mechanism of alkylation of beta-ketoesters; process development and production of steroids and aromatic compounds. Address: Upjohn Co, 7000 Portage Rd, Kalamazoo, MI 49001.

FORSCHER, BERNARD K(RONMAN), b. New York, N.Y, Nov. 15, 27; m. 48; c. 5. BIOCHEMISTRY. B.A, N.Y. Univ, 46; Ph.D.(chem), Northwestern, 52. Res. chemist, Chas. Pfizer & Co, 46-48, chemist, eng. res. & develop. lab, 47; asst. instr, dent. sch, Northwestern, 48-52; coordinator of res, sch. dent, Georgetown, 52-54; chemist, Nat. Inst. Dent. Res, Nat. Insts. Health, 54-57; prof. biochem. & chmn. dept, sch. dent. Univ. Kansas City, 57-62; CONSULT, SECT. PUBL, MAYO CLIN, 62- AAAS; Soc. Exp. Biol. & Med; Am. Soc. Exp. Path. Chemistry of inflammation; chemistry of bone. Address: Section of Publications, Mayo Clinic, 200 First St. S.W, Rochester, MN 55901.

FORSCHER, FREDERICK, b. Vienna, Austria, May 20, 18; nat; m. 44; c. 3. ENGINEERING. B.S. & M.S, Princeton, 47; Ph.D.(applied mech), Columbia, 53. Instr. civil eng, Columbia, 47-52; supvr. mech. metall, atomic power div, Westinghouse Elec. Corp, 52-57; v.pres, Nuclear Mat. & Equip. Corp, 57-67; mgr. adv. fuels, Westinghouse Elec. Corp, 67-71; CONSULT. ENGR, 71- U.S.A, 41-46. Am. Soc. Metals; Am. Soc. Mech. Eng; Am. Nuclear Soc; Am. Soc. Test. & Mat; Am. Inst. Mining, Metall. & Petrol. Eng. Address: 6580 Beacon St, Pittsburgh, PA 15217.

FORSDYKE, DONALD ROY, b. London, Eng, Oct. 9, 38; m. 64; c. 3. BIOCHEMISTRY, IMMUNOLOGY. M.B, B.S, London, 61; Med. Res. Coun. scholar, Cambridge, 62-63, fel, 64-67, B.A, 65, Ph.D.(biochem), 67. House physician, St. Mary's Hosp, London, 61; house surgeon, Addenbrooke's Hosp, Cambridge, 63; sci. officer. exp. path, Inst. Animal Physiol, Babraham, Cambridge, 67-68; ASSOC. PROF. BIOCHEM, QUEEN'S UNIV.(ONT), 68- Can. Biochem. Soc; Brit. Biochem. Soc. Cell control mechanisms, especially lymphoid tissue and nucleic acids; serum factors affecting the transformation of cultured lymphocytes by phytohaemagglutinin and antigens: complement; labelling of nucleic acid with ^{3}H-uridine and ^{3}H-thymidine. Address: Dept. of Biochemistry, Faculty of Medicine, Queen's University, Kingston, Ont, Can.

FORSEN, HAROLD K(AY), b. St. Joseph, Mo, Sept. 19, 32; m. 52; c. 3. PLASMA PHYSICS, NUCLEAR ENGINEERING. B.S, Calif. Inst. Tech, 58, Hughes fel. & M.S, 59; Ph.D.(elec. eng), California, Berkeley, 65. Staff assoc. exp. physics, Gen. Atomic Div, Gen. Dynamics Corp, 59-62; res. assoc. elec. eng, California, Berkeley, 62-65; assoc. prof. NUCLEAR ENG, UNIV. WIS, MADISON, 65-69, PROF, 69-, DIR. PHYS. SCI. LAB, 70- Mem. tech. staff, Hughes Aircraft Co, 58-59; consult, Gen. Atomic Div, Gen. Dynamics Corp, 62-64; Proj. Sherwood, Lawrence Radiation Lab, 64-65; Atomic Energy Comn. grant plasmas & controlled fusion, 66-71; Nat. Sci. Found. grant plasma source develop, 67-73; consult, Oak Ridge Nat. Lab, 69-; Argonne Nat. Lab, 70-; Jersey Nuclear Co, 70-; Battelle Mem. Inst, 71- U.S.A.F, 51-55, S/Sgt. Am. Phys. Soc; Am. Nuclear Soc. Plasma physics; ion beams; plasma sources; thermonuclear fusion; reactor concepts. Address: 1134 Frisch Rd, Madison, WI 53711.

FORSGARD, FREDERICK C(HARLES), b. Philadelphia, Pa, Nov. 16, 27; m. 49; c. 9. PHYSICAL CHEMISTRY. A.B, Pennsylvania, 49, M.S, 50, Ph.D.(chem), 54. Chemist photo prods, E.I. du Pont de Nemours & Co, 53-61; res. specialist, photo & reprod. div, Gen. Aniline & Film Corp, 61-62, sect. mgr, 63, assoc. dir. res. & develop, 63-67; dir. res. & develop, Anken Chem. & Film Corp, 67-69, gen. mgr. prods. div, 69-70; dir. res. & develop, Memorex Corp, Calif, 70-71; DIR. QUAL. CONTROL, ITEK CORP, 71- U.S.C.G, 45-46. Am. Chem. Soc; Soc. Photog. Sci. & Eng. Alkali metal solutions; photosensitive systems; photographic emulsions; color photography. Address: Itek Corp, 10 Maguire Rd, Lexington, MA 02173.

FORSGREN, KLANE F, b. Preston, Idaho, Sept. 10, 36; m. 61; c. 5. CHEMICAL ENGINEERING, POLYMER SCIENCE. B.E.S, Brigham Young Univ, 61; Sun Oil fel, Univ. Ill, 61-62, M.S, 63, Ph.D.(chem. eng), 65. Sr. chemist, ROHM AND HAAS CO, 65-68, LAB. HEAD FIBERS DEVELOP, 68- Physical characterization of polymers as they apply to fiber technology. Address: Rohm and Haas Co, Independence Center, 5000 Richmond St, Philadelphia, PA 19137.

FORSHAM, PETER H(UGH), b. New Orleans, La, Nov. 15, 15; m. 46; c. 3. INTERNAL MEDICINE, ENDOCRINOLOGY. B.S, Cambridge, 37, fel, 38-40, M.A, 41; M.D, Harvard Med. Sch, 43. Res. assoc. physiol. chem, Rockefeller Inst, 40-41; house off. med, Peter Bent Brigham Hosp, Mass, 43-44, asst. resident, 44-46, res. fel, 46-48, assoc, 48-49; instr, Harvard Med. Sch, 49-51; assoc. prof. MED. & PEDIAT, SCH. MED, UNIV. CALIF, SAN FRANCISCO, 51-57, PROF, 57-, DIR. METAB. RES. UNIT, UNIV. HOSP. & GEN. CLIN. RES. CTR, MED. CTR. & CHIEF ENDOCRINOL, UNIV, 57- Res. fel, Harvard Med. Sch, 46-48, assoc, 48-49; consult, Nat. Insts. Health, 54-; chmn. metab. study sect, 58-; consult, U.S. Navy, 57-, Oak Knoll Hosp, Oakland. Dipl, Am. Bd. Internal Med, 51. AAAS; Am. Soc. Clin. Invest; Asn. Am. Physicians; Soc. Exp. Biol. & Med; Endocrine Soc; Am. Diabetes Asn; fel. Am. Col. Physicians; Am. Med. Asn. Metabolic diseases; pathophysiology of the adrenal cortex, mostly in man; relation of pituitary tropic hormones to activity of target glands; metabolic studies of diabetes mellitus; anti-inflammatory agents used in collagen diseases. Address: 267 Hillside Ave, Mill Valley, CA 94112.

FORSHEY, C(HESTER) G(ENE), b. Salem, Ohio, Mar. 21, 25; m. 56; c. 4. POMOLOGY. B.S, Ohio State, 50, Ph.D.(hort), 54. Asst, Ohio Agr. Exp. Sta, 52-54; asst. prof, N.Y. STATE AGR. EXP. STA, 54-58, assoc. prof, 58-66, prof, 66-69, SUPT. HIGHLAND LAB, 69- Mem. staff, Rockefeller Found. Chilean Agr. Prog, 63-64; hon. mem. faculty, Cath. Univ. Chile & Univ. Chile. U.S.N, 43-46. Am. Soc. Hort. Sci; Am. Chem. Soc; Soil Sci. Soc. Am. Nitrogen and mineral nutrition of fruit plants. Address: Highland Lab, New York State Agricultural Experiment Station, Box 476, Highland, NY 12528.

FORSHEY, DAVID R(ONALD), b. Butler, Pa, Sept. 27, 38; m. 59; c. 1. PHYSICAL & THEORETICAL CHEMISTRY. B.S, Carnegie Inst. Technol, 61; M.S, Duquesne Univ, 67, Ph.D.(phys. chem), 70. Chemist, explosives chem. br, explosives res. ctr, U.S. BUR MINES, 63-64, res. chemist, 64-66, group leader, 66-71, STAFF ENGR, 71- Sig.C, U.S.A, 61-63, Res, 63-, Capt. AAAS; Am. Chem. Soc. Computer study of nonsteady state coupled gasdynamics-reaction kinetics of condensed detonation products; development of new explosive formulations; evaluation of sensitivity of new and novel explosive systems; quantum mechanical calculations on heterocyclic organic compounds. Address: Bureau of Mines, U.S. Dept. of Interior, Washington, DC 20240.

FORSHEY, WILLIAM OSMOND, JR, b. Youngstown, Ohio, Dec. 13, 21; m. 43; c. 2. ORGANIC CHEMISTRY. B.S, Grove City Col, 42; M.S, Carnegie Inst. Tech, 43, D.Sc, 48. Asst, Carnegie Inst. Tech, 44; RES. CHEMIST, CENT. RES. DEPT, EXP. STA, E.I. DU PONT DE NEMOURS & CO, INC, 48- U.S.N, 44-46. Am. Chem. Soc. Polymer, synthetic organic and high temperature research; inorganic fiber synthesis; composite materials. Address: 100 Newport St, Richardson Park, Wilmington, DE 19804.

FORSMAN, EARL N, b. Keuterville, Idaho, Oct. 27, 36; m. 62; c. 3. ATOMIC PHYSICS. B.S, Gonzaga Univ, 63; M.S, Univ. Wash, 65, Ph.D.(physics), 70. ASST. PROF. PHYSICS, EAST. WASH. STATE COL, 70- U.S.A.R, 55-62. Am. Inst. Physics; Am. Asn. Physics Teachers. Atomic and molecular physics; gas-phase reactions and spectroscopy; chemiluminescent reactions in the upper atmosphere. Address: Dept. of Physics, Eastern Washington State College, Cheney, WA 99004.

FORSMAN, JAMES P(ARKER), b. St. Louis, Mo, June 30, 21; m. 46; c. 2. ORGANIC CHEMISTRY. A.B, Princeton, 43; Ph.D.(org. chem), Washington (St. Louis), 52. Chemist, plastics div, Firestone Tire & Rubber Co, 43-44; Tretolite Corp, 47-48; res. chemist, Carter Oil Co, 52-58; proj. leader, Esso Res. & Eng. Co, 58-62, res. assoc, 62-71; CONSULT, J. PARKER FORSMAN ASSOCS, 71- U.S.N.R, 44-46, Lt.(jg). Am. Chem. Soc; Am. Soc. Test. & Mat; Soc. Plastics Eng. Polymer chemistry; petroleum geochemistry; oil well chemicals; plastics processing and properties; environmental control. Address: 209 West Shaw, Pasadena, TX 77502.

FORSMAN, M(ARION) E(DWIN), b. Raymondville, Texas, July 19, 12; m. 38; c. 4. ELECTRICAL ENGINEERING. B.S.E.E. & M.S.E.E, Texas, 40; Ph.D.(elec. eng), Iowa State, 54. Supt. construct, Am. Smelting & Refrigeration Co, Texas & Mex, 40-42; field engr, Fischback & Moore of Texas, Inc, 42-43; res. dir, Electronic Chem. Eng. Co, Calif, 46; res. lab. analyst, Northrop Aircraft, 46-47; assoc. prof, Tulane, 47-51; instr, Iowa State, 51-52; elec. engr, Gen. Elec. Co, Wash, 52-55; asst. dir, eng. & indust. exp. sta, UNIV. FLA, 55-64, eng. admin, 64-65, dir, 65-68, PROF. ELEC. ENG. & DIR. ENG. EXTERNAL PROGS, 68- U.S.N, 43-46, Res, 46-, Comdr. Am. Soc. Eng. Educ; Inst. Elec. & Electronics Eng; Nat. Soc. Pro. Eng. Electrical power transmission; instrumentation and control; nuclear power. Address: College of Engineering, University of Florida, Gainesville, FL 32601.

FORSMAN, WILLIAM C(OMSTOCK), b. Grand Rapids, Minn, July 24, 29; m. 56; c. 4. PHYSICAL CHEMISTRY, CHEMICAL ENGINEERING. B.Ch.E, Minnesota, 52; Ph.D.(phys. chem), Pennsylvania, 61. Chem. engr, Hercules Powder Co, 52-54, 56, res. chemist, 61-63; asst. prof. CHEM. ENG, UNIV. PA, 64-68, ASSOC. PROF, 68- U.S.A, 54-56. Am. Chem. Soc; Am. Phys. Soc. Physics and physical chemistry of high-polymer systems; statistical mechanics. Address: School of Chemical Engineering, University of Pennsylvania, Philadelphia, PA 19104.

FORSNES, VICTOR G, b. Bingham Canyon, Utah, Aug. 8, 41; m. 64; c. 3. MECHANICAL ENGINEERING, EDUCATIONAL TECHNOLOGY. B.E.S, Brigham Young Univ, 64, M.S, 65; Procter & Gamble Co. fel, Purdue Univ, 67, Ph.D.(fluid mech), 70. Technician, chem. propulsion div, Hercules, Inc, summer 63; engr, atomic energy div, Phillips Petrol. Co, summer 64; res. asst. MECH. ENG, Brigham Young Univ, 64-65, instr, 65-66; Purdue Univ, 66-69; ASST. PROF, UNIV. MD, COLLEGE PARK, 69- Partic-author, Stanford Univ-Air Force Off. Sci. Res. Internal Flow Prog. Conf. on computation turbulent boundary layers, 68. AAAS; Am. Soc. Mech. Eng; Am. Soc. Eng. Educ; Soc. Automotive Eng.(Ralph R. Teetor Award, 71). Mathematical prediction techniques for low-speed incompressible turbulent boundary layers; droplet shattering prediction and analysis; applications and development of educational technology in engineering education. Address: Dept. of Mechanical Engineering, University of Maryland, College Park, MD 20742.

FORSS, CARL, b. Bellingham, Wash, July 19, 31; m. 53; c. 2. ZOOLOGY, BIOLOGY. B.A, Walla Walla Col, 58, M.A, 59; Ph.D.(zool), Oregon State, 65. Instr. BIOL, La Sierra Col, 60-61; ASSOC. PROF, WALLA WALLA COL, 61- U.S.M.C, 52-54, Sgt. AAAS; Am. Soc. Limnol. & Oceanog. Taxonomy and ecology of oceanic shrimps; decapod larvae. Address: Dept. of Biology, Walla Walla College, College Place, WA 99324.

FORSS, DAVID AUSTIN, b. Adelaide, Australia, June 15, 24; m. 50; c. 2. CHEMISTRY. B.Sc, Melbourne, 45, M.Sc, 46, D.App.Sc, 68. Res. chemist, Nicholas Pty, Ltd, Australia, 46-47; res. off, div. dairy res, Commonwealth Sci. & Indust. Res. Orgn, 48-55, sr. res. off, 56-62; res. assoc. dairy sci, Pa. State Univ, 55-56; Nat. Acad. Sci-Nat. Res. Coun. vis. scientist, pioneering res. div, U.S. Army Natick Labs, Mass, 63-64; prin. res. scientist, div. dairy res, Commonwealth Sci. & Indust. Res. Orgn, 63-67; dir. flavor res, res. & develop. labs, INT. FLAVORS & FRAGRANCES, INC, UNION BEACH, 67-69, ASSOC. DIR. FLAVOR RES. & DEVELOP, 69- Am. Chem. Soc; Inst. Food Technol; Am. Soc. Test. & Mat. Chemistry of flavors. Address: 14 Linden Dr, Fair Haven, NJ 07701.

FORST, HAROLD C(ARL), b. Port Arthur, Tex, Jan. 17, 28; m. 53; c. 1. PHYSICS. B.S, Univ. Tex, 50. Electronics engr, instrumentation sect, ballistics res. labs, ABERDEEN PROVING GROUNDS, 52-59, PHYSICIST, solid state sect, 59-63, U.S. ARMY LAND WARFARE LAB, 63- Ord.C, U.S.A, 50-52. Inst. Elec. & Electronics Eng. Acoustics; infrared; weapon signatures; signal analysis and processing; environmental analysis; prototype hardware development. Address: 808 S. Adams St, Havre de Grace, MD 21078.

FORST, WENDELL, b. Trinec, Czech, Sept. 28, 26; nat. Can; m. 53. PHYSICAL CHEMISTRY. B.Sc, Prague Tech, 48; Alexander McFee fel. McGill, 52-53, Nat. Res. Coun. Can. Studentship, 53-55, Ph.D.(phys. chem), 55. Res. engr, Northeast. Paper Prods, Ltd, Can, 55-56; asst. prof. CHEM, LAVAL UNIV, 56-62, assoc. prof, 62-66, PROF, 66- Res. assoc, Univ. N.C, 58-61; sabbatical leave, Univ. Calif, Berkeley & Free Univ. Brussels, 69-70. AAAS; Am. Chem. Soc; Am. Phys. Soc; Chem. Inst. Can; Fr. Soc. Phys. Chem. Kinetics of gas phase reactions; mass spectrometry; theory of unimolecular reactions; quantum chemistry. Address: Dept. of Chemistry, Laval University, Quebec 10, Que, Can.

FORSTALL, WALTON, (JR), b. Rosemont, Pa, June 26, 09; m. 42; c. 2. MECHANICAL ENGINEERING. B.S, Lehigh, 31, M.S, 43, M.E, 51; Sc.D. (mech. eng), Mass. Inst. Tech, 49. Asst. test engr, Del. sta, Phila. Elec. Co, 30; mem. sci. staff, Franklin Inst, 32-34; eng. asst, Phila. Gas Works Co, 34-40; instr. & asst. prof, Lehigh, 40-44; proj. engr, Clinton Eng. Works, Tenn. Eastman Corp, 44-45; res. assoc. MECH. ENG, Mass. Inst. Tech, 46-49; assoc. prof, CARNEGIE-MELLON UNIV, 49-57, PROF, 57-, ASSOC. HEAD DEPT, 64-, asst. dean eng. & sci, 55-57. Dir, Klein-Logan Co, Pa, 53-68; mem. indust. standards adv. bd, Commonwealth Pa, 64-68. Fel. Am. Soc. Mech. Eng; Am. Soc. Eng. Educ; Am. Phys. Soc. Momentum, mass and temperature diffusion in a free turbulent boundary layer. Address: Dept. of Mechanical Engineering, Carnegie-Mellon University, Pittsburgh, PA 15213.

FORSTAT, HAROLD, b. Brooklyn, N.Y, June 6, 21; m. 47; c. 4. PHYSICS. B.A, Brooklyn Col, 42; M.S, Purdue, 50; Ph.D.(physics), Connecticut, 55. Physicist, Camp Evans Signal Lab, N.J, 42-43; res. physicist, S.A.M. Lab, Columbia, 43-46; metall. lab, Chicago, 46-48; Camp Detrick Biol. Lab, Md, 51-53; instr. PHYSICS, Connecticut, 54-55; asst. prof, MICH. STATE UNIV, 55-61, assoc. prof, 61-67, PROF, 67- Fulbright fel, Trinity Col.(Dublin), 63-64. Fel. Am. Phys. Soc. Hydrodynamics of Helium II; low temperature heat capacities of anti-ferromagnets; measurements of alpha particle energies. Address: Dept. of Physics, Michigan State University, East Lansing, MI 48823.

FORSTER, DENIS, b. Newcastle-on-Tyne, Eng, Feb. 28, 41; m. 64; c. 2. INORGANIC CHEMISTRY. B.Sc, London, 62, Ph.D.(inorg. chem, 65. Fel, Princeton, 65-66; res. chemist, MONSANTO CENT. RES. DEPT, 66-70, GROUP LEADER HOMOGENEOUS CATALYSIS, 70- Transition metal chemistry; vibrational spectroscopy; nuclear magnetic resonance; catalysis. Address: 7427 Tulane Ave, St. Louis, MO 63130.

FORSTER, E(RIC) O(TTO), b. Lemberg, Oct. 24, 18; nat; m; c. 6. PHYSICAL ORGANIC CHEMISTRY. B.S, Columbia, 49, M.A, 50, Ph.D.(phys. org. chem), 51. Res. chemist, Standard Oil Develop. Co, 51-57, res. assoc, ESSO RES. & ENG. CO, STANDARD OIL CO.(N.J), 57-67, SR. RES. ASSOC, 67- Lectr, Columbia Univ, 53-67; adj. prof, Rutgers Univ, 67- AAAS; Am. Chem. Soc; Inst. Elec. & Electronics Eng. Electrochemistry applied to hydrocarbon systems; electric properties of petroleum products. Address: 1997 Duncan Dr, Scotch Plains, NJ 07076.

FORSTER, FRANCIS M(ICHAEL), b. Cincinnati, Ohio, Feb. 14, 12; m. 37; c. 4. CLINICAL NEUROLOGY. B.S, Cincinnati, 35, B.M, 36, M.D, 37. Intern, Good Samaritan Hosp, Mass, 37-38; fel. psychiat, Pa. Hosp, Phila, 38-39; asst. neur, Harvard Med. Sch, 39-40; Rockefeller Found. fel. & res. assoc. physiol, sch. med, Yale, 40-41; instr. neurol, sch. med, Boston, 41-43; asst. prof, Jefferson Med. Col, 43-47, assoc. prof, 47-50; prof, med. center, Georgetown, 50-58, dean sch. med, 53-58; PROF. NEUROL, SCH. MED, UNIV. WIS, MADISON, 58- Res. physician, Boston City Hosp, 39-40; specialist, U.S. Vet. Admin, 46-; consult, hosps; Surg. Gen, U.S. Air Force, 56-; Surg. Gen, U.S. Navy, 58-; v.pres, Am. Bd. Psychiat. & Neurol, 59, pres, 59-60. With U.S. Pub. Health Serv, 44. AAAS; Am. Physiol. Soc; Am. Neurol. Asn; Am. Psychiat. Asn; Am. Asn. Neuropath; fel. Am. Med. Asn; Asn. Res. Nerv. & Ment. Diseases; Am. Electroencephaolog. Soc; Am. Acad. Neurol.(v.pres, 53-55, pres, 56-58). Epilepsy; vascular accidents, multiple sclerosis; muscular dystrophy. Address: Dept. of Neurology, University of Wisconsin School of Medicine, 1954 E. Washington Ave, Madison, WI 53704.

FORSTER, HARRIET H(ERTA), b. Vienna, Austria; nat; m. 42. PHYSICS. M.A, Univ. Calif, 47, Ph.D.(physics), 48. Instr. PHYSICS, UNIV. SOUTH. CALIF, 48-51, asst. prof, 51-56, assoc. prof, 56-64, PROF, 64- Fel. Am. Phys. Soc. Nuclear physics; cosmic rays. Address: Dept. of Physics, University of Southern California, Los Angeles, CA 90007.

FORSTER, J(OHN) H(ESLOP), b. Vancouver, B.C, Aug. 13, 23; m. 51. PHYSICS. B.A, British Columbia, 44, M.A, 46; Ph.D.(physics), Purdue, 53. Lab. asst. physics, British Columbia, 43-46; asst. instr, Purdue, 46-50, asst, 50-53; mem. tech. staff, BELL TEL. LABS, 53-58, supvr, 58-63, head integrated circuits & Mesa Dept, 63-68, bipolar device dept, 68-71, HEAD HYBRID ASSEMBLY TECHNIQUES DEPT, 71- Nucleon irradiation of semiconductors; transistor physics; integrated circuits. Address: Hybrid Assembly Techniques Dept, Bell Telephone Labs, 555 Union Blvd, Allentown, PA 18103.

FORSTER, KURT, b. Vienna, Austria, March 17, 15; nat; c. 2. PHYSICS. Ph.D.(physics), Vienna, 38. Sr. res. engr, jet propulsion lab, Calif. Inst. Tech, 46-47, res. fel. physics, 47-48; asst. prof. ENG, UNIV. CALIF, LOS ANGELES, 48-50, assoc. prof, 50-56, PROF, 56- Guggenheim fel, 58-59; vis. prof, faculty eng, Univ. Tokyo, 58. U.S.A.A.F, 42-46. AAAS; Am. Inst. Aeronaut. & Astronaut; Am. Phys. Soc. Aerodynamics; heat transfer; space dynamics. Address: School of Engineering & Applied Science, University of California, Los Angeles, CA 90024.

FORSTER, LESLIE S(TEWART), b. Chicago, Ill, May 10, 24; m. 46; c. 2. PHYSICAL CHEMISTRY. B.S, California, 47; Ph.D.(chem), Minnesota, 51. Fel, Rochester, 51-52; instr. CHEM, Bates Col, 52-54; asst. prof, UNIV. ARIZ, 55-59, assoc. prof, 59-64, PROF, 64- Nat. Sci. Found. Sci. faculty fel, Copenhagen, 61-62; consult, Nat. Insts. Health, 63-64; U.S. Pub. Health Serv. spec. fel, Weizmann Inst, Israel, 68-69. U.S.A, 43-45. Am. Chem. Soc; Am. Phys. Soc. Luminescence; spectroscopy and photochemistry of complex molecules. Address: Dept. of Chemistry, University of Arizona, Tucson, AZ 85721.

FORSTER, MICHAEL, b. Vienna, Austria, Nov. 20, 20; nat; m. 50; c. 2. ELECTRICAL ENGINEERING, MATHEMATICS. B.A, Univ. Calif, Los Angeles, 43, Ph.D.(eng), 67; cert, Univ. Grenoble, 46; M.S, Southern Methodist, 58. Supvr, oper. design eval. group, Douglas Aircraft Co, 51-55, asst. chief missiles preliminary design, 56; dir. adv. eng, Varo Mfg. Co, Tex, 56-57; chmn. guid. panel, tech. mil. planning oper, Gen. Elec. Co, 57-64, MEM. TECH. STAFF eng. disciplines, Calif, 64-68; GEN. RES. CORP, 68- U.S.A, 43-46. Opers. Res. Soc. Am; Inst. Elec. & Electronics Eng; Am. Inst. Aeronaut. & Astronaut. Applied mathematics; space guidance problems. Address: General Research Corp, Hollister Ave, Goleta, CA 93017.

FORSTER, MICHAEL J(AY), b. Buffalo, N.Y, Feb. 8, 23; m. 48; c. 7. PHYSICS. B.S, Canisius Col, 45; M.S, Notre Dame, 50, Ph.D.(physics), 51. Physicist, E.I. du Pont de Nemours & Co, Inc, 45-46; asst, Notre Dame, 46-51; res. physicist, FIRESTONE TIRE & RUBBER CO, 51-66, group leader, 66-67, MGR. TEXTILE RES, 67- Am. Phys. Soc. Fiber structure and properties; fiber morphology; crystalline structure of high polymers. Address: 1422 Delia Ave, Akron, OH 44320.

FORSTER, R(OBERT) E(LDER), b. St. Davids, Pa, Dec. 23, 19; m. 47; c. 4. PHYSIOLOGY. B.S, Yale, 41; M.D, Pennsylvania, 43. Med. intern, Peter Bent Brigham Hosp, Boston, 44, asst. res, 47; Life Ins. med. res. fel. physiol, Harvard Med. Sch, 48-49; asst. prof. PHYSIOL, grad. sch. med, UNIV. PA, 50-53, assoc. prof, 54-58, prof, 58-67, ISAAC OTT PROF, SCH. MED, 67-, CHMN. DEPT, 70-, grad. sch. med, 59-67. Palmer sr. fel, 54-56; mem. cardiovasc. study sect, Nat. Insts. Health, 60-64, gen. clin. ctr. study sect, 64-67; mem. Nat. Heart Coun. Med.C, 44-46, Capt. Am. Physiol. Soc; Am. Soc. Clin. Invest; Biophys. Soc; Am. Fedn. Clin. Res. Respiratory gas exchange; rapid reactions of hemoglobin; temperature regulation. Address: Dept. of Physiology, University of Pennsylvania School of Medicine, Philadelphia, PA 19104.

FORSTER, ROY P(HILIP), b. Milwaukee, Wis, Sept. 28, 11; m. 35; c. 1. PHYSIOLOGY, BIOCHEMISTRY. B.S, Marquette, 32; Ph.B, Wisconsin, 36, Ph.D.(zool), 38; hon. M.A, Dartmouth, 48. Asst. zool, Marquette, 32-34; Wisconsin, 35-38; instr. ZOOL, DARTMOUTH COL, 38-42, asst. prof, 42-48, prof, 48-64, IRA ALLEN EASTMAN PROF, 64-, LECTR. PHYSIOL, MED. SCH, 64- Dir. Biol. Lab, Mt. Desert Island, summers 40-47, trustee, 40-, v.pres, 61-63, pres, 64-70; sect. ed, Biol. Abstr, 47-; Guggenheim fel, Cambridge, 49; mem, Macy Conf. Renal Function, 49-53; Rockefeller Found. grant, 50-57; Guggenheim fel, zool. sta, Univ. Naples, 56; grant, Nat. Insts. Health, 56-, mem. sci. rev. comt, health res. facilities, 64-68, med. biol. rev. comt, 66-67, ad hoc comt. comp. pharmacol, 66-67, pharmacol-toxicol. rev. comt, 69-70; vis. lectr, sch. med, George Wash. Univ, 59-60; dir. regulatory biol. prog, Nat. Sci. Found, 59-60; consult. res. biologist, Vet. Admin. Ctr, Vt, 63-; mem. Nat. Acad. Sci-Nat. Res. Coun. Comt. Eval. Nat. Sci. Found. grad. fels, 64-65; Vet. Admin. Comt. Res. Lab. Sci. & Med, 64-66; Conf. Current Invests. Dealing with Elasmobranch Physiol, 66; Conf. Urea & Kidney, 68; coun. on circulation, Am. Heart Asn. Fel. AAAS; Am. Soc. Zool; Am. Physiol. Soc; Soc. Gen. Physiol; Am. Soc. Nephrology; Int. Soc. Nephrology. Cellular and comparative physiology of the kidney; renal hemodynamics; transport processes in the renal tubule: nitrogen metabolism and excretion. Address: Dept. of Biological Sciences, Dartmouth College, Hanover, NH 03755.

FORSTER, SIGMUND, b. Lvov, Poland, Feb. 11, 06; U.S. citizen; m. 45; c. 1. PHYSICAL MEDICINE. M.D, Naples, 30; M.D, Vilno, Poland, 35. Dir. sanatorium, Poland, 39-41; physiother. clin, 41-45; chief dept. internal med. & physiother, Austria, 45-46; CLIN. ASSOC. PROF. REHAB. MED, DOWNSTATE MED. CTR, STATE UNIV. N.Y, 62-; DIR. PHYSIOTHER. & REHAB, CONEY ISLAND HOSP, 60-; DIR. REHAB. MED, MAIMONIDES MED. CTR, 67- Fel. Am. Col. Physicians; Acad. Phys. Med. & Rehab; Am. Acad. Cerebral Palsy; N.Y. Acad. Med. Physical medicine and rehabilitation. Address: Dept. of Rehabilitative Medicine, Maimonides Medical Center, 4802 Tenth Ave, Brooklyn, NY 11219.

FORSTER, T(HEODORE) L(ESLIE), b. Man, Can, May 25, 11; U.S. citizen; m. 37; c. 1. DAIRY CHEMISTRY. B.S.A, Manitoba, 33; M.S, Wisconsin, 40, Ph.D.(dairy indust), 50. Instr. dairy sci, Manitoba, 33, lectr, 37, asst. prof, 46; dairy husb, N.Dak. Agr. Col, 49-55; WASH. STATE UNIV, 55-60, assoc. prof, 60-66, PROF, 66-70, FOOD SCI, 70-, chmn. grad. prog, 68, acting chmn. dept. food sci. & technol, 70. Fel. AAAS; Am. Chem. Soc; Am. Dairy Sci. Asn; Int. Asn. Milk, Food & Environ. Sanit; Inst. Food Technol. Wrapping materials for packing butter for cold storage; chemistry of oxidized flavor in milk; lipase activity in milk; mastitis and its control; esterases of milk; bovine plasma arylesterase. Address: 110 E. Webb, Pullman, WA 99163.

FORSTER, WARREN S(CHUMANN), b. Denver, Colo, Aug. 16, 14; m. 41; c. 2. ORGANIC CHEMISTRY. B.S, Denver, 36; M.S, Pa. State, 38, Ph.D. (org. chem), 40. Asst. Chem, Pa. State, 36-40; res. chemist, Bound Brook Lab, AM. CYANAMID CO, 40-58, coord, res. servs. dept, 58-63, TECH. COORD, RES. & DEVELOP. DEPT, BUS. OFF, 63- Am. Chem. Soc. Calorimetry of dimethylamine; aliphatic organic chemistry; fluorescent, vat, soluble vat, synthetic fibre dyestuffs and intermediates; optical bleaches; ultraviolet light absorbers; stabilization of plastics. Address: 62 S. Alward Ave, Basking Ridge, NJ 07920.

FORSTER, WILLIAM H(ALL), b. Belmar, N.J, July 11, 22; m. 45; c. 5. COMMUNICATIONS, ELECTRONICS. A.B, Harvard, 43. Asst. res. div, Philco Corp, 43-48, sect. engr. govt. & indust. div, 48-50, exec. engr, 50-52, res. div, 52-56; assoc. dir. res. solid state electronics, 56-57, dir. res, 57-59, dir. semiconductor mkt. & develop, Philco Int. Div, 59-61, corporate staff, 61-62, dir. eng. & res. commun. & electronics div, 62-66; staff asst. to pres, Int. Tel. & Tel. Corp, N.Y, 66, ITT EUROPE, INC, 66-67, V.PRES. & TECH. DIR, 67- Mem. bd. corporators, Med. Col. Pa. Fel. Inst. Elec. & Electronics Eng; Brit. Inst. Phys. & Phys. Soc. Communications; information processing systems; semiconductor devices and solid state physics as applied to devices useful in electronic devices and systems. Address: ITT Europe, Inc, 11 Blvd. de l'Empereur, Brussels 1000, Belgium.

FORSTER, WILLIAM OWEN, b. Dearborn, Mich, July 2, 27; m. 48; c. 3. ANALYTICAL CHEMISTRY, OCEANOGRAPHY. B.S, Mich. State, 51, M.A, 52; Ph.D.(chem), Hawaii, 66. Anal. chemist, Buick Motor Car Co, 50-52; teacher, high sch, Mich, 52-56; instr. chem, Henry Ford Community Col, 56-61; gen. sci, Hawaii, 61-66; ASST. PROF. CHEM. OCEANOG, ORE. STATE UNIV, 66- Lectr, Kilolani Planetarium, Bishop Mus, 64-66; Oak Ridge Nat. Lab. fel, P.R. Nuclear Ctr, Mayaguez, 69-70, head marine biol. prog, 70- Air C, U.S.N, 45-47. AAAS; Am. Chem. Soc; Am. Geophys. Union; Am. Soc. Limnol. & Oceanog; Soc. Appl. Spectros. Trace element analysis in sea water, biota and sediments; biogeochemistry of marine environments. Address: Puerto Rico Nuclear Center, Mayaguez, PR 00708.

FORSTHOEFEL, PAULINUS F(REDERICK), S.J, b. St. Sebastian, Ohio, Apr. 5, 15. GENETICS. A.B, Loyola (Ill), 39; M.Sc, Ohio State, 51, univ. scholar, 52-53, Ph.D.(zool), 53. Instr. math, Loyola Acad, 41-43; private sch, Ohio, 43-44; BIOL, UNIV. DETROIT, 53-56, asst. prof, 56-59, assoc. prof, 59-63, PROF, 63- Citation for outstanding res. & publ, Mich. Acad. Arts, Sci. & Letters, 71. Nat. Sci. Found. grant, 54-56; U.S. Pub. Health Serv. grant, 57-71; judge, Nat. Sci. Fair, 58, 68; trustee, St. Louis Univ, 67. Fel. AAAS; Genetics Soc. Am. Developmental genetics of mice. Address: Dept. of Biology, Lansing-Reilly Hall, University of Detroit, 4001 W. McNichols Rd, Detroit, MI 48221.

FORSTNER, JAMES ALLAN, b. Baltimore, Md, Feb. 17, 36; m. 60; c. 1. INORGANIC CHEMISTRY. B.S, Loyola Col.(Md), 58; M.S, Carnegie Inst. Technol, 61, Ph.D.(chem), 62; J.D, Univ. Md, 69. Chemist, cent. res. dept, E.I. DU PONT DE NEMOURS & CO, INC, 62-65, patent chemist, LEGAL DEPT, 65-69, PATENT ATTORNEY, 69- Summers, res. lab. technician, Allied Chem. Corp, 57; chemist & info. specialist, U.S. Army Chem. Warfare Labs, 58, tech. ed, 59. Am. Chem. Soc; Sci. Res. Soc. Am; The Chem. Soc; Am. Bar Asn. Halides; phosphorus-nitrogen compounds; polyhedral boranes; chemical patent law; licensing. Address: 207 N. Spring Valley Rd, Greenville DE 19807.

FORSTNER, J(AMES) L(EE), b. Chattanooga, Tenn, May 29, 21; m. 46; c. 2. ANALYTICAL CHEMISTRY. B.S, California, Los Angeles, 48, M.S, 50; Little fel, Mass. Inst. Tech, 51-52, Ph.D.(anal. chem), 52. RES. CHEMIST, E.I. DU PONT DE NEMOURS & CO, INC, 53-61, NUCLEAR SAFETY, 61- C.W.S, 42-46, Capt. AAAS; Am. Chem. Soc. Nuclear safety calculations. Address: 1119 Parsons Lane, Aiken, SC 29801.

FORSYTH, BEN RALPH, b. N.Y.C, Mar. 8, 34; m. 62; c. 3. INTERNAL MEDICINE, INFECTIOUS DISEASES. M.D, N.Y. Univ, 57. Intern & asst. res, Yale New Haven Med. Ctr, 57-60; res. fel, dept. bact. & immunol, Harvard Med. Sch. & Boston City Hosp, 60-61; sr. investr, respiratory virus unit, lab. infectious diseases, Nat. Inst. Allergy & Infectious Diseases, 63-66; assoc. prof. MED, COL. MED, UNIV. VT, 66-71, PROF, 71-, ASSOC. PROF. MED. MICROBIOL, 67-, DIR. INFECTIOUS DISEASES UNIT, 66-, ASSOC. DEAN LONG RANGE PLANNING, DIV. HEALTH SCI, 70-, acting chmn. dept. med. microbiol, 67. Sinsheimer Fund faculty fel, 66-71. Mem, res. reagents comt, Nat. Inst. Allergy & Infectious Diseases, 66-68, chmn, 68- Med.C, U.S.N, 61-63, Lt. Comdr; U.S.P.H.S, 63-66, Sr. Surg. Am. Fedn. Clin. Res; Am. Soc. Microbiol; Infectious Diseases Soc. Am; Soc. Exp. Biol. & Med; Am. Thoracic Soc. Virology; mycoplasma; epidemiology; chronic pulmonary disease. Address: Dept. of Medicine, Given Medical Bldg, University of Vermont College of Medicine, Burlington, VT 05401.

FORSYTH, BILLY JOE, b. Searcy, Ark, July 21, 37; m. 64. ORNITHOLOGY, ECOLOGY. B.S, Ark. State Teachers Col, 60; M.S, Arkansas, 62, Welder Wildlife Found. fel, 63-65, Ph.D.(zool), 67. ASSOC. PROF. ZOOL, IND. UNIV. SOUTHEAST, 67- AAAS; Am. Ornith. Union; Am. Inst. Biol. Sci; Wilson Ornithol. Soc. Waterfowl food habits; population dynamics of small mammals; bird migration. Address: Dept. of Biology, Indiana University Southeast, Warder Park, Jeffersonville, IN 47130.

FORSYTH, F(RANK) R(USSELL), b. Russell, Ont, Mar. 15, 22; m. 45; c. 5. PLANT PHYSIOLOGY. B.A, Queen's (Ont), 49; Ph.D.(plant physiol), Toronto, 52. Res. officer agr. & plant physiologist, PLANT PATH. SECT. CAN. DEPT. AGR, Univ. Manitoba, 52-59, RES. OFF. AGR, PESTICIDE RES. INST, 59-62, KENTVILLE RES. STA, 62- R.C.A.F, 41-45. Can. Soc. Plant Physiol; Agr. Inst. Can; Prof. Inst. Pub. Serv. Can; Scandinavian Soc. Plant Physiol. Biochemical aspects of physiological disorders of fruit in storage. Address: Research Station, Canada Dept. of Agriculture, Kentville, N.S, Can.

FORSYTH, JAMES M, b. Niagara Falls, N.Y, Apr. 21, 42; m. 68. OPTICS. B.S, Univ. Rochester, 64, Ph.D.(optics), 69. ASST. PROF. OPTICS, INST. OPTICS, UNIV. ROCHESTER, 68- Optical Soc. Am; Inst. Elec. & Electronics Eng. Gas lasers; optical-electronic instrumentation. Address: Institute of Optics, University of Rochester, River Campus Station, Rochester, NY 14627.

FORSYTH, J(AMES) S(NEDDON), b. Hamilton, Scotland, Dec. 11, 16; m. 45; c. 1. CHEMICAL ENGINEERING. B.Sc, Glasgow, 38; fel. & Ph.D.(fuel), Leeds, 43. Lectr. CHEM. ENG, Leeds, 45-52; sr. lectr, Durham, 52-57; PROF, UNIV. B.C, 57-, head dept, 57-69. Civilian with Ministries of Home Security & Aircraft Prod, 42-46. Fel. Chem. Inst. Can; Brit. Inst. Chem. Eng.(Moulton medal, 55); Royal Inst. Chem. Separation operations, especially distillation. Address: Dept. of Chemical Engineering, University of British Columbia, Vancouver, B.C, Can.

FORSYTH, JANE L(OUISE), b. Hanover, N.H, Nov. 9, 21. GEOLOGY. A.B, Smith Col, 43; M.A, Cincinnati, 46; Ph.D.(geol), Ohio State, 56. Asst. geol, Cincinnati, 43-46; instr, Miami (Ohio), 46-47; asst, California, Berkeley, 47-48; asst. instr, Ohio State, 48-49, 51-55; pleistocene geologist, Ohio Geol. Surv, 55-65; asst. prof. GEOL, BOWLING GREEN STATE UNIV, 65-68, ASSOC. PROF, 68- Summers, instr, Adams State Col, 47-50. Ed, Ohio J. Sci. Geol. Soc. Am; Nat. Asn. Geol. Teachers. Glacial geology and pleistocene geology; Wisconsin chronology in Ohio; soils, particularly as related to glacial geology studies in Ohio; geomorphology; human environmental geology; ecology, especially the relationship between plant distribution and geology in the midwest. Address: Dept. of Geology, Bowling Green State University, Bowling Green, OH 43403.

FORSYTH, JOHN W(ILEY), b. McKinney, Tex, Mar. 18, 13; m. 43; c. 3. EXPERIMENTAL MORPHOLOGY. B.S, Texas Christian, 35, fel, 34-36, M.S, 37; Sterry jr. fel, Princeton, 38-40, Lapham fel, 40-41, Ph.D.(exp. morphol), 41. Instr, Texas Christian, 36-38; prof, Presby. Col.(S.C), 41-43; adj. prof, South Carolina, 46; asst. prof. BIOL, TEX. CHRISTIAN UNIV, 46-47, assoc. prof, 47-50, PROF, 50- U.S.A.A.F, 42-45, Res, 45-, Col. AAAS; Am. Soc. Ichthyol. & Herpet; Soc. Syst. Zool; Am. Soc. Zool. Amphibian limb regeneration; herpetological studies; food habits and distribution in Ft. Worth region. Address: Dept. of Biology, Texas Christian University, Ft. Worth, TX 76129.

FORSYTH, PAUL F(RANCIS), b. Ogdensburg, N.Y, Apr. 21, 28; m. 51; c. 6. INORGANIC CHEMISTRY. B.S, Canisius Col, 51, M.S, 53. Atomic Energy Comn. asst, Canisius Col, 51-53; res. chemist, Union Carbide Metals Co, 53-61; mat. engr, Bell Aerosyst, 61-62; supv. engr, measurement sect, CARBORUNDUM CO, 62-69, SUPVR. ENGR, PROD. DEVELOP, 69- Med.C, 46-48, Sgt. Am. Chem. Soc. Inorganic synthesis; vacuum techniques; analytical instrumentation; abrasive products and processes. Address: Coated Abrasives Division, Carborundum Co, P.O. Box 477, Niagara Falls, NY 14304.

FORSYTH, PAUL S, b. Detroit, Mich, Apr. 23, 18; m. 49; c. 4. CHEMICAL ENGINEERING. B.S.Ch.E. & M.S, Purdue, 41. Prod. engr, Monsanto Chem. Co, 41-45; researcher, synthetic rubber, Reconstruct. Finance Corp, 45-50; indust. off, Econ. Coop. Admin, 50-51; engr, mat. div, Off. Secy. Defense, Wash, D.C, 52-63; CHEM. ENGR, 63- AAAS; Am. Chem. Soc; Am. Inst. Chem. Eng. Non-metallic materials; polymers; plastics; elastomers; adhesives; reinforced plastics; fibers; energy source materials for thermoelectrics; thermionics; fuel cells; solar cells; isotopic power and nuclear power sources. Address: 3418 Quesada St. N.W, Washington, D.C. 20015.

FORSYTH, P(ETER) A(LLAN), b. Prince Albert, Sask, Mar. 20, 22; m. 44; c. 2. PHYSICS. B.A, Saskatchewan, 42-46, Nat. Res. Coun. Can. bursar & M.A, 47; Nat. Res. Coun. fel. & Ph.D.(physics), McGill, 51. Sci. off. radio physics lab, Defence Res. Telecommun. Estab, Can, 51-53, sect. leader, upper atmospheric physics sect, 53-57, supt. radio physics lab, 57-58; prof. PHYSICS, Saskatchewan, 58-61; prof. & head dept, UNIV. WEST. ONT, 61-67, DIR. CTR. RADIO SCI, 67- Mem. comt. geodet. & geophys, Nat. Res. Coun. Can. R.C.N.V.R, 42-45; R.C.N.R, 47-52, Lt. Can. Asn. Physicists; fel. Royal Soc. Can; fel. Can. Aeronaut. & Space Inst. Physics of the upper atmosphere; propagation of radio waves in ionized media; scattering of radio waves by inhomogenous media. Address: Dept. of Physics, University of Western Ontario, London, Ont, Can.

FORSYTH, RALPH P, b. Brooklyn, N.Y, Aug. 23; m. 61; c. 2. PHYSIOLOGICAL PSYCHOLOGY. B.A, Duke Univ; M.A, Univ. N.C, 58, Ph.D.(psychol), 60. Res. fel. PSYCHOL, interdisciplinary res. training prog, MED. CTR, UNIV. CALIF, SAN FRANCISCO, 60-62, RES. PSYCHOLOGIST, CARDIOVASC. RES. INST, 62-, LECTR. PSYCHIAT, 65-, ASSOC. PROF. MED. PSYCHOL, 70- Nat. Heart Inst. career develop. award, 65-70. U.S.A, 52-54. Am. Psychol. Asn. Cardiovascular effects of chronic stressful experiences; central nervous system control of cardiovascular dynamics; learning and personality theory. Address: Cardiovascular Research Institute, University of California Medical Center, San Francisco, CA 94122.

FORSYTH, THOMAS HENRY, b. Pikeville, Ky, Nov. 8, 42; m. 64; c. 2. CHEMICAL ENGINEERING, POLYMER SCIENCE. B.S, Univ. Ky, 64; Nat. Sci. Found. fel, Va. Polytech. Inst, 64-65, U.S. Dept. Health, Educ. & Welfare fel, 65-67, M.S, 66, Ph.D.(chem. eng), 68. Summers, chem. engr, E.I. du Pont de Nemours & Co, Inc, Va, 63, Ky, 64, Va, 65; Dow Chem. Co, Mich, 67-70; ASST. PROF. CHEM. ENG, UNIV. AKRON, 70- Lectr, Midland, Mich, 69-70. Am. Chem. Soc; Am. Inst. Chem. Eng; Soc. Plastics Eng. Polymer engineering; water pollution; solid waste control. Address: Dept. of Chemical Engineering, University of Akron, Akron, OH 44304.

FORSYTHE, ALAN BARRY, b. Brooklyn, N.Y, Nov. 3, 40; m. 62; c. 2. BIOSTATISTICS. B.S, Brooklyn Col, 62; M.S, Columbia Univ, 64; Ph.D.(biomet), Yale, 67. Res. asst. statist. anal, dept. pediat. & cardiac res, Yale, 64, statistician, dept. obstet. & gynec, 66; asst. res. statistician, DEPT. BIOMATH. & SCH. MED, UNIV. CALIF, LOS ANGELES, 67-68, SUPVRY. STATISTICIAN, 68-, fels, 70-73. AAAS; Am. Statist. Asn; Biomet. Soc; Asn. Comput. Mach. Robust estimation and hypothesis testing, especially regression; use of computers for statistical analysis and teaching. Address: Dept. of Biomathematics, School of Medicine, University of California, Los Angeles, CA 90024.

FORSYTHE, GEORGE E(LMER), b. State College, Pa, Jan. 8, 17; m. 41; c. 2. COMPUTER SCIENCE. A.B, Swarthmore Col, 37; Sc.M, Brown, 38, Ph.D.(math), 41. Instr. math, Brown, 38-41; Stanford, 41-42; res. engr, Boeing Aircraft Co, Wash, 46-47; asst. prof. meteorol, California, Los Angeles, 47-48; mathematician, inst. numerical anal, Nat. Bur. Standards, 48-54; res. mathematician & vis. prof. math, California, Los Angeles, 54-57; prof. STANFORD UNIV, 57-64; PROF. COMPUTER SCI. & HEAD DEPT, 64- Sr. scientist & vis. prof, N.Y. Univ, 55-56; consult, various corps, 54-61; ed,

Prentice-Hall Series Automatic Comput, 61- U.S.A.A.F, 42-46. Fel. AAAS; Am. Math. Soc; Soc. Indust. & Appl. Math; Math. Asn. Am; Asn. Comput. Mach.(pres, 64-66); Brit. Comput. Soc. Numerical analysis; computer science education. Address: Dept. of Computer Science, Stanford University, Stanford, CA 94305.

FORSYTHE, HOWARD Y(OST), JR, b. Aiken, S.C, Oct. 27, 31; m. 59; c. 3. ENTOMOLOGY. B.S, Maine, 58; M.S, Cornell, 60, Allied Chem. Corp. fel, 61-62, Ph.D.(entom), 62. Asst. prof. ENTOM, Ohio Agr. Exp. Sta, 62-66, ASSOC. PROF, Ohio Agr. Res. & Develop. Ctr, 66-69; UNIV. MAINE, ORONO, 69- Nat. Sci. Found. Res. grant, 64-66. U.S.A.F, 50-53. Entom. Soc. Am; Entom. Soc. Can. Control and biology of deciduous fruit tree insects and mites; ecology of mites; control and biology of insects on blueberries; biological statistics. Address: Dept. of Entomology, University of Maine at Orono, Orono, ME 04473.

FORSYTHE, R(ICHARD) H(AMILTON), b. Griswold, Iowa, Dec. 9, 21; m. 43; c. 3. BIOPHYSICAL CHEMISTRY. B.S, Iowa State Col, 43, Ph.D, 49. Asst. prof. poultry husb, Iowa State Col, 48-51; asst. dir. food res, Armour & Co, Ill, 51-53; v.pres. & dir. cent. labs, Henningsen, Inc, 53-60; prof. poultry husb. & head dept, Iowa State, 60-67; V.PRES. FOOD RES, HENNINGSEN FOODS, INC, 67- Inst. Am. Poultry Industs. & Inst. Food Technologist award, 58. U.S.A, 43-45. AAAS; Am. Chem. Soc; Poultry Sci. Asn; Inst. Food Tech.(Monsanto award, 54); Am. Cereal Chem. Asn. Technical service; quality control; egg solids. Address: Henningsen Foods, Inc, 2 Corporate Park Dr, White Plains, NY 10604.

FORSYTHE, WARREN M, b. Kingston, Jamaica, June 26, 34. SOIL PHYSICS. B.S, California, Berkeley, 55, Ph.D.(soil physics), 62. Soil physicist, Sugar Res. Dept, Jamaica, 62-63; soil specialist, INTERAM. INST. AGR. SCI, 64-67, ASSOC. SOIL SCIENTIST (PHYSICS), 67- Soil Sci. Soc. Am. Soil-water relations; arid zone agriculture; soil management in the wet and dry tropics in relation to irrigation, drainage and soil and water conservation. Address: Interamerican Institute of Agricultural Sciences, Turrialba, Costa Rica.

FORT, ARTHUR T(OMLINSON), b. Lumpkin, Ga, Sept. 24, 31; m. 57; c. 4. OBSTETRICS & GYNECOLOGY. B.B.A, Univ. Ga, 52; Memphis State Univ, 57-59; M.D, Univ. Tenn, 62. Intern, Baptist Mem. Hosp, Memphis, Tenn, 62-63; resident OBSTET. & GYNEC, col. med, Univ. Tenn, 63-66, instr, 66-68, asst. prof, 68-70; PROF. & HEAD DEPT, SCH. MED, LA. STATE UNIV, 71- Dipl, Am. Bd. Obstet. & Gynec, 69. U.S.A.F, 52-57, Capt. Fel. Am. Col. Obstet. & Gynec; Am. Med. Asn. Treatment and diagnosis of the unborn child and prenatal genesis of mental subnormality. Address: Confederate Memorial, 1541 Kings Highway, Shreveport, LA 71103.

FORT, RAYMOND C(ORNELIUS), JR, b. Upper Darby, Pa, Mar. 28, 38; m. 61; c. 1. PHYSICAL ORGANIC CHEMISTRY. B.S, Drexel Inst, 61; Allied Chem. Co. & Nat. Sci. Found. fels. & Ph.D.(org. chem), Princeton, 65. Fel. CHEM, Princeton, 64-65; asst. prof, KENT STATE UNIV, 65-70, ASSOC. PROF, 70- AAAS; Am. Chem. Soc; The Chem. Soc. Carbonium ions; influence of geometry on the stability of reactive intermediates; nuclear magnetic resonance spectroscopy. Address: Dept. of Chemistry, Kent State University, Kent, OH 44240.

FORT, TOMLINSON, JR, b. Sumter, S.C, Apr. 16, 32; m. 56; c. 2. PHYSICAL CHEMISTRY. B.S, Georgia, 52; M.S. & Ph.D.(surface chem), Tennessee, 57. Stephens res. fel, Sydney, 57-58; res. chemist, E.I. du Pont de Nemours & Co, 58-61, sr. res. chemist, 61-65; asst. prof. CHEM. ENG. SCI, CASE WEST. RESERVE UNIV, 65-67, assoc. Prof, 67-71, PROF, 71- Am. Chem. Soc; Catalysis Soc. Surface chemistry; adsorption; monolayers and thin films; catalysis; adhesion; interfaces in composite materials. Address: Division of Chemical Engineering Science, Case Western Reserve University, Cleveland, OH 44106.

FORTE, JOHN GAETANO, b. Phila, Pa, Dec. 23, 34; m. 61; c. 3. PHYSIOLOGY. B.A, Hopkins, 56; Ph.D.(physiol), Pennsylvania, 61; Copenhagen, 61. Lab. instr. biol, Pennsylvania, 59, mammalian physiol, 59-61, instr. physiol, 61-62, assoc, 62-64; res. assoc. biochem, Southern California, 64-65; asst. prof. PHYSIOL, UNIV. CALIF, BERKELEY, 65-69, ASSOC. PROF, 69- Guest lectr, Med. Col. Ala, 65. Am. Physiol. Soc; Biophys. Soc. Secretory mechanisms in a variety of tissues, particularly glandular systems of gastrointestinal tract. Address: Dept. of Physiology-Anatomy, University of California, Berkeley, CA 94720.

FORTE, LEONARD RALPH, b. Nashville, Tenn, June 10, 41; m. 62; c. 3. PHARMACOLOGY. B.S, Austin Peay State Col, 63; Nat. Insts. Health fel, Vanderbilt, 64-68, Ph.D.(pharmacol), 69. Res. asst. PHARMACOL, Vanderbilt, 63-64, Nat. Insts. Health fel. & res. assoc, 69; ASST. PROF, UNIV. MO-COLUMBIA, 69- AAAS; Am. Soc. Nephrol. Renal pharmacology; mechanism of action of aldosterone; characterization of kidney plasma membranes in regard to function and molecular action of diuretic agents. Address: Dept. of Pharmacology, University of Missouri-Columbia, Columbia, MO 65201.

FORTENBAUGH, ROBERT B(ERENDT), b. Syracuse, N.Y, Apr. 27, 23; m. 46; c. 4. ORGANIC CHEMISTRY. B.A, Gettysburg Col, 44; Ph.D.(chem), Hopkins, 50. Res. chemist, AM. CYANAMID CO, 49-54, group leader, 54-56, mgr. formulations lab, AGR. DIV, 56-68, sr. res. chemist, 68-69, STAFF ASST. TO DIR. RES. & DEVELOP, 70- U.S.A, 43-46. Am. Chem. Soc. Vat dyes; textile resins; agricultural chemicals. Address: 21 Morningside Court, Pennington, NJ 08534.

FORTESS, FRED, b. Antwerp, Belgium, Sept. 4, 13; nat; m. 39; c. 2. PHYSICAL & ORGANIC CHEMISTRY. Res. chemist, Universal Oil Prod, 37-42; reactions, textile lubrication & sizing, Celanese Corp. Am, 42-47, res. group leader byprod. utilization, 47-50, mgr. dyeing & finishing lab, appl. & prod. develop. div, Celanese Fibers Co, 55-61, mgr. textile prod. develop, appl. & prod. develop, N.C, 62-65, DIR. CONSUMER INFO. & TECH. RELATIONS, CELANESE FIBERS MKT. CO, 65- Collab, south. utilization res. & develop. div, U.S. Dept. Agr, 57-63; consult, Nat. Acad. Sci, 61- Chmn, Gordon Res. Conf. Textiles, 60; mem. Nat. Adv. Comt. for Flammable Fabrics Act; consumer issues comt, U.S. Chamber Commerce; adv. bd. mil. personnel supplies, Nat. Res. Coun; tech. adv. comt, mat. qual. comt. & consumer affairs comt, Am. Apparel Mfrs. Asn. Am. Dyestuff Reporter Award, 56; Olney Medalist, 61. AAAS; Am. Asn. Textile Chem. & Colorists; Am. Asn. Textile Technol; Fiber Soc; Am. Inst. Chem; Am. Chem. Soc. Absorption spectra europium ions in solutions; vapor phase catalytic reactions; fermentation of waste carbohydrates to organic acids; yarn and fiber lubricants and adhesive materials; chemical treatment of textile materials; dyeing and finishing chemical processes; textile fiber applications. Address: Consumer Information & Technical Relations, Celanese Fibers Marketing Co, 522 Fifth Ave, New York, NY 10036.

FORTIER, CLAUDE, b. Montreal, Que, June 11, 21; m. 53; c. 4. PHYSIOLOGY. B.A. & M.A, Montreal, 41, M.D, 48, Ph.D.(exp. med, surg), 52. Asst. prof. exp. med. & surg, Montreal, 50-51; res. consult. med. clinic, Univ. Lausanne, 52-53; res. assoc. dept. neuroendocrinol, inst. psychiat, Brit. Postgrad. Med. Fedn, Maudsley Hosp, Univ. London, 53-55; assoc. prof. PHYSIOL. col. med, Baylor, 55-60, DIR. ENDOCRINE LABS, FACULTY MED, LAVAL UNIV, 60-, PROF. EXP. PHYSIOL, 61-, CHMN. DEPT, 64- Lectr, inst. psychol, Montreal, 47-51, asst, inst. exp. med. & surg, 48-51; res. fel, Life Ins. Med. Res. Fund, 48-50, Am. Heart Asn, 51-52, 53-54; Nat. Res. Coun. Can, 52-53; adv. res. fel, Commonwealth Fund, 54-55; dir. Blue Bird Neuroendocrine Res. Labs, Tex, 55-60. Mem. Med. Res. Coun. Can, 63-68, 70-72, v.chmn, 65-67; med. res. adv. & coord. comts, Defense Res. Bd. Can, 67-70; chmn, Nat. Comt. Can. of Int. Union Physiol. Sci, 70-; mem, Killam comt, Can. Coun, 67; Nat. Cancer Inst. Can, 69-; prov. Med. Res. Coun. Que, 63-70; neuroendocrinol. panel, Int. Brain Res. Orgn, 59-; ed. bd, Can. Jour. Biochem. & Physiol, 61-64; Can. Jour. Physiol. & Pharmacol, 64-69; Rev. Can. Biol, 61-66; adv. med. bd, Muscular Dystrophy Asn; Can, 62-65; bd. dir, Can. Found. Adv. Therapeut, 63-67; consult. physician, hosp. ctr, Univ. Laval, 69-; sci. adv. bd, Montreal Clin. Res. Inst, 69- Companion of the Order of Can, 70. Fel, Royal Col. Physicians Can, 65. AAAS; fel. Royal Soc. Can; Am. Physiol. Soc; Endocrine Soc; Am. Thyroid Asn; Soc. Exp. Biol. & Med; N.Y. Acad. Sci; Can. Physiol. Soc.(pres, 66-67); Am. Asn. Physicians; Can. Soc. Clin. Invest; Biomed. Eng. Soc. Neurohumoral control of adenohypophysial functions; functional interrelationships between the pituitary, thyroid, adrenal cortex and gonads; biostatistics; biocontrol systems. Address: Dept. of Physiology, Faculty of Medicine, Laval University, Que, Can.

FORTIER, YVES OSCAR, b. Quebec, Que, Aug. 17, 14; m. 45; c. 4. GEOLOGY. B.A, Laval, 35, 35-36; B.Sc, Queen's (Ont), 40; M.Sc, McGill, 41; Ph.D.(geol), Stanford, 46; Nat. Defence Col, Can, 50-51. From stud. asst. to party chief, Geol. Surv. Can. & Que. Dept. Mines, 36-42; teaching fel. mineral, Stanford, 42; from technologist to geologist, GEOL. SURV. CAN, 43-50, sect. head Arctic Islands, 55-58, chief, Precambrian div, 58-59, chief econ. geol. div, 59-64, DIR, 64- Chmn. Nat. Adv. Comt. Res. Geol. Sci, 65-; mem. bd. gov, Univ. Ottawa; ex-off. mem. exec. comt, Int. Union Geol. Sci, 68-72; mem. Geol. Found. Can. Univ. Coun. Queen's Univ. Massey Medal, 64. Geol. Soc. Am; Soc. Econ. Geol; for. mem. Geol. Soc. London; for. mem. Geol. Soc. France; Royal Soc. Can; Geol. Asn. Can; Arctic Inst. N.Am; Can. Inst. Min. & Metall. Arctic geological exploration; structural studies; economic geology and geomorphology. Address: Geological Survey of Canada, 601 Booth St, Ottawa, Ont. K1A 0E8, Can.

FORTIN, EMERY, b. Chicoutimi, Que, Dec. 24, 35; m. 63. SOLID STATE PHYSICS. B.A, Laval, 56, B.Sc, 60; M.Sc, Alberta, 62, Ph.D.(physics), 65. Nat. Res. Coun. Can. fel. PHYSICS, Strasbourg, 65-67; ASST. PROF, UNIV. OTTAWA, 67- R.C.A.F.R, 56-60, Lt. Can. Asn. Physicists. Transport and optical properties of semiconductors; nonequilibrium processes such as photoconductivity and photoelectromagnetic effects. Address: Dept. of Physics, University of Ottawa, Ottawa, Ont, Can.

FORTIN, J. A(NDRE), b. Que, Sept. 28, 37; m. 61; c. 5. BOTANY. B.Sc, Laval Univ, 62, Agr. Res. Found. fel. & Ph.D.(forest bot), 66; Wis. Alumni Res. Found. fel. & M.Sc, Univ. Wis, Madison, 64; Pasteur Inst, Paris, 67. PROF. BOT, LAVAL UNIV, 65- Can. Bot. Asn; Can. Phytopath. Soc. Ectomycorrhizae, Endomycorrhizae and lichen with special attention to the hormonal relationships; inoculation of seedling with mycorrhizal fungi in nurseries; plant symbiosis. Address: Dept. of Ecology & Pedology, Laval University, Quebec, Que, Can.

FORTIN, JEAN MARIE, b. Val-Brillant, Que, Nov. 26, 24; m. 52; c. 5. AGRICULTURAL ENGINEERING. B.A, Rimouski Sem, 47; B.Sc.A, Laval, 51; M.Sc.A, Toronto, 53. PROF. AGR. ENG, FACULTY AGR, LAVAL UNIV, 53- Am. Soc. Agr. Eng; Can. Soc. Agr. Eng. Farm machinery and power; tillage and crops. Address: 762 Ave. Chevremont, Ste-Foy, Quebec 10, Que, Can.

FORTMAN, JOHN JOSEPH, b. Dayton, Ohio, Oct. 26, 39; m. 68. INORGANIC CHEMISTRY. B.S, Dayton, 61; Ph.D.(phys. inorg. chem), Notre Dame, 66. Asst. prof. CHEM, WRIGHT STATE UNIV, 65-69, ASSOC. PROF, 69- Res. analyst, aerospace res. labs, Wright-Patterson Air Force Base, 66-70. AAAS; Am. Chem. Soc; Am. Phys. Soc; The Chem. Soc. Electron paramagnetic resonance; nuclear magnetic resonance of inorganic complexes; coordination chemistry; theoretical and physical inorganic chemistry. Address: 961 Vinton Place, Dayton, OH 45431.

FORTMANN, HENRY R(AYMOND), b. Frederic, Wis, Feb. 28, 19; m. 43; c. 3. AGRONOMY. B.S, Wisconsin, 40; M.S, Ore. State Col, 42; Ph.D.(plant breeding), Cornell, 49. Asst. prof. AGRON, PA. STATE UNIV, 49-53, assoc. prof, 53-57, PROF, 57-, ASST. DIR. AGR. EXP. STA, 57- Regional coord, N.E. Asn. Agr. Exp. Stas. Marine C, 42-46, Capt. Am. Soc. Agron; Biomet. Soc. Forage crops breeding; applications of statistical procedures and experimental design to biological research; genetics. Address: 106-E Patterson Bldg, Pennsylvania State University, University Park, PA 16802.

FORTMANN, KARL L(ESLIE), b. Kuhlingen, Ger, July 25, 10; nat; m. 40; c. 3. CEREAL CHEMISTRY. B.S, Nebraska, 40. Spec. technician, Nebraska, 40-42; jr. res. fel, Campbell-Taggart Res. Corp, Mo, 42-45; cereal chemist, Wallace & Tiernan, Inc, 45-54, dir. baking lab, Baker Process Co. Div, 54-66, dir. res. & develop, 66-67, prod. develop. mgr, process div,

67-69; FOOD & AGR. DIV, PENNWALT CORP, 69-71, ASST. TO PRES, 71- Am. Soc. Bakery Eng; Am. Asn. Cereal Chem. Enzymes; starch; wheat gluten protein; wheat flour maturity; cereal and baking technology; rheology. Address: Food & Agriculture Division, Pennwalt Corp, 2120-2156 McCarter Highway, Newark, NJ 07104.

FORTNER, JOSEPH G(ERALD), b. Bedford, Ind, May 30, 21; m. 47; c. 2. SURGERY, BIOLOGY. B.S, Illinois, 44, M.D, 45; M.Sc, Univ. Birmingham, 65. Intern, St. Luke's Hosp, Ill, 45-46; res. path, Charity Hosp, La, 48-49; asst. res. surg, Bellevue Hosp, N.Y, 49-51; MEM. HOSP, 51-52, res, 52-54, asst, SLOAN KETTERING INST, 53-60, clin. asst. surg, gastric & mixed tumor serv, 55-59, head exp. oncol. sect, exp. surg. div, 58-68, assoc, 60-68, assoc. attend. physician, gastric & mixed tumor serv, dept, surg, 66-69, chief div. surg. res. & dir. surg. res, 68-69, ATTEND. SURGEON, GASTRIC & MIXED TUMOR SERV, DEPT. SURG, 69-, CHIEF, 70-, TRANSPLANTA- TION SERV, 69-; ASSOC. PROF. SURG, MED. COL, CORNELL UNIV, 70-, instr, 54-58, asst. prof. clin. surg, 58-65, assoc. prof, 65-70. Trainee, Nat. Cancer Inst, Nat. Insts. Health, 53-54. Dipl, Am. Bd. Surg; Alfred P. Sloan Award, 63. Med.C, 46-48, Capt. AAAS; Am. Radium Soc; Harvey Soc; Soc. Univ. Surg; Am. Med. Asn; Am. Asn. Cancer Res; fel. Am. Col. Surg; N.Y. Acad. Sci; Transplantation Soc; Brit. Soc. Immunol; Reticuloendothelial Soc. Immunology; carcinogenesis; transplantable tumors. Address: Sloan Ketter- ing Institute, Memorial Hospital, 410 E. 68th St, New York, NY 10021.

FORTNER, LIMON E, JR, b. Clinton, Tenn, Oct. 18, 25; m. 47; c. 4. METE- OROLOGY, ELECTRICAL ENGINEERING. B.E.E, Virginia, 50; Chicago, 52-53; Fla. State, 59-61. Chief elec. engr, Va. Metal Prod. Corp, 50-52; v.pres. & gen. mgr, Farm Serv, Inc, Va, 52; U.S. AIR FORCE, 52-, fore- caster, 52-53, off-in-charge, Base Weather Sta, Wright Field, 53-55, Max- well Flight Serv. Ctr, Ala, 57-59, opers. off, 30th Weather Squadron, 62, chief forecaster, Detachment 16, First Weather Wing, 62-64, Detachment 2, Second Weather Group, Langley Air Force Base, Va, 64-65, Fifth Weather Wing, 65-67, Detachment 5, First Weather Wing, APO San Francisco, 67-69, sci. serv. tech. consult, THIRD WEATHER WING, 69-71, CHIEF, SCI. SERV. BR, 70- U.S.A.F, 43-45, 52-, Maj, Res, 46-52. Am. Meteorol. Soc; Am. Geophys. Union. Fog and stratus forecasting; tropical meteorology; short range forecasting; electronic data processing statistical forecast aids. Address: 98 Fairchild Circle, Offutt Air Force Base, NE 68113.

FORTNEY, C(ECIL) G(ARFIELD), JR, b. Amarillo, Tex, Sept. 16, 27; m. 50; c. 6. FOOD CHEMISTRY. B.S, Iowa State, 50, M.S, 53, Ph.D.(food tech), 56. Instr. dairy chem. & dairy eng, Iowa State, 50-56; res. chemist fats & oils, Anderson Clayton & Co, 56-59; proj. leader, cereal dept, GEN. FOODS CORP, 60-61, mgr, Corn Mill Labs, Post Div, Kankakee, Ill, 61-64, mgr, new foods develop, 64-65, lab. mgr. new foods, beverages, Swans Down & indust. wheat utilization, 65-69, SR. LAB MGR. PET FOOD RES, 69- U.S.A, 46-47. Am. Chem. Soc; Am. Oil Chemists' Soc. Milk proteins and milk salt equilibria; fats and oil chemistry, especially emulsifier tech- nology; cereal and starch processing technology related to continuously processing cereal grains. Address: Post Division, General Foods Corp, 275 Cliff St, Battle Creek, MI 49015.

FORTNEY, LLOYD R(AY), b. Enid, Okla. June 22, 36; m. 62; c. 2. HIGH ENERGY PHYSICS. B.S, New Mexico State, 58; Ph.D.(physics), Wisconsin, 62. Res. assoc. HIGH ENERGY PHYSICS, Wisconsin, 62-63; res. assoc, DUKE UNIV, 63-64, asst. prof, 64-70, ASSOC. PROF, 70- Am. Phys. Soc. Experimental high energy physics using hydrogen and heavy liquid bubble chambers. Address: Dept. of Physics, Duke University, Durham, NC 27706.

FORTNUM, DONALD H(OLLY), b. Berlin, Wis, Apr. 2, 32; m. 58; c. 4. PHYSICAL CHEMISTRY. B.S, Carroll Col.(Wis), 54; du Pont fel, Brown, 57-58, Ph.D.(chem), 58. Instr. CHEM, Providence Col, 56-57; asst. prof. Ursinus Col, 58-65; ASSOC. PROF, GETTYSBURG COL, 65- Am. Chem. Soc. Molecular structure; kinetics of inorganic reactions; computer ap- plications in chemistry. Address: Dept. of Chemistry, Gettysburg College, Gettysburg, PA 17325.

FORTUNE, CARL H(ALE), b. Chagrin Falls, Ohio, Sept. 10, 00; m. 26; c. 2. MEDICINE. A.B, Transylvania Col, 22, hon. D.Sc, 61; M.D, Michigan, 26. Instr. path, Michigan, 26-29, asst. res. internal med, univ. hosp, 29-30, instr, 30-31; assoc. chief med. serv, St. Joseph's Hosp, 31-58, chief, 58-64; clin. prof. med, col. med, Kentucky, 65-68; RETIRED. Mem. hon. staff, Good Samaritan Hosps, 31-; St. Joseph's Hosp, 65- Consult, Vet. Admin. Hosp, Lexington; Cent. Baptist Hosp. Med.C, A.U.S, 42-46, Col. Fel. Am. Med. Asn; fel. Am. Col. Physicians. Address: 1853 Fielden Dr, Lexington, KY 40502.

FORTUNE, H. TERRY, b. Ramer, Tenn, Feb. 16, 41; m. 61; c. 1. NUCLEAR PHYSICS. B.S, Memphis State Univ, 63; NASA fel, Fla. State Univ, 63-66, Nat. Sci. Found. fel, 66-67, Ph.D.(physics), 67. Res. assoc. nuclear phys- ics, Argonne Nat. Lab, 67-69; ASST. PROF. PHYSICS, UNIV. PA, 69- Vis, Argonne Nat. Lab, summer 70. AAAS; Am. Phys. Soc; Am. Asn. Physics Teachers. Nuclear structure physics; reaction mechanisms; reactions induced by heavy ions. Address: Dept. of Physics, University of Pennsyl- vania, Philadelphia, PA 19104.

FORTUNE, W(ILLIAM) BROOKS, b. Holmesville, Ohio, July 2, 13; m. 41; c. 3. ANALYTICAL CHEMISTRY. B.S, Mt. Union Col, 34; M.S, Purdue, 36, Ph.D.(anal. chem), 38; hon. D.Sc, Purdue Univ. & Mt. Union Col, 66. Asst. chem, Purdue, 34-38; dir, ELI LILLY & CO, 38-63, v.pres, 63-66, group v.pres, 66-68, GROUP V.PRES. SCI. & MFG, 68- U.S.A, 41-46. Am. Chem. Soc; Am. Pharmaceut. Asn. Medical test kit development; research and development of antibiotics; tests for albumin in urine, sugar in blood, acetone and blood in urine. Address: Eli Lilly & Co, 307 E. McCarty St, Indianapolis, IN 46206.

FORWARD, DOROTHY F(LORENCE), b. Ottawa, Ont, Apr. 15, 03. BOTANY. B.A, Toronto, 26, M.A, 28, Ph.D.(plant path), 31; Ph.D.(plant physiol), Cambridge, 40. Asst. bot, Toronto, 27-33, 35-37; res. fel, Royal Soc. Can, 33-34; spec. lectr, McMaster, 36-37; asst. & demonstr. plant physiol, UNIV. TORONTO, 37-41, lectr. BOT, 41-47, asst. prof, 47-53, assoc. prof, 53-62, prof, 62-71, assoc. chmn. dept, 68-71, spec. lectr, 71-72, EMER.

PROF, 71- Am. Soc. Plant Physiol; Can. Soc. Plant. Physiol.(secy, 59-61, pres, 62-63); Can. Biochem. Soc. Plant pathology; nature of rust resis- tance; plant physiology; metabolism; respiration; growth. Address: Dept. of Botany, University of Toronto, Toronto, Ont, Can.

FORWARD, FRANK A(RTHUR), b. Ottawa, Ont, Mar. 9, 02; m. 27; c. 4. CHEMICAL METALLURGY. B.A.Sc, Toronto, 24; D.Sc, British Columbia, 65. Operator & res. asst, Consol. Mining & Smelting Co, B.C, 24-29; asst. smelter supt, Mt. Isa Mines, 29-34; metallurgist, B.C. Nickel Mines, 34-35; asst. prof. metall, British Columbia, 35-38, assoc. prof, 38-41, prof, 41-45, head dept, 45-64; dir. sci. secretariat, Privy Coun. Off, 64-67; consult. engr, Forward Engrs, Ltd, B.C, 67-69; RES. CONSULT, OFF. OF PRES, UNIV. B.C, 69- Nuffield fel. metall, 50; Warren lectr, Minnesota, 63. Con- sult, Nickel Sumitomo Co, Japan, 37; B.C. Nickel Mines, 38; Algoma Ore Properties, 39; Kelowna Explor. Co, 40; tech. dir, B.C. War Metals Res. Bd, 41-45; consult, Freeport Sulphur Co, 45; Chinese Nat. Resources Comn, Formosa, 46; Sherritt Gordon Mines, Ltd, 47-64; Eldorado Co, 50-55; dir. res, Can. Uranium Res. Found, 60-64; mem, Nat. Res. Coun. Can, 62-64. McCharles prize, Toronto, 55, eng. alumni medal, 63; Mining World achievement award, 59; John Scott award, 60. Am. Inst. Min, Metall. & Petrol. Eng.(James Douglas medal, 65); Can. Coun. Prof. Eng.(pres, 49); fel. Chem. Inst. Can; Eng. Inst. Can.(Leonard medal, 55); Can. Inst. Min. & Metall.(Inco medal, 55, pres. elect, 64, pres, 65); Brit. Inst. Min. & Metall. (Gold medal, 62); fel. Brit. Inst. Metall; Brit. Inst. Metals (medal, 66); fel. Am. Soc. Metals; Can. Res. Mgt. Asn. Development of new hydrometal- lurgical processes for nickel, copper, uranium, zinc and lead utilizing ele- vated pressure techniques. Address: Office of the President, University of British Columbia, Vancouver, B.C, Can.

FORWARD, ROBERT L(ULL), b. Geneva, N.Y, Aug. 15, 32; m. 54; c. 3. PHYSICS. B.S, Maryland, 54; Hughes Aircraft Co. fel, California, Los An- geles, 56-58, M.S, 58; Hughes Aircraft Co. fel, Maryland, 58-62, Ph.D. (physics), 65. Mem. tech. staff physics, HUGHES RES. LABS, 56-57, assoc. dept. mgr, theoret. studies dept, 67-68, MGR. EXPLOR. STUDIES DEPT, 68- Gravity Res. Found. awards, 62, 63, 64, 65. U.S.A.F, 54-56, Capt. AAAS; Am. Phys. Soc; sr. mem. Inst. Elec. & Electronics Eng; Sci. Res. Soc. Am; sr. mem. Am. Astronaut. Soc; assoc. fel. Inst. Aeronaut. & Astro- naut. Experimental investigations of dynamic gravitational fields, gravita- tional gradient sensors, tests of general theory of relativity and gravita- tional radiation; supervising research programs in inertial sensors; laser systems and information processing. Address: Hughes Research Labs, 3011 Malibu Canyon Rd, Malibu, CA 90265.

FORYS, LEONARD J, b. Buffalo, N.Y, July 22, 41; m. 66; c. 2. CONTROL SYSTEMS, COMMUNICATIONS. B.S, Univ. Notre Dame, 63; M.S. & E.E, Mass. Inst. Technol, 65; Ph.D.(elec. eng), Univ. Calif, Berkeley, 68. Acting asst. prof. elec. eng & comput. sci, Univ. Calif, Berkeley, 67-68; MEM. TECH. STAFF, BELL TEL. LABS, 68- Inst. Elec. & Electronics Eng. Control theory; communication theory; stability theory; optimal con- trol theory; identification of nonlinear systems; information theory; air traffic control systems; filtering theory; congestion theory. Address: 82 Samson Ave, Madison, NJ 07940.

FORZIATI, A(LPHONSE) F(RANK), b. Boston, Mass, Feb. 27, 11; m. 45. PHYSICAL CHEMISTRY. B.A, Harvard, 32, M.A, 34, Ph.D.(phys. chem), 39. Lab. asst. chem, Harvard, 32-33; Radcliffe Col, 33-38; asst. phys. chem, Harvard, 39-41; Am. Petrol. Inst. res. assoc, Nat. Bur. Standards, 41-50, Am. Dent. Asn. res. assoc, 50-62; electrochemist, Harry Diamond Lab, 62-63; tech. prog. mgr, Adv. Res. Proj. Agency, U.S. Dept. Defense, 63-66; asst. chief res. div, Fed. Water Pollution Control Admin, 66-71, CHIEF MEASUREMENTS & INSTRUMENTATION BR, DIV. PROCESSES & EFFECTS; OFF. RES. & MONITORING, ENVIRON. PROTECTION AGENCY, 71- AAAS; Am. Chem. Soc; Electrochem. Soc; Soc. Appl. Spectros; Am. Dent. Asn; Int. Asn. Dent. Res. Electrochemistry; electrode potentials; fuel cells; high vacuum technique; physical properties of hydrocarbons; precise determination of and correlation with molecular structure; fluorescence and phosphorescence; technical program management. Address: Office of Research & Monitoring, Environmental Protection Agency, Washington, DC 20242.

FORZIATI, FLORENCE HOOPER, b. Union Co, Ky, Dec. 6, 04; m. 45. CHEMISTRY. B.S, Butler, 26; Ph.D.(plant chem), Iowa State Col, 30. Asst. chem, Iowa State Col, 26-30; Nat. Tuberc. Asn. fel, Yale, 30-32, Metz fel, 32-34; asst. biochemist, State Dept. Health, N.Y, 34-35; Weiss fel. org. chem, Yale, 35-37; microbiologist, cellulose dept, chem. found, Boyce Thompson Inst, 37-39; instr. chem, Iowa State Col, 40; teacher, Stout Inst, 40-42; asst. prof, George Washington, 42-48; chemist, Nat. Bur. Standards, 48-60; chief, clothing and textiles lab, clothing & housing res. div, AGR. RES. SERV, U.S. DEPT. AGR, 60-65, ASST. DIR, CONSUMER & FOOD ECON. RES. DIV, 65- Consult, Adj. Gen. Off, 43-44. Am. Chem. Soc; Fiber Soc; Am. Asn. Textile Chem. & Colorists; Am. Home Econ. Asn. Cellulose; textiles. Address: Consumer & Food Economic Research Division, Agricul- tural Research Service, U.S. Dept. of Agriculture, Federal Center Bldg, Hyattsville, MD 20782.

FOSBERG, F(RANCIS) RAYMOND, b. Spokane, Wash, May 20, 08; m. 35; c. 4. BOTANY. A.B, Pomona Col, 30; M.S, Hawaii, 35; Morris Arboretum fel, Pennsylvania, 37-39, Ph.D.(bot), 39. Asst. botanist in charge herbarium, Los Angeles Mus, 30-32; asst. bot, Hawaii, 32-37; asst. botanist, bur. plant indust, U.S. Dept. Agr, 39-42, sr. botanist, For. Econ. Admin, 42-45, bota- nist, bur. plant indust, 45-46; econ. surv, U.S. Commercial Co, Micronesia, 46; Guggenheim fel, S.Am, 47; vis. prof. bot, Hawaii, 48; research assoc, Catholic Univ, 48-50; botanist, U.S. Geol. Surv, 51-66; SPEC. ADV. TROP. BIOL, U.S. NAT. MUS, SMITHSONIAN, 66- Prof. lectr, George Washington, 48-49. Mem. adv. cmt. humid tropics res, UNESCO, 57-64, chmn, 61-64, chmn, vis. comt. for trop. Herbaria, 61-; mem, Nat. Res. Coun, 60-64. Mem. expeds. to Micronesia, 50, 51, 52, 54. Fermat medal, Toulouse Acad, 61; H.E. Gregory Medal, Pac. Sci. Cong, 71. AAAS; Bot. Soc. Am; Am. Soc. Plant Taxon; Ecol. Soc. Am; Int. Asn. Plant Taxon; Int. Soc. Trop. Ecol.(v.pres, 60-66, pres, 67-). Taxonomy and distribution of higher plants, especially those of the Pacific Islands; Rubiaceae; Cinchona; vegetation of the Pacific Islands; ecology of coral atolls; general and human ecology. Ad- dress: 3077 Holmes Run Rd, Falls Church, VA 22042.

FOSBERG, M(AYNARD) A(XEL), b. Turlock, Calif, July 7, 19; m. 47; c. 2. SOIL SCIENCE. B.S, Wisconsin, 48, M.S, 49, Ph.D.(soils), 63. Asst. prof. SOILS, UNIV. IDAHO, ASSOC. PROF, 58- U.S.A.A.F, 40-45. Soil Sci. Soc. Am; Am. Soc. Range Mgt. Soil genesis and classification; soil-plant relationships. Address: Dept. of Agricultural Biochemistry & Soils, University of Idaho, Moscow, ID 83843.

FOSBERG, MICHAEL A(LLEN), b. Oregon City, Ore, Jan. 11, 38; m. 61; c. 2. METEOROLOGY. B.Sc, Oregon State, 61, M.Sc, 63; U.S. Govt. fel, California, Los Angeles, 64-65. Asst. meteorologist, Pac. Southwest Forest & Range Exp. Sta, U.S. FOREST SERV, 62-63, assoc. meteorologist, 63-64, meteorologist, 64-67, ROCKY MT. FOREST & RANGE EXP. STA, 67-70, PRIN. METEOROLOGIST, 70- Vis. lectr, San Fernando Valley State Col, 64; vis. scientist, Nat. Ctr. Atmospheric Res, 66. AAAS; Am. Meteorol. Soc; Soc. Am. Foresters; Am. Geophys. Union. Local winds; air flow over mountains; atmospheric energy exchanges; water movement in plants. Address: Rocky Mt. Forest & Range Experiment Station, 240 W. Prospect St, Ft. Collins, CO 80521.

FOSBERG, THEODORE M(ICHAEL), b. Seattle, Wash, Dec. 26, 34; m. 58; c. 5. CHEMICAL ENGINEERING. B.S, Washington (Seattle), 59, M.S, 61, Standard Oil Co. fel, 62-63, Ph.D.(chem. eng), 64. Bioscientist, Boeing Co, 64-71; PROCESS ENGR, RESOURCES CONSERV. CO, 71- Am. Chem. Soc; Am. Inst. Chem. Eng. Interphase mass transfer; life support requirements and systems; human factors; process technology for desalination and brine concentrator systems; evaporator technology. Address: Resources Conservation Co, P.O. Box 3999, Seattle, WA 98124.

FOSBURY, DAVID W(ILLIAM), b. Halifax, Eng, Dec. 30, 28; m. 55; c. 2. CHEMICAL ENGINEERING. B.Sc, Birmingham, 49, Dept. Sci. & Indust. Res. fel, 49-52, Anglo-Am. Oil fel, 52-53, Ph.D.(chem. eng), 53. Sci. off. chem. eng, Atomic Energy Res. Estab, U.K. Atomic Energy Auth, 53-56; sr. engr, E.I. DU PONT DE NEMOURS & CO, INC, N.C, 56-64, sr. res. engr, spunbonded prod. res. & develop. lab, 64-65, supvr. nylon tech, 65-70, SUPVR. QIANA PROCESS SECT, 70- Am. Inst. Chem. Eng; Brit. Inst. Chem. Eng. Nonwoven fabrics; high polymers; synthetic fibers. Address: Qiana Process Section, E.I. du Pont de Nemours & Co, Inc, Chattanooga, TN 37401.

FOSCANTE, RAYMOND EUGENE, b. N.Y.C, Mar. 24, 42; m. 64; c. 2. ORGANIC CHEMISTRY. B.S, Manhattan Col, 62; Nat. Insts. Health fel, Seton Hall, 64, Ph.D.(chem), 66. Assoc. chemist, MIDWEST RES. INST, 69-70, SR. CHEMIST, 70- U.S.A.F, 66-69, Res, 69-; Capt. Am. Chem. Soc; The Chem. Soc. Propellant chemistry, formulation and ingredient design; catalysis of organic reactions by metals and organometallics; structure-property relationships; wastewater treatment; oil and water pollution; hydrogenation. Address: 10070 Roe Ave, Overland Park, KS 66207.

FOSCHINI, GERARD J(OSEPH), b. Jersey City, N.J, Feb. 28, 40; m. 62; c. 2. APPLIED MATHEMATICS, SYSTEMS ENGINEERING. B.S.E.E, Newark Col. Eng, 61; M.E.E, N.Y. Univ, 63; Stanley fel, Stevens Inst. Technol, 64-65, Ph.D.(math), 67. MEM. TECH. STAFF, BELL TEL. LABS, INC, 61- Math. Asn. Am. Mathematical physics; communication theory; function theory; measure theory; stochastic processes. Address: Data Transmission Studies Dept, Bell Telephone Labs, Inc, Holmdel, NJ 07733.

FOSCOLOS, ANTHONY E, b. Cairo, Egypt, May 15, 30; Can. citizen; m. 58; c. 2. SOIL & SEDIMENTARY MINERALOGY. B.Ag.E, Univ. Thessaloniki, 53; M.S, Univ. Calif, Berkeley, 64, Ph.D.(clay physics, chem), 66. Tech. off, Kopaës Orgn, Greece, 53-64; res. asst. clay mineral, Univ. Calif, Berkeley, 63-66; RES. SCIENTIST, INST. SEDIMENTARY & PETROL. GEOL, CAN. DEPT. ENERGY, MINES & RESOURCES, 66- Greek Found. Scholars. grant, 60; Nat. Sci. Found. grant, 64. Am. Soc. Agron. Clay physical chemistry, chemistry and mineralogy. Address: Institute of Sedimentary & Petroleum Geology, 3303 33rd St. N.W, Calgary 44, Alta, Can.

FOSDICK, LLOYD D(UDLEY), b. N.Y.C, Jan. 18, 28; m. 58. COMPUTER SCIENCE. Ph.B, Chicago, 46, B.S, 48; M.S, Purdue, 50, Res. Found. fel, 51-53, Ph.D.(physics), 53. Systems evaluation, Control Systs. Lab, 53-54; assoc. head, comput. div, Midwest Univs. Res. Asn, 56-57; res. asst. prof. digital comput. lab, Illinois, 57-61, res. assoc. prof. physics, 61-64, res. prof, 64-70; PROF. COMPUT. SCI. & CHMN. DEPT, UNIV. COLO, BOULDER, 70- Guggenheim fel, 64. U.S.A, 54-56. Asn. Comput. Mach; Soc. Indust. & Appl. Math. Digital computers; statistical mechanics; mathematics of computation. Address: Dept. of Computer Science, University of Colorado, Boulder, CO 80302.

FOSDICK, ROGER L(EE), b. Pontiac, Ill, Nov. 18, 36; m. 56; c. 2. APPLIED MATHEMATICS, MECHANICAL ENGINEERING. B.S, Ill. Inst. Tech, 59; Ph.D.(appl. math), Brown, 63. Asst. prof. MECH, Ill. Inst. Tech, 62-65, assoc. prof, 65-69; PROF, UNIV. MINN, MINNEAPOLIS, 69- Soc. Natural Philos. Continuum mechanics, especially theory of finite elasticity, theory of finite viscoelasticity, and theory of non-linear fluids. Address: Dept. of Aerospace Engineering & Mechanics, University of Minnesota, Minneapolis, MN 55455.

FOSGATE, OLIN T(RACY), b. Peru, N.Y, May 14, 18; m. 48; c. 3. DAIRY SCIENCE. B.S, Wisconsin, 50, M.S, 54, Ph.D.(dairy sci), 56. Instr. dairy sci, Wisconsin, 48-56; asst. prof. animal husb, W.H. Miner Agr. Res. Inst, 56-57; DAIRY SCI, UNIV. GA, 57-62, assoc. prof, 62-68, PROF, 68- Consult, Univ. Tennessee-Atomic Energy Cmn, 58-63. Am. Soc. Animal Sci; Am. Dairy Sci. Asn. Physiology of reproduction, especially hormonal control of estrous cycle; influences of different environments on milk production in dairy cattle. Address: Dept. of Dairy Science, University of Georgia, Athens, GA 30601.

FOSHEE, DONALD PRESTON, b. Albertville, Ala, Jan. 8, 31; m. 51; c. 4. PHYSIOLOGICAL PSYCHOLOGY. A.B, Birmingham-South. Col, 58; M.A, Vanderbilt, 60, Ph.D.(physiol. psychol), 61. Asst. prof. psychol, med. sch, Mississippi, 61-65, chief lab. exp. behav, 62-65; assoc. prof. PSYCHOL, AUBURN UNIV, 65-69, PROF, 69-, COORD. EXP. PROGS, 65- U.S. Pub. Health Serv. fel, Mississippi, 61-63, assoc, 63-65; summer vis. asst. prof,

Univ. P.R. & Lab. Perinatal Physiol, 64. U.S.A.F, 50-54. Am. Psychol. Asn; Animal Behav. Soc. Neonatal brain damage and behavioral development; higher education; administration. Address: Dept. of Psychology, Auburn University, Auburn, AL 36830.

FOSKET, DONALD ELSTON, b. Klamath Falls, Ore, July 20, 36. PLANT PHYSIOLOGY & CELL BIOLOGY. B.A, Idaho, 58, Nat. Defense Ed. Act fel, 59-62, Nat. Sci. Found. fel, 62-63, Ph.D.(plant physiol), 64. Res. assoc. developmental bot, Brookhaven Nat. Lab, 64-65; asst. prof. biol, Mt. Holyoke Col, 65-67; Nat. Sci. Found. fel, Biol. Lab, Harvard, 67-69, Bullard fel, 69-70; ASST. PROF. DEVELOP. & CELL BIOL, UNIV. CALIF, IRVINE, 70- AAAS; Bot. Soc; Am; Soc. Exp. Biol. & Med; Japanese Soc. Plant Physiol; Scandinavian Soc. Plant Physiol; Am. Soc. Plant Physiol. Regulation of cell division and cell differentiation. Address: Dept. of Developmental & Cell Biology, University of California, Irvine, CA 92664.

FOSKETT, D(UDLEY) R(OBERT), b. Saskatoon, Sask, Oct. 30, 14; m. 42; c. 1. FISHERIES BIOLOGY. B.A, Univ. Sask, 39; M.A, Univ. B.C, 50. Sci. asst, Int. Pac. Salmon Fisheries Comn, 41-44; jr. biologist, Pac. Biol. Sta, 44-49, asst. scientist, 49-57; limnologist, Can. Wildlife Serv, 57-65; NATURALIST, NAT. PARKS INTERPRETIVE SERV, 65- Wildlife management; limnology. Address: Box 190, Ucluelet, B.C, Can.

FOSMIRE, GARY JAMES, b. Chico, Calif, Oct. 18, 41; m. 65; c. 3. BIOCHEMISTRY, FOOD TECHNOLOGY. A.B, Univ. Calif, Berkeley, 64, Ph.D. (nutrit), 70. Res. asst. nutrit, Univ. Calif, Berkeley, 64-65; virol, U.S. Pub. Health Hosp, San Francisco, 66-67; RES. ASSOC. BIOCHEM, PIONEERING RES. LAB, DEPT. AGR, BRANDEIS UNIV, 70- Nat. Guard, 64-70. Am. Chem. Soc. Forces responsible for maintaining proteins in their native configuration; nature of protein denaturation. Address: U.S. Dept. of Agriculture Pioneer Research Lab, Dept. of Biochemistry, Brandeis University, Waltham, MA 02154.

FOSS, ALAN STUART, b. Stamford, Conn, Sept. 9, 29. CHEMICAL ENGINEERING. B.S, Worcester Polytech, 52; M.Ch.E, Delaware, 54, Ph.D. (chem. eng), 57. Sr. res. engr, eng. res. lab, E.I. du Pont de Nemours & Co, 56-61; asst. prof. CHEM. ENG, UNIV. CALIF, BERKELEY, 61-65, ASSOC. PROF, 65-, v.chmn. dept, 67-69. Spec. lectr, Univ. Del, 57, 59-60; fel, Univ. Trondheim, 69-70. Am. Inst. Chem. Eng. Chemical process dynamics and control; chemical process optimization. Address: Dept. of Chemical Engineering, University of California, Berkeley, CA 94720.

FOSS, DONALD C, b. Providence, R.I, May 3, 38; m. 60; c. 2. NUTRITION, PHYSIOLOGY. B.S, New Hampshire, 60; M.S, Wisconsin, 61; Ralston Purina fel. & Ph.D.(physiol. & nutrit), Massachusetts, 66. Fel. poultry sci, VERMONT, 66-68, ASST. PROF. ANIMAL SCI, 68- AAAS; Poultry Sci. Asn; Am. Dairy Sci. Asn. Effects of light quality on physiological development; effects of physiologically active agents, feeding patterns and appetite regulation in the efficiency of nutrient utilization. Address: Dept. of Animal Sciences, University of Vermont, Burlington, VT 05401.

FOSS, EDWARD W(ILBUR), b. Laconia, N.H, Dec. 4, 14; m. 38; c. 3. AGRICULTURAL ENGINEERING & EDUCATION. B.S, New Hampshire, 36; M.S.A, Cornell, 47. Teacher, pub. sch, N.Y, 36-39; N.H, 39-42; instr. appl. farming & agr. eng, New Hampshire, 42-45; exten. agr. engr, Maine, 45-49; PROF. AGR. ENG, CORNELL UNIV, 49- Consult-coord, Senaca-Tompkins County area vocational surv, 62-64; exec. comt, N.Y. State Rural Safety Coun; vis. prof, Univ. Ibadan, 68-70. Nat. Fire Protection Asn; Am. Soc. Agr. Eng. Farm mechanics; rural fire protection; equipment for woodlot mechanization; agri-business occupations. Address: Dept. of Agricultural Engineering, Riley Hall, Cornell University, Ithaca, NY 14850.

FOSS, FREDERICK W(ILLIAM), JR, b. Lincoln, Mich, June 3, 33; m. 57; c. 3. INORGANIC CHEMISTRY. B.S, Michigan 55; M.S, Minnesota, Minneapolis, 57; Ph.D.(inorg. chem), Univ. of the Pac, 64. Instr. phys. sci, WINONA STATE COL, 57-63, asst. prof. CHEM, 63-65, assoc. prof, 65-67, PROF, 67-, HEAD DEPT, 66- Sig.C, U.S.A, 57, 2nd Lt. Am. Chem. Soc. Inorganic polarography in non-aqueous solvents. Address: Dept. of Chemistry, Winona State College, Winona, MN 55987.

FOSS, GEORGE J(ULIUS), JR, b. Chicago, Ill, July 11, 13; m. 40; c. 3. CHEMICAL & METALLURGICAL ENGINEERING. B.S, Notre Dame, 35, M.S, 37, fel, 37-40, Ph.D.(metall), 40. Asst, Notre Dame, 35-39; chief metallurgist, east. div, Rheem Mfg. Co, 43-45; mem. staff. metall. & testing labs, U.S. Steel Corp, 45-46; DIR. RES. & DEVELOP, White Cap Co, 46-58; ANCHOR HOCKING CORP, 58- Lectr, Catholic Univ, 41; U.S. Naval Acad. Postgrad. Sch, 41; mem. nonferrous metall. adv. comt, War Dept, 41-43; tech. comt, Glass Container Mfg. Inst, 48-58. U.S.N, 40-43. Am. Chem. Soc; Am. Soc. Metals (past secy-treas); Am. Inst. Mining, Metall. & Petrol. Eng; Inst. Food Technol. Metal closures for glass food containers. Address: Plant 35, Anchor Hocking Corp, W. Fair Ave, Lancaster, OH 43130.

FOSS, JOHN E, b. Whitehall, Wis, May 30, 32; m. 53; c. 2. SOIL GENESIS & CLASSIFICATION. B.S, Wis. State, River Falls, 57; M.S, Minnesota, 59, Ph.D.(soil sci, geol), 65. ASST. PROF. SOILS, Wis. State, River Falls, 60-66; UNIV. MD, 66- Consult, Libby, McNeil & Libby Corp, France, 62. U.S.A, 52-55, Sgt. AAAS; Am. Soc. Agron. Soil development; interpretation and uses of soil surveys. Address: Dept. of Agronomy, University of Maryland, College Park, MD 20740.

FOSS, JOHN F, b. Washington, Pa, Mar. 24, 38; m. 60; c. 2. FLUID MECHANICS. B.S, Purdue, 61, M.S, 62, Ph.D.(mech. eng), 65. Asst. prof. MECH. ENG, MICH. STATE UNIV, 64-68, ASSOC. PROF, 68- Fel, Johns Hopkins Univ, 70-71. AAAS; Am. Soc. Mech. Eng; Am. Soc. Eng. Educ; Am. Inst. Aeronaut. & Astronaut; Am. Phys. Soc. Turbulent shear flow and experimental fluid mechanics. Address: Dept. of Mechanical Engineering, Michigan State University, East Lansing, MI 48823.

FOSS, MARTYN (HENRY), b. Salt Lake City, Utah, May 28, 18; m. 42; c. 6. PHYSICS. B.S, Chicago, 38; Mass. Inst. Tech, 38-40; D.Sc.(physics), Carnegie Inst. Tech, 48. Shift supvr, lab, Ind. Ord. Works, 40-41, chem. engr, 41-43; mem. staff, Manhattan proj, Del, Ill. & Los Alamos, 43-46;

res. physicist, Carnegie Inst. Tech, 48-54; sr. physicist, Argonne Nat. Lab, 55-59, assoc. dir, particle accelerator div, 59-62; assoc. dir, nuclear res. ctr, Carnegie Inst. Tech, 62-70, SR. PHYSICIST, CARNEGIE-MELLON UNIV, 70- AAAS; fel. Am. Phys. Soc. Particle accelerator. Address: 305 Le Roi Rd, Pittsburgh, PA 15208.

FOSS, ROBERT PAUL, b. Chicago, Ill, Aug. 22, 37; m. 62; c. 2. PHYSICAL ORGANIC & POLYMER CHEMISTRY. B.A, Northwestern, 58; Ph.D.(chem), Calif. Inst. Tech, 63. Nat. Insts. Health fel. chem, lab. chem. biodynamics, California, Berkeley, 63-65; RES. CHEMIST, CENT. RES. DEPT, E.I. DU PONT DE NEMOURS & CO, INC, 65- Am. Chem. Soc. Photochemistry and energy transfer involving organic and inorganic compounds; polymer chemistry involving general and photopolymerization studies; high energy radiation chemistry of organic and polymer systems. Address: Bldg. 328-309, Experimental Station, E.I. du Pont de Nemours & Co, Inc, Wilmington, DE 19898.

FOSSAN, DAVID B, b. Faribault, Minn, Aug. 23, 34; m. 64. PHYSICS. B.A, St. Olaf Col, 56; M.S, Wisconsin, 57, Ph.D.(physics), 60. Asst. physics, Wisconsin, 60-61; Ford Found. grant, Niels Bohr Inst, Copenhagen, 61-62; mem. res. staff nuclear physics, Van de Graaff Lab, Lockheed Aircraft Corp, 63-65; asst. prof. PHYSICS, STATE UNIV. N.Y. STONY BROOK, 65-67, ASSOC. PROF, 67- Summer asst, Los Alamos Sci. Lab, 58; Brookhaven Nat. Lab, 66. Am. Phys. Soc. Light nucleineutron and charged particle reactions; excited state lifetime of nuclei. Address: Dept. of Physics, State University of New York at Stony Brook, Stony Brook, NY 11790.

FOSSEL, ERIC THOR, b. Minneapolis, Minn, Dec. 11, 41; m. 64; c. 1. ORGANIC CHEMISTRY, BIOCHEMISTRY. B.A, Yale, 64, M.S, 66, M.Phil, 67; Ph.D.(chem), Harvard, 70. NAT. INSTS. HEALTH RES. FEL. chem, HARVARD, 70-71; BIOCHEM, MED. SCH, 71- Am. Chem. Soc; Int. Union Physiol. Sci. Thermal rearrangements; enzyme mechanisms; microcirculation; muscle action mechanism. Address: Dept. of Biological Chemistry, Harvard Medical School, Boston, MA 02115.

FOSSEL, SPENCER M(ARTEL), b. Elliott, Ill, Dec. 18, 14; m. 37; c. 3. ORGANIC CHEMISTRY, PHARMACOLOGY. A.B, St. Olaf Col, 37; Minnesota, 42; Columbia & N.Y. Univ, 43-47. Med. detailman, Sandoz Pharmaceut, 41-43, head clin. res, 43-48, asst. mgr, 48-53; dir. clin. promotion, Organon, Inc, 53-56; mkt, L.W. Frohlich & Co, 56-57; v.pres. mkt, Warner Chilcott, 57-58; pres. in charge res, Spencer Labs, Inc, 58-62; UNIMED, INC, 62-71, MEM. BD. DIRS. & DIR. BASIC RES, 71-; PRES. & DIR, J.H. GUILD CO, INC, 70- AAAS; Am. Inst. Chem; Newcomen Soc. N.Am; N.Y. Acad. Sci. Histamine; new molecules of value in field of medicine; new molecules to increase microcirculation and to prevent clumping of platelets. Address: Claremont Rd, Bernardsville, NJ 07924.

FOSSIER, MIKE W(ALTER), b. New Orleans, La, Mar. 30, 28; m. 53; c. 3. AERONAUTICAL ENGINEERING. B.S, La. State, 45; M.S, Calif. Inst. Tech, 46, Aero. Eng. 47. Aerodynamicist, Douglas Aircraft Co, 47-50; staff engr, Raytheon Mfg. Co, 50-56, tech. dir. air-to-air missiles, 56-58, chief engr, missile systs. div, 58-65, v.pres. & asst. gen. mgr. tech. dept, RAYTHEON CO, 65-71, V.PRES. & GEN. MGR, STRATEGIC DEFENSE SYSTS. DIV, 71- Am. Inst. Aeronaut. & Astronaut. Missile systems engineering; guided missile and space systems and subsystems, particularly in fields of radar, infrared, missile guidance and control. Address: Strategic Defense Systems Division, Raytheon Co, Crosby Dr, Bedford, MA 01730.

FOSSLAND, ROBERT GERARD, b. Winthrop Harbor, Ill, Oct. 18, 18; m. 60; c. 6. ZOOLOGY, PHYSIOLOGY. B.S, Illinois, 40; Ph.D.(zool), Nebraska, 56. Asst, Nebraska, 40-42, instr, 45-56, asst. prof. dairy sci, Arizona, 56-58, assoc. prof, 58-61; fieldman, Am. Jersey Cattle Club, 61-62; assoc. prof. zool, Milwaukee-Downer Col, 62; BIOL, WIS. STATE UNIV, EAU CLAIRE, 62-65, PROF, 65- U.S.A, 42-45, Res, 40-42, 45-69, Col. Feeding and breeding management of dairy cattle; physiology of reproduction. Address: Dept. of Biology, Wisconsin State University, Eau Claire, WI 54701.

FOSSUM, GUILFORD O, b. Loma, N.Dak, Dec. 17, 18; m. 45; c. 4. CIVIL & SANITARY ENGINEERING. B.S, Univ. N.Dak, 42; M.S, Iowa State Univ, 51. Inspector, U.S. Eng. Dept, C.Z, 42-43; engr, Grand Forks City Eng. Dept, 46; asst. prof. CIVIL ENG, UNIV. N.DAK, 46-54, assoc. prof, 54-61, PROF, 61- Civil Eng.C, U.S.N, 43-46, Ens. Water Pollution Control Fedn; Am. Soc. Civil Eng; Am. Soc. Eng. Educ; Nat. Soc. Prof. Eng. Industrial and municipal wastes and water supplies, including treatment methods. Address: Dept. of Civil Engineering, University of North Dakota, Grand Forks, ND 58201.

FOSSUM, ROBERT, b. El Paso, Tex, Nov. 17, 28; m. 51; c. 3. MATHEMATICS, OPERATIONS RESEARCH. B.S, Idaho, 51; M.S, Oregon, 56; Ph.D, Ore. State Univ, 69. Asst. math, Univ. Oregon, 54-56; sr. engr. opers. res, Sylvania Electronic Defense Lab, Gen. Tel. & Electronics Corp, 56-58, adv. res. engr, 58-60, sr. eng. specialist, 60-63, mgr. adv. anal. lab, 63-65, systs. labs, 65-69; systs. eng, ESL, INC, 69-71, V.PRES, 71- Mathematician, Lincoln Lab, Mass. Inst. Technol, summer 55; res. assoc, Ore. State Univ, 69-71. U.S.M.C, 46-47, U.S.N, 51-54, Lt. Inst. Elec. & Electronics Eng; Am. Meteorol. Soc; Inst. Math. Statist. Applied multiple classification theory; error models for aerospace guidance systems; optimization theory and nonlinear programming; statistical meteorology. Address: ESL, Inc, 495 Java Dr, Sunnyvale, CA 94086.

FOSSUM, ROBERT MERLE, b. Northfield, Minn, May 1, 38; m. 60; c. 2. MATHEMATICS. B.A, St. Olaf Col, 59; A.M, Michigan, 61, Lotta B. Backus fel, 63-64, Ph.D.(math), 65. Asst. prof. MATH, UNIV. ILL, URBANA, 64-68, ASSOC. PROF, 68- Fulbright res. grant, inst. math, Univ. Oslo, 67-68, vis. prof, 68-69; vis. prof, Univ. Aarhus, 71-72. Am. Math. Soc; Math. Asn. Am; Norweg. Math. Soc. Commutative noetherian rings; algebras over commutative noetherian integrally closed integral domains and homological algebra. Address: Dept. of Mathematics, University of Illinois, Urbana, Ill. 61801.

FOSSUM, STEVE P, b. Northfield, Minn, Dec. 26, 41; m. 67; c. 1. SURFACE PHYSICS, VACUUM TECHNOLOGY. B.A, St. Olaf Col, 63; M.A, Univ. Wis,

Madison, 65, Ph.D.(physics), 70. ASST. PROF. PHYSICS, STOUT STATE UNIV, 66- Am. Phys. Soc; Am. Vacuum Soc; Am. Asn. Physics Teachers. Atomic hydrogen reactions on metal surfaces in ultra-high vacuums. Address: Dept. of Physics, Stout State University, Menomonie, WI. 54751.

FOSTER, ALBERT EARL, b. Madison, S.Dak, Apr. 4, 31; m. 52; c. 2. PLANT BREEDING. B.S, S.Dak. State Univ, 54, M.S, 56, Ph.D.(agron), 58. Asst. prof. AGRON, N.DAK. STATE UNIV, 58-64, assoc. prof, 64-70, PROF, 70- Nat. Sci. Found. summer fel. statist, 63. Am. Soc. Agron; Biomet. Soc. Barley genetics; statistics. Address: Dept. of Agronomy, North Dakota State University, Fargo, ND 58102.

FOSTER, ALFRED FIELD, b. Warren, Ohio, Dec. 4, 15; m. 40; c. 2. PHYSICAL CHEMISTRY. B.A, Col. of Wooster, 38; M.A, Ohio State, 40, Ph.D, 50. Process engr, U.S. Rubber Co, N.C, 42-43; asst. prof. physics, Davidson Col, 43-44; CHEM, UNIV. TOLEDO, 46-54, assoc. prof, 54-60, PROF, 60-, ASSOC. DEAN GRAD. SCH, 69-, acting dean, 68-69; assoc. dean col. arts & sci, 62-68. Res. assoc, Ohio State Res. Found, 48-50; partic, Argonne Nat. Lab. Conf, 68, 70. U.S.N, 44-46. Am. Chem. Soc; Am. Crystallog. Asn; N.Y. Acad. Sci. X-ray crystal structure; dipole moments of molecules in solutions; radiochemistry. Address: Graduate School, University of Toledo, Toledo, OH 43606.

FOSTER, ALFRED LEON, b. N.Y.C, July 13, 04; m; c. 4. MATHEMATICS. B.S, Calif. Inst. Tech, 26, M.S, 27; J.S.K. fel, Princeton, 28-30, Ph.D, 30. Instr. MATH, Valparaiso, 27-28; Princeton, 30-31; int. res. fel, Göttingen, 31-33; instr, UNIV. CALIF, BERKELEY, 33-37, asst. prof, 37-43, assoc. prof, 43-50, PROF, 50- Vis. prof, inst. math, Univ. Ferrara, 68. AAAS; Am. Math. Soc; Asn. Symbolic Logic. Abstract algebra; ring theory; universal algebras; structure theory and invariant theory; foundations. Address: Dept. of Mathematics, University of California, Berkeley, CA 94720.

FOSTER, ALVIN GARFIELD, b. Preston, Md, Apr. 7, 34; m. 58; c. 3. VETERINARY MEDICINE & MICROBIOLOGY. B.S, Md. State Col, Princess Anne, 56; D.V.M, Tuskegee Inst, 60; M.S, Wash. State Univ, 66, Nat. Insts. Health fels, 66 & 69, Ph.D.(vet. sci), 69. Vet. meat inspector, meat inspection div, U.S. Dept. Agr, 63-64; Nat. Insts. Health fel, col. vet. med, Wash. State Univ, 64-69; RES. MICROBIOLOGIST, MERCK SHARP & DOHME RES. LABS, 69- U.S.A.F.R, 60-62, Capt. Am. Vet. Med. Asn; Am. Soc. Microbiol. Influence of immune responses on the pathogenesis of Marek's disease in chickens; pathogenesis of equine viral arteritis; in vitro and in vivo systems; pathogenesis of bacterial initiated gastroenteritis in domestic animals. Address: Bldg. 80A, Room 6, Merck Institute for Therapeutic Research, Rahway, NJ 07065.

FOSTER, ARTHUR R(OWE), b. Peabody, Mass, April 22, 24; m. 47; c. 2. MECHANICAL ENGINEERING. B.S, Tufts, 45; M.Eng, Yale, 49. Engr, mat. develop. lab, Pratt & Whitney Div, United Aircraft Corp, 47-48; assoc. prof. MECH. ENG, NORTHEAST. UNIV, 49-61, PROF. & CHMN. DEPT, 61- Mem. Gen. Elec. Profs. Conf, 55. Summers, Atomic Energy Cmn, nuclear eng. inst, Cornell, 58, mem, specialized nuclear studies inst, Argonne Nat. Lab, 61, mat. nuclear reactor inst, Hanford Labs, Gen. Elec. Co, 63. U.S.N.R, 43-46, Lt.(jg). Am. Soc. Mech. Eng; Am. Soc. Eng. Educ; Am. Nuclear Soc. Thermodynamics; nuclear engineering; thermoelectrics; refrigeration. Address: Dept. of Mechanical Engineering, Northeastern University, Boston, MA 02115.

FOSTER, A(UBREY) ALFRED, b. Los Angeles, Calif, Oct. 20, 12; m. 41; c. 3. PLANT PATHOLOGY. B.S, Cornell, 39, Ph.D.(plant path), 45. Plant breeder, Francis C. Stokes Co, N.J, 36-40; asst. plant path, Cornell, 41-45; assoc. plant pathologist, Cent. Fla. Exp. Sta, 46-48; assoc. prof. plant path, Cornell, 48-50; plant pathologist, Southeast. Forest Exp. Sta, U.S. Forest Serv, 53-61; supvr. tree improv, Tenn. Valley Auth, 61-68; mem. Peace Corps, Honduras, 68-70; STAFF FORESTER, TENN. VALLEY AUTH, 70- Faculty fel, England & Holland, 49. AAAS; Am. Phytopath. Soc; Am. Inst. Biol. Sci; Am. Soc. Hort. Sci. Diseases of trees; tree breeding; forest and wildland monitoring. Address: Box 416, Norris, TN 37828.

FOSTER, A(UREL) O(VERTON), b. Marathon, N.Y, Sept. 25, 06; m. 31; c. 2. PARASITOLOGY. A.B, Wesleyan, 29, A.M, 30; Sc.D.(parasitol), Hopkins, 33. Asst. helminthol, sch. hygiene & pub. health, Hopkins, 30-33, instr, 33-34; helminthologist, Gorgas Mem. Lab, 34-39; asst. parasitologist, bur. animal indust, U.S. DEPT. AGR, 39-41, assoc. parasitologist, 41-43, parasitologist, 43-53, animal disease & parasite res. div, AGR. RES. SERV, 53-60, DIR, Beltsville Parasitol. Lab, 60-69, PARASITE TREATMENT SECT, ANIMAL DISEASE & PARASITE RES. DIV, 69- Trustee, Brayton H. Ransom Mem. Trust Found, 53-; lectr, Maryland, 57; mem. expert panel, Joint Food & Agr. Orgn, UN-Int. Off. Epizootics, 58- AAAS; Entom. Soc. Am; Am. Soc. Trop. Med. & Hyg; Am. Soc. Parasitol.(pres, 59); Am. Micros. Soc; Soc. Syst. Zool; Wildlife Disease Asn; Conf. Res. Workers Animal Diseases. Parasites and parasitic diseases of domestic animals; livestock parasite control; chemotherapy of parasitic infections. Address: Parasite Treatment Section, Animal Disease & Parasite Research Division, Agricultural Research Service, Beltsville, MD 20705.

FOSTER, BILLY GLEN, b. Canton, Tex, Mar. 6, 32; m. 54; c. 4. MICROBIOLOGY. B.S, North Texas State, 55, M.S, 62; Ph.D.(prev. med, environ. health), Iowa, 65. Instr. biol, North Texas State, 60-62; res. assoc. MICROBIOL, Iowa, 62-65; asst. prof, TEX. A&M UNIV, 65-70, ASSOC. PROF, 70- U.S.A.F.R, 50-53. AAAS; Am. Soc. Microbiol. Medical and diagnostic microbiology; epidemiology and serology of infectious disease; effect of lunar environment on toxic and proteolytic systems of selected bacterial species; isolation: purification and characterization of endo- and exotoxins of Aeromonas species and their role in pathogenicity and their use as diagnostic tools. Address: Dept. of Biology, Texas A&M University, College Station, TX 77843.

FOSTER, BRUCE ELLSWORTH, b. Colorado Springs, Colo, July 29, 06; m. 55. PHYSICS. B.A, Colo. Col, 27; M.A, Oregon, 29; Ph.D.(physics), Stanford, 35. Asst. sci. aide, NAT. BUR. STANDARDS, 35-38, jr. physicist, 38-40, asst. physicist, 40-42, assoc. physicist, 42-48, mat. engr, 48-62, chief, inorg. building mat. sect, 62-65, codes & standards sect, 65-67,

CONSULT, BLDG. RES. DIV, 68- Dept. of Commerce superior serv. award, 66. Teaching specialist, Army Specialized Training Prog, Stanford Univ, 43-44. Am. Phys. Soc; Am. Soc. Test. & Mat.(Frank E. Richart Award, 69; award of merit, 71); Am. Concrete Inst.(Henry L. Kennedy Award, 69); Int. Union Test. & Res. Labs. Mat. & Struct. X-ray spectroscopy and absorption; concrete durability; concrete admixtures; performance requirements and evaluation for buildings, components and materials. Address: Bldg. Res. Division, National Bureau of Standards, Washington, DC 20234.

FOSTER, BRUCE P(ARKS), b. Mussoorie, U.P, India, June 27, 25; U.S. citizen; m. 47; c. 3. EXPERIMENTAL NUCLEAR PHYSICS. B.S, Baldwin-Wallace Col, 49; M.S, Yale, 51, Ph.D.(physics), 54. Asst. prof. PHYSICS, NORTH TEXAS STATE UNIV, 53-56, ASSOC. PROF, 56- Fulbright lectr, Peshawar, 60-61; lectr, Forman Christian Col, W.Pakistan, 61-63; mem. v.chancellors cmt. strengthening physics dept, W.Pakistan Eng. Univ, 62-63. U.S.A, 43-46. Am. Phys. Soc. Investigation and analysis of gamma-ray decay schemes in nuclear reactions including the development of computer programs for this purpose; gamma-ray spectroscopy; astronomy. Address: Dept. of Physics, North Texas State University, Denton, TX 76302.

FOSTER, CHARLES CARLTON, b. Jacksonville, Fla, Feb. 26, 36; m. 58; c. 3. NUCLEAR PHYSICS. B.S, Tulane, 57, Nat. Defense Educ. Act fel, 59-62; M.S, Indiana, 64, Ph.D.(physics), 67. Res. assoc. PHYSICS, Princeton, 67, instr, 67-70; ASST. PROF, UNIV. MO-ST. LOUIS, 70- U.S.N.R, 57-59, Lt.(jg). Am. Phys. Soc. Nuclear reactions studies, particularly proton polarization measurements in stripping reactions; design of elements of cyclotron beam transport systems; elastic scattering angular distributons at extreme back angles for ^{3}He and ^{4}He. Address: 3061 Andore Dr, St. Louis, MO 63121.

FOSTER, C(HARLES) DAVID O(WEN), b. London, Ont, Oct. 26, 38; m. 60; c. 2. BIOCHEMISTRY. B.Sc, Western Ontario, 60, M.Sc, 62; Ph.D.(biochem), Wisconsin, 67. Nat. Insts. Health fel. BIOCHEM, Princeton, 66-68; ASST. PROF, UNIV. ILL, URBANA-CHAMPAIGN, 68- Hormonal regulation of enzyme activity; biological transport of sugars and amino acids. Address: Animal Genetics Lab, University of Illinois, Urbana-Champaign, Urbana, IL 61801.

FOSTER, C(HARLES) VERNON, b. Manzanola, Colo, June 16, 21; m. 45; c. 3. CHEMICAL ENGINEERING. B.S.Ch.E, Kansas, 47, M.S, 48; fel, Delaware, 48-51, Ph.D.(chem. eng), 53. Asst. instr. math, Kansas, 42-43, 46-47, asst. chem. eng, 47-48; res. engr, design methods, C.F. Braun & Co, Calif, 51-52; process engr. process design, Ethyl Corp, La, 52-55; res. engr, petrochem, Continental Oil Co, 55-56, res. group leader, 56-59; consult. engr, H.C. Schutt, 59-60; tech. dir, PASA, Petroquimica Argentina, S.A, 61-64; chief process engr, CONTINENTAL OIL CO, 64-66, MGR. PROCESS ENG. DEPT, 66- Chem.C, 43-46, 1st Lt. Am. Chem. Soc; Am. Inst. Chem. Eng. Heat transfer; distillation; physical properties; process development of petrochemicals. Address: Continental Oil Co, P.O. Drawer 1267, Ponca City, OK 74601.

FOSTER, DANIEL W, b. Marlin, Tex, Mar. 4, 30; m. 55; c. 3. INTERNAL MEDICINE, METABOLISM. B.A, Tex. West. Col, 51; M.D, Univ. Tex, Dallas, 55. Intern internal med, Parkland Mem. Hosp, 55-56, asst. resident, 56-58, chief resident, 58-59; fel. biochem, Univ. Tex.(Southwest) Med. Sch, 59-60; investr, Nat. Inst. Arthritis & Metab. Diseases, 60-62; instr. INTERNAL MED, UNIV. TEX.(SOUTHWEST) MED SCH, 62-63, asst. prof, 63-67, assoc. prof, 67-69, PROF, 69- Mem. metab. study sect, Nat. Insts. Health, 68-70, chmn. sect, 70-72. U.S.P.H.S, 60-62, Sr. Asst. Surg. Am. Soc. Biol. Chem; Am. Soc. Clin. Invest; Am. Fedn. Clin. Res. Endocrinology; regulation of fatty acid synthesis and ketone body formation. Address: Dept. of Internal Medicine, University of Texas (Southwestern) Medical School, Dallas, TX 75235.

FOSTER, D(AVID) BERNARD, b. Marine City, Mich, May 28, 14; m. 38; c. 3. NEUROLOGY. A.B, Wayne, 35; M.D, Michigan, 38, M.S, 41. Instr. neurol, med. sch, Michigan, 41-44; dir. div. neurol. & neurosurg. & instr. neurol, sch. psychiat, Menninger Found, 47-67, SR. PHYSICIAN, DIV. NEUROL. & PSYCHIAT, MENNINGER CLIN, 67- Consult, Topeka Vet. Admin. Hosp, 47-, acting chief neurol. serv, 67; Topeka State Hosp, 47-; lectr, med. sch, Univ. Kans, 49- Med.C, 44-47, Maj. Am. Neurol. Asn; Am. Med. Asn; Am. Acad. Neurol. Clinical neurology and neuropathology. Address: 404 Woodlawn, Topeka, KS 66606.

FOSTER, DAVID I, b. Eldon, Mo, June 19, 29; m. 52; c. 1. AQUATIC ECOLOGY, FISHERIES BIOLOGY. B.S, Missouri, 53, M.A, 57. Res. asst. fishery biol, Missouri, 56-57; fishery biologist, Ariz. Game & Fish Dept, 57-59, supvr. fishery res, 59-63; asst. leader, state coop. fishery unit, Univ. Mo-Columbia, 63-67; fishery biologist, div. fish hatcheries, BUR. SPORTS FISHERIES & WILDLIFE, U.S. DEPT. INTERIOR, 67-69, SUPVRY. FISHERY BIOLOGIST, DIV. FISHERY SERV, 69- Am. Fisheries Soc; Am. Soc. Limnol. & Oceanog. Ecology of fishes; fish culture. Address: P.O. Box 1306, Albuquerque, NM 87103.

FOSTER, DEAN, b. Bellflower, Ill, June 22, 19; m. 42; c. 4. EXPERIMENTAL PSYCHOLOGY. A.B, Indiana, 42; Ph.D.(psychol), Cornell, 49. Res. assoc, Joseph E. Seagram & Sons, Co, 42-51; dir. sci. res, U.S. Testing Co, 52-60; PROF. PSYCHOL, VA. MIL. INST, 61- Nat. Sci. Found. summer fel, 62. AAAS; Am. Psychol. Asn. Chemistry and psychology of olfaction; psychophysiology of sleep; perception; social psychology; measurement of response; food preference. Address: Route 5, Box 161, Lexington, VA 24450.

FOSTER, DONALD (DE LACY), b. West Torbrook, N.S, Can, Mar. 19, 00; nat; m. 24; c. 3. PHYSICS. B.Sc, Acadia, 20; Loomis fel, Yale, 21-24, Ph.D.(physics), 24. Res. physicist, Eastman Kodak Co, Rochester, 24-25; Bell Tel. Labs, 25-36; Westinghouse Elec. & Mfg. Co, 36-38; asst. prof. math, Stevens Inst. Tech, 39-45, assoc. prof, 45; chief spec. studies lab, Air Force Cambridge Res. Labs, 46-51; res. assoc, Yale, 51-54; sr. scientist, Radio Corp. Am, 55-57; physicist, Air Force Cambridge Res. Labs, 58-69; V.PRES, SPACE DEFENSE CORP, 69- Spec. adv, Nat. Defense Res. Comt, 42; res. assoc, Harvard, 43-45. Fel. Am. Phys. Soc. Spectroscopy; ferromagnetism; metallic crystals; photographic sound recording; radiation from antennas; ignitrons; applied mathematics; airborne fire control; electromagnetic theory. Address: Space Defense Corp, 1600 N. Woodward Ave, Birmingham, MI 48011.

FOSTER, DONALD BARTLEY, b. Jackson, Mich, Nov. 2, 28; m. 57; c. 1. DEVELOPMENTAL BIOLOGY, PLANT MORPHOLOGY. B.S, Michigan, 51, M.S, 52; Ph.D.(bot), Cornell, 64. Teacher, pub. sch, Mich, 51-57; asst. prof, BOT, Ithaca Col, 61-67; ASSOC. PROF, ELMIRA COL, 67- AAAS; Bot. Soc. Am. Growth and development in the fern genus Botrychium, especially in relation to spore germination, gametophyte and embryo growth processes and phylogenetic relationships; physiological relationship of symbiosis in the gametophytes; research in plant tissue culture and aging mechanisms and processes in organisms. Address: Dept. of Biology, Elmira College, Elmira, NY 14901.

FOSTER, DOUGLAS L(AYNE), b. Brookings, S.Dak, Apr. 15, 44; m. 67. REPRODUCTIVE ENDOCRINOLOGY, PHYSIOLOGY. B.S, Univ. Nebr, 66; Nat. Insts. Health traineeship & fel, Univ. Ill, 66-70, Ph.D.(animal sci), 70. RES. ASSOC. REPRODUCTIVE ENDOCRINOL, MED. CTR, UNIV. MICH, ANN ARBOR, 71- Nat. Insts. Health fel. child health & human develop, 71- Soc. Study Reproduction. Physiology of reproduction; neuroendocrinology; fetal and neonatal endocrinology; maternal and fetal endocrine relationships; endocrinology of puberty; developmental physiology. Address: Steroid Research Unit, Dept. of Obstetrics & Gynecology, University of Michigan Medical Center, Ann Arbor, MI 48104.

FOSTER, D(UNCAN) GRAHAM, JR, b. Phila, Pa, Sept. 20, 29; m. 53; c. 4. NUCLEAR PHYSICS. B.A, Swarthmore Col, 51; Ph.D.(exp. physics), Cornell, 56. Res. assoc, Pac. Northwest Lab, Battelle Mem. Inst, 56-69; STAFF MEM, LOS ALAMOS SCI. LAB, 69- Instr, ctr. grad. study, Univ. Wash, 57-66. Am. Phys. Soc. Evaluation of neutron cross sections; fast-neutron total cross sections. Address: T-2, Los Alamos Scientific Lab, Box 1663, Los Alamos, NM 87544.

FOSTER, EDWARD S(TANIFORD), JR, b. Port Deposit, Md, June 9, 13; m. 36; c. 4. APPLIED PHYSICS. B.A, Col. of Wooster, 35; M.S, Washington (St. Louis), 37. Field engr, Subterrex-Explor, Geophysicists, 37-39; Halliburton Oil Well Cementing Co, 39-42; from asst. prof. to assoc. prof. ENG. PHYSICS, UNIV. TOLEDO, 46-58, PROF, 58- Consult, Brush Beryllium Co, 48-58; Argonne Labs, 64- U.S.N.R, 42-46, Res, 46-70, Comdr. (Ret). Am. Phys. Soc; Am. Soc. Eng. Educ; Am. Asn. Physics Teachers. Applied spectroscopy; peaceful uses of nuclear energy; applied meteorology; atmospheric stability; friction. Address: Dept. of Engineering Physics, University of Toledo, Toledo, OH 43606.

FOSTER, EDWIN MICHAEL, b. Alba, Texas, Jan. 1, 17; m. 41; c. 1. BACTERIOLOGY. B.A, N.Texas State Teachers Col, 36, M.A, 37; Alumni Res. Found. scholar, Wisconsin, 37-38, univ. fel, 38-39, Ph.D.(bact), 40. Instr. BACT, Univ. Wis, 40-41; Univ. Tex, 41-42; asst. prof, UNIV. WIS, MADISON, 45-46, assoc. prof, 46-52, PROF, 52-, DIR. FOOD RES. INST, 66- Mem. agr. bd, Nat. Acad. Sci-Nat. Res. Coun, 66-, food protection comt, 70-; expert comt. food hyg, WHO, 67- Pasteur award, Soc. Ill. Bacteriologists, 69. Sanit.C, 42-43, C.W.S, 43-45, Capt. Am. Soc. Microbiol.(secy, 57-61, pres, 69-70); Am. Acad. Microbiol.(secy-treas, 62-65, pres, 66-67); Inst. Food Tech.(Nicholas Appert award medal, 69). Food borne disease; safety of food additives. Address: Food Research Institute, University of Wisconsin, Madison, WI 53706.

FOSTER, ELLIS L(OUIS), b. Louisville, Ky, Oct. 2, 23; m. 50; c. 2. METALLURGICAL ENGINEERING. B.S, Kentucky, 50. Prin. metallurgist, BATTELLE MEM. INST, 50-56, asst. div. chief, 56-66, DEPT. TECH. ADV, 66- Sig.C, 42-46, Sgt. Am. Soc. Metals; Am. Vacuum Soc; Am. Inst. Aeronaut. & Astronaut. Materials and processing research as it applies to reactive and refractory composite materials for use in nuclear, aerospace, and industrial applications. Address: Battelle Memorial Institute, 505 King Ave, Columbus, OH 43201.

FOSTER, E(LTON) GORDON, b. Milwaukee, Wis, Feb. 4, 19; m. 41; c. 1. CHEMICAL ENGINEERING. B.S, Wisconsin, 41, M.S, 42, du Pont fel, 43-44, Ph.D.(phys. chem. & chem. eng), 44. Asst. phys. chem, Wisconsin, 41-43; process engr, E.I. du Pont de Nemours & Co, 44-46, group leader process engr, 46-51, asst. prof. chem. eng, Univ. Louisville, 51-52; engr, Shell Develop. Co, Calif. SHELL OIL CO, 52-56, supvr, 56-66, mgr. process develop. dept, indust. chem. div, Shell Chem. Co, N.Y, 66-68, head, process design-licensing dept, SHELL DEVELOP. CO, CALIF, 68-70, MGR, PROCESS ENG-LICENSING DEPT, 70- Am. Chem. Soc; Am. Inst. Chem. Eng. Process evaluation and design of petrochemical processes. Address: Shell Development Co, 1400 53rd St, Emeryville, CA 94608.

FOSTER, EUGENE A, b. N.Y.C, Apr. 26, 27; m. 52; c. 3. PATHOLOGY. A.B, Washington (St. Louis), 47, M.D, 51. Intern, Salt Lake County Gen. Hosp, 51-52; res. path, Peter Bent Brigham Hosp, Boston, 55-58; fel. surg. path, Barnes Hosp, St. Louis, 58-59; asst. prof. PATH, SCH. MED, UNIV. VA, 59-64, assoc. prof, 64-71, PROF, 71- Teaching fel, Harvard Med. Sch, 57-58; mem. exec. comt. end results group, Nat. Cancer Inst, 62-67, chmn, 65-67; res. worker, Sir William Dunn Sch. Path, Univ. Oxford, 67-68; Nat. Inst. Allergy & Infectious Diseases res. career develop. award, 67- U.S.P.H.S, 52-55, Sr. Asst. Surg. AAAS; Am. Asn. Path. & Bact; Am. Soc. Exp. Path; Int. Acad. Path. Natural history and epidemiology of cancer; experimental urinary tract infection; pathogenesis of staphylococcal infections. Address: Dept. of Pathology, School of Medicine, University of Virginia, Charlottesville, VA 22903.

FOSTER, EUGENE L(EWIS), b. Clinton, Mass, Oct. 9, 22; m. 44; c. 4. MECHANICAL ENGINEERING. B.S, New Hampshire, 44, M.S, 51; Mech.E, Mass. Inst. Tech, 53, Sc.D, 54. Proj. res. engr, Procter & Gamble Co, 46; instr, mech. eng, New Hampshire, 47-49; asst. prof, Mass. Inst. Tech, 50-56; PRES, FOSTER-MILLER ASSOCS, INC, 56- Instr. mech, U.S. Mil. Acad, 52-56. C.Eng, U.S.A, 42-46. AAAS; Am. Soc. Eng. Educ; Am. Soc.

Mech. Eng; Am. Soc. Test. & Mat; N.Y. Acad. Sci. Heat transfer; thermodynamics. Address: Foster-Miller Associates, Inc, 135 Second Ave, Waltham, MA 02154.

FOSTER, FREDERICK C(ALVIN), b. Monmouth, Ill, June 8, 17; m. 41; c. 1. CHEMISTRY. B.S, Monmouth Col, 39; Ph.D.(phys. chem), Columbia, 46. Res. chemist, Hercules Powder Co, Del, 44-46; Firestone Tire & Rubber Co, 46-57; sect. mgr, polymer chems. div, W.R. Grace & Co, 57-61, dir. res, 61-66; V.PRES. RES. & DEVELOP, CHEMPLEX CO, 66- Kinetics of organic reactions; molecular weights of high polymers by osmotic pressure; kinetics of addition copolymerization. Address: 225 Melrose Lane, Crystal Lake, IL 60014.

FOSTER, FREDERICK O(SBON), b. Eng, Mar. 28, 28; m; c. 3. CHEMICAL ENGINEERING. B.Sc, Univ. London, 52, Ph.D.(chem. eng), 55. Res. supvr, E.I. du Pont de Nemours & Co, Inc, 55-68; SECT. HEAD, ESSO ENG. SERV, LTD, 68- R.A.F, 46-48. Process design and development; catalysis; air and water pollution control. Address: Downlands, Benfleet Close, Cobham, Surrey, England.

FOSTER, GEORGE, b. Walden, N.Y, Oct. 8, 26; m. 58; c. 3. ORGANIC CHEMISTRY. B.A, Cornell, 49; M.S, Pennsylvania, 51; Ph.D.(chem), 56. Res. chemist, M.W. Kellogg Co, 54-57; Minn. Mining & Mfg. Co, 57-59; res. planning assoc, res. dept, Mobil Oil Co, Inc, 59-67; dir. planning, Mallinckrodt Chem. Works, 67-69; res. affiliate, Sloan Sch. Mgt, 69-71; SR. STAFF MEM, INT. RES. & TECHNOL, 71- U.S.N, 44-46. Am. Chem. Soc. Research planning. Address: International Research & Technology, 1225 Connecticut Ave. N.W, Washington, DC 20036.

FOSTER, GEORGE A, JR, b. Stockton, Kans, Aug. 31, 38; m. 58; c. 3. BIOCHEMISTRY. B.A, Colorado, 60; M.S, Wisconsin, 62, Ph.D.(biochem), 66. Sr. res. biochemist, Gen. Mills, Inc, 66-69; INFO. SCIENTIST, MILES LABS, INC, 69- Am. Chem. Soc; Drug Info. Asn. Pharmacology of aspirin, analgesics. Address: Miles Labs, Inc, Beardsley Research Bldg, Elkhart, IN 46514.

FOSTER, G(ERALD) L(AWRENCE), b. Colony, Kans, Dec. 27, 27; m. 48; c. 4. ORGANIC CHEMISTRY. B.S, Ottawa (Kans), 50; M.S, Kansas State, 52. Chemist, Dowell Inc, Okla, 52-54, group leader, 54-58; asst. lab. dir, Dowell Div, Dow Chem. Co, 58-64, sr. titled specialist, 64-68; mgr. for. opers, Rainey Corp, 68-69; EUROP. MKT. MGR, T.D. WILLIAMSON, INC, 69- U.S.A.A.F, 45-47. Inhibition of acid corrosion of ferrous metals; emulsion technology; water desalination. Address: T.D. Williamson, Inc, P.O. Box 3409, Tulsa, OK 74101.

FOSTER, HARLAN, b. Dalton, Ga, March 27, 09; c. 1. CHEMISTRY. B.S, Emory, 30, fel, 30-31, M.S, 31; Ph.D.(chem), Washington (St. Louis), 35. Asst. chem, Washington (St. Louis), 31-35; RES. CHEMIST, EXP. STA, E.I. DU PONT DE NEMOURS & CO, INC, 35- Am. Chem. Soc; Am. Soc. Test. & Mat. High pressure technology; nuclear and electronic paramagnetic resonance. Address: E.I. du Pont de Nemours & Co, Inc, Experiment Station, Central Research Dept, Wilmington, DE 19898.

FOSTER, HAROLD D(OUGLAS), b. Tunstall, Eng, Jan. 9, 43; m. 64. GEOMORPHOLOGY, HYDROLOGY. B.Sc, Univ. London, 64, Ph.D.(geog), 67. Instr. GEOG, UNIV. VICTORIA (B.C), 67-68, ASST. PROF, 68- Consult, Ottawa Dept. Energy, Mines & Resources, 68-69; ed, West. Geog. Series, 68- Can. Nat. Res. Coun. Award, 67 & 68. Brit. Geog. Asn; Inst. Brit. Geog; Can. Asn. Geog; Asn. Am. Geog. Pleistocene chronology of Western Europe, particularly the Würm glaciation; eustatic change in the Pacific; social significance of geomorphology: gravel resources in Prince Edward Island and Vancouver Island. Address: Dept. of Geography, University of Victoria, Victoria, B.C, Can.

FOSTER, HAROLD M(ARVIN), b. Passaic, N.J, Aug. 2, 28; m. 54; c. 4. ORGANIC CHEMISTRY. B.S, Lehigh, 50; Nat. Sci. Found. fel. & Ph.D. (chem), Illinois, 53. Res. chemist, Am. Cyanamid Co, 53-61; sr. res. chemist & proj. leader, Mobil Chem. Co, 61-66, res. group leader, colors & chem. dept, SHERWIN-WILLIAMS CO, CHICAGO, 66-70, DIR. PIGMENTS LAB, SHERWIN-WILLIAMS CHEM. DIV, 70- Am. Chem. Soc. Organic synthesis; process research; agricultural chemicals. Address: 202 Hickory St, Park Forest, IL 60466.

FOSTER, HELEN L(AURA), b. Adrian, Mich, Dec. 15, 19. GEOLOGY. B.S, Michigan, 41, M.S, 43, fel, 43-46, Ph.D.(geol), 46. Asst. geol, Michigan, 42-44, instr, Wellesley Col, 46-48; GEOLOGIST, mil. geol. br, U.S. GEOL. SURV, Tokyo, 48-55, chief Ishigaki field party, 55-57, D.C, 57-65, ALASKAN MINERAL RESOURCES BR, CALIF, 65- Geologist, U.S. Geol. Surv, Mich, 43-45; instr, Rocky Mt. Field Sta, Univ. Mich, 47. AAAS; fel. Geol. Soc. Am; assoc. Am. Asn. Petrol. Geol; Am. Geophys. Union. Volcanoes of Japan; geology of Ryukyu Islands; Yukon-Tanana Upland, Alaska. Address: Alaskan Mineral Resources Branch, U.S. Geological Survey, 345 Middlefield,Rd, Menlo Park, CA 94025.

FOSTER, HENRY D(ORROH), b. Timmonsville, S.C, Aug. 14, 12; m. 42; c. 6. CHEMICAL ENGINEERING. B.S, South Carolina, 33; M.S, Illinois, 34, Ph.D.(chem. eng), 37; Pennsylvania, 38-39; Delaware, 40-41. Res. chem. engr, E.I. DU PONT DE NEMOURS & CO. INC, 37-45, develop. chem. engr, 45-46, res. supvr, 46-47, plant process supvr, Ohio & N.J, 47-48, asst. tech. supt, N.J. & Tex, 48, tech. supt, 48-51, asst. process mgr, Grasselli Chem. Dept, 51-55, process mgr, 55-61, ASST. MGR. PLANTS TECH. SECT, INDUST. & BIOCHEMS. DEPT, 61- Civilian with Off. Sci. Res. & Develop, 44. Am. Chem. Soc; Am. Inst. Chem. Eng. Development of chemical manufacturing processes for plastics; insecticides, herbicides, pharmaceuticals, and heavy chemicals; catalytic oxidation in the vapor phase. Address: 1000 Wynnewood Ave, Wilmington, DE 19803.

FOSTER, HENRY L(OUIS), b. Boston, Mass, Apr. 6, 25; m. 48; c. 3. VETERINARY MEDICINE. D.V.M, Middlesex Col, 46. Consult. veterinarian, UNRRA, 46-47; PRES, CHARLES RIVER BREEDING LABS, INC, 47-; CHARLES RIVER MOUSE FARMS, INC, 59-, PRES. DIR. GEN, SOC. DES ELEVAGES CHARLES RIVER FRANCE, S.A, 64- Chmn. husb. transportation cmt, Inst. Lab. Animal Resources div, Nat. Acad. Sci-Nat. Res. Coun, 58-59, mem. prod. & standards cmts, 58-59, gnotobiotics cmt, 59, transportation cmt, 60, mem. adv. coun, 59-64, mem. exec. cmt, 63-64. V.pres, Lab. Animal Breeders Asn, 58-60, pres, 61-62, secy-treas, 64; mem, comt. nomenclature randombred animals, subcomt. gnotobiotes, rabbit and rodent procurement standards and standards for qual. lab. animal feed, Inst. Lab. Animal Resources, 67. Dipl, Am. Col. Lab. Animal Med, 61-; chmn. Charles River U.K, Ltd, England, 70-; pres. Allevamento Lombardo Animali da Laboratorio, s.r.l, Italy, 71- Am. Asn. Contamination Control; Am. Asn. Lab. Animal Sci; Am. Vet. Med. Asn; Am. Soc. Lab. Animal Practitioners; Asn. Gnotobiotics; Am. Inst. Biol. Sci; Am. Soc. Microbiol; N.Y. Acad. Sci. Commercial production of caesarean-originated, barrier-sustained and gnotobiotic rats, mice, rabbits, hamsters and guinea pigs; production methods; elimination of specific diseases; environmental control. Address: Charles River Breeding Labs, Inc, 251 Ballardvale St, North Wilmington, MA 01887.

FOSTER, HERBERT G, JR, b. Rutland, Vt, June 1, 21; m. 47; c. 2. DAIRY CHEMISTRY & BACTERIOLOGY. B.S, Vermont, 47; Ph.D.(dairy bact), Rutgers, 51. Res. chemist dairy, SWIFT & CO, 51-55, head div, 55-65, res. mgr. dairy, egg, ice cream & poultry res, res. lab, 65-68, dairy, poultry & ice cream, 68-71, MKT. MGR. SFP & PROVIDE, SWIFT CHEM. CO, 71- U.S.A, 42-46, Capt. Chemistry and bacteriology of cheese. Address: Swift Chemical Co, 1211 W. 22nd St, Oakbrook, IL 60521.

FOSTER, IRVING GORDON, b. Lynn, Mass, July 15, 12; m. 37; c. 3. PHYSICS. B.S, Va. Mil. Inst, 35; Ph.M, Wisconsin, 37; Ph.D.(physics), Virginia, 48. Res. assoc, Weshburn Observ, Wisconsin, 36-37; instr. physics, Va. Mil. Inst, 37-39, asst. prof, 39-45, assoc. prof, 45-50, prof, 50-59; PROF. PHYSICS & CHMN. DIV. MATH. & NATURAL SCI, FLA. PRESBY. COL, 60- Fulbright lectr, Vidyodaya Univ. Ceylon; consult, Honeywell, Inc. Am. Phys. Soc; Am. Asn. Physics Teachers. Theory and design of mechanical devices; coherent radiation. Address: Dept. of Mathematics & Natural Sciences, Florida Presbyterian College, St. Petersburg, FL 33133.

FOSTER, J. EARL, b. New Albany, Ind, Feb. 21, 29; m. 55; c. 4. MECHANICAL ENGINEERING. B.S, U.S. Merchant Marine Acad, 50; M.S, Iowa, 55, Ph.D.(mech. eng), 58. Engr, Collins Radio Co, Iowa, 57-61; PROF. mech. eng, Univ. Wyo, 61-68; MECH, UNIV. MO-ROLLA, 68- U.S.N, 52-54, Res, 54-, Lt. Comdr. Am. Soc. Mech. Eng; Am. Soc. Eng. Educ. Vibrations; dynamics. Address: Dept. of Engineering Mechanics, University of Missouri-Rolla, Rolla, MO 65401.

FOSTER, JAMES R(USSELL), b. Springfield, Ky, Jan. 9. 10. ENTOMOLOGY. A.B, Kentucky, 33, M.S, 35; Ph.D.(entomol), Ohio State, 54. Curator, Mus. of Archeol. & Anthrop, Kentucky, 35-36; jr. archeologist, Tenn. Valley Auth, 36-40; Nat. Park Serv, 40-41; instr. entomol, UNIV. MD, COLLEGE PARK, 48-50, asst. prof, 50-56, ENTOMOLOGIST, 56- U.S.A, 41-46, 51-53, Res, 53-61, Lt. Col. AAAS; Entom. Soc. Am; Am. Soc. Prof. Biol.(pres, 58-59); Am. Mosquito Control Asn. Insecticides; biological control; mosquito control. Address: Dept. of Entomology, University of Maryland, College Park, MD 20742.

FOSTER, JOHN FARLEY, b. Toledo, Ohio, June 29, 10; m. 33; c. 4. CHEMISTRY. B.A, Ohio Wesleyan, 31; M.S, Syracuse, 32; Victor fel, Stanford, Ph.D.(phys. chem), 35. Asst. chemist, elec. res. sect, works lab, Gen. Elec. Co, Pittsfield, 34-43; res. engr, fuels div, BATTELLE MEM. INST, 43-44, supvr, 45-53, chief div. fuels & phys. chem, 53-60, res. assoc. chem, 60-66, sr. fel, 66-69, SR. TECH. ADV, 69-, biol, life scis, 66-71, ENVIRON. SYSTS. & PROCESSES SECT. & ACTING ASSOC. CHIEF, MAT. & ENVIRON. CHARACTERIZATION DIV, 71- Fel. AAAS; Am. Gas Asn; Am. Chem. Soc. Electrical structure of surfaces; combustion intermediates; fuels; gasification; surface chemistry; colloids; biophysics; life support systems; environmental systems and control processes. Address: Dept. of Biology, Environment and Chemistry, Room 7331, Battelle-Columbus Labs, 505 King Ave, Columbus, OH 43201.

FOSTER, JOHN M(cGAW), b. Phila, Pa, Apr. 22, 28; m. 51; c. 2. BIOCHEMISTRY. B.A, Swarthmore Col, 50; Nat. Found. Infantile Paralysis fel, Harvard, 52-54, M.A, 53, Ph.D.(biochem), 54. Res. assoc. biol, Mass. Inst. Tech, 54-56; asst. prof. biochem, sch. med, Boston Univ, 58-67; asst. prog. dir, sci. curriculum improvement prog, Nat. Sci. Found, 67-68, assoc. prog. dir, 68-69; ASSOC. PROF. BIOL, HAMPSHIRE COL, 69- Summer, mem. staff, Colo. Found. Res. Tuberc, sch. med, Colorado, 58. Chief clin. chem. sect, 406 Med. Gen. Lab, Japan, 56-57, asst. chief, chem. dept, res. & develop. unit, Fitzsimons Army Hosp, 58, Med.Serv.C, 56-58, Res, 59-61, Capt. AAAS; Am. Inst. Biol. Sci. Energy metabolism of blood cells; biochemical control mechanisms. Address: School of Natural Science & Mathematics, Hampshire College, Amherst, MA 01002.

FOSTER, JOHN S(TUART), JR, b. New Haven, Conn, Sept. 18, 22; m. 46; c. 4. PHYSICS. B.S, McGill Univ, 48; Ph.D.(physics), Univ. Calif, Berkeley, 52. Mem. staff, Lawrence Radiation Lab, Univ. Calif, Berkeley, 48-52, div. leader exp. physics, Livermore, 52-58, assoc. dir. nuclear explosives, 58-61, dir, Livermore Lab. & assoc. dir, Berkeley Lab, 61-65; DIR. DEFENSE RES. & ENG, DEPT. DEFENSE, 65- Consult, U.S. Air Force, 42-45; President's Sci. Adv. Comt; mem, Air Force Sci. Adv. Bd; Army Sci. Adv. Panel; ballistic missile defense adv. comt, Advan. Res. Projs. Agency. Ernest Orlando Lawrence Mem. Award, Atomic Energy Comn, 60; distinguished pub. serv. medal, Dept. Defense, 69; James Forrestal Mem. Award, 70. Nat. Acad. Eng. Nuclear and high explosives; hydrodynamics; gaseous discharge; radar. Address: Office of Secretary of Defense, The Pentagon, Washington, DC 20301.

FOSTER, JOHN W(ALLACE), b. Iowa City, Iowa, Dec. 28, 16; m. 42; c. 3. IMMUNOLOGY, VIROLOGY. B.S, Oklahoma, 40; M.S, Maryland, 48, Ph.D. (bact), 50. Asst. prof. immunol, virol. & bact, sch. vet. med, Univ. Ga, 50-59, assoc. prof. microbiol. & prev. med, 59-67, prof. med. microbiol. & mem. staff, inst. comp. med, 67-71; RES. MICROBIOLOGIST, CTR. DISEASE CONTROL, 71-, vis. scientist, 70-71. Consult, zoonoses ctr, Pan-Am. Health Orgn, summer 70. U.S.A, 40-45. AAAS; Am. Soc. Microbiol; N.Y. Acad. Sci. Antigens of Brucella; bacteriophage in animal cells. Address: Trepaenatoses Unit, Center for Disease Control, Atlanta, GA 30333.

FOSTER, JOSEPH F(OSTER), JR, b. Chillicothe, Ohio, July 22, 18; m. 57. MATHEMATICS, ASTRONOMY. B.A, Ohio State, 39; M.S, Iowa, 41, Ph.D, 52; M.A, Harvard, 42. Asst. astron, Iowa, 39-41; Harvard, 41-42; instr, UNIV. ARIZ, 42-44, MATH, 46-53, asst. prof, 53-66, ASSOC. PROF, 66- U.S.A, 44-46. Am. Math. Soc; Math. Asn. Am. Geometry. Address: Dept. of Mathematics, University of Arizona, Tucson, AZ 85721.

FOSTER, JOSEPH F(RANKLIN), b. Marion, Ind, May 17, 18; m. 40; c. 3. CHEMISTRY. B.S, Iowa State Col, 40, fel, 40-43, Ph.D.(chem), 43. Prolamine Found. fel, Harvard Med. Sch, 43-45; res. chemist, Am. Maize Prods. Co, Ind, 45-46; asst. prof. CHEM, Iowa State Col, 46-51, assoc. prof, 51-54; PURDUE UNIV, 54-57, PROF, 57-, HEAD DEPT, 68- Spec. fel, Nat. Insts. Health, Carlsberg Lab, Denmark, 59; consult, Nat. Insts. Health, 62-66; pioneering lab, U.S. Army Natick Labs, 63-65. AAAS; Biophys. Soc; Am. Chem. Soc; Am. Soc. Biol. Chem. Physical chemistry of proteins and other natural molecules; isomerization reactions in proteins; physical biochemistry. Address: Dept. of Chemistry, Purdue University, Lafayette, IN 47907.

FOSTER, K(ENNETH) W(ILLIAM), b. Lansing, Mich, Aug. 31, 24; m. 48; c. 3. SOLID STATE PHYSICS. A.B, Miami Univ, 48; M.S, Ohio State Univ, 62. Res. physicist, MOUND LAB, MONSANTO CO, 48-61, sr. res. physicist, 61-62, res. group leader, 62-66, res. sect. mgr, 66-70, RES. SPECIALIST, 70- U.S.A, 43-45. Am. Phys. Soc. Nuclear phenomena; isotope separation; powder compaction and sintering. Address: Mound Lab, Monsanto Research Corp, Miamisburg, OH 45342.

FOSTER, LAURENCE S(TANDLEY), b. Beverly, Mass, March 17, 01; m. 31; c. 2. CHEMISTRY. A.B, Clark, 22, A.M, 23; Metcalf fel, Brown, Ph.D. (chem), 26. Instr. chem, Vermont, 23-24; Utah, 26-27; res. instr, Brown, 27-29, instr, 29-30, asst. prof, 30-43; investigator, Office Sci. Res. & Develop, 42-43; res. assoc, Chicago, 43-44; staff mem. div. indust. co-op, Mass. Inst. Tech, 44-45; metallurgist, Watertown Arsenal Lab, U.S. Army, 45-46, assoc. dir. lab, phys. chemist & chief chem. processes br, 46-49, chief radiochem. sect, 49-54, nucleonics br, 54-55, atomic energy div, Ord. Mat. Res. Off, 55-59, sr. staff adv, 59-63, chief tech. info. ctr, U.S. Army Mat. Res. Agency, Watertown, 63-69; EXEC. DIR, ACAD. APPL. SCI, INC, 69- Instr, nurses training sch, R.I. Hosp, Providence, 40-42. Fel. AAAS; Am. Chem. Soc. Organometallic compounds of germanium, tin and lead; solutions in liquid ammonia; inorganic chemistry of germanium and gallium, including extraction from ores; ceramics; powder metallurgy; radiochemistry; nuclear reactors; technical information retrieval. Address: 16 West St, Belmont, MA 02178.

FOSTER, L(EIGH) CURTIS, b. Montreal, Que, Can, Aug. 24, 25; U.S. citizen; m. 48; c. 2. PHYSICS, SPECTROSCOPY. B.Sc, McGill, 50, Defense Res. fel. & Ph.D, 56. Res. physicist, Santa Barbara Res. Center, 50-52; Calif. Res. & Develop. Co, 52-54; ZENITH RADIO RES. CORP, MENLO PARK, 56-58, dir. res, 58-69, v.pres, 60-69, DIR, EXEC. V.PRES. & GEN. MGR, 69- Bur. Ord. develop. award, 45. Am. Phys. Soc; Inst. Elec. & Electronics Eng. Low noise microwave tubes; ultrasonics; infrared; electron beam devices; laser communications; video recording techniques. Address: Four Altree Ct, Atherton, CA 94025.

FOSTER, LORRAINE L, b. Los Angeles, Calif, Dec. 25, 38; m. 59; c. 3. MATHEMATICS. B.A, Occidental Col, 60; Woodrow Wilson, Nat. Sci. Found. & Gen. Elec. fels. & Ph.D.(math), Calif. Inst. Technol, 64. Asst. prof. MATH, SAN FERNANDO VALLEY STATE COL, 64-68, ASSOC. PROF, 68- Am. Math. Soc; Math. Asn. Am. Elementary and algebraic number theory; matrix theories. Address: Dept. of Mathematics, San Fernando Valley State College, Northridge, CA 91324.

FOSTER, LOWELL BYRON, b. Cape Girardeau, Mo, Sept. 16, 40; m. 64. BIOCHEMISTRY, CLINICAL CHEMISTRY. B.S, Arkansas State, 62; U.S. Pub. Health Serv. trainee & Ph.D.(biochem), Tennessee, 67. U.S. Pub. Health Serv. res. trainee biochem. endocrinol, St. Jude Children's Res. Hosp, Memphis, Tenn, 67-69; asst. chemist, med. lab. assocs. div, Damon Corp, 69-70, asst. dir. clin. chem, 70-71; CLIN. CHEMIST, PATTERSON-COLEMAN LABS, SMITH KLINE & FRENCH, 71- Instr, Tennessee, Memphis, 67-69; clin. asst. prof, Med. Col. Ala, 69- Am. Asn. Clin. Chem; Am. Chem. Soc. Assay and mechanism of action of steroidal and polypeptide hormones. Address: Patterson-Coleman Labs, 4600 N. Habana, Tampa, FL 33614.

FOSTER, L(UTHER) M(ORRIS), b. Cedar City, Utah, Aug. 22, 18; m. 43; c. 4. PHYSICAL CHEMISTRY. B.S, Hawaii, 40; Ph.D.(phys. chem), Brown, 47. Res. chemist, U.S. Naval Res. Lab, D.C, 42-43; metall. lab, Chicago, 43-45; Manhattan Proj, Los Alamos, 45-46; Alcoa Res. Labs, 47-54, chief phys. chem. div, 54-63; MGR. MAT. RES, THOMAS J. WATSON RES. CTR, IBM CORP, 63- Am. Chem. Soc; Sci. Res. Soc. Am; Electrochem. Soc. Semiconductors; high temperature metallurgy; molten salts; radiochemistry; gas in metals; crystal growth. Address: Thomas J. Watson Research Center, IBM Corp, Yorktown Heights, NY 10598.

FOSTER, MANUS R, b. Canyon, Tex, Mar. 10, 27; m. 52; c. 3. APPLIED MATHEMATICS. B.S, Kansas, 48, Atomic Energy Cmn. fel, 50-52, Ph.D. (math. physics), 52. Physicist, Naval Res. Lab, 48; asst, Kansas, 49-50; sr. res. technologist, Magnolia Petrol. Co, 52-59; res. assoc, Socony Mobil Oil Co. Inc, 59-61, sr. res. assoc, 61-69, SR. SCIENTIST, MOBIL RES. & DEVELOP. CORP, 69- Vis. assoc. prof, South. Methodist Univ, 67- U.S.N.R, 44-48, Ens. Am. Math. Soc; Soc. Indust. & Appl. Math. Geophysical data processing; applied statistics; statistical communication theory. Address: Field Research Lab, Mobil Research & Development Corp, P.O. Box 900, Dallas, TX 75221.

FOSTER, MARGARET C, b. Mar. 24, 35. PHYSICS. B.S, Richmond, 57; Rotary Found. fel, Freiburg & Free Univ. Berlin, 58-59; M.S, Wisconsin, 60, Ph.D, 64. Res. asst, Wisconsin, 60-65; researcher, Europ. Orgn. Nuclear Res, Geneva, 65-67; nuclear physics res. lab, Univ. Liverpool, England, 67-68; ASST. PROF. PHYSICS, STATE UNIV. N.Y. STONY BROOK, 68- Am. Phys. Soc; Am. Asn. Physics Teachers. Experimental high energy physics. Address: Dept. of Physics, State University of New York at Stony Brook, Stony Brook, NY 11790.

FOSTER, MARK G(ARDNER), b. Winfield, Kans, Mar. 17, 14; m. 39; c. 3. PHYSICS. A.B, Miami (Ohio), 35; Ph.D.(physics), Calif. Inst. Tech, 39. Asst. physics, Calif. Inst. Tech, 35-39; physicist, res. dept, Champion Paper & Fibre Co, 39-41; Naval Ord. Lab, Wash, D.C, 41-45; Curtiss-Wright Corp, 45; asst. head, eng. physics dept, Cornell Aeronaut. Lab, 46-50, head, develop. div, 50-56; dir. res, Crosley Div, Avco Mfg. Corp, 56-57; prin. physicist, Cornell Aeronaut. Lab, 57-60; WILLS JOHNSON PROF. ELEC. ENG, UNIV. VA, 60-, chmn. dept, 60-66. AAAS; sr. mem. Inst. Elec. & Electronics Eng; Am. Phys. Soc. Applied dynamics; control systems; engineering education. Address: Dept. of Electrical Engineering, University of Virginia, Charlottesville, VA 22901.

FOSTER, MARY LEE, b. Utica, Miss, Feb. 24, 08. MATHEMATICS. B.A, La. State, 30, summer scholar, 36, M.S, 37, fel, 35-36; fel, Alabama, 33-35. Teacher, pub. schs, La, 29-32; Miss, 36-37; instr. MATH, Henderson State Teachers Col, 37-44; head dept, Huntingdon Col, 44-45; adj. prof, South Carolina, 45-46; assoc. prof, HENDERSON STATE COL, 46-59, PROF, 59-, CHMN. FUNDAMENTAL MATH, GEN. COL, 59- Math. Asn. Am; Am. Math. Soc. Some properties of the central conic in the complex plane; fundamental mathematics. Address: Dept. of Mathematics, Henderson State College, Arkadelphia, AR 71923.

FOSTER, MELVIN S, b. Traer, Iowa, Oct. 20, 33; m. 54; c. 4. PHYSICAL CHEMISTRY. B.S, Iowa State, 57, Ph.D.(phys. chem), 60. Asst. chemist, ARGONNE NAT. LAB, 60-64, ASSOC. CHEMIST, 64- U.S.A, 52-54. Am. Chem. Soc; Sci. Res. Soc. Am. Physical chemistry; computer programming; real time computer applications; laboratory interfacing of mini-computers. Address: 24 W. 678 75th St, R.R. 1, Naperville, IL 60540.

FOSTER, MICHAEL RALPH, b. Indianapolis, Ind, Jan. 12, 43; m. 66; c. 1. FLUID DYNAMICS, AERODYNAMICS. B.S, Mass. Inst. Technol, 65, M.S, 66; Nat. Sci. Found. Inst, Woods Hole Oceanog. Inst, summer 68; Ph.D. (aeronaut. eng), Calif. Inst. Technol, 69. Instr. math, Mass. Inst. Technol, 69-70; ASST. PROF. AERONAUT. & ASTRONAUT. ENG, OHIO STATE UNIV, 70- Am. Inst. Aeronaut. & Astronaut. Theoretical fluid dynamics, especially aspects of geophysical fluid dynamics, rotating and/or stratified fluids, singular perturbation theory. Address: Dept. of Aeronautical & Astronautical Engineering, Ohio State University, 2036 Neil Ave, Columbus, OH 43210.

FOSTER, M(ORRIS), b. New York, N.Y, Dec. 14, 18; m. 49; c. 3. GENETICS. A.B, Brooklyn Col, 41; A.M, Columbia, 48, Ph.D, 51. Fel. genetics, Nat. Cancer Inst, Nat. Insts. Health, U.S. Pub. Health Serv, Chicago, 51-52; instr. zool, Yale, 52-56, res. assoc. & asst. prof. dermat, 56-58; assoc. prof. ZOOL, UNIV. MICH, ANN ARBOR, 58-62, PROF, 62- U.S.A.A.F, 42-46. AAAS; Genetics Soc. Am; Am. Soc. Human Genetics; Am. Soc. Zool; Am. Genetics Asn; Am. Soc. Nat; Soc. Develop. Biol. Physiological and biochemical genetics; mammalian melanogenesis; hormonal control of melanogenic and malignant properties of melanomas; mammalian immunogenetics. Address: Dept. of Zoology, University of Michigan, Ann Arbor, MI 48104.

FOSTER, NEAL R(OBERT), b. Nyack, N.Y, Aug. 13, 37; m. 68. ICHTHYOLOGY. B.A, Cornell Univ, 59, N.Y. State Regents fels, 59-61 & 63-64, M.S, 61, Ph.D.(evolutionary biol), 67. Teaching asst. zool, Cornell Univ, 58-59; biologist, inst. fisheries res, Univ. N.C, summer 59; curatorial asst. fish collection, Cornell Univ, 59-60, asst. vertebrate zool, 60-65; ASST. CURATOR, DEPT. LIMNOL, ACAD. NATURAL SCI. PHILA, 65- Nat. Sci. Found. grant, 67-71. AAAS; Am. Fisheries Soc; Am. Soc. Zool; Am. Littoral Soc; Am. Soc. Ichthyol. & Herpetol; Am. Inst. Biol. Sci; Ecol. Soc. Am; Animal Behavior Soc; Soc. Study Evolution; Soc. Syst. Zool; Soc. Vert. Paleont; Asn. Trop. Biol; Brit. Soc. Bibliog. Natural Hist. Bionomic ichthyology; systematics of fishes; comparative ethology, ecology, morphology and evolution of killifishes; application of behavioral and other bionomic information in the higher classification of fishes; zoogeography and evolution of freshwater fishes; aquariology. Address: Dept. of Limnology, Academy of Natural Sciences of Philadelphia, 19th St. & The Pkwy, Philadelphia, PA 19103.

FOSTER, NORMAN FRANCIS, b. Bristol, Eng, Nov. 6, 30; m. 55; c. 2. PHYSICAL CHEMISTRY. B.S, Bristol, 54, Ph.D.(phys. chem), 57. Fel. heterogeneous catalysis, Nat. Res. Coun. Can, 57-59; mem. tech. staff ultrasonics, BELL TEL. LABS, 60-67, SUPVR, 67- R.E.M.E, 49-51. Inst. Elec. & Electronics Eng; Am. Vacuum Soc; Am. Inst. Physics. Ultrasonics, mainly in frequency range above 100 megacycles; piezoelectric semiconductors, particularly cadmium sulphide and other II-VI compounds; mechanical filters, mainly 60 to 600 hz. Address: Bell Telephone Labs, Inc, 555 Union Blvd, Allentown, PA 18103.

FOSTER, NORMAN G(EORGE), b. Chicago, Ill, Dec. 23, 19; m. 44; c. 5. PHYSICAL CHEMISTRY. B.S, Chicago, 42; Res. Corp. fel, Arkansas, 52-55, Coulter W. Jones summer fel, 53, M.S, 54, & Ph.D.(phys. chem), 55. Control chemist, Sinclair Ref. Co, Ind, 42; anal. chemist, Dearborn Chem. Co, Ill, 43; res. chemist, Whiting res. labs, Standard Oil Co, Ind, 46-51; asst, Arkansas, 51-55; res. chemist, Cities Serv. Res. & Develop. Co, Okla, 55-57; phys. chemist, Bartlesville Petrol. Res. Ctr, U.S. Bur. Mines, 57-65, proj. leader, 63; ASSOC. PROF. CHEM, TEX. WOMAN'S UNIV, 65- U.S.A.A.F, 43-46. Fel. AAAS; Am. Chem. Soc; Coblentz Soc; Am. Soc. Mass Spectrometry; N.Y. Acad. Sci; fel. Am. Inst. Chem. Mass spectrometry; fragmentation mechanism studies by utilization of isotopically labeled molecules; characterization of complex mixtures by means of mass spectrometry; structure elucidation utilizing mass spectrometry, nuclear magnetic resonance and infrared. Address: Dept. of Chemistry, Texas Woman's University, Box 23973, TWU Station, Denton, TX 76204.

FOSTER, PERRY A(LANSON), JR, b. Manchester, N.H, May 18, 25; m. 47; c. 5. PHYSICAL CHEMISTRY. B.A, St. Anselm's Col, 50; M.S, Ga. Inst. Tech, 55. Asst. chem, Ga. Inst. Tech, 50-52, eng. exp. sta, 52-55; res. chemist, ALCOA RES. LABS. DIV, ALUMINUM CO. AM, 55-67, SR. RES. SCIENTIST, 67- U.S.A, 43-45. Am. Chem. Soc; Am. Ceramic Soc; fel. Am. Inst. Chem. High temperature chemistry; molten salts; phase equilibria in non-metallic systems; electrochemical and process development. Address: Alcoa Research Labs, P.O. Box 772, New Kensington, PA 15068.

FOSTER, R(AYMOND) E(DWIN), b. Vancouver, B.C, Can, Apr. 14, 19; m. 44. FOREST PATHOLOGY. B.A, British Columbia, 42, B.S.F, 43; Ph.D.(forest mycol, path), Toronto, 49. Head forest path. sect, forest res. lab, CAN. DEPT. OF THE ENVIRONMENT, 48-65, DIR. FOREST PRODS. LAB, 65- Sampling studies; decay investigations. Address: Forest Products Lab, Canada Dept. of the Environment, 6620 N.W. Marine Dr, Vancouver 8, B.C, Can.

FOSTER, RICHARD A(LBERT), b. Waterloo, Iowa, Sept. 20, 18; m. 48; c. 2. CHEMISTRY. A.B, Loras Col, 39. Res. chemist, Shell Oil Co, 46-59; chemist, Beckman Instruments, Inc, 59-61; instrument engr, FLUOR CORP, LTD, LOS ANGELES, 61-68, SR. INSTRUMENT ENGR, 68- U.S.N.R, 41-46, Lt. Am. Chem. Soc; Instrument Soc. Am; Am. Ord. Asn. Hydrocarbon type analysis; instrumentation; control systems; atomic energy. Address: 650 Linda Ave, La Habra, CA 90631.

FOSTER, RICHARD B(ERGERON), b. Springdale, Wash, Nov. 21, 16; m. 55; c. 2. ENGINEERING. B.A, California, 38, 38-39. Asst. supvr, Douglas Aircraft Co, 40-42; dir. planning div, Am. Aviation, 42-43; chief indust. engr, Globe Aircraft Co, 43-44; estimator, Consol. Vultee Aircraft Corp, 44; mem. staff, Kaiser Shipyards, 44; dist. invest. chief, U.S. Govt. Agencies, 44-47; partner, Foster & Derian, Consults, 47-51, 53-54; exec. asst. & gen. mgr, Marquardt Aircraft, 51-53; DIR. STRATEGIC STUDIES CTR, STANFORD RES. INST, 54- Fel. AAAS; Opers. Res. Soc. Am; Sci. Res. Soc. Am; Inst. Strategic Studies. Philosophy and civil engineering; cost-effectiveness analysis for strategic decisions; values, power and strategy; methods of interdisciplinary research in strategic analysis. Address: Stanford Research Institute, 1611 N. Kent St, Arlington, VA 22209.

FOSTER, RICHARD F(REDERIC), b. Grand Lake Stream, Maine, Mar. 17, 17; m. 42; c. 2. ENVIRONMENTAL SCIENCE. B.S, Washington (Seattle), 38, Ph.D.(fisheries), 48. Biologist, State Pollution Cmn, Wash, 42-43; res. assoc. appl. fisheries, Washington (Seattle), 43-45; mgr. aquatic biol, Gen. Elec. Co, 45-61; mgr. environ. studies, 61-64; mgr. environ. studies & eval, BATTELLE MEM. INST, 65-69, ASSOC. MGR. ENVIRON. & LIFE SCI. DIV, PAC. NORTHWEST LAB, 69- Mem. Bikini resurv, Univ. Wash, 47, spec. lectr, 52-55, 58-60; mem. comt. effects atomic radiation on oceanog. & fisheries, Nat. Acad. Sci. Technol. adv, U.S. del, peaceful uses of atomic energy, Geneva, 55; mem, Nat. Tech. adv. comt. water quality standards, Fed. Water Pollution Control Admin, U.S. Dept. Interior, 67-68; environ. radiation exposure adv. comt, Dept. Health, Educ. & Welfare, U.S. Pub. Health Serv, 65-70. AAAS; Am. Fisheries Soc; Health Physics Soc; Radiation Res. Soc; Water Pollution Control Fedn.(medal, 62); fel. Am. Inst. Fishery Res. Biol. Radiation protection; evaluation of radioactive contaminants in the environment; disposal of radioactive waste; detection and measurement of pollution; effects of radiation on aquatic organisms. Address: Pacific Northwest Lab, Battelle Memorial Institute, Richland, WA 99352.

FOSTER, RICHARD N(ORMAN), b. Cleveland, Ohio, June 10, 41; m. 65. CHEMICAL ENGINEERING. B.E, Yale, 63, M.S, 65, Ph.D, 66; N.Y. Univ, 66-68. Tech. rep. int. mkt. develop, Union Carbide Corp, 66, int. prod-mkt. mgr. chem. mkt. develop, 67-69; mgr. tech. & financial anal, ABT ASSOCS, 69-71, DIR. TECHNOL. MGT. GROUP, TECHNOL. TRANSFER, FIRE SAFETY, RES. PLANNING & EVALUATION, 71- AAAS; Am. Inst. Chem; Am. Chem. Soc. Diffusion limited nonisothermal chemical reactions; surface diffusion; semiconductor catalysis; plasma physics; technological transfer; research management. Address: ABT Associates, 55 Wheeler St, Cambridge, MA 02138.

FOSTER, ROBBIE T, b. Clovis, N.Mex, Feb. 4, 37; m. 58; c. 3. ORGANIC CHEMISTRY. B.A, McMurry Col, 59; M.S, Iowa, 62, Ph.D.(org. chem), 63. Res. assoc, Univ. Ariz, 63-64; RES. CHEMIST, PPG INDUSTS, INC, 64- Am. Chem. Soc. Address: 3213 Sumpter, Corpus Christi, TX 78410.

FOSTER, ROBERT C(ARL), b. Canton, Ohio, July 26, 23; m. 49; c. 3. MATHEMATICS. B.S, Bowling Green State, 52, M.A, 53. Instr. math. & eng. mech, Tri-State Col, 53-55, assoc. prof. math, 57-58; instr. eng, Lockheed Aircraft Corp, 55-57; systems design engr, astronautics oper. div, Convair Div, Gen. Dynamics Corp, 58-60; sr. res. engr, Astronautics Div, GEN. DYNAMICS CORP, San Diego, Calif, 60-64, design specialist-comput. appl, Stromberg-Carlson, Div, 64-66, prod. mgr. software, 66-68, mgr. mkt, STROMBERG DATAGRAPHIX, INC, 68-70, SR. SYSTS. ANALYST, 70- U.S.N, 42-46. Asn. Comput. Mach; Am. Soc. Eng. Educ. Applied mathematics. Address: Stromberg Datagraphix, Inc, P.O. Box 2449, San Diego, CA 92112.

FOSTER, ROBERT E(DWARD), II, b. Milwaukee, Wis, Feb. 4, 20; m. 40; c. 2. PLANT BREEDING. B.S, California, 41; Ph.D.(plant path), Wisconsin, 45. Asst. plant path, California, 41; Alumni Found. fel, Wisconsin, 41-46; asst. prof, Cornell, 46-50; assoc. horticulturist, AGR. EXP. STA, UNIV. ARIZ, 50-54, HORTICULTURIST, 54- Inspector, State Dept. Agr, Calif, 41; plant pathologist, N.Y. Exp. Sta, Geneva, 46-50. With U.S. Dept. Agr; War Food Admin, 43-44. Am. Soc. Hort. Sci; Am. Phytopath. Soc; Am. Genetic Asn. Vegetable breeding; breeding for disease resistance; vegetable genetics; physiology of diseases; seed production; propagation; virus and physiological diseases; melons; lettuce. Address: Box 1308, Mesa, AZ 85201.

FOSTER, R(OBERT) E(LLISON) LEE, b. Willard, Ill, Jan. 31, 07; m. 33; c. 4. RADIOLOGY. Southern Illinois, 23-24; California, Los Angeles, 36-37; M.D, Southern California, 42. Intern, St. Joseph's Hosp, Ariz, 41-42; res, Good Samaritan Hosp, 42-45; radiologist, path. lab, Prof. X-ray & Clin. Lab, 45-51, DIR, 51-63, MED. CTR. X-RAY LAB, 51- Preceptor with Dr. W. Warner Watkins, 42-45. Consult, Tempe Clin. Hosp; Ariz. State Sanitarium. Dipl, Am. Bd. Radiol, 47. Fel. AAAS; Am. Med. Asn; Am. Radium Soc; Am. Roentgen Ray Soc; Radiol. Soc. N.Am; fel. Am. Col. Radiol; fel. Am. Col. Physicians. Medical radiology, especially diagnostic and therapeutic. Address: Medical Center Lab, 1313 N. Second St, Suite Three, Phoenix, AZ 85004.

FOSTER, ROBERT E(VERETT), b. Salina, Kans, Jan. 27, 19; m. 42; c. 5. ORGANIC CHEMISTRY. A.B, Miami (Ohio), 40; Ph.D.(org. chem), Illinois, 44. Asst, Illinois, 40-42, Nat. Defense Res. Comt, 42-44; Comt. Med. Res. & Nat. Defense Res. Comt, Nebraska, 44-45; res. chemist, cent. res. dept, exp. sta, E.I. DU PONT DE NEMOURS & CO, INC, 45-60, sr. res. chemist, 60-62, res. supvr. textile fibers dept, new prod. div, 62-66, SUPVR. RES. & DEVELOP, TEXTILE FIBERS DEPT, TECH. DIV, 66- Fel. AAAS; Am. Chem. Soc. Synthetic fiber and polymer technology; textile technology and end use application research; heterogeneous catalysis; oxidations; organic syntheses; chemical warfare agents. Address: Textile Fibers Dept, Technical Division, E.I. du Pont de Nemours & Co, Inc, Wilmington, DE 19898.

FOSTER, ROBERT H, b. Monroe, Ga, Nov. 4, 20; m. 42; c. 4. BIOGEOGRAPHY. B.S, Univ. Ga, 63; M.S, Brigham Young Univ, 66, Ph.D.(bot), 68. ASSOC. PROF. GEOG, WEST. KY, UNIV, 68- U.S.A.F, 39-60. Asn. Am. Geog. Plant distribution in the U.S. intermountain region. Address: Dept. of Geography & Geology, Western Kentucky University, Bowling Green, KY 42102.

FOSTER, ROBERT JAMES, b. Dolton, Ill, Nov. 17, 15; m. 47; c. 2. CHEMICAL ENGINEERING. B.S, Ill. Inst. Tech, 40; M.S, Michigan, 41, 43. Asst. chem. engr, Armour Res. Found, 38-41; North. Regional Res. Lab, bur. agr. & indust. chem, U.S. Dept. Agr, 41-43; develop. engr, Gen. Mills, Inc, 43-50, head dept. chem. eng, 50-56; asst. dir. mfg, Chemagro Corp, 56-64; dir, Foster Eng. Co, 64-70; CHEM. ENGR, CHEMAGRO CORP, 70- Address: Chemagro Corp, Box 4913, Kansas City, MO 64106.

FOSTER, ROBERT J(OE), b. Glendale, Calif, June 6, 24; m. 51; c. 2. BIOLOGICAL CHEMISTRY. B.S, Calif. Inst. Tech, 48, fel, 51-53, Ph.D.(chem), 52. Res. fel. biol, Calif. Inst. Tech, 53-55; asst. chemist & asst. prof. CHEM, WASH. STATE UNIV, 55-61, ASSOC. PROF. & ASSOC. AGR. CHEMIST, 61- U.S.A.A.F, 43-46. Am. Chem. Soc; Am. Soc. Plant Physiol; Am. Soc. Biol. Chem. Mechanisms of enzyme action and specificity; comparative enzymology; enzymological photochemistry. Address: Dept. of Agricultural Chemistry, Washington State University, Pullman, WA 99613.

FOSTER, ROBERT J(OHN), b. Cambridge, Mass, Apr. 19, 29; m. 51; c. 2. GEOLOGY. S.B, Mass. Inst. Tech, 51; M.S, Washington (Seattle), 55, Ph.D. (geol), 57. Seismic computer, Geophys. Serv, Inc, 51-52; instrumentation engr, Boeing Airplane Co, 53-54; asst, Washington (Seattle), 55-57; asst. prof. geol, Mont. State Univ, 58-61; assoc. prof. PHYS. SCI, SAN JOSE STATE COL, 61-67, PROF, 67- Ord.C, 57, 1st Lt. AAAS; Geol. Soc. Am; Mineral. Soc. Am; Am. Asn. Petrol. Geol; Nat. Asn. Geol. Teachers. Petrology; structural geology. Address: Dept. of Natural Science, San Jose State College, San Jose, CA 95114.

FOSTER, ROBERT L, b. Marion, Ind, Nov. 10, 35; m. 58; c. 2. GEOLOGY. B.A, Williams Col, 58; Minnesota, Duluth, 59-60; M.A, Missouri, 62, Ph.D. (geol), 66. Geologist, U.S. Geol. Surv, 66-68; CHIEF GEOLOGIST, CACHE CREEK EXPLOR. CO, 68- Aruthur Day Award, Soc. Sigma Xi; Penrose grant, Geol. Soc. Am. Geol. Soc. Am; Am. Clay Minerals Soc; Mineral. Soc. Am; Arctic Inst. N.Am; Am. Inst. Mining, Metall. & Petrol. Eng; Mineral. Asn. Can. Field geology; petrology; geochemistry; geophysics. Address: Cache Creek Exploration Co, 701 Welch Rd, Palo Alto, CA 94304.

FOSTER, ROBERT L(INCOLN), b. Monmouth, Ill, Sept. 10, 24; m. 48; c. 2. ORGANIC CHEMISTRY. B.S, Monmouth Col, 48; M.S, Univ. Ill, 49, Ph.D. (chem), 52. CHEMIST, ATLANTIC RICHFIELD CO, 51- Address: Atlantic Richfield Co, Harvey, IL 60426.

FOSTER, SAMUEL P(HILLIP), b. Wilmington, Del, Apr. 1, 25; m. 49; c. 2. CHEMICAL ENGINEERING. B.Ch.E, Yale, 45; M.S, Delaware, 48. Res. engr, E.I. DU PONT DE NEMOURS & CO, INC, 47-56, res. supvr, 56-58, sr. res. supvr, 58-60, res. mgr, 60-62, tech. supt, film dept, 62-70, PROD. MGR, 70- U.S.N.R, 42-46, Ens. Am. Chem. Soc; Soc. Plastics Eng; Am. Inst. Chem. Eng. Applied polymer science; polymer films; polymers derived from olefins. Address: Rd. 2, Box 27E, Hockessin, DE 19707.

FOSTER, THEODORE DEAN, b. Plainfield, N.J, July 25, 29. PHYSICS, OCEANOGRAPHY. Sc.B, Brown, 52; Stevens Inst. Tech, 53-55; teaching fel, Colorado, 55-57, M.S, 58, M.A, 60; Sverdrup fel, California, San Diego, 60-62, Ph.D.(physics), 65. Physicist, Reaction Motors Inc, 52-55; instr. phys. sci, Colorado, 57-60; res. physicist, Scripps Inst, California, 62-65; asst. prof. geophys. & appl. sci, Yale, 65-69; asst. res. physicist, SCRIPPS INST. OCEANOG, 69-71, ASSOC. RES. OCEANOGR, 71- Mem. comt. polar res, panel oceanog, Nat. Acad. Sci. U.S.N, 48-50, Res, Lt. Comdr. Am. Phys. Soc; Philos. Sci. Asn; Am. Geophys. Union. Hydrodynamics; geophysical fluid dynamics; physical oceanography; philosophy of science. Address: Marine Physical Lab, Scripps Institution of Oceanography, La Jolla, CA 92037.

FOSTER, THEODORE T(ILLINGHAST), b. Norfolk, Va, Nov. 27, 23; m. 50; c. 3. ORGANIC CHEMISTRY. A.B, Harvard, 44; fel, Mass. Inst. Tech, 47-48, Ph.D.(org. chem), 49. Asst, Mass. Inst. Tech, 48-49; res. chemist, E.I. du Pont de Nemours & Co, Inc, 49-57, mgr. sales develop, intermediates dyes & chem. div, org. chem. dept, 57-63, tech. supvr, 63-66; mgr. mkt, Arapahoe Chem. Div, Syntex Corp, 66-71; MGR. MKT-CHEM, AEROJET SOLID PROPULSION CO, 71- Am. Chem. Soc. Petroleum chemicals; developed dyes; organic intermediates. Address: Aerojet Solid Propulsion Co, P.O. Box 13400, Sacramento, CA 95813.

FOSTER, THOMAS SALISBURY, b. Stratford, Ont, May 30, 21; m. 41; c. 2. BIOCHEMISTRY. B.Sc, Western Ontario, 48, M.Sc, 49, Ph.D.(biochem), 54. RES. OFF. BIOCHEM, ANIMAL RES. INST, CAN. DEPT. AGR, 53- Can. Army, 39-44, Lt. Can. Biochem. Soc; Brit. Biochem. Soc; Can. Soc. Animal Prod. Precursors of deoxyribonucleic acid; pregnancy hormones; adrenal steroid hormones and their relationship to carbohydrate metabolism, adaptation, and metabolism of mucopolysaccharides; pesticides; residues; metabolites; effects on metabolism. Address: Biochemistry Section, Animal Research Institute, Canada Dept. of Agriculture, C.E.F, Ottawa, Ontario, K1A 0C5, Can.

FOSTER, VIRGINIA, b. Joseph, Ore, Feb. 4, 14. BOTANY. B.S, Washington (Seattle), 49, M.S, 50; Ph.D.(bot, plant path), Ohio State, 54. Assoc. prof. biol, Judson Col, 56-58; Miss. State Col. Women, 58-59; life sci, La Verne Col, 59-60; asst. prof. BIOL. SCI, California Western, 60-61; teacher, PENSACOLA JR. COL, 61-66, asst. prof, 66-70, ASSOC. PROF, 70- Summers, Am. Physiol. Soc. fel, Oregon, 57, res, dept. bot, Imp. Col, London, 59. U.S.W.M.C.R, 44-46. Am. Phytopath. Soc; Soc. Indust. Microbiol. Physiological mycology; physiological relations between parasitic fungi and plant hosts, especially the production and action of wilting toxins. Address: Dept. of Biology, Pensacola Junior College, 1000 College Blvd, Pensacola, FL 32504.

FOSTER, WALTER D(EAN), b. Columbia, Mo, Mar. 21, 17; m. 41; c. 2. MATHEMATICAL STATISTICS. A.B, Grinnell Col, 39; M.S, N.C. State, 49, Ph.D, 50. Biometrician & NE-4 coordinator math. statist, West Virginia, 50-54; math. statistician, U.S. ARMY BIOL. LABS, 54-58, CHIEF prog. res. br, 58-60, exp. design br, 60-62, BIOMATH. DIV, 62- U.S.A, 43-46, Lt. Am. Statist. Asn; Biomet. Soc. Application of experimental design and the analysis of experimental data in aerobiology; mathematical biology. Address: U.S. Army Biological Labs, Ft. Detrick, Frederick, MD 21701.

FOSTER, W(ALTER) E(DWARD), b. Cincinnati, Ohio, Oct. 6, 24; m. 44; c. 2. ORGANIC CHEMISTRY. Ch.E, Cincinnati, 49, M.S, 51, Ph.D.(chem), 53. Res. chemist, ETHYL CORP, 53-57, res. supvr, 57-61, asst. dir, 61-63, dir. chem. res. & develop, 63-65, pioneer res, 65-68, TECH. DIR. RES. & DEVELOP, 68- C.Eng, 43-46, 1st Lt. Am. Chem. Soc; Am. Inst. Chem. Industrial inorganic, inorganic and organometallic research. Address: Ethyl Corp, P.O. Box 341, Baton Rouge, LA 70821.

FOSTER, WALTER H, JR, b. Freehold, N.J, Dec. 29, 33. PHYSICAL & ANALYTICAL CHEMISTRY. B.S, Phila. Textile Inst, 55; Ph.D.(anal. chem), Mass. Inst. Technol, 59. Res. explor. chemist, org. chem. div, AM. CYANAMID CO, BOUND BROOK, 59-66, res. chemist, 66-68, sr. res. chemist, 68-70, SR. SYSTS. ANALYST, RES. & DEVELOP. DEPT, 70- Am. Chem. Soc. Analytical spectroscopy; physical chemistry of dyeing; photochemistry. Address: R.R. 3, Millbrook Lane, Colts Neck, NJ 07722.

FOSTER, WILFRID R(AYMOND), b. Fredericton, N.B, Can, Feb. 14, 13; nat; m. 44. MINERALOGY. B.S, New Brunswick, 34; Knights of Columbus fel, 34-38, M.S, Catholic Univ, 36; Penfield fel, Chicago, 39, Ph.D.(geol), 40. Instr. petrol, Catholic Univ, 40-41; mineral preparation, Pa. State Col, 41-42; ceramic petrographer, Champion Spark Plug Co, 42-52; assoc. prof. MINERAL, OHIO STATE UNIV, 52-57, PROF. & CHMN. DEPT, 57- AAAS; fel. Mineral. Soc. Am; fel. Am. Ceramic Soc; Geochem. Soc; Mineral. Soc. Gt. Brit. & Ireland; Meteoritical Soc; Am. Geophys. Union; Mineral. Asn. Can. Petrography and x-ray diffraction of ceramic raw materials and products; solid-phase reactions; froth-flotation; high temperature phase equilibrium of silicates; the sillimanite minerals; thermal behavior of non-metallic minerals. Address: Dept. of Mineralogy, Ohio State University, 104 W. 19th Ave, Columbus, OH 43210.

FOSTER, WILLIAM B(URNHAM), b. Greenfield, Mass, July 30, 30; m. 54; c. 1. PARASITOLOGY, INVERTEBRATE ZOOLOGY. B.S, Massachusetts, 52, M.A, 54; Ph.D.(parasite physiol), Rice Inst, 57. Instr. gen. biol, invert. zool. & helminthol, RUTGERS UNIV, 57-60, asst. prof, 60-64, assoc. prof. ZOOL, 64-70, PROF, 70- Am. Soc. Parasitol. Physiology and immunology of parasites; protein metabolisms; life histories. Address: Dept. of Zoology, Rutgers, The State University, New Brunswick, NJ 08903.

FOSTER, WILLIAM HALE, b. Los Angeles, Calif, Mar. 3, 28; m. 54; c. 2. PHYSICS, ENGINEERING. B.A, California, Los Angeles, 52. Asst. physicist, West Coast Res. Co, 50-52; electronic engr, Electronic Eng. Co. Calif, 54-58; sr. engr, Aerojet Gen. Co, 58-59; proj. mgr, Librascope Div, Gen. Precision, Inc, 59-60; sr. physicist & dept. mgr, electro optical systs. div, Xerox Corp, 60-67; tech. dir. earth sci, Teledyne Co, 67-69; PRES. & GEN. MGR, HEURISTICS, INC, 69- Guest lectr, 60- U.S.N, 46-48. Electronic engineering; infrared physics; aerospace instrumentation; space physics; project management. Address: Heuristics, Inc, 2361 E. Foothill Blvd, Pasadena, CA 91107.

FOSTER, WILLIAM R(ODERICK), b. Springfield, Mo, June 16, 24; m. 46; c. 5. PHYSICAL CHEMISTRY. B.S, Southwest. Mo. State Col, 47; Ph.D. (chem), Wash. Univ, 50. Sr. res. tech, petrol. prod. res, FIELD RES. LAB, MOBIL RES. & DEVELOP. CORP, 50-55, res. assoc, 55-60, sect. supvr, 60-70, MGR. RESERVOIR MECH. RES, 70- U.S.A.A.F, 42-46, 1st Lt. Am. Inst. Chem. Eng; Soc. Petrol. Eng. Continuum mechanics; fluid mechanics; in porous media; interfacial phenomena; petroleum production. Address: 3917 Holliday Rd, Dallas, TX 75224.

FOSTER, W(ILLIS) R(OY), b. New Orleans, La, Dec. 8, 28; m. 57; c. 3. MEDICINE, BIOCHEMISTRY. B.A, La. State, 50, M.S, & M.D, 57; North Carolina, 50-52; fel, Hopkins, 58-59. Res. assoc. pharmacol, George Washington, 57-58; fel. physiol. chem, Hopkins, 58-59; prfnl. assoc, SCI. INFO. EXCHANGE, SMITHSONIAN INST, WASH, D.C, 59-63, ASSOC. DIR. LIFE SCI, 64- AAAS; Am. Chem. Soc. General medicine; pharmacology. Address: 6117 Greentree Rd, Bethesda, MD 20034.

FOSTVEDT, THORLEIF, b. Wetaskiwin, Alta, July 18, 13. MATHEMATICS. B.Sc, Alberta, 42; M.S, Chicago, 48. Sessional lectr. MATH, UNIV. ALBERTA, 45-50, asst. prof, 50-56, ASSOC. PROF, 56-, ACAD. SECY. DEPT, 64-, asst. dean, faculty grad. studies, 61-64. R.C.A.F, 42-45. Math. Asn. Am; Can. Math. Cong. General mathematics; finance; teaching of mathematics. Address: Dept. of Mathematics, University of Alberta, Edmonton, Alta, Can.

FOTH, H(ENRY) D(ONALD), b. Norwalk, Wis, Feb. 9, 23; m. 48. SOILS. B.S, Univ. Wis, 47, M.S, 48; Ph.D, Iowa State Col, 52. Instr. SOILS, Iowa State Col, 48-52; assoc. prof, Agr. & Mech. Col. Tex, 52-55; MICH. STATE UNIV, 55-60, PROF, 60- Summer consult, Earth Sci. Curriculum Proj, Colo, 64, 65; mem, Int. Soil Sci. Cong. Educ. award, Am. Soc. Agron, 59. U.S.A.A.F, 43-46, 1st Lt. AAAS; Soil Sci. Soc. Am. Morphology and genesis of Brunizem soils; soil fertility and root distribution of field crops. Address: Dept. of Soil Science, Michigan State University, East Lansing, MI 48823.

FOTI, GIUSEPPE, b. Furci Siculo, Italy, Jan. 7, 30. INDUSTRIAL CHEMISTRY. Dr.Sc.(indust. chem), Padua, 55. Instr, indust. chem. lab, E.Molinari Inst. Chem, Italy, 55-56; res. fel, Milan Polytech, 57-59; U.S. Bur. Mines, Okla, 60; supvr. develop. & control, Novamont Corp, W.Va, 61-63; mgr. chem. sect, cent. res. labs, Continental Copper & Steel Indust, 64-65; PROD. MGR, NOVAMONT CORP, N.Y, 65- Am. Chem. Soc; Soc. Plastics Eng. Product and market development of polypropylene plastics; analytical techniques for catalysts; plastics extrusion & rubber vulcanization processes; study of acoustically transparent materials; studies on crude oil & petroleum processes. Address: 922 Lester Ave, Mamaronek, NY 10543.

FOTINO, MIRCEA, b. Bucharest, Rumania, June 6, 27; U.S. citizen; m. 69. BIOPHYSICS. Lic. ès. Sci, Univ. Paris, 51; Ph.D.(high-energy physics), Univ. Calif, Berkeley, 58. Asst. physics, Univ. Calif, Berkeley, 52-58; sr. researcher, Nat. Ctr. Sci. Res, Polytech. Sch, Paris, 58-60; res. physicist & lectr. physics, Univ. Calif, Berkeley, 61; res. fel. physics, Cambridge Electron Accelerator, Harvard, 61-68, res. fel. BIOL, univ, 69-70; ASSOC. PROF, UNIV. COLO, BOULDER, 71- Am. Phys. Soc; N.Y. Acad. Sci. Cosmic-ray pi mesons; K-beams in proton synchrotrons; polarized hydrogen targets; vacuum chamber for electron alternating gradient synchrotrons, beam extraction; absolute calibration and monitoring of high-energy beams; inverse Compton effect and polarized photons; structure of biological materials by high-voltage electron microscopy. Address: Dept. of Molecular, Cellular & Developmental Biology, University of Colorado, Boulder, CO 80302.

FOTLAND, RICHARD ALLEN, b. Cleveland, Ohio, Feb. 17, 33; m. 56; c. 3. PHOTOGRAPHY, INFORMATION SCIENCE. B.S, Case, 54, M.S, 58. Res. assoc, HORIZONS RES. INC, 54-56, proj. supvr, 56-61, DEPT. HEAD PHYSICS, 61-, ASSOC. DIR. RES, 66- Am. Chem. Soc; Soc. Photog. Sci. & Eng. Development of organic photochemical systems and applications to photography; photoconducting in amorphous insulators. Address: Horizons Research Inc, 23800 Mercantile Rd, Cleveland, OH 44122.

FOUBERT, EDW(ARD) L(OUIS), JR, b. Marquette, Mich, Sept. 2, 17; m. 39; c. 3. MICROBIOLOGY. B.S, Gonzaga, 39; fel, Washington (Seattle), 44-46; M.S, Washington (Seattle), 46, Ph.D.(bact), 47. Res. chemist, V.O.D. Oil Co, 39-41; instr. chem, Gonzaga, 41-42, asst. prof. biol, 42-44; bact, Washington (Seattle), 46-47; assoc. prof. biol, Gonzaga, 47-50, prof. & chmn. dept, 50-54; DIR. RES, HOLLISTER-STIER, INC, 53- Control chemist, Inland Empire Refineries, 41-43. AAAS; Am. Soc. Microbiol; Am. Chem. Soc; Am. Acad. Allergy; N.Y. Acad. Sci. Taxonomy of anaerobic cocci; bacterial fermentations and ecology; nature of allergens and allergic response. Address: Hollister-Stier Labs, Box 3145, Terminal Annex, Spokane, WA 99220.

FOUCHAUX, ROBERT DARROW, b. North Haledon, N.J, Jan. 27, 34; m. 56; c. 2. SOLID STATE PHYSICS. B.S. & B.A, Lehigh, 56; M.S, Illinois, 58, Ph.D.(physics), 63. ASST. PROF. PHYSICS, LEHIGH UNIV, 63- Am. Phys. Soc. Defects in solids, particularly equilibrium point defect structure of ionic crystals. Address: Dept. of Physics, Lehigh University, Bethlehem, PA 18015.

FOUCHER, WALTER DAVID, JR, b. Bennington, Vt, Aug. 4, 36; m. 58; c. 2. PHYSICAL INORGANIC CHEMISTRY. A.B, St. Michael's Col.(Vt), 58; M.S, Vermont, 59; Ph.D.(phys. inorg. chem), Florida, 62. Chemist, Texaco Res. Ctr, 62-63, sr. chemist, 63-67, res. chemist, 67-69, GROUP LEADER, LUBRICANTS RES, TEXACO, INC, 69- Vis. instr, State Univ. N.Y. Col. New Paltz, 64-68; vis. lectr, Marist Col. Am. Chem. Soc.(ed, Mid-Hudson Chemist, 63-69). Preparation catalysts and catalyst supports for hydrocarbon conversion; additives and lubricating oils for internal combustion engines, gasoline and diesel. Address: 71 Gold Rd, Wappingers Falls, NY 12590.

FOUGERE, PAUL F(RANCIS), b. Cambridge, Mass, Feb. 29, 32; m. 52; c. 6. PHYSICS. B.S, Boston Col, 52, M.S, 53; Ph.D.(physics), Boston Univ, 65. Physicist, Naval Res. Lab, 53-54; tech. aircraft engr, Gen. Elec. Co, Mass, 54-55; PHYSICIST GEOMAGNETISM, AIR FORCE CAMBRIDGE RES. LABS, 55- Int. Asn. Geomag. & Aeronomy; Am. Geophys. Union. Spherical harmonic analysis of the earth's main magnetic field; electronic structure of atoms and of diatomic molecules; space physics; terrestrial magnetic activity. Address: Air Force Cambridge Research Labs, Hanscom Field, Bedford, MA 01730.

FOUGERON, MYRON GEORGE, b. Morris, Minn, July 20, 32; m. 59; c. 2. PHYSIOLOGY, ENDOCRINOLOGY. B.S, Sam Houston State Col, 59, M.A, 65; Ph.D.(zool), Texas A&M, 67. Teacher, Jr. high sch, Tex, 59-61; participant, acad. year inst. biophys, col. med, Baylor, 66-67; asst. prof. BIOL, KEARNEY STATE COL, 67-70, ASSOC. PROF, 70- Participant, summer inst. radiation biol, Univ. New Mexico, 68. U.S.A, 53-55, Am. Inst. Biol. Sci. Effect of radiation on placental transport; effect of hypophysectomy on the endocrine glands of the American chameleon, Anolis carolinensis. Address: Dept. of Biology, Kearney State College, Kearney, NE 68847.

FOULIS, DAVID J(AMES), b. Hinsdale, Ill, July 26, 30; m. 56, 62; c. 3. MATHEMATICS. B.A, Miami (Fla), 52, M.S, 53; Nat. Sci. Found. fel, Chicago, 54-55; Ph.D, Tulane, 58. Asst. prof. MATH, Lehigh, 58-59; Wayne State, 59-63, assoc. prof, Univ. Fla, 63-65; PROF, UNIV. MASS, AMHERST, 65- Am. Math. Soc; Math. Asn. Am. Semigroup theory; operator algebras; topology. Address: Dept. of Mathematics, University of Massachusetts, Amherst, MA 01002.

FOULK, CLINTON ROSS, b. Wichita, Kans, Jan. 24, 30; m. 58; c. 1. COMPUTER SCIENCE, MATHEMATICS. B.A, Kansas, 51; Lund, 51-52; fel, Illinois, Urbana, 56-58, M.A, 58, Ph.D.(math), 63. Res. asst. comput. prog, digital comput. lab, Illinois, Urbana, 58-62; asst. prof. math, OHIO STATE UNIV, 63-66, COMPUT. & INFO. SCI, 66-68, ASSOC. PROF, 68-, summer res. grant, info. sci. res. ctr, 67. Summer manpower estimator, indust. eng. dept, Boeing Airplane Co, Kans, 57. U.S.A.F, 52-56, S/Sgt. Asn. Comput. Mach. Computer systems programming. Address: Dept. of Computer & Information Science, Ohio State University, 2024 Neil Ave, Columbus, OH 43210.

FOULKE, D(ONALD) GARDNER, b. Burnham, Pa, Aug. 19, 12; m. 40; c. 4. ORGANIC CHEMISTRY, ELECTROCHEMISTRY. B.S, Juniata Col, 34; M.S, Rutgers, 37, Ph.D.(chem), 41; Munich, 37. Asst, Rutgers, 35-38, instr.

chem, 38-40; asst. prof, Beaver Col, 40-42; res. assoc, A. Kenneth Graham & Assoc, 41-42; res. chemist, Jenkintown Lab, United Eng. & Foundry Co, 42; asst. chief chemist, Repub. Steel Corp, 42-43; chief chemist, Houdaille-Hershey Corp, Ill, 43-45; dir. anal. lab, Foster D. Snell, Inc, N.Y, 45-46; process electrochemist & chief chemist, Hanson-Van Winkle-Munning Co, N.J, 46-51; mgr. electrochem. res, 53-59; DIR. RES, SEL-REX CORP, NUTLEY, 59- Tech. dir, Laboratorium, 48-; assoc. chemist, bur. agr. & indust. chem, east. regional res. lab, U.S. Dept. Agr, 42; chmn, Nat. Task Comt. Indust. Wastes; co-ed, Electroplaters Process Control Handbook, 63. With Atomic Energy Comn, 44. Am. Chem. Soc; Am. Electroplaters Soc. (gold medal, 45, 57, 64, exec. secy, 51-53); Am. Soc. Metals; Electrochem. Soc. Electroplating and metal finishing; analytical, colorimetric and instrumental organic chemistry; electroplating of tin from an acid solution; reaction of secondary and tertiary dialkylmagnesiums with epichlorohydrin; reaction of dioxane with the Grignard reagent. Address: 455 Johnston Dr, Watchung, Plainfield, NJ 07060.

FOULKES, ERNEST C(HARLES), b. Germany, Aug. 20, 24; U.S. citizen; m. 46; c. 4. PHYSIOLOGY. B.Sc, Univ. Sydney, 46, M.Sc, 47; D.Phil.(biochem), Oxford, 52. Investr, Nat. Health Med. Res. Coun, Australia, 46-49; assoc, May Inst, 52-65; assoc. prof. ENVIRON. HEALTH & PHYSIOL, UNIV. CINCINNATI, 65-70, PROF, 70- Estab. investr, Am. Heart Asn, 56-61. Biochem. Soc; Biophys. Soc; Am. Soc. Biol. Chem; Am. Physiol. Soc; Soc. Exp. Biol. & Med. Action of heme enzymes; active transport; cell permeability, renal physiology and toxicology. Address: Depts. of Environmental Health & Physiology, University of Cincinnati College of Medicine, Eden Ave, Cincinnati, OH 45219.

FOULKES, J(OHN) D(AVID), b. India, Oct. 11, 24; nat; m. 50; c. 3. ENGINEERING. B.A, Oxford, 49; Ph.D.(eng), Cambridge, 53. Asst. prof. eng, Brown, 54-55; mem. staff, Bell Tel. Labs, 55-61; Arthur D. Little, Inc, 61-68; PRES, COMMUN. TECH. INC, 68- Applied mathematics; electrical engineering. Address: 4 A St, Burlington, MA 01803.

FOULKES, ROBERT H(UGH), b. Wis, Nov. 14, 18; m. 44; c. 1. EXPERIMENTAL ZOOLOGY. A.B, Coe Col, 40; M.S, Iowa, 47, Ph.D.(zool), 51. Instr. zool, Iowa, 47-51; res. fel, Edsel Ford Inst. Med. Res, 51-55; asst. prof. biol, Northern Illinois, 55-56; St. Louis, 56-59; assoc. scientist, res. div, Dr. Salsbury's Labs, 59-61; assoc. prof. biol, WIS. STATE UNIV-PLATTEVILLE, 62-69, PROF. ZOOL, 69- Independent consult, 61- U.S.N.R, 42-45. AAAS; Am. Soc. Zool; Wildlife Disease Asn; Am. Inst. Biol. Sci. Regeneration; neoplasms; histochemistry; toxicology; aerobiology. Address: Dept. of Zoology, Wisconsin State University-Platteville, Platteville, WI 53818.

FOULKS, J(AMES) G(RIGSBY), b. Bay City, Texas, Sept. 18, 16; m. 47; c. 2. PHARMACOLOGY. B.A, Rice Inst, 39; Ph.D.(biol. sci), Hopkins, 43; M.D, Columbia, 50. Lab. asst, Rice Inst, 37-39; Rochester, 39-40; Hopkins, 40-42; instr. anat, Ohio State, 42-43; lab. asst. pharmacol. & Nat. Heart Inst. fel, Columbia, 50-51; PROF. PHARMACOL, UNIV. B.C, 51-, head dept, 51-71. U.S.A.A.F, 43-46, 1st Lt. Am. Physiol. Soc; Soc. Exp. Biol. & Med; Am. Soc. Pharmacol. & Exp. Therapeut; Pharmacol. Soc. Can; Can. Physiol. Soc. Water and electrolyte metabolism; renal and cardiovascular physiology and pharmacology. Address: Dept. of Pharmacology, University of British Columbia, Vancouver 8, B.C, Can.

FOULKS, SIDNEY M(ARSHALL), b. Ness City, Kans, Mar. 15, 20; m. 45; c. 2. MATHEMATICS. B.A, Kansas, 48, M.A, 50; Socony fel, Vienna Tech, 52-55, Dr.Sci, 55. Physicist, Boeing Airplane Co, 40-42; mathematician, field res. lab, Magnolia Petrol. Co, 50-53, 55-64; Socony Mobil Oil Co, 64-68; MGR. EXPLOR. RES. DEVELOP, MOBIL RES. & DEVELOP. CORP, 68- U.S.N, 42-45. Am. Math. Soc; Sci. Res. Soc. Am. Fluid mechanics, especially in porus media; approximate solutions of differential equations; exploration for natural resources. Address: Mobil Research & Development Corp, P.O. Box 900, Dallas, TX 75221.

FOULSER, DAVID A, b. Columbus, Ohio, Apr. 10, 33; m. 56; c. 3. MATHEMATICS. B.A, Ohio State, 55; NATO fel, Oxford, 62-63; Ph.D.(math), Michigan, 63. Instr. MATH, Chicago, 63-65; asst. prof, UNIV. ILL, CHICAGO CIRCLE, 65-68, ASSOC. PROF, 68- U.S.A.F, 56-58, 1st Lt. Am. Math. Soc. Projective planes; group theory. Address: Dept. of Mathematics, University of Illinois at Chicago Circle College of Liberal Arts & Sciences, Box 4348, Chicago, IL 60680.

FOUNTAIN, CLIFFORD W, b. Long Beach, Calif, Sept. 12, 30; m. 55; c. 2. METALS, PHYSICS. B.A, Oregon, 59, M.A, 60. PHYSICIST, U.S. Dept. Army, D.C, 60-62; U.S. Naval Ord. Test Sta, 62-69, MICHELSON LAB, NAVAL WEAPONS CTR, 69- Res. assoc, Univ. Ore, 62. U.S.A.F, 51-55, S/Sgt. Effects of high intensity ultrasound and neutrons on lattice imperfections in metals; proton irradiation of semiconductors. Address: Code 5525, Michelson Lab, Naval Weapons Center, China Lake, CA 93555.

FOUNTAIN, LEONARD D(U BOIS), b. Missouri Valley, Iowa, Jan. 25, 29; m. 59; c. 1. MATHEMATICS. A.B, Chicago, 50, M.S, 53; Ph.D.(math), Nebraska, 60. Instr. MATH, Nebraska, 58-60; asst. prof, SAN DIEGO STATE COL, 60-64, assoc. prof, 64-70, PROF, 70- U.S.A, 53-55. Am. Math. Soc; Math. Asn. Am. Ordinary differential equations; convex functions and their applications to existence theorems for differential equations. Address: Dept. of Mathematics, San Diego State College, San Diego, CA 92115.

FOUNTAIN, MATTHEW KEITH, b. Arcata, Calif, Aug. 30, 18; m. 53. CHEMISTRY. B.S, Univ. Calif, Berkeley, 40. Chemist, Golden State Co, Ltd, 41-42; paint chemist, PAINT LAB, MARE ISLAND NAVAL SHIPYARD, VALLEJO, 42-50, res. chemist, 50-67, SUPVRY. RES. CHEMIST, 67- Am. Chem. Soc. Protective coatings for ships; antifouling, fire resistant, anticorrosive and camouflage paints. Address: 24 Romine Way, Vallejo, CA 94590.

FOUQUETTE, M(ARTIN) J(OHN), JR, b. Phila, Pa, June 14, 30; m. 63; c. 2. ZOOLOGY. B.A, Texas, 51, M.A, 53, Ph.D.(zool), 59. Interim asst. prof. ZOOL, Florida, 59-61; asst. prof, Southwestern Louisiana, 61-65; ASSOC. PROF, ARIZ. STATE UNIV, 65- U.S.A.F, 53-58, Capt. AAAS; Am. Inst. Biol. Sci; Soc. Study Amphibians & Reptiles; Am. Soc. Ichthyol. & Herpet; Soc. Study Evolution; Soc. Syst. Zool. Herpetology; vertebrate speciation and ecology; isolating mechanisms in amphibians and reptiles; bioacoustics; vertebrate biology. Address: Dept. of Zoology, Arizona State University, Tempe, AZ 85281.

FOURNELLE, H(AROLD) J(OHN), b. White Bear, Minn, Feb. 1, 09; m. 45; c. 2. BACTERIOLOGY. B.A, Minnesota, 38, M.S, 41, Ph.D.(bact), 49. Clin. lab. asst, Murphy Labs, St. Paul, 35-39; asst, Minnesota, 40; asst. sanitarian, Minn. State Dept. Health, 40-42; asst, Minnesota, 46-49; bacteriologist, Arctic Health Res. Ctr, U.S. Pub. Health Serv, Anchorage, Alaska, 50-58; with U.S. Opers. Mission, Int. Co-op. Admin, Colombia, S.Am, 59-61; div. res. serv, NAT. INSTS. HEALTH, 61-62, EXEC. SECY, career develop. rev. br, div. res. grants, 62-70, TRAINING GRANTS & AWARDS BR, NAT. INST. NEUROL. DISEASES & STROKE, 70- Sanit.C, 42-46, Capt. AAAS; Am. Soc. Microbiol; Am. Pub. Health Asn; Asn. Mil. Surg. U.S. Clinical, enteric and sanitary bacteriology; training grants and awards administration. Address: National Institute of Neurological Diseases & Stroke, National Institutes of Health, Westwood Bldg, Room 7A14, Bethesda, MD 20014.

FOURNEY, M(ICHAEL) E(UGENE), b. Blue Jay, W.Va, Jan. 30, 36. AERONAUTICS. B.S, West Virginia, 58; M.S, Calif. Inst. Tech, 59, Ph.D.(aeronaut), 63. Aerospace engr, Bölkow Entwicklungen K.G, Ger, 63-64; res. asst. prof. AERONAUT. & ASTRONAUT, UNIV. WASH, 64-69, RES. ASSOC. PROF, 69- Consult, Math. Sci. Northwest Inc, 60- Soc. Exp. Stress Anal; Optical Soc. Am. Solid and experimental mechanics. Address: Dept. of Aeronautics & Astronautics, University of Washington, Seattle, WA 98105.

FOURNIER, GEORGE RICHARD, b. San José, Costa Rica, May 6, 14; U.S. citizen; m. 44; c. 2. PALYNOLOGY, STRATIGRAPHY. B.S, Univ. Costa Rica, 38; B.A, N.Y. Univ, 47, M.A, 50. Acct, Banco Nacional de Seguros, Costa Rica, 39-41; res. micropaleontologist, Am. Mus. Nat. Hist, N.Y, 48-51; micropaleontologist-stratigrapher, Mene Grande Oil Co, Venezuela, 51-56, chief palynologist, 56-64; SECT. HEAD PALYNOLOGY, GULF RES. & DEVELOP. CO, 64- Instr, N.Y. Univ, 48-50; field geologist, Geol. Surv. Newf, 49; res. grant, Am. Mus. Nat. Hist, 49-50; del, First Int. Cong. Palynology, Ariz, 58; Cerro Venamo Exped, Venezuelan Guiana, 63; mem. steering comt, Kremp Palynology Lit. Proj, 67-71. Am. Asn. Petrol. Geol; Am. Asn. Stratig. Palynologists (v.pres, 69, pres, 70); Venezuelan Soc. Geol. Palynology of the Cretaceous, Canada and Africa; nannofossils of the Cretaceous, worldwide; use of computers in palynology; analysis of data and world literature. Address: Gulf Research & Development Co, 11111 Wilcrest, Houston, TX 77036.

FOURNIER, LOUIS B(YRON), b. New Orleans, La, Jan. 11, 43; m. 65; c. 2. ANALYTICAL & INORGANIC CHEMISTRY. B.S, Southeast. La. Univ, 65; Ph.D.(anal. chem), La. State Univ, 71. RES. CHEMIST, ELECTROCHEM. DEPT, CHESTNUT RUN LAB, E.I. DU PONT DE NEMOURS & CO, INC, 70- Pollution abatement technology; control of cyanide in waste effluents; applications of hydrogen peroxide, especially to pollution problems; trimethylsilylation uses; sugar chemistry, especially analytical procedures for solutions. Address: Electrochemicals Dept. Chestnut Run Lab, E.I. du Pont de Nemours & Co, Inc, Wilmington, DE 19898.

FOURNIER, MAURILLE JOSEPH, JR, b. Montpelier, Vt, Jan. 13, 40; m. 64; c. 2. BIOCHEMISTRY. B.A, Vermont, 62; Fla. State, 62-63; Ph.D.(molecular biol), Dartmouth Col, 68. Res. biochemist, Walter Reed Army Med. Ctr, Walter Reed Army Inst. Res, 68-70; AM. CANCER SOC. FEL, NAT. INSTS. HEALTH, 70- Med.Serv.C, U.S.A, 68-70, Res, 70-, Capt. AAAS; Am. Chem. Soc. Transfer ribonucleic acid biosynthesis, structure and function; protein synthesis; mitochondrial autonomy. Address: Lab. of Biochemical Genetics, National Institutes of Health, Bethesda, MD 20014.

FOURNIER, PIERRE WILLIAM, b. Sudbury, Ont, Jan. 17, 27; m. 51; c. 3. MEDICINE. M.D, Ottawa, 53. Pathologist, Ottawa Gen. Hosp, 60-66; DIR. LABS. & CHIEF DEPT. PATH, RIVERSIDE HOSP, OF OTTAWA, 66- Lectr, Ottawa, 60-64, asst. prof, 65. Cert. path, Royal Col. Physicians & Surgeons Can, 61. R.C.A.M.C.R, Maj. Can. Med. Asn; Can. Asn. Path; Can. Soc. Forensic Sci; Can. Cytol. Coun. Exfoliative cytology; medicolegal pathology; toxicology. Address: Dept. of Pathology, Riverside Hospital of Ottawa, 1967 Riverside Dr, Ottawa, Ont, Can. K1H 7W9.

FOURNIER, ROBERT O(RVILLE), b. San Diego, Calif, Jan. 14, 32; m. 60; c. 2. GEOLOGY. A.B, Harvard, 54; fel. & Ph.D.(geol), California, 58. Assoc. prof. lectr. geol, George Wash. Univ, 58-59; GEOLOGIST, U.S. GEOL. SURV, 58- Geol. Soc. Am; Mineral. Soc. Am; Geochem. Soc; Am. Geophys. Union; Soc. Econ. Geol; Int. Asn. Geochem. & Cosmochem; Geochem. Soc. Japan. Geologic and geochemical aspects of geothermal energy; geochemistry of hydrothermal solutions and hydrothermal alteration; experimental studies of solution mineral reactions at high temperatures and high pressures. Address: Geologic Division, U.S. Geological Survey, 345 Middlefield Rd, Menlo Park, CA 94025.

FOURNIER-MASSEY, G. GISELE, b. Amos, Que, May 19, 33; m. 66; c. 3. PNEUMOLOGY. B.A, Univ. Montreal, 53, M.D, 59; M.Sc, McGill Univ, 64. Dir. pulmonary function lab, Notre-Dame Hosp, Montreal, 63-66; ASST. PROF. MED, FACULTY MED. & DIR. PULMONARY FUNCTION LAB, UNIV. HOSP. CTR, UNIV. SHERBROOKE, 66-; ASST. DIR, PULMONARY FUNCTION LAB, HÔPITAL HÔTEL-DIEU, 68- Fed. Prov. Govt. fel, 62-64; Med. Res. Coun. Can. fel, 66-68; Med. Res. Coun. Que. estab. grant, 69; consult. adv, Med. Bd. Physiol. Technol, 71. Am. Thoracic Soc; fel. Am. Col. Chest Physicians; Can. Med. Asn. Pulmonary physiology; pneumoconioses; curriculum evaluation of chest. Address: University Hospital Center, Sherbrooke, Que, Can.

FOURT, LYMAN (EDWIN), b. Aurora, Mo, May 27, 12; m. 37; c. 3. TEXTILE PHYSICS. A.B, Missouri, 33; Ph.D.(zool), Washington (St. Louis), 37. Res. instr. chem, Chicago, 37-39, instr. & Logan fel. bacter. & parasitol, 39-40; res. assoc. pharmacol, Washington (St. Louis), 40-41; Textile Found, Nat. Bur. Standards, 41-45; Harris Res. Labs, 45-57, ASST. DIR, 57-69, HARRIS RES. LABS. DEPT, GILLETTE RES. INST, 69- Sci. investigator, Tech. Indust. Intel. Cmt; Foreign Econ. Admin; U.S. Dept. Commerce, 45. With Office Sci. Res. & Develop; U.S.A, 44. Am. Chem. Soc; Am. Soc. Test. & Mat; Fiber Soc; Am. Asn. Textile Technol; Am. Asn. Textile Chem. & Colorists; biophys. Soc. Physics of textile fibers and fabrics; textile finishing; durability and comfort of clothing; unimolecular films. Address: Harris Research Labs. Dept, Gillette Research Institute, 1413 Research Blvd, Rockville, MD 20850.

FOUSHEE, J. HENRY SMITH, JR, b. Salisbury, N.C, Aug. 13, 23; m. 51; c. 1. PATHOLOGY. M.D, Jefferson Med. Col, 47. Fel. path, North Carolina, 50-51; assoc. pathologist, Vet. Admin. Hosp, Durham, 53-54; instr. path, Duke, 53-54; BOWMAN GRAY SCH. MED, 54-59, asst. prof, 59-61, ASSOC. PROF, 61-71, CLIN. OBSTET. & GYNEC, 71-; DIR. LABS, MED. PARK HOSP, 71- Consult, Vet. Admin. Hosp, Salisbury, 55; Nat. Cancer Inst, 59. Dipl, Am. Bd. Path, 55. U.S.A, 44-46; U.S.A.F, 51-53. AAAS; N.Y. Acad. Sci. Cancer; cytology. Address: Suite 124, Forsyth Medical Park, Winston-Salem, NC 27103.

FOUSS, JAMES L(AWRENCE), b. Warsaw, Ohio, Feb. 22, 36; m. 57; c. 2. AGRICULTURAL ENGINEERING. B.Agr.Eng, Ohio State Univ, 59, M.Sc, 62, Ph.D, 71. RES. AGR. ENGR, U.S. DEPT. AGR, 60-, spec. award, 62, performance award, 68. AAAS; Am. Soc. Agr. Eng; Soil Conserv. Soc. Am. Development of new equipment and materials for the high-speed and low-cost installation of subsurface drains in agricultural cropland. Address: Agricultural Research Service, U.S. Dept. of Agriculture, Ohio State University, 2073 Neil Ave, Columbus, OH 43210.

FOUST, ALAN S(HIVERS), b. Dublin, Tex, June 26, 08; m. 39; c. 4. CHEMICAL ENGINEERING. B.S, Texas, 28, M.S, 30; Ph.D.(chem. eng), Michigan, 38. Tutor chem, Texas, 28-30, 32-33, instr, 33-35; chemist, Magnolia Petrol. Co, 30-32; Tex. Pac. Coal & Oil Co, 32-33; assoc. prof. chem, col. mines & metall, Texas, 35-36; instr. chem. eng, Michigan, 37-39, asst. prof, 39-46, assoc. prof, 46-48, prof, 48-52; prof. CHEM. ENG, LEHIGH UNIV, 52-65, McCANN PROF, 65-, dean, col. eng, 62-65, head dept. chem. eng, 52-62. C.W.S, 42-46, Lt. Col; Legion of Merit, 46. Am. Inst. Chem. Eng. Heat transfer; drying; evaporation. Address: Dept. of Chemical Engineering, Lehigh University, Bethlehem, PA 18015.

FOUST, HAROLD, b. Waynesboro, Pa, Sept. 17, 19; m. 45; c. 2. CHEMICAL ENGINEERING. B.S, Pa. State, 42; Ch.E, Virginia, 43; Princeton, 45-48. Instr. chem. eng, Virginia, 42-45; res. assoc, Knolls Atomic Power Lab, Gen. Elec. Co, 48-54; proj. engr, U.S. Naval Propellant Plant, 54-66; mem. staff, adv. waste treatment br, Fed. Water Pollution Control Admin, 66-70; SPEC. STAFF ASST, DIV. PROCESS RES. & DEVELOP, ENVIRON. PROTECTION AGENCY, WATER QUAL. OFF, 70- Am. Inst. Chem. Eng; Am. Inst. Chem; Am. Chem. Soc. Mixing; facilities planning; solid propellants; water quality management research and development. Address: 9701 Taylor Ave, Washington, DC 20022.

FOUST, RUSSELL A(TWOOD), JR, b. Brooklyn, N.Y, Mar. 23, 23; m. 63; c. 1. ELECTROCHEMISTRY, PHYSICAL CHEMISTRY. B.S, Mass. Inst. Tech, 46. Chem. engr, Grasselli Chem. Dept, E.I. du Pont de Nemours & Co, Del. Tex, 46-48; Arthur D. Little, Inc, Mass, 48-53; sr. chem. engr, Polaroid Corp, 53-55; Clevite Transistor Prod, 55-56; sr. chemist, Ionics, Inc, Mass, 56-58; Midwest Res. Inst, Mo, 58-60; res. div, Philco Corp, Pa, 60-63; SUPVRY. RES. CHEMIST, Allison Div, GEN. MOTORS CORP, Ind, 63-68, ELECTROCHEM. DEPT, MICH, 68- U.S.A, 42-43. Electrochem. Soc; Am. Chem. Soc. Theoretical and experimental electrochemistry; electrochemistry of aqueous and molten salt fuel cells and batteries; development, electrocatalysis and physical and kinetic characterization of gas diffusion and metal electrodes; chemical thermodynamics. Address: Research Labs, General Motors Corp, Dept. 37, 12 Mile & Mound Rds, Warren, MI 48090.

FOUTCH, HARLEY WAYNE, b. Woodlawn, Ill, Sept. 29, 44; m. 70. AGRONOMY, PLANT PHYSIOLOGY. B.S, South. Ill. Univ, 66, M.S, 68; Nat. Defense Educ. Act fel. & Ph.D.(agron), Auburn Univ, 71. ASST. PROF. AGR, MIDDLE TENN. STATE UNIV, 70- Am. Soc. Agron; Weed Sci. Soc. Morphological and physiological response of cool season perennial grasses to temperature; forage crop physiology as affected by management practices; incorporation of herbicides by tillage methods. Address: Dept. of Agricuture, Middle Tennessee State University, Murfreesboro, TN 37130.

FOUTS, EVERETT L(INCOLN), b. Lafayette, Ind, Mar. 12, 00; m. 29, 53; c. 2. DAIRY INDUSTRY. B.S.A, Purdue, 23; M.S.A, Okla. Agr. & Mech. Col, 31; Ph.D.(dairy bacter), Iowa State Col, 39. Instr. dairying, Purdue, 25-27; asst. prof. dairy mfrs, Okla. Agr. & Mech. Col, 28, assoc. prof, 30-35, 37-40; supt, Colverts Ice Cream Co, 29; asst, Iowa State Col, 36; prof. dairy sci. & head dept, Florida, 40-70, dairy technologist, agr. exp. sta, 40-70; CONSULT, 70- U.S.A, 18. Am. Dairy Sci. Asn. Dairy manufacturing and bacteriology; decomposition of butterfat; storage of dairy products. Address: 1021 N. 40 Terr, Gainesville, FL 36201.

FOUTS, JAMES R(ALPH), b. Macomb, Ill, Aug. 8, 29; m. 51; c. 3. PHARMACOLOGY, BIOCHEMISTRY. B.S, Northwestern, 51, fel, 51-54, Ph.D.(biochem), 54. Instr. & asst. chem, Northwestern, 52-54; asst. scientist, Nat. Heart Inst, U.S. Pub. Health Serv, 54-56, sr. asst. scientist, 56; sr. res. biochemist, Wellcome Res. Labs, Burroughs Wellcome & Co, 56-57; asst. prof. pharmacol, col. Med, Iowa, 57-59, assoc. prof, 59-65, prof, 65-70, dir. Oakdale Toxicol. Ctr, 68-70; CHIEF, PHARMACOL-TOXICOL. BR, NAT. INST. ENVIRON. HEALTH SCI, NAT. INSTS. HEALTH, 70- Consult, Dr. Salsbury's Labs, Iowa, 60-66; Smith Kline & French Labs, Pa, 64-70; Hoffman La Roche, Inc, N.J, 66-70; mem. pharmacol. & exp. therapeut. study sect, div. res. grants, Nat. Insts. Health, 62-66, pharmacol-toxicol. rev. comt, 64-65 & 67-68, environ. health sci. nat. adv. comt, Nat. Insts. Environ. Health Sci, 68-70, task force on res. planning in environ. health sci. & chmn. comt. on toxicol, 68-69; comt. on anticonvulsant drugs, Nat. Inst. Neurol. Diseases & Stroke, 69-; mem. sci. group on prin. of pre-clin. testing for drug safety, WHO, 66; Claude Bernard Prof, Inst. Med. & Surg, Univ. Mont, 70; adj. prof. pharmacol, sch. med, Univ. N.C, 70-, entom. & toxicol, sch. agr. & life sci, 71- U.S.P.H.S, 54-56, Sr. Asst. Scientist. AAAS; Soc. Exp. Biol. & Med; Am. Soc. Pharmacol. & Exp. Therapeut.(Abel Award, 64); Soc. Toxicol. Drug metabolizing systems and factors affecting these; correlation of cell structure and enzyme activity; developmental pharmacology and toxicology; comparative pharmacology and toxicology; drug interactions. Address: Pharmacology-Toxicology Branch, National Institute of Environmental Health Sciences, P.O. Box 12233, Research Triangle Park, NC 27709.

FOWELL, ALFRED H(UGH) b. Ind, Aug. 10, 14; m. 41; c. 2. MATHEMATICS. B.A, California, 40. Supvr. blood fractionation, Cutter Labs, 42-46, protein res. chemist, 46-60, clin. res, 60-62, dir. standard procedures, 62-70; RETIRED. Methodology of blood fractionation; coagulation theory; administration. Address: Pine Grove, CA 95665.

FOWELL, ANDREW JOHN, b. Liverpool, Eng, Sept. 27, 36; m. 59; c. 2. FLUID MECHANICS, ACOUSTICS. B.Sc, Nottingham, 57, Ph.D.(mech. eng), 61. Grad. apprentice, English Elec. Co, 60-62, develop. engr, 62; res. scientist, AM. STANDARD CORP, 62-68, supvr. acoustics, 68-69, MGR. ADV. PROD. DEVEL, NEW BRUNSWICK, 69- U.S. rep, working group plumbing noise, Int. Sci. Orgn. Brit. Inst. Mech. Eng; Acoust. Soc. Am; Am. Soc. Heat, Refrig. & Air Conditioning Eng. Building technology; pulsating flow; turbulent diffusion; flow through air moving devices; fluid couplings; air conditioner and plumbing noise. Address: Box 1099 D, Mallard Dr, RD 2, Martinsville, NJ 08836.

FOWELLS, H(ARRY) A(RDELL), b. Portland, Oregon, July 5, 08; m. 30; c. 3. SILVICULTURE. B.S, Oregon State Col, 32, McDonald fel, 32-33, M.S, 33; California, 48-52; Ph.D.(plant physiol), Maryland, 58. Silviculturist, Calif. Forest Exp. Sta, 34-53; forest mgt. res, U.S. Forest Serv, 53-63; chief, br. forest genetics res, 63-64, br. silvicult. res, 64-66; asst. dir, foreign res. & tech. progs. div, Agr. Res. Serv, U.S. Dept. Agr, 66-71; RETIRED. Soc. Am. Foresters; Am. Soc. Plant Physiol. Plant physiology. Address: 10217 Green Forest Dr, Silver Spring, MD 20903.

FOWKES, FREDERICK M(AYHEW), b. Chicago, Ill, Jan. 29, 15; m. 37; c. 4. CHEMISTRY. B.S, Chicago, 36, Procter & Gamble fel, 37-38, Ph.D.(chem), 38; Cornell, 36-37. Chemist, Nat. Aluminate Corp, 37; res. chemist, Continental Can Co, 38-42; Shell Develop. Co, 46-52, res. supvr, 52-59, spec. res. chemist, Shell Oil Co, 59-61, res. supvr, Shell Develop. Co, 61-62; dir. res, Sprague Elec. Co, Mass, 62-68; PROF. CHEM. & CHMN. DEPT, LEHIGH UNIV, 68- Exchange chemist, Koninklijke Shell Lab, Amsterdam, 55-56. U.S.A, 42-46, Res, 46-64. Am. Chem. Soc; sr. mem. Inst. Elec. & Electronics Eng; Electrochem. Soc; Am. Inst. Chem. Charge transfer mechanisms at solid-liquid and solid-solid interfaces; electrokinetic phenomena at surfaces and interfaces; surface states of semiconducting solids; dispersion force interactions at interfaces; protons in oxides. Address: Dept. of Chemistry, Lehigh University, Bethlehem, PA 18015.

FOWLE, C(HARLES) DAVID, b. Victoria, B.C, Mar. 31, 20; m. 44; c. 2. VERTEBRATE ECOLOGY, WILDLIFE MANAGEMENT. B.A, British Columbia, 42, M.A, 44; Ph.D.(zool), Toronto, 53. Ont. Dept. Lands & Forest, in charge wildlife res, 47-60; spec. lectr, Univ. Toronto, 47-62; PROF. BIOL, YORK UNIV, 60-, ACTING DIR. CTR. RES. ENVIRON. QUAL, 71-, chmn. dept. biol, 60-66, master, Vanier Col, 66-71. Wildlife Soc; Can. Soc. Zool; Can. Soc. Wildlife & Fishery Biol. Address: Dept. of Biology, York University, Toronto, Ont, Can.

FOWLER, ALAN B, b. Denver, Colo, Oct. 15, 28; m. 50; c. 4. SOLID STATE PHYSICS. B.S, Rensselaer Polytech, 51, M.S, 52; Ph.D.(appl. physics), Harvard, 58. RES. STAFF MEM, IBM CORP, 58- U.S.A, 46-48, 52-53, 1st Lt. AAAS; Sci. Res. Soc. Am; Am. Vacuum Soc; fel. Am. Phys. Soc; sr. mem. Inst. Elec. & Electronics Eng. Semiconductor research in surface studies; optical properties of heavily doped crystals and photoconductors; injection lasers and thin film devices. Address: Thomas J. Watson Research Center, IBM Corp, Yorktown Heights, NY 10598.

FOWLER, ARNOLD K, b. Exeter, N.H, Aug. 11, 36; m. 59; c. 2. ANIMAL PHYSIOLOGY, GENETICS. B.S, New Hampshire, 58; M.S, Connecticut, 60; Ph.D.(animal physiol), Ohio State, 63. Res. scientist virol, U.S. Air Force Sch. Aerospace Med, 63-64, cellular biol, 64-69; asst. prof. animal sci, Univ. N.H, 69-70; WITH NAT. CANCER INST, 70- U.S.A.F, 56-66, Capt. AAAS; Am. Dairy Sci. Asn. Mammalian reproductive physiology and genetics; cellular physiology. Address: Bldg. 41, National Cancer Institute, National Institutes of Health, Bethesda, MD 20014.

FOWLER, CHARLES A(LBERT), b. Centralia, Ill, Dec. 17, 20; m. 43; c. 2. ELECTRONICS. B.S, Illinois, 42. Mem. staff, radiation lab, Mass. Inst. Tech, 42-45; mem. staff, Airborne Instruments Lab, Inc, 45-66; dep. dir. tactical warfare progs, off. of dir. defense res. & eng, Dept. Defense, 66-70; V.PRES. & MGR. EQUIP. DEVELOP. LABS, EQUIP. DIV, RAYTHEON CO, 70- AAAS; fel. Inst. Elec. & Electronics Eng; assoc. fel. Am. Inst. Aeronaut. & Astronaut. Radar; electronics. Address: Equipment Development Labs, Equipment Division, Raytheon Co, Sudbury, MA 01776.

FOWLER, CHARLES A(RMAN), JR, b. Salt Lake City, Utah, April 23, 12; m. 34; c. 2. PHYSICS. A.B, Utah, 33, M.S, 34; fel, California, 35-39, Ph.D. (physics), 40. Instr. PHYSICS, California, 40-42, asst. prof, 43-46; assoc. prof, POMONA COL, 47-49, PROF, 50-, CHMN. DEPT, 47- Nat. Sci. Found. sr. fel, Univ. Grenoble, France, 60-61; mem. comt. physics faculties in cols, Am. Inst. Phys, 62-65; Nat. Sci. Found. faculty fel, 67-68. Am. Phys. Soc; Am. Asn. Physics Teachers. Magnetism; ferromagnetic domains; magneto-optics; molecular spectroscopy; optics; x-ray diffraction. Address: Millikan Lab, Pomona College, Claremont, CA 91711.

FOWLER, C(LARENCE) M(AXWELL), b. Centralia, Ill, Nov. 26, 18; m. 42; c. 1. PHYSICS. B.S, Illinois, 40; M.S. & Ph.D.(physics), Michigan, 49. Asst. wire res, Am. Steel & Wire Co, 40-43; prof. physics, Kans. State Col, 49-57; MEM. STAFF, LOS ALAMOS SCI. LAB, 57- U.S.N.R, 43-46, Lt. Fel. Am. Phys. Soc. Nuclear spectroscopy; shock waves; high magnetic fields; explosive energy conversion. Address: 3220 Arizona, Los Alamos, NM 87544.

FOWLER, DONA J(ANE), b. Muncie, Ind, May 8, 28; div; c. 1. INVERTEBRATE PHYSIOLOGY. B.S, Purdue, 55, Nat. Heart Found. grant, 56-57, summers, Nat. Insts. Health fel, 61, Res. Found. grant, 62, M.S, 62, Nat. Sci. Found. fel, 62-65, Ph.D, 65. Res. asst. plant physiol, Purdue, 54-55, cardiac res, 56-57; assoc. res. anal. chemist, Eli Lilly Co, 57-60; asst. zool. & biol, Purdue, 60-62, physiol. & ecol, 62-65; instr. BIOL, WEST. MICH. UNIV, 65-66, asst. prof, 66-71, ASSOC. PROF, 71- AAAS; Am. Inst. Biol. Sci; Am. Soc. Zool; N.Y. Acad. Sci. Metabolic regulation; environmental factors that influence the regulatory functions of invertebrates, chiefly arachnids, experimental parameters involved, including the analysis of neurosecretions and locomotion as cyclic phenomena; development of tissue culture techniques. Address: Dept. of Biology, Western Michigan University, Kalamazoo, MI 49001.

FOWLER, DONALD E(UGENE), b. Hampton, N.B, Can, Oct. 15, 05; m. CHEMISTRY. A.B, New Brunswick, 26; M.Sc, McGill, 28. Rubber chem. res, Naugatuck chem. div, U.S. Rubber Co, 28-29, control chemist & head anal. dept, 29-41, mgr. reclaim rubber develop, 36, rubber dispersion dept, 37-41, asst. develop. mgr, 41-44, tech. dir, Pa. Ord. Works, 42-43, Scioto Ord. Plant, Ohio, 42-43, admin. asst. to v.pres, New York, 44-47, mgr. latex dispersion, res. & develop, 47-49, mgr. colloidal prods. develop, 49-53, asst. sales mgr, latex & dispersion, 53-57, sales mgr, colloidal prods, 57-64, distribution-scheduling mgr, chem. div, Uniroyal, Inc, 64-70; RETIRED. Rubber and agricultural chemicals; synthetic rubber; latex; plastics. Address: Uniroyal, Inc, Naugatuck, CT 06770.

FOWLER, DONALD PAIGE, b. Waterbury, Conn, Nov. 26, 32; Can. citizen; m. 55; c. 3. FOREST GENETICS. B.Sc, Univ. N.B, 55; M.F, Yale, 56, Ph.D. (forest genetics), 64. RES. SCIENTIST, Ont. Dept. Lands & Forests, 56-66; MARITIMES FOREST RES. CENTRE, CAN. FORESTRY SERV, 66- Res. assoc, Univ. N.B, 67-, lectr, 67-; N.Am. Forestry Comn. del, Working Group on Forestry Genetics, 65-; chmn, Comt. on Forest Tree Breeding in Can, 70-71. Soc. Am. Foresters; Can. Inst. Forestry; Genetics Soc. Can. Genetics of Pinus resinosa; genetics and tree improvement of Picea and Larix species. Address: Maritimes Forest Research Centre, Canadian Forestry Service, Dept. of the Environment, P.O. Box 4000, Fredericton, N.B, Can.

FOWLER, EARLE C(ABELL), b. Bowling Green, Ky, June 10, 21; m. 50; c. 3. HIGH ENERGY PHYSICS. B.S, Kentucky, 42; Chicago; A.M, Harvard, 47, Ph.D.(physics), 49. Assoc. physicist, Brookhaven Nat. Lab, 49-52; asst. prof. physics, Yale, 52-58, assoc. prof, 58-62, prof, Duke, 62-70; PROF. PHYSICS & HEAD DEPT, PURDUE UNIV, 71- Consult, Brookhaven Nat. Lab, 52-; Fulbright lectr, Univ. Birmingham, Eng, 58-59; Fulbright scholar, Univ. Rome, 67-68; mem. bd. dirs, Triangle Univ. Comput. Ctr, 69-; panel mem, Nat. Sci. Found. Comput. Facilities Div, 69-; consult, Oak Ridge Inst. Nuclear Studies; chmn. exec. comt, Nat. Accelerator Lab. User's Orgn. U.S.A.A.F, 42-46, Res, 46-53, Capt. Am. Phys. Soc. Cosmic rays; high energy particle physics; micrometeorology. Address: Dept. of Physics, Purdue University, Lafayette, IN 47907.

FOWLER, EDWARD HERBERT, b. Stoneham, Mass, Oct. 25, 36; m. 56; c. 2. VETERINARY PATHOLOGY. B.S, New Hampshire, 58; M.S & D.V.M, Mich. State, 62; Ph.D.(vet. path), Ohio State, 65. Asst. prof. vet. path, Ohio State Univ, 66-70, acting asst. dean acad. affairs, vet. col, 70; ASSOC. PROF. LAB. ANIMAL MED. & ASSOC. PROF. PATH, SCH. MED, UNIV. ROCHESTER, 70- Consult, Bur. Drugs, Food & Drug Admin, 71- Dipl, Am. Col. Vet. Path. Nat. Guard, 55-63. AAAS; Am. Vet. Med. Asn; Int. Acad. Path; Am. Soc. Vet. Clin. Path; Histochem. Soc; Am. Asn. Path. & Bact. Enzyme histochemical and biochemical changes of animal neoplasms; etiology and pathogenesis of steroid hormone dependent animal and human neoplasms. Address: Division of Laboratory Animal Medicine, School of Medicine & Dentistry, University of Rochester, 260 Crittenden Blvd, Rochester, NY 14642.

FOWLER, ELIZABETH H(ADDOCK), b. Philadelphia, Pa, July 31, 13. BACTERIOLOGY. B.A, Wilson Col, 35; M.A, Pennsylvania, 37. Bacteriologist, Episcopal Hosp, Phila, 37-40; instr. bact, Med. Col. of S.C, 40-42; res. asst, TEMPLE UNIV, 42-57, instr. BIOL, 57-67, ASST. PROF, 67- AAAS; Am. Soc. Microbiol. Immunology; antigen-antibody reactions, especially reactions in protozoa and the Salmonella group; cytological and serological study of aerobic spore-forming bacilli. Address: Dept. of Biology, Temple University, Philadelphia, PA 19122.

FOWLER, EMIL EUGENE, b. Morgantown, W.Va, Sept. 15, 23; m. 49; c. 3. BIOCHEMISTRY. A.B, West Virginia, 46, M.S, 47; Tennessee; Oak Ridge Inst. Nuclear Studies. Chief, radioisotopes br, U.S. ATOMIC ENERGY COMN, Tenn, 47-56, deputy dir, isotopes div, 56, dep. asst. dir, div. civilian application & off. indust. develop, WASH, D.C, 56-59, dep. dir, DIV. ISOTOPES DEVELOP, 59-65, DIR, 65- AAAS; Am. Nuclear Soc; Soc. Nuclear Med; Health Phys. Soc; Am. Inst. Chem; N.Y. Acad. Sci; Am. Pub. Health Asn; Am. Heart Asn. Accelerating development of widespread applications of radioisotopes and high-intensity radiation; radioisotopes production, process development, pricing and marketing; production and distribution of radioisotopes and isotopes technology training. Address: 5124 Westpath Way, Washington, DC 20016.

FOWLER, ERIC B(EAUMONT), b. Milbank, S.Dak, May 4, 14; m. 42; c. 3. BACTERIOLOGY. B.S, Kansas State, 42, M.S, 44; Ph.D.(chem. & physiol. bact), Iowa State Col, 50. Lab. asst. bact, Kansas State, 39-42, asst. soil conserv, 42-44; instr. bact, Iowa State Col, 44-50, asst. prof. & assoc. prof, 50-56; MEM. STAFF & ALTERNATE GROUP LEADER, LOS ALAMOS SCI. LAB, 56- AAAS; Am. Chem. Soc; Am. Soc. Microbiol; Water Pollution Control Fedn; N.Y. Acad. Sci. Chemical and physiological bacteriology; disposal of biological and industrial wastes; plant uptake and control of radio isotopes in the environment. Address: Los Alamos Scientific Lab, Box 1663, Los Alamos, NM 87544.

FOWLER, FRANK CAVAN, b. Kansas City, Mo, June 15, 18; m. 43; c. 3. CHEMICAL ENGINEERING. B.S, Illinois, 39; M.S, Michigan, 40, Ph.D. (chem. eng), 43. Chem. engr, Phillips Petrol. Co, Okla, 43-46; instr, univ. exten, Oklahoma, 45, assoc. prof. chem. eng, 46-48, prof, 48-51; consult. chem. engr, 51-58; PRES, RES. ENGRS, INC, 58- Vis. prof, Univ. Kans, 52-53, 56-58. Am. Chem. Soc; Sci. Res. Soc. Am; Am. Inst. Chem. Eng. Fluid flow; heat transfer; distillation; mixing of fluids by successive flow through pipes; process design; thermodynamics. Address: Route 30, Kansas City, MO 64149.

FOWLER, FRANK WILSON, b. Portland, Maine, May 16, 41; m. 63. ORGANIC CHEMISTRY. Ph.D.(chem), Univ. Colo, 67. Leverhulme vis. fel, Univ. E.Anglia, 67-68; ASST. PROF. CHEM, STATE UNIV. N.Y. STONY BROOK, 68- Synthesis of interesting and unusual heterocyclic molecules;

aromaticity; valence tantomerism; natural products. Address: Dept. of Chemistry, State University of New York at Stony Brook, Stony Brook, NY 11790.

FOWLER, GEORGE W(RIGHT), b. Stoneboro, Pa, Apr. 7, 12; m. 43; c. 1. ORGANIC CHEMISTRY. B.S, Pa. State, 33; Ph.D.(org. chem), Northwestern, 37. RES. CHEMIST, CHEM. & PLASTICS DIV, UNION CARBIDE CORP, 37- Am. Chem. Soc. Organic synthesis; polymers. Address: Union Carbide Corp, P.O. Box 8361, South Charleston, WV 25303.

FOWLER, GREGORY L, b. Wichita, Kans, Aug. 19, 34; m. 67; c. 2. GENETICS. B.A, Wichita State, 56, M.S, 60; Nat. Insts. Health fels, Kansas, 56-57 & Syracuse, 62-64; Nat. Insts. Health fel. & Ph.D.(genetics), Brown, 68. Lectr. biol, Wichita State, 59-60; instr, Bethany Col, 60-62; Nat. Sci. Found. fel. for col. teachers biol, 62-63; asst. prof. biol, George Wash. Univ, 67-69; assoc. & vis. asst. prof. biol, Univ. Ore, 69-71; DOCENT & HUMBOLDT FEL, INST. GEN. BIOL, UNIV. DÜSSELDORF, 71- Sigma Xi res. grant, 60-61; Nat. Insts. Health trainee, Univ. Ore, 69-70. Genetics Soc. Am. Sperm transfer and sperm storage with particular reference to progeny; sperm ratios in Drosophila melanogaster; genetics and cytology of meiosis in Drosophila; genetic and electron microscope studies of chromosome movement in Drosophila; general area of reproductive biology of Drosophila. Address: Institute for General Biology, University of Düsseldorf, Ullenbergstrasse 127-129, D 4-Düsseldorf, Germany.

FOWLER, HARLAND WADE, JR, b. Arcadia, Fla, July 29, 28; m. 53; c. 3. MEDICAL ENTOMOLOGY, INVERTEBRATE ZOOLOGY. B.S, Univ. Fla, 53; M.S, Univ. Ill, Urbana, 60, Ph.D.(med. entom), 69. U.S. ARMY, 53-, chief entomologist, U.S. Army Hosp, Ft. Jackson, S.C, 53-55, commanding off, 37th Preventive Med. Unit, Korea, 55-56, res. entomologist, 406th Med. Lab, Camp Zama, Japan, 56-58, instr. med. entom, Med. Field Serv. Sch, Ft. Sam. Houston, 58-59, res. entomologist, U.S. Army Environ. Hyg. Agency, Md, 60-62, chief entom. dept, U.S. Army Europe Lab, Ger, 62-65, stud. off, Med. Field Serv. Sch, Tex, 65-66, chief entom. dept, 9th Med. Lab, Vietnam, 69-70, chief entom. res. br, U.S. Army Med. Res. & Develop. Command, 70-71, EXEC. SECY, ARMED FORCES PEST CONTROL BD, 71- Med. entom. consult, chief surgeon, 8th U.S. Army, Korea, 55-56, U.S. Army Europe, 62-65, U.S. Army Vietnam, 69-70 & U.S. Army Med. Res. & Develop. Command, 70-71; U.S. Army del, Int. Cong. Entom. London, 64; chief opers, emergency med. relief, Moroccan Flood Disaster, 63; chief mil. quarantine off, U.S. Army Vietnam, 69-70; mem, quarantine & med. entom. comts. & bd, Armed Forces Pest Control Bd, 70-71; Dept. Defense 1st alternate mem, working group pesticides, Coun. Environ. Qual, 71-; Dept. Defense liaison mem, adv. comt. entom. res, Can. Defense Res. Bd, 71-; mem, Dept. Defense Environ. Pollution Control Comt. 71- Dept. Agr. cert. appreciation, 70; U.S. Pub. Health Serv. cert. appreciation, 70. Med.Serv.C, U.S.A, 53-, Lt. Col; Bronze Star Medal, 70; Army Commendation Medal, 71. Entom. Soc. Am; Am. Mosquito Control.Asn. Bionomics of medically important mosquitoes and development of more effective integrated mosquito control programs. Address: Armed Forces Pest Control Board, Forest Glen Section, Walter Reed Army Medical Center, Washington, DC 20012.

FOWLER, H(ORATIO) SEYMOUR, b. Highland Park, Mich, Mar. 1, 19; m. 45; c. 1. BIOLOGY. B.S, Cornell, 41, M.S, 46, Ph.D.(sci. ed), 51. Teacher, pub. schs, N.Y, 46, 47-49; asst. sci. ed, Cornell, 49-51; asst. prof, South. Oregon Col, 51-52; biol, Iowa State Teachers Col, 52-57; PROF. SCI. EDUC, PA. STATE UNIV, 57-, DIR, PA. CONSERV. LAB, 60-, CHMN. SCI. EDUC. FACULTY, 69- Dir, Iowa teachers conserv. camp, 52-57; Fulbright lectr, Korea, 68-69. U.S.A, 42-45. AAAS; Am. Nature Study Soc. (v.pres, 64, pres. elect, 66, pres, 67); Nat. Asn. Res. Sci. Teaching; Nat. Asn. Biol Teachers(v.pres, 59); Nat. Sci. Teachers Asn. Science education. Address: 1340 Park Hills Ave. W, State College, PA 16802.

FOWLER, H(OWLAND) A(UCHINCLOSS), b. N.Y.C, Jan. 25, 30; m. 62; c. 2. PHYSICS. A.B, Princeton, 52; Socony-Vacuum fel, Brown Univ, 53-54, M.Sc, 55, Corinna Borden Keene fel, 55-56, 56-57, Ph.D.(physics), 57. Nat. Res. Coun. assoc, NAT. BUR. STANDARDS, 57-58, PHYSICIST, 58- Am. Phys. Soc. Electron physics; electron scattering; electron-optical technique; far-UV optical constants; application of Josephson effect to voltage measurements. Address: Institute for Basic Standards, National Bureau of Standards, A353 Physics Bldg, Washington, DC 20234.

FOWLER, IRA, b. La, Apr. 27, 21; m. 52; c. 2. EXPERIMENTAL EMBRYOLOGY. B.S, La. Polytech. Inst, 42; M.S, Louisiana, 49; Ph.D.(zool), Northwestern, 52. Asst, Louisiana, 48-50; Northwestern, 50-52, res. assoc, 52-53; instr. ANAT, sch. med, Univ. N.C, Chapel Hill, 53-55, asst. prof, 55-60, assoc. prof, 60-66, U.S. Pub. Health Serv. sr. res. fel, 57-62; ASSOC. PROF, MED. CTR, UNIV. KY, 66- U.S.N.R, 42-46, Lt. Am. Inst. Biol. Sci; Am. Soc. Zool; Am. Asn. Anat. Cellular responses in auto-immunization. Address: Dept. of Anatomy, University of Kentucky Medical Center, Lexington, KY 40506.

FOWLER, JAMES A, b. N.Y.C, Jan. 30, 23; m. 55; c. 2. VERTEBRATE EMBRYOLOGY. B.S.E, Princeton, 44; M.A, Columbia, 57, Ph.D.(zool), 61. Power engr, West. Union Tel. Co, 47-49; elec. engr, St. Anthony Mining & Develop. Co, 49; lectr. embryol, Columbia, 59, zool, Barnard Col, 59-60; ASST. PROF. BIOL. SCI, STATE UNIV. N.Y. STONY BROOK, 61-, asst. dean col. arts & sci, 64-69, ASSOC. DEAN HEALTH PROF. ADV, 69- Summer lectr, Columbia, 56. U.S.N.R, 44-46, Res, 46-55, Lt.(jg). AAAS; Soc. Study Evolution; Am. Soc. Zool; Am. Soc. Nat; Am. Soc. Ichthyol. & Herpet. Interaction between evolution and embryology; population genetics of development and its evolutionary history. Address: Box L, Coraway Rd, Setauket, NY 11733.

FOWLER, JOHN M(AJOR), b. Eufaula, Ala, Feb. 4, 26; m. 48; c. 7. NUCLEAR PHYSICS. B.A, Earlham Col, 49; fel. & M.S, Oklahoma, 50; Ph.D. (physics), Hopkins, 54. Asst, Hopkins, 50-53; res. assoc, physics, Wash. Univ, 54-56, asst. prof, 56-61, assoc. prof, 61-65; exec. secy, comn. col. physics, Univ. Mich, Ann Arbor, 65-66, dir, 65-67; VIS. PROF. PHYSICS & ASTRON. UNIV. MD, COLLEGE PARK & DIR. COMN. COL. PHYSICS, 67- Mem. sci. adv. bd, Consumer's Union, 60-; bd. mem, Sci. Inst. Pub. Info, 61-; vis. physicist, Saclay Nuclear Res. Ctr, France, 64-65. Millikan Lect.

Award, 69. U.S.A, 44-46. Am. Phys. Soc; Am. Asn. Physics Teachers; Fedn. Am. Sci. Nuclear reactions induced by cyclotron produced particles; angular distributions and polarization of neutrons; protons and deuterons; polarization of cosmic-ray muons; pedagogical development. Address: Dept. of Physics & Astronomy, University of Maryland, College Park, MD 20740.

FOWLER, JOHN RAYFORD, b. Winnfield, La, July 11, 43; m. 64; c. 2. INORGANIC CHEMISTRY. B.A, McMurry Col, 65; univ. summer fels, Univ. Kans, 66-68, Nat. Educ. Act fel, 68, Ph.D.(inorg. chem), 69. Teaching asst. chem, Univ. Kans, 65-68; RES. CHEMIST, TEXTILE RES. LAB, E.I. DU PONT DE NEMOURS & CO, INC, WILMINGTON, 69- Am. Chem. Soc. Transition metal complexes; nonaqueous solvents; cyano complexes; IR spectroscopy; electrochemistry of coordination compounds; synthetic textile fibers; textile technology; finishing of textiles. Address: 217 Kenmark Rd, Newark, DE 19711.

FOWLER, JOSEPH LEE, b. Springfield, Ohio, Nov. 19, 13; m. 45; c. 2. PHYSICS. A.B. & M.S, Tennessee, 38; Ph.D.(physics), Princeton, 43. Sect. leader isotron res, Princeton, 42-43; sect. leader & alternate group leader bomb physics div, Manhattan Dist, Los Alamos, N.Mex, 44-46, group leader in charge cyclotron, 46-50; dir. high voltage lab, PHYSICS DIV, OAK RIDGE NAT. LAB, 51-54, assoc. dir, 54-57, DIR, 57- Fel. Am. Phys. Soc. High energy neutron, proton and deuteron interaction with nuclei; fission fragment mass and energy distributions. Address: Physics Division, Oak Ridge National Lab, P.O. Box X, Oak Ridge, TN 37830.

FOWLER, KENNETH A(RTHUR), b. Buffalo, N.Y, Jan. 10, 16; m. 48; c. 2. MATHEMATICS. B.A, Cornell, 38; M.A, Michigan, 47, Ph.D.(math), 52. Asst. prof. MATH, Arizona, 51-55; prof, Col. Ed, State Univ. N.Y. New Paltz, 55-56; asst. prof, Union (N.Y), 56-57; SAN JOSE STATE COL, 57-59, assoc. prof, 59-65, PROF, 65- Am. Math. Soc; Math. Asn. Am. Algebra; foundations of mathematics; topology. Address: Dept. of Mathematics, San Jose State College, San Jose, CA 95114.

FOWLER, LEWIS, b. Ft. Collins, Colo, Mar. 22, 17; m. 45; c. 3. PHYSICAL & ANALYTICAL CHEMISTRY. A.B, Reed Col, 38; M.S, Washington (Seattle), 46; Ph.D, Columbia, 51. Chemist, Archer-Daniels-Midland Co, 38-41; Puget Sound Navy Yard, 42-44; anal. res. chemist, MONSANTO CO, 50-51, asst. chief chemist, 52-55, GROUP LEADER, RES. INSTRUMENTATION, 55- AAAS; Am. Chem. Soc; Instrument Soc. Am. Analytical instrumentation. Address: Monsanto Co, 1700 S. Second St, St. Louis, MO 63177.

FOWLER, MARY CHARLOTTE, S.C.N, b. Mechanicsville, Md, Aug. 26, 99. MATHEMATICS. A.B, Sister's Col, 27; M.A, Catholic Univ, 35, Ph.D. (math), 38. Prof. math. & physics, Spalding Col, 37-69, chmn. dept, 37-66, pres, 61-69; RETIRED. Am. Math. Soc; Math. Asn. Am; Am. Asn. Physics Teachers. Discriminant of the sextic of double point parameters of the plane rational quartic curve. Address: St. Vincent Home, 631 N. Jefferson St, Roanoke, VA 24016.

FOWLER, MICHAEL, b. Doncaster, Eng, Apr. 30, 38; m. 65. THEORETICAL PHYSICS. B.A, Cambridge, 59, Ph.D.(field theory), 62. Instr. PHYSICS, Princeton, 62-63; asst. prof, Maryland, 63-65; Univ. Toronto, 65-68; ASSOC. PROF, UNIV. VA, 68- Am. Phys. Soc. Analytic methods in potential theory and perturbation theory; electrons in high magnetic fields in metals. Address: Dept. of Physics, University of Virginia, Charlottesville, VA 22901.

FOWLER, MURRAY ELWOOD, b. Glendale, Wash, July 17, 28; m. 50; c. 5. VETERINARY MEDICINE. B.S, Utah State, 52; D.V.M, Iowa State, 55. Private practice VET. MED, 55-57; from instr. to ASSOC. PROF, UNIV. CALIF, DAVIS, 57- Dipl, Am. Bd. Vet. Toxicol. U.S.N, 46-48. Am. Vet. Med. Asn; Am. Asn. Equine Practitioners; Am. Asn. Zoo Vets. Clinical toxicology; teaching and research in problems of zoo animal medicine and wildlife diseases; pyrrolizidine alkaloid poisoning in calves. Address: Dept. of Clinical Sciences, University of California, Davis, CA 95616.

FOWLER, NOBLE O(WEN), b. Vicksburg, Miss, July 14, 19; m. 42; c. 3. INTERNAL MEDICINE, CARDIOVASCULAR DISEASE. Memphis State Col, 36-38; M.D, Tennessee, 41. U.S. Pub. Health Serv. fel. cardiol, Cincinnati, 48-49, trainee, 49-50, Am. Heart Asn. res. fel. & asst. prof. med, 51-52; asst. prof, State Univ. N.Y, 52-54; assoc. prof. med. & chair cardiovasc. res, Emory, 54-57; assoc. prof. clin. med, UNIV. CINCINNATI, 57-59, med, 59-64, PROF. INTERNAL MED, 64-, DIR. DIV. CARDIOL, 70-; DIR. CARDIAC RES. LAB, CINCINNATI GEN. HOSP, 64- Consult, Dayton Vet. Hosp, 49-52; Brooklyn Vet. Hosp, N.Y, 54. Med.C, 42-44, Capt. Fel. Am. Col. Physicians; Am. Physiol. Soc. Physiology and pharmacology of the pulmonary circulation; physiology of regulation of cardiac output; plasma substitutes; mechanism of cardiac filling. Address: Cardiac Research Lab, H-3, Cincinnati General Hospital, Cincinnati, OH 45229.

FOWLER, PETER, b. Salem, Mass, July 13, 31; m. 57; c. 2. PHYSICS. B.S, Yale, 53; M.S, Mass. Inst. Tech, 60. Staff mem, Lincoln Lab, Mass. Inst. Tech, 56, res. asst. elec. eng, 56-57, physics, 57-60, staff mem, div. sponsored res, 60, res. asst, res. lab. electronics, 60-61; physicist, res. div, NAT. RES. CORP, 61-67, sr. res. physicist, Norton Explor. Res. Div, 67-70, PROG. MGR. GAS DYNAMICS, 70- U.S.M.C.R, 49-53; U.S.N.R, 53-55, Res, 55-66, Lt. Am. Phys. Soc; Am. Vacuum Soc; Am. Geophys. Union. Infrared properties of metals; thin film properties research; paramagnetic resonance in solutions; superconductivity in high magnetic field; extreme high vacuum techniques and instrumentation; high velocity impact phenomena. Address: National Research Corp, 70 Memorial Dr, Cambridge, MA 02142.

FOWLER, RICHARD C(ROSMAN), b. Rochester, N.Y, Oct. 15, 15; m. 44; c. 1. MEDICINE. B.S, Mass. Inst. Technol, 37; Dayton, 38; Pittsburgh, 40-41; M.D, Rochester, 44. Engr, Delco Prods. Corp, Ohio, 37-40; Westinghouse Elec. Corp, Pa, 40-41; fel, Rochester, 46-47; instr. physiol, 47-52, Markle scholar, 48-53, asst. prof, 52-55; med. res, univ. hosp, GEORGE WASHINGTON UNIV, 55-58, U.S. Pub. Health Serv. spec. res. fel, 58, asst. prof. MED, SCH. MED, 58-64, ASSOC. PROF, 64- Med. res, Mt. Alto Vet. Admin. Hosp, 55-58. U.S.N.R, 42-46, 53-55, Res, 55- AAAS; Optical Soc. Am; Soc. Appl. Spectros; Am. Med. Asn; Inst. Elec. & Electronics Eng; N.Y. Acad. Sci. Respiration; infrared spectroscopy; vibration; neuro-muscular and rheumatoid diseases; electron microscopy. Address: Dept. of Medicine, George Washington University School of Medicine, Washington, DC 20006.

FOWLER, RICHARD EDMOND, b. Marion, Miss, Dec. 20, 23; wid; c. 5. PEDIATRICS. A.B, Mississippi, 43, M.D, Duke, 45. Intern, Charity Hosp, New Orleans, La, 45, pediat. res, La. State Serv, 48-50; Children's Hosp, Birmingham, Ala, 46; Nat. Heart Inst. trainee PEDIAT, SCH. MED, LA. STATE UNIV, 50-51, instr, 53-55, asst. prof, 55, PROF. & HEAD DEPT, 55- Med.C, 46-47; U.S.P.H.S, 51-52, Surg. Soc. Pediat. Res; Am. Acad. Pediat; Am. Med. Asn; Am. Heart Asn; Am. Pediat. Soc; fel. Am. Col. Cardiol. Various aspects of congenital heart disease. Address: Dept. of Pediatrics, School of Medicine, Louisiana State University, New Orleans, LA 70112.

FOWLER, RICHARD G(ILDART), b. Albion, Mich, June 13, 16; m. 39; c. 4. PHYSICS. A.B, Albion Col, 36; M.S, Michigan, 39, Ph.D.(physics), 41. Asst, Dow Chem. Co, Mich, 36-38; Michigan, 38-40, res. physicist, 41, 42-46; instr. PHYSICS, N.C. State Col, 41-42; asst. prof, UNIV. OKLA, 46-49, assoc. prof, 49-56, prof, 56-61, RES. PROF, 61-, chmn. dept, 55-59, 66-68. Guggenheim fel, 52; Fulbright lectr, Australia, 63; NATO fel, 70. With Off. Sci. Res. & Develop, 44. AAAS; fel. Am. Phys. Soc. Ultraviolet spectrochemical analysis; organic structure determination by infrared spectra; plasma physics and electrically generated shock waves; plasma driven shock tubes; purification of graphite; mechanisms involved in the production of radiation. Address: Dept. of Physics, University of Oklahoma, 440 W. Brooks, Norman, OK 73069.

FOWLER, ROBERT DUDLEY, b. San Francisco, Calif, June 27, 05. PHYSICS, CHEMISTRY. B.S, Univ. Calif, 26; M.S, Univ. Mich, 28, Ph.D.(chem), 30. Instr. chem, Univ. Calif, 30-35; Johns Hopkins Univ, 36, asst. prof, 37-40, assoc. prof, 40-43, prof, 43-52, chmn. dept, 47-52; assoc. div. leader, Los Alamos Sci. Lab, 52-53, alternate leader, chem. & metall. div, 54-56, leader CMF div, 56-70, res. adv, 70-71; VIS. SCHOLAR APPL. PHYSICS, STANFORD UNIV, 71- Contracts at Johns Hopkins Univ. with Nat. Defense Res. Comt. & Manhattan Dist, 40-44; SAM Labs, Columbia Univ, 43-44; trustee & mem. sci. adv. comt, Brookhaven Nat. Lab, 46-49. Am. Chem. Soc; Am. Phys. Soc. Inorganic and physical chemistry; reaction kinetics; mass spectrometry; nuclear physics and chemistry; fluorine chemistry; synthesis of uranium hexafluoride; synthesis of fluorocarbons; chemical and physical properties of fluorocarbons; production of fluorine; chemistry and metallurgy of uranium, plutonium and transuranics; superconductivity. Address: 101 Middlefield Rd, Atherton, CA 94025.

FOWLER, ROBERT L(AWRENCE), b. Roanoke, La, Sept, 16, 10; div; c. 1. AGRICULTURE. A.B, Univ. Calif, Los Angeles, 34, A.M, 35; Ph.D.(plant ecol), Univ. Nebr, 41. Instr. bot, Colo. State Col, 36-38; asst, Univ. Nebr, 39-41; agr. aide, Soil Conserv. Serv, U.S. Dept. Agr, 41, agriculturist, For. Agr. Serv, 43-54; trop. hort. adv, U.S. AGENCY INT. DEVELOP, 54-60, gen. agriculturist, 60-66, chief agr. & rural develop. div, E.Asia Bur, 66-68, area agr. adv, U.S. OPERS. MISSION, BANGKOK, THAILAND, 68-71, DEP. ASST. DIR. AGR. DEVELOP, 71- Sr. instr, War Relocation Auth, 42. Meritorious Serv. citation award, U.S. Agency Int. Develop, 59. Fel. AAAS; Soc. Int. Develop; Asia Soc. Rural economic planning and development. Address: U.S. Operations Mission, APO San Francisco 96346.

FOWLER, R(OBERT) M(cSWAIN), b. Georgetown, Tex, Mar. 6, 06; m. 31; c. 3. INORGANIC & ANALYTICAL CHEMISTRY. A.B, Southwestern (Tex), 27; M.A, George Washington, 31. Jr. chemist, Nat. Bur. Standards, 27-36; res. anal. chemist, Union Carbide & Carbon Res. Labs, 36-42, asst. to mgr, 42-48, chief res. chemist, 48-55, res. consult, tech. dept, Union Carbide Metals Co. Div, 55-63; sr. res. chemist & supt. prod, L.I. Labs, Inc, Cybertek, Inc, 69-71; RETIRED. AAAS; Am. Chem. Soc. Chemistry of columbium, tantalum, tungsten, chromium, silicon, manganese, titanium and cobalt; preparation of pure metals; analysis of metals; gases in metals. Address: 8604 Putnam Dr, Austin, TX 78758.

FOWLER, ROY, b. Enfield, Eng, Mar. 24, 23; U.S. citizen; m. 45; c. 2. AERODYNAMICS, ATOMIC PHYSICS. B.Sc, London, 45. Asst. aerodyn, Nat. Phys. Lab, Teddington, Eng, 40-45; group engr, aircraft div, English Elec. Corp, 45-50; sr. sci. off, Royal Aircraft Estab, 50-51; asst. chief designer, Folland Aircraft Ltd, 51-56; design specialist, Gen. Dynamics/Convair, Calif, 57-62; group dir, concepts & tech, AEROSPACE CORP, 62-70, ASSOC. GEN. MGR. REENTRY SYSTS. DIV, 70- Lectr, Southampton, 53-56. Am. Inst. Aeronaut. & Astronaut. All technology relevant to reentry physics, such as aerodynamics, vehicle dynamics, thermodynamics, chemical kinetics, atomic physics, radar wave propagation and reflection. Address: 2615 Piedmont Dr, Riverside, CA 92506.

FOWLER, SCOTT W(ELLINGTON), b. Berkeley, Calif, May 31, 41; m. 65; c. 1. BIOLOGICAL OCEANOGRAPHY. B.A, California, Riverside, 64; M.S, Oregon State, 66, Atomic Energy Comn. fel, 66-68, Ph.D.(biol. oceanog), 69. Scientist, Battelle-Northwest Labs, 67; Fulbright lectr, Monterrey Inst. Tech, Mex, 69-70; SCIENTIST, INT. ATOMIC ENERGY AGENCY, INT. LAB. MARINE RADIOACTIVITY, OCEANOG. MUS, MONACO, 70- Am. Soc. Limnol. & Oceanog; Nat. Audubon Soc. Transfer of zinc-65 in marine crustacean food chains; accumulation and transfer of radionuclides in marine organisms; trace element studies in marine organisms; metabolic nature of zinc in plankton metabolism; marine pollution, radioactive and non-radioactive. Address: International Lab. of Marine Radioactivity, Oceanographic Museum, Principality of Monaco.

FOWLER, S(TEWART) H(AMPTON), b. St. Paul, Minn, July 20, 22; m. 50; c. 3. PHYSIOLOGY, ANIMAL BREEDING, B.S.A, Florida, 47; M.S, Auburn, 50; Ph.D.(physiol. reproduction), Texas A&M, 54. Instr. Auburn, 48-51; Texas A&M, 51-54; asst. prof. swine husb, Maryland, 54-55; assoc. prof. ANIMAL SCI, Wash. State Univ, 54-58; prof, La. State Univ, 58-69; PROF. & HEAD DEPT, MISS. STATE UNIV, 69- Livestock buyer, Lykes Bros, Fla, 47-48; asst. dir, Stockmen's Sch, Agriservs. Found. U.S.N.R, 43-45, Res, 46-, Lt. Comdr. Fel. AAAS; Am. Genetic Asn; Am. Soc. Animal Sci.

(distinguished teacher award, 70); Am. Soc. Range Mgt; Am. Soc. Study Reproduction; Am. Forage & Grassland Coun; Animal Behav. Soc. Reproductive efficiency of farm animals; inheritance of defects and economically important traits in livestock; factors related to the efficient marketing of livestock. Address: Dept. of Animal Science, Mississippi State University, P.O. Drawer 5228, State College, MS 39762.

FOWLER, T(HOMAS) KENNETH, b. Thomaston, Ga, Mar. 27, 31; m. 56; c. 3. THEORETICAL PHYSICS. B.E, Vanderbilt, 53, M.S, 55; Ph.D. (theoret. physics), Wisconsin, 57. Physicist, Oak Ridge Nat. Lab, 57-65; gen. atomic div, Gen. Dynamic Corp, 65-67; LAWRENCE RADIATION LAB, 67-70, ASSOC. DIR. CONTROLLED THERMONUCLEAR RES, 70- Am. Phys. Soc. Controlled fusion; plasma and nuclear physics, especially scattering theory. Address: Lawrence Radiation Lab, P.O. Box 808, Livermore CA 94550.

FOWLER, WALLACE T(HOMAS), b. Greenville, Tex, Aug. 27, 38; m. 68; c. 2. AEROSPACE ENGINEERING. B.A, Texas, Austin, 60, M.S, 61, Ph.D. (eng. mech), 65. Asst. prof. eng. mech, UNIV. TEX, AUSTIN, 65-67, AEROSPACE ENG, 67-69, ASSOC. PROF, 69- Am. Soc. Eng. Ed-NASA summer faculty fel, Manned Spacecraft Center, summer 65, consult, 66-; sci. programmer specialist, Lockheed Electronics Co, summer 66; consult, Gen. Dynamics/Ft. Worth, 67- Am. Inst. Aeronaut. & Astronaut. Flight mechanics; numerical optimization; guidance and control. Address: Dept. of Aerospace Engineering, University of Texas at Austin, Austin, TX 78712.

FOWLER, W(ARD) S(COTT), b. Summerfield, Kans, Oct. 24, 15; m. 40; c. 2. PHYSIOLOGY. A.B, Swarthmore Col, 37; M.D, Harvard, 41. Assoc. prof. PHYSIOL, grad. sch. med, Pennsylvania, 51-52; MAYO GRAD. SCH. MED, UNIV. MINN, ROCHESTER, 52-56, PROF, 56-; CONSULT. PHYSICIAN, MAYO CLINIC, 52- Am. Col. Physicians fel, 47-48; fel, Nat. Insts. Health, 48-50. Med.C, U.S.A, 42-46. AAAS; Am. Physiol. Soc; Am. Soc. Clin. Invest; Soc. Exp. Biol. & Med. Respiratory physiology, clinical derangements and tests. Address: Mayo Clinic, Rochester, MN 55901.

FOWLER, WILLIAM (ALFRED), b. Pittsburgh, Pa, Aug. 9, 11; m. 40; c. 2. PHYSICS. B.Eng.Phys, Ohio State, 33; Ph.D.(physics), Calif. Inst. Tech, 36. Res. fel, CALIF. INST. TECHNOL, 36-39, asst. prof. PHYSICS, 39-42, assoc. prof, 42-46, prof, 46-70, INST. PROF, 70- Mem. res. staff, Nat. Defense Res. Comt, 41, asst. dir. res, 41-45; tech. observ, off. field serv. & new develop. div, Dept. War, 44; acting supvr. res. & develop, Ord. Div, 45; sci. dir. proj. VISTA, Dept. Defense, 51-52; Guggenheim fel, Cavendish lab, Univ. Cambridge, 54-55, 61-62, St. Johns Col, 61-62; vis, observ, Univ. Cambridge, summer, 64, vis. fel, Inst. Theoret. Astron, summers, 67-71; vis. prof, Mass. Inst. Technol, 66; lectr. at various educ. insts, U.S. & abroad, 54-71; mem. Nat. Sci. Bd, Nat. Sci. Found, 68-, bd. dirs, Am. Friends Cambridge Univ, 70-; space sci. bd, Nat. Acad. Sci, 70-; mem. space prog. adv. coun, NASA, 71- Naval Ord. Develop. award, U.S. Navy, 45; Medal for Merit, U.S. Army, 48; Lamme Medal, Ohio State Univ, 52; Liège Medal, Univ. Liège, 55; Barnard Medal, Columbia Univ, 65; Apollo achievement award, NASA, 69. Nat. Acad. Sci; AAAS; fel. Am. Phys. Soc. (Tom. W. Bonner Prize, 70); Am. Astron. Soc; Am. Philos. Soc; fel. Am. Acad. Arts & Sci; Am. Geophys. Union; N.Y. Acad. Sci; fel. Royal Astron. Soc; Brit. Asn. Adv. Sci; Royal Soc. Arts; Int. Astron. Union. Studies of nuclear forces and reaction rates; nuclear spectroscopy; structure of light nuclei; thermonuclear sources of stellar energy and element synthesis in stars and supernovae; study of general relativistic effects in quasar and pulsar models. Address: Kellogg Radiation Lab, California Institute of Technology, Pasadena, CA 91109.

FOWLER, WILLIAM B(ROWNFIELD), b. Owensboro, Ky, Mar. 22, 24; m. 46; c. 3. PHYSICS. B.S, Kentucky, 47; Ph.D.(physics), Washington (St. Louis), 51. Assoc. physicist, Brookhaven Nat. Lab, 51-55; physicist, radiation lab, California, 55-58, asst. prof. physics, 58-59; PHYSICIST, Brookhaven Nat. Lab, 59-70; NAT. ACCELERATOR LAB, BATAVIA, 70- Sig.C, U.S.A, 42-45. Am. Phys. Soc. High energy physics; hydrogen and heavy liquid bubble chamber design, construction and operation; strange particle physics. Address: R.R. 3, Box 208, St. Charles, IL 60174.

FOWLER, W(ILLIAM) D(ORSEY), Mgt. Sci, see 12th ed, Soc. & Behav. Vols.

FOWLER, W(ILLIAM) FRANK, JR, b. Rochester, N.Y, June 4, 16; m. 47; c. 2. CHEMISTRY. B.S, N.Y. State Col. Forestry, Syracuse, 38, M.S, 40. Res. assoc, EASTMAN KODAK CO, 40-67, sr. res. assoc, 67-70, SR. HEAD LAB, 70- Am. Chem. Soc. Chemistry and oxidation of cellulose; addition and condensation polymers; theory and practice of emulsion polymerization. Address: Eastman Kodak Co, 343 State St, Rochester, NY 14650.

FOWLER, W(YMAN) BEALL, b. Scranton, Pa, June 18, 37; m. 61; c. 3. SOLID STATE PHYSICS. B.S, Lehigh, 59; Ph.D.(physics), Rochester, 63. Res. assoc. PHYSICS, Univ. Rochester, 63; Univ. Ill, 63-66; assoc. prof, LEHIGH UNIV, 66-69, PROF, 69- Physicist, Argonne Nat. Lab, summer, 62, consult, 63-66; Naval Res. Lab, 66- Eastman Kodak sci. award, 63. AAAS; fel. Am. Phys. Soc. Solid state theory; electronic properties of insulators; color centers; band structures. Address: Dept. of Physics, Lehigh University, Bethlehem, PA 18015.

FOWLES, G(EORGE) RICHARD, b. Glenwood Springs, Colo, Apr. 2, 28; m. 54; c. 4. GEOPHYSICS, PHYSICS. B.S, Stanford, 52, M.S, 54, Ph.D. (geophysics), 62. Geophysicist, Phelps Dodge Corp, 54-55; physicist, Poulter Labs, Stanford Res. Inst, 55-62, group head shock wave physics, 62-63, div. dir, 63-66; ASSOC. PROF. PHYSICS, WASH. STATE UNIV, 66- Sr. staff scientist, Physics Int. Co, 69-70; consult, Nat. Mat. Adv. Bd, Nat. Res. Coun, 70; Stanford Res. Inst, 71-; Gen. Motors Corp, 71- U.S.N, 46-48. Am. Geophys. Union; Am. Phys. Soc; Am. Asn. Physics Teachers. Non-linear wave propagation; high pressure behavior of solids. Address: Dept. of Physics, Washington State University, Pullman, WA 99163.

FOWLES, GRANT R(OBERT), b. Fairview, Utah, Sept. 19, 19; m. 42; c. 4. PHYSICS, SPECTROSCOPY. B.S, Utah, 41; Ph.D.(physics), California, 50. From asst. prof. to PROF. PHYSICS, UNIV. UTAH, 50- U.S.N.R, 42-45, Lt. Am. Phys. Soc; Optical Soc. Am. Spectroscopy; hyperfine structure; high resolution spectroscopy; lasers. Address: Dept. of Physics, University of Utah, Salt Lake City, UT 84112.

FOWLES, PATRICK ERNEST, b. Harrow, Eng, Nov. 7, 38; m. 67; c. 1. CHEMICAL ENGINEERING. B.Sc, London, 60; Sc.D.(chem. eng, fluid mech), Mass. Inst. Tech, 66. SR. RES. ENGR, CENT. RES. DIV. LAB, MOBIL RES. & DEVELOP. CORP, MOBIL OIL CORP, 66- Am. Soc. Lubrication Eng; Am. Inst. Chem. Eng. Tribiology; experimental and theoretical research in hydrodynamic and elastohydrodynamic lubrication; rheology, especially rheological properties of lubricants and related fluids; fluid mechanics, especially turbulent flow, and mass and heat transfer in turbulent flow. Address: Central Research Division, Mobil Research & Development Corp, P.O. Box 1025, Princeton, NJ 08540.

FOWLIS, WILLIAM WEBSTER, b. Lanarkshire, Scotland, Jan. 21, 37; m. 70. PHYSICS, GEOPHYSICS. B.Sc, Glasgow Univ, 59; Ph.D.(physics), Univ. Durham, 64. Res. staff, dept. geol. & geophys, Mass. Inst. Technol, 62-64; res. assoc. & lectr. METEOROL, FLA. STATE UNIV, 65-68, ASST. PROF. & ASSOC, GEOPHYS. FLUID DYNAMICS INST, 68- AAAS; Am. Geophys. Union; Am. Meteorol. Soc; fel. Royal Meteorol. Soc. Geophysical fluid dynamics; experimental studies of laboratory models of the general hydrodynamic circulations of planetary atmospheres. Address: Geophysical Fluid Dynamics Institute, Keen Bldg, Room 18, Florida State University, Tallahassee, FL 32306.

FOWLKES, EDWARD B, II, b. Tarboro, N.C, Dec. 22, 36. STATISTICS. B.S, North Carolina, 59; M.S, N.C. State, 64; Columbia, 65-66. Qual. control engr, Westinghouse Elec. Corp, 59-62; MEM. TECH. STAFF, BELL TEL. LABS, 63- U.S.C.G, 61, Res, 62-68. Am. Statist. Asn. Statistical computing; data analysis. Address: Location 2C-473, Bell Telephone Labs, Murray Hill, NJ 07974.

FOWLKS, W(ILLIAM) LOUIS, b. Murray, Utah, Mar. 11, 13; m. 48; c. 3. ORGANIC & BIOLOGICAL CHEMISTRY. B.S, California, 37; Ph.D.(org. chem), Oregon State Col, 55. Res. assoc. biochem. & dermat, sch. med, Oregon, 54-59; asst. prof. EXP. OPHTHAL, UNIV. MINN, MINNEAPOLIS, 59-65, ASSOC. PROF, 65- U.S.A, 45. Am. Chem. Soc; Soc. Exp. Biol. & Med; Asn. Res. Vision & Ophthal. Photosensitization of biological materials; biochemistry and physiology of the eye; growth and its regulation; water and electrolyte transport in biological material. Address: Dept. of Ophthalmology, Box 387 Mayo Bldg, University of Minnesota, Minneapolis, MN 55455.

FOX, ADRIAN S(AMUEL), b. Chicago, Ill, Apr. 3, 36; m. 60; c. 1. ORGANIC & POLYMER CHEMISTRY. B.S, Illinois, 57; Ph.D.(org. chem), Washington, 62. Res. fel, Ohio State, 62-63; res. chemist, plastics div, Union Carbide Corp, N.J, 63-66; staff chemist, res. dept, Raychem Corp, Calif, 66-68; res. chemist, POLYMER RES. DEPT, Pennsalt Chem. Corp, 68-70, PROJ. LEADER, PENNWALT CORP, 70- Am. Chem. Soc; The Chem. Soc; Soc. Plastics Eng. Polymer synthesis and post-polymerization chemistry; mechanisms of oxidation reactions; organometallic chemistry. Address: Polymer Research Dept, Pennwalt Corp, 900 First Ave, King of Prussia, PA 19406.

FOX, ALBERT OLE, b. Livermore, Iowa, Apr. 11, 25; m. 48; c. 2. MATHEMATICS. B.S, Nebr. State Teachers Col, Kearney, 49; M.E, Nebraska, 51; M.S, New Mexico Highlands, 61; summers, Alaska, 58, Kansas, 59. Supt, Rockville Pub. Schs, Nebr, 49-50; prin, Sutherland Pub. Schs, 51-52; supt, Wallace Pub. Schs, 52-55; Bertrand Pub. Schs, 55-60; instr, El Camino High Sch, Calif, 61-62; ASSOC. PROF. MATH, CHADRON STATE COL, 62- Math. Asn. Am. Address: Dept. of Mathematics, Chadron State College, Chadron, NE 69337.

FOX, ALLEN S(ANDER), b. Chicago, Ill, Mar. 5, 21; m. 41; c. 2. GENETICS, BIOCHEMISTRY. B.S, Chicago, 41, Ph.D.(zool), 48. Asst. prof. zool, Ohio State, 48-53; Fulbright prof, Pavia, Italy, 53-54; assoc. prof. zool, Mich. State, 54-59, from assoc. prof. agr. chem. to PROF. biochem, 59-63; GENETICS, UNIV. WIS, MADISON, 63- Vis. prof, Univ. Wis, 58; Univ. Zurich, 68-69; Fulbright sr. res. fel, Univ. Sydney, 61. U.S.A, 42-45. AAAS; Am. Soc. Nat; Genetics Soc. Am; Am. Soc. Zool; Soc. Study Evolution; Soc. Exp. Biol. & Med. Biochemical and developmental genetics; immunogenetics; protein synthesis; tissue culture; differentiation; transformation; Drosophila; Neurospora. Address: Lab. of Genetics, University of Wisconsin, Madison, WI 53706.

FOX, ARTHUR CHARLES, b. Newark, N.J, Sept. 16, 26. MEDICINE. M.D, N.Y. Univ, 48. Intern. med, Bellevue Hosp, 48-49, asst. res, 49-51, res, 51-52; prfnl. asst, div. med. sci, Nat. Res. Council, 53-54; asst. MED, SCH. MED, N.Y. UNIV, 50-52, 54-56, instr, 56-58, asst. prof, 58-60, assoc. prof, 60-68, PROF, 68- Res. fel, Nat. Heart Inst, 54-56; vis. physician, Bellevue Hosp; Univ. Hosp; consult, Vet. Admin. Hosp, Manhattan; section chief cardiol, med. ctr, N.Y. Univ. U.S.A.F, 52-54, Capt. Fel. Am. Col. Physicians; Harvey Soc. Internal medicine; cardiology; myocardial metabolism and coronary blood flow. Address: Dept. of Medicine, New York University School of Medicine, 550 First Ave, New York, NY 10016.

FOX, A(RTHUR) GARDNER, b. Syracuse, N.Y, Nov. 22, 12; m. 38; c. 4. ENGINEERING. B.S, M.S. & E.E, Mass. Inst. Technol, 35. HEAD, DEPT. COHERENT WAVE PHYSICS, BELL TEL. LABS, 36- Fel. Inst. Elec. & Electronics Eng.(ed, Jour. Quantum Electronics). Coherent optical wave techniques; lasers, resonators, optical beams; microwave techniques in centimeter and millimeter wave length ranges; microwave magnetics. Address: Bell Telephone Labs, 4E-418, Holmdel, NJ 07733.

FOX, AUGUSTUS H(ENRY), b. Mansfield, Ohio, Sept. 28, 02; m. 28; c. 1. MATHEMATICS. A.B, Western Reserve, 25; A.M, Oberlin Col, 27; A.M, Harvard, 29; Ph.D.(math), Yale, 35. Instr. MATH, Oberlin, 25-27; Harvard, 27-29; UNION UNIV. (N.Y), 29-31, 32-37, asst. prof, 37-43, assoc. prof, 43-49, prof, 49-68, EMER. PROF, 68- Instr, Yale, 31-32. Am. Math. Soc. Differential equations; mathematical physics; reactor theory; numerical analysis. Address: 1743 Ivy Oak Square, Reston, VA 22070.

FOX, BENNETT L, b. Chicago, Ill, Aug. 13, 38. MATHEMATICS. B.A, Michigan, 60; M.S, Chicago, 62; Ph.D.(opers. res), California, Berkeley, 65. MATHEMATICIAN, RAND CORP, 65- Ford vis. prof, Univ. Chicago, 71-72. Opers. Res. Soc. Am. Reliability theory; dynamic programming. Address: Dept. of Management Science, University of Chicago, Chicago, IL 60637.

FOX, B(ERNARD) LAWRENCE, b. Canton, Ohio, Aug. 18, 40; m. 63. ORGANIC CHEMISTRY. B.S, John Carroll, 62; Ph.D.(org. chem), Ohio State, 66. Asst. prof. CHEM, UNIV. DAYTON, 66-71, ASSOC. PROF, 71- Consult, mat. lab, Wright-Patterson Air Force Base, 67- AAAS; Am. Chem. Soc; The Chem. Soc. Synthesis and reactions of azabicycloalkanes; mechanism of hydrogenolysis of benzylamines; mechanism of lithium aluminum hydride reduction of oxazolidines. Address: Dept. of Chemistry, University of Dayton, Dayton, OH 45409.

FOX, C. J. S, b. Toronto, Ont, Dec. 4, 15; m. 43; c. 3. ENTOMOLOGY. B.Sc.A, Toronto, 44; Western Ontario, 49-50. Entomologist, Ont. Dept. Lands & Forests, 44-45; entomologist & res. scientist, Can. Dept. Agr, N.S, 45-66; biologist, plant protection div, Ont, 66-67; ENTOMOLOGIST, RES. STA, N.S. DEPT. AGR, 67- Entom. Soc. Am; Entom. Soc. Can; Agr. Inst. Can; Int. Soc. Soil Sci; Can. Agr. Pesticide Tech. Soc. Agricultural entomology; soil zoology. Address: Research Station, Nova Scotia Dept. of Agriculture, Kentville, N.S, Can.

FOX, CARROLL WARREN, b. Denver, Colo, Mar. 7, 18; m. 44; c. 1. ANIMAL BREEDING. B.S, Colo. Agr. & Mech. Col, 43; Brownell fel, California, 49-51, Ph.D.(animal genetics), 54. Asst, California, 48-49; asst. prof. animal husb, Colo. Agr. & Mech. Col, 51-56; assoc. prof, Ore. State Univ, 56-69; PROJ. SPECIALIST, FORD FOUND, LEBANON, 69- Livestock consult, Univ. Aleppo, 66-67; Beirut, Lebanon, 67-68. Mem. collab. comt, sheep exp. sta, U.S. Dept. Agr. & West. Sheep Breeding Lab, Idaho. U.S.A, 43-47. AAAS; Am. Soc. Animal Sci. Role of genetics in improving the efficiency of carcass characteristics and wool production in sheep; magnitude of environmental influences on carcass and wool characteristics in sheep. Address: Ford Foundation, P.O. Box 2379, Beirut, Lebanon.

FOX, CHARLES, b. London, Eng, Mar. 17, 97; m. 32; c. 2. MATHEMATICS. B.A, Cambridge, 18, M.A, 22; D.Sc.(math), London, 28. Demonstr. MATH, Imp. Col, London, 19-20; lectr, Birkbeck Col, London, 20-48; assoc. prof, McGill, 49-56, PROF, 56-67, SIR GEORGE WILLIAMS UNIV, 67- Brit. Army, 17-18; civilian with Brit. Aircraft Res, 39-45. Am. Math. Soc; fel. Royal Soc. Can. Mathematical analysis; Fourier transform theory and generalizations; integral equations; gyroscopic apparatus and theory. Address: Dept. of Mathematics, Sir George Williams University, Montreal, Que, Can.

FOX, CHARLES J(UNIUS), b. Detroit, Mich, Nov. 22, 26; m. 46; c. 5. ORGANIC CHEMISTRY. B.Sc, Ohio State, 47, M.Sc, 50, Socony-Vacuum Oil Co. fel, 51-52, Ph.D.(chem), 53. Res. assoc, Kettering Lab. Appl. Physiol, 47-49; res. chemist, Durez Plastics Div, Hooker Electrochem. Co, 53-55; sr. res. chemist, EASTMAN KODAK CO, 55-61, res. assoc, 61-67, LAB. HEAD, PHOTOMAT. DIV, 67- Soc. Photog. Sci. & Eng; Am. Chem. Soc. Organic photoconductors; polymers. Address: Research Lab, Photomaterials Division, Eastman Kodak Co, Kodak Park, Rochester, NY 14650.

FOX, CHARLES L(EWIS), JR, b. N.Y.C, Jan. 16, 08; m. 57; c. 3. MICROBIOLOGY, SURGERY. A.B, Harvard, 29; M.D, L.I. Col. Med, 34. Fel. path, Mallory inst, Boston City Hosp, 34; intern & house physician-surgeon, Jewish Hosp, Brooklyn, 34-36; res. fel. chem, Mt. Sinai Hosp, 36-38; asst. bact, Harvard Med. Sch, 38-39; instr. & assoc, col. physicians & surgeons, Columbia, 40-46, asst. prof, 46-51; assoc. prof. surg, N.Y. Med. Col, Flower & Fifth Ave. Hosps, 52-58, surg. & biochem, 58-60, surg. & physiol, 60; assoc. prof. MICROBIOL, COL. PHYSICIANS & SURGEONS, COLUMBIA UNIV, 60-62, PROF, 62- Assoc. vis. surgeon, Metropolitan Hosp, 53-60; assoc. attending surgeon, Flower & Fifth Ave. Hosps, 55-60; assoc. vis. path, Bellevue Hosp, 60-; career scientist, Health Res. Coun, 62-; consult, St. Barnabas Hosp, N.J, 52- Responsible investr, Off. Sci. Res. & Develop, 42-45. Soc. Exp. Biol. & Med; Harvey Soc; Am. Physiol. Soc; Am. Med. Asn; Am. Asn. Immunol; Am. Fedn. Clin. Res; Am. Asn. Clin. Chem; N.Y. Acad. Sci; N.Y. Acad. Med; Am. Burn Asn. Thermal burns and anaphylaxis; mechanisms of shock; fluid and electrolyte physiology; flame photometry; bacterial metabolism; role of sulfonamides and relation to purine biosynthesis; hemoglobin spectroscopy and metabolism; microbiology; synthesis and development of silver sulfadiazine for prevention and treatment of burn wound infection. Address: College of Physicians & Surgeons, Columbia University, 650 W. 168th St, New York, NY 10032.

FOX, C(HESTER) DAVID, b. Albany, N.Y, Apr. 8, 31; m. 61. PHARMACEUTICAL CHEMISTRY. B.S, Union (N.Y), 58; Am. Found. for Pharmaceut. Ed. fel, Wisconsin, 58-59; M.S, Maryland, 63, Nat. Insts. Health fel, 63-64, Ph.D.(indust. pharm), 65. TECH. ADV. PROD, AYERST LABS, INC, DIV. AM. HOME PROD. CORP, 64- U.S.A.F, 50-54, Sgt. AAAS; Pharmaceut. Mfrs. Asn; Am. Pharmaceut. Asn; fel. Am. Inst. Chem. Industrial pharmacy; development of automated industrial pharmaceutical production processes; development and evaluation of new pharmaceutical production equipment and methods. Address: Production Pilot, Ayerst Labs, Inc, 55 Maple St, Rouses Point, NY 12979.

FOX, CLEMENT A(LPHONSINE), b. Hart, Mich, Apr. 15, 08; m. 39; c. 6. NEUROANATOMY. B.S, Marquette, 31; M.A, Michigan, 36, fel, 36-38; Ph.D.(anat), 38. Asst. zool, Marquette, 33-35; anat, Michigan, 35-36, instr, med. sch, Marquette, 38-42; assoc. neurol, inst. neurol, Northwestern, 43; assoc. prof. ANAT, Temple, 44; asst. prof, Marquette Univ, 44-47, assoc. prof, 47-50, prof, 50-65, assoc. chmn. dept, 58-65; PROF. & CHMN. DEPT, SCH. MED, WAYNE STATE UNIV, 65- Mem. neurol. study sect, Nat. Insts. Health, 59-63, steering comt. neuroanat. sci, 63-, nat. dir. neuroanat. vis. scientists prog, 64-70; sect. ed. neuroanat, Biol. Abstr, 61-; mem, Int. Brain Res. Orgn. Am. Asn. Anat; Soc. Exp. Biol. & Med; Am. Acad. Neurol; Am. Neurol. Asn. Certain cat and monkey forebrain centers; amygdala; olfactory tubercle; septum; hippocampus; cingulum; degenerative methods; oscillographic studies of olfactory system in cat; Golgi and electron microscopic studies of the cerebellar cortex and basal ganglia. Address: Dept. of Anatomy, Wayne State University School of Medicine, Detroit, MI 48201.

FOX, DALE BENNETT, b. Sioux Falls, S. Dak, May 25, 39; m. 64; c. 3. ORGANIC CHEMISTRY. B.S, Hamline Univ, 61; M.S, Univ. Iowa, 68, Petrol. Res. Fund fel, 67-69, Ph.D.(org. chem), 69. Assoc. chemist, res. ctr, Marathon Oil Co, Colo, 62-65; RES. CHEMIST, MONSANTO CO, 69- Am. Chem. Soc; Sci. Res. Soc. Am. Catalysis; catalysts and catalytic conversions, especially with hydrocarbons; monomer synthesis; general organic and organometallic synthesis. Address: Monsanto Co, 800 N. Lindbergh Blvd, St. Louis, MO 63166.

FOX, DANIEL W(AYNE), b. Johnstown, Pa, May 14, 23; m. 48; c. 2. ORGANIC CHEMISTRY. B.S, Lebanon Valley Col, 49; M.S, Oklahoma, 51, fel, 52-53, Ph.D.(org. chem), 53. Chemist, mat. & process lab, GEN. ELEC. CO, 53-59, MGR. prod. develop, chem. develop. opers, 59-62, res. & adv. develop, 63-70, CENT. RES, PLASTIC DEPT, 71- U.S.A.A.F, 43-46, 1st Lt. Am. Chem. Soc. High performance polymers and plastics. Address: 193 Dawes Ave, Pittsfield, MA 01201.

FOX, DAVID, b. Brooklyn, N.Y, Sept. 8, 20; m. 38; c. 3. THEORETICAL PHYSICS. B.A, California, 42, M.A, 50, Ph.D.(physics), 52. Lectr. physics, Israel Inst. Tech, 52-55, sr. lectr, 55-56; lectr, Hebrew Univ, 55; res. assoc, inst. optics, Rochester, 56-57, asst. prof, 57-59; PROF. PHYSICS, STATE UNIV. N.Y. STONY BROOK, 59-, acting dean grad. sch, 63-66. U.S.N.R, 45-46. Am. Phys. Soc; Phys. Soc. Israel. Theoretical solid state physics; statistical theory of eigenvalues. Address: Dept. of Physics, State University of New York at Stony Brook, Stony Brook, NY 11790.

FOX, D(AVID) W(ILLIAM), b. Dubuque, Iowa, Nov. 21, 28; m. 50; c. 2. MATHEMATICS. A.B, Michigan, 51, M.S.E, 52; Ph.D.(math), Maryland, 58. Sr. engr, APPL. PHYSICS LAB, JOHNS HOPKINS UNIV, 53-56, consult, 56-60, mathematician, prin. staff, 60-66, SUPVR, APPL. MATH. RES. GROUP, 66- Res. asst. prof, inst. fluid dynamics & appl. math, Maryland, 59-60; consult, int. div, Battelle Mem. Inst, Switz, 60- Am. Math. Soc. Spectral theory of operators and theory of partial differential equations. Address: Applied Mathematics Research Group, Applied Physics Lab, Johns Hopkins University, Silver Spring, MD 20910.

FOX, DENIS L(EWELLYN), b. Udimore, Eng, Dec. 22, 01; nat; m. 27, 32; c. 4. BIOCHEMISTRY, PHYSIOLOGY. A.B, California, 25; Victor fel, Stanford, 30-31, Ph.D.(biochem), 31. Chemist, res. labs, Standard Oil Co. of Calif, Richmond, 25-29; asst. biochem, Stanford, 29-30, biol, 31; instr. physiol, SCRIPPS INST. OCEANOG, UNIV. CALIF, SAN DIEGO, 31-36, asst. prof, 36-37, MARINE BIOCHEM, 37-42, assoc. prof, 42-48, prof, 48-69, RES. BIOCHEMIST, DIV. MARINE BIOL. & EMER. PROF, 69- Res. fel, Rockefeller Found, Cambridge, 38-39; mem. res. coun, Inst. Comp. Biol, San Diego Zoo, 40-; consult, biochemist, 41-; Guggenheim fel, 45-46; grants, Am. Philos. Soc. 47, Rockefeller Found, 47-54, Nat. Sci. Found, 62-70; distinguished scholar, Cranbrook Inst. Sci, 70-71. Fel. AAAS; Am. Soc. Zool; Am. Soc. Limnol. & Oceanog; Soc. Gen. Physiol. Biochemistry and comparative metabolism of animal biochromes; nutrition, growth and metabolism of marine animals; organic matter in marine waters and sediments; biochemical fossils. Address: Division of Marine Biology, Scripps Institution of Oceanography, University of California at San Diego, La Jolla, CA 92037.

FOX, DONALD E, b. Elberon, Iowa, Jan. 1, 05; m. 36. ORGANIC CHEMISTRY. A.B, State Univ. Iowa, 27, M.S, 30, Ph.D.(chem), 36. Teacher, pub. sch, 27-35; PROF. CHEM, KEARNEY STATE COL, 58-, CHMN. DIV. SCI. & MATH, 66-, head dept. chem, 37-58, dean sch. nat. & social sci, 69-70. Am. Chem. Soc. Condensation of vanillin substitution products with nitromethane. Address: Division of Science & Mathematics, Kearney State College, Kearney, NE 68847.

FOX, EDWARD A(LEXANDER), b. New York, N.Y, Aug. 7, 20; m. 49; c. 3. MECHANICS. B.S, Harvard, 41; B.S, Columbia, 47, Quincy Ward Boese fel. & Ph.D.(eng. mech), 58. Asst. prof. MECH, RENSSELAER POLYTECH. INST, 54-58, assoc. prof, 58-65, PROF, 65- U.S.N.R, 43-46. Am. Soc. Mech. Eng. Mathematical theory of elasticity; stress wave propagation; classical mechanics. Address: Dept. of Mechanics, Rensselaer Polytechnic Institute, Troy, NY 12181.

FOX, EDWARD L, b. Dayton, Ohio, May 30, 38; m. 64; c. 2. EXERCISE PHYSIOLOGY. B.S, Ohio State Univ, 60, M.A, 61, Cent. Ohio Heart Asn. fel, 62-64, Ph.D.(physiol), 65. Nat. Insts. Health fel. anat. & physiol, Ind. Univ, 67-68; asst. prof, OHIO STATE UNIV, 68-70, ASSOC. PROF. EXERCISE PHYSIOL. & STATIST, 70- AAAS; N.Y. Acad. Sci; Am. Physiol. Soc. Environmental physiology; effects of heat on exercise tolerance; metabolic responses during exercise; effects of physical conditioning on cardiorespiratory responses during exercise; application of science and medicine to sports. Address: Exercise Physiology Lab, Ohio State University, 337 W. 17th Ave, Columbus, OH 43210.

FOX, EUGENE N, b. Chicago, Ill, Dec. 9, 27; m. 64; c. 2. MICROBIOLOGY. B.S, Illinois, 49, M.S, 50; Ph.D.(microbiol), Western Reserve, 55. Instr. MICROBIOL, West. Reserve Univ, 58-60; asst. prof, LA RABIDA INST, UNIV. CHICAGO, 60-66, ASSOC. PROF, 66- Sr. investr, Arthritis & Rheumatism Found, 59-64. Chem.C, U.S.A, 55-57. Am. Soc. Microbiol; Am. Asn. Immunol. Immunology. Address: La Rabida Institute, University of Chicago, Jackson Park at 65th St, Chicago, IL 60649.

FOX, EVA FERNANDEZ, b. San Juan, P.R, Oct. 11, 17; m. 45; c. 2. RADIOLOGY. B.S, Chestnut Hill Col, 39; M.D, Med. Col. Pa, 43. Asst. prof. RADIOL, MED. COL. PA, 60-62, ASSOC. PROF, 62-69, PROF. & CHMN. DEPT, 69-, CLIN. ASST. PROF. MED, 60- Consult, Vet. Admin. Hosp, Phila, Pa, 66- Am. Col. Radiol; Am. Med. Adn; Am. Thoracic Soc; Pan-Am. Med. Asn; Am. Heart Asn. Address: Dept. of Radiology, Medical College of Pennsylvania, 3300 Henry Ave, Philadelphia, PA 19129.

FOX, FRANCIS H(ENRY), b. Clifton Springs, N.Y, Mar. 11, 23; m. 46; c. 3. VETERINARY MEDICINE. D.V.M, State Univ. N.Y, 45. Asst. mastitis & vet. med, Cornell, 45-46; instr. vet. med. & surg, Ohio State, 46-47; asst. prof. VET. MED. & OBSTET, STATE UNIV. N.Y. VET. COL, CORNELL UNIV, 47-49, assoc. prof, 49-53, PROF, 53- Am. Vet. Med. Asn. Diseases of large domestic animals, especially the bovine. Address: Dept. of Veterinary Medicine & Obstetrics, State University of New York Veterinary College, Cornell University, Ithaca, NY 14850.

FOX, F(REDERICK) G(LENN), b. Weyburn, Sask, Mar. 6, 18; m. 43; c. 2. GEOLOGY. B.Sc, Alberta, 40, M.Sc, 42; fel, Oklahoma, 47, Ph.D.(geol), 48. Geologist, Imperial Oil, Ltd, 42-46, 48-50; sr. geologist, Hudsons Bay Oil & Gas Co, 50-55; sr. survey & struct. geologist, Triad Oil Co, Ltd, Can, 55-68; SR. STRUCT. GEOLOGIST, PANARCTIC OILS LTD, 68- Fel. Geol. Soc. Am; fel. Geol. Asn. Can. Stratigraphy and structure of Rocky Mountains and the foothills belt; general structural geology; mapping of complex structure. Address: Panarctic Oils Ltd, 703 Sixth Ave. S.W, Calgary 2, Alta, Can.

FOX, GEOFFREY T, b. Chicago, Ill, Feb. 11, 41; m. 64; c. 3. LOW TEMPERATURE PHYSICS. B.S, Santa Clara, 62; Wis. Alumni Res. Found. fels, Wisconsin, 62-64, M.S, 64, univ. fel, 66, Ph.D.(physics), 67. Proj. assoc. PHYSICS, Univ. Wis, Madison, 67-69, instr, 68-69; ASST. PROF, UNIV. SANTA CLARA, 69- Summers, engr. aid, Varian Assocs, Calif, 59 & 60, res. aid, Nat. Sci. Found-Univ. Santa Clara, 61 & Int. Bus. Mach. Corp, 62. Am. Phys. Soc. Thermal conductivity at low temperatures, especially as reveal spin-phonon interactions. Address: Dept. of Physics, University of Santa Clara, Santa Clara, CA 95053.

FOX, G(EORGE) SIDNEY, b. Phila, Pa, Feb. 21, 28; m. 56; c. 2. GEOLOGICAL ENGINEERING. B.S.E, Princeton, 50. Hydraul. engr, U.S. Geol. Surv, 51-55; groundwater geologist, LEGGETTE, BRASHEARS & GRAHAM, 55-67, PARTNER, 67- Geol. Soc. Am; Am. Water Resources Asn; Am. Inst. Mining, Metall. & Petrol. Eng; Am. Inst. Prof. Geol; Am. Geophys. Union. Ground-water geology; hydrology. Address: 33 Deer Hill Dr, Ridgefield, CT 06877.

FOX, GERALD, b. N.Y.C, Apr. 23, 23; m. 55; c. 1. INDUSTRIAL CHEMISTRY. B.Sc, Long Island, 47. Chemist, Fleischmann Labs, N.Y, 46-49; chief chemist, Consol. Laundries Corp, 49-57; SECY. & DIR. RES, Gold Par Prod. Co, Inc, 57-70, GOLD PAR CHEM, INC, 70- Consult, electroplaters & mfrs. Med.C, U.S.A, 43-46. Am. Oil Chem. Soc; Am. Chem. Soc; Am. Asn. Textile Chem. & Colorists. Sanitary chemicals; chemical specialty items; soaps and detergents for laundry, dry cleaning, textile processing, food and beverage, dairy, dishwashing and metal industries. Address: 110 Warren St, Nutley, NJ 07110.

FOX, GERALD W(ILLIS), b. Three Rivers, Mich, Sept. 23, 00; m. 26; PHYSICS. A.B, Michigan, 23, A.M, 24, Ph.D.(physics), 26. Instr. physics, Michigan, 24-26, head dept. physics & chem, univ. high sch, 26-27, asst. prof. PHYSICS, univ, 27-30; assoc. prof, IOWA STATE UNIV, 30-35, prof, 35-66; EMER. PROF, 66-, consult, Inst. Atomic Res, 46-66, head dept, 46-61. Opers. analyst, Japan Air Defense Force, 53-54. Consult, U.S.A. With Off. Sci. Res. & Develop, 44. AAAS; fel. Am. Phys. Soc. Conduction of electricity through gases; x-ray diffraction in piezoelectrically oscillating crystals; crystal growing of non-stoichiometric compounds. Address: R.R. S, Box 100, Yachats, OR 97498.

FOX, HARRY W(ILLIAM), b. N.Y.C, Sept. 4, 12. CHEMISTRY. B.S, Mass. Inst. Tech, 34; Ed.M, Boston, 40. Res. chemist, emulsions & agents, Beacon Co, 36-38; emulsions & protective coating, Daitch & Co, 38-40; surface chem. & lubrication, Mass. Inst. Tech, 41; emulsions & protective coatings, Naval Res. Lab, U.S. DEPT. NAVY, 42-45, surface chem, 45-49, head interface res. unit, 49-55, phys. chemist, OFF. NAVAL RES, 55-69, DIR. CHEM. PROG, 69- Award, Carbide & Carbon Chem. Soc, 55. AAAS; Am. Chem. Soc; Sci. Res. Soc. Am. Surface and colloid chemistry. Address: Office of Naval Research, 800 N. Quincy St, Arlington, VA 22217.

FOX, HAZEL METZ, b. Barton, Md, July 2, 21; m. 50; c. 5. NUTRITION. B.A, West. Md. Col, 43, hon. D.Sc, 69; fel, Iowa State Univ, 45-47, M.S, 47, Ph.D. (nutrit), 54. Teacher, high sch, Md, 43-45; res. assoc, Children's Fund Mich, 47-50; asst, Iowa State Univ, 50-54, instr. nutrition, 54-55; assoc. prof, UNIV. NEBR, LINCOLN, 55-62, prof, 62-68, GEORGE HOLMES PROF. FOOD & NUTRIT, 68-, CHMN. DEPT. FOOD & NUTRIT, 63- AAAS; Am. Inst. Nutrit; Am. Dietetic Asn; Am. Home Econ. Asn. (Borden Award human nutrit, 69). Plant proteins in human nutrition; cultural aspects of diet; nutrition education. Address: Dept. of Food & Nutrition, University of Nebraska, Lincoln, NE 68503.

FOX, HERBERT, b. N.Y.C, May 27, 39; m. 62; c. 2. AEROSPACE & URBAN TECHNOLOGY. B.S, Mass. Inst. Technol, 60; M.S, Polytech. Inst. Brooklyn, 62, Ph.D.(aeronaut, astronaut), 64. Res. asst. aeronaut. & astronaut, aerodyn. lab, Polytech. Inst. Brooklyn, Freeport, 60-63; mem. tech. staff, Aerospace Corp, Calif, summer 63; asst. prof. aeronaut. & astronaut, N.Y. Univ, 64-68, assoc. prof, 68-70; prof. mech, aerospace & indust. technol. & chmn. dept, N.Y. INST. TECHNOL, 70-71, ASSOC. DEAN SCI. & TECHNOL, 71- Consult, Gen. Appl. Sci. Labs, 62-67; Advan. Technol. Labs, 67-; Fox-Kirschbaum-Fox, Inc; Amutech Inc, 68-71; Technicon Inc, 70-71. Am. Inst. Aeronaut. & Astronaut. Low-speed aerodynamics; high-speed gas dynamics; bio-fluid mechanics; transportation technology. Address: Dept. of Aerospace Technology, New York Institute of Technology, 268 Wheatley Rd, Old Westbury, NY 11568.

FOX, HERBERT L(EON), b. Boston, Mass, Jan. 6, 30; m. 52; c. 4. PHYSICS, ECONOMICS. B.A, Boston, 58, fel, 61-62, M.A, 62, Nat. Sci. Found. fel, 62-64. Proj. engr, Farnsworth-Tamari, 57; chief design engr, Tech. Prod. Co, 55-57; SR. PHYSICIST & ECONOMIST, BOLT BERANEK & NEWMAN, 57- Res. asst, Boston Univ, 63-64; consult. comt, Nat. Acad. Remote Atmospheric Probing; lectr, dept. econ, Northeast. Univ. AAAS; Am. Phys. Soc; Am. Asn. Physics Teachers; Acoust. Soc. Am. Atmospheric sound propagation; quantum optics; kinetic theory; nonlinear mechanics; development economics. Address: 9 Walden St, Jamaica Plain, MA 02130.

FOX, HERMAN, b. N.Y.C, Aug. 7, 14; m. 42; c. 3. CHEMICAL ENGINEERING. B.S, Polytech. Inst. Brooklyn, 36. Prod. supvr, Hercules Powder Co, 36-43, supvr. res. & develop, 43-53, consult, Australia, 53, Eng, 54-57, new prod. develop. rep, polymer dept, 57-63, managing dir, Hercules Far East, Ltd, Japan, & Teijin-Hercules, Ltd, 63-67, MGR. develop, int. dept, HERCULES INC, DEL, 67-68, VENTURE PROJS, NEW ENTERPRISE DEPT, 68- Polypropylene. Address: New Enterprise Dept, Hercules Inc, Wilmington, DE 19801.

FOX, H(ERMAN) HERBERT, b. New York, N.Y, Nov. 9, 12; m. 43; c. 2. ORGANIC CHEMISTRY. B.S, Brooklyn Col, 33, Ph.D.(org. chem), Columbia, 39. Asst. chem, Columbia, 35-39; instr. org. chem, Brooklyn Col. & City Col, 39-40; supvr. clin. res, Hoffmann-La Roche, Inc, 40-42, sr. res. chemist, 43-63; v.pres, Cyclo Chem. Corp, Calif, 63-67; PRES. FOX CHEM. CO, 67- Award of Honor, Brooklyn Col, 53. AAAS; Am. Chem. Soc; Sci. Res. Soc. Am; N.Y. Acad. Sci. Arsenicals; anti-histaminics; spasmolytics; antioxidants; antimalarials; vitamins; antimonials; synthetic tuberulostats; isoniazid and its derivatives; monomine oxidase inhibitors; psychic energizers. Address: Fox Chemical Co, 1556 Industrial St, Los Angeles, CA 90021.

FOX, H(OMER) M(cGRADY), b. Batesville, Ark, Apr. 15, 20; m. 48; c. 2. PETROLEUM ENGINEERING. A.B.(math), Hendrix Col, 41; Ga. Sch. Tech. Proj. engr, fuels & combustion res, PHILLIPS PETROL. CO, 46-51, group leader, rocket propellants, 51-52, sr. sect, chief rocket propellants & fundamental combustion, 52-56, MGR. rocket propellants sect, 56-60, ADV. PROCESSES RES, 60- U.S.N.R, 42-46, Res, 46-, Comdr. Electrochem. Soc; Am. Inst. Aeronaut. & Astronaut. Effects of fuels and fuel characteristics on combustion performance in jet engines; petrochemicals as liquid rocket fuels; rubber base composite solid rocket propellants; ammonium nitrate as solid rocket propellant oxidizer; precombustion reactions and their role in reciprocating and continuous flow combustion systems; plasma chemistry; electrochemical fluorination; organic electrochemistry. Address: 728 Winding Way, Bartlesville, OK 74003.

FOX, IRVING, b. Hartford, Conn, Dec. 19, 12; m. 41; c. 1. MEDICAL ENTOMOLOGY. A.B, George Washington, 37, M.A, 38; Ph.D, Iowa State Col, 40. Asst. entomol, Iowa State Col, 37-40; instr. biol, Puerto Rico, 41-42; asst. prof. MED. ENTOM, SCH. MED, UNIV. P.R, SAN JUAN, 46-57, assoc. prof, 57-62, PROF, 62- Collab, bur. entom, U.S. Dept. Agr, 35-42; prog. dir, U.S. Pub. Health Serv. grad. res. training grant, 57-70. Cert. med. & vet. entom, Am. Registry Cert. Entom. Sanit.C, 42-46, Lt. Col. Fel. AAAS; Am. Soc. Parasitol; Entom. Soc. Am; Am. Soc. Trop. Med. & Hyg; Am. Mosquito Control Asn; Water Pollution Control Fedn. Taxonomy, population studies and control of insects; arachnida of medical importance, as fleas, mites, ticks, biting flies, mosquitoes and spiders; molluscicides. Address: Dept. of Medical Zoology, University of Puerto Rico School of Medicine, San Juan, PR 00905.

FOX, IRWIN J, b. Gnoien, Ger, June 26, 26; U.S. citizen; m. 64; c. 3. PHYSIOLOGY. A.B, Princeton, 47; M.D, N.Y. Med. Col, 51; Ph.D.(physiol), Minnesota, 62. Intern, Michael Reese Hosp, Chicago, Ill, 51-52, fel. cardiovasc. res, 52; med. & physiol, Mayo Found, UNIV. MINN, 53-59, res. assoc. PHYSIOL, 59-60, asst. prof, MED. SCH, MINNEAPOLIS, 60-64, ASSOC. PROF, 64- Minn. Heart Asn. fel, 56-57; U.S. Pub. Health Serv. sr. res. fel, 59-60, res. career develop. award, 60-70. AAAS; Soc. Exp. Biol. & Med; Am. Physiol. Soc. Indicator dilution technics, methods and application; effects of polybasic polymers and hypertonic solutions on circulation; cardiovascular control mechanisms. Address: Dept. of Physiology, 440 Millard Hall, University of Minnesota School of Medicine, Minneapolis, MN 55455.

FOX, J. EUGENE, b. Anderson, Ind, Aug. 7, 34; m. 60; c. 4. PLANT PHYSIOLOGY & BIOCHEMISTRY. B.S, Indiana, 56, Ph.D.(bot), 60. Nat. Cancer Inst. fel. BOT, Wisconsin, 60-61; asst. prof, UNIV. KANS, 61-64, assoc. prof, 64-70, PROF. & ASSOC. DEAN COL. ARTS & SCI, 70-, asst. dean, 67-70. AAAS; Bot. Soc. Am; Am. Soc. Plant Physiol; Scandinavian Soc. Plant Physiol; Japanese Soc. Plant Physiol. Growth and development of plants; biochemistry of plant growth regulators; plant tissue culture. Address: Dept. of Botany, University of Kansas, Lawrence, KS 66044.

FOX, JACK J(AY), b. New York, N.Y, Dec. 21, 16; m. 39; c. 2. BIO-ORGANIC CHEMISTRY. A.B, Colorado, 39, Ph.D.(chem), 50. Am. Cancer Soc. fel. nucleic acid chem, Universite Libre de Bruxelles, 50-52; Damon Runyon Mem. Fund fel, SLOAN-KETTERING INST. CANCER RES, 52-54, asst, 54-56, assoc, 56-58, CHIEF DIV. ORG. CHEM, WALKER LAB, 71-, PROF. BIOCHEM, SLOAN-KETTERING DIV, CORNELL UNIV, 65-, assoc. prof, 58-65. Head med. chem. sect, Sloan-Kettering Inst. Cancer Res, 58-71. U.S.A.A.F, 43-45. Am. Soc. Biol. Chem; Am. Chem. Soc; Am. Asn. Cancer Res. Chemistry and biological activity of compounds related to the nucleic acids. Address: Division of Organic Chemistry, Walker Lab, Sloan-Kettering Institute for Cancer Research, 145 Boston Post Rd, Rye, NY 10580.

FOX, J(ACK) LAWRENCE, b. Ann Arbor, Mich, Oct. 10, 41; m. 61; c. 2. BIOPHYSICS, BIOCHEMISTRY. B.A, Fla. State, 62; U.S. Pub. Health Serv. fel. & Ph.D.(chem), Arizona, 66. Guest investr. biochem, Rockefeller Univ, 66-68; ASST. PROF. BIOPHYS, UNIV. TEX, AUSTIN, 68- U.S. Pub. Health Serv. fel, 66-68; Nat. Sci. Found. develop. prog. grant, 68. AAAS; Am. Chem. Soc; Biophys. Soc; Int. Union Biochem. Molecular mechanisms of biological reactions; redox enzyme, especially flavoenzyme; model systems; electronic states of redox cofactors; protein synthesis and chain termination. Address: Dept. of Zoology, University of Texas at Austin, Austin, TX 78712.

FOX, JACKSON LELAND, b. Lewes, Del, Mar. 31, 39; m. 65; c. 2. BIOLOGY. B.S, Bucknell, 61; U.S. Pub. Health Serv. traineeship & M.P.H, Minnesota, 65, U.S. Pub. Health Serv. grant & Ph.D.(environ. health), 69. ASST. PROF. ENVIRON. ENG, UNIV. FLA, 69-, investr, biomed. sci. grant, 69-70. Investr, Fed. Water Pollution Control Admin. demonstration grant, 67-70; Fla. Game & Freshwater Fish Comn, 69-71; consult, Environ. Eng, Inc, Fla. U.S.P.H.S, 62-64, Sr. Asst. Health Off. AAAS; Am. Soc. Limnol. & Oceanog; Water Pollution Control Fedn. Periphyton; eutrophication; phytoplankton; lake restoration; tropical limnology. Address: Dept. of Environmental Engineering, University of Florida, Gainesville, FL 32601.

FOX, JAMES DAVID, b. Gatesville, Tex, May 11, 43; m. 66; c. 1. ANIMAL GENETICS, STATISTICS. B.S, Tex. A&M Univ, 65, M.S, 67; Ph.D.(animal breeding), Ohio State Univ, 70. GENETICIST, DEKALB AGRESEARCH, INC, 71- Am. Soc. Animal Sci; Poultry Sci. Asn; Biomet. Soc. Relationship of mature body weight and efficiency of production in livestock; field testing in poultry. Address: DeKalb AgResearch, Inc, Sycamore Rd, De-Kalb, IL 60115.

FOX, JAMES H(ENRY), b. Paterson, N.J, Feb. 10, 20; m. 42; c. 2. GEOPHYSICS. B.S, Mo. Sch. Mines & Metall, 42; M.S, St. Louis Univ, 53, Ph.D. (geophys), 54. BELLCOMM, INC, MEM. TECH STAFF, WASH, D.C, 68- U.S.A.F, 42-68, Col. Ret. Am. Geophys. Union; fel. Brit. Interplanetary Soc. Astronautics, spacecraft flight operations; earth and planetary physics; cratering; cryptoexplosion structures; tectonophysics. Address: Winchester Rd, Annapolis, MD 21401.

FOX, JAY B, JR, b. Lincoln, Nebr, July 30, 27; m. 52; c. 4. BIOCHEMISTRY. B.S, Col. Puget Sound, 51; U.S. Pub. Health Serv. fel. & Ph.D.(biochem), Washington (Seattle), 55. Assoc. biochemist, Am. Meat Inst. Found. 55-61, biochemist, 61-64; CHEMIST, EAST. MKT. & NUTRIT. RES. DIV, AGR. RES. SERV, U.S. DEPT. AGR, 64- AAAS; Am. Chem. Soc; Am. Inst. Chem; Inst. Food Tech; N.Y. Acad. Sci. Biochemistry of heme pigments. Address: Eastern Marketing & Nutrition Research Division, Agricultural Research Service, U.S. Dept. of Agriculture, 600 E. Mermaid Lane, Philadelphia, PA 19118.

FOX, JEROME L(EWIS), b. New York, N.Y, Nov. 16, 23; m. 49; c. 2. APPLIED MATHEMATICS. B.S, Illinois, 47, M.S, 48; Rockefeller fel, Brown, 50-51, Ph.D.(appl. math), 53. Aeronaut. res. scientist, Lewis Flight Propulsion Lab, Nat. Adv. Comt. Aeronaut, 48-50, sect. chief supersonic propulsion div, 52-53; res. assoc, Brown, 51-52; sr. res. engr, missile develop. div, N.Am. Aviation, Inc, 53-55; mem. tech. staff guided missile res. div, Ramo-Wooldridge Corp, 55-57; sr. staff engr, res. lab, missile & space div, Lockheed Aircraft Corp, 57-58, mgr. thermodyn, 58-60, flight sci, 60-62, tech. planning, 62-63; assoc. prof. ENG, SAN FRANCISCO STATE COL, 63-64, PROF, 64-, chmn. dept, 64-68. Mem. mat. adv. bd. & comt. mat. probs. assoc. with thermal control space vehicles, Nat. Acad. Sci, 59, chmn, mat. probs. assoc. with auxillary power unit space vehicles, 60- U.S.A, 43-46. Am. Inst. Aeronaut. & Astronaut. Missiles, satellites and space vehicles; fluid and flight mechanics; heat transfer. Address: Dept. of Engineering, San Francisco State College, 1600 Holloway, San Francisco, CA 94132.

FOX, JOEL S, N.Y.C, Feb. 7, 39; m. 63. MECHANICAL ENGINEERING. B.M.E, Polytech. Inst. Brooklyn, 59, Nat. Sci. Found. fel, 59-61, M.M.E, 61, Ph.D.(mech. eng), 66. Mem. tech. staff heat transfer, Hughes Aircraft Co, 61-62; instr. MECH. ENG, Polytech. Inst. Brooklyn, 63-66; asst. prof, UNIV. HAWAII, 66-69, ASSOC. PROF, 69- Am. Soc. Mech. Eng; Am. Soc. Eng. Educ. Electric fields and combustion process interaction; thermal conductivity of polymers; freeze-dry preservation of whole blood. Address: Dept. of Mechanical Engineering, University of Hawaii, Honolulu, HI 96822.

FOX, JOHN ARTHUR, b. Toronto, Ont, Feb. 8, 24; U.S. citizen; m. 46; c. 4. MECHANICAL & AEROSPACE ENGINEERING. B.S, Univ. Mich, 48 & 49; M.S, Pa. State, 50, Ph.D.(aeronaut. eng), 60. Asst, Michigan, 48-49; instr. aeronaut. eng, Pa. State, 49-60, assoc. prof. & acting head dept, 60-61, consult, ord. res. lab, 57-61; assoc. prof. mech. & aerospace sci, Univ. Rochester, 61-67; PROF. MECH. ENG. & CHMN. DEPT, UNIV. MISS, 67- Consult, Piper Aircraft Corp. & HRB-Singer, Inc, Pa, 61-; Rochester Appl. Sci. Assocs, N.Y, 64- U.S.A, 42-45, S/Sgt. AAAS; Am. Soc. Eng. Educ; Am. Inst. Aeronaut. & Astronaut. Mechanical and aerospace science; dynamics and celestial mechanics; aerodynamics; aerospace structures; magnetohydrodynamics. Address: Dept. of Mechanical Engineering, University of Mississippi, University, MS 38677.

FOX, JOHN C, b. Portland, Ore, Oct. 1, 27; m. 59; c. 3. MECHANICAL & NUCLEAR ENGINEERING. B.S, Ore. State Univ, 49, M.S, 51. Engr, Hanford Atomic Prod, Gen. Elec. Co, Wash, 51-56, Hanford Labs, 57-62, mgr. design anal, 62-65; eng. anal, PAC. NORTHWEST LABS, BATTELLE MEM. INST, 65-68, MGR. SYSTS. ENG, 68- Vis. assoc. prof, dept. nuclear eng, Univ. Wash, 66- Am. Soc. Mech. Eng; Am. Nuclear Soc. Irradiation effects on structural materials; nuclear reactor and fuel cycle design analysis; economic analysis of processes and services; application of optimization techniques to design and operating problems. Address: Battelle-Northwest, P.O. Box 999, Richland, WA 99352.

FOX, JOHN DANA, b. N.Y.C, Feb. 24, 30. PHYSICS. B.A, Princeton, 52; Ph.D.(physics), Wash. Univ, 64. Res. assoc. physics, Univ. Ill, 64-65; asst. physicist, BROOKHAVEN NAT. LAB, 65-70, ASSOC. PHYSICIST, 70- U.S.N, 52-56, Lt.(jg). Am. Phys. Soc. Accelerator design and development; particle physics. Address: Accelerator Dept, Brookhaven National Lab, Upton, NY 11973.

FOX, JOHN DAVID, b. Huntington, W.Va, Dec. 8, 29; m. 53; c. 5. NUCLEAR PHYSICS. S.B, Mass. Inst. Tech, 51; Fulbright scholar, Groningen, 51-52; M.S, Illinois, 54, Nat. Sci. Found. fel, 55-56, Ph.D, 60. Asst, Illinois, 52-55; asst. physicist, Brookhaven Nat. Lab, 56-59; asst. prof. PHYSICS, FLA. STATE UNIV, 59-63, assoc. prof, 63-65, PROF, 65- Nat. Sci. Found. sr. fel. & guest scientist, Max-Planck Inst. Nuclear Physics, Heidelberg, 68-69. Fel. Am. Phys. Soc. Experimental nuclear physics; low energy nuclear physics; neutron physics in resonance region; particle detectors and instrumentation; nuclear isomerism; photonuclear phenomena; isobaric analogue resonances; charged particle induced nuclear reactions. Address: Dept. of Physics, Florida State University, Tallahassee, FL 32306.

FOX, J(OHN) G(ASTON), b. Biggar, Sask, Can, March 5, 16; nat; m. 47; c. 3. NUCLEAR PHYSICS. B.Sc, Saskatchewan, 35, M.Sc, 37; Ph.D.(physics), Princeton, 41. Res. physicist, Hercules Powder Co, 41-45; Manhattan proj, Los Alamos Sci. Lab, N.Mex, 45-46; asst. prof. PHYSICS, CARNEGIE-MELLON UNIV, 46-49, assoc. prof, 49-56, asst. head dept, 50-56, head dept, 56-61, PROF, 56- Vis. staff mem, Joliet Curie Lab, Orsay, France, 62-63; vis. prof, Kanpur Indo-Am. Prog, Indian Inst. Technol, Kanpur, 67-68, prog. leader, 71-72; consult, St. Francis Hosp, Pittsburgh. With Off. Sci. Res. & Develop; U.S.N, 44. Fel. Am. Phys. Soc; Am. Asn. Physics Teachers; Soc. Nuclear Med. High energy nuclear physics; relativity; nuclear medicine. Address: Dept. of Physics, Carnegie-Mellon University, Pittsburgh, PA 15213.

FOX, J(OHN) G(ERALD), b. Winnipeg, Man, May 31, 25; m. 52; c. 4. PATHOLOGY. M.D, Manitoba, 49; dipl, Toronto, 62. Med. officer, Can. Nat. Rwy, 49-51; asst. res. med, Deer Lodge Hosp, Winnipeg, 51-52, res. path, 53-54; sr. intern, Queen of Angels Hosp, Calif, 52-53; asst. res, St. Boniface Hosp, 54-55; Winnipeg Gen. Hosp, 55-56; asst. dir, FRED T. CADHAM PUB. HEALTH LAB, MAN. DEPT. HEALTH & SOCIAL DEVELOP, 56-65, DIR, 65-; from lectr. to ASST. PROF. MED. MICROBIOL, UNIV. MAN, 70- Can. Asn. Med. Bact; Can. Med. Asn; Can. Asn. Path; Can. Pub. Health Asn; Am. Pub. Health Asn; Am. Soc. Microbiol; Conf. State & Prov. Pub. Health Lab. Dirs. Public health laboratory medicine. Address: Fred T. Cadham Public Health Lab, Medical College Bldg, 770 Bannatyne Ave, Winnipeg 3, Man.

FOX, JOHN PERRIGO, b. Chicago, Ill, Nov. 10, 08; m. 34; c. 4. VIROLOGY, EPIDEMIOLOGY. B.S, Haverford Col, 29; M.D, Chicago, 36, Ph.D.(path), 36; M.P.H, Columbia, 48. Asst. path, Chicago, 33-36; intern, Evanston Hosp, Ill, 37-38; mem. staff, int. health div, Rockefeller Found, 38-49; prof. epidemiol, sch. med, Tulane, 49-58, William Hamilton Watkins prof. & dir. grad. pub. health div, 58-60; chief epidemiol. dept, Pub. Health Res. Inst. of New York, 60-65; prof. prev. med, sch. med, UNIV. WASH, 65-70, PROF. EPIDEMIOL. & INT. HEALTH & ASSOC. DEAN, SCH. PUB. HEALTH & COMMUNITY MED, 70- Adj. prof, sch. pub. health, Columbia & sch. med, N.Y. Univ, 60-65. Mem. rickettsial disease comn, U.S. Armed Forces Epidemiol. Bd, 56-, med. comt, adv. coun, U.S. Army Chem. Corps, 57-61; spec. consult. staff, Ctr. Disease Control, Pub. Health Serv, 56-, grad. training grant comt, Nat. Inst. Allergy & Infectious Diseases, Nat. Insts. Health, 57-59, bd. sci. counsr, 69-73, influenza subcomt, 71-, virus & rickettsial study sect, Div. Res. Grants, 58-64, chmn, 62-64, bd. sci. counsr, Div. Biol. Standards, 59-63, chmn, 62-63, mem. epidemiol. & biomet. training comt, Nat. Inst. Gen. Med. Sci, 65-69. Dipl, Am. Bd. Prev. Med, 50. U.S.P.H.S.R, 56-, Med. Dir. AAAS; Am. Epidemiol. Soc; Am. Soc. Microbiol; Am. Soc. Trop. Med. & Hyg; Soc. Exp. Biol. & Med; Harvey Soc; Asn. Teachers Prev. Med; Am. Asn. Immunol; fel. Am. Pub. Health Asn; N.Y. Acad. Sci; Int. Epidemiol. Asn; hon. fel. Belgian Soc. Trop. Med. Active immunization versus yellow fever, rabies, typhus and poliomyelitis; serologic work in typhus, yellow fever and poliomyelitis; chemotherapy in typhus; epidemiologic research in poliomyelitis, enterovirus infections, respiratory virus infections and typhus; viral tissue culture with yellow fever. Address: Dept. of Epidemiology & International Health, School of Public Health & Community Medicine, University of Washington, Seattle, WA 98195.

FOX, JOHN R, b. London, Eng, May 3, 37; m. 61. ORGANIC CHEMISTRY. B.Sc, Durham, 59, Ph.D.(phys. org. chem), 62. Res. fel. org. photochem, Calif. Inst. Tech, 62-64; from res. chemist to SR. RES. CHEMIST, RES. CTR, UNION OIL CO. CALIF, 64- Am. Chem. Soc; The Chem. Soc; Am. Asn. Petrol. Geol. Organic geochemistry and photochemistry; organic reaction mechanisms; photolysis of azo compounds; linear free energy relations; Arrhenius activation parameters. Address: Union Oil Co. of California, Research Center, P.O. Box 76, Brea, CA 92621.

FOX, JOHN ROBIN, Anthrop, see Suppl. I to 11th ed, Soc. & Behav. Vols.

FOX, JOSEPH M(ICKLE), III, b. Phila, Pa, Nov. 20, 22; m. 49; c. 6. CHEMICAL ENGINEERING. B.S, Princeton, 43, Quakers Oats fel, 46-47, M.S, 47. Engr. tech. serv, Pan Am. Ref. Corp, 43-45; instr. chem. eng, Princeton, 46-47; res. engr, res. & develop. dept, M.W. Kellogg Co. Div, Pullman, Inc, 47-52, supvr, 52-58, res. assoc, 58-61, pilot plant sect. head, 61-66; PROCESS DEVELOP. SPECIALIST, PROCESS SERVS. DEPT, REF. & CHEM. DIV, BECHTEL CORP, 66- Instr, J.F. Kennedy Univ, 69- Am. Inst. Chem. Eng; Am. Chem. Soc. Process scale-up; petroleum and petrochemical processing; catalysis; heat and mass transfer; unusual separation techniques; environmental control. Address: 3396 Angelo St, Lafayette, CA 94549.

FOX, KENNETH, b. Highland Park, Mich, Aug. 16, 35; m. 61. MOLECULAR PHYSICS, ASTRONOMY. B.S, Wayne State, 57; State Col. fel, Michigan, 57-58, M.S, 58, univ. fels, 58-59, 61-62, Mary F. Stevens fel, 59-60, Nat. Sci. Found. fel, 60-61, Ph.D.(physics), 62. Instr. physics, Michigan, 61-62; vis. res. physicist, Inst. Nuclear Physics Res, Amsterdam, 62-63; vis. asst. prof. PHYSICS, Vanderbilt Univ, 63-64; asst. prof, Univ. Tenn, Knoxville, 64-67; Nat. Acad. Sci-Nat. Res. Coun. sr. res. assoc, Jet Propulsion Lab, Calif. Inst. Technol, 67-69; ASSOC. PROF, UNIV. TENN, KNOXVILLE, 69- Consult, Oak Ridge Nat. Lab, 64-; Jet Propulsion Lab, Calif. Inst. Technol, 66-67, 69- Am. Phys. Soc; Am. Astron. Soc. Theoretical and experimental spectroscopy; planetary atmospheres; observational astronomy; mathematical physics; statistical mechanics; interaction of charged particles with molecules; environmental problems such as spectroscopic studies of air pollutants; atmospheric phenomena. Address: Dept. of Physics & Astronomy, University of Tennessee, Knoxville, TN 37916.

FOX, KENNETH IAN, b. Chicago, Ill, Mar. 27, 43. FOOD MICROBIOLOGY & SCIENCE. B.S, Univ. Ill, Urbana, 65; M.S, Mich. State Univ, 67, Ph.D.(food sci), 71. RES. CHEMIST, J.R. SHORT MILLING CO, 71- Am. Soc. Microbiol; Inst. Food Technol. Botulism food poisoning; germination of bacterial spores; dry heat resistance of bacterial spores. Address: 729 Red Oak Lane, Park Forest South, IL 60466.

FOX, KENNETH RUSSELL, b. Lowell, Mass, Feb. 14, 16; m. 41; c. 4. TEXTILE ENGINEERING. B.T.E, Lowell Textile Inst, 38, hon. Sc.D, 54; M.S, Mass. Inst. Tech, 40. Asst. textiles, Mass. Inst. Tech, 40-41, instr, 41-43, asst. prof, 43-45; pres, Lowell Textile Inst, 45-50; v.pres. & tech. dir, Burlington Mills Corp, 50-53; v.chmn. in charge develop, FABRIC RES. LABS, INC, 53-70, CHMN. BD, 70- Mem, Textile Res. Inst. Civilian with U.S.A, U.S.A.A.F; Off. Naval Res, 44. Am. Phys. Soc; Am. Asn. Textile Chem. & Colorists; fel. Brit. Textile Inst; Am. Asn. Textile Technol. Textile microscopy and testing; statistics; process, machine and product development for textile and related fields. Address: Fabric Research Labs, Inc, 1000 Providence Highway, Dedham, MA 02026.

FOX, KEVIN A, b. Nashua, N.H, Feb. 1, 39; m. 66; c. 3. BEHAVIORAL ENDOCRINOLOGY, PSYCHOPHARMACOLOGY. B.A, New Hampshire, 60, M.S, 62; NASA fel. & Ph.D.(zool), Vermont, 67. Instr. zool, New Hampshire, 60-61; Hebron Acad, 61-64; res. technician, reproductive physiol, Vermont, 65-66; U.S. Pub. Health Serv. fel. comp. path, Penrose Res. Lab. & Univ. Pennsylvania, 67-69; res. assoc. path, Penrose Res. Lab, 69-70; ASST. PROF. BIOL, STATE UNIV. N.Y. COL. FREDONIA, 70- Nat. Inst. Ment. Health grants, 70-74. AAAS; Am. Soc. Mammal; Am. Inst. Biol. Sci; N.Y. Acad. Sci. Reproductive physiology. Address: Dept. of Biology, State University of New York College at Fredonia, Fredonia, NY 14063.

FOX, KIRK (B), b. Waterloo, Iowa, Apr. 20, 22; m. 48; c. 3. APPLIED MATHEMATICS, ECONOMETRICS. B.Sc, Chicago, 48, M.A, 50. Asst. economist, N.Trust Co. Bank, Chicago, 50; asst. economet, Cowles Comn. Res. Econ, Univ. Chicago, 50-52; assoc. food indust, Illinois, 52-55; prod. economist, opers. anal, U.S. Atomic Energy Comn, 55-57, opers. analyst off. gen. mgr, 57-59; sr. tech. staff, weapons systs. eval. div, inst. defense anal, Off. Secy. Defense, D.C, 59-64, spec. consult. off. civil defense, econ. & polit. sci. div, 64; dir, nat. civil defense comput. facility, Dept. Army, 64-67; ASST. DIR. PROD, U.S. ATOMIC ENERGY COMN, WASH, D.C, 67- Lectr, sch. commerce, Northwest. Univ, 51-54. U.S.N, 43-46. AAAS; Opers. Res. Soc. Am; Economet. Soc. Operations research; statistics. Address: 10411 Windsor View Dr, Potomac, MD 20854.

FOX, LAURETTA E(WING), b. Clarion, Pa, Apr. 25, 10. PHARMACOLOGY. B.S, Westminster Col.(Pa), 31; fel, Illinois, 31-34, M.S, 32, Ph.D.(biol), 34. Asst. biol, Westminster Col.(Pa), 30-31; prof. & head dept, Alderson-Broaddus Col, 34-35; head dept. sci, Dodd Col, 35-36; asst. prof, Northwest. State Col. La, 36-42, assoc. prof, 42-45; Arthur D. Little fel, sch. med, Vanderbilt, 45-46; asst. prof. biochem, 45-46; assoc. prof. chem, Miss. State Col. for Women, 46-47; assoc. prof. & head biol. sci, Cincinnati Col. Pharm, 47-49; asst. prof. pharmacol, col. pharm, UNIV. FLA, 49-55, assoc. prof, 55-65, ASSOC. PROF. PHARMACOL. & THERAPEUT, COL. MED, 65- Summer consult, biol. div, Oak Ridge Nat. Lab, 59. AAAS; fel. Am. Nuclear Soc; Am. Chem. Soc; Am. Pharmaceut. Asn; fel. Am. Inst. Chem. Sydnones; gamma-aminobutyric acid; intestinal absorption; thiuram disulfides; toxicology of constituents of Florida plants; estrogens; fungicides; cholesterol. Address: Dept. of Pharmacology & Therapeutics, University of Florida College of Medicine, Gainesville, FL 32601.

FOX, LEO, b. Boston, Mass, June 3, 17; m. 43; c. 4. RADIOBIOLOGY, ENVIRONMENTAL PHYSIOLOGY. B.S, Boston Univ, 38, M.A, 48, Ph.D, 66. Jr. sanit. engr, State Dept. Pub. Health, Mass, 46-48, assoc. sanit. biologist, 48-55; chief spec. weapons protection br, Qm. Res. & Eng. Labs, U.S. Army, 55-62, acting asst. sci. dir, 58-59; asst. asn. mgr. & res. dir, trade asn, Wash, D.C, 62-63; head environ. physiol. progs, NASA, 63, chief human res. br, OFF. ADVAN. RES. TECHNOL, HQ, 63-70, DIR. DIV. AERONAUT. LIFE SCI, 70- Consult, Mass. Inst. Technol, 50. Sanit.C, 42-46, 1st Lt. AAAS; Sci. Res. Soc. Am; Am. Chem. Soc; Aerospace Med. Asn; Biophys. Soc. Life science concerned with space program; environmental health related to stream pollution and shellfish sanitation; atomic weapons effects relative to protection of individuals against thermal and ionizing radiation. Address: Division of Aeronautical Life Sciences, Office of Advance Research & Technology, NASA, 600 Independence Ave. S.W, Washington, DC 20546.

FOX, LEONARD P, b. Brooklyn, N.Y, Mar. 13, 28; m. 50; c. 3. CHEMICAL ENGINEERING, ELECTROCHEMISTRY. B.S, Lehigh Univ, 48, M.S, 49; M.S, Franklin & Marshall Col, 56. Develop. engr, tube div, Radio Corp. Am, 49-57, eng. group leader, semiconductor div, 57-64, mgr. prod. eng, integrated circuit dept, RCA CORP, 64-67, printed circuit bd. dept, 67-70, RES. LEADER CHEM. PROCESSING, DAVID SARNOFF RES. LABS, 70- Outstanding achievement award, David Sarnoff Res. Lab, RCA Corp, 71. Am. Chem. Soc; Am. Electrochem. Soc; Int. Soc. Hybrid Microelectronics. Electrodeposition; alloys for semiconductor doping and contacts; corrosion protection; electropolishing of semiconductor surfaces; mechanism of solder adherence to various metals; passivation of semiconductor surfaces and study of surface contamination sources; processing related to the storage of high density recorded information. Address: Process & Materials Applied Research, David Sarnoff Research Lab, RCA Corp, Princeton, NJ 08540.

FOX, LEWIS, b. Norwich, Conn, Aug. 31, 03; m. 55. DENTISTRY. D.D.S, Maryland, 27. Assoc. clin. prof. dent, sch. dent. & oral surg, Columbia, 53-56; assoc. prof. periodont, sch. med, Pennsylvania, 56-63; prof. DENT. & dean SCH. DENT. MED, UNIV. CT, 63-69, UNIV. PROF, 69- Consult, Vet. Bur, Conn; mem, Nat. Adv. Dent. Res. Coun. Himman award; Fones award, Conn. State Dent. Asn, 62; award, Waterbury Dent. Soc. Dipl, Am. Bd. Periodont. Fel. AAAS; fel. Am. Col. Dent; Am. Acad. Periodont; Am. Acad. Oral Path; Am. Asn. Dent. Exam; N.Y. Acad. Sci; fel. Int. Col. Dent; Int. Asn. Dent. Res. Diseases of the gums and associated structures; development of dental education in university and teaching hospital. Address: School of Dental Medicine, Box U-155, Life Sciences Annex, University of Connecticut, Storrs, CT 06268.

FOX, MARJORIE HOPKINS, b. N.Y.C, Aug. 12, 19; m. 45; c. 1. ANATOMY. B.A, Hunter Col, 40; M.A, Mt. Holyoke Col, 42; Abraham Rosenberg fel, California, 44-46, Ph.D, 48. Instr. zool, City Col. San Francisco, 46-49; res. assoc, cardiovascular res. lab, Los Angeles Children's Hosp, 51-53; asst. anat, sch. med, LA. STATE UNIV, NEW ORLEANS, 53-56, instr, 56-59, asst. prof. biol, 59-62, ASSOC. PROF, 62-64, RES, MED. CTR, 64- Lectr, Woods Hole Biol. Lab, summers 45-47; Univ. Calif, summer 48. Teratology Soc; Am. Asn. Anat. Experimental embryology; mammalian congenital cardiovascular defects. Address: Dept. of Medicine, Medical Center, Louisiana State University in New Orleans, New Orleans, LA 70112.

FOX, MARTIN, b. N.Y.C, July 25, 29; m. 51; c. 3. STATISTICS. A.B, Univ. Calif, Berkeley, 51, Ph.D.(statist), 59. Asst. prof. statist, MICH. STATE UNIV, 59-64, assoc. prof, 64-71, PROF. STATIST. & PROBABILITY, 71-, acting chmn. dept. statist. & probability, 66-67. Fulbright lectr, Tel-Aviv Univ, 62-63; vis. res. mem, U.S. Army Math. Res. Ctr, Univ. Wis, 67-68. Fel. Inst. Math. Statist; Am. Math. Soc; Am. Statist. Asn. Mathematical statistics; probability; game theory. Address: Dept. of Statistics & Probability, Michigan State University, East Lansing, MI 48823.

FOX, MARY ELEANOR, S.N.D, b. Bellevue, Ky, Aug. 14, 19. PHYSICS. A.B, Villa Madonna Col, 42; M.S, Cath. Univ. Am, 44; Ph.D.(physics), Univ. Cincinnati, 62. Assoc. prof. PHYSICS, THOMAS MORE COL, 44-67, PROF, 67- Am. Phys. Soc; Am. Asn. Physics Teachers. Mathematical and classical physics; nuclear magnetic resonance broad line studies of crystalline materials in relation to motional narrowing; magnetic anisotropy studies in relation to molecular structure. Address: Dept. of Physics, Thomas More College, P.O. Box 85, Covington, KY 41017.

FOX, M(ATTIE) R(AE) SPIVEY, b. Joy, Tex, Feb. 23, 23; m. 54. NUTRITION, BIOCHEMISTRY. B.S, Texas Woman's Univ, 43; M.S, Iowa State, 47; Ph.D.(biochem), George Washington, 53. Chemist, Humble Oil & Ref. Co, 43-45; nutrit. analyst, U.S. Dept. Agr, 47-49; biochemist, Nat. Insts. Health, 51-62; res. biochemist, FOOD & DRUG ADMIN, 62-66, CHIEF micronutrient res. br, DIV. NUTRIT, 66-71, MINERALS SECT, 71- Fel. AAAS; Am. Inst. Nutrit; Fedn. Am. Socs. Exp. Biol; Am. Chem. Soc; N.Y. Acad. Sci; Poultry Sci. Asn. Nutrition of man and experimental animals; metabolic function trace minerals; amino acids; vitamins. Address: Minerals Section, Division of Nutrition, BF 124, U.S. Food & Drug Administration, 200 C St. S.W, Washington, DC 20204.

FOX, MAURICE S(ANFORD), b. N.Y.C, Oct. 11, 24; m. 55; c. 3. GENETICS. B.S, Chicago, 44, M.S, 51, Ph.D.(chem), 51. Res. assoc, Chicago, 51-53; asst, Rockefeller Inst, 53-56, asst. prof, 56-61, assoc. prof, 61-62; GENETICS, MASS. INST. TECHNOL, 62-66, PROF, 66- Nuffield res. scholar, 57; Lalor fel. award, 59. U.S.A.A.F, 43-46. AAAS. Chemical events following high energy nuclear recoil; mutation; continous culture of microorganisms; biological properties of deoxyribonucleates; microbial genetics; genetic recombination. Address: Dept. of Biology, Massachusetts Institute of Technology, 77 Massachusetts Ave, Cambridge, MA 02139.

FOX, MICHAEL ROBERT, b. Olympia, Wash, Dec. 31, 36; m. 59; c. 1. PHYSICAL CHEMISTRY. B.S, St. Martin's Col, 59; Ph.D.(phys. chem), Washington (Seattle), 65. SR. RES. CHEMIST, IDAHO NUCLEAR CORP, 65-71; ALLIED CHEM. CORP, 70- Mem. faculty, Idaho State Univ, 67-69. Am. Nuclear Soc; Am. Inst. Chem. Eng. Molecular structure determination by x-ray diffraction; fluidized-bed applications to air, water and thermal pollution and desalination of sea-water; thermodynamics of nuclear reactor fuels at high temperature. Address: Allied Chemical Co, P.O. Box 2204, Idaho Falls, ID 83401.

FOX, MILDEN J, JR, Indust. Eng, Labor Rels, see 12th ed, Soc. & Behav. Vols.

FOX, PHYLLIS, b. Denver, Colo, Mar. 13, 23; m. 58; c. 2. MATHEMATICS. A.B, Wellesley Col, 44; B.S, Colorado, 48; M.S, Mass. Inst. Technol, 49, Sc.D.(math), 54. Scientist, Atomic Energy Comn, Courant Inst, N.Y. Univ, 54-58; res. assoc, Mass. Inst. Technol, 58-62; assoc. prof. math, NEWARK COL. ENG, 63-67, PROF. COMPUT. SCI, 67- Am. Math. Soc; Soc. Indust. & Appl. Math; Asn. Comput. Mach. Applications of computers; numerical analysis; applied mathematics. Address: Dept. of Computer Science, Newark College of Engineering, Newark, NJ 07102.

FOX, RAYMOND, b. N.Y.C, July 17, 32; m. 55; c. 2. PHYSICS. B.S, City Col. New York, 53; M.A, Harvard, 55, Ph.D.(nuclear physics), 58. Sr. physicist, Lawrence Radiation Lab, Univ. Calif, 57-61; Nat. Sci. Found. fel, Weizmann Inst. Sci, Israel, 61-62; sr. lectr, dept. physics, ISRAEL INST. TECHNOL, 62-67, ASSOC. PROF. PHYSICS, 67- Consult, Astro Div, Marquardt Corp, 60-61; Tex. Instruments Corp, 60-62. Am. Phys. Soc; Phys. Soc. Israel; Europ. Phys. Soc. Relativity; nuclear physics; solid state physics. Address: Dept. of Physics, Israel Institute of Technology, Haifa, Israel.

FOX, RAYMOND T(HOMAS), b. Corning, N.Y, Aug. 31, 22; m. 51. FLORICULTURE. B.S, Cornell, 47, M.S, 52, N.Y. Florists Club fel. & Ph.D, 56. Exten. specialist, FLORICULT, STATE UNIV. N.Y. COL. AGR, CORNELL UNIV, 47-54, asst. prof, 56-61, ASSOC. PROF, 61-. C.Eng, U.S.A, 43-46. Time and motion studies; keeping quality of flowers; extension education. Address: Dept. of Floriculture, State University of New York College of Agriculture, Cornell University, Ithaca, NY 14850.

FOX, RICHARD CARR, b. Lowell, Mass, Oct. 3, 33. VERTEBRATE PALEONTOLOGY. A.B, Hamilton Col, 55; M.Sc, State Univ. N.Y, 57; Ph.D.(zool), Univ. Kans, 65. Asst. prof. GEOL. & ZOOL, UNIV. ALTA, 65-69, ASSOC. PROF, 69- Med.Serv.C, U.S.A, 57-59. AAAS; Am. Soc. Zool; Am. Soc. Ichthyol. & Herpet; Soc. Syst. Zool; Soc. Study Evolution; Soc. Vert. Paleont; Am. Soc. Mammal; N.Y. Acad. Sci; Am. Soc. Naturalists. Paleozoic reptiles and the origin of reptiles; late Cretaceous mammals, lizards, salamanders; community evolution of late Cretaceous vertebrates. Address: Dept. of Geology, University of Alberta, Edmonton, Alta, Can.

FOX, RICHARD C(HARLES), b. Athens, Mich, Sept. 5, 25; m. 47; c. 3. FOREST ENTOMOLOGY. B.S, Mich. State Col, 48, M.F, 49, Ph.D, 58. Asst, bur. entomol. & plant quarantine, U.S. Dept. Agr, 48; instr. bot, Miami (Ohio), 49-51; forest entomologist, State Conserv. Dept, Mich, 51-55; instr. entomol, Mich. State, 55-58; asst. entomologist, CLEMSON UNIV, 58-64, assoc. prof. ENTOM, 64-68, PROF, 68- U.S.A.A.F, 43-45. Entom. Soc. Am; Soc. Am. Foresters. Forest insect teaching, research and survey. Address: Dept. of Entomology, Clemson University, Clemson, SC 29631.

FOX, R(ICHARD) C(UNEO), b. San Francisco, Calif, Nov. 4, 27; m. 51; c. 4. ORGANIC & PHYSICAL CHEMISTRY. B.S, Mass. Inst. Tech, 50; Sinclair Oil Co. fel, Illinois, 51-52, du Pont fel, 52-53, Ph.D.(chem), 53. RES. CHEMIST, CHEVRON RES. CORP, 53- U.S.A, 46-48. Am. Chem. Soc; The Chem. Soc. Rheology; physics and chemistry of solids; physical sciences; mathematics. Address: 127 Humboldt St, San Rafael, CA 94901.

FOX, RICHARD R(OMAINE), b. New Haven, Conn, Nov. 12, 34; m. 55; c. 3. GENETICS. B.S, Connecticut, 56; M.S, Minnesota, 58, Ph.D.(animal breeding, genetics), 59. Acting swine herdsman, Connecticut, 56; asst. animal breeding, Minnesota, 56-59; fel, JACKSON LAB, 59-60, assoc. staff scientist, 60-65, STAFF SCIENTIST, 65- AAAS; Am. Dairy Sci. Asn; Am. Soc. Animal Sci; Genetics Soc. Am; Am. Genetic Asn; Teratology Soc; Am. Asn. Lab. Animal Sci. Genetics of the rabbit; quantitative genetics; reproductive physiology; germ plasm preservation. Address: Jackson Lab, Bar Harbor, ME 04609.

FOX, ROBERT B(ERNARD), b. Boise, Idaho, May 24, 22; m. 54. POLYMER CHEMISTRY. B.Chem, Minnesota, 43; Ph.D.(chem), Maryland, 59. Res. chemist, Sharples Chem, Inc, Mich, 43-44; CHEMIST, NAVAL RES. LAB, 46-, SECT. HEAD, 52- U.S.A, 44-46. Am. Chem. Soc; Sci. Res. Soc. Am. Organic phosphorus chemistry; photochemistry. Address: Code 6120, Naval Research Lab, Washington, DC 20390.

FOX, ROBERT DEAN, b. Cass City, Mich, Oct. 26, 36; m. 66; c. 6. AGRICULTURAL ENGINEERING, ATMOSPHERIC PHYSICS. B.S, Mich. State, 57, M.S, 58, Ph.D.(agr. eng), 68. Instr. agr. eng. & rural electrification, Mich. State, 63-64; AGR. ENGR, AGR. RES. SERV, U.S. DEPT. AGR, 68- U.S.A.F, 58-63, Res, 64-67, Capt. Am. Soc. Agr. Eng. Diffusion of fine particles in air, specifically the effects of turbulent transport of particles in the region of a plant canopy. Address: Agricultural Engineering Dept, Ohio Agriculture Research & Development Center, Wooster, OH 44691.

FOX, ROBERT EUGENE, b. Glendale, W.Va, Feb. 21, 29; m. 53; c. 3. PETROLEUM GEOLOGY. B.S, Marshall, 52, M.S, Illinois, 53. Geologist, Standard Oil Co. Calif, 52-54; Hunt Int. Petrol. Co, 54-61; consult. geol, 62-64; gen. mgr, PLACID INT. OIL, LTD, 64-70, V.PRES. & MANAGING DIR, WEST. EUROPE, 70- Del, Econ. Comn. Asia & Far East, New Delhi, India, 58. Am. Asn. Petrol. Geol; Geol. Soc. Am; Am. Inst. Min, Metall. & Petrol. Eng. Subsurface geology; stratigraphy; marine geology. Address: Klatteweg 18, The Hague, Netherlands.

FOX, ROBERT H(AMLON), b. Chicago, Ill, Sept. 22, 21; m. 47; c. 4. NUCLEAR PHYSICS. A.B, California, 43, Ph.D.(physics), 50. Physicist, Lawrence Radiation Lab, California, 50-51; asst. group leader microwave develop, Lincoln Lab, Mass. Inst. Technol, 51-54; physicist, Lawrence Radiation Lab, California, 54-62, asst. leader, nuclear propulsion div, 59-62; physicist, INST. DEFENSE ANAL, 62-65, dep. dir, res. & eng. div, 65-67, DIR, SCI. & TECHNOL. DIV, 67-, acting dir, res. & eng. div, 64-65. Ed, J. Defense Res, Series A: Strategic Warfare, 66-71; consult, Aerojet Gen. Nucleonics Co, Calif; Electro-Optical Syst, Inc. U.S.M.C, 43-49. Am. Inst. Aeronaut. & Astronaut. Development of advanced concepts in nuclear propulsion and gas-cooled power reactors; reactor physics; gas dynamics; high temperature chemistry; ballistic missile defense technology. Address: Institute for Defense Analyses, 400 Army-Navy Dr, Arlington, VA 22202.

FOX, ROBERT K(RIEGBAUM), b. Covington, Ohio, April 1, 07; m. 34; c. 3. CHEMISTRY. B.A, Ohio State, 29, M.A, 30, Ph.D.(inorg. & phys. chem), 32. Asst. chem, Ohio State, 29-32; instr, Bethany Col.(W.Va), 32-34, asst. prof, 34-36; Hiram Col, 36-41; partner, Fox Chem. Co, Ohio, 41-45; PRES, LANCASTER GLASS CORP, 45-; IND. GLASS CO, 56-; V.PRES. & TREAS, LANCASTER COLONY CORP, 62- Am.Chem.Soc. Catalytic oxidation of acetylene black; solubility of manganese hydroxide; fabric treating compounds; crystal and colored glasses. Address: Amanda Rd, R.D. 6, Lancaster, OH 43130.

FOX, ROBERT L(EE), b. Fayette, Iowa, Apr. 11, 07; m. 31. CHEMISTRY. A.B, Upper Iowa, 28; Roberts fel, Columbia, 28-34, A.M, 30, Ph.D.(phys. chem), 34. Asst. chem, Columbia, 30-34; prof. chem, Robert Col. Istanbul, 34-41; asst, Columbia, 41-42; res. & eng. div, off. of chief, Chem. Corps, Army of U.S, 46-53, dep. asst, 53-55, asst, toxic chem. warfare, res. & eng. command, 55-56, asst. to dir. res, 56-58, asst. to dir, med. res, chem. res. & develop. labs, 58-65, dep. dir. develop. support, 65-66, dep. chief, chem. res. lab, Edgewood Arsenal, 66-70; RETIRED. Chem.C, A.U.S, 42-46, Res, 46-70, Col.(Ret). Am. Chem. Soc; Sci. Res. Soc. Am. Am. Ord. Asn. Chemistry of columbium and tantalum; inorganic oxidation and reduction reactions; trivalent columbium in sulfuric acid; uranium hexafluoride, incendiary and toxic chemical warfare agents. Address: 1309 Westellen Rd, Baltimore, MD 21204.

FOX, ROBERT LEE, b. Moberly, Mo, May 26, 23; m. 48; c. 5. SOILS. B.S, Missouri, 47, M.A, 50, Ph.D.(soils), 55. Asst. prof. agron. & asst. agronomist, Univ. Nebr, 50-56; assoc. prof, Ankara, 56-58; Nebraska, 58-61; PROF. SOIL SCI. & SOIL SCIENTIST, UNIV. HAWAII, 61- U.S.N, 43-46, Lt.(jg). Fel. AAAS; Am. Soc. Agron; Soil Sci, Soc. Am. Soil fertility and chemistry. Address: Dept. of Agronomy & Soil Science, University of Hawaii, 2525 Varney Circle, Honolulu, HI 96822.

FOX, ROBERT WILLIAM, b. Montreal, Que, July 1, 34; m. 62; c. 2. MECHANICAL ENGINEERING, FLUID MECHANICS. B.S, Rensselaer Polytech, 55; M.S, Colorado, 57; Ph.D.(mech. eng), Stanford, 61. Instr. MECH. ENG, Colorado, 55-57; asst, Stanford, 57-60; asst. prof, PURDUE UNIV, 60-63, assoc. prof, 63-66, PROF, 66-, ASST. HEAD, SCH. MECH. ENG, 71-, chmn. grad. prog, 69-71. Vis. prof, Bradley, 64-65. Consult, Nat. Comt. Fluid Mech. Films, 63-; Owens Corning Fiberglass Corp, Ohio, 63. Am. Soc. Eng. Educ; Am. Soc. Mech. Eng; Am. Inst. Aeronaut. & Astronaut. Turbulent boundary layers in adverse pressure gradients; diffuser flows; pulsating flow. Address: School of Mechanical Engineering, Purdue University, Lafayette, IN 47907.

FOX, ROBIN, Anthrop, see 12th ed, Soc. & Behav. Vols.

FOX, RONALD FORREST, b. Berkeley, Calif, Oct. 1, 43; m. 69. THEORETICAL PHYSICS. B.A, Reed Col, 64; Nat. Sci. Found. fel, Calif. Inst. Tech, 64-65; Ph.D.(theoret. physics), Rockefeller Univ, 69. Miller fel, theoret. physics, Miller Inst. Basic Res. in Sci, California, Berkeley, 69-71; ASST. PROF. PHYSICS, GA. INST. TECHNOL, 71- Group theory—non-equilibrium thermodynamics and models for biological processes. Address: School of Physics, Georgia Institute of Technology, Atlanta, GA 30332.

FOX, RONALD LEE, b. St. Louis, Mo, Oct. 16, 40; m. 60; c. 2. FLUID MECHANICS, ATOMIC PHYSICS. B.S, South. Missionary Col, 62; M.A, Wash. Univ, 64; NASA fel, Univ. Tenn, Knoxville, 65-67, Ph.D.(physics), 67. Res. asst, McDonnell Aircraft, Mo, 62-64; TECH. STAFF MEM, SANDIA CORP, 67- Am. Phys. Soc. Application of multipoint distribution functions to calculation of turbulent parameters; effects of inelastic collisions on fluid transport properties; development of methods for calculation of spectral line shapes at general pressures. Address: Division 9341, Sandia Corp, Alburquerque, NM 87115.

FOX, RUSSELL E(LWELL), b. Richmond, Va, Dec. 28, 16; m. 42; c. 3. PHYSICS. B.S, Hampden-Sydney Col, 38; M.S, Virginia, 39, Ph.D.(physics), 42. Fel, RES. LAB, WESTINGHOUSE ELEC. CORP, 42, res. physicist, 42-57, mgr. physics dept, 57-64, dir. atomic & molecular sci. res. & develop, 64-69, RES. DIR, CONSUMER PRODS, 69- Mem, Atomic Energy Comn; Off. Sci. Res. & Develop, 44. AAAS; Am. Vacuum Soc; Am. Soc. Test. & Mat.(pres, 62-64); Am. Phys. Soc; Illum. Eng. Soc. Ultracentrifuge; separation of isotopes; mass spectrometry; atomic physics. Address: Westinghouse Research Labs, Beulah Rd, Pittsburgh, PA 15235.

FOX, SALLY INGERSOLL, b. Phila, Pa, Oct. 19, 25; m. 49; c. 3. MICROBIOLOGY. B.A, Vassar Col, 46; M.A, Columbia Univ, 52; Ph.D.(biol), Rensselaer Polytech. Inst, 67. Lectr. microbiol, Russell Sage Col, 61; asst. microbiol, Rensselaer Polytech. Inst, 63-66; asst. prof. BIOL, COL. ST. ROSE, 67-71, ASSOC. PROF, 71- Fedn. Am. Sci; Am. Soc. Microbiol. Microflora of acid mine waters, especially leaching areas of copper mines; interactions between indigenous yeast and copper oxidizing thiobacilli. Address: Dept. of Biology, College of St. Rose, Albany, NY 12203.

FOX, SAMUEL L(OUIS), b. Baltimore, Md, Dec. 27, 14; m. 48; c. 2. OPHTHALMOLOGY. Ph.G, Univ. Md, 34, B.S, 36, M.D, 38. From asst. to instr. to assoc. otolaryngol, SCH. MED, UNIV. MD, BALTIMORE CITY, 40-53, assoc. prof, 53-61, instr. physiol, 50-55, asst. prof, 55-64, instr. OPHTHAL, 43-45, asst. prof, 59-62, acting head dept, 59-60, assoc. prof, 62-71, CLIN. PROF, 71-, ASST. PROF. PHARMACOL, 64-, CLIN. ASSOC. PROF. PHARM, SCH. PHARM, 71-, LECTR. PHYSIOL, SCH. DENT, 62- Rotating internship, S.Baltimore Gen. Hosp, 38-39, asst. residency, 39-40, secy. med. staff, 43-46, med. adv. coun, 43-49, dir. dept. ophthal. & otolaryngol, 45-67, chief ophthal. servs, 67-, med. educ, 62-66, chmn. med. staff & med. exec. comt, 57-62, 68-70; residency, Baltimore Eye, Ear & Throat Hosp, 40-41; personal asst. to Lee Cohen, M.D, 40-43; preceptorship, M. Randolph Kahn, M.D, 43-45; ophthalmologist, U.S. Med. Induction Bd, Md, 40-47, consult, 47-49; vis. lectr, sch. pharm, Univ. Md, 50-64, lectr, sch. dent, 62- Dipl, Am. Bd. Otolaryngol, 43; Am. Bd. Ophthal, 61. AAAS; Am. Acad. Ophthal. & Otolaryngol; Am. Soc. Ophthal. & Otolaryngol. Allergy; Am. Acad. Facial Plastic & Reconstruct. Surg; Asn. Am. Med. Col; Am. Med. Asn; Asn. Hosp. Med. Educ; fel. Indust. Med. Asn; N.Y. Acad. Sci; Am. Asn. Hist. Med; Am. Soc. Clin. Pharmacol. & Therapeut; Am. Asn. Ophthal. Neurophysiology of special senses, especially vision and hearing; drug actions in ophthalmology and otolaryngology; industrial ophthalmology. Address: 1205 St. Paul St, Baltimore, MD 21202.

FOX, SAMUEL M(ICKLE), III, b. Andalusia, Pa, Feb. 13, 23; m. 49; c. 4. MEDICINE. B.A, Haverford Col, 44; M.D, Univ. Pa, 47. Intern, Univ. Pa. Hosp, 47-48, sr. resident, 50; asst. instr. med, Univ. Pa, 48-49, instr, 49-50; acting chief gastroenterol, Nat. Naval Med. Center, Md, U.S. Navy, 50-51, from mem. staff to chief cardiol. serv, 53-54, staff med. officer, East. Atlantic & Mediterranean, Eng, 51-53; head, dept. clin. invest, Med. Res. Unit, Egypt, 54-56; chief cardiol. & officer in charge, cardiopulmonary res. lab. U.S. Naval Hosp, Portsmouth, Va, 56-57; responsible investr, sect. cardiodyn, Nat. Heart Inst, Nat. Insts. Health, 57-59, co-chief sect, 59-61, asst. dir, 61-62; dep. chief, heart disease & stroke control prog, U.S. Pub. Health Serv, 63-64, chief, 65-70; PROF. MED, DIV. CARDIOL, SCH. MED, GEORGE WASHINGTON UNIV, 70- Res. fel. med. & gastroenterol, Univ. Pa. Hosp, 48-49; res. assoc, Res. Inst. & Abbassia & Embaba Fever Hosps, Egypt, 54-56; vis. prof, Ein Shams Univ, 55-56; res. assoc, Kasr-el-aini, 55-56. Consult, World Health Orgn. & Asian-Pac. Soc. Cardiol. Mem. NASA res. adv. cmt. biotech. & human res, 64-68; fel. coun. clin. cardiol, Am. Heart Asn; mem, President's Coun. Phys. Fitness & Sports, 70- Dipl, Am. Bd. Internal Med, 55. U.S.N.R, 42-46; Med.C, 49-57; U.S.P.H.S., 58-70, Med. Dir. Fel. Am. Med. Asn; Am. Heart Asn; Am. Col. Physicians; Am. Col. Cardiol.(pres-elect, 71). Clinical problems of disturbed cardiopulmonary physiology, prevention, management, and rehabilitation. Address: Dept. of Medicine, George Washington University Medical Center, 2150 Pennsylvania Ave, Washington DC 20037.

FOX, SERECK H(ALL), b. Phila, Pa, Jan. 27, 00; m. 26; c. 3. PHARMACEUTICAL CHEMISTRY. Ph.G, Phila. Col. Pharm, 21, hon. D.Sc, 50; Pennsylvania, 27. With, Powers, Weightman & Rosengarten, 19; H.K. Mulford Co, 21-29; asst. to supt, Sharp & Dohme, Inc, 29-34, dir. pharmaceut. res, 34-37; tech. dir, R.P. Scherer Corp, 37-53, v.pres. pharmaceut. res. & control, 53-57; prof. INDUST. PHARM, WAYNE STATE UNIV, 57-70; EMER. PROF, 70- Indust. consult, 57- U.S.A, 17-19. Fel. AAAS; Am. Chem. Soc; Am. Pharmaceut. Asn; fel. Am. Inst. Chem; fel. N.Y. Acad. Sci. Establishment of standards in foods and drugs; pharmaceutical development; quality control. Address: 12165 Spencer Rd, Milford, MI 48042.

FOX, SHERWOOD (NORMAN), b. Boston, Mass, June 14, 26. CHEMICAL ENGINEERING. B.S, Mass. Inst. Technol, 48; M.S, Pennsylvania, 49; Purdue, 53-56. Chem. engr, Gen. Elec. Co, 48; Arthur D. Little, Inc, 49-53; instr. Purdue, 53-56; chem. engr, Am. Cyanamid Co, 56-60; SCI. DESIGN CO, INC, 60-61, dir. process develop, 61-63, tech. dir. licensing & contracts, 63-70, ASST. V.PRES, 70- U.S.N, 44-46. Am. Chem. Soc; Am. Inst. Chem. Eng; Chem. Mkt. Res. Asn. Theoretical chemical engineering; technical economics; process development; economic design optimization; venture analysis; licensing. Address: Scientific Design Co, Inc, 2 Park Ave, New York, NY 10007.

FOX, SIDNEY A(LBERT), b. Russia, Jan. 30, 98; nat; m. 31. OPHTHALMOLOGY. A.B, Brown, 19; M.D, St. Louis, 31; Sc.M, Pennsylvania, 36. Attend. ophthalmologist, Bronx Vet. Admin. Hosp, N.Y, 46-52; Goldwater Mem. Hosp, 52-58; CLIN. PROF. OPHTHAL, MED. SCH, N.Y. UNIV, 58-,

ASSOC. OPHTHALMOLOGIST, UNIV. HOSP, 58- Asst. surgeon, ophthal, Bellevue Hosp, 40-; attend. ophthalmologist, Hosp. Joint Diseases, N.Y, 55-59. Consult, Bronx Vet. Hosp, 52-; Goldwater Mem. Hosp, 60-; Hosp. Joint Diseases, 60- U.S.A, 43-46, Lt. Col; Legion of Merit. Fel. Am. Med. Asn; fel. Pan-Am. Asn. Ophthal; fel. Am. Col. Surg; fel. Am. Acad. Ophthal. & Otolaryngol; fel. N.Y. Acad. Med. Ophthalmic plastic surgery. Address: 11 E. 90th St, New York, NY 10028.

FOX, SIDNEY W(ALTER), b. Los Angeles, Calif, Mar. 24, 12; m. 37; c. 3. BIOCHEMISTRY. B.A, California, Los Angeles, 33; fel, Calif. Inst. Tech, 37-40, Ph.D.(biochem), 40. Chemist, Macmillan Petrol. Corp, Calif, 33-34; asst, Rockefeller Inst, 34-35; Calif. Inst. Tech, 35-37; res. chemist, Cutter Labs, 40-41; fel, Michigan, 41-42; res. chemist, F.E. Booth Co, 42-43; asst. prof. chem, Iowa State Col, 43-46, assoc. prof, 46-47, prof, 47-55, head chem. sect, exp. sta, 49-55; prof. chem, Fla. State, 55-64, dir. oceanog. inst, 55-61, inst. space biosci, 61-64; PROF. BIOCHEM. & DIR. INST. MOLECULAR EVOLUTION, UNIV. MIAMI, 64- Consult, Atomic Energy Cmn, 47-55; A.E. Staley Co, 54-60; Priestman lectr, New Brunswick, 64; U.S.A-U.S.S.R. Interacad. lectr, 69. Mem. panel selection Nat. Sci. Found. fels, Nat. Acad. Sci-Nat. Res. Coun, 53-55, 60, chmn. subcmt. nomenclature biochem, Nat. Res. Coun, 56-57; secy, Nat. Cmt. Biochem, 56-59; subchmn, panel selection Nat. Sci. Found. faculty fels, Am. Asn. Cols, 57-58; Nat. Acad. Sci. del, Int. Union Biochem. Symp, Moscow, 57, Fourth Int. Cong. Biochem, Vienna, 58; mem. adv. panel syst. biol, Nat. Sci. Found, 58-60; mem. biosci. subcomt, NASA, 60-66; Comn. Undergrad. Educ. Biol. Sci, 69-71; v.pres, Int. Soc. Study Origin Life, 70- U.S. Dept. Commerce Medal, 62; Fla. Acad. Sci. Honors Medal & Citation, 68. Fel. AAAS; Am. Astron. Soc; Int. Asn. Geochem. & Cosmochem; Geochem. Soc; Am. Chem. Soc.(from off. to chmn, div. biol. chem, 58-59); fel. Am. Inst. Chem; Am. Soc. Biol. Chem; Soc. Study Evolution; Am. Soc. Nat; Am. Inst. Biol. Sci; Am. Soc. Cell Biol. Evolution; amino acids, peptides and proteins; molecular and cellular evolution. Address: Institute of Molecular Evolution, University of Miami, Coral Gables, FL 33134.

FOX, STEPHEN S(ORIN), b. New Haven, Conn, July 15, 33; m. 59; c. 3. PHYSIOLOGICAL PSYCHOLOGY. B.A, Pennsylvania, 55; M.A, Michigan, 57, Ph.D.(psychol), 59. Asst. physiol. psychol, vision res. labs, Michigan, 55-56; res. anatomist, med. sch, California, Los Angeles, 57-59; head animal neurophysiol. & behav. sect, schizophrenia & psychopharmacol. joint res. proj, Michigan, 59-63, assoc. res. psychobiologist, ment. health res. inst, 59-65, asst. prof. PSYCHOL, Univ, 62-65; assoc. prof, UNIV. IOWA, 65-70, PROF, 70- Res. assoc, Ypsilanti State Hosp, Mich, 59-63; investr, Woods Hole Marine Biol. Labs, 61- AAAS; Am. Psychol. Asn; Biophys. Soc; N.Y. Acad. Sci; Biofeedback Res. Soc; Am. Physiol. Soc; Psychonomic Soc; Soc. Neurosci. Behavioral neurophysiology; psychobiology; neurophysiological correlates of behavior; electrophysiology; identification of the structural and functional substrate of behavior; neural coding. Address: Dept. of Psychology, University of Iowa, Iowa City, IA 52240.

FOX, STEVEN K(NOWLTON), JR, b. N.Y.C, Oct. 30, 11. GEOLOGY, PALEONTOLOGY. A.B, Princeton, 33, A.M, 36, Ph.D.(geol, paleont, stratig), 39; Yale, 33-34. Instr. GEOL, West Virginia, 37-38; Princeton, 38-42, asst. prof, 46-48; assoc. prof, RUTGERS UNIV, 48-69, PROF, 69- U.S.N, 42-46, 51-52. Paleont. Soc. Stratigraphy of Cretaceous and early Tertiary of western interior New Jersey; coastal plain stratigraphy. Address: Dept. of Geology, Rutgers, The State University, New Brunswick, NJ 08903.

FOX, THEODORE A(LBERT), b. Chicago, Ill, Feb. 16, 13; m. 36; c. 2. ORTHOPEDIC SURGERY. B.S, Chicago, 33, M.D, 37. Instr. ORTHOP. SURG, UNIV. ILL. COL. MED, 46-50, asst. prof, 50-59, ASSOC. PROF, 59-, ATTEND. ORTHOP. SURGEON, RES. & EDUC. HOSPS, 47- Attend. orthop. surgeon, Ill. Masonic Hosp. Dipl, Am. Bd. Orthop. Surg. Med.C, 41-46, Comdr. AAAS; Am. Geriat. Soc; Asn. Am. Med. Cols; Am. Med. Asn; Am. Med. Writers' Asn; fel. Am. Col. Surg; Am. Acad. Orthop. Surg. Clinical orthopedics. Address: Dept. of Orthopedic Surgery, University of Illinois College of Medicine, Chicago, IL 60680.

FOX, THOMAS A(LLEN), b. Dover, Ohio, Aug. 23, 26; m. 53; c. 2. PHYSICS. B.S, Ohio, 49, M.S, 51. Instr. physics, Ohio, 51-52; from res. scientist to HEAD, exp. reactor physics sect, LEWIS RES. CTR, NASA, 52-68, CRITICAL FACILITY UNIT, 68- U.S.N, 44-46. Am. Nuclear Soc. Experimental reactor physics; reactor operations; first analytical studies; reactor critical facilities. Address: 27522 Dunford Rd, Westlake, OH 44145.

FOX, THOMAS G, JR, b. Union Deposit, Pa, Feb. 19, 21; m. 41; c. 3. CHEMISTRY. B.S, Lebanon Valley Col, 40, hon. D.Sc, 67; fel, Columbia, 42-43, Ph.D. (chem), 43. Instr. chem, Columbia, 43-44; sr. res. chemist, Goodyear Tire & Rubber Co, 46-48; res. assoc. chem, Cornell, 48-50; head lab, Rohm & Haas Co, 50-57; asst. dir. res, MELLON INST, 57-61, dir, 61-62, STAFF FEL, 63-; PROF. CHEM. & POLYMER SCI, CARNEGIE-MELLON UNIV, 67- Instr, Univ. Akron, 46-47; ed, J. Polymer Sci; chmn, Pa. Sci. & Eng. Found; Gov. Sci. Adv. Comt, Pa. U.S.N.R, 44-46. Soc. Rheol; Am. Chem. Soc; fel. Am. Phys. Soc. Melt viscosity and brittle temperature of polymers; intrinsic viscosities and thermodynamics of polymer solutions; kinetics of polymerization. Address: Mellon Institute, Carnegie-Mellon University, 4400 Fifth Ave, Pittsburgh, PA 15213.

FOX, THOMAS W(ALTON), b. Pawtucket, R.I, Mar. 21, 23; m. 48; c. 2. AVIAN GENETICS, PHYSIOLOGY. B.S, Massachusetts, 49, fel, 49-50, M.S, 50; Ph.D.(genetics, physiol), Purdue, 52. Asst. POULTRY, Purdue, 50-52; instr, UNIV. MASS, AMHERST, 52-53, asst. prof, 53-54, PROF. & HEAD DEPT, 54- U.S.A, 43-45, Sgt. AAAS; Am. Genetics Asn; Poultry Sci. Asn; Am. Inst. Biol. Sci; Genetics Soc. Am. Avian genetics and applied breeding; avian physiology. Address: Dept. of Veterinary & Animal Science, University of Massachusetts, Amherst, MA 01002.

FOX, VIRGIL GRANT, b. Des Moines, Iowa, July 22, 39; m. 62; c. 5. CHEMICAL ENGINEERING. B.S, Iowa State, 61; NASA trainee, Kansas State, 63-67, Ph.D.(chem. eng), 67. Asst. prof. CHEM. ENG, UNIV. DENVER, 67-71, ASSOC. PROF, 71- U.S.A, 61-63, 1st Lt. Am. Inst. Chem. Eng. Heat transfer; fluid flow. Address: Dept. of Chemical Engineering & Metallurgy, University of Denver, Denver, CO 80210.

FOX, WALLACE B(URGESS), b. Marshall, Mich, May 21, 11; m. 38; c. 3. ORGANIC CHEMISTRY. B.S, Mich. State Col, 33, M.S, 34; Ph.D.(org. chem), Iowa, 38. Asst, Iowa, 35-38; res. & develop. chemist, nat. aniline div, Allied Chem. & Dye Corp, Buffalo, 38-42, 46-69, Buffalo Res. Labs, Allied Chem. Corp, 69-71; RETIRED. With Off. Sci. Res. & Develop, 44. C.W.S, U.S.A, 42-46, Capt. Am. Chem. Soc. Sulfur and allied colors; reaction of aryl compounds with tertiary aliphatic carbinols in the presence of anhydrous aluminum chloride; geometric isomers of the oximes of some substitution products of vanillin; polymer chemicals; isocyanate and fluorochemical manufacture. Address: 143 Huntington Ct, Hamburg, NY 14075.

FOX, WILLIAM, b. New Haven, Conn, Mar. 15, 14; m. 49; c. 2. PHYSICAL & COLLOID CHEMISTRY. B.S, City Col, 35; M.A, Columbia, 42, Ph.D. (chem), 44. Patrolman, NEW YORK POLICE DEPT, 40-45, detective police lab. & field command, 45-52, sgt. supvr, 52-57, Lt, police acad. & faculty police sci, City Col. New York, 57-61, lt. supvr. field command, 62-66, CAPT, 66-; ASSOC, OAKLAND RES. ASSOCS, 56- Phys. chemist, petrol. exp. sta, Bur. Mines, Okla, 49. Meritorious Police duty award, New York City Police Dept, 51. Am. Chem. Soc. Physics and chemistry of fluid interfaces; force constants of fluid interfaces; spontaneous mass movements of fluids; surface active agents, emulsions; foams; aerosols; colloids. Address: Oakland Research Associates, 657 Oakland Ave, Staten Island, NY 10310.

FOX, WILLIAM B, b. Clifton, N.J, Aug. 12, 28; m. 54; c. 1. INORGANIC CHEMISTRY. B.S, Illinois, 55; Koppers Co. fel, Pa. State, 56-60, Ph.D. (inorg. chem), 60. Res. chemist, gen. chem. div, Allied Chem. Corp, Morristown, 60-61, sr. res. chemist, 61-62, tech. supvr, 62-66, mgr. inorg. mat. res, indust. chem. res. lab, 66-68, dir. inorg. res. & develop, 68-71; HEAD, INORG. CHEM. BR, NAVAL RES. LAB, 71- U.S.A, 50-53, Sgt. Am. Chem. Soc. Synthesis of high energy oxidizers; chemistry of fluorides of oxygen, nitrogen, sulfur and halogens; reactions of boron halides and sub-halides; generation, trapping, characterization of inorganic free radicals; electric discharge synthesis. Address: Inorganic Chemistry Branch, Chemistry Division, Naval Research Lab, Washington, DC 20390.

FOX, WILLIAM C(ASSIDY), b. Homestead, Fla, Oct. 9, 26; m. 55; c. 1. MATHEMATICS. B.A, Grinnell Col, 49; M.A, Michigan, 50, Ph.D.(math), 55. C.L.E. Moore res. instr, Mass. Inst. Technol, 54-56; asst. prof. MATH, Northwestern, 56-60; res. assoc, Tulane, 60-61; ASSOC. PROF, STATE UNIV. N.Y. STONY BROOK, 61- U.S.N.R, 44-46. Am. Math. Soc; Math. Asn. Am. Topology; analytic and harmonic functions; Riemann surfaces. Address: Dept. of Mathematics, State University of New York at Stony Brook, Stony Brook, NY 11790.

FOX, WILLIAM E(LTON), b. Salt Lake City, Utah, Feb. 3, 27; m. 55; c. 3. BACTERIOLOGY. B.S, Utah State, 50, M.S, 52. Supvry. microbiologist, U.S. Army Chem. Corps, 52-60, supvr. microbiologist & asst. chief test br, res. & develop. directorate, U.S. Army Mat. Command, 60-64; phys. sci. adminstr. & asst. chief br. tech, Bur. Commercial Fisheries, U.S. Fish & Wildlife Serv, 64-70; SPEC. ASST. TO DIR, COL. PARK FISHERY PROD. TECHNOL. LAB, NAT. MARINE FISHERIES SERV, NAT. OCEANIC & ATMOSPHERIC ADMIN, 70- U.S.A, 45-46. Am. Soc. Micrbbiol. Aerobiological sampling and assessment; microbiological survey, sampling techniques, Army material testing procedures; microbiological spoilage of seafoods; manufacture of fish protein concentrate. Address: College Park Fishery Products Technology Lab, National Marine Fisheries Service, Regents Dr, University of Maryland, College Park, MD 20740.

FOX, WILLIAM R(OBERT), b. Sevierville, Tenn, June 15, 36; m. 59; c. 3. AGRICULTURAL ENGINEERING, ENGINEERING MECHANICS. B.S, Tennessee, 58, M.S, 59; Ph.D.(agr. eng, eng. mech), Iowa State, 62. Instr, agr. eng, Iowa State, 60-62; asst. prof, MISS. STATE UNIV, 62-65, assoc. prof, 65-67, PROF. & HEAD DEPT. AGR. & BIOL. ENG, 67- AAAS; Am. Soc. Agr. Eng; Am. Soc. Eng. Educ; Nat. Soc. Prof. Eng. Tillage mechanics and machinery; fundamentals of tillage energy applications. Address: Dept. of Agriculture & Biological Engineering, Mississippi State University, State College, MS 39762.

FOX, WILLIAM T(EMPLETON), b. Chicago, Ill, Nov. 15, 32; m. 59; c. 1. GEOLOGY. B.A, Williams Col, 54; M.S, Northwestern, 60, Nat. Sci. Found. fel. & Ph.D.(geol), 61. Instr. GEOL, WILLIAMS COL, 61-63, asst. prof, 63-68, ASSOC. PROF, 68- Nat. Sci. Found. res. grant, 62-64, fel, Stanford Univ, 66-67; Off. Naval Res. grant, 69-71; summers, jr. geologist, Pan-Am. Oil & Gas Co, 54; geologist, Shell Oil Co, 61. U.S.A, 55-57. AAAS; Am. Asn. Petrol. Geol; Geol. Soc. Am; Soc. Econ. Paleont. & Mineral. Stratigraphy; sedimentation; paleoecology; computer applications to geology. Address: Dept. of Geology, Williams College, Williamstown, MA 01267.

FOXHALL, GEORGE FREDERIC, b. Worcester, Mass, Feb. 20, 39; m. 61; c. 2. SEMICONDUCTOR PHYSICS. B.S, Worcester Polytech, 61; M.S, Illinois, 62. MEM. TECH. STAFF, BELL TEL. LABS, 61- AAAS; sr. mem. Inst. Elec. & Electronics Eng. Semiconductor device physics. Address: 5 Plymouth Circle, Colony Park, Reading, PA 19610.

FOXHALL, HAROLD B(ELL), b. Memphis, Tex, Nov. 20, 18; m. 42; c. 2. GEOLOGY. B.A, Texas, 40; M.A, Stanford, 42. Geologist, bauxite invest, U.S. Geol. Surv, 42-44, mil. geol. unit, 44-45; dir, State Geol. Surv, Ark, 45-51; geologist, DOW CHEM. CO, 51-58, SR. GEOLOGIST, 58- Am. Asn. Petrol. Geol; Am. Inst. Mining, Metall. & Petrol. Eng. Industrial minerals; economic geology. Address: Dow Chemical Co, Box 22468, Houston, TX 77027.

FOXWORTHY, BRUCE L, b. Spokane, Wash, Dec. 30, 25; m. 56; c. 4. HYDROLOGY. B.S, Univ. Wash, 50. Geologist, WATER RESOURCES DIV, U.S. GEOL. SURV, Wash, 51-59, dist. geologist, Ore, 59-64, hydrologist in charge, L.I, N.Y, 64-68, sub-dist. chief, 68-70, ASST. DIST. CHIEF, WASH, 70- U.S.N.R, 43-46. Am. Geophys. Union. Water resources inventories; artificial recharge; hydrology of volcanic terranes; urban hydrology. Address: Water Resources Division, U.S. Geological Survey, 1305 Tacoma Ave. S, Tacoma, WA 98402.

FOXWORTHY, JAMES E(RNEST), b. Los Angeles, Calif, Feb. 23, 30; m. 50; c. 6. CIVIL ENGINEERING. B.S, Southern California, 55, M.S, 58, Ph.D, 65. Instr. civil eng, Wisconsin, 55-56; lectr. gen. eng, Southern California, 56-59; assoc. prof. civil eng. & chmn. dept, LOYOLA UNIV. LOS ANGELES, 59-69, PROF. CIVIL ENG. & DEAN COL. ENG, 69-, asst. prof, 58-59. C.Eng, U.S.A, 50-52, Res, 53- Am. Soc. Civil Eng; Am. Soc. Eng. Educ. Sanitary and hydraulic engineering. Address: College of Engineering, Loyola University of Los Angeles, 7101 W. 80th St, Los Angeles, CA 90045.

FOY, C(HARLES) D(ALEY), b. Buena Vista, Ky, Aug. 19, 23; m. 50; c. 1. SOIL SCIENCE. B.S, Tennessee, 48, M.S, Purdue, 53, Ph.D.(soil fertility), 55. Instr. vets. instit. on farm training, Ind, 49-51; asst. prof. agron, Purdue, 55-57; Co-op. agent agron, U.S. DEPT. AGR, Univ. Arkansas, 57-61, SOIL SCIENTIST, SOIL & WATER CONSERV. RES. DIV, AGR. RES. SERV, Ark, 57-61, MD, 61- U.S.A.A.F, 43-46. Am. Soc. Agron; Soil Sci. Soc. Am. Soil fertility and plant nutrition; lime requirements of crops on acid soils of Southeastern United States; the nature of acid soil toxicity to plants; differential aluminum tolerance of plant varieties. Address: Plant Industry Station, Soil & Water Conservation Research Division, Agricultural Research Service, U.S. Dept. of Agriculture, Beltsville, MD 20705.

FOY, CHESTER L(ARRIMORE), b. Dukedom, Tenn, July 8, 28; m. 53; c. 2. PLANT PHYSIOLOGY. B.S, Tennessee, 52; M.S, Missouri, 53; Ph.D.(plant physiol), California, 58. Asst. soil testing, Tennessee, 51-52; asst. instr. field crops, Missouri, 52-53; asst. specialist, chem. weed control, dept. bot, California, Davis, 53-56, asst. plant physiol, 57-58, asst. botanist, 58-64, assoc. prof. bot. & assoc. botanist, 64-66; assoc. prof. PLANT PHYSIOL, VA. POLYTECH. INST. & STATE UNIV, 66-68, PROF, 68- Nat. Acad. Sci-Nat. Res. Coun. resident res. assoc, Ft. Detrick, Md, 64-65. C.Eng, 46-49, Lt. Am. Soc. Agron; Am. Soc. Plant Physiol; Weed Sci. Soc. Am. Plant physiology and agricultural chemicals; chemical weed control; pathways and mechanics of foliar and root absorption, translocation, accumulation; metabolism and fate of herbicides and surfactants; physiological, biochemical, and morphological changes induced by chemicals; detoxification and other plant protective mechanisms; mode of action and bases of selectivity of growth regulators and phytotoxicants. Address: Dept. of Plant Pathology & Physiology, Virginia Polytechnic Institute & State University, Blacksburg, VA 24061.

FOY, HJORDIS M, b. Stockholm, Sweden, June 28, 26; U.S. citizen; m. 56; c. 3. INFECTIOUS DISEASES, PREVENTIVE MEDICINE. M.D, Karolinska Inst, Sweden, 53; M.S, Univ. Wash, 67, Ph.D, 68. Mem. staff, Hosp. Infectious Diseases, Stockholm, 53-54, 54-55; Johns Hopkins Hosp, 56-57, 58-59; sr. fel. prev. med, UNIV. WASH, 63-67, instr, 66-68, ASST. PROF, 68-70, EPIDEMIOL, SCH. PUB. HEALTH, 70- Swed. Red Cross, 54, Capt. Epidemiology of infectious diseases, in particular Mycoplasma pneumoniae infections. Address: Dept. of Epidemiology, School of Public Health, University of Washington, Seattle, WA 98105.

FOY, ROBERT (BASTIAN), b. Goodland, Ind, June 14, 28; m. 50; c. 9. BIOCHEMISTRY, CLINICAL CHEMISTRY. B.S, Central Michigan, 50; M.S, Mich. State, 55, Ph.D.(chem), 60. Technologist, CLIN. CHEM, Hurley Hosp, Flint, Mich, 50-52; EDWARD W. SPARROW HOSP, 52-55, TECH. DIR. LABS, 55- Lectr, Mich. State, 63. Consult, Mem. Hosp, Owosso, Mich, 57-61; McPherson Community Hosp, Howell, 58-69. AAAS; Am. Chem. Soc; Am. Asn. Clin. Chem. Proteins and enzymes, especially blood coagulation; clinical chemical methodology. Address: Suite 102 Medical Arts Bldg, 1322 E. Michigan Ave, Lansing, MI 48912.

FOY, WADE H(AMPTON), b. Richmond, Va, Jan. 26, 25; m. 52; c. 2. ELECTRICAL ENGINEERING. B.S, U.S. Naval Acad, 46; B.E.E, N.C. State Col, 51; M.S.E.E, Mass. Inst. Technol, 55; Nat. Sci. Found. fel, Hopkins, 60-61, D.Eng.(elec. eng), 62. Res. engr, Martin Co, Md, 56-62; sr. res. engr, STANFORD RES. INST, 62-67, PROG. MGR, 68- Lectr, Martin exten. prog, Drexel Inst. Technol, 57-61, adj. prof, 61-62; lectr, Univ. Santa Clara, 63-65, 66- U.S.N, 46-48, Res, 51-53, Lt. Sr. mem. Inst. Elec. & Electronics Eng. Information theory and statistical communication theory; electronic and control system design; applied mathematics. Address: Radio Systems Lab, Stanford Research Institute, Menlo Park, CA 94025.

FOY, WALTER L(AWRENCE), b. West Springfield, Mass, Aug. 6, 21; m. 48; c. 2. PHYSICAL CHEMISTRY. B.S, Am. Int. Col, 41; Connecticut, 42; M.A, Clark, 43, Ph.D.(phys. chem), 47. Teacher, pub. sch, Conn, 41-42; res. chemist, E.I. DU PONT DE NEMOURS & CO, 47-52, supvr, 52-55, chief supvr, 55-57, tech. supt. plant, 57-65, mgr. prod. res, 65-70, MGR. GRAPHIC ARTS & PRINTING PROD. RES, 70- U.S.A, 44-46, Lt. AAAS; Am. Chem. Soc; Soc. Motion Picture & TV Eng. Electrical conductance of solutions; photographic chemistry; electrical conductance of substituted ammonium salts in ethylidene dichloride. Address: Photo Products Dept, E.I. du Pont de Nemours & Co, Cheesequake Rd, Parlin, NJ 08859.

FOYE, LAURANCE V, JR, b. Seattle, Wash, Nov. 26, 25; m. 51; c. 2. MEDICINE. A.B, Univ. Calif, 49, M.D, 52. Asst. chief med. serv, Vet. Admin. Hosp, San Francisco, 58-66, chief cancer chemother. sect, 60-66; chief, cancer ther. & eval. br, Nat. Cancer Inst, Md, 66-68, exec. secy, cancer clin. invest. review comt, 66-70, chief, clin. invests. br, 68-70, mem, grants assocs. bd, Nat. Insts. Health, 69-70; DIR, EDUC. SERV. & DEP. ASST. CHIEF MED. DIR, RES. & EDUC, VET. ADMIN CENT. OFF, 70- Clin. instr, sch. med, Univ. Calif, San Francisco, 57-67, asst. clin. prof, 62-66, res. assoc, Cancer Res. Inst, 62-66; prin. investr, Vet. Admin. cancer chemother study group, 61-; mem. Nat. Adv. Heart & Lung Inst. Coun, 70; exec. comt, interagency bd, U.S. Civil Serv. Exam, 70- U.S.A, 44-46. AAAS; Am. Med. Asn; fel. Am. Col. Physicians; Am. Soc. Clin. Oncol; Asn. Am. Med. Cols; Asn. Hosp. Med. Educ. Clinical chemotherapy of cancer; evaluation of drugs and disease response. Address: Veterans Administration Central Office, Washington, DC 20420.

FOYE, WILLIAM O(WEN), b. Athol, Mass, June 26, 23; div. PHARMACEUTICAL & ORGANIC CHEMISTRY. A.B, Dartmouth Col, 43; M.A, Indiana, 44, Ph.D.(org. chem), 48. Res. chemist, E.I. du Pont de Nemours & Co, 48-49; asst. prof. pharmaceut. chem, Wisconsin, 49-55; assoc. prof. CHEM, MASS. COL. PHARM, 55-63, PROF, 63-, DEAN FACULTY, 70-, chmn. dept. chem, 66-71. Instr, U.S. Navy, 44-46. Res. achievement award pharmaceut. & med. chem, Am. Pharmaceut. Asn. Found, 70. AAAS; Am. Chem. Soc; Am. Pharmaceut. Asn. Antitubercular, antimicrobial and radioprotective agents; biological aspects of metal binding; mechanisms of drug action. Address: Massachusetts College of Pharmacy, 179 Longwood Ave, Boston, MA 02115.

FOYT, ARTHUR GEORGE, JR, b. Austin, Tex, June 17, 37; m. 60; c. 2. SOLID STATE ELECTRONICS. B.S.E.E. & M.S.E.E, Mass. Inst. Technol, 60, Sc.D.(Gunn effect), 65. MEM. TECH. STAFF, transistor develop, Bell Tel. Labs, N.J, 60-62; GUNN EFFECT & ION IMPLANTATION, TECHNOL, LINCOLN LAB, MASS. INST. TECHNOL, 62- Inst. Elec. & Electronics Eng. Ion implantation in compound semiconductors; Gunn effect in GaAs and CdTe. Address: Applied Physics Group, Lincoln Lab, Massachusetts Institute of Technology, 130 Wood St, Lexington, MA 02173.

FOZDAR, BIRENDRA S(INGH), b. Hasanpur, India, July 6, 19; m. 41; c. 2. BIOLOGY, HORTICULTURE. B.Sc, Agra, 38, M.Sc, 40; Ph.D.(veg. crops), Florida, 62. Asst. bot, Indian Agr. Res. Inst, 41-42; plant physiol, Sugarcane Res. Inst, 42-43; demonstr. bot, agr. col, Agra, 43-44, lectr, 44-47, 48-53; sr. asst, Nat. Bot. Garden, 47-48; asst. prof, Cent. Col. Agr, New Delhi, 53-59; asst. geneticist, Indian Agr. Res. Inst, 59; from instr. BIOL. to asst. prof, ST. ANSELM'S COL, 62-70; ASSOC. PROF, 70- Wallace Found Res. grant, dept. hort, Univ. N.H, summer 63; mem. Nat. Sci. Found Teacher-Res. Participation Prog, Univ. Calif, Berkeley, 64-66; res. assoc, Radiation Biol. Inst, Univ. N.Mex, summer 68; teacher res. participation, Univ. Mich, summer 70. Nat. Cadet Corps, India, Lt. AAAS; Am. Inst. Biol. Sci. Cytogenetics; botany; plant breeding; horticultural crops and forest trees. Address: Dept. of Biology, St. Anselm's College, Manchester, NH 03102.

FOZZARD, GEORGE BROWARD, b. Jacksonville, Fla, Apr. 13, 39; m. 69; c. 1. ORGANIC CHEMISTRY. B.S, Washington & Lee, 61; Union Carbide fel, North Carolina, 65-66, Ph.D.(org. chem), 67. Res. asst. org. chem, North Carolina, 63-66; RES. CHEMIST, PHILLIPS PETROL. CO, 66- Am. Chem. Soc. Conformational analysis; hydrogen bonding; fluorochemicals. Address: 2079 S. Dewey, Bartlesville, OK 74003.

FOZZARD, HARRY A, b. Jacksonville, Fla, Apr. 22, 31; m. 54; c. 2. PHYSIOLOGY, INTERNAL MEDICINE. M.D, Wash. Univ, 56. Intern med, Yale, 56-57; asst, Wash. Univ, 59-61, instr, 62-64, asst. prof, 64-66; PROF. MED. & PHYSIOL, SCH. MED, UNIV. CHICAGO, 66- Nat. Heart Inst. fels. cardiol, Wash. Univ, 61-63 & physiol, Univ. Berne, 63-64. Med.C, 57-59, Lt. Comdr. Am. Fedn. Clin. Res; Biophys. Soc; Am. Physiol. Soc. Intracellular cardiac electrophysiology, especially excitation-contraction coupling; cardiovascular hemodynamics. Address: Dept. of Medicine, University of Chicago, Chicago, IL 60637.

FRAAD, LEWIS M, b. Harrison, N.Y, Sept. 3, 07; m. 33; c. 3. PEDIATRICS. M.D, Vienna, Austria, 35. Asst. clin. prof. PEDIAT, med. col, Cornell, 48-55; assoc. prof, ALBERT EINSTEIN COL. MED, YESHIVA UNIV, 55-59, PROF, 59-, ACTING CHMN. DEPT, 70- Med.C, U.S.A, 42-45, Capt. Am. Pediat. Soc; Am. Acad. Pediat; N.Y. Acad. Med. Child health; emotional growth and development; problems of pediatric education. Address: Dept. of Pediatrics, Albert Einstein College of Medicine, Yeshiva University, New York, NY 10461.

FRAAS, ARTHUR P(AUL), b. Lakewood, Ohio, Aug. 20, 15; m. 40; c. 2. MECHANICAL ENGINEERING. B.S, Case, 38; M.S.(aeronaut. eng), N.Y. Univ, 43. Exp. test engr, Wright Aeronaut. Corp, 38-40; instr, Aircraft Power Plants, N.Y. Univ, 41-43; exp. proj. engr, aircraft eng. div, Packard Motor Car Co, 43-45; asst. prof. combustion eng, Case, 45-46; assoc. prof, Inst. Tech. of Aeronaut, Brazil, 47-49; mem. gen. design group, aircraft nuclear propulsion proj, OAK RIDGE NAT. LAB, 50-57, ASSOC. DIR, REACTOR DIV, 57- Sci. Res. Soc. Am; fel. Am. Soc. Mech. Eng; Soc. Automotive Eng; Am. Inst. Aeronaut. & Astronaut. Heat exchangers; stress analysis; pumps and compressors; vibration; combustion engines; nuclear power plants. Address: 1040 Scenic Dr, Knoxville, TN 37919.

FRACHTMAN, H(IRSH) JULIAN, b. Houston, Texas, Sept. 2, 13; m. 41; c. 3. CLINICAL MEDICINE. B.A, Rice, 33; M.D, Texas, 37. Fel. med, med. sch, Tulane, 38-39; asst. prof. CLIN. MED, COL. MED, BAYLOR UNIV, 46-64, ASSOC. PROF, 64- Vis. physician, St. Luke's Hosp; consult. physician, Mem. Hosp; mem. courtesy staff, Hermann, Methodist & Ctr. Pavilion Hosps. Dipl. Am. Bd. Internal Med. Med.C, 40-46, Col; Bronze Star Medal. Am. Soc. Internal Med; Am. Heart Asn; Am. Col. Cardiol. Internal medicine; diagnosis and cardiology. Address: 901 Hermann Professional Bldg, Houston, TX 77025.

FRACKELTON, W(ILLIAM) H(AMILTON), b. Milwaukee, Wis, Apr. 5, 11; m. 38; c. 2. SURGERY. M.D, Harvard, 36. Intern, Columbia Hosp, Milwaukee, Wis, 37; res, Passavant Mem. Hosp, Chicago, Ill, 38-40, MEM. FACULTY, MED. COL. WIS, 41-, clin. prof. plastic surg. & head dept, 58-70. Lectr, Milwaukee Downer Col, 52-64; vis. prof, Univ. Mich, 63; Univ. Tex, Galveston, 64-; med. sch, Baylor Univ, 66; Univ. Guadalajara, Mex, 68; Univ. Ariz, 70; consult. & lectr, U.S. Navy, 68- Pres, Newberry Publishers, Inc, 51-; corp. mem, Boys Club Milwaukee; Milwaukee Symphony Orchestra; Chicago Symphony Orchestra Asn. Dipl, Am. Bd. Surg; Am. Bd. Plastic Surg, examiner, 57-63. Med.C, A.U.S, 41-46, Col; Legion of Merit. Hon. mem. Am. Acad. Orthop. Surg; Am. Asn. Plastic Surg.(pres, 61-62); Am. Asn. Surg. Trauma; Am. Cleft Palate Asn; Am. Col. Surg; Am. Med. Asn; Am. Soc. Plastic & Reconstruct. Surg; Am. Soc. Surg. Hand (pres, 52); Int. Soc. Burn Injuries; Nat. Rehab. Asn; Pan-Pac. Surg. Asn; cor. mem. Japan Soc. Plastic Surg. Address: 2266 N. Prospect Ave, Suite 608, Milwaukee, WI 53202.

FRADIN, FRANK YALE, b. Chicago, Ill, May 14, 41; m. 63; c. 3. PHYSICAL METALLURGY, SOLID STATE PHYSICS. S.B, Mass. Inst. Tech, 63; M.S, Illinois, 64, Ph.D.(metall, physics), 67. METALLURGIST, ARGONNE NAT. LAB, 67- Vis. prof, North. Ill. Univ, 69-70, Northwest. Univ, 70. Am. Phys. Soc; Am. Inst. Mining, Metall. & Petrol. Eng. Diffusion in solids; nuclear magnetic resonance in alloys and intermetallic compounds; magnetic and transport properties of alloys and intermetallic compounds. Address: Materials Science Division, Argonne National Lab, 9700 S. Cass Ave, Argonne, IL 60439.

FRADKIN, CHENG-MEI W(ANG), b. China, May 27, 28; nat; m. 52; c. 3. GENETICS. B.S, California, 52; M.S, Wisconsin, 53, Ph.D.(genetics), 55. Asst. genetics, Wisconsin, 52-55; res. assoc, Ohio State, 55-60; fel. microbial genetics, sch. med, Stanford, 60-63; on leave, 63-65; ASSOC. PROF. BIOL, CHAPMAN COL, 65-, HEAD DEPT, 66- Maize genetics and Drosophila genetics; mutation and gene action. Address: Dept. of Biology, Chapman College, Orange, CA 92666.

FRADKIN, DAVID M(ILTON), b. Los Angeles, Calif, Apr. 20, 31; m. 59; c. 3. THEORETICAL PHYSICS. B.S, California, Berkeley, 54; Trinity Col.(Dublin), 56-57; Ph.D.(physics), Iowa State, 63. Exploitation engr, Shell Oil Co, 54-56; res. assoc. theoret. physics, Ames Lab, Atomic Energy Comn. & Iowa State Univ, 63-64; NATO fel, Marconi Inst. Physics, Univ. Rome, 64-65; asst. prof. PHYSICS, WAYNE STATE UNIV, 65-69, ASSOC. PROF, 69- Am. Phys. Soc. Electron polarization operators; coulomb scattering of relativistic electrons; conservation laws and relativistic wave equations; dynamical groups and symmetries; coherent processes in particle beams. Address: Dept. of Physics, Wayne State University, Detroit, MI 48202.

FRAENKEL, DAN G(ABRIEL), b. London, Eng, May 6, 37; U.S. citizen. BACTERIAL PHYSIOLOGY. B.S, Illinois, 57; Nat. Sci. Found. fel, Harvard, 57-61, Ph.D.(bact), 62. Nat. Found. fel. microbiol, sch. med, N.Y. Univ, 62-63; res. assoc. molecular biol, Albert Einstein Col. Med, 63-65; assoc. bact. & immunol, HARVARD MED. SCH, 65-69, ASSOC. PROF. MICROBIOL. & MOLECULAR GENETICS, 69- Am. Soc. Microbiol; Am. Soc. Biol. Chem. Physiology and genetics of amphibolic pathways in Escherichia coli. Address: Dept. of Microbiology & Molecular Genetics, Harvard Medical School, 25 Shattuck St, Boston, MA 02115.

FRAENKEL, GEORGE K(ESSLER), b. Deal, N.J, July 27, 21; m. 51, 67. CHEMICAL PHYSICS. B.S, Harvard, 42; Nat. Res. fel, Cornell Univ, 46-49, Ph.D.(chem), 49. Res. group leader, Nat. Defense Res. Comt, Oceanog. Inst, Woods Hole, 43-46; instr. CHEM, COLUMBIA UNIV, 49-53, asst. prof, 53-57, assoc. prof, 57-61, PROF, 61-, DEAN GRAD. SCH. ARTS & SCI, 68-, chmn. dept. chem, 66-68. Assoc. ed, J. Chem. Physics, 62-64; mem. post-doctoral fel. comt, Nat. Acad. Sci-Nat. Sci. Found, 64-65; mem. adv. ed. bd, Chem. Phys. Letters, 66-70; chmn, Gordon Res. Conf. Magnetic Resonance, 67; mem. adv. ed, bd, J. Magnetic Resonance, 69- Army-Navy Cert. Appreciation, 48. AAAS; Am. Chem. Soc; fel. Am. Phys. Soc. Electron spin resonance; free radicals; chemical physics. Address: Office of the Dean, 109 Low Memorial Library, Graduate School of Arts & Sciences, Columbia University, New York, NY 10027.

FRAENKEL, GIDEON, b. Frankfurt, Ger, Feb. 21, 32; m. 61; c. 2. CHEMISTRY. B.S, Univ. Ill, 52; M.A, Harvard, 53, Ph.D.(org. chem), 57. Res. fel. CHEM, Calif. Inst. Technol, 57-60; asst. prof, OHIO STATE UNIV, 60-65, assoc. prof, 65-69, PROF, 69- Am. Chem. Soc; Faraday Soc. Mechanisms and reactions in organic chemistry; chemical applications of nuclear magnetic resonance; species in solution. Address: Dept. of Chemistry, Ohio State University, Columbus, OH 43210.

FRAENKEL, G(OTTFRIED) S(AMUEL), b. Munich, Germany, Apr. 23, 01; nat; m. 28; c. 2. ENTOMOLOGY, COMPARATIVE PHYSIOLOGY. Ph.D. (zool), Munich, 25. Fel, Int. Ed. Bd, Zool. Sta, Naples, 26-27; asst, dept. zool, Hebrew Univ, 28-30; privatdozent zool, Zool. Inst, Frankfurt, 31-33; res. assoc, dept. zool, Univ. Col, London, 33-35, lectr. zool, Imp. Col, London, 36-48; PROF. ENTOM, UNIV. ILL, URBANA, 48- Vis. prof, dept. entom, Univ. Minn, 47; res. career award, U.S. Pub. Health Serv, 62- Nat. Acad. Sci; AAAS; Am. Soc. Zool; hon. mem. Royal Entom. Soc. London; Am. Entom. Soc; Am. Inst. Nutrit. Orientation of animals; physiology of insects; comparative physiology and biochemistry. Address: Dept. of Entomology, University of Illinois, Urbana, IL 61801.

FRAENKEL-CONRAT, HEINZ L(UDWIG), b. Breslau, Ger, July 29, 10; nat; m. 39, div; c. 2; m. 64. BIOCHEMISTRY. Vienna, Munich; Geneva; M.D, Breslau, 33; Ph.D.(biochem), Edinburgh, 36. Asst, Rockefeller Inst, 36-37; res. assoc, Butantan Inst, Sao Paulo, Brazil, 37-38; inst. exp. biol, California, 38-42; from assoc. chemist to chemist, west. regional res. lab, bur. agr. & indust. chem, U.S. Dept. Agr, 42-50; Rockefeller fel, England, Denmark, 51; res. biochemist, virus lab, CALIFORNIA, BERKELEY, 52-58, PROF. virol, 58-63, MOLECULAR BIOL, 63- Guggenheim fel, 63, 67; faculty res. lectr, Univ. Calif, Berkeley, 68. Lasker Award, Am. Pub. Health Asn; Calif. scientist of year, 58. AAAS; Am. Chem. Soc; Am. Soc. Biol. Chem. Chemistry and structure of proteins and nucleic acids, especially viruses, enzymes, hormones, toxins; structural requirements for activity. Address: 870 Grizzly Peak Blvd, Berkeley, CA 94708.

FRAENKEL-CONRAT, JANE E, b. Baltimore, Md, Dec. 9, 15. BIOCHEMISTRY. B.A, Goucher Col, 36; Ph.D.(biochem), California, 42. Asst, sch. med, Hopkins, 36-37; inst. exp. biol, California, 38-42, res. assoc, radiation lab, 43, biochem, univ, 45-47, res. chemist, dept. home econ, 48-51; res. biochemist, Children's Hosp. East Bay, Oakland, Calif, 53-63; clin. chemist, Mem. Hosp, San Leandro, 63-64; sr. scientist, Lockheed Missiles & Space Co, 64; dir. lab. serv. & assoc. res. scientist, cancer res. ctr, Ellis Fischel Hosp, Mo, 64-66, dir. res. labs, 66-67; lectr. biol, Seattle Univ, Pine Lake Campus, 67-69; ASSOC. PROF. CHEM, ST. MARY'S SEMINARY COL, 69- AAAS; Am. Chem. Soc; Am. Cancer Soc; Am. Inst. Chem; N.Y. Acad. Sci. Enzyme activity of normal and pathological leukocytes; intermediary protein metabolism; protein chemistry; development of clinical methods; interpretation of clinical chemistry; effect of irradiation on enzyme activity. Address: St. Mary's Seminary College, Maiden Choice Lane, Catonsville, MD 21228.

FRAGA, SERAFIN, b. Madrid, Spain, Feb. 11, 31; m. 56; c. 3. THEORETICAL CHEMISTRY. Lic. sc, Madrid, 54, D.Sc.(chem), 57. Res. assoc. physics, Chicago, 58-61; chem, Alberta, 61-62; asst. prof. physics, Royal Mil. Col.(Que), 62-63; chem, UNIV. ALBERTA, 63-65; assoc. prof. THEORET. CHEM, 65-69, PROF, 69- Juan March Found. fel, 58-59; fel, Alberta, 61-62. Quantum chemistry; theoretical research on atomic and molecular structure. Address: Dept. of Chemistry, University of Alberta, Edmonton, Alberta, Can.

FRAGOLA, CAESAR (FRANCIS), b. Brooklyn, N.Y, June 1, 16; m. 42; c. 5. ENGINEERING. B.E.E, Polytech. Inst. Brooklyn, 37, fel, 39-40, M.E.E, 40. Develop. engr, Root Res. Lab, N.Y, 38-39; asst. proj. engr, Sperry Gyroscope Co, 40-44, proj. engr, 44-48, head, eng. sect, 48-54, eng. dept, 54-63; aircraft reliability mgr, GRUMMAN AIRCRAFT CO, 63-69, STAFF ENGR, 69- Sr. mem. Inst. Elec. & Electronics Eng; Am. Inst. Aeronaut. & Astronaut. Aircraft instrumentation engineering; aircraft flight and navigation instruments; individual components and complete system components for stabilized remotely located aircraft compasses and flight directors; Doppler navigators; navigational systems; head-up windshield aircraft displays. Address: Space Division, Grumman Aircraft, Bethpage, NY 11714.

FRAHM, CHARLES P(ETER), b. Mason City, Iowa, July 7, 38; m. 58; c. 2. HIGH ENERGY PHYSICS. B.S, Ga. Inst. Tech, 61, NDEA fel, 61-64, Ph.D. (high energy physics), 67. Instr. PHYSICS, Ga. Inst. Tech, 65-66, asst. prof, 67-68; res. asst, Tel-Aviv, 66-67; asst. prof, ILL. STATE UNIV, 68-70, ASSOC. PROF, 70- Res. asst, Advan. Res. Corp, 64-68. AAAS; Am. Asn. Physics Teachers; Am. Phys. Soc. Theoretical high energy physics. Address: Dept. of Physics, Illinois State University, Normal IL 61761.

FRAHM, ELMER E(DWARD), b. Davenport, Iowa, Apr. 10, 05; m. 37. CHEMISTRY. B.S, Colo. Agr. Col, 33; fel, Iowa State Col, 33-37, M.S, 35, Ph.D. (soil chem), 38. Instr, Iowa State Col, 37-41; asst. chemist, exp. sta, Agr. & Mech. Col. Texas, 41; asst. prof. agr. chem, Florida, 41-44, assoc. prof, 44; asst. prof. CHEM, EXP. STA, MONT. STATE UNIV, 44-46, assoc. prof, 46-52, prof, 52-70, acting head dept, 65-67, EMER. PROF, 70- Soil phosphorus and fertility. Address: 609 S. 12th Ave, Bozeman, MT 59715.

FRAHM, RICHARD R, b. Scottsbluff, Nebr, Nov. 17, 39; m. 61; c. 2. POPULATION GENETICS, ANIMAL BREEDING. B.S, Univ. Nebr, 61; Nat. Sci. Found. fels, 61-65; M.S, N.C. State Univ, 63, Ph.D.(genetics), 65. Asst. prof. ANIMAL BREEDING, OKLA. STATE UNIV, 67-71, ASSOC. PROF, 71- U.S.A, 65-67, Capt. Am. Soc. Animal Sci; Genetics Soc. Am; Biomet. Soc. Population genetics and animal breeding research with beef cattle and mice; research designed to elucidate basic quantitative genetic principles and evidence as to how most effectively incorporate them into breeding programs to improve performance and productivity. Address: Dept. of Animal Sciences & Industry, Agricultural Experiment Station, Oklahoma State University, Stillwater, OK 74074.

FRAIKOR, FREDERICK JOHN, b. Duquesne, Pa, Apr. 22, 37; m. 62; c. 3. METALLURGY. B.S, Carnegie Inst. Technol, 59; Ph.D.(metall), Ohio State, 65. Teaching asst. metall, Carnegie Inst. Technol, 59-60; metallurgist, Duquesne Works, U.S. Steel Corp, 60; res. asst. metall, Ohio State, 62-65; res. metallurgist, Rocky Flats Div, DOW CHEM. CO, 65-68, SR. RES. MGR, 68- Sig.C, 60-62, Capt. AAAS; Electron Micros. Soc. Am; Am. Inst. Mining, Metall. & Petrol. Eng; Am. Soc. Metals. Vacancy concentration and precipitation in quenched metals; transmission electron microscopy of nuclear metals; corrosion; phase transformations in metals and alloys; joining processes. Address: 8169 Pierson Court, Arvada, CO 80002.

FRAILEY, DENNIS J(OHN), b. Tulsa, Okla, Mar. 5, 44; m. 69. COMPUTER SCIENCE, MATHEMATICS. B.S, Univ. Notre Dame, 66; Nat. Defense Educ. Act fel, Purdue Univ, 66, M.S, 68, Ph.D.(comput. sci), 71. Res. scientist COMPUT. SCI, Ford Motor Co, 66-71; ASST. PROF, INST. TECHNOL, SOUTH. METHODIST UNIV, 71- Asn. Comput. Mach. Compilers; operating systems; data structures; microprogramming; scheduling algorithms; code optimization; large scale computer systems and associated problems. Address: Institute of Technology, Southern Methodist University, Dallas, TX 75222.

FRAIR, WAYNE, b. Pittsburgh, Pa, May 23, 26. BIOLOGY. B.A, Houghton Col, 50; B.S, Wheaton Col.(Ill), 51; M.A.(zool), Massachusetts, 55; Ph.D. (serol), Rutgers, 62. Teacher, private sch, 51-52; asst, Massachusetts, 52-53; Brown, 54-55; instr. BIOL, KING'S COL.(N.Y), 55-58, asst. prof, 58-62, assoc. prof, 62-67, PROF, 67- Asst, Rutgers, 59-60. U.S.N, 44-46. AAAS; Am. Sci. Affiliation; Am. Soc. Ichthyol. & Herpet; Am. Soc. Zool; Soc. Syst. Zool. Animal relationships; reptilian molecular taxonomy. Address: Dept. of Biology, The King's College, Briarcliff Manor, NY 10510.

FRAJOLA, WALTER J(OSEPH), b. Chicago, Ill, Nov. 2, 16; m. 41; c. 2. BIOCHEMISTRY. B.S, Hamline, 38; Minnesota; M.S, Illinois, 47, Ph.D.(chem), 50. Instr, pub. sch, S.Dak, 38-41; Minn, 41-42; asst. chem, Illinois, 46-50; asst. prof. physiol. chem, COL. MED, OHIO STATE UNIV, 50-57, assoc. prof, 57-59, path, 59-60, asst. prof. med. res, 53-60, dir, H.A. Hoster Res. Lab, 52-60, chief div. clin. biochem, 59-62, PROF. PATH. & PHYSIOL. CHEM, 60-; PRES. & LAB. DIR, COMMUNITY LABS OF OHIO, 71- Chief scientist, Columbus div, N.Am. Rockwell Corp, 62-66; pres, Lab. Anal. Blood Studies, Inc, 66-71. U.S.A, 44-46, Res, 46-53, 1st Lt. Am. Chem. Soc; Am. Asn. Clin. Chem; Electron Micros. Soc. Am; N.Y. Acad. Sci. Enzymes; cancer; clinical chemistry. Address: 2558 Onandaga Dr, Columbus, OH 43221.

FRAKER, ANNA CLYDE, b. Chuckey, Tenn, June 25, 35. METALLURGICAL & CERAMIC ENGINEERING. B.S, Furman, 57; M.S, N.C. State, 61, Ph.D. (ceramic eng), 67; Aachen Tech, 62-63. Res. asst. metall, N.C. State, 57-62, res. assoc, 63-67; METALLURGIST, NAT. BUR. STANDARDS, 67- Electron Micros. Soc. Am. Alloy phase studies; interstitial alloys; recrystallization of aluminum; corrosion of titanium and aluminum by thin foil transmission electron microscopy. Address: 401 Muddy Branch Rd, Gaithersburg, MD 20760.

FRAKES, LAWRENCE A(USTIN), b. Pasadena, Calif, Apr. 28, 30; m. 54; c. 1. SEDIMENTOLOGY, MARINE GEOLOGY. B.A, Univ. Calif, Los Angeles, 57, M.A, 59, Atlantic Richfield Oil Corp. fel, 63, Ph.D.(geol), 64. Instr. geol, Villanova Univ, 59-60; geologist, Pa. Geol. Surv, 60-62; asst. res. geologist, Univ. Calif, Los Angeles, 64-67, assoc. res. geologist, 67-69; ASSOC. PROF. GEOL, Univ. N.M, 69-70; FLA. STATE UNIV, 70- Fel. AAAS; fel.

Geol. Soc. Am; Am. Geophys. Union; Am. Asn. Petrol. Geol. Paleoclimatology; distribution and causes of late Paleozoic glaciation; atmospheric and oceanic circulation patterns during the late Paleozoic and Mesozoic; Gondwanaland reconstructions. Address: Dept. of Geology, Florida State University, Tallahassee, FL 32306.

FRAKES, ROD(NEY) V(ANCE), b. Ontario, Ore, July 20, 30; m. 52; c. 2. PLANT BREEDING & GENETICS. B.S, Oregon State, 56, M.S, 57; Ph.D.(plant breeding), Purdue, 60. Instr. forage crop res, Purdue, 57-60; asst. prof. PLANT BREEDING, ORE. STATE UNIV, 60-64, assoc. prof, 64-69, PROF, 69- U.S.C.G, 50-53. Am. Soc. Agron; Crop. Sci. Soc. Am. Breeding of legumes, and forage and turf grasses. Address: Dept. of Farm Crops, Oregon State University, Corvallis, OR 97331.

FRALEY, ELWIN E, b. Sayre, Pa, May 3, 34; c. 6. UROLOGY, PATHOLOGY. B.S, Princeton, 57; M.D, Harvard, 61. Instr. surg, Mass. Gen. Hosp, 66-67; investr. UROL, Nat. Insts. Health, 67-69; PROF, UNIV. MINN, MINNEAPOLIS, 69- Soma Weiss Award, med. sch, Harvard, 63. AAAS; Am. Soc. Exp. Path; Am. Asn. Cancer Res; Am. Urol. Asn.(clin. res. award, 64, res. essay awards, 67, movie award, 69); Soc. Univ. Urol; Soc. Univ. Surg. Nucleic acid and protein metabolism in kidney; relation of viruses to development of human genitourinary neoplasms; human tumor immunology; viral oncology; macromolecular pathology. Address: Dept. of Urology, University of Minnesota Medical Center, Minneapolis, MN 55455.

FRALICK, STANLEY C, b. Wilber, Nebr, June 26, 34; m. 55; c. 3. ELECTRICAL ENGINEERING. M.S, Stanford, 57, Ph.D.(elec. eng), 65. Mem. tech. staff elec. eng, Space Tech. Labs, Thompson Ramo Wooldridge, Inc, 60-61; develop. engr, Sylvania Electronic Defense Lab, Gen. Tel. & Electronics Corp, 61-62, adv. res. engr, 62-65, eng. specialist, 65-69, ASST. DIR, TELECOMMUN. DEPT, STANFORD RES. INST, 69- U.S.A.F, 57-60, Capt. Inst. Elec. & Electronics Eng. Adaptive pattern recognition machines; communication theory; decision theory. Address: 1233 Sesame Ct, Sunnyvale, CA 94087.

FRALISH, HOWARD JOSEPH, b. Berlin, Wis, Feb. 20, 09; m. 40; c. 3. PHYSICS. A.B, Ripon Col, 31; M.Sc, Ohio State, 33, Ph.D.(physics), 36; fel, Battelle Mem. Inst, 34-35. Asst. physics, Ohio State, 31-34; ENGR, INDIANAPOLIS WORKS, WEST. ELEC. CO, 35- Soc. Plastics Eng; Inst. Elec. & Electronics Eng; Am. Vacuum Soc. Thermal conductivity of refractory materials at high temperatures; ceramics; insulating and magnetic materials; reclamation; component apparatus, capacitors and transformers; high vacuum metallizing; low pressure resins; compression and injection molding; die casting; organic and inorganic finishing; thin film circuitry. Address: Indianapolis Works, Western Electric Co, 2525 N. Shadeland Ave, Indianapolis, IN 46206.

FRAM, HARVEY, b. Worcester, Mass, Nov. 23, 18; m. 44; c. 2. FOOD TECHNOLOGY. B.S, Massachusetts, 40, M.S, 42. Asst, Mass. Inst. Technol, 42-48; group leader, Nat. Dairy Res. Labs, 48-60; CHIEF FOOD TECHNOLOGIST, B. MANISCHEWITZ CO, JERSEY CITY, 60- Inst. Food Technol; Am. Asn. Cereal Chem. Radiation sterilization of foods; cultured dairy products; food preservation, canned, baked and frozen. Address: 1108 Belle Ave, Teaneck, NJ 07666.

FRAM, PAUL, b. Worcester, Mass, Sept. 14, 18; m. 47; c. 2. POLYMER CHEMISTRY. B.A, Clark, 40, M.A, 42; fel, Polytech. Inst. Brooklyn, 46-49, Ph.D.(chem), 50. Res. assoc. synthetic rubber, Minnesota, 49-50; res. chemist, E.I. du Pont de Nemours & Co, 50-51; chief resin sect, Army Prosthetics Res. Lab, Walter Reed Army Med. Ctr, 51-55; sr. res. chemist, MINN. MINING & MFG. CO, ST. PAUL, 55-65, res. mgr, org. res. sect, magnetic prod. div, 65-69, SR. RES. SPECIALIST, PATENT LIAISON & INFO. SERV, 69- U.S.A, 42-46, 1st Lt. Am. Chem. Soc; N.Y. Acad. Sci. Physical properties of polymers; kinetics of polymerization; mechanism of emulsion polymerization; low pressure laminating resins; coatings; adhesives; vinyl technology; synthetic fibers; synthetic rubber lattices; paper treatment and production. Address: 3527 Arcwood Rd, White Bear Lake, MN 55110.

FRAME, ELIZABETH G(RAHAM), b. Lunenburg, N.S, Can, Aug. 14, 08; nat. PHYSIOLOGICAL CHEMISTRY. B.A, Dalhousie, 28, M.A, 29; London, 35-36; Ph.D.(physiol. chem), Yale, 42. Instr. zool, Smith Col, 30-37, asst. prof, 37-39; instr. urol, Hopkins Hosp, 42-44; fel, Harvard, 44-46; asst. prof. physiol. chem, Minnesota, 46-53; chief biochem. serv, dept. clin. path, clin. center, NAT. INSTS. HEALTH, 53-59, biochemist, center aging res, gen. med. sci. div, 59-60, exec. secy, training grants br, div. gen. med. sci, 60-63, MEM. STAFF, Nat. Inst. Child Health & Human Develop, 63-64, RES. FELS, BR, NAT. INST. GEN. MED. SCI, 64- AAAS; Am. Chem. Soc. Amino acid metabolism; clinical chemistry. Address: National Institute of General Medical Sciences, National Institutes of Health, Bethesda, MD 20014.

FRAME, GORDON F(LEMMING), b. Lunenburg, N.S, Can, Mar. 11, 06; nat. 44; m. 38; c. 3. ORGANIC CHEMISTRY. B.A, Dalhousie, 27, M.A, 30; Nat. Res. Council Can. bursar, McGill, 30, fel. & Ph.D.(org. chem), 32; Tech. Hochschule Zurich, 32-33. Res. chemist, Imp. Oil, Ltd, 33-36; Shawinigan Chems. Ltd, 37; Eastman Kodak Co, 38-49, exp. supvr. film div, 49-59, sr. tech. assoc, 59-69; RETIRED. Am. Chem. Soc. Synthesis of anthraquinone dyes; photographic emulsion research; gamma ketonic esters; triterpenes. Address: 109 Nob Hill, Rochester, NY 14617.

FRAME, HARLAN D, b. Muscatine, Iowa, Jan. 1, 33; m. 60; c. 2. INORGANIC & PHYSICAL CHEMISTRY. B.A, Univ. Wichita, 55; M.S, Univ. Ill, 58, Ph.D.(inorg. chem), 59. Assoc. chemist, Argonne Nat. Lab, Ill, 59-69; ASST. PROF. CHEM, SOUTHWEST. STATE COL.(OKLA), 69- Consult, chem. div, Argonne Nat. Lab, Ill. AAAS; Am. Chem. Soc. Synthetic inorganic chemistry employing nonaqueous solvents; inorganic fluorine chemistry; nonaqueous solvents; high temperature reactions; chromatography. Address: Dept. of Chemistry, Southwestern State College, Weatherford, OK 73096.

FRAME, J(AMES) SUTHERLAND, b. New York, N.Y, Dec. 24, 07; m. 38; c. 4. MATHEMATICS. A.B, Harvard, 29, A.M, 30, Ph.D.(math), 33; Brown, 41. Instr. math, Harvard, 30-33; Rogers traveling fel, Harvard, Göttingen & Zurich, 33-34; instr. math, Brown, 34-38, asst. prof, 38-42; assoc. prof. & chmn. dept, Allegheny Col, 42-43; PROF, MICH. STATE UNIV, 43-63, MATH. & ENG. RES, 63-, chmn. dept. math, 43-60, proj. dir, conf. bd. math. sci, 61-62. Mem, Inst. Advan. Study, 50-51; consult, Ford Found, Bangkok, Thailand, 70. AAAS; Am. Math. Soc; Math. Asn. Am; Soc. Indust. & Appl. Math; Can. Math. Cong. Theory of representations of finite groups; approximations; matrix theory; continued fractions. Address: 136 Oakland Dr, East Lansing, MI 48823.

FRAME, JOHN W. b. Rolla, Mo, Sept. 28, 16. METALLURGICAL ENGINEERING. B.S, Mo. Sch. Mines, 37; Gotshall scholar. & M.S, Lehigh Univ, 38, Ph.D.(metall. eng), 61. Mem. staff, metall. dept, BETHLEHEM STEEL CORP, Lackawanna, 38-46, engr. res. div, 46-56, from supvr. to assoc. dir. res, phys. metall, 56-64, mgr. forming & finishing res, 64-69, MGR. PROD. RES, HOMER RES. LABS, 69- Am. Soc. Metals; Am. Inst. Mining, Metall. & Petrol. Eng; Am. Iron & Steel Inst; Soc. Automotive Eng. Aging, formability and manufacture of sheet steels; corrosion, welding, forming, machining, alloy development, metal physics, fatigue and fracture of steel; organic coating; tin mill products. Address: Homer Research Labs, Bethlehem Steel Corp, Bethlehem, PA 18016.

FRAME, ROBERT ROY, b. Oak Park, Ill, Aug. 24, 39. ORGANIC CHEMISTRY. B.S, Illinois, 61; Texaco Co. fel, Northwestern, 64-65, Ph.D, 65. Fel. ORG. CHEM, Arkansas, 67-68; VIS. ASST. PROF, UNIV. OKLA, 68- Ord.C, U.S.A, 65-67, Capt. Am. Chem. Soc. Synthetic and mechanistic organic chemistry, including the Favorskii reaction, preparation of haloketones, and certain reactions of acetylenes. Address: Dept. of Chemistry, University of Oklahoma, Norman, OK 73069.

FRAMPTON, E(LON) W(ILSON), b. New York, N.Y, July 27, 24; m. 58; c. 2. MICROBIOLOGY. B.A, Syracuse, 49; M.S, Northwestern, 51; Ph.D.(dairy sci, bact), Illinois, 59. Lab. technician, hosp, Rockefeller Inst, 42-43; microbiologist, Wilson Labs, Ill, 50-54; asst. dairy bact, Illinois, 54-58; res. fel, M.D. Anderson Hosp. & Tumor Inst, Univ. Tex, 59-60, res. assoc, 60-62, asst. radiation biologist, 62-66, assoc. biologist, 66-69; ASSOC. PROF. BIOL. SCI, NORTH. ILL. UNIV, 69- U.S.A, 43-46. AAAS; Am. Soc. Microbiol. Radiation and molecular biology; bacterial physiology. Address: Dept. of Biological Sciences, Northern Illinois University, DeKalb, IL 60115.

FRAMPTON, ORVILLE D(EACY), b. Dawson, N.Mex, Oct. 16, 15; m. 43; c. 2. ORGANIC CHEMISTRY, BIOCHEMISTRY. A.B, California, Los Angeles, 38; M.A, Cornell, 40, Ph.D.(biochem), 43. Asst. biochem, Cornell, 39-42; asst. prof. org. chem, Norwich, 42-43; res. chemist, U.S. Indust. Chem. Co, 43; res. physicist, Calif. Inst. Technol, 43-45; RES. CHEMIST, ORG. CHEM. & BIOCHEM, NAT. DISTILLERS & CHEM. CO, 45- Claisen condensation; amino acids; enzymes, wines; hydrogenation; separations; organometallics. Address: 58 W. Charlotte Ave, Wyoming, Cincinnati, OH 45215.

FRAMPTON, VERNON L(ACHENOUS), b. Springer, N.Mex, Jan. 29, 06; m. 30; c. 3. CHEMISTRY. A.B, California, Los Angeles, 31; Ph.D.(biochem), Minnesota, 36. Chemist, Dixtrol Corp, 30-31; jr. chemist, U.S. Dept. Agr, 32-33; asst. biochem, Minnesota, 34-36; asst. prof. plant path, Cornell, 36-44; chemist, Nat. Cotton Coun. Am, 44-46; dir. basic res. lab, cotton res. comt, Texas, 46-54; HEAD oilseed meals invests, SOUTH. REGIONAL RES. LAB, U.S. DEPT. AGR, 54-69, COMPOSITION & PROPERTIES INVESTS, 69- Nat. Res. Coun. fel, Univ. Wis, 36-37; exchange prof, Am. Asn. Cereal Chem; Am. Asn. Plant Physiol; N.Y. Acad. Sci. Plant viruses; colloids; fats and oils; cellulose; plant proteins; carbohydrates and animal biochemistry and animal nutrition. Address: Southern Regional Research Lab, U.S. Dept. of Agriculture, Box 19687, New Orleans, LA 70119.

FRANCE, EVELYN S. (KALAGHER), b. East Orange, N.J, May 17, 30; m. 68. REPRODUCTIVE PHYSIOLOGY, ENDOCRINOLOGY. A.B, Antioch Col, 53; M.S, Wayne State Univ, 55; Ph.D.(biol), Boston Univ, 63. Lab. asst. nutrit. biochem, Univ. Rochester, 49-50; endocrinol, Ciba Pharmaceut. Prods. Corp, 51-52; sch. dent. med, Harvard, 52-53; asst. Wayne State Univ, 53-55; res. physiologist, Ortho Res. Found, 55-59; res. asst. endocrinol, Rutgers Univ, 59-61; staff scientist reprod. physiol, Worcester Found. Exp. Biol, 61-67; RES. BIOLOGIST, WYETH LABS, 67- AAAS; Am. Inst. Biol. Sci; N.Y. Acad. Sci; Soc. Study Reproduction. Reproductive physiology; mechanism of action of oral contraceptives; induction and inhibition of ovulation. Address: Wyeth Labs, P.O. Box 8299, Philadelphia, PA 19101.

FRANCE, PETER W(ILLIAM), b. Chicago, Ill, Sept. 4, 38; m. 65; c. 2. SOLID STATE PHYSICS, NUCLEAR MAGNETIC RESONANCE. B.S, Wayne State Univ, 62, M.S, 64, Nat. Sci. Found. fel. & Ph.D.(physics), 67. Sr. res. physicist, Bendix Res. Labs, 68; ASST. PROF. PHYSICS, UNIV. LOUISVILLE, 68- Am. Phys. Soc; Am. Asn. Physics Teachers. Application of wide line nuclear magnetic resonance of solids, particularly glass; measurement of physical properties of semiconducting and dielectric glasses, such as resistivities, mobilities and Hall constants. Address: Dept. of Physics, University of Louisville, Louisville, KY 40208.

FRANCE, W(ALTER) DEWAYNE, JR, b. New Haven, Conn, Nov. 9, 40; m. 63; c. 2. MATERIALS SCIENCE. B.E, Yale, 62; Scovill Mfg. Co. fel, Rensselaer Polytech, 62-63, Ph.D.(mat. eng), 66. Asst. corrosion res, Rensselaer Polytech. Inst, 63-66; assoc. sr. res. chemist, RES. LABS, GEN. MOTORS CORP, 66-69, SR. RES. CHEMIST, 69-70, SUPV. SPECIALIZED ACTIVITIES, 70- Engr, Scovill Mfg. Co, summers, 60-62. Mem, Int. Comt. Electrochem. Thermodyn. & Kinetics. Nat. Asn. Corrosion Eng.(A.B. Campbell award, 70); Am. Soc. Test. & Mat; Am. Soc. Metals; Am. Chem. Soc; fel. Am. Inst. Chem. Materials engineering; materials characterization; instrumental chemical analysis; corrosion research; development and application of electrochemical techniques for the study and interpretation of corrosion phenomena; mechanisms and kinetics of material-environment reactions. Address: 3902 Crooks Rd, Troy, MI 48084.

FRANCEL, JOSEF, b. Olomouc, Czech, Nov. 19, 24; m. 50; c. 7. CHEMISTRY. Dipl. Ing, Tech. Univ. Brno, Czechoslovakia, 48; Sc.D.(ceramics), Mass. Inst. Technol, 53. Asst, Tech. Univ, Brno, Czech, 46-48; Mass. Inst. Technol, 50-53; res. chemist, gen. res. div, OWENS-ILL, INC, 53-58, dir. appl. res. sect, Kimble Div, 58-63, RES. MGR, CONSUMER & TECH. PROD. DIV, 63- Res. fel, Naples. Consult, 53- AAAS; Am. Ceramic Soc. High temperature technology; surface chemistry and physics; glass; coatings; refractories; heat transfer; microscopy; interferometry; adhesion; electronics; gas evolution; gas absorption. Address: 1802 Perth St, Toledo, OH 43607.

FRANCES, SAUL, b. Brooklyn, N.Y, Dec. 13, 10; m. 41; c. 2. BACTERIOLOGY. B.S, City Col, 35; M.S, Minnesota, 37; Ph.D.(bact), Columbia, 46. Bacteriologist, Skin Res. Labs, Minn, 37-39; res. bacteriologist & asst. to dir, Pease Labs, Inc, N.Y, 40-43; dir, Coconut Processing Labs, 43-44; bacteriologist, Off. Sci. Res. & Develop. contract, Columbia, 44-46, asst. bact, col. physicians & surg, 46-50; DIR, WELLS LABS, INC, 48- Fel, Dazian Found. Med. Res, 44-46. Consultant, advertising agencies & labs, N.Y, 44- AAAS; Am. Chem. Soc; Am. Soc. Microbiol; Sci. Res. Soc. Am; Soc. Indust. Microbiol; Am. Pub. Health Asn; Asn. Consult. Chemists & Chem. Eng; N.Y. Acad. Sci. Bacteriology of the mouth; physiology of bacteria; anaerobes; antihistaminics; antibiotics; vaccines; chronic infections; cosmetics; cancer research; toxicology. Address: Wells Labs, Inc, 25-27 Lewis Ave, Jersey City, NJ 07036.

FRANCESCHINI, GUY A(RTHUR), b. North Adams, Mass, Apr. 2, 18; m. 47; c. 1. METEOROLOGY, OCEANOGRAPHY. B.S, Univ. Mass, 50; S.M, Univ. Chicago, 52; Ph.D.(meteorol), Tex. A&M Univ, 61. Meteorologist, Nat. Adv. Comt. Aeronaut, 45-47; instr, Univ. Chicago, 52; asst. prof. physics, TEX. A&M UNIV, 52-53, meteorol, 54-60, assoc. prof. OCEANOG. & METEOROL, 61-68, PROF, 69-, RES. SCIENTIST, RES. FOUND, 52- U.S.A.A.F, 40-45, Res, 47-, Maj. Am. Meteorol. Soc; Am. Geophys. Union. Air-sea interactions. Address: Route 3, Box 103, Caldwell, TX 77836.

FRANCESCHINI, REMO, b. New York, N.Y, Apr. 14, 28; m. 53; c. 3. FOOD SCIENCE & TECHNOLOGY. B.S, Fordham, 49; M.S, Massachusetts, 55, Ph.D.(food sci), 59. Mgr. new prod. Libby, McNeill & Libby, 58-61; group leader, THOMAS J. LIPTON, INC, 61-63, coordinator, 63-64, asst. dir. res, 64-66, DIR. PROD. DEVELOP, 66- Med.C, U.S.A, 50-52. Inst. Food Tech; Am. Asn. Cereal Chem. Irradiation of food products; thermal processing; dehydration; utilization of vegetable proteins; new product development; emulsions. Address: Thomas J. Lipton, Inc, 800 Sylvan Ave, Englewood Cliffs, N J 07632.

FRANCESCONI, RALPH P, b. Milford, Mass, Jan. 28, 39; m. 62; c. 3. BIOLOGICAL CHEMISTRY. A.B, Amherst Col, 61; M.S, Boston Col, 63, Ph.D.(cell biol), 66. U.S. Pub. Health Serv. fel. biol. chem, sch. med, Harvard, 66-68; INVESTR. ENVIRON. BIOCHEM, U.S. ARMY RES. INST. ENVIRON. MED, 68- AAAS; Sci. Res. Soc. Am; Am. Physiol. Soc. Enzyme development and enzyme regulation in mammals; effects of environmental stress conditions upon enzyme levels; effects of stressors on human amino acid metabolism. Address: Biochemistry Lab, U.S. Army Research Institute of Environmental Medicine, Natick, MA 01760.

FRANCH, ROBERT H, b. Bessemer, Mich, June 15, 27; m. 58; c. 7. CARDIOLOGY, CARDIOVASCULAR PHYSIOLOGY. A.B, Colorado, 48, M.D, 52. Nat. Heart Inst. trainee cardiovasc. diseases, 55-56; instr. MED, MED. SCH, EMORY UNIV, 56-59, asst. prof, 59-62, assoc. prof, 62-70, PROF, 70-DIR, CARDIOVASC. LAB, UNIV. HOSP, 57- Fel. cardiol, med. sch, Emory & dir. cardiac clin, Grady Hosp, 56-57; exam, cardiovasc. subspecialty bds, Am. Bd. Internal Med, 61 & 62; mem. panel cardiol. specialists, State Div. Voc. Rehab. & cardiac consult, heart disease control prog, State Dept. Pub. Health, Ga, 61-; chmn, diag. treatment facilities sect, div. community serv, Nat. Conf. Cardiovasc. Diseases, 64; fel, coun. clin. cardiol, Am. Heart Asn, 64. U.S.N.R, 44-45. Fel. Am. Col. Physicians; fel. Am. Col. Cardiol. Physiology of the pulmonary vascular bed; anatomy of pulmonary vascular disease; thermodilution technics for measuring and diastolic ventricular volumes; natural history of small ventricular septal defect. Address: Dept. of Medicine, 401 Woodruff Bldg, Emory University School of Medicine, Atlanta, GA 30322.

FRANCIS, C(ECIL) V(ERNON), b. Alma, Mo, Aug. 24, 17; m. 53. ANALYTICAL CHEMISTRY. A.B, Missouri, 38. Tech. sales & serv, Greene Bros, Inc, 41-43; sect. head ANAL. RES, WYANDOTTE CHEM. CORP, 46-57, MGR, 57- U.S.N.R, 43-45. Am. Chem. Soc; Am. Soc. Test. & Mat. Optical crystallography; glycols; detergents; carboxymethylcellulose; polyols, amines. Address: 1741 Waverly Rd, Trenton, MI 48183.

FRANCIS, CHARLES E, b. Perryton, Tex, Jan. 12, 18; m. 44; c. 2. PHYSICS. B.S, W.Tex. State Col, 40; M.A, Texas, 47, Ph.D.(physics), 54. Teacher, pub. schs, Can, 40-41; teaching fel. physics, Texas, 42-43, 46-47, res. scientist, 52-54; physicist, res. lab, Magnolia Petrol. Co, 47-52; mem. staff, Los Alamos Sci. Lab, California, 54-57, assoc. group leader, 57-62; MEM. STAFF, Tucson Res. Labs, Bell Aerosys. Corp, 62-65; AEROSPACE CORP, 65- Vis. lectr, Arizona, 61-62. Sig.C, 43-46, Capt. Am. Phys. Soc; Inst. Elec. & Electronics Eng. Nuclear radiation effects; atomic weapon development; solid state devices. Address: Aerospace Corp, P.O. Box 249, San Bernardino, CA 92402.

FRANCIS, CHESTER WAYNE, b. Creston, Iowa, Feb. 14, 36; m. 63; c. 1. SOIL SCIENCE, ECOLOGY. B.S, Iowa State Col, 58; M.S, Univ. Wis, 64, Am. Cancer Soc. grant, 64-67, Ph.D.(soils), 67. Soil specialist, IRI Res. Inst. N.Y, Brazil, 66-68; SOIL CHEMIST, OAK RIDGE NAT. LAB, 69- AAAS; Soil Sci. Soc. Am; Am. Soc. Agron. Soil chemistry, mineralogy and fertility. Address: Oak Ridge National Lab, P.O. Box X, Oak Ridge, TN 37830.

FRANCIS, DAVID W, b. N.Y.C, Oct. 31, 36; m. 64; c. 2. PROTOZOOLOGY, MYCOLOGY. B.A, Harvard, 57; M.S, Wisconsin, 59, Ph.D.(bot), 62. Nat. Insts. Health fel. biol, Princeton, 62-63, res. assoc, 63-65; asst. prof, Univ. B.C, 65-69; ASSOC. PROF. BIOL. SCI, UNIV. DEL, 69- Soc. Protozool. Cell differentiation in protozoa, especially in Acrasiales; developmental biology. Address: Dept. of Biological Sciences, University of Delaware, Newark, DE 19711.

FRANCIS, D(AVID) W(ESSON), b. N.Y.C, Aug. 17, 18; m. 50; c. 3. POULTRY HUSBANDRY. B.S, Rutgers, 41; M.S, Delaware, 52; Ph.D.(poultry husb), Maryland, 55. Technician, small animals, Lederle Labs, 41-42; farmer, Soldier Hill Farm, N.J, 42-50; asst. POULTRY SCI, Delaware, 50-51, res. instr, 51-53; asst, Maryland, 53-55; assoc. prof, N.MEX. STATE UNIV, 55-58, PROF. & HEAD DEPT, 58- Consult, N.Mex. State Univ-U.S. Agency Int. Develop, Paraguay, 70. Distinguished res. award, col. agr. & home econ, N.Mex. State Univ, 68. U.S.N.R, 41. Fel. AAAS; Poultry Sci. Asn; Am. Asn. Avian Path; World Poultry Sci. Asn. Management; physiology; pathology. Address: Dept. of Poultry Science, New Mexico State University, Las Cruces, NM 88001.

FRANCIS, DAWN E(LIZABETH), b. Detroit, Mich; m. 55. INORGANIC CHEMISTRY. B.S, Wayne Univ, 49; Middlebury Col, 50, 53, 54; M.S. & Ph.D.(chem), Wayne State Univ, 68. Res. asst. chemist, M. W. Freeman Chem. Co, 55-58; chemist, Harper Hosp. Pathol. Labs, 62-63; res. assoc. chem, med. sch, Wayne State Univ, 63-64; res. asst, sci. res. labs, Ford Motor Co, 66; instr, Detroit Inst. Technol, 67-68, asst. prof, 68-70, assoc. prof, 70-71; chmn. div. natural sci. & acad. dean, Shaw Col. Detroit, 71; DIR, FRANCIS LABS, 69-; FOUNDER, DRAKE INST. SCI, 71- Speaker Int. Conf. Coord. Chem, Poland, 70; grant, NATO Advan. Study Int. Optical Rotary Dispersion & Circular Dichroism, 71. Am. Chem. Soc; Soc. Appl. Spectros; Am. Inst. Phys. Absolute configuration and outer-sphere complexation; induced optical activity of physiologically important compounds; modern teaching techniques in science; new considerations of induced dipole moments as observed in circular dichroic studies; coordination chemistry. Address: 818 Professional Plaza, Detroit, MI 48201.

FRANCIS, E(LLIOTT) S, b. New Wilmington, Pa, Feb. 9, 15; m. 38; c. 2. PHYSICAL CHEMISTRY. B.S, Slippery Rock State Col, 37; Carnegie Inst. Tech, 38-50. Technician petrol, GULF RES. & DEVELOP. CO, 39-41, res. chemist, 41-46, group leader, 46-68, SR. RES. CHEMIST, 68-71, PROD. DEVELOP, GULF RES. LAB. N.V, NETHERLANDS, 71- Am. Chem. Soc; Am. Soc. Lubrication Eng. Boundary lubrication and surface phenomena; emulsions; corrosion. Address: Gulf Research Laboratoria; Postbox 7045, Rotterdam, Netherlands.

FRANCIS, EUGENE A, b. Christiansted, Virgin Islands, Oct. 27, 27; m. 55. MATHEMATICS. B.A, Inter-Am. Univ. P.R, 49; M.A, Columbia Univ, 51. Instr. MATH, COL. AGR. & MECH. ARTS, UNIV. P.R, MAYAGUEZ, 51-55, asst. prof, 55-57, assoc. prof, 57-67, PROF. & CHMN. DEPT, 67-, assoc. dir, Nat. Sci. Found. Math. Inst, 59-67. Spec. lectr, Inter-Am. Univ. P.R, 51, 56, 58. U.S.A, 54-56. AAAS; Math. Asn. Am; Soc. Indust. & Appl. Math; Am. Math. Soc. Linear algebra and matrix theory; set theory; ordinary differential equations. Address: Dept. of Mathematics, College of Agriculture & Mechanical Arts, University of Puerto Rico, Mayaguez, PR 00708.

FRANCIS, FAITH ELLEN, b. Batavia, N.Y, Dec. 28, 29. BIOCHEMISTRY. B.A, D'Youville Col, 52; fel, St. Louis Univ, 52-57, Ph.D.(biochem), 57. Res. assoc. internal med, SCH. MED, ST. LOUIS UNIV, 57-59, instr, 59-64, ASST. PROF. BIOCHEM, 64-, GYNEC. & OBSTET, 68- Fel. AAAS; Am. Chem. Soc; Endocrine Soc; N.Y. Acad. Sci. Metabolism of steroid hormones. Address: Dept. of Gynecology & Obstetrics, St. Louis City Hospital, 1515 Lafayette Ave, St. Louis, MO 63103.

FRANCIS, F(REDERICK) J(OHN), b. Ottawa, Ont, Oct. 9, 21; m. 52; c. 2. FOOD SCIENCE. B.A, Toronto, 46, M.A, 48; Ph.D, Massachusetts, 54. Instr. food chem, Toronto, 46-50; lectr. hort, Ont. Agr. Col, 50-54; asst. prof. FOOD SCI. & TECHNOL, UNIV. MASS, AMHERST, 54-58, assoc. prof, 58-62, prof, 62-64, Nicolas Appert prof, 64-71, PROF. & HEAD DEPT, 71- R.C.A.F, 44. Inst. Food Technol; Am. Soc. Hort. Sci; Am. Chem. Soc. Plant biochemistry, color and pigments; food preservation. Address: Dept. of Food Science & Technology, University of Massachusetts, Amherst, MA 01002.

FRANCIS, GEORGE K(ONRAD), b. Warnsdorf, Ger, Mar. 7, 39; U.S. citizen; m. 67; c. 1. MATHEMATICS. B.S, Notre Dame, 58, Wilson Nat. fel, 58-59; univ. fel, Harvard, 59-60, M.A, 60; Ph.D.(math), Michigan, 67. Teaching fel. MATH, Harvard, 60-62; lectr, Regis Col, 62-63; Boston Col, 63-64; Newton Col, 64-65; teaching & res. fel, Univ. Mich, 65-67, A.H. Lloyd fel, 67-68; ASST. PROF, UNIV. ILL, URBANA, 68- Teacher, Pomfret Prep, Conn, summer 64. Am. Math. Soc. Differential and combinatorial topology of smooth loops on manifolds; sufficient jets on Banach manifolds; control theory and dynamical systems; confidence bounds in multivariate statistics; biomathematics of morphogenesis and evolution. Address: Dept. of Mathematics, University of Illinois, Urbana, IL 61801.

FRANCIS, GERALD PETER, b. Seattle, Wash, Feb. 15, 36; m. 64; c. 3. FLUID MECHANICS. B.M.E, Univ. Dayton, 58; M.M.E, Cornell Univ, 60, Ph.D.(eng), 65. Instr. MECH. ENG, Cornell Univ, 61-64; asst. prof, Ga. Inst. Technol, 64-66; STATE UNIV. N.Y. BUFFALO, 66-68, ASSOC. PROF, 68-; CHMN. DEPT, 70- Consult, Lockheed-Ga. Co, Marietta, 65-66; Nat. Sci. Found. grants, 67-70; Heart Asn. Southwest. N.Y. grants, 69-71. Am. Soc. Mech. Eng; Am. Inst. Aeronaut. & Astronaut; Am. Soc. Eng. Educ. Basic turbulent phenomena; turbulent boundary layers in both two- and three-dimensional environments; pulsatile blood flow; instrumentation for bio-fluid measurements. Address: Dept. of Mechanical Engineering, State University of New York at Buffalo, Buffalo, NY 14214.

FRANCIS, HOWARD T(HOMAS), b. St. Louis, Mo, Oct. 22, 17; m. 41; c. 2. PHYSICAL CHEMISTRY. B.S, Mt. Union Col, 38; M.S, Pa. State, 40, Ph.D. (phys. chem), 42. Mgr. electrochem, IIT Res. Inst, 42-71; DIR. BIOMED. ENG, COOK COUNTY HOSP, 71- Am. Chem. Soc; Electrochem. Soc; Nat. Asn. Corrosion Eng; Asn. Advan. Med. Instrumentation. Electrodeposition; electroforming; corrosion; theoretical electrochemistry; electropolishing; electrochemical machining; chemical milling; batteries. Address: Cook County Hospital, 1825 W. Harrison St, Chicago, IL 60612.

FRANCIS, JOHN ELBERT, b. Kingfisher, Okla, Mar. 14, 37; m. 62. MECHANICAL ENGINEERING. B.S, Oklahoma, 60, Continental Oil Co. fel. & M.S, 63, NASA fel. & Ph.D.(mech. eng), 65. Engr, Allis Chalmers Mfg. Co, 60; asst. prof. mech. eng, Missouri, Rolla, 64-66; AEROSPACE & MECH. ENG. UNIV. OKLA, 66-69, ASSOC. PROF, 69-, asst. dean grad. col, 68-71. Summers, asst. res. scientist, Continental Oil Co, 63, Am. Soc. Eng. Ed. faculty fel, NASA-Ames Res. Lab, 65 & 66. Am. Soc. Mech. Eng; Am. Inst. Aeronaut. & Astronaut; Optical Soc. Am. Radiative heat transfer analysis of coatings and surfaces; atmospheric radiation; biological heat transfer. Address: School of Aerospace & Mechanical Engineering, University of Oklahoma, 865 Asp, Norman, OK 73069.

FRANCIS, JOHN E(LSWORTH), b. Toronto, Ont, Jan. 25, 32; m. 59; c. 3. ORGANIC CHEMISTRY. B.A, Queen's Univ.(Ont), 53, Ont. Res. Coun. scholar, 53-54, M.A, 56; Nat. Res. Coun. Can. scholar, Univ. N.B, 56-58, Ph.D.(org. chem), 58. Jr. res. chemist, div. pure chem, Nat. Res. Coun. Can, 54-55; vis. scientist, Nat. Inst. Arthritis & Metab. Diseases, 58-60; res. chemist, J.R. Geigy A.G, Switz, 60-63, Geigy Chem. Corp, 63-67, RES. ASSOC. PHARMACEUT, 67-70, CIBA-GEIGY LTD, 70- Am. Chem. Soc. Aromatic chemistry; organic deuterium compounds; structure elucidation of lycopodium alkaloids; synthesis and selective cleavage of peptides; thiophene derivatives; sulphonamides; nitrofurans; nitrogen heterocyclic compounds. Address: Dept. of Pharmaceutical Research, Ciba-Geigy Ltd, Ardsley, NY 10502.

FRANCIS, LYMAN L(ESLIE), b. Alma, Mo, May 17, 20; m. 42; c. 5. MECHANICAL ENGINEERING. M.S, Missouri, 50. Design engr, Owen-Ill. Glass Co, Ohio, 46-47; jr. engr, Toledo Edison Co, 47-48; instr. MECH. ENG, Missouri, 48-52; ASSOC. PROF, Washington State, 52-63; UNIV. MO-ROLLA, 63- U.S.A, 44-46. Am. Soc. Eng. Educ; Soc. Mfg. Eng; Am. Soc. Mech. Eng. Manufacturing engineering, materials, and design. Address: Dept. of Engineering Technology, 201 Mining Bldg, University of Missouri-Rolla, Rolla, MO 65401.

FRANCIS, MARION D(AVID), b. Campbell River, B.C, Can, May 9, 23; m. 49; c. 2. BIOCHEMISTRY. B.A, British Columbia, 46, M.A, 49; Soc. Anal. Chem. fel, Iowa, 51, U.S. Pub. Health Serv. fel, 51-52, Ph.D.(biochem), 53. RES. BIOCHEMIST, PROCTER & GAMBLE CO, 52- Fel. AAAS; Am. Chem. Soc; Am. Asn. Lab. Animal Sci; N.Y. Acad. Sci; fel. Am. Inst. Chem; Int. Asn. Dent. Res. Mechanism of protein synthesis; membrane permeability studies; chemistry and structure of dental hard tissue; keratin and calcium phosphate chemistry; biochemistry and physiology of the di- and polyphosphonates; calcium and phosphorus metabolism in bone and soft tissue. Address: Miami Valley Labs, Procter & Gamble Co, 235R, P.O. Box 39175, Cincinnati, OH 45239.

FRANCIS, NORMAN, b. Rochester, N.Y, Nov. 27, 22; m. 47; c. 3. THEORETICAL PHYSICS. B.A, Rochester, 48, Ph.D.(physics), 52. Res. assoc, Indiana, 52-55; theoret. physicist, KNOLLS ATOMIC POWER LAB, GEN. ELEC. CO, 55-64, MGR. ADVAN. REACTOR THEORY, 64- U.S.N.R, 44-46. Am. Phys. Soc; Am. Nuclear Soc. Nuclear and reactor theory. Address: 2311 Plum St, Schenectady, NY 12309.

FRANCIS, PETER S(CHUYLER), b. Youngstown, Ohio, Nov. 22, 27; m. 51; c. 3. POLYMER & ORGANIC CHEMISTRY. B.A, Pennsylvania, 51; M.S, Delaware, 53, Ph.D.(org. chem), 55. Lab. technician chem, Smith Kline & French Labs, 49-51; asst, Delaware, 52-54; res. chemist, Hercules Powder Co, 54-63; sr. polymer chemist, NORTH STAR RES. & DEVELOP. INST, 63-65, dir. res. polymer chem, 65-67, tech. dir. CHEM. DEPT, 67-69, DIR, 70-Mem. bd. dir, Germantown Labs, 69- U.S.A, 46-47. Am. Chem. Soc; Sci. Res. Soc. Am; Am. Inst. Physics; Am. Ord. Asn. Chromic acid oxidation kinetics; pharmaceutical formulation and analysis; electrokinetic phenomena; polymer fractionation and characterization; rheology of polymers in bulk and solution; metallizing plastics; shrinkproofing textiles; polymeric membranes for desalting water. Address: Chemistry Dept, Franklin Institute Research Labs, 20th & Race Sts, Philadelphia, PA 19103.

FRANCIS, PHILIP HAMILTON, b. San Diego, Calif, Apr. 13, 38; div; c. 2. SOLID MECHANICS, APPLIED MATHEMATICS. B.S, Calif. State Polytech. Col, 59; M.S, Iowa, 60, NASA trainee fel, 63-65, Ph.D.(appl. mech), 65. Stress analyst, Douglas Aircraft Co, Inc, 60-62; SR. RES. ENGR. DEPT. MECH. SCI, SOUTHWEST RES. INST, 65- Consult, Collins Radio Co, 64; Pan Am. Petrol. Corp, 65; tech. ed, Appl. Mech. Rev. Am. Soc. Mech. Eng; Am. Acad. Mech. Theory of fatigue; theory of elasticity; stress wave propagation; approximate methods for partial differential equations; composite material mechanics. Address: Dept. of Mechanical Sciences, Southwest Research Institute, San Antonio, TX 78206.

FRANCIS, RICHARD L, b. Poplar Bluff, Mo, Feb. 5, 33; m. 65; c. 2. MATHEMATICS. B.S, Southeast Mo. State Col, 55; M.A, Univ. Mo, 62, Ed.D. (math. educ), 65. Instr. MATH, Kemper Sch, 55-61; ASSOC. PROF, SOUTHEAST MO. STATE COL, 65- Math. Asn. Am. Mathematics education. Address: Dept. of Mathematics, Southeast Missouri State College, Cape Girardeau, MO 63701.

FRANCIS, ROBERT D(ORL), b. West Liberty, Ohio, Sept. 28, 20; m. 43. MICROBIOLOGY. A.B, Franklin Col, 42; M.S, Chicago, 45; fel, Michigan, 49-50, Ph.D.(microbiol), 55. Anal. chemist fat & oil, Swift & Co, 42-44; prin. bacteriologist, Emulsol Corp, 47-49; instr. bacter, Michigan, 50-52; sr. asst. sanitarian, U.S. Pub. Health Serv, 53-55, sr. asst. scientist, 55-56, scientist, 56; ASSOC. PROF. MICROBIOL, MED. CTR, UNIV. ALA, BIRMINGHAM, 56-, DERMAT, SCH. MED. & DENT, 71- Consult, Emulsol Corp, 49-52; Bur. Labs, Ala. State Health Dept, 66- U.S.P.H.S, 53-56, Res, 56- AAAS; Am. Soc. Microbiol. Epidemiology and immunology of psittacosis-lymphogranuloma venereum, poliomyelitis and enteric viruses; replication and soluble antigens of herpes viruses; tissue culture; diagnostic virology. Address: Dept. of Microbiology, Schools of Medicine & Dentistry, University of Alabama, Birmingham, AL 35233.

FRANCIS, RONALD, b. Livermore Falls, Maine, Oct. 21, 33. PHOTOGRAPHIC SCIENCE. A.B, Colby Col, 55; Ph.D.(phys. inorg. chem), Mass. Inst. Technol, 64. Sr. chemist, metall. dept, A.D. Little, Inc, Mass, 60-63; govt. consult, 63-64; sr. chemist, chem. lab, Itek Corp, 64-66, mgr. inorg. chem. dept, 65-66; mgr. photog. eng. sect, EG&G, Inc, 66-69; asst. prof, SCH. PHOTOG. ARTS & SCI, ROCHESTER INST. TECHNOL, 70-71, ASSOC. PROF, 71- Summers, chemist, Scott Paper Co, Maine, 54, phys. biochem. lab, Nat. Naval Med. Ctr, Md, 57, physicist, Naval Ord. Lab, Md, 58. Soc. Photog. Sci. & Eng. Relevance of magnetic and spectral properties to inorganic structure; chemical vapor deposition; modification of photoconducting solids; photographic dye sensitization; silver halide and non-silver halide emulsion chemistry; mechanisms of photographic development. Address: School of Photographic Arts & Sciences, Rochester Institute of Technology, Rochester, NY 14623.

FRANCIS, STANLEY A(RTHUR), b. Moundsville, W.Va, Oct. 25, 19; m. 44; c. 3. PHYSICAL CHEMISTRY. B.S, Ohio Univ, 40; Ph.D.(phys. chem), Ohio State Univ, 47. Chemist, Monsanto Chem. Co, 44-45; res. chemist, TEXACO INC, 47-63, supvr. FUNDAMENTAL RES, 63-68, dir, 68-71, ASST. MGR, 71- Am. Chem. Soc; Am. Phys. Soc. Molecular spectroscopy; administration. Address: Texaco Inc, Beacon, NY 12508.

FRANCIS, WARREN C(HARLES), b. Rockville, Conn, June 20, 18; m. 42; c. 2. CHEMICAL ENGINEERING. B.S, Mass. Inst. Technol, 40; Purdue Univ, summer 48; Univ. Idaho, 54-71. Foreman chem. processing, Procter & Gamble Co, 40-42, acting chem. supvr, 46-48; mgr. quality control ceramics, Cambridge Tile Mfg. Co, 48-49, dir. ceramic eng. dept, 49-51, staff asst. to pres, 52-53; chem. engr, atomic energy div, Phillips Petrol. Co, 53-54, group leader eng. develop, 55-56, asst. sect. chief reactor eng, 57-61, sect. chief, 61-64, mgr. reactor eng. br, 64-66, AEROJET NUCLEAR CO, 66-71, MGR. METALL. & MAT. SCI. BR, 71- Instr. radar tech, Coast Artillery Sch, Va, 42-46, exec. officer, Artillery Sch, Tex, 51-52. U.S.A, 42-46, 51-52, Maj. Am. Nuclear Soc; Am. Soc. Nondestruct. Test; fel. Am. Inst. Chem. Nuclear fuels and reactor materials, including radiation effects. Address: Metallurgy & Materials Science Branch, Aerojet Nuclear Co, P.O. Box 1845, Idaho Falls, ID 83401.

FRANCIS, WILLIAM C(ONNETT), b. Denver, Colo, Dec. 23, 22; m. 54; c. 2. ORGANIC CHEMISTRY. B.S, Kansas, 47; Gen. Motors fel, Ohio State, 50-51, Du Pont fel, 51-52, Ph.D.(org. chem), 52. Res. chemist, Plaskon div, Libbey-Owens-Ford Glass Co, 47-48; Fulbright grant, Cambridge, 52-54; sr. staff mem. res. dept, Spencer Chem. Co, 54-57, group leader ORG. RES, 57-60, sect. leader, Spencer Chem. Div, Gulf Oil Corp, Kans, 60-66, dir. res. coord, chem. dept, Tex, 66-69, mgr. develop. div, 69-71, MGR, GULF ADHESIVES DIV, GULF OIL CHEM. CO, 71- U.S.A, 43-46. Am. Chem. Soc. Oxidation of organic compounds; synthesis of fluorinated organic compounds and organic compounds of nitrogen; aminoplast resins. Address: Gulf Adhesives Division, Gulf Oil Chemicals Co, 632 N. Cannon Ave, Lansdale, PA 19446.

FRANCIS, WILLIAM P(ORTER), b. St. Louis, Mo, Mar. 15, 40; m. 62; c. 1. THEORETICAL PHYSICS, QUANTUM STATISTICAL MECHANICS. B.S, Rensselaer Polytech. Inst, 61; Nat. Sci. Found. fel, Cornell Univ, 62-63, Ph.D.(physics), 69. Mem. tech. staff solid state physics, Bell Tel. Labs, N.J, 67-68; tech. consult, lab. atomic & solid state physics, Cornell Univ, summer 68; Nat. Res. Coun. Can. fel. physics, Univ. Windsor, 68-70; ASST. PROF. MATH, MICH. TECHNOL. UNIV, 70- Math. Asn. Am. Calculation of the wave function, Bose-Einstein condensate density, and momentum distribution of the quantum liquid helium four at both zero and greater than zero temperatures. Address: Dept. of Mathematics, Michigan Technological University, Houghton, MI 49931.

FRANCISCO, CECIL J(AY), JR, b. Sioux City, Iowa, Sept. 23, 17; m. 44; c. 5. PETROLEUM. A.B, Columbia Univ, 39, B.S, 40, M.S, 41. Process engr, res. & develop, Sinclair Refining Co, Ill, 41-47, div. dir, 48-52, tech. mgr, 52-58, v.pres. patents & licensing, Sinclair Res. Inc, N.Y, 58-66, v.pres, Sinclair Petrochem, Inc, 67, pres, 68, v.pres. & gen. mgr, chem. div, Sinclair Oil Corp, 68; V.PRES. PETROCHEM, ARCO CHEM. CO, DIV. ATLANTIC RICHFIELD CO, 69- Exec. mgt. seminar, Pa. State Univ, 65. Fel. AAAS; Am. Petrol. Inst; Am. Chem. Soc; Am. Inst. Chem. Eng. Research and development in petroleum exploration, refining and petrochemicals; patents and licensing. Address: ARCO Chemical Co, 260 S. Broad St, Philadelphia, PA 19101.

FRANCISCO, J(ERRY) T(HOMAS), b. Huntingdon, Tenn, Dec. 18, 32; m. 54; c. 2. PATHOLOGY. Lambuth Col, 50-51; M.D, Tennessee, 55. Asst. instr. path, Tennessee, 56-57; dir, labs, U.S. Naval Hosp, Memphis, Tenn, 57-59; instr. PATH, UNIV. TENN, 59-60, asst. prof, 60-64, assoc. prof, 64-67, PROF, INST. PATH, 67- Mem. staff, John Gaston Hosp, 60-; med. exam, Memphis & Shelby County, Tenn, 60-; chief med. exam, Tenn, 63-66, forensic path. consult. for chief med. exam, 66-70, chief med. exam, 70- U.S.R, 57-59. Am. Soc. Clin. Path; Col. Am. Path. Forensic pathology; effect of sickle cell erythrocytes on the in vitro growth characteristics of certain bacteria. Address: Institute of Pathology, University of Tennessee, 858 Madison Ave, Memphis, TN 38103.

FRANCK, KURT, b. Weisswasser, Germany, July 16, 11; U.S. citizen; m. 43; c. 3. ELECTRICAL ENGINEERING, OPTICS. Dipl. elec. eng, Tech. Univ, Berlin, 35. Design engr. sci. lighting equip, HOLOPHANE CO, INC, 35-46, chief engr, 46-48, V.PRES. & CHIEF ENGR, 48- Consult, Holophane Co, Ltd, Can, 42- Fel. Am. Illum. Eng. Soc; Optical Soc. Am. Scientific lighting equipment for industrial, commercial and roadway lighting applications. Address: Holophane Co, Inc, Newark, OH 43055.

FRANCK, RICHARD W, b. Ger, May 15, 36; U.S. citizen; m. 58; c. 2. ORGANIC CHEMISTRY. A.B, Amherst Col, 58; M.A, Wisconsin, 60; Nat. Insts. Health fel, Stanford, 60-62, Ph.D.(chem), 63. Nat. Insts. Health fel. CHEM, Mass. Inst. Technol, 62-63; asst. prof, FORDHAM UNIV, 63-68, ASSOC. PROF, 68- Petrol. Res. Fund int. fel, Cambridge, 70-71. Am. Chem. Soc. Modern mechanistic and synthetic organic chemistry. Address: Dept. of Chemistry, Fordham University, New York, NY 10458.

FRANCK, WALLACE EDMUNDT, b. Alexandria, La, Feb. 1, 33; m. 57; c. 2. MATHEMATICAL STATISTICS. B.S, La. State, 55; M.S, New Mexico, 62, Ph.D.(math), 64. Weapons proj. officer, Kirtland Air Force Base, U.S. Air

Force, 56-58, programmer math, 58-60; mathematician, U.S. Naval Weapons Eval. Facility, 60-62; asst. prof. STATIST, UNIV. MO-COLUMBIA, 64-69, ASSOC. PROF, 69- U.S.A.F, 56-58, Capt. Am. Math. Soc; Inst. Math. Soc; Inst. Math. Statist; Soc. Indust. & Appl. Math. Probability; statistics. Address: Dept. of Statistics, University of Missouri-Columbia, Columbia, MO 65201.

FRANCKE, DON E(UGENE), b. Athens, Pa, Aug. 28, 10; m. 37; c. 5; m. 56. PHARMACY. B.S, Univ. Mich, 36, M.S, 48; D.Sc, Purdue Univ, 51. Asst. prof. pharm, col. pharm, Univ. Mich, 51-62, assoc. prof, 62-63, dir. pharm. serv, Hosp, 44-63; dir, dept. sci. servs, Am. Soc. Hosp. Pharmacists, 63-66; publisher & ed, Drug Intel. & ed, Drug Info. Bull, 66-67; prof. & chmn. dept. hosp. pharm. & dir. inst. studies hosp. pharm, col. pharm, Univ. Cincinnati, 67-71; DIR. PHARM. SERV, VET. ADMIN, D.C, 71- Consult, Surgeon Gen, U.S. Dept. Army, 47-; mem. revision comt, U.S. Pharmacopeia, 50-60; consult, U.S. Vet. Admin, 50-; WHO, 59-; ed, Am. Jour. Hosp. Pharm. & Int. Pharmaceut. Abstract, 63-66; dir. pharm. serv, Cincinnati Gen. Hosp, 67-71. Lascoff Mem. Award, 48; Remington Medal, 70. AAAS; Am. Chem. Soc; Am. Soc. Hosp. Pharmacists (pres, 43-46; ed, Bulletin, 44-57; Jour, 58-66); Am. Pharmaceut. Asn.(pres, 51); fel. Am. Col. Apothecaries; Am. Hosp. Asn; Int. Pharmaceut. Fedn.(v.pres, 59-). Theory and practice of pharmacy, especially as they pertain to hospital practice. Address: 2100 Massachusetts Ave. N.W. 710, Washington, DC 20008.

FRANCLEMONT, JOHN G(EORGE), b. Buffalo, N.Y, Apr. 15, 12. ENTOMOLOGY. B.S, Cornell, 35, Ph.D.(entomol), 53. Asst. entomol, Cornell, 46-47; entomologist, bur. entomol. & plant quarantine, U.S. Dept. Agr, 47-53; assoc. prof. entomol, CORNELL UNIV, 53-59, PROF. ENTOM. & LIMNOL, 59- Sanit.C, 42-46, Maj. Entom. Soc. Can; fel. Entom. Soc. S.Africa. Taxonomy of the Lepidoptera, especially the Noctuoidea; insects affecting men and animals. Address: Dept. of Entomology & Limnology, Cornell University, 305A Comstock, Ithaca, NY 14850.

FRANCO, NICHOLAS BENJAMIN, b. Providence, R.I, Apr. 26, 38; m. 64; c. 2. PHYSICAL INORGANIC CHEMISTRY. B.S, Providence Col, 59, Nat. Insts. Health fel. & M.S, 62; Off. Naval Res. grant, NASA fel. & Ph.D.(phys. chem), Miami (Fla), 68. Sr. res. chemist, Olin Corp, 67-69; consult. chemist, RESOURCE CONTROL, INC, 69, ASST. DIR. RES, 69- Consult. chemist, Nuclear Deactivation Sci, 69. Am. Chem. Soc; Sci. Res. Soc. Am; Air Pollution Control Asn. Chemistry of fused salts, propellants, coordination compounds and organometallics; homogeneous catalysis by inorganic salts and organometallics; air and water pollution control. Address: 37 Fallon Ave, Providence, RI 02908.

FRANCO, VICTOR, b. New York, N.Y, Dec. 15, 37; m. 62; c. 2. PHYSICS. B.S, N.Y. Univ, 58; Nat. Sci. Found. fel, Harvard, 58-62, A.M, 59, Ph.D. (physics), 63. Instr. PHYSICS, Mass. Inst. Technol, 63-64, res. assoc, 64-65; fel, Lawrence Radiation Lab, Univ. Calif, Berkeley, 65-67; Los Alamos Sci. Lab, 67-69; ASSOC. PROF, BROOKLYN COL, 69- Consult, Los Alamos Sci. Lab. Am. Phys. Soc. Theoretical nuclear physics; atomic scattering theory. Address: Dept. of Physics, Brooklyn College, Brooklyn, NY 11210.

FRANCOEUR, ROBERT THOMAS, b. Detroit, Mich, Oct. 18, 31. EMBRYOLOGY, EVOLUTION. B.A, Sacred Heart Col, 53; M.A, St. Vincent Col, 57; M.S, Detroit, 62; Ph.D.(biol), Delaware, 67. Instr. biol. & theol, Mt. St. Agnes Col, 61-62; asst. prof. EMBRYOL, FAIRLEIGH DICKINSON UNIV, 65-71, ASSOC. PROF, 71- Buhl Planetarium award, 60. Acad. Zool; Am. Soc. Zool. Interdisciplinary work centering on evolution as a unifying concept with implications for the behavioral sciences, humanities, philosophy and theology; advances in human reproduction; new technologies and social implications. Address: Dept. of Biology, Fairleigh Dickinson University, 285 Madison Ave, Madison, NJ 07940.

FRANCQ, EDWARD N(ATHANIEL LLOYD), b. Greencastle, Ind, July 5, 34; m. 56; c. 2. VERTEBRATE ECOLOGY, ANIMAL BEHAVIOR. B.S, Univ. Md, College Park, 56; M.S, Univ. Idaho, 62; Ph.D.(zool), Pa. State Univ, 67. Instr. ZOOL, UNIV. N.H, 65-67, ASST. PROF, 67- U.S.N.R, 56-, Comdr. AAAS; Am. Soc. Mammal; Animal Behav. Soc. Behavior and population ecology of vertebrates, especially small mammals; behavioral responses to environment and stressful situations. Address: Dept. of Zoology, Spaulding Life Science Bldg, University of New Hampshire, Durham, NH 03824.

FRANDSEN, HENRY, b. Chicago, Ill, May 21, 33; m. 53; c. 3. MATHEMATICS. B.S, Univ. Ill, 57, M.S, 59, Ph.D.(math), 61. Asst. math, Univ. Ill, 57-61; asst. prof, Clark Univ, 61-66; assoc. prof, Wheaton Col, 66-67; MATH. & MATH. EDUC, UNIV. TENN, KNOXVILLE, 67-71, PROF, 71- Mathematician, Mitre Corp, 63-67. U.S.N.R, 52-70, Lt.Comdr.(Ret). AAAS; Am. Math. Soc; Math. Asn. Am. Algebra; theory of finite groups; mathematics education; secondary school teacher training. Address: Dept. of Mathematics, University of Tennessee, Knoxville, TN 37916.

FRANDSEN, JOHN C(HRISTIAN), b. Salt Lake City, Utah, Aug. 25, 33; m. 65; c. 4. PARASITOLOGY. B.S, Utah, 55, M.S, 56, Ph.D, 60; Thompson mem. scholar, California, 56-57. Asst. zool, Utah, 55-58, asst. Nat. Sci. Found. & univ. res. fel, 58-60; res. parasitologist, regional animal disease lab, AGR. RES. SERV, U.S. DEPT. AGR, 61-66, SR. RES. PARASITOLOGIST, REGIONAL PARASITE RES. LAB, 66- Res. lectr, sch. vet. med, Auburn Univ. Med.Serv.C.Res, 55-, Maj. AAAS; Am. Soc. Parasitol; Am. Micros. Soc; N.Y. Acad. Sci. Applications of histochemistry in parasitology; host-parasite relationship; ecology of endoparasites; biochemistry of parasites. Address: Regional Parasite Research Lab, Agricultural Research Service, U.S. Dept. of Agriculture, P.O. Drawer 952, Auburn, AL 36830.

FRANDSON, ROWEN D(ALE), b. Fremont, Nebr, July 22, 20; m. 50; c. 3. ANATOMY. B.S, Colorado State, 42, D.V.M, 44, M.S, 55; Colorado, summers, 52-54. Practicing veterinarian, 47-48; asst. prof. ANAT, COLO. STATE UNIV, 48-56, assoc. prof, 56-62, PROF, 62- Veterinarian, Colo. Racing Comn, summers, 49-64. Vet.C, 45-47, Capt. AAAS; World Asn. Vet. Anat; Am. Asn. Vet. Anat; Am. Vet. Med. Asn; Am. Asn. Anat. Microanatomy of hypothalamic region; application of audio-visual techniques to medical and biological education. Address: Dept. of Anatomy, Colorado State University, Ft. Collins, CO 80521.

FRANK, ALBERT B(ERNARD), b. Fresno, Ohio, July 7, 39; m. 62; c. 3. PLANT PHYSIOLOGY. B.S, Ohio State Univ, 65, M.S, 66; Ph.D.(agron), N.Dak. State Univ, 69. PLANT PHYSIOLOGIST, NORTH. GREAT PLAINS RES. CTR, AGR. RES. SERV, U.S. DEPT. AGR, 69- U.S.A, 60-66. Am. Soc. Plant Physiol; Am. Soc. Agron; Crop Sci. Soc. Am. Shelterbelt influences as they relate to the water regime of growing plants in the northern Great Plains, especially the direct measurement of water status of plant tissue as influenced by the aerial microclimate of sheltered and non-sheltered environments. Address: U.S. Dept. of Agriculture, Agriculture Research Service, Northern Great Plains Research Center, Box 459, Mandan, ND 58554.

FRANK, ALBERT J(OSEPH), b. St. Louis, Mo, Sept. 4, 14. GEOLOGY. B.S, St. Louis, 37, M.S, 40, Ph.D.(geophys), 48. Lectr. GEOL, ST. LOUIS UNIV, 42-45, instr, 45-49, asst. prof, 49-53, from assoc. prof. to PROF, 53-, instr. physics, Army Specialized Training Prog, 43-44. Am. Soc. Eng. Educ; Am. Geophys. Union; Am. Inst. Mech. Eng; Am. Inst. Min, Metall. & Petrol. Eng. Engineering geophysics, geology, petrology and mineralogy; Pennsylvanian cyclothems; bacteriology of clays and shales; electroosmosis of clays, shales and soils; seismology. Address: Dept. of Geology, St. Louis University, St. Louis, MO 63103.

FRANK, ANDREW J(ULIAN), b. Chicago, Ill, Sept. 17, 25; m. 48; c. 2. ANALYTICAL & INORGANIC CHEMISTRY. B.S, Illinois, 48, M.S, 49, fel, 50-51, Ph.D.(anal. & inorg. chem), 51. Asst. prof. chem, Tulane, 51-52; res. chemist, raw mat. develop. lab, Atomic Energy Cmn, Mass, 52-54; chief anal. res. sect, Watertown Arsenal, Mass, 54-56; chief metals chem. br, metall. div, Denver Res. Inst, 56-60; res. chemist, Allis-Chalmers Mfg. Co, Wis, 60-62; assoc. prof. chem, West. Wash. State Col, 62-66, prof, 66-70, chmn. dept, 62-70; EXEC. DIR, COMPREHENSIVE HEALTH PLANNING COUN, WHATCOM, SKAGIT, ISLAND & SAN JUAN COUNTIES, STATE OF WASH, 71- Instr, Northeast. Univ, 54-56; Denver Res. Inst, 57. U.S.A.A.F, 44-45, Res, 45-53, 2nd Lt. AAAS; Soc. Appl. Spectros; Am. Chem. Soc. Gases in metals; trace analysis; electrochemistry; extractive metallurgy; raw materials utilization. Address: Comprehensive Health Planning Council, Whatcom, Skagit, Island & San Juan Counties, State of Washington, 620 Second Ave, Mt. Vernon, WA 98273.

FRANK, ARLEN W(ALKER), b. Lima, Peru, Nov. 22, 28; nat; m. 58; c. 3. ORGANIC CHEMISTRY. B.Sc, Acadia Univ, 50; Ph.D.(chem), McGill Univ, 54. Fel, div. pure chem, Nat. Res. Coun. Can, 54-55; res. chemist, Carothers Res. Lab, E.I. du Pont de Nemours & Co, 56-59; res. labs, Hooker Chem. Corp, 59-66; fel, Ohio Wesleyan Univ, 66-67; RES. CHEMIST, SOUTH. REGIONAL RES. LAB, U.S. DEPT. AGR, 67- AAAS; Am. Chem. Soc; Am. Asn. Textile Chem. & Colorists; Sci. Res. Soc. Am. Organophosphorus chemistry; textile fibers; flame-retardants for cotton; pulp and paper; alkaloid biogenesis. Address: Southern Regional Research Lab, U.S. Dept. of Agriculture, P.O. Box 19687, New Orleans, LA 70179.

FRANK, ARNE, b. Drammen, Norway, Feb. 1, 25; U.S. citizen; m. 52; c. 2. AIR CONDITIONING, REFRIGERATION. B.S, Purdue, 50, M.S, 51. Sr. develop. engr, Carrier Corp, 52-57; develop. engr. reciprocating compressors, TRANE CO, 57-58, sr. engr, 58-62, chief engr. reciprocating mach, 62-65, RECIPROCATING MACH. & UNITARY PRODS, 65-68, MGR. & CHIEF ENGR, 68- Royal Norweg. Navy. Heat transfer; convection. Address: Trane Co, La Crosse, WI 54601.

FRANK, BARRY, b. Montreal, Que, Mar. 26, 41; m. 60; c. 2. PHYSICS. B.S, McGill, 61, M.S, 62; Ph.D.(theoret. physics), British Columbia, 65. ASST. PROF. PHYSICS, SIR GEORGE WILLIAMS UNIV, 65- Solid state and particle physics. Address: Dept. of Physics, Sir George Williams University, Montreal 25, Que, Can.

FRANK, BERNARD, b. Chicago, Ill, Apr. 19, 15; m. 41; c. 2. BIOSTATISTICS. B.S, Chicago, 37. Statistician health statist, State Dept. Pub. Health, Ill, 46-51; chief spec. studies sect. med. statist, resources & eval. div, Vet. Admin, 51-56; chief biostatist. anal. br, Off. Surgeon Gen, U.S. Air Force, 56-61; acting chief mgt. info. br. air traffic, prog. eval. & statist. div, Fed. Aviation Agency, 61-64; statist. consult. care serv, div. chronic diseases, U.S. Pub. Health Serv, 64-66, asst. chief, prog. anal. br, Nat. Inst. Gen. Med. Sci, 66-68; STAFF ASST, MGT. INFO. & SYSTS, HEALTH SYSTS. RES. & DEVELOP. SERV, VET. ADMIN, 68- U.S.A, 41-46, Capt. AAAS; Am. Statist. Asn; Am. Pub. Health Asn. Information systems; air transport statistics; survey planning and analysis. Address: 11706 Trailbridge Dr, Potomac, MD 20854.

FRANK, BRUCE HILL, b. Hartford, Conn, Oct. 12, 38; m. 61; c. 2. BIOCHEMISTRY. B.S, Trinity Col.(Conn), 60; Toni-Gillette Corp. fel, Northwest. Univ, 62-63, Nat. Insts. Health fel, 63-64, Ph.D.(phys. chem), 64. Nat. Insts. Health fel, Univ. Calif, Berkeley, 64-66; SR. PHYS. CHEMIST, LILLY RES. LAB, 66-; ASST. PROF. BIOCHEM, SCH. MED, IND. UNIV-PURDUE UNIV, INDIANAPOLIS, 69- Summers, res. polymer chemist, Monsanto Chem. Corp, 60; instr, Northwest. Univ, 64. AAAS; Am. Chem. Soc. Physical biochemistry; protein structure and function. Address: Lilly Research Lab, Eli Lilly & Co, Indianapolis, IN 46206.

FRANK, CHARLES E(DWARD), b. Philipsburg, Pa, May 1, 14; m. 39; c. 3. ORGANIC CHEMISTRY. B.S, Pa. State Col, 35; M.S, Ohio State, 36, du Pont del, 37-38, Ph.D.(org. chem), 38. Asst. chem, Ohio State, 35-37; exp. sta, E.I. du Pont de Nemours & Co, 38-48; assoc. prof, grad. dept. applied sci, Cincinnati, 48-53; head applied res, res. div, U.S. INDUST. CHEMS. CO. DIV, NAT. DISTILLERS & CHEMS. CORP, 53-58, ASST. DIR. RES, 58- AAAS; Am. Chem. Soc. Autoxidation; catalysis; polymerization; unsaturated hydrocarbons; sodium. Address: Research Division, U.S. Industrial Chemicals Co, 1275 Section Rd, Cincinnati, OH 45237.

FRANK, CHARLES W(ARREN), b. N.Y.C, May 3, 21; m. 46; c. 2. CARDIOLOGY, INTERNAL MEDICINE. A.B, Columbia, 42, M.D, 44, hon. Med.Sc.D, 52. Mem. staff, col. physicians & surgeons, Columbia, 47-55; ALBERT EINSTEIN COL. MED, 55-58, ASSOC. PROF. MED. & DIR. CARDIOPULMONARY LAB, 58- Dipl, Am. Bd. Internal Med. Med.C, 45-47, Capt. Am. Physiol. Soc; Am. Fedn. Socs. Exp. Biol; Am. Fedn. Clin. Res; Harvey Soc.

Human cardiopulmonary physiology; clinical trials; epidemiology of coronary heart disease. Address: Cardiopulmonary Lab, Albert Einstein College of Medicine, Eastchester Rd. & Morris Park Ave, Bronx, NY 10461.

FRANK, DAVID L(EWIS), b. Kearny, N.J, Apr. 4, 43; m. 64; c. 2. TOPOLOGY. B.A, Columbia Univ, 64; Nat. Sci. Found. fel, Univ. Calif, Berkeley, 64-67, Ph.D.(math), 67. Nat. Sci. Found. fel, 67-68; Moore instr. MATH, Mass. Inst. Technol, 68-70; ASST. PROF, STATE UNIV. N.Y. STONY BROOK, 70- Vector fields on manifolds; differential structures on manifolds. Address: Dept. of Mathematics, State University of New York at Stony Brook, Stony Brook, NY 11790.

FRANK, DONALD JOSEPH, b. Cincinnati, Ohio, Nov. 9, 26; m. 49; c. 4. PEDIATRICS. M.D, Univ. Cincinnati, 51. Instr. pediat, COL. MED, UNIV. CINCINNATI, 54-64, asst. prof, 64-67, ASSOC. PROF. PEDIAT. & ASSOC. DIR. DIV. COMMUNITY PEDIAT, 67- Private practice pediat, 54-64; consult, Margaret Mary Hosp, Batesville, Ind, 54- Am. Acad. Pediat. Clinical problems of the newborn; delivery of health care to children; training of pediatric nurse associates. Address: Good Samaritan Hospital, Cincinnati, OH 45220.

FRANK, EDWARD C(OLMAN), b. Toledo, Ohio, Jan. 16; m; c. 2. PSYCHIATRY. A.B, Michigan, 36; Univ. Col, London, England, 36-37; M.D, Wayne State, 42; cert, Chicago Inst. Psychoanal. Extern, Mt. Carmel Mercy Hosp, Detroit, Mich, 42; intern, Cedars of Lebanon Hosp, Los Angeles, Calif, 42-43; neuropsychiatrist, Michael Reese Hosp, Chicago, Ill, 46-49; psychiatrist-in-charge, Rotman res. lab, Munic. Courts, 49-51; assoc. prof. PSYCHIAT, med. sch, North Carolina, 52-54; ASSOC. CLIN. PROF, MED. SCH, UNIV. LOUISVILLE, 54-, vis. assoc. prof, Kent Sch. Soc. Work, 64- Mem. staff, Family Serv. Orgn, Ky, 50-59; private practice, 53-; consult. psychiatrist, Peace Corps Training; consult, Vet. Admin. Hosp, Louisville, Ky; U.S. Pub. Health Serv; U.S. Army, 54-; vis. assoc. prof, med. sch, Cincinnati, 60-; exec. dir, Ky. Region Eight Ment. Health-Ment. Retardation Bd, Inc. Dipl, Am. Bd. Psychiat. & Neurol, 49. U.S.N.R, 43-46. Am. Psychiat. Asn. Address: Dept. of Psychiatry, University of Louisville Medical School, Louisville, KY 40208.

FRANK, ERNEST, b. Rochester, N.Y, Oct. 2, 19; m. 42; c. 2. ELECTRICAL ENGINEERING. B.E.E, N.Y. Univ, 41; M. S. Pennsylvania, 49, Ph.D.(elec. eng), 53. Asst. nuclear physics, Princeton, 41-42; Chicago, 42, instr. electronics, 42-43; proj. engr, radar design, Sperry Gyroscope Co, 43-45; spec. res. engr, Glenn L. Martin Co, 47; asst. prof. ELEC. ENG, Pennsylvania, 47-56; prof. & exec. officer. dept, George Washington, 56-60; dir. res, Dikewood Corp, 60-62; CONSULT, 62- Res. engr, labs, Franklin Inst, 49; instr, Polytech. Inst. Brooklyn, 44-45, med. elec. eng, univ. hosp, Pennsylvania, 51-56. Consult. scientist, Brookhaven Nat. Lab, 48; consult, Provident Mutual Life Ins. Co, 52-56. Morse medal, 41. Electrocardiography; electromedicine; electromagnetic fields; electrical measurements. Address: P.O. Box 694, Rochester, NY 14603.

FRANK, EUGENE N, b. Venice, Calif, May 23, 31. SOLID STATE PHYSICS. B.S, California, Los Angeles, 55, M.A, 60; Ph.D.(physics), Case, 65. ASST. PROF. PHYSICS, Chaminade Col. Honolulu, 65-66; UNIV. DAYTON, 66- NASA summer res. grant, Case Inst. Tech, 66. U.S.N, 55-57. AAAS; Am. Asn. Physics Teachers; Am. Phys. Soc. Plasma turbulence; transport properties in solids. Address: Dept. of Physics, University of Dayton, Dayton, OH 45409.

FRANK, EVELYN, b. Chicago, Ill. MATHEMATICS. Ph.D, Northwestern, 45. Instr. MATH, Northwestern, 42-46; asst. prof, UNIV. ILL, 46-50, assoc. prof, 50-57, PROF, 57- Soc. Indust. & Appl. Math; Am. Math. Soc; Math. Asn. Am. Analysis; continued fractions; polynomials; location of zeros; stability; special functions; number theory; numerical analysis. Address: P.O. Box 361, Evanston, IL 60204.

FRANK, FLOYD, b. Newark, N.J, Aug. 10, 33. POLYMER PHYSICS, APPLIED MECHANICS. B.S, Lowell Tech. Inst, 55; M.S, Cornell, 57; Int. Wool Secretariat fel, Leeds, 57-61, Ph.D.(mech), 61. Instr. appl. mech, Cornell, 55-57; res. engr, Summit Res. Labs, CELANESE CORP. AM, 61-63, SR. DEVELOP. ENGR, CELANESE FIBERS MKT. CO, 63- AAAS; Fiber Soc; Am. Asn. Textile Tech. Fatigue in fibers; mechanics of textile structures; missile recovery systems; impact loading of engineering structures. Address: Celanese Fibers Co, P.O. Box 1414, Charlotte, NC 28201.

FRANK, FLOYD WILLIAM, b. Fortuna, Calif, Feb. 12, 22; m. 48; c. 2. VETERINARY MEDICINE & MICROBIOLOGY. B.S. & D.V.M, Washington State, 51, Ph.D.(vet. sci), 63. Vet, animal disease eradication br, agr. res. serv, U.S. Dept. Agr, Ore, 51-53; vet. bact, Wyo. State Vet. Lab, 53-55; assoc. vet, vet. res. lab, UNIV. IDAHO, 55-63, res. vet, 63-67, PROF. VET. SCI. & HEAD DEPT, 67- Nat. Insts. Health trainee, 61-62. Mem, Tech. Cmt. Vibriosis Sheep & Tech. Cmt. Urolithiasis Cattle & Sheep. U.S.N.R. & U.S.M.C.R, 41-46, Capt. Am. Vet. Med. Asn; Am. Soc. Microbiol; Am. Asn. Vet. Bact; Am. Soc. Animal Sci. Etiology, transmission, treatment and control of vibriosis of sheep; nutritional factors influencing urolithiasis; etiology, transmission and resistance to enteritis in calves and lambs; prophylaxis of enzootic abortion of ewes and epizootic observations regarding tularemia in sheep. Address: Dept. of Veterinary Science, University of Idaho, Moscow, ID 83843.

FRANK, FORREST JAY, b. Chicago, Ill, Sept. 2, 37; m. 59; c. 1. ORGANIC CHEMISTRY. B.S, Grinnell Col, 59; Ph.D.(org. chem), Purdue, 64. Res. chemist, Rayonier, Inc, 64-65; ASST. PROF. CHEM, ILL. WESLEYAN UNIV, 65- Am. Chem. Soc. N-alkyl sulfonomide synthesis; aryl acetoacetates-keto-enol equilibria. Address: Dept. of Chemistry, Illinois Wesleyan University, Bloomington, IL 61701.

FRANK, FRED R, b. Chaska, Minn, Aug. 13, 26; m. 52; c. 1. PHYSIOLOGY, BIOCHEMISTRY. B.S, Minnesota, 55, M.S, 60, Ph.D.(physiol, biochem), 63. Fel. PHYSIOL, California, Davis, 63-65, RES. ASSOC, 65-67; UPJOHN CO, 67- U.S.A.F, 45-47, Sgt. AAAS. Ion and water metabolism; renal control mechanisms; calcification mechanisms; reversible and irreversible control of reproduction and application of avian and mammalian pest control. Address: Unit 9670, The Upjohn Co, Kalamazoo, MI 49001.

FRANK, GEORGE ANDREW, b. Budapest, Hungary, Apr. 6, 38; U.S. citizen; m. 66. ORGANIC CHEMISTRY. B.S, Colorado State, 60; Nat. Insts. Health fel, Sun Oil Co. fel. & Ph.D.(org. chem), Mass. Inst. Tech, 65. Sr. chemist, res. lab, Rohm & Haas Co, Spring House, 65-69; LAB. HEAD, CENT. RES. LAB, BORDEN CHEM. CO, 69- Lectr, Univ. Pa, 68- N.Y. Acad. Sci; Am. Chem. Soc. Reaction mechanisms; Favorskii rearrangement; Wittig reaction; emulsion polymerization theory; photochemistry; free radical oxidation; adhesive and paint technology; acrylic, vinyl acetate and vinyl chloride polymerization; polyesters. Address: Somerset House, Apt. 303A, Ft. Washington, PA 19034.

FRANK, G(EORGE) B(ARRY), b. Brooklyn, N.Y, Feb. 1, 29; Can. citizen; m. 51; c. 3. PHYSIOLOGY, PHARMACOLOGY. B.S, City Col, 50; M.Sc, Ohio State, 52; Ph.D.(physiol), McGill, 56. Lectr. physiol, McGill, 56-57; asst. prof. PHARMACOL, Manitoba, 57-62, assoc. prof, 62-65; PROF, UNIV. ALTA, 65- U.S. Pub. Health Serv. fel, 56-57, spec. fel. physiol, Univ. Col, London & pharmacol, Lund, 63-64; vis. prof, instr. pharmacol, Univ. Geneva. U.S.A, 52-54, Res, 54-60. AAAS; Am. Physiol. Soc; Am. Soc. Pharmacol. & Exp. Therapeut; Soc. Gen. Physiol; Can. Physiol. Soc; Pharmacol. Soc. Can. Electrical and mechanical activities of skeletal muscle; physiology and pharmacology of the central nervous system; electrical properties and activity of the mammalian cerebral cortex. Address: Dept. of Pharmacology, University of Alberta, Edmonton, Alta, Can.

FRANK, GLENN W(ILLIAM), b. Mayfield Heights, Ohio, Jan. 13, 28; m. 49; c. 3. GEOLOGY. B.S, Kent State, 51; M.S, Maine, 53. Asst. prof. GEOL, KENT STATE UNIV, 53-64, assoc. prof, 64-69, PROF. & ASST. CHMN. DEPT, 69-, DANFORTH ASSOC, 71-, faculty senate, 69-74, secy, 69-70, chmn. faculty senate, 71-72. Consult, various cos; asst. geologist, Maine Geol. Surv, 52. U.S.M.C, 46-47. AAAS; Am. Inst. Prof. Geol; Geol. Soc. Am; Nat. Asn. Geol. Teachers. Address: Dept. of Geology, Kent State University, Kent, OH 44242.

FRANK, HENRY S(ORG), b. Pittsburgh, Pa, Aug. 6, 02; m. 27; c. 3. PHYSICAL CHEMISTRY. B.Chem. & M.S, Pittsburgh, 22; China Med. Bd. fel. & du Pont fel, California, 26-27, Ph.D.(chem), 28; L.H.D, Geneva Col, 69. Instr. physics, Canton Christian Col, 22-25; chem, California, 27-28; assoc. prof, Lingnan Univ, 28-33, prof, 33-51, chmn. dept, 31-47, dean col. sci, 38-51, v.provost, 46-48, provost, 48-51; PROF. CHEM, UNIV. PITTSBURGH, 51-, chmn. dept, 51-63. Vis. prof, Univ. Pittsburgh, 39-40; lectr, Univ. Calif, 42-45; head China sect, Far-East br, div. cult. coop, U.S. Dept. State, 45-46; consult, Int. Coop. Admin, Formosa, summer 59; adj. sr. fel, Mellon Inst, 63-71; consult, Oak Ridge Nat. Lab, 66- U.S. adv. & special chair prof, chem. res. ctr, Nat. Taiwan Univ, 68. AAAS; Am. Chem. Soc.(Pittsburgh award, 64); hon. mem. Chinese Chem. Soc. Adsorption of gases; thermodynamics; statistical mechanics; theory of solutions; electrolyte theory; structure of water and of aqueous solutions. Address: Dept. of Chemistry, University of Pittsburgh, Pittsburgh, PA 15213.

FRANK, HILMER A(ARON), b. St. Paul, Minn, Oct. 26, 23; m. 53; c. 1. BACTERIOLOGY. B.A, Minnesota, 49; M.S, Washington State, 52, Ph.D. (food tech), 54. Asst. bact, Washington State, 50-51, hort, 51-55, Nat. Cancer Inst. res. fel, 55-57; bacteriologist indust. test lab, U.S. Naval Shipyard, Pa, 57; east. regional res. lab, U.S. Dept. Agr, 57-60; asst. prof. FOOD SCI, UNIV. HAWAII, 60-63, assoc. prof, 63-68, PROF, 68- U.S.A, 43-45. Am. Soc. Microbiol; Brit. Soc. Gen. Microbiol; Soc. Indust. Microbiol; Brit. Soc. Appl. Bact. Food microbiology; bacterial spores; food safety. Address: Dept. of Food Science & Technology, University of Hawaii, Honolulu, HI 96822.

FRANK, JAMES A(NTHONY), b. Cleveland, Ohio, Mar. 4, 40; m. 66; c. 1. PLANT PATHOLOGY & PHYSIOLOGY. B.S, Ohio Univ, 63; M.S, Univ. Ill, 69, Ph.D.(plant path), 70. Agr. technician plant path, crops res. div, AGR. RES. SERV, U.S. DEPT. AGR, 64-65, plant pathologist, 65-67, RES. PLANT PATHOLOGIST, PLANT SCI. RES. DIV, 70- Am. Phytopath. Soc.(best res. paper, 70); Potato Asn. Am; Europ. Asn. Potato Res. Host-parasite physiology and biochemistry in relation to mechanisms of host disease resistance. Address: Room 11, Deering Hall, University of Maine, Orono, ME 04473.

FRANK, JAMES LEO, b. Syracuse, N.Y, Apr. 22, 38; m. 57; c. 3. MATHEMATICS. B.S, Va. Polytech. Inst, 60; Ph.D.(math), Univ. Ky, 69. Asst. prof. MATH, W.Va. Inst. Technol, 62-64; asst, Univ. Ky, 64-69, ASST. PROF, VA. POLYTECH. INST. & STATE UNIV, 69- Am. Math. Soc. Complex variables, particularly polynomial expansions of analytic functions. Address: Dept. of Mathematics, Virginia Polytechnic Institute & State University, Blacksburg, VA 24061.

FRANK, JEAN ANN, b. N.Y.C, June 17, 29. CHEMISTRY. B.A, Hunter Col, 51; M.A, Colorado State, 58; Ph.D.(chem), Utah State, 64. Geologist, Atomic Energy Comn, 51-57; instr. CHEM, Wis. State Col, 58-60; res. asst, Brandeis, 63-65; from asst. prof. to ASSOC. PROF, AM. INT. COL, 65-, CHMN. DEPT, 68- Am. Chem. Soc. Chemical kinetics of oxidation-reduction type reactions. Address: Dept. of Chemistry, American International College, Springfield, MA 01109.

FRANK, KARL, b. Toronto, Ont, Aug. 5, 16; m. 41; c. 3. NEUROPHYSIOLOGY. B.S, George Washington, 38; M.S, Cornell, 41; Ph.D.(physiol), Chicago, 51. Physicist, Naval Ord. Lab, 41-46; biophysicist, U.S. Pub. Health Serv. Hosp, Ky, 46-51; head, spinal cord sect, neurophysiol. lab, National Inst. Neurol. Diseases & Blindness, 51-68, CHIEF, NEURAL CONTROL LAB, NAT. INST. NEUROL. DISEASES & STROKE, 68-, acting assoc. dir, intramural res, 63-66. AAAS; Int. Brain Res. Orgn; Am. Physiol. Soc; Am. Biophys. Soc; N.Y. Acad. Sci; Am. Soc. Cybernet. Mechanisms of neural control and social implications. Address: Lab. of Neural Control, National Institute of Neurological Disease & Stroke, Room 5A29, Bldg. 36, National Institutes of Health, Bethesda, MD 20014.

FRANK, LAWRENCE, b. Brooklyn, N.Y, Sept. 12, 15; m. 40; c. 2. MEDICINE. A.B, North Carolina, 36; M.D, L.I. Col. Med, 40. From assoc. prof. to PROF. DERMAT. & DIR. DEPT, COL. MED, DOWNSTATE MED. CTR, N.Y. UNIV, 53-, DIR. & HEAD, UNIV. HOSP, 68- Attend. physician, L.I. Col.

Hosp, 55-, dir. dept. dermat; attend. physician, Kings County Hosp, 57-, dir. & head, div. dermat, 59-; consult, Vet. Admin. Hosp, Brooklyn, N.Y, 59-; coun. drugs, Am. Med. Asn, 59-; Brooklyn Eye & Ear & Calodonian Hosps. Dipl, Am. Bd. Dermat, 46. Fel. Soc. Invest. Dermat; fel. Am. Med. Asn; fel. Am. Col. Physicians; fel. Am. Acad. Dermat; fel. N.Y. Acad. Med. Dermatology. Address: 125 Argyle Rd, Brooklyn, NY 11218.

FRANK, LEONARD H(AROLD), b. New York, N.Y, Jan. 24, 30; m. 52; c. 3. BIOCHEMISTRY. A.B, Oklahoma, 50; U.S. Pub. Health Serv. fel, Hopkins, 55-57, Ph.D.(biochem), 57. Sr. instr. biochem, sch. med, West.Reserve Univ, 57-61; asst. prof, sch. hyg, Johns Hopkins Univ, 61-65, assoc. prof, 65-67; SCH. MED, UNIV. MD, BALTIMORE COUNTY, 67-69, PROF. MED, 70- Am. Soc. Microbiol; Am. Soc. Biol. Chem. Amino acid metabolism and metabolic control; microbial physiology. Address: 660 W. Redwood St, Baltimore, MD 21201.

FRANK, LOUIS, b. N.Y.C, July 19, 22; m. 49; c. 3. METALLURGICAL ENGINEERING, PHYSICAL METALLURGY. B.S, Kentucky, 51; M.S, N.Y. Univ, 54. Asst, power metals group, Armour Res. Found, Ill. Inst. Tech, 51-52; engr. fundamental metall, atomic energy div, Sylvania Elec. Prod, Inc, 52-53, sr. engr, develop. sect, 53-56; unit supvr. fuel elements, nuclear div, Martin-Marietta Corp, 56-58, MGR. mat. res. & develop. sect, 58-63; MAT. DEPT, HITTMAN ASSOCS, INC, 63- U.S.A, 42-45. Am. Inst. Min, Metall. & Petrol. Eng. Nuclear and high temperature materials; strength, corrosion and oxidation resistance of materials when exposed to nuclear and elevated temperature environment. Address: Materials Lab, Hittman Associates, Inc, 9191 Red Branch Rd, Columbus, MD 21043.

FRANK, LOUIS ALBERT, b. Chicago, Ill, Aug. 30, 38; m. 60; c. 2. PHYSICS, SPACE SCIENCES. B.A, Univ. Iowa, 60, M.S, 61, Ph.D.(space sci), 64. Asst.prof. PHYSICS, UNIV. IOWA, 64-67, assoc.prof, 67-71, PROF, 71- Am. Geophys. Union. Measurements of planetary magnetic fields, particles and associated atmospheric phenomena; interplanetary medium; solar phenomena. Address: Dept. of Physics & Astronomy, University of Iowa, Iowa City, IA 52240.

FRANK, LOUIS S, b. Chicago, Ill, Feb. 8, 13; m. 42; c. 5. MEDICINE. B.S, Northwest. Univ, 33, B.M, 37, M.D, 38. Asst. prof. PEDIAT, SCH. MED, UNIV. OKLA, 55-62, ASSOC. CLIN. PROF, 62- Dipl, Am. Bd. Pediat, 46. Med.C, 41-46, Maj. Am. Med. Asn; Am. Acad. Pediat. Pediatrics. Address: Dept. of Pediatrics, University of Oklahoma Medical Center, Oklahoma City, OK 73105.

FRANK, MARTIN J, b. Detroit, Mich, June 4, 28; m. 50; c. 4. INTERNAL MEDICINE, CARDIOLOGY. B.S. & M.D, Michigan, 53. Intern, Wayne County Gen. Hosp, Mich, 53-54, res. med, 56-58, chief res, 58-59; Nat. Insts. Health fel. cardiol, Wayne State, 59-60; N.J. Col. Med. & Dent, 60-61, instr. MED, 61-63, asst. prof, 63-67; assoc. prof, MED. COL. GA, 67-69, PROF, 69-, DIR. HEMODYNAMIC LABS, 67- Staff mem, Eugene Talmadge Mem. Hosp, Ga, 67; consult, Vet. Admin. Hosp, 67; Cent. State Hosp, 68; Univ. Hosp, 69. Dipl, Am. Bd. Internal Med, 62. U.S.N, 54-56, Lt. Am. Heart Asn; Am. Fedn. Clin. Res; fel. Am. Col. Cardiol; Am. Col. Physicians; Fedn. Am. Socs. Exp. Biol. Coronary blood flow and myocardial metabolism; left ventricular function in congenital and acquired valvular heart disease; methods for study of circulation by indicator dilution. Address: Medical College of Georgia, Eugene Talmadge Memorial Hospital, Augusta, GA 30902.

FRANK, MAX, b. Detroit, Mich, Feb. 25, 27; m. 56; c. 4. SOLID STATE ELECTRONICS. B.S, Wayne State, 49, M.S, 61. Instr. elec. eng, Wayne State, 49-50; engr. magnetic amplifier circuit anal, Wayne Eng. Res. Inst, 51-53, sr. staff engr. res. solid state electronics, 53-56, chief engr, 56-57; electronics staff engr, defense eng. div, Chrysler Corp, 57-59; SUPVRY. ENGR. SOLID STATE RADIATION EFFECTS, RES. LABS. DIV, BENDIX CORP, 59- U.S.N, 45-46. Sr. mem. Inst. Elec. & Electronics Eng. Prediction of radiation damage in transistors, diodes and microelectronics; radiation effects on magnetic and insulating materials and electronic components; magnetic amplifier development and analysis; extreme high and low temperature electronics. Address: 32445 Olde Franklin Dr, Farmington, MI 48024.

FRANK, MORTON H(OWARD), b. Portland, Maine, Nov. 15, 27; m. 56; c. 2. PHYSIOLOGY. B.A, Bowdoin Col, 48; M.S, Illinois, 54, Ph.D, 58. Asst. physiol, Illinois, 51-57; fel, Albert Einstein Col. Med, 57-59; ASST. PROF. psychiat, col. med, Ohio State, 59-64; PHYSIOL, N.Y. MED. COL, 64- Res. assoc, Columbus Psychiat. Inst. & Hosp, 59-64. AAAS; Am. Physiol. Soc. Renin, renal hypertension in monkeys; role of kidney in hypertension; central regulation of blood pressure; chemoreceptor reflexes. Address: Dept. of Physiology, New York Medical College, Fifth Ave. & 106th St, New York, NY 10029.

FRANK, OSCAR, b. Trieste, Italy, Mar. 6, 32; U.S. citizen; m. 59; c. 2. BIOCHEMISTRY, NUTRITION. B.S, Brooklyn Col, 55, M.A, 57; Ph.D.(biochem), N.Y. Univ, 61. Assoc. chem, Mt. Sinai Hosp, New York, 57-60; instr. med, Seton Hall Col. Med. & Dent, 60-64; asst. dir. vitamin metab, dept. med. res, Roosevelt Hosp, N.Y.C, 64-66; ASSOC. PROF. MED, COL. MED. & DENT. N.J, NEWARK, 66- Assoc, Haskins Labs, N.Y.C, 56- U.S.A.R, 57-65. AAAS; Soc. Protozool; Am. Inst. Biol. Sci; Am. Soc. Clin. Nutrit. Development and application to clinical medicine of techniques; demonstrating metabolic disorders, drug effects, nutrition, medicine, dietetics and vitamin metabolism. Address: 77 Sussex Rd, Tenafly, NJ 07670.

FRANK, PETER J(OSEPH), b. Berlin, Ger, July 27, 32; nat; m. 54. PHYSICAL CHEMISTRY. B.S, Polytech. Inst. Brooklyn, 52; M.S, Illinois, 53, Henry Strong Found. fel, 55-56, Ph.D.(phys. chem), 57. Asst. chem. dept, Polytech. Inst. Brooklyn, 52; Illinois, 52-57; res. assoc, Geneva, 57-59, from instr. to asst. prof. physics, 58-61; SCI. REP, Europe, Gen. Elec. Res. Lab, 61-64, Japan, 65-69, EUROPE, GEN. ELEC. RES. & DEVELOP. CTR, 69- Res. chemist, Varian Co, Switz, 60-61; consult, Europ. Nuclear Energy Agency, Orgn. Europ. Econ. Coop. Am. Phys. Soc; Brit. Inst. Phys. & Phys. Soc; Fr. Phys. Soc; Swiss Phys. Soc; Phys. Soc. Japan. Magnetic resonance, nuclear and electron; solid state physics. Address: Rossbergstrasse, 9, Zurich, Switz.

FRANK, PETER W(OLFGANG), b. Mainz, Ger, Sept. 24, 23; nat; m. 46; c. 3. ECOLOGY. A.B, Earlham Col, 44; Ph.D, Chicago, 51. Seessel fel, Yale, 51-52; asst. prof. zool, Missouri, 52-57; assoc. prof. BIOL, UNIV. ORE, 57-64, PROF, 64- Ecol. Soc. Am.(zool. ed, Ecol, 64-70). Population, marine and experimental ecology. Address: Dept. of Biology, University of Oregon, Eugene, OR 97403.

FRANK, RICHARD E(RNST), b. Stuttgart, Ger, Oct. 7, 00; nat; m. 57. ANALYTICAL CHEMISTRY. B.S, Tech. Hochsch, Stuttgart, Ger, 21; Univ. Freiburg, 21-25, Ph.D.(chem), 25. Chemist, Degussa, 25-38; Harnischfeger Corp, Wis, 39-48; asst. prof. CHEM, UNIV. N.DAK, 48-56, assoc. prof, 56-65, EMER. ASSOC. PROF, 65-, ASSOC. DIR. INST; ECOL. STUDIES, 71- Summers, res. assoc, Mass. Inst. Technol, 51, 52, 61; mem. N.Dak. Adv. Coun. on Air Pollution Control, 71- Am. Chem. Soc. Food industry waste recycling; air pollution control; improved teaching of qualitative analysis. Address: 1020 Boyd Dr, Grand Forks, ND 58201.

FRANK, ROBERT C(ARL), b. Adams, Wis, Aug. 12, 27; m. 51; c. 3. SOLID STATE PHYSICS. B.A, St. Olaf Col, 50; M.A, Wayne State, 52, Ph.D.(physics), 59. Asst, eng. res. inst, Michigan, 52-54; sr. res. physicist, res. labs, Gen. Motors Corp, 54-64; PROF. PHYSICS & HEAD DEPT, AUGUSTANA COL.(ILL), 64- U.S.N.R, 45-46, Ens. Am. Phys. Soc; Am. Asn. Physics Teachers. Mass spectroscopy and its application to the study of gases in solids; growth of single crystals of metals and semiconductors; fatigue, fracture and internal friction of metals. Address: Dept. of Physics, Augustana College, 3520 Seventh Ave, Rock Island, IL 61202.

FRANK, ROBERT L(OEFFLER), b. Milwaukee, Wis, March 15, 14; m. 43; c. 2. ORGANIC CHEMISTRY. A.B, Dartmouth Col, 36; M.A, Wisconsin, 38, Ph.D.(org. chem), 40. Asst. chem, Wisconsin, 39-40; du Pont asst, Illinois, 40-41, instr. org. chem, 41-42, assoc, 43-45, asst. prof, 45-50; dir. res, Edwal Labs, Inc, 50-53; Ringwood Chem. Corp, 53-54; V.PRES, Morton Int, Inc, 55-71, MORTON-NORWICH PROD, INC, 71- V.pres, Ringwood Chem. Corp, 54-57. With synthetic rubber prog, War Prod. Bd, 44. Am. Chem. Soc. Synthetic organic chemistry; polymer and synthetic rubber chemistry; salt technology; nutrition. Address: 700 Lake Shore Dr, Lake Geneva, WI 53147.

FRANK, ROBERT M(ORRIS), b. N.Y.C, Feb. 2, 20; m; c. 2. THEORETICAL PHYSICS. Ph.D.(theoret. physics), Cornell Univ, 51. Asst. prof. theoret. physics, Fla. State Univ, 50-53; mem. staff, Los Alamos Sci. Lab, Univ. Calif, 53-64; assoc, E.H. Plesset Assocs, Inc, Calif, 62-68; MEM. STAFF, LOS ALAMOS SCI. LAB, 68- U.S.A, 41-45. Am. Phys. Soc; Asn. Comput. Mach. Hydrodynamics; nuclear weapons effects; logical design of computing machines; atmospheric optics. Address: Group C-4, Los Alamos Scientific Lab, P.O. Box 1663, Los Alamos, NM 87544.

FRANK, S(IDNEY) R(AYMOND), b. Minneapolis, Minn, Mar. 16, 19; m. 50; c. 1. METEOROLOGY. B.A, Minnesota, 40; M.A, California, Los Angeles, 41. Lab. asst, California, Los Angeles, 41; forecaster, Trans World Airline, Calif, 41-45; instr. meteorol, Missouri, 45-52; proj. dir, Aerophysics Res. Found, Calif, 52-56; v.pres, Aerometric Res, Inc, 56-68, PRES, SIDNEY R. FRANK GROUP & SRF RES. INST, 68- Ed, Jour. Aeronaut. Meteorol, 45-47; lectr, Univ. Kansas City, 49; v.pres, N.Am. Weather Consults, 56-68; pres, Aerometric Res. Found, 56-58; lectr. & res. assoc. Univ. Calif, Santa Barbara, 65-; trustee, Santa Barbara Commun. Col. Dist, 65-, pres. bd, 71-; meteorol. coord, air pollution control Inst, Univ. South. Calif, 67- Air Transport Asn. awards, 43-49; cert, Am. Meteorol. Soc, 63. U.S.A.A.F, 43-45. AAAS; Air Pollution Control Asn; Am. Meteorol. Soc; Solar Energy Soc; Am. Geophys. Union. Meso-scale, transport and diffusion; turbulence, synoptic and air pollution studies. Address: Sidney R. Frank Group, 1500 Cecil Cook Place, Santa Barbara Municipal Airport, Goleta, CA 93017.

FRANK, SIMON, b. Orange, N.J, 21; m. 45; c. 2. ORGANIC CHEMISTRY. A.B, Drew, 43; Ph.D.(chem), Michigan, 50. Chemist, STAMFORD RES. LABS, AM. CYANAMID CO, 50-56, sr. res. chemist, 56-60, group leader, 60-67, MGR. TECH. INFO. SERV, 67- U.S.A.A.F, 43-45. Am. Chem. Soc. Address: American Cyanamid Co, Stamford Research Lab, 1937 W. Main St, Stamford, CT 06904.

FRANK, STANLEY, b. N.Y.C, Apr. 21, 26; m. 60. MATHEMATICS & EDUCATION. B.S, City Col. New York, 50; M.A, 53; Ph.D.(math), Florida, 60; Simmons Col, 62-64. Teacher, pub. sch, N.Y, 50-53; math. & philos. & logic, St. John's Col.(Fla), 60-61; asst. prof. math. & dir. math. testing, South Florida, 61-62; systs. analyst, Mitre Corp, Mass, 62-64, sr. statistician, dynamics res, 64-65; systs. analyst, Gen. Elec. Co, 65-67; res. dir, Booz-Allen Appl. Res, 67-68; proj. mgr, TRW Systs, 68-70; PRES. & RES. DIR, TANGLEWYLDE RES. INST, 70-; DIR, MATH. & MED. LEARNING LAB, SANTA FE JR. COL, GAINESVILLE, 71- Math. Asn. Am; Opers. Res. Soc. Am; Am. Statist. Asn. Medical science; navigation; information storage and retrieval; reliability; logic; autoregressive analysis; management information systems and design of military weapon systems; training of medical personnel; conservation; learning theory; disabilities in reading and quantitative skills. Address: Tanglewylde Research Institute, Rt. 2, Box 325, Palatka, FL 32077.

FRANK, THOMAS S(TOLLEY), b. Milwaukee, Wis, June 26, 31; m. 52; c. 2. MATHEMATICS. B.A, Lawrence Col, 55; M.A, Syracuse, 57, Ph.D.(math), 62. Instr. MATH, Syracuse, 60-62; asst. prof, Le MOYNE COL.(N.Y), 62-65, ASSOC. PROF, 65- Am. Math. Soc; Math. Asn. Am. Point-set topology; analysis of function on quasigroups. Address: Dept. of Mathematics, Le Moyne College, Syracuse, NY 13214.

FRANK, V(ICTOR) S(AMUEL), b. Hartford, Conn, June 18, 19; m. 44; c. 3. ORGANIC CHEMISTRY. B.S, Mass. Inst. Tech, 42, fel, 46-47, Ph.D.(org. chem), 48. Chemist, spectros. lab, Mass. Inst. Tech, 41-42; Dewey & Almy Chem. Co, 42-46; asst, Mass. Inst. Tech, 47-48; sr. chemist, Merck & Co, Inc, 49-51; group leader org. & polymer res, Dewey & Almy Chem. Div, W.R. GRACE & CO, 51-54, res. dir. org. chem, 54-62, dir. polymer res. RES. DIV, 62-67, org. & polymer res, 67-68, V.PRES. RES, 68- Instr, Northeast. Univ, 52-62. Am. Chem. Soc; Soc. Plastics Eng; fel. Am. Inst.

Chem. Amino acid derivatives and peptide synthesis; steroid chemistry; high polymers. Address: Research Division, W.R. Grace & Co, Clarksville, MD 21029.

FRANK, WALLACE E(VERETT), b. Woodmere, N.Y, Jan. 3, 21. MECHANICAL ENGINEERING. S.B, Mass. Inst. Technol, 42; Stevens Inst. Technol, 42-44; M.M.E, N.Y. Univ, 44; Pennsylvania, 46-48. Jr. engr, Gibbs & Cox, Inc, N.Y, 42-45; asst. engr, U.S. Pub. Health Serv, Ga, 45-46; res. engr, Franklin Inst, 46-52, chief, bioeng. sect, 52-58; exec. v.pres, SPITZ LABS, 58-59, PRES, 59- AAAS; Sci. Res. Soc. Am; Am. Soc. Mech. Eng. Interior ballistics and aids for the partly and fully blind; development of an optical opaque projector scanning system and of an electronic guidance device; pressure measuring devices; tonal Braille; flexible endoscope; dynamic scan devices for improvement of resolution in multichannel optical transmission; omnidirectional accelerometers; optical pressure transducers; force recorders; planetarium projectors; visual simulators. Address: Spitz Labs, Inc, Chadds Ford, PA 19317.

FRANK, WILLIAM BENSON, b. Youngstown, Ohio, July 12, 28. PHYSICAL CHEMISTRY, INFORMATION SCIENCE. B.S, Thiel Col, 50. Res. engr, phys. chem. div, ALCOA RES. LABS, ALUMINUM CO. AM, 53-67, MGR. TECH. INFO DEPT, 67- Chem.C, U.S.A, 51-53. AAAS; Am. Chem. Soc; Am. Soc. Info. Sci; Electrochem. Soc; Am. Inst. Mining, Metall. & Petrol. Eng. Extractive metallurgy of aluminum; systems for handling technical information. Address: Technical Information Dept, Alcoa Research Labs, P.O. Box 2970, Pittsburgh, PA 15230.

FRANK, WILLIAM C(HARLES), b. Grand Rapids, Mich, Oct. 10, 40; m. 64; c. 1. ORGANIC CHEMISTRY. B.S, Valparaiso Univ, 62; Ph.D(org. chem), Univ. Colo, Boulder, 63. Sr. chemist, cent. res. lab, 3M CO, 65-66, sr. emulsion chemist, Minn. 3M Res. Ltd, Eng, 66-67, 3M Italia-Ferrania SpA, Italy, 67-68, res. specialist photog. chem, PHOTO PROD. DIV. LAB, 3M CO, 68-71, RES. & DEVELOP. SUPVR, 71- Soc. Photog. Sci. & Eng; Am. Chem. Soc. Photographic emulsion science and chemistry; chemistry of fluorinated cyclobutene derivitives; sulfonamide polymers; photographic product development. Address: Photo Products Division Lab, 3M Co, 3M Center, St. Paul, MN 55101.

FRANK, WILLIAM M(ORDECAI), b. Brooklyn, N.Y, Mar. 6, 31; m. 60. THEORETICAL PHYSICS. B.A, Yeshiva, 50; M.S, Mass. Inst. Tech, 51, Nat. Sci. Found. fel, 52-53, Ph.D.(physics), 59. Asst. physics, Mass. Inst. Tech, 50-54, res. assoc. nuclear physics, lab. nuclear sci, 56-57, physicist, Lincoln lab, 57-58; Nuclear Develop. Corp. Am, 54-46; res. assoc. nuclear physics, Brookhaven Nat. Lab, 58-59; PHYSICIST, NUCLEAR PHYSICS, U.S. NAVAL ORD. LAB, 59- Fulbright vis. prof, Weizmann Inst, 64-65; summers, res. assoc, lab. nuclear sci, Mass. Inst. Tech, 51, Physicist, Lincoln Lab, 52; assoc. prof, Bar-Ilan Univ, Israel & vis. prof, Weizmann Inst, 65-66. Am. Phys. Soc; Math. Asn. Am. Meson, quantum, field, nuclear and probability theories; classical and quantum mechanics; mathematical physics; differential equations; theory of groups. Address: U.S. Naval Ordnance Lab, Silver Spring, MD 20012.

FRANK, WILSON J(AMES), b. Kansas City, Mo, June 4, 23. PHYSICS. B.S, Illinois, 48; Ph.D.(physics), California, 53. PHYSICIST, LAWRENCE LIVERMORE LAB, UNIV. CALIF, 51- U.S.A, 43-46. Am. Phys. Soc; Asn. Comput. Mach. Nuclear physics. Address: Lawrence Livermore Lab, Plans Office (L-28), University of California, P.O. Box 808, Livermore, CA 94550.

FRANKE, CHARLES H, b. Jersey City, N.J, Dec. 28, 33; m. 59; c. 2. ALGEBRA. A.B, Rutgers, 55, Ph.D.(math), 62; M.A, Yale, 56. Instr. math, Rutgers, 58-62; mem. tech. staff, Bell Tel. Labs, 62-66; PROF. MATH, SETON HALL UNIV, 66- Security Agency, U.S.A, 56-58. Math. Asn. Am; Am. Math. Soc. Galois theory of difference fields obtained by adjoining a fundamental system for a linear homogeneous difference equation to a ground field. Address: Dept. of Mathematics, Seton Hall University College of Arts & Sciences, South Orange, NJ 07079.

FRANKE, ERNEST A, b. Uvalde, Tex, Oct. 22, 39; m. 64. ELECTRICAL ENGINEERING. B.S, Texas A&I, 61, M.S, 63; Ph.D.(eng), Case, 67. Instr. ENG, TEX. A&I UNIV, 62-64, assoc. prof, 67-70, PROF, 70-, DEAN, SCH. ENG, 71-, chmn. dept, 69-71. Am. Soc. Eng. Ed-NASA faculty fel, summer 68. Consult, Cent. Power & Light Co, 67- Inst. Elec. & Electronic Eng; Asn. Comput. Mach; Am. Soc. Eng. Ed. Computer aided design of digital systems. Address: School of Engineering, Texas A&I University, Kingsville, TX 78363.

FRANKE, ERNST K(ARL), b. Breslau, Germany, Feb. 6, 11; nat; m. 47; c. 3. BIOPHYSICS. Dipl. Ing, Inst. Tech, Breslau, Germany, 34; Dr. Ing.(physics), Inst. Tech. Berlin, Germany, 39. Physicist electronics, Telefunken Co, Germany, 34-37; asst. physics, Inst. Tech, Berlin, 37-39; res. physicist acoustics & biophys, Helmholtz Inst, 43-47; res. physicist biophys, aero med. lab, Air Develop. Center, Wright-Patterson Air Force Base, Ohio, 47-56; assoc. prof. BIOPHYS, UNIV. CINCINNATI, 56-63, PROF, 63- Biophys. Soc; Am. Heart Asn. Electrocardiography; mechanics of human body; viscoelastic properties of muscle tissue; bioacoustics; ballistocardiography. Address: Dept. of Physics, University of Cincinnati, Cincinnati, OH 45221.

FRANKE, FREDERICK RAHDE, b. Pittsburgh, Pa, Oct. 14, 18; m. 43; c. 5. MEDICINE. B.S, Pittsburgh, 41, M.D, 43, fel, 44-48; M.Sc, Pennsylvania, 50, D.Sc.(med), 52. Instr. physiol. & pharmacol, MED. SCH, UNIV. PITTSBURGH, 48-49, res. assoc. applied physiol, 49-53, physician in charge therapeut. sect, 53-55, ASST. PROF. MED, 55- Spec. fel. cardiol. & genetics Johns Hopkins Hosp, 59-60. Chief div. med, West. Pa. Hosp, Pittsburgh, 63-67, med. dir, 67- Dipl, Am. Bd. Internal Med, 50; dipl, Am. Bd. Cardiovasc. Diseases, 62- Med.C, U.S.N, 45-46. Fel. Am. Col. Physicians; Soc. Exp. Biol. & Med; Am. Therapeut. Soc; Am. Heart Asn. Cardiovascular diseases; physiologic and pharmacologic research in clinical diseases. Address: Western Pennsylvania Hospital, 4800 Friendship Ave, Pittsburgh, PA 15224.

FRANKE, MILTON EUGENE, b. Springfield, Ill, Apr. 7, 31; m. 55; c. 2. MECHANICAL ENGINEERING. B.M.E, Florida, 52; M.S.M.E, Minnesota, 54; Ph.D.(mech. eng), Ohio State, 67. Engr, Westinghouse Elec. Corp, 52; proj. engr, U.S. Air Force Wright Air Develop. Center, 54-56, sr. proj. engr, 56-57; res. engr, E.I. du Pont de Nemours & Co, 57-59; asst. prof. MECH. ENG, U.S. AIR FORCE INST. TECHNOL, 59-65, assoc. prof, 65-70, PROF, 70- U.S.A.F, 52-56, Res, 56-, Maj. Am. Soc. Mech. Eng; Am. Soc. Eng. Educ. Acoustics; heat transfer; fluid mechanics; fluidics; gas dynamics; propulsion; effects of electrostatic fields on heat transfer; fuels and lubricants; fuel systems. Address: Dept. of Aero-Mechanical Engineering, U.S. Air Force Institute of Technology, Wright-Patterson AFB, OH 45433.

FRANKE, NORMAN H(ENRY), b. Philadelphia, Pa, Aug. 13, 25. PHARMACY. B.S, Temple, 49; M.S, Wisconsin, 52, Ph.D.(hist. pharm), 56. ASSOC. PROF. PHARM, Auburn Univ, 54-60; Univ. Ky, 60-67; SOUTH. COL. PHARM, MERCER UNIV, 67- Am. Pharmaceut. Asn. History of pharmacy in the Confederate States of America. Address: Southern School of Pharmacy, Mercer University, 223 Walton St. N.W, Atlanta, GA 30303.

FRANKE, NORMAN W(ILLIAM), b. Pittsburgh, Pa, Aug. 21, 12; m. 36; c. 2. CHEMICAL ENGINEERING. B.S, Carnegie Inst. Tech, 33, M.S, 37. Asst, coal res. lab, Carnegie Inst. Tech, 33-36; res. chemist, Gulf Res. & Develop. Co, 36-43; mem. staff, coal res. lab, Carnegie Inst. Tech, 43-48; group leader, GULF RES. & DEVELOP. CO, 48-61, SECT. SUPVR, 61- AAAS; Am. Chem. Soc; Am. Inst. Chem. Eng; Soc. Plastics Eng. Alkylation; isomerization; petroleum processing; oxidation of coal to aromatic acids; synthetic chemicals; detergents; plastics; coatings. Address: Gulf Research & Development Co, P.O. Drawer 2038, Pittsburgh, PA 15230.

FRANKE, ROBERT G, b. Muskegon, Mich, June 27, 33; m. 57; c. 3. NATURAL SCIENCE. B.S, Northern Illinois, 56; M.S, Northwestern, 61; Iowa, 60-62; Ph.D.(bot), Texas, 65. Instr. natural sci, Mich. State Univ, 64-65, asst. prof, 65-68; ASSOC. PROF. BOT. & PLANT PATH, IOWA STATE UNIV, 68- U.S.A, 57-58. Am. Inst. Biol. Sci. Taxonomy and natural relationship of Myxomycetes, as disclosed with serological, electropheretic, and related techniques. Address: Dept. of Botany & Plant Pathology, Iowa State University, Ames, IA 50010.

FRANKEL, EDWIN N, b. Alexandria, Egypt, July 3, 28; U.S. citizen; m. 50; c. 5. BIOCHEMISTRY, ORGANIC CHEMISTRY. B.S, Mich. State, 50; M.S, California, Davis, 52, Ph.D.(agr. chem), 56. Jr. specialist dairy chem, California, Davis, 53-56; chemist, North. Regional Res. Lab, U.S. Dept. Agr, Ill, 56-61; group leader, food div, Procter & Gamble Co, Ohio, 61-62; PRIN. CHEMIST, NORTH. REGIONAL RES. LAB, U.S. DEPT. AGR, 62- Res. fel, Israel Inst. Technol, 66-67. Am. Chem. Soc; Am. Oil Chem. Soc. Lipid chemistry; autoxidation and hydrogenation of lipids; homogeneous catalysis and organometallic chemistry. Address: Northern Regional Research Lab, 1815 N. University, Peoria, IL 61604.

FRANKEL, FRED H(AROLD), b. Benoni, S.Africa, Mar. 23, 24; U.S. citizen; m. 47; c. 3. PSYCHIATRY. M.B, Ch.B, Witwatersrand, 48, dipl. psychol. med, 52. Intern surg. & med, Johannesburg Gen. Hosp, S.Africa, 48-49; res. psychiat, Tara Hosp. Nervous Disease, Johannesburg, 50-52; MASS. GEN. HOSP, BOSTON, 52-53, ASST. PSYCHIATRIST, 63-; PSYCHIATRIST, BETH ISRAEL HOSP, BOSTON, MASS, 69-, assoc. psychiatrist, 68-69. Consult. social serv. dept, Transvaal & Orange Free State Chamber of Mines, 54-60; from second asst. neuropsychiatrist to asst. med. sch, Witwatersrand & Johannesburg Gen. Hosp, 54-62; hon. psychiatrist, Witwatersrand Jewish Aged Home, 59-62; instr. psychiat, Harvard Med. Sch, 63-68, clin. assoc, 68-69, asst. prof, 69-; asst. to comnr, Dept. Ment. Health, Mass, 65-68. S.African Med.C, 44-46. Fel. Am. Psychiat. Asn; fel. Royal Soc. Med; Col. Physicians, Surg. & Gynec. S.Africa. Psychiatric education; psychiatric consultation; hypnosis. Address: Beth Israel Hospital, 330 Brookline Ave, Boston, MA 02215.

FRANKEL, FRED ROBERT, b. Baltimore, Md, July 6, 34. MOLECULAR BIOLOGY. B.S, Pa. State, 55, M.S, 57; Ph.D, Florida, 60. Res. assoc, Genetics Res. Unit, Carnegie Inst, 60-63; asst. prof. MICROBIOL, SCH. MED, UNIV. PA, 63-69, ASSOC. PROF, 69- Am. Soc. Biol. Chem; Am. Soc. Microbiol. Growth of bacteriophage; replication of bacterial and phage desoxyribonucleic acid; role of the cell membrane in these processes. Address: Dept. of Microbiology, School of Medicine, University of Pennsylvania, Philadelphia, PA 19104.

FRANKEL, HARRY M(EYER), b. Baltimore, Md, Oct. 11, 27; m. 51; c. 2. PHYSIOLOGY. B.S, Maryland, 49; fel, Iowa, 56-58, Ph.D.(physiol), 58. Physiologists, med. labs, Chem. Warfare Lab, Md, 51-55; asst. radiation res. lab, Iowa, 55-56; physiologist, med. res, chem. warfare lab, Army Chem. Ctr, 58-60; asst. prof. PHYSIOL, RUTGERS UNIV, 60-64, assoc. prof, 64-70, PROF, 70- U.S.A, 46. AAAS; Am. Physiol. Soc; Am. Geront. Soc. Environmental and respiratory physiology; comparative pharmacology. Address: Dept. of Physiology, Rutgers University, New Brunswick, NJ 08903.

FRANKEL, HENRY E, b. Brooklyn, N.Y, May 19, 25; m. 53; c. 3. PHYSICAL METALLURGY. B.S. & M.S, Columbia, 49; Ph.D.(metall), Maryland, 58. Asst. metall, Carnegie Inst. Technol, 49-50; phys. metallurgist, Naval Res. Lab, 50-53; Nat. Bur. Standards, 53-60; CHIEF, ENG. PHYSICS DIV, GODDARD SPACE FLIGHT CTR, NASA, 60- Lectr, Univ. Md; Am. del, comn. IV, Int. Inst. Welding. Award, Goddard Space Flight Ctr, NASA. U.S.N, 43-46. High temperature metallurgy; fatigue of metals; mechanical and physical properties of metals; phase transformations and kinetics; materials in a space environment. Address: 1018 Tracy Dr, Silver Spring, MD 20904.

FRANKEL, HERBERT, b. Harrison, N.J, Feb. 12, 14; m. 41; c. 2. ELECTRICAL ENGINEERING. B.A, State Univ. N.Y, 40; B.S, Washington (St. Louis), 47; M.E.E, Rensselaer Polytech, 53. Engr, DeLaval Separator Co, N.Y, 47-48; ASSOC. PROF. ELEC. ENG, RENSSELAER POLYTECH. INST, 48- Consult, Watervliet Arsenal, N.Y, 56- U.S.A, 43-46. Inst. Elec. &

Electronics Eng. Circuit theory; nondestructive testing of metals. Address: Dept. of Electrical Engineering, Rensselaer Polytechnic Institute, Troy, NY 12181.

FRANKEL, IRWIN, b. New Orleans, La, Nov. 25, 19; m. 45; c. 2. CHEMICAL ENGINEERING. B.Ch.E, Tulane, 42; M.S, Case, 48; D.Ch.E, Rensselaer Polytech, 51. Res. engr, petrochem. & gasoline volatility spex, Beacon Res. Labs, Texaco, Inc, 47-49; proj. leader develop. eng, fine chem, chem. div, Corn Prod. Co, 51-55; sr. engr, res. & develop. dept, Crown Cork & Seal Co, 55-57; chief technologist, energy div, Olin Mathieson Chem. Corp, 57-59, mgr, liquid fuels develop, 59-60; group leader eng. develop, org. chem, Nat. Aniline Div, ALLIED CHEM. CORP, 60-65, res. supvr, 65-66, proj. mgr. indust. chem. div, N.J, 66-69, MGR. pilot plants, fibers div, VA, 69-70, OPERS. SERVS, 70- U.S.A.A.F, 42-46, Lt. Col. Am. Chem. Soc; Am. Inst. Chem. Eng. Process development; semiplant production; production. Address: 4137 Carafe Dr, Richmond, VA 23234.

FRANKEL, J(ACK) W(ILLIAM), b. N.Y.C, Feb. 15, 25; m. 48; c. 3. VIROLOGY. B.A, Brown, 48; Ph.D, Rutgers, 51. Res. fel. virol, Pub. Health Res. Inst, Inc, N.Y, 51-53; res. assoc, Sharp & Dohme Div, Merck & Co, 53-58; dept. microbiol, sch. med, Temple, 58-59; dept. res. therapeut, Norristown State Hosp, Pa, 59-61; head virus res, Ciba Pharmaceut. Co, Summit, 61-68; DEP. DIR, LIFE SCI. INC, 68- Prof, Hunter Col, 61-68. U.S.A, 43-46. AAAS; Am. Soc. Microbiol; Am. Pub. Health Asn; Int. Soc. Chemother; N.Y. Acad. Sci. Viruses, tissue culture and animals; antiviral agents; viral immunology; epidemiology. Address: Life Sciences, Inc, 2900 72nd St. N, St. Petersburg, FL 33710.

FRANKEL, JACOB PORTER, b. Phila, Pa, Sept. 7, 23; m. 46; c. 5. ENGINEERING. B.S, Univ. Calif, Berkeley, 44, M.S, 47; Ph.D.(eng), Univ. Calif, Los Angeles, 51. From instr. to asst. prof. eng, Univ. Calif, Los Angeles, 48-51; lead metallurgist, Calif. Res. & Develop. Corp, 51-54; assoc. prof. metall, Northwest. Univ, 54-56; div. leader, Systs. Corp. Am, 56-57; from assoc. prof. to prof. eng, Univ. Calif, Los Angeles, 57-66; assoc. dean Thayer Sch. Eng, Dartmouth Col, 66-68; DEAN FACULTY, HARVEY MUDD COL, 68- Consult. metall. & nuclear eng, 54-; pres, For. Resource Serv, Inc, 65-; consult, Govt. India & China, 70. U.S.N.R. Civil Eng.C, 43-46, Lt.(jg). AAAS; Am. Soc. Eng. Educ. Industrial economics; materials; nuclear engineering; oceanic anthropology. Address: Harvey Mudd College, Claremont, CA 91711.

FRANKEL, JOHN M(ARTIN), b. St. Paul, Minn, Jan. 5, 19; m. 49; c. 2. DENTISTRY. D.D.S, Illinois, 44, M.S, 51; M.P.H, California, 58. Dir. dept. pedodont, Marquette, 49-51; consult, pub. health dent, For. Opers. Admin, Inst. Inter-Am. Affairs, Brazil, 51-56; asst. regional dent. consult, U.S. Pub. Health Serv, 56-58, dent. surgeon, 58-60, sr. dent. surgeon, 60-61, dent. dir, Ill, 61-66; dir. health serv. off, Off. Econ. Opportunity, Wash, D.C, 66-69; chief primary care systs. br, U.S. Pub. Health Serv, Arlington, Va, 69-70; LECTR. PRIMARY HEALTH CARE, SCH. PUB. HEALTH, UNIV. CALIF, BERKELEY, 70-; ASSOC. PROF. COMMUN. DENT, SCH. DENT, UNIV. PAC, 71- Consult, Pan-Am. Health Orgn, Brazil, 62, Columbia, 64. Dent.C, 44-46, Maj. AAAS; Am. Dent. Asn; fel. Am. Pub. Health Asn; Int. Asn. Dent. Res. Epidemiology of dental diseases; dental care. Address: P.O. Box 46, Elk, CA 95432.

FRANKEL, JOSEPH, b. Vienna, Austria, July 30, 35; U.S. citizen; m. 61. PROTOZOOLOGY, BIOLOGY. B.A, Cornell, 56; Ph.D.(zool), Yale, 60. Nat. Insts. Health fel. cell biol, Biol. Inst. Carlsberg Found, Denmark, 60-62; ASSOC. PROF. ZOOL, UNIV. IOWA, 62- Nat. Insts. Health res. grant, 63-69. Am. Soc. Zool; Soc. Protozool; Am. Soc. Cell Biol. Development in ciliated protozoa. Address: Dept. of Zoology, University of Iowa, Iowa City, IA 52240.

FRANKEL, LARRY, b. N.Y.C, July 8, 28; m. 50; c. 2. INVERTEBRATE PALEONTOLOGY. B.Sc, Brooklyn Col, 50, fel, 50-52; A.M, Columbia, 52; Ph.D.(geol), Nebraska, 56. Asst, Nebraska, 52-54; geologist, U.S. Atomic Energy Comn, 54-55; instr. GEOL, UNIV. CONN, 55-59, asst. prof, 59-63, assoc. prof, 63-68, PROF, 68- Geol. Soc. Am; Am. Paleont. Soc; Am. Asn. Petrol. Geol. Pleistocene Mollusca and geology; foraminifera, estuarine studies. Address: Dept. of Geology, University of Connecticut, Storrs, CT 06268.

FRANKEL, LAWRENCE (STEPHEN), b. N.Y.C, July 26, 41; m. 64; c. 1. PHYSICAL & ANALYTICAL CHEMISTRY. B.A, Hofstra Univ, 63; Ph.D. (phys. chem), Univ. of Mass, 67. GROUP LEADER PHYS. ANAL. CHEM, ROHM AND HAAS CO, 69- Chem.C, U.S.A, 67-69, Capt. AAAS; Am. Chem. Soc. Transition metal chemistry; kinetics of fast reactions; thermal and spectroscopic characterization of polymers; ion exchange resins and adsorbents; analytical aspects of pollution problems; applied spectroscopy. Address: Rohm and Haas Co, 5000 Richmond St, Philadelphia, PA 19137.

FRANKEL, MELVIN, b. N.Y.C, Oct. 1, 17; m. 44; c. 2. NUCLEAR ENGINEERING. B.A, Santa Barbara Col, 40. Asst. scientist, Manhattan Dist, Chicago, 43-44; California, 44-46; mech. eng. asst, City Dept. Water & Power, Los Angeles, 46-53; mech. eng. assoc, 53-56; mem. res. staff, mech. eng, Gen. Atomic div, Gen. Dynamics Corp, 56-58; nuclear eng. assoc, CITY DEPT. WATER & POWER, LOS ANGELES, 58-62, nuclear engr, 62-67, SR. NUCLEAR ENGR, 67- Am. Nuclear Soc; Am. Soc. Mech. Eng. Nuclear engineering; steam power plant engineering. Address: 4210 Hazel Kirk Dr, Los Angeles, CA 90027.

FRANKEL, MILTON B(ERNARD), b. Lawrenceburg, Ind. Sept. 10, 19; m. 53; c. 2. ORGANIC CHEMISTRY. B.A, Cincinnati, 41; M.S, Pa. State Col, 47; Ph.D.(chem), Stanford, 49. Res. chemist, Aerojet Gen. Co, 49-59; Stanford Res. Inst, 59-65; ROCKETDYNE DIV, N.Am. Aviation, Inc, 65-70, MGR. PROPELLANTS EXPLOSIVES & PYROTECHNICS, N.AM. ROCKWELL CORP, 70- U.S.A.A.F, 43-45. Sci. Res. Soc. Am; Am. Chem. Soc. Aliphatic nitro compounds, explosives; propellants; cyano and fluorine compounds; polymer chemistry. Address: 5008 Veloz Ave, Tarzana, CA 91356.

FRANKEL, RICHARD B(ARRY), b. St. Paul, Minn, June 24, 39; m. 60; c. 2. PHYSICS, CHEMISTRY. B.S, Missouri, 61; Nat. Sci. Found. fel, California, Berkeley, 61-64, Ph.D.(chem), 65. Res. asst, Lawrence Radiation Lab, California, 62-65; RES. STAFF MEM, NAT. MAGNET LAB, MASS. INST. TECHNOL, 65- NATO fel, Munich Tech, 67-68. Am. Phys. Soc. Nuclear structure, spectroscopy and alignment; Mössbauer spectroscopy; magnetic properties of solids. Address: National Magnet Lab, Bldg. N.W. 14, Massachusetts Institute of Technology, Cambridge, MA 02139.

FRANKEL, SAUL A(RNOLD), b. New York, N.Y, Oct. 4, 21; m. 47; c. 3. NEUROSURGERY. B.S, Yale, 42; M.D, Duke, 46. Clin. instr. NEUROSURG, col. med, State Univ. N.Y. Upstate Med. Center, 55-56; asst. prof, SCH. MED. YALE, 56-60, asst. clin. prof, 60-68, SR. CLIN. ASSOC, 68- Assoc. neurosurgeon, Grace-New Haven Community Hosp, 56-60, asst. attend. neurosurgeon, 60-68, attend. neurosurgeon, Yale-New Haven Hosp, 68-; West Haven Vet. Hosp, 56-68; asst. attend. neurosurgeon, Hosp. St. Raphael, 60-67, attend. & chief neurosurgeon, 67- Med.C, 47-49, Capt. Am. Asn. Neurol. Surg; Cong. Neurol. Surg. Biology and treatment of human gliomas. Address: 2 Church St. S, New Haven, CT 06519.

FRANKEL, SHERMAN, b. U.S.A, Nov. 15, 22; m. 53; c. 1. HIGH ENERGY PHYSICS. B.A, Brooklyn Col, 43; M.S, Illinois, 47, Ph.D.(physics), 49. Mem. staff, radiation lab, Mass. Inst. Technol, 43-46; asst. prof. PHYSICS, UNIV. PA, 52-56, assoc. prof, 56-60, PROF, 60- Guggenheim fel, 56-57. Fel. Am. Phys. Soc. Elementary particle and nuclear physics. Address: Dept. of Physics, University of Pennsylvania, Philadelphia, PA 19104.

FRANKEL, SIDNEY, b. N.Y.C, Oct. 6, 10; m. 38; c. 1. ELECTRONICS. E.E, Rensselaer Polytech, 31, M.S, 34, Ph.D.(math), 36. Instr. math, Rensselaer Polytech, 31-33; jr. engr, Eclipse Aviation Corp, 37-38; engr. radio transmitter & head dept, Fed. Telecommunications Labs, 38-50; assoc. head, microwave lab, Hughes Aircraft Co, 50-54; head, radar & countermeasures dept, Litton Industs, Inc, 54-58; dir. eng, Sierra Div, Philco Corp, 58-60; TECH. CONSULT. & MGR, SIDNEY FRANKEL & ASSOCS, 60- Fel. Inst. Elec. & Electronics Eng. System design; theory of multiconductor transmission lines and cables. Address: 1165 Saxon Way, Menlo Park, CA 94025.

FRANKEL, SIDNEY A, b. Bridgeport, Conn, Aug. 8, 25; m. 52; c. 2. ORGANIC CHEMISTRY, CHEMICAL ENGINEERING. B.Ch.E, Pratt Inst, 46; M.S, Newark Col. Eng, 51; B.S, Rutgers, 60. Sect. head, org. synthetic pilot plant, Squibb Inst. Med. Res, N.J, 46-52; res. engr, Maxwell House Coffee Div, Gen. Foods Corp, 53-54; rubber chem. res. & develop. dept, AM. CYANAMID CO, 54-59, staff asst. to chief div. engr, org. chem. div, N.J, 59-61, mgt. analyst, commercial develop. div, N.Y, 61, DEVELOP. CHEM. ENGR, RES. & DEVELOP. DEPT, ORG. CHEM. DIV, BOUND BROOK, 61- Am. Chem. Soc; Am. Inst. Chem. Eng; fel. Am. Inst. Chem; assoc. mem. Nat. Soc. Prof. Eng. Process development of rubber chemicals, drugs, fine chemicals and pharmaceuticals; process and material cost evaluations; statistical applications; plant process improvement; plant startup; economics; project evaluation. Address: 2 Roger Rd, Edison, NJ 08817.

FRANKEL, THEODORE T(HOMAS), b. Phila, Pa, June 17, 29; m. 55; c. 3. MATHEMATICS. A.B, California, 50, Ph.D, 55. Instr. MATH, Stanford, 55-57, asst. prof, 57-62; assoc. prof, Brown, 61-65, PROF, UNIV. CALIF, SAN DIEGO, 65- Mem, Inst. Adv. Study, 57-59. Am. Math. Soc. Differential geometry; Morse theory. Address: Dept. of Mathematics, University of California, San Diego, La Jolla, CA 92037.

FRANKEL, VICTOR H, b. Wilmington, Del, May 14, 25; m. 58; c. 5. ORTHOPEDIC SURGERY, BIOENGINEERING. B.A, Swarthmore Col, 46; M.D, Univ. Pa, 51; Dr.Med.(orthop. surg), Univ. Uppsala, 60. Fel, Nelson Nat. Found, 58-60; attend. orthop. surgeon, Hosp. Joint Diseases, N.Y.C, 60-66; assoc. prof. orthop. surg, CASE WEST. RESERVE UNIV, 66-69, PROF. ORTHOP. SURG. & BIOENG, 69- Am. Orthop. Asn. traveling fel, 65; mem. comt. prosthetics res. & develop, Nat. Acad. Sci, 70- Med.C, U.S.A, 52-54, Capt. Am. Orthop. Asn; Asn. Bone & Joint Surg; Am. Col. Surg; Am. Soc. Test. & Mat; Int. Soc. Orthop. Surg. & Traumatol. Application of engineering techniques to orthopedic surgery; development of biomechanics teaching. Address: 2065 Adelbert Rd, Cleveland, OH 44106.

FRANKEN, P(ETER) A(LDEN), b. N.Y.C, Nov. 10, 28; m. 55; c. 3. PHYSICS. B.A, Columbia, 48, M.A, 50, Ph.D.(physics), 52. Lectr. math, Columbia, 48-49, asst, PHYSICS, 50-52; instr, Stanford, 52-56; asst. prof, UNIV. MICH, ANN ARBOR, 56-59, assoc. prof, 59-62, PROF, 62- Dep. dir, Advan. Res. Projs. Agency, U.S. Dept. Defense, Wash, D.C, 67-68. Fel. Am. Phys. Soc.(prize, 67); fel. Optical Soc. Am. Experimental atomic and electron physics. Address: Dept. of Physics, University of Michigan, Ann Arbor, MI 48107.

FRANKEN, PETER A(LLAN), b. N.Y.C, Aug. 11, 30; m. 56; c. 2. PHYSICS. A.B, Hamilton Col.(N.Y), 52; Elihu Root fel, Mass. Inst. Technol, 52-53; Owens-Corning fel, 55-56, Ph.D.(physics), 56. Physicist acoust. res, BOLT BERANEK & NEWMAN INC, Calif, 56-68, v.pres. phys. sci. div, 68-69, DIR. ARCHIT. TECHNOL. DIV, 69- AAAS; Acoust. Soc. Am. Theoretical and experimental acoustics; subjective response to environmental noise. Address: Architectural Technologies Division, Bolt Beranek & Newman, Inc, 50 Moulton St, Cambridge, MA 02138.

FRANKENBERG, DIRK, b. Woodsville, N.H, Nov. 25, 37; m. 60. MARINE ECOLOGY. A.B, Dartmouth Col, 59; Nat. Insts. Health fels, Emory, 60-62, M.S, 60, Ph.D.(biol), 62. Asst. prof. ZOOL, marine inst, Univ. Ga, 62-66; Univ. Del, 66-67; ASSOC. PROF, UNIV. GA, 67- Nat. Sci. Found. res. grant, 63-65 & 67-, dir. biol. oceanog. prog, 70-71. Ecol. Soc. Am; Am. Inst. Biol. Sci; Am. Soc. Limnol. & Oceanog. Biological oceanography; ecology of macro-benthos; isopod systematics. Address: Dept. of Zoology, University of Georgia, Athens, GA 30601.

FRANKENBERG, JULIAN MYRON, b. Chicago, Ill, Jan. 18, 38; m. 62; c. 1. PALEOBOTANY, PLANT MORPHOLOGY. B.S, Illinois, 61, Ph.D.(paleobot), 68; M.S, Minnesota, 63; Cmt. Instnl. Coop. fel, Iowa, 67. Lab. asst, paleobot. lab, Illinois, Urbana, 57-61; teaching asst, Minnesota, 61-63; bot. & biol, UNIV. ILL, URBANA-CHAMPAIGN, 63-68, acting asst. dean col. lib. arts & sci, 68, asst. dean, 68-70, DIR. HEALTH PROF. INFO. OFF,

70- V.chmn, Cent. Asn. Advisors Health Profs, 69-71, chmn, 71-72. AAAS; Bot. Soc. Am; Am. Inst. Biol. Sci; Asn. Am. Med. Cols. Study of petrified Stigmaria from North America; coal-ball flora of the Pennsylvania period. Address: 294 Lincoln Hall, College of Liberal Arts & Sciences, University of Illinois, Urbana-Champaign, Urbana, IL 61801.

FRANKENBURG, PETER E(DGAR), b. Ludwigshafen on Rhine, Ger, Nov. 10, 26; nat; m. 54; c. 4. ORGANIC CHEMISTRY. A.B, Princeton, 49, Ph.D. (org. chem), Rochester, 53. RES. ASSOC, E.I. DU PONT DE NEMOURS & CO, INC, 53- C.Eng, 45-46, Res, 46-53, 2nd Lt. Am. Chem. Soc; Sci. Res. Soc. Am. Polymers for textile use. Address: 2405 Shellpot Dr, Wilmington, DE 19803.

FRANKENFELD, JOHN WILLIAM, b. Mesa, Ariz, Oct. 29, 32; m. 59; c. 2. ORGANIC CHEMISTRY. B.A, Chicago, 52, S.M, 57; Nat. Sci. Found. fel, Mass. Inst. Tech, 60-61, Ph.D.(chem), 62, Res. chemist, ESSO RES. & ENG. CO, 61-66, SR. RES. CHEMIST, 66- U.S.A, 53-55. Sci. Res. Soc. Am. Biological degradation of petroleum hydrocarbons; synthesis of peptides and peptide intermediates; isolation and identification of chemicals from microbiological degradation of hydrocarbons; synthetic foods and food additives. Address: Esso Research & Engineering Co, Linden, NJ 07036.

FRANKENTHAL, ROBERT P(ETER), b. Berlin, Ger, Sept. 11, 30; nat; m. 58; c. 1. PHYSICAL CHEMISTRY. B.S, Rochester, 52; Procter & Gamble Co. fel, Wisconsin, 54-55, Ph.D.(chem), 56. Res. chemist surface chem, appl. res. lab, U.S. STEEL CORP, 56-60, scientist, EDGAR C. BAIN LAB. FUNDAMENTAL RES, 60-68, SR. SCIENTIST, 68- Am. Chem. Soc; Electrochem. Soc; Nat. Asn. Corrosion Eng. Electrochemistry; electrodeposition; corrosion; mechanism of electrode reactions; surface properties of metals. Address: Edgar C. Bain Laboratory for Fundamental Research, U.S. Steel Corp, Monroeville, PA 15146.

FRANKFORT, HANS RUDOLF E(DWARD), b. Djokjakarta, Indonesia, May 19, 36; U.S. citizen; m. 62; c. 2. INORGANIC & PHYSICAL CHEMISTRY. B.S, Florida, 59; Ph.D.(inorg. chem), North Carolina, 64. Res. chemist, E.I. DU PONT DE NEMOURS & CO. INC, 64-70, SR. RES. CHEMIST, 70- Am. Chem. Soc. Metal halides, reaction kinetics; polymer chemistry, product and process development work in textile fibers, especially polyesters. Address: E.I. du Pont de Nemours & Co, Inc, P.O. Box 800, Kinston, NC 28501.

FRANKFURT, BORIS, b. Kiev, Russia, Feb. 2, 03; nat; m. 38. ORGANIC & COLLOID CHEMISTRY. Ch.E, Strasbourg, 28; Ph.D, Basel, 31. Sr. chemist, Pac. Mills, Inc, 42-46; chief chemist, Normandy Print Works, 46-49; Glenlyon Print Works, 49-58; tech. dir. color div, Carbic-Hoechist Corp, 58-71; RETIRED. Am. Chem. Soc; Am. Asn. Textile Chem. & Colorists. Textile chemistry. Address: 86 Bretton Woods Dr, Cranston, RI 02920.

FRANKHOUSER, MARY TWICKLER, b. Louisville, Ky, Aug. 14, 28; m. 61. ANALYTICAL CHEMISTRY. B.S, Louisville, 55; Ph.D.(anal. chem), Illinois, 62. Res. chemist, Tidewater Oil Co, Pa, 62-66; anal. res. chemist, org. chem. dept, E.I. du Pont de Nemours & Co, N.J, 66-71; RES. CHEMIST, WYETH LABS, 71- Am. Chem. Soc. Spectroscopy, infrared, visible, near infrared and ultraviolet; nuclear magnetic resonance; gas chromatography. Address: 249 E. Chelsea Circle, Newtown Square, PA 19073.

FRANKHOUSER, W(ILLIS) W(AYNE), b. U.S.A, Oct. 18, 10; m. 40. BIOCHEM CHEMISTRY. B.S, Franklin & Marshall Col, 33. Chemist, Sharp & Dohme Div, Merck & Co, Inc, 34-40, asst. chief chemist, 40-43, asst. dir. biol. control, 43-57, MGR, 57-61; QUAL. CONTROL, WYETH LABS, INC, 61- Am. Chem. Soc; Biomet. Soc; Am. Soc. Qual. Control. Biology; quality control. Address: Wyeth Labs, Inc, Marietta, PA 17547.

FRANKIE, GORDON WILLIAM, b. Albany, Calif, Mar. 29, 40; m. 69. INSECT ECOLOGY. B.S, Univ. Calif, Berkeley, 63, Ph.D.(entom), 68. Nat. Sci. Found. grant & res. specialist, Orgn. Trop. Studies, Inc, Costa Rica, 68-70; ASST. PROF. ENTOM, TEX. A&M UNIV, 70- Co-prin. investr, Nat. Sci. Found. study grant trop. ecosyst, Orgn. Trop. Studies, Inc, 70-72. AAAS; Soc. Study Evolution; Entom. Soc. Can; Entom. Soc. Am. Insect-plant relations of insects on cypress; pollination biology in the tropics; biological organization of tropical communities with emphasis on plant reproductive biology; ecological studies of soil-inhabiting beetles in Texas; community studies of insects inhabiting insect-induced galls on oak. Address: Dept. of Entomology, Texas A&M University, College Station, TX 77843.

FRANKL, DANIEL R(ICHARD), b. N.Y.C, Sept. 6, 22; m. 51; c. 2. SOLID STATE PHYSICS. B.Ch.E, Cooper Union, 43, Schweinburg scholar; Dyckman Inst. scholar, Columbia, Ph.D.(physics), 53. Process develop. engr, U.S. Rubber Co, 43-50; res. assoc, Columbia, 51-53; eng. specialist, Luminescense, Sylvania Elec. Prod, Inc, 53-58, semiconductors, Gen. Tel. & Electronics Labs, Inc, 58-62; vis. prof. phys. metall, Illinois, 62-63; PROF. PHYSICS, PA. STATE UNIV, 63- Fel. Am. Phys. Soc; Electrochem. Soc. (div. ed, Jour, 61-64). Semiconductor surfaces. Address: Dept. of Physics, Pennsylvania State University, University Park, PA 16802.

FRANKL, WILLIAM S, b. Phila, Pa, July 15, 28; m. 51; c. 2. CARDIOLOGY. B.A, Temple Univ, 51, M.D, 55, M.S, 61. Intern med, Buffalo Gen. Hosp, 55-56; resident, Temple Univ, 56-57 & 59-61; res. fel. cardiol. & instr. med, Univ. Pa, 61-62; instr. MED, TEMPLE UNIV, 62-64, assoc, 64-65, asst. prof, 65-68, ASSOC. PROF, 68-; PROF. & DIR. CARDIOL. DIV, MED. COL. PA, 70- Dir. electrocardiogram sect, cardiol. div, Temple Univ, 66-68, cardiac care unit, 67-68; physician-in-chief dept. med, Springfield Hosp. Med. Ctr, 68-70; consult. cardiol, Phila. Vet. Admin. Hosp, 70- Dipl, Am. Bd. Internal Med, 62. Med.C, U.S.A, 57-59, Capt. AAAS; fel. Am. Col. Physicians; fel. Am. Col. Cardiol; N.Y. Acad. Sci; Am. Fedn. Clin. Res; Am. Heart Asn. Cardiac pharmacology, especially beta adrenergic blocking agents; cardiovascular hemodynamics; electrocardiography; vectorcardiography. Address: Dept. of Medicine, Medical College of Pennsylvania, 3300 Henry Ave, Philadelphia, PA 19129.

FRANKLAND, ALBERT ERNEST, b. Wentworth, Eng, June 21, 13; Can. citizen; m. 40; c. 1. ORGANIC CHEMISTRY. B.Sc, Derby Tech. Col, Eng, 36; Borough Polytech, Eng, 36. Jr. chemist org. anal, Brit. Celanese, Ltd, 31-34; chemist, inorg. process control, Brit. Thomson Houston Co, Ltd, 34-38; petrol. develop, Anglo Iranian Oil Co, Ltd, 38-43; asst. chief chemist, resin & plastics develop, Brit. Resin Prod, Ltd, 43-48; chief chemist, Saunders Roe, Ltd, 48-55; dir. res, Weyerhaeuser Can, Ltd, 55-61; SR. PROJ. SCIENTIST, TECH. CTR, WEYERHAUSER CO, LONGVIEW, 61- Lectr, Borough Polytech, Eng, 45-46. Tech. Asn. Pulp & Paper Indust; Am. Soc. Test. & Mat; fel. Chem. Inst. Can; fel. Royal Inst. Chem. Wood pulp; regenerated cellulose; synthetic fibers; antimicrobials; disposables and non wovens reprographic paper development. Address: 202 Williams Finney Rd, Kelso, WA 98626.

FRANKLIN, ALAN D(OUGLAS), b. Glenside, Pa, Dec. 10, 22; m. 43; c. 2; m. 60; c. 1. PHYSICAL CHEMISTRY, SOLID STATE PHYSICS. A.B, Princeton, 46, Ph.D.(chem), 49. Sect. chief, ferromagnetism, Franklin Inst, 49-55; group leader ferroelect, NAT. BUR. STANDARDS, Wash, D.C, 55-59, chief mineral prod. div, 59-63, theoret. physicist & asst. to dir. inst. mat. res, 63-67, RES. CHEMIST, MD, 67- Gold Medal, Dept. Commerce, 70. U.S.A.A.F, 42-46, 1st Lt. Am. Chem. Soc; fel. Am. Phys. Soc; Sci. Res. Soc. Am; fel. Am. Ceramic Soc. Point defects in crystals; ferromagnetism; ferroelectricity. Address: National Bureau of Standards, Gaithersburg, MD 20234.

FRANKLIN, ALLAN DAVID, b. Brooklyn, N.Y, Aug. 1, 38; div. PHYSICS. A.B, Columbia, 59; Nat. Sci. Found. & univ. fels, Cornell, 59-64, Ph.D. (physics), 65. Res. assoc. PHYSICS, Princeton, 65-66, instr, 66-67; ASST. PROF, UNIV. COLO, BOULDER, 67- Am. Phys. Soc. Experimental high energy physics; strong interactions. Address: Dept. of Physics, University of Colorado, Boulder, CO 80302.

FRANKLIN, ARTHUR E(DMUND), b. Sask, June 25, 21; m. 51; c. 2. BIOCHEMISTRY. B.Sc, McGill, 48, Ph.D.(biochem), 51. Res. assoc, Connaught Med. Res. Labs, UNIV. TORONTO, 51-55, assoc. BACT, FACULTY MED, 55-69, ASSOC. PROF, 69- Res. assoc, Hosp. Sick Children, 52; Nat. Res. Coun. Can, 58- R.C.A.F, 41-45. Can. Soc. Microbiol. Virology; infectious hepatitis; enteroviruses. Address: Dept. of Bacteriology, Faculty of Medicine, University of Toronto, Toronto, Ont, Can.

FRANKLIN, BERYL C(LETIS), b. Colly, Ky, Oct. 29, 23; m. 47. ZOOLOGY. A.B, Ky. Wesleyan Col, 48; M.S, Kentucky, 50; Ph.D, Ohio State, 57. Field rep, Ky. Wesleyan Col, 48, instr. zool. & chem, 49-50; asst. zool, Ohio State, 50-52, asst. instr, 52-55, supvr. grad. assts, 54-57, instr, 55-57; biol, Del Mar Col, 57-59; asst. prof. zool, La. State, 59-60; NORTHEAST LA. UNIV, 60-62, assoc. prof. BIOL, 62-67, PROF, 67- Summers, mem. inst. animal ecol, Nat. Sci. Found, 59, Nat. Sci. Found-Atomic Energy inst. radiation biol, 62, Nat. Sci. Found. Conf. col. teachers endocrinol, 65. U.S.A, 43-45. AAAS; Am. Soc. Zool. Reproduction physiology; endocrinology; physiological zoology. Address: Dept. of Biology, Northeast Louisiana University, Monroe, LA 71201.

FRANKLIN, DeLANCE F(LOURNOY), b. Yakima Co, Wash, Apr. 9, 09; m. 35; c. 2. HORTICULTURE. B.S, Idaho, 42, M.S, 55. Inspector food prods, State Dept. Agr, 28-39; asst. horticulturist, br. exp. sta, UNIV. IDAHO, 42-47, assoc. horticulturist, 47-50, acting assoc. prof. hort, univ, 50-51, SUPT, BR. EXP. STA, 52-, HORTICULTURIST, IDAHO AGR. EXP. STA, 65-; RES. PROF. HORT, 69- Collab, U.S. Dept. Agr, 43- Chmn, Nat. Carrot Breeders Conf, 60. Am. Soc. Hort Sci. Vegetable seed production; hybrid onion and carrot breeding. Address: Branch Experiment Station, University of Idaho, Route 2, Box 40-A, Parma, ID 83660.

FRANKLIN, EDWARD C, b. Richmond, Va, Jan. 20, 02; m. 24; c. 4. INDUSTRIAL ENGINEERING. B.S, Va. Mil. Inst, 23; B.S, Mass. Inst. Tech, 31; Coast Artillery Sch, Va, 31-32; Case, 55-56. Comdr. cadets, pub. sch, Va, 23-24; real estate engr, Allen J. Saville, Inc, 24-25; asst. prof. mil. sci. & tactics, Ga. Sch. Tech, 36-40; asst. to v.pres, Am. Wringer Corp, Iowa, 46-48; plant mgr, Sterling Windows, Inc, Ind, 48-50, v.pres, 50-52; consult. ord. problems, Ambassador Draper, NATO, 53; dean, sch. eng, Youngstown, 54-56; asst. to exec. v.pres. & mgr, refrig. div, Bowser Corp, 56; from assoc. prof. to prof. indust. eng, Ga. Inst. Technol, 57-67; RETIRED. Lectr, Army Indust. Col, 41; exec. gen. mgr, Chamberlain Corp, Iowa, 46-48. Summer, asst. surveyor, dept. survs, Panama C.Z, 23. U.S. rep, int. staff, N.Atlantic Coun, 53. U.S.A, 25-46, Col. Am. Soc. Civil Eng; Am. Ord. Asn; Am. Inst. Indust. Eng. Operations research, process dynamics and electronic analogue computation applied to industrial engineering problems. Address: 2531 Black Forest Trail S.W, Atlanta, GA 30331.

FRANKLIN, EDWARD CARLYLE, b. Richmond, Va, July 11, 41; m. 63; c. 1. FOREST GENETICS. B.S, N.C. State, 63, Ph.D.(genetics), 68; M.S, California, Berkeley, 65. PRIN. PLANT GENETICIST, SOUTHEAST. FOREST EXP. STA, U.S. FOREST SERV, 66- Genetics and improvement of southern pine species. Address: P.O. Box 3, Olustee, FL 32072.

FRANKLIN, EDWARD C(LAUS), b. Berlin, Ger, Apr. 14, 28; nat; m. 56; c. 1. MEDICINE. B.S, Harvard, 46; M.D, N.Y. Univ, 50. Res. assoc, Rockefeller Inst, 55-58; asst. prof. MED, BELLEVUE MED. CTR, N.Y. UNIV, 58-62, assoc. prof, 62-68, PROF, 68- Sr. investr, Arthritis & Rheumatism Found, 58-63. Dipl, Am. Bd. Internal Med, 56. Med.C, 52-54, 1st Lt. Am. Soc. Clin. Invest; Am. Asn. Immunol; Am. Rheumatism Asn; Asn. Am. Physicians. Immunochemistry; role of immune processes in disease and the physicochemical nature of antibodies. Address: Dept. of Medicine, New York University, Medical Center, 550 First Ave, New York, NY 10016.

FRANKLIN, E(VERETT) W(HITNEY), b. Brockville, Ont, Aug. 8, 10; m. 34; c. 3. HORTICULTURE. B.S.A, Toronto, 47, M.S.A, 48. Asst. prof. HORT, ONT. AGR. COL, UNIV. GUELPH, 49-56, PROF, 57- Can. Army, 39-44. Am. Soc. Hort. Sci; Can. Soc. Hort. Sci; Agr. Inst. Can; Can. Inst. Food Tech. Postharvest horticulture. Address: Dept. of Horticultural Science, Ontario Agricultural College, University of Guelph, Guelph, Ont, Can.

FRANKLIN, FRED A(LDRICH), b. Worcester, Mass, July 24, 32. ASTRONOMY. A.B, Harvard, 54, Saltonstall scholar, 54-55, M.A, 56, Agassiz fel, 56-57, Ph.D, 62. PHYSICIST, SMITHSONIAN ASTROPHYS. OBSERV, HAR-

VARD, 57- Am. Astron. Soc. Photometry and dynamics of rings of Saturn. Address: 41 Linnaean St, Cambridge, MA 02138.

FRANKLIN, GENE F(ARTHING), b. Banner Elk, N.C, July 25, 27; m. 52; c. 2. ELECTRICAL ENGINEERING. B.E.E, Ga. Inst. Technol, 50; M.S, Mass. Inst. Technol, 52; Eng.Sc.D, Columbia, 55. Instr. ELEC. ENG, Columbia, 52-55, asst. prof, 55-57; STANFORD UNIV, 57-59, assoc. prof, 59-61, PROF, 61- Consult, industs, 58- U.S.N, 45-47. Inst. Elec. & Electronics Eng; Soc. Indust. & Appl. Math. Automatic control with emphasis on the control of multivariable nonlinear dynamical systems. Address: Dept. of Electrical Engineering, Stanford University, Stanford, CA 94305.

FRANKLIN, GEORGE JOSEPH, b. Osmond, Nebr, May 21, 20; m. 54; c. 4. GEOLOGY. B.A, Nebraska, 47; M.S, Ohio State, 53, Ph.D.(geol), 61. GEOLOGIST, U.S. GEOL. SURV, 62- Stratigraphy; structural geology. Address: U.S. Geological Survey, 254 E. Center St, Madisonville, KY 42431.

FRANKLIN, JAMES McWILLIE, b. North Bay, Ont, Nov 9, 42; m. 68. ECONOMIC GEOLOGY, STRATIGRAPHY. B.S, Carleton Univ, 64, M.S, 67; Ph.D.(geol), Univ. West. Ont, 70. ASST. PROF. GEOL, LAKEHEAD UNIV, 69- Geologist, Mattagami Lake Mines Ltd, 71; trip coord, Int. Geol. Cong, Montreal, 72. Fel. Geol. Asn. Can; Can. Inst. Min. & Metall; Mineral. Asn. Can. Precambrian stratigraphy; chemistry of formation of stratabound copper-zinc massive sulphide deposits in Archean volcanic terrains, effects of metamorphism on these deposits; metallogeny of veins associated with Proterozoic sedimentary sequences; lead isotope studies of Archean and Proterozoic mineral deposits. Address: Dept. of Geology, Lakehead University, Thunder Bay, Ont, Can.

FRANKLIN, JERROLD, b. N.Y.C, June 19, 30; m. 55; c. 2. THEORETICAL PHYSICS. B.E.E, Cooper Union, 52; M.S, Illinois, 53, Ph.D.(physics), 56. Asst. physics, Illinois, 52-56; instr, Columbia, 56-59; asst. prof, Brown Univ, 59-64; asst. to dean, 62-64; physicist, Lawrence Radiation Lab, Univ. Calif, 64-67; assoc. prof. PHYSICS, TEMPLE UNIV, 67-70, PROF, 70- Assoc. ed, Math. Rev, 62-63; vis. prof, Israel Inst. Technol, 70-71. Am. Phys. Soc; Phys. Soc. Israel. Elementary particle physics; S-matrix theory; quark models. Address: Dept. of Physics, Temple University, Philadelphia, PA 19122.

FRANKLIN, JERRY FOREST, b. Waldport, Ore, Oct. 27, 36; m. 58; c. 2. PLANT ECOLOGY, SILVICULTURE. B.S, Oregon State, 59, M.S, 61; Ph.D. (bot), Washington State, 66. Trainee, U.S. FOREST SERV, 57-59, res. forester, 59-65, plant ecologist, 65-68, PRIN. PLANT ECOLOGIST, 68-, DEPT. DIR. CONIFEROUS FOREST BIOME, 70- Japanese govt. award, 70; superior serv. award, U.S. Dept. Agr, 70; distinguished scientist award, Northwest. Sci. Asn, 70. AAAS; Soc. Am. Foresters; Ecol. Soc. Am; Brit. Ecol. Soc. Forest community ecology and succession; alpine communities; vegetation-soil relationships, especially Abies-Tsuga forest types. Address: U.S. Forest Service, P.O. Box 887, Corvallis, OR 97330.

FRANKLIN, J(OE) L(OUIS), JR, b. Natchez, Miss, Aug. 11, 06; m. 35; c. 3. B.S, Texas, 29, M.S, 30, Ph.D.(phys. chem), 34; fel, Mass. Inst. Tech, 30-31. Res. chemist, Humble Oil & Ref. Co, 34-36, asst. sect. head, 36-38, sect. head, 38-45, asst. div. head, 45-47, res. assoc, 47-63; ROBERT A. WELCH PROF. CHEM, RICE UNIV, 63-, Welch vis. scholar, 61-62. Guest scientist, Nat. Bur. Standards, 57-58; Wiley lectr, Purdue, 57; invited speaker, Gordon Res. Conf; Brit. Petrol. Soc. Symp. on mass spectrometry, 58; Tenth Int. Symp. Combustion. Mem. Adv. Bd. for Advances in Petrol. Chem. & Ref, 56-65; adv. comts. res. projs, 50 & 54, Am. Petrol. Inst; mem. eng. coun. prof. develop, educ. & accreditation comt, 62; organizer joint U.S-Japan Mass Spectrometry Symp, Japan, 68. AAAS; fel. Am. Inst. Chem; Am. Soc. Mass Spectrometry (pres, 69-70, dir-at-large, 70); Am. Chem. Soc.(Southwest award, 62; Southeast. Tex. sect. award, 70); Am. Inst. Chem. Eng.(South Tex. sect. pub. award, 49; distinguished serv. award, 62); Faraday Soc; fel. Am. Phys. Soc; Am. Soc. Test. & Mat; Combustion Inst. Electric discharge in gases; thermodynamics; reaction kinetics; ionization and appearance potentials by electron impact; ion molecule reactions; trapped radicals; molecular beams; photoelectron spectrometry. Address: Dept. of Chemistry, Rice University, Houston, TX 77001.

FRANKLIN, JOEL N(ICK), b. Chicago, Ill, Apr. 4, 30; m. 49; c. 1. MATHEMATICS. B.S, Stanford, 50, Ph.D.(math), 53. Instr. math, inst. math. sci, N.Y. Univ, 53-55; asst. prof, Washington (Seattle), 55-56; sr. mathematician, Burroughs Corp, 56-57; assoc. prof. appl. mech, CALIF. INST. TECHNOL, 57-65, PROF. appl. sci, 65-70, APPL. MATH, 70- Consult, atomic energy comn, radiation lab, Univ. Calif, 55, 57; jet propulsion lab, NASA, 62- Am. Math. Soc. Applied mathematics; high speed digital computing. Address: Division of Engineering & Applied Science, California Institute of Technology, Pasadena, CA 91109.

FRANKLIN, KENNETH L(INN), b. Alameda, Calif, Mar. 25, 23; wid; m. 58; c. 3. ASTRONOMY. A.B, California, 48, Ph.D.(astron), 53. Lab. technician, Lick Observ, Calif, 49-50; asst, Leuchner Observ, 53-54; res. fel. radio astron, Carnegie Inst, 54-56; asst. astronr, AM. MUS-HAYDEN PLANETARIUM, 56-57, assoc. astronr, 58-63, ASTRONR, 63-, ASST. CHMN, 68- Adj. prof, Cooper Union, 68-; Vis. prof, Rutgers Univ, 68-; astron. ed, World Almanac, 70-; mem. comn. five, Int. Sci. Radio Union; consult, Grumman Aircraft Co; Kearfott Div, Gen. Precision, Inc; Eclipse-Pioneer Div, Bendix Corp; AIL Div, Cutler-Hammer Corp; Razdow Labs, Int. Tel. & Tel; Martin Co; McGraw-Hill Book Co; Sci. Am; N.Y. Times; Time-Life Inc; CBS-TV; NBC-TV. Sig.C, 42-46, S/Sgt. Fel. AAAS; Am. Astron. Soc; Inst. Elec. & Electronics Eng; fel. Royal Astron. Soc. Binary stars; galactic structure; radio astronomy; astronomy education. Address: American Museum-Hayden Planetarium, 81st & Central Park W, New York, NY 10024.

FRANKLIN, LUTHER EDWARD, b. Birmingham, Ala, Jan. 21, 29; m. 48; c. 2. BIOLOGY. B.S, Alabama, 53; Ph.D.(exp. biol), Fla. State, 63. Res. assoc, inst. space biosci, Fla. State, 64; inst. molecular evolution, Miami (Fla), 64-65; RES. ASSOC. & ASSOC. PROF. REPROD. PHYSIOL, DELTA REGIONAL PRIMATE RES. CTR, TULANE UNIV, 65- Electron microscopist, fertilization gamete training prog, Marine Biol. Lab, Woods Hole, summers 64 & 65. U.S.N, 53-57, Lt. AAAS; Am. Asn. Anat; Am. Soc. Cell Biol; Am. Soc. Zool; Soc. Study Reproduction. Developmental biology; fertilization; cytological aspects and mechanisms; electron microscopy. Address: Delta Regional Primate Research Center, Tulane University, Covington, LA 70433.

FRANKLIN, MERVYN, b. Minehead, Eng, Jan. 13, 32; Can. citizen; m. 63. MICROBIOLOGY. B.Sc, Reading, 55, B.Sc, 56; Ph.D.(biochem), McGill, 59. Demonstr. bact, McGill, 57-58, sr. demonstr, 58-59; J.C. Childs fel. microbiol, Western Reserve, 59-60; lectr. bact, McGill Univ, 60-62, asst. prof, 62-65; microbiol, New York Med. Col, 65-66, assoc. prof, 67-69; DEAN FACULTY SCI, UNIV. N.B, 69- Grants referee, subcomt. bact, Med. Res. Coun. Can, 61-65; consult, Smith Kline & French Inter-Am. Corp, 64- Am. Soc. Microbiol; Can. Soc. Microbiol; Brit. Soc. Gen. Microbiol; Brit. Biochem. Soc. Drug metabolism; bacteriophage. Address: Faculty of Science, University of New Brunswick, Fredericton, N.B, Can.

FRANKLIN, MICHAEL LEON, b. Ft. Lauderdale, Fla, Sept. 20, 42; m. 67; c. 2. ANALYTICAL CHEMISTRY. A.B, Indiana, Bloomington, 64; univ. fel, Illinois, Urbana, 65, M.S, 66, Nat. Sci. Found. trainee, 66-69, Ph.D.(anal. chem), 69. Spectrochemist, Lewis Res. Ctr, NASA, 69-70; INSTR. PEDIAT, MED. SCH, UNIV. COLO, 70- Ord.C, U.S.A, 68-70, Capt. Am. Chem. Soc; Optical Soc. Am. Atomic spectroscopy; spectrophotometry; electronic instrumentation. Address: Dept. of Pediatrics, University of Colorado Medical School, 4200 E. Ninth Ave, Denver, CO 80220.

FRANKLIN, M(URRAY), b. N.Y.C, Nov. 3, 15; m. 51; c. 1. MEDICINE. B.S, City Col. New York, 33; M.D, Western Ontario, 40; fel, Northwestern, 47-48, M.S, 48. Instr. path, Northwestern, 47-48; assoc. med, sch. med, Iowa, 48-51; assoc. prof, col. med, Illinois, 51-55; prof. med. & asst. dean, Cook County Grad. Sch. Med, 53-66; MED. DIR, UNION HEALTH SERV, 66- Attend. physician & med. consult, hosps, 48- Dipl, Am. Bd. Internal Med. Med.C, 42-46, Lt. Col. Am. Med. Asn; fel. Am. Col. Physicians. Hepatic function; endocrine metabolism. Address: Union Health Service, Inc, 1634 W. Polk St, Chicago, IL 60612.

FRANKLIN, PAUL W(INTER), b. Vienna, Austria, Sept. 1, 13; m. 38; c. 3. ELECTRICAL ENGINEERING. Dipl. Ing, Vienna Tech. Univ, 36, Dr. Techn, 67. Div. consult, Naval Air Develop. Ctr, 51-52; dir. eng, Leland Airborne Prod. Div, Am. Mach. & Foundry Corp, 53-69; PROF. ELEC. ENG, UNIV. MO-COLUMBIA, 69- C.Eng, U.S.A, 1st Lt; Bronze Star Medal. Inst. Elec. & Electronics Eng; Am. Inst. Aeronaut. & Astronaut. Rotating electrical machinery; electrical power. Address: Dept. of Electrical Engineering, University of Missouri-Columbia, Columbia, MO 65201.

FRANKLIN, PHILIP J(AQUINS), b. Riverside, Calif, Oct. 25. 08; m. 37; c. 1. PHYSICS. A.B, California, Los Angeles, 31; Southern California, 31-32. Teacher, pub. schs, Calif, 32-42; physicist, Nat. Bur. Standards, 43-53; physicist & chief components, Diamond Ord. Fuze Labs, 53-62, prog. mgr, adv. res. proj. agency, U.S. Dept. Defense, 62-65; phys. sci. adminstr, Nat. Bur. Standards, 65-66, Nat. Bur. Standards chief, Nat. Bur. Standards-Gen. Serv. Admin. Testing Lab, 66-68; DIR. MAT. EVAL. & DEVELOP. LAB, FED. SUPPLY SERV, GEN. SERV. ADMIN, 68- Am. Chem. Soc; Am. Phys. Soc; Inst. Elec. & Electronics Eng. Plastics; electronic instrumentation; components; electrochemistry; casting resins; wax composition; printed circuit techniques; dielectrics; physical science testing. Address: 5907 Massachusetts Ave. Extd, Washington, DC 20016.

FRANKLIN, RALPH E, b. Chicago, Ill, Sept. 14, 34; m. 57; c. 3. SOIL CHEMISTRY. B.S, Arkansas, 55, M.S, 57; univ. develop. fund fel. & Ph.D.(soil chem, plant nutrit), Ohio State, 61. Asst. prof. AGRON, OHIO STATE UNIV. & OHIO AGR. RES. & DEVELOP. CTR, 61-66, assoc. prof, 66-69, PROF, 69- Int. Atomic Energy Agency adv. to Peru, 66-67. Sig.C, 56-58, 1st Lt. AAAS; fel. Am. Inst. Chem; Am. Chem. Soc; Soil Sci. Soc. Am; Am. Soc. Plant Physiol; Int. Soc. Soil Sci. Soil colloidal chemistry; exchange properties of plant roots and soil colloids; mineral absorption by plants; radioisotope methodology; gamma ray spectroscopy; liquid scintillation counting; tobacco nutrition; agricultural pollution. Address: Dept. of Agronomy, Ohio State University, 1885 Neil Ave, Columbus, OH 43210.

FRANKLIN, RAYMOND EMERSON, JR, b. N.Y.C, Apr. 6, 23; m. 58; c. 1. ORGANIC CHEMISTRY. B.S, Polytech. Inst. Brooklyn, 54. Chemist, Herstein Labs, Inc, 59-62; RES. CHEMIST, RES. & DEVELOP. DIV, AMSTAR CORP, 62- Am. Chem. Soc; N.Y. Acad. Sci. Organic synthesis; adhesives; pharmaceuticals; surface coatings; instrumental analysis; radioactive tracers; carbohydrate research and analysis. Address: Research & Development Division, Amstar Corp, 266 Kent Ave, Brooklyn, NY 11211.

FRANKLIN, RICHARD C(RAWFORD), b. Spokane, Wash, Nov. 11, 15; m. 42; c. 2. CHEMISTRY. B.A, Illinois, 37; Ph.D.(chem), Wisconsin, 40. Res. chemist, E.I. DU PONT DE NEMOURS & CO, INC, 40-41, 46-64, RES. SUPVR, 64- U.S.A, 41-46, Capt. Am. Chem. Soc. Dyes; anthraquinone colors and intermediates; phthalocyanines; rubber chemicals; hydrogenation and organic chemicals. Address: 1203 Brook Dr, Normandy Manor, Wilmington, DE 19803.

FRANKLIN, R(ICHARD) M(ORRIS), b. Medford, Mass, Oct. 16, 30; m. 58; c. 2. BIOPHYSICS, MOLECULAR BIOLOGY. B.S, Tufts Col, 51; Higgins fel, Yale, 51-52, Nat. Sci. Found. fel, 52-54, Ph.D, 54. Am. Cancer Soc. res. fel, Calif. Inst. Tech, 54-56; res. assoc, Max Planck Inst, Tubingen, Germany, 56-59; asst. prof. virol, Rockefeller Inst, 59-63; assoc. prof. path, sch. med, Univ. Colo, Denver, 63-65, prof, 65-67; mem, Pub. Health Res. Inst, City of New York, 67-71; PROF. VIROL, UNIV. BASEL, 71- Fulbright fel, 56; adj. prof, sch. med, N.Y. Univ, 67-71; mem. ed. bd, J. Virol; Nat. Insts. Health fel. rev. comt. AAAS; Am. Soc. Microbiol. Molecular biology of RNA virus replication; structure of viruses and other biological supramolecular aggregates; replication of viruses; structure of viral and other membranes. Address: Biozentrum, Universität Basel, Klingelbergstrasse 70, Basel, Switz.

FRANKLIN, ROBERT LOUIS, b. Salina, Kans, Feb. 21, 35; m. 61; c. 2. BIOCHEMISTRY, ORGANIC CHEMISTRY. B.A, Westmar Col, 63; Nat. Insts. Health fel, Mich. State, 66-67, Ph.D.(biochem), 67. Asst. prof. CHEM, WESTMAR COL, 67-70, ASSOC. PROF, 70- U.S.A, 57, 61-62. Am. Chem. Soc. Synthesis and physiological activity of indolic plant growth regulators. Address: Dept. of Chemistry, Westmar College, Le Mars, IA 51031.

FRANKLIN, ROBERT R(AY), b. Wetumka, Okla, Jan. 20, 28; m. 51; c. 4. OBSTETRICS, GYNECOLOGY. B.A, Univ. Tex, 49, M.D, 53. Assoc. prof. OBSTET. & GYNECOL, COL. MED, BAYLOR UNIV, 59-70, PROF, 70- Mem. attend. staff, Methodist Hosp; Jeff Davis Hosp; St. Lukes Hosp. U.S.N.R, 57-59. Am. Med. Asn. Endocrinology; bioassay for luteinizing hormone for clinical use; newborn physiology; transitional distress project. Address: 1009 Medical Towers, Houston, TX 77025.

FRANKLIN, RUDOLPH THOMAS, b. Morristown, N.J, Sept. 29, 28; m. 52; c. 5. ENTOMOLOGY. B.A, Emory, 50; M.S, Georgia, 55; Ph.D.(entom), Minnesota, 64. Forest entomologist, Minn. Dept. Agr, 58-62; entomologist, regional off, south. region, U.S. Forest Serv, Ga, 62-63, zone leader entom, N.C, 63-65; asst. prof. entom, UNIV. GA, 65-70, ASSOC. PROF. ENTOM. & FOREST RESOURCES, 70- U.S.A, 51-53, 2nd Lt. Soc. Am. Foresters; Entom. Soc. Am; Entom. Soc. Can. Ecology of forest insects; biology of bark beetles and weevils and hymenopterous parasites of bark beetles. Address: Dept. of Entomology, University of Georgia, Athens, GA 30601.

FRANKLIN, STANLEY PHILLIP, b. Memphis, Tenn, Aug. 14, 31; m. 51; c. 5. MATHEMATICS. B.S, Memphis State, 59; Nat. Sci. Found. fel, California, Los Angeles, summer 61, M.A, 62, Ph.D.(math), 63. Asst, California, Los Angeles, 61-62, assoc, 62-63; Nat. Sci. Found. fel, Washington (Seattle), 63-64; asst. prof. MATH, Univ. Fla, 64-65; CARNEGIE-MELLON UNIV, 65-67, assoc. prof, 67-71, PROF, 71- Summers, instr, Tulane Univ, 63, asst. prof, Univ. Calif, Los Angeles, 64; managing ed, Gen. Topology & Its Applns. U.S.M.C, 51-53, S/Sgt. Am. Math. Soc; Math. Asn. Am. Categorical topology. Address: Dept. of Mathematics, Carnegie-Mellon University, Pittsburgh, PA 15213.

FRANKLIN, THOMAS C(HESTER), b. Birmingham, Ala, Feb. 5, 23; m. 46; c. 4. PHYSICAL CHEMISTRY. B.S, Howard Col, 44; Ph.D.(chem), Ohio State, 51. Instr. chem, Howard Col, 46-48; asst. phys. chem, Ohio State, 48-49, asst. instr, 49-50; asst. prof. CHEM, Richmond, 51-54; assoc. prof, BAYLOR UNIV, 54-62, PROF, 62- Chem. res. worker, Va. Inst. Sci. Res, 52-53. U.S.N.R, 44-46. Electrochem. Soc; Am. Chem. Soc; Am. Electroplaters Soc. Electrochemistry; electrical methods of analysis; catalysis. Address: 1312 Guthrie Dr, Waco, TX 76710.

FRANKLIN, WILBUR MITCHELL, b. Berlin, Germany, Feb. 28, 33; U.S. citizen; m. 58; c. 4. SOLID STATE PHYSICS, METALLURGY. B.A, Col. Wooster, 54; B.S, Case, 57; Kaiser Aluminum fel. & M.S, Yale, 61; Ph.D. (solid state sci. & tech), Syracuse, 64. Engr, Sikorsky Aircraft Co, 57-59; semiconductor prod. div, Gen. Elec. Co, 60-61; sr. scientist & fel. mat. sci. Univ. Va, 64-66; asst. prof. PHYSICS, KENT STATE UNIV, 66-69, ASSOC. PROF, 69- Am. Phys. Soc. Solid state diffusion theory, including surface diffusion, anharmonic effects in solids, field emission, surface energy and defects in solids; liquid crystal theory. Address: Dept. of Physics, Kent State University, Kent, OH 44240.

FRANKLIN, W(ILLIAM) B(ALFOUR), b. Natchez, Miss, Oct. 7, 08; m. 33; c. 2. CHEMICAL ENGINEERING. B.S, Texas, 30, M.S, 31, Ph.D.(phys. chem), 34. Instr. phys. chem. & chem. eng, Texas, 30-34; chem. engr, HUMBLE OIL & REF. CO, 34-38, sect. head, 38-39, asst. div. head, 39-45, head tech. serv. div, 45-49, exec. asst, 49-50, head res. & develop. div, 50-52, mgr. tech. & res. divs, 52-53, head tech. serv. div, 53-56, asst. process supt, 56-57, mgr. tech. & res. divs, 57-58, tech. div, 58-69, HEAD MATH-COMPUT-SYSTS. FOR REF, REF. DEPT, 69- Distinguished eng. grad. award, Univ. Tex, 65. Am. Chem. Soc; fel. Am. Inst. Chem. Eng. (v.pres, 64, pres, 65, founders award, 68). Effect of the silent electric discharge on methane. Address: Refining Dept, Humble Oil & Refining Co, P.O. Box 2180, Houston, TX 77001.

FRANKLIN, WILLIAM E(LWOOD), b. Wash, D.C, Nov. 22, 31; m. 60. ORGANIC CHEMISTRY. B.Sc, Nebraska, 53, M.Sc, 55; Ph.D.(org. chem), Iowa, 59. Asst, Univ. Iowa, 55-58; asst. prof. chem, Loyola Univ.(La), 58-62, assoc. prof, 62-65; RES. CHEMIST, SOUTH. REGIONAL LAB, SOUTH. UTILIZATION RES. & DEVELOP. DIV, AGR. RES. SERV, U.S. DEPT. AGR, 65- Am. Chem. Soc. Diels-Alder reactions; cellulose crosslinking agents; thermally reversable reactions. Address: Southern Regional Lab, Southern Utilization Research & Development Division, Agriculture Research Service, U.S. Dept. of Agriculture, P.O. Box 19687, New Orleans, LA 70119.

FRANKLIN, WOODROW W(ILSON), b. West Plains, Mo, Sept. 4, 18; m. 38. ECONOMIC ENTOMOLOGY. B.S, McPherson Col, 42; Ph.D.(entom), Kans. State, 50. Teacher, pub. schs, Kans, 42-46; asst. prof. entom, Kans. State & asst. entomologist, agr. exp. sta, 48-53; agriculturalist, for. agr. serv, U.S. Dept. Agr. & For. Opers. Admin. Mission, Liberia, 53-57; entomologist, Int. Coop. Admin, 57-61; entom. adv, Agency for Int. Develop, Dept. State Mission, Somali Repub, 61-64; prof. biol. & head dept, Sterling Col, 64-70; PRES, CSC CORP. & EVERGREEN CHINCHILLA RANCH, 70- Entom. consult. U.S.A, 46-47. AAAS; Entom. Soc. Am. Insects attacking coffee and cacao; tsetse flies; ecology; diseases and nutrition of chinchilla. Address: 314 N. Seventh St, Sterling, KS 67579.

FRANKO, BERNARD V(INCENT), b. West Brownsville, Pa, June 9, 22; m. 46; c. 9. PHARMACOLOGY. B.S, West Virginia, 54, M.S, 55; Nat. Heart Inst. fel, Med. Col. Va, 55-58, Ph.D.(pharmacol), 58. Instr. PHARMACOL, MED. COL. VA, VA. COMMONWEALTH UNIV, 58-60, ASST. PROF, 60-; pharmacologist, BIOL. RES. LABS, A.H. ROBINS CO, INC, 58-68, DIR. PHARMACOL. RES, 71-, assoc. dir, 68-71. Fel. AAAS; Am. Soc. Pharmacol. & Exp. Therapeut; Soc. Toxicol; Soc. Exp. Biol. & Med; Int. Soc. Biochem. Pharmacol. Autonomic, cardiovascular and diuretic drugs; toxicology. Address: Biological Research Labs, A.H. Robins Co, Inc, 1211 Sherwood Ave, Richmond, VA 23220.

FRANKO-FILIPASIC, B(ORIVOJ) R(ICHARD) S(IMON), b. Zagreb, Yugoslavia, Jan. 5, 22; nat; m. 48; c. 3. ORGANIC CHEMISTRY. B.S, Northwestern, 43, Swift fel, 49-52, M.S, 51, Ph.D.(chem), 52. Res. chemist, Pittsburgh Plate Glass Co, 52-53; Mathieson Chem. Corp, 53-56; supvr. org, res. & develop, FMC CORP, 56-66, MGR. PROCESS RES. & DEVELOP, 66- U.S.N.R, 43-46, Lt. Am. Chem. Soc; The Chem. Soc; Am. Inst. Chem. Eng. Fats and oils; high polymers; polyesters; isocyanates; boron fuels; high pressure reactions. Address: FMC Corp, P.O. Box 8, Princeton, NJ 08540.

FRANKOSKY, MICHAEL STEPHEN, b. Wyoming, Pa, Mar. 25, 40; m. 63; c. 2. PHYSICAL CHEMISTRY. B.S, Kings' Col.(Pa), 61; Ph.D.(phys. chem), Pa. State Univ, 66. RES. CHEMIST, ORG. CHEM. DEPT, E.I. DU PONT DE NEMOURS & CO, INC, 66- Am. Chem. Soc. Low temperature calorimetry; nuclear magnetic relaxation; colloid and surface chemistry. Address: Organic Chemicals Dept, Jackson Lab, E.I. du Pont de Nemours & Co, Inc, Box 525, Wilmington, DE 19899.

FRANKS, ALLEN PAUL, b. Cleveland, Ohio, Nov. 12, 36; m. 63; c. 1. CHEMISTRY. B.S, Western Reserve, 59, J.D, 63. Phys. scientist, Crile Vet. Admin. Hosp, 59-60; chemist, Western Reserve, 61-63; patent attorney, B.F. Goodrich Co, 63-65; res. chemist, PPG Industs, Inc, 65-66; RUBBER LAB. MGR, REICHHOLD CHEM, CUYAHOGA FALLS, 66- U.S.C.G.R, 54-62. Am. Chem. Soc; N.Y. Acad. Sci. Organic synthesis of antioxidants, antiozonants and nucleotides; bioassay of enzymes and hormones; protective coatings; dispersions and lattices. Address: 340 Hollywood Ave, Akron, OH 44313.

FRANKS, EDWIN C(LARK), b. Chagrin Falls, Ohio, Jan. 13, 37; m. 58. ZOOLOGY. B.Sc, Ohio State, 58, M.Sc, 60, Nat. Sci. Found. fel, 63-64, Ph.D.(zool, ornith), 65. Lab. technician, Battelle Mem. Inst, 59-61, biologist, 61-62; U.S. Pub. Health Serv. trainee zool, Pa. State, 65-66; asst. prof. BIOL, WEST. ILL. UNIV, 66-70, ASSOC. PROF, 70- Nat. Sci. Found. award, Marine Biol. Lab, Woods Hole, 65. AAAS; Am. Ornith. Union; Wilson Ornith. Soc; Cooper Ornith. Soc; Nat. Audubon Soc; Ecol. Soc. Am; Am. Inst. Biol. Sci. Bird ecology and behavior. Address: Dept. of Biological Sciences, Western Illinois University, Macomb, IL 61455.

FRANKS, ERNEST HUGHES, b. Cleveland, Ohio, June 10, 15; m. 41; c. 2. MECHANICAL ENGINEERING. B.S, Drexel Inst, 41. Mech. engr, indust. test lab, Phila. Naval Shipyard, Pa, 41-49, welding engr, 49-56, supt. metals sect, 56-59; chief welding engr, elec. boat div, Gen. Dynamics Corp, 59-68; PRIN. FIELD APPLN. ENGR. MAT, ATOMIC POWER EQUIP. DIV, GEN. ELEC. CO, 68- Am. Soc. Mech. Eng; Am. Welding Soc. Welding engineering; metallurgy; welding; development welded design. Address: 1586 Wawona Dr, San Jose, CA 95125.

FRANKS, J(OHN) ANTHONY, JR, b. Cleveland, Ohio, Nov. 20, 35; m. 59; c. 3. ORGANIC CHEMISTRY. B.S, Notre Dame, 58; Marquette, 58-59; M.S, Western Reserve, 61, Ph.D.(org. chem), 63. Asst. chem, Western Reserve, 59-63, fel. org. chem, sch. med, 63-64; sr. org. chemist, Eli Lilly & Co, 64-66; group leader appln. res, color & chem. res. dept, Sherwin-Williams Co, 66-71; FACTOR REP, PARCO SCI. CO, WARREN, OHIO, 71- AAAS; Am. Chem. Soc; The Chem. Soc; Soc. Plastics Eng. Investigations on the synthesis and structural elucidations via infrared, ultra-violet, x-ray and nuclear magnetic resonance spectroscopy on benzoxazine systems and their derivatives, cyclopentane tetrols plus derivatives and reactions of thebaine type alkaloids. Address: Cornwall Dr, Rt. 2, Box 20-2, Crete, IL 60417.

FRANKS, JOHN J(ULIAN), b. Pueblo, Colo, Apr. 9, 29; m. 51; c. 5. INTERNAL MEDICINE. B.A, Colorado, 51, M.D, 54. Intern, Cornell med. div, Bellevue Hosp, 54-55; resident internal med, med. ctr, Colorado, 55-58; dep. chief dept. pharmacol-biochem, sch. aviation med, U.S. Air Force, 58-62; staff hematologist, Lackland Air Force Hosp, 62-63; asst. prof. MED, MED CTR, UNIV. COLO, DENVER, 63-68, ASSOC. PROF, 68-, ASSOC. DIR. CLIN. RES. CTR, 70- Res. fel. med, sch. med, Harvard & Mass. Gen. Hosp, 63-64; U.S. Pub. Health Serv. res. career develop. award, 63-69; assoc. chief of staff, Denver Vet. Hosp. U.S.A.F, 54-63, Res, 63-, Lt. Col. AAAS; Am. Fedn. Clin. Res; Am. Physiol. Soc; Am. Gastroenterol. Asn. Plasma Protein metabolism; oncology; biomathematics. Address: University of Colorado Medical Center, 4200 E. Ninth Ave, Denver, CO 80220.

FRANKS, LARRY ALLEN, b. Chesterland, Ohio, July 22, 34; m. 60; c. 2. MOLECULAR PHYSICS. A.B, Hiram Col, 58; U.S. Atomic Energy Comn. fels, Vanderbilt, 58-60, 65-66, M.S, 60, Ph.D.(physics, math), 68. Scientist, EG&G INC, 60-62, sr. scientist, 62-68, SCI. SPECIALIST, 68- Fulbright scholar, Australian Nat. Univ, 68-69. Am. Phys. Soc. Molecular structure and spectroscopy; effect of ionizing radiations on nonconductors; radiation dosimetry. Address: EG&G Inc, 130 Robin Hill Rd, Goleta, CA 93017.

FRANKS, LEWIS EMBREE, b. San Mateo, Calif, Nov. 8, 31; m. 54; c. 3. ELECTRICAL & COMMUNICATIONS ENGINEERING. B.S, Ore. State Univ, 52; M.S, Stanford Univ, 53, Ph.D.(elec. eng), 57. Instr. ELEC. ENG, Stanford Univ, 57-58; mem. tech. staff, Bell Tel. Labs, Inc, 58-62, supvr. data syst, 62-69; assoc. prof, UNIV. MASS, AMHERST, 69-71, PROF, 71- Adj. assoc. prof, Columbia Univ, 65, adj. prof, Northeast. Univ, 67-68. Inst. Elec. & Electronics Eng. Theoretical and design aspects of communication systems, signals, and signal processing equipment; circuit theory and design. Address: Juggler Meadow Rd, Amherst, MA 01002.

FRANKS, NEAL E(DWARD), b. Canton, Ohio, July 24, 36; m. 58; c. 2. ORGANIC CHEMISTRY. B.A, Manchester Col, 58; Ph.D.(org. chem), Ohio State Univ, 63. Sr. res. chemist, Am. Enka Corp, 63-64, prod. res. leader, 65; res. assoc. biochem, Univ. Iowa, 65-67; RES. CHEMIST, MIAMI VALLEY LABS, PROCTER & GAMBLE CO, 67- Am. Chem. Soc; N.Y. Acad. Sci. Carbohydrate chemistry; fibers; enzymes and enzyme technology. Address: 30 Jewel Lane, Cincinnati, OH 45218.

FRANKS, PAUL C, b. New York, N.Y, Nov. 10, 30; m. 54; c. 1. GEOLOGY. A.B, Cornell, 52; M.S, Kansas, 56, Ph.D.(geol), 66. Geologist, U.S. Geol. Surv, 54-56; State Geol. Surv. Kans, 56-66; prof. GEOL, N.Y. Univ, 66-71, chmn. dept, 69-71; ASSOC. PROF, UNIV. AKRON, 71- AAAS; fel. Geol. Soc. Am; Mineral. Soc. Am; Clay Minerals Soc; Soc. Econ. Geol; Soc. Econ.

Paleont. & Mineral. Mineralogy and clay mineralogy; sedimentary petrology; petrology of cratonic alkaline periodotites; petrology and stratigraphy of Kiowa and Dakota formations of midcontinent Cretaceous. Address: Dept. of Geology, University of Akron, Akron, OH 44304.

FRANKS, RICHARD LEE, b. Portland, Ore, Mar. 29, 41; m. 66; c. 2. ELECTRICAL ENGINEERING. B.S.E.E, Univ. Wash, 63; M.S, Univ. Calif, Berkeley, 69, Ph.D.(elec. eng), 70. MEM. TECH. STAFF SYST. THEORY, BELL TEL. LABS, 70- U.S.N, 63-67, Lt. Inst. Elec. & Electronics Eng. System theory. Address: 1M-202, Bell Telephone Labs, Whippany, NJ 07981.

FRANKS, ROBERT KENNETH, b. Lothair, Ky, Dec. 9, 34; m. 55; c. 2. PHYSICS. B.S, Carson-Newman Col, 56; Ph.D.(physics), Va. Polytech. Inst, 64. Aerospace technologist, Langley Res. Ctr, NASA, 64-66; asst. prof. physics & elec. eng, South. Methodist Univ, 66-69; ASSOC. PROF. PHYSICS, APPALACHIAN STATE UNIV, 69- NASA res. grants, 68, 69 & 71; NASA-Am. Soc. Eng. Educ. summer faculty fels, 69 & 70; consult, NASA. Am. Phys. Soc. Optical and electrical properties of semiconducting crystals; resistivity profiles by geoelectric sounding. Address: Dept. of Physics, Appalachian State University, Boone, NC 28607.

FRANKS, W(ILLIAM) R(OUNDING), b. Weston, Ont, Mar. 4, 01; wid; c. 2. PHYSIOLOGY, AVIATION MEDICINE. B.A, Toronto, 24, M.A, 25, M.D, 28. Fel. MED. RES, chair med. res, UNIV. TORONTO, 29-32, asst. prof, 32-38, assoc. prof, 38-47, prof, BANTING & BEST INST, 47-69, EMER. PROF, 69- Mem. assoc. comt, aviation med, Nat. Res. Coun. Can, 41-46; adv. med. comt, Royal Can. Air Force, 46-57, sci. adv, 46-; panel aviation & underwater physiol, Defence Res. Bd. Can, 48-; founders' group, Am. Bd. Prev. Med, 54; joint comt. aviation path, Armed Forces Inst. Path, 55. Off, Order of the Brit. Empire, 43. R.C.A.M.C, 40; R.C.A.F.R, 41-, Capt; Legion of Merit (U.S), 46. Am. Asn. Cancer Res; fel. Aerospace Med. Asn. (Lyster Award, 48, Liljencrantz Award, 62); Can. Fedn. Biol. Soc; Int. Acad. Astronaut. Medical and cancer research; accident investigation. Address: Dept. of Medical Research, Banting Institute, University of Toronto, 100 College St, Toronto 5, Ont, Can.

FRANKTON, C(LARENCE), b. Nottingham, Eng, Feb. 7, 06; m. 48; c. 1. BOTANY. B.Sc, McGill, 36, Ph.D.(bot), 40. Pasture researcher, Macdonald Col, McGill, 37-44; Que. Civil Serv, 44-46; sr. botanist, Plant Res. Inst, Can. Dept. Agr, 46-70; RETIRED. Weed biology; taxonomy of weedy plants of Canada; native Rumex and Cirsium. Address: 2297 Fox Crescent, Ottawa, Ont. K2B 7K5, Can.

FRANS, R(OBERT) E(ARL), b. Louisville, Nebr, Apr. 19, 27; m. 49; c. 3. AGRONOMY. B.S, Nebraska, 50; M.S, Rutgers, 53; Ph.D.(plant physiol), Iowa State, 55. Asst. farm crops, Rutgers, 50-53; plant physiol, Iowa State, 53-55; asst. prof. AGRON, UNIV. ARK, FAYETTEVILLE, 55-59, assoc. prof, 59-64, PROF, 64- U.S.A.R, 44-46. Am. Soc. Plant Physiol; Weed Sci. Soc. Am. Applied physiological usages of growth-active compounds for herbicidal purposes; mechanisms responsible for plant-growth inhibition from biologically active compounds. Address: Dept. of Agronomy, University of Arkansas, Fayetteville, AR 72701.

FRANSEN, JAMES M, b. Clinton, Okla, Feb. 23, 27. ANIMAL PHYSIOLOGY. B.S, Okla. State Univ, 51; univ. fel, Ralston Purina Danforth fel. & M.S, Purdue Univ, 53, Ph.D.(animal physiol), 55. Animal scientist, Rockefeller Found, 55-65; LIVESTOCK & CREDIT SPECIALIST & AGR. RES. ADV, WORLD BANK, INT. BANK FOR RECONSTRUCTION AND DEVELOP, 65- U.S.A, 45-46. Am. Soc. Animal Sci. Address: World Bank, International Bank for Reconstruction & Development, 1818 H St. N.W, Washington, DC 20433.

FRANT, MARTIN S, b. N.Y, July 15, 26; m. 48; c. 2. ANALYTICAL CHEMISTRY. B.S, Brooklyn, 49; M.S, Western Reserve, 51, Ph.D.(org. chem), 53. Asst, Western Reserve, 51-52; sr. res. chemist, Gallowhur Chem. Corp, 52-56; sr. res. assoc, AMP, Inc, 56-62; asst. tech. dir, Prototech, Inc, 63-64; asst. dir. res, ORION RES. INC, 64-70, DIR. RES, 70- Cochmn, Gordon Res. Conf. Electrodeposition, 61. U.S.A, 44-45. Fel. AAAS; Am. Electroplaters Soc; Am. Chem. Soc.(speaker award, 69); Electrochem. Soc. Aromatic mercury and quaternary ammonium compounds; corrosion of electroplated surfaces; electrodeposition; electroanalytical chemistry, ion-sensing electrodes. Address: Orion Research, Inc, Cambridge, MA 02139.

FRANTA, W(ILLIAM) A(LFRED), b. Ligderwood, N.Dak, Mar. 26, 13; m. 40; c. 3. CHEMISTRY. B.S, North Dakota, 33, M.S, 34, fel, 34-35; Rhodes scholar, Oxford, 35, A.B, 37; hon. D.Eng, Univ. N.D, 71. Sales engr, Herbert L. Brown, Ohio, 37-38; res. chemist, Columbia Chem. Div, Pittsburgh Plate Glass Co, Ohio, 38-42; from res. chemist to gen. lab. dir, polychem. dept, E.I. DU PONT DE NEMOURS & CO, INC, 46-53, mgr. develop. & serv, 53-55, mkt, 55-57, prod. mgr. plastics, 57-60, dir. supporting res, RES. & DEVELOP. DIV, PLASTICS DEPT, 60-64, asst. dir, 64, DIR, 64- U.S.A, 42-46, Capt. AAAS; Soc. Plastics Eng; Am. Chem. Soc; Am. Inst. Chem. Eng; The Chem. Soc. Organic polymers; polymer science; plastics processing and application. Address: Plastics Dept, E.I. du Pont de Nemours & Co, Inc, Wilmington, DE 19898.

FRANTTI, GORDON E(ARL), b. Palmer, Mich, July 28, 28; m. 52; c. 7. GEOPHYSICS, SEISMOLOGY. B.S, Michigan Tech, 53, State of Mich. fel. & M.S, 54; Michigan, 60-64. Res. asst. physics, Michigan Tech, 53-54, asst. prof, 59-60; mining engr. & geologist, Copper Range Co, 54-55; geologist & geophysicist, Cleveland Cliffs Iron Co, 55-56; geophysicist, U.S. Bur. Mines, 56-59; res. assoc, Inst. Sci. & Technol, Univ. Mich, 60-64, assoc. res. geophysicist, 64-65, lectr, dept. geol. & mineral, 63-64; ASSOC. PROF. GEOPHYS, MICH. TECHNOL. UNIV, 65- Consult, U.S. Bur. Mines, 59-60; Gen. Elec. Co, 62-63. U.S.N, 46-48. Soc. Explor. Geophys; Am. Geophys. Union; Seismol. Soc. Am. Mining and rock mechanics; theoretical and applied seismology; blasting and vibration studies; seismic earth noise. Address: Dept. of Physics, Michigan Technological University, Houghton, MI 49931.

FRANTZ, FREDERICK S(TRASSNER), JR, b. Lebanon, Pa, Jan. 21, 22; m. 46; c. 4. NUCLEAR PHYSICS. B.S, Lebanon Valley Col, 43; M.S, Pennsylvania, 49. Physicist, nuclear radiation, Nat. Bur. Standards, 49-55; scientist reactor physics, Bettis Atomic Power Lab, WESTINGHOUSE ELEC. CORP, 55-63, supvr, 63-65, sr. scientist, ASTRONUCLEAR LAB, 65-66, supvr, 66-68, MGR, 68- U.S.N.R, 43-46, Lt. Comdr. Am. Phys. Soc; Am. Nuclear Soc. Nuclear reactor physics in both water moderated, low enrichment uranium 235 cores and graphite moderated, high enrichment uranium 235 cores. Address: Astronuclear Lab, Westinghouse Electric Corp, P.O. Box 10864, Pittsburgh, PA 15236.

FRANTZ, IVAN D(ERAY), JR, b. Smithville, W.Va, Jan. 16, 16; m. 42; c. 5. BIOCHEMISTRY. A.B, Duke, 37; M.D, Harvard, 41. Intern, Springfield Hosp, Mass, 41-42; res. fel. med, Harvard, 46-48, asst, 48-50, assoc, 51-54, tutor biochem, 47-54, instr. med, 50-51; CLARK RES. PROF, DEPTS. MED. & BIOCHEM, MED. SCH. UNIV. MINN, MINNEAPOLIS, 54- Am. Cancer Soc. fel, Huntington Mem. Labs, Mass. Gen. Hosp, 46-47, clin. fel. med, 46-50, asst. physician, 50-54; consult, Mass. Inst. Technol, 47-54; mem. coun. arteriosclerosis, Am. Heart Asn. U.S.N, 42-46, Lt. Comdr. Am. Soc. Biol. Chem; Am. Soc. Clin. Invest; Am. Asn. Cancer Res. Bacterial nutrition; enzyme kinetics; protein and lipid metabolism with use of radioactive tracers. Address: Depts. of Medicine & Biochemistry, University of Minnesota Medical School, Minneapolis, MN 55455.

FRANTZ, JOSEPH FOSTER, b. McComb, Miss, Feb. 21, 33; m. 60; c. 3. CHEMICAL ENGINEERING. B.S, La. State, 55, M.S, 56, Ph.D.(chem. eng), 58. Res. chem. engr, Monsanto Co, Ark, 58-60, sr. chem. engr, Mo, 61-62, eng. dept, hydrocarbons div, 62-65; mgr. develop. & mkt, South Hampton Co, Houston, 65-68; PRES, FRANTZ CHEM. CONSULTS, 68- Am. Inst. Chem. Eng.(awards, 63, 64); Am. Chem. Soc. Fluidization; thermal cracking of hydrocarbons; marketing. Address: 6410 Tam O'Shanter, Houston, TX 77036.

FRANTZ, ROBERT L(OUIS), b. Fincastle, Va, Apr. 14, 27; m; c. 1. MINING ENGINEERING. B.S, Va. Polytech, 48; M.S, Pa. State, 50. Mining engr, Warner Collieries Co, 48-49; consult. mining engr, J.W. Woomer & Assocs, 53-56; prod. engr, Pocahontas Fuel Co, 56-57; asst. prof. mining eng, Ohio State, 57-64, consult. mining engr, John T. Boyd & Assocs, 64-67, V.PRES, JOHN T. BOYD CO, 67- U.S.N.R, 45-46. Am. Inst. Mining, Metall. & Petrol. Eng. Mine management; property evaluation and development. Address: John T. Boyd Co, 430 Oliver Bldg, Pittsburgh, PA 15222.

FRANTZ, WENDELIN R, b. Cleveland, Ohio, Apr. 28, 29; m. 52; c. 3. PETROLEUM GEOLOGY, STRATIGRAPHY. B.A, Col. Wooster, 52; M.S, Pittsburgh, 56, Ph.D.(geol), 63. Explor. geologist, Sohio Petrol. Co, 56-60; instr. geol, Capital Univ, 61-64, asst. prof, 64-68; PROF. GEOG. & EARTH SCI. & CHMN. DEPT, BLOOMSBURG STATE COL, 68- U.S.A, 52-54, Sgt. Am. Asn. Petrol. Geol; Nat. Asn. Geol. Teachers; Geol. Soc. Am. Subsurface stratigraphy and sedimentation with particular application to exploration for stratigraphic-type hydrocarbon accumulations. Address: Dept. of Geography & Earth Science, Bloomsburg State College, Bloomsburg, PA 17815.

FRANTZ, WILLIAM L(AWRENCE), b. Canton, Ohio, Nov. 3, 27; m. 50; c. 3. ZOOLOGY. B.Sc, Kent State, 51; M.Sc, Ohio State, 53, Ph.D, 57. ASST. PROF. biol, Drake, 57-60; PHYSIOL. & PHARMACOL, MICH. STATE UNIV, 60- Med.C, U.S.A, 45-47. Am. Soc. Zool; Am. Physiol. Soc. Cellular physiology; intermediary metabolism; membrane transport. Address: Dept. of Physiology & Pharmacology, College of Natural Sciences, Michigan State University, East Lansing, MI 48823.

FRANZ, ANSELM, b. Schladming, Austria, Jan. 21, 00; nat; m. 29; c. 2. MECHANICAL & AERONAUTICAL ENGINEERING. M.S, Tech. Univ. Graz, Austria, 24, hon. Dr, 69; Ph.D.(eng), Tech. Univ. Berlin, 39. Asst. prof. turbomachinery, Tech. Univ. Graz, 24-28; res. engr, Schwarzkopff Werke, Berlin, 29-35; v.pres. eng, Junkers Flugzeug & Motorenwerke, Germany, 36-45; consult. jet propulsion, Wright-Patterson Air Force Base, U.S. Air Force, 46-50; v.pres. & asst. gen. mgr, LYCOMING DIV, AVCO CORP, 51-68, CONSULT, 69- Outstanding civilian serv. medal, Dept. of Army, 68. Austria-Hungarian Army, 18. Fel. Am. Soc. Mech. Eng; Soc. Automotive Eng; Am. Helicopter Soc.(Klemin Award, 66); assoc. fel. Am. Inst. Aeronaut. & Astronaut; Ger. Acad. Aeronaut. Sci. Aerodynamics; thermodynamics; combustion; jet-propulsion; gas turbines. Address: Lycoming Division, Avco Corp, 550 S. Main St, Stratford, CT 06497.

FRANZ, DONALD N(ORBERT), b. Indianapolis, Ind, Sept. 23, 32; m. 58; c. 2. PHARMACOLOGY. B.S, Butler Univ, 54, M.S, 62; Pub. Health Serv. trainee, Univ. Utah, 62-66, Ph.D.(pharmacol), 66. Fel. vet. physiol, Univ. Edinburgh, 66-68; ASST. PROF. PHARMACOL, COL. MED, UNIV. UTAH, 68- U.S.A, 54-56. AAAS. Neurobiology of spinal sympathetic reflexes; role of monoamines in central transmission; effects of cold and drugs on nerve conduction; primary afferent projections to spinocervical tracts; C-fiber input to spinal cord. Address: Dept. of Pharmacology, University of Utah College of Medicine, Salt Lake City, UT 84112.

FRANZ, EDGAR A(RTHUR), b. Staunton, Ill, Dec. 9, 19; m. 46; c. 2. MATHEMATICS. B.A, Iowa, 48, M.S, 49. Instr. MATH, Culver-Stockton Col, 49-52, asst. prof, 52-56, assoc. prof, 56-60, PROF, 60-65; ILL. COL, 65- Sig.C, 42-46, 51-52, Lt. Am. Math. Soc. General mathematics. Address: 348 Sandusky, Jacksonville, IL 62650.

FRANZ, EDMUND C(LARENCE), b. Pittsburgh, Pa, July 8, 20; m. 49; c. 3. PHYSICAL METALLURGY. B.S, Carnegie Inst. Technol, 48; M.S, Case, 53. RES. METALLURGIST, Cleveland Res. Div, ALUMINUM CO. AM, 48-53, RES. LABS, 53- U.S.A.A.F, 43-46. Am. Soc. Metals. Physical metallurgy of aluminum alloys. Address: 25 Nancy Dr, Pittsburgh, PA 15235.

FRANZ, FRANK ANDREW, b. Phila, Pa, Sept. 16, 37; m. 59; c. 1. PHYSICS. B.S, Lafayette Col, 59; M.S, Illinois, 61, Ph.D.(physics), 64. Res. assoc. PHYSICS, coord. sci. lab, Illinois, 64-65; res. fel, Swiss Fed. Inst. Tech, 65-67; asst. prof, IND. UNIV, BLOOMINGTON, 67-70, ASSOC. PROF, 70- Nat. Sci. Found. fel, 65-67; Alfred P. Sloan Found. fel, 69-71. U.S.N.R, 54-62. AAAS; fel. Am. Phys. Soc; Am. Asn. Phys. Teachers. Relaxation phenomena in atomic and solid state physics; optical pumping; collisional interactions between atoms in ground and excited states; magnetic resonance in atomic vapors. Address: Dept. of Physics, Indiana University, Bloomington, IN 47401.

FRANZ, GUNTER NORBERT, b. Backa Palanka, Yugoslavia, Mar. 13, 35; m. 65; c. 1. PHYSIOLOGY, BIOPHYSICS. Dipl. elec. eng, Karlsruhe Tech, 59; NATO fel, Washington (Seattle), 60-62, Ph.D.(physiol, biophysics), 68. ASST. PROF. PHYSIOL. & BIOPHYSICS, MED. CTR, W.VA. UNIV, 68- AAAS; Inst. Elec. & Electronics Eng; Biophys. Soc; Am. Physiol. Soc. Cardiovascular physiology; physiology of receptors; biological control systems; systems biophysics. Address: Dept. of Physiology & Biophysics, Medical Center, West Virginia University, Morgantown, WV 26506.

FRANZ, JOHN E(DWARD), b. Springfield, Ill, Dec. 21, 29; m. 51; c. 4. ORGANIC CHEMISTRY. B.S, Illinois, 51; Gen. Elec. Corp. fel, Minnesota, 53, U.S. Rubber Co. fel, 54, Ph.D.(chem), 55. Res. chemist, MONSANTO CO, 55-59, group leader, 59-62, SCIENTIST, 62- Am. Chem. Soc. Fundamental organic research; reaction mechanisms; molecular structure; stereospecific reactions; oxidation processes; chemistry of azides; polymers; flame inhibition mechanisms; herbicide and plant growth regulator synthesis. Address: Monsanto Co, 800 N. Lindberg Blvd, St. Louis, MO 63166.

FRANZ, JOHN M(ATTHIAS), b. Oak Park, Ill, May 23, 27; m. 51; c. 4. BIOCHEMISTRY. B.S, Illinois, 50; M.S, Iowa, 52, U.S. Pub. Health Serv. fel, 52-55, Ph.D.(biochem), 55. Instr. BIOCHEM, MED. CTR, UNIV. MO-COLUMBIA, 55-57, asst. prof, 57-61, ASSOC. PROF, 61- Res. assoc, Harvard, 65-66. U.S.A, 46-47. Developmental and comparative aspects of metabolic control. Address: Dept. of Biochemistry, Medical Center, University of Missouri-Columbia, Columbia, MO 65201.

FRANZ, JUDITH ROSENBAUM, b. Chicago, Ill, May 3, 38; m. 59; c. 1. SOLID STATE & ATOMIC PHYSICS. B.A, Cornell, 59; M.A, Illinois, 61, Ph.D.(physics), 65. Res. physicist, Int. Bus. Mach. Res. Lab, Switz, 65-67; VIS. ASST. PROF. PHYSICS, IND. UNIV, BLOOMINGTON, 67- Am. Phys. Soc. Interaction of sound waves with spin waves and nuclear spins. Address: Dept. of Physics, Indiana University, Bloomington, IN 47401.

FRANZ, NORMAN C(HARLES), b. Newark, N.J, June 12, 25; m. 49; c. 1. WOOD & PULP SCIENCE. B.S, State Univ. N.Y, 48; M.Wood Tech, Michigan, 50, Schoen-Rene fel, 52-54, Haywood Wakefield fel, 51-52, Ph.D, 56. Res. engr, Eng. Res. Inst, 50-54; instr. wood. tech, Michigan, 54-56, asst. prof, 56-57, assoc. prof, 57-68; PROF. FORESTRY, UNIV. B.C, 68- U.S.A, 44-46. Soc. Wood Sci. & Technol; Forest Prod. Res. Soc; Am. Soc. Mech. Eng; Int. Union Forest Res. Orgn. Forest products engineering; machining of wood and other materials; ultra-high pressure physics and processing. Address: Faculty of Forestry, University of British Columbia, Vancouver 8, B.C, Can.

FRANZ, OTTO G(USTAV), b. Eggenburg, Austria, Feb. 14, 31; m. 62; c. 3. ASTRONOMY. Dr.phil.(astron), Vienna, 55. Asst. astron, univ. observ, Vienna, 53-55; res. assoc, Dearborn Observ, Northwestern, 55-58; ASTRONOMER, U.S. Naval Observ, 58-65; LOWELL OBSERV, 65- Am. Astron. Soc; Int. Astron. Union. Photographic astrometry; photoelectric observations of double stars. Address: Lowell Observatory, Flagstaff, AZ 86001.

FRANZ, RAYMOND A(MEND), b. Dayton, Ohio, Sept. 15, 06; m. 30; c. 2. ORGANIC CHEMISTRY. B.S, Miami (Ohio), 29; Ph.D.(org. chem), Iowa State Col, 36. Instr. chem, Iowa State Col, 29-37; res. chemist, United Gas Improv. Co, 37-44; Alco Oil & Chem. Corp, Pa, 45-46; dir. res, Bowman Gum Co, 47-48; sr. specialist, res. hydrocarbon div, Monsanto Co, 48-71; RETIRED. Am. Chem. Soc. Polymerization of unsaturated hydrocarbons; textile finishes; synthetic nitrogen derivatives; cracking; dehydrogenation. Address: 907 Daventry Dr, Baton Rouge, LA 70808.

FRANZ, R(ICHARD) J(OHN), b. Newark, N.J, Sept. 8, 19; m. 43; c. 2. CHEMICAL ENGINEERING. B.S, Tufts, 39. Jr. engr, AM. CYANAMID CO, N.J, 46-49, dept. process engr, 49-52, suprvy. process engr, 52-55, chief process chemist. 55-58, develop. supvr, FLA, 58-59, eng. mgr, 59-61, tech. mgr, 61-63, QUAL. CONTROL MGR, 63- U.S.N.R, 40-46, Capt. Am. Inst. Chem. Eng. Chemical process design and improvement. Address: American Cyanamid Co, Milton, FL 32570.

FRANZAK, EDMUND G(EORGE), b. Chicago, Ill, June 27, 30; m. 60; c. 3. THEORETICAL PHYSICS. B.S, Fournier Inst. Tech, 52; M.S, New Mexico, 55; M.S, Northwestern, 57, Ph.D.(physics), 60. Mem. staff, Sandia Corp, 52-55; asst. prof. physics, Missouri, 60-61; head neutron tube develop. div, SANDIA CORP, 62-66, MGR, ELECTRONIC COMPONENTS DEPT, 66- Summers, mem. staff, Sandia Corp, 58, 60. Am. Phys. Soc. Neutron and theoretical solid state physics; electron transport in metals. Address: 3410 Inman Court N.E, Albuquerque, NM 87110.

FRANZBLAU, CARL, b. N.Y.C, Sept. 26, 34; m. 58; c. 2. BIOCHEMISTRY. B.S, Univ. Mich, 56; Ph.D.(biochem), Albert Einstein Col. Med, 62. Asst. prof. BIOCHEM, SCH. MED, BOSTON UNIV, 62-66, assoc. prof, 66-71, PROF, 71- Res. collab, Brookhaven Nat. Lab, 62-; estab. investr, Am. Heart Asn, 66-71. Am. Chem. Soc; Am. Soc. Biol. Chem; N.Y. Acad. Sci; Am. Heart Asn. Chemistry of connective tissue proteins; enzymology. Address: Dept. of Biochemistry, Boston University School of Medicine, 80 E. Concord St, Boston, MA 02118.

FRANZBLAU, ROBERT S, Clin. Psychol, see 12th ed, Soc. & Behav. Vols.

FRANZBLAU, SANFORD (A), b. Ozone Park, N.Y, Mar. 15, 18; m. 46; c. 4. PHYSIOLOGY. B.A, Illinois, 39, M.S, 42, M.D, 43, Ph.D.(med), 51. Clin. asst. prof. MED, COL. MED, UNIV. ILL, 54-66, CLIN. ASSOC. PROF, 66-, ATTEND. PHYSICIAN, RES. & EDUC. HOSP, 53- Diplomate, Am. Bd. Internal Med, 50. U.S.A, 43-46. Am. Fedn. Clin. Res; Am. Col. Physicians; Am. Soc. Clin. Path. Aviation medicine; altitude stress, cardiac and respiratory response in normals and patients with cardiorespiratory disease;

immunology, antigenicity of antibodies; ballistocardiography, three-dimensional vector ballistocardiogram. Address: Golf Mill Professional Bldg, Niles, IL 60648.

FRANZEN, DOROTHEA S(USANNA), b. Emporia, Kans, Mar. 17, 12. ZOOLOGY. A.B, Bethel Col, 37; M.A, Kansas, 43, Ph.D.(zool), 46. Instr. biol, Cedar Crest Col, 46-47; asst. prof, Washburn, 47-50, assoc. prof, 50-52; ILL. WESLEYAN UNIV, 52-58, prof, 58-71, GEORGE C. & ELLA BEACH LEWIS PROF. BIOL, 71- Researcher, Univ. Reading, England, 59-60. Fel. AAAS; Am. Zool; Soc. Syst. Zool; Am. Malacol. Union. Distribution and ecology of Cenozoic terrestrial and freshwater Mollusca; fossil and living Pupillidae in Kansas; Succineidae in North America. Address: Dept. of Biology, Illinois Wesleyan University, Bloomington, IL 61702.

FRANZEN, HUGO FRIEDRICH, b. N.Y.C, Aug. 27, 34; m. 56; c. 3. PHYSICAL CHEMISTRY. B.S, California, Berkeley, 57; Nat. Sci. Found. fel, Kansas, 58-60, Ph.D.(chem), 62. Fel, inst. inorg. chem, Stockholm, 63-64; asst. chemist, AMES LAB, U.S. ATOMIC ENERGY CMN, 64-65, assoc. chemist, 65-69, CHEMIST, 69-; ASSOC. PROF. CHEM, IOWA STATE UNIV, 69-, asst. prof, 65-69, instr, 64-65. Summer res. asst, Los Alamos Sci. Lab, 58-59. AAAS; Am. Chem. Soc; Am. Crystallog. Asn. High temperature chemistry; thermodynamics; crystallography; heterogeneous equilibrium; vaporization chemistry. Address: Dept. of Chemistry, Iowa State University, Ames, IA 50010.

FRANZEN, JAMES, b. Chicago, Ill, Jan. 13, 34; m. 61; c. 4. BIOPHYSICAL CHEMISTRY. B.S, Wheaton Col.(Ill), 55; M.S, Illinois, 58, Ph.D.(biochem), 60. U.S. Pub. Health Serv. fel, Northwestern, 60-61; res. assoc. biophys. chem, grad. sch. pub. health, UNIV. PITTSBURGH, 61-62, asst. res. prof, 62-65, ASSOC. PROF. BIOCHEM, 65- Am. Chem. Soc; Am. Soc. Biol. Chem. Protein structure; lipid-protein interactions; cooperative enzyme-substrate interactions. Address: Dept. of Biochemistry, Faculty of Arts & Sciences, Crabtree Hall, University of Pittsburgh, Pittsburgh, PA 15213.

FRANZEN, WILLIAM G(ERALD), b. Springfield, Ohio, Feb. 26, 27; m. 50; c. 3. MATHEMATICS. A.B, Miami (Fla), 49, M.S, 51; Mich. State, 51-54; Ill. Inst. Tech, 57-59; La. State, 59-61. Instr. MATH, Aquinas Col, 54-56, asst. prof, 56-57; instr, Ill. Inst. Tech, 57-59; La. State, 59-61; assoc. prof, St. Mary's Col.(Minn), 61-69, co-chmn. dept, 62-64, chmn, 64-69; PROF. & HEAD DEPT, LEA COL, 69- U.S.N, 45-46. Am. Math. Soc; Math. Asn. Am; London Math. Soc. Matric equations; classical theory of functions. Address: Dept. of Mathematics, Lea College on Lake Chapeau, Albert Lea, MN 56007.

FRANZEN, W(OLFGANG), b. Duesseldorf, Ger. Apr. 6, 22; nat; m. 43. PHYSICS. B.S, Haverford Col, 42; M.A, Columbia, 44; Ph.D, Pennsylvania, 49. Instr. physics, Princeton, 49-53; asst. prof, Rochester, 53-56; sr. physicist, Arthur D. Little, Inc, 56-61; assoc. prof. PHYSICS, BOSTON UNIV, 61-65, PROF, 65- Exchange fel, Basel, 54-55; NATO sr. fel, Toulouse, 69-70. U.S.A, 44. Fel. Am. Phys. Soc. Nuclear reactions and physics; instrumentation; optical pumping; magnetic resonance; electron resonance scattering and polarization. Address: Dept. of Physics, Boston University, Boston, MA 02215.

FRANZINI, JOSEPH B(ERNARD), b. Las Vegas, N.Mex, Nov. 10, 20; m. 46; c. 4. CIVIL ENGINEERING. B.S, Calif. Inst. Tech, 42, M.S, 43, C.E, 44; Ph.D.(civil eng), Stanford, 50. Asst, Calif. Inst. Tech, 42-44; instr. CIVIL ENG, STANFORD UNIV, 46-49, asst. prof, 49-55, assoc. prof, 55-62, PROF, 62- U.S.N, 42-44. Am. Soc. Civil Eng; Am. Soc. Eng. Educ; Am. Geophys. Union. Evaporation suppression; infiltration; porous media flow. Address: Dept. of Civil Engineering, Stanford University, Stanford, CA 94305.

FRANZL, ROBERT E, b. N.Y.C, May 27, 21; m. 52; c. 1. BIOCHEMISTRY. B.S, City Col. New York, 41; M.A, Columbia, 48, Ph.D.(biochem), 52. Asst. org. chem & biochem, Columbia, 46-52, res. assoc. biochem, 53-54; res. assoc. immunochem, immunol. dept, Sloan-Kettering Inst, 54-56; IMMUNOL, ROCKEFELLER UNIV, 56-59, ASST. PROF, 59- Vis. res. assoc, Brookhaven Nat. Labs, 52-53. U.S.A, 42-45. Am. Chem. Soc; N.Y. Acad. Sci; Brit. Biochem. Soc; Am. Asn. Immunol; Am. Soc. Microbiol. Bacterial enzymes; cyclitols; lipids; immunochemistry; antibody synthesis. Address: Dept. of Immunology, Rockefeller University, 66th St. & York Ave, New York, NY 10021.

FRANZMEIER, DONALD PAUL, b. Greenwood, Wis, May 13, 35; m. 60; c. 3. SOIL SCIENCE. B.S, Minnesota, 57, M.S, 58; Ph.D.(soil sci), Mich. State, 62. Soil scientist, soil conserv. serv, U.S. Dept. Agr, 62-67; ASSOC. PROF. AGRON, PURDUE UNIV, 67- Am. Soc. Agron; Soil Sci. Soc. Am; Am. Asn. Quaternary Res; Soil Conserv. Soc. Am; Int. Soc. Soil Sci. Soil mineralogy, chemistry and physics in relation to the genesis and classification of soils. Address: Dept. of Agronomy, Purdue University, Lafayette, IN 47907.

FRANZUS, BORIS, b. Chicago, Ill, July 23, 24; m. 48; c. 3. PHYSICAL & ORGANIC CHEMISTRY. M.S, Chicago, 50; Ph.D.(phys. org. chem), Colorado, 54. Res. chemist, Phillips Petrol. Co, 54-60; sr. chemist, cent. basic res. labs, Esso Res. & Eng. Co, 60-67; assoc. prof. CHEM, E. TENN. STATE UNIV, 67-70, PROF, 70- U.S.A, 43-46. Am. Chem. Soc; The Chem. Soc. Kinetics and mechanisms reactions of organic chemistry. Address: Dept. of Chemistry, East Tennessee State University, Johnson City, TN 37601.

FRAPPIER, ARMAND, b. Valleyfield, Que, Nov. 26, 04; m. 29; c. 4. BACTERIOLOGY, HYGIENE. B.A, Univ. Montreal, 24, M.D, 30, Lic-es-Scis, 31; Dipl, Trudeau Sch, 32; hon. Dr, Univ. Paris, 64, Laval Univ, 71. Rockefeller fel. bact, Univ. Rochester, 31-32; prof. faculty med, UNIV. MONTREAL, 33-71, DIR. & FOUNDER INST. MICROBIOL. & HYG, 38-, founder & dean, sch. hyg, 45-65. Dir. clin. labs, St. Luke's Hosp, 27-43; consult, Health League, Can, 47-; mem. adv. comt. med. res, Nat. Res. Coun. Can, 52-55; panel infection & adv. comt. biol. warfare res, Defence Res. Bd, Can; adv. comt, Pub. Health Res: Can, 54-60; expert comt. tuberc, WHO, 53. Off,

Order of the Brit. Empire, 46; Companion, Order of Can, 69. AAAS; fel. Am. Pub. Health Asn; Am. Asn. Path. & Bact; fel. Royal Soc. Can; Can. Physiol. Soc; Can. Soc. Microbiol.(pres, 54); Can. Pub. Health Asn; Can. Med. Asn; Fr-Can. Asn. Advan. Sci; for. mem. Fr. Acad. Med. Allergy and immunization in tuberculosis using Bacillus Calmette-Guerin vaccine; development of scarification test; experimental tuberculosis using radio-isotopes; gas gangrene mechanism; role of bacterial surface washings in production of immunity against whooping cough; infection promoting factors; poliomyelitis. Address: Institute of Microbiology & Hygiene, C.P. 100, Laval-des-Rapides, Que, Can.

FRAREY, M(URRAY) J(AMES), b. Midland, Ont, Jan. 31, 17; m. 54; c. 2. GEOLOGY. B.A, Western Ontario, 40; M.Sc, Michigan, 51, Ph.D.(geol), 54. GEOLOGIST, Kerr-Addison Gold Mines Ltd, 41-43; GEOL. SURV. CAN, 47- Can. Army, 43-46. Geol. Asn. Can. Precambrian geology. Address: 601 Booth St, Ottawa, Ont, Can.

FRASCHE, DEAN F(REDERIC), b. Council Bluffs, Iowa, Aug. 26, 06; m. 37; c. 3. GEOLOGY. Ph.B, Wisconsin, 33, fel, 37; Iowa, 34-35. Geologist, Philippine Bur. Mines, Manila, 37-38, chief geol. surv. div, 38-41; consult. minerals, Off. Prod. Mgt, Wash, D.C, 41; asst. chief chrome manganese br, War. Prod. Bd, 41-42, 42-43, dep. dir. micagraphite div, 43-44; consult. mining geologist, 44-50; mgr. explor, ore div, UNION CARBIDE CORP, 50-67, DIR, UNION CARBIDE EAST. INC, 67- Mem, Anglo-Am. Econ. Mission, W.Africa & Belg. Congo, 42; adv, U.S. Del. Nat. Resources, Fifth Session Econ. Comn. Asia & Far East, 63; chmn. bd, Thailand Smelting & Ref. Co, Ltd, 64-, chmn. & managing dir, 68; mem, Coun. For. Rels, N.Y, 67; adv, Thailand Del, Int. Tin Coun, 67-71; chmn, Thailand Explor. & Mining Co, Ltd, 70; Tahlarng Mining Co, Ltd, Bangkok, Thailand, 70; assoc. mem, Nat. Res. Coun. Philippines; mem. comt. nat. resources, Nat. Acad. Sci-Nat. Res. Coun. Chevalier, Order of Royal Lion, Belg, 47. AAAS; Soc. Econ. Geol; Min. & Metall. Soc. Am; fel. Geol. Soc. Am; Am. Inst. Min, Metall. & Petrol. Eng; Can. Inst. Min. & Metall. Mining geology with special emphasis on political-economic aspects of mineral resources in foreign countries. Address: Union Carbide Eastern Inc, 270 Park Ave, 48th Floor, New York, NY 10017.

FRASCO, DAVID LEE, b. Brush, Colo, Apr. 8, 31; m. 54; c. 2. PHYSICAL CHEMISTRY, SPECTROSCOPY. A.B, Colo. State Col, 53; M.S, Wash. State Univ, 55, Ph.D.(infrared spectra of solids), 58. Asst. Prof. CHEM, WHITMAN COL, 58-65, ASSOC. PROF, 65-, CHMN. DIV. BASIC SCI, 70-, chmn. dept. chem, 65-70. Consult, Pac. Northwest Labs, Battelle Mem. Inst, 68- AAAS; Am. Chem. Soc. Physical, chemical and electrical properties of thin lipid membranes, especially artificial cell membranes; infrared spectra of molecular solids. Address: Dept. of Chemistry, Whitman College, Walla Walla, WA 99362.

FRASER, DAVID A(LLISON), b. Phila, Pa, Aug. 29, 22; m. 47; c. 2. ENVIRONMENTAL HEALTH. B.A, Pennsylvania, 47; M.S, Xavier (Ohio), 57; Sc.D.(indust. health), Cincinnati, 61. Res. chemist, Chem. Mfg. & Distributing Co, 47-49; chemist, div. indust. hyg, U.S. Pub. Health Serv, Wash, D.C, 49-52, chief aerosol unit, div. occup. health prog, Ohio, 52-61; assoc. prof. INDUST. HYG, UNIV. N.C, CHAPEL HILL, 61-68, PROF, 68- Lectr, Cincinnati, 58-61; consult, div. radiol. health, U.S. Pub. Health Serv, 64- U.S.A.A.F, 42-45, Res, 45-49; Nat. Guard, 49-50, 1st Lt. Fel. AAAS; Am. Chem. Soc; Electron Micros. Soc. Am; Am. Indust. Hyg. Asn; fel. Am. Inst. Chem; Conf. Govt. Indust. Hygienists; fel. Royal Micros. Soc. Industrial health and toxicology; air sampling techniques; physics and sampling of airborne particulates; optical and electron microscopy. Address: 408 Long Leaf Dr, Chapel Hill, NC 27514.

FRASER, (WILLIAM) DEAN, b. Wells River, Vt, Oct. 3, 16; m. 39, 53, 65; c. 7. MOLECULAR BIOLOGY. B.S, Harvard, 38; M.S, Illinois, 39, Ph.D. (org. chem), 41. Res. chemist, Monsanto Chem. Co, Mo, 41-45; res. fel, Calif. Inst. Technol, 46-47; asst. prof. res, Princeton, 47-48; Nat. Res. Coun. growth fel, virus lab, California, 48-50, asst. res. biochemist, 50-52, assoc. res. biochemist, 52-55; assoc. prof. virol, IND. UNIV, BLOOMINGTON, 55-60, prof, 60-70, CHMN. DEPT. MICROBIOL, 70- AAAS; Am. Chem. Soc. Mycoplasma viruses; biochemical and genetic resolution. Address: Dept. of Microbiology, Indiana University, Bloomington, IN 47401.

FRASER, D(ONALD), b. Toronto, Ont, Feb. 14, 21; m. 54; c. 1. PHYSIOLOGY. M.D, Toronto, 44, M.A, 46, Ph.D.(physiol), 50. From assoc. pediat. to ASST. PROF. PEDIAT. & PHYSIOL, UNIV. TORONTO, 55-; RES. MEM, RES. INST, HOSP. FOR SICK CHILDREN, 58-, res. assoc, 53-58. Medal med, Royal Col. Physicians & Surgeons, Can, 56. R.C.N.V.R, 45-46, Lt. Surg. AAAS; Soc. Pediat. Res; fel. Am. Acad. Pediat; Can. Pediat. Soc. Physiology of bone metabolism as applied to children. Address: Dept. of Pediatrics, University of Toronto, Toronto, Ont, Can.

FRASER, DONALD A(LEXANDER), b. Toronto, Ont, Jan. 23, 18; m. 53; c. 2. PLANT PHYSIOLOGY. B.A, Toronto, 40, Ph.D.(bot), 51; Oak Ridge Inst. Nuclear Studies, 55. Asst. zool, Toronto, 39-40, demonstr. bot, 45-48; lectr, Alberta, 48-49; plant ecologist, Can. Dept. Agr, 49-53; tree physiologist, Petawawa Forest Exp. Sta, Can. Dept. Forestry, 53-70; CHMN. DEPT. GEOG, SIR GEORGE WILLIAMS UNIV, 70- Inst. bd. ed, Toronto, 38-40; forest soils surveyor, dept. lands & forests, Ont, 45-47. Assoc. dir, radioisotope course for foresters, Fed. Agr. Orgn-Int. Atomic Energy Agency, UN, Germany, 65-; exchange scientist U.S.S.R, Nat. Res. Coun, 69. R.C.A.F, 37-45, 47-53. Ecol. Soc. Am; Bot. Soc. Am; Soc. Am. Foresters; Am. Soc. Plant Physiol; Can. Soc. Plant Physiol; Can. Inst. Forestry; Brit. Ecol. Soc; Brit. Soc. Soil Sci. Morphology, ecology and physiology of forest trees; use of radioisotopes in forestry research. Address: Dept. of Geography, Sir George Williams University, Montreal, Quebec, Can.

FRASER, D(ONALD) A(LEXANDER) S(TUART), b. Toronto, Ont, Apr. 29, 25. STATISTICS. B.A, Toronto, 46, M.A, 47; M.A, Princeton, 48, Ph.D. (math), 49. Instr. MATH, Princeton, 47-49; asst. prof, UNIV. TORONTO, 49-53, assoc. prof, 53-58, PROF, 58- Fel. AAAS; fel. Am. Statist. Asn; fel. Inst. Math. Statist; fel. Royal Statist. Soc; fel. Royal Soc. Can; Int. Statist. Inst. Mathematical statistics. Address: Dept. of Mathematics, University of Toronto, Toronto, Ont, Can.

FRASER, DONALD B(OYD), b. Teaneck, N.J, Nov. 15, 30; m. 55; c. 2. PHYSICAL CHEMISTRY. B.S, St. Peter's Col, 54; Ph.D.(phys. chem), Rutgers, 60. Chemist, Enjay Labs, Esso Res. & Eng. Co, 60-62; sr. develop. engr, Celanese Plastics Co, N.J, 62-63, group leader, 63-68; assoc. prof. CHEM, ESSEX COUNTY COL, 68-71, PROF, 71-, CHMN. DEPT, 70- Am. Chem. Soc. Address: Dept. of Chemistry, Essex County College, 31 Clinton St, Newark, NJ 07102.

FRASER, DONALD W, b. Manchester, Iowa, May 22, 10; m. 36; c. 1. ELECTRICAL ENGINEERING. B.S, U.S. Naval Acad, 34; M.S, Ga. Inst. Tech, 48, Ph.D, 55. Instr, Admiral Farregut Acad, 35-41; asst. prof. electronic eng, Ga. Inst. Tech, 47-49, res. asst. prof, eng. exp. sta, 53-55; head dept, Rhode Island, 56-57; SR. SCIENTIST, HUGHES AIRCRAFT CO, 58- Consult, Elec. Boat Co, Conn, 56-57. U.S.N, 42-46, 50-52, Comdr. Sr. mem. Inst. Elec. & Electronics Eng. Missile and radar systems; frequency control. Address: 3835 Esmeralda Ave, El Monte, CA 91731.

FRASER, EDWARD C(LEVELAND), b. N.Y.C, Nov. 11, 36; m. 63; c. 3. SYSTEMS & CONTROL ENGINEERING. B.S, Worcester Polytech, 58; M.S, Mass. Inst. Technol, 60; Ph.D.(elec. eng), Stanford, 65. Sr. res. engr, info. & control group, Stanford Res. Inst, 60-69; prog. mgr, MB Assocs, Calif, 69-71; DIR. ADVAN. ELECTRONIC SYSTS, TRACOR, INC, 71- Application of control theory and technology to dynamic control problems. Address: Tracor, Inc, 6500 Tracor Lane, Austin, TX 78721.

FRASER, F(RANK) C(LARKE), b. Norwich, Conn, March 29, 20; nat. Can; m. 48; c. 4. GENETICS. B.Sc, Acadia Univ, 40, hon. D.Sc, 67; Nat. Res. Council Can. bursary, McGill, 40-41, M.Sc, 41, Nat. Res. Council Can. studentship, 41-43, Ph.D.(genetics), 45, M.D, C.M, 50. Demonstr. genetics, McGILL UNIV, 45-46, lectr, 46-50, asst. prof, 50-55, assoc. prof, 55-60, ASSOC. PROF. PEDIAT. & PROF. MED. GENETICS, 60-, DEMONSTR, 54-, teaching fel, 52-54. Molson-McConnel res. fel, 50-51; dir. dept. med. genetics, Montreal Children's Hosp, 50-; clin. fel, Royal Victoria Hosp, 50-; consult, Shriners Hosp. Crippled Children, 54- R.C.A.F, 43-45. Am. Soc. Human Genetics (v.pres, 59, pres, 62); Genetics Soc. Am; Soc. Pediat. Res; Genetics Soc. Can; Can. Pediat. Soc; Royal Soc. Can. Experimental production of congenital defects; inheritance of human diseases; genetic counseling. Address: Dept. of Biology, Stewart Bldg, McGill University, Montreal 110, Que, Can.

FRASER, GEORGE HERBERT, b. Sudbury, Ont, Sept. 14, 37. ELECTROCHEMISTRY. B.A, Toronto, 60, M.A, 61, Ph.D.(chem), 64. Res. scientist, Johnson, Matthey & Mallory Ltd, 64-68, res. mgr, 68-69; RES. CHEMIST, MATTHEY BISHOP, INC, 69- Electrochem. Soc; Chem. Inst. Can. Electrode kinetics, particularly relating to the silver electrode in alkaline solution; tantalum and aluminum capacitors; integrators; catalyst and catalytic electrodes. Address: Matthey Bishop Inc, Malvern, PA 19355.

FRASER, GEORGE ROBERT, b. Uzhorod, Czech; m. 63; c. 2. HUMAN & MEDICAL GENETICS. B.A, Cambridge, 53, M.B, B.Ch, 56, M.A, 60, M.D, 66; Ph.D.(human genetics), London, 60. Sci. off, med. res. coun. pop. genetics unit, Oxford, 59-61; res. fel. & assoc. human genetics, Washington (Seattle), 61-63; lectr, Royal Col. Surgeons, London, 63-66; ASSOC. PROF, Adelaide, 66-68; UNIV. WASH, 68-69, MED. & PREV. MED, 69- Am. Soc. Human Genetics; Brit. Genetical Soc; Royal Soc. Med. Genetics of deafness and blindness in childhood; genetics of thyroid disease; population genetics. Address: Dept. of Medicine & Preventive Medicine, University of Washington, Seattle, WA 98105.

FRASER, HARVEY R(EED), b. Elizabeth, Ill, Aug. 11, 16; m. 40; c. 3. MECHANICS. B.S, U.S. Mil. Acad, 39; M.S, Calif. Inst. Tech, 48; Ph.D.(fluid mechanics), Illinois, 56; dipl, Von Karman Inst. Fluid Dynamics, Belgium, 61. Commanding off, eng. co, U.S. Army, Hawaii, 40-43, eng. combat battalion, Europe, 44-45, opers. off, Oak Ridge, Tenn, 45-46, instr. mech, U.S. Mil. Acad, 48-50, assoc. prof, 50-52, prof, 53-65; dean eng, S.DAK. SCH. MINES & TECHNOL, 65-66, PRES, 66- U.S.A, 39-65, Brig. Gen.(Ret); Bronze Star Medal, 45, Legion of Merit, 46, Oak Leaf Cluster, 65. Soc. Am. Mil. Eng; Am. Soc. Eng. Educ. Fluid mechanics; diffuser flow. Address: Office of the President, South Dakota School of Mines & Technology, Rapid City, SD 57701.

FRASER, H(AVELOCK) F(RANK), b. Sask, Can, Nov. 21, 03; m. 36; c. 3. MEDICINE. A.B, Washington (Seattle), 25; M.D, Cornell, 32. Intern, U.S. Pub. Health Serv, 32-34; off, U.S. Penitentiary, Ga, 34-36; trainee pub. health, Nat. Insts. Health, 36-37, res. nutrit, 37-42, indust. hyg, 42-46; with State Dept, Stuttgart, Ger, 46-49; res, health addiction res. center, Nat. Inst. Ment. Health, U.S. Pub. Health Serv. Hosp, 49-63; mem. staff, Eli Lilly Res. Labs, 63-71; CONSULT, ADDICTION RES. CTR, NAT. INST. MENT. HEALTH, 71- Consult. pharmacol, col. med, Cincinnati, 56-63; col. med, Kentucky, 62-63; col. med, Indiana, 63-71; mem. expert. adv. panel addiction producing drugs, WHO; chmn. comt. prob. drug dependence, Nat. Res. Coun, 71. Am. Chem. Soc; Am. Med. Asn; Am. Soc. Pharmacol. & Exp. Therapeut; Am. Therapeut. Soc. Animal and human research on addiction to opiates, barbiturates and alcohol; intermediate metabolism opiates; development of synthetic compounds with reduced addiction liability. Address: National Institute of Mental Health, Addiction Research Centre, Lexington, KY 40507.

FRASER, IAN McLENNAN, b. Victoria, Australia, June 21, 27; m. 49; c. 3. PHARMACOLOGY. B.Sc, Univ. Sydney, 49; Ph.D.(biol), Cambridge, 52. Lectr. physiol, New S.Wales Univ. Technol, 52-53; instr. PHARMACOL, SCH. MED, LOMA LINDA UNIV, 53-54, asst. prof, 54-60, assoc. prof, 60-67, PROF. 67-, CHMN. DEPT. PHYSIOL, PHARMACOL. & BIOPHYS, 70-, chmn. dept. pharmacol, 67-70. Nat. Insts. Health spec. fel, 66-67. Am. Soc. Pharmacol. & Exp. Therapeut; Mycol. Soc. Am; Bot. Soc. Am. Chemotherapy; drug metabolism; pharmacogenetics. Address: Dept. of Physiology, Pharmacology & Biophysics, Loma Linda University School of Medicine, Loma Linda, CA 92354.

FRASER, J. W, b. Cobden, Ont, Feb. 19, 23; m. 45; c. 2. SILVICULTURE. B.Sc, Univ. Toronto, 49. RES. SCIENTIST, CAN. FOREST SERV, DEPT. ENVIRON, 49- R.C.A.F, 41-45, Sgt. Artificial regeneration; forest autecology; temperature-germination relationships and frost hardiness. Address: Great Lakes Forest Research Centre, Canadian Forest Service, Dept. of Environment, Sault Ste. Marie, Ont, Can.

FRASER, J(AMES) M(ATTISON), b. Bozeman, Mont, July 31, 25; m. 51; c. 3. PHYSICAL & ANALYTICAL CHEMISTRY. B.S, Wisconsin, 53, Ph.D.(phys. chem), 57. Alumni Res. Found. asst, Univ. Wis, 53-56; res. chemist, res. ctr, Pure Oil Co, 56-58, sr. res. chemist, 58-60, group supvr. phys. chem, 60-61, sect. supvr. instrumental anal, 61-62, asst. dir, anal. res. & serv. div, 62-64, dir, 64-65, supvr. spectral anal, 65-69, MGR. ANAL. RES. & SERV, RES. DEPT, UNION OIL CO. CALIF, 69- U.S.A.A.F, 43-46, S/Sgt. Am. Chem. Soc; Soc. Appl. Spectros. Instrumental and chemical analysis and analytical methods development of petroleum and its products. Address: Research Dept, Union Oil Co. of Calif, P.O. Box 76, Brea, CA 92621.

FRASER, JOHN S(TILES), b. Wonsan, Korea, June 23, 21; Can. citizen; m. 44; c. 2. ACCELERATOR PHYSICS. B.Sc, Dalhousie, 42; Ph.D.(physics), McGill, 49. Asst, cyclotron, McGill, 47-49; res. physicist nuclear physics, ATOMIC ENERGY CAN, LTD, 49-70, SR. RES. OFF. ACCELERATOR PHYSICS, 70- Can. Army, 42-45, Capt. Fel. Am. Phys. Soc; Can. Asn. Physicists. Accelerator design; data processing; nuclear instrumentation. Address: Atomic Energy of Canada, Ltd, Chalk River, Ont, Can.

FRASER, J(ULIUS) T(HOMAS), b. Budapest, Hungary, May 7, 23; nat; div; c. 3. ENGINEERING PHYSICS, PHILOSOPHY. B.E.E, Cooper Union, 50; N.Y. Univ, 57-59; Ph.D.(philos), Univ. Hannover, 70. Engr, Mackay Radio & Tel. Co, N.Y, 50-53; res. engr. Westinghouse Elec. Corp, 53-55; staff mem, RES. PHYSICS SECT, SINGER CO, KEARFOTT DIV, 55-58, sr. staff mem, 58-62, SR. SCIENTIST, 62- Res. assoc. physics & astron, Mich. State Univ, 62-65; vis. lectr, Mass. Inst. Technol, 66-67, guest of inst, 67-69; founding secy, Int. Soc. Study of Time, 66-; vis. lectr, Mt. Holyoke Col, 67-69; vis. prof, dept. hist, Univ. Md, 69-70; assoc. prof, Fordham University, 71-; vis. lectr, Yale, 71- Sr. mem. Inst. Elec. & Electronics Eng; Am. Asn. Physics Teachers; fel. Brit. Interplanetary Soc; Am. Astronaut. Soc. Philosophy and history of science; chronosophy; nuclear magnetic resonance; field theory; navigational devices. Address: P.O. Box 164, Pleasantville, NY 10570.

FRASER, LEMUEL A(NDERSON), b. Donora, Pa, June 18, 18; m. 42; c. 1. ZOOLOGY. B.A, American Univ, 39; scholar, Wisconsin, 39-41, M.A, 40, Ph.D.(zool), 44. Asst. ZOOL, Wisconsin, 41-44; instr, Texas, 46-48, asst. prof, 48-49; UNIV. WIS, MADISON, 49-53, assoc. prof, 53-59, PROF, 59-, CHMN. DEPT, 57-62, 64- U.S.N, 44-46. Am. Soc. Zool; Am. Micros. Soc; Am. Soc. Limnol. & Oceanog. Freshwater invertebrates; invertebrate embryology. Address: Dept. of Zoology, University of Wisconsin, Madison, WI 53706.

FRASER, LYNN R, b. St. Paul, Minn, Apr. 7, 43; m. 69. DEVELOPMENTAL BIOLOGY. B.A, Univ. Colo, 65; Nat. Sci. Found. fel. & M.Phil, Yale, 67, Nat. Insts. Health fel. & Ph.D.(develop. biol), 70. FORD FOUND. FEL, OBSTET. & GYNEC, MED. SCH, YALE, 70- Artifical parthenogenesis in frogs; mammalian reproductive biology, especially fertilization and early development. Address: Dept. of Obstetrics & Gynecology, Yale Medical School, New Haven, CT 06510.

FRASER, MARSHALL M, b. Beloit, Wis, June 14, 40. ALGEBRA. B.A. & Porter scholar, Beloit Col, 62; Woodrow Wilson fel, Yale, 62-63; M.A, Univ. Ill, 65, Ph.D.(math), 68. ASST. PROF. MATH, Albion Col, 67-68; UNIV. HAWAII, 68- Am. Math. Soc; Math. Asn. Am. Commutative rings; abstract algebra. Address: Dept. of Mathematics, University of Hawaii, Honolulu, HI 96822.

FRASER, M(URRAY) J(UDSON), b. Yarmouth, N.S, Aug. 21, 30. BIOCHEMISTRY. B.Sc, Dalhousie, 52, M.Sc, 54; Overseas 1851 Exhib. scholar, Cambridge, 54-56, Ph.D.(colloid sci), 57. Asst, Nat. Inst. Res. Dairying, Eng, 56-58; mem. res. staff, McGill-Montreal Gen. Hosp. Res. Inst, Can, 58-59; asst. prof. biochem, faculty med, Univ. Man, 59-63, assoc. prof, 63-64; med. biophysics, Univ. Toronto, 64-67; ASSOC. PROF. BIOCHEM, McGILL UNIV, 67- Head subdiv. biochem, Ont. Cancer Inst, 64-67; ed, Can. J. Biochem, 67- Am. Soc. Biol. Chem; Can. Biochem. Soc; Brit. Biochem. Soc. Isolation of repetitive sequences from DNA; action of nucleases specific for single-stranded nucleic acids. Address: Dept. of Biochemistry, McIntyre Medical Sciences Bldg, McGill University, Montreal 109, Que, Can.

FRASER, OLIVER B(RANIFF) J(OSEPH), b. Brockville, Ont, Dec. 22, 95; nat; m. 23; c. 1. METALLURGICAL ENGINEERING. B.Sc, Queen's (Can), 16. Inspector explosives, Imp. Ministry of Munitions, Can, 16-17; plant res, Int. Nickel Co, N.J, 17-18, from night works supt. to plant res. engr, Can, 18-21, mgr. res. lab, N.J, 23-32, develop. engr, N.Y, 33-34, dir. tech. serv. mill prods, 34-47, asst. mgr. develop. & res. div, 47-60; TECH. CONSULT, 61- Sr. fel, Mellon Inst, 22-23. Can. Army, 18-19. AAAS; Am. Soc. Mech. Eng; Am. Chem. Soc; hon. mem. Am. Welding Soc.(treas, 41-47, v.pres, 47-48, pres, 49, Miller Medal, 51); Electrochem. Soc; Am. Soc. Metals; hon. mem. Am. Soc. Test. & Mat; Mining & Metall. Soc. Am.(secy, 62-64); Am. Ord. Asn; Commercial Chem. Develop. Asn; Chem. Mkt. Res. Asn; Am. Inst. Mining, Metall. & Petrol. Eng.(v.pres, 52-55); Am. Inst. Chem. Eng; fel. Am. Inst. Chem; N.Y. Acad. Sci; fel. Chem. Inst. Can; Can. Inst. Mining & Metall; Soc. Chem. Indust; Brit. Inst. Metals; hon. mem. Soc. Indust. Chem.(pres, Am. sect, 59-60); Soc. Civil Eng. France. Corrosion; electrodeposition; physical metallurgy of nickel alloys; roasting, smelting and other operations in production of nickel from sulfide ores; separation of cobalt from nickel in aqueous solutions; nickel compounds and catalysts; market and economic surveys in minerals, metals and chemicals. Address: 70 Pine St, Room 4010, New York, NY 10005.

FRASER, P(ETER) A(RTHUR), b. Ancon, Ecuador, Aug. 26, 28; nat. Can; m. 52; c. 4. PHYSICS. B.Sc, Western Ontario, 50, Ph.D.(physics), 54; M.S, Wisconsin, 52. Asst. physics, Wisconsin, 50-52; res. assoc, Western Ontario, 52-54; Nat. Res. Coun. Can. fel, Univ. Col, London, 54-56; lectr, UNIV. WEST. ONT, 56-57, asst. prof, 57-59, assoc. prof, 59-63, PROF, 63-70, APPL. MATH, 70- Am. Asn. Physics Teachers; Can. Asn. Physicists; Brit. Inst. Physics & Phys. Soc. Low energy atomic collisions. Address: Dept. of Applied Mathematics, University of Western Ontario, London 72, Ont, Can.

FRASER, ROBERT B, b. Plainfield, N.J, Sept. 3, 36; m. 59; c. 4. MATHEMATICS. B.A, Rutgers, 62, Ph.D.(math), 67. Instr. MATH, Rutgers, 65-67; asst. prof, La. State Univ, 67-69; fel, Dalhousie Univ, 69-70; ASST. PROF, La. State Univ, 70-71; MARIETTA COL, 71- U.S.A, 59-61. Am. Math. Soc; Math. Asn. Am. Topology and analysis, especially metric geometry; Lipschitz functions; contraction maps. Address: Dept. of Mathematics, Marietta College, Marietta, OH 45750.

FRASER, ROBERT GORDON, b. Winnipeg, Man, June 30, 21; m. 45; c. 4. MEDICINE. Upper Can. Col, 29-38; Toronto, 39; M.D, L.M.C.C, Manitoba, 45. Res. RADIOL, Royal Victoria Hosp, 48-50, fel, 51; demonstr, McGILL UNIV, 51-54, lectr, 54-56, asst. prof, 56-62, assoc. prof, 62-68, PROF, 68- Clin. asst, Royal Victoria Hosp, 52, assoc. radiologist, 54-56, radiologist, 57-64, diag. radiologist-in-chief, 64-; consult. radiologist, Royal Can. Air Force, 54-59; Montreal Children's Hosp, 54-; Montreal Neurol. Inst, 55-; adv, Dept. Vet. Affairs, Can, 70-; consult, Can. Forces Med. Coun. Fel, Royal Col. Physicians, Can, 56. R.C.A.M.C, 44-45; R.C.N.V.R, 45-46; R.C.A.F, 52-59, Wing Comdr. Can. Asn. Radiol.(assoc. hon. secy-treas, 57-58, hon. secy-treas, 59-63, pres, 70). Diagnostic radiology. Address: 1212 Pine Ave. W, Apt. 1908, Montreal 112, Que, Can.

FRASER, R(OBERT) R(OWNTREE), b. Ottawa, Ont, Oct. 25, 31; m. 64; c. 4. ORGANIC CHEMISTRY. B.Sc, Western Ontario, 53, Nat. Res. Coun. Can. fel, 53-54, M.Sc, 54; univ. fel, Illinois, 54-55, 56-57, Texas Co. fel, 57-58, Ph.D.(org. chem), 58. Asst. prof. org. chem, Ottawa (Can), 58-62; sr. res. chemist, Bristol Labs. Div, Bristol-Myers Co, 62-64; assoc. prof, ORG. CHEM, UNIV. OTTAWA, 64-70, PROF, 70- Am. Chem. Soc; Chem. Inst. Can; The Chem. Soc. Mechanisms of organic reactions; nuclear magnetic resonance spectroscopy. Address: Dept. of Chemistry, University of Ottawa, Ottawa, Ont. K1N 6N5, Can.

FRASER, ROBERT STEWART, b. Nelson, B.C, Feb. 14, 22; m. 49; c. 4. INTERNAL MEDICINE, CARDIOLOGY. B.Sc, Alberta, 44, M.D, 46, M.Sc, 50; F.R.C.P.C, Royal Col. Physicians & Surgeons, Can, 54. Muttart assoc. prof. med, UNIV. ALTA, 55-64, PROF. CLIN. MED, 64-, CHMN. DEPT. MED, 69- Markle scholar, 53-56. Consult, Charles Camsell Indian Hosp, Edmonton. Can. Army, 44-46; R.C.A.F.R, 55-58. Am. Fedn. Clin. Res; Can. Soc. Clin. Invest; Can. Cardiovasc. Soc.(pres, 64). Clinical cardiology; clinical and experimental hemodynamic studies. Address: Dept. of Medicine, University of Alberta, Clinical Sciences Bldg, Edmonton, Alta, Can.

FRASER, ROBIN T(RIANCE) M(ELDRUM), b. Wellington, N.Z, Feb. 16, 37; m. 59; c. 4. INORGANIC CHEMISTRY. B.Sc, Victoria, N.Z, 57, M.Sc, 58; Bell Tel. Labs. fel. & Ph.D.(inorg. chem), Chicago, 59. Sci. officer, N.Z. Dom. Lab, 57-58; asst. prof. INORG. CHEM, Ottawa (Can), 60-62; UNIV. KANS, 62-64, ASSOC. PROF, 64- Sloan fel, 64-67. The Chem. Soc. Reaction rates and mechanisms of inorganic processes; oxidation-reductions in solution; synthesis of transition metal complexes; composition and structure of metal nitrosyls. Address: Dept. of Chemistry, University of Kansas, Lawrence, KS 66044.

FRASER, R(ONALD) C(HESTER), b. Portage la Prairie, Man, Nov. 6, 19; U.S. citizen; m. 44; c. 4. ZOOLOGY, EMBRYOLOGY. B.S, Minnesota, 50, M.S, 52, Ph.D.(zool), 53. Asst. zool, Minnesota, 50-53; instr. biol, Reed Col, 53-54; asst. prof. ZOOL, UNIV. TENN, KNOXVILLE, 54-58, assoc. prof, 58-61, PROF, 61- Asst, Minnesota, 53-; consult, Atomic Energy Comn, 54- U.S.A.A.F, 42-45. Am. Soc. Zool. Morphogenesis; mouse tumor growth; hemoglobins and serum proteins of the chick embryo. Address: Dept. of Zoology, University of Tennessee, Knoxville, TN 37916.

FRASER, RUSSELL S, b. Park City, Utah, Dec. 20, 14; m. 43. MICROBIOLOGY. B.S, Utah, 39; M.S, Utah State, 52. Serologist, DIV. LABS, UTAH STATE DEPT. HEALTH, 40-43, chief bacteriologist, 46-50, DIR, 50- Clin. instr. sch. prev. med, col. med, Utah, 50-, col. med, 66-; assoc. prof, Utah State, 53-63. Mem, Conf. State & Prov. Pub. Health Lab. Dirs, 50- Sanit.C, 43-46, Res, 46-, Lt. Col. Am. Pub. Health Asn; Asn. State & Territorial Pub. Health Lab. Dirs; Royal Soc. Health. Water bacteriology and the epidemiology of rheumatic fever. Address: Utah State Dept. of Health, 44 Medical Dr, Salt Lake City, UT 84113.

FRASER, THOMAS P(ETIGRU), b. Georgetown, S.C, June 24, 02; m. 26; c. 1. BIOLOGY, SCIENCE EDUCATION. B.S, Claflin Col, 26, hon. D.H, 70; Phelps-Stokes Fund scholar, Columbia, 30, A.M, 30, Gen. Ed. Bd. fel, 35-36, Ed.D.(biol. & sci. ed), 48. Head dept. sci, high sch, Fla, 26-29; prof. biol, Wilberforce, 30-35; supvr. teachers, Mus. Sci. & Indust, N.Y, 36-40; dean, Edward Waters Col, 40-42; dean, personnel dir. & prof. biol, Delaware State Col, 42-47; PROF. BIOL, MORGAN STATE COL, 47-, chmn. dept. sci. educ, 47-67, interim pres. col, 70-71. Dir, Nat. Sci. Found. Inst. Sec. Sch. Teachers Sci. & Math, Morgan State Col, summers 57-71, col. sci. improvement progs, 69-; mem. bd. trustees, Claflin Col, 64-; mem. nat. comn. future of state cols. & univs, Am. Asn. State Cols. & Univs. Fel. AAAS; Nat. Asn. Res. Sci. Teaching (pres, 59, distinguished serv. citation, 59). Science teaching at the college level; science for general education; education of science teachers; economic biology. Address: Dept. of Science Education, Morgan State College, Baltimore, MD 21212.

FRASER, WILLARD S(COTT), b. N.S, Can, June 6, 19; m. 47; c. 3. AGRICULTURAL CHEMISTRY. B.Sc, McGill, 43; M.S, Mich. State Col, 48, Ph.D.(soil chem), 54. Asst. chemist, N.S. Agr. Col, 47-50; supvr. agr. res, Calumet & Hecla, Inc, 52-60; tech. dir, HARDY SALT CO, 60-65, V.PRES, 65- Can. Army, 43-46, Lt. Am. Chem. Soc. Agricultural chemicals; soils. Address: Hardy Salt Co, P.O. Box 449, St. Louis, MO 63166.

FRASER, WILLIAM AVON, b. Lincoln, Nebr, Mar. 16, 35; m. 58; c. 4. ENGINEERING, THEORETICAL PHYSICS. B.S, Univ. Nebr, Lincoln, 56, M.A, 59, Nat. Defense Educ. Act fel, 60-62, Ph.D.(physics), 64; fels, Univ. Colo, summers 59-60. Res. fel, theoret. physics inst, Univ. Alta, 63-64; res. scientist, Kaman Sci. Corp, 64-70; STAFF ENGR, MARTIN MARI-

ETTA CORP, 71- Instr, El Paso Community Col, Colo, 70- Am. Phys. Soc. Instrument development; instrumentation and field experimentation; electromagnetic effects on communication systems; low energy theoretical nuclear physics. Address: 1424 N. Tejon, Colorado Springs, CO 80907.

FRASER, WILLIAM M(cKINLEY), JR, b. Colwyn, Pa, Mar. 16, 27; m. 50; c. 4. INORGANIC CHEMISTRY. B.A, Fla. South. Col, 51, B.S, 52; cert. chem. eng, Int. Correspondence Schs, 58. Lab. technician, Int. Minerals & Chem. Corp, 52-53, from chemist to sr. chemist, prod. develop, 53-57, asst. chief chemist & supvr. anal. lab, 57-59, process chem. engr. prod. improv. & develop, 59-60; process chem. engr, Smith Douglass Co, Inc, 61-64, OPERS. SUPT, SMITH DOUGLASS/BORDEN INC, 64- U.S.A, 45-47. Am. Chem. Soc. Chemistry of phosphates; phosphoric acid; fluorides; phosphate in fertilizers and animal feed ingredients; manufacture of complete fertilizers; chemical engineering in manufacturing of heavy chemicals. Address: 1719 17th Ave. N, Texas City, TX 77590.

FRASER-REID, BERTRAM OLIVER, b. Christiana, Jamaica, Feb. 23, 34; m. 63; c. 2. ORGANIC CHEMISTRY. B.Sc, Queen's (Ont), 59, M.Sc, 61; Ph.D.(chem), Alberta, 64. Res. fel, Imp. Col, London, 64-66; asst. prof. CHEM, UNIV. WATERLOO, 66-71, ASSOC PROF, 71- Am. Chem. Soc; Chem. Inst. Can; The Chem. Soc. Carbohydrate chemistry; photochemistry of imines and related molecules; a synthetic route to spiropentadiene. Address: Dept. of Chemistry, University of Waterloo, Waterloo, Ont, Can.

FRASER-SMITH, ANTONY C(HARLES), b. Auckland, N.Z, July 7, 38; m. 68; c. 2. SPACE PHYSICS. B.S, New Zealand, 59, M.S, 61; Ph.D.(physics), Auckland, 66. Lectr, physics, Auckland, 61-65; assoc. res. scientist, Lockheed Missiles & Space Co, Calif, 66-68; RES. ASSOC, RADIOSCI. LAB, STANFORD UNIV, 68- Consult, Stanford Res. Inst, 70- Royal N.Z. Artil, 56-59, Res, 59-65. Fel. Brit. Inst. Physics; Am. Geophys. Union; Am. Inst. Physics. Experimental and theoretical research into the origin and properties of geomagnetic micropulsations; high frequency radio propagation and ionospheric studies. Address: Radioscience Lab, Stanford University, Stanford, CA 94305.

FRASHER, WALLACE G, JR, b. Los Angeles, Calif, Dec. 2, 20; m. 59; c. 2. CARDIOVASCULAR PHYSIOLOGY. A.B, Southern California, 41, M.D, 51. Head physician, Los Angeles County Hosp, 55-57; res. fel, Los Angeles County Heart Asn, 57-58, estab. investr, 58-59; Nat. Heart Inst. res. fel, 60-61; asst. res. prof. med, SCH. MED, Loma Linda Univ, 61-63, assoc. res. prof, 63-66; ASSOC. PROF. PHYSIOL, UNIV. SOUTH. CALIF, 66- Nat. Heart Inst. res. career develop. award, 61-; res. fel. eng, Calif. Inst. Tech, 61-63, sr. res. fel, 63- U.S.A.A.F, 43-46, 1st Lt. Am. Physiol. Soc; Microcirculatory Soc; Soc. Rheol. Major artery distensibility; flow properties of blood and its constituents in small tubes; microvascular casting. Address: Dept. of Physiology, University of Southern California School of Medicine, 2025 Zonal Ave, Los Angeles, CA 90033.

FRASHIER, LOYD D(OLA), b. Pampa, Tex, Oct. 29, 16; m. 53; c. 3. PHYSICAL CHEMISTRY. B.S, Harding Col, 40; Ph.D.(phys. chem), California, 49. Chemist, E.I. du Pont de Nemours & Co, Inc, 41-45; assoc. prof. CHEM, Ga. Inst. Tech, 49-58; PROF. & CHMN. DEPT, PEPPERDINE UNIV, 58- Am. Chem. Soc. Chemical kinetics. Address: Dept. of Chemistry, Pepperdine University, Los Angeles, CA 90044.

FRASIER, JOHN T, b. Washington, D.C, Feb. 21, 33; m. 63; c. 3. APPLIED MECHANICS. B.S, Va. Polytech, 54; M.S, Pa. State, 56, Du Pont fel, 56-57, Ph.D.(eng. mech), 58. Asst. prof. eng, Brown, 60-62; RES. PHYSICIST, BALLISTIC RES. LABS, ABERDEEN PROVING GROUND, 62- U.S.A, 58-60, 1st Lt. Soc. Exp. Stress Anal. Theory of elasticity; photoelasticity; fracture mechanics; hypervelocity impact; dynamic structural analysis; material properties. Address: Route 1, Box 704, Churchville, MD 21028.

FRASIER, JORDAN D, b. Chicago, Ill, July 10, 27; m. 48; c. 3. ELECTRONIC ENGINEERING. Herzl Jr. Col, 47-49; N.Y. University, 58-60. Instr, high sch, Ill, 44-45; owner, Frasier Indust. Electronics, 50-58; chief engr. & plant mgr, Beck-Lee Corp, 58-61; owner, Jordin Instrument Co, Calif, 61-62; chief engr, DALLONS INSTRUMENTS DIV, INT. RECTIFIER CORP, 62-63, chief engr, & gen. mgr. labs, 63-65, PRES, 65- U.S.N, 45-47. Inst. Elec. & Electronics Eng. Design of electronic instrumentation for medicine. Address: Dallons Instruments Division, International Rectifier Corp, 120 Kansas St, El Segundo, CA 90245.

FRASIER, S. DOUGLAS, b. Los Angeles, Calif, Nov. 29, 32; m. 56; c. 3. PEDIATRIC ENDOCRINOLOGY. B.A, Univ. Calif, Los Angeles, 54, fel, 55-56, M.D, 58. Fel. pediat, sch. med, Univ. Calif, Los Angeles, 63-65, asst. prof, 65-67; PEDIAT. PHYSIOL, SCH. MED, UNIV. SOUTH. CALIF, 67-69, ASSOC. PROF, 69- Med.C, U.S.A.R, 61-63, Capt. AAAS; Soc. Pediat. Res; Endocrine Soc. Growth hormone physiology in children; growth hormone deficiency and therapeutic effects of growth hormone; antigenicity of human growth hormone; endocrine correlates of puberty. Address: School of Medicine, University of Southern California, 2025 Zonal Ave, Los Angeles, CA 90033.

FRASSETTO, ROBERTO, b. Naples, Italy, Nov. 25, 17; U.S. citizen; m. 56; c. 1. PHYSICAL OCEANOGRAPHY, INSTRUMENTATION. Royal Naval Acad, Italy, 37-40; Univs. Florence & Pisa, 36-40, 46-47. Consult, U.S. Off. Naval Res, 50-53; oceanogr, Columbia, 53-60; Saclant Antisubmarine Res. Ctr, 60-67; DIR. RES, OCEANOBOE PROG, COUN. NAT. RES, UNIV. PISA, 67- Dir. lab, Studio Dinamica Grandi Masse, Nat. Res. Coun, Venice, Italy, 69-71. Italian Navy, 40-47, Lt. Comdr. Am. Geophys. Union. Microstructure; oceanographic buoy development; environmental research and administration. Address: Oceanoboe Program, University of Pisa, San Terenzo, La Spezia, Italy.

FRATER, ROBERT WILLIAM MAYO, b. Cape Town, S.Africa, Nov. 12, 28; m; c. 3. THORACIC & CARDIOVASCULAR SURGERY. M.B, Ch.B, Cape Town, 52; Minn. Heart Asn. fel, Minnesota, 59-60, M.S, 61. Intern surg, Groote Schuur Hosp, Cape Town, S.Africa, 53-54; Coun. Sci. & Indust. Res. fel, Univ. Cape Town, 54-55 & Mayo Found, 55-61; sr. lectr. THORACIC SURG, Univ. Cape Town, 62-64; asst. prof, ALBERT EINSTEIN COL. MED, 64-68, ASSOC. PROF, 68-; CHIEF CARDIO-THORACIC SURG, BRONX MUNIC. HOSP. CTR, 68- Noble Found. award, 61; Nat. Insts. Health fels, 65-70; Am. Heart Asn. grant-in-aid, 67. Sr. surgeon, Groote Schuur Hosp. & Red Cross War Mem. Children's Hosp, Cape Town, S.Africa, 62-64. Fel, Royal Col. Surg, Eng, 61. Am. Asn. Thoracic Surg. Artificial heart valves; membrane oxygenators; right ventricular growth. Address: Dept. of Surgery, Albert Einstein College of Medicine, New York, NY 10461.

FRATI, WILLIAM, b. N.Y.C, Sept. 14, 31; m. 63; c. 1. HIGH ENERGY PHYSICS. B.S, Polytech. Inst. Brooklyn, 52; M.A, Columbia, 55, Ph.D.(physics), 60. RES. ASSOC. PHYSICS, Columbia, 60-61; RITTENHOUSE LAB, UNIV. PA, 61- Am. Phys. Soc. High energy particle physics. Address: Rittenhouse Lab, Dept. of Physics, University of Pennsylvania, Philadelphia, PA 19104.

FRATIANNE, DOUGLAS G, b. Cleveland, Ohio, Oct. 19, 37; m. 59; c. 6. PLANT PHYSIOLOGY. B.A, West. Reserve Univ, 59, M.Sc, Ohio State Univ, 61, Ph.D.(plant physiol), 68. Instr. PLANT PHYSIOL, OHIO STATE UNIV, 64-68, ASST. PROF, 68- AAAS; Bot. Soc. Am; Am. Soc. Plant Physiol. Photoperiodism; seed germination; other phytochrome mediated processes. Address: Dept. of Botany, College of Biological Sciences, Ohio State University, Columbus, OH 43210.

FRATIANNI, SAVINO V, b. Brooklyn, N.Y, Oct. 25, 18; m. 46; c. 2. ELECTRONIC & ELECTRICAL ENGINEERING. B.E.E, Polytech. Inst. Brooklyn, 43. Engr. electronics, NAVAL RES. LAB, WASH, D.C, 43-44, proj. leader, 44-55, univ head, 55-57, sect. head, 57-68, BR. HEAD, NAVAL SHIP SYST. COMMAND, 68- U.S.N, 44-45, Res, 45-, Lt. Comdr. Sr. mem. Inst. Elec. & Electronics Eng; Sci. Res. Soc. Am. Electronic systems for communications and navigation; new concepts and systems for naval applications. Address: 4309 Brinkley Rd. S.E, Oxon Hill, MD 20031.

FRATIELLO, ANTHONY, b. Providence, R.I, Mar. 16, 36; m. 63; c. 3. PHYSICAL CHEMISTRY. B.Sc, Providence Col, 57; Ph.D.(chem), Brown, 62. Fel. & mem. tech. staff, Bell Tel. Labs, 62-63; asst. prof. CHEM, CALIF. STATE COL, LOS ANGELES, 63-66, assoc. prof, 66-69, PROF, 69- Vis. fel, Bell.Tel. Labs, 69-70; Nat. Insts. Health res. career develop. award, 69-73. Am. Chem. Soc. Nuclear magnetic resonance; solution complexes; ion hydration. Address: Dept. of Chemistry, California State College at Los Angeles, 5151 State College Dr, Los Angeles, CA 90032.

FRATTA, ITALO DOMINIC, b. Travesio, Italy, Apr. 6, 20; U.S. citizen; m. 50; c. 3. TOXICOLOGY, VETERINARY MEDICINE. D.V.M, Bologna, 43; dipl, Milan, 45; Off. Pub. Health, Padua, 47. Vet, private practice, Italy, 44-51; res. vet, sch. med, Columbia, 52-59; HEAD, ANIMAL SCI, CIBA-GEIGY LTD, 59- Lectr, Sch. Cheese Mfg, Italy, 49-51. Fel. Am. Inst. Chem; Am. Asn. Lab. Animal Soc; Am. Vet. Med. Asn; N.Y. Acad. Sci. Nutritional requirements in laboratory animals; fetal development and pharmacologic agents; laboratory animal diseases, etiology and prophylaxis; pharmacologic agents and their toxicity in laboratory animals. Address: Dept. of Toxicology, Ciba-Geigy Ltd, Saw Mill River Rd, Ardsley, NY 10502.

FRAUENFELDER, HANS (EMIL), b. Neuhausen, Switz, July 28, 22; nat; m. 50; c. 3. PHYSICS. Dipl, Swiss Fed. Inst. Technol, 47, Dr.sc.nat, 50. Asst. PHYSICS, Swiss Fed. Inst. Technol, 46-52; res. assoc, UNIV. ILL, URBANA, 52, asst. prof, 52-56, assoc. prof, 56-58, PROF, 58- Vis. scientist, European Orgn. Nuclear Res, 58, 59 & 63; consult, Los Alamos Sci. Lab. Fel. Am. Phys. Soc; Swiss Phys. Soc. Nuclear and particle physics; Mössbauer effect. Address: Dept. of Physics, University of Illinois, Urbana, IL 61801.

FRAUENGLASS, ELLIOTT, b. Hartford, Conn, Aug. 7, 34; m. 55; c. 3. ORGANIC CHEMISTRY. B.S, Univ. Conn, 56; Ph.D.(org. chem), Cornell Univ, 60. Res. chemist, Eastman Kodak Co, 60-65; POLYMER CHEMIST, LOCTITE CORP, 65- Am. Chem. Soc. Synthetic and polymer organic chemistry. Address: Loctite Corp, 705 N. Mountain Rd, Newington, CT 06111.

FRAUMENI, JOSEPH F, JR, b. Boston, Mass, Apr. 1, 33. INTERNAL MEDICINE, EPIDEMIOLOGY. A.B, Harvard, 54, M.Sc.Hyg, 65; M.D, Duke, 58. Intern med, Hopkins Hosp, 58-59, asst. res, 59-60; sr. asst. res, Cornell Second Div, Bellevue Hosp. & Mem. Center, 60-61; chief res, Mem. Sloan-Kettering Cancer Center, 61-62; med. officer EPIDEMIOL, NAT. CANCER INST, 62-66, HEAD ECOL. SECT, 66- Instr, med. col, Cornell, 61-62; asst. med, Peter Bent Brigham Hosp, 64-65. Dipl, Am. Bd. Internal Med, 65. U.S.P.H.S, 62-, Med. Dir. Am. Pub. Health Asn; Am. Col. Physicians; Am. Epidemiol. Soc; Am. Asn. Cancer Res; Teratology Soc. Cancer research, especially epidemiological studies. Address: Wiscon Bldg, Room 410, National Institutes of Health, Bethesda, MD 20014.

FRAUNFELTER, GEORGE H, b. Hamburg, Pa, June 2, 27; div. GEOLOGY. B.A, Lehigh, 48; A.M, Missouri, 51, Ph.D.(geol), 64; Nat. Sci. Found. summer fel, Texas, 61. Curator geol, Missouri, 51-55; paleontologist, Creole Petrol. Corp, 55-58; curator & asst. prof. geol, SOUTHERN ILLINOIS UNIV, 65-70, ASSOC. PROF. GEOL, 70- Asst, Nat. Sci. Found. Summer Inst, Northeast Mo. State Teachers Col, 64 & short course geol. of Miss. Sound, Millsaps Col, 67. AAAS; Am. Asn. Petrol. Geol; Paleont. Soc; Paleont. Res. Inst; Am. Inst. Prof. Geol. Devonian corals and Pennsylvanian dibunophyllid corals; paleontology and stratigraphy of Middle Devonian of Midwestern United States; Devonian crinoids and Pennsylvanian edrioasteroids. Address: Dept. of Geology, Southern Illinois University, Carbondale, IL 62901.

FRAUTSCHI, S(TEVEN) C(LARK), b. Madison, Wis, Dec. 6, 33; m. 67; c. 1. THEORETICAL PHYSICS. B.A, Harvard, 54; Nat. Sci. Found. fel, Stanford Univ, 55-58, Ph.D.(physics), 58. Nat. Sci. Found. fel, Yukawa Hall, Kyoto, 58-59; asst. PHYSICS, Univ. Calif, Berkeley, 59-61; asst. prof, Cornell Univ, 61-62; CALIF. INST. TECHNOL, 62-64, assoc. prof, 64-66, PROF, 66- Guggenheim fel, 71-72. Am. Phys. Soc. Theory of elementary particles. Address: Dept. of Physics, California Institute of Technology, Pasadena, CA 91106.

FRAUTSCHY, JEFFERY D(EAN), b. Monroe, Wis, June 22, 19; m. 48; c. 3. GEOLOGY. B.A, Minnesota, 42. Assoc. physicist, div. war res, California, 42-46; assoc, Scripps Inst, California, 46-47; geophysicist, U.S. Geol. Surv, 47-49; marine geologist, SCRIPPS INST. OCEANOG, UNIV. CALIF, SAN DIEGO, 49-58, ASST. DIR, 58- Civilian with Off. Sci. Res. & Develop, 44. Geol. Soc. Am; Soc. Econ. Paleont. & Mineral; Am. Asn. Petrol. Geol; Am. Geophys. Union. Marine geology; oceanographic field instruments, equipment and methods; oceanographic vessel outfitting and operation; inshore oceanography and shore processes; coastline planning; water quality control. Address: Scripps Institution of Oceanography, University of California at San Diego, P.O. Box 109, La Jolla, CA 92037.

FRAWLEY, JOHN P(AUL), b. Washington, D.C, Dec. 17, 27; m. 53; c. 2. TOXICOLOGY. B.S. & M.S, Georgetown, 48, Ph.D.(biochem), 50. Instr. chem, Georgetown, 47-48; res. pharmacologist, U.S. Food & Drug Admin, 48-52 & 54-56; CHIEF TOXICOLOGIST, HERCULES INC, 56- Lectr, Georgetown Univ, 49-52; mem. agr. bd, Nat. Res. Coun, 69-72. Lea Hitchner Award, 68; dipl, Am. Bd. Indust. Hyg. Med.C, U.S.A, 52-54. Am. Chem. Soc; Soc. Toxicol; Am. Soc. Pharmacol. & Exp. Therapeut; Am. Indust. Hyg. Asn. Toxicity and safety evaluation of chemicals in food, drugs, cosmetics and food packaging. Address: 111 Danforth Pl, Windybush, Wilmington, DE 19810.

FRAWLEY, THOMAS FRANCIS, b. Rochester, N.Y, June 27, 19; m. 47; c. 3. MEDICINE. A.B, Rochester, 41; M.D, Buffalo, 44. Res. fel. med, sch. med, Buffalo, 47-49; Harvard Med. Sch, 49-51; head sub-dept. endocrinol. & metab, Albany Med. Col, 51-63, prof. med, 59-63; PROF. INTERNAL MED. & CHMN. DEPT, SCH. MED, ST. LOUIS UNIV, 63-, PHYSICIAN-IN-CHIEF, UNIV. HOSPS, 63- Chief endocrine-metab. clin, Albany Hosp, 51-63, attend. physician, 52-63; consult, Albany Vet. Admin. Hosp, 51-63; clin. investr, Nat. Inst. Arthritis & Metab. Diseases, 55-57; mem. sci. rev. comt, Nat. Insts. Health, 70- Dipl, Am. Bd. Internal Med; mem, Nat. Bd. Med. Exam. Med.C, U.S.A, 46-47; U.S.P.H.S, 55-57. Endocrine Soc; Am. Diabetes Asn; Am. Thyroid Asn; Am. Med. Asn; Am. Fedn. Clin. Res; fel. Am. Col. Physicians; fel. N.Y. Acad. Sci; Asn. Am. Physicians; Am. Clin. & Climat. Asn. Clinical and basic investigation of endocrine metabolic disorders, particularly adrenal cortical disorders and carbohydrate metabolism. Address: St. Louis University School of Medicine, Room G10A, 1325 S. Grand Blvd, St. Louis, MO 63104.

FRAWLEY, WILLIAM J(AMES), b. Cleveland, Ohio, Sept. 14, 37; m. 57; c. 3. MATHEMATICAL ANALYSIS. B.S, John Carroll Univ, 58, M.S, 60; fel, Univ. Okla, summer 62, NASA trainee, 66-68, Ph.D.(math), 69. Res. engr, Lewis Res. Ctr, NASA, Ohio, 58-60; systs. analyst, systs. & procedures dept, Cleveland Elec. Illum. Co, summer 60; instr. math, John Carroll Univ, 60-62; sr. res. mathematician, SCHLUMBERGER-DOLL RES. CTR, 62-65, SR. RES. PROJ. MATHEMATICIAN & GROUP LEADER, 68- Lectr, John Carroll Univ, 58-60; comput. use consult, Cleveland Elec. Illum. Co, 60-62. Am. Math. Soc; Soc. Indust. & Appl. Math. Second-order differential systems, particularly those related to electromagnetic fields in media with spatially-varying conductivity and optimization of real time control systems. Address: Schlumberger-Doll Research Center, Schlumberger Ltd, Old Quarry Rd, Ridgefield, CT 06877.

FRAY, ROBERT DUTTON, b. Shepherdstown, W.Va, Feb. 16, 39; m. 62. MATHEMATICS. B.S, Roanoke Col, 61; Ph.D.(number theory), Duke, 65. ASST. PROF. MATH, Fla. State Univ, 65-71, FURMAN UNIV, 71- Am. Math. Soc; Math. Asn. Am. Number theory and combinatorial analysis. Address: Dept. of Mathematics, Furman University, Greenville, SC 29613.

FRAYER, WARREN E(DWARD), b. Manchester, Conn, Sept. 22, 39; m. 60; c. 4. FOREST BIOMETRY, COMPUTER SCIENCE. B.S, Pa. State Univ, 61; M.For, Yale, 62, D.For.(forest biomet), 65. Res. forester, northeast. forest exp. sta, U.S. Forest Serv, Pa, 62-66, math. statistician, 66-67; asst. prof. FOREST BIOMET, COLO. STATE UNIV, 67-70, ASSOC. PROF, 70- Soc. Am. Foresters; Biomet. Soc. Uses of statistical procedures and computers in forestry, particularly in forest inventory designs and analyses. Address: College of Forestry & Natural Resources, Colorado State University, Ft. Collins, CO 80521.

FRAYER, WILLIAM C(ORNELIUS), b. Riverside, Calif, June 26, 20; m. 43; c. 3. OPHTHALMOLOGY. A.B, Brown Univ, 43; M.D, Univ. Mich, 45. Res. ophthalmologist, univ. hosp, Univ. Pa, 49-52, asst. prof. OPHTHAL, sch. med, 52-62; PROF, JEFFERSON MED. COL, 64- Med.C, 46-48, Capt. Fel. Am. Col. Surg; fel. Am. Acad. Ophthal. & Otolaryngol. Ophthalmic pathology; pigment epithelium of the retina. Address: 829 Spruce St, Philadelphia, PA 19107.

FRAYNE, JOHN G(EORGE), b. Wexford Co, Ireland, July 8, 94; nat; m. 18, 46; c. 3. PHYSICS. A.B, Ripon Col, 17; Ph.D.(physics), Minnesota, 21. Res. engr, Am. Tel. & Tel. Co, 19; instr. math. & mech, Minnesota, 19-21, physics, 21-22; prof, Antioch Col, 22-28; Nat. Res. Council fel, Calif. Inst. Tech, 28-29; sound recording engr, West. Elec. Co, 29-38, eng. supvr, 38-49, eng. mgr, 49-59; chief engr, datalab div, Consol. Electrodyn. Corp, 59-61; dir. res. & develop, Marquardt Corp, 61-64; lectr. PHYSICS, CALIF. STATE POLYTECH. COL, KELLOGG-VOORHIS, 64-71, EMER. PROF, 71- Adj. prof, sch. cinema, Univ. South. Calif, 71-72. Berliner award, Audio Eng. Soc. Sig.C, 19, Lt. Fel. Soc. Motion Picture & TV Eng.(Jour. award, 41; medal, 47, Warner medal, 59; ed. v.pres, 51, exec. v.pres, 53, pres, 55-56). Emission and absorption spectra; elements of sound recording; radio telephony; thermionic tubes; piezoelectricity; absorption spectra of metallic vapors; densitometer design; vibration analysis; stereophonic recording of motion pictures and discs. Address: 1580 La Loma Rd, Pasadena, CA 91105.

FRAZEE, CHARLES JOSEPH, b. Springfield, Ill, Nov. 8, 40; m. 65; c. 1. SOIL GENESIS. B.S, West. Ill. Univ, 62; M.S, Univ. Ill, Urbana, 64, Ph.D.(agron), 69. ASST. PROF. SOIL GENESIS, S.DAK. STATE UNIV, 69- Am. Soc. Agron; Soil Sci. Soc. Am; Am. Quaternary Asn. Remote sensing of soils; automatic data processing of soil interpretations; clay mineralogy of soils. Address: Dept. of Plant Science, South Dakota State University, Brookings, SD 57006.

FRAZEE, JERRY D, b. Wichita Falls, Tex, May 26, 29; m. 56; c. 4. PHYSICAL CHEMISTRY. B.S, Texas, 51, M.A, 57, Ph.D.(chem), 59; Mex. City Col, 55. Vis. scientist phys. chem, Rohm & Haas Co, Marshall Space Flight Center, 59; asst. prof. chem, La. Polytech, 59-60; chemist, Rocketdyne Div, N.Am. Aviation, Inc, 60-64, sr. chemist, 64-67; proj. leader & supvr. instrumental anal. sect, chem. dept, Gulf Oil Corp, 67-68; SR. PAINT CHEMIST, TEX. HWY. DEPT, 68- Chem.C, U.S.A, 53-55. AAAS; Am. Chem. Soc; Brit. Oil & Colour Chem. Asn. Pyrolysis of hydrocarbons; analytical chemistry; carbon formation mechanisms; physical properties of solid propellants; mechanical vibration; polymers and resins; spectroscopy; color. Address: M & T Lab, 38th & Jackson Sts, Austin, TX 78703.

FRAZER, AUGUST HENRY, b. New Orleans, La, Nov. 15, 24; m. 48; c. 3. CHEMISTRY. B.S, Tulane, 44, M.S, 45, Eaton fel, 46-47; Ph.D.(org. chem), Syracuse, 48. Asst. chem, Tulane, 44-45; Syracuse, 45-46; res. chemist, Ethyl Corp, La, 47-48; rayon dept, E.I. DU PONT DE NEMOURS & CO, INC, 48-60, RES. ASSOC, TEXTILE FIBERS DEPT, 60-, RES. FEL, 68- Am. Chem. Soc. Polymers and intermediates; synthetic fibers; elastomers; polyaromatic heterocyclics; high temperature resistant polymers and fibers. Address: Experimental Station, Bldg. 302, E.I. du Pont de Nemours & Co, Inc, Wilmington, DE 19803.

FRAZER, B(ENJAMIN) CHALMERS, b. Birmingham, Ala, July 19, 22; m. 51; c. 3. PHYSICS. B.S, Ala. Polytech, 47, M.S, 48; fel, Pa. State Col, 51-52, Ph.D.(physics), 52. Assoc. physicist, Brookhaven Nat. Lab, 52-55; physicist, Westinghouse Res. Labs, 55-58; BROOKHAVEN NAT. LAB, 58-67, SR. PHYSICIST & DEP. CHMN. DEPT, 67- Guest scientist, P.R. Nuclear Center, 62-63. Consult, Westinghouse Res. Labs, 55-62; assoc. ed, Jour. Phys. Chem. Solids, 64- U.S.A.A.F, 43-46, Res, 46-, 1st Lt. Fel. Am. Phys. Soc; Am. Crystallog. Asn. Crystal and magnetic structures and lattice dynamics by neutron scattering; solid state physics. Address: Physics Dept, Brookhaven National Lab, Upton, L.I, NY 11973.

FRAZER, JACK W(INFIELD), b. Forest Grove, Ore, Sept. 9, 24; m. 47; c. 3. CHEMISTRY. B.S, Hardin-Simmons, 48. Anal. chemist, Los Alamos Sci. Lab, 48-51, chemist, 51-53; group leader vacuum anal. chem, LAWRENCE LIVERMORE LAB, UNIV. CALIF, 53-66, assoc. div. leader, GEN. CHEM. DIV, 66-70, DIV. LEADER, 70- U.S.A.A.F, 42-45, Res, 45-55, 1st Lt. Analytical chemistry; vacuum procedures; inorganic and fluorine chemistry; computer control and data acquisition as applied to vacuum analytical chemistry. Address: 6767 Alisal, Pleasanton, CA 94566.

FRAZER, JAMES W, b. Chicago, Ill, Feb. 20, 28; m. 47. PHARMACOLOGY, BIOPHYSICS. B.A, Syracuse, 50, Atomic Energy Comn. scholar, 52-55; Nat. Insts. Health fel. & Ph.D.(pharmacol), State Univ. N.Y. Upstate Med. Center, 65. RES. PHYSIOLOGIST, U.S. AIR FORCE SCH. AEROSPACE MED, 64- U.S.N.R, 55-59, Res, 59-66, Lt.(jg). AAAS; fel. Am. Inst. Chem. Biochemical mechanisms of ion transport; relationship of transport phenomena to intracellular cytochromes; biophysics of cellular membrane motion. Address: U.S. Air Force School of Aerospace Medicine, Regular Army, Brooks Air Force Base, TX 78235.

FRAZER, JOHN P, b. Rochester, N.Y, Sept. 14, 14; m. 50; c. 2. OTOLARYNGOLOGY. M.D, Univ. Rochester, 39. Instr. path, med. col, Cornell Univ, 39-40; surg, L.I. Col. Med, 40-41; OTOLARYNGOL, sch. med, Yale, 41-46, 47; PROF, MED. CTR, UNIV. ROCHESTER, 63- Consult, Tripler Army Hosp, Hawaii Leprosarium & Leahi Tuberc. Hosp, Honolulu, 50-63. Dipl, Am. Bd. Otolaryngol, 49. Am. Laryngol, Rhinol. & Otol. Soc; Am. Col. Surg; Am. Broncho-Esophagol. Asn; Am. Laryngol. Asn. Address: Dept. of Otolaryngology, University of Rochester Medical Center, 260 Crittenden Blvd, Rochester, NY 14642.

FRAZER, J(OHN) RONALD, b. Ottawa, Ont, July 17, 23; U.S. citizen; m. 48; c. 5. INDUSTRIAL ENGINEERING & MANAGEMENT. B.M.E, Clarkson Tech, 45; M.S, Iowa State, 50, Ph.D.(eng, econ), 54. Instr. mech. eng, Clarkson Tech, 45-46; indust. eng, Iowa State, 46-50, asst. prof, 50-53; CLARKSON COL. TECHNOL, 53-54, assoc. prof, 54-60, prof. & chmn. dept, 60-67, dean sch. bus. admin, 67-70, PROF. INDUST. MGT, 70- Summer proj. engr; Aluminum Co. Am, 55, 56 & 57, N.Y. Tel. Co, 58, Gen. Motors Corp, 59. Am. Inst. Indust. Eng; Acad. Mgt; Am. Soc. Eng. Educ. Cost studies; linear programming; operations research. Address: Dept. of Industrial Management, Clarkson College of Technology, Potsdam, NY 13676.

FRAZER, LOWELL K(EITH), b. Nashville, Ind, May 15, 25; m. 45; c. 4. MATHEMATICS. A.B, Ind. Univ, 47, M.A, 49, Ph.D, 51. MATHEMATICIAN, NAT. SECURITY AGENCY, 51- U.S.A.A.F, 43-47, 2nd Lt. Geometry. Address: 15612 Ancient Oak Dr, Rt. 3, Gaithersburg, MD 20760.

FRAZER, W(ILLIAM) DONALD, b. Tampa, Fla, Jan. 9, 37; m. 61; c. 3. COMPUTER SCIENCE. B.S.E, Princeton, 59; M.S, Illinois, 61, Int. Bus. Mach. fel, 61-62, univ. fel, 62-63, Ph.D.(elec. eng), 63. Res. asst, digital comput. lab, Illinois, 59-61; RES. STAFF MEM, THOMAS J. WATSON RES. CTR, IBM CORP, 63- Vis. lectr, Princeton, 67-68; adj. assoc. prof, Courant Inst. Math. Sci, N.Y. Univ, 70- AAAS; Math. Asn. Am; Asn. Comput. Mach. Design and analysis of algorithms for sort, search and optimization; computational problems on graphs; data structures; information theory and coding. Address: Thomas J. Watson Research Center, IBM Corp, P.O. Box 218, Yorktown Heights, NY 10598.

FRAZER, WILLIAM R(OBERT), b. Indianapolis, Ind, Aug. 6, 33; m. 54; c. 2. THEORETICAL PHYSICS. A.B, Carleton Col, 54; Nat. Sci. Found. fel, California, 54-56, Ph.D.(physics), 59; Nat. Sci. Found. fel, Utrecht, 56-57. Physicist, Lawrence Radiation Lab, California, 59; mem. physics dept, Inst. Advan. Study, 59-60; asst. prof. PHYSICS, UNIV. CALIF, SAN DIEGO, 60-63, assoc. prof, 64-67, PROF, 67-, acting provost, third col, 69-70. Sloan Found. fel. Am. Phys. Soc. Theoretical physics of the elementary particles. Address: Dept. of Physics, University of California, San Diego, La Jolla, CA 92037.

FRAZEUR, DEAN R(USSELL), SR, b. Omaha, Nebr, Nov. 11, 24; m. 46; c. 3. FOOD CHEMISTRY. B.S, Minnesota, 49; M.S, Pa. State, 52, Ph.D.(dairy) mfg), 53. Dairy technologist, Golden State Co, Inc, 49-50; Swift & Co, 53-55; asst. prof. dairy mfg, Purdue Univ, 55-59, assoc. prof, 59-67; res. supvr, Monsanto Co, 67-69; MGR. NEW PROD. DEVELOP. FOOD, GRAIN PROCESSING CORP, 69- U.S.A, 43-46. AAAS; Am. Chem. Soc; Am. Dairy Sci. Asn; Inst. Food Technol. New food product development; development and application of protein food ingredients; organoleptic evaluation; sanitation and production of foods; quality control. Address: Grain Processing Corp, 1600 Oregon St, Muscatine, IA 52761.

FRAZIER, DAVID, b. Norwalk, Ohio, Nov. 28, 19; m. 50; c. 5. STATISTICS. A.B, Oberlin, 41; Ph.D.(org. chem), Stanford, 45. Asst. chem, Stanford, 41-44; res. chemist, STANDARD OIL CO, 46-52, OPERS. ANALYST, 52- U.S.N.R, 44-46. AAAS; Am. Chem. Soc; Inst. Math. Statist; Am. Statist. Asn. Structure of triterpenoids; experimental statistics; measurement of characteristics of motor vehicles and motor fuels, lubricants and components; design, analysis and interpretation of complex industrial experiments and interlaboratory studies. Address: Standard Oil Co, 4440 Warrensville Center Rd, Cleveland, OH 44128.

FRAZIER, DONALD THA, b. Martin, Ky, Sept. 26, 35; m. 56; c. 3. PHYSIOLOGY, NEUROPHYSIOLOGY. B.S, Kentucky, 58, U.S. Pub. Health Serv. fel, 59-63, M.S, 60, Ph.D, 64. Instr. NEUROPHYSIOL, sch. med, Univ. N.Mex, 64-65, asst. prof, 65-67, ASSOC. PROF, 67-69; MED. CTR, UNIV. KY, 69- Nat. Insts. Health res. grant, 66-69; Grass Found. summer res. fel, Marine Biol. Labs, Woods Hole, Mass, 67, 69-71. AAAS; Am. Physiol. Soc. Neurosciences. Address: Dept. of Physiology, University of Kentucky Medical Center, Lexington, KY 40506.

FRAZIER, DWIGHT E(AROLL), b. West Palm Beach, Fla, Apr. 13, 23; m. 48; c. 2. BACTERIOLOGY. B.S, Florida, 48, M.S, 50. Bacteriologist, State Bd. Health, Fla, 48-52, dir. Miami Regional Lab, 52-56; v.pres. & gen. mgr, LaHuis Clin. Labs, Inc, 56-62; dir, Miami Regional Lab, Fla. State Bd, Health, 63-66; PRES. & DIR, BIOCHEM. ASSOCS. INT, 66- Mem. faculty, sch. med, Miami (Fla), 64- U.S.A, 43-47, 1st Lt. Am. Soc. Microbiol; Am. Pub. Health Asn. Cultural methods for C. Diphtheriae. Address: Biochemistry Associates International, 1150 N.W. 14th St, Miami, FL 33136.

FRAZIER, E(LERI) ANN JAMES, b. Hatch End, Eng, May 5, 41; m. 68. DEVELOPMENTAL BIOLOGY, CELL PHYSIOLOGY. B.Sc, Bristol Univ, 62; Cert. Educ, Cambridge, 63; M.S, Univ. Wash, 65, fel. & Ph.D.(zool), 70. INSTR. BIOL, TEMPLE UNIV, 68- Am. Soc. Zool; Soc. Develop. Biol. Nucleocytoplasmic interactions in the ciliate Stentor; RNA metabolism during oral morphogenesis; initiation of DNA synthesis by alterations of the nucleocytoplasmic ratio. Address: Dept. of Biology, Temple University, Philadelphia, PA 19122.

FRAZIER, FLOYD WENDELL, b. Walters, Okla, Nov. 26, 11; m. 45; c. 2. PLANT BREEDING, GENETICS. B.S, Okla. State, 54, M.S, 56, Ph.D.(plant breeding, genetics), 59. Asst. agronomist, Colorado State, 58-61; asst. prof. BIOL, CENT. STATE UNIV.(OKLA), 61-65, ASSOC. PROF, 65- U.S.N, 34-38, 41-45. AAAS. Plant breeding, expecially wheat and wheatgrass hybrids and modification of amino acid content in wheat and these hybrids. Address: Dept. of Biology, Central State University, Edmond, OK 73034.

FRAZIER, GEORGE CLARK, JR, b. Cumberland, Va, Apr. 14, 30; m. 53. CHEMICAL ENGINEERING. B.S, Va. Polytech, 52; M.Sc, Ohio State, 56; D.Eng.(chem. eng), Hopkins, 62. Engr. nuclear reactor design, atomic power div, Westinghouse Elec. Corp, 56-59; NATO fel, Cambridge, 62-63; asst. prof. chem. eng, Johns Hopkins Univ, 63-68; ASSOC. PROF. CHEM. & METALL. ENG, UNIV. TENN, KNOXVILLE, 68- Consult, Am. Potash & Chem. Corp, Calif, 64-; appl. physics lab, Hopkins. U.S.A.F, 52-54, 1st Lt. Am. Inst. Chem. Eng. Combustion; interfacial transfer; gaseous diffusion. Address: Dept. of Chemical Engineering, University of Tennessee, Knoxville, TN 37919.

FRAZIER, HOWARD S(TANLEY), b. Oak Park, Ill, Jan. 16, 26; m. 50; c. 4. MEDICINE. Ph.B, Chicago, 47; M.D, Harvard, 53. Res. fel, Harvard Med. Sch, 55-56; physiol. lab, Cambridge, 56-57; fel. cardiol, dept. med. Western Reserve, 57-58; res. fel. MED, HARVARD MED. SCH, 58-60, asst, 60-62, assoc, Mass. Gen. Hosp, 62-65, asst. prof, 65-68, ASSOC. PROF, BETH ISRAEL HOSP, 68- U.S.N, 44-46. Am. Soc. Clin. Invest; Am. Soc. Nephrol. Renal physiology; membrane transport. Address: Dept. of Medicine, Beth Israel Hospital, 330 Brookline Ave, Boston, MA 02215.

FRAZIER, JOHN C(ARROLL), b. Middletown, Ind, Mar. 29, 00; m. 25. PLANT PHYSIOLOGY. A.B, DePauw, 25; M.A, Nebraska, 26; Ph.D.(plant physiol), Chicago, 39. Instr. bot, Kans. State Col, 26-27; asst. prof. biol, Ill. Wesleyan, 27-36; instr. bot, KANS. STATE UNIV, 36-39, asst. prof, 39-45, assoc. prof, 45-46, prof. PLANT PHYSIOL, 46-70, asst. plant physiologist, exp. sta, 36-45, plant physiologist, 45-70, EMER. PROF, 70- Fel. AAAS; Bot. Soc. Am; Am. Soc. Plant Physiol. Plant biochemistry; weed control; nature of the root system of noxious perennial weeds and food reserves of such weeds in relation to their control; effects of low and high temperatures and drought on hard red winter wheat; morphology and physiology of the wheat kernel; mineral nutrition of higher plants. Address: Division of Biology, Ackert Hall, Kansas State University, Manhattan, KS 66502.

FRAZIER, J(OHN) EARL, b. Houseville, Pa, July 4, 02; m. 36; c. 2. CERAMICS. B.S, Washington & Jefferson Col, 22; M.S, Mass. Inst. Technol, 24; Sc.D, Brazil, 38. Instr. gen. chem, Washington & Jefferson Col, 19-20; chem. engr, Berney Bond Glass Co. Div, Owens-Illinois, 24-26; fuel engr, Simplex Eng. Co, 26-28, asst. secy. & treas, 28-31, secy. & treas, 31-38, v.pres. & treas, FRAZIER-SIMPLEX, INC, 38-45, PRES, 45-, TREAS, 67-, secy, 45-67. Mem, Indust. War Co, U.S. Govt, 46; trustee, Washington & Jefferson Col, 60- Greaves-Walker Award, Keramos, 67. Fel. AAAS; fel. Am. Inst. Chem; fel. Brit. Soc. Glass Technol; hon. Benjamin Franklin fel. Royal Soc. Arts; Am. Chem. Soc; fel. Am. Ceramic Soc.(v.pres, 67-68, treas, 68-69, Albert Victor Bleininger Award, 69, pres. elect, 69-70, pres, 70-71); Am. Soc. Test. & Mat; Am. Soc. Heat, Refrig. & Air-Conditioning Eng; Nat. Soc. Prof. Eng; Indust. Heating Equip. Asn; Nat. Inst. Ceramic Eng; Can. Ceramic Soc; fel. Royal Soc; Am. Inst. Mining, Metall. & Petrol. Eng. Melting and annealing of glass by fuel and electric methods; raw materials charging to tank furnaces and to open hearth furnaces, including mixing, handling and storage; tank furnace methods of level control; open hearth furnaces methods of improvements of doors and regenerators. Address: Frazier-Simplex, Inc, P.O. Box 493, Washington, PA 15301.

FRAZIER, L(AURENCE) E(MERSON), b. San Bernardino, Calif, Aug. 8, 10; m. 39; c. 2. BIOCHEMISTRY. B.A, Oregon, 32; M.S, Chicago, 48. Asst. chem, Oregon, 30-31, German, 32-33; teacher, pub. schs, Oregon & Wash, 34-41; chem. asst. path, UNIV. CHICAGO, 42-44, asst, 44-58, ADMIN. ASST, 59-, RES. ASSOC, 65-, DEP. DIR, RES. CHEM. LAB, 69-, dir, 59-65. Nutritive value of proteins; relationship between electrolytes, hormones and protein metabolism; cancer inhibition and tissue lipid analysis in atherosclerosis. Address: 1416 E. 54th St, Chicago, IL 60615.

FRAZIER, MARVIN EUGENE, b. Medford, Ore, Apr. 21, 42; m. 63; c. 4. VIROLOGY, MICROBIOLOGY. B.S, Univ. Portland, 63; M.S, Univ. Ore, 67; Ph.D.(microbiol), Univ. Mont, 71. Norcus fel, Northwest Labs, Battelle Mem. Inst, summer 67; res. asst. porcine leukemia, Univ. Mont, 67-68; RES. SCIENTIST VIROL. & IMMUNOL, NORTHWEST LABS, BATTELLE MEM. INST, 69- AAAS; Am. Soc. Microbiol. Respective roles of radiation, viruses and immune response of the host in induction of leukemia and other types of malignancies. Address: Dept. of Biology, Battelle Memorial Institute Northwest Labs, P.O. Box 999, Richland, WA 99352.

FRAZIER, NORMAN W(ALTER), b. Berkeley, Calif, Jan. 28, 07; m. 46; c. 2. ENTOMOLOGY. B.S, California, 39, M.A, 40, Ph.D.(entom), 43. Tech. asst. plant path, UNIV. CALIF, BERKELEY, 38-41, asst. entom, 41-43, jr. entomologist, 43-47, LECTR. ENTOM. & PARASITOL, 47-, ENTOMOLOGIST, EXP. STA, DIV. ENTOM, OXFORD RES. UNIT, 60-, asst. entomologist, 47-54, assoc. entomologist, 54-60. AAAS; Entom. Soc. Am; Am. Phytopath. Soc. Plant virus diseases, especially of strawberries; taxonomy and biology of the Cicadellidae. Address: Experiment Station, Division of Entomology, Oxford Research Unit, University of California, Berkeley, CA 94720.

FRAZIER, RALPH P(AUL), b. Omaha, Nebr, Sept. 16, 16; m. 39; c. 4. ZOOLOGY. A.B, Colo. State Col, 39, A.M, 41; California, 46-47; Ph.D, Illinois, 56. Supv. teacher sci, New Mexico Highlands, 40-43, prin, univ. sch, 43-46; asst. prof. biol, Monmouth Col, 47-50; instr, Illinois, 50-52; assoc. prof, Monmouth Col, 52-56, prof, 56-59, head dept, 52-59; specialist sci. equip. & mat. sci, math. & for. lang. sect, U.S. Off. Educ, 59-60; prof. & head dept. biol, Kans. State Teachers Col, 60-67; CHMN. DIV. SCI. & MATH, SOUTHWEST MINN. STATE COL, 67- AAAS. Detoxifying factors of Crotaline venoms. Address: Division of Science & Mathematics, Southwest Minnesota State College, Marshall, MN 56258.

FRAZIER, RICHARD H(ENRY), b. Bellevue, Pa, May 29, 00; m. 36; c. 2. ELECTRICAL ENGINEERING. S.B, Mass. Inst. Tech, 23, S.M, 32. Elec. engr, Rwy. & Indust. Eng. Co, 23-25; instr. elec. eng, MASS. INST. TECHNOL, 25-31, asst. prof, 31-37, assoc. prof, 37-61, prof. electromech, 61-65, ELEC. CONSULT, dynamic anal. & control lab, 47-57, CHARLES STARK DRAPER LAB, 57-, EMER. PROF. ELECTROMECH, 65- Instr, Lowell Inst. Sch, 27-31, in charge elec. measurements lab, 31-35; exchange prof, Univ. Kans, 35-36; consult. ed, Irwin-Farnham Publ. Co, Ill, 45-49; Ronald Press, 49-63; consult. engr. Am. Soc. Eng. Educ; fel. Inst. Elec. & Electronics Eng; Soc. Hist. Technol. Electromechanical devices. Address: 7 Summit Ave, Winchester, MA 01890.

FRAZIER, ROBERT C(ARL), b. Guilford Co, N.C, Feb. 14, 32; m. 53; c. 3. MATHEMATICS. A.B, Atlantic Christian Col, 53; M.A, East Carolina, 59; M.S, Illinois, 65; Ed.D.(math. ed), Fla. State, 69. Teacher, high sch, N.C, 53-54, 56-59; assoc. prof. MATH, ATLANTIC CHRISTIAN COL, 59-69, PROF, 69- Sig.C, U.S.A, 54-56. Math. Asn. Am. Comparison of methods of teaching mathematical proof; mathematics education. Address: Dept. of Mathematics, Atlantic Christian College, Wilson, NC 27893.

FRAZIER, SHERVERT HUGHES, b. Shreveport, La, June 12, 21; m. 47; c. 4. PSYCHIATRY, PSYCHOANALYSIS. B.S, Illinois, 41, M.D, 43; M.S, Minnesota, 57; cert. psychoanal. med, Columbia, 63. Hosp. administr, Harrisburg Med. Found, 48-51; fel. internal med, Mayo Found, 51-52, fel. psychiat. & asst. to staff, 53-56, consult, 56-58; chief res. scientist, N.Y. State Psychiat. Inst, 58-61; assoc. psychiat, col. physicians & surgeons, Columbia Univ, 58-59, asst. prof, 59-62; prof. & chmn. dept, col. med, Baylor Univ, 62-68; PROF. PSYCHIAT. & CHMN. GRAD. EDUC. COMT. PSYCHIAT, COL. PHYSICIANS & SURGEONS, COLUMBIA UNIV, 68- Private practice, Ill, 46-50, 53; asst. attend. psychiatrist, Presby. Hosp, N.Y.C, 58-63, dir. in-patient consult. serv. psychiat, 61-62, mem. med. bd. & attend. psychiat; dir, Houston State Psychiat. Inst, 62-65; psychiatrist in chief, Ben Traub Gen. Hosp, consult, Vet. Admin. Hosp. & sr. attend. psychiatrist, Methodist Hosp, Houston, Tex, 62-; consult. psychiatrist, Rice Univ, 63-; state comnr. ment. health & ment. retardation, Tex, 65-66; dir, Am. Bd. Psychiat. & Neurol, 65-, v.pres; dep. dir, N.Y. Psychiat. Inst; attend. psychiat, St. Luke's Hosp, N.Y.C. Dipl, Am. Bd. Psychiat. & Neurol, 56. U.S.N.R, 44-46, Lt. Comdr. Am. Med. Asn; Am. Psychiat. Asn; Am. Col. Physicians; Am. Col. Psychiat; Asn. Res. Nerv. & Ment. Disease. Eating disorders; psychosomatic disorders; headache and pain problems. Address: 722 W. 168th St, New York, NY 10032.

FRAZIER, STEPHEN EARL, b. Spencer, W.Va, Oct. 21, 39; m. 70; c. 1. INORGANIC CHEMISTRY. B.S, Fla. South. Col, 61; M.S, Univ. Fla, 63, Ph.D. (chem), 65. Res. assoc. Case West. Res. Univ, 66-67; res. chemist, res. div, W.R. Grace & Co, 67-69; prof. chem, Polk Jr. Col, 70-71; INDUST. CONSULT, INORG. CHEM, 71- Instr, Baltimore Community Col, 68-69; res. assoc, Univ. Fla, 70-71. Am. Chem. Soc. Inorganic phosphorus chemistry; synthesis of organo-phosphonium salts and phosphonitrilic materials; organo-silicon chemistry; inorganic polymers; chemistry of chloramine and ammonia; heterogeneous catalysis; inorganic materials science. Address: 806 Carolina Ave, Tarpon Springs, FL 33589.

FRAZIER, T(HOMAS) VERNON, b. Tonopah, Nev, Feb. 25, 21; m. 64; c. 2. PHYSICS. A.B, California, Los Angeles, 43, M.A, 49, Ph.D.(physics), 52. Asst. physics, California, Los Angeles, 43-44, 45-49; physicist, Naval Ord. Lab, 44-45; instr. PHYSICS, UNIV. NEV, RENO, 50-52, asst. prof, 52-57, from assoc. prof. to PROF, 57- Vis. Fulbright lectr, Nat. Tsing Hua Univ. & Taiwan Provincial Nor. Univ, 59-61. AAAS; Am. Asn. Physics Teachers; Am. Phys. Soc; Acoust. Soc. Am. Hearing by bone connection. Address: Dept. of Physics, University of Nevada, Reno, NV 89507.

FRAZIER, TODD MEARL, b. Lima, Ohio, Nov. 9, 25; m; c. 4. BIOSTATISTICS. A.B, Kenyon Col, 49; Sc.M, Hopkins, 57. Statistician, Army Chem. Center, Md, 51-54; dir. biostatists, Baltimore City Health Dept, 54-63; chief div. planning, res. & statist, D.C. Dept. Pub. Health, 63-68; ASSOC. PROF. BIOSTATIST, SCH. PUB. HEALTH, HARVARD CTR. COMMUNITY HEALTH & MED. CARE, 68- Instr, Johns Hopkins Hosp, 56- U.S.N, 43-46; U.S.A, 50-51. Public health administration, planning, research and statistics. Address: School of Public Health, Harvard Center for Community Health & Medical Care, 643 Huntington Ave, Boston, MA 02115.

FRAZIER, W(ILLIAM) A(LLEN), b. Carrizo Springs, Tex, Apr. 26, 08; m. 35; c. 3. OLERICULTURE. B.S, Agr. & Mech. Col. Texas, 30; fel, Maryland, 30-33, M.S, 31, Ph.D, 33. Instr. olericult, Maryland, 33-35, assoc. prof, 35-37; assoc. horticulturist, exp. sta, Arizona, 37-39; olericulturist & head dept. veg. crops, Hawaii, 39-49; HORTICULTURIST, OREGON STATE UNIV, 49- AAAS; Am. Soc. Hort. Sci. Breeding vegetable crop plants for disease resistance and improved horticultural characters. Address: 3225 N.W. Crest Dr, Corvallis, OR 97330.

FRAZIER, WILLIAM C(ARROLL), b. Madison, Wis, Sept. 26, 95; m. 24, 52; c. 1. BACTERIOLOGY. B.S, Wisconsin, 17, Ph.D.(agr. bact), 24. Instr, Wisconsin, 19-24; assoc. bacteriologist & sr. bacteriologist, bur. dairy indust, U.S. Dept. Agr, 24-34; prof. BACT, UNIV. WIS, MADISON, 34-66, EMER. PROF, 66-, chmn. dept, 43-53. U.S.A, 17-19. AAAS; Am. Soc. Microbiol.(secy-treas, Soc. Bact, 43-44); Inst. Food Technol; Am. Dairy Sci. Asn. Dairy and food microbiology. Address: 231 Westmorland Blvd, Madison, WI 53705.

FRAZIER, W(ILLIAM) R(OBERT), b. Wash, D.C, Dec. 12, 26; m. 51; c. 3. MICROBIOLOGY. B.S, Wisconsin, 50, M.S, 52. Asst. bact, Wisconsin, 51-52; foreman antibiotic mfg, E.R. Squibb & Sons, 52-53; res. asst, Squibb Inst. Med. Res, 53, res. asst. supvr, 53-69, RES. FEL, E.R. SQUIBB & SONS, 69- U.S.A, 45-47. Am. Soc. Microbiol. Fermentation development and process improvement; antibiotics; vitamins; steroids. Address: 158 Herrontown Rd, Princeton, NJ 08540.

FRAZZA, EVERETT J(OSEPH), b. N.J, Nov. 2, 24; m. 46; c. 4. ORGANIC CHEMISTRY. B.S, Maryland, 48-50, fel, 50-51, Nat. Insts. Health fel, 52-54, Ph.D.(org. chem), 54. Chemist, appl. physics lab, Hopkins, 51-52; res. chemist, AM. CYANAMID CO, 54-58, group leader, indust. chem. dept, 58-60, cent. res. div, 60-69, head biotherapeut. dept, LEDERLE LABS, 69-70, DIR. RES. & DEVELOP, DAVIS & GECK DEPT, 70- U.S.N, 43-46. Am. Chem. Soc.(pres, 50). Aliphatic nitriles; petrochemicals; paper chemicals; monomer and polymer synthesis; medical and biological applications of polymers; surgical sutures; hospital specialties. Address: David & Geck Dept, Lederle Labs, American Cyanamid Co, Pearl River, NY 10965.

FREA, JAMES I(RVING), b. Sturgeon Bay, Wis, Mar. 1, 37; m. 59; c. 3. BACTERIOLOGY, BIOCHEMISTRY. B.S, Wisconsin, 59, Nat. Sci. Found. fel. & M.S, 61, Nat. Sci. Found. fel. & Ph.D.(bact, biochem), 63. Asst. prof. MICROBIOL, OHIO STATE UNIV, 65-69, ASSOC. PROF, 69- Med.Serv.C, 63-65, Capt. AAAS; Am. Soc. Microbiol; Am. Chem. Soc. Staphylococcal toxins; actinomycete nucleic acids; metabolic activity of actinomycetes; host-parasite interactions; microbial proteins and nucleic acids; actinomycete physiology; microbial ecology; biochemical ecology of microorganisms. Address: Dept. of Microbiology, Ohio State University, 484 W. 12th Ave, Columbus, OH 43210.

FREAR, DONALD E(LISHA) H(ARDING), b. Tunkhannock, Pa, Sept. 16, 06; m. 28; c. 3. BIOCHEMISTRY. B.S, Pa. State Col, 26, Ph.D.(agr. biochem), 37; M.S, New Hampshire, 28. Asst. biochem, New Hampshire, 26-28; asst. chemist, exp. sta, R.I. State Col, 28-30; assoc. animal nutrit, inst. animal nutrit, PA. STATE UNIV, 30-33, instr. agr. & biol. chem, 33-36, asst. prof, 36-43, assoc. prof, 43-45, prof. agr. biochem, 45-63, chem. pesticides, 63-69, dir. pesticides res. labs, 65-69, EMER. PROF. CHEM. PESTICIDES, 69- Consult, WHO, 63; mem. coordination & food protection comts. & staff mem. comt. mod. methods handling chem. info, Nat. Acad. Sci-Nat. Res. Coun. With Off. Sci. Res. & Develop, 44. Am. Chem. Soc; Entom. Soc. Am. Chemistry of pesticides; plant chemistry; relation of chemical structure to biological activity; chemical notation systems. Address: Dept. of Entomology, Pennsylvania State University, 531 Kennard Rd, State College, PA 16801.

FREAR, D(ONALD) STUART, b. Wakefield, R.I, Sept. 5, 29; m. 56; c. 4. BIOCHEMISTRY. B.S, Pa. State Univ, 51; M.Sc, Ohio State Univ, 53, Ph.D. (agr. biochem), 55. Res. biochemist, Charles F. Kettering Found, 55-57; assoc. prof. BIOCHEM, N.DAK. STATE UNIV, 57-70, PROF, 70-; RES. BIOCHEMIST, PLANT SCI. RES. DIV, AGR. RES. SERV, U.S. DEPT. AGR, 64- Am. Chem. Soc. Biochemistry of rust fungi; pesticide metabolism in plants. Address: Plant Science Research Division, Agricultural Research Service, U.S. Dept. of Agriculture, State University Station, Fargo, ND 58102.

FREAR, GEORGE L(EWIS), b. State College, Pa, Sept. 29, 01; m. 28; c. 2. CHEMISTRY. B.S, Pa. State, 23; Ph.D.(phys. chem), 26. Fel, Yale, 26-27; res. assoc, Am. Sheet & Tin Plate Co, 27-29; assoc. phys. chemist, U.S. Bur. Mines, 29-33; from assoc. chemist to sr. chemist, Tenn. Valley Authority, 33-45; supvr. carbide res, Air Reduction Sales Co, 45-48; phys. chemist, Barrett Div, Allied Chem. Corp, 48-52, mem. staff prod. develop, nitrogen div, 52-65, mkt. analyst, 65-66; spec. lectr, Newark Col. Eng, 66-71; CONSULT, 66- Am. Chem. Soc; Chem. Mkt. Res. Asn. Physical chemistry of steel making; chemical research on calcium carbide manufacture; chemical research on phosphorus, phosphates, ammonia and ammonium nitrate; rocket propellant. Address: Box 255, R.D. 1, Flemington, NJ 08822.

FREAS, ALAN D('YARMETT), b. Newark, Ohio, Nov. 4, 10; m. 34; c. 3. ENGINEERING. B.S, Wisconsin, 33, M.S, 47, C.E, 52. Instr. civil eng, Wisconsin, 36-39; engr, forest prods. lab, U.S. FOREST SERV, 33-36, 39-42, 45-56, asst. dir. div. forest prods. res, 56-58, asst. to dir, FOREST PROD. LAB, 58-67, CHIEF DIV. SOLID WOOD PROD. RES, 67- Eng. aide, Wis. Hwy. Comn, 37; struct. designer, Off. State Architect, 38-39. U.S.A.A.F, 42-45, Res, 29-42, 45-70, Lt. Col.(Ret). Am. Soc. Civil Eng; Forest Prod. Res. Soc. Strength of wood, modified wood and plywood; strength of glued, laminated wood structures; processing and protection of forest products; research administration. Address: 2618 Park Pl, Madison, WI 53705.

FREAS, DONALD H(AYES), b. Silver Spring, Md, July 13, 33; m. 55; c. 3. ECONOMIC GEOLOGY. B.S, West Virginia, 55; M.S, Wisconsin, 57, Union Carbide fel, 58-59; Ph.D.(geol), 59. Asst. prof. geol, Arizona State, 59-60; MGR. EXPLOR, M&E DIV, INT. MINERALS & CHEM. CORP, 61- Geol. Soc. Am; Am. Inst. Mining, Metall. & Petrol. Eng; Soc. Econ. Geol. Economic geology of metallic and nonmetallic mineral deposits; mineralogy; exploration geochemistry. Address: M&E Division, International Minerals & Chemical Corp, Old Orchard Rd, Skokie, IL 60078.

FREASIER, BEN F(OREST), b. San Patricio, Tex, May 14, 23; m. 44; c. 4. PHYSICAL CHEMISTRY. B.S, Tex. Col. Arts & Indust, 47, M.S, 50; Oklahoma, 47-48; Ph.D, Tex. Tech. Col, 57. Instr. chem, Tex. Col. Arts & Indust, 50-52; Amarillo Col, 53-54; chemist & physicist, atomic energy div, Phillips Petrol. Co, 54-55; sr. nuclear engr, Convair div, Gen. Dynamics Corp, 55-56; instr. chem, Tex. Tech. Col, 56-57; assoc. prof, Tex. Col. Arts & Indust, 57-60; S.Dak. State Col, 60-61; sr. phys. chemist, Southwest Res. Inst, 61-62; assoc. prof. CHEM, LA. POLYTECH UNIV, 62-69, PROF, 69- U.S.M.C, 41-45. Am. Chem. Soc. Kinetics; equilibrium; thermodynamics. Address: Dept. of Chemistry, Louisiana Polytechnic University, Ruston, LA 71270.

FREBERG, C(ARL) ROGER, b. Hector, Minn, March 17, 16; m. 41; c. 2. MECHANICAL ENGINEERING. B.M.E, Minnesota, 38, M.S, 40; Ph.D. (mech. eng), Purdue, 43. Instr. mech. eng, Minnesota, 39-40; Purdue, 40-43, asst. prof. mech. eng. & aeronaut. eng, 43-45; res. engr, Carrier Corp, 45-46; dir, eng. div, South. Res. Inst, 46-49; head equip. res, U.S. Naval Civil Eng. Lab, 49-52; assoc. dir, Borg Warner Res. Ctr, 52-57; PROF. MECH. ENG, UNIV. SOUTH. CALIF, 57- Consult, Studebaker Corp, 44; Carrier Corp, 45; Hughes Aircraft Corp, 59; lectr, NATO, Paris, France, 58. Am. Soc. Mech. Eng; Am. Soc. Eng. Educ; Am. Soc. Metals. Vibrations; noise; mechanical design; research management; applied mechanics. Address: OHE 430, Dept. of Mechanical Engineering, University of Southern California, Los Angeles, CA 90007.

FREBOLD, HANS (WILHELM LUDWIG AUGUST HERMAN), b. Hanover, Ger, July 31, 99; Can. citizen; m. 26; c. 5. GEOLOGY, PALEONTOLOGY. Ph.D. (geol, paleont), Göttingen, 24. Privat-docent geol. & paleont, Greifswald, Germany, 26, prof, 31, hon. prof, 45; sci. res, Geol. Inst. Copenhagen, 33-41; chief Arctic Div, German Sci. Inst, 41-45; hon. prof, Kiel, 49; consult. geologist, Danish Am. Prospecting Co, 47-49; geologist, Geol. Surv. Can, 49, chief div. stratig. paleont, 51-59, sr. res. paleontologist, 59-63, prin. res. scientist, 63-68; CONSULT. GEOLOGIST, 69- Vis. prof, Oklahoma, 63-64. Chief Norwegian Exped, Spitzbergen, 30; party chief Danish exped, N.E, Greenland, 31. Danish Medal Merit, E. Greenland, 35. Fel. Royal Soc. Can; Danish Geol. Soc. Stratigraphy and paleontology, particularly of Arctic regions and Canada. Address: 265 Patricia Ave, Ottawa, Ont. K1Y 0C6, Can.

FRECH, EMIL F(ERDINAND), b. Lenburg, Ill, June 6, 14; m. 41; c. 1. INORGANIC CHEMISTRY. B.S, McKendree Col, 36; M.S, Illinois, 38. Teacher, high sch, Ill, 38-41; tech. supvr, Aluminum Ore, Co, 41; res. chemist, Alcoa Res. Labs, Aluminum Co. Am, 41-61; Reardon Co, 61-65; ASST. CHIEF CHEMIST, NAT. LEAD CO, 65- Am. Chem. Soc; Soc. Appl. Spectros. Bayer processing of alumina ores; salting evaporation; gallium; water thinnable latex paints; paint compounds; oxides of lead and lead pigments; bentone gellants for greases; pigments for electroplating of paints. Address: 122 N. 31st St, Belleville, IL 62221.

FRECH, ROGER; b. Gary, Ind, Mar. 26, 41; m. 64; c. 2. PHYSICAL CHEMISTRY. B.S, Mass. Inst. Technol, 63; Ph.D.(phys. chem), Minnesota, 68. Res. assoc. PHYS. CHEM, Ore. State Univ, 68-70, instr, 69-70; ASST. PROF, UNIV. OKLA, 70- Am. Chem. Soc; Am. Inst. Physics. Infrared spectroscopy of crystals, aqueous systems; solid state and condensed phase infrared spectroscopy; theory of optical and dielectric constants. Address: Dept. of Chemistry, Room 211, University of Oklahoma, 620 Parrington Oval, Norman, OK 73069.

FRECHE, JOHN C(HARLES), b. Minneapolis, Minn, Apr. 29, 23; m. 43. METALLURGY, MECHANICAL ENGINEERING. B.S, Pittsburgh, 43. Jr. engr, Wright Aeronaut. Corp, N.J, 43-44; aeronaut. res. engr, Nat. Adv. Cmt. Aeronaut, 44-48, asst. head turbine cooling sect, 49-57, head alloys sect, LEWIS RES. CTR, NASA, 58-63, chief, fatigue & alloys res. br, 63-71, ASST. CHIEF MAT. & STRUCT. DIV, 71- U.S.A.A.F, 44-47. Fel. Am. Inst. Chem; Am. Soc. Metals (I-R 100 Award, 68); Am. Inst. Aeronaut. & Astronaut; Am. Inst. Mining, Metall. & Petrol. Eng; Soc. Exp. Stress Anal; Am. Soc. Test. & Mat. Materials for air breathing and space propulsion systems; nickel and cobalt base alloys; metal fatigue. Address: Lewis Research Center, NASA, 21000 Brookpark Rd, Cleveland, OH 44135.

FRECHETTE, ALFRED L(EO), b. Groveton, N.H, Aug. 22, 09; m. 30; c. 1. PUBLIC HEALTH. M.D, Vermont, 34; M.P.H, Harvard, 39. Instr, col. med, Vermont, 35-36; private practice, 36-38; dir. venereal disease control, N.H. Dept. Pub. Health, 39-42, comnr, 42-45; dir. pub. health, Brookline, Mass, 45-50; health div, United Community Servs. Metrop. Boston, 50-59; COMNR, MASS. DEPT. PUB. HEALTH, 59- Chief med. off. Tunisian unit, Office For. Relief & Rehabil. Opers, 43-44, chief, mission to Ethiopia, UNRRA, 44-45, U.S. Pub. Health Serv. Res, 43-45; Nat. Guard, 57-69. Am. Med. Asn; Am. Pub. Health Asn. Public health administration. Address: 600 Washington St, Boston, MA 02111.

FRECHETTE, ARTHUR R(OY), b. Schenectady, N.Y, Feb. 11, 07; m. 32; c. 2. DENTISTRY. D.D.S, Southern California, 28. Private practice, 28-36; dent. corps, U.S. Navy, 36-65, commanding off, U.S. Naval Dent. Sch, 61-65; EXEC. SECY, INT. ASN. DENT. RES, 65- Consult. to dir, Nat. Inst. Dent. Res; consult, comn. on dent. res, Int. Dent. Fedn. Am. Col. Prosthodontists; Colombian Asn. Advan. Sci; Am. Dent. Asn; Am. Prosthodont. Soc; fel. Am. Col. Dent; Int. Asn. Dent. Res. Prosthodontics; complete and partial dentures; saliva. Address: International Association for Dental Research, 211 E. Chicago Ave, Chicago, IL 60611.

FRECHETTE, (HOWELLS ACHILLE) VAN DERCK, b. Ottawa, Ont, Jan. 5, 16; nat; m. 40; c. 5. CERAMIC ENGINEERING. B.S, Alfred, 39; M.S, Illinois, 40, Ph.D.(ceramic eng), 42. Asst, eng. exp. sta, Illinois, 38-40; res. physicist, Corning Glass Works, N.Y, 42-44; asst. instr. petrog, STATE UNIV. N.Y. COL. CERAMICS, ALFRED UNIV, 41-42, PROF. CERAMIC SCI. TECHNOL, 44- Chmn. solid state studies, Gordon Res. Conf, 55; Fulbright prof, Inst. Phys. Chem, Göttingen, Ger, 55-56; guest prof, Max Planck Inst. Silicates, 65-66. AAAS; fel. Am. Ceramic Soc; Am. Soc. Eng. Educ; Mineral Soc. Am; Can. Ceramic Soc; Brit. Ceramic Soc; Fr. Ceramic Soc; Swedish Royal Soc. Arts & Sci; Ger. Ceramic Soc. Petrography and mineralogy of ceramic materials; color of crystalline inorganic materials; solid state reactivity; refractories; tempering certain glass products; fractography. Address: State University of New York College of Ceramics, Alfred University, Alfred, NY 14802.

FRECK, PETER G, b. Hinsdale, Ill, Aug. 14, 34; m. 58; c. 3. AERONAUTICAL ENGINEERING. B.S.E, Princeton, 56, M.S.E, 59; M.B.A, Harvard, 62. Aerodynamicist, Douglas Aircraft Corp, Calif, 58-60; aeronaut. engr, Anal. Serv, Inc, Va, 62-64; ASST. DIR, SYSTS. EVAL. DIV, INST. DEFENSE ANAL, 64- Am. Inst. Aeronaut. & Astronaut; Opers. Res. Soc. Am. Aircraft performance, stability and control; systems analysis; operations research. Address: Systems Evaluation Division, Institute for Defense Analyses, 400 Army-Navy Dr, Arlington, VA 22202.

FRECKMANN, ROBERT W, b. Milwaukee, Wis, Dec. 5, 39; m. 71. PLANT TAXONOMY. B.S, Univ. Wis-Milwaukee, 62; Nat. Sci. Found. fel, Iowa State Univ, 65-66, Ph.D.(plant taxon), 67. Asst. curator bot, Milwaukee Pub. Mus, 67-68; ASST. PROF. BIOL, WIS. STATE UNIV, STEVENS POINT, 68-, CURATOR HERBARIUM, MUS. NATURAL HIST, 69- Wis. State Univs. Res. Fund grant, 69-71. Am. Soc. Plant Taxon; Bot. Soc. Am; Int. Asn. Plant Taxon. Taxonomy and biosystematics of Panicum; grasses of Wisconsin; flora of central Wisconsin. Address: Dept. of Biology, Wisconsin State University, Stevens Point, WI 54481.

FRED, EDWIN B(ROUN), b. Middleburg, Va, Mar. 22, 87; m. 13; c. 2. BOTANY, BACTERIOLOGY. B.S, Va. Polytech, 07, M.S, 08; Ph.D.(bact), Göttingen, 11; hon. LL.D, Lawrence Col, 45, Northwestern, 47, Mich. State Col, 55, hon. Sc.D, Marquette, 45, Beloit Col, 46, North Carolina, 46, Northland Col, 46; Wisconsin, 58. Asst. bact, Va. Polytech, 07-08, asst. prof, 12-13; UNIV. WIS, MADISON, 13-14, assoc. prof, 14-18, prof, 18-58, dean grad. sch, 34-43, dean & dir, exp. sta, 43-45, pres, 45-48, EMER. PROF. BACT. & EMER. PRES, 58- Spec. consult, Secy. War. Trustee, Carnegie Found, 46-58. Mem, Nat. Adv. Health Coun, 45-50; U.S. Nat. Sci. Found. Bd, 50-56. U.S. Adv. Comn. Ed. Exchange, 49-54; comn. ed. & int. affairs, Am. Coun. Ed, 58-61. C.W.S, 18, Lt. Nat. Acad. Sci; AAAS; Am. Soc. Microbiol; Am. Philos. Soc. Fermentation products of the growth of microorganisms; rootnodule bacteria. Address: Van Hise Hall, University of Wisconsin, Madison, WI 53706.

FRED, MARK (SIMON), b. Richmond, Ind, June 26, 11; m. 41; c. 2. PHYSICS. B.S, Chicago, 33, M.S, 34, Ph.D.(physics), 37. Consult, Standard Oil Co, Ind, 37-43; chemist, Manhattan Dist. proj, Chicago, 42-45; physicist, Armour Res. Found, 45-48; consult, ARGONNE NAT. LAB, 45-48, SR. CHEMIST, 48- Am. Chem. Soc; fel. Optical Soc. Am; Am. Inst. Chem. Spectrochemical analysis; spectroscopy. Address: Room K 113, Bldg. 20D, Argonne National Lab, 9700 S. Cass Ave, Argonne, IL 60439.

FRED, RICHARD KASSLER, b. Charlotte, N.C, July 18, 35; m. 57; c. 1. BIOPHYSICS, DENTISTRY. D.D.S, Emory, 59; Ph.D.(med. physics), California, Berkeley, 67. Intern dent, hosp, U.S. PUB. HEALTH SERV, Staten Island, N.Y, 59-60, dep. chief, biophys. res. unit, Nat. Ctr. Radiol. Health, 67-68, STAFF SCIENTIST, METAB. STUDIES SECT, BUR. RADIOL. HEALTH, 68- U.S.P.H.S, 59-, Sr. Dent. Surg. AAAS; Radiation Res. Soc; Reticuloendothelial Soc. Biological effects of radiation on various physiological functions including phagocytosis; reticuloendothelial system; biological effects of ultrasonic energy. Address: 12720 Twinbrook Pkwy, Rockville, MD 20852.

FREDEEN, HOWARD T, b. MacRorie, Sask, Dec. 10, 21; m. 53; c. 5. ANIMAL GENETICS, BIOMETRY. B.Sc, Saskatchewan, 43; M.Sc, Alberta, 47; Ph.D.(genetics), Iowa State Col, 52. Lectr. animal husb, Saskatchewan, 43-45; animal husbandman, CAN. DEPT. AGR, 47-55, HEAD LIVESTOCK RES, 55- Mem, Quinquennial Reviero Conf, Commonwealth Agr. Bur, Eng, 55; Nat. Animal Breeding Adv. Comt, 59-64; chmn, Can. Livestock Geneticists Roundtable, 63-64. AAAS; N.Y. Acad. Sci; Am. Soc. Animal Sci; Poultry Sci. Asn; Biomet. Soc; Can. Soc. Animal Sci; Genetics Soc. Can.(sci. ed, Can. J. Genetics & Cytol, 60-64); fel. Agr. Inst. Can.(sci. ed, Can. J. Animal Sci, 63-67, ed, 67-71). Genetics of pigs, cattle and poultry, especially factors influencing the effectiveness of selective breeding. Address: Experimental Farm Dept, Research Branch, Canada Dept. of Agriculture, Lacombe, Alta, Can.

FREDEEN, STURE R(AGNVALD), b. Tidaholm, Sweden, May 24, 09; nat. Can; m. 34; c. 2. MINING ENGINEERING. B.S. & E.M, Mich. Col. Min, 29. Mining eng. & surv. engr, Int. Nickel Co, 29-31, miner, 31-33, mining eng. & surv, 33-34, safety & ventilation engr, 34-37, shaft engr, 38-43, rock burst engr, 43-46; asst. chief engr, KERR-ADDISON MINES, LTD, 46-51, CHIEF MINING ENGR, 51-, GEN. SUPT, 67- Can. Inst. Min. & Metall. Mining. Address: Kerr-Addison Mines, Ltd, Virginiatown, Ont, Can.

FREDELL, WALTER G(EORGE), b. St. Paul, Minn, Jan. 13, 06; m. 27. PHARMACEUTICAL CHEMISTRY. B.S, Minnesota, 29, M.S, 39. Head mfg.

& control, Sargon Labs, Inc, 27-32; pharmacist, 32-37; lab. instr, col. pharm, Minnesota, 37-41; instr, St. Louis Col. Pharm, 41-42; assoc. prof, col. pharm, Drake, 42-45; chief pharmacist, Lambert Pharmacal Co, 45-56; Warner-Lambert Pharmacol Co, 56-61; Am. Med. Asn, 61-62; RES. PHARMACIST, Strong, Cobb, Arner, 62-64; Norwich Pharmacal Co, 64-65; BUR. MED, FOOD & DRUG. ADMIN, 65- Lab. asst, col. pharm, Univ. Minn, 27-29. AAAS; Am. Soc. Microbiol; Am. Chem. Soc; Soc. Cosmetic Chem; Am. Pharmaceut. Asn. Pharmaceutical and cosmetic development and evaluation. Address: 2900 S. Glebe Rd, Arlington, VA 22206.

FREDEN, STANLEY C(HARLES), b. Far Rockaway, N.Y, Dec. 5, 27; m. 57; c. 3. SPACE SCIENCE. A.B, California, Los Angeles, 50, M.A, 52, Ph.D, 56. Asst. physics, California, Los Angeles, 50-54, assoc, 54-56, instr, 56-57; sr. staff physicist, Lawrence Radiation Lab, Livermore, 57-61; sect. head, Aerospace Corp, Calif, 61-66, sr. staff scientist, 66-68; chief space physics div, Manned Spacecraft Ctr, NASA, Tex, 68-70, CHIEF SCIENTIST, LAB. METEOROL. & EARTH SCI, GODDARD SPACE FLIGHT CTR, 70- Guest scientist, Max Planck Inst. Extraterrestrial Physics, 64-65. U.S.N.R, 45-46. AAAS; fel. Am. Phys. Soc; Am. Geophys. Union; Am. Astron. Soc. Particles trapped in the earth's magnetic field; experiments performed with space probes and satellites; acquisition of remotely sensed data and their applications to earth sciences and earth resource survey disciplines, including ecology and environmental quality. Address: Code 650, Goddard Space Flight Center, NASA, Greenbelt, MD 20771.

FREDENBURG, ROBERT LOVE, b. Antwerp, N.Y, Nov. 28, 21; m. 42; c. 5. PHYSICS, SCIENCE EDUCATION. A.B, Syracuse, 54; Esso Found. fel, Wesleyan, 58; M.S, Syracuse, 59, Ph.D.(sci. ed), 65. From assoc. prof. phys. sci. to PROF. GEOL. & PHYS. SCI. & V.PRES. ACAD. AFFAIRS, CHICO STATE COL, 59- U.S.A, 42-46, Res, 46-, Lt. Col. Nat. Sci. Teachers Asn. General education physical science courses at the college level and student interest in these courses. Address: Chico State College, Chico, CA 95926.

FREDENDALL, GORDON L(YLE), b. Kettle Falls, Wash, Dec. 20, 09; m. 31; c. 3. ELECTRICAL ENGINEERING. B.S, Wisconsin, 31, M.S, 32, Ph.D. (elec. eng), 36. RES. ENGR, TV labs, RCA CORP, 36-42, SYSTS. ANAL. & DEVELOP, DAVID SARNOFF RES. CTR, 42- Fel. Inst. Elec. & Electronics Eng. Color television; network theory; transmission systems; communications. Address: 969 Gravel Hill Rd, Southampton, PA 18966.

FREDERICK, CARL LEROY, b. Memphis, Nebr, July 28, 03; m. 22; c. 7. ENGINEERING PHYSICS. A.B, Nebr. Wesleyan, 25, D.Sc.(physics), 50; M.A, George Washington, 27. Instr, George Washington, 25-28; mem. tech. staff, Bell Tel. Labs, 28-34; engr, Fed. Tel. & Tel. Co, 34-35; consult, Am. Soc. Naval Architects, 35; asst. dir. res, Dictaphone Corp, Conn, 36-42; supvr, Navy Ord. Lab, Wash, D.C, 42; head dept. physics, Curtiss-Wright Res. Lab, N.Y, 43-46; Cornell Aeronaut. Lab, 46; v.pres, Frederick Flader, Inc, N.Y, 46-49; pres, Frederick Res. Corp, 51-63; fel. sci, HRB-Singer, Inc, 63-65; sr. staff scientist, Vitro Corp, Md, 65-67; private practice consult, 67-70; INST. SCIENTIST, SOUTHWEST RES. INST, 70- Expert consult, weapons systs. eval. group, Dept. Defense, 49, res. & develop. bd, 50; owner, Carl L. Frederick & Assocs, 50- Fel. Inst. Elec. & Electronics Eng; assoc. fel. Am. Inst. Aeronaut. & Astronaut; Am. Ord. Asn. Address: Apt. 101, 6718 Callaghan Rd, San Antonio, TX 78229.

FREDERICK, DALLAS EDWIN, b. Cleveland, Ohio, Sept. 7, 42; m. 66; c. 1. THEORETICAL PHYSICS. B.A, Ohio Wesleyan Univ, 65; M.S, Univ. Mich, 68, Ph.D.(physics), 71. ASST. PROF. PHYSICS, LAKE FOREST COL, 69- Am. Phys. Soc; Am. Asn. Physics Teachers. Mathematical representations of scattering phenomena. Address: Dept. of Physics, Lake Forest College, Lake Forest, IL 60045.

FREDERICK, DANIEL, b. Elkhorn, W.Va, Apr. 29, 25; m. 52; c. 4. ENGINEERING MECHANICS. B.S, Va. Polytech, 44, fel, 47, M.S, 48; Ph.D.(eng. mech), Michigan, 55. Instr. ENG. MECH, VA. POLYTECH. INST. & STATE UNIV, 48-51, assoc. prof, 51-55, PROF, 55-, HEAD DEPT, 70- Lectr, Nat. Sci. Found. Adv. Mech. Inst, Colorado, 62-63, summers, physicist, Norfolk Naval Shipyard, 56-58, lectr, summer inst, Am. Soc. Eng. Ed-NASA, 64. Consult, structures res. div, NASA, Va; Pac. Missile Range, Calif; Martin-Marietta Corp; Lord Mfg. Co; David Taylor Model Basin; dir. conf. continum. mech, Nat. Sci. Found, 65. U.S.A, 44-46. Am. Soc. Civil Eng. (award, 60); Am. Inst. Aeronaut. & Astronaut; Am. Soc. Eng. Educ; Am. Soc. Mech. Eng; Soc. Eng. Sci; Acoust. Soc. Am. Aerodynamic stability of bridges; continuum mechanics; elasticity; plasticity; plates and shells; mechanics of composite materials. Address: Dept. of Engineering Mechanics, Virginia Polytechnic Institute & State University, Blacksburg, VA 24061.

FREDERICK, DAVID E(UGENE), b. Chicago, Ill, June 10, 31; m. 56; c. 4. NUCLEAR PHYSICS. B.S, Yale, 52; M.S, Univ. Ill, 56, Ph.D.(physics), 62. Res. assoc. physics, Iowa State Univ, 62-63, asst. prof, 63-68; proj. leader nuclear power plant training simulation, Link Div, Singer Co, 69-71; PROJ. MGR. SIMULATION, HARSHMAN ASSOC, INC, 71- A.U.S, 52-54, 2nd Lt. Am. Phys. Soc; Am. Nuclear Soc; Simulation Coun. Experimental nuclear physics; simulation; instrumentation research and development. Address: 957 E. Homestead Rd, Sunnyvale, CA 94087.

FREDERICK, DEAN KIMBALL, b. Providence, R.I, Nov. 11, 34; m. 57; c. 4. ELECTRICAL ENGINEERING. B.E, Yale, 55; Sc.M, Brown, 61; Ph.D.(elec. eng), Stanford, 64. Engr, New Departure Div, Gen. Motors Corp, 57-58; ASSOC. PROF. ELEC. ENG, Clarkson Tech, 64; RENSSELAER POLYTECH. INST, 64- U.S.A, 55-57. Inst. Elec. & Electronics Eng. Automatic control theory; stability of nonlinear systems; dynamic simulation; chemical process control. Address: Systems Engineering Division, Rensselaer Polytechnic Institute, Troy, NY 12181.

FREDERICK, D(ONALD) S(HERWOOD), b. Hamilton, Ohio, Nov. 13, 10; m. 36; c. 4. ORGANIC CHEMISTRY. A.B, Miami Univ, 31; fel, Univ. Ill, 31-34, A.M, 32, Ph.D.(org. chem), 34; Inst. Int. Educ. scholar, Univ. Munich, 29-30. Res. chemist, Rohm & Haas Co, 34-36, sales mgr. plastics div, 36-43, dir. & v.pres, 43-66; dir. Warranteed Pharmaceut, Inc, 63-66; RE-

TIRED. Hyatt medal, 41. Am. Chem. Soc; Soc. Plastics Indust; Mfg. Chem. Asn.(v.pres, 57-59); Mfg. Chem. Asn.(v.pres, Plastics Mat. Mfg. Asn, 46-47, pres, 48). Polymer chemistry; synthetic resins. Address: P.O. Box 327, Rancho Santa Fe, CA 92067.

FREDERICK, EDWARD C, b. Mankato, Minn, Nov. 17, 30; m. 51; c. 5. ANIMAL SCIENCE, PHYSIOLOGY. B.S, Minnesota, 54, M.S, 55, Nat. Sci. Found. fel. & Ph.D.(reprod), 58. Assoc. prof. & dairy specialist, Northwest Sch. & Exp. Sta, UNIV. MINN, 58-64, assoc. prof, South. Sch. & Exp. Sta, 64-66, PROF. ANIMAL SCI, 66-69, TECH. COL-WASECA, 69-, PROVOST, 70-, supt, sch. & sta, 64-69, dir, col, 69-70. AAAS; Am. Dairy Sci. Asn; Am. Soc. Animal Sci. Frozen semen; frequency of semen collection; effects of nutrition on semen production; mastitis; effect of tranquilizers on behavior; fly control studies; dairy-beef feeding trials; high moisture barley studies. Address: University of Minnesota Technical College-Waseca, Waseca, MN 56093.

FREDERICK, GEORGE LEONARD, b. Kitchener, Ont, July 15, 30; m. 50; c. 4. VETERINARY MEDICINE. D.V.M, Ont. Vet. Col, 52; M.Sc, Univ. West. Ont, 53. Res. off, Animal Res. Inst, Can. Dept. Agr, 54-68; SCI. ADV, BUR. SCI. ADV. SERV, DEPT. NAT. HEALTH & WELFARE, CAN, 68- Can. Biochem. Soc; Nutrit. Soc. Can. Non-infectious causes and prevention of reproductive failures and neonatal mortality in farm animals; role of vitamin B_{12} and iron metabolism; evaluation of drug safety and efficiency. Address: Bureau of Scientific Advisory Services, Dept. of National Health & Welfare, Ottawa, Ont, Can. K1A 0L2.

FREDERICK, JOHN E(DGAR), b. Thursday, W.Va, Aug. 10, 40. PHYSICAL CHEMISTRY. B.S, Glenville State Col, 60; Ph.D.(phys. chem), Wisconsin, 64. Chemist, Union Carbide Chem. Co, 60; fel. phys. chem, Stanford Res. Inst, 64-66; ASST. PROF. CHEM. & POLYMER SCI. & RES. ASSOC, INST. POLYMER SCI, UNIV. AKRON, 66- Summers, chemist, Union Carbide Chem. Co, 59, res. assoc, Wisconsin, 60. Am. Chem. Soc; Soc. Rheol. High polymer physics; mechanical properties of high polymers. Address: Dept. of Chemistry, University of Akron, Akron, OH 44304.

FREDERICK, JULIAN ROSS, b. Sioux Falls, S.Dak, June 10, 13; m. 44; c. 5. MECHANICAL ENGINEERING. B.S, Iowa State Univ, 35, M.S, 36; Ph.D. (physics), Michigan, 48. Asst, Michigan, 39-41, res. assoc. ultrasonics, 41-46; asst. prof. physics, Brown, 47-50; lectr. & res. physicist, UNIV. MICH, 50-57, asst. prof. MECH. ENG, 57-64, assoc. prof, 64-70, PROF, 70- Am. Soc. Mech. Eng; Am. Soc. Metals; fel. Acoust. Soc. Am; Soc. Nondestructive Test. Nondestructive testing; manufacturing engineering; fatigue and fracture of materials. Address: Dept. of Mechanical Engineering, East Engineering Bldg, University of Michigan, Ann Arbor, MI 48104.

FREDERICK, KENNETH JACOB, b. Schenectady, N.Y, Dec. 5, 13; m. 36; c. 3. PHYSICAL CHEMISTRY. B.S, Union Col, 36; fel, California, 36-39, Ph.D.(phys. chem), 39. Sr. res. chemist, solvay process div, Allied Chem. & Dye Corp, N.Y, 39-47; group leader, Paraffine Co, Inc, Calif, 47-49; MGR. CORP. SCI. RESOURCES, ABBOTT LABS, 49- AAAS; Am. Inst. Chem; Am. Chem. Soc. Physical chemistry of drugs and drug action; scientific instrumentation and mathematics applied to pharmaceutical research; scientific personnel development and facility planning. Address: 420 Simpson Ave, Lake Bluff, IL 60044.

FREDERICK, LAFAYETTE, b. Friarspoint, Miss, Mar. 19, 23; m. 50; c. 3. PLANT PATHOLOGY, MYCOLOGY. B.S, Tuskegee Inst, 43; M.S, R.I. State Col, 50; Ph.D.(plant path), State Col. Wash, 52. Assoc. prof. BIOL, South. Univ, 52-58, PROF, 58-62; ATLANTA UNIV, 62-, CHMN. DEPT, 63- Carnegie res. grant, 53; Nat. Sci. Found. sci. faculty fel, dept. bot, Univ. Ill, 60-61; biol. field sta, Univ. Mich, summer 61; coun-at-large, Ga. Acad. Sci, 69-; mem, Comn. Undergrad. Educ. Biol, 70-71. U.S.N.R, 44-46. AAAS; Am. Phytopath. Soc; Mycol. Soc. Am; Bot. Soc. Am; Am. Inst. Biol. Sci. Vascular wilt diseases of plants; pathologic cellular growth; taxonomic studies of fungi; developmental studies on conidia and ascospores; systematics of imperfect fungi. Address: Dept. of Biology, Atlanta University, Atlanta, GA 30314.

FREDERICK, LLOYD R(ANDALL), b. Ill, Aug. 5, 21; m. 43; c. 3. SOIL MICROBIOLOGY. B.Sc, Nebraska, 43; Texas Gulf Sulphur Co. fel, Rutgers, 46-49, M.Sc, 47, Ph.D.(microbiol), 50. Asst. microbiologist, Purdue, 49-55; assoc. prof. SOILS, IOWA STATE UNIV, 55-59, PROF, 59- Fulbright res. scholar, Ger, 62; consult, W.R. Grace Inoculant Lab, 67-70; Res. Seeds, Inc, 70- U.S.N.R, 43-46, Lt.(jg). AAAS; fel. Am. Soc. Agron; Soil Sci. Soc. Am; Am. Soc. Microbiol; Brit. Soc. Soil Sci. Transformations of sulfur compounds by soil microorganisms; decomposition of plant residues and chemicals in soil; factors affecting ammonia retention and oxidation; denitrification; effect of temperature on biological soil changes; rhizobia in soils and nodules. Address: Dept. of Agronomy, Iowa State University, Ames, IA 50010.

FREDERICK, MARVIN R(AY), b. Wadsworth, Ohio, April 12, 18; m. 41; c. 4. ORGANIC CHEMISTRY. B.Sc, Ohio State, 41; fel, Purdue, 43-46, Ph.D. (org. chem), 47. Lab. asst, chem, Columbia chem. div, Pittsburgh Plate Glass Co, Ohio, 36-37; asst, Purdue, 41-43; res. chemist, B.F. GOODRICH CO, 46-57, SECT. leader, plastics polymerization, 58-60, mgr. chem. eng. res, 60-69, MGR. TECH. INFO. RES, 69- With Off. Sci. Res. & Develop, 44. Am. Chem. Soc. Organic fluorine chemistry; organic chemicals research; chemistry of monomers and polymerization; chemistry of organic fluorine compounds and their preparation; plastics polymerization. Address: B.F. Goodrich Research Center, 9921 Brecksville Rd, Brecksville, OH 44141.

FREDERICKS, ROBERT J(OSEPH), b. New York, N.Y, Dec. 26, 34. X-RAY CRYSTALLOGRAPHY. B.S, Villanova, 57; M.S, St. Joseph's Col.(Pa), 59; Polytech. Inst. Brooklyn, 63-65; Ph.D.(chem), Lehigh, 65. Res. chemist, cent. res. lab, Gen. Aniline & Film Corp, 60-65, res. specialist, 65-67; RES. SUPVR, CENT. RES. LAB, ALLIED CHEM. CORP, 67- Am. Chem. Soc. lectr, 71- U.S.N, 57-60, Res, 60-, Lt.(jg). AAAS; Am. Chem. Soc; Am. Crystallog. Asn; Soc. Appl. Spectros. X-ray crystallography; crystal structure determination; polymer morphology; polymer structure; heterogeneous catalysis. Address: Central Research Lab, Allied Chemical Corp, Morristown, NJ 07960.

FREDERICKS, WILLIAM J(OHN), b. San Diego, Calif, Sept. 18, 24; m. 42. PHYSICAL CHEMISTRY. B.S, San Diego State Col, 51; fels, Ore. State Col, 51-55, Ph.D.(phys. chem), 55. Fulbright fel, Kamerlingh Onnes Lab, Leiden, Holland, 55-56; chemist, Stanford Res. Inst, 56-59, chmn. solid state dept, 59-62; assoc. prof. CHEM, ORE. STATE UNIV, 62-67, PROF, 67- AAAS; Am. Phys. Soc; Am. Chem. Soc. Solid state chemistry; luminescence; ionic solids; impurity reactions in solids; impurity diffusion; crystal growth and purification. Address: Dept. of Chemistry, Oregon State University, Corvallis, OR 97331.

FREDERICKSEN, JAMES MONROE, b. Blackstone, Va, June 25, 19; m. 48; c. 3. ORGANIC CHEMISTRY. B.S, Richmond, 40; Ph.D.(org. chem), Virginia, 47. Chemist, E.R. Squibb & Co, N.J, 44; sr. chemist, Merck & Co, Inc, 47-53; PROF. CHEM. & CHMN. DEPT, Davis & Elkins Col, 53-54; Hampden-Sydney Col, 54-57; DAVIDSON COL, 57- U.S.N.R, 44-46. Am. Chem. Soc. Quinolines, thiazoles, isoalloxazines and vitamins; synthetic medicinals for tuberculosis and malaria; local anesthetics; synthetic medicinals in the quinoline, isoalloxazines and thiazole series. Address: Dept. of Chemistry, Davidson College, Davidson, NC 28036.

FREDERICKSON, ARMAN FREDERICK, b. Winnipeg, Man, May 5, 18; nat; m. 43; c. 5. GEOLOGY. B.Sc, Washington (Seattle), 40; M.Sc, Mont. Sch. Mines, 42; Sc.D, Mass. Inst. Tech, 47. Miner, west. U.S, 36-40; chief geologist, Cornucopia Gold Mines, Ore, 40-41; instr. & asst, Mont. Sch. Mines, 41-42; engr, Alameda Dry Rock Co, Calif, 42; asst, Mass. Inst. Tech, 42-43, 46-47; prof. geol, Washington (St. Louis), 47-55; supvr. geol. res, Pan Am. Petrol. Corp, Okla, 55-60; prof. earth & planetary sci. & chmn. dept. & dir. oceanog. prog, Pittsburgh, 60-66; v.pres. & dir. res, King Resources Co, 66-69, sr. v.pres. & dir. tech. progs, 69-71; PRES, SORBOTEC, INC, 71- Consult. geologist, geochemist & mining engr, Fulbright res. prof, Oslo, 51-52. Chmn, clay mineral comt, Nat. Res. Coun. With U.S.N, 43-46. Fel. Geol. Soc. Am; Soc. Econ. Geol; Am. Mineral. Soc; Asn. Petrol. Geol; Am. Inst. Mining, Metall. & Petrol. Eng; Clay Mineral Soc; fel. Geol. Soc. Finland. Synthesis of minerals under high press-temperature; production of micas from clays; spectrographic, x-ray, diff-thermal and optical research; structure and genesis of ore deposits; isotope and trace geochemistry of sediments; formation fluids; regional stratigraphy and map analysis by computer methods; organization and management of industrial research; mining and petroleum exploration; marine geology and geophysics; oceanography. Address: Sorbotec, Inc, 1964 W. Gray, Houston, TX 77019.

FREDERICKSON, E(DWARD) A(RTHUR), b. Madison, Wis, Sept. 22, 08; m. 38; c. 2. PALEONTOLOGY, STRATIGRAPHY. B.A, Wisconsin, 30, Ph.D.(geol), 42. Jr. geologist, U.S. Forest Serv, D.C, 35-37; instr. GEOL, Wisconsin, 38-40; spec. instr, Oklahoma, 40-42, asst. prof, 42-45, assoc. prof, 45-51, prof, 51-64; PROF. & CHMN. DEPT. KENT STATE UNIV, 64- U.S.A.A.F, 42-46, 51-53, Res, 53-68, Col.(Ret). AAAS; Paleont. Soc; fel. Geol. Soc. Am; Soc. Econ. Paleont. & Mineral; Am. Asn. Petrol. Geol. Cambrian trilobites and stratigraphy. Address: Dept. of Geology, Kent State University, Kent, OH 44240.

FREDERICKSON, EVAN L(OYD), b. Springreen, Wis, Mar. 1, 22; m. 46; c. 3. ANESTHESIOLOGY. B.S, Wisconsin, 47, M.D, 50; M.S, Iowa, 53. Instr. ANESTHESIOL, med. center, Kansas, 53-54, asst. prof, 54-56; Washington (Seattle), 56-59, assoc. prof, 59; PROF, med. center. Kansas, 59-65; EMORY UNIV, 65- U.S.A, 44-46, 50-51. AAAS; Am. Soc. Anesthesiol; Am. Med. Asn. Effect of drugs on cells; cell membranes; mechanisms of anesthesia. Address: Anesthesia Research, Emory University, Atlanta, GA 30322.

FREDERICKSON, LEO D(WIGHT), JR, b. Thurman, Iowa, Feb. 19, 23; m. 46; c. 5. ANALYTICAL CHEMISTRY. A.B, Iowa, 47, M.S, 48. Anal. chemist, Monsanto Chem. Co, 48-49, res. chemist, 49-51; res. labs, Aluminum Co. of Am, 51-56; Denver res. inst, Denver, 56-58; PRES. & TECH. DIR, SPECTRAN LABS, INC, 58- Med.C, U.S.A, 43-46. Am. Chem. Soc; Sci. Res. Soc. Am. Emission and infrared spectroscopy; gas chromatography; instrumental methods of analysis. Address: Spectran Labs, Inc, 1673 Wadsworth Blvd, Denver, CO 80215.

FREDERIKSE, HANS P(IETER) R(OETERT), b. Hague, Netherlands, July 13, 20; nat; m. 52; c. 3. SOLID STATE PHYSICS. B.S, Leiden, Holland, 41, M.S, 45, Ph.D.(physics), 50. Vis. lectr. physics, Purdue, 50-53; physicist, SOLID STATE PHYSICS SECT, NAT. BUR. STANDARDS, 53-55, CHIEF, 55- Fulbright travel grant, 50-52; Guggenheim fel, 61-62. Except. serv. award, U.S. Dept. Commerce, 62. Fel. Am. Phys. Soc; Fedn. Am. Sci; Netherlands Phys. Soc. Electrical, optical, thermal and magnetic properties of semiconductors and oxides; low temperature physics. Address: National Bureau of Standards, U.S. Dept. of Commerce, Washington, DC 20234.

FREDERIKSEN, NORMAN O(LIVER), b. Vienna, Austria, Aug. 11, 32; U.S. citizen; m. 62; c. 1. PALYNOLOGY, MICROPALEONTOLOGY. B.A, Hamilton Col, 57; M.S, Pa. State Univ, 61; Ph.D.(geol), Univ. Wis, Madison, 69. Res. geologist, Field Res. Lab, Mobil Oil Corp, Tex, 61-63, 65-69; asst. prof. GEOL, SAN DIEGO STATE COL, 69-71, ASSOC. PROF, 71- U.S.A, 52-54, Sgt. Am. Asn. Petrol. Geol; Am. Asn. Stratig. Palynologists. Late Palezoic; Jurassic and Tertiary palynology; paleoecology of Tertiary and Recent foraminifers and ostracodes. Address: Dept. of Geology, San Diego State College, San Diego, CA 92115.

FREDERIKSEN, RICHARD ALLAN, b. Renville, Minn, Aug. 9, 33; m. 58; c. 1. PLANT PATHOLOGY & GENETICS. B.Sc, Minnesota, 55, M.S, 57, Ph.D.(plant path), 61. Res. plant pathologist, U.S. Dept. Agr, 56-63; asst. prof. PLANT PATH, TEX. A&M UNIV, 63-70, ASSOC. PROF, 70- Nat. Guard, 57-60; U.S.A.R, 60-63. Am. Phytopath. Soc. Indian Phytopath. Soc; Int. Soc. Plant Path. Diseases of field crops; genetics of plant pathogens; biological control. Address: Dept. of Plant Sciences, Texas A&M University, College Station, TX 77843.

FREDIANI, H(AROLD) A(RTHUR), b. New York, N.Y, Dec. 23, 11; m. 35; c. 4. CHEMISTRY. A.B, Iowa, 34, fel, 34-35, M.S, 35; fel, La. State, 35-37, Ph.D.(phys. chem), 37. Instr. indust. & anal. chem, La. State, 37-40; asst. dir. develop. & res. chemist, Fisher Sci. Co, 40-42; chief chemist & dir. labs, Eimer & Amend, 42-46; mgr. anal. res, Merck & Co, Inc, 46-51, asst. dir. chem. control, 51-54, process res. & develop, 54-55; exec. dir. control, BRISTOL LABS, INC, 55-69, DIR. TECH. EVAL, 69- Fulbright fel, Rome, 52-53. AAAS; Am. Chem. Soc; Soc. Appl. Spectros; Am. Pharmaceut. Asn; fel. Brit. Asn. Pub. Analysts; Italian Chem. Soc; Asn. Advan. Med. Instrumentation; Am. Soc. Qual. Control; N.Y. Acad. Sci. Instrumental methods of analysis; polarography; emission and adsorption photometry; potentiometric titrations; chemical microscopy. Address: 2638 Pompey Center Rd, Manlius, NY 13104.

FREDIN, REYNOLD A, b. Greenville, Iowa, Feb. 13, 23; m. 44; c. 2. FISHERIES BIOLOGY. B.S, Iowa State Univ, 48, fel, 48-49, M.S, 49. Assoc. fisheries biologist, N.C. Wildlife Resources Comn, 49-50; fishery res. biologist, Bur. Commercial Fisheries, U.S. Fish & Wildlife Serv, 50-70; DIR. BIOMET. INST, NAT. MARINE FISHERIES SERV, NAT. OCEANIC & ATMOSPHERIC AGENCY, U.S. DEPT. COMMERCE, 70- Tech. adv, U.S. sect, Int. N.Pac. Fisheries Comn, 56-; U.S. sect, Int. Pac. Halibut Comn, 66-; fisheries conf, U.S-Can, U.S-Japan & U.S-U.S.S.R, U.S. State Dept, 70-; lectr, Univ. Wash, 69- U.S.A, 43-46. Am. Inst. Fishery Res. Biol. Population dynamics of North American salmon and halibut stocks; biometrics; hatchery evaluation; fisheries and biological statistics of United States salmon stocks. Address: Biometrics Institute, National Marine Fisheries Service, National Oceanic & Atmospheric Agency, 2725 Montlake Blvd. E, Seattle, WA 98102.

FREDKIN, DONALD R(OY), b. N.Y.C, Sept. 28, 35. PHYSICS. A.B, N.Y. Univ, 56; Nat. Sci. Found. fel, Princeton, 56-57, Bell Tel. Labs. fel, 57-58, Charlotte Elizabeth Proctor fel, 58-59, Ph.D.(math, physics), 61. Instr. PHYSICS, Princeton, 59-61; assoc, UNIV. CALIF, SAN DIEGO, 61-63, asst. prof, 63-69, ASSOC. PROF, 69- Consult, Bell Tel. Labs, Inc, 60-64; Aerospace Corp, 62-63; Nat. Acad. Sci-Nat. Res. Coun. fel, Saclay Nuclear Res. Ctr, France, 64-65; Alfred P. Sloan res. fel, 64-67. Am. Phys. Soc; Am. Math. Soc. Solid state and low temperature theoretical physics. Address: Dept. of Physics, University of California, San Diego, La Jolla, CA 92038.

FREDRICK, JEROME F(REDERICK), b. New York, N.Y, Feb. 23, 26; m. 46; c. 3. BIOCHEMISTRY. B.Sc, City Col. New York, 49; M.Sc, N.Y. Univ, 51, Ph.D.(biol), 55. Instr. biol, City Col. New York, 48-49; biochemist, Vet. Admin. Hosp, New York, 49-51; chemist, U.S. Customs Labs, 51-53; asst. dir. res, DODGE CHEM. CO, 53-60, DIR. BIOCHEM. RES, 60-, ASSOC. PROF. BIOCHEM, DODGE INST. ADVAN. STUDIES, 65- Consult, Handbook Biol. Data Comt, Nat. Acad. Sci-Nat. Res. Coun, 57-60; mem. bd. dir, Med. Fund, Inc, N.Y, 61-63; organizer, Conf. Phylogenesis & Morphogenesis in Algae, N.Y, 69. Med. Dept, U.S.N.R, 44-46. AAAS; Am. Chem. Soc; Scandinavian Soc. Plant Physiol; fel. Am. Inst. Chem; Am. Inst. Biol. Sci. Chelation chemistry; enzymology; chemotherapy of cancer. Address: Research Labs, Dodge Chemical Co, 3425 Boston Post Rd, Bronx, NY 10469.

FREDRICK, LAURENCE W(ILLIAM), b. Stroudsburg, Pa, Aug. 27, 27; m. 49; c. 3. ASTRONOMY. B.A, Swarthmore Col, 52, M.A, 54; Ph.D.(astron), Pennsylvania, 59. Asst. astron, Sproul Observ, 52-59; astronr, Lowell Observ, Ariz, 59-63; PROF. ASTRON. & DIR, LEANDER McCORMICK OBSERV, UNIV. VA, 63- Asst, Flower & Cook Observ, 55-59; mem. Nat. Res. Coun, 65-68; U.S. Nat. Comt, Int. Astron. Union & Spitzer Comt, Nat. Space Bd, 65- U.S.N, 45-48. Int. Astron. Union; Am. Astron. Soc.(secy); Am. Meteor Soc.(v.pres). Binary stars; infrared spectroscopy; image tubes; instrumentation. Address: Leander McCormick Observatory, Charlottesville, VA 22903.

FREDRICK, WILLIAM G(EORGE), b. Lockland, Ohio, Jan. 25, 09; m. 36; c. 2. INDUSTRIAL HYGIENE. B.S, Michigan, 30, Mallinckrodt fel, 30-32, M.S, 32; Sc.D.(chem), 36. Res. chemist, Mallinckrodt Chem. Works, 33-34; pediat. & infectious diseases, univ. hosp, Michigan, 35-36; chief chemist, bur. indust. hygiene, Dept. Health, Detroit, 36-46, dir, 46-70; PROF. OCCUP. & ENVIRON. HEALTH, SCH. MED, WAYNE STATE UNIV, 38- Lectr, sch. pub. health, Univ. Mich, 39-, consult, inst. indust. health, 52-62; U.S. Dept. State consult, indust. hygiene, High Comn. for Ger, W.Ger, 52; mem. toxicol. comt, Int. Union Pure & Appl. Chem; Threshold Limits Comt. AAAS; Am. Indust. Hygiene Asn.(secy; Cummins Award); fel. Am. Pub. Health Asn; Am. Conf. Govt. Indust. Hygienists (past pres; award); Am. Chem. Soc. Toxicology; air pollution; gas analysis; trace analysis; toxicity of gases, vapors and dusts; experimental silicosis. Address: Dept. of Occupational & Environmental Health, Wayne State University School of Medicine, 625 Mullett St, Detroit, MI 48226.

FREDRICKS, ROBERT W, b. Honolulu, Hawaii, Dec. 4, 27; m. 58; c. 2. PHYSICS, GEOPHYSICS. B.S, California, Los Angeles, 55, Shell Oil Co. fel, 55-56, M.S, 57, Ph.D.(physics), 59. Asst. res. geophysicist, inst. geophys, California, Los Angeles, 58-59; MEM. TECH. STAFF, Space Electronics Corp, 59; SPACE PHYSICS ANALYSIS DEPT, TRW SYSTS. GROUP, 59- Consult, Nat. Eng. & Sci. Corp. & E.H. Plesset & Assocs, Calif, 58-59. U.S.A, 46-48; U.S.A.F, 51-52, S/Sgt. Am. Geophys. Union; Am. Phys. Soc; Inst. Elec. & Electronics Eng. Space physics; solar-terrestrial interactions; space plasma physics; natural electromagnetic and electrostatic waves; spacecraft experiments; theoretical seismology; elastodynamics; diffraction theory; mathematical physics. Address: 20124 Ruston Rd, Woodland Hills, CA 91364.

FREDRICKS, WALTER W(ILLIAM), b. Phila, Pa, July 19, 35; m. 57; c. 3. BIOCHEMISTRY. B.A, La Salle Col, 57; univ. fel, Hopkins, 57-58, Nat. Insts. Health fel, 58-61, Ph.D.(biochem), 62. U.S. Pub. Health Serv. fel, Nat. Heart Inst, 62-64; asst. prof. physiol, Maryland, 64-65; biochem, SCH. MED, MARQUETTE UNIV, 65-66, BIOL, 66-69, ASSOC. PROF, 69- AAAS; Am. Soc. Microbiol. Photosynthesis; regulation of enzyme activity and regulation of enzyme synthesis. Address: Dept. of Biology, Marquette University, Milwaukee, WI 53233.

FREDRICKSON, ARNOLD G(ERHARD), b. Fairbault, Minn, Apr. 11, 32. CHEMICAL ENGINEERING. B.S, Univ. Minn, 54; M.S, 56; Ph.D.(chem. eng), Univ. Wis, 59. Asst. prof. CHEM. ENG, UNIV. MINN, MINNEAPOLIS, 58-63, assoc. prof, 63-66, PROF, 66- Am. Chem. Soc; Am. Inst. Chem. Eng. Bioengineering; demography. Address: Dept. of Chemical Engineering, University of Minnesota, Minneapolis, MN 55455.

FREDRICKSON, DONALD S(HARP), b. Canon City, Colo, Aug. 8, 24; m. 50. BIOCHEMISTRY. B.S, Michigan, 46, M.D, 49. House off, Peter Bent Brigham Hosp, Boston, 49-50; res. fel. med, Harvard, 50-53; clin. assoc, NAT. HEART & LUNG INST, 53-55, mem. sr. res. staff, 55-61, clin. dir, 61-66, head sect. molecular diseases, lab. metab, 62-66, DIR. INTRAMURAL RES. & CHIEF MOLECULAR DISEASE BR, 66- Clin. instr, sch. med, George Wash. Univ, 56-59, spec. lectr, 59-, lectr, 63-; mem. coun. arteriosclerosis, Am. Heart Asn. Dipl, Am. Bd. Internal Med; int. award for heart & vascular res, James F. Mitchell Found. Med. Educ. & Res, 68; superior serv. award, Dept. Health, Educ. & Welfare, 70, distinguished serv. award, 71; McCollum Award, Am. Soc. Clin. Nutrit. & clin. div, Am. Inst. Nutrit, 71. Nat. Inst. Med; AAAS; Am. Soc. Clin. Invest; Am. Oil Chem. Soc; Am. Heart Asn; Am. Physiol. Soc; Am. Soc. Human Genetics; Asn. Am. Physicians; Am. Col. Cardiol.(Gold Medal, 67); Am. Col. Physicians; Soc. Pediat. Res; Brit. Cardiac Soc; Int. Soc. Cardiol; Swedish Med. Soc. Lipoproteins and lipid transport; lipid metabolism; medical genetics; diseases of lipid storage and metobolism; approaches to atherosclerosis in relation to hyperlipidemia. Address: National Heart & Lung Institute, Bethesda, MD 20014.

FREDRICKSON, JAY W(ARREN), b. Salt Lake City, Utah, Dec. 21, 17; m. 40; c. 3. METALLURGY. B.S, Univ. Utah, 47, Ph.D.(metall), 49. Head dept. metall, Pa. State Univ, 49-52; chief fundamental res, metall. lab, Dow Chem. Co, 52-62, res. dir. & mgr. new bus. develop, metals dept, 62-65, mgr. tech. sales & develop, metals prod. dept, 65-69; DIR, GRAD. INST. TECHNOL, UNIV. ARK, 69- U.S.A, 40-46, Res, 46-, Lt. Col. Am. Soc. Metals; Am. Inst. Mining, Metall. & Petrol. Eng. Extractive and physical metallurgy; research management. Address: Graduate Institute of Technology, University of Arkansas, 1201 McAlmont St, Little Rock, AR 72203.

FREDRICKSON, JOHN E, b. Chicago, Ill, Sept. 12, 19; m. 46; c. 3. PHYSICS. B.S, California, Berkeley, 43; M.S, Southern California, 52, Ph.D.(physics), 56. PROF. PHYSICS, CALIF. STATE COL. LONG BEACH, 62- Am. Phys. Soc; Am. Asn. Physics Teachers. Spectroscopy. Address: 27526 Eastvale Rd, Rolling Hills, CA 90274.

FREDRICKSON, JOHN MURRAY, b. Winnipeg, Man, Mar. 24, 31; m. 56; c. 3. OTOLARYNGOLOGY, NEUROPHYSIOLOGY. B.A, Univ. B.C, 53, M.D, 57. Instr. surg, Univ. Chicago, 63-65; asst. prof. otolaryngol, dept. surg, Stanford Med. Ctr, 65-68; ASST. PROF. PHYSIOL. & ASSOC. PROF. OTOLARYNGOL, UNIV. TORONTO, 68- Vis. investr, Univ. Freiburg, 64-65; consult, Toronto Gen. Hosp; Princess Margaret Cancer Hosp. & Hosp. for Children. Res. award, Am. Acad. Ophthal. & Otolaryngol, 64; Hodge Mem. Award, Can. Otolaryngol. Soc, 65; dipl, Am. Bd. Otolaryngol, 66; fel, Royal Col. Surg. Can. Fel. Am. Col. Surg. Vestibular neurophysiology; tissue and organ transplantation. Address: Dept. of Otolaryngology, University of Toronto, Room 7310, Medical Sciences Bldg, 1 King's College Circle, Toronto, Ont, Can.

FREDRICKSON, LEIGH H, b. Sioux City, Iowa, Mar. 13, 39; m. 65. ZOOLOGY. B.S, Iowa State, 61, M.S, 63, Ph.D.(zool), 67. Instr. zool, Iowa State 64-65; ASST. PROF. BIOL. SCI. & DIR. DIV, UNIV. MO, 67- Wildlife Soc; Ecol. Soc. Am; Am. Ornith. Union; Wilson Ornith. Soc; Cooper Ornith. Soc; Animal Behav. Soc. Parasitology of Catostomid and Cyprinid fishes; marsh ecology; behavior and ecology of waterfowl, especially Cairinini; behavior of Rallidae; factors influencing clutch size; molts and plumages of wood ducks. Address: Gaylord Memorial Lab, University of Missouri, Puxico, MO 63960.

FREDRICKSON, RALPH E. C, b. Minneapolis, Minn, Feb. 7, 13; m. 39; c. 5. CHEMICAL ENGINEERING, ORGANIC CHEMISTRY. B.Ch.E, Minnesota, 35, M.S, 37; Ph.D.(chem. eng), Columbia, 45. Chem. engr, E.I. du Pont de Nemours & Co, 37-40; A.E. Staley Mfg. Co, 42-55, DIR. eng. res, 55-60; spec. projs, corporate develop, Stepan Chem. Co, 61-65; commercial dir, C&I Girdler Inc, 66-69; CONSULT, RAPHAEL KATZEN ASSOCS, 69- Am. Chem. Soc; Am. Inst. Chem. Eng. Process development; fluidization; phthalic anhydride; organic intermediates; starch and vegetable oil processing. Address: 6739 Miami Hills Dr, Cincinnati, OH 45243.

FREDERICKSON, RICHARD WILLIAM, b. Blakesburg, Iowa, Apr. 28, 19; m. 47; c. 2. ENTOMOLOGY, VERTEBRATE ZOOLOGY. A.B, Kansas, 51, M.A, 54, Ph.D.(entom), 61. Lectr. zool, Southern Illinois, 56-58; BIOL, Queens Col.(N.Y), 61-62, instr, 62-63; lectr, City Col. New York, 63-64, asst. prof, 64-67; ASSOC. PROF, ST. JOSEPH'S COL.(PA), 67- U.S.A, 41-45, T/Sgt. Am. Ornith. Union; Wilson Ornith. Soc; Cooper Ornith. Soc. Comparative morphology and systematics of Acarina; evolutionary considerations of Arthropoda, particularly Arachnida; systematics and distribution of birds. Address: Dept. of Biology, St. Joseph's College, Philadelphia, PA 19131.

FREDRICKSON, TORGNY N(ORMAN), b. Toronto, Ont, May 24, 30; m. 56; c. 5. VETERINARY PATHOLOGY. D.V.M, Ont. Vet. Col, 55; M.Sc, Maine, 57; Ph.D.(vet. sci), Wisconsin, 63. Res. vet. Agr. Res. Serv, U.S. Dept. Agr, 60-63; VET. PATHOLOGIST, MASON RES. INST, INC, 63-66; ASSOC. PROF. ANIMAL DISEASES, UNIV. CONN, 66- Am. Vet. Med. Asn; Am. Asn. Lab. Animal Sci; Am. Asn. Avian. Path; Indust. Vet. Asn. Avian pathology; pathology and epizootiology of avian tumor viruses; pathology of murine tumor viruses and chemical carcinogens; toxicology studies in laboratory animals. Address: 114 Windham St, Willimantic, CT 06226.

FREDRICKSON, W(ILLIAM) R(USSELL), b. Chicago, Ill, June 28, 03; m. 30; c. 2. PHYSICS. B.S, Chicago, 24, M.S, 26, Ph.D.(physics), 28. Instr. physics, Syracuse, 28-30, asst. prof, 30-35, assoc. prof, 35-38, prof, 38-71, chmn. dept, 39-65; RETIRED. Am. Phys. Soc; Am. Asn. Physics Teachers. Molecular spectra; solid state. Address: 202 Halton Rd, Syracuse, NY 13224.

FREDRIKSEN, RICHARD L, b. Spokane, Wash, Feb. 20, 30; m. 52; c. 2. SOILS, FORESTRY. B.S.F, Washington (Seattle), 54, M.F, 61; Oregon State, 64-65. Forestry aide, Pac. N.W. Forest & Range Exp. Sta, U.S. Dept. Interior, 59; technician, Weyerhaeuser Timber Co, 59-60; RES. FORESTER, PAC. N.W. FOREST & RANGE EXP. STA, U.S. DEPT. INTERIOR, 60-Chmn. nutrient cycling comt, Int. Biol. Prog, West. Coniferous Biome. U.S.A, 57-59, 1st Lt. Soc. Am. Foresters. Nutrient losses from ecosystems; soil erosion from Pacific Coast forest ecosystems; watershed hydrology. Address: Forestry Sciences Lab, Northwest Forest & Range Experimental Station, 320 Jefferson Way, Corvallis, OR 97331.

FREDRIKSON, KURT A, b. Haparanda, Sweden, Apr. 9, 26; m. 64. GEOCHEMISTRY. Chem.E, Stockholm Inst. Tech, Sweden, 46; Ph.D. (mineral & geol), Stockholm, 55. Consult. engr, Hagconsult Inc, Sweden, 46-52; res. asst. sediment. petrol, oceanog. inst, Gothenburg, 53-55; meteorite mineral, Stockholm, 55-57; geochemist, Geol. Surv. Sweden, 58-60; res. assoc. meteoritics, California, San Diego, 60-64; curator-in-charge, DIV. METEORITES, SMITHSONIAN INST, 64-67, CURATOR & SUPVR, 67- Grants, Australian Nat. Univ, 61, NASA, 64; consult, econ. geol. & inorg. & org. chem, Sweden, 52-60; prin. investr. lunar samples, Apollo XI-XVII. Geochem. Soc; Meteoritical Soc; Swedish Geol. Soc. Meteoritics; phase composition in meteorites, particularly chondrites; origin of meteorites and planets; ore mineralogy; electron microprobe analysis. Address: Division of Meteorites, Smithsonian Institution, Washington, DC 20560.

FREE, ALFRED H(ENRY), b. Bainbridge, Ohio, Apr. 11, 13; m; c. 9. BIOCHEMISTRY. A.B, Miami (Ohio), 34; fel, Western Reserve, 35-39, M.S, 36, Ph.D. (biochem), 39. Asst. biochem, Cleveland Clinic, 34-35; instr, Western Reserve, 39-43, asst. prof, 43-46; head biochem. sect, Ames Res. Lab, 46-59, DIR, 59-64, AMES TECH. SERV, 64- Consult, Ben Venue Labs, Ohio, 43-46. Civilian with Off. Sci. Res. & Develop, 44. AAAS; Am. Soc. Biol. Chem; Soc. Exp. Biol. & Med; Am. Chem. Soc; Am. Diabetes Asn; Am. Inst. Nutrit; Am. Inst. Chem; N.Y. Acad. Sci. Vitamin and protein nutrition; enzymes and gastrointestinal tract; intestinal adsorption; antibiotics; clinical biochemistry and laboratory methodology; radioisotope methology; metabolism of drugs; urinalysis tests. Address: Ames Technical Services, Ames Co, Elkhart, IN 46514.

FREE, CHARLES A(LFRED), b. Cleveland, Ohio, Apr. 19, 36; m. 61; c. 2. BIOCHEMISTRY. B.S, Purdue, 57; U.S. Pub. Health Serv. fel, California, Los Angeles, 60-62, Ph.D. (physiol. chem), 62. Res. fel, Sloan-Kettering Inst. Cancer Res, 62-65; sr. res. scientist, SQUIBB INST. MED. RES, 65-69, SR. RES. INVESTR, 69- U.S. Pub. Health Serv. fel, 63-65. AAAS; Am. Chem. Soc; Am. Inst. Chem. Methods for protein characterization; purification and chemistry of anterior pituitary hormones; enzyme purification; enzyme inhibition; cyclic AMP-mediated biological systems. Address: Dept. of Biochemical Pharmacology, Squibb Institute for Medical Research, New Brunswick, NJ 08903.

FREE, GEORGE, b. Waitsburg, Wash, Feb. 6, 05; m. 27; c. 4. SOIL SCIENCE. B.S, Iowa State Col, 27; M.S, Cornell, 50. Engr, West. Elec. Co, 27-32; soil conservationist, soil conserv. serv, U.S. Dept. Agr, 33-56, soil scientist, Agr. Res. Serv, 56-69; ASSOC. PROF. SOIL TECHNOL, COL. AGR, CORNELL UNIV, 56- Soil Sci. Soc. Am; Am. Soc. Agron; Soil Conserv. Soc. Am; Am. Soc. Agr. Eng. Soil and water conservation and management. Address: Dept. of Agronomy, Cornell University College of Agriculture, Ithaca, NY 14850.

FREE, JOSEPH CARL, b. Cedar City, Utah, May 14, 35; m. 55; c. 6. MECHANICAL ENGINEERING. B.E.S, Brigham Young, 58; M.S, Calif. Inst. Tech, 61; Nat. Sci. Found. fel, Mass. Inst. Tech, 66-67, Ph.D. (nonlinear models), 68. Res. engr, Autonetics Div, N.Am. Aviation, Inc, 58-61; instr. MECH. ENG, Brigham Young, 61-62, asst. prof, 62-64; teaching asst, Mass. Inst. Tech, 64-65; ASSOC. PROF, BRIGHAM YOUNG UNIV, 67- Consult, Rich Bumper Co, 68; Lawrence Radiation Lab, 68- Summer employee, E. H. Plessett Assocs, 61, Hercules Powder, 62 & 63. Am. Soc. Mech. Eng. Nonlinear system modeling; optimum design of engineering systems; efficient computer simulation; automatic controls. Address: 195 W. 400 S, Orem, UT 84057.

FREE, MICHAEL J(OHN), b. Newton Abbot, Eng, Nov. 22, 37; m. 64; c. 2. PHYSIOLOGY. B.Sc, Univ. Nottingham, 64; M.Sc, Ohio State Univ, 65, Ph.D. (physiol. of reproduction), 67. Res. assoc. testis physiol, animal reproduction teaching & res. ctr, Ohio State Univ, 67-69; asst. prof. MAMMALIAN PHYSIOL, CALIF. STATE COL, HAYWARD, 69-71, ASSOC. PROF, 71- R.A.Vet.C, 56-60. Brit. Soc. Study Fertil; Soc. Study Reproduction. Physiology and biochemistry of the testis, particularly aspects of energy and lipid metabolism, effect of temperature and hormones, circulation, in vivo metabolism and hormone production. Address: Dept. of Biological Sciences, California State College, 25800 Hillary St, Hayward, CA 94542.

FREE, SPENCER M(ICHAEL), JR, b. Greensburg, Pa, Jan. 24, 23; m. 48; c. 4. EXPERIMENTAL BIOLOGY. B.A, Washington & Jefferson Col, 47; M.S, N.C. State Col, 52, Moss Tobacco Res. fel, 53-54, Ph.D. (exp. statist), 54. Geophysicist, Seismog. Serv. Corp, 47-48; biochemist, Samuel Roberts Noble Found, 48-50; asst, N.C. State Col, 50-53; res. statistician, SMITH KLINE & FRENCH LABS, 54-66, DIR. BIOSTATIST, 66- Adj. asst. prof, sch. med, Temple Univ, 67. U.S.N.R, 43-46, Lt. (jg). Applications of experimental statistics to the biological sciences. Address: Smith Kline & French Labs, 1500 Spring Garden Rd, Philadelphia, PA 19101.

FREEARK, CLAYTON WAYNE, b. Buffalo Center, Iowa, May 15, 33; m. 61; c. 1. CHEMISTRY. B.S, Missouri, 55, Nat. Insts. Health fel, 62-65, Ph.D. (chem), 67; M.S, Stanford, 57. Assoc. prof. CHEM, MO. VALLEY COL, 58-67, PROF, 67-, CHMN. DEPT, 70- U.S.A, 55, Res, 55-, Maj. AAAS; Am. Chem. Soc. Energy transfer in fluorescent solutions; light scattering properties of casein systems. Address: Dept. of Chemistry, Missouri Valley College, Marshall, MO 65340.

FREEBAIRN, HUGH T(AYLOR), b. Long Beach, Calif, July 29, 26. PLANT BIOCHEMISTRY. B.S, California, Los Angeles, 51; Southern California, 52; Ph.D. (biochem), Oregon State, 55. Instr. plant biochem, Oregon State,

54-55; asst. biochemist, citrus exp. sta, California, Riverside, 55-60; chmn. plant physiol. & biochem. sect, div. trop. res, United Fruit Co, Honduras, 60-63; ASSOC. PROF. BIOL, UNIV. HOUSTON, 63- Consult, Nat. Banana Asn, 64. U.S.A.A.F, 45. Am. Chem. Soc; Am. Soc. Plant Physiol; Am. Hort. Soc; Scandinavian Soc. Plant Physiol. Intermediary metabolism of plants; organic acid, fat, carbohydrate and amino acid metabolism; vitamins; sub-cellular particles; enzymes; gas and liquid chromatography; use of isotopes in research; selective toxicity of gases; fruit ripening and the influence of ethylene on plants. Address: Dept. of Biology, University of Houston, Cullen Blvd, Houston, TX 77004.

FREEBERG, FRED E, b. Windber, Pa, Nov. 5, 37; m. 63; c. 2. ANALYTICAL CHEMISTRY. B.S, Pittsburgh, 59; Monsanto & Armstrong Cork Co. summer fels, Pa. State, 61-63, Ph.D. (chem), 65. Asst. chemist, Koppers Co, Inc, 59-60; teaching asst, Pa. State, 60-65; STAFF RES. CHEMIST, PROCTER & GAMBLE CO, 65- Am. Chem. Soc; Am. Soc. Test. & Mat. General use of thermal methods of analysis to obtain thermodynamic constants as well as application to analysis. Address: 1448 Evencrest Dr, Cincinnati, OH 45231.

FREEBERG, J(OHN) A(RTHUR), b. Kenosha, Wis, July 2, 32; m. 55. BOTANY. A.B, Harvard, 54, fel, 54-57, Ph.D. (biol), 57. Asst. prof. BIOL, Lehigh, 57-62; Boston, 62-66; ASSOC. PROF, UNIV. MASS, 66- Bot. Soc. Am; Int. Soc. Plant Morphol. Morphogenesis of vascular plants; plant tissue culture. Address: Dept. of Biology, University of Massachusetts, 100 Arlington St, Boston, MA 02116.

FREEBURGER, MICHAEL ERIC, b. Chicago, Ill, Feb. 7, 42; m. 64; c. 1. POLYMER & ORGANIC CHEMISTRY. B.S, Univ. Ill, Urbana, 64; M.S, Univ. Iowa, 66, Ph.D. (chem), 68. U.S. AIR FORCE, 68-, RES. SCIENTIST, AEROSPACE RES. LABS, WRIGHT-PATTERSON AFB, 68-; ADJ. PROF, U.S. AIR FORCE INST. TECHNOL, 68- U.S.A.F, 68-, Capt. Am. Chem. Soc. Organic polymer chemistry, particularly synthesis and characterization of new polymeric materials, principally those having high thermal stability; organosilicon chemistry. Address: Aerospace Research Labs. (LJ), Wright-Patterson Air Force Base, OH 45433.

FREED, AUBYN, b. Worcester, Mass, Nov. 1, 26; m. 60: c. 2. MATHEMATICS. B.A, Clark Univ, 49; M.A, Univ. Ill, 52, Ph.D. (math), 56. Asst. MATH, Univ. Ill, 52-56; instr, Smith Col, 56-58, asst. prof, 58-60; staff mathematician, LINCOLN LAB, MASS. INST. TECHNOL, 60-66, PROJ. ANALYST, 66- Vis. lectr, Mt. Holyoke Col, 59-60. U.S.N.R, 44-46, Lt. (jg). Am. Math. Soc; Math. Asn. Am. Satellite orbit-determination. Address: Gleasondale Rd, Stow, MA 01775.

FREED, CHARLES, b. Budapest, Hungary, Mar. 21, 26; U.S. citizen; m. 56; c. 2. ELECTRICAL ENGINEERING. B.E.E, N.Y. Univ, 52; S.M, Mass. Inst. Tech, 54, E.E, 58. Asst. res. lab. electronics, Mass. Inst. Tech, 52-54, 55-58, div. indust. co-op, 54-55, consult, phys. sci. study comt, 58; sr. engr, res. div, Raytheon Mfg. Co, 58-59, Spencer Lab, 59, spec. microwave devices oper, 59-62; MEM. STAFF, LINCOLN LAB, MASS. INST. TECHNOL, 62-, LECTR. ELEC. ENG, 69- Inst. Elec. & Electronics Eng. Microwave electronics; electron devices; low noise amplification; parametric devices; vacuum theory and techniques; electron beams; laser design and applications, intensity fluctuations and frequency stability; optical detection. Address: Lincoln Lab, Massachusetts Insitute of Technology, Wood St, Lexington, MA 02173.

FREED, DEBOW, b. Hendersonville, Tenn, Aug. 26, 25; m. 49; c. 1. NUCLEAR SCIENCE & ENGINEERING. B.S, U.S. Mil. Acad, 46; M.S, Kansas, 61; Atomic Energy Cmn. fel, New Mexico, 64, Assoc. West. Univs. fel, 64, Ph.D. (nuclear sci. & eng). 65. Instr. & various other assignments, U.S. Army, 46-61, chief, nuclear br, Defense Atomic Support Agency, N.Mex, 61-65; prof. in charge elective progs. & opers, dept. physics, U.S. Mil. Acad, 67-69; DEAN, MT. UNION COL, 69- U.S.A, 46-69, Col, Legion of Merit. Am. Nuclear Soc; Opers. Res. Soc. Am; Am. Asn. Physics Teachers. Pulsed neutron technique; physics of nuclear systems; nuclear applications; national security affairs; educational administration. Address: Office of the Dean, Mount Union College, Alliance, OH 44601.

FREED, ELISABETH HERTZ, b. Göttingen, Ger, Aug. 21, 24; nat; m. 70. ORGANIC CHEMISTRY. A.B, Smith Col, 47; M.S, Villanova Univ, 68. RES. CHEMIST, WYETH LABS, INC, 57- Synthetic medicinal chemistry. Address: Wyeth Labs, Inc, Box 8299, Philadelphia, PA 19101.

FREED, HERBERT, b. Phila, Pa, May 7, 08; m. 46; c. 2. PSYCHIATRY. M.D, Temple, 33. Chief res. neuropsychiat, Phila. Gen. Hosp, 35-38; instr. PSYCHIAT, SCH. MED, TEMPLE UNIV, 38-39, assoc, 39-40, asst. prof, 40-43, assoc. prof, 44-57, CLIN. PROF, 58-, DIR. PSYCHOTHER, 69- Vis. chief psychiatrist, Phila. Gen. Hosp, 38-56, chief child psychiat, 54-57, child psychiat. res. unit, 57- Consult, Vet. Admin, 55- Fel. Am. Psychiat. Asn; fel. Am. Med. Asn; Am. Psychoanal. Asn. Child psychiatry; psychopharmacology; psychosurgery; psychoanalysis. Address: 255 S. 17th St, Philadelphia, PA 19103.

FREED, JACK H, b. Brooklyn, N.Y, Apr. 19, 38; m. 61; c. 2. CHEMICAL PHYSICS. B.E, Yale, 58; Gen. Elec. Ed. Fund fel, Columbia, 58-59, M.A, 59, Nat. Sci. Found. fel, 59-62, Ph.D. (chem), 62. Nat. Sci. Found. & Hon. U.S. Ramsay Mem. fels, 62-63; asst. prof. CHEM, CORNELL UNIV, 63-67, ASSOC. PROF, 67- Alfred P. Sloan Found. fel, 66-68; vis. scientist, U.S.-Japan Coop. Sci. Prog, Tokyo Univ, 70-71; sr. Weizmann fel, Weizmann Inst. Sci, 71- Am. Phys. Soc. Applications of magnetic resonance to problems of theoretical chemical interest. Address: Dept. of Chemistry, Cornell University, Ithaca, NY 14850.

FREED, JAMES M(ELVIN), b. Enid, Okla, Apr. 6, 39; m. 69; c. 1. CELL & COMPARATIVE PHYSIOLOGY. B.S, McPherson Col, 61; M.S, Univ. Ill, Urbana-Champaign, 63, U.S. Pub. Health Serv. trainee, 65-69, Ph.D. (physiol), 69. Instr. biol, Manchester Col, 63-65; investr, R/V Alpha Helix, Bering Sea Exped, summer 68; ASST. PROF. ZOOL, OHIO WESLEYAN UNIV, 69- AAAS; Am. Inst. Biol. Sci; Am. Soc. Zool. Biochemical adaptations in poikilotherms to environmental temperature changes. Address: Dept. of Zoology, Ohio Wesleyan University, Delaware, OH 43015.

FREED, JEROME J(AMES), b. N.Y.C, May 4, 28; m. 51; c. 4. CELL BIOL-OGY. B.S, Yale, 49; M.A, Columbia Univ, 51, Ph.D.(zool), 54. Res. assoc, INST. CANCER RES, 53-62, asst. mem, 62-66, ASSOC. MEM, 66-, res. career develop. award, 65-70. AAAS; Histochem. Soc; Am. Soc. Cell Biol; Am. Soc. Zool; Am. Asn. Cancer Res. Heredity in cultured cells; haploid frog cell cultures; fine structure of cultured cells. Address: Institute for Cancer Research, Fox Chase, 7701 Burholme Ave, Philadelphia, PA 19111.

FREED, KARL F, b. Brooklyn, N.Y, Sept. 25, 42; m. 64; c. 2. THEORETI-CAL & PHYSICAL CHEMISTRY. A.M, Harvard, 65, Nat. Sci. Found. fel, 63-67, Ph.D.(chem. physics), 67. NATO fel. theoret. physics, Univ. Man-chester, 67-68; ASST. PROF. CHEM, UNIV. CHICAGO, 68- Co-organizer, Int. Union Pure & Appl. Physics Int. Conf. Statist. Mech, Chicago, 71. Am. Phys. Soc; Faraday Soc. Radiationless processes and photochemistry in polyatomic molecules; electronic structure in disordered systems; statis-tical mechanics of polymer systems; many-body theory and the electronic structure of molecules; quantum chemistry. Address: James Franck In-stitute, University of Chicago, Chicago, IL 60637.

FREED, MEIER E(ZRA), b. Phila, Pa, Oct. 20, 25; m. 70. ORGANIC CHEM-ISTRY. B.Sc, Pa. State Univ, 48, M.Sc, 49; Ph.D.(chem), Univ. Pa, 60. RES. CHEMIST, WYETH LABS, INC, 51- Am. Chem. Soc. Pharmaceuti-cal chemistry; heterocyclic and alicyclic derivatives. Address: Wyeth Labs, Inc, Box 8299, Philadelphia, PA 19101.

FREED, MURRAY M(ONROE), b. Paterson, N.J, Oct. 9, 24; m. 48; c. 4. RE-HABILITATION MEDICINE. A.B, Harvard, 48; M.D, Boston Univ, 52. Nat. Found. Infantile Paralysis fel. phys. med, N.Y. Univ-Bellevue Med. Ctr, 53-56; instr. phys. med. & rehab, SCH. MED, BOSTON UNIV, 56-59, assoc, 59-62, asst. prof, 62-65, assoc. prof. REHAB. MED, 65-67, PROF. & CHMN. DEPT, 67- Asst. chief rehab. med, Univ. Hosp, Boston, Mass, 56-59; chief, 59-; consult. Vet. Admin, 62-; physician-in-chief phys. med. & rehab, Bos-ton City Hosp, 64-; del, Int. Med. Soc. for Paraplegia, 67 & 68; mem. med. adv. bd, Nat. Paraplegia Found, 70- A.U.S, 43-46. Am. Acad. Phys. Med. & Rehab; Am. Cong. Rehab. Med; Am. Col. Physicians; Asn. Acad. Phys-iatrists (pres, 71). Long term effects of spinal cord trauma; rehabilitation potential of patient with spinal cord trauma; rehabilitation potential of individual with amputation as a result of malignancy. Address: 750 Harri-son Ave, Boston, MA 02118.

FREED, MYER, b. Orillia, Ont, Can, May 20, 09; nat; m. 42; c. 2. BIOCHEM-ISTRY. M.A, Toronto, 33, Ph.D.(zymol), 40. Res. chemist, Dawe's Labs, 49-67, dir. chem. tech. serv, Fine Chem. Div, 67-70; SR. CHEMIST, SHEFA PROTEIN INDUST. LTD, 70- U.S.A, 42-45. Am. Chem. Soc. Vitamin production; microbiological assay methods; immunochemistry of anthrax; enzymes related to fats, phospholipids and proteins; meat analogs. Ad-dress: 60 Yehuda St, Apt. 15, Arad, Israel.

FREED, N(ORMAN), b. Phila, Pa, June 11, 36; m. 60; c. 2. THEORETICAL NUCLEAR PHYSICS. B.S, Antioch Col, 58; Woodrow Wilson Found. & Atomic Energy Cmn. fels, Western Reserve, 58-61, M.S, 61, Nat. Sci. Found. fel, 63-64, Ph.D.(theoret. physics), 64. Res. assoc. PHYSICS, Ne-braska, 63-64; Nordic Inst. Theoret. Atomic Physics res. fel, inst. theoret. physics, Lund, 64-65; Ford Found. fel, Bohr Inst, Copenhagen, 65; asst. prof, PA. STATE UNIV, 65-68, ASSOC. PROF, 68- On leave, Res. Inst. Theoret. Physics, Univ. Helsinki, summer 71; Ctr. Nuclear Studies, Saclay, France, 71-72. AAAS; Am. Phys. Soc; Am. Asn. Physics Teachers. Shell model and pairing force calculations. Address: Dept. of Physics, Pennsyl-vania State University, University Park, PA 16802.

FREED, SIMON, b. Lodz, Poland, Nov. 11, 99; nat; m. 43. BIOCHEMISTRY, PHYSICAL CHEMISTRY. S.B, Mass. Inst. Tech, 20; Paris, 20-21; fel, California, 25-27, Ph.D.(chem), 27. Instr. chem, California, 27-28, res. assoc, 28-30; Guggenheim fel, Kammerlingh-Onnes Lab, Leiden, 30-31; instr, Chicago, 31-37, asst. prof, 37-43, 45-46; group leader, s.a.m. lab, Columbia, 43-45; chief chemist, Oak Ridge Nat. Lab, 46-49; sr. scientist, Brookhaven Nat. Lab, 49-65; prof. physiol, Mt. Sinai Med. Ctr, 66-67; RES. PROF. BIOCHEM. & NEUROL, N.Y. MED. COL, 67- Inter-acad. exchange, U.S.S.R, 66, Czech, 67; res. collab, Brookhaven Nat. Lab, 68- AAAS. Optical and magnetic properties; symmetry of electric fields about ions in solutions and crystals; chemistry and biochemistry at low temperatures; resolution of states and reactivities in chemistry and bio-chemistry; endogenous chemistry of animals during learning; radioactivity; physiological chemistry of the nervous system; cryobiochemical analysis of tissue. Address: New York Medical College, Fifth Ave. & 106th St, New York, NY 10029.

FREED, VIRGIL H(AVEN), b. Mendota, Ill, Nov. 18, 19; m. 44; c. 4. BIO-CHEMISTRY. B.S, Ore. State Univ, 43, M.S, 48; Ph.D.(chem), 59. Asst. prof. chem, ORE. STATE UNIV, 44-48, assoc. prof. chem. & assoc. prof. farm crops, 48-54, assoc. prof. CHEM, 54-59, PROF, 60-, HEAD DEPT, AGR. CHEM, 61-, DIR. ENVIRON. HEALTH SCI. CTR, 67- Chmn. res. comt, U.S. Pub. Health Serv, 47; mem, West. Weed Control Conf, 52; Gordon Res. Conf, 58, 65; lectr, Tour Europ. Res. Ctrs, 62; mem, Gov. Adv. Comt. Synthetic Chem. in Environ, Ore, 69-; study sect. comt, EUHS; invitational lectr, Du Pont Seminar Series; spec. consult, environ. sci. training comt, Bur. State Serv; mem. training comt, Nat. Inst. Environ. Health Sci; comt. persistent pesticides, Nat. Insts. Health-Nat. Res. Coun. Governor's North-west Scientists Award, 71. Fel. AAAS; Am. Chem. Soc; Weed Sci. Soc. Am. Mechanism of action of plant growth regulators and herbicides; physical chemistry of compounds in relation to their biological action. Address: Dept. of Agricultural Chemistry, 337 Weniger Hall, Oregon State University, Corvallis, OR 97331.

FREEDBERG, A(BRAHAM) STONE, b. Salem, Mass, May 30, 08; m. 35; c. 2. MEDICINE. A.B, Harvard, 29; M.D, Chicago, 35. House officer med, Mt. Sinai Hosp, Ill, 34-35; res, Cook County Hosp, 35-36; house officer path, R.I. Hosp, 36-37; asst. MED, Beth Israel Hosp, 38-40; res. fel, HARVARD MED. SCH, 41-42, asst, 42-46, instr, 46-47, assoc, 47-50, asst. prof, 50-57, assoc. prof, 58-69, PROF, 69- Summer, house officer, Mass. Mem. Hosp, 35. Jr. vis. physician, Beth Israel Hosp, 40-46, assoc. vis. physi-cian, 46-48, vis. physician, 49-63, physician & dir. cardiol. unit, 64-69,

assoc. med. res, 40-50, assoc. dir, 50-63, Ziskind sr. fel, 56; Guggenheim fel, 67-68. Consult. & mem. thyroid uptake calibration cmt, med, div, Oak Ridge Inst. Nuclear Studies, 55-56; consult, metab. study sect, U.S. Pub. Health Serv, 56-60. Dipl, Am. Bd. Internal Med. AAAS; Am. Physiol. Soc; Am. Soc. Clin. Invest; Am. Heart Asn; Asn. Am. Physicians; Am. Thyroid Asn.(first v.pres, 65-66). Cardiovascular diseases; thyroid in health and disease. Address: 111 Perkins St, Jamacia Plain, MA 02130.

FREEDLAND, RICHARD A, b. Pittsburgh, Pa, May 9, 31; m. 58; c. 2. BIO-CHEMISTRY. B.S, Univ. Pittsburgh, 53; M.S, Univ. Ill, 55; Ph.D.(biochem), Univ. Wis, 58. Res. assoc. pediat, Univ. Wis, 58-60; lectr, biochem, UNIV. CALIF, DAVIS, 60-61, asst. prof. PHYSIOL. CHEM, 61-65, assoc. prof, 65-69, PROF, 69- Fel. AAAS; Am. Soc. Biol. Chem; Am. Inst. Nutrit; Soc. Exp. Biol. & Med; Am. Chem. Soc; Brit. Biochem. Soc; N.Y. Acad. Sci. Enzyme chemistry; induction and suppresion of enzyme systems in higher animals by dietary and hormonal manipulations; particularly the mechan-isms and physiological interpretations. Address: Dept. of Physiological Science, School of Veterinary Medicine, University of California, Davis, CA 95616.

FREEDMAN, AARON D(AVID), b. Albany, N.Y, Jan. 4, 22; m. 48; c. 3. INTERNAL MEDICINE, BIOCHEMISTRY. A.B, Cornell, 42; M.D, Albany Med. Col, 45; Libman fel, Mt. Sinai Hosp, New York, 51-54; U.S. Pub. Health Serv. fel. Columbia, 54-57, Ph.D.(biochem), 58. Instr. biochem, Co-lumbia, 58-59, asst. prof. med, 59-65; dir. dept. med, Menorah Med. Ctr. & dir. exp. med, Danciger Res. Found, 65-69; PROF. MED. & ASSOC. DEAN, SCH. MED, UNIV. PA, 69- Career investr, Health Res. Coun, New York, 64-65; clin. prof. med, sch. med, Univ. Kans, 66-69. Dipl, Am. Bd. Internal Med. Med.C, 46-48, 53, Capt. AAAS; Am. Soc. Biol. Chem; Am. Soc. Cell Biol. Intermediary metabolism; tricarboxylic acid cycle activity; renal metabolism. Address: University of Pennsylvania School of Medicine, 36th St. & Hamilton Walk, Philadelphia, PA 19104.

FREEDMAN, ALFRED MORDECAI, b. Albany, N.Y, Jan. 7, 17; m. 43; c. 2. PSYCHIATRY. A.B, Cornell, 37; M.B, Minnesota, 41, M.D, 42. Intern, Harlem Hosp, N.Y, 41-42; asst. dept. path, Mt. Sinai Hosp, 46; physiologist, med. div, Army Chem. Ctr, Md, 46-48; res, psychiat. div, N.Y. Univ-Belle-vue Med. Ctr, 48-49, asst. alienist, 49-50, jr. psychiatrist, children's serv, 50-51, res. fel, 51-52, sr. psychiatrist, 53-54, clin. instr. psychiat, col. med, 53-55; asst. prof. PSYCHIAT, State Univ. N.Y. Downstate Med. Ctr, 55-57, assoc. prof, 57-60; PROF. & CHMN. DEPT, N.Y. MED. COL, 60- Child psychiatrist, inst. phys. med. & rehab, Bellevue Hosp, 52-53, clin. asst. neuropsychiatrist, 54-55; asst, N.Y. Univ. Hosp, 53-55; asst. pedia-trician, Babies Hosp, 53-60; dir. pediat. psychiat, Kings County Hosp, 55-60; dir. psychiat, Flower & Fifth Ave. Hosp, Metrop. Hosp. & Bird S. Coler Hosp, New York; bd. trustees, Ctr. Urban Educ; consult, WHO Europ. Ment. Health Sect. U.S.A.A.F, 42-46. AAAS; Soc. Biol. Psychiat; fel. Am. Psy-chiat. Asn; fel. Am. Orthopsychiat. Asn; fel. Am. Pub. Health Asn; Asn. Res. Nerv. & Ment. Disease; Am. Acad. Child Psychiat; Acad. Psychoanal; N.Y. Acad. Sci; Am. Psychopath. Asn.(pres, 71-72); Am. Col. Neuropsycho-pharmacol.(pres. elect, 71-72). Effect of anticholinesterases on central nervous system; clinical and biological aspects of child and adult psychia-try; psychiatric education; narcotic addiction. Address: Dept. of psychiatry, New York Medical College, Flower & Fifth Ave. Hospital, Fifth Ave. & 106th St, New York, NY 10029.

FREEDMAN, ALLAN, b. Phila, Pa, May 26, 37; m. 59; c. 2. ORGANIC CHEMISTRY. A.B, Temple, 58; Sun Oil fel. & Ph.D.(org. chem), Pennsyl-vania, 62. Res. chemist plastics, Am. Viscose Div, FMC Corp, 62-64, group leader, plastics res. & explor. cellophane coatings, 64-66; tech. serv. engr, SHELL CHEM. CO, 66-70, PROD. REP. POLYPROPYLENE, 70- Am. Chem. Soc. Preparation of bridgehead nitrogen compounds; emulsion poly-merization of acrylics; formulation and extrusion of thermoplastics. Ad-dress: Shell Chemical Co, P.O. Box 2463, Houston, TX 77002.

FREEDMAN, ALLEN ROY, b. Chicago, Ill, Aug. 18, 40; m. 62; c. 2. MATH-EMATICS. A.B, California, Berkeley, 62; Ph.D.(math), Oregon State, 65. Asst. prof. MATH, SIMON FRASER UNIV, 65-70, ASSOC. PROF, 70- Am. Math. Soc. Number theory; density theory in additive number theory. Address: Dept. of Mathematics, Simon Fraser University, Burnaby, B.C, Can.

FREEDMAN, ARTHUR J(ACOB), b. Brooklyn, N.Y, Dec. 10, 24; m. 64; c. 6. CHEMISTRY. B.A, N.Y. Univ, 45, M.S, 46, Ph.D.(chem), 48. Res. assoc, Mass. Inst. Technol, 48-49; mem. staff, Los Alamos Sci. Lab, 49-50; res. assoc, New Mexico, 50-54; from asst. proj. engr. to sr. proj. supvr, Stan-dard Oil Co.(Ind), 54-59; sect. head, NALCO CHEM. CO, 59-66, res. coord, 66-67, tech. mgr. res, 67-69, TECH. DIR, 69- AAAS; Am. Chem. Soc; Water Pollution Control Fedn. Phase rule; radiochemistry; kinetics; cor-rosion; water treatment; petroleum; water and air pollution control; paper-making chemicals; silica sols. Address: Nalco Chemical Co, 6216 W. 66th Place, Chicago, IL 60638.

FREEDMAN, BERNARD, b. Hudson, Mass, Oct. 22, 19; m. 53; c. 1. CHEM-ICAL ENGINEERING. B.S, Ind. Inst. Tech, 42. Chief chemist & metall. engr, Babcock Printing Press Mfg. Co, Conn, 42-46; asst. chief plastics res. chem. eng, Foster-Grant Co, Mass, 46-49; asst. chief metallurgist, res. & develop, Whiten Mach. Works, 49-51; from group leader to metall. engr, Walworth Valve Co, 51-53; sr. res. chem. engr, Monsanto Chem. Co, 53-63; chief process engr, develop. & eng. dept, plumbing & heating div, Am. Standard, 63-67; head appln. res, Reichhold Chem, Inc, N.Y, 67-70; ASST. MGR. & SR. SCIENTIST, PLASTICS DEPT, NAT. LEAD RES, HIGHTSTOWN, 70- AAAS; Am. Chem. Soc; Am. Soc. Metals; Am. Found-rymen's Soc; Nat. Soc. Prof. Eng; N.Y. Acad. Sci. Materials and process engineering; plastics application in research; metallurgy; plating; forging; coatings; synthetics; stabilizers; flame retardants; lubricants; formulation. Address: 23 Briar Cliff Rd, Upper Saddle River, NJ 07458.

FREEDMAN, BERNARD, b. Wilmington, Del, Oct. 14, 29; m. 57; c. 1. OR-GANIC CHEMISTRY. B.S, Delaware, 51, Ph.D.(chem), Illinois, 57. RES. CHEMIST, Esso Res. & Eng. Co, 57-59; Calif. Spray Chem. Corp, Standard Oil Co. Calif, 59-63; WEST. REGIONAL RES. LAB, U.S. DEPT. AGR, 63-

Chem.C, U.S.A, 51-53. Am. Chem. Soc; Am. Oil Chem. Soc. Fatty acid chemistry. Address: 2688 Wright Ave, Pinole, CA 94564.

FREEDMAN, DANIEL X, b. Lafayette, Ind, Aug. 17, 21; m. 45. PSYCHIATRY. B.A, Harvard, 47; M.D, Yale, 51. Intern pediat, sch. med, Yale, 52-55, res. psychiat, 55, instr, 55-58, chief res, 55-56, asst. prof, 58-61, assoc. prof, 61-64, prof, 64-66, dir. psychopharmacol. unit, 58-66; PROF. PSYCHIAT. & CHMN. DEPT, UNIV. CHICAGO, 66- Attend. psychiatrist, Vet. Admin. Hosp, West Haven, Conn, 55-66; assoc. psychiatrist, Grace-New Haven Community Hosp, 55-66; consult, juvenile courts, 55-57; Fairfield State Hosp, 58-66, U.S. Dept. Army, 65-67; career investr, Nat. Inst. Ment. Health, 57-66, consult. psychopharmacol. study sect, 60-65, mem. drug eval. comt, 65-67, res. scientist, develop. review comt, 70-; mem. comt. on brain sci, Nat. Res. Coun, 70-; chief ed, Archives Gen. Psychiat. U.S.A, 42-46. Am. Psychiat. Asn; Am. Soc. Pharmacol. & Exp. Therapeut; Am. Col. Neuropsychopharmacol; Soc. Psychophysiol. Res; Am. Med. Asn; Group Advan. Psychiat; Int. Brain Res. Orgn; Int. Col. Neuropsychopharmacol. Psychopharmacology; psychoanalytic, neurophysiologic and social investigation in schizophrenia; central nervous system determinants of allergy; drugs, brain function and behavior; methodology of drug studies. Address: Dept. of Psychiatry, University of Chicago, 950 E. 59th St, Chicago, IL 60637.

FREEDMAN, DANIEL Z, b. Hartford, Conn, May 3, 39. THEORETICAL PHYSICS. B.A, Wesleyan, 60; Nat. Sci. Found. fel, Wisconsin, 61-64, M.S, 62, Ph.D.(physics), 64. Res. assoc. physics, Wisconsin, 64; Nat. Sci. Found. fel, Imp. Col, London, 64-66; res. fel, California, Berkeley, 65-66, instr, 66-67; mem. inst. adv. study, Princeton, 67-68; asst. prof. PHYSICS, STATE UNIV. N.Y. STONY BROOK, 68-70, ASSOC. PROF, 70- Alfred P. Sloan Found. fel, 69-71; vis. scientist, dept. physics, Mass. Inst. Technol, 70-71. Am. Phys. Soc. Theory of elementary particles and interactions, particularly strong interactions, dispersion relations, complex angular momentum, approximation methods and phenomenology. Address: Dept. of Physics, State University of New York at Stony Brook, Stony Brook, NY 11790.

FREEDMAN, DAVID ASA, b. Boston, Mass, May 27, 18; m. 47; c. 4. NEUROLOGY, PSYCHIATRY. A.B, Harvard, 39; M.D, Tufts, 43. Rockefeller fel. neurol, Columbia, 47-48; from fel. to assoc. clin. prof. neurol, Tulane, 49-65; assoc. prof. psychiat. & neurol, BAYLOR COL. MED, 65-71, PROF. PSYCHIAT, 71- From instr. to training & supv. analyst, New Orleans Psychoanal. Inst, 54-; clin. prof. psychiat, med. sch, La. State, 69- Med.C, U.S.A, 44-46, Capt. AAAS; Asn. Res. Nerv. & Ment. Disease; Am. Acad. Neurol; Am. Psychiat. Asn; Am. Psychoanal. Asn. Role of congenital and perinatal sensory deprivations in evolution of psychic structure; an approach to the study of ego development. Address: Dept. of Psychiatry, Baylor College of Medicine, 1200 Moursund Ave, Houston, TX 77025.

FREEDMAN, ELI (HANSELL), b. Pittsburgh, Pa, Dec. 12, 27; m. 51; c. 2. PHYSICAL CHEMISTRY. B.S, Carnegie Inst. Tech, 47; Ph.D.(chem), Cornell, 52. Res. assoc. physics dept, Brown, 52-53, instr. CHEM, 53-56; asst. prof, Buffalo, 56-60; res. chemist, chem. br, BALLISTIC RES. LABS, ABERDEEN PROVING GROUND, 60-62, CHIEF, phys. chem. sect, 62-65, chem. phys. br, 65-69, THERMOKINETICS GROUP, 69- Mem, eve. col. faculty, Johns Hopkins Univ, 65- AAAS; Am. Chem. Soc; Am. Phys. Soc; Am. Soc. Test. & Mat. Applications of acoustics to chemistry; chemical reaction in shock tubes. Address: Ballistic Research Labs, IBL, Aberdeen Proving Grounds, MD 21005.

FREEDMAN, GEORGE, b. Boston, Mass, Dec. 11, 21; m. 43; c. 2. PHYSICS, METALLURGY. S.B, Mass. Inst. Tech, 43; M.A, Boston, 52. Asst. metallurgist, RAYTHEON CO, 43, plant metallurgist, 43-51, head semiconductor eng. & develop. sect, 51-55, chief engr. adv. develop, 55-59, chief process engr, 59-60, mgr. mat. & tech. lab, 62-65, group mgr. mat. & tech. eng, 65-69, MGR. NEW PROD. DEVELOP, MICROWAVE & POWER TUBE DIV, 69-, TECH. ED, SEMICONDUCTOR PROD. & SOLID STATE TECHNOL, 61-Pres, Tyco Semiconductor Corp, 60-62; lectr. dent. mat, Harvard Sch. Dent. Med, 65- U.S.N.R, 44-46. Am. Soc. Metals. Development of new business concepts and new products. Address: Five Brook Trail Rd, Wayland, MA 01778.

FREEDMAN, H(AROLD) H(ERSH), b. Malden, Mass, Mar. 5, 24; m. 51; c. 3. ORGANIC CHEMISTRY. B.S, Tufts, 49, M.S, 50; Ph.D.(org. chem), Boston, 56. Chemist, Ionics, Inc, 51-52; res. chemist, EAST. RES. LAB, DOW CHEM. CO, 56-63, ASSOC. SCIENTIST, 63- U.S.A.A.F, 41-43. Am. Chem. Soc. Mechanism and structure in organic chemistry, small ring compounds, stable organic anions and cations. Address: Eastern Research Lab, Dow Chemical Co, Box 400, Wayland, MA 01778.

FREEDMAN, HENRY H(ILLEL), b. New York, N.Y, Dec. 21, 19; m. 48; c. 1. IMMUNOLOGY. A.B, N.Y. Univ, 48, M.S, 50, Ph.D.(physiol), 53. Teaching fel. biol, Wash. Sq. Col, N.Y. Univ, 49-52; res. assoc, Princeton Labs, Inc, 52-64; res. immunologist, inst. microbiol, Rutgers, 65; sr. res. assoc, WARNER-LAMBERT RES. INST, 65-67, mgr. dept. microbiol, 67-68, DIR, 68-69, DEPT. PHYSIOL. & MICROBIOL, 69- Med.Admin.C, U.S.A, 42-46, 1st. Lt. AAAS; Am. Chem. Soc; Soc. Exp. Biol. & Med; Am. Soc. Microbiol; Reticuloendothelial Soc; Transplantation Soc; Soc. Indust. Microbiol; fel. N.Y. Acad. Sci. Immune mechanisms; non-specific host resistance; bacterial lipopolysaccharides; reticuloendothelial system; delayed hypersensitivity; transplantation immunity; immunosuppression. Address: Dept. of Physiology & Microbiology, Warner-Lambert Research Institute, Tabor Rd, Morris Plains, NJ 07950.

FREEDMAN, JACOB, b. Manchester, N.H, March 28, 11; m. 44; c. 2. GEOLOGY. B.S, New Hampshire, 38; A.M, Harvard, 40, Russell scholar & Ph.D. (geol), 48. Asst. instr. geol, New Hampshire, 40-41; geologist, Alaskan br, U.S. Geol. Surv, 42-46, geologist, mil. geol. unit, 47; asst. instr. GEOL, Harvard, 46-47; asst. prof, FRANKLIN & MARSHALL COL, 47-51, assoc. prof, 51-58, PROF, 58-, chmn. dept, 57-59, 61-63. Geologist, Pa. Geol. Surv, 57-64; consult, Am. Geol. Inst. Duluth Conf, 59; Earth Sci. Curriculum Proj, 64-66; explor. geochemist, resources res. br, U.S. Geol. Surv, 66-67; exec. secy, Nat. Asn. Geol. Teachers-U.S. Geol. Surv. Coop. summer field training prog, 67-; councilor, Coun. Educ. Geol. Sci. & chmn, Curriculum Panel, 69- AAAS; fel. Geol. Soc. Am; Geochem. Soc; Nat. Asn. Geol. Teachers. Petrology and petrography of areas in New Hampshire, North Carolina, Alaska, Michigan and Costa Rica; the iron problem; mineral deposits of Israel, Southeastern Pennsylvania and Maryland; structural geology and stratigraphy of Piedmont of Pennsylvania and Maryland and the Northern Blue Ridge Mountains of Pennsylvania. Address: 2414 Helena Rd, Lancaster, PA 17603.

FREEDMAN, JEROME, b. N.Y.C, Aug. 16, 16; m. 46; c. 7. ELECTRICAL ENGINEERING, ELECTRONICS. B.S, City Col. New York, 38; M.S, Polytech. Inst. Brooklyn, 51. Electronics scientist, Watson Lab, N.J, 46-51; dep. chief, Rome Air Develop. Center, Griffiss Air Force Base, 51-52; staff mem, LINCOLN LAB, MASS. INST. TECHNOL, 52-53, group leader, 53-55, div. head, 55-68, ASST. DIR, 68- Mem. Adv. Cmt. Ballistic Missile Defense, Adv. Res. Projs. Agency, U.S. Dept. Defense, 63-67, chmn, 67-68; mem. Re-entry Progs. Rev. Group, U.S. Dept. Defense Res. & Eng, 63-; consult, U.S. Arms Control & Disarmament Agency, 65-67; Inst. Defense Anal, 65-, dir. summer study missile defense, 66; mem. avionics panel, Adv. Group Aerospace Res. & Develop, NATO, 68-; consult, Joint Chiefs of Staff, 68- Sig.C, U.S.A, 42-46, Res, 46-54, 1st Lt. AAAS; Inst. Elec. & Electronics Eng.(editor's award, Inst. Radio Eng, 52). Electronics; radar system design; signal design theory; microwave technology; systems design and analysis in ballistic missile defense and offense systems; radar system design. Address: Lincoln Lab, Massachusetts Institute of Technology, Lexington, MA 02173.

FREEDMAN, L(ARRY) A, b. Phila, Pa, Mar. 29, 27; m. 51; c. 2. ELECTRICAL ENGINEERING. B.S, Drexel Inst, 48; M.S, Rutgers Univ, 50. Asst. elec. eng, Rutgers Univ, 48-50; res. engr, David Sarnoff Res. Ctr, RCA CORP, 50-62, eng. leader, ASTRO-ELECTRONICS DIV, 62-68, MGR, CAMERA DEVELOP, 69- U.S.N.R, 45-46. Am. Inst. Aeronaut. & Astronaut; Inst. Elec. & Electronics Eng. Space electronics; television camera systems. Address: Astro-Electronics Division, RCA Corp, Princeton, NJ 08540.

FREEDMAN, LAWRENCE R(APHAEL), b. New York, N.Y, Dec. 1, 27; m. 55; c. 2. INTERNAL MEDICINE. B.S, Yale, 47, M.D, 51; Brown fel. from Yale, Pennsylvania, 48-49. Asst. path, Hopkins, 55-56; instr. med, SCH. MED, YALE, 57-58, asst. prof, 58-64, assoc. prof, 64-70, PROF. MED. & ED, YALE J. BIOL. & MED, 70- Markle scholar, 57-62; chief med, Atomic Bomb Casualty Comn, Hiroshima-Nagasaki, Japan, 62-64; vis. prof, Swiss Inst. Exp. Cancer Res, 70-71; mem. Sci. adv. bd, Nat. Kidney Found. Med.C, 53-55, 1st Lt. Am. Fedn. Clin. Res; Am. Soc. Clin. Invest; Infectious Diseases Soc. Am. Renal and infectious diseases; experimental pathology. Address: Dept. of Medicine, Yale School of Medicine, New Haven, CT 06525.

FREEDMAN, LAWRENCE ZELIC, b. Gardner, Mass, Sept. 4, 19; m. 55; c. 5. PSYCHIATRY. B.S, Tufts, 41, M.D, 44; dipl, N.Y. Psychoanal. Inst, 50-55. Res. PSYCHIAT, New Haven Hosp. & sch. med, Yale, 46-49, assoc. clin. prof, sch. med, 49-61; PROF, SCH. MED, UNIV. CHICAGO, 61- Vis. lectr. & mem. coop. faculty, sch. law, Yale, 49-57, chmn. study unit psychiat. & law, 53-58; vis. scholar. & sr. res. assoc, Cambridge, 58-59; fel, Center Adv. Study Behav. Sci, 59-60. Assoc. psychiatrist, Grace-New Haven Community Hosp, 49-, physician in charge psychiat. dispensary, 51-52, psychiatrist in charge & consult, univ. servs, hosp, 49-51. Psychiat. consult, Am. Law Inst, 54-; Am. Bar Asn, 59- Permanent del, UN Econ. & Soc. Coun, 49-, consult, 49-50; Yale del, Int. Cong. Psychiat, Paris, 54; Int. Cong. Criminol, Paris, 54. Med.C, 41-46, Lt. AAAS; Am. Psychiat. Asn; fel. Am. Orthopsychiat. Asn; N.Y. Acad. Sci. Psychosomatic medicine; psychosomatic aspects of obstetrics; psychoanalysis; social psychiatry; neurosis and economic factors; non-conformist behavior and social response; delinquent behavior; sex, aggressive and acquisitive deviant behavior. Address: Dept. of Psychiatry, University of Chicago School of Medicine, Chicago, IL 60637.

FREEDMAN, LEON D(AVID), b. Baltimore, Md, July 19, 21; m. 45; c. 2. ORGANIC CHEMISTRY. A.B, Hopkins, 41, M.A, 47, U.S. Pub. Health fel, 48-49, Ph.D.(org. chem), 49. Anal. chemist, Hopkins Hosp, U.S. Pub. Health Serv, 41-44, org. chemist, sch. hyg, 46-48; Nat. Cancer Inst, Nat. Insts. Health, 48-49; North Carolina, 49-61; assoc. prof. CHEM, N.C. STATE UNIV, 61-65, PROF, 65- U.S.N.R, 44-46. AAAS; Am. Chem. Soc. Organophosphorus compounds; oxidation-reduction; relationship between chemical structure and biological activity. Address: 2006 Myron Dr, Raleigh, NC 27607.

FREEDMAN, LEONARD, b. Cape Town, S.Africa, Dec. 8, 23; m. 47; c. 3. VERTEBRATE ZOOLOGY & PALEONTOLOGY. B.Sc, Cape Town, 46, Ph.D, 55. Med. technologist, amoebiasis res. unit, Durban, S.Africa, 49-52, res. off, 55-58; bursar paleontol, Transvaal Mus, Pretoria, S.Africa, 53-55; sr. lectr. anat, Witwatersrand, 58-61; Sydney, 61-66; assoc. prof. anthrop. anat, UNIV. WIS, MADISON, 66-67, PROF. ZOOL, 67- Anti-Aircraft Union Defence Forces S.Africa, 43-46. S.African Asn. Adv. Sci; Australian Soc. Mammal.(treas, 64-65). Amoebiasis; physical anthropology of Australia and New Guinea; fossil and living Cercopithecoidea; taxonomy of bandicoots; vertebrate functional anatomy and taxonomy. Address: Dept. of Zoology, 444 Birge Hall, University of Wisconsin, Madison, WI 53706.

FREEDMAN, M. JOEL, b. Brest Litovsk, Poland, Oct. 15, 03; nat; m. 30; c. 3. DENTISTRY. D.D.S, N.Y. Univ, 27. Instr. PEDODONT, COL. DENT, N.Y. UNIV, 44-45, asst. clin. prof, 45-60, ASSOC. CLIN. PROF, 60- AAAS; Am. Soc. Dent. for Children; Am. Dent. Asn; fel. Am. Pub. Health Asn; Am. Acad. Oral Med; N.Y. Acad. Sci; Am. Col. Dent; fel. Royal Soc. Health; Int. Acad. Orthod. Mass communication; dental health education. Address: 300 W. 23rd St, New York, NY 10011.

FREEDMAN, MARVIN I, b. Boston, Mass, Oct. 4, 39; m. 66. MATHEMATICS B.S, Mass. Inst. Tech, 60; Nat. Defense Ed. Act fel, Brandeis, 60-63, M.A, 62, Nat. Sci. Found. summer fel, 62, Ph.D.(math), 64. Instr. math, California, Berkeley, 64-66; scientist, electronic res. ctr, NASA, 67-70; ASSOC. PROF. MATH, BOSTON UNIV, 70- Vis. asst. prof, Brown, 68-69. Co-winner best paper award, Joint Automatic Control Conf, 68. Math. Asn. Am; Am. Math. Soc. Stability theory; partial differential equations; harmonic and functional analysis; numerical analysis and system theory. Address: Dept. of Mathematics, Boston University, 270 Bay State Rd, Boston, MA 02215.

FREEDMAN, MELVIN S(LEIN), b. Chicago, Ill, May 24, 15; m. 40. CHEMISTRY. B.S, Chicago, 36, Ph.D.(phys. chem), 42. Res. engr, Acme Indust. Co, Ill, 41-43; assoc. chemist, metall. lab, Chicago, 43-46; SR. CHEMIST, ARGONNE NAT. LAB, 46- Fel. Am. Phys. Soc. Nuclear physics; radio chemistry; distribution of electricity on rotating metallic conductors. Address: Argonne National Lab, 9700 S. Cass Ave, Argonne, IL 60440.

FREEDMAN, M(ORRIS) DAVID, b. Toronto, Ont, May 23, 38; m. 62; c. 2. ELECTRICAL ENGINEERING. B.A.Sc, Univ. Toronto, 60; M.S, Univ. Ill, Urbana, 62, Ph.D.(elec. eng), 65. Res. assoc. elec. eng, biol. comput. lab, Univ. Ill, Urbana, 65-66; sr. engr, INFO. SCI. LAB, BENDIX RES. LABS, 66-69, STAFF ENGR, 70- Inst. Elec. & Electronics Eng; Pattern Recognition Soc. Analysis and synthesis of musical tones; digital computer systems—design and applications; pattern recognition—optical character recognition. Address: Bendix Research Labs, Bendix Center, Southfield, MI 48076.

FREEDMAN, MURRAY H, b. Toronto, Ont, Can, Nov. 3, 36; m. 59. BIOCHEMISTRY, IMMUNOCHEMISTRY. B.Sc, Toronto, 59, Warner-Lambert fel, 60-61, M.Sc, 61, Nat. Res. Coun. studentship, 62-64, Ph.D.(biochem), 64. Med. Res. Coun. overseas fel. chem. immunol, Weizmann Inst, 64-66; sr. cancer res. scientist, Roswell Park Mem. Inst. 66-68; ASSOC. PROF. BIOCHEM, FACULTY OF PHARM, UNIV. TORONTO, 68-, FACULTY OF MED, 69- Lectr, State Univ. N.Y. Buffalo, 67-69. Am. Chem. Soc; Am. Asn. Immunol; Can. Soc. Immunol; N.Y. Acad. Sci. Physical and chemical studies on the structure of immunoglobulin molecules; structural and functional studies on biological macromolecules using high resolution ^{1}H and ^{13}C Fourier transform nuclear magnetic resonance spectroscopy. Address: Faculty of Pharmacy, University of Toronto, Toronto 5, Ont, Can.

FREEDMAN, PHILIP, b. London, Eng, June 25, 26; U.S. citizen; m. 54; c. 5. MEDICINE. M.B.B.S, London, 48, M.D, 51. First asst. physician, St. George's Hosp, London, Eng, 59-60, clin. asst. physician, renal study clin, 60-63; assoc. prof. med, Chicago Med. Sch, 63; CHMN. DEPT. MED, MED. CENTER, MT. SINAI HOSP, 66-; CHMN. DEPT. MED, UNIV. HEALTH SCI, CHICAGO MED. SCH, 67- Pollard fel, Univ. Col. hosp. med. sch, London & dept. med, Univ. Illinois, 57-59; chief, Chicago Med. Sch. serv, div. med. & dir. renal unit, Cook County Hosp, 63-66; acting chmn. dept. med, Chicago Med. Sch, 66-67. Consult. physician, Woolwich Hosp. Group & Redhill Hosp. Group, London, Eng, 60-63; consult, Cook County Hosp, 66- R.A.M.C, 51-53, Jr. Med. Specialist. Am. Fedn. Clin. Res; Am. Soc. Nephrology; Soc. Exp. Biol. & Med; fel. Am. Col. Physicians; Med. Res. Soc. London; Royal Col. Physicians; Asn. Profs. Med; Brit. Soc. Immunol. Renal disease, particularly the pathogenesis of glomerulonephritis and the autoimmune diseases; immunologic aspects of renal and systemic disease. Address: Dept. of Medicine, Mt. Sinai Hospital Medical Center, 2755 W. 15th St, Chicago, IL 60608.

FREEDMAN, ROBERT W(AGNER), b. Newark, N.J, Feb. 15, 15; m. 46; c. 2. ORGANIC CHEMISTRY. S.B, Mass. Inst. Tech, 38; Ph.D.(chem), Polytech. Inst. Brooklyn, 51. Res. chemist, Battelle Mem. Inst, 51-52; Balco Res. Corp, 52-54; Colgate Palmolive Co, 54-57; asst. plant mgr, Transition Metals, Inc, 57; sect. head anal. res, Consol. Coal Co, 57-65; PROJ. COORD. ANAL. RES. METHODS, U.S. BUR. MINES, 65- U.S.A.A.F, 44-46, 2nd Lt. Am. Chem. Soc; Am. Inst. Chem.(secy-treas, 59-); The Chem. Soc. Gas chromatography. Address: 5028 Debra Dr, Pittsburgh, PA 15236.

FREEDMAN, STEVEN I(RWIN), b. N.Y.C, June 5, 35; m. 58; c. 3. MECHANICAL ENGINEERING, APPLIED PHYSICS. S.B, Mass. Inst. Technol, 56, S.M, 57, Mech.E, 60, Ph.D.(mech. eng), 61. Instr. mech. eng, Mass. Inst. Technol, 59-61, asst. prof, 61-63; consult. engr, nuclear space power, Gen. Elec. Co, 63-68; asst. chief engr, prod. develop. div, Budd Co, 68-70; lectr, UNIV. PA, 70-71, CHIEF ENGR, NAT. CTR. ENERGY MGT. & POWER, 71- Am. Soc. Mech. Eng. Energy conversion, heat transfer, power generation, thermodynamics; magnetohydrodynamics; thermoelectricity; thermionics; fluid mechanics. Address: 1615 Winston Rd, Gladwyne, PA 19035.

FREEDMAN, STEVEN LESLIE, b. Boston, Mass, Mar. 3, 35; m. 62. NEUROANATOMY, HISTOLOGY. B.S, New Hampshire, 57; Ph.D.(avian physiol), Rutgers, 62. Nat. Insts. Health fel. ANAT, brain res. inst, California, Los Angeles, 62-63; COL. MED, UNIV. VT, 63-64, res. assoc, 64-65, asst. prof, 65-71, ASSOC. PROF, 71- AAAS; Poultry Sci. Asn; Am. Asn. Anat. Neuroanatomical and neurophysiological studies on the avian autonomic nervous system, especially on reproductive processes. Address: Dept. of Anatomy, University of Vermont, Burlington, VT 05401.

FREEDMAN, TOBY, b. New York, N.Y, July 2, 24; m. 50; c. 1. AEROSPACE MEDICINE. A.B, Stanford, 45, M.D, 48. Intern & res, Los Angeles County Gen. Hosp, 47-51; physician, South. Calif. Permanente Med. Group, 54-55; corp. asst. med. dir. & corp. flight surgeon, gen. off, N.Am. Aviation, Inc, 56-65, dir. life sci, space & info. systs. div, 60-65, corp. dir. life sci, 63-65, exec. dir. med. & life sci, 65-69, corp. med. scientist, N.Am. Rockwell Corp, 69-71; MED. DIR, CALIF. MED. GROUP, 71- Clin. assoc. prof, Ohio State Univ. & Univ. Calif, Los Angeles, 61-; nat. consult, U.S. Air Force Off. Surgeon Gen, 64- Dipl, Am. Bd. Internal Med; Am. Bd. Prev. Med. Med.C, 49-54, Res, 54-, Maj. Am. Inst. Aeronaut. & Astronaut; Aerospace Med. Asn; Am. Med. Asn. Aerospace medicine clinical research with test pilots; stress physiology. Address: California Medical Group, 1880 Century Park E, Los Angeles, CA 90067.

FREEH, EDWARD J(AMES), b. Pleasant Valley, Pa, Sept. 18, 25; m. 52; c. 5. CHEMICAL ENGINEERING. B.Ch.E, Dayton, 48; M.S, Mass. Inst. Tech, 50; Ph.D.(kinetics), Ohio State, 58. Process develop. engr, nylon mfg, E.I. du Pont de Nemours & Co, 50-52; res. engr, res. inst, Dayton, 52-55, assoc. dir. res, 59-62; instr. chem. eng, Ohio State, 55-58; petrol. indust. mgr, Indust. Nucleonics Corp, 58-59; PROF. CHEM. ENG, Arizona, 62-68; OHIO STATE UNIV, 68- Staff consult, Indust. Nucleonics Corp, 63- Summer, engr, Oak Ridge Nat. Lab, 49. U.S.N.R, 43-46. Am. Inst. Chem. Eng; Am. Chem. Soc; Am. Soc. Eng. Educ; Instrument Soc. Am. Application of computers to chemical engineering calculations; instrumentation and process control. Address: Dept. of Chemical Engineering, Ohio State University, Columbus, OH 43210.

FREELAND, FORREST DEAN, JR, b. Detroit, Mich, June 25, 23; m. 65. HYDROLOGY, FORESTRY. B.Sc, Michigan, 48, M.F, 49; Ph.D.(forest hydrol. & soils), Mich. State, 56. Forester, cent. states forest exp. sta, U.S. Forest Serv, Ohio, 48-50, res. forester, 50-51; teaching asst. forestry, Mich. State, 51-54; asst. prof, Nat. Univ. Colombia, 54-56; Mich. State, 56-59; res. forester, Rocky Mt. Forest & Range Exp. Sta, U.S. Forest Serv, Colo, 60-61; consult. specialist, Price-Waterhouse & Co, Calif, 61-65; chief hydrologist, Metrop. Water Dist. South. Calif, 66-67; ASSOC. PROF. WATERSHED MGT, HUMBOLDT STATE COL, 67- U.S.M.C, 43-46, 2nd Lt. Soc. Am. Foresters; Am. Geophys. Union; Am. Water Resources Asn. Watershed management; forest influences and soils; forest mensuration; statistics; photogrammetry. Address: Dept. of Watershed Management, Humboldt State College, Arcata, CA 95521.

FREELAND, MAX, b. Browning, Mo, Oct. 20, 20; m. 55; c. 6. ANALYTICAL CHEMISTRY. B.S, Northeast Mo. State Teachers Col, 41; N.Y. Univ; M.S, Iowa State Col, 52, Ph.D.(anal. chem), 55. Teacher, pub. sch, Mo, 46-48; chemist, anal. method develop, Columbia-South. Chem. Corp, 55-57; assoc. prof. CHEM, NORTHEAST MO. STATE TEACHERS COL, 57-66, PROF, 66- Fel. Tex. A&M Univ, 64-65. U.S.N.R, 42-53, Lt. Am. Chem. Soc. Spectrophotometric analysis; high precision spectrophotometry; non-aqueous titrations. Address: Dept. of Chemistry, Northeast Missouri State Teachers College, Kirksville, MO 63501.

FREELAND, R(ALPH) O(RLANDO), b. Jasper Co, Ill, Sept. 27, 99; m. 21; c. 2. PLANT PHYSIOLOGY. B.S, East. Ill. State Teachers Col, 26; M.S, Ohio State, 31, Ph.D.(plant physiol), 34. Prin, high sch, Ill, 21-30; instr. math, East. Ill. State Teachers Col, 24; plant physiol, Ohio State, 31-38, asst. prof, 38-40; assoc. prof. BOT, NORTHWEST. UNIV, 40-70, dir. biol. labs, 60-70, EMER. ASSOC. PROF, 70- Agent, Barberry Eradication, U.S. Dept. Agr, 36, supt. vegetation surv, soil conserv. serv, 38. AAAS. Transpiration; absorption of minerals; factors affecting photosynthesis. Address: Dept. of Biology, Northwestern University, Evanston, IL 60201.

FREELE, HUGH W, b. Silver Creek, N.Y, Dec. 24, 16; m. 42; c. 2. PARASITOLOGY, ENTOMOLOGY. B.S, Cornell, 38; M.S, Col. St. Rose, 63. Jr. technician, STERLING-WINTHROP RES. INST, 46-47, sr. technician, 47-48, res. asst, 48-50, res. assoc, 50-61, assoc. mem, 61-64, RES. BIOLOGIST, 64- Med.C, U.S.A, 41-45. Am. Soc. Parasitol; Entom. Soc. Am; World Asn. Adv. Vet. Parasitol. Laboratory testing of synthetic chemicals as chemotherapeutic agents for treatment and control of malaria, schistosomiasis and intestinal parasites. Address: Sterling-Winthrop Research Institute, Rensselaer, NY 12144.

FREEMAN, AARON E(LIOTT), b. Buena Vista, Va, Mar. 5, 28; m. 52; c 2. CELL PHYSIOLOGY. B.A, George Washington, 51, M.S, 54, Ph.D.(physiol), Cath. Univ. Am, 64. Bacteriologist, U.S. Army Chem. Corps, 53-54; lab. cell biol, Nat. Inst. Allergy & Infectious Diseases, 54-62; dir. qual. control, MICROBIOL. ASSOCS, INC, 62-69, MEM. STAFF, 69- Tissue Cult. Asn; Soc. Exp. Biol. & Med; Am. Soc. Microbiol. Establishment, growth and maintenance of mammalian cells in tissue culture with special interest in nutritional requirements; factors influencing transformation of mammalian cells by oncogenic viruses. Address: Microbiological Associates, 4813 Bethesda Ave, Bethesda, MD 20014.

FREEMAN, ALAN R, b. Atlantic City, N.J, Jan. 16, 37; m. 58; c. 2. PHYSIOLOGY, PHARMACOLOGY. B.Sc, Phila. Col. Pharm, 58; Ph.D.(pharmacol), Hahnemann Med. Col, 62. Instr. pharmacol, Hahnemann Med. Col, 62-63; univ. fel, neurophysiol, med. ctr, Columbia Univ, 63-66; asst. prof, dept. physiol, med. sch, Rutgers Univ, 66-68, assoc. prof, 68-71; ASSOC. PROF. PSYCHIAT. & PHYSIOL, MED. CTR. & DIR. NEUROPHYSIOL. SECT, INST. PSYCHIAT. RES, IND. UNIV, 71- AAAS; Biophys. Soc; Am. Physiol. Soc; Brit. Soc. Gen. Physiol; Soc. Neurosci. Application of biophysical techniques to electrophysiological, osmotic and permeability studies as an approach to understanding the physiology and pharmacology of the nervous system at the level of the cellular membrane. Address: Dept. of Psychiatry, Indiana University Medical Center, 1100 W. Michigan St, Indianapolis, IN 46202.

FREEMAN, A(LBERT) E(UGENE), b. Lewisburg, W.Va, Mar. 16, 31; m. 50; c. 3. ANIMAL BREEDING. B.S, West Virginia, 52, M.S, 54; Ph.D.(animal breeding), Cornell, 57. Asst. dairy husb, West Virginia, 52-54; ANIMAL SCI, Cornell, 54-56; asst. prof, IOWA STATE UNIV, 56-64, assoc. prof, 64-65, PROF, 65- Am. Soc. Animal Sci; Am. Dairy Sci. Asn; Am. Statist. Asn. Genetic improvement of domestic animals, dairy cattle, beef cattle, swine, poultry and sheep; genetics of populations; statistical genetics. Address: 239 Kildee Hall, Iowa State University, Ames, IA 50010.

FREEMAN, ARTHUR, b. Youngstown, Ohio, Jan. 12, 25; m. 55; c. 2. VETERINARY MEDICINE. Stanford, 49-50; D.V.M, Ohio State, 55. Private practice, Pac. Vet. Hosp, Wash, 55-56; dir. prof. rels, Jensen-Salsbery Labs, Inc, Mo, 56-59; ED, J. AM. VET. MED. ASN, 59- U.S.A.A.F, 43-45, Lt. Am. Vet. Med. Asn; U.S. Animal Health Asn; Am. Soc. Vet. Physiol. & Pharmacol; Am. Med. Writers' Asn; Wildlife Disease Asn. Address: 600 S. Michigan Ave, Chicago, IL 60605.

FREEMAN, A(RTHUR) J(AY), b. Lublin, Poland, Feb. 6, 30; nat; m. 52; c. 4. SOLID STATE PHYSICS. B.S, Mass. Inst. Tech, 52, Ph.D.(physics), 56. Asst. physics, Mass. Inst. Tech, 52-56; instr, Brandeis, 55-56; physicist, Ord. Mat. Res. Off, 56-62; assoc. dir. & head theoret. physics group, Nat. Magnet Lab, Mass. Inst. Tech, 62-67; PROF. PHYSICS & CHMN. DEPT, NORTHWEST. UNIV, 67- Lectr, Northeast. Univ, 59-61; dir. NATO Advan. Study Insts, France, 66, Can, 67; Guggenheim fel. & Fulbright-Hays fel, Hebrew Univ. Jerusalem, 70-71; ed, Int. J. Magnetism; consult, Argonne Nat. Lab; IBM Corp; Nat. Magnet Lab, Mass. Inst. Technol; Interactive

Technol, Inc. Fel. Am. Phys. Soc. Quantum theory of atoms, molecules and solids; neutron and x-ray scattering; crystalline field theory; electronic band structure of solids; theory of magnetism; hyperfine interactions. Address: Dept. of Physics, Northwestern University, Evanston, IL 60201.

FREEMAN, BOB A, b. Eastland, Tex, May 7, 26; m. 60; c. 4. MICROBIOLOGY. B.A, Texas, 49, M.A, 50, Ph.D.(bact), 54. Instr. biol, Agr. & Mech. Col. Texas, 50-51; res. scientist brucellosis, Texas, 51-53; instr. bact, Arkansas, 54; MICROBIOL, Chicago, 54-58, asst. prof, 58-64; assoc. prof, UNIV. TENN, 64-66, PROF, 66-, ACTING CHMN. DEPT, 70- U.S.N, 44-46. AAAS; Am. Soc. Microbiol. Host-parasite relationships, effective immunity; antigens of Vibrio cholerae; cholera toxins. Address: Dept. of Microbiology, University of Tennessee Medical Units, Memphis, TN 38103.

FREEMAN, B(URTON) E(DGAR), b. Pasadena, Calif, July 31, 24; m. 46; c. 7. PHYSICS. B.S, Calif. Inst. Tech, 45; M.S, California, Los Angeles, 46; Ph.D.(physics), Yale, 50. Mem. staff, theoret. div, Los Alamos Sci. Lab, 50-58; Gen. Atomic Div, Gen. Dynamics Corp, 58-67; V.PRES. & SR. RES. SCIENTIST, SYSTS, SCI. & SOFTWARE, 67- Consult, Los Alamos Sci. Lab. U.S.N.R, 43-46. Am. Phys. Soc. Coulomb wave functions; resonance phenomena in individual particle model of nucleus; hydrodynamics; radiation transport. Address: Systems, Science & Software, 3347 Industrial Court, San Diego, CA 92121.

FREEMAN, CHARLES EDWARD, JR, b. Ironton, Mo, Aug. 19, 41; m. 63; c. 2. PLANT ECOLOGY. B.S, Abilene Christian Col, 63; M.S, N.Mex. State Univ, 66, fel, 66-68, Ph.D.(plant ecol), 68. Univ. Res. Inst. grants, UNIV. TEX, EL PASO, 68-70, ASST. PROF, BOT, 68- Am. Asn. Quaternary Environ. Pleistocene paleoecology; plant autecology. Address: Dept. of Biology, University of Texas at El Paso, El Paso, TX 79999.

FREEMAN, DARYL E, b. Melbourne, Australia, Feb. 27, 30; U.S. citizen; m. 66. PHYSICAL CHEMISTRY. B.Sc, Melbourne, 51, M.Sc, 55; univ. fel, Sydney, 55-57, Imp. Chem. Industs. fel, 58-59, Ph.D.(chem), 59. Res. officer, Imp. Chem. Industs, Ltd, Australia & N.Z, 51-53; lectr. chem, New South Wales Univ. Tech, 56-57; resident tutor sci, St. Andrew's Col, Sydney, 57-59; res. assoc. chem, Tufts, 60-62; res. fel, Harvard, 62-64; RES. PHYS. CHEMIST, Wentworth Inst, Boston, Mass, 64-68; AIR FORCE CAMBRIDGE RES. LABS, 68- Molecular structure, including infrared, Raman and ultraviolet spectroscopy; molecular vibrational theory; optical Stark effects. Address: Air Force Cambridge Research Labs, L.G. Hanscom Field, Bedford, MA 01730.

FREEMAN, DAVID H(AINES), b. Rochester, N.Y, June 24, 31; m. 56; c. 4. PHYSICAL CHEMISTRY. B.S, Rochester, 52, M.S, Carnegie Inst. Tech, 54; Ph.D.(chem), Mass. Inst. Tech, 57. Res. assoc. phys. chem, Mass. Inst. Tech, 57-60; asst. prof. chem, Washington State, 60-65; res. chemist, ANAL. CHEM. DIV, NAT. BUR. STANDARDS, 65, CHIEF SEPARATION & PURIFICATION SECT, 65- Vis. prof, Univ. Md. Am. Chem. Soc; Am. Phys. Soc; Optical Soc. Am. Interactive gel networks; ion exchange; chromatography; particle metrology; microscopy. Address: Separation & Purification Section, Analytical Chemistry Division, National Bureau of Standards, Washington, DC 20234.

FREEMAN, DONALD C(HESTER), JR, b. Haverhill, Mass, May 15, 30; m. 51; c. 3. PHYSICS. Sc.B, Brown, 51; Ph.D.(chem), Maryland, 55. Asst. mgr. res, Linde Div, UNION CARBIDE CORP, 55-68, dir. technol, mat. systs. div, 68-69, GEN. MGR, ENVIRON. INSTRUMENTS DEPT, ELECTRONICS. DIV, 69- Res. assoc, Duke Univ, 58-59. Am. Phys. Soc. Coordination chemistry; physical properties of zeolites; low temperature physics; superconductivity. Address: Electronics Division, Union Carbide Corp, 5 New St, White Plains, NY 10601.

FREEMAN, ELI S(AUL), b. Brooklyn, N.Y, Jan. 14, 28; m. 50; c. 3. PHYSICAL CHEMISTRY. B.S, Brooklyn Col, 50, M.A, 52; fel, Rutgers, 55-56, Ph.D, 60. Chemist, Kings County Hosp, 50-51; inorg. chem, Nossen Lab, 51-52; res. chemist, Picatinny Arsenal, 52-55; instr. physics, Rutgers, 56-57; res. chemist, Picatinny Arsenal, 57-59, chief basic chem. unit, pyrotechnics lab, 60-64; mgr. phys. chem. res, IIT Res. Inst, 64-66, asst. dir, 66-70; PRES, FREEMAN LABS, INC, ROSEMONT, 70- Am. Chem. Soc; Am. Soc. Test. & Mat; Am. Inst. Chem. Air and water pollution; kinetics of high temperature reactions in liquid and solid states; radiation effects on chemical reactivity of inorganic solids; pre-ignition, ignition and propagative reactions between phrotechnic fuels and oxidants; thermoanalysis; polymer degradation. Address: 216 Aspen Lane, Highland Park IL 60035.

FREEMAN, FILLMORE, b. Lexington, Miss, Apr. 10, 36. PHYSICAL ORGANIC CHEMISTRY. B.Sc, Cent. State Univ, 57; Petrol. Res. Fund fel, Mich. State, 60-62, Ph.D.(phys. org. chem), 62. Res. chemist, Calif. Res. Corp, 62-64; Nat. Insts. Health fel, Yale, 64-65; asst. prof. CHEM, CALIF. STATE COL, LONG BEACH, 65-69, ASSOC. PROF, 69- Summer, jr. chemist, Nat. Aluminate Co, 59; vis. prof, Univ. Paris, 71-72. Am. Chem. Soc; Brit. Chem. Soc. Mechanisms and kinetics of transition metals oxidations; heterocyclic and bio-organic chemistry. Address: Dept. of Chemistry, California State College, Long Beach, CA 90801.

FREEMAN, FRANK E, b. Newport, Ind, Jan. 14, 08. CLINICAL PSYCHOLOGY. B.A, Pennsylvania, 31, M.A, 41; Ph.D.(clin. psychol), London, 52; hon. M.A, Oxford, 53. Instr. psychol, Pennsylvania, 41-42, instr. & asst. personnel off, 46-48; lectr. soc. psychol, Oxford, 50-56; dep. dir. opers, psychol. & spec. warfare, spec. opers. res. off, American Univ, 57-58; consult. psychologist, 58-59; proj. dir. life sci, Opers. Res, Inc, 60-61; exec. secy. ment. health study sect, div. res. grants, Nat. Insts. Health, 62-64, assoc. chief biomed. res. admin, off. res. grants, bur. state serv, U.S. Pub. Health Serv, 64-67, dep. dir. off. res. & develop, Bur. Health Serv, 67-68; COORD. SPEC. FOR. CURRENCY PROG, OFF. INT. HEALTH, DEPT. HEALTH, EDUC. & WELFARE, 68- Sr. consult. res, inst. psychiat, Univ. London, 52-54. Med.Serv.C, 42-46, Res, 46-, Comdr. AAAS; Am. Psychol. Asn. Psychopathology; management control systems; administration of biomedical research programs. Address: Office of International Health, Office of Assistant Secretary for Health & Scientific Affairs, Room 3030, Health, Education & Welfare North Bldg, 330 Independence Ave. S.W, Washington, DC 20201.

FREEMAN, FRED W, b. Logan, Ohio, Aug. 27, 24; m. 46; c. 3. FORESTRY, HORTICULTURE. B.S, Mich. State, 49, M.S, 51, Ph.D.(forestry), 63. Soil scientist, Fed. Bur. Reclamation, 50-51; ranger, Ohio Div. Forestry, 51-53, forester, 53-55; horticulturist, HIDDEN LAKE GARDENS, MICH. STATE UNIV, 55-61, asst. prof. HORT, 61-68, ASSOC. PROF, 68-, CURATOR, 61- Interchange fel. hort, British Isles, 63. U.S.A, 43-46, Sgt. Am. Asn. Bot. Gardens & Arboretums; Am. Soc. Hort. Sci; Royal Hort. Soc; Int. Soc. Hort. Sci. Arboretum development and management; establishment and maintenance of both woody and herbaceous plant collections in arboretum and conservatory; educational programs in the natural sciences for the visiting public. Address: Hidden Lake Gardens, Tipton, MI 49287.

FREEMAN, GEORGE R(OLAND), b. Chattahoochee, Fla, Oct. 30, 18; m. 43; c. 2. AGRICULTURAL ENGINEERING. B.S.A, Florida, 48, M.S.A, 57. Asst. regional engr, Int. Harvester Co, Fla, 48-50; supt. field opers, AGR. EXP. STA, UNIV. FLA, 50-66, ASST. DIR, 66- U.S.A.A.F, 41-46, Res, 46-, Col. Development of research equipment, tools and buildings for all departments, especially agronomy, animal husbandry, plant pathology and entomology. Address: 1021 McCarty Hall, University of Florida, Gainesville, FL 32601.

FREEMAN, G(ORDON) R(USSEL), b. Hoffer, Sask, Aug. 27, 30; m. 51; c. 2. PHYSICAL CHEMISTRY. B.A, Univ. Sask, 52, M.A, 53; Ph.D.(chem), McGill Univ, 55; Exhib. 1851 overseas scholar, Oxford, 55-57, D.Phil, 57. Fel, Saclay Ctr. Nuclear Studies, France, 57-58; asst. prof. CHEM, UNIV. ALTA, 58-62, assoc. prof, 62-65, PROF, 65-, CHMN. DIV. PHYS. CHEM, 66- Radiation Res. Soc; fel. Chem. Inst. Can; Faraday Soc. Radiation chemistry; reaction kinetics. Address: Dept. of Chemistry, University of Alberta, Edmonton 7, Alta, Can.

FREEMAN, GUSTAVE, b. New York, N.Y, July 3, 09; m. 38; c. 3. MEDICINE. Ph.B, Brown, 29; M.D, Duke, 34. Instr. path, Yale, 34-36; instr. & asst. prof. med, Chicago, 36-47; mem. staff, Peter Bent Brigham Hosp, 49-51; chief clin. invest, med. labs, Army Chem. Ctr, 51-57; head clin. pharmacol. & exp. therapeut. sect, Nat. Serv. Ctr, Nat. Cancer Inst, 57-58; CHMN. MED. SCI. DEPT, STANFORD RES. INST, 58- Asst. prof, Hopkins, 52-59; res. assoc, Calif. Inst. Tech, 58-59. Res. assoc, Childrens Hosp, Boston, 49-51, consult, 51-; Nat. Insts. Health, 69- Med.C, 41-46, Maj. AAAS; Am. Soc. Trop. Med. & Hyg; Am. Soc. Hemat; Am. Med. Asn; Am. Fedn. Clin. Res; N.Y. Acad. Sci; Int. Soc. Hemat; Am. Asn. Cancer Res. Thrombocytopenic bleeding; clinical investigation; infectious disease; pathology; cholinesterase biology; cancer chemotherapy; viral tumorigenesis in tissue culture; viral hepatitis; experimental emphysema. Address: Medical Sciences Dept, Stanford Research Institute, 333 Ravenswood Ave, Menlo Park, CA 94025.

FREEMAN, HARLAN GEORGE, b. Minneapolis, Minn, Jan. 18, 33; m. 56; c. 3. WOOD TECHNOLOGY. B.S, Minnesota, 54; M.F, Yale, 59; Fulbright grant, Inst. Tech, Finland, 59-60. Tech. dir. wood prod, Wabash Screen Door Co, Minn, 56-58; RES. SCIENTIST, WEYERHAEUSER CO, 60- U.S.A, 54-56. Forest Prod. Res. Soc. Wood adhesives. Address: Research Division, Weyerhaeuser Co, 3400 13th S.W, Seattle, WA 98134.

FREEMAN, HAROLD A(DOLPH), b. Wilkes-Barre, Pa, July 12, 09; m. 35; c. 2. STATISTICS. B.S, Mass. Inst. Tech, 31; Harvard, 36-38; Guggenheim Mem. fel, Princeton, 52-53; Nat. Sci. Found. fel, North Carolina, 60-61. ASST. STATIST, MASS. INST. TECHNOL, 33-35, instr, 35-39, asst. prof, 39-44, assoc. prof, 44-50, PROF, 50- Consult, Nat. Defense Res. Comt, 43-45; U.S. War Dept, 43-45. Fel. Am. Statist. Asn.(v.pres, 48-50); fel. Am. Soc. Qual. Control; Inst. Math. Statist; fel. Am. Acad. Arts & Sci. Statistical methods. Address: Dept. of Economics, Room 52-383, Massachusetts Institute of Technology, Cambridge, MA 02139.

FREEMAN, HARRY F(REDERICK), b. Kansas City, Kans, Dec. 6, 09; m. 41; c. 3. CHEMICAL ENGINEERING. B.S, Kans. State Col, 36, M.S, 37; Ph.D.(chem. eng), Iowa, 40. Chemist, Swift & Co, 34-35; asst, Kans. State Col, 36-37; asst, Iowa, 37-40; chem. engr, Nat. Aniline div, Allied Chem. & Dye Corp, 40-42; Am. Cyanamid Co, N.Y, 46-47, chief chem. engr, Warners Plant, 47-51, sr. engr, Agr. Chem. Div, 51-58; CHEM. ENGR, PICATINNY ARSENAL, DOVER, 58- U.S.A, 42-45, Maj. Am. Inst. Chem. Eng. Clarification of Iowa river water with bentonite; cyanides; cyanogen and cyanuric chlorides; guanidines; nitrogen chemicals; explosives; ammunition. Address: 1 Rose Terr, Chatham, NJ 07928.

FREEMAN, HARRY W, b. Mt. Pleasant, S.C, Jan. 19, 23; m. 44; c. 2. VERTEBRATE ZOOLOGY. B.S, Charleston Col, 44; M.S, South Carolina, 48; Ph.D.(biol), Stanford, 51. Acting instr. BIOL, Stanford, 50-51; asst. prof, South Carolina, 51-54, assoc. prof, 54-60; PROF, COL. CHARLESTON, 60- Atomic Energy Comn. res. assoc. invest, 51-53. U.S.N.R, 44-46, Lt.(jg). Am. Soc. Ichthyol. & Herpet. Ichthyology; herpetology. Address: Dept. of Biology, College of Charleston, 66 George St, Charleston, SC 29401.

FREEMAN, HERBERT, b. Frankfurt-am-Main, Ger, Dec. 13, 25; U.S. citizen; m. 55; c. 3. ELECTRICAL ENGINEERING. B.S.E.E, Union (N.Y), 46; M.S, Columbia Univ, 48, Eng.Sc.D.(elec. eng), 56. Asst. elec. eng, Columbia Univ, 46-48; head dept, adv. studies eng, Sperry Gyroscope Co, 48-58, data processing, 59-60; vis. prof. ELEC. ENG, Mass. Inst. Technol, 58-59; PROF, N.Y. UNIV, 60-, CHMN. DEPT, 68- Res. grant, Air Force Off. Sci. Res, 61-; mem. cong. comt, Int. Fedn. Info. Processing, 64-65, chmn. U.S. comt, cong, 71; NASA res. grant, 65-; Nat. Sci. Found. fel, 66-67; vis. prof. Swiss Fed. Inst. Technol, 66-67; dir. Cybex Assoc, Inc. AAAS; Asn. Comput. Mach; fel. Inst. Elec. & Electronics Eng; N.Y. Acad. Sci. Digital computers and control systems; logical design, graphical data processing and pattern recognition; general system theory, particularly discrete-time systems; computer science. Address: Dept. of Electrical Engineering, New York University, Bronx, NY 10453.

FREEMAN, HORATIO P(UTNAM), b. Emmitsburg, Md, Mar. 17, 24; m. 51; c. 3. INORGANIC CHEMISTRY. B.Sc, Dickinson Col, 47; George Washington, 49-53. Res. assoc, Bone Char Res. Proj, Nat. Bur. Standards, 48-56; RES. CHEMIST, fertilizer lab, U.S. DEPT. AGR, 56-65, SOILS LAB, 65- U.S.A.F, 43-45, Res, 45-, Maj. Am. Chem. Soc. Cane sugar refining processes; phosphatic fertilizer materials; pesticide chemistry. Address: Soils Lab, U.S. Dept. of Agriculture, Beltsville, MD 20705.

FREEMAN, IRA M, b. Chicago, Ill, Aug. 15, 05; m. 35; c. 2. PHYSICS. B.S, Chicago, 25, M.S, 26, Ph.D.(physics), 28. Inst. Int. Ed. fel, Frankfurt, 28-29; fel, von Humboldt Found, 29-30; assoc. physicist, Nat. Adv. Comt. for Aeronaut, Langley Field, Va, 30-31; vis. prof. PHYSICS, Purdue, 42-43; res. assoc, Princeton, 43-45; assoc. prof, Swarthmore Col, 45-47; RUTGERS, UNIV, 47-59, PROF, 59- With Nat. Defense Res. Comt, 44. Prog. specialist, Dept. Natural Sci. UNESCO, Paris, 50-51. Mem. eclipse exped, Princeton, 45; mem, Sci. Policy Found. Fel. AAAS; Am. Asn. Physics Teachers. Theoretical physics; public education in science. Address: Dept. of Physics, Rutgers University, New Brunswick, NJ 08903.

FREEMAN, IRVING, b. Baltimore, Md, Feb. 25, 12; m. 43; c. 2. INTERNAL MEDICINE. B.S, Univ. Md, 32, M.D, 35. Asst. med, med. sch, Tufts Univ, 39; instr, sch. med, Univ. Md, 39-46, assoc, 46-57, asst. prof, 57-66; chief, med. serv, Lutheran Hosp, Baltimore, Md, 66-70; CHIEF, MED. OUT PATIENT SERV, MARICOPA COUNTY GEN. HOSP, 70- Attend. physician, Vet. Admin. Hosp, Ft. Howard, 47-49, asst. chief med. serv, 49-56, chief, 57-66. Dipl, Am. Bd. Internal Med, 48. Med.C, 41-46, Maj. Am. Med. Asn; fel. Am. Col. Physicians. Electrophoretic patterns and enzyme contents in various diseases; cardiovascular diseases, particularly quinidine in atrial fibrillation. Address: 3056 N. 32nd St, Apt. 345, Phoenix, AZ 85018.

FREEMAN, J(ACOB) J(OACHIM), b. Brooklyn, N.Y, Aug. 30, 13; m. 41; c. 3. PHYSICS. B.Sc, Col. William & Mary, 33; A.M, Columbia, 35; Mass. Inst. Technol, 37-39; Ph.D.(physics), Catholic Univ, 49. Radio physicist, Nat. Bur. Standards, 40-54; electronic scientist, U.S. Naval Res. Lab, 54-56; syst. analyst, Air Navig. Develop. Bd, 56-58; physicist, Vitro Corp. Am. Labs, 58-61; pres, J.J. Freeman Assocs, Consult, 61-66; RES. PHYSICIST, U.S. NAVAL RES. LAB, 66- Spec. lectr, Maryland, 54-61. Inst. Elec. & Electronics Eng; Pattern Recognition Soc. Theory and measurement of radio noise; electromagnetic and circuit theory; systems analysis. Address: 604 Perth Pl, Silver Spring, MD 20901.

FREEMAN, JAMES ALVIN, b. Washington, D.C, Dec. 28, 32; m. 55; c. 3. EXPERIMENTAL PATHOLOGY. B.S, La. State, 53, M.D, 58. Res. assoc. anat, sch. med, La. State, 56-58; mem. staff internal med, U.S. Pub. Health Serv. Hosp, San Francisco, Calif, 60-61; instr. PATH, SCH. MED, LA. STATE UNIV, NEW ORLEANS, 63-64, asst. prof, 64-67, assoc. prof, 67-69, INSTR, 69-, NAT. INSTS. HEALTH SPEC. FEL, 69- Dir. labs, Earl K. Long Hosp, Baton Rouge, 67-; U.S. Pub. Health Serv. trainee teaching fel. anat, 56-58 & spec. fel. path, 62-64. Dipl, Am. Bd. Path, 64, cert. clin. path, 65. U.S.P.H.S, 58-61, Lt. Am. Med. Asn; Am. Asn. Anat; Am. Soc. Cell Biol; Electron Micros. Soc. Am; Asn. Mil. Surg. U.S; Am. Soc. Exp. Path; Am. Soc. Cytol. Academic medicine; experimental hematology; electron microscopy. Address: Dept. of Pathology, School of Medicine, Louisiana State University, 1542 Tulane Ave, New Orleans, LA 70112.

FREEMAN, JAMES H(ARRISON), b. Braddock, Pa, Feb. 11, 22; m. 44; c. 3. ORGANIC & POLYMER CHEMISTRY. B.S, Juniata Col, 44; M.S, Pennsylvania, 49, Ph.D.(org. chem), 50. Jr. res. chemist, Tidewater Associated Oil Co, 44; asst. instr. org. chem, Pennsylvania, 46-50; res. chemist, plastics, WESTINGHOUSE RES. LABS, 50-56, adv. chemist, 56-58, mgr. org. polymer chem. sect, insulation dept, 58-69, MGR. POLYMERS & PLASTICS DEPT, 69- U.S.N.R, 44-46, Lt.(jg). AAAS; Am. Chem. Soc. Heterocyclic organic compounds; mechanism of phenolformaldehyde resin formation; paper chromatographic analysis; high temperature application of polymers; thermally stable polymers; flat wiring systems; reinforced composites; research management. Address: Polymers & Plastics Dept, Westinghouse Research Labs, Pittsburgh, PA 15235.

FREEMAN, JAMES J, b. Erie, Pa, Mar. 11, 40; m. 62; c. 3. ELECTRICAL ENGINEERING, BIOENGINEERING. B.S, Gannon Col, 62; M.S, Univ. Detroit, 64, M.Eng, 67, D.Eng, 68. Instr. eng, Univ. Detroit, 64-68; Nat. Insts. Health Med. fel, Carnegie-Mellon Univ, 68-69; ASST. PROF. ELEC. ENG, UNIV. DETROIT, 69- Systs. consult, Pan Aura Div, Parke Davis Corp, 66-69; investr, Nat. Sci. Found. grant, 70-71; res. assoc, Providence Hosp, Detroit Mich, 71- Am. Soc. Eng. Educ; Inst. Elec. & Electronics Eng; Soc. Advan. Med. Systs. Electrical and medical engineering with special emphasis in electric vehicles, cardiac ultrasonic diagnosis, in vitro oximetry and multi-phasic health testing system analysis. Address: Dept. of Electrical Engineering, University of Detroit, Detroit, MI 48221.

FREEMAN, JAMES R, b. Hamilton, Ont, May 31, 25. OPTICS, SOLID STATE PHYSICS. B.A, McMaster, 48, M.Sc, 49; Ph.D.(physics), N.Y. Univ, 59. Res. scientist PHYSICS, Atomic Energy Can, Ltd, 50-52; res. asst, Air Force contract, N.Y. Univ, 53-59; vis. res. assoc, Munich Tech, 60-62; asst. prof, RUTGERS UNIV, 62-65, ASSOC. PROF, 65- Mass spectrometry; radiation physics; energy transfer, microwave effects, and optical effects in solids. Address: Dept. of Physics, Rutgers University, Newark, NJ 07102.

FREEMAN, JEFFREY V(AN DUYNE), b. Orange, N.J, Sept. 13, 34; m. 56; c. 2. ENTOMOLOGY, FORESTRY. B.S, State Univ. N.Y. Col. Forestry, 57; M.S, Rutgers, 60, Ph.D.(entom), 62. Teacher biol, Windham Col, 62-64; asst. prof. SCI, CASTLETON STATE COL, 64-65, ASSOC. PROF, 65- Entom. Soc. Am; Soc. Am. Foresters; Ecol. Soc. Am; Entom. Soc. Can. Biology and ecology of horse and deer flies; limnobiological studies, Lake Bomoseen, Vermont and tributaries; water conservation. Address: Castleton State College, Castleton, VT 05735.

FREEMAN, JERE E(VANS), b. Martin, Tenn, Oct. 13, 36; m. 62; c. 4. PLANT GENETICS & PHYSIOLOGY. B.S, Univ. Tenn, 58; M.S, Univ. Ill, 61, Ph.D.(agron), 62. Res. asst. plant genetics, Univ. Ill, 58-62; plant physiologist, MOFFETT TECH. CTR, CPC INT, INC, 62-67, SECT. LEADER RES, 67- Nat. Guard, 54-66, 1st Lt. Am. Soc. Agron; Crop Sci. Soc. Am; Am. Asn. Cereal Chem. Genetics, physiology and chemistry of cereal grains. Address: Moffett Technical Center, CPC International, Box 345, Argo, IL 60501.

FREEMAN, J(EREMIAH) P(ATRICK), b. Detroit, Mich, Aug. 3, 29; m. 53; c. 6. ORGANIC CHEMISTRY. B.S, Notre Dame, 50; M.S, Illinois, 51, Atomic Energy Cmn. fel, 51-53, Ph.D.(chem), 53. Anal. chemist, Monsanto Chem. Co, 50; asst, Illinois, 50-51; sr. res. chemist, Rohm & Haas Co, 53-57, head org. chem. group, 57-64; assoc. prof. CHEM, UNIV. NOTRE DAME, 64-68, PROF, 68-, CHMN. DEPT, 70-, asst. head dept, 65-70. Alfred P. Sloan fel, 66- Am. Chem. Soc; Brit. Chem. Soc. Conjugate addition of Grignard reagents involving aromatic nuclei; chemistry of oxidized nitrogen compounds; organic fluorine compounds. Address: 17806 Edgewood Walk, South Bend, IN 46635.

FREEMAN, JOHN A, b. Berkeley, Calif, May 7, 38; m. 57; c. 4. NEUROPHYSIOLOGY, BIOPHYSICS. B.Sc, Trinity Col, 58; fel, McGill, 60-62, M.D, C.M, 62; fel, Mass. Inst. Tech, 65-66, Ph.D.(biophys), 67. Lectr. physiol, faculty med, McGill, 61-62; med. intern, Wilford Hall U.S. Air Force Hosp, San Antonio, Tex, 62-63; chief, in-flight res. unit & flight surgeon, U.S. Air Force Sch. Aerospace Med, 63-64; vis. scientist, Inst. Biomed. Res, Am. Med. Asn, 67-69; marine biol. lab, Woods Hole, 68; res. scientist, aerospace med. res. lab, Wright-Patterson AFB, 69-71; ASST. PROF. ANAT, SCH. MED. VANDERBILT UNIV, 71- Consult. biomed. electronics, Technol. Inc, Ohio. U.S.A.F, 62-71, Lt. Col. AAAS; Am. Physiol. Soc; N.Y. Acad. Sci; Asn. Res. Vision & Ophthal. Neurophysiological mechanisms underlying information processing in the cerebellum; basic visual transduction mechanisms; related problems in biomedical engineering involving electronic design, computer applications and mathematical analysis; design of biomedical instrumentation for patient care. Address: Dept. of Anatomy, Vanderbilt University School of Medicine, Nashville, TN 37203.

FREEMAN, JOHN A(LDERMAN), b. Raleigh, N.C, Aug. 27, 17; m. 41; c. 4. PHYSIOLOGY. B.A, Wake Forest Col, 38, M.A, 40; North Carolina, 41-42; Ph.D.(zool), Duke, 49. Prof. natural sci, Louisburg Col, 42; asst. prof. chem, Wake Forest Col, 42-46; instr. zool, Duke, 47-48; asst. prof. BIOL, Tulane, 48-52; PROF, WINTHROP COL, 52-, CHMN. DEPT, 62- Human blood phospholipids; tissue enzymes; temperature acclimatization in fish; metabolism of the fish brain; mollusk shell growth; differential longevity of sperm. Address: Dept. of Biology, Winthrop College, Rock Hill, SC 29730.

FREEMAN, JOHN C(LINTON), JR, b. Houston, Tex, Aug. 7, 20; m. 47; c. 6. METEOROLOGY, MATHEMATICS. B.A, Rice, 41; M.S, Calif. Inst. Tech, 42; Brown, 46-48; Inst. Adv. Study, 49-50; Ph.D.(meteorol), Chicago, 52. Asst. gas & fluid dynamics, Brown, 46-48; meteorologist, U.S. Weather Bur, 48-49; mem. res, Inst. Adv. Study, 49-50; res. assoc. meteorol, Chicago, 50-52; sr. engr, Cook Res. Lab, 51-53; assoc. prof. meteorol. & oceanog, Texas A&M, 52-55; owner, Gulf Consult, 55-62; prof. math, Houston, 58; UNIV. ST. THOMAS (TEX), 58-66, PROF. PHYSICS & DIR. INST. STORM RES, 66- Tech. dir. meteorol. & oceanog, Nat. Eng. Sci. Co, 62-66. U.S.A.A.F, 41-46, Lt. Col. AAAS; N.Y. Acad. Sci; Meteorol. Soc. Japan; Am. Geophys. Union; Am. Meteorol. Soc.(Meisinger Award, 51; citation for work in estab. of the Tornado Warning Radar Network, 61); Royal Meteorol. Soc; Marine Technol. Soc. Fluid dynamics; applied mathematics; oceanography. Address: Institute for Storm Research, University of St. Thomas, 3812 Montrose Blvd, Houston, TX 77006.

FREEMAN, JOHN DANIEL, b. Clarksville, Tenn, Apr. 16, 41; m. 65; c. 2. SYSTEMATIC BOTANY, PLANT EVOLUTION. B.A, Austin Peay State Univ, 63; Gulf Coast Res. Lab, Ocean Springs, Miss, summer 64; Harvard, fall 64; Nat. Defense Educ. Act fel & Ph.D.(biol), Vanderbilt Univ, 69. ASST. PROF. BIOL. & CURATOR HERBARIUM, AUBURN UNIV, 68- Am. Soc. Plant Taxon; Int. Asn. Plant Taxon. Taxonomy and cytogenetics of Trillium; Liliaceae of Alabama; flora of east-central and southeastern Alabama; poisonous plants of Alabama; eastern Asian-eastern North American floristic relationships. Address: Dept. of Botany & Microbiology, Auburn University, Auburn, AL 36830.

FREEMAN, JOHN H(ARTTERT), JR, b. Evanston, Ill, June 29, 31; c. 1. MECHANICAL ENGINEERING. B.S, Northwestern, 54. Jr. engr, Pure Oil Co. Res. Ctr, 54-57; res. engr, 57-63, sr. res. engr, 63-65; STAFF ENGR, RES. & DEVELOP. ADMIN. STAFF, SUN OIL CO, 65- Chem.C, U.S.A, 55-57. Soc. Automotive Eng; Sci. Res. Soc. Am. Fuel development, combustion systems development, especially charge stratification; fuel systems development, especially gasoline fuel injection for spark-ignition internal combustion engines; on-site power generation with waste heat utilization. Address: Sun Oil Co, Box 426, Marcus Hook, PA 19061.

FREEMAN, JOHN J(EROME), b. Arlington Heights, Ill, Sept. 28, 33; m. 58. PHYSICAL CHEMISTRY. B.Sc, New Mexico, 58, Ph.D.(phys. chem), 64; Woodrow Wilson fel, California, Berkeley, 58-59. Res. asst. biochem, Lovelace Res. Found, 57-58; res. assoc. chem, Brookhaven Nat. Lab, 63-66; Chemstrand Res. Ctr, Inc, 66-68; RES. CHEMIST, MONSANTO CO, 68- Sci. Res. Soc. Am; N.Y. Acad. Sci; Am. Phys. Soc. Visible absorption and emission spectroscopy of molecules and complexed ions; infrared and far-infrared absorption spectroscopy of molecules in the solid state. Address: Monsanto Co, 800 N. Lindbergh Blvd, St. Louis, MO 63166.

FREEMAN, JOHN MARK, b. Brooklyn, N.Y, Jan. 11, 33; m. 56; c. 3. PEDIATRIC NEUROLOGY. A.B, Amherst Col, 54; M.D, Johns Hopkins Univ, 58. From intern to sr. resident pediat, Harriet Lane Home, Johns Hopkins Hosp, 61-64; fel. pediat. neurol, Columbia Presby. Med. Ctr, N.Y.C, 64-66; asst. prof. PEDIAT. & NEUROL, sch. med, Stanford Univ, 66-69; ASSOC. PROF, SCH. MED, JOHNS HOPKINS UNIV, 69-, DIR. PEDIAT-NEUROL. SERV. & BIRTH DEFECTS TREATMENT CTR, HOSP, 69- Consult, perinatal res. br, Nat. Inst. Neurol. Diseases & Stroke; Walter Reed Gen. Hosp; Rosewood State Hosp, Baltimore, Md. Dipl, Am. Bd. Pediat, 63, Am. Bd. Psychiat. & Neurol, 69; Lucy Moses Prize, Columbia Presby. Med. Ctr, 66. U.S.A, 66. Fel. Am. Acad. Pediat; Am. Acad. Neurol; Soc. Pediat. Res; Am. Fedn. Clin. Res. Address: Dept. of Neurology & Pediatrics, Johns Hopkins University School of Medicine, Baltimore, MD 21205.

FREEMAN, JOHN RICHARDSON, b. Murfressboro, Tenn, Aug. 24, 27; m. 64; c. 3. HERPETOLOGY. A.B, North Carolina, 50; M.A, George Peabody Col, 53; Ph.D.(zool), Florida, 63. Instr. BIOL, Jacksonville Jr. College, 53-55; asst. prof, UNIV. TENN, CHATTANOOGA, 59-64, assoc. prof. & head dept, 64-70, PROF, 70- U.S.N.R, 45-46. Am. Soc. Ichthyol. & Herpet. Physiological ecology; respiratory behavior in the salamander Pseudobranchus striatus. Address: Dept. of Biology, University of Tennessee, Chattanooga, TN 37401.

FREEMAN, JOHN WRIGHT, JR, b. Chicago, Ill, July 12, 36; m. 57; c. 2. SPACE SCIENCE. B.S, Beloit Col, 57; U.S. Steel Found. fel, Iowa, 60, M.S, 61, NASA fel, 62, Ph.D.(physics), 63. Staff scientist, off. space sci. & appln, NASA, D.C, 63-64; res. assoc. SPACE SCI, RICE UNIV, 64-65, asst. prof, 65-68, ASSOC. PROF, 68- Consult, NASA, D.C; mem. Nat. Sci. Found. vis. scientist prog, 65-; vis. scientist, Royal Inst. Technol, Stockholm and Univ. Bern, 71-72; prin. investr, Apollo Sci. Exp. Am. Geophys. Union; Int. Union Geod. & Geophys; Am. Asn. Physics Teachers; Int. Asn. Geomag. & Aeronomy. Space radiation studies, particularly the Van Allen or geomagnetically trapped radiation; low energy particle measurements and magnetospheric dynamics; lunar exosphere and solar wind interaction with the moon. Address: Dept. of Space Science, Rice University, Houston, TX 77001.

FREEMAN, JOSEPH T(HEODORE), b. McKeesport, Pa, May 25, 08; m. 43; c. 1. INTERNAL MEDICINE. A.B, Harvard, 30; M.D, Jefferson Med. Col, 34. Asst. physician chest diseases, Phila. Gen. Hosp. & Rush Hosp, Pa, 37-41; chief, dept. geriatrics, Doctor's Hosp, 42-47; clin. asst. prof. med, MED. COL. PA, 56-64, LECTR, 64- Lectr, Phila. Sch. Social Sci, 51-64, spec. lectr, grad. med. sch, Pennsylvania, 56- Consult, Home for Jewish Aged, 55-; U.S. Vet. Admin. Hosp, Coatesville; comn. on geriatrics, Pa. Med. Soc. Meyer B. Strouse award, Moss Rehab. Hosp, 61; Dipl, Am. Bd. Internal Med. Civilian with chem. warfare div, Off. Civilian Defense, 42-45. Fel. Am. Geriatrics Soc.(v.pres, 48-52); fel. Geront. Soc.(pres, 60-, citation of merit, 61); fel. Am. Med. Asn.(recog. award, 71); fel. Am. Col. Physicians; Int. Asn. Geront; fel. Int. Soc. Hist. Med; fel. Int. Col. Angiol; Chilean Soc. Geront.(distinguished Serv. Dipl). Geriatrics; gerontology; medical education in aging; history of gerontology; bio-bibliography of gerontology. Address: 1530 Locust St, Philadelphia, PA 19102.

FREEMAN, KARL BORUCH, b. Toronto, Ont, Can, Jan. 21, 34; m. 55; c. 2. BIOCHEMISTRY. B.A, Toronto, 56, Nat. Res. Coun. Can. fel, 56-59, Ph.D. (biochem), 59. Fel, Toronto, 60-61; Nat. Inst. Med. Res, Eng, 61-63; Ont. Cancer Inst, 64-65; asst. prof. BIOCHEM, McMASTER UNIV, 65-68, ASSOC. PROF, 68- Am. Soc. Biol. Chem; Can. Biochem. Soc. Biogenesis of mitochondria; function and biosynthesis of mitochondrial nucleic acids and proteins. Address: Dept. of Biochemistry, McMaster University, Hamilton, Ont, Can.

FREEMAN, KELLY CAREY, b. Caledonia, Miss, May 27, 19; m. 42; c. 5. SOILS, FIELD CROPS. B.S, Miss. State Univ, 41, M.S, 61. RES. AGRONOMIST, U.S. DEPT. AGR, 61- U.S.A, 41-46, Maj. Agronomic research in sugarcane and sweet sorghum. Address: U.S. Sugar Crops Field Station, Rt. 10, Box 152, Meridian, MS 39301.

FREEMAN, KENNETH A(LFREY), b. McAllaster, Kans, June 29, 12; m. 38; c. 2. ORGANIC CHEMISTRY. B.S, Stetson, 34, M.S, 35, Florida, 36-38; Ph.D.(biochem), Georgetown, 48. Naval stores asst, Florida, 36-38; teacher, high sch, Fla, 38-39; chemist, U.S. Dept. Agr, Food & Drug Admin, La, 39-40, Fed. Security Agency, Wash, D.C, 40-42, chief color certification br, 46-53, Dept. Health, Educ. & Welfare, 53-57, dep. dir. div. cosmetics, 57-64, dir. div. color certification & eval, 64-68; dir. div. colors & cosmetics, 68-70; RETIRED. Vis. lectr, Georgetown Univ, 48-56. U.S.N.R, 42-46, Lt. Comdr. Am. Chem. Soc; Soc. Cosmetic Chem; fel. Am. Inst. Chem. Terpene chemistry; naval stores; synthetic organic dyes; cosmetics; spectrophotometry. Address: P.O. Box 156, Cape Ann, Churchton, MD 20733.

FREEMAN, LEON DAVID, b. Minneapolis, Minn, Oct. 21, 20; m. 43; c. 2. BIOCHEMISTRY. B.A, California, Los Angeles, 43; Ph.D.(biochem), Southern California, 62. Lab. supvr. chem, U.S. Rubber Co, 43-47; chief chemist, So. Calif. Gland Co, 49-60; res. dir, Darwin Labs, 55-60; dir. biochem. sect, Riker Labs, 60-63, assoc. dir. clin. invest, 63-65; v.pres. & dir. biol. res, Calbiochem, 66-71; PRES, MEDIQUEST, 71- Tech. dir, Harvard Labs, 55-60. AAAS; Am. Chem. Soc. Chemistry and biology of mucopolysaccharides; mechanism of action and metabolism; lipid metabolism and coronary heart disease; pharmaceutical research and clinical investigation; new drug design and early human trials. Address: Mediquest, Box 5252, Beverly Hills, CA 90210.

FREEMAN, LESLIE S(HERWOOD), b. Easton, Pa, Dec. 15, 16; m. 43; c. 2. NEUROPSYCHIATRY. B.A, Lafayette Col, 38; M.D, N.Y. Univ, 42. Res. med, Easton Hosp, Pa, 42-44; chief psychiat. serv, William Beaumont Gen. Hosp, 46-47; continued treatment serv, LYONS VET. ADMIN. HOSP, LYONS, N.J, 48-53, chief, 53-57, dir. res. & ed, 57-62, CHIEF OF STAFF, 62- Assoc. clin. prof. psychiat, N.Y. Med. Col, 57-; Rutgers Med. Col, 70- Med.C, 44-47, Capt. Am. Med. Asn; fel. Am. Psychiat. Address: 495 Anlee Rd, Somerville, NJ 08876.

FREEMAN, MARK P(HILLIPS), b. Palembang, Sumatra, June 9, 28; m. 49; c. 5. PHYSICAL CHEMISTRY. B.S, Washington (Seattle), 53, Nat. Sci. Found. fel, 54-56, Ph.D.(chem), 56. Instr. chem, Washington (Seattle), 56; California, 56-58; res. chemist, AM. CYANAMID CO, 58-64, sr. res. chemist, 64-65, RES. ASSOC, 65- Corporate sr. educ. award, Electrophys. Inst. Munich Tech. Univ, 63-64; vis. prof. chem. eng, Mass. Inst. Technol, 67-68. U.S.A.F, 46-49, 50-51, 1st Lt. Am. Chem. Soc; Am. Phys. Soc. Statistical mechanics of long range forces; chemistry of extremely high temperatures; plasma state; infrared photolysis. Address: New Process Dept, American Cyanamid Co, 1937 W. Main St, Stamford, CN 06904.

FREEMAN, M(AX) J(AMES), b. Columbus, Ohio, Aug. 28, 34; m. 59; c. 3. IMMUNOBIOLOGY, IMMUNOPATHOLOGY. D.V.M, Auburn, 58; M.S, Wisconsin, 60, Ph.D.(vet. sci. path), 61. Ralston-Purina Co. res. fel, 59-60; Vet. Med. Asn. res. fel, 60-61; asst. prof, Ohio Agr. Exp. Sta, 61-62; fel. microbiol, Western Reserve, 62-63, U.S. Pub. Health Serv. fel. immunol, 63-64; asst. prof. microbiol, Univ. Kans, 64-67; assoc. prof. vet. microbiol, PURDUE UNIV, 67-70; PROF. IMMUNOL, 70- Am. Vet. Med. Asn; Am. Soc. Microbiol; Am. Asn. Immunol; Am. Soc; Exp. Path. Antibody biosynthesis; function and heterogeneity; immunologic mechanisms in disease. Address: Dept. of Veterinary Microbiology & Pathology, Purdue University, West Lafayette, IN 47907.

FREEMAN, MILTON M(ALCOLM) R(OLAND), Anthrop, Ecol, see Suppl. I to 11th ed, Soc. & Behav. Vols.

FREEMAN, MONROE E(DWARD), b. Washington, D.C, Apr. 1, 06; m. 29; c. 2. BIOCHEMISTRY. B.S, Minnesota, 28, M.S, 29, Ph.D.(biochem), 31. Instr. chem, Arizona, 29-30; asst. prof. biochem, Maine, 30-36; res. prof. chem, Massachusetts, 36-42, prof, 45-47; chief dept. biochem, Walter Reed Army Inst. Res, Med. Serv. Corps, U.S. Army, 48-53, asst. chief, Off. Surg. Gen, 49-54, chief biol. med. sci. br, off. chief res. & develop, 53-56, commanding officer European Res. Off, 56-60, asst. chief, basic sci. sect, adv. res. proj. agency, Off. Secy. Defense, 60-61; DIR. SCI. INFO. EXCHANGE, SMITHSONIAN INST, 61- From pres. to secy, int. cmn. clin. chem, Int. Union Pure & Appl. Chem, 54-62; pres, Int. Fedn. Clin. Chem, 58-62; chmn. cmt. clin. chem, Nat. Acad. Sci-Nat. Res. Coun, 62- Dipl. & Dir. Am. Bd. Clin. Chem. Sanit.C, U.S.A, 42-45; Med.Serv.C, 45-61, Col. AAAS; Am. Chem. Soc. Clinical chemistry; research program management; scientific information. Address: Science Information Exchange, Smithsonian Institution, 1730 M St. N.W, Washington, DC 20036.

FREEMAN, MYRON L, b. Fergus Falls, Minn, Nov. 2, 30; m. 57; c. 3. PLANT TAXONOMY. B.S, Moorhead State Col, 57; Univ. Minn, summers, 57 & 62; M.S, Univ. N.Dak, 62; D.Agr.(bot), Univ. North. Colo, 70. Instr. BIOL, Univ. N.Dak, 60-62; PROF, DICKINSON STATE COL, 62- Guest prof, Univ. N.Dak, summer 64. U.S.A.F. Identification of western North Dakota plants, especially grasses. Address: 959 Park Ave, Dickinson, ND 58601.

FREEMAN, NEIL JULIAN, b. Jersey City, N.J, Nov. 25, 39; m. 62; c. 2. STRUCTURAL MECHANICS, APPLIED MATHEMATICS. B.S, Univ. Miami, 62, Nat. Sci. Found. fels, 63 & 64, NASA traineeship, 64-65, M.S, 65; Ph.D. (theoret. & appl. mech), Northwest. Univ, 66. Structural engr, M.H. Connell Assoc, summers 62 & 63; asst. prof. CIVIL ENG, UNIV. MIAMI, 66-69, ASSOC. PROF, 70- Prin. investr, Nat. Sci. Found. res. initiation grant, 68-69, res. grant, 70-; Nat. Comt. Vehicle Crashworthiness, Dept. Transportation, 68- Am. Soc. Civil Eng. Analytical studies of load transfer, cracks and stress concentrations in composite materials, within the scope of classical elasticity; mixed boundary value problems in elasticity; multidisciplinary vehicle accident investigation. Address: Dept. of Civil Engineering, University of Miami, Coral Gables, FL 33124.

FREEMAN, NORMAN K(EITH), b. Greeley, Colo, Feb. 25, 16; m. 42; c. 3. PHYSICAL CHEMISTRY. A.B, Colo. State Col, 35; Ph.D.(chem), California, 49. Jr. chemist, U.S. Customs Lab, 38-41; Shell Develop. Co, 41-46; asst. chem, UNIV. CALIF, BERKELEY, 46-49, chemist, DIV. MED. PHYSICS, 49-69, RES. ASSOC, 69- Am. Chem. Soc; Am. Oil Chem. Soc; Coblentz Soc. Infrared spectroscopy; molecular structure; lipide chemistry. Address: Donner Lab, University of California, Berkeley, CA 94720.

FREEMAN, PAUL J(OEL), b. Minneapolis, Minn, Sept. 26, 17; m. 54; c. 1. PHYSIOLOGY. A.B, Stanford, 47, fel. & M.A, 48, fel. & Ph.D.(biol), 52. Instr. physiol. & anat, SAN JOSE STATE COL, 51-58, assoc. prof. PHYSIOL, 58-62, PROF, 62- Med.C, U.S.A, 43-46. Photobiology; blood coagulation in invertebrates; comparative physiology of invertebrates. Address: 2146 Mangin Way, San Jose, CA 95122.

FREEMAN, PETER K(ENT), b. Modesto, Calif, Nov. 25, 31; m. 55; c. 4. ORGANIC CHEMISTRY. B.S, Univ. Calif, 53; Ph.D.(chem), Univ. Colo, 58. Res. technologist, Shell Oil Co, 58; res. assoc. org. chem, Pa. State Univ, 58-59; asst. prof. CHEM, Univ. Idaho, 59-62, assoc. prof, 62-65, PROF, 65-68; ORE. STATE UNIV, 68- Am. Chem. Soc. Rearrangements; reaction mechanisms. Address: Dept. of Chemistry, Oregon State University, Corvallis, OR 97331.

FREEMAN, R(AOUL) J(AMES), b. Vienna, Austria, May 15, 33; U.S. citizen; m. 61; c. 3. OPERATIONS RESEARCH, ECONOMICS. B.A, Brooklyn Col, 54; Sci. Res. Coun. fel, Mass. Inst. Technol, 54-55, Ramo-Wooldridge fel, 56, Ph.D.(opers. res, indust. econ), 57. Mathematician and proj. dir, C-E-I-R, Inc, 57-61; tech. dir, Researnalysis Corp, 61-63; mgr, space systs. proj, Rand Corp, 63-65; bus. studies & spec. progs, Gen. Elec. Co, 65-68; PRES. SYSTS. APPLNS, INC, BEVERLY HILLS, 68- Lectr, Univ. Calif, Los Angeles, 58-59, 61-62; vis. prof, Stanford Univ, 67; Oper. Res. Soc. Am. vis. lectr. prog, 68-; lectr, statewide lect. series, Univ. Calif, 69; fels, Nat. Sci. Found, Gen. Elec. Swope, Social Sci. Res. Coun. AAAS; Inst. Elec. & Electronics Eng; Asn. Comput. Mach; Oper. Res. Soc. Am; Inst. Mgt. Sci; Am. Inst. Aeronaut. & Astronaut. Operations research; computer science; economics; environmental control; corporate planning and management; space sciences. Address: 10563 Lindbrook Dr, Los Angeles, CA 90024.

FREEMAN, RAYMOND, b. Long Eaton, Eng, Jan. 6, 32; m. 58; c. 5. PHYSICAL CHEMISTRY. B.A, Oxford, 55, M.A. & D.Phil.(nuclear magnetic resonance), 57. Engr, French Atomic Energy Cmn, 57-59; sr. sci. officer, Nat. Phys. Lab, 59-61; res. fel. nuclear magnetic resonance, instrument div, Varian Assocs, 61-62; sr. sci. officer, Nat. Phys. Lab, Eng, 62-63; MGR. NUCLEAR MAGNETIC RESONANCE BASIC RES, INSTRUMENT DIV, VARIAN ASSOCS, 64- R.A.F, 50-51. Nuclear magnetic resonance spectroscopy; double irradiation techniques and relaxation time studies; Fourier transform spectroscopy; nuclear spin echoes. Address: 271 W. Floresta Way, Menlo Park, Calif. 94025.

FREEMAN, REINO S(AMUEL), b. Virginia, Minn, Aug. 20, 19; m. 50. HELMINTHOLOGY, PARASITOLOGY. B.S, Duluth State Col, 42; M.A, Univ. Minn, 48, Ph.D.(zool), 50. Asst. prof. zool, South. Ill. Univ, 50-52; asst. prof. PARASITOL, UNIV. TORONTO, 52-59, assoc. prof, 59-65, PROF, 65- Sr. res. fel, Ont. Res. Found, 52-64, sr. res. scientist, 64-66, consult, 66-; Fulbright grant, Finland, 63-64. U.S.N.R, 42-45, Lt. Am. Soc. Parasitol; Am. Micros. Soc; Wildlife Disease Asn; Can. Soc. Zool. Taxonomy and life history of cestodes, trematodes and nematodes; life history and ecology of parasitic helminths; parasites of man. Address: Dept. of Parasitology, School of Hygiene, University of Toronto, Toronto 181, Can.

FREEMAN, RICHARD B, b. Allentown, Pa, July 24, 31; m. 54; c. 3. INTERNAL MEDICINE, NEPHROLOGY. B.S, Franklin & Marshall Col, 53; M.D, Jefferson Med. Col, 57. Intern, Pa. Hosp, Phila, 57-58, fel. hypertension, 58-59, resident med, 59-61; fels. NEPHROLOGY, med. ctr, Georgetown Univ, 61 & 63-64, instr, 64-67; asst. prof, MED. CTR, UNIV. ROCHESTER, 67-69, ASSOC. PROF, 69- Consult, hosp. & med. facilities div, U.S. Pub. Health Serv, 67-; mem, Nat. Adv. Comt. Artificial Kidney Chronic Uremia Prog, Nat. Insts. Arthritis & Metab. Diseases, 69-; pres, Nat. Kidney Found, 70- U.S.P.H.S, 63-67, Sr. Surg. AAAS; Am. Fedn. Clin. Res; Am. Heart Asn; Am. Soc. Artificial Internal Organs; Am. Soc. Nephrology; fel. Am. Col. Physicians; Am. Med. Asn. Pathogenesis and course of chronic renal disease; performance characteristics of artificial kidneys; cation metabolism. Address: University of Rochester, Medical Center, Rochester, NY 14620.

FREEMAN, ROBERT C(LARENCE), b. Harrellsville, N.C, Oct. 14, 27; m. 54. ORGANIC CHEMISTRY. B.S, N.C. Col, Durham, 50, M.S, 52; Parke Davis fel, Wayne State, 52-53, Res. Corp. fel, 53-55, U.S. Pub. Health Serv. fel, 55-56, Ph.D.(chem), 56. Res. chemist, Monsanto Chem. Co, 56-62; mem. faculty, Agr. & Tech. Col. N.C, 62-64; RES. CHEMIST, MONSANTO CHEM. CO, 64- Am. Chem. Soc. Acyloin condensation; ketenimine chemistry; epoxyether chemistry; reactions of phosphorous compounds with alpha halocarbonyl compounds; reactions of enamines; synthesis of radioactive compounds. Address: 4647 Penrose St, St. Louis, MO 63115.

FREEMAN, ROBERT D(AVID), b. Nicholson, Ga, Feb. 7, 30; m. 57; c. 2. PHYSICAL CHEMISTRY. B.S, N.Ga. Col, 48; M.S, Purdue, 52, Ph.D.(chem), 54. Phys. chemist, Goodyear Atomic Corp, 54-55; asst. prof. CHEM, OKLA. STATE UNIV, 55-59, ASSOC. PROF, 59- U.S.A.R, 49-63, 1st Lt. AAAS; Am. Chem. Soc; Am. Phys. Soc; Am. Asn. Physics Teachers; Brit. Chem. Soc. Vaporization phenomena and chemistry at high temperatures; molecular flow of rarefied gases; thermochemistry; calorimetry; information theory and thermodynamics. Address: Dept. of Chemistry, Oklahoma State University, Stillwater, OK 74075.

FREEMAN, ROBERT G(LEN), b. Kerrville, Tex, Feb. 3, 27; m. 50; c. 4. PATHOLOGY. M.D, Baylor Univ, 49. Instr. anat, col. med, Baylor Univ, 50-52; Med. Field Serv. Sch, Ft. Sam Houston, 52-54; asst. prof. med. br, Univ. Tenn, 54-55; res. & asst. surg, Vet. Admin. Hosp, 55-56; res. & instr. path, affiliated hosps, Baylor Univ, 57-59, asst. prof, col. med, 59-64, assoc. prof, 64-68; PROF, 68-70; PATH. & INTERNAL MED, UNIV. TEX.(SOUTHWEST) MED. SCH. DALLAS, 70- Consult. dermat, Brooke Army Hosp, Ft. Sam Houston, Tex. Med.C. Res, 50-54, 1st Lt. Am. Med. Asn; Col. Am. Path; Am. Soc. Clin. Path; Am. Acad. Dermat; Am. Soc. Dermatopath; Am. Dermatol. Asn; Soc. Invest. Dermat; Am. Fedn. Clin. Res; Int. Acad. Path. Dermatopathology; effects of ultraviolet on the skin. Address: Dept. of Pathology, University of Texas (Southwestern) Medical School, 5323 Harry Hines Blvd, Dallas, TX 75235.

FREEMAN, ROBERT S, U.S. citizen. MATHEMATICS. B.A.E, N.Y. Univ, 47; Ph.D.(math), Univ. Calif, Berkeley, 59. Mathematician, Lawrence Radiation Lab, 58-62; asst. prof. MATH, Univ. Md, 62-65, ASSOC. PROF, 65-67; UNIV. ORE, 67- Nat. Sci. Found. grant, 63-65. Am. Math. Soc; Math. Asn. Am. Spectral and operation theoretic structure of elliptic boundary value problems. Address: Dept. of Mathematics, University of Oregon, Eugene, OR 97403.

FREEMAN, SALLIE B(OINEAU), b. Ft. Benning, Ga, Oct. 4, 40; m. 62; c. 1. DEVELOPMENTAL BIOLOGY. B.A, Agnes Scott Col, 62; M.S, Emory Univ, 64, Nat. Sci. Found. fel. & Ph.D.(develop. biol), 67. NAT. INSTS. HEALTH FEL. DEVELOP. BIOL. & INSTR, ANAT, UNIV. FLA, 68- Am. Soc. Zool. Nucleocytoplasmic relationships in embryology; fertilization. Address: Dept. of Anatomy, Institute of Anatomical Science, University of Florida, Gainesville, FL 32601.

FREEMAN, S(MITH), b. Joplin, Mo, Aug. 14, 06; m. 37; c. 3. BIOCHEMISTRY. B.A, Park Col, 28; M.S, Northwestern, 30, Ph.D.(biochem), 33, Nat. Res. Coun. fel, 33-34, univ. fel, 34-40, M.D, 38. Asst. biochem, med. sch, Northwestern, 28-33, instr, sch. dent, 34-37, univ, 39-40, asst. prof, 40-42, assoc. prof, 42-45, prof, 45-46; head biochem. sect, Mayo clin, 46-47; prof. exp. med, MED. SCH, NORTHWEST. UNIV, 47-51, prof. BIOCHEM. & chmn. dept, 51-69, EMER. PROF, 69- Consult, Children's Mem. Hosp, 42-46, 47-; Chicago Wesley Mem. Hosp, 47-; sr. consult, Vet. Admin. Hosp, Hines, 45-46, 47-, dir. res, 47-58; mem. staff, Passavant Mem. Hosp, 47-; consult, G.D. Searle & Co, 68- Dir, chem. warfare proj, Off. Sci. Res. & Develop, 41-44. Am. Phys. Soc; Am. Chem. Soc; Am. Soc. Internal Med; Am. Med. Asn. Medical biochemistry; biochemical studies on animals and patients concerned with metabolism and endocrine function; calcium. Address: Route 1, Lyndon Station, WI 53944.

FREEMAN, STANLEY K(NOEL), b. New York, N.Y, May 6, 18; m. 44; c. 3. ORGANIC CHEMISTRY. B.S, Polytech. Inst. Brooklyn, 40, M.S, 45, Ph.D, 50. Textile chemist, Sandoz Chem. Works, 40-42; chemist, chem. warfare dept, U.S. Army, 42-44; chief chemist, Benzol Prod. Co, 44-61; proj. leader instrumental res. group, res. dept, INT. FLAVORS & FRAGRANCES, INC, 61-68, GROUP LEADER, RES. CTR, 68- AAAS; Am. Chem. Soc; Am. Entom. Soc; Soc. Appl. Spectros; Am. Soc. Test. & Mat; Am. Inst. Biol. Sci. Elucidation of structure of natural products; organic molecular spectroscopy; pheromones and physiological effects of odor. Address: 18 Juniper Way, Springfield, NJ 07081.

FREEMAN, THEO(DORE) R(USSELL), b. West Plains, Mo, Dec. 13, 06; m. 34; c. 1. DAIRYING. B.S, Kans. State Col, 29; M.S, Okla. Agr. & Mech. Col, 33; Ph.D.(dairy mfg), Pa. State Col, 37. Asst. buttermaker, Wash. County Co-op. Creamery, Kans, 29-30; instr. high sch, Mo, 30-32; asst, Okla. Agr. & Mech. Col, 32-33; gen. plant work, Quality Milk Prods. Co, Okla, 33-34; ice cream maker, Banner Ice Cream Co, 34-35; asst, Pa. State Col, 35-37; instr. dairy husb, Agr. & Mech. Col. Texas, 37-38, asst. prof, 38-39, assoc. prof, 39-41; assoc. dairy mfrs, dairy prods. lab, Exp. Sta, Florida, 41-46; mgr, Sunshine Dairy Prods, Inc, Fla, 46-48; assoc. prof. DAIRY MFG, UNIV. KY, 48-52, PROF, 52- AAAS; Inst. Food Tech; Am. Dairy Sci. Asn; Int. Asn. Milk & Food Sanit. Storage of dairy products; composition of milk; cheese production; freezing point of milk. Address: Dept. of Animal Sciences, University of Kentucky, Lexington, KY 40506.

FREEMAN, T(HOMAS) E(DWARD), b. Laurel, Miss, Jan. 29, 30; m. 53; c. 2. PLANT PATHOLOGY. B.S, Millsaps Col, 52; M.S, La. State, 54, Ph.D. (plant path), 56. Asst, La. State, 52-56; asst. plant pathologist, UNIV. FLA, 56-63, assoc. plant pathologist, 63-68, PLANT PATHOLOGIST & PROF. PLANT PATH, 68- Am. Phytopath. Soc. Grass diseases; chemical nature of plant diseases; nature of disease resistance in plants. Address: Dept. of Plant Pathology, University of Florida, Gainesville, FL 32601.

FREEMAN, THOMAS J, b. Miami, Fla, Sept. 30, 32; m. 55; c. 2. GEOLOGY. B.S, Univ. Ark, 56, M.S, 57; Ph.D.(geol), Univ. Tex, 62. Jr. geologist, Standard Oil Co. Ohio, 57-58; asst. prof. geol, Univ. Mo, 62-63; field geologist, Ark. Geol. Comn, 63-64; asst. prof. GEOL, UNIV. MO-COLUMBIA, 64-67, ASSOC. PROF, 67- Vis. prof, Univ. Madrid, 69-70; leader, Int. Field Inst, Spain, 71. U.S.M.C, 50-52, Sgt. Am. Asn. Petrol. Geol; Geol. Soc. Am; Soc. Econ. Paleont. & Mineral.(best paper award, 71). Economic aspects of the genesis and diagenesis of carbonate rocks. Address: Dept. of Geology, University of Missouri-Columbia, Columbia, MO 65201.

FREEMAN, T(HOMAS) N(ESBITT), b. Saskatoon, Sask, Oct. 16, 11; m. 38; c. 2. AGRICULTURE. B.S.A, Ont. Agr. Col, 34; M.S, Colorado, 36; Ph.D. (zool), Toronto, 46. Investr, CAN. DEPT. AGR, 35, AGR. SCIENTIST, 35-, co-ordinator north. insect surv, 47-59. Assoc. ed, Biol. Abstracts, 40-41. Entom. Soc. Can. Systematics of Lepidoptera. Address: R.R. 2, Ottawa, Ont, Can.

FREEMAN, THOMAS PATRICK, b. Denver, Colo, Aug. 14, 38; m. 63; c. 2. PLANT ANATOMY & MORPHOLOGY. B.A, Colo. State Univ, 62, M.A, Colo. State Col, 63; Ph.D.(plant anat), Arizona State, 68. Instr. bot, Foothill Col, 63-65; teaching asst, Arizona State, 65-68; ASST. PROF. ANAT, N.DAK. STATE UNIV, 68- Nat. Sci. Found. Instnl. grant, 69. Am. Inst. Biol. Sci; Bot. Soc. Am; Int. Soc. Plant Morphol. Developmental anatomy of the Cactaceae. Address: Dept. of Botany, North Dakota State University, Fargo, ND 58102.

FREEMAN, V(ERNE) C(RAWFORD), b. Bentonville, Ind, Dec. 25, 00; m. 26; c. 1. AGRICULTURAL EDUCATION. B.S.A, Purdue, 23, M.S.A, 26. Teacher, pub. sch, Ind, 23-25; instr. animal husb. & asst. to dean, PURDUE UNIV, 26-35, asst. dean, 35-39, asst. prof. animal husb, 38-42, prof, 42-69, assoc. dean, 39-69, dir. resident instr, SCH. AGR, 58-69, EMER. DIR. RESIDENT INSTR, 69- Consult, Bd. Fundamental Educ; mem. Am. Coun. Educ. Farm Econ. Asn; Am. Soc. Animal Sci. Agricultural personnel and guidance programs. Address: Room 211B, Agricultural Administration Bldg, Purdue University, Lafayette, IN 47907.

FREEMAN, WALTER J(ACKSON), III, b. Wash, D.C, Jan. 30, 27; m. 52; c. 7. PHYSIOLOGY. M.D, Yale, 54. Intern path, Yale, 54-55; med, hosp, Hopkins, 55-56; asst. res. physiologist, California, Los Angeles, 56-59; asst. prof. physiol, UNIV. CALIF, BERKELEY, 59-62, assoc. prof, 62-67, PROF. PHYSIOL. & CHMN. DEPT. PHYSIOL-ANAT, 67- Fels, U.S. Pub. Health Serv, Univ. Calif, Los Angeles, 56-58, Found. Fund Res. Psychiat, 58-60 & Guggenheim, 65-66. U.S.N.R, 45-46. Neurophysiology. Address: Dept. of Physiology, University of California, Berkeley, CA 94720.

FREEMON, FRANK REED, b. Bloomington, Ill, July 18, 38; m. 66. NEUROLOGY. M.D, Univ. Fla, 65. Clin. fel. neurol, Univ. Fla, 66-69; res. fel. sleep, Wash. Univ, 69-70; ASST. PROF. NEUROL, MARQUETTE SCH. MED, 70- U.S.N, 56-60. AAAS; Am. Acad. Neurol; Asn. Psychophysiol. Study Sleep. Sleep research; clinical neurology; function of sleep; brain function. Address: Dept. of Neurology, Marquette School of Medicine, Milwaukee, WI 53226.

FREER, RICHARD J(OHN), b. Poughkeepsie, N.Y, June 2, 42. PHARMACOLOGY. B.A, Marist Col, 64; U.S. Pub. Health Serv. grant & Ph.D. (pharmacol), Columbia Univ, 69. INSTR. BIOCHEM, SCH. MED, UNIV. COLO, DENVER, 69- Investigation of the role of intracellular proteases in the formation and degradation of vasoactive peptide during inflammation; synthesis of analogs of vasoactive peptides to study peptide-receptor interactions; study and synthesis of inhibitors of peptide hormones. Address: Dept. of Biochemistry, University of Colorado School of Medicine, Denver, CO 80220.

FREER, STEPHAN T, b. Akron, Ohio, May 14, 33; m. 59; c. 2. BIOCHEMISTRY, PHYSICAL CHEMISTRY. A.B, California, Berkeley, 59; Ph.D.(biochem), Washington (Seattle), 64. Asst. specialist, chem, UNIV. CALIF, SAN DIEGO, 64-67, ASST. RES. CHEMIST, 67- U.S.N, 52-56. AAAS; Am. Crystallog. Asn; Am. Chem. Soc. Structure and function of biologically significant macromolecules. Address: Dept. of Chemistry, University of California, San Diego, P.O. Box 109, La Jolla, CA 92037.

FREERKS, MARSHALL C(ORNELIUS), b. Wahpeton, N.Dak, Sept. 2, 12; m. 41; c. 3. ORGANIC CHEMISTRY. B.A, Carleton Col, 39, Ph.D.(chem), 49. Org. chemist & res. group leader, MONSANTO CO, 49-61, SCIENTIST, 61- U.S.N.R, 39-45, Capt. Am. Chem. Soc. Fundamental nature of catalysis as a function of atomic structure; physical nature of atomic structure; nature of the chemical bond. Address: Research Division, Monsanto Co, 1700 S. Second St, St. Louis, MO 63104.

FREESE, ERNST, b. Dusseldorf, Ger, Sept. 27, 25; m. 56; c. 2. BIOLOGY. Vordipl, Heidelberg, 48; dipl, Göttingen, 51, Ph.D.(physics), 53. Res. fel. physics, Max Planck Inst, Göttingen, 53-54; inst. nuclear studies, Chicago, 54; biol, Calif. Inst. Tech, 55-56; biophysics, Purdue, 57; biol, Harvard, 57-59; assoc. prof. genetics, Wisconsin, 59-62; CHIEF LAB. MOLECULAR BIOL, NAT. INST. NEUROL. DISEASES & STROKE, 62- Biophys. Soc; Genetics Soc. Am; Am. Soc. Biol. Chem; Am. Soc. Microbiol. Quantum theory; molecular mechanisms of mutation; recombination; genetic function and differentiation. Address: Lab. of Molecular Biology, National Institute of Neurological Diseases & Stroke, Bldg. 36, Bethesda, MD 20014.

FREESE, L(EONARD) R(OY), b. Gaylord, Kans, Feb. 3, 06. BIOLOGY. B.A, Colorado, 32, M.A, 40; Ph.D.(bot), Northwestern, 51. Teacher, pub. schs, Kans, 23-28, 32-33; instr, Ark. State Agr. & Mech. Col, Jonesboro, 33-34; teacher, pub. sch, Colo, 34-39; instr. biol, Tex. Mil. Col, 40-42; Nat. Col. Educ.(Ill), 45-48; from asst. prof. to prof, Houston, 48-58; with Independent Sch. Syst, Houston, 58-60; prof. BIOL, ALASKA METHODIST UNIV, 60-71, EMER. PROF, 71- Med.C, U.S.N, 42-45. AAAS; Phycol. Soc. Am. Diatoms. Address: Dept. of Biology, Alaska Methodist University, Anchorage, AK 99504.

FREESE, RAYMOND WILLIAM, b. Foristell, Mo, Dec. 17, 34; m. 57; c. 3. MATHEMATICS. B.S, Missouri, 56 & 58, Gregory fel, Nat. Sci. Found. coop. & summer fels, 58-61, M.A, 58, Ph.D.(math), 61. Asst. prof. MATH, ST. LOUIS UNIV, 61-64, assoc. prof, 64-67, PROF, 67-, CHMN. DEPT, 71- Am. Math. Soc; Math. Asn. Am. Distance geometry. Address: Dept. of Mathematics, St. Louis University, 221 N. Grand Ave, St. Louis, MO 63103.

FREESE, UWE ERNST, b. Bordesholm, Ger, May 11, 25; U.S. citizen; m. 61; c. 1. OBSTETRICS & GYNECOLOGY. M.D, Univ. Kiel, 52. Instr. & res. assoc. obstet, gynec. & path, Univ. Chicago Lying-in-Hosp, 59-61, asst. prof, 61-66; ASSOC. PROF. OBSTET. & GYNEC, CHICAGO MED. SCH, 66- Consult, Chicago Lying-in-Hosp. & Billings Hosp, Chicago, 64- Fel. Am. Col. Obstet. & Gynec. Human placentology; problems concerning Rh sensitization; gynecological, obstetric and fetal pathology. Address: Chicago Lying-in-Hospital, 5841 S. Maryland Ave, Chicago, IL 60637.

FREESTON, W. DENNEY, JR, b. Orange, N.J, May 8, 36; m. 57; c. 2. MECHANICAL ENGINEERING, TEXTILES. B.S, Princeton, 57, M.S, 58, M.A, 59, Textile Res. Inst. fel, 58-60, Ph.D.(mech. eng), 61. Asst, Princeton, 57-58; sr. res. assoc. textile mech, Fabric Res. Labs, Inc, Dedham, 60-65, asst. dir. appl. mech, 65-69, assoc. dir, 69-71; PROF. A. FRENCH TEXTILE SCH, GA. INST. TECHNOL, 71- Fiber Soc.(award distinguished achievement, 69); Am. Soc. Test. & Mat. Mechanics of flexible fibrous structures; fabric flammability. Address: 2765 Joel Pl, Doraville, GA 30340.

FREEZE, ROY ALLAN, b. Edmonton, Alta, May 23, 39; m. 61; c. 4. HYDROLOGY. B.Sc, Queen's Univ, 61; M.Sc, Univ. Calif, Berkeley, 64, Ph.D.(hydrol), 66. Res. scientist, Inland Waters Br, Can. Dept. Energy, Mines & Resources, 61-69; RES. STAFF MEM. HYDROL, THOMAS J. WATSON RES. CTR, IBM CORP, 70- Am. Geophys. Union; Geol. Soc. Am. Computer simulation of regional groundwater flow systems and hydrologic response models. Address: IBM Corp, Thomas J. Watson Research Center, P.O. Box 218, Yorktown Heights, NY 10598.

FREGEAU, JEROME H(EYDE), b. Columbus, Ohio, May 16, 29; m. 59; c. 3. NUCLEAR PHYSICS. B.S, Yale, 51; Ph.D.(physics), Stanford Univ, 56. Instr. physics, Univ. Mich, 56-59; nuclear physicist, U.S. Off. Naval Res, 59-62, head nuclear physics br, 62-64; prog. dir. elem. particle facilities, NAT. SCI. FOUND, 64-67, asst. for spec. projs. to assoc. dir. res, 67-70, EXEC. ASST. TO DEP. ASST. DIR. RES, 70- Am. Phys. Soc. Scattering of high energy electrons. Address: 3715 Forest Grove Dr, Annandale, VA 22003.

FREGLY, MELVIN J(AMES), b. Patton, Pa, May 26, 25; m. 56. PHYSIOLOGY. B.S. & M.S, Bucknell Univ, 49; Ph.D.(physiol), Univ. Rochester, 52. Instr. PHYSIOL, Harvard Med. Sch, 52-56; asst. prof, COL. MED, UNIV. FLA, 56-60, assoc. prof, 60-65, PROF, 65-, ASST. DEAN GRAD. STUDIES, 67- Travel fels, Int. Physiol. Cong, 56, 59, 62; mem. coun. on high blood pressure, Am. Heart Asn; consult, Strasenburgh Pharmaceut. Co, N.Y, 65-67. U.S.A, 43-46. AAAS; Soc. Exp. Biol. & Med; Am. Physiol. Soc; Am. Soc. Zool; Endocrine Soc; Am. Thyroid Asn; Can. Physiol. Soc. Cardiovascular hypertension; temperature regulation; behavioral physiology. Address: Dept. of Physiology, University of Florida College of Medicine, Gainesville, FL 32601.

FREHN, JOHN, b. Shippensburg, Pa, Mar. 17, 36; m. 60; c. 2. PHYSIOLOGY. B.S, Dickinson Col, 58; M.S, Pa. State, 60, univ. fel, 61, Ph.D.(zool), 62. Asst. prof. PHYSIOL, ILL. STATE UNIV, 62-64, assoc. prof, 64-70, PROF, 70- AAAS; Am. Soc. Zool. Cellular metabolism in cold acclimation and hibernation in various species of mammals. Address: Dept. of Biological Sciences, Illinois State University, Normal, IL 61761.

FREI, EMIL, III, b. St. Louis, Mo, Feb. 21, 24; m. 48; c. 5. INTERNAL MEDICINE. M.D, Yale, 48. Intern, univ. hosp, St. Louis, 48-49, res. path, 52-53, internal med, 53-55; from head chemother. serv. to assoc. sci. dir, Nat. Cancer Inst, 55-65; ASSOC. DIR, M.D. ANDERSON HOSP. & TUMOR INST, 65- U.S.N, 43-45, Med.C, 50-52, Lt. Am. Asn. Cancer Res.(pres, 71-72); Am. Soc. Clin. Invest. Biochemistry and biology of clinical cancer chemotherapy. Address: University of Texas M.D. Anderson Hospital & Tumor Institute, Houston, TX 77025.

FREI, J(AROSLAV) V(ACLAV), b. Prague, Czech, Mar. 7, 29; Can. citizen; m. 55; c. 5. PATHOLOGY. M.U.C, Charles Univ, Prague, 49; M.D, C.M, Queen's Univ.(Ont), 56; Life Ins. Med. Res. Fund fel, McGill Univ, 59-61, M.Sc, 60, Nat. Cancer Inst. Can. fel, 61-62, Ph.D.(path), 62. Asst. prof. PATH, McGill Univ, 63-66; cancer res. lab, UNIV. WEST. ONT, 66-70, ASSOC. PROF, 70- Nat. Cancer Inst. Can. res. assoc, 63-66; Eleanor Roosevelt fel, Med. Res. Coun. Toxicol. Unit, U.K, 66. Am. Asn. Cancer Res; Am. Soc. Exp. Path; Am. Soc. Cell Biol; Can. Soc. Cell Biol; Can. Asn. Path. Experimental two stage epidermal carcinogenesis in mice; nitroso compound carcinogenesis; oncogenic virus activation; computers in medicine. Address: Dept. of Pathology, University of Western Ontario, London 72, Ont, Can.

FREI, ROLAND W, b. Geneva, Switz, Aug. 20, 36; m. 62; c. 2. ANALYTICAL CHEMISTRY. Dipl, Burgdorf-Bern Col, 60; Geneva, 60-61; Ph.D.(chem), Hawaii, 64. Chem. engr, Union Carbide Europe S.A, Geneva, 60-61; instr. chem, Hawaii, 64-65; res. fel, DALHOUSIE UNIV, 65-66, asst. prof. CHEM, 66-70, ASSOC. PROF, 70- Coordinator, Atlantic Prov. Inter-Univ. Cmt. Sci, 65; ed-in-chief, J. Environ. Anal. Chem. Am. Chem. Soc; Swiss Chem. Soc; Chem. Inst. Can. Investigation of adsorption phenomena with reflectance spectroscopy; microanalysis of metals and pesticides by spectroscopic and chromatographic methods and application to pollution problems; preparation and investigation of new metal chelates. Address: Dept. of Chemistry, Dalhousie University, Halifax, N.S, Can.

FREIBERG, GEORGE W(ILLIAM), b. Eitzen, Minn, May 22, 92. PLANT PATHOLOGY, PHYSIOLOGY. B.S, S.Dak. State Col, 13; Lackland fel, Mo. Bot. Garden, 14-16; Ph.D, Washington (St. Louis), 17; LL.B, Benton Col. Law, St. Louis, Mo, 32. Asst. bot, Missouri, 13-14; Mo. Bot. Garden, 16-17; plant supt, Commercial Solvents Corp, Ind, 20-22; instr. bot, Washington (St. Louis), 22-24; city bacteriologist, St. Louis, Mo, 25-27; head, biol. div, res. dept, Buckeye Incubator Co, Ohio, 28-29; dept. microbiol, ANHEUSER-BUSCH, INC, 29-40, COORD, RES. & PATENT INFO, 40- Sanit.C, 17-19, Lt. AAAS; Am. Soc. Microbiol; Am. Water Works Asn. Microbiology; patent law; mosaic diseases; biochemistry. Address: 6352 Alexander Dr, St. Louis, MO 63105.

FREIBERG, LESLIE A(LAN), b. Chicago, Ill, May 29, 36; m. 58; c. 3. ORGANIC CHEMISTRY. B.S, Illinois, 58; Ph.D.(org. chem), Wayne State, 62. Sr. res. scientist, ABBOTT LABS, 62-70, ASSOC. RES. FEL, 70- Am. Chem. Soc. Steroid total synthesis and natural product chemistry; conformational analysis; organic reaction mechanisms. Address: Abbott Labs, Dept. 482, North Chicago, IL 60064.

FREIBERG, S(AMUEL) R(OBERT), b. Staten Island, N.Y, Apr. 14, 24; m. 49; c. 2. PLANT PHYSIOLOGY, BIOLOGY. B.Sc, Rutgers, 48, Ph.D.(plant physiol), 51. Res. assoc. hort, Rutgers, 51-52; plant physiologist, div. trop. res, United Fruit Co, Honduras, 52-57, head plant physiol, cent. res. labs, Mass, 58-60, asst. dir. res, 60-62, dir. labs, 62-65; dir. res, IRI RES. INST, INC, 65-66, V.PRES, 66-, consult, 65. Vis. fel. plant physiol, Cornell Univ, 57-58. C.Eng, U.S.A, 43-46. AAAS; Am. Soc. Plant Physiol; Am. Soc. Hort. Sci; Inst. Food Technol; Asn. Trop. Biol. Host-parasite relationships; nitrogen and urea metabolism; plant nutrition and growth; polyphenols and polyphenoloxidases; post harvest fruit physiology; plant and animal fruit productivity; fruit flavor volatiles. Address: IRI Research Institute, Inc, One Rockefeller Plaza, New York, NY 10020.

FREIBERGER, WALTER F(REDERICK), b. Vienna, Austria, Feb. 20, 24; nat; m. 56; c. 2. APPLIED MATHEMATICS. B.A, Melbourne, 47, M.A, 49; Australian Dept. Supply overseas fel, Cambridge, 50-53, Ph.D.(math), 53. Sci. res. officer, Aeronaut. Res. Lab, Dept. Supply, 47-49, sr. sci. res. off, 53-54; res. assoc, APPL. MATH, BROWN UNIV, 55-56, asst. prof, 56-58, assoc. prof, 58-64, PROF, 64-, DIR. CTR. COMPUT. & INFO. SCI, 68-, comput. lab, 63-68. Tutor, dept. math, Univ. Melbourne, 47-49; Fulbright fel, 55; John Simon Guggenheim Mem. Found. fel, inst. math. statist, Univ. Stockholm, 62-63; managing ed, Quart. Appl. Math, 66-; ed-in-chief, Int. Dictionary Appl. Math. Australian Army, 43-45. Am. Math. Soc; Asn. Comput. Mach; Inst. Math. Statist; Soc. Indust. & Appl. Math. Computer science; computational probability and statistics; pattern recognition. Address: 24 Alumni Ave, Providence, RI 02906.

FREIBURG, RICHARD E(IGHME), b. Milwaukee, Wis, Apr. 2, 23; m. 50; c. 4. ZOOLOGY, ECOLOGY. B.A, Univ. Kans, 49, M.A, 51; Ph.D.(zool), Ore. State Col, 54. Asst. instr. zool, Univ. Kans, 49-51; Ore. State Col, 51-54; asst. prof. BIOL, Washburn Univ. Topeka, 54-57; from asst. prof. to PROF, MacMURRAY COL, 57-, HEAD DEPT, 70- U.S.N, 42-46. Am. Soc. Mammal; Am. Soc. Ichthyol. & Herpet; Ecol. Soc. Am. Herpetology; ecological studies on reptiles and amphibians. Address: Dept. of Biology, MacMurray College, Jacksonville, IL 62650.

FREID, SHELDON H, b. Brooklyn, N.Y, July 28, 39; m. 63; c. 3. INORGANIC & NUCLEAR CHEMISTRY. B.S, Brooklyn Col, 60; M.S, Purdue, 62; Ph.D.(nuclear chem), Fla. State, 66. RES. ASSOC. REACTOR CHEM, OAK RIDGE NAT. LAB, 66- Am. Chem. Soc; Am. Nuclear Soc. Reactor chemistry; nuclear safety and mass spectrometry. Address: 107 Newcrest Lane, Oak Ridge, TN 37830.

FREIDLINE, CHARLES E(UGENE), b. San Francisco, Calif, Oct. 5, 37; m. 60. INORGANIC CHEMISTRY. B.A, Westmont Col, 60; M.S, Minnesota, 63, Ph.D.(inorg. chem), 66. ASSOC. PROF. CHEM, CENT. METHODIST COL, 65- Nat. Acad. Sci. grant. Am. Chem. Soc. Determination of stability constants and structure of complex ions in solution using potentiometric and Raman spectroscopic techniques, especially of group (IV) and organometallic cations. Address: Dept. of Chemistry, Central Methodist College, Fayette, MO 65248.

FREIENMUTH, WILLIAM L(ELAND), b. Tonganoxie, Kans, Aug. 15, 20; m. 43; c. 3. ELECTRICAL ENGINEERING. Radio engr, A.D. Ring & Co, 47-48; engr, VITRO CORP. AM, 48-50, sect. leader, 50-53, group leader, 53-57, asst. dept. head, 57-60, asst. mgr. tech. opers, 60-62, MGR. RES. & DEVELOP. BR, 62- Sig.C, 42-46, Capt. Sr. mem. Inst. Elec. & Electronics Eng. Management and administration research; development; data processing and manufacturing. Address: 22501 Robin Court, Laytonsville, MD 20760.

FREIER, ESTHER F(AY), b. Hibbing, Minn, Mar. 3, 25. PHYSIOLOGICAL CHEMISTRY. B.S, Univ. Minn, 46, M.S, 56. Instr. MED. TECH, UNIV. MINN, MINNEAPOLIS, 51-58, asst. prof, 58-64, assoc. prof, 64-68, PROF, 68-, HOSP. CHEMIST, 57- AAAS; Am. Chem. Soc; Am. Soc. Med. Technol; Am. Asn. Clin. Chem. Clinical chemistry methodology and quality control; proteins and enzymes. Address: Dept. of Lab. Medicine, University of Minnesota, Minneapolis, MN 55455.

FREIER, GEO(RGE) D(AVID), b. Ellsworth, Wis, Jan. 22, 15; m. 43; c. 2. ATMOSPHERIC PHYSICS. B.S, Wis. State Col.(River Falls), 38; M.A, Minnesota, 44, Ph.D.(physics), 49. Res. physicist, Naval Ord. Lab, 44-46; asst. prof. PHYSICS, UNIV. MINN. MINNEAPOLIS, 50-58, from assoc. prof. to PROF, 59- AAAS; Am. Phys. Soc; Am. Asn. Physics Teachers;

Am. Geophys. Union; Am. Meteorol. Soc. Atmospheric electricity. Address: 238 Physics Bldg, University of Minnesota, Minneapolis, MN 55455.

FREIER, HERBERT E(DWARD), b. Delmont, S.Dak, Mar. 19, 21; m. 55; c. 2. ORGANIC CHEMISTRY. B.A, Yankton Col, 43; Ph.D.(org. chem), Illinois, 46. Asst. chem, Illinois, 43-44, spec. asst, 44-46; asst. prof, North Dakota, 46-50, assoc. prof, 50; mem. staff, cent. res, MINN. MINING & MFG. CO, 50-54, supvr. anal. sect, 54-55, org. sect, 55-57, sect. leader, tech. info. serv, 57-60, MGR. RES. SERV, 60- Civilian with Off. Sci. Res. & Develop, 44. Am. Chem. Soc. Organic synthesis and analysis. Address: 3M Center, P.O. Box 33221, St. Paul, MN 55133.

FREIER, J(EROME) B(ERNARD), b. N.Y.C, May 6, 16. MATHEMATICS. B.S, City Col, 39; Ph.D.(math), N.Y. Univ, 58. Asst. physics, N.Y. Univ, 47-49; instr. MATH, St. Peter's Col, 50-53; asst. prof, Rensselaer Polytech, 53-65; ASSOC. PROF, SOUTHEAST. MASS. UNIV, 65- AAAS; Am. Phys. Soc; Am. Math. Soc. Analysis; applied mathematics. Address: Dept. of Mathematics, Southeastern Massachusetts University, North Dartmouth, MA 02747.

FREIER, PHYLLIS S, b. Minneapolis, Minn, Jan. 19, 21; m. 43; c. 2. PHYSICS. B.S, Minnesota, 42, M.A, 44, Ph.D.(physics), 50. Physicist, Naval Ord. Lab, 44-45; res. assoc. PHYSICS, UNIV. MINN, MINNEAPOLIS, 50-70, ASSOC. PROF, 70- AAAS; Am. Astron. Soc; Am. Geophys. Union; fel. Am. Phys. Soc. Cosmic rays. Address: Dept. of Physics, University of Minnesota, Minneapolis, MN 55455.

FREIFELDER, DAVID, b. Phila, Pa, July 19, 35; m. 65; c. 2. MOLECULAR BIOLOGY. B.S, Chicago, 57, Ph.D.(biophys), 59. Physicist, Diamond Ord. Fuze Lab, 56-58; res. assoc. biophys, Mass. Inst. Tech, 60-61; U.S. Pub. Health Serv. fel, Univ. Inst. Microbiol, Copenhagen, 62; res. assoc. biophysics, Mass. Inst. Tech, 63; Donner Lab, California, Berkeley, 63-66; U.S. PUB. HEALTH SERV. CAREER DEVELOP. AWARD, BRANDEIS UNIV, 66-, ASSOC. PROF. BIOCHEM, 70- Synthesis and physical properties of nucleic acids. Address: Dept. of Biochemistry, Brandeis University, Waltham, MA 02154.

FREIFELDER, MORRIS, b. Phila, Pa, Jan. 23, 07; m. 28; c. 1. ORGANIC CHEMISTRY. Temple. Anal. chemist, Abbott Labs, 26-37, org. res. chemist, sulfa drugs & related compounds, 37-45, in charge pressure lab, org. res. dept, 45-58, supvr. chem. autoclave res, 58-67, CONSULT. IN HYDROGENATION, 67- Am. Chem. Soc. Investigation in catalytic hydrogenations and pressure type reactions. Address: 9 Captain Parker Arms, Lexington, MA 02173.

FREILICH, GERALD, b. Brooklyn, N.Y, Dec. 29, 26; m. 53; c. 2. MATHEMATICS. B.S, City Col, 46; M.S, Brown, 47, Ph.D.(math), 49. Asst. MATH, Brown, 46-48, instr, 49-50; City Col. New York, 50-54, asst. prof, 54-60, assoc. prof, 60-67, prof, 67-71, chmn. dept, 66-70; PROF, QUEENS COL. (N.Y), 71- U.S.N.R, 45, Lt.(jg). Am. Math. Soc; Math. Asn. Am. Measure theory; theory of convex sets; operations research. Address: 1619 E. 21st St, Brooklyn, NY 11210.

FREILICH, JOSEPH K(ENNETH), b. Chicago, Ill, Feb. 10, 18; m. 46; c. 3. INTERNAL MEDICINE. Asst. prof, MED, Chicago Med. Sch, 48-49, ASSOC. PROF, 59-71; STRITCH SCH. MED, LOYOLA UNIV, 71-; ATTEND. PHYSICIAN & DIR, DEPT. OF INHALATION THERAPY & PULMONARY PHYSIOL. LAB, ST. JOSEPH HOSP, 71- Assoc. med, Mt. Sinai Hosp, 54-71; adj, chest dept, Michael Reese Hosp, 51-59, attend. physician, 59-71. Med.C, 42-46, Capt. Fel. Am. Col. Physicians; fel. Am. Col. Chest Physicians. Internal medicine, especially chest diseases. Address: 55 E. Washington St, Suite 1345, Chicago, IL 60602.

FREILING, EDWARD C(LAWSON), b. San Francisco, Calif, Aug. 11, 22; m. 48; c. 7. PHYSICAL & NUCLEAR CHEMISTRY. B.S, San Francisco, 43; M.S, California, 47; Ph.D.(chem), Stanford, 51. Asst. prof. chem, St. Mary's Col. (Calif), 49-51; sr. investigator, U.S. NAVAL Radiol. Defense Lab, 51-68, HEAD, ANAL. BR, WEAPONS LAB, 69- Superior civilian serv. award, Chief Naval Mat, 68. U.S.N.R, 43-46, Lt(jg). Ion exchange; radiochemical analysis: nuclear detonation phenomena; fused salt chemistry: kinetics. Address: U.S. Naval Weapons Lab, Code FCA, Dahlgren, VA 22448.

FREIMAN, CHARLES, b. N.Y.C, June 17, 32; m. 55; c. 4. COMPUTER SCIENCE. A.B, Columbia Univ, 54, B.S, 55, M.S, 56, Sc.D.(eng), 61; Brooklyn Col, 50; N.Y. Univ, 60-61. Instr. elec. eng, Columbia Univ, 56-60; mem. res. staff, T.J. WATSON RES. CTR, IBM CORP, 60-65, develop. engr, systs. develop. div, 65-68, MEM. RES. STAFF COMPUTER SCI, 68- AAAS; Asn. Comput. Mach; Inst. Elec. & Electronic Eng; Int. Fedn. Info. Processing (ed, Info. Processing, 71). Discrete information theory; computer arithmetic; computer system maintainability. Address: Computer Sciences Dept, T.J. Watson Research Center, IBM Corp, Yorktown Heights, NY 10598.

FREIMAN, DAVID G(ALLAND), b. New York, N.Y, July 1, 11; m. 49; c. 2. PATHOLOGY. A.B, City Col. N.Y, 30; M.D, L.I. Col. Med, 35; hon. A.M, Harvard, 62. Intern & res. path, Montefiore Hosp, 38-43; asst. pathologist, Mass. Gen. Hosp, 44-50; asst. prof. PATH, col. med, Cincinnati, 50-52, assoc. prof, 52-56; clin. prof, HARVARD MED. SCH, 56-62, prof, 62-69, MALLINCKRODT PROF, 69-; PATHOLOGIST-IN-CHIEF, BETH ISRAEL HOSP, 56- Instr, med. sch, Tufts Univ, 47 & 48; Harvard Med. Sch, 49 & 50; attend. pathologist, Cincinnati Gen. & Drake Mem. Hosps, 52-56; Vet. Admin. Hosps, Ohio & Ky, 54-56; consult, Boston, 62- AAAS; Am. Soc. Clin. Path; Am. Soc. Exp. Path; Histochem. Soc; Am. Asn. Path. & Bact; Int. Acad. Path; Int. Soc. Thrombosis & Haemostasis. Histochemistry; pulmonary disease; sarcoidosis; cardiovascular and thromboembolic disease. Address: Dept. of Pathology, Beth Israel Hospital, Boston, MA 02215.

FREIMAN, GERALD, b. New York, N.Y, June 11, 22; m. 48; c. 3. PSYCHIATRY. A.B, N.Y. Univ, 43; M.D, Middlesex, 46; cert. psychoanal, State Univ. N.Y, 58. Intern, St. Johns L.I. City Hosp, 46-48; res. neurologist, Goldwater Mem. Hosp, N.Y, 49-50; res. psychiatrist, Kings County Hosp, 50-52; instr. PSYCHIAT, COL. MED, STATE UNIV. N.Y. DOWNSTATE MED. CENTER, 52-55, asst. prof, 55-60, clin. asst. prof, 60-70, CLIN. ASSOC. PROF, 70-, CLIN. ASST. PROF. PSYCHOANAL, DIV. PSYCHOANAL, 60- Asst. vis. neurologist, Goldwater Mem. Hosp, 50-53; asst. vis. psychiatrist, Kings County Hosp, 55-64, dir. psychother. clin, 64-; chief psychiatrist, Kingston Ave. Hosp, N.Y, 55-57. Med.C, Res, 51-, Maj. Fel. Am. Psychiat. Asn; Am. Psychoanal. Asn; Am. Psychosom. Soc; Am. Orthopsychiat. Asn; fel. N.Y. Acad. Med. Psychiatry psychoanalysis. Address: Dept. of Psychiatry, State University of New York Downstate Medical Center, 450 Clarkson Ave, Brooklyn, NY 11203.

FREIMAN, STEPHEN WEIL, b. Alexandria, La, Jan. 21, 42; m. 69. CERAMICS. B.Ch.E, Ga. Inst. Tech, 63, M.S, 66; Ph.D.(metall, mat. eng), Florida, 68. Assoc. res. scientist, IIT Res. Inst, 68-70; MEM. STAFF, OCEAN TECHNOL. DIV, NAVAL RES. LAB, 70- Am. Inst. Mining, Metall. & Petrol. Eng; Am. Ceramic Soc; Brit. Soc. Glass Technol. Structure and properties of glass ceramics; nucleation and growth phenomena; structure of glass; mechanical properties of glasses. Address: Ocean Technology Division, Naval Research Lab, Washington, DC 20390.

FREIMANIS, ATIS K, b. Riga, Latvia, Mar. 28, 25; U.S. citizen; m. 51; c. 3. RADIOLOGY. Dr.Med, Univ. Hamburg, 51. Instr. RADIOL, col. med, Ohio State Univ, 58-59, asst. prof, 59-61, assoc. prof, 61-65, prof, 65-70; PROF. & CHMN. DEPT, MED. COL. OHIO AT TOLEDO, 70- Consult, Juvenile Diag. Ctr, 51-; Brown Vet. Admin. Hosp, Dayton, 63-; Chillicothe Vet. Admin. Hosp, 64-70. Med.C, 53-55, 1st Lt. Am. Col. Radiol; Radiol. Soc. N.Am; Asn. Univ. Radiol; Am. Med. Asn; Am. Roentgen Ray Soc; Am. Inst. Ultrasonics in Med. Ultrasonic diagnosis of abdominal diseases; teaching programs in radiology. Address: Dept. of Radiology, Medical College of Ohio at Toledo, P.O. Box 6190, Toledo, OH 43614.

FREIMER, EARL HOWARD, b. New York, N.Y, Nov. 15, 26; m. 48; c. 4. MICROBIOLOGY, INFECTIOUS DISEASES. A.B, Michigan, 48; M.D, State Univ, N.Y, 55. Intern, Columbia Med. Serv, Bellevue Hosp, 55-56, asst. resident, 56-57; res. assoc, Rockefeller Inst, 57-61; asst. prof. Rockefeller Univ. & assoc. physician, Hosp, 61-68; PROF. INTERNAL MED, DIR. DIV. INFECTIOUS DISEASES & PROF. MICROBIOL. & CHMN. DEPT, MED. COL. OHIO, TOLEDO, 68- Vis. assoc. prof, State Univ. N.Y. Downstate Med. Ctr. & assoc. vis. physician, Kings County Hosp, Ctr, 67-68; vis. prof, col. med, Pa. State, 68- U.S.N, 44-46. AAAS; Am. Soc. Microbiol; Am. Asn. Immunol; Infectious Diseases Soc. Am; fel. Am. Col. Cardiol. Biology of group A streptococcus; pathogenesis of rheumatic fever; bacterial L-forms and protoplasts; bacterial cell walls and membranes; immunochemistry of bacterial antigens; mechanisms of action of antimicrobial agents; immunocytochemistry of cardiac muscle; biology of the pneumococcus. Address: Dept. of Microbiology, Medical College of Ohio at Toledo, P.O. Box 6190, Toledo, OH 43614.

FREIMER, MARSHALL LEONARD, b. N.Y.C, May 6, 32; m. 61; c. 2. MATHEMATICS. A.B, Harvard, 53, A.M, 54, Ph.D.(math), 60. Mem. staff, Lincoln Lab, Mass. Inst. Tech, 57-61; mem. tech. staff, Inst. Naval Studies, 61-63; ASSOC. PROF. BUS. ADMIN, UNIV. ROCHESTER, 63- Ford Found. faculty fel, 65-66. Inst. Math. Statist; Math. Asn. Am; Inst. Mgt. Sci. Operations research, especially mathematical programming and decision analysis. Address: Graduate School of Management, University of Rochester, Rochester, NY 14627.

FREIMUTH, HENRY CHARLES, b. New York, N.Y, June 24, 12; m; c. 5. CHEMISTRY. B.S, City Col, 32; M.S, N.Y. Univ, 33, fel, 35-37, Ph.D. (chem), 38. Asst. instr. chem, Wash. Sq. Col, N.Y. Univ, 37-38, asst. therapeut, sch. med, 38-39; from jr. chemist to prin. chemist, fed. bur. invest, U.S. Dept. Justice, Wash, D.C, 39-44; TOXICOLOGIST, STATE POST-MORTEM EXAMS, 44-; ASSOC. PROF. LEGAL MED, SCH. MED, UNIV. MD, 57-, ADJ. ASSOC. PROF, DEPT. PHARMACOL. & TOXICOL, SCH. PHARM, 70-, asst. prof. legal med, sch. med, 53-57. Instr, Loyola Col.(Md), 46-56, prof. lectr, 56-68, adj. prof, 68-; assoc, div. forensic path, sch. hyg. & pub. health, Hopkins, 65- Consult, Baltimore Poison Control Centers, 56- AAAS; Am. Chem. Soc; Am. Acad. Forensic Sci. Carbon monoxide poisoning; alcoholic intoxication; detection of organic poisons in tissues; drowning tests; asphyxia; boric acid poisoning. Address: 1402 Gibsonwood Rd, Catonsville, MD 21228.

FREINKEL, NORBERT, b. Mannheim, Ger, Jan. 26, 26; m. 55; c. 3. INTERNAL MEDICINE, ENDOCRINOLOGY. A.B, Princeton, 45; M.D, N.Y. Univ, 49. Intern & asst. resident med, third med. div, Bellevue Hosp, N.Y, 49-50; res. fel, Harvard Med. Sch. & Thorndike Mem. Lab, Boston City Hosp, 52-55; Agr. Res. Coun, Inst. Animal Physiol, Cambridge, Eng, 55-56; from instr. to asst. prof. med, Harvard Med. Sch, 56-66; KETTERING PROF. MED, CHIEF SECT. ENDOCRINOL. & METAB. & DIR. ENDOCRINE CLINS, NORTHWEST. UNIV-McGAW MED. CTR, 66-, PROF. BIOCHEM, 69- Am. Cancer Soc. fel, 53-55; Nat. Found. Infantile Paralysis fel, 55-56; investr, Howard Hughes Med. Inst, 56-65; asst. physician & dir. diabetes & metab. div, Thorndike Mem. Lab, Boston City Hosp, 57-66; vis. prof, Wash. Univ, 64; vis. scientist, Agr. Res. Coun, Inst. Animal Physiol, Cambridge, 69-70. Consult, Qm. Corps, U.S. Army, 57-62, Surgeon Gen, 62- Mem. metab. study sect, div. res. grants, Nat. Insts. Health, 67-69, chmn. 70, nat. adv. coun. alcoholism, Nat. Inst. Ment. Health, 68- Hon. mem. high table, King's Col, Cambridge, 69- U.S.N.R, 43-45; Med.C, A.U.S, 50-52, Capt. Asn. Am. Physicians; Am. Soc. Clin. Invest; Endocrine Soc; Am. Physiol. Soc; Soc. Exp. Biol. & Med; Am. Diabetes Asn. (Lilly Medal & Award, 66); Am. Thyroid Asn. Hormone transport; gluconeogenic regulation; metabolism of endogenous fuels; alcohol; hypoglycemic disorders; intermediary metabolism in pregnancy; peptide hormone action. Address: Dept. of Medicine, Northwestern University-McGaw Medical Center, 303 E. Chicago Ave, Chicago, IL 60611.

FREINKEL, RUTH KIMMELSTIEL, b. Hamburg, Germany, Dec. 26, 26; U.S. citizen; m. 55; c. 3. MEDICINE. A.B, Randolph Macon Col, 48; M.D, Duke, 52. Res. fel. biochem, Harvard Med. Sch, 54-55; Cambridge, 55-56; DERMAT, Harvard Med. Sch, 58-60, instr, 60-61, assoc, 61-64, asst. prof, 64-66; ASSOC. PROF, MED. SCH, NORTHWEST. UNIV, 66- Dipl, Am. Bd. Dermat, 61. Am. Soc. Clin. Invest; Soc. Invest. Dermat; Am. Acad. Dermat.

Intermediate and lipid metabolism of skin; pathogenesis of acne. Address: Dept. of Dermatology, Northwestern University, 303 E. Chicago Ave, Chicago, IL 60611.

FREIREICH, A(BRAHAM) W(ALTER), b. N.Y.C, July 27, 06; m. 32; c. 2. INTERNAL MEDICINE. B.S, City Col, 28; M.D, N.Y. Univ, 32. Asst. toxicologist to Dr. A.O. Gettler, N.Y, 32-38; toxicologist, NASSAU COUNTY MED. EXAM. OFF, 38-66, CHIEF TOXICOLOGIST, 66- Asst. prof. clin. med, post-grad. med. sch, N.Y. Univ, 46-60, assoc. attend. physician, univ. hosp, 52-60; assoc. vis. physician, Bellevue Hosp, 46-60; chief med, Brunswick Hosp, Amityville, 48-; consult. physician, Southside Hosp, Bay Shore, 53-; Nassau Hosp, Mineola, 54-; Long Beach Mem. Hosp, 54-; St. Francis Hosp. & Sanitorium, Roslyn, 56-62; dir. div, internal med, Meadowbrook Hosp, 56-66, dir. & consult. toxicologist, poison control ctr, 58-65, chmn. dept. internal med. & emer. physician, 66-; consult, Mercy Hosp, Rockville Centre, 62-; South Nassau Community Hosp, Oceanside, 62- Dipl, Am. Bd. Internal Med, 44. Fel. Am. Col. Physicians; Am. Acad. Forensic Sci. (pres, 54-55). Toxicology; thrombophlebitis; thiocyanate therapy of hypertension; hydrogen sulfide poisoning; tetanus. Address: 180 Hempstead Ave, Malverne, NY 11565.

FREIREICH, EMIL J, b. Chicago, Ill, Mar. 16, 27; m. 53; c. 4. HEMATOLOGY, INTERNAL MEDICINE. B.S, Illinois, 47, M.D, 49. Intern, Cook County Hosp, 49-51; res. internal med, Presby. Hosp, Chicago, Ill, 51-53; asst. med, Boston, 53-55; sr. investr, Nat. Cancer Inst, 55-65, head leukemia serv, 64-65; PROF. MED, ASST. HEAD DEPT. DEVELOP. THERAPEUT. & CHIEF SECT. RES. HEMAT, UNIV. TEX. M.D. ANDERSON HOSP. & TUMOR INST, 65- Asst, Univ. Ill, 51-53; res. assoc, Evans Mem. Hosp, 53-55. Dipl, Am. Bd. Internal Med, 57. U.S.P.H.S, 55-65. AAAS; fel. Am. Col. Physicians; Am. Soc. Hemat; Am. Asn. Cancer Res; Am. Med. Asn; Am. Fedn. Clin. Res; Int. Soc. Hemat; Am. Soc. Clin. Invest; Am. Soc. Clin. Oncol. Chemotherapy and natural history of human acute leukemia; platelet and leukocyte transfusion and physiology. Address: Dept. of Developmental Therapeutics, University of Texas M.D. Anderson Hospital & Tumor Institute, Medical Center, 6723 Bertner Ave, Houston, TX 77025.

FREIRE-MAIA, A(DEMAR), b. Boa Esperança, Brazil, Feb. 14, 32; m. 62; c. 3. HUMAN GENETICS. B.S, Fed. Univ. Paraná, 54, L.S, 55; Ph.D.(human genetics), Univ. São Paulo, 68. Fel. & res. asst, human genetics lab, Fed. Univ. Paraná, 53-62; asst. prof. biol, Cath. Univ. Paraná, 55-56; prof, Araraquara Sch. Philos, 62-63; PROF. HUMAN GENETICS, BOTUCATÚ SCH. MED. & BIOL. SCI, 63-, HEAD DEPT. GENETICS, 66-, supvr. sect. biol. sci, 66-70. Brazilian Nat. Coun. Res. fel, 53-60; Nat. Atomic Energy Comn. fel. & grant, 60-62; adv, São Paulo State Found. Aid to Res, 63; Nat. Insts. Health grant, 64-67; mem, São Paulo State Coun. Educ, 68-69, 70-71; São Paulo State Permanent Comn. Full Time Regime, 67-71; dir. coun, State Univ. Campinas, 70-71; lectr, Fed. Univ. Paraná, Cath. Univ. Paraná, Univ. Minas Gerais, State Univ. Campinas & Univ. São Paulo. AAAS; Brazilian Soc. Advan. Sci; Brazilian Genetics Soc; Soc. Study Evolution; Am. Eugenics Soc; Soc. Study Reproduction; Japan Soc. Human Genetics; N.Y. Acad. Sci; Brazilian Acad. Sci; Brazilian Asn. Med. Schs; Brazilian Soc. Biochem; Int. Asn. Anthropobiol; Latin-Am. Genetics Asn. Inbreeding studies, especially inbreeding effects in man; effect of background radiation; endemic goiter. Address: Dept. of Genetics, Botucatú School of Medical & Biological Sciences, Botucatú, São Paulo, Brazil.

FREIRE-MAIA, NEWTON, b. Boa Esperanca, Brazil, June 29, 18; m. 48; c. 4. HUMAN GENETICS. D.D.S, Sch. Pharm. & Ondontol, Brazil, 45; Rockefeller Found. fel, Michigan, 56-57; Ph.D, Univ. Brazil, 60. Asst, Univ. São Paulo, 46-47, teacher & researcher, 48-50; teacher & res. chief, UNIV. PARANA, 51-69, PROF. GENETICS, 69- Lectr, Univ. Minas Gerais, 54 & 58; mem. study group on effect of radiation on human genetics, WHO, Copenhagen, 56; lectr, Univ. São Paulo & Buenos Aires, 59; Cath. Univ. Parana & Univs. Bahia & Rio de Janeiro, 63; WHO scientist, 70-71. Brazilian Genetics Soc.(pres, 51-52). Etiology of congenital malformations; malformation syndromes; geographic distribution and genetic effects of consanguineous marriages; radiation effects and genetic load in man. Address: Dept. of Genetics, University of Parana, Caixa Postal 756, Curitiba, Parana, Brazil.

FREIS, EDWARD DAVID, b. Chicago, Ill, May 13, 12; m. 34; c. 3. MEDICINE. B.S, Arizona, 36; M.D, Columbia, 40. Intern med, Mass. Mem. Hosp, Boston, 40-41; sr. intern & house physician, Boston City Hosp, 41-42; asst. res, Evans Mem. Hosp, 46-47, res. fel. cardiovasc. disease, 47-49; adj. clin. prof. MED, SCH. MED, GEORGETOWN UNIV, 49-57, assoc. prof, 57-63, PROF, 63-, CHIEF CARDIOVASCULAR RES. LAB, UNIV. HOSP, 49-; SR. MED. INVESTR, VET. ADMIN. HOSP, 59-, asst. chief med, 49-54, chief, 54-59. Instr, sch. med, Boston, 47-49. Med.C, U.S.A.A.F, 42-45. Am. Soc. Clin. Invest. Clinical evaluation and hemodynamic analysis of hypotensive drugs; blood and fluid volume changes in disease; cardiovascular physiology in man. Address: Veterans Administration Hospital, 50 Irving St. N.W, Washington, DC 20422.

FREISE, EARL J, b. Chicago, Ill, Dec. 30, 35; m. 58; c. 4. MATERIALS SCIENCE, METALLURGY. B.S, Ill. Inst. Tech, 58; M.S, Northwestern, 59; Ph.D.(metall), Cambridge, 62. Asst. prof. MAT. SCI, NORTHWEST. UNIV, 62-66, ASSOC. PROF, 66- Am. Soc. Metals; Am. Inst. Mining, Metall. & Petrol. Eng; Am. Soc. Eng. Educ. Phase transformations in materials; physical and mechanical properties of high temperature metallic and nonmetallic materials. Address: Dept. of Materials Science, Technological Institute, Northwestern University, Evanston, IL 60201.

FREISER, HENRY, b. New York, N.Y, Aug. 27, 20; m. 42; c. 3. ANALYTICAL CHEMISTRY. B.S, City Col, 41; M.A, Duke, 42, Ph.D.(phys. chem), 44. Prof. anal. & phys. chem. & chmn. dept, N.Dak. State Col, 44-45; res. fel, Mellon Inst, 45-46; instr. anal. chem, Pittsburgh, 46-50, asst. prof, 50-53, assoc. prof, 53-58; PROF. CHEM, UNIV. ARIZ, 58-, head dept, 58-67. Mem. comn. equilibrium data, anal. div, Int. Union Pure & Appl. Chem; O.M. Smith lectr, 68. Am. Chem. Soc; Am. Soc. Test. & Mat; fel. The Chem. Soc. Analytical separations processes and solvent extraction; trace analysis; metal chelates. Address: Dept. of Chemistry, University of Arizona, Tucson, AZ 85721.

FREISER, MARVIN J(OSEPH), b. Brooklyn, N.Y, Feb. 9, 26; m. 49; c. 1. THEORETICAL PHYSICS. B.S, Brooklyn Col, 48; M.S, Purdue, 51, Ph.D. (physics), 55. Asst. prof. physics, Worcester Polytech, 55-56; physicist, Midwest. Univs. Res. Asn, 56-57; assoc. physicist, res. lab, IBM CORP, 57-64, RES. PHYSICIST, WATSON RES. CTR, 64- Sig.C, U.S.A, 46-47. Am. Phys. Soc. Solid state physics; theory of magnetism; statistical mechanics; liquid crystals. Address: IBM Watson Research Center, Box 218, Yorktown Heights, NY 10598.

FREISHEIM, JAMES H(AROLD), b. Tacoma, Wash, July 19, 37; m. 58; c. 2. BIOCHEMISTRY. B.A, Pacific Lutheran, 60; Ph.D.(biochem), Washington, 66. Res. assoc. BIOCHEM, Scripps Clin. & Res. Found, 66-69; ASST. PROF, COL. MED, UNIV. CINCINNATI, 69- Nat. Insts. Health training grant, 66-67; Am. Cancer Soc. fel, 67-68. AAAS; Am. Chem. Soc. Relationship of protein structure to function in proteolytic enzymes and zymogens; molecular properties and mechanism of action of folate-dependent enzymes; mechanism of drug resistance to folate antagonists. Address: Dept. of Biochemistry, University of Cincinnati College of Medicine, Cincinnati, OH 45219.

FREITAG, DEAN R(ICHARD), b. Ft. Dodge, Iowa, Oct. 1, 26; m. 52; c. 4. CIVIL ENGINEERING, SOIL MECHANICS. B.S, Iowa State, 49; M.S, Harvard, 51; Secy. Army fel, Auburn, 61-62, Ph.D.(agr. eng), 65. Civil engr, U.S. ARMY ENGR. WATERWAYS EXP. STA, 51-55, supv. res. civil engr, 55-70, ASST. TECH. DIR, 70- Engr, mat. & res. lab, Calif. Div. Hwys, 53-54. U.S. Army Meritorious Civilian Serv. Award. Int. Soc. Terrain-Vehicle Systs; Am. Soc. Civil Eng; Am. Soc. Agr. Eng. Mechanics of soil-vehicle systems; behavior of soils under dynamic loading; soil stabilization; roads and airfields; environment-compatible civil engineering. Address: U.S. Army Engineer Waterways Experiment Station, Box 631, Vicksburg, MS 39180.

FREITAG, HARLOW, b. N.Y.C, Apr. 17, 36. COMPUTER SCIENCE. A.B, N.Y. Univ, 55; M.S, Yale, 57, Ph.D.(chem), 59. Assoc, data processing div, Int. Bus. Mach. Corp, 58-59, mgr. chem, advan. systs. develop. div, 59-61, mem. staff, res. div, 61-63, MGR. design automation, COMPUT. SYSTS. DEPT, THOMAS J. WATSON RES. CTR, IBM CORP, 63-67, SUBSYSTS. & INTEGRATION, 67- U.S.A.R, 61-67. AAAS; Asn. Comput. Mach; Inst. Elec. & Electronics Eng. Digital computers. Address: Computing Systems Dept, Thomas J. Watson Research Center, IBM Corp, P.O. Box 218, Yorktown Heights, NY 10598.

FREITAG, HERTA T(AUSSIG), b. Vienna, Austria, Dec. 6, 08; nat; m. 50. MATHEMATICS. Dipl, Realgymnasium, Vienna, 27; M.A, Columbia, 49, Ph.D.(math), 53. Prof. math. & physics, Realgymnasium, Vienna, 34-35, teacher, pub. sch, 37-38; head dept. MATH, Mt. Sch, Eng, 41-44; Greer Sch, N.Y, 44-48; prof. & chmn. dept, HOLLINS COL, 48-71, EMER. PROF, 71- Asst, Columbia Univ, 46-49; vis. prof, Univ. Tenn, 65-66; consult. & lectr, Univ. Va. grad. TV course. Fel. AAAS; Am. Math. Soc; Math. Asn. Am. Mathematical education; history of mathematics; theory of numbers. Address: 7076 Brookview Rd, Hollins, VA 24019.

FREITAG, JULIA L(OUISE), b. Allentown, Pa, Nov. 29, 27. PREVENTIVE MEDICINE, EPIDEMIOLOGY. A.B, Cornell, 49, M.D, 53; M.P.H, Harvard, 57. Epidemiologist, STATE DEPT. HEALTH, N.Y, 57-58, asst. dir, off. epidemiol, 58-66, DIR. off. epidemiol, 66-70, OFF. MED. MANPOWER, 70- Lectr, Rensselaer Polytech. Inst, 62-70; Albany Med. Col, Union Univ. (N.Y), 70- Communicable diseases; population studies and outbreak investigation; genetics; inheritance of blood groups. Address: 84 Holland Ave, Albany, NY 12208.

FREITAG, J(ULIUS) H(ERMAN), b. Berkeley, Calif, Jan. 6, 08; m. 35; c. 4. ENTOMOLOGY. B.S, California, 31, M.S, 32, Ph.D.(entom), 35. Jr. entomologist, EXP. STA, UNIV. CALIF, BERKELEY, 35-42, asst. entomologist & asst. prof. entom. & parasitol, 42-48, assoc. entomologist & assoc. prof, 48-54, ENTOMOLOGIST & PROF. ENTOM. & PARASITOL, 54-, instr, 39-42. AAAS; Entom. Soc. Am; Am. Phytopath. Soc; Am. Inst. Biol. Sci; Brit. Asn. Appl. Biol. Insect transmission of plant viruses; virus diseases of cucurbits and celery. Address: Dept. of Entomology & Parasitology, University of California, Berkeley, CA 94720.

FREITAG, ROBERT FREDERICK, b. Jackson, Mich, Jan. 20, 20; m. 41; c. 4. AERONAUTICAL & ASTRONAUTICAL ENGINEERING. B.S.E, Michigan, 41; Mass. Inst. Tech, 41-42. Aerodyn. officer, bur. aeronaut, Navy Dept, D.C, 42-48; intel. officer develop. tech. intel. plans, Off. Naval Attache, Eng, 48-49; chief tech. systs. labs, U.S. Air Force Missile Test Center, Cape Canaveral, Fla, 49-51; prog. plans officer, guided missiles div, bur. aeronaut, Navy Dept, 51-53, dir. surface launched missiles br, 53-55, ballistic missile br, 55, prog. officer, off. chief naval opers, 55-57, astronaut. officer, bur. naval weapons, 59-63; dir. plans & requirements, U.S. Navy Pacific Missile Range, Calif, 57-59; dir. launch vehicles & propulsion, OFF. MANNED SPACE FLIGHT, NASA, 63, manned space flight ctr. develop, 63-70, SPEC. ASST. TO ASSOC. ADMINR. MANNED SPACE FLIGHT, 70- Mem. subcmt. propellers, Nat. Adv. Cmt. Aeronaut, 44-46, spec. cmt. space tech, 58-59; Joint Army-Navy Ballistic Missile Cmt, 55-57; spec. cmt. adequacy range facilities, Secy. Defense, 56-58; res. adv. cmt. missile & spacecraft aerodyn, NASA, 60-63; launch vehicles panel, aeronaut. & astronaut. coord. bd, Joint Defense Dept-NASA, 60-64. Exceptional serv. medal, NASA, 69. U.S.N, 41-63, Capt; Legion of Merit, 59; Commendation Medal, 63. Assoc. fel. Am. Inst. Aeronaut. & Astronaut; fel, Royal Aeronaut. Soc. Aeronautics and astronautics, especially in aerodynamics, guided missile guidance, rocket propulsion, range testing and instrumentation. Address: Office of Manned Space Flight, National Aeronautics & Space Administration, 600 Independence Ave. S.W, Washington, DC 20546.

FREITAG, WALTER O(TTO), b. Laureldale, Pa, June 26, 28; m. 53; c. 4. PHYSICAL & INORGANIC CHEMISTRY. B.S, Pennsylvania, 51, M.S, 52, Du Pont fel, 53-54, Ph.D, 55. Res. chemist, Foote Mineral Co, 54-56; sr. invest. & fel, Pennsylvania, 56-58; sr. res. chemist, Foote Mineral Co, 58-60; supvr. mat. res. group, UNIVAC DIV, SPERRY RAND CORP, 60-66, MGR. MAT. RES, 66- Am. Chem. Soc; Electrochem. Soc; Am. Vacuum Soc. Thin film microcircuits; vacuum evaporation and sputtering; electrodeposition; preparative inorganic chemistry; infrared spectroscopy; semiconductor materials; magnetic films. Address: 1613 Kenmare Dr, Dresher, PA 19025.

FREMLING, CALVIN R, b. Brainerd, Minn, Nov. 13, 29; m. 54; c. 1. LIMNOLOGY, ENTOMOLOGY. B.S, St. Cloud State Col, 51, M.S, 55; Ph.D. (zool), Iowa State, 59. Sci. teacher, high sch, Minn, 51-52; ecologist, Univ. Utah at Dugway Proving Ground, 52-54; instr. zool. & bot, Eveleth Jr. Col, 55-56; PROF. BIOL, WINONA STATE COL, 59- Minn. Acad. Sci. vis. scientist, high schs, 50-; Nat. Sci. Found. res. grant, 61-64, 69-70; consult, U.S. Pub. Health Serv, 62-; consult, Int. Joint Comn, 62; Am. Inst. Biol. Sci. vis. scientist, cols, 63-71; consult, Metrop. Structures of Can, Montreal, 66-69; Fed. Water Pollution Control Admin. grant, 66-70; consult, Nasco Inc, Wis, 67-; summer aquatic biologist, Minn. Conserv. Dept, 55. U.S.A, 52-54, S/Sgt. AAAS; Entom. Soc. Am; Am. Soc. Limnol. & Oceanog; Nat. Asn. Biol. Teachers; Wildlife Soc; Am. Fisheries Soc; Int. Soc. Limnol; Am. Inst. Biol. Sci. Ecology of the Mississippi River; biology of Hexagenia mayflies and hydropsychid caddisflies; water pollution and floods. Address: Dept. of Biology, Winona State College, Winona, MN 55987.

FREMMING, BENJAMIN DeWITT, b. Minneapolis, Minn, Oct. 27, 24; m. 55; c. 2. PHYSIOLOGY. D.V.M, Colo. State Univ, 46; M.P.H, Univ. Calif, Berkeley, 52. Scientist virol-serol, Walter Reed Res. & Grad. Ctr, 52-53; chief radiobiol, vet. res. group, radiobiol. lab, Univ. Tex, 53-56; proj. mgr. physiol, life sci. sect, Westinghouse Res. Develop. Ctr, 61-64; scientist adminr, Nat. Heart Inst, Nat. Insts. Health, 65-67; prof. path. & dir. animal care ctr, UNIV. TEX. MED. SCH. SAN ANTONIO, 67-71, PROF. LAB. ANIMAL MED, 71-, ANESTHESIOL, 71-, CHMN. DEPT. LAB. ANIMAL MED, 68- Mem, Inst. Lab. Animal Resources, Nat. Res. Coun, 53-58, chmn. coun. non-human primates, 53-58; consult, off. inspector gen, U.S. Dept. State, 62-64. Dipl, Am. Col. Lab. Animal Med, 56, pres, 59-62; dipl, Am. Bd. Vet. Pub. Health. U.S.A, 46-48; U.S.A.F, 48-56. Aerospace Med. Asn; Am. Vet. Med. Asn; Am. Asn. Lab. Animal Sci. Radiobiology; epidemiology; experimental surgery; laboratory animal medicine. Address: Dept. of Lab. Animal Medicine, University of Texas Medical School, 7703 Floyd Curl Dr, San Antonio, TX 78229.

FREMONT, C(LAUDE), b. Que, Aug. 18, 22; m. 53. PHYSICS. B.A, Laval Univ, 43, B.App.Sc, 47, M.Sc, 48. Lectr. physics, LAVAL UNIV, 48-50, assoc. prof. geophys, 50-53, geophys. & physics, 53-63, prof, asst. lectr. & adj. prof. sch. teacher orientation, 63-70, PROF. PHYSICS, 70- Am. Phys. Soc; Can. Asn. Physicists; French-Can. Asn. Advan. Sci; Royal Astron. Soc; Brit. Interplanetary Soc. Semi-transparent thin films; magnetism. Address: Dept. of Physics, Laval University, Quebec, Que, Can.

FREMONT, HENRY ALBERT, b. Lakewood, Ohio, Feb. 23, 17; m. 44; c. 6. CHEMICAL ENGINEERING. B.S, Case, 39, Dow fel, 41-42, M.S, 43; Ph.D, Rensselaer Polytech, 50. Chem. engr, Nat. Starch Prod. Co, N.Y, 39-41; instr. chem, Case, 41-43; res. assoc, res. lab, Gen. Elec. Co, 43-48, Knolls Atomic Power Lab, 48-50, mgr. combustion, aircraft gas turbine div, 50-56, consult. opers. res. & synthesis, 56-61; mgr. develop. servs, Champion Papers, Inc, 61-65, ASSOC. DIR. RES. & DEVELOP, U.S. PLYWOOD-CHAMPION PAPERS, INC, 65- Mem. sub-cmts. aircraft fuels & combustion, Nat. Adv. Cmt. Aeronaut, 53-56. With Nat. Defense Res. Cmt, 42-43; Atomic Energy Cmn, 46. AAAS; Am. Chem. Soc; Am. Inst. Chem. Eng; Inst. Mgt. Sci; Tech. Asn. Pulp & Paper Indust. Fused salt systems; decontamination of water; heterogeneous reactions; combustion aerothermodynamics; kinetics of combustion; material products; wood and cellulose technology; membrane processes; materials; business and operations research; research planning. Address: 550 Laveta Court, Cincinnati, OH 45215.

FREMONT, HERBERT I(RWIN), b. Brooklyn, N.Y, Nov. 1, 24; m. 46; c. 2. MATHEMATICS. B.A, N.Y. Univ, 49, M.A, 51, Ph.D.(math. ed), 63. Teacher, pub. schs, N.Y, 49-58, chmn. dept. math, high sch, 58-61; assoc. prof. MATH. EDUC, QUEENS COL.(N.Y), 61-71, PROF, 71- Proj. dir. Math. Individual Learning Exp, U.S. Off. Ed, 60-62; math. consult, Bldg. Resources of Instruct. for Disadvantaged Groups, Queens Col.(N.Y), 62-63; North Shore Pub. Schs, Glen Head, 62-65; ed. adv, McGraw-Hill Brook Co, 63-; curriculum consult, Huntington Training Proj, Jamaica, N.Y. & U.S. Dept. Labor, 64-65; dir. summer insts. for teachers of disadvantaged youth, Queens Col. & N.Y. State Educ. Dept, 65, 66. Ord.Dept, U.S.A, 44-46. AAAS; Math. Asn. Am. Techniques of individualizing instruction in mathematics; new mathematics curriculum based on science concepts; aiding slow learners in mathematics through use of multi-media individualized approach. Address: Dept. of Education, Queens College, Flushing, NY 11367.

FREMOUNT, HENRY NEIL, b. Easton, Pa, Sept. 29, 33; m. 57; c. 2. BIOLOGICAL SCIENCES. B.S, East Stroudsburg State Col, 56, M.Ed, 64; Nat. Sci. Found. summer fel, Univ. Md, 60; Nat. Sci. Found. acad. year-in-serv. grant, Pa. State Univ, 63-64; Nat. Insts. Health trainee, Univ. Mich, 65; Nat. Insts. Health trainee, Columbia Univ, 65-66 & 68-70, M.S, 66, Dr.P.H.(parasitic diseases), 70. Teacher & co-chmn. sci. dept, Delaware Valley Joint Sch. Syst, 56-58, teacher, high sch, Belvidere, N.J, 58-65; assoc. prof. BIOL, EAST STROUDSBURG STATE COL, 66-71, PROF, 71- Instr, sch. pub. health, Columbia Univ, 70-; vis. scientist, Gorgas Mem. Lab. Panama, summer 70; Nat. Insts. Health int. fel. trop. med, La. State Univ, summer 70; Nat. Inst. Allergy & Infectious Diseases res. grant, 71-74. AAAS; Royal Soc. Trop. Med. & Hyg; Am. Soc. Trop. Med. & Hygiene; Am. Soc. Parasitol. Biology and pathophysiology of malaria; ultrastructural changes in the host red cell as induced by the parasite. Address: Dept. of Biology, East Stroudsburg State College, East Stroudsburg, PA 18301.

FREMOUW, EDWARD J(OSEPH), b. Northfield, Minn, Feb. 23, 34; m. 60; c. 2. AERONOMY, RADIO PHYSICS. B.S, Stanford, 57; M.S, Alaska, 63, Ph.D.(geophys), 66. Engr, Boeing Co, 57-58 & 60; auroral physicist & auroral discipline chief for U.S. Antarctic Res. Prog. in Antarctica, Arctic Inst. N.Am, 58-59; asst. elec. eng, Univ. Alaska, 60-61, aeronomy, geophys. inst, 61-63, res. assoc, 63-66, asst. prof. geophys, univ, 66-67; physicist, RADIO PHYSICS, STANFORD RES. INST, 67-70, SR. PHYSICIST, 70- Consult, geophys. inst, Alaska, 67- Am. Geophys. Union; Inst. Elec. & Electronics Eng; Int. Radio Sci. Union. Ionospheric and auroral physics; satellite communication and navigation. Address: Radio Physics Lab, Stanford Research Institute, 333 Ravenswood, Menlo Park, CA 94025.

FRENCH, A(DAM) JAMES, b. Van Houten, N.Mex, Sept. 3, 12; m. 37. PATHOLOGY. A.B, Colorado, 33, A.M. & M.D, 36. Asst. physiol, sch. med, Colorado, 34-36; intern, Gen. Hosp, Kansas City, Mo, 36-37; res, Children's Hosp, Colo, 37-38; res. PATH, St. Louis Hosp, 38-40; UNIV. HOSP, UNIV. MICH, ANN ARBOR, 40-41, instr, 41-46, asst. prof, 46-47, assoc. prof, 47-53, PROF, 53-, CHMN. DEPT, 56-, CHIEF CLIN. LAB, 52- Consult, Surgeon Gen, U.S. Dept. Army, 48-53, 57, 66 & 71; Vet. Admin. Hosp, 53; Wayne County Gen. Hosp, 60. Dipl, Am. Bd. Path, 41, trustee, 62-, secy-treas, 64- Med.C, 41-52, Res, 62-, Col. Fel. Am. Asn. Path. & Bact.(secy-treas, 71-); fel. Am. Soc. Clin. Path; Am. Med. Asn; fel. Col. Am. Path.(secy-treas, 69-70); fel. Am. Col. Physicians; fel. Int. Acad. Path.(pres. elect, 65, pres, 66); Am. Acad. Oral Path. Hypophysectomy in rats; sulfahypersensitivity; coronary disease in soldiers; glomerulonephrosis; parotid tumors; chromoblastomycosis; benign disease of breast. Address: Dept. of Pathology, University of Michigan, 1335 E. Catherine St, Ann Arbor, MI 48104.

FRENCH, ALEX(ANDER) M(URDOCH), b. New Bedford, Pa, April 23, 20; m. 47; c. 2. PLANT PATHOLOGY. B.S, Muskingum Col, 42; Ph.D.(plant path), Cornell, 50. Assoc. plant pathologist, STATE DEPT. AGR, CALIF, 50-59, plant nematologist, 59-71, PROG. SUPVR, PLANT PATH-NEMATOL. LAB, 71- Soc. Nematol; Am. Phytopath. Soc. Regulatory plant pathology and plant nematology. Address: California Dept. of Agriculture, 1220 N St, Sacramento, CA 95814.

FRENCH, A(NTHONY) P(HILIP), b. Brighton, Eng, Nov. 19, 20; m. 45; c. 2. PHYSICS. B.A, Cambridge, 42, M.A, 46, Ph.D, 48. With Cavendish Lab, 42-44, demonstr, 48-53, lectr, 53-55; with Manhattan Proj, Los Alamos, N.Mex, 44-46; sci. officer, Atomic Energy Res. Estab, Eng, 46-48; prof. PHYSICS, South Carolina, 55-62, chmn. dept, 56-62; vis. prof, MASS. INST. TECHNOL, 62-64, PROF, 64- Dir. studies nat. sci, Pembroke Col, Cambridge, 49-55, fel, 50-55; Guignard lectr, South Carolina, 58. Phys. Soc. Science education. Address: Dept. of Physics, Massachusetts Institute of Technology, Cambridge, MA 02139.

FRENCH, ARTHUR B(ANCROFT), b. Hanover, N.H, May 18, 18; m. 44; c. 6. INTERNAL MEDICINE. A.B, Dartmouth Col, 40; M.D, Hopkins, 43. Intern, Phila. Gen. Hosp, 43; res. med, Veterans Hosp, Ft. Howard, Md, 46-49; fel, Mass. Gen. Hosp, 49-51; instr, Utah, 51-55; assoc. prof, Wayne State, 55-56; asst. prof. INTERNAL MED, UNIV. MICH, ANN ARBOR, 56-59, assoc. prof, 59-68, PROF, 68-, DIR. CLIN. RES. UNIT, 62- Mem. Gastroenterol. Res. Group. Med.C, 44-46, Res, 46, Maj. AAAS; fel. Am. Col. Physicians; Am. Fedn. Clin. Res; Am. Physiol. Soc; Am. Med. Asn; Gastroenterol. Asn; Radiation Res. Soc; Am. Inst. Nutrit. Gastroenterology particularly intestinal absorption; physiological effects of stress, particularly operation and radiation. Address: Clinical Research Unit W4644, University Hospital, Ann Arbor, MI 48104.

FRENCH, B(ERLIN) CARSON, b. Carlton, N.Y, Oct. 5, 04; m. 38; c. 2. ORGANIC CHEMISTRY. B.S, Wesleyan, 26, M.A, 28; M.S, Yale, 34; Ph.D. (chem), North Carolina, 56. Instr. chem, Juniata Col, 30-32; Arnold Col, 33-34; res. chemist, Nat. Aniline & Chem. Co, N.Y, 34-35; teacher, pub. schs, Mass, 35-48; assoc. prof. CHEM, Salem Col.(N.C), 48-56, prof, 56-67, chmn. dept, 48-67; PROF, CAPE COD COMMUNITY COL, 67- Summers, vis. prof, State Univ. N.Y, 50, Univ. N.C, 57, 60-65; Nat. Sci. Found. fel, Tufts Univ, 59. Am. Chem. Soc; Nat. Sci. Teachers Asn. Chemistry of natural products; naphthylethyl barbiturates; fluoro-riboflavin analogs; polarographic reduction potentials of nitrofluoroxylenes. Address: Cape Cod Community College, West Barnstable, MA 02668.

FRENCH, BEVAN MEREDITH, b. East Orange, N.J, Mar. 8, 37; m. 67; c. 3. GEOCHEMISTRY, PETROLOGY. A.B, Dartmouth Col, 58; M.S, Calif. Inst. Tech, 60; Ph.D.(geol), Hopkins, 64. Nat. Acad. Sci-Nat. Res. Coun. resident res. assoc. geochem, GODDARD SPACE FLIGHT CTR, NASA, 64-65, AEROSPACE TECHNOLOGIST, 65- Vis. prof, Dartmouth Col, 68; co-investr. Apollo XI, XII & XIV lunar samples. Geol. Soc. Am; Mineral Soc. Am; Meteoritical Soc. Shock metamorphism of natural materials; geology of terrestrial meteorite impact craters; mineralogy and shock metamorphism of lunar samples; equilibrium relations in natural and artificial solid-gas systems; experimental synthesis and stability studies of carbonate minerals; mineralogy and petrology of sedimentary and metamorphosed iron formations. Address: 7408 Wyndale Lane, Chevy Chase, MD 20015.

FRENCH, C(HARLES) CLEMENT, b. Phila, Pa, Oct. 24, 01; m. 25; c. 2. CHEMISTRY. B.S, Pennsylvania, 22, M.S, 23, Ph.D.(phys. chem), 27; LL.D, Punjab, Pakistan, 55, Whitworth Col.(Wash), 56, Wash. State Univ, 66; hon. Litt.D, Pacific Lutheran, 60. Asst. chem, Pennsylvania, 22-23, instr, 23-30; prof. & head dept, Randolph-Macon Woman's Col, 30-49, dean, 36-49; v.pres, Va. Polytech, 49-50, dean, Agr. & Mech. Col. Tex, 50-52; pres, WASH. STATE UNIV, 52-66, EMER. PRES, 66- Pres, Land-Grant Cols. & State Univs, 58-59, chmn. exec. comt, 59-60. With U.S.A.A.F; Off. Naval Res, 42. AAAS; Effect of neutral salts with hydrogen ion catalysis. Address: 305 Sunset Dr, Pullman, WA 99163.

FRENCH, C(HARLES) STACY, b. Lowell, Mass, Dec. 13, 07; m. 38; c. 2. PLANT PHYSIOLOGY. S.B, Harvard, 30, M.A, 32, Ph.D.(biol), 34. Asst. gen. physiol, Radcliffe Col, 30-31; Harvard, 31-33; res. fel. biol, Calif. Inst. Tech, 34-35; guest worker, Kaiser Wilhelm Inst, 35-36; Austin teaching fel. biochem, Harvard Med. Sch, 36-38; instr. chem, Chicago, 38-41; asst. prof. bot, Minnesota, 41-45, assoc. prof, 45-47; DIR. DEPT. PLANT BIOL, CARNEGIE INST, 47-, PROF. BIOL. BY COURTESY, 64- Nat. Acad. Sci; AAAS; Bot. Soc. Am; Am. Soc. Plant Physiol; Am. Soc. Biol. Chem; Biophys. Soc; Soc. Gen. Physiol.(pres, 55); Optical Soc. Am; Am. Acad. Arts & Sci; Leopold Carol German Acad. Res. Natural Sci. Cellular respiration; photosynthesis of purple bacteria, leaves and algae; characteristics, spectroscopy and functions of plant pigments. Address: Dept. of Plant Biology, Carnegie Institution, Stanford, CA 94305.

FRENCH, CHESTER L(EROY), b. Greenfield, Mass, Aug. 26, 11; m. 39; c. 2. CHEMISTRY. B.S, Mass. State Col, 34, M.S, 38; Ph.D.(phys. chem), Missouri, 40. Asst. chem, Mass. State Col, 34-36; Missouri, 36-40; chemist, MALLINCKRODT CHEM. WORKS, 40-43, sect. head, anal. lab, Manhattan proj, 43-45, in charge anal. lab, 45-54, head qual. & related probs. group, 54-64, tech. comt. specialist, 64-66, sr. chemist, 66-68, SR. RES. ASSOC,

69- Am. Chem. Soc; Acad. Pharmaceut. Sci; Am. Pharmaceut. Asn. Analytical and physical chemistry; colorimetrics and spectrophotometrics of ferric thiocyanate solutions; ferric thiocyanate and related equilibria; absorption of copper sulfate in mixtures of ordinary and heavy water. Address: 121 S. Maple Ave, Webster Groves, MO 63119.

FRENCH, DAVID M(ILTON), b. Alexandria, Va, July 11, 14; m; c. 2. PHYSICAL CHEMISTRY. B.S, Virginia, 36, Ph.D.(chem), 40. Chemist, U.S. Rubber Co, 40-46; res. engr, eng. exp. sta, Florida, 46-48; Nat. Bur Standards, 49-52; Acme Backing Corp, 53-56; Wyandotte Chem. Corp, 56-59; U.S. NAVAL ORD. STA, 62-67, BR. HEAD, 67- Polymer chemistry; polymerization; prepolymers; propellant binders. Address: 703 S. Fairfax St, Alexandria, VA 22314.

FRENCH, DAVID N(ICHOLS), b. Newton, Mass, Jan. 24, 36; m. 60; c. 4. PHYSICAL METALLURGY. B.S, Mass. Inst. Tech, 58, M.S, 59, Sc.D. (metall), 62. Res. metallurgist, Linde Div, Union Carbide Corp, 62-63; mem. tech. staff, Ingersoll-Rand Res. Center, 63-68; PHYS. METALLURGIST, ABEX CORP. RES. CTR, MAHWAH, 68- Am. Soc. Metals; Am. Inst. Mining, Metall. & Petrol. Eng. Mechanical properties and solidification of sea ice; heat flow and transfer; mechanical behavior, x-ray stress analysis and manufacture of composites. Address: 881 Hillcrest Rd, Ridgewood, NJ 07450.

FRENCH, DAVID W(ESTON), b. Mason City, Iowa, Nov. 10, 21; m. 44; c. 3. FOREST PATHOLOGY. B.S, Minnesota, 43, M.S, 49, Ph.D, 52. Instr, PLANT PATH, UNIV. MINN, ST. PAUL, 50-53, asst. prof, 53-57, assoc. prof, 57-63, PROF, 63- U.S.A, 42-46, Capt. Am. Phytopath. Soc; Forest Prod. Res. Soc; Soc. Am. Foresters; Mycol. Soc. Am; Am. Forestry Asn. Products pathology; mycology. Address: Dept. of Plant Pathology, University of Minnesota, St. Paul, MN 55101.

FRENCH, DEXTER, b. Des Moines, Iowa, Feb. 23, 18; m. 39; c. 6. BIOCHEMISTRY. B.A, Dubuque, 38, hon. D.Sc, 60; fel, Iowa State Univ, 38-42, Ph.D.(plant chem), 42. Corn Prod. Co. fel, Harvard Med. Sch, 42-44; res. chemist, Corn Prod. Co, 44-45; asst. prof. chem, IOWA STATE UNIV, 46-51, assoc. prof, 51-55, PROF, 55-60, biochem, 60-71, CHEM. & BIOCHEM, 71-, DISTINGUISHED PROF. AGR, 68-, chmn. dept. biochem. & biophys, 63-71. Nat. Sci. Found. res. fel, Univ. London & Univ. Paris, 62-63. Am. Chem. Soc.(Hudson Award, 64); Brit. Biochem. Soc; Am. Soc. Biol. Chem; Am. Asn. Cereal Chem. Carbohydrates; starch; amylases. Address: Dept. of Biochemistry, Iowa State University, Ames, IA 50010.

FRENCH, EDWARD P(ERRY), b. Boise, Idaho, Aug. 9, 24; m. 49; c. 2. PHYSICAL CHEMISTRY, METALLURGY. B.S, Stanford, 48, M.S, 50, Ph.D. (metall), 52. Group supvr. ramjet engines, Marquardt Aircraft Co, 52-58; MEM. TECH. STAFF, SPACE DIV, N.AM. ROCKWELL CORP, DOWNEY, 58- Instr, eng. exten, Univ. Calif, Los Angeles, 57 & 62, lectr, col. eng, 65-66. U.S.A.A.F, 43-45. Soc. Eng. Sci; Combustion Inst; Am. Inst. Aeronaut. & Astronaut; Sci. Res. Soc. Am. Aircraft and space propulsion; combustion; aerothermochemistry; thermodynamics; heat transfer. Address: 15988 El Soneto Dr, Whittier, CA 90603.

FRENCH, ELLERY W(ALTER), b. Cranston, R.I, Feb. 20, 18; m. 50; c. 5. ENTOMOLOGY, ECOLOGY. B.S, Rhode Island, 48; M.S, Hawaii, 50; Ph.D. (entom), Illinois, 53. Mem. staff agr. chem. prod. develop, Rohm & Haas Co, Pa, 53-63; ASST. PROF. ZOOL, DELAWARE VALLEY COL, 63- Sr. researcher, herbicide res. grant, Smith Kline & French Labs, 64- U.S.A.A.F, 40-45, Sgt. Entom. Soc. Am; Am. Entom. Soc. Long-range effects of various pesticides' residues on various soil dwelling organisms. Address: Dept. of Biology, Delaware Valley College, Doylestown, PA 18901.

FRENCH, ERNEST W(EBSTER), b. Osnabrock, N.Dak, July 19, 29; m. 54; c. 2. AGRICULTURAL ENGINEERING. B.S, N.Dak. State, 51, M.S, 56. Salesman, Standard Oil Co, 54-55; asst. agr. engr, N.DAK. STATE UNIV, 57-59, asst. prof. agr. eng, 59-60, SUPT, WILLISTON BR. EXP. STA, 60- U.S.A, 51-54. Am. Soc. Agr. Eng. Soil and water conservation research and application. Address: Williston Branch Experimental Station, North Dakota State University, Box 1445, Williston, ND 58801.

FRENCH, FRANCIS WILLIAM, b. Brooklyn, N.Y, Dec. 28, 27; m. 67; c. 3. AEROSPACE ENGINEERING, APPLIED MECHANICS. B.S, Polytech. Inst. Brooklyn, 51, M.S, 56, Ph.D.(aeronaut. eng), 59. Struct. draftsman, Grumman Aircraft, 51-52; stress analyst, aerophysics lab, N.Am. Aviation, Inc, 52-53; res. asst. aerospace eng. & appl. mech, Polytech. Inst. Brooklyn, 53-55, res. assoc, 55-59; sr. engr, Technik, Inc, 59-60; sr. staff mem, Allied Res. Assocs, 60-61, chief appl. mech. group, 61-62; mem. tech. staff, space systs. dept, Mitre Corp, Mass, 62-65; sr. consult. engr, sci. satellite proj. off, AVCO CORP, 65-67, prin. res. engr, Avco Everett Res. Lab, 67-70, sr. consult. scientist, Avco Systs. Div, 70-71, PRIN. RES. ENGR, AVCO EVERETT RES. LAB, 71- U.S.A, 46-47. Assoc. fel. Am. Inst. Aeronaut. & Astronaut; sr. mem. Am. Astronaut. Soc. Laser systems; manned and unmanned spacecraft; structural mechanics. Address: Avco Everett Research Lab, 2385 Revere Beach Pkwy, Everett, MA 02149.

FRENCH, F(RANK) E(DWARD), JR, b. Cincinnati, Ohio, May 8, 22; m. 46; c. 3. CHEMICAL ENGINEERING. B.S, Mass. Inst. Tech, 43, Sc.D.(chem. eng), 48. Res. engr, Grasselli Chem. Dept, E.I. DU PONT DE NEMOURS & CO, INC, 48-50, res. supvr, 50-53, mgr. eng. develop. sect, 53-54, asst. tech. supt, 55-56, mem. develop. dept, 56-59, mgr. new prod. & mkt. develop, 59-61, sales mgr. indust. chem, 62-67, MGR. BUS. & SYSTS. ANAL, ORG. CHEM. DEPT, 67- U.S.N.R, 43-46, Lt. Am. Chem. Soc; Sci. Res. Soc. Am; Am. Inst. Chem. Eng. Specialty chemicals; marketing research; economic analysis; computer science. Address: Organic Chemicals Dept, E.I. du Pont de Nemours & Co, Inc, Box 525, Wilmington, DE 19899.

FRENCH, FRANK E(LWOOD), JR, b. Lubbock, Tex, Feb. 20, 35; m. 58; c. 2. ENTOMOLOGY, PARASITOLOGY. B.S, Tex. Tech, Col, 57; M.S, Iowa State, 58, Ph.D.(entom), 62. Res. assoc. med. entom, Queen's Univ. (Ont), 66-68; ASST. PROF. BIOL, GA. SOUTH. COL, 68- Med.Serv.C, U.S.A, 63-66, Res, 66-, Capt. Entom. Soc. Am. Acarina and Insecta of medical and veterinary importance, ectoparasites of mammals; allergic skin reaction to insect bites; Demodex hair follicle mites; life history, host aquisition, host's pathologic response. Address: Dept. of Biology, Georgia Southern College, Statesboro, GA 30458.

FRENCH, FREDERIC ALEXIS, b. Berkeley, Calif, Mar. 19, 17; m. 37; c. 2. CHEMOTHERAPY. A.B, California, 42. Jr. chemist, Shell Develop. Co, 40-42, chem. engr, 42-45; res. chemist chemother, Harold Brunn Res. Inst, Mt. Zion Hosp, 44-50, consult, chemother. res, 50-56, res. assoc. cancer chemother, MT. ZION HOSP. & MED. CENTER, 56-61, DIR. CHEMOTHER. RES, 61- Res. Chemist, U.S. Naval Radiol. Defense Lab, 51-56. AAAS; N.Y. Acad. Sci; Am. Chem. Soc; Am. Asn. Cancer Res. Organic analysis and synthesis; organic group analytical research; thermodynamics; chemotherapy of tuberculosis, malaria and cancer. Address: 2 Le Roy Ave, Portola Valley, CA 94026.

FRENCH, GILBERT M(ORSE), b. Buffalo, N.Y, Jan. 3, 28; m. 56; c. 3. PSYCHOLOGY. B.A, Maine, 52; M.S, Wisconsin, 54, Ph.D.(psychol), 56. Nat. Sci. Found. fel, Calif. Inst. Technol, 56-57; asst. prof. PSYCHOL, California, Berkeley, 57-63, assoc. prof, 63-67; PROF. & CHMN. DEPT, UNIV. S.DAK, 67- U.S. Pub. Health Serv. res. grants, 61-67. Psychol. consult, Vet. Admin, 68- U.S.A, 46-47. AAAS; Am. Psychol. Asn; Ecol. Soc. Am. Psychobiology; brain-behavior correlations, particularly on frontal lobe functions as they relate to adaptive behavior in primates. Address: Dept. of Psychology, University of South Dakota, Vermillion, SD 57069.

FRENCH, GORDON N(ICHOLS), b. Washington, D.C, March 14, 19; m. 42; c. 4. INTERNAL MEDICINE. A.B, Yale, 41; M.D, Tufts, 44. Intern path, Boston City Hosp, 44-45; fel. pharmacol, Harvard, 46-47; res. med, Veterans Admin. Hosp, Boston, 47-48; Bellevue Hosp, N.Y, 48-49; physician, Green Mountain Clinic, Vt, 49-53; instr. med, sch. med, Tufts, 54-59; asst. physician, Harvard, 55-59, res. assoc, sch. pub. health, 57-59; dir. med, Misericordia Hosp, 59-67; ASST. PROF. CLIN. MED. & ASSOC. DEAN, SCH. MED, UNIV. PA, 67- Consult, Lemmuel Shattuck Hosp, Boston, 55-59. U.S.N.R, 42-46, 53-54. Fel. Am. Col. Physicians. Cardiovascular physiology; ventricular pressure; volume relationships and oxygen consumption in fibrillation and arrest. Address: University of Pennsylvania School of Medicine, Philadelphia, PA 19104.

FRENCH, HOBERT W(ARD), JR, b. Chelsea, Mass, Aug. 16, 11; m. 34; c. 1. OPTICS, PHYSICS. A.B, Harvard, 32; M.S, Mass. Inst. Tech, 35; Ph.D. (optics), Rochester, 45. Asst, U.S. Dept. Agr, Mass, 36-39; asst. solar, Rochester, 39-41, instr, 41-45, asst. prof, 45; chief design engr. in charge res. & new design, Argus, Inc, 45-50; engr, instrument div, Am. Optical Co, 50-52, mgr. develop, 52-56, spec. prod, 56-62; mgr. optical develop, Link Div, Gen. Precision, Inc, 62-63; CHIEF PHOTO-OPTICAL ENGR, ITEK CORP, 63- With Off. Sci. Res. & Develop, 44. Am. Phys. Soc; assoc. Optical Soc. Am. Optical instrument design; astrophysics; electronics; antivibration mounts for optical instruments; cameras and associated equipment; mechanical vibrations in optical systems. Address: 1 Ministerial Dr, West Concord, MA 01781.

FRENCH, HUGH MORTON, b. U.K, Feb. 2, 43. GEOGRAPHY. B.A, Southampton, 64, Ph.D.(geog), 67. ASST. PROF. GEOG, UNIV. OTTAWA, 67- Quantitative geomorphology and climatology; periglacial features of the middle-latitudes of the world. Address: Dept. of Geography, University of Ottawa, Ottawa 2, Ont, Can.

FRENCH, IAN P, b. Cuenca, Ecuador, Apr. 22, 35; m. 59; c. 2. MICROWAVE & PLASMA PHYSICS. B.Sc, St. Andrews, 56, Hons, 58; McGill, 58-62; California, Santa Barbara, 63-65, M.S, 67. Elec. engr, Canadair, Ltd, Can, 58-59; mem. sci. staff plasma physics, RCA Victor Co. Ltd, 59-62; SR. RES. PHYSICIST, DELCO ELECTRONICS, GEN. MOTORS CORP, 62- Plasma diagnostics, particularly by microwave methods; turbulence and radar scatter from plasma. Address: Delco Electronics, 6767 Hollister Ave, Goleta, CA 93107.

FRENCH, IAN W(ILFRED), b. Chilliwack, B.C, Nov. 11, 33; m. 56; c. 2. BIOCHEMISTRY. B.S.P, British Columbia, 57; Nat. Res. Coun. Can. fels, Toronto, 59-63, Ph.D.(biochem), 63. Nat. Res. Coun. Can. overseas fel, 63-65; asst. prof. physiol, Ottawa (Ont), 65-67; SR. BIOCHEMIST, Smith Kline & French Res. Ctr, Que, 67-70; NUCRO-TECHNICS LTD, 70- Med. Res. Coun. Can. res. grants, 65-68; Muscular Dystrophy res. grant, 66-67. Can. Biochem. Soc; Can. Physiol. Soc; Can. Asn. Lab. Animal Sci; Brit. Biochem. Soc. Muscle metabolism and effect of adrenal steroids; effect of cardiac hypertrophy and hormones on nucleic acid metabolism; microbial metabolism; synthetic polynucleotides. Address: Nucro-Technics Ltd, 2000 Ellesmere Rd, Unit II, Scarborough 722, Ont, Can.

FRENCH, JAMES AUSTIN, b. Memphis, Tenn, Aug. 13, 45; m. 67; c. 2. TOPOLOGY. B.A, David Lipscomb Col, 67; M.S, Auburn Univ, 68, Ph.D. (math), 69. ASST. PROF. MATH, La. State Univ, Baton Rouge, 69-70; DAVID LIPSCOMB COL, 70- Am. Math. Soc. Point set topology; coverings and their relation to dimension in topological spaces. Address: Dept. of Mathematics, David Lipscomb College, 3901-4001 Granny White Pike, Nashville, TN 37203.

FRENCH, JAMES C, b. Detroit, Mich, Apr. 25, 30; m. 56; c. 1. ORGANIC CHEMISTRY. B.S, Wayne State, 51, U.S. Pub. Health Serv. fel, 52-54, Ph.D. (chem), 54. U.S. Pub. Health Serv. fel, Harvard, 54-56; RES. CHEMIST, PARKE, DAVIS & CO, 56- Am. Chem. Soc. Nitrogen analogs of ketenes; isolation and chemistry of antibiotics. Address: 20009 Blackburn St, St. Clair Shores, MI 48080.

FRENCH, J(OHN) BARRY, b. Toronto, Ont, Aug. 22, 31; m. 51; c. 4. AEROSPACE ENGINEERING. B.Sc, Univ. Toronto, 55, Ph.D.(low density plasmas), 61; M.Sc, Univ. Birmingham, 57. Attached scientist, ramjets, Nat. Gas Turbine Estab, 55-56; lectr. AEROSPACE ENG. SCI, INST. AEROSPACE STUDIES, UNIV. TORONTO, 61-62, asst. prof, 62-64, assoc. prof, 64-68, PROF, 68- Past pres. Aerospace Eng. & Res. Consultants Ltd; consult, Martin Marietta Corp. & Bristol Aerospace Ltd; mem. assoc. comt. aerodynam, Nat. Res. Coun. Assoc. fel. Can. Aeronaut. & Space Inst; Am. Inst. Aeronaut. & Astronaut; Am. Phys. Soc. Space simulator development; gas-surface and vehicle-planetary atmospheric interactions; atmospheric instrumentation for satellites; outgassing and contamination; space materials testing; molecular beams; mass spectroscopy; instrumentation for trace gas analysis. Address: Institute for Aerospace Studies, University of Toronto, Toronto 5, Ont, Can.

FRENCH, JOHN D(ONALD), b. New Orleans, La, Feb. 19, 23; m. 48; c. 4. PHYSICS. B.S, La. State, 48, M.S, 52, Ph.D.(physics), 58. Physicist, U.S. Geol. Surv, 53-55; asst. prof. PHYSICS, AUBURN UNIV, 58-63, ASSOC. PROF, 63- U.S.A, 43-46. Am. Phys. Soc. Nuclear physics. Address: Dept. of Physics, Auburn University, Auburn, AL 36830.

FRENCH, JOHN DOUGLAS, b. Los Angeles, Calif, Apr. 11, 11. NEUROSURGERY. A.B, California, Los Angeles, 33; M.D, Southern California, 37. Intern, internal med, univ. hosp, California, 37-38; asst. res. surg, Strong Mem. Hosp, 38-41; instr, sch. med, Rochester, 41-43, asst. prof. neurosurg, 43-46; neuropsychiat. inst, Illinois, 46-47; assoc. clin. prof. surg, MED. SCH, UNIV. CALIF, LOS ANGELES, 49-58, PROF. ANAT. & CLIN. PROF. SURG, 58-, DIR, BRAIN RES. INST, 60- Intern & asst. neurosurg, Strong Mem. Hosp, 38-39, assoc. res, 41-42, chief res. surg, 42-43, acting head div. neurosurg. & asst. surgeon, 43-46; chief neurosurg, Vet. Admin. Hosp, Long Beach, 48-58, acting chief, neuropsychiat, 50-58, dir. invest. med, 54-58; mem. ed. adv. bd, Commun. in Behav. Biol, 68-71; Progress in Brain Res. J, 65-70. Dipl, Am. Bd. Surg, 43; Am. Bd. Neurol. Surg, 47. Am. Asn. Neurol. Surg; Soc. Univ. Surg; Am. Med. Asn; Am. Acad. Neurol. Surg; Soc. Neurol. Surg; Am. Neurol. Asn; Soc. Neurosci. Function and disorder of the nervous system. Address: Brain Research Institute, University of California Medical Center, Los Angeles, CA 90024.

FRENCH, JOSEPH H, b. Toledo, Ohio, July 4, 28; m; c. 4. PEDIATRICS, NEUROLOGY. B.A, Ohio State, 50, M.D, 54. John Hay Whitney Found. fel, 54-55; sr. clin. traineeship fel, Nat. Inst. Neurol. Diseases & Blindness, 57-61; asst. prof. PEDIAT. & NEUROL, sch. med, Colorado, 61-64; ALBERT EINSTEIN COL. MED, 64-69, ASSOC. PROF, 69-, ASST. DEAN, 70- Assoc. attend, Montefiore Hosp. & Med. Ctr, 64-; assoc. vis. pediatrician, Morrisania City Hosp, 64-; asst. vis. neurologist, Bronx Munic. Hosp, 64-; consult, Jewish Mem. Hosp, 66-; Commonwealth Fund fel, 70. Dipl, Am. Bd. Pediat, 60; dipl. neurol, Am. Bd. Psychiat. & Neurol, 65. U.S.A, 45-47. Fel. Am. Acad. Pediat; fel. Am. Acad. Neurol; Soc. Pediat. Res. Neurochemistry and clinical pediatric neurology. Address: Montefiore Hospital & Medical Ctr, 111 E. 210th St, Bronx, NY 10461.

FRENCH, JUDSON C(ULL), b. Wash, D.C, Sept. 30, 22; m. 51; c. 1. APPLIED PHYSICS. B.S, American Univ, 43; Hopkins, 43-44; George Washington, 44-45; M.S, Harvard, 49. Instr. physics, Hopkins, 43-44; George Washington, 44-47; proj. leader gaseous electronics, NAT. BUR. STANDARDS, 48-50, group leader, 51-56, SOLID STATE DEVICES, 56-64, asst. chief, ELECTRON DEVICES SECT, 64-68, CHIEF, 68- Silver medal, Dept. Commerce, 64; Edward Bennett Rosa Award, Nat. Bur. Standards, 71. Am. Phys. Soc; Inst. Elec. & Electronics Eng; Am. Soc. Test. & Mat. Gaseous electronics and semiconductors; microwave gas switching tubes; measurements and research on semiconductor devices and materials. Address: Electron Devices Section, National Bureau of Standards, Washington, DC 20234.

FRENCH, LESLIE HOWSON, b. London, Eng, Mar. 8, 95; nat; m. 29. PHYSIOLOGY. M.D, George Washington, 24. Assoc. prof. embryol. & histol, sch. med, George Washington, 22-24, prof. physiol. & head dept, 25-33; assoc. prof. clin. med, sch. med, Georgetown, 34-60; dir. med. ed. & res, Sibley Mem. Hosp, 63-66; CONSULT, 66- Chief dept. med, Prince Georges Gen. Hosp, 45-58, chief cardiologist & dir. heart sta, 45-60, consult, 45- Dipl, Am. Bd. Internal Med. Ordoneau scholar, George Washington Univ. Fel. Am. Col. Physicians; fel. Am. Col. Cardiol; Am. Col. Chest Physicians; fel. Am. Soc. Internal Med; fel. Am. Col. Angiol; fel. Asn. Hosp. Med. Educ. Human physiology; electrocardiography; graduate medical education. Address: 6803 Pineway, University Park, Hyattsville, MD 20782.

FRENCH, LYLE ALBERT, b. Worthing, S.Dak, Mar. 26, 15; m. 41; c. 3. NEUROSURGERY. B.S, Minnesota, 36, M.B, 39, M.D, 40, M.S, 46, Ph.D. (neurosurg), 47. Instr. surg, MED. SCH, UNIV. MINN, MINNEAPOLIS, 47-48, asst. prof, 48-52, assoc. prof, 52-57, PROF. NEUROSURG, 57-, DIR. DIV, 60-, V.PRES. HEALTH SCI, UNIV, 70- Dipl, Am. Bd. Neurol. Surg, 48. Med.C, U.S.A, 42-46. Am. Med. Asn. Peripheral nerve injuries; cerebral edema; brain tumors in children. Address: University Hospitals, Minneapolis, MN 55455.

FRENCH, NORMAN R(OGER), b. Kankakee, Ill, Mar. 7, 27; div; c. 2. ZOOLOGY. A.B, Illinois, 49; M.A, Colorado, 51; Ph.D.(zool), Utah, 54. Asst, univ. mus, Colorado, 49-51; instr. zool, Nebraska, 51-52; biol, Utah, 54-55; ecologist, nat. reactor test sta, Atomic Energy Comn, 55-59; res. ecologist, lab. nuclear med. & radiation biol, Univ. Calif, Los Angeles, 59-69; PROF. BIOL, NAT. RESOURCE ECOL. LAB, COLO. STATE UNIV, 69- Curator, Nebr. State Mus, 51-52. U.S.N, 48-49. Fel. AAAS; Wildlife Soc; Am. Inst. Biol. Sci; Ecol. Soc. Am; Am. Ornith. Union; Cooper Ornith. Soc. Desert and alpine ecology, birds and mammals; radiobiology; physiological ecology; computer simulation. Address: Natural Resource Ecology Lab, Colorado State University, Ft. Collins, CO 80521.

FRENCH, ORVAL C, b. Geneseo, Kans, Jan. 3, 08; m. 32; c. 2. AGRICULTURAL ENGINEERING. B.S, Kans. State Col, 30, M.S, 31. Agr. engr, Black-Sivals & Bryson, Mo, 30-31; asst, Kans. State Col, 31; instr. agr. eng, California, 31-39, asst. agr. engr, 40-46, mech. res. engr, Manhattan Dist. proj, radiation lab, 41-45, assoc. prof. AGR. ENG, 47; PROF. & HEAD DEPT, CORNELL UNIV, 57- Vis. prof, Univ. Philippines, Los Baños, 58-59; mem. col. conf. bd, United-Coop, Inc, Ohio. Fel. AAAS; fel. Am. Soc. Agr. Eng.(pres. elect, 65-66, pres, 66-67); Am. Soc. Eng. Educ. Agricultural power and machinery. Address: Dept. of Agricultural Engineering, Riley-Robb Hall, Cornell University, Ithaca, NY 14850.

FRENCH, PARK, b. New Middletown, Ohio, May 3, 26; m. 52; c. 7. NUCLEAR PHYSICS. B.S, Case, 51, M.S, 54, Ph.D.(physics), 58. Reactor physicist, nat. reactor testing sta, atomic energy div, Phillips Petrol. Co, 57-59; eng. specialist, new devices labs, TRW Inc, 59-63, staff engr, equip. labs, 63-70; consult. magnetics & nuclear criticality safety, 70-71. U.S.N.R, 43-46. High-energy particle acceleration and focusing; high-efficiency ion sources; magnetomechanical devices; magnetic materials; dynamoelectric machinery. Address: 59 S. Chillicothe Rd, Aurora, OH 44202.

FRENCH, PRESTON W, b. Avoca, N.Y, Aug. 16, 13; m. 36; c. 2. CERAMIC ENGINEERING. B.S, Alfred, 36; M.S, Ohio State, 37; Pittsburgh, 37-42. Fel, Mellon Inst, 37-40, indust. fel, 40-42; head optics dept, GLASS DIV. RES. CTR, PPG INDUSTS, 42-62, asst. head properties dept, 62-63, SR. RES. ASSOC, 64- Am. Ceramic Soc; Am. Inst. Ceramic Eng; Optical Soc. Am. Physics and chemistry of glass surfaces; spectrophotometry and colorimetry; optical instrument design; thin optical films; laser glass; nondestructive stress measurement; interferometry. Address: Glass Division Research Center, Advanced Research Division, PPG Industries, Box 11472, Pittsburgh, PA 15238.

FRENCH, R(AY) P(ALMER) C(URTIS), b. Pilley's Island, Newf, Aug. 11, 09; m. 32; c. 3. BIOCHEMISTRY. B.Sc, Dalhousie, 30; M.A, Toronto, 32, fel, 33, Ph.D.(biochem), 35. Asst. biochem, Connaught Med. Res. Labs, Toronto, 34-42, res. assoc, 42-55; chemist, Dept. Nat. Health & Welfare, Can, 56-61; res. assoc. ophthal, FACULTY MED, UNIV. TORONTO, 61-63, ASSOC. PROF. BACT, 63- Can. Soc. Microbiol. Antigens and antibodies; poliovirus; bacteriophage. Address: Dept. of Bacteriology, Faculty of Medicine, University of Toronto, Toronto, Ont, Can.

FRENCH, RICHARD C(OLLINS), b. Camden, N.J, Dec. 11, 22. PLANT PHYSIOLOGY. B.S, Rutgers, 47, M.S, 48; univ. res. found. fel, Purdue, 52-53, Ph.D.(plant physiol), 53. PLANT PHYSIOLOGIST, biol. warfare labs, Ft. Detrick, 53-57; biol. sci. br, agr. mkt. serv, U.S. Dept. Agr, 57-62; biol. labs, crops div, U.S. ARMY, 62-68, PLANT SCI. LAB, 68- U.S.A.A.F, 43-46. AAAS; Am. Chem. Soc; Am. Soc. Plant Physiol; Bot. Soc. Am; Am. Phytopath. Soc; Am. Soc. Hort. Sci; fel. Am. Inst. Chem. Seed and spore physiology. Address: Epiphytology Research Lab, Plant Science Research Division, U.S. Dept. of Agriculture, Box 1209, Ft. Detrick, Frederick, MD 21701.

FRENCH, ROBERT DEXTER, b. Springfield, Mass, Oct. 26, 39; m. 65; c. 2. PHYSICAL METALLURGY, SURFACE PHYSICS. B.Sc, Northeast. Univ, 62, M.Sc, 64; Nat. Sci. Found. fel. & Ph.D.(eng), Brown Univ, 67. Res. asst. crystal growth, Northeast. Univ, 62-64; asst. phys. metall, Brown Univ, 64-67; instr, 67, res. assoc, 67-68; METALLURGIST, ARMY MAT. & MECH. RES. CTR, 68- U.S.A, 67-69, Capt. Am. Inst. Min. & Metall. Eng; Am. Soc. Metals; Am. Crystallog. Soc. Study of metal structure and metal surfaces through electron and field ion microscopy; diffusion of interstitials; creep and stress-rupture in single and two-phase alloys. Address: Metals Division, Army Materials & Mechanics Research Center, Watertown, MA 02172.

FRENCH, ROBERT LEWIS, b. Henry Co, Tenn, Sept. 23, 28; m. 52; c. 3. RADIATION PHYSICS, COMPUTER SCIENCES. B.S, Murray State Col, 54; U.S. Atomic Energy Comn. fel, Vanderbilt Univ, 54-55, M.S, 55. Nuclear group engr, Gen. Dynamics Corp, 55-63; V.PRES. RES, RADIATION RES. ASSOCS, INC, 63- Pres, Comd. Systs. Corp, 69-; mem. adv. comt. civil defense, Nat. Acad. Sci, 69-; consult, Oak Ridge Nat. Lab, 71- U.S.M.C, 46-50. AAAS; Am. Nuclear Soc; Health Physics Soc; Asn. Comput. Mach. Development of mathematical models and analysis techniques for evaluation of, and protection from, radiation fields produced by nuclear reactors and nuclear weapons; development of computer-automated vehicular systems. Address: 5667 Worrell Dr, Ft. Worth, TX 76133.

FRENCH, R(OWLAND) B(ARNES), b. Haverhill, Mass, Dec. 20, 96; m. 24; c. 2. BIOCHEMISTRY. B.S, Dartmouth Col, 20; M.S, Mass. Col, 22; fel, Yale, 31; Ph.D.(biochem), Iowa, 33. Asst. chemist, inst. animal nutrit, Pa. State Col, 22-26, assoc. chemist, 26-30, fel, Iowa, 34; from assoc. chemist, to biochemist, AGR. EXP. STA, UNIV. FLA, 35-67, EMER. BIOCHEMIST, 67- With Off. Sci. Res. & Develop, 44. Sig.C, U.S.A, 17-19. Am. Chem. Soc. Nutrition of farm animals; nutritive value of food; human nutrition; fat antioxidants; royal jelly; mineral nutrition; gerontology. Address: 1225 N.E. 5th Terrace, Gainesville, FL 32601.

FRENCH, THAYER CARLTON, b. Pittsburgh, Pa, Mar. 2, 35. ENZYMOLOGY, ORGANIC CHEMISTRY. B.S, Mass. Inst. Tech, 57, Gen. Foods Corp. fel, 57, Nat. Sci. Found. fel, 57-60, Nat. Insts. Health fel, 60-61, Ph.D.(biochem), 63. Instr. biochem, Mass. Inst. Tech, 61-63; fel. chem, Cornell, 63-64; Nat. Inst. Gen. Med. Sci. fel, MASS. INST. TECHNOL, 64-65, ASST. PROF. CHEM, 65- Am. Chem. Soc. Biochemical genetics in Neurospora crassa labeling of enzyme active sites; model enzyme chemistry; fast reaction techniques. Address: 29 Staunton Rd, Belmont, MA 02178.

FRENCH, WALTER R(USSELL), JR, b. Inman, Nebr, Sept. 29, 23; m. 45; c. 3. PHYSICS. A.B, Nebr. Wesleyan, 48; M.A, Iowa, 50; Ph.D.(physics), Nebraska, 57; Univ. Wis, 65-66. Instr. PHYSICS, Nebr. State Teachers Col. (Peru), 50-51; asst. prof, NEBR. WESLEYAN UNIV, 51-52, assoc. prof, 52-56, prof, 56-62, E.C. AMES DISTINGUISHED PROF, 62-, HEAD DEPT, 52-, chmn. sci. div, 56-62. Nat. Sci. Found. faculty fel, Wisconsin, 65-66; dir. & lectr, Nat. Sci. Found. in-serv. insts, 60-61, 61-62, 62-63, dir, 64-65; co-dir, Nebr. Acad. Sci. vis. scientist prog, 56-64; participant, Oak Ridge Nat. Labs, 63; summers, lectr, summer insts, Minnesota, 58-59, dir. & lectr, Nat. Sci. Found. Summer Insts, 60, 61, 62, dir, 63, 65, 67-71. Consult, Oak Ridge Inst. Nuclear Studies, Atomic Energy Comn, 62- Woods outstanding teacher, Nebr. Wesleyan, 61. U.S.A.A.F, 42-46, 2nd Lt. Am. Phys. Soc; Am. Asn. Physics Teachers. Experimental nuclear physics; applications of nuclear spectroscopy techniques. Address: Dept. of Physics, Nebraska Wesleyan University, Lincoln, NE 68504.

FRENCH, WARREN NEIL, b. Waverley, Ont, June 27, 35; m. 61; c. 3. ORGANIC CHEMISTRY. B.S.A, Ont. Agr. Col, 56, M.S.A, 57; Ph.D.(org. chem), McMaster, 60. Univ. fel, Toronto, 60-62; CHEMIST PHARMACEUT, FOOD & DRUG DIR, DEPT. NAT. HEALTH & WELFARE, 62- Chem. Inst. Can. Pharmaceutical chemistry. Address: Food & Drug Directorate, Dept. of National Health & Welfare, Ottawa, Ont, K1A 0L2, Can.

FRENCH, W(ILBUR) L(ILE), b. Hammond, Ind, Mar. 16, 29; m. 54; c. 3. GENETICS, CYTOGENETICS. B.S, Illinois, 56, M.S, 57, Ph.D.(cytol, genetics), 62; Nat. Sci. Found. fel, Oregon, 59. Instr. biol, Eastern Illinois, 58-59; res. assoc. GENETICS, Illinois, 62-63; U.S. Pub. Health Serv. Fel, California, Riverside, 63-64; Univ. Mainz, 64-65; asst. prof. to ASSOC. PROF, LA. STATE UNIV, 65- AAAS; Am. Mosquito Control Asn. Mosquito genetics and cytogenetics. Address: Dept. of Genetics, Louisiana State University, Baton Rouge, LA 70803.

FRENCH, WILLIAM E(DWIN), b. Jackson, Mich, Nov. 17, 36; m. 58; c. 2. OCEANOGRAPHY, MARINE GEOLOGY. B.S, Univ. Mich, 58, M.S, 60, Ph.D. (oceanog), 65. Asst. res. geologist, Great Lakes res. div, Univ. Mich, 59-66; oceanographer, Marine Geophys. Surv, U.S. Navy Oceanog. Off, D.C, 66-68; ASST. PROF. GEOL, HOPE COL, 68- U.S.A.R, 54-62. Am. Soc. Limnol. & Oceanog; Soc. Econ. Paleont. & Mineral; Geol. Soc. Am; Am. Geophys. Union. Measurement of sedimentary activity and near-bottom current regime in Great Lakes; Great Lakes estuarine circulation. Address: Dept. of Geology, Hope College, Holland, MI 49423.

FRENCH, WILLIAM STANLEY, b. Colfax, Iowa, Sept. 17, 40; m. 68; c. 6. GEOPHYSICS, MATHEMATICS. B.S, Iowa State Univ, 62; Ph.D.(geophys), Ore. State Univ, 70. Asst. phys, Ore. State Univ, 62-64, geophysics, 64-68; RES. GEOPHYSICIST, GULF RES. & DEVELOP. CO, GULF OIL CORP, 68- Soc. Explor. Geophys; Am. Geophys. Union; Seismol. Soc. Am. Application of mathematical theory of elastic wave propagation to problems in earthquake seismology and petroleum exploration; oceanographic seismology; gravity and magnetic exploration; ultrasonic modeling. Address: 2429 Foxfield Dr, Glenshaw, PA 15116.

FRENKEL, ALBERT W, b. Berlin, Ger, Jan. 1, 19; nat; m. 48; c. 3. PLANT PHYSIOLOGY. B.A, California, 39, Ph.D.(plant physiol), 42. Asst, California, 39-42; Calif. Inst. Tech, 42-44; assoc. radiol, Rochester, U.S. Army, Manhattan Dist. & Atomic Energy Comn. contract, 45-47; asst. prof. BOT, UNIV. MINN, MINNEAPOLIS, 47-51, assoc. prof, 51-55, PROF, 55- Res. fel, Mass. Gen. Hosp, 54; vis. scientist, Johns Hopkins Univ. Marine Sta, 67-68. Med.C. & Eng.C, U.S.A, 45-46. Fel. AAAS; Am. Soc. Plant Physiol; Am. Chem. Soc; Am. Soc. Microbiol; Am. Soc. Biol. Chem; Am. Soc. Oceanog; Japanese Soc. Plant Physiol. Biochemistry; photosynthesis; regulation of microbial metabolism. Address: Dept. of Botany, University of Minnesota, Minneapolis, MN 55455.

FRENKEL, CHAIM, b. Tel Aviv, Israel, Mar. 16, 34. HORTICULTURE. B.S, Hebrew Univ, Israel, 58; M.S, Massachusetts, Amherst, 61; Ph.D. (hort), Washington State, 66. FEL, Mich. State, 66-68; RUTGERS UNIV, 68- Israeli Armed Forces, 52-55, Lt. Am. Soc. Plant Physiol. Post harvest physiology; carbon dioxide interaction with cellular metabolism of harvested pome fruits; ripening of pome fruits in relation to protein synthesis; isozymic polymorphism in relation to lateral root initiation. Address: Dept. of Horticulture, Rutgers University, New Brunswick, NJ 08903.

FRENKEL, EUGENE P(HILLIP), b. Detroit, Mich, Aug. 27, 29; m. 58; c. 1. INTERNAL MEDICINE, HEMATOLOGY. B.S, Wayne, 49, M.D, Michigan, 53. Intern, Wayne County Gen. Hosp, Mich, 53-54; res, Boston City Hosp, Mass, 54-55; med. center, Michigan, 57-59, res. assoc. hemat, 59-60, instr, 60-62; asst. prof. INTERNAL MED, SOUTHWEST. MED. SCH, UNIV. TEX, 62-66, assoc. prof, 66-69, PROF, 69-, CHIEF SECT. HEMAT, 62- Consult, Lisbon Vet. Admin. Hosp, 62-; St. Paul Hosp, 64-; Brooke Army Hosp, 65- U.S.A.F, 55-57, Maj. Fel. Am. Col. Physicians; Am. Soc. Hemat; Int. Soc. Hemat; Am. Fedn. Clin. Res; Soc. Nuclear Med; Am. Asn. Cancer Res; Am. Soc. Clin. Oncol. Cancer chemotherapy. Address: Dept. of Internal Medicine, Southwestern Medical School, University of Texas, 5323 Harry Hines Blvd, Dallas, TX 75235.

FRENKEL, J(ACOB) K(ARL), b. Darmstadt, Ger, Feb. 16, 21; nat; m. 54; c. 3. PATHOLOGY. A.B, California, 42, M.D, 46, Ph.D.(comp. path), 48. Asst. zool, California, 40-42, 43, bact, 42-43; anat, 43-44, intern path, univ. hosp, 46-47, clin. asst, med. sch, 47-48; pathologist, Rocky Mt. lab, U.S. Pub. Health Serv, 48-52; instr, med. sch, Tennessee, 51-52; asst. prof. PATH, SCH. MED, UNIV. KANS, 52-57, assoc. prof, 57-60, PROF, 60- Res, path. lab, Nat. Insts. Health, 50-51; Fulbright fel. & vis. prof, Nat. Univ. Mex, 63-64; mem, subcomt. comp. path, div. med. sci, Nat. Res. Coun; sci. panel, Lunar Receiving Lab. U.S.A, 43-46. AAAS; Wildlife Disease Asn; Reticuloendothelial Soc; Soc. Exp. Biol. & Med; Soc. Psychol. Study Social Issues; Am. Soc. Exp. Path; Am. Asn. Path. & Bact; N.Y. Acad. Sci; Int. Acad. Path; Infectious Diseases Soc. Am; Am. Soc. Trop. Med. & Hyg. Pathogenesis of infection with obligate intracellular organisms; adrenal infection and necrosis; effects of corticoids on immunity and hypersensitivity; cellular immunity; toxoplasmosis. Address: Dept. of Pathology & Oncology, University of Kansas Medical Center, Kansas City, KS 66103.

FRENKEL, LOTHAR, b. Vienna, Austria, Oct. 10, 23; U.S. citizen; m. 48; c. 3. PHYSICS. B.Sc, London, 49, Hons, 52; Ph.D.(physics), Maryland, 64. PHYSICIST, Tektronix Inc, 56-58; Nat. Bur. Standards, 58-64; Martin Co, Fla, 65-66; Electronics Res. Ctr, NASA, 66-71; TRANSPORTATION SYSTS. CTR, U.S. DEPT. TRANSPORTATION, CAMBRIDGE, 71- AAAS; Am. Phys. Soc. Electron ballistics; dielectric measurements; nuclear acoustical resonance; orientational relaxation in gases; microwave spectra and absorption; absolute laser frequency measurements. Address: 27 Greystone Park, Lynn, MA 01902.

FRENKEL, RENE, b. Santiago, Chile, Sept. 1, 32; m. 59; c. 4. BIOCHEMISTRY. B.S. & M.S, Chile, 56; U.S. Pub. Health Serv. fel, Cornell, 60-64, Ph.D.(biochem), 64. First asst. biochem, Chile, 56-57; res. asst, Sloan-Kettering Inst. Cancer Res, N.Y, 57-60; fel. biophys, Johnson Res. Found, Pennsylvania, 64-67, res. assoc, 67-68, ASST. PROF, 68; BIOCHEM, SOUTHWEST. MED. SCH, UNIV. TEX, 68- AAAS; Am. Soc. Biol. Chem. Metabolic control; enzyme kinetics and interactions; integrated metabolic sequences. Address: Dept. of Biochemistry, University of Texas Southwestern Medical School, Dallas, TX 75235.

FRENKIEL, FRANCOIS N, b. Warsaw, Poland, Sept. 19, 10; nat; m. 62; APPLIED MATHEMATICS, FLUID DYNAMICS. Mech. Eng, Ghent, 33, Aero. Eng, 37; Ph.D.(physics), Lille, 46. Res. engr, Tech. Serv. Aeronaut, Belgium, 37-38; sci. collab, Ghent, 39; res. assoc, inst. fluid mech, Lille, 39-40; sci. collab, French Group Aeronaut. Res, Toulouse, 40-43, from res. assoc. to chief lab, Aerodyn. Res. Center, 45-47; mem. res. staff, grad. sch. aeronaut. eng, Cornell, 47-48; sr. res. assoc, U.S. Naval Ord. Lab, 48, chief theoret. & appl. mech. subdiv, 49-50; sr. res. physicist, res. center, appl. physics lab, Johns Hopkins Univ, 50-52, mem. prin. staff, 52-60; SR. RES. SCIENTIST, COMPUT. & MATH. DEPT, NAVAL SHIP RES. & DEVELOP. CTR, 60-, consult. physicist, 56-60. Lectr, Univ. Md, 50; res. master, grad. coun, George Wash. Univ, 52-; prof, Univ. Minn, 63-64. Consult, U.S. Weather Bur, 52-60; appl. physics lab, Johns Hopkins Univ, 57-60. Ed, Physics of Fluids, Am. Inst. Physics, 57- Chmn, U.S. Nat. Comt. Theoret. & Appl. Mech, 65-66, secy, 70- Fel. AAAS; fel. Am. Phys. Soc; Am. Meteorol. Soc; fel. Am. Geophys. Union; assoc. fel. Am. Inst. Aeronaut. & Astronaut. Atmospheric physics; turbulence; fluid dynamics; mathematical modeling of urban pollution. Address: Dept. of Computation & Mathematics, Naval Ship Research & Development Center, Washington, DC 20034.

FRENSDORFF, H(ANS) KARL, b. Hannover, Ger, Apr. 7, 22; nat. PHYSICAL CHEMISTRY. B.S, Rensselaer Polytech, 49; A.M, Princeton, 51, Ph.D.(phys. chem), 52. RES. CHEMIST, E.I. DU PONT DE NEMOURS & CO, INC, 52- U.S.A, 43-46. AAAS; Am. Chem. Soc. Structure and properties of high polymers; polymerization statistics; sorption and diffusion; macrocyclic polyethers. Address: Elastomer Chemicals Dept, Experimental Station, E.I. du Pont de Nemours & Co, Inc, Wilmington, DE 19898.

FRENSTER, JOHN H, b. Chicago, Ill, Oct. 14, 28; m. 58; c. 3. INTERNAL MEDICINE, HEMATOLOGY. B.S, Illinois, 50, M.D, 54. Intern, Cook County Hosp, Chicago, Ill, 55; res. fel. hemat, Res. & Ed. Hosps, Univ. Illinois, 56-57, resident med, 55-58; Am. Cancer Soc. fel. & guest investr. cell biol, Rockefeller Inst, 58-60, asst. prof, 62-65; cell radiobiologist, Walter Reed Army Inst. Res, Wash, D.C, 60-62; ASSOC. PROF. MED, SCH. MED, STANFORD UNIV, 65- Asst. hemat, Hopkins Hosp, Md, 60-62; U.S. Pub. Health Serv. res. career develop. award, 62-67. Med.C, 60-62, Capt. Fel. Am. Col. Physicians; Am. Econ. Asn; Am. Soc. Hemat; Am. Asn. Cancer Res; Am. Soc. Cell Biol; Electron Micros. Soc. Am; Soc. Gen. Syst. Res. Structure and function of the cell nucleus; clinical and biological aspects of leukemia and lymphomas; control of RNA synthesis; human systems analysis; quantitation of health or disease within individual human systems. Address: S-025, Dept. of Medicine, Stanford University School of Medicine, Palo Alto, CA 94305.

FRENZEL, HUGH N, b. Madison, Wis, Apr. 21, 18; m. 45; c. 4. PETROLEUM GEOLOGY. B.A, Wisconsin, 40, M.A, 41. Geologist, Standard Oil Co, Tex, 46-49, dist. geologist, 49-52; geologist, Ryan, Hayes & Burke, 52-54; Ralph Lowe, 54-62, CHIEF GEOLOGIST, 62-65; RALPH LOWE ESTATE, 65- U.S.A.A.F, 41-45, S/Sgt; Legion of Merit, 44. Soc. Econ. Paleont. & Mineral; Am. Asn. Petrol. Geol; fel. Geol. Soc. Am. Petroleum geology, stratigraphy, sedimentation and structure of Permian Basin. Address: 1118 Mogford, Midland, TX 79701.

FRENZEL, L(OUIS) D(ANIEL), JR, b. San Antonio, Tex, Aug. 22, 20; m. 45; c. 3. BIOLOGY, ECOLOGY. B.S, N.Tex. State Col, 47, fel, 47-48, M.S, 48; fel, Minnesota, 46-47, Ph.D.(wildlife mgt), 57. Instr. biol, Ely Jr. Col, Minn, 48-54; asst, Minnesota, 54-56; assoc. prof. Macalester Col, 57-69; PROF. ENTOM, FISHERIES & WILDLIFE, UNIV. MINN, ST. PAUL, 69- Med. Dept, U.S.N.R, 41-45. Wildlife Soc; Am. Soc. Mammal; Ecol. Soc. Am. Ecology of terrestrial vertebrates, especially of avian and mammalian populations; field and general biology; wildlife ecology. Address: Dept. of Entomology, Fisheries & Wildlife, University of Minnesota, St. Paul, MN 55101.

FRENZEN, PAUL, b. Oak Park, Ill, Sept. 4, 24; m. 51; c. 4. METEOROLOGY, FLUID MECHANICS. B.S, Chicago, 49, M.S, 51, Ph.D.(meteorol), 64. Weather officer, U.S. Army Air Force, 44-46; res. asst, hydrodyn. lab, dept. meteorol, Chicago, 51-56; ASSOC. METEOROLOGIST, RADIOL. PHYSICS DIV, ARGONNE NAT. LAB, 56-, HEAD ATMOSPHERIC PHYSICS SECT, 71- Vis. res. off, div. meteorol. physics, Commonwealth Sci. & Indust. Res. Orgn, Australia, 62-63 & 68-69; prof. lectr, dept. geophys. sci, Univ. Chicago, 70- U.S.A.F, 43-46, Res, 46-71, Col. Am. Meteorol. Soc; Royal Meteorol. Soc. Meteorological modeling; statistical theories of turbulent diffusion; laboratory experiments and field measurements of the structure of atmospheric turbulence. Address: Atmospheric Physics Section, Argonne National Lab, Argonne, IL 60439.

FRERE, MAURICE HERBERT, b. Sheridan, Wyo, Sept. 8, 32; m. 57; c. 3. SOIL CHEMISTRY. B.S, Wyoming, 54, M.S, 58; Ph.D.(soils), Maryland, 62. RES. SOIL SCIENTIST, SOIL & WATER CONSERV. DIV, U.S. DEPT. AGR, 58- Sig.C, U.S.A, 54-56. AAAS; Am. Soc. Agron; Soil Sci. Soc. Am; Am. Chem. Soc. Systems analysis of soil-water-plant relations, especially pollution; soil chemistry; mineral nutrition. Address: U.S. Agricultural Water Quality Management Lab, Durant, OK 74701.

FRERICHS, RUDOLF, b. Koeln, Ger, Apr. 9, 01; nat; m. 35; c. 2. PHYSICS. Ph.D.(physics), Bonn, 24. Asst. physics, Bonn, 24-27; physicist, Physikal. Tech. Reichsanstalt Berlin-Charlottenburg, 27-28, 31-35, lectr, Tech. Hochsch, 31-45; Int. Ed. Bd. fel, Michigan & Calif. Inst. Technol, 28-30; Osram Lamp Works, Berlin, 35-41; A.E.G. Res. Inst, 41-45; prof. physics, Tech. Univ. Berlin-Charlottenburg, 45-47; physicist, Kaiser Wilhelm Inst, Berlin, 45-47; res. assoc. physics, NORTHWEST. UNIV, 47-54, lectr, 54-56, prof. ELEC. ENG, TECHNOL. INST, 56-69, EMER. PROF, 69- Consult, x-ray dept, Gen. Elec. Co, Wis. Fel. Am. Phys. Soc. Spectroscopy bands and lines; vacuum spectroscopy; physics of light sources and phosphors; photoconductivity; cadmiumsulfidephotocell; infrared transmittant sulfide glasses; thin film superconductors. Address: 512 Florence Ave, Evanston, IL 60202.

FRERICHS, WAYNE MARVIN, b. Bloomington, Nebr, Apr. 9, 33; m. 57; c. 2. VETERINARY SCIENCE, BIOCHEMISTRY. B.S. & D.V.M, Kans. State Univ, 57; Ph.D.(vet. sci), Wash. State Univ, 66. RES. VET, NAT. ANIMAL

PARASITOL. LAB, U.S. DEPT. AGR, 66- AAAS; Am. Vet. Med. Asn; Am. Soc. Microbiol. Leptospira antigenic variations; immunology and biology of Babesia caballi, B. equi, B. rodhaini and B. procyoni. Address: National Animal Parasitological Lab, Beltsville, MD 20705.

FRERICHS, WILLIAM EDWARD, b. Des Moines, Iowa, Mar. 30, 39; m. 63; c. 2. MICROPALEONTOLOGY. B.S. & M.S, Iowa State Univ, 63; Ph.D. (geol), Univ. South. Calif, 67. Res. geologist, Esso Prod. Res. Co, 66-68; ASST. PROF. GEOL, UNIV. WYO, 68- Nat. Sci. Found. grant, 70-72. AAAS. Foraminiferal paleoecology; geopolarity history of the Cretaceous; vertical movements related to continental drift. Address: 1917 Thornburgh Dr, Laramie, WY 82070.

FRESCO, JACQUES R(OBERT), b. N.Y.C, May 30, 28; m. 57; c. 3. BIOCHEMISTRY. B.A, N.Y. Univ, 47, M.S, 49, fel, 49-52, Ph.D.(biochem), 53. Asst, Lebanon Hosp, N.Y, 46-48; instr. chem, col. med, N.Y. Univ, 53-54, pharmacol, 54-56; res. fel. CHEM, Harvard, 56-60; asst. prof, PRINCETON, 60-62, assoc. prof, 62-65, PROF, FRICK LAB, 65- Fel, Sloan-Kettering Inst. Cancer Res, 52-54; U.S. Pub. Health Serv, 52-54; Lalor Found. fel, Cavendish Lab, Cambridge & Inst. Biol. Phys. Chem, Paris, 57; tutor, Harvard, 57-60; estab. investr, Am. Heart Asn, 58-63; Guggenheim Found. fel, Med. Res. Coun. Lab. Molecular Biol, Eng, 69-70. Am. Chem. Soc; Am. Soc. Biol. Chem. Molecular biology; biochemistry of nucleic acids; genetics; configuration of biomacromolecules. Address: Dept. of Biochemical Sciences, Frick Lab, Princeton University, Princeton, NJ 08540.

FRESCO, JAMES M(ARTIN), b. Yonkers, N.Y, Sept. 29, 26. ANALYTICAL CHEMISTRY. A.B, N.Y. Univ, 49; M.S, Polytech. Inst. Brooklyn, 56; Ph.D. (chem), Arizona, 61. Chemist, health & safety div, N.Y. Opers. Off, U.S. Atomic Energy Comn, 49-56; res. assoc. CHEM, Arizona, 61-62; asst. prof, Nevada, 62-64; chemist, U.S. Naval Radiol. Defense Lab, 64; asst. prof, Tex. Technol. Col, 64-65; McGILL UNIV, 65-69, ASSOC. PROF, 69- U.S.A, 44-46, Sgt. Am. Chem. Soc; The Chem. Soc. Radiochemistry; infrared spectroscopy; chemistry of coordination compounds; polarography; chemical separation processes. Address: Dept. of Chemistry, McGill University, Montreal, Que, Can.

FRESCO, RAOUL, b. Cairo, Egypt, Sept. 8, 27; U.S. citizen. EXPERIMENTAL PATHOLOGY. M.B.B.Ch, Cairo, 58. Intern, MT. SINAI HOSP, 59-60, resident path, 60-63, res. fel. exp. path, 63-65, res. assoc. pathologist, 65-67, RES. ASSOC. PATHOLOGIST, 67- Asst. prof, Chicago Med. Sch, 68-71, assoc. prof, 71- Am. Soc. Clin. Path; Electron Micros. Soc. Am; Int. Acad. Path; Am. Soc. Cell Biol; Reticuloendothelial Soc. Ultrastructural pathology; electron microscopy; immunopathology; kidney diseases. Address: Mt. Sinai Hospital, Chicago, IL 60608.

FRESE, FREDERICK J(OSEPH), JR, b. Savannah, Ga, Dec. 10, 12; m. 39; c. 5. AEROSPACE MEDICINE. B.S, Fordham Univ, 34; M.D, St. Louis Univ, 38. Chief surg, Savannah Army Air Base Hosp, U.S. Air Force, 41, surgeon, 13th Air Force, S.Pac, 43-44, sr. instr, Command & Gen. Staff Col, Ft. Leavenworth, Kans, 45-46, instr, Armed Forces Staff Col, 46-48, dir. res, Sch. Aviation Med, 49-50, dep. commandant, 51-53, surgeon, Air Univ, 53-54, proj. off. in planning, designing & construct. of Aerospace Med. Ctr, Brooks AFB, Tex, 54-59, comdr, Kindley AFB Hosp, Bermuda, 59-62, chief med. & biol. res, Off. Secy Defense, Wash, D.C, 62-66, dir. bioastronaut, Hq. Air Force East. Test Range, Patrick AFB, Fla, 66-70; MED. DIR. COMPUT. APPLNS. STUDY GROUP, WUESTHOFF MEM. HOSP, 70- V.chmn. life sci. sub panel, aeronaut. & astronaut. coord. bd, NASA, 62-66. Med.C, U.S.A.F, 39-70, Col. Fel. Aerospace Med. Asn; fel. Am. Col. Prev. Med; Am. Inst. Aeronaut. & Astronaut; Am. Hosp. Asn; Am. Med. Asn. Medical and biological research; bioastronautics. Address: Computer Applications Study Group, Wuesthoff Memorial Hospital, P.O. Box 6, Rockledge, FL 32955.

FRESEMAN, WILLIAM L(ANGFITT), b. Pittsburgh, Pa, Dec. 1, 01; m. 47. ELECTRONIC ENGINEERING, TELECOMMUNICATIONS. B.S, U.S. Naval Acad, 22; M.S, Harvard, 29; cert, U.S. Naval War Col, 35. Dir. eng, sales & distribution of spec. prods, Midtown Motors Co, Calif, 48-53; prof. elec. eng. & dir. radar res. lab, Miami (Fla), 52-57, lectr, 56-57; dir. int. field commun. projs, hqs, Int. Tel. & Tel. Corp. & v.pres, Int. Standard Elec. Corp. Div, 57-61; ASST. TO PRES, RADIO ENG. LABS, 61-, ASST. TO EXEC. V.PRES, DYNAMICS CORP. AM, 63- U.S.N, 18-48, Rear Adm; Legion of Merit; Bronze Star Medal; Navy Commendation Pendant; French Croix de Guerre; Brazilian War Serv. Medal. Sr. mem. Inst. Elec. & Electronics Eng. Engineering of telecommunications systems; management of field engineering projects; business management of electronic and engineering firms; development of radio and radar systems of expanded functions and improved performance; corporate public relations. Address: Dynamics Corp. of America, 501 Fifth Ave, New York, NY 10017.

FRESH, JAMES W, b. Toccoa, Ga, Jan. 9, 26; m. 57; c. 2. PATHOLOGY. B.A, Lenoir-Rhyne Col, 49; M.P.H, North Carolina, 50, M.D, 57. Instr. physiol, North Carolina, 52-54, path, 57-58; U.S. NAVY, 58-, pathologist, Marine Corps Air Facility, New River, N.C, 58-59, Naval Hosp, St. Albans, N.Y, 59-62, head path, Naval Med. Res. Unit 2, Taipei, Taiwan, 62-69, commanding off, Naval Med. Res. Unit 1 & head path. sect, Naval Biomed. Res. Lab, 69-71, COMMANDING OFF, NAVAL MED. RES. UNIT 3, 71- Vis. prof, col. med, Taiwan Univ, 64-69, Nat. Defense Med. Col, Taiwan, 65-68 & Taipei Med. Col, 65-69. Consult, Chinese Navy. U.S.N, 58-, Comdr. Am. Soc. Clin. Path; Col. Am. Path; Asn. Mil. Surg. U.S; Am. Med. Asn; Am. Pub. Health Asn; Royal Soc. Health. Clinical research on malignancies, infectious diseases, nutritional deficiencies and coronary artery disease. Address: U.S. Naval Medical Research Unit 3, FPO New York 09527.

FRESIA, E(LMO) JAMES, b. Pittsfield, Mass, Sept. 10, 31; m. 58; c. 3. INORGANIC CHEMISTRY. B.S, Massachusetts, 53; M.S, Connecticut, 59. Proj. leader high reliability develop, SPRAGUE ELEC. CO, 59-62, sect. head, solid state capacitors res. & develop, 62-69, PROJ. MGR, ELECTROCHEM. PROD. DEVELOP. LAB, 69- U.S.A.F, 54-56, 1st Lt. Preparation and structure determination of ternary oxides; development of solid state capacitors, electrolytic type. Address: Electrochemical Development Lab, Sprague Electric Co, North Adams, MA 01247.

FRESTON, JAMES W, b. Mt. Pleasant, Utah, July 20, 36; m. 56; c. 4. INTERNAL MEDICINE, GASTROENTEROLOGY. U.S. Pub. Health Serv. grant, Univ. Utah, 59-61, M.D, 61, Nat. Insts. Health grant, 64-65, Ph.D.(med), 67- Nat. Inst. Arthritis & Metab. Diseases fel, dept. med, Royal Free Hosp, London, Eng, 65-67; asst. prof. MED. & PHARMACOL, COL. MED, UNIV. UTAH, 67-71, ASSOC. PROF, 71-, CHIEF DIV. CLIN. PHARMACOL, 69-, CHMN. DIV. GASTROENTEROL, 70- Clin. investr, Vet. Admin. Hosp, Salt Lake City, Utah, 67-69; staff physician, med. ctr, Univ. Utah, 67-; Burroughs-Wellcome scholar, 69; vis. prof, Univ. Man, 70. U.S.A.F, Maj. AAAS; Am. Med. Asn; Am. Asn. Study Liver Disease; Am. Col. Physicians; Am. Soc. Internal Med; Am. Gastroenterol. Asn. Pathogenesis of gallstones; drug toxicity. Address: Division of Gastroenterology, Room 4E504, University of Utah Medical Center, Salt Lake City, UT 84112.

FRETER, KURT RUDOLF, b. Hamburg, Ger, Jan. 26, 29; Can. citizen; m. 59; c. 4. ORGANIC CHEMISTRY. Hauptdiplom, Frankfurt, 53, Dr. rer. nat, 55. Vis. scientist, Nat. Insts. Health, 56-57; group leader med. chem, C.H. Boehringer, Ger, 57-64; HEAD CHEM. DEPT, PHARMA RES. CAN. LTD, 64- Am. Chem. Soc; Chem. Inst. Can; Soc. German Chem. Peptides; Heterocyclic Chemistry. Address: 250 Hymus Blvd, Pointe Claire, Que, Can.

FRETER, ROLF (GUSTAV), b. Hamburg, Ger, Jan. 5, 26; U.S. citizen; m. 55; c. 4. BACTERIOLOGY. Ph.D.(bact), Goethe Univ, Frankfurt, Ger, 51. Res. assoc. bact, Biol. Budesanstalt, Braunschweig, Ger, 51; Logan fel. & res. assoc, Chicago, 52-54; instr. bact, Loyola (Ill), 54-57; assoc. prof. MICROBIOL, Jefferson Med. Col, 57-65; PROF, UNIV. MICH, ANN ARBOR, 65- AAAS; Am. Soc. Microbiol; fel. Am. Acad. Microbiol; Am. Asn. Immunol; Soc. Exp. Biol. & Med. Oral enteric vaccines; ecology of normal enteric flora of man; bacterial toxins and enzymes; experimental enteric animal infections; anaerobic bacteria. Address: Dept. of Microbiology, University of Michigan, 6734 Medical Science Bldg. II, Ann Arbor, MI 48104.

FRETTER, WILLIAM B(ACHE), b. Pasadena, Calif, Sept. 28, 16; m. 39; c. 3. PHYSICS. A.B, Univ. Calif, 37, Ph.D.(physics), 46. Asst. physics, Univ. Calif, 37-41; res. assoc, Mass. Inst. Technol, 41; res. engr, Westinghouse Elec. Co, Pa, 41-44; Manhattan Dist. proj, radiation lab, UNIV. CALIF, BERKELEY, 45-46, instr. PHYSICS, 46-47, asst. prof, 47-50, assoc. prof, 50-55, PROF, 55-, dean col. letters & sci, 62-67. Fulbright res. scholar, France, 52-53, 60-61; Guggenheim fel, 60-61. Chevalier, Legion of Honor, France. With U.S.N; Off. Sci. Res. & Develop, 44. Fel. Am. Phys. Soc. High power microwaves; isotope separation; cosmic rays; mass of cosmic ray mesotrons; penetrating showers, heavy mesons and hyperons; elementary particle physics. Address: 1120 Cragmont Ave, Berkeley, CA 94708.

FRETWELL, CHARLES C, b. Williamstown, Mo, June 20, 36; m. 59; c. 2. ENGINEERING MECHANICS, COMPUTER SCIENCE. B.S, Iowa, 59, M.S, 60; Ph.D.(theoret. & appl. mech), Illinois, 65. Res. assoc. theoret. & appl. mech, Illinois, 60-62, instr, 63-65; asst. prof. eng. mech, Ohio State, 65-68; v.pres, Integrated Data Systs, Inc, 68-69; appln. engr, Measurement Instruments, Inc, 69-70; PROJ. DIR. COMPUT. SYSTS, DESIGN ELEMENTS, INC, 70- Res. contracts worked on, Univ. Illinois, Rock Island Arsenal, U.S. Army, 59-62, Redstone Arsenal & Rohm & Haas Co, 62-63, summers, Univ. Illinois, NASA, 63, Nat. Sci. Found. grant, 64, Ohio State Univ, Air Force Contract A, 66, eng. exp. sta, 67. C.Eng, 60, Res, 60-, Capt. Engineering mechanics, specifically elasticity and vibrations; computer programming and numerical analysis. Address: Design Elements, Inc, 1356 Norton Ave, Columbus, OH 43212.

FRETWELL, LYMAN JEFFERSON, JR, b. Rockford, Ill, Oct. 8, 34; m. 63; c. 1. PHYSICS. B.S, Calif. Inst. Tech, 56, Ph.D.(physics), 67. Mem. tech. staff, BELL TEL. LABS, INC, 66-68, SUPVR, 68- AAAS; Am. Phys. Soc. Computational physics techniques in plasma physics and magnetohydrodynamics with modeling of results for practical systems applications. Address: Bell Telephone Labs. Inc, Whippany, NJ 07981.

FRETWELL, STEVE D, b. Harrisonburg, Va, Jan. 15, 42; m. 63; c. 2. POPULATION ECOLOGY. B.S, Bucknell, 64; Nat. Insts. Health fel, N.C. State, 64-68, Ph.D.(biomath), 68. Fel, Princeton, 68-69; ASST. PROF. THEORET. ECOL, KANS. STATE UNIV, 69- Wilson Ornith. Soc; Am. Ornith. Union; Am. Inst. Biol. Sci. Role of behavior in population control; population control in a seasonal environment; role of population control in evolution of behavior. Address: Division of Biology, Ackert Hall, Kansas State University, Manhattan, KS 66502.

FREUDENSTEIN, FERDINAND, b. Ger, May 12, 26; nat; m. 59. MECHANICAL ENGINEERING. M.S, Harvard, 48; DuPont fel, Columbia, 52-54, Ph.D. (mech. eng), 54. Develop. engr, Am. Optical Co, N.Y, 48-50; mem. tech. staff, Bell. Tel. Labs, Inc, 54; asst. prof. MECH. ENG, COLUMBIA UNIV, 54-57, from assoc. prof. to PROF, 57-, chmn. dept, 58-64. Guggenheim fels, 61-62, 67-68; indust. consult. U.S.A, 44-46. Am. Soc. Mech. Eng.(jr. award, 55). Engineering design; mechanisms; kinematic analysis and synthesis. Address: Dept. of Mechanical Engineering, Columbia University, New York, NY 10027.

FREUDENTHAL, ALFRED M(ARTIN), b. Stryj, Poland, Feb. 12, 06; nat; m. 39; c. 1. CIVIL ENGINEERING. C.E, Prague Tech. Univ, 29, D.Sc.(eng), 30; M.A, Charles Univ, Prague, 30. Design engr, Prague, 30-34; consult. engr, 34-35; from lectr. to prof. civil eng, Hebrew Inst. Technol, 36-49; prof, Columbia Univ, 49-69; PROF. CIVIL & MAT. ENG, GEORGE WASH. UNIV, 69- From engr. to res. eng, Port of Tel Aviv, Palestine, 35-44; consult. eng, 44-47; vis. prof, Univ. Ill, 47-50; Swiss Fed. Inst. Technol, 70- Medal, Swed. Soc. Aeronaut, 56. Am. Soc. Civil Eng.(Norman Medal, 48, 57; Vonkarman Medal, 71); Soc. Rheol; Am. Soc. Test. & Mat; Int. Asn. Bridge & Struct. Eng. Fatigue of metals and non-metals; inelastic behavior of engineering materials; theory of plasticity; structural design; statistical methods in engineering. Address: Dept. of Civil, Mechanical & Environmental Engineering, 314 Tompkins Hall, George Washington University, Washington, DC 20006.

FREUDENTHAL, HUGO D(AVID), b. Brooklyn, N.Y, Mar. 29, 30; m. 55; c. 2. MARINE MICROBIOLOGY, AEROSPACE SCIENCES. B.S, Columbia Univ, 53, M.S, 55; Ph.D.(protozool), N.Y. Univ, 59. Assoc. prof. BIOL, C.W.

POST COL, L.I. UNIV, 59-65, PROF. & CHMN. GRAD. DEPT. MARINE SCI, 65-; MGR. LIFE SCI, FAIRCHILD REPUB. DIV, FAIRCHILD INDUSTS, INC, 66- Assoc. dir, Living Foraminifera Lab, Am. Mus. Natural Hist, 61-69; res. assoc, Nat. Bur. Standards, 70-; independent consult. life sci. AAAS; Soc. Protozool; Am. Soc. Limnol. & Oceanog; Am. Micros. Soc; Am. Soc. Microbiol; Marine Technol Soc; Aerospace Med. Asn; Torrey Bot. Club; N.Y. Acad. Sci; Brit. Soc. Gen. Microbiol; Marine Biol. Asn. U.K. Physiology and ecology of planktonic Foraminifera; calcification and pressure studies on marine microorganisms; ecology and taxonomy of zooxanthellae; photomicrography of planktonic organisms; microbiology of polluted waters; aerospace life sciences. Address: 2911 Carlyle Rd, Wantagh, NY 11793.

FREUDENTHAL, PETER, b. N.Y.C, Aug. 12, 34; m. 56; c. 2. ENVIRONMENTAL HEALTH, METEOROLOGY. B.A, N.Y. Univ, 54, U.S. Pub. Health Serv. fel. & M.S, 63, Ph.D.(environ. health sci), 70; B.S, Columbia Univ, 60. Meteorologist, air weather serv, 55-57; asst. res. scientist, environ. health, med. ctr, N.Y. Univ, 63-66; phys. scientist, environ. studies div, health & safety lab, U.S. Atomic Energy Comn, 66-70; ENGR, AIR QUAL. CONTROL DIV, CONSOL. EDISON CO. N.Y, 70- Asst. res. scientist, inst. environ. med, med. ctr, N.Y. Univ, 66-70; adj. asst. prof, Long Island Univ, 68-; mem. pub. utilities comt, Air Pollution Control Asn, 70- U.S.A.F, 55-57, Res, 57-68, Maj. AAAS; Am. Meteorol. Soc; Air Pollution Control Asn; Health Physics Soc. Air pollution; meteorology, epidemiology, control techniques; cooling tower environmental effects; radioactive fallout transport and deposition; aerosol sizing and deposition. Address: Office of Environmental Affairs, Consolidated Edison Co. of New York, 4 Irving Pl, New York, NY 10003.

FREUDENTHAL, RALPH IRA, b. N.Y.C, Aug. 27, 40. BIOCHEMICAL PHARMACOLOGY. B.S, N.Y. Univ, 63; Ph.D.(biochem. pharmacol), State Univ. N.Y. Buffalo, 69. BIOCHEM. PHARMACOLOGIST, RES. TRIANGLE INST, 69- AAAS; Int. Soc. Biochem. Pharmacol; N.Y. Acad. Sci; Brit. Biochem. Soc. Isolation and characterization of enzymes; drug-enzyme interactions; drug metabolism with emphasis on steroidal agents, including the separation and identification of metabolites; whole body autoradiography. Address: Chemistry & Life Sciences Lab, Research Triangle Institute, P.O. Box 12194, Research Triangle Park, NC 27709.

FREUND, GERHARD, b. Frankfurt, Ger, Apr. 21, 26; U.S. citizen; m. 55; c. 2. INTERNAL MEDICINE, ENDOCRINOLOGY. M.D, Univ. Frankfurt, 51; M.S, McGill Univ, 57. Resident internal med, Augustana Hosp, Chicago, 52-53; Res. & Educ. Hosp, Univ. Ill, 53-55; res. fel. endocrinol, McGill Univ, 55-57; clin. instr. internal med, col. med, Univ. Ill, 57-60, asst. clin. prof, 60-63; res. assoc. endocrinol, COL. MED, UNIV. FLA, 63-64, asst. prof. INTERNAL MED, 64-70, ASSOC. PROF, 70-; CHIEF ENDOCRINOL, VET. ADMIN. HOSP, GAINESVILLE, 67- AAAS; fel. Am. Col. Physicians; Am. Med. Asn; Am. Diabetes Asn; Am. Fedn. Clin. Res; Endocrine Soc. Effects of intermediary metabolites on systemic diseases; ketoacidosis and its mechanism; effects of chronic ethanol ingestion and acetaldehyde metabolism on brain function in man and experimental animals. Address: Dept. of Medicine, University of Florida, Gainesville, FL 32601.

FREUND, HANS-ULRICH H(ERBERT), b. Waldenburg, Ger, July 7, 39; m. 65; c. 2. NUCLEAR & ATOMIC PHYSICS. Dipl. physics, Munich Tech, 65, Dr. rer. nat.(exp. nuclear physics), 67. RES. FEL. NUCLEAR & ATOMIC PHYSICS, GA. INST. TECHNOL, 68- Am. Phys. Soc. Low energy nuclear physics; physics of the inner atomic shells. Address: Nuclear Research Center, Georgia Institute of Technology, Atlanta, GA 30332.

FREUND, HARRY, b. Tulsa, Okla, Nov. 21, 17; m. 45; c. 3. ANALYTICAL CHEMISTRY. B.S, City Col, 40; M.S, Michigan, 41, Ph.D.(chem), 45. Asst, anal. lab, dept. eng. res, Michigan, 41-42, res. assoc, 42-45, res. chemist, 45-47; instr. CHEM, ORE. STATE UNIV, 47-49, asst. prof, 49-54, assoc. prof, 54-60, PROF, 60- Chemist anal. problems, U.S. Bur. Mines, 48- Award, N.Y. Cocoa Exchange, 40. Am. Chem. Soc. Inorganic chemistry; instrumental analysis; chemical instrumentation. Address: Dept. of Chemistry, Oregon State University, Corvallis, OR 97330.

FREUND, ISAAC, b. N.Y.C, Aug. 8, 38; m. 60. PHYSICAL CHEMISTRY. B.S, City Col. New York, 59; M.A, Columbia Univ, 60, Ph.D.(chem), 63. Res. assoc. chem, Columbia Univ, 63-65; MEM. TECH. STAFF, BELL TEL. LABS, 65- Am. Chem. Soc. Infrared and Raman spectroscopy of the solid state; nonlinear optics. Address: 850 W. Grand St, Elizabeth, NJ 07202.

FREUND, JACK, b. N.Y.C, Nov. 19, 17; m. 46; c. 3. PHARMACOLOGY. B.S, N.Y. Univ, 37; Univ. Va, 41-42; M.D, Med. Col. of Va, 46. Intern, Hosps, Med. Col. of Va, 46-47; res. path, Beth Israel Hosp, N.Y, 47-48; asst. therapeut, dept. med, N.Y. Univ-Bellevue Med. Ctr, 49; res. med, Vet. Admin. Hosp, Bronx, 49-50, sr. res. chest & cardiol, 50-51; lectr. pharmacol. & assoc. med, MED. COL, VA, 51-58, clin. assoc. med, 58-61, asst. clin. prof. med, 61-65, assoc. clin. prof. med, 65-70, ASST. PROF. PHARMACOL, 58-, CLIN. PROF. MED, 70-; V.PRES, A.H. ROBINS CO, INC, 64-, asst. dir. clin. res, 55-58, dir, 58-60, med. dir, 60-62, v.pres. & med. dir, 62-64. U.S.A.F, 53-55, Capt. Fel. Am. Col. Physicians; fel. Am. Soc. Clin. Pharmacol. & Therapeut; fel. Am. Col. Cardiol; Soc. Toxicol. Clinical evaluation of drugs; peripheral vascular disease. Address: 310 Old Bridge Lane, Richmond, VA 23229.

FREUND, J(OHN) E(RNST), b. Berlin, Ger, Aug. 6, 21; nat; m. 49; c. 2. MATHEMATICAL STATISTICS. B.A, California, Los Angeles, 43, M.A, 44; Ph.D.(math), Pittsburgh, 52. Prof. math, Alfred Univ, 46-54; statist, Va. Polytech. Inst, 54-57; prof. MATH, ARIZ. STATE UNIV, 57-71, EMER. PROF, 71- Am. Math. Soc; Am. Statist. Asn; Math. Asn. Am; Inst. Math. Statist. Address: 7035 N. 69th Pl, Scottsdale, AZ 85253.

FREUND, LAMBERT BEN, b. McHenry, Ill, Nov. 23, 42; m. 65; c. 1. APPLIED MECHANICS. B.S, Illinois, 64, M.S, 65; Ph.D.(theoret. & appl. mech), Northwestern, 67. Fel. eng, BROWN UNIV, 67-68, teaching & res. fel, 68-69, ASST. PROF. APPL. MECH, 69- Am. Soc. Mech. Eng; Seismol. Soc. Am. Propagation of elastic waves; constitutive equations for elastic plastic materials at finite strain; surface waves; fracture mechanics. Address: Division of Engineering, Brown University, Providence, RI 02912.

FREUND, LOUIS E(DWARD), b. St. Louis, Mo, Dec. 30, 40; m. 64; c. 1. INDUSTRIAL ENGINEERING. M.S.I.E, Washington Univ, 65; Kellogg Found. fel, Univ. Mich, 65-68, Ph.D.(indust. eng), 69. Res. assoc. indust. eng. & hosp. admin, Univ. Mich, 68-69; ASST. PROF, eng. design plan, opers. res. U.S. Army-Baylor Prog. in Hosp. Admin, 69-70, INDUST. ENG, UNIV. MO-COLUMBIA, 71- Consult, Tex. Hosp. Asn, 70; Lutheran Gen. Hosp, San Antonio, Tex, 69-70. Med.Serv.C, U.S.A, 69-70, Capt. Am. Inst. Indust. Eng; Am. Hosp. Asn; Opers. Res. Soc. Am; Human Factors Soc; Am. Soc. Eng. Educ. Health care and management systems design and analysis; human factors engineering; man-machine interactive systems. Address: Dept. of Industrial Engineering, 106 Electrical Engineering Bldg, University of Missouri-Columbia, Columbia, MO 65201.

FREUND, MATTHEW J, b. New York, N.Y, Aug. 3, 28; m. 52; c. 2. PHYSIOLOGY, PHARMACOLOGY. B.A, N.Y. Univ, 48; M.Sc, Nebraska, 50; Ph.D. (physiol), Rutgers, 57. Asst. dairy husb, Rutgers, 55-56; anat, med. col, Cornell, 56-58; instr. physiol. & pharmacol, N.Y. MED. COL, 58-60, asst. prof, 60-63, assoc. prof. pharmacol, 64-67, ASSOC. PROF. OBSTET-GYNEC, 64-, PROF. PHARMACOL, 68- Health Res. Coun. City of New York res. grant & career scientist, 62-; Nat. Insts. Health grants; res. partic, Oak Ridge Inst. Nuclear Studies, summer 58. AAAS; Am. Physiol. Soc; Am. Soc. Pharmacol. & Exp. Therapeut; Am. Fertil. Soc; Am. Soc. Cell Biol; Soc. Develop. Biol; Soc. Exp. Biol. & Med; Soc. Cryobiol; Geront. Soc; Asn. Gnotobiotics; Am. Genetic Asn; Am. Dairy Sci. Asn; Am. Soc. Animal Sci; Soc. Sci. Study Sex; Asn. Comput. Mach; Am. Asn. Lab. Animal Sci; Asn. Am. Med. Cols; Brit. Soc. Study Fertil; Int. Fertil. Asn; Harvey Soc; Animal Behav. Soc; Am. Soc. Animal Sci. Physiology and pharmacology of reproduction fertility and infertility; cryobiology. Address: Dept. of Pharmacology, New York Medical College, 1 E. 105th St, New York, NY 10029.

FREUND, PETER GEORGE OLIVER, b. Temesvar, Rumania, Sept. 7, 36; m. 63. THEORETICAL PHYSICS. Dipl. eng, Polytech. Inst. Temesvar, 58; Ph.D.(physics), Vienna, 60. Res. assoc. PHYSICS, inst. theoret. physics, Vienna, 61; res. assoc, inst. theoret. physics, Geneva, 61-62; res. assoc, Enrico Fermi Inst. Nuclear Studies, UNIV. CHICAGO, 62-64, asst. prof, PHYSICS & ENRICO FERMI INST. NUCLEAR STUDIES, 64-70, ASSOC. PROF, 70- Mem, inst. adv. study, Princeton, 64-65. Am. Phys. Soc; Austrain Phys. Soc; Italian Phys. Soc. Quantum field theory; dispersion theory; symmetries of elementary particle interactions. Address: Dept. of Physics, University of Chicago, Chicago, IL 60637.

FREUND, RICHARD A, b. N.Y.C, Nov, 14, 24; m. 63; ENGINEERING, STATISTICS. B.A, Columbia, 47, M.S, 49. Qual. control engr, Camera Works, EASTMAN KODAK CO, 48-49, statist. analyst, color tech. div, 49-52, statist. engr. color print & processing, 53-57, film testing div, 58-60, STAFF CONSULT, MGT. SYSTS. DEVELOP, 60- U.S.A.A.F, 42-46, 1st Lt. Fel. AAAS; fel. Am. Soc. Qual. Control (Brumbaugh Award, 60, 62, v.pres, 67-70, pres-elect, 71-72); fel. Am. Statist. Asn; Am. Soc. Test. & Mat. Design of experiments; quality control techniques and data analysis interpretation. Address: Eastman Kodak Co, Kodak Park, MSDD-B56, Rochester, NY 14650.

FREUND, ROBERT STANLEY, b. Newark, N.J, Jan. 26, 39; m. 62; c. 2. CHEMICAL PHYSICS. B.S, Wesleyan, 60; Nat. Sci. Found. fel, Harvard, 60-61, M.A, 62, Nat. Insts. Health fel, 62-65, Ph.D.(chem. physics), 65. Res. fel. chem, Harvard, 65-66; MEM. TECH. STAFF, BELL TEL. LABS, 66- AAAS; Am. Phys. Soc; Am. Chem. Soc. Electronic spectroscopy of molecules; molecular beams. Address: Bell Telephone Labs, Murray Hill, NJ 07974.

FREUND, RUDOLF J(AKOB), b. Kiel, Germany, Mar. 3, 27; nat; m. 48; c. 3. STATISTICS, AGRICULTURAL ECONOMICS. M.A, Chicago, 51, Ph.D.(exp. statist), 55. Asst. prof. statist, Va. Polytech, 55, assoc. prof, 55-62; ASSOC. DIR. INST. STATIST, TEX. A&M UNIV, 62- Vis. res. scholar, Univ. Okla, 60. U.S.A, 45-46. Am. Statist. Asn. Use of computers in statistics; use of statistics and mathematics in economics; linear programming. Address: Institute of Statistics, Texas A&M University, College Station, TX 77843.

FREUND, THOMAS, b. Philadelphia, Pa, Sept. 28, 26; m. 70; c. 4. PHYSICAL CHEMISTRY. A.B, Princeton, 47; Ph.D.(chem), Catholic Univ, 54. Asst. chem, Catholic Univ, 47-51; res. assoc, Northwestern, 51-53, instr, 52-53; N.Y. Univ, 53-57; staff scientist, sci. res. lab, Convair Div, Gen. Dynamics Corp, 57-62; phys. chemist, Stanford Res. Inst, 62-69; MEM. TECH. STAFF, DAVID SARNOFF RES. CTR, RCA CORP, 69- U.S.N.R, 45-46. Am. Chem. Soc. Heterogeneous catalysis; borohydrides; reaction mechanisms; solid state; electrophotography. Address: David Sarnoff Research Center, RCA Corp, Route 1, Princton, NJ 08540.

FREUND, THOMAS STEVEN, b. N.Y.C, Jan. 11, 44; m. 66; c. 2. BIOCHEMISTRY, MICROBIOLOGY. B.S, Lehigh Univ, 65, Ph.D.(biochem), 69. Teaching asst. chem, Lehigh Univ, 65-66, res. asst. marine sci. & biochem, 66-69; Nat. Insts. Health trainee, ophthal, col. physicians & surgeons, Columbia Univ, 69-70; RES. ASSOC. ORAL BIOL, SCH. DENT. MED, UNIV. CONN, 70- Am. Chem. Soc; Am. Soc. Microbiol. Proteins and proteolytic enzymes, their structure and function; cellular metal ion requirements and transport; microbial biochemistry; biologic regulation; marine microbiology. Address: Dept. of Oral Biology, University of Connecticut, Box U155, Storrs, CT 06268.

FREUNDLICH, MARTIN, b. N.Y.C, Dec. 15, 30; m. 52; c. 4. MICROBIOLOGY. B.A, Brooklyn Col, 55; M.S, Long Island, 57; Ph.D.(microbiol), Minnesota, 61. U.S. Pub. Health Serv. fel, Cold Spring Harbor Lab. Quant. Biol, 61-64; asst. prof. microbiol, Dartmouth Med. Sch, 64-66; biol. sci, STATE UNIV. N.Y. STONY BROOK, 66-69, ASSOC. PROF. BIOCHEM, 69- U.S. Pub. Health Serv. res. grant, 64-67 & 69-72, career develop. award, 70-75; Lederle med. fel, 65-66; ed, J. Bact, 66-70; N.Y. State Res. Found. grant, 68-69. U.S.A, 53-55. AAAS; Am. Soc. Microbiol; Am. Soc. Biol. Chem. Biochemistry and genetic control in branched biosynthetic pathways in microorganisms. Address: Dept. of Biochemistry, State University of New York at Stony Brook, Stony Brook, NY 11790.

FREUNDLICH, MARTIN M(ORRIS), b. Goerlitz, Ger, Nov, 23, 05; nat; m. 47; c. 1. ELECTRICAL ENGINEERING. Dipl.Ing, Tech. Univ, Berlin, 29, D.Ing. (eng), 33. Asst, Tech. Univ, Berlin 33-34; Royal Tech. Col. Scotland, 35; mem. staff, Pye Radio Ltd, Eng, 35-36; Columbia Broadcasting Syst, 36-44, 45-49; N.Am. Philips, 44-45; asst. supv. eng. consult, AIL Div, Cutler-Hammer, Inc, 49-70; INDEPENDENT CONSULT, 70- AAAS; Am. Astron. Soc; Inst. Elec. & Electronics Eng. Tube development, oscillographs for lightning investigations, electron microscopes; cathode ray tubes for monochrome and color television, measurements of properties of phosphors; storage tubes; experiments on color television systems; materials in space environments; space lubrication; vacuum technology. Address: 16 Suydam Dr, Mellville, NY 11746.

FREVEL, LUDO K(ARL), b. Frankfurt am Main, Ger, May 31, 10; nat; m. 37; c. 3. CHEMISTRY. Ph.D.(chem), Hopkins, 34. Nat. res. fel. chem, Calif. Inst. Tech, 34-36; res. chemist, DOW CHEM. CO, 36-69, LAB. DIR. CHEM. PHYSICS, 69- With Naval Res. Lab; Field Info. Agencies Technol. AAAS; Am. Chem. Soc; Am. Crystallog. Asn. X-ray studies of substances under pressure; crystal structure; identification of compounds by x-ray and electron diffraction methods; catalysis; iterated function. Address: 1205 W. Park Drive, Midland, MI 48640.

FREVERT, RICHARD KELLER, b. Odebolt, Iowa, Feb. 26, 14; m. 47; c. 1. AGRICULTURAL ENGINEERING. B.S, Iowa State Col, 37, M.S, 40, Ph.D. (agr. eng, soils), 48. Instr. agr. eng, Iowa State Col, 37-42, asst. prof, 46-48, assoc. prof, 48-49, prof, 49-58; DIR. AGR. EXP. STA, UNIV. ARIZ, 58- Asst. dir, agr. exp. sta, Iowa State Col, 52-58. U.S.A.A.F, 42-46, Capt. Fel. AAAS; fel. Am. Soc. Agr. Eng; Soil Conserv. Soc. Am; Am. Geophys. Union. Permeability of soils; irrigation; drainage; erosion control; soil and water losses from watersheds. Address: Agricultural Experiment Station, University of Arizona, Tucson, AZ 85721.

FREY, ALBERT JOSEPH, b. Urnaesch, Switz, Apr. 23, 27; m. 56; c. 2. ORGANIC & MEDICINAL CHEMISTRY. B.S, State Col. Trogen, Switz, 47; Chem. Engr, Swiss Fed. Inst. Tech, 51, Ph.D.(steroid synthesis), 53. Res. fel, Swiss Fed. Inst. Tech, 53-55; Harvard, 55-56; res. chemist, Sandoz Ltd, Switz, 56-60, res. group leader, 60-62, dir. res, SANDOZ-WANDER, INC, 62-64, v.pres. in charge res, 64-70, PRES, 71- Swiss Mil. Serv, Capt. AAAS; Am. Chem. Soc; Swiss Chem. Soc. Synthetic organic chemistry especially applied to natural products; drug research in general. Address: Sandoz-Wander, Inc, Route 10, Hanover, NJ 07936.

FREY, ANTHONY L(OCKWAY), b. Whitehall, Wis, Nov. 19, 37; m. 63; c. 2. CHEMICAL ENGINEERING. B.S, Wisconsin, 59, M.S, 60; Nat. Sci. Found. fel, 62-63, Ph.D.(chem. eng), 66. Instr. chem. eng, Wisconsin, 60-61, proj. asst, 61-62; systs. develop. engr, Dow Chem. Co, 65-67; asst. prof. chem. eng, Iowa State Univ, 67-71; fel, Tech. Univ. Norway, 71; ASSOC. PROF. AGR. ENG, COLO. STATE UNIV, 71- Food processing equipment dynamics; mathematical programming; food industry waste control. Address: Dept. of Agricultural Engineering, Colorado State University, Ft. Collins, CO 80521.

FREY, CARL, b. New York, N.Y; m. 55; c. 3. ENGINEERING. B.M.E, N.Y. Univ, 49; M.A, Columbia, 51. Asst. exec. secy, Eng. Manpower Comn, 60, exec. secy, 61-64; secy, ENGRS. JOINT COUN, 65-67, EXEC. DIR, 67- Adv, U.S. Dept. Labor, 62; mem. comt. specialized personnel, Off. Emergency Planning, Off. of the President, 62-64, mem. exec. res, 62-; adv. panel, select comt. govt. res, House of Rep, 64-; treas, U.S. Comt. Large Dams & U.S. Nat. Comt, World Power Conf, 65- U.S.N, 42-45. AAAS; Am. Soc. Eng. Educ. Policies in field of engineering and scientific manpower; professional society activities. Address: Engineers Joint Council, 345 E. 47th St, New York, NY 10017.

FREY, CELESTE, b. Long Beach, Calif, July 9, 27. MICROBIOLOGY. A.B, Immaculate Heart Col, 55; Nat. Insts. Health fel, St. Louis, 58-61, Ph.D. (microbiol), 64. Teacher, parochial sch, Calif, 54-56; ASSOC. PROF. BIOL. SCI, IMMACULATE HEART COL, 65- Nat. Sci. Found. sci. faculty fel, Univ. Calif, Santa Barbara, 69-70. Am. Soc. Microbiol. Bacteriophage genetics. Address: Dept. of Biological Sciences, Immaculate Heart College, 2021 N. Western Ave, Los Angeles, CA 90027.

FREY, CHRIS(TIAN) M(ILLER), b. Cumberland, Md, Feb. 26, 23; m. 43; c. 2. MECHANICAL ENGINEERING. B.S, Maryland, 51. Supvr. gen. design group, Allegany Ballistics Lab, 51-53, design res. group, 53-59; chief engr, UNITED TECHNOL. CTR, 59-67, MGR. RES. & ADVAN. TECHNOL. DEPT, 67- Chmn, Missile Booster Mat. Comt, 56-59; consult, mat. adv. bd, Nat. Acad. Sci, 58-60; Nat. Aeronaut. & Space Admin, 59-60; lectr, Stanford Univ. U.S.A.A.F, 42-44, Res, 44-46, Lt. Am. Soc. Mech. Eng; Am. Soc. Test. & Mat; Am. Ord. Asn. Rocket propulsion; high temperature materials; high strength materials, including fiberglass and boron structures; unique fabrication techniques and rocket design. Address: Research & Advanced Technology Dept, United Technology Center, 1050 E. Arques Ave, Sunnyvale, CA 94086.

FREY, DAVID ALLEN, b. Mendota, Ill, Nov. 26, 35; m. 57; c. 2. ORGANIC & POLYMER CHEMISTRY. B.A, Monmouth Col.(Ill), 57; M.S, Iowa, 59, Ph.D.(org. chem), 61. Fel. high temperature polymers under C.S. Marvel, Univ. Arizona, 61-62; RES. CHEMIST, Phillips Petrol. Co, 62-64; MORTON CHEM. CO, 64- Am. Chem. Soc. Inter-intra polymerizations, high temperature polymers and emulsion and solution polymerizations using free radical and ionic catalysts. Address: Morton Chemical Co, 1275 Lake Ave, Woodstock, IL 60098.

FREY, DAVID G(ROVER), b. Hartford, Wis, Oct. 10, 15; m. 48; c. 3. LIMNOLOGY. B.A, Wisconsin, 36, M.A, 38, Ph.D.(zool), 40. Asst, Conserv. Dept, Wis, 35-40; jr. aquatic biologist, U.S. Fish & Wildlife Serv, Wash, 40-42, asst. aquatic biologist, Md, 42-43, assoc. aquatic biologist, 43-45; assoc. prof. ZOOL, North Carolina, 46-50; IND. UNIV, BLOOMINGTON, 50-55, PROF, 55- Fulbright & Guggenheim fels, Austria, 53-54; instr, Food & Agr. Orgn. Fisheries Training Center, Java, 55; Nat. Acad. Sci-Nat. Res. Coun. Exchange to Soviet Union, 62; summer vis. prof, Univ. Virginia Biol. Sta, 59; Univ. Michigan Biol. Sta, 61; Ford Found. consult, Mindanao State Univ, 67-68. U.S.N.R, 45-46, Lt.(jg). Am. Soc. Limnol. & Oceanog.(pres, 55; ed. jour); Am. Micros. Soc.(v.pres, 70); Ecol. Soc. Am.(aquatic ed. jour); Am. Quaternary Asn.(pres. elect, 71-72); Int. Union Quaternary Res; Am. Soc. Zool; Soc. Syst. Zool; Int. Asn. Limnol; Brit. Ecol. Soc; Brit. Freshwater Biol. Asn; Marine Biol. Asn. India. Development history of lakes and micropaleontology of freshwater deposits; vegetational history of southeastern United States. Address: Dept. of Zoology, Indiana University, Bloomington, IN 47401.

FREY, DELTON R(UBEN), b. Tiffin, Ohio, Dec. 19, 10; m. 36; c. 1. CHEMICAL ENGINEERING. B.S, Case, 32, Ph.D.(chem. eng), 45. Operator, Gen. Chem. Co, Ohio, 32-33; chemist, Addressograph-Multigraph Corp, 33-34; chief chemist, Cleveland Indust. Res, 34-43; proj. dir, Case, 43-45; develop. engr, B.F. Goodrich Chem. Co, 45-46; fuels & lubricants engr, Anderson-Pritchard Oil Co, 46-49; gen. mgr. prod. develop. & qual. control, Kerr-McGee Oil Industs, Inc, 49-66; ASST. PROF. CHEM, CENT. STATE COL.(OKLA), 66- Am. Chem. Soc; Soc. Automotive Eng. Chemistry of detergents and antioxidants applied to petroleum products; petroleum processing; uses and applications of asphalts; solvents; lubricating oils and petroleum chemicals. Address: 1501 Andover Ct, Oklahoma City, OK 73120.

FREY, DONALD AUSTIN, b. Phila, Pa, Mar. 8, 36; m. 65; c. 2. THEORETICAL PHYSICS. B.S, Stanford Univ, 58; Ph.D.(physics), Univ. Colo, 64. Res. assoc. PHYSICS, Univ. Rennes, 64; lectr, Theoret. Inst, Uppsala, Sweden, 65; asst. prof, Univ. P.R, 65-66; ROBERT COL, ISTANBUL, 66-69, ASSOC. PROF, 69- Summers, mem. Univ. Pa-Nat. Geog. Underwater Exped, Turkey, 69, tech. dir, Nat. Geog. Underwater Surv, Greece, 70, assoc. dir. Univ. Pa. Underwater Surv, Turkey, 71; Am. Coun. Learned Soc. grant, res. lab. archaeol, Oxford, 71-72. Am. Asn. Physics Teachers. Theory of the interaction of radiation with atomic systems; quantum mechanics; archaeomagnetism. Address: Dept. of Physics, Robert College, Bebek P.K. 8, Istanbul, Turkey.

FREY, DONALD N(ELSON), b. St. Louis, Mo, Mar. 13, 23; m. 42; c. 6. MECHANICAL ENGINEERING. B.S, Michigan, 47, Ph.D.(metall), 50. Asst. eng, Michigan, 47-48, res. assoc, 48-49, instr. metall. eng, col. eng, 49-50, asst. prof. chem. & metall. eng, 50-51; assoc. dir, sci. lab, Ford Motor Co, 51-57; asst. chief engr, Ford Div, 57-61, prod. planning mgr, 61, asst. gen. mgr, 62-65, v.pres. & gen. mgr, 65-67, v.pres. prod. develop, 67-68; pres, Gen. Cable Corp, 68-71; CHMN, BELL & HOWELL CO, 71- Ord.C, U.S.A, 43-46. Nat. Acad. Eng; fel. Am. Soc. Metals; Soc. Automotive Eng; Am. Inst. Mining, Metall. & Petrol. Eng. Metallurgy of high temperature alloys; general metallurgy including iron and steel making; general automotive engineering; general management. Address: Bell & Howell Co, 7100 McCormick Rd, Chicago, IL 60645.

FREY, ELMER J(ACOB), b. Buffalo, N.Y, Jan. 3, 18; m. 45, 63; c. 2. MATHEMATICS. B.S, City Col, 37; M.S, N.Y. Univ, 40; Ph.D.(math), Mass. Inst. Tech, 49. Teacher, pub. sch, N.Y, 40-41; instr. math, MASS. INST. TECHNOL, 46-49, mathematician, instrumentation lab, 49-53, group leader, 53-55, asst. dir, 55-57, deputy assoc. dir, 57-69, MEM. STAFF, CTR. SPACE RES, 70-, LECTR, AERONAUT. & ASTRONAUT, 62-, assoc. dir, measurement systs. lab, 65-70. Mem, U.S. Defense Dept. Ad Hoc Comt. Inertial Guidance, 63; vis. prof, Spec. Sch. Aeronautics, Paris, 63-64; consult. engr, France, 63-64; consult, U.S. Air Force Sci. Adv. Bd, 63-65, chief scientist, 64-65; NATO Adv. Group Aerospace Res. & Develop, 64 & 69; U.S. Dept. Transportation lectr, Univ. Naples, Cath. Univ. Louvain & Nat. Sch. Advan. Aeronaut. Studies, Paris, 69-70. Am. Geophys. Union; assoc. fel. Am. Inst. Aeronaut. & Astronaut; Soc. Indust. & Appl. Math. Applied mathematics; geophysics; systems engineering; stochastic processes; control systems; servomechanisms; geodesy; dynamic gravimetry; satellite altimetry; aircraft altimetry; inertial navigation; gyroscopes; accelerometers; gravimeters; navigation systems; hurricane observation systems; meteorological instruments. Address: Massachusetts Institute of Technology, Room N51-305, Cambridge, MA 02139.

FREY, FREDERICK AUGUST, b. Milwaukee, Wis, Apr. 1, 38. GEOCHEMISTRY. B.S, Wisconsin, 60, Ph.D.(phys. chem), 66. Res. chemist, Hercules Chem. Co, 60-61; ASST. PROF. GEOCHEM, MASS. INST. TECHNOL, 66- AAAS; Am. Geophys. Union; Geochem. Soc. Elemental distribution in geologic systems. Address: Dept. of Earth & Planetary Sciences, Room 54-1220, Massachusetts Institute of Technology, Cambridge, MA 02139.

FREY, F(REDERICK) W(OLFF), JR, b. New Orleans, La, Sept. 30, 30; m. 52; c. 5. INORGANIC CHEMISTRY. B.S, Loyola (La), 50; M.S, Tulane, 52, U.S. Army Ord. fel, 52-54, Ph.D.(chem), 54. Chemist, Mallinckrodt Chem. Works, 54-55; SUPVR. CHEM. RES, ETHYL CORP, 55- U.S.N.A.R, 49-57. Am. Chem. Soc. Metal hydride chemistry; organometallics. Address: Ethyl Corp, P.O. Box 341, Baton Rouge, LA 70821.

FREY, HAROLD J(OSEPH), b. Benton Harbor, Mich, Oct. 9, 20; m. 49; c. 3. PHYSICAL CHEMISTRY. B.S, Loyola (Ill), 41; Ph.D.(phys. chem), Catholic Univ, 48. Chemist, polychem. dept, E.I. DU PONT DE NEMOURS & CO, INC, 48-53, res. supvr, 53-58, INDUST. SPECIALIST, POLYOLEFINS, 58- U.S.N, 44-46. Am. Chem. Soc. Polymer chemistry. Address: E.I. du Pont de Nemours & Co, Inc, Wilmington, DE 19898.

FREY, JAMES R, b. De Young, Pa, Feb. 27, 32; m. 53; c. 2. BACTERIOLOGY, IMMUNOLOGY. B.S, Defiance Col, 52; M.A, Miami (Ohio), 57; Tulane, 55-58; Ph.D.(virol), Mich. State, 61. Asst. bacteriol, Tulane, 55-58; Mich. State, 58-59, virol, 59-61; asst. prof. BIOL, DEFIANCE COL, 61-67, assoc. prof, 67-70, PROF, 70-, HEAD DEPT, 68-, DIV. CHMN, NATURAL SYSTS. STUDIES, 69- Vis. scientist, Nat. Sci. Found, 62-64. AAAS; Am. Pub. Health Asn; Am. Soc. Microbiol; Am. Inst. Biol. Sci. Quantitative study of the enteric viruses in sewage; immuno-genetics approach to study of gene differences. Address: Dept. of Biology, Defiance College, Defiance, OH 43512.

FREY, JEFFREY, b. N.Y.C, Aug. 27, 39; m. 66. ELECTRICAL ENGINEERING, PHYSICAL ELECTRONICS. B.E.E, Cornell Univ, 60; Charles Legeyt Fortescue fel, Univ. Calif, Berkeley, 60-61, Howard Hughes fel, 61-65,

M.S, 63, Ph.D.(elec. eng), 65. Mem. tech. staff, microwave semiconductor devices, Watkins-Johnson Co, Calif, 65-66; NATO fel, Rutherford High Energy Lab, Eng, 66-67; Res. assoc. ion implantation, U.K. Atomic Energy Res. Estab, Harwell, 67-69; ASST. PROF. ELEC. ENG, CORNELL UNIV, 70- Inst. Elec. & Electronic Eng. Plasma instabilities and beam-plasma interactions; microwave semiconductor devices and circuits; microwave integrated circuits. Address: Dept. of Electrical Engineering, Phillips Hall, College of Engineering, Cornell University, Ithaca, NY 14850.

FREY, JOHN ERHART, b. Chicago, Ill, May 6, 30; m. 57; c. 4. INORGANIC CHEMISTRY, EDUCATION. B.S, Northwest. Univ, 52; M.S, Univ. Ill, 55; Ph.D.(inorg. chem), Univ. Chicago, 56. Res. chemist, Univ. Chicago, 56-57; instr. CHEM, Bowdoin Col, 57-59, asst. prof, 59-60; Ill. Inst. Technol, 60-63; West. Mich. Univ, 63-66; assoc. prof, NORTH. MICH. UNIV, 66-71, PROF, 71-, ASST. DEAN. COMMON LEARNING, 69- Am. Chem. Soc. Boron hydrides and halides. Address: Dept. of Chemistry, School of Arts & Sciences, Northern Michigan University, Marquette, MI 49855.

FREY, JOHN H, U.S. citizen. GEOPHYSICS, GEOLOGY. A.B, Harvard, 55; M.S, Boston Col, 59. Res. geophysicist, Weston Observ, Boston Col, 59-63; res. dir. geophys, phys. res. div, Emmanuel Col, 63-67; sr. scientist & res. dir. space physics, Sea Farm Res. Found, 67-70; consult, SCI. RESOURCES FOUND, 70, RES. SPECIALIST EARTH & SPACE SCI, 71- Consult, astrogeol. sect, U.S. Geol. Surv, 67-68; pres, Sci. Serv. Co, 69- U.S.A, 55-57, Sgt. AAAS. Relationships between seismicity and tectonophysics; magnetohydrodynamics and dynamo mechanisms of solar phenomena; polar cap aeronomy; basic geomagnetism, especially hydromagnetic wave phenomena and solar-terrestrial physics; analytical techniques applicable to data analysis. Address: 26 Windmill Dr, Marlborough, MA 02172.

FREY, JOHN T, b. Milwaukee, Wis, Jan. 26, 39; m. 60; c. 3. ORGANIC CHEMISTRY. B.S, Marquette, 60; Ph.D.(org. chem), Iowa State, 64. Asst. prof. chem, Black Hawk Col, 64-66, assoc. prof, 66-68, Am. Coun. Ed. fel, 68-69; DEAN INSTR, WORTHINGTON STATE JR. COL, 69- Fel. Am. Inst. Chem; Am. Chem. Soc. Chemical education. Address: Worthington State Junior College, Worthington, MN 56187.

FREY, KENNETH J(OHN), b. Charlotte, Mich, Mar. 23, 23; m. 45; c. 3. AGRONOMY. B.S, Mich. State, 44, M.S, 45; fel, Iowa State, 45-48, Ph.D. (plant breeding), 48. Asst, Mich. State, 44-45, asst. prof. farm crops, 48-53; assoc. prof. agron, IOWA STATE UNIV, 53-56, prof, 56-70, C.F. CURTIS DISTINGUISHED PROF. AGR, 70-, asst. dean grad. col, 67-70, acting v.pres. res. & dean grad. col, 70-71. Fulbright scholar, Australia, 68. Fel. AAAS; fel. Am. Soc. Agron; Genetics Soc. Am. Plant breeding methodology for self-pollinated crops; biochemistry of cereal grains. Address: Dept. of Agriculture, Iowa State University, Ames, IA 50010.

FREY, KURT, b. Berlin, Ger, Jan. 15, 01; nat; m. 28; c. 1. MECHANICAL ENGINEERING. Dipl.Ing, Tech. Hochschule, Hannover, 26; Dr.Ing, Tech. Hochschule, Danzig, 31. Res. engr, Tech. Univ, Danzig, 27-33; engr, Junkers Airplane Co, 34-36; I.G. Farben-Industry, Hoechst-am-Main, 37-39; Messerschmitt Co, Augsburg, 39-45; consult. engr, 45-51; res. engr, eng. res. inst, Michigan, 52-54; Armour Res. Found, Ill. Inst. Tech, 55-56; prof. eng. mech, UNIV. DEL, 57-66, EMER. PROF. CIVIL ENG. & SPEC. CONSULT, DEPT, 66- Consult. with Prof. H. Foettinger, 29-45; consult. engr, Ger. Air Ministry, 35-36; rep. engr, spec. study group, Ger. Air Industs, 42-45. Am. Soc. Mech. Eng; Am. Soc. Eng. Educ; Am. Soc. Civil Eng. Control of subsonic engineering fluid flow. Address: 201 Aronimink Dr, Newark, DE 19711.

FREY, MAURICE G, b. Cincinnati, Ohio, July 26, 13; m. 45; c. 2. STRUCTURAL & PETROLEUM GEOLOGY. B.S, Cincinnati, 36; M.S, Minnesota, 37, Ph.D.(geol), 39. Party chief, gravity meter crew, Chevron Oil Co. Div, Standard Oil Co. Calif, 39-41, seismologist, 42-45, supvr. geophys, 45-46, dist. geologist, 46-47, explor. res. supvr, 47-48; assoc. prof. geol, Cincinnati, 48-52; mem. staff geol. & geophys. explor, CHEVRON OIL CO. DIV, STANDARD OIL CO. CALIF, 52-54, chief geologist, 55-67, ASST. TO V.PRES, 67- Am. Asn. Petrol. Geol; Soc. Explor. Geophys; fel. Geol. Soc. Am. Exploration for oil and gas in relation to origin and development of salt domes. Address: 800 California Co. Bldg, 1111 Tulane Ave, New Orleans, LA 70112.

FREY, MERWIN LESTER, b. Manhattan, Kans, Apr. 20, 32; m. 61; c. 2. VETERINARY MICROBIOLOGY. B.S. & D.V.M, Kansas State, 56; M.S, Wisconsin, 61, Ph.D.(vet. sci), 66. Res. asst, vet. sci, Wisconsin, 59-61, proj. assoc, 61-64; Nat. Insts. Health trainee, 64-66; ASSOC. PROF. VET. MICROBIOL, IOWA STATE UNIV, 66- U.S.A.F, 56-58, Capt. AAAS; Am. Vet. Med. Asn; Am. Asn. Avian Path. Respiratory and other diseases of cattle, chickens and turkeys, especially viruses and mycoplasmas as causes of respiratory disease and arthritis. Address: Iowa State University Veterinary Medical Research Institute, Ames, IA 50010.

FREY, PAUL J, b. Lawrence, Nebr, May 16, 27; m. 64; c. 4. AQUATIC BIOLOGY. B.S, Illinois, 56, M.A, 58. Biologist, Va. State Comn. Game & Inland Fish, 58-59; res. biologist, U.S. Fish & Wildlife Serv, 59-63; AQUATIC BIOLOGIST, Water Pollution Control, Dept. Health, Ed. & Welfare, 63-65; Fed. Water Pollution Control Admin, U.S. Dept. Interior, 65-71; WATER QUAL. OFF, ENVIRON. PROTECTION AGENCY, 71- U.S.A, 51-52. Effect of pesticides on aquatic fauna; effects of industrial and domestic influences on ecology of arctic and subarctic aquatic environments. Address: Southeast Water Lab, College Station Rd, Athens, GA 30601.

FREY, PAUL R(EHEARD), b. Wrightsville, Pa, Apr. 30, 02; m. 38. PHYSICAL CHEMISTRY. B.S, Albright Col, 22; M.S, Colorado, 30; Ph.D.(chem), Oregon State, 36. Asst. res. biochemist, Carnegie Inst, 22-24; prin. & instr. pub. sch, N.Y, 24-26; prof. phys. sci, York Col, 30-33; instr. CHEM, COLO. STATE UNIV, 36-38, asst. prof, 38-44, assoc. prof, 44-51, prof, 51-67, EMER. PROF, 67- Fel. AAAS; Am. Chem. Soc; assoc. Soc. Exp. Biol. & Med. Utilization of carotene and vitamin A in the animal body; dipole moments of hydrazine derivatives. Address: Dept. of Chemistry, Colorado State University, Ft. Collins, CO 80521.

FREY, PERRY ALLEN, b. Plain City, Ohio, Nov. 14, 35; m. 61; c. 2. BIOCHEMISTRY, ORGANIC CHEMISTRY. B.S, Ohio State, 59; Cincinnati, 61-63; Nat. Insts. Health fel, Michigan, 64; Nat. Insts. Health fel. & Ph.D.(biochem), Brandeis, 68. Chemist, U.S. Pub. Health Serv, 60-64; Nat. Insts. Health res. fel. CHEM, Harvard, 67-68; ASST. PROF, OHIO STATE UNIV, 69- U.S.A, 54-56, Res, 56-62. Am. Chem. Soc. Chemical mechanism of action of enzymes and coenzymes. Address: Dept. of Chemistry, Ohio State University, 140 W. 18th Ave, Columbus, OH 43210.

FREY, PETER W, Psychol, see 12th ed, Soc. & Behav. Vols.

FREY, SHELDON E(LLSWORTH), b. Wheelerville, Pa, Apr. 29, 21; m. 47; c. 2. ORGANIC CHEMISTRY. B.S, Pa. State Col, 43; M.S, Tennessee, 50; Atomic Energy Cmn. fel, Illinois, 51-53, Ph.D.(chem), 53. Jr. engr. mass spectrom, Kellex Corp, N.Y, 43-44, vacuum test, Tenn, 44; from tech. supvr. to assoc. chemist process control, Carbide & Carbon Chem. Div, Union Carbide & Carbon Corp, 44-50; res. chemist, E.I. du Pont de Nemours & Co, 53-62; COORD. OPERS. IMPROV, ALLIED CHEM. CORP, 62- Am. Chem. Soc. Fluorocarbon polymers; organic chemistry of plastics; elastomers; polymers; hindered ketones; products of formaldehyde and hydroxybenzoic acid; fluorinated hydrocarbons; tetraethyl lead; dispersed dyes; cumene hydroperoxide; phenol; phthalic anhydride. Address: 404 Kings Highway, Moorestown, NJ 08057.

FREY, SHERWOOD C(HARLES), b. Chicago, Ill, Oct. 31, 16; m. 41; c. 2. PHYSICS. B.S, De Paul, 37; M.S, Northwestern, 40. Physicist, Eastman Kodak Co, N.Y, 41; Naval Ord. Lab, Md, 41-49; sci. warfare adv, weapon systs. eval. group, Off. Secy. Defense, Wash, D.C, 49-51; chief develop. planning, Lockheed-Calif. Co, 51-64; dir. naval warfare anal. group, ctr. naval anal, Franklin Inst, 64-67; V.PRES, SCI. INDUST. RES, INC, ROCKVILLE, MD, 68- Consult, Proj. Nobska, Nat. Acad. Sci, 56; Ctr. Naval Anal, 63-64. AAAS. Defense and management systems analyses. Address: 6321 Beachway Dr, Falls Church, VA 22044.

FREY, THOMAS G, b. Eugene, Ore, Sept. 24, 43; m. 64; c. 2. ORGANIC CHEMISTRY. B.A, Univ. Ore, 65; Ph.D.(org. chem), Univ. Idaho, 71. ASST. PROF. CHEM, CALIF. STATE POLYTECH. COL, SAN LUIS OBISPO, 70- Am. Chem. Soc. Study of base catalyzed nucleophilic additions to activated acetylenes. Address: Dept. of Chemistry, California State Polytechnic College, San Luis Obispo, CA 93401.

FREY, WILLIAM C(ARL), b. Newark, N.J, Aug. 21, 23; m. 47; c. 2. STATISTICS, CHEMISTRY. B.A, Upsala Col, 43; M.S, Rutgers, 54. Control chemist, BRISTOL-MYERS CO, 43-45, asst. to purchasing agent, 45-47, supvr. anal. unit, control dept, 47-53, statist. unit, 53-57, head statist. serv. dept, 57-66, dir. tech. serv, 66-68, DIR. QUAL. ASSURANCE & REGULATORY CONFORMANCE, 68- Adj. instr. grad. sch, Rutgers Univ, 58- Am. Statist. Asn; fel. Am. Soc. Qual. Control. Applied statistics; application of statistical methods in the treatment of experimental data, control of quality, production improvement and in assorted management functions. Address: Bristol-Myers Co, 225 Long Ave, Hillside, NJ 07207.

FREY, WILLIAM FRANCIS, b. Bristol, Va, Nov. 23, 33; m. 55; c. 2. PHYSICS. A.B, King Col, 55; M.S, Vanderbilt, 57, Ph.D.(physics), 60. Asst. prof. PHYSICS, DAVIDSON COL, 60-64, ASSOC. PROF, 64- Beta-ray spectroscopy; internal conversion coefficients; photoelectric angular distributions; fluorescent yields. Address: Dept. of Physics, Davidson College, Davidson, NC 28036.

FREYBERGER, WILFRED L(AWSON), b. Newark, N.J, Feb. 28, 28; m. 51; c. 3. MINERAL ENGINEERING, SURFACE CHEMISTRY. S.B, Mass. Inst. Technol, 47, Sc.D.(metall), 55. Res. engr, N.J. Zinc Co, Pa, 55-60; res. metallurgist, Am. Cyanamid Co, Conn, 60-64; assoc. prof. metall. & res. engr, inst. mineral res, MICH. TECHNOL. UNIV, 64-68, prof. metall. eng, 68-70, DIR. INST. MINERAL RES, 70- Mem. mineral task force, Upper Great Lakes Regional Comn. AAAS; Am. Inst. Mining, Metall. & Petrol. Eng; Am. Soc. Eng. Educ. Flotation collector chemistry; flotation kinetics; developmental studies in the practice of mineral engineering. Address: Institute of Mineral Research, Michigan Technological University, Houghton, MI 49931.

FREYBURGER, W(ALTER) A(LFRED), (JR), b. Phila, Pa, May 14, 20; m. 47; c. 5. PHARMACOLOGY. B.S, Bucknell, 42; fel, Michigan, 45-46, Ph.D.(pharmacol), 51. Asst. pharm, Michigan, 46-50; pharmacologist, UPJOHN CO, 50-57, sect. head, cardiovasc-renal pharmacol, 57-68, MGR. CARDIOVASC. DISEASES RES, 68- Mem, coun. high blood pressure res. & circulation, Am. Heart Asn. Am. Soc. Pharmacol. & Exp. Therapeut. Cardiovascular and autonomic nervous system physiology and pharmacology. Address: Upjohn Co, Kalamazoo, MI 49001.

FREYD, PETER J(OHN), b. Evanston, Ill, Feb. 5, 36; m. 57; c. 2. MATHEMATICS. A.B, Brown, 58; Wilson fel, Princeton, 58-59, Ph.D.(math), 60 Consult, Batton, Barton, Durstine & Osborn, 58-60; Ritt instr. MATH, Columbia, 60-62; asst. prof, UNIV. PA, 62-64, assoc. prof, 64-68, PROF, 68-, ASSOC. CHMN. DEPT, 64- Am. Math. Soc. Categorical algebra; theory of functors; Abelian categories and their embeddings; representation in Abelian categories; existence of adjoints; applications to relative homological algebra, stable homotopy, model theory and foundations. Address: Dept. of Mathematics, University of Pennsylvania, Philadelphia, PA 19104.

FREYERMUTH, HARLAN B(ENJAMIN), b. Muscatine, Iowa, Sept. 15, 17; m. 46; c. 1. ORGANIC CHEMISTRY. B.A, Iowa, 38, M.S, 40, Ph.D.(org. chem), 42. Asst, Univ. Iowa, 40-42; tech. assoc, GAF CORP, 42-69, MGR. COL. RELS. & TECH. EMPLOYMENT, 69- Am. Chem. Soc. Organic research in dyes and dye intermediates; formation and properties of uretidinedione; textile finishes; catalytic hydrogenation; diisocyanates; optical bleaching agents; ultra violet absorber. Address: GAF Corp, 140 W. 51st St, New York, NY 10020.

FREYGANG, WALTER H(ENRY), JR, b. Jersey City, N.J, Dec. 27, 24; m; c. 3. PHYSIOLOGY. M.E, Stevens Inst. Tech, 45; M.D, Pennsylvania, 49. Intern & asst. med. res, Bellevue Hosp, 49-51; asst. res. neurol, Columbia-

Presby. Med. Ctr, 51-52, asst. neurologist, 52, vis. fel. neurol. & Nat. Found. Infantile Paralysis fel, Columbia, 52; neurophysiologist, Nat. Insts. Health, 52-59; vis. scientist, Cambridge, 59; chief, sect. membrane physiol, Nat. Inst. Ment. Health, 60-67; guest prof, Univ. Heidelberg, 67-69; MEM. STAFF, DIV. BIOL. & BIOCHEM. RES, NAT. INST. MENT. HEALTH, 69- U.S.P.H.S, 52-, Med. Dir; Commendation medal, 1966. AAAS; Soc. Gen. Physiol; Biophys. Soc; Am. Physiol. Soc; Marine Biol. Asn. U.K; Asn. Res. Nerv. & Ment. Disease. Muscle; central nervous system; peripheral nerve. Address: 6247 29th St. N.W, Washington, DC 20015.

FREYHAN, FRITZ ADOLF, b. Berlin, Ger, Nov. 24, 12; U.S. citizen; m; c. 1. PSYCHIATRY. M.D, Univ. Berlin, 37. From assoc. to adj. assoc. prof. psychiat, sch. med, Univ. Pa, 50-60; clin. prof, sch. med, George Washington Univ, 60-66; dep. chief in charge & dir. clin. studies, neuropharmacol. res. ctr, Nat. Inst. Ment. Health, St. Elizabeths Hosp, 61-66; ASSOC. CLIN. PROF. PSYCHIAT, N.Y. UNIV. & DIR, RES. DEPT. IN PSYCHIAT, ST. VINCENT'S HOSP. MED. CTR, 66- Clin. dir. & dir. res, Del. State Hosp, 50-60; ed, Comprehensive Psychiat. Fel. AAAS; fel. Am. Psychiat. Asn; fel. Am. Col. Neuropsychopharmacol; Am. Psychopath. Asn.(past pres); Am. Med. Asn; Int. Col. Neuropsychopharmacol. Clinical and social psychiatry, especially schizophrenia; clinical psychopharmacology; rationale for and effectiveness of modern treatments in psychiatry; concept and function of comprehensive psychiatric treatment centers. Address: Research Dept. in Psychiatry, St. Vincent's Hospital Medical Center, 153 W. 11th St, New York, NY 11204.

FREYMAN, STANISLAW, b. Warsaw, Poland, Feb. 4, 36; Can. citizen; m. 65; c. 2. AGRICULTURE, AGRONOMY. B.S.A, Pretoria, 59; M.S.A, British Columbia, 63, Ph.D.(agron), 67. Lab. technician, British Columbia, 62-63; RES. SCIENTIST, CAN. AGR. RES. STA, Kamloops, B.C, 66-69, LETHBRIDGE, ALTA, 69- S.African Army, 55. Crop Sci. Soc. Am; Am. Soc. Range Mgt; Am. Soc. Agron; Can. Soc. Agron; Agr. Inst. Can. Icesheet injury to perennial forage crops; increasing productivity of forages on range lands; cultural and ecological aspects of production of corn and other forage crops in southern Alberta. Address: Canada Agriculture Research Station, Lethbridge, Alta, Can.

FREYMANN, JOHN GORDON, b. Omaha, Nebr, Apr. 9, 22; m. 50; c. 4. MEDICINE. B.S, Yale, 44; M.D, Harvard, 46. Intern med, Mass. Gen. Hosp, 46-47; fel. internal med, Mayo Found, Minnesota, 49-50; asst. res. med, Mass. Gen. Hosp, 50-51, Nat. Cancer Inst. clin. & res. fel, Huntington Lab, 51-53; Damon-Runyon fel, Harvard Med. Sch, 53-54, asst, 54-56, instr, 56-60; asst. prof. med, sch. med, Tufts Univ. & dir. med. educ. & physician, Mem. Hosp, Worcester, Mass, 59-65; gen. dir, Boston Hosp. Women & lectr. prev. med, Harvard Med. Sch, 65-69; DIR. EDUC, HARTFORD HOSP. & ASSOC. PROF. HEALTH EDUC. RES, SCH. MED. & DENT, UNIV. CONN, 69- Asst, Mass. Gen. Hosp, 54-60, clin. assoc, 61-69; pres, Educ. Coun. For. Med. Grads, 70-72. Dipl, Am. Bd. Internal Med, 55. U.S.N.R, 43-45; U.S.P.H.S.R, 47-, Sr. Surgeon. Radiation Res. Soc; Am. Soc. Hemat; Am. Asn. Cancer Res; Am. Fedn. Clin. Res; Asn. Hosp. Med. Educ.(v.pres, 70-72); Asn. Am. Med. Cols; Soc. Med. Adminr. Chemotherapy of cancer. Address: Hartford Hospital, 80 Seymour St, Hartford, CT 06115.

FREYMANN, MOYE W(ICKS), b. Omaha, Nebr, Sept. 2, 25; m. 56; c. 3. PUBLIC HEALTH. B.S, Yale, 45; M.D, Hopkins, 48; M.P.H, Harvard, 56, Dr.P.H, 60. Fel. virol, med. sch, Yale, 48-49, intern. internal med, univ. hosp, 49-51; trainee, U.S. Pub. Health Serv, 51; health officer, U.S. Tech. Coop. Mission, Iran, 52-55; chief consult. health & family planning, India Off, Ford Found, 57-66; PROF. HEALTH ADMIN, SCH. PUB. HEALTH & DIR, CAROLINA POP. CTR, UNIV. N.C, CHAPEL HILL, 66- Mem. adv. comt. pop. dynamics, Pan-Am. Health Orgn; consult, WHO; spec. asst. to asst. secy. health & sci. affairs, Dept. Health, Educ. & Welfare, 71-; consult, UN Adv. Comt. on Application Sci. & Technol. to Develop. U.S.N.R, 43-46; U.S.P.H.S.R, 46-, Surg. AAAS; fel. Am. Pub. Health Asn; fel. Am. Sociol. Asn; Am. Soc. Trop. Med. & Hyg; Am. Soc. Pub. Admin; Int. Union Sci. Study Pop; Pop. Asn. Am; Soc. Int. Develop; Am. Eugenics Soc. Development of population programs, international technical assistance and public health administration; population studies. Address: Carolina Population Center, University of North Carolina at Chapel Hill, University Square, Chapel Hill, NC 27514.

FREYMUTH, PETER, b. Warmbrunn, Ger, Dec. 4, 36; m. 65; c. 3. AEROSPACE ENGINEERING. M.Physics, Berlin Tech, 62, Dr.Eng, 65. Res. assoc. aerodynamics, inst. turbulence res, German Exp. Estab. Air & Space Res, Berlin, 62-65; AEROSPACE ENG. SCI, UNIV. COLO, BOULDER, 65-67, asst. prof, 67-70, ASSOC. PROF, 70- Erich Trefftz Award, German Soc. Flight Sci, 66. Am. Phys. Soc; German Soc. Aerospace Sci. Aerospace engineering sciences, especially annealing of radiation effects in quartz crystals, hydrodynamic stability, theory and design of hot-wire anemometers and experimental investigation of turbulent flows. Address: Dept. of Aerospace Engineering Sciences, University of Colorado, Boulder, CO 80302.

FREYRE, RAOUL MANUEL, b. Gibara, Cuba, Jan. 18, 31. PHYSICS, MATHEMATICS. B.S, Inst. Holguin, Cuba, 49; Ph.D, Havana, 55. Asst. physics, Inst. Holquin, Cuba, 53-54, asst. prof. math, 54-55, prof. & head dept, 55-57; instr. physics, N.C. State Col, 57-58, asst. prof, 58-63; res. physicist, Nat. Co, Mass, 63; head dept. physics, Col. Adv. Sci, Canaan, N.H, 63-64, dean, 64; asst. prof. math. & physics, Lowell Technol. Inst, 64-66; assoc. prof. MATH, BOSTON STATE COL, 66, PROF, 67- Am. Phys. Soc; Am. Nuclear Soc; Am. Math. Soc; Math. Asn. Am. Lasers. Address: Dept. of Mathematics, Boston State College, 625 Huntington Ave, Boston, MA 02115.

FREYTAG, PAUL H(AROLD), b. Laramie, Wyo, Dec. 3, 34; m. 67; c. 2. ENTOMOLOGY. B.S, Wyoming, 56; M.Sc, Ohio State, 60, Ph.D.(entom), 63. Res. assoc. ENTOM, Ohio State Univ, 63-64, asst. prof, 64-66; Ark. State Col, 66-67; ASSOC. PROF, UNIV. KY, 67- Nat. Sci. Found. grant, 64-72. U.S.A, 57-59. AAAS; Soc. Syst. Zool; Entom. Soc. Am; Ecol. Soc. Am. Taxonomy of the Idiocerinae and Gyponinae; taxonomic studies of aquatic insects with special reference to the Plecoptera. Address: Dept. of Entomology, University of Kentucky, Lexington, KY 40506.

FREZON, SHERWOOD EARL, b. Highland Park, Mich, Nov. 28, 21. GEOLOGY. B.S, Michigan, 50, M.S, 63. GEOLOGIST, U.S. GEOL. SURV, 51- U.S.A.A.F, 40-45, Sgt. Am. Asn. Petrol. Geol; Geol. Soc. Am; Paleont. Soc; Soc. Econ. Paleont. & Mineral. Paleozoic stratigraphic studies in Oklahoma and Arkansas. Address: U.S. Geological Survey, Denver Federal Center, Bldg. 25, Denver, CO 80225.

FRIAR, BILLY W(ADE), b. Rose Hill, Va, July 18, 31. MECHANICAL ENGINEERING. A.B, Berea Col, 53; B.S, Va. Polytech. Inst, 58; Standard Oil (Ohio) fel, Ohio State Univ, 58-59, M.Sc, 59, univ. fels, 63-64, 65-66, Ph.D. (mech. eng), 70. ASST. PROF. mech. eng, Va. Polytech. Inst, 60-62; ENG, WRIGHT STATE UNIV, 70- Mech. engr, Babcock & Wilcox Co, 60; facilities eng. sect, U.S. Army Chem. Ctr, 61. U.S.A, 53-55, Sgt. AAAS; Thermodynamics; measurement of gas density; ionization of gases by beta-particle radiation. Address: Dept. of Engineering, Wright State University, Dayton, OH 45431.

FRIAR, CLYDE LUTHER, b. Cornelia, Ga, June 1, 22; m. 43; c. 3. CHEMISTRY, CHEMICAL ENGINEERING. B.S, Kent State, 42; M.S, Mass. Inst. Technol, 55. CHEM. CORPS, U.S. ARMY, 42-, asst. chief air force munitions br, Edgewood Arsenal, Md, 48-50, exec. officer, munitions div, biol. labs, Ft. Detrick, 51-53, chief indust. engr, Rocky Mt. Arsenal, Colo, 55-58, asst. chem. off, Hq. U.S. Army, Pac, Ft. Shafter, Hawaii, 59-62, chief defense br, chem. & biol. off, Off. of Chief of Res. & Develop, Hq. Dept. of Army, Wash. D.C, 63-64, dir. defense develop. & eng. labs, Edgewood Arsenal, 65-68, commanding off, Pine Bluff Arsenal, 68-70, CHIEF, FORCE DEVELOP. DIV, HQ. U.S. ARMY, PAC, FT. SHAFTER, 70- U.S. rep, NATO Working Group AC/196, 63-64. Amos Fries Gold Medal, Am. Ord. Asn, 68. Chem.C, U.S.A, 42-, Col. Sci. Res. Soc. Am. Chemical and biological research; chemical, mechanical and ordnance engineering; military science; chemical and biological weapons and defense of all types. Address: Force Development Division, Headquarters U.S. Army, Pacific, Ft. Shafter, Honolulu, HI 96823.

FRIAR, ROBERT E(DSEL), b. Warren, Ind, Dec. 30, 33; m. 61; c. 3. ANIMAL PHYSIOLOGY. B.S, Purdue, 56, M.S, 59, Ph.D.(physiol), 68. Instr, high sch, Ind, 56-58, 59-64; asst. prof. PHYSIOL, FERRIS STATE COL, 67-70, ASSOC. PROF, 70- Am. Soc. Animal Sci; Am. Inst. Biol. Sci; Soc. Study Reproduction. Physiological effects of the phytogenetic estrogens; affinity of various estrogenic compounds for the estrogen receptor; human anatomy and physiology; animal physiology. Address: Dept. of Biology, Ferris State College, Big Rapids, MI 49307.

FRIARS, GERALD W, b. Sussex, N.B, Apr. 26, 29; m. 54; c. 3. POULTRY BREEDING. B.Sc, McGill, 51; M.Sc, Purdue, 55, Ph.D.(genetics), 61. Asst. GENETICS, Ont. Agr. Col, 51-55, lectr, 55-61, res. scientist, 61-63, asst. prof, 63-64, ASSOC. PROF, UNIV. GUELPH, 64- Nat. Res. Coun. Can. grants quant. genetics, 64-; res. grants, Can. Dept. Agr, Ont. Turkey Bd; mem, Can. Poultry Breeding Comt, 64- Biomet. Soc; Poultry Sci. Asn; Genetics Soc. Can. Quantitative genetics of economic and physiological traits of chickens and turkeys; quantitative and population genetics of Tribolium castaneum used as a pilot organism. Address: Dept. of Poultry Science, Ontario Agricultural College, University of Guelph, Guelph, Ont, Can.

FRIAUF, JAMES J(OSEPH), b. Toledo, Ohio, Feb. 15, 14; m. 44; c. 2. ZOOLOGY. B.S, Toledo, 36; M.A, Michigan, 37, Hinsdale scholar, 37-38; Ph.D.(zool), Florida, 42. Instr. biol, Florida, 41-42; asst. prof. ZOOL, VANDERBILT UNIV, 46-50, assoc. prof, 50-68, PROF, 68-, mem. exec. cmt, dept. biol, 58-60. Ford faculty fel, 54-55. Mem, Univ. Michigan exped. to Mex, 41. U.S.C.G, 42-46, Res, 46-66, Comdr. AAAS; Soc. Syst. Zool; Am. Inst. Biol. Sci; Am. Micros. Soc; Am. Soc. Zool. Ecology and taxonomy of Dictyoptera; ecology and systematics of marine meiobenthic fauna. Address: Dept. of Biology, Vanderbilt University, Nashville, TN 37203.

FRIAUF, ROBERT J(AMES), b. Pittsburgh, Pa, March 31, 26; m. 49; c. 3. SOLID STATE PHYSICS. B.S, Duke, 47; S.M, Chicago, 51, Atomic Energy Comn. fel, 51-53, Ph.D.(physics), 53. Asst. prof. PHYSICS, UNIV. KANS, 53-60, assoc. prof, 60-64, PROF, 64- Summers, res. physicist, Westinghouse Elec. Corp, 57, Elizabeth Watkins scholar, Kansas, 58, mem. staff, Los Alamos Sci. Lab, 59, res. engr, aircraft nuclear propulsion dept, Gen. Elec. Co, 60, lectr, Vis. Sci. Prog, Physics, 64-; Fulbright fel, Univ. Stuttgart, 65-66. U.S.N.R, 44-46. Am. Chem. Soc; Am. Phys. Soc; Am. Asn. Physics Teachers. Dielectric properties, ionic conductivity, diffusion and color centers in ionic crystals. Address: Dept. of Physics, University of Kansas, Lawrence, KS 66044.

FRIBERG, MARTIN S(AMUEL), b. Superior, Wis, Aug. 16, 10; m. 48; c. 3. ANALYTICAL MATHEMATICS. B.Ed, Wis. State Col, 36; Dipl, Wisconsin, 37, M.Ph, 46; Ph.D.(math), Minnesota, 51. Chief document div, Wis. State Hist. Library, 40-43; tech. asst. MATH, Wisconsin, 45-46, instr, 46-47; tech. asst, Minnesota, 47-49; instr, Hamline, 49-50; asst. prof, N.MEX. INST. MINING & TECHNOL, 51-57, assoc. prof, 57-66, PROF, 66- U.S.A.A.F, 43-45. Am. Math. Soc. Conformal mapping; partial differential equations. Address: Dept. of Mathematics, New Mexico Institute of Mining & Technology, Campus Station, Socorro, NM 87801.

FRIBOURG, HENRY A(UGUST), b. Paris, France, Mar. 10, 29; nat; m. 56; c. 2. AGRONOMY. B.S, Wisconsin, 49; M.S, Cornell, 51; Ph.D.(agron), Iowa State, 54. Asst. agronomist, forage crop prod. res, UNIV. TENN, KNOXVILLE, 56-57, assoc. agronomist, 57-70, PROF. AGRON, 70- Interpreter, Int. Grassland Cong, Pa. State, 52; chief interpreter, Inter-Am. Meeting Livestock Prod, Brazil, 52; food & agr. meeting on exten. methods Caribbean area, Jamaica, UN, Jamaica, 54; pres, South. Pasture Forage Crops Improv. Conf; South. Appalachian Sci. Fair. Chem.C, U.S.A, 54-56, Res, 56- Am. Soc. Agron; Am. Meteorol. Soc. Digital computer use in agronomic research; forage crop ecology and management; crop climatology. Address: Dept. of Agronomy, University of Tennessee, Knoxville, TN 37916.

FRIBOURGH, JAMES H, b. Sioux City, Iowa, June 10, 26; m. 55; c. 3. ZOOLOGY, SCIENCE EDUCATION. B.A. & M.S, Univ. Iowa, 49, Ph.D.(zool, sci. educ), 57. Instr. biol, UNIV. ARK, LITTLE ROCK, 49-56, assoc. prof, 57-59, prof. & chmn. dept, 59-69, v.pres. acad. affairs, 69-70, V.CHANCELLOR ACAD. AFFAIRS, 70- Res. biologist, fish farming exp. sta, U.S. Dept. Interior, 60-; vis. scientist, Nat. Sci. Found. vis. scientist prog, Ark. Acad. Sci, 60-; consult, radioisotope serv, Vet. Admin. Hosp, Little Rock, 60- Fel. AAAS; Nat. Asn. Biol. Teachers (state dir, 63-); Am. Fisheries Soc; Ecol. Soc. Am. Fisheries biology and culture; experimental embryology. Address: University of Arkansas, 33rd & University Ave, Little Rock, AR 72204.

FRICK, CHARLES H(AROLD), b. Chapin, S.C, Nov. 25, 09; m. 33; c. 2. MATHEMATICS. B.S, South Carolina, 30; M.S, Iowa State Col, 31; Washington (Seattle), 38; Duke, 39; Ph.D.(math), North Carolina, 41; Catholic Univ, 47; Yale, 60. Asst. elec. eng, Iowa State Col, 30-31; instr. math, Valparaiso, 31-34, asst. prof, 34-37; instr, Mont. State Col, 37-40; prof, Mary Wash. Col, Va, 41-43, 46-55; mathematician, U.S. Naval Weapons Lab, 55-64; prof. math, Univ. S.D, 62-63, 64-67; MATHEMATICIAN, U.S. NAVAL WEAPONS LAB, 67- U.S.N, 43-46. Math. Asn. Am; Soc. Indust. & Appl. Math. Current limiting circuits; columns; growth; numerical methods; exterior ballistics. Address: Code KXF, U.S. Naval Weapons Lab, Dahlgren, VA 22448.

FRICK, KENNETH E(UGENE), b. San Jose, Calif, Apr. 26, 17; m. 42; c. 2. ENTOMOLOGY. A.B, San Jose State Col, 41; Ph.D.(entom), Calif, 50. Asst. entomologist, Washington State, 49-57, assoc. entomologist, 57-61; MEM. STAFF. entom. res. div, biocontrol weeds invests, U.S. DEPT. AGR, 61-70, SOUTH. SEED SCI. LAB, 70- U.S.A, 41-42, Sig.C, 42-44, Med.C, 44-45. AAAS; Entom. Soc. Am. Ecology and host specificity of insects that feed upon certain weedy plants. Address: Southern Weed Science Lab, P.O. Box 225, Stoneville, MS 38776.

FRICK, LYMAN P(HILLIP), b. Salem, Ind, June 24, 15; m. 41; c. 1. PARASITOLOGY. A.B, Kansas City, 27; M.S, Kans. State Univ, 41; Ph.D.(parasitol), Tulane Univ, 53. Chief, dept. med. zool, 406th med. gen. lab, Med. Serv. Corps, U.S. Army, 53-56, 6th Army Med. Lab, 56-61, med. zool. div, Trop. Res. Med. Lab, 61-66, asst. chief res. div, Army Med. Serv. Res. & Develop. Command, 66-67, spec. asst. to dir, Walter Reed Army Inst. Res, 67-70, RETIRED. Med.Serv.C, U.S.A, 42-70, Col.(Ret). Am. Soc. Trop. Med. & Hyg; Am. Soc. Parasitol. Parasite immunology; biology of Endamoeba histolytica. Address: 520 Appleberry Dr, San Rafael, CA 94903.

FRICK, N(EIL) H(UNTINGTON), b. Rockville Centre, N.Y, July 14, 33; m. 60; c. 4. PHYSICAL & POLYMER CHEMISTRY. B.A, Col. Wooster, 60; M.A, Princeton, 62, Ph.D.(phys. chem), 64. Sr. res. chemist, PPG INDUSTS, INC, 64-67, res. assoc. CHEM, 67-69, SR. RES. ASSOC, 69- U.S.A, 55-58. Am. Chem. Soc. Polymer characterization; electrophoretic deposition of organic coatings. Address: PPG Industries, Inc, Coatings & Resins Research, Springdale, PA 15144.

FRICK, OSCAR L, b. N.Y.C, Mar. 12, 23; m. IMMUNOLOGY, PEDIATRICS. A.B, Cornell Univ, 44, M.D, 46; M.Med.Sci, Univ. Pa, 60; Ph.D.(microbiol), Stanford Univ, 64. ASSOC. PROF. PEDIAT, SCH. MED, UNIV. CALIF, SAN FRANCISCO, 64- Mem. sub-bd. allergy, Am. Bd. Pediat, 67-73. Med.C, U.S.N.R, 47-49, Lt. Am. Asn. Immunol; Am. Acad. Allergy: Am. Acad. Pediat; Int. Asn. Allergol. Hypersensitivity, especially immediate type related to immunoglobulins and allergy; adaptation of clinical situations to laboratory evaluation. Address: Dept. of Pediatrics, School of Medicine, University of California, San Francisco, CA 94122.

FRICK, R(ICHARD) H(ENRY), b. Los Angeles, Calif, Dec. 6, 16; m. 43; c. 2. PHYSICS. A.B, California, Los Angeles, 37, fel, 40-41, Ph.D.(physics), 42. PHYSICIST sound transmission, Nat. Defense Res. Comt, California, Los Angeles, 40-42; sound ranging, Duke, 42-45; contact noise, Bell Tel. Labs, 45-46; AIR FORCE RES, RAND CORP, 46- Acoustics; applied mechanics. Address: Rand Corp, 1700 Main St, Santa Monica, CA 90406.

FRICKE, ARTHUR LEE, b. Huntington, W.Va, Mar. 6, 34; m. 54; c. 3. CHEMICAL ENGINEERING. Ch.E, Cincinnati, 57; Warf fel, Shell fel. & M.S, Wisconsin, 59, Esso fel. & Ph.D.(chem. eng), 61. Proj. engr, Gardner, Bd. & Carton, Gardner-Nat, Ohio, summer 57; instr. chem. eng, Wisconsin, Madison, 59-60; res. engr, Shell Develop. Co, Calif, 61-63, group leader mech. eng. res, 63-65, asst. dept. mgr. mkt. develop. prod, 65-66, sr. technologist, process develop, N.Y, 66-67; ASST. PROF. CHEM. ENG, VA. POLYTECH. INST. & STATE UNIV, 67- V.pres. develop. Polytron Corp. Va, 68-69; res. engr, Celanese Fibers Co, N.C, summer, 70. Am. Chem. Soc; Am. Inst. Chem. Eng; Soc. Plastics Eng. Polymer foaming; mass and heat transfer in polymers; phase change in polymers; composities; economic analysis. Address: Room 158, Randolph Hall, Virginia Polytechnic Institute & State University, Blacksburg, VA 24061.

FRICKE, EDWIN FRANCIS, b. Mackay, Idaho, July 25, 10; m. 42; c. 5. NUCLEAR PHYSICS. B.S, Idaho, 35; Rogers fel. & M.A, California, Los Angeles, 37, Ph.D.(physics), 40. Design engr, Stone & Webster Engr. Corp, Mass, 40-43; engr, Manhattan Proj, Kellex Corp, N.Y, 43-44; sr. engr, Sylvania Elec. Prod, Inc, 44-45; phys. chemist, Gen. Chem. Co, 45-46; physicist, Repub. Aviation Corp, 46-49; nuclear physicist & staff engr, Argonne Nat. Lab, 50-56; sr. nuclear physicist, nuclear prod. div, ACF Industs, 56-59; sr. develop. engr. & nuclear physicist, Repub. Aviation Corp, 59-65; res. scientist, Bell Aerosysts. Co, 65-66; sr. staff scientist, Sanders Assocs, Nashua, 66-68; prin. engr, Jackson-Moreland Engrs, 68-70; NUCLEAR ENG. CONSULT, 70- Instr, Fournier Inst. Technol, 50-55. AAAS; Am. Phys. Soc; Am. Chem. Soc; Am. Nuclear Soc; Acoustical Soc. Am; Sci. Res. Soc. Am. Adsorption of sound in five triatomic gases; statistical thermodynamics applied to chemical kinetics. Address: County Rd, Merrimack, NH 03054.

FRICKE, HOWARD H(ENRY), b. Idaho Falls, Idaho, Oct. 3, 16; m. 47; c. 2. BIOCHEMISTRY. B.S, State Col, Wash, 37, M.S, 38; Abbott res. fel, Pittsburgh, 39-40, Swift & Co. fel, 42-43, Ph.D.(biochem), 43. Pharmacist, Owl Drug Co, Wash, 37-38; asst, Pittsburgh Col. Pharm, 38-39 & 40-42; res. chemist, ABBOTT LABS, 43-57, biochem. group leader, 57-66, sect. head microbiol. res, 66-70, MGR. DIAG. RES, ABBOTT SCI. PROD. DIV, 70- Abbott Labs. Meritorious Res. Award for Sci. Achievement, 50. Pharmacist, drug stores, Pa, 38-43. AAAS; Am. Chem. Soc; Am. Inst. Chem. Development of diagnostic test systems for clinical or research laboratories. Address: D-473, Abbott Scientific Products Division, Abbott Labs, 14th St. & Sheridan Rd, North Chicago, IL 60064.

FRICKE, HUGO, b. Aarhus, Denmark, Aug. 15, 92; nat; m. 49. PHYSICS. Ph.D.(x-rays), Copenhagen, 16; Lund, 18. Asst, inst. theoret. physics, Copenhagen, 16-17; Am-Scandinavian Found. fel, Columbia, 19; asst, Harvard, 20; biophysicist, Cleveland Clin. Found, 21-27; biol. lab, Cold Spring Harbor, 28-55; res. assoc, Argonne Nat. Lab, 55-57, CONSULT, 57-66; ATOMIC ENERGY COMN, DENMARK, 66- Co-founder, Victoreen Instrument Co, 25. Consult, dept. phys. med, Pennsylvania, 53-56. Mem. cmt. high level dosimetry, adv. bd, Qm. res. & develop, Nat. Res. Coun, 56-58. Commemorative issue Radiation Res, Sept, 62. Fel. Am. Phys. Soc; Radiation Res. Soc. X-ray and ultraviolet vacuum spectroscopy; x-ray dosimetry; electric conductance and dielectric constant of heterogenous systems; radiation chemistry and biology. Address: P.O. Box 171, Cold Spring Harbor, NY 11724.

FRICKE, MARTIN P(AUL), b. Franklin, Pa, May 18, 37; m. 59. NUCLEAR PHYSICS. B.S, Drexel Inst, 61; M.S, Minnesota, 64, Ph.D.(physics & math), 67; Atomic Energy Cmn. fel, Oak Ridge Assoc. Univs, 64-67. Res. asst. physics, Univ. Minn. 61-64; fel, Univ. Mich, 67-68; staff physicist, defense sci. dept, Gulf Gen. Atomic Inc, 68-70, STAFF PHYSICIST & CROSS SECT. GROUP LEADER, GULF RADIATION TECHNOL. DIV, GULF ENERGY & ENVIRON. SYSTS. CO, 70- Employee, Oak Ridge Nat. Lab, summers 61 & 62; assoc. res. scientist, Res. Lab, Honeywell Corp, Minn, 62-64. Am. Phys. Soc. Experimental and theoretical research in nuclear reactions. Address: Gulf Radiation Technology Division, Gulf Energy & Environmental Systems Co, P.O. Box 608, San Diego, CA 92112.

FRICKE, WERNER, b. Erfurt, Ger, Sept. 7, 06; U.S. citizen; m. 34; c. 2. APPLIED PHYSICS. Ph.D.(appl. physics), Jena, 32. Asst. prof. appl. physics, Jena, 32; res. physicist, fusing systs, Rheinmetall-Borsig, Ger, 34-35, sect. chief ballistic instrumentation, 35-40, exp. ballistics, 40-43, proj. mgr. missile develop, 43-45; pres, Tool Mach. Co, 45-54; sect. chief environ. studies, Bell Aerosysts. Co, 54-68, ASST. CHIEF ENGR, BELL AEROSPACE. CO, 68- Lilienthal Soc. Award, 39. Acoust. Soc. Am; Am. Phys. Soc. Ballistic instrumentation; stereophotogrammetry; design and testing of guided missiles; induced shock, vibration; noise and space environments. Address: 620 Orchard Pkwy, Niagara Falls, NY 14301.

FRICKE, WILLIAM G(EORGE), JR, b. Pittsburgh, Pa, May 10, 26; m. 48; c. 4. METALLURGY. B.S, Pa. State, 50, M.S, 51; Ph.D.(metall. eng), Univ. Pittsburgh, 61. Res. metallurgist, ALCOA RES. LABS, ALUMINUM CO. AM, 52-67, SR. RES. ENGR, 67- Templin Award, Am. Soc. Test. & Mat, 55. U.S.A, 44-46, 51-52. Am. Soc. Metals; Sci. Res. Soc. Am; Am. Inst. Mining, Metall. & Petrol. Eng; Int. Soc. Stereology. Physical metallurgy and metallography; mechanisms of metal fatigue; deformation and plastic flow; electron microprobe analysis; electron microscopy. Address: Physical Metallurgy Division, Alcoa Research Labs, Aluminum Co. of America, P.O. Box 2970, Pittsburgh, PA 15230.

FRICKEN, RAYMOND L(EE), b. New Orleans, La, June 25, 37. HIGH ENERGY PHYSICS. B.S, Loyola (La), 59; Nat. Sci. Found. fel, La. State, 59-63, Ph.D. (physics), 63. PHYSICIST, RES. DIV, U.S. ATOMIC ENERGY COMN, 63- U.S.A, 59-65, 1st Lt. Am. Phys. Soc. Interactions of primary cosmic rays; high energy particle accelerators. Address: Research Division, U.S. Atomic Energy Commission, Germantown, MD 20545.

FRICKEY, PAUL HENRY, b. Syracuse, N.Y, Nov. 14, 31; m. 56; c. 2. MICROBIOLOGY, VIROLOGY. B.S, Syracuse, 54, M.S, 57; Nat. Insts. Health fel, Rochester, 60-62, Ph.D.(microbiol), 63. Res. virologist, biol. process & prod. improv. dept, Lederle Labs. Div, Am. Cyanamid Co, 62-64, virus & rickettsial res. sect, 64-70; DIR. PROD. & DEVELOP, FLOW LABS, INC, 70- Med.Serv.C, 56-58, Capt. AAAS; Am. Soc. Microbiol. Factors affecting multiplication of various human respiratory viruses in primate and avian tissues and the development of vaccines from such viruses; identification and anti-viral activity of antibodies in nasal secretions using immunoelectrophoresis; development of viral disgnostics. Address: Flow Labs, Inc, 1710 Chapman Ave, Rockville, MD 20852.

FRIDAY, JOHN R(OBERT), b. Dallas, Tex, Jan. 14, 35; m. 58; c. 2. CHEMICAL ENGINEERING. B.S, Okla. State Univ, 57; Ph.D.(chem. eng), Purdue Univ, 63. Asst. chem. engr, Humble Oil & Ref. Co, Tex, 57-59; res. engr, CONTINENTAL OIL CO, 63-67, group leader, ref, 67-70, SUPT. PROCESS LAB, 70- Am. Inst. Chem. Eng; Am. Chem. Soc. Petroleum refining; needle coke production; catalytic processing of refining processes; activated carbon manufacture; separation processes. Address: Process Lab, Continental Oil Co, Ponca City, OK 74601.

FRIDEN, JAMES E(RICK), b. Pittsburgh, Pa, Aug. 25, 23; m. 44; c. 3. CHEMICAL ENGINEERING. B.S, Clarkson Tech, 47; Standard Oil Co. (Ind). fel, Carnegie Inst. Tech, 47-48, M.S, 48. From asst. chem. engr. to asst. personnel supvr, Am. Oil Co, 48-57, gen. foreman, maintenance & construct. res. & develop. dept, 57-64; dir. prod. qual, Avon Prod, Inc, 64-66, mfg. control mgr, 66-68, dir. res. admin, 68-70; ASST. DIR. RES. & DEVELOP, MERLE NORMAN COSMETICS, 71- U.S.N.R, 43-45. Am. Inst. Chem. Eng; Soc. Cosmetic Chem. Research and development administration; distillation and extraction; equipment design and construction; design of laboratories. Address: Merle Norman Cosmetics, 9130 Bellanca Ave, Los Angeles, CA 90045.

FRIDHANDLER, L(OUIS), b. Kishinev, Bessarabia, Jan. 3, 24; U.S. citizen; m. 52; c. 2. BIOCHEMISTRY. B.Sc, McGill, 47, M.Sc, 51. Can. Packers fel. & Ph.D.(biochem), 53. Fel, Montreal Gen. Hosp. Res. Inst, 53-54; mem. staff biochem, Worcester Found, 54-63; asst. prof, sch. med, California, Los Angeles, 63-68, ASSOC. RES. BIOCHEMIST, UNIV. CALIF, IRVINE,

68-, with dept. nuclear med. & radiation biol, 59-60. AAAS; Am. Physiol. Soc. Metabolism of mammalian ova and blastocysts in the preimplantation stages; intermediary metabolism and lipid biosynthesis in rat yolk sac; serum amylase and nature of macroamylase. Address: Dept. of Medicine, University of California, Irvine, CA 92664.

FRIDINGER, TOMAS LEE, b. Wash, D.C. Dec. 21, 40; m. 63; c. 2. ORGANIC CHEMISTRY. B.S, Col. William & Mary, 62; Mass. Inst. Technol, 62-63; NASA fel, Maryland, 65-67, Ph.D.(org. chem), 67. Sr. res. chemist, MINN. MINING & MFG. CO, 67-70, RES. SPECIALIST, 70- Am. Chem. Soc; Weed Sci. Soc. Am. Synthetic approaches to azirinones; synthesis of potential agri-chemicals. Address: 3M Center, Minnesota Mining & Manufacturing Co, St. Paul, MN 55101.

FRIDLEY, ROBERT BRUCE, b. Burns, Ore, June 6, 34; m. 55; c. 3. AGRICULTURAL ENGINEERING, APPLIED MECHANICS. B.S, California, Berkeley, 56, M.S, Davis, 60. Asst. specialist AGR. ENG, UNIV. CALIF, DAVIS, 56-60, asst. prof, 60-67, assoc. prof, 67-69, PROF, 69- Charles G. Woodbury Award, Am. Soc. Hort. Sci, 66. Am. Soc. Agr. Eng.(award, 66 & 69). Development of methods, equipment and systems for mechanical harvest of tree fruits and nuts; investigation of physical properties of agricultural materials. Address: 1219 Aspen Pl, Davis, CA 95616.

FRIDLUND, PAUL R(USSELL), b. Minneapolis, Minn, Jan. 3, 20; m. 49; c. 4. PLANT PATHOLOGY. B.A, Augsburg Col, 42; M.S, Minnesota, 52, Ph.D. (plant path), 54. Asst, Minnesota, 46-49; supvr, sect. plant path, State Dept. Agr, Minn, 49-55; assoc. plant pathologist, irrigation exp. sta, WASH. STATE UNIV, 55-66, PLANT PATHOLOGIST, IRRIGATED AGR. RES. & EXTEN. CTR, 66- U.S.N.R, 42-46, Lt. Am. Phytopath. Soc. Virus diseases of deciduous fruit trees. Address: Irrigated Agriculture Research & Extension Center, Washington State University, Prosser, WA 99350.

FRIDOVICH, IRWIN, b. N.Y.C, Aug. 2, 29; m. 51; c. 2. BIOCHEMISTRY. B.S, City Col. New York, 51; Nat. Insts. Health fel, Duke, 54-55, Ph.D. (biochem), 55. Nat. Insts. Health fel, 55-56; instr. BIOCHEM, MED. CTR, DUKE UNIV, 56-58, assoc. 58-63, asst. prof, 63-66, assoc. prof, 66-71, PROF, 71- Nat. Insts. Health sr. res. fel, 59, career develop. award, 61-, mem. biochem. study sect, 66-70, assoc. dir, med. scientist training prog, 68-; assoc. chemist, Harvard, 61-62. Am. Soc. Biol. Chem. Biological chemistry; enzyme mechanisms; oxidative enzymes; mechanism of specific anion effects on enzymes; oxygen toxicity; mechanism and function of superoxide dismutase; sulfite oxidase. Address: Dept. of Biochemistry, Duke University Medical Center, Durham, NC 27706.

FRIDY, JOHN ALBERT, b. Lancaster, Pa, Sept. 30, 37; m. 59; c. 2. MATHEMATICS. B.S, Pa. State, 59, M.A, 61; Ph.D.(math), North Carolina, 64. Asst. prof. MATH, Rutgers Univ, 64-66; ASSOC. PROF, KENT STATE UNIV, 67- Nat. Sci. Found. res. grant, 65-66. Am. Math. Soc; Math. Asn. Am. Summability theory; number theory. Address: Dept. of Mathematics, Kent State University, Kent, OH 44240.

FRIED, BERNARD, b. Chicago, Ill, Apr. 18, 12; m. 36; c. 2. MECHANICS. B.S, Illinois, 34; Chicago, 34-35; M.S, Ohio State, 36, Ph.D.(physics), 39. Asst. physics, Ohio State, 35-38; res. engr, eng. exp. sta, 39-40, physicist, 40-41; asst. prof. mech. eng, State Col. Wash, 41-44, 45-47, assoc. prof, 47-54, prof, 54-55; res. engr, Consol. Vultee Aircraft Corp, San Diego, 44-45; stress & vibration engr, AiResearch Mfg. Co. of Ariz, 55-58, eng. specialist, 58-67; consult. engr, 67-68; RES. SPECIALIST, BOEING CO, 68- Prof. eng, Ariz. State Univ, 57-58. Civilian with Nat. Adv. Comt. Aeronaut; Office Naval Res, 44. Soc. Exp. Stress Anal. Theoretical and experimental atomic spectra; photoelasticity and photo-viscosity; behavior of metals under combined stress; behavior of partially elastic-partially plastic materials; space technology; energy conversion. Address: Boeing Co, Kent, WA 98031.

FRIED, BERNARD, b. N.Y.C, Aug. 17, 33; m. 59; c. 1. PARASITOLOGY. A.B, N.Y. Univ, 54; M.S, Univ. N.H, 56; Ph.D.(zool), Univ. Conn. 61. Asst. zool, Univ. N.H, 54-56; res. technician, Archbold Biol. Sta, Fla, 57; instr. parasitol, sch. med, Yale, 59; asst. zool, Univ. Conn, 59-61; Nat. Insts. Health res. fel. parasitol, Emory Univ, 61-63; asst. prof. BIOL, LAFAYETTE COL, 63-69, assoc. prof, 69-70, ACTING HEAD DEPT, 70- Am. Soc. Parasitol. Biology and physiology of endoparasitic trematodes. Address: Dept. of Biology, Lafayette College, Easton, PA 18042.

FRIED, BURTON D(AVID), b. Chicago, Ill, Dec. 14, 25; m. 47; c. 2. THEORETICAL PHYSICS. B.S, Ill. Inst. Tech, 47; M.S, Chicago, 50, Ph.D. (physics), 52. Instr. physics, Ill. Inst. Tech, 48-52; res. physicist, radiation lab, California, 52-54; mem. sr. staff, TRW Space Tech. Labs, Inc, 54-60, dir. res. Thompson-Ramo-Wooldridge Comput. Div, 60-62, SR. STAFF PHYSICIST, TRW SYSTS. GROUP, 62-; PROF. PHYSICS, UNIV. CALIF, LOS ANGELES, 64-, assoc. prof, 63. Physicist consult, Naval Ord. Lab, 51-55. U.S.N.R, 44-46. Fel. Am. Phys. Soc. Physics of elementary particles; quantum field theory; theory of ballistic missile trajectories; on-line computing; magnetohydrodynamics; plasma physics; controlled fusion. Address: Dept. of Physics, University of California, Los Angeles, CA 90024.

FRIED, DAVID L, b. Brooklyn, N.Y, Apr. 13, 33; m. 61; c. 3. PHYSICS. B.A, Rutgers, 57, M.S, 59, Ph.D.(physics), 62. Engr, astro-electronic div, Radio Corp. Am, 57-59; sr. tech. specialist, space & info. systs. div, N.Am. Rockwell Corp, 61-66, Autonetics Div, 66-67, chief, sensor technol. sect, electrooptical lab, 67-68, mgr. avionic systs. sect, 69-70; OWNER, OPTICAL SCI. CONSULT, 70- Consult. mem, Army Sci. Adv. Panel, 68- U.S.A, 54-55. Am. Phys. Soc; fel. Optical Soc. Am; Inst. Elec. & Electronics Eng. Quantum field theory; optical propagation in stochastic media; electrooptic and mechanooptic interactions; infrared systems. Address: 5362 S. Ohio St, Yorba Linda, CA 92686.

FRIED, GEORGE H, b. N.Y.C, Apr. 16, 26; m. 54; c. 3. PHYSIOLOGY. B.A, Brooklyn Col, 47; fel. & M.S, Tennessee, 49, fel. & Ph.D.(zool), 52. Fel. physiol, N.Y. Univ, 53-54; lectr, BROOKLYN COL, 57-64, from asst. prof. to PROF. BIOL, 64- Res. assoc, Levy Found, Beth Israel Hosp, 54-; lectr,

dent. col, N.Y. Univ, 58- AAAS; Am. Soc. Exp. Path; N.Y. Acad. Sci; Am. Physiol. Soc. Metabolic studies in obesity; cellular physiology; tissue enzyme levels as a reflection of difference in metabolic intensity in animals of different sizes; enzymatic basis for psychopharmacology; histochemical studies with tetrazolium salts. Address: Dept. of Biology, Brooklyn College, Brooklyn, NY 11210.

FRIED, HERBERT M(ARTIN), b. N.Y.C, Sept. 22, 29; m. 52; c. 1. THEORETICAL PHYSICS. B.S, Brooklyn Col, 50; M.S, Connecticut, 52; Ph.D.(physics), Stanford, 57. Nat. Sci. Found. fel. physics, Paris, 57-58; res. lectr, California, Los Angeles, 58-63; vis. mem, Courant Inst. Math. Sci, N.Y. Univ, 63-64; asst. prof. PHYSICS, BROWN UNIV, 64-66, assoc. prof, 66-69, PROF, 69- Consult, Rand Corp, 58- U.S.A, 52-54. Am. Phys. Soc. Quantum field theory. Address: Dept. of Physics, Brown University, Providence, RI 02912.

FRIED, JERROLD, b. N.Y.C, Mar. 3, 37; m. 65. BIOPHYSICS. B.S, Calif. Inst. Technol, 58; M.S, Stanford, 60, U.S. Pub. Health Serv. fel, 63-64, Ph.D.(biophys), 64. Res. assoc. biol, Hunter Col, 64-65; BIOPHYS. DIV, SLOAN-KETTERING INST. CANCER RES, 65-67, ASSOC, 68- Muscular Dystrophy Asn. Am, Inc. fel, 65; asst. prof, grad. sch. med. sci, Cornell Univ, 68-; Leukemia Soc. Am. spec. fel, 71-73. AAAS; Biophys. Soc; Am. Asn. Cancer Res. Cell proliferation kinetics; mathematical models of cell populations; chemotherapy of acute leukemia; radiation biology. Address: Division of Biophysics, Sloan-Kettering Institute for Cancer Research, 410 E. 68th St, New York, NY 10021.

FRIED, JOHN, b. Leipzig, Ger, Oct. 7, 29; U.S. citizen; m. 55; c. 3. ORGANIC CHEMISTRY. A.B, Cornell, 51, Visking fel, 54-55, Ph.D.(org. chem), 55. Fel, Columbia, 55-56; sect. head steroid chem, Merck & Co, N.J, 56-64; dept. head, Syntex Inst. Steroid Chem, 64-65, assoc. dir, 65-67, V.PRES. SYNTEX RES, SYNTEX INST. ORG. CHEM, 67-, DIR, 67- Am. Chem. Soc; The Chem. Soc. Organic synthesis; correlation of structure with biological activity; chemistry of natural products; fluorine chemistry. Address: Institute of Organic Chemistry, Syntex Research Division, 3401 Hillview Ave, Palo Alto, CA 94301.

FRIED, JOHN H, b. Linz, Austria, Oct. 9, 24; m. 51; c. 1. MICROBIOLOGY, CHEMISTRY. B.S, Connecticut, 49; M.S, Syracuse, 51. MICROBIOLOGIST, Stauffer Chem. Co, 51-57; Chas. Pfizer & Co, 57-71, PFIZER INC, 71- Med.C, U.S.A, 43-46. Am. Soc. Microbiol; Am. Chem. Soc. Microbiologically derived products; development of commercial fermentation processes. Address: 35 Tiffany Ave, Waterford, CT 06385.

FRIED, JOSEF, b. Przemysl, Poland, July 21, 14; nat; m. 39; c. 1. ORGANIC CHEMISTRY. Leipzig, 34-37; Zurich, 37-38; Ph.D.(org. chem), Columbia, 41. Eli Lilly fel, Columbia, 40-42; res. chemist, Givaudan Res. Inst, N.Y, 43; head dept, Squibb Inst. Med. Res, N.J, 44-59, dir, sect. org. chem, 59-63; PROF. CHEM. & BIOCHEM, DEPT. CHEM. & PROF, BEN MAY LAB. CANCER RES, UNIV. CHICAGO, 63- Chmn, Gordon Res. Conf. Steroids & Related Natural Prod, 55-57; Knapp Mem. lectr, Wisconsin, 58; mem. med. chem. study sect, Nat. Insts. Health, 63-67 & 68-72; comt. arrangements, Laurentian Hormone Conf, 64- N.J. Outstanding Patent Award, 68. Nat. Acad. Sci; fel. AAAS; Am. Chem. Soc; Am. Soc. Biol. Chem; fel. N.Y. Acad. Sci; Brit. Chem. Soc; Swiss Chem. Soc. Chemistry of steroids; prostaglandins. Address: Dept. of Chemistry, University of Chicago, Chicago, IL 60637.

FRIED, MAURICE, b. New York, N.Y, Nov. 6, 20; m. 43; c. 5. SOIL CHEMISTRY. B.S, Cornell, 41, M.S, 45; fel, Connecticut, 41-42; fel, Purdue, 46-48, Ph.D.(soil chem), 48. Asst. soil chem, Cornell, 44-45; instr. soils, Purdue, 47-48; prin. res. scientist, bur. plant indust, soils & agr. eng, U.S. Dept. Agr, 48-53, agr. res. serv, 53-61; head agr. sect, Int. Atomic Energy Agency, 61-64; DIR, JOINT FOOD & AGR. ORGN-INT. ATOMIC ENERGY AGENCY DIV, ATOMIC ENERGY IN AGR, 64- Am. Soc. Agron; Am. Soc. Plant Physiol; Am. Chem. Soc; N.Y. Acad. Sci; Soil Sci. Soc. Am. Poor crop growth in acid soils; sufficiency of sulfur for plant growth; radioactive tracers in soil and mineral nutrition investigations. Address: International Atomic Energy Agency, P.O. Box 645, Vienna, Austria A-1011.

FRIED, MELVIN, b. Brooklyn, N.Y, May 28, 24; m. 47; c. 3. BIOCHEMISTRY. B.S, Florida, 48, M.S, 49; Atomic Energy Cmn. fel, Yale, 50-52, Ph.D.(biochem), 52. Childs Fund fel. med. res, Cambridge, 52-53; instr. BIOCHEM, Washington (St. Louis), 53-56; asst. prof, COL. MED, UNIV. FLA, 56-64, assoc. prof, 64-67, PROF, 67- Nat. Insts. Health sr. res. fel, 57-62; vis. res. prof, inst. biol. chem, Univ. Aix-Marseille, 68-69. U.S.A, 42-46. Am. Soc. Biol. Chem; Am. Chem. Soc; Brit. Biochem. Soc; Soc. Exp. Biol. & Med. Proteolytic enzymes; protein biosynthesis; nucleic acid chemistry; metal-peptide complexes; chemistry and metabolism of serum proteins; marine biochemistry. Address: Dept. of Biochemistry, College of Medicine, University of Florida, Gainesville, FL 32601.

FRIED, RAINER, b. Worms, Germany, July 28, 24; U.S. citizen; m. 51; c. 6. BIOCHEMISTRY. B.Sc, São Paulo, 45; Brazilian Nat. Res. Coun. fel, 47-52, Ph.D.(biochem), 52. Res. assoc. BIOCHEM, med. sch, São Paulo, 47-57; med. sch, Northwestern, 57-59; Vet. Admin. Hosp, Tupper Lake, N.Y, 59-61; asst. prof, sch. med, Indiana, 61-64; SCH. MED, CREIGHTON UNIV, 64-65, ASSOC. PROF, 65- Asst. prof, Escola Paulista de Medicina, Brazil, 46-47, assoc. prof, 47-50; Brazilian Nat. Res. Coun. fel, 52-57; Rockefeller Found. fel, 54-55; Am. Cancer Soc. res. fel, 55. AAAS; Am. Chem. Soc; Am. Neurochem. Soc; Int. Soc. Neurochem. Neurochemistry; intermediary metabolism; amino acids; purines; vitamins; enzymes; biochemical pharmacology. Address: Dept. of Biochemistry, Creighton University Medical School, Omaha, NE 68131.

FRIED, VOJTECH, b. Lozin, Czech, Aug. 27, 21; m. 51; c. 1. PHYSICAL CHEMISTRY. Chem.Engr, Univ. Chem. Tech, Prague, 51, Dr.Sc.(phys. chem), 53, Dr.Ch.Sc.(phys. chem), 57. Instr. phys. chem, Univ. Chem. Tech, Prague, 50-53, asst. prof, 53-63, assoc. prof, 63-64; PROF. CHEM, BROOKLYN COL, 65- Czech. State Prize in Sci, 63. Am. Chem. Soc; Czech. Chem. Soc; fel. Am. Inst. Chem; N.Y. Acad. Sci. Thermodynamic and statistical theories of solutions of nonelectrolytes; experimental studies in the field of phase equilibria. Address: Dept. of Chemistry, Brooklyn College, Bedford Ave. & Ave. H, Brooklyn, NY 11210.

FRIEDBERG, A(RTHUR) L(EROY), b. River Forest, Ill, Mar. 25, 19; m. 44; c. 2. CERAMIC ENGINEERING. B.S, Illinois, 41, M.S, 47, Ph.D.(ceramic eng), 52; Chicago, 43; California, 44. From res. asst. to assoc. prof, UNIV. ILL, URBANA-CHAMPAIGN, 46-57, PROF. CERAMIC ENG. & HEAD DEPT, 57- Consult, Ferro Corp, Ohio. U.S.N, 43-46, Lt. Fel. Am. Ceramic Soc; Brit. Soc. Glass Technol; Am. Soc. Test. & Mat. Ceramic research; porcelain enamels; high temperature coatings. Address: Dept. of Ceramic Engineering, 203 Ceramics, University of Illinois, Urbana-Champaign, Urbana, IL 61801.

FRIEDBERG, CARL E, U.S. citizen. EXPERIMENTAL HIGH ENERGY PHYSICS. B.A, Harvard, 64; NASA traineeship, Princeton, 66-68, M.A. & Ph.D. (physics), 69. INSTR. PHYSICS, PRINCETON, 69- Am. Phys. Soc. Tests of time reversal invariance by reciprocity and polarization measurements. Address: Dept. of Physics, Jadwin Hall, Princeton University, Princeton, NJ 08540.

FRIEDBERG, ERROL CLIVE, b. Johannesburg, S.Africa, Oct. 2, 37; m. 61; c. 1. BIOCHEMISTRY, PATHOLOGY. B.Sc, Witwatersrand, 58, M.B. & B.Ch, 61. Intern. med. & surg, King Edward VIII Hosp, Univ. Natal, S.Africa, 62-63; registr. path, Witwatersrand, 63-65; res. & fel. path, Cleveland Metrol. Gen. Hosp. & sch. med, Case Western Reserve, 65-66; fel. biochem, sch. med, Case Western Reserve, 66-68; res. investr, Walter Reed Army Inst. Res, 69-70; ASST. PROF. PATH, SCH. MED, STANFORD UNIV, 70- Grants, Atomic Energy Comn; Nat. Insts. Health; Am. Cancer Soc. Cert, Ed. Coun. For. Med. Grad, 69. Med.C, U.S.A, 68-70, Maj. Am. Med. Asn; Biophys. Soc; N.Y. Acad. Sci; Radiation Res. Soc; Am. Chem. Soc. Enzymes in deoxyribonucleic acid metabolism; repair of radiation damage to deoxyribonucleic acid; role of DNA repair in carcinogenesis. Address: Dept. of Pathology, School of Medicine, Stanford University, Stanford, CA 94305.

FRIEDBERG, FELIX, b. Copenhagen, Denmark, Apr. 3, 21; nat; m. 71. BIOCHEMISTRY. B.S, Denver, 44; Rosenberg fel, California, 46-47, Ph.D.(biochem), 47. Asst. biochem, California, 44-46, sr. fel, U.S. Pub. Health Serv, 47-48; instr. BIOCHEM, COL. MED, HOWARD UNIV, 48-52, asst. prof, 53-57, assoc. prof, 57-61, PROF, 61- Vis. lectr, Cath. Univ. Am, 50-52; Commonwealth Fund fel, Howard Univ, 62-63. Lederle Med. Faculty Award, 57. Am. Soc. Biol. Chem. Protein metabolism and structure. Address: Dept. of Biochemistry, Howard University College of Medicine, Washington, DC 20001.

FRIEDBERG, RICHARD MICHAEL, b. N.Y.C, Oct. 8, 35; m. 63. THEORETICAL PHYSICS. B.A, Harvard, 56; M.A, Columbia, 61, Ph.D.(physics), 62. Mem, Inst. Adv. Study, 62-64; asst. prof. PHYSICS, COLUMBIA UNIV, 64-70, ASSOC. PROF, BARNARD COL, 70- Sloan res. fel, 61-65; visitor, European Orgn. Nuclear Res, Geneva, Switz, 64-65. Elementary particles. theoretical physics; mathematical logic; artificial intelligence. Address: Dept. of Physics, Barnard College, Columbia University, New York, NY 10027.

FRIEDBERG, SIMEON A(DLOW), b. Pittsburgh, Pa, July 7, 25; m. 50; c. 3. PHYSICS. A.B, Harvard, 47; M.S, Carnegie Inst. Tech, 48, Westinghouse fel, 50-51, D.Sc.(physics), 51. Fulbright grant, Leiden, 51-52; res. physicist, CARNEGIE-MELLON UNIV, 52-53, asst. prof. PHYSICS, 53-57, assoc. prof, 57-62, PROF, 62- Alfred P. Sloan res. fel, 57-61; Guggenheim fel, 65-66. U.S.A, 43-46, Res, 46-53. Fel. Am. Phys. Soc. Solid state and low temperature physics; thermal, magnetic and transport properties; cooperative behavior in magnetic crystals. Address: Dept. of Physics, Carnegie-Mellon University, Pittsburgh, PA 15213.

FRIEDBERG, WALLACE, b. N.Y.C, Apr. 12, 27; m. 57; c. 3. PHYSIOLOGY. A.B, Hope Col, 49; M.S, Mich. State, 51, Ph.D.(physiol), 53. Asst, Mich. State, 49-53; Nat. Insts. Health res. fel, Indiana, 53-54; res. assoc, Children's Hosp. Phila, Univ. Pa, 54-55; biol. div, Oak Ridge Nat. Lab, 55-56, Nat. Insts. Health res. fel, 57-58, assoc. biologist, 58-59, biologist, 59-60; CHIEF RADIOBIOL. RES, PHARMACOL-BIOCHEM. LAB, CIVIL AEROMED. INST, FED. AVIATION ADMIN, 60- Asst. prof, med. sch, Univ. Okla, 61-64, assoc. prof, 64-69, prof, med. sch. & res. prof, sch. health, 69-, adj. prof, univ, 71-; assoc, Oklahoma City Univ, 68-; loanee, Oak Ridge Nat. Lab, 69- U.S.N, 45-46. Am. Chem. Soc; Soc. Exp. Biol. & Med; Am. Physiol. Soc; Transplantation Soc. Biological effects of radiation; mechanisms of immunity. Address: Dept. of Transportation, Federal Aviation Administration, Civil Aeromedical Institute, Pharmacology-Biochemistry Lab, AC-114, P.O. Box 25082, Oklahoma City, OK 73125.

FRIEDE, JOHN DAVIS, b. Albuquerque, N.Mex, Mar. 3, 41; m. 66; c. 2. BIOCHEMISTRY, MICROBIOLOGY. B.S, St. Benedict's Col.(Kans), 63; assistantship & M.S, Univ. N.Mex, 66; Nat. Insts. Health trainee & Ph.D. (biochem), Univ. Minn, St. Paul, 71. RES. ASSOC. BIOCHEM, OKLA. STATE UNIV, 71- Am. Soc. Microbiol. Lysine and 5-hydroxylysine transport in Streptococcus faecalis; lysine and 5-hydroxylysine degradation in Pseudomonas fluorescens; hydrocarbon metabolism in microorganisms and production of emulsifying agents by these organisms when grown on hydrocarbons. Address: Dept. of Biochemistry, Oklahoma State University, Stillwater, OK 74074.

FRIEDE, REINHARD L, b. Jaegerndorf, Czech, May 12, 26; U.S. citizen; m. 53; c. 2. NEUROPATHOLOGY, HISTOCHEMISTRY. M.D, Vienna, 51. Res, City Hosp, St. Poelten, Austria, 51-52; intern, neurol. inst. & clin. Univ. Vienna, 53; mem. staff, clin. neurosurg, Univ. Freiburg, 53-57; with civil serv, Wright Air Develop. Center, Ohio, 57-59; instr. psychiat, Michigan, 59-60, asst. prof. histochem, 60-62; assoc. prof. path, 62-65; PROF. NEUROPATH, INST. PATH, CASE WEST. RESERVE UNIV, 65- Civil Service Award, 61; dipl, Am. Bd. Path, 63. Am. Asn. Neuropath. Histochemistry of nervous system; experimental pathology; chemical cytology of nervous system. Address: Institute of Pathology, Case Western Reserve University, Cleveland, OH 44106.

FRIEDEL, ARTHUR W, b. Pittsburgh, Pa, Nov. 14, 37. INORGANIC CHEMISTRY. B.S, Pittsburgh, 59, M.Ed, 63; Nat. Sci. Found. fel, Ohio State, 63-64, Ph.D.(sci. ed), 68. Teacher, pub. schs, Pa, 59-63; asst. sci. ed, Ohio State, 64-65, CHEM, 65-67; instr, PURDUE UNIV, 67-68, ASST. PROF, 68- Consult, East Allen County Sch. Dist, Bishop Dwenger High Sch. sci. dept. & Ft. Wayne community schs, 67- Am. Chem. Soc; Nat. Sci. Teachers Asn. Chemical education; boroxine chemistry. Address: Dept. of Chemistry, Purdue University, Ft. Wayne, IN 46805.

FRIEDEL, ROBERT A(UGUSTINE), b. Kenton, Ohio, Aug. 14, 17; m. 42; c. 2. PHYSICAL CHEMISTRY. B.A, Ohio State, 39; M.S, Carnegie Inst. Tech, 40, D.Sc.(phys. chem), 43. Asst. chem, Carnegie Inst. Tech, 39-41; RES. CHEMIST, Shell Oil Co, Houston, 43-45; U.S. BUR. MINES, 45- Mem. staff Los Angeles County Air Pollution Dist, 50; Guggenheim Found. fel. & guest scientist, Australian Commonwealth Sci. & Indust. Res. Orgn, 64-65. Mem. comt. spectral absorption data & phys. chem. subcomt. standards, Nat. Res. Coun; prog. comt. 10th Int. Spectros. Conf; local chmn, 6th Int. Carbon Conf; co-chmn, 1st Pittsburgh Conf. Anal. Chem. & Appl. Spectros; mem, Nat. Bur. Standards-Am. Soc. Test. & Mat. joint comt. phys. data; chmn, Comn. Mass Spectrometry, 58-60; Conf. on Nuclear Magnetic Resonance, 63. Pittsburgh Spectros. Award, 64; U.S. Dept. Interior Gold Medal, 66. Fel. AAAS; Optical Soc. Am; Soc. Appl. Spectros; Am. Chem. Soc.(H.H. Storch Award, 66, Pittsburgh Award, 67); Am. Soc. Test. & Mat; Coblentz Soc; Geochem. Soc. Infrared, ultraviolet, nuclear and electron magnetic resonance and mass spectrometry; molecular structure; coal; carbons; catalytic synthesis. Address: U.S. Bureau of Mines, 4800 Forbes Ave, Pittsburgh, PA 15213.

FRIEDELL, GILBERT H, b. Minneapolis, Minn, Feb. 28, 27; m. 50; c. 5. MEDICINE, PATHOLOGY. B.S, Minnesota, 47, M.B, 49, M.D, 50. Intern, Minneapolis Gen. Hosp, 49-50; fel. & asst. res, Mallory Inst. Path, 50-52; Am. Cancer Soc. fel. path, Free Hosp. Women, 52-53; res, Salem Hosp, 53-54; Pondville Hosp, 54-55; from asst. to assoc, Mass. Mem. Hosps, Boston, 57-62; pathologist, New Eng. Deaconess Hosp. & res. assoc, Cancer Res. Inst, Boston, 62-67; assoc. pathologist, Mallory Inst. Path, Boston City Hosp, 67-69; CLIN. PROF. PATH, SCH. MED, UNIV. MASS, WORCESTER, 70-; CHIEF PATH. DEPT, ST. VINCENT HOSP, 69- Teaching fel. path, Harvard Med. Sch, 52-53, asst, 57-61, instr, 62-; U.S. Pub. Health Serv. spec. fel, Strangeways Res. Lab, Eng, 61-62; instr, Boston Univ, 62-67, lectr, 67-69, assoc. prof, sch. med, 67-71, lectr, 71-; asst. pathologist, Mallory Inst. Path, Boston City Hosp, 66-; lectr, Harvard Med. Sch, 67- Dipl, Am. Bd. Path, 55. Am. Asn. Cancer Res; Am. Soc. Exp. Path; Am. Soc. Clin. Path; Am. Soc. Cytol; Am. Soc. Clin. Oncol; James Ewing Soc. Clinical and experimental studies of tumor-host relationships with special reference to breast, cervix and bladder cancer. Address: Pathology Dept, St. Vincent Hospital, 25 Winthrop St, Worcester, MA 01610.

FRIEDELL, HYMER L(OUIS), b. St. Petersburg, Russia, Feb. 6, 11; nat; m. 35; c. 3. RADIOLOGY. B.S, Minnesota, 31, M.B, 35, M.D, 36, Ph.D. (radiol), 40. Nat. Cancer Inst. fel, Chicago Tumor Inst, Mem. Hosp, New York, 39-40; univ. hosp, California, 40-41, instr. radiol, univ, 41-42; PROF. RADIOL. & DIR. DEPT, UNIV. HOSPS, CASE WEST. RESERVE UNIV, 46- Consult, Nat. Adv. Comt. Aeronaut; chmn, radiation study sect, Nat. Insts. Health; chmn, comt. allocation of isotopes for human use & mem. reactor safeguard comt, Atomic Energy Comn; chmn. subcomt. radiobiol. & mem. comt. radiol, Nat. Res. Coun; mem. subcomt. permissable external dose, Nat. Bur. Standards; coun. exec. bd, Argonne Nat. Lab; cent. adv. comt, radioisotope sect, res. & educ. serv, U.S. Vet. Admin; res. & develop. bd, Joint Panel on Med. Aspects of Atomic Warfare; partic, Int. Cong. Radiol; mem. vis. comt. for med. dept, Brookhaven Nat. Lab. U.S.A, 43-46. AAAS; Am. Radium Soc; Soc. Exp. Biol. & Med; Radiol. Soc. N.Am; Am. Roentgen Ray Soc; Am. Med. Asn; fel. Am. Col. Radiol; Radiation Res. Soc.(pres). Biological effects of radioisotopes; use of radiation and radioisotopes for therapy and diagnosis; radiation protection and radiation hazards. Address: Case Western Reserve University Hospitals, 2065 Adelbert Rd, Cleveland, OH 44106.

FRIEDELL, JOHN C, b. Dubuque, Iowa, Nov. 2, 29. PURE MATHEMATICS. B.A, Loras Col, 51; S.T.L, Gregorian Univ, 55; M.S, Iowa, 58; Nat. Sci. Found. fel, Catholic Univ, 61-62, Ph.D.(math), 62. Instr. MATH, LORAS COL, 57-63, asst. prof, 63-68, ASSOC. PROF, 68- Mem, Nat. Sci. Found. Summer Inst, Princeton, 63; prog. res. participation for col. teachers, Oklahoma, summer 65. Am. Math. Soc; Math. Asn. Am. Linear and topological algebra; Banach algebras, specifically H* algebras. Address: Dept. of Mathematics, Loras College, Dubuque, IA 52001.

FRIEDEMANN, THEODORE E(DWARD), b. Kiel, Okla, Feb. 22, 96; m. 22; c. 3. BIOCHEMISTRY, BACTERIOLOGY. B.S, Okla. State, 15; A.M, Missouri, 21; Ph.D.(biochem), Washington (St. Louis), 23. Instr. chem, Mich. State, 15-17, asst. chemist, exp. sta, 17-18; Missouri, 20-21; biochem. sch. med, Washington (St. Louis), 21-23, instr, 23-27; asst. prof. res. bact, med. sch, Northwestern, 27-29; chem. bact, dept. med, Chicago, 29-40; assoc. prof. physiol. & nutrit, med. sch, Northwestern, 40-51, dir. lab, Abbott Fund, 40-49; sci. dir, Army Med. Res. & Nutrit. Lab, 51-59; mem. biochem. res. staff, Univ. Colo, Boulder, 59-67; RETIRED. Consult. to Surgeon Gen, U.S. Army, 45-46, 58-; mem. metab. & nutrit. study sect, Nat. Insts. Health, 51-61, consult, 59-61; mem, Res. & Develop. Assoc. Food & Container Inst; consult. Med.C, U.S.A, 18-19. AAAS; Soc. Exp. Biol. & Med; Am. Soc. Biol. Chem; Am. Chem. Soc; Am. Inst. Nutrit; Am. Inst. Food Technol. Microbiology; nutrition and food chemistry; high altitude and work physiology; intermediary metabolism; analytical chemistry. Address: 1503 Balsam Ave, Boulder, CO 80302.

FRIEDEN, B(ERNARD) ROY, b. Brooklyn, N.Y, Sept. 10, 36; m. 62; c. 2. OPTICAL PHYSICS. B.S, Brooklyn Col, 57; M.S, Pennsylvania, 59; Ph.D. (optics), Rochester, 66. Physicist, Gen. Elec. Co, 60-61; mathematician, Bausch & Lomb, Inc, N.Y, 61-62; res. asst. optics, Rochester, 62-63; asst. prof. OPTICAL SCI, UNIV. ARIZ, 66-70, ASSOC. PROF, 70- Consult, Elgeet Optical Co, N.Y, 65; Tropel, Inc, N.Y, 66; RCA Corp, N.J, 69. AAAS; Optical Soc. Am. Optical, photographic image formation; information theory; image enhancement; apodizing, super-resolving pupils; synthetic apertures; numerical, statistical analysis; special mathematical functions. Address: Optical Science Center, University of Arizona, Tucson, AZ 85721.

FRIEDEN, CARL, b. New Rochelle, N.Y, Dec. 31, 28; m. 53; c. 3. BIOCHEMISTRY. B.A, Carlton Col, 51; U.S. Rubber Co. fel, Univ. Wis, 54-55, Ph.D. (chem), 55. Fel, WASH. UNIV, 55-57, instr. BIOCHEM, 57-60, asst. prof, 60-63, assoc. prof, 63-67, PROF, 67- AAAS; Am. Chem. Soc; Am. Soc. Biol. Chem. Enzymes and enzymatic kinetics; physical chemistry of proteins. Address: Dept. of Biochemistry, Washington University School of Medicine, St. Louis, MO 63130.

FRIEDEN, E(ARL), b. Norfolk, Va, Dec. 31, 21; m. 42; c. 2. BIOCHEMISTRY. B.A, California, Los Angeles, 43; M.S, Southern California, 47, Ph.D. (biochem), 49. Lab. supvr. anal. chem, Rubber Reserve Co, U.S. Rubber Co, 43-45; res. biochemist, Bedwell Labs, 45-47, instr, Southern California, 48; asst. prof. CHEM, FLA. STATE UNIV, 49-52, assoc. prof, 52-57, PROF, 57-, chmn. dept, 62-68. U.S. Pub. Health Serv. spec. fel, Carlsberg Labs, Denmark, 57-58; Lalor award, inst. enzyme res, Wisconsin, 55. Am. Soc. Biol. Chem; Am. Chem. Soc.(Florida Award, 68). Chemistry and mechanism of enzymes; copper enzymes and catalysis; biochemistry of amphibian metamorphosis; role of thyroxine in vitro and in vivo systems. Address: Dept. of Chemistry, Florida State University, Tallahassee, FL 32306.

FRIEDEN, EDWARD H(IRSCH), b. Norfolk, Va, Jan. 4, 18; m. 41; c. 5. BIOCHEMISTRY. A.B, California, Los Angeles, 39, M.A, 41, Ph.D.(biochem), 42. Asst. chem, California, Los Angeles, 39-42; Lalor Found. fel, Texas, 42-43, instr. biochem, sch. med, 43-44, res. assoc, 45-46; res. fel, biol. labs, Harvard, 46-52, instr. biol. chem, sch. med, 48-52; asst. prof. biochem, med. sch, Tufts, 52-60, assoc. prof, 60-64; PROF. CHEM, KENT STATE UNIV, 64- Guggenheim fel, California, Los Angeles, 53; coord. res, Boston Dispensary, 57-64. Am. Chem. Soc; Am. Soc. Biol. Chem; Endocrine Soc; Soc. Exp. Biol. & Med. Effects of steroid hormones on protein and nucleic acid synthesis; chemistry of relaxin; biosynthesis of pyridoxine. Address: Dept. of Chemistry, Kent State University, Kent, OH 44242.

FRIEDENBERG, RICHARD M, b. New York, N.Y, 26; m; c. 3. RADIOLOGY. A.B, Columbia, 46; M.D, State Univ. N.Y, 49. Asst. prof. RADIOL, Albert Einstein Col. Med, 55-66, assoc. clin. prof, 66-68; PROF. & CHMN. DEPT, METROP. HOSP. CENTER, N.Y. MED. COL, 68- Dir. & chmn. dept. radiol, Bronx-Lebanon Hosp. Center, 57-68. U.S.A.F. Fel. Am. Col. Radiol; Radiol. Soc. N.Am; Am. Roentgen Ray Soc; fel. N.Y. Acad. Med. Address: Dept. of Radiology, New York Medical College, 1249 Fifth Ave, New York, NY 10029.

FRIEDENBERG, ROBERT M, b. Brooklyn, N.Y, May 9, 30. PHARMACEUTICAL CHEMISTRY, CHEMICAL PHYSICS. B.A, Park Col, 53; M.S, Mississippi, 56; Ph.D.(pharmaceut. chem), Connecticut, 63. Asst. res. prof. theoret. biol, State Univ. N.Y. Buffalo, 63-65; assoc. res. prof. theoret. neuro-biol, psychiat. inst, sch. med, Maryland, 65-69; DEP. TECH. DIR, HITTMAN ASSOCS, INC, 69- AAAS; Am. Chem. Soc. Cosmetic chemistry; lipstick removing compositions; aerosol shaving creams; organic synthesis; thyroxin analogs; ultrapurity and ultrapurification of organics; analytical techniques and zone melting; thermal analysis; chemical physics of model membrane systems; theoretical biology; differential thermal analysis. Address: Hittman Associates, Inc, 9190 Red Branch Rd, Columbia, MD 21043.

FRIEDENSTEIN, HANNA, b. Vienna, Austria; nat. CHEMISTRY. B.Sc, London, 41; M.S, Simmons Col, 50. Res. chemist, Phillips Elec. Ltd., Eng, 42-46; asst. intel. officer, Brit. Oxygen Co, 46-47; res. librn, CABOT CORP, 47-57, HEAD TECH. INFO. SERV, 57-68, MGR, INFO. CTR, 68- Am. Chem. Soc; Am. Soc. Info. Sci; Spec. Libr. Asn. Chemical documentation; communication and retrieval of information; library science. Address: Performance Chemicals Group, Technical Center, Cabot Corp, Concord Rd, Billerica, MA 01821.

FRIEDERICH, ALLAN G(EORGE), b. Wood River, Ill, Jan. 1, 22; m. 45; c. 3. MECHANICAL ENGINEERING. B.S, Illinois, 47, M.S, 53. Loftsman, Curtiss-Wright & Corp, Mo, 42-45; instr. gen. eng, UNIV. ILL, URBANA-CHAMPAIGN, 47-53, asst. prof, 53-56, ASSOC. PROF. MECH. ENG, 56- Consult, N.E. Newmark & Assocs, 53-; U.S. Govt, 53- Am. Soc. Mech. Eng; Am. Soc. Eng. Educ. Machine design and graphics. Address: 340 Mechanical Engineering Bldg, University of Illinois at Urbana-Champaign, Urbana, IL 61801.

FRIEDERICI, H(ARTMANN) H. R, b. Asuncion, Paraguay, Jan. 25, 27; U.S. citizen; m. 58; c. 3. MEDICINE, PATHOLOGY. B.S, Goethe Col, Paraguay, 46; M.D, La Plata, 53. Asst. PATH, Bonn, 55-56; res, col. med, Illinois, 47-49, instr, 60-61, asst. prof, 61-66, assoc. prof, 66-69; PROF, SCH. MED, NORTHWEST. UNIV, 69-, BIOL. SCI, COL. ARTS & SCI, 70-; HEAD DEPT. PATH, EVANSTON HOSP, 71- Assoc. pathologist, Res. & Educ. Hosp, 66-69. AAAS; Int. Acad. Path; Am. Asn. Path. & Bact; Am. Soc. Exp. Path; Am. Soc. Cell Biol; Am. Soc. Clin. Path; Latin Am. Soc. Path. Anat. Study of ultrastructure of blood and lympathic capillaries under physiologic and pathologic circumstances in man and experimental animals; cell surfaces. Address: Dept. of Pathology, Evanston Hospital, 2650 Ridge Ave, Evanston, IL 60201.

FRIEDERS, ROBERT B, b. Aurora, Ill, July 13, 19. ZOOLOGY, ENDOCRINOLOGY. B.A, St. Meinrad Col. Lib. Arts, 42; M.S, Catholic Univ, 49, Ph.D.(biol), 54. Prof. biol, St. Meinrad Col. Lib. Arts, 54-64; mem. staff biol. res, Loveland Pet Prod, 61-66; ASSOC. PROF. BIOL, MONTGOMERY JR. COL, 66- Asst. prof, St. Benedict Col.(Ind), 60-64; summers, assoc. prof, Catholic Univ, 56-64. Int. Fedn. Aquarium Socs. Award, 63. Ecology; ichthyology. Address: Dept. of Biology, Montgomery Junior College, Rockville, MD 20850.

FRIEDES, JOSEPH L(EONARD), b. Brooklyn, N.Y, Dec. 4, 34; m. 54; c. 2. NUCLEAR & HIGH ENERGY PHYSICS. B.A, Cornell, 56; M.S, Illinois, 58, Int. Bus. Mach. fel, 60-61, Ph.D.(physics), 62. Instr. physics, Illinois, 56-62; asst. physicist, Brookhaven Nat. Lab, 62-66, assoc. physicist, 66-70; PRES, PERIPHONICS CORP, 70- Am. Phys. Soc. Breakup of new nuclear systems; neutron-proton charge exchange at high energies; nuclear physics using one billion electron volt proton probes. Address: 15 Highland Down, Shoreham, NY 11786.

FRIEDHOFF, ARNOLD J(EROME), b. Johnstown, Pa, Dec. 26, 23; m. 46; c. 3. PSYCHIATRY. M.D, Pennsylvania, 47. Intern psychiat, W.Pa. Hosp, 47-48; jr. staff psychiatrist, Mayview State Hosp, Pa, 48-51; res. psychiat. div, Bellevue Hosp. & Clin, med. ctr, N.Y. UNIV, 53-54, clin. asst. PSYCHIAT, COL. MED, 55-56, clin. instr, 56-57, instr, 57-58, asst. prof, 58-66, PROF, 66-, HEAD PSYCHOPHARMACOL. RES. UNIT, 56-, DIR, CTR. STUDY PSYCHOTIC DISORDERS, 64-, ASST. VIS. NEUROPSYCHIATRIST, UNIV. HOSP. & CLIN, 57-, jr. psychiatrist, 54-57. Consult, prof. exam. serv, Am. Pub. Health Asn; dir, Millhauser Labs; mem. clin. proj. rev. comt, Nat. Inst. Ment. Health. U.S.A, 51-53. Harvey Soc, Asn. Res. Nerv. & Ment. Diseases (asst. secy); Am. Psychiat. Asn; N.Y. Acad. Sci; Am. Psychopath. Asn.(treas); Am. Col. Neuropsychopharmacol.(v.pres). Neurochemistry; neuropharmacology. Address: Dept. of Psychiatry, New York University School of Medicine, 550 First Ave, New York, NY 10016.

FRIEDKIN, JOSEPH FRANK, b. Brooklyn, N.Y, Oct. 18, 09; m. 37; c. 2. HYDRAULIC ENGINEERING. B.S, Tex. Col. Mines, 32; Miss. State Col, 44. Resident engr, San Diego Field Off, U.S. SECT, INT. BOUNDARY & WATER COMN, U.S. & MEX, 47-52, prin. supvr. engr, HQS, EL PASO OFF, 52-62, COMNR, 62- Mem, Miss. River Stabilization Bd, Miss. River Cmn, 44-45; Bur. Reclamation Consult. Bd, Colo. River Channel Works, Needles, Ariz, 49; Imp. Dam Adv. Bd, Colo. River, 52-60. C.Eng, 42-46, Res, 46-, Maj. Am. Geophys. Union; fel. Am. Soc. Civil Eng; Soc. Am. Mil. Eng. Water control and utilization using dams and streams; planning river regulation; surface waters. Address: International Boundary & Water Commission, P.O. Box 1859, El Paso, TX 79950.

FRIEDKIN, MORRIS ENTON, b. Kansas City, Mo, Dec. 30, 18; m. 43; c. 3. BIOCHEMISTRY. M.S, Iowa State Col, 41; Ph.D.(biochem), Chicago, 48. Chemist, penicillin proj, north. regional res. lab, U.S. Dept. Agr, 41-45; U.S. Pub. Health Serv. fel, Copenhagen, 48-49; instr. pharmacol, sch. med, Washington (St. Louis), 49-52, asst. prof, 51-57, assoc. prof, 57-58; prof. & chmn. dept, sch. med, Tufts Univ, 58-69; PROF. BIOL. & MEM. FACULTY, SCH. MED, UNIV. CALIF, SAN DIEGO, 69- Am. Chem. Soc; Am. Soc. Biol. Chem; Am. Soc. Pharmacol. & Exp. Therapeut; Am. Acad. Arts & Sci. Enzymology; nucleic acid metabolism; biochemical pharmacology. Address: Dept. of Biology, University of California, San Diego, P.O. Box 109, La Jolla, CA 92037.

FRIEDL, FRANK E(DWARD), b. Stewart, Minn, May 29, 31; m. 56; c. 4. INVERTEBRATE PHYSIOLOGY, PARASITOLOGY. B.A, Minnesota, 52, Ph.D.(zool), 58. Asst. zool, Minnesota, 52-58; res. fel, U.S. Pub. Health Serv, Rockefeller Inst, 58-60; asst. prof. ZOOL, UNIV. S.FLA, 60-64, ASSOC. PROF, 64- Fel. trop. med, La. State Univ, summer 65. U.S.N.R, 48-57. AAAS; Am. Soc. Parasitol; Am. Soc. Zool. Comparative biochemistry and physiology; intermediary metabolism in invertebrates; nitrogen catabolism in molluses. Address: Dept. of Biology, University of South Florida, Tampa, FL 33620.

FRIEDL, PAUL J, b. Cleveland, Ohio, Oct. 17, 33; m. 60; c. 4. CHEMICAL ENGINEERING. B.S, Case, 55, M.S, 57, Westinghouse fels, 58-60, Ph.D. (chem. eng), 60. Indust. analyst process control, IBM CORP, 60-61, control systs. rep. control, 61-64, spec. rep. med. servs, 64-65, MGR, high energy physics applns, 65, on-line systs, 65-70, MICROPROGRAMMED COMPUT. SYSTS. DESIGN & EVAL, 70- Adj. asst. prof, Univ. South. Calif, 64- Mem, Simulation Coun, Inc. Analog and digital computers applied to simulation and control of industrial, biomedical, geophysical and military systems. Address: IBM Scientific Center, 2670 Hanover St, Palo Alto, CA 94304.

FRIEDLAENDER, CARLO G(OTTHELF) I(MMANUEL), b. Naples, Italy, May 23, 05; Can. citizen; m. 55; c. 2. PETROGRAPHY, MINERALOGY. B.Sc, Zurich, 23, Ph.D.(geol), 30. Asst. mineral. & petrog, Inst. Eidgenossische Technische Hochsch, 30-34; co-worker, Swiss Geotech. Comn, 34-37, 40-55; geologist, Soc. Forminière, Brussels, 37-40; geologist, Chartered Explor, Rhodesia, 55-56; prof. GEOL, DALHOUSIE UNIV, 57-70, EMER. PROF, 70- AAAS; Geol. Soc. Am; fel, Geol. Asn. Can; Mineral. Asn. Can. (secy); Geol. Soc. S.Africa; Swiss Geol. Soc; Swiss Soc. Nat. Sci; Swiss Soc. Mineral. & Petrog. Petrography of plutonic and metamorphic rocks; geochemistry. Address: 248 Clemow Ave, Ottawa 1, Ont, Can. K1S 2B6.

FRIEDLAENDER, FRITZ J(OSEF), b. Freiburg, Ger, May 7, 25; nat; m. 69; c. 1. ELECTRICAL ENGINEERING. B.S, Carnegie Inst. Tech, 51, M.S, 52, Ph.D.(elec. eng), 55. Asst. ELEC. ENG, Carnegie Inst. Tech, 51-54; asst. prof, Columbia, 54-55; PURDUE UNIV, 55-59, assoc. prof, 59-62, PROF, 62- Guest prof, Max-Planck Inst. Metal Res, 64-65. Consult, Gen. Elec. Co, Ind, 56-58; Components Corp, Ill, 59-61; Lawrence Radiation Lab, Univ. Calif, 67-69. Am. Phys. Soc; Am. Soc. Eng. Educ; fel. Inst. Elec. & Electronics Eng.(rev. ed. jour, 65-67); Swiss Elec. Eng. Soc. Magnetics, magnetic devices and memories. Address: School of Electrical Engineering, Purdue University, Lafayette, IN 47907.

FRIEDLAENDER, JONATHAN SCOTT, b. New Orleans, La, Aug. 24, 40; m. 71; c. 1. PHYSICAL ANTHROPOLOGY. A.B, Harvard, 62, Nat. Sci. Found. fel, 65-67 & grant, 67-68, Ph.D.(anthrop), 69; Pennsylvania, 62-63. Pop. Coun. fel. demog. & pop. genetics, Wisconsin, Madison, 68-69, ASST. PROF. ANTHROP, 69-70; HARVARD, 70- AAAS; Am. Asn. Phys. Anthrop; N.Y. Acad. Sci; Brit. Soc. Study Human Biol; Am. Asn. Human Genetics. Studies of human physical variation over population boundaries; populations on Bougainville Island, Territory of New Guinea. Address: Dept. of Anthropology, Harvard University, Cambridge, MA 02138.

FRIEDLAND, AARON J, b. Spring Lake, N.J, Dec. 1, 29; m. 60; c. 2. CHEMICAL & NUCLEAR ENGINEERING. B.Ch.E, City Col. New York, 51; M.S, Columbia, 54, Eng.Sc.D.(chem. eng), 61. Chem. engr, Brookhaven Nat. Lab, 52-53; ATOMIC POWER DEVELOP. ASSOCS, INC, 60-62, HEAD ENG. ANAL. SECT, 62- U.S.A, 54-56. Am. Soc. Mech. Eng; Am. Nuclear Soc. Heat transfer; fluid flow; chemical and nuclear engineering research and development for liquid-metal cooled fast power breeder nuclear reactors. Address: Atomic Power Development Associates, Inc, 1911 First St, Detroit, MI 48226.

FRIEDLAND, ALLAN B, b. Brooklyn, N.Y, Nov. 18, 37; m. 66. MATHEMATICAL & PLASMA PHYSICS. B.E.E, City Col. New York, 60; Hughes Masters fel, Calif. Inst. Technol, 60-61, M.S.E.E, 61; Nat. Sci. Found. fel, Cornell Univ, 62-64, NASA fel, 64-66, univ. scholar. & Ph.D.(theoret. phys, appl. math), 66; Nat. Insts. Health med. scholar, Yale, 70- Sr. staff scientist, space systems div, Avco Corp, Mass, 66-67; sr. scientist, Am. Sci. & Eng, Mass, 67-70. Sr. scientist consult, Am. Sci. & Eng, Mass, 70- Am. Inst. Phys; Inst. Elec. & Electronics Eng; jr. mem. Am. Med. Asn. Plasma physics; wave propagation in homogeneous media; magnetohydrodynamics; statistical communication theory; physics of fluids; general relativity & gravitational theory; astrophysics; ionized shock waves; singular perturbation theory. Address: 111 Park St, Apt. 2F, New Haven, CT 06511.

FRIEDLAND, BEATRICE L, b. N.Y.C, Feb. 12, 14; m. 39; c. 2. BIOLOGY. B.A, N.Y. Univ, 35, M.S, 38, fel, 38-43, Ph.D.(biol), 43. Instr. BIOL, N.Y. Univ, 43-46; Hunter Col, 47-51; STERN COL, YESHIVA UNIV, 51-55, asst. prof, 55-58, assoc. prof, 58-61, PROF, 61-, chmn. dept, 55-71. Embryological genetics; action of genes at specific times in development. Address: Dept. of Biology, Stern College for Women, Yeshiva University, New York, NY 10016.

FRIEDLAND, BERNARD, b. Brooklyn, N.Y, May 25, 30; m. 59; c. 3. ELECTRICAL ENGINEERING. A.B, Columbia, 52, B.S, 53, M.S, 54, PhD.(elec. eng), 57. Instr. elec. eng, Columbia, 54-57, asst. prof, 57-61; head control systs. lab, Melpar, Inc, 61-62; MGR. SYSTS. RES, KEARFOTT DIV, SINGER-GENERAL PRECISION, INC, 62- Adj. assoc. prof, Columbia Univ, 65-70, adj. prof, 70- Am. Soc. Mech. Eng; Inst. Elec. & Electronics Eng; Am. Inst. Aeronaut. & Astronaut. Modern control theory and application. Address: 36 Dartmouth Rd, West Orange, NJ 07052.

FRIEDLAND, DANIEL, b. Columbus, Ohio, Apr. 5, 16; m. 40; c. 2. CHEMICAL ENGINEERING. B.Ch.E, City Col. New York, 37; M.Ch.E, Polytech. Inst. Brooklyn, 45, D.Ch.E, 48. Asst, M.W, Kellogg Co, 37; chem. engr, Cities Serv. Oil Co, New York, 38-46; v.pres, Truland Chem. Co, 46-59; v.pres. Trubek Labs, East Rutherford, 59-64, exec. v.pres, Trubek Chem. Co, East Rutherford, 64-65, UOP Chem. Co, 65-66, V.PRES. MKT, UOP CHEM. DIV, 66- Am. Chem. Soc; Am. Inst. Chem. Eng; Am. Inst. Chem; Commercial Chem. Develop. Asn. Distillation; extraction; unit operations of chemical engineering; petroleum refining. Address: 1046 Field Ave, Plainfield, NJ 07060.

FRIEDLAND, DAVID J, b. Brooklyn, N.Y, Nov. 18, 42; m. 67. ORGANIC CHEMISTRY. B.A, Brooklyn Col, 63; M.S, Yale, 64, Nat. Insts. Health fel, 64-68, Ph.D.(org. chem), 68. RES. CHEMIST, SPECIALTY CHEM. DIV, ALLIED CHEM. CORP, 68- Am. Chem. Soc. Isolation and identification of natural products; polymer chemistry; chemistry of textile coatings. Address: 319 Evans St, Williamsville, NY 14221.

FRIEDLAND, FRITZ, b. Berlin, Ger, Jan. 2, 10; nat; m. 38. MEDICINE. M.D, Berlin, 34. CHIEF, phys. med, Warren City Hosp, Ohio, 43-44; PHYS. MED. & REHAB. SERV, VET. ADMIN. HOSP, Framingham, 46-53, BOSTON, 53-; asst. clin. prof. PHYS. MED. & REHAB. SCH. MED, TUFTS, 54-61, ASSOC. PROF, 61- Consult, Lemuel Shattuck Hosp; assoc. staff, New Eng. Med. Ctr. Hosps. Med.C, U.S.A, 44-46, Capt. Am. Med. Asn; fel. Am. Col. Physicians; Am. Cong. Rehab. Med. Ultrasound in medicine; medical rehabilitation of paraplegics, amputees, arthritic and poliomelitic patients, cerebrovascular accidents. Address: Physical Medicine & Rehabilitation Service, Veterans Administration Hospital, Boston, MA 02130.

FRIEDLAND, JOAN M(ARTHA), b. Binghamton, N.Y, Feb. 6, 36. BIOCHEMISTRY, NEUROCHEMISTRY. B.S, Cornell, 59; Hopkins, 59-62; M.S, Illinois, 64, Ph.D.(biochem), 68. Res. asst, Hopkins, 59-62; biol. labs, Harvard, 66-67, res. fel, 68; RES. ASSOC. ENZYM. & NEUROCHEM, KINGSBROOK JEWISH MED. CTR, 68- Am. Chem. Soc. Bacterial bioluminescent enzymes, subunit structure; biochemistry of lipid storage diseases, hexosaminidase; isozyme studies on Tay Sachs disease and enzymes; studies in mucopolysacchariodosis; prenatal diagnosis of Tay Sachs disease. Address: Kingsbrook Jewish Medical Center, E. 49th & Rutland Rd, Brooklyn, NY 11203.

FRIEDLAND, M(ELVYN), b. Aug. 24, 32; m. 61; c. 2. BIOCHEMISTRY. B.S, California, Los Angeles, 54; Ph.D.(biochem), Southern California, 63. CLIN. CHEMIST, Bio-Sci. Labs, Los Angeles, 63-67; UPJOHN CO, 67- AAAS; Am. Asn. Clin. Chem; Am. Chem. Soc. Nucleic acid antimetabolites; development of new tests for clinical chemistry; management of laboratory operations. Address: Upjohn Co, 6330 Variel Ave, Woodland Hills, CA 91364.

FRIEDLAND, STEPHEN SCHOLOM, b. N.Y.C, Jan. 25, 21; m. 45; c. 2. NUCLEAR PHYSICS & MEDICINE. B.A, Brooklyn Col, 43; M.A, Pennsylvania, 47; Ph.D.(physics), N.Y. Univ, 48. Res. fel, Sloan-Kettering Inst. Cancer Res, 45-48; asst. prof. physics, New Mexico, 48-49; prof. Connecticut, 49-58; scientist, Hughes Aircraft Co, Calif, 58-60; CHIEF EXEC. OFF, SOLID STATE RADIATIONS, INC, 60- Prof, San Fernando Valley State Col, 63-68; mem. sci. specialists, Int. Atomic Energy Agency, 69; res. fel, Israeli Atomic Energy Comn, 69-70. Am. Phys. Soc; Am. Nuclear Soc; Am. Geophys. Union; Inst. Elec. & Electronics Eng. Detection of nuclear radiation; nuclear instrumentation; mass spectroscopy; upper atmosphere density profile; in vivo applications of radioisotopes. Address: 2261 S. Carmelina Ave, Los Angeles, CA 90064.

FRIEDLAND, WALDO C(HARLES), b. Menasha, Wis, Dec. 18, 23; m. 46; c. 6. CHEMISTRY. B.S, Iowa State Col, 48, Ph.D.(chem), 51. Res. microbiologist, ABBOTT LABS, 51-59, sect. mgr, 59-63, asst. to dir. develop, 63-67, DIR. DEVELOP, 67- U.S.A.A.F, 43-46. AAAS; Am. Chem. Soc. Antibiotics and microbial products. Address: 1020 Gracewood Dr, Libertyville, IL 60048.

FRIEDLANDER, ALAN L, b. Chicago, Ill, Aug. 31, 36; m. 58; c. 3. ELECTRICAL ENGINEERING. B.S, Ill. Inst. Tech, 58; M.S, Case, 63. Aeronaut. res. engr, NASA-Lewis Res. Center, 58-63; SR. ENGR, IIT RES. INST, 63- U.S.A.F, 58-62, 1st Lt. Am. Inst. Aeronaut. & Astronaut. Theoretical analysis and design of space vehicle guidance and control systems; astronautical engineering; trajectory and space mission analysis. Address: 5041 Wright Terr, Skokie, IL 60076.

FRIEDLANDER, G(ERHART), b. Munich, Germany, July 28, 16; nat; m. 41; c. 2. NUCLEAR CHEMISTRY. B.S, California, 39, Ph.D.(radiochem), 42. Asst. chem, California, 42; instr, Idaho, 42-43; chemist & group leader, Los Alamos Sci. Lab, California, 43-46; res. assoc, res. lab, Gen. Elec. Co, N.Y, 46-48; vis. lectr. chem. & physics, Washington (St. Louis), 48; chemist, BROOKHAVEN NAT. LAB, 48-52, SR. CHEMIST, 52-, CHMN. DEPT. CHEM, 68- AAAS; fel. Am. Phys. Soc; Am. Chem. Soc.(Award for Nuclear Applns. in Chem, 67). Nuclear reactions; properties of radioactive nuclides. Address: Chemistry Dept, Brookhaven National Lab, Upton, NY 11973.

FRIEDLANDER, HAROLD, b. Mt. Vernon, N.Y, Feb. 6, 13; m. 37; c. 3. MICROBIOLOGY. B.S, City Col. New York, 34; M.A, George Washington, 39, Ph.D.(bact), 50. Bacteriologist, agr. res. admin, U.S. Dept. Agr, 42-43; Lederle Labs. Div, Am. Cyanamid Co, 46; Vet. Admin. Hosps, 46-48, 51-55; Nat. Insts. Health, 48-51; phys. defense div, U.S. Army Res. Labs, Ft. Detrick, Md, 55-59, chief, bio-detection br, 59-62; SCIENTIST ADMINSTR, DIV. RES. GRANTS, NAT. INSTS. HEALTH, 62- Sanit.C, 43-46, Capt. AAAS; Am. Soc. Microbiol; Sci. Res. Soc. Am; Am. Pub. Health Asn; Int. Asn. Dent. Res. Experimental infections of laboratory animals; Corynebacterium; Streptococcus; Bacillus anthracis; Pasteurella pestis. Address: Division of Research Grants, National Institutes of Health, Bethesda, MD 20014.

FRIEDLANDER, HENRY Z, b. N.Y.C, May 18, 25; div; c. 2. ORGANIC CHEMISTRY. A.B, Oberlin Col, 48; M.S, Univ. Ill, 49, Ph.D.(chem), 52. Res. assoc, Case Inst. Technol, 48; asst, Univ. Ill, 49-52; chemist, Stamford labs, Am. Cyanamid Co, 52-56; sr. chemist, Johnson & Johnson, 57-58; sr. scientist, Springdale Labs, Am. Machine & Foundry Co, 59-64; res. mgr, Dorr-Oliver, Inc, 64-66; MEM. STAFF, UNION CARBIDE RES. INST, 66- U.S.N.R, 44-46. Am. Chem. Soc; Sci. Res. Soc. Am. Polymerization; organic synthesis; electrochemistry; synthetic membranes. Address: Union Carbide Research Institute, Box 278, Tarrytown, NY 10591.

FRIEDLANDER, HERBERT N(ORMAN), b. Chicago Heights, Ill, Mar. 12, 22; m. 43; c. 3. CHEMISTRY. S.B, Chicago, 42, Ph.D.(phys. org. chem), 47. Lab. asst. org. chem, Chicago, 42-44; jr. chemist, metall. labs, Illinois, 44, res. corp, fel. & asst, 47-48; jr. scientist, Los Alamos Labs, N.Mex, 44-46; proj. chemist, res. dept, Standard Oil Co.(Ind), 48-57, leader, res. dept, 59-60; res. assoc, res. dept, Amoco Chem. Corp, 61-62; mgr. polymer sci, basic res. dept, Chemstrand Res. Ctr, Inc, 62-65; dir. res, 65-66, dir. new prod. res. & develop, 66-67, assoc. dir. cent. res. dept, MONSANTO CO, 67-68, V.PRES. & DIR. TECH. OPERS, CHEMSTRAND RES. CTR, INC, 68- Consult, Nat. Coun. Res. & Develop, State of Israel, 62 & 64. AAAS; Am. Chem. Soc. Reaction of organic free radicals; slow neutron cross sections; atoms and free radicals in solution; chemicals from petroleum; catalysis and polymerization; stereo-regulated polymerization with solid catalysts; structure and properties of fiber-forming polymers. Address: Chemstrand Research Center, Inc, P.O. Box 731, Durham, NC 27702.

FRIEDLANDER, JACKSON HARRISON, b. New York, N.Y, Jan. 23, 07; m. 31. INTERNAL MEDICINE. B.S, Alfred, 30; M.D, State Univ. N.Y, 34. Assoc. attend. physician & assoc. cardiologist, King County Hosp, N.Y, 39-42; chief, med. serv, Veterans Admin. Hosp, Northport, N.Y, 47-52; dir, prfnl. servs, Veterans Admin. Hosp, Big Spring, Texas, 52-55, mgr, hosp, 56-60; chief, res. & intern. div, Veterans Admin. Cent. Office, 55-56; mgr. & dir, prfnl. serv, Vet. Admin. Hosp, 60-63; area med. dir, Vet. Admin, Columbus, 63-64; dir. educ. serv, res. & educ. med, Vet. Admin, Wash, D.C, 64-70; CTR. DIR, VET. ADMIN. CTR, 70- Dipl, Am. Bd. Med, 41. Chief cardiovascular diseases, 79th Gen. Hosp, U.S.A, 43-46, Maj. Am. Med. Asn; Am. Col. Physicians; Am. Col. Cardiol. Relationship of schizophrenia to responsiveness of the adrenal cortex; secretion of corticosteroids in schizophrenia. Address: Veterans Administration Center, Bay Pines, FL 33504.

FRIEDLANDER, SHELDON K, b. N.Y.C, Nov. 17, 27; m. 58; c. 4. CHEMICAL & ENVIRONMENTAL HEALTH ENGINEERING. B.S, Columbia, 49; M.S, Mass. Inst. Tech, 51; Ph.D.(chem. eng), Illinois, 54. Asst. prof. chem. eng, Columbia, 54-57; Hopkins, 57-59, assoc. prof, 59-62, PROF, 62-64; CHEM. ENG. & ENVIRON. HEALTH ENG, CALIF. INST. TECHNOL, 64- Fulbright scholar, France, 60-61; indust. & govt. consult; mem. environ. sci. & eng. study sect, U.S. Pub. Health Serv, 65-68; Guggenheim fel, 69-70; mem. air pollution chem. & physics adv. comt, Environ. Protection Agency, 69-; chmn. panel on abatement particulate emissions, Nat. Res. Coun, 70-; mem. comt. power plant siting, Nat. Acad. Eng, 71- U.S.A, 46-47. Am. Inst. Chem. Eng.(Colburn Award, 59); Am. Chem. Soc. Aerosol physics and physical chemistry; air pollution; interfacial transfer; convective diffusion; atmospheric chemistry; cloud physics; bioengineering; diffusion in blood. Address: W.M. Keck Lab, California Institute of Technology, Pasadena, CA 91109.

FRIEDLANDER, WALTER J(AY), b. Los Angeles, Calif, June 6, 19; m. 43; c. 3. NEUROLOGY. M.D, California, 45. Chief electroencephalog. lab, Nat. Insts. Health, 52-53; clin. instr. med, sch. med, Stanford, 53-55, asst. clin. prof. neurol, 55-56; asst. prof, sch. med, Boston, 57-61; assoc. prof, Albany Med. Col, 61-62, prof, 62-66; PROF. NEUROL. & CHMN. DEPT, COL. MED, UNIV. NEBR, 66- Adj. prof, State Univ. N.Y. Albany, 65-66. Dipl, Am. Bd. Psychiat. & Neurol. U.S.A, 51-52. AAAS; fel. Am. Acad. Neurol; Am. Electroencephalog. Soc; Am. Epilepsy Soc; N.Y. Acad. Sci. Neurology; electroencephalography. Address: Dept. of Neurology, University of Nebraska College of Medicine, Omaha, NE 68105.

FRIEDLANDER, WILLIAM S(HEFFIELD), b. Evanston, Ill, Feb. 17, 30; m. 51; c. 5. ORGANIC CHEMISTRY. A.B, Dartmouth Col, 51; M.S, Illinois, 52, Ph.D, 54. Sr. chemist & group supvr, MINN. MINING & MFG. CO, 54-61, asst. mgr, Adv. Res. Proj. Agency proj, 61-62, head, polymer sect, 62-65, dir, contract res. lab, 65-67, TECH. DIR, NEW BUS. VENTURES DIV, 67- Am. Chem. Soc. Synthetic organic chemistry; free radical reactions; chemistry of high energy propellants and rocket fuels; polymer science; fluorochemicals. Address: Minnesota Mining & Manufacturing Co, 3M Center, St. Paul, MN 55101.

FRIEDLI, HANS R(UEDI), b. Bern, Switz, Feb. 3, 31; m. 61; c. 3. CHEMISTRY. D.Sc, Swiss Fed. Inst. Tech, 59. Res. chemist, DOW CHEM. CO, 59-60, Strosacker's Lab, 61-62, chem. physics res. lab, 63-70, RES. MGR, BRITTON RES. LAB, 70- AAAS; Am. Chem. Soc. Heterogeneous catalysis; research and development on new processes and products. Address: 1602 Crane Ct, Midland, MI 48640.

FRIEDLY, JOHN C, b. Glen Dale, W.Va, Feb. 28, 38; m. 62; c. 3. CHEMICAL ENGINEERING. B.S, Carnegie Inst. Technol, 60; Ph.D.(chem. eng), Univ. Calif, Berkeley, 64. Chem. engr, Gen. Elec. Res. Lab, 64-67; asst. prof. CHEM. ENG, Johns Hopkins Univ, 67-68; UNIV. ROCHESTER, 68-71, ASSOC. PROF, 71- Am. Inst. Chem. Eng; Am. Chem. Soc. Dynamics of chemical processes; automatic control as applied to the process industries; dynamics of combustion. Address: Dept. of Chemical Engineering, University of Rochester, Rochester, NY 14627.

FRIEDMAN, ABRAHAM SOLOMON, b. Brooklyn, N.Y, Oct. 25, 21; m. 52; c. 4. CHEMISTRY. B.A, Brooklyn Col, 43; fel, Ohio State, 46-50, Ph.D. (phys. chem), 50. Chem. engr, Manhattan Proj, Decatur, Ill, 44-45; res. chemist, Manhattan Proj, metall. lab, Chicago, 45-46; res. assoc, Ohio State, 50-51; Fulbright res. fel, Van der Walls Lab, Amsterdam Univ, 51-52; phys. chemist, Nat. Bur. Standards, 52-56; chemist, U.S. ATOMIC ENERGY COMN, 56-61, sr. chemist, 61-62, sci. rep, Paris, 62-65, dep. asst. dir. res. chem, D.C, 65-66, DEP. DIR. INT. AFFAIRS, 66- U.S.A, 43-46. AAAS; Am. Phys. Soc; Am. Chem. Soc; Netherlands Phys. Soc. Thermodynamics; chemical physics; isotope effects; nuclear chemistry; international affairs. Address: International Affairs, U.S. Atomic Energy Commission, Washington, DC 20545.

FRIEDMAN, ALAN J(ACOB), b. Brooklyn, N.Y, Nov. 15, 42; m. 66. SOLID STATE PHYSICS. B.S, Ga. Inst. Technol, 64; fel, Fla. State Univ, 68, Ph.D. (physics), 70. Res. asst, eng. exp. sta, Ga. Inst. Technol, 60-64; trainee, U.S. Naval Avionics Facility, Indianapolis, summers 62 & 63; asst. PHYSICS, Fla. State Univ, 64-68; instr, HIRAM COL, 69-70, ASST. PROF, 70-, faculty res. grant, summers 70 & 71. Am. Phys. Soc; Am. Asn. Physics Teachers. Critical phenomena in low temperature magnetic materials; the uses and influence of science in literature and the modern novel in particular. Address: Dept. of Physics, Hiram College, P.O. Box 196, Hiram, OH 44234.

FRIEDMAN, ALEXANDER H(ERBERT), b. Yonkers, N.Y, July 26, 25; m. 61; c. 2. PHARMACOLOGY. B.A, N.Y. Univ, 48; M.S, Illinois, 56, Ph.D.(pharmacol), 59. Asst. PHARMACOL, Yale, 53; col. med, Illinois, 55-59; instr, col. med, Wisconsin, 59-62, asst. prof, 62-65, acting chmn, 63-64; assoc. prof, STRITCH SCH. MED, LOYOLA UNIV. CHICAGO, 66-72, PROF, 72- Lederle Med. Faculty Award, 66-69. Sigma Xi Res. prize, 68. Med.C, U.S.A, 46-47. AAAS; N.Y. Acad. Sci; Am. Soc. Pharmacol. & Exp. Therapeut; Int. Soc. Biochem. Pharmacol. Neuropharmacology; tremor and rigidity-Parkinsonism; autonomic nervous system pharmacology; muscle spindles; modulator effects of drugs and circadian rhythms of biogenic amines as a basis for drug action; vocalization patterns as an index of drug action. Address: Dept. of Pharmacology & Therapeutics, Loyola University Stritch School of Medicine, 2160 S. First Ave, Maywood, IL 60153.

FRIEDMAN, ARNOLD M(ARVIN), b. N.Y.C, June 6, 26; m; c. 2. NUCLEAR CHEMISTRY. Sc.B, Brown, 50; Van Barcolm scholar & Heermans fel, Washington (St. Louis), 52, Ph.D.(chem), 53. Res. assoc, Shell Oil Co, Ill, 52; ASSOC. CHEMIST, ARGONNE NAT. LAB, 53- U.S.N, 44-46. Am. Phys. Soc. Physical and chemical properties of the actinide elements; kinetics of fission; decay schemes; stripping reaction in the octinide elements; heavy ion reactions. Address: Argonne National Lab, Bldg. 200, Argonne, IL 60439.

FRIEDMAN, ARNOLD P, b. Portland, Ore, Aug. 25, 09; m. 39; c. 1. NEUROLOGY. B.A, Southern California, 32, M.A, 34; M.D, Oregon, 39. Asst. neuroanat, Univ. Ore, 38-39; rotating internship, Los Angeles County Hosp, 39-40; resident neurol, 40-42; asst. physician, Boston Psychopathic Hosp, 42-43; instr. NEUROL, COL. PHYSICIANS & SURGEONS, COLUMBIA UNIV, 44-45, assoc, 46, asst. clin. prof, 50-54, assoc. clin. prof, 54-67, CLIN. PROF, 67-; PHYSICIAN-IN-CHARGE, HEADACHE UNIT, MONTEFIORE HOSP. & MED. CTR, NEW YORK, 47-, ATTEND. PHYSICIAN, DIV. NEUROL, 49-; ATTEND PHYSICIAN, NEUROL. INST, PRESBY. HOSP, NEW YORK, 71-, asst. attend. physician, 48, assoc. attending, 49-71. Asst, med. sch, Univ. South, Calif, 41-42; resident-in-charge head injury proj, Off. Sci. Res. & Develop. & res. assoc, Boston City Hosp, 43-44, fel. neurol, Harvard Med. Sch, 43-44; exam. neurol. & psychiat, Induction Ctr, Mass, 43-44; vis. neurologist, Cambridge Hosp, Mass, 44; designated exam. for vet. in neuropsychiat, N.Y, 45-46; asst. neuroroentgenology, Montefiore Hosp. & Med. Ctr, N.Y, 46, assoc. attend. physician, div. neurol, 47; cert. exam. ment. hyg, State of N.Y, 46; neuropsychiatrist, Vet. Admin, N.Y, 46-47; consult, 47-49; rep. Am. Acad. Neurol. to Coun. Med. TV, 60-63; chmn. panel headache, Nat. Inst. Neurol. Disease & Blindness, 60-67, spec. consult, 61-; consult, Am. Med. Asn, 60-, v.chmn. sect. nerv. & ment. diseases, 62-63, chmn, 63-64, acting del, Calif, 64, consult, Jour, 62-; mem. panel neuropsychiat, U.S. Pharmacopeia, 60-; hon. surgeon, New York Police Dept, 61-; dir, Am. Bd. Psychiat. & Neurol, 64, v.pres, 70, pres, 71; mem. sci. adv. panel, Nat. Asn. Broadcasters, 65-66; chmn-secy, res. headache & migraine, World Fedn. Neurol, 67; mem. coun, sect. neurol. & psychiat, N.Y. Acad. Med, 68, ed-in-chief, Res. & Clin. Studies in Headache, 68- Dipl, Am. Bd. Psychiat. & Neurol. Fel. Am. Acad. Neurol; fel. Am. Med. Asn; Am. Neurol. Asn; fel. Am. Psychiat. Asn; Asn. Res. Nerv. & Ment. Diseases; Int. Col. Allergy; fel. N.Y. Acad. Med.(secy, 64-66, chmn, 66-68); fel. Am. Col. Physicians. Headache. Address: 71 E. 77th St, New York, NY 10021.

FRIEDMAN, AVNER, b. Israel, Nov. 19, 32; nat; m. 59; c. 4. MATHEMATICS. M.Sc, Hebrew Univ, Israel, 54, Ph.D, 56. Asst. MATH, Hebrew Univ, Israel, 53-56; res. assoc, Kansas, 56-57; lectr, Indiana, 57-58; asst. prof, California, 58-59; assoc. prof, Minnesota, 59-61; Stanford, 61-62; PROF, NORTHWEST. UNIV, 62- Sloan fels, 62-65; Guggenheim fel. & vis. prof, Tel Aviv Univ, 66-67, vis. prof, 70-71. Am. Math. Soc. Mathematical analysis, especially partial differential equations; potential theory; ordinary differential equations; differential games. Address: Dept. of Mathematics, Northwestern University, Evanston, IL 60201.

FRIEDMAN, BARRY ALAN, b. Columbus, Ohio, Aug. 13, 43; m. 70. MICROBIOLOGY, SANITARY ENGINEERING. B.S, Ohio State Univ, 64, Fed. Water Pollution Control Admin. trainee, 67-68, Ph.D.(microbiol), 68; M.S, Mich. State Univ, 66. MICROBIOLOGIST, LINDE DIV, UNION CARBIDE CORP, 70- Med.Serv.C, U.S.A, 68-70, Capt. AAAS; Am. Soc. Microbiol; Soc. Indust. Microbiol. Fine structure and composition of natural exocellular polymers and their relationship to accumulation of metallic ions and flocculation; effects of high purity oxygen on acitivated sludge; continuous fermentations. Address: Linde Division, Union Carbide Corp, P.O. Box 44, Tonawanda, NY 14150.

FRIEDMAN, BEN I, b. Cincinnati, Ohio, Oct. 18, 26; m. 54; c. 1. NUCLEAR & INTERNAL MEDICINE. Univ. Cincinnati, 43-44, M.D, 48. Fel. hemat. & nutrit, Cincinnati Gen. Hosp, 53-55; instr. med, col. med, Univ. Cincinnati, 55-59, asst. clin. prof, 59-62, asst. prof, 62-65, assoc. prof, 65-68, asst. prof. radiol, 64-68, assoc. dir. nuclear med, 66-68; PROF. RADIOL. & MED. & HEAD NUCLEAR MED, COL. MED, UNIV. TENN, MEMPHIS, 68-, ACTING CHMN. DEPT. RADIOL, 71- Clinician, outpatient dept, Cincinnati Gen. Hosp, 55-68, asst. chief clinician, hemat. clin, 56-68, asst. attend. physician, hosp, 56-61, attend. physician, 61-68; City of Memphis Hosps, 68- Med.C, U.S.A.F, 50-52, Capt. Am. Med. Asn; Am. Soc. Hemat; N.Y. Acad. Sci; Soc. Nuclear Med; Radiol. Soc. N.Am. Hematology; radioisotopes; radiobiology. Address: Dept. of Radiology, University of Tennessee, 865 Jefferson Ave, Memphis, TN 38103.

FRIEDMAN, BENJAMIN, b. Russia, Apr. 28, 04; nat; m. 42. MEDICINE. B.S, City Col, 27; M.D, Washington (St. Louis), 31. Henry res. fel. endocrinol, med. col, Cornell, 34; Sutro fel. cardiovasc. res, Mt. Sinai Hosp, New York, 35-39; instr. MED, med. col, Cornell, 39-42; asst. prof, southwest. med. sch, Texas, 46-47, assoc. prof, 47-49, PROF, 49-55; Med. Col. Ala, 55-58; Univ. Tex. Southwest Med. Sch, 58-66; MED. CTR, UNIV. ALA, BIRMINGHAM, 66-, V.CHMN. DEPT, 70-, dir. div. med. educ, 67-70. Chief med, Vet. Admin. Hosp, Dallas, 46- Med.C, U.S.A, 42-45. Am. Soc. Clin. Invest; fel. Am. Col. Physicians; Asn. Am. Physicians. Cardiovascular physiology; physiology of blood circulation. Address: Medical Center, University of Alabama, 1919 Seventh Ave. S, Birmingham, AL 35233.

FRIEDMAN, BERNARD SAMUEL, b. Chicago, Ill, Jan. 4, 07; m. 38; c. 2. ORGANIC CHEMISTRY. A.B, Illinois, 30, Ph.D.(org. chem), 36. Teacher, pub. sch, Ill, 30-33; asst. instr. chem, Illinois, 33-36; res. chemist, Universal Oil Prods. Co, Ill, 36-45; tech. dir, Reyam Plastic Prods. Co, 45-47; dir. chem. lab, QM Res. & Develop. Labs, 47-48; assoc. dir. org. res. div, SINCLAIR RES. LABS, INC, 48-59, RES. ASSOC, 59- Mem, Chicago Bd. Ed, 62-; prof. lectr, Univ. Chicago, 69- Honor Scroll, Am. Inst. Chem, 59; Merit award, Chicago Tech. Soc. Coun, 63. Am. Chem. Soc; fel. Am. Inst. Chem. Petroleum and petrochemical catalytic chemistry. Address: 7321 S. Shore Dr, Chicago, IL 60649.

FRIEDMAN, (HELEN) CAROL HECHLER, b. Galesburg, Ill, Sept. 17, 33; m. 69. NEMATOLOGY, PLANT PATHOLOGY. B.S, Univ. Ill, Urbana, 56, M.S, 57, Ph.D.(plant path), 65. Res. asst. plant path, Univ. Ill, Urbana, 57-65, res. assoc, 65-67; RES. NEMATOLOGIST, PLANT INDUST. STA, U.S. DEPT. AGR, 67- Soc. Nematol; Soc. Europ. Nematol. Cytology; embryology; morphogenesis; reproduction of soil and freshwater nematodes; taxonomy. Address: Plant Industry Station, U.S. Department of Agriculture, Beltsville, MD 20705.

FRIEDMAN, C(ECIL) A(LFRED), b. Tacoma, Wash, July 28, 10; m. 43; c. 3. ORGANIC CHEMISTRY. B.S, Washington (Seattle), 33, Ph.D, 38. Res. chemist, Nat. Aniline Div, ALLIED CHEM. CORP, 38-52, sect. leader, 52-53, group leader, 53-65, RES. SUPVR, 65-67, INDUST. CHEM. DIV, 67- Detergents; new products. Address: 138 Sterling Ave, Buffalo, NY 14216.

FRIEDMAN, CONSTANCE L(IVINGSTONE), b. Montreal, Que, July 30, 20; m. 40. ANATOMY. B.Sc, McGill, 41, M.Sc, 42, Ph.D.(anat), 48. Demonstr. histol. & biochem, McGill, 43-45, res. asst. & assoc, 45-50; RES. ASSOC. PROF. ANAT, UNIV. B.C, 50- Can. Asn. Anat. Hypertension; endocrinology; aging. Address: Dept. of Anatomy, University of British Columbia, Vancouver 8, B.C, Can.

FRIEDMAN, DAVID BELAIS, b. Far Rockaway, N.Y, May 1, 16; m. 43; c. 3. PEDIATRICS. A.B, Michigan, 37, M.D, 40. Intern, Kings Co. Hosp, Brooklyn, N.Y, 40-42; res. pediat, Los Angeles Co. Gen. Hosp, Calif, 46-48; staff pediatrician, Permanente Med. Group, Oakland, Calif, 48-52; teaching fel. child psychiat, sch. med, Pittsburgh, 52-53; dir. out-patient serv, Permanente Med. Group, Oakland, Calif, 53-55; from clin. instr. to clin. assoc. prof. pediat, SCH. MED, UNIV. SOUTH. CALIF, 55-65, assoc. prof, 65-71, PROF. PEDIAT. & DIR. PEDIAT. EDUC. PROGS, 71- Private practice, Los Angeles, 55-65; assoc. dir. out-patient dept, Los Angeles Col. Gen. Hosp, 65- Consult, Family & Child Study Ctr, Cedars-Sinai Med. Ctr, Los Angeles, 55- Mem. prof. adv. bd, Reiss-Davis Ctr. Child Guid. & Dubnoff Sch. Educ. Therapy, 64-; Frostig Sch. Educ. Ther. Dipl, Am. Bd. Pediat, 50. Med.C, 42-46, Maj. Am. Acad. Pediat; Soc. Res. Child Develop; Am. Orthopsychiat. Asn. Medical education; child behavior and development; pediatric education research. Address: Room 3 E 34, Pediatric Pavilion, LAC-USC Medical Center, University of Southern California School of Medicine, 2025 Zonal Ave, Los Angeles, CA 90033.

FRIEDMAN, DAVID I, b. Minneapolis, Minn, Mar. 27, 38; m. 62; c. 1. GENETICS, MOLECULAR BIOLOGY. B.A, Minnesota, 61, M.D, 64. Nat. Cancer Inst. fel. biochem, Minnesota, 64-65; fel. genetics, Purdue, 65-66; molecular biol, Walter Reed Inst. Res, 66-68; NAT. CANCER INST. spec. fel. genetics, NAT. INSTS. HEALTH, 68-69, GUEST WORKER, 69- Med.C, U.S.A, 66-68, Capt. Structure and function of ribosomes; modifications in deoxyribonucleic acid during phage replication. Address: Lab. of Molecular Biology, Bldg. 2, Room 208, National Institute of Arthritis & Metabolic Diseases, 9000 Rockville Pike, Bethesda, MD 20014.

FRIEDMAN, DON G(ENE), b. Long Beach, Calif, May 26, 25; m. 49; c. 6. METEOROLOGY. B.A, California, Los Angeles, 50; M.S, Mass. Inst. Tech, 51, Sc.D.(meteorol), 54. Asst. meteorol, Mass. Inst. Tech, 50-54; fel. statist, Chicago, 54-55; res. assoc. appl. meteorol. & opers. res, TRAVELERS INS. CO, 55-60, asst. dir. res, 60-66, ASSOC. DIR. RES, 66- U.S.A.A.F, 43-46. Am. Meteorol. Soc; Am. Statist. Asn. Operations research; statistics; insurance; applied meteorology. Address: Travelers Insurance Co, 1 Tower Square, Hartford, CT 06115.

FRIEDMAN, DONALD, b. New York, N.Y; m. 49; c. 6. ELECTRICAL ENGINEERING. B.E.E, Vanderbilt, 48; grad. courses network anal. & synthesis, Polytech. Inst. Brooklyn. Jr. engr, gyro dept, Arma Corp, N.Y, 48-49; proj. engr, sidewinder infrared seeker, Avion Div, ACF Industs, Inc, N.J, 49-54, mgr. contract rels, 54-55, asst. eng. mgr, 55-56, eng. mgr, 56-59, mil. opers. mgr, 59-60; head land opers, GM Defense Res. Labs, Gen. Motors Corp, Calif, 60-67, head commercial projs. dept, res. labs, Mich, 67-68; PRES, MINICARS, INC, 68- Partic, Am. Mgt. Asn. Workshop Seminars. U.S.N.R, 45-46. Soc. Automotive Eng; Inst. Elec. & Electronics Eng. Engineering management; transportation system design; low emission power trains; system analysis; off-the-road, high mobility, terrestrial and lunar vehicles; electric drive systems; infrared guidance and detection and servo systems. Address: Minicars, Inc, 35 La Patera Lane, Goleta, CA 93017.

FRIEDMAN, EDWARD A(LAN), b. Bayonne, N.J, Sept. 29, 35; m. 63; c. 1. SOLID STATE PHYSICS. B.S, Mass. Inst. Tech, 57; Ph.D.(physics), Columbia, 63. Asst. prof. PHYSICS, STEVENS INST. TECHNOL, 63-69, ASSOC. PROF, 69- U.S. Agency Int. Develop. contract loan, Kabul, Afghanistan, 65-67. AAAS; Am. Phys. Soc. Mössbauer measurements of hyperfine fields; inelastic neutron scattering from magnetic materials. Address: Dept. of Physics, Stevens Institute of Technology, Hoboken, NJ 07030.

FRIEDMAN, ELI A, b. N.Y.C, Apr. 9, 33; m. 57; c. 3. INTERNAL MEDICINE, IMMUNOLOGY. B.S, Brooklyn Col, 53; M.D, State Univ. N.Y. Downstate Med. Ctr, 57. Intern med, Peter Bent Brigham Hosp, Boston, 57-58, res. fel. nephrology, 58-60, sr. resident MED, 60-61; instr, Emory Univ, 61-63; asst. prof, STATE UNIV. N.Y. DOWNSTATE MED. CTR, 63-67, assoc. prof, 67-71, PROF, 71- Consult, Vet. Admin, 64-; U.S. Pub. Health Serv, 64-, coord, regional med. prog, 70- Dipl, Am. Bd. Internal Med, 68. U.S.P.H.S, 61-63, Sr. Surg. Fel. Am. Col. Physicians; Transplantation Soc; Am. Soc. Nephrology; Am. Fedn. Clin. Res; Am. Soc. Artificial Internal Organs. Development and application of artificial kidneys; effect and synergistic relationship of immunosuppressive drugs. Address: Dept. of Medicine, State University of N.Y. Downstate Medical Center, 450 Clarkson Ave, Brooklyn, NY 11203.

FRIEDMAN, EMANUEL A, b. New York, N.Y, June 9, 26; m. 48; c. 3. OBSTETRICS, GYNECOLOGY. A.B, Brooklyn Col, 47; M.D, Columbia, 51, Med.Sc.D.(physiol), 59; hon. A.M, Harvard, 69. Intern path, Cornell Med. Div, Bellevue Hosp, New York, 51-52; res. obstet. & gynec, Columbia-Presby. Med. Center, 52-57; instr, faculty med, Columbia, 57-59, assoc, 59-60, asst. prof, 60-62, assoc. prof, 62-63; prof. & chmn. dept, Chicago Med. Sch, 63-69; chmn. div. obstet. & gynec, Michael Reese Hosp. & Med. Ctr, 63-69; PROF. OBSTET, HARVARD MED. SCH, 69-; CHMN. DEPT. OBSTET. & GYNEC, BETH ISRAEL HOSP, BOSTON, 69- Asst, Columbia-Presby. Med. Center, 57-59, asst. attend, 59-62, assoc. attend, 62-63. Joseph Mather Smith Award, Columbia Univ, 58, Commemorative Silver Award, 67; Distinguished Alumnus Merit Award, Brooklyn Col, 64. Dipl, Am. Bd. Obstet. & Gynec. U.S.N.R, 44-46. AAAS; fel. Am. Col. Obstet. & Gynec; fel. Am. Col. Surg; Soc. Exp. Biol. & Med; fel. Int. Col. Surg. Physiology and pathophysiology of human labor phenomena; lactation and milk ejection; placental physiology. Address: Dept. of Obstetrics & Gynecology, Beth Israel Hospital, 330 Brookline Ave, Boston, MA 02215.

FRIEDMAN, EPHRAIM, b. Belvedere, Calif, Jan. 1, 30; m. 54; c. 4. OPHTHALMOLOGY. B.A, California, Los Angeles, 50; M.D, California, San Francisco, 54. Intern, San Francisco City & County Hosp, 54-55; resident OPHTHAL, Mass. Eye & Ear Infirmary, 59-61; instr, Howe Lab. Ophthal, 61-64; PROF, SCH. MED, BOSTON UNIV, 65-, DEAN, 71- Med.C, U.S.A.F, 56-58, Capt. Am. Med. Asn; Asn. Res. Vision & Ophthal. Physiology of the circulation of blood in the eye and related clinical problems. Address: Boston University School of Medicine, 80 E. Concord St, Boston, MA 02118.

FRIEDMAN, GARY D(AVID), b. Cleveland, Ohio, Mar. 8, 34; m. 58; c. 3. EPIDEMIOLOGY. B.S, Univ. Chicago, 56, M.D, 59; M.S, Harvard, 65. Res. fel, med. sch, Harvard, 62-64, res. assoc, 64-66; ASST. CLIN. PROF, MED. SCH, UNIV. CALIF, SAN FRANCISCO, 67-; SR. EPIDEMIOLOGIST, DEPT. MED. METHODS RES, PERMANENTE MED. GROUP, 69- Lectr, sch. pub. health, Univ. Calif, Berkeley, 68-; fel. coun. epidemiol, Am. Heart Asn. Dipl, Am. Bd. Internal Med. 66. U.S.P.H.S, 62-68, Sr. Surg. Fel. Am. Col. Physicians; Soc. Epidemiol. Res; Am. Pub. Health Asn. Epidemiology of non-infectious diseases with emphasis on coronary heart disease, stroke, gall bladder disease and adverse drug reactions. Address: 3779 Piedmont Ave, Oakland, CA 94611.

FRIEDMAN, GEORGE J(ERRY), b. N.Y.C, Mar. 22, 28; m. 53; c. 3. SYSTEMS ANALYSIS, APPLIED MATHEMATICS. B.S, Univ. Calif, Berkeley, 49; M.S, Univ. Calif. Los Angeles, 56, Ph.D.(eng. & appl. sci), 67. Mech. eng. assoc, pub. utility systs. anal, Los Angeles Dept. Water & Power, 49-56; res. & develop. engr, Servomechanisms, Inc, Calif, 56-60; RES. SCIENTIST & MGR. ADV. SYSTS, ELECTRO-MECH. DIV, NORTHROP CORP, ANAHEIM, 60- Lectr. Univ. Calif, Los Angeles, 57; Univ. Ala, Huntsville, summer 69. U.S.A, 46, 50-52. Soc. Gen. Systs. Res; Inst. Elec. & Electronics Eng.(W.R.G. Baker Award, 70); Am. Inst. Aeronaut. & Astronaut. Operations analysis; constraint theory applied to the analysis of complex, multidimensional math models; computer simulation of evolutionary processes; automata theory; systems analysis methodology; artificial intelligence and multidimensional kinematics. Address: 5084 Gloria Ave, Encino, CA 91316.

FRIEDMAN, G(ERALD) M(ANFRED), b. Berlin, Germany, July 23, 21; nat; m. 48; c. 5. SEDIMENTOLOGY, SEDIMENTARY PETROLOGY. B.Sc, London, 45; M.A, Columbia, 50, Ph.D.(geol), 52. Lectr, Chelsea Polytech, London, 44-45; sr. chemist, J. Lyons & Co, 45-46; anal. chemist, E.R. Squibb & Sons, 47-49; asst. geol, Columbia, 50; instr, Cincinnati, 50-53, asst. prof, 53-54; consult. geologist, Sault St. Marie, Can, 54-56; sr. res. geologist, Pan-Am. Petrol. Corp, 56-60, res. assoc. & supvr. sedimentary petrol. res, 60-64; PROF. GEOL, RENSSELAER POLYTECH. INST, 64- Sect. ed, Chem. Abstracts, 62-69; Fulbright sr. vis. lectr, Hebrew Univ, 64; res. scientist, Hudson Labs, Columbia Univ, 65, 66-69; vis. prof. mineral, Univ. Heidelberg, 67; res. assoc. geol, Columbia Univ, 68-; vis. scientist, Geol. Surv. Israel, 70-71; consult. scientist, Inst. Petrol. Res. & Geophys, Israel, 67-71. Fel. AAAS; fel. Geol. Soc. Am; fel. Mineral. Soc. Am; Nat. Asn. Geol. Teachers (treas, 51-55), Int. Asn. Sedimentol.(v.pres, 71-75); Soc. Econ. Paleont. & Mineral.(ed, J. Sedimentary Petrol, 64-70, v.pres, 70-71); Asn. Earth Sci. Ed; Am. Asn. Petrol. Geol; Soc. Econ. Geol; fel. Geol. Asn. Can; fel. Brit. Geol. Soc; Mineral. Soc. Gt. Brit. & Ireland; French Soc. Mineral. & Crystallog; Swiss Mineral. & Petrol. Soc. Carbonate petrology; chemistry of sedimentation; petrology and sedimentology of clastic sediments. Address: Dept. of Geology, Rensselaer Polytechnic Institute, Troy, NY 12181.

FRIEDMAN, HAROLD B(ERTRAND), b. Montgomery, Ala, Oct. 13, 04; m. 53; c. 3. PHYSICAL & INDUSTRIAL CHEMISTRY. A.B, Alabama, 23, fel, Virginia, 24-27, Ph.D.(chem), 27; Columbia, 28-29; Hopkins, 43-44. Teacher, pub. sch, Ala, 23-24; instr. phys. chem, Maine, 27-28; asst. chem, Columbia, 28; asst. prof, Ga. Tech, 29-32, assoc. prof, 32-42; chem. dir, ZEP MFG. CO, 45-63, V.PRES. RES. & DEVELOP, 63- Chem.C.Res, 28-58, Lt. Col. Am. Chem. Soc; fel. Am. Inst. Chem. Solid-gas catalysis; neutral salt action; reaction velocity and kinetics; activity coefficients of electrolytes; history of chemistry; soaps, waxes and detergents. Address: Zep Manufacturing Co, 1310 Seaboard Industrial Blvd. N.W, Atlanta, GA. 30301.

FRIEDMAN, HAROLD L(EO), b. N.Y.C, Mar. 24, 23; m. 45; c. 2. PHYSICAL & INORGANIC CHEMISTRY. B.S, Chicago, 47, Ph.D.(chem), 49. Instr. chem, Southern California, 49-51, asst. prof, 51-54, assoc. prof, 54-59; adv. chemist, Res. Center, Int. Bus. Mach. Corp, 59-65; PROF. CHEM, STATE UNIV. N.Y. STONY BROOK, 65- Guggenheim fel, 57-58; Alfred P. Sloan res. fel, 59-61; adj. prof, Polytech. Inst. Brooklyn, 64-65. U.S.A, 42-45. Am. Chem. Soc; Faraday Soc. Equilibrium and dynamic properties of liquid solutions. Address: Dept. of Chemistry, State University of New York at Stony Brook, Stony Brook, NY 11790.

FRIEDMAN, HARRIS L(EONARD), b. Dover, N.J, Jan. 17, 13; m. 40; c. 2. ORGANIC CHEMISTRY. B.S, N.Y. Univ, 34, Ph.D.(org. chem), 38. Asst. chem, N.Y. Univ, 35-38; res. chemist & dir. div. pure res, Pyridium Corp, 39-47; chief chemist, Reade Mfg. Co, N.J, 47-48; chief chem. div, Lakeside Labs, Inc, 48-53, dir. lab. & tech. res, 53-59, basic res, 59, v.pres. res, 59-68, PROF. MED. CHEM, MED. COL. WIS, 68- Consult. chemist, Galat Chem. Develop. Co, 47-48. AAAS; Am. Chem. Soc; N.Y. Acad. Sci; fel. Am. Soc. Clin. Pharmacol. & Therapeut; Am. Soc. Pharmacol. & Exp. Therapeut. Chemotherapy; heterocyclic organic chemistry; vitamins; hormones; medicinal chemistry, especially structure activity relationships; isosterism. Address: Dept. of Pharmacology, Medical College of Wisconsin, 561 N. 15th St, Milwaukee, WI 53233.

FRIEDMAN, HARRY GEORGE, JR, b. New Orleans, La, Aug. 12, 38; m. 62; c. 3. COMPUTER SCIENCE. B.S, Loyola (La), 59; Nuclear Sci. fel, Fla. State, 59-60, Ethyl Corp. fel, 61-62, Ph.D.(inorg. chem), 66. Asst. prof. COMPUT. SCI, UNIV. ILL, URBANA, 65-70, ASSOC. PROF, 70- U.S.A, 62-64, Res, 64-, Capt. Asn. Comput. Mach. Compilers; executive systems. Address: 1115 Newbury, Champaign, IL 61820.

FRIEDMAN, HARVEY MARTIN, b. Chicago, Ill, Sept. 23, 48. MATHEMATICAL LOGIC & ANALYSIS. Ph.D.(math), Mass. Inst. Tech, 67. Asst. prof. LOGIC, STANFORD UNIV, 67-69, ASSOC. PROF, 69- Am. Math. Soc. Mathematical analysis of informal concepts which arise in the study of mathematics, logic, and philosophy; technical development of mathematical logic. Address: Dept. of Philosophy, Stanford University, Stanford, CA 94305.

FRIEDMAN, HARVEY PAUL, b. New York, N.Y, Dec. 31, 35; m. 70. EMBRYOLOGY, IMMUNOLOGY. B.S, City Col. New York, 57; Hunter Col, 58; Ph.D.(anat), Kansas, 63. Bacteriologist, Sloan-Kettering Inst, 57-58; asst. prof. microbiol, Meharry Med. Col, 65-66; res. assoc. IMMUNOL, Univ. Kans, 66-68; asst. prof, UNIV. MO-ST. LOUIS, 68-71, ASSOC. PROF, 71- Nat. Insts. Health fel, Case West. Reserve Univ, 63-65; Nat. Inst. Neurol. Diseases & Blindness grant; consult, Vet. Admin. Hosp, Topeka, Kans. AAAS; Am. Soc. Neurochem; Soc. Study Develop. Immunological investigation of embryonic development; in vitro synthesis of antibody. Address: Dept. of Biology, University of Missouri-St. Louis, 8001 Natural Bridge Rd, St. Louis, MO 63121.

FRIEDMAN, HELEN L(OWENTHAL), b. New York, N.Y, Jan. 25, 24; m. 46; c. 2. PHYSICS. B.A, Hunter Col, 44; M.S, Purdue, 46; fel, Harvard, 46-47; Ph.D.(physics), Columbia, 51. Asst. PHYSICS, Purdue, 44-46; asst, Columbia, 49-51; lectr, Hunter Col, 52-53; instr, Queens Col.(N.Y), 53-55, lectr, 58-61; asst. prof, HOFSTRA UNIV, 61-68, ASSOC. PROF, 68- AAAS; Am. Phys. Soc; Optical Soc. Am; Am. Asn. Physics Teachers. Physical optics. Address: Dept. of Physics, Hofstra University, Hempstead, NY 11550.

FRIEDMAN, HENRY, b. Brooklyn, N.Y, Mar. 3, 29; m. 53; c. 3. PHYSICAL CHEMISTRY. B.Chem.Eng, City Col, 50; M.S, Clarkson Tech, 52; Ph.D.(chem), Ill. Inst. Technol, 56. Chemist, silicone prod. dept, GEN. ELEC. CO, 55-56, PHYS. CHEMIST, SPACE SCI. LAB, 56- Consult, Educ. Servs, Inc, 62; mem, Franklin Inst; consult, Charles W. Henry Sch, 65- Am. Chem. Soc; Am. Phys. Soc. Mass spectrometer probes for analyzing planetary atmospheres; pyrolysis studies of micro-organisms by mass spectrometic thermal analysis. Address: 527 W. Arbutus St, Philadelphia, PA 19119.

FRIEDMAN, HENRY D(AVID), b. N.Y.C, June 22, 26. MATHEMATICS. B.S, Pa. State Col, 48, Ph.D.(math), 53; M.A, Columbia Univ, 50. Instr. math, City Col. New York, 49-51; Pa. State Univ, 51-53; sr. mathematician, Haller, Raymond & Brown, 52-53; mathematician, Gen. Elec. Co, 53-59; Tech. Opers, Inc, 59-60; Arcon Corp, 60-62; appl. res. lab, Sylvania Electronic Systs. Div, Gen. Tel. & Electronics Corp, 62-65; mgr. data processing, Smithsonian Astrophys. Observ, 65-66; consult, 66-67; LECTR. APPL. MATH, UNIV. SANTA CLARA, 67- U.S.A, 44-47, 2nd Lt. Am. Math. Soc; Math. Asn. Am; Inst. Elec. & Electronics Eng; Opers. Res. Soc. Am. Mathematical statistics; digital computation; operations research. Address: University of Santa Clara, Santa Clara, CA 95053.

FRIEDMAN, H(ENRY) HAROLD, b. New York, N.Y, July 31, 17; m. 43; c. 3. INTERNAL MEDICINE. B.S, N.Y. Univ, 36, M.D, 39. Intern. & res, Jewish Hosp, Brooklyn, N.Y, 39-42, 46; Bellevue Hosp, 47; fel. MED, col. med, N.Y. Univ-Bellevue Med. Ctr, 47; instr, MED. CTR, UNIV. COLO. DENVER, 48-51, asst. clin. prof, 51-64, ASSOC. CLIN. PROF. MED, 64- Attend. physician, Nat. Jewish Hosp, 48-, pres. med. staff, 64-; attend. physician, dir. heart sta. & pres. med. staff, Gen. Rose Mem. Hosp; attend. physician & electrocardiographer, St. Joseph Hosp; consult. cardiologist, Denver Gen, St. Anthony & Nat. Jewish Hosps. Dipl, Am. Bd. Internal Med. Med.C, 42-46, Capt. Fel. Am. Col. Physicians; fel. Am. Col. Cardiol; fel. Am. Col. Angiol; fel. Am. Col. Chest Physicians; fel. coun. clin. cardiol, Am. Heart Asn. Cardiology. Address: 2045 Franklin St, Denver, CO 80205.

FRIEDMAN, HERBERT, b. New York, N.Y, June 21, 16; m. 40; c. 2. PHYSICS, ELECTRONICS. B.A, Brooklyn Col, 36; Ph.D.(physics), Hopkins, 40. Physicist, U.S. NAVAL RES. LAB, 40-43, head electron optics br, 43-58, SUPT, ATMOSPHERE & ASTROPHYS. DIV, 58-, CHIEF SCIENTIST, E.O. HULBURT CTR. SPACE RES, 63- Instr, Hopkins, 39-40; prof, Maryland, 61-; mem. exec. cmt, space sci. bd, Nat. Acad. Sci, 62-, mem. comt. sci. & pub. policy; chmn. Cmt. Space Res. Working Group II for Int. Year Quiet Sun, 62-; v.chmn, Inter-Union Cmt. on Ionosphere, 63-; exec. cmt, Int. Asn. Geomag. & Aeronomy, 63-; bd. trustees, Assoc. Univs, Inc, 66-70; exec. comt, div. phys. sci, Nat. Acad. Sci-Nat. Res. Coun, 69-, mem. adv. panel, atmospheric sci, chmn. comt. solar-terrestrial res, geophysics res. bd; mem. gen. adv. comt. to U.S. Atomic Energy Comn, 69-; pres. comn. 48 on high energy astrophys, Int. Astron. Union, 70-; chmn. int. rels. comt, Space Sci. Bd, 71-; v.pres. Comt. Space Res, 71-; mem, President's Sci. Adv. Comt, 71-; pres, Inter-Union Comn. on Solar-Terrestrial Physics. Navy Distinguished Civilian Serv. Award, 45; Annual Award, Soc. Appl. Spectros, 57; Dept. Defense Distinguished Civilian Serv. Award, 59; Janssen Medal, Fr. Photog. Soc, 62; Navy Award for Distinguished Achievement in Sci, 62; Capt. Robert Dexter Conrad Award, 64; Eddington Medal, Royal Astron. Soc, 64; President's Award for Distinguished Fed. Civilian Serv, 64; Rockefeller Pub. Serv. Award, 67; Nat. Medal Sci, 68; NASA Medal for Exceptional Sci. Achievement, 70. Nat. Acad. Sci; fel. AAAS(v.pres. elect, 71); Int. Acad. Astronaut.(trustee, 64-); Am. Philos. Soc; fel. Am. Acad. Arts & Sci; fel. Am. Phys. Soc; fel. Optical Soc. Am; fel. Am. Inst. Aeronaut. & Astronaut. (dir. Rocket Soc, 60-63; Space Sci. Award, 63); fel. Am. Geophys. Union (v.pres. planetary sci, 64-); fel. Am. Astron. Soc. X-ray spectroscopy and diffraction; electron diffraction and microscopy; nucleonics; upper atmosphere research; electron tubes; astrophysics; radio astronomy. Address: Code 7100, Space Science Division, E.O. Hulburt Center for Space Research, Naval Research Lab, Washington, DC 20390.

FRIEDMAN, HERMAN, b. Phila, Pa, Sept. 22, 31; m. 58. MICROBIOLOGY, IMMUNOLOGY. B.A, Temple, 53, M.A, 55; Am. Cancer Soc. fel, Hahnemann Med. Col, 55-57, Ph.D.(microbiol), 57. Instr. microbiol. dept, Hahnemann Med. Col, 57-58; res. biochemist & chief, allergy dept, Vet. Admin. Hosp, Pittsburgh, 58-59; asst. prof. MICROBIOL, SCH. MED, TEMPLE UNIV, 59-63, assoc. prof, 64-70, PROF, 71-; HEAD DEPT. MICROBIOL, ALBERT EINSTEIN MED. CTR, 59- Am. Heart Found. fel, Childrens Heart Hosp, Phila, 57-58; Hahnemann Med. Col, 57-58; Nat. Insts. Health & Nat. Sci. Found. grants, 60-; Am. Cancer Soc. grant awards, 65-68; mem. comt. immunol, Am. Bd. Med. Microbiol, 67-; del. & session chmn, Int. Cong. Microbiol, Moscow, 66 & Mexico City, 70; consult, Miles Labs, Smith Kline & French Labs. & Wyeth Labs. Dipl, Am. Bd. Microbiol. AAAS; Am. Soc. Microbiol; N.Y. Acad. Sci; Brit. Soc. Gen. Microbiol; Am. Asn. Immunol; Am. Acad. Allergy; Am. Inst. Biol. Sci; Soc. Exp. Biol. & Med; Reticuloendothelial Soc; Am. Pub. Health Asn; Transplantation Soc. Bacterial physiology; nucleic acid synthesis; immunology and immunochemistry; antibody formation; hypersensitivity and allergy. Address: Dept. of Microbiology, Albert Einstein Medical Center, York & Tabor Rd, Philadelphia, PA 19141.

FRIEDMAN, HOWARD S, b. New York, N.Y, Mar. 18, 25; m. 47; c. 2. CLINICAL CHEMISTRY. B.S, City Col. New York, 44; M.A, Boston, 47; Ph.D. (biochem), Georgetown, 53. Clin. lab. technician, Vet. Admin. Hosp, Perry Point, Md, 47-48; Physicians Lab, Hammond, Ind, 49; chem. technician, Mt. Sinai Hosp, Baltimore, Md, 49; chief chemist, Prince Georges County Hosp, Cheverly, Md, 49-51; asst, clin. lab, Tampa Munic. Hosp, Fla, 51-55; U.S. AIR FORCE, 55-, chief clin. chem. dept, Med. Lab. Ctr, South Ruislip, Eng, 57-61, clin. lab, dispensary, Kelly AFB, Tex, 61-63, dir. tech. support dep. for. tech, aerospace med. div, Aerospace Systs. Command, 63-65, tech. adv. for. biomed. sci, 65-66, CHIEF, CLIN. CHEM. BR, epidemiol. lab, Lackland AFB, 66-71, SCH. AEROSPACE MED, BROOKS AFB, 71- U.S.N, 44-46, Res, 46-50; U.S.A.F, 55-, Maj. Am. Chem. Soc; Am. Asn. Clin. Chem; Brit. Asn. Clin. Biochem. Technology and methodology in clinical chemistry, including electrophoresis, immunochemistry, amino acid chromatography; radioassay; statistical applications to normal and abnormal values in clinical chemistry and correlation to clinical medicine. Address: Epidemiology Division, School of Aerospace Medicine, Air Force Systems Command, Brooks Air Force Base, TX 78235.

FRIEDMAN, IRVING, b. N.Y.C, Jan. 12, 20; m. 46. GEOCHEMISTRY. B.S, Mont. State Col, 42; M.S, State Col, Wash, 44; Ph.D.(geochem), Chicago, 50. Chemist, U.S. Naval Res. Lab, 46-48; asst. geol, Chicago, 48-50, res. assoc, Enrico Fermi Inst. Nuclear Studies, 50-52; GEOCHEMIST, U.S. GEOL. SURV, 52- U.S.N.R, 44-46. Am. Chem. Soc; Geol. Soc. Am; Am. Geophys. Union. Phase equilibria in hydrous silicate systems at high temperature and pressure; abundance of stable isotopes applied to geology; volcanology. Address: Branch of Isotope Geology, U.S. Geological Survey, Bldg. 21, Denver Federal Center, Denver, CO 80225.

FRIEDMAN, IRVING A(BRAHAM), b. Chicago, Ill, Feb. 10, 23; m. 46; c. 2. HEMATOLOGY. B.A, Univ. Ill, 43, B.S. & M.D, 45. Assoc. dir. hemat. lab, Hektoen Inst, COOK COUNTY HOSP, 51-68, ATTEND. PHYSICIAN, 51-; CLIN. PROF. HEMAT, STRITCH SCH. MED, LOYOLA UNIV, 70-, MEM. STAFF, HOSP, 70- Chief hemat, clin, Mt. Sinai Hosp, Chicago, 51-58, assoc. attend, 58-70; assoc. staff, Oak Park Hosp, Ill, 51-58, sr. staff, 58-; consult, Hines Vet. Admin. Hosp, Chicago, Edgewater Hosp, Resurrection Hosp, Grant Hosp, Martha Washington Hosp. & Columbus Hosp. Am. Soc. Hemat; Am. Med. Asn; Am. Fedn. Clin. Res; fel. Am. Col. Physicians; Int. Soc. Hemat. Internal medicine. Address: 720 N. Michigan, Chicago, IL 60611.

FRIEDMAN, IRWIN, b. New York, N.Y, Dec. 15, 29; m. 53; c. 3. MEDICINE. B.S, Union Col, 51; M.D, N.Y. Univ, 55. Nat. Heart Inst. fel, 60-61; DIR. PULMONARY FUNCTION LAB, BUFFALO GEN. HOSP, 63-, DIR. RESPIRATORY INTENSIVE CARE UNIT, 68-; ASST. PROF. INTERNAL MED, STATE UNIV. N.Y. BUFFALO, 66- Private practice, 61- Med.C, 56-58, Capt. Am. Thoracic Soc; Am. Heart Asn; Am. Med. Asn. Clinical pulmonary physiology. Address: 85 High St, Buffalo, NY 14203.

FRIEDMAN, JACK P, b. N.Y.C, Sept. 4, 39; m. 62; c. 2. COMPUTER SCIENCE, NUCLEAR PHYSICS. B.S, Rensselaer Polytech. Inst, 60; M.S, Univ. Chicago, 61, Ph.D.(physics), 65. Comput. programmer, IBM Corp, summers 60-63; COMPUT. SCIENTIST, GEN. ELEC. KNOLLS ATOMIC POWER LAB, 65- Am. Phys. Soc; Asn. Comput. Mach; Am. Geophys. Union. Applied mathematics; theoretical reactor physics; atmospheric physics. Address: 2251 Berkely Ave, Schenectady, NY 12309.

FRIEDMAN, JEROME ISAAC, b. Chicago, Ill, Mar. 28, 30; m. 56; c. 3. PHYSICS. A.B, Chicago, 50, M.S, 53, Ph.D.(physics), 56. Res. assoc. PHYSICS, Univ. Chicago, 56-57; Stanford Univ, 57-60; asst. prof, MASS. INST. TECHNOL, 60-64, assoc. prof, 64-67, PROF, 67- Mem. prog. adv. comt, Stanford Linear Accelerator Ctr, 71- Am. Phys. Soc. High energy physics; elementary particles. Address: Dept. of Physics, Massachusetts Institute of Technology, Cambridge, MA 02139.

FRIEDMAN, JULES D(ANIEL), b. Poughkeepsie, N.Y, Oct. 24, 28; m. 59; c. 3. GEOLOGY. A.B, Cornell, 50; M.S, Yale, 52, Ph.D.(geol), 58. Asst. dept. geol, Yale, 50-53; GEOLOGIST, U.S. GEOL. SURV, 53-, REGIONAL GEOPHYS, 69- Mem. panel geodesy & cartography, Comt. Polar Res, Nat. Acad. Sci-Nat. Res. Coun. Geol. Soc. Am; Am. Geophys. Union. Geophysics; volcanology; structural geology; geomorphology; application of aerial and satellite infrared thermography to volcanic geology, geothermal sources and geomorphology, especially neovolcanic zone of Iceland; Mono Basin, California; Cascade Range. Address: U.S. Geological Survey, Dept. of the Interior, Washington, DC 20242.

FRIEDMAN, JULIUS J(AY), b. Brooklyn, N.Y, Mar. 6, 26. PHYSIOLOGY. B.S, Tulane, 49, M.S, 51, Ph.D.(physiol), 53. Res. physiologist, biophys. lab, Tulane, 53-58; asst. prof. PHYSIOL, SCH. MED, IND. UNIV, 58-64, assoc. prof, 64-71, PROF, 71- Lederle med, faculty fel, 60-63. U.S.N, 44-46. AAAS; Am. Physiol. Soc; Am. Inst. Biol. Sci. Tissue blood volumes and hematocrits; hemorrhagic and traumatic shock; peripheral vascular dynamics; trans-capillary exchange; capillary regulation. Address: Dept. of Physiology, Indiana University Medical Center, Indianapolis, IN 46202.

FRIEDMAN, KENNETH J(OSEPH), b. Brooklyn, N.Y, July 28, 43; m. 69. NEUROPHYSIOLOGY, ZOOLOGY. B.A, Lawrence Col, 64; Nat. Defense Educ. Act fel. & Ph.D.(biol. sci), State Univ. N.Y. Stony Brook, 69. Lectr, State Univ, N.Y. Stony Brook, 68-69; Nat. Insts. Health trainee, DEPT. ZOOL, UNIV. CALIF, LOS ANGELES, 69-70; NAT. INSTS. HEALTH FEL, 70- AAAS; Am. Soc. Zool. Electrophysiology of Protozoa, especially paramecia; insect neurophysiology; comparative zoology; effects of d-tubocurarine on nervous tissue; control of cilia; behavior and learning in lower organisms. Address: Dept. of Zoology, University of California, Los Angeles, CA 90024.

FRIEDMAN, LAURENCE F(ISHER), b. New York, N.Y, Nov. 15, 35; m. 61; c. 2. PHYSICAL CHEMISTRY. B.S, Wisconsin, 55; Ph.D.(phys. chem), Rensselaer Polytech, 62; dipl, Inst. Use Radioisotopes, Israel, 62. Res. chemist, labs, Israel Atomic Energy Comn, 62-63; sr. chemist, cent. res. lab, Air Reduction Co, 63-64; chemist, health & safety lab, U.S. Atomic Energy Comn, 64-66; asst. prof. chem, Quinnipiac Col, 66-68; SEWAGE PLANT CHEMIST, DEPT. PUBLIC WORKS, CITY NEW HAVEN, 68- AAAS; Am. Chem. Soc. Sewage plant chemistry. Address: Dept. of Public Works, City of New Haven, 200 Orange St, New Haven, CT 06510.

FRIEDMAN, LAWRENCE A(BRAHAM), b. N.Y.C, Apr. 23, 37; m. 60; c. 3. PERIODONTOLOGY, EPIDEMIOLOGY. B.A, N.Y. Univ, 58; D.D.S, Pennsylvania, 62. Fel. prev. med, Pennsylvania, 64-65, periodont, 65-67, res. assoc, 67-68; asst. mem, DENT. SCI. INST, UNIV. TEX, HOUSTON, 68-70, MEM, 70- U.S.A.F, 62-64, Capt. AAAS; Am. Dent. Asn; Am. Acad. Periodont; Int. Asn. Dent. Res. Clinical research in oral diseases, including methods of detection, control and prevention of dental caries and periodontal disease. Address: 5227 Lymbar, Houston, TX 77035.

FRIEDMAN, LAWRENCE BOYD, b. Minneapolis, Minn, May 9, 39; m. 61; c. 2. INORGANIC CHEMISTRY. B.A, Minnesota, Duluth, 61; Nat. Sci. Found. fel, Harvard, 61-62, M.A, 63, Nat. Insts. Health, 63-65, Ph.D.(chem), 66. Asst. prof. CHEM, Oakland, 66-68; WELLESLEY COL, 68-71, ASSOC. PROF, 71- Am. Chem. Soc; Am. Crystallog. Asn. Boron hydride chemistry; x-ray crystallography. Address: Dept. of Chemistry, Wellesley College, Wellesley, MA 02181.

FRIEDMAN, LAWRENCE D(AVID), b. Newark, N.J, Aug. 25, 32; m. 60; c. 3. GENETICS. B.A, Rutgers, 54; M.S, Northwestern, 55; Ph.D.(zool, genetics), Wisconsin, 60. Asst. genetics, Northwestern, 54-55; zool, Wisconsin, 55-57, genetics, 57-60, proj. assoc, 60-61; asst. prof. BIOL, Hiram Col, 61-66; ASSOC. PROF, UNIV. MO-ST. LOUIS, 66- AAAS; Genetics Soc. Am;

Am. Genetic Asn. Genetics of Drosophila. Address: Dept. of Biology, University of Missouri-St. Louis, 8001 Natural Bridge Rd, St. Louis, MO 63121.

FRIEDMAN, LEO, b. Brooklyn, N.Y, May 18, 15; m. 37; c. 1. FOOD TOXICOLOGY, NUTRITION. B.S, George Washington, 41; M.S, Georgetown, 46, Ph.D.(biochem), 49. Biochemist, food & drug admin, Fed. Security Agency, 41-50, chief biol. br, div. nutrit, food & drug admin, Dept. Health Ed. & Welfare, 50-58, dir. res, div. nutrit, 59-62; assoc. prof. nutrit. & food safety, Mass. Inst. Technol, 62-65, prof, 65-69; DIR, DIV. TOXICOL, BUR. FOODS, FOOD & DRUG ADMIN, 69- Fel. AAAS; Am. Chem. Soc; Soc. Exp. Biol. & Med; Asn. Off. Anal. Chem; Am. Inst. Nutrit; Am. Oil Chemists' Soc; N.Y. Acad. Sci; Soc. Toxicol; Environ. Mutagen Soc. Heated fats; nutrition and biological response; biological assay; physiological effects of food substances; experimental carcinogenesis; evaluation of food safety. Address: Division of Toxicology, BF-150, Office of Science, Bureau of Foods, Food & Drug Administration, Washington, DC 20204.

FRIEDMAN, LEONARD, b. Brooklyn, N.Y, Jan. 27, 29; m. 64. BIOCHEMISTRY. B.A, N.Y. Univ, 51; M.S, Rutgers, 53, Ph.D.(biochem), 59. Fel, Iowa State, 59-61; RES. CHEMIST BIOCHEM, Nat. Insts. Health, 61-62; FOOD & DRUG ADMIN, 62- Med.C, U.S.A, 53-55. AAAS; Soc. Toxicol; fel. Am. Inst. Chem; Am. Chem. Soc. Chemical, physical and enzymic nature of proteolytic enzymes, especially rennin and proteinase; metabolism of malaria; effect of nutrition on enzymes and metabolism of tissues. Address: Division of Nutrition, Bureau of Scientific Research, Food & Drug Administration, Washington, DC 20204.

FRIEDMAN, LESTER, b. New York, N.Y, Sept. 14, 28; m. 57; c. 2. ORGANIC CHEMISTRY. B.S, Purdue, 51; Develop. Fund fel. & Ph.D.(chem), Ohio State, 59. Instr. phys. chem, Capital Univ, 52-53; asst. prof. CHEM, N.Y. Univ, 57-61; CASE WEST. RESERVE UNIV, 61-65, ASSOC. PROF, 65- Consult, Borg-Warner Corp, Monsanto Co. & Farchan Chem. Co. Med.Serv.C, U.S.A, 54-56. AAAS; Am. Chem. Soc; N.Y. Acad. Sci; The Chem. Soc. Reaction mechanisms and syntheses; reactive intermediates; arynes; carbenes; poorley solvated cations; over crowded molecules; organophosphorus chemistry; insect phermones; chemical basis of olfaction. Address: Dept. of Chemistry, Case Western Reserve University, University Circle, Cleveland, OH 44106.

FRIEDMAN, LEWIS, b. Spring Lake, N.J, Aug. 8, 22; m. 48; c. 3. PHYSICAL CHEMISTRY. A.B, Lehigh, 43, A.M, 45; Ph.D.(chem), Princeton, 47. Inst. Nuclear Studies fel, Chicago, 47-48; assoc. chemist, BROOKHAVEN NAT. LAB, 48-52, chemist, 52-64, SR. CHEMIST, 64- Guest scientist, Found. Fundamental Res. Matter Lab. Mass Separation, Amsterdam, Netherlands, 60-61. Electron and ion impact phenomena; high sensitivity mass spectrometry; chemical studies with isotopes. Address: Brookhaven National Lab, Upton, NY 11973.

FRIEDMAN, LIONEL R(OBERT), b. Phila, Pa, May 8, 33; m. 56; c. 2. SOLID STATE PHYSICS. B.S, Swarthmore Col, 55; Ph.D.(physics), Pittsburgh, 61. Scientist, Westinghouse Atomic Power Div, 55-61; res. assoc. SOLID STATE PHYSICS, Univ. Pittsburgh, 61-62; MEM. TECH. STAFF, RCA CORP, 62- Instr, Temple Univ, 64-; Sci. Res. Coun. sr. vis. fel, Cavendish Lab, Cambridge, 71-72. Am. Phys. Soc. Transport phenomena in solids; small polaron transport; organic semiconduction; diamagnetism; magnetic semiconductors; amorphous semiconductors. Address: RCA Labs, David Sarnoff Research Center, Princeton, NJ 08540.

FRIEDMAN, LORRAINE, b. Dawson, N.Mex, Jan. 1, 19. MYCOLOGY. M.P.H, North Carolina, 48; Ph.D.(microbiol), Duke, 51. Bacteriologist, hosp, Hopkins, 46-47; Kellogg Found. fel, 47-48; res. mycologist, dept. bact, Naval Biol. Lab, California, 51-55; PROF. MICROBIOL, SCH. MED, TULANE UNIV, 55- Consult, U.S. Pub. Health Serv, 62-65, mem. study sect, 66-69. Lederle Faculty Award, 55-57. Med.Serv.C, U.S.N, 43-46, Comdr. Am. Pub. Health Asn; Am. Soc. Microbiol; Mycol. Soc. Am. Epidemiology and immunology of mycoses. Address: Mycology Lab, Tulane University School of Medicine, 1430 Tulane Ave, New Orleans, LA 70112.

FRIEDMAN, LOUIS DAVID, b. Washington, Pa, June 16, 15; m. 42; c. 4. CHEMISTRY. B.S, Pittsburgh, 37, M.S, 41; Ph.D.(fuel tech), Pa. State, 51. Chemist, Duquesne Smelting Corp, Am. Metals Co, 41-44; res. chemist, Cities Serv. Oil Co, 44-46; res. asst. fuel tech, Pa. State, 47-50; res. chemist, Texaco, Inc, 51-62; SR. RES. CHEMIST, FMC CORP, 62- Am. Chem. Soc; Am. Inst. Chem. Coal chemistry; synthetic fuels; air and water pollution. Address: FMC Corp, P.O. Box 8, Princeton, NJ 08540.

FRIEDMAN, MARCELLE, b. Newark, N.J; m. 52; c. 2. MATHEMATICS. B.S, Seton Hall, 61; Nat. Sci. Found. fel. & M.S, N.Y. Univ, 63, Nat. Sci. Found. fel. & Ph.D.(math), 66. ASST. PROF. MATH, Seton Hall Univ, 65-71; QUEENSBOROUGH COMMUNITY COL, 71- Ordinary differential equations. Address: Dept. of Mathematics, Queensborough Community College, Bayside, NY 11364.

FRIEDMAN, MARK H(IRSCH), b. Chelsea, Mass, Aug. 25, 24; m. 51; c. 2. VETERINARY MEDICINE. D.V.M, Middlesex, 46. Consult. veterinarian, UN Relief & Rehabil. Admin, 47-48; lab. animal supplier, Charles River Breeding Labs, 48-50; virus res, Vet. Virus Lab, Haifa, Israel, 50-52; ASSOC. MEM, SLOAN-KETTERING INST, NEW YORK, 52- Consult, Hosp. for Spec. Surg, 60-65; med. col, Cornell Univ, 61-65; Vet. Admin. Hosp, Bronx, 65- Dipl, Am. Col. Lab. Animal Med, 61. Am. Vet. Med. Asn; Am. Asn. Lab. Animal Sci. Laboratory animal medicine. Address: 238 Clearmeadow Dr, East Meadow, NY 11554.

FRIEDMAN, MARVIN ALAN, b. Cincinnati, Ohio, Jan. 17, 42; m. 66; c. 1. TOXICOLOGY, PHARMACOLOGY. S.B, Mass. Inst. Technol, 64, S.M, 65, Ph.D.(nutrit, food sci), 67. Res. assoc. nutrit. & food sci, Mass. Inst. Technol, 67; Nat. Insts. Health fel. path, Univ. Pittsburgh, 67-69; chief biochemist, labs. environ. toxicol. & carcinogenesis, Children's Cancer Res. Found, Inc, Mass, 69-71; ASST. PROF. PHARMACOL, MED. COL. VA, 71- AAAS; Environ. Mutagen Soc; Soc. Toxicol. Chemical carcinogenesis; environmental mutagenesis. Address: Box 726, Medical College of Virginia, Richmond, VA 23219.

FRIEDMAN, MARVIN H(AROLD), b. N.Y.C, July 20, 23. PHYSICS. B.S, City Col, 43; M.S, Illinois, 49, Ph.D.(physics), 52. Nat. Sci. Found. fel, Cornell, 52-53; res. assoc. PHYSICS, Columbia, 53-55; asst. prof, Mass. Inst. Tech, 55-61; assoc. prof, NORTHEAST. UNIV, 61-66, PROF, 66- U.S.A, 43-46. Am. Phys. Soc. High energy theoretical physics; statistical mechanics. Address: Dept. of Physics, Northeastern University, Boston, MA 02115.

FRIEDMAN, MAX M(ARTIN), b. Austria, Jan. 24, 07; nat; m. 31; c. 1. CLINICAL CHEMISTRY. B.A, Alabama, 30; Columbia, 30-31; Ph.D.(chem), Polytech. Inst. Brooklyn, 47. Res. assoc. biochem, med. col, N.Y. Univ, 32-39; chemist in charge, Fordham Hosp, N.Y, 39-42, sr. chemist, Queens Gen. Hosp, 42-53; CHEMIST, BRONX-LEBANON HOSP. CTR, 47- Consult. chemist, Pack Med. Found. & Med. Arts Ctr. Hosp, 51-65. Am. Chem. Soc; Am. Asn. Clin. Chem.(secy, 50-59). Carbohydrate metabolism; biochemical methodology; extracellular fluid; blood enzymes; tissue enzymes. Address: Bronx-Lebanon Hospital Center, Bronx, NY 10457.

FRIEDMAN, MELVIN, b. West Orange, N.J, Nov. 14, 30; m. 54; c. 2. GEOLOGY. B.S, Rutgers, 52, M.S, 54; Ph.D, Rice, 61. Res. geologist, Shell Develop. Co, 54-67; assoc. prof. GEOL, CTR. TECTONOPHYS, TEX. A&M UNIV, 67-69, PROF, 69- Summers, geologist, Newf. Geol. Surv, 52; Bear Creek Mining Co, 53. Res. Award, Intersoc, Comt. Rock Mech, 69. AAAS; fel. Geol. Soc. Am; Am. Geophys. Union. Dynamic analysis of tectonic structures through a knowledge of the physical and mechanical properties of minerals and rocks. Address: Center Tectonophysics, Texas A&M University, College Station, TX 77843.

FRIEDMAN, MENDEL, b. Pultusk, Poland, Feb. 13, 33; U.S. citizen; m. 57; c. 3. ORGANIC CHEMISTRY. B.S, Univ. Ill, 54; M.S, Univ. Chicago, 58, Ph.D.(chem), 62. Res. assoc, Univ. Wis, 61-62; prin. chemist, North. Regional Res. Lab, U.S. DEPT. AGR, 62-69, res. chemist, WEST. REGIONAL RES. LAB, 69-70, HEAD, FIBER CHEM. INVEST, WOOL & MOHAIR LAB, Berkeley, 70- Part-time instr, Bradley Univ, 66-67; Eureka Col, 67-69; fel. Intra-Sci. Found. Protein Chem, 71- Intel.C, U.S.A, 55-56. Am. Chem. Soc. Protein chemistry and biochemistry; bio-organic chemistry. Address: 6896 Paseo Grande, Moraga, CA 94556.

FRIEDMAN, MICHAEL E, b. Bronx, N.Y, Aug. 17, 37; m. 64; c. 1.. BIOPHYSICAL & ANALYTICAL CHEMISTRY. A.B, Pennsylvania, 59; M.S, Polytech. Inst. Brooklyn, 63; Ph.D.(biophys. chem), Cornell, 66. Technician CHEM, Pack Med. Group, 58-60; staff fel, Nat. Insts. Health, 66-68; ASST. PROF. DEPT. CHEM, AUBURN UNIV, 68- Am. Chem. Soc. Structural studies of biological polymers and their relationship to the body. Address: Dept. of Chemistry, Auburn University, Auburn, AL 36830.

FRIEDMAN, MISCHA E(LLIOT), b. Worcester, Mass, Nov. 7, 22; m. 56; c. 2. BACTERIOLOGY. B.S, Massachusetts, 48; M.S, Illinois, 49, fel, 51-53, Ph.D.(dairy sci), 53. Res. assoc. dairy sci, Illinois, 53; microbiologist, med. bact. div, U.S. Army Chem. Corps Biol. Labs, Ft. Detrick, 53-70; EXEC. SECY, ALLERGY & IMMUNOL. STUDY SECT, DIV. RES. GRANTS, NAT. INSTS. HEALTH, 70- Secy. Army Res. & Study fel. & vis. lectr, Hadassah Med. Sch, Hebrew Univ, Israel, 64-65. U.S.A.A.F, 43-46. AAAS; Am. Soc. Microbiol. Bacterial nutrition and metabolism; nitrogen metabolism; nutritional inhibitors; bacteriophage; protein synthesis; immunology; science administration. Address: Division of Research Grants, National Institutes of Health, Bethesda, MD 20014.

FRIEDMAN, M(OE) H(EGBY) FRED, b. Montreal, Que, Can, Apr. 28, 09; m. 37; c. 3. PHYSIOLOGY. B.Sc, McGill, 30, fel, 34-36, Libman fel, 36-37, Ph.D.(physiol), 37; M.A, Western Ontario, 32. Demonstr. zool, McGill, 28-29, res. assoc. physiol, 32-33, fel. gastric secretions, 37-38; demonstr, zool, Western Ontario, 30-32; res. assoc. PHYSIOL, Wayne, 38-41; assoc, JEFFERSON MED. COL, 41-43, asst. prof, 43-47, assoc. prof, 47-54, PROF, 54-, HEAD DEPT, 57- Res. worker, Atlantic Biol. Sta, Can, 29-33. Soc. Exp. Biol. & Med; Am. Physiol. Soc; Am. Gastroenterol. Asn; Can. Physiol. Soc; hon. mem. Belgian Soc. Gastroenterol. Effects of low temperatures; experimental shock; digestive enzymes; preparation of secretin and other hormones; experimental therapy of peptic ulcer and ulcerative colitis; gall bladder functions. Address: Dept. of Physiology, Jefferson Hall, Jefferson Medical College, 1020 Locust St, Philadelphia, PA 19107.

FRIEDMAN, MORRIS, b. Radom, Poland, July 1, 11; U.S. citizen. MATHEMATICS. B.S.Ch.E, Wayne State, 34; fel, Chicago, 36-39, Ph.D.(math), 52. Instr. MATH, Wayne State, 39-43; Chicago, 48-51; vis. asst. prof, Tulane 52-53; asst. prof, Emory, 53-55; mathematician, Inst. Air Weapons Res, 55-59; assoc. prof, Central Michigan, 60-64; PROF, Northern Michigan, 65-67; HOFSTRA UNIV, 67- Address: Dept. of Mathematics, Hofstra University, Hempstead, NY 11550.

FRIEDMAN, MORRIS D(AVID), b. Brooklyn, N.Y, May 20, 17; m. 50; c. 2. MATHEMATICS. B.A, Brooklyn Col, 39; M.S, N.Y. Univ, 48; Stanford, 50-53. Theoret. res. dynamicist, Ames Aeronaut Res. Lab, NASA, 49-53; aerodynamicist & mathematician, flight control lab, Mass. Inst. Tech, 53-55, trans. specialist, Lincoln Lab, 56-59; tech. translator, 55-56; tech. dir, Morris D. Friedman, Inc, Mass, 59-61; RES. SPECIALIST, INFO. ANAL. CENTER, LOCKHEED MISSILES & SPACE CO, 62- Consult, Soviet Tech. Ed. Study Proj, Mass. Inst. Tech. U.S.A.A.F, 43-46, 1st Lt; Air Medal, 45. Am. Math. Soc; Am. Inst. Aeronaut. & Astronaut. Reduction of wave drag in supersonic flow. Address: Lockheed Missiles & Space Co, Sunnyvale, CA 94088.

FRIEDMAN, MORTON (BENJAMIN), b. Bayonne, N.J, Mar. 14, 28; m. 56; c. 2. ENGINEERING. B.Aero.Eng, N.Y. Univ, 48, M.Aero.Eng, 50, D.Eng. Sc, 53. Engr. aerodyn, Cornell Aeronaut. Lab, Inc, 48; res. assoc, N.Y. Univ, 53-55; appl. mech, inst. flight structures, COLUMBIA UNIV, 55-56, asst. prof. AERODYN. & APPL. MATH, 56-61, ASSOC. PROF, 61- Field scholar, Found. Instrumentation Ed. & Res, 60; Fulbright lectr, Netherlands, 62-63. AAAS. Gas dynamics; shock diffraction; acoustics; viscous fluids; applied mathematics and mechanics. Address: Dept. of Civil Engineering & Engineering Mechanics, Columbia University, New York, NY 10027.

FRIEDMAN, MORTON H(AROLD), b. New York, N.Y, June 18, 35; m. 61; c. 3. BIOPHYSICS. B.Ch.E, Cornell, 57; M.S, Michigan, 58, Phi Kappa Phi fel, 57-58, Gen. Elec. Found. fel, 58-61, Ph.D.(chem. eng), 61. Sr. chem. engr, cent. res. labs, Minn. Mining & Mfg. Co, 60-65; sr. staff engr, APPL. PHYSICS LAB, JOHNS HOPKINS UNIV, MEM. PRIN. PROF. STAFF, 68-, ASSOC. PROF. OPHTHAL, SCH. MED, 70- Nat. Capital Award, D.C. Coun. Eng. & Archit. Soc, 70. AAAS; Am. Chem. Soc; Am. Inst. Chem. Eng; Biophys. Soc. Chemistry and physics of exothermic processes; fluid mechanics; physiological transport; membrane biophysics; ophthalmology. Address: Applied Physics Lab, Johns Hopkins University, 8621 Georgia Ave, Silver Spring, MD 20910.

FRIEDMAN, MORTON HENRY, b. Uniontown, Pa, Apr. 16, 38; m. 63; c. 2. ANATOMY, CYTOLOGY. A.B, Washington & Jefferson Col, 60; M.A. Hofstra, 64; U.S. Pub. Health Serv. grant & Ph.D.(anat), Tennessee, 69. Instr. ANAT, SCH. MED, W.VA. UNIV, 69, ASST. PROF, 70- Am. Asn. Anat; Electron Micros. Soc. Am; Am. Soc. Cell Biol. Electron microscopy; microanatomy. Address: Dept. of Anatomy, West Virginia University School of Medicine, Morgantown, WV 26506.

FRIEDMAN, NATHAN, b. Newark, N.J, May 18, 12; m. 39. PERIODONTOLOGY, ORAL PATHOLOGY. B.S.D. & D.D.S, Northwest. Univ, 36. Asst. prof. periodont. & oral path, UNIV. SOUTH. CALIF, 51-54, assoc. prof, 54-66, clin. prof. human behav. & periodont, sch. dent, 66, PROF. HUMAN BEHAV. & CHMN. DEPT, 66- Consult, Vet. Admin, Calif. Dipl, Am. Bd. Periodont. Dent.C, U.S.A, 43-46. Am. Dent. Asn; Am. Acad. Periodont; Am. Acad. Oral Path. Clinical research and animal experimentation in the field of periodontal surgery and wound healing. Address: 436 N. Roxbury Dr, Beverly Hills, CA 90210.

FRIEDMAN, NATHAN B(ARUCH), b. N.Y.C, Jan. 30, 11; m. 42, 60; c. 6. PATHOLOGY. B.S, Harvard, 30; M.D, Cornell, 34. Res. pneumonia serv, Harlem Hosp, N.Y, 34-35; intern, Montefiore Hosp, 35-37; res. path, univ. clinics, Chicago, 38-39; Littauer fel, Harvard Med. Sch, 39-40; instr, sch. med, Stanford, 41-42; sr. pathologist, Army Inst. Path, Wash, 46-47; DIR. LABS, CEDARS OF LEBANON HOSP, 48-; CLIN. PROF, SCH. MED, UNIV. SOUTH. CALIF, 59-, assoc. clin. prof, 52-59. Prof. lectr, George Wash. Univ, 47. Med.C, 42-46, Maj. Endocrine Soc; Am. Soc. Exp. Path; Am. Asn. Path. & Bact; Am. Asn. Cancer Res. Pathology of endocrine glands, genitourinary organs and tumors; radiation reactions. Address: Cedars of Lebanon Hospital, 4833 Fountain Ave, Los Angeles, CA 90029.

FRIEDMAN, O(RRIE) M(AX), b. Grenfell, Sask, June 6, 15; nat; m. 50, div, m. 69; c. 3. ORGANIC CHEMISTRY. B.Sc, Manitoba, 35; McGill, 41, Nat. Res. Coun. Can. stud, 42-43, fel, 43-44, Ph.D.(chem), 44. Jr. res. chemist, Nat. Res. Coun. Can, 44-46; res. fel. chem, Harvard, 46-49; res. assoc. surg, Harvard Med. Sch, 49-52, asst. prof. CHEM, 52-53; BRANDEIS UNIV, 53-55, assoc. prof, 55-60, prof, 60-66, ADJ. RES. PROF, 66-; PRES. & SCI. DIR, COLLAB. RES, INC, 62- Assoc, Beth Israel Hosp, 49-54; consult, Harvard Med. Sch, 53-54, 56-57; spec. consult, Nat. Cancer Inst, Nat. Insts. Health, 63-; v.pres, United Chem. Co. Ltd, 65- Fel. AAAS; Am. Chem. Soc; Am. Asn. Cancer Res; Radiation Res. Soc; N.Y. Acad. Sci; The Chem. Soc. Bio-organic chemistry. Address: 49 Warren St, Brookline, MA 02146.

FRIEDMAN, PAUL, b. Brooklyn, N.Y, Oct. 12, 31; m. 54; c. 2. ORGANIC CHEMISTRY. B.S, City Col. New York, 53; M.A, Brooklyn Col, 57; Ph.D. (chem), Stevens Inst. Tech, 63. Sr. res. chemist, Evans Res. & Develop. Corp, 55-60; instr. CHEM, Newark Col. Eng, 60-61; res. assoc, Stevens Inst. Tech, 61-63; Nat. Sci. Found. res. assoc, Southern California, 63-64; asst. prof, PRATT INST, 64-66, assoc. prof, 66-70, PROF, 70- Cottrell grant, 64-65. U.S.A, 56-57. Am. Chem. Soc; fel. The Chem. Soc. Heterocyclic chemistry; non benzenoid aromatics; photochemistry; quantum organic and physical organic chemistry. Address: Dept. of Chemistry, Pratt Institute, Brooklyn, NY 11205.

FRIEDMAN, PAUL J, b. N.Y.C, Jan. 20, 37; m. 60; c. 4. RADIOLOGY. B.S, Univ. Wis, 55; M.D, Yale, 60. James Picker Found. advan. fel. acad. radiol, 66-68; asst. prof. RADIOL, UNIV. CALIF, SAN DIEGO, 68-70, ASSOC. PROF, 70- James Picker Found. scholar. radiol. res, 68-69; John & Mary Markle Found. scholar. acad. med, 69-74. Chief radiol, U.S. Naval Submarine Med. Ctr, Conn, Med.C, U.S.N.R, 64-66, Lt. Comdr. Am. Thoracic Soc. Pulmonary diseases; pulmonary vascular morphology and reactivity in experimental pulmonary hypertension; magnification radiography; tantalum powder bronchography; vascular supply of pulmonary neoplasms; radiologic-pathologic correlation. Address: Dept. of Pathology, University of California, San Diego, P.O. Box 109, La Jolla, CA 92037.

FRIEDMAN, RAYMOND, b. Portsmouth, Va, Feb. 9, 22; m. 45. PHYSICAL CHEMISTRY. B.S, Va. Polytech, 42; M.S, Wisconsin, 43, Ph.D.(chem. eng), 48. Res. engr. elec. insulation, res. labs, Westinghouse Elec. Corp, 43-46, res. scientist, thermodyn. sect, 48-55; dir. kinetics & combustion div, Atlantic Res. Corp, 55-63, v.pres, 63-69; V.PRES. & SCI. DIR, FACTORY MUTUAL RES. CORP, 69- Am. Chem. Soc; Combustion Inst; Am. Inst. Chem. Eng; Soc. Fire Protection Eng. Combustion; flame propagation; fire suppression; flame quenching; temperature distribution in flames; kinetics of gas and surface reactions. Address: Factory Mutual Research Corp, Norwood, MA 02062.

FRIEDMAN, RICHARD M, b. Cleveland, Ohio, Aug. 25, 30; m. 52; c. 4. NUCLEAR & ATOMIC PHYSICS. B.S, Case, 52; M.S, Stanford, 54, Ph.D. (physics), 56. Res. scientist, res. lab, Lockheed Missiles & Space Co, 56-61; mgr. nuclear instrumentation, Vela prog, AEROSPACE CORP, 61-62, proj. leader, infrared measurements, SPACE PHYSICS LAB, 62-63, STAFF SCIENTIST, 63-66, head space tech. support dept, 66-67; PROJ. MGR, TRW SYSTS. GROUP, 67-69, MODEL 35 PROG, VIKING LANDER BIOL. INSTRUMENT, 69- Am. Phys. Soc; Am. Geophys. Union. Development of instrumentation for space applications including detection of life forms on other planets; measurement of solar x-rays; earth's background radiance and nuclear phenomena. Address: Applied Technology Division, TRW Systems Group, One Space Park, Redondo Beach, CA 90278.

FRIEDMAN, ROBERT B(ERNARD), b. Chicago, Ill, June 9, 38; m. 69; c. 1. BIOCHEMISTRY, CARBOHYDRATE CHEMISTRY. Ph.B, Northwest. Univ, 62; Ph.D.(biochem), Univ. Ill, 69. Res. assoc, sch. med, Tufts Univ, 68-70; asst. prof. chem, Boston Univ, 70-71; RES. FEL. BIOCHEM, EUNICE KENNEDY SHRIVER CTR. MENT. RETARDATION, MASS, 71- AAAS. Study of the structure of glycoproteins and polysaccharides; synthetic and analytic carbohydrate chemistry. Address: 110 Lanark Rd, Brookline, MA 02146.

FRIEDMAN, ROBERT H(AROLD), b. Sioux City, Iowa, Jan. 11, 24; m. 45, 66; c. 4. PHYSICAL CHEMISTRY. Ph.B, Chicago, 47, B.S, 49; Carbon & Carbide Co. fel, Texas, 55-56, Ph.D, 57. Sr. res. engr, Humble Oil & Ref. Co, 56-64; RES. SCIENTIST, Tidewater Oil Co, 64-69, GETTY OIL CO, 69- Lectr, Houston, 58- U.S.A.A.F, 43-45, Res, 45-57, Capt. AAAS; Am. Phys. Soc; Am. Chem. Soc; Am. Inst. Mining, Metall. & Petrol. Eng. Theoretical chemistry; operations research; oil recovery from subsurface formations. Address: Getty Oil Co, 3903 Stoney Brook, Houston, TX 77043.

FRIEDMAN, ROBERT MORRIS, b. New York, N.Y, Nov. 21, 32; m. 57; c. 2. PATHOLOGY, VIROLOGY. B.A, Cornell, 54; M.D, N.Y. Univ, 58. Intern med, Mt. Sinai Hosp, New York, 58-59; investr. virol, div. biologics standards, Nat. Insts. Health, 59-61, pathologist, clin. center, 61-63; vis. scientist virol, Nat. Inst. Med. Res, London, Eng, 63-64; INVESTR, NAT. CANCER INST, NAT. INSTS. HEALTH, 64-70, pathologist, 65-70, CHIEF, MOLECULAR PATH. SECT, LAB. MOLECULAR BIOL, 70- Consult, antiviral chemotherapy prog, Nat. Inst. Allergy & Infectious Diseases; Nat. Insts. Health; McLaughlin Lectr, Univ. Tex. Med. Br, Galveston, 71; vis. scientist, biochem, dept, Nat. Inst. Med. Res, London, Eng, 71-72. U.S.P.H.S, 59-66, Res, 66-, Sr. Surg. Am. Soc. Microbiol; Am. Soc. Immunol; Am. Soc. Exp. Path. Experimental pathology; virology; interferon studies; immunology. Address: National Cancer Institute, Nat. Institutes of Health, Bethesda, MD 20014.

FRIEDMAN, ROBERT S, b. Boston, Mass, Jan. 10, 15; m. 41; c. 3. EMBRYOLOGY, CYTOLOGY. B.S, Boston, 36, A.M, 37; Ph.D.(embryol), Harvard, 46. Res. assoc, radiol. res. lab, Off. Sci. Res. & Develop, U.S. Army, 42-45; PROF. BIOL, SUFFOLK UNIV, 46- V.pres. develop, Harodite Finishing Co, Inc, Mass, 52- Development of sensory nerves; comparison of regeneration phenomena and tumor development; influence of visible radiation on amphibian thyroid and pituitary development. Address: Dept. of Biology, Suffolk University, Boston, MA 02114.

FRIEDMAN, SAM, b. Youngstown, Ohio, July 29, 16; m. 41; c. 2. CHEMICAL ENGINEERING. B.Ch.E, Ohio State, 39; Va. Polytech, 43; Mass. Inst. Tech, 43; Pittsburgh, 46-47. Chem. engr, U.S. BUR. MINES, 46-53, supvr, chem. eng, 53-59, chem. res. engr, 59-68, SUPVR. CHEM. ENG, 68- U.S.A, 41-46; Res, 46-50, 1st Lt. Am. Chem. Soc; Am. Inst. Chem. Eng. Conversion of coal to low-sulfur liquid fuels; hydrogenation of coal in pilot plant and bench-scale in high pressure operations; hydrogasification and carbonization of coal; energy conversion and solid organic waste conversion and utilization. Address: 1332 Cordova Rd, Pittsburgh, PA 15206.

FRIEDMAN, S(AMUEL) A(RTHUR), b. Brooklyn, N.Y, Jan. 21, 27; m. 53; c. 3. GEOLOGY. B.S, Brooklyn Col, 50; M.S, Ohio State, 52. GEOLOGIST, Ind. Geol. Surv, 52-67; U.S. Bur. Mines, 67-71; OKLA. GEOL. SURV, 71- Fel. Geol. Soc. Am; Soc. Econ. Paleont. & Mineral. Coal geology and reserves; Pennsylvanian stratigraphy; cyclothems; mapping and sedimentology of channel sandstones. Address: Oklahoma Geological Survey, 830 Van Vleet Oval, Room 163, Norman, OK 73069.

FRIEDMAN, SAMUEL J(OHN), b. Cleveland, Ohio, Jan. 25, 18; m. 51; c. 2. CHEMICAL ENGINEERING. B.S, Case, 39, M.S, 41. Chem. engr, E.I. DU PONT DE NEMOURS & CO, INC, Del, 41-47, indust. engr, N.J, 47-48, chem. engr, Del, 48-50, sr. engr, S.C, 51-52, group leader, 52-53, res. supvr, Va, 53-57, sr. tech. supvr, 57-62, res. mgr, Del, 62-63, tech. supt, OLD HICKORY RES. & DEVELOP. LAB, 63-69, LAB. DIR, 69- Civilian with Atomic Energy Comn; Off. Sci. Res. & Develop; U.S.N, 44. AAAS; Am. Chem. Soc; Am. Soc. Mech. Eng; Am. Inst. Chem. Eng. Heat transfer and drying process equipment; synthetic textile fiber products and processes. Address: Old Hickory Research & Development Lab, E.I. du Pont de Nemours & Co, Inc, Old Hickory, TN 37138.

FRIEDMAN, S(ELWYN) MARVIN, b. N.Y.C, May 17, 29. BIOCHEMICAL GENETICS, MICROBIOLOGY. B.S, Michigan, 51; M.S, Purdue, 53, U.S. Pub. Health Serv. fel, 56-59, Ph.D.(bact), 61. Fel. biochem, Western Reserve, 60-62; cell biol, Albert Einstein Col. Med, 62-63; res. fel. med, col. physicians & surgeons, Columbia, 63-66; asst. prof. BIOL, HUNTER COL, 66-69, ASSOC. PROF, 69- Summer vis. scientist, Leiden, 65. U.S.A, 54-56. AAAS; Am. Soc. Microbiol. Biosynthesis of macrolide antibiotics; metabolism of mammalian cells grown in tissue culture; protein synthesis and the genetic code; physiology of thermophilic bacteria. Address: Dept. of Biological Sciences, Hunter College, 695 Park Ave, New York, NY 10021.

FRIEDMAN, SEYMOUR K, b. N.Y.C, July 1, 28; m. 56; c. 4. ORGANIC & COLLOID CHEMISTRY. B.S, City Col. New York, 48. Group leader chem, cent. res, Stauffer Chem. Co, 53-56; asst. mgr. develop, emulsol div, WITCO CHEM. CO, INC, 57-60, mgr. prod. appln. & planning, detergent div, 61-63, CORP. DIR. COMMERCIAL DEVELOP, 64- Commercial Chem. Develop. Asn. Information techniques; research planning. Address: Technical Center, Witco Chemical Co, Inc, 100 Bauer Dr, Oakland, NJ 07436.

FRIEDMAN, SIDNEY, b. Union City, N.J, Jan. 24, 26; m. 57; c. 3. ORGANIC CHEMISTRY. B.S, Purdue, 49; Gorham Thomas fel, Harvard, 49-50, univ. fel, 52-53, A.M. & Ph.D.(org. chem), 53. Fel. petrol, Mellon Inst, 53-54; RES. CHEMIST, U.S. BUR. MINES, 54- Lectr, Duquesne, 56-57. Bituminous Coal Res. Award, 69. U.S.A, 44-46. Am. Chem. Soc. Organometallic chemistry; catalysis; reaction mechanisms; origin and structure of petroleum and coal; organic spectroscopy; gas chromatography. Address: Bureau of Mines, 4800 Forbes Ave, Pittsburgh, PA 15213.

FRIEDMAN, SIGMUND L, b. N.Y.C, Jan. 28, 09; m. 35, 68; c. 2. MEDICINE. B.S, N.Y. Univ, 29, M.D, 33. Dir, Sydenham Hosp, New York, 47-48; Mt. Sinai Hosp, Cleveland, Ohio, 48-52; div. group practice admin, Health Ins. Plan Greater New York, 52-56; asst. clin. prof. prev. med, N.Y. Med. Col, 56-66; DIR. DIV. PLANNING & CONSULTATION, HEALTH & HOSP. PLANNING COUN. SOUTH. N.Y, 66- Prof. lectr, sch. archit, Pratt Inst, 56-65;

lectr, grad. sch. pub. admin, N.Y. Univ, 61-65; staff consult, Hosp. Rev. & Planning Coun. South. New York, 56-65; prof. & dir. grad. sch, N.Y. Med. Col, 65-66, clin. prof, 66-68. Fel. Am. Pub. Health Asn; Am. Asn. Hosp. Consult; Am. Hosp. Asn; Am. Asn. Hosp. Planning; assoc. Am. Inst. Archit; fel. N.Y. Acad. Med. Hospital planning. Address: 85 E. End Ave, Apt. 9A, New York, NY 10028.

FRIEDMAN, STANLEY, b. N.Y.C, Dec. 11, 25; m; c. 4. INSECT PHYSIOLOGY. B.A, Illinois, 48; Lalor fel, Hopkins, 51-52, Ph.D.(biol), 52. Res. assoc. entom, Illinois, 52-56; biochemist, Nat. Insts. Health, 56-58; asst. prof. ENTOM, Purdue, 58-62, assoc. prof, 62-64; UNIV. ILL, URBANA, 64-67, PROF, 67- U.S.N, 43-46. Am. Soc. Zool; Am. Soc. Biol. Chem; Entom. Soc. Am. Biochemistry and physiology of insects. Address: Dept. of Entomology, University of Illinois, Urbana, IL 61801.

FRIEDMAN, STEPHEN B(URT), b. Amsterdam, N.Y, Mar. 23, 31; m. 64; c. 2. MICROBIOLOGY. B.A, Rochester, 53; M.S, Syracuse, 55; Ph.D.(microbiol), Illinois, 62. Nat. Inst. Health fel. microbiol, State Agr. Univ, Belgium, 62-64; res. assoc. molecular biol, Cold Spring Harbor Lab. Quant. Biol, 64-66; ASSOC. PROF. BIOL, WEST. MICH. UNIV, 66- U.S.A, 55-57. AAAS; Am. Soc. Microbiol; Am. Inst. Biol. Sci. Call regulatory mechanisms and protein synthesis; active transport across biological membranes; membrane structure and function. Address: Dept. of Biology, Western Michigan University, Kalamazoo, MI 49001.

FRIEDMAN, SYDNEY M(URRAY), b. Montreal, Que, Feb. 17, 16; m. 40. MEDICINE. B.A, McGill, 38; M.D, C.M, 40, M.Sc, 41, fel, 41-43, Ph.D. (renal physiol), 46. Demonstr. histol, McGill, 40-41, asst. prof. ANAT, 44-48, assoc. prof, 48-50; PROF. & HEAD DEPT, UNIV. B.C, 50- Asst. physician, Royal Victoria Hosp, 48-50. R.C.A.F, 43-44. Am. Physiol. Soc; Am. Asn. Anat; Can. Asn. Anat.(v.pres, 62-64, pres, 65-66); Can. Physiol. Soc; fel. Royal Soc. Can. Cardiovascular-renal physiology; endocrinology; hormonal hypertension; aging. Address: Dept. of Anatomy, University of British Columbia, Vancouver 8, B.C, Can.

FRIEDMAN, WILLIAM ALBERT, b. Chicago, Ill, May 29, 38; m. 61. PHYSICS. B.E.P, Cornell Univ, 61; Nat. Sci. Found. fel, Mass. Inst. Technol, 61-64, Ph.D.(physics), 66. Nat. Sci. Found. fel, Niels Boyr Inst, Copenhagen, Denmark, 66-67; instr, Princeton, 67-70; ASST. PROF. PHYSICS, UNIV. WIS, MADISON, 70- Am. Phys. Soc. Theoretical nuclear physics, including nuclear reactions and nuclear structure. Address: Dept. of Physics, University of Wisconsin, Madison, WI 53706.

FRIEDMAN, WILLIAM F(OSTER), b. N.Y.C, July 24, 36; m. 57; c. 2. PEDIATRIC CARDIOLOGY. A.B, Columbia Col, 57; M.D, State Univ. N.Y, 61. Intern pediat, Harriet Lane Home, Johns Hopkins Hosp, 61-62, asst. & sr. resident, 62-64; clin. assoc, cardiol. br. & pediat. consult, clin. of surg, Nat. Heart Inst, 64-66, sr. investr. & pediat. cardiologist, cardiol. br, 66-68; asst. prof. PEDIAT. & MED, SCH. MED, UNIV. CALIF, SAN DIEGO, 68-70, ASSOC. PROF, 70, CHIEF PEDIAT. CARDIOL, 68- Consult. to dir. intramural res, Nat. Inst. Dent. Res, 68-70; civilian consult. pediat. cardiol, U.S. Naval Hosp, San Diego, Calif. & Camp Pendleton, 68-; consult. pediat. cardiologist, Grossmont Hosp, Kaiser Found. Hosp. & Children's Health Ctr, San Diego, 69-; mem. cardiovasc. training comt, Nat. Heart & Lung Inst, 71-75; Nat. Heart Inst. res. career develop. award; Benjamin Gasul Mem. lectr, Hektoen Inst. Med. Res. Am. Fedn. Clin. Res; Am. Heart Asn; Soc. Nuclear Med; Soc. Pediat. Res; fel. Am. Col. Cardiol; fel. Am. Acad. Pediat; Am. Physiol. Soc; Am. Soc. Pharmacol. & Exp. Therapeut. Physiology, pharmacology and biochemistry of the developing heart. Address: Dept. of Pediatric Cardiology, University Hospital, University of California, 225 W. Dickinson St, San Diego, CA 92103.

FRIEDMANN, E(MERICH) IMRE, b. Budapest, Hungary, Dec. 20, 21. PHYCOLOGY. B.Sc, Sch. Agr, Kolozsvár, Hungary, 43; M.Sc, Sch. Agr, Magyaróvár, 49; Dr.Phil.(bot), Vienna, 51. Instr. bot, Hebrew Univ, Israel, 52-56, lectr, 57-61, sr. lectr, 61-66, ASSOC. PROF, 66-67; biol, Queen's (Ont), 67-68; BIOL. SCI, FLA. STATE UNIV, 68- Res. fel, Manchester, 56-58; Dept. Sci. & Indust. Res. sr. vis. res. fel, Leeds, 59; res. assoc, Queens Col.(N.Y), 65-66; vis. assoc. prof, Fla. State, 66-67. AAAS; Bot. Soc. Am; Phycol. Soc. Am; Am. Inst. Biol. Sci. Biology of desert algae and cave algae; life history, sexuality, cytology and ecology of marine algae; fine structure of gamete fusion in algae; Phycomycetes parasitic on algae; taxonomy of blue-green algae. Address: Dept. of Biological Science, Florida State University, Tallahassee, FL 32306.

FRIEDMANN, GERHART B, b. Mannheim, Ger, Jan. 10, 29; m. 59. MEDICAL PHYSICS, OPTICS. B.Sc, Madras, 49, M.A, 51; Ph.D.(physics), British Columbia, 58. Res. asst. cosmic ray physics, Tata Inst. Fundamental Res, 51-54; spec. lectr. PHYSICS, UNIV. VICTORIA (B.C), 58-62, asst. prof, 62-70, ASSOC. PROF, 70- Grant radiation physics, B.C. Cancer Clin, 58-59; physicist, Victoria Cancer Clin, 58-; radiol. health off, Royal Jubilee Hosp, 63- Am. Asn. Physics Teachers; Can. Asn. Physicists; Brit. Inst. Radiol. Holography and medical physics. Address: Dept. of Physics, University of Victoria, Victoria, B.C, Can.

FRIEDMANN, HERBERT, b. N.Y.C, Apr. 22, 00; m. 37; c. 1. VERTEBRATE ZOOLOGY, ORNITHOLOGY. B.S, City Col, 20; Ph.D.(ornith), Cornell, 23. Asst. ornith, Am. Mus. Natural Hist, 20; instr. zool, Cornell, 22-23; Nat. Res. Coun. fel, Bussey Inst, Harvard, 23-26; instr, Brown, 26-27; instr. biol, Amherst Col, 27-29; curator div. birds, U.S. Nat. Mus, 29-57, head curator zool, 57-61; Dir, Los Angeles County Mus, 61-70; RETIRED. Expeds, Mex. border, Argentina, South, east & cent. Africa. Del, Int. Ornith. Cong, Oxford, 34, Upsala, 50. Elliot medal, Nat. Acad. Sci, 59; Leidy medal, Acad. Nat. Sci, Phila, 55; Brewster medal, Am. Ornith. Union, 64. U.S.A, 18-19. Nat. Acad. Sci; AAAS (pres. sect. F, 59); Am. Soc. Nat; Am. Soc. Zool; Cooper Ornith. Soc; fel. Am. Ornith. Union (v.pres, 32-38; pres, 38-39); hon. mem. Cuban Soc. Natural Hist; German & S.African Ornith. Socs. Systematic ornithology; brood parasitism; natural history symbolism in medieval and Renaissance art; animal behavior; physiological cycles and cyclical instincts; theoretical biology. Address: 350 S. Fuller Ave, Apt. 12H, Los Angeles, CA 90036.

FRIEDMANN, HERBERT C(LAUS), b. Mannheim, West Ger, June 19, 27; nat; m. 61; c. 2. BIOCHEMISTRY. B.Sc, Univ. Madras, India, 47, M.Sc, 51; fel, Chicago, 54-55, Ph.D.(biochem), 58. Chemist, allergic asthma enquiry, Govt. of Madras, India, 51-54; asst, Chicago, 55-58, res. assoc, 58-59; fel, Damon Runyon, McCollum-Pratt Inst, Hopkins, 59-60; res. assoc, dept. physiol, UNIV. CHICAGO, 60-64, asst. prof. BIOCHEM, 64-69, ASSOC. PROF, 69- Am. Soc. Biol. Chem; Am. Chem. Soc; Am. Soc. Microbiol. Chemical anthropology applied to steroids; enzymes of intermediary metabolism; flavoproteins; vitamin B_{12}; amino acids. Address: Dept. of Biochemistry, University of Chicago, Chicago, IL 60637.

FRIEDMANN, HERMAN H, b. New York, N.Y, Nov. 30, 18; m. 42; c. 2. PHYSICAL CHEMISTRY. B.S, City Col, 41; Polytech. Inst. Brooklyn. Anal. chemist, Joseph E. Seagram & Sons, 41-44; res. biochemist, Schwarz Labs, 46-49; chief chemist, Physiol. Chems. Co, 49-55; proj. leader, TECH. CTR, GEN. FOODS CORP, 55-63, RES. SPECIALIST, 63- U.S.N, 44-45. Am. Chem. Soc; Soc. Appl. Spectros. X-ray diffraction; surface chemistry; infrared and nuclear magnetic resonance spectrometry. Address: Technical Center, General Foods Corp, 555 S. Broadway, Tarrytown, NY 10591.

FRIEDMANN, NORMAN E(RNEST), b. Los Angeles, Calif, Mar. 18, 29; m. 52; c. 3. APPLIED MATHEMATICS. B.S, California, Los Angeles, 50, M.S, 52, Ph.D.(eng), 57. Res. engr, California, Los Angeles, 50-56; prog. mgr, Litton Industs, 56-58; assoc. prog. dir, Space Tech. Labs, Titan Proj, Thompson Ramo Wooldridge, Inc, 58-62; v.pres. & gen. mgr, Fed. Labs, Aerospace, Int. Tel. & Tel. Corp, Calif, 62-63, pres, data & info. systs. div, Paramus, N.J, 64-66; PRES. & CHMN. BD, COMPUT. & SOFT WARE, INC, LOS ANGELES, 66- Nat. Guard, 48-51, Sgt. Systems engineering; computers and automation. Address: 5327 Andasol Ave, Encino, CA 91316.

FRIEDRICH, BENJAMIN C, b. Fond du Lac, Wis, Feb. 2, 29; m. 64. SCIENCE EDUCATION. B.S, St. Cloud State Col, 54; M.S, Indiana, 57; D.Ed, Pa. State, 61. Instr. chem, Luther Jr. Col, 54-56; sci. educ, Indiana, 57-59; asst. prof, Northeastern, 61-66, assoc. prof, DEPT. GEOSCI, JERSEY CITY STATE COL, 66-69, PROF. & CHMN. DEPT, 69- Dir, Nat. Sci. Found. Summer Inst. Progs. Sec. Sch. Sci. Teachers, 62-66. U.S.N, 50-52. AAAS; Nat. Asn. Geol. Teachers. Address: Dept. of Geoscience, Jersey City State College, Jersey City, NJ 07305.

FRIEDRICH, BRUCE H, b. Clinton, Okla, Oct. 20, 36; m. 63; c. 1. PHYSICAL CHEMISTRY. Nat. Sci. Found. fel, Iowa, 60-62, M.S, 61, Ph.D.(chem), 63. Fel. phys. chem, California, Berkeley, 62-63; asst. prof. CHEM, Gustavus Adolphus Col, 63-66; UNIV. IOWA, 66-70, ASSOC. PROF, 70- Summer fels, Univ. Iowa, 63, 64 & 65. AAAS; Am. Chem. Soc; Am. Phys. Soc. Infrared spectra of molecular crystals; spectra of donor-acceptor complexes. Address: Dept. of Chemistry, University of Iowa, Iowa City, IA 52240.

FRIEDRICH, CARL M(ARK), b. Ford City, Pa, May 6, 26. MECHANICAL ENGINEERING. B.S, Carnegie Inst. Tech, 48, M.S, 49, D.Sc.(mech. eng), 52. Instr, Carnegie Inst. Tech, 48-52; engr, ATOMIC POWER DIV, WESTINGHOUSE ELEC. CORP, 52-70, FEL. ENGR, 70- Am. Soc. Mech. Eng. Address: 3633 Willett Rd, Pittsburgh, PA 15227.

FRIEDRICH, EDWIN CARL, b. Woodbury, N.J, Jan. 15, 36; m. 67. ORGANIC CHEMISTRY. B.S, Illinois, Urbana, 57; Ph.D.(chem), California, Los Angeles, 61. Res. assoc. chem, California, Los Angeles, 61-62; res. chemist, Calif. Res. Corp, 62-64; fel. CHEM, Mass. Inst. Technol, 64-65; asst. prof, UNIV. CALIF, DAVIS, 65-69, ASSOC. PROF, 69- Am. Chem. Soc; The Chem. Soc. Kinetics, product studies, salt and solvent effects in carbonium ion reactions of cyclopropylcarbinyl and bridged bicyclic systems; free-radical brominations; cyclopropylcarbinyl-allylcarbinyl radical rearrangements. Address: Dept. of Chemistry, University of California, Davis, CA 95616.

FRIEDRICH, J(OHN) P(HILIP), b. Pekin, Ill, Mar. 28, 32; m. 52; c. 4. ORGANIC CHEMISTRY. B.S, Mo. Sch. Mines, 53, M.S, 55; Carlisle Chem. Co. fel, Okla. State, 57-59, Ph.D.(org. chem), 59. Instr. biochem, Okla. State, 55-56; PRIN. CHEMIST, NORTH. REGIONAL RES. LAB, AGR. RES. SERV, U.S. DEPT. AGR, 59- Am. Chem. Soc. Reactions of materials under high pressure, acetylene and olefins with conjugated double bond systems, and of fats and oils as a general classification. Address: 1815 N. University St, Peoria, IL 61604.

FRIEDRICH, L(AWRENCE) W(ILLIAM), b. Parkston, S.Dak, Dec. 15, 12. SOLID STATE PHYSICS. Ph.L, St. Louis, 41, S.T.L, 49, Ph.D.(physics), 53. Teacher, high sch, Colo, 42-44; instr. physics, Marquette, 53-55, asst. prof, 55-62, assoc. prof, 62-67, dean grad. sch, 60-67; specialist grad. progs, U.S. OFF. EDUC, 67-68, ASST. CHIEF GRAD. ACAD. PROGS. BR, DIV. UNIV. PROGS, BUR. HIGHER EDUC, 68- AAAS; Am. Phys. Soc. Electrical and magnetic properties of metals and organic compounds. Address: Division of University Programs, Bureau of Higher Education, U.S. Office of Education, Washington, DC 20202.

FRIEDRICH, LOUIS ELBERT, b. Wilmington, Del, Sept. 7, 41; m. 65. ORGANIC CHEMISTRY. B.S, Mass. Inst. Technol, 63; Nat. Sci. Found. fel, Univ. Calif, Berkeley, 63-66, Ph.D.(chem), 66. Nat. Sci. Found. fel, chem, Yale, 66-67; ASST. PROF. ORG. CHEM, UNIV. ROCHESTER, 67- Am. Chem. Soc. Mechanisms of organic reactions; carbonium ions; photochemistry; thermal reactions. Address: Dept. of Chemistry, University of Rochester, Rochester, NY 14627.

FRIEDRICH, MARTIN E(DWIN PAUL), b. Hobart, Ind, Jan. 29, 04; m. 29; c. 2. CHEMISTRY. A.B, Augustana Col, 25; M.S, Louisville, 26; Ph.D. (org. chem), Illinois, 30. Asst. chem, Louisville, 25-26; Illinois, 26-29; res. chemist, E.I. du Pont de Nemours & Co, 29-65; ASSOC. PROF. CHEM. CONCORDIA TEACHERS COL, 65- Am. Chem. Soc. Dyes and intermediates; arsonium compounds and acridine derivatives. Address: Dept. of Chemistry, Concordia Teachers College, River Forest, IL 60305.

FRIEDRICH, SEVGI SUMER, b. Ankara, Turkey, Mar. 3, 40; m. 67. PHYSICAL ORGANIC CHEMISTRY. B.S, Am. Col. Girls, Istanbul, 61; M.A,

Smith Col, 63; Nat. Sci. Found. fel, Univ. Calif, Davis, 67-68, Ph.D.(chem), 69. Nat. Sci. Found. fel, UNIV. CALIF, DAVIS, 69-70, LECTR. CHEM, 70- Intramolecular participation in carbonium ion and free radical systems; hydrogen abstraction reactions at aromatic side chains. Address: Dept. of Chemistry, University of California, Davis, CA 95616.

FRIEDRICHS, ANDREW VALLOIS, JR, b. Metarie, La, Apr. 20, 24; m. 52; c. 4. ZOOLOGY. B.S, Tulane, 46; M.S, La. State, 55. Salesman, Lederle Labs, 47-50; teacher, high sch, La, 51-53; marine biologist, La. Wildlife & Fisheries Comn, 55-62; asst. prof. ZOOL, SOUTHEAST. LA. UNIV, 62-66, ASSOC. PROF, 66- Am. Inst. Biol. Sci; Am. Fisheries Soc; Am. Soc. Limnol. & Oceanog. Estuarine ecology, particularly as relates to oysters. Address: 2 Lynn Lane, Whitmar Acres, Hammond, LA 70401.

FRIEDRICHS, K(URT) O(TTO), b. Kiel, Germany, Sept. 28, 01; nat; m. 37; c. 5. MATHEMATICS. Ph.D.(math), Göttingen, 25. Asst, Göttingen, 25-27, privat-docent, 29-30; asst. & privat-docent, Aachen Tech, 27-29; prof. math, Brunswick Tech, 30-37; vis. prof. APPL. MATH, N.Y. UNIV, 37-39, assoc. prof, 39-43, PROF, 43-; assoc. dir, Courant Inst. Math. Sci, 53-66, dir, 66-67. Civilian with Off. Sci. Res. & Develop; U.S.N, 44. Nat. Acad. Sci; Am. Math. Soc; fel. Am. Acad. Arts & Sci. Mathematical physics; partial differential equations; elasticity; fluid dynamics. Address: Dept. of Applied Mathematics, New York University Graduate School of Arts & Sciences, New York, NY 10003.

FRIEL, DANIEL D(ENWOOD), b. Queenstown, Md, Aug. 11, 20; m. 43; c. 4. PHYSICS. B.S, Hopkins, 42. Engr, Okla. ord. works, E.I. du Pont de Nemours & Co, 42-43, group leader, Manhattan Proj, Chicago, 43-45, res. engr, Harford Ord. Works, 44-45, res. supvr, eng. res. lab, 45-56, res. mgr, 56-57, asst. lab. dir, 57-60, mgr. eng. prod, 60-61, mgr. invests, 61-69, pres, Holotron Corp, 69-71, MGR, RISTON DIV, PHOTOPROD. DEPT, E.I. DU PONT DE NEMOURS & CO, INC, 71- Optical Soc. Am; Instrument Soc. Am; Am. Chem. Soc. Optics and electronics; infrared; applied physics and instrumentation. Address: Box 3795, Greenville, DE 19807.

FRIEL, PATRICK J(OSEPH), b. Phila, Pa, Jan. 6, 28; m. 57; c. 4. PHYSICAL CHEMISTRY. B.S, Villanova, 50; Atomic Energy Cmn. fel, Pennsylvania, 50-52, M.S, 52, univ. fel, 53, Ph.D.(phys. chem), 54. Res. chemist, Sun Oil Co, 54-58; engr, reentry systs. dept, Gen. Elec. Co, 58-60, supvry. engr, 60-62, mgr. aerospace physics lab, 62-66; dir. ballistic missile defense, Dept. of Defense, 66-67, dep. asst. secy. army (res. & develop), 67-68; pres, Sadtler Res. Labs, Inc, 69-70; MEM. STAFF, FRIEL & CO, CONSULT, 70- Meritorious civilian serv. medal, Dept. of Army, 68. U.S.A, 46-47, Sgt. Am. Chem. Soc; Am. Inst. Aeronaut. & Astronaut. Reentry physics; high temperature thermochemistry; plasma and space physics; ionization in gases; ablation; combustion phenomena; nuclear weapons effects; strategic systems technology. Address: Friel & Co, Round Hill Rd, Lincoln, MA 01773.

FRIEMAN, EDWARD A(LLAN), b. N.Y.C, Jan. 19, 26; m. 49, 67; c. 5. PHYSICS. B.S, Columbia, 45; M.S, Polytech. Inst. Brooklyn, 48, fel, 48-50, Ph.D. (physics), 51. Instr. physics, Polytech. Inst. Brooklyn, 45-52; res. assoc, 47-49; Proj. Matterhorn, PRINCETON, 52-53, head theoret. div, 53-64, ASSOC. DIR, PLASMA PHYSICS LAB, 64-, PROF, ASTROPHYS. SCI, 61-, DIR. PLASMA PHYSICS PROG, 59- Consult, Lawrence Radiation Lab, California, 53-57, Los Alamos Sci. Lab, 53-64; mem. res. adv. comt. nuclear energy processes, NASA, 59-; John Simon Guggenheim Mem. Found. fel, 70. U.S.N, 43-46, Res, 46-52. AAAS; Am. Phys. Soc; Am. Astron. Soc. Theoretical plasma physics; hydrodynamics stability; astrophysics. Address: Plasma Physics Lab, Box 451, Princeton University, Princeton, NJ 08540.

FRIEND, ALBERT W(ILEY), b. Morgantown, W.Va, Jan. 24, 10; m. 31; c. 3. ELECTRONICS, PHYSICS. B.S, West Virginia, 32, M.S, 36; fel, Harvard, 39-42, Sc.D.(communication eng), 48. Instr. physics, West Virginia, 34-37, asst. prof, 37-44; develop. engr, Radio Corp. Am, 44-47, mem. res. staff, labs, 47-51, dir. eng, Daystrom Indust. div, 51; eng. & develop, Magnetic Metals Co, 51-53; CONSULT. ENGR. & PHYSICIST, A.W. FRIEND ENGRS. & SCIENTISTS, 53-; PRES, ACOUSTEX, INC, 61- Transmission & distribution engr, Ohio Power Co, 33-34; instr, Harvard, 39-41; res. assoc. & mem. staff, radiation lab, Mass. Inst. Tech, 41-42, tech. dir, heat res. lab, 42-44. Eng. consult. radio facilities, 33-39; electronic res, Cruft Lab, Harvard, 46-48. Radio Corp. Am. Labs, Award, 50; Nat. Electronics Conf. award, 55. Consult div. five, Nat. Defense Res. Cmt, 43-44; U.S.A; U.S.N, 44; U.S. govt; res. & develop. labs, Hopkins, Denver; State govt. depts; Inst. Elec. & Electronics Eng. rep. to Am. Nat. Standards Inst; lectr, grad. sch. fine arts, Univ. Pa, 65-66. AAAS; fel. Am. Phys. Soc; Inst. Elec. & Electronics Eng; Am. Ord. Asn; Am. Meteorol. Soc; Audio Eng. Soc; Acoust. Soc. Am; Am. Inst. Physics; Am. Geophys. Union. Communications systems; radar; sound transmission; noise abatement; television; magnetic recording; magnetic materials and circuits; engineering and scientific testimony in legal proceedings; medical electronics. Address: P.O. Box 34420, West Bethesda, (Md.) Branch, Washington, DC 20034.

FRIEND, CHARLOTTE, b. N.Y.C, Mar. 11, 21. MICROBIOLOGY. B.A, Hunter Col, 44; Ph.D.(bact), Yale, 50. Assoc. mem, Sloan-Kettering Inst, 49-66, assoc. prof. microbiol, Sloan-Kettering Div, Med. Col, Cornell Univ, 52-66; PROF. & DIR. CTR. EXP. CELL BIOL, MT. SINAI SCH. MED, 66- Alfred. P. Sloan Award, 54, 57, 62; award, Am. Cancer Soc, 62; Presidential Medal Centennial Award, Hunter Col, 70. U.S.N.R, 44-46, Lt.(jg). Fel. N.Y. Acad, Sci; Am. Asn. Cancer Res; Am. Asn. Immunol; Am. Soc. Hemat; Tissue Cult. Asn; Harvey Soc; Int. Soc. Hemat; Am. Soc. Microbiol. Immunology; virology; viruses in relation to cancer. Address: Center for Experimental Cell Biology, Mt. Sinai School of Medicine, 100th St. & Fifth Ave, New York, NY 10029.

FRIEND, DALE G(ILBERT), b. Missouri Valley, Iowa, Sept. 19, 07; m. 37; c. 3. INTERNAL MEDICINE, PHARMACOLOGY. B.A, Iowa, 30, M.S, 31; M.D, Harvard, 35. Intern & asst. res. med, Peter Bent Brigham Hosp, 35-37; res. fel. med. & biochem, HARVARD MED. SCH, 37-38, instr. pharmacol, 39-51, assoc. MED, 51-57, asst. prof, 57-69, ASSOC. CLIN.

PROF, 69-, asst. dean, 46-47. Mosely traveling fel, London, 38-39, Sr. assoc, Peter Bent Birgham Hosp, 46-, clin. pharmacologist & head div, 51- Consult, Boston Veterans Admin. Hosp; Sturdy Mem. Hosp; Year Book of Drug Therapy. Med.C, 41-46, Col. AAAS; Am. Soc. Pharmacol. & Exp. Therapeut; Am. Soc. Internal Med; Am. Therapeut. Soc; fel. Am. Med. Asn; Am. Heart Asn; fel. Am. Col. Physicians; Am. Fedn. Clin. Res; N.Y. Acad. Sci. Medical treatment of disease; drugs in tissue metabolism; chlorpromazine; peripheral vascular disease; current concepts of drug therapy; prochlorperazine. Address: Deconess Medical Bldg, 110 Francis St, Suite 8D, Boston, MA 02215.

FRIEND, DANIEL S, b. Passaic, N.J, Nov. 20, 33; m. 67; c. 1. PATHOLOGY, CELL BIOLOGY. B.A, N.Y. Univ, 57; M.D, State Univ. N.Y. Downstate Med. Center, 61. Intern, Boston City Hosp, 61-62; resident path, 62-63; res. fel. anat, Harvard Med. Sch, 63-65; PATH, SCH. MED, UNIV. CALIF, SAN FRANCISCO, 65-66, lectr, 66-67, ASST. PROF, 67- U.S. Pub. Health Serv. career develop. award, 67-, res. grant, 68- U.S.A, 52-54, Sgt. AAAS; Am. Soc. Cell Biol; Am. Soc. Exp. Path; Am. Asn. Path. & Bact; Am. Asn. Anat. Electron microscopy; structure and function of the Golgi complex; intracellular transport of macromolecules; cell junctions; intercellular communication; cytochemistry. Address: Dept. of Pathology, University of California School of Medicine, San Francisco, CA 94122.

FRIEND, EARL WILLARD, JR, b. New Brighton, Pa, Apr. 24, 40. ORGANIC CHEMISTRY. B.S, Washington & Jefferson Col, 62; M.S, Hopkins, 65, Ph.D. (org. chem), 67. RES. CHEMIST, E.I. DU PONT DE NEMOURS & CO, 67- AAAS; Am. Chem. Soc. Photochemistry; 1,2,4,7-tetraphenylcyclooctatetraene and related compounds. Address: E.I. du Pont de Nemours & Co, Drawer A, Camden, SC 29020.

FRIEND, ELBERT BARTON, b. Sang Run, Md, Aug. 28, 26; m. 50; c. 2. BIOLOGY, ENDOCRINE PHYSIOLOGY. B.S, Alliance Col, 50; Nat. Sci. Found-Atomic Energy Cmn. Summer Inst, New Mexico, 57; Nat. Sci. Found. Inst. & M.S, Syracuse, 59; Nat. Sci. Found. Inst, Brown, 63-64, Summer Res. Fel. Prog, 65-66; Nat. Sci. Found. Summer Inst, Colorado State, 68. Head dept. sci, high sch, 51-66; ASSOC. PROF. BIOL, ZOOL. & PHYSIOL, EDINBORO STATE COL, 66- Finance C, U.S.A, 45-46. AAAS. Adrenal-gonad hormonal factors involved in sexual dimorphism; suceptibility of C_3HS mice to chloroform induced nephrosis; radioautography and scintillation detection of tritiated thymidine in Chinese hamster ovary cells following cell cycle synchronization and pulse labeling. Address: 210 Canfield St, Cambridge Springs, PA 16403.

FRIEND, JAMES PHILIP, b. Hartford, Conn, Nov. 30, 29; m. 55; c. 2. ATMOSPHERIC CHEMISTRY. S.B, Mass. Inst. Technol, 51; M.A, Columbia Univ, 53, Ph.D.(chem), 56. Asst. chem, Columbia Univ, 53, 55-56; proj. engr, Perkin-Elmer Corp, 56-57; sr. res. scientist, Isotopes, Inc, 57-64, sr. scientific adv, 64-67; ASSOC. PROF. ATMOSPHERIC CHEM, N.Y. UNIV, 67- Independent consult. Chem.C, U.S.A, 53-55. AAAS; Am. Geophys. Union; Am. Meteorol. Soc; Am. Chem. Soc; Air Pollution Control Asn. Atmospheric chemistry and radioactivity; atmospheric diffusion; air pollution chemistry; global cycles and geochemistry of trace materials in the atmosphere. Address: Dept. of Meteorology & Oceanography, New York University, University Heights, Bronx, NY 10453.

FRIEND, JONATHON D, U.S. citizen. VETERINARY MEDICINE. D.V.M, Kans. State Univ, 45, M.S, 59; B.S, Okla. State, 49. From asst. prof. VET. ANAT. to ASSOC. PROF, OKLA. STATE UNIV, 48- U.S.A, 43-44. Am. Asn. Vet. Anat. Regional innervation in the bovine. Address: Dept. of Veterinary Medicine, Oklahoma State University, Stillwater, OK 74075.

FRIEND, LEO, b. N.Y.C, July 16, 10; m. 45; c. 2. CHEMICAL ENGINEERING. B.S, N.Y. Univ, 32, Ch.E, 38; M.S, Michigan, 33. Chem. engr, Catalazuli Mfg. Co, N.Y, 33-34; M.W. KELLOGG CO, 34-50, assoc. dir. chem. eng, 50-61, dir. chem. eng. develop, 61-68, DIR. TECH. SERV, 68-, CONSULT, 71- Civilian with Atomic Energy Comn; Off. Sci. Res. & Develop, 44. Mem. adv. bd, off. critical tables, Nat. Acad. Sci. Cert. distinction, col. eng, N.Y. Univ, 55. Am. Chem. Soc.(Scroll of Honor, div. indust. chem, 68); Am. Inst. Chem. Eng; fel. Am. Inst. Chem; Sci. Res. Soc. Am. Pressure drop in round pipe; liquid-vapor equilibrium; heat exchange and pressure drop; thermodynamics. Address: 7 Merritt Lane, Rocky Hill, NJ 08553.

FRIEND, PATRIC L(EE), b. Iron River, Mich, Sept. 4, 38; m. 62; c. 3. MICROBIOLOGY. B.S, North. Mich. Col, 61; Wayne State, 56-58; Nat. Insts. Health fel, Northwestern, 61-65, Ph.D.(microbiol), 65. Res. asst. MICROBIOL, med. sch, Northwestern, 65-66; ASST. PROF, COL. MED, UNIV. CINCINNATI, 66- Am. Soc. Microbiol. Relationships between betahemolytic streptococci and their bacteriophages. Address: Dept. of Microbiology, University of Cincinnati, Cincinnati, OH 45219.

FRIEND, W(ILLIAM) G(EORGE), b. Toronto, Ont, July 25, 28; m. 53. INSECT PHYSIOLOGY. B.Sc, McGill Univ, 50; Ph.D.(insect physiol), Cornell Univ, 54. Entomologist, Can. Dept. Agr, 50-59; asst. prof. ZOOL, UNIV. TORONTO, 59-61, assoc. prof, 61-66, PROF, 66- Entom. Soc. Am; Entom. Soc. Can; Can. Biochem. Soc; Nutrit. Soc. Can. Insect nutrition and biochemistry. Address: Dept. of Zoology, University of Toronto, Toronto 5, Ont, Can.

FRIERSON, W(ILLIAM) JOE, b. Batesville, Ark, July 8, 07; m. 30; c. 2. ANALYTICAL CHEMISTRY. A.B, Ark. Col, 27; fel, Emory, 27-28, M.S, 28; Ph.D.(inorg. chem), Cornell, 36. Asst. CHEM, Ark. Col, 26-27; asst. prof, Hampden-Sydney Col, 28-36, assoc. prof, 36-44; prof, Birmingham-South. Col, 44-46; AGNES SCOTT COL, 46-69, WILLIAM RAND KENAN, JR. PROF, 69- Fel, Cornell Univ, 35-36; vis. lectr, Univ. Calif, Berkeley, summer 67. Am. Chem. Soc. Chemistry of inorganic nitrogen compounds; organic reagents in analytical chemistry; boiling points of pure compounds under varying pressures; paper chromatography of inorganic ions. Address: Dept. of Chemistry, Agnes Scott College, Decatur, GA 30030.

FRIES, BERNARD A(LBERT), b. Indianapolis, Ind, June 26, 17; m. 39; c. 3. RADIOCHEMISTRY. B.S, California, 36, Ph.D.(physiol, biochem), 41. Chemist viticulture anal, col. agr, California, 36-37, asst. physiol, 37-41,

Rosenberg fel, 41-42, res. neurophysiologist, med. sch, 42-43; res. assoc, metall. lab, Chicago, 43; assoc. chemist, Clinton Eng. Works, Tenn, 43-44; chemist, Hanford Eng. Works, Wash, 44-45; RES. CHEMIST, Calif. Res. Corp, 45-66, CHEVRON RES. CORP, 66- Consult. radiation lab, Univ. Calif, 46. Am. Chem. Soc; Health Physics Soc. Chemistry of plutonium; industrial applications of radioactivity; radioisotopes in process control. Address: Chevron Research Corp, 576 Standard Ave, Richmond, CA 94802.

FRIES, JAMES ANDREW, b. St. Louis, Mo, June 25, 43; m. 61; c. 2. PHYSICAL CHEMISTRY. B.S.Ed, South Dakota, 65; M.S, Iowa, 68, Ph.D.(phys. chem), 69. Asst. phys. chem, Iowa, 65-69; ASST. PROF. CHEM. & HEAD DEPT, NORTH. STATE COL, 69- Am. Chem. Soc. High temperature mass spectrometric studies of the vaporization and thermodynamics of the lanthanide metal sulfides. Address: Division of Science & Mathematics, Northern State College, Aberdeen, SD 57401.

FRIES, R(ALPH) JAY, b. Lancaster, Pa, Oct. 22, 30; m. 50; c. 3. PHYSICAL CHEMISTRY. B.Sc, Pa. State, 52, Anthracite fel, 54; M.Litt, Pittsburgh, 58, Ph.D.(chem), 59. Res. assoc. phys. chem, Mellon Inst, 55-58; MEM. STAFF, LOS ALAMOS SCI. LAB, 58- Lectr, Pittsburgh, 56-57; vis. scientist, Ispra Lab, Europ. Atomic Energy Community, Italy, 67-68. Fel, Am. Inst. Chem; Am. Chem. Soc. Surface and high temperature chemistry; physical measurements. Address: 70 Turquoise St, Los Alamos, NM 87544.

FRIESEM, ALBERT ASHER, b. Haifa, Israel, Jan. 18, 36; U.S. citizen; m. 56; c. 3. ELECTRICAL ENGINEERING, OPTICS. B.S, Michigan, 58, Ph.D. (elec. eng), 68; M.S, Wayne State, 61. Engr, Bell Aircraft Co, N.Y, 58-59; res. labs, Bendix Corp, Mich, 59-63; res. assoc, radar & optics lab, Inst. Sci. & Tech, Michigan, 63-66, assoc. res. eng, 66-68, res. engr, 68-69; PRIN. RES. ENGR, ELECTRO OPTICS CTR, RADIATION INC, 69- Lectr, col. eng, Michigan, summers 66, 67, vis. scholar, 69- Inst. Elec. & Electronics Eng; Optical Soc. Am. Simulation of radar returns with coherent optics; development of image processing equipment; wavefront reconstruction; holographic storage, retrieval and display systems. Address: Electro Optics Center, Radiation Inc, P.O. Box 1084, Ann Arbor, MI 48106.

FRIESEN, BENJAMIN S, b. Garden City, Kans, Mar. 24, 28; m. 53; c. 4. MOLECULAR BIOLOGY, RADIATION BIOPHYSICS. B.A, Univ. Kans, 52, M.A, 54; Ph.D.(biophys), Iowa State Univ, 59. U.S. Pub. Health Serv. fel, 59-60; asst. prof. RADIATION BIOPHYS, UNIV. KANS, 60-64, assoc. prof, 64-70, PROF, 70- AAAS; Health Phys. Soc; Biophys. Soc; Radiation Res. Soc; Am. Soc. Microbiol. Biophysical characterization of viruses, viral components and virus-host relationships; radiation effects in microorganisms and tissue culture; dioxyribonucleic acid repair mechanisms. Address: Nuclear Reactor Center, University of Kansas, W. 15th St, Lawrence, KS 66044.

FRIESEN, DONALD KENT, b. Morrison, Ill, Mar. 31, 41. ALGEBRA. B.A, Knox Col, 63; Nat. Defense Ed. Act fel. & M.A, Dartmouth Col, 65, Ph.D. (math), 66. Res. instr. MATH, Dartmouth Col, 66-67; ASST. PROF, UNIV. ILL, URBANA, 67- Math. Asn. Am. Finite subgroups of orthogonal groups and related problems in theory of finite groups. Address: Dept. of Mathematics, University of Illinois, Urbana, IL 61801.

FRIESEN, EARL W(AYNE), b. Hillsboro, Kans, Jan. 8, 27; m. 50; c. 2. NUCLEAR PHYSICS. A.B, California, 50, Westinghouse fel, 53-54, Ph.D, 54. Instr. PHYSICS, California, 54-55; asst. prof, Indiana, 55-61; assoc. prof, SAN FRANCISCO STATE COL, 61-66, PROF, 66- U.S.N.R, 44-46. Fel. Am. Phys. Soc; Am. Asn. Physics Teachers. Cosmic ray physics; elementary particle physics; high energy nuclear physics. Address: Dept. of Physics, San Francisco State College, 1600 Holloway Ave, San Francisco, CA 94132.

FRIESEN, GEORGE, b. Man, Dec. 11, 26; m. 50; c. 3. AGRONOMY. B.S.A, Manitoba, 49, M.Sc, 52; Ph.D.(agron), Washington State, 56. Asst. agronomist, Can. Dept. Agr, 49-50; asst, Nat. Res. Coun. Can, 50-52; asst, Washington State, 52-54; assoc. prof. plant sci, Univ. Man, 55-66, prof, 66-68; RES. MGR, GEIGY LTD, 68- Pres, West. Can. Weed Control Conf, 59-60; sci. ed, Can. J. Plant Sci, 60-63; chmn. west. sect, Can. Nat. Weed Comt, 62-63. Weed Sci. Soc. Am; Can. Agr. Pesticide Tech. Soc.(v.pres, 59, pres, 60); Can. Soc. Agron; Agr. Inst. Can. Weed control investigations; weed crop ecological studies; physiology of herbicides. Address: Geigy Ltd, 630 Evans Ave, Toronto, Ont, Can.

FRIESEN, HENRY G, b. Morden, Man, July 31, 34; m. 67; c. 1. MEDICINE. B.Sc, & M.D, Manitoba, 58. Intern, Winnipeg Gen. Hosp, 58-59, asst. res. med, 59-60; from instr. to asst. prof. MED, sch. med, Tufts, 60-65; asst. prof, FACULTY MED, McGILL UNIV, 65-68, ASSOC. PROF, 68- Res. fel. endocrinol, New England Centre Hosp, 63. Can. Soc. Clin. Invest; Can. Physiol. Soc. Endocrinology. Address: Room 19, 4 Main, Royal Victoria Hospital, Montreal 112, Que, Can.

FRIESEN, JAMES DONALD, b. Rosthern, Sask, Nov. 4, 35; m. 58; c. 3. MOLECULAR BIOLOGY, MICROBIOLOGY. B.A, Saskatchewan, 56, M.A, 58; Ph.D.(med. physics), Toronto, 62. Nat. Cancer Inst. Can. fel, inst. microbiol, Copenhagen Univ, 62-64; vis. asst. prof. physics, Kansas State, 64-65, asst. prof, 65-67, ASSOC. PROF. BIOL, 67-68; YORK UNIV.(ONT), 69- Regulation of ribonucleic acid synthesis and function in microorganisms. Address: Dept. of Biology, York University, 4700 Keele St, Downsview, Ont, Can.

FRIESEN, RHINEHART F, b. Gretna, Man, Jan. 6, 14; m. 44; c. 4. MEDICINE. M D, Manitoba, 44. Demonstr. OBSTET. & GYNEC, UNIV. MANITOBA, 58-65, lectr. & sr. res. asst, 65-67, ASST. PROF, 67-, asst. pediat, 59-65. Asst. obstetrician & gynecologist, Winnipeg Gen. Hosp, 59. Consult, Man. Rehab. Hosp. Fel, Royal Col. Physicians & Surgeons, Can, 57. R.C.A.M.C, 42-46, Capt. Can. Med. Asn; fel. Am. Col. Obstet. & Gynec. Obstetrics and gynecology; perinatal mortality; fetal transfusions in Rh-sensitized mothers. Address: 409 Medical Arts Bldg, Winnipeg 1, Man, Can.

FRIESEN, STANLEY R(ICHARD), b. Rosthern, Sask, Sept. 8, 18; U.S. citizen; m. 42; c. 4. SURGERY. A.B, Kansas, 40, M.D, 43; Ph.D.(surg), Minnesota, 49. Asst. prof. surg, SCH. MED, UNIV. KANS, 49-52, assoc. prof. surg. & oncol, 52-59, PROF. SURG, 59- Consult, Vet. Admin. Hosp. Dipl, Am. Bd. Surg, 50. U.S.N.R, 41-43. AAAS; Soc. Exp. Biol. & Med; Soc. Univ. Surg; Am. Surg. Asn; fel. Am. Col. Surg; Asn. Thoracic Surg; Am. Asn. Cancer Res; Int. Soc. Surg. Surgical endocrinology and gastroenterology, specifically acid-peptic ulceration and multiple endocrine adenomatosis. Address: University of Kansas School of Medicine, Kansas City, KS 66103.

FRIESER, RUDOLF G(RUENSPAN), b. Vienna, Austria, Apr. 20, 20; U.S. citizen; m. 55; c. 2. INORGANIC & SOLID STATE CHEMISTRY. B.S, Columbia, 50; M.S, Polytech. Inst. Brooklyn, 58. Bacteriologist, U.S. Testing Corp, N.J, 47; clin. chemist, Clinicians Lab, N.Y, 47-51; chemist, Fisher Sci. Corp, 51-52; sr. chemist, res. labs, Interchem. Corp, 52-58; engr, Radio Corp, Am, N.J, 58-60; mem. tech. staff semiconductor mat. chem, Bell Tel. Labs, Inc, N.J, 60-65; sr. res. scientist, res. & develop. lab, Sprague Elec. Co, 65-68; ADV. CHEMIST, IBM CORP, 68- Lectr, eve. div, Mass. State Col. N. Adams, 67-68. Sig.C, U.S.A, 43-45, Res, 42-43. Am. Chem. Soc; Electrochem. Soc. Impurity diffusions in semiconductors; preparation and deposition of thin films of glasses and refractor materials; preparation of inorganic pigments; transparent pigments and surface treatment of pigments; passivation studies of semiconductor junctions; chemistry and physics of surfaces and interfaces of thin solid films. Address: IBM Corp, East Fishkill Route 52, Hopewell Junction, NY 12533.

FRIESINGER, GOTTLIEB CHRISTIAN, b. Zanesville, Ohio, July 4, 29; m. 52; c. 4. MEDICINE, PHYSIOLOGY. B.S, Muskingum Col, 51; M.D, Johns Hopkins Univ, 55. Intern, Osler Med. Serv, Johns Hopkins Hosp, 55-56, asst. resident med, 56-57, 59-60, chief resident, 62, fel, cardiovasc. div, Johns Hopkins Univ, 60-62, instr. med, sch. med, 63-64, asst. prof, 64-67, assoc. prof, 67-71; PROF. MED. & DIR. DIV. CARDIOL, VANDERBILT UNIV, 71- Clayton scholar, Johns Hopkins Univ, 63-71, dir. myocardial infarction unit, univ. hosp, 68-71; mem. coun. on circulation, Am. Heart Asn, 66. Dipl, Am. Bd. Internal Med, 65. Med.C, U.S.N.R, 57-59, Lt. Am. Fedn. Clin. Res; Am. Physiol. Soc. Applied cardiovascular physiology, especially ischemic heart disease including acute myocardial infarction. Address: Dept. of Medicine, Vanderbilt University, Nashville, TN 37203.

FRIESS, SEYMOUR L(OUIS), b. Detroit, Mich, July 1, 22; m. 53; c. 2. PHYSICAL & ORGANIC CHEMISTRY. A.B, California, Los Angeles, 43, M.A, 44, Ph.D.(chem), 47. Res. chemist, Manhattan Eng. Dist, Oak Ridge, 44-45; instr. chem, California, Los Angeles, 47-48; Rochester, 48-51; res. chemist, U.S. NAVAL MED. RES. INST, 51-59, head phys. biochem. div, 59-68, acting dir, physiol. sci. dept, 67-68, DIR, 68-70, ENVIRON. BIOSCI. DEPT, 70- Mem. comt. on toxicol, Nat. Res. Coun, 67- Am. Chem. Soc; Am. Soc. Toxicol. Mechanisms of organic peracid reactions; enzymatic topography; kinetics and catalysis; cholinesterase and conduction in nerve; mechanisms of toxic interactions in tissues; hyperbaric pharmacology; marine toxins. Address: U.S. Naval Medical Research Institute, National Naval Medical Center, Bethesda, MD 20014.

FRIGERIO, NORMAN A(LFRED), b. Rochester, N.Y, Sept. 4, 29; m. 51; c. 5. PHYSICAL CHEMISTRY. B.S, Mass. Inst. Technol, 53; Nat. Sci. Found. fel, Yale, 54-57, Ph.D.(biochem), 57. Chief engr. aviation electronics, Usher Aviation, Inc, 53-57; ASSOC. SCIENTIST BIOPHYS. & BIOCHEM, ARGONNE NAT. LAB, 56- Asst, Yale, 53-54; abstractor, Chem. Abstr, 58-64; prof, St. Procopius Col, 58-65; Am. Univ. Beirut, 70-71. U.S.A.F, 46-49. Am. Chem. Soc; Radiation Res. Soc; Inst. Elec. & Electronics Eng; Sci. Res. Soc. Am; fel. Am. Inst. Chem. Aeronavigation systems; mechanisms of bacteriostasis; scientific instrumentation; enzyme purification and mechanisms; effects of ionizing radiation on organisms; neutron physics; neutron capture tumor therapy; phthalocyanine chemistry. Address: Biology & Medicine Dept, Argonne National Lab, 202-B-225, Argonne, IL 60439.

FRIGYESI, TAMAS L, b. Budapest, Hungary, June 7, 27; U.S. citizen. NEUROPHYSIOLOGY, NEUROANATOMY. M.D, Univ. Budapest, 51. Nat. Inst. Neurol. Diseases & Blindness spec. fel, 62-65; asst. neurol, Columbia Univ, 65-67; asst. prof. anat, Albert Einstein Col. Med, 67-69; ASSOC. PROF. physiol, N.J. Col. Med. & Dent, 69-70; NEUROL, COLUMBIA UNIV, 70- Vis. prof, Col. Med. & Dent. N.J, Newark, 70- Semmelweis Award, Am-Hungarian Med. Asn, 70. Am. Physiol. Soc; Am. Asn. Anat; Am. Electroencephalog. Soc; Am. Acad. Neurol; Soc. Neurosci. Neurobiology of central integration of sensorimotor activities; synaptic organizations in basal ganglia-diencephalon functional linkages. Address: Dept. of Neurology, College of Physicians & Surgeons, Columbia University, 640 W. 168th St, New York, NY 10032.

FRIICHTENICHT, JOSEPH F, b. Matherville, Ill, Feb. 1, 31; m. 53, 70; c. 4. PHYSICS. B.S, Western Illinois, 53; M.S, Iowa, 56. MGR. METEORITICS DEPT, SYSTS. GROUP RES. STAFF, TRW SYSTS. GROUP, 59- Nuclear scientist, Naval Res. Lab, U.S.N, 56-59, Res, 59-, Lt. Low energy nuclear physics; scintillation spectrometry; ion optics; acceleration of particles by electric fields; hypervelocity impact phenomena. Address: Meteoritics Dept, Systems Group Research Staff, TRW Systems Group, Bldg. R-1, Room 1196, One Space Park, Redondo Beach, CA 90278.

FRIIHAUF, EDWARD JOE, b. Cleveland, Ohio, Apr. 29, 36; m. 58; c. 3. ORGANIC & INORGANIC CHEMISTRY. B.S, Kent State, 58; Firestone Tire & Rubber Co. fel, Illinois, 59-60, Nat. Sci. Found. fel, 60-61, Ph.D. (inorg. chem), 61. CHEMIST, J.T. Baker Chem. Co, 61-62; LUBRIZOL CORP, 62- Am. Chem. Soc; Am. Soc. Lubrication Eng. Lubricant additives; coordination chemistry. Address: Lubrizol Corp, Cleveland, OH 44117.

FRIIS, H(ARALD) T(RAP), b. Naestved, Denmark, Feb. 22, 93; nat; m. 27. ENGINEERING. E.E, Royal Tech. Col, Copenhagen, 16, D.Eng, 38. Radio lab. asst, Copenhagen, 16-17; tech. adv, Royal Gun Factory, 17-18; radio res. engr, West. Elec. Co, N.Y, 19-24; Bell Tel. Labs, 25-45, dir. radio res, 46-51, dir. res. in high frequency & electronics, 52-57, consult, 58-69; RETIRED. Valdemar Poulsen gold medal, 54; Stuart Ballantine medal, 58. With Joint Res. & Develop. Bd, 46-49. Fel. Inst. Elec. & Electronics

Eng.(Inst. Radio Eng, Liebmann Mem. prize, 39, Honor medal, 55, Kelly award, 64); Danish Acad. Tech. Scis. Radio recieving; static; amplifiers; generators, direction; microwaves. Address: 30 E. River Rd, Rumson, NJ 07760.

FRILETTE, VINCENT J(OSEPH), b. New York, N.Y, Sept. 21, 16; m. 38; c. 1. ORGANIC CHEMISTRY. B.S, City Col, 38; M.S, Polytech. Inst. Brooklyn, 44, Ph.D.(chem), 47. Sr. res. chemist, printing inks, Frederick H. Levey Co, 38-42; resins, fatty oils, Ridbo Labs, 42-47; mgr. abstracts div, Intersci. Publisher, Inc, 47-53; group leader ion exchange, Permutit Co, 53-56; RES. ASSOC. CATALYSIS, RES. DEPT, MOBIL OIL CORP, 56- Adj. prof, Polytech. Inst. Brooklyn, 47-51. AAAS; Am. Chem. Soc. Physical organic chemistry; catalysis; polymers; electrolytic processes; ion exchange. Address: Research Dept, Mobil Oil Corp, Princeton, NJ 08540.

FRIMPTER, GEORGE W, b. Haverstraw, N.Y, Mar. 17, 28; m. 51; c. 6. MEDICINE. B.A, Williams Col, 48; M.D, Cornell, 52. Res. fel. med, U.S. Pub. Health Serv, 58-59; sr. res. fel, N.Y. Heart Asn, 59-64; estab. investr, Am. Heart Asn, 64-69; asst. prof. med, med. col, Cornell Univ, 61-65, assoc. prof, 65-69; PROF. PHYSIOL. & MED, UNIV. TEX. MED. SCH. SAN ANTONIO, 69- U.S.A.F, 52-55, Res, 55-, Col. Am. Fedn. Clin. Res; Am. Soc. Clin. Invest; fel. Am. Col. Physicians; Aerospace Med. Asn. Internal medicine; metabolic aspects of kidney disease, especially errors of amino acid metabolism in various inherited conditions. Address: 7703 Floyd Curl Dr, San Antonio, TX 78229.

FRIMPTER, MICHAEL H(OWARD), b. New York, N.Y, Dec. 10, 34; m. 62; c. 3. GEOLOGY, HYDROLOGY. B.A, Williams Col, 57; M.A, Boston, 61, fels, 61-62, Ph.D.(geol), 67. Geologist. water resources div, U.S. Geol. Surv, 63-68, hydrologist, 68-69; asst. prof. geol, Wis. State Univ, 69-71; HYDROLOGIST, WATER RESOURCES DIV, U.S. GEOL. SURV, 71- U.S.A, 57-59, Sgt. Geol. Soc. Am; Am. Geophys. Union; Am. Inst. Prof. Geol. Geology of the Hudson Highlands; hydrogeology of aquifers with secondary porosity; geochemistry of surface and ground water; glacial geology and ground water resources, New York and Massachusetts. Address: Water Resources Division, U.S. Geological Survey, John F. Kennedy Federal Bldg, Boston, MA 02203.

FRINGS, CHRISTOPHER STANTON, b. Birmingham, Ala, Aug. 10, 40; m. 65; c. 2. ANALYTICAL CHEMISTRY, BIOCHEMISTRY. B.S, Alabama, 61; Ph.D.(chem), Purdue, 66. Chemist, Shell Chem. Co, La, 61-62; res. asst. biochem, Mayo Clin, 66-67; DIR. CLIN. CHEM, MED. LAB. ASSOCS, 67- Clin. asst. prof, Med. Col. Ala, 67- Am. Chem. Soc; Am. Asn. Clin. Chem; Am. Acad. Clin. Toxicol. Drug, lipid and lipoprotein analysis; spectrophotometry; standards; quality control and automated methods of analysis. Address: 1025 S. 18th St, Birmingham, AL 35205.

FRINGS, HUBERT (WILLIAM), b. Phila, Pa, Jan. 1, 14; m. 36; c. 1. COMPARATIVE PHYSIOLOGY. B.S, Pa. State, 36; M.S, Oklahoma, 37; Ph.D. (zool), Minnesota, 40. Asst. zool, Minnesota, 37-39; asst. prof. biol, Luther Col, 39-40; head dept. sci, Monett Jr. Col, Mo, 40-41; head dept. natural sci, Snead Jr. Col, Ala, 41-43; head dept. physics, W.Va. Wesleyan Col, 43-45, prof. biol, 45-46; head dept, Gustavus Adolphus Col, 46-47; assoc. prof. entom, Pa. State, 47-53, prof. zool, 53-61; Hawaii, 61-66; UNIV. OKLA, 66-71, DAVID ROSS BOYD PROF. ZOOL, 71- Physiologist, Army Chem. Ctr, Md, 45. Trustee, Mt. Desert Island Biol. Lab, 57- Chmn, Int. Comt. Biol. Acoustics. AAAS; Entom. Soc. Am; Am. Soc. Zool; Soc. Protozool; Am. Soc. Human Genetics; Ecol. Soc. Am; Acoust. Soc. Am; Am. Ornith. Union; Brit. Ecol. Soc; Marine Biol. Asn. U.K; Entom. Soc. S.Africa; Int. Union Study Soc. Insects. Chemical senses of insects; effects of sounds on animals; comparative physiology of taste. Address: Dept. of Zoology, University of Oklahoma, 730 Van Vleet Oval, Norman, OK 73069.

FRINGS, MABLE (RUTH), b. Shawville, Pa, Apr. 11, 12; m. 36; c. 1. COMPARATIVE PHYSIOLOGY. B.S, Pa. State, 35, Oklahoma, 36-37. Instr. bot, Snead Jr. Col, 42-43; Gustavus Adolphus Col, 46-47; RES. ASSOC, Pa. State, 49-61; Hawaii, 61-66; ZOOL, UNIV. OKLA, 66- Secy, Int. Cmt. Biol. Acoustics. AAAS; Entom. Soc. Am. Audiogenic seizures in rodents; production and reception of sound by insects; reactions of birds to sounds; sensory physiology of invertebrates. Address: Dept. of Zoology, University of Oklahoma, 730 Van Vleet Oval, Norman, OK 73069.

FRINK, ALINE, b. Torrington, Conn, Mar. 2, 04; m. 31; c. 4. MATHEMATICS. B.A, Mt. Holyoke Col, 24; M.A, Chicago, 27, Ph.D.(math), 30. Teacher physics & algebra, pub. sch, N.Y, 24-26; instr. MATH, Mt. Holyoke Col, 29-30; PA. STATE UNIV, 30-31, asst. prof, 40-50, assoc. prof, 50-62, prf, 62-69, EMER. PROF, 69- Calculus of variations; topology. Address: Box 225, Kennebunkport, ME 04046.

FRINK, CHARLES R(ICHARD), b. Keene, N.H, Sept. 26, 31; m. 53; c. 3. SOIL CHEMISTRY. B.S, Cornell Univ, 53, Ph.D.(soil chem), 60; M.S, Univ. Calif, Berkeley, 57. Asst. soil chemist, CONN. AGR. EXP. STA, 60-64, assoc. soil chemist, 65-67, soil chemist, 67-70, CHIEF, DEPT. SOIL & WATER, 70- U.S.N, 53-56, Lt.(jg). AAAS; Am. Chem. Soc; Soil Sci. Soc. Am; Clay Minerals Soc; N.Y. Acad. Sci. Aluminum chemistry and clay mineralogy in acid soils; cation-exchange; analytical methods; plant nutrition; nutrient cycles in soil, water and lake sediments. Address: Dept. of Soil & Water, Connecticut Agricultural Experiment Station, P.O. Box 1106, New Haven, CT 06504.

FRINK, DONALD W, b. Madison, Ohio, Apr. 25, 33; m. 55; c. 3. MECHANICAL ENGINEERING. B.M.E, Ohio State, 56, M.M.E, 57. Res. engr, BATTELLE MEM. INST, 56-60, proj. leader, 60-62, proj. dir, 62-63, GROUP DIR, 63- Nat. Soc. Prof. Eng; Am. Soc. Mech. Eng. Kinematics; mechanism; dynamics and statistics; mechanism synthesis and analysis. Address: 2309 Johnston Rd, Columbus, OH 43220.

FRIOU, GEORGE JACOB, b. Brooklyn, N.Y, Oct. 5, 19; div; c. 4. IMMUNOLOGY. B.S, Cornell, 40, M.D, 44. Intern internal med, New Haven Hosp, Yale, 44-45; asst. res, 45-46, res. fel, 48-49, chief res, 49-50, instr, sch. med, 49-50, clin. instr, 50-52, clin. asst. prof, 52-58, asst. prof. med, 58-60; assoc. prof. med. & microbiol, sch. med, Oklahoma, 60-64; assoc. prof. MED, SCH. MED, UNIV. SOUTH. CALIF, 64-68, PROF, 68-, CHIEF IMMUNOL. & RHEUMATIC DISEASE SECT, 64- Dipl, Am. Bd. Internal Med, 51. Med.C, 46-47, 52-53, Lt. Am. Soc. Clin. Invest; Am. Asn. Immunol; Am. Rheumatism Asn; fel. Am. Col. Physicians; Am. Fedn. Clin. Res; Heberden Soc; Brit. Soc. Immunol. Rheumatic diseases; immunology; infectious diseases. Address: Dept. of Medicine, Immunology & Rheumatic Disease Section, University of Southern California School of Medicine, 2025 Zonal Ave, Los Angeles, CA 90033.

FRISANCHO, ROBERTO, b. Cuzco, Peru, Feb. 4, 39; m. 64; c. 1. PHYSICAL ANTHROPOLOGY. B.H, Cuzco, 62; M.A, Pa. State, 66, Ph.D.(anthrop), 68. Res. asst. anthrop, Pa. State, 63-67, instr, 67-68; ASSOC. PROF. ANTHROP. & RES. ASSOC. CTR. HUMAN GROWTH & DEVELOP, UNIV. MICH, ANN ARBOR, 68- Fel. AAAS; Brit. Soc. Study Human Biol; Am. Asn. Phys. Anthrop. Human growth and development; physical and physiological developmental adaptation to environmental stress. Address: Center for Human Growth & Development, 611 Church St, Ann Arbor, MI 48104.

FRISBY, EMILY MARY, b. Eng, Sept. 13, 07; U.S. citizen. METEOROLOGY. B.A, Wales, 29, M.A, 52; Ph.D.(climat), Reading, 63. Dir. res. climat. & meteorol, Am. Inst. Aerological Res, Colo, 52-57; prof. weather eng, S.Dak. State Col, 57-60; head meteorol. dept. & dir. res, Raven Industs. S.Dak, 60-66; res. meteorologist, atmospheric sci. div, U.S. Army Electronics Labs, Ft. Monmouth, N.J, 66-69; RETIRED. Consult, North. States Power Co, Minn, 57-69. W.R.N.S, 41-45. Royal Meteorol. Soc; Inst. Brit. Geog. High stratosphere; hailstorms of mid and tropical latitudes. Address: 10 The Larches, London Rd, Headington, Oxford, England.

FRISBY, JAMES CURTIS, b. Bethany, Mo, Oct. 22, 30; m. 69. AGRICULTURAL ENGINEERING. B.S, Missouri, 52 & 56; M.S, Iowa State, 63, Ph.D. (agr. eng), 65. Classroom instr. math. sci, ed. & training dept, Caterpillar Tractor Co, Ill, 56-57, tech. writer, serv. dept, 57-58, mkt. analyst, engine div, 58-60; asst. mgr, farm serv. dept, Iowa State, 61-63, instr. AGR. ENG, 63-66; asst. prof, UNIV. MO-COLUMBIA, 66-69, ASSOC. PROF, 69- U.S.A, 52-54, 1st Lt. Am. Soc. Agr. Eng; Am. Soc. Eng. Educ. Application of operations research techniques to machine systems used for agricultural enterprises. Address: Dept. of Agricultural Engineering, 100 Agricultural Engineering Bldg, University of Missouri-Columbia, Columbia, MO 65201.

FRISCH, ARTHUR W(AIN), b. Chisholm, Minn, Mar. 3, 10; m. 41; c. 1. BACTERIOLOGY. A.B, Wisconsin, 31, A.M, 33, Ph.D, 35, M.D, 37. Mem. dept. bacter. & clin. path, col. med, Wayne State, 37-46; from assoc. prof. to PROF. BACT, SCH. MED, UNIV. ORE, 46-, chmn. dept. microbiol, 56. Attend. physician, U.S. Vet. Hosp. Dipl, Clin. Path, Am. Bd. Path, 46; Am. Bd. Med. Microbiol. Med.C, U.S.A, 42-46. Am. Soc. Microbiol; Am. Soc. Clin. Invest; Am. Soc. Clin. Path; Am. Asn. Immunol. Inhibition of bacteriophage by bacterial extracts and Salmonella; multiplication of bacteriophage; group A streptococci in normal throats; blood groups and their medicolegal applications; sputum in pneumonia; virus diseases; hepatitis; meningococcal meningitis; immunosuppression. Address: Dept. of Medical Microbiology, University of Oregon Medical School, 3181 S.W. Sam Jackson Park Rd, Portland, OR 97201.

FRISCH, DAVID H(ENRY), b. N.Y.C, Mar. 12, 18; m. 40; c. 2. PHYSICS. B.A, Princeton, 40; Ph.D.(physics), Mass. Inst. Technol, 47. Asst, Wisconsin, 40-43; jr. physicist, Manhattan proj, Los Alamos, N.Mex, 43-46, res. assoc, 46-48; asst. prof, PHYSICS, MASS. INST. TECHNOL, 48-52, assoc. prof, 52-58, PROF, 58- Fulbright & Guggenheim fel, 54; Sloan fel, 57-61; Nat. Sci. Found. fel, 60. Fel. Am. Phys. Soc; fel. Am. Acad. Arts & Sci. Elementary particle physics. Address: Room 24-036, Massachusetts Institute of Technology, Cambridge, MA 02139.

FRISCH, DAVID MARVIN, b. Chicago, Ill, Dec. 3, 21; m. 55; c. 2. BIOCHEMISTRY. B.S, California, Berkeley, 43; M.S, Southern California, 51, Ph.D.(biochem), 60. Jr. rubber technologist, Mare Island Naval Shipyard, 43-44; paint chemist, Amercoat Div. Am. Pipe & Construct. Co, 44-46; anal. chemist, U.S. Naval Ord. Test Sta, 51-53; instr. chem, Los Angeles Harbor Col, 53-59; asst. prof. BIOCHEM, CALIF. STATE COL, LOS ANGELES, 59-63, assoc. prof, 63-71, PROF, 71- AAAS; Am. Chem. Soc; Brit. Biochem. Soc. Nucleic acid metabolism in plants; synthesis and biological activity of nucleic acid inhibitors; clinical chemistry. Address: Dept. of Chemistry, California State College, Los Angeles, 5151 State College Dr, Los Angeles, CA 90032.

FRISCH, H(ARRY) L(LOYD), b. Vienna, Austria, Nov. 13, 28; nat; m. 50, div; c. 2. PHYSICAL CHEMISTRY. A.B, Williams Col.(Mass), 47; Ph.D.(phys. chem), Polytech. Inst. Brooklyn, 52. Res. assoc. phys. chem, Polytech. Inst. Brooklyn, 51-52; physics, Syracuse, 52-54; instr. chem, Southern California, 54-55, asst. prof, 55-56; mem. tech. staff, Bell Tel. Labs, 56-67; PROF. CHEM, STATE UNIV. N.Y. ALBANY, 67-, ASSOC. DEAN COL. ARTS & SCI, 69- Vis. assoc. prof, Yeshiva, 62-; vis. mem, Courant Inst. Math. Sci, N.Y. Univ, 64-65; assoc. ed, J. Chem. Phys, 64-66. Am. Chem. Soc; fel. Am. Phys. Soc. Statistical mechanics and kinetic theory; colloid and high polymer chemistry; solid state chemistry and physics. Address: Dept. of Chemistry, State University of New York at Albany, 1400 Washington Ave, Albany, NY 12203.

FRISCH, I(VAN) T, b. Budapest, Hungary, Sept. 21, 37; U.S. citizen; m. 62. ELECTRICAL ENGINEERING. B.S, Queens Col.(N.Y), 58; B.S, Columbia, 58, M.S, 59, Ph.D.(elec. eng), 62. Asst. prof. elec. eng, Univ. Calif, Berkeley, 62-65, 66-68, assoc. prof, 68-69; Ford Found. resident eng. practice, Bell Tel. Labs, 65-66; Guggenheim sr. scientist, NETWORK ANAL. CORP, 69-70, V.PRES, 70- Summers, electronics engr, Harrison Labs, Inc, 58 & Sperry Gyroscope Co, Inc, 59; consult, Collins Radio Co, Inc, 62-; off. emergency planning, Exec. Off. President, 68-; ed-in-chief, Networks. Inst. Elec. & Electronics Eng. Theory of active and passive circuits; communication nets and nonlinear systems. Address: Network Analysis Corp, Beechwood, Old Tappan Rd, Glen Cove, NY 11542.

FRISCH, JOSEPH, b. Vienna, Austria, Apr. 21, 21; nat; m. 51; c. 3. MECHANICAL ENGINEERING. B.S.M.E, Duke, 46; M.S, California, 50. Sr. eng. draftsman, static testing, Glenn L. Martin Co, 46; sr. engr, dept. pub.

works, Baltimore, 47; asst. prof. eng. design, UNIV. CALIF, BERKELEY, 47-57, assoc. prof. MECH. ENG, 59-63, PROF, 63-, CHMN. DEPT. MECH. DESIGN, 66-, asst. dir, inst. eng. res, 63-66. Am. Soc. Mech. Eng; Soc. Exp. Stress Anal. Machine design; materials behavior and processing. Address: Dept. of Mechanical Engineering, College of Engineering, University of California, Berkeley, CA 94720.

FRISCH, KURT CHARLES, b. Vienna, Austria, Jan. 15, 18; nat; m. 46; c. 3. CHEMISTRY. B.S, Realgymnasium, Austria, 35; M.A, Vienna, 38; Brussels, 38-39; M.A, Columbia, 41, Hopkinson fel, 41-44, Ph.D.(org. chem), 44. Anal. & res. chemist, Am. Dietaids Co, N.Y, 41; res. chemist, Gen. Elec. Co, 44-52; asst. mgr. res, E.F. Houghton & Co, 52-56; dir. polymer res. & develop, Wyandotte Chems. Corp, 56-68; PROF. POLYMER ENG. & CHEM. & DIR. POLYMER INST, UNIV. DETROIT, 68- Am. Chem. Soc; N.Y. Acad. Sci; fel. Am. Inst. Chem. Polymer research on polyurethanes; silicones; phenolics; vinyls; organic synthetic and application research on textile and paper chemicals; synthetic lubricants; antimalarials. Address: University of Detroit, 4001 McNichols Rd, Detroit, MI 48221.

FRISCH, M. ELIZABETH, O.S.B, b. Covington, Ky, Oct. 18, 01. MATHEMATICS. A.B, Marygrove Col, 23; M.S, Notre Dame, 27; Pittsburgh, 28; Ph.D.(math), Catholic Univ, 40. Teacher, high sch, Ky, 24-35, 40-43; instr. MATH, Villa Madonna Col, 43-66, PROF, 66-67; THOMAS MORE COL, 67- Am. Math. Soc. Power plant engineering; general biology and anatomy; electrical apparatus and machinery; determination of a set of independent relations characterizing a certain system consisting of a conic and quartic curve. Address: Dept. of Mathematics, Thomas More College, Box 85, Covington, KY 41017.

FRISCH, NORMAN W(ILLIAM), b. New York, N.Y, Dec. 8, 23; m. 49; c. 3. CHEMICAL ENGINEERING. B.Ch.E, City Col, 48; Res. Corp. fel, Yale, 50-51, Du Pont fel, 51-52, D.Eng.(chem. eng), 54; Princeton, 61-62. Res. chem. engr, res. labs, Rohm & Haas Co, 52-60, res. assoc, Princeton Chem. Res, Inc, 60-64, dir. catalyst res, 64-67; INDEPENDENT CHEM. CONSULT, 67-; DIR. RES, COTTRELL ENVIRON. SYSTS. DIV, RES-COTTRELL, INC, 70-, mgr. chem. process develop, 68-70. U.S.A, 43-45. AAAS; Am. Chem. Soc; Am. Inst. Chem. Eng. Air and water pollution control technology; particulate collection mechanisms; electrostatic precipitation; absorption; catalysis; heterogeneous reactions; surface chemistry; applied mathematics; adsorptions; kinetics; diffusion mechanisms; chemical reaction analysis; ion exchange. Address: 145 Ridgeview Circle, Princeton, NJ 08540.

FRISCHE, CARL A(LFRED), b. Freeport, Kans, Aug. 13, 06; m; c. 3. PHYSICS. A.B, Miami (Ohio), 28, hon. D.Sc, 55; M.S, Iowa, 31, Ph.D.(physics), 32; hon. D.Sc, Mitchel Col, 64. Asst. physics, Iowa, 28-32; fel, Columbia, 32-33; from. engr. to exec. v.pres. opers, Sperry Gyroscopy Co, Sperry Rand Corp, 33-58, pres, 58-68, v.pres, 68-71; RETIRED. Consult, & med. sci. adv. bd. to Chief of Staff, U.S. Air Force, 58-59. AAAS; fel. Inst. Elec. & Electronics Eng; assoc. fel. Am. Inst. Aeronaut. & Astronaut. Development of soundproofing and automatic flight control equipment. Address: 114 Wheatley Rd, Glen Head, NY 11545.

FRISCHER, HENRI, b. Brussels, Belgium, Jan. 15, 34; U.S. citizen; m. 61; c. 3. INTERNAL MEDICINE, GENETICS. M.D, Santo Domingo, 58; Ph.D. (genetics), Chicago, 65. Intern, Michael Reese Hosp, Chicago, Ill, 58-59, res. internal med, 59-61, chief res, 61-62; U.S. Pub. Health Serv. trainee genetics, Univ. Chicago, 62-64, instr. med, 64-65, asst. prof, 65-71; ASSOC. PROF. HEMAT, RUSH-PRESBY. MED. SCH, 71- U.S. Pub. Health Serv. spec. fel, 65-66. Med.C, U.S.A, 66-68, Capt. AAAS; Am. Soc. Human Genetics. Biochemical genetics; hereditary hemolytic anemias; glucose-6-phosphate dehydroglucose deficiency; disorders and regulation of pentose phosphate shunt; carbohydrate metabolism. Address: Section of Hematology, Rush Medical Center, 1753 W. Congress Pkwy, Chicago, IL 60612.

FRISCHKNECHT, FRANK C, b. Bicknell, Utah, Oct. 12, 28; m. 67; c. 2. GEOPHYSICS. B.S.E.E, Utah, 50, M.S, 53; M.S, Colorado, 67. Asst. engr, Telluride Power Co, 50-51; airways engr, Civil Aeronaut. Admin, 51; geologist, U.S. GEOL. SURV, 53-54, GEOPHYSICIST, 54- AAAS; Soc. Explor. Geophys; Am. Geophys. Union; Am. Inst. Min, Metall. & Petrol. Eng; Inst. Elec. & Electronics Eng; European Asn. Explor. Geophys. Development of electrical exploration methods, chiefly electromagnetic induction methods; development of instruments for airborne and ground electromagnetic and magnetic surveying. Address: U.S. Geological Survey, Room 1244, Bldg. 25, Federal Center, Denver, CO 80225.

FRISCHKNECHT, NEIL C, b. Manti, Utah, Nov. 12, 18; m. 45; c. 9. RANGE SCIENCE. B.S, Utah State Univ, 43, M.S, 49; Ph.D.(bot), Brigham Young Univ, 68. Range conservationist & in charge Benmore Exp. Range, INTERMT. FOREST & RANGE EXP. STA, U.S. FOREST SERV, 46-62, RANGE SCIENTIST & PROJ. LEADER RES, 62-, DIRS. REP, 67- Lectr, Wash. State Univ, 56; consult, Forest Range Environ. Study, 70. U.S.N.R, 43-46, Lt.(jg). Ecol. Soc. Am; Am. Soc. Range Mgt. Ecology, physiology and management of salt desert shrub, sage brush-grass and pinyon-juniper vegetation types in Utah, Nevada and southwestern Wyoming. Address: Intermountain Forest & Range Experiment Station, U.S. Forest Service, Federal Bldg, 88 W. First N, Provo, UT 84601.

FRISCO, L(OUIS) J(OSEPH), b. Patchogue, N.Y, Aug. 21, 23; m. 50; c. 2. ELECTRICAL ENGINEERING. B.E.S, Hopkins, 49, M.S, 53. Asst. res. contract dir, dielec. lab, Hopkins, 50-58, res. contract dir, 58-64; prog. mgr. dielec. mat, adv. tech. labs, Gen. Elec. Co, N.Y, 64-67; mgr. TECH. SERV. LABS, RAYCHEM CORP, Redwood City, 67-70, DIR, MENLO PARK, 70- Mem. conf. elec. insulation, Nat. Acad. Sci-Nat. Res. Coun; U.S. del, Int. Electrotech. Comn. U.S.A, 42-45. Inst. Elec. & Electronics Eng; Am. Soc. Test. & Mat. Electrical insulation and dielectric phenomena. Address: Technical Services Labs, Raychem Corp, 300 Constitution Dr, Menlo Park, CA 94025.

FRISELL, WILHELM RICHARD, b. Two Harbors, Minn, Apr. 27, 20; m. 48; c. 2. BIOCHEMISTRY. B.A, St. Olaf Col, 42; M.A, Hopkins, 43, Ph.D.(org. chem), 46. Jr. instr. chem, Hopkins, 42-46, res. assoc, 46-47, instr. chem, sch. med, 47-51; asst. prof. biochem, sch. med, Colorado, 51-58, assoc. prof, 58-64, prof, 64-69, assoc. dean grad. sch, 59-69; PROF. BIOCHEM. & CHMN. DEPT, COL. MED. & DENT. N.J, NEWARK, 69- Am-Scand. fel, Upsala, 49-50; mem. int. res. adv. comt, Nat. Insts. Health, 67-71, for. fels. panel, off. int. res. With Off. Sci. Res. & Develop, 44. Fel. AAAS; Am. Chem. Soc; N.Y. Acad. Sci; Harvey Soc; Am. Soc. Biol. Chem. Organic chemistry synthesis and biological analogies; enzyme chemistry; photochemical reactions; biochemical structure and function. Address: College of Medicine & Dentistry of New Jersey at Newark, 100 Bergen St, Newark, NJ 07103.

FRISHKOPF, L(AWRENCE) S(AMUEL), b. Phila, Pa, June 26, 30; m. 60; c. 3. BIOPHYSICS. A.B, Univ. Pa, 51; fel, Mass. Inst. Technol, 53-55, Ph.D. (physics), 56. Mem. res. staff commun. biophys, Mass. Inst. Technol, 55-57; Nat. Insts. Health fel. biophys, Rockefeller Inst, 57-58; mem. tech. staff res, Bell Tel. Labs, 59-68; PROF. ELEC. ENG, MASS. INST. TECHNOL, 68- AAAS; fel. Acoustical Soc. Am. Physiology and anatomy of acousticolateralis system; relation to perception and behavior; physiology and anatomy of sensory systems; animal communication. Address: Room 20B-225, Dept. of Electrical Engineering, Massachusetts Institute of Technology, Cambridge, MA 02139.

FRISHMAN, AUSTIN MICHAEL, b. Brooklyn, N.Y, May 28, 40; m. 62; c. 2. ENTOMOLOGY. B.S, Cornell, 62, M.S, 64; Ph.D.(entom), Purdue, 68. Res. asst. livestock entom, Cornell, 62-64; exten. asst. entom, Purdue, 64-67, instr. pest control & entom, 67-68; asst. prof. ENTOM, BOT. & BIOL, STATE UNIV. N.Y. AGR. & TECH. COL. FARMINGDALE, 68-70, ASSOC. PROF, 70- Res. asst, Purdue Univ, summer 64; Nat. Sci. Found. res. grant & consult, Huntington Comput. Proj, Brooklyn Polytech. Inst, 68-69; training dir, Copesan Serv. Inc, 69-71; Nat. Sci. Found. res. grant comput, 70-71; N.Y. State grant, summer 70; adj. assoc. prof, Post Col, L.I. Univ, summer 71. Entom. Soc. Am. Structural and industrial control of pests; extermination; pest control; livestock and medical entomology; extension entomology. Address: Dept. of Biology, State University of New York Agriculture & Technical College at Farmingdale, Farmingdale, NY 11735.

FRISHMAN, DANIEL, b. Brooklyn, N.Y, Oct. 19, 19; m. 42; c. 4. CHEMISTRY. B.A, Brooklyn Col, 40; M.S, Catholic Univ, 47; Ph.D, Georgetown, 50. Anal. chemist, Navy Yard, Wash, D.C, 40-42; asst, Catholic Univ, 42-43; res. assoc, textile found, Nat. Bur. Standards, 43-44; tech. adv, Fercleve Corp, Tenn, 44-45; res. assoc, Harris Res. Labs, 45-49, proj. leader, 51-55; dir. res, A. Hollander & Son, N.J, 49-51; dir. res. & develop, Malden Mills, Mass, 55-62; pres. & dir. res. Fibresearch Corp, 62-65; TECH. ADV, REID-MEREDITH INC, LAWRENCE, 65- Civilian with U.S.A; U.S.N, 44. AAAS; Am. Chem. Soc; Am. Asn. Textile Chem. & Colorists; Fiber Soc; N.Y. Acad. Sci. Lead-acid storage batteries; thermal diffusion of uranium isotopes; chemistry and physics of textile fibers, animal fibers, fur and leather; coated and pile fabrics; synthetic furs. Address: 14 Castle Heights Rd, Andover, MA 01810.

FRISHMAN, FRED, b. N.Y.C, Aug. 4, 23; m. 48; c. 4. MATHEMATICAL STATISTICS. B.B.A, City Col. New York, 47; A.B, George Wash. Univ, 56, M.A, 57, Ph.D, 71. Enumerator, U.S. Bur. Census, N.Y, 48; statistician, Bd. Educ, N.Y, 48-49; eng. statistician, Naval Inspector Ord, 49-51, Bur. Ord, Dept. Navy, 51-54, head appl. math. & statist. group, U.S. Naval Propellant Plant, 54-60; CHIEF MATH. BR, OFF. CHIEF RES. & DEVELOP, HQ, DEPT. ARMY, 60- Assoc. statist, col. gen. studies, George Wash. Univ, 55-59, lectr, 60-64, asst. prof. lectr, 66- U.S.A, 42-46. Inst. Math. Statist; Math. Asn. Am; Am. Statist. Asn; Int. Asn. Statist. in Phys. Sci. Statistical design of experiments; development of sampling techniques; applications of statistics in the physical sciences. Address: Mathematics Branch, Office of Chief of Research & Development, Headquarters, Dept. of the Army, Washington, DC 20310.

FRISINGER, H. HOWARD, II, b. Ann Arbor, Mich, Feb. 28, 33; m. 54; c. 4. MATHEMATICS, METEOROLOGY. B.S. & B.B.A, Univ. Mich, Ann Arbor, 56, M.S, 61, D.Educ.(math), 64; Mass. Inst. Technol, 56-57. ASSOC. PROF. MATH, COLO. STATE UNIV, 64-, faculty improv. comt. grant, 64-65. U.S.A.F, 56-60, Capt. Am. Math. Soc; Am. Meteorol. Soc; Math. Asn. Am. History of science, especially the contributions of mathematics and mathematicians to the development of the science of meteorology. Address: Dept. of Mathematics, Colorado State University, Ft. Collins, CO 80521.

FRISKEN, WILLIAM R(OSS), b. Hamilton, Ont, Can, May 29, 33; m. 56; c. 3. NUCLEAR PHYSICS. B.Sc, Queen's (Ont), 56, Nat. Res. Coun. Can. Bursary & M.Sc, 57; R.S. McLaughlin traveling fel, Birmingham, 57-58, Exhib. of 1851 overseas scholar, 58-60, Ph.D.(physics), 60. Teaching fel. physics, McGill, 60-62, asst. prof, 62-64; assoc. physicist, exp. planning div, accelerator dept, Brookhaven Nat. Lab, N.Y, 64-66; ASSOC. PROF. PHYSICS, CASE WEST. RESERVE UNIV, 66- Adj. asst. prof, McGill Univ, 64-66. AAAS; Am. Phys. Soc; Int. Asn. Great Lakes Res. High energy particle physics, particularly scattering experiments to probe nucleonic structure; design of experimental facilities for new accelerators; physics of the earth and the atmosphere including long-term environmental implications. Address: Dept. of Physics, Case Western Reserve University, University Circle, Cleveland, OH 44106.

FRISONE, GINO J(OSEPH), b. Poughkeepsie, N.Y, June 18, 27; m. 48; c. 4. ORGANIC & ANALYTICAL CHEMISTRY. B.S, Clarkson Tech, 51; M.S, Lehigh, 52; Ph.D, Univ. Pa, 65. Res. anal. chemist, Atlas Powder Co, 53-55; Rohm & Haas Co, 55-65, group leader struct. anal, 65-68; SUPVR. INSTRUMENTAL ANAL. DIV, M.W. KELLOGG CO, 68- U.S.N, 45-46. Am. Chem. Soc; N.Y. Acad. Sci. Analytical methods; instrumental development; physical-chemical investigations, especially polymer systems. Address: Research & Engineering Development Division, M.W. Kellogg Co, Piscataway, NJ 08854.

FRISQUE, A(LVIN) J(OSEPH), b. Wis, Jan. 27, 23; m. 50; c. 2. ANALYTICAL & PHYSICAL CHEMISTRY. B.S, Wisconsin, 48, Pure Oil Co. fel, 53-54, Ph.D, 54; M.S, Iowa, 51. Chemist, labs, Colgate-Palmolive-Peet Co, N.J, 48-50; sr. chemist, Am. Oil Co, 54-61; group leader, NALCO CHEM. CO, 61-69, dir. anal. facilities, 69, V.PRES, INDUST. CHEM. DIV, 69-

U.S.A.A.F, 43-46, 1st Lt; Air Medal; Croix de Guerre. Am. Chem. Soc. Electroanalytical chemistry; spectroscopy; chromatography. Address: Industrial Chemicals Division, Nalco Chemical Co, 6216 W. 66th Pl, Chicago, IL 60638.

FRISSEL, HARRY FREDERICK, b. Alphen aan de Rhine, Netherlands, Mar. 29, 20; U.S. citizen; m. 43; c. 3. NUCLEAR PHYSICS. B.A, Hope Col, 42; M.S, Iowa State, 43, Ph.D.(physics), 54. Res. physicist, Cornell Aeronaut. Lab, 43-48; PROF. PHYSICS, HOPE COL, 48-, CHMN. DEPT, 63- Mem, Denver Conf. Undergrad. Physics, 61- Am. Asn. Physics Teachers; Am. Sci. Affiliation. Beta-ray spectroscopy; internal conversion in L subshells. Address: Dept. of Physics, Hope College, Holland, MI 49423.

FRISSELL, SIDNEY STEWART, JR, b. Keene, N.H, Sept. 13, 38; m. 59; c. 3. FORESTRY. B.S, Minnesota, 60, M.S, 63. Forester, U.S. Forest Serv, Dept. Agr, 60-61; res. asst. FORESTRY, Minnesota, 61-65, instr, 65-67; ASST. PROF, UNIV. MONT, 67- Soc. Park & Recreation Educators. Problems of preserving and managing wildlands for outdoor recreation. Address: School of Forestry, University of Montana, Missoula, MT 59801.

FRISSELL, WARREN JOSEPH, b. Dubuque, Iowa, June 25, 23; m. 44; c. 2. CHEMICAL & PLASTICS ENGINEERING. B.S, Iowa State, 48. Anal. chemist, Tenn. Eastman Corp, 44-46; chem. engr, plastics div, Union Carbide Corp, 48-56, group leader raw mat, 56-59, tech. serv, chem. div, 59-62; plasticizer res, Rohm & Haas Res. Labs, 62-66; res. prod. specialist, DOW CHEM. CO, 66-68, sect. head tech. serv. & develop, 68-69, RES. MGR. STYRENE MOLDING POLYMERS RES. & DEVELOP, 69- U.S.A, 43-46. Soc. Plastics Eng. Raw materials for use in plastics; applications research in fields of synthetic latex coatings, plasticizers for vinyl polymers; acrylic resins for vinyl topcoatings; vinyl resins; styrene based polymers. Address: 672 Bldg, Dow Chemical Co, Midland, MI 48640.

FRIST, RAMSEY HUDSON, b. Meadville, Pa, Aug. 16, 36; m. 62; c. 3. BIOPHYSICS. B.S, Allegheny Col, 59; M.S, Pittsburgh, 62, Ph.D.(biophys), 65. U.S. Pub. Health Serv. fel, Virus res. unit, Agr. Res. Coun, Eng, 65-67; fel, biophys. lab, Univ. Wis, Madison, 67-69; ASST. PROF. BIOL, W.VA, UNIV, 69- Biophys. Soc. Structure of viruses; primary structure of nucleic acids; physical chemistry of proteins. Address: Rt. 7, Box 160, Morgantown, WV 26505.

FRISTOE, HAROLD T(RYON), b. Windsor, Mo, June 4, 09; m. ELECTRICAL ENGINEERING. B.S, Mich. State Norm. Col, 33; B.E.E, Arkansas, 41, E.E, 47; M.S, Okla. State, 47; Ph.D.(elec. eng), Agr. & Mech. Col. Texas, 53. Head radio sch, John Brown Univ, 33-39; curriculum coordinator elec. eng. & radio mech. sch, U.S. Navy, OKLA. STATE UNIV, 42-45, PROF. ELEC. ENG, 41- Acting assoc. prof, Agr. & Mech. Col, Texas, 52-53. Am. Soc. Eng. Ed; Audio Eng. Soc; Inst. Elec. & Electronics Eng; Nat. Soc. Prof. Eng. Electron tubes and circuits; study of surges in hydraulic systems using electrical analogies; transistor circuits; electronic instrumentation. Address: Dept. of Electrical Engineering, Oklahoma State University, Stillwater, OK 74075.

FRISTROM, JAMES W, b. Chicago, Ill, July 7, 36; m. 66. GENETICS. B.A, Reed Col, 59; Ph.D.(genetics), Rockefeller, 64. Nat. Sci. Found. fel, biol. div, Calif. Inst. Technol, 64-65; asst. prof. GENETICS, UNIV. CALIF, BERKELEY, 65-69, ASSOC. PROF, 69- Vis. lectr, Univ. Sydney, 69. Developmental genetics; chemical analysis of morphological mutants and biochemistry of imaginal discs in Drosophila Melanogaster. Address: Dept. of Genetics, University of California, Berkeley, CA 94720.

FRISTROM, R(OBERT) M(AURICE), b. Portland, Oregon, May 26, 22; m. 57; c. 1. CHEMISTRY, PHYSICS. A.B, Reed Col, 43; A.M, Oregon, 45; Ph.D. (chem), Stanford, 48. Res. fel. chem, Harvard, 48-51; PRIN. MEM. STAFF CHEM. & PHYSICS, APPL. PHYSICS LAB, JOHNS HOPKINS UNIV, 51- Parson's fel. chem. eng, Johns Hopkins Univ, 59-60, lectr, 60-61; ed, Fire Res. Abstracts & Rev, 65; mem. comt. fire res, Nat. Acad. Sci, 70; prin. investr. fire probs, Nat. Sci. Found. grant, 70. Hillebrand Prize, Chem. Soc. Wash, 66. U.S.N.R, 44-46. Am. Chem. Soc; Am. Phys. Soc; Combustion Inst.(Silver Combustion Medal, 66). Microwave spectroscopy; combustion; molecular beams; chemical kinetics; fire research. Address: Applied Physics Lab, Johns Hopkins University, 8621 Georgia Ave, Silver Spring, MD 20910.

FRITCHLE, FRANK P(AUL), b. Chicago, Ill, Aug. 27, 22; m. 49; c. 6. PHYSICS. B.S, De Paul, 49, M.S, 50; M.B.A, Santa Clara, 65. Physicist instrument design, Cent. Sci. Co, 50-53, asst. to dir. res, 54; group leader prod. & equip. design, Helipot Div, BECKMAN INSTRUMENTS, INC, 55-58, chief equip. design engr, 58-59, mgr. prod. develop, SPINCO DIV, 59-60, MGR. ENG, 60- Sig.C, U.S.A, 43-46, 1st Lt. AAAS; Am. Phys. Soc; Inst. Elec. & Electronics Eng. Design and development of scientific instruments; electronics; precision mechanics; optics; servo systems; precision component design including potentiometers. Address: Spinco Division, Beckman Instruments, Inc, 1117 California Ave, Palo Alto, CA 94304.

FRITCHMAN, HARRY K(IER), II, b. Portland, Oregon, Sept. 11, 23; m. 55; c. 3. ZOOLOGY. B.A, California, 48, M.A, 51, Ph.D, 53. Acting instr. biol, California, 53; ZOOL, Washington (Seattle), 54; instr, BOISE STATE COL, 54-67, PROF. & CHMN. DEPT. BIOL, 67- Summers, vis. asst. prof, Calif. Inst. Tech, 55-56, Washington (Seattle), 58-59, vis. instr, California, Berkeley, 60-61; consult, Am. Inst. Biol. Sci. Film Series, 60; lectr, Nat. Sci. Found. Marine Inst, Ore, 62-64. U.S.A.A.F, 43-45, Lt. Natural history of marine invertebrates; metamorphosis and development of stylasterine hydrocorals. Address: Dept. of Biology, Boise State College, Boise, ID 83707.

FRITSCH, ALBERT JOSEPH, S.J, b. Maysville, Ky, Sept. 30, 33. ORGANIC CHEMISTRY. B.S, Xavier Univ.(Ohio), 55, M.S, 56; West Baden Col, 59-61; Ph.D.(chem), Fordham Univ, 64; S.T.L. Loyola Univ. Chicago, 68. Res. assoc. chem, Loyola Univ. Chicago, 67-68; res. fel, Univ. Tex, Austin, 69-70; tech. consult, Ctr. Study Responsive Law, 70-71; DIR, CTR. SCI. IN PUB. INTEREST, 71- Consult, Ctr. Study Responsive Law, 70-; adv, Appalachian Res. & Defense Fund Environ. Ctr, 71- AAAS; Am. Chem. Soc. Nitrogen and boron-nitrogen heterocyclic chemistry; environmental effects of fuel additives; synthesis of anti-bacterial agents; dimethyl sulfoxide as a reacting medium; heavy metals as chemical pollutants. Address: Center for Science in the Public Interest, Room 812, 1346 Connecticut Ave, N.W, Washington, DC 20036.

FRITSCH, ARNOLD R(UDOLPH), b. Passaic, N.J, Mar. 28, 32; m. 53; c. 4. NUCLEAR CHEMISTRY. B.S, Rochester, 53; Ph.D.(chem), California, 57. Atomic Energy Cmn. asst. nuclear chem, California, 53-56; sr. engr. nuclear physics, Westinghouse Elec. Corp, 56-59; br. chief, div. int. affairs, U.S. Atomic Energy Comn, 59-61, spec. asst. to chmn, 61-68; mgr. tech. eval. dept, Gulf Gen. Atomic Inc, Calif, 68-71; PRES, GULF UNITED NUCLEAR FUELS, INC, 71- Am. Phys. Soc; Am. Chem. Soc; Am. Nuclear Soc. Nuclear fuel; reactor technology. Address: Gulf United Nuclear Fuels, Inc, Grasslands Rd, Elmsford, NY 10523.

FRITSCH, CARL W(ALTER), b. N.Y.C, July 21, 28; m. 54; c. 2. BIOCHEMISTRY. A.B, Blackburn Col, 52; Ph.D.(agr. biochem), Ohio State, 55. Sect. leader, dept. food processing, CENT. RES. LABS, GEN. MILLS, INC, 55-67, RES. ASSOC, CEREAL DEVELOP. DEPT, 67- Am. Chem. Soc; Am. Oil Chemists' Soc. Nutrition; food product development; flavor preference testing; autoxidation and antioxidants; food engineering. Address: Cereal Development Dept, Central Research Labs, General Mills, Inc, 9000 Plymouth Ave, Minneapolis, MN 55427.

FRITSCH, CHARLES A(NTHONY), b. Maysville, Ky, Mar. 9, 36; m. 63; c. 1. MECHANICAL ENGINEERING. B.M.E, Dayton, 58; Trane Co. fel. & M.S, Purdue, 60, Ph.D.(mech. eng), 62. Summer engr. design, res. inst, Univ. Dayton, 58; mem. tech. staff, BELL TEL. LABS, INC, 61-65, SUPVR. FLUID MECH. & HEAT TRANSFER GROUP, 65- Am. Soc. Mech. Eng. Thermodynamics and heat transfer; applied mechanics. Address: Bell Telephone Labs, Inc, Murray Hill, NJ 07974.

FRITSCHE, RICHARD T, b. Dallas, Tex, Jan. 29, 36; m. 59; c. 2. MATHEMATICS. B.S, St. Louis, 57, M.S, 59; Texas Christian, 61-62; Ph.D.(math) Arizona, 67. Instr. MATH, Arizona, 60-61; Dallas, 61-66, asst. prof, 66-68; ASSOC. PROF, NORTHEAST LA. UNIV, 68- Dir. summer sessions, Dallas, 64-68. Am. Math. Soc; Math. Asn. Am. Topological structures for probabilistic metric spaces. Address: Dept. of Mathematics, Northeast Louisiana University, Monroe, LA 71201.

FRITSCHEN, LEO J, b. Salina, Kans, Sept. 14, 30; m. 53; c. 6. METEOROLOGY. B.S, Kans. State Col, 52; New Mexico, 52-53; M.S, Kansas State, 58; Ph.D.(agr. climat), Iowa State, 60. Res. meteorologist, U.S. Water Conserv. Lab, U.S. Dept. Agr, 60-66; ASSOC. PROF. FOREST METEOROL, COL. FORESTRY, UNIV. WASH, 66- U.S.A.F, 52-56, Capt. Am. Meteorol. Soc; Am. Soc. Agron; Am. Soil Sci. Soc. Agricultural climatology; micrometeorological research and instrumentation. Address: College of Forestry, University of Washington, Seattle, WA 98105.

FRITSCHY, J(OHN) MELVIN, b. Tucson, Ariz, Aug. 23, 21; m. 50; c. 2. METALLURGICAL ENGINEERING. B.S, Arizona, 44. Asst. test engr, Phelps Dodge Corp, 44-45, test engr, 45-46; jr. chem. engr. flotation res, POTASH CO. AM, 46-51, chem. engr, 51-56, plant res. & develop, 56-69, PROCESS ENGR, 69- Am. Inst. Mining, Metall. & Petrol. Eng. Mineral beneficiation, especially of potash ores by flotation process. Address: Plant Dept, Potash Co. of America, P.O. Box 31, Carlsbad, NM 88220.

FRITTON, DANIEL DALE, b. Cheyenne Wells, Colo, Oct. 1, 42; m. 65; c. 4. SOIL PHYSICS. B.S, Colorado State, 64; M.S, Iowa State, 66, Ph.D.(soil physics, agr. climat), 68. Res. assoc. SOIL PHYSICS, Iowa State, 66-68; ASST. PROF, Cornell Univ, 68-71; PA. STATE UNIV, 71- Soil Sci. Soc. Am. Heat, water, and ion movement in soil; measurement and modification of soil physical properties; land disposal of waste effluents. Address: Dept. of Agronomy, Pennsylvania State University, University Park, PA 16802.

FRITTS, C(RAWFORD) E(LLSWORTH), b. Hudson, N.Y, Mar. 2, 27; m. 53; c. 3. GEOLOGY. B.S, Union (N.Y), 48; B.S, Michigan Tech, 50, M.S, 52; fel, Michigan, 54-55, Ph.D, 62. Asst. geologist, iron mining div, Inland Steel Co, Mich, 50-51; Geologist, U.S. Geol. Surv, 56-67; supvry. geologist, heavy metals prog, U.S. Bur. Mines, Denver, 67-68; mining geologist, div. mines & minerals, ALASKA STATE DEPT. NATURAL RESOURCES, 68-71, ACTING CHIEF GEOLOGIST, DIV. GEOL. SURV, 71- Summer asst. geologist, Newf. Geol. Surv, 52-54. U.S.N, 44-46. Geol. Soc. Am. Structural geology; stratigraphy; petrography; metamorphism. Address: 2731 Talkeetna Ave, Fairbanks, AK 99701.

FRITTS, HAROLD C(LARK), b. Rochester, N.Y, Dec. 17, 28; m. 55; c. 2. PLANT ECOLOGY, DENDROCHRONOLOGY. A.B, Oberlin Col, 51; M.Sc, Ohio State, 53, fel, 54-56, Ph.D.(bot), 56. Asst. prof. bot, Eastern Illinois, 56-60; DENDROCHRONOL, UNIV. ARIZ, 60-64, assoc. prof, 64-69, PROF, LAB. TREE RING RES, 69- Mem. Nat. Sci. Found. prog, Inst. Marine Biol, Univ. Ore, summer 57; John Simon Guggenheim fel, 68-69. AAAS; Ecol. Soc. Am; Tree Ring Soc; Am. Meteorol. Soc; Am. Asn. Quaternary Environ. Tree growth and forest tree physiology; paleoclimatology; microenvironment; soils. Address: Lab. of Tree Ring Research, University of Arizona, Tucson, AZ 85721.

FRITTS, HARRY W(ASHINGTON), JR, b. Rockwood, Tenn, Oct. 4, 21; m. 49; c. 3. MEDICINE. B.S, Mass. Inst. Tech, 43; M.D, Boston, 51. Mem. res. staff, Mass. Inst. Tech, 46-47; instr. elec. eng, Northeastern, 47-51; assoc. MED, COL. PHYSICIANS & SURGEONS, COLUMBIA UNIV, 56-57, asst. prof, 57-60, assoc. prof, 60-67, PROF, 67- Guggenheim fel, 59. Assoc. vis. physician, Bellevue Hosp, 58-; attend. physician, Manhattan Veterans Admin. Hosp, 58-; Presby. Hosp, 68- U.S.N.R, 43-46. Am. Soc. Clin. Invest; Harvey Soc; Am. Physiol. Soc. Diseases of the heart and lungs. Address: Cardio-Respiratory Lab, Presbyterian Hospital, 630 W. 168th St, New York, NY 10032.

FRITTS, ROBERT W(ASHBURN), b. Rochester, N.Y, Oct. 26, 24; m. 47; c. 3. PHYSICS. A.B, Oberlin Col, 47; M.S, Northwestern, 48, Milwaukee Gas

Specialty Co. fel, 49-50, Ph.D.(physics), 50. Asst. dir. res, Milwaukee Gas Specialty Co, Wis, 50-57; supvr. thermoelec. mat. group, Minn. Mining & Mfg. Co, 57-59, mgr. thermoelec. proj, 59-66, sr. res. specialist, energy conversion, 66-68; TECH. DEVELOP. MGR, NAT. ADVERTISING CO, 68- U.S.N, 43-46, Res, 46-, Ens. Am. Phys. Soc. Semiconductor research on intermetallic compounds; thermoelectric effects and transport phenomena; thermoelectric generator devices and thermoelectric power supply systems; traffic control devices and systems; visual display systems. Address: National Advertising Co, 3M Center, Bldg. 794, St. Paul, MN 55101.

FRITZ, ANDREA, b. Zurich, Switz, Apr. 7, 39; m. 66; c. 3. POLYMER CHEMISTRY. B.S, Swiss Fed. Inst. Technol, 61, M.S, 64, assistantship, 64-67, Ph.D.(polymer chem), 67. RES. CHEMIST, PLASTICS DEPT, E.I. DU PONT DE NEMOURS & CO, INC, 67- Swiss Army Res, Lt. Thermodynamics and kinetics of polymerizations; synthesis of monomers and polymerizations, condensations; polymer physics and polymer characterizations. Address: Plastics Dept, E.I. du Pont de Nemours & Co, Inc, Wilmington, DE 19898.

FRITZ, CAROL S, b. Gaffney, S.C, Nov. 9, 40; m. 61; c. 3. MATHEMATICS. B.S, South Carolina, 61, Nat. Defense Educ. Act fel, 61-64, Ph.D.(math), 65. ASST. PROF. MATH, Calif. State Col. Hayward, 66-68; MUNDELEIN COL, 68- Am. Math. Soc. Investigations of initial and final structures in categories. Address: Dept. of Mathematics, Mundelein College, 6363 Sheridan Rd, Chicago, IL 60626.

FRITZ, CHARLES G(ERHARD), b. Shanghai, China, Oct. 3, 30; m. 57. ORGANIC CHEMISTRY. B.S, Gonzaga Univ, 52; Ph.D.(org. chem), Univ. Wash, 56. Fel, Univ. Minn, 56-57; res. chemist, polychem. dept, E.I. du Pont de Nemours & Co, Inc, 57-63, sr. res. chemist, plastics dept, 63-69; MGR. POLYMER RES. DEPT, ETHICON, INC, 69- Organic chemistry of polymers and monomers. Address: Polymer Research Dept, Ethicon, Inc, Somerville, NJ 08876.

FRITZ, FRED ARTHUR, b. Wyoming, Pa, May 19, 24; m. 47. PHYSICAL CHEMISTRY. B.S, Scranton, 50; M.S, Bucknell, 52; Res. Corp. fel, Delaware, 58-59, Ph.D.(chem), 63. Mass spectroscopist, RES. CENTER, HERCULES POWDER CO, WILMINGTON, 52-54, infrared spectroscopist, 54-55, polymer chemist, 55-58, res. chemist, 60-70, SR. RES. CHEMIST, 70- U.S.A, 43-46. Am. Chem. Soc. Chemical kinetics; chemical and chemical engineering instrumentation. Address: Box 185J, R.D. 2, Alexis Ct, Canterbury Hills, Hockessin, DE 19707.

FRITZ, GAROLD FREDERIC, b. Toledo, Ohio, Apr. 21, 43; m. 64; c. 2. SOLID STATE PHYSICS. B.S, Univ. Toledo, 66; NASA fel, Mich. State Univ, 66-69, M.S, 68, Ph.D.(physics), 70. RES. PHYSICIST, RES. LABS, EASTMAN KODAK CO, 70- Am. Phys. Soc. Coupling between pressure and temperature waves in liquid helium; photoconductivity and electrophotographic systems. Address: 47 Sierra Dr, Rochester, NY 14616.

FRITZ, GEORGE J(OHN), b. N.Y.C, Feb. 27, 19; m. 57. PLANT PHYSIOLOGY. B.S, Montana State, 39; M.S, California, 51; Purdue Res. Found. fel, Purdue, 52-54, Ph.D.(bot), 54. Fel. plant physiol, Duke, 54-55; asst. prof. BOT, Pa. State, 55-60; ASSOC. PROF, UNIV. FLA, 60- Atomic Energy Comn. res. grant, 57, 61-68; Sigma Xi-Sci. Res. Soc. Am. grant, 58; Nat. Sci. Found. grant, 62. U.S.N.R, 43-46, Lt. AAAS; Am. Soc. Plant Physiol; Scandinavian Soc. Plant Physiol. Oxygen fixation by plants. Address: Dept. of Botany, University of Florida, Gainesville, FL 32601.

FRITZ, GEORGE RICHARD, JR, b. Detroit, Mich, Mar. 28, 32; m. 60; c. 2. PHYSIOLOGY, ENDOCRINOLOGY. B.S, Mich. State, 54, M.S, 58; Ph.D. (dairy sci), Illinois, 63. Nat. Insts. Health fel. PHYSIOL, SCH. MED, UNIV. PITTSBURGH, 62-65, instr, 65-66, res. assoc, 66-67, RES. ASST. UNIV. PROF. & ASST. DIR. PRIMATE RES. LAB, 67- U.S.A, 54-56. Am. Soc. Animal Sci; Brit. Soc. Study Fertil; Am. Asn. Lab. Animal Sci; Soc. Study Reproduction. Physiology of reproduction, especially regulation of gonadal function and control of parturition. Address: Primate Research Lab, University of Pittsburgh, 709 New Texas Rd, Pittsburgh, PA 15239.

FRITZ, HENRY EDWARD, b. Enderlin, N.Dak, Mar. 21, 22; m. 46; c. 4. ORGANIC CHEMISTRY. B.S. & M.S, Illinois, 47; Ph.D.(org. chem), Minnesota, 53. Chemist, W.S. Merrell Co, 47-49; res. chemist, Union Carbide Chem. Co, 53-60, group leader, olefins div, UNION CARBIDE CORP, 60-66, mgr. admin. for silicones div. res, develop. & tech. serv, 66-68, ASST. DIR. CHEM. & PLASTICS RES. & DEVELOP, 68- U.S.A, 43-46. Paraffin, olefin and other hydrocarbon research. Address: Tarrytown Research & Development Lab, Union Carbide Corp, Tarrytown, NY 10591.

FRITZ, H(ERBERT) IRA, b. N.Y.C, May 31, 35; m. 62; c. 2. NUTRITION, PHYSIOLOGY. A.B, California, Davis, 58, Ph.D.(nutrit), 64. Res. asst. nutrit, California, Davis, 58-64; Nat. Insts. Health fel, Pennsylvania, 64-66; asst. prof. BIOL, WRIGHT STATE UNIV, 66-69, ASSOC. PROF, 69- AAAS; Am. Soc. Cell Biol; Soc. Study Reproduction. Embryo nutrition, avian, reptilian and mammalian; nutrition in tissue and organ cultures; reproduction and biochemical taxonomy of American marsupials; comparative and experimental teratology. Address: Dept. of Biology, Wright State University, Colonel Glenn Hwy, Dayton, OH 45431.

FRITZ, I(RVING) B(ANDAS), b. Rocky Mount, N.C, Feb. 11, 27; m. 50; c. 3. PHYSIOLOGY, BIOCHEMISTRY. D.D.S, Med. Col. Va, 48; Zoller fel, Chicago, 49-51, Ph.D.(physiol), 51. U.S. Pub. Health Serv. fel, Inst. Med. Physiol, Copenhagen, 53-55; asst. dir. dept. metab. & endocrine res, med. res. inst, Michael Reese Hosp, 55-56; asst. prof. PHYSIOL, Univ. Mich, Ann Arbor, 56-60, assoc. prof, 60-64, prof, 64-68; PROF. & CHMN. BANTING & BEST DEPT. MED. RES, BEST INST, UNIV. TORONTO, 68- Dent.C, 51-53, 1st Lt. Am. Physiol. Soc; Endocrine Soc; Brit. Biochem. Soc; Am. Soc. Cell Biol; Can. Biochem. Soc. Control of fat metabolism; carnitine; hormonal control of spermatogenesis. Address: Banting & Best Dept. of Medical Research, Best Institute, University of Toronto, 112 College St, Toronto 101, Ont, Can.

FRITZ, JAMES C(LARENCE), b. Berlin, Pa, May 15, 10; m. 33; c. 2. NUTRITION. B.S, Pa. State Col, 29; New Hampshire, 29-30; Maryland, 30-33. Asst, New Hampshire, 29-30; jr. biologist, bur. animal indust, U.S. Dept. Agr, Beltsville, Md, 30-37, asst. biochemist, 37; lab. dir, Borden Co, 37-51; dir. nutrit. res. Dawe's Labs, Inc, 52-65; SUPVRY. RES. CHEMIST, FOOD & DRUG ADMIN, DEPT. HEALTH, EDUC. & WELFARE, 65- AAAS; Am. Chem. Soc; Poultry Sci. Asn; Am. Dairy Sci. Asn; Am. Soc. Animal Sci; Soc. Exp. Biol. & Med; Am. Inst. Nutrit; Am. Inst. Chem; Am. Asn. Cereal Chem; Animal Nutrit. Res. Coun.(chmn, 62, secy-treas, 64-). Nitrogen metabolism; physiology of digestion; nutritional requirements; protein quality; vitamin stability; pigmentation of poultry and eggs; nutrient availability; influence of stress on nutritional requirements. Address: 12314 Madeley Lane, Bowie, MD 20715.

FRITZ, J(AMES) J(OHN), b. Sunbury, Pa, Sept. 21, 20; m. 43; c. 4. PHYSICAL CHEMISTRY. B.S, Pa. State, 39; M.S, Chicago, 40; Ph.D.(chem), California, 48. Asst. chem, California, 43-48; res. assoc. phys. chem, Ohio State, 48-49; asst. prof. CHEM, PA. STATE UNIV, 49-53, assoc. prof, 53-62, PROF, 62- Guggenheim fel, Oxford, 61-62. With Off. Sci. Res. & Develop, 43-45. Am. Chem. Soc. Low temperature phenomena; solutions of electrolytes. Address: Dept. of Chemistry, 218 Pond Lab, Pennsylvania State University, University Park, PA 16802.

FRITZ, JAMES S(HERWOOD), b. Decatur, Ill, July 20, 24; m. 49; c. 4. ANALYTICAL CHEMISTRY. B.S, James Millikin, 46; M.S, Illinois, 46, Ph.D. (chem), 48. Asst. prof. CHEM, Wayne State, 48-51; IOWA STATE UNIV, 51-55, assoc. prof, 55-60, PROF, 60- Am. Chem. Soc. Titrations in nonaqueous solvents; analytical methods involving chelate formation; ion exchange separations. Address: Dept. of Chemistry, Iowa State University, Ames, IA 50010.

FRITZ, JOSEPH N, b. Klein, Mont, Dec. 27, 31; m. 57; c. 2. SOLID STATE PHYSICS. B.S, Mont. State Col, 53; Eastman Kodak fel, Cornell, 59-60, Ph.D.(physics), 61. STAFF MEM, LOS ALAMOS SCI. LAB, 61- Instr, Cornell, summer 60. Am. Phys. Soc. Theoretical solid state physics; solid state physics at high and very high pressures. Address: Los Alamos Scientific Lab, P.O. Box 1663, Gmx-6, Los Alamos, NM 87544.

FRITZ, KATHERINE E(LIZABETH), b. Omaha, Nebr, June 24, 18; m. 40; c. 2. PATHOLOGY, IMMUNOLOGY. B.A, Univ. Omaha, 39; M.S, Albany Med. Col, 61, Ph.D.(path), 66. Res. assoc. PATH, ALBANY MED. COL, 61-63, instr, 66-69, ASST. PROF, 69- Res. biologist, Vet. Admin. Hosp, Albany, N.Y, 66-; fel. coun. on arteriosclerosis, Am. Heart Asn, 71. Am. Soc. Cell Biol; Electron Micros. Soc. Am; Am. Soc. Exp. Path. Development of arteriosclerosis as influenced by certain serum factors, and by the synergism of minimal arterial injury and elevated serum cholesterol levels. Address: 1360 Valencia Rd, Schenectady, NY 12309.

FRITZ, K(ENNETH) E(ARL), b. Monroeville, Ohio, Oct. 17, 18; m. 40; c. 2. METALLURGY. B.S, Ohio State, 42; M.S, Wisconsin, 51. METALL. ENGR, Naval Res. Lab, 42-45; Bucyrus-Erie Co, 45-55; locomotive & car equip. dept, GEN. ELEC. CO, 55-56, mat. & process lab, 56-69, GAS TURBINE DEPT, 69- U.S.N, 44-45. Am. Soc. Metals. Ultra high strength materials; statistical evaluation of data; precipitation hardening process; high temperature properties of materials. Address: Gas Turbine Dept, Bldg. 53-337, General Electric Co, One River Rd, Schenectady, NY 12305.

FRITZ, MADELEINE A(LBERTA), b. Saint John, N.B. PALEONTOLOGY. B.A, McGill, 19; Ph.D.(stratig. paleont), Univ. Toronto, 26. Asst. PALEONT, UNIV. TORONTO, 24-35, lectr, 35-37, asst. prof, 37-45, assoc. prof, 45-51, prof, 51-65, SPEC. LECTR. & EMER. PROF, 65- Mus. asst, Royal Ont. Mus, 27-36, acting dir, 36-37, asst. dir. invert. paleont, 37-43, assoc. dir, 45-55, curator, 55-57, res. assoc, dept. invert. palaeont, 70- Paleont. Soc; Geol. Soc. Am; Geol. Asn. Can; fel. Royal Soc. Can. Invertebrate paleontology. Address: Royal Ontario Museum, 100 Queens Park, Toronto 181, Ont, Can.

FRITZ, MICHAEL E, b. Boston, Mass, Feb. 26, 38; m. 60; c. 3. PERIODONTOLOGY, CELL PHYSIOLOGY. D.D.S, Univ. Pa, 63, cert. peridont. & M.S, 65, Ph.D.(physiol), 67. Fel. physiol, sch. med. & instr. periodont, sch. dent, Univ. Pa, 63-67; ASSOC. PROF. PERIODONT. & CHMN. DEPT, SCH. DENT, EMORY UNIV. 67- Nat. Inst. Dent. Res. grant, 68-71; consult, U.S. Vet. Admin. Hosp, Atlanta, 67-; health ctr, Univ. Ala, 68-; Ft. Benning, Ga, 70- AAAS; Int. Asn. Dent. Res; Am. Dent. Asn; Am. Acad. Periodont; Fedn. Am. Socs. Exp. Biol. Physiology of salivary glands; bone pathology; virus infection of cells; clinical dentistry. Address: Dept. of Periodontology, Emory University School of Dentistry, Atlanta, GA 30322.

FRITZ, NORMAN L(ISLE), b. Hartford, Mich, Apr. 30, 18; m. 42; c. 4. PHYSICS. B.S, Cent. Mich. State Teachers Col, 40; M.S, Mich. State Col, 42. Mem. staff, Mich. State Col, 40-41, asst. physics, 41-42; res. physicist, Eastman Kodak Co, N.Y, 42-44; tech. supvr, Clinton Eng. Works & Tenn. Eastman Corp, Tenn, 44-45; RES. ASSOC, EASTMAN KODAK CO, 45- Am. Phys. Soc; Am. Soc. Photogram.(Autometric Award, 68); Soc. Photog. Sci. & Eng. Characteristics of aerial photographs; materials and methods for aerial photography. Address: Research Labs, Eastman Kodak Co, 343 State St, Rochester, NY 14650.

FRITZ, PAUL J(OHN), b. Belleville, Ill, May 17, 29; m. 56; c. 4. BIOCHEMISTRY. A.B, Washington (St. Louis), 51; Ph.D.(biochem), Auburn, 62. Instr. chem, Auburn, 60-62; U.S. Pub. Health Serv. fel. biochem, biol. div, Oak Ridge Nat. Lab, 62-64; asst. prof. pharmacol, Auburn Univ, 64-65, assoc. prof, 65-66; asst. prof. biochem. & sr. investr, molecular biol. lab, med. ctr, Univ. Ala, Birmingham, 66-69; ASSOC. PROF. PHARMACOL, MILTON S. HERSHEY MED. CTR, PA. STATE UNIV, 69- U.S.N, 51-56, Lt. AAAS; Am. Chem. Soc; Am. Soc. Biol. Chem. Enzymatic control of metabolism; mechanisms of enzyme action; physical and chemical properties of enzymes; factors controlling synthesis and degradation of enzymes. Address: Dept. of Pharmacology, Milton S. Hershey Medical Center, Pennsylvania State University, Hershey, PA 17033.

FRITZ, PETER, b. Stuttgart, Ger, Mar. 18, 37; m. 66; c. 2. GEOLOGY, GEOCHEMISTRY. Diplom, Univ. Stuttgart, 62, Dr. rer. nat, 65; Euratom scholar, Univ. Pisa, 62, Nat. Res. Coun. Italy scholar, 64. NATO res. fel,

Univ. Paris, 65-66; fel, Univ. Alta, 66-68, res. assoc. isotope geol, 68-71; ASSOC. PROF. GEOCHEM, UNIV. WATERLOO, 71- Geochem. Soc; Geol. Asn. Can. Geochemistry of stable isotopes in groundwater, carbonates and hydrothermal ore deposits. Address: Dept. of Earth Sciences, University of Waterloo, Waterloo, Ont, Can.

FRITZ, ROBERT J(ACOB), b. New Orleans, La, June 5, 23; m. 47; c. 4. MECHANICAL & NUCLEAR ENGINEERING. B.E.E, Tulane Univ. La, 44; M.S, Union Univ.(N.Y), 50, M.E.E, 52; Princeton, 44; Mass. Inst. Technol, 44; D.Eng.(mech. eng), Rensselaer Polytech. Inst, 70. With test prog, GEN. ELEC. CO, 46-47, heat transfer engr, KNOLLS ATOMIC POWER LAB, 47-52, mech. analyst, 52-53, supvr. mech. anal, 53-55, sr. specialist, 55, supvr. eng. evaluation, 55-57, consult. eng. heat transfer & mech, 57-61, supvr. & mgr, reactor core heat transfer sect, 61-63, CONSULT. ENGR, rotating equip. & mech, 63-66, STRUCT. MECH. & DYNAMICS, 66- U.S.N.R, 44-46. Am. Soc. Mech. Eng. Electrical engineering; development of practical nuclear power systems, especially nuclear power reactors. Address: 2511 Whamer Lane, Schenectady, NY 12309.

FRITZ, RODGER LEE, b. Altoona, Pa, Nov. 27, 35; m. 60; c. 2. ELECTRICAL ENGINEERING. B.S, Pa. State, 57, M.S, 61, Ph.D.(elec. eng), 64. Instr. elec. eng, Pa. State, 57-64, asst. prof, 64-65; staff engr, IBM CORP, 65-68, DEVELOP. ENGR-MGR, ECM SYSTS. ENG, 68- Inst. Elec. & Electronics Eng. Simulation of hybrid analog computers; minimization of switching functions; library automation; digital computer performance evaluation; digital computer operating systems. Address: Dept. L11, IBM Corp, Owego, NY 13827.

FRITZ, ROY F(REDOLIN), b. Oakland, Calif, Nov. 15, 15; m. 39; c. 2. ENTOMOLOGY, EPIDEMIOLOGY. B.S, Kans. State Col, 37, M.S, 39; M.P.H, California, 48. Asst. entomologist, agr. exp. sta, Kans. State Col, 39-42; malaria control in war areas, U.S. Pub. Health Serv, 42-43, dist. entomologist, 43-44, asst. chief entom. div, 44-46; typhus control entomologist, 46-47, res, California, 47-49, rep. communicable disease ctr, Region X, 50, chief mosquito control & invest. eng. br, 51-52, vector-borne disease unit, epidemiol. br, 52-55, acting chief, surveillance sect, Ga, 54-55; malariologist adv, Int. Coop. Admin, Mex. Govt, 55-57; malariologist & chief, Malaria Eradication Br, U.S. Agency Int. Develop, 58-63; SCIENTIST, prog. & planning, malaria eradication div, WHO, 63-66, ANOPHELINE RES, VECTOR BIOL. & CONTROL, 66-, MEM. EXPERT PANEL MALARIA, 60-, report expert comt. malaria, 62. U.S.P.H.S, 42-70. Sci. Res. Soc. Am; Am. Soc. Prof. Biol.(pres, 48); Entom. Soc. Am; Am. Mosquito Control Asn; fel. Am. Pub. Health Asn; fel. Royal Soc. Trop. Med. & Hyg. Medical entomology; epidemiology of vector-borne diseases; ecology; biological control; environmental entomology. Address: World Health Organization, 50 Ave Appia, 1211 Geneva, Switz.

FRITZ, SAMUEL H(ENRY), b. Bison, Kans, Aug. 18, 11; m. 41; c. 5. SURGERY. B.A, Walla Walla Col, 40; M.D, Loma Linda, 48. Res. surg, White Mem. Hosp, 53; instr. SURG, SCH. MED, LOMA LINDA UNIV, 54-57, asst. clin. prof, 57-59, asst. prof, 59-61, ASSOC. PROF, 61-; ASSOC. CLIN. PROF, CALIF. COL. MED, 70- Secy, tumor bd, White Mem. Hosp, 55-, dir, cent. tumor registry, 55-, secy, med. staff, 57-, v.chmn, 58-59, chmn, 59-60; sr. attend. surg. Dipl, Nat. Bd. Med. Exam; mem. Am. Bd. Surg. Med.C, U.S.A, 53-55. AAAS; Am. Med. Asn; fel. Am. Col. Surg. Clinical and experimental research in chemotherapy and malignancy. Address: Dept. of Surgery, White Memorial Medical Center, 1720 Brooklyn Ave, Los Angeles, CA 90033.

FRITZ, SIGMUND, b. Brooklyn, N.Y, June 9, 14; m. 46; c. 2. METEOROLOGY. B.S, Brooklyn Col, 34; U.S. Weather Bur. scholar, Mass. Inst. Tech, 40-41, 51-52, M.S, 41, Sc.D, 53. Observer, U.S. Weather Bur, 37-42, METEOROLOGIST, Wash, D.C, 46-67; NAT. ENVIRON. SATELLITE SERV, NAT. OCEANIC & ATMOSPHERIC ADMIN, 67- Vis. prof, Univ. Md. U.S.N, 42-46. Fel. Am. Meterol. Soc; fel. Am. Geophys. Union. Solar radiation; albedo of ground; albedo and absorption; atmospheric ozone measurements; meteorological satellites. Address: National Environmental Satellite Service, National Oceanic & Atmospheric Administration, F.O.B. 4, Suitland, MD 20233.

FRITZ, THOMAS E(DWARD), b. Detroit, Mich, May 24, 33; m. 66. PATHOLOGY, INFECTIOUS DISEASES. B.S, Mich. State, 55, D.V.M, 57; M.S, Illinois, 60. Instr. path, col. vet. med, Illinois, 57-62; supvr, diag. res. lab, State Dept. Agr. & Univ. Ill, 62-63; ASSOC. PATHOLOGIST, DIV. BIOL. & MED. RES. ARGONNE NAT. LAB, 63- AAAS; Am. Vet. Med. Asn; Sci. Res. Soc. Am; Am. Asn. Lab. Animal Sci; Radiation Res. Soc. Comparative pathology of diseases of domestic and laboratory animals; pathology of radiation and isotope toxicity. Address: Division of Biological & Medical Research, Bldg. D-202, Argonne National Lab, 9700 S. Cass Ave, Argonne, IL 60439.

FRITZ, W(ILLIAM) BARKLEY, b. Baltimore, Md, Oct. 29, 24; m. 50; c. 5. MATHEMATICS. Ph.B, Loyola Col.(Md), 43; fel, Georgetown, 43-44; M.A, Hopkins, 48. Instr. math, Loyola Col.(Md), 46-47; comput. programmer, Ballistics Res. Labs, Md, 48-50, from numerical analyst to acting chief anal. & comput. br, 51-55; sr. engr, comput. math, air arm div, WESTINGHOUSE ELEC. CORP, 55-57, fel. engr, eng. appln. digital comput, 57-59, adv. engr. & tech. dir. comput. anal. group, 59-61, MGR. info. processing dept, 61-64, info. systs. & prog. dept, 64-67, tech. planning, 67-68, systs. & opers, 68-70, DATA BASE SERV, WESTINGHOUSE TELE-COMPUT. SYSTS. CORP, 70- Mem. subcomt. meteorol. probs, Nat. Adv. Comt. Aeronaut. 55; subcomt. X3L8 data elements, Am. Nat. Standards Inst, X3K5 info. processing vocabulary, v.chmn, 59-70; instr, Johns Hopkins Univ, 62-67; cert, Data Processing Mgt. Asn, 64; comput. scientist & consult. U.S.N.R, 44-46, Lt.(jg). Asn. Comput. Mach; Am. Nat. Standards Inst. Numerical analysis; programming and application of automatic digital computers; systems design and evaluation; computer languages and simulation; flow chart symbols; computer terminology; information systems; management of automatic data processing facilities; information storage; retrieval technology; electronic data processing standards; documentation. Address: 421 Radcliffe Dr, Pittsburgh, PA 15235.

FRITZ, WILLIAM H(AROLD), b. Cathlamet, Wash, Aug. 24, 28; m. 58; c. 1. PALEONTOLOGY. B.S, Washington (Seattle), 52, M.S, 58, Ph.D.(geol), 60. Nat. Sci. Found. fel, 60-61; explor. geologist, Shell Oil Co, 61-64; CAMBRIAN PALEONTOLOGIST, GEOL. SURV. CAN, 64-, asst. party chief, summer 55. Res. scientist, Nat. Sci. Found, fall 61- U.S.A.F, 53-55, 1st Lt. Geol. Soc. Am; Am. Paleont. Soc; Brit. Palaeont. Asn. Structure and stratigraphy; Cambrian paleontology. Address: Geological Survey of Canada, 601 Booth St, Ottawa, Ont, K1A 0E8, Can.

FRITZE, CURTIS W(ILLIAM), b. LeSueur, Minn, June 2, 23; m. 48; c. 3. ELECTRONICS. B.S.E.E, Univ. Minn, 47. Res. & design engr, Minn. Electronics Corp, 47-50; sr. engr, Eng. Res. Assoc, Inc, 50-54; eng. dept. mgr, Remington Rand Univac, 54-57, dir. spec. prod. eng, 57-59; v.pres. & gen. mgr, Monarch Electronics Co, 59-60; systs specialist, corp. staff mkt, CONTROL DATA CORP, 60-62, asst. to v.pres. indust. group, 62-65, dir. planning, indust. & govt. group, 65-66, dir. CORP. PLANNING, 66-68, V.PRES, 68- Consult, Lab. Psychol. Hyg, 47-57; mem. bd. trustees, Sci. Mus. Minn; bd. dirs, Am. Nat. Standards Inst. U.S.A, 42-45. Technological and corporate planning systems. Address: Corporate Planning, Control Data Corp, 8100 34th Ave. S, Minneapolis, MN 55440.

FRITZE, KLAUS, b. Dresden, Ger, Apr. 22, 26; m. 53; c. 1. ANALYTICAL CHEMISTRY. Dipl, Johannes Gutenberg Univ. Mainz, 52, Dr. rer. nat, 55. Asst, Johannes Gutenberg Univ, Mainz, 54-55; fel, McMASTER UNIV, 55-58, res. chemist, McMaster reactor, 58-67, assoc. prof. CHEM, 67-71, PROF, 71- Neutron activation analysis, especially applied to trace elements in biological and geological matrices; comparison with other methods in trace element analysis, particularly flame emission and atomic absorption. Address: Dept. of Chemistry, McMaster University, Hamilton, Ont, Can.

FRITZLEN, THOMAS L(EO), b. Indianapolis, Ind, Oct. 21, 05; m. 48; c. 4. METALLURGY. B.S.Ch.E, Purdue Univ, 27. Chief plant metallurgist, Aluminum Co. Am, Pa, 27-41; extrusion metallurgist, Ky. & dir. metall. eng. div, Reynolds Metals Co, Va, 41-65; ASST. DIR. & CONSULT, INDUST. RES. CTR, UNIV. MO-ROLLA, 66- Independent consult, Tex. Aluminum Co, 68-; rep, Am. Schiess Corp, 70- Am. Soc. Metals; Am. Inst. Mining, Metall. & Petrol. Eng; Brit. Inst. Metals; Nat. Soc. Prof. Eng. Aluminum and aluminum alloys, especially processes and products; patents and articles on aluminum alloys; metallurgical engineering and physical metallurgy of aluminum and its alloys. Address: 11 McFarland Dr, Rolla, MO 65401.

FRITZSCHE, H(ELLMUT), b. Berlin, Ger, Feb. 20, 27; U.S. citizen; m. 52; c. 4. PHYSICS. Dipl, Göttingen, 52; Ph.D.(physics), Purdue, 54. Asst. prof. PHYSICS, Purdue, 55-57; UNIV. CHICAGO, 57-61, assoc. prof, 61-63, PROF, JAMES FRANCK INST, 63- Fel. Am. Phys. Soc. Electronic properties of semiconductors and metals at low temperatures. Address: James Franck Institute, University of Chicago, 5640 Ellis Ave, Chicago, IL 60637.

FRITZSCHE, H(ERBERT) W(ILLIAM), b. Westville, Fla, Mar. 2, 20; m. 43; c. 6. PHYSICAL CHEMISTRY. B.S, Elmhurst Col, 42; M.S, Chicago, 48. Food technologist, Qm. Food & Container Inst, 49-51, veg. prods, plant prod. br, 51-55, fruit & veg. sect, 55-56, appln. eng. br, food div, 56-57, food technologist & head br, 57-58, acting sr. technologist, 58, sr. technologist, 58-59, chief fruit & veg. prod. br, 59-63; PRES, SPACE AGE FOODS LAB, FRITZSCHE ENTERPRISES, 63- Secy. Army Res. & Study fel, 60. U.S.N.R, 42-46; U.S.A.R, 46-49, Lt. Am. Chem. Soc; Inst. Food Technol. Food preservation; freeze-drying. Address: 4601 Downers Dr, Downers Grove, IL 60515.

FRITZSCHE, OSCAR HAROLD, b. Hamilton, Ohio, Jan. 15, 14; m; c. 3. SPECTROCHEMISTRY. Ph.B, Univ. Cincinnati, 34. From sampler to spectrochemist, ARMCO STEEL CORP, 34-68, SR, SPECTROCHEMIST, SPECTROCHEM. LABS, RES. CTR, 68- Wet chemistry including sample preparation, ferrous and nonferrous metals and nonmetals and method development; spectrography including qualitative and quantitative analysis, method development in x-ray emission analysis of such things as furnace bricks, slags and fluxes; x-ray diffraction analysis; electron microprobe analysis. Address: Spectrochemical Labs, Research Center, Armco Steel Corp, 703 Curtis St, Middletown, OH 45042.

FRIZ, CARL T, b. Elmhurst, Ill, July 9, 27; m. 63. ANATOMY, BIOCHEMISTRY. B.S, Illinois, 51, M.S, 52; Ph.D.(anat), Minnesota, 59. U.S. Pub. Health Serv. fel. biol, Carlsberg Lab, Copenhagen, 59-62; instr. ANAT, Univ. Minn, 62-64; asst. prof, UNIV. B.C, 64-71, ASSOC. PROF, 71- U.S.N.R, 45-59, Lt. Biophys. Soc; Soc. Protozool; Am. Asn. Anat. Physical and chemical studies of DNA and biochemical analysis of the large, free-living amoebae. Address: Dept. of Anatomy, University of British Columbia, Vancouver 8, B.C, Can.

FRIZZELL, DON(ALD) L(ESLIE), b. Bellingham, Wash, Oct. 19, 06; m. 38. PALEONTOLOGY. B.S, Washington (Seattle), 30, M.S, 31; Jacobs fel, Stanford, 31-32, scholar, 33-34, Jordan fel, 34, Ph.D.(paleont), 36. Paleontologist, Shell Oil Corp, 36-37; geologist, Int. Petrol. Co, S.Am. 37-44; consult. paleontologist, Wash, 44-45; assoc. prof. GEOL, Texas, 45-48; UNIV. MO-ROLLA, 48-52, PROF, 52- Fel. Geol. Soc. Am; Paleont. Soc; Soc. Econ. Paleont. & Mineral; Soc. Study Evolution; Soc. Syst. Zool; Am. Asn. Petrol. Geol; cor. mem. Peruvian Geol. Soc. Fish otoliths; classification of teleostean fishes; foraminifera; fossil holothurians; general micropaleontology. Address: Dept. of Geology, University of Missouri at Rolla, Rolla, MO 65401.

FRIZZELL, LAURENCE DAVID, b. South Portland, Maine, Nov. 18, 03; m. 46; c. 5. ANALYTICAL CHEMISTRY. B.S, Bowdoin Col, 25; M.A, Harvard, 31, Ph.D.(anal. chem), 33. Asst. chem, A.D. Little, Inc, 25; teacher, high sch, Mass, 25-26; asst. chem, Radcliffe Col, 28-32; Harvard, 33-35; res. chemist, Norton Co, Mass, 36-37; asst. CHEM, Harvard, 38-39; instr. Northwestern, 40-45, asst. prof, 45-49; prof. & chmn. dept, MERRIMACK COL, 49-66, EMER. PROF, 66- AAAS; Am. Chem. Soc. Determination of atomic weights; aqueous pressures of crystal hydrates; behavior of precipitates; surface tension of solutions of electrolytes; exchange adsorbers. Address: West Boxford, MA 01885.

FRLAN, LAURA BRILLIANTINE, b. Trenton, N.J, Nov. 16, 19; m. 48. BAC-TERIOLOGY. A.B, West Virginia, 40, M.S, 41; Ph.D, Southern California, 49. Chief microbiologist, Childrens Hosp, Los Angeles, 48-51; res. investr, George Russell Carr Found, 52; asst. prof. BACT, IMMACULATE HEART COL, 53-57, assoc. prof, 57-62, PROF, 62- Res. grant, U.S. Pub. Health Serv, 59-68; res. fel, Calif. Inst. Technol, 62, sabbatical assoc. prof, 68-69. AAAS; Am. Soc. Microbiol; N.Y. Acad. Sci. Immunology; bacteriology; biology. Address: Dept. of Bacteriology, Immaculate Heart College, 2021 N. Western Ave, Los Angeles, CA 90027.

FROBISH, LOWELL T, b. Flanagan, Ill, Aug. 3, 40; m. 60; c. 1. ANIMAL NUTRITION, BIOCHEMISTRY. B.S, Illinois, Urbana, 62; M.S, Iowa State, 64, Ph.D.(animal nutrit), 67. Assoc, Iowa State, 66-67; RES. ANIMAL HUS-BANDMAN, SWINE RES. BR, ANIMAL SCI. RES. DIV, U.S. DEPT. AGR, 67- Am. Soc. Animal Sci. Utilization of energy by gravid animals and the neo-natal pig. Address: Swine Research Branch, Animal Science Research Division, U.S. Dept. of Agriculture, Beltsville, MD 20705.

FRODYMA, MICHAEL M(ITCHELL), b. Holyoke, Mass, March 3, 20; m. 51; c. 1. ANALYTICAL CHEMISTRY. B.S, Massachusetts, 42; A.M, Colum-bia, 47; M.S, Hawaii, 49; fel, George Washington, 49-52, Ph.D.(chem), 52. Asst. chem, Univ. Hawaii, 47-49, asst. prof, 52-58, assoc. prof, 58-67, prof, 67; DIR. ACAD. YEAR STUDY PROG, NAT. SCI. FOUND, 65-66, 67- Exchange asst. prof, Vassar Col, 57-58, lectr 58; faculty fel, Nat. Sci. Found, 58-61. U.S.A, 42-46, Res, 46-53, 1st Lt. AAAS; Am. Inst. Chem; Am. Chem. Soc; The Chem. Soc. Microchemistry; oceanographic chemis-try; organic polarography; analytical aspects of spectral reflectance. Ad-dress: Academic Year Study Program, National Science Foundation, Wash-ington, DC 20550.

FROEB, HERMAN F, b. Forest Hills, N.Y, Aug. 9, 24; m. 52; c. 3. PHYS-IOLOGY, MEDICINE. Princeton, 42-44; M.D, Duke, 47. Intern, Bellevue Hosp, Columbia Div, New York, N.Y, 47-48; med. resident, Columbia Res. Div, Goldwater Hosp, Welfare Island, 48-50; med. center, Colorado, 50-51; chest disease resident, Columbia Chest Serv, Bellevue Hosp, 53-54; Govt. of France fel, Nancy, 55; Nat. Tuberc. Asn. fel, Cardiovasc. Lab, Southern California & Hosp. Good Samaritan, 55-56; res. fel. physiol, sch. pub. health, Harvard, 63-64; res. assoc. med, UNIV. CALIF, SAN DIEGO, 66-68, assoc. res. pulmonary physiologist, sch. med, 67-68, ASSOC. CLIN. PROF. MED, 68- Mem. sr. staff, Scripps Mem. Hosp. & vis. mem, Scripps Clin. & Res. Found. Med.C, 51-52, Capt. Am. Physiol. Soc; Am. Col. Phy-sicians; Am. Col. Chest Physicians; Am. Fedn. Clin. Res; Am. Thoracic Soc. Pulmonary physiology; chest medicine. Address: 9844 Genesee, La Jolla, CA 92037.

FROEBE, LARRY R(YAN), b. Dayton, Ohio, May 4, 43. INORGANIC & CO-ORDINATION CHEMISTRY. A.B, Wittenberg Univ, 65; M.S, Univ. N.Dak, 67; Nat. Defense Educ. Act fel. & Ph.D.(chem), Univ. Pittsburgh, 70. Nat. Res. Coun. res. assoc, Bur. Mines, U.S. Dept. Interior, 70-71; RES. ANA-LYST CHEM, TECHNOL, INC, 71- AAAS; Am. Chem. Soc. Absolute con-figurations of metal chelates using nuclear magnetic resonance and circular dichroism spectroscopy; asymmetric catalytic interactions. Address: Aerospace Research Labs.(LJ), Bldg. 450, Wright-Patterson Air Force Base, OH 45433.

FROEDE, HARRY CURT, b. Cortez, Colo, Sept. 9, 34; m. 64; c. 3. PHAR-MACOLOGY, BIOCHEMISTRY. B.S, Colorado, 58, M.S, 61; Ph.D.(pharma-col), Washington (St. Louis), 65. Fel. pharmacol, Wash. Univ, 55-66; sch. med, Stanford Univ, 66-69; ASST. PROF. PHARMACOL. & TOXICOL, SCH. PHARM, UNIV. COLO, BOULDER, 70-, RES. ASSOC. CHEM, UNIV, 68- Enzyme mechanisms and control of enzyme activity. Address: School of Pharmacy, University of Colorado, Boulder, CO 80302.

FROEHLICH, CECILIE, b. Cologne, Ger, Nov. 21, 00; nat. ELECTRICAL ENGINEERING. Maedchengymnasium, Cologne, Germany, 13-19; Ph.D. (math), Univ. Bonn, 25. Tech. sci. asst, German Gen. Elec. Co, 26-37; engr. & consult, Studios of Elec. Construct, Charleroi, Belgium, 37-40; prof. elec. eng, City Col. New York, 42-65; PROF. MATH, PAC. UNIV, 70-, chmn. dept, 65-69. Consult, Comput. Sci. Corp, 69-70. Am. Soc. Eng. Ed; sr. mem. Inst. Elec. & Electronics Eng. Electrical engineering analysis; networks; systems; electromagnetic fields. Address: Dept. of Mathematics, Pacific University, Forest Grove, OR 97116.

FROEHLICH, F(RITZ) E(DGAR), b. Germany, Nov. 12, 25; nat; m. 49; c. 3. PHYSICS. B.S, Syracuse, 50, M.S, 52, Ph.D.(physics), 55. Asst. physics, Syracuse, 50-53, asst. instr, 53-54; mem. tech. staff, BELL TEL. LABS, 54-56, supvr. commun. tech, 56-63, HEAD, wideband data & spec. systs. dept, 63-66, data systs. dept, 66-67; TEL. TECHNOL. DEPT, 67- Instr, Utica Col, 52-54. A.U.S, 44-46. AAAS; sr. mem. Inst. Elec. & Electronics Eng; Am. Phys. Soc. Techniques of digital and voice communication. Ad-dress: Room 1C-637, Bell Telephone Labs, Holmdel, NJ 07733.

FROEHLICH, REIMAR, b. Jena, Ger, Jan. 4, 28; m. 57; c. 2. REACTOR PHYSICS, NUMERICAL ANALYSIS. Vordiplom, Jena, 48, Diplom, 51, Dr. (math. & physics), 55. Lectr. math, Jena, 55-58; staff mem, Inst. Neutron Physics, Karlsruhe, Ger, 58-59; MGR. reactor physics & numerical anal, Interatom, Bensberg, 59-65; REACTOR PHYSICS & METHODS DEVELOP, GULF GEN. ATOMIC, INC, 65- Am. Nuclear Soc; Ger. Math. Asn; Ger. Soc. Appl. Math. & Mech. Mathematical and computer methods for the solution of reactor physics and engineering problems; transport theory, diffusion theory, reactor dynamics, error analysis, stability theory, optimi-zation methods, variational methods, Galerkin methods, radiative transfer. Address: 705 Chalcedony, San Diego, CA 92109.

FROELICH, ALBERT JOSEPH, b. Cleveland, Ohio, Aug. 2, 29; m. 58; c. 2. GEOLOGY. B.S, Ohio State, 52, M.S, 53. Geologist, U.S. Geol. Surv, 53-54; geologist-party chief, San Jose Oil Co, Inc, 56-60; sr. geologist, United Canso Oil & Gas, Inc, 60-65; chief geologist, Magellan Petrol. Corp, 65-67; geol. consult, 67-68; geologist, U.S. GEOL. SURV, Ky, 68-71, MEM. STAFF URBAN GEOL, NEW CITIES PROJ, WASH, D.C, 71- C.Eng, U.S.A, 54-56.

Am. Asn. Petrol. Geol. Geology, particularly international petroleum ex-ploration in Philippines, western and northern Canada and Australia; envi-ronmental studies. Address: New Cities Project, U.S. Geological Survey, Washington DC 20242.

FROELICH, ERNEST, b. Vienna, Austria, Dec. 7, 12; nat; m. 47; c. 1. MI-CROBIOLOGY, CHEMOTHERAPY. D.V.M, Zagreb, 37. Vet. asst, Vet. Inst, Belgrade, 38-39; head vet, Vet. Serum Labs, Zemun, 39-40; Biol. Con-trol Labs, 40-41; UNRRA fel, 46-47; res. assoc, microbiol. & chemotherapy, STERLING-WINTHROP RES. INST, 48-50, head, chemotherapy lab, 50-62, DIR. RES. & TECH. SERV, VET. DEPT, 62- Yugoslav Army, 41-45. Am. Soc. Microbiol; Am. Vet. Med. Asn; N.Y. Acad. Sci. Chemotherapy of bac-terial, viral & rickettsial diseases; immunological studies of diseases of domestic animals. Address: 174 Tampa Ave, Albany, NY 12208.

FROELICH, HERMAN C(HRISTIAN), b. Berlin, Ger, July 26, 07; nat; m. 42; c. 2. PHYSICAL CHEMISTRY. Dr.Ing, Inst. Tech. Berlin, 31. Asst, Inst. Tech. Berlin, 31-33; res. chemist, Harshaw Chem. Co, 33-41; ENGR, GEN. ELEC. CO, 41- Am. Chem. Soc; Electrochem. Soc. Gas kinetics; nickel catalysts for hydrogenation; luminescence; fluorescent lamps; preparation and development of new phosphors, and new phosphor treatments to in-crease efficiency. Address: General Electric Co, Nela Park, Cleveland, OH 44112.

FROELICH, JEAN S(MALL), b. Southbridge, Mass, Dec. 20, 28; m. 59; c. 5. EMBRYOLOGY. A.B, Massachusetts, 51; Fulbright grant, Naples Zool. Sta, 51-52; U.S. Pub. Health Serv. fel, Brown, 55-56, Ph.D.(biol), 56. Am. Can-cer Soc. fel, Yale, 56-58; INSTR. ANAT, sch. med, Wash. Univ, 58-60; SCH. MED, CASE WEST. RESERVE UNIV, 61- AAAS; Am. Soc. Zool. Cellular differentiation in tissue culture. Address: 14807 Shaker Blvd, Cleveland, OH 44120.

FROEMKE, JON, b. Sioux Falls, S.Dak, June 23, 41; m. 63; c. 1. MATHE-MATICS. B.A, Univ. Nebr, Lincoln, 62, Woodrow Wilson fel, 62-63, Nat. Sci. Found. fel, 62-64, M.A, 63; Ph.D.(math), Univ. Calif, Berkeley, 67. Asst. prof. MATH, OAKLAND UNIV, 67-71, ASSOC. PROF, 71- Partic, Conf. Universal Algebra, Math. Res. Inst, Ger, summer 71. AAAS; Am. Math. Soc; Math. Asn. Am. General algebraic systems. Address: Dept. of Mathematics, Oakland University, Rochester, MI 48063.

FROEMSDORF, DONALD H(OPE), b. Cape Girardeau, Mo, Mar. 4, 34; m. 54. ORGANIC CHEMISTRY. B.S, Southeast Missouri State Col, 55; Ph.D.(org. chem), Iowa State, 59. Asst. proj. chemist, res. & develop. dept, Standard Oil Co, Ind, 59-60; assoc. prof. CHEM, SOUTHEAST MO. STATE COL, 60-66, PROF, 66-, CHMN. DIV. SCI. & MATH, 70- AAAS; Am. Chem. Soc; The Chem. Soc. Physical organic chemistry; organic reaction mechanisms, es-pecially alpha and beta elimination reactions; structure and properties of high polymers. Address: Division of Science, Southeast Missouri State Col-lege, Cape Girardeau, MO 63701.

FROESCHLE, JAMES E, b. Santa Ana, Calif, Nov. 18, 29; m. 56; c. 2. VI-ROLOGY, PEDIATRICS. A.B, California, 51; M.D, Rochester, 55; M.P.H, Harvard, 59. Lectr. epidemiol, Univ. Calif, 60-63; RES. MED. OFF, CTR. DISEASE CONTROL, U.S. PUB. HEALTH SERV, GREELEY, 63- Instr, Emory Univ, 63- Med.C.Res, Capt. Am. Pub. Health Asn. Medical virol-ogy. Address: 1025 Lemay, Ft. Collins, CO 80521.

FROESCHNER, RICHARD C(HARLES), b. Chicago, Ill, Mar. 8, 16; m. 40; c. 2. ENTOMOLOGY. B.S, Missouri, 41; M.S, Iowa State Col, 51, Ph.D, 54. Taxonomic entomologist, State Dept. Agr, Mo, 40-41, asst. entomolo-gist, 41-45; chief curator mus. sci, Acad. Sci, St. Louis, 46-48; asst. zool, Iowa State Col, 48-54; asst. prof, Mont. State Col, 54-59, assoc. prof, 59-61; res. entomologist, U.S. Dept. Agr, 61-62; assoc. prof. zool, Montana State, 62-63; ASSOC. CURATOR IN CHARGE, DIV. HEMIPTERA, DEPT. ENTOM, SMITHSONIAN INST, 63- Specialist, agr. res. serv, U.S. Dept. Agr, summer 58; Nat. Sci. Found. travel grant, 59-61. U.S.A.A.F, 45-46. Entom. Soc. Am; Soc. Syst. Zool. Systematic entomology; hemiptera. Address: Dept. of Entomology, Division of Hemiptera, Smithsonian Institution, Wash-ington, DC 20560.

FROESE, ARNOLD, b. Halbstadt, Ukraine, Mar. 18, 34; Can. citizen; m. 69; c. 1. IMMUNOCHEMISTRY. B.S, Univ. West. Ont, 57; fel, McGill Univ, 62-64, Ph.D.(chem), 63. Lectr, McGill Univ, 63-64; res. assoc. immuno-chem, 67-69; Max Planck Inst. Phys. Chem, 64-67; ASST. PROF. IM-MUNOL, UNIV. MAN, 69- Scholar, Med. Res. Coun. Can, 68, res. grant, 68- Chem. Inst. Can; Can. Biochem. Soc; Can. Soc. Immunol; Am. Asn. Immunol. Kinetics of antibody-hapten reactions; structure and function of immunoglobulins. Address: Dept. of Immunology, University of Manitoba, Winnipeg 3, Man. Can.

FROESE, CHARLOTTE, Appl. Math, see FISCHER, CHARLOTTE.

FROESE, GERD, b. Saporoshje, U.S.S.R, May 18, 26; Can. citizen; m. 53; c. 3. BIOPHYSICS. B.A, Saskatchewan, 54; M.Sc, Western Ontario, 56, Ph.D.(biophys), 58. PHYSICIST, MAN. CANCER TREATMENT & RES. FOUND, 60- Donner res. fel, Max Planck Inst. Biophys, Ger, 58-59 & res. unit radiobiol, Brit. Empire Cancer Campaign, Middlesex, 59-60. Biophys. Soc; Can. Physiol. Soc; Brit. Asn. Radiation Res. Mammalian temperature regulation; radiation physics; radiobiology and cellular biology. Address: Manitoba Cancer Treatment & Research Foundation, 700 Bannatyne, Winni-peg 3, Man, Can.

FROHLICH, EDWARD DAVID, b. New York, N.Y, Sept. 10, 31; m. 59; c. 3. INTERNAL MEDICINE. A.B, Washington & Jefferson Col, 52; Nat. Insts. Health fel, Maryland, 55-56, M.D, 56; M.S, Northwestern, 63. Intern. med, D.C. Gen. Hosp, 56-57; res. internal med, 57-58; fel. cardiovasc. res. George-town, 58-59, res. internal med, Georgetown Univ. Hosp, 59-60; clin. investr. internal med. & cardiovasc. res. Vet. Admin. Res. Hosp, Northwestern, 62-64; staff mem, res. div. Cleveland Clin, Ohio, 64-69; assoc. prof, MED. CTR, UNIV. OKLA, 69-71, ASSOC. PROF. PHARMACOL. & PROF. MED.

& PHYSIOL. & BIOPHYS, 71- Mem. med. adv. bds, coun. on circulation, Am. Heart Asn, 64-, coun. high blood pressure res, 68, coun. basic sci, 69; spec. consult, cmt. on hypertension, Am. Col. Chest Physicians, 67- Dipl. Am. Bd. Internal Med, 65. Chief circulation sect, Army Med. Res. Lab, Ft. Knox, Ky, U.S.A, 60-62, Capt. Fel. AAAS; Am. Soc. Clin. Pharmacol. & Therapeut; fel. Am. Col. Cardiol; fel. Am. Col. Physicians; Am. Soc. Pharmacol. & Exp. Therapeut; Am. Fedn. Clin. Res; Soc. Exp. Biol. & Med. Cardiovascular research; hypertension; clinical pharmacology. Address: Dept. of Medicine, University of Oklahoma Medical Center, 800 N.E. 13th St, Oklahoma City, OK 73104.

FROHLICH, GERHARD J, b. Simmern, Ger, Feb. 20, 29; U.S. citizen; m. 58; c. 2. CHEMICAL ENGINEERING, PHYSICAL CHEMISTRY. Dipl. chem, Darmstadt Tech. Univ, 53; M.Ch.E, Polytech. Inst. Brooklyn, 54, D.Ch.E, 57; Stevens Inst. Technol, 64-65. Chem. engr, Vulcan-Cincinnati, Inc, Ohio, 55-59; sr. chem. engr, St. Paul Ammonia Prod, Inc, Minn, 59-61, chief process engr, 61-62, mgr. res. & develop, 62-64; sr. chem. engr, HOFFMANN-LA ROCHE, INC, NUTLEY, 64-70, MGR. CHEM. ENG. DEVELOP, 70- Am. Inst. Chem. Eng; Am. Chem. Soc; Electrochem. Soc; Faraday Soc; Nat. Soc. Prof. Eng. Chemical process design and development; electrochemical engineering; heterogeneous catalysis; liquid-liquid extraction. Address: 50 N. Irving St, Ridgewood, NJ 07450.

FROHLICH, HANS P(ETER), b. Zurich, Switz, June 26, 24; m. 53; c. 2. PLANT PATHOLOGY. Dipl, Fed. Inst. Tech, Switz, 50. Biologist, Dr. R. Maag, A.G. Chem. Co, Switz, 50-52; PLANT PATHOLOGIST, RES. LABS, ROHM AND HAAS CO, 52- Swiss Army. Am. Phytopath. Soc. Fungicides. Address: Rohm and Haas Co, Research Labs, Spring House, PA 19477.

FROHLICH, M(OSES) M(ICHAEL), b. Peczenizyn, Austria, Oct. 18, 02; nat; m. 46; c. 2. PSYCHIATRY. A.B, Michigan, 28, M.D, 32. Instr. internal med, MED. SCH, UNIV. MICH, 34-36, PSYCHIAT, 37-45, asst. prof, 45-47, assoc. prof, 47-51, PROF, 51-, CLIN. DIR. DEPT, 62-, lectr, sch. social work, 47-52. Consult. psychiatrist, Vet. Admin. Hosp, 46- Med.C, 42-46, Res, 46-, Col. Am. Med. Asn; Am. Psychiat. Asn; Am. Psychoanal. Asn; Am. Geriat. Soc. Psychotherapy; classification and nomenclature of mental illness. Address: University of Michigan Hospital, Ann Arbor, MI 48104.

FROHLIGER, JOHN O(WEN), b. Indianapolis, Ind, Dec. 21, 30; m. 52; c. 3. ANALYTICAL CHEMISTRY. B.S, Purdue, 57; M.S, Iowa, 59, Ph.D. (anal. chem), 61. Asst. prof. chem, Duquesne Univ, 61-67; INDUST. HEALTH & AIR CHEM, GRAD. SCH. PUB. HEALTH, UNIV. PITTSBURGH, 67-70, ASSOC. PROF, 70- U.S.M.C.R, 50-52. AAAS; Am. Chem. Soc; Air Pollution Control Asn; Am. Inst. Chem. Identification of chemical compounds in the environment; liquid chromatography; thermal analytical techniques. Address: Graduate School of Public Health, University of Pittsburgh, 130 De Soto St, 519 Parran Hall, Pittsburgh, PA 15213.

FROHMADER, STANLEY H(ARRISON), b. Rockford, Ill, Oct. 14, 12; m. 41; c. 4. ORGANIC CHEMISTRY. B.S, Beloit Col, 36, M.S, 37; Wisconsin, 40-41. Prod. supvr, Origin Inc, Ill, 37; head dept. sci, Wayland Acad. & Jr. Col, Wis, 37-40; instr. chem, Wisconsin, 40-41; res. chemist & sales engr, Res. Prods. Corp, Wis, 41-42; tech. asst. mfg. opers, Badger Ord. Works, Hercules Powder Co, Wis, 42-45; asst. dir. res, RES. PRODS. CORP, 45-51, head, develop. & control dept, 51-56, CHIEF CHEM. ENGR, 56- Am. Chem. Soc. Resin technology; cation exchange resin; dispersion in carriers; surface active agents; air filter adhesives and their production; air purification and water treatment. Address: Research Products Corp, 1015 E. Washington Ave, Madison, WI 53701.

FROHMAN, CHARLES E(DWARD), b. Columbus, Ind, Oct. 25, 21; m. 46; c. 4. PHYSIOLOGICAL CHEMISTRY. B.S, Indiana, 47, A.M, 48; Ph.D.(phys. chem), Wayne State, 51. Res. assoc, Kresge Eye Inst, 51-52; instr. PHYSIOL. CHEM, COL. MED, WAYNE STATE UNIV, 52-56, ASST. PROF, 56-; LAB. DIR. & BIOCHEMIST, LAFAYETTE CLIN, 55- Med.C, U.S.A, 43-46. Am. Soc. Biol. Chem; Soc. Biol. Psychiat. Intermediary carbohydrate metabolism; schizophrenia; diabetes; chromatography; analytical biochemistry; comparative biochemistry. Address: Lafayette Clinic, 951 E. Lafayette, Detroit, MI 48207.

FROHMBERG, RICHARD P, b. Newburgh Heights, Ohio, Mar. 30, 20; m. 45; c. 4. PHYSICAL METALLURGY, MATERIALS SCIENCE. B.S, Case, 42, M.S, 48, Ph.D.(phys. metall), 54. Instr. phys. metall, Case, 48-51, res. assoc. metals, 51-55; chief prod. develop. lab, Rocketdyne Div, N.Am. Aviation, Inc, 55-60, mat. res, 60-70; CHIEF ENGR, ADVAN. DEVELOP. & MAT. ENG, BENDIX CORP, 70- Henry Marion Howe Award, 55. U.S.A.A.F, 42-45, 1st Lt. AAAS; fel. Am. Inst. Aeronaut. & Astronaut; Am. Soc. Metals. High temperature materials sciences, including physical metallurgy, fabrication, ceramics and polymer science. Address: Bendix Corp, P.O. Box 1159, Kansas City, MO 64141.

FROHNE, WILLIAM C(ARRINGTON), b. Nyack, N.Y, July 23, 08; m. 35, 59; c. 5. ENTOMOLOGY. B.A, Michigan, 30, M.A, 35, Ph.D.(entom), 37; Inst. Int. Ed. exchange fel, Tübingen, 30-31; Cornell, 35. Jr. entomologist, U.S. Pub. Health Serv, Ga, 36-39; chief aquatic biologist, Mo. Conserv. Cmn, 39-42; assoc. entomologist & sanit. scientist, malaria control in war areas & commun. disease ctr, U.S. Pub. Health Serv, 42-49, scientist dir, Arctic Health Res. Ctr, 49-56; med. zoologist, WHO, Philippines, 56-58; chief Malaria adv, U.S. Mission to Ethiopia, 60-62; asst. chief career develop. rev. br, Nat. Insts. Health, 62-63; chief labs, Lake Erie Field Sta, Great Lakes-Ill. River Basins Proj, 63-64; MEM. FACULTY BIOL, ALASKA METHODIST UNIV, 64- Mem. mission to Greece, UNRRA, 45. AAAS; Am. Soc. Prof. Biol; Am. Soc. Limnol. & Oceanog; Am. Soc. Microbiol; Am. Soc. Trop. Med. & Hyg; Am. Mosquito Control. Asn. Mosquitoes; malaria; tropical butterflies. Address: Faculty of Biology, Alaska Methodist University, Anchorage, AK 99504.

FROHNSDORFF, GEOFFREY JAMES CARL, b. London, Eng, Feb. 4, 28; U.S. citizen; m. 56; c. 3. PHYSICAL CHEMISTRY. B.Sc, St. Andrews, 53; M.S, Lehigh, 56; Ph.D.(phys. chem), London & dipl, Imp. Col, 59. Res. fel. chem, Royal Mil. Col.(Ont), 59-60; mgr. res. & develop, Am. Cement Corp, 60-70; GROUP LEADER, GILLETTE RES. INST, INC, 70- Mem. comt. res. cement & concrete, Hwy. Res. Bd, Nat. Acad. Sci-Nat. Res. Coun. R.A.F, 46-49. Am. Chem. Soc; Am. Ceramic Soc. Rheology of dispersions in liquids; infrared spectra and thermodynamic properties of sorbed phases; adsorption in charcoals; cement compounds and their hydration; silicate chemistry; metal surfaces. Address: Gillette Research Institute, Inc, 1413 Research Blvd, Rockville, MD 20850.

FROHRIB, DARRELL A, b. Oshkosh, Wis, June 25, 30; m. 55; c. 3. MECHANICAL ENGINEERING, MECHANICS. S.B, Mass. Inst. Tech, 52, S.M, 53; Ph.D.(mech), Minnesota, Minneapolis, 66. Engr, Sperry Gyroscope Co, N.Y, 53-59; lectr. MECH. ENG, UNIV. MINN, MINNEAPOLIS, 59-66, asst. prof, 66-68, ASSOC. PROF, 68-, DIR. DESIGN CTR, 71- Am. Petrol. Soc. fel, 63-65; Fulbright-Hays sr. fel, India, 71. Am. Soc. Mech. Eng; Am. Soc. Eng. Educ; N.Y. Acad. Sci. Shock and vibration; engineering design; dynamics; mathematical modeling of regional development systems; automation. Address: 2144 Princeton Ave, St. Paul, MN 55105.

FROILAND, S(VEN) G(ORDON), b. Astoria, S.Dak, May 4, 22; m. 43; c. 6. BIOLOGY, ECOLOGY. B.S, S.Dak. State, 43; M.A, Colorado, 51, Ph.D, 57. Instr. BIOL, Augustana Col, 46-49; Colorado, 49-53; assoc. prof, AUGUSTANA COL, 53-57, PROF, 57-, CHMN. DEPT, 53-, DIV. NAT. SCI, 59-, DIR, BLACK HILLS NATURAL SCI. FIELD STA, 70- Vis. scholar, Univ. Ariz, 70-71. U.S.A, 42-46, Capt. AAAS; Ecol. Soc. Am; Am. Inst. Biol. Sci; Nat. Asn. Biol. Teachers; Soc. Study Evolution. Morphology of genus betula; taxonomy and ecology of genus salix in Black Hills of South Dakota. Address: 1910 S. Duluth Ave, Sioux Falls, SD 57105.

FROILAND, THOMAS GORDON, b. Henderson, Ky, Dec. 9, 43; m. 66; c. 1. DEVELOPMENTAL GENETICS. B.A, Augustana Col, 65; M.S, Univ. Nebr, 67, Ph.D.(zool), 70. Instr. BIOL, Kans. State Univ, 70-71; ASST. PROF, WAYNE STATE COL, 71- Control of pigmentation in genetic systems; ultrastructural relationships of microtubules to pigment. Address: Dept. of Biology, Wayne State College, Wayne, NE 68787.

FROJMOVIC, MAURICE MONY, b. Brussels, Belg, Feb. 2, 43; Can. citizen; m. 66; c. 2. SURFACE CHEMISTRY. McGill Univ, 63, Nat. Res. Coun. Can. scholar, 63-67, Ph.D.(org. chem), 67. Nat. Res. Coun-NATO fel, chem. biodynamics lab, McGILL UNIV, 66-68, ASST. PROF. PHYSIOL, 68- AAAS; Am. Chem. Soc. Interactions at the blood-material interface; materials with physically and chemically characterized surfaces studied for their effects on blood proteins, clotting factors and cells, in hope of identifying the nature of a blood-compatible surface; blood clotting and thrombosis. Address: Dept. of Physiology, McIntyre Medical Bldg, McGill University, Montreal 110, Can.

FROLANDER, HERBERT F(ARLEY), b. Providence, R.I, Sept. 29, 22; m. 50; c. 4. BIOLOGY. Ed.B, R.I. Col. Ed, 46; Sc.M, Brown, 50, Ph.D.(biol), 55; fel, Rhode Island, 49-52. Instr. OCEANOG, Washington (Seattle), 52-56, asst. prof, 57-59; assoc. prof, ORE. STATE UNIV, 59-65, PROF, 65-, COORD. MARINE SCI. & TECHNOL. PROG, 68-, asst. dean grad. sch, 66-67, acting chmn. dept. oceanog, 67-68. Pres-elect, Asn. Sea Grant Prog. Insts, 70-71, pres, 71- U.S.A, 43-46. Am. Soc. Limnol. & Oceanog; Am. Micros. Soc. Marine zooplankton; population dynamics. Address: Sea Grant Administration Office, Administrative Services Bldg. A320, Oregon State University, Corvallis, OR 97331.

FROLICH, PER K(EYSER), b. Kristiansand, Norway, June 29, 99; nat; m. 27; c. 2. CHEMISTRY, CHEMICAL ENGINEERING. B.S, Norway Inst. Tech, 21; Am-Scandinavian Found. fel, Mass. Inst. Tech, 22-23, M.S, 23, Sc.D, 25; hon. D.Sc, Rutgers, 43; hon. D.Eng, Lehigh, 43. Asst. chem, Norway Inst. Tech, 19-21; instr, Kristiansand Bus. Col, 21-22; asst, Mass. Inst. Tech, 23-25, res. assoc. & div. dir, res. lab. appl, chem, 25-27, asst. dir. res. lab. appl. chem. & asst. prof, 27-29, assoc. prof, 29; res. chemist, Standard Oil Develop. Co, 29-31, asst. dir. res. labs, 31-33, dir, 33-35, chief chemist, 35-36, dir. chem. div, Esso Labs, Esso Res. & Eng. Co, 36-46; coordinator res, Merck & Co, Inc, 46-47, dir. res. & develop, 47-48, v.pres, 48-52, v.pres. & assoc. sci. dir, 52-53, v.pres. sci. activities, chem. div, 53-54; dep. chief chem. officer. sci. activities, Off. chief chem. officer hqs. & chief scientist, chem. corps, U.S. Dept. Army, 54-60; TECH. CONSULT, 60- Consult, Rubber Reserve Co, off. rubber reserve & rubber dir, 42-46. Trustee, Merck Inst, 49-54. Mem. chem. adv. cmt, Rutgers, 40-54, adv. bd, res. coun, 44-63; vis. cmt, dept. biol, Mass. Inst. Tech, 45-56; exec. cmt, chem. div, Nat. Res. Coun, 41-45, mem. chem. div, 58-60; Am. Chem. Soc. cmt. adv. to Chem. Corps, 47-54; adv. cmt, dept. chem. eng, Princeton, 48-56; Chem. Corps, 47-54; adv. cmt, dept. chem. eng, Princeton, 48-56; Chem. Corps Adv. Coun, 50-52. AAAS; Am. Chem. Soc.(pres, 43); Soc. Chem. Indust.(Grasselli medal, 30); Am. Inst. Chem; hon. mem. Norweg. Chem. Soc; Norweg. Tech. Acad. Sci. Hydrocarbon and polymer chemistry; microbiology, nutrition; pharmaceuticals. Address: 1160 Wychwood Rd, Westfield, NJ 07090.

FROLIK, ELVIN FRANK, b. DeWitt, Nebr, June 9, 09; m. 38; c. 3. AGRONOMY. B.S, Nebraska, 30, M.S, 32; Ph.D, Minnesota, 48. Exten. agronomist, UNIV. NEBR, LINCOLN, 36-45, assoc. prof. AGRON, 46-51, PROF, 51-, DEAN COL. AGR, 60-, assoc. dir. agr. exp. sta, 55-60, chmn. dept. agron, univ, 52-55. Chem.C, U.S.A.R, Maj.(Ret). AAAS; Am. Soc. Agron; Soil Conserv. Soc. Am; assoc. Int. Crop Improv. Asn.(pres, 45-47). Maize genetics; radiation genetics of crop plants. Address: College of Agriculture, 202 Agricultural Hall, University of Nebraska, Lincoln, NE 68503.

FROM, CHARLES A(UGUSTUS), JR, b. Chicago, Ill, April 12, 15; m. 40; c. 4. CHEMICAL ENGINEERING. B.S, Michigan, 36. Anal. chemist, E.I. du Pont de Nemours & Co, 36-37; develop. engr, raw mat. develop, WEST. ELEC. CO, 37-42, plastics develop, 46-55, DEPT. CHIEF, 55-59, non-metallic raw mat. develop, 59-61, ORG. FINISHING, INSULATING & ENCAPSULATION DEVELOP, 61- Ord. Dept, 42-46, Capt. Am. Chem. Soc; Am. Inst. Chem. Eng; Soc. Plastics Eng; Am. Watchmakers Inst. Plastics; non-metallic raw materials; organic finishing; mechanical finishing; adhesives. Address: 241 Kenmore Ave, Elmhurst, IL 60126.

FROMAN, DAROL (KENNETH), b. Harrington, Wash, Oct. 23, 06; nat; m. 31; c. 2. NUCLEAR PHYSICS. B.Sc, Alberta, 26, M.Sc, 27, LL.D, 64; Nat. Res. Coun. Can. bursary, 27-28; fel, Chicago, 28-29, Ph.D.(physics), 30. Asst. physics, Chicago, 29-30; lectr, Alberta, 30-31; Macdonald Col, McGill, 31-36, asst. prof, 36-39, univ, 39-41; prof, Denver, 41-42; group leader radio & sound lab, U.S. Navy, San Diego, 42; res. assoc. Manhattan Dist. Proj, metall. lab, Chicago, 42-43; group leader, Los Alamos Sci. Labs, 43-45, div. leader, 45-48, asst. dir. weapon develop, 49-51, tech. assoc. dir, 51-62; PRIVATE CONSULT, 62- Dir, Mt. Evans High Altitude Lab, 41; sci. dir, atomic weapons tests, Eniwetok, 48; consult. prof, New Mexico, 54-61; mem. sci. adv. comt. ballistic missiles, Secy. Defense, 55-60; sci. directorate, Douglas Aircraft Co, 63-69; gen. adv. comt, Atomic Energy Comn, 64-66; dir. develop, Espanola Hosp, 67-70; chmn. bd, First Nat. Bank Rio Arriba, 71- Fel. Am. Phys. Soc; fel. Am. Nuclear Soc. Supersonics; x-rays; cosmic rays; electronics applied to nuclear physics. Address: Pajarito Village, Rt. 1, Box 428, Espanola, NM 87532.

FROMAN, JAY, b. New York, N.Y, June 7, 12; m. 46; c. 2. PHYSICS. B.S, City Col. New York, 35; Columbia, 39-40; California, Berkeley, 46-47. Instr. radar theory, U.S. Army Air Force Radio Sch, 41-42, tech. adv, 42-43; physicist, OFF. NAVAL RES, 47-54, phys. sci. coord, 54-57, DEP. CHIEF SCIENTIST, 57-, NAT. CONSULT. ELECTRON DEVICES, 63- U.S.N.R, 43-46, Res, 46-, Comdr. AAAS; Am. Phys. Soc; sr. mem. Inst. Elec. & Electronics Eng. Microwave physics and high power klystrons; evaluation of physics and electronics programs; infrared physics; detectors and image forming sensors. Address: Office of Naval Research, 50 Fell St, San Francisco, CA 94102.

FROMAN, SEYMOUR, b. N.Y.C, May 19, 20; m. 46; c. 3. MICROBIOLOGY. B.A, N.Y. Univ, 46; M.A, Univ. Calif, Los Angeles, 49, Ph.D, 52. Asst. clin. prof. MICROBIOL. & IMMUNOL, SCH. MED, UNIV. CALIF, LOS ANGELES, 64-65, ASSOC. PROF-IN-RESIDENCE, 65-; DIR. MICROBIOL. RES. LAB, OLIVE VIEW HOSP, 64- Consult, tuberc. unit, WHO; clin. lab, Univ. Calif, Los Angeles. Dipl, Am. Bd. Microbiol, 63. U.S.A, 42-46. Am. Soc. Microbiol; Am. Thoracic Soc; fel. Am. Pub. Health Asn; N.Y. Acad. Sci; Int. Union Against Tuberc. Microbiology of tuberculosis. Address: Olive View Medical Center, Sylmar, CA 91342.

FROME, JULIUS, b. N.Y.C, Nov. 10, 15; m. 37; c. 3. ORGANIC CHEMISTRY, INFORMATION SCIENCE. B.S, City Col. New York, 36; LL.B, American Univ, 45, J.D, 68. Patent exam. org. chem, U.S. Patent Off, 41-56, patent res. specialist info. sci, res. & develop, 56-61; dep. sci. & tech, U.S. Air Force, 61-63; head, info. processing unit, NAT. INSTS. HEALTH, 63-66, MEM. FACULTY, GRAD. SCH, 63-; SUPVRY. PATENT EXAM, U.S. PATENT OFF, 66- Silver medal, U.S. Dept. Commerce, 58. Am. Chem. Soc. Research in documentation; information storage and retrieval, both in the physical and social sciences. Address: 12912 Middlevale Lane, Silver Spring, MD 20906.

FROMHOLD, ALBERT T(HOMAS), JR, b. Birmingham, Ala, Nov. 25, 35; m. 60; c. 2. SOLID STATE PHYSICS. B.Eng.Phys, Auburn, 57, Atomic Energy Comn. fel, 57-58, M.S, 58; Avco Corp. fel, Cornell, 58-59, Nat. Sci. Found. fel, 59-60, Ph.D.(eng. physics), 61. Mem. res. staff, Sandia Corp, 61-65; assoc. res. prof. PHYSICS, AUBURN UNIV, 65-69, ALUMNI PROF, 70- Vis. scientist, Nat. Bur. Standards, D.C, 69-70. Am. Phys. Soc. Theory of oxide film formation; optical properties of metals; transient nuclear magnetic resonance; nuclear relaxation in metals and magnetic insulators; solid state transport. Address: Dept. of Physics, Auburn University, Auburn, AL 36830.

FROMM, ELI, b. Niedaltdorf, Germany, May 7, 39; U.S. citizen; m. 62; c. 3. BIOMEDICAL ENGINEERING, PHYSIOLOGY. B.S, Drexel Univ, 62, M.S, 64; Ph.D.(physiol, biomed. eng), Jefferson Med. Col, 67; Nat. Insts. Health fels, 64, 67. Engr, missile & space div, Gen. Elec. Co, 62-63; eng. physics lab, E.I. du Pont de Nemours & Co, 63; teaching asst. physics, DREXEL UNIV, 63-64, asst. prof. BIOMED. ENG. & BIOL. SCI, 67-70, ASSOC. PROF, 70- Lalor Found. grant, 68-70; Nat. Sci. Found, 69-71; Nat. Insts. Health, 69- Consult, Goddard Space Flight Ctr, NASA, summer 67; several indust. co, 68- Inst. Elec. & Electronics Eng. Physiologic function by telemetry from the free subject; rhythmic responses of physiologic and biophysical parameters; development of transduction and transmission techniques for biologic variables. Address: Dept. of Biological Sciences, Drexel University, 32nd & Chestnut Sts, Philadelphia, PA 19104.

FROMM, HERBERT J(EROME), b. N.Y.C, Apr. 5, 29; m. 64; c. 4. BIOCHEMISTRY. B.S, Mich. State Univ, 50; Ph.D.(biochem), Loyola Univ. (Ill), 54. Asst. prof. BIOCHEM, sch. med, Univ. N.Dak, 54-59, assoc. prof, 59-64, PROF, 64-66; IOWA STATE UNIV, 66- Am. Chem. Soc; Am. Soc. Biol. Chem. Protein metabolism; enzyme chemistry. Address: Dept. of Biochemistry & Biophysics, Iowa State University, Ames, IA 50010.

FROMM, PAUL O(LIVER), b. Ramsey, Ill, Dec. 2, 23; m. 47; c. 2. COMPARATIVE PHYSIOLOGY. B.S, Univ. Ill, 49, M.S, 51, Ph.D.(physiol), 54. Asst. PHYSIOL, Univ. Ill, 51-54; instr, MICH. STATE UNIV, 54-59, asst. prof, 59-62, assoc. prof, 62-65, PROF, 65- Fulbright res. scholar, Oceanog. Inst, Monaco, 63-64; vis. prof, Ariz. State Univ, 71. U.S.M.C, 43-46. Seasonal aspects of frog metabolism; physiological effects of various pollutants on aquatic life; physiology of the thyroid of telecosts; eye disease in hatchery trout. Address: Dept. of Physiology, Michigan State University, East Lansing, MI 48823.

FROMM, WINFIELD E(RIC), b. Haddonfield, N.J, Jan. 18, 18; m. 44; c. 3. ELECTRONIC ENGINEERING. B.S.E.E, Drexel Inst, 40; M.E.E, Polytech. Inst. Brooklyn, 48. Aircraft radio engr, Transcontinental & West. Air, Inc, 40-41; electronic engr, Airborne Instruments Lab, 45-49, asst. supv. engr, 49-55, dept. head, 55-61, div. dir, res. syst. eng. div, 61-64, v.pres, 64, group v.pres, 64-68, EXEC. V.PRES, AIL, DIV. CUTLER-HAMMER, INC, 68- Mem. staff, off. sci. res. & develop, Columbia Univ, 41-45; lectr, Hofstra Col, 51. Fel. Inst. Elec. & Electronics Eng; assoc. Am. Inst. Aeronaut. & Astronaut. Magnetic airborne detection; low and medium frequency vacuum tube circuits; microwave equipment development, including special components and strip transmission lines; electronic and microwave systems for aerospace applications. Address: AIL, Division of Cutler-Hammer, Inc, Comac Rd, Deer Park, NY 11729.

FROMME, JOSEPH ARCHIBALD, b. Washington, Ind, Oct. 9, 37; m. 60; c. 3. THEORETICAL & APPLIED MECHANICS. B.S.A.E, Purdue, 59; M.Sc, Ohio State, 63, Ph.D.(eng. mech), 67. Dynamics engr, N.Am. Aviation, Inc, Ohio, 59-63, sr. dynamics engr, 63-66; instr. math. & eng. mech, Ohio State, 60-67; res. scientist, Kaman Nuclear Div, Kaman Aircraft Corp, 67-70; PROF. MATH, OHIO UNIV, 70- Applied mathematics; solid and fluid mechanics; aeroelasticity; unsteady aerodynamics; vibrations. Address: Dept. of Mathematics, Ohio University, Athens, OH 45701.

FROMMER, DONALD W(ALTER), b. Chesterfield, Mo, June 25, 21; m. 43; c. 4. METALLURGICAL ENGINEERING. B.S, Missouri, 44. Corrosion engr, Aluminum Res. Labs, Pa, 46-48; metallurgist MINERAL DRESSING, U.S. BUR. MINES, Mo, 48-58, SUPVRY. METALLURGIST, 58- UN expert low grade iron ore beneficiation, Arg, 71. C.Eng, 44-46, Res, 50-59, Capt. Flotation and other beneficiation methods on rutile, barite, manganese, talc, phosphate, lead-zinc, taconite and other iron ores. Address: U.S. Bureau of Mines, P.O. Box 1660, Twin Cities, MN 55111.

FROMMER, GABRIEL PAUL, b. Budapest, Hungary, Apr. 27, 36; m. 58; c. 2. PSYCHOLOGY. B.A, Oberlin Col, 57; Sc.M, Brown, 59, Ph.D.(psychol), 61. From asst. health serv. off. to sr. asst. scientist, Nat. Insts. Health, 60-62; U.S. Pub. Health Serv. fel, Yale, 62-64; asst. prof. PSYCHOL, IND. UNIV, BLOOMINGTON, 64-69, ASSOC. PROF, 69- U.S.P.H.S.R, Sr. Asst. Scientist. AAAS; Am. Psychol. Asn; Soc. Neurosci. Neural mechanisms in behavior; sensory psychophysiology. Address: Dept. of Psychology, Indiana University, Bloomington, IN 47401.

FROMMER, JACK, b. New Haven, Conn, Jan. 21, 18; m. 44; c. 4. ANATOMY. B.S, Connecticut, 40, M.S, 46; Schenley fel, Brown, 52-53, Ph.D.(biol), 54. Instr. zool, Connecticut, 47-48, 49-50; asst. res. physiol, Yale, 48-49; instr. ANAT, MED. SCH, TUFTS UNIV, 53-54, asst. prof, 54-67, ASSOC. PROF, 67- U.S.A.A.F, 42-45, Lt. AAAS; Am. Asn. Anat. Temporomandibular joint; mandible development; cleft palate; osteoclasts; teratology; radioautography. Address: 39 Whittemore Rd, Framingham, MA 01701.

FROMMER, PETER LESLIE, b. Budapest, Hungary, Feb. 13, 32; U.S. citizen; m. 53; c. 4. CARDIOLOGY, BIOMEDICAL ENGINEERING. E.E, Cincinnati, 54; M.D, Harvard Med. Sch, 58. Intern, med. center, Cincinnati, 58-59, asst. res. med, 61-63; jr. investr, lab. tech. develop, NAT. HEART & LUNG INST, 59-61, sr. investr, cardiol. br, 63-66, asst. chief MYOCARDIAL INFARCTION BR, 66-67, acting chief, 67-69, CHIEF, 69- Mem, Joint U.S. Comt. Eng. Med. & Biol, Nat. Res. Coun, 60-65, chmn. comt, 64, mem, U.S. Nat. Comt. Eng. Med. & Biol, 66-68; admin. coun, Int. Fedn. Med. & Biol. Eng, 65-, v.pres, 69- U.S.P.H.S, 59-61, Sr. Asst. Surg. AAAS; Am. Fedn. Clin. Res; Am. Heart Asn; Am. Physiol. Soc; Inst. Elec. & Electronics Eng; Am. Col. Cardiol; Biomed. Eng. Soc. Cardiovascular physiology and myocardian infarction; instrumentation; research planning and administration. Address: Myocardial Infarction Branch, National Heart & Lung Institute, Bethesda, MD 20014.

FROMMEYER, WALTER BENEDICT, JR, b. Cincinnati, Ohio, Nov. 23, 16; m. 44; c. 2. INTERNAL MEDICINE. A.B, Cincinnati, 39, M.D, 42. Intern, Cincinnati Gen. Hosp, 42-43, jr. asst. res, 46-47, sr. asst. res, 47-48; res. fel, Thorndike Mem. Lab, 48-49; dir, blood bank & tumor clin, univ. hosp. & Hillman Clin, med. center, Alabama, 50-53; chief med. serv, Vet. Admin. Hosp, Birmingham, Ala, 53-54; assoc. dean, MED. CTR, UNIV. ALA, BIRMINGHAM, 54-57, PROF. MED, 57-, DISTINGUISHED PROF, UNIV, 68-, DISTINGUISHED FACULTY LECTR, MED. CTR, 71-, chmn. dept. med. & physician-in-chief, univ. hosp. & Hillman Clin, 57-68, co-chief staff, hosp. & clin, 62-67. Consult, Vet. Admin. Hosp; St. Vincent's Hosp; Birmingham Baptist Hosps. Med.C, 43-46, Maj; Bronze Star Medal & Oak Leaf Cluster. AAAS; Am. Heart Asn.(v.pres, 63-67, pres, 68-69); Asn. Profs. Med; fel. Am. Col. Physicians; Am. Fedn. Clin. Res; Asn. Am. Physicians. Hematology. Address: 2920 Cherokee Rd, Birmingham, AL 35223.

FROMMHAGEN, LAURENCE H, b. Pittsburgh, Pa, June 26, 29. BIOCHEMISTRY, VIROLOGY. B.A, Gettysburg Col, 51; M.A, California, Berkeley, 55, Ph.D.(biochem), 58. Chemist physiol, Lederle Labs, 51-53; virol, Calif. Health Dept, 58-62; RES. SCIENTIST BIOCHEM, AMES RES. CTR, NASA, 62- Lectr, Calif. Med. Sch, 60-63; res. assoc, dept. microbiol, Stanford, 62- Biochemistry and immunology of myxoviruses and enteroviruses; chemistry of immunoglobulins; fluorescent antibody analysis of viral and microbial antigens. Address: Ames Research Center, NASA, Moffett Field, CA 94035.

FROMMHOLD, LOTHAR WERNER, b. Würzburg, Germany, Apr. 20, 30; m. 58; c. 2. ATOMIC & PLASMA PHYSICS. Dipl, Hamburg, 56, Ph.D.(gas discharges), 61, Dr. habil, 64. Res. assoc. PHYSICS, Hamburg, 56-63, instr, 61-63, asst. prof, 64; res. assoc. & instr, Pittsburgh, 64-66, res. prof, 66; assoc. prof, UNIV. TEX, AUSTIN, 66-69, PROF, 69- Fulbright travel grant, Pittsburgh, 64, res. fel, 64-66. Fel. Am. Phys. Soc. Basic processes in gas discharges; gaseous electronics; atomic and molecular physics; plasma physics and diagnostics; millimicrosecond pulse techniques. Address: Dept. of Physics, Physics Bldg. 122, University of Texas at Austin, Austin, TX 78712.

FRONABARGER, C(ARL) V(ALENTINE), b. Oak Ridge, Mo, Feb. 14, 09; m. 37; c. 3. MATHEMATICS. B.S, Southeast Mo. State Teachers Col, 32; M.A, Peabody Col, 36; Ph.D.(math. ed), Missouri, 51. Teacher, pub. schs, Mo, 27-29, 32-35, prin, 29-30; teacher, Ky, 35-41; instr. math, SOUTHWEST MO. STATE COL, 41-45, asst. prof, 46-49, assoc. prof, 50-51, prof, 51-, head dept, 58-67, dir. DIV. SCI. & TECH, 67-68, DEAN, 68- Math. Asn. Am. Undergraduate mathematics curriculum. Address: Office of the Dean, Division of Science & Technology, Southwest Missouri State College, Springfield, MO 65802.

FRONDEL, CLIFFORD, b. N.Y.C, Jan. 8, 07; m. 41; c. 2. MINERALOGY. Geol. Eng, Colo. Sch. Mines, 29; A.M, Columbia, 36; fel, Mass. Inst. Tech, 37-39, Ph.D.(crystallog), 39. Res. assoc. MINERAL, HARVARD, 39-46, assoc. prof, 46-54, PROF, 54-, CHMN. DEPT. GEOL. SCI, 65-; PRES, CRYSTAL RES, INC, 69- Sr. physicist, U.S. War Dept, 42-43; res. dir, Reeves Sound Labs. & Reeves-Ely Labs, 43-45; corr. mem, Am. Mus. Nat. Hist; Hist. Mus. Vienna. Becke medal, Austrian Mineral. Asn, 58; distinguished serv. medal, Colo. Sch. Mines, 64; Boricky Medal, Charles Univ, Prague, 68. With Off. Sci. Res. & Develop; U.S.N, 44. Fel. Am. Mineral. Soc.(pres, 56, Roebling medal, 64); fel. Geol. Soc. Am; Am. Crystallog. Asn; Am. Acad. Arts & Sci; Geochem. Soc; hon. mem. Mineral. Soc. Gt. Brit. & Ireland; German Mineral. Soc; French Soc. Mineral. & Crystallog; Italian Mineral. Soc; for. mem. Nat. Acad. Lincei; for. mem. German Soc. Nature Study; for. mem. Austrian Acad. Sci. Descriptive mineralogy; crystal synthesis. Address: 20 Beatrice Circle, Belmont, MA 02178.

FRONDEL, JUDITH W, b. Phila, Pa, Oct. 23, 12; m. 49; c. 1. GEOLOGY, MINERALOGY. B.A, Temple, 34; M.A, Bryn Mawr, 45, fels, 46-48, Ph.D. (geol), 49. Relief investr, Phila. County Relief Bd, 34-36; mus. docent natural hist, Acad. Natural Sci. Phila, 36-42; crystallographer, Phila. Signal Corps Depot, 42-43; geologist, U.S. Geol. Surv, D.C, 48-49, part time, 49-61, RES. ASSOC. MINERAL, Atomic Energy Comn. contract, HOFFMAN LAB, HARVARD, 61-70, NASA CONTRACT, 70- Fel, Radcliffe Inst. Independent Study, 65-66, 66-67; summers, crystallographer, Philco Corp, Pa, 43, 44. AAAS; fel. Mineral. Soc. Am; Am. Geochem. Soc. Mineralogical and geochemical investigation of radioactive and rare-earth bearing minerals using optical, x-ray diffraction and x-ray spectrographic techniques; investigation of origin of amber, using all mineralogical techniques. Address: 20 Beatrice Circle, Belmont, MA 02178.

FRONEK, ARNOST, b. Topolčany, Czech, Aug. 8, 23; m. 57; c. 2. PHYSIOLOGY. M.D, Charles Univ, Prague, 49; cert, Czech Acad. Sci, Prague, 55. Intern. med, County Hosp, Most, Czech, 49-51; inst. exp. physiol, Charles Univ, Prague, 51-52; res. fel. cardiovasc. physiol, Inst. Cardiovasc. Res, Prague, 52-64; asst. prof, Bockus Res. Inst, Univ. Pa, 65-68, vis. asst. prof, 62-63; assoc. prof. AEROSPACE & MECH. ENG, SCI, SCH. MED, UNIV. CALIF, SAN DIEGO, 68-71, PROF, 71- Czech Army, Brit. Forces, 43-45, Lt. Czech. Soc. Cardiol.(hon. secy, 61-64); Czech. Soc. Physiol; Czech. Soc. Med. Electronics. Cardiovascular physiology; local thermodilution; cardiac energetics. Address: Dept. of Aerospace & Mechanical Engineering, Division of Bioengineering, School of Medicine, University of California, San Diego, P.O. Box 1090, La Jolla, CA 92037.

FRONEK, KITTY, b. Grenoble, France, Mar. 23, 25; m. 51; c. 2. HUMAN PHYSIOLOGY. M.D, Charles Univ, Prague, 51; C.Sc.(physiol), Czech. Acad. Sci, 60. Instr. pharmacol, med. sch, Charles Univ, Prague, 50-51; sr. investr. physiol. & clin. res, Inst. Cardiovasc. Res, 51-60; head physiol. div, nuclear lab, Inst. Clin. & Exp. Surg, 60-64; res. assoc. cardiovasc. res, med. sch, Temple Univ, 65-68; ASSOC. RES. BIOENGR, SCH. MED, UNIV. CALIF, SAN DIEGO, 68- Head, physiol. lab, Episcopal Hosp, Phila, Pa, 67-68. Am. Soc. Physiol; Am. Heart Asn. Control and regulation of the cardiovascular system under physiological and pathophysiological conditions; relationship between cardiac output, blood pressure and blood flow in several peripheral regions. Address: AMES-Basic Science Bldg, Room 5024, School of Medicine, University of California, La Jolla, CA 92037.

FRONING, GLENN WESLEY, b. Gray Summit, Mo, Sept. 8, 30; m. 62; c. 1. FOOD TECHNOLOGY, BIOCHEMISTRY. B.S, Missouri, 53, M.S, 57; Ph.D. (food tech), Minnesota, 61. Asst. prof, food sci, Rutgers, 61-63; POULTRY SCI, Univ. Ct, 63-66; PROF, UNIV. NEBR, LINCOLN, 66- U.S.A, 54-55, 1st Lt. Poultry Sci. Asn; Inst. Food Tech. Egg white proteins; binding and emulsification properties of poultry meat and poultry meat myoglobin. Address: Dept. of Poultry Science, University of Nebraska, Lincoln, NE 68503.

FRONING, H R(OBERT), b. Bushton, Kans, Sept. 8, 21; m. 46; c. 3. PHYSICAL CHEMISTRY. B.S, Ottawa (Kans), 43; M.A, Indiana, 44, All-Univ. fel, 48-49, Ph.D.(chem), 49. Chemist, Pan-Am. Petrol. Corp, 49-52, sr. chemist, 52-60, sr. res. engr, 60-63, res. assoc, 63, staff res. scientist, 64-69, RES. GROUP SUPVR, AMOCO PROD. CO, 69- U.S.N.R, 44-52, Lt. Am. Chem. Soc; Soc. Petrol. Eng. Secondary recovery of crude oil; surface chemistry; natural gas processing. Address: Research Center, Amoco Production Co, P.O. Box 591, Tulsa, OK 74102.

FRONING, J(OSEPH) FENDALL, b. Columbus, Ohio, Aug. 9, 16; m. 40; c. 5. ORGANIC CHEMISTRY. B.S, Notre Dame, 37, M.S, 38, Ph.D.(org. chem), 40. Res. chemist Jackson Lab, E.I. DU PONT DE NEMOURS & CO, INC, 40-52, mfg. div, org. chem. dept, 52-62, SUPT. Ponsol Prod. Area, 62-69, CHEM. AREA, 69- Am. Chem. Soc; Am. Inst. Chem. Eng. Surfactants; petroleum additives; rubber chemicals; dyes. Address: P.O. Box 391, R.D. Three, Kennett Square, PA 19348.

FRONK, W(ILLIAM) DON, b. Odgen, Utah, Aug. 30, 20; m. 51; c. 3. ECONOMIC ENTOMOLOGY. B.S, Utah State Agr. Col, 42; M.S, Iowa State Col, 49, Ph.D.(entomol), 53. Asst. entomologist, Va. Agr. Exp. Sta, 46-49; assoc. & instr. ENTOMOL, Iowa State Col, 50-54; assoc. prof, agr. exp. sta, Univ. Wyo, 54-64, prof, 64-67; PROF. & HEAD DEPT, COLO. STATE UNIV, 67- Med.C, 43-44, Sanit.C, 44-46, Capt. AAAS; Entom. Soc. Am; Ecol. Soc. Am. Control of insects attacking western farm crops. Address: 1104 Stover, Ft. Collins, CO 80521.

FRONTERA-REICHARD, JOSE GUILLERMO, b. Aguadilla, P.R, Jan. 20, 19; wid; c. 3. NEUROANATOMY. B.S, Puerto Rico, 40; Puerto Rico scholar, Michigan, 45-48, M.S, 46, Rackham Sch. Grad. Studies fel, 47-48, Ph.D. (anat), 48. Instr. comp. vert. anat, Nat. Univ. Panama, 41-43; biol. sci, UNIV. P.R, 43-45, assoc. prof. biol. & chmn. dept, 48-50, asst. prof. ANAT, SCH. MED, 50-53, assoc. prof, 53-63, PROF, 63- Spec. res. fel. U.S. Pub. Health Serv, col. physicians & surg, Columbia, 55; consult, perinatal physiol. lab, U.S. Pub. Health Serv, San Juan, P.R, 56. Am. Asn. Anat; Am. Acad. Neurol. Mammalian vascular anomalies; the anuran diencephalon; function and connections of insular region of macaque's brain; neurohistological techniques; effects of fixatives, storage, and dehydrating fluids on measurements of macaque brains. Address: Dept. of Anatomy, University of Puerto Rico School of Medicine, San Juan, P.R. 00931.

FROSCH, ROBERT A(LAN), b. New York, N.Y, May 22, 28; m. 57; c. 2. PHYSICS. A.B, Columbia, 47, M.A, 49, Ph.D.(theoret. physics), 52. Res. scientist, theoret. physics, Hudson Labs, Columbia, 51-53, asst. dir. theoret. div, 53-54, assoc. dir, 54-56, dir, 56-63; nuclear test detection, adv. res. proj. agency, Off. Secy. Defense, 63-65, dep. dir, 65-66; ASST. SECY. OF NAVY FOR RES. & DEVELOP, DEPT. OF NAVY, 66- Chmn, Interagency Comt. Oceanog, 66-67; mem, Interagency Comt. Marine Res, Educ. & Facilities, 67-69; chmn. U.S. del, Intergovt. Oceanog. Comt, UNESCO, Paris, 67 & 70; Dept. Defense mem, Comt. for Policy & Rev. of Nat. Coun. Marine Resources & Eng. Develop, 69-; mem. vis. comt. earth sci, Mass. Inst. Technol. Arthur S. Flemming Award, 66. Nat. Acad. Eng; fel. AAAS; fel. Acoustical Soc. Am; Am. Phys. Soc; fel. Inst. Elec. & Electronics Eng; Am. Geophys. Union; Soc. Explor. Geophys; Seismol. Soc. Am. Theoretical physics; acoustical oceanography; marine physics; seismology; system analysis and design. Address: Dept. of the Navy, Room 4E736, The Pentagon, Washington, DC 20350.

FROSCH, R(OBERT) PETER, b. Summit, N.J, Apr. 27, 37; m. 68. PHYSICAL CHEMISTRY, SPECTROSCOPY. B.S, Union Col.(N.Y), 59, Woodrow Wilson fel, 59-60; Nat. Sci. Found. fel, Calif. Inst. Technol, 62-63, Ph.D.(phys. chem), 65. Res. assoc. phys. chem, Enrico Fermi Inst, Univ. Chicago, 64-66; asst. prof. CHEM, Univ. Calif, Berkeley, 66-71; ASSOC. PROF, UNION COL,(N.Y), 71- Am. Chem. Soc; Am. Phys. Soc. Electronic absorption and emission spectra of molecules trapped in inert solids; electron paramagnetic resonance of organic triplet states; theory of nonradiative relaxation of electronically excited molecules. Address: Dept. of Chemistry, Union College, Schenectady, NY 12308.

FROSETH, JOHN A(LLEN), b. Eau Claire, Wis, July 18, 42; m. 61; c. 2. ANIMAL NUTRITION. B.S, Wis. State Col, 64; M.S, Purdue Univ, 66, Ph.D. (animal nutrit), 70; Ford Found. grant, Nat. Univ. South, Arg, 67-69. Instr. ANIMAL SCI, Purdue Univ. & Nat. Univ. South, Arg, 67-69; ASST. PROF. & ASST. ANIMAL SCIENTIST, WASH. STATE UNIV, 69- AAAS; Am. Soc. Animal Sci; Am. Dairy Sci. Asn. Selenium and vitamin E metabolism in the pig; effects of age, sex and nutrition on swine carcass characteristics; nutritive value of forages; Northwest grains for swine. Address: Dept. of Animal Science, Washington State University, Pullman, WA 99163.

FROSHEISER, FRED I(MANUEL), b. Keeline, Wyo, Sept. 23, 13; m. 46. PLANT PATHOLOGY. B.S, Wyoming, 41, M.S, 49; fel, Minnesota, 54-55, Ph.D.(plant path), 55. Asst. county agr. exten. agent, Lander, Wyo, 41-42; instr. agron, Wyoming, 46-49; Veteran's on-the-farm training, Minn, 49-51; PLANT PATHOLOGIST, AGR. RES. SERV, U.S. DEPT. AGR, UNIV. MINN, ST. PAUL, 55- U.S.A, 42-45. Am. Phytopath. Soc. Alfalfa improvement, disease control; crop improvement. Address: Dept. of Plant Pathology, University of Minnesota, St. Paul, MN 55101.

FROSLIE, HAROLD M(ILTON), b. Philip, S.Dak, Nov. 6, 16; m. 42; c. 4. PHYSICS. B.A, Augustana Col, 40; M.S, Iowa, 42; Ph.D.(physics), Wisconsin, 47. Asst. physics, Iowa, 40-41, asst, 41-42; res. engr. in charge testing lab, Sylvania Elec. Prods, N.Y, 42-45; asst. physics, Wisconsin, 45-47; asst. prof, Kans. State Col, 47-49; PROF. ENG. PHYSICS & HEAD DEPT. PHYSICS, S.DAK. STATE UNIV, 49- Civilian with Off. Sci. Res. & Develop; U.S.A, 44. Nuclear physics; microwave propagation; molecular spectroscopy. Address: Dept. of Physics, South Dakota State University, University Station, SD 57006.

FROST, ALBERT D(ENVER), b. Mass, Feb. 12, 22; m. 56; c. 4. ELECTRICAL ENGINEERING. B.S, Tufts Univ, 44; A.M, Harvard, 47; Sc.D.(appl. physics), Mass. Inst. Technol, 52. Instr. physics, Tufts, 47-53, asst. prof, 53-57; from assoc. prof. to PROF. ELEC. ENG, UNIV. N.H, 57-, DIR. ANTENNA SYSTS. LAB, 58-, CHMN. Ph.D. ENGR. SIGNAL PROCESSING, 68- Res. assoc, acoust. lab, Mass. Inst. Tech, 49-53; engr, Bolt Beranek & Newman, 51-53; consult, Arthur D. Little, Inc, 56-57; asst. dir. res, Transistor Appln, Inc, 59-61; staff scientist, Inst. Defense Anal, 63-64; vis. prof, Jodrell Bank Radio Astron. Lab, Univ. Manchester, 64-65; consult, Stanford Res. Labs, 68-71. U.S.N.R, 44-46, Lt.(jg). Acoust. Soc. Am; Am. Soc. Eng. Educ; sr. mem. Inst. Elec. & Electronics Eng. Measurement of upper atmosphere tides and winds using meteor trails; radar; interferometer observations of ionospheric irregularities; radio astronomy; physical acoustics and noise control; antenna systems; piezoelectricity; electromagnetic wave guides. Address: Dept. of Electrical Engineering, Antenna Systems Lab, University of New Hampshire, Durham, NH 03824.

FROST, ARTHUR A(TWATER), b. Onarga, Ill, Aug. 3, 09; m. 34; c. 3. PHYSICAL CHEMISTRY. B.S, California, 31, Ph.D.(phys. chem), Princeton, 34. Res. fel, Harvard, 34-36; instr. CHEM, NORTHWEST. UNIV, 36-42, asst. prof, 42-48, assoc. prof, 48-54, PROF, 54-, chmn. dept, 57-62. AAAS; Am. Chem. Soc; Am. Phys. Soc. Molecular quantum mechanics. Address: Dept. of Chemistry, Northwestern University, Evanston, IL 60201.

FROST, BETTINA M(ARY), b. Ithaca, N.Y, Nov. 21, 16. MICROBIOLOGY. A.B, Cornell, 39, M.S, 40; Ph.D.(bacter), Rutgers, 58. Agent, bur. animal indust, Cornell, 41-42; med. technologist, Presby. Hosp, N.J, 42-44; asst. chemotherapy, Merck Inst. Therapeut. Res, 44-50, res. assoc. bact, 50-66, RES. FEL. MICROBIOL, MERCK SHARP & DOHME RES. LABS, 66- AAAS; Am. Soc. Microbiol; N.Y. Acad. Sci. Chemotherapy of bacterial infections. Address: 126 Salter St, Springfield, NJ 07081.

FROST, BRUCE W(ESLEY), b. Brunswick, Maine, Mar. 8, 41; m. 63; c. 2. BIOLOGICAL OCEANOGRAPHY. B.A, Bowdoin Col, 63; Ph.D.(oceanog), Univ. Calif, San Diego, 69. ASST. PROF. OCEANOG, UNIV. WASH, 69- Nat. Sci. Found. res grant, 70-72. AAAS; Am. Soc. Limnol. & Oceanog; Soc. Syst. Zool. Ecology and systematics of marine zooplankton. Address: Dept. of Oceanography, University of Washington, Seattle, WA 98105.

FROST, DAVID, b. Brooklyn, N.Y, Dec. 19, 25; m. 46; c. 2. EMBRYOLOGY. B.S, City Col. New York, 46, M.S, 52; Ph.D, N.Y. Univ, 60. Tutor biol, City Col. New York, 46-49; instr, private sch, 49-52; biol. sci. Rutgers Univ, 52-56, asst. prof, 56-59; MGR. SCI. ED. SECT, SQUIBB INST. MED. RES, 59- Lectr, Rutgers Univ, 53- AAAS; Coun. Biol. Ed. Genetic control of axolotl pigmentation; inhibition of lens regeneration in Diemictylus viridescens. Address: Squibb Institute for Medical Research, New Brunswick, NJ 08903.

FROST, DAVID C(REGEEN), b. Ormskirk, Eng, Mar. 27, 29; m. 60. PHYSICAL CHEMISTRY. B.Sc, Liverpool, Eng, 53, Ph.D.(chem), 58. PROF.

CHEM, UNIV. B.C, 59- Fel. Am. Chem. Soc; Can. Inst. Chem. Photoelectron spectroscopy; ionization and dissociation of molecules by electron and photon impact. Address: Dept. of Chemistry, University of British Columbia, Vancouver, B.C, Can.

FROST, DOUGLAS VAN ANDEN, b. Pittsburgh, Pa, Oct. 31, 10; m. 40; c. 4. BIOCHEMISTRY. A.B, Illinois, 33; M.S, Wisconsin, 38, Ph.D.(biochem), 40. Res. & anal. chemist, Pacini Labs, Chicago, 34-35; chemist, Rival Packing Co, 35-36; asst. biochem, Wisconsin, 36-40; res. biochemist, Abbott Labs, 40-45, head nutrit. res, 46-59, res. specialist, 60-66; res. assoc, med. sch, Dartmouth Col. & Brattleboro Hosp, Vt, 66-69; CONSULT. NUTRIT. BIOCHEM, 69- Consult, selenium-tellurium develop. asn, 61-; EPA Water Qual. Off, 71-; indust. task force agr. arsenical pesticides, Nat. Agr. Chem. Asn, 70; mem. amino acids adv. bd, U.S. Pharmacopeia; Agr. Res. Inst; comt. selenium in nutrit, Nat. Acad. Sci-Nat. Res. Coun; subpanel arsenic, Off. Sci. & Technol, 71. AAAS; Am. Chem. Soc; Am. Soc. Biol. Chem; Am. Inst. Nutrit.(treas, 62-65); Am. Soc. Animal Sci; Animal Nutrit. Res. Coun; Metric Asn.(pres, 68-70); N.Y. Acad. Sci. Nutrition; pharmaceutical and agricultural chemistry; vitamins trace elements; arsenic and selenium; safety evaluation. Address: 48 High St, Brattleboro, VT 05301.

FROST, FREDERICK HAZARD, b. Hanover, N.H, Jan. 11, 02; m. 24; c. 3. PAPER TECHNOLOGY. B.S, Chicago, 23; Ph.D.(bot), California, 27. Nat. Res. Coun. fel, Harvard, 27-29; asst, S.D. Warren Co, 29-32, asst. supt. coating dept, 32-35, supt, 35-40, res. mgr, 40-48, res. dir, 48-52, mem. bd. dirs, 52-67, v.pres, 53-67; RETIRED. Tech. Asn. Pulp & Paper Indust. Lithography; paper coatings; letterpress printing; fundamentals of paper making; botany. Address: 1366 Westbrook St, Portland, ME 04102.

FROST, H(AROLD) BONNELL, b. Ft. Washakie, Wyo, Dec. 3, 23; m. 46; c. 4. ELECTRONICS. B.S, Nebraska, 48; S.M, Mass. Inst. Tech, 50, Sc.D. (elec. eng), 54. Asst, Lincoln Lab, Mass. Inst. Tech, 48-54; MEM. TECH. STAFF, BELL TEL. LABS, N.J, 54-63, PA, 63- U.S.N.R, 42-46. AAAS; sr. mem. Inst. Elec. & Electronics Eng. Engineering applications of digital computers; characterization of solid state devices. Address: Nine Bluebird Dr, Wyomissing, PA 19610.

FROST, HERBERT H(AMILTON), b. N.Y.C, Jan. 22, 17; m. 48; c. 5. VERTEBRATE ZOOLOGY. B.A, Brigham Young Univ, 41, M.S, 47; Ph.D, Cornell Univ, 55. Teacher & head dept. biol. scis, Ricks Col, 47-60, chmn. div. math. & natural scis, 55-60; assoc. prof. ZOOL, BRIGHAM YOUNG UNIV, 60-67, PROF, 67- Med. Dept, 42-46, M/Sgt. AAAS; Wilson Ornith. Soc. Ornithology; natural history; conservation. Address: Dept. of Zoology, Brigham Young University, Provo, UT 84601.

FROST, J(ACKIE) G(ENE), b. Feb. 18, 37; U.S. citizen; m. 63. CHEMISTRY, POLAROGRAPHY. B.S, Eastern Illinois, 58; Du Pont fel, Duke, 60-61, Tenn. Eastman Co. fel, 61-62, Ph.D.(polarography), 62. Res. assoc, North Carolina, 62-63; develop. chemist, anal. instrumentation, HALLIBURTON CO, 63-66, res. chemist, 66-69, SR. RES. CHEMIST, 69- Am. Chem. Soc. Organic polarography; complex ion chemistry; potentiometry. Address: Halliburton Co, Duncan, OK 73533.

FROST, JOHN K(INGSBURY), b. Sioux Falls, S.Dak, Mar. 12, 22; m. 49; c. 7. MEDICINE, PATHOLOGY. B.A, California, 43, M.D, 46; cert, Harvard Med. Sch, 48, Armed Forces Inst. Path, 51, Army Grad. Sch. Med, 52. Intern, San Francisco Hosp, California, 47, fel. med. & path, hosp. & instr, sch. med, 48, instr. path. & jr. res. pathologist, sch. med. & cancer res. inst, 53-56; ASST. PROF. gynecol, SCH. MED, JOHNS HOPKINS UNIV, 56-60, GYNECOL. & OBSTET, 60-, ASSOC. PROF. PATH. & DIR. POSTGRAD. INST. CYTOPATH, 59-, HEAD, DIV. CYTOPATH, 56-, PATHOLOGIST & HEAD DEPT. CYTOPATH, HOSP, 59- Spec. scholar, Calif. Pub. Health Serv, 48; assoc. prof. path. & head, div. cytopath, sch. med, Maryland, 56-59. Consult, Cent. Identification Lab, Hawaii, 50-52; U.S. Army, 55-56, 60-; U.S. Pub. Health Serv, 59-; Am. Bd. Path, 62- Dipl, Am. Bd. Path, 53. Med.C.Res, 42-61, Lt. Col. AAAS; fel. Am. Soc. Clin. Path; Am. Soc. Cytol.(pres, 64-65); Am. Med. Asn; Asn. Am. Med. Cols; Am. Fedn. Clin. Res; fel. Col. Am. Path; N.Y. Acad. Sci; Int. Acad. Cytol. Cytology; cytopathology; carcinogenesis; hormonal effects; Trichomonas; pulmonary fine structure; bronchoalveolarcytogenesis; early cancer diagnosis; television microscopy. Address: 610 Pathology Bldg, Johns Hopkins Hospital, Baltimore, MD 21205.

FROST, JOHN W, b. Monongahela, Pa, May 30, 20; m. 44; c. 4. MEDICINE, HEMATOLOGY. M.D, Pennsylvania, 44. Intern univ. hosp, Pennsylvania, 44-45, resident, sch. med, 45-48, fel. hemat, 48-49; res. assoc. MED, Eli Lilly & Co, 49-50; assoc, sch. med, Pennsylvania, 50-52, asst. prof, 52-58, assoc. prof, 58-65, PROF, 65-68; SCH. MED, UNIV. MINN, MINNEAPOLIS, 68-; DIR. DEPT. INTERNAL MED, ST. PAUL RAMSEY HOSP, 68- Fel. Am. Col. Physicians; Am. Soc. Hemat. Clinical research; internal medicine. Address: Dept. of Internal Medicine, St. Paul Ramsey Hospital, St. Paul, MN 55101.

FROST, LAWRENCE W(ILLIAM), b. Fredonia, N.Y, Dec. 2, 20; m. 42; c. 2. POLYMER CHEMISTRY. A.B, Allegheny Col, 41; Ph.D.(org. chem), Purdue, 44. Res. Found. fel, Purdue, 44-46; res. chemist, WESTINGHOUSE ELEC. CORP, 46-59, FEL. CHEMIST, 59- AAAS; Am. Chem. Soc. Organic fluorine and organo silicon compounds; aromatic polyimides; high temperature electrical varnishes and wire enamels; laminates. Address: Research Labs, Westinghouse Electric Corp, Pittsburgh, PA 15235.

FROST, L(ESLIE) S(WIFT), b. Pittsburgh, Pa, May 7, 22; m. 47; c. 2. ELECTRICAL ENGINEERING. B.S, Carnegie Inst. Tech, 46, M.S, 48, D.Sc.(elec. eng), 49. RES. ENGR. PHYSICS, WESTINGHOUSE RES. LABS, 49- U.S.A, 43-46, 1st Lt. Am. Phys. Soc; Am. Inst. Elec. & Electronics Eng. Feasibility of cesium vapor ignitrons; studies of low pressure helium positive column; interpretation of electron transport data; metal vapor arc lamps; experimental and theoretical studies of gas-blast circuit breaker arcs. Address: Westinghouse Research Lab, Pittsburgh, PA 15235.

FROST, PAUL D(AVIS), b. Beverly, Mass, Aug. 9, 16; m. 43; c. 2. METALLURGY. B.Met.Eng, Rensselaer Polytech. Inst, 40. Metallurgist, Republic Steel Corp, N.Y, 40-43; instr. metall, Cornell, 41-45, sr. process engr, airplane div, Curtiss-Wright, 43-45; res. engr, BATTELLE MEM. INST, 46-53, chief light metals div, 53-60, sr. res. adv. metal prod. planning, 60-70, SR. ADV. TECH. & BUS. PLANNING SECT, DEPT. SOCIAL & MGT. SYSTS, 70- Am. Soc. Metals; Am. Foundrymen's Soc; Am. Inst. Mining, Metall. & Petrol. Eng; Magnesium Asn. Ferrous and nonferrous metallurgy; technical economic research in metals, processes and business planning. Address: Battelle, 505 King Ave, Columbus, OH 43201.

FROST, ROBERT EDWIN, b. Gowanda, N.Y, Feb. 1, 32; m. 58; c. 3. INORGANIC CHEMISTRY. B.S, Allegheny Col, 53; A.M, Harvard, 55, Ph.D. (chem), 57. Res. chemist, res. ctr, B.F. Goodrich Co, Ohio, 57-61; assoc. prof. CHEM, STATE UNIV. N.Y. ALBANY, 61-64, PROF, 64- Vis. lectr, Illinois, 65-66. Am. Chem. Soc. Transition metal complexes; organometallic chemistry. Address: Dept. of Chemistry, State University of New York at Albany, Albany, NY 12203.

FROST, ROBERT H(ARTWIG), b. Riverside, Calif, July 2, 17; m. 44; c. 2. PHYSICS. A.B, California, 39, M.A, 45, Ph.D.(physics), 47. Asst. PHYSICS, California, 41-45; asst. prof, Missouri, 47-53; asst. prof, CALIF. STATE POLYTECH. COL, SAN LUIS OBISPO, 53-57, assoc. prof, 57-63, PROF, 63-, HEAD DEPT, 71- C.W.S, U.S.A, 45-46. AAAS; Am. Asn. Physics Teachers; Am. Phys. Soc. Specific ionization of electrons; cloud chamber investigation of cosmic radiation. Address: Dept. of Physics, California State Polytechnic College, San Luis Obispo, CA 93401.

FROST, ROBERT R(EX), b. Rochester, Minn, June 14, 40. PHYSICAL CHEMISTRY. B.A, Mankato State Col, 62; Ph.D.(phys. chem), Iowa State Univ, 68. Res. scientist, plant foods res. div, Continental Oil Co, 68-69; ASST. PHYS. CHEMIST, ILL. STATE GEOL. SURV, 69- Am. Chem. Soc. Surface chemistry; adsorption of gases and vapors by solid adsorbents; sulfur dioxide removal from power plant stack gases by limestone injection process. Address: 394 Jefferson St, Route 1, Mahomet, IL 61853.

FROST, ROBERT T, b. Towson, Md, Sept. 14, 24; m. 48; c. 5. PHYSICS. A.B, Hopkins, 49, Atomic Energy Cmn. fel, 51-53, Ph.D, 53. Jr. instr. physics, Hopkins, 49-51; res. assoc, Knolls Atomic Power Lab, GEN. ELEC. CO, 53-55, mgr. critical assemblies groups, 55-57, adv. reactor physics, 57-59, adv. concepts, 59-61, consult, SPACE SCI. LABS, 61-62, MGR. SPACE PHYSICS, 62- Mem. space & atmos. physics comt, Am. Inst. Aeronaut. & Astronaut. U.S. Merchant Marine, 43-45, Ens. Am. Phys. Soc; Am. Nuclear Soc; Am. Geophys. Union. Reactions of light nuclei; nuclear power reactors; space physics; geophysics; development of airborne and satellite experiments for remote sensing of earth and atmosphere, cosmic rays, zero gravity studies. Address: General Electric Co, P.O. Box 8555, Philadelphia, PA 19101.

FROST, ROGER A(NTHONY), b. York, Eng, Nov. 30, 44; m; c. 1. PLANT ECOLOGY. B.Sc, Univ. London, 65, A.R.C.S, Imp. Col. Sci. & Technol, 65; Ph.D.(plant ecol), Univ. West. Ont, 71. Instr. BOT, ERINDALE COL, UNIV. TORONTO, 70-71, ASST. PROF, 71- Autecology of plants; ecology of the weeds of arable crops studied at the species and population levels. Address: Dept. of Botany, Erindale College, University of Toronto, 3359 Mississauga Rd, Clarkson, Ont, Can.

FROST, STANLEY H, b. Amboy, Ill, May 7, 37; m. 62; c. 1. GEOLOGY, PALEONTOLOGY. B.S, Northern Illinois, 61; M.S, Illinois, 63, Ph.D.(paleont, geol), 66. Asst. prof. GEOL, NORTH. ILL. UNIV, 65-69, ASSOC. PROF, 69- Paleont. Soc; Geol. Soc. Am. Carbonate petrology of Silurian and Devonian, Indiana and Nevada Devonian brachiopods and corals; southeastern Nevada Tertiary larger Foraminifera and corals; northern Central America Tertiary biostratigraphy of western Caribbean. Address: Division of Geology, Dept. of Earth Science, Northern Illinois University, DeKalb, IL 60115.

FROST, THOMAS ROGERS, b. Portland, Ore, Sept. 20, 23; m. 49; c. 3. FOREST PRODUCTS, CHEMISTRY. B.A, Lewis & Clark Col, 48; M.S, Oregon State, 50. Technologist, spec. prod. div, WEYERHAEUSER CO, 50-57, res. scientist, res. div, 58-61, sect. chief composite prod, 61-64, dept. mgr, 64-68, MGR, panel & molded prods. develop. dept, 68-70, REGIONAL SERV, WOOD PRODS. RES, DEVELOP. & PROCESS ENG, 70- Assoc. mem. tech. studies adv. cmt. characteristics exterior wall cladding mat. & cladded bldg. components, bldg. res. adv. bd, Nat. Acad. Sci, 62-63. U.S.A.A.F, 42-46. Forest Prod. Res. Soc. Particleboard, hardboard, plywood, doors, molded products, fire testing and fire rated products; wood hydrolysis and production of levulinic acid; by-product utilization, especially bark and wood fiber. Address: Regional Services, Wood Products Research, Weyerhaeuser Co, Longview, WA 98632.

FROST, WALTER, b. Edmonton, Alta, Apr. 6, 35; m. 62; c. 2. MECHANICAL ENGINEERING, HEAT TRANSFER. B.S, Washington (Seattle), 61, M.S, 63, Nat. Defense Educ. Act fel. & Ph.D.(mech. eng), 65. ASSOC. PROF. MECH. ENG, SPACE INST, UNIV. TENN, 65- Am. Soc. Mech. Eng; Am. Inst. Aeronaut. & Astronaut. Boiling heat transfer and two phase flow; radiation and convection heat transfer from finned surfaces; natural convection from finite horizontal surfaces; heat transfer in porous media. Address: University of Tennessee Space Institute, Tullahoma, TN 37388.

FROST, WALTER S(PRAGUE), b. Roxbury, Mass, Jan. 25, 90; m. 45; c. 1. PHARMACEUTICAL CHEMISTRY. B.S, Tufts, 12; Ph.D.(inorg. chem), Cornell, 23. Asst. chemist, Corn Prods. Ref. Co, N.J, 12-13; Exp. Sta, Massachusetts, 13-14; asst. & instr. chem, Cornell, 15-19; instr, West Virginia, 19-20; asst. prof, New Hampshire, 20-26; chemist, Burnham Soluble Iodine Co, 29-50; proprietor, W.S. Frost Co, 51-52; pres, treas. & dir, Frost Labs, Inc, 52-71; RETIRED. Instr, Lincoln Tech. Inst, 37-42; asst. prof, Northeastern, 42-43; lectr, Tufts, 47-49. AAAS; Am. Chem. Soc; fel. Am. Inst. Chem. Ammonium trinitride; medical uses of iodine; amino acid addition compounds; iodine water sterilizing tablets; chloramine-T. Address: Box 66, Auburndale, MA 02166.

FROSTICK, FREDERICK CHARLES, JR, b. Maxton, N.C, Aug. 3, 22; m. 53; c. 2. ORGANIC CHEMISTRY. B.S, Duke, 43, Ph.D.(chem), 51. Res. assoc. org. chem, RES. & DEVELOP, UNION CARBIDE CORP, 50-56, group leader, 56-58, asst. to dir. res, 58-64, assoc. dir. admin, 64-70, SITE ADMINSTR, 70- U.S.N.R, 43-46, Lt. AAAS; Am. Chem. Soc. Oxidations of organic compounds; synthetic organic chemistry; research administration. Address: Union Carbide Corp, S. Charleston Technical Center, P.O. Box 8361, S. Charleston, WV 25303.

FROTHINGHAM, THOMAS ELIOT, b. Boston, Mass, June 21, 26; m. 54; c. 4. TROPICAL MEDICINE, PUBLIC HEALTH. M.D, Harvard Med. Sch, 51. Teaching fel. pediat, Harvard, 56-57, res. fel, 57-58; asst. prof. epidemiol, Tulane, 59-60; assoc. mem, Pub. Health Res. Inst, City of New York, Inc, 60-61; asst. prof. trop. pub. health, Harvard, 61-65, assoc. prof, 66-69; MEM. STAFF, CORVALLIS CLIN, ORE, 69- Am. Soc. Trop. Med. & Hyg. Infectious diseases; clinical, laboratory and public health aspects. Address: Corvallis Clinic, 530 N.W. 27th St, Corvallis, OR 97330.

FROUNFELKER, ROBERT E, b. West Allis, Wis, Apr. 20, 25; m. 45; c. 4. ENGINEERING SCIENCE. B.M.E, Marquette, 45, M.S, 48 & 63. Asst. physics, Marquette, 46-48, instr. math, 48-53, asst. prof, 53-63; assoc. prof. ENG, SCI, TENN. TECHNOL. UNIV, 63-66, PROF, 66- Consult. engr, Bayley Blower Co, 58-63, Sheldons Eng. Ltd. & Clarage Fan Co, 59-63; comput. consult, Johnson Serv. Co, 60-63. U.S.N, 43-46, Lt.(jg). Materials and computer science; computer techniques for rating capacities of air moving equipment; determination of the cohesive and surface energies of ionic crystals. Address: Dept. of Engineering Science, Tennessee Technological University, Cookeville, TN 38501.

FROYD, JAMES DONALD, b. Brooklyn, N.Y, May 25, 39; m. 63; c. 2. PLANT PATHOLOGY. B.S, Denison, 61; M.S, Minnesota, 64, Ph.D.(plant path), 67. Res. asst. plant diseases, Minnesota, St. Paul, 61-65, exten. plant pathologist, 65-67; SR. PLANT PATHOLOGIST, ELI LILLY & CO, 67- Am. Phytopath. Soc. Ecology of the dissemination of forest pathogens; diseases of ornamentals; chemical control of plant diseases; systemic fungicides. Address: R.R. 1, Box 16A, Fountaintown, IN 46130.

FRUEH, ALFRED J(OSEPH), JR, b. Passaic, N.J, Sept. 2, 19; m. 43; c. 3. CRYSTALLOGRAPHY, MINERALOGY. B.S, Mass. Inst. Technol, 42, fel, 46-49, M.S, 47, Ph.D.(mineral), 49. Res. assoc, Chicago, 49-52, asst. prof. mineral. & crystallog, 52-58; vis. prof, Oslo, 58-59; asst. prof. crystallog, McGill Univ, 59-62, assoc. prof, 62-68, prof, 68-69; PROF. GEOL. & CHMN. DEPT, UNIV. CONN, 69- Chmn. teaching comn, Int. Union Crystallog, 60-66, Int. Union Crystallog. rep, Int. Coun. Sci. Unions, 63-66. U.S.N.R, 42-46, Lt. Mineral. Soc. Am; Geol. Soc. Am; Geochem. Soc; Am. Crystallog. Asn; Mineral. Asn. Can; Fr. Soc. Mineral. & Crystallog; Mineral. Soc. Gt. Brit. & Ireland. X-ray crystallography; mineral structures; solid state physics and chemistry applied to minerals. Address: Dept. of Geology & Geography, University of Connecticut, Storrs, CT 06268.

FRUH, E. GUS, b. N.Y.C, Jan. 6, 39; m. 65; c. 2. ENVIRONMENTAL HEALTH ENGINEERING, WATER CHEMISTRY. B.C.E, Manhattan Col, 61; M.S, Wisconsin, 63; U.S. Pub. Health Serv. fel, 63-65, Ph.D.(water chem), 65. U.S. Pub. Health Serv. trainee, Wisconsin, 61-63, fel. lake ecol, 65-66; ASST. PROF. CIVIL ENG, UNIV. TEX, AUSTIN, 66- Consult, Galveston Bay Ecol-Biol. Comt, summer 67; Proj. Mem. Adv. Bd, Jamaica Bay, N.Y. Study, 68- Am. Water Pollution Control Fedn; Am. Water Works Asn. Water chemistry, pollution control and treatment. Address: Dept. of Civil Engineering, University of Texas, Austin, TX 78712.

FRUHMAN, GEORGE JOSHUA, b. Boston, Mass, Oct. 17, 24. ANATOMY. A.B, N.Y. Univ, 48, M.S, 52, Ph.D,54. Fel, Damon Runyon Found, N.Y. Univ, 54-56; asst. prof. biol, Stern Col. for Women, YESHIVA UNIV, 55-58, ANAT, ALBERT EINSTEIN COL. MED, 56-70, ASSOC. PROF, 70- Lectr, N.Y. Univ. U.S.A, 43-46. Fel. N.Y. Acad. Sci; Am. Asn. Anat; Am. Zool. Soc; Reticuloendothelial Soc; Soc. Exp. Biol. & Med; Am. Soc. Hemat. Experimental hematology; histology. Address: Dept. of Anatomy, Albert Einstein College of Medicine, New York, NY 10461.

FRUMIN, ABRAHAM M(AURICE), b. Passaic, N.J, Feb. 20, 15; m. 50; c. 2. MEDICINE. A.B, Michigan, 36; M.D, Temple, 42. Resident & fel. path. & internal med, Queen's Gen. Hosp, 46-48; fel. hematol, J.H. Pratt Diagnostic Hosp, 48-49; clin. asst, MED, MED. COL. OF PA, 49-50, clin. instr, 50-51, instr, 51-53, assoc, 53-55, asst. prof, 55-62, CLIN. ASSOC. PROF, 62- Consult, Vet. Admin. Hosp, Phila. Dipl. Am. Bd. Internal Med. Med.C, 43-46, Capt. AAAS; Soc. Int. Med; Am. Soc. Hemat; Am. Fedn. Clin. Res; Am. Col. Physicians; Int. Soc. Hemat; Int. Soc. Internal Med. Hematology. Address: 515 Howe Rd, Merion Station, PA 19066.

FRUMIN, M(ORRIS) JACK, b. Passaic, N.J, Sept. 5, 19; m. 43; c. 3. ANESTHESIOLOGY. A.B, Temple, 40, M.D, 46. Intern, City Hosp, Welfare Island, N.Y, 46-47; res. ANESTHESIOL, Presby. Hosp, 47-49; instr, col. physicians & surgeons, Columbia, 49-52, assoc, 52-54, asst. prof, 54-59, assoc. prof, 59-60; prof, Jefferson Med. Col, 60; clin. prof, ALBERT EINSTEIN COL. MED, 61-67; ASSOC. PROF, 68- Asst, Presby. Hosp, 49-52, assoc, 52-54, asst. attend. anesthesiologist, 54-; dir. anesthesiol, Beth El Hosp, Brooklyn, 61-63; assoc. attend. anesthesiologist, Mt. Sinai Hosp, 63-68, assoc. clin. prof, Mt. Sinai Sch. Med, 66-68; attend. anesthesiologist, Bronx Munic. Hosp. Ctr, 68- Harvey Soc; Am. Soc. Anesthesiol; Am. Physiol. Soc; Am. Soc. Pharmacol. & Exp. Therapeut; N.Y. Acad. Sci. Peridural anesthesia; respiratory mechanisms; spinal anesthesia; artificial respiration; automatic maintenance of anesthesia; carbon dioxide homeostasis; apneic oxygenation; amnesia; central action curare; acid-base balance. Address: Dept. of Anesthesiology, Albert Einstein College of Medicine, Bronx, NY 10461.

FRUMKES, THOMAS EUGENE, b. Rochester, N.Y, July 25, 41. PHYSIOLOGICAL PSYCHOLOGY, NEUROPHYSIOLOGY. A.B, Cornell, 63; U.S. Pub. Health Serv. fels, Syracuse, 64-67, Ph.D.(physiol. psychol), 67. Asst, Syracuse, 63-64; Nat. Insts. Health fel, QUEENS COL.(N.Y), 67-69, lectr. PSYCHOL, 68-69, ASST. PROF, 69- Res. assoc, dept. neurosurg, Mt. Sinai Hosp, City Univ. New York, 69-70; dept. ophthal, col. physicians & surgeons, Columbia Univ, 70- AAAS; Optical Soc. Am; Asn. Res. Vision & Ophthal; N.Y. Acad. Sci; Am. Psychol. Asn. Vision; electrophysiology; psychophysics; sensory processes; central nervous system; cerebral cortex. Address: Dept. of Psychology, Queens College, Flushing, N.Y. 11367.

FRUMKIN, ROBERT M(ARTIN), Rehab. Psychol, Behav. Sci, see Suppl. I to 11th ed, Soc. & Behav. Vols.

FRUSH, CHARLES O(LIN), JR, b. Oskaloosa, Iowa, Oct. 20, 19; m. 41; c. 4. MINING ENGINEERING. B.S, Iowa State Col, 41, M.S, 55. Jr. mining engr, Chile Explor. Co, 41-44; asst. field engr. mineral explor, U.S. Smelting, Ref. & Mining Co, 44; engr, Frush Mining Co, 44-46; instr. MINING ENG, Iowa State Col, 46-56; asst. prof, eng. exp. sta, 50-56; ASSOC. PROF, COLO. SCH. MINES, 56- Am. Inst. Mining, Metall. & Petrol. Eng. Mineral technology. Address: Dept. of Mining Engineering, Colorado School of Mines, Golden, CO 80401.

FRUSH, HARRIET L(OUISE), b. Knoxville, Iowa, July 3, 03. ORGANIC CHEMISTRY. B.A, Cent. Col.(Iowa), 24, hon. Sc.D, 53; M.S, Iowa, 28; Ph.D.(org. chem), Maryland, 41. Teacher, high sch, Iowa, 24-26, 28-29; Colo, 26-27; chemist carbohydrate res. Nat. Bur. Standards, 29-71; RETIRED. Meritorious serv. award, U.S. Dept. Commerce, 59. AAAS; Am. Chem. Soc. Rare sugars and their derivatives; polyhydroxy acids; mutarotation reactions; effect of neighboring groups in the course of chemical reactions; methods for separation of uronic acids from natural products; synthesis of radioactive carbohydrates. Address: 4912 New Hampshire Ave. N.W, Washington, DC 20011.

FRUTH, LESTER S(YLVESTER), JR, b. Seneca Co, Ohio, July 16, 38; m. 63; c. 3. GEOLOGY, SEDIMENTOLOGY. B.S, Bowling Green State Univ, 60; M.A, Columbia Univ, 65, Ph.D, 67. Res. asst. GEOL, Columbia Univ, 65-67; RES. ASSOC, UNIV. ILL, URBANA, 67- Geol. Soc. Am. Experimental rock deformation; experimental diagenesis of carbonate sediments under high pressure. Address: Dept. of Geology, University of Illinois, Urbana, IL 61801.

FRUTHALER, G(EORGE) J(AMES), JR, b. New Orleans, La, Aug. 8, 25; m. 48; c. 3. MEDICINE. B.S, Tulane, 46, M.D, 48. Intern, Charity Hosp, La, 48-49; pediat, hosp, Vanderbilt, 49-50; fel, Ochsner Med. Found, 50-51, 53; MEM. PEDIAT. STAFF, OCHSNER CLIN, 53-; PROF. CLIN. PEDIAT, TULANE UNIV, 68-, assoc. prof, 65-68, asst. prof, 57-65, instr, 54-57. Asst. vis. physician, Charity Hosp, 50-68, vis. physician, 68- Dipl, Am. Bd. Pediat, 54, mem, 66-72. U.S.N.R, 43-46, 51-53, Lt.(jg). Am. Med. Asn; Am. Acad. Pediat. Pediatrics; allergy. Address: Ochsner Clinic, 1514 Jefferson Hwy, New Orleans, LA 70121.

FRUTON, JOSEPH S(TEWART), b. Czestochowa, Poland, May 14, 12; nat; m. 36. BIOCHEMISTRY. B.A, Columbia, 31, Gies fel, 32-33, Ph.D.(biochem), 34; hon. M.A, Yale, 50. Asst. biochem, col. physicians & surg, Columbia, 33-34; fel. chem, Rockefeller Inst, 34-35, asst, 35-38, assoc, 38-45; assoc. prof. physiol. chem, YALE, 45-50, prof. BIOCHEM, 50-57, EUGENE HIGGINS PROF, 57-, chmn. dept, 51-67, dir. div, sci, 59-62. Spec. fel, Rockefeller Found, 48; Commonwealth Fund fel, 62-63; vis. prof, Rockefeller Univ, 68-69. Chmn. panel enzymes, cmt. growth, Nat. Res. Coun, 46-49, mem. for biochem, adv. cmt, chem. biol. co-ord. center, 46-51, div. chem. & chem. tech, 50-52, fel. bd, 53-60, chmn, 58-60, mem. exec. cmt, div. med, sci, 60-63; Harvey lectr, 55; Dakin lectr, 62; mem, Int. Union Pure & Appl. Chem-Int. Union Biochem, 64-; consult, Anna Fuller Fund, 51- With Nat. Defense Res. Comt, 44-45. Nat. Acad. Sci; fel. AAAS; Am. Chem. Soc.(Lilly award, 44); Am. Soc. Biol. Chem; Am. Hist. Sci. Soc; Harvey Soc; Am. Acad. Arts & Sci; N.Y. Acad. Sci.(v.pres, 45-46); Am. Philos. Soc; Brit. Biochem. Soc; Brit. Chem. Soc; Benjamin Franklin fel. Royal Soc. Arts. Chemistry and metabolism of amino acids, peptides and proteins; enzymes. Address: 350 Kline Biology Tower, Yale University, New Haven, CT 06520.

FRY, ALBERT J(OSEPH), b. Phila, Pa, May 12, 37; m. 66; c. 2. ORGANIC CHEMISTRY. B.S, Univ. Mich, 58; Ph.D.(org. chem), Univ. Wis, 63. Res. fel. CHEM, Calif. Inst. Technol, 63-64; WESLEYAN UNIV, 64-65, ASST. PROF, 65- Am. Chem. Soc; The Chem. Soc; Int. Electrochem. Soc. Nonbenzenoid aromatic species; synthetic and mechanistic organic electrochemistry. Address: Hall-Atwater Lab. of Chemistry, Wesleyan University, Middletown, CT 06457.

FRY, ANNE E(VANS), b. Phila, Pa, Sept. 11, 39. ZOOLOGY, DEVELOPMENTAL BIOLOGY. A.B, Mt. Holyoke Col, 61; M.S, Univ. Iowa, 63; Ph.D. (zool), Univ. Mass, 69. Instr. biol, Carleton Col, 63-65; ASST. PROF. ZOOL, OHIO WESLEYAN UNIV, 69- AAAS; Am. Inst. Biol. Sci; Am. Soc. Zool; Soc. Develop. Biol. Amphibian limb regeneration; effects of temperature on amphibian metamorphosis; histochemical changes during amphibian metamorphosis. Address: Dept. of Zoology, Ohio Wesleyan University, Delaware, OH 43015.

FRY, ARTHUR (JAMES), b. Dodson, Mont, March 10, 21; m. 47; c. 3. ORGANIC CHEMISTRY. B.S, Mont. State Col, 43; fel, California, 48-51, Ph.D. (chem), 51. Assoc. chemist, Oak Ridge Nat. Lab, 46-48; asst. prof. CHEM, UNIV. ARK, FAYETTEVILLE, 51-55, assoc. prof, 55-59, PROF, 59-, chmn. dept, 64-67. Vis. prof, Univ. Auckland & Univ. Adelaide, 69-70. U.S.N.R, 44-46. AAAS; Am. Chem. Soc. Organic reaction mechanisms; isotope effects on rates of chemical reactions; acid catalyzed ketone rearrangements. Address: Dept. of Chemistry, University of Arkansas, Fayetteville, AR 72701.

FRY, CLEOTA G(AGE), b. Shoshone, Idaho, Dec. 30, 10. MATHEMATICS. B.A, Reed Col, 33; M.S, Purdue, 36, Ph.D.(math), 39. Asst. instr. math, PURDUE UNIV, 39-40, instr. physics, 41-45, MATH, 45-47, asst. prof, 47-55, ASSOC. PROF, 55-, asst. to dean sch. sci, 52-61. Am. Phys. Soc; Am. Math. Soc. Mathematical analysis in field of complex variables; acoustics; theoretical physics; calculation of atomic form factors; applied mathematics. Address: Dept. of Mathematics, Purdue University, Lafayette, IN 47907.

FRY, DAVID JOHN ILLINGWORTH, b. Leek, Eng, Aug. 7, 37; m. 68; c. 1. PHYSICS. B.Sc, Bristol, 58, Ph.D.(physics), 61. Lectr. PHYSICS, McGill, 61-64; ASST. PROF, UNIV. CALGARY, 64- Am. Asn. Physics Teachers; Can. Asn. Physicists; Royal Astron. Soc. Can. Electron paramagnetic resonance and electron-nuclear double resonance; design of spectrometer systems; transition and rare-earth ions in single crystals of inorganic and biological materials. Address: Dept. of Physics, University of Calgary, Calgary 44, Alta, Can.

FRY, DAVID L(LOYD GEORGE), b. Detroit, Mich, Sept. 22, 18; m. 42; c. 3. PHYSICS. B.A, Kalamazoo Col, 40; Kettering Found. fel, Antioch, 40-42; M.S, Ohio State, 42. Asst, Kalamazoo Col, 39-40; res. physicist, RES. LABS, GEN. MOTORS CORP, 42-52, SUPVR. spectros, 52-56, chem. physics, 56-65, CHEM. PHYSICS & MAGNETICS, 65- Fel. AAAS; Am. Phys. Soc; Optical Soc. Am. Emission and absorption spectroscopy in ultraviolet, visible and infrared; mass spectroscopy; diffusion of gases in solids; nuclear magnetic resonance; internal friction; electro-optics; magnetics. Address: Research Labs, General Motors Corp, Warren, MI 48090.

FRY, DONALD (LEWIS), b. Des Moines, Iowa, Dec. 29, 24; m. 57; c. 4. PHYSIOLOGY. M.D, Harvard, 49. Intern, Med, Univ. Hosps, Minnesota, 49-50, res. internal med. inst, 50-52, fel, Variety Club Heart Hosp, 52-53; independent investr, NAT. HEART & LUNG INST, 53-58, HEAD SECT. CLIN. BIOPHYS, 58- U.S.N.R, 43-46; U.S.P.H.S, 59-, Med. Dir. AAAS; Am. Physiol. Soc; Biophys. Soc; Am. Soc. Clin. Invest. Physiology and biophysics of the blood-vascular interface, with particular emphasis on mechano-chemical events associated with endothelial degeneration, transvascular lipoprotein transport and the genesis of atherosclerosis. Address: National Heart & Lung Institute, National Institutes of Health, Bethesda, MD 20014.

FRY, DONALD H(UME), JR, b. San Francisco, Calif, Sept. 2, 05; m. 37; c. 4. FISHERIES, BIOLOGY. A.B, Stanford, 27, M.A, 28. Asst. fisheries biologist, BUR. MARINE FISHERIES, STATE DIV. FISH & GAME, CALIF, 28-31, sr. fisheries researcher, 31-43, SR. MARINE BIOLOGIST, 43-, SUPVR. RES. & ANAL. SALMON & STEELHEAD INVESTS, 58-, RES. ANALYST, 59-, state marine fisheries invests, North. Calif, 47-58. Fisheries expert, Food & Agr. Orgn, UN, 57-58; Calif. state rep, Pacific Marine Fisheries Cmn, 48-57. Fel. Am. Inst. Fishery Res. Biol. Life history and conservation of marine and anadromous fishes; ocean waters and low elevation streams of California; Uganda, East Africa fisheries. Address: 1417 La Sierra Dr, Sacramento, CA 95825.

FRY, EDWARD I(RAD), b. U.S, Jan. 7, 24; m. 50. PHYSICAL ANTHROPOLOGY. B.A, Texas, 49, M.A, 50; Hemenway fel, Harvard, 52, univ. fels, 52-53, 54-55, Fulbright traveling fel, 53-54, Ph.D.(anthrop), 58. Office coordinator, Rimrock Values Study, Harvard, 50-51; asst. prof. anthrop. & tech. dir, anthropomet. proj, Antioch Col, 55-56; instr. ANTHROP, Univ. Nebr, Lincoln, 56-58, asst. prof, 58-62, assoc. prof, 62-66; PROF, SOUTH. METHODIST UNIV, 66- Fulbright res. fel, Univ. Hong Kong, 63-64. Field consult, Carnegie Inst, Mex, 55. U.S.A.F, 42-46, Res, 50-55, 2nd Lt. AAAS; Am. Anthrop. Asn; Am. Asn. Phys. Anthrop.(secy-treas); Soc. Study Human Biol; N.Y. Acad. Sci. Human biology, especially growth, body components and serology; Polynesia; Southeast Asia. Address: Dept. of Anthropology, Box 339, Southern Methodist University, Dallas, TX 75222.

FRY, FRANCIS J(OHN), b. Johnstown, Pa, Apr. 2, 20; m. 46; c. 9. ELECTRICAL ENGINEERING. B.S, Pa. State Univ, 40; M.S, Univ. Pittsburgh, 46. Design engr, Westinghouse Elec. Corp, 40-46; res. assoc. ELEC. ENG, UNIV. ILL, URBANA, 46-50, res. asst. prof, 50-57, res. assoc. prof, 57-68, ASSOC. PROF, 68-; SECY. & CHMN. BD. DIRS, INTERSCI. RES. INST, 70-, v.pres, 57-68, pres, 68-70. Artificial hearts, blood flow; effects of ultrasound on biological systems; ultrasonic soft tissue visualization and tissue modifying systems; neuroscience, quantitative aspects of structural organization in brain; relations between structure and function. Address: Biophysical Research Lab, University of Illinois, Urbana, IL 61803.

FRY, FRANKLIN HORNOR, b. Woodbury, N.J, Jan. 1, 37; m. 57; c. 5. INORGANIC & PHYSICAL CHEMISTRY. B.A, Princeton, 60, Sayre fel, 60-61, Esso Ed. Found. fel, 62-63, Ph.D.(chem), 64. Sr. scientist, Princeton Lab, AM. CAN CO, 64-67, res. assoc, 67-68, ASSOC. DIR. EXPLOR. RES, WIS, 68- Am. Chem. Soc. Inorganic reaction kinetics and reaction mechanisms; fluorescence and spectroscopy of coordination compounds; laser applications; disposable product development. Address: American Can Co, 333 N. Commercial St, Neenah, WI 54956.

FRY, F(REDERIC) S(UMMERVILLE), b. Pierce, Colo, March 28, 10; m. 36; c. 2. MECHANICAL ENGINEERING. B.S, Colorado State, 32; M.S, Colorado, 52. Self employed, 32-36; hydraul. engr, bur. agr. econ, U.S. Dept. Agr, 36-42; instr. aircraft drafting, Denver, 43-44; engr. prod. application, Gates Rubber Co, 44-45; hydrol, Bur. Reclamation, U.S. Dept. Interior, 45-46; asst. prof. MECH. ENG, UNIV. DENVER, 46-52, ASSOC. PROF, 52-, RES. ENGR. & CONSULT, DENVER, DENVER RES. INST, 54- Am. Soc. Mech. Eng; Am. Soc. Eng. Educ; Soc. Exp. Stress Anal. Internal combustion engines; experimental stress analysis; applied mechanics; ordnance. Address: 2727 S. Ogden St, Englewood, CO 80110.

FRY, F(REDERICK ERNEST JOSEPH), b. Surrey, England, Apr. 17, 08; Can. citizen; m. 35; c. 3. LIMNOLOGY. A.B, Toronto, 33, A.M, 35, Ph.D.(ichthyol), 36; D.Sc, Univ. Manitoba, 70. Assoc. prof. limnol, dept. zool, UNIV. TORONTO, 48-56, PROF. ZOOL, 56- Mem, Fisheries Res. Bd. Can, 64-69; comnr, Int. Great Lakes Fishery Comn, 69- Mem, Order of the Brit. Empire, 44; Govt. Can. Centennial Medal, 68. R.C.A.F, 41-45. Fel. Royal Soc. Can.(Flavelle Medal, 62); Am. Soc. Limnol. & Oceanog.(pres, 51); Am. Fisheries Soc.(pres, 66; gold medal, 71); Can. Soc. Zool.(pres, 66). Relation of fish to factors in their environment. Address: Dept. of Zoology, University of Toronto, Toronto 181, Ont, Can.

FRY, GLENN A(NSEL), b. Wellford, S.C, Sept. 10, 08; m. 35; c. 3. PHYSIOLOGICAL OPTICS. A.B, Davidson Col, 29; M.A, Duke, 31, Ph.D.(psychol), 32; hon. D.O.S, North. Ill. Col. Optom, 38; hon. D.Sci, Pa. Col. Optom. & hon. D.Nat. Sci, Univ. Munich, 69. Nat. res. fel, psychol, sch. med, Washington (St. Louis), 32-34, asst. ophthalmol, 34-35; asst. prof. PHYSIOL. OPTICS, OHIO STATE UNIV, 35-42, assoc. prof, 42-46, prof. & dir. sch. optom, 46-66, REGENTS PROF, COL. OPTOM, 66- Mem, Inter-Soc. Color Coun, 45-; U.S. Nat. Comt, Int. Comn. Optics; U.S. Nat. Comt, Int. Comn. Illum; Nat. Acad. Sci-Nat. Res. Coun. Comt. Vision. Fel. Optical Soc. Am. (Tillyer Medalist, 61); fel. Illum. Eng. Soc.(gold medalist, 69); Am. Optom. Asn.(Appollo Award, 69); fel. Am. Acad. Optom.(Prentice Award, 64); fel. Brit. Optical Asn. Electro physiology of the retina; color vision; visual acuity; accommodation and convergence. Address: College of Optometry, The Ohio State University, 338 W. Tenth Ave, Columbus, OH 43210.

FRY, HAROLD, b. Pierce, Colo, Oct. 16, 15; m. 39; c. 2. MECHANICAL ENGINEERING. B.S, Colorado State, 37; M.E, Wyoming, 50; M.S, Colorado, 57. Motor engr, Westinghouse Elec. Corp, 37-40; instr. machine design, Kansas State, 40-42; from asst. prof. to prof. mech. eng, Wyoming, 42-58; ASSOC. PROF. ENG, ARIZ. STATE UNIV, 58- Elec. engr, Nat. Adv. Comt. Aeronaut, 44-45. U.S.A.A.F.R, 44-45. Am. Soc. Mech. Eng; Am. Soc. Eng. Educ. Automotive engines; causes and corrections of bearing failures; wear rates of engine parts under adverse operating conditions. Address: Dept. of Mechanical Engineering, College of Engineering, Arizona State University, Tempe, AZ 85281.

FRY, JACK L(EROY), b. Thomas, Okla, Dec. 24, 30; m. 52; c. 3. FOOD TECHNOLOGY. B.S, Okla. State, 52, M.S, 56; Ph.D.(food tech), Purdue, 59. Asst. prof, Kans. State Univ, 59-64; assoc. prof. POULTRY SCI, UNIV. FLA, 64-70, PROF, 70-, faculty develop. grant, 70. Inst. Am. Poultry Industs. award, 69. U.S.A, 52-54, Res, 54-62, Capt. Poultry Sci. Asn; World Poultry Sci. Asn; Inst. Food Tech. Poultry products technology. Address: Dept. of Poultry Science, University of Florida, Gainesville, FL 32601.

FRY, JAMES L(ESLIE), b. Fostoria, Ohio, May 24, 41; m. 64. ORGANIC CHEMISTRY. B.S, Bowling Green State, 63; Ph.D.(org. chem), Mich. State, 67. Nat. Insts. Health fel. org. chem, Princeton, 67-69; ASST. PROF. CHEM, UNIV. TOLEDO, 69- Chemist, exp. sta, E.I. du Pont de Nemours & Co, summers, 63 & 64. Am. Chem. Soc. Carbonium ions; solvolvolysis mechanisms; structure and reactivity studies; kinetic isotope effects; asymmetric syntheses. Address: Dept. of Chemistry, University of Toledo, Toledo, OH 43606.

FRY, JOHN CRAIG, b. Salem, Ore, Dec. 11, 26; m. 49; c. 3. PHYSICAL OCEANOGRAPHY, ACOUSTICS. B.S, U.S. Naval Acad, 47; M.S, Univ. Calif, 52. Prog. off. acoustics, Naval Underwater Sound Lab, U.S. Navy, 56-59, proj. off, Cruiser Destroyer Flotilla Three, 60-62, head requirements br, oceanog. div, Off. Chief Naval Opers, 62-65; tech. asst. oceanog, Off. Sci. & Technol, Exec. Off. of President, 65-67, sr. staff mem, Nat. Coun. Marine Resources & Eng. Develop, 67-69; V.PRES, OCEAN DATA SYSTS, INC, 69- U.S.N, 47-67, Comdr. Am. Geophys. Union. Underwater acoustics; research administration. Address: 7200 Fairfax Rd, Bethesda, MD 20014.

FRY, JOHN SEDGWICK, b. Phila, Pa, Oct. 22, 29; m. 51; c. 2. ORGANIC CHEMISTRY. B.S, Duke Univ, 51, M.A, 55. Proj. scientist, plastics div, UNION CARBIDE CORP, 55-68, RES. SCIENTIST, RES. & DEVELOP. DEPT, 68- U.S.M.C, 51-53, Capt. Am. Chem. Soc. Polymers and resins and derived products. Address: Research & Development Dept, Union Carbide Corp, 1 River Rd, Bound Brook, NJ 08805.

FRY, KEELIN TILLMAN, JR, b. Wilmington, Del, May 14, 33; m. 58; c. 3. BIOCHEMISTRY. B.S, Delaware, 55; Nat. Sci. Found. fel, Harvard, 55-56, M.A, 57, Dow Chem. Co. fel, 58-59, U.S. Pub. Health Serv. fel, 59-60, Ph.D. (chem), 61. U.S. Pub. Health Serv. fel, McCollum Pratt Inst, Hopkins, 60-62; fel, Charles F. Kettering Res. Lab, 62-63, staff scientist biochem, 63-68; CHEMIST, CENT. RES. DEPT, EXP. STA, E.I. DU PONT DE NEMOURS & CO, INC, 68- Am. Chem. Soc. Mechanism of thiamine action, photosynthesis and protein structure; nitrogen fixation. Address: Central Research Dept, Experimental Station, E.I. du Pont de Nemours & Co, Wilmington, DE 19898.

FRY, KENNETH A(LVIN), b. Topeka, Kans, Oct. 20, 14; m. 64; c. 4. MICROBIOLOGY. A.B, Kansas State Teachers Col, 35, M.S, 36; Iowa State, 48; summer, Oak Ridge Inst. Nuclear Studies, 49; Purdue, 49, 51-53, South. Faculty fel, 56, Nat. Sci. Found. grant, 59-60, Ph.D, 60. Teacher, pub. sch, 36-41, prin, 41-44; instr. bact, Martin Col, Tennessee, 46-47; asst. prof. biol, Chattanooga, 47-60, prof. & head dept, 60-63; head fel, off, Oak Ridge Inst. Nuclear Studies, 64-65; PROF. BIOL. & CHMN. DEPT, TEX. WOMEN'S UNIV, 65- Consult, Erlanger Hosp, Chattanooga, 50-63; Chattanooga Med. Col. & Indust. Res. Inst, 56-63. U.S.N.R, 44-46, Lt.(jg). Am. Acad. Microbiol. Bacteriology; physiology; biochemistry; radiation. Address: Dept. of Biology, Texas Women's University, Denton, TX 76204.

FRY, KENNETH E, b. Niskayuna, N.Y, Apr. 18, 25; m. 56. PLANT PHYSIOLOGY. B.S, Cornell, 50; M.S, Washington (Seattle), 60, Ph.D.(plant physiol), 65. Asst. bot, Washington (Seattle), 54-56; sci. technician, West. Wash. State Col, 57-59; asst. plant physiol, Washington (Seattle), 60-65, instr, summer, 63; PLANT PHYSIOLOGIST, U.S. Dept. Agr, N.C. State Univ, 65-70; WEST. COTTON RES. LAB, 70- U.S.A, 43-46, Sgt. AAAS; Am. Inst. Biol. Sci; Ecol. Soc. Am; Am. Soc. Plant Physiol; Am. Soc. Agron; Crop Sci. Soc. Am. Environmental stresses in cotton affecting plant metabolism and physical functions. Address: Western Cotton Research Lab, 4135 E. Broadway, Phoenix, AZ 85040.

FRY, LOUIS RUMMEL, b. N.Y.C, Aug. 8, 28; m. 65. ORTHOPEDIC SURGERY. B.A, Denison, 51; M.D, Temple, 55. Intern, sch. med, Temple, 56; instr. anat, med. sch, Michigan, 57-58, resident orthop, 61, instr. ORTHOP. SURG, 61-62; SCH. MED, UNIV. WASH, 62-65, asst. prof, 65-70, ASSOC. PROF, 71- Nat. Insts. Health training grant, 64-65. Dipl, Am. Bd. Orthop. Surg. U.S.N, 46-48. AAAS; Orthop. Res. Soc; Am. Med. Asn; Asn. Am. Med. Cols. Cell morphology; cartilage; ultrastructure; bone ultrastructure. Address: Dept. of Orthopedics, School of Medicine, University of Washington, Seattle, WA 98105.

FRY, PEGGY C(ROOKE), b. Conroe, Tex, Oct. 24, 28; m. 50. NUTRITION. B.S, Univ. Tex, Austin, 49; Fulbright fel, N.Z. & Cook Island, 53-54; univ. fel, Harvard, 54-55, M.P.H, 55; Olin-Mathiesen Chem. Co. grant, Univ. Nebr, Lincoln, 58, univ. fel, 64-66, Ph.D.(nutrit), 67; U.S. Dept. Agr. For. Agr. Serv. fel, Univ. Hong Kong, 63-64. Am. Dietetic Asn. internship, Aetna Life Ins. Co, Conn, 49-50; asst. dietitian, Rice Univ, 50; asst. admin. dietitian, Mt. Auburn Hosp, Cambridge, Mass, 51; nutritionist, Forsyth Dent. Infirmary for Children, Boston, 51-53; org. chemist, Charles F.

Kettering Found. & nutrit. consult, Yellow Springs Med. Clin, Ohio, 55-56; instr. food & nutrit, Univ. Nebr, Lincoln, 56-60, ASST. PROF, 60-63; PEDIAT, SOUTHWEST. MED. SCH, UNIV. TEX, DALLAS, 68- Consult, interdepartmental comt. on nutrit. for nat. defense, Nat. Insts. Health, Wash, D.C, 62-63; Inst. for Cross-Cult. Res, 68-; panel mem, White House Conf. on Food, Nutrit. & Health, 69; allied health consult. to attend. staff, Children's Med. Ctr, Dallas, Tex, 69- Effie L. Raitt Award, Am. Home Econ. Asn, 53. Am. Inst. Nutrit; Am. Dietetic Asn. Metabolic interrelationships between amino acids and minerals in humans; weight reduction, nitrogen excretion and subcutaneous fat alterations in children and young adult females; nutritional status of humans in Massachusetts, Nebraska, Texas, Hong Kong and the Cook Islands, South Pacific. Address: Dept. of Pediatrics, University of Texas Southwestern Medical School, 5323 Harry Hines Blvd, Dallas, TX 75235.

FRY, RICHARD JEREMY MICHAEL, b. Dublin, Ireland, July 8, 25; m. 56; c. 3. PHYSIOLOGY, RADIATION BIOLOGY. B.A, Dublin, 46, M.B, B.Ch. & B.A.O, 49, M.D, 62. Lectr. physiol, Dublin, 52-59; resident res. assoc. radiobiol, Argonne Nat. Lab, 59-61; lectr. physiol, Dublin, 61-63; assoc. scientist RADIOBIOL, ARGONNE NAT. LAB, 63-70, SR. SCIENTIST, 70- Radiation Res. Soc; Am. Asn. Cancer Res; Reticuloendothelial Soc. Cell proliferation; cell renewal in the intestinal tract and the effects of irradiation. Address: Division of Biological & Medical Research, Argonne National Lab, Argonne, IL 60439.

FRY, THOMAS R, b. Franklin, Pa, Dec. 10, 23; m. 44; c. 3. ELECTRICAL ENGINEERING. B.S, Pittsburgh, 49. Test engr, Porcelain Prods, Inc, W.Va, 49-51, chief engr, Parkersburg & Carey plants, 51-59; A.B. CHANCE CO, 59-67, MGR. ENG, UTILITY SYSTS. DIV, 67- Consult, Monongahela Power Co, W.Va, 53; Am. Casualty Co, 53-58; Puritan Pottery Co, Pa, 57. U.S.A.A.F, 42-45. Nat. Soc. Prof. Eng; sr. mem. Inst. Elec. & Electronics Eng. Design and development of electrical porcelain insulators. Address: Utility Systems Division, A.B. Chance Co, 210 N. Allen St, Centralia, MO. 65240.

FRY, THORNTON C(ARL), b. Findlay, Ohio, Jan. 7, 92. MATHEMATICS. A.B, Findlay Col, 12, hon. D.Sc, 58; M.A, Wisconsin, 13, Ph.D.(math, physics, astron), 20. Mathematician, West. Elec. Co, 16-24; mem. tech. staff, Bell Tel. Labs, 24-40, math. res. dir, 40-44, dir. switching res, 44-47, dir. switching res. & eng, 47-49, asst. to exec. v.pres, 49-51, asst. to pres, 51-56; v.pres. & dir, Univac Eng, Remington Rand Div, Sperry Rand Corp, 57-60; CONSULT. TO DIR, NAT. CTR. ATMOSPHERIC RES, 61-68, 71-; CONSULT, GRANVILLE-PHILLIPS CO, 64-, mem. bd. dirs, 66- Lectr, Mass. Inst. Technol, 27; Princeton, 29-30; consult. Boeing Sci. Res. Labs, 64-70. Presidential cert. of Merit, 48. With Off. Sci. Res. & Develop, 40-44, chief, sect. 7.2 (math), 42-44, dep. chief, appl. math. panel, 42-45. Fel. AAAS (v.pres, sect, U, 65); fel. Am. Phys. Soc; fel. Inst. Math. Statist; fel. Inst. Elec. & Electronics Eng; Am. Math. Soc; Math. Asn. Am; Am. Astron. Soc; Am. Soc. Eng. Educ; Economet. Soc. Theory of probability; electromagnetic theory; other areas of applied mathematics. Address: Apt. 708, 500 Mohawk Dr, Boulder, CO 80303.

FRY, WAYNE L(YLE), b. Inwood, Iowa, Oct. 6, 22. PALEOBOTANY. B.Sc, Minnesota, 47; Cornell exchange fel, Glasgow, 50-51; Shell fel, Cornell, 51-52, Ph.D.(bot. geol), 53. Asst. bot, Minnesota, 47-49; Cornell, 49-50, instr, 52-53; geologist, Geol. Surv. Can, 53-57; asst. prof. PALEONT, UNIV. CALIF, BERKELEY, 57-61, ASSOC. PROF, 61-, CURATOR PALEOBOT, MUS. PALEONT, 57-, dir. mus. & chmn. dept, 69-70, faculty fel, 59-62. Dir, Summer Inst. Earth Sci, 65-67, 69-; assoc. prog. dir. & for. affairs coord, pre-col. div, Nat. Sci. Found, 67-69. U.S.A, 43-45. Carboniferous and Devonian petrifications; Mesozoic and Tertiary floras of British Columbia. Address: Dept. of Paleontology, University of California, Berkeley, CA 94720.

FRY, WILLIAM EARL, b. Lincoln, Nebr, July 6, 44; m. 70. PLANT PATHOLOGY. B.A, Nebr. Wesleyan Univ, 66; univ. fel, Cornell Univ, 66-67, Nat. Sci. Found. fel, 67-70; Ph.D.(plant path), 70. ASST. PROF. biol, Cent. Conn. State Col, 70-71; PLANT PATH, CORNELL UNIV, 71- AAAS; Am. Phytopath. Soc; Am. Soc. Plant Physiol. Biological factors affecting plant disease control; nature of disease resistance in plants. Address: Dept. of Plant Pathology, Cornell University, Ithaca, NY 14850.

FRY, W(ILLIAM) F(REDERICK), b. Carlisle, Iowa, Dec. 16, 21; m. 43; c. 2. EXPERIMENTAL PHYSICS. B.S, Iowa State Col, 43, Ph.D.(physics), 51. Atomic Energy Cmn, Chicago, 51-52; asst. prof. PHYSICS, UNIV. WIS, MADISON, 52-58, PROF, 58- Physicist, Naval Res. Lab, 43-47; Fulbright lectr, Italy, 56-57. Fel. Am. Phys. Soc. Elementary particle physics using bubble chambers. Address: Dept. of Physics, University of Wisconsin, Madison, WI 53706.

FRY, WILLIAM JAMES, b. Ann Arbor, Mich, Mar. 21, 28; m. 49; c. 2. GENERAL SURGERY. M.D, Michigan, 52. Instr. SURG, MED. SCH. UNIV. MICH, 59-61, asst. prof, 61-64, assoc. prof, 64-67, PROF, 67-, HEAD SECT. GEN. SURG, 67-, asst. surg, dept. postgrad. med, 60-66, chief red surg. serv, med. ctr, 64-67. Attend. physician, Ann Arbor Vet. Admin. Hosp, 60-61, chief surg, 61-64, consult, 64-; Wayne Co. Gen. Hosp, 67- U.S. Pub. Health Serv. grant. Distinguished serv. award, med. sch, Michigan, 63, sr. award, 64. Dipl, Am. Bd. Surg, 60. U.S.N, 54-56, Lt. Am. Surg. Asn; Am. Med. Asn; Soc. Univ. Surg; fel. Am. Col. Surg; Soc. Surg. Alimentary Tract; Soc. Vascular Surg; Int. Cardiovasc. Soc; Asn. Acad. Surg. Vascular physiology. Address: Dept. of Surgery, University Hospital, Ann Arbor, MI 48104.

FRYAR, ROBERT M(ARSHALL), b. Spokane, Wash, Nov. 10, 21; m; c. 1. MECHANICAL & NUCLEAR ENGINEERING. B.S, Idaho, 47, hon. M.E, 55; M.S, Purdue, 48, Ph.D.(heat transfer, thermodyn), 50. Supt. mil. construct, Hawaii, 41-43; instr. eng, Purdue, 47-50; mgr. reactor eng, Gen. Elec. Co, 50-63; assoc. mgr. advan. high temperature gas-cooled reactor div. prog, Gen. Atomic Div, Gen. Dynamics Corp, Calif, 63-66; gen. mgr, NUCLEAR DIV, KERR-McGEE CORP, 66-67, v.pres, div, 67-69, V.PRES, NUCLEAR OPERS, 69- Lectr, Washington (Seattle), 50-63; mem. sr. staff, Space Tech. Labs, Inc. Div, Thompson-Ramo-Wooldridge, Inc, Calif, 62. U.S.A, 43-45. Nuclear power research and development. Address: Kerr-McGee Corp, Kerr-McGee Bldg, Oklahoma City, OK 73102.

FRYBURG, GEORGE C(RUMBACK), b. Phila, Pa, June 25, 19; m. 50; c. 5. PHYSICAL CHEMISTRY. B.S, Franklin & Marshall Col, 41; M.S, Pa. State, 44, E.I. du Pont fel, 47-48, Ph.D.(phys. chem), 48. AERONAUT. RES. SCIENTIST, LEWIS RES. CTR, NASA, 48- AAAS; Am. Chem. Soc; fel. Am. Inst. Chem. Oxidation of metals at high temperatures; investigation of fundamental properties of liquid crystals using electron paramagnetic resonance spectroscopy. Address: Lewis Research Center, NASA, 21000 Brookpark Rd, Cleveland, OH 44135.

FRYD, MICHAEL, b. Wolomin, Poland, Sept. 13, 36; U.S. citizen; m. 59; c. 1. ORGANIC CHEMISTRY. B.S, City Col. New York, 58; M.S, N.Y. Univ, 62, Ph.D.(org. chem), 64. Res. asst. chem, N.Y. Univ, 57-61; lectr, Hunter Col, 61-62; instr. & res. assoc. biochem. & endocrinol, Hahnemann Med. Col, 62-63; res. chemist, fabric & finishes dept, E.I. DU PONT DE NEMOURS & CO, INC, 63-69, develop. assoc, 69-70, RES. ASSOC, 70- AAAS; Am. Chem. Soc; fel. Am. Inst. Chem. Mechanisms of free radical reactions; mechanism and kinetics of free radical polymerization; synthesis and properties of graft copolymers. Address: Marshall Lab, E.I. du Pont de Nemours & Co, Inc, 3500 Grays Ferry Ave, Philadelphia, PA 19146.

FRYDENDALL, MERRILL J, b. Portis, Kans, Mar. 28, 34; m. 59; c. 2. VERTEBRATE ECOLOGY, ANIMAL BEHAVIOR. B.S, Ft. Hays Kans. State Col, 56, M.S, 60; Nat. Insts. Health fel, Utah State, 64-66, Ph.D.(zool), 67. Instr. high sch, Kans, 56-57, 60-62; ornith, Utah State, 65; ASSOC. PROF. BIOL, MANKATO STATE COL, 67- U.S.A, 67-69. Am. Ornith. Union; Ecol. Soc. Am. Vertebrate ecology and behavior, especially activity patterns and utilization by mammals and aves. Address: Dept. of Biology, Mankato State College, Mankato, MN 56001.

FRYE, ALVA L(EONARD), b. Gray, Okla, July 19, 22; m. 43; c. 2. CHEMICAL ENGINEERING. B.S, Iowa State Col, 43. Control chemist, Shell Chem. Co, Texas, 43-44; process engr, Nat. Synthetic Rubber Corp, Ky, 44-47; sect. leader, Minn. Mining & Mfg. Co, 47-57, mgr, cent. res. pilot plant, 57-62, tech. dir. paper prod. div, 62-68; v.pres. res. & commercial develop, Inmont Corp, 69-70, dir. RES. & DEVELOP, ALADDIN INDUST, 70-71, V.PRES, 71- Am. Chem. Soc; Am. Inst. Chem. Eng; Tech. Asn. Pulp & Paper Indust. Synthetic polymers; process development; fluoro-chemical and pilot plant; specialty papers and new products. Address: Aladdin Industries, 703 Murfreesboro Rd, Nashville, TN 37201.

FRYE, B(ILLY) E(UGENE), b. Clarkesville, Ga, June 26, 33; m. 58; c. 2. ENDOCRINOLOGY. B.S, Piedmont Col, 53; John Hay Whitney Found. fel, Emory, 53-54, M.S, 54, Nat. Sci. Found. fel, 55-56, Ph.D.(biol), 56. Nat. Sci. Found. fel, Princeton, 56-57; prof. biol, Piedmont Col, 57-58; vis. asst. prof, Virginia, 58-61; asst. prof, UNIV. MICH, ANN ARBOR, 61-65, assoc. prof, 65-69, PROF. ZOOL, 69- Res. grant, Nat. Sci. Found, 59-60, Nat. Insts. Health, 60- AAAS; Am. Soc. Zool. Metamorphosis; functional and morphological differentiation of the islets of Langerhans and other embryonic endocrine glands; diabetes and pregnancy; developmental biology. Address: Dept. of Zoology, University of Michigan, Ann Arbor, MI 48104.

FRYE, CECIL LEONARD, b. Dearborn, Mich, Apr. 3, 28; m. 52; c. 4. ORGANIC CHEMISTRY. B.S, Michigan, 50, M.S, 51; Dow Corning Corp. fel. & Ph.D.(org. chem), Pa. State, 60. Res. chemist, DOW CORNING CORP, 51-56, proj. leader, RES. DEPT, 60-63, lab. supvr, 63-70, MGR, SEALANTS RES. UNIT, 70- U.S.A, 46. Am. Chem. Soc; Sci. Res. Soc. Am. Silicon stereochemistry; extra-coordinate silicon compounds; polysiloxanes. Address: 2424 Pinehurst Ct, Midland, MI 48640.

FRYE, CHARLES ISAAC, b. Peterboro, N.H, Dec. 15, 35; m. 65; c. 2. SEDIMENTARY PETROLOGY, STRATIGRAPHY. B.A, Univ. N.H, 58; M.S, Univ. Mass, Amherst, 60; Ph.D.(geol), Univ. N.Dak, 67. Asst. prof, GEOL, MUSKINGUM COL, 65-70, ASSOC. PROF, 70-, CHMN. DEPT. GEOL-GEOG, 69- Paleont. Soc; Am. Asn. Petrol. Geol. Stratigraphy and sedimentation of Hell Creek formation and related beds, Montana, North Dakota, South Dakota and of the Conemaugh formation in southeastern Ohio; sources of glacial stream gravels in western North Dakota. Address: Dept. of Geology-Geography, Muskingum College, New Concord, OH 43762.

FRYE, C(LIFTON) G(EORGE), b. Port Clinton, Ohio, Dec. 13, 18; m. 43; c. 2. CHEMICAL ENGINEERING. Ch.E, Cincinnati, 41; M.S, Mass. Inst. Tech, 47. Sr. chem. engr, petrochem. res, Pan Am. Petrol. Co, 47-58; sr. res. engr, PETROL. REF. RES, Standard Oil Co. Ind, 58-61; RES. ASSOC, AM. OIL CO, 61- U.S.A.F, 42-45, Res, 45-53, Maj. Am. Meteorol. Soc; Am. Inst. Chem. Eng; Am. Chem. Soc. Application of thermodynamics and kinetics to the development of new catalytic processes. Address: American Oil Co, Box 431, Whiting, IN 46394.

FRYE, GLENN M(cKINLEY), JR, b. Ithaca, Mich, Apr. 20, 26; m. 48; c. 3. PHYSICS. B.S.E, Michigan, 46, M.S, 47, Ph.D.(physics), 50; Glasgow, 50-51. Mem. staff, physics div, Los Alamos Sci. Lab, 51-58; physicist, physics br, res. div, Atomic Energy Cmn, 58-60; ASSOC. PROF. PHYSICS, CASE WEST. RESERVE UNIV, 60- Guest lectr, Minnesota, 57; prof, New Mexico, 58. U.S.N.R, 44-46. Am. Phys. Soc. Nuclear reactions; neutron physics; high energy physics; cosmic rays. Address: Dept. of Physics, Rockefeller Physics Bldg, Case Western Reserve University, Cleveland, OH 44106.

FRYE, GRAHAM E(UGENE), b. Portland, Ore, Nov. 18, 32; m. 57; c. 1. PHYSICS. A.B, California, Berkeley, 55, Ph.D.(physics), 60. Res. asst. prof. PHYSICS, Washington (Seattle), 60-62; assoc. res. scientist, N.Y. Univ, 62-64; asst. prof, City Col. New York, 64-67; ASSOC. PROF, YESHIVA UNIV, 67- Am. Phys. Soc. Theory of capture of K-mesons; K-meson electromagnetic structure; pion-K-meson scattering; K-nucleon and K-nucleon scattering and reactions; partial wave dispersion relations; diffraction scattering. Address: Dept. of Physics, Belfer Graduate School of Science, Yeshiva University, 186th & Amsterdam Ave, New York, NY 10033.

FRYE, HERSCHEL G(ORDON), b. Long Beach, Calif, Apr. 6, 20; m. 40; c. 2. INORGANIC & ANALYTICAL CHEMISTRY. A.B, Col. of Pacific, 47, M.A, 49; Ph.D.(chem), Oregon, 57. Chemist, Permanente Metals Corp, 42-44; chief chemist, Kaiser Magnesium Co, 51-52; head sci. dept, high sch, 52-54; asst. prof. CHEM, UNIV. OF THE PACIFIC, 56-59, assoc. prof, 59-62, PROF, 62- Res. Corp. grants, 58, 60; Am. Philos. Soc. grants, 59, 63, 64. Med. Dept, 44-46, S/Sgt. AAAS; Am. Chem. Soc; Am. Inst. Chem. Absorption spectrophotometry; reaction kinetics in non-aqueous media; non-aqueous polarography; organic ligand synthesis; synthesis of coordination compounds. Address: Dept. of Chemistry, University of the Pacific, Stockton, CA 95204.

FRYE, JENNINGS BRYAN, JR, b. Springhill, La, Sept. 3, 18; m. 40; c. 4. DAIRY SCIENCE. B.S, La. State, 35; Danforth fel, Iowa State, 38, M.S, 40; Ph.D.(dairy cattle nutrit), 45. Assoc. prof. DAIRY SCI, Georgia, 45-48; PROF. & HEAD DEPT, LA. STATE UNIV, BATON ROUGE, 48- Spec. dairy indust. consult, Venezuela, 53, spec. study, Dairy Indust, 57; Breeding Res, Cuba, 58. U.S.A, 42-46. Am. Forage & Grassland Coun; Am. Dairy Sci. Asn. Nutrition of dairy cattle; influence of soybeans on the flavor of milk, cream and butter and on the body and texture of butter; heat tolerance of dairy cattle; bloat in dairy cattle; silage, including use of various preservatives and methods of self feeding; feeding green forage to cattle. Address: Dept. of Dairy Science, Louisiana State University, Baton Rouge, LA 70803.

FRYE, JOHN C(HAPMAN), b. Marietta, Ohio, July 25, 12; m. 36; c. 3. GEOLOGY. A.B, Marietta Col, 34, hon. Sc.D, 55; Ohio State, 33, 34-35; M.S, Iowa, 37, Ph.D.(physiog), 38. Asst. geol, Iowa, 35-38; jr. geologist, div. ground water, U.S. Geol. Surv, Kans, 38-40, asst. geologist, 40-41; asst. state geologist & asst. dir, State Geol. Surv, Kans, 42-45, exec. dir, 45-54, state geologist, 52-54, CHIEF, STATE GEOL. SURV, ILL, 54-; PROF. GEOL, UNIV. ILL, URBANA, 63- Asst. prof, Univ. Kans, 42-45, assoc. prof, 45-52, prof, 52-54; del, Int. Geol. Cong, Algiers, 52; mem, comt. geol. aspects radioactive waste disposal, Nat. Acad. Sci-Nat. Res. Coun, 55-64, chmn, 62-64, chmn. adv. comt, earth resources remote sensing to U.S. Dept. Int, 66-69, mem. comt. mineral sci. & technol. to U.S. Bur. Mines, 66-70, radioactive waste mgt. to U.S. Atomic Energy Comn, 68-70, chmn, 70-; mem. Sci. Manpower Comn, 56-58; Am. Comn. Stratig. Nomenclature, 56-; chmn, 57-59; mem. Nat. Res. Coun, 58-70; mem. adv. comt. health physics, Oak Ridge Nat. Lab, 59-; adv. comt, U.S. Geol. Surv, 60-66; exec. comt, Ill. Ctr. Water Resources Res, 63-; U.S. Nat. Comn. for UNESCO, 68-, v.chmn. comt. man & his environ, 70-; mem. exec. adv. comt. future oil prospects, Nat. Petrol. Coun, 68-70; spec. comt. probs. environ, Int. Coun. Sci. Unions, 69-; nat. adv. bd, Desert Res. Inst, Univ. Nev, 70- Nat. Acad. Eng; AAAS; fel. Geol. Soc. Am; Soc. Econ. Geol; Soc. Econ. Paleont. & Mineral (v.pres, 65-66); Am. Asn. State Geol. (ed, 56-57, secy-treas, 57-58, v.pres, 58-59, pres, 60-61); Am. Inst. Prof. Geol; Am. Geophys. Union; Am. Asn. Petrol. Geol; Am. Inst. Mining, Metall. & Petrol. Eng; Am. Geol. Inst. (pres, 66). Physiography; Cenozoic and ground water geology. Address: Illinois State Geological Survey, 121 Natural Resources Bldg, Urbana, IL 61801.

FRYE, JOHN H, JR, b. Birmingham, Ala, Oct. 1, 08; m. 35; c. 3. PHYSICAL METALLURGY. A.B, Howard Col, 30; M.S, Lehigh, 34; D.Phil.(phys. sci), Oxford, 42. Engr, Am. Cast Iron Pipe Co, Ala, 34-35; instr. metall, Lehigh, 35-37, from asst. prof. to assoc. prof, 40-44; res. engr, Bethlehem Steel Co, 44-48; DIR. metall. div, OAK RIDGE NAT. LAB, 48-62, METALS & CERAMICS DIV, 62- Lectr, grad. sch, Tennessee, 50-; adj. prof, col. eng, Alabama, 64-66. Lincoln gold medal, Am. Welding Soc, 43. Civilian with Off. Sci. Res. & Develop, 44. Fel. AAAS; fel. Am. Soc. Metals; Am. Nuclear Soc; Am. Inst. Mining, Metall. & Petrol. Eng; Brit. Inst. Metals. Rates of reaction solids; phase equilibria; nuclear materials. Address: Metals & Ceramics Division, Oak Ridge National Lab, P.O. Box X, Oak Ridge, TN 37830.

FRYE, JOHN R(OBERT), b. Asheville, N.C, Apr. 17, 17; m. 37; c. 4. ORGANIC CHEMISTRY. B.S, North Carolina, 38, Ph.D.(org. chem), 42. Chemist, Union Carbide Chems. Co. Div, UNION CARBIDE CORP, W.Va, 42-43, chem. engr, 43-44, asst. dept. head fine chem, 44-46, dept. head, 46-47, assoc. chemist, Linde Co. Div, N.Y, 47-52, dept. head, pilot prods. plant, chems. div, 52-55, area supvr. new chem. prod, 55-59, area prod. supt, 60-62, prod. mgr, mkt, 62-63, midwest regional mgr, 63-66, mgr. agr. chem. & subsidiaries, 67-68, mgr. mkt. res, 68-69, DIR. MKT, 69- AAAS; Am. Chem. Soc; Am. Inst. Chem. Eng. Development of miscellaneous fine chemicals; synthetic lubricants; synthesis of some polyhydroxy chalcones. Address: Chemicals & Plastics Operations Division, Union Carbide Corp, 270 Park Ave, New York, NY 10017.

FRYE, KEITH, b. Columbus, Ohio, July 17, 35; m. 65. GEOCHEMISTRY, MINERALOGY. A.B, Oberlin Col, 57; M.S, Minnesota, 59; Calif. Inst Technol, 59-60; Ph.D.(geochem), Pa. State, 65. Chemist, Hyman labs, Inc, 61-62; asst. prof. GEOL, Georgia, 65-67; ASSOC. PROF, OLD DOMINION UNIV, 67- U.S.A, 60. AAAS; Am. Geophys. Union; Geol. Soc. Am; Mineral. Soc. Am. High-pressure synthesis of aromatic hydrocarbons; effects of pressure on crystal defects; distribution of trace elements and of minor minerals in granites; interaction between man and his geological environment. Address: Dept. of Geophysical Sciences, Old Dominion University, Norfolk, VA 23508.

FRYE, O(ZRO) E(ARLE), JR, b. Petersburg, Tenn, Oct. 8, 17; m. 49; c. 2. BIOLOGY. B.S, Florida, 39, fel, 39-40, M.S, 41, Ph.D.(biol), 54; Agr. & Mech. Col, Texas, 41-42. Asst. for res. & quail mgt, State Coop. Wildlife Res. Unit, Ala, 40, food habits of predatory mammals & fur interests, Texas, 41-42; asst. biol, Florida, 40-41; wildlife biologist, STATE GAME & FRESH WATER FISH COMN, FLA, 46-47, chief wildlife biologist, 47-51, asst. dir, 51-65, DIR, 65- U.S.N.R, 42-46. Wildlife Soc; Ecol. Soc. Am; Am. Soc. Ichthyol. & Herpet; Am. Ornith. Union; Wilson Ornith. Soc; Am. Soc. Mammal. Ecology of bobwhite quail in southern Florida; ecology of vegetation in south Florida pine lands; bobwhite quail populations in Florida. Address: State Game & Fresh Water Fish Commission, Tallahassee, FL 32304.

FRYE, ROBERT S(MITH), b. Laura, Ill, Apr. 30, 10; m. 36; c. 1. CHEMICAL ENGINEERING. B.S, Illinois, 33. Develop. chemist, Abbott Labs, 34-43, mgr. antibiotic extraction, 43-54, tech. adv, 54-57, mgr. standards & methods, 57-61, opers. mgr, serv. & supply, 61-68; SUPVR. CHEM. MFG, G.D. SEARLE & CO, 68- Am. Chem. Soc. Address: G.D. Searle & Co, P.O. Box 5110, Chicago, IL 60680.

FRYE, ROYAL M(ERRILL), b. Milford, N.H, May 27, 90; m. 15, 70. PHYSICS. A.B, Boston Univ, 11, A.M, 12, Ph.D.(physics), 34; Harvard, 12-13; Mass. Inst. Technol, 16-27; hon. Sc.D, Belknap Col, 68. Instr. physics, Boston Univ, 13-14, 32-36, chem, 14-15, asst. prof. physics, 36-42, prof, 42-50; instr, Worcester Polytech. Inst, 26-27; Mass. Inst. Technol, 15-31; prof, Simmons Col, 50-59; col. adv. sci, 59-63, dean col, 59-63; pres, BELKNAP COL, 63-69, CHANCELLOR, 69- Instr, Lincoln Tech. Inst, eve. grad. sch, Northeastern, 30-46, 52-60, army specialized training prog. Sci. consult, Bikini, U.S. Army, 46; dir. res. proj, air mat. command, U.S. Air Force, 47-48; pres, Wood Prod. Chem. Co, Inc, 70- Relativity theory; chemistry of wood. Address: Box 129, Center Harbor, NH 03226.

FRYE, VIRGINIA B(RIGHAM), b. Boston, Mass, Mar. 20, 15; m. 70. SPECTROSCOPY. A.B, Boston Univ, 36, A.M, 45, Ph.D.(physics), 52; hon. Sc.D, Belknap Col, 69. Instr. physics, Boston Univ, 43-49; Simmons Col, 50-52, asst. prof, 52-58, assoc. prof, 58-61; prof. & asst. dean, Col. Advan. Sci, 61-63; v.pres. acad. affairs, Belknap Col, 63-70; PHYSICIST, WOOD PROD. CHEM. CORP, INC, FITZWILLIAM, 70- Am. Phys. Soc. Address: Old Meredith Rd, Center Harbor, NH 03226.

FRYE, WILBUR W(AYNE), b. Finger, Tenn, Aug. 6, 33; m. 57; c. 2. SOIL CHEMISTRY & MINERALOGY. B.S, Univ. Tenn, Knoxville, 61, M.S, 64; Nat. Sci. Found. fel, Va. Polytech. Inst. & State Univ, 67-68, Ph.D, 69. Instr. AGRON, TENN. TECHNOL. UNIV, 63-64, asst. prof, 64-67, ASSOC. PROF. & CHMN. DEPT, 70- U.S.A.F, 53-57, S/Sgt. AAAS; Am. Soc. Agron; Soil Sci. Soc. Am; Int. Soc. Soil Sci; Soil Conserv. Soc. Am; Am. Forestry Asn; Clay Minerals Soc. Off-season nitrogen fertilization; nitrogen transformations and movement in soils; residual soil nitrogen; non-exchangeable ammonium in soils; soil temperature under sod-planted corn. Address: Dept. of Agronomy, Box 5102, Tennessee Technological University, Cookeville, TN 38501.

FRYE, WILLIAM E(MERSON), b. Detroit, Mich, June 20, 17; m. 42; c. 2. PHYSICS. A.B, Illinois, 37, M.S, 38; Ph.D.(physics), Chicago, 41. Group leader, airborne radio div, Naval Res. Lab, Wash, 42-45, asst. sect. head, 45-46; group leader, aerophysics lab, North. Am. Aviation, Inc, Calif, 46-48; physicist, Rand Corp, 48-56; mgr. dept, LOCKHEED MISSILE & SPACE CO, 56-59, consult. scientist, 59-62, 64-68, SR. MEM. RES. LAB, 68- Mem. adv. comt. control, guidance & navig, NASA, 60-64. Am. Phys. Soc; Am. Inst. Aeronaut. & Astronaut; Am. Astronaut. Soc. Space systems and scientific instrumentation. Address: 536 Lincoln Ave, Palo Alto, CA 94301.

FRYE, WILLIAM W(ESLEY), b. North English, Iowa, July 26, 03; m. 29; c. 5. MEDICINE. B.S, Iowa Wesleyan Col, 26, hon. Sc.D, 57; M.S, Iowa State Col, 27, Ph.D, 31; M.D, Vanderbilt, 39. Asst, Iowa State Col, 26-28, instr. zool. & entomol, 28-31; asst. prev. med. & pub. health, sch. med, Vanderbilt, 31-37, instr, 37-40, asst. prof, 40-42, assoc. prof, 42-45, prof. obstet. & head dept, 45-48; prof. trop. med. & pub. health, asst. dean & dir, div. grad. med, sch. med, Tulane, 48-49; dean sch. med, La. State Univ, 49-65, prof. trop. med, 49-70, v.pres, Univ, 59-65, chancellor, med. ctr, 65-70; PROF. TROP. MED, TEX. TECH UNIV, 70- Asst. vis. physician, dept. obstet, sch. med, Vanderbilt, 43-45, vis. physician, 45-48, dir, sch. pub. health, 46-48. Special consult, U.S. Pub. Health Serv, 46-, consult, city dept. health, New Orleans, 48-50; civilian consult, La. Installations, Fourth Army, 58- Mem. cholera comn, UN Relief & Rehabil. Admin, 45-46; deputy dir. comn. enteric infections, Armed Forces Epidemiol. Bd, 48-49, mem, 59-; chmn. trop. med. study sect, res. grants, U.S. Pub. Health Serv, 51-56, mem. Nat. Adv. Allergy & Infectious Diseases Coun, Nat. Insts. Health, 58-62; mem. adv. council inst. grants, Am. Cancer Soc, 58-60. Dipl, Am. Bd. Prev. Med. Am. Epidemiol. Soc; Am. Soc. Test. & Mat.(pres-elect, 59, pres, 61); Am. Soc. Parasitol; Am. Pub. Health Asn; fel. Am. Med. Asn; Am. Gastroenterol. Asn; Am. Col. Prev. Med; fel. Am. Acad. Microbiol; fel. Am. Col. Physicians; Royal Soc. Trop. Med. & Hyg. Amoebiasis and tropical medicine; maternal and child health programs. Address: Texas Tech University School of Medicine, P.O. Box 4390, Lubbock, TX 79409.

FRYER, CHARLES W, b. Springfield, Mo, May 4, 28; m. 53; c. 1. GEMMOLOGY. Grad. gemologist, Gemol. Inst. Am, 63; Gemmol. Asn. Gt. Brit. fel, 63. Plant mgr, C. Holle Glass Co, 62-64; mgr, R & B Artcraft Co, 64-66; instr. GEM IDENTIFICATION, GEMOL. INST. AM, 66-67, LAB. SUPVR, 67- Cert. gemologist, Am. Gem Soc, 67. U.S.A, 50-52. X-ray powder diffraction identification of gem materials and their inclusions; optical and physical identification of gem materials and their substitutes; x-ray analysis of pearls to determine natural or cultured origin. Address: Gemological Institute of America, 11940 San Vicente Blvd, Los Angeles, CA 90049.

FRYER, EDWARD MONTGOMERY, b. Spadra, Calif, July 12, 16; m. 44. PHYSICS. B.A, Pomona Col, 37; Engr, Stanford, 40, Ph.D.(physics), 43. Asst. physics, Pomona Col, 37-38; Stanford, 39-42; asst. prof, Pomona Col, 46-49, assoc. prof, 49-56, prof, 56-65; gen. mgr, quantum electronics div, Varian Assocs, 65-68. Staff mem, Los Alamos Sci. Lab, 52-53. Liaison, Off. Sci. Res. & Develop; U.S.N; U.S.N.R, 42-46, Lt. Am. Phys. Soc; Am. Asn. Physics Teachers. Atmospheric haze; neutron reaction cross sections; transmission of velocity selected neutrons through magnetized iron; magneto optics and ferromagnetic domains. Address: 45 Tagus Ct, Portola Valley, CA 94025.

FRYER, ELSIE BETH, b. Kopperl, Tex, June 25, 25; m. 66. FOOD TECHNOLOGY, NUTRITION. B.S, Univ. N.Mex, 45; M.S, Ohio State Univ, 49; Ph.D.(foods & nutrit), Mich. State Univ, 59. Teacher, high sch, N.Mex, 45-48; asst. prof foods & nutrit, S.Dak. State Col, 49-56; ASSOC. PROF. NUTRIT, KANS. STATE UNIV, 59- Am. Dietetic Asn; Am. Asn. Cereal Chem; Am. Home Econ. Asn. Food habit and nutritional status surveys of women and children; quality of cereal proteins; human metabolic studies concerned with weight reduction, lipid metabolism and nitrogen balance. Address: Dept. of Foods & Nutrition, Kansas State University, Manhattan, KS 66502.

FRYER, H(OLLY) C(LAIRE), b. Carlton, Ore, Dec. 6, 08; m. 34, 66; c. 2. BIOLOGICAL STATISTICS. B.S, Oregon, 31; M.S, Ore. State Col, 33; Illinois, 35-37; Ph.D.(statist), Iowa State Col, 40. Instr. math, Iowa State, 37-40; asst. prof, Kansas State, 40-42, assoc. prof. & statistician, exp. sta, 42-44; assoc. res. mathematician, Columbia, 44-45; prof. math, KANS. STATE UNIV, 45-59, HEAD DEPT. STATIST, 59-, DIR. STATIST. LAB, 46-, STATISTICIAN, EXP. STA, 45- With Nat. Defense Res. Comt, 44. Biomet. Soc; Am. Statist. Asn; Inst. Math. Statist. Designing biometric experiments; mathematical statistics. Address: Dept. of Statistics, Kansas State University, Manhattan, KS 66502.

FRYER, JOHN L(OUIS), b. Ft. Worth, Tex, July 4, 29; m. 52; c. 1. MICROBIOLOGY, FISHERIES. B.S, Oregon State, 56, M.S, 57, Ph.D.(microbiol), 64. Instr. fisheries, Oregon State, 57-58; fish pathologist, res. div, Ore. Fish Cmn, 58-60, state fisheries pathologist, 60-63; res. assoc, ORE. STATE UNIV, 63-64, asst. prof. MICROBIOL. & FISHERIES, 64-70, ASSOC. PROF, 70- U.S.M.C, 50-52. AAAS; Am. Soc. Microbiol; Am. Inst. Fishery Res. Biol; Am. Fisheries Soc; Tissue Cult. Asn. Medical microbiology, virology, immunology and tissue culture in relation to infectious diseases of cold blooded animals; methods for prevention, detection and control of diseases in populations of fishes; fish pathology. Address: Dept. of Microbiology, Oregon State University, Corvallis, OR 97331.

FRYER, MINOT P(ACKER), b. Conn, Mar. 16, 15; m. 42; c. 2. SURGERY. A.B, Brown Univ, hon. D.Sc, 71; M.D, Johns Hopkins Univ. 40. Assoc. prof. clin. surg, med. sch. & maxillofacial surg, dent. sch, WASH. UNIV, 57-67, PROF. CLIN. SURG, MED. SCH. & MAXILLOFACIAL SURG, DENT. SCH, 67- Asst. surgeon, Barnes, McMillan & St. Louis Children's Hosps, 48-; mem. staff, De Paul Hosp, 48-; consult, Vet. Admin. Hosp, 49-; v.chmn, Am. Bd. Plastic Surg, 67-68. Med.C, 44-46, Res, 46-, Lt. Am. Soc. Plastic & Reconstruct. Surg; Am. Asn. Plastic Surg.(v.pres, 66-67, pres, 67-68); fel. Am. Asn. Surg. of Trauma; fel. Am. Col. Surg; Soc. Head & Neck Surg; N.Y. Acad. Sci; Am. Surg. Asn; Pan-Pac. Surg. Asn. Plastic and reconstructive surgery. Address: 4989 Barnes Hospital Plaza, St. Louis, MO 63110.

FRYER, RODNEY IAN, b. London, Eng, Mar. 13, 30; U.S. citizen; m. 54; c. 4. ORGANIC & MEDICINAL CHEMISTRY. B.S, California, Los Angeles, 57; Ph.D(chem), Manchester, 60. Sr. chemist pharmaceut. res, HOFFMANN-LA ROCHE, INC, 60-63, asst. group chief, 63-65, group chief pharmaceut. res, 65-69, SECT. CHIEF, RES. DEPT, 69- U.S.A, 53-55. AAAS; Am. Chem. Soc; The Chem. Soc. Biosynthesis of naturally occurring compounds; synthesis and transformations of 1,4-benzodiazepinones and other heterocyclic compounds of potential medicinal interest. Address: Research Dept, Hoffmann-La Roche, Inc, Nutley, NJ 07110

FRYKLUND, VERNE C(HARLES), JR, b. Greeley, Colo, July 2, 20; m. 43; c. 4. GEOLOGY. B.S, Minnesota, 44, M.S, 47, Longyear fel, 47-48, Ph.D. (geol), 49. Instr. Idaho, 48, asst. prof, 49-51; field asst, U.S. Geol. Surv, 43; jr. geologist, 43-45, geologist, 51-62; chief, lunar & planetary sci. br, manned space sci. div, Nat. Aeronaut. & Space Admin, 62-64; chief mil. geol. br, U.S. Geol. Surv, 64-66; prog. mgr, ADVAN. RES. PROJS. AGENCY, OFF. SECY. DEFENSE, 66-68, DEP. DIR. NUCLEAR MONITORING RES. OFF, 68- U.S.A, 42-43. Fel. Geol. Soc. Am; Soc. Econ. Geol; Geochem. Soc; Am. Inst. Mining, Metall. & Petrol. Eng. Management. Address: 6805 Broyhill St, McLean, VA 22101.

FRYLING, ROBERT H(OWARD), b. Danville, Pa, Nov. 17, 21; m. 43; c. 2. MATHEMATICS. B.A, Gettysburg Col, 43; M.S, Pittsburgh, 51. Instr. math, GETTYSBURG COL, 47-50, dean of men, 52-56, asst. prof. MATH, 58-69, ASSOC. PROF, 69- U.S.M.C, 43-46, Res, 46-64, Maj. Math. Asn. Am. Boundaries and existence of random variable centers. Address: Dept. of Mathematics, Gettysburg College, Gettysburg, PA 17325.

FRYMAN, LEO RAY, b. Noble, Ill, Feb. 8, 20; m. 41; c. 2. DAIRY SCIENCE. B.S, Univ. Ill, 48, M.S, 50; Ph.D, Purdue Univ, 71. Assoc. prof. DAIRY SCI. EXTEN, UNIV. ILL, URBANA, 48-68, PROF, 68- U.S.A.A.F, 44-45. Am. Dairy Sci. Asn. Dairy cattle management, feeding and breeding. Address: 338 Animal Science Lab, University of Illinois, Urbana, IL 61801.

FRYREAR, DONALD W, b. Haxtum, Colo, Dec. 8, 36; m. 56; c. 2. AGRICULTURAL ENGINEERING. B.S, Colorado State, 59; M.S, Kansas State, 62. Agr. engr, Cent. Great Plains Field Sta, U.S. DEPT. AGR, 59-60, wind erosion lab, 60-62, Blackland Conserv. Exp. Sta, 62-63, res. agr. engr, 63-65, SUPT. & RES. AGR. ENGR, BIG SPRING FIELD STA, AGR. RES. SERV, 65- Am. Soc. Agr. Eng; Nat. Soc. Prof. Eng; Sci. Res. Soc. Am. Dryland water conservation in Colorado; application of annual barriers for wind erosion control; land modifications for controlling erosion; development of equipment for measuring erosion rates. Address: Agricultural Research Service, U.S. Dept. of Agriculture, Big Spring Field Station, Big Spring, TX 79720.

FRYSINGER, GALEN ROYER, b. Harrisburg, Pa, Aug. 21, 31; m. 53; c. 4. PHYSICAL CHEMISTRY. B.S, Juniata Col, 53; M.S, Yale, 55, Monsanto Chem. Co. fel, 55-56, Ph.D.(phys. chem), 56. Fulbright scholar, Max Planck Inst. Phys. Chem, Göttingen, 56-57, Nat. Sci. Found. fel. phys. chem, 57-58; res. assoc, inst. natural sci, North Carolina, 58-60; sr. phys. chemist, Arthur D. Little, Inc, Mass, 60-63; chief res. br, elec. power div, U.S. Army Engr. Res. & Develop. Labs, Va, 63-66; chief power sources div, electronic components lab, U.S. Army Electronics Command, N.J, 66-69; dir. res, res. ctr, ESB, Inc, Pa, 69-71; DIR. ENG. RES, EDISON BATTERY DIV, McGRAW-EDISON CO, 71- Mem. power sources panel, undersea warfare comt, Nat. Acad. Sci, 67. Am. Chem. Soc; Electrochem. Soc. Electrochemistry; adsorption and reaction on solid surfaces; fuel cell; storage battery; energy conversion. Address: Edison Battery Division, McGraw-Edison Co, Bloomfield, NJ 07003.

FRYSTAK, RONALD WAYNE, b. Chicago, Ill, Sept. 25, 41; m. 65; c. 1. PHYSICAL & ENVIRONMENTAL CHEMISTRY. B.S, Millikin Univ, 63;

Atomic Energy Comn. grant, Iowa State Univ, summer 66; NASA fel, Univ. Hawaii, 66-68, Ph.D.(phys. chem), 68. Qual. control analyst, A.E. Staley Mfg. Co, summers 62 & 63; ASST. PROF. CHEM, HAWAII LOA COL, 68- Nat. Sci. Found. fel. col. teachers, summer 71. Am. Chem. Soc. A physical interpretation of the He-He interaction through the use of the associated density matrices; saving of Hawaiian beaches in case an accidental oil spillage occurs. Address: Division of Science & Mathematics, Hawaii Loa College, Kaneohe, HI 96744.

FRYXELL, F(RITIOF) M(ELVIN), b. Moline, Ill, Apr. 27, 00; m. 28; c. 2. GEOLOGY. A.B, Augustana Col.(Ill), 22; M.A, Illinois, 23; summers, Colorado, 23, Iowa, 24-25; Rockefeller fel, Chicago, 26, Ph.D.(geol), 29; hon. Sc.D, Wittenberg, 60; Upsala Col, 60. Asst, Chicago, 27-28; asst. prof. GEOL, AUGUSTANA COL.(ILL), 23-26, assoc. prof, 26-29, PROF. & CURATOR MUS, 29-, DIR. RES. FOUND, 47-, GEOL. MUS, 68-, chmn. sci. div, 46-51. Naturalist, Grand Teton Nat. Park, Wyo, 29-34, geologist, mus. planning staff, Nat. Park Serv, 35-37; sr. geologist, Philippine Govt, 39-40; geologist, mil. geol. unit, U.S. Geol. Surv, 42-46; Am-Scandinavian Found. traveling fel, 48; lit. exec, Francois E. Matthes, 49-65; dir, Am. Geol. Inst, 50-51; Guggenheim Found. fel, 54; Nat. Sci. Found. res. grant, Augustana Col, 59-61, 64. Trustee, Davenport Pub. Mus, 41- Miner award, 53, Meritorious award, Augustana Col, 58. AAAS; fel. Geol. Soc. Am; fel. Am. Geog. Soc; Nat. Asn. Geol. Teachers (pres, 38). Geomorphology; glacial and military geology; history of geology. Address: Geology Museum, Augustana College, Rock Island, IL 61201.

FRYXELL, PAUL A(RNOLD), b. Moline, Ill, Feb. 2, 27; m. 47; c. 3. BOTANY. A.B, Augustana Col, 49; M.S, Iowa State, 51, Ph.D.(genetics), 55. Asst. agron, agr. exp. sta, N.Mex, 52-55; asst. prof. bot, Wichita, 55-57; from geneticist to PRIN. RES. GENETICIST, COTTON BR, AGR. RES. SERV, U.S. DEPT. AGR, 57- Mem. grad. faculty, Tex. A&M Univ. Cotton genetics res. award, 67. U.S.A.A.F, 45-46. Fel. AAAS; Soc. Study Evolution; Asn. Trop. Biol; Am. Soc. Plant Taxon.(ed, J. Brittonia); Int. Asn. Plant Taxon; Am. Soc. Nat; Asn. Taxon. Study Trop. African Flora. Systematics of Malvaceae; phylogeny of the tribe Gossypieae; breeding systems and speciation in phanerogams. Address: Dept. of Soil & Crop Sciences, Texas A&M University, College Station, TX 77843.

FRYXELL, ROBERT E(DWARD), b. Moline, Ill, Mar. 24, 23; m. 61; c. 3. PHYSICAL CHEMISTRY. B.A, Augustana Col, 44; M.S, Chicago, 49, Ph.D (chem), 50. Chemist, Manhattan Proj, metall. lab, Chicago, 43-44; Los Alamos Sci. Lab, California, 44-46; anal. chemist, inst. study metals, Chicago, 46-50; chemist, M & P lab, transformer div, GEN. ELEC. CO, 50-59, prin. engr, aircraft nuclear propulsion dept, 59-61, nuclear mat. & propulsion oper, 61-64, mgr, high temp. fuels res, 64-69, SR. PHYS. CHEMIST, AIRCRAFT ENGINE GROUP, 69- AAAS; Am. Chem. Soc. Separation procedures in analytical chemistry; electrochemistry; reactions of non metallic impurities in metals; high temperature reactions; corrosion. Address: 7355 Drake Rd, Cincinnati, OH 45243.

FRYXELL, RONALD C, b. Moline, Ill, Aug. 31, 38; m. 59; c. 1. MATHEMATICS. A.B, Augustana Col.(Ill), 60; Nat. Defense Ed. Act fel, Washington State, 60-63, M.A, 62, Nat. Sci. Found. fel, 63, Ph.D.(math), 64. Asst. prof. MATH, ALBION COL, 64-70, ASSOC. PROF, 70- Am. Math. Soc; Math. Asn. Am. Finite geometry, particularly finite planes of square order. Address: Dept. of Mathematics, Albion College, 701 E. Porter, Albion, MI 49224.

FU, CHUEN-CHENG, b. China, Dec. 25, 30; m. 63; c. 3. APPLIED MECHANICS. B.S, Taiwan Normal Univ, 55; M.S, Univ. Minn, 60; Ph.D.(appl. mech), 61. Res. assoc. appl. mech, Johns Hopkins Univ, 61-63; MEM. TECH. STAFF, INGERSOLL-RAND RES, INC, PRINCETON, 63- Elastic waves in solids; theory of elasticity; theory of vibrations. Address: 1228 Indian Pl, North Brunswick, NJ 08902.

FU, JERRY HUI MING, b. Hupeh, China, July 15, 32; U.S. citizen; m. 64; c. 2. PLASMA & SPACE PHYSICS. B.S, Taiwan, 56; M.S, Northwestern, 61; summer, Nat. Sci. Found. fel, Plasma Physics Inst, Princeton, 64; Ph.D. (aerospace sci) Michigan, 67. Fel, inst. fluid dynamics & appl. math, Maryland, 67-68, res. assoc, 67-70; SR. SCIENTIST, EG&G, INC, 70- AAAS; Am. Phys. Soc; Am. Geophys. Union. Shock wave in collisionless plasma and microstructure of the earth's bow shock; surface potential distribution near a satellite in interplanetary space. Address: EG&G, Inc, Los Alamos, NM 87544.

FU, KING-SUN, b. Nanking, China, Oct. 2, 30; m. 58; c. 3. ELECTRICAL ENGINEERING. B.S, Nat. Taiwan Univ, 53; M.A.Sc, Toronto, 56; Ph.D. (elec. eng), Illinois, 59. Demonstr, Toronto, 54-55; asst, Illinois, 55-59; res. engr, Boeing Aircraft Co, 59-60; asst. prof. ELEC. ENG, PURDUE, 60-63, assoc. prof, 63-66, PROF, 66- Vis. prof, Univ. Calif, Berkeley, 67-68. Fel. Inst. Elec. & Electronics Eng; Soc. Indust. & Appl. Math; Am. Soc. Eng. Educ. Computer and information sciences; pattern recognition; bionics. Address: Dept. of Electrical Engineering, Purdue University, Lafayette, IN 47907.

FU, KUAN-CHEN, b. Nanking, China, Feb. 2, 33; m. 63; c. 2. CIVIL & STRUCTURAL ENGINEERING. B.S, Taiwan Prov. Col. Eng, 55; M.S, Univ. Notre Dame, 59, asst, 57-59, 64-67, Ph.D.(civil eng), 67. Struct. engr, Chas. Cole & Sons, 59-63; ASST. PROF. CIVIL ENG, UNIV. TOLEDO, 67- Prin. investr, Nat. Sci. Found. res. grant, 69- Chinese Air Force, 55-57, 2nd Lt. Assoc. mem. Am. Soc. Civil Eng. Optimization of structural configurations under deterministic and probabilistic loading conditions. Address: Dept. of Civil Engineering, University of Toledo, Toledo, OH 43606.

FU, SHOU-CHENG JOSEPH, b. Peiping, China, Mar. 19, 22; nat; m. 51; c. 3. CHEMISTRY. B.S, Cath. Univ. Peiping, China, 41, M.S, 44; Peiping Union Med. Col, 41-42; Ph.D.(chem), Johns Hopkins Univ, 49. Asst. chem, Cath. Univ. Peiping, 42-44; jr. instr, Johns Hopkins Univ, 47-49; res. fel, Nat. Cancer Inst, U.S. Pub. Health Serv, 49-51, vis. scientist, 51-54; Bissing fel. from Johns Hopkins Univ. to Univ. Col, Univ. London, 55; chief enzyme & bio-org. chem. lab, Children's Cancer Res. Found, Boston, 56-66; prof. chem. & chmn. div, Chinese Univ. Hong Kong, 66-70, vis. prof. ophthal. col. physicians & surgeons, Columbia Univ, 70-71; PROF. BIOCHEM, COL. MED.

& DENT. N.J, 71- Res. assoc. Children's Hosp. Med. Ctr. & Harvard Med. Sch, 56-66; dean sci. faculty, Chinese Univ. Hong Kong, 67-69. Fel. AAAS; Am. Chem. Soc; Biophys. Soc; Am. Asn. Cancer Res; Am. Soc. Biol. Chem; N.Y. Acad. Sci; The Chem. Soc. Organic chemistry; chemistry of amino acids and peptides; proteins and enzymes; chemical kinetics and reaction mechanism. Address: Dept. of Biochemistry, College of Medicine & Dentistry of New Jersey, 100 Bergen St, Newark, NJ 07103.

FU, TIM TSE-MIN, b. Peking, China, Jan. 9, 32; U.S. citizen; m. 59; c. 2. MECHANICAL ENGINEERING. B.S, Nat. Taiwan Univ, 54; M.S, Univ. Ill, Urbana, 59; Ph.D.(mech. eng), Univ. Wash, 70. Design engr, Yue Loong Eng. Co, Ltd, Taiwan, 54-57; assoc. engr, Boeing Co, Wash, 59-63; res. physicist, north. forest fire lab, U.S. Forest Serv, Mont, summer 67; RES. MECH. ENGR, NAVAL CIVIL ENG. LAB, 69- Am. Inst. Aeronaut. & Astronaut; Combustion Inst. Fire research, especially thermal environment, gross behavior, flow field, detection and extinguishment. Address: Code L-63, Naval Civil Engineering Lab, Port Hueneme, CA 93043.

FU, WEI-NING, b. Huang Hsien, China, Feb. 24, 25; m. 55; c. 3. GENETICS. B.S, Nat. Honan Univ, China, 49; M.S, Okla. State, 60, Ph.D.(plant breeding, genetics), 63. Teacher, high sch, Taiwan, 49-51; assoc. agronomist, Taiwan Tobacco Res. Inst, 52-57; asst. prof. GENETICS & CYTOL, CENT. CONN. STATE COL, 63-69, ASSOC. PROF, 69- Nat. Sci. Found. grant. AAAS; Am. Soc. Agron; Crop Sci. Soc. Am; Am. Genetic Asn; Agr. Asn. China. Tobacco breeding and chemical analysis; corn and sorghum breeding; chromosomal aberrations induced with X-ray and thermal neutrons in Sorghum vulgare; evolutionary pathways in Tripsacum. Address: Dept. of Biological Sciences, Central Connecticut State College, New Britain, CT 06050.

FU, WHAI-SANG, b. Yunyang, China, Sept. 17, 39. THEORETICAL & APPLIED MECHANICS, CIVIL ENGINEERING. B.S, Nat. Taiwan Univ, 62; for. scholar. & Univ. assistantship, Univ. Wash, 62-63; res. assistantship, Northwest. Univ, 63-67, M.S, 65, Ph.D.(theoret. & appl. mech), 67. Trainee reinforced concrete bldg. design, Taiwan Pub. Works Bur, China, summer 61; asst. prof. ENG. MECH, OHIO STATE UNIV, 67-71, ASSOC. PROF, 71- Res. mech. engr, Naval Res. Lab, Dept. Navy, Wash, D.C, summer 69; Nat. Sci. Found. res. grant, 69-71. Award, Naval Res. Lab, Dept. Navy, 70. Am. Soc. Mech. Eng; Am. Soc. Eng. Educ. Correlation between dislocation and the mathematical theory of plasticity; crack and punch problems in thermoelasticity; plastic flow and fracture. Address: Dept. of Engineering Mechanics, Ohio State University, 155 W. Woodruff, Columbus, OH 43210.

FU, YUAN C(HIN), b. Formosa, Feb. 16, 30; U.S. Citizen; m. 60; c. 2. PHYSICAL CHEMISTRY, FUEL ENGINEERING. B.S, Nat. Taiwan Univ, 53; Ph.D.(fuels eng), Univ. Utah, 61. Res. engr, Union Indust. Res. Inst, Formosa, 53-56; res. engr, Phillips Petrol. Co, 61-64; res. assoc, Univ. South. Calif, 64-65; RES. CHEMIST, U.S. BUR. MINES, 65- Instr, Univ. Pittsburgh, 67-69. Am. Chem. Soc; Chem. Soc. Japan. Chemical reactions in electrical discharge; chemical kinetics; chemistry of coal and other fossil fuels; conversion of cellulosic wastes to fuel. Address: Pittsburgh Energy Research Center, U.S. Bureau of Mines, Pittsburgh, PA 15213.

FU, YUMIN, b. Peking, China, May 15, 29; m. 64. ELECTRICAL ENGINEERING. B.S, Taiwan, 55; M.S, Illinois, 60, Ph.D.(elec. eng), 62. Asst. prof. ELEC. ENG, Kansas, 62-64; ASSOC. PROF, SOUTH. METHODIST UNIV, 64- Inst. Elec. & Electronics Eng. Network theory in electrical engineering. Address: Dept. of Electrical Engineering, Southern Methodist University, Dallas, TX 75222.

FUBINI, EUGENE G(HIRON), b. Turin, Italy, Apr. 19, 13; nat; m. 45; c. 6. ENGINEERING. Inst. Tech. Turin, 29-31; Dr. Physics, Rome, 44; hon. LL.D, Polytech. Inst. Brooklyn, 68; hon. D.Eng, Pratt Inst, 67; hon. Sc.D, Rensselaer Polytech. Inst. Res. assoc, Nat. Inst. Electrotechnics, Rome, 35-38; engr. in charge microwave & int. broadcasting, CBS, Inc, 38-42; res. assoc. develop. electronic countermeasures, radio res. lab, Harvard, 42-44; with Airborne Instruments Lab, 45-61, div. head to v.pres, 60-61; asst. secy. defense & dep. dir. defense res. & eng, 61-65; v.pres. & group exec, IBM Corp, 65-69; DIR. & OFF. BD, TEX. INSTRUMENTS, INC, 70- Spec. lectr, Harvard, 56; consult, IBM Corp, 69-; President's Sci. Adv. Comt, 57-61, 69- Mem. adv. coun. advan. sci. res. & develop, N.Y. State, 58-; panel sci. adv. bd, Nat. Security Agency, 58-61; chmn. electromagnetic warfare adv. group, Air Res. & Develop. Command, 58-61; adv. group spec. projs, Dept. Defense, 58-61; President's Comn. Law Enforcement, 65-67; Defense Sci. Bd, 66-69; sci. adv. comt, Am. Newspaper Publ. Asn, 69-; defense spec. projs. group, 70-; Defense Intel. Agency, 65-, chmn, 65-70; bd. dirs, Volunteers Int. Tech. Assistance, Inc, 69-; trustee, Urban Inst, 69-; vis. comt, comput. ctr, Harvard; sch. eng, Stanford Univ; George Wash. Univ. Presidential Cert. Merit, 46; defense medal, Dept. Defense, 66; exceptional serv. medal, Defense Intel. Agency, 70. Civilian with Off. Sci. Res. & Develop; U.S.A.A.F; U.S.N, 44. Nat. Acad. Eng; fel. Inst. Elec. & Electronics Eng; N.Y. Acad. Sci. Advanced development of special electronic devices; non-conventional antennas and microwave devices; radar; radar countermeasures; computers. Address: 2300 Hunter Mill Rd, Vienna, VA 22180.

FUCHIGAMI, LESLIE H, b. Lanai City, Hawaii, June 11, 42; m. 63; c. 3. HORTICULTURE, PLANT PHYSIOLOGY. B.S, Univ. Hawaii, 64; M.S, Univ. Minn, St. Paul, 66, Ph.D.(plant physiol), 70. ASST. PROF. HORT, ORE. STATE UNIV, 70- Am. Soc. Hort. Sci; Int. Plant Propagators Soc. Environmental, physiological and chemical control of cold acclimation in Cornus stolonifera; Meloidogyne hapla versus Treflan; rooting and establishment of Douglas fir; storage of ornamentals; forcing of colored lilies; root regeneration of nursery crops. Address: Dept. of Horticulture, Oregon State University, Corvallis, OR 97331.

FUCHS, ALBERT FREDERICK, b. Philadelphia, Pa, Feb. 15, 38; m. 63; c. 2. BIOMEDICAL ENGINEERING. B.S.E.E, Drexel Inst, 60, M.S, 61; Ph.D. (biomed. eng), Hopkins, 66. Nat. Inst. to Combat Blindness fel, Hopkins, 66-67; Nat. Sci. Found. fel, Freiburg, 67-68; ASST. PROF. PHYSIOL. & BIOPHYS, DEPT. PHYSIOL. & BIOPHYS. & REGIONAL PRIMATE RES. CTR, UNIV. WASH, 69- Samuel A. Talbot Award, group on biomed. eng, Inst. Elec. & Electronics Eng, 69. Soc. Neurosci. Oculomotor system of primates. Address: Regional Primate Research Center, I-421 Health Sciences Bldg, University of Washington, Seattle, WA 98105.

FUCHS, FRANKLIN, b. New York, N.Y, July 1, 31; m. 57; c. 2. PHYSIOLOGY. A.B, Michigan, 53; Ph.D.(physiol), Tufts, 62. Res. fel. PHYSIOL, sch. med, Tufts, 58-62; U.S. Pub. Health Serv. fel, Inst. Neurophysiol, Copenhagen, 62-64; instr, SCH. MED, UNIV. PITTSBURGH, 64-66, asst. prof, 66-71, ASSOC. PROF, 71- Lederle Med. Faculty Award, 67-70. AAAS; Am. Physiol. Soc; Biophys. Soc. Physiology and biochemistry of muscle. Address: Dept. of Physiology, University of Pittsburgh School of Medicine, Pittsburgh, PA 15213.

FUCHS, FRITZ F(RIEDRICH), b. Frederiksberg, Denmark, Nov. 27, 18; m. 48; c. 4. OBSTETRICS, GYNECOLOGY. M.D, Copenhagen, 45, Dr.Med. Sci, 57. Second asst. surgeon, Kommunehosp, Copenhagen, 53-55; second asst. obstetrician & gynecologist, Rigshosp, 55-56, first asst. obstetrician & gynecologist, 56-58; gynecologist-in-chief, Kommunehosp, 58-64; GIVEN FOUND. PROF. OBSTET. & GYNEC. & CHMN. DEPT, MED. COL, CORNELL UNIV, 65-; OBSTETRICIAN & GYNECOLOGIST-IN-CHIEF, N.Y. HOSP, 65- Assoc. prof, Copenhagen Univ, 56-64; consult, Rockefeller Univ, 68- Med.C, Danish Brigade, Allied Forces, 45, 1st Lt. Fel. Am. Gynec. Soc; fel. Am. Col. Obstet. & Gynec; fel. Am. Fertil. Soc; fel. Perinatal Res. Soc. Permeability of placenta; endocrinology of pregnancy; biology of reproduction. Address: Dept. of Obstetrics & Gynecology, Cornell University Medical College, 1300 York Ave, New York, NY 10021.

FUCHS, H(ENRY) O(TTEN), b. Strasbourg, France, 07; U.S. citizen; m. 34; c. 1. MECHANICAL ENGINEERING. B.A, Strasbourg, France, 24; M.E. Tech. Univ. Karlsruhe, Ger, 29, Dr.Eng, 33. Sr. design engr, Gen. Motors Corp, 33-45; chief res. engr, Preco Inc, 45-54; pres, Metal Improv. Equip. Co, 54-61; PROF. MECH. ENG, STANFORD UNIV, 64- Soc. Automotive Eng; Am. Soc. Mech. Eng; Am. Soc. Test. & Mat. Metal fatigue; vehicle dynamics; engineering design and development. Address: Dept. of Mechanical Engineering, Stanford University, Stanford, CA 94305.

FUCHS, IRVIN J, b. Brooklyn, N.Y, Mar. 23, 26; m. 50; c. 3. ENGINEERING. B.S, Pa. State, 50. Staff mem. creative eng. prog, Gen. Elec. Co, 50-53, develop. engr, air conditioning div, 53-56, mgr. eng. lab, 56-58; V.PRES. ENG, U.S. TESTING CO, INC, 58- U.S.A, 44-46. Nat. Soc. Prof. Eng; Am. Soc. Mech. Eng; Soc. Automotive Eng; Am. Soc. Heat, Refrig. & Air-Conditioning Eng. Administration of laboratory and field testing organizations. Address: U.S. Testing Co, Inc, 1415 Park Ave, Hoboken, NJ 07030.

FUCHS, JACOB, b. New York, N.Y, May 7, 23; m. 46; c. 2. ANALYTICAL CHEMISTRY. A.B, N.Y. Univ, 44; M.S, Illinois, 47, Ph.D.(chem), 50. Asst. CHEM, Illinois, 48-52; asst. prof, ARIZ. STATE UNIV, 52-56, assoc. prof, 56-59, PROF, 59-, EXEC. OFF. DEPT, 61- A.U.S, 44-45. Am. Chem. Soc; Soc. Appl. Spectros; fel. Am. Inst. Chem. X-ray diffraction and spectroscopy; ultraviolet and infrared spectroscopy. Address: Dept. of Chemistry, Arizona State University, Tempe, AZ 85281.

FUCHS, LASZLO, b. Budapest, Hungary, June 24, 24. MATHEMATICS. M.S. & Ph.D.(math), Budapest, 47. Asst. MATH, Eötvös Lóránd, Budapest, 49-52, docent, 52-54, PROF, 54-68; TULANE UNIV, 68- Vis. prof, Tulane, 61-62; New South Wales, 65; Miami (Fla), 66-68. Am. Math. Soc; Math. Asn. Am; Hungarian Math. Soc.(treas, 51-63, secy. gen, 63-66); Ger. Math. Asn. Abstract algebra, particularly commutative groups, ring theory and partially ordered algebraic structures. Address: Dept. of Mathematics, Tulane University, New Orleans, LA 70118.

FUCHS, MORTON S, b. New York, N.Y, Nov. 16, 32; m. 60; c. 2. BIOCHEMICAL GENETICS. B.S, Mich. State, 58, M.S, 60, Ph.D.(biochem), 67; Wisconsin, Madison, 63-66. Asst. prof. BIOL, UNIV. NOTRE DAME, 66-69, ASSOC. PROF, 69- Nat. Commun. Disease Control Ctr grant, 68- U.S.A, 51-54, Sgt. AAAS; Genetics Soc. Am; Entom. Soc. Am. Biochemical and genetic control of differentiation; reproductive physiology of insects. Address: Dept. of Biology, University of Notre Dame, Notre Dame, IN 46556.

FUCHS, NORMAN H, b. Newark, N.J, Aug. 2, 38; m. 59; c. 2. THEORETICAL PHYSICS. George Westinghouse scholar. & B.S, Carnegie Inst. Tech, 59; Nat. Sci. Found. fel. & Ph.D.(physics), Mass. Inst. Tech, 64. Res. assoc. PHYSICS, Mass. Inst. Technol, 64; res. investr, Univ. Pa, 64-66; asst. prof, PURDUE UNIV, 66-69, ASSOC. PROF, 69- Am. Phys. Soc. Symmetries and their breakdown; elementary particle physics. Address: Dept. of Physics, Purdue University, West Lafayette, IN 47907.

FUCHS, RICHARD, b. Baltimore, Md, Dec. 29, 26. ORGANIC CHEMISTRY. A.B, Cornell, 49; univ. fel, Kansas, 51-52, Ph.D.(chem), 53. Asst. instr. chem, Kansas, 49-53; fel, Iowa State Col, 53-54; asst. prof. CHEM, Alabama, 54-55; instr, Texas, 55-58, asst. prof, 58-63; ASSOC. PROF, UNIV. HOUSTON, 63- U.S.N.R, 45-46. Am. Chem. Soc. Solvation effects on rates and equilibria; electronic transmission within molecules. Address: Dept. of Chemistry, University of Houston, Houston, TX 77004.

FUCHS, RICHARD E(ARL), b. Milan, Tenn, July 26, 36; m. 61; c. 2. CHEMICAL ENGINEERING. B.S, Tennessee, 58; M.S, La. State, 62, Ph.D.(chem. eng), 64. Chem. engr, Esso Res. Labs, 58-61; asst. prof. chem. eng, Mississippi, 64; SR. RES. ENGR, COMPUT. PROCESSES, OLINKRAFT, INC, 64- Summers, chem. engr, Nat. Coun. Stream Improv, 62, 63. Ord.C, 59, U.S.A.R, 58-66, Capt. Tech. Asn. Pulp & Paper Indust. Decolorization of pulp mill bleaching effluents; forest products; process control. Address: Olinkraft, Inc, P.O. Box 488, West Monroe, LA 71291.

FUCHS, RONALD, b. Los Angeles, Calif, Jan. 27, 32; m. 63; c. 2. PHYSICS. B.S, Calif. Inst. Tech, 54; Ph.D.(physics), Illinois, 57. Fulbright fel, Stuttgart Tech, 57-59; physicist, div. sponsored res, lab. insulation res. Mass. Inst. Tech, 59-61; asst. prof. PHYSICS, IOWA STATE UNIV, 61-66, ASSOC. PROF, 66- Am. Phys. Soc. Theoretical solid state physics; optical properties; lattice dynamics. Address: Dept. of Physics, Iowa State University, Ames, IA 50010.

FUCHS, W(OLFGANG) H(EINRICH) J(OHANNES), b. Munich, Germany, May 19, 15; nat; m. 43; c. 3. PURE MATHEMATICS. B.A. Cambridge, 36, Ph.D.(math), 41. Teacher, Brit. Univs, 40-49; assoc. prof. MATH. CORNELL UNIV, 50-58, PROF, 58-, vis. assoc. prof. 48-49. Theory of functions. Address: 1105 Trumansburg Rd, Ithaca, NY 14850.

FUCHSMAN, CHARLES H(ERMAN), b. New York, N.Y, June 12, 17; m. 37; c. 3. CHEMISTRY. B.S, City Col, 36; Ph.D.(org. chem), Western Reserve. 65. Technologist, U.S. Bur. Mines, 42-45; res. chemist, potash ref, Int. Minerals & Chems. Corp, 45-51; res. group leader, micro-pilot plant develop, Columbia South. Chem. Corp, 51-56; dir. res. & develop, Ferro Chem. Corp, 56-66, Ferro Chem. Div, FERRO CORP, 66-69, ASSOC. DIR. RES. ORG. CHEM, BEDFORD, 69- AAAS; Am. Chem. Soc; Soc. Plastics Eng; Am. Inst. Mining, Metall. & Petrol. Eng; The Chem. Soc; N.Y. Acad. Sci. Organic chemical synthesis; polymer chemistry; history of organic chemistry; extractive metallurgy; reaction mechanisms. Address: 3441 Washington Blvd, Cleveland Heights, OH 44118.

FUCHSMAN, WILLIAM H(ARVEY), b. N.Y.C, June 2, 41; m. 64; c. 2. BIOCHEMISTRY. B.A, Harvard, 63; Ph.D.(biochem). Hopkins, 67. Asst. prof. chem, South Florida, 67-68; fel, E.I. du Pont de Nemours & Co, 68-70; ASST. PROF. CHEM, OBERLIN COL, 70- AAAS; Am. Chem. Soc; The Chem. Soc. Chemistry of porphyrins, metalloporphyrins and hemeproteins; nitrogen fixation. Address: Dept. of Chemistry, Oberlin College, Oberlin, OH 44074.

FUCIK, JOHN E(DWARD), b. Waukegan, Ill, May 30, 28; m. 56; c. 3. HORTICULTURE, PLANT PHYSIOLOGY. B.S, Illinois, 49, M.S, 57, Ph.D.(hort), 63. Asst. prod. mgr, Pfister Assoc. Growers, Inc, 49-51; supvr. & teacher HORT, Univ. Ill, 57-65; ASSOC. PROF, CITRUS CTR, TEX. A&I UNIV, 65- Nat. Sci. Found-Atomic Energy Comn. grant, Oak Ridge Inst. Nuclear Studies, summer 64. U.S.A.F.R, 51-53, Lt. Col. Am. Soc. Hort. Sci; Am. Soc. Plant Physiol; Am. Pomol. Soc; Int. Soc. Hort. Sci. Physiology of horticultural tree crops; tree-soil-environment relationships. Address: Citrus Center, Texas A&I University, Weslaco, TX 78596.

FUDA, MICHAEL GEORGE, b. Albany, N.Y, Oct. 31, 38; m. 62; c. 2. NUCLEAR PHYSICS. B.S, Rensselaer Polytech. Inst, 60, Ph.D.(physics), 67. Res. physicist, Knolls Atomic Power Lab, 62-64; ASST. PROF. PHYSICS, STATE UNIV. N.Y. BUFFALO, 67- Am. Phys. Soc. Scattering theory with applications to nuclear physics; theory of three-particle systems. Address: Dept. of Physics, State University of New York at Buffalo, Buffalo, NY 14214.

FUDALI, ROBERT F, b. Minneapolis, Minn, July 7, 33; m. 56; c. 3. GEOCHEMISTRY, PETROLOGY. B.A, Univ. Minn, Minneapolis, 56; Nat. Sci. Found. fel, Pa. State Univ, 59-60, Ph.D.(geochem), 60. Res. fel, Pa. State Univ, 60-62; staff scientist, Bellcomm Inc, 62-66; RES. SCIENTIST, DEPT. MINERAL SCI, SMITHSONIAN INST, 66- AAAS; Geochem. Soc; Meteoritical Soc. Genesis of igneous and metamorphic rocks and meteorites; genesis of lunar rocks and landforms; role of large cometary and meteorite impacts in the development of planetary surfaces. Address: Dept. of Mineral Sciences, Division of Meteorites, Smithsonian Institution, Washington, DC 20560.

FUDENBERG, H. HUGH, b. New York, N.Y, Oct. 24, 28; m. 55; c. 4. HEMATOLOGY, IMMUNOLOGY. A.B, California, Los Angeles, 49; M.D, Chicago, 53; M.A, Boston, 57. Intern med, Utah, 53-54; fel. hemat, sch. med, Tufts, 54-56; asst. res. med, Mt. Sinai Hosp, N.Y, 56-57; Peter Bent Brigham Hosp, Boston, Mass, 57-58; res. assoc. immunol, Rockefeller Inst, 58-60; asst. prof. MED, SCH. MED, UNIV. CALIF, SAN FRANCISCO, 60-62, assoc. prof, 62-66, PROF, 66-, CHIEF HEMAT. UNIT, 62-, PROF. BACT. & IMMUNOL, BERKELEY, 66-, assoc. prof. microbiol, Berkeley, 65-66. Mem. expert comt. immunol, WHO, 62- Pasteur Medal, Inst. Pasteur, Paris, 62; Robert A. Cooke Mem. Medal, Am. Acad. Allergy, 67. Fel. AAAS; Am. Asn. Immunol; Am. Soc. Human Genetics; Am. Soc. Clin. Invest; Genetics Soc. Am; Brit. Soc. Immunol; Asn. Am. Physicians; Fedn. Am. Soc. Exp. Biol. Antigenic, biologic, and physico-chemical properties of antibody molecules and related proteins; genetic control of normal antibody synthesis and genetically-determined aberrations predisposed to infection. Address: Dept. of Medicine, University of California School of Medicine, San Francisco, CA 94122.

FUEHRING, HOWARD DALE, b. Seward, Nebr, Oct. 20, 24; m. 47; c. 3. SOIL FERTILITY, PLANT NUTRITION. B.S, Nebraska, 48, M.S, 49, Ph.D. (agron), 60. Instr. soil sci, Nebraska, 56-59; asst. prof. soil fertil, Am. Univ. Beirut, 59-62, assoc. prof, 62-67, prof, 67-68, head div. soils & irrig, 62-68; ASSOC. PROF. SOIL FERTIL, N.MEX. STATE UNIV, 69- Am. Soc. Agron; Soil Sci. Soc. Am. Soil fertility, plant nutrition, plant growth regulation, and water management in relation to obtaining maximum sustained yields of crops. Address: 1632 Jonquil Park Dr, Clovis, NM 88101.

FUENNING, SAMUEL ISAIAH, b. Ft. Morgan, Colo, Sept. 20, 16; m. 44; c. 4. MEDICINE. B.Sc, Nebraska, 40, M.S, 41, M.D, 45. Asst. bot, UNIV. NEBR, LINCOLN, 40-41, ASSOC. PROF. pub. health & assoc. cellular res, 50-62, PREV. MED, 62-, MED. DIR. UNIV. HEALTH SERVS. & HEALTH CTR, 47- Med.C, 42-46, Lt. AAAS; Am. Med. Asn; Am. Col. Health Asn.(pres, 60-61). Clinical medicine in the college age group; stress; cellular research. Address: University Health Services & Health Center, University of Nebraska, Lincoln, NE 68508.

FUERHOLZER, JAMES J, b. Peru, Ill, Mar. 5, 36; m. 57; c. 4. POLYMER & ORGANIC CHEMISTRY. B.S, Bradley Univ, 58; Ph.D.(org. chem), Univ. Nebr, 65. Res. chemist, Morton Chem. Co, 57-60; res. asst, Univ. Nebr. 60-65; res. chemist, Morton Int, Inc, 65-67, RES. SUPVR. POLYMER COATINGS, PACKAGING INST, MORTON CHEM. CO, 65- Am. Chem. Soc. Reaction of amines; adhesives and coatings. Address: Packaging Institute. Morton Chemical Co, 1275 Lake Ave, Woodstock, IL 60098.

FUERST, HAROLD T(HEODORE), b. N.Y.C, May 21, 09; m. 40; c. 1. EPIDEMIOLOGY. A.B, Cornell Univ, 29; M.D. Jefferson Med. Col, 33; M.P.H, Columbia Univ, 58. Asst. clin. prof. prev. med, N.Y. MED. COL, 55-58,

assoc. clin. prof. 58-65, pediat, 59-65, clin. prof. 65-68, PROF. COMMUNITY & PREV. MED. & ASSOC. PROF. PEDIAT, 68-; CHIEF PREV. MED. SERV. & VIS. PEDIATRICIAN, METROP. HOSP, N.Y, 68-; asst. comnr, Preventable & Chronic Disease Serv, New York Dept. Health, 64-68, dir. bur. prev. diseases, 60-64, chief. div. epidemiol, 55-60. Asst. pediatrician, Vanderbilt Clin, 37-54; vis. physician, Willard Parker Hosp, 40-55; asst. pediatrician, Flower-Fifth Ave. Hosp, 55-68; lectr, grad. med. sch, N.Y. Univ-Bellevue Med. Ctr, 56-68; adj. asst. prof, Columbia Univ, 60-68. Dipl. Am. Bd. Prev. Med. U.S.A, 42-46. AAAS; Am. Med. Asn; Am. Pub. Health Asn; N.Y. Acad. Sci; N.Y. Acad. Med; Soc. Epidemiol. Res; Am. Heart Asn. Communicable diseases; epidemiological problems. Address: 510 E. 77th St, New York, NY 10021.

FUERST, ROBERT, b. Vienna, Austria, Jan. 12, 21; nat; m. 46; c. 2. GENETICS. B.S, Houston, 44; M.A, Texas, 48, Ph.D.(zool), 55. Asst. prof. genetics, Univ. Tex, 55-57, res. scientist biochem, M.D. Anderson Hosp. & Tumor Inst, 49-52, res. scientist, genetics found, 52-55, asst. biologist in charge microbiol. sect, 55-57; assoc. prof. BIOL, TEX. WOMAN'S UNIV, 57-64, PROF, 64-, HEAD MICROBIOL. RES, 57- AAAS; Am. Soc. Human Genetics; Soc. Indust. Microbiol; Am. Asn. Lab. Animal Sci; Genetics Soc. Am; Am. Soc. Microbiol; N.Y. Acad. Sci; Am. Inst. Biol. Sci; Am. Chem. Soc. Microbial genetics; radiation; biology. Address: Dept. of Biology, Texas Woman's University, Box 22757, TWU Station, Denton, TX 76204.

FUERSTENAU, D(OUGLAS) W(INSTON), b. Hazel, S.Dak, Dec. 6, 28; m. 53; c. 3. METALLURGY. B.S, S.Dak. Sch. Mines & Tech, 49; M.S. Mont. Sch. Mines, 50; Sc.D.(metall), Mass. Inst. Tech, 53. Asst. prof. mineral. eng, Mass. Inst. Tech, 53-56; res. engr, Union Carbide Metals Co, 56-58; mgr. mineral eng, Kaiser Aluminum & Chem. Corp, 58-59; assoc. prof. METALL, UNIV. CALIF, BERKELEY, 59-62, PROF, 62-, CHMN. DEPT. MAT. SCI. & ENG, 70- Am. Chem. Soc; Am. Inst. Mining, Metall. & Petrol. Eng.(Hardy Gold Medal, 57, Raymond Award, 61); Am. Inst. Chem. Eng. Mineral processing; applied colloid and surface chemistry; properties of particulate materials. Address: Dept. of Materials Science & Engineering, University of California, Berkeley, CA 94720.

FUERSTENAU, M(AURICE) C(LARK), b. Watertown, S.Dak, June 6, 33; m. 53; c. 3. GEOLOGICAL ENGINEERING, METALLURGY. B.S, S.Dak. Sch. Mines & Tech, 55; M.S, Mass. Inst. Tech, 57, Sc.D.(metall), 61. Res. assoc. metall, Mass. Inst. Tech, 60-61; res. engr, N.Mex. Bur. Mines, 61-63; asst. prof, Colo. Sch. Mines, 63-64, assoc. prof, 64-68; Univ. Utah, 68-70, prof, 70; PROF. METALL. ENG. & HEAD DEPT, S.DAK. SCH. MINES & TECHNOL, 70- U.S.A.R, 55-, Capt. Am. Inst. Mining, Metall. & Petrol. Eng. Surface chemistry and adsorption phenomena; kinetics and reaction mechanisms involved in hydrometallurgy; mechanisms involved in froth flotation; fundamentals of sedimentation. Address: Dept. of Metallurgical Engineering, South Dakota School of Mines & Technology, Rapid City, SD 57701.

FUESS, FREDERICK W(ILLIAM), III, b. Syracuse, N.Y, Nov. 5, 27; m. 52; c. 2. AGRONOMY. B.S, Cornell, 52, M.Ed, 55; Ph.D, Michigan State, 63. Teacher, pub. sch, 52; asst. prof. agron, State Univ. N.Y. Agr. & Tech. Inst, Morrisville, 55-60; asst, Michigan State, 60-63; asst. prof, ILL. STATE UNIV, 63-65, assoc. prof, 65-69, PROF. PLANT & SOIL SCI, 69- U.S.A, 52-54. Am. Soc. Agron; Am. Forestry Asn; Crop Sci. Soc. Am. Crop physiology and management. Address: R.R. 1, Normal, IL 61761.

FUEST, RONALD W(ALTER), b. Irvington, N.J, Feb. 4, 36; m. 62; c. 2. ORGANIC & PHYSICAL CHEMISTRY. B.S, Seton Hall, 58; Ph.D.(org. chem), Rutgers, 63. Res. chemist, Trubek Chem. Co, 62-63; RES. SCIENTIST, U.S. Rubber Co, 63-71, RES. CTR, UNIROYAL, INC, 71- Am. Chem. Soc. Reactions catalyzed by transition metals; organic reaction mechanisms; synthetic fibers. Address: Uniroyal Inc. Research Center, 1361 Alps Rd, Wayne, NJ 07470.

FUGASSI, (JAMES) PAUL, b. Trafford City, Pa, Feb. 1, 09; m. 40. PHYSICAL CHEMISTRY. B.S, Carnegie Inst. Tech, 30, fel, 30-33, M.S, 31; Coffin fel, Wisconsin, 31-33, univ. fel, 33-34, Ph.D.(phys. chem), 34. Asst. CHEM, Carnegie Inst. Tech, 30-31; Wisconsin, 34-35; instr, CARNEGIE-MELLON UNIV, 35-38, asst. prof, 38-44, assoc. prof, 44-49, PROF, 49-, DIR. COAL RES. LAB, 59- With Off. Sci. Res. & Develop; U.S.A, 44. Assoc. mem. Am. Chem. Soc; assoc. mem. Electrochem. Soc; fel. N.Y. Acad. Sci; assoc. mem. Faraday Soc. Kinetics of gaseous decompositions; photochemistry; electrochemistry; polymerization; synthetic rubber; kinetics solution reactions. Address: Dept. of Chemistry, Carnegie-Mellon University, Pittsburgh, PA 15213.

FUGATE, KEARBY JOE, b. Dallas, Tex, Aug. 6, 34; m. 62; c. 2. MICROBIOLOGY, BIOCHEMISTRY. B.A, Baylor, 56, M.S, 63, Ph.D.(microbiol), 67. Res. asst. microbiol, J.K. & Susie Wadley Res. Inst, 60-63; instr, dent. sch, Baylor, 64-67; MICROBIOLOGIST, U.S. PUB. HEALTH SERV, 67- Med.Serv.C, U.S.A, 57-60, Sgt. AAAS; Am. Soc. Microbiol; Am. Pub. Health Asn; fel. Am. Inst. Chem. Immunochemistry of bacterial cell wall constituents; immunochemistry of antigen-antibody interactions; immunology of murine leukemia-virus transmission. Address: Dept. of Health Education & Welfare, U.S. Public Health Service, 3032 Bryan St, Dallas, TX 75204.

FUGATE, WESLEY O(RLEAN), b. Providence, Ky, June 10, 14. ORGANIC CHEMISTRY. B.S, West. Ky. Univ, 33; fel, Illinois, 37-39, Ph.D.(org. chem), 39. Teacher, pub. sch, Ill, 33-36; asst. chem, Illinois, 36-37; assoc. chemist, Minnesota, 39-40; instr. org. chem, Columbia, 40-41; res. chemist, Barrett div, Allied Chem. & Dye Corp, N.J, 41-43; Inter-chem. Corp, N.Y, 43-46; AM. CYANAMID CO, 46-52, employee training coord, 52-57, group leader, 57-62, col. relations rep, 62-69, MGR. TECH. PLACEMENT SERV, 69- Am. Chem. Soc; Am. Soc. Eng. Educ. Magnesium derivatives of hindered ketones; vitamin E; coal tar chemicals; amino acids; catalytic reactions; petrochemicals; industrial relations. Address: American Cyanamid Co, Wayne, NJ 07470.

FÜGER, KARL EMIL, b. San Salvador, El Salvador, Sept. 22, 31; m. 60; c. 1. ORGANIC CHEMISTRY. Dipl. ing, Swiss Fed. Inst. Tech, 55, Ph.D.(tech.

org. chem), 58. Res. & develop. chemist, J.R. Geigy Ag, Switz, 58-60, Geigy Chem. Corp, Ala, 60-61; RES. CHEMIST, Sinclair. Res, Inc, Ill. 61-64; Inrescor Ag, Switz, 64-67; Sinclair Res, Inc, Ill. 67-69, ATLANTIC RICHFIELD CO, 69- Am. Chem. Soc. Synthesis of monomers in the field of polyurethane chemistry. Address: 500 S. Ridgeway Ave, Glenolden, PA 19036.

FUGET, C(HARLES) R(OBERT), b. Rochester, Pa, Dec. 15, 29; m. 56; c. 1. PHYSICAL CHEMISTRY. B.S, Geneva Col, 51; M.S, Pa. State, 53, Ph.D. (phys. chem), 56. Res. chemist, Esso Res. & Eng. Co, N.J, 55-56; asst. prof. chem, Geneva Col, 56-59, assoc. prof, 59-63; res. chemist, phys. & theoret, Callery Chem. Co, 57-59; prof. sci, State Univ. N.Y. Col. Buffalo, 63-64; prof. physics & chmn. dept, Geneva Col, 64-71; PROF. PHYSICS & DIR. DIV. NATURAL SCI. & MATH, IND. UNIV. PA, 71- Am. Chem. Soc; Am. Phys. Soc. Thermodynamic properties; reaction calorimetry; electrochemistry. Address: Division of Natural Sciences & Mathematics, 230 Weyandt Hall, Indiana University of Pennsylvania, Indiana, PA 15701.

FUGGER, J(OSEPH), b. Jesenice, Yugoslavia, Feb. 11, 21; nat; m. 53; c. 6. PHYSICAL & ORGANIC CHEMISTRY. B.S, Pittsburgh, 46, M.S, 48, Ph.D. (chem), 52. Res. intern, North. Regional Lab, U.S. Dept. of Agr, 49-50; asst. prof. res, Antioch Col, 52-53; res. chemist, Buckeye Cellulose Corp, 54-55; fel. chem, Harvard, 55-56; res. group leader, Thiokol Chem. Corp, 57-58; res. specialist gas dynamics, Boeing Airplane Co, 58-59; staff scientist res, opers, aeronutronic div, Ford Motor Co, 59-60; res. scientist, missiles & space div, Lockheed Aircraft Corp, 61-62; res. group leader, Westreco, Inc, Nestle Int, 63-64, head, basic res. sect, 64-67; consult. chemist, Hops Extract Corp. Am, Wash, 69-70; CONSULT. CHEMIST, 70- Private lessee, oil, gas & geothermal steam properties in Colo-Wyo. area, 67- U.S.A.F, 42-45, 1st Lt. Am. Chem. Soc; fel. The Chem. Soc. Coffee and tea chemistry. Address: 739 Greenleaf Dr, Monroeville, PA 15146.

FUGLISTER, FREDERICK C(HARLES), b. N.Y.C, Aug. 1, 09; m. 39; c. 3. OCEANOGRAPHY. From observer to PHYS. OCEANOGR, WOODS HOLE OCEANOG. INST, 40-, chmn. dept. phys. oceanog, 62-67. Agassiz Medal, Nat. Acad. Sci, 69. Fel. Am. Geophys. Union. Thermohaline structure of the Atlantic Ocean with special emphasis on the Gulf Stream system; physical oceanography. Address: Woods Hole Oceanographic Institution, Woods Hole, MA 02543.

FUGMANN, RUTH A(DELE), b. Baltimore, Md, Sept. 7, 23. IMMUNOCHEMISTRY, MICROBIOLOGY. B.S, Hopkins, 50; M.S, Miami (Fla), 64, Ph.D. (cancer immunol), 68. Technician, clin. lab, Mercy Hosp, Baltimore, Md, 42-44; sr. technician, Army Chem. Ctr, 44-48, hematologist, 48-50; res. asst. cancer, Col. Physicians & Surgeons, Columbia, 50-58; Miami (Fla), 58-61; immunochem, Howard Hughes Med. Inst, Miami, Fla, 61-65; res. asst. immunochem, Variety Children's Res. Found, 65-68, res. assoc. cancer immunol, 68-69; CO-DIR. CANCER IMMUNOL, CATH. MED. CTR. OF BROOKLYN & QUEENS, INC, 69- Instr, Univ. Miami, 68-70. AAAS; Am. Soc. Microbiol; Am. Asn. Cancer Res; Am. Asn. Immunol. Cancer and transplantation immunology; cancer chemotherapy. Address: Dept. of Surgery, Catholic Medical Center of Brooklyn & Queens, Inc, 8825 153rd St, Jamaica, NY 11432.

FUGO, NICHOLAS W(ILLIAM), b. Syracuse, N.Y, Sept. 15, 13; m. 40; c. 1. OBSTETRICS & GYNECOLOGY. A.B, Syracuse, 35; M.S, Iowa, 37, Ph.D (endocrinol), 40; Jones scholar, Biol. Lab, Cold Spring Harbor, 39; M.D, Chicago, 50. Res. assoc. zool, Iowa, 39-40, instr. pharmacol, med. labs, 40-43; res. assoc. OBSTET. & GYNECOL, Chicago, 46-52, instr, 52-56, asst. prof, 56-58, assoc. prof, 58-60; PROF, SCH. MED, W.VA. UNIV, 60-, MARGARET HIGGINS SANGER CHAIR FAMILY PLANNING & REPROD. PHYSIOL, 67-, chmn. dept. obstet. & gynec, 60-66. Dipl, Am. Bd. Obstet. & Gynec. U.S.N.R, 43-46, Res, 46-53, Lt.(jg). Soc. Exp. Biol. & Med; Am. Soc. Pharmacol. & Exp. Therapeut; Am. Fertil. Soc; Am. Med. Asn; Am. Fedn. Clin. Res; fel. Am. Col. Obstet. & Gynec. Endocrinology of sex; human reproduction. Address: Dept. of Obstetrics & Gynecology, West Virginia University School of Medicine, Morgantown, WV 26506.

FUGUITT, ROBERT E(UGENE), b. Boone Grove, Ind, July 17, 17; m. 39, 53; c. 2. CHEMISTRY. B.S, Florida, 37, B.A, 38, M.S, 40, Ph.D.(phys. org. chem), 43. Asst. chem, Florida, 37-40, naval stores, 40-43; res. chemist, Distillation Prods, Inc, 43-47; asst. dir. res, org. chem. div, Glidden Co, 47-49, gen. supt, 49-56, tech. & admin. asst. to mgr, 56-58, chief process engr, 58-59; consult, 59-63; distillation specialist, Int. Flavors & Fragrances, 63-69; CONSULT, 69- Am. Chem. Soc; Am. Inst. Chem. Eng. Reaction kinetics; terpenes and natural oils; distillation; vacuum technology; process development. Address: 108 Ridge Rd, Fair Haven, NJ 07701.

FUHLHAGE, DONALD W(AYNE), b. Virgil, Kans, Sept. 2, 31; m. 61; c. 2. ORGANIC CHEMISTRY. B.S, Kansas, 53, Am. Petrol. Inst. fel, 54-58, Ph.D.(org. chem), 58. Sr. res. chemist, Tidewater Oil Co, Calif, 58-62, res. assoc, Pa, 62-63; supvr. process develop, THOMPSON-HAYWARD CHEM. CO, PHILIPS ELECTRONICS & PHARMACEUT. INDUSTS. CORP, 63-70, SECT. LEADER PROCESS DEVELOP. & RESIDUE ANAL, 70- Am. Chem. Soc; Instrument Soc. Am. Pyrrole chemistry; gas chromatographic analysis; synthesis of pesticides. Address: 7407 Belleview, Kansas City, MO 64114.

FUHR, IRVIN, b. Sharon, Pa, Jan. 16, 13; m. 40; c. 2. BIOCHEMISTRY. B.S, Wisconsin, 37, M.S, 39, Ph.D.(biochem), 42. Toxicologist, Army Chem. Center, U.S. War Dept, Md, 43-48; exec. secy. biochem. study sect, DIV. RES. GRANTS, NAT. INSTS. HEALTH, 48-55, EXEC. SECY. BIOPHYSICS & BIOPHYS. CHEM. STUDY SECT, 55- Biophys. Soc. Toxicology of drugs and chemical warfare agents; vitamin and mineral metabolism; anemia and rickets; development of experimental diets and chemical methods; development of rodenticide cartridge. Address: Division of Research Grants, National Institutes of Health, Bethesda, MD 20014.

FUHRIMAN, D(EAN) K(ENNETH), b. Ridgedale, Idaho, June 6, 18; m. 41; c. 5. CIVIL ENGINEERING. B.S, Utah State Col, 41, M.S, 50; Ph.D.(civil eng), Wisconsin, 52. Dept. asst, exp. sta, Utah State Col, 37-41; jr. engr, U.S. Corps Engrs, 41; instr, civil eng, Utah State Col, 41-43; asst. irrig. engr, soil conserv. serv, U.S. Dept. Agr, 46-48, agr. engr, P.R, 48-50; assoc. prof. civil eng, Colo. Agr. & Mech. Col, 51-52; irrig. & drainage engr, Utah State Agr. Col, 52-54; CIVIL ENG, BRIGHAM YOUNG UNIV, 54-56, PROF, 56-, chmn. dept, 58-61. Pres. & prin. engr, Fuhriman, Rollins & Co, 56-66; tech. adv, U.S. Water Pollution Control Admin, Wash, D.C, 67-68; pres, Fuhriman, Barton & Assoc, Consult. Engrs, 70-; mem. U.S. comt, Int. Conf. Irrig. & Drainage. U.S.N.R, 43-46. Am. Soc. Civil Eng; Am. Soc. Eng. Educ; Nat. Soc. Prof. Eng; Water Pollution Control Fedn. Water resources engineering; irrigation; drainage; agricultural engineering; environmental engineering. Address: College of Engineering, Brigham Young University, Provo, UT 84601.

FUHRKEN, GEBHARD, b. Frankfurt, Germany, Feb. 10, 30. MATHEMATICS. Münster, 51-57; Ph.D.(math), California, Berkeley, 62. ASST. PROF. MATH, UNIV. MINN, MINNEAPOLIS, 62- Am. Math. Soc; Asn. Symbolic Logic. Mathematical logic; theory of models. Address: School of Mathematics, University of Minnesota, Minneapolis, MN 55455.

FUHRMAN, ALBERT W(ILLIAM), b. Brooklyn, N.Y, Jan. 13, 21; m. 43; c. 2. ORGANIC CHEMISTRY. B.S, City Col. New York, 42; Columbia, 42; M.S, Purdue, 44, Am. Chem. Soc. fel, 46-48, Ph.D.(org. chem), 48. Res. chemist, chems. div, Glenn L. Martin Co, 48-50; res. & develop. chemist, Naugatuck Chem. Div, U.S. Rubber Co, 50-55; plant mgr, plastics & chem. div, Great Am. Plastics Co, 55-59, V.PRES, 59-69, GREAT AM. CHEM. CORP, 69- Civilian with Off. Sci. Res. & Develop, 44. U.S.N.R, 44-46. Am. Chem. Soc. Ketene reactions; vinyl resins; vinyl polymerization; reaction of ketene with certain carbonyl compounds; vinyl compounding. Address: Great American Chemical Corp, Fitchburg, MA 01420.

FUHRMAN, FREDERICK A(LEXANDER), b. Coquille, Oregon, Aug. 13, 15; m. 42. PHYSIOLOGY. B.S, Oregon State Col, 37, M.S, 39; exchange student, Freiburg (Germany), 37-38; Washington (Seattle), 39-41; Ph.D. (physiol), Stanford, 43. Res. assoc. physiol, STANFORD UNIV, 41-44, instr, 44-49, asst. prof, 49-52, assoc. prof, 52-57, PROF, 57-59, EXP. MED, 59-, dir. Fleischmann Labs. Med. Sci, 59-70. Vis. investr, zoophysiol. lab, Copenhagen, 49, Guggenheim fel, 51-52; Nat. Sci. Found. fel, 58-59; Donner lab, California, 58-59; Commonwealth Fund fel, 65-66; vis. investr, Hopkins Marine Sta, 71-72. Consult, tech. info. div, Library of Congress, 56. With Off. Sci. Res. & Develop, 44. AAAS; Am. Physiol. Soc; Soc. Exp. Biol. & Med; fel. N.Y. Acad. Sci; Am. Soc. Pharmacol. & Exp. Therapeut. Drugs and tissue respiration; temperature and drug action; experimental frostbite; tissue changes following ischemia; ion transport; pharmacology of marine and amphibian toxins. Address: P.O. Box 313, Pebble Beach, CA 93953.

FUHRMAN, NATHAN, b. New York, N.Y, July 27, 25; m. 51; c. 4. PHYSICAL CHEMISTRY. B.Ch.E, Rensselaer Polytech, 49; fel, Polytech. Inst. Brooklyn, 51-53, Ph.D.(chem), 53. Res. assoc. polymer chem, Polytech. Inst. Brooklyn, 53-54; sr. engr. nuclear fuel res, atomic energy div, Sylvania Elec. Prod, Inc, 54-57, adv. res. engr, Sylvania-Corning Nuclear Corp, 57; eng. group supvr, silicon process develop, Landsdale Tube Co. div, Philco Corp, 57-59; group supvr. nuclear phys. chem, metall. labs, Olin Mathieson Chem. Corp, 59-62; develop. div, New Haven Res. Labs, United Nuclear Corp, 62-65, adv. scientist, RES. & ENG. CTR, 65-69, MGR. CHEM. & CERAMICS DEPT, 69-71, GULF UNITED NUCLEAR FUELS CORP, 71- U.S.A, 44-46. Am. Chem. Soc. Chemical metallurgy; high temperature materials particularly for nuclear power application; preparation, fabrication and processing of nuclear fuels. Address: Chemistry & Ceramics Dept, Research & Engineering Center, Gulf United Nuclear Fuels Corp, Elmsford, NY 10523.

FUHRMAN, RALPH E(DWARD), b. Kansas City, Kans, Sept. 6, 09; m. 35; c. 2. CIVIL & SANITARY ENGINEERING. B.S, Kansas, 30; M.S, Harvard, 37; D.Eng, Hopkins, 54. Asst. pub. health engr, Mo. State Bd. Health, 31 & 37; supt, Springfield Water Pollution Control Plant, Mo, 31-36; asst. supt, D.C. Water Pollution Control Plant, 37-42, supt, 42-53; dep. dir, D.C. Sanit. Eng. Dept, 53-54; exec. secy, Water Pollution Control Fedn, 55-69; ASST. DIR, NAT. WATER COMN, 69- Prof. lectr, George Wash. Univ, 41-60. Fel. Am. Soc. Civil Eng; fel. Am. Pub. Health Asn; Am. Water Works Asn; Am. Acad. Environ. Eng; hon. mem. Water Pollution Control Fedn. (pres, 50-51, ed, jour, 55-64); hon. fel. Brit. Inst. Water Pollution Control; hon. fel. Brit. Inst. Pub. Health Eng. Wastewater technology; control of water pollution through proper collection and treatment of domestic and industrial wastewater. Address: 2917 39th St. N.W, Washington, DC 20016.

FUHRMANN, ROBERT, b. Cernauti, Rumania, Mar. 9, 30; U.S. citizen; m. 54; c. 2. ORGANIC & PHYSICAL ORGANIC CHEMISTRY. B.S, Sorbonne, 51, Ph.D.(chem), 54. Res. chemist, Carrol Dunham Smith Pharmaceut. Co, 55-56; E.F. Drew Chem. Co, N.J, 56-57; cent. res. lab, ALLIED CHEM. CORP, 57-60, sr. scientist, 60-64, dir. lab. res, 64-68, TECH. SUPVR, CORP. CHEM. RES. LAB, 68- Award, Inst. Tech. Res, Paris, France, 55. Am. Chem. Soc. Stereospecific polymerization; biodegradable surfactants; free radical reactions, especially oxydation; chemical modification polymers; petrochemical intermediates; amino acids; homogenous catalysis. Address: 32 Cross Rd, Morris Plains, NJ 07950.

FUHS, ALLEN E(UGENE), b. Laramie, Wyo, Aug. 11, 27; m. 51; c. 1. MECHANICAL ENGINEERING. B.S, New Mexico, 51; M.S, Calif. Inst. Tech, 55, Guggenheim fel, 56-57, Ph.D.(mech. eng), 58. Asst, Calif. Inst. Tech, 54-55, lectr. jet propulsion, 57-58; private consult, 56-57; asst. prof. mech. eng, Northwestern, 58-59; mem. tech. staff, phys. res. lab, space tech. labs, Thompson Ramo Wooldridge, Inc, 59-60; staff scientist, plasma res. lab, Aerospace Corp, 60-66; prof. aeronaut, Naval Postgrad. Sch, 66-68, chmn. dept, 67-68; chief scientist, Air Force Aero Propulsion Lab, Wright-Patterson AFB, Ohio, 68-70; PROF. AERONAUT, NAVAL POSTGRAD. SCH, 70- Vis. fel, Joint Inst. Lab. Astrophysics & vis. assoc. prof, Colorado, 64-65. U.S.N, 51-54, Res, 54-, Comdr. Am. Inst. Aeronaut. & Astronaut; Am. Phys. Soc; Am. Soc. Mech. Eng; Optical Soc. Am; Am. Soc. Eng. Educ; Am. Asn. Physics Teachers; Combustion Inst. Magnetohydrodynamics; spectroscopy; combustion; jet propulsion; re-entry physics; instrumentation for high speed plasma flow; aircraft gas turbines; combustion; high energy lasers. Address: Dept. of Aeronautics, Naval Postgraduate School, Monterey, CA 93940.

FUHS, G(EORG) WOLFGANG, b. Cologne, Ger, May 19, 32; m. 60; c. 3. MICROBIOLOGY, LIMNOLOGY. Dipl. biol. & Dr. sci. nat.(biol), Univ. Bonn, 56. Sci. employee bot, Univ. Frankfurt, 57-58; hyg. & med. parasitol, Univ. Bonn, 58-63; Ger. Res. Asn. career develop. award genetics, Univ. Cologne, 63-64; sr. res. scientist, DIV. LABS. & RES, N.Y. STATE DEPT. HEALTH, 64-68, PRIN. RES. SCIENTIST, ENVIRON. HEALTH CTR, 68- Res. assoc, sch. pub. health, Univ. Minn, Minneapolis, 70. Am. Soc. Microbiol; Ger. Soc. Hyg. & Microbiol; Netherlands Soc. Microbiol; Int. Asn. Theoret. & Appl. Limnol; Am. Soc. Limnol. & Oceanog; Water Pollution Control Fedn; Am. Pub. Health Asn. Cell structure of bacteria and Cyanophyceae; physiological ecology of bacteria and algae; water pollution and eutrophication; sanitary microbiology. Address: Division of Labs. & Research, New York State Dept. of Health, New Scotland Ave, Albany, NY 12201.

FUJII, AKIRA, b. Nagano-ken, Japan, Oct. 29, 42; m. 69; c. 1. BIOCHEMISTRY, MEDICINAL CHEMISTRY. B.S, Shinshu Univ, Japan, 65; M.S, Inst. Divi Thomae, 69, Ph.D.(biochem), 70. Res. engr, Nippon Soda Co, Ltd, Japan, 65-67; FEL. & LECTR. BIOCHEM, ST. THOMAS INST, 70- Am. Chem. Soc; Chem. Soc. Japan; Japanese Biochem. Soc. Antistaphylococcal and antifibrinolytic activities of dipeptides. Address: Dept. of Chemistry & Biochemistry, St. Thomas Institute, 1842 Madison Rd, Cincinnati, OH 45206.

FUJII, CHARLES T(ATSUMI), b. Honolulu, Hawaii, May 20, 30. ANALYTICAL & PHYSICAL CHEMISTRY. B.A, Hawaii, 52, N.Y. Res. Corp. fel. & Ph.D.(chem), 58; M.S, Duquesne, 54. RES. CHEMIST, PHYS. METALL. BR, U.S. NAVAL RES. LAB, 58- Nat. Acad. Sci-Nat. Res. Coun. fel, 58-60. Am. Chem. Soc; Am. Soc. Metals. Behavior of complex ions in solution; high temperature gas-solid equilibria; pure metals and alloy oxidation; corrosion mechanisms. Address: U.S. Naval Research Lab, Code 6320, Washington, DC 20390.

FUJIKAWA, CLIFF Y(ASUO), b. Honolulu, Hawaii, May 11, 27. INORGANIC CHEMISTRY. B.S, Hawaii, 49, M.S, 57; Ph.D.(inorg. chem), Univ. Ill, 61. Sr. res. engr, Rocketdyne Div, N.Am. Aviation, Inc, 61-69; PROGRAMMER, RCA Corp, 69-71; WEST. AIRLINES, 71- Sig.C, 51-54, 2nd Lt. Am. Chem. Soc. Light metal and boron hydrides; inorganic polymers; metal organics; radioactive tracers. Address: 6517 Kester Ave, Apt. 3, Van Nuys, CA 91401.

FUJIMOTO, GEORGE I(WAO), b. Seattle, Wash, July 1, 20; m. 49; c. 3. BIOCHEMISTRY. B.A, Harvard, 42; M.S, Michigan, 45, Ph.D.(chem), 47. Fel, chem, Calif. Inst. Tech, 47-49; asst. res. prof. BIOCHEM, sch. med, Utah, 49-55; ASSOC. PROF, ALBERT EINSTEIN COL. MED, YESHIVA UNIV, 55- AAAS; Am. Chem. Soc; Am. Soc. Biol. Chem; Endocrine Soc. Steroid chemistry and endocrinology. Address: 101 Carthage Rd, Scarsdale, NY 10583.

FUJIMOTO, JAMES (MASAO), b. Vacaville, Calif, May 10, 28. PHARMACOLOGY. A.B, California, 51, M.S, 53, U.S. Pub. Health Serv. fel, 55-56, Ph.D, 56. Asst. PHARMACOL, California, 51-55; instr, sch. med, Tulane Univ, 56-58, asst. prof, 58-61, assoc. prof, 61-66, prof, 66-68, acting chmn. dept, 64-68; PROF, MED. COL. WIS, 68- Soc. Exp. Biol. & Med; Am. Soc. Pharmacol. & Exp. Therapeut; Soc. Toxicol. Drug metabolism; toxicology. Address: Dept. of Pharmacology, Medical College of Wisconsin, 561 N. 15th St, Milwaukee, WI 53233.

FUJIMOTO, MINORU, b. Takasago, Japan, Feb. 11, 26; m. 55; c. 3. CHEMICAL PHYSICS. B.Sc, Osaka, 48; Ph.D.(physics), Southampton, 59. Res. assoc. PHYSICS, Maryland, 59-61; asst. prof, Clark, 61-63; Univ. Man, 63-67; ASSOC. PROF, UNIV. GUELPH, 67- Am. Phys. Soc; Phys. Soc. Japan. Physics and chemistry of solids as studied by paramagnetic resonance. Address: Dept. of Physics, University of Guelph, Guelph, Ont, Can.

FUJIMURA, ROBERT, b. Seattle, Wash, July 28, 33; m. 62; c. 3. BIOCHEMISTRY. B.S, Washington (Seattle), 56; M.S, Wisconsin, 59, Ph.D.(biochem), 61. Nat. Insts. Health fel. biochem, Inst. Protein Res, Osaka, Japan, 61-62; fel, biophys, Wisconsin, 63; MEM. STAFF BIOCHEM, BIOL. DIV, OAK RIDGE NAT. LAB, 63- Lectr, Univ. Tenn. Am. Chem. Soc; Am. Soc. Biol. Chem; Am. Soc. Microbiol. Interaction of bacteriophages with their hosts; biosynthesis of small bacteriophages and their nucleic acids; bacteriophage T5 DNA repair and replication; DNA recombination; state of viral DNA inside the host cell. Address: Biology Division, Oak Ridge National Lab, Oak Ridge, TN 37830.

FUJINO, KAZUO, b. Tokyo, Japan, Sept. 22, 25; m. 55; c. 2. IMMUNOGENETICS, POPULATION GENETICS. B.Agr, Tokyo, 50, D.Agr, 62. Sr. scientific officer, Whales Res. Inst, Tokyo, Japan, 50-64; CHIEF SUBPOP. PROG, HAWAII AREA FISHERY RES. CTR, NAT. OCEANIC & ATMOSPHERIC AGENCY, 64- Mem. affiliate grad. faculty, Univ. Hawaii, 65- Mem, Whaling Cmns. Japan, 55-64. Fel. AAAS; Genetics Soc. Am; Japanese Soc. Sci. Fisheries. Genetic studies of proteins and enzymes of fishes by means of immunology and biochemistry, their application to identification of isolated breeding populations and population genetics. Address: Hawaii Area Fishery Research Center, National Oceanic & Atmospheric Agency, P.O. Box 3830, Honolulu, HI 96812.

FUJIOKA, GEORGE S(ATSUKI), b. Vashon, Wash; m. 52; c. 2. INORGANIC CHEMISTRY. B.S, Washington (Seattle), 49, Nat. Sci. Found. fel, 55-56, Ph.D.(chem), 56. Eng. asst, Gen. Elec. Co, 51-53; asst, Washington (Seattle), 53-55; RES. CHEMIST, DOW CHEM. CO, 56- AAAS; Am. Chem. Soc. Inorganic fluorine compounds; inorganic olefin catalyst; high energy compounds; inorganic nitrogen compounds; olefin polymerization. Address: Dow Chemical Co, 2800 Mitchell Dr, Walnut Creek, CA 94598.

FUJITA, SHIGEJI, b. Oita City, Japan, May 15, 29; m. 58; c. 4. THEORETICAL PHYSICS. B.S, Kyushu, 53; Ph.D.(physics), Maryland, 60. Res. asst. physics, Kyushu, 53-56; Maryland, 56-58; res. assoc, Northwestern, 58-60; sr. res. assoc. phys. chem, Brussels, 60-65; vis. assoc. prof. PHYSICS, Oregon, 65-66; assoc. prof, STATE UNIV. N.Y. BUFFALO, 66-68, PROF, 68- Vis. assoc. prof, Pa. State, 64-65. Am. Phys. Soc; Phys. Soc. Japan. Non-equilibrium statistical mechanics. Address: 74 Mahogany Dr, Williamsville, NY 14221.

FUJITA, TETSUYA T, b. Japan, Oct. 23, 20; m. 48; c. 1. METEOROLOGY. B.S, Meiji Inst. Tech, Japan, 43; D.Sc.(meteorol), Tokyo, 53. Asst, Meiji Inst. Tech, Japan, 43, asst. prof, 43-50; Kyushu Inst. Tech, 50-53; vis. prof, UNIV. CHICAGO, 53-56, from dir. mesometeorol. res. to assoc. prof. METEOROL, 56-69, PROF, 69- Consult, Ill. State Water Surv, 54-58. Okada Award, 59; Kamura Award, 65. Am. Meteorol. Soc; Am. Geophys. Union; Optical Soc. Am; Am. Soc. Photogram; Meteorol. Soc. Japan. Mesometeorology; severe local storms; aerial photogrammetry; satellite meteorology. Address: Dept. of Geophysical Sciences, University of Chicago, 5734 Ellis Ave, Chicago, IL 60637.

FUKADA, MINORU, b. Kobe, Japan, Oct. 17, 26; m. 52; c. 2. ELECTRICAL ENGINEERING. B.S, Tokyo, 51; Fulbright grant, California, Berkeley, 60-61, M.S, 61, Ph.D.(elec. eng), 64. Res. engr, Yokogawa Elec. Works, Ltd, Japan, 51-60; res. asst, California, Berkeley, 61-64; ASSOC. PROF. ELEC. ENG, McGILL UNIV, 64- Summers, mem. tech. staff, Bell Tel. Labs, 62, San Jose Res. Lab, Int. Bus. Mach. Corp, Inc, 64. Inst. Elec. & Electronics Eng. Communication, coding and network theories. Address: Dept. of Electrical Engineering, McGill University, Montreal, Que, Can.

FUKANO, KIYOSHI GEORGE, b. King Co, Wash, Sept. 24, 16; m. 47; c. 1. FISHERIES BIOLOGY. B.S, Washington (Seattle), 39, fel, 41-42; Cornell, 44-45. Biol. aide, U.S. Fish & Wildlife Serv, Seattle, 41; teacher, high sch, Idaho, 42; fisheries technician, inst. fisheries res, Michigan, 45, fisheries biologist, 45-64; fisheries reporting specialist, U.S. BUR. COMMERCIAL FISHERIES, 64-65, FISHERY BIOLOGIST, 65- AAAS; Am. Fisheries Soc. (ed, 52-55). Creel census; freshwater biology. Address: U.S. Bureau of Commercial Fisheries, 2725 Montlake Blvd. E, Seattle, WA 98102.

FUKUDA, YOICHIRO, b. Hitachi, Ibaraki, Japan, Oct. 23, 28; U.S. citizen; m. 57. MATHEMATICAL STATISTICS. B.A, Pepperdine Col, 53; M.A, California, Los Angeles, 55, Ph.D.(math), 60. Res. mathematician, cargo handling res. proj, California, Los Angeles, 55-58, mgt. sci. res. proj, 58-60; assoc, Planning Res. Corp, 60-65; mathematician, Syst. Develop. Corp, 65-66; sr. assoc, Planning Res. Corp, 66-67; MEM. PROF. STAFF, SYSTS. GROUP, TRW INC, 67- Inst. Mgt. Sci; Opers. Res. Soc. Am; Asn. Comput. Mach. Mathematical programming, statistics and probability theory; operations research. Address: Systems Group, TRW Inc, One Space Park, Redondo Beach, CA 90278.

FUKUI, GEORGE M(ASAAKI), b. San Francisco, Calif, May 25, 21; m. 44. MICROBIOLOGY. B.S, Connecticut, 45, M.S, 48; Ph.D, Cornell, 52. Instr. bact, Connecticut, 48-49; res. bacteriologist, Ft. Detrick, 52-60; RES. MICROBIOLOGIST, WALLACE LABS, 60- Commendation, Sci. Res. Soc. Am, 59. U.S.A, 45-47. AAAS; Am. Acad. Microbiol; N.Y. Acad. Sci; Am. Soc. Microbiol. Basis for endotoxin elicited nonspecific immunity; chemotherapy of immunologic diseases. Address: 329 Prospect Ave, Princeton, NJ 08540.

FUKUI, H(ATSUAKI), b. Yokohama, Japan, Dec. 14, 27; m. 54; c. 2. ELECTRICAL ENGINEERING. Grad, Miyakojima Tech. Col, 49; D.Eng, Osaka Univ, 61. Res. assoc, Osaka City Univ, 49-54; engr, Shimada Phys. & Chem. Indust. Co, 54-55; sr. engr, semiconductor div, Sony Corp, 55-59, supvr, 59-61, mgr. eng. div, 61-62; mem. tech. staff, BELL LABS, 62-69, SUPVR, 69- Lectr, Tokyo Metrop. Univ, 62. Inada Prize, Inst. Elec. Eng, Japan, 59. Sr. mem. Inst. Elec. & Electronics Eng; Am. Phys. Soc; Electrochem. Soc; Inst. TV Eng. Japan. Image pickup and display devices; thin films; transistors; Esaki-diodes; avalanche diodes; bulk-effect devices; microwave tubes; microwave circuits; solid-state radio and television circuits; videophone subsystems. Address: Room 2A427, Bell Labs, Mountain Ave, Murray Hill, NJ 07974.

FUKUNAGA, KEINOSUKE, b. Japan, July 23, 30; m. 57; c. 2. ELECTRICAL ENGINEERING. B.S, Kyoto, 53, Ph.D.(elec. eng), 62; M.S, Pennsylvania, 59. Res. engr, res. lab, Mitsubishi Elec. Co, Amagasaki-shi, Japan, 53-57, sect. head. res. comput. control, 59-65, develop. of comput, Kamakura-shi, 65-66; asst. instr. ELEC. ENG, Pennsylvania, 57-59; ASSOC. PROF, PURDUE UNIV, 66- Summer res. employee, Int. Bus. Mach. Corp, N.Y, 67-69. Inst. Elec. & Electronics Eng. Information processing; computer system; computer control. Address: Dept. of Electrical Engineering, Purdue University, Lafayette, IN 47907.

FUKUSHIMA, DAVID K(ENZO), b. Fresno, Calif, Aug. 24, 17; m. 42; c. 2. BIOCHEMISTRY. B.A, Whittier Col, 39; M.A, California, Los Angeles, 43; Ph.D.(org. chem), Rochester, 46. Fel, Sloan-Kettering Inst, 46-47, asst, 47-51, assoc, 51-60, mem, 60-63; SR. INVESTR, INST. STEROID RES, MONTEFIORE HOSP. & MED. CTR, 63-; PROF. BIOCHEM, ALBERT EINSTEIN COL. MED, 66- Am. Chem. Soc; Endocrine Soc; Am. Soc. Biol. Chem; Swiss Chem. Soc; Brit. Soc. Endocrinol; Pharmaceut. Soc. Japan. Biochemistry of steroid hormones in man; steroid chemistry. Address: Institute for Steroid Research, Montefiore Hospital & Medical Center, 111 E. 210th St, Bronx, NY 10467.

FUKUSHIMA, EIICHI, b. Tokyo, Japan, June 3, 36; U.S. citizen; m. 63; c. 2. SOLID STATE & CHEMICAL PHYSICS. A.B. & S.B, Chicago, 57; M.A, Dartmouth Col, 59; Nat. Sci. Found. fel, Washington (Seattle), 61, Ph.D. (physics), 67. STAFF MEM, LOS ALAMOS SCI. LAB, 67- Am. Phys. Soc; Am. Asn. Physics Teachers. Nuclear magnetic resonance studies of spin-lattice and transferred hyperfine interactions of phase transitions and of hindered molecular motion. Address: 4873A Yucca, Los Alamos, NM 87544.

FUKUSHIMA, TOSHIYUKI, b. Tacoma, Wash, Sept. 26, 21; m. 51; c. 6. MECHANICAL ENGINEERING. B.S, Swarthmore Col, 51; Mass. Inst. Tech; M.S, Pennsylvania, 59. Engr, Ultra-Mechanisms, Inc, 53; Prewitt Aircraft Corp, 53-54; Thermal Res. & Eng. Corp, 54-56; instr. mech. eng, Swarthmore Col, 56-61; asst. prof, Drexel Inst, 61-65; sr. engr. theoret. aerodyn, Dynasci. Corp, 65-67; sr. engr. aerodynamics res, Vertol Div, Boeing Co, Pa, 67-70; TEACHER MATH, DELAWARE COUNTY AREA VOC-TECH. SCHS, 70- Summer engr, Gen. Elec. Co, 56, Vertol Div, Boeing Co, 60, 61

& 71; lectr, PMC Cols, 65- Am. Soc. Eng. Educ; Am. Soc. Mech. Eng; Am. Inst. Aeronaut. & Astronaut. Fluid mechanics and heat transfer; thermodynamics and magnetohydrodynamics as applied to energy conversion. Address: 218 Lafayette Ave, Swarthmore, PA 19081.

FUKUTA, NORIHIKO, b. Tokoname, Japan, May 11, 31; m. 66. CLOUD PHYSICS, ATMOSPHERIC SCIENCES. B.Sc, Nagoya, 54, M.Sc, 56, Ph.D. (cloud physics), 59. Res. asst, chem. inst, Nagoya, 59-61; vis. res. fel, Commonwealth Sci. & Indust. Res. Orgn, Sydney, Australia, 62-64; head microphys. lab, Meteorol. Res. Inc, Calif, 66-67, dir. microphys. lab, 67-68; PROF. ENVIRON. ENG. & HEAD CLOUD PHYSICS LAB, DENVER RES. INST, UNIV. DENVER, 68- Vis. scientist, Imp. Col, London, 61-62; consult, atmospheric res. group, Meteorol. Res, Inc, summer 68. Am. Meteorol. Soc; Meteorol. Soc. Japan; Am. Geophys. Union. Ice nucleation; organic ice nuclei; development of non-AgI cloud seeding generators; development of automatic ice nucleus counters; convective cloud seeding; ice crystal growth; hydrometeor growth kinetics; Venusian atomosphere. Address: Cloud Physics Lab, Denver Research Institute, University of Denver, Denver, CO 80210.

FUKUTO, T(ETSUO) ROY, b. Los Angeles, Calif, Dec. 15, 23; m. 53; c. 4. ORGANIC CHEMISTRY. B.S, Univ. Minn, 46; Ph.D, Univ. Calif, Los Angeles, 50. Res. fel, Univ. Ill, 50-51; develop. chemist, Aerojet Eng. Corp, 51-52; asst. insect toxicologist, CITRUS RES. CTR. & AGR. EXP. STA, UNIV. CALIF, RIVERSIDE, 52-57, assoc. insect toxicologist, 57-63, PROF. ENTOM. & CHEM. & INSECT TOXICOLOGIST, 63- Consult, toxicol. study sect, U.S. Pub. Health Serv, 62-66. Am. Chem. Soc; Entom. Soc. Am. Chemistry and mode of action of insecticides. Address: Citrus Research Center & Agricultural Experiment Station, University of California, Riverside, CA 92507.

FUKUYAMA, KIMIE, b. Tokyo, Japan, Dec. 11, 27. DERMATOLOGY. M.D, Tokyo Women's Med. Col, 49, Ph.D, 64; M.S, Michigan, 58. Intern, Tokyo Med. Sch, 49-50, resident & asst. DERMAT, 50-56; res. assoc, Michigan, 58-61; asst, Tokyo Women's Med. Col, 61-63, lectr, 64-65; SCH. MED, UNIV. CALIF, SAN FRANCISCO, 65-67, ASST. PROF. IN RESIDENCE, 67- Vis. res. asst, inst. protein res, Osaka Univ, 64. Japanese Dermat. Asn; Japanese Women's Med. Asn. Address: Division of Dermatology, 1186 Moffitt Hospital, University of California, San Francisco, CA 94122.

FUKUYAMA, THOMAS T, b. Juneau, Alaska, Dec. 30, 27; m. 60; c. 3. MICROBIOLOGY, BIOCHEMISTRY. B.S, Washington, 50, M.S, 53; U.S. Pub. Health Serv. fel, Pennsylvania, 60, Ph.D.(microbiol), 61. Res. fel, MICROBIOL, Harvard Med. Sch, 60-63; res. assoc, sch. med, UNIV. SOUTH. CALIF, 63-64, instr, 64-65, asst. prof, 65-69, SCH. PHARM, 69-71, ASSOC. PROF, 71- U.S. Pub. Health Serv. fel, 61-63, res. grants, 66; Southern California gen. res. support grant, 66. U.S.A, 53-55. AAAS; Am. Soc. Microbiol. Microbial physiology; enzyme action and regulation; mechanisms of antibiotic action. Address: Dept. of Biopharmacy, School of Pharmacy, University of Southern California, Los Angeles, CA 90007.

FULBRIGHT, HARRY WILKS, b. Springfield, Mo, Sept. 19, 18; m. 44. NUCLEAR PHYSICS. A.B, Washington (St. Louis), 40, M.S, 42, Ph.D.(physics), 44. Physicist in charge cyclotron, Washington (St. Louis), 42-44; physicist & group leader, Manhattan dist. proj, California, Los Alamos, 44-46; asst. prof. PHYSICS, Princeton, 46-50; UNIV. ROCHESTER, 50-52, assoc. prof, 52-56, PROF, 56-, consult, med. sch, 54-57. Fulbright & Guggenheim fel, Inst. Theoret. Physics, Copenhagen, 56-57; consult, Gen. Atomic Co, 58-60; Tropel, Inc, 61-64. Fel. Am. Phys. Soc. Nuclear reactions and structure; nuclear accelerator design. Address: Dept. of Physics, University of Rochester, Rochester, NY 14627.

FULCHER, O(SCAR) HUGH, b. Sandidges, Va, Aug. 29, 01; m. 36. NEUROSURGERY. B.S, Col. William & Mary, 22; M.D, Univ. Va, 26; M.S, Univ. Minn, 31. Fel. surg, Mayo Found, 28-33; chief, Grace Hosp, Welch, W.Va, 33-37; assoc. prof. NEUROL. SURG, SCH. MED, GEORGETOWN UNIV, 37-46, prof, 47-68, CLIN. PROF, 68- Chief neurol. surg, hosps; attend. & consult. neurol. surgeon, hosps; U.S. Pub. Health Dispensary; clin. ctr, Nat. Insts. Health. Dipl, Am. Bd. Surg; Am. Bd. Neurol. Surg. Med.C, U.S.N.R, 41-46, Capt. Am. Asn. Neurol. Surg; Am. Med. Asn; fel. Am. Col. Surg; Am. Acad. Neurol; fel. Int. Col. Surg. Use of tantalum in surgery; endogenous protein metabolism of muscles and of the liver in dogs and swine during various stages of nutrition; treatment of communicating hydrocephalus; functioning of the choroid plexus as a potential third kidney of the body; diagnosis and treatment of low back pains. Address: 5081 Lowell St. N.W, Washington, DC 20016.

FULCO, ARMAND J, b. Los Angeles, Calif, Apr. 3, 32; m. 55; c. 4. BIOCHEMISTRY. B.S, California, Los Angeles, 57, Ph.D.(lipid biosynthesis), 60. U.S. Pub. Health Serv. res. fel, lipid labs, California, Los Angeles, 60-61; Nat. Insts. Health res. fel. chem, Harvard, 61-63; asst. prof. in residence, UNIV. CALIF, LOS ANGELES, 65-70, ASSOC. PROF. BIOL. CHEM. & ASSOC. RES. BIOCHEMIST, LAB. NUCLEAR MED. & RADIATION BIOL, 70-, asst. res. biochemist, dept. biol. chem. & dept. biophys. & nuclear med, 63-70. U.S.A, 52-54. AAAS; Am. Chem. Soc; Am. Oil Chemists' Soc; Am. Soc. Biol. Chem. Pathways, mechanisms and enzymology of unsaturated fatty acid biosynthesis; comparative biochemistry; biosynthetic control mechanisms. Address: Dept. of Biological Chemistry, University of California School of Medicine, Los Angeles, CA 90024.

FULCO, JOSE R(OQUE), b. Buenos Aires, Arg, Dec. 5, 27; m. 49; c. 5. PHYSICS. C.E, Argentine Army Tech. Sch, 55; Bariloche Inst. Physics, 55-56; Ph.D.(physics), Buenos Aires, 62. Argentine Army vis. fel. PHYSICS, Lawrence Radiation Lab, California, 57-59; prof, Buenos Aires, 59-62; asst. res. physicist, UNIV. CALIF, San Diego, 62-64, assoc. prof, SANTA BARBARA, 64-69, PROF, 69- Prof, La Plata, 62. Argentine Army, 43-54, Lt. Col. Am. Phys. Soc. Theoretical high energy physics. Address: Dept. of Physics, University of California, Santa Barbara, CA 93106.

FULD, GEORGE J(OSEPH), b. Baltimore, Md, Nov. 8, 32; m. 55; c. 3. RADIATION CHEMISTRY, MICROBIOLOGY. S.B, Mass. Inst. Tech, 53, Swope fel. & Sc.D.(biochem. eng), 56. Instr. biochem. eng, Mass. Inst. Tech, 55-57, asst. prof. food eng, 57-60; v.pres, Fuld Bros, Inc, 60-63; head radiation res, Goodyear Tire & Rubber Co, 63-67; med. engr, Hittman Assocs, Inc, 67-69; v.pres. mfg, Enzymes Int, Inc, 69-71; CONSULT, RADIATION CHEM, MICROBIOL. & POLLUTION, 71- Consult, Fuld Bros, Inc, 54-60; Atlantic Sugar Ref, Ltd, 56-60; Outstanding Young Men Am, 65. AAAS; Am. Chem. Soc; Am. Nuclear Soc; Am. Soc. Microbiol; Inst. Food Tech; Soc. Plastics Eng. Radiation research, fermentation dynamics; automatic control application in fermentation; fermentation equipment design. Address: P.O. Box 5745, Baltimore, MD 21208.

FULDA, MYRON O(SCAR), b. N.Y.C, Mar. 18, 30; m. 61; c. 1. ANALYTICAL CHEMISTRY. B.S, Iowa State Col, 53, M.S, 55. Chemist, E.I. DU PONT DE NEMOURS & CO, 55-64, res. chemist, 64-70, SR. CHEMIST, 70- Am. Chem. Soc. Non-aqueous, complexiometric and electrometric titrmetry; radiochemistry; analytical chemistry of textile fibers; dyeability of acrylic fibers. Address: 2106 Burns Lane, Camden, SC 29020.

FULDE, ROLAND CHARLES, b. Chicago, Ill, Nov. 23, 26; m. 52; c. 2. MICROBIOLOGY, BIOCHEMISTRY. B.S, Mich. State Univ, 48, M.S, 49, Ph.D, 53. Res. bacteriologist, Swift & Co, 53-62; DIV. HEAD, PROCESS BIOCHEM, CAMPBELL SOUP CO, 62- U.S.A, 42-45. AAAS; Inst. Food Technol; Soc. Indust. Microbiol; Am. Soc. Microbiol; Am. Chem. Soc. Industrial biochemical processes. Address: 78 Knollwood Dr, Cherry Hill, NJ 08034.

FULEKI, TIBOR, b. Budapest, Hungary, June 28, 31; Can. citizen; m. 71; c. 1. FOOD SCIENCE, BIOCHEMISTRY. B.Sc, Col. Hort. & Viticult, Budapest, 53; M.Sc, McGill Univ, 61; Ph.D.(food chem), Univ. Mass, Amherst, 67. RES. SCIENTIST, res. sta, Can. Dept. Agr, N.S, 61-67; res. labs, Food & Drug Directorate, Ont, 67-68; HORT. PROD. LAB, HORT. RES. INST. ONT, 68- Can. Inst. Food Technol; Inst. Food Technol; Am. Chem. Soc; Can. Soc. Hort. Sci; Can. Soc. Oenol; Am. Soc. Enol. Chemical composition of fruits, vegetables and their products; tristimulus colorimetry of horticultural crops; anthocyanin composition of economic plants; chemistry and technology of wine making; food analysis. Address: Horticultural Products Lab, Horticultural Research Institute of Ontario, Vineland Station, Ont, Can.

FULENWIDER, JOHN E, b. Phoenix, Ariz, Feb. 4, 29; m. 55; c. 2. ELECTRICAL ENGINEERING. B.S, Northwestern, 52, M.S, 57. Engr, Sargent & Lundy, Engr, 52-55; consult. electronics, Booz-Allen Appl. Res, Inc, 55-59; res. asst. visual syst. dynamics, Northwestern, 59-61; supvr. tech, Automatic Elec. Labs, Inc, div, Gen. Tel. & Electronics Corp, 61-62, mgr, 63-64, dir. res, Ill, 64-68, DEPT. MGR. COMMUN. LAB, GEN. TEL. & ELECTRONICS LABS. INC, 68- Walter P. Murphy fel, 59-60; Nat. Insts. Health grant, 60-61. Med.Serv.C, U.S.A, 46-48. Inst. Elec. & Electronics Eng. Model studies of cat retinal ganglion cell system, limulus visual system; computer memory systems of twistor, ferrite core; speech data switching and control with time division multiplex; space matrices. Address: Communication Lab, General Telephone & Electronics Labs, Inc, 208-20 Willets Point Blvd, Bayside, NY 11360.

FULFORD, GEORGE D(ENNISON), JR, b. Jamaica, W.I, Aug. 16, 36. CHEMICAL ENGINEERING. B.Sc, Birmingham, 59, Ph.D.(chem. eng), 62. Res. engr, photo prod. dept, E.I. du Pont de Nemours & Co, Inc, 62-66; asst. prof. chem. eng, Waterloo, 66-69; SR. PROCESS ENGR, ALPART, 69- Am. Inst. Chem. Eng; Am. Chem. Soc; Soc. Hist. Technol; sr. mem. Chem. Inst. Can; assoc. Brit. Inst. Chem. Eng. Fluid flow; heat and mass transfer; drying; air and water pollution; dimensional analysis; translation of Russian technical literature; solar energy; utilization of tropical natural products. Address: Hope, Spur Tree P.O, Jamaica, W.I.

FULFORD, MARGARET H(ANNAH), b. Cincinnati, Ohio, June 14, 04. BOTANY. B.A, Cincinnati, 26, B.E, 27, M.A, 28; Chicago, 29; Ph.D.(bot), Yale, 35. Instr. bot. & curator, UNIV. CINCINNATI, 27-40, asst. prof. BOT, 40-46, assoc. prof, 46-54, PROF, 54-, fel, grad. sch, 58. Guggenheim fel, Harvard, Yale & N.Y. Bot. Garden, 41; mem. staff, biol. sta, Michigan, 47-53. AAAS; Bot. Soc. Am; Am. Soc. Plant Taxon; Am. Bryol. & Lichenological Soc; Soc. Study Evolution; Torrey Bot. Club; Int. Soc. Plant Morphol. Hepatics; leafy hepatics of Latin America; sporeling development and regeneration of hepatics; nutrient studies in a leafy hepatic. Address: Dept. of Biological Sciences, University of Cincinnati, Cincinnati, OH 45221.

FULFORD, PHILLIP JAMES, b. Winnipeg, Man, Oct. 18, 35; m. 62; c. 3. NUCLEAR ENGINEERING. B.Sc, Manitoba, 57; M.Sc, Birmingham, 58; cert. bus. admin, London Sch. Econ, 59; Ph.D.(nuclear eng), Purdue, 68. Adv. proj. engr, Atomic Energy Can, Ltd, 60-63; engr, Dilworth, Secord, Meagher, 63-64; asst. prof. NUCLEAR ENG, PURDUE UNIV, 68-71, ASSOC. PROF, 71- Am. Nuclear Soc. Nuclear fuel management. Address: Dept. of Nuclear Engineering, Purdue University, Lafayette, IN 47907.

FULGER, CHARLES VON, b. Budapest, Hungary, Sept. 27, 32. FOOD CHEMISTRY & TECHNOLOGY. B.Sc, Univ. Budapest, 56; Wool Res. Bd. fel. & M.S, Univ. Melbourne, 60; Nat. Insts. Health fel. & Ph.D.(food sci), Univ. Mass, 67. Res. anal. chemist, Univ. Melbourne, 57-60; asst. biochemist, Univ. Calif, 60-61; res. fel. food sci, Univ. Mass, 63-67; proj. leader FOOD RES, KELLOGG CO, 67-68, dir. labs, 68-69, ASST. DIR. RES, 69- Res. award, Univ. Melbourne, 60. Am. Chem. Soc; Inst. Food Technol. Microbiological vitamin synthesis in the rumen; metabolism of flavor formation in Brassica; stereospecificity of triglyceride heat hydrolysis; experimental design food systems. Address: Research Dept, Kellogg Company, Battle Creek, MI 49016.

FULGHUM, ROBERT SCHMIDT, b. Washington, D.C, Mar. 3, 29; m. 53; c. 3. BACTERIOLOGY. B.S, Roanoke Col, 54; M.S, Va. Polytech, 59, Ph.D.(bact), 65. Res. asst. biol, Va. Agr. Exp. Sta, 56-60; instr. biol, Susquehanna, 60-63, asst. prof, 63-64; bact, N.Dak. State Univ, 64-68, assoc. prof, 68; asst. prof. oral biol, col. dent, Univ. Ky, 68-71; DIR. ANAEROBIC PROD, ROBBIN LABS. DIV, SCOTT LABS, 71- Summer resident vet. sci. with Dr. W.E.C. Moore, Va. Polytech. Inst, 61; Nat. Inst. Dent. Res. grant, 71-72. U.S.A.F, 52-56, Res, 56-59. Am. Soc. Microbiol; Brit. Soc. Gen. Microbiol; Int. Asn. Dent. Res. Anaerobic bacteriology; anaerobic bacteria of medical importance; rumen bacteriology; cecal bacteriology; oral bacteriology; antibiotic susceptibilities of bacteria; bacterial nutrition; bacterial flora-host animal ecology; methodology in anaerobic bacteriology. Address: Robbin Labs. Division, Scott Labs, P.O. Box 808, Chapel Hill, NC 27514.

FULGINITI, VINCENT A(NTHONY), b. Philadelphia, Pa, Aug. 8, 31; m; c. 4. PEDIATRICS, IMMUNOLOGY. A.B, Temple, 53, M.D, 57, M.S, 61. Asst. pediat, St. Christopher's Hosp, Phila, Pa, 60-61; instr, Univ. Colorado Med. Center, Denver, 62-64, asst. prof, 64-67, assoc. prof, 67-68; PROF. PEDIAT. & HEAD DEPT, COL. MED, UNIV. ARIZ, 69- Fulbright scholar; Markle scholar acad. med, summer 64; Waldo E. Nelson lectr, 59; fel. pediat. infectious diseases, Univ. Colorado Med. Center, Denver. Consult, Tucson Med. Ctr; Pima County Hosp; Davis-Monthan Hosp. First prize pediat. res, Phila. Pediat. Soc, 60; Ross res. award, West. Soc. Pediat. Res, 65. AAAS; Infectious Diseases Soc. Am; Am. Soc. Microbiol; Am. Acad. Pediat; Am. Med. Asn; Am. Pub. Health Asn; Am. Soc. Pediat. Res. Pediatric virology; measles virus, immunization and reaction; smallpox and vaccination. Address: Dept. of Pediatrics, University of Arizona College of Medicine, Tucson, AZ 85724.

FULKERSON, D(ELBERT) R(AY), b. Ill, Aug. 14, 24; m. 47; c. 2. MATHEMATICS. B.A, Southern Illinois, 47; M.S, Wisconsin, 48, Ph.D, 51. Mathematician, Rand Corp, 51-71; MAXWELL M. UPSON PROF. ENG. & PROF. APPL. MATH. & OPERS. RES, CORNELL UNIV, 71- Vis. prof, Univ. Calif, Berkeley, 63; Stanford Univ, 66; Univ. Waterloo, 71. Ford Prize, Math. Asn. Am, 67. U.S.A.A.F, 43-46. AAAS; Soc. Indust. & Appl. Math; Math. Soc. Am; Oper. Res. Soc. Am. Linear and mathematical programming; combinatorial analysis; network flow theory; graph and matroid theory. Address: Operations Research Dept, Cornell University, Ithaca, NY 14850.

FULKERSON, JOHN F(REDERICK), b. Los Angeles, Calif, Feb. 20, 22; m. 53; c. 2. MICROBIOLOGY, PLANT PATHOLOGY. B.S, Western Reserve, 49; M.S, N.C. State Col, 51, Ph.D.(plant path), 57. Asst. biol, Western Reserve, 41-42, 46-49; N.C. State Col, 49-51, 53-56; assoc. entomologist & plant pathologist, West Virginia, 51-53; res. pathologist, U.S. DEPT. AGR, 56-60, PLANT PATHOLOGIST & MICROBIOLOGIST, 60- U.S.A, 42-46. Fel. AAAS; Am. Phytopath. Soc. Phytobacteriology; microbial physiology; disease physiology. Address: Cooperative State Research Service, U.S. Dept. of Agriculture, Washington, DC 20250.

FULKERSON, ROBERT SERPELL, b. Tillonsburg, Ont, Nov. 28, 22; m. 46; c. 2. AGRONOMY. B.S.A, Ont. Agr. Col, 46; M.S.A, Toronto, 48. From lectr. to ASSOC. PROF. FIELD CROPS, ONT. AGR. COL, UNIV. GUELPH, 48- Am. Agron. Soc; Agr. Inst. Can. Forage crops establishment; hay production and utilization; seed production. Address: Dept. of Crop Science, Ontario Agricultural College, University of Guelph, Guelph, Ont, Can.

FULKERSON, W(ILLIAM), b. Baltimore, Md, May 26, 35; m. 57. CHEMICAL ENGINEERING, SOLID STATE PHYSICS. B.A, Rice, 57, Ph.D.(chem. eng), 62; Oak Ridge Inst. Nuclear Studies, 58-61. Metallurgist, OAK RIDGE NAT. LAB, 62-70, DIR. MAT. RESOURCES & RECYCLING GROUP, OAK RIDGE NAT. LAB-NAT. SCI. FOUND. ENVIRON. PROG, 70- Am. Soc. Metals; Am. Ceramic Soc. Thermophysical property measurements, especially mechanisms underlying high temperature heat transport in solids; correlation of electrical properties of semiconducting films with gaseous environment and doping. Address: Oak Ridge National Lab-National Science Foundation Environmental Program, Oak Ridge National Lab, P.O. Box X, Oak Ridge, TN 37830.

FULKS, W(ATSON), b. Ark, Jan. 24, 19; m. 43; c. 3. MATHEMATICS. B.S, Ark. State Teachers Col, 40; M.S, Arkansas, 41; Brown, 44-45; Ph.D.(math), Minnesota, 49. Instr. MATH, Arkansas, 41-44; Minnesota, 45-49, asst. prof, 50-56, assoc. prof, 56-60; PROF, Ore. State Col, 60-63; UNIV. COLO, BOULDER, 63- Asst, Calif. Inst. Tech, 49-50. AAAS; Am. Math. Soc; Math. Asn. Am. Partial differential equations; asymptotics. Address: Dept. of Applied Mathematics, University of Colorado, Boulder, CO 80304.

FULLAGAR, PAUL DAVID, b. Ft. Edward, N.Y, Dec. 19, 38; m. 59; c. 2. GEOLOGY. A.B, Columbia, 60; fel, Illinois, 61-62, Shell fel, 62-63, Ph.D. (geol), 63. Asst. prof. GEOL, Old Dom. Col, 63-67; UNIV. N.C, CHAPEL HILL, 67-69, ASSOC. PROF, 69- Geochem. Soc. Rubidium-strontium geochronology; origin of ore deposits. Address: Dept. of Geology, University of North Carolina, Chapel Hill, NC 27514.

FULLAM, HAROLD THOMAS, b. Tacoma, Wash, June 4, 27. CHEMICAL ENGINEERING. B.S, Washington (Seattle), 51, M.S, 52, Ph.D.(chem. eng), 56. Design engr, Standard Oil Co. Calif, 52; res. engr, Martinez Ref, Shell Oil Co. Calif, 56-57; group leader, Richmond Res. Lab, Stauffer Chem. Co, 57-63; SR. NUCLEAR ENGR, Hanford Atomic Prod. Opers, Gen. Elec. Co, 63-65; PAC. NORTHWEST LAB, BATTELLE MEM. INST, 65- U.S.N, 45-46; U.S.A.F, 52-53, 2nd Lt. Am. Chem. Soc; Electrochem. Soc; Am. Ord. Asn. Fused salt electrochemistry; inorganic process development; high temperature thermodynamics, actinide chemistry and processing. Address: 1500 Torthay Pl, Richland, WA 99352.

FULLENLOVE, T(H)OM(AS) M(cCLELLAN), b. Louisville, Ky, Apr. 6, 10; m. 32; c. 1. RADIOLOGY. M.D, Louisville, 34. Intern, Louisville City Hosp, 34-35; private practice, Ill, 35; Ky, 35-38; res. RADIOL, Ventura County Hosp, Calif, 39-40; asst. res, univ. serv, San Francisco Hosp, UNIV. CALIF, SAN FRANCISCO, 40-41, clin. instr, SCH. MED, 41-53, asst. clin. prof, 53-66, ASSOC. CLIN. PROF, 66- Radiologist, Franklin Hosp, 41-60; vis. radiologist, San Francisco Gen. Hosp, 41-; mem. courtesy radiol. staff, Univ. Hosp, California & Herbert C. Moffitt Hosp, 46-; radiologist, St. Francis Mem. Hosp, 59-71. Private practice, 41- Dipl, Am. Bd. Radiol, 41. Med.C, 42-45, Lt. Col. AAAS; Am. Med. Asn; fel. Am. Col. Radiol; Radiol. Soc. N.Am; Am. Cancer Soc.(v.pres, 63-64); Am. Roentgen Ray Soc.(pres-elect, 70-71, pres, 71-72). Angiography; sterility; neuroradiology; gastroenterology. Address: 450 Sutter St, San Francisco, CA 94108.

FULLER, ALFRED L(EE), b. Fullerton, Calif, May 9, 22; m. 45; c. 3. CHEMICAL ENGINEERING. B.E, Southern California, 43. Control chemist, A.R. Maas Chem. Co, 46-47; process engr, Gen. Elec. Co, 47-51; sr. res. chem. engr, Fluor Corp, Ltd, 51-60, chief res. engr, 60-63; sr. engr, Space-Gen. Corp, 63-64; sr. proj. engr, Fluor Corp, Ltd, 64-70, PRIN. MECH. ENGR, FLUOR CORP, 70- Mem. subcomt. fired heaters, Am. Petrol. Inst. U.S.N.R, 43-45, Lt.(jg). Am. Inst. Chem. Eng; fel. Am. Inst. Chem; Am. Petrol. Inst. Evaporative water cooling; heat and mass transfer processes; heat transfer equipment evaluation; conceptual design and evaluation of combustion equipment including fired process heaters and boilers for refining and process industries. Address: Mechanical Engineering Dept, Fluor Corp, 2500 Atlantic Blvd, Los Angeles, CA 90022.

FULLER, BENJAMIN FRANKLIN, JR, b. St. Paul, Minn, Aug. 7, 22; m. 45; c. 3. MEDICINE. B.A, Univ. Minn, 43, M.D, 45, M.S, 50. Clin. asst. prof. internal med, MED. CTR, UNIV. MINN, MINNEAPOLIS, 53-66, asst. prof, 66-67, assoc. prof, 67-70, PROF. MED, 70-, DIR. DIV. FAMILY MED. & COMMUNITY HEALTH, UNIV. HOSPS, 67-, consult, med. sch. Med.C, 46-53, Capt. Fel. Am. Col. Physicians. Peripheral vascular disease. Address: Division of Family Medicine & Community Health, University of Minnesota Medical Center, Minneapolis, MN 55455.

FULLER, DEREK JOSEPH HAGGARD, b. London, Eng, June 17, 17. MATHEMATICS. B.Sc, South Africa, 48, B.A, 53, B.Sc, 56, M.Sc, 60; B.Sc.(eng), Witwatersrand, 50; M.A. & Ph.D.(math), California, Los Angeles, 63. Lectr. math, Pius XII Col, Roma, Basutoland, 50-59, 63; Univ. Basutoland, Bechuanaland Protectorate & Swaziland, 64, sr. lectr, 65; asst. prof, CREIGHTON UNIV, 65-66, assoc. prof. MATH, 66-69, PROF, 69-, CHMN. DEPT, 67-, acting chmn. dept, 66-67. R.A.F, 40-46. Am. Math. Soc; Math. Asn. Am. Analytic functions on Riemann surfaces. Address: Dept. of Mathematics, Creighton University, Omaha, NE 68131.

FULLER, D(ONALD) L(EASK), b. Duluth, Minn, Nov. 12, 06; m. 38; c. 2. PHYSICAL CHEMISTRY. B.Ch.E, Minnesota, 29, Goodrich fel, 29, Shevlin fel, 32-33, Ph.D.(chem), 33. Res. chemist, Am. Cyanamid Co, 35-38, tech. dir, 52-55; res. chemist, Shell Develop. Co, 38-42; assoc. dir. cent. res. lab, Gen. Aniline & Film Corp, 42-52; dir. res, res. div, Wash. Res. Center, W.R. Grace & Co, D.C, 55-61, v.pres, 61-64; SCI. ATTACHÉ, U.S. STATE DEPT, INDIA, 64- Fel, Minnesota, 33-35. Tech. consult, Field Info. Agency, U.S. Dept. of Commerce, 46. Am. Chem. Soc; Am. Math. Soc. Catalysis; petrochemistry; acetylene chemistry; high pressure reactions; research management; science and public policy. Address: Executive Section, Physical Science Office, American Embassy, Shanti Path, Chanakyapuri 21, New Delhi, India.

FULLER, DOROTHY L(ANGFORD), b. Cincinnati, Ohio, Dec. 17, 18. BIOLOGY. A.B, Stetson Univ, 38, M.A, 39. Instr. BIOL, STETSON UNIV, 41-43, asst. prof, 43-47, assoc. prof, 47-63, PROF, 63- Nat. Sci. Found. grant, 57. AAAS; Am. Inst. Biol. Sci. Development of embryo sac and germination in Yucca; developmental anatomy. Address: Box 418, 345 N. Clara Ave, De Land, FL 32720.

FULLER, DUDLEY D(EAN), b. Woodhaven, N.Y, Feb. 8, 13; m. 45; c. 1. MECHANICAL ENGINEERING. B.M.E, City Col. N.Y, 41; M.S, Columbia, 45. Instr. MECH. ENG, City Col. N.Y, 41-44; COLUMBIA UNIV, 43-47, from asst. prof. to assoc. prof, 47-54, PROF, 54-, chmn. dept, 64-70. Prin. engr, Franklin Inst, 54-69; mem. bearing panel, high-temperature bearings, Nat. Acad. Sci, 59; chmn, Int. Gas Bearing Symposium, Off. Naval Res, 59; mem. bearing panel, Inst. Defense Anal, 62; bearing panel, proj. forecast, U.S. Army-Air Force, 63. Hon. mem. Am. Soc. Lubrication Eng.(award, 57); fel. Am. Soc. Mech. Eng.(Richards Mem. Award, 62); Soc. Automotive Eng; inst. fel, Franklin Inst; Brit. Inst. Mech. Eng. Lubrication and bearing design; gas bearing research. Address: Dept. of Mechancial Engineering, 236 Seeley W. Mudd, Columbia University, New York, NY 10027.

FULLER, E. LOREN, JR, b. Alliance, Nebr, Sept. 9, 30; m. 60; c. 2. PHYSICAL CHEMISTRY. B.A, Chadron State Col, 57; M.S, Nebraska, 60, Ph.D. (chem), 62. CHEMIST, OAK RIDGE NAT. LAB, 62- U.S.A, 52-54. AAAS; Am. Chem. Soc. Calorimetry of aqueous systems; surface chemistry; calorimetry of surface reactions; microgravimetric analyses; infrared spectroscopy. Address: Oak Ridge National Lab, Oak Ridge, TN 37830.

FULLER, EDWARD C, b. Helena, Mont, Aug. 8, 07; m. 37; c. 2. PHYSICAL CHEMISTRY. B.S, Mont. State Col, 28; Ph.D.(phys. chem), 41. Instr. chem. & chem. eng, Mont. State Col, 28-31; asst. chem, Columbia, 31-34; from instr. to prof, Bard Col, 35-44; admin. aide, Manhattan dist. atomic energy proj, s.a.m. labs, Columbia, 44-45; prof. chem, Bard Col, 45-46, pres, 46-50; prof. chem. & dir, area natural sci. & math, Champlain Col, 50-53; PROF. CHEM. & CHMN. DEPT, BELOIT COL, 53- AAAS; Am. Chem. Soc. Teaching integrated physics and chemistry. Address: Dept. of Chemistry, Beloit College, Beloit, WI 53511.

FULLER, EDWARD NOEL, b. Murray, Utah, Apr. 10, 36; m. 61; c. 3. PHYSICAL CHEMISTRY. B.S, Univ. Utah, 61, Ph.D.(phys. chem), 66. SR. PHYS. CHEMIST, res. & develop. dept, Phillips Petrol. Co, 66-68; SYSTS. RES. DEPT, APPL. AUTOMATION, INC, 68- U.S.A, 59; Nat. Guard, 59-64. AAAS; Am. Chem. Soc. Gas phase diffusion and chromatography. Address: Systems Research Dept, Applied Automation, Inc, Bartlesville, OK 74004.

FULLER, ELLEN O(NEIL), b. Providence, R.I; m. 46; c. 4. CARDIOVASCULAR PHYSIOLOGY. B.S, Med. Col. Ga, 60; M.N, Emory Univ, 60, U.S. Pub. Health Serv. fel, 61-67, M.Sc, 64, Ph.D.(physiol), 68. Assoc. prof. PHYSIOL, Ga, State Univ, 68-70; ASST. PROF, EMORY UNIV, 70- Grants, Ga. Heart Asn, 69-70, Am. Nurses Found, 69-72 & Nat. Insts. Health, 71-74; consult, sch. nursing, St. Louis Univ, 71; vis. lectr, sch. nursing, Med. Col. Ga, 71. AAAS. Hemodynamics of the uterine circulation; perfusion of the pregnant sheep uterus; fetal responses to changes in the uterine circulation. Address: Dept. of Physiology, Emory University, Atlanta, GA 30322.

FULLER, EUGENE GEORGE, b. Reno, Nev, May 12, 38; m. 66; c. 2. EMBRYOLOGY, HISTOLOGY. B.S, Nevada, 60, M.S, 63; Ph.D.(zool), Oregon State, 66. Instr. ZOOL, Oregon State, 66-67; asst. prof, BOISE STATE COL, 67-70, ASSOC. PROF, 70- U.S.M.C.R, 55-63. AAAS; Am. Soc. Zool.

Histochemistry of the crustacean antennal gland in relation to its function; histochemistry, histology and morphogenesis of the rodent placenta. Address: Dept. of Biology, Boise State College, Boise, ID 83701.

FULLER, EVERETT G(LADDING), b. Springfield, Mass, Dec. 6, 20; m. 47; c. 3. NUCLEAR PHYSICS. B.S, Amherst Col, 42; M.A, Illinois, 47, Ph.D. (physics), 50. Asst. physics, Illinois, 49-50; PHYSICIST, NAT. BUR. STANDARDS, 50- U.S.A.A.F, 42-46, Capt. Fel. Am. Phys. Soc. Photonuclear interaction. Address: 9016 Honeybee Lane, Bethesda, MD 20034.

FULLER, EVERETT J, b. Twin Falls, Idaho, July 3, 29; m. 52; c. 4. PHYSICAL CHEMISTRY. B.S, Idaho State Col, 51; Corning Glass fel, Utah, 58-59, Eastman Kodak fel, 59-60, Ph.D.(chem), 60. Chemist, atomic energy div, Am. Cyanamid Co, 51-53 & Phillips Petrol. Co, 53; ESSO RES. & ENG. CO, STANDARD OIL CO. N.J, 60-63, sr. chemist, 63-67, RES. ASSOC, 70- U.S.A.F, 53-57, S/Sgt. Am. Chem. Soc; Enzyme model systems; theoretical statistical mechanics; radiochemistry; separations. Address: Corporate Research Labs, Esso Research & Engineering Co, Linden, NJ 07036.

FULLER, FORST D(ONALD), b. Stroh, Ind, Apr. 25, 16; m. 37; c. 2. PHYSIOLOGY. B.A, DePauw, 38; M.S, Purdue, 41, Ph.D.(zool), 52. Physiologist, Armour Labs, Ill, 42-43; instr. ZOOL, Purdue, 46-47; DePAUW, 47-48, asst. prof, 48-52, assoc. prof, 52-58, PROF, 58- U.S.N.R, 43-46, Lt. Comdr. Vertebrate and invertebrate physiology. Address: R.R. 3, Greencastle, IN 46135.

FULLER, F(RANCIS) B(ROCK), b. Eugene, Ore, July 8, 27; m. 57; c. 1. MATHEMATICS. A.B, Princeton, 49, Ph.D, 52. Instr. MATH, Princeton, 51-52; CALIF. INST. TECHNOL, 52-55, asst. prof, 55-59, assoc. prof, 59-66, PROF, 66- Fulbright res. scholar, Univ. Strasbourg, 67-68. Am. Math. Soc. Applications of algebraic topology, especially fixed point theory; global theory of ordinary differential equations; mechanics of DNA molecules. Address: Dept. of Mathematics, California Institute of Technology, Pasadena, CA 91109.

FULLER, FRANKLYN BELMONT, b. San Jose, Calif, Dec. 22, 21; m. 43; c. 2. APPLIED MATHEMATICS. A.B, San Jose State Col, 46; M.S, Stanford Univ, 49, Ph.D.(eng. mech), 64. Res. scientist fluid mech, Ames Res. Ctr, NASA, 47-70; asst. prof. MATH, SAN JOSE STATE COL, 70-71, ASSOC. PROF, 71-, lectr, 64-70. U.S.A.F, 42-46, Lt. AAAS; Math. Asn. Am; Soc. Indust. & Appl. Math. Numerical methods in fluid mechanics, particularly computer simulation of flows about bodies at high speeds. Address: Dept. of Mathematics, San Jose State College, San Jose, CA 95114.

FULLER, GENE B(OB), b. Overton, Tex, Aug. 4, 39; m. 60; c. 3. ENDOCRINOLOGY, REPRODUCTIVE PHYSIOLOGY. B.S, Sam Houston State Univ, 62; M.S, Okla. State Univ, 65; Ph.D.(endocrinol), Purdue Univ, 67. Nat. Insts. Health fel, dept. animal sci, Cornell Univ, 67-69; ASST. PROF. reproductive physiol, Univ. N.H, 69-71; ENDOCRINOL, UNIV. SOUTH. MISS, 71- AAAS; Soc. Study Reproduction; Am. Soc. Animal Sci; Am. Soc. Zool. Factors controlling life-span of corpus luteum in rabbit and sheep; role of endocrine system in regulating maternal behavior in the rabbit; ovulation in the rat. Address: Dept. of Biology, University of Southern Mississippi, Hattiesburg, MS 39401.

FULLER, GEORGE CHARLES, b. Detroit, Mich, May 15, 37; m. 59; c. 3. BIOCHEMICAL PHARMACOLOGY. B.S, Wayne State, 59, M.S, 63; Ph.D. (pharmacol), Purdue, 67. Asst. prof. PHARMACOL, UNIV. R.I, 66-70, ASSOC. PROF, 70- R.I. Heart Asn. res. grant, 67-71, Nat. Insts. Health res. grant, 67-71. AAAS; N.Y. Acad. Sci; Soc. Toxicol; Am. Soc. Pharmacol. & Exp. Therapeut. Enzyme induction—stress induction of drug metabolism enzymes; relation of collagen synthesis to experimental atherosclerosis; mechanisms of hepatotoxicity. Address: Dept. of Pharmacology, University of Rhode Island, Kingston, RI 02881.

FULLER, GERALD M(AXWELL), b. Beaumont, Tex, Sept. 13, 35; m. 63; c. 3. MARINE BIOCHEMISTRY. B.A, Univ. Tex, 58; M.A, Sam Houston State Univ, 60; Ph.D.(marine biol), Univ. Calif, San Diego, 68. Res. assoc, Mass. Inst. Technol, 68-70; ASST. PROF. GENETICS, UNIV. TEX. MED. BR, GALVESTON, 70- AAAS; Am. Soc. Human Genetics. Evolution of fibrinogen; control of fibrinogen synthesis. Address: Dept. of Human Genetics, University of Texas Medical Branch, Galveston, TX 77550.

FULLER, GLENN, b. Lancaster, Calif, May 18, 29; m. 54; c. 2. ORGANIC CHEMISTRY. B.S, Stanford, 50; M.S, Illinois, 51, Ph.D.(chem), 53. Chemist, Shell Develop. Co, 53-64; asst. prof. chem, Mills Col, 64-65; res. chemist, WEST. REGIONAL RES. LAB, U.S. DEPT. AGR, 65-71, CHIEF FRUIT LAB, 71- AAAS; Am. Chem. Soc; Inst. Food Technol; Am. Oil Chemists' Soc; The Chem. Soc. Chemistry of fats and oils; reductions of α-aminoketones; chemistry of free radicals; antioxidants; lubricants; preservation of fruit and fruit products. Address: 1060 Cragmont St, Berkeley, CA 94708.

FULLER, HAROLD Q, b. Waynetown, Ind, Apr. 21, 07; m. 32; c. 3. PHYSICS. A.B, Wabash Col, 28, Campbell fel, 28; A.M, Illinois, 30, fel, 31-32, Ph.D. (physics), 32. Res. physics, Illinois, 32-33; asst. prof. math. & physics, Ill. Col, 33-37; instr. PHYSICS, Illinois, 37-38; from asst. prof. to assoc. prof, Albion Col, 38-44, PROF, 45-47; UNIV. MO-ROLLA, 47-, DEAN COL. ARTS & SCI, 70-, chmn. dept. physics, 48-70, acting dean sch. sci, 66-67. Sr. physicist, process improvement div, Tenn. Eastman Corp, Oak Ridge, Tenn, 44-45. With Manhattan Dist, 44. AAAS; Am. Phys. Soc; Am. Soc. Eng. Educ; Am. Asn. Physics Teachers. Spectroscopy; photochemistry; soft x-rays. Address: College of Arts & Sciences, University of Missouri at Rolla, Rolla, MO 65401.

FULLER, HARRISON W, b. Grand Rapids, Mich, Nov. 17, 25; m. 52; c. 4. APPLIED PHYSICS. B.S, Worcester Polytech, 46; M.A, Harvard, 50, Ph.D. (appl. physics), 56. Res. assoc, computation lab, Harvard, 46-47; jr. engr, Fairchild Pilotless Plane Div, 48-49; proj. engr, Lab. for Electronics, Inc, 50-56, asst. chief engr, Int. Computers Corp, 56-57, mgr. appl. physics lab, computer prods. div, 57-61, dir. solid state electronics lab, res. div, 61-62, mgr, LFE Electronics Div, 62-66, assoc. dir. advan. technol, 66-69; RES. SCIENTIST, SANDERS ASSOCS, INC, 69- U.S.N, 44-46, Res, 46-, Lt. Inst. Elec. & Electronics Eng; Am. Phys. Soc. Analog and digital computer devices, circuits and systems; magnetic memory and display techniques and devices; thin magnetic film switching phenomena including use of electron microscopy for viewing magnetization distribution; communication theory. Address: Corporate Staff, Sanders Associates, Inc, 95 Canal St, Nashua, NH 03060.

FULLER, HENRY L(ESTER), b. Andreasky, Alaska, June 25, 16; m. 46; c. 2. POULTRY NUTRITION. B.S, State Col. Wash, 40; M.S, Iowa State Col, 41; fel, Purdue, 49-51, Ph.D.(poultry nutrit), 51. Salesman livestock feeds, Hales & Hunter Co, 46-48; dir. ed. sales, feed mill div, Glidden Co, 48-49; assoc. prof. POULTRY NUTRIT, UNIV. GA, 51-57, PROF, 57- Indust. consult. U.S.A, 41-46, Maj. Poultry Sci. Asn; Am. Inst. Nutrit; World Poultry Sci. Asn. Effects of restricted feeding of young chickens on subsequent egg production characteristics and longevity; nutrition requirements of chickens. Address: 209 Pine Valley Dr, Athens, GA 30601.

FULLER, JACK C(AVITT), b. Palestine, Tex, Aug. 19, 32; m. 53; c. 2. PHYSICS. B.S, Baylor, 52, M.S, La. State, 54, Ph.D.(physics), 57. Nuclear res. engr, Atomic Int, 57; asst. prof. PHYSICS, Baylor, 57-59; staff mem, LOS ALAMOS SCI. LAB, 59-70, GROUP LEADER, 70- Soft x-rays; extreme ultraviolet; nuclear weapons and weapons x-ray effects. Address: Los Alamos Scientific Lab, P.O. Box 1663, Los Alamos, NM 87544.

FULLER, J(AMES) OSBORN, b. Chaumont, N.Y, Aug. 14, 12; m. 39; c. 3. GEOLOGY. A.B, Lehigh, 34; Ph.D.(geol), Columbia, 41. Asst. petrol, Columbia, 36-37, asst. econ. geol, 37-39; asst. prof. geol, Mt. Union Col, 39-41; instr, Ohio State, 41-43; asst. prof, West Virginia, 43-44; asst. geologist, U.S. Geol. Surv, Va, 44-45; asst. prof. geol, West Virginia, 45-46; assoc. prof, Ohio State Univ, 46-48, prof, 48-67, acting dean col. arts & sci, 51-52, assoc. dean, 52-57, secy. adv. res. coun, 55-57, dean col. arts & sci, 57-67; PRES, FAIRLEIGH DICKINSON UNIV, 67- AAAS; fel. Geol. Soc. Am; Am. Asn. Petrol. Geol. Economic and petroleum geology; field mapping of Sharon conglomerate and Lee County, Virginia, oil field; ore petrography and polishing; water resources of Ohio. Address: Office of the President, Fairleigh Dickinson University, Rutherford, NJ 07070.

FULLER, JERRY, b. Palestine, Tex, June 2, 34; m. 58; c. 2. PHYSICS. B.S, Baylor, 54, M.S, 55; Ph.D.(physics), La. State, 61. Assoc. prof. physics, Baylor, 60-66; mem. staff comput. applns, TRW SYSTS, 66-67, mem. tech. staff, 67-70, MEM. PROF. STAFF, SYSTS. ENG. LAB, 70- AAAS; Am. Phys. Soc; Am. Asn. Physics Teachers. Theoretical studies on hydrogen absorption line profiles in the atmospheres of white dwarf stars. Address: TRW Systems, Space Park Dr, Houston, TX 77058.

FULLER, JOHN B(URT), b. Burlington, Vt, Aug. 29, 20; m. 46; c. 2. CHEMISTRY. B.S, Hampden-Sydney Col, 40; M.D, Med. Col. of Va, 43. Res. assoc. & instr. PATH, Univ. Ill. Med. Ctr, 50-51, asst. prof, 51-54, assoc. prof, 54-59, PROF, 59-68; UNIV. TEX. MED. BR, GALVESTON, 68- Med.C, 44-46, Capt. Am. Soc. Clin. Path; Am. Med. Asn. Biological effects of ionizing radiation; clinical biochemistry and clinical metabolic studies. Address: Dept. of Pathology, University of Texas Medical Branch, Galveston, TX 77550.

FULLER, JOHN L(ANGWORTHY), Psychobiol, see 12th ed, Soc. & Behav. Vols.

FULLER, JOSEPH A(LLEN), (JR), b. Eureka, Kans, Nov. 4, 22; m. 46; c. 3. ORGANIC CHEMISTRY. B.S, Wichita, 48; M.S, Illinois, 49, Ph.D.(org. chem), 51. Res. chemist, CHEVRON RES. CO, Standard Oil Co, Calif, 51-56, staff asst, 56-57, personnel rep, 57-58, sr. analyst, 58-64, asst. to lab. dir, La Habra Lab, 64-68, STAFF EMPLOYEE ADV, RICHMOND LAB, 68- U.S.N.R, 42-43; U.S.M.C.R, 43-46. Am. Chem. Soc. Emulsion polymerization; petrochemicals. Address: Chevron Research Co, 576 Standard Ave, Richmond, CA 94802.

FULLER, KENT RALPH, b. Northfield, Minn, Feb. 15, 38; m. 58; c. 1. MATHEMATICS. B.S, Mankato State Col, 60, M.S, 62; M.A, Oregon, 65, Ph.D.(math), 67. Asst. prof. MATH, UNIV. IOWA, 67-70, ASSOC. PROF, 70- Am. Math. Soc. Algebra, especially ring theory. Address: Dept. of Mathematics, University of Iowa, Iowa City, IA 52240.

FULLER, LEONARD E(UGENE), b. Casper, Wyo, July 25, 19; m. 43. MATHEMATICS. B.A, Wyoming, 41; M.S, Wisconsin, 47, Ph.D.(math), 50. Asst, Wisconsin, 46-50, instr, 50-51; mathematician, Goodyear Aircraft Corp, 51-52; asst. prof. MATH, KANS. STATE UNIV, 52-56, assoc. prof, 56-59, PROF, 59- U.S.N.R, 42-45, Lt. Am. Math. Soc; Math. Asn. Am. Applications of matrix theory. Address: Dept. of Mathematics, Kansas State University, Manhattan, KS 66502.

FULLER, M(ACK) F(RANCIS), b. Bowdon, Ga, Oct. 11, 18; m. 50; c. 1. ORGANIC CHEMISTRY. A.B, Emory, 40, M.S, 42. Res. chemist, EXPLOSIVES DEPT, E.I. DU PONT DE NEMOURS & CO, INC, 41-55, tech. assoc, 55-61, RES. ASSOC, 61- Am. Chem. Soc. Military explosives; nitric acid oxidation of organic compounds; water-soluble cellulose derivatives; chemical blowing agents; polyamides. Address: 106 W. Buttonwood St, Wenonah, NJ 08090.

FULLER, MARIAN J(ANE), b. Scottsbluff, Nebr, Jan. 9, 40. PLANT TAXONOMY, GENETICS. B.S, Univ. Nebr, Lincoln, 62, Ph.D.(plant taxon), 67. Asst. prof. BIOL, MURRAY STATE UNIV, 67-70, ASSOC. PROF, 70- Am. Soc. Plant Taxon; Int. Asn. Plant Taxon; Bot. Soc. Am. Relationships among members of the genus Carduus in Nebras; relationships among members of the genus Spiranthes. Address: Dept. of Biology, Murray State Univ, Murray, KY 42071.

FULLER, MARTIN E(MIL), II, b. Inglewood, Calif, Sept. 15, 30; m. 61; c. 2. PHYSICAL CHEMISTRY. B.S, California, Los Angeles, 52; Nat. Sci. Found. fel, Mass. Inst. Tech, 53-54, 55-56, Union Carbide Co. fel, 54-55, Ph.D. (chem), 56. Asst. phys. chem, Mass. Inst. Tech, 52-53; asst. prof. chem, Pomona Col, 56-61; res. asst, Florida, 61-63; assoc. prof, Colo. Sch. Mines,

63-68; Prescott Col, 68-70; teacher, Colo. Rocky Mountain Sch, 70-71; ASSOC. PROF. CHEM, FT. LEWIS COL, 71- Am. Chem. Soc; Am. Phys. Soc; Faraday Soc. Dielectric and nuclear magnetic relaxation processes; dielectric properties of polypolar polymers and solutions; induced chemical reactions; science education; science and society. Address: Dept. of Chemistry, Ft. Lewis College, Durango, CO 81301.

FULLER, M(ARTIN) LUTHER, b. Phila, Pa, Oct. 25, 04; m. 24; c. 2. METALLURGY. B.S, Pennsylvania, 26. Anal. chemist, N.J. Zinc Co, 26-27, investr, x-ray diffraction, 27-40, chief x-ray & spectrographic sect, 40-50, minerals res, 50-68, asst. gen. mgr. res, 68-70, mgr. res, 70-71. RETIRED. Am. Inst. Mining, Metall. & Petrol. Eng. X-rays; spectrographic analysis; electron microscopy; ore dressing. Address: 155 Princeton Ave, Palmerton, PA 18071.

FULLER, MELVIN OTIS, b. Waterman, Ill, Aug. 27, 14; m. 41; c. 3. PHYSICS. B.A, Florida, 35; M.A, Colorado, 41; Ph.D.(physics), California, Berkeley, 55. Asst. prof. physics, Sacramento State Col, 49-51; res. asst, Lawrence Radiation Lab, California, 51-52; asst. prof, Sacramento State Col, 52-55, assoc. prof, 55-57; physicist, Forrestal Res. Labs, Princeton, 57-58; assoc. prof. PHYSICS, SACRAMENTO STATE COL, 58-60, PROF, 60- U.S.A, 41-46, Capt. Am. Asn. Physics Teachers. Electrophysics. Address: Dept. of Physics, Sacramento State College, 6000 J St, Sacramento, CA 95819.

FULLER, MELVIN S(TUART), b. Livermore Falls, Maine, May 5, 31; m. 55; c. 3. BOTANY, MYCOLOGY. B.S, Maine, 53; M.S, Nebraska, 55; Nat. Insts. Health fel, California, 58-59, Ph.D, 59; M.S.(ad eundem), Brown, 63. Instr. bot, Brown, 59-60, asst. prof, 60-63, assoc. prof, 63-64; asst. prof, Univ. Calif, Berkeley, 64-66, assoc. prof. & dir. electron microscope lab, 66-68; PROF. BOT. & HEAD DEPT, UNIV. GA, 68- Consult. ed, McGraw-Hill. Mycol. Soc. Am; Bot. Soc. Am; Soc. Develop. Biol. Biology of the fungi; aquatic Phycomycetes. Address: Dept. of Botany, University of Georgia, Athens, GA 30601.

FULLER, MICHAEL D, b. London, Eng, June 10, 34. GEOPHYSICS. B.A, Cambridge, 58, Ph.D.(geophys), 61. Fel. geophys, Scripps Inst, California, 61-62; res. geophysicist, Gulf Res. & Develop. Co, Pa, 62-64; assoc. prof. GEOPHYS, UNIV. PITTSBURGH, 65-69, PROF, 69- R.N.V.R, Sub. Lt. Physical process of magnetization of rocks in nature; interpretation of geological structure from aeromagnetic surveys. Address: Dept. of Earth & Planetary Science, University of Pittsburgh, Pittsburgh, PA 15213.

FULLER, MILTON E, b. Mesa, Ariz, Aug. 27, 26; m. 52; c. 3. PHYSICAL CHEMISTRY. B.S, Arizona State, 48; Ph.D.(phys. chem), Northwestern, 56. Chemist, Shell Develop. Co, 56-60; staff chemist, Int. Bus. Mach. Corp, 60-61; asst. prof. CHEM, Univ. of the Pacific, 61-64; assoc. prof, CALIF. STATE COL. HAYWARD, 64-71, PROF, 71-, chmn. dept, 68-69. Fulbright lectr, Pakistan, 71-72. U.S.A, 43-45; U.S.A.F, 50-51. Am. Chem. Soc. Solid state surface effects; rheological properties of thermoplastics. Address: Dept. of Chemistry, California State College at Hayward, Hayward, CA 94542.

FULLER, NORMAN A, b. Madurai, India, June 10, 29; m. 67; c. 2. IMMUNOCHEMISTRY. M.A, Shembaganur Jesuit Col, S.India, 55; M.S, Loyola Col, Madras, India, 58; S.T.L, St. Marys Jesuit Col, Kurseong, Darjeeling, India, 63; Europ. Molecular Biol. Orgn. fel, Helsinki, Finland, summer 66; Dr. (immunochem), Sorbonne & Pasteur Inst, Paris, 67. Lectr. chem, St. Xavier's Col, India, 58-59; adminr, Archdiocese of Calcutta & Archdiocese of Madurai, 59-64; U.S. Pub. Health Serv. fel, sch. med, Johns Hopkins Univ, 67-70; res. scientist, blood res. prog, Am. Nat. Red Cross, 70-71; EXEC. DIR. COMPREHENSIVE HEALTH SERV, MEMPHIS HEALTH CTR, 71- Am. Soc. Microbiol; Am. Chem. Soc; Fr. Soc. Microbiol. Bacterial surface antigens; viral induced neo-antigens; specificity of cell surfaces; glycoproteins in human platelets; structure and biosynthesis of lipopolysaccharides. Address: 1063 Winchester Rd, Memphis, TN 38116.

FULLER, RAY W, b. Dongola, Ill, Dec. 16, 35; m. 56; c. 2. BIOCHEMISTRY. B.A, Southern Illinois, 57, M.A, 58; Ph.D.(biochem), Purdue, 61. Dir, biochem. res. lab, Ft. Wayne State Sch, Ind, 61-63; sr. pharmacologist, RES. LABS, ELI LILLY & CO, 63-67, res. scientist, 67-68, head dept. metab. res, 68-71, RES. ASSOC, 71- AAAS; Am. Chem. Soc; Am. Soc. Biol. Chem; Am. Soc. Pharmacol. & Exp. Therapeut; Am. Soc. Neurochem; N.Y. Acad. Sci; Am. Sci. Affiliation. Biochemistry of mental function and dysfunction; mechanism of drug action on nerve activity; metabolism of biogenic amines; enzyme inhibition. Address: Research Labs, Eli Lilly & Co, Indianapolis, IN 46206.

FULLER, RICHARD C, b. Lyons, Kans, Mar. 15, 40; m. 64; c. 1. THEORETICAL NUCLEAR PHYSICS. B.S.E, Michigan, 62; M.S, Wisconsin, 64, fel, 64-67, Ph.D.(physics), 68. RES. ASST. PHYSICS, INST. SCI. TECHNOL, UNIV. MINN, MINNEAPOLIS, 68- AAAS; Am. Phys. Soc. Reaction theory in nuclear physics. Address: Dept. of Physics, Institute of Science Technology, University of Minnesota, Minneapolis, MN 55455.

FULLER, RICHARD E(UGENE), b. New York, N.Y, June 1, 97; m. 51. GEOLOGY. Ph.B, Yale, 18; B.S, Washington (Seattle), 24, M.S, 25, Ph.D, 30; LL.D, Wash. State Col, 44. Asst. prof. geol, UNIV. WASH, 30-34, res. assoc. prof, 34-40, RES. PROF, 40- Pres. & dir, Seattle Art Mus, 33- Chmn. U.S. cmt. for study of Paricutin Volcano, Nat. Res. Council, Mex, 44-49. U.S.A, 42-43, Maj. AAAS; fel. Geol. Soc. Am; fel. Mineral. Soc. Am; Am. Geophys. Union. Volcanic rocks and basin range structure; geomorphology and volcanic sequence of Steens Mountain, Oregon; petrology of volcanic and plutonic rocks. Address: 3801 Prospect St, Seattle, WA 98102.

FULLER, RICHARD H, b. San Francisco, Calif, Mar. 15, 28; m. 60; c. 1. COMPUTER SCIENCE. B.S, Calif. Inst. Technol, 52; M.S, Mass. Inst. Technol, 54; Ph.D.(comput. sci), California, Los Angeles, 63. Sect. head instrumentation & controls, Pacific Semiconductors Inc, 55-58; mem. tech. staff, comput. div, Thompson-Ramo-Wooldridge, Inc, 58-63; dir. adv. tech, Librascope Group, Gen. Precision Inc, 63-68; dir. res, Univac Fed. Systs.

Div, 68-69, dir. eng. develop, 69-70; GEN. MGR, SPERRY RAND RES. CTR, 70- Lectr, California, Los Angeles, 56-60, 63-65. U.S.N, 46-47. Inst. Elec. & Electronics Eng; Asn. Comput. Mach. Advanced computer organizations including highly parallel cellular structures; thin film magnetic memories; semiconductor devices and circuits. Address: Sperry Rand Research Center, 100 North Rd, Sudbury, MA 01776.

FULLER, RICHARD M, b. Crawfordsville, Ind, July 23, 33; m. 55; c. 3. PHYSICS. B.A, DePauw, 55; M.A, Minnesota, 60; Ph.D.(physics), Mich. State, 65. Instr. PHYSICS, Alma Col.(Mich), 59-61, asst. prof, 61-66, assoc. prof, 66-68; GUSTAVUS ADOLPHUS COL, 68-70, PROF, 70- AAAS; Am. Asn. Physics Teachers; Am. Phys. Soc. Low temperature physics; liquid helium phenomena; thin films; optical properties of solids; infrared physics. Address: Dept. of Physics, Gustavus Adolphus College, St. Peter, MN 56082.

FULLER, R(OBERT) A(RTHUR), b. Moosomin, Sask, Sept. 7, 26; m. 51; c. 3. BIOCHEMISTRY. B.A, Saskatchewan, 49, M.A, 50; Ph.D.(biochem), Minnesota, 55. Agr. res. off, dom. entom. lab, Can. Dept. Agr, 50-51; asst. biochem, Minnesota, 51-55; dir. pharmaceut. res. sect, Johnson & Johnson, Ltd, 55-60, dir. res, 61-62, V.PRES. RES. & DEVELOP, 62-66, JOHNSON & JOHNSON DOMESTIC OPER. CO, N.J, 66- Sr. agr. asst, Can. Dept. Agr, summers 45-50. Chem. Inst. Can. Physical biochemistry; protein chemistry; formulation and development of toiletries and pharmaceuticals; research administration. Address: Johnson & Johnson Domestic Operating Co, Route 1, New Brunswick, NJ 08903.

FULLER, ROBERT G(OHL), b. Crawfordsville, Ind, June 7, 35; m. 61; c. 2. SOLID STATE PHYSICS. B.S, Missouri, Rolla, 57; Nat. Sci. Found. fel, Illinois, Urbana, 57-58, M.S, 58, Ph.D.(physics), 65. Teacher, high sch, Burma, 59-61; res. asst. physics, Illinois, Urbana, 61-65; Nat. Res. Coun-Nat. Acad. Sci. res. fel, Naval Res. Lab, 65-67, physicist, 67-69; ASSOC. PROF. PHYSICS, UNIV. NEBR, LINCOLN, 69- Am. Asn. Physics Teachers; Am. Phys. Soc. Diffusion and pulse radiolysis in ionic solids; electrical conductivity of ionic solids. Address: Dept. of Physics, University of Nebraska, Lincoln, NE 68508.

FULLER, ROBERT W, b. Summit, N.J, Oct. 26, 36; m. 59; c. 2. PHYSICS. Ph.D.(physics), Princeton, 61. Instr. physics, Columbia Univ, 61-63, asst. prof, Barnard Col, 63-65, Columbia Univ, 65-66; mem. faculty, ctr. advan. study, Wesleyan Univ, 66-67; mem. res. staff, Battelle Mem. Inst, 67-68; prof. & dean faculty, Trinity Col.(Conn), 68-70; PRES, OBERLIN COL, 70- Fission; relativity; biophysics. Address: Oberlin College, Oberlin, OH 44074.

FULLER, ROY J(OSEPH), b. Little Rock, Ark, June 19, 39. MATHEMATICS. B.S.E.E, Arkansas, 61, M.S, 63; Ph.D.(math), Princeton, 67. Elec. engr, U.S. Naval Ord. Lab, Md, summers 61-64, mathematician, summers 64-66; ASST. PROF. MATH, UNIV. ARK, FAYETTEVILLE, 67- Am. Math. Soc. Non-Abelian Gaussian sums and their connection with Hecke operators; estimation of damage to aircraft due to fragmenting-warhead projectiles. Address: Dept. of Mathematics, University of Arkansas, Fayetteville, AR 72701.

FULLER, R(UEBEN) GLEN, b. Stillwater, Okla, Aug. 3, 10; m. 35; c. 2. BOTANY. A.B, Bethel Col.(Kans), 38; fel, State Col. Wash, 38-40, M.S, 41. Agronomist, Rogers Canning Co, Oregon, 41-43; instr. aerial navigation & assoc. coordinator, Whitman Col, 43-44; plant physiologist, BATTELLE COLUMBUS LABS, 44-50, mgr. North Fla. res. sta, 50-54, asst. chief, physiol. & biophys. div, 55-67, assoc. fel, 67-69, ASSOC. ADV. ECOL. & ENVIRON. SYSTS. DIV, 69- Vaughan Mem. Award, Am. Soc. Hort. Sci, 46. AAAS. Physiology of selenium in plants; marine biology, especially of fouling and wood-destroying organisms; deterioration of materials in marine environments; ecology. Address: Ecology & Environmental Systems Division, Battelle Columbus Labs.(Las Vegas Office), 2957 S. Highland Dr, Las Vegas, NV 89102.

FULLER, R(UFUS) CLINTON, b. Providence, R.I, Mar. 5, 25; m. 46; c. 4. MICROBIOLOGY, BIOCHEMISTRY. A.B, Brown, 45; A.M, Amherst Col, 48; Nutrit. Found. fel, Stanford, 49-51, Ph.D.(biol), 52; hon. M.A, Dartmouth Col, 61. Teaching asst. biol, Brown, 45-46; Amherst Col, 46-48; Stanford, 48-50, asst. microbiol, 51-52; res. microbiologist, Lawrence Radiation Lab, Univ. Calif, 52-55; assoc. plant physiologist, Brookhaven Nat. Lab, 55-58, plant biochemist, 58-59; prof. microbiol. & chmn. dept, Dartmouth Med. Sch, 60-65; prof. biomed. sci. & dir. grad. sch. biomed. sci, Univ. Tenn-Oak Ridge Nat. Lab, 66-71; PROF. BIOCHEM. & CHMN. DEPT, UNIV. MASS, AMHERST, 71- Vis. prof, dept. life sci, Univ. Calif, Riverside, 66; consult, biol. div, Oak Ridge Nat. Lab, 66- Sigma Xi sr. fel, Nat. Sci. Found, Oxford, Eng, 59-60; mem. med. scientists training comt, Nat. Inst. Gen. Med. Sci, 63-65; cell biol. study sect, Nat. Insts. Health, 65-69; microbiol. training comt, Nat. Inst. Gen. Med. Sci, 69- U.S.N.R, 43-45. AAAS; Am. Soc. Plant Physiol; Am. Soc. Microbiol; Am. Soc. Biol. Chem. Comparative biochemistry of photosynthesis; cellular biochemistry as related to cellular structures; developmental aspects of microbial ultrastructure; control mechanisms in photosynthesis; membrane structure and function. Address: Dept. of Biochemistry, University of Massachusetts, Amherst, MA 01002.

FULLER, THOMAS C(HARLES), b. Evanston, Ill, Aug. 2, 18; m. 45; c. 2. BOTANY. B.S, Northwestern, 40; M.S, New Mexico, 42; Ph.D.(cytol), Chicago, 47. Asst. bot. & zool, New Mexico, 40-41; instr. bot, R.I. State Col, 46-48; prof, Hanover Col, 48-49; asst. prof, Southern California, 49-53; jr. plant pathologist, CALIF. DEPT. AGR, 53-54, asst. plant pathologist, 54-57, BOTANIST, 57- U.S.A, 42-45. Cytology; mitosis; effects of several sulfa compounds on nuclear and cell division; diseases and culture of ornamentals; distribution of weeds in California. Address: 171 Westcott Way, Sacramento, CA 95825.

FULLER, VERNON J(ACK), b. Wash, D.C, Sept. 11, 28; m. 64; c. 2. BACTERIOLOGY. B.S, Maryland, 51; Sanders fel, George Washington, 51-56, M.S, 53, Ph.D.(bact), 58. BACTERIOLOGIST, Walter Reed Army Inst. Res, 56-61; lab. germfree animal res, Nat. Inst. Allergy & Infectious Diseases, NAT. INSTS. HEALTH, 61-63, LAB. CONTROL ACTIVITIES, DIV. BIOL.

STANDARDS, 63- U.S.A.R, 48-61, U.S.P.H.S, 61-, Sci. Dir. Am. Soc. Microbiol. Development of new or improved test procedures for the control, standardization and stability of biological products. Address: Lab. of Control Activities, Division of Biologics Standards, National Institutes of Health, Bethesda, MD 20014.

FULLER, WALLACE H(AMILTON), b. Old Hamilton, Alaska, Apr. 15, 15; m. 39; c. 1. BIOCHEMISTRY, BACTERIOLOGY. B.S, State Col. Wash, 38, M.S, 39; Ph.D.(soils chem), Iowa State Col, 42. Res. assoc, State Col. Wash, 37-39; soil scientist, soil conserv. serv, U.S. Dept. Agr, 39-40; res. assoc, Iowa State Col, 40-45; bacteriologist, bur. plant indust. & agr. eng, U.S. Dept. Agr, 45-47, soil scientist, 47-48; biochemist & assoc. prof. CHEM, UNIV. ARIZ, 48-56, PROF. & BIOCHEMIST, 56-, HEAD DEPT. AGR. CHEM. & SOILS, 56- AAAS; Am. Soc. Agron. Soil microbiology; cellulose decomposition; chemistry of soil organic matter; soil fertilizers; plant nutrition; plant decomposition; soil phosphorus; plant nutrition; plant decomposition and nutrient release. Address: 740 E. Mescal Pl, Tucson, AZ 85718.

FULLER, WAYNE A(RTHUR), b. Brooks, Iowa, June 15, 31; m. 56; c. 2. AGRICULTURAL ECONOMICS, STATISTICS. B.S, Iowa State Univ, 55, M.S, 57, Ph.D.(agr. econ), 59. Asst. agr. econ, IOWA STATE UNIV, 55-56, res. assoc, 56-59, asst. prof. STATIST, 59-62, assoc. prof, 62-66, PROF, 66- Nat. Sci. Found. fel, 64-65. Am. Agr. Econ. Asn; Am. Statist. Asn; Inst. Math. Statist; Economet. Soc. Survey sampling, estimation and econometrics. Address: Dept. of Statistics, Iowa State University, Ames, IA 50010.

FULLER, W(ILLIAM) A(LBERT), b. Moosomin, Sask, May 10, 24; m. 47; c. 4. VERTEBRATE ECOLOGY. B.A, Saskatchewan, 46, Nat. Res. Coun. bursary, 46-47, M.A, 47; Alumni Res. Found. fel, Wisconsin, 49-50, Ph.D.(ecol), 57. Mammalogist, Can. Wildlife Serv, 47-59; asst. prof. ZOOL, UNIV. ALTA, 59-63, assoc. prof, 63-67, PROF, 67-, ACTING CHMN. DEPT, 69- Mem. exec. bd, Int. Union Conserv. Nature & Natural Resources, 64-70. AAAS; Am. Soc. Mammal; Wildlife Soc; Arctic Inst. N.Am. Ecology of mammals, especially in the taiga in winter. Address: Dept. of Zoology, University of Alberta, Edmonton, Alta, Can.

FULLER, WILLIAM R(ICHARD), b. Indianapolis, Ind, Oct. 27, 20; m. 43; c. 2. MATHEMATICS. B.S, Butler, 48; M.S, Purdue, 51, Ph.D.(math), 57. Instr. math, Butler, 48-49; asst, Purdue, 49-51; mathematician, U.S. Naval Ord. Plant, Ind, 51-54; instr. math, PURDUE UNIV, 54-57, asst. prof, 57-59, from assoc. prof. & acting head dept. math; & statist. to prof. & acting head div. math. sci, 59-61, 63-64, ASSOC. DEAN SCH. SCI, 65- Consult, U.S. Naval Avionics Facility, 58-61; Radio Corp. Am. Serv. Co, Patrick AFB, Fla, 59; Gen. Elec. Co, 60-61. U.S.A, 42-45. Am. Math. Soc; Math. Asn. Am. Nonlinear differential equations. Address: Division of Mathematics Sciences, Mathematical Sciences Bldg, Purdue University, Lafayette, IN 47906.

FULLERTON, ALBERT L, JR, b. Boston, Mass, Aug. 25, 21; m. 44; c. 4. PHYSICS. A.B, Harvard, 47; M.S, Colorado, 51. Staff mem. commun, Lincoln Lab, Mass. Inst. Tech, 52-54; proj. engr. mil. systs, Melpar, Inc, 54-57; proj. mgr, logistic data processing, Sylvania Gen. Tel. & Electronics Corp, 57-61; tech. staff mem. commun. & data processing, Inst. Naval Studies, Franklin Inst. Boston, 61-65; PRELIMINARY DESIGN DEPT, SANDERS ASSOCS, N.H, 65- U.S.A.A.F, 42-46, Sgt. Sr. mem. Inst. Elec. & Electronics Eng; Asn. Comput. Mach. Data processing; naval command, control, and communications systems. Address: Blueberry Lane, Lincoln Center, MA 01773.

FULLERTON, CHARLES M(ICHAEL), b. Oklahoma City, Okla, Mar. 10, 32; m. 54; c. 2. CLOUD PHYSICS. B.S, Univ. Okla, 54; Nat. Sci. Found. fel, High Altitude Observ, Univ. Colo, summer 60; M.Sc, N.Mex. Inst. Mining & Technol, 64, Nat. Sci. Found. fels, 64-66, Ph.D.(geophys), 66. Instr. physics & math, Col. St. Joseph (N.Mex), 57-61; asst. geophysicist & asst. prof. physics, CLOUD PHYSICS OBSERV, HAWAII INST. GEOPHYS, UNIV. HAWAII, HILO, 66-70, ASSOC. GEOPHYSICIST & ASSOC. PROF. PHYSICS, 70-, acting dir, 69-71, DIR. OBSERV, 71- Prin. investr, U.S. Dept. Interior Off. Water Resources res. grant, 71-72. U.S.A, 54-57, 1st Lt. Am. Geophys. Union; Am. Meteorol. Soc. Precipitation physics; solar coronal emission; electrical effects and coalescence processes in warm rain; ice nuclei concentrations in relation to volcanic activity; microbarometric oscillations; distribution of high intensity rainfall. Address: Cloud Physics Observatory, University of Hawaii, Hilo, HI 96720.

FULLERTON, H(ERBERT) P(ALMER), b. Philadelphia, Pa, Aug. 14, 12; m. 34; c. 2. MECHANICAL ENGINEERING. B.S, Pennsylvania, 33, M.E, 45; M.A, Buffalo, 44. With Gen. Elec. Co, 33-36; Am. Eng. Co, 36-41; assoc. prof. eng, Buffalo, 41-45; mach. design, Virginia, 45-48; develop. & design engr, GEN. ELEC. CO, 48-62, proj. engr, 62-68, CONSULT. ENGR, 68- Adj. prof, Drexel Inst, 48-64. Am. Soc. Mech. Eng; Am. Soc. Eng. Educ; Soc. Indust. & Appl. Math; Asn. Comput. Mach; Inst. Mgt. Sci. Mathematical analysis of engineering and business systems. Address: General Electric Co, 6901 Elmwood Ave, Philadelphia, PA 19142.

FULLERTON, RICHARD, b. Phila, Pa, Sept. 16, 28; m. 50; c. 4. ANALYTICAL CHEMISTRY. B.S, Purdue, 55; Ph.D, Iowa State, 59. Asst, Iowa State, 55-59; chemist, Gen. Elec. Co, 59-65; res. scientist, chem. dept, Pac. Northwest Lab, Battelle Mem. Inst. Wash, 65-66; sr. res. chemist, Idaho Nuclear Corp, 66-69; ASST. PROF. CHEM, HASTINGS COL, 69- U.S.A.R, 49-52, Med.Serv.C, 50-51. Am. Chem. Soc. Chelate chemistry; radiation effects on solids; separation chemistry; analysis of gases in metals and ceramics; analytical methods development. Address: 411 E. Fifth St, Hastings, NE 68901.

FULLERTON, THOMAS M, b. Wilberton, Okla, Oct. 11, 36; m. 58; c. 5. CROP PHYSIOLOGY. B.S, Okla. State Univ, 59; M.S, Univ. Ark, Fayetteville, 64, Ph.D.(agron), 69. Res. asst. AGRON, Univ. Ark, Fayetteville, 64-69; ASST. PROF, Univ. Nebr. mission to Colombia, 69-71; UTAH STATE UNIV. WATER MGT. RES. PROG, COLOMBIA, 71- Ecol. Soc. Am; Weed Sci. Soc. Am. Herbicide effects on winter hardiness of bermuda grass;

weed and brush control in pasture and rangeland areas; crop response to irrigation and fertilizer treatments. Address: 304 S. 14th, Fort Smith, AR 72901.

FULLERTON, W(ILLIAM) WARDLE, b. Belfast, North. Ireland, Mar. 31, 39; m. 71. PROTEIN CHEMISTRY, X-RAY CRYSTALLOGRAPHY. B.A, Trinity Col.(Dublin), 64, Med. Res. Coun. Ireland fels, 64-68, M.A. & Ph.D.(biochem), 68. Med. Res. Coun. Ireland res. worker biochem, Trinity Col. (Dublin), 68; NAT. INST. HEALTH & NAT. SCI. FOUND. RES. ASSOC. PROTEIN CHEM, COLUMBIA UNIV, 68- AAAS; Brit. Biochem. Soc; Am. Chem. Soc; Am. Inst. Physics; Am. Asn. Crystal Growth. The physical and chemical properties of fatty acids, their role in blood clotting, atherosclerosis and cancer; purification, crystallization, chemical modification and x-ray diffraction studies of several proteins and peptides. Address: Dept. of Biochemistry, Columbia University, 630 W. 168th St, New York, NY 10032.

FULLHART, LAWRENCE, JR, b. Mystic, Iowa, Sept. 14, 20; m. 42; c. 2. CHEMISTRY. A.B, William Jewell Col, 42; fel, Iowa State Col, 42-46, Ph.D.(org. chem), 46. Asst, William Jewell Col, 41-42; chemist, E.I. DU PONT DE NEMOURS & CO, 46-57, tech. rep, 57-62, develop. specialist, 62-70, MKT. RES. REP, 70- With Off. Sci. Res. & Develop, 44. AAAS; Am. Chem. Soc; N.Y. Acad. Sci. Organic sulfur compounds; synthetic antimalarial and antitubercular compounds; synthetic vitamin D; nutritional biochemistry; amino acids and proteins; polymer dispersions. Address: Electrochemicals Dept, E.I. du Pont de Nemours & Co, Room 3161, DuPont Bldg, Wilmington, DE 19898.

FULLILOVE, S(USAN) L(OUISE), b. Shreveport, La, Sept. 15, 41. DEVELOPMENTAL BIOLOGY. B.A, South. Methodist Univ, 63; M.A, Univ. Tex, Austin, 65, univ. fel, 66-68, Ph.D.(zool), 68. Instr. ZOOL, UNIV. TEX, AUSTIN, 68, ASSOC. RES. SCIENTIST, 68- Soc. Develop. Biol. Tissue interactions during amphibian heart induction; ultrastructure of the early Drosophila egg as correlated with developmental events; cytology and ultrastructure of Drosophila embryonic lethals. Address: Dept. of Zoology, University of Texas at Austin, Austin, TX 78712.

FULLILOVE, WILLIAM THOMAS, b. Watkinsville, Ga, Apr. 17, 06; m. 38; c. 3. AGRICULTURAL ECONOMICS. B.S.A, Georgia, 27; Iowa State Col, 38. Cotton mkt. specialist, GA. EXP. STA, UNIV. GA, 27-34, head agr. econ. dept, 34-57, dir, 57-68, PROF. AGR. ECON. & AGR. ECONOMIST, 68- Chief consult, Piedmont Field Exp. Sta, 38-; consult, Callaway Found, 44-47. Am. Agr. Econ. Asn. Cotton grade and staple statistics; market price studies; farm management and marketing problems. Address: University of Georgia College of Agriculture Experiment Stations, Experiment, GA 30212.

FULLING, ROGER WILLIAM, b. Princeton, Ind, March 5, 08; m. MECHANICAL ENGINEERING. B.S, Delaware, 32. Construct. engr, eng. dept, E.I. DU PONT DE NEMOURS & CO, 34-36, asst. field proj. mgr, 36-38, field proj. mgr, 38-41, dir. supt, 41-45, special asst. to gen. dir, indust. eng. & develop. eng. div, 45-46, mgr. planning div, 46-48, asst. mgr. indust. eng. div, 48-51, atomic eng, 51-54, mgr, 54-55, from staff asst, mech. develop. lab. to asst. mgr, develop. eng. div, 56-58, asst. div. dir, 58-59, MEM. STAFF, DEVELOP. DEPT, 59- Dir. construct, Office Asst. Secy. Defense, Dept. Defense, 55, acting asst. secy. defense for properties & installations, 56; civilian aide to Secy. Army, State Del. U.S.A.R, 32, Capt. AAAS; Am. Soc. Mech. Eng. Engineering research and development for chemical industry comprising chemical engineering unit operations, applied physics, materials technology, mechanical and electrical engineering. Address: Development Dept, E.I. du Pont de Nemours & Co, Wilmington, DE 19898.

FULLINGTON, J. GARRIN, b. Peoria, Ill, May 25, 40. BIOCHEMISTRY. B.A, Bradley, 62; M.S, Indiana, 64; California, 65-68. CHEMIST, North. Regional Lab, U.S. DEPT. AGR, 60-63, WEST. REGIONAL LAB, 63- Am. Asn. Cereal Chem. Oil and fatty ester ozonolysis; phospholipid-metal complexes; phospholipid-protein interactions; orthoester hydrolysis. Address: Western Regional Research Lab, U.S. Dept. of Agriculture, 800 Buchanan, Albany, CA 94710.

FULLMAN, R(OBERT) L(OUIS), b. Sewickley, Pa, Sept. 13, 22; m. 44; c. 2. PHYSICAL METALLURGY. B.Eng, Yale, 43, D.Eng.(metall), 50. Instr. metall, New Haven Y.M.C.A. Jr. Col, 47-48; res. assoc, GEN. ELEC. CO, 48-55, mgr. mat. & processes studies, 55-59, metal studies, 60-63, fuel cell studies, 64-65, mgr. properties br, 65-68, MGR. PLANNING & RESOURCES, MAT. SCI. & ENG, 69- Vis. lectr, Rensselaer Polytech. Inst, 51-56, adj. prof, 56-65; secy-treas. bd. gov, Acta Metallurgica, 65- U.S.N, 42-45. Am. Soc. Metals; Am. Inst. Mining, Metall. & Petrol. Eng. Deformation of metals; interfacial energies in solids; crystal growth; origin of microstructures; recrystallization and grain growth; relationships between microstructure and properties of metals. Address: Corporate Research & Development, General Electric Co, P.O. Box 8, Schenectady, NY 12301.

FULLMER, G(EORGE) C(LINTON), b. Tucson, Ariz, Feb. 17, 22; m. 46; c. 2. PHYSICS. B.S, Washington (Seattle), 47. Physicist, Hanford Atomic Prod. Oper, Gen. Elec. Co, 47-53, supvr. pile physics, 53-56, mgr. oper. physics, 56-65; mgr. instrumentation, Pac. Northwest Labs, Battelle Mem. Inst, 66-67; mgr. physics & reactor physics & irradiation technol, Douglas United Nuclear, Inc, 67-71; PRIN. ENGR, NUCLEAR ENERGY DIV, GEN. ELEC. CO, 71- U.S.A.A.F, 43-46, 1st Lt. Am. Phys. Soc; Am. Nuclear Soc. Reactor operational control of reactivity and flux distribution; reactor safety control and instrumentation; reactor shielding. Address: Nuclear Energy Division, General Electric Co, San Jose, CA 95125.

FULLMER, HAROLD M(ILTON), b. Gary, Ind, July 9, 18; m. 42; c. 2. HISTOCHEMISTRY. B.S, Indiana, 42, D.D.S, 44; Tulane. Intern & res, Charity Hosp, New Orleans, 46-48; assoc. prof. gen. & oral. path. & head dept. path, sch. dent, Loyola (La), 48-53; prin. investr, lab. histol. & path, Nat. Inst. Dent. Res, Nat. Insts. Health, 53-64, chief, sect. histochem. & exp. path, 65-66, sect. histochem, 66-70, exp. path. br, 68-70; DIR. INST. DENT. RES, UNIV. ALA. MED. CTR, 70-, PROF. PATH, 70-, DENT, 70-, ASSOC. DEAN, SCH. DENT, 70- Ed-in-chief, J. Oral Path, 72- Dipl. Am. Bd. Oral Path. Dent.C, 44-46, Capt. Fel. AAAS; fel. Am. Col. Dent; Histochem. Soc; Am.

Soc. Cell Biol; Am. Dent. Asn; Biol. Stain Comn; Int. Acad. Path; Int. Asn. Dent. Res. Histochemistry and microchemistry of connective tissues, bones and teeth; mechanisms of staining reactions; cytological changes with development and age. Address: Institute of Dental Research, University of Alabama Medical Center, 1919 Seventh Ave. S, Birmingham, AL 35233.

FULLMER, JUNE Z(IMMERMAN), b. Peoria, Ill, Dec. 16, 20; m. 53. HISTORY OF SCIENCE, CHEMICAL KINETICS. B.S, Ill. Inst. Tech, 43, M.S, 45; fel, Bryn Mawr Col, 46-48, Ph.D, 48. Instr. chem, Hood Col, 45-46; asst. prof, Pa. Col. Women, 49-52; res. chemist, metall. eng, Carnegie Inst. Tech, 53-54; vis. asst. prof. chem, Newcomb Col, Tulane, 56-57, asst. prof, 57-59, assoc. prof. & head dept, 59-64; vis. assoc. prof, Ohio Wesleyan, 64-65; adj. assoc. prof. HIST, OHIO STATE UNIV, 66-69, assoc. prof, 69-71, PROF, 71- Berliner fel, Oxford, 48-49; Am. Coun. Learned Socs. fel, 60-61; Guggenheim fel, 63-64; hon. fel, Univ. Wisconsin, 63-64. Fel. AAAS; Am. Chem. Soc. History of science. Address: 781 Latham Ct, Columbus, OH 43214.

FULLWOOD, RALPH R, b. Hereford, Tex, Sept. 16, 28; m. 54; c. 3. PHYSICS. B.S, Tex. Tech. Col, 52; A.M, Harvard, 55; Pennsylvania, 58-60; Ph.D. (nuclear eng), Rensselaer Polytech, 65. Physicist, Knolls Atomic Power Lab, Gen. Elec. Co, 56-57; res. assoc. physics, Pennsylvania, 57-60; nuclear eng. & sci, Rensselaer Polytech, 60-65, assoc. prof, 65-66; STAFF MEM, LOS ALAMOS SCI. LAB, 66- Consult, Los Alamos Sci. Lab. & NASA, 66. Chem.C, U.S.A, 54-56. Am. Phys. Soc; Am. Nuclear Soc; Inst. Elec. & Electronics Eng. Reactor physics; neutron cross section measurements. Address: 352 Venado, Los Alamos, NM 87544.

FULMER, CHARLES V, b. Council Bluffs, Iowa, Nov. 15, 20; m. 47; c. 4. GEOLOGY. B.S. & M.S, Washington (Seattle), 47; Ph.D.(geol, paleont), California, Berkeley, 56. Geologist, Standard Oil Co. Calif, 51-53, field geologist geol. mapping, 53-56, stratigrapher, Wash. & Ore, 56-59, Alaska, 59-60, div. stratigrapher, Wash, Ore. & Alaska, 60-62; RES. ENGR. appl. res, BOEING CO, 62-64, SPACE EXPLOR, 64- U.S.A, 42-46, 1st Lt. Geol. Soc. Am; Am. Asn. Petrol. Geol; Asn. Eng. Geol. Tertiary stratigraphy of Washington and Oregon; space exploration. Address: 6174 N.E. 187th Pl, Seattle, WA 98155.

FULMER, CLYDE B(ENSON), b. Lowndes Co, Ga, Nov. 7, 24; m. 54; c. 2. PHYSICS. B.S, Berry Col, 48; M.S, Emory, 49; Ph.D.(eng. physics) N.C. State Col, 57. Asst. prof. physics, Jacksonville State Col, 49-51; physicist, Redstone Arsenal, 51-52; instr. physics, N.C. State Col, 52-56; PHYSICIST, OAK RIDGE NAT. LAB, 56- U.S.A, 43-46. Am. Phys. Soc; Am. Asn. Physics Teachers. Medium energy nuclear physics. Address: Physics Division, Oak Ridge National Lab, P.O. Box X, Oak Ridge TN 37830

FULMER, GLENN ELTON, b. Istanbul, Turkey, Aug. 3, 28; U.S. citizen; m. 52; c. 4. PHYSICAL CHEMISTRY, PHYSICS. B.A, Oberlin Col, 49; M.A, Hopkins, 56. Chemist, Nalco Chem. Co, 49-50; sr. engr, Martin Marietta Corp, 56-58; SR. RES. PHYSICIST, RES. DIV, W.R. GRACE & CO, 58- U.S.A, 50-52. Soc. Rheol; Am. Soc. Test. & Mat; Am. Chem. Soc. Rheological research; failure of materials and development of superior materials; testing of nuclear fuel elements and nuclear fallout; evaluation of ion exchange resins. Address: 11505 Crows Nest Rd, Clarksville, MD 21029.

FULMER, HUGH SCOTT, b. Syracuse, N.Y, June 18, 28; m. 52; c. 3. PREVENTIVE MEDICINE. A.B, Syracuse, 48; M.D, State Univ. N.Y, 51; M.P.H, Harvard, 61. Instr. internal med, sch. med, State Univ. N.Y. Syracuse, 57; res. assoc. pub. health & prev. med, Cornell, 58-60; asst. prof. community med, col. med, Univ. Ky, 60-62, assoc. prof, 62-66, prof, 66-68; tech. rep. health progs, Peace Corps, Malaysia, 68-69; PROF. COMMUNITY MED. & HEAD DEPT, COL. MED, UNIV. MASS, 69- U.S.A.F, 52-54, Capt. Am. Med. Asn; Am. Pub. Health Asn. Epidemiology of non-infectious disease; medical care. Address: Dept. of Community Medicine, College of Medicine, University of Massachusetts, Worcester, MA 01604.

FULMER, RICHARD H, b. Syracuse, N.Y, Oct. 24, 38; m. 64; c. 1. NUCLEAR PHYSICS. B.S, LeMoyne Col, 60; A. Mellon & Nat. Sci. Found. fels. & Ph.D. (nuclear struct), Pittsburgh, 64. PHYSICIST, KNOLLS ATOMIC POWER LAB, GEN. ELEC. CO, 64- Am. Phys. Soc; Am. Nuclear Soc. Nuclear structure; reactor physics. Address: Knolls Atomic Power Lab, General Electric Co, Schenectady, NY 12301.

FULMER, RICHARD W(ARREN), b. Istanbul, Turkey, Jan. 23, 30; U.S. citizen; m. 47; c. 4. ORGANIC CHEMISTRY. A.B, DePauw, 52; univ. fel. & Nat. Sci. Found. fel, Illinois, 54-55, Ph.D.(chem), 55. Chemist & proj. leader, Gen. Mills Inc, 55-64; mgr. resin res. & develop, CARGILL, INC, 64-67, MGR. CENT. RES. LAB, 67- Am. Chem. Soc. Fine chemicals; organic synthesis; intermediates; coatings; polymers. Address: Central Research Labs, Cargill, Inc, Cargill Bldg, Minneapolis, MN 55402.

FULMER, ROBERT E(LLERY), b. Ames, Iowa, Dec. 17, 22; m. 48; c. 2. ORGANIC CHEMISTRY. B.S, Iowa State Col, 46; M.S, Minnesota, 50; Ph.D. (org. chem), Cincinnati, 52. Chemist, Manhattan proj, Iowa State Col, 42-44; Oak Ridge, Tenn, 44-46; chemist & group leader, Lederle Labs. Div, Am. Cyanamid Co, 51-54; prin. chemist, Battelle Mem. Inst, 54-59; from asst. ed. to SR. ASSOC. INDEXER, CHEM. ABSTRACTS SERV, 59- AAAS; Am. Chem. Soc. Chemical literature and documentation. Address: 273 Eastmoor Blvd, Columbus, OH 43209.

FULMOR, WILLIAM, b. Philadelphia, Pa, July 3, 13; m. 42; c. 3. ORGANIC CHEMISTRY. B.S, Fairleigh Dickenson, 61. Mem. staff, micro anal. lab, LEDERLE LABS, AM. CYANAMID CO, 46-52, supvr, spectros. lab, 52-63, GROUP LEADER SPECTROS, 63- C.Eng, 41-45, Capt. Am. Chem. Soc; Soc. Appl. Spectros; Coblentz Soc. Application of absorption spectroscopy to elucidation of structures of organic compounds; methods of information retrieval for spectroscopic data. Address: Ferris Lane, Nyack, NY 10960.

FULOP, MILFORD, b. N.Y.C, Nov. 7, 27; m. 57; c. 2. INTERNAL MEDICINE. A.B, Columbia Univ, 46, M.D, 49. Asst. prof. MED, ALBERT EINSTEIN COL. MED, 56-61, assoc. prof, 61-68, PROF, 68-; DIR. MED. SERV, BRONX MUNIC. HOSP. CTR, 70- Med.C, 51-53, Capt. Am. Fedn. Clin. Res. Renal diseases; metabolic disorders. Address: Dept. of Medicine, Albert Einstein College of Medicine, Yeshiva University, New York, NY 10461.

FULP, RONALD OWEN, b. Trinity, N.C, June 29, 36; m. 59; c. 3. ALGEBRA. B.S, Wake Forest Col, 58; M.A, Univ. N.C, Chapel Hill, 61; Ph.D.(math), Auburn Univ, 65. Part time instr. MATH, Univ. N.C, 58-61; instr, Auburn Univ, 61-62; asst. prof, Ga. State Col, 63-65; Univ. Houston, 65-68, ASSOC. PROF, 67-69; N.C. STATE UNIV, 69- Am. Math. Soc; Math. Asn. Am. Theory of characters of both algebraic and topological semigroups; homological methods applied to algebraic and topological semigroups, especially theory of extensions and tensor products; homological methods applied to the theory of topological groups. Address: Dept. of Mathematics, North Carolina State University, Raleigh, NC 27607.

FULRATH, RICHARD M(ERLE), b. Princeton, Ill, Aug. 30, 24; m. 47; c. 4. CERAMICS. B.S, Illinois, 50, M.S, 51; Oak Ridge Sch. Reactor Tech, 52; D.Eng, California, 60. Res. engr, Calif. Res. & Develop. Co, 52-54; assoc. CERAMIC ENG, UNIV. CALIF, BERKELEY, 54-57, acting asst. prof, 57-60, asst. prof, 60-62, assoc. prof, 62-67, PROF, 67- U.S.A.A.F, 43-45, Res, 51-58. Fel. Am. Ceramic Soc; Am. Soc. Metals; Am. Nuclear Soc; Nat. Inst. Ceramic Eng. Behavior of nuclear materials and ceramics; chemistry and physics of ceramics. Address: 1156 Sterling Ave, Berkeley, CA 94708.

FULS, ELLIS, b. Hammonton, N.J, Dec. 8, 31; m. 59. ATOMIC PHYSICS. B.S, Upsala Col, 53; M.S, Connecticut, 55, Ph.D, 57. Asst, Connecticut, 55-57; MEM. TECH. STAFF DEVICE DEVELOP, BELL TEL. LABS, 57- Am. Phys. Soc. Atomic collisions at kilovolt energies; luminescent and photoconductive phenomena; semiconductor technology. Address: Box 653, Lindabury Ave, Bernardsville, NJ 07924.

FULTON, ALBERT I(RVIN), b. Sunbury, Pa, Jan. 29, 21. CHEMICAL ENGINEERING. B.S, Grove City Col, 51. Chem. analyst, standard steel div, Baldwin Locomotive Works, 41-44; Midvale Steel Co, 45, 47; chem. engr, res. & develop. dept, Am. Cyanamid Co, 51-52, acid area supvr, 53-55; supvr. quality control, Westwood Plant, ALLEGHENY LUDLUM STEEL CORP, 56-66, CHIEF WORKS CHEMIST, CHEM. LAB, QUAL. CONTROL DIV, BRACKENRIDGE PLANT, 66- U.S.A.A.F, 45-47. Am. Chem. Soc. Quality control in the steel industry. Address: 255 White Oak Dr, New Kensington, PA 15068.

FULTON, ALBERT STEWART, b. Brawley, Calif, Jan. 16, 24. COMMUNICATION & CONTROL ENGINEERING. B.S, Calif. Inst. Tech, 45; California, Berkeley, 46-47. Mem. tech. staff guid, navig. & control, Hughes Aircraft Co, 47-53; asst. mgr. eng, Servomechanisms, Inc, 53-56; sr. staff mem. commun. theory & controls, Ramo-Wooldridge Div, TRW SYSTS, 56-61, dept. mgr. electrooptics, phys. res. div, 61-65, sci. payload mgr. voyager spacecraft, 65-66, dept. mgr. electrooptics, electronic systs. div, 66-67, asst. lab. mgr. sensor systs, 67-70, PROG. MGR, 70- U.S.N, 42-46, Res, 46-55, Ens. Inst. Elec. & Electronics Eng; Optical Soc. Applied research in sensor devices; image data processing; laser systems; noise theory and experimental measurements. Address: TRW Systems, Bldg. R2-Room 2104, 1 Space Park, Redondo Beach, CA 90278.

FULTON, CHANDLER M(ONTGOMERY), b. Cleveland, Ohio, Apr. 17, 34; m. 55; c. 3. CELL & DEVELOPMENTAL BIOLOGY. B.A, Brown Univ, 56; Ph.D.(biol), Rockefeller Univ, 60. Instr. BIOL, BRANDEIS UNIV, 60-62, asst. prof, 62-66, ASSOC. PROF, 66- Nat. Sci. Found. grants, 60- Soc. Develop. Biol; Am. Soc. Cell Biol; Genetics Soc. Am. Analysis of molecular and cellular events of cell differentiation in the amebo-flagellate Naegleria gruberi; invertebrate development; microbial genetics. Address: Dept. of Biology, Brandeis University, Waltham, MA 02154.

FULTON, C(HARLES) DARBY, JR, b. Kobe, Japan, July 16, 18; U.S. citizen. MECHANICAL ENGINEERING, THERMODYNAMICS. B.E, Vanderbilt, 40; Ill. Inst. Tech, 40-42; Sc.D.(mech. eng), Mass. Inst. Tech, 50. Asst, res. lab, Gen. Elec. Co, 42-47; asst. prof. mech. eng, Duke, 50-57, Nat. Sci. Found. res. grant, 55-57; design engr, aircraft nuclear propulsion dept, Gen. Elec. Co, 58-61; pres. & engr, Fulton Cryogenics, Inc, 61-68, V.PRES. RES, VORTEC CORP, 68- Vortex tubes; ram jets; fuel spray nozzles; heat switches for magnetic cooling; steam-jet ejectors; air flow in nuclear reactor; combustion chambers. Address: 440 Beech Tree Dr, Cincinnati, OH 45224.

FULTON, CHARLES L, b. Minneapolis, Minn, Apr. 2, 25; m. 52; c. 2. PHYSICS. B.S, Maryland, 51. Ord. engr, U.S. Naval Ord. Lab, Md, 51-56; physicist, U.S. ARMY FRANKFORD ARSENAL, 56-60, sect. chief ballistic ranges test & eval, 60-62, proj. mgr. spec. weapons, 62-64, chief ballistics & supporting res. br, 64-65, appl. ballistics lab, 65-66, supt, N.Am. Regional Test Ctr, NATO Small Caliber Ammunition, 66-71, CHIEF TEST EVAL. CTR, 71- U.S.A, 43-46. Am. Ord. Asn; Sci. Res. Soc. Am. Research design, development, test and evaluation of small arms, recoilless rifles, propellant actuated devices, and special ordnance devices for sabotage and guerilla warfare. Address: U.S. Army Frankford Arsenal, SMUFA-K3000, Philadelphia, PA 19137.

FULTON, CURTIS M(AXWELL), b. Stuttgart, Ger, July 4, 10; nat. MATHEMATICS. Grad, Munich, 33, Ph.D.(math), 36. Prof. MATH, Escuela Nor. Superior, Colombia, 38-46; lectr, Univ. Calif, Los Angeles, 46-47; instr, UNIV. CALIF, DAVIS, 47-49, asst. prof, 49-55, assoc. prof, 55-61, PROF, 61- Am. Math. Soc; Math. Asn. Am. Non-Euclidean geometry; spaces of constant curvature. Address: Dept. of Mathematics, University of California, Davis, CA 95616.

FULTON, DAWSON GERALD, b. Bass River, N.S, Can, Dec. 23, 05; nat; m. 37. MATHEMATICS. B.A, Acadia, 29; fel, Michigan, 29-32, M.Sc, 30, Ph.D.(math), 32. Teacher, pub. sch, 33-37; teaching fel, Michigan, 37; instr. MATH, Armour Inst. Tech, 37-39; asst. prof, Ohio Northern, 39-41, prof. & head dept, 41-43; asst. prof, New Hampshire, 43-44; TUFTS UNIV, 44-46, assoc. prof, 46-50, PROF, 50- Am. Math. Soc. Generalizations of the Cauchy integral formula. Address: Dept. of Mathematics, Tufts University, Medford, MA 02155.

FULTON, GEORGE P(EARMAN), b. Milton, Mass, June 3, 14; m. 42; c. 4. PHYSIOLOGY. B.S, Boston, 36, M.A, 38, fel, 38-41, Ph.D.(physiol), 41. Instr. biol, Boston, 41-42; res. physiologist, Arthur D. Little, Inc, Mass, 46-47; asst. prof. BIOL, BOSTON UNIV, 47-49, assoc. prof, 50-52, prof, 53-60, SHIELDS WARREN PROF, 60-, HEAD DEPT, 56- Vis. prof, sch. med, Stanford, 58-59; mem. staff, Childrens Cancer Res. Found, Boston, 64-; consult, biophys. lab, aeromed. lab, Wright-Patterson AFB; div. nursing, U.S. Pub. Health Serv; mem. adv. bd, Sea Farms Found; sci. adv. bd, New Eng. Aquarium; founding ed, Microvascular Res. U.S.A.A.F, 42-46, Res, 46-, Lt. Col. Am. Physiol. Soc; Am. Soc. Zool; Soc. Exp. Biol. & Med; Radiation Res. Soc; Gerontol. Soc; fel. Am. Col. Angiol.(v.pres, 57-60); Microcirc. Soc.(chmn, 54-55); Am. Asn. Anat; fel. Am. Acad. Arts & Sci. Blood capillary circulation; innervation of blood vessels; skin temperature and heat tolerance work; topical effects of irritant chemicals on skin; thromboembolism; vascular effects of irradiation; petechial formation; hamster cheek pouch as a site for blood vessel and tumor growth studies. Address: Dept. of Biology, Biological Science Center, Boston University, Boston, MA 02215.

FULTON, J(AMES) C(ALVIN), b. Sunbury, Pa, Oct. 17, 23; m. 46; c. 5. METALLURGY. B.S, Pennsylvania, 50; S.M, Mass. Inst. Tech, 52, Sc.D.(metall), 53. Asst. metall, Mass. Inst. Tech, 50-53; res. metallurgist, ALLEGHENY LUDLUM STEEL CORP, 53-54, develop. metallurgist, 54-56, assoc. dir. res, 56-57, chief res. metallurgist, 57-61, mgr. melting technol. dept, 61-65, mgr. melting res. & sci. serv. dept, 65-71, MGR. PROCESS RES. & DEVELOP. DEPT, 71- U.S.C.G.R, 43-46, Ens. Am. Inst. Mining, Metall. & Petrol. Eng; Am. Soc. Metals. Slag-metal reactions; open hearth and electric furnace development; solidification; vacuum melting. Address: Research & Development Labs, Allegheny Ludlum Steel Corp, Brackenridge, PA 15014.

FULTON, J(AMES) M(cCULLOUGH), b. Debert, N.S, Mar. 29, 26; m. 51; c. 2. SOIL PHYSICS & CHEMISTRY. B.Sc, McGill Univ, 47; M.S.A, Univ. Toronto, 52; Ph.D.(soil sci), Mich. State Univ, 63. Soil scientist, RES. BR, CAN. DEPT. AGR, 47-57, HEAD, soil sci. sect, 57-71, HORT. & SOIL SCI. SECT, 71- Soil Sci. Soc. Am; Am. Soc. Agron; Can. Soc. Soil Sci.(sci. ed, Can. J. Soil Sci, 65); Int. Soc. Soil Sci. Effect of soil moisture, aeration and fertility on plant growth, nutrition and metabolism. Address: Horticultural & Soil Science Section, Research Station, Canada Dept. of Agriculture, Harrow, Ont, Can.

FULTON, JAMES W(ILLIAM), b. Oklahoma City, Okla, Dec. 2, 28; m. 62; c. 2. CHEMICAL ENGINEERING. B.A, Harvard, 51; M.S, Oklahoma, 61, Ph.D.(chem. eng), 64. Serv. engr. oil well treating, Dowell, Inc, 55-56; process engr, Monsanto Chem. Co, 57; instr. CHEM. ENG, Oklahoma, 58-59; asst. prof, Okla. State, 63-66; GROUP SUPVR, MONSANTO CO, 66- Med.C, 52-54. Am. Inst. Chem. Eng. Reaction kinetics and catalysis; heterogeneous catalysts; chemical reactor design; biochemical process design; heat and mass transfer in chemical reactors; distillation; applied statistics; economic evaluations. Address: 1902 Fairwind, Houston, TX 77058.

FULTON, JOHN DAVID, b. Norton, Va, Dec. 4, 37; m. 59; c. 1. MATHEMATICS. B.S, N.C. State, 60, M.S, 63, Ph.D.(math), 65. Instr. math, N.C. State, 65-66; res. assoc, math. div, Oak Ridge Nat. Lab, 66-67; asst. prof. MATH, CLEMSON UNIV, 67-71, ASSOC. PROF, 71- Am. Math. Soc; Math. Asn. Am. Combinatiorial mathematics. Address: Dept. of Mathematics, Clemson University, Clemson, SC 29631.

FULTON, JOHN D(ONALDSON), b. St. Joseph, Mo, Jan. 14, 16; m. 42; c. 4. BIOLOGY. B.S, St. Mary's Col.(Minn), 38; M.S, St. Louis, 40, Ph.D, 53. Instr, St. Louis, 38-41; asst. res. biologist, Midwest Res. Inst, 46-47; res. biologist, Sch. Aviation Med, 49-57, chief, dept. microbiol. & cellular biol, 57-59, chief, dept. environ. med, Arctic Aeromed. Lab, 59-61, comdr, Arctic Aeromed. Lab, 61-62, chief, biosci. br, U.S. Air Force Sch. Aerospace Med, 62-68; CHMN, DEPT. BIOL, LAREDO JR. COL, 68- U.S.A.F, 41-68, Col.(Ret). AAAS; Soc. Exp. Biol. & Med; Am. Asn. Immunol; Aerospace Med. Asn. Aerobiology; radiobiology; space biology. Address: Dept. of Biology, Laredo Junior College, Laredo, TX 78040.

FULTON, JOSEPH P(ATTON), b. Princeton, Ind, July 1, 17; m. 45; c. 2. PLANT PATHOLOGY. A.B, Wabash Col, 39; M.A, Illinois, 41, Ph.D.(plant path), 47. Asst. bot, Univ. Ill, 39-42, 46-47; asst. prof. PLANT PATH, UNIV. ARK, FAYETTEVILLE, 47-51, assoc. prof, 51-54, PROF, 54-, head dept, 59-64. U.S.A, 42-46. AAAS; Bot. Soc. Am; Am. Phytopath. Soc.(pres, 71); Am. Inst. Biol. Sci. Diseases of vegetables and strawberries; virus diseases. Address: Dept. of Plant Pathology, University of Arkansas, Fayetteville, AR 72701.

FULTON, LEWIS M(acLEOD), JR, b. Sydney, N.S, Nov. 27, 18; nat; m. 48; c. 1. APPLIED MATHEMATICS. Ph.D.(math), Duke Univ, 50. Instr. math, Duke Univ, 49-51; res. assoc, Johns Hopkins Univ, 51-52, res. scientist, 52-57; mgr. appl. sci, IBM CORP, 57-63, asst. to dir. sci. comput, 63-65, PROG. MGR. INDUST. DEVELOP, 66- Vis. prof, New Col, Fla, 65-66. AAAS; Am. Math. Soc. Computer program development; mathematics and statistics. Address, 34 Reynal Rd, White Plains, NY 10605.

FULTON, MACDONALD, b. Oconto, Wis, Sept. 24, 08; m. 31; c. 1. BACTERIOLOGY. B.A, Carroll Col.(Wis), 28; A.M, Brown, 30; Ph.D.(bact), 35. Instr. biol, Franklin & Marshall Col, 31-32; asst. prof, Middlebury Col, 32-33; instr. bact, Brown, 35-36; sr. instr, sch. med, St. Louis, 36-39; asst. prof, col. med, Baylor, 39-42, assoc. prof, 42-43; prof, Southwest. Med. Col, 43-45; vis. prof. pediat. res, sch. med, Texas, 45-46; dir. dept. bact, Bowman Gray Sch. Med, 46-48; prof. microbiol, Stritch Sch. Med, Loyola (Ill), 49-62; res. prof. trop. med. & microbiol, sch. med, La. State Univ, 62-65; PROF. MICROBIOL, MISS. STATE COL. WOMEN, 65- Dipl, Am. Bd. Microbiol, 61. Am. Soc. Microbiol; Wildlife Disease Asn; Asn. Trop. Biol. Taxonomy of enteric bacilli; diagnostic methods; bacteria of reptiles and amphibians; microbial ecology. Address: Dept. of Biological Sciences, Mississippi State College for Women, Columbus, MS 39701.

FULTON, N(EIL) D(OUGLAS), b. Sinnamahoning, Pa, Sept. 23, 09; m. 44. PLANT PATHOLOGY. B.S, Arkansas, 49; Ph.D.(plant path), Wisconsin, 54. Instr. plant path, Arkansas, 49-51; asst, Wisconsin, 51-54; asst. prof. PLANT PATH, UNIV. ARK, FAYETTEVILLE, 54-58, assoc. prof, 58-62, PROF, 62- U.S.A, 42-46. Am. Phytopath. Soc; Mycol. Soc. Am. Diseases of forage legumes; vascular wilts and seedling blight of cotton. Address: Dept. of Plant Pathology, University of Arkansas, Fayetteville, AR 72701.

FULTON, NORMAN D(UDLEY), JR, b. Attleboro, Mass, June 3, 18; m. 43; c. 3. ORGANIC CHEMISTRY. Sc.B, Brown, 39. Tech. supvr, Milan Ord. Depot, 41-45; head anal. lab, chem. div, PROCTER & GAMBLE CO, 50-59, perfume develop, soap prod. div, 59-66, head anal. & perfume factory serv, 66-71, HEAD HOME PERFORMANCE TESTING, 71- Am. Chem. Soc; Am. Oil Chemists' Soc. Fats; oils; detergents. Address: 6330 Parkman Pl, Cincinnati, OH 45213.

FULTON, PAUL F(RANKLIN), b. Irwin, Pa, Mar. 28, 16; m. 48. PETROLEUM ENGINEERING. B.S, Univ. Pittsburgh, 38, M.S, 51; Ph.D, Pa. State Univ, 64. Instr. PETROL. ENG, UNIV. PITTSBURGH, 47-50, asst. prof, 50-53, assoc. prof, 53-56, PROF, 56-, ASSOC. CHMN. DEPT, 65- Res. engr, Gulf Res. & Develop. Co, 49-59; Nat. Sci. Found. sci. faculty fel, 60-61. Am. Inst. Mining, Metall. & Petrol. Eng. Petroleum reservoir engineering; core analysis research; thermal methods of oil recovery; role of wettability in oil recovery. Address: 1248 Benedum Engineering Hall, University of Pittsburgh, Pittsburgh, PA 15213.

FULTON, ROBERT A(VERY), b. Corvallis, Ore, Aug. 29, 03; m. 32; c. 1. PHYSICAL & ORGANIC CHEMISTRY. B.S, Ore. State Col, 25; M.S, Wisconsin, 27; univ. fel, Stanford, 28, Du Pont fel, 29. Agent chem, U.S. Dept. Agr, 29-36, assoc. entomologist, 36-40, chemist, 40-46, sr. chemist, 46-53, prin. chemist, 53-64; CHEM. CONSULT, 64- AAAS. Insecticides; insect physiology; liquefied gas aerosol for insect control and gaseous sterilization. Address: 530 Merrie Dr, Corvallis, OR 97330.

FULTON, R(OBERT) B(URWELL), III, b. Washington, D.C, Oct. 24, 21; m. 49; c. 5. GEOLOGY. A.B, Hopkins, 43; fel. & Ph.D.(geol), Stanford, 49. Asst. geologist field mapping, N.J. Zinc Co, 47, geologist, geochem. prospecting, 48-49, gen. mineral exp, 49-52, res. geologist, supv. explor, 52-53, asst. geol. chief, 53-57; geologist, E.I. DU PONT DE NEMOURS & CO, INC, 57-65, asst. purchasing agent minerals & ores, 66-68, planning asst. purchasing dept, 69, ECON. GEOLOGIST & MINERAL EVAL, NEW BUS. VENTURES, 70- Asst, Stanford Univ, 43; indust. adv, UN Lead-Zinc Study Group; mem. panel on gold, Nat. Mat. Adv. Bd. U.S.A, 43-46, Maj. Soc. Econ. Geol; Asn. Explor. Geochem; Can. Inst. Mining & Metall; Am. Inst. Mining, Metall. & Petrol. Eng; Am. Inst. Prof. Geol. Investigation and application of geochemical and geophysical methods to mineral exploration; study of occurrence of various mineral raw materials; economic evaluation of mineral projects; development of new business ventures. Address: Box 131, RD 3, Kaolin Rd, Kennett Square, PA 19348.

FULTON, ROBERT E(ARLE), b. Dothan, Ala, Jan. 23, 31; m. 53; c. 3. STRUCTURAL ENGINEERING, APPLIED MECHANICS. B.Sc, Auburn Univ, 53; M.S, Univ. Ill, Urbana, 58, Ph.D.(civil eng), 60. Struct. designer, Chicago Bridge & Iron Co, Ala, 53-54; asst. prof. civil eng, Univ. Ill, Urbana, 60-62; aerospace engr, NASA LANGLEY RES. CTR, 62-65, HEAD AUTOMATED METHODS SECT, 65- Instr, Va. Polytech. Inst, 62-65; Univ. Va, 62-68; prof. lectr, George Washington Univ, 68-; adj. prof, Old Dominion Univ, 70; N.C. State Univ, 71. U.S.A.F, 54-57, Res, 57-62, Capt. Am. Soc. Mech. Eng; Am. Inst. Aeronaut. & Astronaut; Int. Asn. Shell Struct; Am. Soc. Civil Eng. Structural mechanics including shell structures, stability theory, vibrations and numerical methods; use of computers for analysis and design of complex structures occurring in aerospace and civil engineering. Address: Structures Division, NASA Langley Research Center, Hampton, VA 23365.

FULTON, ROBERT F, b. Des Moines, Iowa, Oct. 1, 34; m. 56; c. 1. ORGANIC & POLYMER CHEMISTRY. B.A, St. Olaf Col, 56; M.S, Purdue, 58, Ph.D.(org. chem), 60. SR. RES. CHEMIST, ADHESIVE COATINGS & SEALANTS DIV, MINN. MINING & MFG. CO, 60- Am. Chem. Soc. New polymerization initiators and procedures; new family of polymers; silicone polymerizations; vinyl polymers; research and product development of polyurethanes as sealants and coatings. Address: R.R. 3, River Falls, WI 54022.

FULTON, ROBERT J(OHN), b. Birtle, Man, May 27, 37; m. 63; c. 3. GEOLOGY, ENGINEERING. B.Sc, Univ. Man, 59; Ph.D.(geol), Northwest. Univ, 63. Geologist, GEOL. SURV. CAN, 63-67, RES. SCIENTIST QUATERNARY GEOL, 67- Geol. Asn. Can; Geol. Soc. Am. Mapping of Quaternary deposits; Quaternary history; delta and lake sedimentation. Address: Geological Survey of Canada, 601 Booth St, Ottawa 4, Ont, Can. K1A OE8.

FULTON, ROBERT L(ESTER), b. Weymouth, Mass, May 13, 35; m. 65. CHEMICAL PHYSICS. Sc.B, Brown, 57; Amsterdam, 57-58; A.M, Harvard, 60, Soc. of Fels, 61-64, Ph.D.(chem. physics), 64. Res. fel. CHEM, Harvard, 64-65; asst. prof, FLA. STATE UNIV, 65-69, ASSOC. PROF, 69- Am. Phys. Soc. Interaction of electromagnetic radiation with matter; relaxation phenomenon; light scattering by macromolecules; macroscopic quantum electrodynamics; crystal optics. Address: Dept. of Chemistry, Florida State University, Tallahassee, FL 32306.

FULTON, ROBERT WATT, b. Sistersville, W.Va, Jan. 29, 14. PLANT PATHOLOGY. A.B, Wabash Col, 35; Ph.D, Wisconsin, 40. Instr. bot, Wabash Col, 35-37; asst. hort, UNIV. WIS, MADISON, 37-42, asst. prof, 47-55, PLANT PATH, 55-56, assoc. prof, 56-60, PROF, 60- Sanit.C, 42-46, 1st Lt. AAAS; fel. Am. Phytopath. Soc.(former ed-in-chief). Viruses and virus diseases of plants. Address: Dept. of Plant Pathology, University of Wisconsin, Madison, WI 53706.

FULTON, THOMAS, b. Budapest, Hungary, Nov. 19, 27; nat; m. 52; c. 2. THEORETICAL PHYSICS. B.A, Harvard, 50, M.A, 51, Ph.D, 54. Mem. & Jewett fel, Inst. Adv. Study, 54-55, Nat. Sci. Found. fel, 55-56; asst. prof. PHYSICS, JOHNS HOPKINS UNIV, 56-59, assoc. prof, 59-64, PROF, 64- Fulbright sr. res. scholar & Guggenheim fel, Inst. Theoret. Physics, Vienna, 64-65; consult, Res. Inst. Advan. Study, Inc, 57; res. collab, Brookhaven Nat. Lab, summers, 54, 62; assoc. ed, J. Math. Physics, 68-71. Vis. scientist,

Univ. Calif, Berkeley, 59; Stanford Linear Accelerator Ctr, summer 67; Argonne Nat. Lab, summer 68; Europ. Orgn. Nuclear Res, 69-70. Lectr, Brandeis Summer Inst, 62; Aspen Inst. Humanistic Studies, summers, 63, 66, 67, 68, 71. U.S.A, 46-47. Am. Phys. Soc. Quantum theory of fields; elementary particle physics; scattering theory. Address: Dept. of Physics, Johns Hopkins University, Baltimore, MD 21218.

FULTS, JESS LAFAYETTE, b. Colorado Springs, Colo, Jan. 15, 10; m. 32; c. 4. PLANT PHYSIOLOGY. B.Sc, Colo. Agr. & Mech. Col, 31; fel, Iowa State Col, 31-33, M.Sc, 32; Ph.D.(bot), Nebraska, 41. Asst. bot, Iowa State Col, 31-33; asst. forest pathologist, Civilian Conserv. Corps, Iowa, 33-34; asst. nurseryman, soil conserv. serv, U.S. Dept. Agr. Iowa, 34-35, assoc. agronomist, Nebr, 35-39, Colo, 39-41, Texas, 41-45; assoc. prof. bot, COLO. STATE UNIV, 45-53, prof. bot. & plant path. & head dept, 53-65, PROF. BOT. & PLANT PHYSIOL, 65- Consult, Velsical Chem. So, Ill, 59-60; Scotts, The Lawn People, 65-71. Hon. forester, Colo. State Univ. 54. Am. Soc. Agron; Weed Sci. Soc. Am. Agronomy; weed control; methods of eradicating mesquite; cytology of grasses; plant hormones; turf management; herbicides; infrared detection of plant stress; turfgrass growth inhibitors; herbicide soil residues; Columbine selection and breeding. Address: Weed Research Lab, Dept. of Botany & Plant Pathology, Colorado State University, Ft. Collins, CO 80521.

FULTYN, ROBERT V(ICTOR), b. Chicago, Ill, Nov. 8, 33; m. 55; c. 1. PHYSICS, MATHEMATICS. B.S, Northwestern, 54, M.S; 55; M.S, Harvard, 58, Sc.D. (indust. hyg), 61. STAFF MEM, LOS ALAMOS SCI. LAB, UNIV. CALIF, 63- U.S.N, 55-63, Lt. Am. Indust. Hyg. Asn; Air Pollution Control Asn. Atmospheric physics, specifically dispersion of airborne radioactive materials released from point and jet sources. Address: 1472 A, 40th St, Los Alamos, NM 87544.

FULTZ, DAVE, b. Chicago, Ill, Aug. 12, 21; m. 46; c. 3. METEOROLOGY. S.B, Chicago, 41, Ph.D.(meteorol), 47. Asst. U.S. Weather Bur, Chicago Sta, 42; res. assoc, Chicago & P.R, 42-44; opers. analyst, U.S. Air Force, 45; res. assoc, UNIV. CHICAGO, 46-47, instr. METEOROL, 47-48, asst. prof. 48-53, assoc. prof. 53-60, PROF, 60-, IN CHARGE HYDRODYN. LAB, 46- Guggenheim fel, 50-51; sr. fel, Nat. Sci. Found, 57-58; mem. sci. adv. bd, U.S. Air Force, 59-63; Nat. Comt. Fluid Mech. Films, 62-71; res. grants adv. comt, Air Pollution Control Off, 70- With U.S.N. Fel. Am. Meteorol. Soc.(Meisinger Award, 51, Rossby Res. Medal, 67); fel. Am. Geophys. Union. Geophysical experimental fluid mechanics; convectional flows in stationary and rotating systems; synoptic study of the upper air, cloud forms; upper air trajectories in weather forecasting. Address: Dept. of Geophysical Sciences, University of Chicago, Chicago, IL 60637.

FULTZ, SARA ANN, b. Royal Center, Ind, Nov. 10, 29. BOTANY, MYCOLOGY. B.S, Purdue, 51; M.S, Michigan, 53, Nat. Insts. Health fel, 62-64, Ph.D.(bot), 65. Instr. BOT, Michigan, 64, Rackham fel, 65; ASST. PROF, UNIV. MASS, AMHERST, 65- Mycol. Soc. Am; Am. Soc. Microbiol. Physiology of lower plants; fungal cell wall structure and formation. Address: Dept. of Botany, University of Massachusetts, Amherst, MA 01002.

FULTZ, S(TANLEY) C(HARLES), b. Winnipeg, Man, Can, June 27, 18; nat; m. 50; c. 3. NUCLEAR PHYSICS. B.Sc, Manitoba, 41, M.Sc, 43; Nat. Cancer Inst. fel, Ohio State, 50-52, Ph.D.(physics), 54. Res. physicist, Nat. Res. Coun. Can, 44, 46-47; lectr, Sir George Williams Col, 45; asst, McGill, 48; Ohio State, 49; from asst. prof. to assoc. prof. physics, Rensselaer Polytech, 53-56; RES. PHYSICIST, LAWRENCE LIVERMORE LAB, UNIV. CALIF, 56- Fel. Am. Phys. Soc. Neutron physics; photonuclear research; nuclear accelerators; nuclear engineering. Address: 10727 Foothill Rd, Sunol, CA 94586.

FULWYLER, MACK J, b. Nampa, Idaho, July 6, 36; m. 56; c. 3 BIO-PHYSICS. B.S, Idaho State Col, 60; Univ. N.Mex, 62-65; Ph.D.(biophys), Univ. Colo, 69. Engr, nat. reactor test. sta, U.S. Atomic Energy Comn, Idaho, 58-60; MEM. STAFF, LOS ALAMOS SCI. LABS, UNIV. CALIF, 62- Chem.C, U.S.A, 60-62, 1st Lt. Nuclear radiation spectrometry and instrumentation; biomedical instrumentation; physical properties of biological cells; electronic cell separation; mammalian cell biology. Address: 226 Rover Blvd, Los Alamos, NM 87544.

FUN, F(AY), b. China, July 19, 34; m. 60; c. 4. CHEMICAL ENGINEERING. B.S, Cheng Kung Univ, Taiwan, 56; M.S, Case, 61, Ph.D.(chem. eng), 63. Res. engr, E.I. du Pont de Nemours & Co, 62-65; sr. res. engr, 65-69; RES. SECT. HEAD, APPL. RES. LAB, U.S. STEEL CORP, 69- Am. Inst. Chem. Eng; Am. Chem. Soc. Pyrochemical and plasma reactions; ore beneficiation and reduction; fluidization and fluidized-bed technology. Address: M.S. 56, Applied Research Lab, U.S. Steel Corp, Monroeville, PA 15146.

FUNCK, DENNIS L(IGHT), b. Palmyra, Pa, Nov. 23, 26; m. 49; c. 2. ORGANIC CHEMISTRY. B.S, Lebanon Valley Col, 49; M.S, Delaware, 50, Du Pont fel, 51-52, Ph.D.(org. chem), 52. Res. chemist, process develop. E.I. DU PONT DE NEMOURS & CO, 52-62, SR. RES. CHEMIST, PROD. DEVELOP, 62- U.S.A, 44-46. Am. Chem. Soc. Chromic acid oxidation of secondary and tertiary alcohols; free radical chemistry; polymer process and product development, synthesis and oxidation; acoustics; radiation; applications scouting. Address: 104 Monticello Rd, Fairfax, Wilmington, DE 19803.

FUNCK, LARRY LEHMAN, b. Hershey, Pa, Dec. 25, 42; m. 64; c. 2. INORGANIC CHEMISTRY. B.S, Lebanon Valley Col, 64; Pittsburgh, 64-65; Nat. Sci. Found. fel, Lehigh, 66-69, Ph.D.(inorg. chem), 69. ASST. PROF. CHEM, WHEATON COL.(ILL), 69- Am. Chem. Soc. Visible and ultraviolet spectra of transition metal complexes; solution studies of complex equilibria. Address: Dept. of Chemistry, Wheaton College, Wheaton, IL 60187.

FUNCKES, ARNOLD J(AY), b. Holland, Mich, Nov. 11, 26; m. 49; c. 5. BIOCHEMISTRY. A.B, Hope Col, 50; Ph.D, Missouri, 53, M.D, 58. Instr. biochem, Missouri, 53-58; intern, Youngstown Hosp. Asn, Ohio, 58-59; chief dept. toxicol, U.S. Pub. Health Serv, Ariz, 59-62; res. asst. microbiol, California, 62-63; res. path, VET. ADMIN. HOSP, Pa, 63-66, TUCSON, 66-

69, ACTING CHIEF LAB. SERV, 69- U.S.N.R, 44-46. Protein and cytochemistry. Address: Veterans Administration Hospital, Tucson, AZ 85713.

FUNDERBURG, JOHN BROADUS, JR, b. Wilmington, N.C, Dec. 16, 21; m. 53; c. 3. ANIMAL ECOLOGY, VERTEBRATE ZOOLOGY. B.Sc, E.Carolina Col, 55; M.Sc, N.C. State Col, 57, Ph.D.(ecol), 60. Instr. zool, N.C. State Col, 56; Duke, 59-60; asst. prof. biol, Fla. South. Col, 60-63, assoc. prof, 63-71; PROF. BIOL. & CHMN. DEPT, RANDOLPH-MACON COL, 71- U.S.A, 42-46, 51-53, M/Sgt; Nat. Guard, 46-51. Am. Ornith. Union; Am. Soc. Mammal; Soc. Syst. Zool. Ecology, distribution, speciation and evolution of southeastern Coastal Plain vertebrates. Address: Dept. of Biology, Randolph-Macon College, Ashland, VA 23005.

FUNDERBURK, CULLIE FRANKLIN, b. Union Co, N.C, Sept. 6, 36. PHYSIOLOGY. B.S, Wake Forest Col, 58; Bowman Gray Sch. Med, 58-61; Ph.D. (physiol), Univ. Tenn, 66. Instr. & res. assoc. PHYSIOL, col. med, Univ. Tenn, 66-68; ASST. PROF, SCH. MED, ST. LOUIS UNIV, 68- Thiocyanate metabolism as related to thyroid physiology. Address: Dept. of Physiology, St. Louis University School of Medicine, 1402 S. Grand Blvd, St. Louis, MO 63104.

FUNDERBURK, HENRY HANLY, JR, b. Carrollton, Ala, June 19, 31; m. 53; c. 2. PLANT PHYSIOLOGY. B.S, Auburn, 53, M.S, 58; Ph.D.(bot), La. State, 61. Asst. prof. plant physiol, AUBURN UNIV, 61-63, assoc. prof, 63-66, alumni assoc. prof, 66-68, V.PRES, MONTGOMERY, 68- Mem, Weed Res. Coun. U.S.A, 53-55, 1st Lt. Weed Sci. Soc. Am. Fate and mode of action of herbicides. Address: Office of the Vice President, Auburn University at Montgomery, Montgomery, AL 36109.

FUNDERBURK, WILLIAM H(ENRY), b. Nevada, Mo, Mar. 12, 17; m. 38; c. 4. PHARMACOLOGY. B.S, Univ. Ky, 39; Ph.D.(pharmacol), Univ. Ill, 51. Electroencephalographer, Univ. Chicago, 42-48; Traverse City State Hosp, Mich, 51-57; pharmacologist, Miles-Ames Res. Labs, 57-59; Chas. Pfizer Co, 59-61; ASSOC. DIR. PHARMACOL, A.H. ROBINS CO. INC, 61- Lectr, Univ. Ill, 56-57; Med. Col. Va, Va. Commonwealth Univ, 62- Am. Soc. Pharmacol. & Exp. Therapeut; Soc. Neurosci. Neuropharmacology; anticonvulsant, muscle relaxant, tranquilizer, anti-depressant, analeptic, analgesic and anti-inflammatory drugs. Address: A.H. Robins Co, Inc, 1211 Sherwood Ave, Richmond, VA 23220.

FUNER, ROLF E, b. Chicago, Ill, July 23, 40; m. 65; c. 1. ORGANIC CHEMISTRY. B.S, Loyola (Ill), 61; Ph.D.(org. chem), Wisconsin, 66. Res. chemist, E.I. DU PONT DE NEMOURS & CO, INC, PHILA, 65-68, RES. SUPVR. POLYMER CHEM, 68- Am. Chem. Soc. Synthesis of natural products and new polymers. Address: 205 Friendship Rd, Drexel Hill, PA 19026.

FUNG, ADRIAN K, b. Liuchow, Kwangsi, China, Dec. 25, 36; m. 66. ELECTRICAL ENGINEERING. B.Sc, Nat. Taiwan Univ, 58; M.Sc, Brown Univ, 61; fel, Univ. Kans, 62, Ph.D.(elec. eng), 65. Res. engr, Ctr. for Res, Inc, 62-65; asst. prof. ELEC. ENG, UNIV. KANS, 65-68, ASSOC. PROF, 68- Nat. Sci. Found. grant, 66-68; mem. comn, U.S. Nat. Comt, Int. Sci. Radio Union, 66- Inst. Elec. & Electronics Eng. Scattering of waves by rough surfaces; simulation of electromagnetic scattering. Address: Dept. of Electrical Engineering, University of Kansas, Lawrence, KS 66044.

FUNG, BING-MAN, b. Hong Kong, Aug. 15, 39. PHYSICAL CHEMISTRY. Dipl.Sci, Chung Chi Col, Hong Kong, 63; Ph.D.(chem), Calif. Inst. Tech, 67. ASST. PROF. CHEM, TUFTS UNIV, 66- Am. Phys. Soc; Am. Chem. Soc; N.Y. Acad. Sci. Magnetic resonance. Address: Dept. of Chemistry, Tufts University, Medford, MA 02155.

FUNG, DANIEL Y(EE) C(HAK), b. Hong Kong, May 15, 42; m. 68. MICROBIOLOGY, FOOD TECHNOLOGY. B.A, Int. Christian Univ, Tokyo, 65; univ. assistantship, Univ. N.C, Chapel Hill, 65, M.S.P.H, 67; univ. assistantship, Iowa State Univ, 67, Soc. Sigma Xi grant-in-aid, 68, Ph.D.(food technol), 69. Res. asst. environ. microbiol, Univ. N.C, Chapel Hill, summer 67; ASST. PROF. MICROBIOL, PA. STATE UNIV, 69- Nat. Sci. Found. instnl. grant & agr. exp. sta. res. grant, Pa. State Univ, 70- AAAS; Am. Soc. Microbiol; Inst. Food Technol. Development of miniaturized microbiological methods for diagnostic microbiology; enterotoxigenesis of Staphylococcus aureus; detection of Salmonella; effects of modern food processing on bacteria survival in foods; Clostridium perfringens sporulation problems. Address: Dept. of Microbiology, College of Science, Pennsylvania State University, University Park, PA 16802.

FUNG, FRANCIS C(HUN) W(HA), b. Hong Kong, China, Feb. 14, 40; U.S. citizen; m. 62; c. 1. FLUID MECHANICS, HEAT TRANSFER. B.S, Brown Univ, 60; M.S, Johns Hopkins Univ, 62; Ph.D.(mech. eng), Univ. Notre Dame, 70. Res. engr. fluid mech, Cornell Aeronaut. Lab, Inc, 64-65; sr. engr, Gen. Dynamics Corp, 67-68; asst. prof, Univ. Nebr, Lincoln, 69-70; MECH. ENGR. HEAT TRANSFER & FLUID MECH, FIRE RES. SECT, NAT. BUR. STANDARDS, 70- Hydrofoils; aerodynamics; biomedical engineering; low gravity fluid mechanics; magnetohydrodynamics; fire research. Address: Fire Research Section, National Bureau of Standards, Washington, DC 20234.

FUNG, HENRY C, JR, b. San Francisco, Calif, Feb. 5, 39; m. 61; c. 3. IMMUNOLOGY. B.A, California, 59; M.A, San Francisco State Col, 62; Ph.D.(bact), Washington State, 66. Asst. prof. MICROBIOL, CALIF. STATE COL. LONG BEACH, 66-70, ASSOC. PROF, 70- Collab. scientist, City of Hope Nat. Med. Ctr. AAAS; Am. Pub. Health Asn; Am. Soc. Microbiol; Tissue Cult. Asn. Cancer immunology; cellular immunity; antigenic mosaic of microorganisms influenced by their environment. Address: Dept. of Microbiology, California State College at Long Beach, 6101 E. Seventh St, Long Beach, CA 90801.

FUNG, HO-LEUNG, b. Hong Kong, Nov. 17, 43; m. 70. PHARMACEUTICS. Cert, Victorian Col. Pharm, Australia, 66; Ph.D.(pharmaceut), Univ. Kans, 70. ASST. PROF. PHARMACEUT, STATE UNIV. N.Y. BUFFALO, 70- AAAS; Am. Chem. Soc; Am. Pharmaceut. Asn. Application of fundamental physicochemical principles to the optimization of drug delivery in the human body. Address: Dept. of Pharmaceutics, School of Pharmacy, State University of New York at Buffalo, Buffalo, NY 14214.

FUNG, HONPONG, b. Hong Kong, July 29, 20; nat; m. 47; c. 2. CIVIL ENGINEERING. B.Sc, Lingnan Univ, 42; M.Sc, Iowa State Univ, 48, Ph.D, 56. Asst. mechs. surv, Nat. Chaio-tung Univ, China, 42-46; res. assoc, eng. exp. sta, IOWA STATE UNIV, 51-55, asst. prof. RES, BITUMINOUS RES. LAB, 55-63, ASSOC. PROF, 63-, ASST. PROF. HWY. TRANSPORTATION, DEPT. CIVIL ENG, 55- Mem, Hwy. Res. Bd, 46- Asn. Asphalt Paving Technol; Am. Road Builders Asn. Planning of highway transportation; bituminous paving materials; technology of asphalt pavement construction and quality control of the bituminous paving materials. Address: 1516 Roosevelt Ave, Ames, IA 50010.

FUNG, SUI-AN, b. Chekiang, China, Dec. 18, 22; m; c. 5. MECHANICAL ENGINEERING. B.S, Nat. Cent. Univ. Nanking, 48; M.S, Univ. Rochester, 56; Ph.D, Cornell Univ, 65. Mech. engr. & supvr, Signal Equip. Co, 48-52; asst. prof. mech. eng, Univ. Evansville, 56-59; assoc. prof, Tex. Tech Univ, 59-62; MEM. STAFF, SPACE DIV, N.AM. ROCKWELL, INC, 65- Summers, test engr, Pfauder Co, 53, mach. design engr, Dixie Cup Co, 56, consult, engr, RCA Whirlpool Refrig, Inc, 59. AAAS; Am. Soc. Mech. Eng; Am. Soc. Eng. Educ; Am. Inst. Aeronaut. & Astronaut. Thermodynamic properties; heat transfer; fluid mechanics; applied mathematics and low-g propellant behavior. Address: 325 S. Doheny Dr, Beverly Hills, CA 90211.

FUNG, YUAN-CHENG B(ERTRAM), b. China, Sept. 15, 19; m. 49; c. 2. BIOENGINEERING, STRUCTURAL DYNAMICS. B.S, Nat. Cent. Univ.(China), 41, M.S, 43; fel, China Bur. Aeronaut. Res, 43-45; fel, Calif. Inst. Technol, 45-51, Ph.D.(aeronaut), 48. Instr. mech, Nat. Cent. Univ.(China), 41-43; asst. prof. aeronaut, Calif. Inst. Technol, 51-55, assoc. prof, 55-59, PROF, 59-66; BIOENG. & APPL. MECH, UNIV. CALIF, SAN DIEGO, 66- Am. Inst. Aeronaut. & Astronaut; Am. Soc. Mech. Eng; Am. Physiol. Eng. Physiology; circulation; respiration; elasticity; aeroelasticity; dynamics. Address: Dept. of Bioengineering & Applied Mechanics, University of California at San Diego, La Jolla, CA 92037.

FUNK, ALBERT G(AIL), b. Sterling, Utah, Feb. 18, 25; m. 63; c. 2. PHYSICAL CHEMISTRY. B.S, Brigham Young Univ, 52; Ph.D, Univ. Utah, 57. Res. fel. chem, Univ. Utah, 57-58; chemist, Thiokol Chem. Corp, 58-59; res. prof. metall, Univ. Utah, 59-64; res. scientist, IRECO CHEM. CO, 64-69, asst. res. dir, 69-70, RES. DIR, 70- U.S.A, 46-47. Explosives design and development; study of phenomena accompanying detonation. Address: IRECO Chemical Co, 3000 W. 8600 South, West Jordan, UT 84084.

FUNK, C(YRIL) REED, JR, b. Richmond, Utah, Sept. 20, 28; m. 51; c. 3. PLANT BREEDING. B.S, Utah State, 52, M.S, 55; Iowa State, 56; Ph.D. (plant breeding), Rutgers, 62. Instr. farm crops, RUTGERS UNIV, 56-61, asst. res. specialist TURFGRASS BREEDING, 61-64, assoc. res. specialist, 64-69, RES. PROF, 69- Qm.C, 52-54, 1st Lt. Am. Soc. Agron; Am. Genetic Asn. Field corn breeding, production and management; ecology of crop mixtures; seed quality; turfgrass breeding and genetics; apomixis. Address: Dept. of Soils & Crops, Rutgers University, New Brunswick, NJ 08903.

FUNK, DAVID CROZIER, b. Wilmington, Del, Sept. 24, 22; m. 47; c. 4. PHYSIOLOGY. B.S, Emory, 43, M.D, 46. Intern, hosps, UNIV. IOWA, 46-47, res. INTERNAL MED, 49-52, clin. instr, COL. MED, 52-54, clin. asst. prof, 55-61, clin. assoc. prof, 61-70, ASSOC. PROF, 70- Clin. investr, Vet. Admin, 57-60; chief cardiovasc. lab, Vet. Admin. Hosp, Iowa City, 57-; res. fel, cardiovasc. res. inst, med. ctr, Univ. Calif, 59-60. Dipl, Am. Bd. Internal Med, 54. Med.C, U.S.N.R, 43-45, 47-49. AAAS; fel. Am. Col. Physicians. Cardiovascular and pulmonary physiology. Address: Dept. of Internal Medicine, University of Iowa College of Medicine, Iowa City, IA 52240.

FUNK, DAVID TRUMAN, b. Greensburg, Ind, Oct. 17, 29; m. 56; c. 1. FOREST GENETICS. B.S, Purdue, 51, M.S, 56; Ph.D, Mich. State, 71. Res. forester, cent. states forest exp. sta, U.S. FOREST SERV, 56-65, plant geneticist, N.CENT. FOREST EXP. STA, 65-70, PRIN. PLANT GENETICIST, 70- Chmn, Cent. States Forest Tree Improv. Conf, 68-71. U.S.N, 51-55. AAAS; Soc. Am. Foresters; Am. Soc. Plant Taxon. Strip-mine reclamation and reforestation research; population genetics; hardwood tree breeding. Address: Forestry Sciences Lab, Southern Illinois University, Carbondale, IL 62901.

FUNK, EDWARD C, b. Walla Walla, Wash, June 13, 24; m. 49; c. 2. ORAL SURGERY & PATHOLOGY. Puget Sound, 42-44; D.M.D, Oregon, 47, B.S, 55; M.S, Minnesota, 56. Instr. path, dent. sch, Oregon, 50-51, ASST. PROF, 51-52; ORAL SURG, UNIV. WASH, 65- Attend. oral surgeon Univ, Harborview & Children's Orthop. Hosps, Seattle, Wash, 65- Consult. to Surgeon Gen, U.S. Air Forces, Europe, 59-62. U.S.A.F, 55-65, Lt. Col. AAAS; Am. Soc. Oral Surg; Am. Dent. Asn; Am. Med. Asn; Int. Asn. Oral Surg. Osteitis deformans of the facial bones. Address: Dept. of Health Sciences, B-348, University of Washington, Seattle, WA 98105.

FUNK, EDWARD R(OSS), b. Wooster, Ohio, May 10, 25; m. 51. METALLURGY. B.S, Worcester Polytech, 46; M.S, Mass. Inst. Tech, 48, Sc.D. (mech. metall), 51. Asst. prof. metall, Mass.Inst. Tech, 51-53; eng. consult, Goodyear Aircraft Corp, 53-55; pres, Johnston & Funk Metall. Corp, 55-60; Astro Metall. Corp, Ohio, 60-66; assoc. prof. WELDING ENG, OHIO STATE UNIV, 66-67, PROF, 67- U.S.N.R, 46-47, Ens. Surface tension of solid metals; hydromechanics of brazing; scientific basis of welding; titanium fabrication. Address: 567 Welling Way, Worthington, OH 43085.

FUNK, E(MERSON) G(ORNFLOW), JR, b. Highland Park, Mich, Jan. 27, 31; m. 53; c. 3. NUCLEAR PHYSICS. A.B, Wayne State, 53; M.A, Michigan, 54, Ph.D.(physics), 58. Instr. PHYSICS, Michigan, 58; asst. prof, NOTRE DAME UNIV, 58-64, assoc. prof, 64-71, PROF, 71- Am. Phys. Soc. Nuclear spectroscopy; investigation of nuclear level schemes by gamma and beta ray spectroscopy and nuclear reaction techniques. Address: Dept. of Physics, Notre Dame University, Notre Dame, IN 46556.

FUNK, GREGORY L(EE), b. Erwin, W.Va, Sept. 4, 17; m. 40; c. 2. ORGANIC CHEMISTRY. B.S, W.Va. Wesleyan Col, 39. Group leader, specifications, Carbide & Carbon Chems. Co, div. UNION CARBIDE CORP, 41-42, 47-50, asst. works chemist, 42-45, works chemist, 45-47, group leader, methods & specifications, tech. supvr, develop, Chem. Co, 55-57, asst. dir, res. & develop, 57-63, prod. mgr, POLYOLEFINS, PLASTICS DIV, 63-66, OPERS. MGR, 66- AAAS; Am. Chem. Soc; Soc. Plastics Eng. Polymer chemistry, especially production, process and product development. Address: 39 Highlander Dr, Scotch Plains, NJ 07076.

FUNK, HELEN B(EATRICE), b. Waverly, Iowa, May 23, 13. MICROBIOLOGY. B.A, Iowa State Teachers Col, 35; M.S, Iowa, 36; univ. fel, 42-43; fel, Wisconsin, 48-49, Ph.D.(bact), 55. Teacher, pub. sch, Ill, 36-42; instr. bact. & zool, Milwaukee-Downer Col, 43-46; teaching fel, Wisconsin, 46-48, 49-50; asst. prof. bot, Barnard Col, Columbia, 50-56; assoc. prof. BIOL. SCI, GOUCHER COL, 56-61, chmn. dept, 58-61, PROF, 61- Fulbright lectr, Teheran, 61-62. AAAS; Am. Soc. Microbiol; Soc. Protozool. Physiology; soil microbiology; vitamin metabolism. Address: Dept. of Biological Sciences, Goucher College, Baltimore, MD 21204.

FUNK, JAMES ELLIS, b. Cincinnati, Ohio, Nov. 8, 32; m. 55; c. 5. MECHANICAL & CHEMICAL ENGINEERING. Chem.E, Cincinnati, 55; M.S, Pittsburgh, 58, Ph.D.(chem. eng), 60. Sr. engr, Bettis Atomic Power Lab, Westinghouse Elec. Corp, 55-63; group leader, Allison Div, Gen. Motors Corp, 63-64; assoc. prof. mech. eng, Univ. Ky, 64-67, prof, 67-70, assoc. dean grad. progs, 68-70; dir. tech. activities, indust. group, Combustion Eng, Inc, 70-71; ACTING DEAN COL. ENG, UNIV. KY, 71- AAAS; Am. Inst. Chem. Eng. Chromatography; systems analysis; fluid mechanics; thermodynamics. Address: College of Engineering, University of Kentucky, Lexington, KY 40506.

FUNK, JOHN CHARLES, b. Peoria, Ill, June 12, 41; m. 62; c. 1. FLUID DYNAMICS. B.S.Ch.E, Tulane Univ, 63; M.S. & Shell Oil Co. grant, Vanderbilt Univ, 68, Ph.D.(chem. eng) & NASA trainee, 70. Engr, E.I. du Pont de Nemours & Co, Inc, 63-65; RES. ENGR, BURLINGTON INDUSTS, INC, 70- Am. Inst. Chem. Eng. Use of tracer and pulse testing techniques for the investigation and characterization of flow, particularly as related to the development of appropriate mathematical models; transport phenomena. Address: Research Center, Burlington Industries, Inc, 410 Swing Rd, Greensboro, NC 27409.

FUNK, JOHN L(EON), b. Coschocton, Ohio, Nov. 15, 09; m. 33; c. 1. FISHERIES BIOLOGY. B.S, Kent State, 32; M.A, Michigan, 39. Aquatic biologist, Inst. Fisheries Res, Mich. Dept. Conserv, 40-44; Wash. State Pollution Control Cmn, 44-45; fishery biologist, MO. DEPT. CONSERVATION, 45-59, supvr. fisheries res, 59-64, SUPT. FISHERIES RES. & TRAINING, FISH & GAME RES. CTR, 64- Ord. Dept, 42-44, Capt. Am. Fisheries Soc; Am. Soc. Limnol. & Oceanog; fel. Am. Inst. Fishery Res. Biol. Warm-water stream fisheries; ecology of fishes of warm-water streams; migration of fishes; measurement of the harvest of fish by anglers, especially warm water streams; training in fishery biology. Address: Fish & Game Research Center, Missouri Dept. of Conservation, 1110 College Ave, Columbia, MO 65201.

FUNK, WILLIAM H(ENRY), b. Phoenixville, Pa, Oct. 15, 16; m. 39; c. 4. CIVIL ENGINEERING. B.S, Drexel Inst, 39. Engr, welded steel prods, Lukenweld, Inc, 39-44; develop. engr, LUKENS STEEL CO, 44-48, asst. mgr, develop. eng. div, 48-52, mgr. tech. serv. dept, 52-58, RES. ADMINR, STEEL PROD. & PROCESS RES, 58- Am. Welding Soc; Am. Ord. Asn; Am. Iron & Steel Inst. Carbon and alloy steel development; ore reduction and steel process development; alloy steel fabrication. Address: Lukens Steel Co, Coatesville, PA 19320.

FUNK, WILLIAM HENRY, b. Ephraim, Utah, June 10, 33; m. 64; c. 1. LIMNOLOGY, SANITARY BIOLOGY. B.S, Utah, 55, M.S, 63, U.S. Pub. Health Serv. trainee, 63-66, Ph.D.(zool), 66; Nat. Sci. Found. grant, Brigham Young, 59. Instr, high schs, Utah, 57-63; ASSOC. PROF. SANIT. SCI, WASH. STATE UNIV, 66- Consult, lake asns. & industries on water quality. U.S.N, 55-57, Res, 57-, Comdr. Water Pollution Control Fedn. (ed, Newsletter, Pac. Northwest Sect, 68-); Am. Soc. Limnol. & Oceanog; Am. Micros. Soc. Nature and causes of Eutrophication of lakes and reservoirs; development of multidisciplinary research and inter-university cooperation on water research. Address: Dept. of Sanitary Engineering, 141 Sloan Hall, Washington State University, Pullman, WA 99163.

FUNKE, PHILLIP T, b. Bend, Ore, Nov. 1, 32; m. 70. MASS SPECTROMETRY, ORGANIC CHEMISTRY. B.S, Univ. Puget Sound, 54; M.S. & Robert Crooks Stanley fel, Stevens Inst. Technol, 56, Ph.D.(phys. chem), 62. Instr. chem, Newark Col. Eng, 60-63; res. scientist MASS SPECTROMETRY, Stevens Inst. Technol, 63-70; RES. INVESTR, SQUIBB INST. MED. RES, 70- Vis. lectr, Stevens Inst. Technol, 63-71; consult, Sandoz Pharmaceut, Inc, 66-69. Am. Chem. Soc; Am. Soc. Mass Spectrometry. Organic structure determination by mass spectrometry; ion-molecule reactions; analysis of thermal degradation products of polymers. Address: Squibb Institute for Medical Research, New Brunswick, NJ 08903.

FUNKENBUSCH, WALTER W(ILLIAM), b. Canton, Mo, Feb. 13, 18; m. 45; c. 4. MATHEMATICS. B.A, Culver-Stockton Col, 40; M.S, Oregon State Col, 50. Asst. math, Oregon State Col, 40-41, instr, 42-44; seismograph comput, West Geophys. Co, 44; instr. MATH, Mich. Col. Min. & Tech, 44-45, 45-49; asst. prof, MICH. TECHNOL. UNIV, 49-58, assoc. prof, 58-67, PROF, 67-, proj. dir. undergrad. partic, Nat. Sci. Found, 59-60. Instr, Mich. State Col, 45. Eng. aide, Kinross AFB, Eng.C, U.S.A, 52. Math. Asn. Am. Probability and game theory. Address: Dept. of Mathematics, Michigan Technological University, Houghton, MI 49931.

FUNKHOUSER, JOHN T(OWER), b. Paterson, N.J, Dec. 19, 28; m. 55; c. 3. ANALYTICAL CHEMISTRY. A.B, Princeton, 50; Ph.D.(chem), Mass. Inst. Tech, 54. Chemist, E.I. du Pont de Nemours & Co, 54-62, ARTHUR D. LITTLE, INC, 62-63, group leader anal. res, 63-69, DIR. ENVIRON. SCI, RES. & DEVELOP. DIV, CAMBRIDGE, 71- AAAS; Am. Chem. Soc. Microwave spectrometry; environmental chemistry. Address: 68 Westland Rd, Weston, MA 02193.

FUNKHOUSER, JOHN W(ILLIAM), b. Beaverdam, Va, Aug. 28, 26; m. 50; c. 2. GEOLOGY, BIOLOGY. A.B, Washington & Lee, 48; summers, Colorado, 47, Virginia, 48; Atomic Energy Cmn. fel, Stanford, 48-51, Ph.D. (biol), 51; Richmond Prof. Inst, 66-67. Instr. biol, Stanford, 51-52, res.

assoc, 52-54; res. geologist, Carter Oil Co, 54-58, Jersey Prod. Res. Co, Standard Oil Co, N.J, 58-63; sr. paleontologist, Int. Petrol.(Colombia) Ltd, 63-66; PROF. GEOL, JOHN TYLER COMMUNITY COL, 67- On loan, Creole Petrol. Corp, 60-62; mem, Int. Union Biol. Sci; Int. Comt. Paleobot. Nomenclature. U.S.N, 45-46, Res, 46- Int. Asn. Plant Taxon; Geol. Soc. Am; Am. Inst. Biol. Sci. Palynology; biostratigraphy; micropaleontology; general biology and geology. Address: John Tyler Community College, Chester, VA 23831.

FUNNELL, JOHN E(MSLEY), b. Providence, R.I, Apr. 2, 18; m; c. 3. MATERIALS ENGINEERING, MINERAL TECHNOLOGY. B.S, Va. Polytech, 41. Qual. control engr. steel prod, Carnegie-Ill. Steel Corp, 41; res. ceramic engr, Corning Glass Works, 41-43, res. ceramist, 46-47; sr. ceramic engr, Midwest Res. Inst, 47-50; supvr. mineral tech. dept, SOUTHWEST RES. INST, 50-56, mgr, 56-59, dir, 59-62, ASST. DIR. DEPT. MAT. ENG, 62- U.S.N.R, 43-46, Res, 46-53, Lt.(jg). Am. Ceramic Soc; Sci. Res. Soc. Am; fel. Am. Geog. Soc; Nat. Inst. Ceramic Eng; Am. Soc. Metals. Am. Concrete Inst. Properties, processing and uses of mineral substances; ceramic processes and products; expanded clay and shale aggregates; characterization and utilization of solid mineral wastes; glass technology; industrial minerals technology; cement, lime and aggregates. Address: 121 Wagon Trail Rd, San Antonio, TX 78231.

FUNSTEN, HERBERT, b. Richmond, Va, Oct. 28, 30; m. 60; c. 2. NUCLEAR PHYSICS. B.A, Virginia, 53, M.A, 55, Ph.D.(physics), 60. Res. assoc. PHYSICS, Princeton, 60-63; ASSOC. PROF, COL. WILLIAM & MARY, 63-; ASST. DIR, SPACE RADIATION EFFECTS LAB, 69- Chem.C, 56-58, 1st Lt. Am. Phys. Soc. Low and medium energy nuclear physics. Address: Space Radiation Effects Lab, 11970 Jefferson Ave, Newport News, VA 23606.

FUNT, B(ORIS) LIONEL, b. Warsaw, Poland, Jan. 20, 24; nat, Can; m. 47; c. 3. POLYMER CHEMISTRY. B.Sc, Dalhousie Univ, 44, M.Sc, 46; Nat. Res. Coun. Can. fel, McGill Univ, 48, Ph.D.(phys. chem), 49. Lectr. chem, Dalhousie Univ, 46-47; asst. prof, Univ. Man, 50-53, assoc. prof, 53-59, prof, 59-68, dean grad. studies, 64-68; PROF. CHEM. & DEAN SCI, SIMON FRASER UNIV, 68- Res. consult, Nuclear Enterprises, 54-, dir, Scotland, 56-, Can, 60-, U.S, 68-; mem. bd. dirs, Asn. Univs. & Cols. Can, 66-69; Univs. Grants Comn. Man, 67-69. Fel. Chem. Inst. Can.(secy, 50-52). Dielectric studies of polymers; organic scintillators and scintillation mechanisms; kinetics of polymerization; electrically initiated polymerizations. Address: Dept. of Chemistry, Simon Fraser University, Burnaby 2, B.C, Can.

FUORTES, M(ICHELANGELO) G(IORGIO) F(ILIPPO), b. Bologna, Italy, Dec. 27, 17; m. 46; c. 3. NEUROPHYSIOLOGY. M.D, Torino, Italy, 41. Asst. prof. neurol, Univ. Torino, Italy, 41-48, chief, electroencephalog. sect, 48-49; vis. prof, physiol, N.Y. State Med. Center, 50-51; neurophysiologist, Walter Reed Army Med. Center, 51-56; head, dept. neurophysiol, ophthal. br, NAT. INST. NEUROL. DISEASES & STROKE, NAT. INSTS. HEALTH, U.S. PUB. HEALTH SERV, 56-69, CHIEF, LAB. OF NEUROPHYSIOL, 69- G.H. Bishop lectr, St. Louis, 58. Am. Physiol. Soc; Am. Electroencephalog. Soc; Asn. Research Nerv. & Ment. Diseases. Neurophysiology of spinal cord and vision. Address: Room 2C02, Bldg. 36, National Institute of Neurological Diseases & Stroke, National Institutes of Health, Bethesda, MD 20014.

FUOSS, RAYMOND M(ATTHEW), b. Bellwood, Pa, Sept. 28, 05; m. 26, 47; c. 1. PHYSICAL CHEMISTRY. Sc.B, Harvard, 25; Sheldon fel. from Harvard, Munich, 25-26; Ph.D.(chem), Brown, 32. Res. chemist, Skinner, Sherman & Esselen, Inc, Mass, 27-30; res. instr, Brown, 32-33; int. res. fel, Leipzig & Cambridge, 33-34; asst. res. prof. chem, Brown, 34-36; res. chemist, Gen. Elec. Co, N.Y, 36-45; STERLING PROF. CHEM, YALE, 45- With Off. Sci. Res. & Develop; Nat. Defense Res. Comt; Off. Naval Res, 44. Nat. Acad. Sci; Am. Chem. Soc.(award, 35); Am. Acad. Arts & Sci. Experimental and theoretical studies of properties of electrolytes, dielectrics and polymers. Address: Dept. of Chemistry, Yale University, New Haven, CT 06520.

FUQUA, B. BROWN, b. Bowling Green, Ky, Apr. 27, 38; m. 62; c. 3. CHEMICAL ENGINEERING. B.E, Vanderbilt, 60; univ. fel, Purdue, 63, Nat. Sci. Found. fel, 64, Esso fel, 66, Ph.D.(chem. eng), 67. SR. RES. ENGR, ESSO RES. LABS, HUMBLE OIL & REF. CO, 67- U.S.M.C, 60-63, Maj. Am. Inst. Chem. Eng; Am. Chem. Soc. Petroleum processing research. Address: 1156 Havenwood Dr, Baton Rouge, LA 70815.

FUQUA, MARY ELIZABETH, b. Dresden, Tenn, Sept. 12, 22. FOODS, NUTRITION. B.S, Tennessee, 44; M.S, Ohio State, 48, Am. Home Econ. Asn. scholar, 50, Ph.D.(food & nutrit), 52. Therapeut. dietician, med. center, Indiana, 45-47; instr. FOODS & NUTRIT, Ohio State, 48-49; asst. prof, Illinois, 51-53; assoc. prof, Pa. State Univ, 53-63; PROF, PURDUE UNIV, 63-, head dept, 63-66. Am. Inst. Nutrit. Calcium metabolism. Address: School of Home Economics, Purdue University, Lafayette, IN 47907.

FUQUAY, JAMES J(ENKINS), b. Montesano, Wash, May 18, 24; m. 46; c. 4. METEOROLOGY, CLIMATOLOGY. B.S, Washington (Seattle), 50, M.S, 52. Jr. res. meteorologist, atmospheric diffusion, Washington (Seattle), 50-51, res. meteorologist, 51-52; atmospheric physics oper, Hanford Labs, Gen. Elec. Co, 52-60, mgr, 60-65, atmospheric physics sect, physics & instruments dept, PAC. NORTHWEST LAB, BATTELLE MEM. INST, 65-66, environ. & radiol. sci. dept, 66-68, ASSOC. MGR. ENVIRON. & LIFE SCI. DIV, 68- Sig.C, U.S.A, 42-46, Res, 46-49. Am. Meteorol. Soc; Am. Geophys. Union; Air Pollution Control Asn. Micrometeorology; microclimatology; application of meteorology in industrial plant operation and dispersing of stack effluents. Address: Pacific Northwest Labs, Battelle Memorial Institute, P.O. Box 999, 3000 Stevens Dr, Richland, WA 99352.

FUQUAY, JOHN WADE, b. Burlington, N.C, July 31, 33; m. 70; c. 1. ANIMAL PHYSIOLOGY & NUTRITION. B.S, N.C. State Univ, 55, M.S, 66; Ph.D. (dairy sci), Pa. State Univ, 69. Herd mgr. dairy cattle, Fuquay's Jersey Farm, 59-64; asst. dairy cattle physiol, N.C. State Univ, 64-66; dairy cattle nutrit, Pa. State Univ, 66-69; ASST. PROF. DAIRY CATTLE PHYSIOL, MISS. STATE UNIV, 69- U.S.A.F, 56-59, Capt. Am. Dairy Sci. Asn; Am. Soc. Animal Sci. Dairy cattle, especially effects of energy intake on reproduction and causes of reproductive failure, histamine metabolism, environmental stress and performance. Address: Dept. of Dairy Science, Drawer DD, Mississippi State University, State College, MS 39762.

FURANO, ANTHONY, b. Stamford, Conn, Nov. 8, 36. BIOCHEMISTRY. B.S, Tufts, 58; M.D, Yale, 62. Holbrook res. fel. pharmacol, sch. med, Yale, 62-63; STAFF BIOCHEMIST, NAT. INSTS. HEALTH, 63- U.S.P.H.S, 63-, Surg. Am. Soc. Biol. Chem. Address: National Institutes of Health, Dept. of Biochemistry, Bethesda, MD 20014.

FURBISH, WILLIAM J, b. Rudolph, Wis, July 30, 17; m. 50; c. 4. MINERALOGY, PETROLOGY. B.S, Wisconsin, 51, M.S, 53. Explor. geologist, Jones & Laughlin Steel Corp, 53-54; instr. GEOL, DUKE UNIV, 54-60, asst. prof, 60-66, ASSOC. PROF, 66- Mineral. Soc. Am; Mineral. Asn. Can; Geol. Soc. Am; Am. Inst. Mining, Metall. & Petrol. Eng. Mineralogy of minerals formed at low temperature and pressure. Address: Dept. of Geology, Duke University, Box 6665, College Station, Durham, NC 27708.

FURBY, NEAL W(ASHBURN), b. Hanford, Calif, Apr. 20, 12; m. 37; c. 3. CHEMISTRY. B.S, California, 39. Res. chemist, CALIF. RES. CORP, 39-54, sr. res. chemist, 54-58, supv. res. chemist, 58-64, SR. RES. ASSOC, 64- Am. Chem. Soc; Am. Soc. Test. & Mat; Am. Soc. Lubrication Eng. Petroleum chemistry; lubricating oils; lubricants; hydraulic fluids; engine oils; synthetic fluids. Address: California Research Corp, Box 1627, Richmond, CA 94707.

FURCHGOTT, ROBERT F(RANCIS), b. Charleston, S.C, June 4, 16; m. 41; c. 3. PHARMACOLOGY, BIOCHEMISTRY. B.S, North Carolina, 37; Ph.D. (biochem), Northwestern, 40. Res. fel. med, med. col, Cornell, 40-43, res. assoc, 43-47, instr. physiol, 43-48, asst. prof. med. biochem, 47-49; asst. prof. PHARMACOL, med. sch, Washington (St. Louis), 49-52, assoc. prof, 52-56; PROF. & CHMN. DEPT, STATE UNIV. N.Y. DOWNSTATE MED. CTR, 56- Mem. pharmacol. training comt, U.S. Pub. Health Serv, 61-64, pharmacol-toxicol. rev. comt, 65-68, spec. fel, 71-72; Commonwealth fel, 62-63; vis. prof, Geneva, 62-63; mem. bd. sci. coun, Nat. Heart Inst, 64-68; ed, Pharmacol. Rev, 64-69; mem. metab. rev. panel, New York City Health Res. Coun, 65-70; adv. coun. res, N.Y. Heart Asn, 67-70; vis. prof, Univ. Calif, San Diego, 71-72. With Off. Sci. Res. & Develop, 44. AAAS; Am. Chem. Soc; Am. Soc. Biol. Chem; Am. Soc. Pharmacol. & Exp. Therapeut. (ed, Jour, 53-62, pres, 71-72); Harvey Soc; fel. N.Y. Acad. Sci; Soc. Gen. Physiol; Cardiac Muscle Soc. Physical chemistry of red cell structure; infrared spectra of steroids; circulatory shock and hypertension; pharmacology and biochemistry of cardiac and smooth muscle; adrenergic mechanisms; theory of drug-receptor interactions. Address: Dept. of Pharmacology, State University of New York Downstate Medical Center at Brooklyn, Brooklyn, NY 11203.

FURCHNER, J(OHN) E(MIL), b. Brooklyn, N.Y, Dec. 5, 15; m. 45; c. 1. RADIOBIOLOGY. B.S.(biol) & B.S.(ed), Southwest. Mo. State Col, 49; M.S, New Mexico, 51, Ph.D.(biol), 55. Asst. RADIOBIOLOGY, LOS ALAMOS SCI. LAB, 51-54, MEM. STAFF, 54- U.S.A, 41-45. Health Physics Soc. Physiology; radiobiology. Address: 106 Rover St, Los Alamos, NM 87544.

FURCHTGOTT, ERNEST, b. Zlate Moravce, Czech, Nov. 2, 22; nat; m. 53; c. 3. PHYSIOLOGICAL PSYCHOLOGY. A.B, California, Los Angeles, 46, M.A, 48, Ph.D.(psychol), 50. Asst. prof. PSYCHOL, Tennessee, 49-53, assoc. prof, 53-59, prof, 59-69; PROF. & HEAD DEPT, UNIV. S.C, 69- Consult, Vet. Admin; Sch. Aerospace Med, 64-66. Mem. comt. biol. effects of atomic radiation, Nat. Res. Coun, 63-65, adv. comt. to Fed. Radiation Coun, 70-72; psychopharmacol. study sect, Nat. Insts. Health, 64-67, neurol. study sect, 68-72, radiol. animal res. adv. comt, U.S. Pub. Health Serv, 66-68; U.S. del. to UN Comt. Effects of Atomic Radiation, 67-69: U.S.A, 43. AAAS; Am. Psychol. Asn; Radiation Res. Soc; Geront. Soc; Int. Soc. Develop. Psychobiol. Behavioral effects of ionizing radiations; drugs; developmental anomalies; aging. Address: Dept. of Psychology, University of South Carolina, Columbia, SC 29208.

FURCOLOW, MICHAEL L, b. Alliance, Ohio, June 8, 07; m. 42; c. 4. PUBLIC HEALTH. M.D, Yale, 34; M.A, Cincinnati, 38; hon. D.Sc, Mt. Union Col, 64. Commissioned off, U.S. Pub. Health Serv, 38-64, med. dir, field sta, Kans. City, 52-64; PROF. COMMUNITY MED. & PEDIAT, COL. MED, UNIV. KY, 64- Tuberculosis and fungal diseases of the lungs. Address: Dept. of Community Medicine, University of Kentucky College of Medicine, Lexington, KY 40506.

FURDYNA, JACEK K, b. Kamionka, Poland, Sept. 6, 33; U.S. citizen; m. 60; c. 4. SOLID STATE PHYSICS. B.S, Loyola Univ. Chicago, 55; Ph.D.(physics), Northwest. Univ, 60. Res. assoc, Northwest. Univ, 60-62; res. physicist, Francis Bitter Nat. Magnet Lab, Mass. Inst. Technol, 62-66; ASSOC. PROF. PHYSICS, PURDUE UNIV, 66- Am. Phys. Soc. Physics of semiconductors and metals; galvano-magnetic phenomena; magneto-optical phenomena at microwave frequencies; plasma effect in solids. Address: Dept. of Physics, Purdue University, Lafayette, IN 47907.

FURESZ, JOHN, b. Miskolc, Hungary, Oct. 13, 27; Can. citizen; m. 64; c. 3. VIROLOGY. M.D, Univ. Budapest, 51 & McGill Univ, 61. Med. off. VIROL, State Inst. Hygiene, Budapest, 51-56; biologist, Lab. of Hyg, Ottawa, 56-64; MED. OFF, CAN. COMMUNICABLE DISEASES CTR, 64- Can. Soc. Microbiol; Can. Asn. Med. Microbiol; Am. Soc. Microbiol; Int. Asn. Microbiol. Socs. Antigenic structure of influenza viruses; genetic markers of polioviruses; measles, German measles and mumps vaccines in the laboratory and field trials; slow virus infections. Address: Canada Communicable Disease Centre, Tunney's Pasture, Ottawa, Ont. K1A 0K9, Can.

FUREY, ROBERT L(AWRENCE), b. Canton, Ohio, June 25, 41; m. 64; c. 2. ORGANIC CHEMISTRY. B.S, Kent State Univ, 63, NASA fel, 63-66, Goodyear fel, 66-67, Ph.D.(org. chem), 67. Res. chemist, res. labs, Edgewood Arsenal, Md, 67-69; ASSOC. SR. RES. CHEMIST FUELS, RES. LABS, GEN. MOTORS CORP, 69- U.S.A, 67-69, Capt. Am. Chem. Soc; Soc. Automotive Eng. Organic photochemistry of N-substituted imines; effects of automotive fuels on vehicle emissions and air quality. Address: Fuels & Lubricants Dept, General Motors Research Labs, 12 Mile & Mound Rds, Warren, MI 48090.

FUREY, ROGER JOSEPH, b. Boston, Mass, Oct. 9, 32; m. 58; c. 4. FLUID MECHANICS, HEAT TRANSFER. B.S, Boston, 60; M.S, Cath. Univ, 62, Ph.D.(fluid mech), 69. Aeronaut. engr, AERODYN. LAB, NAVAL SHIP RES. & DEVELOP. CTR, 60-65, acting res. br. head, 65-67, RES. BR. HEAD, 67- U.S.N, 51-55. Am. Inst. Aeronaut. & Astronaut. Application of optimization theory to hypersonic shapes; numerical solutions to supersonic and hypersonic flow fields. Address: 2519 Villanova Dr, Vienna, VA 22180.

FURFINE, CHARLES S(TUART), b. St. Louis, Mo, Apr. 26, 36; m. 58; c. 2. BIOLOGICAL CHEMISTRY; B.A, Washington (St. Louis), 57, Ph.D.(biochem), 62. Res. fel. BIOCHEM, Albert Einstein Col. Med, 62-63, instr, 63-64, ASST. PROF, 64-70; GEORGETOWN UNIV, 70- Nat. Insts. Health grant, 65- Am. Chem. Soc. Effect of substrates on the physical chemical parameters of proteins; nature of allosteric effects and its relation to phenomena observed in vivo. Address: Dept. of Chemistry, Georgetown University, 37th & O Sts, Washington, DC 20007.

FURGASON, ROBERT ROY, b. Spokane, Wash, Aug. 2, 35; m. 64. CHEMICAL ENGINEERING. B.S, Idaho, 56, M.S, 58; Ph.D.(chem. eng), Northwestern, 61. Instr. CHEM. ENG, UNIV. IDAHO, 57-59, asst. prof, 59-62, assoc. prof, 62-67, PROF, 67-, HEAD DEPT, 65-, acting head dept, 63-64. Consult, Minute Maid Corp, 58-59; J R. Simplot Co, 63-; Nat. Sci. Found. grant, 64-; develop. consult, B.F. Goodrich Chem. Co, 69-70, continuing consult, 70- Am. Inst. Chem. Eng; Am. Chem. Soc. Heat transfer in chemically reacting systems, especially nitrogen tetroxide-nitrogen dioxide and ozone-oxygen decomposing systems; physical properties of reacting systems. Address: Dept. of Chemical Engineering, University of Idaho, Moscow, IA 83843.

FURGASON, WALDO H(AMLET), b. Canby, Minn, Apr. 25, 02. ZOOLOGY. A.B, St. Olaf Col, 24; univ. fel, Stanford, 33-34, Ph.D.(microbiol), 36, 46-47; Am-German exchange fel, zool. inst, Munich, 34-35. Asst. instr. biol, Calif. State Teachers Col, San Diego, 26-28, instr, 30-31; from asst. instr. to acting instr, Stanford, 28-30, asst, 32-34, 35-36; asst. prof, Whitman Col, 36-38; asst. prof. ZOOL, Wabash Col, 38-40; Missouri, 40-42; assoc. prof, Wabash Col, 47-49; UNIV. CALIF, LOS ANGELES, 49-54, prof, 54-69, EMER. PROF, 69-, lectr, 46, 48. Leader biol. surv, U.S. Bur. Fisheries, 34. U.S.A.A.F, 42-46. Fel. AAAS; Am. Soc. Zool; Soc. Protozool; Am. Micros. Soc; Am. Inst. Biol. Sci. Morphology and taxonomy of ciliates; protoplasmic reorganization and cell division; history of science. Address: Dept. of Zoology, University of California, Los Angeles, CA 90024.

FURGERSON, W(ILLIAM) T(HOMAS), b. Knoxville, Tenn, Mar. 27, 21; m. 46; c. 4. FLUID MECHANICS, THERMODYNAMICS. B.Sc, Tennessee, 43. Jr. engr, Linde Air Co. Lab, Union Carbide Corp, 44-45, res. engr, gaseous diffusion plant, 45-51, sr. develop. engr, 51-55; prin. engr, Oak Ridge Nat. Lab, 55-58; assoc. proj. mgr, fluid mech. & thermoheat transfer, gen. atomic div, Gen. Dynamics Corp, 58-62, proj. mgr. exp. beryllium oxide reactor, Calif, 62-66, res. & develop. staff mem, 66-67; res. consult, YORK DIV, BORG-WARNER CORP, 67-68, assoc. dir. res, 68-71, DIR. ENG, 71- Private consult, 54-58; consult, U.S. Air Force, 56-58. Sci. Res. Soc. Am. Stability of fluid flow systems; secondary and higher order flows in two and three dimensional flow; fluid machinery design. Address: 20 Rainier Ct, York, PA 17402.

FURGIUELE, ANGELO R(ALPH), b. Washington, Pa, Apr. 14, 29; m. 52; c. 2. PHARMACOLOGY. B.S, Duquesne, 51; M.S, Pittsburgh, 59, Nat. Insts. Health fel, 60-62, Ph.D.(pharmacol), 62. Sr. res. scientist, Squibb Inst. Med. Res, 62-64, sci. coord. biol, Squibb-Int. Div, Olin Mathieson Chem. Corp, 64-67, DIR. BIOL. RES, E.R. SQUIBB & SONS INC, 67- Med.Serv.C, U.S.A, 54-56. AAAS; N.Y. Acad. Sci; Am. Pharmaceut. Asn; Am. Soc. Pharmacol. & Exp. Therapeut; Am. Soc. Toxicol. Central nervous system pharmacology; toxicology; product planning and development; research management. Address: E.R. Squibb & Sons Inc, 909 Third Ave, New York, NY 10022.

FURIA, JOHN J(OSEPH), b. White Plains, N.Y, Oct. 1, 93; m. 17; c. 4. INDUSTRIAL ENGINEERING. A.B, Columbia, 16, A.M, 17, Ph.D.(indust. mgt), 22; M.S, N.Y. Univ, 20; I.E, Manhattan Col, 27. Instr. physics, Manhattan Col, 15, prof. indust. eng. & head dept. & dir. personnel, 23-36; instr. physics, Columbia, 15-17; sch. eng, N.Y. Univ, 17-20; fed. coord, City Col. New York, 20-23; exam, City Civil Serv. Comn, New York, 36-39, dir. div. war training, exec. off. of mayor, 39-44, chief, prof. sci. & admin. bur, 44-58, asst. dir. exams, 58-62; RETIRED. With. Indust. Res. & Eng. Corp, 17-20; pres. & dir, Queensboro Tire Co, 19; Queensboro Mfg. & Sales Corp, 23-27; consult. indust. engr, 23-70; nat. mgt. coun. del. & U.S. Govt. del, Int. Cong. Sci. Mgt, Eng, 35, gen. secy, Wash, D.C, 37; lectr, grad. sch, N.Y. Univ, 36- coord, practical politics, 54-56, war training; consult, Nat. Roster Sci. Personnel, 41-47; dir. personnel surv, Citizens Budget Comn, N.Y, 47-48; div. training & secy. mayor's coun. pub. serv. training; consult, U.S. Dept. Army, 48-; U.S. Off. Educ; N.Y. State Civil Serv. Comn; U.S. Dept. Labor; Nat. Resources & Nat. Security Resources Bd, war manpower comn; David Bogen Co; Transitron Elec. Corp; E. Kalish, Inc. Consult, U.S. Depts. War & Navy, 43-45. AAAS; Am. Inst. Indust. Eng; Am. Soc. Eng. Educ; Nat. Soc. Prof. Eng; Am. Soc. Pub. Admin; Am. Mgt. Asn; Nat. Voc. Guid. Asn; Inst. Elec. & Electronics Eng. Address: 28 McKenna St, Blauvelt, NY 10913.

FURLONG, CLEMENT E(UGENE), b. Detroit, Mich, Sept. 30, 39; m. 66; c. 2. BIOCHEMISTRY. B.A, San Jose State Col, 63; U.S. Pub. Health Serv. fel, Univ. Calif, Davis, 66-67, Ph.D.(comp. biochem), 68. U.S. Pub. Health Serv. fel. BIOCHEM, Cornell Univ, 68-70; ASST. PROF, UNIV. CALIF, RIVERSIDE, 70- Proteins involved in membrane transport systems; metabolic regulation. Address: Dept. of Biochemistry, University of California, Riverside, CA 92502.

FURLONG, IRA E, U.S. citizen; b. June 2, 31. GEOLOGY. A.B, Boston, 53, M.S, 54, Ph.D.(geol), 60. Instr. GEOL, Marshall, 58-59; lectr, Boston, 59-60; instr, BRIDGEWATER STATE COL, 60-62, asst. prof, 62-65, assoc.

prof, 65-69, PROF, 69- C.Eng, U.S.A, 54-56. AAAS; Mineral. Soc. Am; Geol. Soc. Am; Nat. Asn. Geol. Teachers (v.pres, 65). Genesis of granite plutons and their relationship on resulting geomorphology. Address: Dept. of Geology, Bridgewater State College, Bridgewater, MA 02324.

FURLONG, LeROY R(OBERT), b. East Hartford, Conn, May 17, 21; m. 45. SOLID STATE & MOLECULAR PHYSICS. B.S, Trinity Col.(Conn), 43; fel, Hopkins, 43-44; Ph.D, Catholic Univ, 59. Jr. instr. physics, Hopkins, 43-44; physicist, Manhattan Proj, 44-45; U.S. Naval Res. Lab, 45-54; asst, Catholic Univ, 55-58; asst. prof. physics, Georgetown, 58-61; supvry. res. physicist & proj. coord, Col. Park Metall. Res. Ctr, 61-66; res. dir, Rolla Metall. Res. Ctr, U.S. BUR. MINES, Mo, 66-68, DIR. METALL. RES, WASH. D.C, 68- AAAS; Am. Ceramic Soc; Am. Phys. Soc. Solid state physics; molecular structure; spectra; optics. Address: U.S. Bureau of Mines, 18th & C Sts. N.W, Washington, DC 20242.

FURLONG, NORMAN BURR, JR, b. Norwalk, Ohio, Jan. 6, 31; m. 56; c. 3. BIOCHEMISTRY. A.B. & B.S, Southern Methodist, 52; M.S, Stanford, 54; Ph.D.(chem), Texas, 60. U.S. Pub. Health Serv. fel, biol. div, Oak Ridge Nat. Lab, 60-61; UNIV. TEX. M.D. ANDERSON HOSP. & TUMOR INST, 61-62, ASSOC. PROF. BIOCHEM, GRAD. SCH. BIOMED. SCI. & ASSOC. BIOCHEMIST, 66-, ASSOC. DEAN CURRICULUM DEVELOP, 70-, asst. biochemist, 62-66, asst. prof. biochem, grad. sch. biomed. sci, 64-66. U.S.A.F, 52-57, Capt. AAAS; Am. Asn. Cancer Res. Biosynthesis of DNA, enzymology and mechanism of DNA replication; tumor-host relationships; oligonucleotide chemistry; histochemical methodology in enzyme localization; experimental graduate curricula and teaching methods. Address: Dept. of Biochemistry, University of Texas M.D. Anderson Hospital & Tumor Institute, Houston, TX 77025.

FURLONG, RICHARD W, b. Norwalk, Ohio, Mar. 30, 29; m. 51; c. 2. STRUCTURAL ENGINEERING. B.S, Southern Methodist, 52; M.S, Washington (St. Louis), 57; Ford Found. fel, Texas, 61-62, Nat. Sci. Found. fel, 62-63, Ph.D.(struct), 63. Engr, McDonnell Aircraft Corp, Mo, 52-53; Petrol. Equip. Co, 53-55; F. Ray Martin, Inc, 55-58; asst. prof. civil eng. & struct, UNIV. TEX, AUSTIN, 58-65, assoc. prof. CIVIL ENG, 65-71, PROF, 71- Lectr, Wash. Univ, 54-56. Am. Soc. Civil Eng; Nat. Soc. Prof. Eng; Am. Concrete Inst. Analysis and design of structures, especially reinforced concrete and limit analysis of continuous frames; design of metal and concrete structures. Address: Dept. of Civil Engineering, 221B Taylor Hall, University of Texas, Austin, TX 78712.

FURLONG, ROBERT B, b. Malone, N.Y, Jan. 19, 34; m. 60. MINERALOGY, GEOCHEMISTRY. B.A, Harpur Col, 62; M.S, Illinois, Urbana, 65, Ph.D. (clay mineral), 67. ASST. PROF. GEOL, WAYNE STATE UNIV, 66- Clay Minerals Soc; Mineral. Soc. Am; Electron Micros. Soc; Am. Geochem. Soc. Use of electron microscopy and electron diffraction to study high temperature changes in the clay minerals; clay mineralogy of deep sea sediment. Address: Dept. of Geology, Wayne State University, Detroit, MI 48202.

FURLOW, LEONARD T(HOMPSON), b. Madison, Ga, Jan. 18, 02; m. 26; c. 2. NEUROSURGERY. B.S, Emory, 23, M.D, 25. Asst. prof. CLIN. NEUROSURG, SCH. MED, WASH. UNIV, 37-39, assoc. prof, 39-66, prof, 66-70, EMER. PROF, 70-; PROF, UNIV. FLA, 70- Past. secy. & chmn, Am. Bd. Neurol. Surg, past chmn. study comn. U.S.N, 42-46, Capt. Am. Asn. Neurol. Surg.(past pres); Soc. Neurol. Surg.(past pres); Am. Neurol. Asn. Neurological surgery. Address: Route 1, Box 111, Crystal River, FL 32629.

FURLOW, W(ILLIAM) M(ERIWETHER), JR, b. Albany, Ga, Feb. 13, 17; m. 41; c. 3. PHYSICS. B.S, Ga. Inst. Tech, 38; Polytech. Inst. Brooklyn; Maryland. Engr. control systems, Gen. Elec. Co, 40-41; electronic scientist, Naval Res. Lab, 46-51; proj. engr, Melpar, Inc, Va, 51-55, staff asst. to chief engr, 55-57; chief of staff, airborne electronics dept, MARTIN MARIETTA CORP, 57, mgr. phys. sci. lab, 57-64, acting mgr. new concepts dept, 64-69, PRIN. STAFF ENGR, AEROSPACE DIV, 69- U.S.N.R, 42-46. AAAS; Inst. Elec. & Electronics Eng; Optical Soc. Am. Applications of optics and physics to military system design; coherent optical processes; applications of millimeter wave phenomena. Address: Martin Marietta Corp, Aerospace Division, P.O. Box 5783, Orlando, FL 32808.

FURMAN, DEANE P(HILIP), b. Richardton, N.Dak, June 4, 15; m. 38; c. 3. PARASITOLOGY, ENTOMOLOGY. B.S, California, 37, Ph.D.(med. entom), 42. Entomologist, U.S. Pub. Health Serv, 46; asst. prof. parasitol. & asst. entomologist, EXP. STA, UNIV. CALIF, BERKELEY, 46-52, assoc. prof. & assoc. entomologist, 52-58, PROF. & ENTOMOLOGIST, 58-, CHMN. DIV. PARASITOL, 63- Nat. Insts. Health spec. fel, 64-65; guest investr, U.S. Naval Med. Res. Unit-3, Egypt, 64-65; chmn, Interdisciplinary Grad. Group Parasitol. U.S.A, 42-46, Maj. AAAS; Am. Soc. Parasitol; Entom. Soc. Am; Am. Soc. Trop. Med. & Hyg; Wildlife Disease Asn. Control of parasitic arthropods; systematics of parasitic mites; biology of helminths; arthropod vectors of diseases and parasites of man and animals. Address: Division of Parasitology, University of California, Berkeley, CA 94720.

FURMAN, GERSHON G(EORGE), b. Tel Aviv, Israel, Oct. 30, 30; U.S. citizen; m. 57; c. 1. ELECTRICAL ENGINEERING, SYSTEMS ANALYSIS. B.E.E, City Col. New York, 57; S.M, Mass. Inst. Tech, 59; Fulbright grant, Tech. Univ. Denmark, 59-60; Raytheon fel, California, Berkeley, 60-63, Ph.D.(elec. eng), 64. Mem. eng. res, instrumentation lab, Mass. Inst. Tech, 57-59; asst. elec. eng, electronics res. lab, California, Berkeley, 60-64; mem. tech. staff, res. acoustics & vision, Bell Tel. Labs, 64-65; mem. tech. staff & consult, Gen. Res. Corp, 65-68; SR. RES. ENGR, STANFORD RES. INST, 67- Consult, Rand. Corp, Calif, 62; mem. tech. staff, Bell Tel. Labs, summer 63. AAAS; Opers. Res. Soc. Am; Inst. Mgt. Sci; Inst. Elec. & Electronics Eng. Operations research; health systems; linear and dynamic programming; computer modeling and simulation; resource allocation; physiological modeling and hypothesis testing. Address: Stanford Research Institute, Menlo Park, CA 94025.

FURMAN, ROBERT HOWARD, b. Schenectady, N.Y, Oct. 23, 18; m. 45; c. 4. CARDIOVASCULAR DISEASES. A.B, Union Col.(N.Y), 40; M.D, Yale, 43. Asst. med, sch. med, Yale, 44-45, intern, 44, asst. res. physician, 45; instr. physiol. & asst. med, sch. med, Vanderbilt, 46-48, Lilly fel, 46-47,

Nat. Res. Coun. fel. med. scis, 47-48, asst. res. physician, 48-49, res. physician, 49-50, instr. med, 49-50, asst. prof, 50-52; assoc. prof. res. med, sch. med, Univ. Okla, 52-66, prof, 66-71, head cardiovasc. sect, Okla. Med. Res. Found, 52-70, assoc. dir. res, 58-70; EXEC. DIR. CLIN. RES, ELI LILLY & CO, 70-; PROF. MED, SCH. MED, IND. UNIV, 70- Mem. cardiovasc. study sect, Nat. Insts. Health, 60-63; heart spec. proj. comt, adv. heart coun, coun. arteriosclerosis, Am. Heart Asn. U.S.N.R, 42-46, 55-57, Comdr. Endocrine Soc; Soc. Exp. Biol. & Med; Am. Physiol. Soc; Wilson Ornith. Soc; Am. Heart Asn; fel. Am. Col. Physicians; Am. Fedn. Clin. Res; N.Y. Acad. Sci; Am. Soc. Clin. Pharmacol. & Therapeut. Nutritional-endocrinologic-lipid metabolic interrelationships in atherogenesis. Address: Eli Lilly & Co, 307 E. McCarty St, Indianapolis, IN 46206.

FURMAN, SEYMOUR, b. N.Y.C, July 12, 31; m. 57; c. 3. SURGERY. Wash. Sq. Col, N.Y. Univ, 51; M.D, State Univ. N.Y, 55. Intern med, Montefiore Hosp. & Med. Ctr, N.Y, 55-56, res. surg, 56-60; thoracic surg, Baylor Univ, 62-63; adj. attend. surgeon, Montefiore Hosp. & Med. Ctr, 63; clin. assoc. surg, ALBERT EINSTEIN COL. MED, 64-66, assoc. surgeon, 66-67, asst. prof. SURG, 68-71, ASSOC. PROF, 71-, ASSOC. ATTEND. SURGEON, MONTEFIORE HOSP. & MED. CTR, 70- Instr, dept. surg, Baylor, 63; assoc. attend. surgeon, Polyclin. Med. Sch. & Hosp, 66-67. Med.C, U.S.N.R, Lt. Comdr. Am. Med. Asn; Am. Soc. Artificial Internal Organs; fel. Am. Col. Surg; Asn. Advan. Med. Instrumentation; Am. Col. Cardiol; Soc. Thoracic Surg. Cardiothoracic surgery; cardiac pacemaker; cardiac support systems. Address: 111 E. 210th St, Bronx, NY 10467.

FURMAN, S(YDNEY) C(LARK), b. Bakersfield, Calif, Mar. 22, 23. PHYSICAL & RADIOCHEMISTRY. B.S, California, Los Angeles, 48, Coffin fel, 50-51, Ph.D.(chem), 51. Res. assoc, Knolls Atomic Power Lab, GEN. ELEC. CO, 51-57, chemist, Vallecitos Atomic Lab, 57-61, MGR, radioactive mat. lab, 61-69, TECH. SERV, VALLECITOS NUCLEAR CTR, 70-. U.S.A.A.F, 43-46. Am. Chem. Soc; Am. Nuclear Soc. Vanadium solution chemistry; complexions; radiochemistry; isotopic exchange; fission product chemistryL metal-water reactions; gas chromatography; post-irradiation examination of materials; radioisotopes; nuclear medicine; membrane filtration. Address: Vallecitos Nuclear Center, General Electric Co, Box 846, Pleasanton, CA 94566.

FURMAN, THOMAS deS(AUSSURE), b. Milledgeville, Ga, Nov. 8, 15; m. 40; c. 4. SANITARY ENGINEERING. B.S, The Citadel, 36; M.S.E, Florida, 50. Draftsman, inspector & instrumentman, State Hwy. Dept, S.C, 36-42; chief of party & asst. proj. engr, Harland Bartholomew & Assocs, 42-43; design engr. & v.pres, Quattlebaum Eng. Co, 46-51; asst. prof. CIVIL ENG, UNIV. FLA, 51-53, assoc. prof, 53-64, PROF, 64- Design consult, Black, Crow & Eidsness, Inc, Fla. Dipl, Am. Acad. Sanit. Eng. U.S.N.R, 43-46, Res, 46-, Lt. Nat. Soc. Prof. Eng; Am. Water Works Asn; fel. Am. Soc. Civil Eng. Design, operation and control of water and waste water treatment. Address: Dept. of Civil Engineering, University of Florida, Gainesville, FL 32601.

FURMAN, WALTER L, b. Charlotte, N.C, Nov. 30, 13. MATHEMATICS, PHYSICS. B.S, The Citadel, 33; M.S, Florida, 41, Ph.D.(math), 61; S.T.L, St. Louis, 51; U.S. State Dept. fel, Jesuit Univ, Bogota, 59-60. Teacher, high sch, S.C, 33-34; Rugby Acad, La, 36-37; instr. physics, Spring Hill Col, 43-46, 51-53; phys. sci, Florida, 55-57; asst. prof. MATH, SPRING HILL COL, 57-59, 60-63, assoc. prof, 63-66, PROF, 66- AAAS; Math. Asn. Am; Soc. Indust. & Appl. Math; Am. Math. Soc. Mathematics in the Latin American universities. Address: Dept. of Mathematics, Spring Hill College, Mobile, AL 36608.

FURNAS, DAVID W(ILLIAM), b. Caldwell, Idaho, Apr. 1, 31; m. 56; c. 3. PLASTIC & RECONSTRUCTIVE SURGERY. A.B, California, 52, M.D, 55, M.S, 57. Asst. pharmacol, California, 55, intern surg, univ. hosp, 55-56, asst. res, 56-57; Nat. Insts. Ment. Health fel. & asst. res. psychiat, Langley Porter Neuropsychiat. Inst, 57-60; res. surg, Gorgas Hosp, C.Z, 60-61; plastic surg, N.Y. Hosp, 61-62; registrar, Glasgow Royal Infirmary, 63-64; assoc. SURG, Univ, Iowa, 64-69; ASSOC. PROF. & CHIEF DIV. PLASTIC SURG, UNIV. CALIF, IRVINE, 69- Res, Vet. Admin. Hosp, Bronx, N.Y, 62-63; mem, Plastic Surg. Res. Coun. Dipl, Am. Bd. Surg, 66; Am. Bd. Plastic Surg. Chief surg, 6580th Air Force Hosp, Holloman AFB, N.Mex, U.S.A.F, 57-59, Res, 59-63, Capt. Am. Soc. Plastic & Reconstruct. Surg.(scholar. award, 69); Am. Asn. Plastic Surg; Am. Soc. Surg. of Hand (res. award, 70); Soc. Univ. Surg; Am. Cleft Palate Asn; Soc. Head & Neck Surg; fel. Royal Col. Surg; fel. Am. Col. Surg; fel. Royal Soc. Med; Brit. Asn. Plastic Surg. Skeletal development; psychiatric aspects of plastic surgery; microsurgery; naso-orbital surgery and anatomy; hand surgery and anatomy. Address: Division of Plastic Surgery, University of California, Irvine, CA 92664.

FURNESS, GEOFFREY, b. Blackburn, Eng, Aug. 2, 19; m. 41; c. 2. MICROBIOLOGY. B.Sc, Leeds, 48; dipl, Manchester, 49, fel, 49-51, Ph.D.(microbiol), 51. Lectr. microbiol, Trinity Col.(Dublin), 51-53; Fleming fel, Wright Fleming Inst, London, 54-56, scientist, 56-59; Med. Res. Coun, 59-62; head virol. sect, Twyford Labs, Ltd, 62-66; PROF. virol, Univ. Tex. M.D. Anderson Hosp. & Tumor Inst, 66-67; MICROBIOL, COL. MED. & DENT. N.J, NEWARK, 67-, vis. prof, 66, secy. grad. sch. biomed. sci, 67-70. Ciba Anglo-French Med. bursary, 55; vis. res. assoc, Pittsburgh, 57-59; vis. scientist, animal health div, Commonwealth Sci. & Indust. Res. Orgn, Melbourne, Australia, 71. Brit. Inst. Biol; Brit. Soc. Gen. Microbiol; Brit. Soc. Appl. Bact; Brit. Soc. Cell Biol. Bacterial genetics; natural immunity of animals to salmonellae; replication in cell cultures of viruses, especially polioviruses, vaccinia and the lymphogranuloma venereum-tric agents; mycoplasmas. Address: Dept. of Microbiology, College of Medicine & Dentistry of New Jersey at Newark, 100 Bergen St, Newark, NJ 07103.

FURNISH, W(ILLIAM) M(ADISON), (JR), b. Tipton, Iowa, Aug. 17, 12; m. 38; c. 5. GEOLOGY. B.A, Iowa, 34, M.S, 35, Ph.D.(geol), 38. Res. assoc. paleont, Iowa, 38-40; instr. geol, Okla. Agr. & Mech. Col, 40-41; geologist, Shell Oil Co, 41-44; dist. geologist, Creole Petrol. Corp, 46-49; div. geologist, Arabian-Am. Oil Co, 50-53; assoc. prof. GEOL, UNIV. IOWA, 53-56, PROF, 56-, acting head dept, 56-59, chmn, 59-62. Geol. Soc. Am; Paleont. Soc; Soc. Econ. Paleont. & Mineral. Petroleum geology; fossil cephalopods; conodonts. Address: Dept. of Geology, University of Iowa, Iowa City, IA 52240.

FURNIVAL, GEORGE MASON, b. Johnson City, Tenn, May 1, 25; m. 46; c. 2. FORESTRY. B.S.F, Georgia, 48, M.F, Duke, 52, D.F, 57. Res. forester, Miss. State Col, 48-50; U.S. Forest Serv, 52-55; instr. forest mensuration, sch. forestry, Yale, 55-57, asst. prof, 57-61, assoc. prof, 61-64; dir. biomet. studies, U.S. Forest Serv, 64-65; PROF. FOREST BIOMET, YALE, 65- U.S.A, 43-45. Soc. Am. Foresters; Am. Statist. Asn. Application of statistical methods in forestry. Address: Dept. of Forest Biometry, Yale University, 1303 A, New Haven, CT 06520.

FURNIVAL, G(EORGE) M(ITCHELL), b. Winnipeg, Man, July 25, 08; m. 37; c. 4. ECONOMIC GEOLOGY. B.Sc, Manitoba, 29; M.A, Queen's (Can), 34; scholar, Mass. Inst. Tech, 33-35, Ph.D.(econ. geol), 35. In charge field parties, Nipissing Mining Co, 29-30; asst. geol, Manitoba, 30-31; geol. asst, Man. Dept. Mines, 31; asst. geol, Queen's (Can), 31-33; geologist, Geol. Surv. Can, 31-32; Bear Explor. & Radium Ltd, 33; Dept. Mines, Ont, 34; O'Brien Gold Mines, 35-36; asst. supt. and geologist, Cline Lake Gold Mines, 36-39; geologist, Geol. Surv. Can, 39-42; sr. geologist, Standard Oil Co, B.C, Ltd, 42-43; dist. geologist, Dom. Oil Co, Ltd, 43; Calif. Standard Co, 43-45, field supt, 45-46; dir. mines, Prov. Man, 46-48; supt. land & lease, Calif. Standard Co, 48-49, mgr. land & lease, 49-50, dir, 50-51, dir. & v.pres. in charge legal, crude oil sales & pub. rels, 51-55, v.pres. & dir, Calif. Explor. Co, Standard Oil Co, Calif, 56-63; chmn. bd. & managing dir, W. Australian Petrol. Pty, Ltd, 63-70; CONSULT, 70- Pres, Dom. Oil Co, Ltd, 52-55; v.pres. & dir; Cuba Calif. Co; Bahama Calif. Co; Richmond Oil Co. Columbia; Calif. Petrol. Guatemala; Calif. Ecuador Co; Bolivia Calif. Co; Richmond Co. Peru. Mem, Dom. Provincial Cmt. Aerial Photo, Topog, Geol. & Geophys. Survs, 46-48. Secy, Inter-provincial Mines Minister's Conf, Winnipeg, 46; mem. Man. del, Mines Minister's Conf, Nova Scotia, 47; Alta. del, British Col, 50, Sask, 51. Am. Asn. Petrol. Geol; fel. Geol. Soc. Am; Soc. Econ. Geol; fel. Mineral. Soc. Am; fel. Royal Soc. Can; fel. Geol. Asn. Can; Eng. Inst. Can; Can. Inst. Min. & Metall.(v.pres, 52). Silver-pitchblende deposits of Great Bear Lake; ore deposits of the Canadian Precambrian rocks; petroleum geology; sedimentary and structural geology of Western Canada, carribean area, Central and South America, Australia, East Indies, Middle East, North and West Africa and Western Europe. Address: Apt. 405 Renfrew House, Rideau Towers Apts, Calgary, Alta, Can.

FURR, AARON KEITH, b. Salisbury, N.C, Mar. 5, 32; m. 58; c. 4. NUCLEAR PHYSICS. B.A, Catawba Col, 54; M.S, Emory, 55; fel, Oak Ridge Inst. Nuclear Studies, 59-60; Ph.D.(nuclear physics), Duke, 62. Asst. prof. physics, VA. POLYTECH. INST. & STATE UNIV, 60-63, assoc. prof, 63-70, PROF. physics & nuclear eng, 70-71, NUCLEAR SCI. & ENG, 71- Summer consult, Savannah River Proj, 62. Nuclear level measurements; neutron spectroscopy; activation analysis. Address: Dept. of Mechanical Engineering, Virginia Polytechnic Institute & State University, Blacksburg, VA 24061.

FURR, HOWARD L(EE), b. Pontotoc, Miss, Oct. 31, 15; m. 46; c. 3. CIVIL ENGINEERING. B.S, Miss. State Col, 41; M.S, Agr. & Mech. Col, Texas, 48; South. Fels. Fund fel, Texas, 55-56, Ph.D.(civil eng), 58. Designer & detailer, Sverdrup & Parcel, Inc, Mo, 49-51; asst. prof. CIVIL ENG, Mississippi, 51-55, PROF, 56-59; Mo. Sch. Mines, 59-61; TEX. A&M UNIV, 61- Summers, designer, Sverdrup & Parcel, Inc, 52; engr, Humble Oil & Ref. Co, 57; Arnold Eng. Develop. Center, ARO, Inc, 59; appl. physics lab, Hopkins, 60, 61. Recog. award, Gen. Dynamics, 69. U.S.A, 41-46, Capt. Am. Soc. Civil Eng; Am. Soc. Eng. Educ; Am. Concrete Inst. Structural design and mechanics. Address: Dept. of Civil Engineering, Texas A&M University, College Station, TX 77843.

FURR, J(OE) R(OUDOLPH), b. Belen, Miss, Oct. 22, 00; m. HORTICULTURE. B.S, Miss. Agr. & Mech. Col, 24; Ph.D.(pomol), Cornell, 32. From asst. horticulturist to physiologist, div. fruit & veg. crops & diseases, bur. plant indust, U.S. Dept. Agr, Calif, 32-43, physiologist, soils & agr. eng, Fla, 43-46, sr. horticulturist, 46-53, hort. crops res. br, agr. res. serv, 53-58, res. horticulturist & supt, U.S. Date & Citrus Sta, 58-70; RETIRED. AAAS; Am. Soc. Hort. Sci; Bot. Soc. Am; Am. Soc. Plant Physiol. Production and breeding of citrus and dates; water relations of plants. Address: 81-242 Alberta Ave, Indio, CA 92201.

FURR, R(ANDLE) E(LIAS), b. Wesson, Miss, Aug. 1, 25; m. 49; c. 3. ENTOMOLOGY. B.S, Millsaps Col, 49; M.S, Miss. State, 51; Ph.D.(entomol), Okla. State, 55. Asst. entomologist, Miss. State, 51-54; ENTOMOLOGIST, U.S. DEPT. AGR, 55- U.S.N, 43-46, Res, 46-54. Cotton insect research; taxonomy of Tetranychidae. Address: P.O. Box 828, Leland, MS 38756.

FURRER, JOHN D, b. Walton, Nebr, Jan. 23, 20; m. 51; c. 4. AGRONOMY. B.S, Nebraska, 47, M.S, 52. Exten. agronomist, UNIV. NEBR, LINCOLN, 47-64, exten. specialist & assoc. prof. agron, 65-70, PESTICIDE SPECIALIST & PROF. AGRON, 70- U.S.A, 41-45, Sgt. Weed Sci. Soc. Am. Herbicides for perennial weed control; pre-emergence herbicides for annual weed control in corn, sorghum and soybeans and for lawn weed control. Address: Dept. of Agronomy, College of Agriculture, E. Campus, University of Nebraska, Lincoln, NE 68503.

FURRER, MAX A, b. Grenchen, Switz, May 26, 20; m. 58; c. 3. PALEONTOLOGY. Ph.D, Basel, 48. Micropaleontologist, Socony Mobil Oil Co, Colombia, 49; paleontologist & stratigrapher, Iran Oil Co, Iran, 50-55; res. assoc. micropaleont, Stanford, 55-56; paleontologist & stratigrapher, Cuba Calif. Oil Co, Cuba, 56-57; Guatemala Calif. Oil Co, Guatemala, 57; Calif. Ecuador Petrol. Co, Ecuador, 57-58; Calif. Explor. Co, 58-59; res. geologist, Calif. Res. Corp. Div, Standard Oil Co, Calif, 59; CHIEF PALEONTOLOGIST, Dom. Oil, Ltd, W.I. 60-67; CREOLE PETROL. CORP, STANDARD OIL CO, 67- Mem, Cushman Inst. Foraminiferal Res, 53- Swiss Army, 40-45. AAAS; Geol. Soc. Am; Soc. Econ. Paleont. & Mineral; Soc. Syst. Zool. Ecology and stratigraphic and geographic distribution of planktonic foraminifera and larger foraminifera. Address: Creole Petroleum Corp, Standard Oil Co, Apartado 889, Caracas, Venezuela.

FURROW, C(LARENCE) L(EE), b. Galesburg, Ill, Nov. 15, 28; m. 53; c. 3. ORGANIC CHEMISTRY. A.B, Knox Col.(Ill), 50; M.S, Iowa, 52, Allied Chem. Corp. fel, 53-54, Ph.D.(org. chem), 54. Res. chemist, Ethyl Corp, 54-57; PHILLIPS PETROL. CO, 57-71, TECH. ADV, PATENT DIV, 71- Am. Chem. Soc. Structure of lignin; radiation chemistry; fuels, lubricants and combustion; benzyl ethers; photochemistry. Address: Patent Division, Phillips Petroleum Co, Bartlesville, OK 74003.

FURROW, ROBERT DANIEL, b. Glen Morgan, W.Va, May 13, 32; m. 57; c. 3. VETERINARY & PATHOLOGICAL MEDICINE. D.V.M, Ohio State, 60. Vet, Lewisberg Vet. Hosp, W.Va, 60-61; vet. poultry inspector, U.S. Dept. Agr, D.C, 61-62, path. trainee, Md, 62-65, pathologist, 65-67; res. assoc. vet. path, Univ. Missouri, 67-68; HEAD PATH. GROUP, LAB. SERV. DIV, CONSUMER & MKT. SERV, U.S. DEPT. AGR, 68- U.S.N, 50-54. AAAS; Am. Asn. Avian Path. Avian leukosis complex; comparative pathology of blood related neoplasms; fluorescent antibody serological typing of avian Pasteurella species bacteria. Address: Lab. Services Division, Consumer & Marketing Service, U.S. Dept. of Agriculture, Washington, DC 20250.

FURROW, STANLEY DONALD, b. Bangor, Maine, Mar, 6, 34; m. 61; c. 2. PHYSICAL CHEMISTRY. B.S, Maine, 56, M.S, 62, Ph.D.(chem), 65; California, Berkeley, 56-57. Instr. CHEM, Maine, 63-64; res. asst, Exeter, 65-66; ASST. PROF, Univ. Maine, 66-69; PA. STATE UNIV, 69- U.S.A, 57-59. Am. Chem. Soc. Non-electrolyte solution thermodynamics; calorimetry; air pollution particulate analysis. Address: Dept. of Chemistry, Berks Campus, Pennsylvania State University, 814 Hill Ave, Wyomissing, PA 19610.

FURRY, BENJAMIN K, b. Wadsworth, Ohio, Nov. 21, 23; m. 45; c. 3. RUBBER CHEMISTRY. B.S, Muskingum Col, 44. Lab. technician adhesives, Firestone Tire & Rubber Co, 44-46; asst. chemist, Seiberling Latex Prods, 46-51, chief chemist latex polymers, 51-67; develop. scientist, B.F, Goodrich Chem. Co, 67-68; V.PRES. RES. & DEVELOP, SEIBERLING LATEX PROD, 68- Am. Chem. Soc. Dipping compounds in natural and synthetic lactices; foam polymers; dipping plastisols. Address: 3617 N.W. 68th St, Oklahoma City, OK 73116.

FURRY, DONALD E(DWARD), b. Cleveland, Ohio, Feb. 8, 34; m. 60; c. 2. ANATOMY, PHYSIOLOGY. B.S, John Carroll, 56, fel, 56-57, M.S, 57; fel, Cincinnati, 57-59; Kansas, 60. Res. assoc, Children's Hosp, Cincinnati, 59; aviation physiologist, U.S. Naval Sch. Aviation Med, 59-64; instr. appl. physiol, col. med, Cincinnati, 64-65; res. aviation physiologist, NAVAL MED. RES. INST, 65-69, AEROSPACE PHYSIOLOGIST, 69- AAAS; assoc. fel, Aerospace Med. Asn. Microanatomy; primate anatomy; pulmonary physiology; hyperbaric-radiation biology. Address: Naval Medical Research Institute, Naval Aerospace Medical Center, Pensacola, FL 32512.

FURRY, RONALD B(AY), b. Niagara Falls, N.Y, Oct. 22, 31; m. 53; c. 3. AGRICULTURAL ENGINEERING. B.S, Cornell, 53, M.S, 55; Ph.D, Iowa State Univ, 65. Instr. drafting & descriptive geometry, CORNELL UNIV, 53-56, asst. prof. agr. exten. eng, 56-60, AGR. ENG, 60-62, ASSOC. PROF, 62-, GRAD. FIELD REP. & COORD. GRAD. INSTR, 69-, teaching & dir. plan. serv, 60-63. Nat. Sci. Found. sci. faculty fel, 63-65. U.S.A.F.R, 53-56, 1st Lt. Am. Soc. Agr. Eng; Am. Soc. Eng. Educ. Environment in farm structures; structural design of farm structures. Address: Dept. of Agricultural Engineering, Riley-Robb Hall, Cornell University, Ithaca, NY 14850.

FURRY, W(ENDELL) H(INKLE), b. Prairieton, Ind, Feb. 18, 07; m. 31; c. 2. PHYSICS. A.B, DePauw, 28; A.M, Illinois, 30, fel, 31-32, Ph.D.(physics), 32; hon. A.M, Harvard, 42. Asst. physics, Illinois, 28-31; Nat. Res. fel, California & Calif. Inst. Tech, 32-34; instr, Harvard, 34-37, asst. prof, 37-40, assoc. prof, 40-43; res. assoc, radiation lab, Mass. Inst. Technol, 43-45; assoc. prof. PHYSICS, HARVARD, 45-62, PROF, 62- Guggenheim Mem. fel, 50. With Nat. Defense Res. Comt; Off. Sci. Res. & Develop, 44. AAAS; Am. Acad. Arts & Sci; Am. Asn. Physics Teachers; fel. Am. Phys. Soc. Theory of molecular energies, microwave propagation and of isotope separation; positron theory; quantum field theories; quantum theory of measurement. Address: Dept. of Physics, Harvard University, Cambridge, MA 02138.

FURSE, CLARE TAYLOR, b. Salt Lake City, Utah, May 18, 31; m. 55; c. 5. ANALYTICAL CHEMISTRY. B.S, Utah, 57, Nat. Sci. Found. fel. & Ph.D. (anal. chem), 61. Res. chemist, Esso Res. & Eng. Co, 61-64; ASSOC. PROF. CHEM, MERCER UNIV, 64- Dir, Nat. Sci. Found. Summer Sec. Sch. Insts, 65-68, U.S.A, 53-55. Am. Chem. Soc. Square-wave polarography; electrode kinetics; ultraviolet and fluorescence spectroscopy; separation and identification of polynuclear aromatics. Address: Dept. of Chemistry, Mercer University, Macon, GA 31207.

FURSHPAN, E(DWIN) J(EAN), b. Hartford, Conn, Apr. 18, 28; m. 57; c. 3. NEUROBIOLOGY. B.A, Connecticut, 50; Ph.D.(animal physiol), Calif. Inst. Tech, 55; A.M.(hon), Harvard Med. Sch, 67. Fel. & hon. asst, Univ. Col, London, 55-58; instr. neurophysiol, med. sch, Hopkins, 58-59; assoc.neurophysiol. & neuropharmacol, HARVARD MED. SCH, 59-62, asst. prof. NEUROBIOL, 62-67, assoc. prof, 67-69, PROF, 69- U.S.A, 46-48. Am. Physiol. Soc; Tissue Cult. Soc. Electrophysiology and chemistry of excitable cells; cell interaction. Address: Dept. of Neurobiology, Harvard Medical School, 25 Shattuck St, Boston, MA 02115.

FURST, ARTHUR, b. Minneapolis, Minn, Dec. 25, 14; m. 40; c. 4. MEDICINAL CHEMISTRY, TOXICOLOGY. A.B, California, Los Angeles, 37, M.A, 40; California, 42; Ph.D.(chem), Stanford, 48. Asst, California, Los Angeles, 38-39; teacher, Pacific Mil. Acad, 39-40; petrol. inspection & org. chem, California, 42-45; teacher chem, City Col. of San Francisco, 40-47; asst. prof, San Francisco, 47-49, assoc. prof, 49-52; med. chem, sch. med, Stanford, 52-57, prof, 57-61; PROF. CHEM. & DIR. INST. CHEM. BIOL, UNIV. SAN FRANCISCO, 61- Grants, Res. Corp, U.S. Pub. Health Serv. & Am. Cancer Soc; res. assoc, Mt. Zion Hosp, 50-; clin. prof, col. physicians & surgeons, Columbia Univ, 69-70. AAAS; Am. Chem. Soc; Am. Asn. Cancer Res; Am. Soc. Pharmacol. & Exp. Therapeut; Soc. Toxicol; fel. N.Y. Acad. Sci. Synthesis of possible antimalarial quinoline compounds and of possible growth inhibitors; chemotherapy of cancer and virus; central nervous system drugs; carcinogenesis. Address: Institute of Chemical Biology, University of San Francisco, San Francisco, CA 94117.

FURST, MILTON, b. New York, N.Y, Sept. 10, 21; m. 45; c. 2. PHYSICS. B.S, City Col. New York, 42; M.S, N.Y. Univ, 48, Ph.D, 52. Physicist, N.Y. Naval Shipyard, 47-50, asst. PHYSICS, N.Y. Univ, 50-52; instr, HUNTER COL, 55-58, asst. prof, 58-62, assoc. prof, 62-67, PROF, 67- Res.

assoc, N.Y. Univ, 52-63, res. scientist, 63-67; consult. & researcher, Saclay Nuclear Res. Ctr, France, 61-62. U.S.A.A.F, 42-46. AAAS; Am. Phys. Soc. Fluorescence and energy transfer in liquid organic systems under high energy and light excitations. Address: Dept. of Physics, Hunter College, 695 Park Ave, New York, NY 10021.

FURST, ULRICH RICHARD, b. Vienna, Austria, Jan. 18, 13; nat; m. 44; c. 2. PHYSICS. E.E, Inst. Tech, Vienna, 35, Ph.D.(physics), 38. Engr, Keystone Mfg. Co, Mass, 38-40; Rehtron Corp, Ill, 40-41; electronic engr, Offner Electronics, 41-42; chief electronic engr, Russell Electric Co, 42-46; pres, Furst Electronics, Inc, 46-56; chief electronics engr, Elec. Eye Equip. Co, 56-58; chief missile opers. unit, Bomarc Proj, aero-space div, Boeing Co, 58-62; SECT. MGR, SYST. ENG. DEPT, MISSILE SYSTS. DIV, HUGHES AIRCRAFT CO, 62- Lectr, Northwestern, 46-49. Sr. mem. Inst. Elec. & Electronics Eng. Missile systems. Address: 17785 Alonzo Pl, Encino, CA 91316.

FURSTE, WESLEY L(EONARD), II, b. Cincinnati, Ohio, Apr. 19, 15; m. 42; c. 3. SURGERY. A.B, Harvard, 37; M.D, Harvard Med. Sch, 41. Intern & res. surg, Hosp, Ohio State & St. Francis Hosp, 41-42, res, 49-50, chief res, 50-51; fel. & asst. surg, col. med, Cincinnati, 45-49; from instr. SURG. to clin. asst. prof, COL. MED, OHIO STATE UNIV, 49-69, CLIN. ASSOC. PROF, 69-, MEM. COURTESY SURG. STAFF, UNIV. HOSP, 51- Mem. courtesy surg. staff, St. Anthony Hosp, 51-; Grant Hosp, 51-; Children's Hosp, 51-; sr. attend. staff, White Cross Hosp, 54-62; Mt. Carmel Hosp, 54-; Riverside Methodist Hosp, 62- Chmn. med. adv. cmt, Am. Red Cross Regional Blood Center, 58-67; founder, Digestive Disease Found, 70; mem. med. adv. comt, Med. Alert Found. Int, 71. Surg. consult, Columbus State Sch, 51-; Benjamin Franklin Tuberc. Hosp, 53-; Dayton Vet. Admin. Hosp, 54-; Mercy Hosp, 54-; Ohio State Penitentiary, 57- Mem. Second Int. Conf. Tetanus, Switzerland, 66, third, Brazil, 70. Dipl, Am. Bd. Surg, 53. Med.C, 42-46, Res, 50-52, Maj. AAAS; Am. Med. Asn; Am. Med. Writers Asn; Am. Asn. Surg. of Trauma; fel. Am. Col. Surg; Am. Pub. Health Asn; Soc. Surg. Alimentary Tract; Asn. Am. Med. Cols; N.Y. Acad. Sci; Pan Am. Med. Asn. Surgery with particular emphasis on the etiology, diagnosis and treatment of acute abdominal pain, trauma, gas gangrene, transmetatarsal amputations, radical surgery for cancer, tracheostomy, tetanus prophylaxis, submucosal gastro-intestinal lipomata. Address: 3534 Olentangy River Rd, Columbus, OH 43214.

FURSTMAN, LAWRENCE L, b. Chicago, Ill, Feb. 28, 09; m. 33; c. 2. ORTHODONTICS, ANATOMY. D.D.S, Univ. South. Calif, 29, M.S, 64, Ph.D.(anat), 69; cert, Univ. Ill, 34. Instr. histol, sch. dent, Univ. South. Calif, 34-36, fel. anat, sch. med. & spec. lectr, grad. sch. orthod, 61-69, res. assoc. anat, 69-70; lectr, SCH. DENT, CTR. HEALTH SCI, UNIV. CALIF, LOS ANGELES, 70-71, ADJ. PROF, 71- Consult, Cedars Sinai Hosp, 66-; res. assoc, Univ. South. Calif, 69- Los Angeles County Health Dept. medal, 29. Dent.C, 42-46, Maj. Am. Asn. Orthod.(Milo Hellman Res. Award, 63); fel. Am. Col. Dent; Am. Asn. Anat; Int. Asn. Dent. Res; Int. Soc. Cranic-facial Biol. Growth and development of the face and head; development and normal age changes in the temporo-mandibular joint and hormonal, nutritional and functional disturbances. Address: 6-3-048, Center for Health Sciences, University of California School of Dentistry, Los Angeles, CA 90024.

FURTADO, VICTOR C(UNHA), b. Elizabeth, N.J, Mar. 21, 37; m. 58; c. 4. HEALTH PHYSICS, ENVIRONMENTAL HEALTH ENGINEERING. B.S.C.E, Newark Col. Eng, 58; M.Biorad, Univ. Calif, Berkeley, 63; Ph.D.(civil eng, environ. health sci), N.Y. Univ, 71. U.S. AIR FORCE, 58-, sanit. & indust. hyg. engr, 810th med. group, Fairchild AFB, Wash, 58-61, health physicist, 392nd med. group, Vandenberg AFB, Calif, 63-64, 6595th aerospace test wing, 64-65, bioenviron. engr, aerospace med. div, Brooks AFB, Tex, 65-66, HEALTH PHYSICIST, RADIOL. HEALTH LAB, WRIGHT-PATTERSON AFB, 69- U.S.A.F, 58-, Maj. Health Physics Soc; Am. Conf. Govt. Indust. Hygienists. Evaluation of low levels of iodine-131 in nuclear power reactor environments. Address: U.S. Air Force Radiological Health Lab, Wright-Patterson Air Force Base, Dayton, OH 45431.

FURTER, W(ILLIAM) F(REDERICK), b. North Bay, Ont, Apr. 5, 31; m. 66; c. 2. CHEMICAL ENGINEERING. R.M.C, Royal Mil. Col. Can, 53; B.A.Sc, Toronto, 54; scholar. & S.M, Mass. Inst. Technol, 55; Nat. Res. Coun. fels. & Ph.D.(chem. eng), Toronto, 58; N.D.C, Nat. Defence Col. Can, 70. Asst, Mass. Inst. Technol, 54-55; Toronto, 55-58; res. engr. & sr. tech. investr, res. & develop. dept, Du Pont of Can. Ltd, 58-60; asst. prof. CHEM. ENG, ROYAL MIL. COL. CAN, 60-61, assoc. prof, 61-66, PROF, 66-, HEAD CHEM. ENG. SECT, DEPT. CHEM. & CHEM. ENG, 60-, SECY. GRAD. SCH, 67-, spec. lectr, 58-60. Consult. engr, 60-; res. grant, Defence Res. Bd. Can, 62-; Dominion scholar; consult. engr, Hexcel Corp, Calif; Air Liquide Ltd, Can. Lt. Gen. Ont. Silver Medal; 2 Gov-Gen. Medals; Eng. Inst. Can. prize; Royal Can. Sch. Mil. Eng. Prize. R.C.E.R, 53-70, Capt. Fel. Chem. Inst. Can; Can. Soc. Chem. Eng; Can. Nuclear Asn. Mass transfer; vapor-liquid phase equilibria; thermodynamics of ternary electrolytic solutions; extractive distillation; gas-liquid tray design; packed tower design; nuclear chemical engineering; rocket propulsion; high polymer research and engineering; engineering economics and administration. Address: Dept. of Chemical Engineering, Royal Military College of Canada, Kingston, Ont, Can.

FURTH, ADOLPHE, b. Strakonice, Bohemia, May 30, 97; nat; m. 22. PHYSICAL & INORGANIC CHEMISTRY. Ph.D.(chem), Vienna Univ, 22. Asst, Polytech. Inst, Vienna, 22-24; res. & tech. serv, hydrogen peroxide, Austrian Chem. Works, 34-38; Union Chem. Belge, 38-40; res, phosphates & fluosilicates, I.P. Thomas & Son Co, 42-48; teacher silicon fluoride res, Assumption Col, 48-52; prof. chem, N.C. Col. Durham, 52-62; St. Augustine's Col, 62-70; RETIRED. Am. Chem. Soc. Hydrogen peroxide; phosphates; fluosilicates. Address: R.D. 7, Box 371, Durham, NC 27707.

FURTH, ENRIQUE, b. Buenos Aires, Argentina, Aug. 4, 28; U.S. citizen; m. 55; c. 2. OPERATIONS RESEARCH, MATHEMATICS. Telecommun. engr, Buenos Aires, 54; Syracuse, 56-58; N.Y. Univ, 64-69. Assoc. engr, adv. systs. div, Int. Bus. Mach. Corp, 56-59; sr. mem. tech. staff opers. res, systs. lab, Radio Corp. Am, N.Y, 59-65; chief scientist, systs. sci. div, Dunlap & Assocs, Inc, 65-69; V.PRES. PHILLIPS STEWART TURNER ASSOCS, INC, 69- Lectr, mgt. inst, N.Y. Univ, 68- Sr. mem. Inst.

Elec. & Electronics Eng; Opers. Res. Soc. Am; Inst. Mgt. Sci; Asn. Comput. Mach. Operations research; mathematics of transportation and communication; systems analysis; cost-effectiveness. Address: Phillips Stewart Turner Associates, Inc, 370 Lexington Ave, New York, NY 10017.

FURTH, EUGENE D(AVID), b. Phila, Pa, Jan. 25, 29; m. 52; c. 2. MEDICINE, ENDOCRINOLOGY. A.B, Wesleyan Univ, 50; M.D, Cornell Univ, 54. Asst. prof. med. & radiobiol, col. med, Cornell Univ, 63-67; assoc. prof. MED, ALBANY MED. COL, 67-71, PROF, 71- Asst. dir. radioisotope lab, N.Y. Hosp, 62-67. Dipl, Am. Bd. Internal Med. U.S.A, 55-57, Capt. Am. Fedn. Clin. Res; Am. Thyroid Asn; Endocrine Soc. Thyroid gland physiology and pathophysiology. Address: Dept. of Medicine, Albany Medical College, Albany, NY 12208.

FURTH, FRANK W(ILLARD), b. Trenton, N.J, Sept. 27, 22; m. 45; c. 3. INTERNAL MEDICINE, HEMATOLOGY. B.S, Rutgers, 43; M.D, Rochester, 47. Instr. radiation biol, Rochester, 50-52, internal med, 54-56; asst. prof. & coord. cancer ed, col. med, State Univ. N.Y. Upstate Med. Ctr, 56-62; dir. med. serv. & educ, Community Gen. Hosp. Greater Syracuse, 62-67; assoc. prof. med, State Univ. N.Y. Upstate Med. Ctr, 67-68; ASST. REGIONAL HEALTH DIR, SYRACUSE REGIONAL OFF, N.Y. STATE DEPT. HEALTH, 68- Dipl, Am. Bd. Internal Med, 56. U.S.A, 43-45, Med.C, 52-54, Res, 54-, Capt. AAAS; Am. Soc. Hemat; Am. Fedn. Clin. Res. Hematology. Address: Syracuse Regional Office, New York State Dept. of Health, 677 S. Salina St, Syracuse, NY 13202.

FURTH, F(REDERICK) R(AYMOND), b. Seattle, Wash, Oct. 13, 01; m. ELECTRONICS. B.S, U.S. Naval Acad, 24; M.S, Yale, 32. Ship assignments, U.S. Navy, 24-30, radio off, battleship div, 32-35, naval commun, 35-37, U.S. Fleet Commun. Off, 38-40, Off. Chief Naval Opers, 40-43, radar mission, U.K, 43, dep. chief electronics, 44-46, electronics off, Puget Sound Naval Shipyard, 46-48, dir, Naval Res. Lab, 49-52; asst. chief, Bur. Ships, 52-53, chief, Naval res, 54-56; v.pres, Farnsworth Electronics Co, 56-57; asst. dir. res. & develop, Int. Tel. & Tel. Co, 57-58, v.pres. & dir. res. & develop, 58-60, mil. electronics develop, Farnsworth Res. Corp, Conn, 60-62, v.pres, 60-67, v.chmn. & gen. mgr, 62-67; INDEPENDENT CONSULT, 68- Mem, Inst. Aeronaut. Sci. U.S.N, 24-56, Rear Adm.(Ret). AAAS; Am. Inst. Aeronaut. & Astronaut; Am. Soc. Naval Eng; Sci. Res. Soc. Am; Soc. Naval Archit. & Marine Eng; Inst. Elec. & Electronics Eng. Address: Carter Rd, Kent, CT 06757.

FURTH, HAROLD P(AUL), b. Vienna, Austria, Jan. 13, 30; nat; m. 59; c. 1. PHYSICS. A.B, Harvard, 51, Ph.D, 60. Physicist, Lawrence Radiation Lab, Univ. Calif, Berkeley, 56-67; PROF. ASTROPHYS. SCI. & CO-HEAD EXP. GROUP, PLASMA PHYSICS LAB, PRINCETON, 67- Fel. Am. Phys. Soc. Plasma physics; controlled thermonuclear research. Address: Plasma Physics Lab, Princeton University, Princeton, NJ 08540.

FURTH, J(ACOB), b. Miskolcz, Hungary, 96; nat. PATHOLOGY. Fel, Ger. Univ, Prague, 20-21, M.C, 21; hon. D.Sc, Univ. Pa, 68. Asst, hyg. inst, Ger. Univ, 21-22; fel, Henry Phipps Inst, Pennsylvania, 24-25, asst, 25-27, assoc, 28-32; path, med. col, Cornell, 32-33, asst. prof, 33-38, assoc. prof, 38-45, prof, 45-49; chief lab, br. 10, U.S. Vet. Admin, 47-49, chief path. & physiol. sect, biol. div, Atomic Energy Cmn, Oak Ridge Nat. Lab, 49-53; assoc. dir. res, Children's Cancer Res. Found, Harvard Med. Sch, 54-59; dir. exp. path, Roswell Park Mem. Inst, Buffalo, 59-61; prof. PATH, COLUMBIA UNIV, 61-67, EMER. PROF. & SPEC. LECTR, 67- Dir path. lab, Francis Delafield Hosp, 61-68. Clin. prof, Harvard Med. Sch, 58-59; acting dir. inst. cancer res, Columbia Univ, 68-69. Am. Med. Asn. gold medal, 31; Bertner Award, M.D. Anderson Hosp. & Tumor Inst, 58; Robert Roessler de Villiers Award, 59; Semmelweis Medal, 62. Dipl, Am. Bd. Path. AAAS (Rosenthal Award, 67); Am. Asn. Cancer Res.(pres, 57-58, Cloves Medal, 62); Am. Soc. Exp. Path.(pres, 59-60). Typhoid; tuberculosis; antigens; leukemia; blood; tumors; general pathology; radiation biology; endocrine neoplasia. Address: Institute of Cancer Research, Columbia University, 99 Ft. Washington Ave, New York, NY 10032.

FURTH, JOHN J, b. Phila, Pa, Jan. 25, 29; m. 59; c. 2. BIOCHEMISTRY, PATHOLOGY. B.A, Cornell, 50; Yale, 50-51. Intern. med. path, Cornell, 58-59; res. path, N.Y. Univ, 59-60, fel. biochem, sch. med, 60-62; assoc. PATH, SCH. MED, UNIV. PA, 62-65, asst. prof, 65-68, ASSOC. PROF, 68- U.S. Pub. Health Serv. fel, 60-62, res. career develop. award, 62- Roche Award, sch. med, Duke Univ, 56. Qm.C, 61-63, 2nd Lt. RNA synthesis with particular emphasis on the DNA dependent RNA polymerase. Address: Dept. of Pathology, University of Pennsylvania School of Medicine, Philadelphia, PA 19104.

FURTICK, WILLIAM R, b. Salina, Kans, Jan. 8, 27; m. 59. AGRONOMY. B.S, Kansas State, 49; M.S, Oregon State, 52, Ph.D, 58. Instr, exten, ORE. STATE UNIV, 49-50, FARM CROPS, 50-57, asst. prof, 57-59, assoc. prof, 59-64, PROF, 64-, DIR. INT. PLANT PROTECTION CTR, 69- Proj. mgr, Food & Agr. Orgn. Plant Protection Ctr, UN Develop. Prog, Taipei, Taiwan, 71- U.S.A, 51-52. AAAS; Weed Sci. Soc. Am.(pres. elect, 64, pres, 65); Crop Sci. Soc. Am. Weed control; herbicides; plant growth regulators and crop physiology and ecology. Address: International Plant Protection Center, Gilmore Annex, Oregon University, Corvallis, OR 97331.

FURTSCH, E(DWARD) F(RANK), b. Traverse City, Mich, Apr. 23, 06; m. 37; c. 2. ANALYTICAL CHEMISTRY. B.S, Michigan, 28, M.S, 29; Ph.D. (chem), Pittsburgh, 36. Instr. CHEM, Uniontown center, Pittsburgh, 29-31; VA. POLYTECH. INST, 36-38, asst. prof, 38-45, assoc. prof, 45-57, prof, 57-71, EMER. PROF, 71- Am. Chem. Soc. Specific heat measurements; metallic corrosion. Address: 1302 Oak Rd, Blacksburg, VA 24060.

FURUKAWA, DAVID HIROSHI, b. San Pedro, Calif, Mar. 26, 38; m. 64; c. 2. CHEMICAL ENGINEERING. B.S.Ch.E, Colorado, 60. Chem. engr, saline water demineralization sect, Bur. Reclamation, 60-64, supvr. sect, 64-66, head sect, 66-69; MGR. res. & develop, Havens Int, 69-70, COMMERCIAL DEVELOP. DEPT, CALGON-HAVENS SYSTS, 70- Am. Inst. Chem. Eng; Am. Chem. Soc; Am. Water Works Asn; Tech. Asn. Pulp & Paper Indust; Inst. Food Technol. Research and development in field of desalting, particularly reverse osmosis but also electrodialysis and transport depletion; characterization of permselective and semipermeable membranes. Address: Commercial Development Dept, Calgon-Havens Systems, 8133 Aero Dr, San Diego, CA 92123.

FURUKAWA, GEORGE T(ADAHARU), b. Calif, May 25, 21; m. 51; c. 2. PHYSICAL CHEMISTRY. A.B, Cent. Col.(Mo), 43; Ph.D.(chem), Wisconsin, 48. Instr. chem. & physics, Cent. Col.(Mo), 43-45; PHYSICIST, BUR. STANDARDS, 48- Prof. lectr, George Wash. Univ, 64-68. Am. Chem. Soc; Am. Phys. Soc. Low temperature heat capacity; vapor pressure; latent heats; surface tension; gas heat capacity; heterogeneous phase equilibria; temperature scale and thermometry. Address: 1712 Evelyn Dr, Rockville, MD 20852.

FURUMOTO, AUGUSTINE S, b. Honolulu, Hawaii, Aug. 12, 27; m. 65; c. 2. GEOPHYSICS, SEISMOLOGY. B.S, Univ. Dayton, 49; M.Sc, Univ. Tokyo, 55; Ph.D.(geophys), St. Louis Univ, 61. Asst. prof. geophys. & seismol. & res. asst, UNIV. HAWAII, 61-67, assoc. prof. GEOPHYS, 67-71, PROF. & SEISMOLOGIST, INST. GEOPHYS, 71-, assoc. seismologist, 67-71. Summers, Nat. Sci. Found. fel, Woods Hole Oceanog. Inst, 60, res. asst, 61. AAAS; Am. Geophys. Union; Seismol. Soc. Am; Seismol. Soc. Japan; Volcanological Soc. Japan; Nat. Asn. Corrosion Eng. Exploration of the crust and upper mantle in the Pacific area by explosion seismic techniques with special interest in Hawaii and Melanesia; seismicity of Hawaii; tsunamigenic earthquakes. Address: Institute of Geophysics, University of Hawaii, 2525 Correa Rd, Honolulu, HI 96822.

FURUMOTO, HORACE W(ATARU), b. Honolulu, Hawaii, Dec. 13, 31; m. 59; c. 2. PHYSICS. B.S, Calif. Inst. Tech, 55; Ph.D.(physics), Ohio State, 63. Res. physicist, res. & adv. develop. div, Avco Corp, 63-66; NASA Electronics Res. Ctr, 66-70; GEN. ENGR, DEPT. TRANSPORTATION, CAMBRIDGE, 70- U.S.A.F, 55-57, 1st Lt. AAAS; Am. Phys. Soc; Optical Soc. Am; Inst. Elec. & Electronics Eng. High power lasers; laser radiation interactions with solids and gases; plasma diagnostics with lasers; x-ray diffraction by liquids; electronics-high speed pulse techniques; organic dye and high power lasers; laser interactions; instrumentation; environmental measurements. Address: 22 Belair Rd, Wellesley, MA 02181.

FURUMOTO, HOWARD HOOSAKU, b. Ninole, Hawaii, July 13, 21; m. 46; c. 7. VETERINARY MEDICINE, VIROLOGY. B.S, Kansas State, 47, M.S, 48, D.V.M, 50; Nat. Insts. Health fel, Illinois, 64-66, Ph.D.(virol, vet. med), 66. Intern vet. med, Angell Mem. Animal Hosp, Mass, 50-51; asst. prof. surg. & med, Kansas State, 51-52; vet. practice, Care Animal Clin, Hawaii, 52-63; supvr. vet. med, Atlas Chem. Industs, Del, 66-67; assoc. prof. animal path, Univ. Hawaii, 67-69; SR. PARTNER, CARE ANIMAL MED. CTR, 69- Consult, Hawaii Dept. Agr, 68. Mil.Intel, U.S.A, 42-46, Res, 46-51, 2nd Lt. Am. Soc. Trop. Med. & Hyg; Am. Vet. Med. Asn; Am. Soc. Lab. Animal Practitioners. Parasitology, including helminths of cats in Kansas; susceptibility studies with St. Louis encephalitis and other arthropod-borne viruses; metabolism, including pathogenesis of atherosclerosis; biochemical mechanisms and related tissue changes. Address: Care Animal Medical Center, 1135 Kapahulu Ave, Honolulu, HI 96816.

FURUMOTO, WARREN A(KIRA), b. Honolulu, Hawaii, Dec. 12, 34; m. 62. BIOLOGY. B.S, Calif. Inst. Tech, 57; Ph.D.(bot. sci), California, Los Angeles, 61. Instr. bot, Chicago, 60-62; asst. prof. BIOL, SAN FERNANDO VALLEY STATE COL, 62-66, assoc. prof, 66-70, PROF, 70- Nat. Sci. Found. res. grants, 60-65. AAAS. Studies on the infective process of tobacco mosaic virus. Address: Dept. of Biology, San Fernando Valley State College, Northridge, CA 91324.

FURUSAWA, EIICHI, b. Japan, Jan. 25, 28; m; c. 1. CHEMOTHERAPY, VIROLOGY. M.D, Osaka, 54, Ph.D, 59. Res. assoc, res. inst. microbial diseases, Osaka, 55-59; fel. microbiol, Stanford, 59-61, res. assoc, 61-64; assoc. pharmacologist, Pac. Biomed. Ctr, UNIV. HAWAII, 64-65, assoc. prof. PHARMACOL, SCH. MED, 65-70, PROF, 70- Fel. microbiol, Columbia, 60; Nat. Insts. Health Res. grant, 67-70; Leukemia Soc. res. grant, 70-71; Am. Med. Asn. res. grant, 71-; Am. Cancer Soc. res. grant, 71- Am. Soc. Microbiol; Soc. Japanese Virol. Virus chemotherapy and search for antiviral agents from natural products. Address: School of Medicine, University of Hawaii, Honolulu, HI 96822.

FURUTA, OTTO KAMEYOSHI, b. Rivers, Ariz, Mar. 4, 43. ORGANIC CHEMISTRY. B.S, Univ. Calif, Berkeley, 65; Ph.D.(org. chem), Univ. Colo, Boulder, 68. SR. RES. CHEMIST, MONSANTO CO, 68- Am. Chem. Soc. Synthesis of polyfluorocycloalkenyl phosphonates; reactions of aromatic olefins; determination of reaction parameters for synthesis of thiolcarbamates; kinetics of the gas phase reactions of carbon monoxide and sulphur. Address: Agricultural Research Division, T402, Monsanto Co, 800 N. Lindbergh Blvd, St. Louis, MO 63166.

FURUTA, TOKUJI, b. La Mesa, Calif, Mar. 3, 25; m. 50; c. 5. ENVIRONMENTAL HORTICULTURE. B.S, Ohio State, 48, M.Sc, 49, Ph.D.(hort), 51. Asst, Ohio State, 49-51; assoc. prof. hort, Auburn, 51-62, prof, 62-65; EXTEN. SPECIALIST ORNAMENTAL HORT, UNIV. CALIF, RIVERSIDE, 65- Assoc. horticulturist, agr. exp. sta, Auburn, 51-62, horticulturist, 62-65. U.S.A, 44-46. AAAS; Int. Plant Propagators Soc; Am. Soc. Hort. Sci. Environmental planning, analysis and maintenance; behavior basis for environmental development; nutrition and propagation of floricultural and ornamental plants; morphogenesis of plants; systems analysis for plant production; economics of production and marketing. Address: Dept. of Plant Science, University of California, Riverside, CA 92502.

FURY, LAWRENCE A, JR, b. Chicago, Ill, Jan. 22, 38. ORGANIC CHEMISTRY. B.S, Southwestern at Memphis, 60; Ph.D.(org. chem), Vanderbilt, 64. Sr. res. chemist, Monsanto Co, 63-64; DIR. MKT. RES, HUMKO PRODUCTS DIV, KRAFTCO CORP, 64- Am. Chem. Soc; Am. Oil Chemists' Soc. Organic chemical marketing research; chemical long range planning for new business development. Address: Humko Products Div, Krafto Corp, P.O. Box 398, Memphis, TN 38101.

FUSARI, SALVATORE A(NTHONY), b. N.Y.C, Apr. 3, 22; m. 45; c. 4. PHYSIOLOGICAL CHEMISTRY. B.S, City Col, 43; M.S, Ohio State, 48, Ph.D.

(physiol. chem), 50. Sr. res. chemist, antibiotics develop, PARKE DAVIS & CO, 50-64, MGR. ANAL. & SPECIFICATIONS DEPT, CONTROL DEVELOP, 64- U.S.A, 43-46. Am. Chem. Soc. Antibiotics and chemistry of natural products. Address: Parke, Davis & Co, Analytical & Specifications Dept, P.O. Box 118, Detroit, MI 48232.

FUSARO, BERNARD A, b. Charleston, W.Va, Aug. 9, 24; m. 53. MATHEMATICS. B.A, Swarthmore Col, 50; M.A, Columbia Univ, 54; Ph.D.(math), Univ. Md, 65. Instr. physics & math, Ripon Col, 51-52; asst. MATH, Columbia Univ, 52-54; instr, Middlebury Col, 54-57; Univ. Md, 57-61; vis. asst. prof, Univ. Okla, 61-62; asst. prof. to assoc. prof, Univ. South Fla, 62-67; prof. & chmn. dept, QUEENS COL.(N.C), 67-69, DANA PROF, 69- Lectr, Nat. Sci. Found. Inst, Univ. Okla, 61-62; Fulbright prof, Nat. Taiwan Univ, 70-71; summers, mathematician, Ballistics Res. Lab, Aberdeen Proving Grounds, 54, Nat. Sci. Found. Insts, Univ. Mich, 56, Am. Univ, 60, Soc. Sci. Res. Inst, Stanford Univ, 57, vis. asst, Nat. Sci. Found. Inst, N.Mex. Highlands Univ, 65. U.S.M.C, 43-46, Sgt. Am. Math. Soc; Math. Asn. Am; Soc. Indust. & Appl. Math. Linear and hyperbolic second order differential equations, particularly the generalized Euler-Poisson-Darboux equation; harmonic Riemannian spaces. Address: Dept. of Mathematics, Queens College, Charlotte, NC 28207.

FUSARO, RAMON MICHAEL, b. Brooklyn, N.Y, Mar. 6, 27; m. 51; c. 2. DERMATOLOGY. B.A, Univ. Minn, 49, B.S, 51, M.D, 53, M.S, 58, Ph.D, 65. Intern, Minneapolis Gen. Hosp, Minn, 53-54; resident, Minneapolis Gen. Hosp-Univ. Minn. Hosp, 54-57; instr. DERMAT, med. sch, Univ. Minn, 57-65, asst. prof, 65-66, assoc. prof, 66-70; PROF. & CHMN. DEPT, MED. CTR, UNIV. NEBR, 70- Am. Acad. Dermat; Am. Fedn. Clin. Res; Am. Med. Asn; Soc. Invest. Dermat. Clinical dermatology; carbohydrate metabolism; photosensitivity, immunology. Address: Dept. of Dermatology, University of Nebraska Medical Center, 42nd & Dewey Ave, Omaha, NE 68105.

FUSCALDO, ANTHONY ALFRED, b. N.Y.C, Nov. 11, 39; m. 63; c. 2. VIROLOGY, GENETICS. B.S, St. John's Univ.(N.Y), 61, M.S, 63; univ. fel, Nat. Insts. Health fel. & Ph.D.(microbiol), Ind. Univ, Bloomington, 67. Prin. investr. viral genetics, U.S. Army Biol. Labs, 67-71; RES. ASSOC, MERRELL NAT. LABS DIV, RICHARDSON-MERRELL, INC, 71- Am. Soc. Microbiol. Biochemical and biophysical analysis of viruses; viral replication, morphogenesis and genetics; virus purification. Address: Dept. 53, Merrell National Labs Division, Richardson-Merrell, Inc, Swiftwater, PA 18370.

FUSCALDO, KATHRYN E(LIZABETH), b. N.Y.C, Jan. 4, 31. GENETICS. B.S, Queens Col.(N.Y), 52; M.A, Hofstra Col, 55; Ph.D, Mich. State, 60. Jr. bacteriologist immunol, N.Y. State Dept. Health, 52-53; asst, Carnegie Inst, 55-56; asst. genetics, Mich. State, 56-60; asst. prof, St. John's (N.Y), 60-63; ANAT, HAHNEMANN MED. COL, 63-65, ASSOC. PROF, 65-, RES. ASSOC. PROF. MICROBIOL, 66- Instr, Hofstra Col, 55-56; guest investr, Carnegie Inst, 61-63; vis. lectr, Med. Col. Pa, 71- AAAS; Genetics Soc. Am; Am. Soc. Microbiol; Am. Soc. Cell Biol; N.Y. Acad. Sci. Biochemical genetics; immunologists; genetic control of protein synthesis. Address: Division of Genetics, Dept. of Anatomy, Hahnemann Medical College, Philadelphia, PA 19102.

FUSCHILLO, NICHOLAS, b. Saviano, Italy, Feb. 15, 27; nat; m. 54; c. 2. PHYSICS, ELECTRICAL ENGINEERING. B.Sc, London, 48, M.S, 50, Ph.D. (physics) Leeds, 52. Tech. off. high polymer physics, Brit. Nylon Spinners, 53; res. assoc. eng. physics, Cornell, 53-54; asst. prof. physics, Pa. State, 54-57; head, magnetics & semiconductors br, Franklin Inst, 57-59; mgr, phyics dept, Columbia Broadcasting Syst, 59-61; head, solid state lab, Melpar Inc, 61-64, tech. dir. appl. sci. ctr, 65-67; PROF. ELEC. ENG, RUTGERS UNIV, 67- Consult, Litton Systs; TRW Electronics; Armco Steel, Allied Chem. Co. Electronics; thin films; energy conversion; materials research; electro-optics; mos transistors. Address: 2908 Wesley Ave, Ocean City, NJ 08226.

FUSCO, ANTHONY MICHAEL, b. New Haven, Conn, Mar. 17, 31; m. 62; c. 1. ORGANIC CHEMISTRY. B.S, Yale, 53; M.S, Purdue, 57, Ph.D.(org. chem), 64. SR. CHEMIST, INTERCHEM. CORP, 59- Stereospecific polymerization; mechanism of urea; melamine-formaldehyde condensation reactions; photothermography; synthesis of polyhydric phenols; heterocyclic intermediates; disperse dyestuffs; nuclear magnetic resonance. Address: Interchemical Corp, 1255 Broad St, Clifton, NJ 07015.

FUSCO, GABRIEL CARMINE, b. Pittsburgh, Pa, Nov. 11, 36; m. 60; c. 3. ORGANIC CHEMISTRY. B.S, Duquesne, 58, M.S, 60; Ph.D. (org. chem), Colorado, 65. Res. chemist, Jackson Lab, E.I. du Pont de Nemours & Co, N.J, 65-67; asst. prof. CHEM, CALIFORNIA STATE COL.(PA), 67-68, ASSOC. PROF, 68- Am. Chem. Soc; Brit. Chem. Soc. Carbonium ion rearrangements; addition and elimination reactions; substitution reactions of saturated carbons. Address: Dept. of Chemistry, California State College, California, PA 15419.

FUSCO, JAMES V(INCENT), b. Bristol, R.I, Feb. 21, 29; m. 51; c. 4. PHYSICAL & ORGANIC CHEMISTRY. B.S, Brown, 51. Res. chemist, Esso Res. & Eng. Co, 51-57; mkt. develop. engr, ENJAY CHEM. CO, 58-62, res. & new prod. coord, 63-65, new prod. develop. MGR, 65-66, ADHESIVES INTERMEDIATES DIV, ELASTOMERS DEPT, 66- Dir, Adhesives & Sealants Coun, 66-, chmn. tech. comt, 69-71, bd. gov, 70-71. Am. Chem. Soc. Petrochemicals; synthetic elastomers. Address: Adhesives Intermediates Division, Enjay Chemical Co, P.O. Box 3272, Houston, TX 77001.

FUSCO, M(ADELINE) M, b. Waterbury, Conn, Nov. 7, 24. PHYSIOLOGY. B.S, Ohio State, 48, fel, 48-49, M.S, 49; fel, Pennsylvania, 55-59, Ph.D. (physiol), 59. Vis. lectr. PHYSIOL, Goucher Col, 49-50, instr, 50-52; asst. instr, Pennsylvania, 52-55; instr, Vassar Col, 54-55; from instr. to asst. prof, Michigan, 59-66, assoc. prof, 66-67; Med. Col. Pa, 67-71; PROF, SCH. BASIC SCI, STATE UNIV. N Y. STONY BROOK, 71- AAAS; Am. Physiol. Soc. Animal calorimetry; temperature regulation, especially in hypothalamus; temperature regulation; neural control of energy exchange; behavior; neurophysiology. Address: Dept. of Anatomy, School of Basic Sciences, State University of New York at Stony Brook, Stony Brook, NY 11790.

FUSFELD, HERBERT I(RVING), b. Brooklyn, N.Y, Feb. 13, 21; m. 43; c. 2. PHYSICS. B.A, Brooklyn Col, 41; M.A, Pennsylvania, 45, Ph.D.(physics), 50. From res. physicist to head physics & math. div, Frankford Arsenal, 41-53; sr. physicist, Am. Mach. & Foundry Co, 53-55, dir. cent. res. lab, 55-59, DIR. RES, 59-63, KENNECOTT COPPER CORP, 63- Vis. lectr, Univ. Pa, 52-53, mem. adv. comn, sch. mat. sci, 68-71; gov. bd, Am. Inst. Physics, 67-70; bd. dirs, Indust. Res. Inst, 68-71; v.pres, 71-; adv. comn, metall. div, Nat. Bur. Standards, 69-; numerical data adv. bd, Nat. Res. Coun, 70- Am. Phys. Soc; Sci. Res. Soc. Am; Am. Inst. Mining, Metall. & Petrol. Eng; Am. Inst. Aeronaut. & Astronaut. Internal friction of metals; plastic deformation and fracture; solid state physics; organization of general physical research; industrial research management. Address: 45 Mohawk Trail, Stamford, CT 06905.

FUSHIMI, FRED C(HIKASHI), b. Seattle, Wash, Jan. 29, 33; m. 58; c. 4. INORGANIC CHEMISTRY. B.A, Utah, 59, Ph.D.(inorg. chem), 64. Sr. res. chemist, MOUND LAB, MONSANTO RES. CORP, 63-65, group leader inorg. chem, 65-66, nuclear chem, 66-69, RES. SPECIALIST CHEM, 69- Sig.C, U.S.A, 53-54. Reaction kinetics and mechanisms of inorganic systems; fine particle size determination; process control computer systems; environmental control systems. Address: Mound Lab, Monsanto Research Corp, Miamisburg, OH 45342.

FUSHTEY, S(TEPHEN) G(EORGE), b. Wasel, Alta, Sept. 17, 24; m. 51; c. 4. PLANT PATHOLOGY. B.Sc, Alberta, 47, M.Sc, 50, Agr. Inst. Can. scholar, 52; Ph.D.(plant path), London, 53. Asst. plant pathologist, plant path. lab, Can. Dept. Agr, 47-51; lectr. BOT. & PLANT PATH, UNIV. GUELPH, 53-57, asst. prof, 57-64, ASSOC. PROF, 64- Am. Phytopath. Soc; Soc. Nematol; Can. Phytopath. Soc; Agr. Inst. Can. Diseases of cereal crops; nematology; turf grass diseases. Address: Dept. of Botany, University of Guelph, Guelph, Ont, Can.

FUSILLO, M(ATTHEW) H(ENRY), b. N.J, Aug. 10, 21; m. 47; c. 4. MICROBIOLOGY. B.S, Maryland, 48; M.S, George Washington, 57. Supv. bacteriologist, antibiotic res, Walter Reed Army Med. Ctr, 48-55; chief lab. sect, infectious diseases, Wash, D.C. Gen. Hosp, 55-64; CHIEF MICROBIOLOGIST, VET. ADMIN. HOSP, WASH, D.C, 64-; PROF. LECTR, GRAD. SCH, U.S. DEPT. AGR, 63- Instr, med. sch, Georgetown, 59-62; res. assoc, George Washington, 56-64. U.S.A.A.F, 43-46. AAAS; Am. Soc. Microbiol; Tissue Cult. Asn. Metabolism and genetics of antibiotic resistance; immunology of tuberculosis and staphylococcal diseases; automation in microbiology; immunoglobulins. Address: 5009 Corkran Lane, Temple Hills, MD 20031.

FUSON, NELSON, b. Canton, China, Sept. 4, 13; U.S. citizen; m. 45; c. 2. SPECTROSCOPY. A.B, Col. Emporia, 34; M.A, Univ. Kans, 35; Rackham fel, Univ. Mich, 37-38, Ph.D.(physics), 39. Lab. instr. physics, Univ. Mich, 35-37; instr, Rutgers Univ, 38-41; res. physicist, Off. Sci. Res. & Develop, Univ. Mich, 45; res. assoc, Rockefeller Found. Proj, Johns Hopkins Univ, 46-48; asst. prof. PHYSICS, Howard Univ, 48-49; assoc. prof, FISK UNIV, 49-52, PROF, 52-, DIR. FISK INFRARED SPECTROS. INST, 50- Dir, Latin Am. Fisk Infrared Spectros. Inst, São Paulo, Brazil, 65; consult, AMP, Inc, Pa, 55-57; res. assoc, Univ. Bordeaux, 56-57, vis. prof, faculty of sci, 57-59; Vanderbilt Univ, summer 60; dir. coop. study, Nashville Univ. Ctr. Coun, 69-71. Fel. AAAS; Am. Chem. Soc; Am. Phys. Soc; Am. Soc. Physics Teachers; Coblentz Soc; Soc. Social Responsibility in Sci. Applications of infrared spectroscopy to problems in chemical physics such as inter-molecular interactions, carcinogenic properties, inorganic ions in alkali halide matrices, and solid solutions; teaching of infrared spectroscopy short courses. Address: Dept. of Physics, Fisk University, Nashville, TN 37203.

FUSON, R(EYNOLD) C(LAYTON), b. Wakefield, Ill, June 1, 95. ORGANIC CHEMISTRY. B.A, Montana, 20, hon. D.Sc, 46; M.A, Univ. Calif, 21; Ph.D. (org. chem), Univ. Minn, 24; hon. D.Sc, Univ. Ill, 66. Nat. res. fel. CHEM, Harvard, 24-26, instr, 26-27; assoc, UNIV. ILL, URBANA, 27-28, asst. prof, 28-29, assoc. prof, 29-32, prof, 32-63, mem. ctr. advan. study, 59-63, EMER. PROF, 63-; EMER. DISTINGUISHED VIS. PROF, UNIV. NEV, RENO, 70-, vis. prof, 63-66. Vis. prof, Rice Univ, 47-48. With Off. Sci. Res. & Develop, 44. Outstanding achievement award, Univ. Minn, 51; John R. Kuebler Award, 64. Nat. Acad. Sci; AAAS; Am. Chem. Soc.(Nichols Medal, 53). Chemistry. Address: Dept. of Chemistry, University of Nevada, Reno, NV 89507.

FUSON, ROBERT L, b. Indianapolis, Ind, Mar. 12, 32; m. 59; c. 2. THORACIC & CARDIOVASCULAR SURGERY. M.A, DePauw Univ, 56, M.A, 57; M.D, Ind. Univ, 61. V.pres. res, Hemathermatrol Corp, 58-62; resident, med. ctr, Duke Univ, 62-69; MGR. SURG. PROD. RES. & DEVELOP. DEPT, ETHICON, INC, 69- Intern, med. ctr, Ind. Univ, 61-62; Nat. Insts. Health fel, 63-65; asst. prof. surg, Rutgers Univ, 71- Dipl, Am. Bd. Surg, 70. Am. Soc. Artificial Internal Organs. Development of biomedical devices; clinical and experimental surgical research. Address: Surgical Products Research & Development Dept, Ethicon, Inc, Route 22, Somerville, NJ 08876.

FUSON, ROGER BAKER, b. Hazard, Ky, Mar. 7, 16; m. 48. IMMUNOLOGY, ANATOMY. B.S, Kentucky, 39; B.S, Utah, 51, M.S, 52, Ph.D.(anat, microbiol), 58. Res. bacteriologist, Vet. Admin. Hosp, Salt Lake City, Utah, 52-58; assoc. dir. exp. med. lab, Deaconess Hosp, Great Falls, Mont, 58-61; scientist adminstr. res. grants br, NAT. INST. GEN. MED. SCI, 61-63, HEAD PREDOCTORAL FELS. SECT, 63- U.S.A.F, 42-46, Res, 46-, Lt. Col. AAAS; Am. Soc. Cell Biol; Am. Soc. Microbiol; N.Y. Acad. Sci; Am. Asn. Anat. Inhibition of hyaluronidase activity by blood sera as a function of neoplasia and cytotoxins elicited by transplanted tumors and normal tissues. Address: Predoctoral Section, Fellowships Branch, National Institute of General Medical Sciences, National Institutes of Health, Bethesda, MD 20014.

FUSSELL, CATHARINE P(UGH), b. Phila, Pa, July 13, 19. CELL BIOLOGY, BOTANY. A.B, Colby Col, 41; M.S, Cornell, 58; U.S. Pub. Health Serv. fel, Columbia, 60-66, Ph.D.(cell biol), 66. Admin. asst. shipping & purchasing dept, Am. Friends Serv. Cmt, Phila, 47-55; res. asst. BIOL, Brookhaven Nat. Lab, 57-60; res. assoc, Inst. Cancer Res. Phila, 66-67; Nat. Insts.

Health res. fel, Fels Res. Inst, sch. med, Temple, 67-68; ASST. PROF, PA. STATE UNIV, McKEESPORT COMMONWEALTH CAMPUS, 68- Nat. Sci. Found. instnl. res. grant, Pa. State, 69-70. AAAS; Am. Soc. Cell Biol; Bot. Soc. Am. Molecular genetics; relationship between chromosome structure and chromosome function; changes in macromolecular components of chromosomes during cell division and cell differentiation; extra nuclear DNA. Address: Dept. of Biology, McKeesport Commonwealth Campus, Pennsylvania State University, McKeesport, PA 15132.

FUSSELL, DELBERT DEAN, b. Geneva, Nebr, Aug. 17, 37; m. 59; c. 2. CHEMICAL & PETROLEUM ENGINEERING. B.S, Nebraska, Lincoln, 60, M.S, 61; Ph.D.(chem. eng), Rice, 65. SR. RES. ENGR, RES. DEPT, AMOCO PROD. CO, 67- C.Eng, U.S.A, 65-67, Capt. Am. Inst. Chem. Eng; Am. Inst. Mining, Metall. & Petrol. Eng; Soc. Petrol. Eng. Numerical solution of the boundary layer equations; effect of ultrasonics on heat and mass transfer; numerical solution of reservoir fluid flow equations including compositional effects on phase properties. Address: Research Dept, Amoco Production Co, P.O. Box 591, Tulsa, OK 74102.

FUSTER, J(OAQUIN) M(ARIA), b. Barcelona, Spain, Aug. 17, 30; m. 57; c. 3. NEUROPHYSIOLOGY. M.D, Univ. Barcelona, 53. Intern, psychiat, sch. med, Univ. Barcelona, 52-53; Balmes fel. & asst. resident, neuropsychiat. clin, Innsbruck Univ, 54; asst. resident, inst. preventive psychiat, Univ. Barcelona, 55-56; assoc. res. psychiatrist, MED. CTR, UNIV. CALIF, LOS ANGELES, 57-64, res. psychiatrist, 64-67, PROF. PSYCHIAT, 67- Del Amo fel, 56; Nat. Inst. Ment. Health career develop. award, 60-70, career scientist award, 70- AAAS; N.Y. Acad. Sci; Soc. Neurosci; Am. Psychiat. Asn. Neurophysiological basis of behavior; biological psychiatry. Address: Dept. of Psychiatry, University of California Medical Center, Los Angeles, CA 90024.

FUTCH, ARCHER H(AMNER), b. Monroe, N.C, Mar. 21, 25; m. 53; c. 3. PHYSICS. B.S, North Carolina, 49, M.S, 51; Ph.D.(physics), Maryland, 56. PHYSICIST, E.I. du Pont de Nemours & Co, 53-58; LAWRENCE RADIATION LAB, 59- U.S.A, 44-46. Am. Phys. Soc; Am. Nuclear Soc. Plasma, atomic, and nuclear physics. Address: Lawrence Radiation Lab, Box 808, Livermore, CA 94550.

FUTCH, DAVID G(ARDNER), b. Schofield Barracks, Hawaii, Aug. 31, 32; m. 67. ZOOLOGY. B.A, North Carolina, 55; M.A, Texas, 61, Ph.D.(zool), 64. Res. fel. genetics, Calif. Inst. Technol, 64-65; Inst. Animal Genetics, Edinburgh, 65-67; City of Hope Med. Ctr, 67; ASST. PROF. BIOL, SAN DIEGO STATE COL, 67- U.S.A, 56-58, Res, 58-62. Genetics Soc. Am; Soc. Study Evolution; Am. Genetic Asn. Population genetics and evolution; genetic and cytological studies of evolution in Drosophila. Address: Dept. of Biology, San Diego State College, San Diego, CA 92115.

FUTCHER, PALMER HOWARD, b. Baltimore, Md, Sept. 13, 10; m. 42; c. 2. MEDICINE. A.B, Harvard, 32; M.D, Hopkins, 36. Intern, Hopkins Hosp, 36-39, res, 41; fel. & asst. res. physician, Rockefeller Inst. Hosp, 39-41; asst. prof. med, sch. med, Wash. Univ, 46-48; assoc. prof, Johns Hopkins Univ, 48-66, dir. personnel health clin, Hopkins Med. Insts, 62-66; ASSOC. PROF. CLIN. MED, SCH. MED, UNIV. PA, 67- Exec. dir, Am. Bd. Internal Med, 67- U.S.N.R, 42-46. Am. Soc. Clin. Invest; Endocrine Soc; Am. Diabetes Asn; Am. Med. Asn; Am. Col. Physicians; Am. Clin. & Climat. Asn. Evaluation of clinical competence of physicians; administrative medicine. Address: 3930 Chestnut St, Philadelphia, PA 19104.

FUTRELL, JEAN H, b. Dry Prong, La, Oct. 20, 33; m. 55; c. 2. PHYSICAL CHEMISTRY. B.S, La. Polytech, 55; Nat. Sci. Found. fel, California, 55-56, Allied Chem. & Dye Corp. fel, 57-58, Ph.D.(chem), 58. Res. chemist, Humble Oil & Ref. Co, 58-59; sr. res. chemist & group leader, Aero-Space Res. Labs, Ohio, 61-68; PROF. CHEM, UNIV. UTAH, 68- Sloan fel, 68-72; Nat. Insts. Health career develop. award, 69-; mem. sci. adv. panel, pub. works comt, U.S. Senate, 70- U.S.A.F, 59-61, Capt. AAAS; Am. Chem. Soc; Am. Phys. Soc; Faraday Soc; Am. Soc. Mass Spectros. Chemical kinetics; mass spectrometry; ion-molecule reactions. Address: Dept. of Chemistry, Chemistry Bldg. 146, University of Utah, Salt Lake City, UT 84112.

FUTRELL, MARY FELTNER, b. Cadiz, Ky, Jan. 5, 24; m. 47; c. 2. BIOCHEMISTRY, HUMAN NUTRITION. B.S, Austin Peay State, 44; M.S, Wisconsin, 49, Ph.D.(human nutrit), 52. Teacher, grade sch, Tenn, 42-43; high sch, Tenn, 44-46, Ky, 47-49; res. asst. nutrit, Wisconsin, 48-52; res. assoc. biochem, Texas A&M, 52-54, asst. prof, home econ, 54-56; lectr, Ahmadu Bello Univ, Nigeria, 64-66; ASSOC. PROF. NUTRIT, MISS. STATE UNIV, 67- Fel. Am. Inst. Chem; Am. Home Econ. Asn; Am. Dietetic Asn. Amino acids in self-selected diets; ascorbic acid requirements; nutritional status of preschool children. Address: P.O. Drawer DT, State College, MS 39762.

FUTRELL, MAURICE C(HILTON), b. Cadiz, Ky, Jan. 28, 23; m. 47; c. 2. PLANT PATHOLOGY. B.S, West. Ky. State Col, 47; M.S, Univ. Wis, 49, Ph.D.(plant path, agron), 52; hon. Ph.D, Univ. Coahuila, 67. Instr. biol, West. Ky. State Col, 47-48; asst. plant path, Univ. Wis, 48-52; agent, U.S. Dept. Agr, Tex. A&M Univ, 52-53, plant pathologist, 53-66, mem. grad. faculty, 58-66; RES. PLANT PATHOLOGIST, U.S. DEPT. AGR. & MISS STATE UNIV, 66- With U.S. Agency Int. Develop, Ahmadu Bello Univ, Nigeria, 64- U.S.A, 43-45. Am. Soc. Agron; Am. Phytopath. Soc; Bot. Soc. Am. Fungal mycoplasma; epidemiology of Southern Corn Leaf Blight; interaction of virus and fungal diseases of corn. Address: Dept. of Plant Pathology & Weed Science, Mississippi State University, State College, MS 39762.

FUTRELLE, ROBERT PEEL, b. Wash, D.C, Apr. 23, 37; m. 62; c. 2. THEORETICAL & CHEMICAL PHYSICS. B.S, Mass. Inst. Technol, 59, Ph.D. (physics), 66. Mem. tech. staff theoret. physics, Sci. Ctr, N.Am. Rockwell Corp, 65-69, staff engr. optical physics, electrooptical lab, autonetics div, 69-71; VIS. FEL, JOINT INST. LAB. ASTROPHYS, UNIV. COLO-NAT. BUR. STANDARDS, 71- Chmn, Gordon Res. Conf. Atomic & Molecular Interactions, 70-71. AAAS; Am. Phys. Soc; Am. Asn. Physics Teachers; Asn. Comput. Mach; Inst. Elec. & Electronics Eng. Nonequilibrium statistical mechanics; kinetic theory of liquids; atomic and molecular collisions; spectral line shapes; optical propagation; syntax analysis; real-time systems;

computer graphics; models and simulation in developmental biology. Address: Joint Institute for Lab. Astrophysics, University of Colorado, Boulder, CO 80302.

FUTTERMAN, SIDNEY, b. Baltimore, Md, July 21, 29; m. 51; c. 4. BIOCHEMISTRY. B.S, George Washington, 50, M.S, 52, Ph.D.(biochem), 54. Biochemist, Nat. Insts. Health, 55-57; asst. prof. biol. chem, Harvard Med. Sch, 63-66; ASSOC. PROF. OPHTHAL, SCH. MED, UNIV. WASH, 66- Biochemist, Mass. Eye & Ear Infirmary, 57-66. U.S.P.H.S, 55-57. AAAS; Am. Soc. Biol. Chem; Am. Chem. Soc; Asn. Res. Vision & Ophthal. Carbohydrate metabolism; metabolism of the retina, and vitamin A; lipid metabolism; visual pigments. Address: Dept. of Ophthalmology, University of Washington School of Medicine, Seattle, WA 98105.

FUTTERMAN, WALTER I(RVING), b. San Francisco, Calif, Aug. 17, 25; m. 69. THEORETICAL PHYSICS. B.A, Pomona Col, 47; fel, California, Los Angeles, 52-54; Ph.D.(physics), Southern California, 55. Res. physicist, Lawrence Radiation Lab, California, 54-55; Fulbright grant, Univ. Rome, 55-56, Univ. Naples, 56-57, lectr, 57; res. physicist, Lawrence Radiation Lab, California, Berkeley, 57-62; Lockheed Missiles & Space Co, 62-68, STAFF SCIENTIST, LOCKHEED PALO ALTO LABS, 68- Ed, Propagation & Instabilities in Plasmas, Stanford Univ. Press, 63. Am. Phys. Soc. Nuclear physics; scattering; plasma physics. Address: Dept. 52-14, Bldg. 201, Lockheed Palo Alto Labs, 3251 Hanover St, Palo Alto, CA 94304.

FUZEK, JOHN F(RANK), b. Knoxville, Tenn, Dec. 21, 21; m. 43; c. 3. PHYSICAL CHEMISTRY. B.S, Tennessee, 43, M.S, 45, Hercules Powder Co. fel, 47, Ph.D.(phys. chem), 47. Chem. eng. aide, Tenn. Valley Authority, 40-42, chemist, Hercules Powder Co, Wilmington, 43-44; Off. Naval Res. fel, Tenn, 47-48; res. chemist, Beaunit Fibers Div, Beaunit Corp, 48-55, head res. physics, 55-66; sr. res. chemist, TENN. EASTMAN CO, 66-70, RES. ASSOC, 70- Oak Ridge Inst. res. award, 49. Fel. AAAS; Am. Chem. Soc; Am. Crystallog. Asn; fel. Am. Inst. Chem; Am. Asn. Textile Chem. & Colorists; Fiber Soc. Catalysis; kinetics of heterogeneous reactions; absorption from solution; cellulose chemistry; physical chemistry of polymers; kinetics of catalytic hydrogenation of terpenes; x-ray diffraction of polymers; analytical instrumentation. Address: Research Labs, Tennessee Eastman Co, Kingsport, TN 37662.

FYE, PAUL M(cDONALD), b. Johnstown, Pa, Aug. 6, 12; m. 42; c. 2. PHYSICAL CHEMISTRY. B.S, Albright Col, 35, hon. Sc.D, 55; univ. fel, Columbia, 37-38, Ph.D.(phys. chem), 39; hon. D.Sc, Tufts Univ, 70; hon. D.Sc, Southeast. Mass. Univ, 70. Lab. asst. chem, Albright Col, 32-35; statutory asst. Columbia, 35-39; asst. prof, Hofstra Col, 39-41; res. assoc. high explosives, Nat. Defense Res. Cmt. Proj, Carnegie Inst. Tech, 41-42; res. supvr, underwater explosives res. lab, Woods Hole Oceanog. Inst, 42-44, dep. res. dir, 44-45, res. dir, 45-47; assoc. prof. chem, Tennessee, 47-48; dep. chief, Naval Ord. Lab, 48-51, chief explosives res. dept, 51-56, assoc. tech. dir. res, 56-58; DIR, WOODS HOLE OCEANOG. INST, 58-, PRES, 61- Mem. steering task group, Polaris, 56-58, ad hoc group long range res. & develop, 60-65; Undersea Res. & Develop. Planning Coun, 59-; comt. oceanog, Nat. Acad. Sci, 61-70; bd. trustees, State Cols. Mass, 66; vis. comt, geol. sci. dept, Harvard, 67-; U.S. rep. sci. comn, NATO Res. Ctr, La Spezia, Italy, 68-; bd. dirs, A.D. Little, Inc, 69-; Textron, Inc, 69-; mem. corp, Marine Biol. Lab; trustee, Bermuda Biol. Sta; Woods Hole Oceanog. Inst; mem, President's Task Force Oceanog, 69; ocean affairs bd, Nat. Acad. Sci, 70- Presidential Cert. Merit, 48; U.S. Navy Meritorious Award, 51, Cert. Commendation, 60 & 66; Bur. Ord. develop. award, 46. Consult, U.S.N, 44. Fel. AAAS; Am. Chem. Soc; Am. Phys. Soc; Am. Geophys. Union; Marine Technol. Soc.(pres, 68-69). Oceanography; gas kinetics; photochemistry; purification of gases; high explosives; underwater photography; liquid state. Address: Woods Hole Oceanographic Institution, Woods Hole, MA 02543.

FYE, R(OBERT) E(ATON), b. Cresco, Iowa, Jan. 19, 24. ENTOMOLOGY. B.S, Iowa State Col, 49; M.S, Washington State, 51; Ph.D, Wisconsin, 54. Asst. entomologist, New Mexico State, 54-55; entomologist, entom. res. div, Agr. Res. Serv, U.S. Dept. Agr, 55-59; res. off, Can. Dept. Forestry, 60-65; ENTOMOLOGIST, COTTON INSECT BIOL. CONTROL LAB, ENTOM. RES. DIV, AGR. RES. SERV, U.S. DEPT. AGR, 65- U.S.A, 43-46, Sgt. Entom. Soc. Am; Ecol. Soc. Am. Biology and ecology of cotton insects, pollinators, native bees and forage insects; wasp predation; toxicology of insecticides; laboratory and field screening of insecticides; insect population dynamics; bioclimatology. Address: Cotton Insects Biological Control Lab, 2000 E. Allen Rd, Tucson, AZ 85719.

FYFE, FOREST W(ILLIAM), b. Aberdeen, Scotland, June 21, 13; m. 43; c. 4. ANATOMY. M.A, Aberdeen, Scotland, 33, M.B. & Ch.B, 37. House physician & surgeon, Royal Infirmary, Blackburn, Eng, 37-38; house surgeon, Royal Nat. Orthop. Hosp, Stanmore, Eng, 38-39; from asst. to lectr. ANAT, Aberdeen, 39-55; assoc. prof, FACULTY MED, DALHOUSIE UNIV, 56-64, PROF, 64- Am. Asn. Anat; Can. Asn. Anat; Anat. Soc. Gt. Brit. & Ireland; Royal Soc. Arts. Anatomical illustration; larynx; bone growth; connective tissues; transition and scanning electron microscopy. Address: Dept. of Anatomy, Tupper Medical Bldg, Dalhousie University, Halifax, N.S, Can.

FYFE, I(AN) MILLAR, b. Glen Ridge, N.J, Nov. 13, 25; m. 51; c. 1. AERONAUTICAL ENGINEERING, APPLIED MECHANICS. A.R.T.C, Royal Col. Sci. & Tech, 51; M.M.E, Delaware, 54; Ph.D.(mech), Stanford, 58. Res. engr. dynamics, Boeing Co, 57-60; asst. prof. aeronaut, UNIV. WASH, 60-62, assoc. prof, 62-69, PROF. AERONAUT. & ASTRONAUT, 69- NATO sr. fel, 68. U.S.A, 46-47. Am. Soc. Mech. Eng; Am. Inst. Aeronaut. & Astronaut; Am. Soc. Eng. Educ. Wave propagation in solids and fluids; impact dynamics. Address: 207 Guggenheim Hall, University of Washington, Seattle, WA 98105.

FYFE, RICHARD ROSS, b. Binghamton, N.Y, Nov. 19, 41; m. 66. c. 1. ELECTROCHEMISTRY, CHEMICAL ENGINEERING. B.S, & B.A, Lafayette Col, 64; Shell fel, Columbia Univ, 64-65, Quiney Ward Bosee fel, 65-66, M.S, 66, Samuel Ruben fel, summer 68, D.Eng.Sc.(chem. eng), 69. Chem. engr, Am. Cyanamid, Conn, summer 64; Shell Chem. Co, N.Y, summers 65 & 66; res. asst, Columbia Univ, summer 67; chem. engr, Alcorn Combustion Co, 68-69; RES. CHEM. ENGR, U.S. ARMY, PICATINNY ARSENAL, 69- Ord.C,

U.S.A, 69-, Capt. Am. Inst. Chem. Eng; Am. Chem. Soc; Electrochem. Soc; Faraday Soc. Electrochemistry; colloid chemistry; kinetics; electrostatics; shock waves; metastable and explosive materials characterization; surface chemistry; reactor design; multiple contactor separations. Address: Explosives Lab, Picatinny Arsenal, Dover, NJ 07801.

FYFE, ROBERT A(NDREW), b. Glenwood Landing, N.Y, Mar. 28, 10; m. 36, 58; c. 1. MARINE ARCHITECTURE & MARINE ENGINEERING. B.S, Mass. Inst. Tech, 32. Jr. designer, Burgess & Donaldson Yacht Designers, 32-34; hull draftsman, Newport News Shipbldg. & Dry Dock, 34-35; asst. naval archit, Naval Shipyard, Phila, 35-37; N.Y, 37-38; head boat & small craft design, Bur. Ships, U.S. Dept. Navy, 38-57; eng. div, MINE DEFENSE LAB, U.S. NAVY, 57-67, NAVAL ARCHITECT & MARINE ENGR, 67- Meritorious Civilian Serv. Award, U.S. Navy, 45. Am. Soc. Naval Eng. Development of underwater towed vehicles; hydrofoil; planning and displacement hull forms; fabrication techniques for plastic, light metal, inflatable fabric and advanced wood boat construction; light weight propulsion systems; naval architecture. Address: U.S. Navy Mine Defense Lab, 2824 Canal Dr, Panama City, FL 32401.

FYFE, WILLIAM S(EFTON), b. N.Z, June 4, 27; m. 50; c. 2. GEOCHEMISTRY. B.Sc, Univ. Otago, N.Z, 47, scholar. & M.Sc, 48, Ph.D.(chem), 52. Lectr. chem, Univ. Otago, N.Z, 48-52; res. geologist, Univ. Calif, 53-55; sr. lectr. chem, Univ. Otago, N.Z, 55-57, reader, 57-59; from assoc. prof. to prof. geol, Univ. Calif, Berkeley, 59-66; ROYAL SOC. RES. PROF. GEOCHEM, VICTORIA UNIV. MANCHESTER, 66- Geochem. Soc; Am. Chem. Soc; hon. fel. Geol. Soc. Am; fel. Royal Soc; hon. fel. Royal Soc. N.Z; cor. mem. Brazilian Acad. Sci; Mineral. Soc. Am.(award, 64); The Chem. Soc; assoc. N.Z. Inst. Chem. High pressure temperature; chemistry of complex ions. Address: Dept. of Geology, Victoria University of Manchester, Manchester, England.

FYFFE, DAVID EUGENE, b. Washington, Ind, June 29, 25; m. 65; c. 2. INDUSTRIAL ENGINEERING, OPERATIONS RESEARCH. B.S.M.E, Purdue, 50, M.S.I.E, 55; Ph.D, Northwestern, 64. Mgr. qual. control, appliance motor dept, Gen. Elec. Co, 57-61; assoc. prof. INDUST. ENG, GA. INST. TECHNOL, 64-67, PROF, 67- Consult, mfg. ed. serv, Gen. Elec. Co, N.Y, 65- U.S.A, 43-46. Opers. Res. Soc. Am; Inst. Mgt. Sci. Operations research methodology and applications for the analysis and optimization of man-machine systems. Address: Dept. of Industrial Engineering, Georgia Institute of Technology, Atlanta, GA 30332.

FYLES, JAMES THOMAS, b. Vancouver, B.C, Dec. 22, 24; m. 50; c. 4. GEOLOGY. B.A.Sc, British Columbia, 47, M.A.Sc, 49; Ph.D.(geol), Columbia, 54. Asst. geologist, B.C. DEPT. MINES & PETROL. RESOURCES, 48-54, GEOLOGIST, 54- Can. Inst. Min. & Metall; Geol. Asn. Can. Economic geology of metallic mineral deposits; structural geology; mineral resources and land use in British Columbia. Address: 1720 Kingsberry Crescent, Victoria, B.C, Can.

FYLES, JOHN GLADSTONE, b. Vancouver, B.C, Can, Feb. 27, 23; m. 50; c. 3. GEOLOGY. B.A.Sc, British Columbia, 46, M.A.Sc, 50; Ph.D.(geol), Ohio State, 56. Tech. off, GEOL. SURV. CAN, 50-56, geologist, 56-68, CHIEF DIV. QUATERNARY RES. & GEOMORPHOL, 68- Geol. Soc. Am. Pleistocene geology; geomorphology; engineering geology. Address: Division of Quaternary Research & Geomorphology, Geological Survey of Canada, 601 Booth St, Ottawa, Ont, Can. K1A 0E8.

FYMAT, ALAIN L, b. Casablanca, Morocco, Dec. 7, 38; m. 60; c. 2. METEOROLOGY, ASTROPHYSICS. B.A, Nat. Superior Sch. Meteorol, Paris, France, 59; Govt. France fel, Paris, 59-60; M.A, Sorbonne, 60; M.S, Bordeaux, 63; Ford Found. fel, California, Los Angeles, 64, U.S. Agency Int. Develop. fel, 64-67, univ. fel, 65-67, Ph.D.(meterol), 67. Staff engr, Weather Bur. Morocco, 60-63; res. meteorologist, Univ. Calif, Los Angeles, 64-67, lectr. meteorol, 67-70; MEM. TECH. STAFF, JET PROPULSION LAB, SPACE SCI. DIV, CALIF. INST. TECHNOL, 70-, sr. res. scientist, 67-70. Del, World Meteorol. Orgn, Toronto, 62; lectr, summer faculty prog, Columbia Univ, 65; sr. lectr, Univ. South. Calif, 70; vis. prof, Univ. Lille, 70-71. AAAS; N.Y. Acad. Sci; Am. Inst. Physics; Am. Astron. Soc; Optical Soc. Am; Am. Geophys. Union; Am. Meteorol. Soc; Coblentz Soc; Royal Astron. Soc. Hydrogen lyman alpha geocorona; radiative transfer in planetary atmospheres; nonconservative scattering in gaseous media; interferometric polarimetry; spectral line formation in scattering atmospheres; integral equations theory. Address: Jet Propulsion Lab, Space Sciences Division, California Institute of Technology, 4800 Oak Grove Dr, Pasadena, CA 91103.

FYNN, P(ERCY) J(AMES), b. Chicago, Ill, Feb. 21, 10; m. 32; c. 1. ORGANIC & PHYSICAL CHEMISTRY. B.S, Tulane, 32. Mgr. chem, supplies & equip, Tulane, 33-42; glass blower, south. regional lab, U.S. Dept. Agr, 42-45, chemist textiles, 45-49; asst. dir, res. lab, J.C. Penney Co, Inc, 49-56, dir, N.Y, 56-70; ASST. TO DIR. SOUTH. MKT. & NUTRIT. RES. DIV, U.S. DEPT. AGR, 71- Chmn. consumer coun, Am. Nat. Standards Inst, 68. Nat. Retail Merchants Asn. leadership award, 67; Am. Nat. Standards Inst. citation, 68. Am. Chem. Soc; Am. Soc. Test. & Mat; Am. Asn. Textile Chem. & Colorists (v.pres, 63-64, Harold C. Chapin Award, 69); Am. Asn. Textile Technol. Textile technology and applications to apparel and other consumer goods. Address: Southern Marketing & Nutrition Research Division, U.S. Dept. of Agriculture, 1100 Robert E. Lee Blvd, New Orleans, LA 70119.

FYSTROM, DELL O, b. Minneapolis, Minn, Aug. 29, 37; m. 63; c. 2. ATOMIC PHYSICS. B.A, St. Olaf Col, 59; Ph.D.(physics), Univ. Colo, Boulder, 69. ASST. PROF. PHYSICS, WIS. STATE UNIV-LA CROSSE, 69- Am. Asn. Physics Teachers. Magnetic moment; precision measurements; proton moment; nuclear magnetons. Address: Dept. of Physics; Wisconsin State University-La Crosse, La Crosse, WI 54601.

FYTELSON, MILTON, b. Bridgeport, Conn, Nov. 15, 17; m. 46; c. 2. CHEMISTRY. B.S, Yale, 37, Ph.D.(org. chem), 41. Pfizer fel, Columbia, 41-42; res. chemist, Yale, 42-43; chemist, Am. Quinine Co, Bogota, Colombia, S.Am, 43; fel, Mellon Inst, 44-45; res. chemist, E.I. du Pont de Nemours & Co, 46-58; group leader, Toms River Chem. Corp, 58-67; mgr. process develop, Otto B. May, Inc, 67-68; PRES, FYTELSON & ASSOCS, CHEM. & ENG. CONSULT, 68- Asst. chem. dept, Manhattan Col. With Off. Sci. Res. & Develop; Bd. Econ. Warfare, 44. U.S.N, 45. Am. Chem. Soc. Synthesis of vitamin A; synthesis of synthetic lubricants; synthesis and applications of organic pigments; metallo-organic complexes; process development and engineering; sulfur and chromium chemistry. Address: 859 Dewey St, Union, NJ 07083.

G

GAAFAR, S(AYED) M(OHAMMED), b. Tanta, Egypt, Jan. 18, 24; nat; m. 49; c. 4. PARASITOLOGY. B.V.Sc, Cairo, 44; Egyptian Govt. scholar, Kans. State Col, 47-50, M.S, 49, Ph.D, 50; D.V.M, Agr. & Mech. Col. Tex, 55. Veterinarian, Vet. Serv, Egypt, 44-46; asst. parasitologist, Vet. Path. Lab, Egypt, 46-47, parasitologist, 50-51; veterinarian, Rutheford Vet. Hosp, 52-54; instr, Agr. & Mech. Col. Tex, 55-56, ASST. PROF, 56-58; VET. SCI, PURDUE UNIV, 58- Soc. Parasitol; Am. Vet. Med. Asn. Resistance against parasites as affected by mineral supplements in the food; surveys on parasitic infestations; pathology of helminth parasites in domestic animals; biology of Demodex sp in domestic animals and in vitro. Address: Dept. of Veterinary Microbiology, School of Veterinary Science & Medicine, Purdue University, Lafayette, IN 47907.

GAAL, ILSE L(ISL) NOVAK, b. Vienna, Austria, Jan. 17, 24; nat; m; c. 2. MATHEMATICS. A.B, Hunter Col, 44; Whitney fel, Radcliffe Col, 44, Maltby fel, 47-48, M.A, 44, Ph.D.(math), 48. Asst, Mass. Eye & Ear Infirmary, 44-46; instr. MATH, Wellesley Col, 48-50; Jewett fel, 50-52; instr, Cornell, 52-53, asst. prof, 54-59; RES. ASSOC, Yale, 59-60; UNIV. MINN, MINNEAPOLIS, 60-, LECTR, 64- Am. Math Soc; Math. Asn. Am; Asn. Symbolic Logic. Mathematical logic; Galois theory. Address: Dept. of Mathematics, University of Minnesota, Minneapolis, MN 55455.

GAAL, STEVEN ALEXANDER, b. Budapest, Hungary, Feb. 22, 24; U.S. citizen; m. 52. MATHEMATICS. Ph.D.(math), Budapest Univ, 47. Instr. MATH, Szeged, 46-48; asst. prof, Budapest Univ, 48; mem. res. fel, Nat. Ctr. Sci. Res, Paris, 48-50; mem. Inst. Adv. Study, 50-52; instr, Cornell, 53-54, asst. prof. MATH, 54-59; res. assoc, Yale, 59-60; vis. assoc. prof, UNIV. MINN, MINNEAPOLIS, 60-61, assoc. prof, 61-63, PROF, 63- Am. Math. Soc; Math. Asn. Am; Math. Soc. France; London Math. Soc. Mathematical analysis; theory of numbers; complex variables; topology; algebra. Address: Dept. of Mathematics, University of Minnesota, Minneapolis, MN 55414.

GAALSWYK, ARIE, b. Alvord, Iowa, June 14, 18; m. 43; c. 3. APPLIED MATHEMATICS. B.A, Luther Col, 42; Chicago, 42; M.S, Wisconsin, 47; California, Los Angeles, 48-50; Ph.D.(math), Minnesota, 63. Instr. math, Luther Col, 47-48; prin. scientist, mech. div, Gen. Mills, Inc, Minn, 50-59; res. assoc. MATH, Minnesota, 59-60; assoc. prof, AUGUSTANA COL. (S.DAK), 60-70, PROF, 70- Consult, Raven Indust, S.Dak, 60- U.S.A.A.F, 42-46, Lt. Col. Am. Math. Soc; Am. Meteorol. Soc. Combustion shock waves; mathematical models for problems in mechanics and geophysics. Address: Dept. of Mathematics, Augustana College, Sioux Falls, SD 57101.

GAARDER, NEWELL THOMAS, b. La Crosse, Wis, Feb. 17, 39; m. 63; c. 1. ELECTRICAL ENGINEERING. B.A, Wisconsin, 61; M.S, Stanford, 62, Ph.D. (elec. eng), 65. Res. engr, Stanford Res. Inst, 63-65; asst. prof. ELEC. ENG, Cornell, 65-67; ASSOC. PROF, UNIV. HAWAII, 67- Summer res. engr, aeronaut. lab, Cornell, 61, Lincoln Lab, Mass. Inst. Tech, 62. AAAS; Inst. Elec. & Electronics Eng. Statistical decision theory; statistical communication theory; information sciences. Address: Dept. of Electrical Engineering, University of Hawaii, 2565 The Mall, Honolulu, HI 96822.

GAARDER, SYDNEY R(UST), b. Oshkosh, Wis, Oct. 9, 21; m. 48; c. 2. CHEMISTRY. S.B, Chicago, 43. Asst. metall. lab, Chicago, 43-44; Clinton Labs, Oak Ridge, 44; jr. technologist, E.I. du Pont de Nemours & Co, Wash, 44-45; Argonne Nat. Lab, 46-48; chemist, Atomic Energy Comn, Ill, 48-56, D.C, 56-67, chief, grants & mat. loan br, div. nuclear educ. & training, 62-67; training sect, Int. Atomic Energy Agency, 67-69; MEM. STAFF, U.S. ATOMIC ENERGY COMN, 70- AAAS; Am. Chem. Soc. Use of radioactive tracers; radiation effects; radioactive materials handling; civilian uses of atomic energy. Address: U.S. Atomic Energy Commission, Washington, DC 20545.

GABAI, HYMAN, b. Phila, Pa, Jan. 26, 26. MATHEMATICS. B.S, Temple Univ, 58; M.A, Univ. Pa, 60, Ph.D.(math), 63. Asst. prof. math. & educ, Univ. Ill, Urbana, 63-67, assoc. prof, 67-68; MATH, YORK COL.(N.Y), 67-70, PROF, 71- Vis. asst. prof. math, City Col. New York, 66-67. U.S.N, 44-46. Am. Math. Soc; Math Asn. Am. Mathematics teaching; teacher training programs. Address: Dept. of Mathematics, York College City University of New York, 150-14 Jamaica Ave, Jamaica, NY 11432.

GABALLAH, SAEED S, b. Oct. 16; U.S. citizen; m. 60; c. 3. BIOCHEMISTRY, MOLECULAR BIOLOGY. B.S, Cairo, 46; Ph.D.(biochem), Wisconsin, 54. Asst. prof. Cairo, 55-57; res. assoc. biochem, col. med, Illinois, 57-61, asst. prof, 62-63; Chicago Col. Osteop, 63-65; HEAD NEUROPSYCHIAT. LAB, VET. ADMIN. HOSP, DOWNEY, 65- AAAS; Soc. Nuclear Med; Brit. Biochem. Soc; Am. Chem. Soc; N.Y. Acad. Sci. Medical and biological research, especially central nervous system; organ and cell structure. Address: 221 W. Sheridan Pl, Lake Bluff, IL 60044.

GABAY, J(ACK) J(OSEPH), b. New York, N.Y, Nov. 1, 21; m. 52; c. 3. RADIOCHEMISTRY. B.A, N.Y. Univ, 48; Polytech. Inst. Brooklyn, 48-55. Chemist, Polychrome Corp, 49-50; Sheppard Baking Co, 50-51; Picatinny Arsenal, 51; radiochemist, Can. Radium & Uranium Corp, 51-52; N.Y. Opers. Off, U.S. Atomic Energy Cmn, 52-55; lab. supvr, Nuclear Develop. Corp. Am, 55-60; SR. RES. SCIENTIST, DIV. LABS. & RES, N.Y. STATE

DEPT. HEALTH, 60- U.S.A, 42-45. AAAS; Am. Chem. Soc; Am. Nuclear Soc; Health Physics Soc; Am. Pub. Health Asn. Radiological health and application of countermeasures to reduce public exposure to ionizing radiation; analytical chemistry; hot laboratory design and operation for handling gamma and alpha-gamma emitters. Address: 463 Bruno St, Schenectady, NY 12306.

GABAY, SABIT, b. Istanbul, Turkey, Mar. 18, 22; nat; m. 52; c. 3. BIOCHEMISTRY, PHARMACOLOGY. B.A, Galatasaray Col, Turkey, 43; B.S, Istanbul, 46; M.S, Texas A&M, 54; Ph.D.(biochem), Madrid, 58. Asst. chemist, Med. Specialties Labs, Turkey, 44-48; res. asst, Texas A&M, 53-54; res. biochemist, Philip R. Park, Inc, Calif, 54-55; Southern California, 55-59; dir. clin. chem, York-Regency Med. Labs, N.Y, 59-60; sr. res. biochemist, Columbia & Rockland State Hosp, 60-61; DIR. BIOCHEM. RES. LABS, VET. ADMIN. HOSP, 61-; ASST. PROF. PHARMACOL, SCH. DENT. MED, HARVARD, 70- Del Amo Found. sr. res. fel, postgrad. med. sch, Univ. Madrid, 57-59; asst. prof, Boston Univ, 68-70; travel awards, Sweden, Denmark, Spain, Italy, USSR, Romania & France, 58-71; secy-gen, Int. Conf. Phenothiazine Metab, France, 62; consult, Mo. Psychiat. Inst, 68-; Marcy State Hosp, 70- Soc. Biol. Psychiat; Int. Soc. Neurochem; Int. Soc. Biochem. Pharmacol; Am. Soc. Neurochem; Asn. Res. Nerv. & Ment. Disease. Neurobiochemistry; biochemical psychopharmacology and neuropharmacology encompassing drug enzymology and their metabolic mechanisms; neurochemistry; molecular pharmacology; drug-protein binding. Address: Biochemical Research Lab, Veterans Administration Hospital, Brockton, MA 02401.

GABBARD, FLETCHER, b. Sand Gap, Ky, Sept. 13, 30; m. 57; c. 2. NUCLEAR PHYSICS. B.S, Kentucky, 51; M.A, Rice, 57, Ph.D.(physics), 59. Physicist, U.S. Naval Ord. Lab, 51-52; Nat. Bur. Standards, 52-53; asst. prof. PHYSICS, UNIV. KY, 59-62, assoc. prof, 62-70, PROF, 70- Fel, Oak Ridge Inst. Nuclear Studies, summer 60; fel, Oak Ridge Assoc. Univ, summer 71. Chem.C, U.S.A, 53-55. AAAS; Am. Phys. Soc. Energy levels in light nuclei; neutron induced reactions; neutron producing reactions in medium weight nuclei. Address: Dept. of Physics, University of Kentucky, Lexington, KY 40506.

GABBARD, R(ICHARD) BRUCE, b. Bryan, Tex, Nov. 12, 28. ORGANIC CHEMISTRY, PHARMACY. B.S, Texas, 50; M.S, Wisconsin, 54, Ph.D.(pharm), 56. Hosp. pharmacist, Terrell State Hosp, Tex, 50-52; res. assoc, Ben May Lab. Cancer Res, Chicago, Ill, 56-58; SR. ORG. CHEMIST, OCHSNER MED. FOUND, 58- AAAS; Am. Chem. Soc. Pharmaceutical chemistry; biochemistry of steroids; steroid synthesis; cancer chemotherapy. Address: Ochsner Medical Foundation, Research Bldg, 1520 Jefferson Hwy, New Orleans, LA 70121.

GABBAY, EDMOND J, b. Baghdad, Iraq, Dec. 15, 38; U.S. citizen; m. 63. ORGANIC CHEMISTRY, BIOCHEMISTRY. B.S, City Col. New York, 60; Ph.D.(chem), Columbia, 65. Asst. prof. CHEM, Rutgers Univ, 65-69; ASSOC. PROF, UNIV. FLA, 69- Am. Soc. Biol. Chem; Am. Chem. Soc. Application of physical organic chemistry to current biochemical problems. Address: Dept. of Chemistry, University of Florida, Gainesville, FL 32601.

GABBAY, KENNETH HESKEL, b. Baghdad, Iraq, Oct. 18, 36; U.S. citizen; m. 63; c. 3. MEDICINE, BIOCHEMISTRY. B.S, City Col. New York, 56; M.D, Rochester, 61. Intern med, Sinai Hosp. Baltimore, Inc, 61-62, resident, 62-63; res. fel. pediat, Albert Einstein Col. Med, 63-64; fel. med, Mass. Gen. Hosp. & Harvard Med. Sch, 64-66; chief cell biol. unit, diabetes & arthritis br, field res. sect, U.S. PUB. HEALTH SERV, 66-68, DIR. CELL BIOL. UNIT & DEP. CHIEF DIABETES & ARTHRITIS FIELD SECT, 68- Asst. in med, Boston City Hosp. & Harvard Med. Sch, 66- U.S.P.H.S, 66-, Surg. AAAS; Am. Diabetes Asn. Diabetes and metabolic diseases; etiology and biochemistry of diabetic complications; role of accessory pathways of glucose metabolism in the development of neuropathy, retinopathy and nephropathy. Address: U.S. Public Health Service, Diabetes & Arthritis Branch, Field Research Section, 745 Massachusetts Ave, Boston, MA 02118.

GABBERT, PAUL GEORGE, b. Brownsville, Tex, Dec. 3, 35; m. 59; c. 2. BIOCHEMISTRY, TOXICOLOGY. B.A, Stanford, 58; Ph.D.(biochem), California, San Francisco, 67. Res. asst. biochem, res. & develop. serv, Letterman Gen. Hosp, San Francisco, 59-61, proj. supvr. pharmacol. res, 61-65; asst. biochem, sch. med, California, San Francisco, 65-67; res. biochemist, Huntingdon Res. Ctr. Inc. Div, Becton-Dickinson & Co, 67-68, dir. dept. chem, 68-71; BIOCHEMIST-TOXICOLOGIST, CENT. LABS. ASSOC. MD. PATHOLOGISTS, LTD, 71- U.S.A, 59-61. Am. Chem. Soc; fel. Am. Inst. Chem. Hepatic lipid transport; hepatic carbohydrate metabolism; effect of drugs on pharmacodynamic parameters of isolated organ systems; detection of toxic substances in medical devices and biological material; methods development. Address: Central Labs of Associated Maryland Pathologists, Ltd, 1526 York Rd, Timonium, MD 21093.

GABBY, J(OHN) LESTER, b. Chicago, Ill, Sept. 30, 09; m. 33; c. 1. FOOD TECHNOLOGY. B.S, Illinois, 30, M.S, 31. Res. chemist, Armour & Co, Ill, 32-39; Glidden Co, 39-49, prod. mgr. fine chems. dept, 45-51; dir. nutrit, Blue Ribbon Mills, Ore, 51-52; dir. res. & exp. farm, O.A. Cooper Co, Nebr, 52-53; dir. nutrit, Honeymead, Inc, Iowa, 53-55; sect. leader nutrit. prod. develop, res. ctr, MEAD JOHNSON & CO, 55-67, sect. leader food prod. develop, 67-69, ASSOC. DIR. CEREAL PROD. DEVELOP, NUTRIT. DIV, 69- Am. Oil Chem. Soc; Inst. Food Tech; Am. Asn. Cereal Chem. Soya products in nutrition; development of human food specialties. Address: Food Product Development, Mead Johnson & Co, 2404 Pennsylvania Ave, Evansville, IN 47721.

GABEL, ALBERT A, b. Fremont, Ohio, Mar. 3, 30; m. 54; c. 6. VETERINARY SURGERY. D.V.M, Ohio State Univ, 54, M.Sc, 59. Ambulatory clinician vet. med, COL. VET. MED, OHIO STATE UNIV, 54-55, instr. VET. SURG, 57-60, asst. prof, 60-63, assoc. prof, 63-69, PROF, 69-, univ. develop. fund grant, 58-59. Wyeth Lab. res. grant, 61-63. Dipl, Am. Col. Vet. Surg; Borden Award, 54. U.S.A.F, 55-57, Res, 54-55 & 57-59, Capt; Commendation Medal. Am. Col. Vet. Surg; Am. Vet. Med. Asn. Anesthesia and orthopedics of horses and cattle. Address: 2578 Kenny Rd, Columbus, OH 43210.

GABEL, J(AMES) RUSSEL, b. Pottstown, Pa, Aug. 21, 18; m. 44; c. 1. PROTOZOOLOGY. B.S, Pa. State Teachers Col. Lock Haven, 47; Ph.D.(zool), Pennsylvania, 53. Asst. instr. zool, Pennsylvania, 47-53; asst. prof, Fisk, 53-56; assoc. prof, W.Liberty State Col, 56-59; asst. prof, SAN FRANCISCO STATE COL, 59-64, ASSOC. PROF. BIOL, 64- U.S.A.A.F, 42-46, 2nd Lt. Am. Micros. Soc. Protozoan parasitology; histology. Address: Division of Science, Mathematics & Engineering, San Francisco State College, 1600 Holloway Ave, San Francisco, CA 94132.

GABELMAN, IRVING J(ACOB), b. Brooklyn, N.Y, Nov. 12, 18; m. 49; c. 2. ELECTRICAL ENGINEERING. B.A, Brooklyn Col, 38; B.E.E, City Col. New York, 45; M.E.E, Polytech. Inst. Brooklyn, 48; Ph.D.(elec. eng), Syracuse, 61. Radio engr, Watson Labs, Red Bank, N.J, U.S. Dept. Air Force, 45-51; electronic scientist, ROME AIR DEVELOP. CTR, GRIFFISS AFB, 51-59, dir. advan. studies, 59-66, chief plans, 67-70, CHIEF SCIENTIST, 71- U.S. mem, avionics panel, Adv. Group Aeronaut. Res. & Develop, NATO, 63-69, dep. chmn, 69-71, chmn, 71- Fel. AAAS; fel. Inst. Elec. & Electronics Eng. Switching circuits, especially threshold element logical design; electronic computers. Address: Rome Air Development Center, Code XP, Griffiss Air Force Base, Rome, NY 13440.

GABELMAN, JOHN W(ARREN), b. Manila, Philippines, May 18, 21; m. 45; c. 2. GEOLOGY. Geol.E, Colo. Sch. Mines, 43, M.S, 48, D.Sc.(geol. eng), 49. Jr. engr. & geologist, N.J. Zinc Co, 43-44, 46; instr. geol, Colo. Sch. Mines, 46-49; geologist, Colo. Fuel & Iron Corp, 49-52; Am. Smelting & Ref. Co, 52-54; U.S. ATOMIC ENERGY COMN, 54-62, chief resource appraisal br, 62-71, CHIEF TECH. SERV. BR, 71- U.S.N.R, 44-46. Geol. Soc; Am. Soc. Econ. Geol; Asn. Petrol. Geol; Am. Inst. Min, Metall. & Petrol. Eng; Am. Geophys. Union; Peruvian Geol. Soc; Mex. Geol. Soc; Am. Inst. Prof. Geol. Structural geology and tectonics; ore deposits; hydrothermal rock alteration; uranium geology and mining. Address: Division of Raw Materials, U.S. Atomic Energy Commission, Washington, DC 20545.

GABELMAN, WARREN H(ENRY), b. Tilden, Nebr, Apr. 18, 21; m. 45. PLANT GENETICS. B.Sc, Nebraska, 42, fel, 46; Yale, 46-49. Asst. hort, exp. sta, Nebraska, 38-42; fel. plant genetics in charge veg. breeding program, Conn. Exp. Sta, 46-49; asst. prof. HORT, UNIV. WIS, MADISON, 49-56, assoc. prof, 56-60, PROF, 60-, CHMN. DEPT, 65- U.S.N.R, 42-46, Lt. Fel. AAAS; Genetics Soc. Am; fel. Am. Soc. Hort. Sci. Cytoplasmic inheritance of male sterility in corn, onions, beets, and carrots; byosynthesis of carotenes in carrots; genetics of mineral nutrition efficiencies in higher plants. Address: Dept. of Horticulture, University of Wisconsin, Madison, WI 53706.

GABELNICK, HELENE SEEDER, b. Allegan, Mich, July 23, 43; m. 65. PHYSICAL CHEMISTRY. B.S, Michigan, 64; Anthony fel, California, Berkeley, 67-68, Ph.D.(phys. chem), 68. Asst. prof. chem, Chicago State Col, 68-71. Infrared and Raman spectroscopy; liquids. Address: 10447 S. Bell Ave, Chicago, IL 60643.

GABELNICK, HENRY LEWIS, b. Boston, Mass, May 10, 40; m. 62; c. 2. CHEMICAL ENGINEERING. B.S, Mass. Inst. Tech, 61, Sloan fel, 61-62, M.S, 62; Textile Res. Inst. fel, Princeton, 62-66, Ph.D.(chem. eng), 66. Sr. chem. engr, res. dept, Monsanto Co, Mass, 66-68; CHEM. ENGR, BIOMED. ENG. BR, NAT. INSTS. HEALTH, 68- Am. Inst. Chem. Eng; Am. Chem. Soc; N.Y. Acad. Sci. Kinetics of decomposition reactions; physical properties of polymers; blood rheology; kinetics of drug distribution in vivo; biomaterials. Address: Biomedical Engineering Branch, National Institutes of Health, Bethesda, MD 20014.

GABER, BRUCE PAUL, b. Chicago, Ill, Oct. 15, 41; m. 66; c. 1. PHYSICAL BIOCHEMISTRY. B.A, Hendrix Col, 63; Ph.D.(biochem), Univ. South. Calif, 68. Fel, IBM Watson Res. Lab, Columbia Univ, 68-70; T.J. Watson Res. Ctr, 70-71; ASST. PROF. CHEM, UNIV. MICH-DEARBORN, 71- AAAS; Am. Chem. Soc; N.Y. Acad. Sci. Physical biochemistry of metalloproteins; application of magnetic resonance to biochemical problems; role of dithiols in enzymatic reactions. Address: Dept. of Natural Science, University of Michigan at Dearborn, Dearborn, MI 48128.

GABERSON, HOWARD A(XEL), b. Detroit, Mich, Apr. 11, 31; m. 69. APPLIED MECHANICS. B.S.M.E, Michigan, 55; S.M, Mass. Inst. Technol, 57, Ph.D.(appl. mech), 67. Mech. consult, Raytheon Co, 57-59; asst. prof. mech. eng, Lowell Tech. Inst, 59-60; Boston, 60-64; proj. engr, mat. res, Teledyne Inc, 67; assoc. prof. mech. eng, Hawaii, 67-68; SR. PROJ. ENGR, NAVAL CIVIL ENG. LAB, 68- Consult, Lessells & Assocs, 59-61; Brewer Eng. Labs, 61-64; Woods Hole Oceanog. Inst, 62-64; summers, Cambridge Acoustical Assocs, 61, Space Tech. Labs, 63, Los Angeles Div, N.Am. Aviation Inc, 64, Instrumentation Labs, Mass. Inst. Technol, 65. Am. Soc. Mech. Eng; Soc. Exp. Stress Anal; Am. Soc. Eng. Educ; Nat. Soc. Prof. Eng; Acoustical Soc. Am; Sci. Res. Soc. Am. Vibration, shock and dynamics analysis; experimental mechanics; nonlinear effects; oscillating conveyors; ship slamming; equipment dynamic test philosophy; ocean and deep ocean structural dynamics. Address: Naval Civil Engineering Lab, Port Hueneme, CA 93043.

GABERT, AUGUST CARL, b. Sturgeon Bay, Wis, Dec. 23, 37; m. 68; c. 1. PLANT BREEDING & GENETICS. B.S, Univ. Wis, Madison, 59, M.S, 61, Ph.D.(genetics), 63. PLANT SCIENTIST, FERRY-MORSE SEED CO, PUREX CORP, LTD, 63- Am. Soc. Agron; Am. Soc. Hort. Sci; Am. Inst. Biol. Sci. Haploidy as a tool in plant science; ploidy levels of vegetable crops; varietal development in cucumbers, squash, table beets and storage onions; inheritance of desirable characteristics in vegetable crops. Address: 428 S. Lewis St, Columbus, WI 53925.

GABLE, C(LARENCE) L(OUIS), b. Detroit, Mich, May 17, 21; m. 47; c. 2. ORGANIC CHEMISTRY. B.S, Wayne State, 43. Group leader adhesives, Minn. Mining & Mfg. Co, 41-52; res. group leader, appln. elastomers & rubber chems, Monsanto Co, 52-61; res. specialist appln. polurethanes & polycarbonates, MOBAY CHEM. CO, 61-65, sr. group leader thermoplastics appln. res, 65-67, MGR. plastics appln. res, 67-71, THERMOPLASTICS DEVELOP, 71- U.S.A, 43-46. Am. Inst. Chem; Am. Chem. Soc. Adhesives; elastomers; rubber chemicals; polyurethanes; polycarbonates. Address: 1265 Sun Ridge Dr, Pittsburgh, PA 15241.

GABLE, JAMES JACKSON, JR, b. Oklahoma City, Okla, Apr. 3, 18; m. 41; c. 5. INTERNAL MEDICINE. B.S, Univ. Okla, 40, M.D, 42. Asst. prof. MED, SCH. MED, UNIV. OKLA, 50-61, ASSOC. PROF, 61- Attend. physician, Vet. Admin. Hosp, 53-; chief med. serv, Presby. Hosp, 62-67, mem. trustees, 64. Dipl, Am. Bd. Internal Med, 53. Med.C, U.S.A, 43-45, 50-52. Fel. Am. Col. Physicians; N.Y. Acad. Sci. Clinical aspects of internal medicine. Address: Dept. of Medicine, Oklahoma City Clinic, 301 N.W. 12th St, Oklahoma City, OK 73103.

GABLE, RALPH WILLIAM, b. San Antonio, Tex, Sept. 27, 29; m. 53; c. 3. PHYSICAL CHEMISTRY. B.S, Univ. Tex, 50; M.A, Duke Univ, 53, Am. Cyanamid Co. fel, 53-54, Ph.D.(phys. chem), 56. Asst. prof. CHEM, Pfeiffer Col, 55-57, assoc. prof, 57-60, head dept, 55-60; asst. prof, DAVIDSON COL, 60-64, ASSOC. PROF, 64- Res. assoc, Fla. State Univ, 68-69. AAAS; Am. Chem. Soc. Ion exchange; non-aqueous electrolyte solutions; water structure. Address: Dept. of Chemistry, Davidson College, Davidson, NC 28036.

GABLER, ROBERT EARL, b. Lodi, Ohio, Nov. 22, 27; m. 50; c. 3. PHYSICAL GEOGRAPHY. B.S, Ohio, 49; M.S, Pa. State, 51; Ed.D.(sci), Columbia, 57. Teacher, high schs, Ohio, 50-55; lectr. GEOG, Hunter Col, 55-57; asst. prof, WEST. ILL. UNIV, 57-61, assoc. prof, 61-64, PROF. & CHMN. DEPT, 64-, dir. Nat. Defense Ed. Act Geog. Inst, 65-68. Consult, geog. inst. progs, U.S. Off. Educ, 65-66; dir. coord, Nat. Coun. Geog. Educ, 63-69; mem. nominating comt, 68-69, const. revision comt, 68-, mem. exec. bd, 69-, joint comt, Nat. Coun. Geog. Educ-Asn. Am. Geog, 70- U.S.A, 46-47. Asn. Am. Geog. Physical geography, especially physiography, with strong regional interests in the geography of Asia; application of geography in American education. Address: Dept. of Geography, Western Illinois University, Macomb, IL 61455.

GABLER, WALTER LOUIS, b. Chicago, Ill, May 30, 31; m. 52; c. 4. BIOCHEMISTRY. Univ. Ill, 49-52; D.D.S, Northwest. Univ, 56, Ph.D.(chem), 64. Instr. pedodontics, dent. sch, Northwest. Univ, 58-59, biochem, 60-64; asst. prof. biochem. pedodontics, dent. sch, Univ. Ore, 64-65, ASSOC. PROF, 65-67; Univ. Ky, 67-69; ORAL BIOL. & BIOCHEM, DENT. SCH, UNIV. ORE, 69-, AFFILIATE BIOCHEM, MED. SCH, 71- Nat. Heart Inst. fel, 61-64; Pharmaceut. Mfrs. Asn. grant, 70-71; Advan. Inst. Dent. Res, 71; partic, Northwest Environ. Health Conf, 71; Epilepsy Found. Am. grant, 71-72; vis. scientist, Ore. Regional Primate Res. Ctr. Dent.C, 56-58, Capt. AAAS; Int. Asn. Dent. Res; N.Y. Acad. Sci. Biochemistry of inflammation; metabolism of Collagen; drug metabolism during pregnancy. Address: 2 Bartok Pl, Lake Oswego, OR 97034.

GABLIKS, JANIS, b. Nitaure, Latvia, Nov. 1, 24; nat; m. 50; c. 2. MICROBIOLOGY. D.D, Baltic Univ, Ger, 49; M.S, Rutgers, 57, Ph.D, 63. Dent. surgeon, Int. Refugee Org. Eutin, Ger, 49-51; asst. path. & virol, E.R. Squibb & Sons, N.J, 52-55; biochem, bur. biol. res, Rutgers, 56-57; res. assoc. virol, Schering Co, 57-60; instr. bact, Rutgers, 60-63; asst. prof. cell biol, Mass. Inst. Technol, 63-67; ASSOC. PROF. BIOL, NORTHEAST. UNIV, 67- Am. Soc. Microbiol. Bacterial toxins; carcinogens; nutrition and viral infections; insecticides; cell cultures. Address: Dept. of Biology, Northeastern University, Boston, MA 02356.

GABLIKS, MAIGONIS, b. Riga, Latvia, May 26, 23; U.S. citizen; m. 57; c. 1. ORGANIC CHEMISTRY. B.S, Rutgers, 57. CHEMIST, Petro-Tex Chem. Corp, 57-65; FMC CORP, PRINCETON, 66- Am. Chem. Soc. Catalytic polymerization of olefines; catalytic dehydrogenation of hydrocarbons; organometallic compounds and polyurethanes. Address: 220 Grant Ave, Highland Park, NJ 08904.

GABOR, ANDREW J(OHN), b. Budapest, Hungary, June 2, 35; m. 61; c. 3. NEUROLOGY, NEUROPHYSIOLOGY. B.A, George Washington Univ, 56, M.S, 58; Ph.D.(anat), Duke Univ, 62, M.D, 64. Instr. neuroanat, med. ctr, Duke Univ, 62-64, 66, resident neurol, 65-67; clin. assoc, Electroencephalog. & clin. Neurophysiol. Br, Nat. Insts. Health, 67-69; DIR. ELECTROENCEPHALOG. LAB, SACRAMENTO MED. CTR. & ASST. PROF. NEUROL, SCH. MED, UNIV. CALIF, DAVIS, 69- U.S.P.H.S, 67-69. AAAS; Am. Acad. Neurol; Am. Epilepsy Soc. Morphological changes associated with dietary cataract in albino mice and electrographic and behavioral manifestations of stimulation of claustrum of cats; clinical neurology and clinical and electrographic manifestations of seizure disorders; cortical organization with special reference to the underlying mechanisms of epilepsy. Address: Dept. of Neurology, School of Medicine, University of California, Davis, CA 95616.

GABOR, DENNIS, b. Budapest, Hungary, June 5, 00; Brit. citizen; m. 36. PHYSICAL OPTICS, ELECTRONICS. Dipl.Ing, Tech. Univ, Berlin, 24, Dr.Ing, 27; D.Sc.(sci), London, 64; hon. Dr, Univ. Southampton, 70, Delft Univ. Technol, 71. Res. engr, Siemens & Halske, Germany, 27-33; Brit. Thomson-Houston, Eng, 34-48; reader electronics, IMP. COL, UNIV. LONDON, 49-57, prof. appl. electron physics, 58-67, SR. RES. FEL, 67-; STAFF SCIENTIST, CBS LABS, 67- Vis. prof, State Univ. N.Y. Stony Brook, 68-69. Cristoforo Colombo Prize and Medal, Int. Inst. Commun, Italy, 67; Albert Michelson Medal, Franklin Inst, 68; Comdr, Order of Brit. Empire, 70; Nobel Prize for Physics, 71. Hungarian Army, 18. Fel. Royal Soc.(Rumford Medal, 68); fel. Brit. Inst. Physics (Thomas Young Medal, 67); fel. Brit. Inst. Elec. Eng; hon. mem. Hungarian Acad. Sci; French Phys. Soc. (Prix Holweck, 71); Inst. Elec. & Electronics Eng.(Medal of Honor, 70). Electrical transients; electrical discharges and electronics devices; communication theory; holography. Address: CBS Labs, 227 High Ridge Rd, Stamford, CT 06905.

GABOR, JOHN DEWAIN, b. Chicago, Ill, Aug. 8, 32; m. 61; c. 2. CHEMICAL ENGINEERING. B.S, Illinois, 54; Standard Oil Co. Ind, fel, Cornell, 56-57, Ph.D.(chem. eng), 57. Asst. chem. engr, ARGONNE NAT. LAB, 57-64, ASSOC. CHEM. ENGR, 64- Inst. Chem. Eng; Am. Chem. Soc; Sci. Res. Soc. Am. Fluidization; heat transfer; fluid mechanics; process development for nuclear fuel reprocessing; chemical reactors. Address: Argonne National Lab, D208, 9700 S. Cass Ave, Argonne, IL 60439.

GABOR, THOMAS, b. Budapest, Hungary, June 28, 25; U.S. citizen; m. 63; c. 2. PHYSICAL CHEMISTRY. B.Sc, Univ. Sci, Hungary, 48; Ph.D.(phys. chem), London, 59. RES. CHEMIST org. chem, Alco Gand, Belgium, 49-50; Taubmans Chems. Co, Australia, 51-52; Monsanto Chem. Co, Australia, 53-54; phys. chem, Commonwealth Sci. & Indust. Res. Orgn, 55-56; res. labs, Westinghouse Elec. Corp, 60-63; Battelle Mem. Inst, 64-69; RES. SPECIALIST, CENT. RES. LABS, 3M CO, 69- Crystal growth; surface chemistry. Address: Central Research Labs, 3M Co, St. Paul, MN 55101.

GABOUREL, JOHN D(USTAN), b. San Francisco, Calif, Oct. 16, 28; m. 51; c. 5. PHARMACOLOGY. B.S, California, 50; M.S, San Francisco, 51; Ph.D. (pharmacol), Rochester, 57. Res. assoc, atomic energy proj, Rochester, 55-57; instr. PHARMACOL, med. sch, Stanford, 57-60, asst. prof, 60-64; assoc. prof, MED. SCH, UNIV. ORE, 64-71, PROF, 71- Consult. toxicol, Univ. Rochester, 56- Chem.C, 53-55, Res, 55-61, Capt. AAAS; Am. Chem. Soc; Soc. Pharmacol. & Exp. Therapeut. Cancer research; physiological factors which limit growth; effect of adrenal steroids on lymphoid tissue; drug metabolism; metabolism of atropine; anticonvulsants. Address: Dept. of Pharmacology, University of Oregon Medical School, 3181 S.W. Sam Jackson Park Rd, Portland, OR 97201.

GABRIEL, CEDRIC J(OHN), b. Gustine, Calif, Mar. 25, 35; m. 64; c. 1. SOLID STATE PHYSICS. A.B, Fresno State Col, 56; Ph.D.(physics), California, Berkeley, 64. RES. PHYSICIST, Naval Ord. Lab, Corona, 64-70; NAVAL ELECTRONICS LAB. CTR, 70- AAAS; Am. Phys. Soc. Nuclear quadrupole resonance spectroscopy; magnetooptics in solids. Address: Code 2600, Naval Electronics Lab. Center, 271 Catalina Blvd, San Diego, CA 92152.

GABRIEL, DAVID SAMUEL, b. Lakewood, Ohio, Oct. 1, 19; m. 43; c. 3. MECHANICAL ENGINEERING. B.M.E, Akron, 43. With NASA, 43-58, chief propulsion syst. div, 58-61, nuclear syst. div, 61-63, mgr, Centaur proj, 63-66; chief engr. propulsion systs, Bell Aerosysts. Co, N.Y, 66-69; DEP. MGR, SPACE NUCLEAR PROPULSION, ATOMIC ENERGY COMN, NASA, 69- Assoc. fel. Am. Inst. Aeronaut. & Astronaut. Propulsion systems. Address: Atomic Energy Commission, NASA, Washington, DC 20545.

GABRIEL, EDWIN Z, b. Union City, N.J, Aug. 26, 13. ELECTRICAL ENGINEERING. B.S, Newark Col. Eng, 36, M.E, 39, M.S, 52; Harvard, 48-49; Mass. Inst. Tech, 49-50; Stevens Inst. Tech, 53-54. Heating engr, Webster Tallmadge & Co, N.J, 38-39; efficiency & mech. engr, Prudential Ins. Co. Am, 39-41; asst. mech. engr, U.S. Engr. Off, N.Y, 41-42, Manhattan dist, Mass, 42-43; assoc. mech. engr, Watson Labs, U.S. Air Force, N.J, 45-48, Cambridge Res. Center, 48-50; electronic engr, Signal Corps Eng. Labs, N.J, 50-52; proj. engr, Curtiss-Wright Corp, 52-53; proj. engr. & consult, Kearfott Co, Inc, 53-55; asst. prof. elec. eng, Lehigh, 55-56; elec. & mech. eng, Villanova, 56-60; elec. eng, Fairleigh Dickinson, 60-62; assoc. prof, weapons dept, U.S. Naval Acad, 62-64; writing textbook, 64-65; independent comput. design, develop. & mfr, 65; PROJ. ENGR. AVIONICS LAB, ELECTRONICS COMMAND, U.S. ARMY, 65- Award, U.S. Army, 67. U.S.A.A.F, 43-45. Am. Soc. Mech. Eng; Am. Soc. Eng. Educ; Inst. Elec. & Electronics Eng. Study and design of automatic controls and analog and digital components and systems; use of teaching aids for effective presentation of the principles of physics. Address: 318 B. South St, Eatontown, NJ 07724.

GABRIEL, GARABET J(ACOB), b. Basrah, Iraq, Feb. 15, 35; U.S. citizen. ELECTRICAL ENGINEERING, PHYSICS. B.S, St. Louis, 56; M.S, Ill. Inst. Tech, 60; Ph.D.(elec. eng. physics), Northwestern, 64. Engr, Motorola Inc, Ill, 56-57; instr. elec. eng, Ill. Inst. Tech, 57-61; res. asst. microwave physics, Northwestern, 61-64; staff scientist, Hallicrafters Co, 64-65; asst. prof. ELEC. ENG, UNIV. NOTRE DAME, 65-69, ASSOC. PROF, 69-, STAFF MEM, RADIATION LAB, 65- Res. assoc, res. inst, Chicago Med. Sch, 60; summer vis. scientist, Stritch Sch. Med, Loyola (Ill), 67. Inst. Elec. & Electronics Eng. Electromagnetic wave propagation in arbitrary, anisotropic, inhomogeneous dissipative media, perturbation and variation methods; statistical theoretical analysis of radiation scattering in fluctuating media. Address: Dept. of Electrical Engineering, University of Notre Dame, Notre Dame, IN 46556.

GABRIEL, HENRY, b. Berlin, Ger, Apr. 28, 14; nat; m. 38. INORGANIC & PHYSICAL CHEMISTRY. B.S, Long Island, 34; M.S, George Washington, 49; Ph.D.(chem), Stanford, 51. Prof. German & asst. dir, Berlitz Sch. Langs, 36-43; assoc. chem, George Washington, 46-49; instr, Santa Clara, 49-51; asst. prof, Fisk, 51-54; assoc. prof, Siena Col, 54-56; mgr. tech. info, PHILLIPS PETROL. CO, 56-63, DEVELOP. ENGR, PATENT DIV, 63- Carnegie Found. grant, Fisk, 51-53. U.S.A, 43-46. Am. Chem. Soc. Rare earth elements, separation and compounds; preparation, properties and reactions of silicon compounds; ion exchange and adsorption; information storage and retrieval systems. Address: 1948 S. Sante Fe, Bartlesville, OK 74003.

GABRIEL, JOHN R, b. Leeds, Eng, Apr. 30, 31. APPLIED MATHEMATICS, COMPUTER SCIENCE. B.S.(pure & appl. math) & B.S.(physics & radio physics), Univ. Otago, N.Z, 52, Shirtcliffe fel, 52-53, M.S, 53. Asst. lectr. physics, Univ. Otago, N.Z, 54-55, Imp. Chem. Industs. fel, 55-57; theoret. physicist, Inst. Nuclear Sci, N.Z, 57-58; sr. spec. res. fel. theoret. phys, U.K. Atomic Energy Auth, Eng, 58-62; vis. res. fel, solid sci. div, ARGONNE NAT. LAB, 62-65, asst. head comput. ctr, APPL. MATH DIV, 65-69, ASSOC. COMPUT. SCIENTIST, 69- Fel. Brit. Inst. Phys. & Phys. Soc; Am. Phys. Soc; Inst. Elec. & Electronics Eng; Asn. Comput. Mach; Soc. Indust. & Appl. Math; Am. Math. Soc. Group theory and quantum mechanics; shell model calculations; general and special purpose programming languages; mathematical biology; hydrodynamics and thermal pollution. Address: Applied Mathematics Division, Bldg. 221, Argonne National Laboratory, 9700 S. Cass Ave, Argonne IL 60439.

GABRIEL, KARL L(EONARD), b. Phila, Pa, July 27, 29; m. 52; c. 4. PHARMACOLOGY, TOXICOLOGY. A.B, Pennsylvania, 51, V.M.D, 56; Ph.D, Jefferson Med. Col, 64; Nat. Insts. Health fel, Drexel Inst, 63-65, M.S, 65. Asst. dir, Indust. Biol. Res. & Testing Lab, Inc, Pa, 56-61; v.pres. & dir. res, AME Assocs, 65-66; ASSOC. PROF. biol. sci. & environ. eng, Drexel Inst. Technol, 66-71; PHARMACOL, MED. COL. PA, 71-, vis. asst. prof,

65-71. Instr, sch. vet. med, Univ. Pa, 60-63, asst. prof, 63-65. Am. Chem. Soc; Am. Soc. Microbiol; Soc. Cosmetic Chem; Am. Vet. Med. Asn; Soc. Toxicol; N.Y. Acad. Sci; Am. Asn. Lab. Animal Sci. Applied microbiology; biomathematics. Address: P.O. Box 8598, Philadelphia, PA 19101.

GABRIEL, LESTER H, b. Brooklyn, N.Y, Mar. 17, 28; m. 50; c. 2. CIVIL ENGINEERING. B.S.C.E, Cooper Union, 49; M.S.C.E, Polytech. Inst. Brooklyn, 56; Ph.D, Univ. Calif, Berkeley, 71. Civil engr, U.S. Bur. Reclamation, 49-51; struct. engr, Farkas & Barron, 51-52; Severud-Elstad-Krueger, 52-55; sr. struct. engr, Kaiser Engrs, 55-57; asst. prof. CIVIL ENG, SACRAMENTO STATE COL, 57-62, assoc. prof, 62-67, PROF, 67-, chmn. dept, 63-68. Nat. Sci. Found. sci. fel, California, 61-; mem. comt. buried struct, hwy. res. bd, Nat. Acad. Sci-Nat. Res. Coun, 64-67. Am. Soc. Civil Eng; Am. Concrete Inst; Am. Soc. Eng. Educ. Soil-structure interaction for static and dynamic loads on buried structures; concrete materials and materials of manufacture. Address: Dept. of Civil Engineering, Sacramento State College, 6000 Jay St, Sacramento, CA 95819.

GABRIEL, MORDECAI LIONEL, b. New York, N.Y, March 18, 18; m. 45; c. 2. BIOLOGY. B.A, Yeshiva Col, 38; A.M, Columbia, 38, univ. fel, 42-43, Ph.D. (zool), 43. Asst. zool, Columbia, 38-41, lectr, 41-42; instr. genetics, Connecticut, 43-45; BIOL, BROOKLYN COL, 45-50, asst. prof, 50-55, assoc. prof, 55-63, PROF, 63-, DEAN SCH. SCI, 71-, chmn. dept, 65-71. Faculty fel, Ford Found, 54-55; vis. prof, Columbia, 55; Fulbright lectr, Tel-Aviv Univ, 59-60. AAAS; Soc. Vert. Paleont; Am. Soc. Zool; Soc. Study Evolution; Am. Asn. Anat; N.Y. Acad. Sci. Comparative myology of Plectognath fishes; meristic variation of fishes; embryology of polydactylism in fowl. Address: Dept. of Biology, Brooklyn College, Brooklyn, NY 11210.

GABRIEL, R. OTHMAR, b. Vienna, Austria, Jan. 10, 25; U.S. citizen; m. 49; c. 2. BIOCHEMISTRY. Ph.D.(chem), Vienna, 54. Res. assoc. BIOCHEM, Vienna, 54-58; assoc, med. ctr, Columbia Univ, 58-60; vis. scientist, NAT. INSTS. HEALTH, 60-64, res. biochemist civil serv, 64-65, GUEST WORKER, BETHESDA, MD, 65-; PROF. BIOCHEM, MED. & DENT. SCH, GEORGETOWN UNIV, 70-, clin. asst. prof, 61-64, prof. lectr, 64-65, assoc. prof, 65-70. Am. Soc. Biol. Chem; Am. Soc. Microbiol; Soc. Exp. Biol. & Med; Am. Chem. Soc; Brit. Biochem. Soc; Austrian Biochem. Soc; Austrian Chem. Soc. Phosphorylated intermediates in yeast; separation and characterization of mono- and polysaccharides; precursors for the biosynthesis of polysaccharides; mechanism of enzyme action. Address: Dept. of Biochemistry, Georgetown University Medical & Dental School, Washington, DC 20007.

GABRIEL, RICHARD F(RANCIS), b. New Rochelle, N.Y, Nov. 30, 20; m. 48; c. 2. MATHEMATICS. A.B, Fordham, 43; M.A, Columbia, 47; Ph.D.(math), Rutgers, 55. Instr. math, pub. sch, 46-47; ed, therapist, Vet. Admin, 47-48; instr. MATH, St. Francis Col.(N.Y), 48-50; ASSOC. PROF. & asst. dir, comput. center, Rutgers, 50-62; DIR. COMPUT. CTR, SETON HALL UNIV, 62- Nat. Sci. Found. grant, 57; consult, Esso Res. & Eng. Co; State Rehab. Comn; chmn, Nat. Sci. Found. Numerical Anal. & Electronic Comput. Conf. U.S.A.R, 58-62. AAAS; Soc. Indust. & Appl. Math; N.Y. Acad. Sci; Asn. Comput. Mach; Am. Math. Soc; Math. Asn. Am. Complex variable; numerical analysis; electronic digital computers; evaluation of programming systems and equipment configurations. Address: 236 Clairmont Terr, Orange, NJ 07050.

GABRIEL, VITTALI GAVRILOVICH, b. Irkutsk, Russia, Oct. 23, 95; nat; m. GEOPHYSICS. B.S, California, 25; Mass. Inst. Tech, 28-29; fel, Colo. Sch. Mines, 29-30, M.S, 31, Sc.D.(geol), 33. Asst. seismol, Mt. Wilson Observ, Carnegie Inst, Calif, 25-27; seismologist, Shell Oil Co, 27-28; in charge magnetic & torsion balance parties, Plains Explor. Co, 30-31; geophysicist, Fohe Oil Co, Tex, 34-36; consult. geophysicist, 38-40; asst. geologist, U.S. Dept. Engrs, 41-43; res. analyst, Consolidated Vultee Aircraft Corp, 46-48; assoc. prof. geophys, sch. mines & metall, Missouri, 49-55; prof. physics, W.Va. Inst. Technol, 57-62; physicist, Libr. Cong, 62-64; hydrologist, U.S. Geol. Surv, 69-70; private practice, 70- Civilian with U.S.N; Nat. Adv. Comt. Aeronaut, 44. Russian White Army, 17-21, Lt. Am. Geophys. Union. Magnetic geophysics; seismology; gravity; structural geology. Address: 540 Ocean Ave, Brooklyn, NY 11226.

GABRIEL, WILLIAM FRANCIS, b. Sault Ste. Marie, Mich, Oct. 17, 25; m. 48; c. 2. ELECTRICAL ENGINEERING. B.S, Wisconsin, 45, M.S, 48, Ph.D. (elec. eng), 50. Instr, Wisconsin, 49; electronic scientist, Naval Res. Lab, 50-56, head scanning systems sect, 56-59; sr. res. engr, Stanford Res. Inst, 59-61; consult, Aero Geo Astro Corp, Va, 61-64; sr. engr, NASA, Goddard Space Flight Ctr, Md, 64-67; engr, Scanwell Labs, Inc, Va, 67-69; MEM. STAFF, DELEX SYSTS, INC, 69- U.S.N.R, 43-46. Int. Sci. Radio Union; Inst. Elec. & Electronics Eng. Microwave antennas and components, and related instrumentation; servomechanisms. Address: Delex Systems, Inc, 1701 N. Fort Meyer Dr, Arlington, VA 22209.

GABRIELE, ORLANDO FREDERICK, b. North Providence, R.I, June 6, 27; m. 60; c. 4. RADIOLOGY. B.A, Brown, 50; M.D, Yale, 54. Instr. RADIOL, sch. med, Yale, 57-59, lectr, 59-65, asst. prof, 65-66; assoc. prof, SCH. MED, UNIV. N.C, CHAPEL HILL, 66-71, PROF, 71- U.S.A, 45-47. Radiol. Soc. N.Am; Am. Col. Radiol; Am. Roentgen Ray Soc; Asn. Univ. Radiol. Cardiovascular radiology. Address: Dept. of Radiology, School of Medicine, University of North Carolina, Chapel Hill, NC 27514.

GABRIELE, THOMAS L, b. York, Pa, Sept. 7, 40; m. 65; c. 2. ELECTRICAL ENGINEERING. B.S.E.E, Lehigh Univ, 62; Nat. Sci. Found. fel, Johns Hopkins Univ, 62-66, M.S, 64, Ph.D.(elec. eng), 68. Eng. specialist, Martin Marietta Corp, 66-67; PROJ. ENGR, COMMUN. DIV, BENDIX CORP, TOWSON, 67- Inst. Elec. & Electronics Eng; Pattern Recognition Soc. Pattern recognition; adaptive information systems; modulation and coding techniques; automated decision systems; computer assisted analysis, simulation and design via interactive graphic displays. Address: Cardigan Rd, Timonium, MD 21093.

GABRIELI, ELEMER RUDOLPH, b. Budapest, Hungary, Jan. 6, 19; nat; m. 55; c. 2. PATHOLOGY. M.D, Budapest, Hungary, 41. Res. fel, sch. med, Yale, 51-55; res. assoc. Pfizer Therapeut. Inst, 56-57; clin. pathologist & dir. res, Millard Fillmore Hosp, 58-62; DIR. clin. labs, E.J. MEYER MEM. HOSPS, N.Y, 62-67, CLIN. INFO. CTR, 67-; ASSOC. CLIN. PROF. PATH, STATE UNIV. N.Y. BUFFALO, 68-, asst. prof, 62-68. Am. Heart Asn. fel, Newark Beth Israel Hosp, 57-58. Am. Asn. Path. & Bact; Soc. Exp. Biol. & Med; Am. Soc. Exp. Path; Sci. Res. Soc. Am. Liver functions; reticulo-endothelial functions; electronic data processing. Address: Clinical Information Center, E.J. Meyer Memorial Hospital, State University of New York at Buffalo, 462 Grider St, Buffalo, NY 14215.

GABRIELSE, H(UBERT), b. Golden, B.C, Mar. 1, 26; m. 55; c. 2. GEOLOGY. B.A.Sc, British Columbia, 48, M.A.Sc, 50; Ph.D.(geol), Columbia, 55. GEOLOGIST, GEOL. SURV. CAN, 53- Geol. Soc. Am; N.Y. Acad. Sci; fel. Geol. Asn. Can; jr. mem. Can. Inst. Mining & Metall. Regional stratigraphy, structure and tectonics. Address: Geological Survey of Canada, 100 W. Pender St, Vancouver 3, B.C, Can.

GABRIELSEN, BERNARD L, b. Woodland, Wash, May 29, 34; m. 66; c. 3. CIVIL & STRUCTURAL ENGINEERING. B.S, Oregon State, 56; M.S, Stanford, 61, Ph.D.(civil eng), 66. Engr-scientist, Lockheed Missiles & Space Co, 58-61; sr. engr, West. Develop. Labs, Philco Corp, 61-63; acting asst. prof. CIVIL ENG, Stanford, 63-65; asst. prof. SAN JOSE STATE COL, 65-70, ASSOC. PROF, 70-; PRIN. STRUCT. ENGR, URS CORP, 67- Private consult, 61-; consult, Stanford Res. Inst, 65-66; Walter V. Sterling, Inc, 65- U.S. Coast & Geod. Surv, 56-58, Lt.(jg). Am. Soc. Civil Eng; Am. Concrete Inst. Structural research on the dynamic failure of building panels; application of statistics to structural problems. Address: Dept. of Civil Engineering, San Jose State College, San Jose, CA 95114.

GABRIELSEN, BJARNE, b. Brooklyn, N.Y, Oct. 22, 41. ORGANIC CHEMISTRY. B.S, Wagner Col, 62, M.S, State Univ. N.Y, Stony Brook, 64, Ph.D. (phys. org. chem), 69. Instr. CHEM, WAGNER COL, 64-65, ASST. PROF, 69- Am. Chem. Soc. Effect of pressure on the rates of organic reactions in general, solvolysis reactions in particular; deduction of reactive intermediates via measurement of activation volumes. Address: Dept. of Chemistry, Wagner College, 631 Howard Ave, Staten Island, NY 10301.

GABRIELSEN, TRYGVE O, b. Vest-Agder, Norway, Mar. 27, 30; U.S. citizen; m. 55; c. 4. RADIOLOGY. B.S, Washington (Seattle), 53, M.D, 56. Asst. chief diag. RADIOL, Brooke Army Med. Ctr, 60-62; instr, MED. SCH, UNIV. MICH, 62-64, asst. prof, 64-68, assoc. prof, 68-71, PROF, 71- Asn. Univ. Radiologists travel award, 68. Med.C, U.S.A, 60-62, Capt. Am. Med. Asn; Radiol. Soc. N.Am; Asn. Univ. Radiol; Am. Soc. Neuroradiol. Diagnostic radiology, particularly neuroradiology. Address: Dept. of Radiology, S4453 University Hospital, University of Michigan, Ann Arbor, MI 48104.

GABRIELSON, IRA N(OEL), b. Sioux Rapids, Iowa, Sept. 27, 89; m. 12; c. 3. BIOLOGY. B.A, Morningside Col, 12, LL.D, 41; hon. Sc.D, Oregon State Col, 36. Teacher, pub. sch, Iowa, 12-15; biol. aide, bur. biol. surv, U.S. Dept. Agr, 15-18, leader rodent control, 18-31, regional supvr, 31-35, asst. chief div. wildlife res, 35, chief bur, 35-40; dir. fish & wildlife serv, U.S. Dept. Interior, 40-46; pres, Wildlife Mgt. Inst, 46-70; RETIRED. Pres, World Wildlife Fund, 61- Hon. mem. Wildlife Soc; Am. Soc. Mammal; Cooper Ornith. Soc; fel. Am. Ornith. Union; Wilson Ornith. Soc. Ornithology; wildlife management and general conservation. Address: 2500 Leeds Rd, Oakton, VA 22124.

GABRIELSON, R(ICHARD) L(EWIS), b. Riverside, Calif, Feb. 12, 31; m. 52; c. 4. PLANT PATHOLOGY. B.A, San Diego State Col, 52; Campbell Soup fel, California, Davis, 58-60, Ph.D.(plant path), 61. Asst. plant pathologist, WEST. WASH. EXP. STA, WASH. STATE UNIV, 60-66, ASSOC. PLANT PATHOLOGIST, 66- U.S.N, 52-55, Res, 55-, Lt.(jg). Am. Phytopath. Soc. Etiology, epidemiology and control of vegetable diseases. Address: Western Washington Research & Extension Center, Washington State University, Puyallup, WA 98371.

GABRILOVE, J(ACQUES) LESTER, b. New York, N.Y, Sept. 21, 17; m. 46; c. 2. MEDICINE, PHYSIOLOGY. B.S, City Col, 36; M.D, N.Y. Univ, 40. Intern path, Mt. Sinai Hosp, 40-43, res. med, 43-44; clin. asst. prof, col. med, State Univ. N.Y. Downstate Med. Ctr, 57-59, clin. assoc. prof, 59-66, clin. prof. med, 66-69; CLIN. PROF. MED, MT. SINAI SCH. MED. & ATTEND. PHYSICIAN, HOSP, 68- Practicing physician, internal med; Libman fel, sch. med, Yale, 45; Blumenthal fel, Mt. Sinai Hosp, 46-48, asst, 49-51, asst. vis. physician, 51-60, assoc. attend. physician, 60-; prof. lectr, col. med, State Univ. N.Y. Downstate Med. Ctr, 69- Consult, Vet. Admin. Hosp, East Orange, N.J, 58-66; Bronx Vet. Admin. Hosp, N.Y, 69-; Elizabeth A. Horton Hosp, Middletown, N.Y. Mem. panel metabolic & rheumatoid diseases, U.S. Pharmacopeia XVI, 56. Mem, Am. Bd. Internal Med. AAAS; Am. Fedn. Clin. Res; Endocrine Soc; Am. Diabetes Asn; Am. Med. Asn; Am. Col. Physicians; Royal Soc. Med; hon. mem. Peruvian Endocrine Soc. Physiological chemistry; adrenal cortex; thyroid; diabetes mellitus; endocrine metabolic diseases. Address: Mt. Sinai School of Medicine, 1 E. 100th St, New York, NY 10029.

GABRON, FRANK, b. Pittsfield, Mass, May 3, 30; m. 57; c. 1. MECHANICAL ENGINEERING, THERMOPHYSICS. B.S, Univ. R.I, 53; M.S, Pa. State Univ, 55. Engr, res. labs, Tex. Co, N.Y, summer 53; res. asst. mech eng, Pa. State Univ, 54-55; combustion engr, res. labs, United Aircraft Corp, Conn, 55-60; GROUP LEADER APPL. THERMODYN, ENG. DIV, ARTHUR D. LITTLE, INC, 60- Lectr, Univ. Calif, Los Angeles, spring 67. Am. Inst. Aeronaut. & Astronaut. Heat transfer as applied to spacecraft and spacecraft experiments; research and development of devices for providing cryogenic cooling of components. Address: Engineering Division, Arthur D. Little, Inc, Acorn Park, Cambridge, MA 02140.

GABRUSEWYCZ-GARCIA, NATALIA, b. Kiev, Ukraine, Nov. 14, 34; U.S. citizen; m. 61. CELL BIOLOGY, CYTOLOGY. B.S, Sao Paulo, 58; O'Higgins fel, Columbia, 59-60, U.S. Pub. Health Serv. fel, 62-63, Ph.D.(zool), 64. Instr. histol. & cytol, São Paulo, 58-59; RES. ASSOC. PHARMACOL, STATE UNIV. N.Y. UPSTATE MED. CTR, 64- Co-investr, U.S. Pub. Health Serv. grant, 64-67. Am. Soc. Cell Biol. Structure and nucleic acids metabolism of chromosomes, especially of polytene chromosomes. Address: Dept. of Anatomy, State University of New York Upstate Medical Center, Syracuse, NY 13210.

GABRYSH, ANDREW F(RANCIS), b. Ralphton, Pa, Sept. 29, 21. PHYSICS, METALLURGY. B.C.E, Catholic Univ, 50; M.S, 51; Oak Ridge Sch. Reactor Tech, 53-54; Ph.D.(phys. metall), Utah, 60. Apprentice tool-die maker, Essex Tool-Die, N.J, 38-42; tool-die maker, Springfield Tool-Die Co, N.J, 46; sci. aide, geophys. sect, U.S. Geol. Surv, 47-49; res. assoc, Catholic Univ, 49-51; engr, Wash, D.C. Dist, U.S. Army Corps Engrs, 51-52; physicist, Oak Ridge Nat. Lab, 52-55; consult. civil engr, 55-56; physicist, Univ. Calif. Radiation Lab. for Pratt-Whitney, 56-58; res. assoc, Utah, 58-61, assoc. prof, inst. study rate processes & dept. metall, 61-64; physicist, U.S. Bur. Mines, Pittsburgh, 65-71; CONSULT, RES. & WRITING, 71- Summer vis. prof, inst. geophys, California, Los Angeles, 60. U.S.N.R, 42-46. Fel. AAAS; fel. Am. Inst. Chem; Am. Phys. Soc; Am. Soc. Civil Eng; Am. Soc. Test. & Mat. Cosmic rays; x-rays; rheology; ultrasonic energy in gas; optical properties of single crystals; high-pressure effects on materials; thermoluminescense in solids; radiation damage; diffusion of gas in metals; solid state of matter; particle accelerator studies; rock mechanics; environmental studies, air and mine drainage; radiation caused aging and biological processes of irreversible damage. Address: P.O. Box 91, Irvona, PA 16656.

GABUZDA, GEORGE J(OSEPH), b. Freeland, Pa, Jan. 26, 20; m. 46; c. 3. CLINICAL MEDICINE. A.B, Lehigh, 41; M.D, Harvard, 44. Intern, Pa. Hosp, Phila, 44-45; res. med, Mary Fletcher Hosp, Vt, 45-46; U.S. Pub. Health Serv. fel, Harvard Med. Sch. & Thorndike Mem. Lab, Boston City Hosp, 48-50, Richardson res. fel, 50-51, instr, 51-52, Welch fel, Nat. Res. Coun, 51-54, assoc, 52-54; asst. prof. MED, CASE WEST. RESERVE UNIV, 54-57, assoc. prof, 57-64, PROF, 64- Consult, Vet. Admin. Hosp, 54- Med.C, 46-48, Capt. AAAS; Am. Soc. Clin. Nutrit; Am. Inst. Nutrit; Am. Soc. Clin. Invest; Soc. Exp. Biol. & Med; Am. Asn. Study Liver Diseases (pres, 60); Am. Fedn. Clin. Res. Nutrition and metabolism; hepetology; metabolic aspects of liver disease. Address: Cleveland Metropolitan General Hospital, 3395 Scranton Rd, Cleveland, OH 44109.

GABY, W(ILLIAM) L(AURENCE), b. Hot Springs, N.C, June 15, 17; m. 40; c. 3. BACTERIOLOGY. B.A, Tennessee, 39, M.S, 40; Ph.D.(bact), St. Louis, 56. Sr. bacteriologist, State Dept. Pub. Health, Tenn, 40-41; bacteriologist, Winthrop Chem. Co, N.Y, 41-42; sr. bacteriologist, Bristol Labs, Inc, 46-49; asst. prof. bact, Hahnemann Med. Col. & Hosp, 49-52, assoc. prof, 53-64; PROF. MICROBIOL. & CHMN. DEPT. HEALTH SCI, E. TENN. STATE UNIV, 64- Commercial Solvents award, 52. Dipl, Am. Bd. Microbiol. With Off. Sci. Res. & Develop, 44. AAAS; Am. Soc. Microbiol; Am. Soc. Biol. Chem; Am. Asn. Immunol; fel. Am. Acad. Microbiol; N.Y. Acad. Sci. Dissociation of bacteria; antigen; antibody response; penicillin production and antibiotic activity; mold mutation and metabolism; lipid and phospholipid role in metabolism. Address: College of Health, East Tennessee State University, Johnson City, TN 37601.

GAC, NORMAN A, b. Buffalo, N.Y, Aug. 3, 37; m. 61; c. 3. PHYSICAL CHEMISTRY. B.S.Ch.E, Purdue, 59; Am. Petrol. Inst. & Union Carbide fels. & Ph.D.(phys. chem), Rensselaer Polytech, 64; Cath. Univ. P.R, 65. Chem. engr, Gen. Elec. Co, 59-60; sr. res. engr, Rocketdyne Div, N.Am. Aviation, Inc, 64-65; phys. sci. consult, St. Louis Univ-U.S. Agency Int. Develop. Proj. Univ. Assistance, Quito, Ecuador, 65-67; res. assoc. thermochem. & chem. kinetics under Dr. S.W. Benson, Stanford Res. Inst, 67-69; asst. prof. phys. chem, St. Louis Univ, 69-71; GROUP MGR. POLYMER DEVELOP, THERMOFIT DIV, RAYCHEM CORP, 71- Consult, St. Louis Univ-Int. Progs, 69-71. Am. Chem. Soc. Bond strengths and reaction mechanisms; flame retardancy; irradiation and plasma treatment of polymers. Address: Research & Development Bldg, Raychem Corp, 300 Constitution Dr, Menlo Park, CA 94025.

GACULA, MAX C, JR, b. Butuan City, Philippines, Oct. 3, 36. ANIMAL BREEDING, GENETICS. B.S.A, Philippines, 59; M.S, Arkansas, 63; summer, Nat. Sci. Found. fel, Brown, 66; Ph.D.(animal breeding), Massachusetts, 67. Instr. animal sci, Philippines, 59-61; HEAD BIOMET. SECT, FOOD RES. LAB, ARMOUR & CO, 67- Am. Genetic Asn; Biomet. Soc; Am. Soc. Animal Sci. Biometrics; design of experiments; experimental evalution of statistical methods; quantitative inheritance; electronic data processing. Address: Food Research Lab, Armour & Co, 801 W. 22nd St, Oak Brook, IL 60521.

GADAIRE, CHARLES R(ICE), b. Brookfield, Mass, Aug. 16, 11; m. 35; c. 4. BIOLOGY. B.A, Clark, 32; Ph.D.(biol), Toronto, 35. Demonstr. biol, Toronto, 34-35; asst. prof. biol, Am. Int. Col, 35-37, prof. & chmn. dept, 37-42; teacher, pub. schs, Mass, 42-46; prof. biol. & chmn. dept, AM. INT. COL, 46-52, PROF. NATURAL SCI, 52-, DEAN CONTINUING EDUC, 67-, CHMN. DEPT. NATURAL SCI, 71-, dir. student activities, 52-54, dean student activities, 54-57, dean students, 57-65. Vis. prof, Our Lady of the Elms Col, 48. AAAS; Nat. Asn. Biol. Teachers. Histology; embryology. Address: Dept. of Natural Science, American International College, 170 Wilbraham Rd, Springfield, MA 01109.

GADAMER, ERNST O(SCAR), b. Berlin, Germany, Nov. 1, 24; Can. citizen; m. 54; c. 2. APPLIED MATHEMATICS & STATISTICS. Dipl. physics, Frankfurt, 51; M.A, Toronto, 56, Ph.D.(aerophys), 62. Data reduction engr, de Havilland of Can. Co, Ont, 58-59; res. fel, inst. aerophys, Toronto, 56-61; asst. res. officer hypersonics, Nat. Res. Coun. Can, 61-62; ASST. PROF. ENG. ANAL, McMASTER UNIV, 62- German Air Force, 43-45, Sgt. Low-density aerodynamics; applied statistics and applied mathematics. Address: Dept. of Applied Mathematics, McMaster University, Hamilton, Ont, Can.

GADBERRY, HOWARD M(ILTON), b. Kansas City, Mo, July 25, 22; m. 52; c. 2. CHEMICAL ENGINEERING. B.S, Kansas, 43. Chemist, Phillips Petrol. Co, 43-46; assoc. chem. engr, MIDWEST RES. INST, 46-50, sr. chem. engr, 50-54, head indust. chem. sect, 54-58, asst. mgr, div. chem. & chem. eng, 58-61, asst. dir, econ. develop. div, 61-63, SR. ADV. TECH, 63- Am. Chem. Soc; Am. Inst. Aeronaut. & Astronaut; Sci. Res. Soc. Am; Am. Asn. Textile Chem. & Colorists; Am. Ord. Asn. Advanced industrial technology; industrial applications of government research results; technological forecasting; econometric analysis of new technology; information systems; detergents and surface active materials; cleaning processes; surface chemistry of thin films and colloids; commercial chemical specialties; plastics, adhesives and protective coatings. Address: Midwest Research Institute, 425 Volker Blvd, Kansas City, MO 64110.

GADD, CHARLES W(INFORD), b. Spokane, Wash, Apr. 6, 15. BIOMECHANICS. B.S, Mass. Inst. Technol, 37. SUPVR. BIOMECH. & PROTECTION, RES. LAB, GEN. MOTORS CORP, 53- Am. Soc. Mech. Eng. Human impact tolerance; vehicle crash protection; general engineering mechanics. Address: 3773 Indian Trail, Orchard Lake, MI 48033.

GADD, JOHN DALE, b. Akron, Ohio, Mar. 28, 36; m. 56; c. 2. METALLURGY. B.S, Case Inst. Tech, 57, M.S, 60, Jones & Laughlin fel, 63-64, Ph.D.(metall), 64. Metallurgist, equip. group, TRW, INC, 57-63, res. metall, 64-66, sect. mgr, 66-69, MGR. TECH. DEVELOP. & CONTROL, JET & ORD. DIV, 69- Mem, mat. adv. bd. comt. on coatings, Nat. Acad. Sci, 68- Am. Soc. Metals; Am. Soc. Test. & Mat. High temperature coatings for refractory metals and superalloys; aerospace and aircraft gas turbines applications. Address: Jet & Ordnance Division, TRW, Inc, 1400 N. Cameron St, Harrisburg, PA 17105.

GADD, NELSON R(AYMOND), b. Ft. Frances, Ont, Sept. 22, 23; m. 47; c. 4. GEOLOGY. B.Sc, Western Ontario, 46; M.Sc, Laval, 48; Ph.D, Illinois, 55. GEOLOGIST, CAN. GEOL. SURV, 48- Geol. Soc. Am. Pleistocene stratigraphy in eastern Canada, St. Lawrence lowland, pleistocene geology. Address: Geological Survey of Canada, Ottawa, Ont, Can.

GADDIE, DONALD WAYNE, b. Louisville, Ky, Dec. 19, 33; m. 54; c. 2. ORGANIC CHEMISTRY. B.S, Louisville, 55, Ph.D.(org. chem), 59. Chemist, Devoe & Raynolds Co, 58-63, sr. chemist, S.C. Johnson & Son, Inc, 63-64; CHEMIST, Celanese Fibers Mkt. Co, 64-66; ARIZ. CHEM. CO, 66- Am. Chem. Soc; Am. Oil Chem. Soc; Sci. Res. Soc. Am. Reactions of gem-dinitroparaffins; polymers for coatings applications; synthesis of epoxy resins. Address: 826 Brandeis Ave, Panama City, FL 32401.

GADDIE, ROBERT S(TANLEY), b. Sugar City, Idaho, Nov. 4, 09; m. 33; c. 3. CHEMISTRY. B.S, Utah, 32. Asst. lectr, Utah, 32; res. chemist, Kalunite Corp, 33; special analyst, UTAH-IDAHO SUGAR CO, 34, prod. foreman, 34-40, chief chemist, Toppenish Plant, 40-41, Cent. Lab, 42-43, asst. gen. chemist, 43-46, GEN. CHEMIST, 46-, GEN. SUPT, 70- Fel. AAAS; Am. Chem. Soc; Am. Soc. Sugar Beet Technol.(meritorious serv. award); fel. Am. Inst. Chem; Inst. Food Technol. Various problems relating to the production, refining and analysis of the sugars, particularly sucrose. Address: 905 Military Dr, Salt Lake City, UT 84108.

GADDIS, ALVIS MATHEW, b. Mt. Pleasant, Tex, Aug. 31, 05; m. 33; c. 2. MECHANICAL ENGINEERING. B.A, Austin Col, 30. Prin. & teacher, pub. schs, Texas, 28-34, athletic dir, 34-42; asst. prof, naval training sch, Agr. & Mech. Col, Tex, 42-45; engr, Mt. Pleasant, Tex, 45-46; asst. prof. mech. eng, Texas A&M Univ, 46-56, assoc. prof, 56-69; private practice, 69- Summers, sr. design engr, Boeing Airplane Co, Wash, 51-52, syst. engr, Chance Vought Aircraft, Tex, 52-61; part-time mem. staff res. & develop, Tex. Transportation Inst, 61-69. Soc. Exp. Stress Anal. General engineering. Address: 800 S. Dexter, College Station, TX 77840.

GADDY, OSCAR, b. Republic, Mo, July 18, 32; m. 53; c. 3. ELECTRICAL ENGINEERING. B.S, Kansas, 57, M.S, 59; Ph.D.(elec. eng), Illinois, 62. Instr. & res. asst. ELEC. ENG, Kansas, 57-59; res. asst, UNIV. ILL, URBANA-CHAMPAIGN, 59-62, asst. prof, 62-65, assoc. prof, 65-69, PROF, 69- Sr. mem. Inst. Elec. & Electronics Eng. Optical communication; quantum electronics; electron devices; infrared devices; subnanosecond optical pulse generation and detection. Address: Dept. of Electrical Engineering, University of Illinois, Urbana-Champaign, Urbana, IL 61801.

GADE, DANIEL WAYNE, Geog, see Suppl. I to 11th ed, Soc. & Behav. Vols.

GADE, EDWARD H(ERMAN) H(ENRY), III, b. St. Joseph, Mo, Feb. 19, 36; m. 60; c. 2. MATHEMATICS. B.A, Valparaiso, 58; M.S, Purdue, 60; Ph.D.(math), Pittsburgh, 65. ASST. PROF. MATH, WIS. STATE UNIV, OSHKOSH, 66- Summability methods analysis. Address: Dept. of Mathematics, Wisconsin State University, Oshkosh, WI 54902.

GADE, SANDRA ANN, b. Waterbury, Conn, Oct. 27, 37; m. 60; c. 2. PHYSICS. B.S, Valparaiso, 59; Nat. Sci. Found. summer fel, Pittsburgh, 64, Ph.D.(physics), 66. ASST. PROF. PHYSICS, WIS. STATE UNIV-OSHKOSH, 66- Atomic physics; nuclear magnetic and electron paramagnetic resonance. Address: Dept. of Physics, Wisconsin State University-Oshkosh, Oshkosh, WI 54901.

GADEBUSCH, HANS H(ENNING), b. Charlottenburg, Germany, Jan. 8, 24; nat; m. 49; c. 5. MICROBIOLOGY. B.S, Detroit, 49; M.S, Michigan, 51; Ph.D, Univ. Mich, 65. Asst. bact, Michigan, 49-51; res. microbiologist, Irwin, Neisler & Co, Ill, 51-53; clin. bacteriologist, Detroit Dept. Health, 53; chief bacteriologist, Vet. Admin. Hosp, 53-57, coord. gen. med. res, 57-62, head microbiol-immunol. res. sect, 57-66, chief med. microbiol, SQUIBB INST. MED. RES, 66-71, ASST. DIR. DEPT. MICROBIOL, 71- Med.C, U.S.A, 43-46. AAAS; Am. Asn. Lab. Animal Care; Am. Soc. Microbiol; Med. Mycol. Soc. Am; Soc. Exp. Biol. & Med; N.Y. Acad. Sci. Immunology; immunochemistry; mycology; bacteriology; biochemistry; analytical chemistry. Address: Squibb Institute for Medical Research, Dept. of Microbiology, New Brunswick, NJ 08903.

GADECKI, FILON ALEXANDER, b. Poland, Feb. 26, 32; U.S. citizen; m. 54; c. 6. PHYSICAL ORGANIC CHEMISTRY. B.S, Illinois, 54; Ph.D.(phys. org. chem), Washington (Seattle), 57. Nat. Res. Coun. grant, Swiss Fed. Inst. Tech, 57-58; res. chemist, E.I. DU PONT DE NEMOURS & CO, INC, 58-62, sr. res. chemist, 62-63, tech. supvr, 63-68, SR. SUPVR, RES. & DEVELOP, 68- Am. Chem. Soc. Theoretical organic chemistry; natural products; polymer and radiation chemistry; fiber technology. Address: 2108 Davie Lane, Camden, SC 29020.

GADEK, FRANK JOSEPH, b. Troy, N.Y, Oct. 1, 41; m. 70. ORGANIC CHEMISTRY. B.S, Siena Col.(N.Y), 63; Nat. Cancer Inst. assistantship, Cath. Univ. Am, 64-68, Ph.D.(org. chem), 69. Asst, Cath. Univ. Am, 68; ASST.

PROF. ORG. CHEM, ALLENTOWN COL, 68- Frederick Gardner Cottrell res. grant-in-aid, 71-72. Am. Chem. Soc. Synthesis and the investigation of the properties of new heterocyclic aromatic compounds which are analogs of azulene and quinoline using organometallic reagents and novel dehydrogenating agents. Address: Dept. of Chemistry, Allentown College, Center Valley, PA 18034.

GADEKAR, SHREEKRISHNA M, b. Bombay, India, Sept. 23, 20; m. 48; c. 4. ORGANIC CHEMISTRY. B.S, Bombay Univ. 44; Tata scholar, Maryland, 46-49, M.S, 48, Am. Found. Pharmaceut. Ed. grant, 48-49, Ph.D.(pharmaceut. chem), 49. Pharmacologist, Lederle Labs, 49-50, org. res. chemist, 50-54, sr. res. scientist, 54-67; sr. chem. pharmacologist, Carter-Wallace Inc, 67-69; assoc. dir. pharmaceut. chem, AFFILIATED MED. ENTERPRISES INC, 69-70, DIR. PHARMACEUT. & ANAL. CHEM, 70- AAAS; Am. Chem. Soc; Soc. Cosmetic Chem; The Chem. Soc. Organic and medicinal chemistry; biochemistry; pharmacology; pharmaceutical chemistry; cosmetic chemistry. Address: Affiliated Medical Enterprises, Inc, Princeton Pike, P.O. Box 57, Princeton, NJ 08540.

GADEN, ELMER L(EWIS), JR, b. Brooklyn, N.Y, Sept. 26, 23; m. 64; c. 2. CHEMICAL & BIOCHEMICAL ENGINEERING. B.S, Columbia, 44, M.S, 47, Ph.D.(chem. eng), 49. Biochem. eng. head, Chas. Pfizer & Co, 48-49; asst. prof. CHEM. ENG, COLUMBIA UNIV, 49-54, assoc. prof, 54-58, PROF, 58-, CHMN. DEPT, 60-69 & 71- Tech. dir, Biochem. Processes, Inc, 58- U.S.N.R, 43-46, Lt.(jg). Am. Chem. Soc; Am. Soc. Microbiol; Am. Inst. Chem. Eng. Biochemical engineering; fermentation; industrial biochemistry; enzyme technology. Address: Dept. of Chemical Engineering, Columbia University, New York, NY 10027.

GADS, LEONARD E(USTACE), b. Bukhara, Russia, Apr. 30, 07; nat; m. 44; c. 2. ASTRONOMY, CARTOGRAPHY. B.Sc, Alberta, 39. Demonstr, civil eng, Alberta, 39-41; indust. engr. labor standards, Burns & Co, 41-42; interpreter Russian, Control Cmn, Germany, 45-46; asst. prof. CIVIL ENG, UNIV. ALBERTA, 46-56, PROF, 56-, ASSOC. DEAN ENG, 59-, secy. faculty, 59-69. Researcher, Nat. Geog. Inst, Paris, France, 60-61. R.C.A.F, 42-45, Res, 46-47, Wing Comdr. Am. Soc. Eng. Educ; Royal Astron. Soc. Can; Eng. Inst. Can; Can. Inst. Surv. Applied astronomy and cartography; geodesy; engineering education. Address: Dept. of Civil Engineering, University of Alberta, Edmonton, Alta, Can.

GADSDEN, RICHARD H(AMILTON), b. Denver, Colo, June 25, 25; m. 53; c. 5. BIOCHEMISTRY. B.S, Col. of Charleston, 50; fel, Med. Col. S.C, 51-54, M.S, 52, Ph.D.(biochem), 56. Instr. org. chem. & biochem, Med. Col. S.C, 54-56, asst. prof. biochem, 56-65, assoc. prof, 65-69, PROF. BIOCHEM. & CLIN. PATH. & DIR. CLIN. CHEM, MED. UNIV. S.C, 69-, interim chmn. dept. chem, 67-69. U.S.N.R, 43-46. AAAS; Am. Chem. Soc; Am. Asn. Clin. Chem; Asn. Clin. Sci. Clinical chemistry; toxicology. Address: Dept. of Clinical Pathology, Medical University of South Carolina, Charleston, SC 29401.

GADZALA, A(NTONI) EDWARD, b. Sudbury, Ont, Can, Aug. 6, 31; m. 59; c. 2. PHYSICAL PHARMACY. B.Sc.Phm, Toronto, 58, M.Sc.Phm, 60; Ph.D.(phys. pharm), Ohio State, 64. Phys. chemist, AVON PROD, INC, 64-67, sr. phys. chemist, 67-69, SR. RES. PHYS. CHEMIST, PROD. RES. & DEVELOP. DEPT, 69- AAAS; Am. Chem. Soc; Am. Pharmaceut. Asn; Soc. Cosmetic Chem; Can. Pharmaceut. Asn. Structure and behavior of keratins, especially as related to hair and nails; microscopy; differential thermal analysis; coulter counter; rheology; physical and chemical changes produced in proteinaceous materials on interaction with micro or macromolecules. Address: Avon Products, Inc, Product Research & Development Dept, Suffern, NY 10901.

GADZUK, JOHN W(ILLIAM), b. Philadelphia, Pa, Mar. 28, 41; m. 68; c. 1. THEORETICAL SOLID STATE PHYSICS. B.S, Mass. Inst. Technol, 63, M.S, 65, Ph.D.(solid state physics), 68. Physicist, Hughes Res. Labs, summer 66; Electronics Res. Center, NASA, summer 67; instr. physics, Mass. Inst. Technol, 67-68; PHYSICIST, NAT. BUR. STANDARDS, 68- Am. Phys. Soc. Theory of solids; solid surfaces; tunneling phenomena; impurities in solids and other properties of solids. Address: Optical Physics Division, Room A-251, National Bureau of Standards, Washington, DC 20234.

GAEBLER, O(LIVER) H(ENRY), b. Swiss, Mo, Nov. 14, 95; m. 28; c. 2. BIOCHEMISTRY. A.B, Cent. Wesleyan Col, 17; A.M, Missouri, 20; Chicago, 20; fel, Toronto, 20-22, Ph.D.(path. chem), 22; Hopkins, 22-23; M.D, Cornell, 31. Asst. anat, Missouri, 18-20; asst. physiol, Rochester, 23-24; assoc. biochem. & asst. path. chemist, Univ. hosps, Iowa, 24-25, asst. prof, 25-27; assoc. in charge chem, Henry Ford Hosp, Detroit, 28-47; head dept. BIOCHEM, EDSEL B. FORD INST. MED. RES, 47-65, EMER. MEM. & CONSULT, 66- Prof. lectr, Wayne State, 34- Mem. Am. Bd. Clin. Chem, 49-56, v.pres, 52, secy-treas, 53-56. Bischoff award, 59. U.S.A, 17-18. AAAS; Am. Chem. Soc; Soc. Exp. Biol. & Med; Am. Soc. Biol. Chem; Endocrine Soc; Am. Asn. Clin. Chem.(pres, 58); Am. Inst. Chem; Can. Biochem. Soc; Can. Soc. Clin. Chem; Can. Physiol. Soc. Analytical methods, blood and urine; mass spectrometry; metabolic effects of hormones and vitamins; creatine and creatinine; antimetabolites; tissue enzymes during induced growth; metabolism of N^{15} from individual sources; metabolic effects of x-irradiation. Address: 18410 Northlawn, Detroit, MI 48221.

GAEDKE, RUDOLPH MEGGS, b. Dallas, Tex, Apr. 4, 38; m. 60; c. 3. NUCLEAR PHYSICS. B.A, Rice, 60; Nat. Defense fel, South Carolina, 60-63, Oak Ridge Inst. Nuclear Studies, fel, 63-65, Ph.D.(physics), 65. Asst. prof. physics, Trinity (Tex), 65-67; sr. staff mem, electro-nuclear div, Oak Ridge Nat. Lab, 67; asst. prof. PHYSICS, TRINITY UNIV.(TEX), 67-70, ASSOC. PROF, 70-, CHMN. DEPT, 68- Summer res. scientist, Texas, 66. Nuclear reaction induced by heavy ions; gamma spectroscopy. Address: Dept. of Physics, Trinity University, San Antonio, TX 78212.

GAEKE, G(OTTLIEB) C(HARLES), JR, b. Goose Creek, Tex, Sept. 11, 28; m. 52; c. 2. ANALYTICAL CHEMISTRY. B.S, Houston, 50; Mine Safety Appliances Co. fel, La. State, 53-54, M.S, 56. Asst. chem, Houston, 48-50; prev. med, med. br, Texas, 50-52; lab. instr. chem, La. State, 52-53; gen. mgr. Kem-Tech. Labs, Inc, 54-60, asst. prof. chem, La. State, 60-61; RES.

ASSOC, ETHYL CORP, 61- Fel. Am. Inst. Chem; Am. Chem. Soc. Trace, organic and organometallic analysis; gas-liquid chromatography. Address: Ethyl Corp, P.O. Box 341, Baton Rouge, LA 70821.

GAENSLEN, GEORGE J, b. Milwaukee, Wis, Oct. 18, 11; m. 37; c. 1. GEOLOGY. B.A, Wisconsin, 33. Geologist, Amerada Petrol. Corp, 37-43; Standard Oil Co.(N.J), 44-49, Egypt, 44-49, Kans, 50, Venezuela, 51-62, France, 63-66; ASST. CURATOR GEOL, MILWAUKEE PUB. MUS, 67- Geol. Soc. Am; Am. Asn. Petrol. Geol. Address: 2711 N. Avondale Blvd, Milwaukee, WI 53210.

GAENSLER, E(DWARD) A(RNOLD), b. Vienna, Austria, Feb. 5, 21; nat; m. 53; c. 2. SURGERY, PHYSIOLOGY. B.S, Haverford Col, 42; M.D, Harvard, 45. From instr. to PROF. SURG, SCH. MED, BOSTON UNIV, 48- U.S. Pub. Health Serv. fel, 48-50; Trudeau fel, 55-59; lectr, Harvard Med. Sch, & sch. med, Tufts, 60-; Nat. Insts. Health res. career award, 64- Vis. thoracic surgeon, Boston City Hosp. & Univ. Hosp; consult, Chelsea Naval Hosp; Vet. Admin. Hosp, Boston. Med.C, 53-55, Capt. Fel. Am. Col. Surg; fel. Am. Col. Chest Physicians; Am. Thoracic Soc; Am. Soc. Thoracic Surg; Am. Fedn. Clin. Res; Am. Physiol. Soc. Pulmonary physiology; physiology in thoracic surgery; chest radiology and pathology; interstitch and occupational lung disease. Address: Boston University Medical School, 80 E. Concord St, Boston, MA 02118.

GAER, MARVIN C(HARLES), b. Milwaukee, Wis, Apr. 28, 35; m. 60; c. 2. MATHEMATICAL ANALYSIS. B.S, Wisconsin, 57, M.S, 62; Ph.D.(math), Illinois, 68. Physicist, Allen-Bradley Co, Wis, 57-58; comput. analyst, AC Electronics Div, Gen. Motors Corp, 58-62; instr. MATH, UNIV. DEL, 67-68, ASST. PROF, 68- Am. Math. Soc; Math. Asn. Am. Complex variable theory; measure theory; harmonic analysis. Address: Dept. of Mathematics, University of Delaware, Newark, DE 19711.

GAERTNER, ERIKA E(VA), b. Trutnov, Bohemia, Sept. 3, 21; Can. citizen; m. 53; c. 2. ECONOMIC BOTANY, FORESTRY. B.S.A, Ont. Agr. Col, 44; M.S, Cornell Univ, 45, Ph.D.(bot), 49. Scientist, Geneva Agr. Exp. Sta, N.Y, 49-50; lectr. bot, McMaster Univ, 50-53; botanist, Petawawa Forest, Ont, 53-71; INVITED LECTR. ECON. BOT, SIR GEORGE WILLIAMS UNIV, 71- Can. Coun. res. grant, 71. Can. Bot. Asn; Soc. Econ. Bot; Soc. Study Evolution; Agr. Inst. Can. Biology of Cuscuta; tree growth; seed classification; utilization of wild foods. Address: 617 Berwick Ave, Town of Mount Royal, Montreal, Que, Can.

GAERTNER, RICHARD F(RANCIS), b. Pittsburgh, Pa, Aug. 10, 33; m. 62; c. 2. CHEMICAL ENGINEERING. B.S, West Virginia, 55, M.S, 57; Dow Chem. Co. fel, Illinois, 58-59, Ph.D.(chem. eng), 59. Res. assoc, Gen. Elec. Res. Lab, GEN. ELEC. CO, 59-68, MGR. tech. mkt, polymer prod. oper, 68-69, MFG, PLASTICS DEPT, 69- Am. Inst. Chem. Eng. Heat transfer associated with change of phase; boiling phenomena; process engineering of polymers. Address: Plastics Dept, General Electric Co, Noryl Ave, Selkirk, NY 12158.

GAERTNER, ROBERT A(NTHONY), b. Baltimore, Md, May 26, 27; m. 56; c. 3. SURGERY. A.B, Hopkins, 48; M.D, 52. Instr. SURG, SCH. MED, JOHNS HOPKINS UNIV, 60-61, ASST. PROF, 61- U.S.P.H.S, 54-56. Am. Med. Asn; Am. Col. Surg. Cardiovascular research, especially treatment of congenital and acquired cardiac disease. Address: 550 N. Broadway, Baltimore, MD 21205.

GAERTNER, V(AN) R(USSELL), b. Centralia, Ill, July 4, 24; m. 52; c. 3. ORGANIC CHEMISTRY. B.S, Bradley, 45; fel, Illinois, 47-48, Ph.D.(org. chem), 48. Teacher inorg. chem, Illinois, 45-47; Nat. Insts. Health fel, Ohio State, 48-49; asst. prof. chem, Oregon, 49-52; res. chemist & group leader, MONSANTO CO, 52-66, sr. res. specialist, 66-67, scientist, 67-70, SCI. FEL, 70- Am. Chem. Soc. Organometallic reactions; synthesis of carcinogenic hydrocarbons; heterocycles; Diels-Alder reactions of quinones; biological toxicants; surfactants; epoxyamines; paper chemicals; reactive polymers; small nitrogen heterocycles. Address: Technology Dept, Research Center, Monsanto Co, St. Louis, MO 63166.

GAERTNER, WOLFGANG WILHELM, b. Vienna, Austria, July 5, 29; U.S. citizen; m. 55; c. 3. SOLID STATE PHYSICS, ELECTRONICS. Ph.D. (physics), Vienna, 51; dipl. eng, Vienna Tech, 55. Physicist, Siemens & Halske, Austria, 51-53; solid state physics, U.S. Army Signal Corps. Res. & Develop. Labs, N.J, 53-59, chief scientist, solid state div, 59-60; v.pres. solid state physics & electronics, Columbia Broadcasting Syst, Inc, 60-65; PRES, W.W. GAERTNER RES. INC, 65- Am. Phys. Soc; sr. mem. Inst. Elec. & Electronics Eng. Semiconductor devices; microelectronics; ultrasonics; adaptive electronics; system design and software. Address: W.W. Gaertner Research Inc, 205 Saddle Hill Road, Stamford, CT 06903.

GAERTTNER, ERWIN R(UDOLF), b. Denver, Colo, Feb. 27, 11; m. 40; c. 2. PHYSICS. B.S, Denver, 32; M.A, Michigan, 33, Ph.D.(physics), 37. Nat. Res. Coun. fel, Calif. Inst. Tech, 37-38, Rackham fel, 38-39; instr. physics, Ohio State, 40-42, asst. prof, 44; mem. staff, radiation lab, Mass. Inst. Tech, 42-46; res. assoc, Gen. Elec. Co, 46-51, Knolls Atomic Power Lab, 51-58; PROF. NUCLEAR ENG. & SCI, RENSSELAER POLYTECH. INST, 58-, HEAD DEPT, 60-, DIR. LINEAR ACCELERATOR RES. LAB, 58- Fel. Am. Phys. Soc; fel. Am. Nuclear Soc. Nuclear physics. Address: Dept. of Nuclear Science, Rensselaer Polytechnic Institute, Troy, NY 12181.

GAETH, JOHN H(ENRY), b. Fremont, Nebr, Sept. 19, 13; m. 39; c. 2. AUDIOLOGY. B.A, Nebraska, 40, M.A, 42; Ph.D.(audiol), Northwestern, 48. Assoc. prof. speech & dir. hearing clinic, Denver, 48-49; from asst. prof. to assoc. prof. & dir. hearing clinic, Northwestern, 49-56; prof. & dir. hearing clin, WAYNE STATE UNIV, 57-65, PROF. AUDIOL. & CHMN. DEPT, SCH. MED, 65- Consult, Vet. Admin, 55- U.S.N.R, 44-46; Med. Serv. Corps Res, 48-52, Lt. Acoustical Soc. Am; Am. Psychol. Asn; fel. Am. Speech & Hearing Asn. Psychophysics of audition, especially in hard-of-hearing; verbal learning in normal-hearing and hard-of-hearing children. Address: Dept. of Audiology, School of Medicine, Wayne State University, 261 Mack Blvd, Detroit, MI 48201.

GAETJENS, ERIC, b. Port-au-Prince, Haiti, Mar. 10, 32; U.S. citizen. BIOCHEMISTRY. B.S, Polytech. Inst. Brooklyn, 54, Ph.D.(chem), 60. Fel, Brookhaven Nat. Lab, 60-62; ASST. MEM. BIOCHEM, INST. MUSCLE DISEASE, 62- U.S.A, 54-56. AAAS; Am. Chem. Soc. Kinetic and mechanism of organic reactions; enzymes; structure of proteins. Address: Institute for Muscle Disease, 515 E. 71st St, New York, NY 10021.

GAFARIAN, ANTRANIG VAUGHN, b. Fresno, Calif, Dec. 26, 24; m. 51; c. 2. MATHEMATICAL STATISTICS, MECHANICAL ENGINEERING. B.S.(eng. math) & B.S.(mech. eng), Michigan, 47; Southern California, 50-53; Ph.D. (math), California, Los Angeles, 59. Aerodynamicist, N.Am. Aviation, Inc, 47-51; Northrop Aircraft, Inc, 51-52; aerodyn. engr, Aerophys. Develop. Corp, 52-53; mem. tech. staff, Hughes Aircraft Co, 56-59; sr. mathematician, SYST. DEVELOP. CORP, 59-66, sr. scientist, 66-69, head math. & opers. res. prog. staff, 67-69, MGR. TRANSPORTATION & TELECOMMUN. DEPT, 69- Teacher, phys. sci. exten. prog, California, Los Angeles, 56-65; assoc. prof, San Fernando Valley State Col, 61-65. U.S.N, 43-46, Lt. (jg). Inst. Math. Statist; Opers. Res. Soc. Am; Math. Asn. Am; Am. Statist. Asn. Application of the mathematical theory of probability and mathematical statistics to the analysis of random phenomena. Address: System Development Corp, 2500 Colorado St, Santa Monica, CA 90406.

GAFFAR, ABDUL, b. Dec. 10, 39; U.S. citizen. IMMUNOLOGY, IMMUNOCHEMISTRY. B.S, Karachi, 56; M.S, Brigham Young, 65; Ph.D.(microbiol), Ohio State, 67. Res. assoc. biochem, Pakistan Res. Coun, 60-63; res. asst. bact, Brigham Young, 64-65; immunol, Ohio State, 65-67; res. microbiologist, COLGATE-PALMOLIVE RES. CTR, 67-70, SR. RES. MICROBIOLOGIST, 70- AAAS; N.Y. Acad. Sci; Am. Soc. Microbiol. Immunochemistry of tissue antigens and microbial products. Address: 255 Powers St, New Brunswick, NJ 08902.

GAFFEY, CORNELIUS T(HOMAS), b. Philadelphia, Pa, Aug. 24, 28; m. 55. BIOPHYSICS. B.A, La Salle Col, 49; fel, Tennessee, 49-51, M.S, 51; fel, Purdue, 52-58, Ph.D.(biophys), 58. Asst. physiol, Purdue, 51-52, instr. physics, 58; BIOPHYSICIST PHYSICS, DONNER LAB, LAWRENCE BERKELEY LAB, UNIV. CALIF, 58- Biophys. Soc; Am. Astronaut. Soc; Radiation Res. Soc; Soc. Neurosci; Tissue Cult. Asn. Effects of irradiation on the nervous system; computer analysis of brain electrical activity; microelectrode techniques with tissue cultures; molecular biology; excitation phenomenon in plant cell membranes. Address: Biophysical Division, Donner Lab, Lawrence Berkeley Lab, University of California, Berkeley, CA 94720.

GAFFEY, WILLIAM R(OBERT), b. Jersey City, N.J, Feb. 10, 24; m. 49; c. 3. BIOSTATISTICS, BIOMETRY. A.B, California, 48, Ph.D.(math. statist), 54. Asst. res. biostatistician, California, 54-55, instr. biostatist, 55-57, asst. prof, 57-60; statist. consult, Calif. Dept. Pub. Health, 60-69; sr. biostatist. consult, inst. med. sci, Pac. Med. Ctr, 69-71; SPEC. CONSULT, CALIF. STATE DEPT. PUB. HEALTH, 71- U.S.A, 42-45. Fel. Am. Pub. Health Asn; Am. Statist. Asn; Inst. Math. Statist. Problems of statistical methodology, particularly hypothesis testing in biology, medicine and public health. Address: California State Dept. of Public Health, 2151 Berkeley Way, Berkeley, CA 94704.

GAFFIELD, WILLIAM, b. Chicago, Ill, Dec. 26, 35; m. 61; c. 2. ORGANIC CHEMISTRY. B.S, Illinois, 57; Ph.D.(chem), Iowa, 63. Res. assoc. ORG. CHEM, New Hampshire, 62-64; RES. CHEMIST, WEST. REGIONAL RES. LAB, U.S. DEPT. AGR, 64- Am. Chem. Soc; The Chem. Soc. Application of chiroptical methods to the determination of configuration and conformation of natural products; organic stereochemistry. Address: Western Regional Research Lab, Albany, CA 94710.

GAFFNEY, BARBARA JEAN, b. Houston, Tex, Dec. 31, 44; m. 66. ORGANIC CHEMISTRY, BIOCHEMISTRY. B.A, Rutgers Univ, 66, Nat. Defense Educ. Act fel, 66-69, Ph.D.(org. chem), 70. Res. assoc, Inst. Microbiol, RUTGERS UNIV, 69-70, LECTR. CHEM, DOUGLASS COL, 70- Am. Chem. Soc. Address: Dept. of Chemistry, Douglass College, Rutgers, The State University, New Brunswick, NJ 08903.

GAFFNEY, EDWIN V, II, b. Greensburg, Pa, Sept. 1, 41; m. 64; c. 4. CELL BIOLOGY. B.A, St. Vincent Col, 63; M.S, Cath. Univ. Am, 65, Ph.D.(physiol), 68. Am. Cancer Soc. fel, Sloan-Kettering Inst. Cancer Res, 68-70; ASST. PROF. BIOL, PA. STATE UNIV, 70- AAAS; Tissue Cult. Asn. Am. Soc. Cell Biol. Control mechanisms of cell growth; SV40 transformation of human amnion cells; the inhibition of malignant cell growth by interferon. Address: Dept. of Biology, Pennsylvania State University, University Park, PA 16802.

GAFFNEY, F(RANCIS) J(OSEPH), b. Middleton, England, June 27, 12; nat; m. 38; c. 3. ENGINEERING. B.S, Northeastern, 35; Tufts, 38-39; Mass. Inst. Tech, 42-43; Polytech. Inst. Brooklyn, 46-48. Chief engr, Browning Labs, Inc, 37-41; mem. staff, radiation lab, Mass. Inst. Tech, 41-45; gen. mgr, Polytech. Res. & Develop. Co, 45-53; dir. eng, Fairchild Guided Missiles Div, 53-55; v.pres, Teleregister Corp, 55-59; v.pres. & gen. mgr, FXR, Inc, 59; tech. dir, N.AM. PHILIPS CORP, 60-67, dir. corp. prod. planning, 67-71, PRES, COMMUN. SYSTS. DIV, 71- Mem, Int. Sci. Radio Union; consult, Off. Asst. Secy. Defense. Am. Phys. Soc; fel. Inst. Elec. & Electronics Eng. Design of radio and radar equipment; measuring instruments; microwave equipment; guidance and control systems; engineering management. Address: North American Philips Corp, Communications Systems Division, 91 McKee Dr, Mahwah, NJ 07430.

GAFFNEY, PAUL C(OTTER), b. Du Bois, Pa, May 12, 17; m. 44; c. 7. MEDICINE. B.S, Pittsburgh, 40, M.D, 42. Instr. PEDIAT, UNIV. PITTSBURGH, 51-52, asst. prof, 52-53, assoc. prof, 53-62, PROF, 61- Sr. staff, Childrens Hosp, 53-; Magee Hosp, 63- Med.C, U.S.A, 43-46. Hematology. Address: Children's Hospital, 125 De Sota St, Pittsburgh, PA 15213.

GAFFNEY, PETER E(DWARD), b. Carbondale, Pa, Nov. 24, 31; m. 55; c. 3. MICROBIOLOGY. B.S, Scranton, 53; M.S, Syracuse, 54; fel. & Ph.D. (environ. sci), Rutgers, 58. Asst. prof. appl. biol. res. asst. prof, eng. exp. sta, Ga. Inst. Technol, 58-62, assoc. prof, 62-65; ASSOC. PROF. MICROBIOL. & COORD. MICROBIOL. SECT, GA. STATE UNIV, 65- Fulbright lectr, Trinity Col.(Dublin), 67-68; consult, indust. microbiol. AAAS; Am. Soc. Microbiol; Water Pollution Control Fedn. Microbial physiology; growth kinetics; stream pollution; waste treatment; microbial deterioration of industrial products; industrial fermentations. Address: Dept. of Biology, Georgia State University, 33 Gilmer St, Atlanta, GA 30303.

GAFFNEY, THOMAS EDWARD, b. East St. Louis, Ill, Nov. 5, 30; m. 54; c. 3. PHARMACOLOGY. A.B, Missouri, 51, M.S, 53; M.D, Cincinnati, 57. Intern, Harvard Med. Serv, Boston City Hosp, 58-59; asst. res, Mass. Gen. Hosp, 59-60; instr. pharmacol. & asst. med, col. med, Cincinnati, 60-61; clin. assoc, cardiol. br, Nat. Heart Inst, 61-62; asst. prof. med, COL. MED, UNIV. CINCINNATI, 62-65, assoc. prof. pharmacol, 62-67, assoc. prof. MED, 65-69, PROF, 69-, PHARMACOL, 67-, DIR. DIV. CLIN. PHARMACOL, 62- Clinician, outpatient dept, & asst. attend. physician, Cincinnati Gen. Hosp, 62-64, res. career develop. award, 62-, dir. hypertension clin, 64-; mem. med. adv. bd, Coun. High Blood Pressure Res; prog. review comt, pharmacol. & toxicol, Nat. Inst. Gen. Med. Sci, Nat. Insts. Health. U.S.P.H.S, 60-62. Soc. Exp. Biol. & Med; Am. Soc. Pharmacol. & Exp. Therapeut; cor. mem. Am. Fedn. Clin. Res; Am. Heart Asn; Am. Soc. Clin. Invest. Cardiovascular autonomic and clinical pharmacology; hypertension. Address: University of Cincinnati College of Medicine, Cincinnati, OH 45219.

GAFFORD, EDWARD L(EIGHMAN), b. Montgomery, Ala, Oct. 22, 33; m. 63; c. 1. GEOLOGY, X-RAY DIFFRACTION. B.A, Univ. Wichita, 62, M.S, 65; Nat. Defense Educ. Act fel, Univ. Okla, 65-69, Ph.D.(geol), 69. RES. SCIENTIST RADIOCHEM. & X-RAY DIFFRACTION, PAC. NORTHWEST LABS, BATTELLE MEM. INST, 68- Soc. Econ. Paleont. & Mineral; Geochem. Soc; Mineral. Soc. Am; Nat. Asn. Geol. Teachers. Research and development of x-ray diffraction analysis of particulates; heavy isotope fractionation and disequilibrium in natural systems; optical microscopy; petrographical analysis of natural material; geochemistry; mineralogy; lunar geology. Address: Environmental & Life Sciences Division, Radiological Sciences Dept, Pacific Northwest Labs, Battelle Memorial Institute, P.O. Box 999, Richland, WA 99352.

GAFFORD, ROBERT D(OSTER), b. Dawson, N.Mex, Dec. 23, 20; m. 42; c. 2. BIOLOGICAL SCIENCES. B.S, New Mexico, 47; M.A, Stanford, 55; Ph.D. (biol. sci), U.S. Air Force Sch. Aerospace Med, 57. Res. biologist, U.S. Air Force School of Aerospace Med, 55-58; assoc. res. scientist, Denver Div, Martin Co, 58-61, mgr. life sci. labs, 61-63; life sci, space eng. dept, BECKMAN INSTRUMENTS, INC, 63-64, projs. mgr, 64-66, MGR. advan. technol. opers, 66-69, MARINE PROD, 69- U.S.A.F, 42-46, 51-58. Assoc. fel. Am. Inst. Aeronaut. & Astronaut; Am. Astronaut. Soc; Am. Soc. Microbiol; Aerospace Med. Asn; Soc. Indust. Microbiol; Aerospace Indust. Life Sci. Asn.(v.pres, 64-65, pres, 66-67). Radiation biology; photosynthetic gas exchange; closed ecological systems for support of manned space flight; biochemical instrumentation. Address: Beckman Instruments, Inc, 2500 Harbor Blvd, Fullerton, CA 92634.

GAFFORD, WILLIAM R(ODGERS), b. Dawson, N.Mex, May 26, 24; m. 49; c. 1. CIVIL ENGINEERING. B.S, New Mexico, 45; Tex. Tech. Col, summer 48; M.S, Texas, 51. Instr. archit. eng, UNIV. N.MEX, 46-50, asst. prof, 51-57, assoc. prof. CIVIL ENG, 57-65, PROF, 65- Summers, draftsman, archit. firms, N.Mex, 46, 52, bldg. inspector, City of Albuquerque, 53, real estate appraiser, Fed. Savings & Loan Asn, 56, 57, archit. engr, U.S. Bu. Indian Affairs, 58, res. assoc. engr, Air Force Shock Tube Facility, 62, 63. U.S.N.R, 42-66, Lt.(jg), (Ret). Am. Soc. Eng. Educ; Am. Inst. Archit. Digital computer programming; building construction; engineering graphics. Address: Dept. of Civil Engineering, University of New Mexico, Albuquerque, NM 87106.

GAFFRON, HANS, b. Lima, Peru, May 17, 02; nat; m. 32; c. 1. BIOCHEMISTRY. Ph.D.(chem), Berlin, 25. Asst, Kaiser Wilhelm Inst. Biol, 25-30, 35-37; Kaiser Wilhelm Inst. Biochem, 32-35; res. assoc, Hopkins Marine Sta, 38-39; chem, Chicago, 39-41, asst. prof, 41-46, assoc. prof, dept. chem. & biochem, 46-49, biochem. & res. insts, 49-52, prof, 52-60; res. prof. BIOCHEM. & PLANT PHYSIOL, INST. MOLECULAR BIOPHYS, FLA. STATE UNIV, 60- Guest instr, Calif. Inst. Tech, 31. Mem, Inst. Radiobiol. & Biophys, 48-60. AAAS; Bot. Soc. Am; Am. Soc. Biol. Chem; Soc. Gen. Physiol; Biophys. Soc; Am. Soc. Plant Physiol.(award, 65). Plant physiology; photosynthesis; general biochemistry; photochemistry; metabolism of purple bacteria; exobiology. Address: Institute of Molecular Biophysics, Florida State University, Tallahassee, FL 32306.

GAFFRON, MERCEDES, b. Lima, Peru, July 2, 08. PSYCHOLOGY. Ph.D. (comp. psychol), Berlin, Germany, 34; M.D, Munich, Germany, 38. Asst. res. prof. PSYCHOL, DUKE UNIV, 57-58, ASSOC. RES. PROF, 58- Am. Psychol. Asn. Comparative and physiological psychology; visual perception; psychology of art. Address: Dept. of Psychology, Duke University, Durham, NC 27706.

GAGE, CLARKE L(YMAN), b. Mason City, Iowa, Apr. 20, 21; m. 44; c. 3. ORGANIC CHEMISTRY. B.S, Antioch Col, 44; Kettering scholar, Ohio State Univ, 46-48, Kettering fel, 48-51, Ph.D.(chem), 51. Res. chemist, polystyrene copolymers, Monsanto Chem. Co, 43-44; asst. porphyrins, C. F. Kettering Found, 46; Vernay fel, 52; asst. prof. CHEM, ST. LAWRENCE UNIV, 52-58, assoc. prof, 58-66, PROF, 66- U.S.N.R, 44-46. Am. Chem. Soc. Pyrrole chemistry; spirane synthesis; stereochemistry. Address: 6 Elm St, Canton, NY 13617.

GAGE, DONALD S(HEPARD), b. Evanston, Ill, June 10, 30; m. 56; c. 3. ELECTRICAL ENGINEERING. B.S.E.E, Northwestern, 53; Nat. Sci. Found. fel, Stanford, 53-55, M.S.E.E, 54, Ph.D.(elec. eng), 58. Asst. ELEC. ENG, Stanford, 55-58; asst. prof, Northwestern, 58-62, assoc. prof, 62; Mich. State, 63-66; PROF, UNIV. COLO, COLORADO SPRINGS, 70-, ASSOC. CHMN, 67- Mem. bd. dir, Nat. Electronics Conf, 58- Inst. Elec. & Electronics Eng. Explanation of semiconductor devices through an understanding of applied solid state physics with special interest in avalanche and transient radiation effects. Address: Dept. of Electrical Engineering, University of Colorado, Cragmor Rd, Colorado Springs, CO 80907.

GAGE, FREDERICK W(ORTHINGTON), b. Cleveland, Ohio, Dec. 27, 12; m. 40; c. 2. CHEMISTRY. B.S, Ill. Wesleyan, 34; M.S, Northwestern, 37. Res. supvr, Columbia-South. Chem. Corp, 36-54; tech. dir, Dayton Chem. Prod. Labs, Inc, WEST ALEXANDRIA, 54-58, tech. dir. & v.pres, 58-70, GEN. MGR, DAYTON CHEM. PROD. DIV, WHITTAKER CORP, 70- Am. Chem. Soc. Rubber pigments; heavy chemicals; caustic soda; calcium bleach; chlorine; sodium bicarbonate; calcium chloride; general analytical methods; preparation of calcium carbonate and calcium silicate; use of rubber pigments; purification caustic soda; purification titanium tetrachloride; rubber to metal bonding agents. Address: 106 W. Peach Orchard Rd, Dayton, OH 45419.

GAGE, KENNETH SEAVER, b. Boston, Mass, Nov. 11, 42; m. 69. GEOPHYSICS, METEOROLOGY. A.B, Brandeis, 64; Ford Found. fel, Chicago, 64-65, M.S, 66, Ph.D.(geophys. fluid dynamics), 68. ASST. PROF. METEOROL, UNIV. MD, COLLEGE PARK, 68- Am. Meteorol. Soc; Am. Geophys. Union. Geophysical fluid dynamics; hydrodynamic stability and turbulence theory; stability of thermally stratified parallel flows. Address: Institute for Fluid Dynamics & Applied Mathematics, University of Maryland, College Park, MD 20742.

GAGE, R(OBERT) S(TANLEY), b. Windsor, Ont, Oct. 25, 20; nat; m. 42; c. 5. BIOPHYSICS. B.S.A, Univ. Toronto, 49, M.S.A, 52; Ph.D.(biophys), Iowa State Univ, 58. Lectr. PHYSICS, Ont. Agr. Col, UNIV. GUELPH, 52-57, asst. prof, 57-60, ASSOC. PROF, UNIV, 60- R.C.A.F, 41-46. Biophys. Soc; Can. Asn. Physicists. Energy transformation in photosynthesis; macromolecular structure by electron microscopy and small angle x-ray scattering. Address: Dept. of Physics, University of Guelph, Guelph, Ont, Can.

GAGE, STEPHEN JOHN, b. Palisade, Nebr, Sept. 27, 40; m. 61; c. 2. NUCLEAR ENGINEERING. B.S, Nebraska, 62; M.S, Purdue, 64, Ph.D.(nuclear eng), 66. Asst. prof. mech. eng, UNIV. TEX. AUSTIN, 65-70, ASSOC. PROF. MECH. ENG. & COORD. NUCLEAR ENG. PROG, 70-, DIR. NUCLEAR REACTOR LAB, 67-, acting dir, 66-67. White House fel, Wash. D.C, 71-72. AAAS; Am. Nuclear Soc; Am. Soc. Mech. Eng. Nuclear reactor engineering; coupled-core reactor kinetics; nuclear desalting; evaporator plant dynamics; nuclear engineering laboratory development; multipurpose nuclear plant complexes. Address: Dept. of Nuclear Engineering, University of Texas at Austin, Austin, TX 78712.

GAGE, THOMAS B(ARTON), b. Oklahoma City, Okla, Jan. 2, 14; m. 41; c. 1. ORGANIC CHEMISTRY. B.S, Cent. State Col.(Okla), 40; U.S. Pub. Health Serv. fel, Oklahoma, 47-50, M.S, 48, Ph.D.(chem), 50. RES. CHEMIST, res. inst, Oklahoma, 50-51; E.I. DU PONT DE NEMOURS & CO, INC, 51- U.S.A, 40-46, Maj. Am. Chem. Soc. Textile fibers. Address: Experimental Station, Pioneering Research Division, E.I. du Pont de Nemours & Co, Inc, Wilmington, DE 19898.

GAGE, TOMMY W(ILTON), b. Stamford, Tex, Oct. 6, 35; m. 56; c. 4. PHARMACOLOGY, PHYSIOLOGY. B.S, Univ. Tex, Austin, 57; D.D.S, Baylor Univ, 61, Ph.D.(physiol), 69. Nat. Insts. Health spec. fel, 66-69; ASSOC. PROF. PHARMACOL. & CHMN. DEPT, COL. DENT, BAYLOR UNIV, 69- Dent.C, U.S.A, Maj. AAAS; Am. Dent. Asn; Int. Asn. Dent. Res. Cellular responses to oxygen and oxygenating agents, limited to tissues in the oral cavity; experimental edema. Address: Dept. of Pharmacology, Baylor University College of Dentistry, 800 Hall St, Dallas, TX 75226.

GAGE, WALTER H(ENRY), b. Vancouver, B.C, Mar. 5, 05. MATHEMATICS. B.A, Univ. B.C, 25, M.A, 26, hon. LL.D, 58. Asst. math, Univ. B.C, 26-27; instr, Victoria Col.(B.C), 27, asst. prof, 28-33, registr, 29-33; asst. prof. MATH, UNIV. B.C, 33-36, assoc. prof, 36-43, PROF, 43-, DEAN INTER-FACULTY & STUD. AFFAIRS, 48-, PRES, 69-, co-dir. Can. Army Course, 43-44, dir. summer session, 45, asst. to dean arts & sci, 45-48, dir. spec. winter session, 46, acting dean col. educ, 56-57, dep. to pres, 66-67, dep. pres, 68-69, acting pres, 67-68 & 69. Asst, Calif. Inst. Technol, 39-40. Am. Math . Soc; Math. Asn. Am; Royal Astron. Soc. Can; Can. Math. Cong. (v.pres, 48-51). Theory of numbers, especially formulas of the Liouville type. Address: Office of the President, University of British Columbia, Vancouver 8, B.C, Can.

GAGEN, JAMES EDWIN, b. Elyria, Ohio, Dec. 27, 35; m. 59; c. 4. ORGANIC CHEMISTRY. B.S, Kent State Univ, 57; M.S, Case West. Reserve Univ, 64, NASA traineeship, 65-67, Ph.D.(org. chem), 67. Chemist, B.F. Goodrich Chem. Co, 59-65; ASST. PROF. CHEM, UNIV. TENN, MARTIN, 67- Am. Chem. Soc. Aromatic substitution by sulfonyl peroxides. Address: Dept. of Chemistry, University of Tennessee at Martin, Martin, TN 38237.

GAGEN, WALTER L(EONARD), b. Dayton, Ky, May 15, 29; m. 51; c. 3. PHYSICAL BIOCHEMISTRY. Cincinnati, 47-51. Res. chemist, Procter & Gamble Co, 47-66; sect. head protein res, res. dept, OGILVIE FLOUR MILLS CO, LTD, 66-68, admin. & tech. serv, 68-71, MGR. ANAL. SERV, 71- U.S.A, 50-51. AAAS; Am. Chem. Soc; Chem. Inst. Can; Am. Asn. Cereal Chem. Protein chemistry; ultracentrifugation; electrophoresis; biophysical techniques; atomic absorption spectroscopy; gas-liquid chromatography; color technology. Address: Ogilvie Flour Mills, 995 Mill St, Montreal, Que, Can.

GAGER, F(ORREST) L(EE), JR, b. Phila, Pa, Apr. 23, 22; m. 50; c. 2. ORGANIC CHEMISTRY. B.S, Haverford Col, 49; A.M, Indiana, 51. Res. chemist, Merck & Co, Inc, 51-55; PHILIP MORRIS, INC, 55-57, supvr. org. sect, 57-59, res. assoc, 59-60, res. scientist, 60-63, SR. SCIENTIST, 63- Vis. fel, Univ. Manchester, 65-66. U.S.A.A.F, 43-46, 1st Lt. AAAS; Am. Chem. Soc; The Chem. Soc; Brit. Inst. Petrol. Chemistry of natural products; flavors and aromas; tobacco chemistry; chromatography; biosynthesis; isotope tracer techniques. Address: Philip Morris U.S.A. Research Center, P.O. Box 26583, Richmond, VA 23261.

GAGER, WILLIAM B(ALLANTINE), b. Columbus, Ohio, April 18, 28; m. 56; c. 2. PHYSICS. A.B, Bowdoin Col, 49; M.A, Ohio State, 51, Ph.D.(physics), 56. Physicist, Nat. Bur. Standards, 56-58; Battelle Mem. Inst, 58-67; ASSOC. PROF. PHYSICS, JACKSONVILLE UNIV, 67- Am. Phys. Soc. Paramagnetic resonance; nuclear magnetic resonance; very low temperatures; solid state physics. Address: Dept. of Physics, Jacksonville University, Jacksonville, FL 32211.

GAGGE, A(DOLF) P(HARO), b. Columbus, Ohio, Jan. 11, 08; m. 36; c. 4. BIOPHYSICS, PHYSIOLOGY. B.A, Virginia, 29, M.A, 30; scholar, Yale, 31-32, Coffin fel, 31-33, Ph.D.(physics), 33. Instr. math, Virginia, 28-30; asst. physics, Yale, 30-31, fel, 33-35, instr. biophys, 36-39, asst. prof, 39-41; chief biophys. br, aero med. lab, U.S. Air Force, Wright Field, 42-45, aeromed. res. & opers, 45-50, med. res. div, Off. Surgeon Gen, 50-51, chief human factors div. & dir. res. & develop, 51-55, dep. comdr. sci, Off. Sci. Res, 55-60, comdr, 60; prog. mgr. Adv. Res. Proj. Agency, Off. Secy. Defense, 60-63; assoc. prof. physiol, SCH. MED, YALE, 63-69, PROF. EPIDEMIOL, 69-, DEP. DIR, JOHN B. PIERCE FOUND. LAB, 71-, fel, 63-64. Asst, Univ. Va, 29-30; res. physicist, John B. Pierce Found, Conn, 33-41. Mem. subcomt, altitude chambers, Nat. Res. Coun, 41; panel aviation med, Aeronaut. Bd, 47; Res. & Develop. Bd, 50-53; comt. hearing, bioacoustics & biomech, Nat. Acad. Sci-Nat. Res. Coun, 66-67. U.S.A.F, 42-60, Col; Commedation Ribbon, 45; Legion of Merit, 46, 60. AAAS; Am. Phys. Soc; Am. Physiol. Soc; Biophys. Soc; fel. Aerospace Med. Asn; assoc. fel. Am. Inst. Aeronaut. & Astronaut. Scattering of electrons in gases; atmospheric ionization; environmental physiology; partitional calorimetry; aviation of physiology; respiration and metabolism; bio-astronautics; biophysics. Address: John B. Pierce Foundation Lab, 290 Congress Ave, New Haven, CT 06519.

GAGGIOLI, RICHARD A, b. Lake Forest, Ill, Dec. 3, 34; m. 57; c. 5. MECHANICAL ENGINEERING. B.S.M.E, Northwestern, 57, Nat. Sci. Found. fel, 57-58, M.S, 58; Coffin fel, Wisconsin, 58-59, Rice fel, 59-60, Nat. Sci. Found. fel, 60-61, Ph.D.(mech. eng), 61. Nat. Sci. Found. fel. chem. eng, Univ. Wis, Madison, 61-62, asst. prof. mech. eng, 62-66, assoc. prof, 66-69; res. mem, U.S. Army Math. Res. Ctr, 65-67; PROF. MECH. ENG. & CHMN. DEPT, MARQUETTE UNIV, 69- Vis. fel, Battelle Mem. Inst, 68-69. Am. Soc. Eng. Educ; Am. Soc. Mech. Eng; Am. Inst. Chem. Eng; Soc. Indust. & Appl. Math; Soc. Natural Philos. Thermodynamics of non-equilibrium processes; applied mathematics. Address: Dept. of Mechanical Engineering, Marquette University, 1515 W. Wisconsin Ave, Milwaukee, WI 53233.

GAGLIANI, JOHN, b. Whitewater, Wis, Feb. 10, 26; m. 52; c. 4. ORGANIC & POLYMER CHEMISTRY. Ph.D.(chem), Pisa, 51. Instr. metab, N.Y. Univ. Med. Center, 52-55; asst. dir. synthesis, Gamma Chem. Corp, 55-60; res. dir. polymers, Synvar Corp, 60-66; mgr. res. & develop, G.T. Schjeldahl Co, 66-68; STAFF SCIENTIST, IBM CORP, 68- Am. Chem. Soc; Am. Mgt. Asn. Synthesis of organic chemicals, monomers and polymers; physical properties of polymers and relationship to molecular structure; high temperature polymers. Address: 1012 Northern Heights Dr, Rochester, MN 55901.

GAGLIANO, L(OUIS) J(OHN), b. Jamestown, N.Y, Aug. 4, 17; m. 45; c. 4. INORGANIC CHEMISTRY. S.B, Chicago, 39. Res. chemist inorg. chem, Imp. Color Chem. & Paper Dept, Hercules Powder Co, 39-47, res. supvr, 48-65, res. mgr, Imp. Color & Chem. Dept, HERCULES, INC, 65-71, CHEM. SUPT. IMP. DIV, COATINGS & SPECIALTIES PROD. DEPT, 71- AAAS; Am. Chem. Soc. Research supervision for chemical and pigment development in both inorganic and organic fields. Address: Imperial Division, Coatings & Specialties Products Dept, Hercules, Inc, 51 Kensington Rd, Glens Falls, NY 18201.

GAGLIANO, NICHOLAS CHARLES, b. New Orleans, La, Apr. 5, 27; m. 51; c. 2. PEDIATRICS, PREVENTIVE MEDICINE. B.S, Loyola (La), 48; M.D, La. State, 52. Intern, Charity Hosp. La, New Orleans, 52-53, res, 53-55; practicing pediatrician, 55-60; assoc. prof. pediat, SCH. MED, LA STATE UNIV, 60-70, PROF. PEDIAT. & PREV. MED, 70-, assoc. prof. prev. med, 64-70. Asst. proj. dir. collab. child develop. prog, Charity Hosp. La, 61-64. Dipl, Am. Bd. Pediat, 61. U.S.N.R, 45-46. Am. Acad. Pediat. Preventive and ambulatory pediatrics. Address: Dept. of Pediatrics, Louisiana State University School of Medicine, 1542 Tulane Ave, New Orleans, LA 70112.

GAGLIANO, SHERWOOD M(ONEER), b. New Orleans, La, Dec. 10, 35; m. 61. PHYSICAL GEOGRAPHY, ARCHAEOLOGY. B.S, La. State Univ, 59, M.A, 63, Ph.D.(geog), 67. Supvr. sediment lab, COASTAL STUDIES INST, LA. STATE UNIV, 60-64, field investr, coastal geol, 64-65, instr. coastal morphol, 65-67, asst. prof. COASTAL GEOG, 67-69, ASSOC. PROF, 69-, ASST. PROF. MARINE SCI, UNIV, 69-, instr. geog. & anthrop, 63-67, asst. prof, 67-68. Consult, Nat. Acad. Sci-Nat. Res. Coun, summer 65. U.S.A.R, 59. AAAS; Geol. Soc. Am; Am. Asn. Petrol. Geol; Soc. Econ. Paleont. & Mineral; Soc. Am. Archaeol; Asn. Am. Geog. Geology, sedimentology, geomorphology and archaeology of coastal areas, especially deltas and low-lying coasts; comparative studies and process-form relationships in deltas and archaeology of early man. Address: Coastal Studies Institute, Center for Wetland Resources, Louisiana State University, Baton Rouge, LA 70803.

GAGLIARDI, GEORGE N(ICHOLAS), b. Brooklyn, N.Y, May 17, 30; m. 56; c. 6. CHEMICAL ENGINEERING. B.Ch.E, Pratt Inst, 52; M.Ch.E, N.Y. Univ, 61. Chem. engr, process develop, AM. CYANAMID CO, 52-56, res. engr, 56-59, group leader process res. agr. chem, 59-66, mgr. process develop, agr. div, 66-68, PROD. MGR. PESTICIDES, 68- Am. Inst. Chem. Eng; Am. Chem. Soc. Process research on and manufacture of organic chemicals scaleup; techniques. Address: American Cyanamid Co, Box 31, Linden, NJ 07036.

GAGLIARDI, ROBERT M, b. New Haven, Conn, Apr. 7, 34; m. 57; c. 3. ELECTRICAL ENGINEERING. B.S.E.E, Connecticut, 56; M.S, Yale, 57, Ph.D.(elec. eng), 60. Staff engr, Hughes Aircraft Co, 60-61; asst. prof. ENG, UNIV. SOUTH. CALIF, 61-70, ASSOC. PROF, 70- Consult, Hughes Aircraft Co, 61- Inst. Elec. & Electronics Eng. Problems of communication theory, information theory, telemetry and data handling system studies. Address: Dept. of Electrical Engineering, University of Southern California, University Park, CA 90007.

GAGNE, JEAN-MARIE, b. Alma, Que, July 12, 32; m. 59; c. 1. SPECTROSCOPY, OPTICS. B.Sc, Univ. Montreal, 58, M.Sc, 59; D.Sc.(physics), Univ. Paris, 65. Asst. prof. physics, Polytech. Sch, Univ. Montreal, 59-63; fel. spectros, Aimé-Cotton Lab, 63-65; ASSOC. PROF. PHYSICS & ENG. & HEAD OPTICAL LAB, POLYTECH. SCH, UNIV. MONTREAL, 65-, HEAD DEPT. PHYS. ENG, 70- AAAS; Can. Asn. Physicists; Optical Soc. Am; Spectros. Soc. Can; French-Can. Asn. Advan. Sci; Soc. Photo-Optical Instrument. Eng. Hyperfine structure in line spectra and influence of isotopes on the hyperfine of atomic spectral lines; essentials of a problem os spectroscopy, especially Fabry-Pérot spectrometers; detection of flux and spectrometers photon noise and detection noise. Address: Dept. of Engineering Physics, University of Montreal, C.P. 6128, Montreal, Que, Can.

GAGNÉ, RAYMOND J, b. Meriden, Conn, Aug. 27, 35; m. 63; c. 2. ENTOMOLOGY. B.A, Connecticut, 61; M.S, Iowa State, 63; Ph.D.(entom), Minnesota, 67. RES. ENTOMOLOGIST, SYST. ENTOM. LAB, U.S. DEPT. AGR, 65- U.S.A, 55-58. AAAS; Entom. Soc. Am; Soc. Syst. Zool. Systematics of gall midges and fungus gnats. Address: Systematic Entomology Lab, U.S. Dept. of Agriculture, U.S. National Museum, Washington, DC 20560.

GAGNE, ROBERT M(ILLS), b. North Andover, Mass, Aug. 21, 16; m. 42; c. 2. EXPERIMENTAL PSYCHOLOGY. A.B, Yale, 37; M.S, Brown, 39, Ph.D. (psychol), 40. Instr. psychol, Conn. Col, 40-41, from asst. to assoc. prof, 46-49; asst. prof, Pa. State, 45-46; res. dir. perceptual & motor skills lab, U.S. Air Force, 49-53, tech. dir. maintenance lab, Personnel & Training Res. Center, 53-58; prof. psychol, Princeton, 58-62; dir. res, Am. Inst. Res, Pa, 62-66; PROF. EDUC. PSYCHOL, Univ. Calif, Berkeley, 66-69; FLA. STATE UNIV, 69- U.S.A.A.F, 41-45, 1st Lt. AAAS; fel. Am. Psychol. Asn. Human learning; intellectual functions; human factors engineering; psychological factors in education and training. Address: Dept. of Educational Research, Florida State University, Tallahassee, FL 32306.

GAGNEBIN, ALBERT PAUL, b. Torrington, Conn, Jan. 23, 09; m. 35; c. 2. METALLURGY. B.S, Yale, 30, M.S, 32. Res. metallurgist, res. lab, INT. NICKEL CO, 32-49, metallurgist in charge ductile iron, develop. & res. div, 49-55, asst. mgr, nickel sales dept, 54-56, mgr, 56-58, asst. v.pres, 57-58, v.pres. & mgr, primary nickel dept, 58-64, EXEC. V.PRES, 64- V.pres, Int. Nickel Co. Can, Ltd, 60-64, exec. v.pres, 64-67, pres, 67- Am. Soc. Metals; Am. Foundrymen's Soc.(Simpson Gold Medal, 52); Am. Soc. Mech. Eng; Am. Inst. Min, Metall. & Petrol. Eng. Development of nickel containing materials. Address: International Nickel Co, Inc, One New York Plaza, New York, NY 10004.

GAGNON, ANDRÉ, b. Quebec, Que, Can, Nov. 2, 21; m. 50; c. 6. PHYSIOLOGY. B.A.Sc, Laval, 47; Ph.D.(zool, physiol), Pennsylvania, 53. Lectr. GEN. PHYSIOL, sch. med, LAVAL UNIV, 51-62, asst. prof, SCH. SCI, 62-66, PROF, 66- Cell division; intestinal absorption; osmoregulation in fishes. Address: Dept. of Biology, Laval University, Quebec, Que, Can.

GAGNON, ARTHUR, b. Montreal, Que, May 14, 13; m. 48; c. 5. BIOCHEMISTRY. M.D, Univ. Montreal, 39, Rockefeller Found. fel, & L.Sc, 41. PROF. BIOCHEM, FACULTY MED, UNIV. MONTREAL, 43- AAAS; N.Y. Acad. Sci; Can. Soc. Biol. Vitamines and enzymes. Address: Dept. of Biochemistry, University of Montreal, P.O. Box 6128, Montreal, Que, Can.

GAGNON, EUGENE GERALD, b. Revere, Mass, Feb. 20, 36; m. 67; c. 2. ELECTROCHEMISTRY, ELECTROCHEMICAL ENGINEERING. B.Sc, Loyola Col.(Que), 57; Westinghouse fel, Stevens Inst. Technol, 57-60, M.S, 60; Ph.D, Pa. State Univ, 70. Asst, Stevens Inst. Technol, 58-60; res. chem. eng, Socony Mobil Oil Co, 60-66; res. asst, Pa. State Univ, 66-69; asst. res. dir, C&D Batteries Div, Eltra Corp, 69-70; ASSOC. SR. RES. CHEMIST, ELECTROCHEM. DEPT, GEN. MOTORS CORP. RES. LABS, 70- Instr, Rutgers Univ, 64-66; consult, Harry Diamond Labs, Army Mat. Command, 68-69. Am. Chem. Soc; Electrochem. Soc. Electrochemical studies on air, depolarized air cathodes; mathematical modeling of distributed reactions in porous electrodes; fundamental studies on the lead-acid battery system; kinetics of porous Ag/Ag_2O electrodes at low temperatures in KOH. Address: Electrochemistry Dept, General Motors Corp. Research Labs, 12 Mile & Mound Rds, Warren, MI 48090.

GAGNON, LEO PAUL, b. Milford, N.H, Oct. 25, 29; m. 57; c. 6. PHARMACY. B.S, Mass. Col. Pharm, 52; M.S, Purdue, 54, Am. Found. Pharmaceut. Ed. fel, 54-56, Ph.D, 57. Res. pharmacist, pharm. res. lab, Miles Labs, Inc, 56-58, group leader, 58-59, sect. head, 59-63; CHIEF, NORWICH PROD. DEVELOP. SECT, NORWICH PHARM. CO, 63- AAAS; Soc. Cosmetic Chem; Am. Pharmaceut. Asn; Acad. Pharmaceut. Sci; N.Y. Acad. Sci. Pharmaceutical product development; ethical and proprietary medicinals. Address: Norwich Product Development Section, Pharmaceutical Research Division, Norwich Pharmacal Co, Norwich, NY 13815.

GAGNON, MARCEL, b. St. Moise, Que, Jan. 17, 28; m. 54; c. 3. FOOD TECHNOLOGY. B.A, Laval, 49, B.S, 53; M.S, Massachusetts, 55, Ph.D. (food tech), 57. Asst. biologist, Que. Dept. Maritime Fisheries, Can, 50, technologist, 52-53, asst. technologist, econ. div, Can. Dept. Maritime Fisheries, Ont, 51; technologist, Fisheries Res. Bd. Can, 54-55; res. instr. food tech, Massachusetts, 55-56, asst. res. prof, 57; prod. mgr. & dir. res. & develop, Alphonse Raymond, Ltd, 58-61, v.pres. prod. & res, 61-66, v.pres. & gen. mgr, 66-68; v.pres. opers, R.J. Reynolds Foods, Ltd, 68-70; v.rector, UNIV. QUE, MONTREAL, 70-71, DIR. FOOD RES, 71- Lectr, Montreal Inst. Technol, 60-; head, food mission to Europe, 64; Que. Food Industs. rep, Int. Food Salon, Paris, 64; mem. bd. dir, Univ. Que, Montreal, 70-71. AAAS; Am. Chem. Soc; Inst. Food Technol; Can. Inst. Food Technol.(v.pres, 62); Can. Food Processors Asn.(v.pres, 66-67). Food biochemistry; enzyme biochemistry; food management; environment. Address: University of Quebec, P.O. Box 3050 Succ. B, Montreal 110, Que, Can.

GAGNON, PAUL E(DOUARD), b. Kingsey, Que, Feb. 26, 01. CHEMISTRY. B.A, Laval, 21, Price scholar, 24-26, B.A.Sc, 26, Ph.D, 33; Que. Prov. Govt. scholar, 26-30; D.ès Sci, Sorbonne, 29; D.I.C, London, 31; LL.D, Bathurst, 49; D.Sc, McMaster, 51; D.Sc, Toronto, 53. Lectr. CHEM, LAVAL UNIV, 31-32, asst. prof, 32-35, prof, 35-70, head dept, 38-56, dean grad. sch. & gov. univ, 40-60, head dept. chem. eng, 41-45, EMER. PROF, 70- Mem. coun, Chem. Inst. Can, 34-37; adv, Wartime Bur. Tech. Personnel, 41-45; Can. Sci. Del. to Ger, 45; mem. coun, Eng. Inst. Can, 45-46; Nat. Res. Coun. Can, 45-51, spec. asst. to ed-in-chief of Can. Jours. Res, 62-66; Can. del, Empire Sci. Conf, London, Eng, 46; mem. Defence Res. Bd. Can, 46-52; Atomic Energy Control Bd. Can, 46-60; Fisheries Res. Bd. Can, 50-60; Nuffield Found. traveling fel, 51; Can. del, Brit. Commonwealth Sci. Off. Conf, Australia, 52; Int. Conf. Peaceful Uses of Atomic Energy, Geneva, Switz, 55 & 58; sci. adv, Dept. Mines, Que, 56-60; dir. div. exchange & training scientists & experts, Int. Atomic Energy Agency, Vienna, Austria, 60-62; mem. Can. Govt. Comt. of Can. Pavilion at Expo, 67; emer. mem, Prof. Inst. Pub. Serv. Can, 69. Prix d'Action Intellectuelle, Prov. Que, 30 & 35; Coronation Medal, 38 & 53; Prix David, 42. Can. Army, 23-36, Maj; C.D, 62. Fel. Royal Soc. Can.(v.pres, sect. III, 52, pres, 53); fel. The Chem. Soc; hon. fel. Chem. Inst. Can.(hon. treas, 34-45, v.pres, 46-47, pres, 47); Eng. Inst. Can. Organic and inorganic chemistry; indene and anthracene derivatives; amino acids and pyrazolones. Address: 200 Rideau Terr, Ottawa, Ont. K1M 0Z3, Can.

GAGNON, REAL, b. Montreal, Que, May 9, 24; m. 52; c. 3. ANATOMY. B.A, Montreal, 45, M.D, 51; Ph.D.(anat), Michigan, 55. Asst. prof. ANAT, UNIV. MONTREAL, 54-58, assoc. prof, 58-64, PROF, 64- Can. Asn. Anat; French Asn. Anat. Gross anatomy; human embryology; anthropology. Address: Dept. of Anatomy, Faculty of Medicine, University of Montreal, P.O. Box 6128, Montreal, Que, Can.

GAGOSIAN, ROBERT BERJ, b. Medford, Mass, Sept. 17, 44; m. 67. ORGANIC CHEMISTRY. S.B, Mass. Inst. Technol, 66; Nat. Sci. Found. trainee, Stanford Univ, 66-67; Ferguson fel, Columbia Univ, 67-68, IBM fel, 69-70, Ph.D. (org. chem), 70. NAT. INSTS. HEALTH FEL. CHEM, UNIV. CALIF, BERKELEY, 70- AAAS; Am. Chem. Soc; The Chem. Soc. Organic photochemistry; mechanisms of excited state reactions; small ring chemistry; synthesis involving new techniques. Address: Dept. of Chemistry, University of California, Berkeley, CA 94720.

GAHAN, JAMES B(ONNET), b. Berwyn, Md, July 19, 09; m. 37. ENTOMOLOGY. B.S, Maryland, 30, M.S, 32. Field asst, bur. entom. & plant quarantine. U.S. Dept. Agr, Md, 30-35, jr. entomologist, 35-37, Fla, 37-43, asst. entomologist, 43-44, entomologist, 44-53, entom. res. div, Agr. Res. Serv, 53-69; RETIRED. With Off. Sci. Res. & Develop, 43-45; U.S.N, 48-51. AAAS; Entom. Soc. Am; Am. Mosquito Control Asn. Insect toxicology; development of new insecticides. Address: 3845 S.W. Third Ave, Gainesville, FL 32601.

GAHLER, A(RNOLD) R(OBERT), b. Portland, Ore, Sept. 6, 19; m. 42; c. 2. ANALYTICAL CHEMISTRY. A.B, Pacific, 41; Ore. State Col, 41-42; Nat. Insts. Health fel, Purdue, 48-50, M.S, 49. Asst. anal. chem, Purdue, 46-48; anal. res. chemist, metal res. labs, Electro Metall. Co, Union Carbide & Carbon Corp, 50-59, sr. develop. chemist, Union Carbide Metals Co, 59-61, asst. chief chemist, tech. dept, metals div, Union Carbide Corp, 61-63, alloy plant, 63-64; asst. biochem, Oregon State, 65; anal. chemist, PAC. NORTHWEST WATER LAB, U.S. PUB. HEALTH SERV, 65-67, RES. CHEMIST, ENVIRON. PROTECTION AGENCY, 67- U.S.N.R, 43-46. Am. Chem. Soc; Soc. Appl. Spectros; Water Pollution Control. Fedn; Int. Asn. Gt. Lakes Res. Analytical research in metallurgical inorganic fields; water analysis, especially trace analysis, spectrophotometry and physical methods; eutrophication; lake restoration methods; sediment-water nutrient interchange. Address: 1120 N.W. 11th St, Corvallis, OR 97330.

GAHM, W(ALLACE) LEROY, b. Jackson Co, Ohio, Feb. 13, 19; m. 42. ELECTRICAL ENGINEERING. B.S, Ohio, 40. Draftsman, Trumbull Elec. Mfg. Co, Gen. Elec. Co, 40; inspector, Naval Aircraft Factory, 40-42, resident inspector, field serv, inspection div, Bur. Aeronautics, 42-43, prin. inspector, 43-44; elec. engr, Curtiss-Wright Corp, 46-49, 50; engr, Columbia Res. & Develop. Corp, 50-59; sr. elec. engr, Battelle Mem. Inst, 59-70; SR. DEVELOP. ENGR, I-T-E IMPERIAL CORP, 70- U.S.N.R, 44-46, Lt. (jg). Nat. Soc. Prof. Eng; Numerical Control Soc. Servomechanisms; automatic control systems; solid state devices; numerical control. Address: Industrial Control Dept, I-T-E Imperial Corp, 811 N. Main St, Bellefontaine, OH 43311.

GAIDIS, JAMES MICHAEL, b. Baltimore, Md, Oct. 17, 40; m. 63; c. 3. ORGANOMETALLIC CHEMISTRY. A.B, Harvard, 63; Ph.D.(inorg. chem), Wisconsin, Madison, 67. RES. CHEMIST, Dow Chem. Co, 67-70; W.R. GRACE & CO, CAMBRIDGE, 71- Am. Chem. Soc. Silicon and organometallic chemistry. Address: 891 Old Connecticut Path, Framingham, MA 01701.

GAIDOS, JAMES A, b. Clarksburg, W.Va, July 15, 36; m. 59; c. 2. PHYSICS. A.B, West Virginia, 58; Ph.D.(physics), Wisconsin, 63. Res. assoc. PHYSICS, Wisconsin, 63-65; ASST. PROF, Hamilton Col, 65-69; PURDUE UNIV, 69- Am. Phys. Soc; Italian Phys. Soc. Elementary particles. Address: Dept. of Physics, Purdue University, West Lafayette, IN 47907.

GAILANI, SALMAN, b. Baghdad, Iraq, May 25, 26; U.S. citizen; m. 56; c. 3. MEDICINE, CANCER. M.B, Ch.B, Univ. Baghdad, 49. RES. ASST. PROF. MED. & RES. ASSOC. PROF. PHARMACOL, GRAD. SCH, STATE UNIV. N.Y. BUFFALO, 70-; ASSOC. CHIEF MED, ROSWELL PARK MEM. INST, 69-, sr. cancer res. internist, 61-65, assoc. cancer res. internist, 65-69. Am. Fedn. Clin. Res; Am. Asn. Cancer Res; Am. Soc. Clin. Oncol; Am. Inst. Nutrit. Cancer chemotherapy; nutrition. Address: Dept. of Medicine, Roswell Park Memorial Institute, 666 Elm St, Buffalo, NY 14203.

GAILAR, N(ORMAN) M(ILTON), b. Hornell, N.Y, Feb. 20, 18; m. 69. PHYSICS. B.A, Syracuse, 48, M.S, 50; Ph.D.(physics), Ohio State, 58. Physicist, Nat. Bur. Standards, 50-52; Naval Res. Lab, 52-53; asst. prof. PHYSICS, UNIV. TENN, KNOXVILLE, 58-63, ASSOC. PROF, 63- U.S.A.A.F, 43-45, 2nd Lt. Optical Soc. Am. Molecular and infrared spectroscopy; molecular structure. Address: Dept. of Physics, University of Tennessee, Knoxville, TN 37916.

GAILAR, OWEN H, b. Rochester, N.Y, Nov. 10, 25; m. 52; c. 2. PHYSICS. B.S, Rochester, 46; Eastman Kodak fel, Purdue, 48-49, M.S, 49, Ph.D.(exp. nuclear physics), 56. Asst. physics, Purdue, 46-56; supvr. reactor physics, statics, Combustion Eng, Inc, 57-62; ASSOC. PROF. NUCLEAR PHYSICS, PURDUE UNIV, 62- Physicist, Nat. Bur. Standards, 51-52; consult, Pac. Gas & Elec. Co, Calif, 69-70; Commonwealth Edison. Am. Soc. Eng. Educ; Am. Nuclear Soc. Reactor design; application of digital computers to reactor design and analysis; integration of power reactors into utility grids; nuclear fuel cycle; reactor physics; computer application. Address: Dept. of Nuclear Engineering, Duncan Annex, Purdue University, West Lafayette, IN 47906.

GAILEY, FRANKLIN B(RYAN), b. Atlanta, Ga, Oct. 18, 18; m. 48; c. 4. BIOLOGY, CHEMISTRY. B.S, Ga. Tech, 40; M.S, Wisconsin, 42, Ph.D.(biochem), 46. Asst. biochem, Wisconsin, 40-46; instr. chem. & biol, Lees Jr. Col, 46-48; asst. prof. biol, BEREA COL, 48-51, assoc. prof, 51-57, PROF. BIOL. & CHEM, 57-, CHMN. DEPT. BIOL, 56- With Off. Prod. Res. & Develop, 44. AAAS; Am. Chem. Soc; Am. Soc. Plant Physiol. Differentiation and separation of hog mucosa peptidases; production of penicillin by fermentation in pilot tanks; greening of dark-grown seedlings; protoplasmic streaming in slime mold. Address: Dept. of Biology, Berea College, Berea, KY 40403.

GAILEY, JOSEPH A, b. York, Pa, Feb. 27, 30; m. 52; c. 3. ANALYTICAL CHEMISTRY, MOLECULAR SPECTROSCOPY. B.S, Haverford Col, 52; M.S, Wisconsin, 55. Chemist, RES. CTR, HERCULES, INC, 56-69, RES. CHEMIST, 69- Soc. Appl. Spectros. Molecular spectroscopy; computer assisted analytical chemistry. Address: Hercules Research Center, Wilmington, DE 19899.

GAINER, ALVIS BERYL, b. Brady, Tex, Nov. 26, 34; m. 55; c. 2. ORGANIC & ANALYTICAL CHEMISTRY. B.S, Texas A&M, 56, M.S, 59; Nat. Sci. Found. fel, Oklahoma, 60-61, Ph.D.(anal. & org. chem), 62. Instr. gen. chem, Oklahoma, 61-62; develop. chemist, res. & tech. lab, Mobil Chem. Co, 62-65, sr. develop. chemist, 65-67; lab. mgr, Merichem Co, 67-70; PRES, ANAL. & TESTING LAB, INC, 70- U.S.A.R, 62-64, 1st Lt. Am. Chem. Soc. Absorption spectroscopy; polarography; organometallic syntheses; high temperature organic syntheses; catalyst preparation; fixed-bed catalysis; air and water pollution; petrochemicals; pharmaceuticals; foods; metallurgy; trace metals; corrosion; microbiology. Address: Analytical & Testing Lab, Inc, 6001 Clinton Dr, Houston, TX 77020.

GAINER, FRANK EDWARD, b. Waynesboro, Ga, June 18, 38; m. 61; c. 2. ANALYTICAL CHEMISTRY. B.S, Morehouse Col, 60; Army Res. Off. fel, Tuskegee Inst, 60-62, M.S, 62; M.S, Iowa State, 64, Ph.D.(chem), 67. SR. ANAL. CHEMIST, ANAL. DEVELOP. DEPT, ELI LILLY & CO, 67- Am. Chem. Soc. Broad spectrum pharmaceutical analysis; developing control and stability assay procedures for new pharmaceutical compounds; solving analytical problems associated with pharmaceutical pilot plant and production operations; qualitation and quantitation of impurities. Address: 1810 W. Kessler Blvd, Indianapolis, IN 46208.

GAINER, GORDON C(LEMENTS), b. Edmonton, Alta, Aug. 25, 20; nat; m. 44; c. 3. ORGANIC CHEMISTRY. B.Sc, Alberta, 42; Ph.D.(org. chem), Iowa State, 46. Instr. chem, Iowa State, 42-46; chemist, res. lab, WESTINGHOUSE ELEC. CORP, 46-52, supvr. chem. develop. sect, mat. lab, 52-55, mgr. insulation & chem. eng. dept, 55-61, advan. planning, RES. LABS, 61-69, CONSULT. SCIENTIST, 69- Am. Chem. Soc. Synthesis of antimalarial and antituberculous compounds; organometallic reactions; organic syntheses; silicone monomers, polymers and lubricants; polymers for electrical insulation. Address: Westinghouse Research Labs, Pittsburgh, PA 15235.

GAINER, HAROLD, b. New York, N.Y, Sept. 16, 23; m. 47; c. 5. ORGANIC CHEMISTRY. B.S, City Col. New York, 45; M.S, Polytech. Inst. Brooklyn, 52, Ph.D.(org. chem), 58. Chemist, Hoffmann-La Roche, Inc, 47-55; sr. chemist, Wyandotte Chem. Corp, 57-62; sr. res. chemist, Chapman Chem. Co, 63-66; plant lab. mgr, CIBA-GEIGY LTD, 66-67, GROUP LEADER, DEVELOP. & PILOT PLANT DEPT, 67- U.S.A.A.F, 45-46, Sgt. Am. Chem. Soc. Fine organic chemicals syntheses; heterocylic compounds; polyethers; polyurethanes; chlorination; industrial process development. Address: Ciba-Geigy Ltd, Box 2055, Providence, RI 02905.

GAINER, HAROLD, b. New York, N.Y, Aug. 6, 35; m. 65. NEUROBIOLOGY. B.S, City Col. New York, 56; Nat. Insts. Health fel, California, Berkeley, 57-59, Ph.D.(physiol), 59. Res. fel. physiol, California, Berkeley, 59-60; U.S. Pub. Health Serv. res. fels. electrophysiol, Columbia, 60-63; asst. prof. zool, Univ. Md, 63-66, assoc. prof, 66-69; RES. PHYSIOLOGIST, NAT. INST. CHILD HEALTH & HUMAN DEVELOP, 69- Lectr, sch. med, California, San Francisco, 59-60; U.S. Pub. Health Serv. res. grant, 63-; vis. prof, Tel-Aviv Univ, 69. AAAS; Am. Physiol. Soc; Am. Soc. Zool. Electrophysiology; physiological and biochemical basis of electrogenesis in biological systems. Address: Behavioral Biology Branch, National Institutes of Child Health & Human Development, Bethesda, MD 20014.

GAINER, JOHN LLOYD, b. Grafton, W.Va, July 19, 38. CHEMICAL ENGINEERING. B.S.Ch.E, West Virginia, 60; M.S, Mass. Inst. Tech, 61; Ph.D.(chem. eng), Delaware, 64. Fel. chem. eng, Delaware, summer 64; res. chem. engr, silicones div, Union Carbide Corp, 64-66; asst. prof. CHEM. ENG, UNIV. VA, 66-68, ASSOC. PROF, 68- Vis. fel, Karolinska Inst, Sweden, 71-72. Am. Inst. Chem. Eng; Am. Chem. Soc; Am. Soc. Eng. Educ. Diffusion in liquids; polymer and surface chemistry; biological mass transfer. Address: Dept. of Chemical Engineering, Thornton Hall, University of Virginia, Charlottesville, VA 22901.

GAINER, JOSEPH H(ENRY), b. Atlanta, Ill, Oct. 24, 24; m. 54; c. 5. VIROLOGY. D.V.M, Ohio State, 46, M.S, 47, Michigan, 58. Instr, Ohio State, 47-49; asst. comp. path, Mayo Clinic, 49-50; res. assoc. med, Chicago, 50-51; asst. prof. vet. sci, Arkansas, 51-53; vet. virologist, Fla. Dept. Agr, 59-66; sr. vet. off, Nat. Cancer Inst, 66; VIROLOGIST & VET. DIR, U.S. PUB. HEALTH SERV, NAT. INST. ENVIRON. HEALTH SCI, 67- Adj. prof, dept. of animal sci, N.C. State Univ, 68- Dipl, Am. Col. Vet. Microbiol, 67. U.S.A, 53-55, Capt. AAAS; N.Y. Acad. Sci; Conf. Res. Workers Animal Diseases; Am. Soc. Microbiol; Am. Vet. Med. Asn; Int. Acad. Path. Ovine ketosis; experimental tuberculosis and influenza chemotherapy; radiation sickness; salmonellosis; chemical warfare; encephalomyocarditis virus and arbovirus infections of animals. Address: U.S. Public Health Service, National Institute of Environmental Health Sciences, P.O. Box 12233, Research Triangle Park, NC 27709.

GAINES, ALAN McCULLOCH, b. Asheville, N.C, Nov. 13, 38; div; c. 2. GEOCHEMISTRY. B.S, Chicago, 60, M.S, 63, Ph.D.(geochem), 68. Lectr. chem, Illinois, Chicago, 60-62; phys. sci, Univ. Chicago, 62-64, res. asst. GEOCHEM, 64-68, res. assoc, 68-69; ASST. PROF, UNIV. PA, 69- AAAS; Mineral Soc. Am; Am. Geophys. Union; Geochem. Soc; Int. Asn. Geochem. & Cosmochem. Kinetics and mechanisms of mineral reactions; geochemistry of carbonate minerals; crystal growth mechanisms. Address: Dept. of Geology, University of Pennsylvania, Philadelphia, PA 19104.

GAINES, ALBERT L(OWERY), b. Selma, Ala, Feb. 28, 20; m. 42; c. 4. THERMODYNAMICS. B.M.E, Auburn, 46; M.S, Missouri, 50. Mech. engr, Phillips Petrol. Co, Okla, 47; asst. prof. mech. eng, Auburn, 47-48; mech. engr, Humble Oil & Ref. Co, Tex, 48; instr, mech. eng, Missouri, 49-50; develop. engr, Union Carbide Nuclear Co. div, Union Carbide Corp, Tenn, 50-56; supvr, thermo group, COMBUSTION ENG, INC, Chattanooga, 56-58, spec. prods. eng. sect, 59-60, proposition eng. sect, 60-66, mgr. desalination eng, CONN, 66-67, mgr. mech. design sect, nuclear power dept, 67-69, exec. asst. to dir. power eng, 69-70, PROJ. MGR. WATERFORD STEAM ELEC. STA. NUCLEAR PLANT, 70- U.S.A, 43-46, 1st Lt. Am. Soc. Mech. Eng; Am. Nuclear Soc; Am. Inst. Chem. Eng; Nat. Soc. Prof. Eng. Design and fabrication of very large pressure vessels for nuclear reactors. Address: 15 Pasture Lane, West Simsbury, CT 06092.

GAINES, DONALD FRANK, b. Caldwell, Idaho, July 26, 36; m. 60; c. 2. INORGANIC CHEMISTRY. B.S, Col. Idaho, 58; Ph.D.(inorg. chem), Indiana, 63. Res. assoc. INORG. CHEM, Indiana, 63-64; Manchester, 64-65; asst. prof, UNIV. WIS, MADISON, 65-71, ASSOC. PROF, 71- Am. Chem. Soc; The Chem. Soc. Boron hydrides; organo-group III compounds; boron-group III & IV compounds; boron-nitrogen compounds. Address: Dept. of Chemistry, University of Wisconsin, 1101 University Ave, Madison, WI 53706.

GAINES, EDMUND PENDLETON, JR, b. Wash, D.C, Aug. 30, 25; m. 60; c. 2. PHYSICS. B.S, Univ. Chicago, 50; M.S, Georgetown Univ, 61; Air War Col, Air Univ, 66-67. U.S. AIR FORCE, 44-, aircraft maintenance, Air Transport Command, 45-46, nuclear physicist, Armed Forces Spec. Weapons Command, 50-56, chief nuclear analyses group & nuclear physicist, Hqs, 56-60, chief geophys. div. & physicist, Air Force Off. Sci. Res, 60-64, chief electronics div, 65-66, chief physics br, Defense Atomic Support Agency, Lawrence Radiation Lab, 67-68, dep. chief nuclear br, Arms Control & Disarmament Agency, D.C, 68-71, DIR. DESIGN & DEVELOP. COMMAND & MGT. COMPUT. SYSTS, ELECTRONIC SYSTS. DIV, L.G. HANSCOM FIELD, 71- U.S.A.F, 46-, Col. Am. Inst. Aeronaut. & Astronaut; Am. Phys. Soc; Sci. Res. Soc. Am. General physics and computer sciences. Address: Electronic Systems Division, L.G. Hanscom Field, Bedford, MA 01730.

GAINES, EDWARD M(cCULLOCH), b. Pullman, Wash, Sept. 30, 13; m. 34; c. 2. FORESTRY. B.S, State Col. Wash, 34; California, 34-35. Jr. forester, U.S. FOREST SERV, Tenn, 35-37, timber mgt. asst, N.C, 37-40, Tenn, 40-41, timber mgt. specialist, Ga, 41-46, silviculturist, Ark, 46, res. center leader, Ala, 46-51, Ariz, 51-60, leader, west. pine log & tree grade proj, Calif, 60-66, prog. mgr, Proj. Flambeau, Calif, 66-67, ASST. DIR, PAC. SOUTHWEST FOREST & RANGE EXP. STA, 67- AAAS; Soc. Am. Foresters; Soc. Range Mgt. Direction and administration of research for protection and multiple use management of forests and rangelands. Address: Pacific Southwest Forest & Range Experiment Station, U.S. Forest Service, P.O. Box 245, Berkeley, CA 94701.

GAINES, GEORGE L(OWEREE), JR, b. New Haven, Conn, Mar. 7, 30; m. 54; c. 3. PHYSICAL CHEMISTRY. B.S, Yale, 50, M.S, 52, Ph.D.(chem), 54. Chemist, E.I. du Pont de Nemours & Co, 50-51; asst. chem. res, Yale, 52-54; PHYS. CHEMIST, RES. & DEVELOP. CTR, GEN. ELEC. CO, 54- Lectr, Rensselaer Polytech. Inst, 70- Am. Chem. Soc. Surface chemistry; ion exchange; silicate minerals; adsorption; monolayers; photosynthesis; polymer surface props. Address: Research & Development Center, General Electric Co, P.O. Box 8, Schenectady, NY 12301.

GAINES, G(ORDON) B(RADFORD), b. Fitzgerald, Ga, Aug. 10, 23; m; c. 1. PHYSICS. B.S, Georgia, 48, M.S, 49. Res. engr. phys. electronics, BATTELLE MEM. INST, 50-52, asst. div. chief, solid state devices, 52-62, res. assoc, ELECTRONIC MAT. & DEVICES DIV, 62-65, fel, 65-66, sr. fel, 66-69, CHIEF, 69- Physical electronics; electron physics; solid state materials and devices; gas discharges; electron paramagnetic resonance, dielectrics. Address: Battelle Memorial Institute, 505 King Ave, Columbus, OH 43201.

GAINES, J. H, b. Luling, Tex, Mar. 30, 31; m. 52; c. 3. ENGINEERING MECHANICS, AERONAUTICAL ENGINEERING. B.S, Texas, Austin, 57, M.S, 59, Ph.D.(eng. mech), 66; Texas Christian, 59; Southern Methodist, 60-61. Instr. eng. mech, Texas, Austin, 58-59; struct. engr, Gen. Dynamics, Ft. Worth, 59-61; lectr. civil eng, grad. sch, Southern Methodist, 61; instr. eng. mech, Univ. Tex, Austin, 61-66; asst. prof, UNIV. TEX, ARLINGTON, 66-68, ASSOC. PROF. AERONAUT. & MECH. ENG, 68- U.S.M.C, 50-53. Am. Soc. Civil Eng; Am. Inst. Aeronaut. & Astronaut; Am. Soc. Eng. Educ. Solid mechanics; structural analysis; vibrations; dynamics of structures. Address: Dept. of Aeronautical & Mechanical Engineering, University of Texas at Arlington, Arlington, TX 76010.

GAINES, JACK R(AYMOND), b. Bozeman, Mont, May 9, 27; m. 57; c. 2. ORGANIC CHEMISTRY. B.S, Mont. State Col, 49, M.S, 50, Ph.D.(chem), 56. Instr. chem. & physics, West. Mont. Col. Ed, 50-51; res. chemist, Phillips Petrol. Co, 56-57; assoc. prof. ORG. CHEM, S.DAK. SCH. MINES & TECHNOL, 57-66, PROF, 66- Vet.C, U.S.A, 51-53. Am. Chem. Soc. Basic organic research in heterocyclic compounds. Address: Dept. of Chemistry, South Dakota School of Mines & Technology, Rapid City, SD 57701.

GAINES, J(AMES) A(BNER), b. San Antonio, Tex, Aug. 5, 27; m. 57; c. 6. GENETICS. B.S, Agr. & Mech. Col. Texas, 49, M.S, 54; Ph.D.(animal breeding, genetics), Iowa State, 57. ASSOC. PROF. ANIMAL HUSB, VA. POLYTECH. INST. & STATE UNIV, 56- U.S.M.C, 45-46; U.S.A, 50-52. Am. Soc. Animal Sci; Genetics Soc. Am. Animal genetics and husbandry; statistics. Address: Dept. of Animal Science, Virginia Polytechnic Institute & State University, Blacksburg, VA 24061.

GAINES, JAMES R, b. Cincinnati, Ohio, Sept. 8, 35; m. 67; c. 2. SOLID STATE PHYSICS. A.B, Berea Col, 56; Ohio Oil fel, Washington (St. Louis), 58, Nat. Sci. Found. fel, 59-61, Ph.D.(physics), 61. Asst. prof. PHYSICS, OHIO STATE UNIV, 61-64, assoc. prof, 64-67, PROF, 67- Consult, Avco Corp, 64-65; Alfred P. Sloan fel, 64-67; vis. scientist, Atomic Energy Comn, Saclay, France, 65-66; lectr, Col. France, 65-66; consult, Malaker Industs, 65-66; vis. distinguished scholar, Univ. Pa, 67; consult, Gardner Cryogenics Corp, 68- Am. Phys. Soc. Nuclear magnetic resonance on liquid and solid He_3, solid H^2, D^2, HD at temperatures below 4°K; properties of semiconductors. Address: Dept. of Physics, Ohio State University, Columbus, OH 43210.

GAINES, RICHARD V(ENABLE), b. Poughkeepsie, N.Y, Jan. 25, 17; m. 49; c. 4. ECONOMIC GEOLOGY, MINERALOGY. E.M, Colo. Sch. Mines, 40; A.M, Harvard, 49, Ph.D.(econ. geol, mineral), 51. Resident mgr, Explor, Inc, 52-53; explor. geologist, Res. Inc, 54-55; mgr. west. opers, Gen. Minerals Corp, 55-57; mining geologist, Dresser Indust, 58; explor. geologist, Perforadora Latina, S.A, 59-63; Cia. Minera de Cerralvo, S.A, 64-67; MGR. EXPLOR. & MINING, KAWECKI BERYLCO INDUSTS, INC, BOYERTOWN, 67- Res. mineralogist, inst. geol, Nat. Univ. Mex, 62-67; consult. geologist & mineralogist. C.Eng, U.S.A, 41-45. Mineral. Soc. Am; Soc. Econ. Geol; Am. Inst. Mining, Metall. & Petrol. Eng; Mineral. Asn. Can; Mineral. Soc. Gt. Brit. Exploration geology; mineralogical research; economic mineralogy. Address: Hoffecker Rd, Route 1, Pottstown, PA 19464.

GAINES, ROBERT D, b. Bozeman, Mont, Sept. 4, 33; m. 57; c. 2. BIOCHEMISTRY. B.S, Mont. State Col, 55, Nat. Sci. Found. grant, 58, Ph.D.(biochem), 60. Res. chemist, Minn. Mining & Mfg. Co, 54-57; sr. chemist, Pillsbury Co, 60-61; asst. prof. CHEM, CENT. WASH. STATE COL, 61-62, assoc. prof, 63-68, PROF, 68-, chmn. dept, 62-66. Carbohydrate chemistry; plant metabolism; microbial and animal physiology. Address: Dept. of Chemistry, Central Washington State College, Ellensburg, WA 98926.

GAINES, ROBERT E(ARL), b. Champaign, Ill, Aug. 16, 41; m. 61; c. 1. MATHEMATICS. B.S. & Nat. Sci. Found. fel, Univ. Ill, Urbana, 62, M.S, 63; NASA traineeship, Univ. Colo, Boulder, 64-67, Ph.D.(math), 67. ASSOC. PROF. MATH, COLO. STATE UNIV, 67- Math. Asn. Am; Am. Math. Soc. Boundary value problems for nonlinear ordinary differential equations; periodic solutions of nonlinear parabolic equations. Address: Dept. of Mathematics, Colorado State University, Ft. Collins, CO 80521.

GAINES, S(IDNEY), b. Cleveland, Ohio, July 15, 17. BACTERIOLOGY. B.A, Ohio State, 41, M.S, 43, Ph.D.(bact), 50. U.S. ARMY, 43-, bacteriologist & serologist, 168th Gen. Hosp, Europe, 44-45, chief lab. serv, 348th Sta. Hosp, Europe, 45-46, bacteriologist & serologist, 97th Gen. Hosp, Europe, 46-47, Brooke Gen. Hosp, 47-48, res. bacteriologist, surg. res. unit, Brook Army Med. Ctr, 51-52, div. immunol, Walter Reed Army Inst. Res. Walter Reed Army Med. Ctr, 52-55; chief, dept. microbiol, 56-61, dept. bact. & immunol, med. res. lab, Southeast Asia Treaty Orgn, Thailand, 61-63, asst. to dir, Walter Reed Army Inst. Res, 63-65, chief, enteric bact. lab, Pasteur Inst. Vietnam, 65-67, bacteriologist, div. commun. disease & immunol, WALTER REED ARMY INST. RES, 67-68, NAT. LAB. ADV, U.S. AGENCY INT. DEVELOP-PUB. HEALTH, VIETNAM, 68- Dipl, Am. Bd. Microbiol. Med.Serv.C, U.S.A, 43-, Col; Army Commendation Medal, Legion of Merit. Am. Soc. Microbiol; Am. Asn. Immunol; fel. Am. Acad. Microbiol. Microbiological vitamin assays; bacterial nutrition and physiology; endotoxins; immunizing agents; experimental typhoid fever in chimpanzees; bacterial virulence; enterobacteriaceae. Address: Walter Reed Army Institute of Research, Walter Reed Army Medical Center, Washington, DC 20012.

GAINES, THOMAS B(LANTON), b. Proctor, Tex, Apr. 21, 16, m. 40; c. 2. ZOOLOGY. B.A, Texas, 53. Biologist, tech. develop. labs, commun. disease ctr, U.S. Pub. Health Serv, Ga, 46-55, PHARMACOLOGIST, toxicol. sect, 55-70; ENVIRON. PROTECTION AGENCY, 70- AAAS; Sci. Res. Soc. Am. Toxicity and mechanism of action of pesticides in laboratory animals and the relating of research findings to the possible hazard of pesticides to man and measures necessary for human safety. Address: Environmental Protection Agency, 4770 Buford Hwy, Chamblee, GA 30341.

GAINOR, CHARLES, b. N.Y.C, Feb. 5, 16; m. 41; c. 2. MICROBIOLOGY. B.S, Alfred, 36; M.S, Maryland, 39; Egg Inst. fel, Mich. State, 40-41, Parke Davis Co. fel, 46-47, Ph.D.(bact), 48. Nat. Sanit. Found. res. instr, Mich. State, 47-48; asst. prof. biol. sci, Pittsburgh, 48-52, assoc. prof, 52-63; BIOL, NORTHEAST. UNIV, 63-69, PROF, 69- Sig.C, 43-46, Capt. AAAS; Am. Soc. Microbiol; Brit. Soc. Gen. Microbiol. General microbiology; immunology; crown gall. Address: Dept. of Biology, Northeastern University, Boston, MA 02115.

GAINSFORTH, BURDETTE L(IVINGSTON), b. Holdrege, Nebr, Nov. 14, 11; m. 43; c. 2. ORTHODONTICS. D.D.S, Nebraska, 35; cert. & M.S, Iowa, 45. Instr. oper. dent, Iowa, 42-43, orthod, 43-45, asst. prof, 45-46; pedodontics, COL. DENT, UNIV. NEBR. 47-54, ORTHOD, 54-58, ASSOC. PROF, 58- Vis. lectr, Toronto, 50-51; vis. lectr, San Miguel, GTO, Mex, 70. Dent.C. Res, U.S.A, 35-41. Am. Dent. Asn; Am. Asn. Orthod; fel. Am. Col. Dent. Tissue response to orthodontic forces; space control and sculpture related to orthodontics. Address: 710 N. Spruce St, Ogallala, NE 69153.

GAINTNER, JOHN RICHARD, b. Lancaster, Pa, Feb. 18, 36; m. 61; c. 3. INTERNAL MEDICINE. B.A, Lehigh Univ, 58; M.D, Johns Hopkins Univ, 62. Nat. Insts. Health fel. hemat, Johns Hopkins Univ. Hosp, 66-67; asst. prof. MED, SCH. MED, UNIV. CONN, 67-69, ASSOC. DEAN CONTINUING EDUC, 69-; CHIEF OF STAFF, McCOOK DIV, UNIV. HOSP, 69- Mem. adv. bd, Conn. Regional Med. Prog; adv. comt. continuing educ. for health prof, New Eng. Ctr. Continuing Educ; med. adv. comt, State Welfare Dept; trustee, Ambulatory Health Care Planning; Health Planning Coun, Inc. Borden Res. Award, 62. Med.C, U.S.A, 64-66, Capt. Asn. Am. Med. Col; Asn. Hosp. Med. Educ. Health care delivery; continuing medical education; hematology, coagulation and blood platelets; malaria. Address: University of Connecticut-McCook Hospital, 2 Holcomb St, Hartford, CT 06112.

GAIR, JACOB E(UGENE), b. Pittsfield, Mass, Apr. 1, 22; m. 44; c. 3. GEOLOGY. A.B, Rochester, 46; Ph.D.(geol), Hopkins, 49. Asst. prof. geol, Oregon, 49-52; GEOLOGIST, U.S. GEOL. SURV, 52- U.S.A.A.F, 43-45, 1st Lt. Geol. Soc. Am; Soc. Econ. Geol. Petrography and stratigraphy of Precambrian of northern Michigan, and of iron region of Minas Gerais, Brazil; structural geology; central Appalachians; petrography; volcanic rocks; iron exploration of Turkey; tungsten exploration of North Carolina. Address: U.S. Geological Survey, Washington, DC 20242.

GAISER, R(OMEY) ARTHUR, b. Elmira, N.Y, July 10, 10; m. 31; c. 3. INORGANIC CHEMISTRY. B.S, Alfred, 33, Guggenheim fel. & M.S, 39; Buffalo, 34-35; Toledo, 46. Teacher & prin, pub. schs, N.Y, 33-34, 35-42; res. chemist, Libby-Owens-Ford Glass Co, 42-50, asst. dir. res, 50-55, assoc. dir. res, 55; dir. res. & develop, Ball Bros. Co, 55-58, v.pres, BALL CORP, 58-69, CORP. V.PRES. & DIR, 69- V.pres, Ball Bros. Res. Corp, 58-67, dir, 58-, exec. v.pres, 67-68, pres, 68-69, v.chmn. bd, 69-, chmn. bd. & dir, Ball Bros. Service Corp; dir, Casper Tin Plate Co; Kent Plastic Corp; Pantek Corp. Fel. Am. Ceramic Soc; fel. Am. Inst. Chem; assoc. fel, Am. Inst. Aeronaut. & Astronaut. Electrical conducting films and lubricating coatings on glass. Address: Ball Corp, 1509 Macedonia Ave, Muncie, IN 47302.

GAIT, ROBERT I, b. Johannesburg, S.Africa, Sept. 12, 38. GEOLOGY, MINERALOGY. B.Sc, Univ. Witwatersrand, 58, Hons, 59; M.Sc, Univ. Man, 64, Ph.D.(mineral), 67. Geologist, Williamson Diamonds, Ltd, Tanzania, 60-62; lectr. geol, Univ. Man, 66-67; asst. curator MINERAL, DEPT. MINERAL, ROYAL ONT. MUS, 67-71, ASSOC. CURATOR, 71- Dept. Univ. Affairs, Ont. grant-in-aid res, 70-71. Mineral Soc. Am; Mineral Asn. Can; fel. Geol. Asn. Can; Geol. Soc. S.Africa. Feldspar mineralogy; detailed crystal structural implications; general mineralogy. Address: Dept. of Mineralogy, Royal Ontario Museum, 100 Queen's Park, Toronto, Ont, Can.

GAITHER, ROBERT BARKER, b. North Bay, Ont, Aug. 12, 29; U.S. citizen; m. 54; c. 3. MECHANICAL ENGINEERING. B.M.E, Auburn, 51; M.S.M.E, Illinois, 57, Ford Found. fel, 59-61, Ph.D.(mech. eng), 62. Instr, MECH. ENG, Illinois, 57-62; assoc. prof, UNIV. FLA, 62-66, PROF, 66-, CHMN. DEPT, 64- U.S.N, 51-54, Lt. Am. Soc. Mech. Eng; Am. Soc. Eng. Educ. Statistical thermodynamics; gas dynamics; plasma diagnostics; transport properties. Address: Dept. of Mechanical Engineering, University of Florida, Gainesville, FL 32601.

GAITHER, THOMAS WALTER, b. Great Falls, S.C, Nov. 12, 38; m. 68; c. 1. BOTANY. B.S, Claflin Col, 60; M.S, Atlanta Univ, 64; scholar, Univ. Iowa, 66-68, Ph.D.(bot), 68. Teaching asst. life sci, Univ. Iowa, 64-66, phycol, summer 66, gen. bot, 66-67, mycol, 67-68, ASSOC. PROF. GEN. BIOL, GEN. BOT. & NONVASCULAR PLANT MORPHOL, SLIPPERY ROCK STATE COL, 68-, microbiol, summer 70. AAAS; Mycol. Soc. Am; Bot. Soc. Am. Ultrastructure of myxomycetes; morphology and development of capillitium; ultrastructural changes in angiosperm leaves throughout the growing season; mycology. Address: Dept. of Biology, Slippery Rock State College, Slippery Rock, PA 16057.

GAITHER, WILLIAM SAMUEL, b. Lafayette, Ind, Dec. 3, 32; m. CIVIL ENGINEERING. B.Sc.E, Rose Polytech, 56; M.S.E, Princeton, 62, M.A, 63, Ph.D.(civil eng), 64. Chief party, Ayrshire Collieries Corp, Ind, 54, construct. inspector, 55; from field engr. to res. engr, Dravo Corp, Pa, 56-60; from field engr. to field supt, Meyer Corp, Wis, 60-61; asst, Princeton, 61-63, lectr, 64; assoc. prof. coastal eng, Univ. Fla, 64-65; from supv. engr. to chief engr, Bechtel Corp, 65-67; from assoc. prof. to PROF. CIVIL ENG, UNIV. DEL, 67-, DEAN COL. MARINE STUDIES, 70- Arthur Le Grand Doty fel, 61-62; Ford Found. fel. port planning, 62-64. Am. Soc. Civil Eng; Soc. Naval Archit. & Marine Eng. Marine structures; ocean engineering. Address: College of Marine Studies, University of Delaware, Newark, DE 19711.

GAITO, JOHN, b. Kernersville, N.C, June 25, 23; m. 48; c. 2. MOLECULAR PSYCHOBIOLOGY. A.B, Pennsylvania, 51, Ph.D, 59; A.M, Temple, 52. Physiol. & exp. psychologist, air crew equip. lab, U.S. Naval Base, Pa, 54-58; asst. prof, Wilkes Col, 58-60; Lake Forest Col, 60-61; physiol. psychol, Kansas State, 61-64; assoc. prof. molecular psychobiol, YORK UNIV. (ONT), 64-66, PROF. PSYCHOL, 66- U.S.M.C, 41-46. Am. Psychol. Asn. Human engineering; biochemical correlates of behavior; molecular psychobiology; physiological psychology. Address: Dept. of Psychology, York University, Toronto, Ont, Can.

GAITONDE, MANGESH R, b. Bombay, India, Aug. 21, 25; U.S. citizen; m. 62. PSYCHIATRY. M.D, Bombay, 50, dipl. psychol. med, 54; Menninger Sch. Psychiat, 57. From house physician to registr, K.E.M. Hosp, Bombay, 50-52, Indian Coun. Med. Res. fel. psychiat, 52-54; res, Worcester City Hosp, Mass, 54-55; Topeka State Hosp, Kans, 55-57; instr. PSYCHIAT, MED. CTR, UNIV. KANS, 57-61, asst. clin. prof, 61-62, asst. prof, 62-64, ASSOC. PROF, 64- Asst. dir, outpatient clin, Osawatomie State Hosp, Kans, 57-59, dir, 59-61. Dipl, Am. Bd. Psychiat. & Neurol, 61. Fel. Am. Psychiat. Asn; Asn. Am. Med. Cols; Indian Psychiat. Asn; Indian Med. Asn. Address: 4643 Wyandotte, Kansas City, MO 64112.

GAIZAUSKAS, V(ICTOR), b. Toronto, Ont, Sept. 18, 30; m. 54; c. 1. ASTROPHYSICS. B.A, Univ. Toronto, 51, M.A, 52, Nat. Res. Coun. Can. stud, 52-54, Ph.D.(physics), 55. ASTROPHYSICIST, Dom. Observ, 55-70; ASTROPHYS. BR, NAT. RES. COUN. CAN, 70- Am. Astron. Soc; Royal Astron. Soc. Can; Int. Astron. Union. Solar physics. Address: Astrophysics Branch, M-50, National Research Council, Ottawa, Ont, Can.

GAJ, BERNARD J(OSEPH), b. Swoyerville, Pa, Sept. 21, 27; m. 50; c. 6. ORGANIC CHEMISTRY. B.S, Lafayette Col, 54; Du Pont summer fel, Iowa State Univ, 58, Ph.D.(organometallic synthesis), 60. Res. chemist, Esso Res. & Eng. Co, 60-64; group leader, J.P. Stevens & Co, Inc, 64-71;

CHIEF ORG. CHEMIST, FISHER SCI. CO, 71- U.S.A, 46-48. AAAS; Am. Chem. Soc; Am. Inst. Chem; Am. Asn. Textile Chem. & Colorists. Organometallic chemistry; polymer modification; textile finishing chemicals; organophosphorous flame retardants; antistats; wood modifiers; durable press wash-wear resins; textile chemicals. Address: 14 Harrison Ave, Montclair, NJ 07042.

GAJAN, RAYMOND JOSEPH, b. Missoula, Mont, Sept. 30, 20; m. 50; c. 3. ANALYTICAL & ORGANIC CHEMISTRY. B.A, Univ. Mont, 43; M.S, Canisius Col, 48. Chemist, Nat. Aniline Div, Allied Chem. & Dye Corp, 43-49; inspection equip. agency, U.S. Army Chem. Ctr, Md, 50-54, chem. & radiol. lab, 54-57; U.S. Bur. Mines, Md, 57-60; RES. CHEMIST, div. food chem, bur. sci, U.S. FOOD & DRUG ADMIN, 60-71, DIV. CHEM. & PHYSICS, OFF. SCI, BUR. FOODS, 71- U.S.A, 44-46, Sgt. Am. Chem. Soc; Asn. Off. Anal. Chem. Development of polarographic procedures for the determination of pesticide residues, drugs, food additives and other contaminants when present in foods in less than microgram amounts. Address: U.S. Food & Drug Administration, 200 C St, S.W, Washington, DC 20204.

GAJDUSEK, D(ANIEL) CARLETON, b. Yonkers, N.Y, Sept. 9, 23. PEDIATRICS, VIROLOGY. B.A, Rochester, 43; M.D, Harvard Med. Sch, 46. Intern pediat, Columbia-Presby Med. Ctr, N.Y, 46-47; res, Children's Hosp, Ohio, 47-48; sr. fel. phys. chem, Calif. Inst. Tech, 48-49; clin. fel. & res. fel, Boston Children's Hosp, Harvard, 49-51; sr. investr. virus & rickettsial diseases, Pasteur Inst. Iran, 54-55; investr. ethnopediat. studies, Australia & Melanesia, 55-58; PEDIATRICIAN, VIROLOGIST & NEUROLOGICAL SCIENTIST, NAT. INST. NEUROL. DISEASES & STROKE, 58- Fel, Children's Hosp, Calif, 48-49; investr, med. mission, Ger, 48; res. fel, Harvard Med. Sch, 50-51, sr. fel, Children's Med. Ctr & Harvard Med. Sch, Nat. Found. Infantile Paralysis, 50-52; sr. investr, Walter & Eliza Hall Inst. Med. Res, Australia, 55-57. Mead Johnson award, Am. Acad. Pediat, 63. Med. off, dept. virol, Walter Reed Army Inst. Res, 52-54. Am. Pediat. Soc; Soc. Pediat. Res; Am. Anthrop. Asn; Am. Acad. Neurol; Genetics Soc. Am. Protein physical chemistry; mammalian virology; pathophysiology of autoimmune diseases and neurological degenerative disorders; human evolutionary studies in isolated populations; child behavior, development, nervous system patterning and learning in primitive cultures. Address: 4 Laurel Parkway, Chevy Chase, MD 20015.

GAJENDAR, N(ANDIGAM), b. Nellore, India, Nov. 29, 40. APPLIED MATHEMATICS, COMPUTER SCIENCE. B.A, Sri Venkateswara Univ, India, 59, M.S, 61; Ph.D.(appl. math), Indian Inst. Technol, Kharagpur, 65. Lectr. MATH, Indian Inst. Technol, 65-70; ASST. PROF, GRAMBLING COL, 70- Grant, Manned Spacecraft Ctr, NASA, 70-71. Indian Soc. Theoret. & Appl. Mech; Soc. Indust. & Appl. Math; Asn. Comput. Mach. Static and dynamic behavior of elastic plate and shell structures under kinetic heating; thermal buckling of elastic structures; numerical applications to structural problems; hydromagnetics in higher altitudes. Address: Dept. of Mathematics, Grambling College, Grambling, LA 71245.

GAJEWSKI, FRED J(OHN), b. New York, N.Y, May 2, 12; m. 39; c. 2. CHEMISTRY. B.S, N.Y. Univ, 34, scholar & Ph.D.(chem), 38. Asst. chem, N.Y. Univ, 34-37; res. chemist, Calco Chem. Co, 37-38; area supvr, res. & develop, GAF Corp, 38-55, mgr. process res. & develop, 55-60, tech. dir. Antara Div, 60-62, asst. to v.pres. & gen. mgr. dyestuff & chem. div, 62-64, tech. adminr. res. & develop, 64-68, dir. shareholder rels, 68-70; DIR. TECH. OPERS, AZOPLATE CORP, 70- AAAS; Am. Chem. Soc; fel. Am. Inst. Chem. Surfactants; acetylene derivatives; dyestuffs; pigments; intermediates; metal carbonyls; metal powders; graphic arts. Address: 30 Westbrook Rd, Westfield, NJ 07090.

GAJEWSKI, JOHN EDMUND, b. Green Bay, Wis, Oct. 5, 15; m. 44; c. 3. PHARMACOLOGY. B.A, St. Norbert Col, 37; Ph.D.(pharmacol), Wisconsin, 44, M.D, 46. Instr. chem, St. Norbert Col, 37-39; asst. pharmacol, Wisconsin, 40-44; intern, univ. hosp, Kansas, 46-47; head pharmacol. facility, Naval Med. Res. Inst, 47-49; ASSOC. PHYSICIAN, DEPT. CLIN. INVEST, PARKE DAVIS & CO, 49- U.S.N, 42-46. Experimental chemotherapy; mechanisms of drug action; mechanisms of relapse in avian malaria; chemotherapy of experimental malaria; clinical pharmacology. Address: Dept. of Clinical Investigation, Parke Davis & Co, P.O. Box 118, General Post Office, Detroit, MI 48232.

GAJEWSKI, JOSEPH J, b. Hammond, Ind, Nov. 7, 39; m. 62; c. 2. ORGANIC CHEMISTRY. B.S, Loyola Univ. Chicago, 61; Univ. South. Calif, 61-62; Dow Co. fel. & Ph.D.(org. chem), Univ. Wis, 65. Nat. Sci. Found. fel. org. chem, Columbia Univ, 65-66; asst. prof. CHEM, IND. UNIV, BLOOMINGTON, 66-69, ASSOC. PROF, 69- Alfred P. Sloan fel, 71-73. Am. Chem. Soc; The Chem. Soc. Energetics and stereochemistry of chemical reactions; application of molecular orbital theory to organic chemistry. Address: Dept. of Chemistry, Indiana University, Bloomington, IN 47401.

GAJEWSKI, W(ALTER) M(ICHAEL), b. Hartford, Conn, Apr. 4, 23; m. 49; c. 3. ENGINEERING. B.S, Connecticut, 49, M.S, 51. Engr, Bettis Atomic Power Lab, 51-55, sr. engr. & fel. engr, 56, supvry. engr, 56-59, sect. mgr, 59-66, plant mgr, 66-68, asst. proj. mgr, Westinghouse-Bettis Atomic Power Plant, Pa, 68-70; ENG. MGR. FAST FLUX TEST FACILITY PROJ, WADCO CORP, 70- Sig.C, U.S.A, 43-46. Inst. Elec. & Electronics Eng; Am. Nuclear Soc; Am. Soc. Mech. Eng. General engineering; reactor plant analysis and systems design; overall reactor plant design, development and evaluation. Address: WADCO Corp, P.O. Box 1970, Richland, WA 99352.

GAJJAR, JAGDISHCHANDRA T(RIKAMJI), b. Bombay, India, May 23, 40; m. 66; c. 1. ELECTROOPTICS, ELECTRICAL ENGINEERING. B.E, Univ. Bombay, 60 & 61; M.E.E, Univ. Okla, 63; fel, Univ. Houston, 67-70, Ph.D. (elec. eng), 70. Proj. engr, Fischbach & Moore Systs. Inc, Tex, 63-64; instr. ELEC. ENG, Univ. Tulsa, 66-67; ASST. PROF, UNION COL.(N.Y), 70- Prin. investr, Nat. Sci. Found. eng. res. initiation grant, 71-72. Inst. Elec. & Electronics Eng; Optical Soc. Am. Optical information processing; system theory and system diagnostics; applied instrumentation; atmospheric probing. Address: Dept. of Electrical Engineering, Union College, Schenectady, NY 12308.

GAKENHEIMER, WALTER C(HRISTIAN), b. Baltimore, Md, July 28, 16; m. 41. PHARMACEUTICAL CHEMISTRY. B.S, Maryland, 38, M.S, 41, Ph.D.(pharmaceut. chem), 43; Cornell, 39; N.Y. Univ, 48. Asst. instr. pharm, Maryland, 38-42; synthetic org. res. chemist, Minerec Corp, Md, 42-45; sr. chemist pharmaceut. res, Merck & Co, Inc, 45-50, mgr. tech. serv, 50-53, mgr. med. mkt, 53-57; sci. asst. to pres, Stuart Co, 57-59, admin. v.pres, 59-63; TECH. DIR. INT. DIV, ATLAS CHEM. INDUSTS, INC, 63- L.S. Williams award. AAAS; Am. Chem. Soc; Am. Pharmaceut. Asn; Inst. Food Technol; N.Y. Acad. Sci. Pharmaceutical research and development; synthesis of aminoalkanols of pharmacological interest. Address: Atlas Chemical Industries, Inc, Wilmington, DE 19899.

GAKSTATTER, JACK H, b. Indianapolis, Ind, Jan. 25, 39; m. 59; c. 4. AQUATIC BIOLOGY. A.B, Indiana, 61; M.S.P.H, North Carolina, 63, Ph.D. (environ. biol), 66. Aquatic biologist, Southeast Water Lab, Fed. Water Pollution Control Admin, U.S. Dept. Interior, 66-68; PRIN. LIMNOLOGIST, STATE HYG. LAB, UNIV. IOWA, 68- AAAS; Am. Fisheries Soc; Water Pollution Control Fedn; Am. Soc. Limnol. & Oceanog; Am. Inst. Biol. Sci; Am. Water Works Asn. Effects of water pollutants on the aquatic ecosystem; uptake, distribution and metabolism of organic insecticides by fish. Address: State Hygienic Lab, E. Seventh & Court Ave, Des Moines, IA 50309.

GAL, ANDREW E(UGENE), b. Budapest, Hungary, July 14, 18; nat; m. 51; c. 3. ORGANIC CHEMISTRY. Chem. Eng, Swiss Fed. Inst. Tech, 43, Sc.D. (org. chem), 47. Res. chemist, Cruet Labs, France, 48-50; Roques, 50-53; sr. chemist, Nat. Drug Co, 53-62; supvr. org. chem, Hazleton Labs, 62-64; RES. CHEMIST, NAT. INST. NEUROL. DISEASES & STROKE LABS. OF NEUROCHEM, 64- Am. Chem. Soc. Synthesis of new organic chemicals; synthetic estrogens; alkaloids; barbituric acids; heterocyclic compounds; sphingolipids; radiochemicals; analytical biochemistry; neurochemistry. Address: 707 Ware St. S.W, Vienna, VA 22180.

GAL, GEORGE, b. Pecel, Hungary, July 18, 21; m. 45; c. 1. ORGANIC CHEMISTRY. Ph.D.(chem), Pazmany Peter Univ, Hungary, 44. Res. chemist. explosives, Nitrochem. Factory, Hungary, 44-46; pharmaceut, United Pharmaceut. Factory, 46-52, mgr. res, 52-56; SR. RES. CHEMIST, MERCK SHARP & DOHME RES. LABS, 57- Am. Chem. Soc. Reduction with complex metalhydrides; synthesis of amino alcohols, amino acids, heterocyclic compounds and steroids. Address: 5 Timberline Way, Watchung, NJ 07060.

GALA, RICHARD R, b. Bayonne, N.J, July 2, 35; m. 60; c. 2. PHYSIOLOGY, ENDOCRINOLOGY. B.S, Rutgers, 57, fel, 60-63, Ph.D.(neuro-endocrinol), 63; Maine, 57-58. Asst. reprod. physiol, Maine, 57-58; bact, Rutgers, 58-60; res. assoc. & fel. endocrinol. & biochem, sch. med, Louisville, 63-65; asst. prof. PHYSIOL, SCH. MED, Boston Univ, 65-71; ASSOC. PROF, WAYNE STATE UNIV, 71- AAAS; Soc. Exp. Biol. & Med; N.Y. Acad. Sci; Endocrine Soc; Am. Physiol. Soc. Relationship between nervous system and anterior pituitary; reproductive physiology. Address: Dept. of Physiology, Wayne State University School of Medicine, 540 E. Canfield, Detroit, MI 48201.

GALAGAN, DONALD J, b. Buffalo, Iowa, Apr. 27, 14; m. 39; c. 3. PREVENTIVE DENTISTRY. D.D.S, Iowa, 37; M.P.H, California, 50. From intern to various positions in European Theater Opers, U.S. Pub. Health Serv. Hosps, 37-44, dent. administrator, U.S. Pub. Health Serv, 45-65; PROF. DENT. & DEAN COL. DENT, UNIV. IOWA, 66- Dipl, Am. Bd. Dent. Pub. Health. U.S.P.H.S, 37-65, Rear Adm. AAAS; Am. Dent. Asn; Am. Pub. Health Asn; Int. Asn. Dent. Res. Effectiveness of topical fluorides; environmental influences on fluid intake and effect on optimum fluoride concentration; effective utilization of dental auxiliaries; national care programs and health insurance; dental manpower requirements. Address: College of Dentistry, University of Iowa, Iowa City, IA 52240.

GALAMBOS, JANOS, b. Zirc, Hungary, Sept. 1, 40; m. 64. STATISTICS, NUMBER THEORY. M.Sc. & Ph.D.(probability), Eötvös Lóránd Univ, Budapest, 63. Asst. prof. probability & statist, Eötvös Lóránd Univ, 63-65; lectr. MATH, Univ. Ghana, 65-69; Univ. Ibadan, 69-70; asst. prof, TEMPLE UNIV, 70-71, ASSOC. PROF, 71- Del, Int. Cong. Mathematicians, Moscow, 66, Austria, 68, France, 70; Brit. Math. Colloquium, 68; vis. res. fel, statist. lab, Cambridge, 68; del, Int. Statist. Inst, London, 69. Hungarian Math. Soc; Am. Math. Soc; Inst. Math. Statist. Probabilistic number theory; combinatorics; probabilistic inequalities; order statistics; sequential methods of statistics; asymptotic distribution of functions of a random number of random variables. Address: Dept. of Mathematics, Temple University, Philadelphia, PA 19122.

GALAMBOS, JOHN T(HOMAS), b. Budapest, Hungary, Oct. 29, 21; nat; m; c. 3. MEDICINE. B.S, Georgia, 48; M.D, Emory, 52. Intern med, Barnes Hosp, St. Louis, Mo, 52-53; res, Billings Hosp, Chicago, Ill, 53-54; res. fel, U.S. Pub. Health Serv, Chicago, 54-55; fel. MED, SCH. MED, EMORY UNIV, 55-57, assoc, 57-58, asst. prof, 58-61, assoc. prof, 61-67, PROF, 67-, IN CHARGE GASTROENTEROL. TEACHING PROG, 58-, DIR. DEPT. MED, DIV. DIGESTIVE DISEASES, 68- Dir, gastroenterol. clinic, Grady Mem. Hosp, 57-; assoc. physician, univ. hosp, Emory, 58-; consult, Veterans Admin. Hosp, Atlanta, Ga. & Tuskegee, Ala; Martin Army Hosp, Ft. Benning, Ga. U.S.P.H.S, 55-57. AAAS; N.Y. Acad. Sci; Am. Gastroenterol. Asn; Am. Col. Physicians; Am. Fedn. Clin. Res; Am. Asn. Study Liver Diseases; Int. Asn. Study Liver. Liver function and alcoholic liver disease; metabolism of adult human liver culture and glycosaminoglycan metabolism. Address: Dept. of Medicine, Division of Digestive Diseases, Emory University School of Medicine, 69 Butler St, S.E, Atlanta, GA 30303.

GALAMBOS, ROBERT, b. Lorain, Ohio, Apr. 20, 14; m. 39; c. 3. PHYSIOLOGY, PSYCHOLOGY. A.B, Oberlin Col, 35, M.A, 36; A.M, Harvard, 38, fel, 39-41, Ph.D, 41; M.D, Rochester, 46. Instr. & jr. invest. physiol, Harvard Med. Sch, 42-43; intern, univ. hosp, Emory, 46, asst. prof. anat, med. sch, 46-47; res. fel, psycho-acoustic lab, Harvard, 47-51; chief, dept. neurophysiol, Walter Reed Army Inst. Res, 51-62; Higgins Prof. psychol. & psysiol, Yale, 62-68; PROF. NEUROSCI, SCH. MED, UNIV. CALIF, SAN DIEGO, 68- Tutor, Harvard, 41-42 & 47-48. Nat. Acad. Sci; Am. Physiol. Soc; Am. Acad. Arts & Sci; Acoust. Soc. Am; Am. Psychol. Asn. Hearing;

obstacle avoidance by bats; neurophysiology of learning. Address: Dept. of Neurosciences, School of Medicine, University of California, San Diego, La Jolla, CA 92037.

GALAMBOS, THEODORE V, b. Budapest, Hungary, Apr. 17, 29; U.S. citizen; m. 57; c. 4. CIVIL ENGINEERING. B.S, North Dakota, 53, M.S, 54; Ph.D. (civil eng), Lehigh, 59. Stress analyst, Babcock & Wilcox Co, Ohio, 54-56; res. asst, Lehigh, 56-58, res. assoc, 58-59, asst. prof. CIVIL ENG, 59-62, assoc. prof, 62-65; prof, WASH. UNIV, 65-68, HAROLD R. JOLLEY PROF, 68-, CHMN. DEPT. CIVIL & ENVIRON. ENG, 70- Chmn. Column Res. Coun, 70-73. U.S.A, 54-56. Am. Soc. Civil Eng; Column Res. Coun; Int. Asn. Bridge & Struct. Eng. Inelastic behavior of metal structures and structural elements; static instability of members and frames. Address: Dept. of Civil & Environmental Engineering, School of Engineering & Applied Science, Washington University, St. Louis, MO 63130.

GALAN, LOUIS, b. Pineres, Asturias, Spain, Aug. 10, 28; nat; m. 59; c. 2. AERONAUTICAL ENGINEERING. B.S, Mass. Inst. Technol, 51; M.S, Univ. Mich, 54, 55. Test engr, aircraft power plants, Wright Air Develop. Ctr, 51-53, proj. engr, advan. flight control systs, 55-58; asst. head, flight sci. dept, SYSTS. DIV, BENDIX CORP, 58-64, mgr. vehicle eng, lunar mobile lab. prog, 64-70, MGR. LUNAR EJECTA & METEORITES EXP. PROG, 70- U.S.A.F, 51-58, Res, 58-, Capt. Aerodynamics; supersonic and hypersonic flow; system performance; stability and control; propulsion; soil mechanics. Address: 4030 W. Loch Alpine Dr, Ann Arbor, MI 48103.

GALANE, IRMA B(ERESTON), b. Baltimore, Md, Aug. 23, 21; div; c. 1. ELECTRONIC ENGINEERING. B.A, Goucher Col, 40; Hopkins, 40-42; Mass. Inst. Tech. Radiation Lab, 43, 45. Asst. math, sch. eng, Hopkins, 41-42; physicist, Naval Ord. Lab, 42-43; electronic engr, bur. ships, U.S. Navy, 43-49; Off. Chief Signal Officer, U.S. Army, 49-51; bur. aeronaut, U.S. Navy, 51-56; electronic scientist, Air Res. & Develop. Command, U.S. Air Force, 56-57; electronic engr, Fed. Commun. Cmn, 57-60; res. engr, Goddard Space Flight Center, NASA, 60-62; supvry. electronic engr, U.S. Coast Guard Hqs, 62-64; eng. specialist, Library Cong, 64-66; GEN. ENGR, U.S. DEPT. NAVY, 66- Instr, Commercial Radio Inst, Md, 41-42; Navy mem. & secy, res. & develop. bd. radome subpanel, Dept. Defense, 51-56, mem. int. radio consult. comt, Int. Telecommun. Union, 51-56; assoc, Smithsonian Inst. AAAS; sr. mem. Inst. Elec. & Electronics Eng; Nat. Soc. Prof. Eng; Am. Inst. Aeronaut. & Astronaut; Am. Ord. Asn; Marine Technol. Soc. Satellite communication, radar and navigational systems; antennas; propagation; nuclear radiation detection instrumentation; infrared applications; missile radomes; oceanography. Address: 4201 Cathedral Ave. N.W, Washington, DC 20016.

GALANTAY, EUGENE ERVIN, b. Budapest, Hungary, Mar. 18, 28; U.S. citizen; m. 56; c. 2. ORGANIC & MEDICINAL CHEMISTRY. Dipl, Budapest Tech, 50; Ph.D.(org. chem), Swiss Fed. Inst. Tech, 59. Res. chemist, res. inst, Pharmaceut. Indust, Budapest, 50-56; res. fel, Hopkins, 59-60; sr. res. chemist, Squibb Inst. Med. Res, N.J, 60-63; res. group leader med. chem, SANDOZ PHARMACEUT. DIV, SANDOZ-WANDER, INC, 63-69, SECT. HEAD RES. DEPT, 69- Am. Chem. Soc; Swiss Chem. Soc. Organic chemistry of natural products and of other medicinally interesting compounds. Address: Research Dept, Sandoz Pharmaceuticals Division, Sandoz-Wander, Inc, Hanover, NJ 07936.

GALARNEAULT, THOMAS P, b. St. Cloud, Minn, June 25, 22; m. 53; c. 4. BACTERIOLOGY. B.S, St. John's (Minn), 48; M.S, Loyola (Ill), 51, Ph.D. (microbiol), 55. Instr. microbiol, Stritch Sch. Med, Loyola (Ill), 53-57, asst. prof, 57-60, assoc. prof, 60-64, asst. dean, 54-61; assoc. prof. BIOL, ST. JOHN'S UNIV.(MINN), 64-66, PROF, 66-, CHMN, DEPT, 70- Consult, Augustana Hosp, Chicago, 55-56; Resurrection Hosp, 61-64. U.S.N.R, 41-46. Am. Soc. Microbiol. Bacterial nomenclature and taxonomy. Address: Dept. of Biology, St. John's University, Collegeville, MN 56321.

GALASSO, FRANCIS S(ALVATORE), b. Monson, Mass, Apr. 26, 31; m. 50; c. 2. SOLID STATE & INORGANIC CHEMISTRY. B.S, Massachusetts, 53; M.S, Connecticut, 57, Ph.D.(chem), 60. Res. asst. solid state chem, Connecticut, 56-60; res. scientist, RES. LABS, UNITED AIRCRAFT CORP, 60-62, res. supvr, mat. synthesis group, 62-67, CHIEF MAT. SYNTHESIS SECT, 67- Sci. & eng. adv. to U.S. Rep. Emilio Daddario, Conn; consult, NASA space exp. U.S.A.F, 53-55, 1st Lt. Am. Chem. Soc; Am. Ceramic Soc; Am. Inst. Mining, Metall. & Petrol. Eng. Ordering in oxides; x-ray crystallography; superconducting, pyrolytic, laser, ferroelectric and ferromagnetic, fiber and composite, thermoelectric, and infrared optical materials; single crystal growth; perovskite type oxides. Address: Research Labs, United Aircraft Corp, East Hartford, CT 06108.

GALASSO, GEORGE JOHN, b. New York, N.Y, June 3, 32; m. 58; c. 3. MICROBIOLOGY, VIROLOGY. B.S, Manhattan Col, 54; Ph.D.(bact), North Carolina, 60. Trainee VIROL, North Carolina, 60-62, res. assoc, 62-63, res. asst. prof, 63-64; assoc. prof, sch. med, Univ. Va, 64-68; mem. grants assocs. prog, NAT. INSTS. HEALTH, 68-69, ACTING CHIEF INFECTIOUS DISEASE BR. & HEAD ANTIVIRAL SUBSTANCES PROG, NAT. INST. ALLERGY & INFECTIOUS DISEASES, 69- U.S.A, 54-56. AAAS; Am. Soc. Microbiol; Electron Micros. Soc; Soc. Exp. Biol. & Med; Tissue Cult. Asn. Interferon and antiviral research; virus particle counts in quantitation of animal virus-cell relationship; inhibition; toxicity; multiplicity reactivation; immunology and aggregation with vaccinia; psittacosis and vesicular stomatitis virus in tissue culture. Address: Room 7A-06, Bldg. 31-A, National Institute of Allergy & Infectious Diseases, Bethesda, MD 20014.

GALASYN, VALENTINE D(AVID), b. Hartford, Conn, Feb. 25, 28; m. 55; c. 4. MEDICINE. B.S, Teachers Col, Conn, 54; M.S, Illinois, 57, Ph.D.(chem), 58; M.D, Tennessee, 65. Res. chemist, Am. Cyanamid Co, Conn, 58-59; asst. prof. chem, Arizona State, 59-62; WITH MED. CORPS, U.S. NAVY, 65- U.S.N, 45-46, 50-52. Am. Chem. Soc. Inorganic and analytical chemistry; cardiology; nuclear medicine; nonaqueous solvents; electrochemistry; rare earths; carbides; solid propellant oxidizers; submarine medicine. Address: Buck Hill Rd, Canterbury, CT 06331.

GALATI, WILLIAM, b. New York, N.Y, Apr. 23, 41; m. 67. NUCLEAR PHYSICS. B.S, Polytech. Inst. Brooklyn, 62; M.S, Kentucky, 66, Ph.D.(nuclear physics), 69. Res. asst, Univ. Ky, 64-69, res. assoc, Univ. Md, 69-71; SR. SCIENTIST, RAFF ASSOCS, INC, 71- Am. Phys. Soc. Nuclear structure physics; low energy experimental research; undersea sound propagation. Address: Raff Associates, Inc, 912 Thayer Ave, Silver Spring, MD 20910.

GALBIATI, LOUIS J, b. Vineland, N.J, Feb. 17, 25; m. 53; c. 4. ELECTRICAL ENGINEERING, MATHEMATICS. B.E, Hopkins, 51; M.S, Cornell, 56, Ph.D.(elec. eng), 60; M.Ed, 67. Engr, Gen. Elec. Co, Pa, 51-54; instr. elec. eng, Cornell, 54-56; prin. engr, Kimble Glass Co, Ohio, 56-58; scientist, aero lab, Cornell, 59, asst, 59-60; prof. elec. eng. & head dept. eng, Merrimack Col, 60-62; mgr. space payloads, Radio Corp. Am, Mass, 62; mem. tech. staff, Mitre Corp, Mass, 62-68; PROJ. MGR. & ASST. CONTROLLER, SERV. TECHNOL. CORP, 68- Engr, N.Am. Aviation, Inc, Calif, summer 60; mem. instrumentation eng. staff, Avco Corp, Mass, 61-62; Merrimack Col. rep, cmt. comput. center, New Eng. Col, 61-62; mem. Andover Sch. Cmt, 65-68. Sig.C, 44-46, Sgt. Am. Soc. Eng. Educ; Inst. Elec. & Electronics Eng; Am. Geophys. Union; Instrument Soc. Am. Tropospheric refraction effects; nuclear instrumentation; educational techniques; adaptive control systems; arcs and magnetic fields. Address: Service Technology Corp, 55 Broadway, Cambridge, MA 02142.

GALBRAITH, A(LAN) S(TUART), b. Guelph, Ont, July 15, 04; nat; m. 41; c. 2. MATHEMATICS. B.Sc, Alberta, 28; A.M, Harvard, 30, Ph.D.(math), 37. Instr. math, Alberta, 28-29; Harvard, 30-33; Colby Col, 33-36; asst. prof, 41-46; instr, Rochester, 37-41; mathematician, Aberdeen Proving Ground, 46-56, supv. physicist, air proving ground center, Eglin Air Force Base, Fla, 56-60; assoc. chief data systs. div, Goddard Space Flight Center, Md, 60-61; DIR. MATH. DIV, U.S. ARMY RES. OFF-DURHAM, 61- Am. Math. Soc; Math. Asn. Am. Ordinary differential equations; conformal mapping; ballistics; missile and satellite motion. Address: U.S. Army Research Office-Durham, Box CM, Duke Station, Durham, NC 27706.

GALBRAITH, DONALD BARRETT, b. McDonald, Pa, Mar. 10, 37; m. 57; c. 3. BIOLOGY. B.S, Grove City Col, 58; Sc.M, Brown Univ, 60, U.S. Pub. Health Serv. fel, 60-62, Corinna Borden Keen fel, 61-62, Ph.D.(biol), 62. Res. assoc, Brown Univ, 63; Nat. Sci. Found. res. grants genetics, TRINITY COL.(CONN), 64-70, ASSOC. PROF. BIOL, 70- AAAS; Am. Soc. Zool; N.Y. Acad. Sci. Physiological genetics; experimental embryology; radiation biology; expression of the agouti locus in mice. Address: Dept. of Biology, Trinity College, Hartford, CT 06106.

GALBRAITH, E(RNAL) P(OWELL), b. Blanding, Utah, Aug. 14, 17; m. 42; c. 4. ANALYTICAL CHEMISTRY. B.S, Utah State, 40; M.S, Kansas State, 42. Anal. chemist, Remington Arms Co, 42-43; E.I du Pont de Nemours & Co, 43-46; mgr. anal. labs, Gen. Elec. Co, 46-56, MGR. PROF. PLACEMENT, 56-65; PAC. NORTHWEST LAB, BATTELLE MEM. INST, 65- Am. Chem. Soc; Am. Soc. Eng. Educ. Effective utilization of engineering and scientific personnel by industry. Address: Pacific Northwest Labs, Battelle Memorial Institute, Box 999, Richland, WA 99352.

GALBRAITH, HARRY W(ILSON), b. Detroit, Mich, Apr. 8, 18. ORGANIC CHEMISTRY. B.S, Wayne, 40, M.S, 42; Ph.D.(org. chem), Purdue, 49. Asst. res. chemist, Children's Fund, Mich, 40-43; asst, Cornell & Purdue, 43-46; analyst chem, Purdue, 46-50; HEAD, GALBRAITH LABS, INC, 50- Am. Chem. Soc. Organic microanalysis. Address: Galbraith Labs, Inc, P.O. Box 4187, Lonsdale, Knoxville, TN 37921.

GALBRAITH, JAMES GARBER, b. Anniston, Ala, May 28, 14; m. 42; c. 4. NEUROSURGERY. B.S, St. Louis, 36, M.D, 38. Intern, Lloyd Noland Hosp, Fairfield, Ala, 38-39, res. gen. surg, 39-40; neurol. surg, neurol. inst, Columbia, 40-43, instr. neurol, univ, 42-43; assoc. prof. neurol. surg, MED. COL. ALA, 46-54, PROF. SURG, 54-, CHMN. DIV. NEUROL. SURG, 65- Consult, Vet. Admin. Hosps, Birmingham, Tuscaloosa & Montgomery, Ala; Lloyd Noland, St. Vincent's & Children's Hosps, S. Highland Infirmary, Birmingham, Ala. Dipl, Am. Bd. Neurol. Surg. Med.C, 43-46, Lt. Soc. Neurol. Surg; Am. Asn. Neurol. Surg; Am. Acad. Neurol. Surg; Asn. Res. Nerv. & Ment. Disease. Surgical aspects of cerebral vascular disease. Address: Medical College of Alabama, 1919 Seventh Ave. S, Birmingham, AL 35233.

GALBRAITH, JAMES NELSON, JR, b. Phila, Pa, Apr. 26, 36; m. 60; c. 1. GEOPHYSICS. S.B, Mass. Inst. Technol, 58, Ph.D.(geophys), 63. Sr. scientist, GEOSCI. INC, 63-67, V.PRES, 67- Am. Geophys. Union; Soc. Explor. Geophys; Seismol. Soc. Am; Inst. Elec. & Electronics Eng. Computer applications to geophysical problems, including time series analysis and optimum single and multichannel filtering of seismic and magnetic data and solution to boundry value problems. Address: Geoscience Inc, 199 Bent St, Cambridge, MA 02141.

GALBRAITH, RALPH A(RTHUR), b. Ash Grove, Mo, Aug. 1, 11; m. 43; c. 2. ELECTRICAL ENGINEERING. B.S, Missouri, 34; Tau Beta Pi fel, Yale, 36-37, Ph.D, 37. Res. engr. & ed, Detroit Edison Co, 37-38; instr, Missouri, 38; asst. prof. & assoc. prof, Texas, 39-44; mem. staff, radar sch, Mass. Inst. Technol, 44-45; prof, Ga. Inst. Technol, 46; chmn. dept. elec. eng, col. eng, SYRACUSE UNIV, 46-51, dean, 51-58, exec. v.pres, 58-69, V.PROVOST PLANNING, 69- Consult, Willow Run Res. Ctr, Michigan, 53; dir, Crouse-Hinds Co, 62- Distinguished serv. award, Univ. Missouri, 63. AAAS; Am. Soc. Eng. Ed. Operations research. Address: Syracuse University, Syracuse, NY 13210.

GALBRAITH, RUTH LEGG, b. Lecompte, La, Nov. 5, 23; m. 50; c. 1. TEXTILES. B.S, Purdue, 45, fel, 48-50, Ph.D.(textile chem), 50. Chemist orlon res, E.I. du Pont de Nemours & Co, 45-46; textile chemist, detergent res, Gen. Elec. Co, 46-47; asst. chem, Purdue, 47-48; prof, textiles, Tennessee, 50-55; assoc. prof, Univ. Ill, Urbana, 56-64, prof, 64-70; PROF. & HEAD DEPT. CONSUMER AFFAIRS, AUBURN UNIV, 70- Mem. nat. adv. comt, Fed. Flammable Fabrics Act, 70-72. Am. Soc. Test & Math; Am.

Asn. Textile Chem. & Colorists; Am. Chem. Soc; fel. Am. Inst. Chem. Textile chemistry; detergents; textile fiber and fabric properties. Address: 368 Singleton, Auburn, AL 36830.

GALBREATH, EDWIN C(ARTER), b. Ashmore, Ill, March 18, 13; m. 55; c. 1. VERTEBRATE PALEONTOLOGY, GEOLOGY. B.Ed, East. Ill. State Col, 41; Ph.D.(zool), Kansas, 51. Asst. prof. anat, med. sch, Kansas, 53-57; assoc. prof. ZOOL, SOUTH. ILL. UNIV, 57-66, PROF, 66- U.S.N.R, 36-45. Soc. Vert. Paleont; Geol. Soc. Am. Soc. Study Evolution. Cenozoic vertebrate paleontology and geology; Pleistocene faunas of eastern Illinois; Oligocene and Miocene stratigraphy and paleontology of northeastern Colorado; vertebrate morphology. Address: Dept. of Zoology, Southern Illinois University, Carbondale, IL 62901.

GALBREATH, W(ILLIAM) W(ILSON), JR, b. Youngstown, Ohio, May 31, 19. CERAMIC ENGINEERING. B.S, Illinois, 43; M.S, Ohio State, 47. Ceramic engr, power pile div, Oak Ridge Nat. Lab, 47-48; staff engr, naval reactor div, Argonne Nat. Lab, 48-51, mat. group leader, reactor eng. div, 51-54, asst. dir, 54-55; proj. engr, Vitro Corp. Am, 55-56; atomic energy div, Babcock & Wilcox Co, 56-57, acting mgr, mat. & testing dept, 57-60, tech. adv. res. & develop. planning, 60-62; consult, 62-63; PRES, VA. KYANITE CORP, 63- Mem. Atomic Indust. Forum. Am. Nuclear Soc; Am. Ceramic Soc; Nat. Inst. Ceramic Eng. Materials and fabrication procedures for components for nuclear reactors with emphasis on metals and oxides for fuel elements; high temperature ceramics; development and testing; mining, processing and purification of industrial minerals for ceramic industry. Address: Virginia Kyanite Corp, 2029 Royal Oak Dr, Lynchburg, VA 24503.

GALDSTON, IAGO, b. Russia, Dec. 8, 95; nat; m. 20; c. 4. MEDICINE. B.S. & M.D, Fordham Univ, 21; Univ. Vienna, 25, 29, 34, 38. Dir. health div, Community Coun, New York, 18-20, educ. dir. & med. off, Union Health Ctr, 20-22; dir. div. health educ, N.Y. Tuberc. Asn, 21-30; secy, med. info. bur, N.Y. Acad. Med, 27-62; dir. resident training, CONN. DEPT. MENT. HEALTH, HARTFORD, 62-, CHIEF PSYCHIAT. TRAINING, 62- Prof, Fordham Univ; lectr, N.Y. Univ; N.Y. Med. Col, Flower & Fifth Ave. Hosps; N.Y. Training Sch. Teachers; res. assoc, Wenner-Gren Found. Anthrop. Res, N.Y, 60- AAAS; Hist. Sci. Soc; fel. Am. Psychiat. Asn; fel. Am. Pub. Health Asn; Acad. Psychoanal; fel. Acad. Psychiat; fel. N.Y. Acad. Sci. Social medicine and psychiatry; psychiatry; psychoanalysis; history of medicine; psychosomatic medicine; cultural anthropology. Address: 69 Orange St, Brooklyn, NY 11201.

GALDSTON, MORTON, b. N.Y.C, Nov. 2, 12; m. 41; c. 3. MEDICINE. B.S. N.Y. Univ, 32, M.D, 37; Columbia, 32-33. N.Y. Acad. Med. Bowen-Brooks scholar med, Hopkins Hosp, 41-42; asst, COL. MED. N.Y. UNIV, 42-46, instr, 46-50, asst. prof. clin. med, 50-54, MED, 54-55, ASSOC. PROF, 55-, RES. ASSOC, 46-, asst, 42-43. From clin. asst. vis. physician to vis. physician, Goldwater Mem. Hosp, 43-62; asst. vis. physician, French Hosp, N.Y, 49-54, asst. attend. physician, 54-58; jr. asst. physician, cardiac clin, Lenox Hill Hosp, 48-52, sr. asst. physician, 52-58; asst. vis. physician, N.Y. Univ. Hosp, 52-64, assoc. vis. physician, 64-; assoc. vis. physician, Bellevue Hosp, 55- Civilian with Off. Sci. Res. & Develop, 42-43. Med.C, 43-46, Maj. Am. Physiol. Soc; Harvey Soc; Soc. Clin. Invest; Am. Heart Asn; Col. Physicians; fel. N.Y. Acad. Med; Am. Med. Asn; Thoracic Soc. Clinical research; physiology of respiration; circulation in general and of heart and kidneys; essential and experimental hypertension; humans under stress. Address: New York University College of Medicine, 550 First Ave, New York, NY 10003.

GALE, A(LFRED) JOHN, b. Swindon, England, March 21, 15; nat; m. 39; c. 1. PHYSICS. B.Sc, London, 36. Physicist, Scophony, Ltd, England, 37-43; Precision Develops, Ltd, 43-45; Airmec Labs, 45-49; gen. mgr, Scophony-Baird, Ltd, 49-50; V.PRES. & DIR. APPL. PHYSICS, HIGH VOLTAGE ENG. CORP, 50-; PRES, ION PHYSICS CORP, 59- Dir. Diffraction Ltd, 63- AAAS; Am. Inst. Aeronaut. & Astronaut; Am. Vacuum Soc.(pres, 58-59). Particle accelerators; electrical propulsion systems for space. Address: Box 98, Burlington, MA 01803.

GALE, BENNETT T(YLER), b. Greenville, N.H, Oct. 28, 06; m. 35; c. 3. GEOLOGY. B.S, Antioch Col, 31; Harvard, 32. Chief field party, Tenn. Valley Authority, 34; park naturalist, Grand Teton, NAT. PARK SERV, Wyo, 38-41, Petrified Forest, Ariz, 41-45, Carlsbad Caverns, N.Mex, 45-52, chief geologist, Wash, D.C, 52-58, regional chief interpretation, Calif, 58-62, asst. to regional dir, 62-65, supt, Olympic Nat. Park, Wash, 65-69, ASSOC. REGIONAL DIR, 69- U.S.N.R, 42-45. Geol. Soc. Am. Geomorphology; origin and development of limestone caves; petrification of wood. Address: 16631 N.E. 91st St, Redmond, WA 98052.

GALE, CHARLES, b. Wyandotte, Mich, July 7, 26; m. 50; c. 2. VIROLOGY, VETERINARY MEDICINE. D.V.M, Mich. State, 52; M.P.H, Minnesota, 55, Ph.D.(virol), 58. Instr. vet. bact. & virol, Minnesota, 52-56, asst. head diag. lab, 53-56; asst. res. prof, Ohio Agr. Exp. Sta, 56-57, assoc. res. prof, 57-62, assoc. prof. & adv, grad. sch, Ohio State Univ, 60-62; sr. res. virologist, ELI LILLY & CO, 62-71, RES. ASSOC, 71- Mem, Conf. Vet. Diagnosticians; bd. mem, Am. Col. Vet. Microbiol; instr, eve. div, Ind. Cent. Col. Am. Vet. Med. Asn; Conf. Res. Workers Animal Diseases; Am. Asn. Avian Path; U.S. Animal Health Asn. Viral respiratory diseases, especially of cattle and companion animals; biological and pharmaceutical evaluations. Address: Eli Lilly & Co, Box 708, Greenfield, IN 46140.

GALE, CHARLES C, JR, b. Cleveland, Ohio, Sept. 28, 26; m. 58; c. 2. PHYSIOLOGY. B.A, Arizona State, 51; Ph.D.(physiol), Pennsylvania, 60; Fil. Lic, Stockholm, 63, Fil. Dr.(physiol), 64. Asst. instr. PHYSIOL, sch. med, Pennsylvania, 56-58, instr, 60-61; Nat. Insts. Health res. fel, Royal Vet. Col. Sweden, 61-64; res. asst. prof, SCH. MED, UNIV. WASH, 64-65, asst. prof, 65-71, ASSOC. PROF, 71- U.S.N.R, 44-45. Am. Physiol. Soc: Int. Soc. Biometeorol; Endocrine Soc. Neuroendocrinology, role of the central nervous system in regulation of the pituitary gland; thermoregulation, interaction of central nervous and endocrine systems; reproduction. gestation and lactation. Address: Dept. of Physiology, School of Medicine, University of Washington, Seattle, WA 98105.

GALE, DAVID, b. N.Y.C, Oct. 5, 15; m. 37. BACTERIOLOGY. B.S, City Col. New York, 35; Ph.D.(bact), Univ. Calif, 51. Asst. bact, Univ. Calif, 47-51; instr, sch. dent, Wash. Univ, 51-53; serologist, Vet. Admin. Hosp, Durham, N.C, 53-54, bacteriologists, Albuquerque, N.Mex, 54-67; RETIRED. Asst. prof. microbiol, sch. med, Univ. N.Mex, 65-67. Dipl, Am. Bd. Med. Microbiol, 63. U.S.N, 43-46. Fel. AAAS; Am. Thoracic Soc; Am. Soc. Microbiol; N.Y. Acad. Sci. Bacteriology and immunology of the tubercle bacillus and systemic mycotic infections; all aspects of the host-parasite relationships. Address: 7915 Bosque St. N.W, Albuquerque, NM 87114.

GALE, DAVID, b. N.Y.C, Dec. 13, 21; m. 54; c. 2. MATHEMATICS. B.S, Swarthmore Col, 43; M.A, Michigan, 47; Ph.D.(math), Princeton, 49. Mem. staff, radiation lab, Mass. Inst. Tech, 43-45; instr. math, Princeton, 49-50; asst. prof, Brown, 50-57, assoc. prof, 57-61, prof, 61-66, chmn. dept, 60-66; PROF. MATH, ECON. & OPER. RES, UNIV. CALIF, BERKELEY, 66- Nat. Sci. Found. res. grant, 52-53; Fulbright res. scholar, Denmark, 53-54; Guggenheim fel. & vis. prof, Osaka, 62-63; Nat. Sci. Found. sr. fel, Univ. Copenhagen, 68-69. Consult, Rand Corp, 55- Am. Math. Soc; Math. Asn. Am; Economet. Soc. Mathematical economics; theory of games; geometry of convex sets; combinatorial problems. Address: 791 Hilldale Ave, Berkeley, CA 94708.

GALE, DAVID MARK, b. Chicago, Ill, Aug. 21, 38; m. 61; c. 2. ORGANIC CHEMISTRY. B.S, Illinois, 60; Nat. Sci. Found. summer fel, Mass. Inst. Tech, 61, Nat. Insts. Health fel, 61-63, Ph.D.(org. chem), 63. RES. CHEMIST, CENT. RES. DEPT, E.I. DU PONT DE NEMOURS & CO, INC, 63- Am. Chem. Soc. Polymer chemistry; organofluorine chemistry; reaction mechanisms; spectroscopic methods of structure proof. Address: E.I. du Pont de Nemours & Co, Inc, Central Research Dept, Experimental Station, Wilmington, DE 19898.

GALE, GEORGE OSBORNE, b. Brooklyn N.Y, May 3, 31; m. 53; c. 2. MICROBIOLOGY, BIOCHEMISTRY. B.A, Hofstra, 53; fel, Purdue, 53-54, M.S, 57. Res. asst. microbiol, Purdue, 54-56; biochemist, Lederle Labs, AM. CYANAMID CO, 56-59, res. bacteriologist, AGR. DIV, 59-64, GROUP LEADER, CLIN. DEVELOP. LAB, 64-, MGR. NUTRIT. & PHYSIOL, 70- AAAS; Am. Soc. Microbiol; Am. Soc. Animal Sci; N.Y. Acad. Sci. Reproductive physiology; bacterial resistance to antibiotics; chemotherapy of experimental infections; veterinary toxicology. Address: Agricultural Division, American Cyanamid Co, P.O. Box 400, Princeton, NJ 08540.

GALE, GLEN ROY, b. Florence, S.C, Dec. 1, 29; m. 53; c. 4. PHARMACOLOGY. B.A, Duke, 50, M.A, 52, Ph.D.(pharmacol), 54. Physiologist, Vet. Admin. Hosp, Durham, 53-55; res. assoc. PHARMACOL, Duke, 57-59, assoc, 59-65; asst. prof, MED. UNIV. S.C, 65-67, assoc. prof, 67-70, PROF, 70-; PHARMACOLOGIST, VET. ADMIN. HOSP, 65-, Durham, N.C, 59-65. U.S. Pub. Health Serv. res. grant, 61- Med.Serv.C, 55-57, Capt. AAAS; Am. Soc. Pharmacol. & Exp. Therapeut; Soc. Exp. Biol. & Med; N.Y. Acad. Sci. Mechanisms of action of antimicrobial agents and antitumor drugs; electron microscopy; biochemical pharmacology. Address: Veterans Administration Hospital, Charleston, SC 29403.

GALE, GRANT O(SCAR), b. Prentice, Wis, Dec. 29, 03; m. 29; c. 3. ELECTRICAL ENGINEERING. B.S, Wisconsin, 26; M.S, Michigan, 33, Mem. eng. dept, Ill. Bell Tel. Co, Chicago, 26-27; estimator Kewaunee Mfg. Co, Wis, 27-28; PROF. PHYSICS & CHMN. DEPT, GRINNELL COL, 29- Fulbright lectr, col. arts & sci, Baghdad, 54-55, Jamia Col, Pakistan, 63-64; summer vis. prof, teacher training insts, Taiwan Norm. Univ, Taipei & Tokyo, Japan, 64; vis. prof, Haile Sellassie I Univ, 69-70. Staff consult, Am. Inst. Physics, N.Y, 57-58. AAAS; Am. Phys. Soc; Am. Asn. Physics Teachers. Joule-Thomson effect in metals; resistance strain gages; elastic hysteresis: temperature changes accompanying the adiabatic expansion and compression of metal wires; magnetomechanical effects. Address: Dept. of Physics, Grinnell College, Grinnell, IA 50112.

GALE, HOYT RODNEY, b. Boston, Mass, Aug. 1, 04; m. 29, 40, 52; c. 4. PALEONTOLOGY, ANTHROPOLOGY. A.B, Harvard, 26; Ph.D.(geol), Stanford, 29; M.A, California, Los Angeles, 36. Paleont. & geol. consult, West. Gulf Oil Co, Calif, 29; field asst. geol, Gulf Prod. Co, Tex, 30-31; asst. geologist & spec. agent, U.S. Gen. Land Off. Colo. 31-34; consult. geologist, 34-37; asst. California. Los Angeles, 36-37; teacher, Pasadena Jr. Col, 38-44; vis. asst. prof. Southern California, 44-47; teacher geol, Pasadena City Col. 47-64, assoc. prof, 64-70; RES. & WRITING, 70- AAAS; Paleont. Soc; Asn. Petrol. Geol. Marine Pliocene and Pleistocene Mollusca of California; causes of business cycles; philosophical and sociological significance of the paleontological record of evolution. Address: 669 Sturtevant Dr, Sierra Madre, CA 91024.

GALE, JAMES L(YMAN), b. Boston, Mass, Dec. 31, 34; m. 66; c. 2. EPIDEMIOLOGY, PUBLIC HEALTH. A.B, Harvard, 57; M.D, Columbia Univ, 61; M.S, Univ. Wash, 69. Intern, Bellevue Hosp, N.Y.C, 61-62; resident, Bellevue & Mem. Hosps, 62-64; fel. prev. med, UNIV. WASH, 67-69, ASST. PROF. EPIDEMIOL. & INT. HEALTH, SCH. PUB. HEALTH & COMMUNITY MED, 69- Vis. assoc. prof, sch. med, Nat. Taiwan Univ, 69-; consult, Tri-Serv. Gen. Hospital, Taipei, Taiwan, 69-70; U.S. Pub. Health Serv. career develop. award, 69-74. U.S.P.H.S, 64-67, Surgeon. Am. Pub. Health Asn; Am. Soc. Microbiol; Am. Soc. Trop. Med. & Hyg; Soc. Epidemiol. Res. Epidemiology of infectious disease, especially rubella, respiratory and genital disease. Address: Dept. of Epidemiology & International Health, RD 96, University of Washington School of Public Health & Community Medicine, Seattle, WA 98195.

GALE, LAIRD HOUSEL, b. San Francisco, Calif, Jan. 24, 35; m. 61; c. 1. PHYSICAL ORGANIC CHEMISTRY. B.S, San Diego State Col, 56; Convair fel, California, 56-57, Du Pont Co. summer fel, 57, Allied Chem. & Dye Corp. fel, 58-59, Ph.D.(org. chem), 59. Res. technologist RADIATION CHEM, Martinez Res. Lab, SHELL OIL CO, 59-62, RES. CHEMIST, EMERYVILLE RES. CTR, SHELL DEVELOP. CO, 62- AAAS; Am. Chem. Soc. Radiation chemistry and free radical chemistry; stereochemical studies of organic reactions and conformational analysis. Address: Emeryville Research Center, Shell Development Co, Shell Oil Co, Emeryville, CA 94608.

GALE, LAWRENCE JUDD, b. Chicago, Ill, Aug. 6, 23; m. 47; c. 2. MECHANICAL ENGINEERING. B.S, Northwestern, 44; Xavier, 59-60. Aeronaut. res. scientist, Nat. Adv. Comt. Aeronaut, 44-52; sr. aeronaut. engr, spec. devices ctr, Off. Naval Res, 52-54; sr. proj. engr, Lycoming Div, Avco Corp, 54-55; chief engr, asst. to pres. & dir. sales, Burtek, Inc, 55-62; mgr. space prog, Reflectone Div, Universal Match Corp, 62-63; dir. mkt. & corp. planning, Gen. Appl. Sci. Labs, Inc, 63-71; DIR. MKT, APPL. DEVICES CORP, HAUPPAUGE, 71- Soc. Automotive Eng; Am. Soc. Mech. Eng. Aerospace operation and ground support equipment. Address: 75 Salem Ridge Dr, Huntington, NY 11743.

GALE, NORD LORAN, b. Phoenix, Ariz, Feb. 21, 38; m. 60; c. 3. MICROBIOLOGY, BIOCHEMISTRY. M.S, Brigham Young Univ, 64, Nat. Sci. Found. fel, 64-67, Ph.D.(bact), 67. Mem. tech. staff microbiol, TRW Inc, Calif, 66-68; ASST. PROF. LIFE SCI, UNIV. MO-ROLLA, 68- AAAS; Am. Soc. Microbiol. Autotrophy; cation transport across microbial membranes; extra terrestrial life detection; waste treatment. Address: Dept. of Life Sciences, University of Missouri-Rolla, Rolla, MO 65401.

GALE, STEPHEN BRUCE, b. Syracuse, N.Y, June 21, 40; m. 63; c. 3. SANITARY & CHEMICAL ENGINEERING. B.S.Ch.E, Syracuse Univ, 62, M.S, 64, Ph.D.(sanit. eng), 69. SANIT. ENGR, AIR POLLUTION ENG. DIV, U.S. ARMY ENVIRON. HYG. AGENCY, 69- Med.Serv.C, U.S.A, 69-, Capt. Am. Inst. Chem. Eng; Am. Chem. Soc; Air Pollution Control Asn. Kinetics of oxidation of sulfites by dissolved oxygen; kinetics of photochemical oxidation of sulfur dioxide in dilute gas-air mixtures; air pollution instrumentation. Address: Air Pollution Engineering Division, U.S. Army Environmental Hygiene Agency, Edgewood Arsenal, Edgewood, MD 21010.

GALE, WALTER W, b. Jamaica, N.Y, Dec. 22, 36; m. 62; c. 1. ORGANIC CHEMISTRY. Sc.B, Brown, 58; M.S, Illinois, 60, Phillips Petrol. Co. fel, 60-61, Ph.D.(org. chem), 61. RES. CHEMIST, Esso Res. & Eng. Co, STANDARD OIL CO.(N.J), 61-64, Jersey Prod. Res. Co, 64-65, ESSO PROD. RES. CO, 65- Am. Chem. Soc; Soc. Petrol. Eng. Nitrogen sulfur heterocycles; new recovery methods for petroleum. Address: 13831 Kimberley Lane, Houston, TX 77024.

GALE, WILLIAM ARTHUR, Econ, Numerical Anal, see 12th ed, Soc. & Behav. Vols.

GALEANO, CESAR, b. Montevideo, Uruguay, Apr. 8, 26; m. 51; c. 2. NEUROPHYSIOLOGY. M.D, Univ. of the Republic, Uruguay, 61. Asst. neurophysiol, Inst. Res. Biol. Sci, Montevideo, Uruguay, 51-60, head electrophysiol, 61-65; int. fel. NEUROPHYSIOL, Brain Res. Inst, Mexico City, Mex, 65; Nat. Insts. Health int. fel, sch. med, Stanford Univ, 65-67; asst. prof, SCH. MED, UNIV. SHERBROOKE, 67-69, ASSOC. PROF, 69- Asst. electroencephalog, sch. med, Univ. of the Republic, Uruguay, 51-56. Neuronal mechanisms of learning. Address: Dept. of Physiology, University of Sherbrooke School of Medicine, Sherbrooke, Que, Can.

GALEANO, SERGIO F(RANCIS), b. Havana, Cuba, Apr. 7, 34; U.S. citizen; wid; c. 3. ENVIRONMENTAL ENGINEERING. B.S, Univ. Havana, 57; M.S.E, Univ. Fla, 64, Ph.D.(bioenviron. eng), 66. Proj. engr, Ingenieria Vame S.Am, 56-58; chief design sect, Comision Nacional Acueductos, 59-60, head eng. div, 60-61; process develop. eng, OWENS-ILL, INC, 66-69, PROJ. MGR. NEW SYSTS. DEVELOP, 69- Dipl, Intersoc. Bd. Environ. Eng. Am. Inst. Chem. Eng; Acad. Environ. Eng; Sci. Res. Soc. Am; Air Pollution Control Asn; Nat. Soc. Prof. Eng. Deep well hydrology; water supply systems; environmental control; process development drying systems. Address: 2964 Dorian Dr, Toledo, OH 43614.

GALEF, ARNOLD E, b. New York, N.Y, Oct. 28, 25; m. 48; c. 3. ENGINEERING MECHANICS. B.S, Rensselaer Polytech, 47; M.S, Stanford, 51. Jr. engr, Arma Div, Am. Bosch-Arma, 47-48; instr. eng. mech, Maine, 48-50; res. engr, Hughes Aircraft Co, 51-56; sr. engr, Radioplane Div, Northrop Corp, 56-60; mem. sr. staff, Nat. Eng. Sci. Co, 60-67, STAFF ENGR, TRW SYSTS, 68- Mem. comt. shock & vibration specifications, U.S. Air Force, 59. U.S.N, 43-46. Am. Acoust. Soc. Aircraft and missile shock, vibration and fatigue; offshore drilling technology. Address: TRW Systems Group, M-3, 2465, One Space Park, Redondo Beach, CA 90278.

GALEHOUSE, JON SCOTT, b. Doylestown, Ohio, Feb. 16, 39; m. 59; c. 2. GEOLOGY. B.A, Col. Wooster, 62; Nat. Sci. Found. summer fels, California, Berkeley, 64 & 65, univ. fel, 65-66, Ph.D.(geol), 66. Geol. Soc. Am. Penrose bequest, 64, res. grant, 65; Nat. Sci. Found. fel, 66-67; asst. prof. GEOL, SAN FRANCISCO STATE COL, 67-70, ASSOC. PROF, 70- Am. Chem. Soc. Petrol. Res. Fund grant, 67-69. AAAS; Geol. Soc. Am; Soc. Econ. Paleont. & Mineral. Stratigraphy, sedimentology and marine geology. Address: Dept. of Geology, San Francisco State College, San Francisco, CA 94132.

GALEJS, J(ANIS), b. Riga, Latvia, July 21, 23; nat; m. 55; c. 2. ELECTRICAL ENGINEERING. Eng. dipl, Brunswick Tech, Germany, 50; M.S, Ill. Inst. Tech, 53, Ph.D, 57. Engr, Lembeck Radio, Germany, 50; Nat. Video Corp, Ill, 51-52; staff engr, Cook Res. Lab, 52-57; sr. scientist, electronic syst, Sylvania Elec. Prods, Inc, 57-70; RES. ENGR, COMMUN. SCI. DIV, NAVAL RES. LAB, 70- Mem. comn. VI, Int. Sci. Radio Union. Inst. Elec. & Electronics Eng; Am. Geophys. Union. Antennas and propagation theory. Address: Code 5404, Communications Sciences Division, Naval Research Lab, Washington, DC 20390.

GALER, BETTINA BANKS, b. Seattle Wash, Sept. 27, 43. ANATOMY. B.S, Colo. State Univ, 65, M.S, 67, Ph.D.(anat), 71. Lectr. anat. & physiol, med. sch, Univ. Wash, 65-66; ASST. PROF. ANAT, COLO. STATE UNIV, 71- Neuroendocrinology; comparative pathobiology. Address: Dept. of Anatomy, Colorado State University, Ft. Collins, CO 80521.

GALES, ROBERT S(YDNEY), b. Boston, Mass, Dec. 12, 14; m. 42; c. 3. PHYSICS. A.B, California, Los Angeles, 38, M.A, 42. Asst. physics, California, Los Angeles, 40-42; assoc. physicist & group leader, div. war res, California, 42-45; from physicist & leader psychol. physics br. to head listening div, Naval Electronics Lab, 46-67; Naval Undersea Warfare Ctr, 67-69; SUPVRY. PHYSICIST, NAVAL UNDERSEA RES. & DEVELOP. CTR, 69- Civilian with Off. Sci. Res. & Develop, 44. Acoustical Soc. Am. Hearing aids; audio masking; measurements and methods of detection of underwater sounds; noise measurement; voice communication. Address: Naval Undersea Research & Development Center, San Diego, CA 92132.

GALETTO, WILLIAM GEORGE, b. Grass Valley, Calif, Oct. 5, 39; m. 62; c. 2. ORGANIC CHEMISTRY. B.S, Chico State Col, 61; Ph.D.(agr. chem), California, Davis, 67. Res. asst. flavor chem, dept. enol, California, Davis, 62-67; RES. CHEMIST, West. Regional Res. Lab, U.S. Dept. Agr, 67-68; RES. & DEVELOP. LAB, McCORMICK & CO, 68- Nat. Acad. Sci-Nat. Res. Coun. associateship, 67-68. U.S.A.F.R, 62-68, S/Sgt. AAAS; Am. Chem. Soc; Inst. Food Technol; Am. Soc. Enol. Stereochemistry of sesquiterpene lactones; synthesis of natural products; flavor chemistry; gas chromatographic separation of diastereoisomers. Address: McCormick & Co, 204 Wight Ave, Cockeysville, MD 21030.

GALEY, JOHN APT, b. Oak Park, Ill, May 27, 28; m. 52; c. 5. NUCLEAR PHYSICS. B.S, Yale, 50; M.S, Chicago, 54, Ph.D.(physics), 59. Res. assoc. physics, Notre Dame, 59-60; SR. SCIENTIST, BETTIS ATOMIC POWER LAB, WESTINGHOUSE ELEC. CORP, 60- Photonuclear work; 100 million electron volt betatron; low energy physics; Van de Graff accelerators; experimental reactor physics. Address: Bettis Atomic Power Lab, Westinghouse Electric Corp, P.O. Box 79, West Mifflin, PA 15122.

GALGINAITIS, SIMEON VITIS, b. Sheboygan, Wis, Nov. 29, 21; m. 45; c. 4. PHYSICS. B.A, Ripon Col, 43; Ph.D.(physics), Wisconsin, 47. Instr. physics, Ripon Col, 43-44; tech. asst. Tenn. Eastman Corp, Oak Ridge, 44-45; asst. prof. physics, Louisville, 47-54, assoc. prof, Ill. Inst. Tech, 54-56; physicist, Gen. Elec. Co, 56-57; prof. physics & chmn. dept, Rose Polytech, 58-60; MEM. STAFF, RES. LAB, GEN. ELEC. CO, 60- Am. Phys. Soc. Discharges in gases; semiconductors; applied general physics. Address: 913 Ash Tree Lane, Schenectady, NY 12309.

GALIA, LENA N, b. Sicily, Italy, Sept. 8, 12; U.S. citizen. ANATOMY, PHYSIOLOGY. B.S, Columbia, 43, M.A, 48. Instr. sci, St. John's Hosp, L.I, N.Y, 43-46; from instr. to asst. prof. health ed. & sci, JERSEY CITY STATE COL, 46-55, ASSOC. PROF. anat. & physiol, 55-67, SCI, 67- Summers, vis. prof, Columbia, 57, 63. Consult. sci. curriculum, Escambia County, Fla; mem. adv. bd. sci. curriculum, Long Island, 60-65. Improving health education through use and understanding of physical examination. Address: Dept. of Science, Jersey City State College, 2039 Kennedy Blvd, Jersey City, NJ 07305.

GALIANO, FRANCIS R(OSS), b. Kansas City, Mo, July 2, 36; m. 57; c. 2. ORGANIC & POLYMER CHEMISTRY. B.S, Rockhurst Col, 56; Ph.D.(org. chem), Washington (St. Louis), 60. Res. chemist, Spencer Chem. Co, 60-63, Spencer Chem. Div, GULF OIL CO, 63-66, GROUP LEADER, GULF RES. & DEVELOP. CO, 66- Am. Chem. Soc. Reactions of naphthalene negative ion; monomer synthesis; polymerization and copolymerization; formaldehyde chemistry; coating resins; molding and laminating resins; polyamides; polyolefins; nuclear magnetic resonance; gas liquid chromatography. Address: Gulf Research & Development Co, 9009 W. 67th St, Merriam, KS 66204.

GALIANO, ROBERT J(OSEPH), b. St. Louis, Mo, Apr. 1, 31; m. 57; c. 3. PHYSICAL CHEMISTRY. B.S, St. Louis, 53, Ph.D, 57. Analyst, weapons systs. eval. div, Inst. Defense Anal, 57-64; mem. staff, Lambda Div, Defense Res. Corp, 64-65, V.PRES. & TREAS, LAMBDA CORP, 65- AAAS; Opers. Res. Soc. Am. Molecular structure; quantum mechanics; systems analysis; computer sciences. Address: 2733 N. Radford St, Arlington, VA 22207.

GALIBOIS, ANDRE, b. Quebec, Que, Apr. 21, 38; m. 69; c. 1. PHYSICAL METALLURGY, OPERATIONS RESEARCH. B.A, Laval Univ, 57, Que. Prof. Engr. fel, 60, B.A.Sc, 61, Int. Nickel Co. fels, 61-63, D.Sc.(metall), 64. Lectr. eng. mech, Laval Univ, 64; Ford Found. res. fel. metall. & mat. sci, Univ. Toronto, 64-65; asst. prof. MINES & METALL, LAVAL UNIV, 65-68, ASSOC. PROF, 68-, ASST. DIR. DEPT, 70-, DIR. ENG. PHYSICS, 71- Consult, Defence Res. Bd. Can, summer 67, mem, 69-; faculty coun, Laval Univ, 68-; phys. metall. subcomt, Can. Nat. Adv. Comt. for Res. in Mining & Metall. 69-; sr. partner, Opers. Res. Consult. Firm, 69- Am. Soc. Metals; Can. Inst. Mining & Metall. Martensitic transformation and tempering mechanism in extra low carbon steels; grain boundaries migration and grain growth in high purity lead, tin and aluminum and in material doped with impurities; operations research applied to mining ventures. Address: Dept. of Mines & Metallurgy, Laval University, Quebec 10, Que, Can.

GALIL, FAHMY, b. Talkha, Egypt, Oct. 20, 25; m. 59; c. 2. TEXTILE CHEMISTRY, CHEMICAL ENGINEERING. B.Sc, Univ. Cairo, 47, M.Sc, 54; Ph.D.(textile chem), Manchester Col. Sci. & Technol, Eng, 58. Textile chemist, Misr Spinning & Weaving Co, Egypt, 47-50; asst. eng, Univ. Cairo, 50-58, lectr, 58-64, assoc. prof, 64-68; res. fel. polymers, Univ. Mainz, 68-69; RES. CHEMIST, TEXTILES DIV, MONSANTO CO, 69- Alexander von Humboldt fel, Reutlingen, Ger, 62-64. Am. Chem. Soc; sr. mem. Am. Asn. Textile Chem. & Colorists; corp. mem. Brit. Soc. Dyers & Colourists. Polymers; unit processes in organic synthesis. Address: Textiles Division, Monsanto Co, Technical Center, Decatur, AL 35602.

GALIN, MILES A, b. New York, N.Y, Jan. 8, 32; m. 53; c. 6. OPHTHALMOLOGY. A.B, N.Y. Univ, 51, scholar, 51-55, M.D, 55. Intern, Mt. Sinai Hosp, New York, 55-56; asst. ophthal. surg, med. col, Cornell, 56-58, instr, 58-61, clin. asst. prof, 61-63, asst. prof, 63-66; PROF. OPHTHAL. & CHMN. DEPT, N.Y. MED. COL, 66- Asst. resident ophthal. surg, New York Hosp, 56-58, resident, 58-59, surgeon to out-patients, 59-61, asst. attend, 61-64, assoc. attend, 64-66; prin. investr. & co-investr, Nat. Soc. Prev. Blindness & Nat. Coun. Combat Blindness res. award & U.S. Pub. Health Serv. res. award, med. col, Cornell Univ, 59-66, N.Y. City Health Res. Coun. career scientist award, 63-66; consult, Mem. Hosp, New York, 60-66; prin. investr. & co-investr, Nat. Soc. Prev. Blindness & Nat. Coun. Combat Blindness res. award, N.Y. Med. Col, 66-67, U.S. Pub. Health Serv. res. award, 66-; attend ophthalmologist, Flower & Fifth Ave. Hosps, 66-; Metrop. Hosp, 66-; Bird

S. Coier Hosp, 66-; Dr. Henry Balconi Mem. lectr, N.Y, 67; second Culler Mem. lectr, Ohio, 67; First Hermann Hosp. Lectr, Tex, 67; consult, Nat. Multiple Sclerosis Found; U.S. ed, Annali de Ottalmologia; mem, tech. adv. comt, Bur. Handicapped Children. Dipl, Am. Bd. Ophthal, 60. AAAS; Am. Acad. Ophthal. & Otolaryngol.(award of merit, 67); Am. Med. Asn; Asn. Res. Vision & Ophthal; N.Y. Acad. Med.(William Warner Hoppin Award, 59); N.Y. Acad. Sci; Fr. Soc. Ophthal; Israel Ophthal. Soc; Ophthal. Soc. U.K; Pan-Am. Asn. Ophthal; hon. mem. Arg. Ophthal. Soc; hon. mem. Peruvian Asn. Ophthal. Address: Dept. of Ophthalmology, New York Medical College, 1249 Fifth Ave, New York, NY 10029.

GALINAT, W(ALTON) C(LARENCE), b. Manchester, Conn, Dec. 9, 23; m. 45; c. 2. GENETICS, PLANT MORPHOLOGY. B.S, Connecticut, 49; M.S, Wisconsin, 51, Ph.D.(agron, genetics, bot), 53. Asst. genetics, Conn. Agr. Exp. Sta, 48-50; agron, agr. exp. sta, Wisconsin, 50-53; res. fel, BUSSEY INST, HARVARD, 53-63, RES. ASSOC, 63-; assoc. prof, UNIV. MASS, 64-68, PROF, 68- U.S.C.G, 43-46. Genetics Soc. Am; Bot. Soc. Am; Soc. Econ. Bot. Genetics and morphology of maize mutations and maize evolution. Address: Waltham Field Station, University of Massachusetts, Waltham, MA 02154.

GALINDO, ANIBAL H, b. Buga, Colombia, Sept. 11, 29; m. 51; c. 4. ANESTHESIOLOGY, NEUROPHYSIOLOGY. B.Sc, Rosary Col, Bogota, 46; M.D, Nat. Univ. Colombia, 52; Ph.D.(physiol, neurophysiol), McGill Univ, 68. Internship, Univ. Hosp, Bogota, 52-53; private practice, 53-54; resident anesthesia, San Jose Hosp, Nat. Univ. Colombia, 54-56, instr, univ, 58-59; vis. scientist, Nat. Inst. Neurol. Diseases & Blindness, 59-63, head sect. neuroanesthesia, 60-63; asst. prof. ANESTHESIOL, sch. med, McGill Univ, 64-68; ASSOC. PROF, SCH. MED, UNIV. WASH, 68- Am. Physiol. Soc; Am. Soc. Pharmacol. & Exp. Therapeut. Pharmacology of anesthetic drugs; effect of various anesthetics on cardiac excitability, cerebral and hepatic circulation; neuropharmacology, especially the effects of muscle relaxants and anesthetics on synaptic transmission. Address: Dept. of Anesthesiology, University of Washington School of Medicine, Seattle, WA 98195.

GALINDO, PEDRO, b. Panama City, Panama, Oct. 27, 17; m. 64; c. 1. ENTOMOLOGY. B.S, Loyola (Calif), 39; M.S, California, Berkeley, 44. Field investr. arboviruses, George Williams Hooper Found, 43-44; malariologist, Dept. Pub. Health, Panama, 45-47, chief antimalaria campaign, 47-50; RES. ENTOMOLOGIST, GORGAS MEM. LAB, 50- Hon. asst. prof. trop. med, med. sch, Panama, 62- Consult, Gorgas Mem. Lab, 47-50; Yellow Fever Conf, U.S. Pub. Health Serv, 54; conf. on birds as hosts of arboviruses, Am. Cmt. Arboviruses, 62. Mem. expert cmt. malaria, WHO, 47-51; exec. cmt. eradication malaria, Dept. Pub. Health, Panama, 64- Ecology, epidemiology and control of arthropod-borne diseases, especially malaria and yellow fever; taxonomy and zoogeography of neotropical mosquitoes. Address: Gorgas Memorial Lab, P.O. Box 2016, Balboa Heights, CZ.

GALINSKY, ALVIN M, b. Chicago, Ill, Oct. 14, 31. PHARMACEUTICAL CHEMISTRY. B.S, Illinois, 54, univ. fel, 56-58, M.S, 57, Ph.D.(pharmaceut. chem), 62. Instr. org. medicinals, col. pharm, Columbia, 60-61, asst. prof, 61-63; phys. pharm, SCH. PHARM, DUQUESNE UNIV, 63-64, assoc. prof, 64-68, PROF. PHARM. & CHMN. DEPT, 68- AAAS; Am. Chem. Soc; Am. Pharmaceut. Asn; Am. Asn. Cols. Pharm. Structure-activity relationships; local anesthetics; antifungal agents; dosage form bioavailability; kinetics and stability of pharmaceutical dosage forms. Address: Dept. of Pharmacy, Duquesne University School of Pharmacy, 600 Forbes Ave, Pittsburgh, PA 15219.

GALINSKY, IRVING, b. N.Y.C, June 15, 21; m. 48; c. 2. CYTOLOGY, GENETICS. B.Sc, McGill, 44, MacDonald Col. Alumni scholar, 44-45, M.Sc, 45; Ph.D.(cytogenetics), Wisconsin, 48. Asst, Wisconsin, 45-48; Hite cancer fel, Texas, 48-49; Nat. Cancer fel, col. med, Baylor, 49-51; res. assoc. bact. genetics, Carnegie Inst, 51-53; asst. prof. genetics & cytol, Delaware, 53-54; res. assoc, Biochem. Res. Found, 54-59; PROF. BIOL, HOFSTRA UNIV, 59-, CHMN. DEPT, 63- AAAS; Genetics Soc. Am; Am. Genetic Asn; Am. Asn. Cancer Res. Cytology of meiosis and mitosis; bacterial genetics; cancer research; mitotic abnormalities in plant and animal cells. Address: Dept. of Biology, Hofstra University, Hempstead, NY 11550.

GALITZ, DONALD S, b. Chicago, Ill, May 28, 35; m. 60; c. 2. PLANT PHYSIOLOGY. B.A, Monmouth Col, 56; M.S, Illinois, 60, Ph.D.(agron), 61. Asst. prof. biol. sci, West. Ill. Univ, 61-68; ASSOC. PROF. BOT, N.DAK. STATE UNIV, 68- Res. assoc, dept. agron, Univ. Ill, 67-68. Am. Soc. Plant Physiol; Weed Sci. Soc. Am. Seed physiology; stress physiology; plant physiology; root initiation; physiology of initiating roots. Address: Dept. of Botany, North Dakota State University, Fargo, ND 58102.

GALITZINE, NICHOLAS, b. Moscow, Russia, May 28, 04; nat; m. 36; c. 1. ANALYTICAL CHEMISTRY. Ing.Chem, Sch. Indust. Chem, Lyon, 28; M.S, Michigan, 40. Anal. chemist, Gen. Elec. Co, 40-52, supv. chemist anal. unit, 52-53, specialist Anal. chem, 53-56, leader, 56-60, mgr, 60-68; RETIRED. Am. Chem. Soc; Am. Microchem. Soc. Histology of plant fibers; inorganic impurities in metals; relation between chemical composition and electrical properties of insulation. Address: 3302 Ingle Ave, Louisville, KY 40206.

GALIVAN, JOHN H, b. Albany, N.Y, June 19, 39; m. 65; c. 1. BIOCHEMISTRY. B.S, Union Univ.(N.Y), 60; Ph.D.(biochem), Albany Med. Col, 67; M.S, State Univ. N.Y. Albany, 63. Res. asst. biochem, Albany Med. Col, 64-67; Nat. Insts. Health fel, Scripps Clin. & Res. Found, 67-70; SR. RES. SCIENTIST, DIV. LABS. & RES, N.Y. STATE DEPT. HEALTH, 70- AAAS. Enzymology; folate and vitamin B_{12} metabolism; regulation of cell division; pyrimidine metabolism; cytoxic drugs. Address: Division of Labs. & Research, New York State Dept. of Health, New Scotland Ave, Albany, NY 12201.

GALKOWSKI, THEODORE T(HADDEUS), b. Worcester, Mass, Nov. 9, 21; m. 49; c. 2. ORGANIC CHEMISTRY. B.S, Col. of Holy Cross, 47, M.S, 48; Corn Industs. Res. Found. fel, Ohio State, 48-51, Ph.D.(chem), 51. Org. chemist, Nat. Bur. Standards, 51-52; asst. prof. CHEM, PROVIDENCE COL, 52-55, assoc. prof, 55-60, PROF, 60-, COORD. RES, 67- U.S.A, 43-46. AAAS; Am. Chem. Soc; fel. Am. Inst. Chem. Structure of starch; proof of structure of carbohydrates; synthesis of C^{14} labeled carbohydrates; configurations of branched carbohydrates; carbohydrates in natural products. Address: Dept. of Chemistry, Providence College, Providence, RI 02918.

GALL, CARL EVERT, b. Burlington, Ont, Can, Dec. 17, 31; m. 55; c. 4. CHEMICAL ENGINEERING. B.A.Sc, Toronto, 55; M.Sc, Queen's (Ont), 62; Ph.D.(chem. eng), Minnesota, 66. Lectr. chem, Royal Mil. Col, 53-54; tech. rep, Imp. Oil Ltd, 55-56; asst. prof. math, Haile Sellassie I Univ, 56-59; Royal Mil. Col, 59-61, CHEM. ENG, 61-62; res. fel, Minnesota, 62-64; asst. prof, UNIV. WATERLOO, 64-66, ASSOC. PROF, 66- Control science; applied mathematics; chemical reaction engineering. Address: Dept. of Chemical Engineering, University of Waterloo, Waterloo, Ont, Can.

GALL, D(ONALD) A(LAN), b. Reddick, Ill, Sept. 13, 34; m. 60; c. 3. BIOMEDICAL ENGINEERING. B.S, Univ. Ill, 56; S.M, Mass. Inst. Technol, 58, Mech.E, 60, Sc.D.(mech. eng), 64. Exp. res. engr, Gen. Motors Corp, 56-57; staff engr, Dynatech Corp, 59-60, mgr. control systs, 62-63; eng. specialist, Thompson Ramo Wooldridge, Inc, 60-62; asst. prof. automatic controls, Carnegie-Mellon Univ, 64-68, assoc. prof. mech. eng, 68-69; res. asst. prof. surg, SCH. MED, UNIV. PITTSBURGH, 68-69, RES. ASSOC. PROF. SURG. & ANESTHESIOL, 69- Taylor Medal, Int. Conf. Prod. Res, 71. AAAS; Inst. Elec. & Electronics Eng; Am. Soc. Mech. Eng. Automatic controls; medical computer systems; engineering systems analysis; transient behavior of engineering systems; biological servomechanisms. Address: School of Medicine, University of Pittsburgh, Pittsburgh, PA 15213.

GALL, EDWARD A(LFRED), b. N.Y.C, June 10, 06; m. 33; c. 2. PATHOLOGY. M.D, Tulane, 31. Intern, Sydenham Hosp, N.Y, 31-33; fel. med, Tufts Col, 33-35, instr. path, 35-40; Harvard Med. Sch, 40-41; pathologist, Bethesda Hosp, 41-48; asst. prof, COL. MED, UNIV. CINCINNATI, 41-48, Mary E. Emery prof. path, 48-71, V.PRES. & DIR. MED. CTR, 71- Dist. physician, Boston Dispensary, 33-35; res. path, Mass. Gen. Hosp, 35-37, asst. pathologist, 37-40; surg. pathologist, Cincinnati Gen. Hosp, 46- Consult, Armed Forces Inst. Path; Surgeon Gen, U.S. Army. Med.C, 42-46, Lt. Col. Soc. Exp. Biol. & Med; fel. Am. Soc. Clin. Path; Am. Soc. Exp. Path; Am. Asn. Path. & Bact.(secy, 55-57; ed-in-chief, Am. Jour. Path, 57-66; pres, 63-64); Int. Acad. Path.(pres, 68-69); hon. mem. Peruvian Soc. Path. Anat; hon. mem. Japanese-Am. Soc. Path; Am. Asn. Cancer Educ.(pres, 71-72). Hematopoietic system; benzol poisoning; malignant lymphoma; effects of irradiation; infectious mononucleosis; mumps; neoplasm of alimentary tract; hepatic disease; cardiovascular disorders. Address: Medical Center, University of Cincinnati, Cincinnati, OH 45229.

GALL, GRAHAM A. E, b. Moose Jaw, Sask, Sept. 2, 36; m. 60; c. 3. BIOCHEMICAL GENETICS. B.Sc, Alberta, 60, M.Sc, 63; Ph.D.(animal genetics), Purdue, 66. Res. asst. genetics, Alberta, 63; Purdue, 63-66; ASST. PROF. ANIMAL SCI, UNIV. CALIF, DAVIS, 66-, ASST. ANIMAL GENETICIST, EXP. STA, 66- Genetics consult, Calif. Dept. Fish & Game, 67- Am. Soc. Animal Sci; Genetics Soc. Am. Biochemical genetics of growth in mice and Tribolium castaneum; quantitative inheritance of rainbow trout; fish genetics. Address: Dept. of Animal Science, University of California, Davis, CA 95616.

GALL, JAMES WILLIAM, b. Taylorville, Ill, Apr. 22, 42; m. 66; c. 2. PHYSICAL CHEMISTRY. Nat. Air Pollution Control Asn. fel, Ohio State Univ, 65-69, Ph.D.(phys. chem), 69. Teaching asst. chem, Ohio State Univ, 64-65; RES. SCIENTIST CHEM, PHILLIPS PETROL CO, 69- Am. Chem. Soc; Soc. Petrol. Eng. Photochemistry; gas phase kinetics; chemistry of atmospheric pollutants; interaction of aqueous polymer solutions; oxidation. Address: 3600 Dana Dr, Bartlesville, OK 74003.

GALL, JOHN F(REDERICK), b. Chicago, Ill, April 15, 13; m. 41; c. 2. PHYSICAL CHEMISTRY. B.S, Northwestern, 34; univ. fel, Chicago, 36-37, Ph.D. (phys. chem), 39. Asst, Chicago, 37-38; res. phys. chemist, Pa. Salt Mfg. Co, 38-42, group leader, 42-46, asst. res. supvr, 46-48, res. supvr, 48-52, dir. inorgan. res, 52-58, asst. mgr. res. Pennsalt Chem. Corp, 58-60, mgr, res. prod. develop. dept, 60-68; PROF, PHILA. COL. TEXTILES & SCI, 68- AAAS; Am. Chem. Soc; Electrochem. Soc. Electrochemistry; thermodynamics; calorimetry; electrolytic processes; percompounds; fluorine chemistry; organic halogen compounds; agricultural chemicals; industrial cleaners; industrial chemical processes; rocket propellants; high energy chemicals; research administration; inorganic chemistry; surface chemistry. Address: 128 Fairview Rd, Narberth, PA 19072.

GALL, JOSEPH G(RAFTON), b. Wash, D.C, Apr. 14, 28; m. 55; c. 2. CYTOLOGY. B.S, Yale, 48, Ph.D.(zool), 52. Instr. zool, Minnesota, 52-55, asst. prof, 55-58, assoc. prof, 58-64; PROF. BIOL, YALE, 64- Jr. Lalor fel, Marine Biol. Lab, Woods Hole, 54. AAAS; Am. Soc. Cell Biol; Am. Soc. Zool; Genetics Soc. Am. Chromosome structure. Address: Dept. of Biology, Yale University, New Haven, CT 06520.

GALL, LORRAINE S(IBLEY), b. Binghamton, N.Y, June 16, 15. BACTERIOLOGY. B.S, Cornell, 38, Ph.D.(animal nutrit), 46. Res. technician, Lederle Labs, Am. Cyanamid Corp, N.Y, 38-41; Borden Co, 42-43; asst. rumen bacteria, Cornell, 44-46; fel. nutrit, Yale, 46-47; asst, Ohio Exp. Sta, 47-48; res. microbiologist, Nat. Dairy Res. Corp, 48-53; Fulbright Sr. Res. A, Wallaceville Animal Res. Sta, N.Z, 54-55; coordinator int. sales ed, Lederle Labs, Am. Cyanamid Corp, 55-61; assoc. scientist, Repub. Aviation Corp, 61-65; adv. microbiologist, IBM Corp, 65-66, sr. microbiologist, 66-67, mgr. biosci, 67-70; br. mgr. automated microbiol, Becton, Dickinson Res. Ctr, 70-71; CHIEF MICROBIOL, MOSES H. CONE MEM. HOSP, 71- Am. Soc. Microbiol; Soc. Indust. Microbiol. Effect of space flight on indigenous microflora of man and chimpanzee; automated microbiology. Address: 1101 N. Elm St, Greensboro, NC 27401.

GALL, WALTER G(EORGE), b. Passaic, N.J, Mar. 11, 29; m; c. 2. ORGANIC CHEMISTRY. B.S, Carnegie Inst. Tech, 50, M.S, 50; Nat. Sci. Found. fel, Rochester, 52-53, Ph.D.(chem), 53. Res. chemist, org. high polymer chem, EXP. STA, E.I. DU PONT DE NEMOURS & CO, 53-62, sr. res. chemist, PLASTICS DEPT, 63-69, RES. ASSOC, 69- Sci. Res. Soc. Am; Am. Chem. Soc; fel. Am. Inst. Chem. Bridgehead nitrogen heterocycles; quinolizine;

high polymer chemistry; stereospecific polymerizations; high temperature polymers; polymer flammability. Address: Plastics Dept, Experimental Station, E.I. du Pont de Nemours & Co, Wilmington, DE 19898.

GALLA, STEPHEN J(OSEPH), b. Detroit, Mich, Apr. 26, 27. MEDICINE, ANESTHESIOLOGY. B.S, Notre Dame, 49; M.D, Hopkins, 53. Asst. anesthesia, Hopkins, 54-55; surg, Peter Bent Brigham Hosp, 57-59; sr. instr. ANESTHESIOL, sch. med, Western Reserve, 59-61, asst. prof, 61; SCH. MED, UNIV. PITTSBURGH, 61-67, assoc. res. prof, 67-69, ASSOC. PROF, 69-, V.CHMN. DEPT, 70-, acting chmn, 69-70, trainee metab. & nutrit, grad. sch. pub. health, 63-65. Asst. vis. anesthesiologist, Metrop. Gen. Hosp, 59-61; Nat. Insts. Health res. grant, 60-; sr. staff anesthesiologist, Presby-Univ. Hosp, 61- Dipl, Am. Bd. Anesthesiol. U.S.N, 45. Am. Soc. Anesthesiol; Am. Med. Asn; Am. Col. Anesthesiol; Asn. Univ. Anesthetists. Pharmacology; physiology; biochemistry. Address: 1081 Scaife Hall, University of Pittsburgh, Pittsburgh, PA 15213.

GALLACHER, LAWRENCE V, b. Brooklyn, N.Y, Jan. 6, 34; m. 58; c. 4. PHYSICAL CHEMISTRY. B.S, Manhattan Col, 55; M.S, Adelphi, 61, Ph.D. (phys. chem), 65. Chemist, Am. Bosch Arma Corp, 56-63; res. chemist, AM. CYANAMID CO, 64-69, SR. RES. CHEMIST, 69-, PROJ. LEADER, CENT. RES. DIV, 70- Am. Chem. Soc; Soc. Rheol. Polymer physics; relationship between properties of polymers and molecular structure; relaxation processes in polymers; high-strain behavior of polymeric systems. Address: Central Research Division, American Cyanamid Co, 1937 W. Main St, Stamford, CT 06904.

GALLAGER, H(ARRY) STEPHEN, b. Chester, Pa, June 5, 22; m. 67. PATHOLOGY. A.B, Temple Univ, 43, M.D, 46. Asst. pathologist, Germantown Hosp, Phila, Pa, 53-54; chief lab. serv, U.S. Army Hosp, Ft. Knox, Ky, 54-56; asst. prof. PATH, grad. sch. biomed. sci, UNIV. TEX, HOUSTON, 56-62, ASSOC. PROF. & ASSOC. PATHOLOGIST, M.D. ANDERSON HOSP. & TUMOR INST, 62- Chmn. path. working group, Nat. Breast Cancer Task Force, 70- U.S.A, 43-46, Res, 46-48, 54-56, Maj. Am. Soc. Clin. Path; Am. Med. Asn; Col. Am. Path; Int. Acad. Path; Am. Asn. Path. & Bact. Pathology of malignant diseases. Address: Dept. of Pathology, University of Texas M.D. Anderson Hospital & Tumor Institute, Houston, TX 77025.

GALLAGHAN, JOHN A(RTHUR), b. Oakland, Calif, Oct. 28, 13; m. 42; c. 6. ORGANIC CHEMISTRY. B.S, California, 36, 36-37; Ph.D.(org. chem), Virginia, 46. Asst. org. prep, Shell Develop. Co, Calif, 37-38; jr. chemist, U.S. Naval Powder Factory, 41-43, asst. chemist, 43-44, assoc. chemist, 44-45, chemist, 45-48, sr. chemist & head org. sub. div, 48-58, head org. br, Naval Propellant Plant, 52-58; res. scientist, MISSILES & SPACE DIV, LOCKHEED AIRCRAFT CORP, 58-65, STAFF SCIENTIST, 65- Assoc. Am. Chem. Soc. Synthesis of organic compounds of possible use in solid propellants; synthesis of phenanthridine derivatives; the phenanthridine series; high energy solid propellants; explosives. Address: 320 Larita Dr, Ben Lomond, CA 95005.

GALLAGHAR, ROBERT G(EORGE), b. Camden, N.J, Apr. 17, 24; m. 49; c. 5. PHYSICS. A.B, Stanford, 47; Atomic Energy Comn. fel, Oak Ridge Inst. Nuclear Studies, 48-49; Cincinnati; Hahnemann Med. Col. Res. biologist, Qm. Corps, U.S. Dept. Defense, 48-49; health physicist, U.S. Pub. Health Serv, 49-54; Liberty Mutual Ins. Co, Mass, 54-60; asst. mgr, dept. biol. & med, Nuclear Sci. & Eng. Corp, Pa, 60-62; PRES, APPL. HEALTH PHYSICS, INC, 62- Lectr, sch. pub. health, Harvard, 56-58; asst. prof, Pittsburgh, 60- Consult, Atomic Energy Comn, Los Alamos, 51-52. Dir, Iso/serve, Inc. Dipl, Am. Bd. Health Physics; Am. Bd. Indust. Hyg. U.S.A, 42-45, U.S.P.H.S, 48-54, Lt. Health Physics Soc.(treas, 56-59); Am. Soc. Nondestruct. Test; Am. Soc. Safety Eng; Am. Acad. Indust. Hyg; Am. Indust. Hyg. Asn; Am. Nuclear Soc; Am. Chem. Soc; N.Y. Acad. Sci. Health physics; radiological decontamination; radiochemistry; radiobiology; management and control of radioisotope accidents; effect of certain chemicals upon selected strains of fungi; nuclear energy public liability and property damage insurance inspection. Address: Applied Health Physics, Inc, 2986 Industrial Blvd, Bethel Park, PA 15102.

GALLAGHER, ALAN C, b. Oak Park, Ill, June 14, 36; m. 58; c. 2. ATOMIC PHYSICS. B.E.S, Purdue, 58; Ph.D.(physics), Columbia, 64. Res. assoc. physics, IBM Watson Lab, 64; JOINT INST. FOR LAB. ASTROPHYS, UNIV. COLO, BOULDER, 64-; PHYSICIST FOR NAT. BUR. STANDARDS, 67- Lectr, Colorado, 67- Am. Phys. Soc. Atomic structure; atom-atom collisions; electron-atom collisions. Address: Joint Institute for Laboratory Astrophysics, University of Colorado, Boulder, CO 80302.

GALLAGHER, BERNARD T(HOMAS), b. N.Y.C, Jan. 28, 22; m. 51; c. 2. CHEMICAL ENGINEERING, NATIONAL DEFENSE. Dipl. command & staff, Air Univ, 62; dipl. nuclear weapons, Defense Atomic Support Agency, N.Mex, 63; dipl. chem. biol. & radiol, U.S. Army Dugway Proving Ground, Utah, 64; dipl. mgt. nat. defense, Indust. Col. Armed Forces, 69. Comdr. 2857 Test Squadron, Olmsted Air Force Base, U.S. Air Force, Pa, 58-62, chief spec. flights br, Hq. Air Force, Andrews Air Force Base, 63-64, disaster control off, Hq. Air Force, the Pentagon, 64-65; chief plans & progs. br, SPEC. FACILITIES DIV, OFF. EMERGENCY PREPAREDNESS, EXEC. OFF. OF PRESIDENT, 65-66, dep. chief div, 66-68, CHIEF DIV, 68- U.S. mem. & chmn, Quadrapartite Standardization Coord. Comt. dealing with Nuclear Biol. & Chem. Defense Measures, tech. adv. to U.S. rep, NATO on Working Group for Protection against Nuclear, Biol. & Chem. Warfare & NATO on Interserv. Working Party on Nuclear Biol. & Chem. Warfare, U.S. rep, Air Force Subgroup, NATO AC-196 Comt. on Standardization of Nuclear, Biol. & Chem. Defense, 64-65. U.S.A.F, 42-65, Col. National Defense Policy related to development of doctrine, organizational concepts and policy guidance for nuclear, biological and chemical warfare; development of attack analysis and damage assessment techniques; Federal Government emergency operations. Address: Route 2, Box 88B, Leesburg, VA 22075.

GALLAGHER, BRENT S, b. Greenfield, Mass, Nov. 3, 39; m. 58; c. 2. PHYSICAL OCEANOGRAPHY. B.S, California, Los Angeles, 62; U.S. Bur. Commercial Fisheries fel, 64-65; Ph.D.(oceanog), Scripps Inst, California, 65. Asst. res. oceanographer, Inst. Geophysics & Planetary Physics, California, San Diego, 66-67; asst. prof. PHYS. OCEANOG, UNIV. HAWAII, 67-71, ASSOC. PROF, 71- Consult, U.S. Naval Radiological Defense Labs, 67-68. Nonlinear aspects of ocean waves; fine-scale structure of physical variables in the ocean. Address: Dept. of Oceanography, University of Hawaii, Honolulu, HI 96822.

GALLAGHER, BRIAN BORU, b. Chicago, Ill, Sept. 2, 34; m. 58; c. 2. NEUROLOGY. B.S, Notre Dame, 56; U.S. Pub. Health Serv. fel, Chicago, 57-60, Ph.D.(biol. psychol), 60, M.D, 63. Intern med, Chicago, 63-64; res. NEUROL, Yale-New Haven Hosp, 64-67, instr, SCH. MED, YALE, 67-68, asst. prof, 68-71, ASSOC. PROF, 71- AAAS; Am. Acad. Neurol; Am. Soc. Neurochem; Soc. Neurosci; N.Y. Acad. Sci. Neurochemistry, particularly in relation to metabolism and epilepsy. Address: Dept. of Neurology, Yale University School of Medicine, 333 Cedar St, New Haven, CT 06520.

GALLAGHER, C(HARLES) E(DWARD), b. Doylestown, Pa, Feb. 1, 19; m. 41; c. 2. ENGINEERING. B.S, Pennsylvania, 41. Mech. engr, Naval Aircraft Factory, Phila, 41-42; aeronaut. engr. & supt, automatic & remote controls div, Naval Air Exp. Sta, 42-48, consult. engr, 48; proj. engr, Naval Air Develop. Cent, 48-54, asst. supt. control & guid. div, aeronaut, elec. & electronics lab, 54-56; mgr. polaris guid. program, missile & ord. systems dept, Gen. Elec. Co, Pa, 56-57, ord. dept, Mass, 57-63; Raytheon Co, 63-65; mgr. adv. guid. systs, 65; dir. res, AM. STERILIZER CO, 65-68, dir. res. & develop, 68-69, GEN. MGR. EQUIP. DIV, 69- Airborne and spaceborne guidance and navigation systems and related computers, Apollo, Polaris and Poseidon programs; development and manufacture of hospital equipment. Address: 601 Pasadena Dr, Erie, PA 16505.

GALLAGHER, C(HARLES) J(OSEPH), b. Phila, Pa, Oct. 16, 17; m. 43; c. 2. PHYSICS. B.S, Temple, 38, fel, 38-40, M.A, 40; Pennsylvania, 38-40; Ph.D. (physics), Notre Dame, 42. Asst. physics, Notre Dame, 40-42; res. assoc, radio res. lab, Harvard, 43-45; physicist, res. lab, GEN. ELEC. CO, 45-67, res. adminr, RES. & DEVELOP. CTR, 67-68, proj. develop. mgr. progs. & systs, 68-69, TECH. ADMINR, GEN. PHYSICS LAB, 69- With Off. Sci. Res. & Develop, 44. Am. Phys. Soc.(secy, 61). Vibration mode of clarinet reed; thermionic emission; noise in gaseous discharges; design of wide band transformers; mechanism of arc cathode spot; semiconductors high pressure arcs. Address: General Physics Lab, General Electric Research & Development Center, P.O. Box 8, Schenectady, NY 12301.

GALLAGHER, D(UDLEY) M(ICHAEL), b. St. Paul, Minn, Aug. 14, 16; m. 48; c. 6. CHEMISTRY. B.S, Col. St. Thomas, 38, M.A, 40; Ph.D.(chem), Missouri, 42. RES. CHEMIST, U.S. Rubber Co, 42-43; Sharples Chems, Inc, 43-44; Corn Prods. Ref. Co, 46-54; Beaunit Mills, 54-58; Tee-Pak, Inc, 58-61; DeBell & Richardson, 61-62; United Merchants, 62-63; SOUTH. REGIONAL LAB, U.S. DEPT. AGR, 63- U.S.A, 44-46. Polymerization; textiles; organic synthesis. Address: P.O. Box 19687, New Orleans, LA 70119.

GALLAGHER, EDWARD HENRY, O.P, b. Providence, R.I, Sept. 16, 09. MATHEMATICS. M.S, Catholic Univ, 41; Ph.D.(math), Cincinnati, 48; hon. D.Sc, Providence Col, 65. Instr. MATH, PROVIDENCE COL, 39-44, asst. prof, 48-53, assoc. prof, 53-66, PROF, 66-, chmn. dept, 66-71. Am. Math. Soc; Math. Asn. Am. Fourier and divergent series; summability of divergent series. Address: Dept. of Mathematics, Providence College, Providence, RI 02918.

GALLAGHER, GEORGE A(RTHUR), b. Paterson, N.J, Feb. 11, 23; m. 48; c. 2. ORGANIC CHEMISTRY. A.B, Cornell Univ, 43; M.S, Univ. Pa, 50, Ph.D.(chem), 54. Chemist, Socony Mobile Oil Co, Inc, 46-47; res. chemist, Atlantic Ref. Co, 47-53; CHEMIST, org. chem. dept, E.I. DU PONT DE NEMOURS & CO, 54-57, ELASTOMER CHEM. DEPT, 57- Ord. Dept, U.S.A, 43-46. Am. Chem. Soc. Elastomer research. Address: 832 Surrey Lane, Media, PA 19063.

GALLAGHER, GERALD J(OSEPH), b. Williamsport, Pa, Mar. 4, 26; m. 50; c. 3. PHYSICS. B.S, Pa. State Col, 50; M.S, Drexel Inst, 55. Physicist, Army Qm. Res. & Develop. Lab, Pa, 50-52; DEVELOP. ENGR, E.I. DU PONT DE NEMOURS & CO, 52- U.S.N.R, 44-46. Inst. Elec. & Electronics Eng. Development and analysis of engineering models, usually by digital computer. Address: Church Hill, Hockessin, DE 19707.

GALLAGHER, JAMES A, b. Chicago, Ill, July 12, 26; m. 57; c. 4. ORGANIC CHEMISTRY. B.S, St. Louis, 49; M.A, Missouri, 51, Ph.D.(org. chem), 55; Washington (St. Louis), 52-53. Chemist, Lubrizol Corp, Ohio, 51-52; Esso Res. & Eng. Co, 55-64; BASF WYANDOTTE CORP, 65-69, SUPVR. POLYMER RES, 69- U.S.A.A.F, 44-45. AAAS; Am. Chem. Soc. Synthetic resin development; synthesis and applications research on organic polymers, chiefly for surface coating, including cure mechanisms, surface chemistry. Address: Polymer Research & Development, BASF Wyandotte Corp, Wyandotte, MI 48192.

GALLAGHER, JAMES D(ANIEL), b. Mahonoy City, Pa, Dec. 26, 22; m. 49; c. 4. MEDICINE. B.S, Chicago, 46, M.D, 49. Assoc. dir. clin. develop, LEDERLE LABS, AM. CYANAMID CO, 50-53, clin. res, 53-56, asst. to dir. labs, 56, dir. med. res. sect, 56-65, dir. planning, 65-69, DIR. MED. RES, CYANAMID INT, 69- U.S.A, 42-46. Am. Geriat. Soc; Am. Med. Asn; Am. Heart Asn; Asn. Am. Med. Cols. Enzyme inhibitors; antibiotics; oncolytic agents. Address: Cyanamid International, Pearl River, NY 10965.

GALLAGHER, J(AMES) E(MERSON), b. Gibsonia, Pa, Nov. 21, 20; m. 43; c. 3. METEOROLOGY. B.S, Pa. State Teachers Col, 42; N.Y. Univ, 43; Harvard, 55; Mass. Inst. Technol, 57. Teacher, pub. sch, Pa, 42-43; asst. prof. math, Westminster Col.(Pa), 46-47; chief weather sta. rehab, Off. Mil. Govt, Ger, 47-49; dir. progs. div, geophys. res. directorate, Air Force Cambridge Res. Ctr, Mass, 49-58; v.pres. programming, Geophys. Corp. Am, 58-65, SR. V.PRES. OPERS, GCA CORP, 65- Consult, Air Force Res. & Develop. Mgt, 52-53; spec. study group geophys, Nat. Acad. Sci, 56-58. U.S.A.A.F, 42-46, Res, 46-, Capt. Am. Meteorol. Soc; Am. Inst. Aeronaut. & Astronaut; Am. Mgt. Asn; Am. Geophys. Union. Technical management; physics of atmosphere and space; geophysics. Address: 181 Follen Rd, Lexington, MA 02173.

GALLAGHER, JAMES GERARD, b. Chicago, Ill, Apr. 30, 41; m. 66; c. 2. MEDICAL MICROBIOLOGY, VIROLOGY. B.S, Loyola Univ. Chicago, 63; Off. Res. Med. Educ. fel, Univ. Ill, 66-67, M.S, 67, Ph.D.(med. microbiol), 69. ASST. PROF. MED. MICROBIOL, COL. MED, UNIV. VT, 69- AAAS; Am. Soc. Microbiol; Tissue Cult. Asn. Sensitivity of adenoviruses to interferons; tumor viruses and transformation; relationship between genetic diseases and susceptibility to tumor viruses. Address: Dept. of Medical Microbiology, University of Vermont, Burlington, VT 05401.

GALLAGHER, JAMES J, b. Albany, N.Y, Nov. 15, 22; m. 58; c. 5. PHYSICS. B.S, Siena Col, 48; Rensselaer Polytech, 48-49; M.S, Columbia, 52; Hopkins, 52-59. Asst. proj. engr, Sperry Gyroscope Co, N.Y, 51-52; assoc. res. physicist, Hopkins, 52-59; sr. res. scientist millimeter spectros, Martin-Marietta Corp, 59-66, res. chief, 66-69, lab. chief, electromagnetics dept, 69-70; PRIN. RES. PHYSICIST, ENG. EXP. STA, GA. INST. TECHNOL, 70- Instr, Rollins Col, 62-66, adj. prof, 66-70. Am. Phys. Soc; sr. mem. Inst. Elec. & Electronics Eng. Molecular and atomic spectroscopy, especially phenomena observed in the far infrared and millimeter wavelength regions; laser technology. Address: Engineering Experiment Station, Georgia Institute of Technology, Atlanta, GA 30332.

GALLAGHER, JAMES P(ATRICK), b. Ft. Worth, Tex, Aug. 30, 31; m. 55; c. 3. ORGANIC CHEMISTRY. Ph.B, Univ. Chicago, 50; B.S, Univ. Ill, 55. Chemist, Sinclair Res, Inc, 55-57, res. chemist, 57-69, SR. CHEMIST, HARVEY TECH. CTR, ATLANTIC RICHFIELD CO, 69- U.S.A, 52. Am. Chem. Soc. Catalytic processing of hydrocarbons and derivatives. Address: Atlantic Richfield Co, Harvey Technical Center, 400 E. Sibley Blvd, Harvey, IL 60426.

GALLAGHER, JAMES W(ELDON), b. Elgin, Ill, Feb. 24, 28; m. 52; c. 1. CLIMATOLOGY, GEOGRAPHY. B.S, Ill. State Norm. Univ, 51, M.S, 52; Ph.D, Illinois, 59. Instr. phys. geog, Belleville Jr. Col, 52-54; asst, Illinois, 54-55, meteorol, 55-58; assoc. prof. climat, meteorol. & geog, East. Mich. Univ, 58-69; PROF. GEOG, ORE. COL. EDUC, 69- Teacher, pub. sch, Ill, 52-54; summers, instr, Illinois, 57, 58, dir, Nat. Sci. Found-Nat. Defense Educ. Act. Inst, 63, 64, 65. V.chmn, Ypsilanti Twp. Planning Comn, 61-63; mem. exec. comt, Nat. Coun. Geog. Educ, ed, Geog. Bull. U.S.A.F, 47-48. Asn. Am. Geog; Nat. Coun. Geog. Educ. Applied climatology. Address: 943 Margaret St, Monmouth, OR 97361.

GALLAGHER, JOHN JOSEPH, b. Phila, Pa, Mar. 30, 14; m. 47. ECOLOGY. B.A, Univ. Pa, 49, Ph.D.(zool), 55; Univ. Tenn, Knoxville, 67-68. Res. assoc, Acad. Natural Sci, Phila, 51; Univ. Pa, 55-57; Idaho State Univ, 57-60; Northeast La. Univ, 60-67; sr. res. assoc, State Univ. N.Y. Col. Brockport, 68-71; ASST. PROF. ECOL, LEWIS COL, 71- Consult, 52-67; sr. res. assoc, Fancher lake proj, Off. Water Resources Res, Dept. of Interior, 68; assoc. dir. proj. develop. performance measures, U.S. Off. Educ, 69; partic. res. training sessions, Am. Educ. Res. Asn, 69, 70, mem. spec. interest group comput. aids. U.S.A.A.F, 42-45, T/Sgt. AAAS; Int. Asn. Theoret. & Appl. Limnol; Am. Inst. Biol. Sci; Am. Micros. Soc; Am. Soc. Limnol. & Oceanog; Ecol. Soc. Am; Soc. Gen. Systs. Res; Soc. Syst. Zool; Am. Educ. Res. Asn. Ecology of the Rotifera; complexity of cyclomorphosis; shore-influenced methods of rotifer collecting; generic classification of Rotatoria; rotifer population variations; new species; Idaho & Louisiana. Address: Dept. of Ecology, Lewis College, Lockport, IL 60441.

GALLAGHER, JOHN M(ICHAEL), JR, b. Charleston, W.Va, Feb. 26, 27; m. 53; c. 6. ELECTRICAL & NUCLEAR ENGINEERING. B.E.E, Rensselaer Polytech, 51; M.S, Mass. Inst. Tech, 54, E.E, 56. Asst. & res. engr, dynamic anal. & control lab, Mass. Inst. Tech, 51-56; sr. engr, comput. anal. group, atomic power dept, WESTINGHOUSE ELEC. CO, 56-59, supvry. engr, systs. transient anal. group, 59-63, mgr. systs. anal, West. Atomic Power Plant, 63-67, control & elec. systs, 67-69, consult. engr, NUCLEAR ENERGY SYSTS, 70-71, MGR. INSTRUMENTATION & CONTROL DEVELOP, 71- Mem. int. electro-tech. comn, Am. Nat. Standards Inst. U.S.N, 45-46. Am. Nuclear Soc; Inst. Elec. & Electronics Eng. Development, design and testing of instrumentation; control electrical equipment and systems for nuclear-power plants. Address: Nuclear Energy Systems, Westinghouse Electric Co, P.O. Box 355, Pittsburgh, PA 15230.

GALLAGHER, MILTON, b. Peru, Ill, May 13, 04; m. 39; c. 2. CHEMISTRY. B.S, Univ. Ill, 26, Ph.D.(phys. chem), 34; M.S, Univ. Pittsburgh, 28. Asst. chem, Univ. Pittsburgh, 26-28; res. chemist, Atmospheric Nitrogen Corp, N.Y, 28-29; asst. chem, Univ. Ill, 30-33; res. chemist, Tenn. Eastman Corp, 34-37; Joseph E. Seagram & Sons, Ky, 37-42; tech. asst, test. div, Owens-Corning Fiberglas Corp, Ohio, 42-45; res. chemist, indust. res. inst, Univ. Chattanooga, 45-56; res. dir, GA. MARBLE CO, 56-70, CONSULT, 70- With U.S.A.A.F; U.S.N, 44. Am. Chem. Soc; fel. Am. Inst. Chem; Tech. Asn. Pulp & Paper Indust; Soc. Plastics Eng. Properties of calcium carbonate extenter pigments; development of marble products. Address: P.O. Box 252, Tate, GA 30177.

GALLAGHER, NEIL I(GNATIUS), b. Cleveland, Ohio, Oct. 12, 26; m. 56; c. 4. INTERNAL MEDICINE, HEMATOLOGY. B.S, Santa Clara Univ, 47; M.A, Univ. Ariz, 51; M.D, St. Louis Univ, 54. Intern, St. Louis City Hosp, Mo, 54-55; asst. resident, St. Louis Univ. Hosp, 55-57; instr. INTERNAL MED, SCH. MED, ST. LOUIS UNIV, 59-61, sr. instr, 61-62, asst. prof, 62-65, assoc. prof, 65-70, PROF. & V.CHMN. DEPT, 70; STAFF MEM, ST. LOUIS UNIV. HOSP, 59-; DIR. ST. LOUIS UNIV. MED. SERV, VET. ADMIN. HOSP, 61-, fel, hemat, 57-59, clin. investr, 59-61, in charge radioisotope lab, 61-68, assoc. chief of staff res, 63-66, chief of staff, 66-67, med, 66-68. Staff physician, Univ. Group Hosps, 59- Dipl, Am. Bd. Internal Med, 62. Am. Fedn. Clin. Res; Am. Soc. Hemat; Am. Med. Asn; Int. Soc. Hemat; Soc. Exp. Biol. & Med; Am. Physiol. Soc; fel. Am. Col. Physicians. Cell proliferation; humoral regulation of erythropoiesis; pathophysiology of dyserythropoiesis. Address: Veterans Administration Hospital, St. Louis, MO 63135.

GALLAGHER, P(ATRICK) K(ENT), b. Waukegan, Ill, Mar. 17, 31; m. 53; c. 2. INORGANIC & PHYSICAL CHEMISTRY. B.S, Wisconsin, 53, M.S, 54, Ph.D. (inorg. chem), 60. MEM. TECH. STAFF, BELL TEL. LABS, INC, 59- U.S.M.C, 54-57, Res, 57-59, Capt. Am. Chem. Soc. Am. Ceramic Soc; Am. Phys. Soc. Complex ion equilibria; thermal analysis; Mössbauer spectroscopy; solid state reactions and kinetics. Address: Room 1B-314, Bell Telephone Labs, Inc, Murray Hill, NJ 07974.

GALLAGHER, PATRICK XIMENES, b. Elizabeth, N.J, Jan. 2, 35; m. 61; c. 1. MATHEMATICS. A.B, Harvard, 56; Ph.D.(math), Princeton, 59. Asst. math, Princeton, 57-59; instr, Mass. Inst. Tech, 59-61; asst. prof, Columbia Univ, 62-64; mem, Inst. Advan. Study, 64-65; assoc. prof. MATH, BARNARD COL, 65-68, PROF, 68-, GRAD. FACULTIES, COLUMBIA UNIV, 70- Am. Math. Soc. Analytic number theory; finite groups. Address: Dept. of Mathematics, Barnard College, Columbia University, New York, NY 10027.

GALLAGHER, RICHARD HUGO, b. New York, N.Y, Nov. 17, 27; m. 52; c. 5. CIVIL ENGINEERING. B.C.E, N.Y. Univ, 50, M.C.E, 55; Ph.D.(civil eng), State Univ. N.Y. Buffalo, 66. Civil engr, U.S. Dept. Commerce, Civil Aeronaut. Admin, 50-52; struct. designer, Tex. Co, 52-55; struct. engr, Bell Aerosysts. Co, 55-59, group leader struct. res, 59-65, asst. chief engr, 65-67; PROF. CIVIL ENG, CORNELL UNIV, 67-, CHMN. DEPT. STRUCT. ENG, 70- Consult, adv. group aeronaut. res. & develop, NATO, 60-62; Bell Aerosysts. Co, 67- U.S.N.R, 45-47. Fel. Am. Soc. Civil Eng; assoc. fel. Am. Inst. Aeronaut. & Astronaut; Soc. Exp. Stress Anal. Solid mechanics, particularly the development of finite element techniques; development of methods of optimum design. Address: Dept. of Structural Engineering, Cornell University, College of Engineering, Ithaca, NY 14850.

GALLAGHER, R(OBERT) T(AYLOR), b. Johnstown, Pa, July 17, 05; m. 34; 65; c. 2. MINING. B.S, Pa. State, 27; M.A, Missouri, 38; D.E.M, Colo. Sch. Mines, 41. Student engr, Bethlehem Steel Co, 27-29; instr. mining, Pa. State Col, 29-31; commercial acct, Mo, 31-38; instr. MINING, Colo. Sch. Mines, 38-42; asst. prof, LEHIGH UNIV, 42-45, assoc. prof, 45-49, PROF, 49-, ASSOC. DEAN, COL. ENG, 64-, asst. dir, mat. res. ctr, 63-64, head dept. mining eng, 51-63. Soc. Explor. Geophys; Am. Soc. Eng. Educ; Mining & Metall. Soc. Am; Am. Asn. Petrol. Geol; Am. Inst. Mining, Metall. & Petrol. Eng. Mining subsidence; underground storage liquid petroleum products. Address: College of Engineering, Packard Lab, Lehigh University, Bethlehem, PA 18015.

GALLAGHER, T(HOMAS) F(RANCIS), b. Chicago, Ill, Dec. 29, 05; m. 30; c. 3. BIOCHEMISTRY. A.B, Fordham, 27; fel, Chicago, 28-30, Ph.D.(biochem), 31; Gen. Ed. Bd. fel, Tech. Hochsch, Free City of Danzig, 36; Kaiser Wilhelm Inst. Biochem, Germany, 37. Asst. biochem, Chicago, 28-30, res. assoc, 30-36, asst. prof, 37-41, assoc. prof, 41-47; mem, Sloan-Kettering Inst, 47-63; CHIEF INST. STEROID RES, MONTEFIORE HOSP, 63-; PROF. BIOCHEM, ALBERT EINSTEIN COL. MED, 63- AAAS; Endocrine Soc; Am. Soc. Biol. Chem; Am. Chem. Soc; Soc. Exp. Biol. & Med; Am. Asn. Cancer Res. Biochemistry and chemistry of steroid hormones. Address: 136 E. 64th St, New York, NY 10021.

GALLAGHER, WILLIAM J(OSEPH), b. San Francisco, Calif, Dec. 21, 23; m. 43; c. 6. ELECTRICAL ENGINEERING. B.S, Univ. Calif, 51; Stanford Univ, 54. Engr, Rogers Eng. Co, Calif, 51-53; res. engr, Hewlett-Packard Co, 53-54; res. assoc, Hansen Labs, Stanford, 54-60; Ecole Normalé Superiéure, Paris, 60-62; sr. engr, Litton Industs, Inc, 62-64; DIR. RES, DIV. HIGH VOLTAGE ENG, APPL. RADIATION CORP, 64- Consult, Varian Assocs, 56-60; Compagnie Francaise Thomson-Houston, France, 60-62; consult, Bechtel Eng. Co, Calif, 68-71; vis. scientist, Argonne Nat. Lab, 71. U.S.N, 41-45. Am. Astron. Soc; Am. Meteor. Soc; Inst. Elec. & Electronics Eng; Royal Astron. Soc. Microwave engineering; electron linear accelerators; instability of dense electron beams; radiography; use of artificial satellites; heavy ion accelerators. Address: 525 Dover Rd, Walnut Creek, CA 94596.

GALLAGHER, WILLIAM J(OSEPH), b. Allentown, Pa, Jan. 13, 31; m. 56; c. 1. MECHANICAL ENGINEERING. B.S, Drexel Inst, 53; Westinghouse Elec. Corp. fel, Lehigh Univ, 54, M.S, 55; Atomic Energy Comn. fel, Univ. Pittsburgh, 57, Ph.D.(mech. eng), 62. Engr, Pa. Power & Light Co, 53-54; assoc. engr. thermal & hydraul. design, Westinghouse Elec. Corp, 57-62, sr. engr, 62-64, supvr, Bettis Atomic Power Lab, 64-66; mgr. eng. anal, NUS Corp, 66-69, dir. tech. opers. Europe, Ger, 69-71; MANAGING DIR, NUKLEAR INGENIEUR SERVICE, GmbH, 71- U.S.A, 55-57, 1st Lt. Nuclear reactor heat transfer and fluid flow. Address: Nuklear Ingenieur Service GmbH, Hanau, Haussmann Str. 23, German Federal Republic.

GALLAHER, B(EATRICE) SHANNON, b. Phila, Pa, June 5, 20. INTERNAL MEDICINE. A.B, Temple, 46; M.D, Hahnemann Med. Col, 50. Rotating intern Univ. Hosp, Augusta, Ga, 50-51, sr. & chief res, 53-54; asst. res. internal med, St. Louis City Hosp, Mo, 51-53; instr. med, Med. Col. Ga, 54-56, assoc, 56-58, asst. prof, 58-59, asst. clin. prof, 59-64, assoc. clin. prof, 64; clin. dir, St. Barnabas Hosp, 64-65; ASSOC. CLIN. PROF. MED, SCH. MED, TULANE UNIV. LA, 65-; DIR. DIV. PULMONARY DISEASES & SR. ASSOC, MED. STAFF, TOURO INFIRMARY, 66-, med. educ. & mem. med. staff, 65-66. Clinician, tuberc. clin, Aiken County Dept. Health, S.C, 53-62; consult, Milledgeville State Hosp, 55-58; attend. physician, Forest Hills Div, Va. Hosp, Augusta, Ga, 55-59; Battey State Hosp, Rome, 56-59; Gracewood State Hosp, 57-58; private practice, 59-64; mem. vis. staff, Charity Hosp, New Orleans, 65-; trustee, found. educ. & res, Am. Asn. Inhalation Therapists, 70; clin. med. dir, Stroke Rehab. Prog, Ga; mem. Ga. Interagency Tuberc. Comt; regular staff, Univ, St. Joseph's & Eugene Talmadge Mem. Hosps, Augusta, Ga. Dipl, Am. Bd. Internal Med, 58. Am. Med. Asn; Am. Heart Asn; Am. Thoracic Soc; Am. Med. Women's Asn; fel. Am. Col. Chest Physicians; fel. Am. Col. Physicians; fel. Pan-Am. Med. Asn; Am. Asn. Inhalation Therapists. Chest disease, particularly pulmonary insufficiency and improving pulmonary function in such people. Address: Division of Pulmonary Diseases, Touro Infirmary, 1401 Foucher St, New Orleans, LA 70115.

GALLAHER, D(ONALD) F(REDERICK), b. Vancouver, B.C, Jan. 1, 36; m. 59; c. 1. THEORETICAL PHYSICS. B.A.Sc, Univ. B.C, 59, M.Sc, 63; M.A, Univ. Toronto, 60; Ph.D.(physics), Univ. Wash, 67. Meteorologist, meteorol. div, Dept. Transport, Uplands AFB, Ottawa, Ont, Can, summer 60, ground observations supvr. precipitation physics proj, McWatters, Que, summer 61; asst. prof. physics, Acadia Univ, 62-63; res. asst, plasma physics res. group, Univ. B.C, summer 63; res. fel. theoret. physics, Queen's Univ.(Belfast), 67-69; vis. res. assoc, theoret. physics div, U.K. Atomic Energy Auth, 68; ASST. PROF. PHYSICS, UNIV. WEST. ONT, 69- Nat. Res. Coun. Can. res. grant-in-aid, 69-72. Am. Phys. Soc; Can. Asn. Physicists; fel. Brit. Inst. Physics & Phys. Soc. Convergence properties of various expansion bases in ion-atom collision theory; pseudo-state basis set predictions for electron and positron hydrogen elastic scattering and for He and H^- autoionization states. Address: Dept. of Physics, University of Western Ontario, London, Ont, Can.

GALLAHER, LAWRENCE JOSEPH, b. St. Louis, Mo, May 31, 25; m. 54; c. 7. PHYSICS, COMPUTER SCIENCE. B.S, Rensselaer Polytech, 50; Fulbright fel, Leiden, 53-54; Ph.D.(physics), Washington (St. Louis), 55. Lectr, physics, Minnesota, 55; asst. prof, Ohio, 55-60, assoc. prof, 60-63; RES. PHYSICIST, GA. INST. TECHNOL, 63- Am. Phys. Soc. Theoretical physics; applications of digital computers. Address: Rich Electronic Computer Center, Georgia Institute of Technology, Atlanta, GA 30332.

GALLANDER, JAMES F(RANCIS), b. Peoria, Ill, Apr. 17, 37; m. 63; c. 1. FOOD TECHNOLOGY. B.S, Ohio State Univ, 60, Ph.D.(food technol), 64. Instr. FRUIT & VEGETABLE PROCESSING, OHIO AGR. RES. & DEVELOP. CTR, 62-64, asst. prof, 64-68, ASSOC. PROF, 68- Inst. Food Technol; Am. Soc. Enol. Freezing and canning of pomological crops; wine fermentation. Address: Dept. of Horticulture, Ohio Agricultural Research & Development Center, Wooster, OH 44691.

GALLANT, DONALD, b. Brooklyn, N.Y, Aug. 9, 29; m. 54; c. 1. PSYCHIATRY, NEUROLOGY. B.S, Tulane, 51, M.D, 55. Instr. PSYCHIAT. & NEUROL, SCH. MED, TULANE UNIV. LA, 61-62, asst. prof, 62-65, assoc. prof, 65-68, PROF, 69- Prin. investr, Tulane Psychopharmacol. Serv. Ctr. grant, 62-; consult, La. State Alcoholism Prog, 62- U.S.A.F, 59-61, Capt. Am. Col. Neuropsychopharmacol; Am. Psychiat. Asn. Investigation and evaluation of neuropsychopharmacologic compounds; alcoholism. Address: Dept. of Psychiatry & Neurology, School of Medicine, Tulane University of Louisiana, New Orleans, LA 70118.

GALLANT, JONATHAN A, b. New York, N.Y, Sept. 23, 37; m. 61; c. 1. MOLECULAR BIOLOGY. B.S, Haverford Col, 57; Ph.D.(biochem), Hopkins, 61. Asst. prof. GENETICS, UNIV. WASH, 61-65, assoc. prof, 65-70, PROF, 70- Nat. Insts. Health res. grants, 62-65, 66-70 & 71-; Nat. Insts. Health spec. fel, Inst. Biophys. & Biochem, Paris, France, 64-65; dir. sci. & gas, Grosser Seattle, 69-; Guggenheim fel, 71. AAAS; Genetics Soc. Am; Fedn. Am. Sci. Recombination in Escherichia coli merodiploids; regulation of enzyme synthesis; regulation of RNA synthesis; biology of aging. Address: Dept. of Genetics, University of Washington, Seattle, WA 98105.

GALLANT, MORRIS, b. New York, N.Y, Nov. 4, 16; m. 48; c. 2. CHEMISTRY. B.S, City Col, 37; M.S, Polytech. Inst. Brooklyn, 53. Biochemist, N.Y. Post-Grad. Hosp, 37-39; clin. bacteriologist & chemist, New York Dept. Health & Hosps, 39-42; anal. chemist, Atlas Powder Co, 42-44; res. anal. chemist, Kellex Corp, 44-45; res. chemist, M.W. Kellogg Co, 45-47; anal. chemist, Gen. Servs. Admin, 47-50, chief chemist, 50-58; chief anal. sect, Hoboken Lab, Chemetron Corp, 58-65; SR. ANAL. CHEMIST, LUMMUS CO, 65- Am. Chem. Soc. Analytical and organic chemistry; development of new methods; refinement of existing methods. Address: 33-34 Crescent St, Long Island City, NY 11106.

GALLARDO DIAZ, JOSE ARTURO, b. Naguabo, P.R, June 2, 09; m. 44; c. 4. OPHTHALMOLOGY, BIOLOGY. B.S, George Washington, 31, M.A, 33; M.D, Lausanne, 38; D.Sc, Neuchâtel, 38; London & Paris, 38. Med. health off, Dept. Health, P.R, 38-39; ophthalmologist, Fajardo Dist. Hosp, 39-40; San Patricio Vet. Admin. Hosp, 47-48; Rodriguez Gen. Hosp, 48-49; asst. clin. prof. ophthal, med. sch, Univ. P.R, San Juan, 51-71. Ophthalmologist, San Juan City Hosp, 39-40, 45-; Teachers Asn, P.R, 46-52; mem. staff, Doctor's, San Juan City & Univ. Hosps; practicing ophthalmologist, 45- Med.C, 40-45, Capt. Asn. Mil. Surg. U.S; Am. Med. Asn; N.Y. Acad. Sci; P.R. Ophthal. Soc; P.R. Med. Asn; Pan-Am. Asn. Ophthal. Ichthyology. Address: P.O. Box 13343, Santurce, PR 00908.

GALLATI, WALTER W(ILLIAM), b. Brooklyn, N.Y, Dec. 7, 27; m. 58; c. 2. ZOOLOGY. A.B, Drew Univ, 50; M.S, Univ. Miami, 52; Ph.D.(zool), Ohio State Univ, 57. Asst. zool, Univ. Miami, 50-51; Ohio State Univ, 52-54, asst. instr, 54-55, instr, 55-57; assoc. prof. sci, INDIANA UNIV. PA, 57-59, PROF. BIOL, 59- U.S.A, 45-46. AAAS; Am. Soc. Parasitol; Am. Micros. Soc; Am. Inst. Biol. Sci. Parasitology. Address: Dept. of Biology, Indiana University of Pennsylvania, Indiana, PA 15701.

GALLAUGHER, ARTHUR F(REDERICK), b. Londonderry, North. Ireland, June 14, 05; m. 41; c. 2. ORGANIC CHEMISTRY. B.A, British Columbia, 26, M.S, 28; Ph.D.(chem), McGill, 32. Asst. chem, British Columbia, 26-28; asst. chemist, Powell River Co, 28; instr. chem, Haverford Col, 28-29; chief chemist, Interlake Tissue Mills, Ltd, 31-33; joint managing dir, West. Chem. Industs, Ltd, 34-58; PRES, ROYAL FISHERIES, LTD, 58- Physical and chemical properties of the polyethylene glycols and their derivatives; industrial chemistry of British Columbia fish oils and fish liver oils; freezing, cold storage and canning preservation of fisheries products. Address: 6090 Blink Bonnie Rd, S.S. 1, West Vancouver, B.C, Can.

GALLAWAY, BOB MITCHEL, b. Kosciusko, Miss, Oct. 14, 16; m. 41; c. 3. CIVIL ENGINEERING. B.S, Texas A&M, 43, M.S, 46, M.E, 56. Instr. war training in eng, TEX. A&M UNIV, 43-44, eng. drawing & descriptive geom, 44-46, asst. prof, 46-48, CIVIL ENG, 48-56, assoc. prof, 56-59, PROF, 59- Summer, lectr, Asphalt Inst, 58; res. engr. & head hwy. mat. dept, Tex. Transportation Inst; mem. Hwy. Res. Bd; pres, Consult. & Res. Serv, Inc, 67-; mem. bd. consults, study 4-10, Nat. Coop. Hwy. Res. Prog; Transportation Ctr, Univ. P.R. Nat. Soc. Prof. Eng; Am. Soc. Test. & Mat; Am. Soc. Eng. Educ; Am. Concrete Inst; Asn. Asphalt Paving Technol. Materials research with particular interest in asphalt paving, portland cement, concrete and soil stabilization; skid resistance; waste solids utilization; synthetic aggregate. Address: Dept. of Civil Engineering, Texas A&M University, College Station, TX 77843.

GALLAY, WILFRED, SR, b. Hawkesbury, Ont, June 10, 06; m. 32; c. 4. ORGANIC & COLLOID CHEMISTRY. B.S, McGill Univ, 27, Nat. Res. Coun. Can. stud. & M.Sc, 28, Moyse traveling fel. & Ph.D, 30; Univ. Leipzig, 30; Kaiser Wilhelm Inst, 31. Head sect. colloids & plastics, Nat. Res. Coun. Can, Ont, 32-44; consult, 44-53; DIR. RES, E.B. EDDY CO, 53- Secy-Gen, Int. Union Pure & Appl. Chem, 71; mem, Spec. Comt. on Probs. Environ. Bolton awards, 44, 53, 56; Plummer Medal, Eng. Inst. Can, 54. AAAS; Am. Chem. Soc; Can. Pulp & Paper Asn.(tech. serv. medal, 54); Chem. Inst. Can. Organic colloids; high polymers; cellulose; pulp and paper. Address: E.B. Eddy Co, Hull, Que, Can.

GALLE, KURT R(OBERT), b. Newton, Kans, July 19, 25; m. 46; c. 2. MECHANICAL ENGINEERING. B.S, Purdue, 46, B.S, 47, M.S, 49, Ph.D.(mech. eng), 51. Instr. mech. eng, Purdue, 48-50; res. engr, Boeing Co, Wash, 51-58, sr. group engr, 58-60; ASSOC. PROF. MECH. ENG, UNIV. WASH, 60- Summer fels, Cardiovasc. Res. Training Prog, Univ. Wash, 63, 64. U.S.N, 43-46, Res, 46-, Lt. Am. Inst. Aeronaut. & Astronaut; Instrument Soc. Am; Am. Soc. Eng. Educ; Biomed. Eng. Soc; Simulation Coun. Instrumentation research in bioengineering; systems analysis and simulation. Address: Dept. of Mechanical Engineering, University of Washington, Seattle, WA 98195.

GALLEGLY, M(ANNON) E(LIHU), b. Mineral Springs, Ark, Apr. 11, 23; m. 47; c. 3. PLANT PATHOLOGY. B.S, Univ. Ark, 45; M.S, Univ. Wis, 46, Ph.D.(plant path), 49. Asst. prof. PLANT PATH, W.VA. UNIV, 49-55, assoc. prof, 55-60, PROF, 60-, DIR. DIV. PLANT SCI, 70- U.S.A, 46-47. Am. Phytopath. Soc; Potato Asn. Am. Vegetable diseases; physiologic specialization and resistance to tomato and potato late blight; sexuality in the genus Phytophthora. Address: Division of Plant Sciences, West Virginia University, Morgantown, WV 26506.

GALLEGOS, EMILIO J(UAN), b. Del Norte, Colo, June 24, 32; m. 63; c. 1. PHYSICAL CHEMISTRY. B.S, Regis Col, 54; Ph.D.(phys. chem), Kansas State, 61. RES. CHEMIST, CHEVRON RES. CORP, STANDARD OIL CO. CALIF, 61- U.S.A, 56-57. Am. Chem. Soc; Electron Micros. Soc. Am. Mass spectrometry; electron and optical microscopy; plasma. Address: Chevron Research Corp, Room 2104, Richmond, CA 94803.

GALLEN, WILLIAM J, b. Columbus, Ohio, July 4, 24; m. 54; c. 3. MEDICINE. B.A, Ohio State, 45, M.D, 48. Intern, Harper Hosp, Detroit, 48-50, res, 50-51; pediat, Milwaukee Children's Hosp, 53-55; instr, hosp, Hopkins, 55-56; trainee, Nat. Heart Inst, Nat. Insts. Health, Karolinska Inst, Sweden, 56-57; from instr. to asst. prof. PEDIAT, MED. COL. WIS, 57-68, ASSOC. PROF, 68-; CHIEF, DEPT. PEDIAT, MILWAUKEE CHILDREN'S HOSP, 70-, dir, cardiac diagnostic unit, 57-70, Fairchild Cardiac Study Ctr, 67-70. Fel, Crippled Children's Bur, Johns Hopkins Univ. Hosp, 55-56. Dipl, Am. Bd. Pediat, 57, cert. cardiol, 61. U.S.A, 43-44; Med.C, 51-53. Am. Med. Asn; Am. Heart Asn. Pediatrics; pediatric cardiology. Address: Dept. of Pediatrics, Milwaukee Children's Hospital, 1700 W. Wisconsin Ave, Milwaukee, WI 53233.

GALLENT, JOHN B(RYANT), b. Wylam, Ala, Mar. 28, 02; m. 26. CHEMISTRY. B.S, Davidson Col, 25; M.S, North Carolina, 28, Ph.D.(chem), 30. Teacher, pub. schs, N.C, 25-27; North Carolina, 27-30; prof. CHEM, Jonesboro Agr. & Mech. Col, 30-31; Brenau Col, 31-42; PROF, DAVIDSON COL, 42-, CHMN. DEPT, 62- Faculty fel, Nat. Sci. Found, Univ. Col, London, 57-58. Am. Chem. Soc. Sulfonation of vegetable oils; preparation of the ethers of p-di-hydroxybenzene and their sulfonates. Address: Dept. of Chemistry, Davidson College, Daivdson, NC 28036.

GALLER, BERNARD A(ARON), b. Chicago, Ill, Oct. 3, 28; m. 51; c. 4. COMPUTER SCIENCE, MATHEMATICS. Ph.B, Univ. Chicago, 46, B.S, 47, Ph.D. (math), 55; A.M, Univ. Calif, Los Angeles, 49. Instr. math, UNIV. MICH, ANN ARBOR, 55-58, asst. prof, 59-62, assoc. prof, 62-66, PROF. COMPUT. & COMMUN. SCI. & MATH. & ASSOC. DIR. COMPUT. CTR, 66- U.S.A, 52-53. AAAS; Asn. Comput. Mach.(pres, 68-70). Digital computers; automatic programming; mathematical logic; linear programming. Address: 1056 Ferdon Rd, Ann Arbor, MI 48104.

GALLER, SIDNEY R(OLAND), b. Baltimore, Md, Nov. 9, 22; div; c. 4. ECOLOGY, LIMNOLOGY. B.S, Maryland, 44, fel, 44-46, M.S, 47, Ph.D.(limnol), 48. Asst, agr. exp. sta, Maryland, 42-43, asst. zool, 46-48; consult. human ecol. & biophys. & acting head biophys. br, Off. Naval Res, 48-50, head ecol. sect, biol. br, 50-51, biol. br, 51-65; asst. secy. for sci, SMITHSONIAN INST, WASH, D.C, 65-71, DEP. ASST. SECY. COMMERCE FOR ENVIRON. AFFAIRS, 71- Collab, U.S. Fish & Wildlife Serv, 47. U.S. Navy Distinguished Civilian Serv. Medal, 65; Smithsonian Exceptional Serv. Medal, 71. Nat. Guard, 38-40; U.S.A, 42-44. Fel. AAAS; Marine Technol. Soc; Sci. Res. Soc. Am; Am. Inst. Biol. Sci. Chemical, physical and biological investigations of acid ponds; polluted streams; development of microtechnique for cytological studies of marine organism; research administration; pollution control; research policy and program planning. Address, 6242 Woodcrest Ave, Baltimore, MD 21209.

GALLER, WILLIAM SYLVAN, b. Chicago, Ill, June 12, 29; m. 55; c. 2. SANITARY ENGINEERING, OPERATIONS RESEARCH. B.S, Ill. Inst. Tech, 51, M.S, 61; Ph.D.(civil eng), Northwestern, 65. Jr. sanit. engr, water purification div, City of Chicago, 51-53, sr. sanit. engr, 53-61; asst. prof. CIVIL ENG, N.C. STATE UNIV, 64-68, ASSOC. PROF, 68- Am. Water Works Asn; Am. Water Resources Asn; Opers. Res. Soc. Am. Systems analysis approach to problems in sanitary engineering. Address: Dept. of Civil Engineering, North Carolina State University, Box 5993, Raleigh, NC 27607.

GALLETTA, GENE J(OHN), b. Phila, Pa, July 3, 29; m. 57; c. 2. GENETICS. B.S, Maryland, 51; M.S, Rutgers, 53; Ph.D.(genetics), California, 59. Asst. hort, Rutgers, 51-53; pomol, California, 53-54, 56-59, pomologist, 56; asst. prof. HORT. SCI, N.C. STATE UNIV, 59-64, assoc. prof, 64-71, PROF, 71-, ASSOC. MEM. FACULTY GENETICS, 70- U.S.A, 54-56, Res, 56-62. Bot. Soc. Am; Am. Soc. Hort. Sci; Am. Genetic Asn; Genetics Soc. Am; Am. Pomol. Soc. Fruit crop breeding; cytogenetics; evolution; plant and fruit morphology and anatomy; physiology of perennial plants; inheritance of quantitative characters and disease resistance; plant propagation. Address: Dept. of Horticultural Science, North Carolina State University, Raleigh, NC 27607.

GALLETTI, PIERRE M(ARIE), b. Monthey, Switz, June 11, 27; U.S. citizen; m. 59; c. 1. PHYSIOLOGY, CARDIOLOGY. B.A, St. Maurice Col, Switz, 45; M.D, Univ. Lausanne, 51, Ph.D.(physiol), 54, D.Sc.(physiol), 55. Instr. physiol, Univ. Lausanne, 52-54; resident med, Zurich, 54-56; fel. cardio-vasc. res, Cedars of Lebanon Hosp, Los Angeles, Calif, 57-58; asst. prof. physiol, sch. med, Emory Univ, 58-62, assoc. prof, 62-66, PROF, 66-67; MED. SCI, BROWN UNIV, 67-, CHMN. DIV. BIOL. & MED. SCI, 68- Lilienthal lectr, Mt. Sinai Hosp, N.Y.C, 64; Int. Union Against Cancer fel, tumor ctr, Palermo, 64-65; mem. physiol. training comt, Nat. Insts. Health, 68- Am. Physiol. Soc; Am. Soc. Artificial Internal Organs; Am. Col. Cardiol. Cardiorespiratory physiology; artificial hearts, lungs and kidneys; physiology of death and resuscitation; bioengineering of artificial organs. Address: Division of Biological & Medical Sciences, Brown University, Providence, RI 02912.

GALLEZ, BERNARD, b. Charleroi, Belg, June 17, 38; m. 61; c. 2. HYDRAULIC ENGINEERING. C.E, Cath. Univ. Louvain, 61; M.Sc.A, Univ. Liege, 63, D.Sc.A, 68. Asst, hydraulic lab, Univ. Liege, 61-63; lectr. hydraulics, Sherbrooke Univ, 63-64, asst. prof, 64-66; asst, hydraulic lab, Univ. Liege, 66-68; asst. prof. hydraulics, UNIV. SHERBROOKE, 68-70, assoc. prof, 70-71, ASSOC. PROF. CIVIL ENG. & CHMN. DEPT, 71- Alexandre Galopin Found. Laureat Award, 70. Int. Asn. Hydraul. Res. Hydraulic instabilities; turbulence and sediment movement; ice problems related to spillways operation. Address: Dept. of Civil Engineering, University of Sherbrooke, Sherbrooke, Que, Can.

GALLI, JOHN R(ONALD), b. Salt Lake City, Utah, Oct. 10, 36; m. 60; c. 2. SOLID STATE PHYSICS. B.S, Utah, 58, M.A, 60, Ph.D.(physics), 63. Physicist, Aerojet-Gen. Corp. Div, Gen. Tire & Rubber Co, 63; asst. prof. PHYSICS, WEBER STATE COL, 63-67, ASSOC. PROF, 67-, chmn. dept, 64-70. Summers, physicist, Naval Ord. Test Sta, Calif, 58, 59. Am. Asn. Physics Teachers. Basic mechanisms responsible for mechanical properties of solids. Address: Dept. of Physics, Weber State College, Ogden, UT 84403.

GALLICCHIO, VINCENT, b. Farrell, Pa, Apr. 13, 20; m. 51; c. 2. ZOOLOGY. B.S, Michigan, 50; M.S, Illinois, 51, Ph.D.(zool), 56. Asst. zool, Illinois, 53-55, instr, KENT STATE UNIV, 56-59, asst. prof. biol, 59-64, assoc. prof, 64-67, PROF. BIOL. & DIR. GRAD. STUDIES, 67- U.S.A.A.F, 42-45. Am. Soc. Parasitol; Am. Micros. Soc; Am. Soc. Zool. Parasitology; life histories, ecology and physiology of helminths; tissue culture. Address: Dept. of Biological Sciences, Kent State University, Kent, OH 44240.

GALLIE, T(HOMAS) M(UIR), b. New York, N.Y, Aug. 25, 25; m. 45; c. 4. COMPUTER SCIENCE. A.B, Harvard, 47; fel, Texas, 47-49, M.A, 49, Rice Inst, 52, Ph.D.(math), 54. Teacher, private sch, 49-50; asst, Rice Inst, 51-54; res. engr, Humble Oil & Ref. Co, 54, 45-56; res. instr. math, DUKE UNIV, 54-55, asst. prof, 56-62, assoc. prof, 62-67, prof, 67-71, PROF. COMPUT. SCI. & DIR. COMPUT. SCI. PROG, 71-, dir. comput. lab, 58-64. Visitor, Swiss Fed. Inst. Technol, Zurich, 62-63; head educ. res. & training sect, off. comput. activities, Nat. Sci. Found, 68-69. Asn. Comput. Mach; Math. Asn. Am. Translation of mechanical languages; computer programming theory; numerical analysis. Address: Computer Science Program, Duke University, Durham, NC 27706.

GALLIGAN, JAMES M, b. Far Rockaway, N.Y, May 13, 31; m. 58; c. 2. PHYSICAL METALLURGY. B.Met.E, Polytech. Inst. Brooklyn, 55; M.S, Illinois, 57; Ph.D.(metall), California, Berkeley, 63. Res. asst. elec. eng, Illinois, 55-57; res. engr. METALL, E.C. Bain Lab, U.S. Steel Corp, 57-58; Lawrence Radiation Lab, California, 58-62; asst. prof, Columbia, 63-64, assoc. prof, 64-67; SCIENTIST, BROOKHAVEN NAT. LAB, 67- Consult, Brookhaven Nat. Lab, 65-67; vis. scientist, Max Planck Inst. Physics, 67. Am. Inst. Min, Metall. & Petrol. Eng; Am. Phys. Soc. Thin film research; defects in solids; hardening of crystals; liquids. Address: Brookhaven National Lab, Upton, NY 11973.

GALLIGAN, JOHN D(ONALD), b. Washington, D.C, Oct. 9, 32; m. 58; c. 5. PHYSICAL CHEMISTRY. B.S, Manhattan Col, 55; Emory, 55-56; Catholic Univ, 56-58. Chemist, Harris Res. Labs, Inc, 57-58, sr. chemist, 58-62; proj. mgr. phys. chem, GILLETTE CO, 62-65, res. supvr, Harris Res. Labs, Inc, 65-68, group leader, GILLETTE RES. INST. INC, 68, MGR. PHYS. SCI. DEPT, 68- AAAS; Am. Chem. Soc. Surface and polymer chemistry; lubrication; adsorption; electrochemistry; adhesion; chemical modification of textiles. Address: Physical Science Dept, Gillette Research Institute Inc, 1413 Research Blvd, Rockville, MD 20850.

GALLIHER, H(ERBERT) P(ARRISH), JR, b. Wash, D.C, Apr. 24, 19; m. 44, 67; c. 4. MATHEMATICS. B.A, Yale, 40, M.A, 50, Ph.D.(logic), 52. Asst. prof. math, New Haven State Teachers Col, 49-53; mathematician, Arthur D. Little, Inc, 53-45; mem. div. indust. coop. staff, Mass. Inst. Technol, 54-56, asst. dir. opers. res. ctr, 56-63; PROF. INDUST. ENG, UNIV. MICH, ANN ARBOR, 63- Govt, mil. & indust. consult. U.S.A, 40-45, Res, 45-52, Capt. Fel. AAAS; Am. Math. Soc; Opers. Res. Soc. Am.(ed, Int. Abstr. in Opers. Res, 60-68). Probability; operations research; biomathematics. Address: Dept. of Industrial Engineering, University of Michigan, Ann Arbor, MI 48104.

GALLINI, JOHN B(ATTISTA), b. Detroit, Mich, June 5, 34; m. 57; c. 5. CHEMICAL ENGINEERING. B.Ch.E, Detroit, 56; M.S, Michigan, 58, Ph.D. (chem, eng), 61. Res. engr, plastics dept, E.I. DU PONT DE NEMOURS & CO, INC, 59-65, group mgr, venture develop. sect, film dept, 65-66, STAFF ENGR, SPRUANCE FILM RES. & DEVELOP, 66- Am. Chem. Soc. High polymers; polymerization kinetics; physical and molecular properties of polymers; processing technology for thermoplastic materials. Address: 2425 Triton Rd, Richmond, VA 23235.

GALLIVAN, JAMES B(ERNARD), b. Sydney, N.S, Aug. 9, 38; m. 61; c. 4. PHYSICAL CHEMISTRY. B.Sc, St. Francis Xavier, 60, M.A, 62; Atomic Energy Cmn. grant, Notre Dame, 62-65, Atomic Energy Cmn. fel, radiation lab, 64-65, Ph.D.(radiation chem), 65. Res. chemist, AM. CYANAMID CO, 65-70, SR. RES. CHEMIST, 70- AAAS; Am. Chem. Soc. Radiation chemistry; transients trapped in organic glasses at low temperatures; photochemistry; electronic spectroscopy, particularly luminescence properties of organic systems. Address: American Cyanamid Co, 1937 Main St, Stamford, CT 06904.

GALLIZIOLI, STEVE, b. Riva, Italy, July 25, 24; U.S. citizen; m. 49; c. 3. WILDLIFE MANAGEMENT. B.S, Oregon State, 50. Dist. wildlife biologist, ARIZ. GAME & FISH DEPT, 50-55, res. biologist, 55-57, res. supvr, 57-66, RES. CHIEF, 66- Partic, Food & Agr. Orgn, UN, assignment to Venezuela, 69. Am. Motors Conserv. Award, 67. U.S.N.R, 43-46. AAAS; Wildlife Soc; Cooper Ornith. Soc. Population dynamics of mule deer; investigation of factors controlling Gambel and scaled quail populations; development of inventory technique for Gambel quail, whitewing doves. Address: 4722 W. Crittendon Lane, Phoenix, AZ 85031.

GALLO, ANTHONY EDWARD, JR, b. Apr. 7, 31; U.S. citizen; c. 2. NEUROSURGERY. B.S, Tufts Univ, 52; M.D, Harvard, 56. Intern surg, Boston City Hosp, Mass, 56-57, sr. asst. resident neurosurg, 57-58; mem. staff, Madigan Gen. Hosp, Tacoma, Wash, 58-59; resident neurol. & neurosurg, Letterman Gen. Hosp, San Francisco, Calif, 59-61; chief resident & teaching fel. pediat. neurosurg. & physiol, hosps. & med. sch, Univ. Pittsburgh, 61-63; dir. intern training & chief neurosurg, Madigan Gen. Hosp, Tacoma, Wash, 63-68; PROF. NEUROSURG, MED. SCH, UNIV. ORE, 68- Fel. & asst, Univ. Calif, San Francisco, 59-60; investr. with Dr. Paul Yakovlev, Boston, 63; prof. pro-tem, Univ. Saigon, 64-65; chief neurosurg. training team, Cong Hoa Hosp, Saigon, 64-65; consult, Madigan Gen. Hosp, 68-; myeomeningocele clin. crippled childrens div, Univ. Ore, 68-; liaison, U.S. Army to Univ. Ore. Med. Sch, 70- David W. E. Baird Award, Univ. Ore. Med Sch, 69. U.S.A, 58-68, Lt. Col; Commendation Medal, 65, Oak Leaf Cluster, 68. Cong. Neurol. Surg; Am. Asn. Neurol. Surg. Development of hydrocephalic beagles; surgical treatment of vascular lesions and complications of cerebrovascular disease; psychological evaluation of carotid occlusion; prefabricated cranioplasty. Address: Dept. of Neurosurgery, University of Oregon Medical School, 3181 S. W. Sam Jackson Park Rd, Portland, OR 97201.

GALLO, CHARLES F(RANCIS), JR, b. Mt. Vernon, N.Y, July 22, 35; m. 57; c. 1. PHYSICS. B.S, Rensselaer Polytech, 57. Jr. engr, res. labs, Westinghouse Elec. Corp, 57-62, eng. specialist, 62-64; sr. physicist, XEROX CORP, 64-67, Assoc. scientist, 67-68, SCIENTIST, WEBSTER, 68- Sci. consult, Inner City Schs, Rochester, N.Y. Am. Phys. Soc. Solid state physics; transport properties of solids; energy conversion; xerography; coronas; gas discharges; light sources; injection electroluminescence. Address: 51 Coachman Dr, Penfield, NY 14526.

GALLO, DUANE G(ORDON), b. Aberdeen, S.Dak, May 15, 26; m. 52; c. 10. BIOCHEMISTRY. B.S, North Dakota, 51, M.S, 53, Ph.D.(biochem), 55. Asst, North Dakota, 52-55; chemist, MEAD JOHNSON & CO, 55-57, assoc. sr. chemist, 57-58, sr. chemist, 59-61, group leader, 61-68, sr. res. assoc, 68-70, PRIN. INVESTR, 70- U.S.A, 44-46. AAAS; Soc. Study Reproduction; Soc. Exp. Biol. & Med. Phosphatide, cholesterol and drug metabolism; lipid metabolism; endocrinology; reproductive physiology and biochemistry. Address: Dept. of Pharmacology, Mead Johnson Research Center, Evansville, IN 47721.

GALLO, FRANK J, b. Iselin, Pa, July 29, 21; m. 44; c. 6. STRUCTURAL ENGINEERING, ENGINEERING MECHANICS. B.Struct.E, Fenn Col, 43; Case Inst. Technol, 49-51; M.S.C.E, Cleveland State Univ, 71. Stress analyst, Fisher-Cleveland Aircraft Div, Gen. Motors Corp, 43-45; instr. CIVIL ENG. & MECH. ENG, CLEVELAND STATE UNIV, 46-51, asst. prof, 51-62, ASSOC. PROF, 62- Struct. consult, Barber & Hoffman, Inc, 49- U.S.A.A.F. Fel. Am. Soc. Civil Eng. Structural design of buildings in steel and reinforced concrete. Address: Dept. of Civil Engineering, Cleveland State University, 1983 E. 24th St, Cleveland, OH 44115.

GALLO, ROBERT C, b. Waterbury, Conn, Mar. 23, 37; m. 61; c. 2. CELL BIOLOGY, BIOCHEMISTRY. B.S, Providence Col, 59; summer fels, Jefferson Med. Col, 61-63, M.D, 63. Clin. clerk, metab. sect, Yale Med. Sch, 62-63; from intern to resident med, Univ. Chicago, 63-65; clin. assoc, med. br, NAT. CANCER INST, 65-68, sr. investr, HUMAN TUMOR CELL BIOL. BR, 68-69, HEAD SECT. ON CELLULAR CONTROL MECHANISMS, 69- Consult, M.D. Anderson Hosp. & Tumor Inst, 70-71; vis. prof, Univ. Minn, 71; Bryan Priestman Mem. lectr, Univ. N.B, 71-72. U.S.P.H.S, 65-68, Surg. AAAS; Am. Soc. Hemat; Am. Fedn. Clin. Res; Am. Asn. Cancer Res; Biochem. Soc; Am. Soc. Pharmacol. & Exp. Therapeut; Am. Soc. Biol. Chem; Am. Soc. Microbiol. Oncology; hematology; mechanisms involved in control of cell growth and differentiation and in particular how these apply or fail to apply in neoplasia; viral and chemical oncogenesis; human oncogenesis; role of inciting agents; new approaches to chemotherapy of cancer. Address: National Institutes of Health, Bldg. 10, Room 6B16, Bethesda, MD 20014.

GALLO, S(ALVATORE) GEORGE, b. Atlantic City, N.J, May 6, 17; m. 44; c. 1. CHEMISTRY. B.A, Oberlin Col, 40; Conoco fel. & Ph.D.(anal. chem), Illinois, 43. Asst. to city bacteriologist, Oberlin Twp, Ohio, 39; lectr, E.I. du Pont de Nemours & Co, N.J, 41; res. chemist, Standard Oil Develop. Co, N.J, 43-52, employment specialist, 52-53; Creole Petrol. Corp, 53-54, training supvr, 54-59, head col. rels. group, 59-70, U.S. rep, Creole Found, 59-70; COORD. PROF. EMPLOY, STANDARD OIL CO.(N.J), 71- Mem. Greater N.Y. Coun. For. Stud. Bd, 61-63. Am. Chem. Soc; Sci. Res. Soc. Am; Nat. Asn. For. Stud. Affairs; fel. Am. Inst. Chem. Lube oil additives; analytical methods; petrochemicals; employment and placement; training and relations. Address: Employee Relations Dept, Room 2261, Standard Oil Co. of New Jersey, 30 Rockefeller Plaza, New York, NY 10020.

GALLOP, PAUL MYRON, b. N.Y.C, Nov. 24, 27; m. 64; c. 3. PROTEIN CHEMISTRY. A.B, Univ. Pa, 48; Ph.D.(biophys), Mass. Inst. Technol, 53. Instr. biophys, Mass. Inst. Technol, 53-54; biophysicist, L.I. Jewish Hosp, 54-59; vis. asst. prof, ALBERT EINSTEIN COL. MED, 57-59, assoc. prof.

BIOCHEM, 59-62, PROF, 62- Nat. Insts. Health career investigatorship award, 63. AAAS; Am. Chem. Soc; Biophys. Soc; Am. Soc. Biol. Chem. Collagen structure; proteolytic enzymes; collagenase; mechanism of enzyme action; peptide synthesis; connective tissue structure; mass spectrometry. Address: Dept. of Biochemistry, Albert Einstein College of Medicine, 1300 Morris Park Ave, Bronx, NY 10461.

GALLOPO, ANDREW ROBERT, b. Passaic, N.J, Mar. 23, 40. ORGANIC CHEMISTRY, BIOCHEMISTRY. A.B, Rutgers Univ, 62; Ph.D.(org. chem), Brown Univ, 67. Fel, Univ. Wis, 66-68; asst. mgr, Philip Hunt Chem. Corp, 68-69; ASST. PROF. CHEM, MONTCLAIR STATE COL, 69- Nat. Insts. Health fel, 67-69. Am. Chem. Soc. Organic chemical kinetics; enzymic kinetics; enzyme purification. Address: Dept. of Chemistry, Montclair State College, Upper Montclair, NJ 07043.

GALLOWAY, A(RTHUR) L(YLE), b. Eaton, Ohio, Mar. 10, 04; m. 30; c. 1. CHEMISTRY. B.S, Tri-State Col, 26. Chemist, Tobacco By-Prod. & Chem. Corp, 26-30, poultry res. dept, 30-37, res. assoc, 37-42, asst. chief res, 43-45, chief res. & consult. mfg, 45-49, mgr. develop. dept, Black Leaf Prod. Div, Va-Carolina Chem. Corp, 49-55; res. & develop. dept, Diamond Alkali Co, 55-58, group leader agr. & biol. chem. res, 58-69, consult, biochem. div, Diamond Shamrock Corp, 69-71; RETIRED. AAAS; Am. Chem. Soc; Entom. Soc. Am; Weed Sci. Soc. Am. Pesticides. Address: 7443 Sherwood Dr, Mentor, OH 44060.

GALLOWAY, DALE O(SCAR), b. Green Forest, Ark, Jan. 6, 13; m. 37; c. 1. BACTERIOLOGY. B.S, Cent. State Col, 35; M.S, Tennessee, 48, fel, 53-54. Instr. pub. schs, Tenn, 39-46; instr. bact, Tennessee, 46-51, asst. prof, 51-58; chief biol. develop. sect, directorate biol. opers, Pine Bluff Arsenal, 58-62; PROJ. OFF, U.S. ARMY COMBAT DEVELOP. COMMAND CHEM-BIOL-RADIOL. AGENCY, FT. McCLELLAN, 62- Med.C, U.S.N, 42-45. AAAS; Am. Soc. Microbiol. Developmental phases of detection and identification of microorganisms. Address: 2000 Henry Rd, Anniston, AL 36201.

GALLOWAY, ETHAN CHARLES, b. Howell, Mich, Oct. 31, 30. ORGANIC CHEMISTRY. B.Sc, Mich. State, 51; Ph.D.(chem), California, Berkeley, 54. Res. chemist, Dow Chem. Co, 54-58, mem. staff, tech. serv. & develop. dept, 58-60, head polymer intermediates, 60-61, head specialty chem, 61-62; dir. res, plastics div, Nopco Chem. Co, 62-65; mgr. prod. develop, STAUFFER CHEM. CO, 65-66, asst. dir, EAST. RES. CTR, 66-67, dir, 67-69, dir. res, 69-70, V.PRES. RES, 70- Am. Chem. Soc; Sci. Res. Soc. Am; Indust. Res. Inst; Soc. Chem. Indust. Natural products; condensation polymers; specialty organics. Address: 73-12 Courtland Ave, Stamford, CT 06092.

GALLOWAY, GORDON L(YNN), b. Pottstown, Pa, Sept. 25, 36; m. 62; c. 2. INORGANIC CHEMISTRY. B.S, Franklin & Marshall Col, 57; Monsanto fel, Mich. State, 60-61, Nat. Sci. Found. summer fel, 61, Ph.D.(inorg. chem), 62. Mem. staff, Los Alamos Sci. Lab, 61-63; asst. prof. chem. & asst. to dean col, St. Lawrence Univ, 63-67; asst. prof. CHEM, DENISON UNIV, 67-69, ASSOC. PROF, 69- Summers, res. asst, Los Alamos Sci. Lab, 59 & 60; partic, Nat. Sci. Found. res. prog. col. teachers, 64 & grant, 64-66; Nat. Sci. Found. Undergrad. res. partic. grant, summer 69. AAAS; Am. Chem. Soc. Chemistry of the interaction of metal ions with barbituric acid and its derivatives; synthesis of species containing boronium ions. Address: Dept. of Chemistry, Denison University, Granville, OH 43023.

GALLOWAY, HARRY M, b. Prospect Park, Pa, Nov. 3, 14; m. 39; c. 3. SOIL SCIENCE. B.S, Pa. State, 36; M.S, Wisconsin, 38; Mich. State, 42-43; Okla. State, 55-57. Field asst, exp. sta, U.S. Forest Serv, Pa, 38, jr. soil surveyor, soil conserv. serv, 38-39, soil surveyor, lands div, dept. conserv, 39-46; planning specialist, State Mich, 46-47; soil surv. party chief, Okla. State Univ. & Bur. Plant Indust, Soils & Agr. Eng, 47-52; Okla. State Univ. & U.S. Soil Conserv. Serv, 52-57, soil interpretation specialist, 57-58; ASSOC. PROF. AGRON. & EXTEN. AGRONOMIST, PURDUE UNIV, 58- Vis. prof, Fed. Univ. Viçosa, Brazil, 68-70. U.S.N.R, 44-46, Lt.(jg). Am. Soc. Agron; Soil Sci. Soc. Am; fel. Soil Conserv. Soc. Am. Soil classification for conservation programs; planning use of public lands; adapting soil survey information for use in land use planning; teaching soil characteristics which affect soil management and conservation; soil tillage-management systems; soil drainage research. Address: Dept. of Agronomy, Purdue University, Lafayette, IN 47906.

GALLOWAY, JOSEPH H(OMER), b. Atlanta, Ga, Feb. 21, 18; m. 42; c. 1. VETERINARY MEDICINE, ANIMAL SCIENCE. B.S, Mich. State, 50, M.S, 53; B.V.Sc, Queensland, 58. Veterinarian, Ohio, 58-59; asst. state veterinarian, Div. Vet. Serv, State of Ore, 59-60; in charge animal quarantine sect, Plum Island Animal Disease Res. Lab, U.S. Dept. Agr, N.Y, 60-62; assoc. prof. animal sci. & univ. vet, Arizona State Univ, 62-68; ASST. PROF. PHYSIOL. & BIOPHYS. & DIR. VIVARIUM, GEORGETOWN UNIV. SCH. MED, 68- Mem, Nat. Coun. Animal Transportation. Dipl, Am. Col. Lab. Animal Med, 64. U.S.A.A.F, 42-47, Capt. AAAS; U.S. Animal Health Asn; Am. Asn. Lab. Animal Sci; Am. Col. Lab. Animal Med; Am. Vet. Med. Asn; Am. Soc. Lab. Animal Practitioners; Royal Col. Vet. Surg. Endocrinology; mineral metabolism; parasitic diseases of domestic animals. Address: 3200 N. George Mason Dr, Arlington, VA 22207.

GALLOWAY, KENNETH FRANKLIN, b. Columbia, Tenn, Apr. 11, 41; m. 59; c. 2. HIGH ENERGY PHYSICS. A.B, Vanderbilt, 62; Ph.D.(physics), South Carolina, 66. Res. assoc. HIGH ENERGY PHYSICS, IND. UNIV, BLOOM-INGTON, 66-67, ASST. PROF, 67- Am. Phys. Soc; Am. Asn. Physics Teachers. Pion-nucleon and kaon-nucleon interactions at high energy. Address: Dept. of Physics, Indiana University College of Arts & Sciences, Bloomington, IN 47401.

GALLOWAY, LOUIE A, III, b. Pine Bluff, Ark, Feb. 3, 36; m. 58; c. 2. NU-CLEAR PHYSICS. A.B, Hendrix Col, 58; Nat. Sci. Found. summer fel, Case Inst. Technol, 59-60, M.S, 61, Ph.D.(physics), 66. Asst. Prof. PHYSICS, Col. William & Mary, 63; assoc. prof, CENTENARY COL, 66-69, PROF, 69- Lectr. & Consult, NASA, Langeley Field, aerospace technologist, Manned Spacecraft Ctr, 67, prin. investr, NASA contract, development of a low energy/charge spectrometer, 68-70; del, Conf. Neutron Cross Sections &

Technol, 71. Am. Phys. Soc; Am. Asn. Physics Teachers. Neutron total cross section measurements using time-of-flight techniques to measure neutron energies; development of a low energy/charge spectrometer for use in space measurements of proton and electron particle fluxes. Address: Dept. of Physics, Centenary College, Shreveport, LA 71104.

GALLOWAY, RAYMOND A(LFRED), b. Arbutus, Md, May 12, 28. PHYSIOL-OGY. B.S, Maryland, 52, M.S, 56, Ph.D.(bot), 58. Asst. prof. PHYSIOL, UNIV. MD, 58-64, assoc. prof, 64-69, PROF, 69- U.S.M.C, 52-54, Res, 54-64, Maj. Bot. Soc. Am; Am. Soc. Plant Physiol; Phycol. Soc. Am. Enzymology; heterotrophy in estuarine algae; physiology of algae; CO_2 metabolism. Address: Dept. of Botany, University of Maryland, College Park, MD 20740.

GALLOWAY, RICHARD T(HOMAS), b. Hartford, Ala, July 20, 23; m. 52; c. 3. PHYSICS. B.E.E, Ala. Polytech, 49; M.S, Fla. State, 50. Instr. math. & eng, Florence State Col, 50-51; proj. leader electronics & navig, Mine Defense Lab, U.S. NAVY, 51-67, head navig. command & control div, NAVAL SHIP RES. & DEVELOP. LAB, 67-69, HEAD, MINESWEEPING & NAVIG. DIV, 69- Superior accomplishment awards, 61 & 64; Commanding Off. Award for Sci. Achievement, 65. U.S.A.A.F, 43-46. Am. Inst. Navig. Mine countermeasures and navigation equipment development; command support; analysis of information and operations. Address: Naval Ship Research & Development Lab, Panama City, FL 32401.

GALLOWAY, ROBERT E, b. Birmingham, Ala, Feb. 16, 21; m. 45; c. 2. BIOCHEMISTRY, ANALYTICAL CHEMISTRY. B.S, Howard Col, 50; M.S, Alabama, 52. Instr. chem, Alabama, Birmingham, 52-54; assoc. scientist, South. Res. Inst, Ala, 54-57; supvry. biochemist, Vet. Admin. Hosp, Birmingham, 57-64; res. assoc. thyroid res, med. ctr, Univ. Ala, Birmingham, 64-66; BIOCHEMIST, Med. Lab. Assocs, 66-68; Carraway Methodist Hosp, 68-69; COLUMBUS MED. CTR, GA, 70- Cert, Nat. Registry Clin. Chem, 69. U.S.N, 42-46, Res, 46-63, Lt. Am. Inst. Chem; Am. Chem. Soc; Asn. Clin. Chem. Clinical chemistry. Address: 4130 Cliff Rd, Birmingham, AL 35222.

GALLOWAY, WILLIAM J(OYCE), b. Chicago, Ill, Sept. 15, 24; m. 46; c. 2. PHYSICS. B.S, California, Los Angeles, 49, M.S, 50, Ph.D.(physics), 53. Physicist, res. staff, eng. labs, Signal Corps, 51-52; V.PRES. & PRIN. CONSULT, BOLT BERANEK & NEWMAN, INC, 53- Sig.C, 41-46, 1st Lt. Fel. Acoust. Soc. Am; Am. Inst. Aeronaut. & Astronaut. Acoustics; cavitation in liquids; aircraft, rocket and traffic noise. Address: 21120 Vanowen St, Canoga Park, CA 91303.

GALLUB, ARNOLD M, b. N.Y.C, Sept. 19, 13. PHYSICS. B.S.S, City Col. N.Y, 33; Columbia Univ, 33-34; N.Y. State Vet. Scholar, 46; M.S, N.Y. Univ, 52, Ph.D.(sci. ed), 63. Instr. physics, Newark Col. Eng, 52-55; asst. prof. math. & physics, Dickinson Col, 55-56; Wagner Col, 56-60; lectr. PHYSICS, Queen's Col.(N.Y), 60-61; instr, L.I. Univ, 61-63; ASSOC. PROF, Nassau Community Col, 63-67; KINGSBOROUGH COMMUNITY COL, 67- Consult. physicist, Aircraft-Marine Prod, Inc, Pa, 55-56; Hygeia Electronics, Inc, N.Y, 61-63; lectr, Brooklyn Col, 63-; N.Y. Univ, 64- U.S.A, 42-44. Am. Asn. Physics Teachers. Effects of ionized air on mental performance. Address: 639 West End Ave, New York, NY 10025.

GALLUN, ROBERT L(OUIS), b. Milwaukee, Wis, Feb. 21, 24; m. 49; c. 2. ENTOMOLOGY. B.S, Mich. State, 48, M.S, 50; Ph.D, Purdue, 60. Entomologist, bur. entom. & plant quarantine, U.S. DEPT. AGR, 50-52, RES. ENTO-MOLOGIST, ENTOM. RES. DIV, AGR. RES. SERV, 53-; PROF. ENTOM, AGR. RES. STA, PURDUE UNIV, 71-, assoc. prof, 70-71. U.S.A, 43-45. Entom. Soc. Am; Am. Soc. Agron. Host plant resistance to insects; biological races and genetics of the Hessian fly. Address: Dept. of Entomology, Agricultural Experiment Station, Purdue University, Lafayette, IN 47907.

GALLUP, A(VERY) H(OUSELEY), b. National City, Calif, Aug. 3, 18; m. 44; c. 4. PLANT PHYSIOLOGY. A.B, San Diego State Col, 47; M.A, Claremont Cols, 49; Newcombe fel, Michigan, 49-51, Ph.D.(bot), 52. Asst. prof. zool, SAN DIEGO STATE COL, 52-57, assoc. prof. BOT, 57-60, PROF, 60- U.S.M.C, 42-46. Am. Soc. Plant Physiol. Plant growth sunstances; herbicides. Address: Dept. of Botany, San Diego State College, San Diego, CA 92115.

GALLUP, DeVERE M(ARION), b. Muskegon, Mich, Mar. 30, 20; m. 43; c. 3. MICROBIOLOGY. B.S, Wayne, 44; M.S, Michigan, 52, fel, 57-59, Ph.D. (bact), 62. Res. assoc. chem, Ford Motor Co, 41-43; jr. res. microbiologist, Parke, Davis & Co, 52-57; res. assoc. microbiol, Michigan, 59-62; process develop. microbiologist, MERCK & CO, INC, 62-64, sr. microbiologist, 64-66, SECT. LEADER MICROBIOL, 66- U.S.N.R, 42-45, Ens. Am. Chem. Soc; Am. Soc. Microbiol. Microbial physiology and metabolism; mechanisms of fermentation; production of fine chemicals by fermentation. Address: Merck & Co, Inc, Danville, PA 17821.

GALLUP, DONALD NOEL, b. Plainfield, N.J, July 28, 31; m. 57; c. 2. LIM-NOLOGY, ZOOLOGY. B.S, Rutgers Univ, 63; M.S, Univ. N.H, 65, Fed. Water Pollution Control Admin. fel, 67-69, Ph.D.(limnol, zool), 69. Heavy equip. mech, Ehrbar Equip. Corp, N.J, 55-56; cost analyst, Worthington Pump Corp, N.J, 56-57; eng. aid, U.S. Soil Conserv. Serv, N.J, 57; lab. equip. maintainer, Nat. Starch Prod, N.J, 57-58; painter & decorator, self-employed, N.J, 59-61; forestry aid, U.S. Forest Serv, Pa, 62; res. asst. forestry, Univ. N.H, 63-65; proj. asst. zool, 65-67; FEL. & LECTR. LIM-NOL. & ZOOL, UNIV. ALTA, 69- U.S.M.C, 52-55, Sgt. Am. Soc. Limnol. & Oceanog; Am. Inst. Biol. Sci; Can. Soc. Zool; Ecol. Soc. Am; Brit. Freshwater Biol. Asn; Int. Asn. Theoret. & Appl. Limnol. Effects of thermal effluent on the biota of a prairie-parkland lake; effects of heat on the population dynamics, production and turnover rates of the crustacean zooplankton; zooplankton energetics; zooplankton-zhytoplankton relationships; northern zooplankton distribution, ecology and taxonomy; phytoplankton production and ecology; epipelic animal production; general pollution effects on aquatic ecosystems. Address: Dept. of Zoology, University of Alberta, Edmonton, Alta, Can.

GALLUP, GORDON GRAHAM, JR, Psychol, see Suppl. I to 11th ed, Soc. & Behav. Vols.

GALLUP, HOWARD F(REDERICK), b. New London, Conn, Nov. 17, 27; m. 49; c. 3. EXPERIMENTAL PSYCHOLOGY. A.B, Rutgers, 50; M.A, Pennsylvania, 53, Ph.D, 57. Asst. instr, Pennsylvania, 51-56; instr. PSYCHOL, Hobart & William Smith Cols, 56-58; asst. prof, LAFAYETTE COL, 58-62, ASSOC. PROF, 62- Asst. to personnel officer, Pennsylvania, 53-56; res. psychologist, Phila. Navy Yard, 55-56. U.S.N.R, 45-46. AAAS; Am. Psychol. Asn. General experimental psychology, particularly in perception and thinking. Address: Dept. of Psychology, Lafayette College, Easton, PA 18042.

GALLY, J(OSEPH) A(NTHONY), b. Las Vegas, Nev, Feb. 9, 38. BIOCHEMISTRY, GENETICS. B.A, Pomona Col, 60; Ph.D.(molecular biol), Rockefeller Inst, 64. Asst. prof. biochem, Pomona Col, 64-66; Fulbright lectr, Ain Shams Univ, Cairo, 66; guest investr. immunochem, Rockefeller Univ, 67-69; ASST. PROF. MICROBIOL. & BIOCHEM, MEHARRY MED. COL, 69- Structure and genetics of immunoglobulins; theories of antibody formation. Address: Dept. of Biochemistry, Meharry Medical College, Nashville, TN 37208.

GALMARINO, ALBERTO R(AÚL), b. Buenos Aires, Argentina, Sept. 23, 28; m. 61; c. 1. MATHEMATICS. Lic. math, Buenos Aires, 55; Ph.D.(math), Mass. Inst. Tech, 61. Instr. algebra & topology, Buenos Aires, 57-58; res. assoc. MATH, Northeastern, 61-62; assoc. prof, Buenos Aires, 62-63; asst. prof, NORTHEAST. UNIV, 63, ASSOC. PROF, 63- Summer res. asst, Mass. Inst. Tech, 61. Math. consult, Argentine Navy, 62. Am. Math. Soc; Argentine Math. Soc. Probability theory; stochastic processes; theory of games; mathematical analysis. Address: Dept. of Mathematics, Northeastern University, Boston, MA 02115.

GALONIAN, GEORGE E, b. Cohoes, N.Y, Nov. 10, 23; m. 47. PHYSICAL CHEMISTRY. B.S, Siena Col, 50; Rensselaer Polytech. Inst. Corrosion engr, KNOLLS ATOMIC POWER LAB, GEN. ELEC. CO, 50-68, PROJ. ENGR, 68- Knolls Atomic Power Lab. rep, comt. fundamental stress corrosion studies, Atomic Energy Comn, comt. steam generator develop. U.S.N, 42-46. Nat. Asn. Corrosion Eng; Am. Inst. Chem. Eng. Corrosion of nuclear power plant materials; water treatment and control. Address: Knolls Atomic Power Lab, General Electric Co, Schenectady, NY 12304.

GALONSKY, A(ARON) I(RVING), b. Brooklyn, N.Y, Apr. 18, 29; m. 51; c. 3. NUCLEAR PHYSICS. B.A, Brooklyn Col, 50; M.S, Wisconsin, 51, Ph.D, 54. Physicist, Oak Ridge Nat. Lab, 54-59; group leader, Midwest Univs. Res. Asn, 59-64; assoc. prof, PHYSICS, MICH. STATE UNIV, 64-66, PROF, 66-, dir. cyclotron lab, 67-69. Nuclear reactions; scattering; beta-ray polarization; accelerators; neutrons. Address: Dept. of Physics, Michigan State University, East Lansing, MI 48823.

GAL-OR, BENJAMIN, b. Afula, Israel, Aug. 8, 33; m. 59; c. 2. CHEMICAL & AERONAUTICAL ENGINEERING. B.Sc, Israel Inst. Tech, 59, M.Sc, 61, D.Sc.(chem. eng), 64. Fel, Hopkins, 64-65, asst. prof. CHEM. ENG, 65-66; ASSOC. PROF, UNIV. PITTSBURGH, 66-; AERONAUT. ENG, ISRAEL INST. TECHNOL, 68- AAAS; N.Y. Acad. Sci. Thermodynamics; hydrodynamics; heat and mass transfer in multiphase systems; bubble and drop phenomena; acid waste disposal; reacting boundary layers; combustion; aerosols; shock wave structure; origins of irreversability and time asymmetrics; history and philosophy of science. Address: Dept. of Chemical Engineering, University of Pittsburgh, Pittsburgh, PA 15213.

GALPER, M(ILTON) J(EROME), b. Chicago, Ill, Oct. 18, 26; m. 53; c. 4. PHYSICS. A.B, California, Los Angeles, 50, M.A, 51; Oak Ridge Sch. Reactor Tech, 51-52. Scientist reactor physics, BETTIS ATOMIC POWER DIV, WESTINGHOUSE ELEC. CORP, 52-55, supvr. scientist physics, 55-57, sect. mgr. nuclear design, 57-66, MGR. reactor thermal & nuclear design, 66-68, NUCLEAR ENG, 69- U.S.A, 44-45, U.S.A.A.F, 46. Am. Nuclear Soc. Analytical design of advanced pressurized water cooled and moderated power reactors; improved analytical methods. Address: Bettis Atomic Power Lab, Westinghouse Electric Corp, Box 79, West Mifflin, PA 15122.

GALPERIN, IRVING, b. Buffalo, N.Y, Dec. 3, 26; m. 58. PHYSICAL CHEMISTRY. A.B, Alfred, 48; M.S, Canisius Col, 52; Ph.D.(phys. chem), Western Reserve, 57. Chemist, Continental Can Corp, Ill, 58-60; Visking Div, Union Carbide Corp, 60-62; Plastics Div, N.J, 62-64; sr. chemist, Interchem. Corp, Clifton, 64-67; MEM. TECH. STAFF, Bell Tel. Labs, 67-69; GEN. CABLE CORP, 69- Am. Chem. Soc; Soc. Plastics Eng; Instrument Soc. Am; Am. Inst. Chem. Electrochemistry; structure and properties of polymers. Address: General Cable Corp, Union, NJ 07083.

GALPIN, DONALD R, b. Butte, Mont, Apr. 1, 33; m. 57; c. 2. MEDICINAL CHEMISTRY, PHARMACY. B.S, Montana, 57, M.S, 62; Am. Found. Pharmaceut. Educ. fel, Washington (Seattle), 62-66, Ph.D.(pharmaceut. chem), 66. ASST. PROF. PHARM, COL. PHARM, WASH. STATE UNIV, 66- Am. Pharmaceut. Asn. Medicinal chemistry; drug metabolism; nuclear magnetic resonance; optical rotatory dispersion and circular dichroism; configurational and conformational analysis. Address: College of Pharmacy, Washington State University, Pullman, WA 99163.

GALSKY, ALAN GARY, b. Chicago, Ill, Mar. 6, 42; m. 66. PLANT PHYSIOLOGY, MICROBIOLOGY. B.S, Roosevelt, 64; M.S, Northwestern, 67, Ph.D. (biol), 69. ASST. PROF. BIOL, BRADLEY UNIV, 69- Am. Soc. Plant Physiol. Role of 3', 5'-cyclic adenosine monophosphate in plants; mechanism of gibberellic acid action; production of plant hormones by phytopathogenic bacteria. Address: Dept. of Biology, Bradley University, Peoria, IL 61614.

GALSTAUN, LIONEL S(AMUEL), b. Kediri, Java, Dec. 17, 13; nat; m. 50. PHYSICAL CHEMISTRY. B.S, Dayton, 33; M.S, Mass. Inst. Tech, 34, Ph.D. (phys. chem), 36. Reader & asst. chem, Mass. Inst. Tech, 34-36; res. chemist, Tidewater Assoc. Oil Co, 36-46, asst. supvr. res, 46, supvr, 46-58; prin. engr, Bechtel Corp, 58-64, mgr. appl. technol. dept, 64-66, MGR. PROCESS ENG, BECHTEL ASSOCS, 66- Leader, chem. ministerial team,

strategic bombing surv, Pac. Theater Opers, U.S. War Dept, 45-46. Am. Chem. Soc; Am. Inst. Chem. Eng; Am. Inst. Chem. System palladium-hydrogen; petroleum refining and products; process engineering; chemicals; saline water conversion; coal gasification; hydrometallurgy; air and water pollution control. Address: Bechtel Associates, 485 Lexington Ave, New York, NY 10017.

GALSTER, RICHARD W, b. Seattle, Wash, May 13, 30; m. 51; c. 2. ENGINEERING GEOLOGY. B.S, Washington (Seattle), 52, M.S, 56. GEOLOGIST, Grant County Pub. Utility Dist, Wash, 54-55; CORPS ENGRS, U.S. ARMY ENGR. DIST, 55- U.S.A, 52-54. Asn. Eng. Geol; Geol. Soc. Am. Geomorphology; hydrogeology; rock mechanics; rock mechanics instrumentation; seismic instrumentation. Address: 18233 13th N.W, Seattle, WA 98177.

GALSTER, WILLIAM ALLEN, b. Kenosha, Wis, Apr. 11, 32; m. 55; c. 5. COMPARATIVE PHYSIOLOGY, BIOCHEMISTRY. B.S, Wisconsin, 58, M.S, 61. Chemist, Wis. State Lab. Hyg, 56-57; asst. prof. biol, St. Benedict's Col.(Kans), 61-64; ASST. PROF. COMP. PHYSIOL. & COORD. ANAL. SERV, INST. ARCTIC BIOL, UNIV. ALASKA, 64- U.S.A, 55-57. AAAS; Am. Soc. Mammal; Am. Zool. Soc; Am. Inst. Chem; Int. Soc. Mammalian Hibernation. Bioenergetics of natural populations exposed to environmental extremes; effects of critical cold stress on microtine rodents; seasonal changes in Arctic hibernators; human physiological adjustments to altitude and cold stressors; toxicology. Address: Institute of Arctic Biology, University of Alaska, College, AK 99701.

GALSTON, ARTHUR W(ILLIAM), b. New York, N.Y, Apr. 21, 20; m. 41; c. 2. PLANT PHYSIOLOGY. B.S, Cornell, 40; M.S, Illinois, 42, Ph.D.(bot), 43. Res. fel. biol, Calif. Inst. Tech, 43-44, sr. res. fel, 47-50, assoc. prof. biol, 51-55; PROF. plant physiol, YALE, 55-65, BIOL, 65-, chmn. dept. bot, 61-62, dir. div. biol. sci, 65-66. Guggenheim fel, Stockholm, 50-51; mem. metab. biol. panel, Nat. Sci. Found, 59-60; Fulbright fel, Australia, 60-61; mem, Nat. Res. Coun, 64-; Nat. Sci. Found. sr. faculty fel, London, 68; consult, cent. res. dept, E.I. du Pont de Nemours & Co, Inc. U.S.N.R, 44-46, Lt.(jg). Am. Soc. Plant Physiol.(secy, 55-57, v.pres, 57-58, pres, 62-63); Bot. Soc. Am.(pres, 67-68, merit award, 69); Int. Asn. Plant Physiol.(secy-treas). Plant growth hormones; photobiology; differentiation and morphogenesis. Address: Dept. of Biology, 902 Kline Biology Tower, Yale University, New Haven, CT 06520.

GALSWORTHY, PETER R(OBERT), b. Montreal, Que, June 13, 39; m. 63; c. 2. BIOCHEMISTRY, GENETICS. B.Sc, Queen's Univ.(Ont), 62; Ph.D. (biochem), Univ. Wis, Madison, 68. Nat. Insts. Health res. fel. BIOCHEM, Princeton, 68-70; ASST. PROF, UNIV. WEST. ONT, 70- Med. Res. Coun. Can. res. grant, 70-72. AAAS; Can. Biochem. Soc; Brit. Biochem. Soc; Am. Chem. Soc; Am. Soc. Microbiol. Membrane structure and function; membrane transport proteins; energy-coupling mechanisms for active transport; phospholipids and membrane structure in relation to transport; role of transport systems in differentiation. Address: Dept. of Biochemistry, University of Western Ontario, London 72, Ont, Can.

GALT, JOHN (ALEXANDER), b. Toronto, Ont, Mar. 8, 25; m. 55; c. 2. ASTROPHYSICS. B.A, Toronto, 49, Nat. Res. Coun. Can. bursar, 50-51, stud, 51-52, M.A, 52, Nat. Res. Coun. Can. fel, 52-53, Ph.D.(physics), 56. Res. physicist, Du Pont of Can, 56-57; ASTROPHYSICIST, DOM. RADIO ASTROPHYS. OBSERV, 57- Res, Jodrell Bank, Univ. Manchester, 58. R.C.N.V.R, 44-45. AAAS; Am. Astron. Soc; Royal Astron. Soc. Can; Can. Asn. Physicists; Inst. Elec. & Electronics Eng; Royal Astron. Soc. Physics; spectroscopy; high pressures; electronics; optics; radio astronomy; twenty-one centimeter research; long baseline interferometry; pulsars. Address: Dominion Radio Astrophysical Observatory, Box 248, Penticton, B.C, Can.

GALT, JOHN K(IRTLAND), b. Portland, Ore, Sept. 1, 20; m. 49; c. 1. PHYSICS. A.B, Reed Col, 41; fel, Mass. Inst. Tech, 41-43, Ph.D.(physics), 47. Res. assoc, Mass. Inst. Tech, 45-47; Nat. Res. Coun. fel, Bristol, Eng, 47-48; mem. tech. staff, BELL TEL. LABS, 48-61, DIR. SOLID STATE ELECTRONICS RES, 61- Mem, Nat. Acad. Comt. Adv. to Air Force Systs. Command, 71- Civilian with Off. Sci. Res. & Develop, 43-45. Fel. Am. Phys. Soc; sr. mem. Inst. Elec. & Electronics Eng. Mechanical and magnetic properties of solids; band structure of metals; lasers, nonlinear optics, luminescence and optical properties of solids. Address: Bell Telephone Labs, Murray Hill, NJ 07974.

GALTIERI, ANGELA BARBARO, b. Palmi, Italy, Oct. 23, 34; m. 58; c. 1. PARTICLE PHYSICS. Ph.D.(physics), Rome, 57. Res. physicist, Rome, 57-61; PHYSICIST, LAWRENCE BERKELEY LAB, UNIV. CALIF, 61- Nat. Comt. Res. fel, Italy, 58-59. Am. Phys. Soc; Italian Phys. Soc. Experimental research in strong and weak interactions of elementary particles using high energy accelerators. Address: Lawrence Berkeley Laboratory, University of California, Berkeley, CA 94704.

GALTON, SUZANNE A, b. Budapest, Hungary; U.S. citizen; m. 52. ORGANIC & POLYMER CHEMISTRY. B.A, Hunter Col, 53; fel, Polytech. Inst. Brooklyn, 59-63, M.S, 60, Ph.D.(org. & polymer chem), 63. Res. asst. steroids, Worcester Found. Exp. Biol, 53-54; synthetic med, Chas. Pfizer & Co, Inc, 54-58, staff chemist, 58-59; Nat. Cancer Inst. fel. org. chem, Polytech. Inst. Brooklyn, 63-65; asst. mem. nucleic acid chem, Inst. Muscle Disease, N.Y, 65-66; asst. prof. org. chem, COL. PHARMACEUT. SCI, COLUMBIA UNIV, 66-70, ASSOC. PROF. CHEM, 70-; AAAS; Am. Chem. Soc; The Chem. Soc. Nucleoside and nucleotide analogs, chemical and physical properties; mechanism of arylation with diaryliodonium salts; synthesis and properties of iodonium salts; synthesis of organic medicinals; isolation and identification of steroids; Clemmensen reduction mechanism. Address: Dept. of Chemistry, Columbia University College of Pharmaceutical Science, 115 W. 68th St, New York, NY 10023.

GALTON, VALERIE ANNE, b. Louth, Eng, May 6, 34; wid; c. 2. ENDOCRINOLOGY. B.Sc, London, 55, Ph.D.(physiol), 58. Res. assoc. endocrinol, Nat. Inst. Med. Res, London, 55-58; Thorndike Mem. Lab, Harvard Med. Sch, 59-61; instr. PHYSIOL, DARTMOUTH MED. SCH, 61-63, asst. prof, 63-67, ASSOC. PROF, 67- Milton res. fel. med, Harvard Med. Sch, 59-60; Life Ins. med. res. fel, 61-63; U.S. Pub. Health Serv. res. grants, 62-, res.

career develop. award, 65-70. Endocrine Soc; Am. Thyroid Asn. Mode of action of the thyroid hormones, nature of their peripheral metabolism and relation between hormonal action and metabolism. Address: Dept. of Physiology, Dartmouth Medical School, Hanover, NH 03755.

GALTSOFF, PAUL S(IMON), b. Moscow, Russia, Mar. 28, 87; nat; m. 11. ZOOLOGY. Grad, Moscow State, 10; Ph.D.(invert. zool), Columbia, 25. Instr. zool, Moscow, 10-14; privat-docent, Univ. Crimea, Russia, 18; sr. zoologist in charge, Sebastapol Biol. Sta, Russian Acad. Sci, 17-21; naturalist, Albatross, Bur. Fisheries, 22-25, biologist, 25-30, sr. biologist, U.S. Fish & Wildlife Serv, 40-48, res. biologist, U.S. Shellfish Lab, Woods Hole, 48-64; RETIRED. Guest invester, biol. lab, Nat. Marine Fisheries Serv, 67-71. Dir. biol. sta, Kossino, Russia, 10-14; pearl oyster invests, Hawaii, 30, Gulf of Panama, 48, Venezuela, 48; res. assoc. grad. coun, George Washington, 42; observer, Bikini, 46. Exped, Russian Acad. Sci. to Black Sea & Bosporus, 14. Consult, Marine Lab, Miami (Fla); Fed. Water Pollution Control Admin, 67-68. Trustee, Bermuda Biol. Sta; Marine Biol. Lab, Woods Hole. Distinguished serv. award & Gold Medal, Dept. Interior, 62. AAAS; Am. Soc. Nat; Am. Soc. Zool; Am. Soc. Limnol. & Oceanog; Soc. Gen. Physiol; fel. N.Y. Acad. Sci. Fresh-water biology; oceanographical observations along Atlantic Coast and Gulf of Mexico; regeneration of sponges; physiology and ecology of the oyster; physiology of reproduction and sex change in oysters; sponge mortality in the British West Indies. Address: P.O. Box 167, Woods Hole, MA 02543.

GALVIN, AARON A, b. Brooklyn, N.Y, Apr. 13, 32; m. 56; c. 3. ELECTRONIC ENGINEERING. B.S. & M.S, Mass. Inst. Tech, 55. Engr, Lincoln Lab, Mass. Inst. Tech, 55-59, group leader, 59-68; V.PRES. ADVAN. DEVELOP, AEROSPACE RES, INC, 68- Inst. Elec. & Electronics Eng. Research and development in the field of radar; advanced radar system development, particularly optimal signal processing; radar and ultrasonic intrusion alarms. Address: Aerospace Research, Inc, 130 Lincoln St, Boston, MA 02135.

GALVIN, CYRIL JEROME, JR, b. Jersey City, N.J, June 16, 35. OCEANOGRAPHY, GEOLOGY. B.S, St. Louis Univ, 57; S.M, Mass. Inst. Technol, 59, Ph.D.(geol), 63. Res. asst, hydrodyn. lab, Mass. Inst. Technol, 59-63; phys. oceanogr, U.S. ARMY COASTAL ENG. RES. CTR, 63-70, CHIEF COASTAL PROCESSES BR, 70- Summer geologist, Minerva Oil Co, 56; U.S. Geol. Surv, 57, 58; res. resident, math. res. ctr, Univ. Wis, 65-66. AAAS; Am. Geophys. Union; Geol. Soc. Am; Am. Soc. Civil Eng.(Huber Res. Prize, 69; Norman Medal, 70); Int. Asn. Hydraul. Res; Soc. Econ. Paleont. & Mineral. Coastal processes; experimental and field studies of waves, currents, and sediment transport on beaches; inlet and barrier island formation; analysis of geologic and topographic maps; geomorphology; history of science. Address: U.S. Army Coastal Engineering Research Center, 5201 Little Falls Rd. N.W, Washington, DC 20016.

GALVIN, THOMAS J(OSEPH), b. Cisco, Tex, Mar. 14, 34; m. 52; c. 3. PARASITOLOGY, VETERINARY MEDICINE. N.C. State Col, 57-58; D.V.M, Texas A&M, 57, B.S. & M.S, 61; Ph.D.(parasitol), Tulane, 64. Sta. veterinarian, N.C. State Col, 57-58; instr. VET. PARASITOL, TEX. A&M UNIV, 58-60, asst. prof, 60-64, assoc. prof, 64-71, PROF, 71- Nat. Insts. Health fel, 61-62; lectr, Univ. E.Africa & Univ. Col, Nairobi, Kenya, 65-67. Wildlife Disease Asn; Am. Vet. Med. Asn; Am. Soc. Vet. Parasitol; Am. Soc. Parasitol; Am. Soc. Trop. Med. & Hyg; World Asn. Adv. Vet. Parasitol. Biology, control and treatment of helminth parasites of domestic and laboratory animals, especially those species which may affect human health. Address: Dept. of Veterinary Parasitology, Texas A&M University, College Station, TX 77843.

GALYON, G(EORGE) TIPTON, b. Port Chester, N.Y, Mar. 4, 39; m. 63; c. 3. METALLURGY. B.Sc, Lehigh Univ, 61; M.Sc, Univ. Pa, 63; Stevens Inst. Technol, 65; Ph.D. Mass. Inst. Technol, 70. Res. metallurgist, aerospace res. labs, Gen. Precision Inc, N.J, 63-70; MEM. STAFF, IBM COMPONENTS DIV, 70- Summers, tech. trainee, Bethlehem Steel Corp, 60 & asst, Int. Nickel Res. Labs, N.J, 61- Am. Inst. Mining, Metall. & Petrol. Eng. Physical and mechanical metallurgy; internal friction and mechanical behavior of materials with respect to defect structure; development management in integrated circuit component field. Address: IBM Components Division, IBM Corp, East Fishkill, NY 12524.

GALYSH, FRED T(HEODORE), b. Cleveland, Ohio, Apr. 17, 29; m. 51; c. 2. PHARMACOLOGY. B.S, Pittsburgh, 52; Am. Found. Pharmaceut. Ed. fel, Ohio State, 52-55, M.S, 54, Ph.D.(pharmacol), 55. Prof. pharmacol, N.Dak. State Col, 56-59; sr. res. pharmacologist, BAXTER LABS, INC, 59-66, HEAD CARDIOVASC. SECT, 66- AAAS; Asn. Advan. Med. Instrumentation; N.Y. Acad. Sci. Cardiovascular and renal pharmacology; pharmacology of narcotic and analgetic agents; artificial organs; biomedical instrumentation. Address: Baxter Labs, Inc, 6301 Lincoln Ave, Morton Grove, IL 60053.

GAMBAL, D(AVID), b. Old Forge, Pa, Dec. 16, 31; m. 60; c. 3. BIOCHEMISTRY. B.S, Pa. State, 53; fel, Purdue, 53-57, M.S, 56, Ph.D.(biochem), 57. Asst, Purdue, 53-57; fel, McCollum-Pratt Inst, Hopkins, 57-59; asst. prof, vet. med. res. inst, Iowa State, 59-63, assoc. prof. BIOCHEM, 63-65; SCH. MED, CREIGHTON UNIV, 65-70, PROF, 70- AAAS; Am. Chem. Soc; Soc. Exp. Biol. & Med. Biosynthesis of phospholipides; metabolism and function of essential fatty acids; hormonal control of cellular metabolism and spermatogenesis; vitamin D and bone calcification. Address: Dept. of Biochemistry, Creighton University School of Medicine, Omaha, NE 68131.

GAMBESCIA, JOSEPH MARION, b. Phila, Pa, June 10, 19; m. 44; c. 16. INTERNAL MEDICINE, GASTROENTEROLOGY. B.S, Phila. Col. Pharm, 39; Villanova Univ, 41; M.D, Hahnemann Med. Col, 44. Assoc. gastroenterol, HAHNEMANN MED. COL. & HOSP, 50-52, asst. prof. med, 52-55, dir. res, dept. gastroenterol, 51-61, clin. prof. MED, 61-70, PROF, 70-; CHMN. DEPT. MED. & HEAD GASTROENTEROL. SECT, ST. AGNES HOSP, 67-, dir. educ, 54-60. Instr, div. grad. med, Univ. Pa, 54-; asst, G.I. Clin, Phila. Gen. Hosp, 56-60; pres, Phila. Nutrit. Coun, 70. Chief lab, Army Hepatitis Res. Ctr, 120th Sta. Hosp, Ger, U.S.A, 46-48, Capt. Am. Col. Gastroenterol; Am. Soc. Clin. Invest; Am. Med. Asn.(Cert. of Merit, 55); fel. Am. Col. Physicians; Am. Fedn. Clin. Res; fel. Am. Gastroenterol. Asn. Hepato pancreatic biliary disease. Address: 141 N. Highland Ave, Bala-Cynwyd, PA 19004.

GAMBILL, ROBERT A(RNOLD), b. Indianapolis, Ind, Feb. 20, 27; m. 50; c. 2. MATHEMATICS. A.B, Butler, 50; M.S, Purdue, 52, Nat. Sci. Found. fel. & Ph.D.(math), 54. Head, theoret. anal. br, math. div, U.S. Naval Avionics Facility, 54-58; sr. mathematician, Gen. Motors Corp, 58-60; assoc. prof. MATH, PURDUE UNIV, 60-66, PROF. & ASST. HEAD. DEPT, 66- U.S.N, 45-46. Am. Math. Soc; Math. Asn. Am; Soc. Indust. & Appl. Math. Ordinary and functional differential equations; calculus of variations; optimal control. Address: Division of Mathematical Sciences, Purdue University, Lafayette, IN 47907.

GAMBINO, S(ALVATORE) RAYMOND, b. Brooklyn, N.Y, Oct. 13, 26; m. 53; c. 2. CLINICAL PATHOLOGY & CHEMISTRY. B.S, Antioch, 48; M.D, Rochester, 52. Assoc. pathologist, St. Lukes Hosp, Milwaukee, Wis, 57-61; asst. prof. PATH, COL. PHYSICIANS & SURGEONS, COLUMBIA UNIV, 61-69, PROF. & DIR. CLIN. CHEM. LABS, 69- Asst. prof, Marquette Univ, 59-61; dir. labs, Englewood Hosp, N.J, 61-69. U.S.N.R, 45-46. AAAS; Am. Soc. Clin. Path; Am. Chem. Soc; Am. Asn. Clin. Chem; Col. Am. Path; Am. Med. Asn. Measurement and interpretation of blood pH, blood gases and serum bilirubin; diagnostic laboratory methodology. Address: College of Physicians & Surgeons, Columbia University, 630 W. 168th St, New York, NY 10032.

GAMBLE, CHARLES N(ORTHAM), b. Albert Lea, Minn, Aug. 18, 28; m. 54; c. 3. PATHOLOGY. B.A, Minnesota, 51, B.S. & M.D, 55. Am. Cancer Soc. trainee path, Minnesota, 57-58, Nat. Insts. Health med. fel. specialist path. & histochem, 58-60; assoc. pathologist, Scripps Mem. Hosp, La Jolla, Calif, 62-63, assoc. exp. path, Scripps Clin. & Res. Found, 63-65; assoc. prof. ophthal, med. ctr, California, San Francisco, 65-66, assoc. clin. prof. path, 66-69; PARTNER, SACRAMENTO CLIN. LAB, 69- Am. Soc. Clin. Path. res. award, 55. Nat. Insts. Health trainee immunopath, 63-65. U.S.N, 60-62, Res, 60-, Lt. Comdr. Histochemistry; immunopathology; ocular immunology. Address: Sacramento Clinical Lab, 2600 Capitol Ave, Sacramento, CA 95816.

GAMBLE, DEAN F(RANKLIN), b. McDonald, Pa, Aug. 6, 20; m. 46; c. 3. ORGANIC CHEMISTRY. B.S, Pa. State, 42, Ph.D.(chem), 53. Chem. librn, Nat. Insts. Health, 53-56, head sect. doc, records & pubs, cancer chemother, nat. serv. ctr, Nat. Cancer Inst, 56-60; dir. dept. sci. info, Miles Labs, Inc, Ind, 60-66, acting dir, info. dept, 66-71; HEAD FOOD & NUTRIT. INFO. & EDUC. MAT. CTR, NAT. AGR. LIBR, 71- Mem. comt, codification, ciphering & punched card techniques, Nat. Res. Coun, 59-61. U.S.A.A.F, 43-46. Am. Chem. Soc; Am. Soc. Info. Sci; Soc. Nutrit. Educ. Chemical documentation; information processing, storage and retrieval; correlation of chemical structure and biological activity; use of punched cards and computers in information work. Address: Food & Nutrition Information & Educational Materials Center, National Agricultural Library, Beltsville, MD 20705.

GAMBLE, DEAN L(A FEVER), b. Olean, N.Y, Dec. 11, 92; m. 16, 49; c. 4. VERTEBRATE ZOOLOGY. B.S, Cornell, 16, Ph.D.(zool), 21. Lab. asst, zool, Cornell, 14-16, instr, 16-20, asst. prof, 21-24; v.pres, Gen. Biol. Supply Co, Ill, 24-31; pres, Wards Natural Sci. Estab, Inc, 31-62, chmn. bd, 62-70; RETIRED. Morphology of vertebrates; morphology of ribs and transverse process of Necturus maculosus. Address: 26116 Mesa Dr, Carmel, CA 93921.

GAMBLE, DEAN PHILIP, b. Iowa City, Iowa, Dec. 17, 22; m. 47; c. 4. PHYSICS. B.S, California, Los Angeles, 44, 49. Chemist, radioisotope unit, Vet. Admin. Hosp, Long Beach, Calif, 49-52, physicist, Los Angeles, 52-54; reactor physicist, dept. radiol, sch. med, California, Los Angeles, 54-56; sr. res. engr, atomics int. div, N.Am. Aviation Inc, 56-60; PHYSICIST, LAWRENCE RADIATION LAB, UNIV. CALIF, 60- Consult, Litton Industs, 56-60. U.S.A.A.F, 43-45, Res, 45-58, Capt. Am. Chem. Soc; Am. Nuclear Soc; Soc. Nuclear Med. Nuclear weapon design and vulnerability; nuclear reactor kinetics, safety and operation of medical research reactor; cancer therapy with pure Beta ray radioisotopes; medical use of radioisotopes; health physics. Address: 752 Adams Ave, Livermore, CA 94550.

GAMBLE, E(DMUND) LEE, b. Haymarket, Va, June 10, 06; m. 37; c. 1. INORGANIC CHEMISTRY. B.S, Washington & Lee, 29; M.S, Mass. Inst. Technol, 30, Ph.D.(inorg. chem), 32; Sorbonne, 32-33. Res. assoc. INORG. CHEM, MASS. INST. TECHNOL, 33-36, instr, 36-37, asst. prof, 37-43, assoc. prof, 43-64, prof, 64-71, EMER. PROF, 71- Master, Baker House, 62-68. With Office Sci. Res. & Develop, 44. Boron; fluorine; silicon. Address: Box 176, North Falmouth, MA 02556.

GAMBLE, EDWARD HOLLAND, b. East Liverpool, Ohio, Sept. 27, 20; m. 42; c. 3. SYSTEMS ENGINEERING. B.Sc, Ohio, 41; M.Sc, Ohio State, 42; Dr.E.E.(electro-physics), Polytech. Inst. Brooklyn, 47. Lab. instr. physics, Ohio, 40-41; asst, Ohio State, 41-42; mem. tech. staff, Bell Tel. Labs, N.J, 42-46, 47-48; lectr, electronics & physics, Polytech. Inst. Brooklyn, 46-47; chief res. engr, Curtiss-Wright Corp, 48-49, head res. & electronics dept, 49-50, chief engr, electronics prods, 51-52; controls engr, jet engine dept, Gen. Elec. Co, 52-53, mgr. controls, flight propulsion lab. dept, 53-59, consult. engr, flight propulsion div, 59-63, Missiles & Space Div, 63-64, PROF. elec. eng, OHIO UNIV, 64-67, SYSTS. ENG, 67- Sr. res. fel, Microwave Res. Inst, N.Y, 46-47; consult, Polytech. Res. & Develop. Co, Brooklyn, 46-47; vis. prof, Purdue Univ, 60-61, prof. mech. eng, 60-64; mem. subcomt. power plant controls, Nat. Adv. Comt. Aeronaut; design & systs. reliability consult, Goodyear Atomic Corp, 69- Projs. for Off. Sci. Res. & Develop; U.S.A; U.S.N; U.S.A.A.F. Inst. Elec. & Electronics Eng. Electronics; servo-mechanisms; computers; semiconductors; stress analysis; response of planar and cylindrical thermionic diodes to applied signals; gas turbine and nuclear power controls; aircraft guidance, stabilization and control; optimization of large complex systems; prediction of off-design performance of mechanical devices; design of information-energy systems. Address: College of Engineering, Engineering Bldg. 319, Ohio University, Athens, OH 45701.

GAMBLE, F(RANCIS) TREVOR, b. Montpelier, Vt, July 10, 28; m. 51; c. 3. PHYSICS. A.B, Colgate, 58; M.A, Connecticut, 60, Ph.D.(physics), 63. Res. asst. PHYSICS, Connecticut, 62-63; asst. prof, DENISON UNIV, 63-65, assoc. prof, 65-70, PROF. & DEAN STUD, 70-, chmn. dept. physics, 69-70. Consult, Battelle Mem. Inst, 64- U.S.N.A.F, 48-56, Res, 57-, Comdr. Am. Asn. Physics Teachers; Am. Phys. Soc; N.Y. Acad. Sci. Electron spin resonance in solids; radiation damage in solids. Address: Dean of Students, Denison University, Granville, OH 43023.

GAMBLE, FRED R(IDLEY), JR, b. Dallas, Tex, Apr. 24, 41; m. 64; c. 2. SOLID STATE CHEMISTRY & PHYSICS. B.A, Harvard, 64; Nat. Sci. Found. fel, Stanford Univ, 65-68, Ph.D.(chem. physics), 68. Sr. Chemist, Syva Corp, 68-71; GROUP LEADER, CHEM. PHYSICS, ESSO RES. & ENG. CO, 71- Am. Chem. Soc; Am. Phys. Soc. New superconducting materials; intercalation compounds; interactions between metals and molecules. Address: Corporate Research Laboratories, Esso Research & Engineering Co, P.O. Box 45, Linden, NJ 07036.

GAMBLE, JAMES LAWDER, JR, b. Boston, Mass, Jan. 8, 21; m. 48; c. 6. PHYSIOLOGY, BIOCHEMISTRY. B.S, Harvard, 43, M.D, 45. Intern pediat, univ. hosp, Hopkins, 45-46, asst. res, sch. med, 48-50; clin. investr. physiol, Brookhaven Nat. Lab, 50-52; Nat. Insts. Health fel. pediat. & biochem, SCH. MED, JOHN HOPKINS UNIV, 53-57, Am. Heart Asn. estab. investr. pediat. & physiol, 57-62, asst. prof. PHYSIOL, 61-67, ASSOC. PROF, 67- U.S.A.A.F, 46-57; U.S.A, 53, Capt. Soc. Pediat. Res; Am. Pediat. Soc; Am. Physiol. Soc. Electrolyte and fluid space physiology; mitochondrial electrolytes and ion transport. Address: 17 Blythewood Rd, Baltimore, MD 21210.

GAMBLE, JESS FRANKLIN, b. Pollack, Mo, Feb. 14, 14; m. 41; c. 3. INTERNAL MEDICINE, HEMATOLOGY. B.S, Nebraska, 38, M.D, 40. Intern, Walter Reed Gen. Hosp, 40-41; res. internal med. & hemat, Ohio State Univ. Hosp, 46-49, instr. hemat, 48-49; asst. chief med, Vet. Admin. Hosp, Houston, Tex, 49-51, chief med, 51-53; ASSOC. PROF. MED. & ASSOC. INTERNIST MED. & HEMAT, UNIV. TEX. M.D. ANDERSON HOSP. & TUMOR INST, 54- Asst. prof. med, Baylor, 49-66. Dipl, Am. Bd. Internal Med, 51. Med.C, U.S.A, 41-46, Col. Am. Med. Asn; Am. Soc. Internal Med. Address: University of Texas M.D. Anderson Hospital & Tumor Institute, Houston, TX 77025.

GAMBLE, JOHN F(RANCIS), b. Lynn, Mass, Aug. 30, 24; m. 53; c. 5. ECOLOGY, SPECTROSCOPY. B.S, New Hampshire, 50, M.S, 54; Ph.D.(soil genesis), Rutgers, 64. Res. asst. clay mineral. soil surv, Conn. Agr. Exp. Sta, 50-51; asst. soils, New Hampshire, 51-53; asst. dir. res, Cent. Aguirre Sugar Co, P.R, 54-55; supvr. dept. fabrication & cane res, United Fruit Sugar Co, Cuba, 56-60; asst. soils, spec. lab, Rutgers, 60-61, instr, 61-64; sr. res. scientist, Isotopes, Inc, 64-66; proj. dir. & interim assoc. prof. soils, int. prog, UNIV. FLA, 66-70, RES. ASSOC. ECOL, 70- Asst. pedologist, res. exped, Arctic Slope, summer 52; mem, Symposium Radioecol, Oak Ridge, Tenn. U.S.N.R, 43-46. Tropical ecology; nutrient cycling in mature, terrestrial systems; radionuclide movement and transfer within and among ecosystems; nuclear power reactor siting studies; soil genesis. Address: Ecology Section, Dept. of Botany, 3165 McCarty Hall, University of Florida, Gainesville, FL 32601.

GAMBLE, LEON W(ALTER), b. Grand Cane, La, July 4, 13; m. 36; c. 4. ANALYTICAL CHEMISTRY. B.A, La. State Normal Col, 34; fel, La. State, 37-39, M.S, 39. Teacher, pub. sch, La, 34-37; res. chemist, ESSO RES. LABS, HUMBLE OIL & REF. CO, 39-67, INSTR. PROCESS TRAINING, 66-, SR. RES. CHEMIST, 67- AAAS; Am. Chem. Soc.(Best Paper Award, 65); Am. Inst. Chem. Emission spectroscopy; microscopy; analytical chemistry; plastics; elastomers. Address: 766 Nelson Dr, Baton Rouge, LA 70808.

GAMBLE, MICHAEL I, b. Everett, Washington, Dec. 19, 35; m. 57; c. 2. PHYSICS. B.S, Univ. Wash, 57. Assoc. engr, Boeing Co, 56-59, res. engr, 59-62; prog. mgr. environ. physics, Tulsa Div, AVCO CORP, 62-64, mgr. eng, instrument div, 64-66, mgr. prog. develop, Tulsa Oper, 66-70, MKT. MGR. SPACE PROGS, 70- Nat. Guard, 53-62, Capt. Assoc. fel. Am. Inst. Aeronaut. & Astronaut. Nuclear weapons effects; space environment effects on materials; ionospheric physics related to satellite attitude sensing. Address: Avco Corp, 8939 S. Sepulveda, 400, Los Angeles, CA 90045.

GAMBLE, ROBERT OSCAR, b. Greensboro, N.C, Nov. 20, 35; m. 63; c. 3. MATHEMATICS. B.S.M.E, Duke Univ, 59; M.S, Clemson Univ, 63, Ph.D.(math), 71. Develop. engr, Celanese Fibers Co, S.C, 59-62; instr. MATH, WINTHROP COL, 63-66, ASST. PROF, 70- U.S.A.R, 59-60, Res, 60-62. Am. Math. Soc; Math. Asn. Am. Investigation of ring-theoretic properties of matrices over finite local rings. Address: Dept. of Mathematics, Winthrop College, Rock Hill, SC 29730.

GAMBLE, SAMUEL J(AMES) R(EEVES), b. Pennsauken Township, N.J, Dec. 15, 16; m. 43; c. 3. BIOCHEMISTRY. B.S, Va. Polytech, 47, M.S, 51. Instr. bact. & biochem, Va. Polytech, 49-51; res. microbiologist, Merck & Co, 51-58; ASSOC. PROF. CHEM, LYNCHBURG COL, 58- Nat. Insts. Health fel, Pasteur Inst, Paris, 64-65; res. assoc, Harvard Univ. Wheat Fortification Proj, Tunisia, 70-71. Chevalier de la Republique de Tunisie. U.S.A, 41-46, Maj. Biochemistry of soil microorganisms; industrial fermentations, especially antibiotics, vitamins and steroids; natural products chemistry; plant flavanoids. Address: Dept. of Chemistry, Lynchburg College, Lynchburg, VA 24504.

GAMBLE, STANLEY JOSEPH, b. Detroit, Mich, Jan. 30, 27; m. 58; c. 3. HORTICULTURE, PLANT PHYSIOLOGY. B.S, Mich. State, 51, M.S, 58, Ph.D.(hort), 63. Technician, Mich. State, 58-63; exten. horticulturist & asst. prof. hort, Purdue, 63-65; assoc. prof. BIOL, FERRIS STATE COL, 65-69, PROF, 69- U.S.N.R, 45-46. Am. Soc. Hort. Sci; Int. Soc. Hort. Sci. Mineral nutrition of plants; water requirements of tree fruit crops. Address: Dept. of Biology, Ferris State College, Big Rapids, MI 49307.

GAMBLE, WILBERT, b. Greenville, Ala, June 19, 32; m. 57; c. 1. CHEMISTRY. B.S, Wayne State Univ, 55, Ph.D, 60. Asst. physiol. chem, Wayne State Univ, 55-59, Nat. Insts. Health res. fel, 59-62; asst. prof, ORE. STATE UNIV, 62-68, ASSOC. PROF. BIOCHEM. & BIOPHYS, 68- Vis. assoc. prof. & Nat. Insts. Health spec. fel, Johnson Res. Found, Univ. Pa, 68-69; Fulbright fel, Univ. Sci. & Technol, Ghana, 71-72. AAAS; Am. Chem. Soc; Am. Soc. Biol. Chem. Enzymes and metabolism of vascular tissue; study of synthesis of steroids and ribonuclease in vascular tissue; computer simulation; pharmacy. Address: Dept. of Biochemistry & Biophysics, Oregon State University, Corvallis, OR 97331.

GAMBLE, WILLIAM LEO, b. Elkhart, Kans, Nov. 25, 36; m. 62; c. 3. STRUCTURAL ENGINEERING. B.S, Kansas State, 59; M.S, Illinois, Urbana, 61, Ph.D.(civil eng), 62. Res. asst. struct, Illinois, Urbana, 59-62; Fulbright res. fel, div. bldg. res, Commonwealth Sci. & Indust. Res. Orgn, Australia, 62-63; sr. engr, Bechtel Corp, 64-65; asst. prof. CIVIL ENG, UNIV. ILL, URBANA, 63-69, ASSOC. PROF, 69- Engr. aide, Kans. Hwy. Comn, summers 57, 58. Am. Concrete Inst; Am. Soc. Civil Eng; Am. Soc. Test. & Mat; Am. Rwy. Eng. Asn. Strength and behavior of reinforced concrete floor slab systems; long-term behavior of prestressed concrete bridges; thick reinforced concrete slabs. Address: Dept. of Civil Engineering, 2209 Civil Engineering Bldg, University of Illinois at Urbana-Champaign, Urbana, IL 61801.

GAMBORG, OLUF LIND, b. Denmark, Nov. 9, 24; Can. citizen; m. 53; c. 3. PLANT BIOCHEMISTRY. B.Sc, Univ. Alta, 56, M.Sc, 58; Ph.D.(plant biochem), Univ. Sask, 62. RES. OFF. PLANT BIOCHEM, PRAIRIE REGIONAL LAB, NAT. RES. COUN. CAN, 58- Am. Soc. Plant Physiol; Tissue Cult. Asn; Can. Soc. Plant Physiol; Int. Asn. Plant Tissue Cult. Plant cell culture; suspension culture of plant cells; asexual production of plants from cultured cells and protoplasts by embryogenesis and organogenesis; development of hybrid plants from somatic cells; plant physiology; morphogenesis. Address: Prairie Regional Lab, National Research Council of Canada, Saskatoon, Sask, Can.

GAMBRELL, CARROLL B(LAKE), JR, b. Birmingham, Ala, Dec. 1, 24; m. 44; c. 2. INDUSTRIAL ENGINEERING. B.S, Clemson, 49; univ. exp. sta. grant, Florida, 51-52, M.S, 52; univ. res. found. Ph.D. grant, Purdue, 57-58, Ph.D, 58. Instr. textile mgt, Clemson, 49-51; asst. prof. indust. eng, Lamar State Col, 52-55; instr, Purdue, 55-58, asst. prof, 58-59; prof. eng, Arizona State, 59-67, chmn. dept. indust. eng, 59-67; v.pres. acad. affairs, FLA. TECHNOL. UNIV, 67-71, EXEC. V.PRES, 71- Consult, Gulf States Utilities Co; C&D Battery Co; West. Elec. Co; Sperry Phoenix Co; U.S. Army Sci. Adv. Panel. C.Eng, 43-46; U.S.A.R, 47-, Maj. Am. Soc. Eng. Educ; Am. Inst. Indust. Eng. Human engineering; system simulation; operations research; engineering economic analysis. Address: Florida Technological University, P.O. Box 25000, Orlando, FL 32816.

GAMBRELL, LYDIA J(AHN), b. Cleveland, Ohio, May 18, 04; m. 32; c. 2. BIOLOGY. B.A, Ohio State, 27, M.A, 28, Ph.D.(entom), 32. Asst, dept. zool. & entom, Ohio State, 27-30; instr. bact. & physiol, Lindenwood Col, 30-32; tech. asst. entom, N.Y. Agr. Exp. Sta, 35-38; field agent, Endicott Jr. Col, 39-43; instr. BIOL, Hobart Col, 47; KEUKA COL, 45, 47-54, assoc. prof, 54-57, PROF, 57-, head dept, 57-69. Insect anatomy and embryology. Address: Dept. of Biology, Keuka College, Keuka Park, NY 14478.

GAMBRELL, SAMUEL C, JR, b. Owings, S.C, Sept. 15, 35; m. 57; c. 3. ENGINEERING MECHANICS. B.S, Clemson Univ, 57, M.S, 61; Ph.D.(eng. mech), W.Va. Univ, 65. Instr. ENG. MECH, Clemson Univ, 59-61, asst. prof, 61-62; instr, W.Va. Univ, 62-63; asst. prof, UNIV. ALA, TUSCALOOSA, 65-67, ASSOC. PROF, 67-, DIR. SOLID. MECH. DIV, 69- U.S.A, 57-59, Res, 59-, Maj. Am. Soc. Eng. Educ; Soc. Exp. Stress Anal. Experimental stress analysis; photoelasticity; fatigue; experimental mechanics. Address: Dept. of Aerospace Engineering, Mechanical Engineering & Engineering Mechanics, Box 6307, University of Alabama, University, AL 35486.

GAMBRILL, C(HARLES) M(cDONALD), b. Baltimore, Md, Aug. 19, 01; m. 26; c. 1. CHEMISTRY. B.S, Maryland, 24; Western Reserve, 36; Wayne State, 36. Chemist, Hagen Corp, Pa, 24-25; asst. works chemist, Mathieson Alkali Works, Inc, N.Y, 25-28; res. chemist, Ethyl Corp, N.Y, 28-32, res. & anal. chemist, Mich, 32-36, head anal. sect, 36-52, mgr. anal. res. & servs, 52-54, anal. coord, 54-69; RETIRED. Am. Chem. Soc; Am. Soc. Test. & Mat.(Merit award, 60); Asn. Anal. Chem.(award, 58). Technical service and use of analytical methods and development of methods for analysis of basic materials for manufacture of tetraethyl lead and use of that product in fuels and in combustion engines. Address: 612 Knollcrest Place, Cockeysville, MD 21030.

GAMERTSFELDER, G(EORGE) R(OYCE), b. Naperville, Ill, July 11, 16; m. 39; c. 2. PHYSICS. B.A, N.Cent. Col.(Ill), 37; M.S, Univ. Ill, 39, Ph.D.(physics), 42. Asst. physics, Univ. Ill, 37-42; mem. staff, radiation lab, Mass. Inst. Technol, 42-46; engr, GPL div, SINGER-GEN. PRECISION, INC, 46-51, head res. dept, 51-57, dir. res, 57-61, RES. CONSULT, SINGER-KEARFOTT, 61- With Off. Sci. Res. & Develop, 44. Inst. Elec. & Electronics Eng; Optical Soc. Am. Slow neutrons; microwaves; electronic circuitry; reproducible neutron standard; phase shifting condenser; Doppler navigation; optical data processing; optical instrumentation; correlators; helium speech. Address: Singer-Kearfott, 63 Bedford Rd, Pleasantville, NY 10570.

GAMET, MERRILL B(ARTLETT), b. Chicago, Ill, Jan. 9, 05; m. 30, 37, 48; c. 2. SANITARY ENGINEERING. B.S, Northwestern, 27, C.E, 28; M.S, Wisconsin, 38. Instr. civil eng, tech. inst, Northwestern, 28-38, asst. prof, 38-43; assoc. prof, 43-51, prof, 51-62, acting chmn. dept, 45-47, 51-53, dir. eng, sci. & mgt. war training, 43-44, dir. summer surv. camp, 50-57; sr. sanit. engr. & spec. consult, U.S. Pub. Health Serv, 57-60, sanit. engr. dir. & chief water qual. sect, region V, 60-66, regional prog. coord, FED. ACTIVITIES COORD. BR, Fed. Water Pollution Control Admin, Great Lakes Region, 66-71, CHIEF, FED. ACTIVITIES COORD. BR, SURVEILLANCE & ANAL. DIV, ENVIRON. PROTECTION AGENCY, REGION V, 71- Supvr. water supplies, Serv. Command Engr. Off, Dallas, 44-45; chmn. res. comt, West Shore Water Producers Asn, 57- Am. Soc. Eng. Educ; Am. Soc. Photogram; Am. Water Works Asn; Am. Cong. Surv. & Mapping. Design of water hammer arresters; sterilization of water; activated sludge process of sewage treatment; hydraulics of open channels; determination of bulk modulus of elasticity of crude petroleum products; analysis of water distribution systems by electronic methods; study of Lake Michigan water to provide more effective treatment; effects of algae on filter runs with Great Lakes water. Address: Federal Activities Coordination Branch, Surveillance & Analysis Division, Environmental Protection Agency, 1 N. Wacker Dr, Chicago, IL 60606.

GAMM, STANFORD, b. Chicago, Ill, Aug. 14, 17; m. 43; c. 3. PSYCHIATRY. A.B, Illinois, 39, M.D, 43; Chicago. Asst. dir, outpatient psychiat. clinic, Michael Reese Hosp, Chicago, Ill, 49-51, dir, 51-54; ASST. PROF. PSYCHIAT, MED. SCH, NORTHWEST. UNIV, 56- Consult, Jewish Family & Community Serv, 49-51; res. fel, inst. psychiat. & psychosom. res. & training, Michael Reese Hosp, 49-51, assoc. attend. psychiatrist, hosp, 51-60, attend. psychiatrist, 60-; Vet. Admin. Hosp, 56-; clin. assoc, Chicago Inst. Psychoanal, 57- U.S.N.R, 44-46, Lt.(jg). Am. Psychosom. Soc; Am. Med. Asn; fel. Am. Psychiat. Asn. Family health; healthy personality development; psychosomatic processes. Address: 1631 Sunnyside, Highland Park, IL 60035.

GAMMAGE, RICHARD BERTRAM, b. Whitby, Eng, Nov. 5, 37; m. 64. SURFACE CHEMISTRY, HEALTH PHYSICS. B.Sc, Univ. Exeter, 60, Ph.D.(chem), 64. Nat. Sci. Found. fel, Univ. Fla, 64-67; res. scientist oxide surfaces, OAK RIDGE NAT. LAB, 67-70, HEALTH PHYSICIST, 70- Res. assoc, Imp. Col, Univ. London, 64. Am. Chem. Soc; The Chem. Soc; Faraday Soc; Health Physics Soc. Surface and structural properties of crystalline and deformed calcium carbonate; adsorption on ceramic oxides; isotherms spectroscopy and calorimetry exoelectron emission from beryllium oxide and lunar materials. Address: Oak Ridge National Lab, P.O. Box X, Oak Ridge, TN 37830.

GAMMAL, ELIAS BICHARA, b. Cairo, Egypt, Nov. 18, 30; Can. citizen; m. 61; c. 4. OBSTETRICS & GYNECOLOGY, ANATOMY. M.B, B.Ch, Ain Shams, Cairo, 55; Ph.D.(med. res), Western Ontario, 66. Intern, Ain Shams Univ. Hosps, Egypt, 56-57; St. Joseph's Infirmary, Atlanta, Ga, 57-58, resident obstet. & gynec, 58-61; fel. gynec. cancer, Emory, 61-62; med. res, Collip Lab, UNIV. WEST. ONT, 62-66, lectr. OBSTET. & GYNEC, 67, ASST. PROF, 67-, ANAT, 69-, lectr, 68-69. N.Y. Acad. Sci; Can. Asn. Anat. Mammary carcinogenesis; environmental effects of tissue growth and early embryogenesis. Address: Dept. of Anatomy, Health Sciences Centre, University of Western Ontario, London, Ont, Can.

GAMMANS, WILLIAM J(AMES), b. San Antonio, Tex, Aug. 22, 37; m. 60; c. 2. ORGANIC CHEMISTRY. B.S, Southwest Tex. State Univ, 58; Welch fel, Univ. Tex, Austin, 61-62, Ph.D.(org. chem), 63. SR. CHEMIST, TEX. EASTMAN CO, 63- Am. Chem. Soc. Preparation of nitrogen heterocyclics; catalytic oxidations; organic synthesis. Address: Texas Eastman Co, Box 7444, Longview, TX 75601.

GAMMEL, JOHN L(EDEL), b. Austin, Tex, July 9, 24; m. 47; c. 5. THEORETICAL PHYSICS. B.S, Univ. Tex, 44, M.A, 46; Ph.D.(theoret. physics), Cornell Univ, 50. Tutor physics, Univ. Tex, 42-45, instr. math, 45-46; asst. physics, Cornell Univ, 46-50; mem. staff, Los Alamos Sci. Lab, 50-63; prof. physics, Tex. A&M Univ, 63-67; MEM. STAFF, LOS ALAMOS SCI. LAB, 67- Fulbright fel, 57-58; mem. staff, Aere Harwell, Eng, 61-62. Instr, Univ. Calif, Los Angeles, 52. Fel. AAAS. Theoretical nuclear physics. Address: Group T-9, Los Alamos Scientific Lab, Los Alamos, NM 87544.

GAMMEL, WALTER ARTHUR, SR, b. Chicago, Ill, Nov. 21, 17; m. 43; c. 3. ENGINEERING, POLYMER CHEMISTRY. B.S, Minnesota, 52. Inspector, Detroit Ord. Dist, Mich, 41-45; specialist, Reconstruct. Finance Corp, 45-46; develop. engr, West. Elec. Co, Inc, 46-54; div. sales mgr. & proj. engr, Essex Wire Corp, 54-58; gen. mgr, Automatic Process Control, Inc, 58-59; dir. eng, Nat. Connector Corp, 60-61; pres. & chmn. bd, Modular Electronics, Inc, 61-65; Flexible Prod, Inc, 68-70; EXEC. V.PRES. & MEM. BD. DIR, LEAF, INC, 70- Mem. bd, Bus. Radio, Inc, 63-66; Zodiac Electronics, Inc, 64-; Reo Tool & Plastic, Inc, 64-66. Consult, Int. Plastics Indust, 62-; lectr, Univ. Ala, Huntsville. Sr. mem. Am. Chem. Soc; Am. Ord. Asn; Am. Soc. Test. & Mat; sr. mem. Soc. Automotive Eng; sr. mem. Soc. Plastics Eng. Electrical insulation; encapsulation; techniques for handling multiphase adhesives; epoxy resins, systems and formulation; printed circuits. Address: Leaf, Inc, Box 98, Goulds, FL 33170.

GAMMILL, STEPHEN L, b. Bude, Miss, Jan. 1, 36; m. 67. MEDICINE. B.A, Univ. Miss, 57, B.S, 60, M.D, 62; Univ. Tex, 63-66. Intern, Univ. Tex, 62-63, resident RADIOL, 63-66, instr, 66-67; asst. prof, SCH. MED, TULANE UNIV. LA, 67-70, ASSOC. PROF, 70- Dipl, Am. Bd. Radiol. Army Nat. Guard, 59-65. Am. Med. Asn. Research in a new method of staining Pap smears; clinical radiology; new methods of teaching medicine, particularly programmed teaching. Address: Dept. of Diagnostic Radiology, Charity Hospital, Tulane University, New Orleans, LA 70116.

GAMMON, JAMES R(OBERT), b. Sparta, Wis, Apr. 24, 30; m. 53; c. 4. BIOLOGY, ECOLOGY. B.S, Wis. State Col, Whitewater, 56; M.S, Univ. Wis, 57, Danforth fel, 57-61, Ph.D.(zool, bot), 61. Asst. prof. ZOOL, DePAUW UNIV, 61-65, ASSOC. PROF, 65- U.S.N, 48-49, 51-52. Am. Fisheries Soc; Am. Soc. Limnol. & Oceanog. Fish ecology; radiation effects on fishes; role of external metabolites in aquatic ecology. Address: Dept. of Zoology, DePauw University, Greencastle, IN 46135.

GAMMON, NATHAN, JR, b. Cheyenne, Wyo, June 22, 14; m. 41; c. 2. SOIL CHEMISTRY. B.S, Maryland, 36, M.S, 39; Ph.D.(soils), Ohio State, 41. Asst. soils, Maryland, 36-39; agron, Ohio Exp. Sta, 38-42; PROF. SOIL CHEM, INST. FOOD & AGR. SCI, UNIV. FLA, 46- U.S.N, 42-46, Lt. AAAS; Am. Chem. Soc; Soil Sci. Soc. Am; Am. Soc. Agron. Ion exchange; plant nutrition; pasture soils and fertility maintenance; flame photometry; micronutrients; pecan and peach production. Address: Dept. of Soil Science, Institute of Food & Agricultural Sciences, University of Florida, Gainesville, FL 32601.

GAMMON, RICHARD ANTHONY, b. Lackawanna, N.Y, May 6, 37; m. 63; c. 2. MICROBIOLOGY, BIOLOGY. B.S, St. Bonaventure, 59, Ph.D.(biol), 65. Asst. BIOL, St. Bonaventure, 60-64; asst. prof, GANNON COL, 64-70, ASSOC. PROF, 70- Res. asst, Am. Sterilizer Co, 66-; Nat. Insts. Health res. grant, 66-68. AAAS; Am. Soc. Microbiol. Bacteriophages for the thermophile, Bacillus coagulans; kinetics of ethylene oxide sterilization. Address: Dept. of Biology, Gannon College, Perry Square, Erie, PA 16501.

GAMMON, ROBERT WINSTON, b. Wash, D.C, Sept. 1, 40; m. 57; c. 2. PHYSICS. A.B, Hopkins, 61, Ph.D.(physics), 67; M.S, Calif. Inst. Tech, 63. Mem. tech. staff, Hughes Res. Labs, 62-63; res. assoc. PHYSICS, Hopkins, 66-67; asst. prof, CATH. UNIV. AM, 67-71, ASSOC. PROF, 71- Am. Phys. Soc; Optical Soc. Am. Experimental solid state physics, especially lattice dynamics, thermal properties of solids and elasticity; optics, including light scattering spectroscopy. Address: Dept. of Physics, Catholic University of America, Washington, DC 20017.

GAMMON, WILLIAM H(UGH), b. St. Louis, Mo, Mar. 8, 26; m. 48; c. 3. CHEMICAL ENGINEERING. B.S, Missouri, 49. Chem. engr, Sinclair Res. Labs, Inc, Ill, 49-51, 53-55, foreman, 51-53; supvr. res. & develop, Ashland Oil & Ref. Co, 55-60, asst. dir, 60-63, mgr, United Carbon Co, 63, dir, 64, v.pres, United Carbon Co, 64, pres, 64-67, sr. v.pres, Ashland Chem. Co, 67-70, ADMIN. V.PRES, ASHLAND OIL, INC, 70- U.S.M.C, 44-46. Am. Chem. Soc; Am. Inst. Chem. Eng. Processes and products in petroleum and petrochemical industry. Address: Ashland Oil, Inc, P.O. Box 391, Ashland, KY 41101.

GAMO, HIDEYA, b. Ueda, Japan, Apr. 1, 24; m. 56; c. 2. PHYSICS. B.S, Tokyo, 46, D.Sc.(physics), 58. Res. asst. physics, Tokyo, 46-49, res. assoc. & lectr, 49-58; consult. physicist, T.J. Watson Res. Ctr, Int. Bus. Mach. Corp, 58-59, res. physicist, 59-63; vis. prof. ELEC. ENG, Univ. Rochester, 63-64, PROF, 64-68; UNIV. CALIF, IRVINE, 68- Chmn, Electronics Eng. Group, 71- Inst. Elec. & Electronics Eng; fel. Optical Soc. Am; Am. Phys. Soc; Phys. Soc. Japan. Statistical properties of laser radiation; intensity correlation interferometry; laser light scattering; optical-electronic devices such as infrared isolator; gas laser plasma; air-pollution measurements; optical communication and information processing. Address: School of Engineering, University of California, Irvine, CA 92664.

GAMOTA, GEORGE, b. Lviv, Ukraine, May 6, 39; U.S. citizen; m. 61; c. 3. LOW TEMPERATURE PHYSICS. B.Phys, Univ. Minn, 61, M.S, 63; Ph.D. (physics), Univ. Mich, 66. Res. asst. PHYSICS, Univ. Minn, 59-63; Univ. Mich, 63-66, res. assoc, 66-67; MEM. TECH. STAFF, BELL TEL. LABS, 67- Am. Phys. Soc. Liquid and solid helium. Address: Bell Telephone Labs, Murray Hill, NJ 07974.

GAMOW, RUSTEM IGOR, b. Washington, D.C, Nov. 4, 35; m. 61. BIOENGINEERING, PHYSIOLOGY. B.A, Univ. Colo, 61, M.B.S, 63, Ph.D.(microbiol), 67. Teaching asst. phys. sci, Univ. Colo, 61-63; Nat. Insts. Health res. fel. biol, Calif. Inst. Technol, 67-68; ASST. PROF. BIOENG, UNIV. COLORADO, BOULDER, 68- U.S.C.G.R, 53-59. Am. Soc. Microbiol; Am. Soc. Plant Physiol. Bacteriophage; kinetics; conformational changes in proteins; light response of Phycomyces. Address: Dept. of Aerospace Engineering Sciences, University of Colorado, Boulder, CO 80302.

GAMSON, BERNARD W(ILLIAM), b. Chicago, Ill, Aug. 18, 17; m. 14, 52; c. 4. CHEMICAL ENGINEERING. B.S, Ill. Inst. Tech, 38; M.S, Michigan, 39; Ph.D.(chem. eng), Wisconsin, 43. Develop. engr, Socony Vacuum Oil Co, N.J, 39-41; res. engr, War Prod. Bd, Wisconsin, 42-43; group leader, Great Lakes Carbon Corp, 43-49, chief process engr, 49-51, dir. res. & develop, 51-55; mgr. nuclear fuel, Gen. Eelc. Co, 55-56; assoc. dir, res. ctr, Borg-Warner Corp, Ill, 56-60, v.pres, res. & eng, oil field prod, Byron Jackson Div, Calif, 60-65; consult, chem. engr. & scientist, 65-70; V.PRES, HARVEY ALUMINUM CO, TORRANCE, 70- Am. Chem. Soc; Am. Inst. Chem. Eng. Petroleum refining; petro- and heavy chemicals; metallurgy of iron, aluminum and light metals; carbon technology; thermodynamics; sulfur recovery; nuclear reactor technology; oil well logging; thermoelectrics. Address: 129 S. Alta Vista Blvd, Los Angeles, CA 90036.

GAMSON, EDWARD PHILIP, b. Chicago, Ill, Apr. 14, 43; m. 68; c. 1. ORGANIC CHEMISTRY. B.S, Trinity Col.(Conn), 65; Ph.D.(chem), Northwest. Univ, 70. RES. CHEMIST, PERSONAL CARE DIV, GILLETTE CO, 69- Am. Chem. Soc. Mechanistic organic photochemistry and mechanistic studies of oxidative dyeing. Address: 2823 Summit Ave, Highland Park, IL 60035.

GAN, JOSE C(AJILIG), b. Iloilo, Philippines, Nov. 30, 33; m. 60; c. 2. BIOCHEMISTRY. B.S, Wisconsin, 57; M.S, Iowa, 59; Ph.D.(biochem), Illinois, 64. Asst. res. physiologist, California, Berkeley, 64-66; asst. res. biochemist, hormone res. lab, med. center, California, San Francisco, 66-68; ASST. PROF. BIOCHEM, MED. BR, UNIV. TEX, 68- San Francisco Heart Asn. fel, 65-67. AAAS; Soc. Exp. Biol. & Med. Plasma protein and amino acid metabolism; biosynthesis of glycoproteins; chemistry and biological activity of pituitary gonadotropic hormones. Address: Dept. of Biochemistry, University of Texas Medical Branch, Galveston, TX 77550.

GANAPHATHY, RAMACHANDRAN, b. Tellicherry, India, Jan. 16, 39. COSMOCHEMISTRY, NUCLEAR CHEMISTRY. B.Sc, Govt. Arts Col, Madras, 59; Ph.D.(nuclear chem), Univ. Ark, Fayetteville, 67. Sci. off. radiochem, Atomic Energy Estab, Bombay, 60-63; res assoc. COSMOCHEM, ENRICO FERMI INST, UNIV. CHICAGO, 67-70, SR. RES. ASSOC, 71- Geochem. Soc. Geochronology, particularly determination of age and origin of meteorites by studying the abundance of volatile chemical elements and isotopic composition of noble gases; radiochemical investigation of the distribution of mass in fission. Address: Enrico Fermi Institute, University of Chicago, 5640 S. Ellis Ave, Chicago, IL 60637.

GANAWAY, JAMES RIVES, b. East St. Louis, Ill, Jan. 2, 27; m. 50; c. 3. VETERINARY MEDICINE, MICROBIOLOGY. B.S. & D.V.M, Univ. Mo-Columbia, 53; M.P.H, Johns Hopkins Univ, 58. Base veterinarian, U.S. Air Force, 53-56, assoc. virologist, sch. hyg. & pub. health, Johns Hopkins Univ, 56-58, virologist, Armed Forces Inst. Path, Walter Reed Army Med. Ctr, 58-61; MICROBIOLOGIST, COMP. PATH. SECT, LAB. AIDS BR, DIV. RES. SERV, NAT. INSTS. HEALTH, 61- Dipl, Am. Bd. Vet. Pub. Health, 60. U.S.A.F, 53-61, Capt. Am. Vet. Med. Asn; Am. Soc. Microbiol; Am. Asn.

Lab. Animal Sci. Investigations of the naturally occurring diseases of laboratory animals and their comparative aspects with human diseases, with emphasis on the infectious diseases, their etiology, pathogenesis, control and/or prevention. Address: Comparative Pathology Section, National Institutes of Health, Bldg. 28A, Room 103, Bethesda, MD 20014.

GANCHOFF, JOHN C(HRISTOPHER), b. Wauwatosa, Wis, Aug. 15, 33; m. 66; c. 2. ANALYTICAL & INORGANIC CHEMISTRY. B.S, Marquette, 55, M.S, 57; Ph.D.(chem), Ga. Inst. Tech, 63. ASST. PROF. CHEM, Rutgers, 62-66; ELMHURST COL, 66- Rutgers Univ. & Res. Coun. grants, 63-64; Nat. Sci. Found. summer res. partic. grant & acad. year exten. U.S.A. Am. Chem. Soc. Titrations, especially with spectrophotometric end point location, in both aqueous and non-aqueous solvents using complexing agents as titrants. Address: Dept. of Chemistry, Elmhurst College, Elmhurst, IL 60126.

GANCHROW, DONALD, b. Brooklyn, N.Y, Dec. 30, 40; m. 67; c. 1. BIOLOGICAL PSYCHOLOGY. B.S, Brooklyn Col, 61; U.S. Pub. Health Serv. traineeship, Duke Univ, 65-67, Res. Triangle Found. award, 68-69, Ph.D.(psychol), 69. Nat. Acad. Sci-Nat. Res. Coun. vis. scientist, behav. sci. div, pioneering res. lab, U.S. Army Natick Labs, Mass, 69-71; FEL. ANAT, UNIV. WIS, MADISON, 71- AAAS. Phylogenesis of taste; taste behavior and electrophysiological correlates; evolution of sensory systems in mammals. Address: Dept. of Anatomy, University of Wisconsin, Madison, WI 53706.

GANCHROW, JUDITH RUTH JAY, b. DuQuoin, Ill, Oct. 28, 41; m. 67; c. 1. ANATOMY, PHYSIOLOGICAL PSYCHOLOGY. A.B, Carleton Col, 63; Nat. Inst. Ment. Health fel. & S.M, Brown Univ, 65; Nat. Inst. Ment. Health fel. & Ph.D.(psychol), Duke Univ, 69. RES. FEL. PSYCHOL, SCH. PUB. HEALTH, HARVARD, 69- Sensory physiology; psychophysics of taste; behavioral correlates of taste; electrophysiological correlates of taste; sensory coding; anatomy of gustation. Address: Dept. of Nutrition, Harvard School of Public Health, 665 Huntington Ave, Boston, MA 02115.

GANDER, FREDERICK W(ILLIAM), b. N.Y.C, Jan. 14, 21; m. 42; c. 3. CHEMICAL ENGINEERING. S.B, Mass. Inst. Technol, 42, S.M, 46. Res. eng, Yerkes Res. Lab, E.I. DU PONT DE NEMOURS & CO, 46-53, res. supvr, 53-55, res. mgr, 55-57, lab. dir, 57-62, res. & develop. mgr, 62-70, RES. FEL, FILM DEPT, EXP. STA, 70- U.S.N.R, 42-46, Lt. Am. Chem. Soc; Am. Inst. Chem. Eng. Polymer synthesis; chemical modification of polymers; polymer fabrication. Address: Film Dept, Experimental Station, E.I. du Pont de Nemours & Co, Wilmington, DE 19898.

GANDER, GEORGE WILLIAM, b. Hamilton, Mont, June 27, 30; m. 58; c. 3. BIOCHEMISTRY. B.S, Mont. State Col. 53; M.S, Cornell Univ, 55, Ph.D. (dairy chem), 59. Res. assoc. dairy chem, Univ. Conn, 59-61; BIOCHEM, Albany Med. Col, 61-63; asst. prof, MED. COL. VA, VA. COMMONWEALTH UNIV, 63-67, ASSOC. PROF, 67- Am. Chem. Soc; Am. Soc. Exp. Path; N.Y. Acad. Sci. Mechanism of action of pyrogens. Address: Dept. of Academic Pathology, Medical College of Virginia, Virginia Commonwealth University, Richmond, VA 23219.

GANDER, JOHN E, b. Roundup, Mont, Mar. 9, 25; m. 51; c. 3. BIOCHEMISTRY. B.Sc, Montana State Col, 50; M.Sc, Minnesota, 54, Ph.D.(agr. biochem), 56. Asst. prof. chem, Montana State, 55-58; BIOCHEM, Ohio State, 58-62, assoc. prof, 62-64; UNIV. MINN, ST. PAUL, 64-68, PROF, 68- Mem, Plant Phenolics Group N.Am. U.S.A.A.F, 43-46. AAAS; Am. Chem. Soc; Am. Soc. Biol. Chem; Biophys. Soc. Pathways of biosynthesis of lactose and polygalactofuranosides; pathways of tartrate metabolism in fungi; tyrosine metabolism in Sorghum vulgare; mechanism of galactokinase, phosphoglucose isomerase and uridine diphosphate glucose pyrophosphorylase catalyzed reactions; characterization of fungal glycopeptides. Address: Dept. of Biochemistry, University of Minnesota, St. Paul, MN 55101.

GANDER, R(OBERT) J(OHNS), b. Eagle River, Wis, Sept. 12, 18; m. 48; c. 2. ORGANIC CHEMISTRY. B.S, Wisconsin, 40, M.S, 42; Ph.D.(org. chem), Illinois, 44. Asst. Nat. Defense Res. Comt. proj, Wisconsin, 40-42; Office Sci. Res. & Develop. synthetic rubber proj, Illinois, 42-45; chemist, Firestone Plastics Co, 45-50; asst. dir. surg. adhesives res, JOHNSON & JOHNSON, 50-66, MGR. POLYMER RES, DOMESTIC OPERATING CO, 66- Am. Chem. Soc. Polymer synthesis, especially synthetic elastomers and vinyl chloride resins; technology of plasticized vinyl film and pressure sensitive adhesives. Address: Johnson & Johnson Research Center, North Brunswick, NJ 08903.

GANDHI, CHANDRAVADAN I, b. Gandevi, Gujarat, India, Nov. 23, 28; m. 55; c. 3. CHEMICAL ENGINEERING. B.Sc, Bombay, 49; B.S, Wisconsin, 52; M.Ch.E, Louisville, 53, Ph.D.(chem. eng), 64. Chemist, Premier Chromate & Chem, India, 49-50; sales chemist & engr, Esso Eastern, 53-59; instr. math, Louisville, 63-64; proj. scientist, packing res. lab, Reynolds Metals Co, 64-67; PROJ. ENGR, TECH. CTR, UNION CARBIDE CORP, 67- Organic coatings; synthesis of latexes and evaluations of fundamental processing conditions; process development of organic coatings on aluminum metal, foils and sheets. Address: Technical Center, Bldg. 701-107, Union Carbide Corp, South Charleston, WV 25303.

GANDHI, JEET-MAL, b. Banswara, India, May 1, 31; m. 52; c. 3. PURE MATHEMATICS, THEORETICAL PHYSICS. B.S, Univ. Rajasthan, 53, M.S, 55, Ph.D.(physics), 64. Lectr. physics, Lingraj Col, Belguam, India, 55-57; Jain Eng. Col, Panchkoola, 57-58; Thapar Inst. Eng, Patiala, 58-60; Govt. Col, Bhilwara, 60-62; Univ. Rajasthan, 62-63, reader, 63-66; fel. MATH, Univ. Alta, 66-67; assoc. prof, Univ. Man, 67-68; York Univ.(Ont), 68-69; PROF, WEST. ILL. UNIV, 69- Grants, Univ. Grant Comn. India, 65-66; Nat. Res. Coun. Can, 67-69; Univ. Res. Coun, 69-70; reader, Univ. Rajasthan, 66-68; del, Int. Cong. Math, Moscow, Russia, 66 & Nice, France, 70. Indian Math. Soc; Am. Math. Soc; Am. Asn. Math; fel. Royal Astron. Soc. Stability problems in magneto-hydro dynamics and plasma physics; theory of numbers, diophantine equations and theory of partitions; theory of relativity. Address: Dept. of Mathematics, Western Illinois University, Macomb, IL 61455.

GANDRUD, WILLIAM BENTLEY, b. Birmingham, Ala, Aug. 18, 39. APPLIED PHYSICS. B.S, Alabama, 61; Ph.D.(physics), Hopkins, 68. MEM. TECH STAFF LASER RES, BELL TEL. LABS, 68- Am. Phys. Soc; Inst. Elec. & Electronics Eng. Ion-ion interactions in solids; infared quantum counters; nonlinear optics. Address: Bell Telephone Labs, Whippany, NJ 07981.

GANDY, H(AROLD) W(ELLS), b. San Francisco, Calif, June 19, 23; m. 46; c. 2. SOLID STATE PHYSICS. A.B, Univ. Calif, 49; Univ. Okla, 49-50; fel, Univ. Mo, 51-53, Ph.D.(physics), 53. Instr. physics, Univ. Mo, 50-51; res. physicist, res. labs, Westinghouse Elec. Corp, 53-56; electronics lab, Gen. Elec. Co, 56-59; res. supvry. physicist, U.S. Naval Res. Lab, 59-67; physicist, U.S. Govt, 67-69; CONSULT. PHYSICIST, U.S. NAVAL RES. LAB, 69- Award for Group Achievement, U.S. Naval Res. Lab, 66. U.S.N.R, 42-46. Am. Phys. Soc; Sci. Res. Soc. Am. Optical and electronic properties of crystalline insulators; optical properties of glasses; laser materials research; laser physics; applied optics; systems synthesis; management and direction of research and development. Address: 2000 S. Eads St, Apt. 404, Arlington, VA 22202.

GANDY, WOODROW W(HEELER), b. Bryan, Tex, July 4, 15; m. 40; c. 3. ELECTRICAL ENGINEERING. B.S, Agr. & Mech. Col. Tex, 36, M.S, 38, Ph.D.(elec. eng), 52; Missouri, 38-39; Harvard, 44; Mass. Inst. Tech, 45. Asst. math, Agr. & Mech. Col, Tex, 36-38, instr, 39-41, 48-51; Missouri, 38-39; asst. prof, Mo. Sch. Mines, 41-44, 46; assoc. prof, Northwest. State Col.(La), 46-48; design group engr, Convair Div, Gen. Dynamics Corp, 51-62, chief penetration aids & mission & traffic control, Ft. Worth Div, 62-65, eng. staff specialist, 65-71; MEM. STAFF, U.S. ARMY, HQ, MASSTERS, WEST FT. HOOD, 71- Adj. prof, eve. col, Tex. Christian Univ, 53-56. U.S.N.R, 44-46, Res, 44-53. Math. Asn. Am; Inst. Elec. & Electronics Eng. Circuit analysis and synthesis; electronic countermeasures; fire control systems; missile systems; reconnaissance systems and radomes; analyses in the field of operational research. Address: Hq, MASSTERS, West Ft. Hood, Killen, TX 76544.

GANESAN, ADAYAPALAM T, b. Madras, India, May 15, 32; m. MOLECULAR BIOLOGY, GENETICS. M.A, Annamalai Univ, Madras, 53; Nat. Insts. Health fel, Stanford Univ, 59-63, Ph.D.(genetics), 63. Res. fel. biochem, Indian Inst. Sci, Bangalore, 53-55; res. asst. bot, Indian Agr. Res. Inst, New Delhi, 55-57; res. fel. physiol, Carlesberg Lab, Denmark, 57-59; res. assoc. GENETICS, SCH. MED, STANFORD UNIV, 63-64, asst. prof, 65-70, ASSOC. PROF, 70- Nat. Insts. Health res. grant, 66-69, 71- Genetics Soc. Am; Am. Microbiol. Soc. Fermentation genetics; cytogenetics; molecular biology of DNA replication and recombination. Address: 102 Santa Maria Ave, Portola Valley, CA 94025.

GANESAN, ANN K, b. Denver, Colo, July 25, 33; m. 63. MICROBIAL GENETICS. B.A, Wilson Col, 54; Nat. Insts. Health fel. & M.S, Wisconsin, 59; Nat. Insts. Health fel. & Ph.D.(genetics), Stanford, 61. Res. assoc. microbiol, Palo Alto Med. Res. Found, 61-62; biochem, Syntex Inst. Molecular Biol, 62-65; Nat. Insts. Health fel. radiol, med. ctr, STANFORD UNIV, 65-66, RES. ASSOC, 66-71, BIOL, 71- Biochemical genetics of bacteria. Address: Dept. of Biology, Stanford University, Stanford, CA 94305.

GANGAL, MUKUND D, b. Poona, India, Mar. 30, 40; m. 67; c. 1. APPLIED MECHANICS, MACHINE DESIGN. B.E, Univ. Poona, 61; M.S, Univ. Rochester, 64, Ph.D.(mech. eng), 67. MEM. TECH. STAFF, INGERSOLL-RAND RES. INC, 66- Am. Soc. Mech. Eng. Mechanics; elasticity; plasma physics; numerical methods; finite element methods; rock mechanics. Address: Solid Mechanics Section, Ingersoll-Rand Research, Inc, P.O. Box 301, Princeton, NJ 08540.

GANGAROSA, EUGENE J, b. Rochester, N.Y, Aug. 7, 26; m. 50; c. 3. EPIDEMIOLOGY. A.B, Rochester, 50, M.D, 54, Life Ins. Med. Res. Fund fel, 54-55, M.S, 55. Asst. prof. med. & microbiol, sch. med, Maryland, 61-64; chief epidemic intel. serv, Commun. Disease Ctr, 64-65, chief enteric diseases sect, bact. diseases br, EPIDEMIOL. PROG, 65-70, DEP. CHIEF, BACTERIAL DISEASES BR, CTR. FOR DISEASE CONTROL, 70- Vis. assoc. prof, Jefferson Med. Col, 62; dir, Pakistan Med. Res. Ctr, Lahore, 62-64. U.S.P.H.S, 64-, Med. Dir. Am. Soc. Trop. Med; Am. Pub. Health Asn. Clinical investigation; cholera; shigellosis; salmonellosis; botulism; food poisoning; gastroenterology; hematology; drug toxicity. Address: Bacterial Diseases Branch, Center for Disease Control, Atlanta, GA 30333.

GANGAROSA, LOUIS P(AUL), SR, b. Rochester, N.Y, June 8, 29; m. 50; c. 4. PHARMACOLOGY. B.A, Univ. Rochester, 52, M.S, 61, Nat. Inst. Health grant & Ph.D.(pharmacol), 65; D.D.S, Univ. Buffalo, 55. Private practice, 58-61; asst. prof. dent. res, Univ. Rochester, 65-68, instr. pharmacol, 65-66, asst. prof, 66-68; ASSOC. PROF. PHARMACOL, MED. COL. GA, 68-, PROF. ORAL BIOL, 71-, assoc. prof, 68-71. Lectr, Eastman Dent. Ctr, 63-65, clin. res. assoc, 65-68; Nat. Inst. Dent. Res. grant, 67-, consult, training grant comt, 69-; mem. Am. Asn. Dent. Schs. Dent.C, U.S.A.F, 55-58, Capt. Am. Soc. Pharmacol. & Exp. Therapeut; Int. Asn. Dent. Res; Am. Dent. Asn. Dental research; salivary gland-endocrine relationships; roles of neural system and thyroid in epinephrine hyperglycemia; local anesthetic and sympathomimetic effects on subcutaneous isotope clearances; comparison of subcutaneous and oral submucosal isotope clearances. Address: School of Dentistry, Medical College of Georgia, Augusta, GA 30902.

GANGEMI, FRANCIS A, b. Syracuse, N.Y, Feb. 20, 29. PHYSICS. B.S, Univ. Notre Dame, 54; M.S, Cath. Univ. Am, 59, Zahm Found. fel. & Ph.D. (physics), 62. Asst. prof. PHYSICS, Univ. Portland, 62-65; ASSOC. PROF, South. Ore. Col, 65-67; OHIO NORTH. UNIV, 67- Nat. Sci. Found. grant, Cornell Conf. Relativity, 63; Nat. Sci. Found. res. grant, 63-64; Shell Found. res. grant, summer 64. U.S.M.C, 48. Am. Phys. Soc; Faraday Soc. Quantum chemistry; theoretical calculation of dipole movements of polyatomic molecules; particle physics. Address: 801 S. Gilbert St, Ada, OH 45810.

GANGI, ANTHONY F(RANK), b. Newark, N.J, Feb. 19, 29; m. 61; c. 4. GEOPHYSICS. B.S, California, Los Angeles, 53, M.S, 54, Shell Found. fel, 57-58, Ph.D.(physics, geophys), 60. Sr. electronics technician, inst. geophys, California, Los Angeles, 54-60; mem. tech. staff, Space Electronics Corp, Calif, 60-62; mgr. antenna dept, Space-Gen. Corp, 62-64; assoc. prof. GEOPHYS, Mass. Inst. Technol, 64-67; TEX. A&M UNIV, 67-70, PROF, 70- U.S.A, 46-48. AAAS; Inst. Elec. & Electronics Eng; Am. Geophys.

Union; Seismol. Soc. Am; Soc. Explor. Geophys. Seismology; elastic and radio wave propagation; antenna and antenna array theory; boundary valve problems and mathematical physics; theoretical geophysics. Address: Dept. of Geophysics, Texas A&M University, College Station, TX 77843.

GANGSTAD, EDWARD O(TIS), b. Chippewa Falls, Wis, Dec. 18, 17; m. 45; c. 4. AGRONOMY. B.S, Wisconsin, 42, M.S, 47; Ph.D.(agron), Rutgers, 50. Asst. biochem, Wisconsin, 46-47; agron, Rutgers, 47-50; agronomist, Everglade exp. sta, U.S. Dept. Agr, Fla, 50-51, res. agronomist, 51-53, assoc. agronomist, 53-54; agronomist, Tex. Res. Found, 54-59, sr. agronomist, 59-62, prin. agronomist, 63-66; mgt. agronomist, OFF. CHIEF ENGRS, U.S. ARMY, 66-69, CHIEF, AQUATIC PLANT CONTROL PROG, 69- Cert. serv, U.S. Army, 68, cert. achievement, 71. U.S.A.A.F, 42-45, Res, 45-52, Capt. AAAS; Am. Soc. Agron; Weed Sci. Soc. Am; Am. Genetic Asn; Am. Statist. Asn. Plant growth, breeding, production and utilization; forage crops for livestock production in the Southwest; management of military lands; aquatic plant control. Address: Office, Chief of Engineers, U.S. Army, Forrestal Bldg, Room 4E-070, Washington, DC 20314.

GANGULEE, AMITAVA, b. Rajshahi, Brit. India, Apr. 26, 41. PHYSICAL METALLURGY, SOLID STATE PHYSICS. B.E, Univ. Calcutta, 61; Sc.M, Brown Univ, 64; Sc.D.(metall, mat. sci), Mass. Inst. Technol, 67. Metallurgist, Steel & Allied Prod. Ltd, India, 61-62; consult, Metal Eng. & Treatment Co, 62-63; mem. staff, div. sponsored res, Mass. Inst. Technol, 67; sr. assoc. metallurgist, components div, IBM CORP, 67-68, RES. STAFF MEM, T.J. WATSON RES. CTR, 68- Fel. AAAS; Am. Phys. Soc; Am. Soc. Metals; Am. Crystallog. Asn; jr. mem. Am. Inst. Mining, Metall. & Petrol. Eng. Mechanical and transport properties of solids; thermodynamics; x-ray diffraction; thin films; relation of structure with properties of solids. Address: T.J. Watson Research Center, IBM Corp, P.O. Box 218, Yorktown Heights, NY 10598.

GANGULI, AMAL(ENDU), b. Dacca, E. Pakistan, Jan. 1, 30; m. 63. METALLURGY. B.E, Univ. Calcutta, 52; Ph.D.(metall), Univ. London, 60. Apprentice, Indian Aluminum Co, 52; steel foundry asst, Bird & Co, Ltd, India, 53-56; res. asst. ceramics, Univ. Surrey, 56-59; tech. off, metal-ceramics, Ferodo Ltd, Eng, 59-60; scientist, Nat. Coal Bd, 60-66; STAFF ENGR, BENDIX CORP, 66- Am. Inst. Min, Metall. & Petrol. Eng; Am. Soc. Metals; Soc. Appl. Spectros; Electron Probe Anal. Soc. Am. Friction and wear of sintered metal-ceramic composites and cemented carbides; properties of steels, aluminum alloys and brazing alloys; x-ray diffraction and spectrographic analysis; thermal behavior of silicate bonded oxide-ceramics. Address: Energy Controls Division, Bendix Corp, 717 N. Bendix Dr, South Bend, IN 46620.

GANGULI, GOURANGA, b. Calcutta, India, Dec. 1, 35; m. 67; c. 1. ORGANIC & NATURAL PRODUCTS CHEMISTRY. B.S, Univ. Calcutta, 54, M.S, 56, Indian Coun. Sci. & Indust. Res. fel, 61-64, Ph.D.(chem), 65. Prof. chem, Maharaja Manindra Chandra Col, Calcutta, 57-59; lectr, Scottish Church Col, Calcutta, 59-61; DumDum Motijheel Col, 64-67; res. assoc, Duke Univ, 67-68; prof. chem. & chmn. div. sci. & math, Rust Col, 68-69; fel. CHEM, Memphis State Univ, summer 69; PROF, EDWARD WATERS COL, 69- Am. Chem. Soc; Indian Sci. Cong. Asn; Indian Chem. Soc. Structure elucidation of natural products, especially alkaloids and their biosynthesis. Address: Dept. of Chemistry, Edward Waters College, Jacksonville, FL 32209.

GANGULI, MAYA (GUHA), b. Silchar, India, Feb. 13, 36; m. 67: c. 1. ORGANIC CHEMISTRY. B.S, Univ. Calcutta, 55 & B.S.(honors), 56, M.S, 58, Coun. Sci. & Indust. Res. fel, 59-62, Univ. Grants Comn. fel, 62-63, Ph.D.(chem), 63. Lectr. chem, Jogamaya Devi Col, Calcutta, 63-64; West Bengal Govt. Educ. Serv, 64-67; res. assoc. org. chem, Duke Univ, 67-68; ASSOC. PROF. CHEM, Rust Col, 68-69; EDWARD WATERS COL, 69- AAAS; Indian Chem. Soc; Indian Sci. Cong. Asn. Synthesis of diterpenes; Robinson-Mannich condensation; chemical constituents of corals; synthesis of organo-mercury compounds with liquid crystalline properties. Address: Dept. of Chemistry, Edward Waters College, Jacksonville, FL 32209.

GANGULY, ACHINTYA K(UMAR), b. Dacca, Bengal, India, Dec. 3, 30; m. 66. SOLID STATE PHYSICS. B.Sc, Presidency Col, 49; M.Sc, Calcutta, 52; Ph.D.(physics), N.Y. Univ, 65. Res. asst. physics, Inst. Nuclear Physics, Calcutta, 52-53; lectr, Scottish Church Col, Calcutta, India, 53-54; M.B.B. Col, Agartala, India, 54-61; res. asst, N.Y. Univ, 61-65, res. assoc, 65-67; ENG. SPECIALIST, GEN. TEL. & ELECTRONICS LABS, 67- Instr. physics, N.Y. Univ, 63-65, adj. asst. prof, summer 66. Am. Phys. Soc; Sci. Res. Soc. Am. Optical properties of solids; transport properties of solids; electron-phonon interactions; atomic structure. Address: General Telephone & Electronics Labs, Inc, Bayside, NY 11360.

GANGULY, ASHIT K, b. New Delhi, India, Aug. 9, 34; m. 66; c. 1. ORGANIC CHEMISTRY. B.Sc, Univ. Delhi, 53, M.Sc, 55, Ph.D.(org. chem), 58; Ph.D. (org. chem), Univ. London & dipl, Imp. Col, 61. Res. asst. ORG. CHEM, Univ. Delhi, 55-57; lectr, 57-59; scientist, Glaxo Labs, India, 62-63; Ciba Res. Centre, Bombay, 63-67; Res. Inst. Med. & Chem, Cambridge, Mass, 67-68; sr. scientist, SCHERING CORP, 68-70, prin. scientist, 70-71, RES. FEL, 71- Exhib. 1851 scholar; Glaxo fel; partic. & lectr, Int. Union Pure & Appl. Chem, Riga, U.S.S.R. The Chem. Soc; Am. Chem. Soc. Chemistry of natural products; alkaloids, terpenes, carbohydrates, flavonoids, antibiotics and photochemistry. Address: Research Division, Schering Corp, Bloomfield, NJ 07003.

GANGULY, JIBAMITRA, b. Calcutta, India, Oct. 24, 38; m. 66. GEOLOGY, GEOCHEMISTRY. B.Sc, Calcutta, 58; M.Sc, Jadavpur Univ, India, 60; Ph.D. (geophys. sci), Chicago, 67. Sci. off, Atomic Energy Estab, India, 61-62; MEM. RES. STAFF, Yale, 67-69; Jadavpur Univ, India, 69-71; Birla Inst. Technol. & Sci, India, 71; INST. GEOPHYS. & PLANETARY PHYSICS, UNIV. CALIF, LOS ANGELES, 72- Phase equilibria in geochemical systems and crystal chemistry of rock forming minerals. Address: Institute of Geophysics & Planetary Physics, University of California, Los Angeles, CA 90024.

GANGWERE, STANLEY K(ENNETH), b. Canton, Ohio, Nov. 12, 25; m. 49; c. 1. ZOOLOGY. A.B, Michigan, 50, fel, 50-55, M.S, 52, E.S. George fel, 54, Herbert Boynton fel, 55, Ph.D.(zool), 57. Asst, Michigan, 51-55; instr, WAYNE STATE UNIV, 55-59, asst. prof. BIOL, 59-62, assoc. prof, 62-67, PROF, 67- Fulbright sr. lectr, Valencia, 61; Fulbright res. scholar, Span. Entom. Inst, Madrid, 62. U.S.A.A.F, 44-46. Am. Entom. Soc; Entom. Soc. Am. General behavior of orthopteroid insects, with emphasis on feeding; insect ecology. Address: Dept. of Biology, Wayne State University, Detroit, MI 48202.

GANIS, FRANK M(ICHAEL) (GANGAROSA), b. Rochester, N.Y, Nov. 26, 24; m. 49; c. 2. BIOCHEMISTRY. A.B, Rochester, 49, Ph.D.(biochem), 56. Asst, Rochester, 50-51, res. assoc, 51-56, U.S. Pub. Health Serv. fel, 56-58, instr. biochem, 56-62, radiation biol, 59-61, asst. prof, 61-62; dir. labs, clin. study ctr, UNIV. MD, BALTIMORE CITY, 62-66, CHMN. DEPT. BIOCHEM, 66- U.S.A.F, 43-46, Res, 56-, Lt. Col. Intermediary metabolism of steroid hormones. Address: Dept. of Biochemistry, School of Dentistry, University of Maryland, Baltimore City, Baltimore, MD 21201.

GANIS, SAM EUGENE, b. Comiso, Italy, Apr. 4, 07; nat; m. 33; c. 2. MATHEMATICS. A.B, Rochester, 31, M.A, 32; M.S, Michigan, 36; J.D, John Marshall Law Sch.(Ill), 47, M.P.L, 48. Instr. math, Rochester Collegiate Center, N.Y, 32-36; asst. to actuary, Wash. Nat. Inst. Co, Ill, 37-41; designer electronic develop, Zenith Radio Corp, 41-42. chief engr. prod. develop, Barnes & Reinecke, Inc, 42-47; instr. math, Wilson Jr. Col, 47-48; mech. engr, Armour Res. Found, 48-49; asst. chief engr. & attorney, Consol. Elec. Corp, 49-51; proj. engr. prod. design, Dominion Elec. Corp, Ohio, 51-54; PROF. MATH. & ENG. DRAWING, OHIO WESLEYAN UNIV, 54- Consult, Radio Free Europe, Germany, 50-51. Actuarial science; insurance. Address: Dept. of Mathematics, Ohio Wesleyan University, Delaware, OH 43015.

GANLEY, OSWALD H(AROLD), b. Amsterdam, Holland, Jan. 28, 29; nat; m. 55; c. 2. BACTERIOLOGY, PHYSIOLOGY. A.B, Hope Col, 50; M.S, Michigan, 51, Ph.D, 53; M.P.A, Harvard, 65. Asst, med. bact, Walter Reed Inst. Res, 53-55; res. assoc. allergy & immunol, Merck Inst, 55-60, asst. dir. sci. rels, Merck Sharp & Dohme Res. Labs, 60-64; fel. sci. & pub. policy, Harvard, 64-65; spec. asst. to sci. dir, Agency Int. Develop, Md, 65-66; chief, tech. div, int. sci. & tech. affairs, U.S. DEPT. STATE, D.C, 66-69; SCI. ATTACHE, 69- U.S.A, 53-55, Lt. Microcirc. Soc; Asn. Mil. Surg. U.S; Am. Soc. Microbiol; N.Y. Acad. Sci; fel. Am. Acad. Microbiol; Am. Physiol. Soc. Shock, surgical infections, allergy and host resistance. Address: American Embassy, Rome & Bucharest, APO New York 09794.

GANLEY, W(ILLIAM) PAUL, b. North Tonawanda, N.Y, Apr. 1, 34; m. 70. PHYSICS. B.A, Buffalo, 55, Ph.D.(physics), 60. Assoc. physicist, Cornell Aeronaut. Lab, 60-61; asst. prof. PHYSICS, Bryn Mawr Col, 61-66; ASSOC. PROF. & CHMN. DEPT, WILSON COL, 66- Am. Phys. Soc; Am. Asn. Physics Teachers. Nuclear physics; aerial reconnaissance systems analysis; coherent optical processing; gaseous discharges; electroluminescence. Address: Dept. of Physics, Wilson College, Chambersburg, PA 17201.

GANN, DONALD S(TUART), b. Baltimore, Md, Feb. 25, 32; m. 59; c. 4. PHYSIOLOGY, SURGERY. A.B, Dartmouth Col, 52; Henry Strong Denison fel, Hopkins, 54-56, M.D, 56. Investr. endocrinol, Nat. Heart Inst, 58-60; instr. surg, Med. Col. Va, 63-64; sr. instr. surg. & physiol, Western Reserve, 64-65, asst. prof, 65-66, assoc. prof. surg, prof. physiol, prof. & dir. biomed. eng, 67-70; ASSOC. PROF. SURG. & PROF. BIOMED. ENG, SCH. MED, JOHNS HOPKINS UNIV, 70- Spec. fel, Nat. Heart Inst, 63-64, res. career develop. award, 65-67; asst. surgeon, Univ. Hosp. Cleveland, 64-70; surgeon, Johns Hopkins Hosp, 70- U.S.P.H.S, 58-60, Sr. Asst. Surgeon. AAAS; Am. Physiol. Soc; Endocrine Soc; Soc. Exp. Biol. & Med; Am. Fedn. Clin. Res; Biomed. Eng. Soc.(pres, 71-72); Soc. Univ. Surg. Endocrine physiology; electrolyte metabolism; mathematical models in biology and medicine. Address: Dept. of Biomedical Engineering, Johns Hopkins University School of Medicine, Baltimore, MD 21205.

GANNON, JOHN JAMES, b. Pittsburgh, Pa, May 31, 44. ORGANIC CHEMISTRY. B.S, Duquesne Univ, 64; Nat. Sci. Found. fel, Univ. Notre Dame, summer 65, Ph.D.(org. chem), 68. RES. CHEMIST, CHEVRON RES. CO, STANDARD OIL CO. CALIF, 68- Am. Chem. Soc. Organo-nitrogen heterocycles; fuel additive research and development. Address: Fuel Additive Division, Chevron Research Co, 576 Standard Ave, Richmond, CA 94802.

GANNON, WALTER FRANCIS, b. Medford, Mass, Jan. 26, 35; m. 63; c. 2. ORGANIC CHEMISTRY. A.B, Harvard, 56; Ph.D.(org. chem), Mass. Inst. Technol, 59. Sr. chemist, McNeil Labs, Inc, Pa, 59-64; dir. res. org. chem, REGIS CHEM. CO, 64-70, V.PRES. & TECH. DIR, 70- Am. Chem. Soc. Medicinal chemistry. Address: 2225 Simpson St, Evanston, IL 60201.

GANNON, WILLIAM E, b. Brooklyn, N.Y, Jan. 18, 23; m. 57; c. 1. RADIOLOGY. B.S, St. Francis Col.(N.Y), 44; M.A, Brooklyn Col, 48; M.D, State Univ. N.Y, 52. Instr. RADIOL, STATE UNIV. N.Y. DOWNSTATE MED. CTR, 56-57, asst. prof, 57-62, ASSOC. PROF, 62- Consult, U.S. Naval Hosp, St. Albans, N.Y, 61-; Methodist & Vet. Admin. Hosps, Brooklyn, 64- U.S.A, 44-46, Sgt. Am. Col. Radiol; Am. Roentgen Ray Soc; Am. Soc. Neuroradiol; Radiol. Soc. N.Am. Neuroradiology. Address: Dept. of Radiology, State University of New York Downstate Medical Center, 450 Clarkson Ave, Brooklyn, NY 11203.

GANO, JAMES EDWARD, b. Cleveland, Ohio, Sept. 6, 41; m. 65; c. 1. ORGANIC CHEMISTRY, PHOTOCHEMISTRY. A.B, Miami (Ohio), 63, M.S, 66; Ph.D.(chem), Illinois, 67. Asst. prof. CHEM, UNIV. TOLEDO, 67-71, ASSOC. PROF, 71- Am. Chem. Soc. res. grant, 68-70. Am. Chem. Soc; The Chem. Soc. Mechanistic organic photochemistry; short-lived reaction intermediates, their structures and properties. Address: Dept. of Chemistry, University of Toledo, Toledo, OH 43606.

GANONG, WILLIAM FRANCIS, b. Northampton, Mass, July 6, 24; m. 48; c. 4. PHYSIOLOGY. A.B, Harvard, 45, M.D, 49. Intern med, Peter Bent Brigham Hosp, 49-50, jr. asst. res, 50-51; res. fel. surg, Harvard Med. Sch, 52-53, dir. surg. res. lab. & res. fel. med, 53-55; asst. prof. PHYSIOL, SCH. MED, UNIV. CALIF, SAN FRANCISCO, 55-60, assoc. prof, 60-64, PROF, 64-, CHMN. DEPT, 70-, faculty res. lectr, 68. Consult, State Dept. Ment. Hyg, Calif; mem, Int. Brain Res. Orgn. Prize, Boylston Med. Soc,

49; Med.C, 43-46, 51-52, Capt. AAAS; I.F.I. Golden Hippocrates Award, Italy, 70. Endocrine Soc; Am. Physiol. Soc; Am. Soc. Zool; Soc. Exp. Biol. & Med; Nat. Soc. Med. Res; N.Y. Acad. Sci; Royal Soc. Med. Neuroendocrinology; interrelation between endocrine and brain function. Address: Dept. of Physiology, University of California, San Francisco, CA 94122.

GANS, BENJAMIN J, b. Poland, June 6, 23; nat; m. 48; c. 2. HISTOCHEMISTRY. B.S. & D.D.S, St. Louis, 46; M.S, Illinois, 51. Asst, Illinois, 48-50; asst. prof. ORAL SURG, Loyola (Ill), 51-55; assoc. prof, dent. sch, Northwest. Univ.(Ill), 55-65; asst. prof, sch. dent. & clin. asst. prof. surg, sch. med, UNIV. ILL. MED. CTR, 65-66, ASSOC. PROF. ORAL SURG, SCH. DENT, 66-, SURG, COL. MED, 68-, clin. assoc. prof, 66-68. Chief oral surg, Michael Reese Hosp, dir. advan. educ. oral surg; consult, Zeller Clin, Univ. Chicago. Dipl, Am. Bd. Surg. Dent.C, 46-48, Capt. AAAS; fel. Am. Col. Dent; Am. Dent. Asn; Int. Asn. Dent. Res. Ground substance of connective tissues; growth and development. Address: 2376 E. 71st St, Chicago, IL 60649.

GANS, CARL, b. Hamburg, Germany, Sept. 7, 23; nat; m. 61. BIOLOGY. B.M.E, N.Y. Univ, 44, M.S, Columbia, 50; Nat. Sci. Found. fel. & Ph.D.(biol), Harvard, 57. Asst. proj. mgr, Babcock & Wilcox Co, N.Y, 47-51, serv. engr, 51-55, contract engr, 55; fel. biol, Florida, 57-58; asst. prof, State Univ. N.Y. Buffalo, 58-62, assoc. prof, 62-66, prof, 66-71, chmn. dept, 70-71; PROF. ZOOL. & CHMN. DEPT, UNIV. MICH, ANN ARBOR, 71- Guggenheim Mem. fel, Brazil, 53-54; res. assoc, Carnegie Mus, Pa, 52-; Am. Mus. Natural Hist, 59-; consult, Buffalo Mus. Sci, 59-66; sci. fel, N.Y. Zool. Soc, 70- C.Eng, U.S.A, 44-46. Fel. AAAS; Am. Asn. Anat; Am. Soc. Mech. Eng; Soc. Study Evolution; Soc. Syst. Zool; Am. Soc. Zool; Am. Soc. Ichthyol. & Herpet; Soc. Vert. Paleont; Ecol. Soc. Am; Am. Physiol. Soc; Int. Soc. Toxicol. Evolution; comparative anatomy; functional morphology; physiology; behavioral aspects of amphibians and reptiles; feeding and burrowing adaptations. Address: Dept. of Zoology, University of Michigan, Ann Arbor, MI 48104.

GANS, DAVID, b. New York, N.Y, Apr. 10, 07; m. 45. MATHEMATICS. B.S, N.Y. Univ, 28, Ph.D.(math), 48; Shattuck fel, Harvard, 29-30, A.M, 30. Instr. MATH, N.Y. Univ, 28-42; Illinois, 45; WASH. SQUARE COL, N.Y. UNIV, 46-48, asst. prof, 49-54, ASSOC. PROF, 55- Faculty fel, Fund Adv. Ed, 53-54. Civilian instr. radio eng, U.S. War Dept, 42-45. Math. Asn. Am; Am. Math. Soc. Modern geometry, especially euclidean, non-euclidean, projective. Address: Dept. of Mathematics, Washington Square College, New York University, Washington Square, New York, NY 10003.

GANS, DAVID M(ANUS), b. Russia, May 5, 05; nat; m. 26; c. 2. CHEMISTRY. B.S, Chicago, 26, M.S, 27, Swift fel. & Ph.D.(chem), 29. Instr. phys. chem, Chicago, 29-36; res. chemist, Interchem. Corp, N.Y, 36, sr. chemist, 36-39, asst. dir. res, 39-45; tech. dir, Quaker Chem. Prods. Corp, Pa, 45-49; dir. res. Arco Div, Am. Marietta Co, Ohio, 49-59, v.pres, 59-62; DIR, COATINGS RES. GROUP, INC, CLEVELAND, 62- With Atomic Energy Comn; Off. Sci. Res. & Develop. AAAS; Am. Chem. Soc; Fedn. Socs. Paint Technol; Am. Soc. Metals; fel. Am. Inst. Chem. Colloid chemistry and surface activity; protective coatings; nuclear disintegration; spectroscopy; applied surface chemistry and colloids. Address: 3311 Warrensville Center Rd, Shaker Heights, OH 44122.

GANS, EUGENE H(OWARD), b. New York, N.Y, Dec. 17, 29; m. 53; c. 2. PHARMACY, CHEMISTRY. B.S, Columbia, 51, M.S, 53; Ph.D.(pharm), Wisconsin, 56. Lab. asst, col. pharm, Columbia, 51-53; Alumni Res. Found. fel, pharmaceut. res, sch. pharm, Wisconsin, 55-56; sr. scientist group leader, Hoffman-LaRoche, Inc, N.J, 56-60; head new prod. develop. sect, Vick Div. Res. & Develop. Labs, Richardson-Merrell, N.Y, 60-64, asst. dir. develop, 64-67, dir, 67-71; ASSOC. DIR, ALZA INST. PHARMACEUT. CHEM, 71- Am. Pharmaceut. Asn; Am. Chem. Soc; Sci. Res. Soc. Am. Pharmaceutical research and development; corporate research and development management; development of pharmaceutical and proprietary products; advanced therapeutic and drug delivery systems; drug stability; absorption and metabolism; activity and potentiation; solubilization. Address: 2133 Terrace Rd, Lawrence, KS 66044.

GANS, HENRY, b. Zevenaar, Netherlands, July 1, 25; U.S. citizen; m. 58. SURGERY, PHYSIOLOGICAL CHEMISTRY. M.D, State Univ. Utrecht, 52; D.Med.Sc, Roman Cath. Univ. Nijmegen, 55; Ph.D.(surg), Univ. Minn, 64. Instr. anat, Roman Cath. Univ. Nijmegen, 54-55; resident SURG, sch. med, Univ. Minn, 56-61, instr, 61-64, asst. prof, 64-68; ASSOC. PROF, MED. COL, CORNELL UNIV, 68-; ASSOC. SURGEON, NEW YORK HOSP, 68- U.S. Pub. Health Serv. fel, 60-61, career develop. award, 67-70. Dipl, Am. Bd. Surg, 65. AAAS; Am. Col. Surg; Am. Med. Asn; Soc. Exp. Biol. & Med; Am. Chem. Soc; Reticuloendothelial Soc; Am. Soc. Artificial Internal Organs; Harvey Soc. Anatomy of intrahepatic structures; hepatic physiology and surgery; mechanisms which preserve blood fluidity and their relationship to thrombosis. Address: New York Hospital-Cornell Medical College, 535 E. 68th St, New York, NY 10021.

GANS, JOSEPH H(ERBERT), b. Hartford, Conn, Dec. 29, 22; m; c. 3. PHARMACOLOGY. V.M.D, Univ. Pa, 46; Ph.D.(physiol), Jefferson Med. Col, 58. Prof. PHARMACOL, State Univ. N.Y. Vet. Col, Cornell Univ, 57-61; assoc. prof, sch. med, Indiana Univ, 61-67; COL. MED, UNIV. VT, 67-69, PROF, 69- AAAS; Am. Soc. Vet. Physiol. & Pharmacol; Am. Physiol. Soc; Am. Soc. Pharmacol. & Exp. Therapeut; Am. Soc. Nephrology. Cholesterol metabolism; renal metabolism; polysaccharide metabolism. Address: Dept. of Pharmacology, University of Vermont, Burlington, VT 05401.

GANS, PAUL J(ONATHAN), b. Chicago, Ill, May 1, 33; m. 59; c. 2. CHEMICAL PHYSICS. B.Sc, Ohio State, 54; univ. fel, Case, 56-58, Veazey fel, 58-59, Ph.D.(chem), 59. Res. assoc. CHEM, Illinois, 59-62, instr, 61-62; asst. prof, N.Y. UNIV, 62-66, ASSOC. PROF, 66-, asst. chmn. dept, 65-67, acting chmn, 67-68, chmn, 68-70. AAAS; Am. Chem. Soc; Am. Phys. Soc; Asn. Comput. Mach. Statistical mechanics; phase transitions; polymeric systems; digital computation; Monte Carlo techniques. Address: Dept. of Chemistry, New York University, Washington Square, New York, NY 10003.

GANSCHOW, ROGER E(LMER), b. Buffalo, N.Y, Mar. 21, 37; m. 59; c. 2. BIOCHEMISTRY, GENETICS. B.A, Valparaiso, 59; Ph.D.(biol), State Univ. N.Y, Buffalo, 67. Am. Cancer Soc. fel. BIOCHEM, sch. med, Stanford, 67-68; RES. ASSOC, CHILDREN'S HOSP. RES. FOUND, 68- Asst. prof, med. sch, Univ. Cincinnati, 68-71, assoc. prof, 71-; Nat. Inst. Arthritis & Metab. Diseases res. grant, 70-73. Genetic control of enzymes in animal cells. Address: Children's Hospital Research Foundation, Cincinnati, OH 45229.

GANSLEN, R(ICHARD) V(ICTOR), b. Newark, N.J, Feb. 15, 17; m. 51; c. 5. PHYSIOLOGY, HEALTH EDUCATION. B.S, Columbia, 39; M.Ed, Springfield Col, 40; Ph.D, Illinois, 52; Oklahoma, 60. Asst. instr, Springfield Col, 39-40; instr. anat. & physiol, Rutgers, 46-48; instr. & asst. prof. kinesiology & res. & supvr. phys. fitness res. lab, Univ. Ill, 48-52; assoc. prof. physiol, anat. & kinesiology, Arkansas, 52-62; acting dir. human performance res. lab, California, Los Angeles, 63; physiologist aerospace med, McDonnell Douglas Aircraft Corp, Mo, 63-67; prof. health, phys. educ. & recreation, Tex. Woman's Univ, 67-71; DIR. HEALTH EDUC. & TRAINING, DALLAS CITY HEALTH DEPT, 71- U.S.A.R, Lt. Col. Aerospace Med. Asn; Am. Inst. Aeronaut. & Astronaut. Scientific analysis of sports skills utilizing metabolic or kinesiological principles; work in pharmacology and physiology of exercise; fatigue and training effects; biochemistry of muscle; aerodynamics of sports implements; analysis of motor skills via high speed cinematographical techniques; life support function in aircraft and Gemini spacecraft; supervision of ejection seat testing; cockpit geometry; escape and survival systems; extensive work anthropometry on college women. Address: Dallas City Health Dept, 1936 Amelia Ct, Dallas, TX 75235.

GANSOW, OTTO ALPHONSE, b. St. Louis, Mo, Oct. 5, 40. INORGANIC CHEMISTRY, BIOCHEMISTRY. A.B,,Wash. Univ, 62; Ph.D.(chem), Northwest. Univ, 66. Fel. CHEM, Univ. Wis, 66-67; Mass. Inst. Technol, 67-68; ASST. PROF, RICE UNIV, 68- Am. Chem. Soc; The Chem. Soc. Application of ^{23}Na, ^{13}C, ^{15}N, ^{31}P, ^{1}H nuclear magnetic resonance to studies of structure and chemical bonding in inorganic and biological systems. Address: Dept. of Chemistry, Rice University, Houston, TX 77001.

GANT, FRED ALLAN, b. Howard, Ala, Aug. 7, 36; m. 70; c. 1. PHYSICAL CHEMISTRY, THERMODYNAMICS. B.S, Alabama, 62, Atomic Energy Cmn. summer grant, 63, M.S, 65, NASA grant, 64-66, Ph.D.(phys. chem), 67. Chemist, cent. labs, Swift & Co, 60-61; asst. prof. CHEM, Mobile Col, 66-67; ASSOC. PROF, JACKSONVILLE STATE UNIV, 67- Nat. Guard, 54-62, S/Sgt. Am. Chem. Soc. Thermodynamic studies of inorganic compounds using a copper block calorimeter; fused salt; reaction calorimetry. Address: Dept. of Chemistry, Jacksonville State University, Jacksonville, AL 36265.

GANT, JAMES QUINCY, JR, b. Detroit, Mich, May 26, 06; m. 38, 62. DERMATOLOGY. B.A, Ohio State, 30, M.Sc, 31; M.D, Med. Col. Va, 35. Intern, Stuart Circle Hosp, Richmond, Va, 35-36; ship surgeon, S.S. Exochorda, 36-37; intern, Bellevue Hosp, New York, N.Y, 37-38; mem. staff, U.S. Dept. Agr, 38-39; U.S. Pub. Health. Serv, 39-46; U.S. Penitentiaries, Ft. Leavenworth, Kans. & Atlanta, Ga, 39-40; venereal disease res, dermatoses sect, Nat. Insts. Health, 41-46; chief skin & allergy clin, Vet. Admin. Regional Off, 46-66; EMER. PROF. CLIN. DERMAT. & SYPHILOL, SCH. MED, GEORGE WASHINGTON UNIV, 71- Mem. staff, U.S. Food & Drug Admin, 38-39; emer. sr. attend. dermatologist, Children's Hosp, D.C; sr. attend. dermatologist, Doctor's Hosp, D.C. Dipl, Am. Bd. Clin. Immunol. & Allergy, 66. U.S.P.H.S.R, 46-, Med. Dir. AAAS; fel. Am. Acad. Dermat; Am. Acad. Allergy; Am. Med. Asn; Am. Pub. Health Asn; Am. Venereal Disease Asn; Asn. Mil. Surg. U.S; Am. Geophys. Union; N.Y. Acad. Sci; Int. Lunar Soc.(pres, 58-60, secy-gen, 60-); Int. Asn. Planetology; Brit. Astron. Soc; Brit. Interplanetary Soc; Royal Astron. Soc. Can; Astron. Soc. Mex. Industrial skin disease; corticosteroid in various skin diseases; griseofulvin in fungus infections; astronomy; lunar research and mapping. Address: 1801 Eye St. N.W, Washington, DC 20006.

GANTHER, HOWARD EDWARD, b. Adrian, Mo, Jan. 17, 37, m. 64; c. 2. BIOCHEMISTRY. B.S, Missouri, 58; M.S, Wisconsin, 61, Babcock fel, 62-63, Ph.D.(biochem), 63. Res. assoc. biochem, Michigan, 63-64; assoc. staff scientist, Jackson Lab, 64-65; asst. prof. BIOCHEM, Univ. Louisville, 65-69; ASSOC. PROF, UNIV. WIS, MADISON, 69- AAAS; Am. Soc. Biol. Chem; Am. Inst. Nutrit. Biochemistry of sulfur, selenium and heavy metals; trace element nutrition. Address: Dept. of Nutritional Sciences, University of Wisconsin, 1270 Linden Dr, Madison, WI 53706.

GANTNER, GEORGE E, JR, b. St. Louis, Mo, June 7, 27; m; c. 7. MEDICINE, PATHOLOGY. B.S, St. Louis, 49, M.D, 53. Assoc. prof. PATH, SCH. MED, ST. LOUIS UNIV, 62-69, PROF, 69-, PATHOLOGIST & DIR. LABS, UNIV. HOSPS, 58- Chief med. exam, St. Louis County, Mo, 69- U.S.N.R. Am. Med. Asn; Col. Am. Path; Am. Soc. Clin. Path; Am. Acad. Forensic Sci; Am. Rheumatism Asn. Chemistry of body after death; time of death; criteria of cell viability; data processing systems; drug effects on cytogenetics; clinical pathology. Address: Dept. of Pathology, St. Louis University School of Medicine, St. Louis, MO 63105.

GANTT, CLARENCE LEROY, b. Asheville, N.C, Jan. 25, 28; m; c. 2. INTERNAL MEDICINE. B.S, Wake Forest Col, 49; M.D, Bowman Gray Sch. Med, 52; M.S, Ohio State, 55. Intern, Atlantic City Hosp, 52-53; asst. resident path, Ohio State, 53-55, med, 55; Georgetown, 55-56; Univ. Virginia Hosp, 56-57; asst. prof. med, col. med, Illinois, 57-61; asst. prof. med. & asst. dir. clin. res. unit, hosp, Ohio State, 61-63; asst. prof. MED, COL. MED, UNIV. ILL, 63-67, assoc. prof, 67-71, PROF, 71-; DIR. CORP. RES. DEVELOP, ABBOTT LABS, 71- Asst. dir. div. clin. res, G.D. Searle & Co, 57-61; asst. prog. dir, clin. res. ctr, col. med, Univ. Ill, 63-67, chief, sect. nephrol, 67-71, co-dir, renal transplantation ctr, 68-71. Am. Fedn. Clin. Res; Am. Soc. Pharmacol. & Exp. Therapeut; Am. Soc. Clin. Pharmacol. & Chemother. Address: Corporation Research Development, Abbott Labs, North Chicago, IL 60064.

GANTT, ELISABETH, b. Gakovo, Yugoslavia, Nov. 26, 34; m. 58 c. 1. CELL BIOLOGY, ELECTRON MICROSCOPY. B.A, Blackburn Col, 58; M.Sc, Northwest. Univ, 60, Nat. Insts. Health fel, 61-63, Ph.D.(biol), 63. NAT. INSTS. HEALTH RES. ASSOC. MICROBIOL, med, sch, Dartmouth Col,

63-66; RADIATION BIOL. LAB, SMITHSONIAN INST, 66- AAAS; Am. Soc. Cell Biol; Bot. Soc. Am; Am. Soc. Plant Physiol; Phycol. Soc. Am. Structure of photosynthetic apparatus in algae; localization of phycobiliproteins; membrane structure. Address: Radiation Biology Lab, Smithsonian Institution, 12441 Parklawn Dr, Rockville, MD 20852.

GANTT, RALPH RAYMOND, b. Chicago, Ill, Apr. 2, 36; m. 58. BIOCHEMISTRY. B.A, Blackburn Col, 58; Ph.D.(biochem, org. chem), Illinois, Chicago, 64. Am. Cancer Soc. fel, Dartmouth Med. Sch, 63-66; CHEMIST, NAT. CANCER INST, 66- Am. Chem. Soc; Tissue Cult. Asn. Nucleic acid and protein synthesis; carcinogenesis. Address: National Cancer Institute, Bldg. 37, Room 4D05, National Institutes of Health, Bethesda, MD 20014.

GANTT, W(ILLIAM) HORSLEY, b. Wingina, Va, Oct. 24, 93; m. 34; c. 2. NEUROPHYSIOLOGY, PSYCHIATRY. B.Sc, North Carolina, 16; Miller scholar, Virginia, 10, 11-13, M.D, 20; Kaiser Wilhelm Inst. für Hirnforschung, Berlin, 33. Instr. anat, Virginia, 17-18; intern surg, Univ. Hosp Maryland, 19-20, med, 20-21, med. & clin. lab, 21-22; chief petrograd. unit, med. div, Am. Relief Admin, 22-23; res. path, med. sch, Univ. Col, London, 23-24; collab, Pavlov's Physiol. Labs, Russia, 25-29; res. psychiat, Phipps Psychiat. Clin, SCH. MED, JOHNS HOPKINS UNIV, 29-32, from assoc. to assoc. prof. PSYCHIAT, 32-58, EMER. PROF, 58-, DIR. PAVLOVIAN LAB, 32- Intern surg, Union Mem. Hosp, 19-20; Church Home & Infirmary, 29-30; collab, Insts. Exp. Med, Russia & Mil. Med. Acad, 25-29; consult, U.S. Vet. Admin, 49-; vis. prof, Univ. P.R, 54-55; lectr, U.S.S.R. Acad. Sci, 57; chief scientist, psychophysiol. lab, U.S. Vet. Admin. Hosp, Md, 58-; mem. adv. bd, Medico, 61-; ed, Pavlovian J. Res, 65-; Conditional Reflex J, 66-; Soviet Neurol. & Psychiat, 69-; pres, Collegium Internationale Activitatas Nervosae Superioris sect, World Psychiat. Asn, 69- Award, Am. Heart Asn, 51, 54; Lasker Award, 56. AAAS; Am. Physiol. Soc; Am. Psychosom. Soc; Am. Soc. Pharmacol. & Exp. Therapeut; Soc. Biol. Psychiat.(v.pres, 59-60, pres, 60-61, gold medal award, 71); assoc. Am. Neurol. Asn; Am. Psychopath. Asn.(pres, 60-61); Am. Psychiat. Asn; fel. Am. Med. Asn; Pavlovian Soc. N.Am.(pres, 55-65); Am. Acad. Neurol; Royal Soc. Med; hon. mem. Czech. Med. Soc. Liver and gastrointestinal diseases; secretions of the digestive glands; conditional reflexes and behavior; anatomy of conditional reflex pathways; experimental neurosis; constitutional factors in disease; public health; effect of war and revolution in Russia on diseases; cardiac conditional reflexes; visceral functions and learning capacity in psychogenic and organic disorders; objective measures of susceptibility to nervous breakdown in the human; application of physiological methods to dynamics of human psychopathology; preventive psychiatry. Address: Pavlovian Research Lab, Veterans Administration Hospital, P.O. Box 7, Perry Point, MD 21902.

GANTZ, RALPH L(EE), b. Anthony, Kans, Sept. 16, 32; m. 61; c. 2. PLANT PHYSIOLOGY. B.S, Kansas State, 54; M.S, Illinois, 56, Ph.D.(agron), 58. Asst. agron, Illinois, 54-58, exten. agronomist, 58-59; plant physiologist, Tex. Div, DOW CHEM. CO, 59-63, field agriculturist, plant sci. res. & develop, Mich, 63-64, field agriculturist, Minn, 65-66, AGR. PROD. FIELD RES. STA. MGR, CALIF, 66- Am. Soc. Agron; Weed Sci. Soc. Am. Weed control; herbicide research and development. Address: Dow Chemical Co, Rt. 1, Box 1313, Davis, CA 95616.

GANTZEL, PETER KELLOGG, b. Pasadena, Calif, June 23, 34; m. 56; c. 3. PHYSICAL CHEMISTRY. B.A, Colorado, 56; Ph.D.(crystallog), Univ. Calif, Los Angeles, 62. STAFF MEM, GULF GEN. ATOMIC CO. DIV, GULF ENERGY & ENVIRON. SYSTS. INC, 62- Am. Chem. Soc; Am. Crystallog. Asn. X-ray diffraction and fluorescence analysis; electron diffraction and microscopy, computer programming for these areas; gamma-ray spectroscopy. Address: 8308 Paseo del Ocaso, La Jolla, CA 92037.

GANZ, AARON, b. New York, N.Y, Feb. 4, 24; m. 49; c. 2. RESEARCH ADMINISTRATION, HUMANISTIC PSYCHOLOGY. B.S, Chicago, 47, Lederle fel, 47-49, Atomic Energy Comn. fel, 49-50, Ph.D.(pharmacol), 50. Instr. pharmacol, med. units, Tennessee, 50-52, asst. prof, 52-55, assoc. prof, 55-61; exec. secy, res. career award comt, Nat. Inst. Gen. Med. Sci, NAT. INSTS. HEALTH, 62-63, head res. career sect, res. fels. br, 63-64, training grants & fels. officer, off. dir, 64-68, assoc. dir. prog. planning & eval, NAT. INST. DENT. RES, 68-70, CHIEF GEN. ORAL SCI. PROG, 70- U.S.A, 43-46. Fel. AAAS; Am. Soc. Pharmacol. & Exp. Therapeut. Medical and dental research, education and administration; humanistic science administration. Address: 6800 Breezewood Terr, Rockville, MD 20852.

GANZ, WILLIAM, b. Kosice, Czech, Jan. 7, 19; m. 45; c. 2. CARDIOLOGY. M.D, Charles Univ, Prague, 47; C.Sc, Czech. Acad. Sci, 60. Sr. investr, Inst. Cardiovasc. Res, Prague, 51-53, head coronary res. group, 53-66; SR. RES. SCIENTIST CARDIOL, CEDARS-SINAI MED. CTR, 66-; ASSOC. PROF. MED, UNIV. CALIF, LOS ANGELES, 70- Coord. coronary res. in Czech, 60-66. Fel. Am. Col. Cardiol. Coronary circulation in health and disease; measurement of blood flow–methods. Address: Dept. of Cardiology, Cedars of Lebanon Hospital, 4833 Fountain Ave, Los Angeles, CA 90029.

GAPOSCHKIN, CECILIA P(AYNE), b. Wendover, Eng, May 10, 00; nat; m. 34; c. 3. ASTRONOMY. A.B, Cambridge, 23, M.A. & D.Sc, 50; Ph.D, Radcliffe Col, 25; hon. D.Sc, Wilson Col, 42, Smith Col, 43, Western Col, 51, Colby Col, 58. With HARVARD OBSERV, 23-38, Phillips Astronr, 38-67, Phillips Prof. ASTRON, 56-67, EMER. PROF, 67-; MEM. STAFF, SMITHSONIAN ASTROPHYS. OBSERV, 67- Chmn. dept. astron, Harvard, 56-67. Award of Merit, Radcliffe Col, 52. Am. Astron. Soc; Am. Philos. Soc; Am. Acad. Arts & Sci; Royal Astron. Soc. Variable stars; stellar evolution, galactic structure and novae. Address: Harvard Observatory, 60 Garden St, Cambridge, MA 02138.

GAPOSCHKIN, E(DWARD) M(ICHAEL), b. Boston, Mass, May 29, 35; m. 59; c. 3. GEODESY, GEOPHYSICS. B.S, Tufts Univ, 57; Dipl, Cambridge 59; Ph.D.(geophys), Harvard, 69. PRIN. SCIENTIST SATELLITE GEOPHYS. GROUP, SMITHSONIAN ASTROPHYS. OBSERV, HARVARD, 59- Lectr, Yale Summer Inst. Dynamical Astron, 68-69; consult, adv. comt. geodesy & cartography, NASA, 68-70; lectr, inst. geodetic sci, Ohio State Univ, 69; res. assoc, Harvard Col. Observ, 69- Asn. Comput. Mach; Am. Geophys. Union; Royal Astron. Soc. Satellite geodesy; satellite orbit analysis; celestial mechanics; digital computer techniques for literal algebra and numerical methods; dynamics of the earth, especially those which can be studied with satellite techniques such as the mass motion and tectonic displacements; solid earth geophysics. Address: 55 Farmcrest Ave, Lexington, MA 02173.

GAPOSHKIN, SIRGAY, b. Eupatoria, Russia, July 12, 98; nat; m. 34; c. 3. ASTRONOMY. Ph.D.(Russian humanities), Univ. Berlin, 28, Ph.D. (Ger. sci), 32. Asst, HARVARD OBSERV, 33-39, res. assoc, 39-48, ASTRONOMER, 48- Variable stars; galactic and extragalactic eclipsing binaries; stellar photometry; globular clusters; spectroscopic binaries; novae; galaxies; Milky Way; Magellanic Clouds. Address: 74 Shade St, Lexington, MA 02173.

GAPSKI, G(EORGE) ROBERT, b. Chicago, Ill, Feb. 22, 34. ORGANIC CHEMISTRY. B.S, Loyola Univ. Chicago, 56; M.S, Northwest. Univ, 61; Ph.D. (org. chem), Ohio Univ. 66. Org. chemist, William Wrigley, Jr. Co, 60-61; fel. org. chem, Salk Inst. Biol. Studies, 65-67; dept. biochem, Scripps Clin. & Res. Found, 67-70; MEM. STAFF, TERRA-MARINE BIORES, 70- U.S.A, 57-59. Am. Chem. Soc. Heterocyclic chemistry and natural products. Address: Terra-Marine Bioresearch, P.O. Box 2208, La Jolla, CA 92037.

GARA, ROBERT, b. Santiago, Chile, Dec. 16, 31; m. 58; c. 2. FOREST ENTOMOLOGY. B.S, Utah, 53; M.S, Oregon State, 62, Boyce Thompson Inst. Plant Res. fel. & Ph.D.(entom), 64. Forester, Kirby Lumber Corp, 57-60; res. asst. forest entom, Boyce Thompson Inst, plant res, 60-62, sr. scientist, 62-63, proj. leader, 63-66; asst. prof. FOREST ENTOM, col. forestry, Syracuse Univ, 66-68; ASSOC. PROF, COL. FOREST RESOURCES, UNIV. WASH, 68- Consult, Food & Agr. Orgn, Turrialba, Costa Rica, 69-70. U.S.A.F, 53-57, Capt. Soc. Am. Foresters; Entom. Soc. Am. Flight behavior of bark beetles; host selection of the southern pine beetle. Address: Dept. of Forest Enotomology, College of Forest Resources, University of Washington, Seattle, WA 98105.

GARABEDIAN, H(ENRY) L(ESLIE), b. Dorchester, Mass, Nov. 22, 01; m. 26; c. 1. MATHEMATICS. B.S, Tufts Col, 22; M.A, Harvard, 23; Ph.D.(math), Princeton, 30. Instr. math, Harvard, 23-26; Rochester, 26-27; Northwestern, 27-28; Princeton, 28-30; Northwestern, 30-36, asst. prof, 36-40, assoc. prof, 40-46; prin. physicist, Oak Ridge Nat. Lab, 46-48; chief, res. reactors sect, div. reactor develop, U.S. Atomic Energy Comn, Wash, D.C, 48-49; consult. scientist, Bettis Atomic Power Div, Westinghouse Elec. Corp, 49-56; asst. head nuclear power eng. dept, res. labs, Gen. Motors Corp, 56-60, head math. dept, 60-67; prof. math. & energy eng, Univ. Ill, Chicago Circle, 67-70; RETIRED. Sr. res. mathematician, Nat. Defense Res. Coun, 44-45; res. assoc, Brown, 45-46. Am. Math. Soc; fel. Am. Nuclear Soc. Theory of matrix and integral transformations; mathematical analysis; numerical analysis; reactor physics. Address: 2394-1E Via Mariposa W, Laguna Hills, CA 92653.

GARABEDIAN, MICHAEL ED, b. Los Angeles, Calif, Aug. 17, 39; m. 66; c. 3. PHYSICAL & POLYMER CHEMISTRY. B.Sc, Univ. Calif, Los Angeles, 61; Du Pont fel, Univ. South. Calif, 65-66, Ph.D.(phys. chem), 67. Res. asst, Univ. South. Calif, 62-64; res. chemist, elastomers dept, exp. sta, E.I. du Pont de Nemours & Co, Inc, 67-70; sr. res. chemist, Int. Playtex Inc, 70-71; MGR. DEVELOP. RES, ARBROOK INC, 71- Am. Chem. Soc. Research and development of products based on elastomeric materials; adhesives, compounding and theory; correlation of basic physical param eters with end-use properties. Address: 1801 Crestridge Ct, Arlington, TX 76013.

GARABEDIAN, P(AUL) R(OESEL), b. Cincinnati, Ohio, Aug. 2, 27; div. MATHEMATICS. A.B, Brown, 46; A.M, Harvard, 47, Ph.D.(math), 48. Nat. Res. Coun. fel, 48-49; asst. prof. MATH, California, 49-50; Stanford, 50-52, assoc. prof, 52-55, PROF, 55-59; N.Y. UNIV, 59- Am. Math. Soc; Am. Acad. Arts & Sci. Functions of a complex variable; hydrodynamics; partial differential equations. Address: Courant Institute, New York University, 251 Mercer St, New York, NY 10003.

GARASCIA, RICHARD J(OSEPH), b. Detroit, Mich, Dec. 25, 17; m. 42; c. 7. CHEMISTRY. B.S, Detroit, 40; M.S, Michigan, 41; Ph.D.(chem), Cincinnati, 50. Instr. math, Detroit, 41-42; CHEM, XAVIER UNIV.(OHIO), 42-46, asst. prof, 46-52, assoc. prof, 52-59, PROF, 59-, chmn. dept, 61-66. Res. chemist, Cook Paint & Varnish Co, Detroit, 41-42. Am. Chem. Soc. Organic synthesis; organic arsenic and phosphorus compounds; fluorene and acenapthene chemistry. Address: Dept. of Chemistry, Xavier University, Cincinnati, OH 45207.

GARAY, GUSTAV JOHN, b. Carteret, N.J, May 24, 33; m. 58; c. 2. ENTOMOLOGY, MICROBIOLOGY. A.B, Columbia, 55; M.S, Rutgers, 62, Ph.D. (med. entom), 64. Res. asst. immunol, Rockefeller Univ, 59; entom, Rutgers, 59-64; DIR. BIOL. DIV, WARD'S NATURAL SCI. ESTAB, 64- Asst. prof, Rochester, summer, 65. U.S.A.F, 55-59, Res, 59-, Capt. Am. Soc. Microbiol; Soc. Protozool. Mass rearing of insects; laboratory rearing of mosquitoes; Protozoan and Algae culture; photomicrography. Address: Biology Division, Ward's Natural Science Establishment, P.O. Box 1712, Rochester, NY 14603.

GARAY, LESLIE A(NDREW), b. Hosszuheteny, Hungary, Aug. 6, 24; nat. TAXONOMY. M.Sc, Tufts, 61, Ph.D, 64. Asst, Toronto, 49-51, asst. curator, 52-58; CURATOR, ORCHID HERBARIUM OAKES AMES, BOT. MUS, HARVARD, 58-, lectr. biol, univ, 65-70. Guggenheim fel, Can, 57-58; mem. bd. freshman adv, Harvard, 60-63; faculty of arts & sci, 63-, chmn, int. orchid cmn. classification, nomenclature & registration; mem, World Orchid Conf, London, 60; Singapore, 63; Int. Bot. Cong. Montreal, Edinburgh, 64; field work in Colombia, Ecuador, Venezuela, Jamaica, Fiji, New Caledonia, New Guinea, Malaya, Ceylon. Int. Asn. Plant Taxon. Taxonomy, phylogeny and evolution of the entire orchid family; orchids of Colombia, Ecuador, Haiti and Okinawa. Address: Ames Orchid Herbarium, Botanical Museum, Harvard University, Oxford St, Cambridge, MA 02138.

GARB, SOLOMON, b. Brooklyn, N.Y, Oct. 19, 20; m. 54. PHARMACOLOGY. A.B, Cornell, 40, M.D, 43. N.Y. Heart Asn. res. fel, 49-51; asst. prof. clin. pharmacol, med. col, Cornell, 52-56; assoc. prof. pharmacol, Albany Med. Col, 57-61; med. sch, Missouri, 61-66, prof. pharmacol. & assoc. prof. community health & med, 66-70; SCI. DIR, AM. MED. CTR, 70- Am. Heart Asn. res. fel, 52-54; U.S. Pub. Health Serv. sr. res. fel, 57-61, Nat. Cancer Inst. career develop. award, 62-67. Med.C, 44-46, Capt. Am. Soc. Pharmacol. & Exp. Therapeut; fel. Am. Soc. Clin. Pharmacol. & Therapeut; Soc. Exp. Biol. & Med; fel. Am. Col. Physicians. Cancer; clinical pharmacology; disaster prevention and management. Address: American Medical Center, 6401 W. Colfax Ave, Denver, CO 80214.

GARBACCIO, DONALD HOWARD, b. Paterson, N.J, June 29, 30; m. 52; c. 4. MECHANICAL ENGINEERING. B.S.M.E, Newark Col. Eng, 51; Wallace Mem. fel. & M.S.E, Princeton, 53; Consol. Eng. Corp. fel. & Ph.D.(eng. mech), Stanford Univ, 55. Res. engr, Calif. Res. Corp, 55-58; sr. engr, Rocketdyne Div, N.Am. Aviation, Inc, 58-60; sr. staff mem, Nat. Eng. Sci. Co, 60-64; sr. res. engr, Sci. Eng. Assocs. Div, Kaman Aircraft Corp, 64-69; SR. STAFF ENGR, ACTRON INDUSTS, INC, 69- Am. Soc. Mech. Eng. Structural dynamics; engineering oceanography. Address: Actron Industries, Inc, 700 Royal Oaks Dr, Monrovia, CA 91016.

GARBACIK, THEODORE JOHN, b. West Hazleton, Pa, June 10, 40; m; c. 3. ORGANIC CHEMISTRY, WATER RESOURCES. B.S, Pa. State Univ, 61 & 62; Ph.D.(chem), Univ. Vt, 70. Instr. chem, Wells Col, 68-69; Univ. Vt, 69-70; CHEMIST, DEPT. WATER RESOURCES, STATE VT, 71- Am. Chem. Soc. Relative reactivity of enamines; effect of structure on reaction rate; detection and effect of pesticides on aquatic life. Address: Dept. of Water Resources, Montpelier, VT 05602.

GARBACZ, ROBERT J, b. Buffalo, N.Y, Sept. 12, 33. ELECTRICAL ENGINEERING. B.S, Univ. Buffalo, 55; M.S, Ohio State Univ, 57, Ph.D.(electromagnetic scattering), 68. ASST. PROF. ELEC. ENG, OHIO STATE UNIV, 68-, ASST. SUPVR. ELECTRO SCI. LAB, 55- Inst. Elec. & Electronics Eng. Electromagnetic scattering by antennas; characteristic modal expansions of fields scattered by obstacles of arbitrary shape. Address: Dept. of Electrical Engineering, Ohio State University, 2015 Neil Ave, Columbus, OH 43210.

GARBARINI, GEORGE S, b. Manchester, Conn, June 2, 31; m. 50; c. 2. GEOLOGY. A.B, Univ. Conn, 53; Proctor fel, Princeton, 55-56, Ph.D. (geol), 57. Geologist, SUN OIL CO, 57-70, DIST. GEOL. SUPVR, 70- Am. Asn. Petrol. Geol. Structural and stratigraphic geology of Rocky Mountains; structural geology of Beartooth Range, Montana; atomic waste disposal potential of Denver Basin; oil exploration in Colorado. Address: P.O. Box 1798, Denver, CO 80201.

GARBARINI, ROBERT F, b. Woodside, N.Y, Dec. 31, 18; m. 46; c. 5. NAVIGATION. M.E, Stevens Inst. Technol, 40, M.S, 45. From asst. proj. engr. to eng. mgr, Sperry Gyroscope Co, 41-59, chief engr, air armament div, 59-63; dep. assoc. admin. space sci. & appln, NASA, 63-67; asst. v.pres. & Telex & Mailgram prog. mgr. exec, WEST. UNION TEL. CO, 67-69, v.pres. prog. mgt. off. exec, 69-71, GROUP V.PRES. SWITCHED EXCHANGE SERV, 71- Alternate, sub-panel airborne surveillance, navig. & bombing systs, radar panel comt. electronics, res. & develop. bd, Dept. Defense, 50-51, consult, ad hoc panel on troop carrier navig, Off. Asst. Secy, Defense Tech. Adv. Panel Electronics, 55-57; mem. U.S. Air Force Indust. Team for surv. of inertial guid. activity, U.K, 56, consult. mem. & adv, guid. & control panel sci. adv. bd, 60-67. Execptional Serv. Medal, NASA, 67 & 69. Inst. Elec. & Electronics Eng. Research and development management of airborne electronic devices and systems for flight navigation and guidance; management of terrestrial and satellite communications systems developments and operations. Address: Western Union Telegraph Co, 60 Hudson St, New York, NY 10013.

GARBARINI, VICTOR C, b. N.Y.C, May 24, 26; m. 48; c. 4. ELECTROCHEMISTRY. B.S, Manhattan Col, 44; Ph.D.(chem), N.Y. Univ, 56. Engr. & chemist, E.I. du Pont de Nemours & Co, Inc, Del, 51-55; engr, Esso Res. & Eng. Co, 55-59; MEM. TECH. STAFF, BELL TEL. LABS, 59- Am. Chem. Soc; Electrochem. Soc. Semiconductor device chemistry; contamination control; photochemistry; polymer chemistry; analytical chemistry as applied to semiconductor device process development and control. Address: Bell Telephone Labs, 555 Union Blvd, Allentown, PA 18103.

GARBARINO, J(OSEPH) J(OHN), b. N.Y.C, Jan. 21, 29; m. 55; c. 2. ANALYTICAL CHEMISTRY. B.S, St. Johns (N.Y), 50, M.S, 56; M.B.A, N.Y. Univ, 61. Chemist, Army Criminal Invest. Lab, Ft. Gordon, 51-53; anal. chemist, Nat. Lead Co, 53-54; detective & chemist, lab, N.Y.C. Police Dept, 54-56; anal. proj. chemist, org. chem. div, Am. Cyanamid Co, 56-59, mkt. analyst, 59-62; mgr. commercial develop, Ariz. Chem. Co, 62-65, mgr. commercial develop. & planning, 65-68; SALES MGR, INDUST. CHEM. & PLASTICS DIV, AM. CYANAMID CO, 68- U.S.C.G.R, Lt. Comdr. Commercial Develop. Asn; Chem. Mkt. Res. Asn; Am. Chem. Soc. Instrumental methods of analysis; cyclopropyl carbinols; chemical tests for intoxication. Address: Chemicals & Plastics Division, American Cyanamid Co, Berdan Ave, Wayne, NJ 07470.

GARBELLANO, DAVID W(ESLEY), b. Niagara Falls, Ont, Feb. 11, 15; nat; m. 39; c. 2. ATOMIC PHYSICS. B.A, Cornell, 37; M.A, N.Y. Univ, 39. Mem. staff, radiation lab, California, 46-50, Bevatron group, 50-52, Greenhouse tests in Pacific, 52, Atomic test in Nev. & Pacific, 53-55; V.PRES, APPL. RADIATION CORP, BERKELEY, 54-; PRES, ENG. DEVELOP. CORP, 54- Consult. & dir, Berkeley Sci. Capital Corp; sci. dir, Winfield Growth Industs. Fund, Inc; dir, Antipodes Sci. Corp; v.pres. & dir, Tri-Ocean, Inc; dir, Wincap Fund; consult, radiation lab, California, 54-58; Sargent-Raymont Co, 54-; Systron, Inc, 56-; Omega Corp, 58- Sig.C, 42-47, Maj. AAAS; Am. Inst. Aeronaut. & Astronaut; Am. Nuclear Soc; Soc. Enol. Eng. High energy particle accelerators; radiation detection instruments; underwater equipment. Address: Rt. 2, Box 1565, Grass Valley, CA 95945.

GARBER, CALVIN S(AMUEL), b. Grier City, Pa, Oct. 29, 24; m. 47; c. 3. PHYSICAL CHEMISTRY. B.S, Ursinus Col, 47; Ph.D.(chem), Pa. State Col, 51. Res. chemist, EASTMAN KODAK CO, 51-57, sr. res. chemist, 57-62; RES. ASSOC, ROCHESTER, 62- U.S.A, 44-46. Am. Chem. Soc; Soc. Photog. Sci. & Eng. Photographic processes; chemistry of development; patent liaison. Address: 684 Lake Rd, Webster, NY 14581.

GARBER, CHARLES A, b. Rock Island, Ill, May 23, 41; m. 64. POLYMER PHYSICS. B.S, Univ. Ill, Urbana, 63; M.S, Case Inst. Technol, 65, Petrol. Res. Fund del, 65-67, Ph.D.(polymer solid state physics, morphol), 67. Res. fel, Case Inst. Technol, 63-67; res. physicist, Plastics Dept, E.I. du Pont de Nemours & Co, Del, 67-70; PRES, STRUCT. PROBE, INC, 70- Instr, Cleveland State Univ, 66-67, adj. prof, Drexel Inst. Tech, 68-69; Phila. Col. Textiles & Sci, 69-70. Am. Chem. Soc; Am. Inst. Chem. Eng; Am. Phys. Soc; Electron Micros. Soc. Am; Res. Soc. Am. Solid State structure and morphology of polymers; heterogeneous catalysts; microelectronic devices; ceramics; biological materials; particulate pollutants; scanning and transmission electron microscopy. Address: Structure Probe, Inc, 535 E. Gay St, West Chester, PA 19380.

GARBER, C(LARENCE) ZENT, b. Plymouth, Ohio, Nov. 19, 96; m. 35; c. 2. PATHOLOGY. A.B, Oberlin Col, 18; M.D, Hopkins, 23. Asst. chemist, Mansfield Tire & Rubber Co, Ohio, 18; chemist, Ohio Brass Co, 19; asst. path, Hopkins, 23-25; assoc. pathologist, Henry Ford Hosp, Mich, 25-28; Peking Union Med. Col, China, 29-30; surgeon exped, Am. Mus. Natural Hist, Mongolia, 30; vol. asst, path-inst, Univ. Munich, 31-32; pathologist & dir. labs, Fifth Ave. Hosp, N.Y, 32-35; dir. clin. labs, Roosevelt Hosp, 36-37, dir. labs, 37-39; pathologist, N.Y. Orthop. Hosp, 39-51; assoc. prof. PATH, COLUMBIA UNIV, 51-62, SPEC. LECTR, 62-, asst. prof, 47-51. Summers, jr. physiologist, Chem. Warfare Serv, 20, 21; asst. med, Metrop. Life Ins. Co, 22; res, med. col, Cornell Univ, 36-39; assoc. attend. orthop. pathologist, Presby. Hosp, 51-62. Jr. chemist, gas mask res. div, C.W.S, U.S.A, 18. AAAS; Am. Soc. Clin. Path; Am. Soc. Trop. Med. & Hyg; Am. Chem. Soc; Col. Am. Path; Am. Med. Asn; N.Y. Acad. Sci; N.Y. Acad. Med. Silicosis and transportation of particulate matter by tracheal cilia; bone growth; bone bank; pathology and chemistry of diseases of bone. Address: Dept. of Pathology, Columbia University, 630 W. 168th St, New York, NY 10032.

GARBER, DONALD I, b. Cleveland, Ohio, July 8, 36. NUCLEAR PHYSICS. B.S, Carnegie Inst. Tech, 58; M.S, Case, 60, Ph.D.(nuclear physics), 64. Instr. physics, Case West. Reserve Univ, 64-66, asst. prof, 66-67; asst. physicist, BROOKHAVEN NAT. LAB, 67-70, ASSOC. PHYSICIST, 70- Am. Phys. Soc. Elastic and inelastic scattering of neutrons; polarization measurements of neutrons produced in deuteron reactions; radiative capture; automated nuclear physics publications. Address: 35 Marion Ave, Stony Brook, NY 11790.

GARBER, EDWARD D(AVID), b. N.Y.C, Mar. 22, 18; m. 43; c. 3. CYTOGENETICS. B.S, Cornell, 40; M.S, Minnesota, 42; Ph.D.(genetics), California, 49. Asst. res. scientist & microbial geneticist, Naval Biol. Lab, 49-53; asst. prof. BOT, UNIV. CHICAGO, 53-58, assoc. prof, 58-61, PROF, 61- U.S.A, 42-46, 1st Lt. Genetics Soc. Am; Bot. Soc. Am; Am. Soc. Microbiol; Brit. Soc. Gen. Microbiol. Cytotaxonomy and cytogenetics of sorghum and collinsia; genetics of virulence; fungal genetics. Address: Dept. of Biology, University of Chicago, 1101 E. 57th St, Chicago, IL 60637.

GARBER, HAROLD J(EROME), b. Cleveland, Ohio, March 12, 13; m. 45; c. 5. CHEMICAL ENGINEERING. Ch.E, Cincinnati, 35. Asst. chem. eng, Cincinnati, 35-36, instr, 36-40, asst. prof, 40-44, assoc. prof, 44-47; prof. Tennessee, 47-55; mgr. chem. eng. sect, atomic power div, Westinghouse Elec. Corp, 55-59, chem. develop. dept, 59; dir. plutonium facility, NUCLEAR MAT. & EQUIP. CORP, 59-62, DIR. ADVAN. PROJ. & TECH. ASST. TO PRES, 62- Consult. engr, Gen. Air Condit. Corp. & Adler Co, Wright Field, 42-46; Holabird & Root, Chicago; Hamilton Mfg. Co, Wis, 39; Carbide & Carbon Chems. Corp, Tenn, 49-55; Jensen Specialties Co, 52- Hochstetter prize, Ohio. AAAS; fel. Am. Inst. Chem; Am. Inst. Chem. Eng; Am. Nuclear Soc. Nuclear materials technology; plutonium technology; applied radiochemistry; applied chemical reaction kinetics; energy and mass transport; energy conversion technology; process engineering and plant design; isotope powered heart and cardiac pacemakers. Address: 5515 Darlington Rd, Pittsburgh, PA 15217.

GARBER, H(IRSH) NEWTON, b. Philadelphia, Pa, March 16, 30, m. 51; c. 5. OPERATIONS RESEARCH. B.S, Pennsylvania, 52; S.M, Mass. Inst. Tech, 53, Nat. Sci. Found. fel. & Sc.D.(elec. eng), 56. Oper. res. analyst, RCA CORP, 56-65, sr. scientist, 66-69, MGR. OPERS. RES, 69- AAAS; Opers. Res. Soc. Am; Soc. Indust. & Appl. Math; Am. Math. Asn; Inst. Elec. & Electronics Eng; Inst. Mgt. Sci. Application of scientific techniques to the problems of industrial management of complex systems. Address: 28 Red Berry Rd, Levittown, PA 19056.

GARBER, J. NEILL, b. Dunkirk, Ind, Nov. 3, 09; m. 45; c. 3. ORTHOPEDIC SURGERY. B.S, Indiana, 30, M.D, 32; Sc.D.(orthop. surg), Columbia, 38. PROF ORTHOP. SURG, SCH. MED, IND. UNIV, INDIANAPOLIS, 57- Attend. staff, Methodist Hosp, 40; Community & Univ. Hosps. Med.C, 42-46, Maj. Clin. Orthop. Soc; Am. Orthop. Asn; Am. Med. Asn; Am. Acad. Orthop. Surg; hon. mem. Brit. Orthop. Asn. Address: 7036 N. Pennsylvania, Indianapolis, IN 46220.

GARBER, JOHN D(OUGLAS), b. Minneapolis, Minn, May 12, 20; m. 43; c. 3. ORGANIC CHEMISTRY. B.S, Pa. State Col, 40; Ph.D.(chem), Univ. Ill, 43. Res. chemist, Standard Oil Develop. Co, 43-47; res. dir, E.M. Wanderman & Co, 47-48; res. chemist, Merck & Co, Inc, 48-55, mgr. agr. & indust. org. chem. develop, 55-64; asst. to dir, res. & develop, indust. chem. div, Am. Cyanamid Co, 64-65, dir, 65-66; gen. mgr. basic & appl. res, Moffett Tech. Ctr, CPC INT, INC, 66-69, SCI. V.PRES, DEVELOP. DIV, 69- Am. Chem. Soc. Conversion of carbohydrates to furans and their utilization as industrial organics; high temperature polymers and fluids; systemic approaches to plant agricultural chemicals; petrochemicals including specialty resins and organics; food components. Address: 154 Chestnut St, Englewood, NJ 07631.

GARBER, LAWRENCE L, b. Goshen, Ind, July 4, 42; m. 65. INORGANIC CHEMISTRY. B.A, Goshen Col, 63; Nat. Insts. Health fel, Mich. State Univ, 63-67, Ph.D.(chem), 67; Univ. Notre Dame, 67-68. ASST. PROF. CHEM, Goshen Col, 68-69; IND. UNIV, SOUTH BEND, 69- Ind. Univ. Res. Found. Grant, 70- Am. Chem. Soc; The Chem. Soc. Synthesis and characterization of transition metal complexes; normal coordinate analysis of small inorganic compounds. Address: Dept. of Chemistry, Indiana University at South Bend, South Bend, IN 46615.

GARBER, M(EYER), b. Phila, Pa, June 6, 28. PHYSICS. B.S, Univ. Pa, 49; M.S, Univ. Ill, 50, Ph.D.(physics), 54. Fulbright fel, Univ. Leiden, Netherlands, 54-55; Nat. Res. Coun. fel, Ottawa (Can), 55-57; prof. physics, Mich. State Univ, 58-66; PHYSICIST, DEPT. APPL. SCI, BROOKHAVEN NAT. LAB, 66- Mem. staff, div. sponsored res, Mass. Inst. Technol, 61-63; vis. physicist, Brookhaven Nat. Lab, 64. Am. Phys. Soc. Low temperature physics. Address: Dept. of Applied Science, Brookhaven National Lab, Upton, NY 11973.

GARBER, M(ORRIS) J(OSEPH), b. N.Y.C, Nov. 6, 12; m. 43; c. 2. BIOMETRY, COMPUTER SCIENCE. Ph.D.(genetics), Agr. & Mech. Col. Tex, 51. Asst. prof. genetics, Agr. & Mech. Col. Tex, 47-56; BIOMETRICIAN & PROF. STATIST, UNIV. CALIF, RIVERSIDE, 56- Med. Dept, A.U.S, 41-45, S/Sgt. AAAS; Asn. Comput. Mach; Biomet. Soc; Am. Statist. Asn; Am. Genetic Asn; Pattern Recognition Soc. Statistical design and analysis in agriculture; computer programming. Address: Dept. of Statistics, University of California, P.O. Box 112, Riverside, CA 92502.

GARBER, R(ICHARD) H(AMMERLE), b. Beaver Falls, Pa, June 22, 21; m. 45; c. 4. PLANT PATHOLOGY. B.S, Geneva, 47; M.S, Colorado State, 50; Ph.D.(plant path), California, 60. Asst. bot. & plant path, Colorado State, 48-50, resident supt, San Luis Valley exp. sta, 50-52; PLANT PATHOLOGIST, AGR. RES. SERV, U.S. DEPT. AGR, UNIV. CALIF, 54- Mem, Cotton Disease Coun. U.S.A.A.F, 42-45. Am. Phytopath. Soc. Ecology of plant diseases; seed and soil treatments, fungicides. Address: U.S. Cotton Research Station, 17053 Shafter Ave, Shafter, CA 93263.

GARBER, T(HEODORE) B(RUCE), b. Cleveland, Ohio, June 30, 26; m. 54; c. 3. PHYSICS. B.S, Mass. Inst. Tech, 47, M.S, 52. Mem. staff, div. indust. co-op, Mass. Inst. Tech, 48-51; tech. instr. aeronaut, 53-54; PHYS. SCIENTIST, RAND CORP, 54- Am. Phys. Soc; Am. Inst. Aeronaut. & Astronaut. Guidance and control; applied mechanics. Address: Rand Corp, 1700 Main St, Santa Monica, CA 90406.

GARBISCH, EDGAR W, JR, b. N.Y.C, Oct. 3, 32; m. 57; c. 2. ORGANIC CHEMISTRY. B.S, North Carolina, 55; Ph.D.(chem), Northwestern, 61. Nat. Sci. Found. fel, 61-62; asst. prof. CHEM, Chicago, 62-63; UNIV. MINN, MINNEAPOLIS, 64-65, ASSOC. PROF, 65- Sloan res. fel, 65-67. U.S.N, 55-57, Lt.(jg). Am. Chem. Soc. Conformational analysis; nuclear magnetic resonance spectroscopy; stereochemistry; strain effects on chemical reactivities; catalytic hydrogenolysis; reaction mechanisms. Address: Dept. of Chemistry, University of Minnesota, Minneapolis, MN 55455.

GARBRECHT, WILLIAM LEE, b. Grand Rapids, Mich, Apr. 18, 23; m. 47; c. 3. ORGANIC CHEMISTRY. A.B, Kalamazoo Col, 48, Upjohn scholar, 47-49, M.S, 49; Parke, Davis fel, 51-53, Ph.D.(chem), Mich. State Col, 53. Org. chemist, ELI LILLY & CO, 53-60, develop. assoc, 60-68, RES. ASSOC, 68- U.S.N.R, 43-47, Lt.(jg). Am. Chem. Soc. Chemistry of 5-amino tetrazole derivatives; chemistry of ergot alkaloids; chemistry of cephalosporin antibiotics; tetrazole sweeteners. Address: 4114 Ponderosa Blvd, Indianapolis, IN 46250.

GARBUNY, M(AX), b. Koenigsberg, Ger, Nov. 22, 12; nat; m. 47; c. 3. PHYSICS. Dipl.Ing, Tech. Univ. Berlin, 36, Dr. Ing, 38. Physicist, Allen-Bradley Co, 39-43; instr. physics, Princeton, 43-44; develop. engr, WESTINGHOUSE ELEC. CORP, 44-46, sr. res. physicist, 46-52, mgr, optical physics sect, RES. LABS, 52-60, CONSULT, OPTICAL PHYSICS, 60- Summer lectr, Univ. Calif, Los Angeles, 59-; nat. exec. comt, Infrared Info. Symposia, 63-; mem. sci. adv. panel, U.S. Army, 64-, electronics adv. group, Army Electronics Command, 69-; N.Y. State vis. prof, Univ. Rochester, 68-69. Most meritorious patent award, Westinghouse Elec. Corp. Fel. Am. Phys. Soc; fel. Am. Optical Soc. Atomic physics; microwave devices; spectroscopy; solid state physics; infrared devices; low temperature physics; optics. Address: 2305 Marbury Rd, Pittsburgh, PA 15221.

GARBUTT, JOHN T(HOMAS), b. Janesville, Wis, Apr. 19, 29; m. 57; c. 3. BIOCHEMISTRY. B.S, Beloit Col, 51; M.S, Univ. Wis, Madison, 56; Ph.D. (biochem), 58. SECT. LEADER BIOCHEM, GRAIN PROCESSING CORP, 58- U.S.N, 52-54, Res, 54- Am. Chem. Soc. Isolation and application of proteases and amylases for industrial use; industrial applications of carbohydrates and proteins. Address: Dept. of Biochemistry, Grain Processing Corp, Muscatine, IA 52761.

GARCELON, GEORGE F(RANK), b. Wilkinsburgh, Pa, July 31, 11; m. 38; c. 2. ORGANIC CHEMISTRY. B.S, Mass. Inst. Tech, 33. Chemist, ALTHOUSE CHEM. DIV, CROMPTON & KNOWLES CORP, 34-50, chief chemist, 50-54, DIR. RES, 54- Am. Chem. Soc. Dyestuffs and textile auxiliary products. Address: 1126 Albright Ave, Wyomissing, PA 19610.

GARCIA, ALFREDO MARIANO, b. Itati-Corrientes, Arg, Sept. 12, 27; U.S. citizen; m. 61. BIOLOGY, ANATOMY. M.D, Univ. Buenos Aires, 53, Dr. Med, 58; Ph.D.(zool), Columbia Univ, 62. Res. fel. hemat, Mt. Sinai Hosp, 57-59; instr. biol, Columbia Univ, 59, lectr. zool, 59-60, instr, 61-62; asst. prof. ANAT, STATE UNIV. N.Y. UPSTATE MED. CTR, 62-68, ASSOC. PROF, 68- Nat. Insts. Health fel, 60-62 & career develop. award, 66-70; guest lectr, Univ. Chicago, spring 65 & fall 68. Arg. Army, 48-49. Histochem. Soc. Quantitative cytochemistry; fine structure and nucleic acid metabolism of mammalian blood cells. Address: Dept. of Anatomy, State University of New York Upstate Medical Center at Syracuse, 766 Irving Ave, Syracuse, NY 13210.

GARCIA, CARLOS E(RNESTO), b. Las Vegas, N.Mex, May 14, 36; m. 65; c. 3. MECHANICAL ENGINEERING. B.S, New Mexico State, 58, M.S, 62, fel, 65, D.Sc.(mech. eng), 66. Assoc. engr, Douglas Aircraft Co, 58-60; asst. mech. eng, New Mexico State, 60-62, instr, 62-65; assoc. res. engr, N.Mex. Inst. Mining & Technol, 65-66, res. engr. & asst. prof. fluid dynamics, 66-67; sr. scientist, Ling-Temco-Vought, 67-70; TECH. CONTRACT ANALYST, ATOMIC ENERGY COMN, 71- Am. Inst. Aeronaut. & Astronaut. Hydromechanical missile control systems; shock wave phenomena; gas dynamics; thermodynamics; heat transfer; underground nuclear explosions; shock tubes; supersonic wind tunnels; subsonic and supersonic diffusers; boundary layer bleed; thermoelectrics. Address: Space & Special Programs Division, Atomic Energy Commission, P.O. Box 5400, Albuquerque, NM 87115.

GARCIA, CELSO-RAMON, b. N.Y.C, Oct. 31, 21; m. 50; c. 2. GYNECOLOGY, OBSTETRICS. B.S, Queens Col.(N.Y), 42; fel, N.Y. Univ, 42; M.D, State Univ. N.Y, 45. Intern, Norweg. Lutheran Hosp, Brooklyn, N.Y, 45-46; res. path, Cumberland Hosp, 48-49, res. fel. obstet. & gynec, 49-50, res, 50-53; assoc, sch. med. & trop. med, Univ. P.R, 53-54, asst. prof, 54-55; asst. dir, Rock Reprod. Clin, Inc, 56-58, co-dir, 58-61; dir. training prog. physiol. of reprod, Worcester Found. Exp. Biol, 60-62, sr. scientist, 60-65; assoc. prof. obstet. & gynec, SCH. MED, UNIV. PA, 65-67, prof, 67-70, WILLIAM SHIPPEN JR. PROF. HUMAN REPROD, 70-, CHIEF INFERTIL. CLIN, HOSP. UNIV. PA, 65- Res. fel. gynec, Harvard Med. Sch, 55-56, asst, 58-59, obstet. & gynec, 59-60, instr, 60-64, clin. assoc, 64-65. Assoc, San Juan City Hosp, 53-55; res. fel, Free Hosp. Women, 55-57, courtesy staff, 57-58, asst. surgeon, 58-60, assoc. surgeon, 60-65; asst. obstetrician & gynecologist, Boston Lying-in Hosp, 56-65; courtesy staff, Faulkner Hosp, 56-57, assoc. staff, 57-65; courtesy staff, Glover Mem. Hosp, 58-65; Newton Wellesley Hosp, 63-65; consult, Worcester State Hosp, 61-65; asst. surgeon & chief infertil. clin, Mass. Gen. Hosp, 62-65. Dipl, Am. Bd. Obstet. & Gynec; Carl Hartman Award, 61. Med.C, 46-48, Capt. AAAS; Endocrine Soc; Am. Fertility Soc; Am. Med. Asn; Asn. Am. Med. Cols; fel. Am. Col. Obstet. & Gynec; fel. Am. Col. Surg; Am. Physiol. Soc; Int. Fertil. Asn. Reproductive physiology; infertility. Address: Hospital of the University of Pennsylvania, 3400 Spruce St, Philadelphia, PA 19104.

GARCIA, EDWARD E(RNEST), b. New Haven, Conn, Nov. 21, 35; m. 62; c. 3. ORGANIC CHEMISTRY. B.S, Fairfield Univ, 57; Ph.D.(org. chem), Fordham Univ, 61. Fel, Princeton, 61-64; SR. CHEMIST, HOFFMANN-LA ROCHE, INC, 64- Am. Chem. Soc. Heterocyclic chemistry, with particular emphasis on purines, pyrimidines and pyridine compounds; Indoles. Address: Hoffmann-La Roche, Inc, Nutley, NJ 07110.

GARCIA, EUGENE N, b. Guadalajara, Mex, Oct. 27, 25; U.S. citizen; c. 3. BIOCHEMISTRY. A.B, Gonzaga Univ, 48; M.S, Univ. San Francisco, 51; Calif. Inst. Technol, 52-54; Ph.D.(physiol. chem), Univ. Calif, Los Angeles, 61. Chemist org. synthesis, Calif. Corp. Biochem. Res, 54-55; res. asst. BIOCHEM, med. ctr, Univ. Calif, Los Angeles, 55-60; asst. prof, Calif. Col. Med, Univ. Calif, Irvine, 61-69; PARTNER, PROGRAMMEDIA ASSOCS, INC, 70- Consult. biomed. educ, 69-; lectr, Univ. Calif, Los Angeles, 70- AAAS; Am. Chem. Soc. Ehrlich ascites carcinoma; irradiation effects and development of immunity in mice; lipids in Ehrlich ascites carcinoma. Address: ProgramMedia Associates, Inc, 15612 Claretta Ave, Norwalk, CA 90650.

GARCIA, JOHN, b. Santa Rosa, Calif, June 12, 17; m. 43; c. 3. PHYSIOLOGICAL PSYCHOLOGY. B.A, Univ. Calif, Berkeley, 48, M.A, 49, Ph.D.(psychol), 65. Exp. physiol. psychologist, U.S. Naval Radiol. Defense Lab, 51-58; asst. prof. psychol, Calif. State Col. Long Beach, 59-65; lectr. neurosurg, Harvard Med. Sch, 65-68; PROF. PSYCHOL, STATE UNIV. N.Y. STONY BROOK, 68- Assoc. biologist, Mass. Gen. Hosp, 65-68. Summers, consult, Vet. Admin. Hosp, Long Beach, 60, prin. investr, Nat. Insts. Health grant, 65. U.S.A.A.F, 43-46. AAAS; Am. Psychol. Asn; Radiation Res. Soc. Effect of x-rays, toxins and drugs upon behavior. Address: Dept. of Psychology, State University of New York at Stony Brook, Stony Brook, NY 11790.

GARCIA, JOSE DOLORES, JR, b. Santa Fe, N.Mex, Jan. 3, 36; m. 60; c. 2. ATOMIC PHYSICS. B.S, New Mexico State, 57; Fulbright fel, Göttingen, 57-58; M.A, California, Berkeley, 59; Ph.D.(physics), Wisconsin, 66. NASA fel. PHYSICS, Pittsburgh, 66-67; asst. prof, UNIV. ARIZ, 67-70, ASSOC. PROF, 70- Summer res. asst, Los Alamos Sci. Lab, Univ. Calif, 57, consult, Lawrence Radiation Lab, Livermore, 70-; consult, Air Force Weapons Lab, Kirtland Air Force Base, 67. U.S.A.F, 60-63, 1st Lt. Atmospheric physics; atomic bound state theory; atomic scattering theory. Address: Dept. of Physics, University of Arizona, Tucson, AZ 85721.

GARCIA, JULIO H, b. Armenia, Colombia, Dec. 22, 33; nat; m. 66; c. 2. NEUROPATHOLOGY, ELECTRON MICROSCOPY. B.S, Col. St. Bartholomew, Colombia, 51; M.D, Nat. Univ. Colombia, 58. Intern path, Hosp. San Juan de Dios, Colombia, 58-59; res. physician, L.I. Jewish Hosp, 59-60; Kings County Hosp, N.Y, 60-64; asst. prof. path, Med. Col. Va, 64-67; assoc. prof. path. & neurol, Univ. Tenn, Memphis, 67-70; Baylor Col. Med, 70-71; HEAD NEUROPATH. DIV, SCH. MED, UNIV. MD, 71- Instr, State Univ. N.Y, 62-64; consult, East. State Hosp, Va, 64-66; Off. Chief Med. Exam, 64-66; Vet. Admin. Hosp, Richmond, Va, 64-66; Baptist Mem. Hosp, Tenn, 67-; W.Tenn. Psychiat. Hosp. & Inst, 67-; U.S. Pub. Health Serv. grant, 69; fel. coun. cerebrovascular disease, Am. Heart Asn, 70, mem. res. comt. I, 71-73; consult, Vet. Admin. Hosp, Baltimore, Md, 71- Dipl, Am. Bd. Path, 64. N.Y. Acad. Sci; AAAS; Am. Asn. Neuropath; Am. Asn. Path. & Bact; Asn. Res. Nerv. & Ment. Disease; Am. Soc. Exp. Path; Electron Micros. Soc. Am; Colombian Soc. Path. Ultrastructural changes of primates' brain after experimental production of regional ischemia; ultrastructural studies of mechanisms of nerve cell damage after ischemia, shock and trauma; effects of methanol poisoning on the brain. Address: Dept. of Pathology, University of Maryland School of Medicine, 32 S. Greene, Baltimore, MD 21201.

GARCIA, MANUEL MARIANO, b. Dumaguete City, Philippines, Nov. 25, 38; m. 70. SOIL MICROBIOLOGY, BACTERIAL PHYSIOLOGY. B.S.A, Philippines, 59, fel, 60-62, M.Sc, 62; Nat. Res. Coun. Can. grant, Guelph, 65-67, Ph.D.(microbiol, bact. physiol), 67. Res. instr, soil microbiol, Philippines, 62-65; RES. SCIENTIST SOIL MICROBIOL. & BACT. PHYSIOL, ANIMAL DISEASES RES. INST, 67- AAAS; Am. Soc. Microbiol; Can. Soc. Microbiol. Growth and survival of animal pathogens in soil; effects of herbicides on soil bacteria; physiology of rhizobia, anaerobic bacteria and L-forms; microbial toxins; mycobacteriophages; ecology of soil fungi; protein synthesis by bacteria. Address: Animal Diseases Research Institute, P.O. Box 1400, Hull, Que, Can.

GARCIA, MARIANO, b. Naguabo, P.R, Sept. 13, 18; m. 40; c. 2. MATHEMATICS. B.S, Washington & Jefferson Col, 39, M.A, 40; Ph.D.(math), Virginia, 44. Instr. MATH, Richmond, 44; from asst. prof. to PROF. & HEAD DEPT, COL. AGR. & MECH. ARTS, UNIV. P.R, MAYAGUEZ, 44- Am. Math. Soc; Math. Asn. Am. Topology and theory of numbers. Address: Dept. of Mathematics, University of Puerto Rico, Mayaguez, PR 00708.

GARCIA, OSCAR NICOLAS, b. Havana, Cuba, Sept. 10, 36; U.S. citizen; m. 62; c. 1. ELECTRICAL ENGINEERING, COMPUTER SCIENCE. B.S.E.E, N.C. State Univ, 61, M.S.E.E, 64; Nat. Sci. Found. fel, Univ. Md, 68-69, Ph.D. (elec. eng), 69. Asst. elec. eng, N.C. State Col, 61-62, instr, 62; elec. engr, IBM Glendale Develop. Labs, 62-63; asst. prof. elec. eng, Old Dominion Col, 63-66; instr, Univ. Md, 66-67, res. asst, 67-68; Am. Soc. Eng. Educ-NASA summer faculty fel, Goddard Space Flight Ctr, 69; ASSOC. PROF. ELEC. ENG, Old Dominion Univ, 69-70; UNIV. S.FLA, 70- Nat. Sci. Found. res. initiation grant prin. investr, 70-71. Inst. Elec. & Electronics Eng; Am. Soc. Eng. Educ; Asn. Comput. Mach. Application of coding theory to improved computer reliability and speed; computer architectural design and simulation of digital systems for design and diagnostic tests. Address: Dept. of Electrical & Electronic Engineering, College of Engineering, University of South Florida, Tampa, FL 33620.

GARCIA, PILAR A, b. Manila, P.I, Nov. 4, 26. NUTRITION. B.S, Philippines, 49; M,S, Michigan, 50; M.S, Iowa State, 52, Ph.D.(nutrit), 55. Asst. nutrit, IOWA STATE UNIV, 50-55, assoc. & instr, 55-57, from asst. prof. to ASSOC. PROF. FOOD & NUTRIT, 57- Human nutrition; energy expenditure of adult women; nutrition and aging of adult women; nutrition during adolescent pregnancy. Address: Dept. of Food & Nutrition, Iowa State University, Ames, IA 50010.

GARCIA, RICHARD, b. Sebastopol, Calif, Apr. 26, 30; m. 53; c. 2. PARASITOLOGY, MEDICAL ENTOMOLOGY. B.S, Univ. Calif, Berkeley, 57, Nat. Insts. Health fel, 60-63, Ph.D.(parasitol), 63. U.S. Pub. Health Serv. fel. arbovirus res, Rocky Mt. Lab, Mont, 63-65; asst. res. parasitiologist, George Williams Hooper Found, med. Ctr, UNIV. CALIF, San Francisco, 65-69, ASSOC. ENTOMOLOGIST, BERKELEY, 69- U.S.A.F, 50-54. Entom. Soc. Am; Am. Soc. Trop. Med. & Hyg; Wildlife Disease Asn. Behavior of bloodsucking arthropods to external stimuli and ecological studies of arboviruses in vector populations; biological control of mosquitoes. Address: Division of Biological Control, University of California, 1050 San Pablo Ave, Albany, CA 94706.

GARCIA-BENGOCHEA, FRANCISCO, b. Havana, Cuba, Dec. 15, 17; m. 53; c. 2. NEUROSURGERY. M.D, Univ. Havana, 41; M.D, Tulane Univ. La, 49. Res. asst. neurol, col. physicians & surgeons, Columbia Univ, 44-49, resident neurosurg, Presby. Med. Ctr, 48-49; instr. neurol. & neurosurg, sch. med, Tulane Univ. La, 49-50, asst. prof, 50-51; instr. NEUROSURG, col. med, Univ. Fla, 60-61; asst. prof, sch. med, Univ. Kans, 61-62; assoc. prof, COL. MED, UNIV. FLA, 62-69, PROF, 70- Traveling fel, sch. med, Univ. Havana, 43-45; surgeon, Greystone Brain Res. Proj, Columbia Univ, 48-49; neurosurgeon, Charity Hosp. New Orleans, Tulane Univ. La, 49-51, Markle scholar. med. sci, sch. med, 50-51. Am. Asn. Neurosurg; Cong. Neurol. Surg; Neurosurg. Soc. Am. Address: Division of Neurological Surgery, College of Medicine, University of Florida, Gainesville, FL 32601.

GARCIA-BENITEZ, CARLOS R(AFAEL), b. Vieques, P.R, Dec. 22, 14. BIOLOGY. S.B, Puerto Rico, 34; S.M, Chicago, 39, Ph.D.(bot), 41; cert. radiobiol, Argonne Nat. Lab, 57; cert. radioisotopes tech, P.R. Nuclear Center, 59. Asst. instr. BIOL, UNIV. P.R. 34-37, instr, 37-40, asst. prof, 40-42, PROF, 42-, chmn. dept, 42-45, 50-59. Assoc. scientist, P.R. Nuclear Center, 59-62, hon. assoc. scientist, 62-; vis. investr, cytol. & genetics group, Oak Ridge Nat. Lab, 60-61, tissue culture group, summer 63. Fel. AAAS; Bot. Soc. Am. Morphology, taxonomy and anatomy of Pteridophyta; radiation effects on chromosomes, especially Tradescantia and Vicia; mammalian cytogenetics; especially human chromosomes. Address: Dept. of Biology, University of Puerto Rico, Rio Piedras, PR 00931.

GARCIA-COLIN, LEOPOLDO S(CHERER), b. Mex, Nov. 27, 30; m. 57; c. 3. PHYSICS, THERMODYNAMICS. B.Sc, Mexico, 53,& 54; Ph.D.(physics), Maryland, 59. Asst. physics, Maryland, 56-57, inst. fluid dynamics & appl. math, 57-59, res. assoc, inst. fluid dynamics, 59-60; assoc. prof, Nat. Polytech. Inst, Mex, 60-63; prof, Univ. Puebla, 64-66; res. prof. physics, reactor nuclear, Nat. Nuclear Energy Comn, 66-67; HEAD APPL. RES. DIV, MEX. PETROL. INST, 67- Res. asst, Nat. Inst. Sci. Res, Mex, 53-62; consult, Nuclear Energy Comn, Mex, 60-; lectr, Sch. Mil. Eng, 61-62; Nat. Univ. Mex, 61-62, part-time prof, 67- Sci. Award, Acad. Sci. Res. Mex, 65. AAAS; Am. Phys. Soc; Am. Asn. Physics Teachers, Mex. Chem. Soc; Mex. Physics Soc. Statistical mechanics of equilibrium and non-equilibrium phenomena; superfluids; superfluid model of the nuclear matter; lattice vibrations. Address: Av. de Los Cien Metros, Núm. 500, Mexico 14, D.F.

GARCIA DE QUEVEDO, JOSE LUIS, b. Santurce, P.R, Mar. 5, 20; m. 43; c. 3. PHYSICS. B.S, Univ. P.R, 39; M.E.E, Rensselaer Polytech, 40; Ph.D. (physics), Duke Univ, 48. Instr. math, COL. AGR. & MECH. ARTS, UNIV. P.R, 40-41, elec. eng. & physics, 41-42, physics, 42-45, asst. prof, 45-48, assoc. prof. ELEC. ENG, 48-52, PROF, 52-57 & 65-, DIR. NUCLEAR ENG. DEPT, NUCLEAR CTR, 63-, head dept. elec. eng, univ, 49-57, head reactor div, nuclear ctr, 57-60, chief scientist & acting dir, 59-60, assoc. dir, 60-63. Sr. mem. Inst. Elec. & Electronics Eng; Am. Phys. Soc; Col. Eng. P.R; P.R. Soc. Elec. Eng. Frequency stabilization of microwave oscillators by spectrum lines. Address: Dept. of Electrical Engineering, College of Agriculture & Mechanical Arts, University of Puerto Rico, Mayaguez, PR 00708.

GARCIA-MOLINARI, OVIDIO, b. Hatillo, P.R, Nov. 22, 13; m. 46; c. 8. AGROSTOLOGY. B.S, Puerto Rico, 37; M.S, Nebraska, 43, Ph.D,(bot), 48. Jr. agron. aide, soil conserv. serv, U.S. Dept. Agr, P.R, 37-38, Rio Piedras exp. sta, 38-40, acting dir, 41, jr. soil conservationist, 41-42, Virgin Islands & P.R, 42; agrostologist, inst. trop. agr, UNIV. P.R, MAYAGÜEZ, 42, prin. botanist, 44, chief ecologist, 44-45, prof. ad honorem, COL. AGR. & MECH. ARTS, 45, PROF. AGRON, 45-, HEAD DEPT, 45-, DEAN AGR, 46-, DIR. INT. PROGS, AGR, 68- Mem. exped. to Andes, 40; mem. bd. dirs, Baltimore Dist, Fed. Land. Bank P.R, 70-; adv. comt. multiple use of nat. forests & nat. grasslands, U.S. Secy. Agr, 70- AAAS; Ecol. Soc. Am; Am. Soc. Range Mgt; Am. Soc. Agr. Sci.(award, 41); Col. P.R. Soil conservation; erosion control and pasture grasses; plant ecology; grasslands and grasses of Puerto Rico. Address: College of Agricultural & Mechanical Arts, University of Puerto Rica, Mayagüez, PR 00708.

GARCIA-MORIN, MANUEL, b. Cienfuegos, Cuba, Aug. 17, 14; U.S. citizen; m. 50; c. 1. PHYSICAL & ANALYTICAL CHEMISTRY. B.S, Puerto Rico, 38; M.A, Columbia, 39; Du Pont fel, Duke, 46-48, Ph.D.(chem), 48. Instr. CHEM, UNIV. P.R, RIO PIEDRAS, 39-41, asst. prof, 41-47, assoc. prof, 47-51, PROF, 51-, chmn. dept, 62-67. Guggenheim fel, Duke, 55-56; sr. scientist, Gen. Motors Corp, 57-58; resident res. assoc, Argonne Nat. Lab, 66-67. Am. Chem. Soc. Structure of electrolytic solutions; thermodiffusion and Soret coefficient of electrolytes; nuclear and electron magnetic resonance; trace analysis of alcoholic beverages by gas chromatography; properties of chlorophyll systems. Address: Dept. of Chemistry, University of Puerto Rico, Rio Piedras, PR 00931.

GARCIA-MUNOZ, MOISES, b. Valencia, Spain, May 21, 22; m. 55; c. 1. ATOMIC & NUCLEAR PHYSICS. M.S, Valencia, 47; Ph.D.(physics), Madrid, 57. Instr. phys. chem, Valencia, 49-50, asst, physics div, Spanish Atomic Energy Cmn, 51-56, investr, 56-59; RES. ASSOC. atomic physics, ENRICO FERMI INST. NUCLEAR STUDIES, UNIV. CHICAGO, 59-64, LAB. ASTROPHYSIC & SPACE RES, 64- Am. Phys. Soc. Atomic and molecular processes; space research. Address: University of Chicago, Enrico Fermi Institute of Nuclear Studies, 5630 Ellis Ave, Chicago, IL 60637.

GARCIA-PALMIERI, MARIO R, b. Adjuntas, P.R, Aug. 2, 27; m. 59; c. 1. INTERNAL MEDICINE, CARDIOLOGY. B.S, Univ. P.R, 47; M.D, Univ. Md, 51. Intern, Fajardo Dist. Hosp, 51-52; res. med, Bayamon Dist. Hosp, 52-53; asst. med, sch. med, Univ. P.R, 53-54, Nat. Heart Inst. fel. cardiol, 54-55; head dept, Fajardo Dist. Hosp, 55-56; instr. MED, SCH. MED, UNIV. P.R, 55-56, assoc, 56-58, asst. prof, 58-60, assoc. prof, 60, PROF, 61-, HEAD DEPT, 68-, CHIEF SECT. CARDIOL, 61-, dir. comprehensive med. prog, 56-59, out patient dept, 59-61, head dept. med, 61-66, lectr. cardiovasc. epidemiol, dept. prev. med. & pub. health. Res. med, San Patricio Vet. Admin. Hosp, 53-54; head dept. med, Univ. Dist. Hosp, 61; dir. undergrad. & postgrad. cardiovasc. training prog, sch. med, Univ. P.R, 61-; vis. prof, Seton Hall Col. Med. & sch. med, Univ. Fla. Gainesville, 63; vis. lectr, sch. med, Ind. Univ, 63; Brooklyn Jewish Hosp, 64; Cent. Univ. Venezuela, 64; lectr, Dominican Repub, 66 & 68; consult, San Patricio Vet. Admin, Presby, San Jorge, San Juan City, Auxilio Muto, Doctors and Teachers Hosps; fel. coun. clin. cardiol. and coun. epidemiol, Am. Heart Asn. Dipl, Am. Bd. Internal Med, 58, cert. Cardiovasc. Disorders, 62; cert. Merit, Fajardo Dist. Hosp, 65; Cert. Distinction, Hosp. Asn. P.R, 70. AAAS; fel. Am. Col. Physicians; fel. Am. Col. Cardiol; Am. Fedn. Clin. Res; Am. Soc. Trop. Med. & Hyg; Asn. Profs. Med; Am. Soc. Internal Med; Am. Asn. Med. Col; P.R. Med. Asn.(ed, Bull, 60-66, cert. merit); P.R. Soc. Cardiol.(pres, 68 & 69); P.R. Soc. Gastroenterol; Am. Pub. Health Asn; P.R. Pub. Health Asn; Soc. Epidemiol. Res; Royal Soc. Health; P.R. Acad. Arts & Sci; hon. mem, Dominican Soc. Cardiol; Inter-Am. Soc. Cardiol.(v.pres, 68-72); Asn. Am. Physicians; Asn. Univ. Cardiol. Tropical diseases; study of different electrocardiographical alternations, vectorcardiogram and coronary atherosclerosis. Address: Dept. of Medicine, University of Puerto Rico School of Medicine, San Juan, PR 00905.

GARCIA RAMOS, J(UAN), b. Queretaro, Qro, June 26, 15; m. 38; c. 9. PHYSIOLOGY. M.D, Army Med. Sch, Mex, 36; Johns Hopkins Univ, 49, 51-52; Sci.D, Nat. Polytech. Inst, Mex, 64. Asst. prof. physiol, Army Med. Sch, Mex, 40-42, assoc. prof, 42-58, pharmacol, 53, PROF, phys. chem. & gen. physiol, 52-58, PHYSIOL, 58-61; RES. CTR. ADVAN. STUDY, NAT. POLYTECH. INST, MEX, 61-, assoc. prof, 42-44. Investr, Inst. Cardiol, 44-53; vis. investr, Rockefeller Inst, 48-49; Guggenheim fel, 48-49, 51-52; sr. res. fel, Calif. Inst. Technol, 52; head dept. physiol, Inst. Neumol, 53-57. Carnot Award, 52. Mex. Army Res, 31-56, Lt. Col. Neurophysiol. Address: Dept. of Physiology, Research Center for Advanced Study, National Polytechnical Institute, Mexico 14, D.F, Mex.

GARD, D(ON) I(RVIN), b. Beaver Crossing, Nebr, June 18, 26. ANIMAL NUTRITION. B.S, Nebraska, 50; M.S, Okla. State, 52; Ph.D.(animal sci), Illinois, 54. Asst, Okla. State, 50-51; Illinois, 52-54; dir. res. & nutrit, Crete Mills, Lauhoff Grain Co, Nebr, 54-57; SR. ANIMAL NUTRITIONIST, ELI LILLY & CO, 57- Am. Soc. Animal Sci; Poultry Sci. Asn; Animal Nutrit. Res. Coun; World Poultry Sci. Asn. New antibiotic and organic compound effects on poultry growth, layer production, egg quality, fertility and hatchability. Address: Eli Lilly & Co, Animal Science Field Research, P.O. Box 708, Greenfield, IN 46104.

GARD, L(EAVITT) N(ELSON), b. Athens, Ohio, Jan. 7, 11; m. 36; c. 3. ANALYTICAL CHEMISTRY. A.B, Ohio, 32. Chemist, W.M. Welch Sci. Co, Ill, 34-36; chemist, res. anal. sect, chem. div, BARBERTON TECH. CTR, PPG INDUSTS, INC, 42-62, SUPVR, TECH. SERV. ANAL. SECT, 62- AAAS; Am. Chem. Soc; Am. Soc. Test. & Mat. Development of analytical methods applicable to organic and inorganic products; analysis of food crops for herbicide residues. Address: 420 E. Tuscarawas Ave, Barberton, OH 44203.

GARD, L(ELAND) E(DWARD), b. Bone Gap, Ill, Sept. 27, 04; m. 33; c. 4. AGRONOMY, SOIL SCIENCE. B.S, Illinois, 28, M.S, 29; Bonn, 29-30. Sales supvr, Am. Agr. Chem. Co, Ill, 30-32; farmer, 33-34; agronomist, soil conserv. serv, U.S. Dept. Agr, 35-36, soil surveyor, 36-37, res, 37-50, ASSOC. PROF. AGRON, DIXON SPRINGS AGR. CTR, UNIV. ILL, 50- Am. Soc.

Agron; Soil Sci. Soc. Am; Soil Conserv. Soc. Am. Soil conservation; soil management. Address: Dixon Springs Agricultural Center, University of Illinois, Simpson, IL 62985.

GARD, O(LIVER) W(ILLIAM), b. Berea, Ky, Oct. 2, 21; m. 43; c. 5. MECHANICAL ENGINEERING. B.S, Kentucky, 48; M.S, Ga. Inst. Tech, 51. Instr. MECH. ENG, UNIV. KY, 48-52, asst. prof, 52-56, ASSOC. PROF, 56- U.S.A, 42-46, Capt. Am. Soc. Mech. Eng. Work simplification; time study; production engineering; statistical quality control; plant layout; machine design. Address: Dept. of Mechanical Engineering, University of Kentucky, Lexington, KY 40506.

GARD, ORIN P(ENETON), b. Tremont City, Ohio, Dec. 6, 09; m. 38; c. 4. OPERATIONS RESEARCH. A.B, Wittenberg Col, 31; M.S, Ohio State, 32. Asst. physics, Ohio State, 31-32; instr, Muskingum Col, 34-35; seismic res, U.S. Bur. Mines, 35-36; asst. geophysicist, Gulf Res. & Develop. Co, 37; physicist aeronaut. systs. div, 37-60; OPERS. RES. ANALYST, AERONAUT. SYSTS. DIV, XROL, WRIGHT-PATTERSON AFB, 60- Opers. Res. Soc. Am; Am. Phys. Soc; Optical Soc. Am. Operations research; effectiveness of aerospace systems; analytical mechanics; ballistics. Address: 2014 Ewalt Ave, Dayton, OH 45420.

GARD, RICHARD, b. Alhambra, Calif, July 6, 28; m. 63. ZOOLOGY. A.B, California, 50, M.A, 53, Ph.D.(zool), 58; Southern California, 50-51. Res. zoologist, California, 56-58, jr. res. zoologist, 58, lectr. zool, 58-59, jr. res. zoologist, 59-60, asst. res. zoologist, 60-62; res. biologist, U.S. Bur. Commercial Fisheries, 62-65; assoc. res. zoologist, Univ. Calif, 69-70, Belvedere Sci. Fund grant, 70-71; RES. BIOLOGIST, NAT. MARINE FISHERIES SERV, 71- Wildlife Soc; Am. Fisheries Soc; Am. Soc. Mammal. Trout taxonomy; stream ecology; life history and dynamics of sockeye salmon; life history of marine mammals. Address: National Marine Fisheries Service, Box 155, Auke Bay, AK 99821.

GARDELLA, JOSEPH WARREN, b. Medford, Mass, Feb. 18, 17; m. 42; c. 5. BIOCHEMISTRY. B.S, Harvard, 41; M.D, Johns Hopkins Univ, 44. Intern & asst. resident med, Mass. Gen. Hosp, 44-46; fel. med. & res, Peter Bent Brigham Hosp, 47-48; resident med. & res. fel, Mary I. Bassett Hosp, N.Y, 48-50; clin. assoc. med, MED. SCH, HARVARD, 50-63, asst. dean STUD. AFFAIRS, 56-61, assoc. dean, 61-68, DEAN, 68-, LECTR. MED, 63- Res. assoc, Mass. Gen. Hosp, 51-56, asst. physician, 56- Dipl, Am. Bd. Internal Med, 54. Med.C, 46-47, Capt. Radiation Res. Soc; Am. Fedn. Clin. Res. Biochemistry of normal, malignant and irradiated tissues. Address: Harvard Medical School, 25 Shattuck St, Boston, MA 02115.

GARDELLA, LIBERO ANTHONY, b. Chicago, Ill, July 24, 35; m. 65; c. 3. PHARMACEUTICAL CHEMISTRY. B.S, Univ. Ill, 59, Ph.D.(pharmaceut. chem), 62. Fel. org. chem, Princeton, 62-63; res. pharmacist, pharmaceut. div, Abbott Labs, 63-67, hosp. prod. div, 67-69, prog. mgr. prod. develop, 69; SECT. HEAD, ARNAR-STONE LABS, AM. HOSP. SUPPLY CORP, 69- Am. Pharmaceut. Asn; Acad. Pharmaceut. Sci; Am. Chem. Soc. Medicinal chemistry; product development in pharmaceutical dosage forms. Address: Arnar-Stone Labs, 601 E. Kensington Rd, Mt. Prospect, IL 60056.

GARDER, A(RTHUR) O(RIS), JR, b. Kansas City, Mo, Dec. 17, 25; m. 53; c. 2. MATHEMATICS. B.S, Chicago, 48; M.A, Washington (St. Louis), 50, Ph.D. (math), 54. Asst. math, Washington (St. Louis), 49-52; mathematician, United Gas Corp, 52-55; programmer utility routines, Int. Bus. Machines Corp, 55-56; mathematician numerical anal, Humble Oil & Ref. Co, 56-64; ASSOC. PROF, dept. comput. sci, Wash. Univ, 64-66; MATH, SOUTH. ILL. UNIV, 66- U.S.A.A.F, 45-47. Am. Math. Soc; Soc. Indust. & Appl. Math. Convolution transforms with totally positive kernals; solution of partial differential equations of elliptic and parabolic type by difference methods. Address: Dept. of Mathematics, Southern Illinois University, Edwardsville, IL 62025.

GARDIER, R(OBERT) W(OODWARD), b. Scranton, Pa, May 17, 27; m. 51; c. 3. PHARMACOLOGY. B.S, Scranton, 49; fel, Tennessee, 49-51, M.S, 52, U.S. Pub. Health Serv. fel, 52-53, Ph.D.(pharmacol), 54. Pharmacologist, Pitman-Moore Co, 53-58; asst. prof. pharmacol. & dir. res. anesthesiol, sch. med, Indiana, 59-61; assoc. prof. pharmacol, med. br, Texas, 61-63; assoc. prof. pharmacol. & anesthesia res. dir, col. med, Ohio State Univ, 63-67, prof, 67-69; dir. biol. res, Bristol Labs, 69-71; PROF. PHARMACOL. & ANESTHESIOL, COL. MED, OHIO STATE UNIV, 71- Mem. med. div, Inst. Nuclear Studies, Oak Ridge, 51, consult, 51-52. Hosp.C, U.S.N, 45-46. AAAS; Soc. Pharmacol. & Exp. Therapeut; Soc. Exp. Biol. & Med; Soc. Toxicol. Drugs related to anesthesia. Address: Dept. of Pharmacology & Anesthesiology, College of Medicine, Ohio State University, 333 W. Tenth Ave, Columbus, OH 43210.

GARDINER, DONALD A(NDREW), b. Buffalo, N.Y, Feb. 2, 22; m. 43; c. 3. MATHEMATICAL STATISTICS. B.S, Buffalo, 43, M.B.A, 48; Ph.D.(exp. statist), N.C. State Col, 56. Lectr. statist, Buffalo, 46-48; asst. prof, Tennessee, 48-51; asst. statistician, N.C. State Col, 55-56; statistician phys. & eng. sci, OAK RIDGE NAT. LAB, 56-67, ASST. DIR. MATH. DIV, 67- Assoc. prof, Univ. Tenn, 65-; vis. prof. Fla. State Univ, 66-67; ed-elect, Technometrics, 71, ed, 72- U.S.N.R, 43-46, 51-53, Lt. Comdr.(Ret). Biomet. Soc; fel. Am. Statist. Asn; Inst. Math. Statist; Int. Asn. Statist. in Phys. Sci. Experimental statistics; design of experiments for physical sciences; statistical analysis of experiments in physical sciences; probability models. Address: Statistics Division, Oak Ridge National Lab, P.O. Box Y, Bldg. 9704-1, Oak Ridge, TN 37830.

GARDINER, E(ARL) E(DWIN), b. Thorndike, Maine, Sept. 28, 34; m. 52; c. 2. NUTRITION, PHYSIOLOGY. B.S, Univ. Maine, 56; M.S, Purdue Univ, 58, Ph.D.(nutrit), 60. Res. off. poultry nutrit, Can. Dept. Agr, 60-61; asst. prof, Univ. R.I, 61-65; RES. SCIENTIST, ANIMAL SCI. SECT, CAN. DEPT. AGR, 65- AAAS; Poultry Sci. Asn; World Poultry Sci. Asn; Can. Biochem. Soc; Can. Soc. Animal Prod. Mineral interrelationships; food consumption. Address: Animal Science Section, Canada Agricultural Research Station, Lethbridge, Alta, Can.

GARDINER, JOHN ALDEN, b. Providence, R.I, Feb. 9, 38; m. 60; c. 3. ANALYTICAL CHEMISTRY. B.S, N.C. Univ, 60; Mershon fel. & M.S, Ohio State Univ, 62, Allied Chem. fel. & Ph.D.(anal. chem), 64. Res. chemist, INDUST. & BIOCHEM. DEPT, E.I. DU PONT DE NEMOURS & CO, INC, 64-67, sr. res. chemist, 67-69, RES. SUPVR, 69- Am. Chem. Soc. Metabolism and degradation of pesticides in soil, plants, animals and water, including frequent use of C-14 labeled materials, thin layer, gas and liquid chromatography. Address: 2004 Eden Rd, N. Graylyn Crest, Wilmington, DE 19810.

GARDINER, J(OHN) BROOKE, b. Bryn Mawr, Pa, Nov. 9, 29; m. 56; c. 1. ORGANIC CHEMISTRY. A.B, Haverford Col, 51; Ph.D.(org. chem), North Carolina, 57. Chemist prod. res. div, ESSO RES. & ENG. CO, 57-59, high energy propellant proj, 59-64, sr. chemist, 64-66, proj. leader rubber adhesion, Enjay Polymer Labs, 66-68, staff planner prog. & budget, 68-70, PROG. MGR, ENJAY NEW VENTURE ADDITIVES LAB, LINDEN, 70-, res. assoc, 71. AAAS; Am. Chem. Soc.(Best Paper Award, 68); Sci. Res. Soc. Am; fel. Am. Inst. Chem. Optical isomerization; anthracene chemistry; synthetic motor oils; viscosity index improvers for motor oils; synthesis of high energy oxidizers-monomers-binders; scale-up formulation and micro rocket firing; rubber adhesion; microinterferometry. Address: 1364 Stony Brook Lane, Mountainside, NJ 07092.

GARDINER, KENNETH W(ILLIAM), b. Chicago, Ill, Feb. 10, 19; m. 42; c. 3. PHYSICAL & ANALYTICAL CHEMISTRY. A.B, Stanford, 39, M.A, 40; Ph.D.(instrumental anal. chem), Mass. Inst. Tech, 52. Sr. res. chemist, Lever Bros. Co, 41-46; Firestone Tire & Rubber Co, 46-49; asst, Mass. Inst. Tech, 50-52; dir. res, Gardiner Instrument Res. Lab, 52-56; gen. chem. lab, cent. res. & eng. div, Continental Can Co, Ill, 56-59; chief res. chemist, asst. dir, Cent. Res. Div, Consol. Electrodynamics Corp. Div, Bell & Howell Co, 59-60, dir. chem. res, Bell & Howell Res. Center, 60-64; gen. mgr, anal. systs. co, Teledyne Systs. Corp, 64-70, PRES. & GEN. MGR, TELEDYNE ANAL. INSTRUMENTS, TELEDYNE INC, 70- Consult, 52-56; res. assoc, Mass. Inst. Technol, 53. Am. Chem. Soc; Am. Phys. Soc. Technical management; instrumental analytical chemistry; physical and instrumental methods in research and chemical analysis. Address: 1125 Mesita Rd, Pasadena, CA 91101.

GARDINER, LION F(REDERICK), b. Glen Cove, N.Y, June 21, 38; m. 71. MARINE ZOOLOGY. B.S, Wheaton Col.(Ill), 60; M.S, Michigan, 64; summer, Duke, 65; Nat. Sci. Found. summer fel, Rhode Island, 66, Woods Hole Oceanog. Inst. fel, 66-69. Res. asst. marine invert. systs, Sapelo Island Res. Found, summer 63; instr. biol, Delta Col, 64-65; ASST. PROF. ZOOL, RUTGERS UNIV, 69- Chem.C, U.S.A, 60-62, 1st Lt. AAAS; Am. Inst. Biol. Sci; Ecol. Soc. Am; Am. Soc. Limnol. & Oceanog; Am. Sci. Affiliation. Biology of the deep-sea fauna; systematics and biology of the Tanaidacea; marine benthic ecology. Address: Dept. of Zoology & Physiology, Rutgers University, 195 University Ave, Newark, NJ 07102.

GARDINER, ROBERT ARCHIE, b. Winnipeg, Man, Oct. 12, 42; m. 66; c. 1. ORGANIC & PETROLEUM CHEMISTRY. B.S, Univ. Alta, 64; univ. fel, Univ. Ill, Urbana, 65-66, M.S, 66, Allied Chem. Co. fel, 66-67, Nat. Insts. Health fel, 67-69, Ph.D.(org. chem), 70. CHEMIST, JACKSON LAB, E.I. DU PONT DE NEMOURS & CO, INC, 69- Am. Chem. Soc. Chemistry of lubrication and petroleum additives. Address: 5110 New Kent Rd, Wilmington, DE 19808.

GARDINER, WILLIAM CECIL, b. Exeter, Ont, Nov. 14, 04; nat; m. 31; c. 3. PHYSICAL CHEMISTRY. B.A, Queen's (Ont), 26, M.A, 27; Ph.D.(phys. chem), Princeton, 29. Res. chemist, Comstock & Westcott, Inc, N.Y, 29-32; Mathieson Alkali Works, 32-40, electrochem. eng. dept, 40-42, supt. electrolytic dept, Mathieson Magnesium Plant, La, 42-44, chem. eng. develop. dept, Olin Mathieson Chem. Corp, 44-49, supt, electrochem. eng, 49-52, assoc. dir. res. & develop, 52-54, mgr. res. eng, res. & develop. dept, chem. div, 54-60, mgr. electrochem. res, 60-67, sci. adv, Olin Corp, 67-69; CONSULT. & DIR. ELECTROCHEM. DEVELOP, CRAWFORD & RUSSELL, INC, 69- Sci. consult, tech. indust. intel. bd, U.S. Dept. Commerce, 46; Atomic Energy Comn, 51-58; chmn. ad hoc mercury comt, Chlorine Inst. Mem. Award, Chem. Mkt. Res. Asn. AAAS; Am. Chem. Soc; Electrochem. Soc.(prize, 29, pres, 59-60, div. ed, Electrochem. Tech); Am. Inst. Chem. Eng. Chlorine metallurgy; industrial electrochemistry; mercury pollution abatement and recovery; graphite and metal anodes; chlorates; alkali-chlorine cells; sodium amalgam utilization; brine purification; chemical chlorine; hydrochloric acid electrolysis; fuel cells; electrolytic manganese; magnesium cells; alternating current to direct current rectifiers. Address: 283 Great Oak Rd, Orange, CT 06477.

GARDINER, WILLIAM CECIL, JR, b. Niagara Falls, N.Y, Jan. 14, 33; m. 59; c. 2. PHYSICAL CHEMISTRY. A.B, Princeton, 54; Fulbright fel, Heidelberg, 54-55; Nat.Sci. Found. fel. & Ph.D.(chem), Harvard, 60. Res. assoc. CHEM, Max-Planck Inst. Phys. Chem, Göttingen, 55-57; instr, UNIV. TEX, AUSTIN, 60-62, asst. prof, 62-66, ASSOC. PROF, 66- Am. Phys. Soc; Am. Chem. Soc; Faraday Soc; Combustion Inst. Chemical kinetics; combustion; electron spin resonance spectroscopy; laser photochemistry. Address: Dept. of Chemistry, University of Texas, Austin, TX 78712.

GARDLUND, ZACH(ARIAH) G(UST), b. Lake City, Minn, Sept. 12, 37; m. 63; c. 3. POLYMER & ORGANIC CHEMISTRY. B.A, Carleton Col, 59; Socony-Mobil fel, Univ. Ariz, 62-64, Ph.D.(org. chem), 64. Assoc. sr. res. chemist, POLYMERS DEPT, RES. LAB, GEN. MOTORS TECH. CTR, 64-67, sr. res. chemist, 67-69, SR. RES. CHEMIST & SUPVR. ORG. CHEM. SECT, 69- Am. Chem. Soc; The Chem. Soc. Monomer-polymer synthesis; polymer structure-property relationship; block and graft polymers; photochemistry; organometallics. Address: Polymers Dept, Research Labs, General Motors Technical Center, Warren, MI 48089.

GARDNER, ALVIN F(REDERICK), b. Chicago, Ill, Mar. 22, 20; m. 42; c. 1. PATHOLOGY. Florida, 37-40; D.D.S, Emory, 43; cert, Univ. Kansas City, 46; Nat. Insts. Dent. Res. fel, Iowa, 54-55, Illinois, 55-57; M.S, 57; Nat. Inst. Dent. Res. fel, Georgetown, 57-59, Ph.D.(path), 59. Res. assoc. & instr. oral path, Illinois, 57; resident oral path, dent. & oral br, Armed

Forces Inst. Path, 57-59; assoc. prof. path. & oral path, sch. dent, Univ. Maryland, 59-63; pathologist, BUR. DRUGS, FOOD & DRUG ADMIN, DEPT. HEALTH, EDUC. & WELFARE, WASH, D.C, 63-67, dent. officer, off. drug surveillance, 67-69, ORAL PATHOLOGIST, 69- Consult, Vet. Admin, 60-; Nat. Insts. Health, U.S. Army res. & develop. command, Am. Cancer Soc. & Sigma Xi res. grants; vis. scientist, Nat. Bur. Standards; staff dentist, Kadlec Hosp, Hanford Works, Wash; mem. dent. serv, Stockton State Hosp, Calif; consult, Stedman's med. dictionary. Dent.C. Res, 42-50, Capt. AAAS; Am. Nutrit. Soc; fel. Am. Pub. Health Asn; Am. Med. Writers' Asn; Am. Dent. Asn; fel. Int. Asn. Anesthesiol; Int. Asn. Dent. Res; Am. Acad. Oral Path; Am. Acad. Oral Med; Int. Col. Appl. Nutrit; N.Y. Acad. Sci; Royal Soc. Health. Experimental Lathyrism; disturbances in the metabolism of connective tissue; nutritional disturbance in mesoderm; oral pharmacology, effects of drugs on oral tissues. Address: 9039 Sligo Creek Pkwy, Silver Spring, MD 20901.

GARDNER, ANDREW L(EROY), b. Ogden, Utah, Feb. 6, 19; m. 41; c. 5. PHYSICS. B.S, Utah State, 40; Ph.D.(physics), California, Berkeley, 55. Commun. asst, Idaho Nat. Forest, U.S. Dept. Agr, 41; radio engr, Off. Chief Sig. Officer, U.S. War Dept, 42-44; mem. staff, radiation lab, Mass. Inst. Tech, 44-45; res. asst. & assoc, inst. eng. res, California, 46-54, physicist, Lawrence Radiation Lab, 54-64; assoc. prof. PHYSICS, BRIGHAM YOUNG UNIV, 64-66, PROF, 66- Consult, Inst. Plasma Physics, Japan, 62; Lawrence Radiation Lab, 68- Fel. Am. Phys. Soc. Experimental plasma physics; microwave circuitry; electronics; high voltage switching. Address: 555 E. 2950 N, Provo, UT 84601.

GARDNER, ARTHUR WENDEL, b. Cedar City, Utah, Oct. 23, 24. GENETICS, ZOOLOGY. B.S, Utah State, 49; M.S, Kansas State, 54, Ph.D.(genetics), 56. Instr. genetics, Kansas State, 55, BIOL, Russell Sage Col, 61-64; asst. prof, Washburn Univ, 64-67; ASSOC. PROF, W.GA. COL, 67-, acting head dept. biol, 68-69. U.S.A.F.R, 43-46, 50-51, 1st Lt. AAAS; Am. Soc. Animal Sci. Genetics and physiology of the Syrian hamster. Address: Dept. of Biology, West Georgia College, Carrollton, GA 30117.

GARDNER, BERNARD, b. Brooklyn, N.Y, Oct. 1, 31; m. 54; c. 3. BIOCHEMISTRY. A.B, N.Y. Univ, 52, M.D, 56. Asst. prof. SURG, STATE UNIV. N.Y. DOWNSTATE MED. CTR, 65-68, ASSOC. PROF, 68-, DIR. SURG. & ONCOL, KINGS COUNTY HOSP, 70- John & Mary R. Markle scholar. acad. med, 68-; mem. bd. dir, res. found, State Univ. N.Y, 68- U.S.A.F, 58-60, Capt. AAAS; Am. Fedn. Clin. Res; Asn. Acad. Surg; Am. Asn. Cancer Educ; Soc. Exp. Biol. & Med; Soc. Univ. Surg; Am. Soc. Clin. Oncol; Am. Soc. Artificial Internal Organs; Soc. Surg. Alimentary Tract; Int. Soc. Surg; fel. Am. Cancer Soc; James Ewing Soc. Tumor metastases; metabolic effects of tumor, particularly the relationship between tumor growth and calcium and phosphate metabolism; the suspension stability of bile and its relationship to the electro-chemistry of the cholesterol-bile salt-lecithin micelle. Address: Dept. of Surgery, State University of New York Downstate Medical Center, 450 Clarkson Ave, Brooklyn, NY 11203.

GARDNER, BERTRAM W(ALLACE), JR, b. Baldwin City, Kans, Aug. 25, 15; m. 41; c. 2. FOODS. B.S, Kans. State Univ, 41; M.S, Univ. Ill, 43. Mem. faculty, Univ. Ill, 41-43; mem. exten. staff, Kans. State Univ, 43; chief animal prod. br, Q.M. Food & Container Inst, Chicago, 46-54, assoc. chief animal prod. div, 54-58, head cured, smoked and canned meats & sausage prod. lab, 58-63; head mammalian & marine prod. br, U.S. ARMY NATICK LABS, 63-69, TECH. DATA RES. FOR DIR, 69- AAAS; Inst. Food Technol; N.Y. Acad. Sci; Am. Meat Sci. Asn; Am. Soc. Qual. Control. Address: 5 Richard Rd, Cochituate, MA 01778.

GARDNER, BRYANT ROGERS, b. McNary, Ariz, Sept. 19, 30; m. 53; c. 4. SOIL CHEMISTRY, PLANT NUTRITION. B.S, Ariz. State Univ, 58; M.S, Univ. Ariz, 60, Ph.D.(agr. chem), 63. Res. assoc, UNIV. ARIZ, 62-63, ASST. AGR. CHEMIST, 63- U.S.A.F, 51-55, 1st Lt. Am. Soc. Agron. Soil fertility; plant physiology. Address: Dept. of Agricultural Chemistry & Soils, University of Arizona, R.R. 1, Box 587, Yuma, AZ 85364.

GARDNER, CHARLES H, b. Wausaw, Wis, Mar. 7, 20; m. 45; c. 2. MICROBIOLOGY. B.S, Wisconsin, 47, M.S, 48. Prod. supvr, Merck & Co, Inc, 48-51, staff microbiologist, 51-54, microbiologist, 54-61; v.pres. opers, Rachelle Labs, Inc, 61-66; MGR. FERMENTATION RES, RES. & DEVELOP, GRAIN PROCESSING CORP, 66- U.S.A.A.F, 40-45, Capt. Am. Soc. Microbiol; Am. Chem. Soc. Agricultural bacteriology; biosynthesis of antibiotics and chemicals; fermentation technology, including continuous fermentation. Address: Research & Development, Grain Processing Corp, 1600 Oregon St, Muscatine, IA 52761.

GARDNER, CHARLES N(ORMAN), b. Brooklyn, N.Y, Dec. 4, 14; m. 43; c. 2. POLYMER CHEMISTRY. Polytech. Inst. Brooklyn; Pratt Inst. Asst. to S. Pellerano, consult. chemist, N.Y, 36-40; asst. to pres, George Morrell Corp, Mich, 45-49; chem. engr, res. & develop. br, Off. Qm Gen, U.S. DEPT. ARMY, 49-52, acting chief & asst. chief chems. & plastics br, res. & develop. div, 52-53, CHIEF, develop. br, 53-62, lab. br, res. div, RES. & DEVELOP. DIRECTORATE, HQ, ARMY MAT. COMMAND, 62-, CHIEF INDIVIDUAL EQUIP. BR, 66- Res. Dirs. Award, Qm. Res. & Develop. Orgn, U.S. Dept. Army, 51, meritorious civilian serv. award, 59, 62 & 67. U.S.A, 40-45. Industrial chemistry, especially synthetic resins and plastic compositions; molded plastics; bombs and pyrotechnics; helmets and body armor and other protective devices. Address: 4108 Suitland Rd, Suitland, MD 20023.

GARDNER, C(HARLES) O(LDA), b. Tecumseh, Nebr, March 15, 19; m. 47; c. 4. GENETICS. B.Sc, Nebraska, 41, M.S, 48; M.B.A, Harvard, 43; Ph.D. (agron), North Carolina, 51. Asst. exten. agronomist, UNIV. NEBR, 46-48, assoc. prof. AGRON, 52-57, prof, 57-70, MEYER KATZMAN PROF, 70-, chmn. statist. lab, 58-68, consult. biometrician, dept. agron. Asst. statistician, N.C. State Col, 51-52. U.S.A, 43-46, Capt. AAAS; Genetics Soc. Am; fel. Am. Soc. Agron; Biomet. Soc; Am. Genetic Asn. Quantitative inheritance studies in plants; application of statistical methods in research; biometrical genetics. Address: Dept. of Agronomy, University of Nebraska, Lincoln, NE 68503.

GARDNER, CHARLES W(ILLIAM), b. Detroit, Mich, July 18, 26; m. 50; c. 1. MECHANICAL ENGINEERING, MATHEMATICS. B.S, Detroit Inst. Tech, 50; Minnesota, 51, 54; California, Los Angeles, 58, 62, 63. Fel. math, Minnesota, 50-51; test engr, aero div, Minneapolis Honeywell Regulator Co, 53-55; proj. engr, Summers Gyroscope Co, 55-57; sr. res. engr, Rocketdyne Div, N.Am. Aviation, Inc, 57-59; assoc, Planning Res. Corp, 59-61; sr. mem, adv. prog. staff, Gen. Precision, Inc, 61-63; staff engr, adv. projs. labs, aeronaut. systs. div, Hughes Aircraft Co, 63-64; staff mem, weapons systs. eval. div, Inst. Defense Analyses, 64-69; SR. STAFF ENGR, AERONAUT. SYSTS. DIV, HUGHES AIRCRAFT CO, 69- U.S.N.R, 51-53, Lt.(jg). Opers. Res. Soc. Operations research for weapon systems evaluation. Address: 3165 Hodler Dr, Topanga, CA 90290.

GARDNER, CLARENCE E(LLSWORTH), JR, b. Bucyrus, Ohio, Feb. 27, 03; m. 28; c. 1. SURGERY. A.B, Wittenberg Col, 24, D.Sc, 51; M.D, Hopkins, 28. Asst. SURG, Hopkins, 29-30; from assoc. prof. to prof, DUKE UNIV, 32-69, EMER. PROF, 69-, chmn. dept, 60-64. Med.C, U.S.A, 42-45. Mem. exam. bd, Am. Bd. Surg, 51-57. Fel. Soc. Univ. Surg; fel. Am. Med. Asn; fel. Am. Surg. Asn; fel. Am. Col. Surg. Arterial injuries; localization of foreign bodies in the soft parts; surgical treatment of peptic ulcer; chest injuries; hyper parathyroidism; anomalies of intestinal rotation. Address: Duke Hospital, Durham, NC 27706.

GARDNER, C(LARENCE) GERALD, b. Waynesboro, Miss, Jan. 14, 33; m. 54; c. 6. APPLIED PHYSICS. B.S, Miss. State, 54; univ. scholar, Vanderbilt, 54-55, fel, 55-56, Ford Found. fel, 56-58, Ph.D.(physics), 59. Res. assoc. PHYSICS, Oak Ridge Nat. Lab, 59; physicist, Lawrence Radiation Lab, California, 60; asst. prof. physics, Tex. Tech. Col, 60-62, assoc. prof, 62-64; SR. RES. PHYSICIST, SOUTHWEST RES. INST, 64- Am. Phys. Soc; Soc. Nondestructive Test. Solid state; nondestructive evaluation. Address: Southwest Research Institute, San Antonio, TX 78284.

GARDNER, CLIFFORD S, b. Ft. Smith, Ark, Jan. 14, 24; m. 67. APPLIED MATHEMATICS. A.B, Harvard Col, 44; Ph.D.(math), N.Y. Univ, 52. Physicist, Nat. Adv. Cmt. Aeronaut, 44-46; mathematician, Control Instrument Co, 47-48; physicist, Calif. Res. & Develop. Co, 52-54; radiation lab, California, 54-56; res. scientist, Courant Inst, N.Y. Univ, 56-62; physicist, Radio Corp. Am, 62-64; vis. res. prof. physics, plasma physics lab, Princeton, 64-68; PROF. MATH, UNIV. TEX, AUSTIN, 68- Am. Math. Soc. Aerodynamics; plasma physics. Address: 3415 Shinoak Dr, Austin, TX 78731.

GARDNER, DAVID A(RNOLD), b. Ithaca, N.Y, June 19, 39; m. 59; c. 3. CELL BIOLOGY, BIOCHEMISTRY. B.S, Univ. Rochester, 61, Ph.D.(biochem), 67. Nat. Insts. Health res. fel. biochem, Brandeis Univ, 67-69; RES. SCIENTIST CELL BIOL, RES. DIV, MILES LABS, INC, ELKHART, 69- Asst. faculty fel, Univ. Notre Dame, 69- Tissue Cult. Asn. Regulation of cell division in tissue culture; host cell response to viruses; regulation of pyridine nucleotide metabolism in adrenal tumor cell cultures; metabolism of isolated mouse liver cells. Address: 1912 Trent Way, South Bend, IN 46614.

GARDNER, DAVID GODFREY, b. Darlington, Eng, Feb. 24, 36; Can. citizen; m. 60; c. 3. ORAL PATHOLOGY. D.D.S, Univ. Toronto, 58; Nat. Res. Coun. Can. fel, Ind. Univ, 63-65, M.S.D, 65. Asst. prof. oral med, Univ. B.C, 65-66; ASSOC. PROF. PATH, UNIV. WEST. ONT, 66-, CHMN. DIV. ORAL PATH, 70- Consult. oral path. & oral med, Children's Psychiat. Res. Inst, London, Ont, 66-; oral path, St. Thomas Psychiat. Hosp, Ont, 67-; mem. consult. panel, Can. Tumour Registry, Nat. Cancer Inst. Can, 68- Dipl, Am. Bd. Oral Path, 69. Dent.C, Can. Army, 56-63, Capt. Fel. Am. Acad. Oral Path; Can. Dent. Asn; Can. Acad. Oral Path.(secy, 66-); Int. Asn. Dent. Res; Can. Soc. Forensic Odontol. Oral manifestations of systemic disease. Address: Dept. of Pathology, Health Sciences Centre, University of Western Ontario, London, Ont, Can.

GARDNER, DAVID L, b. Winesburg, Ohio, May 28, 38; m. 65; c. 2. BIOMEDICAL ENGINEERING, PHYSIOLOGY. B.A, Kent State Univ, 60, M.A, 63, Ph.D.(physiol), 69. Res. chemist, Goodyear Tire & Rubber Co, 64-66; dept. res, Akron City Hosp, 67-68; RES. BIOCHEMIST, BATTELLE MEM. INST, 69- AAAS; Am. Soc. Artificial Internal Organs. Development and fabrication of artificial arteries and hearts; dialysis by the oral ingestion of microencapsulated adsorbents in an artificial kidney program. Address: Dept. of Biochemistry & Biomedical Engineering, Battelle Memorial Institute, 505 King Ave, Columbus, OH 43201.

GARDNER, DAVID M(ILTON), b. Cleveland, Ohio, June 21, 28; m. 55; c. 4. PHYSICAL CHEMISTRY. Sc.B, Brown, 50; M.S, Pennsylvania, 52, Ph.D. (chem), 54. Proj. leader, Reaction Motors, Inc, 54-56; GROUP LEADER, PENNWALT CORP, 57- U.S.A, 46-48, Sgt. AAAS; Am. Chem. Soc; Am. Inst. Aeronaut. & Astronaut. Thermodynamics; halogens; nitrogen; metallo-organic chemistry; rocket fuels and oxidizers; equilibria and kinetics. Address: Pennwalt Corp, 900 First Ave, King of Prussia, PA 19406.

GARDNER, DAVID R, b. London, Eng, Aug. 10, 42. NEUROPHYSIOLOGY. B.Sc, Univ. Southampton, 63, Sci. Res. Coun. grant & Ph.D.(neurophysiol), 66. Sci. Res. Coun. res. fel. neurophysiol, Univ. Southampton, 66-67; ASST. PROF. BIOL, CARLETON UNIV.(CAN), 67- Brit. Soc. Exp. Biol. Ionic requirements of action potentials from Helix Aspersa ganglia nerve cells; effect pesticides on the nervous system; temperature regulation in fish. Address: Dept. of Biology, Carleton University, Ottawa, Ont, K1S 5B6, Can.

GARDNER, DONALD G(LENN), b. Chicago, Ill, Sept. 25, 31; m. 53; 69; c. 2 NUCLEAR & RADIATION CHEMISTRY. B.S, Illinois, 53; M.S, Michigan, 54, Eastman Kodak fel. & Ph.D.(nuclear chem), 57. Chemist, Westinghouse Elec. Corp, 57-59; asst. prof. chem, Arkansas, 69-61; Ill. Inst. Tech, 61-64, assoc; prof, 64-68; SR. CHEMIST, LAWRENCE LIVERMORE LAB, UNIV. CALIF, 68-, mem. staff, 65-67. Consult, Argonne Nat. Lab, 62-64. Am. Phys. Soc; Am. Chem. Soc. Nuclear reactions; cross sections; statistical theory; nuclear decay schemes; radiation damage in polymers; optical properties of irradiated glasses; energy transport in noncrystalline solids;

radiation effects in biological systems; applied mathematics. Address: Lawrence Livermore Lab, University of California, Livermore, CA 94550.

GARDNER, DONALD M(URRAY), b. Hartford, Conn, Dec. 17, 28; m. 51; c. 3. PHYSICAL CHEMISTRY. A.B, Hamilton Col, 50; M.A, Columbia Univ, 54, Ph.D.(chem), 56; M.B.A, Am. Int. Col, 69. Res. chemist, Shawinigan Resins Corp, 55-61, GROUP LEADER, 61-64; MONSANTO CO, 64- Am. Chem. Soc. Chemical physics; electron magnetic resonance spectroscopy; sulfur chemistry; instrumental analysis; water soluble polymers; surface chemistry; detergents; polymerization; adhesives; reprographics. Address: Monsanto Co, Bircham Bend Plant, P.O. Box 2130, Springfield, MA 01101.

GARDNER, E(ARL) W(ILLIAM), JR, b. Houston, Tex, July 31, 28; m. 62; c. 2. MICROBIOLOGY. B.S, Baylor, 50; M.A, Texas, 54, Ph.D.(bact), 58. Asst. prof. BIOL, TEX. CHRISTIAN UNIV, 58-61, assoc. prof, 61-68, PROF, 68- Vis. asst. prof, Univ. Tex, 60. Am. Soc. Microbiol; Am. Inst. Biol. Sci. Antigenicity and pathogenicity of vibrio comma. Address: Dept. of Biology, Texas Christian University, Ft. Worth, TX 76129.

GARDNER, EDWARD, JR, b. Charleston, W.Va, July 28, 25; m. 49; c. 3. IMMUNOLOGY. B.S, Morris Harvey Col, 50; M.Sc, Ohio State, 52, Ph.D. (bact, immunol), 55. Asst. bacter, Ohio State, 52-54, med, 54-55; res. assoc, div. hemat, Med. Col. Ga, 55-58, asst. res. prof, 58-62, assoc. prof. med. & assoc. prof. med. microbiol. & pub. health, 62-70; SCIENTIST/ADMINISTRATOR, CHIEF RES. & TRAINING BR. & EXEC. SECY, ENVIRON. SCI. TRAINING COMT, NAT. INST. ENVIRON. HEALTH SCI, 70- Dipl, Am. Bd. Microbiol. U.S.A.A.F, 43-45. AAAS; Am. Soc. Microbiol; Soc. Exp. Biol. & Med; Can. Soc. Immunol; N.Y. Acad. Sci. Immunology; autoimmune disease; erythropoietin. Address: Research & Training Branch, National Institute of Environmental Health Sciences, P.O. Box 12233, Research Triangle Park, NC 27709.

GARDNER, EDWARD E(UGENE), b. Somerset, Pa, Aug. 3, 23; m. 48; c. 4. PHYSICS. S.B, Mass. Inst. Tech, 48; M.A, Minnesota, 50; Ph.D.(physics), Catholic Univ, 55. Mem. res. staff, div. indust, Mass. Inst. Tech, 48-49; instr. gen. physics, Va. Polytech, 50-51; asst. prof, U.S. Naval Acad, 51-55; asst. prof. elec. eng. & physics, Lehigh, 55-58; res. physicist, Whirlpool Corp, Mich, 58-62; adv. physicist, IBM CORP, 62-69, SR. PHYSICIST, COMPONENT DIV, 69- Summers, mem. tech. staff, Bell Tel. Labs, 56; prof, Gen. Elec. Co, 57; spec. lectr, Mich. State, 59- Sig.C, U.S.A, 43-46. AAAS; Electrochem. Soc; Am. Phys. Soc; Inst. Elec. & Electronics Eng. Solid state physics; electromagnetic theory; characterization of semiconductor materials; semiconductor materials measurement technique development. Address: R.D. 2, Ticonderoga Rd, Shelburne, VT 05482.

GARDNER, EDWARD M(ARKHAM), b. London, England, June 23, 01; nat; m. 35; c. 1. ELECTRICAL ENGINEERING. B.Sc, London, 23; M.S, Calif. Inst. Tech, 38. Elec. engr, N.Y. Tel. Co, 28-37; asst. prof. elec. eng, Univ. of the Pacific, 38-39, assoc. prof, 39-42; asst. prof. elec. eng. & supvr. eng. sci. & mgt. war training program, California, 42-46; elec. engr, U.S. Navy, Calif, 47; mem. teaching staff elec. eng, San Francisco City Col, 47-48; assoc. prof, U.S. Naval Post-Grad. Sch, 48-52, prof, 52-71; RETIRED. Sr. mem. Inst. Elec. & Electronics Eng. Electrical apparatus and machinery; power generation. Address: Dept. of Electrical Engineering, U.S. Naval Postgraduate School, Monterey, CA 93940.

GARDNER, ELDON J(OHN), b. Logan, Utah, June 5, 09; m. 39; c. 6. ZOOLOGY. B.S, Utah State, 34, M.S, 35; Thompson scholar, California, 38-39; Ph.D.(zool), 39. Instr. biol. & dean lower div, Salinas Jr. Col, 39-46; from asst. prof. to assoc. prof. ZOOL, Utah, 46-49; PROF, UTAH STATE, 49-, DEAN SCH. GRAD STUDIES, 67-, faculty res. lectr, 54, dean col. sci, 62-67. Vis. investr, Univ. Calif, 57-58; Brit. Mus. & Univ. London, 71; mem. health res. facilities sci. rev. comt, health res. facilities br, Bur. Educ. Manpower Training, 67-71, chmn, 69-71. AAAS; Am. Soc. Nat; Genetics Soc. Am; Am. Soc. Human Genetics (secy, 55-58, v.pres, 61); Am. Genetic Asn; Am. Eugenics Soc. General genetics; history of biology; cytology; evolution. Address: School of Graduate Studies, Utah State University, Logan, UT 84321.

GARDNER, ELIZABETH B, b. Boston, Mass, Oct. 22, 40; m. 65. DEVELOPMENTAL BIOLOGY. A.B, Vassar Col, 62; M.Sc, Brown, 64, Ph.D.(biol), 65. Instr. biol, Queen's Col.(N.Y), 65-66; Wellesley Col, 66-67; CHMN. DEPT. BIOL. & PHYS. SCI. & TEACHER BIOL, PINE MANOR JR. COL, 67- AAAS; Am. Soc. Zool. Problems of maternal-fetal relationships as investigated by experiments on regeneration and hormone interactions. Address: Dept. of Biological & Physical Sciences, Pine Manor Junior College, 400 Heath St, Chestnut Hill, MA 02167.

GARDNER, ELIZABETH MOORHEAD, b. Findlay, Ohio, June 12, 39; m. 66. NUCLEAR CHEMISTRY. B.S, Bowling Green State, 60; M.A, Columbia, 61, univ. scholar, Union Carbide fel, Nat. Sci. Found. summer fel. & Ph.D, 64. Res. assoc. mech. inorg. reactions, Brookhaven Nat. Lab, 64-66; ASST. PROF. CHEM, DOWLING COL, 66-, ASST. DEAN ACAD. AFFAIRS, 69- Res. collaborator, Brookhaven Nat. Lab, 67- Am. Chem. Soc. Compound-nucleus reactions; inorganic chemistry, including kinetics and mechanisms of fast reactions in aqueous solutions. Address: Dept. of Chemistry, Dowling College, Idle Hour Blvd, Oakdale, NY 11769.

GARDNER, ERNEST (DEAN), b. Maltby, Wash, Jan. 3, 15; m. 39; c. 2. ANATOMY. B.S, Univ. Wash, 34; M.D, Stanford Univ, 41. Asst. ANAT, Stanford Univ, 37-38, 40-41; Univ. South. Calif, 43-45; SCH. MED, WAYNE STATE UNIV, 45-50, PROF, 50-, dean, 63-70, assoc. dean, 61-63, chmn. dept, 50-63. Mem. study sect. neurol, Nat. Insts. Health, 64-68; comt. skeletal diseases, Nat. Res. Coun, 64-67; neurol. disorders prog. proj. comn, Nat. Insts. Health, 68-69, chmn, 69-72. With Off. Sci. Res. & Develop, 44. Am. Physiol. Soc; Orthop. Res. Soc; Am. Asn. Anat; Am. Neurol. Asn; Am. Acad. Neurol. Neuroanatomy and neurophysiology; sensory pathways; anatomy and physiology of joints. Address: School of Medicine, Wayne State University, 1400 Chrysler Freeway, Detroit, MI 48207.

GARDNER, E(RNEST) HUGH, b. Saskatoon, Sask, Apr. 20, 20; m. 45; c. 2. SOIL SCIENCE. B.S.A, British Columbia, 50; fel, Oregon State, 57-60, M.S, 59, Ph.D.(soil sci), 60. Res. officer, Can. Dept. Agr, 50-56, 60-61; assoc. prof. soil sci, Univ. B.C, 61-66; PROF. SOIL FERTILITY, ORE. STATE UNIV, 66- R.C.A.F, 41-46, Flight Lt. Can. Soc. Soil Sci; Am. Soc. Agron. Soil fertility; field plot experimentation; soil-plant relationships; soil and plant analysis; soil chemical properties. Address: Dept. of Soil Science, Oregon State University, Corvallis, OR 97331.

GARDNER, FRANK HERBERT, b. San Bernardino, Calif, Sept. 21, 19. MEDICINE, HEMATOLOGY. B.S, Northwestern, 41, M.D, 45. Asst. prof. MED, Harvard Med. Sch, 57-61, assoc. clin. prof, 61-66; PROF, UNIV. PA. SCH. MED, 66- Consult, Surgeon Gen, U.S. Army, 55-; dir. med, Presby Univ. Pa. Med. Ctr, 68- Med.C, 53-55, Capt. Am. Soc. Clin. Invest; Am. Fedn. Clin. Res; Am. Soc. Hemat. Internal medicine; hemolytic anemias; tropical sprue; platelet physiology; blood. Address: Presbyterian-University of Pennsylvania Medical Center, 51 N. 39th St, Philadelphia, PA 19104.

GARDNER, FRANK H(UGH), JR, b. Atlanta, Ga, March 17, 19; m. 42; c. 2. CHEMISTRY, CHEMICAL ENGINEERING. B.S, Ga. Inst. Tech, 41. Res. chemist & acid area supvr, Hercules Powder Co, 41-52, CHEM. SUPT, 52-67, HERCULES, INC, 67- Am. Chem. Soc; Am. Inst. Chem. Eng. Naval stores; terpenes; technology. Address: Hercules, Inc, Hattiesburg, MS 39401.

GARDNER, FRANK J(OHNSON), b. Ft. Towson, Okla, Oct. 6, 15. GEOLOGY. B.A, Texas, 36, M.A, 38, Ph.D.(geol), 42. Chief geologist, Rinehart Oil Publications, Texas, 40-42, Rinehart Oil News Co, 46-50; pres, Petrol. News Corp, 50-54; EXPLOR. ED, OIL & GAS JOUR, 54- U.S.A, 42-46, Capt. Am. Asn. Petrol. Geol; Brit. Inst. Mech. Eng. History of oil development of Texas; oil exploration in the United States. Address: Oil & Gas Journal, 16 E. 48th St, New York, NY 10017.

GARDNER, FRANK S(TREETER), b. Baltimore, Md, Dec. 9, 16; m. 41; c. 4. PHYSICAL METALLURGY. S.B, Mass. Inst. Tech, 38, Sc.D.(metall), 41. Metallurgist, Am. Brake Shoe Co, N.J, 41-46; Gen. Elec. Co, 46-53, supvr. magnetic mat. res, transformer div, 53-58; proj. mgr, Nuclear Metals, Inc, 58-60; MAT. SCIENTIST, OFF. NAVAL RES, 60- With Off. Sci. Res. & Develop, 44. Am. Soc. Metals; Am. Inst. Min, Metall. & Petrol. Eng. Metallography; pressure welding; metallurgy of soft magnetic materials; mechanical metallurgy; magnetic transformations; research programming. Address: Office of Naval Research, 495 Summer St, Boston, MA 02210.

GARDNER, F(RANKLIN) P(IERCE), b. Hillsville, Va, Mar. 20, 24; m. 43; c. 3. AGRONOMY. B.S, Va. Polytech. Inst, 49; M.S, Iowa State Univ, 50, Ph.D. (plant physiol, crop sci), 52. Instr. crop sci, Iowa State Univ, asst. prof, Univ. Ga, 52-54; Ohio State Univ, 54-55; assoc. prof, Iowa State Univ, 55-62, prof, 62-63; prof. agron. & head dept, Okla. State Univ, 63-68; PROF. AGRON. & DEAN COL. APPL. SCI, WEST. ILL. UNIV, 68- U.S.A, 43-46, S/Sgt. Fel. Am. Soc. Agron. College administration; effect of photoperiod and temperature on development and flowering of perennial grasses and legumes; effect of cultural treatments on yield and quality of silage; effect of cultural treatments on photosynthetic efficiency and production. Address: College of Applied Sciences, Western Illinois University, Macomb, IL 61455.

GARDNER, FRED MARVIN, b. Kansas City, Kan, July 4, 22; m. 63; c. 4. PHYSICS. B.S, St. Mary's Col.(Minn), 45; M.S, St. Louis, 52; Nat. Sci. Found. fel, Notre Dame, 57-58, Ph.D.(physics), 62. Instr, Christian Bros. Mil. High Sch, Mo, 45-52; asst. prof. physics, St. Mary's Col.(Minn), 52-57, assoc. prof, 61-62; res. scientist, United Aircraft Res. Labs, 62-64, sr. res. scientist, 64-69; v.pres, High Tech. Indust, 69-70; PROF. PHYSICS & CHMN. DEPT, UNIV. HARTFORD, 70- Am. Phys. Soc; Inst. Elec. & Electronics Eng. Electron physics. Address: Dept. of Physics, University of Hartford, West Hartford, CT 06117.

GARDNER, FREDERICK ALBERT, b. Middletown Springs, Vt, Nov. 23, 27; m. 49; c. 6. ORGANIC CHEMISTRY, MICROBIOLOGY. B.S, Vermont, 53; M.S, Agr. & Mech. Col, Tex, 55; Ph.D.(poultry sci), Missouri, 60. Instr. POULTRY SCI, Agr. & Mech. Col, Tex, 54-55; asst, Iowa State Col, 55-56; Missouri, 56-58, instr, 58-59; asst. prof, TEX. A&M UNIV, 59-63, ASSOC. PROF, 63- U.S.N, 45-48. AAAS; Poultry Sci. Asn; Inst. Food Technol; Am. Chem. Soc. Chemistry and microbiology of poultry and egg products with specific interest in fundamental product characterization and in the maintenance of product quality. Address: Dept. of Poultry Science, Texas A&M University, College Station, TX 77843.

GARDNER, G(ERALD) H(ENRY) F(RASER), b. Ireland, Mar. 2, 26; m. 50. MATHEMATICS. B.A, Trinity Col. (Dublin), 47; M.Sc, Carnegie Inst. Tech, 48; Ph.D.(math), Princeton, 53. Lectr. math, Trinity Col. (Dublin), 49-54; instr, Cornell, 54-55; asst. prof, Carnegie Inst. Tech, 55-56; sect. head, GULF RES. & DEVELOP. CO, 56-66, SR. SCIENTIST, EXPLOR. & PROD, 66- Am. Math. Soc; Math. Asn. Am; Am. Inst. Min. Metall. & Petrol. Eng. Relativity; mathematical physics and the properties of matter. Address: Gulf Research & Development Co, P.O. Box 2038, Pittsburgh, PA 15230.

GARDNER, G(ERARD), b. Acton Vale, Que, Aug. 5, 97. BIOLOGY. B.A. & L.Sc, Montreal, 27; D.Sc.(biol), Paris, 31. Lectr, natural sci, GRAD. SCH. COMMERCE, UNIV. MONT, 27-43, BIOL, 28, assoc. prof, 35-43, prof, 43-66, curator commercial & indust. mus, 45-56, EMER. PROF, 66-, DIR. ARCTIC RES. CTR, 66- Am. Polar Soc; Royal Soc. Arts; Bot. Soc. France. Spirochaetes; geology and flora of Labrador, Hudson Bay and James Bay. Address: Graduate School of Commerce, University of Montreal, 5255 Decelles Ave, Montreal 250, Que, Can.

GARDNER, HAROLD WAYNE, b. Carlisle, Pa, June 19, 35; m. 60; c. 4. BIOCHEMISTRY. B.S, Pa. State, 57, M.S, 63, Ph.D.(biochem), 65. Assoc. biochemist, Pineapple Res. Inst, 65-66; asst. res. plant biochemist, Univ. Calif, Los Angeles, 66-67; CHEMIST, NORTH. REGIONAL LAB, U.S. DEPT. AGR, PEORIA, ILL, 67- U.S.N, 58-61, Lt.(jg). Am. Chem. Soc; Am. Oil Chem. Soc. Oxidation of unsaturated fatty acids by plant systems; lipid hydroperoxides; photosynthetic and photochemical processes. Address: Northern Regional Lab, U.S. Dept. of Agriculture, Peoria, IL 61604.

GARDNER, HERBERT COLBY, b. Hinton, Ky, May 17, 30; m. 50; c. 4. RADIOLOGY. B.S, Tennessee, 50, M.D, 53. Intern, U.S. Naval Hosp, San Diego, Calif, 54; res. RADIOL, COL. MED, UNIV. TENN, 57-60, instr, 60-62, asst. prof, 62-64, assoc. prof, 64-68, CLIN. ASSOC. PROF, 68- Dipl, Am. Col. Radiol, 63. U.S.N, 54-57, Lt. Radiol. Soc. N.Am; dipl. mem, Pan-Am. Med. Asn. Address: Dept. of Radiology, Baptist Memorial Hospital, 899 Madison Ave, Memphis, TN 38103.

GARDNER, HERBERT R(EED), b. Logan, Utah, Nov. 1, 28; m. 51; c. 4. SOIL SCIENCE. B.S, Utah State, 52, M.S, 55; Cornell, 54-56; Ph.D.(soil sci), Colorado State, 62. RES. SOIL SCIENTIST, SOIL & WATER CONSERV. RES. DIV, U.S. DEPT. AGR, 56- U.S.A, 46-48, 52-53, 2nd Lt. Am. Soc. Agron; Soil Sci. Soc. Am. Plant root-soil compaction interactions; dryland moisture conservation. Address: 1106 Skyline Dr, Ft. Collins, CO 80521.

GARDNER, HOWARD SHAFER, b. Brooklyn, N.Y, Sept. 18, 08; m. 31; c. 2. CHEMICAL ENGINEERING. S.B, Mass. Inst. Tech, 30, S.M, 31, Sc.D. (chem. eng), 46. Staff chem. engr, Eastman Kodak Co, N.Y, 31-36; asst. prof. chem. eng. & dir. Bangor field sta, Mass. Inst. Tech, 36-38; assoc. prof. chem. eng. & chmn. dept, Rochester, 38-47; dir. res. & develop, Fibreboard Corp, Calif, 47-61; sr. res. assoc. & chmn, eng. & tech. sect, Inst. Paper Chem, Lawrence Univ, 62-64, admin. staff, 64-65; PROF. PULP & PAPER TECHNOL. & CHEM. ENG, UNIV. WASH, 66- Private consult, 38-47, 66-; mem. staff, div. indust. coop. & res, Mass. Inst. Technol, 45. Am. Chem. Soc; fel. Tech. Asn. Pulp & Paper Indust; Am. Inst. Chem. Eng; Am. Soc. Eng. Educ; Air Pollution Control Asn; Can. Pulp & Paper Asn. Chemical engineering; pulp and paper technology. Address: College of Forest Resources, University of Washington, Seattle, WA 98195.

GARDNER, IRWIN J(EROME), b. N.Y.C, Aug. 9, 29; m. 53; c. 2. PHYSICAL & POLYMER CHEMISTRY. B.S, Columbia, 53, M.A, 57, Ph.D.(phys. org. chem), 59. Sr. polymer chemist, cent. basic res. labs, ESSO RES. & ENG. CO, 57-70, RES. ASSOC, ENJAY POLYMER LABS, LINDEN, 70- Am. Chem. Soc. Polymer catalyst structure and mechanisms; polymerizatic kinetics; polymer synthesis, structure determination, characterization and use evaluation; methods and mechanisms of elastomer vulcanization. Address: 3 Poplar Pl, Fanwood, NJ 07023.

GARDNER, JAMES H(AMILTON), b. Salt Lake City, Utah, May 14, 24; m. 50; c. 3. PHYSICAL-ORGANIC CHEMISTRY. B.Ch.E, Utah, 47; A.M, Harvard, 48, Austin fel, 48-49, U.S. Rubber Co. fel, 49-50, Ph.D.(chem), 50. Ref. technologist, Shell Oil Co, 50-51; res. supvr. petrochem, Nat. Res. Corp, 51-53, asst. dir, 54-56, asst. dir. res, 56-58, gen. mgr. metals div, 58-61, dep. dir. defense res. & eng, Dept. Defense, 62-63; exec. v.pres, Nat. Res. Corp, 63-69; MEM. STAFF, ARMOUR INDUST. CHEM. CO, 69- U.S.A, 43-46, 1st Lt. Am. Chem. Soc; Faraday Soc; Am. Inst. Chem. Eng. Hydrocarbon chemistry; oxidation; process research; technical management. Address: Armour Industrial Chemical Co, Box 1805, 8401 W. 47th St, Chicago, IL 60690.

GARDNER, JAMES HERBERT, b. Magnolia, Ark, Nov. 21, 40; m. 61; c. 3. ORGANIC CHEMISTRY. B.S, Ark. A&M Col, 62; M.S, Memphis State Univ, 64; Ph.D.(org. chem), Miss. State Univ, 69. RES. CHEMIST, AM. ENKA CO, 68- Am. Chem. Soc. Synthesis of heterocyclic compounds; fiber forming polymers. Address: P.O. Box 235, Enka, NC 28728.

GARDNER, J(OHN) D(AVID), b. Oildale, Calif, Sept. 6, 21; m. 48; c. 3. ORGANIC CHEMISTRY. B.S, Stanford Univ, 48; Ph.D.(chem), Univ. Wash, 52. Chemist, CHEVRON RES. CO, 52-53, res. chemist, 53-62, sr. res. chemist, 62-71, SR. RES. ASSOC, 71- U.S.A.F, 42-45, 1st Lt. Am. Chem. Soc. Chemistry of surface active agents and plastics; unsaturated polyesters and alkyds; process improvement. Address: Chevron Research Co, 576 Standard Ave, Richmond, CA 94802.

GARDNER, JOHN H(ALE), b. Logan, Utah, Aug. 24, 22; m. 43; c. 8. MAGNETIC RESONANCE. B.S, Utah State Agr. Col, 43; fel, Harvard, 46-49, A.M, 47, Ph.D.(physics), 50. Mem. staff, radiation lab, Mass. Inst. Tech, 43-46; asst. prof. PHYSICS, BRIGHAM YOUNG UNIV, 49-52, assoc. prof, 52-55, 57-58, PROF, 58-, CHMN. DEPT, 61-63, 64- Mem. tech. staff, Thompson-Ramo-Wooldridge Corp, 55-57, consult, space tech. labs, 57-63, 64-, mem. tech. staff, 63-64. AAAS; Am. Phys. Soc; Am. Asn. Physics Teachers; fel. Brit. Inst. Physics & Phys. Soc. Nuclear magnetic moments; nuclear masses and relative abundances; soil moisture dynamics; shaped beam antennas at microwave frequencies; electromagnetic propagation; magnetic resonance; gaseous electronics; quantum electronics. Address: Dept. of Physics, 296 ESC, Brigham Young University, Provo, UT 84601.

GARDNER, JOHN O(MEN), b. Chicago, Ill, Sept. 14, 27; m. 53. ANALYTICAL INSTRUMENTATION. B.S, Illinois, Ph.D.(anal. chem), 53. Asst, Illinois, 49-53; res. chemist, Calif. Res. Corp, Standard Oil Co, Calif, 53-57; scientist, Dow Chem. Co, 57-61; ELECTRON MICROSCOPIST, Gen. Atomic Div, Gen. Dynamics Corp, 61-68; RES. DIV, PHILLIPS PETROLEUM CO, 68- U.S.N.R, 45-46. Am. Chem. Soc; Electron Micros. Soc. Am. Electrochemical and x-ray methods of analysis; electron microscopy and diffraction applied to chemistry, physics, and metallurgy. Address: Phillips Petroleum Co, Research Division, Room 134 RBI, Bartlesville, OK 74003.

GARDNER, J(OHNNY) B(ERTEN), b. Shamrock, Tex, Aug. 31, 28; m. 50; c. 4. POLYMER CHEMISTRY. B.A, Bethany-Nazarene Col, 51; M.S, Agr. & Mech. Col. Tex, 58. Chemist, Pan-Am. South. Ref. Co, 51-53; TEX. DIV, DOW CHEM. CO, 53-57, res. chemist, 57-60, SR. RES. CHEMIST, 60- Am. Chem. Soc. Catalysis; Mössbauer spectroscopy. Address: 520 Circle Way, Lake Jackson, TX 77566.

GARDNER, J(OSEPH) A(RTHUR) F(REDERICK), b. Nakusp, B.C, Aug. 17, 19; m. 45; c. 2. ORGANIC CHEMISTRY. B.A, British Columbia, 40, Nat. Res. Coun. Can. stud. & M.A, 42; Nat. Res. Coun. Can. fel, McGill, 43, Ph.D, 44. Res. assoc, McGill, 44-45; res. chemist, Howard Smith Paper Mills, Ont, 45-47; head wood chem. sect, Forest Prod. Lab, 47-62, dir, 62-65; DEAN FACULTY FORESTRY, UNIV. B.C, 65-, hon. lectr, 53, hon. prof, 64. Am.

Chem. Soc; Tech. Asn. Pulp & Paper Indust; Forest Prod. Res. Soc; Int. Acad. Wood. Sci; fel. Chem. Inst. Can; Can. Pulp & Paper Asn. Chemistry of wood and its components, especially lignin and phenolic extractives. Address: Faculty of Forestry, University of British Columbia, Vancouver 8, B.C, Can.

GARDNER, K(ARL) A(LBERT), b. Ashland, Mass, Aug. 2, 12; m. 36; c. 2. HEAT TRANSFER, CHEMICAL ENGINEERING. B.S, Mass. Inst. Tech, 34; Columbia. Engr, Cities Serv. Ref. Co, 34-36; Griscom-Russell Co, 36-49, asst. chief engr, 49-52, chief engr, 52-59; v.pres. eng, Yuba Consol. Industs, 59-62; eng. consult, M.W. Kellogg Co, 62-68; SR. STAFF CONSULT, LIQUID METAL ENG. CTR, ATOMICS INT. DIV, N.AM. ROCKWELL, INC, 68- Lectr, Univ. Del, 47, 53; Stanford Univ, 61; consult, Tubular Exchanger Mfrs. Asn; mem. adv. ed. bd, Heat Transfer—Soviet Res, 68-; Heat Transfer—Japanese Res, 71- Am. Soc. Mech. Eng.(mem. award, 64); Am. Inst. Chem. Eng. Equipment engineering; fluid mechanics; stress analysis; pressure vessel design. Address: 9500 Vanalden Ave, Northridge, CA 91324.

GARDNER, KARL E(DRICK), b. Chicago, Ill, Feb. 11, 13; m. 38; c. 3. DAIRY SCIENCE. B.S, Purdue, 36; M.S, Cornell, 39, Ph.D.(dairy prod), 40. Assoc. & dairy exten. mgr, UNIV. ILL, URBANA, 40-43, asst. prof. dairy prod, 46-49, assoc. prof, 49-53, PROF. DAIRY SCI, 53-, ASSOC. DEAN, COL. AGR, 59- Consult, Interdepartmental Cmt. on nutrit. in Nat. Defense, 56-; chief of party U.S. Agency Internat. Develop-Univ. Illinois estab. univ. in Sierra Leone, 63-64; adv. to dean agr, J. Nehru Agr. Univ, India, 67. Sanit.C, U.S.A, 43-46. Fat requirements of cattle; endocrines for milk production; calf feeding. Address: College of Agriculture, University of Illinois, Urbana, IL 61803.

GARDNER, KENNETH DRAKE, JR, b. San Francisco, Calif, Oct. 3, 29; m. 54; c. 4. INTERNAL MEDICINE. B.M.S, Stanford Univ, 51, M.D, 55. Instr. MED, sch. med, Univ. Pa, 60-61; sch. med, Stanford Univ, 63-64, asst. prof, 64-69; PROF, SCH. MED, UNIV. HAWAII, 69-, ASSOC. DEAN, 70-, CHMN. DEPT. MED, 71- Daland res. fels. clin. med, 59-60, 61-63; consult, U.S. Army Tripler Gen. Hosp, Honolulu. Med.C, 56-58, Capt. Am. Fedn. Clin. Res; fel. Am. Col. Physicians; Am. Physiol. Soc; Am. Soc. Nephrology. Effect of hormones on molecular movement across collecting tubular walls of the mammalian kidney; clinical renal disease; renal cystic diseases and pathophysiology of human kidney disease. Address: Dept. of Medicine, University of Hawaii School of Medicine, 1960 East West Rd, Honolulu, HI 96822.

GARDNER, LYTT I(RVINE), b. Reidsville, N.C, Oct. 1, 17; m. 42; c. 5. PEDIATRICS. A.B, North Carolina, 38, M.A, 40; M.D, Harvard, 43. Instr, sch. med, North Carolina, 49-50; res. fel, Harvard Med. Sch, 48-49; asst. prof. PEDIAT, sch. med, Hopkins, 50-52; assoc. prof, col. med, State Univ. N.Y. Upstate Med. Ctr, 52-56; PROF, sch. med, Yale, 56-57; COL. MED, STATE UNIV. N.Y. UPSTATE MED. CTR, 57- Med.C, 44-46, Capt. Soc. Pediat. Res.(pres, 62-63); Am. Pediat. Soc; Endocrine Soc; Europ. Soc. Paediat. Endocrinol; hon. mem. Latin-Am. Soc. Pediat. Res. Pediatric endocrinology; genetics; chromosome abnormalities in children; effects of maternal deprivation on endocrine system; steroid metabolism of fetal and infant adrenal cortex. Address: Dept. of Pediatrics, State University of New York Upstate Medical Center, 750 E. Adams St, Syracuse, NY 13210.

GARDNER, MARJORIE H(YER), b. Logan, Utah, Apr. 25, 23; m. 47; c. 2. SCIENCE EDUCATION, CHEMISTRY. B.S, Utah State, 46; M.A, Ohio State, 58, Ph.D.(sci. ed, chem), 60. Teacher, high sch. Utah, 47-49; Nev, 49-53; tutor, 53-56; instr. chem. & sci. ed, Ohio State, 58-60; dir. vistas sci, Nat. Sci. Teachers Asn, 61, asst. exec. secy. & dir. vistas sci. 62-64; asst. prof. CHEM. & SEC. EDUC, UNIV. MD, COLLEGE PARK, 64-67, assoc. prof, 67-71, PROF, 71- Mem. summer writing team, Earth Sci. Curriculum Proj, 64-66, dir. teacher prep, 67-69; mem. Columbia Univ. & Nat. Sci. Found. summer insts, India, 65-66, 68 & 69; del, Int. Conf. & Cong, Wash, D.C, 66, Bulgaria, 68, Brazil, 71; dir, Nat. Sci. Found. Inserv. Insts, Leadership Conf. & Coop. Col-Sch. Sci. progs, 67-; Interdisciplinary Approaches to Chem. Proj, 70- Fel. AAAS; Nat. Sci. Teachers Asn; Am. Chem. Soc.(vis. scientist award, 71); Nat. Asn. Res. Sci. Teaching; Am. Inst. Chem. Curriculum development; evaluation; teacher preparation; instructional methods and materials. Address: Science Teaching Center, University of Maryland, College Park, MD 20742.

GARDNER, MAX W(ILLIAM), b. Lansing, Mich, May 11, 90; m. 22; c. 2. BOTANY, PLANT PATHOLOGY. B.S, Mich. State Col, 12, D.Sc, 50; M.S, Wisconsin, 15, Ph.D.(plant path), 18. Instr. plant path, Michigan, 17-18; asst. pathologist, bur. plant indust, U.S. Dept. Agr, 18-19; assoc. botanist, exp. sta, Purdue, 19-29, chief in bot, 29-32; prof. plant path. & plant pathologist, exp. sta, UNIV. CALIF, BERKELEY, 32-57, EMER. PROF. & EMER. PLANT PATHOLOGIST, 57- Mem. div. biol. & agr, Nat. Res. Coun, 39-42. AAAS; Am. Soc. Nat; Am. Phytopath. Soc.(v.pres, 30, pres. 31); Bot. Soc. Am; Mycol. Soc. Am. Diseases of fruit and truck crops. Address: 1441 Hawthorne Terr, Berkeley, CA 94708.

GARDNER, MURRAY BRIGGS, b. Lafayette, Ind, Oct. 5, 29; m. 61; c. 4. PATHOLOGY, ONCOLOGY. B.A, California, 51, M.D. 54. Asst. prof. PATH, SCH. MED, UNIV. SOUTH. CALIF, 63-68, ASSOC. PROF, 68- Pathologist, Univ. Southern California-U.S. Pub. Health Serv. Air Pollution Proj, 63-68; prin. investr, Nat. Cancer Inst-Univ. Southern California Res. Contract, 68-; dep. vet, Los Angeles County, 68- U.S.N, 55-57, Lt. AAAS; Int. Acad. Path; Am. Med. Asn. Extrinsic factors in carcinogenesis; the etiology and epidemiology of cancer in humans and domestic pets; biological effects of urban air pollution. Address: Dept. of Pathology, University of Southern California School of Medicine, 2025 Zonal Ave, Los Angeles, CA 90033.

GARDNER, MURRAY CURTIS, b. Brooklyn, N.Y, Oct. 5, 32; m. 59; c. 2. GEOLOGY. B.S, Brooklyn Col, 53; Ph.D. (geol), Univ. Ariz, 64. Petrol. geologist, Monarch Logging Co, 56; mining geol. asst, San Manuel Copper Mines, 57; instr. petrol. & petrog, Univ. Ariz, 59-60; field geologist, South.

Pac. Land Co, 60-61; geologist, U.S. Geol. Surv, 61-64; sr. scientist & asst. proj. dir, Teledyne Isotopes, Inc, 64-66, scientist & dir. field opers, 66-70, staff scientist & mgr. indust. projs, 70-71; ASST. PROF. GEOL, SOUTH. ORE. COL, 71- Summer cartographer, Mus. State Ariz, 58. U.S.M.C, 53-55, Capt. Geol. Soc. Am. Diffusion paths in rock and soil; structural and engineering geology; petrology and petrography of volcanic rocks; tectonics; hydrologic tracers; nuclear geology; relationship of matrix to underground atomic detonations; geothermal resources evaluation; deep well injection of wastes. Address: Dept. of Geology, Southern Oregon College, Ashland, OR 97520.

GARDNER, PAUL J(AY), b. Wichita, Kans, May 25, 29; m. 49; c. 4. ANATOMY. A.B, Wichita, 51, fel, 54-55, M.S, 55; Ph.D.(anat), Nebraska, 64. Asst. instr. anat, Kansas, 55-56; prof. biol. & head dept, Vincennes, 56-60; asst. prof. biol, Omaha, 60-63; U.S. Pub. Health Serv. trainee, MED. CTR, UNIV. NEBR, OMAHA, 63-64, instr. ANAT, 64-65, asst. prof, 65-70, ASSOC. PROF, 70- AAAS; Am. Asn. Anat; Electron Micros. Soc. Gross anatomy; electron microscopy; ultrastructure. Address: Dept. of Anatomy, University of Nebraska Medical Center, Omaha, NE 68105.

GARDNER, PETE D, b. Salt Lake City, Utah, Jan. 17, 27; m. 50; c. 3. ORGANIC CHEMISTRY. B.S, Utah, 49, M.S, 50, Ph.D.(chem), 53. Chemist, res. & develop, Merck & Co, Inc, 51-52; asst. prof. CHEM, Texas, 53-57, assoc. prof, 57-62, PROF, 63-65; UNIV. UTAH, 65-, DEAN SCI, 70- U.S.A, 44-45. Am. Chem. Soc. Chemistry of small and medium ring compounds; thermal, photochemical and base-catalyzed rearrangements. Address: Office of the Dean of Science, University of Utah, Salt Lake City, UT 84112.

GARDNER, PHILLIP JOHN, b. Pomona, Calif, July 28, 41; m. 63; c. 2. PHYSICAL CHEMISTRY. B.A, California, Riverside, 64; Ph.D.(phys. chem), Fla. State, 69. MEM. TECH. STAFF, BAYSIDE RES. CTR, GTE LABS, 69- Am. Chem. Soc; Am. Phys. Soc. Theoretical and experimental studies of radiative and non-radiative electronic transitions in polyatomic molecules; experimental studies of atomic discharge systems. Address: Bayside Research Center, GTE Labs, 208-20 Willets Point Blvd, Bayside, NY 11360.

GARDNER, P(RESCOTT) E(LLIOTT), b. Liverpool, N.S, Oct. 1, 32; m. 57; c. 2. ORGANIC CHEMISTRY. B.Sc, Acadia, 54; Sensenbrenner fel, McGill, 54-55, Nat. Res. Coun. assistantship, 55-57, Ph.D.(chem), 58. Fel, Nat. Res. Coun, Can, 57-59; RES. CHEMIST, INT. CELLULOSE RES, LTD, 59- Chem. Inst. Can. Reactions and structure of carbohydrates and lignin; cellulose-plastics combinations. Address: 580 Allen St, Hawkesbury, Ont, Can.

GARDNER, RALPH A(LEXANDER), b. Cleveland, Ohio, Dec. 3, 22; m. 45; c. 1. PHYSICAL CHEMISTRY. B.S, Illinois, 43; M.S, Western Reserve, 52, Ph.D, 59. Chemist, Argonne Nat. Labs, 43-47; Standard Oil Co, Ohio, 49-68; ASSOC. PROF. CHEM, CLEVELAND STATE UNIV, 68- Am. Chem. Soc. Infrared spectroscopy, heterogeneous catalysis. Address: Dept. of Chemistry, Cleveland State University, 24th & Euclid, Cleveland, OH 44115.

GARDNER, REED McARTHUR, b. St. George, Utah, Oct. 24, 37; m. 59; c. 4. BIOPHYSICS, ELECTRICAL ENGINEERING. B.S.E.E, Univ. Utah, 60, Nat. Defense Educ. Act fel, 60-61, Nat. Insts. Health fel, 63-65, Ph.D.(biophys, bioeng), 68. ASST. PROF. BIOPHYS. & BIOENG, UNIV. UTAH, 65-; DIV. CHIEF COMPUT. MONITORING PROJ, INTERMOUNTAIN REGIONAL MED. PROG, 67- Consult, Univ. Kiel, summer 69; mem. adv. comt, NASA & Dept. Health, Educ. & Welfare Gen. Elec. Rev. Comt, 70; consult, NASA Life Sci. Adv. Comt, 71. U.S.A, 61-62, S/Sgt. Inst. Elec. & Electronics Eng; Biomed. Eng. Soc. Application of bioengineering principles to solution of medical problems, computer applications in intensive care, cardiovascular laboratories and multiphasic screening centers. Address: Biophysics & Bioengineering Dept, Latter-day Saints Hospital, 325 Eighth Ave, Salt Lake City, UT 84103.

GARDNER, RICHARD A, b. Foley, Ala, Jan. 21, 41; m. 69; c. 1. INORGANIC CHEMISTRY, CERAMICS. B.S, Col. William & Mary, 64; Ph.D.(inorg. chem), Brown Univ, 69. Res. asst. chem, Brown Univ, 65-68; staff chemist, IBM CORP, 68-70, ADV. CHEMIST, 70- Solid-state inorganic chemistry—preparation of transition metal and rare earth oxides, chalcogenides and halides and the electrical, magnetic, optical and crystallographic characterization of the same; electronic ceramics. Address: IBM Corp, East Fishkill Facility, Route 52, Hopewell Junction, NY 12533.

GARDNER, RICHARD A, b. Oak Park, Ill, Dec. 6, 41; m. 64; c. 1. FLUID MECHANICS, HEAT TRANSFER. B.S, Purdue Univ, 63, Douglas fel. & M.S, 65, Ph.D.(fluid mech), 69. Instr. aeronaut, astronaut. & eng. sci, Purdue Univ, 68-69, ASST. PROF, 69; MECH. ENG, WASH. UNIV, 69- Ralph R. Teetor Award, Soc. Automotive Eng, 71. Am. Inst. Aeronaut. & Astronaut; Air Pollution Control Asn. Magneto-fluid-mechanics; environmental engineering; urban meteorology; blood flow. Address: Dept. of Mechanical Engineering, School of Engineering & Applied Science, Washington University, Box 1185, St. Louis, MO 63130.

GARDNER, RICHARD LYNN, b. Clear Lake, Okla, June 4, 34; m. 54; c. 3. BIOCHEMISTRY. B.S, Panhandle Agr. & Mech. Col, 57; Ph.D.(chem), Colo. State Univ, 63. Instr. math. & chem, Panhandle Agr. & Mech. Col, 57-60; res. asst. CHEM, Colorado State, 60-61, Nat. Sci. Found. coop. fel, 61-62, temporary instr, 62-63; PROF. & HEAD DEPT, PANHANDLE STATE COL, 63- Am. Chem. Soc; Phytochem. Soc. N.Am. Phenols in plant disease resistance; plant sterols and cyclic triterpenes. Address: Dept. of Chemistry, Panhandle State College, Goodwell, OK 73939.

GARDNER, ROBERT A(LEXANDER), b. Pleasanton, Calif, May 29, 12; m. 36; c. 5. SOIL SCIENCE. B.S, Univ. Calif, 36, M.S, 39, Ph.D.(soil sci), Berkeley, 67. Assoc. soil tech, Univ. Calif, Berkeley, 36-43, in charge soil survs, 40-43, asst. inspector & soil scientist, div. soil surv, bur. plant indust, U.S. Dept. Agr, 43-46, sr. soil scientist, 46-54, proj. chief. soil-veg. surv, Pac. Southwest Forest & Range Exp. Sta, 54-59, soil scientist, Berkeley, 59-61; mem, Food & Agr. Orgn, UN, 61-65; SOIL SCIENTIST, ENG. CONSULTS, INC, 65- Consult, Royal Irrigation Dept, Govt. Thailand, 65- Int. Soc. Soil Sci; Soil Sci. Soc. Am; Sci. Res. Soc. Am. Soil characteristics in relation to crop production irrigability and reclamation; soil classification and productivity; soil-vegetation relationships; land classification; soil ecosystems. Address: Royal Irrigation Dept, Engineering Consultants, Inc, P.O. Box 1010, Bangkok, Thailand.

GARDNER, ROBERT B, b. Tarrytown, N.Y, Feb. 27, 39; m. 62; c. 2. GEOMETRY. A.B, Princeton, 59, summer, Nat. Sci. Found. grant, 59; M.A, Columbia Univ, 60; Ph.D.(math), Univ. Calif, Berkeley, 65. Res. asst. math, Univ. Calif, Berkeley, 62-65; vis. mem, Nat. Sci. Found. & Sloan grants, Courant Inst. Math. Sci, N.Y. Univ, 65-67; asst. prof, Columbia Univ, 67-70; Nat. Sci. Found. grant, Inst. Advan. Study, 70-71; res. mathematician & Nat. Sci. Found. grant, Univ. Calif, Berkeley, 71; ASSOC. PROF. MATH, UNIV. N.C, CHAPEL HILL, 71- Am. Math. Soc; Math. Asn. Am. Necessary and sufficient conditions for an arbitrary C^{∞}Cauchy problem; reduction of the isometric immersion problem for compact manifolds to a variational principle; rigidity and uniqueness theorems for hypersurfaces; characterizations of isometries among volume preserving diffeomorphisms; differential geometry; partial differential equations. Address: Dept. of Mathematics, University of North Carolina, Chapel Hill, NC 27514.

GARDNER, ROBERT N, b. Winslow, Ariz, Aug. 21, 24; m. 49; c. 4. CHEMISTRY, CIVIL ENGINEERING. B.S, Arizona, 50. State dept. tech. adv, Agency Int. Develop, U.S. Geol. Surv, Pakistan, 64-65, proj. engr, U.S. GEOL. SURV, 65-67, ASST. CHIEF BR. FIELD SURV, 67- C.Eng, 42-45, 1st Lt. Am. Cong. Surv. & Mapping; Am. Soc. Photogram. Topographic mapping. Address: 26096 Todd Lane, Los Altos Hills, CA 94022.

GARDNER, ROBERT WAYNE, b. St. George, Utah, July 24, 28; m. 51; c. 5. ANIMAL NUTRITION. B.S, Utah State, 59; M.S, Cornell, 62, Ph.D.(animal nutrit), 64. Res. nutritionist, Cornell, 63-64; asst. prof. dairy sci, Arizona, 64-66; ASSOC. PROF. ANIMAL SCI, BRIGHAM YOUNG UNIV, 66- Am. Soc. Animal Sci; Am. Dairy Sci. Asn; Am. Inst. Nutrit. Energy requirements of animals for milk production; body chemical composition related to growth; interrelationships between selenium, vitamin E and muscular dystrophy. Address: Dept. of Animal Science, 353 Widtsoe Bldg, Brigham Young University, Provo, UT 84601.

GARDNER, ROBIN P(IERCE), b. Charlotte, N.C, Aug. 17, 34; m. 58. CHEMICAL ENGINEERING, NUCLEONICS. B.Ch.E, N.C. State Col, 56, M.S, 58; Ph.D.(fuel tech), Pa. State, 61. Res. asst. fuel tech, Pa. State, 56-61; scientist, Oak Ridge Inst. Nuclear Studies, 61-63; res. engr, Res. Triangle Inst, 63-67; assoc. prof. NUCLEAR ENG, N.C. STATE UNIV, 67-70, PROF, 70- Adj. asst. prof, N.C. State, 64- Consult, Oak Ridge Inst. Nuclear Studies, 63-64; mem, Hwy. Res. Bd. Cmt. Nuclear Principles & Applns, Nat. Acad. Sci-Nat. Res. Coun, 64- C.Eng, 56, 1st Lt. Am. Nuclear Soc; Am. Inst. Chem. Eng; Am. Chem. Soc; Am. Soc. Test. & Mat. Development of tracing and gauging techniques with radioisotopes; mathematical treatment of chemical engineering unit operations, particularly comminution. Address: Dept. of Nuclear Engineering, North Carolina State University, Raleigh, NC 27607.

GARDNER, RULON B, b. Ogden, Utah, June 24, 23; m. 47; c. 5. CIVIL ENGINEERING. B.S, Utah State, 49; Michigan Tech, 62-63. Hydraul. engr, water resources div, U.S. Geol. Surv, Utah, 48-51, U.S. Bur. Reclamation, 51-52; Los Angeles County Flood Control Dist, Calif, 52-54; supvry. hwy. engr, region IV, U.S. FOREST SERV, Utah, 54-55, forest engr, Targhee Nat. Forest, Idaho, 55-60, br. chief, div. eng, hydraul. & struct, Alaska, 60-61, ENGR, FOREST ENG. LAB, Michigan Tech, 61-64; MONT. STATE UNIV, 64- U.S.N.R, Lt.(jg). Nat. Soc. Prof. Eng; Am. Soc. Civil Eng. Forest engineering research; adapting systems engineering approach to logging and regeneration of forested lands. Address: Forestry Sciences Lab, Montana State University, Bozeman, MT 59715.

GARDNER, SHERWIN, b. N.Y.C, July 31, 28; m. 54; c. 2. MECHANICAL ENGINEERING, OPERATIONS RESEARCH. B.M.E, City Col. New York, 50; Polytech. Inst. Brooklyn, 54-58. From jr. engr. to engr, William L. Gilbert Clock Corp, 50-51; engr, res. & develop. labs, Bulova Watch Co, 54-56; prod. engr, Kay Mfg. Corp, 56; sr. engr. & prin. engr, Ford Instrument Co, Sperry Rand Corp, 56-58, proj. supvr, 58-62, standards mgr, 62-64; proj. engr, Booz Allen Appl. Res. Inc, 64-66, res. dir, 66-69, assoc, Booz Allen Systs, Inc, 69-70; ASST. COMNR. PLANNING & EVAL, U.S. FOOD & DRUG ADMIN, 70- Chem.C, U.S.A, 52-54. Nat. Soc. Prof. Eng; Opers. Res. Soc. Am. System engineering analyses; management information systems; organizational and facility planning and evaluation; technological economic analysis; mathematical modeling and computer simulation. Address: 1403 Fallsmead Way, Rockville, MD 20854.

GARDNER, WALTER H(ALE), b. Beaver, Utah, Feb. 24, 17; m. 48; c. 5. SOILS. B.S, Utah State Univ, 39, Cent. Sci. Co. fel, 39-40, univ. fel, 46-48, 49-50, M.S, 47, Ph.D.(soil physics), 50. Asst. soil physics, Cornell Univ, 40-41; spec. instr. math, Utah State Univ, 48-49; asst. prof. soil physics, WASH. STATE UNIV, 50-53, assoc. prof, 53-58, PROF, 58-70, AGRON, SOILS & BIOPHYS, 70- Guggenheim fel, 64-65; Am. Soc. Agron. fel, 66; mem, Am. Soc. Agron-Nat. Sci. Found. Vis. Scientist Prog, 66-68. U.S.A.A.F, 41-46, Maj. AAAS; Am. Soc. Agron; Soil Sci. Soc. Am.(ed-in-chief, Proc, 65-69); Am. Geophys. Union. Physics of the soil with emphasis on soil water retention and flow and their effect on plant growth. Address: 1301 Upper Dr, Pullman, WA 99163.

GARDNER, WARREN H(ENRY), b. Ottumwa, Iowa, March 23, 95; m. 42; c. 2. SPEECH. A.B, Harvard, 18; Ph.D.(speech path), Iowa, 36. Supvr. traveling hearing clin, Iowa, 36-38; traveling speech & hearing clin, Indiana, 38-40; consult. hearing & vision, State Dept. Health, Ore, 40-42; hearing conserv. specialist, State Dept. Health, Calif, 42-45; prof. hearing & speech therapy, Western Reserve, 45-54; chief hearing & speech therapy, Cleveland Hearing & Speech Ctr, 45-54; audiol. & speech path, Cleveland Clin. Found, 54-65; AUDIOLOGIST & SPEECH PATHOLOGIST, 65- Prof, Bunts Educ. Inst, 55-

65. Founder & dir, Int. Asn. Laryngectomees, 52- U.S.N, 17-19. Fel. Speech & Hearing Asn. Voice pathology; speech pathology; corrective handwriting. Address: 776 Woodview Rd, Cleveland Heights, OH 44121.

GARDNER, WAYNE SCOTT, b. Clifton, Colo, Jan. 11, 20; m. 44; c. 4. PLANT PATHOLOGY, VIROLOGY. B.S, Utah State, 50, M.S, 51; Ph.D. (plant path), California, Davis, 67. Asst. plant path, Utah State, 49-51; instr. agr, Mesa Col, 51; plant pathologist, lab. br, crops div, tech. opers. Dugway Proving Ground, Utah, 51-52, crops div, biol. warfare facilities, 52-54; agr. technician, agr. div, Columbia-Geneva Steel Div, U.S. Steel Corp, 54-61, chem. unit, Fairless Works, Pa, 61-63; res. asst. plant path, California, Davis, 63-65, lab. technician, 65-67; assoc. prof. plant path, S.DAK. STATE UNIV, 67-71, PROF. PLANT SCI, 71- U.S.A.A.F, 42-46, S/Sgt. AAAS; Am. Phytopath. Soc; Air Pollution Control Asn. Plant virology and electron microscopy; ultrastructure of plant pathogen, host and environment interaction; effects of air pollutants on plants; cereal and forage crop virus diseases; aerobiology and epiphytology. Address: Dept. of Plant Science, South Dakota State University, Brookings, SD 57006.

GARDNER, WESTON D(EUAIN), b. Cresco, Iowa, Jan. 6, 17; m. 44; c. 2. ANATOMY. B.S, Pa. State Col, 38; M.D, Pittsburgh, 42. Intern, St. Francis Hosp, Pittsburgh, 42-43; practicing physician, 45-46; asst. ANAT, Wisconsin, 46-47; instr, MED. COL. WIS, 47-51, asst. prof, 51-55, ASSOC. PROF, 55- Dir. med. educ, Deaconess Hosp, 55-70; asst. exec. dir, Educ. Coun. For. Med. Grad, 60-65; med. dir, Curative Workshop Rehab. Ctr, Milwaukee, 71- Med.C, U.S.A, 43-45. AAAS; Am. Med. Asn; Am. Asn. Anat; Asn. Am. Med. Cols; Asn. Hosp. Med. Educ; Nat. Soc. Med. Res. Embryology of human ear; degeneration studies on the cingulum; repair of bone to experimental fractures; venous patterns of thorax and breast by infrared photographic methods; relation of superficial veins and thorax to breast tumors; development of broncho pulmonary segments in human lungs; segmental veins in human lungs; audiovisual communications; medical illustration. Address: Dept. of Anatomy, Medical College of Wisconsin, 561 N. 15th St, Milwaukee, WI 53233.

GARDNER, WILFORD R(OBERT), b. Logan, Utah, Oct. 19, 25; m. 49; c. 3. PHYSICS. B.S, Utah State Agr. Col, 49; M.S, Iowa State Col, 51, Ph.D. (physics), 53. Asst. physics, Iowa State Col, 49-51, res. assoc, Inst. Atomic Res, 51-53; physicist, SOIL PHYSICS, U.S. Salinity Lab, U.S. Dept. Agr, Calif, 53-66; PROF, UNIV. WIS, MADISON, 66- Sr. fel, Nat. Sci. Found, Cambridge, 59; Fulbright lectr, Ghent, 71-72. C.Eng, U.S.A, 43-46. AAAS; Am. Phys. Soc; Soil Sci. Soc. Am; fel. Am. Soc. Agron.(award, 62); Am. Geophys. Union; Am. Phys. Soc. Measurement of soil moisture by neutron scattering; soil physics; movement of fluids in porous media; soil-water-plant relations; soil salinity; plant biophysics; environmental physics. Address: Dept. of Soils, University of Wisconsin, Madison, WI 53706.

GARDNER, WILLIAM H, b. Plain Grove, Pa, Apr. 17, 29; m. 50; c. 5. ORGANIC CHEMISTRY. B.S, Grove City Col, 50; M.S, Purdue, 52. Asst, Hercules Powder Co, 52-54, res. specialist, 54-56, sr. chemist, 56-58, group supvr, 58-67, res. dept. supt, Allegany Ballistics Lab, HERCULES, INC, 67-70, mgr. technol. mkt, 70-71, MGR. SOLID WASTE SYSTS, INDUST. SYSTS. DEPT, 71- Am. Chem. Soc; Nat. Speleol. Soc. Propellant chemistry and polymers; product and process development in propellant and polymer applications; solid waste management and reclamation. Address: Industrial Systems Dept, Hercules, Inc, 910 Market St, Wilmington, DE 19899.

GARDNER, W(ILLIA)M HOWLETT, b. N.Y.C, Sept. 25, 02; m. 32; c. 3. CHEMISTRY, CHEMICAL ENGINEERING. B.Chem, Cornell, 23, Ph.D.(inorg. chem), 27; M.S, Dartmouth Col, 25. Instr. chem, Dartmouth Col, 23-26; res. chemist, Vitreous Enameling Co, Cleveland, 27; fel, shellac res. bur, Polytech. Inst. Brooklyn, 28-31, asst. res. prof. chem. eng, 31-34, res. prof, 34-42, supvr. shellac res. bur, 34-42; chief specification sect, conserv. div, War Prod. Bd, Wash, D.C, 42, chem. materials sect, 43, chem. materials br, 43-44; new prods. div, Nat. Aniline Div, Allied Chem. Corp, 44-50, mgr. chem. lit, 50-67; CHEM. CONSULT, 67- Am. Chem. Soc; Am. Soc. Test. & Mat; Am. Inst. Chem. Eng; fel. Am. Inst. Chem; Fedn. Socs. Paint Technol; Inst. Food Technol. Paint and varnish technology; resin chemistry; chemistry of high polymers; manufacture of pigments; maleic anhydride derivatives; aniline; food acidulants. Address: 29 Merriam Ave, Bronxville, NY 10708.

GARDNER, WILLIAM LEE, b. Carlisle, Pa, June 8, 40; m. 65; c. 1. PHYSICAL & INORGANIC CHEMISTRY. B.S, Pa. State Univ, 62; Ph.D.(phys. inorg. chem), Purdue Univ, 68. SR. RES. CHEMIST, RES. LABS, EASTMAN KODAK CO, 68- Am. Chem. Soc. Thermodynamic properties of high-temperature aqueous solutions; solution and titration calorimetry; adsorption and surface phenomena within an aqueous medium. Address: Eastman Kokak Co. Research Labs, 343 State St, Rochester, NY 14650.

GARDNER, WILLIAM REAVIS, b. Temple, Tex, July 14, 40; m. 61. PHYSICAL CHEMISTRY. B.S, Texas, Austin, 61; Ph.D.(phys. chem), California, Berkeley, 66. MEM. TECH. STAFF, TEX. INSTRUMENTS, INC, 66- Cryogenics; high vacuum; thin films; sputtering. Address: 3616 Douglas Ave, Dallas, TX 75219.

GARDNER, W(ILLIAM) U(LLMAN), b. Kinbrae, Minn, b. Nov. 11, 07; m. 34. ANATOMY. B.S, S.Dak. State Col, 30, hon. D.Sc, 60; fel, Missouri, 30-32, M.A, 31, Gregory fel, 32-33, Ph.D, 33; hon. M.A, Yale, 43; hon. Dr. Med. & Surg, Univ. Perugia, 69. Fel, Nat. Res. Coun. & instr. ANAT, SCH. MED, YALE, 33-35, instr, 35-37, asst. prof, 37-38; assoc. prof. & res. assoc, 38-41, prof. & chmn. dept, 43-60, E.K. HANT PROF, 60- Mem. med. fel, bd. Nat. Res. Coun, 45-52; nat. adv. cancer coun, U.S. Pub. Health Serv, 47-54; chmn, cmt. fels, Int. Union Against Cancer, 60, v.pres, 58-62; pres, 70-74; mem, bd. sci. counsr, Nat. Cancer Inst, 62-66. AAAS; Endocrine Soc; Soc. Exp. Biol. & Med; Soc. Study Develop. & Growth; Am. Cancer Soc; Am. Asn. Cancer Res.(secy-treas, 42-45; pres, 46-47); Am. Asn. Anat. (pres-elect, 71-72); fel. N.Y. Acad. sci. Physiology of reproduction; influence of hormones in abnormal and malignant growth. Address: Dept. of Anatomy, Yale University School of Medicine, New Haven, CT 06510.

GARDOCKI, JOSEPH F, b. Brooklyn, N.Y, Sept. 5, 26; m. PHARMACOLOGY. Ph.D, Georgetown Univ, 51. Pharmacologist, Food & Drug Admin, 47-48; Hazelton Labs, 48-51; sr. pharmacologist, Pfizer Therapeut. Inst, 52-57; res. assoc, Squibb Inst. Med. Res, 58-59; PHARMACOLOGIST & HEAD NEUROPSYCHOPHARMACOL, McNEIL LABS, INC, 60- AAAS; Am. Soc. Pharmacol. & Exp. Therapeut; N.Y. Acad. Sci. Intravenous anesthetics; tranquilizers; diuretics; analgesics; muscle relaxants; neurophysiological correlates of behavior; toxicology; blood chemistry; central nervous system stimulants; bioassay; operant conditioning. Address: McNeil Labs, Inc, Camps Hill Rd, Ft. Washington, PA 19034.

GARDON, JOHN L(ESLIE), b. Budapest, Hungary, June 5, 28; nat; m. 51; c. 2. PHYSICAL CHEMISTRY. Dipl, Swiss Fed. Inst. Tech, Zurich, 51; Anglo-Can. scholar, McGill, 52-54, Nat. Res. Coun. Can. fel, 54-55, Ph.D.(chem), 55. Res. chemist, Indust. Cellulose Res. Ltd. Div, Int. Paper Co, 55-58; Rohm & Haas Co, 58-63, res. assoc, 63-66, lab. head, 66-69; DIR. CORP. RES, M&T CHEM, INC, 69- Am. Chem. Soc; Chem. Inst. Can; Fedn. Socs. Paint Technol; Soc. Plastics Eng. Polymers; emulsion polymerization; adhesion; coatings; finishes; textiles; plastic additives; cullose; lignin; polymer solutions; organotins; water pollution abatement; laminates. Address: M&T Chemicals, Inc, Randolph & Woodbridge Rds, Rahway, NJ 07065.

GARDON, ROBERT, b. Sarvar, Hungary, Aug. 29, 23; m. 51; c. 2. MECHANICAL ENGINEERING. B.Sc, London, 45, Ph.D.(eng), 59; M.E, Yale, 50. Engr, Imp. Chem. Indust, Ltd, Eng, 46-49; res. engr, Mass. Inst. Tech, 50-53; fel, Mellon Inst, Pa, 54-58; sr. group leader, glass res. ctr, Pittsburgh Plate Glass Co, 58-60; res. mgr. glass div, FORD MOTOR CO, 61-62, prin. res. engr, appl. res. off, 62-69, MGR. CERAMICS & GLASS DEPT, 69- Am. Soc. Mech. Eng; fel. Am. Ceramic Soc.(Purdy Award, 58, Meyer Award, 60); Brit. Inst. Mech. Eng; Brit. Soc. Glass Technol; Ger. Soc. Glass Technol. Heat transfer and glass technology, notably heat treatment of glass. Address: Scientific Research Staff, Ford Motor Co, Box 2053, Dearborn, MI 48121.

GAREAU, ROGER, b. Montreal, Que, June 30, 21; m. 51; c. 4. PATHOLOGY. M.D, Univ. Montreal, 48. ASSOC. PROF. PATH, UNIV. MONTREAL, 52-; CHIEF DEPT. PATH, HOTEL DIEU HOSP, 70-, mem. staff, 48-70. Int. Acad. Path. Cancer of stomach; experimental arthritis; trichinosis; carcinoma of the prostate gland; lesions of lymph nodes; connective tissue reaction to carboxymethyl cellulose and muscle lesions by paraphenylenediamine, in rats. Address: Dept. of Pathology, Hotel Dieu Hospital, 3840 St. Urbain, Montreal, Que, Can.

GARELICK, DAVID ARTHUR, b. Woonsocket, R.I, Nov. 17, 37; m. 60; c. 1. PHYSICS. B.S, Mass. Inst. Tech, 59, Ph.D.(physics), 63. Res. staff, lab. nuclear sci, Mass. Inst. Technol, 63-67; assoc. physicist, Brookhaven Nat. Lab, 67-69; ASSOC. PROF. PHYSICS, NORTHEAST. UNIV, 69- Am. Physics Soc. Elementary particles experimentation. Address: Dept. of Physics, Northeastern University, 109 Dana, Boston, MA 02115.

GARELIS, EDWARD, b. Hamtramck, Mich, July 13, 23; m. 50; c. 3. CHEMICAL ENGINEERING, MATHEMATICS. B.S.E.(chem. eng) & B.S.E.(math), Michigan, 47, M.S.E, 49. Chem. engr. res. & design, Charles Pfizer & Co, Inc, 49-52; chem. mathematician, Ethyl Corp, 52-55; nuclear engr, Atomic Power Develop. Assocs, 55-59; sr. physicist, Vallecitos Atomic Lab, Gen. Elec. Co, 59-70; PHYSICIST, LAWRENCE LIVERMORE LAB, 70- Asst, Univ. Mich, 49. U.S.A, 44-46. Am. Nuclear Soc; Math. Asn. Am. Symmetry coordinate analysis; reactor physics; core analysis; pulsed neutron source research. Address: Lawrence Livermore Lab, P.O. Box 808, Livermore, CA 94550.

GAREN, ALAN, b. Brooklyn, N.Y, May 26, 26; m. 59; c. 2. DEVELOPMENTAL BIOLOGY. Ph.D.(biophysics), Colorado, 53. Res. fel. virol, Carnegie Inst, 52-55; res. assoc. biophysics, Purdue, 55-57; sr. res. assoc, Mass. Inst. Tech, 57-60; from assoc. prof. to prof. biol, Pennsylvania, 60-63; PROF. MOLECULAR BIOPHYS. & BIOCHEM, YALE, 63- Nat. Acad. Sci; Genetics Soc. Am. Genetic control of Drosophila development. Address: Dept. of Molecular Biophysics & Biochemistry, Yale University, New Haven, CT 06520.

GAREY, C(ARROLL) L(AVERNE), b. Ft. Collins, Colo, Nov. 9, 17; m. 41; c. 3. CHEMISTRY. B.Sc, Nebraska, 39, M.Sc, 47; Ph.D.(soils), Purdue, 52. Jr. engr, State Hwy. Dept, Nebr, 40-42; instr. soils, Nebraska, 46-49; asst. prof. Arkansas, 51-57; RES. ASSOC. & PHYS. CHEMIST, INST. PAPER PAPER CHEM, 57- Chem.C, U.S.A, 42-46, 1st Lt. AAAS; Soc. Rheol; Clay Minerals Soc; Am. Chem. Soc; Tech. Asn. Pulp & Paper Indust. Evaluation of clays and other pigments for use as paper coatings and fillers; study of starches, proteins and polymers as adhesives and for use in paper manufacture, sizing and conversion; rheology and physical chemical problems of paper coating suspensions and influences on paper conversion processes; use of x-ray diffraction in study of cellulose, and structure of paper and coating. Address: Institute of Paper Chemistry, Appleton, WI 54911.

GAREY, MICHAEL RANDOLPH, b. Manitowoc, Wis, Nov. 19, 45; m. 65. MATHEMATICS, COMPUTER SCIENCE. B.S, Univ. Wis, Madison, 67, M.S, 69, Ph.D.(comput. sci), 70. MEM. TECH. STAFF, MATH. RES. CTR, BELL TEL. LABS, 70- Math. Asn. Am; Asn. Comput. Mach; Soc. Indust. & Appl. Math. Design and analysis of combinatorial algorithms; graph theory; operations research. Address: Mathematics Research Center, Bell Telephone Labs, Murray Hill, NJ 07974.

GARFIELD, EUGENE, b. N.Y.C, Sept. 16, 25; m; c. 4. CHEMISTRY, INFORMATION SCIENCE. B.S, Columbia, 49, Grolier Soc. fel, 53-54, M.S, 54; Ph.D.(chem. ling), Pennsylvania, 61. Res. chemist, Evans Res. & Develop. Corp, 49-50; chem, Columbia, 50-51; staff mem. mach. indexing proj, Hopkins, 51-53; PRES, INST. SCI. INFO, 56- Lectr, Univ. Pennsylvania, 63- Consult, Smith, Kline & French Labs, Biol. Abstracts, Nat. Library Med. & Encyclop. Americana, 54-58; mem. adv. comt. to cardiovasc. lit. proj, Nat. Acad. Sci. Founder, publisher and editor of Current Contents, Index Chemicus and Science Citation Index; Who Is Publishing in Science; Chemical Substructure Index. U.S.A, 43-45. Fel. AAAS; Am. Soc. Info. Sci; Am.

Inst. Biol. Sci; Am. Library Asn; Drug Info. Asn; Asn. Comput. Mach; Asn. Comput. Ling; Am. Chem. Soc; Coun. Biol. Ed; Fedn. Am. Sci; Am. Aging Asn; Int. Fedn. Document; Inst. Elec. & Electronics Eng; fel. Brit. Inst. Info. Sci; Med. Library Asn; Optical Soc. Am; Soc. Hist. Technol; Spec. Libraries Asn; N.Y. Acad. Sci. Address: Institute for Scientific Information, 325 Chestnut St, Philadelphia, PA 19106.

GARFIELD, L(AWRENCE) J(AMES), b. Minneapolis, Minn, Jan. 1, 31; m. 52; c. 4. PHYSICAL CHEMISTRY. B.S, Minnesota, 54, Ph.D.(chem), 59. Sr. res. chemist, EASTMAN KODAK CO, 59-67, RES. ASSOC, 67- Soc. Rheol; Am. Chem. Soc; Am. Phys. Soc. High polymer physics; nuclear magnetic resonance; valence theory. Address: Research Labs, Eastman Kodak Co, Rochester, NY 14650.

GARFIN, LOUIS, b. Mason City, Iowa, June 7, 17; m. 43; c. 2. MATHEMATICS. B.A, Iowa, 38, M.S, 39, Ph.D.(math), 42; Minnesota, 41. Asst. math, Iowa, 39-42; assoc. instr. radio operating, training sch, Army Air Force, Scott Field, 42-43; instr. math. in charge U.S. Army radio program, Ill. Inst. Tech, 43; U.S. Army pre-flight program, Minnesota, 43-44; actuary, state dept. ins, Ore, 46-52; assoc. actuary, PAC. MUTUAL LIFE INS. CO, 52-62, actuary, 62-64, V.PRES. & CHIEF ACTUARY, 64- Dir, Comput. Commun, Inc, 68- U.S.N, 44-45. Am. Math. Soc; fel. Soc. Actuaries; Am. Acad. Actuaries; Int. Actuarial Asn. Pension funds; theoretical and practical bases and valuation; linear integral equations. Address: Pacific Mutual Life Insurance Co, 523 W. Sixth St, Los Angeles, CA 90054.

GARFINKEL, ARTHUR FREDERICK, b. New York, N.Y, Nov. 13, 34; m. 63; c. 2. HIGH ENERGY PHYSICS. B.A, Columbia, 56, M.S, 58, Ph.D.(physics), 62. Vis. scientist, Res. Estab. Risö, Denmark, 62-64; proj. assoc. PHYSICS, Wisconsin, Madison, 64-67; ASST. PROF, PURDUE UNIV, 67- Am. Phys. Soc. Experimental particle physics research, primarily making use of bubble chamber and counter techniques to study particle reactions. Address: Dept. of Physics, Purdue University, Lafayette, IN 47907.

GARFINKEL, BORIS, b. Moscow, Russia, Nov. 18, 04; nat. ASTRONOMY. B.S, City Col. N.Y, 27; M.A, Columbia, 26; Ph.D.(astron), Yale, 43. Instr. physics, Yale, 43-46; mathematician, ballistic res. lab, Aberdeen Proving Ground, 46-60, dep. chief comput. lab, 60-63, chief res. scientist, 63-67; SR. RES. ASSOC. & LECTR. ASTRON, YALE, 67- Lectr, Univ. Del, 48-56; res. assoc, Yale, 58-, vis. prof, 66-67; adv. scientist, Lockheed Missile & Space Co, 61, 62; Nat. Acad. Sci. sr. res. assoc, 63-64; mem. celestial mech. comn, Int. Astron. Union. R.H. Kent Award, 59. Am. Astron. Soc; Math. Asn. Am. Celestial mechanics; artificial satellite theory; the ideal resonance problem; astronomical refraction; calculus of variations. Address: Dept. of Astronomy, Yale University, New Haven, CT 06520.

GARFINKEL, DAVID, b. New York, N.Y, May 18, 30; m. 60; c. 2. BIOCHEMISTRY. A.B, California, 51; fel, Harvard, 52-53, Nat. Sci. Found. fel, 53-54, Ph.D.(biochem), 55. Fel. biophysics, U.S. Pub. Health Serv, Pennsylvania, 55-57, Nat. Res. Council, 57-58; res. biochemist, N.Y. State Psychiat. Inst, Columbia, 58-60; res. assoc. BIOPHYSICS, UNIV. PA, 61-63, asst. prof, 63-65, ASSOC. PROF, 65- Mem, comput. res. study sect, Nat. Insts. Health, 60-62, res. career develop. award, 61-70. Am. Chem. Soc; Inst. Elec. & Electronics Eng; Asn. Comput. Mach; Am. Soc. Biol. Chem; Am. Physiol. Soc; Simulation Coun; Biomed. Eng. Soc; N.Y. Acad. Sci. Application of computers and computational techniques to biological areas, especially metabolic control, enzyme kinetics, other biochemistry and physiology, and to health services, clinical laboratory and environmental problems. Address: Johnson Research Foundation, University of Pennsylvania, Philadelphia, PA 19104.

GARFINKEL, HARMON M, b. Brooklyn, N.Y, May 20, 33; m. 56; c. 2. PHYSICAL CHEMISTRY. B.A, Brooklyn Col, 57; Ph.D.(phys. chem), Iowa State, 60. Sr. chemist, TECH. STAFF DIV, CORNING GLASS WORKS, 60-64, MGR, 64- Am. Chem. Soc; Am. Phys. Soc; fel. Am. Inst. Chem. Diffusion in crystalline and non-crystalline silicates; electrochemistry; strength of materials; chemical kinetics; thermodynamics; ion exchange; biomaterials. Address: Corning Glass Works, Technical Staff Division, Sullivan Park, Corning, NY 14830.

GARFINKEL, LAWRENCE, b. N.Y.C, Jan. 11, 22; m. 48; c. 2. EPIDEMIOLOGY, BIOSTATISTICS. B.B.A, City Col. New York, 47; M.A, Columbia Univ, 49. Biostatistician, AM. CANCER SOC, 47-59, CHIEF FIELD & SPEC. PROJS, 59- Asst. res. scientist, col. dent, N.Y. Univ, 62-69, asst. clin. prof, 70-; from res. consult to sr. med. investr, Vet. Admin. Hosp, East Orange, N.J, 65-; mem. epidemiol. adv. comt, Third Nat. Cancer Surv, Nat. Cancer Inst, 68-; assoc. prof, Mt. Sinai Sch. Med, 70. U.S.A, 43-45. Design and analysis of epidemiologic and pathologic studies in smoking and health; analysis of trends in cancer mortality, morbidity and survival. Address: American Cancer Society, 219 E. 42nd St, New York, NY 10017.

GARFINKEL, SAMUEL B(ERNARD), b. Detroit, Mich, Mar. 17, 24; m. 49; c. 2. PHYSICS. B.S, Michigan, 47, M.S, 48. Physicist mech. instruments sect, NAT. BUR. STANDARDS, 51-57, PROJ. LEADER RADIOACTIVITY STANDARDS, RADIOACTIVITY SECT, 58- Consult, subcomt, Nat. Comt. Radiation Protection & Measurement. Sig.C, U.S.A, 43-46. Am. Phys. Soc; Am. Instrument Soc; Health Physics Soc; Inst. Elec. & Electronics Eng. Standardization of beta and gamma emitting and electron-capturing radionuclides; nuclear detection instrumentation. Address: Radioactivity Section, National Bureau of Standards, Washington, DC 20234.

GARFUNKEL, IRVING M(INTURN), b. Jersey City, N.J, July 14, 25; m. 47; c. 2. MATHEMATICS. B.S, N.Y. Univ, 46, M.S, 48. Teacher, pub. sch, N.Y, 47-48; res. assoc. math, Willow Run Res. Labs, Michigan, 48-51; mathematician, Naval Ord. Test Sta, Calif, 51-54; mathematician & chief analyst, res. & develop. labs, Rheem Mfg. Co, 54-58; sr. mathematician, Syst. Develop. Corp, 58-59; sr. assoc, Planning Res. Corp, Calif, 59-63; asst. mgr. opers. anal, systs. div, Autonetics Div, N.Am. Aviation, Inc, 63-64; mem. tech. staff, Inst. Defense Anal, 64-66; SR. STAFF ENGR, SATELLITE SYSTS. DIV, AEROSPACE CORP, 66- Opers. Res. Soc. Am. Applied mathematics; operations research; systems analysis; weapons systems evaluation; command and control analyses. Address: 209 21st Pl, Santa Monica, CA 90402.

GARFUNKEL, M(YRON) P(AUL), b. New York, N.Y, June 17, 23; m. 46; c. 3. PHYSICS. B.S, Rutgers, 47, Ph.D.(physics), 51. Physicist, res. lab, Westinghouse Elec. Corp, 51-59; PROF. PHYSICS, UNIV. PITTSBURGH, 59- U.S.A, 43-46. Low temperature physics; superconductivity; metals. Address: Dept. of Physics, University of Pittsburgh, Pittsburgh, PA 15213.

GARG, BHAGWAN DASS, b. Dhuri, India, Aug. 14, 40; m. 67. ZOOLOGY, ELECTRON MICROSCOPY. B.S.(Hons), Panjab, India, 61, M.S, 62; Nat. Res. Coun. fel. & Ph.D.(biol), McMaster, 66. Lab. instr. zool, Panjab, India, 61-62; biol, McMaster, 63-66; res. assoc. orthop. surg, Case Western Reserve, 66-67; fel. obstet. & gynec, Col. Physicians & Surgeons, Columbia, 67-68, surg, 68-69; ASST. PROF, INST. EXP. MED. & SURG, UNIV. MONTREAL, 69- Lectr, Hunter Col, 68-69. N.Y. Acad. Sci; Am. Inst. Biol. Sci; Am. Asn. Anat. Anatomy; hormones; drugs and liver ultrastructure; endocrinology. Address: Institute of Experimental Medicine & Surgery, University of Montreal, Montreal, Que, Can.

GARG, DEVENDRA PRAKASH, b. Roorkee, India, Mar. 22, 36; m. 61; c. 2. MECHANICAL ENGINEERING, AUTOMATIC CONTROL SYSTEMS. B.S, Agra Univ, 54; B.Eng, Univ. Roorkee, 57; U.S. Agency Int. Develop. fel, Univ. Wis, 59-60, M.S, 60; Ph.D.(mech. eng), N.Y. Univ, 69. Lectr. MECH. ENG, Univ. Roorkee, 57-62, reader, 62-65; instr, N.Y. Univ, 65-69; asst. prof, MASS. INST. TECHNOL, 69-71, ASSOC. PROF, 71-, chmn. eng. projs. lab, 71-72. Am. Soc. Mech. Eng. Design of controllers for nonlinear systems using computational approach; dynamic modeling, simulation and control of socioeconomic systems. Address: Dept. of Mechanical Engineering, Room 3-453A, Massachusetts Institute of Technology, Cambridge, MA 02139.

GARG, JAGADISH B(EHARI), b. Kanpur, India, July 7, 29; m. 55; c. 2. NUCLEAR PHYSICS. B.Sc, Allahabad, 48; M.Sc, Lucknow, 51; D.Sc.(physics), Paris, 58. Physicist, Indian Atomic Energy Dept, 51-55; fel. PHYSICS, lab. atomic & molecular physics, Col. of France, 55-58; Turner & Newall fel, Manchester, 58-61; sr. res. assoc, Columbia, 61-66; PROF, STATE UNIV. N.Y. ALBANY, 66- DIR. NUCLEAR ACCELERATOR LAB, 71- Chmn, Int. Conf. Statist. Properties of Nuclei, 71. AAAS; fel. Am. Phys. Soc; fel. Brit. Inst. Physics & Phys. Soc; N.Y. Acad. Sci. Reaction mechanism induced by charged particles at intermediate energies; high resolution neutron resonance spectroscopy. Address: Nuclear Accelerator Lab, State University of New York, Western Ave, Albany, NY 12203.

GARG, KRISHNA MURARI, b. Lucknow, India, Aug. 5, 32; m. 66. MATHEMATICS. B.Sc, Lucknow, 52, M.Sc, 55, Govt. India Min. Sci. Res. grant, 59-61, Comn. India univ. grants, 61-62, Ph.D.(math), 63. Lectr. math, Kanyakubja Col, Lucknow, 57-58, asst. prof, 62-63, Govt. India Coun. Sci. & Indust. Res. sr. res. fel, 63-64; asst. prof, Alberta, 64-65; study & res, Inst. Henri Poincaré, Paris, France, 65-66; asst. prof. MATH, UNIV. ALTA, 66-67, ASSOC. PROF, 67- Am. Math. Soc; Math. Asn. Am; Can. Math. Cong; Math. Soc. France. Nature of derivates and structure of level sets of real functions in general and nowhere monotone functions in particular. Address: Dept. of Mathematics, University of Alberta, Edmonton, Alta, Can.

GARGANO, FREDIE PATRICK, b. Elizabeth, N.J, Mar. 22, 26; m. 53; c. 4. RADIOLOGY. B.S, George Washington, 47, M.D, 52. Instr. radiol, Vet. Admin. Hosp, Coral Gables & sch. med, Miami (Fla), 58-59, asst. prof, 59-61, assoc. prof, 61-62; fel. neuroradiol, Columbia Presby. Hosp, New York, 62-63; assoc. prof. RADIOL, SCH. MED, UNIV. MIAMI, 63-70, PROF, 70-, DIR. NEURORADIOL, 63- Consult. radiol, Vet. Admin. Hosp. 59-; neuroradiol, Variety Children's Hosp, 63-; Broward Gen. & Hollywood Mem. Hosps, 70- Am. Col. Radiol; Radiol. Soc. N.Am; Asn. Univ. Radiol; Am. Soc. Neuroradiol; Am. Asn. Neurol. Surg. Neuroradiology with emphasis on vascular disease. Address: Dept. of Radiology, University of Miami School of Medicine, Miami, FL 33124.

GARGUS, JAMES L, b. Dalton, Ark, Oct. 27, 22; m. 43; c. 5. BIOLOGY, CYTOLOGY. B.S, George Washington, 50, M.S, 54; Rutgers, 54-55. Res. asst. tissue culture, Warwick Clin, 50-54; inst. microbiol, Rutgers, 54-55; lab. supvr. APPL. BIOL, HAZLETON LABS, INC, 55-60, dept. chief, 61-65, res. coord, 65-68, DEPT. DIR, 69- U.S.A, 43-45. AAAS; Electron Micros. Soc. Am; Am. Asn. Cancer Res; Tissue Culture Asn; N.Y. Acad. Sci. Supervision and research management in applied biology and toxicology; carcinogenesis, including bioassay procedures and ultrastructural changes induced by carcinogens; experimental cancer chemotherapy and toxicology. Address: 7108 Wayne Dr, Annandale, VA 22003.

GARIBALDI, JOHN A(TTILIO), b. San Francisco, Calif, Apr. 3, 16; m. 59; c. 2. BIOCHEMISTRY. B.S, California, 38, Ph.D.(biochem), 58. Chemist, WEST. REGIONAL RES. LAB, U.S. DEPT. AGR, 46-52, BIOCHEMIST, 55- Ord.Dept, 41-45, Capt. Am. Soc. Microbiol. Microbial biochemistry; mineral nutrition of microorganisms; process development for the microbial production of antibiotics and vitamins; iron nutrition of microbes; shell egg microbiology. Address: Western Regional Research Lab, U.S. Dept. of Agriculture, 800 Buchanan St, Albany, CA 94706.

GARIBOTTI, DOMENICK J(OHN), b. Cleveland, Ohio, Feb. 22, 25; m. 52; c. 3. MICROELECTRONICS. B.S, Fenn Col, 49; Westinghouse Elec. Corp. fel, Case, 50-51, M.S, 51, Ph.D.(phys. metall), 55. Asst. phys. metall, Case, 51-55; res. metallurgist, Crucible Steel Co. Am, 55-56; sr. res. metallurgist, Continental Can Co, Inc, 56-60; sr. scientist, Hamilton Standard Div, United Aircraft Corp, 60-65; microcircuit group head, AC Spark Plug Div, Gen. Motors Corp, 65-68, sect. head res. & develop. microelectronics, AC Electronics Div, 68-69, dept. head, 69-70; PLANT MGR, MICROCIRCUIT ENG. FACILITY, ZENITH RADIO CORP, ELK GROVE VILLAGE, 70- Am. Inst. Mining, Metall. & Petrol. Eng; Am. Soc. Metals; Electrochem. Soc; Am. Vacuum Soc. Microcircuits; hybrid integrated circuits; thin and thick film materials and processes; vacuum technology, development of linear large scale integration electron beam techniques for microcircuits; solid state devices. Address: 629 Indian Way, Barrington, IL 60010.

GARIBOTTI, JOSEPH F(ORTUNATO), b. Cleveland, Ohio, Feb. 14, 34; m. 56; c. 3. ENGINEERING MECHANICS, MATHEMATICS. B.S.C.E, Case,

55, Ph.D.(eng. mech), 63; Southern California, 55-56; M.S, Ohio State, 59. Stress analyst, missile systs. div, Lockheed Aircraft Corp, 55-56; Columbus Div, N.Am. Aviation, Inc, 56-57; instr. eng. mech, Ohio State, 57-59; exec. adv. struct. mech, MISSILE & SPACE SYSTS. DIV, DOUGLAS AIRCRAFT CO, 62-63, br. chief solid mech. res, 63-64, dep. br. chief STRUCT. RES, 64-66, BR. CHIEF, 66- Am. Inst. Aeronaut. & Astronaut. Thin shell theory; stability of elastic systems; management of research in structural engineering, particularly aerospace structures. Address: 1816 Jamaica Rd, Costa Mesa, CA 92626.

GARIK, VALDEMAR L, b. Berlin, Ger, Mar. 25, 13; nat; m. 44; c. 1. PHYSICAL CHEMISTRY. B.S, Polytech. Inst. Brooklyn, 44, M.S, 47; Ph.D, Connecticut, 53. Assoc. prof. phys. chem, Iona Col, 56-64; asst. prof. CHEM, MONTCLAIR STATE COL, 64-69, ASSOC. PROF. 69- Am. Chem. Soc. Hydrogenation of nitrocompounds with Raney nickel; kinetics of the decomposition of methyl in propyl ketone. Address: Dept. of Chemistry, Montclair State College, Upper Montclair, NJ 07043.

GARIN, DAVID L, b. N.Y.C, June 14, 39. ORGANIC CHEMISTRY. B.S, City Col. New York, 60; Ph.D.(org. chem), Iowa State Univ, 64. Van Leer fel, Weizmann Inst. Sci, 64, Nat. Insts. Health fel, Weizmann Inst. Sci. & Ind. Univ, 64-66; asst. prof. CHEM, UNIV. MO-ST. LOUIS, 66-71, ASSOC. PROF. 71- Petrol. Res. Fund grant, 67; Res. Corp. Cottrell grant, 68. Am. Chem. Soc; The Chem. Soc. Synthesis of strained ring systems; photochemistry; rearrangement reactions; reaction mechanisms. Address: Dept. of Chemistry, University of Missouri-St. Louis, 8001 Natural Bridge, St. Louis, MO 63121.

GARIN, GEORGE ILLICHEVSKY, b. Odessa, Russia, Apr. 9, 02; nat; m. 33; c. 5. FORESTRY. B.S, Idaho, 29, M.S, 30; Ph.D.(forest soils), Yale, 42. Forest ranger, Indian Forest Serv, Mont, 31-33; proj. mgr, Indian Field Serv, 33-38; asst, exp. sta, Connecticut, 40-41; FORESTER, Indian Forest Serv, Klamath Agency, Oregon, 41-43; Navajo Agency, Ariz, 43-48; AGR. EXP. STA, AUBURN UNIV, 48- Soc. Am. Foresters. Silviculture; forest management; silvics; forest soils. Address: Agricultural Experiment Station, Auburn University, Auburn, AL 36830.

GARING, JOHN S(EYMOUR), b. Toledo, Ohio, Nov. 6, 30; m. 52; c. 2. PHYSICS. B.Sc, Ohio State, 51, M.Sc, 54, fel, 57-58, Ph.D.(physics), 58. Asst. physics, Ohio State, 51-53; physicist, geophysics res. directorate, Air Force Res. Div, 58-61, chief, infrared physics br, 61-63; DIR, OPTICAL PHYSICS LAB, AIR FORCE CAMBRIDGE RES. LABS, BEDFORD, MASS, 63- U.S.A.F, 53-57, Res, 57-61, 1st Lt. Fel. AAAS; fel. Optical Soc. Am. Infrared optics and spectroscopy; atmospheric transmission and absorption; molecular structure and interactions; lasers; non-thermal atmospheric phenomena; spectroscopic and interferometric instrumentation and techniques. Address: 157 Cedar St, Lexington, MA 02173.

GARINTHER, GEORGES ROBERT, b. Montreal, Que, May 2, 34; m. 57; c. 3. ELECTRICAL ENGINEERING. B.S.E.E, Gannon Col, 57. RES. ENGR, ACOUSTICAL RES. BR, HUMAN ENG. LABS, 57- Mem. comt. hearing & bioacoustics & biomech, Nat. Acad. Sci-Nat. Res. Counc, 63-; partic, V Int. Cong. Acoust, Belgium, VI, Japan & VII, Hungary. U.S. Army res. & develop. award, 71. Ord.C, 57-59, Capt. Acoustical Soc. Am. Effects of noise on man including hearing loss, speech interference, annoyance; measurement of impulse noise and its effect on hearing. Address: Acoustical Research Branch, Human Engineering Labs, U.S. Army Aberdeen Research & Development Center, Aberdeen Proving Ground, MD 21005.

GARIZIO, JOHN ERNEST, b. New York, N.Y, July 27, 13; m. 40; c. 2. PHARMACEUTICAL CHEMISTRY. B.S, Columbia Univ, 35. Head chemist, Drug Prods. Co, N.Y, 35-43; asst. to dir, Warner Inst. for Therapeut. Res, 43-45; asst. to pres, Marvin R. Thompson Co, Conn, 45-48; applied res, Sheffield Farms Co, N.Y, 48-49; asst. to pres, Reheis Co, Inc, 49-60, v.pres. & bd. dirs, 60-68; V.PRES. & TECH. DIR, J.H. WALKER & CO, INC, 68- With Off. Sci. Res. & Develop, 44. Mem. revision comt, U.S. Pharmacopoeia; Nat. Vitamin Found. Soc. Cosmetic Chem; Am. Pharmaceut. Asn. Pharmaceuticals; medicine; water-soluble vitamin K solution for parenteral solutions; calcium salt of 2,4:1-methyl napthoquinone for blood clotting; cosmetic chemicals. Address: J.H. Walker & Co, Inc, 22 W. First St, Mt. Vernon, NY 10550.

GARLAND, CARL W(ESLEY), b. Bangor, Maine, Oct. 1, 29; m. 55; c. 2. PHYSICAL CHEMISTRY. B.S, Rochester, 50; Ph.D.(chem), California, 53. Instr. CHEM, California, 53; MASS. INST. TECHNOL, 53-55, asst. prof, 55-59, assoc. prof, 59-68, PROF, 68- Sci. ed, Optics & Spectros, 60-; Guggenheim fel, 63-64. Am. Chem. Soc; Am. Phys. Soc; fel. Am. Acad. Arts & Sci. Lattice dynamics; low temperature elastic constants and heat capacities; ultrasonic studies of phase transitions and critical points; bulk properties of solids at high pressures; dynamical aspects of cooperative phenomena. Address: 13-2054 Massachusetts Institute of Technology, Cambridge, MA 02139.

GARLAND, CHARLES E, b. Haverhill, Mass, June 5, 26; m. 48; c. 1. ORGANIC CHEMISTRY. A.B, Colby Col, 50; M.S, New Hampshire, 52. Instr. chem, New Hampshire, 50-51; res. chemist anthraquinone dyes, E.I. DU PONT DE NEMOURS & CO, 51-66, COLOR MEASUREMENT & CONTROL, 66-70, SR. RES. CHEMIST, 70- U.S.N, 44-46. Am. Chem. Soc; Am. Asn. Textile Chem. & Colorists; Inter-Soc. Color. Coun. U.S.N, 44-46. Polarographic reduction of diazonium compounds; research in anthraquinone chemistry leading to new dyes for cotton and polyester fibers; measurement of color in solutions and dyed fabrics and computer shade matching. Address: General Analytical Lab, Chambers Works, E.I. du Pont de Nemours & Co, Deepwater, NJ 08023.

GARLAND, CLYNE FREDERICK, b. Elizabeth, Colo, Mar. 14, 03; m. 27; c. 3. MECHANICAL ENGINEERING. Colorado, 23; M.S, Yale, 30. Jr. engr, Westinghouse Elec. Corp, 23-24; instr. mech. eng, Colorado, 25-29; lab. asst, Yale, 29-30; asst. prof, Univ. Calif, Berkeley, 30-40, assoc. prof. eng. design, 40-49, prof, 49-58, chmn. div, 47-58, prof. mech. eng. & assoc. dean col. eng, 58-62, chmn. dept. mech. eng, 58-60, prof. mech. eng. & assoc. dean col. eng, UNIV. CALIF, DAVIS, 62-69, EMER. PROF.

MECH. ENG, 69- U.S.N.R, 41-45, Capt. Am. Soc. Mech. Eng. Mechanical vibration; machine design. Address: 3112 Tice Creek Dr, Apt. 2, Walnut Creek, CA 94595.

GARLAND, FRED M(cKEE), b. Corsicana, Tex, Mar. 16, 12; m. 39; c. 2. CHEMISTRY. B.S, Trinity (Tex), 34; M.S, Tex. Tech. Col, 36; Ph.D.(org. chem), Texas, 39. Asst. chem, Tex. Tech. Col, 34-36; instr, Texas, 36-39; prof, Trinity (Tex), 39-41; res. chemist, res. labs, Armour & Co, 41-43; PROF. CHEM, TEX. A&I UNIV, 46-, CHMN. DEPT, 50- Sanit.C, U.S.A, 43-46. Am. Chem. Soc. Isolation and identification of the nitrogen bases in petroleum; the isolation and identification of acids in petroleum; fatty acids. Address: Dept. of Chemistry, Texas A&I University, Kingsville, TX 78363.

GARLAND, GEORGE D(AVID), b. Toronto, Ont, June 29, 26; m. 49; c. 2. B.A.Sc, Toronto, 47, M.A, 48; Ph.D.(geophysics), St. Louis, 51. Lectr. geophysics, Toronto, 49-52; geophysicist, Dom. Observ, Can, 52-54; assoc. prof. geophysics, Alberta, 54-60, PROF, 60-63; PHYSICS, UNIV. TORONTO, 63- Secy-gen. Int. Union Geod. & Geophys. Gravity; structure of the earth's crust; magnetic and electric fields of the earth. Address: Geophysics Lab, University of Toronto, Toronto, Ont, Can.

GARLAND, HEREFORD, b. Lake Bluff, Ill, Jan. 2, 05; m. 40; c. 3. FOREST PRODUCTS. B.S, California, 31, M.S, 32; fel, Washington (St. Louis), 35-38, Ph.D.(plant physiol), 38. Tech. asst. forestry, California, 31-34; jr. forester, Calif. Forest Exp. Sta, U.S. Forest Serv, 34-35, asst. conservationist, 40-42, assoc. forest prod. technologist, 42-45; instr. forestry, Arkansas, 39-40; assoc. prof. FOREST PROD. RES, MICH. TECHNOL. UNIV, 45-47, PROF, 47-, forest prod. res. div, 47-64, dir, inst. wood res, 64-71. Soc. Am. Foresters; Forest Prod. Res. Soc; Am. Soc. Eng. Educ; Soc. Wood Sci. & Technol; Am. Soc. Test. & Mat; Soc. Res. Adminr. Mechanical properties of wood; anatomical studies of wood; coniferous wood in relation to its strength properties; forest products; wood production and economics. Address: Dept. of Forest Products Research, Michigan Technological University, Houghton, MI 49931.

GARLAND, HOWARD, b. Detroit, Mich, Oct. 27, 37; m. 61; c. 2. MATHEMATICS. B.S, Chicago, 57; M.S, Wayne State, 59; Nat. Sci. Found. fels, California, Berkeley, 57-58, 60-62, Ph.D.(math), 64. Instr. MATH, Yale, 64-65; asst, Inst. Adv. Study, 65-66; asst. prof, Yale, 66-69; assoc. prof, Cornell Univ, 69-71; PROF, COLUMBIA UNIV, 71- Am. Math Soc. Discrete subgroups of Lie groups. Address: Dept. of Mathematics, Columbia University, New York, NY 10027.

GARLAND, JAMES C, b. Columbia, Mo, Aug. 11, 42; m. 65; c. 1. SOLID STATE PHYSICS. A.B, Princeton, 64; Ph.D.(physics), Cornell Univ, 69. Nat. Sci. Found. fel, PHYSICS, Cambridge, 69-70; ASST. PROF, OHIO STATE UNIV, 70- Am. Phys. Soc. Low temperature electronic properties of metals, including transport and galvanomagnetic effects. Address: Dept. of Physics, Smith Lab, Ohio State University, Columbus, OH 43210.

GARLAND, JAMES W, JR, b. Wash, D.C, Aug. 1, 33; m. 58; c. 2. SOLID STATE PHYSICS. M.S, Chicago, 58, Nat. Sci. Found. fel, 60-63, Ph.D. (physics), 65. Acting asst. prof. PHYSICS, Univ. Calif, Berkeley, 63-65, asst. prof, 66-67; assoc. prof, UNIV. ILL, CHICAGO CIRCLE, 67-70, PROF, 70- Alfred P. Sloan Found. fel, 64-66; vis. lectr, Cambridge, 65; consult, Argonne Nat. Lab, 67-, assoc. physicist, 69-70. U.S.A, 54-56. Am. Phys. Soc. Theory of metals; superconductivity; magnetism; transition metals. Address: 6040 Carpenter, Downers Grove, IL 60515.

GARLAND, JOHN KENNETH, b. Cadillac, Mich, Dec. 27, 35; m. 58; c. 5. CHEMISTRY. B.S, Univ. Ill, 57; Okla. State Univ, 57-59; Nat. Sci. Found. fels, Univ. Kans, summer 60, 60-61, 62-63, Ph.D.(chem), 63. Asst. res. chemist, Continental Oil Co, Okla, 57-59; asst. prof. CHEM, Univ. Mo-Columbia, 63-70; ASSOC. PROF, WASH. STATE UNIV, 70- Res. fel, Univ. Mo, summer 64. U.S.A.R, 59-67. Am. Chem. Soc. Chemical education; hot atom chemistry, particularly recoil tritium. Address: Dept. of Chemistry, Washington State University, Pullman, WA 99163.

GARLAND, MICHAEL McKEE, b. Clarksville, Tenn, Jan. 12, 39; m. 58; c. 2. SOLID STATE PHYSICS. B.A, Austin Peay State Col, 61; Ph.D.(physics), Clemson, 65. Asst. prof. PHYSICS, MEMPHIS STATE UNIV, 65-69, ASSOC. PROF, 69- Am. Asn. Physics Teachers; Am. Vacuum Soc. Superconducting behavior of thin films; superconductive tunneling between superimposed films. Address: Dept. of Physics, Memphis State University, Memphis, TN 38111.

GARLAND, ROBERT B(RUCE), b. Chicago, Ill, Nov. 6, 32; m. 55; c. 3. ORGANIC CHEMISTRY. B.S, Illinois, 53; Nat. Sci. Found. fel, Mass. Inst. Tech, 53-55, Knudsen fel, 55-56, Ph.D.(chem), 57. RES. CHEMIST, G.D. SEARLE & CO, 59- Am. Chem. Soc. Synthetic organic chemistry, primarily steroidal hormones. Address: Chemical Research, G.D. Searle & Co, P.O. Box 5110, Chicago, IL 60680.

GARLAND, STEPHEN J(AY), b. Cincinnati, Ohio, Nov. 25, 41; m. 67; c. 1. MATHEMATICAL LOGIC, COMPUTER SCIENCE. A.B, Dartmouth Col, 63; M.A, California, Berkeley, 65, Ph.D.(math. logic), 67. ASST. PROF. MATH. & ASST. DIR. KIEWIT COMPUT. CTR, DARTMOUTH COL, 67- Dartmouth Col. faculty fel, 70-71; vis. asst. prof, Univ. Calif, Los Angeles, 70-71. Am. Math. Soc; Math. Asn. Am; Asn. Symbolic Logic. Hierarchy theory; theory of definability; model theory; recursive function theory; models for computation; programming languages, compilers; and time-sharing systems. Address: Dept. of Mathematics, Dartmouth College, Hanover, NH 03755.

GARLICH, JIMMY DALE, b. Okawville, Ill, Feb. 18, 36; m. 65; c. 1. NUTRITION, BIOCHEMISTRY. B.S, Illinois, Urbana, 58, M.S, 59; Ph.D.(animal nutrit), Cornell, 64. Nat. Heart Inst. fel. human nutrit, sch. pub. health, Pittsburgh, 64-65, sch. med, St. Louis, 65-66; ASST. PROF. NUTRIT, N.C. STATE UNIV, 66- U.S.A, 59-60, 1st Lt. Poultry Sci. Asn. Pharmacological effects of amino acids on lipid metabolism in human subjects; effect of plant proteolytic enzyme inhibitors on digestion by chicks; hormonal regulation of calcium metabolism in avian species. Address: Dept. of Poultry Science, North Carolina State University, Raleigh, NC 27607.

GARLICK, G(EORGE) DONALD, b. Lusaka, Zambia, Nov. 29, 34; m. 64. GEOCHEMISTRY, PETROLOGY. B.S, Witwatersrand, 56; Ph.D.(geochem), Calif. Inst. Tech, 65. Geologist, New Consol. Gold Fields, S.Africa, 56-59; geochemist, Columbia, 65-66, asst. prof. GEOL, 66-69; ASSOC. PROF, HUMBOLDT STATE COL, 69- Am. Geochem. Soc; Geol. Soc. Am; Geophys. Union. Oxygen isotope geochemistry and petrology. Address: Dept. of Geology, Humboldt State College, Arcata, CA 95521.

GARLICK, GEORGE FOREST, b. McCook, Nebr, July 17, 36; m. 60; c. 2. ELECTRICAL ENGINEERING, SOLID STATE PHYSICS. Mobil Oil Co. fel. & B.S, S.Dak. Sch. Mines & Tech, 58; Hughes Aircraft Co. fel. & M.S, Southern California, 60; alumni fel. & Ph.D.(solid state physics), Iowa State, 62. Sr. engr. solid state circuit design, Hughes Aircraft Co, Calif, 58-60; electronics, Hanford Labs, Gen. Elec. Co, 62-64; mgr. res, Pac. Northwest Lab, Battelle Mem. Inst, 64-68; dir, Ctr. Grad. Study, Wash, 68-71; PRES, HOLOSONICS, INC, 71- Summers, jr. engr, aviation div, Sundstrand Corp, Ill, 57, mem. res. prog. Int. Bus. Mach. Corp, N.Y, 61, res. proj. dir, Iowa State, 62. Management of applied solid state physics research; semiconductor device development. Address: Holosonics, Inc, 2950 George Washington Way, Richland, WA 99352.

GARLICK, NORMAN L(EE), b. Tacoma, Wash, Apr. 11, 16; m. 38; c. 2. VETERINARY MEDICINE, COMPARATIVE PATHOLOGY. B.S, Wash. State Univ, 40, D.V.M, 41; Med. Univ. S.C, 51-52. Vet, Button Vet. Hosp, Tacoma, Wash, 41-50; dist. vet, U.S. Dept. Agr, Calif, 55-58, asst. chief staff vet, Wash, D.C, 58-63, chief staff vet, 63-68; PROF. LAB. ANIMAL MED. & CHMN. DEPT, MED. UNIV. S.C, 68- Vet, Bur. Prisons, Dept. Justice, 43-51; mem, subpanel intensification animal prod, President's Sci. Adv. Comt. World Food Probs, 66-67; consult, panel vet. terminology, Nat. Libr. Med, U.S. Dept. Health, Educ. & Welfare, 67-70; U.S. Vet. Admin. Hosp, Charleston, S.C, 68-; coun. accreditation, Am. Asn. Accreditation of Lab. Animal Care, 71- Vet.C, U.S.A, 52-54, Capt. N.Y. Acad. Sci; Am. Vet. Med. Asn; U.S. Animal Health Asn; Am. Soc. Lab. Animal Practitioners; Am. Asn. Lab. Animal Sci; Asn. Gnotobiotics; Microcirculatory Soc; Am. Col. Vet. Toxicol; Wildlife Disease Asn; Int. Acad. Path; Am. Inst. Biol. Sci; Am. Asn. Vet. Parasitol. Fluorosis in livestock; parasitology; immunology, including graft rejection phenomena; cancer in animals; diseases of laboratory animals. Address: Dept. of Lab. Animal Medicine, Medical University of South Carolina, 80 Barre St, Charleston, SC 29401.

GARLID, KERMIT L(EROY), b. Ellsworth, Wis, May 10, 29; m. 54; c. 4. CHEMICAL & NUCLEAR ENGINEERING. B.S, Wis. State Col, River Falls, 50; B.Ch.E, Minnesota, 56, Ph.D.(chem. eng), 61. Engr. qual. control, aero div, Minneapolis-Honeywell Regulator Co, 53-54; instr. chem. eng, Minnesota, 56-60; asst. prof, UNIV. WASH, 60-66; assoc. prof, 66-71, PROF. NUCLEAR & CHEM. ENG, 71- Vis. prof, Tech. Univ, Munich, 68-69; consult, Hanford Atomic Power Oper, Gen. Elec. Co, 63-68; Battelle N.West Labs, 65-68; Electronic Assoc, Inc, 68; Thermodynamics, Inc, 70-; Atlantic Richfield Hanford Co, 71-; R.W. Beck & Assoc, 71- U.S.A, 51-53, Res, 53-58, Sgt. AAAS; Am. Inst. Chem. Eng; Am. Nuclear Soc. Nuclear reactor theory; dynamic analysis of nuclear and chemical processes, especially using pulsed analysis; control and optimization of processes; two-phase flow. Address: Dept. of Nuclear Engineering, University of Washington, Seattle, WA 98105.

GARLINGTON, WILLIAM D(RAKE), b. Topeka, Kans, May 10, 24; m. 49; c. 3. CHEMICAL ENGINEERING. B.E, Yale, 45, M.E, 48. Chem. engr, high pressure res, polychems. res. div, E.I. DU PONT DE NEMOURS & CO, INC, 48-51, cost estimation res, develop. sect, FILM DEPT, 51-52, develop. supvr, tech. sect, Columbia Sponge Plant, 52-56, STAFF ENGR, FILM RES. LAB, 56- U.S.N.R, 43-46, Ens. Am. Inst. Chem. Eng. High pressure polymerization; plastic films; cellulose sponge. Address: 209 Lister Dr, Hyde Park, Wilmington, DE 19808.

GARLOCK, EDWARD A(LLEN), b. New London, Conn, June 9, 18; m. 39; c. 2. ORGANIC CHEMISTRY. B.S, George Washington, 42. Org. chemist drug res, Nat. Insts. Health, 40-45; antibiotic res, Food & Drug Admin, 45-49; tech. rep, Fisher Sci. Co, 49-54; regional mgr, Perkin-Elmer Corp, 54-59; res. appl. specialist, Hazleton Labs, Inc, 59-61, res. mgr, 61-63, res. coord, Va, 63-68; ASST. DIR. CLIN. SCI, GILLETTE RES. INST, 68- U.S.A.R, 49-57, Capt. Am. Chem. Soc; Am. Inst. Chem. Organic synthesis; antibiotic analysis; instrumental methods of analysis; clinical sciences, design and development of clinical protocols and evaluation of clinical data. Address: Medical Evaluations Dept, Gillette Research Institute, 1413 Research Blvd, Rockville, MD 20850.

GARMAISE, D(AVID) L(YON), b. Montreal, Que, Mar. 26, 23; m. 50; c. 3. ORGANIC CHEMISTRY. B.Sc, McGill, 42; Ph.D.(chem), 45. Assoc. prof. chem, New Brunswick, 45-50; Brit. Empire Cancer Soc. res. fel, Wales, 50-52; res. sect. head, Monsanto Can. Ltd, 52-63; MGR. ORG. CHEM. RES, ABBOTT LABS. LTD, 63- Am. Chem. Soc; Chem. Inst. Can. Synthetic organic chemistry; medicinal chemistry; history of science. Address: 4021 Marcil Ave, Montreal 260, Que, Can.

GARMAN, JOHN A(NDREW), b. Berlin, Pa, Aug. 2, 21; m. 45; c. 2. ORGANIC CHEMISTRY. B.S, Franklin & Marshall Col, 43; E.I. du Pont de Nemours fel, Maryland, 46-47, Ph.D.(org. chem), 48. Res. chemist, Firestone Plastics Co. div, Firestone Tire & Rubber Co, 47-50; U.S. Indust. Chems. Co, 50-53, head org. chems. sect, 53-54; Fairfield Chem. Div, FMC Corp, 54-55, asst. dir, Fairfield Br, cent. chem. res, 56-57, mgr. org. chem. res, org. chem. div, 57-58, chem. & plastics div, 58-62, dir. res. & develop, org. chem. div, 62-69; DIR. RES. & DEVELOP, GREAT LAKES CHEM. CORP, 70- Am. Chem. Soc. Organic synthesis; agricultural chemicals; pharmaceuticals; fine organic chemicals, polymers and plastics. Address: Great Lakes Chemical Corp, P.O. Box 2200, West Lafayette, IN 47906.

GARMAN, W(ILLARD) H(ERSHEL), b. Cherry Tree, Pa, Oct. 21, 12; m. 38; c. 2. AGRICULTURE. B.S, Pa. State Col, 33, M.S, 34, Ph.D.(agron), 39. Asst. agr. & biol. chem, Pa. State Col, 33-34, soils chem. & morphol, 36-39; asst. chemist, Agr. & Mech. Col. Tex, 34-36; asst. prof. agron, Univ. Ga, 39-40, assoc. prof, 41-42; soil scientist, exp. sta, Clemson Col, 42-47; prof. agron. & head dept, Univ. Ark, 47-49; prin. administr. soil technol, U.S. Off. Exp. Stas, 49-54; chief agriculturist, Nat. Plant Food Inst, 54-62, v.pres. div. sci. serv. & ed, Plant Food Rev, 63-71; AGR. CHEM. SPECIALIST, U.S. DEPT. OF STATE, 71- Chmn, Nat. Soil Res. Comt, 53. U.S.N, 44-46. Fel. AAAS; Am. Chem. Soc; fel. Am. Soc. Agron; Soil Sci. Soc. Am; Am. Soc. Plant Physiol; Soil Conserv. Soc. Am. Plant nutrition; soil technology; fertilizers; environment and agriculture. Address: 3423 Woodside Rd, Alexandria, VA 22310.

GARMAN, W(ILLIAM) L(EE), b. Wagoner, Okla, Oct. 24, 17; m. 42; c. 4. INORGANIC CHEMISTRY. B.S, Okla. Agr. & Mech. Col, 39, M.S, 46; Ph.D. (soils), Ohio State, 54. Asst. soil scientist, soil surv, soil conserv. serv, U.S. Dept. Agr, 40-42; asst. prof. soils, Okla. Agr. & Mech. Col, 46-50; Cornell, 50-55; agr. serv. mgr. & agronomist, Grand River Chem. Div, Deere & Co, Okla, 55-56; pres. & gen. mgr, Best Fertilizers Co, Lathrop, 56-64; V.PRES, OCCIDENTAL CHEM. CO, WEST. DIV, LATHROP, 64- U.S.A.A.F, 42-46, Capt. Soil Sci. Soc. Am; Am. Soc. Agron. Soil association surveys; potassium supplying power of soils; nitrogen utilization. Address: 1249 Stratford Circle, Apt. 21, Stockton, CA 95207.

GARMEZY, R(OBERT) H(ARPER), b. Manila, Philippines, Dec. 8, 23; m; c. 4. MECHANICAL & ELECTRICAL ENGINEERING. B.E.E, Cornell, 43, B.M.E, 45; M.A.E, Chrysler Inst. Eng, 47. Instr, elec. lab, Cornell, 43-44; student engr, Chrysler Corp, 45-47, lab. engr, 47-51; head radiator lab, BLACKSTONE CORP, 51-60, dir. eng, AUTOMOTIVE DIV, 60-68, V.PRES. ENG, 68- Instr, night sch, Lawrence Inst. Technol, 46-51. Am. Soc. Mech. Eng; Soc. Automotive Eng; Am. Ord. Asn; Inst. Elec. & Electronics Eng. Heat transfer; automotive radiators; heater cores. Address: 12 Whitehill Ave, Jamestown, NY 14701.

GARMIRE, ELSA MEINTS, b. Buffalo, N.Y, Nov. 9, 39; m. 61; c. 2. PHYSICS. A.B, Radcliffe Col, 61; Ph.D.(physics), Mass. Inst. Tech, 65. Res. fel. physics, Mass. Inst. Tech, 65-66; scientist, electronics res. ctr, NASA, 66; RES. FEL. ELEC. ENG, CALIF. INST. TECHNOL, 66-, PART-TIME SR. RES. FEL. APPL. SCI, 70-, part-time res. fel, 69-70. Pres, Laser Images, Inc. Am. Phys. Soc; Exp. Art & Tech. Lasers; integrated optics; nonlinear optics; spectroscopy; quantum electronics. Address: Dept. of Electrical Engineering, California Institute of Technology, Pasadena, CA 91109.

GARMIRE, GORDON PAUL, b. Portland, Ore, Oct. 3, 37; m. 61; c. 2. PHYSICS. A.B, Harvard, 59; Ph.D.(physics), Mass. Inst. Tech, 62. Mem. staff div. sponsored res, Mass. Inst. Technol, 62-64; asst. prof. PHYSICS, 64-66, assoc. prof, 67-68; sr. fel, CALIF. INST. TECHNOL, 66-67, ASSOC. PROF, 68- Mem. astron. subcomt, NASA, 68-70. Int. Astron. Union. Geomagnetically trapped radiation; x-ray and gamma ray astronomy; cosmic rays. Address: 320-47, Dept. of Physics, California Institute of Technology, Pasadena, CA 91109.

GARMON, LUCILLE BURNETT, b. Johnstown, Pa, July 1, 36; m. 56; c. 2. PHYSICAL CHEMISTRY, SOLID STATE PHYSICS. B.S, Richmond, 56, M.S, 60; Ph.D.(chem), Virginia, 66. Res. chemist, Va. Inst. Sci. Res, 56-61; assoc. prof. chem, E.Carolina Col, 64-66; asst. prof. physics & res. assoc, Auburn, 66-68, fel. solid state physics, 66-67; ASST. PROF. PHYSICS, W.GA. COL, 68- AAAS; Am. Chem. Soc; Am. Phys. Soc; Am. Asn. Physics Teachers; Electron Micros. Soc. Am; Nat. Sci. Teachers Asn; N.Y. Acad. Sci. Oxidation of metals, especially epitaxial relationship between metal and oxide on single crystal metal specimens. Address: Dept. of Physics, West Georgia College, Carrollton, GA 30117.

GARMON, RONALD GENE, b. Charlotte, N.C, Mar. 13, 34; m. 55; c. 3. ANALYTICAL CHEMISTRY. B.S, North Carolina, 58, Ph.D.(chem), 61. Res. chemist, CHEMSTRAND RES. CTR, INC, 61-65, sr. res. chemist, 65-69, GROUP LEADER, 69- U.S.A.F, 53-55. Am. Chem. Soc. Analytical chemistry of polymers; radiochemistry; kinetic methods of analysis. Address: Chemstrand Research Center, Box 731, Durham, NC 27702.

GARMONG, GREGORY OTIS, b. Gary, Ind, Dec. 15, 43. METALLURGY. S.B, Mass. Inst. Technol, 66, Ph.D, 69. MEM. TECH. STAFF, SCI. CTR, N.AM. ROCKWELL CORP, 69- Am. Inst. Mining, Metall. & Petrol. Eng; Am. Soc. Metals. Composite materials; mechanical properties; plasticity; solidification; computer control. Address: P.O. Box 1085, Thousand Oaks, CA 91360.

GARN, PAUL D(ONALD), b. Freemont, Ohio, July 7, 20; m. 45; c. 3. ANALYTICAL & PHYSICAL CHEMISTRY. B.S, Ohio State Univ, 48, M.S, 49, Ph.D.(chem), 52. Mem. tech. staff, Bell Tel. Labs, Inc, 52-63; assoc. prof. CHEM, UNIV. AKRON, 63-67, PROF, 67- Consult, Apparatus Mfrs, Inc, 63-69; for. lectr, Japanese Soc. Calorimetry & Thermal Anal, Japan, 70. Sig.C, 39-41, 42-46, 1st Lt. AAAS; Am. Inst. Chem; Am. Chem. Soc; N.Am. Thermal Anal. Soc.(pres, 69); Int. Confedn. Thermal Anal. Thermoanalytical techniques; mechanisms of solid-solid transitions; liquid-crystalline transitions; kinetics of thermal decompositions; kinetics of reversible and irreversible high temperature reactions; environmental studies. Address: Dept. of Chemistry, University of Akron, Akron, OH 44304.

GARN, STANLEY MARION, b. New London, Conn, Oct. 27, 22; m. 50; c. 2. PHYSICAL ANTHROPOLOGY. A.B, Harvard, 42, A.M, 47, Ph.D.(phys. anthrop), 48. Res. assoc, Mass. Inst. Tech, 42-44; tech. ed, Polaroid Corp, 44-46, consult, 46; instr. anthrop, Harvard, 48-52; assoc. prof, Antioch Col, 52-59, prof; 60-68, chmn. dept. growth & genetics, fels res. inst, 52-68; PROF. HEALTH DEVELOP, SCH. PUB. HEALTH & FEL, CTR, HUMAN GROWTH & DEVELOP, UNIV. MICH, ANN ARBOR, 68- Res. fel, Mass. Gen. Hosp, 46-50; Forsyth Dent. Infirmary, 47-52; Int. Univ. Training Prog, 58; vis. prof, Chicago, 58; mem. vis. staff, Inst. Nutrit. Cent. Am. & Panama, 62; guest lectr, inst anthrop, Colorado, summer 60. AAAS; Am. Soc. Nat; Am. Anthrop. Asn; Am. Asn. Phys. Anthrop; Am. Inst. Nutrit; Int. Asn. Dent. Res. Growth and development of body tissues; applied physical anthropology; human evolution. Address: Center for Human Growth & Development, University of Michigan, 611 Church St, Ann Arbor, MI 48104.

GARNAR, THOMAS E(DWARD), JR, b. Vineland, N.J, June 24, 22; m. 54. MINERAL ENGINEERING. B.S, West Virginia, 50, M.S, 51. Asst, West

Virginia, 48-51; res. geologist, res. div, Int. Minerals & Chem. Corp, 51-56; mining engr, Humphreys Gold Corp, 56-57; develop. engr, pigments dept, E.I. DU PONT DE NEMOURS & CO, INC, STARKE, 57-64, sr. res. geologist, 64-69, TECH. SUPVR, 69- U.S.A.A.F, 42-46. Geol. Soc. Am; Am. Inst. Mining, Metall. & Petrol. Eng. Mineralogy of iron, aluminum, calcium and rare earth phosphates; potash minerals; clays; perlite; micas; feldspar; barite; fluorite; gravity, electrostatic, high tension and magnetic concentration of titanium minerals, zircon and aluminum silicates; new uses for mineral products; process and quality control. Address: P.O. Box 417, Keystone Heights, FL 32656.

GARNEAU, FRANÇOIS XAVIER, b. Montreal, Que, May 6, 36; m. 63; c. 3 ORGANIC CHEMISTRY. B.Sc, Loyola Col. Montreal, 62; univ. fel, Col. of the Holy Cross, 62-63, M.Sc, 63; Prov. of Ont. fels, Univ. Toronto, 67-68, Ph.D.(photochem), 69. Fels, Univ. Alta, 68-70; ASST. PROF. ORG. CHEM, UNIV. QUE, CHICOUTIMI, 70- Am. Chem. Soc; Fr-Can. Asn. Advan. Sci. Monovalent carbon intermediates; organometallic chemistry; photochemistry of chromic esters. Address: Dept. of Chemistry, University of Quebec, 930 E. Jacques Cartier St, Chicoutimi, Que. Can.

GARNEAU, ROBERT (PAUL), b. Paris, France, Aug. 4, 26; nat. Can; m. 51; c. 1. PATHOLOGY. B.A, Jesuit's Col, Can, 45; M.D, Laval, 50; F.R.C.P, Royal Col. Physicians, Can, 56. Sr. intern, Hôtel-Dieu de Que, 50-51; trainee PATH, Laval, 51-53; Inst. Cancer, France, 53-54; Lyon, 54; Radcliffe infirmary, Oxford, 54-55; assoc. prof, MED. SCH, LAVAL UNIV, 55-63, prof. agrege, 63-68, PROF. TITULAIRE, 68- Asst, St. Sacrement Hosp, 55-62, dir, anat. path. lab, 62- Can. Med. Asn; Can. Asn. Path; Int. Acad. Path. Surgical pathology; post-mortem examinations. Address: Faculty of Medicine, Laval University, Quebec, Que, Can.

GARNER, ALBERT Y, b. Wash, D.C, May 8, 25; m. 49; c. 4. ORGANIC CHEMISTRY. B.S, Howard, 50, M.S, 51; Ph.D.(org. chem), Pa. State, 56. Instr, Howard, 51-52, res. assoc, 52-53; res. chemist, Monsanto Chem. Co, 56-62, MONSANTO RES. CORP, 62-65, res. specialist, 64-65, PROJ. LEADER, 65-, GROUP LEADER, 65- U.S.A.A.F, 43-46. Am. Chem. Soc; Am. Inst. Chem. Organic synthesis; reaction mechanisms; organophosphorus chemistry; structure determination; reactive intermediates. Address: 690 Omar Circle, Yellow Springs, OH 45387.

GARNER, BRUCE L(ELAND), b. Huntington Park, Calif, June 15, 22; m. 48; c. 3. PHYSICAL ORGANIC CHEMISTRY. B.A, California, Los Angeles, 43, Am. Chem. Soc. fel. & Ph.D.(phys. org. chem), 52. Res. chemist, corrosion inhibitors fuels, Calif. Res. Corp, 52-56; group leader prod. eval, Los Angeles Soap Co, 56-58; prod. mgr, Geigy Chem. Corp, N.Y, 58-63; PLASTICS RES. & DEVELOP, ORG. MAT. DIV, LAWRENCE LIVERMORE LAB, UNIV. CALIF, LIVERMORE, 63- Mem. U.S. nat. comt, tech. comt, Int. Standards Orgn. U.S.N.R, 44-46, Lt.(jg). Am. Chem. Soc; Soc. Plastics Eng; Am. Soc. Test. & Mat. Permanence properties of plastics. Address: Organic Materials Division, Lawrence Livermore Lab, Box 808, L-402, University of California, Livermore, CA 94550.

GARNER, CLIFFORD S(YMES), b. Newark, N.J, Oct. 4, 12; m. 37. PHYSICAL & INORGANIC CHEMISTRY. B.S, Calif. Inst. Tech, 35, Ph.D.(chem), 38. Asst. anal. chem, Calif. Inst. Tech, 35-36, fel, 36-38; Noyes res. fel. phys. chem, 38-39; instr. chem, Texas, 39-41, asst. prof, 41-46; res. assoc, Nat. Defense Res. Cmt, California, 42-43; group leader, Manhattan Proj, Los Alamos Lab, N.Mex, 43-46; asst. prof. CHEM, UNIV. CALIF, LOS ANGELES, 46-47, assoc. prof, 47-53, PROF, 53- Guggenheim Mem. fel, Copenhagen, 59. AAAS; Am. Chem. Soc; Am. Phys. Soc. Physical, inorganic and radiochemistry; chemistry of coordination compounds, especially kinetics and mechanisms of electron-transfer, substitution and isomerization reactions; synthesis of new transition-metal complexes; chemical fate of recoil atoms. Address: Dept. of Chemistry, University of California, Los Angeles, CA 90024.

GARNER, CYRIL WILBUR LUTHER, b. Scotland, Ont, Mar. 20, 40; m. 67. PURE MATHEMATICS. B.Sc, New Brunswick, 61; Woodrow Wilson fel. & M.A, Toronto, 62, Nat. Res. Coun. stud. & Ph.D.(math), 64. Asst. prof. MATH, CARLETON UNIV.(ONT), 64-68, ASSOC. PROF, 68- Mem, Ont. Math. Comn, 65- Can. Math. Cong; Ger. Math. Asn. Regular polyhedra in hyperbolic space; finite geometries and the foundations of geometry with particular emphasis upon hyperbolic geometry. Address: Dept. of Mathematics, Carleton University, Ottawa 1, Ont, Can.

GARNER, F. M, b. Chicago, Ill, Nov. 5, 22; m. 45; c. 3. VETERINARY PATHOLOGY. B.S, Washington State, 48; D.V.M, 50. U.S. ARMY, 51-, res. vet. path, ARMED FORCES INST. PATH, 58-60, vet. lab. officer, 60-61, asst. chief DIV. VET. PATH, 61-62, 63-64, acting chief, 62-63, CHIEF, 64- Dipl, Am. Col. Vet. Path. U.S.A, 40-45, 51-, Col. Am. Vet. Med. Asn. Veterinary and comparative pathology, including laboratory animals. Address: Veterinary Pathology Division, Armed Forces Institute of Pathology, Washington, DC 20305.

GARNER, GEORGE B(ERNARD), b. Kirksville, Mo, Dec. 7, 27; m. 48; c. 4. BIOCHEMISTRY, NUTRITION. B.S, Northeast Mo. State Teachers Col, 49; M.S, Missouri, 51, Ph.D.(agr. chem), 57. Teacher, pub. sch, 51-53; instr, AGR. CHEM, UNIV. MO-COLUMBIA; 53-57, asst. prof, 57-70, ASSOC. PROF, 70- Fulbright Res. scholar, 62-63. Med.C, U.S.A, 46-47. AAAS; Am. Chem. Soc; Am. Soc. Animal Sci. Rumen nutrition and physiology; nitrate toxicity and physiologically active constituents of forages; analytical methods applicable to agricultural products. Address: Dept. of Agricultural Chemistry 111 Schweitzer Hall, University of Missouri-Columbia, Columbia, MO 65201.

GARNER, HAROLD K(ARL), b. Porterville, Calif, Apr. 8, 21; m. 49. ORGANIC CHEMISTRY. B.S, Calif. Inst. Tech, 43, Noyes fel, 48-49, Ph.D. (org. chem), 49. Res. scientist, RES. CTR, U.S. Rubber Co, 49-61, sr. res. scientist, 61-69, MGR. PERSONNEL, UNIROYAL INC, 69- U.S.A.A.F, 43-45. Am. Chem. Soc. Role of neighboring groups in ionic organic reactions; free radical polymerizations; polymer chemistry; stereospecific polymerization; adhesion chemistry; inorganic polymers. Address: 105 Chestnut Dr, Wayne, NJ 07471.

GARNER, HARRY RICHARD, b. East Liverpool, Ohio, Feb. 4, 35; m. 57; c. 2. ANALYTICAL CHEMISTRY. B.S, Kent State, 57; M.S, Western Reserve, 62. Chemist, HARSHAW CHEM. CO. DIV, KEWANEE OIL CO, 57-59, group leader, 59-63, unit mgr, instrumental anal. lab, 63-66, asst. sect. mgr, CENT. ANAL. LAB, 66-68, sect. mgr, 68-69, TECH. DIR. METAL FINISHING RES, 69- Am. Chem. Soc; Soc. Appl. Spectros.(treas, 66-67, secy, 67-68, v.pres, 68-69); Am. Electroplaters Soc. Electrodeposition of metals; emission spectroscopy; x-ray diffraction; x-ray spectroscopy; absorption spectroscopy; electron microscopy; instrumental color evaluation; colorimetric analysis; wet chemical analysis. Address: Harshaw Chemical Co. Division, Kewanee Oil Co, 1945 E. 97th St, Cleveland, OH 44106.

GARNER, HARVEY L(OUIS), b. Lake, Colo, Dec. 23, 26; m. 50; c. 2. ELECTRICAL ENGINEERING. B.S, Denver, 49, M.S, 51; Ph.D.(elec. eng), Michigan, 58. Res. assoc, cosmic radiation lab, Denver, 49-51; assoc. res. engr, digital comput. dept, Willow Run Labs, Michigan, 51-53, asst. head dept, 53-55, instr. ELEC. ENG, 55-58, asst. prof, 58-60, assoc. prof, 60-63, prof, 63-70, dir. info. syst. lab, 60-64; PROF. & DIR. MOORE SCH. ELEC. ENG, UNIV. PA, 70- U.S.N.R, 45-46. AAAS; Am. Soc. Eng. Educ; Asn. Comput. Mach; Inst. Elec. & Electronics Eng. Digital computation; machine number systems and arithmetic; organization and design of digital computing machines. Address: 719 King of Prussia Rd, Radnor, PA 19087.

GARNER, H(ESSLE) F(ILMORE), b. Creston, Iowa, Feb. 24, 26; m. 54. PHYSICAL GEOLOGY. B.S, Iowa State Col, 50; M.S, Iowa, 51, Ph.D.(geol), 53. Asst. phys. geol, Iowa, 50-51, paleont, 52-53; geologist, Richmond Petrol. Co. Calif, 53, Calif-Ecuador Petrol. Co, 54-56; asst. prof. GEOL, Arkansas, 56-60, assoc. prof, 61-67; PROF, RUTGERS UNIV, 67- Attend. mem, 19th Int. Geol. Cong, Algiers. U.S.N, 44-46. Geol. Soc. Am; Paleont. Soc; Am. Asn. Petrol. Geol. Invertebrate paleontology; paleozoic and mesozoic cephalopoda; tertiary stratigraphy and structure of Ecuador; Andes mountain geomorphology and climatic sedimentation; global drainage developments; paleozoic stratigraphy of north Arkansas. Address: Dept. of Geology, Rutgers University, Newark, NJ 07102.

GARNER, JACKIE B(ASS), b. Jonesboro, La, Aug. 21, 34; m. 57; c. 2. MATHEMATICS. B.S, La. Polytech, 55; M.S, Auburn, 57, Ph.D.(math), 60. Instr. MATH, LA. TECH UNIV, 57-58, asst. prof, 60-62, assoc. prof, 62-65, PROF, 65- Nat. Sci. Found. res. grant, 63-64. Am. Math Soc; Math. Asn. Am. Ordinary and partial differential equations. Address: Dept. of Mathematics, Louisiana Tech University, Ruston, LA 71270.

GARNER, JAMES G(REGORY), b. Astoria, N.Y, Dec. 21, 38; m. 64; c. 2. CYTOGENETICS, MICROBIOLOGY. A.B, Providence Col, 60; M.S, Long Island, 63; Ph.D.(biol), St. John's (N.Y), 67. Teaching fel. BIOL, Long Island, 60-62; teaching asst, St. John's (N.Y), 62-65; instr, C.W. POST COL, L.I. UNIV, 65-67, asst. prof, 67-70, ASSOC. PROF, 70- Am. Soc. Microbiol; Am. Soc. Cell Biol. Cytogenetics, sex chromatin in vertebrates and invertebrates; microbiology action of plant hormones on bacteria. Address: Dept. of Biology, C.W. Post College, Long Island University, Greenvale, NY 11548.

GARNER, JAMES W(ILLIAM), b. Detroit, Mich, May 24, 26; m. 50; c. 5. CHEMICAL ENGINEERING. B.Ch.E, Detroit, 49. Chem. engr, Gage Prod. Co, 45-50; head control & develop. labs, Grow Solvent Co, Inc, 50-71, V.PRES. RES. & DEVELOP, GROW CHEM. CO, 71- Lectr, J. Berg Found, 58- Am. Chem. Soc; Instrument Soc. Am; Fedn. Socs. Paint Technol; Soc. Plastics Eng. Organic solvents and coatings. Address: Grow Chemical Co, 14100 Stansbury, Detroit, MI 48227.

GARNER, JASPER H(ENRY) B(ARKDOLL), b. Bulsar, India, Nov. 7, 21; U.S. citizen; m. 54; c. 1. MYCOLOGY. B.A, Manchester Col, 48; M.A, Indiana, 53; Ph.D.(bot), Iowa, 55. Asst. prof. bot, Nebraska, 55-56; instr, Kentucky, 56-57, asst. prof, 57-67; assoc. prof. biol, East. Tenn. State Univ, 67-69; res. assoc. plant path, N.C. State Univ, 69-71; BOTANIST, OFF. AIR PROGS, ENVIRON. PROTECTION AGENCY, 71- Univ. Ky-Int. Coop. Admin. Prog. vis. prof, col. agr. & vet. sci, Univ. Indonesia, 57-61. Mycol. Soc. Am; Bot. Soc. Am; Torrey Bot. Club; Am. Phytopath. Soc. Gasteromycetes; forest pathology; interrelationships between natural gas pollution of soil and death of woody plants. Address: Room K-210, Environmental Protection Agency, Research Triangle Park, NC 27711.

GARNER, JOHN H, b. Mullin, Tex, Apr. 22, 30; m. 50; c. 6. MATHEMATICS. B.S. & M.S, Tex. Tech. Col, 52. Instr, high sch, Reagan County, 54-56; MATH, Tyler Jr. Col, 56-63; ASSOC. PROF, TARLETON STATE COL, 63- U.S.A.F, 52-54, 1st Lt. Math. Asn. Am. Topology, paracompact spaces. Address: Dept. of Mathematics, Tarleton State College, Stephenville, TX 76401.

GARNER, LaFORREST D, b. Muskogee, Okla, Aug. 20, 33; m. 64; c. 3. ORTHODONTICS. D.D.S, Indiana, 57, M.S.D, 59, cert, 61. Asst. pedodontics, SCH. DENT, IND. UNIV, 57-58, res. asst, 58-59, instr. ORTHOD, 59-61, asst. prof, 61-67, ASSOC. PROF, 67-, CHMN. DEPT, 70- Am. Dent. Asn; Am. Asn. Orthod; Am. Soc. Dent. for Children; Int. Asn. Dent. Res; fel. Am. Col. Dent. Growth and development; posture of tongue in children with normal occlusions; cleft lip and palate rehabilitation; pedodontics. Address: School of Dentistry, Indiana University, 1121 W. Michigan St, Indianapolis, IN 46202.

GARNER, LYNN E, b. Ontario, Ore, July 19, 41; m. 60; c. 3. MATHEMATICS. B.S, Brigham Young, 62; M.S, Utah, 64; Danforth grant, Cornell, 66-67; Ph.D.(math), Oregon, 68. Instr. MATH, BRIGHAM YOUNG UNIV, 64-66, ASST. PROF, 68- Am. Math. Soc. Algebra; commutative algebra; projective and algebraic geometry. Address: Dept. of Mathematics, Brigham Young University, Provo, UT 84601.

GARNER, MERIDON VESTAL, b. Belton, Tex, Sept. 20, 28; m. 56; c. 3. MATHEMATICS. M.Ed, Sul Ross State Col, 56; Texas A&M, 56-63; Tex. Tech. Col, 57; Univ. Tex, Austin, 59; Ed.D, North Texas State, 63. Assoc. prof. MATH, Sul Ross State Col, 56-63; asst. prof, N.TEX. STATE UNIV, 63-69, ASSOC. PROF, 69- U.S.M.C, 46-48, Res, 49-51. Math. Asn. Am.

Preparation of subject-content material in mathematics for future elementary teachers. Address: Dept. of Mathematics, North Texas State University, Denton, TX 76203.

GARNER, NORMAN R(OBERT), b. Sarahsville, Ohio, July 14, 23; m. 45; c. 3. STATISTICS. B.A, Rochester, 49; M.S, North Carolina, 51; M.S, N.C. State Col, 51. Asst. instrumentation errors, N.C. State Col, 50-51; chief qual. assurance dept, Gen. Testing Lab, U.S. Govt, Pa, 51-53; asst. to chief statistician & consult. statistician, Thiokol Chem. Corp, Ala, 53-55; consult. statistician qual. surveillance, U.S. Naval Powder Factory, 55-57; tech. specialist, Aerojet-Gen. Corp, Div, Gen. Tire & Rubber Co, 57-65; HEAD STATIST. ANAL. SECT, RELIABILITY ASSURANCE DIV, POWER SYSTS. DIV, TRW SYSTS, INC, 65- U.S.A.A.F, 42-45. Am. Soc. Qual. Control. Statistics in research; quality control; decision and cost functions. Address: 17516 La Bonita Way, Cerritos, CA 90701.

GARNER, R(AYMOND) L(ORAINE), b. Louisiana, Mo, Mar. 5, 06; m. 33; c. 3. ORGANIC CHEMISTRY & BIOCHEMISTRY. A.B, Westminster Col.(Mo), 27; Chicago, 28-29; Ph.D.(biol. chem), Hopkins, 32. Teacher, pub. schs, Ill, 27-28; spec. chemist, U.S. Dept. Agr, Hopkins, 29-31, biochemist med, hosp, 32-35; assoc. prof. biochem. & biochemist, med. sch, Michigan, 35-56; PROF. BIOCHEM. & CHMN. DEPT, COL. MED. & DENT. N.J, NEWARK, 56-, ASSOC. DEAN SCH. DENT, 68-, asst. dean, 65-68. AAAS; Am. Chem. Soc; Am. Soc. Biol. Chem; Soc. Exp. Biol. & Med; N.Y. Acad. Sci; Brit. Biochem. Soc. Immunochemistry; protein metabolism; tissue metabolism of carbohydrate. Address: College of Medicine & Dentistry of New Jersey at Newark, Jersey City, NJ 07304.

GARNER, R(EUBEN) JOHN, b. Oundle, Eng, Feb. 4, 21; m. 42; c. 2. RADIOBIOLOGY, BIOCHEMISTRY. B.A, Cambridge, 42, M.A, 46; M.R.C.V.S, 45, F.R.C.V.S, 52; M.V.Sc, Liverpool, 52, D.V.Sc, 61; A.R.I.C, Royal Inst. Chem, 56; Churchill Found. fel, Royal Vet. Col, Denmark, 56. Vet. res. officer, Vet. Res. Lab, N.Nigeria, 46-50; lectr. vet. biochem, Liverpool, 50-53; sr. lectr. chem. path, Bristol, 53-56; head radiobiol. lab, inst. res. animal diseases, Agr. Res. Coun, U.K, 57-60; head pub. health sect, health & safety br, radiol. protection div, U.K. Atomic Energy Authority, 65; DIR. COLLAB. RADIOL. HEALTH LAB, COLO. STATE UNIV, 65- Consult, Food & Agr. Orgn. & Int. Atomic Energy Agency, 60-65. AAAS; Brit. Biochem. Soc; Radiation Res. Soc; Health Physics Soc; Brit. Inst. Biol; Brit. Vet. Asn; Brit. Asn. Vet. Teachers & Res. Workers. Fission-product metabolism and toxicity in farm animals; effects of early irradiation on development and aging. Address: Collaborative Radiological Health Lab, Colorado State University, Ft. Collins, CO 80521.

GARNER, RICHARD G(ORDON), b. Alto, Tenn, Feb. 16, 23; m. 47; c. 4. FOOD TECHNOLOGY. B.S. & M.S, Tennessee, 48; Ph.D.(food tech), Illinois, 53. Asst. lab. instr, food processing lab, Tennessee, 48; asst. gen. chemist, Tenn. Agr. Exp. Sta, 49-50; asst, Illinois, 51-53; assoc. food technologist, cent. labs, Gen. Foods Corp, 53-55; agr. adminr, State Exp. Sta. Div, Agr. Res. Serv, U.S. DEPT. AGR, 55-59, acting asst. dir. utilization div. and prin. food technologist, 59-62, dir. utilization div, COOP. STATE RES. SERV, 63-71, DIR. FOOD SCI. PROGS, 71- U.S. Dept. Agr. Superior Serv. Award, 70. U.S.A.A.F, 42-46. AAAS; Inst. Food Technol; Poultry Sci. Asn. Chemistry of foods; food quality, freezing; canning and dehydration of foods; food product and process development; research administration. Address: Cooperative State Research Service, U.S. Dept. of Agriculture, Washington, DC 20250.

GARNER, RICHARD LEWIS, b. Nacogdoches, Tex, Nov. 1, 38; m. 62; c. 3. PHYSICAL CHEMISTRY. B.S, Stephen F. Austin State Univ, 60; M.S, Tex. Tech. Univ, 62, Welch Found. fel, 61-64, univ. scholar, summer 63, Ph.D. (chem), 65. Instr. CHEM, Panhandle State Col, 64-65; asst. prof, Wayland Baptist Col, 65-67, ASSOC. PROF, 67-68; HARDIN-SIMMONS UNIV, 68- Welch fel, Tex. Tech. Univ, summer, 65; Nat. Sci. Found. col. teacher res. partic, Ga. Inst. Technol, summer 68; Hardin-Simmons Univ, 68-70, Welch Found. grant 71- Am. Chem. Soc. Adsorption of gases on solids at low pressures; kinetics of solid state reactions. Address: Dept. of Chemistry, Hardin-Simmons University, Abilene, TX 79601.

GARNER, ROBERT H(ENRY), b. Mobile, Ala, Jan. 7, 33; m. 61; c. 3. CHEMISTRY. B.A, Vanderbilt, 54; Ph.D.(chem), Rice Inst, 58. Fel. CHEM, Yale, 58-59; asst. prof, UNIV. ALA, 59-68, ASSOC. PROF, 68- Am. Chem. Soc. Organic chemistry. Address: Dept. of Chemistry, Box H, University of Alabama, University, AL 35486.

GARNER, WILLIAM, b. Buffalo, N.Y, Dec. 15, 23; m. 47; c. 4. WATER CHEMISTRY. B.A, Buffalo, 49, M.A, 52, Ph.D.(chem), 59. Res. assoc. chem, Buffalo, 53-54; res. chemist, Allied Chem. Co, 54-55; asst. prof. pharmaceut. chem, Buffalo, 55-59, assoc. pediat, 59-61, asst. prof. biochem, 60-61; chief anal. chemist, John H. Breck, Inc, 61-62; assoc. prof. sanit. sci, New Mexico State, 62-66; PRIN. ENVIRON. SCIENTIST, MIDWEST RES. INST, 66- U.S.A.A.F, 42-46. Am. Water Works Asn; Water Pollution Control Fedn; Am. Chem. Soc. Uric acid metabolism; cancer chemotherapy; enzymology; detection of environmental contaminants; technology of water and wastewater processing. Address: Midwest Research Institute, 425 Volker Blvd, Kansas City, MO 64110.

GARNER, WILLIAM E(VERETTE), b. Washington, D.C, July 19, 23; m. 51; c. 2. ELECTRONIC ENGINEERING. B.E.E, Catholic Univ, 44. Electronic engr, radio frequency interference, U.S. NAVAL RES. LAB, D.C, 44-49, electronic scientist, 49-50, radio propagation, 50-58, electronic engr. & sect. head, 58-67, HEAD ELECTROMAGNETIC PROPAGATION BR, 67- Head, U.S. Navy Very Low Frequency Propagation Center, 62- U.S.N.R, 44-45, Ens. Inst. Elec. & Electronics Eng; Sci. Res. Soc. Am. Tropospheric propagation; electromagnetic wave propagation; radio communications. Address: 9609 McAlpine Rd, Silver Spring, MD 20901.

GARNER, WILLIAM V(AUGHN), b. Hartford, Conn, Aug. 1, 23; m. 50; c. 2. ENTOMOLOGY. B.S, Ursinus Col, 47; M.A, Boston, 48; M.S, Pa. State Col, 49; Ph.D.(entom), California, 54. Asst. prof. entom, Iowa State Col, 54-57; from asst. prof. to PROF. BIOL. & CHMN. DEPT, MONMOUTH COL.(N.J), 57- U.S.N, 42-46. AAAS; Entom. Soc. Am; Soc. Syst. Zool; Soc. Study Evolution; Am. Soc. Zool. Systematic entomology; taxonomy and biology of coleopterous larvae. Address: Dept. of Biology, Monmouth College, West Long Branch, NJ 07764.

GARNET, HYMAN, b. Brooklyn, N.Y, Apr. 4, 20; m. 44; c. 2. APPLIED MECHANICS & MATHEMATICS. B.S, N.Y. Univ, 51; M.A, Columbia, 52; Ph.D.(appl. mech), Polytech. Inst. Brooklyn, 62. Struct. engr, Repub. Aviation Corp, N.Y, 52-57; mech. engr, mat. lab, Brooklyn Navy Yard, 57-58; struct. engr, GRUMMAN AIRCRAFT ENG. CORP, 58-59, RES. SCIENTIST, 59- Lectr, dept. eng. sci, Hofstra Univ, 65- U.S.A, 43-45. Am. Soc. Mech. Eng; Am. Acad. Mech. Solid mechanics; statics and dynamics of shells; stress wave propagation. Address: Research Dept, Grumman Aircraft Engineering Corp, Plant 35, Bethpage, L.I, NY 11714.

GARNETT, RICHARD WINGFIELD, JR, b. Albemarle Co, Va, Mar. 27, 15; m. 41; c. 5. PSYCHIATRY. B.S, Virginia, 36, M.D, 40, M.S, 49. Asst. prof. NEUROL. & PSYCHIAT, SCH. MED, UNIV. VA, 49-52, assoc. prof, 52-57, PROF, 57-, acting chmn. dept, 55-57, 63-64. WHO fel. community psychiat, Gt. Brit. & West. Europe, 63; mem. sr. faculty seminars, Harvard Med. Sch, 65-67. Consult, Vet. Admin. Med.C, 41-47, Comdr. Fel, Am. Psychiat. Asn; Am. Med. Asn. Psychosomatic medicine; academic and community psychiatry. Address: Dept. of Psychiatry, School of Medicine, University of Virginia, Charlottesville, VA 22901.

GARNIER, B(ENJAMIN) J(OHN), b. China, Apr. 6, 17; m. 56; c. 1. GEOGRAPHY. B.A, Cambridge, 39, M.A, 43. Chmn. dept. GEOG, Otago, N.Z, 46-51; Ibadan, Nigeria, 51-61; prof, Indiana, 62-66; PROF, McGILL UNIV, 67- Am. Meteorol. Soc; Am. Geog. Soc; Asn. Am. Geog; Am. Geophys. Union; Royal Meteorol. Soc; Royal Geog. Soc. Climatology, particularly with reference to radiation and surface energy budgets and their ecological applications. Address: Dept. of Geography, McGill University, Montreal, Que, Can.

GARNJOST, MARGARET ALSTON, b. Ashtead, Eng, Jan. 23, 29; m. 66. PHYSICS. B.Sc, Liverpool, 51, Hons, 52, Ph.D.(physics), 55. Demonstrator physics, Univ. Liverpool, 54-56, Imp. Chem. Industs. res. fel, 56-58; PHYSICIST, LAWRENCE RADIATION LAB, UNIV. CALIF, 59- Am. Phys. Soc. High energy particle physics. Address: Lawrence Radiation Lab, University of California, Berkeley, CA 94720.

GARNSEY, STEPHEN M(ICHAEL), b. Oceanside, Calif, Aug. 3, 37; m. 58; c. 2. PLANT PATHOLOGY. B.A, California, Riverside, 58, Ph.D.(plant path), Davis, 64. Lab. technician plant path, California, Riverside, 58-59, res. asst, Davis, 59-63; RES. PLANT PATHOLOGIST, PLANT SCI. RES. DIV, U.S. DEPT. AGR, 63- Assoc. prof, Univ. Fla, 69- AAAS; Am. Phytopath. Soc. Mechanical transmission and purification of plant viruses; identification and properties of citrus viruses; development of virus tolerant citrus rootstocks. Address: Plant Science Research Division, U.S. Dept. of Agriculture, 2120 Camden Rd, Orlando, FL 32803.

GAROFALO, F(RANK), b. Italy, Apr. 8, 21; nat; m. 42; c. 3. METALLURGY. B.S, Pa. State, 43, U.S. Steel Corp. fel, 46-48, Ph.D.(metall), 49. Asst, res. lab, Carnegie Inst. Tech, 44-45; Pa. State, 45-46; res. metallurgist, res. lab, U.S. Steel Corp, 48-56, head, mech. metall. sect, Edgar C. Bain Res. Lab, 56-65; asst. mgr. res. ctr, INLAND STEEL CO, 65-67, ASSOC. MGR. RES. DEPT, 67- Am. Soc. Metals; Soc. Exp. Stress Anal; Am. Inst. Mining, Metall. & Petrol. Eng. Elasticity; plasticity; fracture; creep; creep rupture. Address: Research Dept, Inland Steel Research Labs, 3001 E. Columbus Dr, East Chicago, IN 46312.

GAROIAN, GEORGE, b. Deadwood, S.Dak, July 23, 27; m. 54; c. 2. PARASITOLOGY. A.B, Washington (St. Louis), 49; M.S, Illinois, 51, Ph.D.(zool), 56. Asst. zool, Illinois, 49-55, vet. med, 55-56; asst. prof. ZOOL, SOUTH. ILL. UNIV, 56-64, ASSOC. PROF, 64-, ACTING CHMN. DEPT, 71-, asst. chmn. dept, 58-61. U.S.N.R, 45-46. Am. Soc. Parasitol; Soc. Protozool; Am. Soc. Zool. Helminthology. Address: Dept. of Zoology, Southern Illinois University, Carbondale, IL 62901.

GARON, OLIVIER, b. Quebec, Que, Jan. 24, 28; m. 55; c. 2. COMPARATIVE ANATOMY. B.A, Laval, 50; D.M.V, Montreal, 55, M.Sc, 61, Ph.D, 64. PROF. ANAT. & BIOL, SCH. VET. MED, UNIV. MONTREAL, 57-, HEAD DEPT. BASIC SCI, 61- Domestic and wild animals. Address: Dept. of Anatomy & Biology, University of Montreal School of Veterinary Medicine, St. Hyacinthe, Que, Can.

GARONO, LOUIS E(DWARD), b. Buffalo, N.Y, Apr. 23, 11; m. 51; c. 5. CHEMICAL ENGINEERING. B.S, Mass. Inst. Tech, 35, M.S, 36; Pennsylvania, 36-39. Instrument supt, E.I. du Pont de Nemours & Co, 36-42; chief engr, Chem. Warfare Serv, Pine Bluff Arsenal, 42-45; eng. supt, Atlantic Gelatin Div, Gen. Foods Corp, 45-51; chief engr, chem. corps eng. agency, U.S. ARMY CHEM. CENTER, 51-65, dir. eng. & indust. servs, EDGEWOOD ARSENAL, 65-66, CHIEF ENGR, tech. support directorate, 66-71, DEVELOP. & ENG, 71- Lectr, Northeast. Univ, 50-51. Exceptional civilian award, U.S. War Dept, 44. Am. Chem. Soc; Am. Inst. Chem. Eng; Instrument Soc. Am; Am. Ord. Asn. Personnel utilization and management; drying of heavy leathers; separation of barytes from drilling muds; continuous extraction and purification of gelatin. Address: Directorate, U.S. Army, Edgewood Arsenal, MD 21010.

GAROUTTE, BILL (CHARLES), b. Absarokee, Mont, Mar. 15, 21; m. 48; c. 4. NEUROPHYSIOLOGY. A.B, Univ. Calif, 43, M.D, 45, Ph.D.(biophys), 54. Intern, San Diego County Hosp, 45-46; asst. resident neurol, Univ. Hosp, UNIV. CALIF, SAN FRANCISCO, 48, 51-52, from lectr. to assoc. prof. ANAT. & NEUROL, 49-66, PROF, 66- Fulbright scholar, Inst. Neurol, London, 50-51; vis. asst. prof, faculty med, Univ. Indonesia, 56-57; vis. investr, Inst. Brain Res, Tokyo, 63. Med.C, 46-47, Lt.(jg). AAAS; Am. Epilepsy Soc; Am. Electroencephalog. Soc; Am. Med. Soc; Am. Asn. Anat; Am. Acad. Neurol; Royal Soc. Med. Function of the nervous system. Address: Dept. of Anatomy, University of California, San Francisco, CA 94122.

GARR, CARL ROBERT, b. Olean, N.Y, Apr. 4, 27; m. 47; c. 3. PHYSICAL METALLURGY. B.S, Kent State, 50; M.S, Case 53, Ph.D.(metall), 57. Sr.

engr, Bettis Plant, Westinghouse Elec. Corp, 56-58; supt. tech. serv, Olin Mathieson Chem. Corp. 58-62; dir. appl. res. & develop, Albuquerque Div, ACF Industs, Inc, 62-66, dir. eng, N.Mex, 66-68, v.pres, 68-70; PRES, POLYMER CORP, 70- U.S.N. 44-46. Am. Soc. Metals; Am. Inst. Mining, Metall. & Petrol. Eng; Soc. Plastics Indust; Newcomen Soc. Materials research in both metals and nonmetals; development of fabrication processes and testing techniques for both metal and plastic products, largely for nuclear reactor components. Address: Polymer Corp, 2120 Fairmont Ave, Reading, PA 19603.

GARRARD, STERLING D(AVIS), b. Chicago, Ill, Nov. 10, 19; m. 45; c. 3. PEDIATRICS. M.D, Illinois, 45, B.S. 48. Instr. PEDIAT, col. med, Illinois, 50-52; asst. prof, STATE UNIV. N.Y. UPSTATE MED. CTR, 55-62, assoc. prof, 62-65, PROF, 65-, acting chmn. dept, 65-68. Mem. ment. hyg. coun, N.Y. State Dept. Ment Hyg. U.S.A. 43-45, Med.C, 46-48. AAAS; fel. Am. Asn. Ment. Deficiency; Am. Acad. Pediat; Am. Pediat. Soc; Soc. Res. Child Develop; N.Y. Acad. Sci; Am. Pub. Health Asn. Mental retardation. Address: Dept. of Pediatrics, State University of New York Upstate Medical Center, Syracuse, NY 13210.

GARRARD, VERL G(RADY), b. Burley, Idaho, July 21, 23; m. 62; c. 3. PHYSICAL & ANALYTICAL CHEMISTRY. B.S, Univ. Idaho, 45, M.S, 52; Ph.D, Univ. Utah, 67. Instr. CHEM, UNIV. IDAHO, 47-54, asst. prof, 54-70, ASSOC. PROF. 70- U.S.N. 44-46. AAAS; Am. Chem. Soc. Chemical kinetics. Address: Dept. of Chemistry, University of Idaho, Moscow, ID 83843.

GARRARD, W(ILFRED) C(HARLES) J(AMES), b. Sanderstead, Eng, Oct. 29, 17; m. 57; c. 3. AERONAUTICS. B.Sc, London, 39, Ph.D.(aerodyn), 41. Res. engr, Handley Page, Ltd, Eng, 41-45; sr. aerodynamicist, Gloster Aircraft Co, Ltd, England, 45-46; chief aerodynamicist, Cunliffe-Owen Aircraft, Ltd, Eng, 46-47; sr. aerodynamicist, Saunders-Roe, Ltd, Eng, 48; sales engr, Canadair, Ltd, Can, 48-51; sr. aerodyn. engr, Chance-Vought Aircraft Corp, Tex, 51-54; div. engr, preliminary design, Lockheed Aircraft Corp, 54-68, chief preliminary design engr, LOCKHEED GA. CO, 68-71, PRELIMINARY DESIGN ENGR, 71- Wright Brothers Medal, 65. Am. Inst. Aeronaut. & Astronaut. Vertical and short takeoff and landing aircraft; subsonic airplane design; automobile design. Address: Dept. 72-09 Z455, Lockheed Georgia Co, 86 S. Cobb Dr, Marietta, GA 30060.

GARRARD, WILLIAM LASH, JR, b. Waco, Tex, Nov. 7, 40; m. 65. ENGINEERING MECHANICS. B.S, Texas, 62, Ph.D.(eng. mech), 68. ASST. PROF. AERONAUT. & ENG. MECH, UNIV. MINN, MINNEAPOLIS, 68- Nat. Sci. Found. grant, 68-69. Inst. Elec. & Electronic Eng. Control theory; stability and control of dynamical systems. Address: Dept. of Aeronautics, University of Minnesota, Minneapolis, MN 55455.

GARRATT, GEORGE A(LFRED), b. Brooklyn, N.Y, May 7, 98; m. 22; c. 2. FORESTRY. B.S, Mich. State Col, 20, M.F, Yale, 23, Ph.D.(forestry), 33; D.Sc, Univ. of the South, 57. Instr. forestry, Mich. State Col, 20-22; prof. forestry & eng, Univ. of the South, 23-25; asst. prof. forest prods, sch. forestry, YALE, 25-31, assoc. prof, 31-39, mfrs. asn. prof. lumbering, 39-55, Pinchot prof. forestry, 55-66, EMER. PINCHOT PROF. FORESTRY, 66-, EMER. DEAN, SCH. FORESTRY, 65-, asst. dean, 36-39, dean, 45-65. Chief div. tech. serv. training, forest prod. lab, U.S. Forest Serv, 42-45; dir. packaging training ctr, Transportation Corps, U.S. Army, France, 45; chmn, Conn. State Park & Forest Comn, 51-71; mem, nat. forestry res. adv. comt, U.S. Dept. Agr, 58-64; chmn, Conn. Coun. Agr. & Natural Resources, 61-65; dir, Found. Prof. Forestry, 63-71; chmn, 69-71; dir, Can. Forestry Educ. Study, 65-71; educ. consult, self-employed, 66- Am. Forest Prod. Industs. distinguished serv. award, 67. Fel. Soc. Am. Foresters (v.pres, 56-57, pres, 58-59; Schlich Medal, 66); Forest Prod. Res. Soc.(v.pres, 47, pres, 48); Forest Hist. Soc.(v.pres, 69-70, pres, 70-72); Am. Forestry Asn. Wood technology and preservation. Address: 421 Ridge Rd, Hamden, CT 06517.

GARRAWAY, MICHAEL OLIVER, b. Roseau, Dominica, Brit. W.I, Apr. 29, 34; U.S. citizen; m. 66; c. 2. PLANT PATHOLOGY. B.Sc, McGill, 59, M.Sc, 62; Ph.D.(plant path), California, Berkeley, 66. Asst. res. plant pathologist, California, Berkeley, 66-68; asst. prof. BOT. PLANT PATH, Ohio State Univ, 68-71, ASSOC. PROF, OHIO STATE UNIV. & OHIO AGR. RES. & DEVELOP. CTR, 71- Fred C. Gloeckner Found. Inc. res. grant, diseases of ornamentals. AAAS; Am. Phytopath. Soc; Am. Inst. Biol. Sci; Can. Phytopath. Soc; Int. Soc. Plant Path. Relation of nutrition to rhizomorph initiation and growth in Armillaria mellea (Vahl) Quel; nutritional and environmental factors affecting fungal spore germination and growth; influence of plant nutrition on disease susceptibility. Address: Dept. of Plant Pathology, Ohio State University, Botany & Zoology Bldg, 1735 Neil Ave, Columbus, OH 43210.

GARRELL, MARTIN HENRY, b. Brooklyn, N.Y, Jan. 4, 39; m. 65. ENVIRONMENTAL PHYSICS. A.B, Princeton, 60; Nat. Sci. Found. fel, Univ. Ill, 60-61, M.S, 62, Ph.D.(physics), 66. Volkswagen Found. res. fel. PHYSICS, Deutsches Elektronen Synchrotron, 66-68; vis. asst. prof, Univ. Ill, Chicago Circle, 68-70; ASST. PROF, ADELPHI UNIV, 70- Am. Phys. Soc. Molecular physics; high energy physics; population models; air, water and pesticides pollution. Address: Dept. of Physics, College of Arts & Sciences, Adelphi University, Garden City, L.I, NY 11530.

GARRELS, ROBERT M(INARD), b. Detroit, Mich, Aug. 24, 16; m. 40, 70; c. 3. GEOCHEMISTRY. B.S, Michigan, 37; fel, Northwestern, 38, 39, M.S, 39, Ph.D.(geol), 41; hon. D.Sc, Univ. Brussels, 69. Dept. asst, Northwestern, 37, 40, instr. geol, 41-44, asst. prof, 44, 45-47, assoc. prof, 48-52; assoc. geologist, U.S. Geol. Surv, 44-45, geologist, 52-55; assoc. prof. geol, Harvard, 55-57, prof, 57-65, chmn. dept, 63-65; prof, Northwest. Univ, 65-69; Scripps Inst. Oceanog, 69-71; CAPT. JAMES COOK PROF. OCEANOG, UNIV. HAWAII, 72- Henri Speciael chair appl. sci, Univ. Brussels, 62-63; mem, Int. Comt. Electrochem. Thermodyn. & Kinetics, 62-63. Nat. Acad. Sci; fel. Geol. Soc. Am; Soc. Econ. Geol; fel. Am. Mineral. Soc; Am. Acad. Arts & Sci; Geochem. Soc.(pres, 62); Am. Chem. Soc. Crystallization of minerals; reactions among minerals; ionic diffusion through rocks; electrode techniques; chemistry of seawater; geochemistry of sediments. Address: Dept. of Oceanography, University of Hawaii, Honolulu, HI 96822.

GARRELTS, JEWELL MILAN, b. McPherson, Kans, Oct. 25, 03; m. 24; c. 3. CIVIL ENGINEERING. B.S, Valparaiso, 24; M.S, Columbia, 33. Draftsman, Ill. Steel Co, 24-25; instr. struct. eng, Cornell, 25-27; mech, COLUMBIA UNIV, 27-38, asst. prof. civil eng, 38-39, assoc. prof, 39-46, prof. & exec. off. dept, 46-57, PROF. ENG, CHMN. DEPT. & ASSOC. DEAN COL. ENG, 57- Assoc. engr, Hardesty & Hanover, N.Y, 36-51; consult. engr, 51- AAAS; Am. Soc. Eng. Educ; Am. Soc. Civil Eng; Am. Concrete Inst; Int. Asn. Asn. Bridge & Struct. Eng. Structural engineering and design. Address: Dept. of Engineering, Room 610, S.W. Mudd Bldg, Columbia University, New York, NY 10027.

GARREN, HENRY W(ILBURN), b. Hendersonville, N.C, Apr. 2, 25; m. 46; c. 2. PHYSIOLOGY, ENDOCRINOLOGY. A.B, North Carolina, 47, B.S. 49; M.S, Maryland, 51, Ph.D.(physiol), 53. Asst, Maryland, 49-52; physiologist, med. labs, Army Chem. Ctr, Md, 52-53; assoc. prof. endocrinol, N.C. State, 53-60, prof. poultry sci. & head dept, 60-68; DEAN & COORD, COL. AGR, UNIV. GA, 68- Poultry sci. res. award, 53. U.S.N.R. 43-46, Lt.(jg). Am. Physiol. Soc; Poultry Sci. Asn; Soc. Exp. Biol. & Med. Physiological response of animals to various stress stimuli, including disease, and conditions, nutritional and otherwise, affecting this response. Address: 100 Conner Hall, College of Agriculture, University of Georgia, Athens, GA 30601.

GARREN, KENNETH H(OWARD), b. Asheville, N.C, Nov. 26, 12; m. 45; c. 1. PLANT PATHOLOGY. A.B, Duke, 34, fel, 35-38, M.A, 37, Ph.D.(forest path), 38. Asst. prof. biol, Ala. State Teachers Col, Jacksonville, 38-41; assoc. botanist, exp. sta, Georgia, 41-42, 45-47; assoc. prof. bot, Ala. Polytech, 47-54; plant pathologist, U.S. Overseas Mission, El Salvador, 54-55; PLANT SCI. RES. DIV, AGR. RES. SERV, U.S. DEPT. AGR, 55-64, PROJ. LEADER, 64- Plant pathologist, Spec. U.S. Agency Int. Develop. Mission, W.Pakistan; 71- U.S.N, 42-45, Res, Lt.(Ret). Am. Phytopath. Soc. Peanut diseases; microbiology of peanut fruit; ecology of soil fungi. Address: Tidewater Research Station, Holland, VA 23391.

GARREN, LEONARD DAVID, b. N.Y.C, Sept. 14, 28; m. 56; c. 2. MEDICINE, ENDOCRINOLOGY. B.S, City Col. New York, 48; M.S, Wisconsin, 50; D.M.D, Harvard, 54, M.D, 56. Teaching asst. zool, Wisconsin, 49-50; intern med, Duke, 56-57; asst. resident, Mass. Mem. Hosp, 57-58; clin. assoc, Nat. Insts. Health, 58-60; asst, Peter Bent Brigham Hosp, Harvard, 60-61; asst. resident, Mass. Gen. Hosp, 61-62; adv. fel. molecular biol, Nat. Inst. Health, 62-64, sr. investr. exp. endocrinol, 64-66; assoc. prof. med, Yale, 66-68; PROF. MED. & DIR. DIV. ENDOCRINOL, SCH. MED, UNIV. CALIF, SAN DIEGO, 68- U.S.P.H.S, 58-60, Surg. Am. Fedn. Clin. Res; Am. Soc. Clin. Invest; Endocrine Soc; Am. Soc. Biol. Chem. Mechanism of action of hormones. Address: Dept. of Medicine, School of Medicine, University of California at San Diego, La Jolla, CA 92037.

GARREN, RALPH, JR, b. Rutland, Iowa, June 10, 21; m. 42; c. 3. HORTICULTURE. B.S, Ore. State Col, 50, M.S, 54; Ph.D, Purdue, 61. Asst, ORE. STATE UNIV, 50-51, res. asst. & instr. HORT, 51-57, asst. prof, 57-62, ASSOC. PROF, 62-, EXTEN. SPECIALIST SMALL FRUITS, 70- Res. found. fel, Purdue, 57-59. C.Eng, U.S.A, 39-46. Am. Soc. Hort. Sci; Int. Soc. Hort. Sci. Small fruits physiology and production problems. Address: Dept. of Horticulture, Oregon State University, Corvallis, OR 97331.

GARRET, MARTA, b. Rzeszow, Poland, Oct. 27, 16; U.S. citizen; m. 39. MEDICINE, PATHOLOGY. M.D, Univ. J. Kazimierz, Poland, 40. Am. Cancer Soc. fel, 56-57; dir. cytol. lab, Kings County Hosp. Ctr, 57-67; HEAD CYTOPATH. LAB, STATE UNIV. N.Y. HOSP, 67-, ASSOC. PROF. PATH, COL. MED, STATE UNIV. N.Y. DOWNSTATE MED. CTR, 67-, asst. prof, 60-67. Spec. consult, Nat. Cancer Inst, 60-62; chief investr, Nat. Cancer Inst. grant, 61-65. Dipl. Am. Bd. Path, 55. Am. Med. Asn; fel. Col. Am. Path; Am. Soc. Cytol. Early detection of cancer; experimental pathology in carcinogenesis. Address: Dept. of Pathology, State University of New York Downstate Medical Center, 450 Clarkson Ave, Brooklyn, NY 11203.

GARRET, RUDOLPH, b. Lvov, Poland, May 29, 14; U.S. citizen; m. 39. PATHOLOGY. Poitiers, 32-33; M.D, Univ. Stefana Batorego Wydzial Lekarski, Poland, 39. Assoc. pathologist, St. Luke's Hosp, New York, 54-60; CHIEF DEPT. PATH, ROOSEVELT HOSP, 60-; PROF. PATH, COL. PHYSICIANS & SURGEONS, COLUMBIA UNIV, 69-, asst. prof, 60-69. AAAS; fel. Am. Soc. Clin. Path; fel. Col. Am. Path. Address: Roosevelt Hospital; 428 W. 59th St, New York, NY 10019.

GARRETSON, CRAIG M(ARTIN), b. Glendale, N.Y, Sept. 14, 24; m. 49; c. 3. ELECTROPHYSICS. B.E.E, Cooper Union, 49; M.E.E, Polytech. Inst. Brooklyn, 53, Ph.D.(electrophys), 69. Jr. engr, power substa, N.Y.C. Bd. Transportation, 46-50; Nat. Union Radio Corp, 50-51; sr. engr, Sylvania Elec. Prod, 51-56; engr, Sperry Gyroscope Co, 56-63; asst. prof. PHYSICS & ENG, C.W. POST COL, L.I. UNIV, 63-69, ASSOC. PROF, 69-, COORD, DEPT. ENG. SCI, 66- U.S.M.C. 44-46. AAAS; Am. Asn. Physics Teachers; Am. Asn. Eng. Educ; Inst. Elec. & Electronics Eng. Electron devices; development of charged particle devices including mass spectrometers, beam deflection tubes, klystrons, and millimeter wavelength electron tubes. Address: Dept. of Physics & Engineering, C.W. Post College, Long Island University, Brookville, NY 11548.

GARRETSON, HAROLD H, b. Tacoma, Wash, Mar. 3, 11; m. 36; c. 3. CHEMISTRY. A.B, Whitman Col, 32; M.S, Washington (Seattle), 33, Ph.D.(chem), 40. Asst. prof. CHEM, Agr. & Mech. Col, Texas, 38-43; New Mexico, 43-45; PROF, LYNCHBURG COL, 45-, HEAD DEPT, 64- Consult, Oak Ridge Nat. Labs. Am. Chem. Soc. Thermodynamic ionization constants of sulfurous acid; electrometric titrations; stable isotope separations. Address: Dept. of Chemistry, Lynchburg College, Lynchburg, VA 24501.

GARRETT, ALFRED B(ENJAMIN), b. Glencoe, Ohio, June 28, 06; m. 34; c. 3. CHEMISTRY. B.S, Muskingum Col, 28, hon. D.Sc, 58; M.S, Ohio State, 31, Ph.D.(chem), 32; hon. D.Sc, Ohio Wesleyan, 62; Denison Univ, 66. Teacher, pub. sch, Pa, 28-29; asst. chem, Ohio State, 29-32; assoc. prof, Kent State Col, 32-35; instr, OHIO STATE UNIV, 35-37, asst. prof, 37-40, assoc. prof, 40-44, prof, 44-71, chmn. dept. chem, 58-62, v.pres. univ, 62-69, EMER. PROF. CHEM, 71- Governor's award, 64; Am. Chem. Soc. award, 64;

NASA Apollo 11 award, 70; Ohioana Award, 70. Nat. Sci. Teachers Asn. (pres, 69-70). Photovoltaic cells; ionic equilibria in solution; physical and organic chemistry; low temperature studies of electrolytes; alkyl derivatives of boron hydrides. Address: Dept. of Chemistry, 140 W. 18th Ave, Ohio State University, Columbus, OH 43210.

GARRETT, ARTHUR RANDOLPH, JR, b. Birmingham, Ala, Oct. 3, 39; m. 65. PLANT ECOLOGY. A.B, Ala. Col, 61; Woodrow Wilson & Nat. Sci. Found. fels, Georgia, 61, M.S, 63; Ph.D.(biol), Emory, 68. Res. assoc. radioecol, Emory, 65-66; ASST. PROF. BIOL, UNIV. S. ALA, 68- Chief plant invest. sect, Southeast. Radiol. Health Lab, U.S.P.H.S, 66-68, Lt. Comdr. Inst. Am. Biol. Sci. Structure, operation and maintenance of ecological systems; distribution and effect of environmental radioactivity; ecology of the Gulf Coast. Address: Dept. of Biological Sciences, University of South Alabama, Mobile, AL 36688.

GARRETT, BARRY B, b. Waco, Tex, Nov. 10, 35; m. 57; c. 2. PHYSICAL & INORGANIC CHEMISTRY. B.S, Texas, 59, M.A, 62, Ph.D.(chem), 63. Jr. chemist, Gen. Dynamics/Convair, 56-57; technician, Tex. Instruments Inc, 57-58; res. assoc. phys. chem, Illinois, 63-64; ASST. PROF. INORG. CHEM, FLA. STATE UNIV, 64- Am. Chem. Soc. Electron spin resonance and relaxation in solids and solution; theory of transition metal complexes; structure of solution. Address: Dept. of Chemistry, Florida State University, Tallahassee, FL 32306.

GARRETT, BERNARD R(OBERT), b. Brooklyn, N.Y, Feb. 23, 26; m. 50; c. 2. ELECTRONIC ENGINEERING. B.S, N.Y. Univ, 48. Proj. engr, Reeves Instrument Corp, 48-53; dir. eng, Sterling Precision Instrument Corp, 53-55; sr. staff engr, Am. Bosch Arma Corp, 55-57; dir. eng, Loral Electronics Corp, 57-60, v.pres. eng, 60-64; INSTRUMENT SYSTS. CORP, 64-69, EXEC. V.PRES, 69- U.S.A, 43-45. Inst. Elec. & Electronics Eng; N.Y. Acad. Sci. Radar tracking systems; missile guidance; microwave antenna systems; video mapping; airborne anti-submarine warfare systems; receiving systems for electronic countermeasures; multiplexing systems for aircraft passenger entertainment and service; multiplexing telephone communications. Address: Instrument Systems Corp, 410 Jericho Turnpike, Jericho, NY 11753.

GARRETT, BEVERLEY ROSS, b. Woodlawn, Pa, Sept. 30, 20; m. 44; c. 3. ORGANIC & POLYMER CHEMISTRY. B.A, Montana State, 47; M.S, Syracuse, 49; Ph.D.(org. chem), Delaware, 59. Res. chemist, paint div, Pittsburgh Plate Glass Co, Wis, 51-52; Am. Viscose Corp, Pa, 52-55; polychem. div, Budd Co, Del, 55-59, res. group leader, 60-62, mgr. polymer res, 62-64; mgr. mat. & polymer res, Hexcel Prod, Inc, Calif, 64-70; mgr. prod. & process develop, res. & develop. div, Whittaker Corp, 70-71; PRES, GARRETT SYSTS, 71- Res. Corp. fel. U.S.A.F, 43-46, Res, 46-, Maj. Am. Chem. Soc. Metal bonding and structural applications; plastics, adhesives, prepregs and heat resistant polymers; honeycomb structures; ionic and free radical polymerization; carbon and graphite reinforced composites; electronic and technical ceramics, capacitors. Address: Garrett Systems, 5980 La Jolla Corona Dr, La Jolla, CA 92037.

GARRETT, BOWMAN S(TAPLES), b. Baton Rouge, La, July 8, 22; m. 44; c. 3. PHYSICAL CHEMISTRY. B.S, Louisiana, 40, M.S, 42; Oak Ridge Inst. Nuclear Studies fel, Oak Ridge Nat. Lab, 53; Ph.D, Arkansas, 54. Shift supvr, Flintkote Co, 42; control chemist, Esso Standard Oil Co, 43-45; staff engr, fuels lab, Socony-Vacuum Co, 45-49; asst. prof. chem, Arkansas, 50-52; sr. phys. chemist, ROHM & HAAS, 53-57, lab. head, 57-61, res. supvr, 61-66, ASST. DIR. RES, RES. DIV, 66- AAAS; Soc. Rheol; Am. Chem. Soc. Neutron diffraction; polymer physics; industrial polymer applications. Address: Research Division, Rohm & Haas, Spring House, PA 19477.

GARRETT, C(HARLES) G(EOFFREY) B(LYTHE), b. Ashford, Kent, England, Sept. 15, 25. PHYSICS. B.A, Cambridge, 46, Trinity Col. sr. scholar, 47, Twisden studentship of Trinity Col, 49, M.A, 50, Ph.D.(physics), 50. Asst. low temperature physics, Royal Soc. Mond Lab, Cambridge, 46-50; instr. physics, Harvard, 50-52; mem. tech. staff, BELL TEL. LABS, 52-60, head, optical electronics res. dept, 60-68, mat. sci. res. dept, 68-69, DIR. ELECTRON DEVICE PROCESS & BATTERY LAB, 69- Fel. Am. Phys. Soc. Solid state; optical masers; paramagnetics; surface physics. Address: 41 Elm St, Morristown, NJ 07960.

GARRETT, C(YRIL), b. Sutherland, Sask, May 1, 21; m. 45; c. 4. PHYSICS. B.Sc, Saskatchewan, 42, M.Sc, 47. Res. off, div. appl. physics, NAT. RES. COUN. CAN, 49-53, head x-rays & nuclear radiations, 53-69, DIV. ADMIN, SPEC. ASSIGNMENTS, 69- R.C.N, 43-45. Can. Asn. Physicists. Radiation and nuclear physics. Address: Division of Administration, Montreal Rd. Labs, National Research Council, Ottawa, Ont, Can.

GARRETT, DONALD E(VERETT), b. Long Beach, Calif, July 5, 23; m. 46; c. 4. CHEMICAL ENGINEERING. B.S, Univ. Calif, 47; M.S, Ohio State Univ, 48, Shell Oil Co. fel, 49-50, Ph.D.(chem. eng), 50. Asst. chem. eng, Ohio State Univ, 47-50; res. & develop. engr. & group leader, Dow Chem. Co, Calif, 50-52; Union Oil Co, 52-55; mgr. res, Am. Potash & Chem. Co, 55-60; pres, GARRETT RES. & DEVELOP. CO, 60-, EXEC. V.PRES. RES. & DEVELOP, OCCIDENTAL PETROL. CORP, 68- Pres, Assoc. Chem. Co, Calif, 60-64; mem. gen. tech. adv. comt, off. coal res, U.S. Dept. Interior. Kirkpatrick Chem. Plant achievement award, 61-62. C.Eng, U.S.A, 43-46. Am. Chem. Soc; Am. Inst. Chem. Eng. Inorganic chemistry; research management; crystallization; evaporation; saline mineral processing. Address: Occidental Petroleum Corp, 1855 Carrion Rd, La Verne, CA 91750.

GARRETT, EDGAR R(AY), b. Lordsburg, N.Mex, Aug. 14, 21; m. 42; c. 4. SPEECH PATHOLOGY. B.S, Western New Mexico, 42; Rockefeller fel, North Carolina, 46-48, M.A, 48; Ph.D.(speech path), Denver, 54. Instr. speech, N.MEX. STATE UNIV, 48-52, asst. prof, 52-57, assoc. prof, 57-63, prof. in charge speech & dir. speech & hearing ctr, 63-65, asst. dean col. arts & sci, 69-71, HEAD DEPT. SPEECH, 65- Res. automated speech correction systs. & prog. language for deaf, coop. res. br, U.S. Off. Educ, 64- U.S.A.F, 42-46, Maj. Fel. AAAS; Am. Speech & Hearing Asn.(Sci. Exhibit award, 63, 67). Speech pathology and audiology; psychology of learning; programmed instruction. Address: Dept. of Speech, New Mexico State University, Las Cruces, NM 88001.

GARRETT, EDWARD R(OBERT), b. New York, N.Y, Apr. 9, 20; m. 41; c. 3. PHYSICAL ORGANIC & PHARMACEUTICAL CHEMISTRY. B.S, Mich. State, 41, M.S, 48, Hinman fel, 49-50, Ph.D.(chem), 50. Asst. foreman heavy chem. prod, Gen. Chem. Co, 41; acid prod. & heavy chem, Keystone Ord. Works, 42; chem. process engr, Gen. Tire & Rubber Co, 43-45; asst. plant mgr, sulfuric acid prod, Stauffer Chem. Co, 45-46; asst, Mich. State, 46-49; sr. res. scientist, Upjohn Co, 50-61; GRAD. RES. PROF. PHARM, UNIV. FLA, 60- Vis. prof, Wisconsin, 59; pres, Latin-Am. Conf. Biochem. & Indust. Pharm, 62; vis. prof, Univ. Calif, 63; consult, Smith, Kline & French Co, 63-; vis. prof, Univ. Buenos Aires, 65; ed, Int. J. Clin. Pharmacol. Upjohn Award, 59; Ebert prize, 63; J.E. Purkyne Medal, Czech. Med. Soc, 72. AAAS; Am. Chem. Soc; N.Y. Acad. Sci; Am. Pharmaceut. Asn. (res. achievement award phys. pharmaceut. chem, 63, pharmaceut. anal. chem, 70); Am. Soc. Microbiol; hon. mem. Arg. Soc. Indust. Pharm. & Biochem; hon. mem. Chilean Soc. Indust. Pharm. & Biochem. Kinetics and mechanisms of reactions; prediction of stability of pharmaceuticals and antibiotics; pharmacokinetics of drug absorption, distribution and excretion in vivo; kinetic evaluation of antibiotic activity. Address: J. Hillis Miller Health Center, University of Florida College of Pharmacy, Gainesville, FL 32601.

GARRETT, FREDERIC D(AUGHERTY), b. Oil City, Pa, July 3, 11. ANATOMY. A.B, Cornell, 33, Ph.D, 39. Instr. ANAT, col. med, Nebraska, 39-48; asst. prof, col. med, Ohio State, 48-51; assoc. prof, sch. med, Miami (Fla), 52-66, PROF, 66-69; UNIV. B.C, 69- Teleostean endocrines; segmental innervation. Address: Dept. of Anatomy, University of British Columbia, Vancouver 8, B.C, Can.

GARRETT, G(EORGE) A(LVIN), b. Sardis, Miss, Nov. 29, 10; m. 34; c. 1. GEOPHYSICS, MATHEMATICS. B.A, Univ. Miss, 31; fel, Rice Univ, 31-35, M.A, 33, Ph.D.(math), 35. Geophys. comput. & seismologist, Independent Explor. Co, Tex, 35-39, party chief, 39-42; res. assoc, radiation lab, Mass. Inst. Technol, 42-45; sr. admin. physicist & head theoret. anal. dept, gas diffusion plant, Carbide & Carbon Chem. Co, 46-50, chief res. scientist, 50-54, supt. opers. anal. div, Union Carbide Nuclear Co. Div, Union Carbide Corp, 54-62; dir. info. processing, Lockheed Missiles & Space Co, Calif, 62-69; SR. CONSULT, NUCLEAR DIV, UNION CARBIDE CORP, 69- Res. assoc, Oak Ridge Inst. Nuclear Studies. With Off. Sci. Res. & Develop, 44. AAAS; Sci. Res. Soc. Am; Soc. Explor. Geophys; Am. Phys. Soc; Am. Math. Soc; Asn. Comput. Mach. Potential theory; metric geometry; isotope separation; radar scanning system; data processing. Address: A.E.C.O.P, Nuclear Division, Union Carbide Corp, P.O. Box S, Oak Ridge, TN 37830.

GARRETT, HOWARD L(EE), b. Porterville, Calif, Sept. 8, 24; m. 49; c. 2. GEOLOGY, ENGINEERING. G.E, Colo. Sch. Mines, 49, M.S, 50. Field geologist, SHELL OIL CO, 50-53, supvr. field crews, 53-57, field geologist, 57-62, expl. geochemist, Can, 62-70, REG. GEOLOGIST, 70- U.S.A.A.F, 43-45, 1st Lt. Am. Asn. Petrol. Geol; Geol. Soc. Am; Am. Inst. Prof. Geol; Am. Inst. Mining, Metall. & Petrol. Eng. Petroleum exploration in Rocky Mountains; geochemical exploration of Great Basin; aerial, structural, stratigraphic and historical geology and geochemistry. Address: 10925 W. 23rd Ave, Lakewood, CO 80215.

GARRETT, J. MARSHALL, b. Cleveland, Tenn, Nov. 18, 32; m. 54; c. 2. GASTROENTEROLOGY, INTERNAL MEDICINE. A.B, Chattanooga, 56; M.D, Tennessee, 58; M.S, Minnesota, 64. Intern med, John Gaston Hosp, Memphis, Tenn, 59; staff physician, United Mine Workers Hosp, Wise, Va, 60; res. internal med, Mayo Found, 60-63, fel. gastroenterol, Mayo Clin, 63-64; chief gastroenterol, Vet. Admin. Hosp, 64-70, chief of staff, 69-70; DIR. GASTROENTEROL. DEPT, ST. VINCENT'S HOSP, 70-; CLIN. ASSOC. PROF. MED, MED. CTR, UNIV. ALA, BIRMINGHAM, 70-, instr, 64-65, asst. prof, 65-68, assoc. prof, 68-70. Dipl. Am. Bd. Internal Med, 67. Hosp.C, U.S.N.R, 51-53. AAAS; Am. Med. Asn; Am. Fedn. Clin. Res; Am. Col. Physicians. Motility of the gastrointestinal tract. Address: 1023 S. 20th St, Birmingham, AL 35205.

GARRETT, JAMES M, b. Magnolia, Ark, Aug. 3, 41; m. 66; c. 3. ORGANIC CHEMISTRY. B.S, Arlington State Col, 63; Ph.D.(org. chem), Texas, 66. Fel, Florida, 66-67; asst. prof. CHEM, STEPHEN F. AUSTIN STATE UNIV, 67-71, ASSOC. PROF, 71- Am. Chem. Soc. Synthetic organic photochemistry; chemistry of small ring systems; stable boron cations. Address: Dept. of Chemistry, Stephen F. Austin State University, Box 3006, Stephen F. Austin Station, Nacogdoches, TX 75961.

GARRETT, JAMES R(ICHARD), b. Landrum, S.C, May 4, 17; m. 46; c. 3. MATHEMATICS. A.B, Lenoir-Rhyne Col, 40; B.S, Calif. Inst. Tech, 41, M.S, 52; A.M, Duke, 47, Ph.D.(math), 50. Asst. prof. math, Ga. Inst. Tech, 50-53, assoc. prof, 53-60, res. assoc, Rich Comput. Ctr, 58-60; mgr. math. serv, Radio Corp. Am. missile test proj, Patrick AFB, Fla, 60-67, MGR, DIAG. & TEST SYSTS, INFO. SYSTS. DIV, RCA CORP. 67- U.S.N.R, 41-46, Lt. Comdr. Am. Math. Soc; Math. Asn. Am; Asn. Comput. Mach; Soc. Indust. & Appl. Math. Satellite and missile orbits and trajectories; mathematical problems. Address: 245 Nicholson Dr, Moorestown, NJ 08057.

GARRETT, J(ERRY) D(ALE), b. Springfield, Mo, Oct. 1, 40; m. 65. EXPERIMENTAL NUCLEAR PHYSICS. B.S, Univ. Mo, Columbia, 62; M.S, Univ. Pa, 67, Ph.D.(physics), 70. RES. ASSOC. physics, tandem accelerator lab, Univ. Pa, 70-71; NUCLEAR PHYSICS, LOS ALAMOS SCI. LAB, 71- U.S.N, 62-66, Lt. AAAS; Am. Phys. Soc. Single-nucleon, two-nucleon, alpha-particle and heavy-ion transfer reactions. Address: P Division, Los Alamos Scientific Lab, P.O. Box 1663, Los Alamos, NM 87544.

GARRETT, J(ULIUS) B(ENJAMIN), JR, b. Calhoun, La, June 18, 13; m. 40; c. 3. STRATIGRAPHY, PALEONTOLOGY. B.S, La. State, 32, M.S, 33. Lab. asst, La. State, 33-34; micropaleontologist, United Gas Syst, Tex, 34-35; paleontologist, Stanolind Oil & Gas Co, 35-42, CHIEF PALEONTOLOGIST & SUPVR. PALEONT. LAB, 46-57, AMOCO PROD. CO, 57- U.S.A, 42-46. Soc. Econ. Paleont. & Mineral.(v.pres, 48); fel. Geol. Soc. Am; Am.

Asn. Petrol. Geol. Micropaleontology, lithology and stratigraphy of the Mesozoic and Cenozoic strata of the Gulf Coast area. Address: Amoco Production Co, P.O. Box 3092, Houston, TX 77001.

GARRETT, L(UTHER) W(EAVER), JR, b. Corsicana, Tex, Apr. 26, 25; m. 47; c. 2. CHEMICAL ENGINEERING. B.S, Texas, 47; Polytech. Inst. Brooklyn, 47. Chem. engr, M.W. Kellogg Co, 47-50, process design engr, & asst. to mgr. synthol div, 50-55, acting mgr. synthol. div, 56-58, chief oper. eng, 58-60, develop. eng, 60-62, mgr. iron & steel dept, 62-63; mgr, proj. dept, Swindell-Dressler Co, div. Pullman, Inc, 63-66, v.pres, equip. opers, 66-69; ENG. MGR, BECHTEL CORP, 69- U.S.N.R, 44-45. Am. Chem. Soc; Am. Inst. Chem. Eng; Am. Inst. Mining, Metall. & Petrol. Eng; fel. Am. Inst. Chem. Catalysis in the field of hydrocarbon synthesis; processing synthesis; processing synthetic hydrocarbon oils; ore reduction and metals processing. Address: Bechtel Corp, 50 Beale St, San Francisco, CA 94119.

GARRETT, MARION H, b. Centre, Ala, Jan. 6, 27; m. 50; c. 2. BIOLOGY. A.B, Huntingdon Col, 48; M.S, Alabama, 50, Ph.D.(anat, physiol, biochem), 62. Teacher, county sch. syst, Ala, 48-49, jr. high sch, 50-51; instr. sci. & biol, Howard Col, 54-57; asst. instr. biol, Yale, 62-63; res. assoc, Siena Col.(Tenn), 63-64, prof, 64-71. Grant, med. ctr, Univ. Tenn, 71-72. AAAS. Anatomy; histology; uptake of radioactive elements by microorganisms; autonomic nervous system in rhesus monkey; cutaneous sensory organs in bats; sinus hairs and genital corpuscles in mice; electron microscopy. Address: 3029 Flint Dr, Memphis, TN 38118.

GARRETT, REGINALD HOOKER, b. Roanoke, Va, Sept. 24, 39; m. 57; c. 3. BIOCHEMISTRY. B.S, Hopkins, 64, Nat. Insts. Health fel, 64-68, Ph.D. (biol), 68. Res. asst. biochem, McCollum-Pratt Inst, Hopkins, 56-64, fel, 68; ASST. PROF. BIOL, UNIV. VA, 68- Electron transport enzymes; enzymology of nitrate assimilation; chemical and physical properties of Neurospora crassa pyridine nucleotide nitrite reductase. Address: Dept. of Biology, University of Virginia, Charlottesville, VA 22903.

GARRETT, RICHARD E, b. Chester, Pa, Sept. 9, 33; m. 55; c. 2. MECHANICAL ENGINEERING. B.S.M.E, Delaware, 56; M.S.M.E, Florida, 63; Ford Found. fel, NASA fel, & Ph.D.(mech. eng), Purdue, 67. Develop. engr, Hamilton Standard Div, United Aircraft Corp, 56-59; asst. prof. MECH. ENG, Florida, 59-67; assoc. prof, PURDUE UNIV, 67-71, PROF, 71- Eng. consult, Midwest Appl. Sci. Corp, 66-68; consult. & mem. bd. dir, TecTran, Inc, 68- U.S.C.G.R, 56-58, Lt. Assoc. mem. Am. Soc. Mech. Eng; Soc. Exp. Stress Anal. Computer-aided design and computer graphics; optimization of mechanical devices; bio-medical engineering. Address: School of Mechanical Engineering, Purdue University, Lafayette, IN 47907.

GARRETT, RICHARD E(DWARD), b. Roanoke, Va, Feb. 17, 22; m. 47. NUCLEAR PHYSICS. B.S, Roanoke Col, 42; M.S, Ga. Inst. Tech, 50; du Pont sr. fel. & Ph.D.(nuclear physics), Virginia, 53. Instr. math. & physics, Roanoke Col, 42-43, 46-48; PHYSICS, Ga. Inst. Tech, 48-50; Virginia, 50-53, asst. prof, Hollins Col, 53-56, ASSOC. PROF, 56-63; UNIV. FLA, 63- Spec. instr, Newport News Shipbldg. & Drydock Co, summer 52; consult, radiation lab, Univ. Calif, 58-59; vis. lectr, Univ. Va, summer 60, res. assoc, 63; vis. lectr, Va. Polytech. Inst. & State Univ, 61. U.S.N.R, 43-46, Lt. AAAS; Am. Asn. Physics Teachers. Nature of nuclear emulsions, physical properties and their use in high energy particle physics; research in teaching - development of new material; lecture demonstrations and laboratory experiments. Address: Dept. of Physics, University of Florida, Gainesville, FL 32601.

GARRETT, ROBERT AUSTIN, b. Indianapolis, Ind, Jan. 25, 19; m. 46; c. 4. UROLOGY. A.B, Miami (Ohio), 40; M.D, Indiana, 43. Instr. UROL, MED. CTR, UNIV. IND, INDIANAPOLIS, 48-49, asst. prof, 49-51, assoc. prof, 51-54, PROF. & CHMN. DEPT, 54- Mem. staff, Vet. Admin. Hosp; Indianapolis Gen. Hosp; Indianapolis Methodist Hosp. U.S.A, 46. Am. Med. Asn; Am. Urol. Asn; Am. Col. Surg; Am. Asn. Genito-Urinary Surg. Pediatric urology. Address: Dept. of Urology, Medical Center, Indiana University, 1200 W. Michigan St, Indianapolis, IN 46202.

GARRETT, ROBERT L(EE), b. Bowden, Ga, Nov. 11, 03; m. 32; c. 1. MATHEMATICS. B.S, Georgia, 26; M.A, North Carolina, 30. Prof. math, Bowdon State Col, 26-29; fel, North Carolina, 30-31, instr, 31-37; prin, pub. sch, 39-40; prof. math. & physics, Pearl River Jr. Col, 41-43; MATH, Ark. Agr. & Mech. Col, 43-45; Mars Hill Col, 45-46; prof. & head dept, Athens Col, 46-51; head dept, pub. sch, Ga, 51-54; prof, MID. GA. COL, 55-71, head dept, 64-71, EMER. PROF, 71- Am. Math. Soc; Math. Asn. Am. Mathematical physics and applied mathematics. Address: R.F.D. 2, Bowdon, GA 30108.

GARRETT, ROBERT OGDEN, b. Berkeley, Calif, Jan. 11, 33; m. 55; c. 2. PHYSICS. B.A, Whitman Col, 54; M.S, Cornell Univ, 60; Ph.D.(physics), Univ. Ore, 64. Asst. prof. PHYSICS, BELOIT COL, 64-69, ASSOC. PROF, 69-, CHMN. DEPT, 70- Res. assoc, Univ. Ore, 69-70. U.S.N.R, 54-56, Lt.(jg). Am. Asn. Physics Teachers. Pressure broadening of spectral lines of atoms perturbed by foreign gases. Address: Dept. of Physics, Be'oit College, Beloit, WI 53511.

GARRETT, ROBERT R(OTH), b. Asheville, N.C, Nov. 29, 21; m. 53; c. 2. PHYSICAL CHEMISTRY. B.S, Duke, 44; M.S, Louisville, 51; Ph.D.(chem), Cornell, 57. Asst, Louisville, 50-51; Cornell, 52-56; RES. CHEMIST, E.I. DU PONT DE NEMOURS & CO, INC, 57- U.S.N.R, 44-46, Lt. Am. Chem. Soc. Phase transitions in high polymers; physical chemistry of elastomers. Address: Elastomer Chemistry Dept, E.I. du Pont de Nemours & Co, Inc, Wilmington, DE 19898.

GARRETT, RONALD D, b. Maryville, Mo, Jan. 25, 34; m. 60; c. 3. PHARMACOGNOSY. B.A, Texas, 55, M.A, 58, Welch fel, 58-60, Ph.D.(org. chem), 60. Res. chemist, Pittsburgh Plate Glass Co, Tex, 60-61; asst. prof. chem, Tex. Lutheran Col, 61-63, assoc. prof, 63-64, chmn. dept, 64-65; ASST. PROF. BIOCHEM, med. units, Tennessee, 65-68; COL. PHARM, UNIV. TEX. AUSTIN, 68- Petrol. Res. Found. grant, 61-64; Nat. Sci. Found. res. participation grant, 62-; Nat. Insts. Health grant, 63; summer, Nat. Sci. Found. participation grant, Okla. State, 65; summer, fel, Oak Ridge Inst.

Nuclear Sci, 68. Am. Chem. Soc. Investigation of the correlation of physiological activity of organic compounds with their structure, especially hypnotics, anti-spasmodics and steroid compounds; investigation of biogenetic pathways involved in the in vivo production of terphenyl quinones and alkyl substituted citric acid derivatives. Address: University of Texas at Austin School of Pharmacy, Austin, TX 78712.

GARRETT, THOMAS A, b. Phila, Pa, June 1, 08; m. 54; c. 2. CLINICAL MEDICINE, PEDIATRICS. A.B, Villanova, 31; M.D, Temple, 39. Intern, Holy Name Hosp, Teaneck, N.J, 39-40; resident pediatrician, New York Foundling Hosp, 40-41; L.I. Col. Hosp, Brooklyn, 41-42; contagious disease, Charles Chapin Mem. Hosp, Providence, R.I, 42; attend. pediatrician, Holy Name Hosp, Teaneck, 46-52; assoc. med. dir, Chas. Pfizer & Co, N.Y, 52-54; med. dir, J.B. Roerig & Co, Ill, 54-56; Irwin Neisler & Co, 56-59; v.pres. & med. dir, BAXTER LABS, INC, 59-67, V.PRES. MED. AFFAIRS, 67- Private practice, 46-52; assoc. pediatrician, Mercy Hosp, Stritch Sch. Med, Loyola Univ. Chicago, 55-56. Med.C, U.S.A, 42-46, Maj. Am. Fedn. Clin. Res; Am. Soc. Artificial Internal Organs; Asn. Am. Med. Cols; Am. Med. Asn; Am. Med. Writers Asn; World Med. Asn; N.Y. Acad. Sci. Erythroblastosis fetalis; new drugs. Address: Baxter Labs, Inc, 6301 Lincoln Ave, Morton Grove, IL 60053.

GARRETT, THOMAS P(INKSTON), b. Washington, Ga, Apr. 24, 26; m. 50; c. 4. PHYSICAL & INORGANIC CHEMISTRY. B.S, N.Ga. Col, 50; fel, Tennessee, 52-55, Ph.D.(chem), 55. Asst, Tennessee, 50-52; res. chemist, Savannah River lab, E.I. DU PONT DE NEMOURS & CO, INC, 55-58, east. lab, 58-63, SR. RES. CHEMIST, 63-65, explosion hazards lab, 65-71, EAST. LAB, 71- U.S.N.R, 44-46. AAAS; Am. Chem. Soc. Molecular structure studies by infrared spectroscopy; kinetics, specifically the thermal decomposition of uranyl nitrate; thermochemical studies by means of rotating bomb calorimetry; explosion hazards testing and evaluation. Address: Eastern Lab, E.I. du Pont de Nemours & Co, Inc, Gibbstown, NJ 08027.

GARRETT, WILLIAM N(ORBERT), b. Cresson, Pa, June 8, 26; m. 54; c. 2. ANIMAL NUTRITION. B.S, Pa. State Univ, 50, M.S, 51; Ph.D.(nutrit), Univ. Calif, 58. Assoc. animal husb, UNIV. CALIF, 53-56, asst. animal husbandman, 58-63, assoc. animal husbandman, DAVIS, 63-65, assoc. prof. ANIMAL SCI, 65-69, PROF, 69- U.S.N, 44-46. Ruminant nutrition; energy metabolism. Address: Dept. of Animal Science, University of California, Davis, CA 95616.

GARRETT, W(ILLIAM) RAY, b. Warrior, Ala, Oct. 17, 37; m. 57; c. 3. THEORETICAL PHYSICS. B.S, Alabama, 60, M.S, 62, Ph.D.(physics), 63. Res. assoc. physics, res. inst, Alabama, 63-65, asst. prof, 65-66; PHYSICIST, OAK RIDGE NAT. LAB, 66- Am. Phys. Soc. Theoretical atomic and molecular physics. Address: Health Physics Division, Oak Ridge National Lab, P.O. Box X, Oak Ridge, TN 37830.

GARRETTSON, GARRETT AQUILA, b. San Francisco, Calif, July 20, 43; m. 67. COMPUTER SCIENCE, PHYSICS. Atomic Energy Comn. fel, Stanford Univ, 65-68, M.S, 66, Ph.D.(nuclear eng), 69. Sci. programmer, IBM Systs. Res. & Develop. Ctr, Calif, 66-68, math. physicist, 68; res. asst, Stanford Univ, 68-69; ASST. PROF. PHYSICS, NAVAL POSTGRAD. SCH, 69- U.S.N, 69-, Lt. Am. Phys. Soc; Am. Nuclear Soc. Multidimensional neutron transport theory; bubble transport in the upper ocean; computer applications in reactor physics; numerical simulation of laser-produced plasmas. Address: Dept. of Physics, Naval Postgraduate School, Monterey, CA 93940.

GARRICK, B(ERNELL) JOHN, b. Eureka, Utah, Mar. 5, 30; m. 52; c. 3. PHYSICS, ENGINEERING. B.S, Brigham Young Univ, 52; Atomic Energy Comn. scholar, Oak Ridge Sch. Reactor Technol, 54-55; M.S, Univ. Calif, Los Angeles, 62, Ph.D.(eng), 68. Physicist, atomic energy div, Phillips Petrol. Co, Idaho, 52-54; physicist & sr. scientist, reactor hazards eval. br, Atomic Energy Comn, Wash, D.C, 55-57; V.PRES. TECHNOL, HOLMES & NARVER, INC, LOS ANGELES, 57- Tech. adv. & Atomic Energy Comn. rep, Int. Conf. Peaceful Uses Atomic Energy, Switz, 58; mem. reactor safety comt, Atomic Indust. Forum, 60, steering comt. pub. understanding, 63, ad hoc comt. reactor regulation, 65; mem. & chmn. adv. panel on reactor safety for Pakistan, Int. Atomic Energy Agency, 62; consult, Adv. Comt. on Reactor Safeguards, 67. Am. Nuclear Soc. Systems analysis; nuclear engineering and applied physics. Address: 18757 Wells Dr, Tarzana, CA 91356.

GARRICK, I(SADORE) E(DWARD), b. Chicago, Ill, Mar. 3, 10; m. 37; c. 3. MATHEMATICS, PHYSICS. B.S, Chicago, 30. Jr. & asst. physicist, LANGLEY RES. CTR, NASA, 30-37, assoc. physicist & physicist, 37-43, sr. & prin. physicist, 43-47, chief physicist, 47-48, aeronaut. res. scientist, 48-49, chief, dynamic loads div, 49-70, CHIEF MATH. SCIENTIST, 70- Mem. appl. math. adv. coun, Nat. Bur. Standards, 48-50; Hunsaker prof, Mass. Inst. Technol, 56-57; mem; NASA Res. Adv. Comts, 58-; NASA liaison mem. to div. math. sci, Nat. Res. Coun, 68-; adj. prof, George Wash. Univ. 69- Except. serv. award, NASA, 64, Langley Res. Ctr. Sci. Achievement award, 65. Am. Phys. Soc; Soc. Indust. & Appl. Math; fel. Am. Inst. Aeronaut. & Astronaut. Theoretical aerodynamics; aeroelasticity; gas dynamics; acoustics; applied mathematics. Address: Langley Research Center, M.S. 115, NASA, Hampton, VA 23365.

GARRICK, MICHAEL D, b. Newport News, Va, July 25, 38; m. 61, 70. GENETICS. B.A, Hopkins, 59, Nat. Sci. Found. fel, 59-61, Nat. Insts. Health fel, 61-63, Ph.D.(biol), 63. Fel. biochem. genetics, Hopkins, summer 63, asst. prof. genetics, McCoy Col. & fel. med. genetics, univ. hosp, 63-64; asst. prof. molecular genetics, Univ. Va, 64-69, biol, 69-70; ASST. PROF. BIOL. & RES. ASST. PROF. PEDIAT. & BIOCHEM, STATE UNIV. N.Y. BUFFALO, 70- AAAS; Genetics Soc; Am. Inst. Biol. Sci; Am. Soc. Microbiol. Biochemical and human genetics; gene action; protein biosynthesis; modulation; immunochemistry; immunogenetics. Address: Bell Facility, State University of New York at Buffalo, P.O. Box U, Station B, Buffalo, NY 14207.

GARRIGA-RODRIGUEZ, FRANCISCO, b. Santiago, Spain, April 3, 12; nat; m. 41; c. 5. MATHEMATICS. B.S, Puerto Rico, 32; A.B, Chicago, 44, M.S, 49; North Carolina, 51; Texas, 53-56; Princeton, 59; Ph.D., Madrid,

65. Teacher, pub. sch, P.R, 32-41, prin, 41-42; instr. MATH, UNIV. P.R, 42-48, asst. prof, 48-54, assoc. prof, 54-65, PROF, 65-, acting head dept, 57-58, chmn, 61-66, asst. dean sci, 59-60, assoc. dean studies, 60-62. Consult, P.R. Dept. Ed, 50-60; P.R. Develop. Co, 59-60; WIPR-TV, 59-60; Govt. Personnel Off, 59-60. Am. Math. Soc; Math. Asn. Am. Correlation analysis; science evaluation; statistics. Address: Dept. of Mathematics, University of Puerto Rico, Box 22152, Rio Piedras, PR 00931.

GARRIGUS, UPSON S(TANLEY), b. Willimantic, Conn, July 2, 17; m. 42; c. 2. ANIMAL SCIENCE. B.S, Connecticut, 40; M.S, Illinois, 42, Ph.D.(animal sci), 48. Asst. ANIMAL SCI, UNIV. ILL, URBANA, 40-42, 46-48, instr, 48-49, asst. prof, 49-50, assoc. prof, 51-55, PROF, 55-, head ruminant div, 64-70. Mem. comt. sheep nutrit, Nat. Res. Coun, 53-, comt. use of non-protein nitrogen compounds as protein replacement for animals, 70-; Moorman res. travel award, 70. U.S.A, 42-46, Maj. Fel. AAAS; Am. Soc. Animal Sci; Am. Inst. Nutrit. Use of sulfur, antibiotics, arsenicals and non-protein nitrogen in lamb feeding; pelleting of ruminant rations; commercial ruminant feeding; farm flock feeding; breeding and management of ruminants. Address: University of Illinois, 103 Stock Pavilion, Urbana, IL 61801.

GARRIGUS, W(ESLEY) P(ATTERSON), b. Storrs, Conn, June 16, 09; m. 33; c. 3. AGRICULTURE. B.S, Conn. Agr. Col, 31; M.S, Illinois, 33, Ph.D. (animal husb), 35. Asst. animal husb, Illinois, 31-36; agronomist, soil conserv, U.S. Dept. Agr, 36-37; instr. ANIMAL HUSB, UNIV. KY, 37-39, asst. prof, 39-40, assoc. prof, 40-41, PROF, 41-, CHMN. DEPT. ANIMAL SCI, 62-, chmn. animal indust. group, 41-61, assoc. dir, agr. exp. sta, 51-62. Am. Soc. Animal Sci.(pres, Soc. Animal Prod, 59-60). Pasture utilization; animal nutrition and husbandry. Address: 227 Shady Lane, Lexington, KY 40503.

GARRIGUS, WOODFORD (McDOWELL), b. Toledo, Ohio, May 10, 23; m. 58; c. 4. GEOGRAPHY. A.B, Middlebury Col, 49; M.A, Clark, 55, Ph.D, 58. Asst. geol, Middlebury Col, 49-52; Clark, 54-55; asst. prof. GEOG, E.Carolina Col, 58-61; Univ. Victoria (B.C), 61-65; PROF, ASHLAND COL, 65- U.S.A.A.F, 42-45. Fel. Am. Geog. Soc; fel. Asn; Am. Geog. Morphology and genetic morphology of land surface; land utilization; associations between economic and physical conditions; particularly those of land surface; urban and economic geography. Address: Earth Science Dept. Ashland College, Ashland, OH 44805.

GARRINGTON, GEORGE EVERETT, b. Poplar Branch, N.C, June 1, 27; m. 53; c. 4. DENTISTRY, ORAL PATHOLOGY. D.D.S, Maryland, 53; M.P.H, Hopkins, 60; M.S, Georgetown, 64. U.S. PUB. HEALTH SERV, 53-, dent. officer, hosp, San Francisco, 54-56, outpatient clin, Wash, D.C, 56-58, dent. pub. health trainee, regional off, Atlanta, 58-59, asst. to chief dent. officer, hq, 60-62, res. path, Georgetown Univ, 62-64, oral path, Armed Forces Inst. Path, 64-65, oral pathologist, NAT. INST. DENT. RES, 65-68, acting clin. dir, 68-69, DEP. DIR, INTRAMURAL RES, 69- Dipl, Am. Bd. Oral Path. U.S.A.A.F, 44-46, Sgt. Am. Dent. Asn; fel. Am. Acad. Oral Path. Oral pathology, particularly malignant bone tumors; gingival hyperplasias, dental implantation and transplantation. Address: National Institute of Dental Research, Bethesda, MD 20014.

GARRIOTT, OWEN KAY, b. Enid, Okla, Nov. 22, 30; m. 52; c. 4. PHYSICS. B.S, Univ. Okla, 53; M.S, Stanford Univ, 57, Ph.D.(elec. eng), 60. Res. assoc. elec. eng, Stanford Univ, 59-60; Nat. Sci. Found. fel, Cambridge Univ. & Radio Res. Sta, 60-61; asst. prof. elec. eng, Stanford Univ, 61-62, assoc. prof, 62-65; SCIENTIST-ASTRONAUT, MANNED SPACECRAFT CTR, NASA, 65- Consult, Lockheed Missiles & Space Co, 60; ionospheric & radio physics subcomt, NASA, 62-66, manned space sci. div, 63-66; regional ed, Planetary & Space Sci, 64-66; secy, U.S. Comn. III, Int. Sci. Radio Union, 64-67. U.S.N, 53-56, Lt.(jg). Radio investigations of the ionosphere. Address: 1902 Back Bay Ct, Houston, TX 77058.

GARRISON, ALLEN K, b. Lake Wales, Fla, Oct. 24, 31; m. 57; c. 2. PHYSICS. B.S, Davidson Col, 53; Danforth fel, Duke Univ, 53-58, Ph.D.(physics), 58. Asst. prof. PHYSICS, EMORY UNIV, 58-63, assoc. prof, 63-71, PROF, 71- Nat. Res. Coun. fel, Naval Res. Lab, 64-65. Am. Phys. Soc. Microwave spectroscopy; solid state physics. Address: 1370 Springdale Rd, Atlanta, GA 30306.

GARRISON, ARTHUR WAYNE, b. Greenville, S.C, Sept. 9, 34; m. 56; c. 2. ORGANIC & WATER CHEMISTRY. B.S, The Citadel, 56; M.S, Clemson, 58; U.S. Dept. Health, Ed. & Welfare trainee, Emory, 63-65, Ph.D.(org. chem), 66. Chemist, dept. agr. chem, Clemson, 61-62; anal. chemist, pesticide pollution lab, div. water supply & pollution control, U.S. Pub. Health Serv, 62-65; RES. CHEMIST, SOUTHEAST WATER LAB, ENVIRON. PROTECTION AGENCY, 65- Ord.C, U.S.A, 58-60, 1st Lt. Am. Chem. Soc; Am. Soc. Mass Spectrometry. Organophosphorus chemistry; organic mass spectrometry; nuclear magnetic resonance spectrometry of pesticides and related compounds; analysis of organic pollutants in water; analytical chemistry. Address: Southeast Water Lab, Environmental Protection Agency, Athens, GA 30601.

GARRISON, BETTY B(ERNHARDT), b. Danbury, Ohio, July 1, 32; m. 68; c. 1. MATHEMATICS. B.S.Ed. & B.A, Bowling Green State Univ, 54; M.A, Ohio State Univ, 56; Nat. Sci. Found. fels, Ore. State Univ, 60-62, Ph.D.(math), 62. Instr. MATH, Ohio Univ, 56-57; SAN DIEGO STATE COL, 57-59, asst. prof, 62-69, PROF, 69- Am. Math. Soc; Math. Asn. Am. Extensions of Schnirelmann density to sets of lattice points. Address: Dept. of Mathematics, San Diego State College, 5402 College Ave, San Diego, CA 92115.

GARRISON, DELNA W(ILSON), b. Detroit, Mich, Aug. 8, 11; m. 40; c. 2. MICROBIOLOGY. B.S, Michigan, 33, M.S, 44, Ph.D, 60. Bacteriologist, Mich. Dept. Health, 33-40; instr. bact, Wayne State, 44-45; res. assoc. immunol, Univ. Mich, Ann Arbor, 50-51, instr. bact, 51-60, asst. prof. Microbiol, 60-68, assoc. prof, sch. med, 68-71; RETIRED. Dipl, Am. Bd. Microbiol, 68. AAAS; Am. Soc. Microbiol. Pathogenic microbiology; tumor immunology; host-parasite relationships; burns and pseudomonas; urinary tract. Address: Aneth, UT 84510.

GARRISON, EARL R(AYMOND), b. Centralia, Ill, Sept. 18, 00; m. 30; c. 2. DAIRY BACTERIOLOGY. B.S, Illinois, 26; M.A, Missouri, 28; Ph.D.(dairy bact), Iowa State Col, 40. Asst. instr. dairy husb, Missouri, 26-28, instr, 28-30, asst. prof, 30-45; res. supt, Golden State Co, Ltd, Calif, 45-48; assoc. prof. ANIMAL HUSB, UNIV. ARK, FAYETTEVILLE, 49-50, prof, 51-68, EMER. PROF, 68- Am. Dairy Sci. Asn; Inst. Food Technol. Optical determination of lactose; classification of fluorescent bacteria; sources and biochemical characteristics of Oospora lactis; lactose fermenting yeasts; rancidity in cream; lipolytic yeasts in cream; lipolytic species of Clostridium in milk and cream lipolytic staphylocci in udder of dairy cows; fatty acids utilized by lipolytic microorganisms. Address: Dept. of Animal Industry, University of Arkansas, Fayetteville, AR 72701.

GARRISON, GEORGE A(LFRED), b. Lincoln, Nebr, Apr. 6, 17; m. 42; c. 3. ECOLOGY. B.Sc, Nebraska, 40, M.Sc, 47. Prin. plant ecologist, PAC. NORTHWEST FOREST & RANGE EXP. STA, U.S. FOREST SERV, 47-65, res. center leader, 56-63, RES. PROJ. LEADER, 64- U.S.N, 42-46. Fel. AAAS; Am. Soc. Range Mgt; Ecol. Soc. Am; Am. Inst. Biol. Sci; Soil Conserv. Soc. Am. Forest and range ecology; interrelation of timber and forage production; range grass and shrub physiology; grazing management; land use planning. Address: La Grande Unit-Pacific Northwest Forest & Range Experiment Station, U.S. Forest Service, La Grande, OR 97850.

GARRISON, GEORGE N(ELVIN), b. Walhonding, Ohio, Sept. 11, 05; m. 34; c. 1. MATHEMATICS. B.S, Denison, 27; M.A, Ohio State, 29; Ph.D.(math), Princeton, 39. Instr. math, Case, 29-31; teacher, high sch, N.Y, 34-37; instr. MATH, City Col. New York, 37-46; asst. prof, Lehigh, 46-47, assoc. prof, 47-48; asst. prof, CITY COL. NEW YORK, 48-51, assoc. prof, 51-57, prof, 57-64, chmn. dept, 52-64, EMER. PROF, 64- Lectr, Wesleyan Univ, & assoc. dir, grad. summer sch. for teachers, 64-71, emer. lectr, 71- Am. Math. Soc; Math. Asn. Am. Generalized groups; quasi-groups; group theory. Address: 174 Lincoln St, Middletown, CT 06457.

GARRISON, GERALD R(AY), b. Wenatchee, Wash, June 12, 22; m. 47; c. 3. B.S, Univ. Wash, 42, Ph.D.(physics), 52. Assoc. physicist, APPL. PHYSICS LAB, UNIV. WASH, 52-53, physicist, 53-58, SR. PHYSICIST, 58- Am. Phys. Soc. Cosmic rays; oceanography; ultrasonics. Address: Applied Physics Laboratory, University of Washington, Seattle, WA 98105.

GARRISON, JAMES A(RTHUR), b. Rocky, Okla, June 22, 27; m. 50; c. 3. ORGANIC CHEMISTRY. B.S, Northwestern, 50; M.S, Mich. State Col, 51, Parke-Davis fel, 53-54, Ph.D.(chem), 54. Sr. chemist, Mead Johnson & Co, 54-58, prof. employ. mgr, 58-60, sr. chemist, 60-62, group leader, 62-64; asst. prof. chem, Pittsburgh, Greensburg, 64-67; assoc. prof, State Univ. N.Y. Col. Buffalo, 67-70; TECH. V.PRES, E. SHORE CHEM. CO, 70- U.S.N.R, 45-46. Am. Chem. Soc. Polynitrogen heterocycles; medicinal chemicals; diazonium compounds. Address: East Shore Chemical Co, Box 448, Muskegon, MI 49443.

GARRISON, JOHN D(RESSER), b. Salt Lake City, Utah, Aug. 9, 22; m. 50; c. 3; div; m. 68; c. 1. PHYSICS. B.A, California, Los Angeles, 47, M.A, 48; Ph.D.(physics), California, 54. Instr. PHYSICS, Yale, 53-56; asst. prof, SAN DIEGO STATE COL, 56-59, assoc. prof, 59-62, PROF, 62-, chmn. dept, 66-69. Assoc. physicist, Brookhaven Nat. Lab, 62-63; consult, Gen. Atomic/Gen. Dynamics Corp. U.S.A.A.F, 43-46, 2nd Lt. Am. Phys. Soc. Proton-proton scattering; nuclear physics; neutron cross sections. Address: Dept. of Physics, San Diego State College, San Diego, CA 92115.

GARRISON, LOUIS ELDRED, b. West, Tex, July 2, 21; m. 49; c. 2. OCEANOGRAPHY, GEOLOGY. B.S, Tex. Col. Mines & Metall, 49; M.S, California, 51; Ph.D.(oceanog), Rhode Island, 67. Instr, Rhode Island, 51-53, asst. prof, 53-56; explor. geologist, Lion Oil Co, 56-63; MARINE GEOLOGIST, U.S. GEOL. SURV, 67- U.S.N, 43-47, Lt. Comdr. AAAS; Am. Geophys. Union; Soc. Econ. Paleont. & Mineral. N.Y. Acad. Sci. Geologic history and origins of continental margins and island arcs. Address: 746 Monette Dr, Corpus Christi, TX 78412.

GARRISON, MARY M(cCLINTOCK), b. St. Paul, Minn, July 4, 16; m. 47; c. 1. PHYSIOLOGY. B.A, Carleton Col, 37; M.A, Minnesota, 43. Instr. biol, Wayland Baptist Col, 38-43; Bemidji State Col, 43-44; Tulane, 44-47; physiol. chemist, Georgetown, 55-57; PHYSIOLOGIST, NAT. INSTS. HEALTH, 57- Pituitary hormones. Address: National Institutes of Health, Bethesda, MD 20014.

GARRISON, O(LEN) B(RANFORD), b. Columbia, S.C, May 31, 10; m. 39; c. 3. HORTICULTURE. B.S, Clemson Col, 33; M.S, La. State, 34; fel, Cornell, 36-39, Ph.D.(hort), 39. Asst. horticulturist, Edisto Exp. Sta, CLEMSON UNIV, 39-42, assoc. horticulturist, 46-48, PROF. HORT. & HORTICULTURIST, AGR. EXP. STA, 48-, DIR, 54- Mem. Nat. Cotton Res. Coun. C.Eng, U.S. Army, 42-45, Maj. Am. Soc. Hort. Sci. Sweet potatoes; tomatoes; breeding vegetables; irrigation. Address: Agricultural Experiment Station, Clemson University, Clemson, SC 29631.

GARRISON, RHODA, b. Newton, Mass, July 9, 17. BOTANY. B.A, Wellesley Col, 39; A.M, Radcliffe Col, 40, Ph.D.(biol), 48. Asst. bot, Wellesley Col, 40-41, instr, 41-45, asst. prof, 49-55, assoc. prof, 55-58; asst, Harvard, 48-49, res. fel. biol, 57-59; assoc. prof. biol, Wheaton Col.(Mass), 59-63, prof, 63-68; res. assoc. biol, Harvard, 68-70. Res. fel, Radcliffe Col, 51-52. AAAS; Bot. Soc. Am; Soc. Develop. Biol; Int. Soc. Plant Morphol. Plant morphology. Address: 181 Pine Ridge Rd, Waban, MA 02168.

GARRISON, ROBERT EDWARD, b. Dallas, Tex, Oct. 25, 32; m. 63; c. 1. GEOLOGY. B.S, Stanford, 55, M.S, 58; Fulbright grant, Innsbruck, 58-59; William Libbey fel. & Ph.D.(geol), Princeton, 64. Geologist petrol. explor, Sunray D-X Oil Co, 59-61; res. assoc. geol, Princeton, 64-65; asst. prof, California, Santa Barbara, 65-66; vis. asst. prof, British Columbia, 66-68; ASSOC. PROF. NATURAL SCI, UNIV. CALIF, SANTA CRUZ, 68-, CHMN. EARTH SCI. BD, 70- U.S.A.F, 55-57, 1st Lt. AAAS; Geol. Soc. Am; Am. Asn. Petrol. Geol; Soc. Econ. Paleont. & Mineral. Sedimentology and stratigraphy; petrology of carbonate rocks and eugeosynclinal sedimentary rocks; electron microscopy of fine-grained sedimentary rocks. Address: Earth Sciences Board, University of California, Santa Cruz, CA 95060.

GARRISON, ROBERT FREDERICK, b. Aurora, Ill, May 9, 36; m. 57; c. 2. ASTRONOMY, ASTROPHYSICS. B.A, Earlham Col, 60; Wisconsin, 61-62; Ph.D.(astron. & astrophys), Chicago, 66. Res. asst. ASTRON, Yerkes Observ, 60-61; res. assoc, Mt. Wilson-Palomar Observ, 66-68; ASST. PROF, DAVID DUNLAP OBSERV, UNIV. TORONTO, 68- U.S.M.C, 54-56. Am. Astron. Soc; Am. Asn. Variable Star Observers. Direct photography of galaxies and H II regions; stellar spectral classification; clusters and associations; Mira variables. Address: David Dunlap Observatory, University of Toronto, Richmond Hill, Ont, Can.

GARRISON, ROBERT G(ENE), b. Pittsburg, Kans, Aug. 30, 25; m. 58; c. 2. MICROBIOLOGY. B.A, Kans. State Col. Pittsburg, 49; M.S, Kansas State, 51, Ph.D.(bact), 54. Asst. antibiotics, sch. med, La. State, 51-52; bacteriologist, VET. ADMIN. HOSP, Grand Island, Nebr, 54-57, SCIENTIST, KANSAS CITY, 57- Asst. prof, sch. med, Univ. Kans, 61-67, assoc. prof, 67-; consult. bacteriologist, Upsher Labs, Kansas City, 64-; clin. asst. prof, sch. dent, Univ. Mo-Kansas City, 70- Med.C, U.S.A, 43-46. Am. Soc. Microbiol; Am. Pub. Health Asn; N.Y. Acad. Sci. Physiology of pathogenic fungi; microbial decomposition of natural materials. Address: Veterans Administration Hospital, 4801 Linwood Blvd, Kansas City, MO 64128.

GARRISON, WARREN M(ANFORD), b. Seattle, Wash, June 6, 15; m. 42; c. 2. PHYSICAL CHEMISTRY. B.S, California, 37, M.S, 39; Ph.D.(photochem), N.Y. Univ, 42. Res. assoc, metall. lab, Chicago, 42-43, assoc. sect. chief, radiation chem. sect, 43-44; res. chemist, Hanford Eng. Works, Gen. Elec. Co, Wash, 45-46; asst. prof. chem, Wyoming, 46-48; CHEMIST, LAWRENCE RADIATION LAB, UNIV. CALIF, BERKELEY, 48-, asst. dir, Crocker Lab, 58-62. Consult, E.I. du Pont de Nemours & Co, 58; Aerojet-Gen. Nucleonics Div, Gen. Tire & Rubber Co, 62-; chmn, Gordon Res. Conf. Radiation Chem, 59; State Dept. rep, Int. Cong. Nuclear Energy, Italy, 59. AAAS; Am. Chem. Soc; Radiation Res. Soc; Am. Inst. Chem. Reaction mechanism; radiation chemistry. Address: Lawrence Radiation Lab, University of California, Berkeley, CA 94704.

GARRISON, WILLIAM EMMETT, JR, b. Media, Pa, Nov. 29, 33; m. 57; c. 6. ORGANIC & POLYMER CHEMISTRY. B.S, Juniata Col, 55; Ph.D.(org. chem), Illinois, 59. Res. chemist, PLASTICS DEPT, EXP. STA, E.I. DU PONT DE NEMOURS & CO, INC, 58-66, SR. RES. CHEMIST, 66- Am. Chem. Soc. Polymers; product and process development. Address: Plastics Dept, Experimental Station, E.I. du Pont de Nemours & Co, Inc, Wilmington, DE 19898.

GARRITY, MICHAEL K, b. Austin, Minn, Sept. 1, 42; m. 65. MATHEMATICAL PHYSICS. B.S, St. John's (Minn), 64; M.S, Arizona State, 65, Ph.D. (math. physics), 68. ASST. PROF. PHYSICS, ST. CLOUD STATE COL, 67- General relativity and mathematical physics; formulation of mathematical models. Address: Dept. of Physics, St. Cloud State College, St. Cloud, MN 56301.

GARROD, CLAUDE, b. New York, N.Y, Sept. 25, 32; m. 55; c. 3. THEORETICAL PHYSICS. A.B, N.Y. Univ, 57, Ph.D.(physics), 63. Instr. PHYSICS, Manhattan Col, 61-62; res. scientist, Courant Inst. Math. Sci, N.Y. Univ, 62-64; asst. prof, UNIV. CALIF, DAVIS, 62-69, ASSOC. PROF, 69- Am. Phys. Soc. Quantum theory of many-particle systems. Address: Dept. of Physics, University of California, Davis, CA 95616.

GARRON, DAVID C(HARLES), Psychol, see Suppl. I to 11th ed, Soc. & Behav. Vols.

GARROW, ROBERT JOSEPH, b. Buffalo, N.Y, Dec. 24, 29; m. 64; c. 3. MATHEMATICS, PHYSICS. B.S, Ohio State, 61; M.E.D, Xavier, 69. Engr, North Am. Aviation, Inc, 57-60; instr. MATH, Ohio State, 60-61; PROF. & CHMN. DEPT, FRANKLIN UNIV, 61- Pres, Franklin Educ. Serv, Inc. U.S.A.F, 50-54, Sgt. Am. Soc. Eng. Educ. Evaluation of the reliability and validity of an electronics aptitude test; use of the computer as an aid in teaching mathematics and science. Address: 4359 Schirtzinger Rd, Columbus, OH 43220.

GARRY, MARK W(ILLIAM), b. Manawa, Wis, Aug. 8, 06; m. 31; c. 6. INTERNAL MEDICINE. B.S, Marquette, 32, M.D, 34. Gen. practice, Sherwood, Wis, 34-36; investr, Trudeau Found, 36-42; consult, indust. med, Milwaukee, Wis, 42-44; dir. div. tuberc, State Dept. Health, Ohio, 45-46, chief internal med. & tuberc. control, Dept. Pub. Welfare, 46-47; chief med. serv, Vet. Admin. Hosp, Wood, 47-60; assoc. prof. MED, MED. COL. WIS, 54-67, ASSOC. CLIN. PROF, 71- INTERNIST, BLUEMOUND MED. CTR, 67- Consult. & dir, rheumatic disease clin, Milwaukee County Gen. Hosp. & Dispensary, 51-60; dir. univ. health serv, Med. Col. Wis, 61-67. U.S.P.H.S, 44-45, Surgeon. AAAS; Am. Thoracic Soc; Am. Soc. Gastrointestinal Endoscopy; Am. Rheumatism Asn; Am. Med. Asn; N.Y. Acad. Sci; fel. Am. Col. Physicians; Royal Soc. Health. Rheumatic diseases. Address: 6200 W. Bluemound Rd, Milwaukee, WI 53213.

GARSIA, ADRIANO MARIO, b. Tunis, Tunisia, Aug. 20, 28; nat; m. 55; c. 1. MATHEMATICS. Rome, 49-53; Ph.D.(math), Stanford, 57. C.L.E. Moore instr. MATH, Mass. Inst. Tech, 57-59; asst. prof, Minnesota, 59-61; assoc. prof, Calif. Inst. Technol, 61-64, PROF, 65-66; UNIV. CALIF, SAN DIEGO, 66- Am. Math. Soc; Math. Asn. Am. Classical analysis; probability theory; classical differential geometry. Address: P.O. Box 295, Rancho Santa Fe, CA 92067.

GARSIDE, EDWARD THOMAS, b. London, Ont, June 14, 30. ZOOLOGY. B.A, Queen's (Ont), 54; M.A, Toronto, 57, Ph.D.(zool), 60. Supvr. fish culture, Ont. Dept. Lands & Forests, 61-62; asst. prof. zool, Manitoba, 62-65; BIOL, DALHOUSIE UNIV, 65-67, ASSOC. PROF, 67- Am. Fisheries Soc; Am. Inst. Fishery Res. Biol; Am. Soc. Ichthyol. & Herpet; Int. Asn. Theoret. & Appl. Limnol. Embryogenesis and ecology of early stages of fish; limnological productivity. Address: Dept. of Biology, Dalhousie University, Halifax, N.S, Can.

GARSKE, DAVID HERMAN, b. Kalamazoo, Mich, Mar. 2, 37; m. 67; c. 1. MINERALOGY. B.S, Mich. Technol. Univ, 59; M.S, Univ. Mich, 61, Ph.D. (mineral), 70. ASST. PROF. MINERAL. & GEOL, S.DAK. SCH. MINES & TECHNOL, 65- Mineral. Soc. Am; Nat. Speleol. Soc; Mineral. Asn. Can; Am. Crystallog. Asn. Paragenesis and formation of secondary pegmatite phosphates. Address: Dept. of Geology & Geological Engineering, South Dakota School of Mines and Technology, Rapid City, SD 57701.

GARSON, LORRIN RAY, b. Virginia, Minn, Aug. 12, 39; m. 61; c. 1. ORGANIC & MEDICINAL CHEMISTRY. B.A, California, Riverside, 61; M.S, Maine, 64, NASA trainee, 64-66, Ph.D.(org. chem), 67. Chem. technician, Pomona Tile Mfg. Co, Calif, 59; asst. med. chemist, Riker Labs, Inc, 61-62; teaching asst, Maine, 62-64 & 67; res. assoc. MED. CHEM, COL. PHARM, UNIV. TENN, MEMPHIS, 67-68, ASST. PROF, 68- AAAS; Am. Chem. Soc; Am. Inst. Chem. Synthesis and determination of selected physicochemical parameters of peptides and medicinal agents effective against pathogenic or physical impairments inflicted through the skin and periodontal diseases and dental caries. Address: Dept. of Medicinal Chemistry, University of Tennessee College of Pharmacy, Memphis, TN 38103.

GARST, ARTHUR W(ILHELM), b. McPherson, Kans, Mar. 7, 11; m. 36; c. 2. CHEMISTRY. B.S, Tulsa, 33. Chemist, Dowell, Inc, Tulsa, 36-38; Stanolind Oil & Gas Co, 39-57, SR. RES. SCIENTIST, Pan Am. Petrol Corp, 57-71, AMOCO PROD. CO, 71- Consult. chemist. Electron Micros. Soc. Am; Am. Inst. Mining, Metall. & Petrol. Eng; fel. Am. Inst. Chem. Oil well acidization processes; high pressure testing of cement slurries; salt water disposal problems; electron microscopy. Address: 2303 S. Delaware Pl, Tulsa, OK 74114.

GARST, JOHN F(REDRIC), b. Jackson, Miss, May 8, 32; m. 55. PHYSICAL & ORGANIC CHEMISTRY. B.S, Miss. State, 54; Nat. Sci. Found. fel, Iowa State, 55-57, Ph.D.(chem), 57. Instr. CHEM, Yale, 57-58; asst. prof, Univ. Calif, Riverside, 58-63; UNIV. GA, 63-67, ASSOC. PROF, 67- Am. Chem. Soc. Physical organic chemistry; free radicals; solvent and metal effects on organoalkali systems. Address: Dept. of Chemistry, University of Georgia, Athens, GA 30601.

GARST, JOSEPHINE B(URGIS), b. Detroit, Mich, Oct. 23, 04. BIOLOGICAL CHEMISTRY. A.B, Michigan, 26, M.S, 38; Ph.D.(biol. chem), Minnesota, 45. Teacher, pub. sch, Mich, 27-28; private sch, Ky, 28-29; technician, Clin. Lab, Ill, 29-30; teacher, private sch, Mo, 31-34; Northrop Collegiate Sch, Minneapolis, 34-42; instr. med. tech. & head technician, univ. hosps, Minnesota, 42-44; asst. chem, sch. med, Southern California, 44-45, instr, 45-46; res. fel. biochem, Calif. Inst, Tech, 47-48; res. assoc, sch. med, California, Los Angeles, 48-52, asst. res. physiol. chemist, 52-57; RES. BIOCHEMIST, VET. ADMIN. HOSP, 67- AAAS; Am. Chem. Soc; Soc. Exp. Biol. & Med; Am. Soc. Biol. Chem; Endocrine Soc. Biochemistry and physiology of steroid hormones. Address: Veterans Administration Hospital, 10701 East Blvd, Cleveland, OH 44106.

GARST, ROGER HARRY, b. Galesburg, Ill, Oct. 23, 37; m. 67; c. 2. ORGANIC CHEMISTRY. B.A, Col. Wooster, 59; Union Carbide fel, Brown, 62-63, Ph.D.(org. chem), 64. Proj. leader, RES. & DEVELOP. DEPT, CHEM. DIV, UNION CARBIDE CORP, SOUTH CHARLESTON, 64-67, PROJ. SCIENTIST, 67- Am. Chem. Soc; Am. Asn. Textile Chem. & Colorists. Mechanism of aromatic nucleophilic substitution; synthesis vis aryne intermediates of benzocyclobutenes; catalysis of vapor phase reactions; monomer synthesis; flame retardants; dyeing auxiliaries; fiber modifiers. Address: 2607 Winter St, St. Albans, WV 25177.

GARSTANG, MICHAEL, b. Utrecht, Natal, S.Africa, Apr. 4, 30; U.S. citizen; m. 53; c. 2. METEOROLOGY, OCEANOGRAPHY. B.A, Natal, 52, M.A, 58; Woods Hole Oceanog. Inst. fels, Fla. State, 58-60, 61-62, Univ. Corp. Atmospheric Res. fel, 60-61, M.S, 61, Ph.D.(meteorol), 64. Asst. geog, Natal, 51; indust. ed, African Explosives & Chem. Industs, Ltd, 52; meteorologist, Brit. Colonial Serv, 53-56; RES. ASSOC. MARINE METEOROL, WOODS HOLE OCEANOG. INST, 57-; PROF. ENVIRON. SCI, UNIV. VA, 70- Asst. prof, Fla. State Univ, 65-68, assoc. prof, 68-70; mem. adv. coun. to Inst. Trop. Meteorol, UN Spec. Fund Proj, Barbados, 68-; session chmn, Annual Conf. Hurricanes & Trop. Meteorol, 69; mem, Univ. Corp. Atmospheric Res. Eval. & Goals Comt, 69-70; vis. scientist, Coun. Sci. & Indust. Res, S.Africa, 70; consult, nat. data buoy prog, Lockheed Aircraft Co. & Southwest Res. Inst, 70-; prin. investr, trop. meteorol. & oceanog. progs, U.S. Army Res. Off, U.S. Dept. Defense; Environ. Sci. Serv. Admin, U.S. Forest Serv. Tropical meteorology and oceanography, especially problems of energy exchange between sea and air, rainfall distributions, evaporation, sensible heat exchange and the thermodynamic and kinematic structure of the Ekman layer of the ocean and atmosphere. Address: Dept. of Environmental Science, Cabell Hall, University of Virginia, Charlottesville, VA 22903.

GARSTANG, ROY H(ENRY), b. Southport, Eng, Sept. 18, 25; m. 59; c. 2. ASTROPHYSICS, ATOMIC PHYSICS. B.A, Cambridge, 46, M.A, 50, Ph.D. (math), 54. Jr. sci. off, Royal Aircraft Estab, Eng, 45-46; sci. off, Brit. Ministry Works, 46-48; res. assoc. astrophys, Yerkes Observ, Chicago, 51-52; lectr. astron, Univ. Col, London, 52-60, reader, 60-64; asst. dir. univ. observ, 59-64; PROF. ASTROPHYS, JOINT INST. LAB. ASTROPHYS, UNIV. COLO, BOULDER, 64-, chmn. inst. 66-67. Ed, Observ. Mag, 53-60; astron. adv. ed, Chambers' Encycl, 60-66; guest worker, Nat. Bur. Standards, Wash, D.C, 61-62, consult, 64-; chmn. comt. transition probabilities, Int. Astron. Union, 64-, v.pres. comn. 14, 70-; consult, Jet Propulsion Lab, Calif, 66-; Erskine vis. fels, Univ. Canterbury, 71; vis. prof, Univ. Calif, Santa Cruz, 71. Fel. Am. Phys. Soc; Optical Soc. Am; Am. Astron. Soc; Int. Astron. Union; Royal Astron. Soc; fel. Brit. Inst. Physics; Brit. Astron. Asn.(v.pres, 57-60, 63-64); Royal Statist. Soc; Royal Astron. Soc. Can; Royal Liège Soc. Sci. Spectroscopy; spectrum line intensities; forbidden transitions; spectroscopy of sun, stars and planetary nebulae. Address: Joint Institute for Lab. Astrophysics, University of Colorado, Boulder, CO 80302.

GARSTENS, MARTIN AARON, b. N.Y.C, Mar. 9, 11; m. 36; c. 1. SOLID STATE PHYSICS. B.S, City Col. New York, 32; M.S, Columbia, 34; Sc.D. (fluid mech), Mass. Inst. Technol, 41. PHYSICIST, David Taylor Model Basin, 43-45; Naval Res. Lab, 46-61; OFF. NAVAL RES, WASH, D.C, 61- Lectr, George Washington, 47-48; Howard, 62-65. Am. Phys. Soc. Nuclear and electron magnetic resonance; biophysics; foundations of physics. Address: 913 Buckingham Dr, Silver Spring, MD 20901.

GARSTKA, WALTER U(RBAN), b. Warsaw, Poland, May 25, 06; nat; m. 35; c. 2. WATER RESOURCES. B.S, Pa. State Col, 29; Sage fel, Yale, 29-30, M.F, 30; Lathrop Pack fel, California, 33, 45; Mich. State Col, 44, M.S, Colo. Agr. & Mech. Col, 49. Field asst, U.S. Forest Serv, 26, 30; soil mapper, Mich, 28-29; instr. forestry, Pa. State Col, 30-33; assoc. forest conservationist, U.S. Forest Serv, Calif, 34-35; soil technologist, soil conserv. serv, U.S. Dept. Agr, 36-40; proj. supvr, Mich. Hydrol. Res. Proj, 40-44; hydraul. engr, California, 44-45; civil engr, hydraul. data div, Tenn. Valley Auth, 45-46; civil, hydrol, hydraul. & gen. engr. & supvr. gen. phys. sci, U.S. Bur. Reclamation, 46-65, head river regulation sect, hydrol br, proj. invests. div, 54-57, chief chem. eng. lab br, div. eng. labs, 57-62, water conserv. br, 62-64, chief off. atmospheric water resources, off. chief engr, 64-65; PROF. civil eng, COLO. STATE UNIV, 66-68, watershed mgt, 69-70, CIVIL ENG, 70- Mem, West. Snow Conf, 46-; lectr, Yale, 69, 70, vis. prof, 70-C.Eng, 49, Res, Lt. Col.(Ret). Sr. mem. Soc. Am. Foresters; fel. Am. Soc. Civil Eng; Soc. Am. Mil. Eng; Am. Soc. Test. & Mat; Geol. Soc. Am; Am. Geophys. Union; Am. Meteorol. Soc. Hydrology and the national welfare; forest hydrology; wildland hydrology; land use management in relation to the water resource. Address: Route 1, Box 153, Pine, CO 80470.

GART, JOHN J(ACOB), b. Chicago, Ill, Apr. 15, 31; m. 61; c. 4. STATISTICS. B.Sc, DePaul Univ, 53; M.S, Marquette, 55; fel, Oak Ridge Inst. Nuclear Studies, 57-58; Ph.D.(statist), Va. Polytech, 58. Asst. prof. biostatist, sch. hyg. & pub. health, Hopkins, 58-62, assoc. prof. biostatist. & statist, 62-65; mathematician, NAT. CANCER INST, 65-67, HEAD MATH. STATIST. & APPL. MATH. SECT, BIOMET. BR, 67- Vis. res. fel, London, 61-62. Fel. AAAS; Biomet. Soc; fel. Am. Statist. Asn; Inst. Math. Statist; fel. Royal Statist. Soc. Biometrics; mathematical statistics; stochastic processes. Address: Mathematical Statistics & Applied Mathematics Section, Biometry Branch, National Cancer Institute, Bethesda, MD 20014.

GARTEN, WILLIAM, JR, b. Baltimore, Md, July 21, 17; m. 50; c. 2. PHYSICS. Ph.D.(physics), Hopkins, 42. Special res. assoc, Harvard, 41-42; PHYSICIST, geophys. lab, Carnegie Inst, 43-45; APPL. PHYSICS LAB, JOHNS HOPKINS UNIV, 46- Civilian with Off. Sci. Res. & Develop, 44. AAAS; Am. Phys. Soc. Ultrasonics; electronics; jet propulsion; plasma physics. Address: Applied Physics Lab, Johns Hopkins University, Silver Spring, MD 20910.

GARTENHAUS, SOLOMON, b. Ger, Jan. 3, 29. THEORETICAL PHYSICS. B.A, Pennsylvania, 51; Gen. Elec. Co. fel, Illinois, 54-55, Ph.D.(physics), 55. Instr, Stanford, 55-58; asst. prof. PHYSICS, PURDUE UNIV, 58-61, assoc. prof, 61-64, PROF, 64- Am. Phys. Soc. Plasma and nuclear physics. Address: Dept. of Physics, Purdue University, Lafayette, IN 47906.

GARTH, JOHN C(AMPBELL), b. New York, N.Y, Sept. 26, 34; m. 60; c. 2. SOLID STATE PHYSICS. B.S.E, Princeton, 56; M.S, Illinois, 58, Nat. Sci. Found. fel, 59-60, Ph.D.(physics), 65. Res. asst. physics, Illinois, 60-64; asst. prof, Worcester Polytech. Inst, 64-67; RES. PHYSICIST, AIR FORCE CAMBRIDGE RES. LABS, SOLID STATE SCI. LAB, RADIATION EFFECTS BR, 67- Am. Phys. Soc. Photoelectric and secondary electron emission from solids; theory of high energy electron transport and ionization effects in electronic device materials; electron spin resonance and optical properties of defects in solids. Address: Air Force Cambridge Research Labs, Solid State Sciences Lab, Radiation Effects Branch, L.G. Hanscom Field, Bedford, MA 01730.

GARTH, JOHN S(HRADER), b. Los Angeles, Calif, Oct. 3, 09; m. 40; c. 1. ZOOLOGY. B.Mus, Southern California, 32, M.S, 35, Ph.D.(zool), 41. Asst. zool, UNIV. SOUTH. CALIF, 35-37, res. assoc, ALLAN HANCOCK FOUND, 37-42, 46-52, assoc. prof. biol, 52-55, adj. assoc. prof, 55-62, assoc. prof, 62-67, PROF. BIOL. SCI, 67-, CHIEF CURATOR, 70-, entomologist & marine zoologist, Hancock Found. exped, Mex, Cent. & S.Am, & Galapagos Islands, 31-41, exped. leader, Ariz. desert, 42, 46, 47, 48, curator, 63-70. Partic, U.S. Prog. Biol, Int. Indian Ocean Exped, 64; assoc. marine biologist, Eniwetok Marine Biol. Lab, summers 57 & 59; mem. sci. adv. comt, Charles Darwin Found. Civilian instr, Santa Ana Army Air Base, U.S. War Dept, 42-44; Sanit.C, 44-46, Capt. AAAS; Soc. Syst. Zool; Am. Soc. Limnol. & Oceanog. Systematics, distribution and ecology of the brachyuran Crustacea, particularly of the Eastern and Indo-West Pacific regions; biological oceanography; zoogeography. Address: Allan Hancock Foundation, University of Southern California, Los Angeles, CA 90007.

GARTH, RICHARD E(DWIN), b. Knoxville, Tenn, Mar. 10, 26; m. 50; c. 6. PHYSIOLOGY, BIOLOGY. A.B, Emory, 49, Ph.D.(biol), 54; M.S, Tennessee, 50. Instr. biol, Bloomfield Col, 50-51; asst. prof, Mt. Union Col, 54-55; E.Tenn. State Col, 55-57, assoc. prof, 57-58; asst. prof, Northwest. State Col.(La), 58-62, assoc. prof, 62-66; prof. biol. sci. & head dept, Miss. State Col. Women, 66-69; PROF. BIOL. & HEAD DEPT, UNIV. TENN, CHATTANOOGA, 69-, DIR. DIV. SCI. & MATH, 71- Asst. prog. dir. sec. sch. progs, Nat. Sci. Found, 63-64, consult. sci. personnel & ed, div, 64- U.S.A, 44-46. AAAS; Am. Inst. Biol. Sci. Autecology of Spanish moss; hypothalamus-gonadotrophin relationships; avian photoperiodism; physiology of development. Address: Dept. of Biology, University of Tennessee, Chattanooga, TN 37401.

GARTHE, WILLIAM A, b. Newark, N.J, May 11, 36; m. 58; c. 2. ZOOLOGY. B.S, Rutgers, 58; M.S, Minnesota, 61; Ph.D.(zool), Cornell, 64. ASST. PROF. ZOOL, NORTH. ILL. UNIV, 64- Entom. Soc. Am. Insect physiology. Address: Dept. of Biological Sciences, Northern Illinois University, DeKalb, IL 60115.

GARTLER, STANLEY M(ICHAEL), b. Los Angeles, Calif, June 9, 23; m. 48. GENETICS. B.S, California, Los Angeles, 48; Ph.D.(genetics), California, 52. Res. assoc. genetics, Columbia, 52-57; res. asst. prof, UNIV. WASH, 57-64, PROF. MED. & GENETICS, 64- U.S. Pub. Health Serv. fel, 52-54, sr. res. fel, 59-, res. career award, 64- U.S.A.A.F, 43-46. Genetics Soc. Am; Am. Soc. Human Genetics; Am. Soc. Nat. Human genetics; mammalian somatic cell genetics. Address: Dept. of Genetics, University of Washington, Seattle, WA 98105.

GARTNER, EDWARD A, b. Milford, Conn, July 9, 28; m. 54; c. 3. ORGANIC CHEMISTRY. B.S, Florida, 51. Process engr, Hercules Powder Co, 51-53, sr. process engr, 55-57; develop. chemist, GLOBE MFG. CO, 58-65, develop. supvr, 65-68, SPEC. PROJS. COORD, FALL RIVER, 68- U.S.A, 53-55. Am. Chem. Soc; Am. Asn. Textile Chem. & Colorists; Am. Soc. Qual. Control. Manufacturing parameters of nitroglycerin; nitrocellulose and solid propellants; mechanism of cold injury; improvements in rubber thread; invention of a spandex fiber; development of dyeing and finishing procedures and optimization of the thread. Address: 117 Mohawk Rd, Somerset, MA 02726.

GARTNER, J(OHN) B(ERNARD), b. Ohio, Mar. 23, 18; m. 43; c. 3. FLORICULTURE & ORNAMENTAL HORTICULTURE. B.S, Ohio State, 42; M.S, Mich. State, 47, Ph.D.(hort, bot), 52. Asst. prof. floricult, Mich. State Col, 46-49; assoc. prof. & exten. horticulturist, N.C. State, 50-53, PROF. hort. & floricult, 54-61; PROF. ORNAMENTAL HORT, UNIV. ILL, URBANA, 61-U.S.N, 42-45, Lt. AAAS; Am. Soc. Hort. Sci. Physiology and nutrition of ornamental plants. Address: Division of Ornamental Horticulture, 100 Floriculture Bldg, University of Illinois, Urbana, IL 61801.

GARTNER, LAWRENCE MITCHEL, b. Brooklyn, N.Y, Apr. 24, 33; m. 56; c. 2. MEDICINE, PHYSIOLOGY. A.B, Columbia, 54; M.D, Hopkins, 58. Intern PEDIAT, Hopkins Hosp, 58-59; resident, Bronx Munic. Hosp. Center, 59-61; asst. instr, ALBERT EINSTEIN COL. MED, 61-62, instr, 62-63, assoc, 63-64, asst. prof, 64-68, ASSOC. PROF, 68-, dir. div. neonatology, 68. Chief resident, Bronx Munic. Hosp. Center, 61-62, asst. dir. premature center, 62-67, dir. center, 67-; U.S. Pub. Health Serv. pediat. res. trainee, 62-64, Nat. Inst. Child Health & Human Develop. spec. fel. & career develop. award, 64-66; Nat. Insts. Health career develop. award, 66-, res. grant, 68-; United Health Found. res. grant, 67-68; Scripps res. fel, inst. comp. biol, California, San Diego, 67. Am. Fedn. Clin. Res; Harvey Soc; Soc. Pediat. Res. Liver function and disease in premature and full-term newborn infants and children; bilirubin metabolism and physiology of bilirubin transport; management of premature and newborn infants; physiology of the newborn and premature infant. Address: Dept. of Pediatrics, Albert Einstein College of Medicine, New York, NY 10461.

GARTNER, STEFAN, JR, b. Hungary, Mar. 28, 37; U.S. citizen; m. 63; c. 2. MARINE GEOLOGY, MICROPALEONTOLOGY. B.A, Connecticut, 60; M.S, Illinois, 62, Ph.D.(geol), 65. Res. geologist, Esso Prod. Res. Co, 65-68; ASST. PROF. MARINE SCI, ROSENSTIEL SCH. MARINE & ATMOSPHERIC SCI, UNIV. MIAMI, 68- Geol. Soc. Am. Micropaleontology and biostratigraphy of calcareous nannofossils. Address: Rosenstiel School of Marine & Atmospheric Sciences, University of Miami, 10 Rickenbacker Causeway, Miami, FL 33149.

GARTON, RONALD R(AY), b. Billings, Mont, Feb. 27, 35; m. 59. AQUATIC BIOLOGY. B.A, Montana, 58, B.S, 63; M.S, Mich. State, 67, Ph.D.(fisheries, wildlife), 68. RES. AQUATIC BIOLOGIST, PAC. NORTHWEST WATER LAB, ENVIRON. PROTECTION AGENCY, 68- U.S.N, 58-61, Res, 61-, Lt. Comdr. Ecol. Soc. Am; Am. Fisheries Soc. Effects of thermal pollution on freshwater organisms. Address: Pacific Northwest Water Lab, Environmental Protection Agency, 200 S. 35th St, Corvallis, OR 97330.

GARTSHORE, IAN STANLEY, b. Calgary, Alta, Apr. 27, 35; m. 62; c. 2. FLUID MECHANICS. B.A.Sc, British Columbia, 57; Athlone fel, London, 57-59, M.Sc, 60; Nat. Res. Coun. studentship, McGill, 62-65, Ph.D.(mech. eng), 65. Sci. off, Nat. Phys. Lab, U.K, 59-60; res. off, Nat. Res. Coun. Can, 61-62; res. dir, McGill, 65-67; asst. prof. MECH. ENG, UNIV. B.C, 67-70, ASSOC. PROF, 70- Assoc. fel. Can. Aeronaut. & Space Inst. Swirling flow phenomena in laminar and turbulent motion; static thrust prediction for propellers; development of turbulent shear flows. Address: Dept. of Mechanical Engineering, University of British Columbia, Vancouver, B.C, Can.

GARTSIDE, ROBERT N(IFONG), b. Fredericktown, Mo, Jan. 1, 18; m. 59; c. 3. CHEMICAL ENGINEERING. B.S, Washington (St. Louis), 39. Chem. engr, east. lab, explosives dept, E.I. DU PONT DE NEMOURS & CO, INC, 39-42, 46-52, tech. asst. tech. div, 52-53, asst. dir, Repauno Process Lab, 53-56, dir, sales develop. lab, 56-59, asst. dir, east. lab, 59-60, DIR, Repauno Develop. Lab, 60-67, ADMIN. ASST, EAST. LAB, GIBBSTOWN, 67- Ord.Dept, 42-46, Capt. Am. Chem. Soc. Process development; administration. Address: 578 High St, Woodbury, NJ 08096.

GARTY, K(ENNETH) T(HOMAS), b. Chicago, Ill, Nov. 4, 16; m. 50; c. 4. ORGANIC CHEMISTRY. B.S, Purdue, 40; M.S, Stevens Inst. Tech, 47. Chemist res, Bakelite Co, 40-48, group leader, 48-52, proj. leader, 52-59, UNION CARBIDE CORP, 59-65, GROUP LEADER, 65- Am. Chem. Soc. Vinyl polymerization and copolymerizations; organosulfur and epoxy polymers; polyethers. Address: Union Carbide Corp, Bound Brook, NJ 08805.

GARVEN, FLOYD C(HARLES), b. Baker, Minn, Mar. 2, 22; m. 45; c. 3. ORGANIC CHEMISTRY. B.S, Moorhead State Teachers Col, 46; M.S, N.Dak. State, 48. Org. res. chemist, antituberculars & hypnotics, ABBOTT LABS, 49-54, plant process, 54-59, org. develop. chemist, process & prod. develop, 59-62, mgr. chem. develop, 62-64, DIR. develop, 64-67, qual. control, 67-69, QUAL. ASSURANCE, 69- U.S.N.R, 43-45, Ens. Am. Chem. Soc. Antitubercular drugs; hypnotics; erythromycin structure work; chemotherapeutic drugs; process development. Address: Quality Assurance, Abbott Labs, 14th & Sheridan Sts, North Chicago, IL 60064.

GARVER, JOHN C, b. Rockford, Ill, Oct. 16, 25; m. 48; c. 3. BIOCHEMICAL ENGINEERING. B.S, Wisconsin, Madison, 46, M.S, 47, Ph.D.(chem. eng), 55. Teaching asst. chem. eng, Wisconsin, Madison, 48-49, instr, 49-51, proj. asst, 51-52, proj. assoc. eng. exp. sta, 52-55, asst. prof. chem. eng, Illinois, 55-57; BIOCHEM, UNIV. WIS, MADISON, 57-60, assoc. prof, 60-66, PROF, 66- Summers, engr, Corn Prod. Refinery Co, 56, biochem. engr, Army Chem. Corps, Ft. Detrik, 57. Am. Chem. Soc; Am. Soc. Microbiol. Kinetics of catalytic cracking of cumene; spray drying of vegetative bacteria and enzymes; large-scale rupturing of microorganisms; behavior of bacterial cultures in continuous fermentation; development of 30-liter continuous fermentor; pilot plant production of glycerol and production of erythritol by osmophillic yeasts. Address: Dept. of Biochemistry, University of Wisconsin, Madison, WI 53706.

GARVEY, GERALD THOMAS, b. New York, N.Y, Jan. 21, 35; m. 59; c. 3. NUCLEAR PHYSICS. B.S, Fairfield, 56; Boston Col, 56-58; Nat. Sci. Found fel. & Ph.D.(physics), Yale, 62. Res. assoc. PHYSICS, Yale, 62-63; instr, Princeton, 63-64; asst. prof, Yale, 64-66; PRINCETON, 66-67, assoc. prof, 67-71, PROF, 71- Sloan Found. fel, 67-69; consult, Brookhaven Nat. Lab, 70-71; mem, Nevis Adv. Panel. Experimental nuclear physics, particularly reactions and isoboric spin studies. Address: Dept. of Physics, Joseph Henry Lab, Jadwin Hall, Princeton University, Princeton, NJ 08540.

GARVEY, JAMES EMMETT, b. Cleveland, Ohio, Nov. 26, 17; m. 46; c. 2. PHYSICS. B.S, Ohio State, 46; Ph.D.(physics), 51. Res. physicist, high vacuum, Distillation Prods, Inc, 46; theoret. physicist, atomic energy res, N.Am. Aviation, Inc, 51-55; warhead res, Rheem Res. & Develop, 55-56; physicist, Army Res. Off, 56-60, Off. Naval Res, Pasadena Br, 60-67; DIR. ACAD. CTR. PASADENA, PAC. INST. ADVAN. STUDIES, 67- U.S.A.A.F, 41-46, Res, 46-, Lt. Col. AAAS; Am. Phys. Soc. Nuclear physics; reactor theory; operations research; methodology of science; research management. Address: Academic Center Pasadena, Pacific Institute for Advanced Studies, 7425 Franklin Ave, Los Angeles, CA 90046.

GARVEY, JAMES R(OSS), b. Pittsburgh, Pa, June 8, 19; m. 45; c. 2. MINING & MECHANICAL ENGINEERING. B.Min.Eng, Ohio State, 41. Mining engr, Pittsburgh Coal Co, Pa, 41-42; maintenance supvr, Capital Airlines, Wash, D.C, 46; from proj. engr. to PRES. & DIR. RES, BITUMINOUS COAL RES, INC, PA, 46- U.S.A.A.F, 42-46, Capt. Am. Soc. Mech. Eng; Am. Inst. Mining, Metall. & Petrol. Eng. Coal research and related technology, particularly preparation and utilization equipment development. Address: Bituminous Coal Research, Inc, 350 Hochberg Rd, Monroeville, PA 15146.

GARVEY, JUSTINE S(PRING), b. Wellsville, Ohio, Mar. 14, 22; m. 46; c. 2. IMMUNOCHEMISTRY. B.S, Ohio State, 44, M.S, 48, Ph.D.(bact), 50. Res. fel. CHEM, CALIF. INST. TECHNOL, 51-57, SR. RES. FEL, 57- AAAS; Am. Asn. Immunol; N.Y. Acad. Sci. Characterization of persisting antigen in animal tissues by physical, chemical and biological techniques; biological studies of soluble antigen-antibody complexes; electron microscopy of isolated chromosomes; radioactive tracer studies of antigen-antibody reactions; in vitro studies of immune response; biomembranes; mechanism of tolerance. Address: Division of Chemistry & Chemical Engineering, California Institute of Technology, Pasadena, CA 91109.

GARVEY, ROY GEORGE, b. Pocatello, Idaho, Jan. 19, 41; m. 63; c. 3. INORGANIC CHEMISTRY. B.A, Utah, 63, Ph.D.(inorg. chem), 66. Asst. prof. INORG. CHEM, N.DAK. STATE UNIV, 66-69, ASSOC. PROF, 69- AAAS; Am. Chem. Soc. Coordination properties of M-D functional groups; kinetics of displacement reactions at transition metal sites; synthesis and physical properties of novel inorganic compounds. Address: Dept. of Inorganic Chemistry, North Dakota State University, Fargo, ND 58102.

GARVIN, DAVID, b. Cleveland, Ohio, Aug. 25, 23. PHYSICAL CHEMISTRY. B.S, Yale, 48; M.A. & Ph.D.(chem), Harvard, 51. Instr. chem, Princeton, 51-55, asst. prof, 55-61; CHEMIST, NAT. BUR. STANDARDS, 61- U.S.A, 43-46, 1st Lt. Am. Chem. Soc; Am. Phys. Soc. Mechanisms of rapid reactions; spectroscopy; information retrieval. Address: B-152, Chemistry Bldg, National Bureau of Standards, Washington, DC 20234.

GARVIN, DONALD FRANK, b. Toledo, Ohio, Mar. 14, 32; m. 51; c. 3. INDUSTRIAL & CLINICAL MICROBIOLOGY. B.S, Wayne State Univ, 64, M.S, 66. Clin. lab. technician, Woodward Gen. Hosp, Highland Park, Mich, 55-59, asst. supvr. clin. lab, 59-65; sr. technologist, William Beaumont Hosp, Royal Oak, Mich, 65-66; RES. BACTERIOLOGIST, Wyandotte Chem. Corp, 66-70, BASF WYANDOTTE CORP, 70- U.S.N, 51-55. Am. Soc. Microbiol; assoc. mem. Asn. Off. Anal. Chem; assoc. mem. Am. Asn. Textile Chem. & Colorists. Identification and isolation of cell wall deficient varients of Mycobacterium tuberculosis and clinical L-forms by gas chromotography, polyacrylamide electrophoresis and fluorescent antibody techniques; application research of germicides and fungicides; environmental effects of carpeting in hospitals and development of laboratory test methods for carpet sanitizing shampoos. Address: Chemical Specialties Research, BASF Wyandotte Corp, Wyandotte, MI 48192.

GARVIN, HUGH L(ESLIE), b. Wilmington, Del, Nov. 18, 28; m. 53; c. 3. ATOMIC & SURFACE PHYSICS. B.S, Rochester, 51; M.A, California, 57, Ph.D.(physics), 59. Asst. atomic beam res, Lawrence Radiation Lab, California, 56-59; mem. res. staff, John Jay Hopkins Lab, Gen. Atomic Div, Gen. Dynamics Corp, 59-62; scientist, energy conversion lab, nuclear div, Martin-Marietta Corp, 62-63; MEM. TECH. STAFF, HUGHES RES. LABS, 63- Officer in charge, naval guided missile test unit, Calif, 53-55, U.S.N, 51-55. Am. Phys. Soc. Plasma acceleration and control; ion beam-surface interactions; thin film phenomena; microelectric development. Address: Hughes Research Labs, 3011 Malibu Canyon Rd, Malibu, CA 90265.

GARVIN, JOHN P(UTNAM), b. Columbus, Ohio, July 24, 19; m. 42; c. 4. ANESTHESIOLOGY. B.A, Ohio State, 41; M.D, Cincinnati, 44. Intern, Cincinnati Gen. Hosp, 44-45, resident anesthesiol, 45-46; instr. surg, OHIO STATE UNIV, 48-49, asst. prof, 49-58, assoc. prof, 58-70, CLIN. ASSOC. PROF. ANESTHESIOL, 70-, resident, univ. hosp, 48-49, asst. dir. dept. anesthesia, 49-51. Dir, Columbus Children's Hosp, 56- Med.C, 46-48, Capt. Am. Soc. Anesthesiol; Am. Med. Asn; Int. Anesthesia Res. Soc; fel. Am. Acad. Pediat. Pediatric anesthesia; causes of death in infants and children. Address: Dept. of Anesthesiology, Ohio State University, Columbus, OH 43210.

GARVIN, PAUL J(OSEPH), JR, b. Toledo, Ohio, Nov. 16, 28; m. 52; c. 6. PHARMACOLOGY. B.S, St. John's, 50; M.S, Minnesota, 59. Asst. pharmacol, Minnesota, 52-54; Sterling-Winthrop Res. Inst, 54-58; pharmacologist, BAXTER LABS, INC, 58-59, SR. RES. PHARMACOLOGIST, 59- AAAS; Soc. Toxicol; Europ. Soc. Study Drug Toxicity. Drug and materials toxicology; safety evaluation; metabolism. Address: Baxter Labs, Inc, Morton Grove, IL 60053.

GARVIN, PAUL L(AWRENCE), b. Dec. 5, 39; U.S. citizen, m. 64; c. 1. MINERALOGY. B.S, Idaho State Univ, 64; Nat. Defense Educ. Act fel, Univ. Colo, Boulder, 65-68, Nat. Sci. Found. fel, 68-69, Ph.D.(geol), 69. Lectr. GEOL, Idaho State Univ, 64-65; field asst, J.R. Simplot Co, summer 65; ASST. PROF, CORNELL COL, 69- AAAS; Mineral. Soc. Am; Mineral. Asn. Can. Sulfide phase relations; mineralogy and genesis of ore deposits. Address: Dept. of Geology, Cornell College, Mt. Vernon, IA 52314.

GARVINE, RICHARD WILLIAM, b. Pottstown, Pa, Jan. 7, 40; m. 66; c. 2. PHYSICAL OCEANOGRAPHY. B.S, Mass. Inst. Technol, 61; Ford Found. fel, Princeton, 61-63, Ph.D.(aerodyn. eng), 65. Theoret. aerodynamicist, space sci. lab, Gen. Elec. Co, 65-69; ASST. PROF. MECH. ENG, MARINE SCI. INST, UNIV. CONN, 69- AAAS; Am. Phys. Soc. Ocean circulation; geophysical fluid dynamics. Address: Marine Sciences Institute, University of Connecticut, Avery Point, Groton, CT 06340.

GARWIN, EDWARD L(EE), b. Cleveland, Ohio, Mar. 22, 33; m. 54; c. 3. PHYSICS. B.S, Case, 54; M.S, Chicago, 55, Nat. Sci. Found. fel, 54-57, Ph.D.(physics), 58. Res. assoc, Chicago, 58-59; res. asst. prof. physics, Illinois, 59-60; prog. mgr. space simulation, Gen. Tech. Corp, 60-62; PHYSICIST, STANFORD LINEAR ACCELERATOR CTR, 62- Consult, Space Technol. Labs, Inc, 59-60; Thompson-Ramo-Wooldridge, Inc, 59-60; Gen. Tech. Corp, 62-64; Rand Corp, 69- Am. Phys. Soc. Secondary emission; surface and high energy physics; ultrahigh vacuum; fast pulse electronics; medical electronics and instrumentation; superconductivity; solid state physics. Address: Stanford Linear Accelerator Center, P.O. Box 4349, Bin 72, Stanford, CA 94305.

GARWIN, RICHARD L(AWRENCE), b. Cleveland, Ohio, Apr. 19, 28; m. 47; c. 3. PHYSICS. B.S, Case West. Reserve Univ, 47, D.Sc, 66; M.S, Univ. Chicago, 48, Ph.D.(physics), 49. Instr. physics, Univ. Chicago, 49-51, asst prof, 51-52; physicist, IBM Watson Lab, Int. Bus. Machines Corp, 52-65, dir. appl. res, THOMAS J. WATSON RES. CTR, 65-66, dir. IBM Watson Lab, 66-67, FEL. IBM CORP, 67- Adj. prof. physics, Columbia Univ, 57-; vis. scientist, Europ. Orgn. Nuclear Res, 59-60; consult, Los Alamos Sci. Lab, 49-; President's Sci. Adv. Comt, 58-62, mem, 62-65, 69-72. Nat. Acad. Sci; Am. Acad. Arts & Sci; fel. Am. Phys. Soc. Liquid and solid helium; general physics. Address: Thomas J. Watson Research Center, IBM Corp, P.O. Box 218, Yorktown Heights, NY 10598.

GARWOOD, DONALD CHARLES, b. Buchanan, Mich, Aug. 30, 36; m. 59. PHYSICAL ORGANIC CHEMISTRY. B.A, Kalamazoo Col, 57; Upjohn fel, Calif. Inst. Tech, 57-58, Nat. Sci. Found. fel, 58-60, Ph.D.(phys. org. chem), 62. Sr. scientist, jet. propulsion lab, Calif. Inst. Tech, 60-61; appl. res. labs, aeronutronic div, Philco-Ford Motor Co, 61-63, sect. supvr. space physics, 63-67, dept. mgr, 67-68; vis. scholar, Univ. Calif, Los Angeles, 68-70; DIR. CHEM. RES. & DEVELOP, SOLAR LABS, 70- Nat. Insts. Health spec. res. fel, 69-70. Am. Chem. Soc. Organosulfur chemistry; photopolymerization; polymers. Address: 153 San Vicente Blvd, Apt. 2C, Santa Monica, CA 90402.

GARWOOD, DOROTHY SEMENOW, Clin. Psychol, see 12th ed, Soc. & Behav. Vols.

GARWOOD, VERNON A(BINGTON), b. Carroll, Nebr, Oct. 29, 24; m. 53; c. 6. ANIMAL GENETICS. B.Sc, Nebraska, 50; M.Sc, 52, Ph.D.(animal breeding), 56. Asst. animal husbandman swine breeding, Nebraska, 54-56; asst. prof. ANIMAL HUSB, PURDUE UNIV, 56-59, ASSOC. PROF, AGR. EXP. STA, 59- Mem. staff, Purdue-U.S. Agency Int. Develop. Prog, Brazil. U.S.N, 43-45. Am. Soc. Animal Sci; Am. Genetic Asn. Animal breeding and physiology; population genetics. Address: Dept. of Animal Husbandry, Agriculture Experiment Station, Purdue University, Lafayette, IN 47907.

GARWOOD, VICTOR P(AUL), b. Detroit, Mich, Sept. 13, 17; m. 42. AUDIOLOGY. B.A, Michigan, 39, M.S, 48, Ph.D.(speech path, exp. phonetics), 52. Clin. asst, speech clin, Michigan, 46-48, chief exam. div, 48-50; instr. AUDIOL, SPEECH-HEARING CLIN, UNIV. SOUTH. CALIF, 50-52, asst. prof, 52-55, assoc. prof, 55-59, asst. dir, clin, 52-59, PROF. & CO-DIR. CLIN, 59-, PROF. OTOLARYNGOL, SCH. MED. & COMMUN. DISORDERS, 60-, chmn. grad. prog. commun. disorders, 67-71. Res. fel, Inst. Neurol. Disease & Blindness, 57-58, spec. res. fel, 61-64; res. assoc, deafness res. lab, Children's Hosp, Los Angeles, 58-61, consult, 64-; Los Angeles County Hosp, 64- Acoustical Soc. Am; Am. Psychol. Asn; Am. Speech & Hearing Asn; Am. Pub. Health Asn. Medical audiology; audition; auditory neurophysiology. Address: Kerckhoff Hall, University of Southern California, 734 W. Adams Blvd, Los Angeles, CA 90007.

GARWOOD, WILLIAM EVERETT, b. Kirkwood, N.J, Oct. 25, 19; m. 46; c. 3. ORGANIC CHEMISTRY. B.A, North Carolina, 42; Temple, 47-54. Res. chemist, Socony Vacuum Res. Labs, 42-55, sr. chemist, MOBIL RES. & DEVELOP. CORP, 55-71, RES. ASSOC, 71- U.S.N, 44-46. Am. Chem. Soc; Catalysis Soc. Chemical catalysis; lubricating oil additives; synthetic lubricants; organophosphorus chemistry; hydrodesulfurization; hydrocracking; zeolite-catalyzed reactions; carbonylation; alkylation. Address: Mobil Research & Development Corp, Paulsboro, NJ 08066.

GARY, HERBERT H(OOVER), b. N.Y.C, June 13, 28; m. 55; c. 3. INORGANIC CHEMISTRY. B.S, City Col. New York, 50; M.A, Brooklyn Col, 60; Ph.D. (chem), Rutgers Univ, 70. Chemist, Montefiore Hosp, 52-54; Morningstar-Paisley, 54-56; anal. chemist, Food & Drug Res. Labs, Inc, N.Y, 56-57; SR. RES. INVESTR, BRISTOL MEYERS INC, 57- U.S.A, 50-52. Solubility of inorganics in ternary systems consisting of salt, water and a nonaqueous solvent. Address: 32 Sharon Ct, Metuchen, NJ 08840.

GARY, JAMES H(UBERT), b. Victoria, Va, Nov. 18, 21; m. 45; c. 4. CHEMICAL ENGINEERING. B.S, Va. Polytech, 42, M.S, 46; Ph.D.(chem. eng), Florida, 51. Group engr. chem. eng, Standard Oil Co, 46-52; asst. prof. chem. eng. & res. dir. eng. exp. sta, Univ. Va, 52-56; assoc. prof, Alabama, 56-59, prof, 59-60; PROF. CHEM. & PETROL. REF. ENG. & HEAD DEPT, COLO. SCH. MINES, 60-, DIR. & TRUSTEE, RES. INST, 70- Res. assoc, Fla. Eng. Exp. Sta, 49-51; consult, U.S. Bur. Mines, 57-60. U.S.A, 42-46, Res, 46-53. Am. Chem. Soc; Am. Inst. Chem. Eng; Am. Inst. Mining, Metall. & Petrol. Eng; Am. Soc. Eng. Educ. Desulfurization of petroleum;

liquid-liquid extraction; distillation; solids mixing; shale oil. Address: Dept. of Chemical & Petroleum Refining Engineering, Colorado School of Mines, Golden, CO 80401.

GARY, JOHN E(VERETT), b. Coquille, Ore, Oct. 22, 16; m. 42; c. 3. MEDICINE. A.B, Willamette, 39; M.D, Oregon, 43. Res, Columbia Presby. Med. Ctr, New York, 47-49; fel. radiol, col. physicians & surgeons, Columbia, 49; RADIOLOGIST, MT. AUBURN HOSP, CAMBRIDGE, 50-, PRES. STAFF, 64-, CHIEF DEPT. RADIOL, 66-; ASST. CLIN. PROF, HARVARD MED. SCH, 68-; MASS. INST. TECHNOL, 69-, ASSOC. RADIOLOGIST, 57- Instr, Harvard Med. Sch, 63-61, clin. assoc, 61-68. Med.C, 43-47, Capt. Am. Roentgen Ray Soc; Am. Med. Asn; fel. Am. Col. Radiol. Radiology; gastrointestinal tract; pulmonary and cardiac disease; radium poisoning in humans; beryllium disease. Address: 1180 Beacon St, Brookline, MA 02146.

GARY, JOHN M(ITCHELL), b. Kalamazoo, Mich, Nov. 30, 30; m. 59. MATHEMATICS, COMPUTER SCIENCE. B.S, Michigan, 52, M.S, 53, Nat. Sci. Found. fel, 53-56, Ph.D.(math), 57. Instr. math, Calif. Inst. Tech, 56-59; asst. prof, Harvey Mudd Col, 59-60; mem, Courant Inst. Math. Sci, N.Y. Univ, 60-62, res. scientist, comput. ctr, 62-63; mem. staff, NAT. CENTER ATMOSPHERIC RES, 63-67, dir. comput. facility, 67-70, SCIENTIST, 70- Vis. prof, Univ. Ill, 69-70. Am. Math. Soc; Math. Asn. Am; Soc. Indust. & Appl. Math; Asn. Comput. Mach. Applied mathematics. Address: National Center for Atmospheric Research, Boulder, CO 80302.

GARY, JULIA THOMAS, b. Henderson, N.C, May 31, 29. PHYSICAL & ANALYTICAL CHEMISTRY. B.A, Randolph-Macon Woman's Col, 51; M.A, Mt. Holyoke Col, 53; Ph.D.(chem), Emory, 58. Instr. CHEM, Mt. Holyoke Col, 53-54; Randolph-Macon Woman's Col, 54-55; asst. prof, AGNES SCOTT COL, 57-60, assoc. prof, 60-71, PROF, 71-, DEAN FACULTY, 69-, asst. dean faculty, 62-69. Am. Chem. Soc. Far ultraviolet absorption spectra; polarography of organic compounds; analytical uses of radioactive isotopes. Address: Agnes Scott College, Decatur, GA 30030.

GARY, NORMAN D(WIGHT), b. Takoma Park, Md, Nov. 23, 22; m. 42; c. 3. MICROBIAL PHYSIOLOGY. B.S, N.Dak, State Col, 48; fel, Indiana, 48-52, M.A, 50, Ph.D.(bact, biochem), 52. Res. bacteriologist, Ft. Detrick, 52-65, chief med. bact. div, U.S. Army, 65-71; EXEC. SECY. SPECIAL STUDY SECT, DIV. RES. GRANTS, NAT. INSTS. HEALTH, 71- Vis. assoc. prof, Wesleyan Univ, 62-63. Dipl, Am. Bd. Med. Microbiol, 65. U.S.A.A.F, 41-46. AAAS; Am. Soc. Microbiol; Am. Acad. Microbiol; Sci. Res. Soc. Am. Tissue culture; nutrition and physiology of bacteria and fungi. Address: Division of Research Grants, National Institutes of Health, Bethesda, MD 20014.

GARY, NORMAN E(RWIN), b. Ocala, Fla, Nov. 1, 33; m. 54; c. 2. APICULTURE, ENTOMOLOGY. B.S, Florida, 55; Ph.D.(apicult), Cornell, 59. Res. assoc. apicult, Cornell, 59-62; asst. prof. ENTOM, UNIV. CALIF, DAVIS, 62-67, ASSOC. PROF, 67- AAAS; Entom. Soc. Am; Bee Res. Asn; Asn. Study Animal Behav; N.Y. Acad. Sci. Behavior of insects, especially social insects; economic entomology. Address: Dept. of Entomology, University of California, Davis, CA 95616.

GARY, ROBERT, b. Baltimore, Md, Apr. 15, 28; m. 59; c. 2. PHYSICAL CHEMISTRY. B.S, Loyola Col.(Md), 50; M.S, Yale, 51, Ph.D.(chem), 54. Res. chemist, E.I. du Pont de Nemours & Co, 54-60; chemist, Nat. Bur. Standards, D.C, 60-66, phys. sci. adminstr, 66-67; independent consult, univ-govt. rels, 67-70; ASST. TO DEP. DIR, OFF. TELECOMMUN, U.S. DEPT. COMMERCE, 70- Am. Chem. Soc. Synthetic fibers in non-garment uses; tire research and development; mixed electrolytes; solvent effects; pH standards in ordinary and heavy water; measurements in amphiprotic solvents operation research; research planning and program development. Address: 132 Claybrook Dr, Silver Spring, MD 20902.

GARY, R(OLAND) THACHER, b. Locker, Tex, April 29, 16; m. 40; c. 2. BIOLOGY. B.S, Southwest Tex. State Teachers Col, 40, M.A, 46; Ph.D. (higher ed), George Peabody Col, 53. Teacher & adminstr, pub. schs, Tex, 37-42; instr. biol, George Peabody Col, 48-49; asst. prof. sci, SOUTHWEST TEX. STATE UNIV, 46-48, biol, 50-54, BIOL. & GEN. SCI, 55-56, PROF, 56- Conserv. ed. consult, 63-64. Med.Serv.C, 43-46, Capt. Nat. Asn. Biol. Teachers. Conservation education; science content of preservice courses for teachers of science in public schools at all levels; ecological studies on land snails. Address: Route 1, Box 327-C, San Marcos, TX 78666.

GARY, S(TEPHEN) PETER, b. Cleveland, Ohio, Oct. 3, 39; m. 66; c. 1. PLASMA PHYSICS. B.S, Case, 61; A.M, Washington (St. Louis), 66, Ph.D. (physics), 67. Instr. PHYSICS, Webster Col, 66-67; res. assoc, Univ. Iowa, 67-68; res. asst, Univ. St. Andrews, 68-69; Leverhulme vis. fel, Univ. Col. N.Wales, 69-70; ASST. PROF. PHYSICS, COL. WILLIAM & MARY, 70- Am. Phys. Soc. Nonlinear, turbulent plasmas. Address: Dept. of Physics, College of William & Mary, Williamsburg, VA 23185.

GASCHKE, MARCEL M(ATHEW), b. Jaroslaw, Poland, Nov. 24, 25; nat; m. 54; c. 2. ORGANIC CHEMISTRY. L.es.Sc, Paris, 51; M.S, Chicago, 53, Ph.D.(chem), 55. Asst, Chicago, 51-55, Shell Oil Co. fel, 55-56; res. chemist fundamental sect, east. res. div, Rayonier Inc, 56-58; explor. sect, M.W. Kellogg Co, 58-61; TAP dept, Ciba Corp, 61-67, SECT. LEADER, CIBA-GEIGY CORP, 67- Am. Chem. Soc. Chemistry of free radicals in solution; reaction mechanisms; organo-metallic compounds; modifications of cellulose; catalysis; chemicals applied in paper; optical brighteners; hair lacquers; epoxy resins, coatings. Address: 16 Cedarwood Dr, Toms River, NJ 08753.

GASCHO, GARY JOHN, b. Bad Axe, Mich, Apr. 9, 41; m. 61; c. 2. PLANT NUTRITION & PHYSIOLOGY. B.S, Mich. State, 63, Ph.D.(soil fertil. & plant physiol), 68; M.S, Illinois, 65. ASST. PROF. PLANT NUTRIT, AGR. RES. & EDUC. CTR, UNIV. FLA, 68- Am. Soc. Agron; Soil Sci. Soc. Am; Crop Sci. Soc. Am; Int. Soc. Sugarcane Technol; Am. Soc. Sugarcane Technol. Sugarbeet nutrition; sugarcane nutrition and physiology; effect of cold stress on sugarcane. Address: Agriculture Research & Education Center, University of Florida, P.O. Drawer A, Belle Glade, FL 33430.

GASCON, ANDRE L, b. Montreal, Que, May 24, 38; m 63; c. 2. PHARMACOLOGY. B.Sc, Univ. Montreal, 60, M.Sc, 61, Nat. Res. Coun. Can. stud, 61-64, Ph.D.(pharmacol), 64. Nat. Res. Coun. Can. fel, FACULTY MED, UNIV. MONTREAL, 64-65, Nat. Insts. Health grant, 65-66, res. asst. PHARMACOL, 66-67, prof. asst, 67-71, PROF. ASSOC, 71-, Med. Res. Coun. Can. scholar, 66-71. Pharmacol. Soc. Can; Am. Soc. Pharmacol. & Exp. Therapeut. Pharmacology of biogenic amines and vasoactive peptides. Address: Dept. of Pharmacology, Faculty of Medicine, University of Montreal, B.O. 6128, Montreal, Que, Can.

GASDORF, EDGAR C(ARL), b. Decatur, Ind, Nov. 27, 31; m. 58; c. 1. ZOOLOGY, ANIMAL PHYSIOLOGY. B.S, Purdue Univ, 53, M.S, 56, Ph.D.(biol. sci), 59. Instr. BIOL, BRADLEY UNIV, 59-61, asst. prof, 61-66, ASSOC. PROF, 66- AAAS; Ecol. Soc. Am; Am. Inst. Biol. Sci. Reptilian physiological ecology. Address: Dept. of Biology, Bradley University, Peoria, IL 61606.

GASH, KENNETH B(LAINE), b. Brooklyn, N.Y, Jan. 2, 33; m. 63; c. 1. ORGANIC CHEMISTRY. B.S, Pratt Inst, 60; Ph.D.(org. chem), Ariz. State Univ, 68. Lab. asst. CHEM, Chas. Pfizer & Co, Inc, N.Y, 50-52, res. asst, 56-60; teacher, pub. schs, N.Y, 60-63; ASSOC. PROF, CALIF. STATE COL, DOMINGUEZ HILLS, 67- U.S.N, 52-56. Am. Chem. Soc. Chemistry of carbonium ions, acyl and aroyl-oxonium ions; investigations of linear free energy relationships; synthesis of novel compounds; redesigning undergraduate organic laboratory programs. Address: Dept. of Chemistry, California State College at Dominguez Hills, 1000 E. Victoria, Dominguez Hills, CA 90246.

GASH, VIRGIL W(ALTER), b. Rock Falls, Ill, June 28, 19; m. 44; c. 2. ORGANIC CHEMISTRY. B.A, Cornell Col, 42; M.S, Illinois, 47, Ph.D.(chem), 52. RES. CHEMIST, ORG. CHEM, William S. Merrell Co, 47-50; MONSANTO CO, ST. LOUIS, 52- U.S.A, 42-46, Res, 46-53. Am. Chem. Soc. Fluorocarbons; nitrogen heterocyclics and unsaturated nitrogen compounds; steroids; oxidations; aromatic substitution; alicyclic stereochemistry; functional fluids; ketene chemistry. Address: 350 Sudbury Lane, Ballwin, MO 63166.

GASIC, GABRIEL J, b. Punta Arenas, Chile, Mar. 18, 12; m. 53; c. 3. PATHOLOGY. M.D, Univ. Chile, 38. Res. fel, John Simon Guggenheim Mem. Found, 43; Carnegie Inst. Res. Univ, 44-46; Rockefeller Univ, 46-47; prof. biol, SCH. MED, Univ. Chile, 48-60, dir. oncol, 60-65; res. prof. PATH, UNIV. PA, 66-67, PROF, 67-, res. assoc, 60-63. Grants, Rockefeller Found, Damon Runyon Mem. Fund, Nat. Cancer Inst, Nat. Sci. Found, Population Coun. AAAS; Am. Soc. Cell Biol; Histochem. Soc; Am. Asn. Cancer Res. Cell surface histochemistry and biology; tumor invasiveness; egg implantation and development. Address: Dept. of Pathology, University of Pennsylvania School of Medicine, Philadelphia, PA 19104.

GASICH, WELKO E(LTON), b. Cupertino, Calif, Mar. 28, 22; m. 47; c. 1. AERONAUTICAL & MECHANICAL ENGINEERING. A.B, Stanford, 43, M.Sc, 47; Aero. Eng, Calif. Inst. Tech, 48. Engr, Douglas Aircraft Co, Inc, 47-50; Rand Corp, 51-53; Norair Div, NORTHROP CORP, Hawthorne, 53-67, corp. v.pres, Beverly Hills, 67, CORP. V.PRES. & GEN. MGR. VENTURA DIV, NEWBURY PARK, 67- Consult, aerospace vehicles panel, sci. adv. bd, Army & Air Force Chiefs of Staff. U.S.N, 43-46, Lt. Am. Inst. Aeronaut. & Astronaut; Soc. Automotive Eng. Development of missiles, aircraft and astronautics; application of laminar flow control to transport aircraft; new concept in lightweight aircraft; tactical fighter in the close support role. Address: Ventura Division, Northrop Corp, 1515 Rancho Conejo Blvd, Newbury Park, CA 91320.

GASIORKIEWICZ, EUGENE C(ONSTANTINE), b. Grabiszew, Poland, Mar. 11, 20; nat; m. 46; c. 2. HORTICULTURE, PLANT PATHOLOGY. A.B, Marquette, 47, M.S, 48; Ph.D.(plant path), Wisconsin, 51. Asst. bot, Marquette, 46-48; plant path, Wisconsin, 48-51, proj. assoc, U.S. Dept. Agr, 51-52; asst. res. prof. bot, Massachusetts, 52-58, asst. prof. plant path, Waltham Field Sta, 58-61; horticulturist & plant pathologist, plant sci. lab, biol. res. ctr, S.C. Johnson & Son, Inc, 61-65; asst. prof. bot, Univ. Wis-Parkside, Racine Campus, 66-67; dir. res. & tech. serv, Can-Am. Plant Co, Ltd, 67-68; ASSOC. PROF. LIFE SCI. & CHMN. DIV. SCI. & DIR. NATURAL SCI. AREAS, UNIV. WIS-PARKSIDE, KENOSHA CAMPUS, 68- Med.C, U.S.A, 42-46. AAAS; Am. Phytopath. Soc. Diseases of greenhouse florist crops; turf and ornamental plants; growth regulants and disease development; pathogen free plants and disease control; ecology of natural areas; Prairie restoration. Address: Division of Science, University of Wisconsin-Parkside, Kenosha, WI 53140.

GASIOROWICZ, STEPHEN G, b. Gdansk, Poland, May 10, 28; nat; m. 53; c. 3. THEORETICAL PHYSICS. A.B, California, Los Angeles, 48, M.A, 49, Ph.D. (theoret. physics), 52. Physicist, Lawrence Radiation Lab, California, 52-60; Nat. Sci. Found. fel, Inst. theoret. physics, Copenhagen & European Orgn. Nuclear Res, 57-58; vis. scientist, Max Planck Inst. Physics & Astrophys, 59-60; assoc. prof. PHYSICS, UNIV. MINN, MINNEAPOLIS, 60-63, PROF, 63- Consult, Argonne Nat. Lab, 61-70; vis. scientist, Nordic Inst. Theoret. Atomic Physics, Copenhagen, 64; Deutsches Elektron-Synchroton, Hamburg, 68-69. Fel. Am. Phys. Soc. Elementary particle physics. Address: Dept. of Physics, School of Physics & Astronomy, University of Minnesota, Minneapolis, MN 55455.

GASKA, R. A, b. Lithuania, Oct. 1, 32; U.S. citizen; m. 60; c. 3. CHEMICAL ENGINEERING. B.S, Illinois, 55; M.S, Pa. State, 57, Ph.D.(chem. eng), 59. Chem. engr, DOW CHEM, U.S.A, 59-64, proj. leader, 64-66, group leader, chem. eng. lab, 66-67, lab. dir, 67-70, DIR. ENVIRON. RES. LAB, MIDLAND DIV, 70- Am. Chem. Soc; Am. Inst. Chem. Eng; Sci. Res. Soc. Am. Separation and purification. Address: Bldg. 1710, Environmental Research Lab, Midland Division, Dow Chemical, U.S.A, Midland, MI 48640.

GASKELL, DAVID R, b. Glasgow, Scotland, Mar. 11, 40; m. 64. METALLURGY. B.Sc, Glasgow, 62; Int. Nickel Co. Can. fel, McMaster, 65-67, Ph.D.(metall), 67. Metallurgist, LaPorte Chem. Ltd, Luton, Eng, 62-64; ASST. PROF. METALL. & MAT. SCI, UNIV. PA, 67- Metall. Soc; sr. mem. Faraday Soc. Physical chemistry of liquid oxide systems; slag-metal chemistry; thermodynamics of chemical metallurgy. Address: School of Metallurgy & Materials Science, University of Pennsylvania, Philadelphia, PA 19104.

GASKELL, PETER, b. Lancashire, England, June 24, 17; m. 40; c. 3. PHYSIOLOGY. M.D, Western Ontario, 50; Life Ins. Med. Res. Fund fel, London, 51-54, Nuffield traveling fel, 54-55, Ph.D.(physiol), 55. Asst. prof. PHYSIOL, UNIV. MAN, 55-64, assoc. prof, 64-70, PROF, 70- Med. res. assoc, Med. Res. Coun. Can, 57-; mem. clin. invest. unit, Winnipeg Gen. Hosp, 57- R.C.A.F, 41-45. Can. Physiol. Soc. Peripheral circulation, especially in the limbs; hypertension. Address: Dept. of Physiology, University of Manitoba, Winnipeg, Man, Can.

GASKELL, ROBERT E(UGENE), b. Grelton, Ohio, Jan. 18, 12; m. 40; c. 2. MATHEMATICS. A.B, Albion Col, 33; M.S, Michigan, 34, Ph.D.(math), 40. Instr. math, Albion Col, 38-39; Alabama, 40-42; res. fel. mech, Brown, 42-43, res. assoc, 43-46; asst. prof. math, Iowa State Col, 47-49, assoc. prof, 49-51; supvr. math. servs. unit, Boeing Airplane Co, 51-59; prof. MATH, Ore. State Univ, 59-66; CHMN. DEPT, NAVAL POSTGRAD. SCH, 66- AAAS; Soc. Indust. & Appl. Math; Math. Asn. Industrial and engineering applications of mathematics. Address: Dept. of Mathematics, Naval Postgraduate School, Monterey, CA 93940.

GASKILL, HERBERT STOCKTON, b. Phila, Pa, Jan. 31, 09; m. 38; c. 4. PSYCHIATRY. A.B, Haverford, 32; M.D, Pennsylvania, 37; Phila. Inst. Psychoanal, 48-49; Chicago Inst. Psychoanal, 49-57. Intern, Pa. Hosp, Phila, 37-39, fel. psychiat, 41-42; res. neurol, Jefferson Med. Col, 39-40, instr, 39-41; assoc. psychiat. & med, Pennsylvania, 46-48, asst. prof. PSYCHIAT, 48-49; prof, sch. med, Indiana, 49-53; PROF. & CHMN. DEPT, SCH. MED, UNIV. COLO, DENVER, 53- Fel. neuropath, Jefferson Med. Col, 40-41. Consult, Fitzsimmons Army Gen. Hosp, Denver, Colo, 53-; Vet. Admin. Hosp, Lowry Air Force Base, 53-. Mem. selection comt. for res. scientist award, Nat. Inst. Ment. Health, 61-64, mem. continuous ed. training comt, 67-70, chmn, 67-68; chmn. ad hoc comt, Nat. Bd. Med. Exam, 61-64; mem. Am. Psychoanal. Asn. ad hoc comt, AAAS, 66-71; mem. adv. comt. residency training, Calif. Dept. Ment. Hyg, chmn, 69- Dipl, Am. Bd. Psychiat. & Neurol, 45. Med.C, U.S.A, 43-46, Maj. Am. Psychoanal. Asn; Am. Psychiat. Asn.(v.pres, 70-71); Am. Psychosom. Soc; Am. Med. Asn; Am. Col. Physicians. Address: Dept. of Psychiatry, Medical Center, University of Colorado, 4200 E. Ninth Ave, Denver, CO 80220.

GASKILL, IRVING E, b. Mt. Holly, N.J, Feb. 24, 22; m. 58; c. 3. MATHEMATICS. B.S, Trenton State Teachers Col, 43; M.A, Pennsylvania, 47; Hopkins, 49-51. Instr. math, Bowling Green State, 47-49; mathematician, Army Map Serv, 51-56, U.S. Army Engr. Math. Comput. Agency, 56-70; DIR. MATH. & COMPUT. LAB, NAT. RESOURCE ANAL. CTR, 70- U.S.A, 43-46. Am. Math. Soc. Mathematical models for computation on electronic computer; economic models; war gaming vulnerability models; nuclear damage assessment models; geodetic network and datum adjustments. Address: 209 Belmont Dr, Leesburg, VA 22075.

GASKILL, JACK DONALD, b. Ft. Collins, Colo, Dec. 9, 35; m. 56; c. 2. ELECTRICAL ENGINEERING, OPTICS. B.S, Colorado State, 57; M.S, Stanford, 65, Ph.D.(elec. eng), 68. Electronics engr, Motorola, Inc, Ariz, 57-58; asst. prof. OPTICAL SCI, OPTICAL SCI. CTR, UNIV. ARIZ, 68-71, ASSOC. PROF, 71- U.S.A.F, 58-63, Capt. Inst. Elec. & Electronics Eng; Optical Soc. Am. Coherent optics; holographic imaging through a randomly inhomogeneous medium; general holography; optical data processing. Address: Optical Sciences Center, University of Arizona, Tucson, AZ 85721.

GASKILL, WILLIAM A(DDISON), b. Holdrege, Nebr, June 7, 21; m. 44; c. 3. ELECTRICAL ENGINEERING. B.S, New Mexico State, 46, M.S, Pittsburgh, 52. Design engr, power circuit breaker develop. sect, Westinghouse Elec. Corp, 46-52, cutout fuse & recloser sect, 52-56; chief, design & develop. sect, South. States Equip. Corp, 56-64; mgr. prod. develop, H.K. Porter Co, 64-67; mgr. eng, HIGH VOLTAGE SWITCHES, ALLIS CHALMERS, 67-69, MERCHANDISING MGR, 69- U.S.A, 43-46. Inst. Elec. & Electronics Eng. High voltage switchgear and substations. Address: Allis Chalmers, Box 23385, Portland, OR 97225.

GASKIN, DAVID EDWARD, b. Croydon, Eng, June 21, 39; m. 62; c. 2. MARINE BIOLOGY, ENTOMOLOGY. B.Sc, Bristol, 61; Ph.D.(entom), Massey Univ, N.Z, 68. Whaling inspector & biologist, Brit. Ministry Agr. Fisheries & Food-Nat. Inst. Oceanog, Wormley, Eng, 61-62, asst. exp. officer fisheries res, Brit. Ministry Agr. Fisheries & Food, Lowestoft, 62; whale fisheries biologist, Fisheries Res. Div, Wellington, N.Z, 62-65; lectr. zool, Massey Univ, N.Z, 65-68; ASST. PROF. MARINE BIOL, DEPT. ZOOL, UNIV. GUELPH, 68- New Zealand Univ. Grants Cmt. res. grant, 65-67; Nat. Res. Coun. Can. res. grant, 69- Consult. taxonomist, N.Z. Dept. Agr, Wellington, 63-64. N.Z. sci. rep, Int. Whaling Cmn, 63-68. Brit. Inst. Biol; fel. Royal Entom. Soc. London; N.Z. Entom. Soc. Ecology and biology of Southern Hemisphere and North West Atlantic cetaceans; systematics and ecology of the family Crambinae; biogeography. Address: Dept. of Zoology, University of Guelph, Guelph, Ont, Can.

GASKINS, FREDERICK H(UDSON), b. Phila, Pa, April 29, 25; m. 49; c. 4. PHYSICAL CHEMISTRY. A.B, Pennsylvania, 51. Anal. chemist, Phila. QM Depot, 51-52; colloid chemist, Franklin Inst, 52-54, rheologist, 54-59; res. proj. leader, Aeroproj, Inc, 59-63; res. phys. chemist, chem. res. & develop. labs, EDGEWOOD ARSENAL, 64-65, RES. CHEMIST, RES. LABS, 65- U.S.A.A.F, 43-46, Res, 50-58, 1st Lt. Am. Chem. Soc; Sci. Res. Soc. Am; Soc. Rheol. Visco-elasticity; physical chemistry of colloidal solutions, polymers, rocket propellants, ceramics and aluminum soap solutions; rheology applied to physical chemical problems; fluid dynamics. Address: Research Labs, Edgewood Arsenal, Box 26, Edgewood Arsenal, MD 21010.

GASKINS, MURRAY H(ENDRICKS), b. Alapaha, Ga, June 9, 27; m. 50; c. 2. HORTICULTURE. B.S, Georgia, 48; M.S, Florida, 56, Ph.D.(agr), 58. Asst. hort, agr. exp. sta, Florida, 56-58; horticulturist, AGR. RES. SERV, U.S. DEPT. AGR, 58, horticulturist in charge, plant introd. sta, 58-64, OFF. IN CHARGE, FED. EXP. STA, 64- U.S.N, 45-46. Am. Soc. Hort. Sci; Am. Soc. Plant Physiol; Soc. Econ. Bot. Fruit crops; tropical agriculture; plant

growth substances. Address: Federal Experiment Station, Agricultural Research Service, U.S. Dept. of Agriculture, Mayaguez, PR 00708.

GASKINS, WAYNE W(ILLIAM), b. Indianapolis, Ind, Mar. 11, 24. FOREST MANAGEMENT. B.S, Mich. State, 47, M.S, 48, fel, State Univ. N.Y, 50-52. Instr. phogrammetry, Mich. State, 47; gen. forestry, Ala. Polytech, 48-50. col. forestry, State Univ. N.Y, 50-52; forester, bur. land mgt, U.S. Dept. Interior, 52-56; asst. prof. gen. forest mgt, from Mich. State Univ. to Colombia Nat. Univ, S.Am, 56-59; FORESTER, WEST. FOREST INDUSTS. ASN, 59- Soc. Am. Foresters. Forest management plans; forest inventory; timber products; harvesting; silvicultural treatments; timber harvesting and marketing in Southeast Asia. Address: Western Forest Industries Association, 1500 S.W. Taylor St, Portland, OR 97205.

GASPAR, MAX R(AYMOND), b. Sioux City, Iowa, May 10, 15; m. 38; c. 5. SURGERY. A.B, Morningside Col, 36; B.S, South Dakota, 38; M.D, Southern California, 41. Assoc. clin. prof. SURG, Loma Linda Univ, 53-61, clin. prof, 62-65; UNIV. SOUTH. CALIF, 65-; SURGEON, HARRIMAN JONES CLIN. HOSP, 48-; CHIEF OF STAFF, ST. MARY'S HOSP, 67- Clin. instr, California, Los Angeles, 52-54; dir. peripheral vascular serv, Los Angeles County Hosp, 54-; consult. vascular surg, U.S. Naval Hosp, Long Beach. Dipl, Am. Bd. Surg. U.S.N, 43-46, Lt. Fel. Am. Col. Surg; Soc. Vascular Surg; Int. Cardiovasc. Soc. Intestinal anastomosis; vascular surgery. Address: 117 E. Eighth St, Long Beach, CA 90813.

GASPAR, PETER P(AUL), b. Brussels, Belg, June 20, 35; U.S. citizen; m. 65; c. 1. PHYSICAL ORGANIC CHEMISTRY, RADIOCHEMISTRY. B.S, Calif. Inst. Tech, 57; California, Los Angeles, 55-56; M.S, Yale, 58, Ph.D.(chem), 61. NATO fel. org. chem, Heidelberg, 61-62; res. fel. CHEM, Calif. Inst. Tech, 62-63; asst. prof, WASH. UNIV, 63-68, ASSOC. PROF, 68- Res. collab, Brookhaven Nat. Lab. Am. Chem. Soc; The Chem. Soc. Reaction mechanisms; carbene and hot atom chemistry; photochemistry; gasphase reactions of free atoms and free radicals. Address: Dept. of Chemistry, Washington University, St. Louis, MO 63130.

GASPER, GEORGE, JR, b. Hamtramck, Mich, Oct. 10, 39; m. 67; c. 1. MATHEMATICS. B.S, Mich. Technol. Univ, 62; M.A, Wayne State Univ, 64, NASA traineeship, 66-67, Ph.D.(math), 67. Nat. Sci. Found. vis. lectr. math, Univ. Wis, Madison, 67-68; Nat. Res. Coun. Can. fel, 68-69; vis. asst. prof. MATH, Univ. Toronto, 69-70; ASST. PROF, NORTHWEST. UNIV, 70- Am. Math. Soc. Analysis; special functions; orthogonal expansions. Address: Dept. of Mathematics, Northwestern University, Evanston, IL 60201.

GASPER, KENNETH ALBERT, b. Duluth, Minn, Sept. 25, 39; m. 61; c. 4. NUCLEAR ENGINEERING. B.S, Wisconsin, 61, M.S, 63, Ph.D.(nuclear eng), 66. Res. asst, Wis. Alumni Res. Found, 62-63; U.S. Atomic Energy Comn, 63-66; lab. scientist/specialist thermionics, DONALD W. DOUGLAS LABS, McDONNELL DOUGLAS CORP, 66-68, SECT. CHIEF, 68- Am. Nuclear Soc. Miniature radioisotope heated thermionic electric power sources and their applications; surface physics; radiation effects on surfaces. Address: Donald W. Douglas Labs, McDonnell Douglas Corp, 2955 George Washington Way, Richland, WA 99352.

GASQUE, MAC ROY, b. Olin, N.C, Jan. 29, 13; m. 39; c. 3. MEDICINE. M.D, Virginia, 44. Instr. Univ. Va, 44-45, intern surg, univ. hosp, 45-46; res, McGuire Vet. Admin. Hosp, 46-47; private practice med, N.C, 47-49; med. dir, OLIN CORP, 49-61, CORP. MED. DIR, N.Y, 61-69, CONN, 69- Lectr. sch. med, Duke; Bowman Gray Sch. Med; assoc. clin. prof, N.Y. Univ. Dipl, Am. Bd. Prev. Med. Med.C, 45-47, 54-55, Res, 55-, Lt. Comdr. AAAS; N.Y. Acad. Sci; Indust. Med. Asn. Alcoholism in industry; industrial medicine; mental health; suicide; medical administration; economics of industrial medical programs; techniques of teaching industrial medicine. Address: 120 Long Ridge Rd, Stamford, CT 06904.

GASS, CLINTON B(URKE), b. Minn, Jan. 9, 20; m. 41; c. 3. MATHEMATICS. A.B, Gustavus Adolphus Col, 41; M.A, Nebraska, 43, Ph.D.(math), 54. Instr. math, Nebraska, 42-43; assoc. prof, Nebraska Wesleyan, 43-46, prof, 46-47, prof. & dean men, 47-53, chmn. div. natural sci, 53-54; assoc. prof. MATH, DePAUW UNIV, 54-56, prof, 56-64, JOHN T. & MARGARET DEAL PROF, 64-, HEAD, DEPT. MATH. & ASTRON, 60- Consult, pub. schs, Ind, 58-59; chmn. state math. adv. comt, Nat. Defense Educ. Act, 59-; assoc. prog. dir. summer insts. prog, Nat. Sci. Found, Wash, D.C, 65-66; math. consult, U.S. Dept. Defense Overseas Schs, Europe, 69-70. U.S.A, 44-46. Am. Math. Soc; Math. Asn. Am. Eigenfunction expansions; mathematical analysis. Address: 707 Highridge Ave, Greencastle, IN 46135.

GASS, FREDERICK STUART, b. Lincoln, Nebr, Apr. 21, 43; m. 66. MATHEMATICS. B.A, DePauw, 64; A.M, Dartmouth Col, 66, Ph.D.(math), 69. ASST. PROF. MATH, MIAMI UNIV, 68- Vis. asst. prof, Talladega Col, 69-70. Math. Asn. Am; Asn. Symbolic Logic. Mathematical logic; recursive function theory; ordinal notation theory. Address: Dept. of Mathematics, Culler Hall, Miami University, Oxford, OH 45056.

GASS, GEORGE H(IRAM), b. Sunbury, Pa, Sept. 23, 24; m. 48; c. 3. ENDOCRINOLOGY, PHARMACOLOGY. B.S, Bucknell, 48; M.S, New Mexico, 52; Ph.D.(physiol), Ohio State, 55. Exp. biologist, Lederle Labs, Am. Cyanamid Co, 48-51; asst. chief, endocrine br, div. pharmacol, Food & Drug. Admin, 55-59; PROF. PHYSIOL. & DIR. ENDOCRINOL. PHARMACOL. RES. LAB, SOUTH. ILL. UNIV, 59- Mem. biol. sci. cmt, grad. sch, U.S. Dept. Agr, 58-60; consult, A.B. Leo Pharmaceut. Co, Sweden; sr. scientist fel, Alexander von Humboldt Found, W.Germany, 67-68. Fel. AAAS; Am. Physiol. Soc. Hormone assay; development of new assay methods; development of knowledge of the physiology and pharmacology of chemical compounds affecting the functions of the endocrine system; carcinogenicity of steroid hormones; mechanism of gastric function. Address: Endocrinologic Pharmacology Research Lab, Southern Illinois University, Carbondale, IL 62901.

GASS, SAUL I(RVING), b. Chelsea, Mass, Feb. 28, 26; m. 46; c. 2. MATHEMATICS. B.S. & M.A, Boston, 49; Ph.D, California, 65. Mathematician, Aberdeen Bombing Mission, 49-51; dir. mgt. anal, Hqs, U.S. Air Force, 52-55; appl. sci. rep, Int. Bus. Mach. Corp, 55-58; chief opers. res. br, C-E-I-R, Inc, 58-60; sr. mathematician, fed. systs. div, Int. Bus. Mach.

Corp, Md, 60-61, systs. mgr, 61-66, mgr. comput. sci. & oper. res, 66-69; v.pres, World Systs. Labs, Inc, Md, 69-70; DIR. OPERS. RES, MATHEMATICA, INC, 70- Secy, Am. Fedn. Info. Processing Socs, 63-65. U.S.A, 44-46. AAAS; Opers. Res. Soc. Am; Soc. Indust. & Appl. Math; Math. Asn. Am; Asn. Comput. Mach; Inst. Mgt. Sci. Linear programing; game theory; operations research; digital computer applications. Address: Mathematica, Inc, 4905 Del Ray Ave, Bethesda, MD 20014.

GASSAWAY, JAMES D, b. Fulton, Miss, Aug. 17, 32. ELECTRICAL ENGINEERING. B.S, Univ. Miss, 57; South. Methodist Univ, 57-59; Ph.D.(elec. eng), Purdue Univ, 64. Design engr. Gen. Dynamics Corp, Tex, 57-59; instr. ELEC. ENG, Purdue Univ, 59-63, asst. prof, 63-65; ASSOC. PROF, Univ. Ala, 65-67; MISS. STATE UNIV. 67- Res. asst, Am. Machine & Foundry, Purdue Univ, 62-63; consult, Wabash Magnetics, Ind, 64; electronic engr, Navy Electronics Lab, San Diego, summers 64 & 65; res. engr, Radiation Inc, Fla, summer 67, consult, 68-69; Am. Soc. Eng. Educ-NASA faculty fel, astrionics lab, Marshall Space Flight Ctr, summers 70-71. U.S.A, 51-52. Am. Soc. Eng. Educ; Inst. Elec. & Electronics Eng. Modeling of semiconductor fabrication processes and semiconductor device behavior using digital computer; development of sensitive electronic instruments; thin magnetic films and magnetic properties of rolled sheets; techniques for reduction of limit cycle oscillations in non-linear feedback systems. Address: Dept. of Electrical Engineering, Drawer EE, Mississippi State University, State College, MS 39762.

GASSAWAY, JOHN DUNCAN, b. Ellicott City, Md, July 23, 33; m. 59; c. 1. GEOCHEMISTRY, CHEMICAL OCEANOGRAPHY. B.S, Georgetown Univ, 56; M.S, George Washington Univ, 61, Ph.D.(geochem), 69. Teaching asst. geol, George Washington Univ, 60-61; res. asst. oceanog, Univ. Wash, 63-65; oceanogr, Inst. Oceanog, Environ. Sci. Serv. Admin, 65-68; RES. OCEANOGR, U.S. NAVAL OCEANOG. OFF, 68- Consult, Ocean Sci. & Eng, 66-67; Ecol. Serv. & Technol, Inc, 70-; consult to Oceanogr. U.S. Navy, 71-; partic. chem. oceanog, Gordon Conf, 70- U.S.A, 56-58. AAAS; Am. Geophys. Union; Geol. Soc. Am; Geochem. Soc; Am. Soc. Oceanog. Using trace elements, radioisotopes and suspended particulate matter to trace water masses in the ocean and determine the degree of mixing of the individual water masses. Address: U.S. Naval Oceanographic Office, Code 7310-RES, Washington, DC 20390.

GASSEL, M. MICHAEL, b. Jersey City, N.J, Mar. 1, 28. NEUROLOGY, NEUROPHYSIOLOGY. B.S, Rutgers, 48; B.M, Chicago Med. Sch, 52, M.D, 53; Ph.D.(neurol), London, 61. Intern med, King's County Hosp, Brooklyn, N.Y, 52-53, res. internal med, 53-54; clin. clerk med, neurol. & neuroanat, Nat. Hosp, Queen Square. & Royal Col. Surgeons, London, Eng, 56-57; house physician neurol, Nat. Hosp. Nervous Diseases, 58, acad. registr, 58-59 & 61, Nat. Inst. Nervous Diseases & Blindness spec. fel, 59-61, inst. neurophysiol, Copenhagen, 61-62, Wellcome Found. res. fel, 62-63; Muscular Dystrophy Asn. Am. res. grant, inst. physiol, Pisa, 63-64; Ger. Res. Asn. res. grant, inst. neurophysiol, Freiburg, 64-65; researcher, neurophysiol. lab, Evangelismos Hosp, Athens, Greece, 65; asst. prof. neurol, sch. med, Univ. Calif, San Francisco, 65-70; private practice, 70- Vis. prof, Univ. Madrid, winter 71. U.S.A.F, 54-56, Res, 57-63, Capt. Diagnosis in clinical neurology; neurophysiology of spinal reflex mechanisms and sleep; visual perception; clinical neurophysiology; oculo-motor mechanisms; meningiomas of the brain. Address: 425 Warren Dr, San Francisco, CA 94131.

GASSER, HEINZ, b. Trelex, Switz, Mar. 23, 32; Can. citizen; m. 59; c. 4. CROP PHYSIOLOGY, PLANT BREEDING. B.Sc, McGill Univ, 59, M.Sc, 62; Ph.D.(crop physiol), Univ. Nottingham, 65. Acting off-in-charge, Ft. Chimo Substa, 59; plant protection off, CAN. DEPT. AGR, 59-60, res. off. forage crops, RES. STA, 64-67, RES. SCIENTIST, 67-, SECT. HEAD GENETICS & PLANT BREEDING, 70- Res. scientist, Can. Dept. Agr. Res. Br. transfer, Lusignan Plant Breeding Res. Sta, France, 70-71. Crop Sci. Soc. Am; Am. Soc. Agron; Can. Soc. Agron. Winter resistance and survival of alfalfa through plant breeding and management; Rhizobium specificity in varieties of forage legumes. Address: Research Station, Canada Dept. of Agriculture, 2560 Chemin Gomin, Ste Foy, Que, Can.

GASSER, RAYMOND FRANK, b. Cullman, Ala, Sept. 13, 35; m. 61; c. 2. ANATOMY, PHYSIOLOGY. B.S, Spring Hill Col, 59; M.S, Alabama, 62, Nat. Insts. Health trainee, 63-64, Ph.D.(anat, physiol, path), 65. Instr. embryol, med. center, Alabama, 65; ANAT, MED. CENTER, LA. STATE UNIV, 65-66, asst. prof, 67-70, ASSOC. PROF, 70- AAAS; Am. Soc. Zool; Am. Asn. Anat. Morphogenesis of the head and neck regions in mammals, especially in man and nonhuman primates. Address: Dept. of Anatomy, Louisiana State University Medical Center, 1542 Tulane Ave, New Orleans, LA 70112.

GASSER, ROBERT J, b. Detroit, Mich, Aug. 24, 28; m. 55; c. 1. ORGANIC CHEMISTRY. B.S, Detroit, 49, fel, 49-51, M.S, 51; fel, Wayne State, 53-57, Ph.D.(org. chem), 57; Sorbonne, 55-56. RES. CHEMIST, U.S. Rubber Co, 51-52; Ethyl Corp, 57-58; MICH. CANCER FOUND, 67- Am. Chem. Soc. Cancer research, especially in chemotherapy of cancer using deoxysugars and nucleotides. Address: 17520 Prest, Detroit, MI 48235.

GASSER, WILLIAM, b. East Conemaugh, Pa, Nov. 22, 23; m. 60; c. 3. ORGANIC CHEMISTRY. B.S, Waynesburg Col, 47; M.S, Michigan, 48; M.S, Maryland, 52, Ph.D.(chem), 55. Instr. chem, Waynesburg Col, 48-49, asst. prof, 51-52, assoc. prof, 52-53; asst, Maryland, 49-51, 53-55; res. chemist, Visking Co, Union Carbide Corp, 55-62; mem. legal staff, Chas. Pfizer & Co, 62-63; asst. prof. CHEM, QUINCY COL, 63-67, assoc. prof, 67-71, PROF, 71- Consult, Blessing Hosp. U.S.N, 42-46, Lt. Comdr. AAAS; Am. Chem. Soc. Organic synthesis; polymers; patent law. Address: Dept. of Chemistry, Quincy College. Quincy, IL 62301.

GASSIE, EDWARD WILLIAM, b. Addis, La, Nov. 29, 25; m. 49; c. 3. EDUCATION, ANIMAL SCIENCE. B.S, La. State Univ, 51, M.S, 58, Ph.D. (agr. educ), 64. Asst. county agent, LA. STATE UNIV, BATON ROUGE, 51-54, assoc. county agent, 54-55, dist. supvr, 55-64, assoc. prof. AGR. EDUC, 64-68, PROF, 68-, TRAINING SPECIALIST, COOP. EXTEN. SERV, 64- Mem, Nat. Exten. Curriculum Develop. Comt, 64- U.S.N, 44-46. Studies of behavorial changes in individuals and groups as a result of planned educational programs and the many variables associated with the extent of these changes. Address: Dept. of Extension Education, Louisiana State University, Baton Rouge, LA 70803.

GASSMAN, MERRILL LOREN, b. Chicago, Ill, Feb. 10, 43; m. 67; c. 1. PLANT PHYSIOLOGY. S.B, Univ. Chicago, 64, S.M, 65, Ph.D.(bot), 67. Guest investr. & U.S. Pub. Health Serv. res. fel, Rockefeller Univ, 67-68; res. plant physiologist, Int. Minerals & Chem. Corp, Ill, 68-69; res. assoc, Argonne Nat. Lab, 69; ASST. PROF. BIOL. SCI, UNIV. ILL, CHICAGO CIRCLE, 69- Consult, Int. Minerals & Chem. Corp, Ill, 69-70. AAAS; Am. Soc. Plant Physiol. Photo induction of chloroplast development; control systems of porphyrin biosynthesis in plants. Address: Dept. of Biological Sciences, University of Chicago at Chicago Circle, Box 4348, Chicago, IL 60680.

GASSMAN, PAUL G, b. Buffalo, N.Y, June 22, 35; m. 57; c. 6. ORGANIC CHEMISTRY. B.S, Canisius Col, 57; Ph.D.(org. chem), Cornell, 60. Asst. prof. CHEM, OHIO STATE UNIV, 61-66, assoc. prof, 66-69, PROF, 69- Alfred P. Sloan fel, 67-69. Am. Chem. Soc.(award petrol. chem, 72); The Chem. Soc. Chemistry of highly strained ring systems; nitrenium ions; carbonium ions; organometallics; transition metal catalyzed rearrangements. Address: Dept. of Chemistry, Ohio State University, 140 W. 18th Ave, Columbus, OH 43210.

GASSMANN, GEORGE J(OSEPH), b. Hanau, Germany, Nov. 2, 13; U.S. citizen; m. 42; c. 2. PHYSICS. Wuerzburg, 32; Vienna, 33; Munich, Germany, 34; Dr. rer. nat, Göttingen, 39. Physicist, German Exp. Inst. Aeronaut, Berlin, 39-43; Agency for High Frequency Res, 43-45; Bayerische Electromech. Works, 45-46, engr, 47-52; physicist & chief, exp. studies sect, Ionospheric Physics Lab, AIR FORCE CAMBRIDGE RES. LABS, 52-60, SUPVR. RES. PHYSICIST, CHIEF BOUNDARY INTERACTIONS BR, 61- Mem, Int. Sci. Radio Union. AAAS; Am. Geophys. Union. Arctic radio propagation; upper atmosphere tide motions; communication effects of natural and manmade disturbances; propagation measurements by airborne techniques. Address: Boundary Interactions Branch, Air Force Cambridge Research Labs, Stop 30, Hanscom Field, Bedford, MA 01730.

GASSNER, EDWARD, b. Utica, N.Y, Aug. 23, 26; m. 57; c. 2. PLANT PHYSIOLOGY. B.S, St. Michael's Col, 50; Ph.D.(biol), Rochester, 60. Mem. staff, Oak Ridge Nat. Lab, 60-62; Res. Inst. Adv. Studies, 62-63; Martin-Marietta Corp, 64; assoc. prof. BIOL, St. John Fisher Col, 66-71, chmn. dept, 64-71; PROF. & CHMN. DEPT, MANSFIELD STATE COL, 71- U.S.A, 45-46. Photosynthesis; interrelationship of Hill reaction and photophosphorilation; new plant pigment found in some blue-green algae; effects of high light intensity on electron transport system in chloroplasts; chemosynthetic bacteria and space life support systems; nature of the tetracycline-hard tissue complex. Address: Dept. of Biology, Mansfield State College, Mansfield, PA 16933.

GAST, JAMES A(VERY), b. New Rochelle, N.Y, Apr. 28, 29; m. 55; c. 3. OCEANOGRAPHY. A.B, Amherst Col, 53; M.S, Washington(Seattle), 57, Ph.D.(oceanog), 59. Asst, Woods Hole Oceanog. Inst, 47-48; Washington (Seattle), 53-58, assoc. & acting instr, 58-59, sr. oceanogr. & exten. asst. prof, 59-60, res. asst. prof, 60-61; asst. prof. OCEANOG, HUMBOLDT STATE COL, 61-65, assoc. prof, 65-70, PROF, 70-, coord, 61-70, dir. marine lab, 64-70. Oceanog. consult, 62- U.S.M.C, 47-52. AAAS; Am. Chem. Soc; Am. Geophys. Union; Am. Soc. Limnol. & Oceanog. Oceanographic education; chemical oceanography. Address: Dept. of Oceanography, Humboldt State College, Arcata, CA 95521.

GAST, JOSEPH H(ENRY), b. New Orleans, La, Apr. 18, 06; m. 28; c. 5. BIOLOGICAL CHEMISTRY. A.B, Michigan, 28, B.S, 36, M.S, 38, Sc.D.(biochem), 40. Instr. physiol. biochem, N.Y. Med. Col, 40-42; asst. prof. biochem, col. med, Baylor, 42-43, assoc. prof. & acting chmn. dept, 42-46, prof, 46-59, dir. west. div, Resources Res, Inc, 59-60; res. prof. chem. & assoc. dir. inst. chem. biol, Univ. San Francisco, 60-68; RES. ASSOC, Mt. Zion Hosp, 64-68, VET. ADMIN. HOSP, 68- Consult, Nat. Insts. Health. Bischoff Award, 57; dipl, Am. Bd. Clin. Chem. Fel. AAAS; Am. Chem. Soc; Soc. Exp. Biol. & Med; fel. Am. Asn. Clin. Chem; N.Y. Acad. Sci. Sulfur metabolism; bile; laboratory methods in clinical chemistry; toxicology; enzymes; subcellular fractions. Address: Veterans Administration Hospital, 5901 E. Seventh St, Long Beach, CA 90801.

GAST, L(YLE) E(VERETT), b. Alden, Ill, Apr. 9, 19; m. 42; c. 1. ORGANIC CHEMISTRY. B.S, Illinois, 41; Ph.D.(org. chem), Wisconsin, 49. Asst. res. chemist, Pa. Salt Mfg. Co, 41-44; res. chemist, NORTH. REGIONAL RES. LAB, U.S. DEPT. AGR, 49-60, HEAD OIL COATINGS INVESTS, 60- U.S.A, 44-46. Am. Chem. Soc; Am. Oil Chemists' Soc. Chlorination of organic compounds; fundamental investigations on higher unsaturated fatty acids. Address: 3027 N. Wilson Dr, Peoria, IL 61604.

GAST, PAUL F(REDERICK), b. St. Paul, Minn, May 29, 16; m. 41; c. 2. PHYSICS. A.B, Ohio State, 37; Ph.D.(physics), Washington (Seattle), 41. Res. physicist, Remington Arms Co, Inc, Conn, 41-43; physicist, E.I. du Pont de Nemours & Co, Del, Tenn. & Wash, 43-46, chief supvr. in charge physics work, Hanford Plutonium Plant, Gen. Elec. Co, 46-51, chief staff physicist, 51-56, mgr. physics & instrument res. & develop, 56-64; sr. scientist, ARGONNE NAT. LAB, 64-67, assoc. dir. liquid metal fast breeder reactor prog. off, 67-70, DIR, 70- Mem. cmt. reactor declassification & adv. cmt. reactor physics, Atomic Energy Cmn. AAAS; fel. Am. Phys. Soc; Am. Nuclear Soc. Cosmic rays; interior ballistics of small arms; reactor physics. Address: Liquid Metal Fast Breeder Reactor Program Office, Argonne National Lab, 9700 S. Cass Ave, Argonne, IL 60439.

GAST, P(AUL) R(UPERT), b. Fitchburg, Mass, Jan. 27, 97; m. 24. BIOPHYSICS. Ph.B, Brown, 20; M.S, Syracuse, 22; Sc.D.(forest biophys), Harvard, 27. Asst. bot, col. forestry, State Univ, N.Y, 20-22; asst, Harvard Forest, 22-24, instr. forestry, Harvard, 24-29, asst. prof, 30-47; physicist, Air Force Cambridge Res. Labs, 48-68; RETIRED. Asst, Harvard, 22-27; agent, U.S. Forest Serv, 24-29; Nat. Res. Coun. fel, Sweden, 29-30; Fulbright res. fel, France, 50-51. Am. Acad. Arts & Sci. Measurement of solar radiation; solar constant; irradiational, meteorological and nutritional factors in growth and development of trees; profile development and nitrogen mobilization and fertility of forest soils; soil exchange reactions; climatological solar irradiation. Address: Red Acre Rd, R.D. Box 246, Stow, MA 01775.

GAST, PAUL W(ERNER), b. Chicago, Ill, Sept. 11, 30; m. 52; c. 3. GEOCHEMISTRY. B.S, Wheaton Col.(Ill), 52; Higgins fel, Columbia, 52-53, M.A, 56, Ph.D.(geol), 57. Res. assoc. geochem, Lamont Geol. Observ, 57-58; asst. prof, Minnesota, 58-61, assoc. prof, 61-65; COLUMBIA UNIV, 65-66, PROF. GEOL, 66- Geochem. Soc; Geol. Soc. Am; Mineral. Soc. Am; Am. Geophys. Union. Isotopic and nuclear processes in geologic problems; meteoritics; chemistry of planet formation; determination of absolute geologic time. Address: Dept. of Geology, 208 Hamilton Hall, Columbia University, New York, NY 10027.

GAST, R(OBERT) C(HARLES), b. Mt. Hope, W.Va, Aug. 12, 29; m. 58. APPLIED MATHEMATICS. B.S, Marshall Col, 51; M.S, Carnegie Inst. Tech, 53, Ph.D.(math), 56. SR. SCIENTIST, BETTIS ATOMIC POWER DIV, WESTINGHOUSE ELEC. CORP, 56- Am. Nuclear Soc. Transport and diffraction theory. Address: Westinghouse Electric Corp, P.O. Box 79, West Mifflin, PA 15122.

GAST, ROBERT GALE, b. Phila, Mo, July 28, 31; m. 54; c. 3. SOIL CHEMISTRY. B.S, Missouri, 53, M.S, 56, Ph.D.(soil chem), 59. Asst. scientist soil chem, agr. res. lab, Atomic Energy Comn. Tennessee, 59-61, assoc. prof, 61-68; res. assoc. SOIL SCI, Mich. State Univ, 68-69; ASSOC. PROF, UNIV. MINN, ST. PAUL, 70- Lectr, Oak Ridge Inst. Nuclear Studies, 63- U.S.A.F, 53-55, Res, 55-62, 1st Lt. Am. Soc. Agron; Am. Chem. Soc; Clay Minerals Soc. Physical chemistry and mineraology of soils. Address: Dept. of Soil Science, University of Minnesota, St. Paul, MN 55101.

GASTEIGER, EDGAR L(IONEL), JR, b. Meadville, Pa, Nov. 25, 19; m. 49; c. 4. NEUROPHYSIOLOGY. A.B, Allegheny Col, 42; M.S, Illinois, 43; Ph.D.(biophys), Minnesota, 52. Res. assoc. physiol, Harvard Med. Sch, 51-53, assoc, 53-54, asst. prof, 54-57; Rochester, 57-61; PROF. PHYS. BIOL, N.Y. STATE VET. COL, CORNELL UNIV, 61- Res. assoc, Mass. Gen. Hosp, 51-57. AAAS; Am. Physiol. Soc; Biophys. Soc. Central nervous system; peripheral nerve and muscle physiology; effects of radiation. Address: Dept. of Physical Biology, New York State Veterinary College, Cornell University, Ithaca, NY 14850.

GASTEN, BURT R, b. Chicago, Ill, Jan. 6, 33; m. 54; c. 2. EXPERIMENTAL PHYSICS. B.S, Ill. Inst. Tech, 54; M.S, Wisconsin, 55, Alumni Res. Found. & Atomic Energy Comn. fels. & Ph.D.(physics), 63. SR. PHYSICIST, Lawrence Radiation Lab, Univ. Calif, Livermore, 63-71; PHYSICS INT. CO, SAN LEANDRO, 71- Am. Phys. Soc. High voltage pulse technology; antennae; electromagnetic propagation; ionospheric and earth media; instrumentation; system studies; nuclear explosive design, especially output and effects; antiballistic missile and reentry vehicle systems, especially vulnerability and hardening; low energy nuclear physics. Address: 564 Tyler Ave, Livermore, CA 94550.

GASTEYER, CHARLES E(ARL), b. Gary, Ind, July 3, 27; m. 59; c. 2. ASTRONOMY. B.S, Chicago, 48; Ph.D.(astron), Northwestern, 52. Asst, Northwestern, 49-52; instr. astron, Yale, 52-56; Wesleyan, 56-57, asst. prof, 57-59; MATHEMATICIAN, ELEC. BOAT DIV, GEN. DYNAMICS CORP, GROTON, 59- Am. Astron. Soc; Hist. Sci. Soc; Royal Astron. Soc. Data processing applications to underwater sound; stellar parallax; double stars; planetary motion; history of astronomy. Address: Burr Rd, Lyme, CT 06371.

GASTIL, R. GORDON, b. San Diego, Calif, June 25, 28; m. 58; c. 3. GEOLOGY. A.B, California, Berkeley, 50, Oak Ridge Inst. Nuclear Studies fel, 51 & 52, Ph.D.(geol), 54. Geologist, Shell Oil Co, Alaska, 54; Can. Javelin Ltd, 56-58; lectr. GEOL, California, Los Angeles, 58-59; asst. prof, SAN DIEGO STATE COL, 59-61, assoc. prof, 62-65, PROF, 65-, CHMN. DEPT, 69- Res. partic, Nat. Sci. Found. grants, 60-61, 62-69, 71; mem. int. geol. field conf, Am. Geol. Inst, E.Africa, 69; Nat. Sci. Found. res. grants, Baja, Calif, 68-70; Sonora, Mex, 71-72. AAAS; Nat. Asn. Geol. Teachers; Geol. Soc. Am; Soc. Econ. Paleont. & Mineral. Regional structural analysis; geochronology; origin and evolution of continents and ocean basins. Address: Dept. of Geology, San Diego State College, 5402 College Ave, San Diego, CA 92115.

GASTINEAU, CLIFFORD FELIX, b. Pawnee, Okla, Dec. 18, 20; m. 51; c. 2. MEDICINE. B.A, Oklahoma, 41, M.D, 43; Ph.D.(med), Minnesota, 50. CONSULT. INTERNAL MED, MAYO CLINIC, 50- Med.C, 53-55, Capt. AAAS; Endocrine Soc; Am. Diabetes Asn; fel. Am. Col. Physicians. Clinical standpoint of diabetes. Address: Mayo Clinic, Rochester, MN 55901.

GASTL, GEORGE C(LIFFORD), b. Shawnee, Kans, Feb. 27, 38; m. 67. TOPOLOGY, ALGEBRA. A.B, Kansas, 60, NDEA fel, 60-62, M.A, 62; Ph.D. (math), Wisconsin, 66. Asst. prof. MATH, UNIV. WYO, 66-70, ASSOC. PROF, 70- Math. Asn. Am; Am. Math. Soc. Abstract topological spaces; extended topology; uniform spaces; proximity spaces. Address: Dept. of Mathematics, University of Wyoming, Laramie, WY 82070.

GASTON, G(ARDNER) E(DMUND), b. Meadville, Pa, Oct. 7, 18; m. 45; c. 2. CHEMICAL ENGINEERING. B.S, Grove City Col, 41; M.S, Pittsburgh, 48. Prod. metallurgist, U.S. Steel Corp, 41-42; chem. engr, GULF RES. & DEVELOP. CO, 42-51, group leader gasoline res, 51-60, acting sect. head FUEL RES, 60-61, SR. RES. ENGR, PETROL. PROD. DEPT, 61- Am. Chem. Soc; Soc. Automotive Eng; Am. Soc. Test & Mat. Petroleum; gasoline development. Address: Petroleum Products Dept, Gulf Research & Development Co, P.O. Drawer 2-38, Pittsburgh, PA 15230.

GASTON, J(ACK) E(VERETT), b. Pittsburg, Kans, Sept. 5, 12; m. 39; c. 5. METALLURGY. B.S, Missouri, 34. Res. chemist, Eagle-Picher Lead Co, 34-42; tech. instr. eng. sci. & mgt. war training, Kansas, 41-42; res. chemist, ARMSTRONG CORK CO, 42-46, mgr. bldg. mat. res, 46-54, gen. mgr, 54-62, TECH. CONSULT, BLDG. PROD. RES. & DEVELOP. CTR, 62- Mem. Bldg. Res. Inst, 54-, prog. chmn, 60-62, v.pres. bd. dirs, 64-65; chmn. standards comt. precoord. bldg. components & systs, Am. Nat. Standards Inst, 66-70. Am. Soc. Test. & Mat. Fundamentals of mineral wool; insulating, acoustical, resilient flooring and decorative building materials research. Address: Research & Development Center, Armstrong Cork Co, Lancaster, PA 17604.

GASTON, LYLE KENNETH, b. Waterloo, Iowa, Nov. 7, 30. ORGANIC CHEMISTRY. B.S, Iowa State, 53; Ph.D.(chem), California, Los Angeles, 60. Fel, Colorado, 60-62; ASSOC. CHEMIST & LECTR. TOXICOL. & PHYSIOL, UNIV. CALIF, RIVERSIDE, 62- U.S.A, 48-49. Am. Chem. Soc; Entom. Soc. Am. Isolation, identification and synthesis of insect sex pheromones; chemistry and analysis of pesticides and their residues. Address: Division of Toxicology & Physiology, University of California, Riverside, CA 92502.

GASTROCK, EDWARD ALVIN, b. New Orleans, La, June 23, 98; m. 20; c. 1. CHEMICAL ENGINEERING. B.E, Tulane, 18. Hydrogenation supt, Phoenix Cotton Oil Co, Tenn, 18; plant supt, Am. Paint Works, La, 19-21; plant mgr, Cook Paint & Varnish Co, Mo, 21-22; asst. supt, South. Cotton Oil Co, La, 22-24; chief chemist, Celotex Corp, 24-37; chem. engr, agr. by-prods. lab, U.S. DEPT. AGR, Iowa, 37-38, prin. chem. engr, south. regional res. lab, bur. agr. & indust. chem, 38-53, head eng. & develop. sect, SOUTH. UTILIZATION DIV, AGR. RES. SERV, 53-57, HEAD CHEM. ENG. INVESTS, 58- U.S.N, 18-19. Am. Chem. Soc; Am. Oil Chem. Soc; Sci. Res. Soc. Am; Nat. Soc. Prof. Eng; Am. Inst. Chem. Eng. Structural insulation from plant fibers; industrial pilot plant scale fermentation; solvent extraction of vegetable oils; vegetable oil processing; pilot plant scale sweet potato starch processing; pilot plant cotton chemical finishing. Address: Southern Utilization Division, Agricultural Research Service, U.S. Dept. of Agriculture, 1100 Robert E. Lee Blvd, New Orleans, LA 70119.

GASTROCK, WILLIAM HENRY, b. New Orleans, La, Feb. 13, 39; m. 61. ORGANIC & MEDICINAL CHEMISTRY. B.S, La. State, 62; Nat. Insts. Health fel, Kansas, 64-67, Ph.D.(med. chem), 67. RES. CHEMIST, AGR. DIV, AM. CYANAMID CO, 67- Am. Chem. Soc. Synthesis of biologically active compounds in agricultural and medicinal fields; heterocyclic chemistry. Address: American Cyanamid Co, Box 400, Princeton, NJ 08540.

GASTWIRT, LAWRENCE E, b. N.Y.C, Mar. 7, 36; m. 60; c. 3. CHEMICAL ENGINEERING, RESEARCH ADMINISTRATION. B.Ch.E, City Col. New York, 57; M.A, Princeton, 59, Ph.D.(chem. eng), 62; M.B.A, N.Y. Univ, 68. Sr. engr, Esso Res. & Eng. Co, 61-67, eng. assoc, 67-68; sr. planning analyst, Standard Oil Co.(N.J), 68-69; ENG. ASSOC. & SECT. HEAD, ESSO RES. & ENG. CO, 69- Am. Inst. Chem. Medal, 57. Am. Econ. Asn; Am. Finance Asn; N.Y. Acad. Sci. Management of polymers research and commercial development; planning and financial evaluation of petrochemical research and development. Address: 12 Gary Court, Scotch Plains, NJ 07076.

GASTWIRTH, JOSEPH L, b. New York, N.Y, Aug. 31, 38. MATHEMATICAL STATISTICS. B.S, Yale, 58; Wilson fel. & M.A, Princeton, 60; Ph.D.(math. statist), Columbia, 63. Res. assoc. STATIST, Stanford, 63-64; asst. prof, JOHNS HOPKINS UNIV, 64-67, ASSOC. PROF, 67- Vis. assoc. prof, Harvard, 70-71; vis. faculty adv, off. statist. policy, Exec. Off. of the President, 71-72. Fel. AAAS; Inst. Math. Statist; Am. Math. Soc; fel. Am. Statist. Asn; Statist. Asn; Royal Statist. Soc. Robust methods of inference; applied probability theory; economic statistics. Address: Dept. of Statistics, Johns Hopkins University, Baltimore, MD 21218.

GASWICK, DENNIS C, b. Rushville, Nebr, Feb. 15, 42; m. 64. INORGANIC CHEMISTRY. B.A, Nebr. Wesleyan, 64; Ph.D.(inorg. chem), Oregon State, 68. Res. assoc, State Univ. N.Y. Stony Brook, 68-69; ASST. PROF. CHEM, ALBION COL, 69- Am. Chem. Soc. Mechanisms of chromium reactions and their intermediates; synthesis of binuclear chromium—cobalt complexes and the mechanisms of electron transfer reactions in coordination chemistry. Address: Dept. of Chemistry, Albion College, 704 E. Porter St, Albion, MI 49224.

GAT, URI, b. Jerusalem, Israel, June 28, 36; m. 61; c. 2. NUCLEAR ENGINEERING. B.Sc, Israel Inst. Technol, 63; Dr. Ing, Aachen Tech. Univ, 69. Fel. scientist nuclear reactor develop, Kernforschungsanlage, Ger, 63-69; ASST. PROF. MECH. ENG, UNIV. KY, 69- Nat. Sci. found. res. initiation grant, 71-72. Israel Air Force, 54-59, Capt. Am. Nuclear Soc; Metric Asn. Liquid fuel reactors; molten salt reactors; reactor evaluations; thermochemical equilibrium evaluation and calculation; phase diagrams; kinetics of chlorination of nuclear fuels; immiscible liquid-liquid flow and heat transfer. Address: Dept. of Mechanical Engineering, University of Kentucky, Lexington, KY 40506.

GATCOMBE, ERNEST K(ENNETH), b. Marion, Maine, Jan. 4, 06; m. 39; c. 1. MECHANICAL ENGINEERING. B.S, Maine, 31; M.S, Purdue, 39; Ph.D. (mech. eng), Cornell, 44. Engr, U.S. Govt. Surv, Maine, 31-33; prin, Wash. Acad, 33-37; instr, Purdue, 37-39; Cornell, 39-44; engr, Pratt & Whitney Aircraft, 44; res, Mass. Inst. Tech, 44-46; assoc. prof. MECH. ENG, NAVAL POSTGRAD. SCH, 46-50, prof, 50-69, EMER. PROF, 69- Asst. chief engr, Jackson & Moreland Engrs. Boston, 44-46; consult, Firestone Tire & Rubber Co, 56-; Dalmo Victor Co, 57- Free piston gas turbine; lubrication characteristics of involute spur gears. Address: Dept. of Mechanical Engineering, Naval Postgraduate School, Monterey, CA 93940.

GATEHOUSE, R. WAYNE, Psychol, see Suppl. I to 11th ed, Soc. & Behav. Vols.

GATELEY, WILSON YORK, b. McFadden, Wyo, May 17, 26; m. 46; c. 6. MATHEMATICS. B.A, Colo. Col, 49; M.S, Mass. Inst. Tech, 56; Ph.D. (math. statist), Okla. State, 62. Tech. rep. electronics, Philco Corp, 51-52; field engr, Bendix Radio Div, 52-55; asst. prof. MATH, COLO. COL, 56-62, assoc. prof, 62-67, PROF, 67-, DIR. COMPUT. CTR, 71-, chmn. dept. math, 65-69. Consult, Kaman Nuclear Div, 61-70; Data Mgt. Assocs, 71- U.S.N.R, 44-46. Math. Asn. Am; Am. Statist. Asn; Asn. Comput. Mach. Mathematical statistics, including reliability and design of experiments; computer science. Address: Computer Center, Colorado College, Colorado Springs, CO 80903.

GATES, ALLEN H(AZEN), JR, b. Rockville, Conn, Nov. 7, 29; m. 65; c. 2. REPRODUCTIVE PHYSIOLOGY, GENETICS. B.S, La. State, 51; Ph.D. (genetics), Edinburgh, 59. Res. asst. develop. biol, Jackson Lab, Maine, 51-53, sr. res. asst. reprod. physiol, 56-59, assoc. staff scientist, 59-60; res. assoc, sch. med, Stanford Univ, 60-64, asst. prof, 64-70; staff researcher, Syntex Res, Calif, 70-71; ASST. PROF. GENETICS, SCH. MED, UNIV. ROCHESTER, 71- Nat. Cancer Inst. consult, 62-68. AAAS; Soc. Study Reproduction; Am. Soc. Zool. Biomedical research; physiologic and genetic mechanisms regulating development of the mammalian egg. Address: Division of Genetics, Dept. of Anatomy, University of Rochester Medical Center, 260 Crittenden Blvd, Rochester, NY 14642.

GATES, BRUCE C(LARK), b. Richmond, Calif, July 5, 40; m. 67; c. 2. CHEMICAL ENGINEERING. B.S, Univ. Calif, Berkeley, 61; Nat. Sci. Found. fels, Univ. Wash, 63-64, 65-66, Ph.D. (chem. eng), 66. Fulbright res. grant, inst. phys. chem, Univ. Munich, 66-67; res. engr, Chevron Res. Co, Calif, 67-69; ASST. PROF. CHEM. ENG, UNIV. DEL, 69- Am. Inst. Chem. Eng; Am. Chem. Soc. Reaction kinetics; catalysis; mass transport in catalysts; catalysis by synthetic polymers; catalyst aging. Address: Dept. of Chemical Engineering, University of Delaware, Newark, DE 19711.

GATES, BURTON N(OBLE), b. Worcester, Mass, Dec. 19, 81; m. 18. ENTOMOLOGY, BOTANY. A.B, Clark, 05, A.M, 06, Ph.D.(biol), 09. Asst. biol, Clark, 06-07; collab. bur. entomol, U.S. Dept. Agr, 07, expert. apicult, 07-10; state inspector apiaries, State Bd. Agr, Mass, 10-18; asst. prof. & assoc. prof. beekeeping, Mass. Col, 10-18; prof. apicult, Ont. Agr. Col. & apiarist, Prov. Ont, 18-19; from inspector apiaries to chief apiary inspector, State Dept. Agr, Mass, 10-52; res, Hadwen Herbarium, Clark Univ, 42-54, res. assoc. biol, 54-71; RETIRED. Special lectr, Mass. Col, 06-10. Entom. Soc. Am. Taxonomic botany; apiculture; statistics, economy and behavior of bees and allied forms; life histories of insects; flora of Worcester County, Massachusetts. Address: 24 Charlotte St, Worcester, MA 01610.

GATES, CHARLES D(ONALD), b. Ashburnham, Mass, Nov. 22, 14; m. 47; c. 3. SANITARY ENGINEERING. B.A, Williams Col.(Mass), 37; Kellogg Found. fel, Harvard, 38, M.S, 38, univ. fel, 54. Jr. sanit. engr. flood control, U.S. Eng. Dept, 39-42; assoc. sanit. engr, water treatment res, Eng. Res. & Develop. Labs, 46-47; asst. prof. SANIT. SCI. & ENG, CORNELL UNIV, 47-49, assoc. prof, 49-60, PROF, 60-, HEAD DEPT. SANIT. ENG, 57-, CHMN. DEPT. WATER RESOURCES ENG, 67- Consult, N.Y. State Dept. Health, 56-; U.S. Pub. Health Serv, 62- Sanit.C, 42-45, 51-52, 1st Lt. Am. Soc. Eng. Educ; Am. Water Works Asn; Water Pollution Control Fedn. Chlorination and biochemical oxygen demand of waste water; environmental health planning. Address: Dept. of Water Resources Engineering, Hollister Hall, Cornell University, Ithaca, NY 14850.

GATES, CHARLES E(DGAR), b. Rapid City, S.Dak, March 6, 26; m. 51; c. 3. AGRICULTURAL STATISTICS. B.S, Iowa State, 50; M.S, N.C. State Col, 52, Ph.D.(exp. statist), 55. Asst. exp. statist, N.C. State Col, 50-53, asst. statistician, 53-54; asst. prof. STATIST, Univ. Minn, St. Paul, 56-60, assoc. prof, 60-65, prof, 65-66, statistician, agr. exp. sta, 56-66; PROF, INST. STATIST, TEX. A&M UNIV, 66- Instr, Louisville, 55-56. U.S.N, 44; U.S.A, 55-56. Biomet. Soc; Am. Statist. Asn; Royal Statist Soc. Statistical genetics; design of agricultural and biological experiments. Address: Institute of Statistics, Texas A&M University, College Station, TX 77843.

GATES, D(ANIEL) W(ILLIAM), b. Chicago, Ill, Oct. 16, 21; m. 45; c. 2. CERAMICS. B.S, Illinois, 48; Orton Found. fel, Ga. Inst. Tech, 49-50, M.S, 51 & 53. With res. & develop, Temco, Inc, 47-49; asst, Eng. Exp. Sta, Ga. Inst. Tech, 50-53; asst. prof. ceramics, Clemson Col, 53-54; aero materials res. engr, Army Ballistic Missile Agency, NASA, 54-60, MAT. RES. ENGR, GEORGE G. MARSHALL SPACE FLIGHT CTR, 60- U.S.A.A.F, 42-46. Am. Ceramic Soc; Nat. Inst. Ceramic Eng; Am. Geophys. Union; fel. Am. Inst. Chem. Geophysical exploration; porcelain enamels; graphite for rockets; materials for space environment; thermal-control coatings for space vehicles. Address: Space Science Lab, George C. Marshall Space Flight Center, NASA, Huntsville, AL 35812.

GATES, DAVID G(ORDON), b. Kansas City, Mo, Mar. 30, 31; m. 50; c. 2. INDUSTRIAL ENGINEERING. B.S, Arkansas, 56, M.S, 59; Ph.D.(eng), Okla. State, 62. Indust. engr, Corning Glass Works, 56-57; instr. INDUST. ENG, Okla. State, 60-62; assoc. prof, Auburn, 62-63; PROF, LAMAR UNIV, 63-, HEAD DEPT, 67- U.S.A, 50-52, Sgt. Am. Inst. Indust. Eng; Am. Soc. Eng. Educ. Methods engineering; work measurement. Address: Dept. of Industrial Engineering, Lamar University, Box 10032, Beaumont, TX 77710.

GATES, DAVID M(URRY), b. Manhattan, Kans, May 27, 21; m. 44; c. 4. BIOPHYSICS. B.S, Michigan, 42, M.S, 44, Ph.D.(physics), 48. Asst, Michigan, 41-44, res. physicist, 42-44; res. asst. prof. physics, Denver, 47-54, assoc. prof, 54-55; sci. dir. & liaison off, Off. Naval Res, Eng, 55-57; asst. chief radio propagation, physics div, Nat. Bur. Standards, 57-60, upper atmosphere & space physics div, 60-61, consult. to dir, 61-64; prof. natural hist, univ. & curator ecol, univ. mus, Univ. Colo, 65; prof. biol, Washington Univ. & dir, Mo. Bot. Garden, 65-71; PROF. BOT. & DIR. BIOL. STA, UNIV. MICH, ANN ARBOR, 71- Mem. oper. anal. stand-by unit, Iowa State Col, 53-55; Univ. Denver, 55-; consult, Air Defense Command, Colo, 53-; ed, Radio Propagation & J. of Res, 61-63; lectr, Univ. Colo, 61-64; vis. prof, Univ. Colo, 65; chmn. environ. studies bd, Nat. Acad. Sci-Nat. Acad. Eng, 70-; mem, Nat. Sci. Bd, 70-; adv. panel, Comn. Sci. & Astronaut, U.S. House Rep, 71-; mem. bd, Conserv. Found; mem. biometeorol. panel, U.S. Nat. Comt. Int. Biol. Prog; chmn. ad hoc comt. environ, Environ. Clearinghouse Inc, Wash, D.C; mem. nat. air quality adv. comt, U.S. Pub. Health Serv; adv. comt. biol. & med. sci, Nat. Sci. Found; ad hoc adv. comt. off. ecol, Smithsonian Inst. Civilian with Off. Sci. Res. & Develop, 44. Fel. AAAS; Optical Soc. Am; Sci. Res. Soc. Am; Am. Geophys. Union; Bot. Soc. Am; Ecol. Soc. Am; Royal Meteorol. Soc. Infrared spectroscopy in the near and far infrared; upper atmosphere research by infrared; geophysical exploration work; ecology; energy exchange for plants; transpiration; photosynthesis. Address: Dept. of Botany, University of Michigan, Ann Arbor, MI 48104.

GATES, DILLARD HERBERT, b. Gates, Nebr, Jan. 23, 25; m. 46; c. 2. RANGE MANAGEMENT, ECOLOGY. B.S, Univ. Nebr, 52, M.S, 53; Ph.D, Utah State Univ, 55. Range conservationist, South. Plains Field Sta, U.S. Dept. Agr, Okla, 55-57, dept. forest range mgt, Washington State, 57-62; range mgt. specialist, ORE. STATE UNIV, 62-70, DIR. RANGE MGT. PROG, 71- Consult, Food & Agr. Orgn, Iraq, 69; coord, bur. land mgt, U.S. Dept. Interior, Calif, 70-71; consult, Develop. & Resources Corp, 71. U.S.C.G, 43-45. Am. Soc. Range Mgt. Integrated management and use of rangeland and related resources; rangeland ecology and vegetation manipulation; long-range planning for development and use of natural resources; remote sensing for rangeland resource analysis. Address: Range Management Program, Oregon State University, Corvallis, OR 97331.

GATES, GEORGE O(SCAR), b. Seiling, Okla, July 26, 05; m. 33. GEOLOGY. A.B, California, 28; Stanford, 36-39. Chemist, Am. Smelting & Ref. Co, Calif, 28-29; Utah Copper Co, 29-30; teacher, Taft Jr. Col, 32-35; Los Angeles City Col, 39-41; jr. geologist, 41, asst. geologist, U.S. Geol. Surv, 41-43, assoc. geologist, 43-44, geologist, 44-52, chief, Alaskan Geol. Br, 52-59, asst. chief geologist, Calif, 59-70; CONSULT, 70- Liaison mem. comt. on Alaska earthquake, Nat. Acad. Sci, 64-70. Distinguished serv. award, U.S. Dept. Interior, 70. Fel. Geol. Soc. Am; Am. Asn. Petrol. Geol; Asn. Eng. Geol. Engineering and earthquake geology; geology and mineral resources of Alaska. Address: 1912 Lexington Ave, San Mateo, CA 94402.

GATES, GERALD OTIS, b. Brewerton, N.Y, Oct. 18, 39. ECOLOGY. B.A, Arizona, 60, Ph.D.(ecol), 63. Asst. prof. BIOL, Univ. of the Pacific 63-66; UNIV. REDLANDS, 66-70, ASSOC. PROF, 70- Ecology and behavior of amphibians and reptiles. Address: Dept. of Biology, University of Redlands, Redlands, CA 92373.

GATES, HALBERT F(REDERICK), b. Milwaukee, Wis, Oct. 30, 19; m. 48; c. 3. PHYSICS. B.S, Wis. State Teachers Col, 40; Ph.M, Wisconsin, 44; Ph.D.(physics), Mich. State Col, 54. Asst. prof. physics, Berea Col, 48-50; asst. prof. & chmn. dept, Cornell Col, 54-55; asst. prof. physics & phys. sci, Illinois, 55-58; assoc. prof. PHYSICS, North. Ariz. Univ, 58-64, PROF. & CHMN. DEPT, 65-66; Slippery Rock State Col, 67-68; BLOOMSBURG STATE COL, 69- Sig.C, 44-46, 2nd Lt. Am. Phys. Soc; Am. Asn. Physics Teachers. Ultrasonics and optics; physical science. Address: 749 E. Fourth St, Bloomsburg, PA 17815.

GATES, HENRY S(TILLMAN), b. Sharon, Pa, Oct. 12, 29; m. 53; c. 5. INORGANIC CHEMISTRY. B.S, Lehigh, 51; Ph.D.(inorg. chem), Wisconsin, 56. Prof. chem, Milton Col, 55-57; assoc. prof, Wis. State Univ, 57-58; asst. prof, Utica Col, 58-62; prof. chem. & chmn. div. natural sci, Milton Col, 62-70; ASSOC. PROF. CHEM, WESTMINSTER COL.(UTAH), 70- Consult, Parker Pen Co, 56-57; summer vis. prof, N.Mex. Highlands Univ, 63; consult, Gibbs Mfg. & Res. Corp, 68-70. AAAS; Am. Chem. Soc. Coordination chemistry; environmental studies. Address: Dept. of Chemistry, Westminster College, Salt Lake City, UT 84105.

GATES, JOHN E(DWARD), b. Parkersburg, W.Va, June 22, 27; m. 51; c. 2. MATERIALS SCIENCE. B.Sc, Ohio State, 53, 53-55. Lab. technician, BATTELLE MEM. INST, 51-53, chemist radiochem, 53-54, proj. leader RADIATION EFFECTS, 54-58, asst. chief, 58-62, div. chief, 62-68, ASSOC. DEPT. MGR, 68- U.S.N, 45-47. Development of nuclear reactor fuels; radiation effects in fuels and other materials; development of radioisotope heat sources, turbine engine coatings and high temperature turbine blade materials. Address: Battelle Memorial Institute, 505 King Ave, Columbus, OH 43201.

GATES, JOHN MANLEY, b. Winona, Minn, July 10, 33; m. 55; c. 2. WILDLIFE ECOLOGY. B.S, Minnesota, 55; M.S, Utah State, 58; Ph.D, Univ. Wis, 71. Wildlife res. biologist, Wis. Dept. Natural Resources, 58-70; ASST. PROF. WILDLIFE & FISHERIES SCI, S.DAK. STATE UNIV, 70- Wildlife Soc; Am. Ornith. Union; Wilson Ornith. Soc; Am. Inst. Biol. Sci. Population ecology and management of migratory waterfowl and gallinaceous birds. Address: Dept. of Wildlife & Fisheries Science, South Dakota State University, Brookings, SD 57006.

GATES, J(OHN) W(ARBURTON), JR, b. Pensacola, Fla, March 5, 14; m. 40. ORGANIC CHEMISTRY. A.B, Stanford, 35, fel, 36-38, A.M, 37, Ph.D. (chem), 38. Asst. chem, Stanford, 35-36; SR. RES. ASSOC, Eastman Kodak Co, 38-43; Clinton Eng. Works & Tenn. Eastman Corp, 43-46, EASTMAN KODAK CO, RES. LABS, COLOR PHOTOG. DIV, 46- With Atomic Energy Cmn, 44. Am. Chem. Soc; N.Y. Acad. Sci. Organic analytical reagents; polyaryl indenes; chemistry of natural proteins; gelatin manufacture; photographic emulsions; sulfur-containing amino acids; thiazolidines; macrocycles; nucleophilic additions to quinoid systems; color photography; photographic developers. Address: Research Labs, Color Photography Division, Eastman Kodak Co, Rochester, NY 14650.

GATES, JOSEPH S(PENCER), b. Des Moines, Iowa, Jan. 18, 35; m. 64; c. 2. HYDROLOGY. Geol. Engr, Colo. Sch. Mines, 56; M.S, Utah, 60. Hydraul. engr, U.S. GEOL. SURV, 56-58, GEOLOGIST, 58- Geologist, U.S. Agency Int. Develop, Cairo, Egypt, 65-67; grad. teaching & res. assoc, grad. sch. training, dept. hydrol. & water resources, Univ. Ariz, 67-71. C.Eng.Res, U.S.A, 56-69, Capt. AAAS; Geol. Soc. Am. Groundwater geology and hydrology of arid regions. Address: 4624 Rolling Stone St, El Paso, TX 79924.

GATES, LESLIE D(EAN), JR, b. Berwyn, Ill, Oct. 10, 22; m. 50; c. 4. MATHEMATICS. B.S, Iowa State Col, 47, M.S, 50, Ph.D.(math), 52. Instr. math, Iowa State Col, 52; mathematician, Armed Forces Spec. Weapons Proj, U.S. Dept. Defense, 52-54; U.S. Naval Proving Grounds, 54-55, head. appl. math. br, 55-58; atomic energy div, Babcock & Wilcox Co, 58-59, chief. math. sect, 59-61; ASSOC. PROF. MATH, SOUTH. ILL. UNIV, 61- U.S.A, 43-46, Res, 46-68, Lt. Col. Am. Math. Soc; Soc. Indust. & Appl. Math; Math. Asn. Am. Numerical analysis. Address: 906 Glenview Dr, Carbondale, IL 62901.

GATES, MARSHALL D(eMOTTE), JR, b. Boyne City, Mich, Sept. 25, 15; m. 41; c. 4. ORGANIC CHEMISTRY. B.S, Rice Inst, 36, M.A, 38; Ph.D. (org. chem), Harvard, 41; hon. D.Sc, MacMurray Col, 63. Asst. prof. chem, Bryn Mawr Col, 41-43; tech. aide, Off. Sci. Res. & Develop, Wash,

D.C, 43-46; assoc. prof. CHEM, Bryn Mawr Col, 46-49; lectr, UNIV. ROCHESTER, 49-52, part-time prof, 52-60, PROF, 60- Tishler lectr, Harvard, 53; mem. comt. drug addiction & narcotics, Nat. Res. Coun, 58-70; Welch Found. lectr, 60. Armed Serv. cert. appreciation, 46. Nat. Acad. Sci; Am. Chem. Soc.(ed, J. Am. Chem. Soc, 62-69); fel. Am. Acad. Arts & Sci. Chemistry of natural products and analgesics. Address: Dept. of Chemistry, University of Rochester, Rochester, NY 14627.

GATES, OLCOTT, b. New York, N.Y, Mar. 19, 19; m. 42; c. 5. GEOLOGY. B.S, Harvard, 41; M.A, Colorado, 50; Ph.D, Hopkins, 56. Asst, Woods Hole Oceanog. Inst, 46; geologist, U.S. Geol. Surv, 49-54; from asst. prof. geol. to assoc. prof, Johns Hopkins Univ, 54-63; U.S. Peace Corps, Ghana, 63-65; PROF. GEOL. & CHMN. DEPT, STATE UNIV. N.Y. COL. FREDONIA, 66- Geologist, Marine Geol. Surv. U.S.C.G, 41-46, Lt. Comdr.(Ret). Geol. Soc. Am; Am. Geophys. Union. Volcanology; petrology; structural geology. Address: Dept. of Geology, State University of New York College at Fredonia, Fredonia, NY 14063.

GATES, RAYMOND D(EE), b. Akron, Ohio, Oct. 10, 25; m. 54; c. 2. POLYMER CHEMISTRY. B.S, Akron, 49, M.S, 51, Ph.D.(chem), 61. Res. chemist, Firestone Tire & Rubber Co, 51-55, synthetic rubber & latex div, 55-58; inst. rubber res, Univ. Akron, 58-60; sr. res. chemist, chem. div, Int. Latex Corp, 60-62, mgr. appl. polymer res, 62-66; res. assoc, PPG Industs, 66-67, res. supvr, 67-71; MGR. CHEM. SERVS, OAK RUBBER CO, 71- U.S.A, 43-46. AAAS; Am. Chem. Soc. Synthesis of elastomeric polymers and halogenated plastics; polymeric structures and the relationship of structural characteristics to physical properties; mechanism of polymeric network degradation. Address: 3183 Silver Lake Blvd, Cuyahoga Falls, OH 44224.

GATES, ROBERT L(EROY), b. Lincoln, Nebr, Dec. 3, 17; m. 43; c. 2. BIOCHEMISTRY. B.S, Nebraska, 39, Ph.D.(chem), 52; M.S, Kans. State Col, 47. Asst, dept. milling indust, Kans. State Col, 46; res. chemist, Farm Crop Processing Corp, 47; asst. agr. chem, Nebraska, 48-52; proj. leader, res. dept, Westvaco Chem. Div, FMC CORP, 52-54, group leader, NIAGARA CHEM. DIV, 54-58, DIR. RES. & DEVELOP. DEPT, 58- Med.C, 40-42, Chem.C, 42-45, Maj. AAAS; Am. Chem. Soc; fel. Am. Inst. Chem; N.Y. Acad. Sci; Entom. Soc. Am; Brit. Soc. Chem. Indust. Precipitation and concentration of amylase; action of amylases on raw starch; gelatinization and retrogradation of starches; role of starch in bread staling; preparation of herbicidally active organic compounds; formulation and toxicology of pesticides; synthesis and development of new pesticides. Address: Research & Development Dept, Niagara Chemical Division, FMC Corp, Middleport, NY 14105.

GATES, ROBERT M(AYNARD), b. Madison, Wis, June 26, 18; m. 48; c. 2. GEOLOGY. B.A, Wisconsin, 41, M.A, 41, Ph.D.(geol), 49. Instr. GEOL, UNIV. WIS, MADISON, 49-50, asst. prof, 50-53, assoc. prof, 53-60, PROF, 60- Geologist, Conn. Geol. Surv, 48- U.S.A.A.F, 42-46, Maj. Fel. Geol. Soc. Am; Mineral Soc. Am; Geochem. Soc. Mineralogy and petrology of igneous and metamorphic rocks; geology of Western Connecticut. Address: Dept. of Geology, 125 Science Hall, University of Wisconsin, Madison, WI 53706.

GATES, RONALD EUGENE, b. Milwaukee, Wis, Sept. 19, 41; m. 66; c. 2. BIOCHEMISTRY. B.A, St. Mary's Col.(Minn), 63; Ph.D.(biochem), Northwest. Univ, 68. FEL. BIOCHEM, Vet. Admin. Hosp, Kansas City, Mo, 68-70; ST. JUDE CHILDREN'S RES. HOSP, 70- Am. Chem. Soc. Physical biochemistry with emphasis on the structure of macromolecular systems. Address: St. Jude Children's Research Hospital, 332 N. Lauderdale, P.O. Box 318, Memphis, TN 38101.

GATES, W(ILLIAM) LAWRENCE, b. South Pasadena, Calif, Sept. 14, 28; m. 51; c. 3. METEOROLOGY. S.B, Mass. Inst. Tech, 50, S.M, 51, Sc.D, 55. Asst, Mass. Inst. Tech, 50-53; res. meteorologist, Air Force Cambridge Res. Ctr, 53-57; asst. prof. meteorol, Univ. Calif, Los Angeles, 57-59, assoc. prof, 59-66; RES. SCIENTIST, RAND CORP, 66- Lectr, Univ. Calif, Los Angeles, 66- Am. Meteorol. Soc; Am. Geophys. Union; Royal Meteorol. Soc. Dynamic meteorology; numerical analysis; numerical weather prediction; physical oceanography. Address: Rand Corp, 1700 Main St, Santa Monica, CA 90406.

GATEWOOD, B(UFORD) E(CHOLS), b. Byhalia, Miss, Aug. 23, 13; m. 40; c. 1. MATHEMATICS. B.S, La. Polytech, 35; M.S, Wisconsin, 37, Ph.D. (math), 39. Asst. math, Wisconsin, 35-39; asst. prof, La. Polytech, 39-42; asst. stress analyst to asst. chief struct. engr, McDonnell Aircraft Corp, Mo, 42-46; struct. res. engr, Beech Aircraft, Kans, 46-47; assoc. prof. mech, Air Force Inst. Tech, Wright Patterson Base, 47-50, prof. & head dept, 50-55, res. coordinator & res. prof, 55-60; PROF. AERONAUT. & ASTRONAUT. ENG, OHIO STATE UNIV, 60- Am. Inst. Aeronaut. & Astronaut; Am. Soc. Mech. Eng; Math. Asn. Am. Shear distribution in diagonal tension beams; thermal stresses in long cylindrical bodies; aircraft structures; buckling of tapered columns; fatigue and thermal stresses. Address: 2150 Waltham Rd, Columbus, OH 43221.

GATEWOOD, CLAUDE W(EST), Sci. Educ, see 4th ed, Leaders in Education.

GATEWOOD, DEAN C(HARLES), b. Iowa City, Iowa, June 29, 25; m. 53; c. 4. BIOCHEMISTRY. B.A, Willamette, 50; M.A, Oregon, 53. Asst. gen. chem, UNIV. ORE, 50-51, biochem, 52-53, endocrinol, med. sch, 54-55, instr. BIOCHEM, DENT. SCH, 55-57, asst. prof, 57-63, ASSOC. PROF, 63- U.S.N, 44-46. AAAS; Am. Chem. Soc. Etiology of dental caries; biochemistry of selenium and other trace elements; metabolism of oral tissues. Address: Dept. of Biochemistry, University of Oregon Dental School, 611 S.W. Campus Dr, Portland, OR 97201.

GATEWOOD, LAËL C(RANMER), b. Cleveland, Ohio, Nov. 16, 38, m. 61; c. 2. BIOMETRY, COMPUTER SCIENCE. B.A, Rockford Col, 59; M.S, Univ. Minn, Minneapolis, 66, fel, 68-71, Ph.D.(biomet), 71. Technician biochem. res, Mayo Clin, 59-61, biophys, 62-67; lab. physiol. hyg, UNIV. MINN, MINNEAPOLIS, 61, scientist health comput. sci. & biomet, 67-68, ASST. PROF. LAB. MED. & BIOMET. & ASST. DIR. DIV. HEALTH COMPUT. SCI, 71- AAAS; Asn. Comput. Mach. Biomedical computation; simulation of dynamic physiological systems using both deterministic and stochastic modeling; techniques of quality assurance and file manipulation of medical information; application of computers to health care delivery. Address: 4932 Stevens, Minneapolis, MN 55409.

GATH, CARL H(ENRY), b. Jewell, Iowa, June 5, 12; m. 35; c. 1. CHEMICAL ENGINEERING. B.S, Iowa State Col, 33, M.S, 34. Jr. engr, EASTMAN KODAK CO, 34-36, sr. engr, 36, sr. asst. engr. & supvr, 37-46, supvr. eng. dept, develop. unit, 46-52, area chief engr, ENG. DIV, 52-53, ASST. DIR, 53- Instr, Rochester, 36-46. Am. Inst. Chem. Eng. Coating and drying of sheet materials. Address: Eastman Kodak Co, Kodak Park, Rochester, NY 14650.

GATHERS, G(EORGE) ROGER, b. Meridian, Okla, Feb. 1, 36; m. 69. SOLID STATE PHYSICS. B.S, Univ. South. Calif, 60; Ph.D.(physics), Univ. Calif, Berkeley, 67. Physicist, LAWRENCE RADIATION LAB, 67-69, asst. group leader physics, 69-70, PHYSICIST, 70- Air Nat. Guard, 54-60; U.S.A.F.R, 60-62. Am. Phys. Soc. Cyclotron resonance in lead; nuclear device diagnostic technology; acoustic geophysical techniques, particularly holography, studies of nuclear event generated ground motion; equation of state solids, specifically nuclear device driven shock hydrodynamics. Address: 1212 Harvest Rd, Pleasanton, CA 94566.

GATHERUM, GORDON E(LWOOD), b. Salt Lake City, Utah, Oct. 22, 23; m. 47; c. 3. SILVICULTURE. B.S, Washington (Seattle), 49; M.S, Utah State, 51; Ph.D.(silvicult, plant physiol), Iowa State, 59. Asst. range mgt, Utah State, 49-51; asst. prof, Texas Tech. Col, 51-53; assoc. prof. FORESTRY, Iowa State, 53-64, prof, 64-69; PROF. & CHMN. DEPT, OHIO STATE UNIV. & OHIO AGR. RES. & DEVELOP. CTR, 69- Summers, range conservationist, U.S. Dept. Agr, 53, instr, Colo. State Univ, 53. U.S.A, 42-45. AAAS; Soc. Am. Foresters; Ecol. Soc. Am. Tree physiology; forest soils. Address: Dept. of Forestry, Ohio State University, 140 Horticulture, Forestry & Food Technology Center, 2001 Fyffe Ct, Columbus, OH 43210.

GATLAND, IAN R(OBERT), b. London, Eng, Feb. 17, 36; m. 63; c. 4. THEORETICAL PHYSICS. B.Sc, London, 57, Ph.D.(theoret. physics), 60. Fel. theoret. physics, European Orgn. Nuclear Res, Geneva, 60-61; staff mem. PHYSICS, Res. Inst. Adv. Study, Md, 61-64; asst. prof, GA. INST. TECHNOL, 64-66, ASSOC. PROF, 66- Am. Phys. Soc. Theoretical elementary particle physics; atomic collisions. Address: School of Physics, Georgia Institute of Technology, Atlanta, GA 30332.

GATLIN, CARL, b. Wichita Falls, Tex, July 9, 24; m. 47; c. 2. PETROLEUM ENGINEERING. B.E, Southern California, 51; M.S, Tulsa, 55; South Penn Oil Co. fel. & Ph.D, Pa. State, 59. Petrol. engr, Phillips Petrol. Co, 51-52; Anderson-Pritchard Oil Corp, 52; Tex. Crude Oil Co, 52-53; asst. prof. petrol. eng, Tulsa, 53-57; assoc. prof, Texas, 59-61, prof, 61-64, chmn. dept, 60-63; prof. mech. eng. & chmn. dept, 63-64; v.pres. res. & dir. grad. studies, Drexel Inst. Technol, 64-65, prof. civil eng. & v.pres. acad. affairs, 65-69; PROF. APPL. SCI. & PRES, STANISLAUS STATE COL, 69- U.S.N, 46, Lt.(jg). Am. Inst. Mining, Metall. & Petrol. Eng; Am. Soc. Mech. Eng. Rock mechanics. Address: Office of the President, Stanislaus State College, 800 Monte Vista, Turlock, CA 95380.

GATLIN, LILA L, b. Hutchinson, Kans; m. 47; c. 4. THEORETICAL BIOLOGY, PHYSICAL CHEMISTRY. B.S, Univ. Tulsa, 57; M.S, Pa. State Univ, 59; Ph.D.(phys. chem), Univ. Tex, Austin, 63. Nat. Insts. Health fel, genetics found, Univ. Tex, Austin, 63-64; asst. prof. phys. chem, Drexel Univ, 64-66; vis. lectr, Bryn Mawr Col, 66-67; RES. BIOPHYSICIST, SPACE SCI. LAB, UNIV. CALIF, BERKELEY, 70- AAAS. Application of information theory to the living system. Address: Space Sciences Lab, University of California, Berkeley, CA 94720.

GATLING, FRANK P(RENTICE), b. Phila, Pa, Sept. 19, 15; m. 43; c. 1. PSYCHOLOGY. B.A, Tennessee, 44; M.A, Ohio State, 45, Carnegie Found. grant, 48, 49, Ph.D.(psychol, 49). Prof. psychol, Col. Charleston, 45-46; Tulane, 48-50; Oklahoma, 50-51; Arkansas, 51-55; head human factors div, Naval Aviation Lab. Ctr, Va, 55-60; MEM. TECH. STAFF, MITRE CORP, 60- Res. grant, Carnegie Found, 50. U.S.N.A.F, 41-42; U.S.A.A.F, 42-44. Experimental psychology; human learning, especially its application to military flying; human factors in the design of computer-centered systems. Address: 7504 Nottoway Pl, Springfield, VA 22150.

GATOS, GEORGE C, b. Athens, Greece, Apr. 15, 23; m. 59; c. 1. ORGANIC & PHARMACEUTICAL CHEMISTRY. M.S, Agr. Sch. Athens, Greece, 47; B.S, Athens, 50; M.S, Delaware, 56, Ph.D.(phys. org. chem), 59. Res. chemist, ATLAS CHEM. INDUSTS, INC, 59-71, SR. RES. CHEMIST, 71- Am. Chem. Soc. Chemistry of carbohydrates; hexitols and anhydrohexitols; conformation analysis and nuclear magnetic resonance analysis. Address: 1107 Dardel Dr, Wilmington, DE 19803.

GATOS, H(ARRY) C(ONSTANTINE), b. Greece, Dec. 27, 21; m. 50; c. 3. MATERIALS SCIENCE. Dipl, Athens, 45; A.M, Indiana, 48; Ph.D.(chem), Mass. Inst. Tech, 50. Instr. inorg. chem, Athens, 42-46; asst. metall, Mass. Inst. Tech, 48-50, res. assoc, 50-51, mem. res. staff, 51-52; res. engr, E.I. du Pont de Nemours & Co, 52-55; leader chem. & metall. group, Lincoln Lab, MASS. INST. TECHNOL, 55-59, assoc. head solid state div, 59-62, head, 64-65, PROF. ELECTRONIC MAT. & MOLECULAR ENG, 66-, metall. & molecular eng, 62-66. Am. Chem. Soc; Electrochem. Soc; Am. Phys. Soc; Am. Inst. Mining, Metall. & Petrol. Eng; Am. Acad. Arts & Sci; Acad. Athens. Electrochemistry; physical metallurgy; semiconductors; superconductors. Address: 20 Indian Hill Rd, Weston, MA 02193.

GATROUSIS, CHRISTOPHER, b. Norwich, Conn, Oct. 8, 28; m. 51; c. 1. NUCLEAR CHEMISTRY, RADIOCHEMISTRY. B.S, DePaul Univ, 57; M.S, Univ. Chicago, 60; Ph.D.(nuclear chem), Clark Univ, 65. Res. asst, Argonne Nat. Lab, 56-61; asst. scientist, Woods Hole Oceanog. Inst, 64-66; CHEMIST, LAWRENCE RADIATION LAB, 66- U.S.M.C, 48-52, Sgt. Am. Phys. Soc; Am. Chem. Soc. Mechanisms of nuclear reactions; nuclear spectroscopy; radiochemistry and geochemistry of fallout radionuclides; detection of low level radioactivity; activation analysis. Address: Lawrence Radiation Lab, Livermore, CA 94550.

GATSLICK, HAROLD B(AILEY), b. N.Y.C, June 30, 22; m. 43; c. 2. WOOD TECHNOLOGY. B.S, State Univ, N.Y, 44, M.S, 48, Ph.D.(wood utilization), 54. Tech. field rep, Monsanto Chem. Co, 48-49; instr. wood utilization, State Univ. N.Y. Col. Forestry, Syracuse, 52-56, asst. prof, 56-58; assoc. prof. forestry, UNIV. MASS, AMHERST, 58-61, PROF. WOOD SCI. & TECH, 61- U.S.A, 43-46, Res, 46-, Col. Soc. Wood Sci. & Tech; Forest Prod. Res. Soc. Wood seasoning; dry kiln engineering; production wood finishing and industrial engineering. Address: Dept. of Forestry, 204 Holdsworth Hall, University of Massachusetts, Amherst, MA 01002.

GATTERDAM, P(AUL) E(SCH), b. La Crosse, Wis, June 27, 29; m. 57; c. 3. ENTOMOLOGY. B.S, Wisconsin, 53, M.S, 57, Ph.D.(entom), 58. Med. entomologist, agr. res. serv, U.S. Dept. Agr, 58-60; res. asst. prof. entom, pesticide residue lab, N.C. State, 60-62; RES. CHEMIST, AGR. RES. CTR, AM. CYANAMID CO, 62- U.S.N.R, 51-53. Am. Entom. Soc. Toxicology, persistence, and metabolism of pesticides in or on plants, animals and soil. Address: American Cyanamid Co, P.O. Box 400, Princeton, NJ 08540.

GATTI, ANTHONY R(OGER), b. Buffalo, N.Y, Sept. 18, 35; m. 57; c. 2. INORGANIC CHEMISTRY. B.S, Brown Univ, 57; Okla. State Univ, 57-58; Ph.D.(chem), Pa. State Univ, 67. Chemist, Arthur D. Little, Inc, Mass, 60-63; res. chemist, HOUSTON RES. LAB, SHELL OIL CO, 67-70, SR. RES. CHEMIST & RES. SUPVR, 70- U.S.A.F, 57-60, Capt. Am. Chem. Soc; Catalysis Soc. Catalysis; the inorganic chemistry and structure of transition metal and noble metal catalysts used in the processing of petroleum products. Address: Houston Research Lab, Shell Oil Co, P.O. Box 100, Deer Park, TX 77536.

GATTI, A(RNO), b. Schenectady, N.Y, Dec. 4, 25; m. 46; c. 2. METALLURGY. B.S, Union (N.Y), 50; M.S, Rensselaer Polytech, 54. METALLURGIST, res. lab, GEN. ELEC. CO, 50-62, SPACE SCI. LAB, 62- U.S.A.A.F, 43-45. Am. Ceramic Soc; Am. Soc. Metals; Am. Inst. Mining, Metall. & Petrol. Eng. Whisker growth; fiber deposition; whisker and fiber composite technology. Address: General Electric Co, Room M9124, P.O. Box 8555, Philadelphia, PA 19101.

GATTINGER, RICHARD L(ARRY), b. Neudorf, Sask, June 28, 37; m. 62; c. 2. PHYSICS, AERONOMY. B.E, Saskatchewan, 60, Nat. Res. Coun. Can. fels, 60-64, M.Sc, 62, Ph.D.(physics), 64. Asst. res. off. PHYSICS, NAT. RES. COUN. CAN, 64-70, ASSOC. RES. OFF, 70- Observation and interpretation of the atmospheric phenomena classes as airglow and aurora, especially in the near infrared region of the spectrum. Address: Astrophysics Branch, National Research Council, Ottawa 7, Ontario, K1A 0R8, Can.

GATTS, ROBERT R(OSWELL), b. Berlin Heights, Ohio, Mar. 2, 25; m. 49; c. 5. MECHANICAL ENGINEERING. B.M.E. & M.Sc, Ohio State, 51, Ph.D. (mech. eng), 59. Engr. plastic film, Visking Corp, Ind, 51-53; res. assoc, Ohio State, 53-58, asst. prof. mech. eng, 58-59; mat. engr, gen. eng. lab, Gen. Elec. Co, 59-61, Knolls Atomic Power Lab, N.Y, 61-63; PROF. MECH. ENG. & CHMN. DEPT, UNIV. KANS, 63- Am. Soc. Mech. Eng; Am. Soc. Eng. Educ; Soc. Mfg. Eng; Soc. Automotive Eng; Soc. Exp. Stress Anal. Mechanics of materials; fatigue of metals; concepts of cumulative damage, mechanical reliability; simulation of engineering, industrial and urban systems. Address: Dept. of Mechanical Engineering, University of Kansas, Lawrence, KS 66044.

GATTS, THOMAS F, JR, b. Kansas City, Mo, Oct. 3, 33; m. 54. ELECTRICAL ENGINEERING. B.S.E.E, Univ. Md, 62, M.S, 66; Nat. Sci. Found. fel, Univ. Iowa, 67-68, Ph.D, 70. Instr. elec. eng, Howard Univ, 62-64; engr, Sylvania Electronics Systs, N.Y, 64-65; asst. prof. ELEC. ENG, Howard Univ, 65-67; ASSOC. PROF, UNIV. ALA, 69- Inst. Elec. & Electronics Eng; Am. Soc. Eng. Educ. Network theory; computer aided design. Address: P.O. Box 6167, University, AL 35486.

GATZ, CAROLE R, b. Omaha, Nebr, Jan. 26, 33. PHYSICAL CHEMISTRY. B.S, Iowa State, 54; fel, Illinois, 59, Ph.D.(phys. chem), 60. Phys. chemist, Stanford Res. Inst, 59-64; asst. prof. CHEM, PORTLAND STATE UNIV, 64-68, ASSOC. PROF, 68- Am. Asn. Univ. Women fel, 70-71. Am. Chem. Soc; Am. Phys. Soc. Quantum chemistry; gas kinetics; isotope effects. Address: Dept. of Chemistry, Portland State University, Portland, OR 97207.

GATZKE, ARNOLD L, b. Vernon, B.C, Aug. 23, 35; m. 57; c. 2. ORGANIC & POLYMER CHEMISTRY. B.A, British Columbia, 57, M.Sc, 59; Ph.D. (chem), Queens(Ont), 63. Lectr. chem, Royal Mil. Col.(Ont), 60-63; fel, Yale, 63-64; res. chemist, DOW CHEM. CO, 65-70, SR. RES. CHEMIST, 70- Am. Chem. Soc; Chem. Inst. Can. Oxidation of organic compounds by transition metal ions; synthesis and mechanism in anionic polymerization; synthesis and physical properties of polymers and copolymers of vinylidene chloride. Address: 1671 Poseyville Rd, Midland, MI 48640.

GATZY, JOHN T, JR, b. Phila, Pa, June 14, 36; m. 58; c. 3. PHARMACOLOGY. B.S, Pa. State, 58; Ph.D.(pharmacol), Rochester, 63. Instr. PHARMACOL, DARTMOUTH MED. SCH, 62-67, ASST. PROF, 67- Bioelectric properties and solute transport of epithlial barriers; cell pharmacology and toxicology. Address: Dept. of Pharmacology & Toxicology, Dartmouth Medical School, Hanover, NH 03755.

GATZY, JOHN T(HOMAS), b. Sharon, Pa, Oct. 25, 03; m. 32; c. 1. BIOLOGY. B.S, Waynesburg Col, 27; M.S, Pittsburgh, 30; D.Ed, Rutgers, 46. Asst. bot, Waynesburg Col, 26-27; teacher, high sch, Pa, 27-31; N.J, 31-46; PROF. BIOL, ZOOL, BOT. & ENTOM, EDINBORO STATE COL, 46- Flower pollination; endocrinology; relationship of visual-auditory perception to the grade placement of sound motion picture films in science. Address: Dept. of Biological Science, Edinboro State College, Edinboro, PA 16412.

GAUCH, HUGH G(ILBERT), b. West Manchester, Ohio, April 5, 13; m. 39; c. 2. PLANT PHYSIOLOGY. A.B, Miami (Ohio), 35; M.Sc, Kans. State Col, 37; Coulter fel, Chicago, 37-39, Ph.D.(bot), 39. Asst. plant physiol, Kans. State Col, 35-37; agent, U.S. Regional Salinity Lab, Calif, 39-43, asst. plant physiologist, 43-44, assoc. plant physiologist, 44-45; asst. prof. bot, Mich. State Col, 45-46; assoc. prof. PLANT PHYSIOL. UNIV. MD, COLLEGE PARK, 46-49, PROF, 49- Am. Soc. Plant Physiol. Plant nutrition and plant composition under saline conditions; boron in relation to plant reproduction and translocation of sugar. Address: Dept. of Botany, University of Maryland, College Park, MD 20742.

GAUCHER, DONALD H(OLMAN), b. Port Arthur, Tex, Aug. 2, 31; m. 57; c. 2. CHEMICAL ENGINEERING. B.A, Rice Inst, 53, B.S, 54; Oak Ridge Sch. Reactor Tech, 54-55; J.D, Houston, 63. Reactor develop. engr, nuclear energy dept, Foster Wheeler Corp, N.Y, 55-57; sr. res. engr, prod. dept, HUMBLE OIL & REF. CO, STANDARD OIL CO, N.J, 57-61, mem. staff, econ. & planning dept, Tex, 61-65, sr. analyst, coord. & planning dept, N.Y, 65-68, GOV. RELS. COUNSR, TEX, 68- Am. Inst. Mining, Metall. & Petrol. Eng. Oil and gas production technology and economics. Address: Humble Oil & Refining Co, P.O. Box 2180, Houston, TX 77001.

GAUCHER, GEORGE MAURICE, b. Edmonton, Alta, Can, Jan. 6, 38; m. 60; c. 3. BIOCHEMISTRY. B.Sc, Alberta, 60; Ph.D.(org. chem), Pennsylvania, 63. Res. assoc. BIOCHEM, Univ. Ill, 63-65; asst. prof, UNIV. CALGARY, 65-70, ASSOC. PROF, 70- Smith Kline & French fel, 63-64. Am. Chem. Soc; Can. Biochem. Soc. Fungal metabolism, enzymology, and regulation of secondary metabolism; radiation chemistry of proteins. Address: Dept. of Chemistry, University of Calgary, Calgary, Alta, Can.

GAUDET, JOHN J(OSEPH), b. Providence, R.I, Nov. 19, 31; m. 65; BOTANY. B.S, Rhode Island, 57, M.S, 59; Fulbright scholar, St. Xavier's Col, India, 59-60; Ph.D.(bot), California, Berkeley, 63. Asst. prof. biol, State Univ. N.Y. Stony Brook, 63-71; SR. LECTR. BOT, MAKARERE UNIV, UGANDA, 71- Res. found. grant-in-aid, State Univ. N.Y. Stony Brook, 64-65, atmospheric sci. res. ctr. summer fel, 64, Nat. Sci. Found. res. grant, 65-66, 68-70, 70-71; Fulbright fel, Univ. Malaya, 66-67; Nat. Geog. Soc. res. grant, 71-72. U.S.A, 52-54. Bot. Soc. Am; Inst. Asn. Theoret. & Appl. Limnol. Growth and development of aquatic vascular plants; control of aquatic weed growth; hydrobiology. Address: Dept. of Botany, Makerere University, P.O. Box 7062, Kampala, Uganda.

GAUDETTE, HENRI EUGENE, b. Boston, Mass, Jan. 26, 32; m. 60; c. 1. GEOLOGY, GEOCHEMISTRY. B.A, New Hampshire, 59; M.S, Illinois, 62, Ph.D.(geol), 63. Res. assoc. clay mineral, Univ. Ill, 63-65; asst. prof. GEOL, UNIV. N.H, 65-69, ASSOC. PROF, 69- U.S.A, 54-57, 1st Lt. Fel. Geol. Soc. Am; Mineral. Soc. Am; Clay Minerals Soc; Geochem. Soc. Inorganic geochemistry; distribution of minor and trace elements in rocks and minerals; clay mineralogy; mechanisms of adsorption by clay minerals. Address: Dept. of Earth Sciences, University of New Hampshire, Durham, NH 03824.

GAUDETTE, LEO E(DWARD), b. South Bellingham, Mass, Mar. 29, 25; m. 54; c. 2. BIOCHEMISTRY. B.S, Col. of Holy Cross, 49, M.S, 50; Ph.D. (biochem), Georgetown, 57. Chemist, Nat. Heart Inst, 54-56; biochemist, Worcester Found. Exp. Biol, 56-58; Nat. Inst. Allergy & Infectious Diseases, 58-60; chief, lab. biochem. pharmacol, Joseph E. Seagram & Sons, 60-62; head neuropharmacol, Riker Labs, 62-63; TECH. DIR, NEN BIOMED. ASSAY LABS, INC, 63- U.S.A.A.F, 43-45; Air Medal; Distinguished Flying Cross. AAAS; Am. Soc. Pharmacol. & Exp. Therapeut; Am. Chem. Soc. Drug metabolism, enzymes and mechanisms of action of central nervous system drugs; alcoholism; endocrinological function; isotope methodology. Address: NEN Biomedical Assay Labs, 575 Albany St, Boston, MA 02118.

GAUDIN, ANTHONY J, b. New Orleans, La, Aug. 11, 38; m. 58; c. 2. HERPETOLOGY, MORPHOLOGY. A.B, Southern California, 59, M.S, 64, Nat. Sci. Found. faculty fel, 68-69, Ph.D.(biol), 69. Teacher, high sch, 60-64; instr. BIOL, Los Angeles Pierce Col, 64-67, ASST. PROF, 67-70; SAN FERNANDO VALLEY STATE COL, 70- Am. Soc. Ichthyol. & Herpet; Soc. Study Amphibians & Reptiles. Amphibian embryology and osteology. Address: Dept. of Biology, San Fernando Valley State College, Northridge, CA 91324.

GAUDIN, A(NTOINE) M(ARC), b. Smyrna, Asia Minor, Aug. 8, 00; nat. 26; m. 26; c. 3. METALLURGY, MINERAL ENGINEERING. B.S, Paris, 17; E.M, Columbia, 21; Sc.D, Montana, 41. Lectr. mining, Columbia, 24-26; assoc. prof. mining & metall. res, Utah, 26-29; res. prof. MINERAL DRESSING, Mont. Sch. Mines, 29-39; RICHARDS PROF, MASS. INST. TECHNOL, 39- Consult. metallurgist, 26-; consult, War Prod. Bd, 42-43; Bd. Econ. Warfare, 42-43; Manhattan Dist, U.S. Corps Eng, 44-46; Atomic Energy Comn, 46-; mem. Marine Bd, Nat. Acad. Eng, U.S. rep, Int. Eng. Comt. Oceanic Resources. AAAS; Am. Soc. Eng. Educ; Mining & Metall. Soc. Am; Am. Chem. Soc; Am. Inst. Mining, Metall. & Petrol. Eng.(Richards Award, 57); fel. Am. Acad. Arts & Sci. Rock and ore crushing; the flotation process; mineragraphy; synthesis of minerals; leaching of ores; adsorption; radioactive tracers. Address: Dept. of Mineral Engineering, Massachusetts Institute of Technology, 77 Massachusetts Ave, Cambridge, MA 02139.

GAUDINO, MARIO, b. Buenos Aires, Arg, May 22, 18; m. 47; c. 2. PHYSIOLOGY, MEDICINE. B.S, Buenos Aires, 34, Millet & Roux fel, 43, M.D, 44, Arg. Nat. Cult. Cmn. fel, 45, U.S. Dept. State fel, N.Y. Univ, 46-48, univ. fel, 46-49, Dazian Found. fel, 47-49, Ph.D.(physiol), 50. Asst. & chief lab, instr. physiol, sch. med, Buenos Aires, 37-44; asst. prof. physiol, med. br, Texas, 49; chmn. dept. biol. physics, sch. med, LaPlata, 50; res. assoc. surg, col. med, N.Y. Univ, 51-55, assoc. prof, 55-57; med. dir, Abbott Labs, Int. Co. & Abbott Universal, Ltd, 57-62; assoc. med. dir, Pfizer Int, Inc, 62-67, assoc. dir. & dir. advan. clin. res. int, MERCK SHARP & DOHME RES. LABS, 67-71, SR. DIR. CLIN. RES. INT, 71- Assoc. dir. med. writing & advert, Lederle Labs. Div, Am. Cyanamid Co, 51-52; estab. investr, Am. Heart Asn, 54-57; clin. asst. prof, med. col, Cornell Univ, 71- Soc. Exp. Biol. & Med; Am. Physiol. Soc; Harvey Soc; Am. Fedn. Clin. Res; Microcirculatory Soc; fel. N.Y. Acad. Sci; Am. Soc. Nephrology; Int. Soc. Nephrology; Asn. Med. Dir. Experimental hypertension; kidney; body and cellular water and electrolyte distribution, exchange and excretion; membrane permeability; biophysics; isotopes; hemodynamics; clinical research; pharmaceutical industry; management. Address: Merck Sharp & Dohme Research Labs. Medical Affairs International, 126 E. Lincoln Ave, Rahway, NJ 07065.

GAUDITZ, ILLO, b. Offenbach-on-Main, West Germany, Sept. 22, 18; nat. PHYSICAL CHEMISTRY. B.S, Halle, 40, M.S, 41, Ph.D.(phys. chem), 44. Asst. prof. phys. chem, inst. phys. chem, Halle, 41-45; tech. consult. chem. indust, Field Info. Agency Tech, 45-47; admin. asst. chem. eng, LURGI Gesellschaft für Waermetech, 47-50; chemist, tech. develop. dept, Pennsalt Chem. Corp, 50-56, admin. asst. chem, 56-57, head chem. anal. sect, 57-60; chem. dept, Hazleton-Nuclear Sci. Corp, 60-61; res. scientist, tech. ctr, WEYERHAEUSER CO, 61-64, RES. CHEMIST, FORESTRY RES. CTR, 64- Soc. German Chem. Pesticide residue analysis and other food and drug laws analysis; wood, pulp and paper service laboratory analysis; phytochemical analysis; bioassay; animal damage control; infrared, ultraviolet and regular gas-liquid chromatography; radio-tracer technique. Address: Forestry Research Center, Weyerhaeuser Co, P.O. Box 54, Centralia, WA 98531.

GAUDRY, ROGER, b. Quebec, Que, Dec. 15, 13; m. 41; c. 5. ORGANIC CHEMISTRY. B.A, Laval, 33, B.Sc, 37, D.Sc, 40; Rhodes scholar, Oxford, 37-39. Lectr. chem, faculty med, Laval, 40-45, asst. prof, 45-50, prof, 50-54; asst. dir. res, Ayerst Labs, Inc. & Ayerst, McKenna & Harrison, Ltd, 54-57, dir, 57-63, v.pres. & dir. res. Ayerst, McKenna & Harrison, Ltd, 63-65; RECTOR, UNIV. MONTREAL, 65- Guest lectr, Sorbonne, Paris, 54-; v.pres, Sci. Coun. Can, 66; mem. Acad. Latin World, Paris, 67; pres. bd, Asn. Univs. & Cols. Can, 69. Pariseau medal, French-Can. Asn. Advan. Sci, 58-; Companion of the Order of Can, 68. Am. Chem. Soc; fel. Royal Soc. Can; Chem. Inst. Can.(pres, 55-56). Amino acid synthesis and metabolism. Address: University of Montreal, P.O. Box 6128, Montreal, Que, Can.

GAUDY, ANTHONY F, JR, b. Jamaica, N.Y, June 16, 25; m. 55. BIOENGINEERING, CIVIL ENGINEERING. B.S, Massachusetts, 51; M.S, Mass. Inst. Tech, 55; U.S. Pub. Health Serv. fel, Illinois, 57-59; Ph.D.(eng), 59. Jr. engr, Metcalf & Eddy & Alfred Hopkins Assoc, 51; engr, E.F. Carlson, Inc, 51-52; Capuano Inc; res. asst, Sedgwick Labs, Mass. Inst. Tech, 53-55; res. engr, Nat. Coun. Stream Improv, 55-57; asst. prof. sanit. eng, Illinois, 59-61; assoc. prof, OKLA. STATE UNIV, 61-63, prof, 63-68, EDWARD R. STAPLEY PROF. CIVIL ENG. & DIR. BIOENG. & WATER RESOURCES PROG, 68-, chmn. prog, 67-68, acting head, sch. civil eng, 66-67. U.S. Pub. Health Serv. grant develop. grad. prog. bioeng, 62-70 & res. grants, 62-68; Sigma Xi lectr, 71-72. U.S.A.A.F, 43-46. Am. Soc. Civil Eng; Water Pollution Control Fedn; Am. Water Works Asn; Am. Soc. Microbiol; Am. Chem. Soc; Am. Soc. Eng. Educ. Shock loading, kinetics and mechanism of activated sludge processes; response of biological systems to physical, chemical and biological environment and engineering control of such response. Address: Bioenvironmental Labs, School of Civil Engineering, Oklahoma State University, Stillwater, OK 74074.

GAUFIN, ARDEN R(UPERT), b. Salt Lake City, Utah, Dec. 25, 11; m. 36; c. 2. ZOOLOGY. B.S, Utah, 35, fel, 35-36, M.S, 37; Michigan, 48; Ph.D. (fisheries biol), Iowa State Col, 51. Instr, Bd. Ed, Salt Lake City, 36-43; ZOOL, UNIV. UTAH, 46-49, assoc. prof, 53-63, PROF, 63- Inspector, Salt Lake City Mosquito Abatement, 35-43; Terminex of Utah, 39-43; in charge stream sanit. res. unit, Environ. Health Center, Cincinnati, 50-53; Salt Lake City Metrop. Water Dist, 54-64; Nat. Insts. Health, 59-63, U.S. Pub. Health Serv, 63-65; asst. dir. biol. sta, Univ. Mont, 63-71, prof, 68-69. Sanit.C, U.S.A, 43-46. Am. Soc. Limnol. & Oceanog; Am. Fisheries Soc; Ecol. Soc. Am; Entom. Soc. Am. Limnological surveys and fisheries investigations; ecology of stoneflies. Address: Dept. of Biology, University of Utah, Salt Lake City, UT 84112.

GAUGER, JOLEROY, b. Lead, S.Dak, Mar. 5, 26; m. 47, 62; c. 4. PHYSICS. B.S, S.Dak. Sch. Mines & Tech, 50; M.S, California, Los Angeles, 52, Ph.D. (physics), 56. Asst. physics, S.Dak. Sch. Mines & Tech, 48-50; California, Los Angeles, 50-56; researcher, Lockheed Missiles & Space Co, Calif, 56-59; STAFF MEM, flight sci. lab, Boeing Sci. Res. Labs, 59-65; environ. sci, Douglas Advan. Res. Labs, 65-70; PHYSICS, UNIV. MELBOURNE, 70- U.S.N, 44-46. Cosmic ray physics; space sciences; magnetohydrodynamics; geophysics; earth strain measurements. Address: Dept. of Physics, University of Melbourne, Parkville, Victoria, Australia.

GAUGER, WENDELL L(EE), b. Eustis, Nebr, Nov. 7, 27; m. 52; c. 4. MYCOLOGY. B.S, Nebraska, 51; M.S, Idaho, 53; Ph.D.(bot), Purdue, 56. Asst. prof. bot, Nebraska, 56-58; assoc. prof. biol, Nebr. Wesleyan, 58-59; asst. prof. BOT, UNIV. NEBR, LINCOLN, 59-65, assoc. prof, 65-67, PROF, 67-, CHMN. DEPT, 65- U.S.C.G, 46-47. Bot. Soc. Am; Mytol. Soc. Am. Genetics and variability of fungi. Address: Dept. of Botany, University of Nebraska, Lincoln, NE 68508.

GAUGH, WILBUR S(ETH), b. Sharon, Pa, Sept. 13, 38. ORGANIC CHEMISTRY. B.A, Thiel Col, 60; Ph.D.(org. chem), Ohio State, 66. RES. SCIENTIST, EASTMAN KODAK CO, 66- Am. Chem. Soc. Synthesis of sterically hindered aromatic systems and cyanine dyes. Address: Eastman Kodak Co, Research Labs, 343 State St, Rochester, NY 14650.

GAUGHAN, EDMUND JEREMIAH, b. Syracuse, N.Y, Jan. 29, 31; m. 57; c. 2. ORGANIC CHEMISTRY. B.S, Le Moyne Col, 53; Ph.D.(org. chem), Fordham, 61. Sr. res. chemist, chem. div, Pittsburgh Plate Glass Co, 60-63; Nat. Insts. Health res. fel. org. chem, California, Riverside, 63-65; res. chemist, STAUFFER CHEM. CO, 65-68, SR. RES. CHEMIST, 68- AAAS; Am. Chem. Soc; The Chem. Soc. Rearrangements of quarternary ammonium salts; organo-metallic chemistry; organo-phosphorus compuonds; agricultural chemicals. Address: Stauffer Chemical Co, 1200 S. 47th St, Richmond, CA 94804.

GAUGHRAN, EUGENE R(OBERT) L(AWRENCE), b. Easton, Pa, Sept. 30, 16; m. 44; c. 2. MICROBIOLOGY. B.A. Lehigh, 39, fel, 39-40, Thorne fel, 40-41, M.S, 41; fel, Mass. Inst. Tech, 41-42, Ph.D.(bacter, biochem), 46. Asst. inst. res, Lehigh, 37-39; sanit. bacteriologist, Eng. Camp, 40; asst. Med. Res. Council, Office Sci. Res. & Develop. & Nat. Defense Res. Cmt, 42-46; asst. prof, bacter, Rutgers, 46-50; assoc. prof, 50-51; sr. bacteriologist, res. dept, JOHNSON & JOHNSON, 51-52; asst. dir. bacter, 52-53; dir, microbial chem, 53-54, microbiol, 54-62, res. found, 54-60, asst. dir. RES. DIV, 62-70, ASSOC. DIR, 70- Asst. Navy V-12, prog 42-46; lectr, Middlesex Gen. Hosp, sch. nursing, 46-50. Dipl, Am. Bd. Microbiol. Fel. AAAS; Am. Soc. Microbiol; Soc. Indust. Microbiol; fel. N.Y. Acad. Sci; fel. Am. Pub. Health Asn; fel. Am. Acad. Microbiol; Brit. Soc. Gen. Microbiol; Brit. Soc. Appl. Bact; Netherlands Soc. Microbiol; Am. Inst. Biol. Sci; Am. Asn. Contamination Control; Int. Asn. Milk, Food & Environ. Sanit. Physiology of thermophilic microorganisms; industrial microbiology; microbial enzymes and enzyme technology; research administration. Address: Research Division, Johnson & Johnson, New Brunswick, NJ 08903.

GAUGHRAN, GEORGE R(ICHARD) L(AWRENCE), b. Pa, Oct. 19, 19; m. 43; c. 1. ANATOMY. B.A, Lehigh, 42; M.S, Michigan, 47, Ph.D.(zool), 52. Res. assoc, Mass. Inst. Tech, 43; instr. ANAT, med. sch, Michigan, 51-57, asst. prof, 58-61; assoc. prof, COL. MED, OHIO STATE UNIV, 61-66, PROF, 66-, V.CHMN. DEPT, 64- Vis. prof, Syracuse Univ, summer, 62. U.S.N.R, 43-46, Lt.(jg). Am. Asn. Anat. Gross human antomy. Address: Dept. of Anatomy, College of Medicine, Ohio State University, Columbus, OH 43210.

GAUGLITZ, ERICH J(OSEF), JR, b. St. Louis, Mo, July 3, 29; m. 55; c. 2. ORGANIC CHEMISTRY. B.S, California, Berkeley, 55; M.S, Washington (Seattle), 60. Asst. org. chem, California, Berkeley, 55; gen. & org. chem, Washington (Seattle), 55-58; chemist, TECHNOL. LAB, Bur. Commercial Fisheries, U.S. Dept. Interior, 58-64, RES. CHEMIST, 64-70, NAT. MARINE FISHERIES SERV, NAT. OCEANIC & ATMOSPHERIC ADMIN, U.S. DEPT. COMMERCE, 70- U.S.A, 46-49, Sgt. Am. Chem. Soc; Am. Oil Chem. Soc. Organic chemical syntheses; chemistry of lipids, especially of marine origin; derivatives of polyunsaturated fatty acids. Address: Technology Lab, National Marine Fisheries Service, 2725 Montlake Blvd, Seattle, WA 98102.

GAUL, RICHARD J(OSEPH), b. Pittsfield, Mass, Oct. 3, 29; m. 53; c. 5. ORGANIC CHEMISTRY. B.S, Spring Hill Col, 49; U.S. Rubber Co. fel, Mass. Inst. Tech, 52-53, Ph.D.(org. chem), 54. Res. chemist, Am. Cyanamid Co, 54-59; assoc. prof. chem. & acting dir. dept, JOHN CARROLL UNIV, 59-62, PROF, 62-, dir, 62-65. Am. Chem. Soc. Synthetic studies related to penicillin; products derived from acrylonitrile; chemistry of sulfur heterocycles; rocket propellants; structure of terreic acid; synthesis and polarographic behavior of polychlorinated propionitriles, acrylonitriles and derivatives. Address: 2365 Fenwood Rd, University Heights, OH 44118.

GAUL, ROY D, b. Toston, Mont, Aug. 5, 32; m. 56; c. 4. PHYSICAL OCEANOGRAPHY. B.S, Texas A&M, 55, M.S, 57, Ph.D.(phys. oceanog), 67. Res. engr, Agr. & Mech. Col, Tex, 55-57; eng. oceanogr, Marine Advisers, Calif, 57-58; phys. oceanogr, U.S. Navy Hydrographic Off, 59-60; sr. res. scientist, Texas A&M, 60-66, mgr. oceanog. res, WESTINGHOUSE OCEAN RES. LAB, 66-69, MGR. & SR. SCIENTIST, 69- Am. Geophys. Union; Am. Soc. Civil Eng; Am. Soc. Limnol. & Oceanog; Sci. Res. Soc. Am. Military oceanography and coastal engineering, especially measurement techniques, surface and internal waves and hydrography and ocean circulation. Address: Westinghouse Ocean Research Lab, 11339 Sorrento Valley Rd, San Diego, CA 92121.

GAULD, JOHN R(OSS), b. Collingwood, Ont, Nov. 6, 28; U.S. citizen; m. 53; c. 2. PREVENTIVE MEDICINE, EPIDEMIOLOGY. B.S, Maryland, 51, M.D, 55; M.P.H, Hopkins, 59; grad, U.S. Army Command & Gen. Staff Col, 70. Intern, Univ. Hosp, Baltimore, Md, 55-56, res. med, 56-57; MED.C, U.S. ARMY, 57-, physician viral diseases, Walter Reed Army Inst. Res, 57-58, res. pub. health, health dept, Contra Costa County, Calif, 59-60, prev. med, Walter Reed Army Inst. Res, D.C. & Army Hosp, Ft. Ord, Calif, 60-61, prev. med. off, med. sect, Hq, Hawaii, 61, 7th Logistical Command, Korea, 61-62, chief dept. epidemiol, Walter Reed Army Inst. Res, Walter Reed Army Med. Ctr, Wash, D.C, 62-66, epidemiologist & dep. staff surgeon med. support & res. div, Atlantic-Pac. Interoceanic Canal Study Comn, Balboa Heights, C.Z, 66-68, epidemiologist, commun. diseases br, prev. med. div, Off. Surgeon Gen, Dept. Army, Wash, D.C, 68-69, CHIEF PREV. MED. DIV, Off. Surg. & Army Med. Command, Vietnam, 70-71, ARMY MED. COMMAND, EUROPE, 71- Dipl, Am. Bd. Prev. Med. & cert. pub. health, 64. Med.C, U.S.A, 57-, Col. Am. Pub. Health Asn. Infectious diseases. Address: 10009 Big Rock Rd, Silver Spring, Md. 20901.

GAULDEN, MARY ESTHER, b. Rock Hill, S.C, Apr. 30, 21; m. 56; c. 2. BIOLOGY. B.S, Winthrop Col, 42; M.A, Virginia, 44, Ph.D.(biol), 48. Res. assoc, Alabama, 45-46; biologist, Nat. Insts. Health, 46-47; instr. zool, Tennessee, 47-48, res. assoc, 48-49; consult, BIOL. DIV, OAK RIDGE NAT. LAB, 47-60, sr. biologist, 49-60, consult, 60-70; EMMA FREEMAN ASSOC. PROF. RADIOL, SOUTHWEST. MED. SCH, UNIV. TEX, 68-, asst. prof, 65-68. Vis. prof, Univ. N.C, 54; lectr, Univ. Tenn, 55-65. AAAS; Am. Soc. Cell Biol; Radiation Res. Soc. Cell biology; low dose effects of radiation and chemicals on cells. Address: Radiation Biology Section, Dept. of Radiology, University of Texas Southwestern Medical School, 5323 Harry Hines, Dallas, TX 75235.

GAULE, GERHART K(ARL), b. Munich, Ger, July 29, 18; U.S. citizen; m. 44. SOLID STATE PHYSICS. Munich, 46-52; M.S, N.Y. Univ, 63. Res. physicist, Sueddeutsch Tel, Ger, 52-54; chief res. & develop. dept, Intermetall, Inc, Ger, 54-56; res. team leader solid state & low temperature physics, U.S. Army Electronics Labs, 56-67, SR. RES. PHYS. SCIENTIST, ELECTRONIC COMPONENTS LAB, U.S. ARMY ELECTRONICS COMMAND, 67- Adj. prof, Fairleigh Dickinson, 64- Co-recipient, Army Sci. Conf. Award, W. Point, N.J, 59, 64. Electrochem. Soc; Metall. Soc; Am. Phys. Soc. Crystal growth and basic properties of silicon and boron; semiconductor devices, boron thermistor pairs for application as neutron sensors; low temperature physics; new superconducting materials; high current superconducting switches. Address: Electronic Components Lab, U.S. Army Electronics Command. Ft. Monmouth, NJ 07703.

GAULL, GERALD E, b. Sept. 17, 30; div; c. 2. PEDIATRICS. B.A, Michigan, 51; M.D, Boston, 55; Harvard, 55-57. Jr. asst. res. path, Peter Bent Brigham Hosp, Boston, Mass, 55-56, sr. asst. res, 56-57; Nat. Insts. Health fel. biochem. & path, Harvard Med. Sch. & resident pre-med. adv, John Winthrop House, Harvard Col, 57-60; jr. asst. resident pediat, Babies Hosp, Columbia-Presby Med. Ctr, 60-61; part time instr, sch. med, Emory Univ,

61-62; Nat. Inst. Neurol. Diseases & Blindness spec. res. fel. human metab, Univ. Col. Hosp. Med. Sch, London, 62-63; teaching fel. pediat, Harvard Med. Sch, 63-64; Nat. Inst. Neurol. Diseases & Blindness spec. res. fel. human metab, neuropsychiat. res. unit, Med. Res. Coun. Labs, Eng, 64-65; res. assoc. neurol, neurol. clin. res. ctr, col. physicians & surgeons, Columbia, 65-67; ASSOC. PROF. PEDIAT, MT. SINAI SCH. MED, 67-; CHIEF DEPT. PEDIAT. RES, N.Y. STATE INST. BASIC RES. MENT. RETARDATION, 67- Sr. resident, Children's Hosp. Med. Ctr, Boston, 63-64; asst. attend. pediatrician, Babies Hosp, Columbia-Presby. Med. Center, 65-67; Italian Nat. Res. Coun. vis. scientist, Univ. Florence, summer 67; attend, Mt. Sinai Hosp, New York, 67- Dipl, Nat. Bd. Med. Exam, 56; Am. Bd. Pediat, 66. U.S.A, 61-62. Soc. Pediat. Res; Am. Soc. Neurochem; Am. Soc. Clin. Nutrit; Am. Inst. Nutrit; Am. Soc. Biol. Chem. Biochemistry; neurochemistry. Address: Institute for Basic Research in Mental Retardation, 1050 Hill Rd, Staten Island, NY 10314.

GAULT, DONALD E, b. Chicago, Ill, Feb. 12, 23; m. 47; c. 3. FLUID MECHANICS, MATHEMATICS. B.S, Purdue, 44; Stanford, 47-48. Res. scientist aerodyn, AMES RES. CTR, NASA, 44-59, ballistics, 59-63, CHIEF PLANETOLOGY BR, 63- Guggenheim fel, 71. Except. sci. achievement medal, NASA, 67. U.S.N, 42-46, Lt.(jg). Am. Geophys. Union; Meteoritical Soc. Viscous and compressible flows; shock wave dynamics; meteoritics; selenology; impact cratering; planetology. Address: NASA Ames Research Center, Moffett Field, CA 94035.

GAULT, FREDERICK P(AUL), b. N.Y.C, Mar. 6, 33; m. 53; c. 3. PHYSIOLOGICAL PSYCHOLOGY. A.B, Rutgers Univ, 54; M.A, Indiana, 57, Ph.D. (physiol. psychol), 59. Jr. res. psychologist, physiol. dept. med. ctr, California, Los Angeles, 58-59, fel, U.S. Pub. Health Serv, 59-60; asst. prof. PHYSIOL. PSYCHOL, Yale, 60-65, ASSOC. PROF, 65-69; WEST. MICH. UNIV, 69- Consult, Long Beach Veterans Admin. Hosp, 59-60. Relationship between central nervous system activity and behavior of organisms; classical conditioning and avoidance conditioning; autonomic and muscular somatic activity and behavior; operant conditioning methods as applicable to the study of central nervous system functions. Address: Dept. of Psychology, Western Michigan University, Kalamazoo, MI 49001.

GAULT, JOHN M, b. French Camaroun, W.Africa, 24. PHYSICS. Ph.B, Chicago, 51, B.S, 57. Asst, Navy Meson Res, Univ. Chicago, 50-51, Inst. Nuclear Studies, 51-52; Fansteel Metall. Corp, 52-57; ASST. DIR. RES. & DEVELOP, INT. RECTIFIER CORP, 57- Am. Phys. Soc; Inst. Elec. & Electronics Eng; Int. Soc. Hybrid Microelectronics. Development of four-layer switch with integrated components; tantalum capacitors; selenium rectifiers; silicon devices. Address: International Rectifier Corp, 233 Kansas St, El Segundo, CA 90245.

GAULT, NEAL L, JR, b. Austin, Tex, Aug. 22, 20; m. 47; c. 3. MEDICINE. B.A, Texas, 50; Baylor; M.B, Minnesota, 50, M.D, 51. Instr. INTERNAL MED, Univ. Minn, Minneapolis, 53-55, asst. prof, 55-59, assoc. prof, 59-67, asst. dean, col. med. sci, 55-64, assoc. dean, 64-67; PROF. & ASSOC. DEAN, SCH. MED, UNIV. HAWAII, 67-, dir. postgrad. med. educ. prog. Ryukyu Islands, 67-69. Med. adv, Seoul Nat. Univ, 59-61; consult, Vet. Admin. Hosp, Minneapolis, Minn, 56-67; China Med. Bd. N.Y, Inc, 63, 71; med. faculty, Univ. Saigon, 64; Agency Int. Develop, 64-67. AOA Hon. Med. Soc, 50; award, Japan Med. Asn, 69. Med.Serv.C, 42-46, Res, 46-51, Capt. AAAS; Asn. Am. Med. Cols; Am. Med. Asn. Rheumatology. Address: 1960 East West Rd, Honolulu, HI 96822.

GAUM, CARL H, b. New York, N.Y, July 29, 22; m. 55; c. 2. CIVIL ENGINEERING. B.S.C.E, Rutgers, 49. Hydraul. engr, U.S. Geol. Surv, 49-53; consult. engr, Gaum Prof. Engrs, 53-55; supvry. hydraul. engr, Phila. Dist, U.S. ARMY CORPS ENGRS, 55-60, asst. chief hydrol. br, D.C. Dist, 60-61, basin planning br, Ohio River Div, 62-69, asst. chief interagency & spec. studies br. & chief tech. assistance & int. sect, planning div, Off. Chief Engrs, 69- Planning assoc, Bd. Engrs. Rivers & Harbors, 61-62; mem, U.S. Comt. Large Dams. U.S.A.F, 42-45, Sgt. AAAS; fel. Am. Soc. Civil Eng; Nat. Soc. Prof. Eng; Permanent Int. Asn. Navig. Cong. Comprehensive water and related land resource planning, including surface and ground water supplies, water quality, navigation, flood control, sedimentation, drainage, irrigation, fish and wildlife, recreation, power and beach protection; environment; economic evaluation; resources management. Address: 9609 Carriage Rd, Kensington, MD 20795.

GAUMER, ALBERT E(DWIN) H(ELLICK), b. Nazareth, Pa, April 27, 26. ECOLOGY. B.S, Moravian Col, 50; M.S, Purdue, 52, fel, 52-54, Ph.D, 54. Asst. instr. BIOL, Purdue, 50; asst. prof, MORAVIAN COL, 54-55, assoc. prof, 55-56, PROF, 56-, CHMN. DEPT, 54- U.S.A, 44-47. AAAS; Ecol. Soc. Am; Am. Soc. Zool. Physiological ecology. Address: 59 New St, Nazareth, PA 18018.

GAUNDER, ROBERT GLENN, b. Newark, Ohio, Mar. 6, 42; m. 66; c. 1. INORGANIC CHEMISTRY. B.S, Denison, 64; Fulbright fel, Leeds, 64-65; Ph.D.(inorg. chem), Stanford, 69. ASST. PROF. CHEM. UNIV. TENN, KNOXVILLE, 69- Am. Chem. Soc. Kinetics and mechanisms of electron transfer reactions and substitution reactions; preparative inorganic chemistry. Address: Dept. of Chemistry, University of Tennessee, Knoxville, TN 37916.

GAUNT, ABBOT STOTT, b. Lawrence, Mass, July 4, 36; m. 63. BIOLOGY, ZOOLOGY. B.A, Amherst Col, 58; Ph.D.(zool), Kansas, 63. Instr. biol, Middlebury Col, 63-66, asst. prof, 66-67; fel, State Univ. N.Y. Buffalo, 67-68, ASST. PROF, 68-69; ZOOL, OHIO STATE UNIV, 69- AAAS; Soc. Study Evolution; Am. Ornith. Union; Wilson Ornith. Soc; Am. Soc. Zool; Soc. Syst. Zool; Cooper Ornith. Soc. Avian vocalization mechanisms; morphology and evolution of burrowing birds; systematics of swallows. Address: Dept. of Zoology, Ohio State University, 1735 Neil Ave, Columbus, OH 43210.

GAUNT, JOHN THIXTON, b. Evansville, Ind, Feb. 29, 36; m. 58; c. 1. STRUCTURAL ENGINEERING. C.E, Cincinnati, 58; fel, Purdue, 58-59, M.S.C.E, 59, Nat. Sci. Found. coop. fel, 62-64, Ph.D.(struct), 66. Design engr, Int. Steel Co, Evansville, Ind, 59-62; instr. STRUCT. ENG, PURDUE UNIV, 64-66, ASST. PROF, 66- Lectr, Evansville, 60-62; consult, Pittsburgh-Des Moines Steel Co, summer, 67. U.S.A, 60. Am. Soc. Civil Eng; Nat. Soc. Prof. Eng; Am. Soc. Eng. Educ. Design and behavior of steel structures; structural analysis; guyed towers. Address: School of Civil Engineering, Purdue University, Lafayette, IN 47907.

GAUNT, PAUL, b. Bootle, Eng, Feb. 23, 32; m. 64; c. 1. SOLID STATE PHYSICS. B.Sc, Sheffield, 53; D.Phil.(metall), Oxford, 58. Lectr. PHYSICS, Sheffield, 57-68; ASSOC. PROF, UNIV. MANITOBA, 68- Fel. Brit. Inst. Physics & Phys. Soc. Physical property and structural changes associated with magnetic and chemical ordering of metals and alloys; hard magnetic materials; dynamical theory of electron diffraction; nerve cell equations. Address: Dept. of Physics, University of Manitoba, Winnipeg 19, Man, Can.

GAUNT, ROBERT, b. Macon, Mo, Apr. 13, 07; m. 33; c. 1. ENDOCRINOLOGY. B.A, Tulsa, 29; M.A, Princeton, 30, fel, 31-32, Ph.D.(biol), 32. Asst. biol, Princeton, 29-31; prof. & chmn. dept, Col. Charleston, 32-35; asst. prof, Wash. Sq. Col, N.Y. Univ, 35-42, assoc. prof, 42-46; prof. zool. & chmn. dept, Syracuse, 46-51; dir. endocrine res, CIBA PHARMACEUT. CO, 51-57, DIR. biol. res, 58-66, BASIC BIOL. SCI, 66- Guggenheim fel, Princeton, 43; vis. prof, Ohio State Univ, 55. Fel. AAAS; Endocrine Soc; Am. Physiol. Soc; Soc. Exp. Biol. & Med; Am. Asn. Anat; fel. N.Y. Acad. Sci; Am. Soc. Zool; assoc. Royal Soc. Med. Physiology of adrenal cortex and gonads; water and electrolyte metabolism; drugs affecting endocrine function and experimental hypertension; research administration. Address: Research Dept, Ciba Pharmaceutical Co, Summit, NJ 07901.

GAUNT, STANLEY NEWKIRK, b. Elmer, N.J, June 20, 15; m. 39; c. 2. ANIMAL SCIENCE & GENETICS. B.S, Rutgers, 38; fel, N.C. State Col, 53, Ph.D.(animal genetics & physiol), 55. Admin. asst, Agr. Adjust. Admin, N.J, 38-39; asst. county agent, Litchfield County exten. serv, Connecticut, 39-43, assoc. county agent, 43-45; PROF. DAIRY SCI, UNIV. MASS, AMHERST, 45- Researcher, N.C. State Col, 51-53; res. grants, Nat. Asn. Artificial Breeders, 56, 57, 65, Hood Found, 57, 58, 59, 65, Abelard Found, 62-71, East. Artificial Breeders Coop, 65-71, Agway grant, 66-67; Fulbright res. scholar, Denmark, 69; guest lectr. univs, Aberdeen, Cambridge, Lisbon, Ljubljana, Thessalonikia, 69. Mem. & chmn, Nat. Res. Comt. Milk Compos, 60-65, 66-67. Am. Dairy Sci. Asn.(secy, 51-52); Am. Soc. Animal Sci; Am. Genetic Asn; N.Y. Acad. Sci. Measures of a dairy sire's genetic merit; programs to maximize genetic progress; genetic and environmental influences on non-fat components of milk; relationships between genetic markers to production and reproduction in dairy cattle. Address: Stockbridge Hall, Room 301, University of Massachusetts, Amherst, MA 01002.

GAUNTT, CHARLES JOHN, b. Granger, Tex, Nov. 23, 37; m. 59; c. 1. MICROBIOLOGY. B.S, Southwestern (Tex), 59; M.A, Texas, Austin, 64, Ph.D.(microbiol), 66. Res. anal. nuclear eng, Off. Tech. Info, Atomic Energy Cmn, 59-61; Nat. Insts. Health fel, Wistar Inst, 66-68, Damon Runyon Mem. Fund fel, 68; ASST. PROF. MICROBIOL, COL. MED, UNIV. ARIZ, 68- Am. Soc. Microbiol. Biological characteristics and biochemical processes involved in the replication of animal viruses in tissue culture; effect of interferon on the replication of animal viruses. Address: Dept. of Microbiology, Arizona Medical Center, University of Arizona, Tucson, AZ 85724.

GAUNYA, WILLIAM S(TEPHEN), b. Conn, Sept. 28, 20; m. 47; c. 3. DAIRY HUSBANDRY. B.S, Univ. Conn, 47; fel, Rutgers Univ, 47-48, M.S, 49, Ph.D, 61. Res. assoc. dairy husb, Rutgers Univ, 48-49; asst. prof, UNIV. CONN, 49-62, ASSOC. PROF. ANIMAL INDUST, 62- U.S.N.R, 42-45. Am. Dairy Sci. Asn. Address: Dept. of Animal Industry, Box U-40, University of Connecticut, Storrs, CT 06268.

GAURI, KHARAITI LAL, b. Narowal, India, Oct. 16, 33; m. 64. PALEONTOLOGY, SEDIMENTOLOGY. B.Sc, Panjab Univ, India, 53, M.A, 55; Ger. Acad. Exchange Serv. scholar, Univ. Bonn, 60-63, Ph.D.(geol), 64. Lectr. geog, D.A.V. Col, Jullundher, 55-58; sci. assoc. GEOL, Calif. Inst. Technol, 65-66; sci. pool off, Coun. Sci. & Indust. Res, New Delhi, India, 66; asst. prof, UNIV. LOUISVILLE, 66-69, ASSOC. PROF, 69- Res. grants, Geol. Soc. Am, 67-68, Res. Corp, 67-68 & 70-71, Kress Found, 70-71. Del, Int. Conf. of Preservation of Stone Statuary, Bologna Italy, 69 & Int. Inst. Conserv, N.Y.C, 70. Stratigraphic paleontology; ultrastructure of shell; conservation of stone statuary. Address: Dept. of Geology, University of Louisville, Louisville, KY 40208.

GAUS, ARTHUR E(DWARD), b. Maplewood, Mo, Nov. 30, 24; m. 50; c. 3. HORTICULTURE. B.S, Univ. Mo, 49, M.S, 50, Ph.D, 57. Asst. instr. hort, Univ. Mo, 51-53; exten. horticulturist, Kans. State Col, 53-54; UNIV. MO-COLUMBIA, 54-66, PROF. HORT, 66- U.S.A, 44-46. Cost of production in vegetable crops. Address: 1-48 Agriculture Bldg, University of Missouri-Columbia, Columbia, MO 65201.

GAUS, MICHAEL P(AUL), b. Chicago, Ill, Dec. 2, 28; m; c. 2. MECHANICS. B.S, Illinois, 54, M.S, 56, Ph.D.(civil eng), 59. Res. assoc, Illinois, 57-59; asst. prof. eng. mech, Pa. State, 59-61, engr, Boeing Airplane Co, 61; DIR, ENG. MECH. PROG, NAT. SCI. FOUND, 61- Sr. struct. designer, Skidmore, Owings & Merrill, summers 55-57. U.S.A, 50-51. Applied mechanics; dynamics; fracture and theoretical properties of materials; structural dynamics, theory and analysis; engineering administration; civil engineering. Address: Division of Engineering, National Science Foundation, 1800 G St, N.W, Washington, DC 20550.

GAUSE, DONALD C, b. Elkhart, Ind, May 4, 34; m. 56; c. 2. COMPUTER SCIENCE. B.S, Mich. State, 56, M.S, 57; Syracuse, 63-65; grad, IBM Systs. Res. Inst, 65. Summer physicist, Naval Avionics Facility, Ind, 56; assoc. engr, Sperry Gyroscope Co, 57-59; proj. engr, Gen. Motors Truck & Coach, Gen. Motors Corp, 59-60, sr. proj. engr, 60-61, sr. res. mathematician, Gen. Motors Res. Lab, 61-62; sr. assoc. programmer, IBM Corp, 62-63, staff engr, 63-68, mgr. prog. educ, 68-70; ASSOC. PROF. COMPUT. SCI, SCH. ADVAN. TECHNOL, STATE UNIV. N.Y. BINGHAMTON, 70-, adj. asst. prof, 67-68, vis. lectr, 68-70. Consult, IBM Corp. Asn. Comput. Mach; Soc. Indust. & Appl. Math; Soc. Gen. Systs. Res. Adaptive, self-organizing and general systems theory; creative processes; group dynamics; computer simulation; heuristic programming; decision theory; creative design; teaching and management of innovation. Address: School of Advanced Technology, State University of New York at Binghamton, Binghamton, NY 13901.

GAUSH, CHARLES R(ICHARD), b. Uniontown, Pa, Nov. 15, 29; m. 61. VIROLOGY. B.S, Waynesburg Col, 51; M.S, George Washington, 55; Ph.D. (microbiol), Pittsburgh, 62. Asst. prof. MICROBIOL, SCH. MED, UNIV. S.DAK, 62-68, ASSOC. PROF, 68- Res. grants, Nat. Inst. Allergy & Infectious Diseases, 63-; S.Dak. Div, Am. Cancer Soc, 63-69 & Fraternal Order Eagles, 71- U.S.A, 51-54, Sgt. AAAS; Am. Soc. Microbiol; Tissue Cult. Asn; Brit. Soc. Gen. Biol. Significance of lipids in virus infected cells; structure and composition of mammalian cell membranes; cell culture. Address: Dept. of Microbiology, University of South Dakota School of Medicine, Vermillion, SD 57069.

GAUSMAN, H(AROLD) W(ESLEY), b. Morris, Minn, Dec. 23, 21; m. 45; c. 1. AGRONOMY. B.S, Maine, 49; M.S, Illinois, 50, Ph.D.(agron), 52. Asst. crop prod, Illinois, 49-52; assoc. agronomist, Agr. & Mech. Col, Texas, 52-54; asst. res. specialist farm crops, Rutgers, 54-55; assoc. agronomist, Univ. Maine, 55-67, prof. soil chem, 59-67; RES. PLANT PHYSIOLOGIST, U.S. DEPT. AGR, AGR. RES. SERV, SOIL & WATER CONSERV. RES. DIV, 67- Nat. Sci. Found. res. grant, 57-59; Atomic Energy Comn. grant; res. fel, Tex. A&M Univ, 64; Nat. Sci. Found. vis. scientist, Am. Soc. Agron, 64-67. U.S.A.F, 42-45. AAAS; Am. Soc. Agron; Am. Soc. Plant Physiol; Am. Inst. Biol. Sci; Scandinavian Soc. Plant Physiol. Plant physiology; histology; microscopy; remote sensing. Address: U.S. Dept. of Agriculture, Agricultural Research Service, Soil & Water Conservation Research Division, P.O. Box 267, Weslaco, TX 78596.

GAUSS, JAMES F(REDERICK), b. Glen Ridge, N.J, Mar. 13, 42; m. 63; c. 3. HORTICULTURE, VEGETABLE CROPS. B.S, Delaware, 65; Ph.D.(hort), Rutgers, 68. ASST. PROF. hort. veg. crops, Ohio Agr. Res. & Develop. Ctr, 68-70; HORT. & FORESTRY, OHIO STATE UNIV, 70- Am. Soc. Hort. Sci; Potato Asn. Am. Physiological and morphological development of flowering in Brassica oleracea, variety italica; growth regulation and fruiting of Lycopersicon esculentum; growth regulation and tuberization of Solanum tuberosum. Address: Dept. of Horticulture & Forestry, Ohio State University, Columbus, OH 43210.

GAUSTER, WILHELM B(ELRUPT), b. Vienna, Austria, Dec. 25, 40; U.S. citizen; m. 69; c. 1. SOLID STATE PHYSICS. A.B, Harvard, 61; Nat. Sci. Found. fel, Tennessee, 63-66, Ph.D.(physics), 66. Res. assoc, Oak Ridge Nat. Lab, 66; MEM. TECH. STAFF, SANDIA LABS, 66- Am. Phys. Soc. Mechanical and thermal properties; ultrasonics; radiation effects. Address: Sandia Labs, Albuquerque, NM 87115.

GAUSTER, W(ILHELM) F(RIEDRICH), b. Vienna, Austria, Jan. 6, 01; nat; m. 40; c. 2. ELECTROPHYSICS. M.S, Vienna Tech, 23, Ph.D, 24, Dr.Habil.(theoret. mech), 27. Mgr, Elin Corp, El. Indust, 24-42; prof, Vienna Tech, 45-50; prof. & dir. high voltage lab, N.C. State Col, 50-57; dir. magnet lab, thermonuclear div, Oak Ridge Nat. Lab, 57-70; CONSULT, 70- Hon. prof, Univ. Technol, Vienna, Austria. Fel. Inst. Elec. & Electronics Eng; fel. Am. Phys. Soc; cor. mem. Austrian Acad. Sci. Applied electrophysics and mathematics; thermonuclear research. Address: 104 Seymour Lane, Oak Ridge, TN 37830.

GAUT, ZANE NOEL, b. Nauvoo, Ala, Aug. 29, 29; m. 55; c. 3. CLINICAL PHARMACOLOGY & NUTRITION. B.S, Birmingham-South. Col, 50; M.D, Tulane, 54, fel, 61-64, Ph.D.(biochem), 64. Intern. med, St. Thomas Hosp, Nashville, Tenn, 54-55; aerospace med. specialist, Gen. Dynamics Corp, 58-60; asst. prof. med. & biochem, Tulane Univ. La, 64-66; STAFF PHYSICIAN, SPEC. TREATMENT UNIT, NEWARK CITY HOSP, 66-; from clin. pharmacol. to DIR. CLIN. NUTRIT, HOFFMANN-LA ROCHE, INC, 66-; CLIN. ASST. PROF, N.J. COL. MED, 67- Nat. Insts. Health res. grant, 63-, fel. nutrit, 64-; attend, Newark Beth Israel Hosp, N.J. U.S.N, 55-58, Lt. AAAS; Am. Soc. Pharmacol. & Exp. Therapeut; Am. Inst. Nutrit; Am. Soc. Clin. Nutrit; Am. Soc. Clin. Pharmacol. & Therapeut; Am. Fedn. Clin. Res; N.Y. Acad. Sci; Am. Med. Asn. Metabolism in human blood platelets; phase I drug evaluation in man; antilipemic drugs. Address: Dept. of Biochemical Nutrition, Hoffmann-La Roche, Inc, Nutley, NJ 07110.

GAUTAM, MANGAL S, b. Danpur, India, July 1, 30; m; c. 4. PHYSICS. B.Sc, Agra, 51; M.Sc, Rajasthan, India, 55; Ph.D.(physics), British Columbia, 66. Asst. prof. PHYSICS, Agra Col, 55-60, assoc. prof, 60-62; res. asst, British Columbia, 62-66; ASST. PROF, ST. FRANCIS XAVIER UNIV, 66- Can. Asn. Physicists; Optical Soc. Am. Plasma physics. Address: Dept. of Physics, P.O. Box 133, St. Francis Xavier University, Antigonish, N.S, Can.

GAUTEREAUX, IONE, b. Sacramento, Calif, Mar. 27, 13. BIOLOGY. B.S, Marylhurst Col, 42; Marine Biol. Lab, Woods Hole, 52; O'Hara fel, Marquette, 53, M.S, 54; Ph.D.(biol), Notre Dame, 58. Instr. biol, Ft. Wright Col, 46-54; Atomic Energy Comn. res. assoc, Notre Dame, 55-60; CHMN, DEPT. SCI, FT. WRIGHT COL, 58- AAAS. Nerve and muscle physiology; radiation biology; cellular physiology. Address: Dept. of Science, Ft. Wright College, Spokane, WA 99204.

GAUTHIER, FERNAND M(ARCEL), b. Soulanges, Que, May 4, 23; m. 48; c. 1. PLANT BREEDING. B.S.A, Laval, 42; M.Sc, McGill, 47; Ph.D, Univ. Manitoba, 67. Cerealist, exp. farm, Can. Dept. Agr, Que, 45-62; from assoc. prof. to PROF. PLANT BREEDING, LAVAL UNIV, 62- Genetics Soc. Can; Agr. Inst. Can. Oat and barley breeding; oat aneuploids. Address: Faculty of Agriculture, Laval University, Quebec 10, Que, Can.

GAUTHIER, GEORGE JAMES, b. Franklin, N.H, July 22, 40; m. 64; c. 3. ORGANIC CHEMISTRY. B.Sc, Notre Dame, 62; univ. fel, New Hampshire, 62-66. Nat. Insts. Health fel, 64-66, Ph.D.(org. chem), 66. Res. assoc. organometallic chem, Frank J. Seiler Lab, Off. Aerospace Res, U.S. Air Force Acad, 66-69; res. chemist, med. res. labs, PFIZER, INC, 69-71, CHEMIST, PFIZER CHEM. DIV, 71- U.S.A.F, 66-69, Capt. Am. Chem. Soc. Investigations of nucleophilic additions to pyridinium salts; synthesis and reactions of metallocenes, ruthenocene, ferrocenes. Address: Pfizer Chemicals Division, Pfizer, Inc, Groton, CT 06340.

GAUTHIER, GERALDINE FLORENCE, b. Haverhill, Mass, May 14, 31. CELL BIOLOGY. B.S, Mass. Col. Pharm, 54, M.S, 55; A.M, Radcliffe, 56, Ph.D.(anat), 62. Res. asst. pharmacol, Harvard Med. Sch, 56-58, teaching fel. anat, 58-59, res. fel, 59-62; instr. biol, Brown, 62-63, asst. prof, 63-64; biol. sci, WELLESLEY COL, 64-68, ASSOC. PROF. BIOL, 68- Fel, Am. Found. Pharmaceut. Ed, 54-57; U.S. Pub. Health Serv. res. award, 63-65 & co-recipient, 64-69, 69-74; Muscular Dystrophy Asns. Am. grant, 69-70, 70-71, 71-72. AAAS; Am. Soc. Cell Biol; Histochem. Soc; Am. Asn. Anat; Int. Soc. Cell Biol. Ultrastructural and cytochemical heterogeneity of mammalian skeletal muscle fibers; cytological basis of absorption and secretion in animal cells. Address: Lab. of Electron Microscopy, Wellesley College, Wellesley, MA 02181.

GAUTHIER, MARCEL, b. Montreal, Que, July 16, 24; m. 59; c. 4. INDUSTRIAL ENGINEERING & STATISTICS. B.Sc.A, Polytech. Sch, Montreal, 59; M.Sc, Univ. Birmingham, 67. Prof. mech. eng, POLYTECH. SCH, MONTREAL, 59-66, ASSOC. PROF. INDUST. ENG, 68- Analyst, Montreal Locomotive Works Ltd, 63-66; Hosp. Ste-Justine, Montreal, 68-70; Montreal Transportation Comn, 71- Can. Oper. Res. Soc. Operations research; computer simulation; statistical quality control; reliability engineering; decision theory. Address: Dept. of Industrial Engineering, Polytechnical School, C.P. 6128, Montreal, Que, Can.

GAUTHIER, P(AUL) M, b. Detroit, Mich, Dec. 11, 40; m. 66; c. 2. MATHEMATICS. B.Sc, Univ. Detroit, 62; M.A, Wayne State Univ, 65, Ph.D, 67. Res. asst, Univ. Mass, 65-66; asst. & instr. MATH, Wayne State Univ, 66-67; fel, UNIV. MONTREAL, 67-68, ASST. PROF, 68- Am. Math. Soc; Can. Math. Cong. Analysis. Address: Dept. of Mathematics, University of Montreal, Box 6128, Montreal 101, Que, Can.

GAUTHIER, ROGER, b. Gardner, Mass, Apr. 3, 06; Can. citizen; m. 42; c. 2. BOTANY. B.A, Montreal, 29, L.S, 37, D.Sc, 52; M.S, Cornell, 47. PROF. BOT, BOT. INST, UNIV. MONTREAL, 38-, secy. faculty pure sci, 50-55. AAAS; Bot. Soc. Am; Int. Soc. Plant Morphol. General botany; morphology. Address: Dept. of Botany, University of Montreal, Montreal 36, Que, Can.

GAUTHIER, YVAN A(LBERT), b. Ste. Elisabeth de Joliette, Que, May 22, 37; m. 64; c. 3. MEDICAL BIOCHEMISTRY. M.D, Univ. Montreal, 63; Med. Res. Coun. Can. fel, Laval Univ, 63-67. DIR. CLIN. CHEM. LAB, BIOCHEM. SERV, ST. LUC HOSP, 67- Can. Biochem. Soc. Dimethylsulfoxide; methodology in clinical chemistry; electrophoresis; chromatography. Address: Biochemistry Service, St. Luc Hospital, 1048 St. Denis St, Montreal, Que, Can.

GAUTHREAUX, SIDNEY ANTHONY, JR, b. Plaquemine, La, Oct. 18, 40; m. 63; c. 2. VERTEBRATE ZOOLOGY, ANIMAL BEHAVIOR. B.S, La. State, New Orleans, 63; M.S, La. State, Baton Rouge, 65, Ph.D.(zool), 68. Instr. biol, La. State, Baton Rouge, 67-68; Stoddard-Sutton res. fel. ZOOL, Univ. Ga, 68-70; ASST. PROF, CLEMSON UNIV, 70- AAAS; Am. Soc. Zool; Animal Behav. Soc; Am. Ornith. Union; Cooper Ornith. Soc; Wilson Ornith. Soc. Comparative physiology; migratory behavior of animals, particularly birds, and physiological mechanisms that underlie the behavior; radar and telescopic studies of bird migration; circadian rhythms. Address: Dept. of Zoology, Clemson University, Clemson, SC 29631.

GAUTIER, T(HOMAS) N(ICHOLAS), JR, b. Miami, Fla, Nov. 12, 13; m. 46; c. 2. PHYSICS. B.S, Florida, 36, M.S, 39; North Carolina, 39-42. Instr. phys. sci, Florida, 36-39; lab. asst. physics, North Carolina, 39-42; physicist, Nat. Bur. Standards, 42-54, chief upper atmosphere physics sect, 54-59, consult, radio propagation physics div, 59-65; chief, ionospheric predictions br, Inst. Telecommunications Sci, Environ. Sci. Servs. Admin, Colo, 65-68, prog. off, res. labs, 68-70, asst. dir, off. geophys. monitoring, environ. res. labs, NAT. OCEANIC & ATMOSPHERIC AGENCY, 70-71, PHYSICIST, SOLAR-IONOSPHERIC CLIMAT. DIV, ENVIRON. DATA SERV, 71- Del, World Aeronaut. Radio Conf, Geneva, 48. Am. Geophys. Union; Int. Sci. Radio Union; Sci. Res. Soc. Am. Ionospheric radio wave propagation; ionospheric physics and climatology. Address: Solar-Ionospheric Climatology Division, Environmental Data Service, National Oceanic & Atmospheric Agency, Boulder, CO 80302.

GAUTIERI, RONALD FRANCIS, b. Providence, R.I, Oct. 10, 33; m. 62; c. 1. PHARMACOLOGY. B.S, R.I. Col. Pharm, 55; M.S, Temple, 57, Smith Kline & French Found. fel, 58-60, Ph.D.(pharmacol), 60. Asst. prof. PHARMACOL, TEMPLE UNIV, 60-66, assoc. prof, 66-70, PROF, 70- Co-investr, Nat. Insts. Health cancer res. grant, 62-63, prin. investr, Nat. Inst. Child Health & Human Develop. grant, 62-64; vis. lectr, Am. Asn. Cols. Pharm, 68- AAAS; Am. Pharmaceut. Asn. Cancer; human placental perfusions; toxicology; teratology; biochemistry; physiology; dental research; gastroenterology; mechanism of action of drugs; fetal pharmacology. Address: 418 Bolton Rd, Glenside, PA 19038.

GAUTRAUD, JOHN A, b. N.Y.C, Sept. 3, 26; m. 49; c. 3. SYSTEMS ENGINEERING. S.B, Mass. Inst. Technol, 46, S.M, 49. Res. asst. instrumentation & control, Mass. Inst. Technol, 47-49, asst. dir. guid. & control, instrumentation lab, 49-59; mgr. guid. & control, Avco Corp, 59-62; dir. systs. eng, off. manned space flight, NASA, 62-63; dir. advan. space systs, Avco Corp, 63-66, develop. & eng, space systs. div, 66-67; exec. asst. to div. pres, systs. ctr, UNITED AIRCRAFT CORP, 67-68, mgr, Hamilton Standard Syst. Ctr, 68-69, gen. mgr. electronic systs, 69-71, MGR. ELECTROMAGNETIC SYSTS, UNITED AIRCRAFT RES. LABS, 71- U.S.N.R, 44-46, Lt.(jg). Laser, radar, electro optic and computer control systems. Address: 64 Paper Chase Trail, Avon, CT 06001.

GAUTREAU, RONALD, b. Newark, N.J, Jan. 21, 40; m. 61; c. 3. PHYSICS. B.S, Lehigh, 61; M.S, Stevens Inst. Tech, 63, Ph.D.(physics), 66. ASSOC. PROF. PHYSICS, NEWARK COL. ENG, 66- Relativity physics with major emphasis on the structure of Weyl gravitational fields. Address: Dept. of Physics, Newark College of Engineering, Newark, NJ 07102.

GAUTSCHI, WALTER, b. Basel, Switzerland, Dec. 11, 27; U.S. citizen; m. 60; c. 4. MATHEMATICS. Ph.D, Basel, 53. Fel, Nat. Inst. Appl. Calculus, Italy, 54-55; comput. lab, Harvard, 55-56; res. mathematician, American

Univ, 56-59; mathematician, Oak Ridge Nat. Lab, 59-63; PROF. MATH, PURDUE UNIV, 63- Res. mathematician, Nat. Bur. Standards, 56-59; vis. prof, Tech. Univ, Munich, Ger, 70-71. Am. Math. Soc; Math. Asn. Am; Soc. Indust. & Appl. Math; Asn. Comput. Mach; Swiss Math. Asn. Numerical analysis; special functions; ordinary differential equations. Address: Dept. of Computer Sciences, Purdue University, Lafayette, IN 47907.

GAUVIN, DOMINIQUE, b. Ancienne-Lorette, Que, July 23, 08; m. 38; c. 2. CHEMISTRY. B.A, Quebec Sem, 28; Price bursar, Laval, 29-31, 32, L.Sc, 30, M.A, 32, Nat. Res. Coun. Can. bursar, 32-33, studentship, 33-35, D.Sc. (chem), 35. Demonstr. chem. & physics, Laval, 31-32; chief chemist, Munic. Lab, Que, 36-47, chief labs, 47-68; PROF. SANIT. MICROBIOL, LAVAL UNIV, 68- Lt-Gov. Silver medal, Que; Prix du Concours sci. de la prov. de Que, 38. Am. Pub. Health Asn; Am. Water Works Asn; fel. Royal Soc. Health; Can. Pub. Health Asn; Can. Inst. Chem. Organic chemistry; biochemistry and bacteriology; polymers and polymerization; constitution of polyindenes and polystyrenes; thermoduric bacteria and clostridium perfringens in milk; silver ions in water treatment. Address: Service de Sante, 2480 Canadiere Rd, Quebec, Que, Can.

GAUVIN, HERVEY P(AUL), b. Pawtucket, R.I, Sept. 21, 18; m. 47; c. 2. PHYSICS, MATHEMATICS. Sc.B, Brown, 43; Columbia, 51-52; Mass. Inst. Tech, 52-53. PHYSICIST, Oak Ridge Nat. Lab, 44-46; Naval Res. Labs, 47-50; acoustics, AIR FORCE CAMBRIDGE RES. LABS, 50-53, UPPER ATMOSPHERIC PHYSICS, 53- Mem. cmt. geophys. & geog, Dept. Defense Res. & Develop. Bd, 52-54; panel thermal radiation, Defense Atomic Support Agency Weapons Effects Bd, 58- U.S.A, 43-46, Sgt. Am. Phys. Soc; Acoust. Soc. Am. Nuclear radiation detectors; upper atmospheric auroral-airglow phenomena induced by artificial stimulation. Address: Air Force Cambridge Research Labs, Laurence G. Hanscom Field, Bedford, MA 01730.

GAUVIN, J. N. L(AURIE), b. Shediac, N.B, Oct. 8, 29; m. 64; c. 2. THEORETICAL PHYSICS. B.Sc, Laval, 54; Rhodes scholar, Oxford, 54-57, Ph.D. (theoret. physics), 57. Asst. prof. physics, Laval Univ, 57-63, assoc. prof, 63-70, prof, 70-71; DIR. COMN. SCI. RES, MINISTRY EDUC, 71- Secy, Que. Comt. Sci. Policy, 71- Am. Phys. Soc; Can. Asn. Physicists. Nuclear structure; nuclear reactions; science policy. Address: Ministry of Education, Government Bldg, Quebec, Que, Can.

GAUVIN, WILLIAM H, b. Paris, France, Mar. 30, 13; Can. citizen; m. 36; c. 1. CHEMICAL & METALLURGICAL ENGINEERING. B.Eng, McGill, 41, M.Eng, 42, Ph.D.(chem), 44; hon. D.Eng, Waterloo, 67. Lectr. chem. eng, McGill, 42-44; plant supt, Frank W. Horner Ltd, Montreal, 44-46; head chem. eng. div, Pulp & Paper Res. Inst, 57-62; mgr, NORANDA RES. CENTRE, 62-70, DIR. RES. & DEVELOP, 70- Assoc. prof, McGill Univ, 47-62, res. assoc, dept. chem. eng, 62-; mem, Nat. Res. Coun. Can, 62-, gen. del, 70-; mem, Sci. Coun. Can, 66- Can. Pulp & Paper Asn. Weldon Medal award, 58; Brit. Inst. Chem. Engrs. sr. Moulton Medal award, 64; Can. Asn. Adv. Sci. Medaille Archambault award, 66; Alcan Award, Can. Inst. Min. & Metall, 70. Chem. Inst. Can.(Paper award, 60 & 61, Jane Mem. lect. award, 63, medal, 66); Can. Soc. Chem. Eng.(pres, 66-67; award, 68); hon. mem. Soc. Indust. Chem; fel. Royal Soc. Can. Electrochemistry; high temperature technology, particle dynamics and fluid dynamics, particularly chemical and metallurgical processes. Address: Noranda Research Centre, 240 Hymus Blvd, Point Claire, Que, Can.

GAVALAS, GEORGE R(OUSETOS), b. Athens, Greece, Oct. 7, 36. CHEMICAL ENGINEERING, APPLIED MATHEMATICS. Dipl. eng, Athens Tech, 58; M.S, Minnesota, 62, Ph.D.(chem. eng), 64. Asst. prof. CHEM. ENG, CALIF. INST. TECHNOL, 64-67, ASSOC. PROF, 67- Consult, Phillips Petrol. Co, 67- Greek Army, 58-60, 2nd Lt. Am. Inst. Chem. Eng; Am. Chem. Soc. Chemical reaction engineering and catalysis; applied mathematics. Address: Dept. of Chemical Engineering, California Institute of Technology, Pasadena, CA 91109.

GAVAN, F(RANCIS) M(ICHAEL), b. Lancaster, Pa, Nov. 6, 08; m. 36; c. 2. PHYSICS. A.B, Dartmouth Col, 31. Physicist, Armstrong Cork Co, 31-41, head phys. test sect, res. labs, 39-41, mgr. phys. test dept, 45-62, gen. mgr, 62-65, phys. standards dept, 65-68, standardization & consumer affairs, 68-70; CONSULT, NAT. BUR. STANDARDS, PROJ. LEAP, 71- C.Eng, 41-45, Res, 37-62, Col; Legion of Merit; Croix de Guerre. AAAS; Am. Chem. Soc; fel. Am. Soc. Test. & Mat.(award of merit); Am. Nat. Standards Inst. Fire tests; packaging; thermal conductivity; weathering; gaskets; floors; walls; ceilings. Address: 712 N. President Ave, Lancaster, PA 17603.

GAVAN, JAMES A(NDERSON), b. Ludington, Mich, July 17, 16; m. 45; c. 2. ANTHROPOLOGY, ANATOMY. B.A, Arizona, 39; M.A, Chicago, 49; Ph.D. (anthrop), 53. Mem. res. staff, Yerkes Labs. Primate Biol, Fla, 50-53; asst. prof. anat, Med. Col. S.C, 53-58, assoc. prof, 58-62; Univ. Fla, 62-67; PROF. ANTHROP, UNIV. MO-COLUMBIA, 67- U.S.A, 42-45. AAAS; Am. Soc. Human Genetics; Am. Asn. Phys. Anthrop; fel. Am. Anthrop. Asn. Growth, development and anatomy of primates; physical anthropology; gross anatomy. Address: Dept. of Anthropology, University of Missouri-Columbia, Columbia, MO 65201.

GAVEN, JOSEPH V(INCENT), JR, b. Bayonne, N.J, Sept. 17, 31; m. 61; c. 1. PHYSICAL CHEMISTRY. S.B, Mass. Inst. Tech, 52, S.M, 53, Ph.D.(phys. chem), 62. Phys. scientist, U.S. Govt, D.C, 53-57; asst. phys. chem, Mass. Inst. Tech, 59-60; phys. scientist, sci. liaison & adv. group, U.S. Dept. Army, Pentagon, 62-68; sr. staff scientist, Perkin-Elmer Corp, 68-70; TECH. CONSULT, 70- Asst. prof. lectr, George Wash. Univ, 68. Chem.C, U.S.A, 53-54. Am. Chem. Soc; fel. Am. Inst. Chem; N.Y. Acad. Sci; Soc. Photog. Sci. & Eng. Nuclear magnetic resonance; transport properties of fluids; informative value of imagery; properties of photosensitive materials; graphic data processing. Address: 8606 Canterbury Dr, Annandale, VA 22003.

GAVENDA, J(OHN) D(AVID), b. Temple, Tex, Mar. 25, 33; m. 52; c. 2. PHYSICS. B.S, Univ. Tex, 54, M.A, 56; Marston fel, Brown Univ, 57-59, Ph.D.(physics), 59. Asst. prof. physics & res. scientist, defense res. lab, UNIV. TEX, AUSTIN, 59-62, assoc. prof, physics 62-67, PROF. PHYSICS & EDUC, 67- Sr. res. fel, inst. study metals, Univ. Chicago, 63; NATO sr. fel. sci, Univ. Oslo, spring,69. AAAS; Am. Asn. Physics Teachers; Am. Phys. Soc. Electronic properties of metals at low temperatures; ultrasonics; physics education. Address: Dept. of Physics, University of Texas, Austin, TX 78712.

GAVER, DONALD P(AUL), b. St. Paul, Minn, Feb. 16, 26. MATHEMATICS. S.B, Mass. Inst. Technol, 50, S.M, 51; Ph.D.(math), Princeton, 56. Mem. staff mil. opers. res, U.S. Navy Opers. Eval. Group, 51-53; systs. anal. res. group, Princeton, 53-56; res. mathematician, res. labs, Westinghouse Elec. Corp, 56-60, supvry. mathematician, dept. math, 60, adv. math, 62-64; assoc. prof. math. & indust. admin, CARNEGIE-MELLON UNIV, 64-70, PROF. STATIST. & INDUST. ADMIN, 70- U.S.N, 44-46. Opers. Res. Soc. Am; Am. Statist. Asn; Inst. Math. Statist. Applications of probability and probability models; statistics; operational research. Address: Carnegie-Mellon University, Pittsburgh, PA 15213.

GAVER, ROBERT CALVIN, b. Chambersburg, Pa, Oct. 2, 38; m. 61; c. 2. BIOCHEMISTRY. B.S, Pa. State, 60; Ph.D.(biochem), Pittsburgh, 64. Res. assoc, Illinois, 64-67; RES. SCIENTIST, BRISTOL LABS, INC, 67- AAAS; Am. Chem. Soc. Lipid chemistry and metabolism; gas-liquid chromatography; sphingolipids; prostaglandins; inflammation; immunology; peritoneal exudates. Address: Bristol Labs, Inc, Box 657, Syracuse, NY 13201.

GAVIN, JOHN BEVAN, b. Matamata, N.Z, May 14, 35; m. 60; c. 4. PATHOLOGY, ORAL BIOLOGY. B.D.S, New Zealand, 59; D.D.S, Otago, 64, Ph.D. (anat), 68. Asst. lectr. dent, dent. sch, Otago, 59-60, lectr. basic dent. sci, 60-65, sr. lectr, 65-68; ASSOC. PROF. anat, Univ. Sask, 68-70; PATH, UNIV. AUCKLAND, 70- U.S. Pub. Health Serv. int. res. fel. anat, med. sch, Northwestern, 66-67. Fel, Australian Col. Dent. Surgeons, 67. Am. Asn. Anat; N.Z. Dent. Asn; N.Z. Orthod. Soc; Int. Asn. Dent. Res. Relationship of thyroid and parathyroid hormones to tooth development; ultrastructure and histophysiology of mucous membranes, especially oral; periodontal disease; cardiac and experimental pathology. Address: Dept. of Pathology, University of Auckland, Auckland, New Zealand.

GAVIN, JOHN J(OSEPH), b. New Brunswick, N.J, Oct. 21, 22; m. 45; c. 9. MICROBIOLOGY. B.S, Rutgers, 49, M.S, 50; Ph.D, 64. Head biol. control, Smith, Kline & French Labs, Pa, 50-55; chief microbiologist, Food Res. Labs, N.Y, 55-57; Fund Res. Therapeut. res. fel. biochem, Norristown State Hosp, 57-64; group leader bact. res, Norwich Pharmacol. Co. & Eaton Labs. Div, 64-66; sr. scientist & head dept. allergy & immunol, Dome Labs, MILES LABS, INC, N.Y, 66-69, dir. biol. prod. develop, 69-71, DIR. MOLECULAR BIOL. RES, 71- U.S.A, 43-45. AAAS; fel. Am. Inst. Chem; Am. Soc. Microbiol; Am. Chem. Soc; Soc. Indust. Microbiol; N.Y. Acad. Sci. Analytical microbiology; cell wall synthesis; nucleic acid metabolism; chemotherapy; molecular biology. Address: 114 W. Sturdy Oak Dr, Elkhart, IN 46514.

GAVIN, ROBERT M, JR, b. Coatesville, Pa, Aug. 16, 40; m. 62; c. 4. PHYSICAL CHEMISTRY. B.A, St. John's (Minn), 62; Nat. Sci. Found. fel, Iowa State, 62-63, Ph.D.(chem), 66. Asst. prof. CHEM, HAVERFORD COL, 66-70, ASSOC. PROF, 70- Res. assoc, Univ. Mich, 66; Nat. Sci. Found. fel, Univ. Chicago, 69-70. Am. Chem. Soc; Am. Phys. Soc. X-ray and electron diffraction; molecular structure; chemical bonding; photochemistry of vision. Address: Dept. of Chemistry, Haverford College, Haverford, PA 19041.

GAVIOLA, (RAMON) ENRIQUE, b. Mendoza, Arg. Repub, Aug. 31, 00; m. 47. EXPERIMENTAL PHYSICS. B.S, Nat. Col. Mendoza, 17; Ph.D, Berlin, 26, Surveyor, La Plata, 21; Int. Ed. Bd. fel, 27-28; asst. physicist, Dept. Terrestrial Magnetism, 28-29; res. assoc, La Plata, 29-30; prof. physics, Buenos Aires, 30-36; La Plata Observ, 36-37; Cordoba Observ, 37-40, dir, 40-47, 56-57; sci. consult, Cristalerias Rigolleau, 47-50; physicist, Gen. Elec. Co, Arg, 52-56; Tucuman Univ, 57-58; PROF. PHYSICS, Buenos Aires, 58-61; Cuyo, 62; BALSERIO INST. PHYSICS, ARG, 63- Arg. Physics Asn. (pres, 44-50, 52-54); Int. Astron. Union. Physical optics; vacuum technique. Address: Bariloche Atomic Center, Balseiro Institute of Physics, Rio Negro, Argentina.

GAVIS, JEROME, b. Hartford, Conn, June 18, 28; m. 54; c. 2. CHEMICAL ENGINEERING. B.Ch.E, Polytech. Inst. Brooklyn, 49; Nat. Sci. Found. fel, Cornell Univ, 52-53, Ph.D.(chem), 53. Asst. prof. CHEM. ENG, JOHNS HOPKINS UNIV, 56-60, ASSOC. PROF, 60- U.S.A, 54-56. Am. Inst. Chem. Eng; Am. Chem. Soc. Transport phenomena. Address: Dept. of Geography & Environmental Engineering, Johns Hopkins University, Baltimore, MD 21218.

GAVLIN, G(ILBERT), b. Chicago, Ill, Jan. 12, 20; m. 47; c. 3. ORGANIC CHEMISTRY. B.S, Illinois, 41; Ph.D.(chem), Cornell, 48. Res. chemist, s.a.m. labs, Columbia, 43-45; Tenn. Eastman Corp, 45-46; assoc. org. chemist, Armour Res. Found, Ill. Inst. Tech, 46-47; asst, Cornell, 47-48; res. org. chemist & dir, nat. registry rare chems, Armour Res. Found, 48-54; sr. scientist, Richardson Co, 54-56, mgr. res. dept, 56-64; PRES, Poly-Synthetix, Inc, 64-69, CUSTOM ORGANICS, INC, 69- Organic fluorine and chlorine compounds; polymer chemistry; mechanism of organic reactions. Address: Custom Organics, Inc, 1445 W. 42nd St, Chicago, IL 60609.

GAVRIL, BRUCE D(AVID), b. Tulsa, Okla, May 13, 27; m. 68. COMPUTER ENGINEERING & SYSTEMS. B.S, Calif. Inst. Tech, 48; S.M, Mass. Inst. Tech, 49, M.E, 51, Sc.D.(mech. eng), 54. Instr. mech. & math, Tulsa, 49-50; mem. staff, div. indust. co-op, Mass. Inst. Tech, 54-55; head thermal anal. group, Nuclear Develop. Corp. Am, 55-59; proj. scientist, Gen. Appl. Sci. Labs, N.Y, 59-64; systs. engr, data processing div, IBM Corp, 64-68, staff mem, comput. sci. dept, res. div, 68-70; COMPUT. SYSTS. DESIGNER, 70- Outstanding contribution award, IBM Data Processing Div, 68. U.S.N.R, 45-46. Asn. Comput. Mach. Digital computers; systems enhancement; data channels and interfaces; multiprocessing systems; microprogramming; data acquisition and control applications. Address: 444 E. 75th St, New York, NY 10021.

GAWARECKI, STEPHEN J(EROME), b. Newark, N.J, July 31, 29; m. 54; c. 2. GEOLOGY. B.S, Rutgers, 51, M.S, 52; Ph.D.(geol), Colorado, 63. Staff mining geologist, N.J. Zinc Co, Colo. & Pa, 52-53; geologist, Doeringsfeld, Amuedo & Ivey, Inc, Colo, 60-62; U.S. GEOL. SURV, D.C, 62-69, PROJ. CHIEF ORBITAL PHOTO ANAL, BR. REGIONAL GEOPHYS, 69- U.S.N.R, 53-57, Lt. AAAS; Am. Soc. Photogram. Structural geology; igneous and metamorphic petrology; photogeology; remote sensing of environment, especially with infrared and ultraviolet portions of spectrum. Address: 7018 Vagabond Dr, Falls Church, VA 22042.

GAWER, ALBERT H(ENRY), b. N.Y.C, July 22, 35. PHYSICAL CHEMISTRY. B.S, Rutgers, 57; A.M, Columbia, 58, Ph.D.(chem), 63; Pa. State Univ, 69. Instr. CHEM, Brooklyn Col, 63-64; ASST. PROF, Barnard Col, Columbia Univ, 64-68; STATE UNIV. N.Y. COL. NEW PALTZ, 69- Summer lectr, Columbia Univ, 63-68. AAAS; Am. Chem. Soc; Am. Phys. Soc. High resolution nuclear magnetic resonance spectroscopy; chemical applications of Mössbauer effect; instrumental methods of analysis. Address: Dept. of Chemistry, State University of New York College at New Paltz, New Paltz, NY 12561.

GAWIENOWSKI, ANTHONY M(ICHAEL), b. Newark, N.J, Oct. 30, 24; m. 55; c. 5. BIOCHEMISTRY. B.S, Villanova, 48; M.S, Missouri, 53, Ph.D.(biochem), 56. Control chemist, Merck & Co, 48; prof. serv. rep. pharmaceut, Schering Corp, 49-52; res. asst, Univ. Mo, 53-56; res. fel, Univ. Tex, 56-57; asst. prof, Kans. State Univ, 57-63; ASSOC. PROF. BIOCHEM, UNIV. MASS, AMHERST, 63- Mem, Human Life Found. U.S.N.R, 43-46, Lt.(jg). AAAS; Am. Chem. Soc; Endocrine Soc; Am. Oil Chem. Soc; Soc. Study Reproduction. Steroids; carotenoids; trace metals. Address: Dept. of Biochemistry, University of Massachusetts, Amherst, MA 01002.

GAWLEY, IRWIN H, JR, b. Union City, N.J, Apr. 20, 27; m. 55; c. 2. CHEMISTRY. A.B, Montclair State Col, 49, A.M, 51; summer, Gen. Elec. Co. fel, Union Col, 52; Ed.D, Columbia, 57. Teacher, pub. schs, N.J, 49-55; from assoc. prof. to PROF. CHEM. & DEAN SCH. MATH. & SCI, MONTCLAIR STATE COL, 55- U.S.N, 45-46. AAAS; Am. Chem. Soc; Nat. Asn. Res. Sci. Teaching; Nat. Sci. Teachers Asn. Chemical education; improvement of teaching of chemistry. Address: Dept. of Chemistry, Montclair State College, Upper Montclair, NJ 07043.

GAWRON, OSCAR, b. N.Y.C, Aug. 14, 14; m. 47; c. 2. BIOCHEMISTRY. B.S, Brooklyn Col, 34; M.A, Columbia, 38; Ph.D.(org. chem), Polytech. Inst. Brooklyn, 45. Chemist, Brooklyn Jewish Hosp, 35-40; chem. supvr, Int. Vitamin Corp, 40-45; res. chemist, Am. Home Prods. Corp, N.Y, 45-46; N.Y. Quinine & Chem. Works, Inc, 46-47; PROF. BIOCHEM, DUQUESNE UNIV, 47- Am. Chem. Soc; Am. Soc. Biol. Chem; N.Y. Acad. Sci. Mechanisms of action of Krebs cycle enzymes; cis-aconitase and succinic dehydrogenase; hydrogen and electron transport; chemistry of sulphur-containing amino acids. Address: Dept. of Biochemistry, Duquesne University, Pittsburgh, PA 15219.

GAY, BEN DOUGLAS, b. Salt Lake City, Utah, Jan. 11, 42; m. 63; c. 2. FLUID MECHANICS, NUMERICAL ANALYSIS. Nat. Defense Educ. Act fel. & Ph.D.(numerical gas dynamics), Univ. N.Mex, 69. ASST. PROF. COMPUT. SCI. & MECH. ENG, BUCKNELL UNIV, 69- Asn. Comput. Mach. Development of numerical procedures for compressible gas dynamics of supersonic flows including shock waves and boundary layers. Address: Freas-Rooke Computing Center, Bucknell University, Lewisburg, PA 17837.

GAY, DAVID LAWRENCE, b. Barbados, W.I, Aug. 7, 38; Can. citizen; m. 65; c. 2. PHYSICAL CHEMISTRY. B.Sc, Univ. W.I, 62, scholar, 62-65, Ph.D. (phys. inorg. chem), 66. Sci. master, Lodge Sch, W.I, 58-59; Nat. Res. Coun. Can. fell 65-67; ASST. PROF. CHEM, XAVIER COL, 67- Am. Chem. Soc; Chem. Inst. Can. Kinetics and mechanisms of inorganic reactions; chemical reactions at high pressures. Address: Xavier College, Box 760, Sydney, N.S, Can.

GAY, FRANK P, b. Denoya, Okla, Jan. 7, 25; m. 57; c. 2. PHYSICAL & ORGANIC CHEMISTRY. B.S, Indiana, 48; Ph.D.(chem), California, 51. Asst. chem, California, 48-51; res. chemist, Calif. Spray Chem. Corp, Standard Oil Co. Calif, 51-53; FILM DEPT. E.I. DU PONT DE NEMOURS & CO, INC, WILMINGTON, 53-57, staff scientist, 57-59, res. supvr, 59-65, RES. ASSOC, 65- U.S.A, 43-46. Am. Chem. Soc. Organometallics; polymer physics and degradation; high temperature polymers; polyesters. Address: Route 2, Box 159 D, Skyline Orchard, Hockessin, DE 19707.

GAY, HELEN, b. Pittsfield, Mass, Aug. 30, 18. BIOLOGY. B.A, Mt. Holyoke Col, 40; fel, Mills Col, 40-42, M.A, 42; Lalor Found fel, Pennsylvania, 51-54, Ph.D, 55. Asst, Carnegie Inst, Dept. Genetics, 42-43; jr. prof. asst, Nat. Insts. Health, 43-45; asst, Carnegie Inst, Dept. Genetics, 45-51, res. assoc, 54-60, assoc. cytogeneticist, 60-62, cytogeneticist, 62; PROF. ZOOL, UNIV. MICH, 62-; CYTOGENETICIST, CARNEGIE INST, 62- Lectr, Adelphi Col, 59-62; guest investr, Brookhaven Nat. Lab. Fel. AAAS; Am. Soc. Nat; Am. Soc. Zool; Genetics Soc. Am; Soc. Develop. Biol; Am. Soc. Cell Biol; Int. Soc. Cell Biol. Cytogenetics of Drosophila; cytochemistry; chromosome structure; electron microscopy. Address: Dept. of Zoology, University of Michigan, Ann Arbor, MI 48104.

GAY, HERMAN P(AUL), b. Baltimore, Md, Oct. 24, 16; m. 45; c. 4. APPLIED MECHANICS. B.S, Hopkins, 41; Delaware, 48-50. Eng. aide, ABERDEEN PROVING GROUND, 37-41, MECH. ENGR, U.S. ARMY BALLISTIC RES. LABS, 41-, CHIEF ENGR, INT. BALLISTIC LAB, 69-, chief appl. mech. br, 52-69. Except. Civilian Serv. medal, 45; Kent award, U.S. Army Ballistic Res. Labs, 68; res. & develop. award, U.S. Army, 69. Am. Soc. Mech. Eng; Am. Ord. Asn. Theoretical and experimental mechanics. Address: U.S. Army Ballistic Research Labs, Aberdeen Proving Ground, MD 21005.

GAY, J(ACKSON) G(ILBERT), b. Selma, Ala, Dec. 27, 32; m. 55; c. 2. SOLID STATE PHYSICS. B.S, Auburn, 55; Nat. Defense Ed. Act fel, Florida, 60-63, Ph.D.(physics), 63. Sr. engr, Pratt & Whitney Aircraft, Div, United Aircraft Co, 55-60; res. assoc. physics, Florida, 63-64; SR. RES. PHYSICIST, GEN. MOTORS RES. LABS, 64- Am. Phys. Soc. Theory of solid surfaces; theory of optical properties of solids. Address: Dept. of Physics, General Motors Research Labs, 12 Mile & Mound Rds, Warren, MI 48090.

GAY, JOHNNY DAN, b. Sylvester, Ga, Oct. 16, 40. PLANT PATHOLOGY & VIROLOGY. B.S.A, Georgia, 62, M.S, 64, Ph.D.(plant path), 67. RES. PLANT PATHOLOGIST, CROPS RES. DIV, AGR. RES. SERV, U.S. DEPT. AGR, 67- Research on cotton seedling disease; specific infectivity of cowpea chlorotic mottle virus in different hosts; diseases of peas and beans, including bacterial, fungal and viral diseases. Address: Crops Research Division, Agricultural Research Service, U.S. Dept. of Agriculture, Georgia Coastal Plain Experiment Station, Tifton, GA 31794.

GAY, LLOYD WESLEY, b. Bryan, Tex, June 26, 33; m. 63; c. 2. FORESTRY. B.S, Colorado State, 55; Fulbright fel, Australian Forestry Sch, Canberra, 55-56, dipl, 59; M.F, Duke, 62, U.S. Pub. Health Serv. fel, 64-65, Ph.D. (forest climat), 66. Forester, Apache Nat. Forest, Ariz, 55, 57; res. forester, Cent. Sierra Snow Lab, Calif, 60-61; asst. prof. forest mgt, ORE. STATE UNIV, 66-70, FOREST CLIMATOL, 70-71, ASSOC. PROF, 71- Nat. Acad. Sci-Polish Acad. Sci. vis. scientist, Inst. Geog, Warsaw, 70; consult, Nat. Cellulose & Paper Orgn, Agr. & Forestry Exp. Ctr, Rome, 70. U.S.A.F, 57-60, Capt. Soc. Am. Foresters; Am. Meteorol. Soc. Influence of forests on heat balance at earth's surface, especially snow and forest hydrology, forest meteorology and evapotranspiration processes. Address: Dept. of Forest Engineering, Oregon State University, Corvallis, OR 97331.

GAY, ROBERT L(AIRD), b. Memphis, Tenn, Mar. 9, 40; m. 63; c. 2. ORGANIC CHEMISTRY. B.S, Southwestern at Memphis, 62; Mass. Inst. Tech, 66-67; Ph.D.(org. chem), Duke, 67. SR. RES. CHEMIST, ROY C. INGERSOLL RES. CTR, BORG-WARNER, INC, 67- Am. Chem. Soc. Organometallic and polymer chemistry. Address: 1434 Ashland, Des Plaines, IL 60016.

GAY, WALTER A, b. Somerville, Mass, Jan. 16, 36; m. 65; c. 2. ORGANIC CHEMISTRY. B.S, Boston Col, 58; M.S, Connecticut, 60; Nat. Insts. Health fel, New Hampshire, 62-65, Ph.D.(org. chem), 65. Res. chemist, Techni-Chem Co, 65-69; SR. RES. CHEMIST, OLIN CORP, 69- Lectr. eve. col, South. Conn. State Col; mem. continuing educ. comn. & tech. info. serv, Olin Corp. Am. Chem. Soc. Custom chemicals; fluoromatic chemistry; aromatic diazotization; hydrofluoric acid chemistry. Address: Olin Corp, 275 Winchester Ave, New Haven, CT 06511.

GAY, WILLIAM I(NGALLS), b. Sussex, N.J, Jan. 25, 26; m. 48. VETERINARY MEDICINE. D.V.M, Cornell, 50. Private practice, 50-52; chief, dept. animal husb, Walter Reed Army Med. Serv, 52-54; animal hosp. sect, NAT. INSTS. HEALTH, 54-63, asst. chief, lab. aids br, 61-63, lab. animal specialist, div. res. facilities & resources, 63-66, prog. dir. comp. med, Nat. Inst. Gen. Med, 66-67, chief res. grants br, 67-70, ASSOC. DIR. EXTRAMURAL PROGS, NAT. INST. ALLERGY & INFECTIOUS DISEASES, 71- Secy-treas, Am. Col. Lab. Animal Med, 64- Vet.C, U.S.A.R, 52-54; U.S.P.H.S.R, 57- Am. Vet. Med. Asn; Am. Asn. Lab. Animal Sci. Laboratory animal medicine; methods of animal experimentation; experimental surgery. Address: National Institute of Allergy & Infectious Diseases, National Institutes of Health, Bethesda, MD 20014.

GAYER, H(UBERT) KENNETH, b. Trinidad, Colo, Sept. 14, 13; m. 37; c. 5. SOCIAL & ENVIRONMENTAL SYSTEMS. A.B, Oberlin Col, 36; Ph.D, Washington (St. Louis), 41. Asst. embryol, Washington (St. Louis), 41-42; instr. biol, Grinnell Col, 42-43, spec. lectr, physics, 43-44; head training pub. sect, Bur. Naval Personnel, 46-49; tech. writer, Atomic Energy Comn, 49-50; dir. res. & develop, Fed. Civil Defense Admin, 50-54; sr. opers. analyst, U.S. Air Force, 54-58, Chief Opers. Anal, Europe, 58-61; dep. dir. appl. sci. div, Mass. Inst. Tech, 61-62, exec. off, neurosci. res. center, 62-63; proj. dir, Inst. Naval Studies, Cambridge, 63-65; chief opers. res. div, Shape Tech. Ctr, 65-67; v.pres, Travelers Res. Ctr, Conn, 67-71; PROG. MGR. RES. APPL. NAT. NEEDS, NAT. SCI. FOUND, 71- U.S.N.R, 44-46. AAAS; Opers. Res. Soc. Am. Research administration; operations research; analysis of air and naval warfare; manpower. Address: Research Applied to National Needs, National Science Foundation, 1800 G St, N.W, Washington, DC 20550.

GAYER, KARL HERMAN, b. Cleveland, Ohio, Aug. 6, 13; m. 50; c. 3. CHEMISTRY. B.S, Case West. Reserve Univ, 43, M.S, 44; Ph.D.(chem), Ohio State Univ, 48. Instr. CHEM, Ohio State Univ, 47-48; asst. prof, WAYNE STATE UNIV, 48-54, assoc. prof, 54-59, PROF, 59-, head inorg. div, 56-65. AAAS; Am. Chem. Soc; Am. Inst. Chem; Calorimetry Conf. Thermochemistry; solution calorimetry; titration calorimetry. Address: Dept. of Chemistry, Wayne State University, Detroit, MI 48202.

GAYLE, JOHN B(EN), b. Scottsboro, Ala, May 26, 24; m. 45; c. 3. PHYSICAL ORGANIC CHEMISTRY, MATHEMATICAL STATISTICS. B.S, Alabama, 49, M.S, 51, Ph.D.(chem), 54. Supvy. chemist & chief coal lab, U.S. Bur. Mines, Ala, 55-60, supvy. chem. engr, 60-61; chief phys. chem. sect. & acting chief appl. chem. sect, Marshall Space Flight Ctr, NASA, 61-65, chief qual. surveillance div, SUPPORT OPER, KENNEDY SPACE CTR, 65-71, CHIEF ANAL. LABS. DIV, 71- Adj. assoc. prof, grad. prog. mgt, Fla. Tech. Univ, Patrick AFB, 67- Am. Chem. Soc; Am. Asn. Contamination Control. Malfunction investigations; material testing; microchemical analyses; prototype development; mechanism of stress corrosion; mechanism of reaction of liquid oxygen with materials; computer simulation of physical and chemical processes. Address: Analytical Labs. Division, Support Operation, NASA, Kennedy Space Center, FL 32899.

GAYLER, C(ECIL),W(INSTON), b. Ft. Payne, Ala, Sept. 2, 16; m. 41; c. 2. CHEMISTRY. A.B, Howard Col, 38; M.S, Ga. Tech, 40; Park Davis fel. & Ph.D.(org. chem), Texas, 43. Asst. chem, Ga. Tech, 38-40; Texas, 40-42; res. chemist, Am. Viscose Co, 43-44, group leader, 44-49, sect. leader, 49-51; tech. supt, Chemstrand Co, 51-56, tech. mgr, 56-57, tech. serv. mgr, 57-58, dir. appln. res. & serv, 58-62; v.pres. & tech. dir, Polythane Corp, 62-64; proj. dir, Chemstrand Co, 62-66; dir. tech. admin, TEXTILES DIV, MONSANTO CO, 66-68, PROJ. DIR, 68- AAAS; Am. Chem. Soc; Am. Asn. Textile Chem. & Colorists. Applied fiber and textile research. Address: Textiles Division, Monsanto Co, 800 N. Lindberg Blvd, St. Louis, MO 63166.

GAYLES, J(OSEPH) N(ATHAN), JR, b. Birmingham, Ala, Aug. 7, 37. PHYSICAL CHEMISTRY. A.B, Dillard, 58; Ph.D.(chem), Brown, 63; Oregon State, 63-64, summer 64. Res. assoc. PHYS. CHEM, Ore. State Univ, 63-64; asst. prof, MOREHOUSE COL, 64-69, PROF, 69- Summer res. assoc, Univ. Iowa, 64; Univ. Uppsala, 65; res. staff scientist, IBM Corp, 66-69; Dreyfus scholar, 70- Am. Phys. Soc; Am. Chem. Soc. Molecular structure and spectroscopy. Address: Dept. of Chemistry, Morehouse College, Atlanta, GA 30314.

GAYLEY, ROBERT I, JR, b. Abington, Pa, May 18, 33; m. 57; c. 3. PHYSICS. B.S, Lafayette Col, 55; M.S, Rutgers, 57, Ph.D.(physics), 61. Instr. PHYSICS, Lafayette Col, 61; res. assoc, Maryland, 61-63; asst. prof, STATE UNIV. N.Y. BUFFALO, 63-67, ASSOC. PROF, 67- Ord.C, 60-61, Res, 61-, Capt. Am. Phys. Soc; Am. Asn. Physics Teachers. Solid state and low temperature physics. Address: Dept. of Physics, State University of New York at Buffalo, Buffalo, NY 14214.

GAYLOR, DAVID W(ILLIAM), b. Waterloo, Iowa, Apr. 8, 30; m. 54; c. 4. STATISTICS. B.S, Iowa State, 51, M.S, 53; Ph.D.(statist), N.C. State, 60. STATISTICIAN, Hanford Atomic Prod. Oper, Gen. Elec. Co, 53-55; Gen. Dynamics/Convair, 55-57; Vallecitos Atomic Lab, Gen. Elec. Co, 60-62; Res. Triangle Inst, 62-68; NAT. INST. ENVIRON. HEALTH SCI, 68- Adj. assoc. prof, N.C. State Univ, 67- Am. Statist. Asn; Biomet. Soc. Statistical design and analysis of experiments. Address: National Institute of Environmental Health Sciences, P.O. Box 12233, Research Triangle Park, NC 27709.

GAYLOR, JAMES L(EROY), b. Waterloo, Iowa, Oct. 1, 34; m. 56; c. 4. BIOCHEMISTRY. B.S, Iowa State, 56; Nat. Insts. Health fel. & M.S, Wisconsin, 58, Ph.D.(biochem), 60. Asst. prof. biochem. GRAD. SCH. NUTRIT, CORNELL UNIV, 60-63, assoc. prof, 63-69, PROF. BIOCHEM. & MOLECULAR BIOL, 69-, CHMN. SECT, DIV. BIOL. SCI, 70- Vis. lectr, Univ. Ill, 64 & 65; vis. mem. staff, dept. biochem, sch. med, Univ. Ore, 66-67. AAAS; Am. Chem. Soc; N.Y. Acad. Sci; Am. Soc. Biol. Chem; Am. Inst. Nutrit. Biosynthesis and metabolism of sterols; microsomal electron transport of mixed function oxidases; isolation and purification of microsomal enzymes. Address: Section of Biochemistry & Molecular Biology, Division of Biological Sciences, Graduate School of Nutrition, Savage Hall, Cornell University, Ithaca, NY 14850.

GAYLORD, EBER WILLIAM, b. Pittsburgh, Pa, Nov. 6, 22; m. 62; c. 1. MECHANICAL ENGINEERING. Ph.D.(mech. eng), Carnegie Inst. Tech, 53. Assoc. prof. mech. eng, Carnegie Inst. Tech, 53-59; RES. ENGR, GULF RES. & DEVELOP. CO, 59- Am. Soc. Mech. Eng; Soc. Automotive Eng. Experimental fluid mechanics; friction and wear dynamics; interface temperature between rubbing metals; momentum and mass transfer in jets. Address: Gulf Research & Development Co, P.O. Box 2039, Pittsburgh, PA 15230.

GAYLORD, EDWIN H(ENRY), b. Youngstown, Ohio, Jan. 16, 03; m. 30; c. 1. CIVIL ENGINEERING. A.B, Wittenberg Col, 24, hon. D.Sc, 59; B.S.C.E, Case, 26; M.S.E, Michigan, 36; fel, Harvard, 48. Struct. detailer, Mt. Vernon Bridge Co, Ohio, 26-27; prof. CIVIL ENG, Ohio (Athens) 27-56; UNIV. ILL, URBANA, 56-71; EMER. PROF, 71- Sr. stress analyst, Goodyear Aircraft Corp, Ohio, 44-45; mem. res. coun, Riveted & Bolted Struct. Joints; column res. coun, Eng. Found, chmn, 62-66. Am. Soc. Eng. Educ; Am. Soc. Civil Eng. Mechanics of materials and applications to design of structures. Address: 27 G.H. Baker Dr, Urbana, IL 61801.

GAYLORD, JOHN WALLACE, b. Pasadena, Calif, Apr. 28, 09; m. 35; c. 3. CHEMICAL ENGINEERING. B.S, Calif. Inst. Technol, 30; M.S, Mass. Inst. Technol, 32. Design engr, STANDARD OIL CO. CALIF, 34-47, sect. supvr. plant design, Calif. Res. Corp, 47-50, tech. asst. to v.pres. res. & develop, Calif. Res. & Develop. Co, 50-54, tech. asst. petrol. process res, Calif. Res. Corp, 54-57, sr. staff engr. atomic energy, 57-65, tech. asst. petrol. process res, 65-71, SR. STAFF ENGR, CHEVRON RES. CO, 71- Am. Inst. Chem. Eng. Sources, conversion, utilization and economics of energy. Address: 181 Deer Hollow Rd, San Anselmo, CA 94960.

GAYLORD, NORMAN G(RANT), b. New York, N.Y, Feb. 16, 23; m. 45; c. 4. POLYMER CHEMISTRY. B.S, City Col. New York, 43; M.S, Polytech. Inst. Brooklyn, 49, Ph.D.(chem), 50. Chemist, Elko Chem. Works, 43-44; Pa. Salt Mfg. Co, 45; Merck & Co Inc, 46-48; res. assoc, Polytech. Inst. Brooklyn, 48-50; res. chemist, film dept, E.I. du Pont de Nemours & Co, 50-55; group leader, resin dept, Interchem. Corp, 55-56, asst. dir. org. chem. dept, 56-59; v.pres, polymer div, West. Petrochem. Corp, N.Y, 59-61; PRES, GAYLORD RES. INST. INC, 61- Polymer consult, 61-; adj. prof, Canisius Col, 51-55; Polytech. Inst. Brooklyn, 55-62; mem. adv. bds, J. Polymer Sci, J. Appl. Polymer Sci. U.S.A.A.F; 45-46. Am. Chem. Soc; Am. Inst. Chem; Soc. Plastics Eng; Tech. Asn. Pulp & Paper Industs; Am. Soc. Test. & Mat. Organic reactions of organometallics and complex metal hydrides; polymer synthesis; polymerization kinetics; allyl polymerization; stereoregular polymers; organic chemistry of high polymers; block and graft copolymerization; charge transfer polymerization. Address: Gaylord Research Institute Inc, 20 Mt. Pleasant Ave, Newark, NJ 07104.

GAYNOR, JOSEPH, b. N.Y.C, Nov. 15, 25; m. 51; c. 4. CHEMICAL ENGINEERING. B.Ch.E, Polytech. Inst. Brooklyn, 50; M.S, Case, 52, Ph.D. (chem. eng), 55. Asst. unit opers. & plastics lab, Case, 50-55; chem. engr, Gen. Elec. Co, 55-59, chem. process engr, 59-64, mgr, info. mat. systs, 64-66; asst. v.pres. res, bus. equip. group, BELL & HOWELL CO, Ill, 66-68, v.pres, 68, DIR. GRAPHIC MEDIA RES, RES. LABS, CALIF, 68- Plenary lectr, Int. Cong. Photog. Sci; prog. chmn, Int. Conf. Electrophotog. Indust. Res. IR-100 awards, 63, 65. U.S.A, 44-46. Fel. AAAS; fel. Am. Inst. Chem; Am. Soc. Photog. Sci. & Eng; Am. Chem. Soc; Am. Inst. Chem. Eng; N.Y. Acad. Sci. Solubility, diffusion, rheology, adhesion and lubrication of high polymers; engineering properties of high polymers; heat transfer; fluid flow; fluidization; physics and chemistry of the solid state; photochemistry; photoelectricity; unconventional image recording processes. Address: Bell & Howell Co, Research Labs, 360 Sierra Madre Villa, Pasadena, CA 91006.

GAYNOR, N(ATHAN), b. Chicago, Ill, Aug. 1, 19; m. 51; c. 2. PHYSICS, ELECTRONICS. B.S, Roosevelt, 49; M.S, Bradley, 50. Physicist, Naval Ord. Lab, 50-52, elec. scientist, Naval Res. Lab, 52-55; elec. engr, ACF Indust, 55-57; ELECTRONICS ENGR, SHIP ACOUST. DEPT, NAVAL SHIP RES. & DEVELOP. CTR, 57- U.S.A, 42-46. Acoust. Soc. Am; Inst. Elec. & Electronics Eng. Evolvement of analytical and data processing techniques having application in acoustical characterization of underwater sounds. Address: Ship Acoustics Dept, Naval Ship Research & Development Center, Bethesda, MD 20034.

GAYTON, WILLIAM F, b. St. Stephen, N.B, Mar. 21, 40; U.S. citizen; m. 62; c. 2. CLINICAL PSYCHOLOGY. B.S, Springfield Col, 63; M.A, Univ. Maine, Orono, 65, Ph.D.(clin. psychol), 68. Intern. clin. psychol, Univ. Minn, Minneapolis, 66-67; asst. prof. psychol, Cent. Conn. State Col, 68-69; clin. psychologist, Wilder Child Guid. Clin, St. Paul, Minn, 69-70; ASST. PROF. PEDIAT. & PSYCHIAT, MED. CTR, UNIV. ROCHESTER, 70- U.S.A, 60, Res, 60-65. Am. Psychol. Asn. Psychological development of the mentally retarded child; family process aspects of mental retardation. Address: Dept. of Pediatrics, University of Rochester School of Medicine & Dentistry, 260 Crittenden Blvd, Rochester, NY 14620.

GAZDA, I(RVING) W(ILLIAM), b. Niagara Falls, N.Y, Nov. 26, 41; m. 66; c. 1. MECHANICAL ENGINEERING, HEAT TRANSFER. B.S, Rensselaer Polytech, 63, M.S, 65, Ph.D.(heat transfer), 69. Group leader electrode develop, Great Lakes Carbon Corp, 60-70, SECT. HEAD, ELECTRODE DEVELOP, GREAT LAKES RES. CORP, 70- Am. Soc. Mech. Eng; Am. Soc. Test. & Mat; Instrument Soc. Am; Am. Soc. Nondestructive Test. Heat transfer in fluids; physical and thermal property determinations for ceramics; thermal shock studies on ceramics. Address: Great Lakes Research Corp, P.O. Box 1031, Elizabethtown, TN 37643.

GAZIN, C(HARLES) LEWIS, b. Colorado Springs, Colo, June 18, 04; m. 27, 43; c. 3. GEOLOGY. B.S, Calif. Inst. Tech, 27, M.S, 28, fel, 29-30, Ph.D. (vert. paleont), 30. Asst. vert. paleont, Calif. Inst. Tech, 27-29; jr. geologist, U.S. Geol. Surv, 30-32; asst. curator vert. paleont, U.S. Nat. Mus, 32-42, assoc. curator, 42-46, curator in charge div. vert. paleont, 46-67; sr. paleobiologist, SMITHSONIAN INST, 67-70, EMER. PALEOBIOLOGIST, 70- Mem, Nat. Res. Council, 48-51, 57-60; dir, Am. Geol. Inst, 56-58. Paleont. expeds, Oregon, Nev. & Calif, Calif. Inst. Tech. & Carnegie Institution; leader expeds, various west. states & Cent. Am, Smithsonian Institution. Legion of Merit, 46. U.S.A.A.F, 42-53, Maj. Fel. Geol. Soc. Am.(prize, 30); fel. Paleont. Soc; Soc. Vert. Paleont.(pres, 49); Am. Soc. Mammal; Soc. Study Evolution; Am. Soc. Zool; Argentine Paleont. Asn. Areal geology and stratigraphy of continental Cenozoic deposits; vertebrate paleontology; Tertiary and Quaternary mammals, particularly Paleocene and Eocene mammalian faunas. Address: 6420 Broad St, Brookmont, MD 20016.

GAZIS, DENOS C(ONSTANTINOS), b. Salonica, Greece, Sept. 15, 30; nat; m. 55; c. 7. APPLIED MATHEMATICS. Dipl, C.E. Tech. Univ. Athens, Greece, 52; Fulbright scholar, Stanford Univ, 53-54, M.S, 54; Eugene Higgins fel, Columbia, 54-55, Ph.D.(eng. mech), 57. Designer engr, Ministry of Pub. Works, Greece, 52-53; asst, Columbia Univ, 55-56; designer engr, Tippetts & Assoc, N.Y, 55, 56-57; sr. res. scientist, res. labs, Gen. Motors Corp, 57-61; res. staff mem, IBM RES. DIV, 61-71, DIR, GEN. SCI. DEPT, 71- Asst, Tech. Univ. Athens, 52-53. AAAS; Opers. Res. Soc. Am.(Lanchester Prize, 59); Am. Phys. Soc; Soc. Natural Philos. Applied mechanics; waves in elastic media; lattice dynamics; theory of traffic flow; computer applications to urban problems. Address: P.O. Box 269, Millwood, NY 10546.

GAZLEY, CARL, JR, b. Rochester, N.Y, Aug. 7, 22; m. 44; c. 2. AERODYNAMICS. B.S, Rochester, 43; Univ. fel, Delaware, 43-44, M.Ch.E, 46, Res. Corp. fel, 45-47, Du Pont fel, 47-48, Ph.D.(chem. eng), 48. Res. chem. engr. heat transfer, Lewis Lab, Nat. Adv. Comt. Aeronaut, 44-45; res. engr. aeronaut. & heat transfer, Gen. Elec. Co, 48-52; ENGR. FLUID MECH, RAND CORP, 52- Lectr, California, Los Angeles, 56-58, prof-in-residence, 66-; vis. prof, Purdue Univ, 70- Consult, materials adv. bd, Nat. Acad. Sci, 58-60. Ed, Int. Jour. Heat & Mass Transfer, 59- Am. Chem. Soc; Am. Soc. Mech. Eng; Am. Inst. Chem. Eng; Am. Inst. Aeronaut. & Astronaut. Hypersonic aerodynamics; various aspects of hypersonic gas dynamics, particularly boundary-layer characteristics; atmospheric re-entry; heat and mass transfer; chemical effects; biological fluid mechanics; rheological phenomena in the microcirculation; image enhancement. Address: Rand Corp, 1700 Main St, Santa Monica, CA 90406.

GAZZANIGA, MICHAEL SAUNDERS, b. Los Angeles, Calif, Dec. 12, 39; m. 63; c. 1. PSYCHOBIOLOGY. A.B, Dartmouth Col, 61; U.S. Pub. Health Serv. fel, Calif. Inst. Technol, 62, Ph.D.(biol), 64. U.S. Pub. Health Serv. res. fel. psychobiol, Calif. Inst. Technol, 64-66; physiol, Inst. Physiol, Pisa, 66; from asst. prof. to assoc. prof. PSYCHOL. & chmn. dept, Univ. Calif, Santa Barbara, 66-69; ASSOC. PROF, GRAD. SCH, N.Y. UNIV, 69- Nat. Inst. Ment. Health res. grant, 67-69. Am. Physiol. Soc; Psychonomic Soc. Cortical mechanisms in visual-motor integration; physiology of cortical commissures. Address: Dept. of Psychology, New York University Graduate School, New York, NY 10003.

GEACH, GEORGE ALWYN, b. England, 1913. MATERIALS SCIENCE. M.Sc, Sheffield, 36, Ph.D.(metall), 39. Res. sect. leader phys. metall, Assoc. Elec. Industs. Ltd, Eng, 41-64; MEM. FACULTY ENG. SCI, UNIV. WEST. ONT, 64- Am. Soc. Metals; Brit. Inst. Metals; fel. Brit. Inst. Metall; Can. Inst. Mining & Metall. Address: Faculty of Engineering Science, University of Western Ontario, London 72, Ont, Can.

GEACINTOV, CYRIL, b. Tarascon, France, Feb. 21, 30; U.S. citizen; m. 53; c. 2. POLYMER & PHYSICAL CHEMISTRY. B.S, State Univ. N.Y. Col. Forestry, Syracuse, 58, Nat. Sci. Found. fel. & Ph.D.(phys. chem), 62. Sr. res. chemist, res. & develop. div, Mobil Chem. Co. Div, Socony Mobil Oil Co, 62-63, proj. leader, 63-66; mgr. spec. projs, Celanese Corp, 66-69; v.pres, Octagon Industs, Inc, 69-70; PRES, DRG INT. ASSOCS, 70- Am. Chem. Soc; Tech. Asn. Pulp & Paper Indust. Kinetics of anionic polymerization systems; Ziegler-Natta olefin polymerization; morphology and crystalline structure of polyolefins. Address: P.O. Box 1178, Mountainside, NJ 07092.

GEACINTOV, NICHOLAS, b. Albi, France, Nov. 9, 35; U.S. citizen. CHEMICAL PHYSICS. B.S, State Univ. N.Y. Col. Forestry, Syracuse, 57, M.S, 59, Ph.D.(phys. chem), 61. Res. assoc. photochem, Polytech. Inst. Brooklyn, 61-63; res. scientist solid state physics, N.Y. UNIV, 63-69, ASST. PROF. CHEM, 69- AAAS; Am. Chem. Soc. Luminescence of organic compounds; electrical conductivity of organic molecular crystals. Address: 100 Bleeker St, Apt. 16 F, New York, NY 10012.

GEAGAN, DONALD W(ILLIAM), b. New Orleans, La, Oct. 6, 26; m. 47; c. 4. BIOLOGY, LIMNOLOGY. B.S, Loyola (La), 49, M.S, 59. Fisheries biologist & proj. leader, La. Wildlife & Fisheries Cmn, 53-63; fisheries biologist & asst. fed. aid supvr, Bur. Sport Fisheries & Wildlife, U.S. FISH & WILDLIFE SERV, Ga, 63-66, asst. fed. aid coord, FLA, 66-69, ASST. CHIEF OFF. FED. AID, NAT. MARINE FISHERIES SERV, 69- U.S.M.C, 44-46. Fishery administration. Address: National Marine Fisheries Service, 144 First Ave. S, St. Petersburg, FL 33701.

GEALER, ROY L(EE), b. Detroit, Mich, Oct. 23, 32; m. 57; c. 2. CHEMICAL ENGINEERING. B.S, Wayne State, 54; M.S, Michigan, 55, Ph.D.(chem. eng), 58. Asst. combustion res, Michigan, 54-58; res. engr, Ethyl Corp, 58-63; prin. res. eng. assoc, FORD MOTOR CO, 63-68, PRIN. STAFF ENGR, 68- Summer partic, Minn. Mining & Mfg. Co, 53. Am. Chem. Soc; Am. Inst. Chem. Eng. Automotive industry product and process research, including friction materials, industrial air pollution control and wastewater treatment. Address: Ford Motor Co, Dept. 9340, Box 2053, Dearborn, MI 48121.

GEALY, ELIZABETH LEE, b. Ft. Worth, Texas, June 22, 23; m. 45; c. 4. GEOLOGY. B.S, Southern Methodist, 44, B.A, 46; res. fel, Oceanog. Inst, Woods Hole, 49-52; M.A, Radcliffe Col, 51, Nat. Sci. Found. fel, 52-53, Ph.D.(geol), 53. Private res, 53-57; assoc. consult, D.R. McCord & Assocs, 58-61, dir. geol. serv, 61-65; partner, Gealy & Gealy, Consult, 65-67; specialist, Scripps Inst. Oceanog, Univ. Calif, San Diego & exec. staff geologist, deep sea drilling proj, 67-70; INSTR. GEOL, SAN DIEGO STATE COL, 70- AAAS; Am. Asn. Petrol. Geol; Geol. Soc. Am; Am. Geophys. Union. Marine geology; sedimentology; petrophysics. Address: 329 Vista De La Playa, La Jolla, CA 92037.

GEALY, JOHN R(OBERT), b. Tokyo, Japan, Dec. 4, 30; m. 64. GEOLOGY. B.S, Southern Methodist, 51; M.S, Yale, 52, Ph.D.(geol), 55. GEOLOGIST, HUMBLE OIL & REF. CO, 55- AAAS; Geol. Soc. Am; Am. Asn. Petrol. Geol. Regional geology. Address: Humble Oil & Refining Co, Box 2180, Houston, TX 77001.

GEALY, WILLIAM J(AMES), b. Tokyo, Japan, Sept. 7, 25; U.S. citizen; m. 45, 70; c. 4. GEOLOGY. B.A, Michigan, 46; M.A, Harvard, 51, fel, 51-53, Ph.D.(geol), 53. Geologist, Standard Oil Co. Calif, 53-56; consult. geologist, 56-69; ASSOC. DIR. DEVELOP, OHIO STATE UNIV. RES. FOUND, 69-, ADJ. ASSOC. PROF. GEOL, UNIV, 70- Geologist, Humble Oil & Ref. Co, summer, 48; lectr. & asst. prof, South. Methodist Univ, 66-68. U.S.A, 44-47, 1st Lt. Geol. Soc. Am; Am. Asn. Petrol. Geol. Areal geology; oil geology. Address: Ohio State University Research Foundation, 1314 Kinnear Rd, Columbus, OH 43212.

GEANANGEL, RUSSELL A(LAN), b. Cadiz, Ohio, Aug. 2, 41; m. 61; c. 2. INORGANIC CHEMISTRY. B.S, Ohio State Univ, 63, Ph.D.(inorg. chem), 68. Fel, Ohio State Univ, summer 68; ASST. PROF. CHEM, UNIV. HOUSTON, 68- Am. Chem. Soc; The Chem. Soc. Synthesis and structural characterization of nonmetal inorganic compounds particularly those with special bonding interests, including compounds of boron, nitrogen and fluorine; photoelectron spectroscopy as a tool to study bonding. Address: Dept. of Chemistry, University of Houston, Houston, TX 77004.

GEANKOPLIS, CHRISTIE J(OHN), b. Minneapolis, Minn, June 18, 21. CHEMICAL ENGINEERING. B.Ch.E, Minnesota, 43; M.S, Pennsylvania, 46, Ph.D. (chem. eng), 49. Develop, design & process engr, Atlantic Ref. Co, 43-47; instr. CHEM. ENG, Pennsylvania, 47-48; asst. prof, OHIO STATE UNIV, 49-53, assoc. prof, 53-60, PROF, 60- Consult. chem. engr, Battelle Mem. Inst, 51-; Gen. Mills Chem, Inc, 66- Am. Chem. Soc; Am. Inst. Chem. Eng. Diffusion and mass transfer; transport processes. Address: Dept. of Chemical Engineering, Ohio State University, Columbus, OH 43210.

GEAR, ADRIAN R. L, b. Pretoria, S.Africa, Aug. 31, 39; m. 64; c. 1. BIOCHEMISTRY. B.A, Oxford, 61, M.A. & D.Phil.(biochem), 65. Fel. BIOCHEM, Johns Hopkins Univ, 65-67; ASST. PROF, SCH. MED, UNIV. VA, 67- N.Y. Acad. Sci. Mitochondria; ion transport; energy coupling; oxidative phosphorylation. Address: Dept. of Biochemistry, School of Medicine, University of Virginia, Charlottesville, VA 22901.

GEAR, CHARLES WILLIAM, b. London, Eng, Feb. 1, 35; c. 2. COMPUTER SCIENCE, MATHEMATICS. B.A, Cambridge, 56; Fulbright fel, Univ. Ill, Urbana, 56-60, M.S, 57, Ph.D.(math), 60. Comput. engr, IBM Brit. Labs, 60-62; asst. prof. COMPUT. SCI, UNIV. ILL, URBANA, 62-65, assoc. prof, 65-68, PROF, 68- Consult, Argonne Nat. Lab, 66-; Brookhaven Nat. Lab, 67-69; Nat. Sci. Found-Agency Int. Develop. Indian Prog, 69; vis. prof, Stanford Univ, 69-70. Soc. Indust. & Appl. Math; fel. Brit. Comput. Soc; Inst. Elec. & Electronics Eng. Numerical analysis; ordinary differential equations; computer systems; on line systems; computer graphics; automatic analysis systems. Address: Dept. of Computer Science, University of Illinois, Urbana, IL 61801.

GEAR, H. S, b. Germiston, S.Africa, July 31, 03; m. 32; c. 3. PREVENTIVE & TROPICAL MEDICINE. B.Sc, Univ. Witwatersrand, 25, M.B. & B.Ch, 28, M.D, 35; D.P.H, Univ. London, 31, D.T.M.H, 32. Off. med, Brit. Colonial Med. Serv, Rhodesia, 29-30; scholar, S.African Govt, 30-32; off. epidemiol, Lester Inst. Med. Res, Shanghai, 32-35; asst. health off, S.African Health Serv, 35-38, dep. chief health off, 38-61; asst. dir. gen, cent. tech. serv, WHO, Geneva, 51-58, consult, 58-59; dir. indust. res, Coun. Sci. & Indust. Res, S.Africa, 60-61; secy. gen. med, World Med. Asn. & World Conf. Med. Educ, 61-66; PROF. PREV. MED. & CHMN. DEPT, FACULTY MED. & PROF. INT. HEALTH, SCH. HYG, UNIV. TORONTO, 67- Del, World Health Conf. to estab. WHO, 46; World Health Assemblies, 48-51; chmn. exec. bd, WHO, 49-50; del. & mem, numerous int. med. orgn. conferences, 46-71. Egyptian Govt. Malaria medal, 44; S.African Med. Asn. gold medal, 62. Brit. Army, 40-44, Lt. Col. Royal Soc. Trop. Med. & Hyg; Royal Soc. Health; Brit. Med. Asn.(Bronze medal, 28); hon. mem. World Med. Asn; hon. mem. Australian Med. Asn. Epidemiology. Address: Faculty of Medicine, University of Toronto, Toronto, Ont, Can.

GEAR, J(AMES) R(ICHARD), b. Kindersley, Sask, Apr. 26, 35; m. 61; c. 1. ORGANIC CHEMISTRY, BIOCHEMISTRY. B.A, Saskatchewan, 56, M.A, 58; Ph.D.(biosynthesis), McMaster, 62. Fel. chem, Minnesota, 62-63; asst. prof. CHEM. & BIOCHEM, UNIV. SASK, REGINA, 63-67, ASSOC. PROF, 67- Chem. Inst. Can. Organic synthesis; biosynthesis and chemistry of natural products. Address: Dept. of Chemistry, University of Saskatchewan, Regina, Sask, Can.

GEARIEN, JAMES E(DWARD), b. Peoria, Ill, Aug. 27, 19; m. 48; c. 2. MEDICINAL & ORGANIC CHEMISTRY. B.S, Univ. Ill, 41; M.S, Univ. Mich, 42, Ph.D.(pharmaceut. chem), 50. Instr. CHEM, UNIV. ILL. COL. MED, 48-50, asst. prof, 50-52, assoc. prof, 52-60, PROF. & HEAD DEPT, 60- U.S.N.R, 44-46. Am. Chem. Soc; Am. Pharmaceut. Asn. Synthesis of organic medicinals; studies of organic structures and medicinal activity relationships; analgesics and ergonovine analogs. Address: 1606 S. Courtland Ave, Park Ridge, IL 60068.

GEARY, CHARLES G(ERALD), b. Woburn, Mass, July 14, 11; m. 43; c. 2. CHEMISTRY. B.S, Tufts Col, 32; M.A, Temple; 34, du Pont fel, Yale, 36-37, Ph.D.(phys. chem), 37. Asst. chem, Tufts Col, 31-32; Temple, 32-34; Yale, 34-36; res. chemist, electrochem. dept, E.I. DU PONT DE NEMOURS & CO, 37-41, group leader, N.Y, 41-46, res. chemist, PHOTO PRODS. DEPT, Patterson screen div, 46-58, PHOTOGRAPHIC FILM, 58-65, sr. process chemist, 65-70, PROCESS ASSOC, 70- Modern pioneer award, Nat. Asn. Mfrs, 40. Civilian with U.S.N, 44. Am. Chem. Soc. Thermodynamics of solutions; ceramic color oxides; alkali metals and cyanides; heat treatment of metals; catalytic oxidation of methanol; preparation of sulfide phosphors; development work on graphic arts, lithographic films, x-ray films and screens; methods for evaluating and improving image quality and coating techniques. Address: Photo Products Dept, E.I. du Pont de Nemours & Co, Parlin, NJ 08859.

GEARY, JACK C, b. Hornell, N.Y, Sept. 29, 20; m. 43; c. 2. VETERINARY RADIOLOGY. D.V.M, Ohio State Univ, 51. Assoc. prof. vet. radiol, Cornell Univ, 55-59; Kans. State Univ, 60; Auburn Univ, 62-66; PROF. VET. RADIOL. & DIR. DEPT, N.Y. STATE VET. COL, CORNELL UNIV, 66- Dipl, Am. Col. Vet. Radiol.(pres, 71-72). Educ. Vet. Radiol. Soc.(pres, 66-67); Am. Vet. Radiol. Soc.(pres, 69-70); Radiol. Soc. N.Am; Am. Vet. Med. Asn; Int. Asn. Vet. Radiol. Roentgenology; radiation therapy. Address: New York State Veterinary College, Cornell University, Ithaca, NY 14850.

GEARY, LEO CHARLES, b. Pittsburgh, Pa, Nov. 19, 42; m. 65; c. 2. ELECTRICAL & SYSTEMS ENGINEERING. B.S, Univ. Pittsburgh, 64, NASA fel, 64-67, M.S, 65, Ph.D.(elec. eng), 68. Res. engr, GULF RES. & DEVELOP. CO, 68-71, SYSTS. ENGR. & SYSTS. ANALYST, 71- Session mem, Spring Joint Comput. Conf, Atlantic City, N.J, 70; Hawaiian Int. Conf. Systs. Sci, 70. Inst. Elec. & Electronics Eng. Research and development of optimal control systems and pattern recognition techniques. Address: 9411 Almar Pl, Pittsburgh, PA 15237.

GEBALA, ALLEN EDMOND, b. St. Paul, Minn, July 26, 42. INORGANIC CHEMISTRY. B.S, Elmhurst Col, 65; Shell fel. & Ph.D.(chem), Vanderbilt Univ, 69. RES. ASSOC. CHEM, Univ. Chicago, 69-70; Univ. Calif, Irvine, 70-71; TEX. A&M UNIV, 71- Am. Chem. Soc; Am. Crystallog. Asn. Synthetic and natural occurring macrocyclic complexes; kinetics and structural determination. Address: 126 Parkview Dr, Northlake, IL 60164.

GEBALLE, RONALD, b. Redding, Calif, Feb. 7, 18; m. 40; c. 8. PHYSICS. B.S, California, 38, M.A, 40, Ph.D.(physics), 43. Physicist, radiation lab, California, 42-43; appl. physics lab, UNIV. WASH, 43-46, asst. prof. PHYSICS, 46-54, assoc. prof, 54-59, PROF. & CHMN. DEPT, 59-, acting exec. officer, 57-59. Guest scientist, lab. mass. separation, Found. Fundamental Res. Matter, Netherlands; mem. adv. panel lab. astrophysics div, Inst. Basic Standards, Nat. Bur. Standards; mem. Comn. Col. Physics, 66-71; secy, Int. Conf. Physics of Electronic & Atomic Collisions, 67-; mem. adv. comt. grants, Res. Corp, 67-; chmn. adv. panel physics, Nat. Sci. Found, 70-71. With Manhattan Dist; Off. Sci. Res. & Develop; U.S.N, 44. AAAS; fel. Am. Phys. Soc; Am. Asn. Physics Teachers (pres, 69-70). Atomic collision processes; physics education. Address: Dept. of Physics, University of Washington, Seattle, WA 98105.

GEBALLE, T(HEODORE) H(ENRY), b. San Francisco, Calif, Jan. 20, 20; m. 41; c. 5. PHYSICS. B.S, California, 40, Ph.D, 50. Res. assoc, California, 50-52; mem. tech. staff, Bell Tel. Labs, Inc, 52-68; PROF. APPL. PHYSICS, STANFORD UNIV, 68- Ord. Dept, 41-46, Capt. Am. Chem. Soc; fel. Am. Phys. Soc.(Buckley Prize, 70). Low temperature physics; superconductivity; materials science. Address: Dept. of Applied Physics, Stanford University, Stanford, CA 94305.

GEBAUER, PETER ANTHONY, b. Albany, Calif, Apr. 15, 43; m. 67; c. 1. ORGANIC CHEMISTRY. B.S, Harvey Mudd Col, 65; Ph.D.(org. chem), Univ. Ill, 70. ASST. PROF. CHEM, IND. UNIV-PURDUE UNIV, INDIANAPOLIS, 70- Am. Chem. Soc. Elimination and substitution reactions employing phosphorus reagents; small ring chemistry. Address: Dept. of Chemistry, School of Science, Purdue University, 1201 E. 38th, Indianapolis, IN 46205.

GEBBEN, ALAN I(RWIN), b. Shelbyville, Mich, July 4, 31; m. 53; c. 4. PLANT ECOLOGY. A.B, Calvin Col, 54; M.A.T, Vanderbilt, 55; M.S, Michigan, 59, Ph.D.(common ragweed ecol), 65. Asst. BIOL, CALVIN COL, 55-58, instr, 61-63, asst. prof, 63-65, assoc. prof, 65-67, PROF, 67- Address: Dept. of Biology, Calvin College, Grand Rapids, MI 49506.

GEBBER, GERARD L, b. New York, N.Y, Feb. 12, 39; m. 61; c. 2. PHARMACOLOGY, NEUROPHARMACOLOGY. B.S, Long Island, 60; U.S. Pub. Health Serv. fel, Michigan, 61-64, Ph.D.(pharmacol), 64. Nat. Insts.

Health res. fel, PHARMACOL, Pennsylvania, 64-65; instr. Tulane, 65-66; asst. prof, MICH. STATE UNIV, 66-70, ASSOC. PROF, 70- AAAS; Soc. Neurosci; N.Y. Acad. Sci; Am. Soc. Pharmacol. & Exp. Therapeut. Central Autonomic reflex pathways; central nervous system control of circulation; ganglionic transmission; nerve physiology. Address: Dept. of Pharmacology, College of Human Medicine, Michigan State University, East Lansing, MI 48823.

GEBBIE, HUGH ALASTAIR, b. Galashiels, Scotland, Jan. 5, 22; m. 57. PHYSICS. B.Sc, Edinburgh 42; Ph.D.(physics), Reading, 52. Mem. staff, dept. astrophys, Hopkins, 55-57; basic physics div, Nat. Phys. Lab, Eng, 57-66, head adv. instrumentation unit, 66-68; sr. res. fel. physics, Nat. Bur. Standards, 68-71; ADJ. PROF. PHYSICS, UNIV. COLO, BOULDER, 69- Brit. Inst. Physics & Phys. Soc.(Duddell medal & award, 65); fel. Royal Astron. Soc. Infrared spectroscopy; high pressure physics; submillimetre wave research. Address: Dept. of Physics & Astrophysics, University of Colorado, Boulder, CO 80302.

GEBBIE, KATHARINE BLODGETT, b. Cambridge, Mass, July 4, 32; m. 57. ASTROPHYSICS. B.A, Bryn Mawr Col, 57; B.Sc, London, 60, fel, 64-66, Ph.D.(astrophys), 65. Res. assoc. astrophys, JOINT INST. LAB. ASTROPHYS, UNIV. COLO, 67-68, ASTROPHYSICIST, NAT. BUR. STANDARDS, 68- Ed, The Observ, 65-67. Int. Astron. Union; Am. Astron. Soc; Royal Astron. Soc. Planetary nebulae and stellar atmospheres. Address: Joint Institute for Lab. Astrophysics, University of Colorado, Boulder, CO 80302.

GEBEL, HARRY, b. Chicago, Ill, June 10, 21; m. 44; c. 2. ORGANIC CHEMISTRY. A.B, Indiana, 43. Anal. chemist, SWIFT & CO, 46-53, head chemist, tech. prod. plant, 53-63, res. chemist, res. & develop. ctr, 63-65, HEAD PILOT PLANT, 65- Intel.C, U.S.A, 44-46. Am. Oil Chem. Soc. (Smalley Found. award, 60). Fats and oils; textile chemicals anti-rust compounds; wetting agents and emulsifiers; steel mill rolling oils and rust preventives. Address: Swift & Co, 1800 165th St, Hammond, IN 46320.

GEBELEIN, CHARLES G, b. Philadelphia, Pa, July 16, 29; m. 51; c. 5. POLYMER & ORGANIC CHEMISTRY. B.A, Temple, 55, M.A, 59; Ph.D. (chem), 67. Chemist, res. labs, Rohm and Haas Co, Pa, 51-59; cent. res. lab, Borden Chem. Co, 59-63, Fels. Res. Inst, Temple, 63-67; asst. prof. CHEM, YOUNGSTOWN STATE UNIV, 67-70, ASSOC. PROF, 70- Am. Chem. Soc. Additions to carbon-carbon double bonds; polymer modification; polymerization; surface chemistry; organophosphorus; isocyanate chemistry. Address: Dept. of Chemistry, Youngstown State University, Youngstown, OH 44503.

GEBELT, ROBERT E(UGENE), b. Rockford, Ill, May 20, 37; m. 62; c. 3. INORGANIC CHEMISTRY. B.S, Illinois, 59; Ph.D.(chem), Mich. State, 65. Res. assoc, Okla. State, 64-66; asst. prof. CHEM, MANKATO STATE COL, 66-70, ASSOC. PROF, 70- AAAS; Am. Chem. Soc. Thermodynamic properties of inorganic materials at high temperatures. Address: Dept. of Chemistry, Mankato State College, Mankato, MN 56001.

GEBER, WILLIAM FREDERICK, b. Rahway, N.J, Oct. 26, 23; m. 46; c. 1. PHYSIOLOGY, PHARMACOLOGY. A.B, Dartmouth Col, 47; M.S, Indiana, 50, Ph.D.(physiol), 54. Teaching assoc. physiol, sch. med, Indiana, 53-54; res. assoc. phys. med, med. col, Minnesota, 54; asst. prof. physiol, sch. med, St. Louis, 54-58; assoc. prof, sch. med, South Dakota, 58-65; PHARMACOL, MED. COL. GA, 65-71, PROF, 71- U.S.N, 42-46. AAAS; Am. Physiol. Soc; Geront. Soc; Am. Chem. Soc. Quantitative measurement of blood flow, hyperemea causes, and drug effects in areas of kidney, intestine, muscle and spleen; vascular aging; cardiovascular responses to weightlessness; environmental causes of congenital malformations; drug induced teratogenesis. Address: Dept. of Pharmacology, Medical College of Georgia, Augusta, GA 30902.

GEBHARD, LOUIS A(UGUST), b. Buffalo, N.Y, June 11, 96; m. 31; c. 1. RADIO RESEARCH. B.S, George Washington, 30; J.D, Georgetown, 24. Mem. staff radio res, U.S. Naval Radio Sta, Ill. & N.J, 17-19; U.S. Naval Aircraft Radio Lab, Wash, D.C, 19-23; head radio transmitter sect, U.S. NAVAL RES. LAB, 23-32, supt. radio eng. dir, 32-34, aircraft div, 34-35, asst. supt. radio div, 34-45, supt, 45-68, CONSULT. ELECTRONICS, 68- Presidential cert. merit, 46. AAAS; fel. Am. Phys. Soc; Sci. Res. Soc. Am; fel. Inst. Elec. & Electronics Eng. Radio communication; navigation; countermeasures; electronics for official United States time and frequency; centralized electronic control. Address: 2142 Branch Ave. S.E, Washington, DC 20020.

GEBHARDT, JOSEPH J(OHN), b. New York, N.Y, Feb. 28, 23; m. 51; c. 2. INORGANIC CHEMISTRY. A.B, Hobart Col, 44; M.Sc, Carnegie Inst. Tech, 49, D.Sc.(chem), 51. Instr. chem, Manhattan Col, 46-47; instr, Carnegie Inst. Tech, 47-49, asst, 49-51; sr. res. chemist, titanium div, Nat. Lead Co, 51-57; Am. Potash & Chem. Corp, 57-59, proj. chemist, 59-60; res. chemist, missile & space div, SPACE SCI. LAB, GEN. ELEC. CO, 60-69; CONSULT. PHYS. CHEMIST, RE-ENTRY & ENVIRON. SYSTS. DIV, 69- U.S.N.R, 42-46, Res, 46-5[illegible], Lt. AAAS; fel. Am. Inst. Chem; Am. Chem. Soc. High temperature m[illegible]erials; vapor deposition; solid state reactions; carbon and graphite; composite materials. Address: Re-entry & Environmental Systems Division, Metallurgical & Ceramic Research Operations, General Electric Co, Box 8555, Philadelphia, PA 19101.

GEBHARDT, LOUIS P(HILIPP, JR), b. Jackson, Calif, Dec. 20, 05; m. 38; c. 3. MICROBIOLOGY. A.B, Stanford, 29, M.A, 34, Ph.D.(virol), 37, M.D, 42. Asst. bact. & exp. path, Stanford, 29-37, res. assoc, 37-38, acting asst. prof, 41-42; assoc. prof. bact. & path, COL. MED, UNIV. UTAH, 42-43, PROF. BACT, 43- Dir. div. bact, Salt Lake Gen. Hosp, 43-57; attending pathologist, U.S. Veterans Admin. Hosp, Utah. Expert civilian consult, U.S. Dept. War, 44; consult, Dugway Proving Grounds, U.S. Army, Utah, 57-62. Dipl, Am. Bd. Med. Microbiol. Am. Soc. Microbiol; fel. Am. Acad. Microbiol; Soc. Exp. Biol. & Med; Am. Asn. Immunol; fel. Am. Pub. Health Asn. Immunology; virus; poliomyelitis; infectious diseases; microbiology; epidemiology. Address: Dept. of Bacteriology, 5C 153 Medical Center, University of Utah College of Medicine, Salt Lake City, UT 84112.

GEBHART, BENJAMIN, b. Cincinnati, Ohio, July 2, 23; m. 68; c. 2. ENGINEERING. B.S, Michigan, 48, M.S, 50; Ph.D, Cornell, 54. Instr. MECH. ENG, Michigan, 49-50; Lehigh, 50-51; CORNELL UNIV, 51-54, asst. prof, 54-57, assoc. prof, 57-63, PROF, 63-, preceptorship award, 55-57, Giordano Found. res. grant, 57-60, Nat. Sci. Found. res. award, 59- Exchange prof, Aix Marseille, 63, 66; vis. prof, Cornell Aeronaut. Lab, 64-65; Univ. Calif, Berkeley, 67. U.S.M.C.R, 42-45. AAAS; Am. Soc. Mech. Eng. Fluid mechanics and heat transfer. Address: Upson Hall, Cornell University, Ithaca, NY 14850.

GEBLER, DOUGLAS PAUL, b. Jersey City, N.J, Mar. 25, 42; m. 64; c. 2. ORGANIC CHEMISTRY, CHEMICAL ENGINEERING. B.E, Yale, 64; Nat. Insts. Health fel, Univ. Wis, Madison, 65; Nat. Insts. Health fel. & Ph.D. (org. chem), Cornell Univ, 69. RES. CHEMIST, ENJAY ADDITIVES LAB, ESSO RES. & ENG. CO, 69- Am. Chem. Soc. Chemistry of petroleum additives including the synthesis, evaluation and analysis of additives. Address: 8 Deer Path, Holmdel, NJ 07733.

GEBURA, STANLEY E(RNEST), b. Buffalo, N.Y, Nov. 8, 23; m. 53; c. 2. ORGANIC & PHYSICAL CHEMISTRY. B.A, Buffalo, 49; Ph.D.(org. & phys. chem), Colorado, 53. Res. chemist, Olin Industs, 52-53; res. assoc. boron chem, Colorado, 53-54; res. chemist, Monsanto Chem. Co, 54-62; sr. res. chemist, Spencer Chem. Co, Kans, 62-65; SR. RES. SCIENTIST, WHARTON RES. LAB, INTERPACE CORP, 65- U.S.A.A.F, 42-45. Am. Chem. Soc; Clay Minerals Soc; Coblentz Soc; Fine Particle Soc. Purine and pyrimidine synthesis; high vacuum synthesis; high pressure synthesis; polymer chemistry; infrared spectroscopy; surface chemistry; particulate technology. Address: 30 Laurelwood Trail, Mountain Lakes, NJ 07046.

GECKLER, RICHARD D(ELPH). CHEMISTRY. A.B, DePauw, 39. Group leader, pilot plant develop, Standard Oil Co.(Ind), 39-45; chief engr, solid engine & chem. div, Aerojet-Gen. Corp, div. Gen. Tire & Rubber Co, 45-53, dir. quality control, 53-55, mgr. solid rocket engine & chem. div, 55-57, solid rocket plant, 57-58, v.pres. & mgr, 58-63, v.pres, future opers, 63-64; asst. dir, strategic weapons, U.S. Dept. Defense, 64-66; v.pres. plans & progs, Aerojet-Gen. Corp, 67-68; chmn. bd. & chief exec, Aerojet Delft Corp, 68-69; exec. v.pres, ANELLUX SYSTS. CORP, EL SEGUNDO, 70-71, CONSULT, 71- U.S. Navy Dept. meritorious pub. serv. citation, 61. Am. Math. Soc; Am. Inst. Chem. Eng; Am. Inst. Aeronaut. & Astronaut; Am. Soc. Qual. Control; Am. Chem. Soc. Petroleum refining processes; chemistry of solid propellants; rocket design; theory of combustion. Address: 135 Belday Rd, Pasadena, CA 91105.

GECKLER, ROBERT P(AYNE), b. Indianapolis, Ind, Sept. 28, 20; m. 44; c. 2. GENETICS. B.S, Indiana, 44, Nat. Insts. Health fel, 47-49, Ph.D.(zool), 49; M.S, Michigan, 46. Lab. asst. biochem, med. sch, Michigan, 45-46; zool, Indiana, 46-49; asst. prof. biol, Vanderbilt, 49-51; physiologist, isotopes div, Atomic Energy Comn, Oak Ridge, 51-52, biologist, res. & med. div, 52-54, isotopes div, 54-55, proj. leader, combat opers. res. group, Va, 55-56; eng. rep, Aerojet Gen. Nucleonics Div, Gen. Tire & Rubber Co, 56-60, dept. head life support systs. div, Aerojet Gen. Corp. Div, 60-68; RES. ASSOC. BIOMATH. PROG, DEPT. STATIST, N.C. STATE UNIV, 68- U.S.N.R, 43. Am. Soc. Nat; Am. Soc. Zool; Aerospace Med. Asn; Soc. Indust. Microbiol. Genetics of paramecium; biological effects of radiation; nuclear reactor development and manufacture; applied biological research for space applications; pollution abatement, biological control of pest and disease organisms. Address: Dept. of Statistics, North Carolina State University, Raleigh, NC 27607.

GECZIK, RONALD J(OSEPH), b. Bronx, N.Y, Mar. 22, 33; m. 61; c. 3. PHYSIOLOGY, PHARMACOLOGY. B.S, Fordham Univ, 54, M.S, 57, Ph.D. (biol), 59; J.D, Seton Hall Univ, 71. Sr. res. scientist, Colgate-Palmolive Co, 59-62, pharmacol. sect, 62-64; asst. to dir. toxicol, path. dept. SQUIBB INST. MED. RES, 64-66, mgr. biol. data, 66-68, DIR. RES. ADMIN, 68- AAAS; N.Y. Acad. Sci. Dental research, especially caries, periodontal disease and calculus; tissue culture; cytology; regeneration and wound healing; toxicology. Address: Squibb Institute for Medical Research, E.R. Squibb & Sons, Georges Rd, New Brunswick, NJ 08903.

GEDANSKY, STANLEY J(EROME), b. New York, N.Y, Oct. 25, 32; m. 54; c. 4. ANALYTICAL CHEMISTRY. B.S, City Col. New York, 53; Du Pont fel, Syracuse, 55-56, Ph.D.(anal. chem), 58. Asst. gen. & anal. chem, Syracuse, 53-54, atomic energy res. contract, 54-55, 56-57; res. technologist anal. chem, res. dept, Mobil Oil Co, N.J, 57-61; anal. supvr. res. & serv, Texus Res. Center, Tex-U.S. Chem. Co, N.J, 61-63; MGR. ANAL. RES. & SERV. GROUP, UNIROYAL INC, 63- Am. Chem. Soc; Sci. Res. Soc. Am. Polymer and elastomer analyses; spectrophotometry; viscometry; osmometry; spectrophotometric titrations; micro analysis; coulometry; gel permeation chromatography; gamma-ray spectrometry; x-ray fluorescence; thermal analyses; gas chromatography; molecular weight; scanning electron microscopy; chelatometry; infrared. Address: Research Center, Uniroyal Inc, Wayne, NJ 07470.

GEDCKE, DALE ALAN, b. Kitchener, Ont, July 20, 39; m. 64; c. 2. INSTRUMENTATION. B.Eng, McMaster Univ, 62; Prov. Ont. fel, Univ. Ottawa, 63-64, M.Sc, 64; Nat. Res. Coun. scholar, Univ. Alta, 65-67, Ph.D. (nuclear physics), 67. Physicist, ORTEC INC, 67-69, DEVELOP. MGR. ANAL. SYSTS, 69- Electron Probe Anal. Soc. Am; Soc. Appl. Spectros. Nuclear and x-ray instrumentation, detectors and electronics; x-ray fluorescence analysis; electron microprobe and scanning electron microscope applications and instrumentation; fast timing nuclear electronics; direct nuclear reactions; gamma-ray spectroscopy. Address: Analytical Systems Research & Development, Ortec Inc, 100 Midland Rd, Oak Ridge, TN 37830.

GEDDES, A(MOS) LESLIE, b. Highland Village, N.S, Can, Jan. 19, 11; nat; m. 36; c. 1. PHYSICAL CHEMISTRY. B.Sc, Dalhousie, 33; M.Sc, 34; Nat. Res. Council Can. bursar, McGill, 34-35, studentship, 35-36, Ph.D.(phys. chem), 36. RES. CHEMIST, Shawinigan Chem, Ltd, Que, 36-39; Eastman Kodak Co, N.Y, 39-46; Tenn. Eastman Corp, 46-47, EASTMAN KODAK CO, 47- Am. Chem. Soc; Am. Phys. Soc; Soc. Applied Spectros. Spectrophotometry; diffusivity; electron microscopy; persistence of the liquid state above the critical temperature; chemical structure; photographic process. Address: Eastman Kodak Co, Rochester, NY 14650.

GEDDES, DAVID DARWIN, b. Haines, Ore, May 17, 22; m. 46; c. 2. BIOLOGY, PHYSIOLOGY. B.S, Willamette Univ, 48; M.S, Brigham Young Univ, 52; Ph.D.(physiol), Univ. South. Calif, 59. Teaching asst. zool, Brigham Young Univ, 49-50, asst. prof. health sci, 50-53; physiologist, U.S. Pub. Health Serv, Los Angeles, 53-55; asst. clin. prof. physiol, Calif. Col. Med, 55-56; chmn. health educ, Brigham Young Univ, 56-59; U.S. Opers. Mission higher educ. adv, Ministry Educ, Iran, 59-61; chmn. dept. phys. educ, Brigham Young Univ, 61-67; fel. higher educ. admin, Univ. Mich, 67-68; PROF. BIOL. SCI. & DEAN COL. SCI. & ARTS, MICH. TECHNOL. UNIV, 69- Physiologist, Los Angeles County Heart Asn, 55-56. Etfekar Medal, His Imp. Majesty Mohammed Reza Pahlavi, Shahanshah of Iran, 61; serv. medal, His Imp. Highness Gholam Reza Pahlavi, Crown Prince of Iran, 61. U.S.A, 42-46, 1st Sgt. Exercise physiology; cardiorespiratory function; human performance; muscle physiology; electrocardiography; manifest anxiety and exercise. Address: College of Sciences & Arts, Michigan Technological University, Houghton, MI 49931.

GEDDES, JOHN A(LBERT), b. Paterson, N.J, Feb. 11, 12; m. 39. CHEMISTRY. B.S, Lafayette Col, 31, Hart fel, 31-32, M.S, 32; Metcalf fel, Brown, 34-35, Ph.D.(chem), 35. Asst. chem, Brown, 32-34; res. chemist, Nat. Carbon Co, Ohio, 35-36; E.I. du Pont de Nemours & Co, Md, 36-39, Del, 39-42; chief, lab. sect, signal intel. div, European Theatre Opers, U.S. Army, 42-45, adj. & dept. chief, Army Security Agency, D.C, 46-49, res. & develop. div, mil. liaison cmt, Atomic Energy Cmn, 51-52, chief, nuclear power div, 52-55, Army Security Agency, Pacific, 57-59, acting dep. chief, res. & develop. div, Off. Chief Signal Officer, 59-61, dep. chief, 62; EXEC. DIR, NORTH. VA. BRIDGE ASSOC, 63- U.S.A, 42-62, Col. Viscous flow; dielectric constants of electrolytic solutions; dipole moments of some electrolytes in benzene. Address: 4535 18th St. N, Arlington, VA 22207.

GEDDES, L(ESLIE) A(LEXANDER), b. Scotland, May 24, 21; m. 45; c. 1. CARDIOVASCULAR PHYSIOLOGY, BIOMEDICAL ENGINEERING. B.Eng, McGill, 45, M.Eng, 53; Ph.D.(physiol), Baylor, 58. Asst. electroencephalog. & neurophysiol. & demonstr. elec. eng, McGill, 45-47; consult. & supvr. tech. equip, Montreal Neurol. Inst. & Royal Victoria Hosp, 46-52; biophysicist, BAYLOR COL. MED, 52, dir. lab. biophys, 53-57, asst. prof. PHYSIOL, 58-65, PROF. & CHIEF DIV. BIOMED. ENG, 65-; DENT. COL, UNIV. TEX, 57- Consult. engr, 49-; partner & consult, Electro-Design Co, 50-52; consult, Nat. Found. Infantile Paralysis, Southwest. Poliomyelitis Respiratory Center, 52-; U.S. Air Force, 58-; prof. vet. physiol. & pharmacol, Tex. A&M Univ, 67-, prof. biomed. eng, 68- Can. Army, 40-45, Lt. Inst. Elec. & Electronics Eng. Electrophysiology; biophysical instrumentation. Address: Baylor College of Medicine, 1200 Moursund Ave, Houston, TX 77025.

GEDDES, RAY L(EWELLYN), b. Wellington, Kans, Jan. 27, 05; m. 28; c. 3. PHYSICAL CHEMISTRY. B.S, Kans. State Col, 27; M.S, Ohio State, 28, fel, 29-30, Ph.D.(phys. chem), 30. Asst. chem, Ohio State, 27-28; chem. engr, Standard Oil Co. of Ind, 30-36; Alco Products, Inc, 36-39; Stone & Webster Eng. Corp, 39-70; RETIRED CONSULT. ENGR. With Off. Sci. Res. & Develop, 42, Am. Chem. Soc; Am. Inst. Chem. Eng. Gas reactions; fractional distillation; chemical engineering design methods. Address: 5157 Selby Dr, Ft. Myers, FL 33901.

GEDEON, GEZA S(CHOLCZ), b. Miskolc, Hungary, June 12, 14; U.S. citizen; m. 41; c. 3. ASTRODYNAMICS. M.S, Budapest Tech, 37, D.Sc.(aero eng), 45. Res. asst. aerodyn, Aerotech. Inst, 39-43; chief test pilot, Repulogepgyar, RT, 43-45; test engr, L.Lang Machine & Eng. Shop, 47-48; aircraft designer, L. Breguet Ateliers d' Aviation, 48-50; lectr. math. & mech, Ind. Tech. Col, 50-55; design specialist, Int. Harvester Co, 55-56; res. scientist, Chance Vought Aircraft, 56-59; Aeronutronic Div, Ford Motor Co, 59-60; head astrodyn, Norair Labs, Northrop Corp, 60-62, chief flight mech, space labs, 62-65; staff engr, TRW SYSTS, INC, 65, mgr. anal. mech. dept, 65-68, SR. SCIENTIST, 68- Lectr, Univ. Calif, Los Angeles, 63-66; ed, j. Celestial Mech, 69- Royal Hungarian Air Force, 37-39, Lt. Assoc. fel. Am. Inst. Aeronaut. & Astronaut; sr. mem. Am. Astronaut. Soc. Astrodynamics related to trajectories; orbit determination and guidance. Address: 2501 Beverly Ave, Santa Monica, CA 90405.

GEDGOUD, JOHN L(EO), b. Chicago, Ill, Feb. 21, 10; m. 34. PEDIATRICS. S.B, Chicago, 30, M.D, 35. Rotating intern, St. Margaret Mem. Hosp, Pittsburgh, 34-35; pediat. intern, Bobs Roberts Mem. Hosp, Chicago, 35-36; asst. res, 36-37, res, 38, instr. PEDIAT, 38-40; asst. prof, col. med, Univ. Nebr, 40-46, assoc. prof, 46-50, PROF, 50-67; SCH. MED, CREIGHTON UNIV, 67- Res. physician, Munic. Contagious Hosp, Chicago, 37-40; pediat. consult, State Bd. Health, Nebr, 40- AAAS; fel. Am. Med. Asn; fel. Am. Acad. Pediat. Carbohydrate absorption in infants; ascorbic acid deficiency in infants; virus pneumonitis; inclusion blennorrhea; lead encephalopathy; rheumatic fever; exercise in children. Address: 3506 Woolworth Ave, Omaha, NE 68105.

GEDULDIG, DONALD S(TANLEY), b. N.Y.C, Oct. 27, 32; m. 62; c. 1. BIOPHYSICS, ELECTROPHYSIOLOGY. B.E.E, Cornell Univ, 55, M.S, 57; Nat. Insts. Health fel, Columbia Univ, 62-65, Ph.D.(biophys), 65. Res. engr. med. electronics, RCA Labs, 57-58; Rockefeller Univ, 58-61; Nat. Insts. Health fel, physiol. lab, Cambridge Univ, 65-66; asst. res. physiologist, Univ. Calif, San Diego, 66-68; ASST. PROF. BIOPHYS, SCH. MED, UNIV. MD, BALTIMORE CITY, 68- Mem. brain res. inst, Univ. Calif, Los Angeles, 66-68. AAAS; Biophys. Soc; Soc. Gen. Physiol. Membrane structure and function; transport of ions through membranes; excitation in nerve and muscle; electrophysiological instrumentation. Address: Dept. of Biophysics, School of Medicine, University of Maryland, Baltimore, MD 21201.

GEE, ALLEN, b. Patterson, Calif, Feb. 23, 24; m. 55; c. 2. PHYSICAL CHEMISTRY. B.S, California, 47; Ph.D.(phys. chem), Mass. Inst. Tech, 51. Asst. chem, California, 47; asst. protein chem, Mass. Inst. Tech, 47-50; res. assoc, Sugar Res. Found, Nat. Bur. Standards, 51-57; sr. process chemist, E.I. du Pont de Nemours & Co, 57-59; sr. proj. engr, Tex. Instruments, Inc, 59-61; mem. tech. staff, Hughes Aircraft Co, 61-67, assoc. mgr. microelectronics lab, Newport Beach Div, 67-69; TECH. CONSULT. & REGISTERED INVESTMENT ADV, 70- Am. Chem. Soc; fel. Am. Inst. Chem; Electrochem. Soc; N.Y. Acad. Sci. Serum proteins; bone, teeth and calcium phosphates; infrared and visible spectrophotometry; chromatography; waste treatment and water pollution; polymers, sugars, cellulose and synthetic fibers; semiconductors; surface effects; process development and control. Address: 2521 Sierra Vista, Newport Beach, CA 92660.

GEE, CHARLES WILLIAM, b. Des Moines, Iowa, Mar. 19, 36; m. 59; c. 3. SCIENCE EDUCATION. B.S, Wisconsin, Madison, 59; M.S, Okla. State, 64; Ph.D.(sci. ed), Mich. State, 67. ASST. PROF. BIOL. & SCI. EDUC, MILLIGAN COL, 67- Nat. Sci. Found. summer inst, Central Michigan, 61 & 62. Nat. Sci. Teachers Asn. Experimentation with techniques of science presentation. Address: Dept. of Biology, Milligan College, TN 37682.

GEE, D(AVID) E(ASTON), b. Ypsilanti, Mich, Oct. 21, 23; m. 44; c. 6. GEOLOGY. B.A, Western Reserve, 47; fel, Texas, 47-48, M.A, 48. Jr. geologist, Humble Oil & Ref. Co, 47; instr. geol. & mineral, Southwestern (Texas), 48-49; asst. div. geologist, Continental Oil Co, 49-53; geologist, Fain & McGaha, 53-54; dist. geologist, Ada Oil Co, Texas, 54-55, mgr, explor. north. div, 55-56, v.pres, Canada, 56, mgr. explor, Westland Oil Develop. Co, 57; partner, SOUTH. CO, 58-64, OWNER, 65-; CAN. ESSEX OIL CO, 65-; CONSULT. GEOL. & EXPLOR. GEOPHYS, 65- Partner, Can. Essex Oil Co, 62-65. U.S.A, 43-46. AAAS; Geol. Soc. Am; Am. Asn. Petrol. Geol. Tectonophysics; structural geology; petroleum geology; oil exploration. Address: 201 Hamilton Bldg, Wichita Falls, TX 76301.

GEE, EDWIN AUSTIN, b. Washington, D.C, Feb. 19, 20; m. 44; c. 3. CHEMICAL ENGINEERING. B.S, George Washington, 41, M.S, 44; Ph.D.(chem. eng), Maryland, 48. Asst. chemist, Naval Res. Lab, D.C, 41-42; chemist, U.S. Bur. Mines, Md, 42-43, phys. chemist, 43-44, Ala, 44-45, chem. engr, Md, 45-46, metallurgist, Wash, D.C, 46-47, asst. chief metall. div, 47-48; metallurgist & chem. engr, E.I. DU PONT DE NEMOURS & CO, 48-50, supvr. res. group, 50-51, mgr, res. sect, 51-53, mgr. plants tech, pigments dept, 53-57, asst. dir. sales, 57-60, develop. dept, 57-63, dir, 63-66, mgr. res. & develop. componate diversification, 66-68, gen. mgr. photo prod. dept, 68-70, V.PRES, DIR. & MEM. EXEC. COMT, 70- Civilian with U.S.A; U.S.A.A.F; U.S.N; Atomic Energy Comn, 46. Am. Chem. Soc; Nat. Soc. Prof. Eng; Inst. Mining, Metall. & Petrol. Eng; Am. Soc. Metals. Organic kinetics; rare metals; titanium and zirconium; extraction of ores; purification of salts; improved method for the acid decomposition of certain silicates; pigments, white and colored; semiconductor materials. Address: One Valmy Lane, Box 3960, Greenville, DE 19807.

GEE, GEORGE F(RANCIS), b. Milton, Mass, Apr. 15, 37; m. 63; c. 2. PHYSIOLOGY, ZOOLOGY. B.V.A, Univ. Mass, 60; M.S, Univ. Maine, 62; Ph.D. (physiol), Univ. Georgia, 67. PHYSIOLOGIST, Sch. Aerospace Med, 65-68; ENDANGERED WILDLIFE RES, PATUXENT WILDLIFE RES. CTR, U.S. DEPT. INTERIOR, 68- U.S.A.F, 65-68, Capt. AAAS; World Poultry Sci. Asn; Poultry Sci. Asn; Am. Soc. Zool. Effects of hypobaric environment in human physiology with particular emphasis on water balance, nutrition and body composition; avian and mammalian reproductive physiology with special emphasis on captive wild animals; comparative physiology of artificial incubation of birds eggs; environmental physiology of captive wild animals; physiological norms in captive wildlife. Address: Patuxent Wildlife Research Center, Endangered Wildlife Research, U.S. Dept. of the Interior, Laurel, MD 20810.

GEE, GLENDON W(ILLIAM), b. Rexburg, Idaho, June 3, 38; m. 58; c. 5. SOIL PHYSICS. B.S, Utah State, 61; Nat. Defense Ed. Act fel, Washington State, 61-64, Ph.D.(soils), 66. Acting instr. SOIL PHYSICS & acting jr. soil scientist, Wash. State Univ, 64-65; ASST. PROF, UNIV. N.H, 66- Res. assoc, Univ. Conn, summers, 68, 69, 70. Soil Sci. Soc. Am. Physics of soil water movement; soil-plant-water relationships; vapor pressure measurements of soil and plant water potentials. Address: Dept. of Soil & Water Science, University of New Hampshire, Durham, NH 03824.

GEE, J. BERNARD L, b. Crewe, Eng, Mar. 13, 27; m. 57; c. 2. MEDICINE, PHYSIOLOGY. B.A, Oxford, 48, B.Sc, 49, M.A, 52, B.M, Ch.B, 53. Jr. demonstr. physiol, Oxford, 48-49; intern surg, Guys Hosp, London, 53-54; MED, Postgrad. Med. Sch, London, 56-57; res, Radcliffe Infirmary, Oxford, 57-59; fel, McGill, 59-61; instr, sch. med, Wisconsin, 61-62, asst. prof, 62-64; sch. med, Pittsburgh, 64-68, ASSOC. PROF, 68-69; SCH. MED, YALE, 69- Consult, Vet. Admin. Hosps, 68- R.A.M.C, 55-57, Capt. AAAS; Am. Thoracic Soc; Am. Fedn. Clin. Res; fel. Am. Col. Physicians; Am. Physiol. Soc; Reticuloendothelial Soc. Pulmonary medicine and physiology; exercise and respiratory physiology; metabolic features of alveolar macrophages. Address: Yale University School of Medicine, 333 Cedar St, New Haven, CT 06510.

GEE, JOHN HENRY, b. New Westminster, B.C, Can, July 25, 36; m. 61. ECOLOGY. B.Com, British Columbia, 59, M.Sc, 61; Commonwealth of Australia scholar, Sydney, 64-66, Ph.D.(zool), 67. Scientist, Fisheries Res. Bd. Can, 61-63; res. fel, UNIV. MANITOBA, 66-67, asst. prof. ZOOL, 67-70, ASSOC. PROF, 70- Res. grants, Fisheries Res. Bd. Can, Nat. Res. Coun. Can. & Univ. Manitoba, 67. Soc. Study Evolution. Ecology and population dynamics of fish and insects. Address: Dept. of Zoology, University of Manitoba, Winnipeg, Man, Can.

GEE, LYNN L(aMARR), b. St. Anthony, Idaho, June 21, 12; m. 33; c. 2. BACTERIOLOGY. B.S, Brigham Young, 35; fel. & M.S, Colo. Agr. & Mech. Col, 37; Ph.D.(bacter), Wisconsin, 41. Asst, Brigham Young, 35; Wisconsin, 41; bacteriologist, Dept. State Conserv, Wis, 39-41; U.S. Civil Serv, 46; soil microbiologist, Purdue, 46-48; prof. BACTER, Agr. & Mech. Col. Texas, 48-54; PROF. & HEAD DEPT, OKLA. STATE UNIV, 54- Bacteriologist, U.S. Dept. Defense, 51-52. U.S.A.A.F, 42-46, U.S.P.H.S.R, Comdr. Am. Soc. Microbiol; Am. Soc. Prof. Biol; Am. Acad. Microbiol. Soil microbiology; aerobiology. Address: Dept. of Microbiology, Oklahoma State University, Stillwater, OK 74075.

GEE, ROBERT E(ARL), b. Olean, N.Y, Aug. 8, 25; m. 45; c. 7. CHEMICAL ENGINEERING. M.Ch.E, Syracuse, 49. Res. chem. engr, polychem. dept,

E.I. DU PONT DE NEMOURS & CO, INC, 49-56, asst. div. supt. Delrin mgr, Wash. works, 56-59, supvr. new develop. group, cent. res. dept, 59-62, CORP. PLANNING, DEVELOP. DEPT, 62- U.S.N, 44-46, Lt.(jg). Catalysis; reaction kinetics; new product development; long range planning and business analysis. Address: Dept. of Development, E.I. du Pont de Nemours & Co, Inc, Wilmington, DE 19898.

GEE, SHERMAN, b. Canton, China, July 18, 37; U.S. citizen; m. 65; c. 1. ELECTRICAL ENGINEERING. B.S, California, Berkeley, 60; M.S, Mass. Inst. Tech, 61; Ph.D.(elec. eng), Stanford, 65. Res. asst. radar astron, Stanford, 63-65; adv. develop. engr, Sylvania Electronic Defense Labs, 61-63 & 65-66; electronic engr, Arnold Eng. Develop. Ctr, 66-67; MGR. ELECTROMAGNETICS RES. DEPT, MB ASSOCS, 69- U.S.A.F, 67-69, Capt. Nat. Security Indust. Asn; Inst. Elec. & Electronics Eng; Int. Union Geod. & Geophys. Electromagnetics; propagation; radiation and scattering; electronic systems analysis and electronic warfare. Address: MB Associates, San Ramon, CA 94583.

GEEHAN, ROBERT W(ILLIAM), b. Yakima, Wash, Dec. 12, 09; m. 32; c. 3. MINING ENGINEERING. E.M, Minnesota, 32. Mining engr, Winston Bros. Co, Mont, 32-34; Cripple Creek Mining Co, Alaska, 34-39; designing engr, Alaska R.R, 39-42; mining engr, U.S. Bur. Mines, Nev. & Va, 42-50, commodity specialist, Wash, D.C, 50-52, asst. chief, br. ferrous metals & ferroalloys, 52-53, asst. chief, div. minerals, 53-56, chief, div. mineral tech, region IV, Mo, 56-59, div. resources, region III, Colo, 59-60, regional dir, 60-63, area dir, area V, 63-68, prog. mgr, bur, 68-71; CONSULT, 71- U.S. rep, Int. Mat. Conf, 52-53; mem. manganese ore comt, Am. Standards Asn-Int. Standards Orgn, Leningrad, USSR, 54, 56; consult, tungsten raw mat. group, Nat. Acad. Sci-Nat. Res. Coun, 58- Am. Inst. Mining, Metall. & Petrol. Eng. Engineering geology; mineral resources; relationship of science and technology to raw materials supply. Address: P.O. Box 267, Black Hawk, CO 80422.

GEEHERN, MARGARET KENNEDY, b. N.Y.C, Feb. 28, 21; m. 64; c. 1. PHYSICS. B.S, Fordham Univ, 41, M.S, 43, Ph.D, 53. Asst, Fordham Univ, 41-42; from instr. to assoc. prof. PHYSICS, Col. Mt. St. Vincent, 45-59; ASST. PROF, LEHMAN COL, 59- Asst. prof, Manhattanville Col, 53-54; grant, biophys. summer conf, Yale, 60. Am. Phys. Soc; Am. Asn. Physics Teachers. Absorption of infrared radiation in various phosphors with simultaneous ultraviolet irradiation. Address: Dept. of Physics, Herbert H. Lehman College, Bronx, NY 10468.

GEELS, EDWIN JAMES, b. Hull, Iowa, Jan. 24, 40; m. 62; c. 2. ORGANIC CHEMISTRY. B.S, Calvin Col, 61; Ph.D.(chem), Iowa State, 65. Fel. Iowa State, 65; ASST. PROF. CHEM, DORDT COL, 65- Petrol. Res. Fund grant, 65-67. Am. Chem. Soc; Brit. Chem. Soc. Electron transfer and free radical reactions of organic compounds. Address: Dept. of Chemistry, Dordt College, Sioux Center, IA 51250.

GEEN, GLEN HOWARD, b. Reston, Man, Can, Oct. 4, 33; m. 56; c. 3. ZOOLOGY, AQUATIC BIOLOGY. B.A, British Columbia, 55, M.A, 58; Ph.D.(biol), Dalhousie, 65. Fisheries biologist, B.C, Game Dept, 56-57; Int. Pac. Salmon Fisheries Cmn, 57-60; asst. prof. BIOL, Dalhousie, 63-66; SIMON FRASER UNIV, 66-68, ASSOC. PROF. & CHMN. DEPT, 68- Am. Soc. Limnol. & Oceanog; Can. Soc. Zool; Int. Soc. Limnol. Primary and secondary production in aquatic ecosystems; energy flow; excretion of inorganic nutrients by zooplankton; diel rhythms; general fish biology. Address: Dept. of Biological Sciences, Simon Fraser University, Burnaby 2, B.C, Can.

GEEN, HENRY C(ORY), b. Denver, Colo, Nov. 8, 19; m. 42; c. 2. CHEMISTRY. Pa. State Col. Lab. technician, resinous prods. div, Rohm and Haas Co, 38-41; asst. to dir. res, Haskelite Mfg. Co, 41-46; partner, F.M. Curran & Assocs, 46-50; v.pres, Tone Mfg. Co, 50-56; tech. asst. to v.pres. res, Simoniz Co, Ill, 56-60, dir. explor. res, 60, dir. res, 60-61, v.pres. res, 61-62; PRES, Chemotronics, Inc, 62-71, CHEMOTRONICS INT, INC, 71- Owner, Geen Lab, 54-56. Am. Chem. Soc. Applications of polymers to the chemical specialties business and to various forms of laminates; surface treatment applications and reticulation of cellular products, especially polyurethanes; thermal deburring process. Address: Chemotronics International, Inc, 2231 Platt Rd, Ann Arbor, MI 48104.

GEER, BILLY W, b. Coin, Iowa, June 6, 35; m. 57. GENETICS, NUTRITION. B.S, Northwest Mo. State Col, 57; M.S, Nebraska, 60; Ph.D.(genetics), California, Davis, 63. Asst. prof. BIOL, KNOX COL.(ILL), 63-67, ASSOC. PROF, 68- Vis. assoc. prof, Ore. State Univ, 68-69; U.S. Pub. Health Serv. spec. fel, 68-69. AAAS; Am. Soc. Zool; Genetics Soc. Am. Inheritance of dietary requirements; behavioral genetics; biochemistry of reproduction. Address: Dept. of Biology, Knox College, Galesburg, IL 61401.

GEER, HARRIET A(LLYN), b. Norwich, Conn, April 29, 09. PHYSICAL CHEMISTRY. B.A, Smith Col, 30; M.A, Kansas, 32, Ph.D.(phys. chem), 35. Asst. chem, Kansas, 30-35; asst. chem, med. sch, Yale, 35-40; chemist, virus div, State Health Lab, Mich, 40-44; tech. aide, insect control cmt, Office Sci. Res. & Develop, Wash, D.C, 44-46; RES. ASSOC, Chem-biol. coordination center, Nat. Res. Council, 46-54; RES. INFO. DEPT, PARKE, DAVIS & CO, 54- Mem. codification cmt, Nat. Res. Coun, 51-59; cmt. modern methods handling chem. info, Nat. Acad. Sci-Nat. Res. Coun, 61-64. Am. Chem. Soc; Am. Soc. Info. Sci. Chemical coding and technical information. Address: Research Lab, Parke, Davis & Co, Ann Arbor, MI 48106.

GEER, IRA W, b. Avoca, N.Y, Jan. 18, 35; m. 64; c. 2. SCIENCE EDUCATION, ATMOSPHERIC SCIENCES. B.S, State Univ. N.Y. Col. Brockport, 57; M.Ed, North Carolina, 50; Ed.D.(sci. ed), Pa. State, 66. Assoc. prof. METEOROL, STATE UNIV. N.Y. COL. BROOKPORT, 61-70, PROF, 70- UNESCO sci. educ. adv, Ministry of Educ, Repub. of Korea, 69-70. U.S.N.R, 53-61. Assoc. mem. Am. Meteorol. Soc. Earth sciences. Address: Dept. of Geology & Earth Science, State University of New York College at Brockport, Brockport, NY 14420.

GEER, JACK CHARLES, b. Galesburg, Ill, Sept. 19, 27; m. 51; c. 5. MEDICINE, PATHOLOGY. B.S, La. State, 50, M.D, 56. Asst, sch. med, La. State Univ, 54-55, res. assoc, 55-57, instr. PATH, 57-60, asst. prof, 60-62, assoc. prof, 62-65, prof, 65-66; S.Tex. Med. Sch, Univ. Tex, 66-67; PROF. & CHMN. DEPT, OHIO STATE UNIV, 67- Sr. res. career develop. award, U.S. Pub. Health Serv, 59-; vis. investr, Rockefeller Inst, 60-61. U.S.N, 45-47. Experimental pathology; electron microscopy. Address: Dept. of Pathology, Ohio State University, 333 W. Tenth Ave, Columbus, OH 43210.

GEER, RICHARD P, b. LaHarpe, Ill, Sept. 23, 38. POLYMER & ORGANIC CHEMISTRY. B.S, Univ. Ill, Urbana, 60; Ph.D.(org. chem), Univ. Rochester, 65. RES. CHEMIST, HERCULES RES. CTR, 64-65 & 67- Med.Serv.C, U.S.A, 65-67, Capt. Am. Chem. Soc. Polymer and monomer synthesis; free radical chemistry. Address: Hercules Research Center, Hercules, Inc, Wilmington, DE 19808.

GEER, ROGER LOREN, b. Marathon, N.Y, June 10, 06; m. 31. METROLOGY. M.E, Cornell, 30. Indust. engr, Perfection Stove Co, Ohio, 30-34; methods engr, Smith-Corona Typewriter Co, N.Y, 35-39; instr. eng. drawing, CORNELL UNIV, 39-41, materials processing, 41-43, asst. prof, 43-46, assoc. prof, 46-68, prof, 68-71, EMER. PROF, 71- Civilian instr, Cornell Univ, 40-43, consult, Hampton Inst, 67-70. Am. Soc. Mech. Eng; Instrument Soc. Am; Soc. Mfg. Eng.(Educ. Citation, 71); Am. Ord. Asn. Materials processing; machine tools capability and control. Address: 105 Clover Lane, Ithaca, NY 14850.

GEERAETS, WALTER J, b. M. Gladbach, Germany, Sept. 27, 22; U.S. citizen; m. 56. OPHTHALMOLOGY, BIOPHYSICS. M.S, Inst. Tech. M. Gladbach, Germany, 43; M.D, Bonn, 50. PROF. OPHTHAL, ASSOC. PROF. BIOPHYS. & DIR. OPHTHAL. RES, MED. COL. VA, 60- Consult, McGuire Vet. Admin. Hosp, 60- AAAS; Am. Med. Asn; N.Y. Acad. Sci; Asn. Res. Vision & Ophthal; Pan Am. Asn. Ophthal. Biological effects of high intensity light, laser and ionizing radiation; ocular syndromes. Address: Health Sciences Center, Virginia Commonwealth University, Box 262, Medical College of Virginia, Richmond, VA 23219.

GEERDES, JAMES D(IVINE), b. Davenport, N.Dak, April 13, 24; m. 47; c. 4. BIOCHEMISTRY, ORGANIC CHEMISTRY. B.S, N.Dak. State, 49, M.S, 50; Ph.D.(biol. chem), Minnesota, 53. Instr. biochem, Minnesota, 50-53; res. chemist, E.I. du Pont de Nemours, 54-58, res. supvr, textile fibers dept, 58-62, res. assoc, 62-64; dir. res, Entoleter, Inc, 64-66, pres, 66-67; asst. to pres, fibers div, Allied Chem. Corp, 67-68, exec. v.pres, 68, pres, 68-70; PRES. & DIR, ALRAC CORP, STAMFORD, 71-; EXEC. V.PRES. & DIR, ACTION CONCEPTS TECHNOL, ROCHESTER, 71- Eng.C, 43-46, Res, 46-53, 1st Lt. AAAS; Am. Chem. Soc. Management and administration of polymer and fiber research; production and marketing operations; chemical process and equipment development. Address: 41 Fanton Hill Rd, Weston, CT 06880.

GEERING, EMIL J(OHN), b. Yonkers, N.Y, Feb. 8, 24; m. 53; c. 4. ORGANIC CHEMISTRY. A.M, Hobart Col, 43; M.S, Polytech. Inst. Brooklyn, 50, Ph.D.(org. chem), 54. Chem. analyst, Best Foods, Inc, 46-47; Interchem. Corp, 50-51; fel. ORG. CHEM, Polytech. Inst. Brooklyn, 52-53; investr, HOOKER CHEM. CORP, 54-57, group leader, 57-59, sr. chemist, 59-62, supvr, 62-64, res. assoc, 64-70, SECT. MGR, 70- U.S.N, 43-46, Lt.(jg). Am. Chem. Soc; The Chem. Soc. Sulfur and chloro compounds; preparation, development and evaluation of organic chemicals and polymers. Address: 4001 West River Parkway, Grand Island, NY 14702.

GEERTSMA, ROBERT H(ENRY), Clin. Psychol, see 12th ed, Soc. & Behav. Vols.

GEES, RUDOLF A(NDREAS), b. Berne, Switz, Jan. 31, 21; U.S. citizen; m. 65. GEOLOGY. B.S, Berne, 43, M.S, 48, Ph.D.(geol), 54. Consult. geol, 48-54; petrol. geol. Moriqui Explor. Co, Calif, 54-55; res. geologist, Union Oil Co. Calif, 56-66; ASSOC. PROF. GEOL, DALHOUSIE UNIV, 66- Swiss Army, 42-45. Geol. Soc. Am; Mineral Soc. Am; Soc. Econ. Paleont. & Mineral; Geochem. Soc; Am. Asn. Petrol. Geol; Swiss Geol. Soc; Swiss Mineral. Soc; Swiss Asn. Petrol. Geol; Ger. Geol. Union. Eugeosynclinal series, sedimentology and structure of continental margins; scanning electron microscopy of surface textures of sedimentary particles. Address: Dept. of Geology, Dalhousie University, Halifax, N.S, Can.

GEESEMAN, GORDON E, b. Fairview, Ill, Mar. 18, 21; m. 50; c. 1. GENETICS, BOTANY. B.S, Illinois, 43, M.S, 46; Ph.D.(genetics, agron), Wisconsin, 49; Oregon State, 60-61. With State Dept. Agr, Wash, 53-57; asst. agronomist, Mont. State Col, 57-60; asst. prof. GENETICS & BOT, WIS. STATE UNIV, STEVENS POINT, 62-67, ASSOC. PROF, 67- U.S.A, 43-45, 2nd Lt. AAAS; Am. Genetic Asn; Am. Soc. Human Genetics; Environ. Mutagen Soc. Plant physiology, anatomy and genetics. Address: Dept. of Biology, Wisconsin State University, Stevens Point, WI 54481.

GEESLIN, ROGER H(AROLD), b. Mt. Healthy, Ohio, May 24, 31; m. 54; c. 3. MATHEMATICS. A.B, Kenyon Col, 53; Nat. Sci. Found. fel, Yale, 53-54, Ph.D.(math), 58. Instr. MATH, Int. Christian Univ, Tokyo, 58-60, asst. prof, 60-65; assoc. prof, UNIV. LOUISVILLE, 65-68, PROF, 68-, CHMN. DEPT, 69- AAAS; Am. Math. Soc; Math. Asn. Am. Diffusion equations; functional analysis; real and complex variables; applications of computers in mathematics and the teaching of mathematics. Address: Dept. of Mathematics, University of Louisville, Louisville, KY 40208.

GEEVER, ERVING FRANCIS, b. Chicago, Ill, Sept. 27, 09; m. PATHOLOGY. B.S, Illinois, 33, M.D, 36; Ph.D.(path), Colorado, 42. Asst. prof. PATH, Colorado, 46-53; assoc. clin. prof, sch. med, George Washington, 55-62; PROF, ALBERT EINSTEIN COL. MED, 62- Med.C, U.S.A, 42-45. Am. Soc. Clin. Path; fel. Am. Med. Asn; Am. Asn. Path. & Bact; Asn. Mil. Surg. U.S. Wound healing; collagen, fluorides, experimental nutrition, and germ-free research. Address: Albert Einstein College of Medicine, 1300 Morris Park Ave, Bronx, NY 10461.

GEFFEN, T(HEODORE) M(ORTON), b. Calgary, Alta, Can, Feb. 22, 22; nat; m. 43; c. 3. PETROLEUM ENGINEERING. B.S, Oklahoma, 43. Res. eng, Petrol. & Natural Gas Conserv. Bd, Alta, 44-45; petrol. engr, Calif. Standard Co, 45-46; jr. engr, Pan Am. Petrol. Corp, 46-47, jr. res. engr, 47-

49, res. engr, 49-51, tech. group leader, 51-53, tech. group supvr, 53-55, res. group supvr, 55-58, res. sect. supvr, 58-70, RES. SECT. MGR, AMOCO PROD. CO, 70- Chmn, oil recovery tech. domain comt, Am. Petrol. Inst, 63-64, Am. Petrol. Inst-Govt. Res. Liaison Comt, 64-65. Am. Inst. Mining Metall. & Petrol. Eng. Oil recovery; multiphase fluid flow in porous material; reservoir engineering. Address: Amoco Production Co, Research Center, P.O. Box 591, Tulsa, OK 74102.

GEFTER, WILLIAM IRVIN, b. Phila, Pa, Jan. 29, 15; m. 39; c. 4. INTERNAL MEDICINE. A.B, Pennsylvania, 35, M.D, 39. Intern, Phila. Gen. Hosp, 39-41, res. med, 41-43; from instr. to William J. Mullen prof. med, Woman's Med. Col. Pa, 43-66, pres. staff, hosp, 58-60, chief MED, col. div, Phila. Gen. Hosp, 59-66; PROF, SCH. MED, TEMPLE UNIV. & DIR. DEPT. MED, EPISCOPAL HOSP, PHILA, 66-, pres. staff, hosp, 70-72. Consult, Vet. Admin. Hosp, Phila, 53-66. Dipl, Am. Bd. Internal Med, 47. Med.C, 43-46, Capt. Am. Heart Asn; Asn. Am. Med. Cols; fel. Am. Med. Asn; fel. Am. Col. Physicians; fel. Am. Col. Cardiol. Clinical cardiology; internal medicine; medical education. Address: 366 Penn Rd, Wynnewood, PA 19096.

GEGEL, HAROLD L(OUIS), b. St. Louis, Mo, Jan. 30, 33; m. 57; c. 3. PHYSICAL METALLURGY. B.S, Univ. Ill, Urbana, 55; M.S, Ohio State Univ, 62, Ph.D.(metall. eng), 65. Develop. engr, Frigidair Div, Gen. Motors Corp, 55-56; proj. engr, AIR FORCE MAT. LAB, 56-59, RES. METALLURGIST, 59- Prof, Dept. Mat. Sci. & Metall, Univ. Cincinnati, 68- U.S.A.F, 56-59, Lt. Am. Soc. Metals; Am. Inst. Min, Metall. & Petrol. Eng; Sci. Res. Soc. Am. Alloy design; thermodynamic and electronic factors which control the phase stability of alpha and beta titanium alloys and the correlation of these factors with the important mechanical properties. Address: 130 E. Greenview Dr, Dayton, OH 45415.

GEHAN, EDMUND A, b. Brooklyn, N.Y, Sept. 2, 29; m. 62; c. 5. STATISTICS, CANCER. B.A, Manhattan Col, 51; M.S, N.C. State Univ, 53, Ph.D.(exp. statist), 57; U.S. Pub. Health Serv. fel, Univ. N.C, 53-55. Instr. biostatist, Univ. N.C, 55-57, asst. prof, 57-58; math. statistician, biomet. br, Nat. Cancer Inst, 58-59, acting head biomet. sect, 59-61, head sect, 61-62, Nat. Cancer Inst. spec. fel. statist, Birkbeck Col, Univ. London, 62-64, math. statistician, biomet. br, Nat. Cancer Inst, 64-67; PROF. BIOMET, UNIV. TEX. M.D. ANDERSON HOSP. & TUMOR INST, 67- Mem. cancer clin. invest. rev. comt, Nat. Cancer Inst, 71-73. Biomet. Soc.(pres-elect, East. N.Am. Region, 71, pres, 72); Am. Statist. Asn; Am. Asn. Cancer Res; Royal Statist. Soc. Clinical trials in cancer research; statistical methodology with applications in cancer research. Address: Dept. of Biomathematics, University of Texas M.D. Anderson Hospital & Tumor Institute, 6723 Bertner Ave, Houston, TX 77025.

GEHATIA, MATATIAHU T, b. Warsaw, Poland, June 1, 11; m. 41. PHYSICAL CHEMISTRY, APPLIED MATHEMATICS. Warsaw Tech, 30-32; Israel Inst. Tech, 33-35; lic, Hebrew Sem, Jerusalem, 40; M.Sc, Hebrew Univ, Israel, 52, Ph.D.(physics), 56; fel, Uppsala, 55-56; fel, Frankfurt, 58-62, Dr. habil. (phys. chem), 62. Civil engr, 35-37; teacher & prin, Bd. Educ, Israel, 40-47; jr. scientist biophys, Weizman Inst, 52-55, intermediate scientist, 56-58; res. chemist, POLYMER BR, MAT. CTR, U.S. AIR FORCE, WRIGHT PATTERSON AIR FORCE BASE, 62-64, GROUP LEADER, 64- Am. Chem. Soc; Sci. Res. Soc. Am; German Colloid Soc. Theoretical and experimental investigation of physical properties of polymers; specific problems and methods; ultracentrifugation; light scattering; viscosity; optical properties; kinetics. Address: 5749 Seven Gables Ave, Dayton, OH 45426.

GEHLBACH, FREDERICK RENNER, b. Steubenville, Ohio, July 5, 35; m. 60; c. 2. VERTEBRATE ZOOLOGY. A.B, Cornell, 57, M.S, 59; Ph.D.(zool, conserv), Univ. Mich, 63. Asst. prof. BIOL, BAYLOR UNIV, 63-68, ASSOC. PROF, 68- Collab, Nat. Park Serv, 59-; Guggenheim fel, 70-71. Samuel T. Dana award, Univ. Mich, 63. Am. Soc. Ichthyol. & Herpet; Ecol. Soc. Am; Soc. Study Evolution. Ecology and behavior of southwestern vertebrates; conservation of natural communities and species. Address: 7717 Delhi Rd, Waco, TX 76710.

GEHLE, MARVIN H(ARLAN), b. Wood River, Nebr, Mar. 21, 32; m. 54; c. 4. POULTRY NUTRITION. B.S, Univ. Nebr, Lincoln, 60, M.S, 61; Ralston Purina res. fel, Iowa State Univ, 62-64, Ph.D.(poultry nutrit), 64. Asst. prof. poultry sci, Iowa State Univ, 64-65; sr. animal nutritionist, Greenfield Labs, Eli Lilly & Co, 65-68; sect. mgr. poultry nutrit, Quaker Oats Co, Ill, 68-69; sect. mgr. layer res, Allied Mills, Inc, 69-71; EXTEN. POULTRY NUTRITIONIST, N.C. STATE UNIV, 71- U.S.A.F, 51-57, 1st Lt. Poultry Sci. Asn; World Poultry Sci. Asn; Am. Soc. Animal Sci. Pyridoxine requirements of broilers; performance of broilers reared sexes separate; chemical suppression of ovulation in chickens; ingredient and nutrient specifications for least-cost linear programming. Address: Dept. of Poultry Science, North Carolina State University, Raleigh, NC 27607.

GEHLEN, PIERRE C(HARLES), b. La Calamine, Belgium, Apr. 29, 39; m. 62; c. 2. METALLURGY. C.E, Liège, 61; Ph.D.(mat. sci), Northwestern, 66. Asst. crystallog, Liège, 61-62; METALLURGIST, BATTELLE MEM. INST, 66- Vis. prof, Univ. Leicester, 70. X-ray work; ordering in binary alloys; computer simulation of defects in crystals and of short and long range order in binary alloys. Address: Battelle Memorial Institute, 505 King Ave, Columbus, OH 43201.

GEHMAN, HARRY MERRILL, b. Norristown, Pa, Jan. 15, 98; m. 22; c. 3. MATHEMATICS. A.B, Pennsylvania, 19, A.M, 20, Ph.D.(math), 25. Instr. math, Pennsylvania, 20-25; Nat. Res. Coun. fel, Texas, 25-26; instr. MATH, Yale, 26-27, asst. prof, 27-29; prof, STATE UNIV. N.Y. BUFFALO, 29-68, head dept, 29-62, EMER. PROF, 68- Prof. & head dept, U.S. Army Univ. (Eng), 45. AAAS; Am. Math. Soc; Math. Asn. Am.(secy-treas, 48-59, treas, 60-67). Topology; continuous curves. Address: 163 Winspear Ave, Buffalo, NY 14215.

GEHMAN, HARRY M(ERRILL), JR, b. Buffalo, N.Y, Jan. 16, 31; m. 54; c. 3. GEOCHEMISTRY. B.S, Union Col, 52; M.S, Cornell, 54; Ph.D.(geol), Minnesota, 57. RES. GEOLOGIST, ESSO PROD. RES. CO, 57- Lectr, Tulsa, 63-64; vis. asst. prof, Minnesota, 65- AAAS; Geol. Soc. Am; Mineral. Soc. Am; Am. Asn. Petrol. Geol. Inorganic geochemistry; mineral solubility; diagnosis of sedimentary rocks; composition of oil-field waters. Address: Esso Production Research Co, P.O. Box 2189, Houston, TX 77001.

GEHRELS, TOM (ANTON MARIE JACOB), b. Haarlemmermeer, Netherlands, Feb. 21, 25; nat; m. 51; c. 3. ASTRONOMY. B.Sc, Leiden, 51; Ph.D.(astron), Chicago, 56, res. assoc. ASTRON, Indiana, 56-61; Chicago, 59-61; assoc. prof, UNIV. ARIZ, 61-67, PROF, 67- Am. Astron. Soc. Minor planets; photopolarimetry; outer planet missions. Address: Lunar & Planetary Lab, University of Arizona, Tucson, AZ 85721.

GEHRI, DENNIS CLARK, b. Beloit, Wis, Jan. 28, 37; m. 61; c. 4. PHYSICAL CHEMISTRY, CHEMICAL ENGINEERING. B.S, Wisconsin, 59, Ph.D.(phys. chem), 68. Mem. jr. staff, Parker Pen Co, fall 59; MEM. SR. STAFF, ATOMICS INT. DIV, N.AM. ROCKWELL CORP, 67- Am. Chem. Soc; Sci. Res. Soc. Am; Am. Inst. Chem; N.Y. Acad. Sci. Experimental thermodynamics and molecular vibrations of gases; sodium chemistry, particularly interactions of carbon with liquid solium; air pollution control of stationary source and automotive emissions. Address: Atomics International, Dept. 737, P.O. Box 309, Canoga Park, CA 91304.

GEHRIG, JOHN D, b. Watson, Minn, Feb. 6, 24; m. 53; c. 4. ORAL SURGERY. D.D.S, Minnesota, 46, M.S, 51. Prof. ORAL SURG, sch. dent, Univ. Kansas City, 52-54; assoc. prof, SCH. DENT, UNIV. WASH, 54-67, PROF, 67-, DIR. GRAD. ORAL SURG. TRAINING PROG, 70-, chmn. dept. oral surg, 56-70. Attend, U.S. Pub. Health Serv. Hosp, Children's Orthop. Hosp, Providence Hosp, Vet. Admin. Hosp, Seattle; Vet. Admin. Hosp, Am. Lake; Consult, Madigan Gen. Hosp, Tacoma; U.S. Army Hq. Dent. Detachment, Ft. Lewis. Dipl, Am. Bd. Oral Surg. Dent.C, 46-48, Capt. Am. Soc. Oral Surg. Transplantation of teeth; development of tooth bank; sclerosing of intramedullary hemangiomas; analyzing two methods of determining anesthesia endpoint; inferior alveolar nerve regeneration on dogs through a Millipore filter sleeve; comparison of ATb sensitivities with ATb choice; blood and fluid volume changes in oral surgery; evaluation of current methods of dental anesthesia. Address: Dept. of Oral Surgery, B348 Health Sciences Bldg, School of Dentistry, University of Washington, Seattle, WA 98105.

GEHRIG, ROBERT F(RANK), b. Manitowoc, Wis, Jan. 3, 28; m. 54; c. 4. MICROBIOLOGY. B.S, Wisconsin, 51, M.S, 58, Ph.D.(bact), 61. Asst. enzyme chem, Merck Inst. Therapeut. Res, N.J, 51-53; asst. prof. BIOL, RUSSELL SAGE COL, 62-66, ASSOC. PROF, 66-, CHMN. DEPT, 70- U.S.A, 53-56. AAAS; Am. Soc. Microbiol; Brit. Soc. Gen. Microbiol. Fatty acid metabolism of the filamentous fungi; physiology of penicillia and aspergilla. Address: Dept. of Biology, Russell Sage College, Troy, NY 12180.

GEHRING, DOUGLAS G, b. Woodbury, N.J, Mar. 13, 32; m. 56; c. 2. ANALYTICAL & PHYSICAL CHEMISTRY. A.B, Bucknell, 54; Temple, 57-58; M.S, Delaware, 65. Chemist, E.I. DU PONT DE NEMOURS & CO, INC, 56-61, sr. chemist, 61-64, RES. CHEMIST, 64- U.S.A, 54-56. Am. Chem. Soc. Nuclear magnetic resonance; gas chromatography; electroanalytical methods; infrared; ultraviolet; colorimetry; trace analysis; polarimetry; qualitative organic analysis. Address: Eastern Lab, Dept. of Explosives, E.I. du Pont de Nemours & Co, Inc, Gibbstown, NJ 08027.

GEHRING, FREDERICK W(ILLIAM), b. Ann Arbor, Mich, Aug. 7, 25; m. 53; c. 2. MATHEMATICS. B.S.E.(elec. eng) & B.S.E.(math), Michigan, 46, M.A, 49; Fulbright fel, Cambridge, 49-51, Ph.D.(math), 52. Benjamin Pierce instr. MATH, Harvard, 52-55; asst. prof, UNIV. MICH, 56-59, assoc. prof, 59-62, PROF, 62- Guggenheim & Fulbright fel, 58-59; Nat. Sci. Found. fel, 59-60; vis. prof, Stanford Univ, 64; Harvard, 64-65; Univ. Minn, 71; Mittag Leffler Inst, Sweden, 72. Anal. ed, Duke Math. Jour, 63-U.S.A, 43-46. Am. Math. Soc; Math. Asn. Am; London Math. Soc; Swiss Math. Soc; Finnish Math. Soc. Analysis. Address: 2001 Shadford Rd, Ann Arbor, MI 48104.

GEHRING, HARVEY T(HOMAS), b. Chicago, Ill, Oct. 27, 11; m. 37; c. 2. CHEMISTRY. B.S, Illinois, 34, Asst. dir. EMULSION RES, SHERWIN WILLIAMS CO, 35-68, DIR, 68- Am. Chem. Soc. Emulsion and water thinned coatings. Address: 11156 Parnell Ave, Chicago, IL 60628.

GEHRING, JOHN WILLIAM, JR, b. Baltimore, Md, Sept. 22, 28; m. 49; c. 3. PHYSICS, METALLURGY. B.S, Loyola Col, 49; U.S. Army Ballistics Inst, 49-57. Res. scientist, Ballistic Res. Labs, 49-54, chief metall. lab, 54-57, chief hyperballistics lab, 56-61; HEAD HIGH VELOCITY IMPACT & METALL. LABS, DEFENSE RES. LABS, GEN. MOTORS CORP, 61- Am. Inst. Aeronaut. & Astronaut; Am. Soc. Metals; Am. Ord. Asn. High strain rate deformation of materials; physics of high explosives; application of meteor physics to the hazards of space flight. Address: General Motors Corp, Delco Electronics, 6767 Hollister Ave, Goleta, CA 93017.

GEHRING, LOIS B(IGGER), b. Collins, Iowa, Jan. 30, 26; m. 53; c. 2. BIOCHEMISTRY. B.A, Cornell Col, 47; M.A, Iowa, 49; Fulbright fel, Cambridge, 49-51, U.S. Pub. Health Serv. fel, 51-52, Ph.D.(biochem, microbiol), 52. Asst. bot, Yale, 53; res. fel. bact, Harvard, 53-55; res. assoc. BIOL. CHEM, MED. SCH, UNIV. MICH, 55-56, INSTR, 56- Res. assoc. biol. dept, Mass. Inst. Tech, 64-65. Brit. Biochem. Soc. Amino acid metabolism in yeast; toxin production by Clostridium welchii; purine metabolism in bacteria. Address: 2001 Shadford Rd, Ann Arbor, MI 48104.

GEHRING, PERRY JAMES, b. Yankton, S.Dak, Mar. 15, 36; m. 59; c. 3. TOXICOLOGY, PHARMACOLOGY. B.S. & D.V.M, Minnesota, Minneapolis, 60, Ph.D.(pharmacol), 65. Res. assoc. toxicol, Iowa State, 60-61; U.S. Pub. Health Serv. fel. pharmacol, Minnesota, Minneapolis, 61-65; pharmacol. toxicologist, Dow Chem. Co, 65-68; assoc. prof. pharmacol, Mich. State Univ, 68-70; ASST. DIR. TOXICOL, DOW CHEM. CO, 70- Vis. prof, dept. pharmacol, Mich. State Univ, 66-68. AAAS; Am. Vet. Med. Asn; Soc. Toxicol; Am. Soc. Pharmacol. & Exp. Therapeut. Toxidynamics; chemical cataractogenesis; metal toxicology; pharmacokinetics. Address: Toxicology Section, Chemical-Biology Research, Dow Chemical Co, Midland, MI 48640.

GEHRINGER, JACK W(ALTON), b. Gretna, Nebr, Apr. 22, 23; m. 46; c. 3. BIOLOGY. B.S, Colo. Agr. & Mech. Col, 50. Fishery res. biologist, gulf fishery invest, U.S. FISH & WILDLIFE SERV, Tex, 50-52, S.Atlantic Fishery Invest, Ga, 52-56, supvr. fishery res. biologist, 56-70, asst. dir. biol. lab, 59-70, acting lab. dir, Bur. Commercial Fisheries, Ga, 67-70, ASSOC. REGIONAL DIR. RESOURCE PROGS, NAT. MARINE FISHERIES SERV, 70- U.S.C.G, 42-45. Am. Fisheries Soc; Am. Inst. Fishery Res. Biol; Gulf & Caribbean Fisheries Inst. Wildlife and marine biology; larval development of marine fishes, ecology and distribution of marine fishes; development of gear for sampling marine zooplankton. Address: National Marine Fisheries Service, 144 First Ave. S, St. Petersburg, FL 33701.

GEHRIS, CLARENCE WINFRED, b. Fleetwood, Pa, Oct. 25, 17; m. 41; c. 2. BOTANY, PLANT ECOLOGY. B.S, Temple, 38, M.Ed, 45; D.Ed.(biol. sci), Pa. State, 64. Instr, pub. sch, Pa, 45-62; assoc. prof. BIOL, STATE UNIV. N.Y. COL. BROCKPORT, 62-71, PROF, 71- AAAS-Nat. Sci. Found. fel, 59-61. Ecol. Soc. Am; Nat. Asn. Biol. Teachers; Nat. Sci. Teachers Asn. Bog ecology; peat development; pollen analysis. Address: Dept. of Biology, State University of New York College at Brockport, Brockport, NY 14420.

GEHRKE, CHARLES W(ILLIAM), b. N.Y.C, July 18, 17; m. 41; c. 3. CHEMISTRY. B.A, Ohio State, 39, M.Sc. & B.Sc, 41, Ph.D.(agr. chem), 47. Asst. bacter, Ohio State, 41; food & dairy inspector, Ohio, 41-42; acting prof. chem, Mo. Valley Col, 42-43, prof. & head dept, 43-45, 46-49; instr. Ohio State Univ, 45-46; assoc. prof. AGR. CHEM, UNIV. MO-COLUMBIA, 49-53, PROF. & SUPVR. EXP. STA. CHEM. LABS, COL. AGR, 54- Co-investr, Apollo 11, 12, 14, 15, lunar samples. Am. Chem. Soc; fel. Asn. Off. Anal. Chem. Physical biochemistry of proteins; gas chromatography of amino acids, genetic molecules, and biological substances; analytical methods development. Address: Experiment Station Chemical Labs, University of Missouri-Columbia, Columbia, MO 65201.

GEHRKE, HENRY, b. Salina, Kans, May 11, 36; m. 56; c. 4. INORGANIC CHEMISTRY. B.S, Okla. State, 58; M.S, Iowa, 63, Ph.D.(inorg. & org. chem), 64. From asst. prof. to ASSOC. PROF. CHEM, S.DAK. STATE UNIV, 64- AAAS; Am. Chem. Soc. Coordination chemistry of rarer elements. Address: Dept. of Chemistry, South Dakota State University, Brookings, SD 57006.

GEHRKE, WILLARD H, b. Belmont, Wis, Jan. 21, 20; m. 44; c. 3. CHEMICAL ENGINEERING. B.S, Wisconsin, 42. Chem. engr, Monsanto Chem. Co, Ohio, 42-47; process engr. mfg. eng, Marathon Div, Am. Can Co, 47-51, supvr, 51, cent. mfg. eng, 51-53, process eng, 53-57, mgr, 57-61, asst. to v.pres. res. & develop. div, 61-62, dir. paper prod. res. & develop, 62-64, rigid container res. & develop, 64-66, dir. fabric bus. develop, 66-68; V.PRES. CO. DEVELOP, CURWOOD INC, 68- Mem, Indust. Res. Inst. Am. Chem. Soc; Tech. Asn. Pulp & Paper Indust. Protective packaging films for foods and other products made from polyester, polyolefins, nylon, vinyl and aluminum foil. Address: Company Development, Curwood Inc, Box 46, New London, WI 54961.

GEHRMANN, WILLIAM HENRY, b. Hoboken, N.J, Aug. 11, 37; m. 60; c. 2. PHYSIOLOGY. B.A, N.Y. Univ, 59; Nat. Insts. Health training grant & Ph.D. (biol), Arizona, 67. Res. asst. endocrine carcinogenesis, sch. med, Stanford, 62-64; Nat. Insts. Health fel. endocrinol, Rutgers, 67-68; ASSOC. PROF. BIOL, TARLETON STATE COL, 68- U.S.A, 59-62. AAAS; Am. Soc. Zool. Neuroendocrine relationships, especially related to thyroid function; endocrinological bases of behavior; environmental physiology. Address: Dept. of Biology, Tarleton State College, Stephenville, TX 76401.

GEIB, IRVING G(EORGE), b. Buffalo, N.Y, Sept. 15, 07; m. 38; c. 2. PHYSICS. B.S, Buffalo, 28; Ph.D, Purdue, 48. Asst. physics, Purdue, 28-33; teacher, pub. schs, N.Y, 33-44; lectr, Buffalo, 43-44; res. physicist, B.F. Goodrich Co, 44-48; assoc. prof. PHYSICS, PURDUE UNIV, 48-61, PROF, 61- AAAS; Am. Phys. Soc; Am. Crystallog. Asn. Properties of rubber; x-ray diffraction. Address: 1809 N. Salisbury St, West Lafayette, IN 47906.

GEIDUSCHEK, E(RNEST) PETER, b. Vienna, Austria, April 11, 28; nat; m. 55; c. 2. BIOPHYSICS, MOLECULAR BIOLOGY. A.B, Columbia, 48; A.M, Harvard, 50, U.S. Pub. Health Serv. fel, 51-52, Ph.D.(chem), 52. Instr, Yale, 52-53, 55-57; asst. prof. chem, Michigan, 57-59; biophys, Chicago, 59-62, assoc. prof, 62-64, PROF, 64-70; BIOL, UNIV. CALIF, SAN DIEGO, 70- Guggenheim Found. fel, 64-65. U.S.A, 53-55. AAAS; Am. Soc. Biol. Chem; Am. Chem. Soc; Biophys. Soc. Macromolecular structure; synthesis and function of nucleic acids; physico-chemical methods applicable to large molecules; virus development. Address: Dept. of Biology, University of California at San Diego, P.O. Box 109, La Jolla, CA 92037.

GEIER, GEORGE, b. N.Y.C, Feb. 2, 18; m. 44; c. 2. OPTICS. B.Ch.E, Cooper Union, 39; M.S, Stevens Inst. Tech, 42. Res. engr, KEUFFEL & ESSER CO, 40-55, qual. control. engr, instruments, 50-55, mgr. res. & develop. optics & metrol, 55-65, DIR. RES. & DEVELOP. INSTRUMENTS, 65-, DEP. TECH. DIR, 69- Indust. Res. Inst; Optical Soc. Am; Am. Soc. Photogram. Photo-optical instruments; metrology; patent law. Address: Keuffel & Esser Co, 20 Whippany Rd, Morristown, NJ 07960.

GEIGER, DONALD R, b. Dayton, Ohio, Feb. 27, 33. PLANT PHYSIOLOGY. B.S, Dayton, 55; M.Sc, Ohio State, 60, Ph.D.(bot), 63. Teacher, Cathedral Latin Sch, 55-60; asst. prof. BIOL, UNIV. DAYTON, 64-67, ASSOC. PROF, 67- Prin. investr, Nat. Sci. Found. res. grant, 64-67; U.S. Atomic Energy Comn, 68-71. AAAS; Am. Soc. Plant Physiol. Translocation of sugar in higher plants using radioisotope tracer techniques. Address: Dept. of Biology, University of Dayton, Dayton, OH 45409.

GEIGER, EDWIN OTTO, b. Chicago, Ill, Apr. 24, 39; m. 63; c. 3. BIOCHEMISTRY. B.S, DePaul, 61; M.S, Loyola, 64, Ph.D.(biochem), 66. Fel. BIOCHEM, Case Western, 65-67; SR. RESEARCH, CPC INT, 67- Medal, Am. Inst. Chem, 61. Am. Chem. Soc. Enzyme chemistry; intermediate metabolism. Address: 15320 Pine Dr, Oak Forest, IL 60452.

GEIGER, FELIX E(UGENE), b. Vienna, Austria, Mar. 3, 21; nat; m. 51. PHYSICS. B.S, Wisconsin, 44, Ph.D.(physics), 50. Fel, Nat. Res. Coun. Can, 50-51; RES. PHYSICIST SOLID STATE PHYSICS, Naval Res. Lab, 51-60; GODDARD SPACE FLIGHT CTR, NASA, 60- Semiconductor solid state physics. Address: 1301 Delaware Ave, Apt. N412, Washington, DC 20024.

GEIGER, GENE E(DWARD), b. Pittsburgh, Pa, Oct. 27, 28; m. 59; c. 2. MECHANICAL ENGINEERING. B.S.M.E, Carnegie Inst. Tech, 50; M.S.M.E, Pittsburgh, 55, Ph.D.(mech. eng), 64. Res. asst. residual stress, Mellon Inst, 51; instr. MECH. ENG, UNIV. PITTSBURGH, 51-55, asst. prof, 55-64, assoc. res. prof, 64-66, assoc. prof, 66-71, PROF, 71-, COORD. GRAD. PROG, 66- Vis. fel, Mellon Inst, 65-69. Summers, res. engr, res. labs, Westinghouse Elec. Corp, 52 & 54-55, engr, atomic power div, 56 & new prod. div, 57, serv. engr, Babcock & Wilcox Co, 53, engr, Univ. Pittsburgh, 58, Boeing Aerospace Co, 59, Joy Mfg. Co, 61. Consult, Pa. Pub. Utility Comn, 64; gas companies west Pa, 65-68; knowledge availability syst, Univ. Pittsburgh, 65-; Anvil Prods, Inc, 67-68; Mine Safety Appliances, Inc, 70- Nat. Guard, 48-50. Am. Soc. Eng. Educ; Am. Soc. Mech. Eng; Nat. Soc. Prof. Eng. Heat transfer; fluid dynamics; thermodynamics. Address: Dept. of Mechanical Engineering, University of Pittsburgh, Pittsburgh, PA 15213.

GEIGER, GORDON HAROLD, b. Chicago, Ill, Apr. 21, 37; m. 60; c. 2. METALLURGICAL ENGINEERING, MATERIALS SCIENCE. B.E, Yale, 59; M.S, Northwestern, 61, Ph.D.(mat. sci), 64. Process engr, Allis-Chalmers Mfg, Co, 60-61; res. asst, Northwestern, 61-63; res. engr, Jones & Laughlin Steel Corp, 64-65; asst. prof. metall. eng, Univ. Wis, Madison, 65-67, assoc. prof, 67-68; MAT. ENG, UNIV. ILL, CHICAGO CIRCLE, 69-71, PROF, 71- Summer engr, U.S. Steel Corp, 59, 65-67. Am. Inst. Mining, Metall. & Petrol. Eng; Nat. Asn. Corrosion Eng.(Campbell award, 66); Am. Soc. Metals; Am. Foundrymen's Soc; Am. Inst. Chem. Eng; Brit. Iron & Steel Inst. Thermodynamics and transport phenomena in process metallurgy; operations research as applied to metallurgical processes; steelmaking; copper production processes; mineral processing. Address: Dept. of Materials Engineering, University of Illinois at Chicago Circle, P.O. Box 4348, Chicago, IL 60680.

GEIGER, H. JACK, b. N.Y.C, Nov. 11, 25; m. 51. COMMUNITY MEDICINE, EPIDEMIOLOGY. Wisconsin, 41-43; Chicago, 47-50; Kettering Found. fel, Western Reserve, 54-58, M.D, 58; Rockefeller Found. scholar, Natal, 57; M.Sci.Hyg, Harvard, 60. Sci. ed, Int. News Serv, 49-54; intern med, sch. med, Harvard, 58-59, Nat. Inst. Ment. Health fel, joint training prog. social sci. & med, dept. social relations, 59-61, instr. prev. med, sch. med, 61-62, asst. med. & resident, 62-64; asst. prof. pub. health, sch. pub. health, 64-65; assoc. prev. med, sch. med, Tufts Univ, 65-66, prof, 66-68, prof. community health & social med. & chmn. dept, 68-71; PROF. COMMUNITY MED. & CHMN. DEPT, SCH. MED, STATE UNIV. N.Y. STONY BROOK, 71- Res. fel, Thorndike Lab, Boston City Hosp, 64; Milbank Mem. Fund faculty fel, 66-71; proj. dir, Tufts Univ-Delta Health Ctr, Mound Bayou, Miss. & Tufts Univ-Columbia Point Health Ctr, Boston, 65-71. Consult, res. policy comt, Peace Corps, 62-64; Rockefeller Found, 69-70; Off. Secy, U.S. Dept. Health, Educ. & Welfare, 68- Mem. bd. gov, Inst. Current World Affairs, 61-, chmn, 71; Nat. Comn. Hunger & Malnutrit. U.S, 67-; mem. bd, Nat. Comn. Inquiry Health Servs. Americans, 69-71; mem. spec. comt. environ. change, AAAS, 69-; planning comt, White House Conf. Youth, 71- U.S. Maritime Serv, 43-47, Lt.(jg). Fel. AAAS; fel. Am. Pub. Health Asn; Soc. Appl. Anthrop; Asn. Teachers Prev. Med; Asn. Am. Med. Cols. Social medicine and change; community health; cultural factors in the epidemiology of hypertension, rheumatoid arthritis and schizophrenia. Address: Dept. of Community Medicine, Health Sciences Center, State University of New York at Stony Brook, Stony Brook, Long Island, NY 11790.

GEIGER, J(ACOB) C(ASSON), b. Alexandria, La, Nov. 18, 85; m; c. 3. PUBLIC HEALTH. A.B. & M.S, Tulane, 05, M.D, 12, Dr.P.H, 19, hon. Sc.D, 44; hon. D.Sc, La. State, 35; LL.D, Santa Clara, 38, California, 63; hon. M.A, Hahnemann Med. Col, 39; hon. Litt.D, Panama, 43; hon. dipl, El Salvador, 45. Asst. dir. & acting dir. labs. & bur. communicable diseases, State Bd. Health, Calif, 13-16; asst. epidemiologist & epidemiologist, U.S. Pub. Health Serv, 16-24; asst. cmnr. in charge med. serv. sect, Dept. Health, Chicago, 24-27, exec. officer, 27-28; assoc. prof. epidemiol, Hooper Found, California, 28-30, prof, 30-32, CLIN. PROF. epidemiol, univ, 32-39; pub. health & prev. med, Stanford, 40-54; EPIDEMIOL, MED. SCH, UNIV. CALIF, SAN FRANCISCO, 55-; HEALTH OFF, OAKLAND, 52- Asst. prof, California, 13-18, res. fel, Hooper Found, 19-22; assoc. prof, Chicago, 22-27, prof. lectr, 27-28; asst. cmnr. health, City of Chicago, 24, exec. officer, 27-39; health officer, city & county San Francisco, 31-32, dir. pub. health, 32-52; prof, Col. Physicians & Surg, San Francisco, 43-54; lectr, Southern California. Staff epidemiologist, Mt. Zion Hosp, San Francisco. Mem. res. consult. staff, Nat. Canners Asn; consult, South. Pac. Ry. Syst; Dollar Steamship Lines; Am. Pres. Lines; Matson Navig. Co, 28-; U.S. Navy. Mem, botulism Cmn, 19-22; hyg. reference bd, Life Exten. Inst, 45. Recipient of 43 honors & awards from foreign govts. for pub. health work done in or for their countries. AAAS; fel. Am. Soc. Trop. Med. & Hyg; fel. Am. Pub. Health Asn; fel. Am. Med. Asn; fel. Am. Col. Physicians; fel. Pan-Am. Med. Asn; fel. Royal Soc. Trop. Med. & Hyg; Egyptian Pub. Health Asn.(hon. v.pres, 45). Botulism; malaria; typhoid fever; food poisoning; rabies; meningitis; brucellosis; chemical poisonings; carbon monoxide and intravenous use of methylene blue. Address: 2166 34th Ave, San Francisco, CA 94116.

GEIGER, JAMES S(TEPHEN), b. Kitchener, Ont, Apr. 5, 29; m. 57; c. 3. PHYSICS. B.Sc, McMaster, 51, M.Sc, 52; M.S, Yale, 53. Sterling fel, Yale, 55-56, Ph.D.(physics), 57. Asst. res. off, NUCLEAR PHYSICS, ATOMIC ENERGY OF CAN, LTD, 56-68, SR. RES. OFF, 68- Am. Phys. Soc; Can. Asn. Physicists. Nuclear physics; Bray spectroscopy and nuclear disintegration schemes; coulomb excitation. Address: Atomic Energy of Canada, Ltd, Chalk River Nuclear Labs, Chalk River, Ont, Can.

GEIGER, JAMES W(OODROW), b. Minneapolis, Minn, Feb. 22, 18; m. 42; c. 2. BIOCHEMISTRY. B.A, Minnesota, 39. Asst, grad. sch, Minnesota, 40-42; head, bact. prod, E.R. Squibb & Sons, 42-46; dir. chem. res. & develop. labs, Geiger Labs, 46-54; chemist, dept. phys. med. & rehab, Minnesota, 54-55; proj. leader, cent. res. div, Gen. Mills, Inc, 55-56, sr. scientist, eng. res. div, 56-57; asst. mgr. res. & develop, Wood Conversion Co, 57-58; staff asst. to v.pres. res, Philip Morris, Inc, 58-61. asst. to dir. purchases, 62-64, dir. purchases, 65-68; pres, Adkem Corp, 68-70; CONSULT, 70- Am.

Soc. Microbiol; Am. Chem. Soc; Chem. Mkt. Res. Asn; Tech. Asn. Pulp & Paper Indust; Am. Mkt. Asn. Product and market development; market research and technical economics in consumer and industrial product areas; research administration and purchasing management; films; fibers; adhesives; plastics; tobacco; confections; biologicals; pharmaceuticals; foods; packaging. Address: 18600-30½ Ave. N, Wayzata, MN 55391.

GEIGER, JOSEPH M, b. N.Y.C, Feb. 16, 33; m. 59; c. 3. THEORETICAL PHYSICS. B.S, Hofstra, 54; M.S, Syracuse, 56, Ph.D.(physics), 60. Proj. assoc, Wisconsin, 59-60; asst. prof. PHYSICS, ST. BONAVENTURE UNIV, 60-62, assoc. prof, 62-69, PROF, 69- Am. Phys. Soc. Quantum field theory; quantum mechanics and electrodynamics; coupling of fermion and meson fields. Address: Dept. of Physics, St. Bonaventure University, St. Bonaventure, NY 14778.

GEIGER, KLAUS W(ILHEIM), b. Berlin, Germany, Apr. 26, 21; Can. citizen; m. 47; c. 2. PHYSICS. Dipl, Tübingen, 49; Ph.D.(physics), Mainz, 51. Res. asst. nuclear physics, Max Planck Inst. Chem, Germany, 49-52; fel, NAT. RES. COUN. CAN, 52-54, RES. OFF. APPL. PHYSICS, 54- Can. Asn. Physicists. Radioactivity; cosmic rays; neutron standardization; neutron spectra. Address: Division of Physics, National Research Council, Ottawa, Ont, Can. K1A 0S1

GEIGER, MARION B(RAXTON), b. Paintsville, Ky, Sept. 4, 03; m. 28; c. 2. CHEMISTRY. B.S, Georgetown Col, 24; Mass. Inst. Tech, 25-26; M.S, Michigan, 30, Ph.D.(chem), 32. Instr. chem, Georgetown Col, 24, physics, 24-25, chem, 27-29; chemist, Oldbury Electrochem. Co, N.Y. 32-35, asst. works mgr, 35-47; works mgr. & secy, 47-50, exec. v.pres, 50-56; dir. gen. develop, Hooker Chem. Corp, 56-58, dir, int. develop, 58-60; ASSOC, CHEM. PROJ. ASSOCS, INC, 60- Am. Chem. Soc; Electrochem. Soc; Am. Inst. Chem. Eng; fel. Am. Inst. Chem. Phosphorus and phosphorus compounds; chlorates and perchlorates; oxalic acid; tautomerism of hydroxy triaryl carbinols; absorption spectra and chemical constitution of organic compounds. Address: 465 Mountain View Dr, Lewiston, NY 14092.

GEIGER, M(ARLIN) G(EORGE), JR, b. South Charleston, W.Va, Oct. 24, 27; m. 49; c. 1. CHEMICAL ENGINEERING. B.S, Purdue, 49, Ph.D.(chem. eng), 54; M.S, Bucknell, 51. Lab. asst, Carbide & Carbon Chem. Co, 46; Proctor & Gamble Co, 47; asst, Bucknell, 49-50; Purdue, 51-54; res. engr, Shell Oil Co, 54-58, res. group leader, 58-61, staff assignment, Royal Dutch Petrol, 61-63, sr. engr, PETROCHEM. DIV, SHELL CHEM. CO, SHELL OIL CO, N.Y, 63-67, MGR. TECH, TEX, 67- Am. Chem. Soc; Am. Inst. Chem. Eng. Process research and development; lubricating oils and wax; catalytic cracking; alkylation; hydroprocesses; petrochemicals; engineering studies; fluidization; two phase transport; process and engineering design; economic evaluation; venture analysis. Address: Petrochemical Division, Shell Chemical Co, P.O. Box 2633, Deer Park, TX 77536.

GEIGER, PAUL FRANK, b. Meadville, Pa, July 12, 32; m. 62; c. 1. PHARMACOLOGY. B.A, Texas, 55, B.S, 58, Armour fel. & M.S, 62, Nat. Insts. Health fel. & Ph.D.(pharmacol), 66. From asst. prof. to ASSOC. PROF. PHARMACOL, NORTHEAST LA. UNIV, 67- Am. Pharmaceut. Asn. Effects of cholinesterase inhibitors and cholinesterase on drugs affecting the central nervous system; biochemical pharmacology and toxicology. Address: Dept. of Pharmacology, Northeast Louisiana University, Monroe, LA 71201.

GEIGER, PAUL JEROME, b. Los Angles, Calif, Jan. 12, 30; m. 55; c. 4. BIOCHEMISTRY. B.S, California, Berkeley, 51; U.S. Pub. Health Serv. scholar, Hopkins, 58-62, Ph.D.(biochem), 62. Res. engr, Jet Propulsion Lab, Calif. Inst. Tech, 62, sr. scientist, 62-68; res. scientist, biosci. lab, Dow Chem. Co, 68-69; Nat. Insts. Health res. fel. PHARMACOL, UNIV. SOUTH. CALIF, 69, ASST. PROF, 69- Consult, jet propulsion lab, Calif. Inst. Technol, 71. U.S.N, 51-55, Res, 55-66, Lt. AAAS; Am. Chem. Soc. Enzymology; kinetics of dehydrogenases; sulfhydryl structures; extraterrestrial biology and soil science; life detection on planets; detection of organic substances in arid soils; analytical biochemistry; mechanism of action of oxydases; biochemical disorders in disease. Address: 931 E. Parkman St, Altadena, CA 91001.

GEIGER, WILLIAM E(BLING), JR, b. Buffalo, N.Y, Feb. 11, 44; m. 65; c. 1. ANALYTICAL CHEMISTRY. B.S, Canisius Col, 65; fel, Cornell Univ, 65-66, Ph.D.(anal. chem), 69; fel, Univ. Calif, Riverside, 68-69. Res. fel, Northwest. Univ, 69-70; ASST. PROF. CHEM, SOUTH. ILL. UNIV, 70- Am. Chem. Soc. Organometallic and transition metal electrochemistry; elucidation of electronic and molecular structure by electron spin resonance; studies of ionic donor-acceptor complexes. Address: Dept. of Chemistry, Southern Illinois University, Carbondale, IL 62901.

GEIL, PHILLIP H, b. Milwaukee, Wis, Sept. 26, 30; m. 55; c. 3. POLYMER PHYSICS. B.S, Wis. State Col.(Milwaukee), 52, M.S, Wisconsin, 54, Ph.D. (physics), 57. Res. physicist, E.I. du Pont de Nemours & Co, 56-62; sr. res. physicist, Res. Triangle Inst, 62-63; assoc. prof. POLYMER SCI. & ENG, CASE WEST. RESERVE UNIV, 63-68, PROF, 68- Ed, Jour. Macromolecular Sci; co-ed, Critical Rev. Macromolecular Sci. AAAS; Am. Phys. Soc; Am. Chem. Soc. Solid state physics; relationship of polymer morphology to physical properties; mechanisms of polymer crystallization and deformation; molecular biophysics. Address: Division of Macromolecular Science, Case Western Reserve University, Cleveland, OH 44106.

GEILER, FREDERICK LINCK, b. Portsmouth, Ohio, Nov. 5, 01; m. 28; c. 2. PHARMACY. B.Sc, Ohio State, 28; M.Sc, West Virginia, 35. Asst. PHARM, Ohio State, 26-28; instr, UNIV. W.VA, 28-37, asst. prof, 37-43, assoc. prof, 43-50, prof, 50-71, EMER. PROF, 71- Pharmacist in charge health dispensary, 28-41. Am. Pharmaceut. Asn. Pharmaceutics and therapeutics. Address: 360 Waitman St, Morgantown, WV 26505.

GEILKER, CHARLES DON, b. Kingston, Mo, Dec. 15, 33; m. 58; c. 2. ASTRONOMY, PHYSICS. A.B, William Jewell Col, 55, Atomic Energy Cmn. fel, 55-56; M.A, Vanderbilt, 57; Mass. Inst. Tech, 59-60; Ph.D.(astron), Case Western Reserve, 68. Instr. radiation physics, U.S. Pub. Health Serv, 57-62; res. assoc. astron, observ, Vanderbilt, 62-64; ASSOC. PROF. ASTRON. & PHYSICS, WILLIAM JEWELL COL, 68- U.S.P.H.S, 57-62, Comdr. Am. Astron. Soc; Am. Asn. Physics Teachers; Health Physics Soc; Am. Sci. Affiliation. Electronic and optical instrumentation; astronomical photoelectric and photographic photometry; gamma spectrometry and radiation dosimetry. Address: Dept. of Physics, William Jewell College, Liberty, MO 64068.

GEIMAN, QUENTIN M(ONROE), b. Glen Rock, Pa, Oct. 16, 04; m. 29; c. 2. PARASITOLOGY. B.S, Gettysburg Col, 27; M.S, Pennsylvania, 31, Ph.D. (protozool), 34. Asst. protozool, Pennsylvania, 31-33, instr. zool, 33-34; fel, Nat. Res. Coun, Harvard Med. Sch, 34-35, asst. comp. path, 35-38, instr, 38-44, bacter, 41-42, asst. prof. trop. diseases, 44-50, assoc. prof. trop. pub. health, sch. pub. health, Harvard, 50-55; prof. prev. med, SCH. MED, STANFORD UNIV, 55-71, EMER. PROF. COMMUNITY & PREV. MED, 71- Chief dept. parasitol, Nat. Inst. Hygiene & Pub. Health, Lima, Peru, 38-39, responsible investigator, U.S. Pub. Health Serv. grant-in-aid, 46-51; projs, Armed Forces Epidemiol. Bd. & Off. Res. & Develop, U.S. Dept. Army, 51-71. Consult, comn. enteric infections; comn. hemorrhagic fever. & comn. malaria, Off. Surg. Gen, U.S. Dept. Army; expert comn. malaria, World Health Orgn; Calif. Dept. Pub. Health & Ment. Hyg. Mem. Int. Cong. Trop. Med. & Malaria, 48; Tenth Pac. Sci. Cong, 61, Eleventh, 66. With Off. Sci. Res. & Develop, 43-45; mem. field team, Armed Forces Epidemiol. Bd, Japan & Korea, 52. AAAS (prize, 46); Am. Soc. Parasitol; Am. Soc. Trop. Med. & Hyg.(secy-treas, 50-52); Royal Soc. Trop. Med. & Hygiene. Medical parasitology; parasitic protozoa of reptiles; parasitic and pathogenic protozoa of man; leishmaniasis; bartonellosis; cultivation and metabolism of malarial parasites; pathogenic spirochetes and amoebae; hemorrhagic fever. Address: 245 E. Edith Ave, Los Altos, CA 94022.

GEIPEL, DAVID H, b. Pittsburgh, Pa, Jan. 23, 28. ENGINEERING. B.S, Carnegie Inst. Tech, 51, M.S, 52, Buhl fel, 53, Ph.D.(elec. eng), 54. Asst, Carnegie Inst. Tech, 52; engr. res, Autonetics Div, N.Am. Aviation, Inc, 54-59, tech. specialist, 59-60; prin. engr, Aeronutronics Div, Ford Motor Co, 60-63; electro-mech. eng. specialist, AUTONETICS DIV, N.AM. ROCKWELL CORP, 63-69, chief scientist, res. & eng. div, 69-70, MEM. TECH. STAFF, AEROSPACE & MARINE PROD. DIV, 70- U.S.N.R, 51-59, Ens. Feasibility, mechanization and performance analyses of avionics; aircraft and missile weapon delivery and space systems. Address: North American Rockwell Corp, Autonetics Division, Aerospace & Marine Production Division, 3370 Miraloma Ave, Anaheim, CA 92803.

GEIPEL, LOTHAR ERNST, b. Joliet, Ill, Jan. 28, 27; m. 58; c. 2. ORGANIC CHEMISTRY. B.S, Illinois, 51; M.S, Iowa, 54, Ethyl Corp. fel, 55-56, Ph.D. (org. chem), 56. Chemist, STAUFFER CHEM. CO, Calif, 56-63, sr. chemist, Anderson Div, Weston, Mich, 63-65, SR. CHEMIST, silicone div, 65-71, SPECIALTY CHEM. DIV, 71- U.S.A.A.F, 45-47, S/Sgt. Am. Chem. Soc. Organometallic chemistry; Ziegler-Natta polyolefin catalysts; titanium compounds; metallo-organic and siloxane polymers. Address: Stauffer Chemical Co, Specialty Chemicals Division, Weston, MI 49289.

GEIS, AELRED D(EAN), b. Chicago, Ill, July 23, 29; m. 51; c. 1. BIOLOGY. B.S, Mich. State, 51, fel, 51-53, M.S, 52, Ph.D, 56. Instr, Mich. State, 53-56; surv. statistician, BUR. SPORT FISHERIES & WILDLIFE, U.S. FISH & WILDLIFE SERV, 56-58, wildlife res. biologist. & asst. chief sect, migratory bird population & distribution studies, 58-61, chief sect. waterfowl population studies, Patuxent Wildlife Res. Center, 61-62, asst. dir. MIGRATORY BIRD POPULATIONS STA, 62-70, MIGRATORY BIRD SPECIALIST, 70- Wildlife Soc. Wildlife population dynamics and biology. Address: Migratory Bird Populations Station, Bureau of Sport Fisheries & Wildlife, Laurel, MD 20810.

GEISE, CHARLES E(DWARD), b. Takoma Park, Md, Nov. 1, 19; m. 47; c. 4. AGRICULTURE. B.S, Purdue, 41; M.S, Iowa State Col, 50, Ph.D.(hort), 52. Sweet corn breeder, Calif. Packing Corp, 52-53; supt, agr. res. & seed dept, 53-56, mgr, agr. res. div, 56-61, mgr, agr. res. & serv, 62-65, assoc. dir. AGR. RES, DEL MONTE CORP, 65-67, DIR, 67- Am. Soc. Hort. Sci. Sweet corn breeding; fruit & vegetable production research; vegetable seed production. Address: Del Monte Corp, Agricultural Research Center, P.O. Box 36, San Leandro, CA 94577.

GEISELMAN, D(OYLE), b. Kewanna, Ind, May 12, 27; m. 51; c. 2. METALLURGICAL ENGINEERING. B.S, Purdue, 51, M.S, 56, Motorola, Inc. fel. & Ph.D.(metall. eng), 58. Plant metallurgist, Wabash div, Raybestos-Manhattan, Inc, 51-54; res. metallurgist, metals res. lab, Union Carbide Metals Co, Union Carbide Corp, 57-63, proj. mgr, 63-65, res. metallurgist, 65-66, group leader, 66-69; DIR. RES. & DEVELOP, ITT-HARPER, INC, 69- Vis. assoc. prof, Purdue Univ, spring, 68. U.S.A, 45-47, M/Sgt. Am. Soc. Metals; Am. Inst. Mining, Metall. & Petrol. Eng; Brit. Inst. Metals. Stainless steels; high temperature alloys; high temperature extrusion. Address: ITT-Harper, Inc, Research & Development, 8200 Lehigh Ave, Morton Grove, IL 60053.

GEISLER, CHARLES H(OOVER), b. Omaha, Nebr, Apr. 8, 30; m. 59; c. 2. PHYSICAL CHEMISTRY, PHYSICS. B.A, Omaha, 56; M.S, Nebraska, 59, Avery Mem. fel, 59-60, Ph.D.(phys. chem), 61. Sr. chemist, MINN. MINING & MFG. CO, 61-66, RES. SPECIALIST, 67- U.S.N. 50-54. Am. Chem. Soc. Electrical properties of semiconductor surfaces; optical and electrical properties of thin films; adsorption phenomena at gas-solid interfaces; photoconductivity and photoeffects in solids; thin film deposition techniques. Address: Duplicating Products Labs, Minnesota Mining & Manufacturing Co, 3M Center, St. Paul, MN 55115.

GEISLER, C(HRIS) D(ANIEL), b. N.Y.C, Jan. 10, 33; m. 61; c. 2. BIOENGINEERING, NEUROPHYSIOLOGY. B.S. & M.S, Mass. Inst. Tech, 56, Sc.D. (elec. eng), 61. Assoc. biocommun, Air Force Res. & Develop. Command, 60-61; mem. tech. staff, Bell Tel. Labs, 61-62; asst. prof. ELEC. ENG. & NEUROPHYSIOL, UNIV. WIS, MADISON, 62-66, ASSOC. PROF, 66- Am. Sci. Affiliation; Inst. Elec. & Electronics Eng. Quantitative study of the brain, including single-neuron recordings and mathematical models; applications of computers to medicine; auditory physiology and neurophysiology. Address: Dept. of Electrical Engineering, University of Wisconsin, Madison, WI 53706.

GEISLER, GEORGE CHARLES, b. Reynoldsville, Pa, Nov. 4, 27; m. 51; c. 5. NUCLEAR & ELECTRICAL ENGINEERING. B.S, Bucknell Univ, 50; M.S, Pa. State Univ, 70. Engr, Honeywell, Inc, 50-55; supvr. reactor opers, Curtiss Wright, 55-58; supvr. plant opers, testing reactor, Westinghouse Elec. Co, 58-62, Plumbrook Opers, 62-64; ASST. DIR. RES. REACTOR, PA. STATE UNIV, 64- Mem. staff, Kewaunee plant, Wis. Pub. Serv, 70-71. C.Eng, 45-47, S/Sgt. Am. Nuclear Soc. Reactor operations; operations research. Address: Nuclear Reactor Facility, Pennsylvania State University, University Park, PA 16802.

GEISLER, GRACE, S.S.J, b. Rochester, N.Y, Dec. 6, 12. BIOLOGY. B.S, Nazareth Col, 39; Joseph Peabody fel, Catholic Univ, M.S, 41, Ph.D.(biol), 44. Instr. BIOL, NAZARETH COL.(N.Y), 43-47, assoc. prof, 47-50, PROF, 50- Summers, Marine Biol. Labs, Woods Hole, 42, 53, Taft. Sanit. & Eng. Center, Ohio, 57, Nat. Sci. Found. Inst. Col. Teachers Zool, Williams Col. (Mass), 58 & 65, med. ctr, Alabama, 60; grant, Am. Physiol. Soc. Am. Soc. Microbiol; Nat. Asn. Biol. Teachers; N.Y. Acad. Sci. Post-embryonic development of Hyalella, a crustacean; effects of humidity on Drosophila melanogaster pupae. Address: Dept. of Biology, Nazareth College of Rochester, Rochester, NY 14610.

GEISLER, MURRAY A(ARON), b. N.Y.C, Mar. 23, 17; m. 41; c. 2. MATHEMATICAL STATISTICS. B.S, City Col. New York, 38; M.A, Columbia, 40; Ph.D, Stanford, 62. Statistician, Nat. Cmt. Maternal Health, N.Y, 39-41; chief income & price forecasting sect, Off. Price Admin, Wash, D.C, 41-42; statist. anal. br, Army Inst. Path, 45-46; opers. analyst, U.S. Dept. Air Force, 46-48, chief standards eval. br. & comput. div, 48-54; mem. logistics dept, RAND CORP, 54-56, mgr, logistics syst. lab, 56-61, asst. head logistic dept, 61-63, head, 63-69, ASST. TO PRES, SANTA MONICA, 69- Consult, Off. Emergency Planning, 65-; res. dir, Joint Logistics Rev. Bd, 69-70. U.S. Air Force Except. Civilian Serv. Award. U.S.A.A.F, 43-45; U.S.A.F.R, 66-, Col. Assoc. mem. Inst. Math. Statist; Am. Statist. Asn; Inst. Mgt. Sci. (pres, 60-61); Opers. Res. Soc. Am. Mathematics; logistics; electronic computers. Address: 1353 Beckwith Ave, West Los Angeles, CA 90049.

GEISMAN, J(EAN) R(ICHARD), b. Ohio City, Ohio, March 20, 33; m. 57; c. 2. HORTICULTURE. B.Sc, Ohio State, 55, M.Sc, 56, Ph.D.(hort), 58. Asst. prof. HORT, OHIO STATE UNIV, 58-63, assoc. prof, 63-67, PROF, 67-, OHIO AGR. RES. & DEVELOP. CTR, 67-, Agr. Exp. Sta, 58-67. Inst. Food Tech; Am. Soc. Hort. Sci. Irradiation of foods; flavors in fermented foods; packaging materials; removal of contaminants from food. Address: 2001 Fyffe Ct, Columbus, OH 43210.

GEISON, RONALD LEON, b. Freeport, Ill, June 22, 39; m. 64; c. 2. NEUROCHEMISTRY, NUTRITION. B.A, Carthage Col, 61; Nat. Insts. Health trainee, Univ. Ill, 61-65, Ph.D.(nutrit. biochem), 65. Nat. Insts. Health trainee neurochem, MED. SCH, UNIV. WIS, MADISON, 65-67, proj. assoc, 67-69, Brittingham fel, 69-70, proj. assoc, 70-71, ASST. PROF. PEDIAT, 71- AAAS; Am. Chem. Soc. Mechanism of formation and synthesis of brain membranes; fractionation and composition of brain membrane fractions; nutritional effects on brain growth and development. Address: 4445 Hillcrest Dr, Madison, WI 53705.

GEISS, GUNTHER R(ICHARD), b. N.Y.C, Oct. 1, 38; m. 62; c. 2. ELECTRICAL ENGINEERING. B.E.E, Polytech. Inst. Brooklyn, 59, M.E.E, 60, Nat. Sci. Found. fel, 59-61, Ph.D.(elec. eng), 64. Part-time instr. elec. tech, Brooklyn Community Col, 60-61; res. engr. control theory, res. dept, Grumman Aircraft Eng. Corp, 61-64, group leader, 64-69; dir. systs. sci. div, Poseidon Sci. Corp, N.Y, 69-71; MGR. N.Y. OFF, SKILLS CONVERSION PROJ, NAT. SOC. PROF. ENGRS, 71- Assoc. engr, marine div, Sperry Gyroscope Co, summer 60; lectr, Polytech. Inst. Brooklyn, 61-; chmn, Oil Spillage Bd, Huntington, N.Y, 61- AAAS; Inst. Elec. & Electronics Eng; Soc. Gen. Systs. Res; Am. Water Resources Asn. Application of systems theory and computer technology to problems of management and urban society; technology of oil spill control and clean up; planning of oil spill combat strategies and modeling, test and evaluation of spill control devices; systems analysis. Address: 8 Meadowlark Lane, Huntington, NY 11743.

GEISSER, SEYMOUR, b. Bronx, N.Y, Oct. 5, 29; m. 55; c. 4. MATHEMATICAL STATISTICS. B.A, City Col, 50; M.A, North Carolina, 52, Ph.D. (math. statist), 55. Sr. asst. scientist, U.S. Pub. Health Serv, 55-57, mathematician, Nat. Inst. Mental Health, Nat. Insts. Health, 57-61, chief, biomet. sect, Nat. Inst. Arthritis & Metab. Diseases, 61-65; prof. math. statist. & chmn. dept, State Univ. N.Y. Buffalo, 65-71; PROF. STATIST. & DIR. SCH, UNIV. MINN, MINNEAPOLIS, 71- Lectr, U.S. Dept. Agr. Grad. Sch, 56-60; vis. assoc. prof, Iowa State Univ, 60; vis. prof, Univ. Wis, 64; prof. lectr, George Wash. Univ, 60-65; Nat. Sci. Found. vis. lectr, 66-67; vis. prof, Univ. Tel-Aviv, Israel, 71. Fel. Am. Statist. Asn; Biomet. Soc; Math. Asn. Am; fel. Inst. Math. Statist; London Math. Soc; Royal Statist. Soc. Biometrics; probability; statistics. Address: School of Statistics, University of Minnesota, Minneapolis, MN 55455.

GEISSINGER, HANS DIETER, b. Mannheim, Ger, Jan. 15, 30; Can. citizen; m. 62; c. 4. PATHOLOGY, PHYSIOLOGY. D.V.M, Toronto, 60, M.V.Sc, 62; Med. Res. Coun. fel, London, 63-66, Ph.D.(vet. path), 66. Res. scientist, ONT. VET. COL, UNIV. GUELPH, 62-63, ASSOC. PROF. PATHOPHYSIOL, 66- Asn. Gnotobiotics; Can. Vet. Med. Asn; Can. Physiol. Soc; Int. Soc. Stereology; Royal Micros. Soc. Pathophysiology of atherosclerosis; pathophysiology and pathology of cardiovascular diseases in man and animals. Address: Dept. of Biomedical Sciences, Ontario Veterinary College, University of Guelph, Guelph, Ont, Can.

GEISSINGER, LADNOR DALE, b. Palm, Pa, Apr. 23, 38; m. 60; c. 3. MATHEMATICS. B.S, Bluffton Col, 59; Nat. Sci. Found. fel, Indiana, 59-62, Ph.D. (math), 63. Asst. prof. MATH, Purdue, 63-67; ASSOC. PROF, UNIV. N.C, CHAPEL HILL, 67- Nat. Sci. Found. Adv. Summer Inst, 66 & 71. Am. Math. Soc; Math. Asn. Am. Algebraic number theory; cohomology of groups; foundations of combinatorial theory. Address: Dept. of Mathematics, University of North Carolina, Chapel Hill, NC 27514.

GEISSLER, ERNST D(IETRICH), b. Chemnitz, Germany, Aug. 4, 15; nat; m. 41; c. 2. AERONAUTICAL ENGINEERING. B.S, Dresden Tech, 36, fel, 37, 39, M.S, 39; Dr.Ing, Darmstadt, 52. Res. engr. control theory, Army Exp. Inst, Peenemuende, Germany, 40-41, sect. chief theory of flight & control, 41-45; aeronaut. res. engr, Ord. Res. & Develop. Agency, Ft. Bliss, Tex, 45-48, group leader aerodyn. & flight mech, 48-50, chief aeroballistics sect, Redstone Arsenal, 50-56, dir. aeroballistics lab, Army Ballistic Missile Agency, 56-59; mem. res. adv. comt. space vehicle aerodyn, NASA, 59-67, DIR. AERO-ASTRODYN. LAB, MARSHALL SPACE FLIGHT CTR, 60- Except. civilian serv. award, U.S. Dept. Army, 59; except. sci. achievement award, NASA, 63, exceptional serv. medal, 68. Fel. Am. Inst. Aeronaut. & Astronaut; fel. Am. Astronaut. Soc. Stability and control; theory of flight; flight mechanics; guidance theory; dynamic analysis, especially flutter and vibration; missile aerodynamics; space mechanics. Address: 3604 Mae Dr. S.E, Huntsville, AL 35801.

GEISSLER, PAUL R(OBERT), b. N.Y.C, Jan. 19, 32; m. 60; c. 2. PHYSICAL CHEMISTRY. B.S, St. Peter's Col, 53; M.S, Fordham, 56; Ph.D.(phys. chem), Univ. Wis, 62. Res. chemist, ESSO RES. & ENG. CO, STANDARD OIL CO.(N.J), 62-67, sr. res. chemist, 67-68, RES. ASSOC, 68- U.S.N, 55-57. Am. Chem. Soc. Effect of neutron activation of organic liquids and solutions; radiation chemistry of hydrocarbon alkyl halide solutions; exploratory aromatic research. Address: Esso Research & Engineering Co, P.O. Box 536, Linden, NJ 07036.

GEISSMAN, T(HEODORE) A(LBERT), b. Chicago, Ill, June 17, 08; m. 36; c. 2. ORGANIC CHEMISTRY. B.S, Wisconsin, 30; Ph.D.(org. chem), Minnesota, 37. Chemist, Standard Oil Co.(Ind), 30-34; univ. fel, Illinois, 37-39; instr. chem, California, Los Angeles, 39-41, asst. prof, 41-44; assoc. dir, cent. eng. lab, Nat. Defense Res. Cmt, Pennsylvania, 43-45; assoc. prof. CHEM, UNIV. CALIF, LOS ANGELES, 44-48, PROF, 48- Guggenheim fel, 50-51, 64-65; Fulbright res. scholar, Australia, 57-58. Am. Chem. Soc; The Chem. Soc; Photochem. Soc. N.Am; hon. mem. Mex. Chem. Soc; Soc. Econ. Bot. Structure of natural plant products; physiological action of organic compounds; chemical-genetics of flower color variation. Address: Dept. of Chemistry, University of California, Los Angeles, CA 90024.

GEIST, JACOB M(YER), b. Bridgeport, Conn, Feb. 2, 21; m. 45; c. 3. CHEMICAL ENGINEERING. B.S, Purdue, 40; M.S, Pa. State, 42; Univ. fel, Michigan, 46-48, Du Pont fel, 47, Eng. Res. Inst. fel, 49, Ph.D.(chem. eng), 50. Instr. chem. eng, Pa. State Col, 43-44; Michigan, 46-48; from instr. to asst. prof, Mass. Inst. Tech, 50-52; sr. lectr, Israel Inst. Tech, 52-55; process mgr, AIR PROD. & CHEM, INC, 55-58, tech. asst. to dir. res. & develop, 58-60, assoc. dir, 60-63, assoc. chief engr, 63-67, DIR. ENG. DESIGN POLICY, 67- Consult, 50-55; lectr, Lehigh Univ, 59-65. U.S.A, 44-46, 2nd Lt. AAAS; Am. Chem. Soc; Am. Inst. Chem. Eng. Low temperature separation processes; cryogenic engineering; natural gas processing; heat transfer; distillation; thermodynamics. Address: 640 Benner Rd, Allentown, PA 18104.

GEIST, J(OHN) C(HARLES), b. Baltimore Co, Md, Sept. 20, 15; m. 38; c. 2. COMMUNICATIONS. B.E.E, Delaware, 37. Test engr, Gen. Elec. Co, 37-38; jr. engr, Hadley Transformer Co, 39; test engr, Westinghouse Mfg. Corp, 40; radio engr, Signal Corps, U.S. Army, 41; systems engr, Link Radio Corp, 46-47; communications engr, applied physics lab, Hopkins, 48; missile systems engr, VITRO CORP. AM, 48-58, mgr. tech. opers, Silver Spring Lab, 58-60, assoc. dir, 60-70, V.PRES. VITRO LABS, 70- Sig.C, 42-46, Maj. Sr. mem. Inst. Elec. & Electronics Eng. Telemetering; missile guidance; television. Address: 2205 Henderson Ave, Silver Spring, MD 20902.

GEIST, JON MICHAEL, b. Springer, N.Mex, Oct. 3, 39; m. 59; c. 3. SOIL CHEMISTRY, PLANT NUTRITION. B.S, Colo. State Univ, 63, M.S, 66, Ph.D. (soil sci), 68. Range conservationist, FOREST SERV, U.S. DEPT. AGR, Coconino Nat. Forest, 63-65, RES. SOIL SCIENTIST, RANGE & WILDLIFE HABITAT LAB, PAC. NORTHWEST FOREST & RANGE EXP. STA, 68- Soc. Range Mgt; Am. Soc. Agron; Soil Sci. Soc. Am. Soil-vegetation ecological relationships; physiological ecology; soil-site delineation studies; nitrogen availability in soils, fertilizer requirement prediction; nitrogen-sulfur relations. Address: Range & Wildlife Habitat Lab, Forest Service, C Ave. & Gekeler Lane, Route 2, Box 2315, LaGrande, OR 97850.

GEIST, VALERIUS, b. Nikolajew, Russia, Feb. 2, 38; Can. citizen; m. 61; c. 3. ZOOLOGY, ETHOLOGY. B.Sc, British Columbia, 60, Ph.D.(zool), 67. ASST. PROF. ZOOL, ENVIRON. SCI. CENTRE, UNIV. CALGARY, 68- Nat. Res. Coun. fel, Max Planck Inst. Physiol. of Behavior, 67-68; mem, subcmt. conserv. terrestrial communities, Can. Cmt. Int. Biol. Prog, 69- Wildlife Soc; Can. Soc. Zool; Can. Soc. Wildlife & Fishery Biol. Behavior and evolution of large mammals, especially ungulates; relation between ecology and social behavior; evolution of Ice Age mammals. Address: Faculty of Environmental Design, University of Calgary, Calgary, Alta, Can.

GEISZLER, ADOLPH O(SCAR), b. Ashley, N.Dak, June 16, 19; m. 45; c. 5. ORGANIC CHEMISTRY. B.S, N.Dak. State Col, 41, M.S, 47; Chicago, 45; fel, Oregon State Col, 48-51, Ph.D.(org. chem), 51. Process specialist, Plum Brook Ord. Works, Trojan Powder Co, 41-44; asst, N.Dak. State Col, 46-47; ABBOTT LABS, 47-48, res. chemist, 51-65, SECT. HEAD, 65- U.S.N.R, 44-46, Lt. Am. Chem. Soc. Reaction mechanisms; molecular rearrangements; plant processes. Address: 270 N. Prairie Ave, Mundelein, IL 60060.

GEITZ, R(OBERT) C(HARLES), b. McKeesport, Pa, Oct. 23, 19; m. 52; c. 5. CHEMICAL ENGINEERING. B.S, Calif. Inst. Tech, 41; Ph.D.(chem. eng), Pittsburgh, 51. Chem. engr, E.I. du Pont de Nemours & Co, 41-43; partner, Calif. Natural Prods, 48-49; sect. chief org. process develop, res. & develop. div, Lever Bros, 49-56; group mgr. res. & develop, Am. Mach. & Foundry Co, 56-61; PRES, GEITZ ENG. CO, 62- U.S.N.R, 43-46, Lt. AAAS; Sci. Res. Soc. Am; Commercial Chem. Develop. Asn; Am. Inst. Chem. Eng; fel. Am. Inst. Chem; Am. Soc. Mech. Eng. Organic chemical development and manufacture of detergents; product and process development; tobacco sheet and paper; application of mechanical engineering techniques to process industries; laboratory equipment; non-soap bars; process plant design and erection; closed die forging. Address: Geitz Engineering Co, P.O. Box 397, East Windsor Hill, CT 06028.

GELABERT, PEDRO ANTONIO, b. Arecibo, P.R, Sept. 10, 33; U.S. citizen; m. 62; c. 2. ENGINEERING GEOLOGY. B.Sc, Tulane, 56; Michigan, 59-60. Geol. field asst, P.R. Econ. Develop. Admin, 56-57; geologist, U.S. Geol. Surv, 57-58; P.R. Dept. Pub. Works, 60-62; chief geologist, eng. geology sect, P.R. Dept. Pub. Works, 62-69; pres, Geol. Serv. P.R, Inc, 69-70; EXEC. SECY. MINING COMN, OFF. GOV, COMMONWEALTH P.R, 70- Exec. secy, natural resources adv. subcomt, Gov. Adv. Coun, Commonwealth P.R. U.S.A, 58, Res, 58- AAAS; Geol. Soc. Am; Asn. Eng. Geol. Construction-material; landslides; mining geology. Address: 400 German Moyer St, Urb. Parque Central, Hato Rey, PR 00918.

GELB, LEONARD L(OUIS), b. Phila, Pa, June 4, 18; m. 57; c. 2. ORGANIC & PHYSICAL CHEMISTRY. B.A, Pennsylvania, 49; B.S, Delaware, 51, Ph.D. (terpene chem), 54. Technician, corporate res. lab, United Gas Improv. Co, Pa, 36-37; res. technician, org. chem. dept, Jackson Lab, E.I. du Pont de Nemours & Co, N.J, 40-49; develop. chemist, Bridesburg Plant, Rohm & Haas Co, Pa, 53-56; Nat. Renderers Asn. fel, east. regional res. lab, U.S. Dept. Agr, 56-59; sr. res. chemist, corporate res. lab, Celanese Corp. Am, N.J, 59-61; supvr. chem. propulsion div, Hercules Powder Co, 61-65; sr. res. chemist, Hercules/Allegany Ballistics Lab, 65-70; SUPVR, APPLN. RES. LAB, W.L. GORE & ASSOC, 70- Summers, mem. staff, Int. Resistance Co, Pa, 51, E.I. du Pont de Nemours & Co, 52. Mem, Gordon Res. Conf. Adhesion, 57. U.S.N, 44-46. Am. Chem. Soc; Inst. Environ. Sci. Research on wire and cable products; laminations of fabrics and metals with expanded, porous polytetrafluoroethylene; adhesive specialties. Address: W.L. Gore & Associates, 555 Paper Mill Rd, Newark, DE 19711.

GELBARD, ELY M(EYER), b. New York, N.Y, Nov. 6, 24; m. 57. THEORETICAL PHYSICS. M.S, Chicago, 49, Ph.D.(physics), 54. Sr. scientist, WESTINGHOUSE ELEC. CORP, 54-56, fel. scientist, 56-59, adv. scientist, 59-67, CONSULT, BETTIS ATOMIC POWER LAB, 67- Ernest Orlando Lawrence Award, 69. U.S.A.A.F, 43-46. Am. Nuclear Soc.(spec. award, 70). Reactor physics; applied mathematics; numerical methods. Address: Westinghouse Electric Corp, Bettis Atomic Power Lab. P.O. Box 79, West Mifflin, PA 15122.

GELBART, ABE, b. Paterson, N.J, Dec. 22, 11; m. 39; c. 4. MATHEMATICS. B.Sc, Dalhousie, 38; Ph.D.(math), Mass. Inst. Tech, 40. Asst, Mass. Inst. Tech, 39-40; instr. math, N.C. State Col, 40-42; res. assoc, Brown, 42; assoc. physicist, Nat. Adv. Cmt. Aeronaut, Langley field, Va, 42-43; asst. prof. math, Syracuse, 43-47, assoc. prof, 47-56, prof, 56-58; dir. inst. math, YESHIVA UNIV, 58-59, dean, BELFER GRAD. SCH. SCI, 59-70, DISTINGUISHED UNIV. PROF. MATH, UNIV, 68-, EMER. DEAN, SCH, 70- Mem, Inst. Advan. Study, 47-48; Fulbright lectr, Norway, 51-52; ed, Scripta Math, 57- Am. Math. Soc; Math. Asn. Am; assoc. fel. Am. Inst. Aeronaut. & Astronaut. Methods of generalizing complex function theory; nonlinear partial differential equations; functions of several complex variables; theory of pseudo-analytic functions; existence theorems in integral equations; fluid dynamics. Address: Dept. of Mathematics, Belfer Graduate School of Science, Yeshiva University, New York, NY 10033.

GELBAUM, BERNARD R(USSELL), b. N.Y.C, Feb. 26, 22; m. 42; c. 4. MATHEMATICS. A.B, Columbia, 43; Nat. res. fel, Princeton, 46-47, M.A, 47, Ph.D.(math), 48. Instr. math, Princeton, 47-48; asst. prof, Minnesota, 48-53, assoc. prof, 53-57, prof, 57-64, prof. & chmn, Univ. Calif, Irvine, 64-68, assoc. dean sch. phys. sci, 68-71; V.PRES. ACAD. AFFAIRS, STATE UNIV. N.Y. BUFFALO, 71- Sig.C, U.S.A, 42-45. Am. Math. Soc. Linear spaces; topological algebra. Address: State University of New York at Buffalo, Buffalo, NY 14214.

GELBEIN, ABRAHAM PERRY, b. Aug. 4, 34; m. 58; c. 2. CHEMICAL ENGINEERING. B.S, Cooper Union, 57; M.S, N.Y. Univ, 61. Chem. analyst, Ledoux & Co, Inc, 52-53, N.Y. Testing Labs, 53-55; qual. control engr, Pall Corp, N.Y, 55-56; res. engr, Gen. Foods Corp, 56- 62; sr. process res. specialist, LUMMUS CO, 62-70, MGR. PROCESS RES, 70- Am. Chem. Soc; Am. Inst. Chem. Eng. Chemical processing; petroleum chemistry; food engineering; heterogeneous catalysis. Address: 916 Sherman Ave, Plainfield, NJ 07063.

GELBERG, ALAN, b. New York, N.Y, May 28, 28; m. 57; c. 3. ORGANIC CHEMISTRY, INFORMATION SCIENCE. B.S, City Col. New York, 50; M.S, Missouri, 53; Delaware, 55-58. Asst. chem, Missouri, 51-52, anal. chemist, agr. exp. sta, 52-53; org. chemist, U.S. Army Chem. Res. & Develop. Labs, Md, 55-57, group leader, 57-59, org. chemist, chem. struct. retrieval prog, 59-61, asst. chief info. retrieval, 61-63; document scientist, Diamond Alkali Co, 64-67; chief chem. info. storage & retrieval staff, sci, info. facility, U.S. FOOD & DRUG ADMIN, 67-70, DIR. MGT. & SCI. INFO. SYSTS. DESIGN DIV, BUR. DRUGS, 70- Mem, U.S. Army Chem. Corps Info. Retrieval Comt, 60-63, liaison rep. to mod. methods comt, div. chem. technol, Nat. Res. Coun, 61-63; mem. tech. adv. bd, J. Chem. Doc, 69-71; prof. lectr, Am. Univ, 69- Chem.C, 53-55, Sgt. Am. Chem. Soc; Sci. Res. Soc. Am; Chem. Notation Asn.(pres, 70). Chemical information and structure retrieval; chemical line notations; automatic data processing equipment. Address: Bureau of Drugs (BD-8), U.S. Food & Drug Administration, 5600 Fishers Lane, Rockville, MD 20852.

GELBOIN, HARRY VICTOR, b. Chicago, Ill, Dec. 21, 29; m. 51; c. 4. BIOCHEMISTRY. A.B, Illinois, 51; M.S, Wisconsin, 56, Ph.D, 58; Nat. Insts. Health fel, Nat. Cancer Inst, 57-58. Develop. chemist, U.S. Rubber Co, 51-54; asst. biochem. & cancer res, Wisconsin, 54-58; biochemist, NAT. INSTS. HEALTH, 58-64, head chem. sect, carcinogenesis studies br, 64-66, CHIEF CHEM. BR. ETIOL, NAT. CANCER INST, 66- Assoc. ed, Cancer Res, 64; keynote speaker, Gordon Res. Conf. Cancer, 65; prin. lectr, Franz Bielschowsky mem, First Int. Symp. Molecular Biol, Carcino, N.Zealand, 66; Claude Bernard award-visit. prof, Univ. Montreal, 70; lectr, Radiol. Soc. N.Am, Ill, 70. Am. Asn. Cancer Res; Am. Soc. Biol. Chem; Am. Soc. Pharmacol. & Exp. Therapeut. Biochemical mechanisms of carcinogenesis; mammalian enzyme induction and protein synthesis. Address: National Cancer Institute, National Institutes of Health, Bethesda, MD 20014.

GELDARD, FRANK A(RTHUR), b. Worcester, Mass, May 20, 04; m. 28; c. 1. PSYCHOLOGY. A.B, Clark, 25, M.A, 26, Ph.D.(psychol), 28; hon. Sc.D, Wash. & Lee Univ, 69. Assoc. prof. PSYCHOL, Virginia, 28-37, prof, 37-62, chmn. dept, 46-60, dean grad. sch. arts & sci, 60-62; STUART PROF, PRINCETON, 62- Chmn. human resources cmt, Res. & Develop. Bd, 50-53, adv. panel personnel & training res, Asst. Secy. Defense, 53-55; adv. panel defense psychol. & chmn. adv. group on human factors, NATO, 59-65; mem, Int. Brain Res. Orgn, UNESCO. U.S.A.A.F, 42-46, Col. AAAS; Soc. Exp. Psychol; Am. Psychol. Asn. Psychophysiology of vision; cutaneous senses. Address: 551 Lake Dr, Princeton, NJ 08540.

GELDART, LLOYD, b. Petitcodiac, N.B, Oct. 20, 14; m. 40; c. 1. GEOPHYSICS. B.A, Mt. Allison Univ, 37; M.A, Univ. Toronto, 41; Ph.D.(physics), McGill Univ, 41; Calif. Inst. Technol, 49. Head dept. physics, Acadia Univ, 42-47; res. geophysicist, Calif. Res. Corp, Standard Oil Co. Calif, 49-52, chief geophysicist, Dom. Oil Ltd, 52-56; Calif. Explor. Co, 56-60; Webster prof. appl. geophys, McGill Univ, 60-69; CHIEF TECH. ADV, UNESCO PROJ. BRA-34, FED. UNIV. BAHIA, 68- AAAS; Soc. Explor. Geophys; Europ. Asn. Explor. Geophys. Gravity interpretation; magneto-tellurics; magnetic micropulsations; telluric currents; dynamic testing of rocks; rock mechanics. Address: Basic Science Centre, Federal University of Bahia, Caixa Postal 1156, Salvador, Bahia, Brazil.

GELDERLOOS, ORIN GLENN, b. Grand Rapids, Mich, July 28, 39; m. 60; c. 2. ECOLOGY. B.A, Calvin Col, 61; Isaak Walton League res. scholar, West. Mich. Univ, 62, M.A, 64; Nat. Sci. Found. fel, Northwest. Univ, 68, Nat. Defense Educ. Act. fel, 68-70, Ph.D.(environ. biol), 70. Instr, high sch, Mich, 62-67; ASST. PROF. EXP. BIOL, UNIV. MICH-DEARBORN, 70- Partic, Nat. Sci. Found. summer inst. field biol, San Diego State Col, 67; NASA bio-space technol. training prog, Wallops Island, 68. Am. Inst. Biol. Sci; Wildlife Soc; Animal Behav. Soc. Biological rhythms; microclimatology; biometeorology; animal orientation; bird migration; environmental physiology. Address: Dept. of Experimental Biology, University of Michigan-Dearborn, Dearborn, MI 48128.

GELDMACHER, R(OBERT) C(ARL), b. Elgin, Ill, Apr. 22, 17; m. 41; c. 3. ENGINEERING. B.E, Northern Illinois, 42; M.S, Purdue, 46; Ph.D.(elec. eng), Northwestern, 59. Asst. prof. eng. mech, Purdue, 47-53, assoc. prof. eng. sci, 53-60; prof. eng. sci. & assoc. dean eng, N.Y. Univ, 60-66; BURCHARD PROF. ELEC. ENG. & HEAD DEPT, STEVENS INST. TECHNOL, 66- Consult, Picatinny Arsenal, 52-; Inter Poly Corp, 67- Inst. Elec. & Electronics Eng; Soc. Indust. & Appl. Math. Magnetomechanical solids; graph theory; network and system analysis and synthesis; applied elasticity. Address: Dept. of Electrical Engineering, Stevens Institute of Technology, Castle Point Station, Hoboken, NJ 07030.

GELDREICH, EDWIN E(MERY), b. Cincinnati, Ohio, May 9, 22; m. 50; c. 2. BACTERIOLOGY. A.B, Cincinnati, 47, M.S, 48. Res. bacteriologist, Robert A. Taft Sanit. Eng. Ctr, U.S. PUB. HEALTH SERV, 48-67, res. microbiologist, Nat. Ctr. Urban & Indust. Health, 67-68, CHIEF BACT. SECT, DIV. WATER HYG, NAT. ENVIRON. RES. CTR, ENVIRON. PROTECTION AGENCY, 68- Tech. dir. bacteriol. sects, Water Hyg. Labs, Ohio, R.I, Ala. & Wash; dir. water bacteriol. lab. eval. serv; microbiol. consult, Pan-Am. Health Orgn, Brazil. Kimble Methodol. res. award, 55. Med.C, U.S.A, 43-46. AAAS; Am. Soc. Microbiol; Am. Pub. Health Asn; Am. Water Works Asn; Water Pollution Control Fedn; Int. Asn. Water Pollution Res. Sanitary bacteriology; membrane filter techniques; rapid methods for the enumeration of bacterial indicators of pollution; biological tests for trace impurities in distilled water; study of heavy metal and organic toxicites on pollution indicators; health criteria and standards for water supply and recreational uses. Address: Division of Water Hygiene, National Environmental Research Center, Environmental Protection Agency, Cincinnati, OH 45268.

GELERINTER, EDWARD, b. N.Y.C, Oct. 27, 36; m. 63; c. 2. SOLID STATE PHYSICS. B.E.E, City Col. New York, 58; Ph.D.(physics), Cornell, 66. Asst. prof. PHYSICS, KENT STATE UNIV, 65-71, ASSOC. PROF, 71- Summers, eng. aide, Atomic Energy Comn, 57 & 58, physicist, Lawrence Radiation Lab, 60, Lincoln Lab, Mass. Inst. Tech, 61, Parma Tech. Center, Union Carbide Corp, 66 & Am. Soc. Eng. Ed-NASA fel, 67 & 68. Am. Phys. Soc; Am. Asn. Physics Teachers. Electron paramagnetic resonance of nitrogen in sodium azide; electron paramagnetic resonance studies of doped liquid crystals. Address: Dept. of Physics, Kent State University, Kent, OH 44242.

GELERNTER, HERBERT L(EO), b. Brooklyn, N.Y, Dec. 17, 29; m. 52; c. 3. PHYSICS, COMPUTER SCIENCE. B.S, Brooklyn Col, 51; Ph.D.(physics), Rochester, 56. Staff physicist, IBM Res, N.Y, 56-58, staff physicist & mgr. theory automata group, 58-60, sr. physicist, 60-64, sr. physicist & mgr. physics & comput. appln. res. group, 64-66; PROF. COMPUT. SCI, STATE UNIV. N.Y. STONY BROOK, 66- Vis. fel, European Orgn. Nuclear Res, 60-61; seminar assoc, Columbia, 66- Mem. ad hoc cmt. on-line data acquisition systs. nuclear physics, Nat. Res. Coun-Nat. Acad. Sci, 68. Am. Phys. Soc. Simulation of intelligent behavior in machines; mathematical biophysics; computer applications in nuclear physics and high energy physics; biomedical computer applications research. Address: Dept. of Computer Science, Division of Mathematical Sciences, State University of New York at Stony Brook, Stony Brook, NY 11790.

GELFAN, SAMUEL, b. Bogopol, Russia, Jan. 16, 03; nat; m. 43; c. 6. PHYSIOLOGY. A.B, California, 25, Ph.D.(biol), 27. Res. assoc. biol, California, 27-28; Donnelly fel. physiol, Chicago, 28-30; asst. prof. physiol. & pharmacol, Alberta, 30-32; Guggenheim fel, Cambridge, 32-33; assoc. physiol, col. med, Illinois, 33-36; dir. res, Va. Patton Pharmaceut. Co, Chicago, 41-44; asst. prof. physiol, col. physicians & surg, Columbia, 44-46; sch. med, Yale, 46-51, dir. aero-med. unit, 47-51; assoc. neurol, NEW YORK MED. COL, 52-60, PROF. NEUROPHYSIOL, 60- AAAS; Am. Physiol. Soc; Harvey Soc; Asn. Res. Nerv. & Ment. Disease; Soc. Exp. Biol. & Med. Studies of electrical properties of unicellular animals with microelectrodes; mechanical and electrical responses of single muscle fibers; aviation physiology; neurophysiology of spinal cord. Address: New York Medical College, Fifth Ave. at 106th St, New York, NY 10029.

GELFAND, HENRY M(ORRIS), b. New York, N.Y, Jan. 7, 20; m. 46; c. 4. EPIDEMIOLOGY, VIROLOGY. B.S, Cornell, 40; M.D, Chicago, 50; M.P.H,

Tulane, 56. Intern, U.S. Pub. Health Serv. Hosp, Staten Island, N.Y, 50-51; med. entomologist, Liberian Inst, W.Africa, 51-53; assoc. prof. epidemiol, sch. med, Tulane, 53-59; chief, enterovirus unit, Commun. Disease Ctr, 59-63, epidemiol. adv, Nat. Inst. Commun. Diseases, Delhi, India, 63-65, spec. asst. res. & eval, smallpox eradication prog, Commun. Disease Ctr, Ga, 65-68; epidemiologist, foreign quarantine prog, London, Eng, 68-70; CHIEF, EVAL. BR, OFF. POP, U.S. AGENCY INT. DEVELOP, & MEM. STAFF, OFF. INT. HEALTH, U.S. PUB. HEALTH SERV, DEPT. HEALTH, EDUC. & WELFARE, 70- Malariologist, W.Africa, India, Burma. Sanit.C, 41-45, Capt; U.S.P.H.S, 59- Am. Epidemiol. Soc; Am. Soc. Trop. Med. & Hyg; Soc. Exp. Biol. & Med; Asn. Teachers Prev. Med; Am. Pub. Health Asn; Int. Asn. Epidemiol; Royal Soc. Trop. Med. & Hyg; Int. Cong. Trop. Med. & Malaria. Epidemiology of infectious diseases; smallpox eradication; foreign quarantine; family planning. Address: Office of International Health, U.S. Public Health Service, Dept. of Health, Education & Welfare, Washington, DC 20201.

GELFAND, NORMAN MATHEW, b. N.Y.C, Jan. 3, 39. EXPERIMENTAL HIGH ENERGY PHYSICS. A.B, Columbia Univ, 59, M.A, 61, Ph.D.(physics), 65. Asst. prof. PHYSICS, UNIV. CHICAGO, 64-70, ASSOC. PROF, 70- Sloan fel, 65-67. Am. Phys. Soc. Particle physics. Address: Enrico Fermi Institute, University of Chicago, 5640 S. Ellis Ave, Chicago, IL 60637.

GELFAND, SAMUEL, b. Norwich, Conn, Jan. 28, 27. ORGANIC CHEMISTRY. B.S, Yale, 50; univ. fel, Illinois, 51-52, U.S. Rubber fel, 52-53, Ph.D.(chem), 53. Res. chemist, HOOKER CHEM. CORP, 53-64, sr. chemist, 64-67, SUPVR. CHEM. RES, INDUST. CHEM. DIV, 67- U.S.A, 45-56. Am. Chem. Soc; Brit. Chem. Soc. Wolff-Kishner reaction; organic fluorine and chlorine chemistry. Address: Research Dept, Hooker Chemical Corp, Niagara Falls, NY 14304.

GELFANT, SEYMOUR, b. N.Y.C, Apr. 14, 22; m. 46; c. 2. CYTOLOGY. B.S, Wisconsin, 48, Ph.D.(zool), 53; M.A, California, Los Angeles, 49. Res. assoc. path, med. sch, Wisconsin, 53-54; British-Am. exchange fel, Am. Cancer Soc, Univ. London, 54-55; asst. prof. ZOOL, SYRACUSE UNIV, 55-60, assoc. prof, 60-64, PROF, 64- U.S.A, 42-46. Am. Soc. Cell Biol; Int. Soc. Cell Biol. Physiology of mitosis; action of hormones on cells; cytochemistry. Address: Dept. of Zoology, Syracuse University, Syracuse, NY 13201.

GELFER, DANIEL H(AROLD). U.S. citizen. CHEMISTRY. B.S, California, Los Angeles, 45, M.S, 48. Asst. phys. & org. chem, California, Los Angeles, 45-48; res. chemist, electroplating, L.H. Butcher Co, 50-51; org. protective coatings, Amercoat Corp, 51-59, lab. mgr. org. & inorg. protective coatings, 59-62, dir. res, 62-64, tech. serv. mgr, 64-69, dir. chem. res, AMERON CORROSION CONTROL DIV, AMERON, INC, 69-71, DIR. RES. & COMMERCIAL DEVELOP, 71- Bausch & Lomb sci. award, 42. AAAS; Am. Chem. Soc; Am. Electroplaters Soc; Nat. Asn. Corrosion Eng. Organic reaction mechanisms; chemistry of organic corrosion protective coatings; mechanisms of corrosion. Address: 3008 Arlington Ave, Fullerton, CA 92631.

GELHAUS, FLOYD ELMER, b. Madison, Wis, Oct. 8, 38; m. 60; c. 2. NUCLEAR ENGINEERING. B.S. & M.S, Univ. Wis, 61; NASA traineeship, Cornell Univ, 64-65, Ph.D.(nuclear sci. & eng), 66. Sr. engr, Radio Corp. Am, 65-67; ENGR, GEN. ELEC. CO, SUNNYVALE, 67- Energy conversion. Address: 656 Canterbury Ave, Livermore, CA 94550.

GELINAS, DOUGLAS ALFRED, b. Nov. 18, 40; U.S. citizen. BOTANY, PHYSIOLOGY. B.S, Fitchburg State Col, 63; Nat. Defense Ed. Act fel, Purdue, 65-68, M.S, 66, Ph.D.(biol), 68. ASST. PROF. BOT, UNIV. MAINE, 68- AAAS; Genetics Soc. Am; Bot. Soc. Am; Am. Soc. Plant Physiol; Am. Genetic Asn. Biochemical basis of genetically determined changes in morphology; developmental physiology. Address: Dept. of Botany, University of Maine, Orono, ME 04473.

GELINAS, LOUIS-de-GONZAGUE, b. Montreal, Que, Mar. 22, 15; m. 43; c. 7. VETERINARY MEDICINE. B.A. & D.M.V, Univ. Montreal, 41, cert. path, 50. Sanit. food inspector, Govt. Can, 41-43; Govt. Que, 43-45, vet. inspector brucellosis control, 45-47; PROF. vet. med, SCH. VET. MED, UNIV. MONTREAL, 47-50, PATH, 50- Can. Vet. Med. Asn. Clinical and veterinary pathology. Address: School of Veterinary Medicine, University of Montreal, St. Hyancinthe, Que, Can.

GELINAS, ROBERT JOSEPH, b. Muskegon, Mich, Sept. 25, 37; m. 60; c. 1. APPLIED PHYSICS, NUCLEAR ENGINEERING. B.S.E, Michigan, 60, M.S.E, 61, Ph.D.(nuclear eng), 65. PHYSICIST, LAWRENCE LIVERMORE LAB, CALIFORNIA, 66- Mark Mills Award, Am. Nuclear Soc, 65. AAAS; Am. Phys. Soc. Quantum statistical physics; radiation and plasma physics; nonequilibrium physics; chemical kinetics. Address: Lawrence Livermore Lab, L-71, Livermore, CA 94550.

GELL, C(HARLES) F(REDRIC), b. Chicago, Ill, June 16, 07; m. 37; c. 4. AEROSPACE MEDICINE. B.S, Loyola (Ill), 34, M.D, 37; M.S, Pennsylvania, 53, D.Sc, 56. Exec. off, Sch. Aviation Med, 47-49, dep. dir, aviation med. acceleration lab, Air Develop. Ctr, 49-53, dir, 53-55, air crew equip. lab, Air Mat. Ctr, 55-58, spec. asst. med. & allied sci, Off. Naval Res, 58-60; dir. life sci, astronaut. div, Ling-Temco-Vought Corp, 60-66; SCI. DIR, SUBMARINE MED. RES. LAB, NAVAL SUBMARINE MED. CTR, 66- Asst. prof. physiol, sch. med, Pennsylvania, 51-55, vis. prof. aviation physiol, 55-60; clin. prof. physiol, southwest. med. sch, Texas, 60; lectr. epidemiol, sch. med, Yale, 68- Mem. exec. coun, comts. bio-astronaut, vision, hearing & bio-acoustics, Armed Forces-Nat. Res. Coun; aeromed. panel, adv. group aeronaut. res. & develop, NATO, 58-; adv. panel med. & biol. sci, Dept. Defense, 60-; elected mem, Int. Acad. Aviation Med, 62; mem. exec. coun, comt. hearing & bioacoustics, Nat. Res. Coun, 63- Citation & pendant, Secy. Navy, 45; cert. except. serv, Surgeon Gen, U.S. Navy, 60. U.S.N, 37-60, Capt. Am. Inst. Aeronaut. & Astronaut.(Jeffries Award, 53); fel. Aerospace Med. Asn.(Liljencrantz Award, 67, Lyster Award, 57); Am. Astronaut. Soc. (Boynton Award, 58); Asn. Mil. Surg. U.S; Am. Col. Prev. Med. Aerospace submarine and diving research management. Address: Submarine Medical Research Lab, Naval Submarine Research Center, U.S. Navy Submarine Base New London, Groton, CT 06340.

GELL, MAURICE L, b. Brooklyn, N.Y, Dec. 1, 37; m. 60; c. 2. METALLURGY. B.A, Columbia, 59, President's fel, 59-60, M.A, 60, Henry Krumb scholar, 56-59, 60-61, B.S, 61; Int. Nickel Co. fels, Yale, 61-62, 64-65, M.S, 63, Ph.D.(metall), 65. Nat. Sci. Found. fel, 65-66; res. assoc, adv. mat. res. & develop. lab, PRATT & WHITNEY AIRCRAFT DIV, UNITED AIRCRAFT CORP, 66-67, sr. res. assoc. & group leader, 67-71, GROUP LEADER, MAT. ENG. & RES. LAB, 71- Am. Soc. Metals; Am. Inst. Mining, Metall. & Petrol. Eng; Am. Soc. Test. & Mat. Mechanical properties of metals including fatigue deformation and fracture, cleavage fracture, hydrogen embrittlement, deformation and fracture of gas turbine engine materials. Address: Materials Engineering & Research Lab, Pratt & Whitney Aircraft, Middletown, CT 06458.

GELL-MANN, MURRAY, b. New York, N.Y, Sept. 15, 29; m. 55; c. 2. THEORETICAL PHYSICS. B.S, Yale, 48, hon. D.Sc, 59; Ph.D.(physics), Mass. Inst. Tech, 51. Mem. sch. math. & physics, Inst. Adv. Study, 51-52; instr. PHYSICS, inst. nuclear studies, Chicago, 52-53, asst. prof, 53-54, assoc. prof, 54-55; CALIF. INST. TECH, 55-56, PROF, 56- Consult. & mem. steering comt, Jason Div, Inst. Defense Anal, 61-; mem, President's Sci. Adv. Comn, 69- Heineman prize, Am. Inst. Physics, 59; Nobel Prize Physics, 69; Res. Corp Award, 69. Nat. Acad. Sci; Am. Acad. Arts & Sci; Am. Phys. Soc. Quantum field theory; elementary particle physics; nuclear physics. Address: Lauritsen Lab. of High Energy Physics, California Institute of Technology, Pasadena, CA 91109.

GELLER, ARTHUR MICHAEL, b. N.Y.C, Dec. 18, 41; m. 63; c. 2. BIOCHEMISTRY. B.S, City Col. New York, 62; Nat. Insts. Health fel, Duke Univ, 64-66, Ph.D.(biochem), 67. ASST. PROF. BIOCHEM, MED. UNITS, UNIV. TENN, MEMPHIS, 68- Am. Cancer Soc. fel, enzyme inst, Univ. Wis, 67-68. AAAS. Enzymology; fructose 1, 6-diphosphatase; gluconeogenesis; control mechanisms. Address: Dept. of Biochemistry, Medical Center, University of Tennessee, Memphis, TN 38103.

GELLER, BERNARD DAVID, b. Brooklyn, N.Y, June 15, 40; m. 62; c. 2. IMMUNOLOGY. B.A, N.Y. Univ, 62; Ph.D.(anat), State Univ. N.Y, 67, M.D, 68. Intern pediat, New York Hosp. & med. center, Cornell, 68-69; staff assoc. immunol, lab. bact. prod, div. biol. standards, Nat. Insts. Health, 69-71; FEL. CLIN. IMMUNOL. & ALLERGY, CHILDREN'S DIV, LOS ANGELES COUNTY-UNIV, S.C. MED. CTR, 71- U.S.P.H.S, 69-71, Surg. AAAS; Reticuloendothelial Soc; Am. Acad. Allergy. Actinomycin D induced alterations in mononuclear cells during the inflammatory response; antibody production; characterization of mouse immunoglobulins produced locally and systemically following intranasal inoculation of Bordetella pertussis. Address: Dept. of Pediatrics, Los Angeles County-University of Southern California Medical Center, Los Angeles, CA 90027.

GELLER, D(AVID) M(ELVILLE), b. Detroit, Mich, Dec. 30, 30. BIOCHEMISTRY. A.B, Amherst Col, 52; fel. & Ph.D.(biochem), Harvard, 57. Instr, biochem, dept. chem, Illinois, 58-59; asst. prof. PHARMACOL, SCH. MED, WASH. UNIV, 59-67, ASSOC. PROF, 67- Fel, Nat. Sci. Found, Oxford, 57-58. Oxidative and photophosphorylation; phosphorylation mechanisms; serum albumin biosynthesis and secretion. Address: Dept. of Pharmacology, Washington University School of Medicine, St. Louis, MO 63110.

GELLER, EDWARD, b. N.Y.C, Dec. 6, 28; m. 52; c. 3. BIOCHEMISTRY. A.B, California, Los Angeles, 47, B.S, 48, M.S, 55, Ph.D.(biochem), 56. Asst. biochem, UNIV. CALIF, LOS ANGELES, 52-55, asst. res. biol. chemist, MED. CTR, 59-65, asst. prof. PSYCHIAT, 65-70, ASSOC. PROF, 70- Res. biochemist, Vet. Admin, 57- U.S.A, 55-57. Fel. AAAS; N.Y. Acad. Sci; Int. Soc. Neurochem; Am. Col. Neuropsychopharmacol; Endocrine Soc; Am. Soc. Neurochem; Int. Soc. Psychoneuroendocrinol. Relation of biochemistry to mental processes; biochemical correlates of behavior. Address: 22907 Gershwin Dr, Woodland Hills, CA 91364.

GELLER, GERALD, b. Brooklyn, N.Y, Apr. 5, 25; m. 46; c. 2. INDUSTRIAL ENGINEERING. B.Ind.Eng, Ga. Inst. Tech, 50. Orgn. & methods exam, Atlanta Gen. Depot, U.S. Army, 51-52, staff indust. engr, 52-54, safety engr, 54-55; chief indust. engr, Warner Robins Air Mat. Area, U.S. Air Force, 55-58; indust. engr. mgt, U.S. Naval Ord. Plant, 58-61; chief mgt. eng. div, U.S. Army Missile Command, 61-63; SATURN V PROJ. COORD, MARSHALL SPACE FLIGHT CTR, NASA, 63- U.S.N, 43-46, Res, 46-57, Lt. Am. Mgt. Asn; Am. Inst. Indust. Eng. Production engineering; labor standards; methods improvement; engineering economy; aerospace program management. Address: 704 Watts Dr. S.E, Huntsville, AL 35801.

GELLER, IRVING, b. Boston, Mass, Oct. 26, 25; m. 51; c. 4. PSYCHOLOGY. B.A, George Washington, 49, M.A, 51; Ph.D, American Univ, 57. Res. psychologist, Walter Reed Army Inst. Res, 52-57; sr. res. scientist & supvr. dept. psychopharmacol, Wyeth Inst. Med. Res, 57-64; assoc. prof. pharmacol, N.Y. Med. Col, 64-66; CHMN. DEPT. EXP. PHARMACOL, SOUTHWEST FOUND. RES. & EDUC, 66- Med.C, U.S.A, 44-46. Am. Soc. Pharmacol. & Exp. Therapeut; Am. Psychol. Asn. Drug effects on behavior; operant conditioning; motivation and learning. Address: Dept. of Pharmacology & Toxicology, Southwest Foundation for Research & Education, San Antonio, TX 78284.

GELLER, IRWIN, b. New York, N.Y, Dec. 1, 21; m. 49; c. 5. FUEL TECHNOLOGY. B.A, Emory & Henry Col, 43; fel, Col. Puget Sound, 53-54, M.S, 54; Ph.D.(fuel tech), Pa. State, 59. Depot mgr, Agelco-Shell Bulk Oil Installation, P.I, 46-49; mgr, Geller Servicenter, Inc, N.Y, 49-53; asst. fuel tech, Pa. State, 54-58; res. chemist, Aerojet-Gen. Div, Gen. Tire & Rubber Co, 58-62; assoc. prof, CHEM, CALIF. STATE POLYTECH. COL, KELLOGG-VOORHIS, 62-71, PROF, 71- U.S.A, 43-46. Am. Chem. Soc. Analytical chemistry; spectroscopy and crystallography. Address: 201 S. Loraine Ave, Glendora, CA 91740.

GELLER, KENNETH N, b. Brooklyn, N.Y, Sept. 22, 30; m. 55; c. 2. PHYSICS. B.S, Brooklyn Col, 52; Ph.D.(physics), Pennsylvania, 60. Res. asst. PHYSICS, Pennsylvania, 55-60, asst. prof, 60-66; ASSOC. PROF, DREXEL UNIV, 66- Sig.C, U.S.A, 53-55. AAAS; Am. Phys. Soc. Study of low energy nuclear reactions; neutron detection techniques. Address: Dept. of Physics, Drexel University, Philadelphia, PA 19104.

GELLER, LAWRENCE E(DWIN), b. Boston, Mass, Mar. 11, 31; m. 54; c. 2. ORGANIC CHEMISTRY. B.A, Brandeis, 52; M.S, Wayne State, 54, Ph.D. (chem), 59. Assoc. chemist, Res. Inst. Med. & Chem, 58-61; head steroid synthesis sect, NEW ENG. NUCLEAR CORP, 61-67, HEAD STEROID & CARBOHYDRATE SYNTHESIS SECT, 67- U.S.A, 54-56. The Chem. Soc. Cactus alkaloids and triterpenes; rotatory dispersion; conformational analysis of bromoketones; synthesis of radioactive steroids. Address: 111 Wallace St, Newton Highlands, Boston, MA 02161.

GELLER, LEONARD, b. N.Y.C, June 19, 25; m. 47; c. 3. MATHEMATICS, PHYSICS. B.A, Brooklyn Col, 48; univ. fel, Mass. Inst. Technol, 49, Atomic Energy Comn. fels, 50, 51, Ph.D.(math), 51. Spec. hazards evaluator, Union Carbide Corp, 51-53; physicist, Cornell Aeronaut. Lab, Inc, 53-55; reactor physicist, Combustion Eng, Inc, N.Y, 55-56; chief reactor physicist, Vitro Eng. Co, 56-60, head nuclear eng. dept, 60-61; sr. assoc. REACTOR DESIGN & ECON. EVAL, S.M. STOLLER ASSOCS, 61-69, V.PRES, 69- U.S.N, 43-46. Am. Math. Soc. Nuclear reactor physics design and safety evaluation; economics of nuclear power; nuclear power fuel cycles, especially fuel management; shielding in complicated geometries. Address: 336 De Mott Ave, Rockville Centre, NY 11570.

GELLER, MILTON, b. New York, N.Y, July 22, 22; m. 49; c. 2. ANALYTICAL & PHARMACEUTICAL CHEMISTRY. B.S, City Col. New York, 44; M.A, Brooklyn, 60. Anal. chemist, Chas. Pfizer & Co, Inc, 43-44, 46-50; chemist, U.S. Signal Corps, 50-51; anal. chemist, Chase Chem. Co, 51; Nepera Chem. Co, 51-58, supvr. qual. control, 58; sr. scientist, Warner Lambert Res. Inst, 58-62, sr. res. assoc, 62-63, dir. Appl. Anal. Res, 63-66; SR. SCIENTIST, HOFFMANN LA-ROCHE, INC, NUTLEY, 66- U.S.N, 44-46. Am. Chem. Soc; Am. Pharmaceut. Asn. Methods development for pharmaceutical dosage forms. Address: 40-10 Kramer Pl, Fairlawn, NJ 07410.

GELLER, MOLLY S, b. N.Y.C, Jan. 16, 11; m. 35; c. 3. BIOLOGY, ORGANIC CHEMISTRY. B.S, N.Y. Univ, 31, M.S, 33, fel, 59-62, Ph.D.(sci. ed), 62. Lectr, sch. ed, N.Y. Univ, 57-59, instr. chem, 62-63; ASSOC. PROF. SCI, WILLIAM PATERSON COL. N.J, 63- Ecologist, Hackensack Meadowlands Develop. Comn, N.J. Am. Chem. Soc; Nat. Asn. Res. Sci. Teaching; Sci. Teachers Asn. Synthetic organic chemistry; science education; ecology of estuaries. Address: Dept. of Science, William Paterson College of New Jersey, 300 Pompton Rd, Wayne, NJ 07470.

GELLER, MURRAY, b. New York, N.Y, Apr. 26, 34; m. 56; c. 2. PHYSICAL & QUANTUM CHEMISTRY. B.S, Brooklyn Col, 55; Dow Chem. Co. fel, Northwestern, 56-57, Nat. Sci. Found. fel, 57-58, Ph.D.(chem), 58. Nat. Sci. Found. fel. chem, Paris, 58-59; from instr. to asst. prof. physics, Howard, 59-62; sr. scientist, Jet Propulsion Lab, 62-65; res. scientist, res. inst. adv. studies div, Martin Co, Md, 65-66; RES. SPECIALIST, JET PROPULSION LAB, 66- Vis. assoc. prof, Southern California, 62-64. Consult, NASA, 61-62. Am. Chem. Soc; fel. Am. Phys. Soc. Development of mathematical and theoretical framework to help to understand the structure of atoms and molecules, the forces between systems and their properties. Address: Jet Propulsion Lab, (183-301), Pasadena, CA 91103.

GELLER, MYER, b. Winnipeg, Man, Can, Oct. 24, 26; U.S. citizen; m. 54. PHYSICS, MATHEMATICS. B.S, Manitoba, 46; M.S, Minnesota, 48; Ph.D. (physics), Mass. Inst. Tech, 55. Mem. tech. staff semiconductors, Hughes Aircraft Co, Calif, 55-60, lasers, 62-64; sr. scientist, Electro Optical Systs. Inc, Calif, 60-62; RES. PHYSICIST, U.S. NAVY ELECTRONICS LAB, 64- Am. Phys. Soc; Optical Soc. Am; Inst. Elec. & Electronics Eng. Coherent optics, especially stimulated emission devices and non-linear optics; spectroscopy, atomic and plasma physics. Address: 1622 Plum St, San Diego, CA 92106.

GELLER, RAYMOND E(VERETT), b. Coffeyville, Kans, Aug. 6, 17; m; c. 1. AERONAUTICAL ENGINEERING. B.S, Oklahoma, 43, M.S, 49. Design engr, Oil Co. Specialties Mfg, 35-40; designer, Menasco Mfg, 46-47, proj. engr, 47-48; Wright Aeronaut. Corp, 48; consult, oil field equip, Kans, Okla. & Tex, 49-50; proj. engr, ord. systs, Bendix Aviation Co, 50-51, chief engr, spec. prod. res. dept, 51-52, dir, 53-56, staff off. of v.pres. eng, 56-59; mgr. base systs. eng, Martin Co, 59-62; DIV. MGR. TECH. ENG, SPACECRAFT, LOCKHEED-CALIF. CO, 62- U.S.N.R, 43-45, Lt. Am. Ord. Asn; Am. Inst. Aeronaut. & Astronaut; Aerospace Med. Asn. Dynamics of lubrication; combustion in subsonic and supersonic flow; cryogenics. Address: 14747 Roscoe Blvd, Apt. 10, Panorama City, CA 91402.

GELLER, SEYMOUR, b. New York, N.Y, Mar. 28, 21; m. 42; c. 2. MATERIALS SCIENCE. A.B, Cornell, 41, Ph.D.(phys. chem), 49. Du Pont fel, Cornell, 49-50; res. chemist, Benger Lab, E.I. du Pont de Nemours & Co, 50-52; struct. chemist, Bell Tel. Labs, Inc, 52-64, struct. chemist & group leader, struct. properties group, N.Am. Rockwell Sci. Ctr, Calif, 64-71; PROF. ELEC. ENG, UNIV. COLO, BOULDER, 71- U.S.A, 43-46, 1st Lt. AAAS; fel. Am. Phys. Soc; Am. Crystallog. Asn; fel. Mineral. Soc. Am; Sci. Res. Soc. Am. Relations of properties to crystal structure; crystal chemistry; magnetic, superconducting, and semiconducting materials; solid electrolytes; high pressure phases; phase transitions; structures of inorganic and intermetallic compounds. Address: Dept. of Electrical Engineering, University of Colorado, Boulder, CO 80302.

GELLERT, MARTIN F(RANK), b. Prague, Czechoslovakia, June 5, 29; m. 55. PHYSICAL CHEMISTRY. B.A, Harvard, 50; Ph.D.(chem), Columbia, 56. Fel. U.S. Pub. Health Serv, Naval Med. Res. Inst, Md, 57-58; asst. prof. biochem, Dartmouth Med. Sch, 58-59; RES. CHEMIST, LAB. MOLECULAR BIOL, NAT. INST. ARTHRITIS & METAB. DISEASES, NAT. INSTS. HEALTH, 59- Am. Phys. Soc; Am. Soc. Biol. Chem. Molecular genetics; physical chemistry of macromolecules. Address: Lab. Molecular Biology, National Institute of Arthritis & Metabolic Diseases, National Institutes of Health, Bethesda, MD 20014.

GELLERT, RONALD J, b. N.Y.C, July 24, 35; m. 59. PHYSIOLOGY. B.A, N.Y. Univ, 57; M.A, California, Berkeley, 59, Nat. Inst. Ment. Health fel, San Francisco, 61-63, Ph.D.(physiol), 63. Nat. Insts. Health fel, California, San Francisco, 63-64, Oxford, 64-65, Harvard Sch. Dent. Med, 65-67; sr. investr, Pac. Northwest Res. Found, 67-70; RES. ASST. PROF. OBSTET. & GYNEC, SCH. MED, UNIV. WASH, 70- AAAS. Neuroendocrinology of reproductive processes; control of onset of puberty; role of pars tuberalis of the pituitary in physiology of reproduction; mechanism of action of certain anti-ovulatory drugs. Address: Dept. of Obstetrics & Gynecology, University of Washington School of Medicine, Seattle, WA 98105.

GELLES, I(SADORE) LEO, b. Phila, Pa, Dec. 15, 25; m. 53; c. 3. PHYSICS. B.A, Temple, 51, M.A, 54. Physicist, Pitman-Dunn Lab, Frankford Arsenal, 51-52; acoust. engr, Radio Corp. Am, 52-53; sr. engr. semiconductors, res. div, Philco Corp, 53-54; mem. staff microwave & optical spectros, res. ctr, Int. Bus. Mach. Corp, 56-61; physicist & group supvr, res. lab, Am-Standard Corp, 61-63; physicist, LEDGEMONT LAB, KENNECOTT COPPER CORP, LEXINGTON, MASS, 63-67, SR. PHYSICIST, 67- Ord. Dept, U.S.A, 54-56. AAAS; Am. Phys. Soc; Sci. Res. Soc. Am. Physical properties of refractory and nonferrous metals; audio spectrum analysis; semiconductor transport properties; magnetic resonance in solids; photoconductivity; ultrasonics in solids; crystal physics; holography. Address: 179 Great Rd, Acton, MA 01720.

GELLES, S(TANLEY) H(AROLD), b. Boston, Mass, Sept. 12, 30; m. 56; c. 2. PHYSICAL METALLURGY. S.B, Mass. Inst. Tech, 52, S.M, 54, Sc.D, 57. Asst. metall, Mass. Inst. Tech, 53-57; proj. leader phys. metall, Nuclear Metals Inc, Mass, 57-60, proj. mgr, 60-63; phys. res. metallurgist, Ledgemont Lab, Kennecott Copper Corp, 63-68; ASSOC. CHIEF, BATTELLE MEM. INST, 68- Consult, Beryllium Comt, Nat. Adv. Bd, Nat. Acad. Sci, 64-67. AAAS; Am. Inst. Min, Metall. & Petrol. Eng; Am. Soc. Metals. Metallurgy of beryllium; phase equilibria; metal deformation; high pressure technology. Address: 2485 Wimbledon Rd, Columbus, OH 43220.

GELLETLY, WILLIAM, b. Edinburgh, Scotland, Dec. 11, 39; m. 65. PHYSICS. B.Sc, Edinburgh, 61, Ph.D.(natural philos), 65. Asst. lectr. physics, Edinburgh, 64-65; Nat. Res. Coun. Can. fel, Chalk River Nuclear Labs, 65-67; asst. physicist, Brookhaven Nat. Lab, 67-69, assoc. physicist, 69-70; LECTR, DEPT. PHYSICS, SCHUSTER LAB, MANCHESTER UNIV, 70- Brit. Inst. Physics & Phys. Soc. Low energy nuclear physics. Address: Dept. of Physics, Schuster Lab, Manchester University, Lancs, U.K. M13 9P2.

GELLHORN, ALFRED, b. St. Louis, Mo, June 4, 13; m. 39; c. 4. CANCER. M.D, Washington (St. Louis), 37. House off. surg, Barnes Hosp, St. Louis, Mo, 37-39; gynec, Passavant Hosp, Chicago, 39-40; res. fel, dept. embryol, Carnegie Institution & Hopkins, 40-43; asst. prof. physiol, col. physicians & surgeons, Columbia, 43-45, pharmacol, 45-46, assoc. prof, 46-48, med, 48-58, prof, 58-68, dir. inst. cancer res, 52-68; PROF. MED. & PHARMACOL, DEAN, SCH. MED. & DIR, MED. CTR, UNIV. PA, 68- Vis. clin. prof, Albert Einstein Col. Med, Yeshiva, 56-68. Chief med. serv, Francis Delafield Hosp, 50-68; assoc. attend. physician, Presby. Hosp, 56-60, attend. physician, 60-68. Mem. adv. comt, U.S. Pub. Health Serv; Am. Cancer Soc; Nat. Res. Coun; pres, Coun. Int. Orgn. Med. Sci, 68- Dipl, Am. Bd. Internal Med. With Office Sci. Res. & Develop, 41-45. AAAS; Am. Asn. Cancer Res.(pres, 62-63); Asn. Am. Physicians; Soc. Exp. Biol. & Med; Am. Soc. Pharmacol. & Exp. Therapeut; Am. Soc. Clin. Invest; Harvey Soc; fel. Am. Col. Physicians; fel. N.Y. Acad. Sci. Placental physiology; circulatory pnarmacology; chemotherapy; infectious disease; clinical research in malignancy; mechanism of action of anti-tumor drugs on clinical cancer chemotherapy; medical aspects of neoplastic disease; lipid metabolism; medical oncology. Address: University of Pennsylvania School of Medicine, Philadelphia, PA 19104.

GELLIS, SYDNEY S(AUL), b. Claremont, N.H, Mar. 6, 14; m. 39; c. 2. MEDICINE. A.B, Harvard, 34, M.D, 38. Instr. PEDIAT, Hopkins, 43-46; asst. prof, Harvard, 46-56; PROF. & CHMN. DEPT, sch. med, Boston, 56-65; SCH. MED, TUFTS UNIV, 65-; CONSULT. PEDIAT, BOSTON CITY HOSP, 65-, dir. pediat, 56-65. Lectr, Harvard Med. Sch, 56-; sch. med, Boston, 65- Physician, Children's Med. Center, Boston, 47-56, consult, 56-; pediatrician-in-chief, Beth Israel Hosp, Boston, 50-56; New Eng. Med. Ctr. Hosps, 65- Consult, Surgeon Gen, 43-47; pediat, U.S. Air Force, 69- Ed, Year Book Pediat, 52-; assoc. ed, Am. Jour. Diseases Children. Med.C, U.S.A, 43-46. Am. Pediat. Soc; Soc. Pediat. Res.(secy, 52-58, pres, 58-59); cor. mem. French Soc. Pediat; hon. mem. N.Z. Pediat. Soc. Liver disease and jaundice; gamma globulin; hepatitis. Address: 20 Ash St, Boston, MA 02111.

GELLMAN, CHARLES, b. N.Y.C, Dec. 18, 16; m. 48; c. 2. INDUSTRIAL ENGINEERING. Columbia, 38. Indust. specialist, War Dept, 42-45; works mgr, Para Equip. Co, 45-47; Heppe Hudson Co, Inc, 47-50; exec. purchasing off. & tech. adv. supply mission, Israel, 50-53; tech. dir, Am. Technion Soc, 53-55; exec. dir. & consult, Grand Cent. Hosp, New York, 55-63; EXEC. DIR, JEWISH MEM. HOSP, 63- Consult, Webb & Knapp Construct. Co. Am. Soc. Metals; Soc. Automotive Eng; Am. Hosp. Asn; Am. Pub. Health Asn; Am. Ord. Asn; Am. Inst. Mgt. Metallurgy. Address: 12 Birch Lane, Green Acres, Valley Stream, NY 11581.

GELLMAN, H(ARVEY) S(AUL), b. Radom, Poland, June 28, 24; nat. Can; m. 46; c. 2. APPLIED MATHEMATICS. B.A, Toronto, 47, M.A, 49, Ph.D. (appl. math), 51. Mathematician, comput. center, Toronto, 48-52, head comput. sect, Atomic Energy Can, Ltd, Ont, 52-54; electronic computer consult, Adalia, Ltd, Que, 54-55; pres, H.S, Gellman & Co, Ltd, Ont, 55-64; v.pres, DCF SYSTS, LTD, 64-66, PRES, 66- Consult, Atomic Energy Can, Ltd, 55-57; Imp. Oil, Ltd, 56-59; Royal Comn. Orgn. Can, 61; Royal Comn. Govt. Admin, Prov. Sask, 64; Air Can; Banks of Can; Banks of Mont; Domtar Ltd; Prov. Ont, Manitoba, Sask, Nova Scotia; Govt. Can; Univ. B.C; Univ. Sask. Asn. Comput. Mach; Inst. Mgt. Sci; Can. Opers. Res. Soc; Can. Info. Processing Soc.(pres, 64-65). Electronic digital computer applications; numerical analysis; operations research. Address: DCF Systems, Ltd, 74 Victoria St, Toronto 210, Ont, Can.

GELLMAN, ISAIAH, b. Akron, Ohio, Feb. 19, 28; m. 47; c. 2. SANITATION. B.Ch.E, City Col. New York, 47; M.S, Rutgers, 50, Nat. Insts. Health fel, 48-51, Ph.D.(sanit), 52. Res. assoc. sanit, Rutgers, 48-51; process engr. air & water, Abbott Labs, 52-56; regional engr. pulp & paper-air & water pollution, Nat. Coun. Stream Improv, 56-67, asst. tech. dir, N.Y, 67-69,

TECH. DIR, NAT. COUN. PAPER INDUST. FOR AIR & STREAM IMPROV, INC, 69- Water Pollution Control Fedn; Air Pollution Control Asn; Am. Soc. Limnol. & Oceanog; Tech. Asn. Pulp & Paper Indust. Air and water pollution control; water resources development; treatment of gaseous and liquid effluents from pulp and paper production to prevent pollution problems. Address: National Council of the Paper Industry for Air & Stream Improvement, Inc, 260 Madison Ave, New York, NY 10016.

GELMAN, CHARLES, b. N.Y.C, Dec. 15, 31; m. 56; c. 3. CHEMISTRY. B.S, Syracuse, 53; M.P.H, Michigan, 58. Res. chemist, Chem. Corps, U.S. Dept. Army, 53-56; field chemist, U.S. Pub. Health Serv. & State of Ky, 56-58; CHMN, GELMAN INSTRUMENT CO, 58- Public health; microchemistry; air pollution measurement. Address: Gelman Instrument Co, 600 S. Wagner Rd, Ann Arbor, MI 48106.

GELMAN, GEORGE, b. Chicago, Ill, Aug. 3, 14; m. 49; c. 3. MICROBIOLOGY, BIOCHEMISTRY. B.S, Chicago, 36, M.B.A, 50; J.D, De Paul, 42. Staff chemist, Wahl-Henius Inst, Chicago, 37-39; consult. chemist, Edwal Labs, 39-40, consult. develop. & planning, 40-42; tech. dir, Qm. Food & Container Inst. Armed Forces, 42-50; v.pres, Vico Prod. Co, 50-58; pres, bioferm corp, 58-61; consult, Int. Minerals & Chem. Corp, Calif, 61-66; chmn. bd, Skymark Airlines, 67-69; MEM. BD. DIRS, ALPHA GROUP INC, 69- Mem. food & nutrit. bd, Nat. Res. Coun, 41-45; food panel res. & develop, U.S. Dept. Defense, 41-45; v.pres, Pac. Yeast Prod, Inc, 50-58; regents lectr, Univ. Calif, Davis, 61; mem, Calif. State Coord. Coun. for Higher Educ, 65-69; chmn. Calif. State Tech. Serv. Prog. Adv. Coun. & Sci. Adv. Comt. to Gov. Calif, 67-69; consult, Mkt. Res. Corp. Am; secy. & mem. comt. food res, Off. Qm. Gen; mem. adv. coun, Southwest Regional Lab. Educ. Res. & Develop. U.S.A, 42-51, Maj. AAAS; Am. Chem. Soc; fel. Am. Inst. Chem; fel. Inst. Food Technol. Psychometrics; microbiology; industrial fermentations; research administration; management. Address: 6633 Kane Way, Bakersfield, CA 93309.

GELMAN, HARRY, b. New York, N.Y, May 23, 35; m. 57; c. 4. PHYSICS. B.S, City Col. New York, 57; Columbia, 57-58; Ph.D.(physics), N.Y. Univ. 64. Asst. physics, Columbia, 57-58; N.Y. Univ, 58-59; instr. math. & physics, U.S. Merchant Marine Acad, 64; staff mem. physics, Sandia Corp, 64-66; MEM. TECH. STAFF, MITRE CORP, 66- Lectr, Northeast. Univ, 67- Am. Asn. Physics Teachers; Am. Phys. Soc. Ionospheric physics; plasma physics; quantum theory of fields; elementary particles. Address: Dept. D-81, MITRE Corp, Bedford, MA 01730.

GELPERIN, ABRAHAM, b. Velez, Russia, Jan. 25, 09; U.S. citizen; m. 38; c. 3. PUBLIC HEALTH. B.M, Cincinnati, 31, M.D, 32; M.P.H, Hopkins, 42, Dr.P.H, 48; M.S.H.A, Northwestern, 58. Intern, St. Joseph's Hosp, Colo, 31-32; res. dermat, Cincinnati Gen. Hosp, 32-33; res. physician, Toledo State Hosp, 33-35; dist. physician, Dept. Health, Cincinnati, 35-41; assoc. clin. prof. pub. health, med. sch, Yale, 48-51; dir. pub. health, Des Moines & Polk County Health Dept, 51-56; health & hosps, Kansas City, Mo, 58-60; med. dir, Michael Reese Hosp, Chicago, Ill, 60-63; dir. health proj, Welfare Coun. Metrop. Chicago, 64-67; ASSOC. PROF. PREV. MED, UNIV. ILL. COL. MED, 67- Dir. bur. communicable & venereal disease control, Dept. Health, New Haven, 48-51. U.S.A, 42-46. Fel. Am. Pub. Health Asn. Natural and acquired immunity in infants and children; community health planning. Address: Dept. of Preventive Medicine, University of Illinois College of Medicine, Chicago, IL 60680.

GELPI-MONTEYS, EMILIO, b. Barcelona, Spain, Aug. 11, 42; m. 65; c. 2. ANALYTICAL BIOCHEMISTRY, ORGANIC GEOCHEMISTRY. B.S, Indust. Tech. Sch, Barcelona, Spain, 63; Ph.D.(chem), Houston, 68. Asst. chem, Houston, 64-68, fel. org. geochem. & cosmochem, 68-69; specialist res. chemist & coinvester. anal. lunar samples, space sci. lab, Univ. Calif, Berkeley, 69-70; ASST. PROF. BIOL, INST. FUNDAMENTAL BIOL, AUTONOMOUS UNIV. BARCELONA, 70- Pres. econ. comt, Inst. Fundamental Biol, 70-; mem. acad. comt. basic med. sci, Autonomous Univ. Barcelona, 71-; consult, ctr. pharmaceut. res, Ferrer-Novag Int. Labs, 71-; vis. res. scientist, dept. biophys. sci, Univ. Houston, 71. Spanish Army Res, 62-64, 2nd Lt. AAAS; Am. Chem. Soc; Am. Soc. Mass Spectrometry; Spanish Soc. Biochem. Instrumental analysis; biochemical, geochemical and biomedical applications of gas chromatography and mass spectrometry; computer applications in analytical organic chemistry; origin and evolution of life; neurochemistry. Address: Institute of Fundamental Biology, Autonomous University of Barcelona, Barcelona, 13, Spain.

GELTMAN, SYDNEY, b. Philadelphia, Pa, May 23, 27; m. 53; c. 3. THEORETICAL PHYSICS. B.S, Yale, 48, M.S, 49, Ph.D.(physics), 52. PHYSICIST, Westinghouse Res. Labs, 52-54; appl. physics lab, Hopkins, 54-57; JOINT INST. LAB. ASTROPHYS, NAT. BUR. STANDARDS, 57- Lectr, Univ. Col, London, 66-67. U.S.N, 45-46. Fel. Am. Phys. Soc. Theory of ionic mobilities; negative ions; atomic scattering processes and ionization; atomic radiative processes. Address: Joint Institute for Laboratory Astrophysics, National Bureau of Standards and University of Colorado, Boulder, CO 80302.

GELZER, JUSTUS, b. Basel, Switz, Nov. 8, 29; m. 60; c. 3. MICROBIOLOGY, IMMUNOLOGY. M.D, Basel, 55. Sr. microbiologist, RES. LABS, pharmaceut. div, Ciba Ltd, Basel, 64-67, dir. microbiol. res, Ciba Pharmaceut. Co, N.J, 67-70, DIR. BIOL. RES, PHARMACEUT. DIV, CIBA-GEIGY LTD, 70- Fel. microbiol, Florida, 57-59; pediat, Children Hosp, Zurich, Switz, 59-62; immunol, dept. microbiol, sch. med, Columbia, 62-64. Mem. comn. exp. cancer chemother, Int. Union Against Cancer, 67- Med.C, Swiss Army Res, 48-, Capt. Am. Soc. Microbiol; N.Y. Acad. Sci. Host-parasite relationship in experimental infections and tumors; infectious immunity and resistance. Address: Ciba-Geigy Research Labs, Pharmaceutical Division, 4000 Basel, Switzerland.

GEMANT, ANDREW, b. Nagyvarad, Hungary, July 27, 95; nat; m. 33. PHYSICAL CHEMISTRY. M.D, Budapest, 19; Ph.D.(physics), Berlin, 22. Res. physicist, Radiologie Inc, Berlin, 23-24; Siemens-Schuckert, 25-31; privat docent, Tech. Univ. Berlin, 29-33; res. mem, Heinrich Hertz Inst, 32-33; res. assoc, Oxford, 34-37; Wisconsin, 38-39; staff physicist, Detroit Edison Co, 40-60; RES. ASSOC, GRACE HOSP, DETROIT, 61- Mem. conf. elec.

insulation, Nat. Res. Coun. Fel. AAAS; fel. Am. Phys. Soc; Electrochem. Soc; German Phys. Soc. X-ray fluorescence; pH of aqueous solutions; high voltage physics; dielectrics; colloids; acoustics; viscosity, internal friction; electrets; electrochemistry of oils; radioactive tracers in solutions; high voltage cables; oxidation and photochemical ions in hydrocarbons; ion-exchange resins in hydrocarbons; solubilization of cholesterol; carcinogenesis; reduction by chemical means of reactivity of DNA. Address: 4501 W. Outer Dr, Detroit, MI 48235.

GEMMELL, GORDON D(OUGLAS), b. Christchurch, N.Z, Sept. 18, 21; U.S. citizen; m. 58; c. 2. PHYSICAL METALLURGY & CHEMISTRY. B.Sc, New Zealand, 42, M.Sc, 43; M.S, Mass. Inst. Tech, 53, Alcoa fel, 53-56, Sc.D. (metall), 56. Physical chemist, Dept. Sci. & Indust. Res, N.Z, 43-51; RES. METALLURGIST, E.I. DU PONT DE NEMOURS & CO, INC, 56- Am. Soc. Metals. Materials science. Address: Experimental Station, E.I. du Pont de Nemours & Co, Inc, Wilmington, DE 19898.

GEMMELL, ROBERT S(TINSON), b. Kenton, Ohio, Apr. 14, 33; m. 55; c. 4. CIVIL ENGINEERING. B.C.E, Ohio State, 56, M.S, 57; U.S. Pub. Health Serv. traineeship, Harvard, 59-60, Ph.D.(eng), 63. Instr. civil eng, Rutgers, 57; lectr. & res. fel, div. eng. & appl. physics & co-dir, U.S. Pub. Health Serv. res. grant, Harvard, 63-64; asst. prof. CIVIL ENG, TECHNOL. INST, NORTHWEST. UNIV, 64-67, ASSOC. PROF, 67-, U.S. Pub. Health Serv. res. grants, 64-68, co-dir, 64-65. Off. Water Resources res. grants, 70-73. Am. Soc. Civil Eng; Am. Water Works Asn; Am. Geophys. Union; Am. Water Resources Asn. Coagulation; water treatment processes; water quality management; environmental health engineering; water resources systems; urban systems engineering. Address: Dept. of Civil Engineering, Technological Institute, Northwestern University, Evanston, IL 60201.

GEMSKI, PETER, JR, b. Bellingham, Mass, Oct. 3, 36; m. 62; c. 2. MICROBIOLOGY, GENETICS. A.B, Brown, 58; M.S, Rhode Island, 60; Ph.D.(microbiol), Pittsburgh, 64. Nat. Insts. Health fel, Lister Inst. Prev. Med, London, Eng, 64-65; dept. med. microbiol, sch. med, Stanford, 66; RES. MICROBIOLOGIST, WALTER REED ARMY INST. RES, 67- AAAS; Am. Soc. Microbiol. Bacterial genetics; conjugation in bacteria; intergeneric bacterial hybridizations; genetic control of lipopolysaccharide biosynthesis. Address: Dept. of Applied Immunology, Walter Reed Army Institute of Research, Washington, DC 20012.

GENAUX, CHARLES T(HOMAS), b. Pullman, Wash, Apr. 8, 27; m. 50; c. 3. BIOCHEMISTRY. B.S, Iowa State Col, 50; M.S, Univ. Rochester, 53; Ph.D. (zoochem), Univ. Alaska, 69. Asst. prof. CHEM, UNIV. ALASKA, 64-70, ASSOC. PROF, 70- U.S.A.A.F, 45-47. Am. Chem. Soc. Polyamino acids; protein systematics. Address: Dept. of Chemistry, University of Alaska, College, AK 99701.

GENCO, JOSEPH MICHAEL, b. Cleveland, Ohio, Apr. 13, 39; m. 67; c. 1. CHEMICAL ENGINEERING, PHYSICAL CHEMISTRY. B.S, Case, 60; M.S, Ohio State, 62, Ph.D.(chem. eng), 65. ASSOC. CHIEF, BATTELLE MEM. INST, 65- AAAS; Am. Inst. Chem. Egn; Am. Chem. Soc. Chemical kinetics and adsorption; physical chemistry; gas scrubbing and environmental science. Address: Battelle Memorial Institute, 505 King Ave, Columbus, OH 43201.

GENCO, ROBERT J, b. Silver Creek, N.Y, Oct. 31, 38; m. 57; c. 3. IMMUNOCHEMISTRY, MICROBIOLOGY. D.D.S, State Univ. N.Y. Buffalo, 63; Ph.D.(microbiol), Pennsylvania, 67. U.S. Pub. Health Serv. fel, 63-66; asst. prof. ORAL BIOL. & PERIDONT, SCH. DENT, STATE UNIV. N.Y. BUFFALO, 67-69, ASSOC. PROF, 69-, DIR. GRAD. PERIODONT, 68- Am. Asn. Immunol; Int. Asn. Dent. Res; Am. Acad. Periodont. Structure-function relationships of the various antibody molecules, especially those present in external secretions. Address: Dept. of Oral Biology, Dental School, State University of New York at Buffalo, 4510 Main St, Buffalo, NY 14226.

GENCSOY, HASAN TAHSIN, b. Turkey, July 4, 24; m. 53; c. 1. MECHANICAL ENGINEERING. B.S, California, 49; M.S, West Virginia, 51. Customer engr, Int. Bus. Machines World Trade Corp, 51-52; prod. engr, Bakir Sanayi Ltd, 53-55; instr. MECH. ENG, W.VA. UNIV, 56-57, asst. prof, 57-62, assoc. prof, 62-67, PROF, 67- Consult, Chamber Indust, Turkey, 53-55. Turkish Army, 52-53, Res, 53-, Lt. Am. Soc. Mech. Eng; Am. Soc. Eng. Educ. Machine design; engineering analysis; engineering systems analysis; similitude in engineering; experimental stress analysis. Address: Dept. of Mechanical Engineering, College of Engineering, West Virginia University, Morgantown, WV 26506.

GENDEL, BENJAMIN R(OBERT), b. N.Y.C, Apr. 29, 11; m. 35; c. 2. INTERNAL MEDICINE. B.S, Tulane, 31, M.D, 35. Asst. med, sch. med, Yale, 37-40, clin. instr, 40-42; asst. prof, col. med, Tennessee, 48-52, assoc. prof, 52-55; clin. prof, sch. med, Emory, 55-57, assoc. prof, 57-58, prof, 58-71; PROF. MED. & ASSOC. CHMN. DEPT, UNIV. TENN, MEMPHIS, 71- Chief hematol. & med, Vet. Admin. Hosp, Memphis, 46-55, med. serv, 71-; med. serv, Atlanta, 55-57; staff mem. cytogenetics, pediat. res. unit, Guy's Hosp. Med. Sch, London, 68-69. Med.C, 42-46, Maj. Am. Soc. Hemat; Am. Soc. Human Genetics; Am. Fedn. Clin. Res; fel. Am. Col. Physicians; fel. Int. Soc. Hemat. Hematology; medical genetics. Address: Medical Service, Veterans Administration Hospital, Memphis, TN 38104.

GENDRON, P(IERRE) R(AOUL), b. St. Hyacinthe, Que, May 1, 16; m. 43; c. 3. PHYSICAL CHEMISTRY. B.Sc, Montreal, 41, Ph.D.(chem), 49, hon. D.Sc, 59; Columbia, 49-50. Asst. prof. chem, Montreal, 46-51; assoc. prof, 51-53; dean faculty pure & appl. sci, Ottawa (Can), 53-62; PRES, Dow Brewery, Ltd, 62-68; PULP & PAPER RES. INST. CAN, 68- Lectr, Columbia Univ, 49-50; mem. Nat. Res. Coun. Can, 57; Defence Res. Bd. Can, 58; Can. del, conf, UNESCO, France, 58; mem, Sci. Coun. Can, chmn. indust. res. & innovation comt. Companion, Order of Can. R.C.N, 41-45, Res, 46-53, Lt. Comdr. Fel. Chem. Inst. Can. Aerosols; nucleation phenomena; adsorption. Address: Pulp & Paper Institute of Canada, 570 St. John's Blvd, Pointe Claire 720, Pointe Claire, Que, Can.

GENECIN, ABRAHAM, b. Minneapolis, Minn, Aug. 21, 18; m. 41; c. 2. INTERNAL MEDICINE, CARDIOLOGY. A.B, Columbia Univ, 39; M.D, Johns

Hopkins Univ, 43. Instr. MED, SCH. MED, JOHNS HOPKINS UNIV, 44-54, asst. prof, 54-66, ASSOC. PROF, 66- Private practice. Med.C, 45-47, Capt. AAAS; Am. Med. Asn; Am. Heart Asn; Am. Col. Physicians. Cardiology. Address: 611 Park Ave, Baltimore, MD 21201.

GENELLY, RICHARD E(MMETT), b. Oakland, Calif, June 3, 16; m. 46; c. 4. VERTEBRATE ZOOLOGY. A.B, California, 50, M.A, 54, Ph.D.(zool), 55. Asst. specialist, insecticide res, California, 53-55, assoc. in zool, 55-56; assoc. prof. WILDLIFE MGT, HUMBOLDT STATE COL, 56-70, PROF, 70- U.S.A.A.F, 42-45. Wildlife Soc; Am. Ornith. Union; Cooper Ornith. Soc. Agricultural chemicals and wildlife; ornithology; African small mammals. Address: Dept. of Wildlife Management, Humboldt State College, Arcata, CA 95521.

GENENSKY, SAMUEL MILTON, b. New Bedford, Mass, July 26, 27; m. 53; c. 2. APPLIED MATHEMATICS. Sc.B, Brown, 49, Ph.D.(appl. math), 58; M.A, Harvard, 51. Mathematician, Nat. Bur. Standards, 51-54; assoc. mathematician, RAND CORP, 58-59, MATHEMATICIAN, 59- Am. Math. Soc. Non-linear continuum mechanics including plasticity, finite elasticity, visco-elasticity and the mechanics of non-Newtonian fluids; classical continuum mechanics, especially elasticity and viscous fluid theory. Address: Rand Corp, 1700 Main St, Santa Monica, CA 90406.

GENERALES, CONSTANTINE D(EMOSTHENES) J(OHN), b. Athens, Greece, Nov. 10, 08; U.S. citizen; m. 38. INTERNAL & AEROSPACE MEDICINE. Univs. Athens, Heidelberg, Zurich & Paris, 28-32; M.D, Univ. Berlin, 36, D.Phil.(zool, bot, genetics, math), 37; Columbia Univ, 58-59. Asst, Univ. Women's Clin, Charité, Berlin, Ger, 34-36; res. asst, Inst. Genetics & Animal Breeding, Berlin-Dahlem, 36-37; instr. med, N.Y. Med. Col, 39-62, asst. prof. space med. & coord. space med. prog, 60-62; RES. ASSOC. & ATTEND. PHYSICIAN, MT. SINAI SCH. MED, 52- Private practice, N.Y.C, 39-; associated with N.Y. Cancer Inst. & Bellevue Hosp, 39-42, Flower & Fifth Ave. Hosp. & Metrop. Hosp, 39-62, Bird S. Coler Hosp, 47-62 & French Hosp, 65-69; consult, David Sarnoff Res. Ctr, Radio Corp. Am, 61; lectr. at various univs. & acad. insts, 62-71; mem. bd. dirs, Coun. on Hosp. Automation, Phila, Pa, 65- Am. Bill of Rights Award, 63; Gold Medallion, City of Thessalonika, Greece, 65; George Photinou Award, Acad. Athens, 69. U.S.A.A.F, 42-46. AAAS; Aerospace Med. Asn; Am. Asn. Hist. Med; sr. mem. Am. Astronaut. Soc; assoc. fel. Am. Col. Angiol; Am. Col. Cardiol; Am. Col. Chest Physicians; Am. Fedn. Clin. Res; Am. Geol. Soc; Am. Geophys. Union; fel. Am. Geriat. Soc; fel. Am. Heart Asn; sr. mem. Am. Inst. Aeronaut. & Astronaut; Am. Med. Asn; Am. Numis. Soc; fel. Brit. Interplanetary Soc; Ger. Genetics Soc; hon. fel. Hellenic Astronaut. Soc; hon. fel. Hermann Oberth Soc; sr. mem. Inst. Elec. & Electronics Eng; sr. mem. Instrument Soc. Am; Marine Technol. Soc; fel. N.Y. Acad. Med; fel. N.Y. Acad. Sci; fel. Royal Soc. Health; Int. Soc. Hist. Med; Soc. Biol. Rhythm. Art and science of care of life in health and illness beyond earth; weightlessness; chest diseases. Address: 115 Central Park W, New York, NY 10023.

GENEST, JACQUES, b. Montreal, Que, May 29, 19; m. 52; c. 5. ENDOCRINOLOGY, METABOLISM. B.A, Jean de Brebeuf Col, 37; M.D, Montreal, 42; hon. LL.D, Queen's Univ.(Ont), 66, Univ. Toronto, 71. Sr. intern, Hotel Dieu Hosp, 42, asst. res. path, 43-44, chief res. med, 44-45; Archbold fel. med, Hopkins Hosp, 45-46, Commonwealth Fund fel, 46-48; with Rockefeller Inst. Med. Res, 48-51; med. surveyor, European Med. Res. Ctrs. for Que. Govt, 51-52; chmn. dept. med, faculty med, Univ. Montreal, 64-68, physician-in-chief, Hotel Dieu Hosp, 64-68; SCI. DIR, CLIN. RES. INST. MONTREAL & DIR. DEPT. NEPHROLOGY-HYPERTENSION, UNIV. MONTREAL HOTEL-DIEU HOSP, 68- Lectr, Royal Col, 61; chmn, Med. Res. Coun. Quebec, 64-69; Sims Commonwealth Traveling Prof, 70. Gairdner Award, Toronto, 63; Stouffer Prize, 69. Endocrine Soc; fel. Am. Soc. Physicians; Am. Clin. & Climat. Asn; Asn. Am. Physicians; fel. Royal Soc. Can; Can. Med. Asn; Royal Soc. Med; Royal Col. Physicians & Surgeons. Human arterial hypertension; relationship of kidneys and adrenals to hypertension and salt regulation; electrolytes and renal function. Address: Clinical Research Institute of Montreal, 110 Pine Ave. W, Montreal 130, Que, Can.

GENET, RENE P. H, b. France, Sept. 4, 20; U.S. citizen. ORGANIC CHEMISTRY. Ph.D.(chem. eng), Swiss Fed. Inst. Tech, 49. DEVELOP. MGR. ORG. CHEM, GIVAUDAN CORP, N.J, 49- Am. Chem. Soc; Swiss Chem. Soc; Am. Inst. Chem. Eng. Chemical engineering. Address: Givaudan Corp, 125 Delawanna Ave, Clifton, NJ 07014.

GENETELLI, EMIL J, b. Brooklyn, N.Y, Feb. 25, 37; m. 60; c. 3. SANITARY ENGINEERING, MICROBIOLOGY. B.C.E, Manhattan Col, 59; M.S, Rutgers, 62, Ph.D.(environ. sci), 65. Instr. ENVIRON. SCI, RUTGERS UNIV, 62-65, asst. prof, 65-70, ASSOC. PROF, 70- U.S.M.C.R, 56-62, Sgt. Microbiology of water and wastewater treatment; water resources; air pollution control; solid waste disposal; aquatic microbiology. Address: Dept. of Environmental Sciences, Rutgers University, New Brunswick, NJ 08903.

GENETTI, WILLIAM ERNEST, b. Ogden, Utah, Mar. 24, 42; m. 65; c. 2. CHEMICAL ENGINEERING. B.S, Univ. Utah, 64; Ph.D.(chem. eng), Ore. State Univ, 68. Res. engr, Texaco Inc, Calif, summer 66; ASST. PROF. CHEM. ENG, MONT. STATE UNIV, 68- Res. engr, Assoc. West. Univs, summer 69; prin. investr, Nat. Sci. Found. grant, 70-71. Am. Inst. Chem. Eng. Heat transfer in fluidized beds; transpirational heat and mass transfer. Address: Dept. of Chemical Engineering, Montana State University, Bozeman, MT 59715.

GENEVESE, FRANK, b. N.Y.C, Nov. 15, 11; m. 41; c. 5. NUCLEAR PHYSICS, MATHEMATICS. A.B, Cornell, 35, M.A, 36; H.H. Rockham fel, Michigan, 46-49, Ph.D.(nuclear physics), 49. Res. physicist, Corning Glass Works, N.Y, 36-40; teaching fel. physics, Michigan, 40-42; dir. new develop. sect, U.S. Army Field Artillery Sch, Okla, 42-46; res. physicist, Kellex Corp, N.Y, 49-50; chief res. & radiation effects, hq, U.S. Air Force, Wash, D.C, 50-56; asst. dir. propulsion & fluids res. div, Armour Res. Found, Ill, 56-59; dep. tech. dir. defense-space, Westinghouse Elec. Corp, Wash, D.C, 59-63; mgr. advan. technol, missile & space div, Gen. Elec. Co, Pa, 63-67; ASSOC. PROF. PHYSICS, UNIV. CONN, 67- U.S. Army commendation award, 46; exceptional civilian serv. award, U.S. Air Force, 57. Sig.C.Res, Lt. Col. Assoc. fel. Am. Inst. Aeronaut. & Astronaut; Am. Phys. Soc; sr. mem. Am. Astronaut. Soc. Experimental nuclear physics; atomic weapons phenomena and effects; operations research; long range technical planning; systems synthesis and evaluations; management of engineering, research, development and advanced technologies. Address: Dept. of Physics, University of Connecticut, Hartford Branch, Trout Brook Rd. & Asylum Ave, West Hartford, CT 06117.

GENGE, C(OLIN) A(RTHUR), b. Edmonton, Alta, Sept. 6, 17; U.S. citizen; m. 39; c. 1. PHYSICAL CHEMISTRY. B.Sc, Alberta, 43, M.Sc, 45; Nat. Res. Coun. Can. stud, McGill, 45-46, fel, 46-47, Ph.D, 47. Asst. chemist, Res. Coun. Alta, 43-45; demonstr. chem, McGill, 45-47; res. chemist anal. div, RES. CTR, HERCULES INC, 47-71, SR. RES. CHEMIST, 71- Am. Chem. Soc; Sci. Res. Soc. Am. Chromatography; automation in analytical research; development in analytical methods. Address: 111 Wayland Rd, Sedgely Farms, Wilmington, DE 19807.

GENGERELLI, J(OSEPH) A(NTHONY), b. Glouster, Ohio, Feb. 2, 05; m. 42; c. 1. PSYCHOLOGY. A.B, Ohio, 25; univ. fel, Wisconsin, 26-27, M.A, 27; Harrison fel, Pennsylvania, 27-28, Ph.D.(psychol), 28. Asst, Ohio, 24-25; Wisconsin, 25-27; Nat. Res. Coun. fel, Yale, 28-29; instr. psychol, California, Los Angeles, 29-32, asst. prof, 32-42; psychologist, Off. Strategic Servs, Wash, D.C, Italy & Austria, 42-45; assoc. prof. PSYCHOL, UNIV. CALIF, LOS ANGELES, 45-50, PROF, 50- Am. Psychol. Asn; Soc. Exp. Biol. & Med. Learning theory; visual perception; physiological psychology. Address: Dept. of Psychology, University of California, Los Angeles, CA 90024.

GENGHOF, DOROTHY SCHAEFER, b. New York, N.Y, Oct. 8, 09; m. 30. MICROBIOLOGY. A.B, Columbia, 29; Ph.D.(med. bact), Cornell, 45. Technician-supvr, Rockefeller Inst. Med. Res, N.Y, 29-33; res. technician, med. col, Cornell, 35-39, asst. bact, 43-46, res. assoc. biochem, 46-55, asst. prof. MICROBIOL. & IMMUNOL, 55-57; ALBERT EINSTEIN COL. MED, 57-68, ASSOC. PROF, 68- Am. Soc. Microbiol; Harvey Soc; N.Y. Acad. Sci. Tuberculosis; bacterial dextrans and levans; ergothioneine in microorganisms; enzymatic synthesis of polysaccharides and oligosaccharides; transglycosylase mechanism. Address: Dept. of Microbiology & Immunology, Albert Einstein College of Medicine, Yeshiva University, 1300 Morris Park Ave, New York, NY 10461.

GENGOZIAN, NAZARETH, b. Racine, Wis, Feb. 13, 29; m. 48; c. 3. IMMUNOLOGY. B.S, Wisconsin, 51, M.A, 53, Ph.D.(immunol), 55. Res. assoc, Oak Ridge Nat. Lab, 55-56, biologist, 57-60, IMMUNOLOGIST, OAK RIDGE ASSOC. UNIVS, 60- Fel, U.S. Pub. Health Serv, Nat. Cancer Inst, 56-57; prof, Univ. Tenn. Am. Asn. Immunol; Radiation Res. Soc; Soc. Exp. Biol. & Med; Transplantation Soc. Radiation immunology; tissue transplantation; antibody formation and immunologic tolerance. Address: Medical Division, Oak Ridge Associated Universities, P.O. Box 117, Oak Ridge, TN 37830.

GENIN, DENNIS JOSEPH, b. Rockford, Ill, Sept. 18, 38; m. 60; c. 3. PHYSICS. B.S, Beloit Col, 60; Ph.D.(physics), Iowa State, 66. Assoc. physics, Argonne Nat. Lab, 66-68; sr. assoc. physicist, Thomas J. Watson Res. Ctr, IBM CORP, 68-71, STAFF PHYSICIST, EAST FISHKILL FACILITY, 71- Am. Phys. Soc. Electric and magnetic fields in solids using magnetic resonance techniques. Address: East Fishkill Facility, IBM Corp, B300-78, D170, Hopewell Junction, NY 12533.

GENIN, JOSEPH, b. Norwalk, Conn, Sept. 9, 30; m. 64; c. 3. SOLID MECHANICS. B.C.E, City Col. New York, 52; M.S, Arizona, 57; Ph.D.(solid mech), Minnesota, 63. Instr. struct. mech, Arziona, 55-58; eng. mech, Minnesota, 58-62; sr. engr, Gen. Dynamics/Ft. Worth, 63-64; assoc. prof. eng. mech, PURDUE UNIV, 64-68, PROF. AERONAUT, ASTRONAUT. & ENG. SCI, 69- Private consult, 55-59. C.Eng, U.S.A, 53-54. Am. Soc. Eng. Educ; Am. Inst. Aeronaut. & Astronaut. Solid mechanics; dynamic stability of discrete and continuous systems, vibrations, material damping, stress waves, structural mechanics; aeroelasticity, and visoelasticity. Address: School of Aeronautics, Astronautics & Engineering Sciences, Purdue University, Lafayette, IN 47907.

GENNARO, ALFONSO R(OBERT), b. Phila, Pa, Dec. 18, 25; m. 49; c. 3. ORGANIC CHEMISTRY. B.Sc, Phila. Col. Pharm, 48; M.Sc, Pennsylvania, 51; Ph.D, Temple, 56. Chemist, E.I. du Pont de Nemours & Co, 51-53; Pa. Salt Mfg. Co, 53-55; asst. prof. CHEM, PHILA. COL. PHARM, 55-58, assoc. prof, 58-65, PROF, 65-, DIR. DEPT, 69-, instr, 48-55. Consult, Samuel P. Sadtler & Son, 55- U.S.N, 44-46. Am. Chem. Soc; Soc. Appl. Spectros; Inst. Elec. & Electronics Eng. Synthetic medicinals; electronic instrumentation; infrared spectroscopy. Address: Dept. of Chemistry, Philadelphia College of Pharmacy & Science, Philadelphia, PA 19104.

GENNARO, A(NTONIO) L(OUIS), b. Raton, N.Mex, Mar. 18, 34; m. 55; c. 3. VERTEBRATE ECOLOGY. B.S, New Mexico State, 57; M.S, New Mexico, 61, Ph.D.(zool), 67. Teacher, high sch, N.Mex, 57-58; dir. grad. teaching asst. BIOL, New Mexico, 61-64; asst. prof, St. John's (Minn), 65-66; EAST. N.MEX. UNIV, 66-70, ASSOC. PROF, 70-, CURATOR, NAT. HIST. MUS, 67- Nat. Sci. Found. summer fels, 61-62. Med.Serv.C, U.S.A, 58, Res, 58-66, Capt. Am. Soc. Mammal. Taxonomy and ecology in mammalogy and herpetology. Address: Dept. of Biology, Eastern New Mexico University, P.O. Box 2056, Portales, NM 88130.

GENNARO, JOSEPH FRANCIS, b. Brooklyn, N.Y, Apr. 9, 24; m. 44; c. 5. ANATOMY. B.S, Fordham, 47; M.S, Pittsburgh, 49, Ph.D.(zool), 52. Asst. biol, Pittsburgh, 47-48, lectr. zool, 48-50, instr, 50-51; asst. prof. biol, col. pharm, St. John's (N.Y), 51-53; instr. anat, col. med, State Univ. N.Y. Downstate Med. Center, 53-56; asst. prof, col. med, Florida, 56-64; assoc. prof, sch. med, Louisville, 64-69; PROF. BIOL, WASH. SQUARE COL, N.Y. UNIV, 69- Res. assoc. Brookhaven Nat. Lab, 51-56; res. fel, Harvard, 64-65. U.S.A, 43-46. Am. Soc. Zool; Radiation Res. Soc; N.Y. Acad. Sci; Am. Asn. Anat. Comparative endocrinology; chemistry of snake venoms and protein toxins; electron microscopy. Address: 651 Brown Bldg, Washington, Square College, New York University, New York, NY 10003.

GENNARO, JOSEPH J(OHN), b. N.Y.C, Apr. 21, 19; m. 46; c. 4. STRUCTURAL ENGINEERING. B.C.E, City Col. New York, 39; M.S, Columbia

Univ, 54. ASSOC. PROF. civil eng, City Col. New York, 46-50; STEVENS INST. TECHNOL, 52-70, APPL. MECH, 70- Structures; civil engineering. Address: Dept. of Applied Mechanics, Stevens Institute of Technology, Hoboken, NJ 07030.

GENOLIO, RAYMOND J(OSEPH), b. San Francisco, Calif, Aug. 5, 33; m. 56; c. 5. THEORETICAL PHYSICS. B.S, San Francisco, 56; M.S, New Mexico State, 60, univ. fel, 61-62, Ph.D.(physics), 63. Asst. prof. PHYSICS, St. John's (N.Y), 63-64; Nat. Acad. Sci-Nat. Res. Coun. resident res. assoc, U.S. Naval Ord. Lab, 64-65; ASST. PROF, UNIV. SAN FRANCISCO, 65- Nat. Sci. Found. summer res. partic, Univ. Md, 64, Univ. Colo, 66, Univ. Calif, Berkeley, 68, Stanford Univ, 69, U.S.A, 56-58, 1st Lt. Am. Phys. Soc; Am. Asn. Physics Teachers. Quantum electronics; molecular physics. Address: 215 Molimo Dr, San Francisco, CA 94127.

GENOVESE, PASQUALE D(ANTE), b. N.Y.C, Oct. 19, 07; m. 36; c. 3. CARDIOLOGY. B.S, Virginia, 29; M.D, L.I. Col. Med, 34. Asst. cardiologist, Vet. Admin. Hosp, Hines, Ill, 41-42, cardiologist, Wichita, Kans, 42-43; instr. MED, SCH. MED, IND. UNIV, INDIANAPOLIS, 50-55, asst. prof, 55-60, assoc. prof, 60-64, PROF, 64-; ASST. CHIEF MED. SERV. & CHIEF CARDIOL. SECT, VET. ADMIN. HOSP, 46- Attend. physician & cardiologist, Marion County Gen. Hosp, 47- U.S.N.R, 43-45, Lt. Comdr. Am. Med. Asn; Am. Heart Asn; fel. Am. Col. Chest Physicians; fel. Am. Col. Physicians; fel. Am. Col. Cardiol. Cardiovascular disease. Address: 1481 W. Tenth St, Indianapolis, IN 46202.

GENOWAYS, HUGH H(OWARD), b. Scottsbluff, Nebr, Dec. 24, 40; m. 63; c. 1. MAMMALOGY, ZOOGEOGRAPHY. A.B, Hastings Col, 63; Fulbright grant, Univ. West. Australia, 64; Ph.D.(syst. & ecol), Univ. Kans, 71. RES. ASSOC, MUS, TEX. TECH UNIV, 71- AAAS; Am. Soc. Mammal; Ecol. Soc. Am; Soc. Syst. Zool; Soc. Study Evolution; Am. Inst. Biol. Sci; Am. Soc. Nat. Systematics, zoogeography and ecology of North American mammals, particularly those occurring on the Great Plains, in Mexico and Central America; Chiroptera and Rodentia. Address: Museum, Texas Tech University, Lubbock, TX 79409.

GENS, THEODORE A, b. Dunkirk, N.Y, Nov. 6, 27; m. 52; c. 3. PHYSICAL CHEMISTRY. B.S, Miami (Fla), 52, M.S, 53; Ph.D.(chem), Florida, 57. Res. chemist, Oak Ridge Nat. Lab, Tenn, 57-66; LINDE DIV, UNION CARBIDE CORP, Tonawanda, 66, sr. res. chemist, 66-69, RES. SCIENTIST, TARRYTOWN RES. CTR, 69- U.S.A, 46-49, Sgt. Am. Chem. Soc. Preparation of ceramic reactor fuel materials; processing of spent reactor fuels; diffusion studies using F^{18} as tracer. Address: Linde Division, Tarrytown Research Center, Union Carbide Corp, P.O. Box 65, Tarrytown, NY 10592.

GENSAMER, MAXWELL, b. Bradford, Pa, June 3, 02; m. 50. PHYSICAL METALLURGY. B.S, Carnegie Inst. Tech, 24, M.S, 31, D.Sc.(metall), 33. Plant metallurgist, Am. Chain & Cable Co, Pa, 24-29; res. metallurgist, Carnegie Inst. Tech, 29-45, asst. prof. metall. eng, 35-38, assoc. prof, 38-43, prof, 43-45; prof. metall. & head dept. mineral tech, Pa. State, 45-47; asst. dir. res, Carnegie-Ill. Steel Corp, 47-50; Howe prof. METALL, COLUMBIA UNIV, 50-71. EMER. HOWE PROF, 71- Consult, Esso Res. & Eng; U.S, Steel Res. Lab. Fel. Am. Soc. Metals (Howe Medal, 32; Alfred E. White distinguished teacher award; Am. Inst. Mining, Metall. & Petrol. Eng; fel. Am. Inst. Mining, Metall. & Petrol. Eng. Properties of alloys, especially steel as controlled by composition and microstructure; mechanical metallurgy, properties, fracture and failure analysis. Address: P.O. Box 512, South Chatham, MA 02659.

GENSLER, WALTER J(OSEPH), b. Minneapolis, Minn, Feb. 24, 17; m. 45; c. 3. ORGANIC CHEMISTRY. B.Ch, Minnesota, 38, M.S, 40, Hormel fel, 41-42, Ph.D.(org. chem), 42. Res. chemist, Barrett div, Allied Chem. & Dye Corp, N.J, 42-43; Off. Sci. Res. & Develop. Proj, Columbia, 43-44, assoc. dir. & co-responsible investr, 44-46, lectr. ORG. CHEM, 46; instr, Harvard, 46-49; asst. prof, BOSTON UNIV, 49-51, assoc. prof, 51-57, PROF, 57- With U.S. Pub. Health Serv, 44; instr, Cooper Union, 44-46; res. assoc, Brookhaven Nat. Labs, 49; fel, Weizmann Inst. Sci, Rehovoth, Israel, 56-57; Nat. Sci. Found. prof. partic, elem. sci. study, Ed. Serv, Inc, 62; U.S. Pub. Health Serv. spec. fel. photosynthesis, Lawrence Radiation Lab, Univ. Calif, Berkeley, 64-65; mem. study sect, Nat. Insts. Health, 67-71; consult, Educ. Develop. Ctr, Mass, 70-; vis. prof, Stanford Univ, 71-72. AAAS; Am. Chem. Soc. Synthesis and structure of natural products; organic reactions. Address: Dept. of Chemistry, Boston University, 675 Commonwealth Ave, Boston, MA 02215.

GENT, ALAN N(EVILLE), b. Leicester, Eng, Nov. 11, 27; m. 49; c. 3. PHYSICS, MECHANICS. B.Sc, London, 46 & 49, Ph.D.(physics), 55. Res. asst, John Bull Rubber Co, 44-45, physicist, Brit. Rubber Prod. Res. Asn, 49-58, prin. physicist, 58-61; PROF. POLYMER PHYSICS, UNIV. AKRON, 61-, ASST. DIR. INST. POLYMER SCI, 64- Chmn, Gordon Res. Conf. Elastomers, 66, Gordon Res. Conf. Cellular Mat, 69; vis. prof, Queen Mary Col, London, 69-70. Corecipient, Mobay Award, 64. Brit. Army, 46-49, Sgt. Fel. Brit. Inst. Rubber Indust. Mechanical behavior of elastomers; deformation; fracture; crystallization; adhesion; friction and wear; stress-cracking. Address: Institute of Polymer Science, University of Akron, Akron, OH 44304.

GENTER, C(LARENCE) F(REDERICK), b. Mason Co, Mich, Dec. 27, 14; m. 40; c. 3. AGRONOMY. B.S, Mich. State Col, 38, M.S, 39; fel, Ohio State, 39-42; Ph.D.(agron), 42. Asst. statistician, bur. agr. econ, U.S. Dept. Agr, Columbia, 42; asst; hort, Illinois, 42-44; mgr. seedstocks orgn, Ill. Seed Prod. Asn, 44-47; agronomist in charge corn breeding, exp. sta, VA. POLYTECH. INST. & STATE UNIV, 47-70, PROF. AGRON, 70- AAAS; Am. Soc. Agron. Genetics of beans; x-ray mutations; vegetable breeding; maize breeding and genetics; inheritance of susceptibility of leaf blight of maize; oil and protein in maize; traits of S_1 lines of maize and their transmission; development of highly productive inbred lines of maize. Address: Dept. of Agronomy, Virginia Polytechnic Institute & State University, Blacksburg, VA 24061.

GENTILE, ADRIAN GEORGE, b. Isle of Capri, Italy, Feb. 11, 26; U.S. citizen; m. 52. ENTOMOLOGY, TAXONOMY. Dr. agr, Naples, 50; M.Sc, California, Davis, 56, Ph.D.(entom), 66. Res. asst. plant breeding, California, Davis, 56-65; res. entomologist, U.S. Dept. Agr, 66-67; U.S. Pub. Health Serv, 67-69; ASST. PROF. ENVIRON. SCI, WALTHAM FIELD STA, UNIV. MASS, 69- Am. Inst. Biol. Sci; Entom. Soc. Am; Am. Mosquito Control Asn. Taxonomy of thysanoptera; plant resistance to insects, especially in solanaceae; biological control of culicines; biological and chemical control of insect pests of ornamentals and vegetable crops. Address: Dept. of Environmental Sciences, Waltham Field Station, University of Massachusetts, Waltham, MA 02154.

GENTILE, ANTHONY L, b. N.Y.C, Apr. 23, 30; m. 57; c. 2. MINERALOGY, CRYSTALLOGRAPHY. B.S, City Col. New York, 50; M.S, N.Mex. Inst. Min. & Tech, 57; Orton, Jr, Ceramic Found. fel, Ohio State, 58-60, Ph.D.(mineral), 60. Ceramic & metall. engr, Aerojet-Gen. Corp, Calif, 60-61; MEM. TECH. STAFF CRYSTAL GROWTH, HUGHES RES. LABS, 61-, HEAD crystal chem. group, CHEM. PHYSICS DEPT, 63-68, ELECTRONIC MAT. SECT, 68- U.S.A.F, 51-54, 1st Lt. Mineral. Soc. Am; Am. Ceramic Soc; Sci. Res. Soc. Am. Crystal growth; application of chemical and physical principles to growth of single crystals, determination of crystal perfection and properties; tailoring of crystal properties by ionic substitution; evaluation of crystal defects. Address: Hughes Research Labs, 3011 Malibu Canyon Rd, Malibu, CA 90265.

GENTILE, ARTHUR C(HRISTOPHER), b. N.Y.C, Nov. 24, 26; m. 49; c. 1. PLANT PHYSIOLOGY. B.S, City Col, 48; Sc.M, Brown, 51; Ph.D.(bot), Chicago, 53. Asst. biol, City Col, 47-48; Brown, 49-51; bot, Chicago, 51-53; univ. fel, Duke, 53, Nat. Cancer Inst. fel, 54-55; plant physiologist, U.S. Forest Serv, 55-56; asst. prof. BOT, UNIV. MASS, AMHERST, 56-60, assoc. prof, 60-64, PROF, 64-, ASSOC. DEAN, GRAD. SCH, 68-, asst. dean, 65-68. U.S.A, 45-46. Am. Soc. Plant Physiol; Scand. Soc. Plant Physiol. Growth and metabolism of neoplastic plant tissues. Address: Graduate School, University of Massachusetts, Amherst, MA 01002.

GENTILE, DOMINICK E, b. Asbury Park, N.J, Jan. 12, 32; m. 58; c. 5. PHYSIOLOGY, BIOPHYSICS. B.S, Notre Dame, 53; M.D, Georgetown, 57. Fel. nephrology, Georgetown, 60-62; instr. med, sch. med, Louisville, 64-65, asst. prof, 65-68, assoc. pediat, 67-68; asst. prof. biophys. & physiol, Mt. Sinai Sch. Med, 68-69; MED, UNIV. CALIF, IRVINE, 69-71, ASSOC. PROF, 71- Med.C, U.S.N, 62-64, Lt. Comdr. Biophys. Soc. Transport physiology and biophysics; renal physiology. Address: Dept. of Medicine, University of California, Irvine, 101 Manchester Ave, Orange, CA 92668.

GENTILE, ENZO R(OMEO), b. Buenos Aires, Argentina, Dec. 14, 28; m. 58; c. 4. MATHEMATICS. D.Sc.(math), Cuyo, 57. Instr. MATH, Rutgers, 57-58, asst. prof, 60; vis. fel, Princeton, 59, asst, inst. adv. study, 60-62; assoc. prof, Nat. Univ. of the South, Argentina, 62-63; UNIV. BUENOS AIRES, 63-70, PROF, 70- Am. Math. Soc; Argentine Math. Union. Algebra; homological algebra; lie algebras. Address: Dept. of Mathematics, Faculty of Exact Sciences, University of Buenos Aires, Peru 222, Buenos Aires, Argentina.

GENTILE, PHILIP, b. N.Y.C, Feb. 27, 23. INORGANIC CHEMISTRY. B.S, City Col, 43; M.S, Polytech. Inst. Brooklyn, 48; Atomic Energy Comn. fel, Texas, 52-55, Ph.D.(chem), 55. Anal. chemist, Ledoux & Co, N.Y, 43-44; res. chemist, Nat. Starch Prods, N.Y, 44-46; supvr, Nat. Lead of Ohio, 55-57; asst. prof. CHEM, FORDHAM UNIV, 57-66, assoc. prof, 66-69, PROF, 69- Am. Chem. Soc. Nonaqueous solvents; kinetics; chelates; inorganic synthesis; solid-solid interactions. Address: Dept. of Chemistry, Fordham University, Bronx, NY 10458.

GENTILE, RALPH G, b. Palermo, Italy, May 13, 14; nat; m. 53. c. 4. ELECTRICAL ENGINEERING. Dr.Eng, Rome, Italy, 38 & 40. Fel. aeronaut. eng, Rome Inst. Advan. Studies, 41; res. engr, U.S. Govt, 43-44; elec. engr, Roger Williams Eng. Co, 44-45; chief engr, TRM Elec. Co, 45-49; fel. nuclear med, Argonne Nat. Lab, 54; res. group leader, Monsanto Chem. Co, 60-63; MGR. PHYSICS SECT, BABCOCK & WILCOX CO, 63- Italian Air Force, 41-43, Lt.(jg). AAAS; Inst. Elec. & Electronics Eng; Am. Phys. Soc; Instrument Soc. Am. Solid state electronics; industrial instrumentation; energy conversion. Address: 415 Vincent Blvd, Alliance, OH 44601.

GENTILE, RICHARD J, b. St. Louis, Mo, June 25, 29. STRATIGRAPHY. B.A, Missouri, Columbia, 56, M.A, 58, Ph.D.(geol), Rolla, 65. Geologist, Mo. Geol. Surv, Rolla, 58-65, chief geologist & head of coal geol. div, 65-66; asst. prof. GEOL, UNIV. MO-KANSAS CITY, 66-70, ASSOC. PROF, 70-, faculty res. grants, 68. U.S.A, 51-52. Am. Asn. Petrol. Geol; Geol. Soc. Am; Asn. Eng. Geol. Mineral resources studies of Missouri, especially coal; paleo sedimentological mapping of Pennsylvanian age strata of western Missouri; relationship of structural movement to sedimentation. Address: Dept. of Geology & Geography, University of Missouri-Kansas City, 5100 Rockhill Rd, Kansas City, MO 64110.

GENTILI, BRUNO, b. Chicago, Ill, Nov. 25, 16; m. 56; c. 2. CHEMISTRY. B.Sc, California, Berkeley, 52. Chemist, West. Precipitation Corp, Calif, 53-54; RES. CHEMIST, AGR. RES. SERV, U.S. DEPT. AGR, 54- U.S. Dept. Agr. Outstanding Performance Award, 65. Med.C, U.S.A, 42-43. Am. Chem. Soc. Basic research on the flavonoid composition of plant species, especially citrus species; preparation of new artificial sweeteners from citrus flavonoids. Address: U.S. Dept. of Agriculture, 263 S. Chester Ave, Pasadena, CA 91106.

GENTLE, KENNETH W, b. Oak Park, Ill, Oct. 27, 40. PLASMA PHYSICS. S.B, Mass. Inst. Tech, 62, Nat. Sci. Found. fel, 62-65, Ph.D.(physics), 66. Instr. PHYSICS, Mass. Inst. Technol, 65-66; asst. prof, UNIV. TEX, AUSTIN, 66-70, ASSOC. PROF, 70- Am. Phys. Soc. Instabilities; linear and nonlinear wave phenomena in plasmas. Address: Dept. of Physics, University of Texas at Austin, Austin, TX 78712.

GENTLEMAN, W(ILLIAM) MORVEN, b. Calgary, Alta, July 6, 42; m. 67; c. 2. MATHEMATICS, COMPUTER SCIENCE. B.Sc, McGill Univ, 63; Woodrow Wilson fel, Princeton, 63, M.A, 64, Ph.D.(math), 66. Mem. Tech. staff, Bell Tel. Labs, 65-69; asst. prof. APPL. ANAL. & COMPUT. SCI, UNIV. WATERLOO, 69-70, ASSOC. PROF, 70- Sr. res. fel, Nat. Phys.

Lab, 68-69. Asn. Comput. Mach; Soc. Indust. & Appl. Math. Numerical algorithms and analysis; symbolic algebraic manipulation; programming language design; computer networks. Address: Dept. of Applied Analysis & Computer Science, University of Waterloo, Waterloo, Ont, Can.

GENTNER, ROBERT F, b. N.Y.C, Oct. 31, 38. PHYSICAL CHEMISTRY, ATOMIC PHYSICS. B.S, St. John's Univ, 60, M.S, 62, Ph.D.(phys. chem), 68; Nat. Defense Educ. Act fel, Polytech. Inst. Brooklyn, 62-63. RES. CHEMIST, PICATINNY ARSENAL, DOVER, N.J, 69- Am. Chem. Soc; Am. Phys. Soc. Quantum mechanical calculations for atomic systems; detonation physics. Address: 20-30 126th St, College Point, Flushing, NY 11356.

GENTNER, WALTER A(NDREW), b. Washington, D.C, April 22, 22; m. 48. PLANT PHYSIOLOGY. A.B, George Washington, 51, M.A, 52, Ph.D, 62. Managing botanist, commercial brush control, R/W Maintenance Corp, N.Y, 52-55; PLANT PHYSIOLOGIST WEED CONTROL, PLANT SCI. RES. DIV, AGR. RES. SERV, U.S. DEPT. AGR, 55- U.S.C.G, 40-46. Weed Sci. Soc. Am; Am. Soc. Plant Physiol. Evaluation of chemicals for herbicidal properties; development of weed control practices and equipment; agronomic ecology; relationships between chemical structure and herbicidal activity. Address: Plant Science Research Division, Agricultural Research Service, U.S. Dept. of Agriculture, Beltsville, MD 20705.

GENTON, EDWARD, b. Norwood, Ohio, Jan. 21, 30; m; c. 3. MEDICINE. B.S, Univ. Cincinnati, 52, M.D, 57. Instr. MED, MED. CTR, UNIV. COLO, DENVER, 62-63, asst. prof, 66-68, ASSOC. PROF, 68-, V.CHMN. DEPT, 69-, CHMN. FACULTY COUN, 70-, intern, 57-58, sr. asst. resident, 59-60, fel. cardiol, 60-62, chief resident, 62-63, acting chmn. dept, 68-69. Jr. asst. resident, Duke Univ, 58-59; res. fel, Wash. Univ, 63-65; mem. coun. clin. cardiol. & mem. exec. comt, coun. thrombosis, Am. Heart Asn; mem. comt. thrombosis, Nat. Heart & Lung Inst. Dipl, Am. Bd. Internal Med; Am. Bd. Cardiovasc. Disease. Am. Fedn. Clin. Res; Am. Col. Physicians; Am. Col. Cardiol; Am. Heart Asn; Int. Soc. Thrombosis & Haemostasis. Cardiovascular and thromboembolic diseases. Address: Dept. of Medicine, University of Colorado Medical Center, 4200 E. Ninth Ave, Denver, CO 80220.

GENTRY, CLAUDE EDWIN, b. Oak Hill, W.Va, Aug. 3, 30; m. 55; c. 3. PLANT PHYSIOLOGY, AGRONOMY. B.S, Kentucky, 58, M.S, 60; Ph.D. (plant path), 68. Assoc. agronomist, BEREA COL, 60-69, ASSOC. PROF. AGRON, 69- Fel, Kentucky, 68. U.S.N, 51-55. Am. Phytopath. Soc. Alkaloid content of tall fescue; plant pathology, including the interrelationship of Rhizoctonia solani, environment and genotype on the alkaloid content of tall fescue. Address: Depts. of Agriculture & Biology, Berea College, Berea, KY 40403.

GENTRY, FRANK C(OOK), b. Mangum, Okla, May 17, 03; m. 41; c. 2. MATHEMATICS. A.B, Oklahoma, 29, M.S, 30; Tulane, 30-32; Ph.D.(math), Illinois, 37. Asst. math, Oklahoma, 29-30, asst. prof, 37-38; instr, Tulane, 30-32; asst, Illinois, 34-37; asst. prof, La. Polytech, 38-41, assoc. prof, 41-42, prof, 45-48; ground sch. instr. physics, Pre-flight Sch, U.S. Navy, 42-43; asst. prof. MATH, New Mexico, 43-45; assoc. prof, Ariz. State Col, 48-49, prof, 49-51; assoc. prof, New Mexico, 51-60, prof, 60-64; assoc. prof, UNIV. OF THE PAC, 64-65, PROF, 65- Math. Asn. Am. Algebraic geometry. Address: Dept. of Mathematics, University of the Pacific, Stockton, CA 95204.

GENTRY, I(VEY) C(LENTON), b. Roxboro, N.C, Apr. 7, 19; m. 43; c. 3. MATHEMATICS. B.S, Wake Forest Col, 40, N.Y. Univ, 43; M.A, Duke, 47, Ph.D.(math), 49. Asst. prof. MATH, WAKE FOREST UNIV, 49-52, assoc. prof, 52-56, PROF, 56- U.S.A.A.F, 42-45. Am. Math. Soc; Math. Asn. Am. Topology. Address: Box 7301, Reynolda Station, Winston-Salem, NC 27106.

GENTRY, J(OHN) T(ILMON), b. St. Louis, Mo, Dec. 31, 21; m. 49; c. 5. PUBLIC HEALTH, HOSPITAL ADMINISTRATION. A.B, Washington (St. Louis), 44, B.S. & M.D, 48; M.P.H, Harvard, 51. Intern, clins, Chicago, 48-49; res. physician, State Dept. Health, N.Y, 49-50; asst. to chief epidemiol. br, Communicable Disease Ctr, 51-52, health off, Great Anchorage Health Dist, Alaska, 52-53; dist. state health off, State Dept. Health, N.Y, 54-57, regional health dir, 57-64; assoc. prof. PUB. HEALTH ADMIN, SCH. PUB. HEALTH, UNIV. N.C, CHAPEL HILL, 64-68, PROF. & DIR. PROG. MED. CARE & HEALTH SERV. ADMIN, 68-, RES. PROF, INST. RES. SOCIAL SCI, UNIV, 70-, asst. dean prog. develop, sch. pub. health, 64-68. Clin. asst. prof, State Univ. N.Y. Upstate Med. Ctr, 55-63, clin. assoc. prof, 63-64; dep. chief health div. & chief med. educ. br, U.S. Agency Int. Develop. mission, India, 61-63; consult, Nat. Comn. Community Health Serv, 64-; adj. prof, grad. prog. hosp, admin, Duke Univ, 70- AAAS; fel. Am. Pub. Health Asn; N.Y. Acad. Sci. Identification of social, psychological and economic factors that enhance or impede the implementation of community health services. Address: School of Public Health, University of North Carolina at Chapel Hill, Chapel Hill, NC 27514.

GENTRY, JOSEPH W(ESLEY), b. Roxboro, N.C, Mar. 3, 23; m. 50; c. 2. ENTOMOLOGY. A.B, North Carolina, 45; N.C. State Col, 52; M.S, George Washington, 56. Control supvr, div. golden nematode control, bur. entom. & plant quarantine, U.S. DEPT. AGR, 47-52, agriculturist in charge reports & records unit, econ. insect. surv. sect, plant pest control div, AGR. RES. SERV, 52-58, asst. in charge insect detection surv. & detection oper, 58-60, asst. coordinator & surv. specialist, Regional Insect Control Proj, Beirut, Lebanon, 60-62, staff specialist prog. anal, 63-64, staff specialist in charge pesticide safety & monitoring, 64-66, chief staff off. surv. & detection opers, 66-68, ASST. DIR. PLANT PROTECTION DIV, 68- Consult, Cent. Treaty Orgn. & Food & Agr. Orgn. Entom. Soc. Am. Detecting insect pests new to the United States. Address: 4207 Wicomico Ave, Beltsville, MD 20705.

GENTRY, KARL RAY, b. Roxboro, N.C, Apr. 13, 38. MATHEMATICS. B.A, Wake Forest Univ, 60; M.A, Univ. Ga, 62, Ph.D.(math), 65. ASSOC. PROF. MATH, UNIV. N.C, GREENSBORO, 65- Am. Math. Soc. General topology. Address: Dept. of Mathematics, University of North Carolina at Greensboro, Greensboro, NC 27412.

GENTRY, ROBERT C(ECIL), b. Paducah, Ky, Nov. 29, 16; m. 48; c. 4. METEOROLOGY. B.S, Murray State Col, 37; Mass. Inst. Tech, 41-42; Chicago, 52; Ph.D, Fla. State, 63. Teacher, pub. sch, Ky, 37-40; res. forecaster, U.S. WEATHER BUR, 42-55, asst. dir, Nat. Hurricane Res. Proj, 55-59, acting dir, 59-61, dir, 61-64, DIR, NAT. HURRICANE RES. LAB, 64-, DIR. PROJ. STORMFURY, 66- Gold medal award for distinguished achievement fed. serv, U.S. Dept. Commerce, 70. Fel. Am. Meteorol. Soc; Am. Geophys. Union. Tropical meteorology, especially hurricanes. Address: National Hurricane Research Lab, P.O. Box 8265, Coral Gables, FL 33124.

GENTRY, ROBERT E(DGAR), JR, b. Denver, Colo, Aug. 19, 27; m. 50; c. 5. ORGANIC CHEMISTRY. Ph.D, Stanford, 54. Res. chemist, G.D. Searle & Co, 54-55; Dow Chem. Co, 55-56, asst. purchasing agent, 56-58; sr. chemist, Aerojet-Gen. Corp. Div, Gen. Tire & Rubber Co, 58-61, mgr. solid rocket opers, D.C, 61-67; DIR. TECH. SERVS, PRINCETON CHEM. RES. INC, 67- Heterocyclics; steroid synthesis; synthetic fibers; solid propellants; raw material purchasing; technical sales management; market analysis. Address: 26 Library Pl, Princeton, NJ 08540.

GENTRY, ROBERT F(RANCIS), b. Topeka, Kans, May 31, 21; m. 42; c. 3. POULTRY PATHOLOGY. D.V.M, Kansas State, 44; M.A, Missouri, 47; Ph.D, Mich. State, 53. Instr. vet. sci, Missouri, 44-47; veterinarian, U.S. Regional Poultry Res. Lab, Mich, 47-53; PROF. VET. SCI, VET. RES. CTR, PA. STATE UNIV, 54- U.S.A, 42-44, Vet.C, Res, 45-, Capt. Am. Vet. Med. Asn; Poultry Sci. Asn; U.S. Animal Health Asn; Am. Asn. Avian Path; Conf. Res. Workers Animal Diseases. Avian diseases with particular emphasis on differential diagnosis using fluorescent antibody techniques; the relationship of avian pleuropneumonialike organisms and bacteria L-forms; etiology and control of chronic respiratory disease; factors influencing the development of immunity; the nature of the virus of avian visceral lymphomatosis. Address: Veterinary Research Center, Pennsylvania State University, University Park, PA 16802.

GENTRY, ROBERT VANCE, b. Chattanooga, Tenn, July 9, 33; m. 53; c. 3. PHYSICS. B.S, Florida, 55, M.S, 56; Southern Methodist, 56-57; Texas Christian, 57-58; Ga. Inst. Tech, 62. Nuclear engr, Gen. Dynamics/Convair, Tex, 56-57, aerophys. engr, 57-58; sr. engr, Martin Co, Fla, 58-59; instr. math, Florida, 59-61; Walla Walla Col, 61-62; physics, Ga. Inst. Tech, 62-64; res. physicist, Archaeol. Res. Found, 65-66; RES. PROF. GEOPHYS, COLUMBIA UNION COL, 66- Nat. Sci. Found. Modern Physics Inst. summer fel, Oak Ridge Inst. Nuclear Studies, 62; guest scientist, chem. div, Oak Ridge Nat. Lab, 71- AAAS; Am. Phys. Soc; Am. Geophys Union; Am. Sci. Affiliation. Radioactive halos with regard to the age of the earth, by the invariance of the decay constant, and their cosmological implications. Address: Dept. of Physics, Columbia Union College, Takoma Park, MD 20012.

GENTRY, WILLARD M(AX), JR, b. Omaha, Nebr, May 2, 23; m. 49; c. 4. ORGANIC CHEMISTRY. A.B, Harvard, 43, A.M, 48; Ph.D.(chem), Boston, 51. Chemist, DOW CHEM. CO, 51-63, group leader, 63-70, ANAL. COORD, 70- U.S.A, 43-46, Res, 46-68, Lt. Col. Am. Chem. Soc; Sci. Res. Soc. Am. Reactions of colored isocyanates with fabrics; development of new organic chemicals and pharmaceuticals; agricultural chemicals residue analysis. Address: 713 Crescent Dr, Midland, MI 48640.

GENTZLER, ROBERT E, b. York, Pa, Aug. 24, 43; m. 65; c. 2. PHYSICAL CHEMISTRY. M.A, Dartmouth Col, 67; Ph.D.(chem), Univ. Mass, 70. RES. CHEMIST, ELECTROCHEM. DEPT, CHESTNUT RUN LAB, E.I. DU PONT DE NEMOURS & CO, INC, 70- Am. Chem. Soc. Nuclear magnetic resonance studies of probe nuclei in solvation and inorganic complex environments. Address: Electrochemicals Dept, Chestnut Run Lab, E.I. du Pont de Nemours & Co, Inc, Wilmington, DE 19898.

GENUA, ALBERT JOHN, b. Waterbury, Conn, Nov. 13, 10; m. 34; c. 2. PHYSICAL SCIENCE. B.S, Catholic Univ, 34; M.A, Columbia, 42; Ph.D. (sci. educ), Fordham, 52. PROF. physics, Seton Hall, 45-50; PHYS. SCI, WESTFIELD STATE COL, 57-, CHMN. DEPT, 52- Vis. lectr, Univ. Mass, 66. AAAS; Am. Inst. Physics. Physics; elementary and secondary science methods. Address: Dept. of Physical Science, Westfield State College, Westfield, MA 01085.

GENUNG, LEO B(LUNT), b. Osage, Iowa, Sept. 7, 06; m. 29; c. 2. CHEMISTRY. B.A, Cornell Col.(Iowa), 28; fel, Brown, 28-29, Sc.M, 29; Ph.D. (chem), Ohio State, 33. Asst. chem, Ohio State, 29-33; res. chemist, Eastman Kodak Co, 33-35, sect. supvr, cellulose tech. div, 35-67, polymer tech. div, 67-71; RETIRED. Am. Chem. Soc; Am. Soc. Test. & Mat. Analysis, composition and properties of cellulose esters and synthetic resins. Address: 57 Harvington Dr, Rochester, NY 14617.

GENYS, JOHN B, b. Marijampole, Lithuania, Aug. 12, 23; U.S. citizen; m. 65; c. 2. FOREST GENETICS. Dipl, Göttingen, 49; Fox Trust Fund fel, 58; Ph.D.(forestry), Mich. State, 60. Res. aid forestry, Lake States Forest Exp. Sta, U.S. Dept. Agr, Minn, 55-57; asst, Mich. State, 57-60; instr. forest soils, Wisconsin, 60-61; asst. res. prof. NATURAL RESOURCES INST, UNIV. MD, COLLEGE PARK, 61-66, RES. ASSOC. PROF, 66- Soc. Am. Foresters. Forest genetics, including studies of racial variation, polyploidy, artificial hybridization, tree introduction. Address: Natural Resources Institute, University of Maryland, College Park, MD 20742.

GENZER, JEROME D(ANIEL), b. N.Y.C, July 23, 25; m. 50; c. 2. ORGANIC CHEMISTRY. B.A, N.Y. Univ, 47; M.A, Ind. Univ. Bloomington, 48. Jr. chemist, WARNER-LAMBERT CO, 48-53, scientist, 53-56, sr. scientist, 56-63; SR. RES. ASSOC, CHEM. DEVELOP, 63- U.S.N, 44-46. Am. Chem. Soc. Organic synthesis; process research and development of organic chemicals for medicinal use from laboratory through pilot plant in preparation for production, including chemical and equipment design and evaluation and cost evaluation. Address: Warner-Lambert Co, 170 Tabor Rd, Morris Plains NJ 07950.

GENZLINGER, BRYCE S(HERMAN), b. Huntingdon Valley, Pa, Apr. 17, 28; m. 53; c. 5. MANAGEMENT SCIENCE, COMPUTER SYSTEMS. B.S, Okla. State, 51; M.S, Va. Polytech, 56; Nat. Sci. Found. fel. & Ford Found. fel, Northwestern, 61-63. Proj. engr, Honeywell Co, 51, 54; asst. prof. indust. eng, Va. Polytech, 54-56; res. dir. & asst. prof, Syracuse, 56-60; assoc. prof, Drexel Inst. Tech, 61-63; mgr. opers. anal, Burroughs Corp, 63-66, dir. opers. anal, West. Union Info. Systs. Div, 66-67; v.pres. info. & comput. systs, Banco Credito, 67-69; mem. bd. dir. & treas, Scott Res. Labs, 69-70; V.PRES. COMPUT. CONSULT. SERV, FRANKLIN COMPUT. ASSOCS, N.Y.C, 71- U.S.A.F, 52-53, 1st Lt. Am. Soc. Eng. Educ; Am. Inst. Indust. Eng; Opers. Res. Soc. Am; Inst. Mgt. Sci; Asn. Comput. Mach. Management information systems; operations analysis; business computer systems; financial administration; market planning and new business ventures. Address: 693 Woodward Dr, Huntingdon Valley, PA 19006.

GEOFFRION, C(LAUDE), b. Quebec, Que, Mar. 17, 18; m. 49; c. 4. PHYSICS. B.A, Seminaire de Que, 39; B.Sc.A, Laval, 44, M.Sc, 47, D.Sc.(physics), 51. Lectr. physics, LAVAL UNIV, 44-45, asst. prof, 45-50, assoc. prof, 50-55, PROF, 55-69, NUCLEAR PHYSICS, 69-, dean faculty sci, 61-69. Am. Phys. Soc; Can. Asn. Physicists. Beta-ray spectrometry. Address: Dept. of Nuclear Physics, Laval University, Quebec, Que, Can.

GEOKEZAS, MELETIOS, b. Erythrai, Greece, June 10, 36; U.S. citizen; m. 63; c. 2. INFORMATION SCIENCE, ELECTRICAL ENGINEERING. B.S, Univ. Wash, 60, M.S, 63, Ph.D.(elec. eng), 68. Res. engr, Boeing Co, 61-63, 65-68; PRIN. RES. SCIENTIST, HONEYWELL, INC, 68- Inst. Elec. & Electronics Eng. Spectral analysis and classification of underwater acoustic signals; digital filtering and error analysis of digital filtering; digital simulation of energy detectors; scattering coefficient of electromagnetic waves from rough surfaces; information theory. Address: Systems & Research Center, Honeywell, Inc, 2345 Walnut St, St. Paul, MN 55113.

GEORAS, HARRY STEVE, b. Bluefield, W.Va, Mar. 17, 24; m. 58; c. 2. CIVIL ENGINEERING, APPLIED MECHANICS. Dipl, Eng. Univ. Athens, Greece, 52; Polytech. Inst. Brooklyn, 54-56; fel, Michigan, 56-57, M.S, 58; Ph.D.(appl. mech), California, Berkeley, 64. Stress analyst, Grumann Aircraft Eng. Corp, 54-56; asst. appl. mech, Michigan, 57-58; California, Berkeley, 58-63; sr. stress engr, United Tech. Ctr, 63-65; mathematician, Shell Develop. Co, 65-68; ASSOC. PROF. GEN. ENG, UNIV. P.R, MAYAGUEZ, 68- Applied mechanics, particularly plates and shells; theory of elasticity; plasticity; continuum mechanics. Address: Dept. of General Engineering, University of Puerto Rico, Mayaguez, PR 00708.

GEORG, LUCILLE K(ATHERINE) (MRS. W. L. PICKARD), b. Ann Arbor, Mich, Oct. 9, 12; m. 50. MYCOLOGY. B.S, Univ. Mich, 33, M.S, 34; Ph.D.(bact), Columbia Univ, 48. Asst. mycol, col. physicians & surgeons, Columbia Univ, 46-48; ASST. PROF. MICROBIOL, SCH. MED, EMORY UNIV, 52-; ASST. CHIEF MYCOL. SECT, CTR. DISEASE CONTROL, HEALTH SERV. & MENT. HEALTH ADMIN, U.S. PUB. HEALTH SERV, U.S. DEPT. HEALTH, EDUC, & WELFARE, 49- Adj. assoc. prof, Ga. State Univ, 71. U.S. Dept. Health, Educ. & Welfare Supvr. Serv. Award, 61; Dipl, Am. Bd. Med. Microbiol, 62. Diagnostic methods in medical mycology; microaerophilic actinomycetes. Address: Mycology Section, Center for Disease Control, Health Services & Mental Health Administration, U.S. Public Health Service, U.S. Dept. of Health, Education, & Welfare, Atlanta, GA 30333.

GEORGAKIS, CONSTANTINE, b. Vonitsa, Greece, Mar. 14, 37; U.S. citizen. MATHEMATICS, STATISTICS. B.S, DePaul Univ, 61, M.S, 63; Ph.D.(math), Ill. Inst. Technol, 69. Instr. MATH, DePAUL UNIV, 62-67, ASST. PROF, 68- Dir. undergrad. res. prog, Nat. Sci. Found, 68-70. Am. Math. Soc; Math. Soc. Am. Fourier analysis on groups, probability theory and mathematical statistics. Address: 2827 N. Cambridge Ave, Chicago, IL 60657.

GEORGE, A(LBERT) EL DEEB, b. Alexandria, Egypt, May 1, 36. PETROLEUM CHEMISTRY. B.Sc, Univ. Cairo, 57, M.Sc, 62, Ph.D.(petrol. chem), 67; dipl. petrol. ref, Enrico Mattei Inst, Milan, Italy, 69. Res. asst, petrol chem. sect, Nat. Res. Ctr, Cairo, Egypt, 58-67, res. supvr. petrol. technol. sect, 67-69; NAT. RES. COUN. CAN. FEL, FUELS RES. CTR, 69- Ital. Govt. training grant, ENI Petrol. Corp, Italy, 68-69. Am. Chem. Soc. Chemistry of heavy petroleum fractions; analysis of hydrocarbons and sulfur compounds in petroleum distillates; hydro-desulfurization of heavy crude oils and their different fractions using high pressure catalytic process and different catalysts; gas chromatographic analysis of sulfur compounds in bitumen heavy distillates. Address: c/o Fuels Research Center, 555 Booth St, Ottawa 7, Ont, Can.

GEORGE, A(LBERT) R(ICHARD), b. N.Y.C, Mar. 12, 38; m. 59; c. 3. AEROSPACE ENGINEERING. B.S.E, Princeton, 59, Guggenheim fel, 59-60, Nat. Sci. Found. fel, 60-63, M.A, 61, Ph.D.(aerospace & mech. sci), 64. Res. asst. aerospace eng, Princeton, 63-64, res. assoc, 64; asst. prof. AEROSPACE ENG, GRAD. SCH. AEROSPACE ENG, CORNELL UNIV, 64-69, ASSOC. PROF, 69- Vis. asst. prof, Univ. Wash, 64-65; vis. sr. res. fel, Southampton Univ, U.K, 71-72. Am. Inst. Aeronaut. & Astronaut; Am. Phys. Soc; Am. Meteorol. Soc. Aerodynamics; fluid and gas dynamics; acoustics; sonic boom; automobile dynamics; hypersonic and rotational flow. Address: Graduate School of Aerospace Engineering, Grumman Hall, Cornell University, Ithaca, NY 14850.

GEORGE, BOYD W(INSTON), b. Burlington, Iowa, Mar. 17, 25; m. 49; c. 3. ENTOMOLOGY. B.A, Iowa, 48, M.S, 50; Nat. Sci. Found. fel, Iowa State Col, 56, Ph.D.(entom), 57. Instr. zool, South Dakota, 50-54; Iowa State, 56-57, asst. prof, 57-61; entomologist, North. Grain Insects Res. Lab, ENTOM. RES. DIV, AGR. RES. SERV, U.S. DEPT. AGR, 61-65, dir. & invests. leader, lab, 65-68, ASST. CHIEF VEG. & SPECIALTY CROPS INSECT RES. BR, PLANT INDUST. STA, 68- U.S.A.A.F, 43-45, Res, 45-55, 1st Lt. AAAS; Entom. Soc. Am. Physiology of insects, and relationships between insects and their host plants. Address: U.S. Dept. of Agriculture, Entomology Research Division, Plant Industry Station, Beltsville, MD 20705.

GEORGE, CARL JOSEPH WINDER, b. Cincinnati, Ohio, Oct. 24, 30; m. 62. MARINE ECOLOGY. B.S, Michigan, 56; Ph.D.(biol), Harvard, 60. Fishery biologist, Woods Hole Oceanog. Inst, spring & summer 56; Friday Harbor Biol. Labs, San Juan Islands, summer 57; Woods Hole Oceanog. Inst, summer 58; asst. prof. BIOL, San Fernando Valley State Col, 60-61; American Univ. Beirut, 61-67, Rockefeller Found. grants, 63-67; ASSOC. PROF, UNION COL.(N.Y), 67- Fishery biologist, Stone Labs, summer 61; partic. fel, UNESCO Int. Cong, Moscow, 66; Nature Conserv. fel, summer 68; Smithsonian Inst. res. support grant fisheries in U.A.R, 68- Ord.C, U.S.A, 51-53. Am. Soc. Ichthyol. & Herpet; Ecol. Soc. Am; Am. Soc. Limnol. & Oceanog. Influence of man-made structures on the ecology of the Eastern Mediterranean Sea; influence of the Sadd el Aali on fisheries; ecology of fishes of the Hudson River; ecological implications of the proposed sea-level canal in Panama. Address: Dept. of Biological Sciences, Union College, Schenectady, NY 12308.

GEORGE, CHARLES FLOYD, JR, b. Brownwood, Tex, Dec. 12, 37; m. 63. ELECTRICAL ENGINEERING, MATHEMATICS. B.S, Texas, 61, univ. fel, 61-62, Nat. Sci. Found. fel, 62-63, Ph.D.(elec. eng, math), 63. Sr. res. engr, Atlantic Ref. Co, 63-67, PRIN. RES. ENGR, RES. & DEVELOP. DEPT, ATLANTIC RICHFIELD CO, 67- Engr, Tex. Instruments, Inc, summers 61 & 62. Am. Geophys. Union; Inst. Elec. & Electronics Eng; Soc. Explor. Geophys; Soc. Petrol. Eng. Communication theory; geophysics. Address: Research & Development Dept, Atlantic Richfield Co, P.O. Box 2819, Dallas, TX 75221.

GEORGE, CHARLES REDGENAL, b. Faison, N.C, July 21, 38; m. 61; c. 2. ENTOMOLOGY, PARASITOLOGY. B.S, A&T Col. N.C, 60, Nat. Sci. Found. stipend, summer 63; M.S, Okla. State Univ, 65; Nat. Insts. Health trainee, Cornell Univ, 67-70, Ph.D.(entom), 70. Teacher, high sch, N.C, 60-64; partic, Nat. Sci. Found. Acad. Year Inst, Okla. State Univ, 64-65; instr. biol, Fayetteville State Col, 65-66; res. asst. insect path, Cornell Univ, 66-67; ASSOC. PROF. BIOL, N.C. CENT. UNIV, 70- Am. Soc. Parasitol; Entom. Soc. Am; Soc. Invert. Path. Effects of malnutrition on growth and mortality of the red rust flour beetle, Tribolium castaneum parasitized by Nosema whitei Weiser. Address: Dept. of Biology, North Carolina Central University, Durham, NC 27707.

GEORGE, DANIEL E(UGENE), b. Idaho Falls, Idaho, Mar. 13, 35; m. 58; c. 2. ORGANIC CHEMISTRY. B.S, Idaho, 56, Nat. Defense Ed. Act. fel, 59-62, Ph.D.(org. chem), 63. CHEMIST, Monsanto Co, 58-59; PLASTICS DEPT, E.I. DU PONT DE NEMOURS & CO, INC, 62- U.S.A, 56-58, Res, 58-65, Capt. Am. Chem. Soc. Carbanion rearrangements; polymer synthesis; polyimide properties; high temperature polymers. Address: E.I. du Pont de Nemours & Co, Inc, Plastics Dept, Experimental Station, Wilmington, DE 19898.

GEORGE, DICK L(EON), b. Oklahoma City, Okla, Mar. 10, 36; m. 57; c. 2. MATHEMATICS. B.S, Okla. State, 58; Ph.D.(math), Duke, 62. Instr. MATH, N.C. State Col, 61-62, asst. prof, 62-63; assoc. prof, Charlotte Col, 63-65; Trinity Univ.(Tex), 65-68; PROF. & CHMN. DEPT, GA. COL. MILLEDGEVILLE, 68- Am. Math. Soc; Math. Asn. Am; Soc. Indust. & Appl. Math. Mixed boundary value problems in thermoelasticity. Address: Dept. of Mathematics, Georgia College at Milledgeville, Milledgeville, GA 31061.

GEORGE, DONALD W(AYNE), b. Topeka, Kans, May 1, 21; m. 43; c. 2. PLANT BREEDING. B.S, Kans. State Col, 48, M.S, 49. Asst. agronomist, Texas Agr. Exp. Sta, 49-51; asst. plant breeder, Arizona, 51-54; AGRONOMIST, Pendleton Br. Exp. Sta, PLANT SCI. RES. DIV, AGR. RES. SERV, U.S. DEPT. AGR, 54-65, WASH. STATE UNIV, 65- U.S.A, 44-46. Cold and frost hardiness; vernalization, photoperiod and temperature influence on development; crown placement; coleoptile tiller and secondary crown development; adaptation to early seeding for erosion-pollution control; post harvest dormancy of wheat. Address: Dept. of Agronomy, 119 Johnson Hall, Washington State University, Pullman, WA 99163.

GEORGE, EDWARD THOMAS, b. North Adams, Mass, Dec. 27, 25; m. 55; c. 4. CHEMICAL ENGINEERING. B.S, Worcester Polytech, 47, M.S, 49; D.Eng.(chem. eng), Yale, 53. Res. scientist, B.F. Goodrich Chem. Co, Ohio, 53-57; eng. develop. engr, Sci. Design Co, N.Y, 57-59, comput. dept. mgr, 59-60; res. develop. mgr. comput. dept. dir, Quantum, Inc, Conn, 60-62; pres, founder & owner, Conn. Sci. Ctr, Inc, 62-69; ASSOC. PROF. INDUST. ENG, UNIV. NEW HAVEN, 70- Teaching assignments, New Haven Col, 64-70; chmn. air & water conserv. comt, Chamber of Commerce, 66- N.Y. Acad. Sci; fel. Am. Inst. Chem. Address: 39 Edgemere Rd, Hamden, CT 06517.

GEORGE, ELMER, JR, b. Kanosh, Utah, Apr. 15, 28; m. 55; c. 4. MICROBIOLOGY, BIOCHEMISTRY. B.S, Utah State, 54, M.S, 56; Ph.D.(dairy indust), Minnesota, 64. Creamery foreman, instr. & res, Utah State, 54-55; res. asst, Minnesota, 55-58, res. & teaching fel, 58-60; LAB. DIR, Qual. Control Cmt, St. Paul, Minn, 60-64; N.Y. STATE FOOD LAB, 64- Consult, Health, Educ. & Welfare-Food & Drug Admin. U.S.A, 46-48. Am. Dairy Sci. Asn; Am. Soc. Microbiol; Asn. Off. Anal. Chem. Applied microbiology; chemistry of foods. Address: Dept. of Agriculture & Markets, N.Y. State Food Lab, Bldg. 7, State Campus, Albany, NY 12226.

GEORGE, FREDERICK W, III, b. Pittsburgh, Pa, June 25, 23; div; c. 4. RADIOLOGY, RADIOTHERAPY. B.S, Univ. Pittsburgh, 44, M.D, 47. Resident radiother, Argonne Cancer Res. Hosp, Univ. Chicago, 54-55; mem. staff, U.S. Naval Hosp, San Diego, Calif, 55-57, head dept. radiol, 57-61, 63-66, chief radiol. serv, Long Beach, 66-67; PROF. RADIOL. & DIR. RADIATION THER, SCH. MED, UNIV. SOUTH. CALIF, 67- Consult, U.S. Naval Hosp, Long Beach; Surgeon Gen, U.S. Navy; Nat. Cancer Inst. Med.C, U.S.N, 48-67, Capt. AAAS; Am. Nuclear Soc; Am. Radium Soc; Am. Fedn. Clin. Res; Am. Soc. Therapeut. Radiol; Am. Med. Asn; Radiation Res. Soc; Asn. Mil. Surg. U.S; Radiol. Soc. N.Am; Am. Col. Radiol; Soc. Nuclear Med. Clinical research in radiotherapy, particularly prostate cancer, testicle cancer, special time dose technics, computer analysis and dosimetry and computer-controlled radiotherapy systems; investigation of newer cancer teaching systems, particularly video taping and teaching modules; neutron radiobiology, particularly activation analysis of trace elements in tissue. Address: Radiation Therapy, Room 1P-2, Los Angeles County-University of Southern California Medical Center, 1200 N. State St, Los Angeles, CA 90033.

GEORGE, HARVEY, b. New York, N.Y, Apr. 28, 35; m. 57; c. 3. BIOCHEMISTRY, CLINICAL PATHOLOGY. B.A, Cornell Univ, 57; M.S, Univ. Tenn, 61, Monsanto summer fel. & Ph.D.(biochem), 63. Res. fel. biochem, sch. med, Tufts Univ, 64-67; sr. biochemist, Collab. Res, Inc, Mass, 67-68, dir. biochem. res, 68-70; DIR. CLIN. LABS, LAHEY CLIN. FOUND, 70- Asst. res. prof, med. sch, Boston Univ, 67-69. AAAS; Am. Chem. Soc; N.Y.

Acad. Sci; Am. Soc. Microbiol; Am. Soc. Clin. Path. Protein and nucleic acid biosynthesis. Address: Clinical Labs, Lahey Clinic Foundation, 605 Commonwealth Ave, Boston, MA 02215.

GEORGE, HARVEY F(RANKLIN), b. Jamaica, N.Y, Sept. 17, 23; m. 48; c. 3. MECHANICAL ENGINEERING. B.S, City Col. New York, 45; M.S, N.Y. Univ, 52. Stress analyst & struct. engr, Fairchild Airplane & Engine Corp, 45-47; develop. engr. Stirling Cycle Engines, Philips Labs. Div, N.Am. Philips Co, Inc, 47-49; res. engr. & head graphic arts res. sect, Mergan-thaler Linotype Co, 49-55; RES. DIR. & ASST. SECY-TREAS, GRAVURE RES. INST, 55- Am. Soc. Mech. Eng; assoc. Tech. Asn. Pulp & Paper Industry; Tech. Asn. Graphic Arts (v.pres, 64-66, pres, 66-67). Graphic arts; printing equipment; management of research and development; industrial management. Address: Gravure Research Institute, 22 Manhasset Ave, Port Washington, NY 11050.

GEORGE, JAMES E, b. Pittsburgh, Pa, July 25, 38; m. 63; c. 4. INORGANIC CHEMISTRY. B.S, Allegheny Col, 60; Ph.D.(chem), Illinois, 64. Asst. prof. CHEM, Oberlin Col, 63-65; DePAUW UNIV, 65-69, ASSOC. PROF, 69- AAAS; Am. Chem. Soc. Chemical education; structure of coordination compounds; coordination chemistry of biological compounds. Address: Dept. of Chemistry, DePauw University, Greencastle, IN 46135.

GEORGE, J(AMES) H(ENRY) B(RYN), b. Swansea, Wales, Feb. 5, 29; nat; m. 63; c. 2. PHYSICAL CHEMISTRY, CHEMICAL ENGINEERING. B.A, Oxford, 49, M.A. & Ph.D.(phys. chem), 52; Rotary Int. fel, Mass. Inst. Tech, 52-53, S.M, 53. Instr. chem. eng, Mass. Inst. Tech, 53; chem. engr, Ionics, Inc, 53-54; sr. phys. chemist, ARTHUR D. LITTLE, INC, 54-60, group leader, 60-66, SECT. HEAD phys. chem, 66-69, CHEM. SYSTS, 69- Am. Chem. Soc; Soc. Chem. Indust. Thermodynamics; electrochemistry; ion exchange; solid state chemistry; infrared and raman spectroscopy; technology and economics of saline water conversion; hydrometallurgy; stability of complexes in solution; fuel cells; battery technology. Address: Arthur D. Little, Inc, 15 Acorn Park, Cambridge, MA 02140.

GEORGE, JOHN ALLEN, b. Swift Current, Sask, July 27, 29; m. 54; c. 3. ENTOMOLOGY. B.S.A, Saskatchewan, 52; M.S.A, Toronto, 54; Ph.D.(entom), Western Ontario, 66. Res. scientist, Vineland Res. Sta, Can. Dept. Agr, 54-67; ASSOC. PROF. ZOOL, UNIV. WEST. ONT, 67- Entom. Soc. Am; Entom. Soc. Can. Insect pheromones. Address: Dept. of Zoology, University of Western Ontario, London 72, Ont, Can.

GEORGE, JOHN ANGELOS, b. Sault Sainte Marie, Mich, Sept. 10, 34; m. 59; c. 3. PHYSICS, AEROSPACE ENGINEERING. B.S, St. Louis, 55, Ph.D. (physics), 67; M.S, Calif. Inst. Tech, 56. Flight test engr, McDonnell Aircraft Corp, 58-59; asst. prof. AEROSPACE ENG, PARKS COL. AERONAUT. TECHNOL, ST. LOUIS UNIV, 59-66, assoc. prof, 66-70, PROF, 70-, acting chmn. dept. gen. sci, 68-70. Res. assoc, St. Louis Univ, 65-; consult, spec. projs. off, U.S. Army Aviation Command, 66-67. U.S.A.F, 56-58, 1st Lt. Am. Inst. Aeronaut. & Astronaut; Am. Soc. Eng. Educ. Trapping of particles in the earth's geomagnetic field from natural and artificial sources; systems studies for aircraft integrated data systems; teaching in areas of gas dynamics, aerodynamics and flight mechanics. Address: Dept. of Aerospace Engineering, Parks College of Aeronautical Technology, Cahokia, IL 62206.

GEORGE, JOHN CALEEKAL, b. Kerala, India, June 16, 21; m. 50; c. 3. ZOOLOGY, PHYSIOLOGY. B.Sc, Bombay, 42, Ph.D.(zool), 48. Demonstr. zool, I.Y. Col, India, 45-48; lectr, Inst. Sci, Bombay, India, 48; zoologist, Dept. Anthrop, Govt. India, 48-50; reader & head ZOOL, Baroda, 50-56, prof. & head, 57-67; assoc. prof, UNIV. GUELPH, 67-68, PROF, 68- Fulbright-Smith-Mundt fel, Pennsylvania, 53-54; ed, Jour. Animal Morphol. & Physiol, 56-; mem. int. teamwork embryol. & Dutch Govt. scholar, Holland, 58; Dorabji Tata travel grant to Holland, 58; Fulbright res. scholar & lectr, Washington State, 61-62; ed. & founder, Pavo, Indian Jour. Ornith, 63-; res. grants, Muscular Dystrophy Asn. Am, 64-67, U.S. Dept. Agr, 65-67; mem. biol. res. comt, Coun. Sci. & Indust. Res, Govt. India, 65-67; food & agr. comt, Govt. India Atomic Energy Comn, 67; negotiated develop. grant, Nat. Res. Coun. Can, 70- N.Y. Acad. Sci; Am. Ornith. Union; Histochem. Soc; Can. Soc. Zool; fel. Zool. Soc. India; Indian Soc. Animal Morphol. & Physiol. Vertebrate anatomy; herpetology; comparative physiology; muscle physiology; avian and insect physiology; histochemistry; embryology. Address: Dept. of Zoology, University of Guelph, Guelph, Ont, Can.

GEORGE, JOHN EDWIN, b. Pampa, Tex, Apr. 1, 35; m. 56; c. 3. ENTOMOLOGY. B.S, West Texas State, 57; M.S, Tex. Tech. Col, 60; Ph.D.(entom), Kansas, 64. Asst. prof. med. entom. & ecol, inst. int. med, sch. med, Univ. Md, Baltimore County, 64-67; BIOL, TEX. TECH UNIV, 67-70, ASSOC. PROF, 70- Am. Soc. Zool. Medical entomology; host-parasite relationships; ecology and sensory physiology of ticks. Address: Dept. of Biology, Texas Tech University, Lubbock, TX 79409.

GEORGE, JOHN HAROLD, b. Bucyrus, Ohio, Nov. 29, 35; m; c. 3. MATHEMATICS. B.S, Ohio State, 57; M.A, Alabama, 61, Ph.D.(math), 66. Aerospace scientist, guid. & control lab, U.S. Army Ballistic Missile Agency, Ala, 57-60; aerospace scientist & sect.chief missile guid. & control, Astrionics Lab, Marshall Space Flight Ctr, NASA, 60-66, spec. asst. to chief res. MATH, aero-astrodynamics lab, Ala, 66-67; ASSOC. PROF, UNIV. WYO, 67- NASA summer fel, 68. Am. Math. Soc; Math. Asn. Am; Soc. Indust. & Appl. Math; Inst. Elec. & Electronics Eng. Geometric theory of differential equations, especially Liapunov stability theory; space vehicle applications of advanced control; analysis techniques. Address: 2455 Park Ave, Laramie, WY 82070.

GEORGE, JOHN L(OTHAR), b. Milwaukee, Wis, Apr. 17, 16; m. 44; c. 3. BIOLOGY. B.S, Michigan, 39, fel, 39-42, 46-47, M.S, 41, Rackham fel, 47-50, Ph.D.(zool), 52. 4H county camp dir, State Agr. Exten. Serv, W.Va, 39; asst, Michigan, 39-42, 46-47; asst. prof. zool, Vassar Col, 50-57; assoc. curator mammals, N.Y. Zool. Soc, 57-58; biologist, U.S. Fish & Wildlife Serv, 58-63; ASSOC. PROF. forestry, PA. STATE UNIV, 63-70, WILDLIFE MGT, 70- Ranger naturalist, Great Smokies Nat. Park, 40 & 41; biologist, U.S. Fish & Wildlife Serv, 46 & 47; chmn. comt. ecol. effects of chem. controls, Int. Union Conserv. Nature & Natural Resources, Switz, 63- U.S.N.R, 42-46, Lt. AAAS; Wildlife Soc; Wilderness Soc; Am. Soc. Mammal; Wilson Ornith. Soc; Cooper Ornith. Soc; Am. Ornith. Union. Avian ecology; effects of pesticides on wild life; avian and mammal populations and life histories. Address: 4 Forestry Bldg, Pennsylvania State University, University Park, PA 16802.

GEORGE, JOHN RONALD, b. Pasco, Wash, Apr. 28, 40; m. 62; c. 1. PLANT PHYSIOLOGY. B.S, Washington State, 62; M.S, Purdue, 64, Ph.D.(crop physiol), 67. AGRONOMIST, AM. POTASH INST, 66- AAAS; Am. Soc. Agron; Crop Sci. Soc. Am; Soil Sci. Soc. Am. Nitrate accumulation in forage crops. Address: 212 Parkridge Circle, Ames, IA 50010.

GEORGE, JOHN W(ARREN), b. Newark, Ohio, July 19, 27; m. 57; c. 3. INORGANIC CHEMISTRY. A.B, Princeton, 48; M.A, North Carolina, 50; Ph.D. (chem), Mass. Inst. Tech, 58. Chemist, res. center, Johns-Manville Corp, 50-52; asst. prof. CHEM, Colorado, 58-61; UNIV. MASS, AMHERST, 61-65, ASSOC. PROF, 65- U.S.N.R, 45-46. Am. Chem. Soc. Volatile halides; chemistry of sulfur, selenium and tellurium. Address: Dept. of Chemistry, University of Massachusetts, Amherst, MA 01002.

GEORGE, JOSEPH J(OHNSON), b. West Plains, Mo, June 20, 09; m. 37; c. 4. METEOROLOGY. California, Los Angeles, 26-29; Calif. Inst. Tech, 33-34. Chief meteorologist, West. Air Express, 29-34; EAST. AIRLINES, INC, 34-42, supt. METEOROL, 46-62, DIR, 62- Consult. to adminstr, Fed. Aviation Agency, 62-; chmn, Adv. Cmt. Weather Servs, 53; mem, President's Cmt. Weather Control, 53. Losey award, Inst. Aeronaut. Sci, 43. Consult, Off. Sci. Res. & Develop. U.S.A.A.F, 42-45, Res, 45-, Brig. Gen. Am. Meteorol. Soc. (v.pres, 50-51, Meisinger award, 40, award, 56). Meteorology and weather forecasting with emphasis on operation of aircraft. Address: Eastern Air Lines, Inc, Meteorology Dept, Miami International Airport, Miami, FL 33148.

GEORGE, KALANKAMARY PILY, b. Kerala, India, June 13, 33; m. 58; c. 1. SOIL & STRUCTURAL ENGINEERING. B.E, Nat. Inst. Eng, India, 56; M.S, Iowa State, 61, Ph.D.(civil eng), 63. Dist. asst. engr, Pub. Works Dept, Kerala, India, 56-59; res. assoc. soils eng, eng. exp. sta, Iowa State, 59-63; asst. prof. struct. eng. & soils, UNIV. MISS, 63-66, assoc. prof, 66-68, PROF. CIVIL ENG, 68-, res. engr, 63-68. State Hwy. Dept. res. grant, 63-69, proj. dir. hwy. res, 63-; Nat. Sci. Found. grant, 71- Am. Soc. Civil Eng. Soil stabilization; shrinkage in soil-cement pavements; design of soil-cement bases; deformation of cracked pavements. Address: Dept. of Civil Engineering, Box 525, University of Mississippi, University, MS 38677.

GEORGE, KENNETH D(UDLEY), b. Eltham, N.Z, Oct. 31, 16; U.S. citizen; m. 43; c. 2. PHYSICS. B.Sc, Auckland, 39, scholar. & M.Sc, 40. Physicist, radio develop. lab, N.Z. Dept. Sci. & Indust. Res, 40-42, sci. liaison officer, D.C, 42-44; sr. sci. officer, U.K-Can. Atomic Energy Proj, Can, 44-48; proj. engr, Sperry Gyroscope Co, N.Y, 48-49; asst. head health radiation br, Nat. Res. Coun. Can, 49-50; engr, Ballantine Labs, Inc, N.J, 50-51; chief exp. unit, U.S. Army Munitions Command, Picatinny Arsenal, 51-52, phys. res. sect, 52-58, asst. nuclear co-ord, 58-59, dep. chief reactor requirements off, 59-62, chief, 62-64; reactor supvr, res. ctr, UNION CARBIDE CORP, TUXEDO, N.Y, 64-66, supt. nuclear opers, 66-68, SR. RES. SCIENTIST, 68- Sci. adv, N.Z. Armed Serv. Mission, U.S, 42-44. Am. Phys. Soc; Am. Nuclear Soc. Medical and industrial applications of radioisotopes and nucleonics; nuclear reactor science. Address: R.D. 3, Box 278, Boonton, NJ 07005.

GEORGE, LEON Y, b. Mosul City, Iraq, July 11, 33; U.S. citizen; m. 58; c. 3. CROP PHYSIOLOGY, PLANT PATHOLOGY. M.Sc, Univ. Baghdad, 56; M.Sc, Univ. Calif, Davis, 60, Ph.D.(plant physiol), 63. Field crop specialist, Govt. Saudi Arabia, 64-65; prof. plant physiol, Nat. Univ. Tucumán, 65-67; res. technician, Univ. Calif, 68-70; PLANT PATHOLOGIST, CALIF. STATE DEPT. AGR, 70- Am. Soc. Agron; Arg. Plant Physiol. Soc. Crop-salinity relations; crop-soil-water and nutrients relations. Address: California State Dept. of Agriculture, 2550 Mariposa Ave, Fresno, CA 93721.

GEORGE, MELVIN DOUGLAS, b. Wash, D.C, Feb. 13, 36; m. 58; c. 2. MATHEMATICS. B.A, Northwestern, 56; Nat. Sci. Found. fel, Princeton, 57-59, Ph.D.(math), 59. Res. assoc, inst. fluid dynamics & appl. math, Maryland, 59-60; asst. prof. math, Missouri, 60-64, assoc. prof, 64-67, prof, 67-70, assoc. dean grad. sch, 67-69; PROF. MATH. & DEAN COL. ARTS & SCI, UNIV. NEBR, LINCOLN, 70- Am. Math. Soc; Math. Asn. Am. Mathematical economics; partial differential equations; functional analysis. Address: 1223 Oldfather Hall, University of Nebraska, Lincoln, NE 68508.

GEORGE, M(ERTON) B(ARON) T(ISDALE), b. Pope, Man, Can, Oct. 24, 20; nat; m. 45; c. 2. AERONAUTICAL ENGINEERING. B.Eng, McGill, 49; Que. scholar & Curtiss-Wright Corp. fel, Cornell, 49-51, McMullen scholar, 51-52, Ph.D.(aeronaut. eng), 53. Group leader design drafting, Noorduyn Aviation, Ltd, Que, 41-45; engr, Can. Car & Foundry, Ltd, 46-49; aeronaut. engr, Canadair, Ltd, Que, 49; asst. aerodyn. res, Cornell, 49-53; sr. engr, Douglas Aircraft Co, Calif, 53-55; prin. res. scientist, Avco-Everett Res. Labs. Div, AVCO CORP, 55-58, dir. plans & progs. & assoc. dir. adv. projs, res. & adv. develop. div, 58-64, V.PRES. PLANS & PROGS, 64-66, GOVT. PRODS. GROUP, 66- Am. Inst. Aeronaut. & Astronaut; Eng. Inst. Can. Missiles and space vehicles, especially preliminary design of vehicles and systems; aerodynamics; structures; controls; management and product evaluation; business planning. Address: Government Products Group, Avco Corp, 201 Lowell St, Wilmington, MA 01887.

GEORGE, N(ICHOLAS), JR, b. Council Bluffs, Iowa, Oct. 29, 27; m. 47; c. 1. ENGINEERING PHYSICS. B.S, California, 49; M.S, Maryland, 56; Hughes fel, Calif. Inst. Technol, 56-59; Ph.D.(elec. eng, physics), 59. Physicist, Nat. Bur. Standards, Wash, D.C, 49-52; proj. leader, Diamond Ord. Fuze Labs, 52-54; chief physics sect, Emerson Res. Labs, 54-56; sr. staff physicist, Hughes Aircraft Co, 56-60; ASSOC. PROF. ELEC. ENG, CALIF. INST. TECHNOL, 59- Sig.C, U.S.A, 46-47. Am. Phys. Soc; Inst. Elec. & Electronics Eng. Lasers; noise theory; microwave thermal radiation processes;

network analysis and synthesis; guided missile systems analysis and electronic circuits. Address: Dept. of Electrical Sciences, California Institute of Technology, Pasadena, CA 91109.

GEORGE, P. F(REDERICK), b. Wolverine, Mich, Jan. 27, 11; m. 33; c. 2. CHEMICAL & MATERIALS ENGINEERING. B.S, Mich. Col. Min, 32. Anal. chemist, DOW CHEM. CO, 34-36, plant metallurgist, 36-41, magnesium metallographer, 41-47, magnesium battery res, electrochem, 47-51, cathodic protection, 51-56, sect. leader magnesium tech. serv. & develop, 56-62, asst. tech. dir. metall. lab, 62-65, group mgr. tech. serv. & develop, Mich, 65-70, METALLURGIST, 70- Lincoln Arc Welding Found. res. grant, 47. Dow Mem. award, 53. Nat. Asn. Corrosion Eng; Am. Soc. Metals; Electrochem. Soc. Magnesium technology, especially metallography, anodes, forming, welding, finishing, casting, extruding, rolling and application; desalination. Address: 109 Redbud Lane, Lake Jackson, TX 77566.

GEORGE, PAUL J(OHN), b. Cleveland, Ohio, April 11, 23; m. 47; c. 1. ORGANIC CHEMISTRY. B.S, Case, 44, M.S, 51, Ph.D.(chem), 53. Instr. chem, Case, 48-54, asst. prof, 54-55; proj. leader, plastics res, B.F. GOODRICH CO, 55-68, RES. ASSOC, RES. CTR, 68- Am. Chem. Soc. Plastics research; chemistry of polymerization catalysts; organic synthesis; organometallic chemistry. Address: Research Center, B.F. Goodrich Co, Brecksville, OH 44141.

GEORGE, P(HILIP), b. Maidstone, Eng, Jan. 30, 20; m. 46; c. 6. BIOPHYSICAL CHEMISTRY. B.A, Cambridge, 41, M.A, 44, fel, 44-47, Ph.D, 45. Asst. tutor, Christ's Col, Cambridge, 45-47; Brotherton res. lectr. phys. chem, Leeds, 47-49; asst. dir. res, dept. colloid sci, Cambridge, 49-55; RES. PROF. BIOPHYS. CHEM, UNIV. PA, 55- Fel, Christ's Col, Cambridge, 53-55. Civilian with Petrol. Warfare Dept, H.M. Govt, Gt. Brit, 40-45. AAAS; Biophys. Soc; Am. Chem. Soc; Am. Soc. Biol. Chem; Hist. Sci. Soc; Faraday Soc; The Chem. Soc; Brit. Biochem. Soc; Brit. Soc. Hist. Sci. Coordination chemistry; hemoprotein reactions; biochemical thermodynamics; history of chemistry. Address: Dept. of Biology, University of Pennsylvania, Philadelphia, PA 19104.

GEORGE, PHILIP D(ONALD), b. Baltimore, Md, June 8, 21; m. 49; c. 2. CHEMISTRY. B.S, Mt. St. Mary's Col.(Md), 43, M.S, Pa. State Col, 44, Ph.D.(org. chem), 48. Asst. chem, Pa. State Col, 42-45; res. assoc, GEN. ELEC. CO, 46-56, MGR. insulation & plastics behavior, 56-59, plastics, 59-61, advan. develop. lab, 61-69, ENG. & MFG. FILM PROD, 69- With U.S.A, War Prod. Bd, 43-46. AAAS; Am. Chem. Soc; Soc. Plastics Eng; Am. Mgt. Asn; fel. Am. Inst. Chem; Inst. Elec. & Electronics Eng; Am. Inst. Chem. Eng. Penicillin; boron hydrides; silicones; materials behavior; liquid and solid dilectrics; plastic film and capacitors. Address: General Electric Co, Hudson Falls, NY 12839.

GEORGE, RAYMOND ARTHUR, b. Port Arthur, Tex, Aug. 29, 28; m. 48; c. 1. PHYSICAL CHEMISTRY. B.A, Texas, 51, M.A, 53. Res. technologist, field res. labs, Mobil Oil Corp, 53-57; reservoir engr, Mobil Oil De Venezuela, 57-61; sr. res. technologist, FIELD RES. LABS, MOBIL RES. & DEVELOP. CORP, MOBIL OIL CORP, 61-65, ENG. ASSOC. OIL PROD. RES, 65- Soc. Petrol. Eng. Miscible flood recovery methods and improved waterfloods. Address: Field Research Labs, Mobil Research & Development Corp, P.O. Box 900, Dallas, TX 75221.

GEORGE, RAYMOND S, b. San Bernardino, Calif, Sept. 4, 36; m. 63; c. 2. NUCLEAR CHEMISTRY. B.A, California, Riverside, 58; Ph.D.(anal. chem), Northwestern, 62. Fulbright fel, H.C. Ørsteds Inst, Copenhagen, 62-63; mem. staff org. chem, Los Alamos Sci. Lab, 63-70; ACCOUNTABILITY OFF, ALBUQUERQUE OPERS. OFF, NUCLEAR MAT. MGT. DIV, U.S. ATOMIC ENERGY COMN, 71- U.S.A.R, 52-62. Am. Chem. Soc. Boric acid complexes; inorganic complexation chemistry; analytical research and development; analytical instrumentation; explosives chemistry; crime laboratory establishment and techniques; radiation chemistry. Address: Albuquerque Operations Office, Nuclear Materials Management Division, U.S. Atomic Energy Commission, P.O. Box 5400, Albuquerque, NM 87115.

GEORGE, R(ICHARD) S(TANLEY), b. Sandy Lake, Pa, Mar. 4, 15; m. 47; c. 1. CHEMISTRY. B.S, Grove City Col, 35; fel, Pa. State Col, 39-42, M.S, 40, Ph.D.(org. chem), 43. Anal. chemist, Jones & Laughlin Steel Corp, Pa, 36; chemist, Sun Oil Co, 36-38; Socony-Vacuum Oil Co, N.J, 38-39; asst. dir, exp. sta, Hercules Powder Co, 49-51, assoc. tech. dir, 51-52, mgr. develop, naval stores dept, 52-56, oxychem. div, 56-61, dir. sales, org. chem, 61-66, ASST. GEN. MGR, PINE & PAPER CHEM. DEPT, HERCULES INC, 66- With Petrol. Indust. War Coun, 44. AAAS; Am. Chem. Soc; Soc. Chem. Indust. Hydrocarbon oxidation, cracking and chlorination; hydroperoxide chemistry; rosin and terpene chemistry; agricultural chemicals. Address: Pine & Paper Chemicals Dept, Hercules Inc, Wilmington, DE 19899.

GEORGE, R(OBERT), b. Turlock, Calif, Feb. 10, 23; m. 58; c. 1. PHARMACOLOGY. A.B, Oregon, 49; Ph.D.(physiol), California, Berkeley, 53. Asst. physiol, California, Berkeley, 50-53; jr. res. pharmacologist, University of California Med. Center, San Francisco, 53-56; asst. res. pharmacologist & asst. prof. PHARMACOL, 58-61; assoc. prof, CTR. HEALTH SCI, UNIV. CALIF, LOS ANGELES, 61-67, PROF, 67- U.S. Pub. Health Serv. fel. neuroendocrinol, Maudsley Hosp, Univ. London, 56-58. U.S.N, 43-46. AAAS; Am. Soc. Pharmacol. & Exp. Therapeut; Brit. Soc. Endocrinol; Am. Physiol. Soc. Analgesics and neuroendocrine function; neural control of anterior pituitary; diabetes mellitus; pharmacology and pathology of tremor. Address: Dept. of Pharmacology, Center for the Health Sciences, University of California, Los Angeles, CA 90024.

GEORGE, ROBERT E(UGENE), b. Bowling Green, Ohio, Nov. 24, 29; m. 52; c. 7. RADIATION BIOLOGY, HEALTH PHYSICS. B.Sc, Ohio State, 52; M.Sc, Rochester, 61; Ph.D.(bionucleonics), Purdue, 66. MED. SERV. CORPS, U.S. NAVY, 52-, chief pharm. serv, Naval Hosp, Quantico, Va, 53-56, Naval Hosp, Newport, R.I, 56-60, instr. nuclear, chem. & biol. weapons, Naval Unit, Army Chem. Sch, 61-64, res. projs. group dir, ARMED FORCES RADIOBIOL. RES. INST, 66-67, CHMN. DEPT. RADIATION BIOL, 67- Med.Serv.C, U.S.N, 52-, Comdr. Radiation Res. Soc; Health Physics Soc. Mortality and performance decrement responses of mammals to neutron, gamma and mixed radiation fields; dependence of acute responses on dose rate and radiation quality; modification of acute responses to radiation. Address: Dept. of Radiation Biology, Armed Forces Radiobiology Research Institute, Bethesda, MD 20014.

GEORGE, ROBERT PORTER, b. San Rafael, Calif, June 18, 37; m. 67; c. 2. DEVELOPMENTAL BIOLOGY, INVERTEBRATE ZOOLOGY. B.A, Univ. Calif, Berkeley, 61; M.S, Univ. Hawaii, 67, Nat. Insts. Health fel, 65-68, Ph.D.(microbiol), 68. Res. fel. bacteriol, Univ. Wis, Madison, 68-70; ASST. PROF. ZOOL, UNIV. WYO, 70- Soc. Protozool; Soc. Develop. Biol; Am. Soc. Cell Biol; Am. Inst. Biol. Sci. Productivity of marine benthic communities; microcrystalline structure of cellulose; transmission and scanning electron microscopy of cellular slime molds; autoradiographic study of stalk formation in Dictyostelium; effect of inhibitors and chemotactic substances on morphogenesis in Dictyostelium. Address: Dept. of Zoology, University of Wyoming, Laramie, WY 82070.

GEORGE, RONALD BAYLIS, b. Zwolle, La, Nov. 17, 32. INTERNAL MEDICINE, PHYSIOLOGY. B.A, Alabama, 54; M.D, Tulane, 58. Asst. prof. internal med, sch. med, Tulane Univ. La, 66-69, assoc. prof. med, 69-72; ASSOC. PROF. MED. & HEAD PULMONARY DISEASES SECT, SCH. MED, MED. CTR, LA. STATE UNIV, SHREVEPORT, 72- Dipl, Am. Bd. Internal Med, 65. U.S.A.F, 60-62, Capt. Am. Thoracic Soc; Am. Col. Chest Physicians; Am. Fedn. Clin. Res. Pulmonary physiology; pathology and clinical appearance of viral and mycoplasmal pneumonias and their x-ray appearance; regional pulmonary ventilation perfusion relationships in normal people and various disease conditions. Address: 510 E. Stoner Ave, Shreveport, LA 71101.

GEORGE, SIMON, b. India, May 10, 31; nat. PHYSICS. B.S, Travancore, 51; M.S, Saugar, 54; Ph.D.(physics), British Columbia, 62. Lectr. PHYSICS, Hislop Col, Nagpur, 54-55; Gauhati, India, 55-57; British Columbia, 59-60; asst. prof, CALIF. STATE COL. LONG BEACH, 61-64, assoc. prof, 64-69, PROF, 69- Optical Soc. Am; Am. Asn. Physics Teachers; assoc. Brit. Inst. Physics & Phys. Soc. Atomic spectroscopy; Fabry Perot interferometry; energy levels in spectra and laser spectroscopy. Address: Dept. of Physics, California State College at Long Beach, Long Beach, CA 90801.

GEORGE, T. ADRIAN, b. Darlington, Eng, Feb. 1, 42; m. 68. ORGANOMETALLIC & INORGANIC CHEMISTRY. B.S, Manchester Col. Sci. & Technol, Eng, 63; Ph.D.(chem), Univ. Sussex, 66. Assoc. CHEM, Univ. Calif, Riverside, 66-68; ASST. PROF, UNIV. NEBR, LINCOLN, 68- Univ. Nebr. Res. Coun. fel, summer 70. The Chem. Soc; Am. Chem Soc. The preparation of organometallic compounds containing metal-metal bonds and a study of their chemical and physical properties; fixation of dinitrogen using molybdenum complexes as the active specie. Address: Dept. of Chemistry, University of Nebraska, Lincoln, NE 68508.

GEORGE, TED MASON, b. Lynnville, Tenn, Sept. 22, 22; m. 60. NUCLEAR PHYSICS, ELECTRONICS. B.A, Vanderbilt, 49, M.A, 57, Nat. Sci. Found. fel, 60-61, Ph.D.(physics), 64. Asst. prof. PHYSICS, Murray State, 56-59; Furman, 63-64; PROF, EAST. KY. UNIV, 64- Sig.C, U.S.A, 42-45. Am. Asn. Physics Teachers. Gamma and beta ray spectroscopy. Address: Dept. of Physics, Eastern Kentucky University, Richmond, KY 40475.

GEORGE, THEODORE ALEXANDER, b. Detroit, Mich, Nov. 1, 26; m. 54. ENGINEERING, MATHEMATICS. B.A, George Washington, 51; B.M.E, Catholic Univ, 58, M.A.E, 61. Aeronaut. engr, Off. Chief of Staff, Dept. Army, 51-58; prog. mgr, Proj. Discoverer, adv. res. proj. agency, Dept. Defense, 59-60, dept. dir. nuclear test detection, 60-64; mgr. earth resources prog, NASA, 64-67; earth resources satellite prog, 68-71; SPEC. ASST. TO COMNR. WATER QUAL, ENVIRON. PROTECTION AGENCY, 71- Guest lectr, Catholic Univ, 62-64; Univ. Va, 66- Exec. secy, Proj. Vela Adv. Sci. Comt, 60-62. Mil. Intel, 46-59, Capt. Am. Inst. Aeronaut. & Astronaut; Soc. Indust. & Appl. Math; N.Y. Acad. Sci; Nat. Soc. Prof. Eng. Atmosphere reentry and problems connected with optimization of space vehicle trajectories; methods of nuclear test detection. Address: Environmental Protection Agency, Washington, DC 20242.

GEORGE, THEODORE S(AMUEL), b. Grove City, Pa, Oct. 10, 11; m. 42; c. 3. APPLIED MATHEMATICS. B.S, Grove City Col, 32; M.A, Duke, 36, Ph.D.(math), 42; summer, Brown, 41; Pennsylvania, 46-48. Instr. math, Florida, 38-42; consult. engr. & head consult. mathematician, Philco Radio Corp, 46-51; chief, opers. anal, U.S. Air Force Missile Test Center, Patrick Air Force Base, 51-56; PROF. ELEC. ENG, UNIV. FLA, 56- Sci. adv, Comdr. in Chief, Pac, 69-70. U.S.N, 42-46, Lt. Comdr. Sr. mem. Inst. Elec. & Electronics Eng; Int. Sci. Radio Union. Applied mathematics in communications; statistics of noise in electronic equipment; statistical communications theory; operations analysis. Address: 619 N.W. 23rd St, Gainesville, FL 32601.

GEORGE, THOMAS D, b. Robstown, Tex, Mar. 3, 40; m. 70. MATERIALS SCIENCE, ANALYTICAL CHEMISTRY. B.S, Tex. Tech Univ, 62, M.S, 65; Rotary Int. fel, Univ. Liverpool, 62-63; Ph.D.(mat. sci), Northwest. Univ, 68. Mem. tech. staff, cent. res. labs, TEX. INSTRUMENTS, INC, 68-69, MGR. ANAL. LABS, QUAL. & RELIABILITY ASSURANCE, COMPONENTS GROUP, 69- Address: Quality & Reliability Assurance, Analytical Lab, Texas Instruments, Inc, Box 5012, Dallas, TX 75222.

GEORGE, (THOMAS) WALLER, b. Kansas City, Mo, Feb. 1, 19; m. 45; c. 4. PHYSICS. A.B, Kansas City, 41; M.A, Illinois, 43; Maryland, 45-46. Asst. physics, Illinois, 41-43; mem. staff, Naval Res. Lab, 43-56; sr. res. assoc, res. labs, Celanese Corp. Am, 56-69; ASSOC. PROF. TEXTILE TECHNOL, SCH. TEXTILES, N.C. STATE UNIV, 69- Head armor mat. sect, Naval Res. Lab, 48-56. U.S.N.R, 44-45, Ens. Am. Phys. Soc; Am. Soc. Metals; Fiber Soc; N.Y. Acad. Sci. Armor materials; fragment penetration dynamics; high strength fibers; mechanics of plastic flowing and fracturing; cigarette smoke chemistry and selective filtration; biophysics of ciliary activity; toxicology of tobacco smoke. Address: School of Textiles, North Carolina State University, Raleigh, NC 27607.

GEORGE, WILLIAM, b. Santa Cruz, Calif, Feb. 2, 25. ORNITHOLOGY, ZOOLOGY. B.A, Arizona, 57, M.S, 58, Ph.D.(zool), 61. Chapman fel, Am. Mus. Natural Hist, 61-62; Nat. Sci. Found. grant, 62-64; ASST. PROF. ZOOL, SOUTH. ILL. UNIV, CARBONDALE, 64- U.S.N.A.F, 43-46. Am. Ornith. Union; Wilson Ornith. Soc; Cooper Ornith. Soc; Am. Soc. Zool. Systematics. Address: Dept. of Zoology, Southern Illinois University, Carbondale, IL 62901.

GEORGE, WILLIAM ARTHUR, b. Pittsburgh, Pa, Jan. 29, 10; m. 36; c. 3. DENTISTRY. B.S. & D.D.S, Pittsburgh, 32. Private practice dent, 32-43, 46-58; PROF. PROSTHODONT. & CHMN. DEPT, SCH. DENT, UNIV. PITTSBURGH, 58-, ASSOC. DEAN, 68-, DIR. POST-GRAD. DIV. & ASSOC. DIR. GRAD. DIV, 64-, instr, 47-57, asst. prof, 57-58, asst. dean, 64-68. Consult, Vet. Admin. Hosp, cent. off, Leech Farm Hosp, 59-; Univ. Dr. Hosp, 60- U.S.N, 43-46, Res, 46-, Capt. Am. Dent. Asn; fel. Am. Col. Dent; Am. Prosthodont. Soc. Tissue reactions to materials used in prosthetic appliances for maxillo-facial deformities. Address: School of Dental Medicine, University of Pittsburgh, 3501 Terrace St, Pittsburgh, PA 15213.

GEORGE, WILLIAM JACOB, b. Houtzdale, Pa, June 19, 38; m. 64; c. 2. BIOCHEMICAL PHARMACOLOGY. B.S, Pa. State, 60; Darbaker scholar. award, Pittsburgh, 61-64, B.S, 64; univ. fel, Michigan, 64-68, Ph.D.(pharmacol), 68. Fel. PHARMACOL, Minnesota, 68-70; ASST. PROF, SCH. MED, TULANE UNIV, 70- Merck Found. award, 70. AAAS; N.Y. Acad. Sci. Drug metabolism; intermediary metabolism; cyclic nucleotides; hormonal control of metabolic processes. Address: Dept. of Pharmacology, Tulane University Medical School, 1430 Tulane Ave, New Orleans, LA 70112.

GEORGE, WILLIAM LEO, JR, b. Riverside, N.J, June 1, 38; m. 60; c. 2. PLANT GENETICS & BREEDING. B.S, Del. Valley Col, 60; M.S, Rutgers, 62, Ph.D.(genetics), 66. Res. asst. genetics, Rutgers, 60-66; asst. geneticist, Conn. Agr. Exp. Sta, 66-71; ASSOC. PROF. HORT, OHIO STATE UNIV. & OHIO AGR. RES. & DEVELOP. CTR, 71- Genetics Soc. Am; Bot. Soc. Am; Am. Genetic Asn; Am. Soc. Hort. Sci. Genetics and developmental genetics of sexuality and unstable gene systems in higher plants; development of new breeding systems in vegetable crops; breeding green house vegetable crops. Address: Dept. of Horticulture, 2001 Fyffe Ct, Ohio State University, Columbus, OH 43210.

GEORGE, WILLIAM L(IVINGSTON), b. Melrose, Mass, Jan. 21, 17; m. 40; c. 3. ORGANIC CHEMISTRY. B.S, Rensselaer Polytech, 38; M.S, Stevens Inst. Tech, 53. Control chemist, Rogers Paper Mfg. Co, 38-39; res. chemist, Arnold Hoffman & Co, 39-42; Hercules Powder Co, 42-43; anal. & res. chemist, Am. Hardware Corp, 43-44; res. chemist, JOHNSON & JOHNSON, 44-54, res. supvr, CHICOPEE MFG. CORP, 54-59, prod. dir, 59-69, group prod. dir, 69-70, MERCHANDISING MGR, NON WOVEN FABRICS DIV, 70- Am. Chem. Soc. Textiles; textile finishing agents; chemical sterilization; hospital products. Address: 23 Meadowbrook Lane, Piscataway, NJ 08854.

GEORGE, WILLIAM LLOYD, b. Tulsa, Okla, Nov. 9, 42; m. 62; c. 2. SOLID STATE ELECTRONICS, MATERIALS SCIENCE. B.S.Met.E, Univ. Okla, 64; Nat. Sci. Found. fel. & Ph.D.(met. eng), Purdue Univ, 68. Sr. engr, MOTOROLA SEMICONDUCTOR PROD. DIV, MOTOROLA, INC, 68-69, sect. mgr. DEVICE RES, 69-71, GROUP MGR, 71- Inst. Elec. & Electronics Eng. Physics of solid state electronic devices, including field effect and bipolar transistors, diodes and thyristors; nuclear radiation effects in semiconductor devices; reliability of electronics. Address: 6902 E. Jenan Dr, Scottsdale, AZ 85254.

GEORGES, JOEL S(AMUEL), b. Iran, May 15, 94; nat; m. 18; c. 3. MATHEMATICS. A.B, Maryville Col.(Tenn), 20; A.M, Chicago, 23, Ph.D.(math), 26. Prin, pub. sch, Ky, 20-23; instr. MATH, Chicago, 24-31; teacher & head dept, Wright Br, Chicago City Jr. Col, 31-59; asst. prof, Mundelein Col, 59-63; assoc. prof, De Paul, Univ, 63-67; VIS. PROF, CAMPBELL COL, 67- Lectr, Loyola Univ.(Ill), 42-63. U.S.A, 17-19. Math. Asn. Am. Associativity conditions for division algebras; teaching mathematics; writing texts. Address: Dept. of Mathematics, Campbell College, Buies Creek, NC 27506.

GEORGHIOU, G(EORGE) PAUL, b. Famagusta, Cyprus, Nov, 23, 25; m. 52; c. 2. ENTOMOLOGY, TOXICOLOGY. B.S, Cornell, 52, M.S, 53; Ph.D.(entom), California, Berkeley, 60. Govt. entomologist, Dept. Agr, Cyprus, 54-58; jr. specialist ENTOM, UNIV. CALIF, RIVERSIDE, 58-60, lectr, 60-69, PROF, 69-, ASSOC. ENTOMOLOGIST, 66-, asst. entomologist, 60-66. Nat. Insts. Health res. grant, 64-67; WHO, 65, 66; U.S. Dept. Agr, 66-69. AAAS; Entom. Soc. Am; Am. Phytopath. Soc. Insect resistance to insecticides; genetics of resistance; insect toxicology. Address: Dept. of Entomology, University of California, Riverside, CA 92502.

GEORGI, CARL E(DWARD), b. Milwaukee, Wis, Feb. 18, 06; m. 36; c. 2. MICROBIOLOGY, BIOCHEMISTRY. B.S, Wisconsin, 30, fel, 30-31, M.S, 32, Ph.D.(agr. biochem), 34. Asst. agr. bact. & agr. biochem, Wisconsin, 31-34, anal. chem, 34-35; instr. bact, UNIV. NEBR, LINCOLN, 35-38, asst. prof, 38-43, assoc. prof, 43-47, PROF. MICROBIOL, 47-, regents prof, 64-71, chmn. dept, 53-71. Sterling fel, Yale, 35; Fulbright scholar, Sorbonne, 51-52. Dipl, Am. Bd. Med. Microbiol. AAAS; Am. Soc. Microbiol; Am. Soc. Biol. Chem; Am. Soc. Cell Biol; Soc. Exp. Biol. & Med; Brit. Soc. Gen. Microbiol; Electron Micros. Soc. Am; Am. Acad. Microbiol. Biochemistry and physiology of thermophilic bacteria; rumen microbiology. Address: Dept. of Microbiology, 316 Lyman Hall, University of Nebraska, Lincoln, NE 68508.

GEORGI, JAY R, b. N.Y.C, Nov. 9, 28; m. 52; c. 4. VETERINARY MEDICINE. D.V.M, Cornell, 51, Ph.D, 62. Asst. prof. phys. biol, N.Y. STATE VET. COL, CORNELL UNIV, 65-66, assoc. prof. PARASITOL, 66-69, PROF, 69- U.S.A.F, 50-53, 1st Lt. AAAS; Am. Vet. Med. Asn. Applications of radioactive isotopes in the study of host-parasite relationships. Address: Dept. of Parasitology, New York State Veterinary College, Cornell University, Ithaca, NY 14850.

GEORGIADE, NICHOLAS G(EORGE), b. Lowell, Mass, Dec. 25, 18; m. 42; c. 3. PLASTIC SURGERY. Fordham, 37-41; D.D.S, Columbia, 44; M.D. & B.S, Duke, 49. Intern oral surg, Kings County Hosp, 44; intern & asst. res. gen. surg, SCH. MED, DUKE UNIV, 49-52, asst. res. & res. plastic surg, 52-54, from instr. to PROF. PLASTIC, MAXILLOFACIAL & ORAL SURG, 54- Nat. Cancer Inst. clin. fel, 52-54; consult, plastic, maxillofacial & oral surgeon, Vet. Admin. Hosp, Durham; consult, U.S. Army & U.S. Air Force; res. proj, Nat. Inst. Health. Mem, Plastic Surg. Res. Coun. Dipl, Am. Bd. Plastic Surg; dipl, Am. Bd. Oral Surg. Med. Dept, U.S.A, 44-46. Am. Soc. Plastic & Reconstruct. Surg; Am. Soc. Oral Surg; Am. Asn. Plastic Surg; fel. Am. Col. Surg; Soc. Cryobiol; Soc. Head & Neck Surg; Int. Soc. Surg; Am. Soc. Maxillofacial Surg.(pres, 63); Am. Cleft Palate Asn; Am. Burn Asn. Plastic, maxillofacial and oral surgery; tissue preservation; burns; maxillofacial growth and development. Address: Box 3098, Duke University School of Medicine, Durham, NC 27710.

GEORGIADIS, MINAS P, b. Athens, Greece, Feb. 2, 25; nat; m. 58; c. 4. ORGANIC & MEDICINAL CHEMISTRY. B.Sc, Nat. Univ. Athens, 53; M.Sc, Univ. Ill, Urbana, 60; Ph.D.(org. chem), Ind. Univ, Bloomington, 64. Lab. instr. indust. org. chem, Nat. Univ. Athens, 53-57; chemist, State Chem. Labs, Athens, 57-58; res. assoc. antibiotics, inst. microbiol, Rutgers Univ, 63-65; SR. RES. CHEMIST, AYERST RES. LABS, AM. HOME PROD. CORP, 65- Greek Army, 48-51. Am. Chem. Soc. Organic synthesis; antibiotics. Address: Ayerst Research Labs, P.O. Box 6115, Montreal, Que, Can.

GEORGIAN, V(LASIOS), b. Quincy, Mass, Sept. 5, 19; m. 49; c. 2. ORGANIC CHEMISTRY. S.B, Harvard, 41, M.A, 43, fel, 44-45, Ph.D.(chem), 50. Res. chemist, Polaroid Corp, 42-44; asst, Harvard, 45-46; instr. CHEM, Northwestern, 51-54, asst. prof, 54-57, res. assoc, 57-60; asst. prof, TUFTS UNIV, 60-63, ASSOC. PROF, 63- U.S. Pub. Health Serv. fel, Harvard, 50-51; consult, Smith Kline & French Labs, 60- Am. Chem. Soc; Am. Acad. Arts & Sci; N.Y. Acad. Sci; The. Chem. Soc. Synthesis of small and strained ring systems; additions to cyclooctatetraene; synthesis of polyunsaturated ring systems with valency tautomerism possibilities; molecular rearrangements; steroid syntheses and transformations; syntheses of natural products. Address: Dept. of Chemistry, Tufts University, Medford, MA 02155.

GEORGIEV, STEVEN, b. Sofia, Bulgaria, Jan. 5, 34; U.S. citizen. AEROPHYSICS. B.S, Cornell, 57; M.B.A, Mass. Inst. Technol, 69. Assoc. engr. aerophysics, Avco-Everett Res. Lab, AVCO CORP, 57-59, sr. staff mem, 59-61, sect. chief, res. & adv. develop. div, 61-62, mgr. aerophysics dept, 62-63, adv. space projs, 63-67, dir. space systs. prog. off, space systs. div, 67-69, DIR. ADVAN. SYSTS. DEVELOP, SYSTS. DIV, 69- Am. Inst. Aeronaut. & Astronaut. High temperature gas dynamics; hypersonic heat transfer and ablation phenomena; space vehicle design. Address: Avco Corp, Avco Systems Division, 201 Lowell St, Wilmington, MA 01887.

GEPHART, LANDIS STEPHEN, b. Dayton, Ohio, Dec. 31, 17; m. 41; c. 5. OPERATIONS RESEARCH, APPLIED MATHEMATICS. B.S, Univ. Dayton, 40, M.A, 48; M.S, Miami Univ, 49; Ph.D.(appl. math. & statist), Univ. Fla, 55. Teacher, high sch, 40-44; asst. prof. math, Univ. Dayton, 45-48; res. mathematician, U.S. Air Force, 48-55, chief, U.S. Army Europ. Res. Off, Frankfort, Ger, 55-59, chief exp. res, Off. Secy. Defense, 59-60; dir, off. reliability & qual. assurance, NASA, 60-62; dir. prod. assurance, Lockheed Aircraft Corp, 62-64; sr. opers. res. analyst, Hq. Air Force Logistics Command, 64-67; PROF. INDUST. ENG, UNIV. DAYTON, 67-, DIR. ENG. MGT. GRAD. PROG, 70- Consult, Hq. NASA, 62-64; Hq. Air Force Systs. Command, 63-64; Duke Univ, 64; Martin-Orlando Co, 64-65; Univ. Pittsburgh, 66-67; Globe Industs. Div, TRW Inc, 68-; Koehler-Dayton Inc, 68-; Cox Coronary Heart Inst, 68-; N.Am. ed, Indust. Abstracts, 61-64. Am. Inst. Aeronaut. & Astronaut; Am. Inst. Indust. Eng. Management science; mathematical modeling; stochastic linear programming; simulation models; experimental design; applied mathematics. Address: Dept. of Industrial Engineering, University of Dayton, Dayton, OH 45409.

GEPPERT, DONOVAN (VERLOE), b. Teague, Tex, Jan. 4, 26; m. 45; c. 4. ELECTRONICS, PHYSICS. B.S, Texas, 45, M.S, 48, Arkansas, 49; Syracuse, 51; Stanford, 54-60. Instr. elec. eng, Texas, 45-48; Arkansas, 48, asst. prof, 49-50; res. engr, Gen. Elec. Co, N.Y, 50-51; Motorola Res. Lab, Ariz, 51-54; electronic defense lab, Sylvania Elec. Prod, Inc, Calif, 54-56, microwave tube lab, 56-60; res. engr. solid state devices, STANFORD RES. INST, 60-62, sr. res. engr, 62-67, chmn. electronic mat. & devices dept, 67-69, MGR. ELECTRONIC DEVICES PROG, 69- Inst. Elec. & Electronics Eng. Electromagnetic structure of photons and electron-photon interactions; cold cathodes; microwave filters, tubes, diodes and transistors. Address: Electron Devices Program, Stanford Research Institute, 333 Ravenswood Ave, Menlo Park, CA 94025.

GERACE, MICHAEL J, b. Brooklyn, N.Y, Jan. 11, 44; m. 68. PHYSICAL CHEMISTRY. B.S, L.I. Univ, 65; Ph.D.(chem), Tufts Univ, 70. RES. ASSOC. CHEM, DARTMOUTH COL, 70- Am. Chem. Soc. Conformational analysis of cyclohexane derivatives; liquid crystal solutions; nuclear magnetic resonance studies; physical polymer chemistry; molecular chain dynamics. Address: Dept. of Chemistry, Dartmouth College, Hanover, NH 03755.

GERACE, PAUL L(OUIS), b. Batavia, N.Y, Aug. 20, 34; m. 65; c. 2. INORGANIC & ANALYTICAL CHEMISTRY. B.S, Notre Dame, 56, Du Pont fel, 58-59, Nat. Sci. Found. summer fel, 59, P.C. Reilly Co. fel, 59-60, Ph.D. (chem), 61. Teaching fel. chem, Notre Dame, 56-58; res. chemist, Solvay Process Div, Allied Chem. Corp, N.Y, 61-66; SCIENTIST, XEROX CORP, 66- Chemist, Linde Co. Div, Union Carbide Corp, summer 57. Am. Chem. Soc. Coordination and chromium chemistry; organic analytical reagents; inorganic and watersoluble polymers; oxidation catalysis; inorganic, metal-organic and organo-metallic synthesis; electrochemistry; spectrophotometry; thermogravimetry; inorganic and organic photoconductors; surface coatings. Address: 72 Hallmark Rd, Rochester, NY 14625.

GERACI, J(OSEPH) E, b. Newark, N.J, Feb. 24, 16; m. 49; c. 1. INTERNAL MEDICINE. Michigan, 36; M.D, Marquette, 40; fel, Minnesota, 45-49, M.S, 49. PROF. MED, MAYO GRAD. SCH. MED, UNIV. MINN, ROCHESTER, 62-, CONSULT, MAYO CLIN, 51- Am. Med. Asn; Am. Col. Physicians; Am. Col. Chest Physicians; Am. Fedn. Clin. Res; Infectious Disease Soc. Am. Infectious disease. Address: Mayo Clinic, Rochester, MN 55901.

GERACI, JOSEPH R, b. Lawrence, Mass, Jan. 16, 38; m. 63; c. 2. ENVIRONMENTAL & PATHOLOGICAL PHYSIOLOGY. B.Sc, Suffolk Univ, 59; D.V.M, Univ. Pa, 63; N.Y. Univ, 64-66; McConnell Mem. award, McGill Univ, 69-70, Ph.D.(marine sci), 70. Chmn, Annual East. Col. Sci. Conf, Boston, 58-59; asst. instr. clin. med, sch. vet. med, Univ. Pa, 63-64; res. assoc. fish path, Osborn Labs. Marine Sci, N.Y. Zool. Soc, 64-66, assoc. curator, N.Y. Aquarium, 65-66; curator & pathologist, Montreal Aquarium, Can, 66-69; ASSOC. PROF. ZOOL, UNIV. GUELPH, 69- Res. assoc, dept. path, Coney Island Hosp, Brooklyn, 65-66; lectr, Nat. Sci. Found. Summer Inst. Biol. Marine Organisms, Suffolk Univ, 68-70. U.S.M.C, 57, Res, 57-62. AAAS; Am. Soc. Zool; N.Y. Acad. Sci; Am. Inst. Biol. Sci; Int. Asn. Aquatic Animal Med. Pathology of fishes and marine mammals; nutritional pathology of marine mammals, especially dolphins and seals; hematology and blood chemistry of marine mammals; marine mammal environmental physiology; marine mammal conservation. Address: Dept. of Zoology, University of Guelph, Guelph, Ont, Can.

GERAGHTY, JAMES J(OSEPH), b. New York, N.Y, Nov. 20, 20; m. 42; c. 2. GEOLOGY. B.S, City Col, 49; M.S, N.Y. Univ. 53. Geologist, water resources div, ground water br, U.S. Geol. Surv, 49-55; GROUND WATER GEOLOGIST, Leggette, Brashears & Graham, 55-57; GERAGHTY & MILLER, PORT WASHINGTON, 57-; TECH. ADV, UN, 62- Lectr, Hofstra Col, 52-55; State Univ. N.Y, 58; N.Y. Univ, 62- U.S.A, 45-46. Geol. Soc. Am; Am. Water Works Asn; Am. Asn. Petrol. Geol; Am. Geophys. Union; Int. Asn. Hydrogeol; Am. Soc. Civil Eng. Ground water geology; hydrology. Address: 101 Clinton Ave, Mineola, NY 11501.

GERAGHTY, MICHAEL A, b. Chicago, Ill, May 15, 30; m. 60; c. 4. MATHEMATICS. B.Sc, Notre Dame, 52, Ph.D.(math), 59. Off. Naval Res. res. assoc. MATH, Northwestern, 59-60, asst. prof, 60-62; vis. assoc. prof, res. inst, Alabama, 62-64; asst. prof, UNIV. IOWA, 64-65, ASSOC. PROF, 65- Am. Math. Soc; Math. Asn. Am. Topology. Address: 1719 Rochester Ct, Iowa City, IA 52240.

GERALD, CURTIS F, b. Omaha, Nebr, May 22, 15; m. 70; c. 5. CHEMICAL ENGINEERING, COMPUTER SCIENCE. B.S, Iowa State, 36; M.S, Cincinnati, 38; Sc.D.(chem. eng), Mass. Inst. Tech, 41. Res. engr, R.R. Donnelley & Sons Co, 40-42; res. chem. engr, Universal Oil Prod. Co, 42-47, chem. engr, 51-60; asst. prof. chem. eng, Washington (Seattle), 47-51; assoc. dir. res, El Paso Natural Gas Prod. Co, 60-63; PROF. COMPUT. SCI, CALIF. STATE POLYTECH. COL, 64-, HEAD DEPT, 69- Am. Inst. Chem. Eng. Catalytic reactions in petroleum chemistry; numerical methods in engineering applications. Address: Dept. of Computer Science & Statistics, California State Polytechnic College, San Luis Obispo, CA 93401.

GERALD, JERRY W, b. Van Horn, Tex, Feb. 14, 40. VERTEBRATE BIOLOGY, ANIMAL BEHAVIOR. B.S, Tex. Tech Univ, 62; M.S, Mont. State Univ, 65; Ph.D.(zool), Univ. Tex, Austin, 70. ASST. PROF. biol, City Col. New York, 69-71; PHYSIOL, SAN FRANCISCO STATE COL, 71- Guest investr, dept. animal behav, Am. Mus. Natural Hist, N.Y.C, 69-71. Am. Soc. Zool; Am. Inst. Biol. Sci; Animal Behavior Soc; Am. Fisheries Soc; Am. Soc. Ichthyol. & Herpet. Physiological aspects of animal communication, especially sound production and hearing in fishes; physiology of aquatic respiration; species isolating mechanisms. Address: Dept. of Physiology & Behavioral Biology, San Francisco State College, San Francisco, CA 94132.

GERALD, MICHAEL C(HARLES), b. N.Y.C, Nov. 20, 39; m. 65; c. 2. PHARMACOLOGY. B.S, Fordham Univ, 61; U.S. Pub. Health Serv. fel, Ind. Univ, Bloomington, 65-68, Ph.D.(pharmacol), 68. U.S. Pub. Health Serv. fel. psychiat. & pharmacol, Univ. Chicago, 68-69; ASST. PROF. PHARMACOL, OHIO STATE UNIV, 69- Consult, Am. Sch. Health Asn. Med.Serv.C, U.S.A.F, 1st Lt. AAAS; sr. mem. Acad. Pharmaceut. Sci; Am. Pharmaceut. Asn; Am. Asn. Cols. Pharm. Brain histamine and behavior; antihistamine-oxotremorine interactions; spironolactone induction of liver microsomal drug metabolizing enzyme systems; psychopharmacology; neuropharmacology; drug metabolism. Address: College of Pharmacy, Ohio State University, 500 W. 12th Ave, Columbus, OH 43210.

GERALD, PARK S, b. Omaha, Nebr, June 30, 21; m. 56; c. 3. PEDIATRICS. B.S, Iowa State Col, 43; M.D, Creighton, 47. Instr. PEDIAT, HARVARD MED. SCH, 58-59, assoc, 59-62, asst. prof, 62-65, assoc. clin. prof, 65-67, assoc. prof, 67-70, PROF, 70-; CHIEF CLIN. GENETICS DIV, CHILDREN'S HOSP. MED. CTR, 66- Nat. Heart Inst. spec. res. fel, 55-59; mem, joint Comn. Ment. Health of Children, Inc, 67-69; chmn. ment. retardation res. & training comt, Nat. Inst. Child Health & Human Develop, 69-72. Mead-Johnson award, Am. Acad. Pediat, 62. Pediatrician, 11th Field Hosp, Augsburg, Ger, Med.C, U.S.A, 51-53. Soc. Pediat. Res; Am. Soc. Clin. Invest; Am. Pediat. Soc; Am. Soc. Human Genetics. Clinical genetics; cytogenetics; inherited variants of proteins. Address: Clinical Genetics Division, Children's Hospital Medical Center, 300 Longwood Ave, Boston, MA 02115.

GERALDSON, CARROLL M(ORTON), b. Manitowoc, Wis, Apr. 8, 18; m. 49; c. 7. SOIL CHEMISTRY. B.A, St. Olaf Col, 40; Ph.D.(soils, plant physiol), Wisconsin, 51. PROF. SOIL CHEM, INST. FOOD & AGR. SCI, AGR. RES. & EDUC. CTR, UNIV. FLA, 69-, SOIL CHEMIST, 51- Fla. Fruit & Vegetable Award, 56. U.S.N, 44-46. Am. Soc. Agron; Am. Soc. Hort. Sci. (Vaughan Award, 55). Nutrition of vegetable crops; control of physiological disorders such as black heart of celery and blossom-end rot of tomatoes and peppers; development and utilization of the intensity and balance soil solution testing procedure for evaluating the ionic root environment for optimal production; maintenance of 3-dimensional gradients; establishment in the soil profile by surface application of nutrients with a mulch covering and constant source of water. Address: Institute of Food & Agricultural Science, Agricultural Research & Education Center, University of Florida, 5007 60th St. E, Bradenton, FL 33505.

GERAMITA, A. V, b. N.Y.C, Aug. 4, 42; m. 68. MATHEMATICS. B.S, City Col. New York, 63; Regents fel, Syracuse Univ, 63, M.A. & NASA trainee, 65, Ph.D.(math), 68. Asst. prof. MATH, State Univ. N.Y. Col. Oswego, 68; instr, Syracuse Univ, 68-69; ASST. PROF. & RES. ASSOC, QUEEN'S UNIV.(ONT), 69- Am. Math. Soc; Math. Asn. Am. Commutative and homological algebra. Address: Dept. of Mathematics, Queen's University, Kingston, Ont, Can.

GERARD, CLEVELAND J(OSEPH), b. Milton, La, Sept. 25, 24. SOIL SCIENCE. B.S, Southwest. La. Inst, 48; M.S, Kansas State, 50; Ph.D.(soil physics), Agr. & Mech. Col, Texas, 55. Soil scientist, Agr. Res. Serv, U.S. Dept. Agr, Oregon State Col, 54-57; SOIL PHYSICIST, TEX. AGR. EXP. STA, 57- U.S.N, 43-46. Soil Sci. Soc. Am. Soil chemistry; soil physics and soil-plant relationships. Address: Texas Agricultural Experiment Station, Weslaco, TX 78596.

GERARD, F(ITZGERALD) A(DOLPHUS), b. Brighton, Eng, Oct. 7, 07; m. 40. CIVIL ENGINEERING. B.A, London, 45, M.A, 49, Ph.D.(struct. eng), 56. Lectr. eng, Stockport Col, Eng, 48-49; Crewe Tech. Col, 50-51; Croydon Tech. Col, 51-57; assoc. prof. civil eng, Saskatchewan, 57-61; prof. mech. eng, New Mexico, 61-65; PROF. ENG, SIR GEORGE WILLIAMS UNIV, 65- Eng. Inst. Can; Brit. Inst. Struct. Eng. Structural analysis; elasticity; design of plates and shells; matrix analysis of structures. Address: Faculty of Engineering, Sir George Williams University, Montreal, Que, Can.

GERARD, JESSE T(HOMAS), b. Windsor, Ont, Mar. 19, 41; m. 62; c. 2. ANALYTICAL CHEMISTRY, COSMOCHEMISTRY. B.Sc, Univ. Windsor, 64, Nat. Res. Coun. Can. fels, 64-68, Ph.D.(anal. chem), 68. Res. faculty mem. & coinvestr. Apollo lunar samples, dept. chem, Cornell Univ, 68-71; RES. CHEMIST & NAT. ACAD. SCI-NAT. RES. COUN. INHOUSE RESIDENT RES. ASSOC, THEORET. STUDIES BR, LAB. FOR SPACE PHYSICS, GODDARD SPACE FLIGHT CTR, NASA, 71- Fel. AAAS; fel. Am. Chem. Soc; fel. Geochem. Soc. Neuron activation analysis; radiochemistry; x-ray fluorescence analysis; classical chemical analysis; separations; ultra trace, trace, minor and major element analysis; lunar chemistry, geochemistry; remote analysis of lunar geology. Address: Theoretical Studies Branch, Lab. for Space Physics, Goddard Space Flight Center, NASA, Greenbelt, MD 20771.

GERARD, R(ALPH) W(ALDO), b. Harvey, Ill, Oct. 7, 00; m. 22, 55; c. 1. NEUROPHYSIOLOGY. B.S, Chicago, 19, Ph.D, 21; M.D, Rush Med. Col, 25; hon. D.Sc, Maryland, 52, McGill Univ, 68; hon. M.D, Leiden, 62; hon. LL.D, St. Andrews, 64; hon. Litt.D, Brown, 64. Asst. physiol, Chicago, 18-21, asst. prof, 28-29, assoc. prof, 29-41, prof, 41-52; prof. & head dept, South Dakota, 21-22; head dept, Hahnemann Med. Col, 22-24; fel, Nat. Res. Coun, London, 25; Kaiser Wilhelm Inst, 26-27; prof. neurophysiol, neuropsychiat. inst, col. med, Illinois, 52-55; ment. health res. inst, Univ. Mich, 55-64; prof. biol. sci, Univ. Calif, Irvine, 64-70, dean grad. div. & dir. spec. studies, 64-69; RETIRED. Arthur lectr, 38; ed, J. Neurophysiol, 39-45; mem. med. teaching mission, Czech, 46; govt. adv. & first vis. prof, Australian Nat. Univ, 47; chmn. physiol. adv. panel, Off. Naval Res, 47-53; mem. med. teaching mission, Greece, 48; Gregory lectr, 48; ed, J. Electroencephalog, 48-; consult, Chief Naval Res. & Opers. Res. Off, 50-52; mem. stress comn, Nat. Res. Coun, 51-, biol. coun, 54-; Eastman lectr, 52; prof, Univ. Chicago, 54; fel, Ford Found, 54-55; praelector, Univ. St. Andrews, Scotland, 58; Hertzstein lectr, 58; consult. sr. scientist, ment. health res. inst, Univ. Mich, 64-; consult, Off. Surgeon Gen, Nat. Insts. Health. Medal, Charles Univ, Prague, 46; Order of White Lion, Czech, 46; Stanley R. Dean Award, 64; Medal, Univ. Chicago Alumni Asn, 67; dir. spec. war res, 42-46. Nat. Acad. Sci; Am. Acad. Arts & Sci; Am. Soc. Nat; Am. Physiol. Soc.(ed, Physiol. Revs, 35-50, Am. J. Physiol, 50-52; pres, 51); Nat. Soc. Med. Res. (secy-treas, 54); Am. Electroencephalog. Soc; Asn. Res. Nerv. & Ment. Diseases; Am. Neurol. Asn; Brit. Physiol. Soc; Brit. Biochem. Soc; Soc. Biol. Psychiat.(pres, 67); Soc. Neurosci.(hon. pres); hon. fel. Royal Soc. Edinburg. Nerve and brain metabolism and electrical properties; mitochondria metabolism; muscle membrane potential and contraction; organismic theory; respiratory irritant gases; relation of biology to social and ethical problems; computers in education; health education and care. Address: 1007 Goldenrod Ave, Corona del Mar, CA 92625.

GERARDE, HORACE W(ILLIAM), b. Rockford, Ill, Oct. 12; m. 42; c. 3. MEDICINE, BIOCHEMISTRY. B.S, Beloit Col, 40, M.S, 42; M.D, Wisconsin, 48; Am. Col. Physicians fel, Iowa, 49-50, Am. Cancer Soc. fel, 50-52, Ph.D. (biochem), 51. Instr. chem, Beloit Col, 40-42; asst. physiol, Wisconsin, 42-47; intern, Univ. Hosps, Iowa, 48-49, res. assoc. biochem, 50-52; chief toxicologist, Esso Res. & Eng. Co, 52-66; med. dir, Becton, Dickinson Div, BECTON, DICKINSON & CO, RUTHERFORD, 66-69, CORP. MED. DIR. OCCUP. HEALTH, 69- Res. specialist, bur. biol. res, Rutgers, 54-; assoc. prof, sch. med, N.Y. Univ; vis. lectr, sch. pub. health, Harvard; adj. prof, sch. dent, Fairleigh Dickinson Univ, 66- Consult, comt. toxicol, Nat. Res. Coun. Am. Chem. Soc; Am. Med. Asn; Indust. Med. Asn; Am. Indust. Hyg. Asn. Industrial toxicology and medicine; pharmacology; toxicology and biochemistry of hydrocarbons. Address: 41 Knoll Rd, Tenafly, NJ 07670.

GERARDO, HENRY A, b. Holyoke, Mass, Nov. 29, 28; m. 54; c. 5. NUCLEAR PHYSICS. B.S, Massachusetts, 50; M.S, Pennsylvania, 52; Ph.D.(nuclear eng. physics), Purdue, 64. Res. asst. nuclear physics, Pennsylvania, 50-52; sr. engr. radar anal, Westinghouse Corp, 56-57; supvr. aircraft nuclear propulsion shielding, Gen. Elec. Co, 57-61; asst. mgr. adv. systs, Radio Corp. Am, 61-62; mgr. nuclear sci, Gen. Motors Corp, 62-64; consult. & mgr. nuclear vulnerability & hardening, Gen. Elec. Co, 65-67; PRES, Universal Signal Corp, 67-69; GENII INDUST, 69- Consult, Mobile Compact Reactor Prog, 62-64; Re-entry Systs, 65- U.S.A.F, 52-56, 1st Lt. Am. Nuclear Soc; Am. Phys. Soc. Space environmental systems involving integration of nuclear power, propulsion, shielding, and radiation effects in maneuverable vehicles; general management with emphasis on organization and development of new ventures, products, policies, programs and acquisitions. Address: 428 Manington Place, West Covina, CA 91791.

GERARDO, JAMES BERNARD, b. Toluca, Ill, Oct. 18, 36; m. 63. ELECTRICAL ENGINEERING, PLASMA PHYSICS. B.S, Univ. Ill, 59, M.S, 60, Ph.D. (elec. eng), 63. Res. asst. elec. eng, Univ. Ill, Urbana, 59-63, res. assoc, 63-67; mem. res. staff, org. 5100, SANDIA LABS, SANDIA CORP, 66-67, SUPVR. DIV. 5243, 67- Am. Phys. Soc. Energy state of gaseous plasmas; gaseous electronics. Address: Division 5243, Sandia Labs, Sandia Corp, Albuquerque, NM 87115.

GERATHEWOHL, SIEGFRIED JOHANNES, b. Ebersbach, Ger, Sept. 11, 09; U.S. citizen; m. 41; c. 2. PSYCHOLOGY, PHYSIOLOGY. B.S. & M.S, Dresden Tech, 33, Ph.D.(psychol), 36; dipl. psychol, Munich, 44. Chief, Aircrew Selection & Test Ctr, Ger, 39-42; indust. psychol. div, BMW Munich, 42-44; res. scientist, Aeromed. Ctr, 45-46; U.S. Air Force Sch. Aviation Med, 47-57; chief scientist, off. bioastronaut, Army Ballistic Missile Agency, 58-60; chief oper. develop, NASA Hq, 60-61, biotech. div, Ames Res. Ctr, 61-63, mgr, life sci. prog, NASA Hq, 64-66; CHIEF RES. PLANNING BR, FED. AVIATION AGENCY HQ, 66- Mem. Armed Forces Comt. Vision, Nat. Acad. Sci-Nat. Res. Coun, 57-58, 64-, comt. bioastronaut, 58-61; lectr, Stanford Univ, 62-63. Ger. Armed Forces, 36-39. Int. Acad. Astronaut; Aerospace Med. Asn.(Arnold D. Tuttle Award, 58); Am. Inst. Aeronaut. & Astronaut; Ger. Soc. Rockets & Space Flight; Ger. Aerospace Med. Asn. Psychology and physiology of flight; flying safety; radar; orientation; navigation; hypoxia; sealed cabins; habitability of closed systems; zero gravity; weightlessness; man-machine relationships. Address: 5208 Albemarle St, Washington, DC 20016.

GERATZ, JOACHIM DIETER, b. Gloethe, Ger, July 3, 29; U.S. citizen; m. 61; c. 3. PATHOLOGY. M.D, Frankfurt, 53. Asst. path, Frankfurt, 54-55; intern, Jefferson Hosp, Roanoke, Va, 55-56; res. PATH, UNIV. N.C, CHAPEL HILL, 56-60, instr, 60-63, asst. prof, 63-67, ASSOC. PROF, 67- AAAS; Int. Acad. Path; Am. Asn. Path. & Bact; Am. Soc. Clin. Path; Int. Soc. Thrombosis & Haemostasis. Blood coagulation; inhibitors of proteolytic enzymes; physiology and pathology of the pancreas. Address: Dept. of Pathology, University of North Carolina, Chapel Hill, NC 27514.

GERBER, ARTHUR H, b. N.Y.C, Feb. 27, 32; m. 57; c. 2. ORGANIC & POLYMER CHEMISTRY. B.S, City Col. New York, 53; M.S, Columbia, 54, Am. Cyanamid fel, 56-57, Ph.D.(org. chem), 59. Res. chemist, Esso Res. Eng. Co, N.J, 57-60; res. assoc. chemist, Lord Corp, Pa, 60-66, sr. res. assoc. chemist, 66-70; SR. RES. ASSOC, HORIZONS RES. INC, 70- Am. Chem. Soc. Organic synthesis; polymerization; reaction mechanism. Address: Chemistry Dept, Horizons Research Inc, 23800 Mercantile Rd, Beachwood, OH 44122.

GERBER, BERNARD ROBERT, b. New York, N.Y, May 31, 35; m. 57; c. 3. PHYSICAL CHEMISTRY, BIOLOGY. A.B, Hunter Col, 55; M.S, N.Y. Univ, 58 & 61, U.S. Pub. Health Serv. fel, 58-64, Ph.D.(phys. chem), 64. Operator comput, Atomic Energy Comn. facility, inst. math. sci, N.Y, 55-58; Helen Hay Whitney Found. fel, 64-67; res. assoc. chem. contractile proteins, State Univ. N.Y. Downstate Med. Ctr, 67-68; ASST. PROF. BIOL, UNIV. PA, 68- John Polachek Found. Med. Res. fel, 68; Biomed. Sci. support grant, 69-70; Nat. Sci. Found. instnl. grant, 69-71, res. grant, 71-72. AAAS; N.Y. Acad. Sci; Biophys. Soc; Soc. Gen. Physiol; Am. Inst. Chem. Static and dynamic aspects of the three dimensional structure of biological macromolecules; self-assembly processes; connective tissue proteins and polysaccharides; contractile proteins; bacterial flagella. Address: Dept. of Biology, University of Pennsylvania, Philadelphia, PA 19104.

GERBER, CHARLES E(DWIN), b. Marietta, Ohio, Sept. 9, 19; m. 42; c. 2. ENTOMOLOGY. B.S, Ohio State, 49, M.S, 50. Field res. specialist entom. & plant path, Ortho Div, CHEVRON CHEM. CO, 51-64, supvr. agr. pesticides, EAST. FIELD RES. STA, 64-69, SR. RES. SPECIALIST, 69- U.S.A, 42-45, S/Sgt. Entom. Soc. Am; Weed Sci. Soc. Am. Agricultural chemicals including fungicides, insecticides, herbicides, nematocides and growth regulators. Address: Eastern Field Research Station, Chevron Chemical Co, N. Church St, Moorestown, NJ 08057.

GERBER, DONALD A(LBERT), b. New York, N.Y, Apr. 10, 32; m. 64; c. 1. INTERNAL MEDICINE. A.B, Columbia, 53, M.D, 57. Intern, Osler Med. Serv, Hopkins Hosp, Baltimore, Md, 57-58, asst. resident, 58-59, asst. MED, 58-59; asst. resident, Presby. Hosp, New York, 59-60; Arthritis Found. vis. fel, col. physicians & surgeons, Columbia, 60-63; instr, STATE UNIV. N.Y. DOWNSTATE MED. CTR, 63-64, asst. prof, 64-69, ASSOC. PROF, 69- Spec. investr, Arthritis Found, 63-66; career scientist award, Health Res. Coun, City of New York, 65- Dipl, Am. Bd. Internal Med. Am. Rheumatism Asn; Am. Fedn. Clin. Res; Harvey Soc; N.Y. Acad. Sci; fel. Am. Col. Physicians; Soc. Exp. Biol. & Med. Metabolic abnormalities in rheumatoid arthritis; mechanism of action of anti-rheumatic drugs; the role of L-histidine, copper, and sulfhydryl groups in rheumatic disease. Address: Dept. of Medicine, State University of New York Downstate Medical Center, 450 Clarkson Ave, Brooklyn, NY 11203.

GERBER, EDUARD A, b. Fuerth, Ger, Apr. 3, 07; U.S. citizen; m. 34; c. 3. PHYSICAL ELECTRICS. M.S, Inst. Tech, Munich, Ger, 31, Ph.D.(physics), 34. Physicist res. & develop, Siemens & Halske, Ger, 34-35; mem. sci. staff & head lab. piezoelec. crystals, Carl Zeiss Works, 35-45, geom. optics, 46-47; consult. frequency control, Sig. Corps Eng. Labs, U.S. ARMY, FT. MONMOUTH, N.J, 47-54, dir, frequency control div, Sig. Res. & Develop. Lab, 54-61, solid state & frequency control div, 61-63, ELECTRONIC COMPONENTS LAB, U.S. ELECTRONICS COMMAND, 63-70, CONSULT, LAB, 70- Fel. Inst. Elec. & Electronics Eng; Am. Phys. Soc. Development of electronic materials; electron tubes; solid state, frequency control and selective devices; quantumelectronics; power sources; passive component parts and component assemblies; integrated electronics. Address: 11 Community Dr, West Long Branch, NJ 07764.

GERBER, EUGENE H(ENRY), b. Paris, France, Nov. 26, 27; U.S. citizen; m. 53; c. 6. PHYSICS. B.A, Buffalo, 47, Ph.D.(physics), 52. Asst. physics, Buffalo, 48-52; asst. res. physicist, Cornell Aeronaut. Lab, 52, assoc. res. physicist, 52-55; scientist, Lockheed Missile Systs. Div, Lockheed Aircraft Corp, 55-56; from prin. physicist to BR. HEAD, CORNELL AERONAUT. LAB, INC, 56- Am. Phys. Soc. Nuclear physics; systems design. Address: Cornell Aeronautical Lab, Inc, P.O. Box 235, Buffalo, NY 14221.

GERBER, H. JOSEPH, b. Vienna, Austria, Apr. 17, 24; U.S. citizen; m. 54; c. 2. AERONAUTICAL ENGINEERING. B.A.E, Rensselaer Polytech, 47. Anal. engr, Hamilton Standard Div, United Aircraft Corp, Conn, 48-51; PRES. & DIR, GERBER SCI. INSTRUMENT CO, 47- Mem. adv. bd. for eng. & mgt. adv. bd, Rensselaer Polytech. Inst; chmn, Gerber Sci-Europe S.A, Brussels; Gerber Sci-U.K. Ltd, London; dir, Gerber Garment Technol. Inc, Conn; Beta Eng. & Develop. Ltd, Beer-Sheba, Israel; Appl. Programming Technol, Mass; Boston Digital Corp; Phoenix Mutual Fund; Mfrs. Asn. Hartford County, Inc; mem. assoc. bd. dirs, Hartford br. off, Conn. Bank & Trust Co; corporator, Inst. Living. Numerical Control Soc. Graphics; graphical numerical computing instruments; data reduction and plotting machines; servo stepping motors; digital positioning devices. Address: Gerber Scientific Instrument Co, 83 Gerber Rd, South Windsor, CT 06074.

GERBER, JAY D, b. Dodge City, Kans, Apr. 1, 41; m. 71. IMMUNOLOGY, BIOCHEMISTRY. B.S, St. Benedict's Col, 63; summer fel, Duke Univ, 65; Ph.D.(zool), Univ. Kans, 68. Res. fel. physiol, sch. med, Stanford Univ, 68-69; IMMUNOLOGIST, MYCOSIS SECT, CTR. DISEASE CONTROL, 69- AAAS; Am. Inst. Biol. Sci; Am. Soc. Microbiol; Soc. Syst. Zool. Development of immunity to parasitic infections, particularly myoctic infections; anaphylactic inducing properties of bacterial and higher animal toxins; immunotaxonomy. Address: Center for Disease Control, 2002 W. 39th St, Kansas City, KS 66103.

GERBER, JOHN F(RANCIS), b. Versailles, Mo, Dec. 13, 30; m. 55; c. 3. AGRICULTURAL METEOROLOGY. B.S, Univ. Mo, 56, M.S, 57, Ph.D. (soils), 60. Instr. soils, Univ. Mo, 59-60; asst. prof. FRUIT CROPS, UNIV. FLA, 60-66, assoc. prof, 66-69, PROF, 69-, ASST. DEAN RES, AGR. EXP. STAS, 71- Consult, Corps Eng, U.S. Army, 65-68; faculty develop. grant from Univ. Fla. & vis. prof, dept. hort, Pa. State Univ, 69-70. Med.C. U.S.A, 53-55. Am. Soc. Hort. Sci.(rev. ed, jour); Am. Meteorol. Soc. Soils; climatology; cold protection of plants; heat budget studies; agricultural climatology. Address: Institute of Food & Agricultural Science, University of Florida, Room 1041, McCarty Hall, Gainesville, FL 32601.

GERBER, LEON E, b. Brooklyn, N.Y, Sept. 5, 41; m. 64; c. 3. MATHEMATICS. B.S, Brooklyn Col, 60; Nat. Sci. Found. fels, Yeshiva, 60-61 & 62-65, M.A, 62, Ph.D.(math), 68. Programmer, Brookhaven Nat. Lab, 60; instr. MATH, ST. JOHN'S UNIV.(N.Y), 66-68, ASST. PROF, 68- Math. Asn. Am. Geometry of n-dimensions; asymptotic relations between solutions of differential equations and difference equations. Address: 1636-50th St, Brooklyn, NY 11204.

GERBER, L(OUIS) P, b. Cardiff, Wales, May 9, 04; nat; m. 34; c. 2. CHEMISTRY. B.S, Illinois, 25; M.S, Purdue, 29, Ph.D.(biochem), 33; fel, Iowa State Col, 29-30. Asst. chem, Purdue, 27-33; res. chemist, William S. Merrell Co, Ohio, 33-36; biochemist, St. Francis & Methodist Hosps, 37-40; res. chemist, Hiram Walker & Sons, Inc, 40-42; A.E. Staley Mfg. Co, 42-46; asst. to res. dir, Schenley Labs, Inc, 46-52; tech. dir, William T. Thompson Co, 59-63; Indag Labs, Inc, Calif, 63-65; dir. clin. lab, Calbiochem, 65-69; INDEPENDENT CONSULT, 69- Am. Chem. Soc. Clinical chemistry; nutrition; industrial fermentation including antibiotics; separation of amino acids; preparation of enzymes; pharmaceuticals. Address: 26314 N. Long Oak Dr, Newhall, CA 91321.

GERBER, MARCIA GETZ, b. New York, N.Y, Feb. 17, 42; m. 64; c. 1. MEDICINE. A.B, Vassar Col, 63; M.D, Columbia, 67. Intern INTERNAL MED, STATE UNIV. N.Y. DOWNSTATE MED. CTR, 67-68, instr, 68, PART-TIME INSTR, 69- Cause and treatment of rheumatoid arthritis. Address: Student Health Service, State University of New York Downstate Medical Center, 450 Clarkson Ave, Brooklyn, NY 11203.

GERBER, NANCY N(ICHOLS), b. Chicago, Ill, June 27, 29; m. 53; c. 2. ORGANIC CHEMISTRY. A.B, Oberlin Col, 50; M.A, Columbia, 52; Ph.D.(org. chem), Rutgers, 57. Res. assoc. org. chem, Rutgers, 52-54, 57-58; res. chemist, Nopco Chem. Co, 58-60; vis. investr, INST. MICROBIOL, RUTGERS UNIV, 60-63, ASST. RES. SPECIALIST, 63- Am. Chem. Soc. Chemistry of natural products; biosynthesis; organic synthesis. Address: Box 779B, R.R. 1, 70 Hillcrest Rd, Martinsville, NJ 08836.

GERBER, PAUL, b. Vienna, Austria, June 7, 16; nat; m. 46; c. 2. MICROBIOLOGY. B.S, Roosevelt, 52; M.S, Chicago, 53, Ph.D.(microbiol), 55. Res. assoc. prev. med, Chicago, 55-56; chemotherapy, Squibb Inst. Med. Res, 56-58; RES. MICROBIOLOGIST, NAT. INSTS. HEALTH, 58- Seymour Coman fel, Chicago, 55-56. Med.C, U.S.A, 41-45. Soc. Exp. Biol. & Med. Viral genetics and biology of viruses. Address: National Institutes of Health, Bethesda, MD 20014.

GERBER, ROBERT K(ING), b. Salt Lake City, Utah, Feb. 18, 10; m. 34; c. 3. HORTICULTURE. B.S, Utah State Agr. Col, 32, M.S, 35; Potash fel, Ohio State, 34-36. Field agronomist, Am. Potash Inst, 36-40; ed. adv. civilian conserv. corps, U.S. Dept. Army, 40-41; control chemist, Remington Arms, Salt Lake City, 41-43; instr. physics, UTAH STATE UNIV, 43-44, agent & res. asst, exp. sta, U.S. Dept. Agr, 44-47, asst. prof. hort, 47-62, asst. foreman campus & grounds, 62-64, asst. supt, HOWELL FIELD STA. HORT. RES, DEPT. PLANT SCI, 64-67, SUPT, 67- Hort. adv, Int. Coop. Admin, Iran, 60-62. Am. Soc. Hort. Sci. Pruning and fertilizing of stone fruits; varieties of deciduous fruits; fruit juices and purees; gamma irradiation of fruits and vegetables. Address: Dept. of Plant Science, Utah State University, Logan, UT 84321.

GERBER, SAMUEL M(ICHAEL), b. New York, N.Y, June 21, 20; m. 53; c. 2. ORGANIC CHEMISTRY. B.S, City Col, 42; M.A, Columbia, 48, Ph.D. (chem), 52. Asst. chem, Columbia, 47-51; chemist, AM. CYANAMID CO, 51-55; asst. to tech. dir, ORG. CHEM. DIV, 56-58, group leader, 58-68, CHIEF CHEMIST, 68- U.S.A, 42-46, Res, 46-53, 1st Lt. Am. Chem. Soc. Brit. Soc. Dyers & Colourists; The Chem. Soc. Aliphatic and aromatic diazo compounds; azo dyes and intermediates; dye and dye intermediates; process development; textile chemistry and finishing. Address: Organic Chemicals Division, American Cyanamid Co, Bound Brook, NJ 08805.

GERBERG, EUGENE J(ORDAN), b. N.Y.C, June 1, 19; m. 41; c. 5. ENTOMOLOGY. B.S, Cornell, 39, M.S, 41; Ph.D, Maryland, 54. Entomol. technician, State Conserv. Dept. N.Y, 40-41; asst. entomologist, U.S. Pub. Health Serv, 41-43; PRES, CORNELL CHEM. & EQUIP. CO, 48-; AM. BIO-CHEM. LAB, INC, 48- DIR, INSECT CONTROL & RES, INC, 46- Special surv, Ministry of Agr, Venezuela, 50; collab, U.S. Dept. Agr, 54- Trop. agr. specialist, U.S. Mkt. & Bus. Develop. Mission, Nigeria, 61, Pakistan, 68; consult, WHO, 69; proj. leader, E.Africa Aedes Res. Unit, Tanzania, 69, 70. Sanit.C, U.S.A, 43-46, U.S.A.R, 46-, Lt. Col. Entom. Soc. Am; Am. Phytopath. Soc; Weed Sci. Soc. Am; Am. Mosquito Control Asn; Inst. Food Tech; Am. Soc. Trop. Med. & Hyg; Royal Soc. Trop. Med. & Hyg. Tropical and medical entomology; food plant sanitation; insect ecology; coleoptera. Address: Insect Control & Research, Inc, 1111 N. Rolling Rd, P.O. Box 3149, Baltimore, MD 21228.

GERBERICH, H(AROLD) ROBERT, b. Wooster, Ohio, May 18, 33; m. 58; c. 2. PHYSICAL CHEMISTRY. B.A, Col. Wooster, 55; Ph.D.(chem), Rochester, 60. Res. chemist, Celanese Chem. Co, 59-61; fel. catalysis, Mellon Inst, 61-66; RES. ASSOC, CELANESE CHEM. CO, 66- Am. Chem. Soc. Kinetics of liquid phase oxidation reactions. Address: Celanese Chemical Co, Box 9077, Corpus Christi, TX 78408.

GERBERICH, J(OHN) B(ARNES), b. Wooster, Ohio, Apr. 21, 16; m. 48; c. 1. MICROBIOLOGY. B.S, Kent State, 39, M.A, 41; Ph.D, Ohio State, 51. Instr. zool, Ohio State, 44-46; biol, Mich. State Col, 46-47; zool, Minnesota, Duluth, 47-53, insect control res. prods, 53-54; asst. prof. zool, WIS. STATE UNIV-EAU CLAIRE, 54-58, assoc. prof, 58-61, prof, 61-67, PROF. BIOL. & DIR. ALLIED HEALTH PROGS, 67- Consult, WHO, summer, 65. Entom. Soc. Am. Biological control methods of insects; immature insects; insect microbiology. Address: Dept. of Biology, Wisconsin State University, Eau Claire, WI 54701.

GERBES, OTTO, b. San Antonio, Tex. Oct. 10, 09; m. 44. CHEMICAL ENGINEERING. B.S, Texas, 31, M.S, 32. Partner, San Antonio Ref. Co, Texas, 33-38, owner, 38-39; chem. engr, Humble Oil & Ref. Co, 39-43, sr. chem. engr, 43-62, staff engr, 62-70; CONSULT, 70- Am. Inst. Chem. Eng. Alkylation; polymerization; petroleum processing; catalytic cracking. Address: 705 Maplewood Dr, Baytown, TX 77520.

GERBODE, FRANK, b. Placerville, Calif, Feb. 3, 07; m. 31; c. 4. SURGERY. A.B, Stanford, 32, M.D, 36; hon. M.Surg, Nat. Univ. Ireland, 61; hon. M.D, Thessaloniki, 64; hon. M.D, Uppsala, 65. Resident & asst. path, Munich, Ger, 37; asst. surg. res, Stanford Hosps, 38, asst. resident surg, 38-39, resident, 40; assoc, St. Bartholomew's Hosp. & Med. Sch, London, 49; clin. prof. SURG, SCH. MED, STANFORD UNIV, 52-71; EMER. CLIN. PROF, 71-; CHIEF CARDIOVASC. SURG, PACIFIC MED. CTR, 60-; CLIN. PROF. SURG, SCH. MED, UNIV. CALIF, SAN FRANCISCO, 64- Guest prof, Royal N.Shore Hosp, Sydney, Australia, 53; Ball guest prof, Indiana, 57; guest prof, St. Thomas' Hosp, London, 58, Free Univ. Berlin, 60, New South Wales, 63 & Heidelberg, 64; lectr. & vis. surgeon, Karolinska Hosp, Stockholm, Sweden, 64. Consult, Letterman Army Hosp, San Francisco; Calif. State Bd. Pub. Health. Spec. consult. to chief div. gen. med. sci, Nat. Insts. Health, 60-63, mem, clin. res. training comt, 63-67, surg. training comt, 66-67, therapeut. eval. comt, 67-71; mem. comt. surg, Nat. Res. Coun, 50-51, comt. cardiovasc. diseases, 55-61. Dipl, Am. Bd. Surg; dipl, Am. Bd. Thoracic Surg; Comdr, Order St. John of Jerusalem; hon. perpetual student St. Bartholomew's Hosp, London; hon. fel, Royal Col. Surg. Eng. Med.C, 42-45, Lt. Col. AAAS; Soc. Thoracic Surg; Am. Col. Surg; Am. Heart Asn; Am. Med. Asn; Am. Surg. Asn; Soc. Clin. Surg; Soc. Univ. Surg; Soc. Vascular Surg; Ger. Surg. Soc; Int. Cardiovasc. Soc; Int. Soc. Surg. Cardiovascular surgery. Address: Pacific Medical Center, Clay & Webster Sts, San Francisco, CA 94115.

GERDEEN, JAMES C, b. Escanaba, Mich, July 16, 37; m. 60; c. 3. ENGINEERING MECHANICS. B.S.M.E, Michigan Tech, 59; M.S.E.M, Ohio State, 62; Battelle fel. & Ph.D.(eng. mech), Stanford, 66. Res. engr, appl. mech. div, Battelle Mem. Inst, Ohio, 59-63, sr. res. engr, adv. solid mech. div, 65-68; ASSOC. PROF. ENG. MECH, MICH. TECHNOL. UNIV, 68- Guest lectr, Ohio State, 67; mem. subcmt. shells, pressure vessel res. cmt, Welding Res. Coun, 67- Soc. Exp. Stress Anal; Am. Soc. Mech. Eng. Stress analysis of thin plate and shell structures, particularly pressure vessels; plastic deformation in structures and metal working operations; inelastic behavior and rock mechanics. Address: Dept. of Mechanical Engineering & Engineering Mechanics, Michigan Technological University, Houghton, MI 49931.

GERDEL, ROBERT W(ALLACE), b. St. Louis, Mo, Oct. 4, 01; m. 27; c. 1. GEOPHYSICS. B.S, Mich. State, 23; M.S, Ohio State, 25, Ph.D.(biochem), 29. Asst. farm crops, Ohio State. 24-25, biochemist, exp. sta, 25-33; asst. soil scientist, soil conserv. serv, U.S. Dept. Agr, 33-39, assoc. soil scientist, 39-40, head soil mgt. sect, regional agron. div, 40-42, physicist, microclimatic res. ctr, 42-43; physicist & dir, cent. Sierra snow res. lab, U.S. Weather Bur, 43-45; tech. supvr, co-op. snow invest, Corps Engr, U.S. Army & U.S. Weather Bur, 45-50; chief climatic & environ. res. br, snow, ice & permafrost res. estab, U.S. Army, 50-60, environ. res. br, cold regions res. & eng. lab, 60-65, consult, Calif, 65-67; sr. staff scientist, Aerojet-Gen. Corp, 67-68; DIR. RES, WEATHER MEASURE CORP, 68- Am. Soc. Civil. Eng; Am. Meteorol. Soc; fel. Inst. Environ. Sci; Am. Geophys. Union. Thermodynamics of snow and ice; cold regions environmental engineering and atmospheric physics. Address: 8435 Oak Knoll Dr, Roseville, CA 95678.

GERDEMANN, J(AMES) W(ESSEL), b. Warrenton, Mo, Nov. 13, 21; m. 49; c. 3. PLANT PATHOLOGY. B.A, Missouri, 45, M.A, 46; Ph.D.(plant path), California, 48. Asst. Missouri, 45-46; California, 46-48; from instr. to asst. prof. crop path, UNIV. ILL, URBANA, 48-55, assoc. prof, 55-59, PROF. PLANT PATH, 59- Am. Phytopath. Soc; Mycol. Soc. Am; Brit. Mycol. Soc. Soil borne and forest tree diseases; mycorrhiza. Address: Dept. of Plant Pathology, 241 Davenport Hall, University of Illinois, Urbana, IL 61801.

GERDES, JOHN W(ILLIAM), b. Hackensack, N.J, May 4, 26; m. 49; c. 4. PHYSICS, ELECTRONIC ENGINEERING. B.S, Boston, 50, M.A, 52; M.S, Northeastern, 55. Head dept. electronics phys. res. lab, Boston, 52-56; asst. mgr, appl. sci. div, Melpar, Inc, 56-60; info. sci. lab, Litton Systs, Inc, Mass, 60-66, mgr. signal processing dept, data syst. div, Calif, 66-69; DIR. RES. & DEVELOP, OPTICAL SYSTS. DIV, ITEK CORP, 69- U.S.N, 44-46. Inst. Elec. & Electronics Eng. Battlefield surveillance systems and techniques; reconnaissance systems; missile fuzing systems; acoustics; seismics; interference in communications systems; automatic photo interpretation equipment. Address: 21 Page Rd, Bedford, MA 01730.

GERDES, RAYMOND A, b. San Antonio, Tex, Aug. 7, 29; m. 54; c. 2. GENETICS. B.S, Texas A&M, 53, Ph.D.(genetics), 67; summers, Nat. Insts. Health fel, Nat. Sci. Found. Inst, Georgia, 61, 62; M.N.S, Oklahoma, 65. ASST. PROF. BIOL, TEX. WOMAN'S UNIV, 67- U.S.A, 46-49, Res, 49-61, 1st Lt. Genetics Soc. Am; Am. Genetic Asn; Am. Asn. Lab. Animal Sci; fel. Int. Soc. Fluoride Res. Mutagenic effects of air pollutants. Address: Dept. of Biology, Texas Woman's University, TWU Station 23971, Denton, TX 76204.

GERDES, WILLIAM HERMAN, b. Oceanside, N.Y, Nov. 9, 35; m. 62; c. 1. ANALYTICAL CHEMISTRY. B.S, Wagner Col, 57; Ph.D.(chem), Rutgers, 61. From res. engr. to ANAL. GROUP LEADER, CATALYSTS & ADSORBENTS, CHEM. PROCESS PRODS. DIV, NORTON CO, OHIO, 61- Am. Chem. Soc. Chemical analysis of abrasive and refractory type materials; characterization of catalyst carriers; catalysts and adsorbents via measurement of chemical and physical properties. Address: Chemical Process Products Division, Chamberlain Labs, Norton Co, 3840 Fishcreek Rd, Stow, OH 44224.

GERDING, THOMAS G, b. Evanston, Ill, Feb. 11, 30; m. 55; c. 4. PHARMACEUTICAL CHEMISTRY. B.S, Purdue, 52, M.S, 54, Ph.D.(pharm), 60. Instr. pharm, Purdue, 57-60, asst. prof, 60-61; sr. res. pharmacist, Pitman-Moore Co. Div, Dow Chem. Co, 62-63, asst. dir. prod. develop, 63, head prod. develop, 63-65; tech. dir, Glenbrook Labs. Div, STERLING DRUG, INC, 65-67, DIR. PROD. DEVELOP. DIV, STERLING-WINTHROP RES. INST. DIV, 67- Med.Serv.C, U.S.A, 54-56. AAAS; Am. Chem. Soc; Am. Pharmaceut. Asn; N.Y. Acad. Sci. Proprietary drug development; ethical pharmaceutical dosage form; packaging development. Address: Sterling-Winthrop Research Institute, Columbia Turnpike, Rensselaer, NY 12144.

GERE, BREWSTER H(UNTINGTON), b. Syracuse, N.Y, Dec. 5, 10; m. 37; c. 3. MATHEMATICS. B.A, Yale, 30; scholar, Syracuse, 33-34, M.A, 34; Ph.D.(math), Mass. Inst. Tech, 38. Asst. math, Syracuse, 34-35; instr, Mass. Inst. Tech, 36-39, Herzl Jr. Col, 39-42; asst. prof. math. & mech, U.S. Naval Postgrad. Sch, 46-47; assoc. prof. MATH, HAMILTON COL, 47-53, PROF, 53-, chmn. dept, 50-69. Vis. prof, U.S. Naval Postgrad. Sch, 62-63; dept. statistics, Univ. N.C, Chapel Hill, 70-71. U.S.N.R, 42-46, 62-63, Comdr.(ret). Am. Math. Soc; Math. Asn. Am. Mathematics analysis; applied mathematics. Address: Dept. of Mathematics, Hamilton College, Clinton, NY 13323.

GERE, DENNIS R, b. Randall, Iowa, Aug. 22, 38; m. 56; c. 2. ANALYTICAL CHEMISTRY. B.S, Iowa State, 60; M.S, Kansas State, 62, Ph.D.(anal. chem), 65. APPLN. CHEMIST, VARIAN AEROGRAPH, 67- U.S.A.F, 64-67, 1st Lt. Am. Chem. Soc. Liquid-liquid solvent extraction; metal chelate chemistry; gas chromatography; physiochemical measurements by gas chromatography and high performance liquid chromatography. Address: Varian Associates, 2700 Mitchell Dr, Walnut Creek, CA 94598.

GERE, JAMES MONROE, b. Syracuse, N.Y, June 14, 25; m. 46; c. 3. STRUCTURAL ENGINEERING, ENGINEERING MECHANICS. B.C.E, Rensselaer Polytech, 49, M.C.E, 51; Nat. Sci. Found. fels, Stanford, 52-54, Ph.D.(eng. mech), 54. Instr. STRUCT. ENG, Rensselaer Polytech, 49-50, res. assoc, 50-52; asst. prof. STANFORD UNIV, 54-57, assoc. prof, 57-62, PROF, 62-, EXEC. HEAD DEPT. CIVIL ENG, 67- U.S.A.A.F, 43-46. Am. Soc. Civil Eng; Am. Soc. Eng. Educ; Nat. Soc. Prof. Eng. Vibrations and buckling of structural components; analysis of framed structures; minimum weight analysis of structures. Address: Dept. of Civil Engineering, Stanford University, Stanford, CA 94305.

GERE, WILLARD C(ALVIN), b. Hutchinson, Kans, Oct. 27, 20; m. 46. ECONOMIC GEOLOGY. B.A, Southern California, 49, 49-51. From asst. geologist to assoc. geologist, ECON. GEOL, conserv. div, U.S. GEOL. SURV, Calif, 48-52, dist. geologist, Colo, 52-68, REGIONAL GEOLOGIST, 68- Summer jr. geologist, fuels br, 48. U.S.A, 42-46. Geol. Soc. Am; Soc. Econ. Paleont. & Mineral; Am. Asn. Petrol. Geol. Petroleum geology; stratigraphy. Address: Conservation Division, U.S. Geological Survey, Room 7744 Federal Bldg, Los Angeles, CA 90012.

GEREBEN, ISTVAN B, b. Sopron, Hungary, Jan. 17, 33; U.S. citizen; m. 56; c. 3. GEOPHYSICS, OCEANOGRAPHY. M.S, Budapest Tech, 56; Hopkins, 62-65. Res. asst. geophys, Hungarian Acad. Sci, 55-56; field engr, Nat. Admin. Geophys. & Geod. Hungary, 56-57; res. asst, Lamont Geol. Observ, 59-62; res. engr, underseas div, Westinghouse Elec. Corp, 62-66; Hydrospace Res. Corp, 66-67, mgr. acoust. dept, 67-71; PROJ. DIR, TRACOR INC, 71- Am. Geophys. Union; Marine Technol. Soc. Tellurical current micropulsation; response of fixed or free floating bodies or structures to ocean wave forces; bearing capacity of ocean bottom sediments; hydrodynamical studies and experimental tests of deep towed bodies; underwater acoustics; submarine silencing; sonar technology; acoustic systems management. Address: 4101 Blackpool Rd, Rockville, MD 20853.

GERECHT, J(OHN) FRED, b. New York, N.Y, Nov. 8, 15; m. 44; c. 1. CHEMISTRY. B.S, Polytech. Inst. Brooklyn, 42, M.S, 45, Ph.D.(org. chem), 48. Lab. helper, E.R. Squibb & Sons, N.Y, 37-39; technician, Rockefeller Inst, 39-40; chemist, Schering Corp, N.J, 40-41; res. chemist, Colgate-Palmolive-Peet Co, 41-49, group leader, COLGATE-PALMOLIVE CO, 49-57, RES. ASSOC, 57- Instr, Fairleigh Dickenson, 60-63; Rutgers, 63- Am. Chem. Soc; Am. Oil Chemists' Soc; The Chem. Soc. Synthesis of pharmaceuticals; ployeptides and hormones; polymerization and oxidation of fatty acids; thermal polymerization of olefinic materials. Address: Colgate-Palmolive Co, 909 River Rd, Piscataway, NJ 08854.

GERENCSER, MARY ANN (AIKEN), b. Macon, Ga, Mar. 24, 27; m. 57. BACTERIOLOGY. B.S, Ga. Col. Milledgeville, 48; M.A, Smith Col, 50; Ph.D. (bact), Univ. Ky, 58. Technician, Ga. State Dept. Health, 50-51; res. technician, Communicable Disease Ctr, U.S. Pub. Health Serv, 51-54; res. asst. bact, Univ. Ky, 54-57; dir, Consolidated Labs, 57-59; supvr. clin. lab. microbiol, Michael Reese Hosp, Chicago, Ill, 59-61; RES. ASSOC. MICROBIOL, SCH. MED, W.VA. UNIV, 62- Am. Soc. Microbiol. Clinical microbiology; genus Actinomyces; taxonomy; serology; dental microbiology. Address: Dept. of Microbiology, West Virginia University School of Medicine, Morgantown, WV 26506.

GERENCSER, VINCENT F(REDERIC), b. New Brunswick, N.J, Jan. 17, 27; m. 57. BACTERIOLOGY. B.S, Fordham, 51; Ph.D.(bact), Kentucky, 58. Asst. bact, Kentucky, 52-57; res. assoc. MICROBIOL, col. med, Illinois, 57-59, instr, 59-61, asst. prof, SCH. MED, W.VA. UNIV, 61-66, ASSOC. PROF, 66- U.S.N, 45-46. AAAS; Am. Soc. Microbiol; Brit. Soc. Gen. Microbiol. Aquatic microbiology; microbial ecology; taxonomy; genetics; morphology; cytology. Address: Dept. of Microbiology, West Virginia University School of Medicine, Morgantown, WV 26506.

GERFEN, CHARLES O(TTO), b. Breese, Ill, April 10, 20; m. 48; c. 4. PHYSICAL CHEMISTRY. B.S, Ill. State Nor. Univ, 42; fel, Missouri, 46-51, Ph.D. (chem), 51. Chemist, control lab, Atmospheric Nitrogen Corp, Ky, 42-43; res. chemist, inorg. res. dept, MALLINCKRODT CHEM. WORKS, 51-55, group leader, 55-57, asst. dir, 57-60, DIR. gen. res, 60-63, spec. prod. dept, 63-71, NARCOTICS & DANGEROUS DRUGS, 71- U.S.A.A.F, 43-45. AAAS; Am. Chem. Soc; Am. Inst. Chem. Chemistry of group IV and V elements, niobium, tantalum; titanium; zirconium and hafnium; ore beneficiation; chemistry of opium and opiates. Address: Narcotics & Dangerous Drugs, Mallinckrodt Chemical Works, 3600 N. Second St, St. Louis, MO 63160.

GERGEL, MAX GUSTAVE, b. Phila, Pa, July 24, 21; m. 64; c. 3. ORGANIC CHEMISTRY. B.S, South Carolina, 42. Chemist, S.C. Pub. Serv. Authority, 42-43; instr. chem, South Carolina, 44-45; PRES, COLUMBIA ORG. CHEM. INC, 45- Consult, Chemetron Corp, 62-; Amcel Div, Celanese Corp, 64-66; S.N.P.A, France, 64-65; Dead Sea Works, Israel, 64- Civilian with Manhattan Dist. Engrs, 42-46. Am. Chem. Soc. Synthesis of alkyl halides and their derivatives, particularly sulfur compounds. Address: P.O. Box 5273, Columbia, SC 29205.

GERGELY, J(OHN), b. Budapest, Hungary, May 15, 19; nat; m. 45; c. 8. BIOCHEMISTRY. M.D, Budapest, Hungary, 42; British Coun. scholar, Leeds Univ, 46-48, Ph.D.(phys. chem), 48. Asst. prof. pharmacol, med. sch, Bupest, Hungary, 42-45, asst. prof. biochem, 45-48; New Sch. for Social Res, 48-50; sr. trainee, Nat. Heart Inst, Wisconsin, 50-51; res. assoc. med, HARVARD MED. SCH, 51-62, TUTOR BIOCHEM. SCI, 57-, asst. prof. BIOL. CHEM, 62-71, ASSOC. PROF, 71-; BIOCHEMIST, MASS. GEN. HOSP, 69-; DIR. DEPT. MUSCLE RES, BOSTON BIOMED. RES. INST, 70- Spec. res. fel, Nat. Insts. Health, 48-50; estab. investr, Am. Heart Asn, 51-58, asst. biochemist, 53-54; assoc. biochemist, Mass. Gen. Hosp, 54-69; dir. dept. muscle res, Retina Found, 61-70. Am. Soc. Biol. Chem; Biophys. Soc; Am. Chem. Soc; N.Y. Acad. Sci; Brit. Biochem. Soc. Biochemistry of muscle contraction; enzymes; nuclear magnetic resonance; physical chemistry of proteins; electron spin resonance. Address: Boston Biomedical Research Institute, 20 Staniford St, Boston, MA 02114.

GERGEN, JAMES B(ERNARD), b. Hastings, Minn, Nov. 19, 22; m. 44; c. 3. ORGANIC CHEMISTRY. B.S, St. Thomas Col, 43; Purdue, 43-44; M.S, Minnesota, 49. Chemist & analyst, Socony-Vacuum Oil Co, Minn, 42-43; asst, Purdue, 43-44; res. chemist, Los Alamos Sci. Lab, 44-46; asst, Naval Ord. proj, Minnesota, 46-47; instr. org. chem, St. Thomas Col, 47-49; sr. chemist, new prod. develop, MINN. MINING & MFG. CO, 49-54, supvr, new tape develop, 54-57, tech. mgr. film prod. group, 57-60, prog. coord, 61-66, PROJS. MGR. MICROFILM PROD. DIV, 66- Pres, Space Structures, Inc, 60-61. U.S.A, 44-46. Am. Chem. Soc; Soc. Photog. Sci. & Eng. Inorganic chemistry of uranium and plutonium; development and promotion of new products; laboratory management. Address: 2570 Olson Lake Rd, St. Paul, MN 55109.

GERGEN, JOHN A, b. Cambridge, Mass, Aug. 7, 32; m. 54, 70; c. 9. NEUROPHYSIOLOGY, PSYCHIATRY. B.S, Yale, 53; M.D, Harvard Med. Sch, 57. Asst. anat, sch. med, Duke, 52-53; physiol, Harvard Med. Sch. & Marine Biol. Lab, 54-55; Nat. Paraplegia Found. fel, Univ, 55-57; intern med, Duke Univ. Hosp, 57-58, asst. res. neurol. & instr. physiol, sch. med, Duke, 58-59; res. assoc. neurophysiol, Nat. Inst. Ment. Health, 59-61; instr. sci, U.S. Dept. Agr. Grad. Sch. & Found. Adv. Ed. in Sci, Inc, 61-62; asst. prof. physiol, Bowman Gray Sch. Med, 62-67, assoc. prof, 67-68; mem. res. staff, hosp, DUKE UNIV, 68-71, ASST. PROF. PSYCHIAT, MED. CTR, 71-; MEM. STAFF, DURHAM VET. ADMIN. HOSP, 71- Clin. assoc, electroencephalog. br, Nat. Inst. Neurol. Diseases & Blindness, 61-62. U.S.P.H.S, 59-62, Surg. Correlation of electrophysiological activities of the central nervous system with behavior in sub-human primate and man; functions of hippocampal formation; clinical electroencephalography; individual and family psychotherapy; alcoholism. Address: Dept. of Psychiatry, Duke University Medical Center, Durham, NC 27706.

GERGEN, JOHN L, b. Hastings, Minn, Sept. 23, 27; m. 60; c. 2. ATMOSPHERIC PHYSICS. B.S, Minnesota, 52, M.S, 56, Ph.D.(physics), 60. Jr. scientist, Minnesota, Minneapolis, 50-54, asst. scientist, 54-60, asst. prof, PHYSICS, 60-64, assoc. prof, UNIV. MINN, DULUTH, 64-68, PROF, 68-, DIR. COMPUT. CTR, 70- Dir. res, G.T. Schjeldahl Co, 58; consult, 57; U.S. Air Force, 61; Winzen Res, 62. U.S.A.A.F, 44-48, Sgt. Am. Geophys. Union; Inst. Elec. & Electronics Eng; Am. Meteorol. Soc; Am. Phys. Soc. High altitude balloon development; atmospheric infrared radiometry; real-time computer operating systems. Address: Dept. of Physics, University of Minnesota, Duluth, MN 55812.

GERGES, R(ICHARD) D(ANIEL), b. Phila, Pa, Nov. 13, 18; m. 43; c. 2. CHEMICAL ENGINEERING. B.S, Mass. Inst. Tech, 40, M.S, 41. Asst. dept. head, prod. unit, Carbide & Carbon Chem. Corp, 41-42; develop. engr, ROHM & HAAS CO, 46-53, head chem. eng. sect, Redstone Arsenal res. div, 53-58, sr. process engr, Bristol, 58-62, PROCESS ENG. SUPVR, ENG. DIV, 62- U.S.A, 42-46, Lt. Col. Am. Inst. Chem. Eng. Process development and design; organic chemicals; solid rocket propellants. Address: Engineering Division, Rohm and Haas Co, P.O. Box 584, Bristol, PA 19007.

GERHARD, EARL R(OBERT), b. Louisville, Ky, Aug. 9, 22; m. 47; c. 5. CHEMICAL ENGINEERING. B.Ch.E, Louisville, 43, M.Ch.E, 47, Ph.D. (chem. eng), Illinois, 53. Technologist, CHEM. ENG. Shell Oil Co, 43-44; asst. prof, UNIV. LOUISVILLE, 51-54, assoc. prof, 54-64, PROF, 64-, CHMN. DEPT, 70- U.S.A, 44-46. Am. Chem. Soc; Am. Soc. Eng. Educ;

Am. Inst. Chem. Eng. Transport phenomenon; reaction kinetics. Address: Dept. of Chemical Engineering, University of Louisville, Louisville, KY 40208.

GERHARD, GLEN CARL, b. Albion, N.Y, Mar. 1, 35; m. 57; c. 4. ELECTRONIC ENGINEERING. B.E.E, Syracuse Univ, 56; M.Sc, Ohio State Univ, 58, Ph.D.(elec. eng), 63. Engr, Gen. Elec. Co, 56; asst. elec. eng, Ohio State Univ, 56-57; develop. engr, Eastman Kodak Co, 57; res. asst. elec. eng, Ohio State Univ, 57-58, instr. elec. eng. & res. assoc. electron devices, 58-62; res. engr, electronics lab, Gen. Elec. Co, 62-63 & 64-67; asst. prof. ELEC. ENG, UNIV. N.H, 67-71, ASSOC. PROF, 71- Consult, Gen. Elec. Co, 67-68; Kidder Press Div, Moore Bus. Forms, 68-70. U.S.A.R, 56-65, Capt. Inst. Elec. & Electronics Eng. Semiconductor and optoelectronic devices and photo sensors, both visible and infrared; multispectral image sensor arrays; remote sensing applications; solid state devices. Address: Dept. of Electrical Engineering, University of New Hampshire, Durham, NH 03824.

GERHARD, JACOB ESTERLY, b. McAdoo, Pa, May 17, 26; m. 51; c. 3. GEOLOGY. B.S, Pa. State, 55; M.S, 58. Res. technologist, FIELD RES. LAB, Socony Mobil Oil Co, 58-67, SR. RES. GEOLOGIST, MOBIL RES. & DEVELOP. CORP, 67- U.S.A, 44-46, Sgt. Am. Asn. Stratig. Palynologists. Palynology; stratigraphy. Address: Field Research Lab, Mobil Research & Development Corp, Box 900, Dallas, TX 75221.

GERHARD, LEE C, b. Albion, N.Y, May 30, 37; m. 64; c. 1. STRATIGRAPHY, PETROLOGY. B.S, Syracuse, 58; M.S, Kansas, 61, Haworth scholar, 62, Ph.D.(geol), 64. Explor. geologist, Sinclair Oil & Gas Co, 64-65, region stratigrapher, 65-66; asst. prof. GEOL, SOUTH. COLO. STATE COL, 66-70, ASSOC. PROF, 70- Sig.C, U.S.A, 58-60, 1st Lt. Am. Asn. Petrol Geol; Geol. Soc. Am; Soc. Econ. Paleont. & Mineral. Structural geologic history; carbonate petrography; stratigraphy; sedimentary petrology. Address: 4036 Hillside Dr, Pueblo, CO 81008.

GERHARD, RINERT J, b. Chicago, Ill, Apr. 6, 25; m. 51; c. 3. DENTISTRY. D.D.S, Loyola Univ. Chicago, 50. Instr. PROSTHODONTICS, DENT. SCH, LOYOLA UNIV. CHICAGO, 50-53, asst. prof, 53-58, ASSOC. PROF, 58-, DIR. CLIN. PROSTHODONTICS, 69- U.S.N, 43-46, Lt.(jg). Am. Prosthodontic Soc; Am. Dent. Asn. Prosthodontics. Address: Loyola University School of Dentistry, 2160 S. First Dr, Maywood, IL 60153.

GERHARD, S(HERMAN) L(EIDICH), b. Quakertown, Pa, May 25, 04; m. 34; c. 2. PHYSICS. B.S, Pennsylvania, 24; Pub. Health Inst. fel, Northwestern, 25-26, M.S, 26; Ph.D.(physics), Michigan, 32. Asst. physicist, Eastman Kodak Co, 26-28; instr. physics, math. & elec. eng, Wyomissing Polytech. Inst, 33-35; asst. physicist, explosives div, U.S. Bur. Mines, 36-39; supvr. physics res, textile div, U.S. Rubber Co, 39-45; physicist, gen. labs, N.J, 45-47; asst. prof. physics, Newark Col. Eng, 47-52; PHYSICIST, PICATINNY ARSENAL, 52- Adj. prof, Polytech. Inst. Brooklyn, 47-50; Stevens Inst. Tech, 52-53. Fel. Am. Phys. Soc; Fiber Soc.(pres, 46); Am. Asn. Physics Teachers. X-ray crystal structure analysis; infrared spectra; ignition of firedamp by explosive discharges; physical properties of textiles and high explosives; stress analysis; heat conduction; aeroballistics. Address: 317 Hillside Ave, Nutley, NJ 07110.

GERHARDT, GEORGE W(ILLIAM), b. Shaler Twp, Pa, Nov. 7, 15. ORGANIC CHEMISTRY. B.S, Pittsburgh, 36, Ph.D.(chem), 51. From fel. to adv. fel, Mellon Inst, 36-59; asst. tech. dir, Stoner-Mudge Div, Mobil Finishes Co, Inc, 59-66; PACKAGING COATINGS DEPT, MOBIL CHEM. CO, 66-71, LAB. DIR, 71- Am. Chem. Soc; Inst. Food Technol; Fedn. Soc. Paint Technol; Master Brewers Asn. Am. Organic coatings; packaging; resin manufacture. Address: Cole Rd, R.D. 1, Wexford, PA 15090.

GERHARDT, JOHN R(ANDOLPH), b. Omaha, Nebr, Apr. 29, 18; c. 3. METEOROLOGY. B.S, Ill. Inst. Tech, 40; M.S, N.Y. Univ, 52. Res. meteorologist, elec. eng. res. lab, Texas, 46-48, asst. dir, 48-63; ASSOC. DIR. ED. PROG, AM. METEOROL. SOC, 63-, TECH. ED, J. ATMOS. SCI, J. APPL. METEOROL, J. PHYS. OCEANOG. & METEOROL. MONGR, 66- Mem. Nat. Comt. Radio Propagation, Int. Sci. Radio Union. U.S.A.A.F, 42-46. Am. Meteorol. Soc; Am. Geophys. Union. Educational meteorology; micrometeorology; radio meteorology. Address: American Meteorological Society, 45 Beacon St, Boston, MA 02108.

GERHARDT, KLAUS OTTO, b. Drengfurt, Ger, Aug. 6, 35. ORGANIC & ANALYTICAL CHEMISTRY. Bayer AG fel, Tech. Univ. Berlin, 63, Diplom Chemiker, 64, Dr. rer. nat.(anal. chem), 67. Fel, Univ. Mo-Columbia, 67-68; asst. prof. phys. & gen. chem, Lincoln Univ.(Mo), 68-69; RES. ANAL. CHEMIST, UNIV. MO-COLUMBIA, 69- Alkali-flame detectors; specific detectors for gas liquid chromatography; development of analytical methods for pesticide residue analysis; thin-layer chromatography. Address: R. 4 Agriculture Bldg, University of Missouri, Columbia, MO 65201.

GERHARDT, LESTER A, b. Bronx, N.Y, Jan. 28, 40; m. 61; c. 2. ELECTRICAL & SYSTEMS ENGINEERING. B.E.E, City Col. New York, 61; M.S, State Univ. N.Y. Buffalo, 64, Ph.D.(commun. systs), 69. Sr. elec. engr. avionics systs, BELL AEROSPACE CORP, 61-64, sect. head, signal & info. processing res, 64-69, ASST. TO DIR. ADVAN. RES. & CONSULT, 69-; ASSOC. PROF, SYSTS. ENG. DIV, RENSSELAER POLYTECH. INST, 69- Inst. Elec. & Electronics Eng.(ed, Prism. Mag, 70-). Adaptive systems research with applications to communications, control and pattern recognition; voice and image processing; digital, signal and information processing; biomedical signal and image processing. Address: Systems Engineering Division, Rensselaer Polytechnic Institute, Troy, NY 12181.

GERHARDT, PAUL D(ONALD), b. Riverside, Calif, July 10, 17; m. 42; c. 1. ECONOMIC ENTOMOLOGY. B.S, California, 40, M.S, 41, Ph.D.(entomol), 49. Asst. entomol, California, 40-41, assoc, exp. sta, Riverside, 46-49, jr. entomologist, 49-51, asst. entomologist, 51-54; UNIV. ARIZ, 55-59, assoc. entomologist, 59-63, ENTOMOLOGIST, 63-, PROF. ENTOM, 68- U.S.N.R, 42-45, Lt. Entom. Soc. Am; Lepidop. Soc. Biology and control of insects attacking vegetable crops; field crops and citrus; laboratory and field studies on resistance of mites and thrips to organic insecticides; use of insecticides; residue problems and development of resistance by certain insects in Arizona; Hymenoptera; Mutillidae; Lepidoptera, Papillionidae. Address: Dept. of Entomology, University of Arizona, P.O. Box 1308, Mesa, AZ 85201.

GERHARDT, PHILIPP, b. Milwaukee, Wis, Dec. 30, 21; m. 45; c. 3. MICROBIOLOGY. Ph.B, Wisconsin, 43, Wis. Alumni Res. Found. fel, 46-47, M.S, 47, U.S. Pub. Health Serv. fel, 47-49, Ph.D.(bact), 49. Asst. prof. MICROBIOL, Oregon State, 49-51; Michigan, 53-56, assoc. prof, 56-59, prof, 59-65; PROF. & CHMN. DEPT, MICH. STATE UNIV, 65- Consult, Chem. Corps, U.S. Army. Dipl, Am. Bd. Microbiol. Chem.C, U.S.A, 43-46, supt, labs. biol. develop, Pine Bluff Arsenal, 51-52. AAAS; Am. Soc. Microbiol. (secy, 61-67); fel. Am. Acad. Microbiol; Brit. Soc. Gen. Microbiol. Medical and physiological microbiology; industrial fermentation; dialysis culture; membrane permeability and ultrastructure; spores. Address: Dept. of Microbiology & Public Health, Michigan State University, East Lansing, MI 48823.

GERHARDT, RICHARD W, b. Hillsboro, Ill, July 6, 25; m. 46; c. 3. ENTOMOLOGY, ZOOLOGY. B.S, Wyoming, 49, M.S, 51; Ph.D.(entom), California, Davis, 57. Res. entomologist, Calif. Mosquito Control Assoc, 52-54; vector control specialist, bur. vector control, Calif. Dept. Pub. Health, 54-58, admin, 58-60; asst. prof. zool, Adams State Col, 60-62; entom, S.Dak. State Univ, 62-63, assoc. prof, 63-66; sr. scientist, aedes aegypti eradication br, commun. disease ctr, U.S. Pub. Health Serv, Ga, 66-69; PROJ. OFF, PESTICIDES OFF, DIV. COMMUNITY STUDIES, ENVIRON. PROTECTION AGENCY, 69- U.S.A, 43-46. Am. Mosquito Control Asn. Mosquito ecology; oviposition responses by mosquitoes; control of mosquitoes; limnology of shallow water. Address: Pesticides Office, Environmental Protection Agency, 4770 Buford Hwy, Chamblee, GA 30341.

GERHART, H(OWARD) L(EON), b. Boyertown, Pa, Sept. 3, 09; m. 42; c. 4. CHEMISTRY. B.S, Franklin & Marshall Col, 31, D.Sc, 53; Ph.D.(chem), Northwestern, 35. Asst. chem, Northwestern, 32-35; res. chemist, Standard Oil Co. of Ind, 35-36; United Gas Improvement Co, 36-37; Pittsburgh Plate Glass Co, 37-47, dir. res, paint div, 47-58, dir. res. & develop, paint & brush div, 58-68, V.PRES. & DIR. RES. & DEVELOP, COATINGS & RESINS DIV, PPG INDUSTS, INC, 68- Am. Chem. Soc.(ed, Jour, 68-); Am. Inst. Chem; Paint Res. Inst. High polymers; paints and plastics; research management; creative problem solving; polymerization; polymer coatings technology. Address: Coatings & Resins Division, PPG Industries, Inc, One Gateway Center, Pittsburgh, PA 15222.

GERHART, JAMES B(ASIL), b. Pasadena, Calif, Dec. 15, 28; m. 58; c. 2. NUCLEAR PHYSICS. B.S, Calif. Inst. Tech, 50; M.A, Princeton, 52, Ph.D. (physics), 54. Asst. PHYSICS, Princeton, 50-54, instr, 54-56; asst. prof, UNIV. WASH, 56-61, assoc. prof, 61-65, PROF, 65- AAAS; Am. Phys. Soc; Am. Asn. Physics Teachers. Beta and gamma ray spectroscopy; nuclear scattering and reactions. Address: Dept. of Physics, University of Washington, Seattle, WA 98105.

GERHART, JOHN C, b. Cincinnati, Ohio, Mar. 27, 36; m. 64. BIOCHEMISTRY. A.B, Harvard, 58; Ph.D.(biochem), California, Berkeley, 62. Asst. prof. MOLECULAR BIOL. & VIROL, UNIV. CALIF, BERKELEY, 62-67, ASSOC. PROF, 67- Cell growth and regulation; control of enzyme activity; metazoan development. Address: Dept. of Molecular Biology, University of California, Berkeley, CA 94720.

GERHAUSER, JOHN M(AYNOR), b. Middleton, Idaho, Dec. 29, 24. CHEMICAL PHYSICS. B.S, Oregon State, 51; M.A, Texas, 54, Ph.D, 56. Res. scientist, computers sect, mil. physics res. lab, Texas, 55-56; lead engr. systems anal, Chance Vought Aircraft, Inc, 56-58; sr. physicist, Bendix Prods. Div, Bendix Aviation Corp, 58-61; rocketdyne div, N.Am. Aviation, 61-67; lectr. PHYSICS, San Fernando Valley State Col, 67-68; PROF, AM. UNIV. CAIRO, 68- AAAS; Am. Phys. Soc; Am. Astronaut. Soc. Theoretical computations of molecular properties and the calculations of processes derivable from molecular functions. Address: 113 Sharia Kasr El Aini, Cairo, Egypt.

GERHOLD, GEORGE A, b. Kewanee, Ill, Mar. 17, 37; m. 58. PHYSICAL CHEMISTRY. B.S, Illinois, 58; Nat. Sci. Found. fel, Washington (Seattle), 60-62, Ph.D.(chem), 63. Nat. Sci. Found. fel. CHEM, Univ. Col, London, 63-65; ASST. PROF, Univ. Calif, Davis, 65-70; WEST. WASH. STATE COL, 70- Electronic and crystal spectra; excitons. Address: Dept. of Chemistry, Western Washington State College, Bellingham, WA 98225.

GERHOLD, HENRY D(IETRICH), b. Mahwah, N.J, Feb. 1, 31; m. 56; c. 3. FORESTRY. B.S, Pa. State, 52, M.F, 54; Strathcona fel, Yale, 54-55, Hartford fel, 55-56, Ph.D.(forest genetics), 59. Soil conserv. aid, soil conserv. serv, U.S. Dept. Agr, 49, fire control aid, forest serv, Mont, 51, forester, Idaho, 52-53; res. forester, Northeast. Forest Exp. Sta, 54-55; instr. FORESTRY, PA. STATE UNIV, 56-60, asst. prof, 60-65, assoc. prof, 65-69, PROF, 69- Nat. Sci. Found. travel grant, World Consultation Forest Genetics, UN Food & Agr. Orgn, 64; NATO sr. sci. fel, 70; chmn, Northeast. Forest Tree Improvement Conf, 70-72; chmn. genetic resistance to diseases & insects subject group, Int. Union Forest Res. Orgns; dir, Pennsylvan Tree Improvement Found. Soc. Am. Foresters; Genetics Soc. Am; Am. Inst. Biol. Sci. Forest genetics; Christmas tree production; resistance to diseases, insects and air pollutants. Address: 306 Forest Resources Lab, Pennsylvania State University, University Park, PA 16802.

GERICKE, OTTO LUKE, b. San Francisco, Calif, July 16, 07; m. 34; c. 4. PSYCHIATRY. A.B, California, 29, M.D, 33; Pennsylvania, 39; Sch. Mil. Neuropsychiat, 43. Intern, San Francisco Hosp, 32-33; asst. res, St. Joseph's Hosp, San Francisco, Calif, 33-34, res, 34-35; private practice med, Calif, 35-36; asst. dist. surgeon, dist. 36, Ft. Douglas Civilian Conserv. Corps; physician & psychiatrist, Mendocino State Hosp, Talmage, Calif, 36-42; asst. supt, Stockton State Hosp, 45-46; MED. DIR, PATTON STATE HOSP, 46- Asst. clin. prof, Loma Linda, 47-58, assoc. clin. prof, 58-67, clin. prof, 67- Dipl, Am. Bd. Psychiat. & Neurol, 50. Chief med. serv. & psychiat, sta. hosp, Camp Cooke, Calif, 42-44, psychiatrist, W.Coast processing ctr, 9th serv. command spec. training ctr, 44-45, Med.C, 42-45, Res, 45-67, Col.(Ret). Am. Med. Asn; fel. Am. Psychiat. Asn; Pan-Am. Med. Asn. Address: Dept. of Mental Hygiene, Patton State Hospital, Patton, CA 92369.

GERICKE, OTTO R(EINHARD), b. Detmold, Germany, Sept. 7, 21; U.S. citizen; m. 52; c. 1. PHYSICS. B.S, Göttingen, 44, M.S, 50; Basel, 46-47, summer, Bern, 48. Physicist, Siemens-Reiniger Co, Germany, 51-54, Siemens & Halske Co, 54-58; U.S. Army Mat. Res. Agency, 58-63, res. physicist, 63-66, chief appl. physics br, 66-69, HEAD NONDESTRUCTIVE TESTING BR, U.S. ARMY MAT. & MECH. RES. CTR, 69- Mem. ultrasonics cmt, ord. corps, U.S. Army, 59-62, mat. command, 59-62, chmn, 62-, mem. tech. working group test & eval, 63- Cert. outstanding achievement, sci. conf, U.S. Army, 62. German Army, 41-43. Soc. Nondestructive Test; Acoust. Soc. Am. Nondestructive testing; studies of various types of physical phenomena to determine their potential usefulness for nondestructive evaluation of materials including ultrasonic pulse spectroscopy, electronic radiography and image storage, one-sided infrared inspection. Address: Nondestructive Testing Branch, U.S. Army Materials & Mechanics Research Center, Watertown, MA 02172.

GERIG, FRANK A, JR, b. Memphis, Tenn, Aug. 28, 18; m. 41; c. 2. CIVIL ENGINEERING. B.S, U.S. Mil. Acad, 41; M.S, Calif. Inst. Tech, 48; U.S. Army Eng. Sch, 52, Command & Gen. Staff Col, 54; Ph.D.(civil eng), Tex. A&M Univ, 67. Prof. phys. sci, U.S. Mil. Acad, 43-47, chief bridge br, U.S. Army Eng. Sch, 52-53, dep. engr, Phila. Eng. Dist, 57-59; assoc. prof. CIVIL ENG, UNIV. MO-ROLLA, 61-68, PROF, 68-, DIR. TRANSPORTATION INST, 70- C.Eng, 41-61, Lt. Col. Am. Soc. Civil Eng; Soc. Am. Mil. Eng; Am. Soc. Eng. Educ; Nat. Soc. Prof. Eng. Bridge and traffic engineering. Address: Dept. of Civil Engineering, University of Missouri at Rolla, Rolla, MO 65401.

GERIG, JOHN THOMAS, b. Windham, Ohio, Nov. 7, 38; m. 61; c. 2. ORGANIC CHEMISTRY. B.A, Col. Wooster, 60; Ph.D.(chem), Brown, 64. Asst. ORG. CHEM, Brown, 60-64; res. fel, Calif. Inst. Technol, 64-66; ASSOC. PROF, UNIV. CALIF, SANTA BARBARA, 66- Am. Chem. Soc. Nuclear magnetic resonance spectroscopy; protein chemistry; enzymatic reactions. Address: Dept. of Chemistry, University of California, Santa Barbara, CA 93106.

GERIN, JOHN LOUIS, b. St. Paul, Minn, Sept. 28, 37; m. 60; c. 1. VIROLOGY, BIOCHEMISTRY. B.S, Georgetown, 59; M.S, Tennessee, Knoxville, 61, Ph.D.(zool), 64. Res. scientist, sci. div, Abbott Lab, 64-66, group leader biochem. & biophys. virol, 66-67; HEAD ROCKVILLE LAB, MOLECULAR ANAT. PROG, OAK RIDGE NAT. LAB, 67- AAAS; Am. Soc. Microbiol; N.Y. Acad. Sci. Effect of thyroid hormones on protein synthetic mechanisms of mammalian cell; biochemical and biophysical characteristics of animal viruses, especially respiratory viruses and hepatitis-associated antigens; purification of viral antigens for vaccine production. Address: Molecular Anatomy Program, Rockville Lab, Oak Ridge National Lab, 5640 Fisher Lane, Rockville, MD 20852.

GERING, ROBERT L(EE), b. Parker, S.Dak, Feb. 18, 20; m. 45; c. 2. INVERTEBRATE ZOOLOGY. A.B, Utah, 47, M.A, 48, Ph.D.(invert. zool), 50. Chmn, nat. sci. div. & biol. dept, Bethel Col, 48-53; asst. dir. ecol. res. proj, Utah, 53-54; assoc. prof. biol, Wells Col, 54-59, prof. & chmn. dept, 59-65; INDEPENDENT RES. & DEVELOP. EDUC. PROD, 65-; PRES, INFO. APPLNS, INC, 66- Vis. prof. Ward's Natural Sci. Estab, 63-64; Univ. Rochester, 65-66; prof. biol, Rochester Inst. Technol, 66-68; coord. computerized multi-media instr, Nat. Tech. Inst. for Deaf, 68-69. Res. Award, Am. Cancer Soc, 51. Med.C, U.S.A, 40-46. AAAS; Soc. Syst. Zool; Asn. Comput. Mach; N.Y. Acad. Sci; Nat. Asn. Biol. Teachers. Morphology and behavior study of spiders; genetics; advanced audio-visual systems. Address: Information Applications, Inc, 2169 Baird Rd, Penfield, NY 14526.

GERJUOY, E(DWARD), b. Brooklyn, N.Y, May 19, 18; m. 40; c. 2. PHYSICS. B.S, City Col. New York, 37; M.A, California 40, Ph.D.(physics), 42. Res. physicist, off. sci. res. & develop, Columbia, 42-46; asst. dir. sonar anal. group, Off. Sci. Res. & Develop, 46; asst. prof. physics, Southern California, 46-49, assoc. prof, 49-52; Pittsburgh, 52-58, prof, 58; mem. res. staff, Gen. Atomic Div, Gen. Dynamics Corp, 58-61; E.H. Plesset Assocs, 61-62; dir. plasma & space appl. physics, Defense Electronics Prod. Div, Radio Corp. Am, 62-64; PROF. PHYSICS, SPACE RES. COORD. CTR, UNIV. PITTSBURGH, 64- Mem. adv. comt, Army Res. Off, Nat. Acad. Sci, 65-68; health physics vis. comt, Oak Ridge Nat. Lab, 68-; vis. fel, Joint Inst. Lab. Astrophys, Colo, 70; consult, Westinghouse Res. Labs; Rand Corp; Inst. Defense Anal; Lockheed Electronics Div; RCA Corp. Am. Defense Electronic Prod. AAAS; fel. Am. Phys. Soc; fel. Brit. Inst. Physics & Phys. Soc; Nat. Sci. Teachers Asn. Theoretical physics, especially atomic collision theory. Address: Dept. of Physics, Space Research Coordination Center, University of Pittsburgh, Pittsburgh, PA 15213.

GERKE, JOHN R(OYAL), b. New York, N.Y, May 29, 27; m. 48; c. 2. MICROBIOLOGY. B.A, Duke, 47; M.S, Illinois, 49; Ph.D, Rutgers, 64. Res. asst, State Water Surv, Ill, 48-51; sr. scientist, E.R. Squibb & Sons, 51-64; sr. microbiologist, Hoffman La Roche, N.J, 64-67; ASSOC. PROF. MICROBIOL, PAC. UNIV, 67- U.S.N.R, 44-45. Am. Soc. Microbiol; Am. Chem. Soc. Ocular diseases, pseudomonas diseases; analytical microbiology; microbiological chemistry; microbiological transformations of steroids; antibiotics. Address: Dept. of Microbiology, College of Optometry, Pacific University, Forest Grove, OR 97116.

GERKEN, GEORGE M(ANZ), b. Hackensack, N.J, July 12, 33; m. 56; c. 2. NEUROPSYCHOLOGY. B.S, Mass. Inst. Tech, 55; Ph.D.(physiol. psychol), Chicago, 59. Asst. prof. psychol, Virginia, 59-67; res. assoc, CALLIER HEARING & SPEECH CTR, 67-70, RES. SCIENTIST, 70- Am. Psychol. Asn; Psychonomic Soc; Acoustical Soc. Am. Brain function; neuropsychology; hearing. Address: Callier Hearing & Speech Center, 1966 Inwood Rd, Dallas, TX 75235.

GERKIN, ERNEST HUGH, b. Larwill, Ind, Mar. 31, 98; m. 27; c. 2. PHYSICAL CHEMISTRY. A.B, Indiana, 22, M.A, 33, Ph.D.(phys. chem), 37. Teacher, pub. sch, 25-39; instr. CHEM, EXTEN. DIV, IND. UNIV, SOUTH

BEND, 39-46, asst. prof, 46-53, assoc. prof, 53-68, EMER. ASSOC. PROF, 68- Res. chemist, U.S. Rubber Co, Ind, 44. Am. Chem. Soc. Grid design in storage battery plates. Address: 918 E. Bowman St, South Bend, IN 46613.

GERKING, SHELBY DELOS, b. Elkhart, Ind, Nov. 16, 18; m. 43; c. 3. ZOOL-OGY. A.B, DePauw, 40; Michigan, 39, 41; Ph.D.(zool), Indiana, 44. Res. assoc. physiol, Ind. Univ, Bloomington, 44-46, instr. zool, 46-49, asst. prof, 49-54, assoc. prof, 54-59, prof, 59-67, dir. biol. sta, 59-67, assoc. dir. water resources res. ctr, 63-67; PROF. ZOOL. & CHMN. DEPT, ARIZ. STATE UNIV, 67- Res. assoc, lake & stream surv, State Dept. Conserv, Ind, 46-53; Ciba grant, 59; Nat. Sci. Found. grant & sci. faculty fel, 59, dir. summer inst. teachers high sch. biol, 56-58, 60; coord. mem. & dep. con-venor, int. biol. prog. biol. basis of freshwater fish prod, Nat. Res. Coun, Eng, 66; mem. adv. panel environ. biol, Nat. Sci. Found, 66-68; Ariz. State Univ. rep. founding insts, Inst. Ecol; consult, inst. limnol, Czech. Acad. Sci. With Off. Sci. Res. & Develop, 44. Fel. AAAS; fel. Am. Inst. Fishery Res. Biol; Am. Soc. Zool; Am. Soc. Ichthyol. & Herpet; Am. Fisheries Soc; Wild-life Soc; Am. Soc. Limnol. & Oceanog; Ecol. Soc. Am.(Mercer Award, 55; treas, 69-); Int. Asn. Theoret. & Appl. Limnol. Distribution of fishes; fish populations in lakes and streams; fish nutrition; fish production. Address: Dept. of Zoology, Arizona State University, Tempe, AZ 85281.

GERLACH, ALAN M(EYER), b. Milwaukee, Wis, Apr. 24, 19; m. 43; c. 4. GEOPHYSICS. B.S, Marquette, 41; Chicago, 43, 46; A.M, Harvard, 48, Ph.D.(philos), 51. Instr. philos, Boston, 48-51; mem. staff, geophys. res. directorate, AIR FORCE CAMBRIDGE RES. LABS, 51-58, chief, prog. div, 58-61, dep. dir, 61, DEP. FOR TECH. PLANS & OPERS, 61- U.S.A.A.F, 42-45, Capt. AAAS; Am. Geophys. Union; Inst. Elec. & Electronics Eng; Sci. Res. Soc. Am. Philosophy of research management. Address: Air Force Cambridge Research Labs, Laurence G. Hanscom Field, Bedford, MA 01730.

GERLACH, A(LBERT) A(UGUST), b. Columbus, Ohio, May 22, 20; m. 43; c. 5. ELECTRICAL ENGINEERING, APPLIED MATHEMATICS. B.S, Ohio State, 42; M.S, Ill. Inst. Tech, 48, M.S, 50, Ph.D, 58. Sr. engr. & asst. to chief engr, Rowe Eng. Corp, 46-48; sr. engr, Motorola, Inc, 48; res. engr, Armour Res. Found, Ill. Inst. Tech, 48-53; exec. engr. & mgr, res. sect, Cook Res. Labs. Div, Cook Elec. Co, 53-61, asst. dir. labs, Tech-Ctr. Div, 61-65, assoc. dir, 65-69, dir. res, 69-70; U.S. NAVAL RES. LAB, 70-71, HEAD SIGNAL PROCESSING BR, 71- Sig.C, 42-46, 1st Lt. AAAS; Am. Ord. Asn; Inst. Elec. & Electronics Eng; Acoust. Soc. Am. Circuit and net-work theory; theory of modulation; integral transforms; information theory and computers; electronic instrumentation. Address: 123 Quay St, Alex-andria, VA 22314.

GERLACH, EBERHARD, b. Berlin, Ger. Mar. 10, 34. MATHEMATICS. A.M, Indiana, 59; Ph.D.(math), Kansas, 64. Res. asst. math, Univ. Kans, 62-64; asst. prof, Univ. B.C, 64-71; ASSOC. ED, MATH REVIEWS, UNIV. MICH, ANN ARBOR, 71- Fel, Univ. Edinburgh, 69-70. Am. Math. Soc; Math. Asn. Am; Can. Math. Cong. Functional analysis, in particular, Hilbert spaces, linear operators and applications to differential problems. Address: Mathe-matical Reviews, University of Michigan, Ann Arbor, MI 48103.

GERLACH, HOWARD G, JR, b. Cheektowaga, N.Y, Nov. 30, 40; m. 64; c. 2. ORGANIC CHEMISTRY. B.S, Cleveland State, 63; Ph.D.(org. chem), Case Western Reserve, 66. RES. CHEMIST, EXP. STA, E.I. DU PONT DE NE-MOURS & CO, INC, WILMINGTON, DEL, 66- Am. Chem. Soc; The Chem. Soc. Identification and synthesis of alkaloids; photochromic agents; photo-polymerization systems; non-silver photographic systems. Address: 55 Greentree Dr, West Chester, PA 19380.

GERLOFF, ELDEAN D, b. Omaha, Nebr, Dec. 21, 33; m. 56; c. 2. AGRON-OMY, BIOCHEMISTRY. B.S, Nebraska, 60; M.S, Wisconsin, 63, Ph.D. (agron), 66. PROJ. LEADER PLANT PHYSIOL, NORTH. GRAIN INSECT RES. LAB, U.S. DEPT. AGR, 65-; ASST. PROF. PLANT SCI, S.DAK. STATE UNIV, 68- U.S.A, 53-56. AAAS; Am. Soc. Agron; Am. Soc. Plant Physiol. Plant physiology; entomology. Address: Crops Research Division, U.S. Dept. of Agriculture, Northern Grain Insect Research Lab, Brookings, SD 57006.

GERLOFF, GERALD C(ARL), b. Aurora, Nebr, Jan. 26, 20; m. 49; c. 2. BOTANY. B.S, Nebraska, 41; Ph.D.(soils), Wisconsin, 48. Proj. assoc. BOT, UNIV. WIS, MADISON, 48-49, asst. prof, 49-55, assoc. prof, 55-59, PROF, 59- AAAS; Am. Soc. Plant Physiol; Scand. Soc. Plant Physiol. Min-eral nutrition of plants, plant physiology and nutritional ecology. Address: Dept. of Botany, Birge Hall, University of Wisconsin, Madison, WI 53706.

GERLOFF, ROBERT K(AY), b. Aurora, Nebr, Aug. 6, 22; m. 46. MICRO-BIOLOGY, PUBLIC HEALTH. B.Sc, Nebraska, 44, M.A, 48; Ph.D.(micro-biol), Minnesota, 62. Asst. bact, Nebraska, 46-48; asst. bacteriologist serol, ROCKY MT. LAB, U.S. PUB. HEALTH SERV, 48-49, sr. asst. san-itarian VIROL, 49-55, sanitarian, 55-62, sr. scientist, 62-67, SCIENTIST DIR, 67- U.S.N, 43-46. Am. Soc. Microbiol; Am. Pub. Health Asn. Bio-logic properties of chlamydiae; growth of chlamydiae and rickettsiae in tissue culture; radioisotope precipitation test for antibody. Address: Rocky Mt. Lab, U.S. Public Health Service, Hamilton, MT 59840.

GERLOUGH, DANIEL L(AUDER), b. San Diego, Calif, May 31, 16; m. 39; c. 1. ENGINEERING. B.S, Calif. Inst. Tech, 37; M.S, California, 48; Ph.D.(eng), California, Los Angeles, 55. Chief, geophys. field party, Mott-Smith Corp, 37-40; res. & methods analyst, N.Am. Aviation, Inc, 40-42; res. & qual. control engr, Plomb Tool Co, 42-44; qual. control engr, Pettit Eng. Co, 44-45; supvr. lab. opers, Menasco Mfg. Co, 45-47; asst. res. engr, inst. trans-portation & traffic eng, California, Los Angeles, 48-55, assoc. res. engr, 55-59; head automobile traffic sect, Ramo-Wooldridge Div, Thompson-Ramo-Wooldridge, Inc, 59-63; mgr. traffic systs. sect, Planning Res. Corp, Calif, 63-67; PROF. TRANSPORTATION ENG, UNIV. MINN, MINNEAPOLIS, 67- With ground systs. labs, Hughes Aircraft Co, 55-57, consult, airborne systs. lab, 57-58; assoc. prof, Univ. Calif, Los Angeles, 56-60; chmn. comt. theory traffic flow, hwy. res. bd, Nat. Acad. Sci-Nat. Res. Coun, 57-64; con-sult, Aeroneutronic Systs, Inc, 58-59. Am. Soc. Eng. Educ; Asn. Comput.

Mach; Inst. Traffic Eng; Inst. Elec. & Electronics Eng. Automobile traffic flow; digital simulation; applications of digital computers. Address: Dept. of Civil Engineering, University of Minnesota, Minneapolis, MN 55455.

GERMAIN, LAWRENCE S(EYMOUR), b. Fresno, Calif, Oct. 26, 23; m. 49; c. 3. PHYSICS. A.B, California, 44, M.A, 47, Ph.D.(physics), 49. Instr. physics, Reed Col, 49-51, asst. prof, 51-54; sr. physicist, LAWRENCE RADIATION LAB, UNIV. CALIF, 53-62, assoc. div. leader, 62-65, DEP. DIV. LEADER, 65-, consult, 49-51. Consult, Dept. of Defense, 62-65; De-fense Atomic Support Agency, 65- Am. Phys. Soc; Am. Geophys. Union. Cosmic rays; nuclear physics; photographic emulsion and cloud chamber techniques; neutron physics; neutronics; hydrodynamics. Address: B-Division, Lawrence Radiation Lab, P.O. Box 808, Livermore, CA 94551.

GERMAIN, LEO (JOSEPH FREDERIC MARCEL), b. Shawinigan, Que, Oct. 24, 12. CHEMISTRY. B.Sc, Sir George Williams Col, 36. Polymer res. chem-ist, Shawinigan Chem, Div. Gulf Oil Can, 31-71; TECH. CONSULT. POLY-MERS METHOD MFR. & APPLN, 71- Am. Chem. Soc; fel. Chem. Inst. Can. New polymers; methods of manufacture; applications. Address: 552 St. Maurice Blvd, Shawinigan, Que, Can.

GERMAINE, GREG R(ITHER), b. Stillwater, Minn, May 16, 41. MICROBI-OLOGY, BIOCHEMISTRY. B.A, Minnesota, 63, M.S, 66, Ph.D.(microbiol), 68. RES. MICROBIOLOGIST, N.Star Res. & Develop. Inst, 68-70; DIV. FOOD RES, COMMONWEALTH SCI. & INDUST. RES. ORGN, 70- Metabolic control mechanisms; radiobiology of bacteria and bacterial spores. Ad-dress: Commonwealth Scientific & Industrial Research Organization, P.O. Box 43, Ryde, N.S.W, Australia.

GERMAN, JAMES L(AFAYETTE), III, b. Sherman, Tex, Jan. 2, 26; m. 56; c. 2. MEDICINE. B.S, La. Polytech, 45; M.D, Southwest. Med. Col, 49. Intern, Cook County Hosp, Ill, 49-51; res. physician internal med, Vet. Ad-min. Hosp, McKinney, Tex, 52-55; clin. investr, Nat. Insts. Health, 56-58; res. assoc. & asst. physician, Rockefeller Inst, 58-62, asst. prof. & assoc. physician, 63; assoc. prof, dept. pediat. & dir. div. human genetics, MED. COL, CORNELL UNIV, 63-68, ASSOC. PROF, DEPT. ANAT, 65-, CLIN. ASSOC. PROF, 68-; INVESTR. & DIR. HUMAN GENETICS, N.Y. BLOOD CTR, 68- Dipl. Am. Bd. Internal Med, 58. U.S.N.R, 43-46; U.S.P.H.S, 55-58. Am. Soc. Human Genetics; Genetics Soc. Am; Tissue Cult. Asn; Am. Soc. Cell Biol; Am. Col. Physicians; Harvey Soc; Int. Soc. Cell Biol; Am. Soc. Clin. Invest. Human genetics. Address: New York Blood Center, 310 E. 67th St, New York, NY 10021.

GERMAN, JOHN D(EE), b. Wilkes-Barre, Pa, May 17, 14; m. 38; c. 2. SUR-GERY. B.A, Wisconsin, 35; M.D, Virginia, 39. Intern, Virginia Mason Hosp. & Clin, Seattle, Wash, 39-40; intern surg, Univ. Virginia Hosp, 40-41, jr. asst. res, 41-42, sr. asst. res, 42-43, instr. path, 43-, res. surg, 44; private practice, W.Va, 46-49, Wis, 49-55; chief of surg, Miner's Mem. Hosp. Asn, 55-62; asst. prof. SURG, SCH. MED, Univ. Pittsburgh, 62-66; UNIV. NEBR, OMAHA, 66-70, PROF, 70-; MEM. SURG. SERV, VET. AD-MIN. HOSP, 66- Consult, Vet. Admin. Hosp, Iron Mountain, Mich, 50-55; sr. surgeon, Man Mem. Hosp, W.Va, 55-62; assoc. chief surg, Vet. Admin. Hosp, Pittsburgh, Pa, 62-66. Dipl, Am. Bd. Surg, 47. Med.C, 44-46, Capt. Fel. Am. Col. Surg; Soc. Surg. Alimentary Tract. General surgery; gyne-cology. Address: Veterans Administration Hospital, Omaha, NE 68105.

GERMAN, JOHN P(AUL), b. Livingston, Tex, June 10, 17; m. 41; c. 1. ELEC-TRICAL ENGINEERING. B.S, Texas, 40, M.S, 49, Ph.D, 55. Radio engr, elec. eng. res. lab, Texas, 50-55; assoc. prof. ELEC. ENG, Purdue, 55-58; PROF, TEX. A&M UNIV, 58-, RES. ENGR, EXP. STA, 58- Sig.C, 42-46, Res, 46-53, Capt. Am. Soc. Eng. Educ; Inst. Elec. & Electronics Eng. Electromagnetic fields. Address: Dept. of Electrical Engineering, Texas A&M University, College Station, TX 77843.

GERMAN, L(ESLIE), b. Dayton, Ky, May 10, 09; m. 44; c. 1. CHEMISTRY. A.B, Centre Col, 26; E.I. du Pont de Nemours & Co. fel. & M.S, Lafayette Col, 27; Ph.D, Cincinnati, 33. Instr. chem, Va. Mil. Inst, 28-30; res. chem-ist, Sinclair Ref. Co, 33-35; asst. prof. chem, Va. Mil. Inst, 35-40, assoc. prof. & acting head dept, 40-42, prof. & head dept, 42-68; prof, Brevard Col, 68-71; RETIRED. AAAS; Am. Chem. Soc. Electrode potential of co-balt; solvent extraction of oils. Address: 317 E. Beverly St, Staunton, VA 24401.

GERMAN, VICTOR FREDERICK, b. Coffeyville, Kans, Nov. 17, 36; m. 62; c. 2. ORGANIC CHEMISTRY, BIOCHEMISTRY. B.S, Univ. Richmond, 58; Ph.D. (org. chem), Univ. Ill, 63. Fel, Univ. Calif, Berkeley, 63-64; SR. RES. CHEMIST, A.H. ROBINS CO, 64- Lectr, Va. Commonwealth Univ, 67-68. Am. Chem. Soc. Isolation and characterization of biologically active com-ponents from natural products; biochemistry and mechanism of action of antipepsin and antiulcer drugs; biochemical changes in gastric functions under ulcer promoting conditions. Address: Research Labs, A.H. Robins Co, 1211 Sherwood Ave, Richmond, VA 23220.

GERMAN, WILLIAM J(OHN), b. McKeesport, Pa, Oct. 28, 99; m. 33, 47; c. 4. NEUROSURGERY. A.B, California, 22, M.A, 23; M.D, Harvard, 26; M.A, Yale, 48. Asst. physiol, California, 21-22, assoc, 22-23; surg. intern, Peter Bent Brigham Hosp, 26-27; fel. plastic surg, Hopkins, 28; Cushing fel. neurosurg, SCH. MED, YALE, 29-30, instr. SURG, 30-32, asst. prof, 32-38, assoc. prof, 38-48, prof, 48-68, EMER. PROF, 68- Asst. res. surg, New Haven Hosp, 28-29, res. surg, 30-31, chief neurosurgeon, 33- Med.C, 44-46, Comdr. Soc. Neurol. Surg.(v.pres, 55, pres, 56-57); Soc. Univ. Surg; Harvey Cushing Soc.(pres, 53); Am. Neurol. Asn; Asn. Res. Nerv. & Ment. Diseases; Am. Med. Asn; Cong. Neurol. Surg; Asn. Am. Med. Cols. Neuro-surgery and allied basic sciences. Address: 2 Church St, South New Haven, CT 06519.

GERMANN, ALBERT F(REDERICK) O(TTOMAR), b. Peru, Ind, Feb. 18, 86; m. 14; c. 4. NUTRITION, BIOCHEMISTRY. A.B, Indiana, 09, A.M, 10; Wis-consin, 10; D.Sc, Geneva, 12; Berlin, 12. Asst. chem, Wisconsin, 09-10; instr, Western Reserve, 13-15, asst. prof, 15-21, assoc. prof, 21; asst. prof, Stanford, 21-25; dir. res. lab, Lab. Prods. Co, 25-26; prof. chem. & head dept, Valparaiso, 26-28; dir. res, SMA Corp, 27-35; PRES. & GEN. MGR,

NUTRIT. RES. ASSOCS, INC, 36- Acting pres. univ. & acting dean col. pharm, Valparaiso, 27. AAAS; Am. Chem. Soc. Physical chemistry of gases; dairy chemistry; infant foods; extraction of carrot oil from carrots; vitamin A and carotene; applications of carotene to food industries; dehydrated vegetables; stabilization of carotene on dry carriers; development of improved vitamin concentrates for poultry and livestock feeds; vitamins for human use; relation of vitamins to human health. Address: Box 385, South Whitley, IN 46787.

GERMANN, ALBERT F(REDERICK) O(TTOMAR), II, b. Cleveland, Ohio, Jan. 4, 29; m. 54; c. 3. ANIMAL NUTRITION. B.S, Purdue, 51, M.S, 56, Ph.D, 58. V.PRES, NUTRIT. RES. ASSOCS, INC, 58- U.S.A, 52-54. AAAS; Am. Soc. Animal Sci. Relationship of lysine requirement to protein level of weanling swine; nutrient requirements of the chinchilla. Address: South Whitley, IN 46787.

GERMANN, D(ONALD) P(ITT), b. N.Y.C, Mar. 29, 12; m. 36; c. 3. CHEMISTRY. B.S, Vermont, 34. Chemist, Ganes Chem. Works, 36-37; Foster D. Snell, Inc, 37-39; sci. dir, CLARK-CLEVELAND, INC, 39-64, v.pres. res, 64-69, TECH. MGR, VICK MFG. DIV, 69- AAAS; Am. Chem. Soc; fel. Am. Inst. Chem. Natural gums; synthetic hydrophilic high polymers. Address: Vick Manufacturing Division, Clark-Cleveland, Inc, 20 Wall St, Binghamton, NY 13902.

GERMANN, PAUL J(ULIAN), b. Naperville, Ill, April 11, 16; m. 42; c. 9. BIOLOGY, BOTANY. B.S, St. Mary's Col, 37; M.S, De Paul, 42; Ph.D.(bot), Minnesota, 53. Teacher, pub. sch, 37-42; instr. biol, Englewood Jr. Col, 41-42; teacher, pub. sch, Ill, 45-46; from instr. to PROF. BIOL. & CHMN. DEPT, COL. ST. THOMAS, 46-, DIR. DIV. SCI. & MATH, 70- U.S.N.R, 42-46, Lt. AAAS; Ecol. Soc. Am; Nat. Asn. Biol. Teachers. Morphological analysis and chronological significance of growth layers of trees from southwestern United States. Address: Dept. of Biology, College of St. Thomas, St. Paul, MN 55101.

GERMANN, RICHARD P(AUL), b. Ithaca, N.Y, Apr. 3, 18; m. 42; c. 1. ORGANIC CHEMISTRY. B.A, Univ. Colo, 39, fel, 41; Naval fel, West. Reserve Univ, 41-43. Chief anal. chemist, Taylor Ref. Co, Tex, 43-44; res. develop. chemist, Alrose Chem. Co. Div, Geigy Chem. Corp, 52-55; new prod. develop. chemist, res. div, W.R. Grace & Co, Md, 55-60; chief chemist, soap & cosmetic div, G.H. Packwood Mfg. Co, 60-61; coord. chem. prod. develop, Abbott Labs, 61-71; CONSULT. CHEMIST, 71- Mem, Int. Sci. Found. AAAS; Am. Chem. Soc; Am. Pharmaceut. Asn; Am. Asn. Textile Chem. & Colorists; Commercial Develop. Asn; Am. Mgt. Asn; Am. Inst. Mgt; The Chem. Soc; Chem. Mkt. Res. Asn; Am. Inst. Chem; World Future Soc. Vitamin nutrition; trace element use in growth of agricultural crops; biocides; pollution control. Address: 3940 Elm Lane, Waukegan, IL 60085.

GERMANY, A(RCHIE) H(ERMAN), b. Dixon, Miss, Nov. 18, 17; m. 43; c. 3. ORGANIC CHEMISTRY. B.A, Miss. Col, 39; fel, North Carolina, 41-42, Ethyl-Dow fel, 42-43, Ph.D.(org. chem), 43. Lab. asst. chem, North Carolina, 39-41; res. assoc, metall. lab, Chicago, 43-44; chemist, Clinton Labs, Oak Ridge, 44-46; assoc. prof. chem, MISS. COL, 46-49, prof, 49-60, head dept, 60-61, CHMN. DIV. SCI. & MATH, 61- AAAS; Am. Chem. Soc. Synthetic organic chemistry. Address: 803 E. Leake St, Clinton, MS 39056.

GERMANY, WILLIAM W, JR, b. Glenmora, La, July 14, 33; m. 60; c. 2. MICROBIOLOGY, CLINICAL PATHOLOGY. B.S, Southwest. La. Inst, 55; M.A, Indiana, 58; Ph.D.(microbiol), Tennessee, 62. Asst. dir. labs, LeBonheur Children's Hosp, Memphis, Tenn, 58-60; asst. prof. path, med. col. & dir. clin. labs, microbiol. div, univ. hosp, Univ. Ala, Birmingham, 62-65; ASST. TO DIR, CLIN. LABS, ST. JOSEPH HOSP, 65- Dipl, Am. Bd. Med. Microbiol, 70. Med.C, U.S.A, 54-56. Am. Soc. Microbiol. Cancer immunology; clinical microbiology. Address: Clinical Labs, St. Joseph Hospital, Memphis, TN 38101.

GERMESHAUSEN, KENNETH J(OSEPH), b. Woodland, Calif, May 12, 07; m. 35; c. 1. ELECTRONICS. S.B, Mass. Inst. Tech, 31. Partner, Edgerton, Germeshausen & Grier, 32-58, pres, 54-65, CHMN. BD. & DIR. RES, EG&G, INC, BEDFORD, 65- Res. assoc, Mass. Inst. Tech, 35-, mem. staff radiation lab, 41-45, sect. chief, 45-46. Nat. Soc. Prof. Eng; fel. Am. Acad. Arts & Sci; fel. Inst. Elec. & Electronics Eng. Gaseous conduction; hydrogen thyratrons; strobotrons; electric flash lamps; electronic control and instrumentation. Address: 240 Highland St, Weston, MA 02193.

GERMINO, FELIX JOSEPH, b. New York, N.Y, July 14, 30; m. 52; c. 7. CARBOHYDRATE & ORGANIC CHEMISTRY. B.S, Fordham, 52; N.Y. Univ, 55-57; St. John's, 61-63. Food inspector, Food Inspection Serv, U.S. Dept. Agr, N.Y, 52; asst. chemist, Gen. Foods Tech. Ctr, 54-59; assoc. chemist, Morehead Patterson Res. Ctr, Am. Mach. & Foundry Co, 59-64; proj. leader carbohydrate chem, Corn Prod. Co, ARGO, 64-71, sect. leader foods & paper textiles, 65-71, ASST. MGR, CPC INT, INC, 71- Med.C, U.S.A, 52-54. Am. Chem. Soc; Am. Asn. Cereal Chem. Physical structure of starch; chemistry of corn sugar; synthesis of polysaccharide derivatives for use in textiles, paper and food related fields; physical chemistry of starch and starch fractions; environmental sciences. Address: 12414 S. 83rd Ave, Palos Park, IL 60464.

GERMONPREZ, RAYMOND LEO, b. Topeka, Kans, July 17, 44; m. 66; c. 2. POLYMER & ORGANIC CHEMISTRY. B.S, Univ. Kans, 66; Nat. Defense Educ. Act fel, Univ. Notre Dame, 66-69, Ph.D.(polymer chem), 70. RES. CHEMIST, SPRUANCE FILM RES. & DEVELOP. LAB, E.I. DU PONT DE NEMOURS & CO, INC, 70- Am. Chem. Soc. Thermally stable polymers; flexible films and adhesives. Address: Spruance Film Research & Development Lab, E.I. du Pont de Nemours & Co, Inc, Richmond, VA 23261.

GERMUTH, FREDERICK G(EORGE), JR, b. Baltimore, Md, Sept. 28, 21. PATHOLOGY. A.B, Hopkins, 42, M.D, 45. Asst. pathologist, Peter Bent Brigham Hosp, Boston, Mass, 53-54; assoc. pathologist, Johns Hopkins Hosp, Baltimore, Md, 54-55, pathologist, 55-58; dir. labs. & pathologist-in-chief, Charlotte Mem. Hosp, N.C, 58-64; Highsmith Mem. Hosp, Fayetteville, 64-65; dir. labs, Aultman Hosp, Canton, Ohio, 65-66; prof. path. & chmn. dept, sch. med, St. Louis, 66-68; DIR. DEPT. LAB. MED, ST. JOHN'S MERCY HOSP, 68- Asst. prof. path, sch. med, Harvard, 53-54; sch. med, Hopkins, 54-55, assoc. prof, 55-58; vis. assoc. prof, sch. med, North Carolina, 59-65. Consult. to Surgeon Gen. & mem. allergy & immunol. study sect, U.S. Pub. Health Serv, 59-63. Cert. anat. path, 57 & clin. path, 64, Am. Bd. Path. Am. Asn. Path. & Bact; Am. Asn. Immunol; Am. Soc. Exp. Path; Col. Am. Path. Pathology and pathogenesis of immune complex disease. Address: Dept. Lab. Medicine, St. John's Mercy Hospital, 615 S. New Ballas Rd, St. Louis, MO 63141.

GERNES, DONALD C(ONSTANT), b. Wilson, Minn, June 1, 10; m. 35; c. 3. CHEMICAL ENGINEERING. B.Ch.E, Minnesota, 31, M.S, 32, Ph.D.(chem. eng), 35. Chem. engr, Northwest Res. Inst, Minnesota, 35-39; Tenn. Valley Auth, Ala, 39-43; U.S. Bur. Mines, Colo. & N.Dak, 43-46; Standard Oil Co, Ind, 46-50; Kaiser Aluminum & Chem. Corp, Calif, 50-69, res. assoc, 69-70; RETIRED. Electrochem. Soc. Fused salts; alumina; microspherical aluminum; catalyst production; dust removal; gasification of lignite; synthetic polymers; titanium; inorganic fluorides; preparation of cuprous chlorid; electrolyte for deposition of copper and copper alloys; electrodeposition of metals and alloys from thiosulfate solutions. Address: Box 38B, Star Route 3, Garden Valley, CA 95633.

GERNETH, DAL CHARLES, b. Gainesville, Tex, Feb. 5, 22; m. 50; c. 1. MATHEMATICS. B.S, Texas, 46; M.S, Okla. State, 47, Ph.D.(math), 53. Instr. math, Okla. State, 46-53; sr. aerophys. engr, Convair div, Gen. Dynamics Corp, 53-56; staff engr, Chance Vought Aircraft, Inc, 56-58; scientist, Temco, Inc, 58-60; tech. asst, Schlumberger, Ltd, 60-64; consult. appl. math, 64-67; SCIENTIST, LTV ELECTROSYSTS, DALLAS, 67- Asst. prof, Miss. South. Col, 49-50. U.S.N.R, 43-46, Lt. Am. Math. Soc. Applied mathematics. Address: 2519 Little Creek, Richardson, TX 75080.

GERNON, GERALD D(ELAND), b. Champaign, Ill, June 10, 26. FOOD SCIENCE. B.S, Illinois, 49, M.S, 51; fel. & Ph.D, Ohio State, 55. Chemist & food technologist, cured meats div, res. labs, Swift & Co, 55-56; food technologist, food radiation preservation div, Qm. Food & Container Inst, 57-60; assoc. prof. food tech, Tennessee, 60-65; FOOD TECHNOLOGIST, FOOD PROD. DIV, R.J. REYNOLDS TOBACCO CO, 65- U.S.N, 44-46. Am. Chem. Soc; Inst. Food Technol; Am. Asn. Cereal Chem; Am. Dairy Sci. Asn. Meats and cured meats; radiation preservation of foods; development of irradiation sterilized meats; biological assay of insecticides in processed vegetables; biochemical aspects of food processing; studies relating enzymatic activity to the acceptability of processed vegetables; food product and process development. Address: Product Development Dept, R.J. Reynolds Tobacco Co, Winston-Salem, NC 27102.

GERNS, FRED R(UDOLPH), b. Mannheim, Ger, Nov. 28, 25; nat; m. 56; c. 2. ORGANIC CHEMISTRY. B.A, Ohio State, 48; M.S, Syracuse, 51; Smith, Kline & French Labs. fel, Virginia, 57-59, Ph.D.(chem), 59. Jr. med. chemist, Smith, Kline & French Labs, 52-56; sr. org. chemist, Burroughs Wellcome & Co, Inc, 59-63; chemist, Chas. Pfizer & Co, Conn, 63-65; SR. RES. CHEMIST, GREAT LAKES CHEM. CORP, 65- U.S.N, 44-46, 51-52. Am. Chem. Soc. Nitrogen and sulfur heterocycles; halogen chemistry. Address: 248 Connolly St, West Lafayette, IN 47906.

GERO, ALEXANDER, b. Budapest, Hungary, May 26, 07; nat; m. 35; c. 2. CHEMISTRY. Ph.D.(chem), Vienna, 30. Asst. org. chem, Inst. Tech. Berlin, 32-34; res. chemist, Syngala, Inc, Vienna, 35-36; Dr. Wander, Inc, Budapest, 36-38; Dr. Roussel Labs, Paris, 38-39; Silva-Araujo-Roussel Labs, Rio de Janeiro, 41-42; chief chemist, Berkeley Chem. Corp, N.J, 42-45; chem. dir, Nat. Foam System & Purocaine, Inc, Pa, 45-47; asst. prof. chem, Villanova Col, 47-48, assoc. prof, 48-52; PHARMACOL, HAHNEMANN MED. COL, 52-66, PROF, 66- Fulbright prof, Valladolid & Oviedo, 62-63. French Army, 40. Am. Chem. Soc; Am. Soc. Pharmacol. & Exp. Therapeut. Drug synthesis; mechanism of drug action; optical isomerism; electronic mechanisms of biological reactions. Address: Dept. of Pharmacology, Hahnemann Medical College, Philadelphia, PA 19102.

GEROCH, ROBERT P(AUL), b. Akron, Ohio, June 1, 42; m. 65. THEORETICAL PHYSICS. B.S, Mass. Inst. Tech, 63; Nat. Sci. Found. fel, Princeton, 63-67, Procter fel, 65-66, Ph.D.(physics), 67. Air Force Off. Sci. Res. fel, Birkbeck Col, 67-68, Nat. Sci. Found. fel, 68-69; fel. physics, Syracuse Univ, 69-70; ASSOC. PROF, Univ. Tex, Austin, 70-71; PHYSICS & MATH, ENRICO FERMI INST, UNIV. CHICAGO, 71- Am. Phys. Soc. General relativity. Address: Enrico Fermi Institute, University of Chicago, 933 E. 56th St, Chicago, IL 60637.

GEROLD, NICOLAS J(OHN), b. N.Y.C, Jan. 1. 19; m. 49; c. 2. HISTOCHEMISTRY. B.A, Brown, 42, M.S, 48; Ph.D.(zool), Cornell, 51. Asst. prof. BIOL. HAMILTON COL, 51-57, assoc. prof, 57-64, PROF, 64-, CHMN. DEPT, 66- U.S.A, 42-46. AAAS; Am. Soc. Zool; N.Y. Acad. Sci; Nat. Asn. Biol. Teachers. Am. Asn. Med. Col. Cell division. Address: Dept. of Biology, Hamilton College, Clinton, NY 13323.

GERONE, PETER J(OHN), b. Oakfield, N.Y, Apr. 11, 28; m. 51; c. 7. VIROLOGY. B.A, Buffalo, 49, M.A, 51; Sc.D.(microbiol), Hopkins, 54. Instr. biol, Buffalo, 50-51; supvry. microbiologist, U.S. Army Biol. Labs, 54-71; DIR, DELTA REGIONAL PRIMATE RES. CTR, TULANE UNIV, LA, 71- Mem. biohazards control & containment working group, Nat. Cancer Inst. Dept. Army meritorious civilian serv. award, 68. Dipl, Am. Bd. Med. Microbiol. AAAS; Sci. Res. Soc. Am; Am. Soc. Microbiol. Respiratory virus infection. Address: Delta Regional Primate Research Center, Tulane University, Covington, LA 70433.

GEROW, CLARE W(ILLIAM), b. Detroit, Mich, Oct. 8, 27; m. 51; c. 13. ORGANIC CHEMISTRY. B.S, Detroit, 51; Ph.D.(org. chem), Iowa State, 56. Res. polymer chemist, film dept, E.I. DU PONT DE NEMOURS & CO, INC, 56-61, tech. mkt. eval. investr, 61-63, res. polymer chemist, 63-67, STAFF SCIENTIST, Yerkes Res. & Develop. Lab, 67-71, SPRUANCE FILM PLANT, 71- Mem. adj. faculty, Va. Commonwealth Univ, 71- U.S.A, 46-47. Am. Chem. Soc. Organogermanium and organosilicon chemistry; polymer chemistry, including polyolefins, polythio ketones and aldehydes and polyimides. Address: Spruance Film Plant, E.I. du Pont de Nemours & Co, Inc, P.O. Box 27222, Richmond, VA 23261.

GERPHEIDE, JOHN H, b. Manitowoc, Wis, Sept. 17, 25; m. 51; c. 3. MECHANICAL ENGINEERING, AERONAUTICS. B.S, Calif. Inst. Tech, 45, M.S, 48. Engr, U.S. Naval Ord. Test Sta, Inyokern, 46-47; JET PROPULSION LAB, CALIF. INST. TECH, 48-53, proj. engr, 53-59, flight test engr, 54-55, sect. mgr. spacecraft develop, 60-62, consult. Apollo support, 62-63, staff specialist proj. planning, 64, proj. mgr, develop. Mars Landing Craft, 67-68, SECT. MGR. SYST. DESIGN & INTEGRATION, 64- U.S.N, 43-46, Lt.(jg). Development of advanced designs, new technologies and system approaches to exploration of space. Address: Jet Propulsion Lab, 4800 Oak Grove Dr, Pasadena, CA 91103.

GERRARD, DOUGLAS J, b. Chesley, Ont, May 23, 38; m. 63; c. 2. FORESTRY, BIOMETRICS. B.Sc.F, Toronto, 60, M.Sc.F, 63; Ph.D.(forestry), Mich. State, 68. Lectr. photogram, Toronto, 60-64; instr. FOREST BIOMET, Mich. State, 64-68; ASST. PROF, UNIV. MINN, ST. PAUL, 68- Soc. Am. Foresters; Am. Soc. Photogram. Aerial photogrammetry; forest measurements; estimation of insect population density; analysis of inter-tree competition in a forest; sequential sampling theory; mathematical modelling of tree form development. Address: College of Forestry, University of Minnesota, St. Paul, MN 55101.

GERRARD, J(OHN) W(ATSON), b. Kasenga, N.Rhodesia, Apr. 14, 16; m. 41; c. 3. PEDIATRICS. B.A, Oxford, 38, B.M. & B.Ch, 41, D.M, 51. Lectr. PEDIAT, Univ. Birmingham, 48-51, chief asst, 51-55; PROF, UNIV. HOSP, UNIV. SASK, 55-, head dept, 55-71. Fel, Royal Col. Physicians Can, 56; John Scott Award, Phila. City Trusts, 62; Enuresis Found. Award, 68; fel, Royal Col. Physicians, 68. R.A.M.C, 42-45, Maj. Can. Pediat. Soc; Am. Acad. Pediat; Am. Pediat. Soc; Can. Soc. Immunol; Nutrit. Soc. Can. Gastrointestinal and genito-urinary allergies. Address: Dept. of Pediatrics, University Hospital, University of Saskatchewan, Saskatoon, Sask, Can.

GERRARD, THOMAS AQUINAS, b. La Crosse, Wis, Feb. 7, 33; m. 58; c. 2. GEOLOGY. B.S, Cincinnati, 56; Pa. State, 56-57; M.S, Miami (Ohio), 59; Ph.D.(geol), Arizona, 64. Explor. geologist, Chevron Oil Co, 64-66; asst. prof. GEOL, WITTENBERG UNIV, 66-71, ASSOC. PROF, 71- Lectr, Tulane, 65-66; Nat. Sci. Found. summer participation grant, Inst. Astrogeol, 67; Nat. Sci. Found. summer grants, 68. Am. Asn. Petrol. Geol; Soc. Econ. Paleont. & Mineral; Nat. Asn. Geol. Teachers. Sedimentary petrology and geochemistry; regional stratigraphy; marine geology; astrogeology. Address: Dept. of Geology, Wittenberg University, Springfield, OH 45501.

GERRATH, J(OSEPH) F(REDRICK), b. Saskatoon, Sask, June 25, 36; m. 66; c. 1. BOTANY, PHYCOLOGY. B.A, British Columbia, 59, B.Sc, 63, M.Sc, 65, Ph.D.(bot), 68; Commonwealth scholar, London, 65-66. ASST. PROF. BOT, UNIV. GUELPH, 68- Can. Bot. Asn; Int. Phycol. Soc; Phycol. Soc. Am; Brit. Phycol. Soc. Taxonomy and cytology of desmids. Address: Dept. of Botany, University of Guelph, Guelph, Ont, Can.

GERRAUGHTY, ROBERT J(OSEPH), b. Newton, Mass, Aug. 30, 28; m. 53; c. 4. PHARMACY. B.S, Mass. Col. Pharm, 50, fel, 50-52, M.S, 52; Ph.D.(pharm), Connecticut, 59. Asst. PHARM, Connecticut, 55-58; asst. prof, Rutgers, 58-60; assoc. prof, UNIV. R.I, 60-68, PROF, 68- U.S.A.F, 52-55, Res, 55-, Capt. Am. Pharmaceut. Asn. Ultrasonics; pharmaceutical formulation. Address: College of Pharmacy, University of Rhode Island, Kingston, RI 01142.

GERRIE, JOHN W(ILFRID), b. Stratford, Ont, Jan. 13, 05; m. 29; c. 4. PLASTIC SURGERY. B.A, Alberta, 24, D.D.S, 27; M.D, C.M, McGill, 31. PROF. ORAL SURG. & asst. prof. to ASSOC. PROF. SURG, McGILL UNIV, 50- Dir. plastic surg, Montreal Gen. Hosp; Queen Mary Vet. Hosp; consult, Montreal Children's Hosp. R.C.A.M.C, 41-45. Soc. Plastic & Reconstruct. Surg; Am. Asn. Plastic Surg; Can. Soc. Plastic Surg; Can. Soc. Oral Surg; British Soc. Plastic Surg. Clinical plastic and oral surgery. Address: 1414 Drummond St, Montreal, Que, Can.

GERRIE, NORMAN F(ORBES), b. Fergus, Ont, Mar. 18, 07; U.S. citizen; m. 33. c. 2. DENTISTRY, PUBLIC HEALTH. D.D.S, Northwestern, 31; M.P.H, Michigan, 46. Field dentist, Utah State Dept. Health, 37-40; dir, dent. div, Mont. State Dept. Health, 40-43; dent. consult, U.S. Pub. Health Serv, Chicago, Kansas City, Denver & Wash, D.C, 43-54, chief div. dent. pub. health, D.C, 56-60, disease control br, div. dent. pub. health & resources, 61-62, prog. planning, Nat. Inst. Child Health & Human Develop, 62-63, dir. human commun. prog, Md, 63-69; prof. social dent, sch. dent. med, Tufts Univ, 69-71; RETIRED. Lectr, sch. dent, Georgetown, 64- Dipl, Am. Bd. Dent. Pub. Health, 50, mem. bd, 62-66; pres, 66. U.S.P.H.S, 43-66. Am. Dent. Asn; fel. Am. Col. Dent; fel. Am. Pub. Health Asn. Fluoride-caries relationships; dental epidemiology; dental public health program and research administration; speech and language development; reading acquisition. Address: 9139 McDonald Dr, Bethesda, MD 20034.

GERRIETS, C(ARL) JOHN, b. Clay Center, Kans, Mar. 31, 24; m. 61; c. 2. MATHEMATICS. B.A, Kansas, 52; Wyoming, 57; M.S, Stanford, 58; Iowa, 61-63. Teacher, pub. sch. Kans, 52-57; ASST. PROF. MATH, Utah State, 58-61; KANS. STATE TEACHERS COL, 63- U.S.A, 46-48. Math. Asn. Am. Mathematics education. Address: Dept. of Mathematics, Kansas State Teachers College, Emporia, KS 66801.

GERRING, IRVING, b. Bridgeport, Conn, Apr. 16, 09; m. 44; c. 3. ENVIRONMENTAL SCIENCES, PUBLIC HEALTH ADMINISTRATION. B.S, Connecticut, 31; M.S.P.H, Columbia, 35; Michigan, 39-41. Teacher, pub. sch, Conn, 32; dir. div. environ. health, Bridgeport, 35-39; assoc. pub. health engr, U.S. Pub. Health Serv, 41-43, sanitarian, 44-46, exec. secy, pub. health & med. res. admin, NAT. INSTS. HEALTH, 47-56, parasitol, radiation & pop. res. study sects, 56-71, HEALTH SCIENTIST ADMINR, DIV. RES. GRANTS, 71- Spec. asst, War Assets Admin, 47. Fel. Am. Pub. Health Asn; Water Pollution Control Fedn. Bactericology; public health; air and water pollution; occupational health; food technology. Address: Division of Research Grants, National Institutes of Health, Bethesda, MD 20014.

GERRISH, E(VERETT) E(LMER), b. Lewiston, Maine, Oct. 2, 26; m. 53; c. 3. PLANT GENETICS. B.S, Maine, 50; M.S, Minnesota, 54, Ph.D.(plant genetics), 56. Asst, Minnesota, 50-55; CORN BREEDER & GENETICIST, CARGILL RES. LAB, 56- U.S.A.F, 45-46. Am. Soc. Agron. Developmental phases in the production of commercially feasible dent corn hybrids. Address: Cargill Research Lab, Cargill, Inc, Box 359, Grinnell, IA 50112.

GERRISH, OLIVER BENJAMIN, b. Edgley, N.Dak, May 29, 18; m. 38; c. 1. FOOD TECHNOLOGY, INDUSTRIAL CHEMISTRY. B.S, Kans. State Col. Pittsburg, 58. Supv. plant chemist, Spencer Chem. Co, Kans, 42-44, lab. chemist, 56-59; chief chemist, Midwest Solvents Co, 44-55; res. asst, med. ctr, Kansas, 55; sr. chemist, Midwest Res. Inst, 59-63, head food technol. & nutrit, Mo, 63-69; mgr. contract res, prod. develop. serv, Pet Inc, Ill, 69-71; GROUP LEADER CEREAL CHEM. RES, RES. CTR, FAR-MAR CO, INC, 71- Mem. Am. Food for Peace Coun, 63-65. Inst. Food Tech; Sci. Res. Soc. Am. Microbiology; industrial fermentations; research administration. Address: Research Center, Far-Mar Co, Inc, 960 N. Halsted, Hutchinson, KS 67501.

GERRITS, ROGER J, b. Green Bay, Wis, Feb. 8, 32; m. 55; c. 5. PHYSIOLOGY. B.S, Wis. State, River Falls, 58; M.S, Minnesota, 60, Ph.D.(dairy husb), 63. Mem. staff animal sci, Univ. Minn, 62-63; invest. leader physiol, ANIMAL SCI. RES. DIV, U.S. DEPT. AGR, 63-67; AGR. ADMINR. & CHIEF SWINE RES. BR, 67- U.S.A.F, 51-54. Am. Dairy Sci. Asn; Am. Soc. Animal Sci; Am. Meat Sci. Asn; Soc. Study Reproduction. Physiology of reproduction in farm animals; semen evaluation of bulls and boars; estrous and ovulation control; related studies in physiology of growth and development in swine. Address: Animal Science Research Division, Agricultural Research Center, U.S. Dept. of Agriculture, Beltsville, MD 20705.

GERRITSEN, A(LEXANDER) N(ICOLAAS), b. The Hague, Netherlands, Nov. 29, 13; m. 43; c. 2. PHYSICS. Drs, State Univ. Leiden, 37, Dr, 48. Govt. asst. physics, State Univ. Leiden, 37, head & instr. physics lab, 43, scientist, Found. Fundamental Res. Matter, 47, sr. scientist, 47, 56; vis. prof. PHYSICS, PURDUE UNIV, 54, assoc. prof, 56-60, PROF, 60- Dutch Army, 33-53. Fel. Am. Phys. Soc; Netherlands Phys. Soc; Netherlands Asn. Sci. Invest.(secy, 48-53). Transport phenomena in metals; low temperatures. Address: Dept. of Physics, Purdue University, Lafayette, IN 47907.

GERRITSEN, FRANCISCUS, b. Dordrecht, Netherlands, Apr. 23, 23; m. 48; c. 4. COASTAL & OCEAN ENGINEERING. M.S, Delft Univ. Technol, 50. Hydraul. engr, Delft Univ. Technol, 48-51; res. engr, Royal Netherlands Bd. Rd. & Waterways, 51-56; asst. prof. coastal eng, Univ. Fla, 56-59, assoc. prof, 59-62; chief engr, Royal Netherlands Bd. Rd. & Waterways, 62-69; PROF. OCEAN ENG, UNIV. HAWAII, 69- Consult. for for. govts. & private practice, 56-; lectr, Int. Course Hydraul. Eng, 67-69. Netherlands Royal Inst. Eng; Am. Soc. Civil Eng; Int. Asn. Hydraul. Res; Permanent Int. Asn. Navig. Cong. Harbor engineering, coastal processes, estuaries, construction, transportation; wave mechanics, ocean environment, air-sea interaction. Address: Dept. of Ocean Engineering, University of Hawaii, 2565 The Mall, Honolulu, HI 96822.

GERRITSEN, GEORGE C(ONTANT), b. Passaic, N.J, Dec. 28, 26; m. 50; c. 1. ENDOCRINOLOGY, BIOCHEMISTRY. A.B, Hope Col, 50; M.S, Mich. State, 55, Nat. Insts. Health fel, 58-60, Ph.D.(physiol), 60. Res. instr. agr. biochem, Mich. State, 50-55; sr. scientist, Mead Johnson & Co, 60-62; RES. SCIENTIST, DIABETES RES. DEPT, UPJOHN CO, 62- U.S.N.R, 44-59, Lt. AAAS; Am. Chem. Soc; Am. Diabetes Asn. Etiology and pathogenesis of diabetes; hypoglycemic agents; metabolic interrelationships between carbohydrate and lipid metabolism; diabetic animals and prediabets. Address: Diabetes Research Dept, Upjohn Co, Kalamazoo, MI 49001.

GERRITSEN, H(ENDRICK) J(URJEN), b. The Hague, Netherlands, Jan. 19, 27; c. 4. PHYSICS, CHEMISTRY. B.S, Leiden, Holland, 48, Ph.D.(phys-ics, chem), 55. Asst. prof. low temperature res, State Univ. Leiden, 52-55; res. physicist, res. labs, Radio Corp. Am, Zurich, 55-57, res. physicist & mem. tech. staff, low temperature magnetism, 57-67; ASSOC. PROF. PHYSICS, BROWN UNIV, 67- Assoc. prof, Chalmers Tech, Sweden, 61-62. Dutch Army, 49-51, Sgt. Swiss Phys. Soc. Microwave properties of solids, particularly at low temperatures and in magnetic materials; gaseous electronics; optics, spectroscopy; nonlinear optics and holography. Address: Dept. of Physics, Brown University, Providence, RI 02912.

GERRITSEN, T(HEO), b. Nijmegen, Netherlands, May 5, 22; U.S. citizen; m. 47; c. 3. BIOCHEMISTRY. B.Sc, Utrecht, 45, M.Sc, 48, Dr.Sc.(physiol. chem), 51. Lectr. physiol. chem, Utrecht, 49-51; clin. chemist, S.African Inst. Med. Res, 51-53; res. off, Nat. Chem. Res. Lab, Johannesburg, S. Africa, 53-56; sr. res. off, Nat. Nutrit. Res. Inst, Pretoria, 56-58; res. assoc. N-metab, Elgin State Hosp, Ill, 58-60; asst. prof. PEDIAT. & PHYSIOL. CHEM, JOSEPH P. KENNEDY JR. LAB, MED. CTR, UNIV. WIS, MADISON, 60-66, ASSOC. PROF, 66-, ACTING DIR, 71- Sr. Kennedy scholar, 62-; consult. biochem, Cent. Wis. Colony, 62- Am. Asn. Clin. Chem; Am. Soc. Biol. Chem. Biochemistry of metabolic abnormalities, especially those causing mental retardation. Address: Joseph P. Kennedy Jr. Lab, University of Wisconsin Medical Center, Madison, WI 53706.

GERRY, EDWARD T, b. Boston, Mass, Sept. 7, 38; m. 60; c. 2. QUANTUM ELECTRONICS. B.S, Col. William & Mary, 59; M.S, Cornell, 62; Ph.D.(nuclear eng), Mass. Inst. Technol, 65. Chmn. laser res. comt, Avco Everett Res. Lab, 61-70, dir. laser prog. off, 70-71; CHIEF LASER TECHNOL. DIV, ADVAN. RES. PROJ. AGENCY, DEPT. DEFENSE, 71- AAAS; Am. Phys. Soc. Physics of fully ionized plasmas; physics of gas lasers; chemical kinetics. Address: 1804 Briar Ridge Ct, McLean, VA 22101.

GERRY, HAROLD T(IRRELL), b. Hartford, Conn, Feb. 6, 08; m. 33; c. 2. PHYSICAL CHEMISTRY. S.B, Mass. Inst. Tech, 29, Ph.D.(phys. chem), 32. Asst, Mass. Inst. Tech, 31-33, res. assoc. & instr. chem, 33-40; res. chemist, nitrogen div, Allied Chem. & Dye Corp, 40-51, lab. dir, 51-61, planning supvr, Allied Chem. Corp, 61-70; CONSULT, 70- Am. Chem. Soc. Chemical thermodynamics; catalysis; process development. Address: 1828 Varina Ave, Petersburg, VA 23805.

GERRY, HENRY, b. Lewiston, Minn, Dec. 24, 20. ORGANIC CHEMISTRY. B.S, Mont. State Col, 43; Nat. Sci. Found. fel, Ohio State, 61-62, Ph.D.(org. chem), 64. Instr. CHEM, Mont. State Col, 46-52, asst. prof, 52-59; instr,

Ohio State, 60-61; asst. prof, MONT. STATE UNIV, 62-66, ASSOC. PROF, 66- A.U.S, 43-46, Capt. Am. Chem. Soc. Synthesis and resolution of intramolecularly hindered organic compounds; reaction mechanisms; stereochemistry. Address: Dept. of Chemistry, Montana State University, Bozeman, MT 59715.

GERRY, MICHAEL C(HARLES) L(EWIS), b. Victoria, B.C, Nov. 8, 39; m. 67. PHYSICAL CHEMISTRY. B.A, Univ. B.C, 60, Nat. Res. Coun. Can. scholar, 60-62, M.Sc, 62; Exhib. 1851 overseas scholar, Cambridge, 62-65, Ph.D. (phys. chem), 65. Fel. physics, Duke Univ, 65-67; ASST. PROF. CHEM, UNIV. B.C, 67- Am. Phys. Soc; The Chem. Soc. Electron spin resonance of irradiated solids; microwave spectroscopy of gases; nuclear quadrupole resonance spectroscopy. Address: Dept. of Chemistry, University of British Columbia, Vancouver 8, B.C, Can.

GERRY, RICHARD W(OODMAN), b. Lewiston, Maine, Nov. 23, 14; m. 37; c. 3. POULTRY NUTRITION. B.S, Maine, 38; M.S, Purdue, 46, Ph.D. (animal nutrit), 48. Asst. poultry husb, Purdue, 43-48; assoc. prof, UNIV. MAINE, 48-56, PROF. POULTRY SCI, 56- Poultry Sci. Asn. Mineral and vitamin nutrition of poultry; potato products; marine products; cereal grains in poultry feed; restricted feeding and force molting of laying hens. Address: Dept. of Animal & Veterinary Sciences, Hitchner Hall, University of Maine, Orono, ME 04473.

GERSBACHER, W(ILLARD) M(ARION), b. Springerton, Ill, Mar. 25, 06; m. 38; c. 5. ZOOLOGY, ECOLOGY. Ed.B, South. Ill. State Nor. Univ, 26; M.A, Illinois, 28, Ph.D. (zool), 32. Asst. zool, Illinois, 27-29; instr. biol, South. Ill. State Nor. Univ, 29-30; prof. sci. & math. & head dept, East. N.Mex. Jr. Col, 34-35; instr. ZOOL, East. Ill. Col, 35-36; asst. prof, SOUTH. ILL. UNIV, 36-38, assoc. prof, 38-47, prof, 47-66, head dept, 38-55, EMER. PROF, 66-; PROF, SOUTHEAST MO. STATE COL, 66- AAAS; fel. Ecol. Soc. Am; Am. Soc. Limnol. & Oceanog; Am. Micros. Soc; Wildlife Soc. Ecology of plants and animals; fresh water biology; development of stream and lake communities; methods in biology teaching; nature conservancy. Address: Dept. of Biology, Southeast Missouri State College, Cape Girardeau, MO 63701.

GERSCH, HAROLD A(RTHUR), b. New York, N.Y, Jan. 8, 22; m. 47; c. 3. PHYSICS. B.S, Ga. Inst. Tech, 48; Ph.D. (physics), Hopkins, 53. Asst. prof. PHYSICS, GA. INST. TECHNOL, 54-56, assoc. prof, 56-61, PROF, 61- Vis. lectr, Hopkins, 56-57; consult, Oak Ridge Nat. Lab, 58- U.S.N, 40-46. AAAS; fel. Am. Phys. Soc. Phase transitions; statistical mechanics; quantum mechanics. Address: School of Physics, Georgia Institute of Technology, Atlanta, GA 30332.

GERSCH, WILL, b. New York, N.Y, Jan. 24, 29. ENGINEERING SCIENCE. B.E.E, City Col. New York, 50; M.S, N.Y. Univ, 56; Dr.Eng.Sc, Columbia, 61. Jr. engr, res. div, Philco Corp, Ford Motor Co, Pa, 50-51; engr, W.L. Maxson Corp, N.Y, 51-53; math. inst, N.Y. Univ, 53-56; sr. res. engr, electronic res. lab, Columbia, 56-61; Nat. Acad. Sci-Nat. Res. Coun. fel. eng, Imp. Col, London, 61-62; sr. res. engr, electronic res. lab, Columbia Univ, 62-63; assoc. prof. STOCHASTIC PROCESSES, Purdue Univ, 63-70; PROF, UNIV. HAWAII, 70- Vis. prof, dept. eng. mech, Stanford Univ, 66-67, Nat. Insts. Health spec. training & res. fel. neurol, 68-70, consult, 69. AAAS; Soc. Indust. & Appl. Math; Inst. Elec. & Electronics Eng. Analysis and modeling of stochastic processes; applications to dynamical systems; neurophysiology; electroencephalogram and electrocardiogram analysis and modeling. Address: Information Science Program, University of Hawaii, Honolulu, HI 96822.

GERSCHENSON, LAZARO E, b. Buenos Aires, Arg, Apr. 25, 36; m. 62; c. 2. MOLECULAR BIOLOGY, CANCER. M.D, Univ. Buenos Aires, 59, fel, 60-62, Ph.D. (physiol), 63. Asst. res. med, dr, inst. cardiol, Nat. Acad. Med, Arg, 62-63; fel. biochem, lab. nuclear med. & radiation biol, Univ. Calif, Los Angeles, 63-66; chief instr, biol. chem. dept, Univ. Buenos Aires, 67-68; asst. res. biochemist, lab. nuclear med. & radiation biol, UNIV. CALIF, LOS ANGELES, 69-71, ASSOC. PROF. PATH, MED. SCH. & ASSOC. RES. BIOLOGIST, LAB, NUCLEAR MED. & RADIATION BIOL, 71- Nat. Coun. Sci. Res, Arg. for. res. fel, 63-65, career res. award, 67-68. Argentine Biol. Soc; Argentine Biochem. Asn; Tissue Cult. Asn; Am. Soc. Cell Biol; Soc. Develop. Biol. Atherosclerosis; metabolism of the arterial wall; developmental biology of cells in culture; hormonal mechanism of action; cancer research. Address: Lab. of Nuclear Medicine & Radiation Biology, University of California, Los Angeles, CA 90024.

GERSH, EILEEN S(UTTON), b. Bishop's Stortford, Eng, July 8, 13; nat; m. 44; c. 2. BIOLOGY. B.A, Oxford, 34; Ph.D. (genetics), London, 39. Res. worker genetics, John Innes Hort. Inst, Eng, 35-38; asst. Drosophila cytogenetics, Carnegie Inst, 38-42; lectr. cytogenetics, McGill, 42-43; instr. biol, Hopkins 43-46; res. assoc. zool, Chicago, 54-63; ANIMAL BIOL, SCH. VET. MED, UNIV. PA, 63-68, res. asst. prof, 68-71, RES. ASSOC. PROF, 71- Vis. lectr, Swarthmore Col, 67-68. Genetics Soc. Am; Am. Soc. Nat. Cytogenetics of Drosophila. Address: Dept. of Animal Biology, University of Pennsylvania School of Veterinary Medicine, Philadelphia, PA 19104.

GERSH, ISIDORE, b. Brooklyn, N.Y, Oct. 6, 07; m. 44; c. 2. ANATOMY. B.A, Cornell, 28; Stieglitz fel, Chicago, 30-32, Ph.D. (anat), 32. From instr. to assoc. prof. anat, sch. med, Hopkins, 33-46; path, col. med, Illinois, 46-49; from assoc. prof. to prof. ANAT, Chicago, 49-64; RES. PROF, SCH. VET. MED, UNIV. PA, 63- Guggenheim fel, Karolinska Inst, Sweden, 39; prin. biologist, Naval Med. Res. Inst, Md; vis. prof, Birmingham, 52; Oslo, 56; Chile, 57; Fulbright fel, 56. U.S.N.R, 43-46, Lt. Comdr. Am. Soc. Exp. Path; Biophys. Soc; Histochem. Soc; Am. Asn. Anat; Int. Inst. Refrig. Cryobiology; histochemistry and cytochemistry for light and electron microscopes; cytology and cytochemistry of kidney, thyroid, pituitary, nerve; ground substance of connective tissues; freezing and drying; autoradiography. Address: Dept. of Anatomy, University of Pennsylvania School of Veterinary Medicine, 3800 Spruce St, Philadelphia, PA 19104.

GERSHAN, BERNARD S(AMUEL), b. New York, N.Y, June 6, 29; m. 55; c. 2. MECHANICAL ENGINEERING. B.M.E, City Col. New York, 51; Maryland, 52; George Washington, 59-65. Mech. engr, Reed Res, Inc, D.C, 51; Nat. Bur. Standards, 51-53; Chem. Corps Eng. Agency, Army Chem. Center, Md, 53-54; proj. engr, armament lab, Air Res. & Develop. Command, Wright Patterson Air Force Base, Ohio, 54-56; armament develop. lab, Air Force Armament Center, Eglin Air Force Base, Fla, 56; sr. engr, air armament div, Westinghouse Corp, Md, 56-59; mech. engr, ANAL. SERV. INC, 59-63, chief adv. anal. br, 63-64, res. & tech. br, 64-70, MGR. SUPPORT SYSTS. DIV, 70- U.S.A.F, 53-56, Capt. Am. Inst. Aeronaut. & Astronaut. Long range planning of air force research and development programs based on analysis of state-of-the-art; forecast of technical possibilities and optimum allocation of resources to provide advanced capabilities to perform future missions; engineering administration. Address: Support Systems Division, Analytic Services Inc, 5613 Leesburg Pike, Falls Church, VA 22041.

GERSHANIK, SIMON, b. Argentina, Aug. 1, 07; m. 35; c. 2. SEISMOLOGY. C.Eng, La Plata, 33; grant from La Plata, Geophys. Inst, Göttingen, 35-36. PROF. geophys, LA PLATA ASTRON. OBSERV, 36-46, SEISMOL, 47-, HEAD DEPT, 44-, ACTING DIR, 64-, PROF. ENG, LA PLATA NAT. UNIV, 71- Mem. comt. seismol, Pan Am. Union Geog. & Hist, 50, comt. solid earth, 71-; pres, Arg. Upper Mantle Comt. Arg. Army. Int. Asn. Seismol. & Physics Earth's Interior; Arg. Asn. Geophys. & Geod. (first pres, 60-62, pres, 62-66); Latin Am. Asn. Seismol. & Earthquake Eng. Geomagnetism; gravimetry; earthquake engineering; seismic loads on buildings; seismographs; seismic rays; focus determination. Address: Observatorio Astronomico, La Plata, Argentina.

GERSHBEIN, LEON L(EE), b. Chicago, Ill, Dec. 22, 17. ORGANIC CHEMISTRY, BIOCHEMISTRY. S.B, Chicago, 38, M.S, 39; Off. Sci. Res. & Develop. fel, Northwestern, 42-43, Pittsburgh Plate Glass Co. fel. & Ph.D. (chem), 44. Res. assoc. org. chem, Northwestern, 45-47; asst. prof. biochem, col. med, Illinois, 47-53; assoc. prof, Ill. Inst. Technol, 53-59; DIR, NORTHWEST INST. MED. RES, 58- Adj. prof, Ill. Inst. Technol, 59- AAAS; Am. Chem. Soc; N.Y. Acad. Sci; fel. Am. Inst. Chem; Soc. Exp. Biol. & Med; Soc. Cosmetic Chem; Soc. Appl. Spectros; Am. Inst. Physics; Am. Oil Chem. Soc; Am. Fedn. Clin. Res; Am. Med. Writers Asn; Am. Asn. Clin. Chem; Am. Asn. Cancer Res. Chemistry of natural products; biochemical pharmacology; sulfur compounds; endocrine metabolism; growth promotors and deccelerators; liver regeneration; electron transfer systems; tumorigenesis; lipid metabolism; sebaceous glandular secretions. Address: Northwest Institute for Medical Research, 5656 W. Addison, Chicago, IL 60634.

GERSHBERG, HERBERT, b. New York, N.Y, Dec. 1, 17; m. 47. INTERNAL MEDICINE. B.S, City Col. New York, 37; M.S, Maryland, 37; M.D, Med. Col. Va, 41. Fel. physiol. chem, sch. med, Yale, 46-48; internal med, COL. MED, N.Y. UNIV. MED. CTR, 48-50, instr, 50-54, asst. prof. MED, 54-65, ASSOC. PROF, 65- Dir. diabetes & endocrine clins, Bellevue Hosp, 61-, assoc. attend, 65-; Univ. Hosps, 65- U.S.A, 42-46, Maj. Soc. Exp. Biol. & Med; Endocrine Soc; Am. Physiol. Soc. Metabolism, nutrition and endocrinology; pituitary, adrenal cortex and renal function; diabetes; growth hormone. Address: New York University Medical Center, 560 First Ave, New York, NY 10016.

GERSHENFELD, L(OUIS), b. Phila, Pa, Dec. 25, 95; m; c. 2. BACTERIOLOGY, HYGIENE. Pharm.D, Phila. Col. Pharm, 15, Clayton fel, 16, B.S, 17, Pharm.M, 20, Sc.D, 40; Jefferson Med. Col, 16-18; Pennsylvania, 19. Asst. prof. bact. & hyg, PHILA. COL. PHARM, 17-18, acting prof, 19-20, prof, 20-68, dir. bact. & clin. chem. labs, 17-68, HON. CHMN. FACULTY COUN, 68-, EMER. PROF. BACT. & EMER. DIR. DEPT, 68- Dir. labs, dept. med. & sanit, Emergency Fleet Corp. Hog Island, 17-18; bacteriologist, intel. dept, U.S. Army & Food Admin, 17-19; dir. Gershenfeld Lab, 19-68; sci. consult, Upper Darby Health Dept, 30-66; chmn. lab. reagent comn, Nat. Formulary VII, 34; comn. bact. & immunol, Nat. Coun. Pharmaceut. Res, 34; past secy, Dropsie Univ, mem. bd, v.pres; mem. sterile adv. bd, U.S. Pharmacopoeia XII, XIII & XIV. AAAS; Am. Soc. Microbiol; Am. Chem. Soc; Am. Pharmaceut. Asn; Am. Pub. Health Asn; Biol. Stain Comn. (secy, 44-45); N.Y. Acad. Sci. Phenol coefficient tests; disinfectants; insecticides; snake venom; sterilization of medicaments; parenteral solutions; clinical chemistry; sanitation; air and atmospheric conditions; surfaceacting agents; urine and urinalysis; iodine; biological products; hematology; historical and sanitary science; emergency disinfection. Address: 1101 N. 63rd St, Philadelphia, PA 19151.

GERSHENOWITZ, HARRY, N.Y.C, Mar. 27, 26. HISTORY & PHILOSOPHY OF SCIENCE. B.S, St. John's Univ. (N.Y), 48; B.A, L.I. Univ, 54, M.S, 57; E.D.D. (sci. educ), Columbia Univ, 67. Instr. biol, Panzer Col, 55-58; sci, Fairleigh Dickinson Univ, 58-62; asst. prof. biol, Wilkes Col, 62-65; PROF. SCI, GLASSBORO STATE COL, 65- Am. Technion Soc; Nat. Sci. Teachers Asn; Am. Inst. Aeronaut. & Astronaut; Nat. Hist. Soc; Am. Bd. Dipl. Pharm. The Darwinian Age. Address: Dept. of Life Sciences, Glassboro State College, Glassboro, NJ 08028.

GERSHENSON, HILLEL H(ALKIN), b. New York, N.Y, Mar. 27, 35; m. 62; c. 3. MATHEMATICS. B.A, Wisconsin, 55; Nat. Sci. Found. fel, Harvard, 55-56; Alumni Res. Found. fel. & M.A, Wisconsin, 57; Ph.D. (math), Chicago, 61. Instr. MATH, Princeton, 61-63; asst. prof, Cornell Univ, 63-68; ASSOC. PROF, UNIV. MINN, MINNEAPOLIS, 68- Vis. lectr, Aarhus Univ, 66-67. Am. Math. Soc. Algebraic topology; homological algebra. Address: School of Mathematics, University of Minnesota, Minneapolis, MN 55455.

GERSHENZON, M(URRAY), b. Brooklyn, N.Y, Nov. 17, 28; m. 52; c. 3; SOLID STATE ELECTRONICS. B.S, City Col, 49; A.M, Columbia, 53, Ph.D. (chem), 57. Mem. tech. staff, solid state physics, Bell Tel. Labs, N.J, 57-66; PROF. MAT. SCI. & ELEC. ENG, UNIV. SOUTH. CALIF, 66- U.S.A, 53-55. Am. Phys. Soc; Int. Elec. & Electronics Eng; Electrochem. Soc. Radiative recombination in semiconductors. Address: Dept. of Materials Science, University of Southern California, University Park, Los Angeles, CA 90007.

GERSHFELD, NORMAN L(EONARD), b. Bronx, N.Y, June 27, 28; m. 53; c. 4. PHYSICAL CHEMISTRY. A.B, Hofstra Col, 49; M.S, Polytech. Inst. Brooklyn, 52; Ph.D. (chem), Rutgers, 55. Asst, Rutgers, 52-54; chemist, Shell Develop. Co, 54-55; sr. asst. scientist, NAT. INSTS. HEALTH, 55-59,

CHEMIST, NAT. INST. ARTHRITIS & METAB. DISEASES, 59- Am. Chem. Soc. Solution properties of polyelectrolytes; electrochemistry of synthetic and biological membranes; surface chemistry. Address: 9411 Elsmere Ct, Bethesda, MD 20014.

GERSHINOWITZ, HAROLD, b. New York, N.Y. Aug. 31, 10; m. 35; PHYSICAL CHEMISTRY. B.S, City Col, 31; A.M, Harvard, 32, Ph.D.(chem), 34. Parker traveling fel. from Harvard to Princeton, 34-35; res. assoc. chem, Columbia, 35-36; Harvard, 36-38; petrol. technologist, Shell Oil Co. Inc, Mo, 38-39, dir. res. lab, Houston, 39-42, dir. mfg. res. east of Rockies, 42-45, dir. explor. & prod. res. div, 45-51, v.pres. explor. & prod. tech. div, 51-53, pres, Shell Develop. Co, 53-62, chmn. res. coun. & res. coord, Royal Dutch/Shell, 62-65; INDEPENDENT CONSULT, 66- Consult, Orgn. Econ. Coop. & Develop, Paris, 66-70; chmn. environ. studies bd, Nat. Acad. Sci-Nat. Acad. Eng, 67-70; affiliate, Rockefeller Univ, 67-; dir. Bataafse Petrol. Maatschappij N.V; Shell Int. Res. Maatschappij N.V, Shell Res, Ltd. & Shell Res. N.V. Fel. AAAS; Am. Chem. Soc. Economics and administration of research; reaction kinetics from standpoint of quantum and statistical mechanics. Address: 25 Sutton Pl. S, New York, NY 10022.

GERSHMAN, HOWARD, b. Phila, Pa, Apr. 2, 43; m. 68; c. 1. DEVELOPMENTAL BIOLOGY, BIOCHEMISTRY. B.A, Temple, 64; Princeton, 66-68; Ph.D. (develop. biol), Hopkins, 68. Nat. Insts. Health fel. BIOCHEM, BRANDEIS UNIV, 68-71, RES. ASSOC, 71- Am. Soc. Zool. Cell adhesion; the cell surface as related to morphogenesis; biochemistry of B_{12}-coenzyme metabolism; kinetics of alcohol dehydrogenase. Address: Dept. of Graduate Biochemistry, Brandeis University, Waltham, MA 02154.

GERSHMAN, LOUIS L(EO), b. Nov. 5, 20; U.S. citizen; m. 48; c. 1. ANALYTICAL CHEMISTRY. B.S, City Col. New York, 41; M.S, Polytech. Inst. Brooklyn, 57. Chemist, U.S. FOOD & DRUG ADMIN, 48-58, supv. chemist, 60-66, LAB. DIR, 67- U.S.A.F, 42-47, Res, 47-, Lt. Col. Am. Chem. Soc; Asn. Off. Anal. Chem. Infrared determination of endrin residues. Address: U.S. Food & Drug Administration, 585 Commercial St, Boston, MA 02109.

GERSHMAN, MELVIN, b. Hartford, Conn, Aug. 24, 27; m. 50; c. 2. BACTERIOLOGY. B.Sc, Ohio State, 54; M.Sc, Massachusetts, 57. Instr. BACT, Smith Col, 56-57; Springfield Hosp. Nursing Sch, Mass, 57; asst. prof, UNIV. MAINE, 58-63, ASSOC. PROF, 63- U.S.A, 45-49. Am. Soc. Microbiol. Diagnostic bacteriology; enteric diseases. Address: Dept. of Microbiology, Hitchner Hall, University of Maine, Orono, ME 04473.

GERSHO, A(LLEN), b. Que, Can, Jan. 18, 40; m. 60; c. 1. ELECTRICAL ENGINEERING. S.B, Mass. Inst. Tech, 60; univ. & Gen. Dynamics/Electronics fels. & M.S, Cornell, 61, Ph.D.(elec. eng), 63. MEM. TECH. STAFF, BELL TEL. LABS, 63- Inst. Elec. & Electronics Eng. Characterization of time-varying linear systems; nonlinear filters; general system theory; statistical communication theory; adaptive signal processing. Address: Bell Telephone Labs, Mountain Ave, Murray Hill, NJ 07974.

GERSHOFF, STANLEY N(ORTON), b. New York, N.Y, Apr. 26, 24. BIOCHEMISTRY. B.A, Wisconsin, 43, M.Sc, 48, Ph.D.(biochem), 51. Proj. assoc. biochem, Wisconsin, 51-52; res. assoc. NUTRIT, SCH. PUB. HEALTH, HARVARD, 52-56, asst. prof. 56-64, ASSOC. PROF, 65- Consult, U.S. Pub. Health Serv, 60- Mem. subcomt. lab. animals, comt. animal nutrit, Nat. Res. Coun, 54. U.S.A, 43-46. Relationship of nutrition to kidney stone formation; endocrine metabolism and immune response; interrelationships of nutrients; nutritional requirements of cats; comparative nutrition; nutrient fortification of rice in Thailand; nutritional status of Americans. Address: Dept. of Nutrition, Harvard School of Public Health, Boston, MA 02115.

GERSHON, HERMAN, b. Brooklyn, N.Y, Jan. 27, 21; m. 55; c. 2. BIOCHEMISTRY. B.A, Brooklyn Col, 42; M.S, Fordham, 47; fel, Colorado, 47-50, Ph.D.(biochem), 50. Chemist, Food Res. Labs, Inc, 42-43; Dr. R.J. Block Lab, 46-47; biochemist, Vet. Admin. Hosp, Northport, N.Y, 50-51; dir. res. & develop, pharmaceut. & fine chem, United Org. Corp, 51-55; biochem. res, Pfister Chem. Works, Inc, 55-62; SR. ORG. CHEMIST, BOYCE THOMPSON INST. PLANT RES, INC, 62- U.S.A, 43-45. AAAS; Am. Chem. Soc; N.Y. Acad. Sci; Am. Soc. Microbiol; Am. Inst. Chem. Amino acid antagonists; synthesis of pyrimidines, quinolines, and fluorinated metabolite analogues; mode of action of antifungal agents. Address: 98 De Haven Dr, Yonkers, NY 10703.

GERSHON, RICHARD K, b. Brooklyn, N.Y, Dec. 24, 32. PATHOLOGY, IMMUNOLOGY. A.B, Harvard, 54; M.D, Yale, 59. Fel, sch. med, Yale, 59-60, intern path, 60-61; acting chief virol, U.S. Army Med. Gen. Lab. 406-Japan, 62-63; asst. residence PATH, SCH. MED, YALE, 63-64, instr, 64-66, asst. prof, 66-70, ASSOC. PROF, 70- Nat. Cancer Inst. spec. fel, 66-69, career develop. award, 69-; vis. prof, Chester Beatty Res. Inst, London, Eng, 67-68. AAAS; Transplantation Soc; Am. Soc. Exp. Path; Brit. Soc. Immunol; Am. Asn. Immunol. Immune response to tumor grafts; cellular basis of the immune response, especially thymus derived lymphocytes. Address: 310 Cedar St, New Haven, CT 06510.

GERSHON, S(OL) D, b. Chicago, Ill, Oct. 18, 10; m. 34; c. 2. CHEMISTRY. B.S, Chicago, 34, M.S, 35, Ph.D.(chem), 38. Asst. chem, col. pharm, Illinois, 30-38, instr, 38-41, assoc, 41-42, asst. prof, 42-43; res. chemist, Pepsodent Co, 43-47, dir. new prods. develop, Pepsodent div, LEVER BROS. CO, 47-48, res. mgr, 49-52, asst. dir. res, prod. improv. & develop, 52-60, develop. mgr. household prod, 60-63, assoc. res. dir, 63-65, asst. dir. develop, 65-68, TECH. PLANNING DIR, EDGEWATER, 68- Am. Chem. Soc; Am. Oil Chemists' Soc; Soc. Cosmetic Chem(v.pres, 51, pres, 52, medal award); Am. Pharmaceut. Asn; Int. Asn. Dent. Res. Chemotherapy; synthesis of organic medicinals; drug assay; carbohydrates; cosmetic, dentifrice, detergent and edible product development. Address: 1363 Mercedes St, Teaneck, NJ 07666.

GERSHOWITZ, HENRY, b. N.Y.C, Sept. 22, 24; m. 49; c. 4. GENETICS. B.A, Brooklyn Col, 49; U.S. Pub. Health Serv. fel, Calif. Inst. Tech, 52, Ph.D. (genetics), 54. Res. fel. immunogenetics, Wisconsin, 54-56; res. assoc. HUMAN GENETICS, UNIV. MICH-ANN ARBOR, 57-61, asst. prof, 61-67, assoc. prof, 67-70, PROF, 70- Consult, blood bank, Univ. Hosp, Michigan, 57- Ord. Dept, U.S.A, 43-46. AAAS; Am. Soc. Human Genetics; Am. Asn. Immunol. Blood group inheritance and correlations; genetic control of immunoglobulin structure and antibody specificity. Address: Dept. of Human Genetics, University of Michigan, Ann Arbor, MI 48104.

GERSHUN, THEODORE LEONARD, b. Council Bluff, Iowa, Feb. 19, 24; m. 48; c. 3. MECHANICAL ENGINEERING. B.S, Iowa, 48, Standard Oil Co.(Ind) fel, 50-52; M.S, Washington (Seattle), 50; Ph.D.(mech. eng), Minnesota, 55. Instr. mech. eng, Washington (Seattle), 48-50; Minnesota, 52-55; assoc. prof, Southern California, 55-57; proj. engr, nuclear reactor safety prog, Atomics Int. Div, N.Am. Aviation, Inc, 57-60; supvr. tech. staff gas turbine res, indust. prod. div, Boeing Airplane Co, 60-61; STAFF SCIENTIST, SPACE & INFO. SYSTS. DIV, N.AM. ROCKWELL CORP, INC, DOWNEY, 61- Consult, Thompson-Ramo-Wooldridge Corp, Calif, 56-57; lectr, Univ. South. Calif, 65. U.S.A.A.F, 43-46, Res, 46-53, 2nd Lt. Am. Soc. Mech. Eng; Am. Soc. Eng. Educ; Soc. Automotive Eng; Am. Nuclear Soc. Heat transfer and fluid flow; thermodynamics; combustion. Address: 5081 Somerset St, Buena Park, CA 90620.

GERSON, M(ELVIN) M, b. Detroit, Mich, June 7, 17; m. 56; c. 1. ORGANIC CHEMISTRY. B.S, Wayne State, 40. Chemist, Ditzler Color Co, 41-50; res. chemist, Ford Motor Co, 50-53, mgr. qual. control & develop, paint & chem. prod, 53-57; tech. serv. mgr, pigment div, Sandoz, Inc, 57-65; V.PRES, PODELL INDUSTS, INC, 65- Spec. lectr, col. eng, Wayne State, 52-54; consult, Wayne Eng. Res. Inst, 52-55. U.S.N.R, 43-46, Lt.(jg). Am. Chem. Soc; Soc. Plastics Eng; Fedn. Socs. Paint Technol; Inter-Soc. Color Coun. Organic coatings; vinyl plastics; pigmentation of organic coatings, inks and plastics. Address: 13-63 Abbott Rd, Fairlawn, NJ 07410.

GERSON, NATHANIEL C(HARLES), b. Boston, Mass, Oct. 15, 15; m. 46; c. 5. PHYSICS. B.S, Puerto Rico, 44; M.S, N.Y. Univ, 47. Asst. chief tech. invest. sect, U.S. Weather Bur, 44-46; asst. propagation, low frequency loran system, Watson Labs, U.S. Air Force, 46-48; chief ionospheric physics lab, U.S. Air Force Cambridge Res. Ctr, 48-56; CONSULT. PHYSICIST, PHYS. RES. ASSOCS, 57- Secy, U.S. Nat. Comt, Int. Geophys. Year, 53-57; consult, Lincoln Lab, Mass. Inst. Tech, 58; Adv. Res. Projs. Agency, Wash, 62-; res, Syracuse Univ, 66-68; Mitre Corp, Bedford, 68. AAAS; Sci. Res. Soc. Am; Am. Meteorol. Soc; Arctic Inst. N.Am; Am. Geophys. Union; Can. Asn. Physicists. Upper atmospheric physics; radio wave propagation; ionospheric physics. Address: Trapelo Rd, R.F.D. 3, Lincoln, MA 01773.

GERSON, RAYMOND E, b. N.Y.C, Feb. 9, 45. ENVIRONMENTAL & BIOMEDICAL ENGINEERING. B.S, Lehigh Univ, 66; NASA fel, Mass. Inst. Technol, 68-69, Ph.D.(chem. eng), 70. PROG. ANALYST, ENVIRON. PROTECTION ADMIN, N.Y.C, 70- Chem. award, Am. Inst. Chem, 66. Am. Chem. Soc. Synthesis of non-trombogenic dialysis membrane for use in artificial kidney; new technologies for urban solid waste disposal. Address: 39 Gramercy Park N, New York, NY 10010.

GERSON, ROBERT, b. New York, N.Y, Dec. 5, 23; m. 48; c. 3. PHYSICS. B.Ch.E, City Col. New York, 43; Ph.D.(phycics), N.Y. Univ, 54. Asst, N.Y. Univ, 51-52; physicist, Erie Resistor Corp, Pa, 53-56; sr. physicist, Clevite Res. Ctr, Ohio, 56-62; PROF. PHYSICS, UNIV. MO-ROLLA, 62- U.S.A, 43-46. Am. Phys. Soc. Dielectric and semiconducting materials; ferroelectricity; ferroelectric-ferromagnetic interaction; electrets; Mossbauer effect. Address: Dept. of Physics, University of Missouri-Rolla, Rolla, MO 65401.

GERSPER, PAUL LOGAN, b. Columbus, Ohio, Oct. 12, 36; m. 56; c. 4. SOIL MORPHOLOGY & MINERALOGY. B.Sc, Ohio State, 61, M.Sc, 63, Ph.D. (soil sci), 68. Res. assoc. SOIL SCI, Ohio State, 61-68; ASST. PROF, UNIV. CALIF, BERKELEY, 68- Eng.C, U.S.A, 54-57. Am. Soc. Agron; Soil Sci. Soc. Am; Am. Polar Soc; Ecol. Soc. Am; Soil morphology, development and classification; interactions of soil forming factors and their effects on soil development; distributions of radioactive fallout on landscapes; ecosystem studies. Address: Dept. of Soils & Plant Nutrition, University of California, Berkeley, CA 94720.

GERST, IRVING, b. New York, N.Y, May 30, 12; m. 37; c. 2. MATHEMATICS. B.S, City Col. New York, 31; M.A, Columbia, 32, Ph.D.(math), 47. Teacher, Bd. Ed, N.Y, 38-42; instr, U.S. Air Force Tech. Sch, Keesler Field, Miss, 42-44; tech. consult, Transportation Corps, U.S. Army Serv. Forces, N.Y, 44-46; mathematician & head appl. analysis group, Control Instrument Co. Div, Burroughs Corp, 46-58; sr. proj. mem. & leader, networks group, Radio Corp. Am, 58-61; PROF. APPL. MATH, STATE UNIV. N.Y. STONY BROOK, 61- Lectr, City Univ. New York, 58-61; consult, Sperry-Rand, Inc, 61-63. Am. Math. Soc; Math. Asn. Am. Network theory; complex variable; functional equations; operational methods; number theory. Address: Dept. of Applied Mathematics & Statistics, State University of New York at Stony Brook, Stony Brook, NY 11790.

GERST, PAUL HOWARD, b. Sept. 24, 27; U.S. Citizen; m. 57; c. 3. SURGERY, PHYSIOLOGY. A.B, Columbia, 48, M.D, 52. Instr. physiol, Pennsylvania, 55-56; instr. SURG, COL. PHYSICIANS & SURGEONS, COLUMBIA UNIV, 62-64, ASST. PROF, 64-; DIR. SURG, BRONX-LEBANON HOSP. CTR, 64- U.S. Pub. Health Serv. res. fel, 55-56 & res. career develop. award, 63-64; Am. Col. Surgeons award, 60-63. Med.C, 53-55, 1st Lt. Am. Physiol. Soc; Biophys. Soc; Am. Col. Chest Physicians. Thoracic and cardiovascular diseases. Address: Bronx-Lebanon Hospital Center, 1276 Fulton Ave, New York, NY 10456.

GERSTEIN, BERNARD C(LEMENCE), b. Monticello, N.Y, Oct. 18, 32; m. 58; c. 4. PHYSICAL CHEMISTRY. B.S, Purdue, 53; Ph.D.(phys. chem), Iowa State, 60. Res. assoc. phys. chem, IOWA STATE UNIV, 60-61, asst. prof. CHEM, 61-67, ASSOC. PROF, 67- Chem.C, 53-65,1st Lt. AAAS; Am. Chem. Soc; Am. Phys. Soc. Chemical binding and magnetism via heat capacity, magnetic susceptibility, and magnetic resonance studies. Address: Dept. of Chemistry, 229 Research, Iowa State University, Box 14A, Station A, Ames, IA 50010.

GERSTEIN, GEORGE L(EONARD), b. Berlin, Ger, Apr. 12, 33; m. 59; c. 1. NEUROPHYSIOLOGY. B.A, Harvard, 52, M.A, 54, Ph.D.(physics), 58. Nat.

Insts. Health fel. biophys, Mass. Inst. Tech, 58-60, instr. physics, 60-61, res. assoc. commun. sci, 61-63; mem. staff, ctr comput. tech, 63-64; asst. prof. biophys, UNIV. PA, 64-66, assoc. prof. BIOPHYS. & PHYSIOL, 66-69, PROF, 69- Mem. neurol. A study sect, Nat. Insts. Health, 67-71. AAAS; Am. Phys. Soc; Biophys. Soc. Electrical activity of the nervous system; auditory system; mathematical analysis and computer simulation in neurophysiology. Address: Dept. of Biophysics & Physiology, University of Pennsylvania, Philadelphia, PA 19104.

GERSTEIN, IRA S(TEPHEN), b. N.Y.C, Feb. 24, 37. THEORETICAL PHYSICS. B.S, Mass. Inst. Technol, 58, Ph.D.(physics), 63. Res. assoc. PHYSICS, Univ. Pa, 63-65, asst. prof, 65-66; MASS. INST. TECHNOL, 66-69, ASSOC. PROF, 69- Am. Phys. Soc. Theory of elementary particles. Address: Dept. of Physics, Massachusetts Institute of Technology, Cambridge, MA 02139.

GERSTEIN, LARRY J, b. Leavenworth, Kans, Aug. 28, 40; m. 69. MATHEMATICS. A.B, Columbia Col, 62; M.S, Notre Dame, 63, Ph.D.(math), 67. ASST. PROF. MATH, UNIV. CALIF, SANTA BARBARA, 67- Univ. Calif. summer faculty fel, 68; vis. asst. prof, Mass. Inst. Technol, 70-71. Am. Math. Soc; Math. Asn. Am. Algebraic number theory; quadratic and hermitian forms. Address: Dept. of Mathematics, University of California, Santa Barbara, CA 93106.

GERSTEIN, MELVIN, b. Chicago, Ill, May 8, 22; m. 44; c. 1. CHEMISTRY. B.S, Chicago, 42, Ph.D.(chem), 45. Asst. instr, army specialized training prog, Chicago, 42-44, jr. chemist, metall. proj, 44, res. assoc, 44-46; chemist, NASA, 46-49, head combustion fundamentals sect, 49-54, chief chem. br, 54-57, asst. chief propulsion chem. div, 57-59; chief phys. sci. div, jet propulsion lab, Calif. Inst. Tech, 59-60; v.pres, Dynamic Sci. Corp, 60-64, pres, 64-66; PROF. MECH. ENG. & CHMN. DEPT. UNIV. SOUTH. CALIF, 66-, ASSOC. DEAN COL. ENG, 70- Lectr, Fenn Col, 48-49; sr. lectr, Calif. Inst. Tech, 62-; v.pres. res. & develop, Ginter Corp, 69- Ed, Isotopics, 55-58. Sci. rep, adv. group aeronaut. res. & develop, NATO, Rome, 52, Cambridge, 53, mem. combustion panel, 54-57, combustion & propulsion panel, 57-64. Outstanding achievement award, Cleveland Tech. Socs. Coun, 57. U.S.N, 45-46. Fel. Am. Chem. Soc; Am. Inst. Aeronaut. & Astronaut. Chemistry of fuels and propellants; hydride chemistry; acid-base theory; combustion theory and applications; propulsion. Address: 1661 E. Mendocino St, Altadena, CA 91001.

GERSTEL, D(AN) U(LRICH), b. Berlin-Dahlem, Ger, Oct. 23, 15; nat; m. 38; c. 2. GENETICS. A.B, California, 40, M.S, 42, Ph.D.(genetics), 45. Asst. bot, California, 42-44, assoc. genetics, 44-46; assoc. geneticist, res. inst, Stanford, 47; natural rubber plant res. sta, U.S. Dept. Agr, 47-49; res. fel, Calif. Inst. Tech, 49-50; asst. prof. agron, N.C. STATE UNIV, 50-53, assoc. prof, 53-56, prof. field crops, 56-63, REYNOLDS PROF. CROP SCI, 64- Vis. prof, Weizmann Inst, 61-62. Am. Soc. Nat; Genetics Soc. Am; Bot. Soc. Am; Soc. Study Evolution; Am. Genetic Asn. Cytogenetics and speciation of Nicotiana, Gossypium and Parthenium; interspecific hybridization and genetic instability; origin and breeding of cultivated crops. Address: Dept. of Crop Science, North Carolina State University, Raleigh, NC 27607.

GERSTELL, RICHARD, b. Ardmore, Pa, July 30, 10; m. 36; c. 2. ECOLOGY. A.B, Dartmouth Col, 33; Cramer fel. & univ. fel, Michigan, 38-39, Ph.D. (forestry), 42. Chief div. res, State Game Comn, Pa, 33-42; contractor, U.S. Navy, 46; dir. slaes res, Animal Trap Co. Am, 47-48; radiol. defense consult, off. Secy. Defense, Wash, D.C, 48-49; atomic & biol. warfare consult, Nat. Security Resources Bd. & Fed. Civil Defense Admin, 49-50; DIR. CIVIL DEFENSE, COMMONWEALTH OF PA, 51- U.S.N, 42-46, Lt. Comdr. Am. Soc. Mammal; Wildlife Soc.(pres, 41); Am. Ornith. Union. Animal ecology with particular reference to effects of environmental factors on physiology; radiological aspects of atomic warfare. Address: 1046 Buchanan Ave, Lancaster, PA 17603.

GERSTEN, JEROME W(ILLIAM), b. New York, N.Y, Apr. 20, 17; m. 41; c. 5. PHYSIOLOGY. B.S, City Col, 35; M.D, N.Y. Univ, 39; Baruch fel, Mass. Inst. Tech, 46; Columbia, 46-47; M.S, Minnesota, 49. Asst, Mayo Clin, 47-49; asst. prof. PHYS. MED. & REHAB, SCH. MED, UNIV. COLO, DENVER, 49-51, assoc. prof, 51-57, PROF. & HEAD DEPT, 57- U.S.A, 41-46. AAAS; Am. Physiol. Soc; Soc. Exp. Biol. & Med; Am. Asn. Electromyog. & Electrodiag; Am. Cong. Rehab. Med.(pres, 69), Am. Inst. Ultrasonics in Med. Muscle physiology; ultrasound. Address: University of Colorado School of Medicine, 4200 E. Ninth Ave, Denver, CO 80220.

GERSTEN, JOEL IRWIN, b. New York, N.Y, Mar. 18, 42; m. 64; c. 2. THEORETICAL PHYSICS. B.S, City Col. New York, 62; M.A, Columbia, 63, Ph.D.(physics), 68. Mem. tech. staff PHYSICS, Bell Tel. Labs, 68-70; ASST. PROF, CITY COL. N.Y, 70- Consult, Bell Tel. Labs, 70- Am. Phys. Soc. Theoretic atomic physics; radiation processes; low energy electron diffraction; nonlinear optical processes; solid state physics. Address: Dept. of Physics, City College of New York, New York, NY 10031.

GERSTEN, STEPHEN M, b. Utica, N.Y, Dec. 2, 40. TOPOLOGY, ALGEBRA. A.B, Princeton, 61; Ph.D.(math), Cambridge, 65. Instr. MATH, Princeton, 63-64; Rice, 64-65; Nat. Sci. Found. fel, Oxford, 65-66; asst. prof, RICE UNIV, 66-69, ASSOC. PROF, 69- Am. Math. Soc. Algebraic topology; homological algebra; projective class groups and Whitehead groups of algebras and geometric applications. Address: Dept. of Mathematics, Rice University, Houston, TX 77001.

GERSTENBERG, DIETER, b. Essen, Ger, Apr. 17, 29; U.S. citizen; m. 58. SOLID STATE PHYSICS. Dipl. physics, Marburg, 56, Ph.D.(physics), 58. Res. assoc. metal physics, Marburg, 58-59; mem. staff THIN FILM TECHNOL, BELL TEL. LABS, 59-66, SUPVR, 66- Electrochem. Soc; Am. Vacuum Soc. Magnetic properties of palladium and palladium alloys with other transition metals; thin film technology; physical and structural properties of sputtered metal and dielectric films; thin film component development. Address: Bell Telephone Labs, 555 Union Blvd, Allentown, PA 18100.

GERSTENHABER, MURRAY, b. Brooklyn, N.Y, May 6, 27; m. 56; c. 3. MATHEMATICS. B.S, Yale, 48; M.S, Chicago, 49, Ph.D.(math), 51. Asst. Cowles Comn. Res. Econ, 49; Jewett fel, 51-53; asst. prof. MATH, UNIV. PA, 53-58, assoc. prof, 58-61, PROF, 61- Mem, Inst. Adv. Study, 57-59, 62, 65-66; Nat. Sci. Found. sr. fel, 58-60; mem. staff, Inst. Defense Anal, 61-62. U.S.A, 45-47. Am. Math. Soc.(ed, Bull, 65-); Math. Asn. Am; Soc. Indust. & Appl. Math. Algebra; algebraic geometry. Address: 237 Hamilton Rd, Menon Station, PA 19066.

GERSTL, BRUNO, b. Neunkirchen, Austria, Apr. 12, 01; nat; m. 35; c. 1. PATHOLOGY. M.D, Vienna, 27. Res. fel. path, sch. med, Yale, 39-40, asst. & instr, 40-44; dir, Cent. Lab, Path. & Res, Conn, 44-47; asst. clin. prof. PATH, SCH. MED, STANFORD UNIV, 47-61, assoc. prof, 61-, EMER. PROF, 66-; CHIEF LAB. SERV, VET. ADMIN. HOSP, 61-, Oakland, 47-61. Consult, State Dept. Pub. Health, Calif. Am. Thoracic Soc; Am. Fedn. Clin. Res; Am. Acad. Neurol. Pulmonary tuberculosis and immunology of granulomatous diseases; pathogenesis and lipid chemistry of multiple sclerosis. Address: Lab. Services, Veterans Administration Hospital, 3801 Miranda Ave, Palo Alto, CA 94304.

GERSTLE, KURT H, b. Munich, Ger, Nov. 11, 23; U.S. citizen; m. 51; c. 4. STRUCTURAL ENGINEERING. B.S, California, Berkeley, 49, M.S, 52; Swiss Fed. Inst. Tech, 49-50; Ph.D.(civil eng), Colorado, 56. From instr. to PROF. CIVIL ENG, UNIV. COLO, BOULDER, 52- Nat. Sci. Found. sci. faculty fel, Brown, 59-60; vis. prof. struct. eng, SEATO Grad. Sch. Eng, Thailand, 63-64; Nat. Sci. Found. consult, Adv. Eng. Summer Inst, India, 68, 69; Fulbright lectr, Munich Tech. Univ, 70-71. U.S.A, 43-46. Am. Soc. Civil Eng; Am. Concrete Inst.(Wason Medal, 64). Elastic and inelastic analysis and behavior of structures; behavior of reinforced concrete structures. Address: 3650 Fourth St, Boulder, CO 80302.

GERSTNER, ROBERT, b. New York, N.Y, Nov. 7, 06; m. 40. ANATOMY, TISSUE CULTURE. A.B, N.Y. Univ, 46, fel, 46-54, M.S, 48, fel. & Ph.D, 53. Instr. ANAT, N.Y. UNIV, 54-57, asst. prof, 57-60, assoc. prof, 60-67, PROF, 67- Res. assoc. Guggenheim Found. Inst. Dent. Res, 55- Am. Asn. Anat; Tissue Cult. Asn; fel. Royal Micros. Soc. Endocrinology; hormonal and glandular physiology; hemopoiesis; effects of cold and freezing on cells, organs and tissues; fetal organ development; tissue culture. Address: Tissue & Organ Culture Lab, New York University, 339 E. 25th St, New York, NY 10010.

GERSTNER, ROBERT W(ILLIAM), b. Chicago, Ill, Nov. 10, 34; m. 58; c. 2. STRUCTURAL ENGINEERING. B.S, Northwestern, 56, M.S, 57, Ph.D.(civil eng), 60. Asst. prof. STRUCT. MECH, UNIV. ILL, 60-63, assoc. prof, 63-69, PROF, 69- Nat. Sci. Found. Res. grant, 64-66. AAAS; Am. Soc. Civil Eng; Am. Concrete Inst; Am. Soc. Eng. Educ. Interface adjustment techniques and numerical methods in solution of problems in structural mechanics and elasticity; stress distributions in layered and sandwich systems. Address: Dept. of Architecture, University of Illinois, Chicago, IL 60680.

GERTEIS, ROBERT L(OUIS), b. San Diego, Calif, Sept. 1, 36; m. 62; c. 2. INORGANIC CHEMISTRY. B.S, Wichita, 58; M.S, Illinois, 61, Ph.D.(inorg. chem), 63. Res. chemist, Esso Res. & Eng. Co, 63-68; RES. SCIENTIST; N.J. ZINC CO, PALMERTON, 68- Am. Chem. Soc. Physical chemistry of lithium alkyls; titanium dioxide and zinc oxide pigments. Address: 121 Penn Hills Dr, Schnecksville, PA 18078.

GERTEISEN, THOMAS J(ACOB), b. Owensboro, Ky, Oct. 21, 43. ORGANIC CHEMISTRY. B.A, Brescia Col, 66; Ph.D.(chem), Univ. Tenn, Knoxville, 70. ASST. PROF. CHEM, BRESCIA COL, 70- Am. Chem. Soc. Physical properties of fused ring organic compounds; instrumental analysis—infrared hydrogen-bonding studies, mass spectroscopy, nuclear magnetic resonance. Address: Dept. of Chemistry, Brescia College, Owensboro, KY 42301.

GERTJEJANSEN, ROLAND O, b. Vesta, Minn, May 7, 36; m. 57; c. 3. WOOD SCIENCE & TECHNOLOGY. B.S, Minnesota, 61, M.S, 62, Ph.D.(pulp & paper), 66. Technologist, U.S. Forest Prod. Lab, 62-63; instr. WOOD SCI. & TECH, COL. FORESTRY, UNIV. MINN, ST. PAUL, 63-66, asst. prof, 66-70, ASSOC. PROF, 70- U.S.N, 54-57. Tech. Asn. Pulp & Paper Indust; Forest Prod. Res. Soc; Soc. Wood Sci. & Technol. Wood permeability; wood pulp drainage and permeability; strength properties of paper; physical and mechanical properties of wood fiber and particle products. Address: Dept. of Forest Products, College of Forestry, University of Minnesota, St. Paul, MN 55101.

GERTLER, MENARD M, b. Saskatoon, Sask, May 21, 19; nat; m. 43; c. 3. INTERNAL MEDICINE. B.A, Saskatchewan, 40; M.D, C.M, McGill, 43, fel, 45-47, M.Sc, 46; fel. Harvard Med. Sch, 47-50; Nat. Heart Inst. fel, N.Y. Univ, 54-56, Office Voc. Rehab. fel, 57-58, D.Sc, 58. Demonstr. physiol, med. sch, McGill, 45-47; resident cardiol. & exec. dir, coronary res. proj, Mass. Gen. Hosp, 47-50; instr. MED, col. physicians & surg, Columbia, 50-54; assoc. prof, INST. REHAB. MED, N.Y. UNIV, 58-66, PROF, 66-, DIR. CARDIOVASC. RES, 58- Asst, Presby. Hosp, N.Y, 50-54; asst. attend. physician & physician-in-charge cardiovasc. diseases, Francis Delafield Div, Columbia-Presby. Med. Center, 51-54; consult. & lectr, St. Albans Naval Hosp. Can. Army, 42-44. AAAS; Am. Chem. Soc; Harvey Soc; fel. Am. Col. Physicians; Am. Fedn. Clin. Res; N.Y. Acad. Sci; N.Y. Acad. Med. Cardiovascular diseases and biochemistry; atherosclerosis and epidemiology of heart disease; biochemistry of congestive heart failure. Address: Institute of Rehabilitation Medicine, New York University Medical Center, 400 E. 34th St, New York, NY 10016.

GERTNER, SHELDON B(ERNARD), b. New York, N.Y, Feb. 16, 27; m. 60; c. 3. PHARMACOLOGY. B.S, Brooklyn Col, 48; Ph.D, Yale, 53. Rockefeller fel, Nat. Inst. Med. Res, London, Eng, 53-55; Inst. Superiore di Sanita, Rome, Italy, 55; assoc. PHARMACOL, col. physicians & surgeons, Columbia, 55-57; asst. prof, COL. MED. & DENT. N.J. NEWARK, 57-60, assoc. prof, 60-67, PROF, 67- U.S.N, 45-46, Res, 46-50. AAAS; Am. Soc. Pharmacol. & Exp. Therapeut; Am. Chem. Soc; N.Y. Acad. Sci; Soc. Exp. Biol. & Med. Autonomic pharmacology; neuromediators at ganglionic synapse; histamine. Address: Dept. of Pharmacology, College of Medicine & Dentistry of New Jersey at Newark, 100 Bergen St, Newark, NJ 07103.

GERTSMAN, SOL L, b. Montreal, Que, Apr. 28, 17; m. 40; c. 5. PHYSICAL METALLURGY. B.A, Queen's Univ.(Ont), 39, M.A, 40. Head mat. lab, Can. Dept. Nat. Defence, 40-41; technologist phys. metall. res, Bur. Mines, Can. Dept. Mines & Resources, 41-45; dir. res, Hull Iron & Steel Foundries, Que, 45-46; head ferrous sect, Can. Dept. Mines & Tech. Surv, 46-57; CHIEF DIV. PHYS. METALL, CAN. DEPT. ENERGY, MINES & RESOURCES, 57- Rep, NATO Steel for Weapons Group, 53-61, World Metall. Soc. Conf, London, 58; partic, World Metals Conf, Chicago, 60; chmn. metals panel, Tech. Coop. Prog, 61-; mem. adv. coun, Queen's Univ.(Ont), 62-64 & 67-68; Orgn. Econ. Coop. & Develop, 66-; chmn. defense res. bd, Univ. Grants Comt. Struct. & Mat. Res, 64-70; nat. leader tech. comt. chain, Int. Standards Orgn, 67-; mem. bd. ctr. metal & mineral sci, Queen's Univ.(Ont), 69-; mem. comt. uranium, Nat. Acad. Sci. & Eng, 69- Steel Castings Inst. Can. Medal, 57. R.C.A.F, 43-45, Flying Officer. Fel. Am. Soc. Metals; Can. Inst. Mining & Metall; Am. Foundrymen's Soc; Brit. Iron & Steel Inst. Ferrous metallurgy; all aspects of steel foundry research, including melting, casting and solidification of steel. Address: Physical Metallurgy Division, Dept. of Energy, Mines & Resources, 568 Booth St, Ottawa, Ont, Can.

GERUGHTY, RONALD MILLS, b. San Francisco, Calif, Aug. 9, 32; m. 55; c. 4. PATHOLOGY. A.A, City Col. San Francisco, 57; D.D.S, California, 61, Ph.D.(path), 65. Asst. dir. clins, sch. dent, California, 61-62; training grant, Nat. Insts, Health, 62-66; ASST. PROF. PATH, COL. MED, MED. UNIV. S.C, 66-, PROF. ORAL PATH, COL. DENT. MED, 71-, CHMN. DEPT, 66-, CHIEF DIV. HEAD & NECK PATH, 68-, assoc. prof, oral path, 68-71. Consult, Vet. Admin. Hosp, Charleston, S.C, 66-; U.S. Army, Ft. Jackson, 66-; Columbia, 70; St. Francis Xavier Hosp, Charleston, 70. Dipl, Am. Bd. Oral Path, 67. U.S.N, 51-55. AAAS; Am. Dent. Asn; Am. Acad. Oral Path; Am. Bronchoesophagol. Asn; N.Y. Acad. Sci; Int. Acad. Path; Tissue Cult. Asn. Immunopathology; study of cellular immune mechanisms, including transplantation and tumor immunity; head and neck pathology, particularly cancer and its biological behavior. Address: Dept. of Pathology, Medical University of South Carolina, 80 Barre St, Charleston, SC 29041.

GERULAT, BERNARD F, b. Kearney, N.J, 27. BIOCHEMISTRY, IMMUNOCHEMISTRY. B.S, St. Peter's Col, 50, Ph.D, Iowa, 58. Res. assoc, Edsel B. Ford Inst. Med. Res, 58-60; res. ctr, Gen. Foods Corp, 60-61; asst. prof. microbiol, sch. med. & dent, Seton Hall Univ, 61-68; ASST. PROF. PATH. & MICROBIOL. & DIR. CLIN. BIOCHEM, MARTLAND HOSP, UNIT, COL. MED. & DENT. N.J, NEWARK, 68- U.S.A, 45-47. AAAS; Am. Chem. Soc; N.Y. Acad. Sci. Antigens and antibodies; antigenicity of synthetic polypeptides. Address: Dept. of Pathology & Microbiology, College of Medicine & Dentistry of New Jersey at Newark, 100 Bergen St, Newark, NJ 07104.

GERUS, THEODORE FRANK, b. Tidioute, Pa, Feb. 7, 33; m. 55; c. 3. DYNAMICS. B.S, Pa. State, 55; Case Inst. Tech, 59-61. Eng. trainee, RCA, 55-56; aerospace res. engr, Lewis Flight Propulsion Lab, Nat. Adv. Comt. Aeronaut, 56-58, aerospace scientist, LEWIS RES. CTR, NASA, 58-63, head E stand sect, dynamics test, 63-66, HEAD DYNAMIC ANAL. SECT, 66- Sig.C, U.S.A.R, 56, 1st Lt. Am. Inst. Aeronaut. & Astronaut. Flexible body dynamics of launch vehicles and their interraction with control dynamics when forced by wind, transient and vibratory loads. Address: 19630 S. Sagamore Rd, Fairview Park, OH 44126.

GERVAIS, PAUL, b. St. Barthelemy, Que, Aug. 27, 15; m. 55; c. 4. FORAGES. B.S.A, Laval, 37; M.Sc, McGill, 48; Ph.D, Wisconsin, 58. Res. off. cereals & forages, exp. farm, Can. Dept. Agr, 39-60, legumes & pastures, 60-62; PROF. FORAGES, LAVAL UNIV, 62- Am. Soc. Agron; Can. Soc. Agron.(pres, 63-64); Agr. Inst. Can. Management and physiology of forage crops. Address: Faculty of Agriculture, Laval University, Quebec 10, Que, Can.

GERVASI, JAY A(NTHONY), b. Brooklyn, N.Y, Jan. 10, 28; m. 53; c. 2. ORGANIC CHEMISTRY. A.B, Cornell, 49; U.S. Naval Ord. fel, Allied Chem. Corp. fel. & Ph.D.(chem), Duke, 54. Chemist, M.W. Kellogg Co, 54-57; Union Carbide Corp, 57-62; Res. Triangle Inst, 62-67; sr. res. chemist, Celanese Res. Co, 67-69; Burlington Industs, Inc, 69-70; SECT. LEADER, ALRAC CORP, 70- Sci. Res. Soc. Am; Am. Chem. Soc. Polymer synthesis including vinyl, olefin and condensation. Address: Alrac Corp, 649 Hope St, Stamford, CT 06907.

GERVAY, JOSEPH EDMUND, b. Dec. 29, 31; U.S. citizen. ORGANIC CHEMISTRY. B.S, Univ. Montreal, 61; M.S, Univ. B.C, 63, Ph.D.(org. chem), 65. RES. CHEMIST, RES. DIV, PHOTO PROD. DEPT, E.I. DU PONT DE NEMOURS & CO, INC, 66- Am. Chem. Soc; Soc. Photog. Sci. & Eng. Oxo reaction, Fischer-Tropsch synthesis, phenol oxidations and biosynthesis of alkaloids and steroids in vivo and in vitro using isotopic labels, photopolymers; principles, processes and materials, photoresists, unconventional photographic systems, photographic chemistry; organic reaction mechanisms. Address: Research Division, Photo Products Dept, E.I. du Pont de Nemours & Co. Inc, Parlin, NJ 08859.

GERWE, R(AYMOND) D(ANIEL), b. Cincinnati, Ohio, May 28, 04; m. 33; c. 2. CHEMISTRY. B.S, Miami (Ohio), 27; M.A, Cincinnati, 29, Lloyd fel, 30-31, Ph.D.(org. chem), 32. Instr. chem, Oxford Col, 27-28; in charge res. & develop. sect, Kroger Food Found, 32-38; dir. res, Fla. Div, FMC Corp, 38-70; RETIRED. Mem, Citrus Prod. Res. Coun; Am. Chem. Soc; Inst. Food Tech. Food technology, processing and chemistry; chemical education; photochemistry as applied to organic chemistry. Address: 2131 Reaney Rd, Lakeland, FL 33803.

GERWE, RODERICK DANIEL, b. Cincinnati, Ohio, Jan. 5, 38; m. 61; c. 2. ORGANIC CHEMISTRY. B.S, Duke, 60; Ph.D.(org. chem), Fla. State, 65. NATO fel, Karlsruhe, Ger, 65-66, Alexander von Humboldt fel, 66-67; chemist, ORG. CHEM. DIV, TENN. EASTMAN CO, 67-70, SR. CHEMIST, 70- Am. Chem. Soc. Syntheses and study of bicyclo$_{2.2.0}$ hexadienes, cyclobutadienes and other small ring compounds. Address: 601 Meadow Lane, Kingsport, TN 37663.

GERWIG, W(ALTER) H(ENRY), b. Parkersburg, W.Va, Oct. 26, 10; m. 39; c. 5. SURGERY. A.B, Univ. W.Va, 31; M.D, Univ. Md, 35; Univ. Pa, 42-43. Intern, asst. resident surgeon, first asst. resident surgeon & chief resident surgeon, Univ. Hosp, Baltimore, 35-40; asst. chief, surg. serv, sta. hosp, Ft. Meade, Md, U.S. Army, 40-41, chief, surg. serv, sta. hosp, Ft. Monroe, Va, 41-42, 28th gen. hosp, Europ. Theater Opers, 43-45; assoc. prof. surg, sch. med. George Wash. Univ, & assoc. surg, univ. hosp, 48-55, assoc. clin. prof. surg, sch. med, 55-58; chief surg. serv. & assoc. chief staff res. & educ, Vet. Admin. Hosp, Clarksburg, W.Va, 58-67; prof. surg, sch. med. Univ. W.Va, 60-67, mem. deans comt, 61-67; prof. surg, sch. med, Wayne State Univ, 67-69; chief surg, Vet. Admin. Hosp, Allen Park, Mich, 67-69; DIR. EDUC, SANTA BARBARA GEN-COTTAGE HOSPS, CALIF, 70- Attend. surg, Mt. Alto Vet. Admin. Hosp, D.C, 46-55; surg. consult. & exec. secy. deans comt. to Vet. Admin. Ctr, George Wash. Univ, 48-58; consult, Walter Reed Gen. Hosp, 48-; regional evaluator, conf. comt. grad. training in surg, 54-; consult. ed, Med. Annals D.C, 55-57. Dipl, Am. Bd. Surg, 43. U.S.A, 40-45, Lt. Col; Bronze Star Medal. Am. Med. Asn; fel. Am. Col. Surg; fel. Am. Surg. Asn; Soc. Surg. Alimentary Tract (treas, 68-); Int. Soc. Surg. Gastrointestinal physiology. Address: Santa Barbara General Cottage Hospitals, Santa Barbara, CA 93105.

GERWIN, BRENDA ISEN, b. Boston, Mass, May 2, 39; m. 60; c. 3. BIOCHEMISTRY. B.A, Radcliffe Col, 60; Nat. Insts. Health trainee, Chicago, 60-64, Ph.D.(biochem), 64. Res. assoc. biochem, Rockefeller Inst, 64-66; instr, sch. med, Case West. Reserve Univ, 66-69; biochemist, anat. prog, Oak Ridge Nat. Lab, 69-71; SR. STAFF FEL, NAT. CANCER INST, 71- Enzymology; protein chemistry. Address: National Cancer Institute, Bldg. 41, Suite 300, Bethesda, MD 20014.

GERWIN, HARRY L(EWIS), b. Rush Hill, Mo, Feb. 2, 15; m. 43; c. 5. MECHANICAL ENGINEERING. B.S, Missouri, 38. Expeditor aircraft mfg, Curtiss Wright Corp, 38; operator power plant, Seagrams Distilling Corp, Ky, 38-40; boiler inspector, Hartford Steam Boiler Ins. Co, Conn, 40-41; sect. chief res, Naval Res. Lab, 45-52; from div. chief to assoc. dir. develop. prod. eng, diamond ord. fuze labs, Nat. Bur. Standards, 52-66; PROJ. MGR, GODDARD SPACE FLIGHT CTR, NASA, GREENBELT, 66- Consult, Am. Ord. Asn, 59. Citation, U.S. Navy, 46; Diamond Ord. Fuze Lab, 54. U.S.N, 42-45, Lt. Comdr. Am. Ord. Asn; Inst. Elec. & Electronics Eng. Fire control radar and proximity fuzes; production of proximity fuzes. Address, 14305 Ansted Rd, Silver Spring, MD 20904.

GERWING, JULIA, Microbiol, see LEVY, JULIA GERWING.

GERWITZ, DAVID L, b. Buffalo, N.Y, July 18, 37; m. 57; c. 4. PLANT PATHOLOGY. B.S, Mich. State, 58; M.S, Minnesota, 61, Ph.D.(plant path), 62. Res. specialist, MONSANTO CO, 62-68, group leader, 68-69, MGR. TECH. APPRAISAL & PLANNING, AGR. DIV, 69- Rep, Agr. Res. Inst 70. Am. Phytopath. Soc; Am. Soc. Plant Physiol. Identification and evaluation of agricultural needs; field evaluation of pesticides and plant growth regulators, worldwide. Address: Agricultural Division, Monsanto Co, 800 N. Lindbergh, St. Louis, MO 63166.

GERZON, KOERT, b. Amsterdam, Netherlands, Jan. 27, 13; nat; m. 44; c. 4. ORGANIC CHEMISTRY. B.Sc, Amsterdam, 36; Ph.D.(org. chem), Cornell, 49. Res. chemist, RES. LABS, ELI LILLY & CO, 49-59, res. assoc, 59-69, RES. ADV, 69- Royal Netherlands Army, 39-46. AAAS; Am. Chem. Soc. Medicinal chemistry; antibiotic structure; parasiticidal agents; cancer chemotherapy. Address: Lilly Research Labs, Indianapolis, IN 46206.

GESCHWIND, GARY I(RA), b. N.Y.C, Jan. 28, 38; m. 61; c. 2. MATERIALS SCIENCE, METALLURGY. B.Eng, N.Y. Univ, 59; M.S, Columbia Univ, 62, D.Eng.Sc.(metall), 66. Res. scientist, GRUMMAN AEROSPACE CORP, 66-69, GROUP LEADER MAT. RES, 69- Am. Inst. Mining, Metall. & Petrol. Eng; Am. Soc. Metals; Brit. Inst. Metals; Nat. Asn. Corrosion Eng; Brit. Corrosion & Protection Asn. Metal matrix composites; solid state reactions; oxidation of refractory metals; thermal analysis; stress corrosion of aluminum alloys; nondestructive testing; grain boundary diffusion; internal friction; liquid metal lubrication. Address: Research Dept, Plant 26, Grumman Aerospace Corp, Bethpage, NY 11714.

GESCHWIND, IRVING I, b. New York, N.Y, Dec. 20, 23; m. 48; c. 2. ENDOCRINOLOGY, BIOCHEMISTRY. B.S, City Col, 45; Ph.D.(endocrinol), California, 49. Lectr. anat, UNIV. CALIF, Berkeley, 50-52, jr. res. endocrinologist, 50-51, asst. res. endocrinologist, 51-57, assoc. res. endocrinologist, 57-60, assoc. prof. ANIMAL SCI, DAVIS, 60-66, PROF, 66- Sr. fel, Nat. Sci. Found, Carlsberg Lab, Copenhagen, 58-59; Guggenheim fel, Nat. Inst. Med. Res, London, 71-72. Mem. endocrine study sect, U.S. Pub. Health Serv, 60-64, 67-71, chmn, 69-71. Endocrine Soc; Am. Soc. Zool; Am. Soc. Biol. Chem; Brit. Biochem. Soc; Brit. Soc. Endocrinol. Purification and structure of protein hormones; mechanism of hormone action. Address: Dept. of Animal Science, University of California, Davis, CA 95616.

GESCHWIND, NORMAN, b. N.Y.C, Jan. 8, 26; m. 56; c. 3. NEUROLOGY. A.B, Harvard, 47, M.D, 51. Moseley traveling fel, Nat. Hosp, Eng, 52-53, U.S. Pub. Health Serv. res. fel, 53-55; resident neurol, Boston City Hosp, 55-56; res. assoc. biol, Mass. Inst. Technol, 56-63; assoc. prof. NEUROL, Boston Univ, 63-66, prof. & chmn. dept, 66-68; PROF, MED. SCH, HARVARD, 69- U.S.A, 42-44. Am. Acad. Neurol; Am. Neurol. Asn. Neurological basis of language; aphasia. Address: Neurological Unit, Boston City Hospital, Boston, MA 02118.

GESCHWIND, STANLEY, b. Brooklyn, N.Y, Nov. 22, 21; m. 57; c. 3. PHYSICS. B.S, City Col. New York, 43; M.S, Illinois, 47; Ph.D.(physics), Columbia, 51. Res. physicist, Columbia, 51-52; physicist, BELL TEL. LABS, MURRAY HILL, 52-66, HEAD QUANTUM & SOLID STATE PHYSICS DEPT, 66- U.S.A, 43-46. Am. Phys. Soc. Microwave spectroscopy; millimeter wave generation; magnetism; paramagnetic resonance; optical spectra of solids; microwave optical double resonance in solids; light scattering. Address: 70 Deep Dale Dr, Berkeley Heights, NJ 07922.

GESE, EDWARD C(HARLES), b. Buffalo, N.Y, Oct. 2, 18; m. 42; c. 2. EMBRYOLOGY. B.A, Buffalo, 40, M.A, 42; Ph.D.(zool), N.Y. Univ, 53. Asst. Buffalo, 39-42, instr. zool, 46; biol. & comp. anat, N.Y. Univ, 42-43, asst. biol, comp. vert. anat, histol. & embryol, 46-50; instr. biol, genetics, bot.

& comp. vert. anat, Lafayette Col, 50-52, asst. prof, 52-58; res. fel. anat, Med. Col, S.C, 58-60; PROF. BIOL, WESTMINSTER COL.(PA), 60-, chmn. dept, 60-69. U.S.N, 43-46. Embryology of the Japanese beetle. Address: Dept. of Biology, Westminster College, New Wilmington, PA 16142.

GESELOWITZ, DAVID B(ERYL), b. Phila, Pa, May 18, 30; m. 53; c. 3. BIOMEDICAL ENGINEERING. B.S, Univ. Pa, 51, M.S, 54, Ph.D.(elec. eng), 58. Asst. prof. elec. eng. in med, Univ. Pa, 58-64, assoc. prof, 64-71; PROF. BIOENG, PA. STATE UNIV, 71- Consult, Provident Mutual Life Ins. Co, 59-; Burroughs Corp, 61-64; Vet. Admin. Hosp, Wash, D.C, 62-; Nat. Insts. Health fel. elec. eng. & vis. assoc. prof, Mass. Inst. Technol, 65-66. AAAS; Biophys. Soc; Inst. Elec. & Electronics Eng.(ed, trans. biomed. eng, 67-71); Am. Phys. Soc; Biomed. Eng. Soc. Electrocardiography; cardiac electrophysiology. Address: 328 Hammond Hall, Pennsylvania State University, University Park, PA 16802.

GESHNER, ROBERT ANDREW, b. Chicago, Ill, Feb. 8, 28; m. 52; c. 2. PHYSICS, MATHEMATICS. A.B, Cornell, 52; Illinois, 53; Rochester, 57. Engr, West. Elec. Co, 52-56; dept. head photog. & printed wire develop, Gen. Dynamics Corp, 56-61; PRIN. ENGR, GOVT. & COMMERCIAL SYSTS. DIV, RCA CORP, 61- Instr. Printed Circuits President's award, 66. U.S.A, 46-47, Sgt. Sr. mem. Inst. Elec. & Electronics Eng. Printed wiring manufacturing and artwork; microphotography; microelectronic packaging. Address: Government and Commercial Systems Division, RCA Corp, Bldg. 1-6-5, Camden, NJ 08102.

GESINSKI, RAYMOND MARION, b. Monesson, Pa, July 16, 32; m. 66. CELL BIOLOGY, PHYSIOLOGY. B.S, Kent State Univ, 60, fel, 60-62, M.A, 62, summer res. fel, 67-68, Ph.D.(biol. sci), 68; vis. scholar, Bayside Lab, Univ. Del, Lewes, 65. Instr. BIOL SCI, KENT STATE UNIV, 62-68, ASST. PROF, 68-, RES. FEL. 70- Tuscarawas County Univ. Found. res. grant, 70; NASA-Am. Soc. Eng. Educ. fel, summer 71. U.S.N, 52-56. AAAS; Exp. Hemat. Soc; Am. Soc. Cell Biol. Influence of physical and chemical micro-environment modifications on hemic cellular metabolism; homoestasis of blood cell differentiation, maturation, and release. Address: Dept. of Biological Sciences, Kent State University, Kent, OH 44242.

GESLER, ROBERT M(OSHER), b. Evanston, Ill, Oct. 23, 26; m. 47; c. 5. PHARMACOLOGY. B.S, New Mexico, 47; M.S, Northwestern, 50, fel, 50-52, Ph.D.(pharmacol), 52. Asst. pharmacol, Northwestern, 48-51; res. assoc, Sterling-Winthrop Res. Inst, 54-58; DIR. PHARMACOL. RES, BAXTER LABS, INC, 58- U.S.N.R, 44-46, 52-54, Lt. AAAS; Am. Soc. Pharmacol; N.Y. Acad. Sci. Histamine; biological assay; neuromuscular blockade; toxicology. Address: 565 Juneberry, Deerfield, IL 60015.

GESNER, BRUCE D, b. Fall River, Mass, May 7, 38; m. 59; c. 4. ORGANIC CHEMISTRY. B.S, Bradford Durfee Col. Tech, 60; Nat. Defense Ed. Act fel, Idaho, 60-63, Ph.D.(org. chem), 63. Polymer chemist, Bell Tel. Lab, 63-69, supvr. mat. & microconnections group, 69-71, SUPVR. MAT. CHEM. GROUP, BELL LABS, INC, 71- Am. Chem. Soc. Organic reactions mechanisms, composition and structure of polyblends. Address: Room 5B-103, Bell Labs. Inc, Murray Hills, NJ 07974.

GESSAMAN, JAMES A, b. Dayton, Ohio, Dec. 10, 39; m. 62; c. 2. PHYSIOLOGICAL ECOLOGY, AVIAN PHYSIOLOGY. M.S, Illinois, Urbana, 64, Ph.D.(zool), 68; Wisconsin, Madison, 65. ASST. PROF. PHYSIOL, UTAH STATE UNIV, 68- Bioenergetics; thermoregulation. Address: Dept. of Zoology, Utah State University, Logan, UT 84321.

GESSEL, STANLEY P(AUL), b. Utah, Oct. 14, 16; m. 47; c. 2. FORESTRY, SOILS. B.S, Utah State Agr. Col, 39; Ph.D.(soils), California, 50. Asst, California, 46-48; instr. FOREST SOILS, UNIV. WASH, 48-51, asst. prof, 51-59, assoc. prof, 59-62, PROF, 62-, ASSOC. DEAN COL. FORESTRY, 64- Nat. Sci. Found. lectr, 63; dir, west. coniferous forest biome, Int. Biol. Prog. U.S.A.A.F, 42-45, Capt. AAAS; Soil Sci. Soc. Am; Soc. Am. Foresters; Am. Soc. Range Mgt; Am. Geophys. Union. Forest soil classification, growth, ecology and soil fertility; tree nutrition; tropical soils. Address: 2026 N. E. 120th St, Seattle, WA 98105.

GESSER, H(YMAN) D(AVIDSON), b. Montreal, Que, Apr. 24, 29; m. 52; c. 3. PHYSICAL CHEMISTRY. B.Sc, Loyola Col.(Can), 49; Ph.D.(phys. chem), McGill, 52. Fel. Photochem, Rochester, 52-54; Nat. Res. Coun. Can. fel, Ottawa (Can), 54-55; assoc. prof. CHEM, UNIV. MAN, 55-67, PROF, 67- Nuffield Found. Can. summer fel, Sheffield Univ, 58; res. fel, Israel Inst. Technol, 61-62; vis. scientist, Whiteshell Nuclear Res. Estab, summer 67; UN Develop. Prog. tech. asst. expert, Ctr. Indust. Res, Israel, 68-69. Am. Chem. Soc; fel. Chem. Inst. Can; The Chem. Soc. Atomic, thermal and photochemical kinetics; gas chromatography; surface reactions. Address: Dept. of Chemistry, University of Manitoba, Winnipeg, Man, Can.

GESSERT, CARL F(REDERICK), b. St. Louis, Mo, Apr. 14, 23; m. 58; c. 2. PHARMACOLOGY. A.B, Washington (St. Louis), 49; Ph.D.(biochem), Wisconsin, 55. Asst, sch. med, Washington (St. Louis), 55-58, res. instr, 58-62; asst. prof. PHARMACOL, COL. MED, UNIV. NEBR, OMAHA, 62-67, ASSOC. PROF, 67-, acting chmn. dept, 67-69. U.S.A, 43-46, S/Sgt. AAAS; Am. Chem. Soc; N.Y. Acad. Sci. Drug absorption, distribution, biotransformation and excretion; microsomal enzyme induction; drug interactions. Address: Dept. of Pharmacology, University of Nebraska College of Medicine, Omaha, NE 68105.

GESSERT, ROLAND A(RTHUR), b. Detroit, Mich, Jan. 14, 21. VETERINARY MEDICINE, AGRICULTURE. B.S, Mich. State Col, 42, D.V.M, 50; Maryland, 53. Private practice, Mich, 50-52; veterinarian, Oakland County Health Dept, 52; res. assoc, dairy dept, Maryland, 53-55; asst. vet. med. dir, U.S. Food & Drug Admin, D.C, 55-58; veterinarian, vet. med. dept, Upjohn Co, 58-67, res. & develop, 67-69; REGULATORY LIAISON, AYERST LABS, 69- U.S.A, 42-46; U.S.P.H.S, 57-, Vet. Am. Soc. Vet. Physiol. & Pharmacol.(secy-treas, 60-66); Am. Vet. Med. Asn; Am. Dairy Sci. Asn. Bovine ketosis; animal nutrition and physiology; diseases of farm animals. Address: Ayerst Labs, 685 Third Ave, New York, NY 10017.

GESSERT, WALTER L(OUIS), b. Detroit, Mich, May 26, 19; m. 44; c. 3. PHYSICS. B.S, Eastern Michigan, 44; M.S, Wayne State, 47, Ph.D.(physics), Mich. State, 54. Instr. gen. physics, Wayne State, 46-50; asst. ultrasonics res, Mich. State, 51-54; physicist tire noise, U.S. Rubber Co, 54-57, group leader in charge passenger tire design, 57-61; assoc. prof. PHYSICS & ASTRON, EAST. MICH. UNIV, 61-64, PROF, 64- U.S.A, 44-45. Acoust. Soc. Am; Am. Asn. Physics Teachers; Optical Soc. Am. Ultrasonics; instrumentation; optics. Address: Dept. of Physics & Astronomy, Eastern Michigan University, Ypsilanti, MI 48197.

GESSLER, ALBERT M(URRAY), b. Brooklyn, N.Y, Nov. 10, 18; m. 43; c. 2. ORGANIC CHEMISTRY. B.S, Cornell Univ, 42. Chemist SYNTHETIC RUBBER, Standard Oil Develop. Co, 42-58, res. assoc, ESSO RES. & ENG. CO, 58-66, SR. RES. ASSOC, CHEM. RES. DIV, 66- Am. Chem. Soc. Elastomer and high polymer chemistry and technology, reinforcement with carbon blacks. Address: Chemical Research Division, Esso Research & Engineering Co, P.O. Box 51, Linden, NJ 07036.

GESSLER, JOHANNES, b. Basel, Switz, Oct. 19, 36; m. 62; c. 4. FLUID MECHANICS, HYDRAULICS. B.S, Swiss Fed. Inst. Technol, 60, Ph.D. (hydraul), 65. Jr. engr, Swisselectra, Basel, 60-61; res. engr, lab. hydraul. res, Swiss Fed. Inst. Technol, 61-66; asst. prof. CIVIL ENG, COLO. STATE UNIV, 66-70, ASSOC. PROF, 70- Am. Soc. Civil Eng; Swiss Eng. & Archit. Soc; Int. Asn. Hydraul. Res. Fluid mechanics, especially turbulence, diffusion and dispersion processes in open channels; river mechanics, especially sediment transport. Address: Dept. of Civil Engineering, Colorado State University, Ft. Collins, CO 80521.

GESSNER, ADOLF WILHELM, b. Berlin, Ger, Aug. 26, 28; m. 53; c. 2. CHEMICAL ENGINEERING. B.A, Williams Col, 52; Sc.D.(chem. eng), Mass. Inst. Tech, 54. Process engr, Chemische Werks Huls, W.Ger, 54-55; develop. engr, Jones & Laughlin Steel Corp, Pa, 55-57; process engr. & mgr. chem. eng. sect, Sci. Design Co, N.Y, 57-61; sr. develop. engr, Lummus Co, N.J, 61-67; supvr. process develop, Foster Wheeler Corp, 67-70; DIR. ENG. & DEVELOP, GIVAUDAN CORP, CLIFTON, 70- Lectr, Polytech. Inst. Brooklyn, 61-63, adj. prof, 63- Am. Chem. Soc; Am. Inst. Chem. Eng; Tech. Asn; Pulp & Paper Indust. Thermodynamics; unit operations. Address: 190 Park St, Montclair, NJ 07042.

GESSNER, FREDERICK B(ENEDICT), b. Newark, N.J, June 11, 37; m. 62; c. 3. MECHANICAL ENGINEERING. B.S, Lehigh, 59; Eng. Exp. Sta. fel, Purdue, 59-62, M.S, 60, Shell fel, 62-63, Ph.D.(mech. eng), 64. Res. scientist, res. div, Am. Radiator & Standard Sanit. Corp, 63-65; asst. prof. MECH. ENG, Va. Polytech, 65-67; UNIV. WASH, 67-71, ASSOC. PROF, 71- NASA-Nat. Guard Regulations res. grant, 66-67; consult, res. div, Am. Radiator & Standard Sanit. Corp, 66-67; Nat. Sci. Found. res. grant, 68-71. Am. Soc. Mech. Eng; Am. Soc. Eng. Educ. Fluid mechanics; heat transfer; thermodynamics; secondary flow in non-circular channels; subsonic flow in diffusers; pressure-flow behavior in distensible tubes; fluid dynamic studies of flow in the lower urinary tract. Address: Dept. of Mechanical Engineering, University of Washington, Seattle, WA 98105.

GESSNER, IRA H(AROLD), b. Rockville Center, N.Y, June 23, 31; m. 59; c. 3. PEDIATRICS. A.B, State Univ. Iowa, 52; M.D, Univ. Vt, 56. Intern pediat, Ohio State Univ, 56-57; resident, col. med, Univ. Fla, 60-61, Am. Heart Asn. advan. res. fel, 62-64; Wenner-Gren Inst, Stockholm, 64-65; chief resident, PEDIAT, COL. MED, UNIV. FLA, 62, instr, 62-65, asst. prof, 65-67, assoc. prof, 67-70, PROF, 70- Nat. Insts. Health career develop. award, 67; mem. coun. rheumatic fever & congenital heart disease, Am. Heart Asn. Dipl, Am. Bd. Pediat, 64, cert. cardiol, 66. U.S.A.F, 58-60, Flight Surg. AAAS; Soc. Pediat. Res; Teratology Soc; Am. Acad. Pediat; fel. Am. Col. Cardiol; Am. Heart Asn. Address: Dept. of Pediatrics, Division of Pediatric Cardiology, University of Florida College of Medicine, Gainesville, FL 32601.

GESSNER, PETER K, b. Warsaw, Poland, May 3, 31; m. 59; c. 2. PHARMACOLOGY. B.Sc, London, 55, Ph.D.(biochem), 58. Res. assoc, res. div, Cleveland Clin, 58-61, asst. staff mem, 61-62; asst. prof. PHARMACOL, STATE UNIV. N.Y. BUFFALO, 62-67, ASSOC. PROF, 67- AAAS; Am. Soc. Pharmacol. & Exp. Therapeut; Am. Chem. Soc; N.Y. Acad. Sci; Brit. Biochem. Soc. Characterization of drug interactions including investigation of concurrent changes in the metabolic fate of the drugs and other biochemical events to determine mechanism; study of interaction of drugs and ethanol; phenomenology and mechanism of action of hallucinogens. Address: Dept. of Pharmacology, School of Medicine, State University of New York at Buffalo, Buffalo, NY 14214.

GESSOW, ALFRED, b. Jersey City, N.J, Oct. 13, 22; m. 47; c. 4. PHYSICS, APPLIED MATHEMATICS. B.C.E, City Col. New York, 43; M.Aero.Eng, N.Y. Univ, 44. Aeronaut. res. scientist, Langley Res. Center, Nat. Adv. Cmt. Aeronaut, Va, 44-59, head fluid & space physics sect, NASA HQ, 59-61, chief fluid physics br, 61-67, asst. dir. res. div, 67-71, CHIEF AERODYN. & FLUID MECH, AERODYN. & VEHICLE SYSTS. DIV, OFF. ADVAN. RES. & TECHNOL, 71- Lectr, grad. exten. ctr, Univ. Va, Hampton, 45-58; Adv. Group Aeronaut. Res. & Develop. helicopter consult. to France & Ger, 59; exec. secy, adv. comt. fluid mech, NASA, 59-63, mem. res. & tech. subcomt. fluid mech, 67-, subcomt. electrophys. & adv. coun. basic res, 68-; adj. prof, N.Y. Univ, 68-; Cath. Univ. Am, 70-; chmn. indust. & prof. adv. coun, dept. aerospace eng, Pa. State Univ, 70- U.S.A.A.F, 44-46. Assoc. fel. Am. Inst. Aeronaut. & Astronaut; Am. Helicopter Soc.(founding ed, jour, 55). Rotating-wing aerodynamics; fluid physics; electrophysics; aerodynamics. Address: Code RAA, Aerodynamics & Vehicle Systems Division, Office of Advanced Research & Technology, NASA Headquarters, Washington, DC 20546.

GEST, H(OWARD), b. London, Eng, Oct. 15, 21; nat; m. 41; c. 3. MICROBIOLOGY. B.A, California, Los Angeles, 42; fel, Vanderbilt, 42; Am. Cancer Soc. fel, Washington (St. Louis), 47-49, Ph.D.(microbiol), 49. Asst. metall. lab, Chicago, 43; from jr. chemist to assoc. chemist, Clinton Labs, Tenn, 43-46; asst. radiol, sch. med, Washington (St. Louis), 46-49; instr. microbiol, sch. med, Western Reserve, 49-51, asst. prof, 51-53, assoc. prof, 53-59; prof. microbiol, Henry Shaw Sch. Bot, Wash. Univ, 59-64, dept. zool, 64-66; PROF. MICROBIOL, IND. UNIV, BLOOMINGTON, 66-, chmn. dept, 66-70. Spec. res. fel, U.S. Pub. Health Serv, Calif. Inst. Technol, 56-57; mem. adv. panel metab. biol, Nat. Sci. Found, 63-66; Nat. Sci. Found.

sr. fel, Nat. Inst. Med. Res, London, 65-66; mem. study sect. bact. & mycol, Nat. Insts. Health, 66-68, chmn. study sect. microbiol. chem, 68-69; mem. comt. microbiol. probs. man in extended space flight, Nat. Acad. Sci-Nat. Res. Coun, 67-69; Guggenheim fel, Imp. Col, Univ. London, Univ. Stockholm, Univ. Tokyo, 70; vis. prof, Univ. Tokyo & Japanese Soc. Promotion Sci, 70. Am. Soc. Microbiol; Am. Soc. Biol. Chem; Brit. Soc. Gen. Microbiol. Physiology and intermediary metabolism of microorganisms; photosynthesis; metabolism of molecular hydrogen and nitrogen; electron transport mechanisms; metabolic regulatory mechanisms. Address: Dept. of Microbiology, Jordan Hall 436, Indiana University, Bloomington, IN 47401.

GESTELAND, RAYMOND FREDERICK, b. Madison, Wis, Apr. 2, 38; m. 60; c. 4. BIOCHEMISTRY, MOLECULAR BIOLOGY. B.S, Wisconsin, 60, M.S, 61; Nat. Insts. Health fel. & Ph.D.(biochem), Harvard, 66. Nat. Sci. Found. fel. biochem, inst. molecular biol, Geneva, 66-67; ASST. PROF. BIOL, STATE UNIV. N.Y. STONY BROOK, 67-; ASST. DIR, COLD SPRING HARBOR LAB, 67- Nat. Insts. Health career develop. award, 68- AAAS. In vitro protein synthesis and its use to study control mechanisms and the replication of viruses. Address: Cold Spring Harbor Lab, Cold Spring Harbor, NY 11724.

GESTELAND, ROBERT CHARLES, b. Madison, Wis, July 1, 30; m. 61; c. 3. NEUROPHYSIOLOGY, ELECTRICAL ENGINEERING. B.S, Wisconsin, 53; S.M, Mass. Inst. Tech, 57, Nat. Insts. Health fel. & Ph.D.(neurophysiol), 61. Engr, Gen. Radio Co, 53-54; mem. staff Harvard-Peabody-Smithsonian Exped, Kalahari Desert, 57-58; mem. res. staff, electronics res. lab, Mass. Inst. Tech, 61-62, res. assoc. biol, 62-65; mem. res. staff life sci, Sci. Eng. Inst, 62-65; ASSOC. PROF. elec. eng. & biol, NORTHWEST. UNIV, 65-67, BIOL. SCI, 67- Consult, Arthur D. Little Co, Inc; Mass. Ment. Health Ctr; Invention Group Inc; Unilever N.V. AAAS; Am. Soc. Zool; Am. Phys. Soc; Am. Physiol. Soc. Sensory neurophysiology; electrode processes; electronic circuit theory. Address: Dept. of Biological Sciences, Northwestern University, Evanston, IL 60201.

GESUND, HANS, b. Vienna, Austria, Sept. 18, 28; nat; m; c. 2. STRUCTURAL ENGINEERING. B.Eng, Yale, 50, M.Eng, 53, D.Eng, 58. Instr. civil eng, Yale, 53-58; PROF. STRUCT. ENG, UNIV. KY, 58- Consult, C.Eng.Res, 48-68, Maj. Am. Soc. Civil Eng; Am. Soc. Eng. Educ; Int. Asn. Bridge & Struct. Eng; Am. Concrete Inst; Int. Asn. Shell Struct. Structures; mechanics and reinforced concrete; structural mechanics; limit and ultimate load design. Address: Dept. of Civil Engineering, University of Kentucky, Lexington, KY 40506.

GETCHELL, B(ASSFORD) C(ASE), b. Baring, Maine, July 5, 04; m. 34. MATHEMATICS. A.B, Colby Col, 27; A.M, Harvard, 29; Ph.D.(math), Michigan, 34. Instr. math, Case, 28-31; Brown, 35-36; Butler, 36-37, asst. prof, 37-43; analyst, NAT. SECURITY AGENCY, 43-58, MATHEMATICIAN, 58- Mem. Case eclipse exped, Maine, 32. AAAS; Am. Inst. Aeronaut. & Astronaut. Integration of interval functions; celestial mechanics. Address: 16301 Bond Mill Rd, Laurel, MD 20810.

GETCHELL, NELSON F(LETCHER), b. Lowell, Mass, Aug. 26, 16; m. 42. TEXTILES. B.S, Lowell Textile Inst, 38. Lab. technician, Ciba Co, Inc, 38-40; chemist, Goodall Worsted Co, 40-43; group leader, fiber res, Ludlow Mfg. & Sales Co, 43-46, asst. mgr, 46-51; chemist, tech. sect, Nat. Cotton Coun. Am. 51-57, MGR, 57-70; PROCESS APPLNS. RES, COTTON INC, 70- Mem. Brit. Textile Inst. AAAS; Am. Chem. Soc; Am. Soc. Test. & Mat; Fiber Soc; Am. Asn. Textile Chem. & Colorists. Physical, chemical and mechanical properties of cotton and other textile fibers; dyeing and chemical finishing of fabrics; processing of fibers into yarns and fabrics; textile chemistry. Address: Cotton Inc, 1200 18th St. N.W, Washington, DC 20036.

GETOOR, RONALD KAY, b. Royal Oak, Mich, Feb. 9, 29; m. 59; c. 1. MATHEMATICS. A.B, Michigan, 50, M.S, 51, Ph.D.(math), 54. Fine instr. MATH, Princeton, 54-56; asst. prof, Univ. Wash, 56-60, assoc. prof, 60-64, PROF, 64-66; UNIV. CALIF, SAN DIEGO, 66- Nat. Sci. Found. fel, 59-60; vis. prof, Hamburg, summer 64; Stanford, 64-65. Am. Math. Soc; Inst. Math. Statist. Probability theory, especially general theory of Markov processes and their associated potential theory. Address: Dept. of Mathematics, University of California, San Diego, P.O. Box 109, La Jolla, CA 92037.

GETTENS, RUTHERFORD JOHN, b. Mooers, N.Y, Jan. 17, 00; m. 30; c. 1. CHEMISTRY. B.S, Middlebury Col, 23; M.A, Harvard, 29. Instr. chem, Colby Col, 23-27; tech. res. fel, Fogg Mus. of Art, Harvard, 30-49, chief tech. res, 49-51; assoc. tech. res, FREER GALLERY OF ART, SMITHSONIAN INST, 51-58, curator, res. lab, 58-61, head curator, 61-68, CONSULT, TECH. RES, 68- Lectr, Harvard, 48-51; Belgian Am. Ed. Found. fel, Royal Mus. Arts & Hist, Brussels, 48. Tech. consult, fed. art proj, Works Progress Admin, Boston, 37-41; consult, Atomic Energy Cmn, California, 47; consult, fel, N.Y. Univ. Conserv. Ctr, 60-; v.pres, Int. Inst. Conserv. Hist. & Artistic Works, 63-68, pres, 68-71, ed, I.I.C. Abstracts, 58-; sect. ed, Chem. Abstracts, 62-; Fulbright lectr, Greece, 71. Mem. staff, U.S. eng. proj, Manhattan Dist, Los Alamos, 44-45. Am. Chem. Soc; Am. Asn. Mus; Am. Inst. Archaeol. Chemistry and technical study of materials of art and archeology. Address: 6011 Broad Branch Rd. N.W, Washington, DC 20015.

GETTES, BERNARD C(HARLES), b. Phila, Pa, Oct. 3, 12; m. 35; c. 2. MEDICINE. M.D, Temple Univ, 36. Asst. prof. OPHTHAL, grad. sch. med, Univ. Pa, 48-67; CLIN. PROF, SCH. MED, TEMPLE UNIV, 67-; DIR. VISION PHYSIOL, WILLS EYE HOSP, 67- Ophthalmologist, Stetson Hosp, 40-55; asst. surg, Wills Eye Hosp, 42-57, chief refraction dept, 46-55, 63-67, sr. asst. surgeon, 57-62, assoc. surgeon, 62-67, attend. surgeon, 67-; ophthalmologist, Phila. Gen. Hosp, 54-59; St. Joseph's Hosp, 60- Dipl, Am. Bd. Ophthal, 42. Med.C, U.S.N.R, 44-46, Res, 46-52, Lt. Asn. Am. Med. Cols; Asn. Res. Vision & Ophthal; Am. Acad. Ophthal. & Otolaryngol.(serv. award, 59); Refraction and optics. Address: 1930 Chestnut St, Philadelphia, PA 19103.

GETTING, I(VAN) A(LEXANDER), b. New York, N.Y, Jan. 18, 12; m. 37; c. 3. PHYSICS. B.S, Mass. Inst. Tech, 33; Rhodes scholar, Oxford, 33-35, D.Phil.(astrophys), 35; hon. D.Sc, North-eastern, 54. Jr. fel, Harvard, 35-40; mem. radiation lab, Mass. Inst. Tech, 40-45, assoc. prof. elec. eng, 43-47, prof, 47-50; asst. develop. planning, dep. chief staff develop, U.S. Air Force, 50-51; v.pres. eng. & res, Raytheon Mfg. Co, 51-60; PRES, AEROSPACE CORP, 60- Mem, sci. adv. bd, U.S. Air Force, 45-; mem, Res. & Develop. Adv. Coun, Sig. Corps, 52-60; consult, President's Sci. Adv. Comt, 61-; chmn, Naval Warfare Panel, 71-; mem. undersea warfare cmn, Nat. Acad. Sci. Presidential Medal for Merit, 48; Naval Ord. Develop. Award; Air Force Exceptional Serv. Award, 60. Civilian with Off. Sci. Res. & Develop; sect. chief naval fire control, Nat. Defense Res. Cmt, 43-45; spec. consult. to secy. War, 43-45. AAAS; Nat. Acad. Eng; fel. Am. Phys. Soc; fel. Inst. Elec. & Electronics Eng; fel. Am. Acad. Arts & Sci; sr. mem. Am. Inst. Aeronaut. & Astronaut. Particle accelerators; nuclear physics; radar; fire control; gaseous discharges; astrophysics; multivibrator synchronization for accurate timing of long intervals; automatic tracking of targets by radar; rapid scanning radar antennas. Address: 605 Tigertail Rd, Los Angeles, CA 90049.

GETTING, VLADO A(NDREW), b. Pittsburgh, Pa, July 20, 10; m. 37; c. 2. PUBLIC HEALTH. A.B, Hopkins, 31; M.D, Harvard, 35, M.P.H, 39, Dr.P.H, 40. Asst. resident, Mattapan Sanatorium, Mass, 35; contract surgeon, U.S. Army, Ft. Ethan Allen, Vt, 35; intern, City Hosp, Worcester, 35-37; asst. epidemiologist, State Dept. Pub. Health, Mass, 37-39, tech. dir. mosquito surv, 39, epidemiologist, 39-40, asst. dist. health officer, 40-41, dist. health officer, 41-42, city cmnr, pub. health, Worcester, 42-43, state cmnr, Mass, 43-53; prof. pub. health practice, SCH. PUB. HEALTH, UNIV. MICH, 53-60, PROF. PUB. HEALTH ADMIN. & CHMN. DEPT. COMMUNITY HEALTH SERV, 61-, acting chmn. dept. pub. health practice, 59-61. Asst, med. sch. & sch. prev. med, Harvard, 40-43, lectr, sch. pub. health, 43-47, clin. prof, 47-53; lectr, Boston Univ, Boston Col. & Simmons Col, 46-53. Consult. to Surgeon Gen, U.S. Air Force, 63-; consult. & dir. admin. & prog. study, Dept. Pub. Health, N.S, Can, 63- Chmn, New Eng. Interstate Water Pollution Control Cmn, 48; secy-treas, Asn. Schs. Pub. Health, 58- Dipl, Am. Bd. Prev. Med. U.S.P.H.S.R, 58-, Dir. Med. AAAS; fel. Am. Med. Asn; fel. Am. Col. Prev. Med; Asn. State & Territorial Health Officers (secy-treas, 45-47); Asn. Teachers Prev. Med. Surveys and evaluations of city, county and state health departments; community programs for the chronically ill and the aged; administration of community health services. Address: Dept. of Community Health Service, University of Michigan School of Public Health, Ann Arbor, MI 48104.

GETTINGER, RAYMOND, b. New York, N.Y, Nov. 24, 05; m. 37; c. 2. PATHOLOGY. B.S, City Col, 26; M.D, Cornell, 32. Asst. path, Mem. Hosp, N.Y, 32-33; morbid anat, Mt. Sinai Hosp, 32-34, surg. path, 34-35, path, 35-38; lectr, Nat. Cmt. Resettlement For. Physicians, 39-40; pathologist & dir. lab, Crown Heights Hosp, Brooklyn, 40-43; pathologist & dir. labs, St. John's Hosp, 43-53; pathologist, St. Vincent's Hosp, 53-66; DIR. PATH. & CLIN. LABS, ST. JOSEPH'S HOSP, 66- Rev. physician, Life Exten. Inst, N.Y, 34-39; pathologist, Lister Hosp, 37; pathologist & dir. lab, N.Y. Inst. Clin. Oral Path, 35-40. Ed, Int. Abstracts Oral Path, Archives Clin. Oral Path, 38-40. Dipl, Am. Bd. Path; Michaelis Prize, Alpha Omega Alpha; first prize, Am. Dental Asn, 39. AAAS; fel. Am. Soc. Clin. Path; Am. Asn. Path. & Bact; fel. Am. Med. Asn; fel. Col. Am. Path; fel. N.Y. Acad. Med; Int. Acad. Path. Pathological anatomy, histology, physiology and chemistry; clinical pathology; medical bacteriology; oncology; radiosensitivity of tumors. Address: Pathology & Clinical Labs, St. Joseph's Hospital, 127 S. Broadway, Yonkers, NY 10701.

GETTLER, JOSEPH D(ANIEL), b. Brooklyn, N.Y, Mar. 5, 16; m. 55; c. 4. PHYSICAL ORGANIC CHEMISTRY. B.A, Columbia, 37, M.A, 39, Ph.D.(chem), 43. Res. chemist, Air Reduction Co, 43-46; instr. CHEM, N.Y. UNIV, 46-48, asst. prof, 48-54, ASSOC. PROF, 54- Tech. adv, Syn-Zyme Labs. Am. Chem. Soc; The Chem. Soc. Solution kinetics; condensation reactions; molecular rearrangements; statistical analysis. Address: 209 Jennifer Lane, Yonkers, NY 10710.

GETTNER, MARVIN, b. Rochester, N.Y, July 21, 34; m. 59; c. 2. PHYSICS. B.S, Rochester, 56; Ph.D.(physics), Pennsylvania, 61. Res. assoc. PHYSICS, Pennsylvania, 60-61; asst. prof, NORTHEAST. UNIV, 61-69, ASSOC. PROF, 69- Am. Phys. Soc; Am. Asn. Physics Teachers. Experimental elementary particle physics. Address: Dept. of Physics, Northeastern University, Boston, MA 02115.

GETTY, ROBERT J(OHN), b. St. Louis, Mo, Dec. 30, 22; m. 50. CHEMICAL ENGINEERING. B.S, Washington (St. Louis), 48, M.S, 49, D.Sc, 55. Jr. engr, piping layouts, Midwest Piping & Supply Co, 42; res. chem. engr, RES. LAB, ALUMINUM CO. AM, 49-59, sr. res. engr, 59-63, asst. chief, 63-66, tech. mgr, chem. prods, 66-70, MGR. CHEM. PROD, 70- U.S.A.F, 43-46. Am. Soc. Heat, Refrig. & Air Conditioning Eng; Sci. Res. Soc. Am; Am. Inst. Chem. Eng. Adsorption; chromatography; dehydration of liquids and gases; alumina processes; manufacture and application of alumina chemicals. Address: Refining Dept, 1501 Alcoa Bldg, 425 Sixth Ave, Pittsburgh, PA 15219.

GETTY, WARD DOUGLAS, b. Detroit, Mich, Aug. 8, 33; m. 55; c. 2. ELECTRICAL ENGINEERING. B.S.(math). & B.S.(elec. eng), Michigan, 55, Gen. Elec. Ed. & Charitable Fund fel, 55-56, M.S, 56; Fed. Telecommun. Lab. fel, Mass. Inst. Tech, 56-57, Sc.D.(elec. eng), 62. Asst. prof. ELEC. ENG, Mass. Inst. Technol, 62-66; ASSOC. PROF, UNIV. MICH, ANN ARBOR, 66- Ford Found. fel, 62-64. Consult, Raytheon Co, 63- Inst. Elec. & Electronics Eng. Interaction of electron beams and plasma; plasma physics in application to controlled thermonuclear fusion; electron beam sources. Address: Dept. of Electrical Engineering, 2500 E. Engineering Bldg, University of Michigan, Ann Arbor, MI 48104.

GETTYS, B(RIGGS), b. Nashville, Tenn, Oct. 23, 04; m. 36; c. 5. ENGINEERING. B.S, Yale, 27. Oil chemist, Indian Ref. Co, 27-30; engr, Mason & Hanger, 30-31; physicist cerebral dominance, Neurol. Inst. N.Y, 32-35; engr, transformer div, Gen. Elec. Co, 35-54, physicist, maj. appliance div, 54-57, mgr, appl. physics lab, maj. appliance labs, 57-68; RETIRED. Naval Ord. develop. award, 45. Acoust. Soc. Am; Optical Soc. Am. Administrative engineering; applied physics; instrumentation; magnetic measurements and magnetostriction; thermoelectric materials; acoustics and noise control. Address: 2426 Newburg Rd, Louisville, KY 40205.

GETZ, GODFREY S, b. Johannesburg, S.Africa, June 18, 30; m. 55; c. 4. BIOCHEMISTRY, PATHOLOGY. M.B, B.Ch, Witwatersrand, 54, B.Sc, 55, D.Phil.(biochem), Oxford, 63. Lectr. chem. path, Witwatersrand, 56, 59-63; demonstr. biochem, Oxford, 56-59; res. assoc, Harvard Med. Sch, 63-64; asst. prof. path. & res. assoc. biochem, UNIV. CHICAGO, 64-67, ASSOC. PROF. PATH. & BIOCHEM, 67- Brit. Biochem. Soc; Am. Soc. Biol. Chem. Lipids and membrane biogenesis, especially interaction of lipid biosynthesis and mitochondrial formation; assembly and secretion of plasma lipoproteins. Address: 5523 S. Kimbark Ave, Chicago, IL 60637.

GETZ, HORACE R(AYMOND), b. Mt. Carroll, Ill, Aug. 28, 07; m. 36. MEDICINE. B.S, Wisconsin, 28, M.D, 33; Illinois, 28-29. Asst, nutrit. div, animal husb. dept, col. agr, Illinois, 28-29; intern, Wis. Gen. Hosp, 33-34; Wis. Alumni Res. Found. asst. med. bact, sch. med, Wisconsin, 34-35, instr, 35-39; med, Henry Phipps Inst, Pennsylvania, 39, res. assoc, 39-45; dir. labs, Hastings Found, 45-61, med. dir, 48-61; assoc. clin. prof. infectious diseases, California, Los Angeles, 53-61; chief tuberc. control sect, Nev. State Div. Health, 61-71; RETIRED. Acting med. dir, Hastings Found, 47-48. AAAS; fel. Am. Med. Asn. Effect of nutrition on the resistance to tuberculosis; vitamin A nutrition. Address: 1899 Berkeley Dr, Reno, NV 89502.

GETZ, J. ALTON, b. Lock Haven, Pa, Aug. 15, 00; m. 33; c. 1. CHEMISTRY. B.S, Phila. Col. Pharm, 22. Chemist, dyes, Am. Aniline Prods. Co, 22-26; rubber chem, U.S. Rubber Co, 26-36, chief chemist, 36-65; TECH. ADV, ROYAL RUBBER CO, SOUTH BEND, 69- Fuel cells for military and civilian aircraft; expulsion diaphragms and insulators for missiles; storage tanks for fuels, oils and chemicals; vapor conservation devices for fuel and chemicals; flexible missile components. Address: 713 N. Mason St, Mishawaka, IN 46544.

GETZ, LOWELL L(EE), b. Chesterfield, Ill, Sept. 21, 31; m. 53; c. 2. ZOOLOGY. B.S, Illinois, 53; M.S, Michigan, 59, Ph.D.(zool), 60. Res. assoc. ecol, Michigan, 59-61; instr. ZOOL. Univ. Conn, 61-62, asst. prof, 62-66, assoc. prof, 66-69; PROF, UNIV. ILL, URBANA, 69- U.S.A, 53-55, Res, 55-, Maj. Am. Soc. Mammal; Brit. Ecol. Soc; Ecol. Soc. Am; Soc. Study Evolution. Ecology of mammals and mollusks. Address: Dept. of Zoology, Vivarium Bldg, University of Illinois, Wright & Healey Sts, Champaign, IL 61820.

GETZ, RALPH WAYNE, b. Savanna, Ill, July 17, 34; m. 60; c. 3. METALLURGY. B.S, Illinois, 57; M.S, Ohio State, 60. Prin. metall. engr, Battelle Mem. Inst, 57-65; SR. SCIENTIST, OWENS-CORNING FIBERGLAS CORP, 65- Am. Soc. Metals; Am. Inst. Min, Metall. & Petrol. Eng; Brit. Inst. Metall. High temperature metallurgy; carbide-refractory metal reactions; precious metals alloy development; nickel-chromium superalloys. Address: Owens-Corning Fiberglas Corp, Granville, OH 43023.

GETZEN, FORREST W(ILLIAM), b. Stuart, Fla, Feb. 28, 28; m. 56; c. 3. PHYSICAL CHEMISTRY. B.S, Va. Mil. Inst, 50; Allied Chem. & Dye Corp. fel, Mass. Inst. Tech, 55-56, Ph.D.(chem), 56. Instr. chem, Va. Mil. Inst, 50-51; asst, Mass. Inst. Tech, 53-55; res. engr, Humble Oil & Ref. Co, 56-61; ASSOC. PROF. CHEM, N.C. STATE UNIV, 61- Mem. U.S. Eng. Team, Kabul, Afghanistan, 65-67. U.S.A.F, 52-53, 1st Lt. AAAS; Am. Chem. Soc; Am. Soc. Qual. Control; Am. Inst. Mining, Metall. & Petrol. Eng; fel. Am. Inst. Chem. Petroleum reservoir fluid behavior; phase behavior of hydrocarbon mixtures; compressibility of gaseous argon; interfacial phenomena; surface and colloid chemistry; solution thermodynamics. Address: 2009 Banbury Rd, Raleigh, NC 27608.

GETZENDANER, MILTON E(DMOND), b. Grandview, Wash, Apr. 17, 18; m. 41; c. 2. BIOCHEMISTRY. A.B, Whitman Col, 40; M.S, Washington (Seattle), 45; Ph.D.(biochem), Texas, 49. Res. chemist, Washington (Seattle), 44-46; res. scientist, concentration growth factor, Texas, 48-49; biochemist, Hanford Works, Gen. Elec. Co, 49-53; agr. chem. res, DOW CHEM. CO, 53-59, group leader RESIDUE RES, bioprod. dept, 59-69, RES. DIR, AGR. ORGANICS DEPT, 69- Jr. chemist, Chem. Warfare Serv, U.S. Army, 43-46. Am. Chem. Soc; Asn. Off. Anal. Chem. Effect of radiation on bacterial growth; metabolite destruction by ionizing radiations; concentration of growth factor; lignin research; methods for and analysis of agricultural chemical residues; protocols for studies on crops, animals, soil, water, elucidating residues of agricultural chemicals to establish safety and tolerances through United States Environmental Protection Agency. Address: 3412 Greenway Dr, Midland, MI 48640.

GETZIN, LOUIS W(ILLIAM), b. Milwaukee, Wis, Oct. 22, 33; m. 57; c. 4. ENTOMOLOGY. B.S, Wisconsin, 55, M.S, 57, Ph.D.(entom), 58. Assoc. entomologist, Agr. & Mech. Col, Tex, 58-60; asst. entomologist, WASH. STATE UNIV, 61-64, assoc. entomologist, WEST. WASH. EXP. STA. & EXTEN. CTR, 64-69, ENTOMOLOGIST, 69- Entom. Soc. Am. Metabolism and persistence of insecticides in soil; applied entomology and malacology. Address: Dept. of Entomology, Western Washington Research & Extension Center, Puyallup, WA 98371.

GETZIN, PAULA MAYER, b. N.Y.C, Oct. 6, 41; m. 65; c. 2. THEORETICAL CHEMISTRY. B.A, Radcliffe Col, 61; M.A, Columbia Univ, 62, Ph.D.(chem), 67. Fel. CHEM, Rutgers Univ, 67-69; ASST. PROF, NEWARK STATE COL, 69- Am. Phys. Soc. Theoretical chemical calculations. Address: Dept. of Chemistry, Newark State College, Union, NJ 07083.

GETZINGER, RICHARD W(ILLIS), b. Hammond, Ind, Dec. 16, 37; m. 61; c. 2. CHEMICAL ENGINEERING. B.S, California, Los Angeles, 60, M.S, Berkeley, 62, Nat. Sci. Found. fels, 61-64, Ph.D.(chem. eng), 64. STAFF MEM. RES, LOS ALAMOS SCI. LAB, 64- Sr. res. fel, Univ. Southampton, 70-71. AAAS; Am. Chem. Soc; Am. Inst. Chem. Eng; Combustion Inst. Multicomponent gaseous diffusion; gaseous detonations; high temperature chemical kinetics of gases in shock tubes. Address: Los Alamos Scientific Lab, P.O. Box 1663, Los Alamos, NM 87544.

GEURIN, H(OBART) B(EACH), b. Bonita, La, Feb. 20, 23; m. 52; c. 3. ANIMAL NUTRITION. B.S, Purdue, 47, M.S, 49, Ph.D.(animal nutrit), 50. Asst. animal husb, Purdue, 48-50; mgr, livestock res. dept, Ralston Purina Co, Mo, 50-67; DIR. FEED RES, AGR. PROD. DIV, W.R. GRACE & CO, 67- U.S.A, 43-46, Capt. Am. Soc. Animal. Sci. Livestock and dairy nutrition. Address: Feed Research, Agricultural Products Division, W.R. Grace & Co, 9348 Dielman Industrial Dr, St. Louis, MO 63132.

GEUZE, EMMERICUS C. W. A, b. Dordrecht, Netherlands, Mar. 27, 06; m. 34; c. 1. CIVIL ENGINEERING. C.E, Delft, 31. Res. asst, Delft, 31-34, lab. soil mech, 34-41, head res. dept, 41-48, dir. res, 48-60, sr. lectr. soil mech, univ, 48-51, prof, 51-60; prof. soil mech. & found. eng, RENSSELAER POLYTECH. INST, 60-69, WILLIAM WEIGHTMAN WALTER PROF. CIVIL ENG, 69-, CHMN. DEPT, 60- Lectr. various univs. & insts, U.S. & abroad, 47-64; UN Tech. Adv. Asn. adv. to Govt. Israel, 51-59; gen. reporter, Int. Conf. Soil Mech. & Found. Eng, Switz, 53, panel mem, Sect. I, Paris, 61; adv, NATO Comt. Runway Construct, 55; Bataafsche Petrol. Mij, France & Venezuela, 57; Netherlands Govt. adv. to Govt. Japan, 57-59; prof, Netherlands Univ. Found. Int. Coop, 57-60; mem, Nat. Res. Coun. adv. comt, U.S. Army Res. Off-Durham, 60-; rev. panel div. math, phys. & eng. sci, Nat. Sci. Found, 60-; consult, Raymond Int. Inc, N.Y, 61-; dept. bldg. construct, Gen. Elec. Co, 62-; Mech. Tech. Inc, 62-; res. div, U.S. Geol. Surv, Wash, D.C, 62-; mem. comt. rock & soil properties, hwy. res. bd, Nat. Acad. Sci-Nat. Res. Coun, 64- Am. Soc. Civil Eng; Am. Soc. Test. & Mat; Am. Soc. Eng. Educ; Brit. Soc. Rheol. Soil mechanics; foundation engineering; hydrology; hydraulic engineering. Address: Dept. of Civil Engineering, Rensselaer Polytechnic Institute, 110 Eighth St, Troy, NY 12181.

GEVANTMAN, L(EWIS) H(ERMAN), b. New York, N.Y, Sept. 12, 21; m. 48; c. 2. PHYSICAL CHEMISTRY. B.E, Hopkins, 42; Ph.D.(chem), Notre Dame, 51. Chem. operator, Bethlehem Steel Co, 42; Hopkins, 42-43; assoc. chemist, Clinton Labs, Oak Ridge Nat. Labs, 43-46; supvry. chemist, radiation chem, U.S. Naval Radiol. Defense Lab, 51-64; sr. sci. adv, U.S. Mission, UN Int. Atomic Energy Agency, 64-67; PROG. MGR, OFF. STANDARD REFERENCE DATA, NAT. BUR. STANDARDS, 67- Consult, Nuclear Sci. & Eng. Corp, 56-60. AAAS; Am. Chem. Soc; Radiation Res. Soc; N.Y. Acad. Sci. Effect of ionizing radiation on the rates of chemical reactions; distribution of absorbed energy in matter and energy transfer mechanisms; radiation dosimetry, nuclear weapons effects; chemical kinetics; solid state. Address: Office of Standard Reference Data, National Bureau of Standards, Washington, DC 20234.

GEVARTER, WILLIAM B, Cybernet, see 12th ed, Soc. & Behav. Vols.

GEVECKER, VERNON A(RTHUR) C(HARLES), b. St. Louis, Mo, Jan. 19, 09; m. 32; c. 2. CIVIL ENGINEERING. B.S.C.E, Missouri, 31, C.E, 50; M.S.C.E, Calif. Inst. Tech, 37. Surveyman & stud. engr, U.S. Eng. Dept, Mo, 31-34; asst, Mo. Sch. Mines, 34-35; Calif. Inst. Tech, 35-37; plant eng. trainee, Procter & Gamble Mfg. Co, 37-38; from instr. to PROF. CIVIL ENG, UNIV. MO-ROLLA, 38-, asst. dean of faculty, 53-59. C.Eng, A.U.S, 41-46, Res, 46-71, Lt. Col.(Ret). Am. Soc. Civil Eng; Nat. Soc. Prof. Eng. Open channel flows; particle size effects on certain phenomena. Address: Dept. of Civil Engineering, University of Missouri-Rolla, Rolla, MO 65401.

GEVER, GABRIEL, b. New York, N.Y, Feb. 19, 17; m. 45; c. 6. ORGANIC CHEMISTRY. Sc.B, Brown, 38; Columbia, 40-41. Res. assoc. underwater explosives, Oceanog. Inst, Woods Hole, 45-46; res. chemist, EATON LABS, 46-54, chief chem. sect, 54-61, asst. dir. res. chem, 61-64, coord. res. scheduling & planning, 64-65, DIR. chem. div, 65-69, DIV. VET. RES, 69- U.S.A, 41-46. Am. Chem. Soc. Furans; hydrazines; thiophenes; chemotherapeutics; operations research. Address: 15 Ridgeland Rd, Norwich, NY 13815.

GEVIRTZ, ARTHUR HAROLD, b. Brooklyn, N.Y, Aug. 13, 39; m. 67; c. 1. ORGANIC CHEMISTRY. B.S, Brooklyn Col, 60; M.S, Cornell, 62, Ph.D.(org. chem), 65. Sr. res. chemist, chem. div, U.S. Rubber Co, 65-68; OTTO B. MAY CO, 68-69, DIR. CHEM. SERV, 69- Asst. prof. eve. div, South. Conn. State Col, 66-67. Am. Chem. Soc; N.Y. Acad. Sci. Stereochemistry of Diels-Alder additions; Michael addition of hydrazines; synthesis of biologically active compounds; synthesis of chemical intermediates process development. Address: Otto B. May Co, 52 Amsterdam St, Newark, NJ 07105.

GEWANTER, HERMAN L(OUIS), b. Bronx, N.Y, May 26, 27; m. 66; c. 1. ORGANIC CHEMISTRY. B.S, Long Island, 52; Off. Naval Res. grant, Florida, 56-58, Nat. Insts. Health grant, 60-61, Ph.D.(fluorocarbons), 62. Chemist, Standard Chem. Prod, Inc, 52-56; res. asst, Florida, 56-61; proj. leader org. synthesis, res. & develop. chem. div, Union Carbide Corp, 62-66; staff scientist tech. serv. & prod. develop. PFIZER INC, 66-69, MGR. TECH. SERV, TEKCHEM, 69- U.S.A.A.F, 45-46. AAAS; Sci. Res. Soc. Am; Am. Chem. Soc. Fluorocarbon chemistry; fluoro-organic synthesis; alkyl amines and polyalkylene amines and derivatives; dimer acid based polyamides; polymer intermediates; detergent additives; chelation. Address: Tekchem, Pfizer Inc, 630 Flushing Ave, Brooklyn, NY 11206.

GEWARTOWSKI, J(AMES) W(ALTER), b. Chicago, Ill, Nov. 10, 30; m. 56; c. 5. ELECTRONIC ENGINEERING. B.S, Ill. Inst. Tech, 52; S.M, Mass. Inst. Tech, 53; Ph.D.(elec. eng), Stanford, 58. Res. asst, electronics lab, Stanford, 54-57; mem. tech. staff, BELL TEL. LABS, 57-62, supvr. microwave source group, 62-71, SUPVR. MICROWAVE INTEGRATED CIRCUITS & AMPLIFIER GROUP, 71- Inst. Elec. & Electronics Eng.(Thompson Mem. Award, Inst. Radio Eng, 60). Microwave solid state circuits. Address: Microwave Integrated Circuits & Amplifier Group, Bell Telephone Labs, 555 Union Blvd, Allentown, PA 18103.

GEWIRTZ, ALLAN, b. Brooklyn, N.Y, May 30, 31; m. 54; c. 3. MATHEMATICS. B.S, Brooklyn Col, 59, M.A, 64; Ph.D.(math), City Univ. New York, 67. Standards engr, West. Elec. Corp, 59-61; electronics proj. leader, Veeco Instruments Corp, 61-64; assoc. prof. math, Pace Col, 64-68; asst. prof, BROOKLYN COL, 68-71, ASSOC. PROF. MATH. & ASST. DEAN SCH. GEN. STUDIES, 71-, lectr, 59-64. U.S.A.F, 51-53. Am. Math. Soc; Math. Asn. Am; fel. N.Y. Acad. Sci; Soc. Indust. & Appl. Math. Combinatorial mathematics, including graph theory, block designs and game theory; low & direct current detection, including mass spectrometry and ion gauges. Address: Dept. of Mathematics, Brooklyn College, Brooklyn, NY 11210.

GEWIRTZMAN, LEONARD, b. Albany, N.Y, Jan. 19, 31; m. 51; c. 6. MATHEMATICS. B.A. & M.S, Hofstra Col, 56; Nat. Defense Ed. Act fel, Rutgers, 59-62, M.S, 61, Ph.D.(math), 62. Asst. prof. MATH, Long Island, 62-63; RUTGERS UNIV, 63-69, ASSOC. PROF, 69- Assoc. dir, Nat. Sci. Found. Inst. High Sch. & Col. Math. Teachers, 63- Am. Math. Soc. Relationship between the structures of modules having isomorphic or anti-isomorphic endomorphism rings. Address: Dept. of Mathematics, Rutgers, The State University, New Brunswick, NJ 08903.

GEYER, ALAN R(AYMOND), b. Ephrata, Pa, Jan. 23, 30; m. 53; c. 2. ECONOMIC GEOLOGY. B.S, Franklin & Marshall Col, 51; M.S, Michigan, 56. Geologist, Pa. Geol. Surv, 53-57, asst. state geologist, 57-68, CHIEF ENVIRON GEOL. DIV, BUR. TOPOG. & GEOL. SURV, 68- U.S.A, 53-55, Res, 55-61. Geol. Soc. Am; Nat. Asn. Geol. Teachers. Geology of non-metallic mineral deposits; structure and stratigraphy of the Cambrian and Ordovician rocks of Pennsylvania. Address: Dept. of Environmental Resources, Bureau of Topographic & Geologic Survey, Harrisburg, PA 17120.

GEYER, BRADFORD P(EARSON), b. Boston, Mass, April 23, 13; m. 41. ORGANIC CHEMISTRY. B.S, Northeastern, 35; Univ. fel, Washington (Seattle), 36-41, Ph.D.(chem), 41. Res. chemist, Shell Develop. Co, Shell Oil Co, 41-59, mem. dir. staff, chem. res, 59-60, staff tech. asst, patent div, 60-71; RETIRED. Am. Chem. Soc; fel. Am. Inst. Chem; N.Y. Acad. Sci. Synthetic organic chemistry; surface-active agents; synthetic polymers; petrochemicals. Address: 5520 Proctor Ave, Oakland, CA 94618.

GEYER, JOHN CHARLES, b. Neosho, Mo, Aug. 11, 06; m. 33; c. 1. SANITARY ENGINEERING. B.S, Michigan, 31; Austin fel, Harvard, 31-34, M.S, 33; D.Eng, Hopkins, 43. From instr. to asst. prof. sanit. eng, North Carolina, 34-37; assoc. civil eng, Hopkins, 37-42; asst. chief engr, health & sanit. div, Off. Inter-Am. Affairs, D.C, 42-43; assoc. prof. sanit. eng, JOHNS HOPKINS UNIV, 46-48, PROF. ENVIRON. ENG, 48-, chmn. dept. geog. & environ. eng, 57-69. Summers, mem. staff, Chesapeake Bay & Susquehanna Drainage Basin Comts. & Hampton Roads Water Supply Study, Nat. Resources Planning Bd, D.C, 40-42. Engr, Md. Water Resources Comn, 38; comnr, Md. Dept. Geol, Mines & Water Resources, 55- Prin. investr, Water Filtration Proj, 47-51; waste disposal projs, Atomic Energy Comn, 48-; Storm Drainage Res. Proj, 49-; low flow augmentation proj, Nat. Insts. Health, 57-63; ground water measurement res, 62-; sanit. sewerage res. proj, Fed. Housing Admin, 59-63, residential water use proj, 59-; cooling water res. proj, Edison Elec. Inst, 63- Consult, nat. res. resources comt, Hoover comn, 48; Joint Res. & Develop. Bd, 49-52; Md. State Planning Dept, 49-; Gulick Bd. Study New York Water Supply, 51; bur. Water Supply, Md, 52-; WHO & sch. pub. health, Chile, 55-56; Interstate Comn. Potomac River Basin, 56-57; Baltimore Regional Planning Coun, 58-59; Patuxent River Valley Regional Sewerage Study, 59-61; Phila. Elec. Co, 59-; Metrop. Wash. D.C. Pollution Study, 60-62; Baltimore Gas Elec. Co; U.S. Pub. Health Serv, 62- Mem. tech. comt. water supply, Interstate Comn. Potomac River Basin, 48-; subcomt. water supply, Nat. Res. Coun, 49-, adv. comt. small sewers, bldg. res, adv. bd, 56-57, comt. ed. objectives, 57; Adv. Comt. Spec. Weapons Defense; Eng. Joint Coun-Am. Water Works Asn. rep, comt, Nat. Water Policy, 57-; study sect. environ. sci. & eng, Nat. Insts. Health, 59-63; adv. comt. reactor safeguards, Atomic Energy Comn, 64, v.pres, 64. U.S.N.R, 43-46, Res, 46-53, Lt. Comdr. AAAS; Am. Soc. Civil Eng; Am. Water Works Asn; Water Pollution Control Fedn; Am. Pub. Health Asn; Am. Geophys. Union; Acad. Environ. Eng; Royal Soc. Health. Textile waste treatment and recovery; industrial wastes; ground water in Baltimore industrial area; water supply and waste water disposal. Address: Dept. of Geography & Environmental Engineering, Ames 511, Johns Hopkins University, Baltimore, MD 21218.

GEYER, J(OHN) HUBERT, b. New Albany, Ind, May 17, 00; m. 28. ANATOMY. B.S, Louisville, 23, M.S, 24; Washington (St. Louis), 28; Minnesota, 37. Prof. biol, Kans. Wesleyan, 29-32; Ill. Col, 32-34; instr. zool. & physiol, Illinois, 46-49; ASSOC. PROF. biol, Franklin Col, 49-50; ANAT. & PHYSIOL, BAYLOR UNIV, 50- AAAS; Soc. Exp. Biol. & Med. Animal behavior; micro-anatomy. Address: 5126 Homer St, Dallas, TX 75206.

GEYER, RICHARD A(DAM), b. N.Y.C, Oct. 27, 14; m. 40; c. 2. OCEANOGRAPHY. B.S, N.Y. Univ, 37, M.S, 40; Fordham, 38; Columbia, 38; M.A, Princeton, 50, Ph.D.(geophysics), 51. Res. geophysics & geol, Standard Oil Co, N.J, 38-42; physicist-in-charge degaussing range, bur. ord, U.S. Navy Dept, R.I, 42-44, sr. field instr, Oceanog. Inst, Woods Hole, 44-45; sr. res. geophysicist, Humble Oil & Ref. Co, 45-48, head oceanog. sect, 49-54; chief geophysicist, gravity dept, Geophys. Serv, Inc, Tex. Instruments, Inc, 54-59, mgr, 59-66, tech. dir. oceanog, geosci. dept, 63-66; HEAD DEPT. OCEANOG, TEX. A&M UNIV, 66- Instr, Princeton, 39-42; asst. prof, Univ. Houston, 48-; mem. oceanwide surv. panel, comt. oceanog, Nat. Acad. Sci, 61-; v.chmn, President's Comn. Marine Sci. Eng. & Resources, 67-69; chmn. adv. comt, int. decade ocean explor, Nat. Sci. Found, 70-; consult, U.S. Coast & Geodetic Surv. Civilian with Off. Sci. Res. & Develop, 44. Soc. Explor. Geophys.(ed, 49-51); Am. Geophys. Union; Nat. Oceanog. Asn; Am. Soc. Oceanog; Marine Technol. Soc. Exploration geophysics; application of oceanographic science to marine engineering operations and to military aspects of underwater sound. Address: Dept. of Oceanography, Texas A&M University, College Station, TX 77843.

GEYER, ROBERT L(EE), b. Chula Vista, Calif, Feb. 6, 15; m. 39, 48; c. 3. SEISMOLOGY. A.B, Univ. Calif, Berkeley, 38; M.S, La. State Univ, 51. Computer, Seismograph Serv, Okla, 38-40; Shell Oil Co, 40-41, asst. seismologist, 41-44; loft mathematician, Rohr Aircraft Corp, Calif, 44-46; seismologist, Seismograph Surv. Corp. of Del, Venezuela, 46-48; instr. geol. & geophys, La. State Univ, 48-51; geophysicist, Pan Am. Petrol. Corp, 51-52, sr. res. engr, 52-59, res. assoc, 59-65, res. group supvr, 65-67; PERSONNEL TRAINING MGR, SEISMOGRAPH SERV. CORP, 67- Soc. Explor. Geophys; Europ. Soc. Explor. Geophys; Can. Soc. Explor. Geophys.(awards, 61, 69); Seismol. Soc. Am; Am. Asn. Petrol. Geol; Am. Soc. Training & Develop. Exploration seismology; quality control in seismic exploration; seismic field research in the generation, propagation and reception of elastic waves in the earth and their relation to the geology. Address: Seismograph Service Corp, P.O. Box 1590, Tulsa, OK 74102.

GEYER, ROBERT P(ERSHING), b. Racine, Wis, Sept. 28, 18; m. 45; c. 2. BIOCHEMISTRY. B.S, Wisconsin, 41, M.S, 43, fel. & Ph.D.(biochem), 46. Fel, SCH. PUB. HEALTH, HARVARD, 46-48, asst. prof. NUTRIT, 49-55, assoc. prof, 56-71, PROF, 71- Mem. nutrit. sci. training comt, Nat. Inst. Gen. Med. Sci; coun. thrombosis, Am. Heart Asn; Int. Conf. Biochem. of Lipids. Fel. AAAS; Am. Chem. Soc; Am. Asn. Cancer Res; Am. Inst. Nutrit; Tissue Cult. Asn; Soc. Exp. Biol. & Med. Development and study of artificial blood substitutes; nutritional, biochemical and chemical studies on oils and fats; parenteral nutrition and the metabolic fate of parenteral nutrients; tissue culture biochemistry. Address: Nutrition Dept, Harvard School of Public Health, 665 Huntington Ave, Boston, MA 02115.

GEYER-DUSZYNSKA, IRENE, b. Warsaw, Poland, Feb. 18, 24; wid. DEVELOPMENTAL GENETICS, CYTOGENETICS. M.Biol, Warsaw, 49, Ph.D. (biol. sci), 59. Sr. lectr. biol, Acad. Phys. Ed, Poland, 51-54; cytol, Warsaw, 54-64, docent & sr. lectr, 65; res. assoc. biol, Geneva, 65-67; MED. COL, CORNELL UNIV, 67-68, INSTR. ANAT, 68- Rockefeller Found. fel. biophys, Univ. Chicago, 59-60; zool, Columbia, 60-61. AAAS; Genetics Soc. Am; Am. Soc. Cell Biol; Am. Inst. Biol. Sci; Swiss Zool. Soc. Role of chromosomes and cytoplasm in development and differentiation, especially the elimination of chromosomes in Cecidomyiidae; T-locus in Mus musculus; nuclear transplantation in Drosophila melanogaster. Address: Dept. of Anatomy, Cornell University Medical College, 1300 York Ave, New York, NY 10021.

GEYLING, F(RANZ) TH(OMAS), b. Tientsin, China, Sept. 7, 26; nat; m. 61; c. 1. ENGINEERING MECHANICS. B.S, Stanford, 50, M.S, 51, Ph.D.(eng. mech), 54. Instr, Stanford, 50-52; mem. tech. staff, mech. res, BELL TEL. LABS, 54-60, HEAD ANAL. MECH. & ENG. PHYSICS, 60- Am. Soc. Mech. Eng; Soc. Exp. Stress Anal; Am. Inst. Aeronaut. & Astronaut; Int. Asn. Bridge & Struct. Eng. Celestial and structural mechanics; elasticity. Address: Post House Rd, Morristown, NJ 07960.

GEYMER, DOUGLAS O(LIVER), b. Tacoma, Wash, Feb. 17, 33; m. 54; c. 6. PHYSICAL CHEMISTRY. B.S, Washington (Seattle), 54, Nat. Sci. Found. fel, Duke, 54-55, Du Pont fel, 56-57, Ph.D.(chem), 58. RES. CHEMIST, E.I. du Pont de Nemours & Co, 56; RES. DEPT, Monsanto Chem. Co, 57-60; SHELL DEVELOP. CO, 61- Am. Chem. Soc. Radiation chemistry; reaction kinetics. Address: Research Dept, Shell Development Co, Emeryville, CA 94608.

GEZON, HORACE M(ARTIN), b. Grand Rapids, Mich, Nov. 12, 14; m; c. 2. MICROBIOLOGY, EPIDEMIOLOGY. A.B, Calvin Col, 38; M.D, Chicago, 40. Res. fel. pediat. path, Chicago, 46-47, instr. pediat, 47-49, asst. prof, 49-52; assoc. prof. epidemiol, Univ. Pittsburgh, 52-58, PROF. epidemiol. & microbiol, 58-66; PEDIAT, SCH. MED, BOSTON UNIV, 66-, chmn. dept, 66-70. Vis. prof, Am. Univ, Beirut, 50-51; consult. to Surgeon Gen, U.S. Army; dir. comn. enteric infections, Armed Forces Epidemiol. Bd, 63-70; dir. pediat. serv, Boston City Hosp, 66-70; lectr. pediat, Harvard Med. Sch, 67-; microbiol, Harvard Sch. Pub. Health, 67-; consult. pediat, Mass. Gen. Hosp, 67- U.S.N, 42-46, Comdr. Soc. Exp. Biol. & Med; Soc. Pediat. Res; Am. Epidemiol. Soc; Am. Pediat. Soc; Am. Asn. Immunol; Infectious Disease Soc. Am. Action of antibiotics on bacteria; epidemiology of streptococcal, staphylococcal and enteric diseases; bacterial metabolism. Address: Boston City Hospital, 818 Harrison Ave, Boston, MA 02118.

GFELLER, BARBARA, S.N.J.M, b. Lind, Wash, Nov. 14, 26. BIOLOGY. B.A, Ft. Wright Col. Holy Names, 48; Marquette grant, Woods Hole Marine Biol. Sta, 57; M.S, Marquette, 58; Nat. Sci. Found. fel, Washington (Seattle), 60; Ph.D.(biol), Oregon, 65. Instr. BIOL, MARYLHURST COL, 58-71, ASSOC. PROF, 71- Stanford Shell fel, 70. Genetics Soc. Am; Nat. Asn. Biol. Teachers. Action of genes concerned with the development of eye color in Drosophila melanogaster; experimental study of tissue interaction in developing chick wing bud. Address: Dept. of Biology, Marylhurst College, Marylhurst, OR 97036.

GFELLER, EDUARD, b. Aarburg, Switz, Sept. 11, 37; nat; m. 59; c. 2. NEUROANATOMY, PSYCHIATRY. Dr.Med, Univ. Berne, 64. Haus fel. endocrinol, Univ. Berne, 64-65; instr. NEUROANAT, JOHNS HOPKINS UNIV, 65-66, ASST. PROF, 66-; RES. PSYCHIATRIST, SHEPPARD-ENOCH PRATT HOSP, 71- AAAS; Am. Asn. Anat; Biophys. Soc; Am. Soc. Cell Biol; Soc. Neurosci; Am. Soc. Neurochem. Comparative neuroanatomy of primate midbrain; endocrine factors influencing brain development; catecholamine metabolism in brain; active transport of biogenic amines and electrolytes in epithelia and nerve endings. Address: Dept. of Anatomy, Johns Hopkins University, 709 N. Wolfe St, Baltimore, MD 21205.

GHADIMI, HOSSEIN, b. Meshed, Iran, May 30, 22; U.S. citizen; m. 50; c. 4. MEDICINE, PEDIATRICS. M.D, Teheran, 47. Chmn. dept. PEDIAT, med. sch, Shiraz, 56-59; sr. res. fel, res. inst, Hosp. Sick Children, Toronto, 59-61; asst. prof, STATE UNIV. N.Y. DOWNSTATE MED. CTR, 61-67, assoc. prof, 67-69, PROF, 69-; DIR. PEDIAT, METHODIST HOSP. BROOKLYN, 67- Res. fel. pediat, Children's Med. Ctr, Harvard, 57-59. AAAS; Am. Soc. Clin. Nutrit; Soc. Pediat. Res; Am. Pediat. Soc; Am. Med. Asn. Inborn errors of amino acid metabolism; descriptions of histidinemia and hyperlysinemia; biochemical causes of mental retardation. Address: Dept. of Pediatrics, Methodist Hospital of Brooklyn, 506 Sixth St, Brooklyn, NY 11215.

GHAFFARI, A(BOLGHASSEM), b. Teheran, Iran, June 15, 09. MATHEMATICS. B.Sc, Univ. Nancy, France, 32, M.Sc, 34; D.Sc, Paris, 36; British Coun. scholar, London, 46-47, Ph.D.(math, physics), 48. Assoc. prof. math, Tehran Univ, Iran, 37, prof, 42; asst, King's Col, London, 47-48; Fulbright scholar & res. assoc, Harvard, 50-51; Princeton, 51-52; mathematician, Nat. Bur. Standards, 56-57, aeronaut. res. scientist, 57-64; sr. aerospace scientist, Goddard Space Flight Ctr, NASA, 64-71; PROF. MATH, TEHRAN UNIV, 71- Mem, Inst. Adv. Study, 51-52. Apollo Achievement Award. AAAS; Am. Math. Soc; Math. Asn. Am; Am. Astron. Soc; fel. N.Y. Acad. Sci. Mathematical analysis; astronomy; celestial mechanics; fluid dynamics; applied mathematics. Address: Faculty of Sciences, Tehran University, Tehran, Iran.

GHALLA, MANJU D, b. Bombay, India, June 10, 40; m. 69. ELECTRICAL ENGINEERING. M.Sc, Univ. Bombay, 62; M.S, Univ. Okla, 64, Ph.D.(elec. eng), 71. ASST. PROF. ELEC. ENG, CLEVELAND STATE UNIV, 68- X-ray photoconductivity of single crystal anthracene; superconductivity, especially flux-trapping in superconductors using microwave techniques. Address: Dept. of Electrical Engineering, Cleveland State University, Euclid at 24th St, Cleveland, OH 44115.

GHALY, THARWAT SHAHATA, b. Cairo, Egypt, Oct. 12, 39; m. 65; c. 2. GEOLOGY, PETROLOGY. B.Sc, Ain Shams, Cairo, 59; Ph.D.(igneous & metamorphic petrol), Glasgow, 65. Instr. geol, faculty sci, Ain Shams, Cairo, 59-61; res. asst, Glasgow, 62-65; mineral, Thermal Syndicate Ltd, Wallsend, Eng, 66-67; ASST. PROF. GEOL, EAST TEXAS STATE UNIV, 67- Geol. Soc. Am. Igneous and metamorphic petrology with mineralogy and geochemistry; structures, petrology and metamorphic differentiation of Precambrian rocks. Address: Dept. of Earth Sciences, East Texas State University, Commerce, TX 75428.

GHANDHI, SORAB KHUSHRO, b. Allahabad, India, Jan. 1, 28; U.S. citizen; m. 50; c. 3. ELECTRICAL ENGINEERING. B.Sc, Benares Hindu Univ, 47; Tata fel, Illinois, 47-51, M.S, 48, univ. fel, 48-51, Ph.D, 51. Mem. tech. staff, electronics lab, Gen. Elec. Co, 51-60; res. mgr, Philco Corp, Ford Motor Co, 60-63; PROF. ELEC. ENG, RENSSELAER POLYTECH. INST, 63-, CHMN. DIV. ELECTROPHYS, 67- Consult, Sprague Elec. Co, Mass. Sci. Res. Soc. Am; fel. Inst. Elec. & Electronics Eng. Solid state devices, processes and materials; microelectronics. Address: 7 Linda Lane, Niskayuna, Schenectady, NY 12309.

GHARRETT, JOHN T(UTT), b. Tacoma, Wash, May 5, 09; m. 40; c. 3. FISHERIES. B.S, Washington (Seattle), 40. Asst. scientist, Int. Pac. Halibut Comn, 40-45; asst. dir. res, Fish Comn, Ore, 45-49; res. coord, Pac. Marine Fisheries Comn, 49-55; asst. adminr, Alaska Commercial Fisheries, U.S. Fish & Wildlife Serv, 57-58, regional dir, Bur. Commercial Fisheries, Dept. of Interior, Alaska Region, 58-60, N.Atlantic Region, 60-69; staff asst. to dir, NAT. MARINE FISHERIES SERV, DEPT. COMMERCE, Wash, D.C, 69-71, SPEC. ASST. TO DIR, REGION ONE, SEATTLE, 71- Am. Inst. Fisheries Res. Biol. Administration of fishery research. Address: National Marine Fisheries Service, Dept. of Commerce, 6116 Arcade Bldg, 1319 Second Ave, Seattle, WA 98101.

GHASSEMI, MASOOD, b. Tehran, Iran, Mar. 7, 40; m. 68. ENVIRONMENTAL ENGINEERING. B.S, Univ. Wash, 61, M.S, 63, Ph.D.(sanit. eng), 67. Proj. engr, Havens & Emerson Engrs, Ohio, 67-68; MEM. TECH. STAFF, ATOMICS INT, N.AM. ROCKWELL CORP, 68- Am. Water Works Asn; Water Pollution Control Fedn; Am. Chem. Soc. The chemical nature of color-causing organics in natural waters; the mechanism of coagulation of organic color and turbidity in natural waters by hydrolyzing salts; chemical precipitation of phosphates from wastewaters; advanced waste treatment. Address: Chemistry Technology Dept, Atomics International, P.O. Box 309, Canoga Park, CA 91304.

GHATE, MADHAV R, b. Karamba, India, Dec. 13, 34; c. 1. PHYSICAL CHEMISTRY, CHEMICAL ENGINEERING. B.Sc, Univ. Poona, 56, Hons, 57, M.Sc, 58; Ph.D.(phys. chem), Univ. Bombay, 64. Sci. off. CHEM, Atomic Energy Estab, India, 58-65; RES. ASSOC, Yeshiva Univ, 65-67; COLUMBIA UNIV, 67- Am. Chem. Soc. Stable isotope separation by chemical exchange methods; mass spectrometry; process development in separation techniques; thermodynamics of ion exchange processes in mixed solvents; gas chromatography; instrumental methods of chemical analysis; high vacuum techniques. Address: Dept. of Chemistry, Columbia University, New York, NY 10027.

GHATE, P(RABHAKAR) B(HIMRAO), b. Terdal, India, May 23, 33; m. 64. SOLID STATE PHYSICS. B.Sc, Karnatak Univ, India, 53; M.Sc, Bombay, 55; Ph.D.(solid state physics), Rensselaer Polytech, 63. Demonstr. physics, Inst. Sci, Bombay, 53-55; asst. lectr. phys. math, Ismail Yusuf Col, Bombay, 55-58; res. asst. physics, Rensselaer Polytech. Inst, 58-62; res. assoc. mat. sci, Cornell Univ, 62-63, researcher & instr, 63-66; MEM. TECH. STAFF, SEMICONDUCTOR RES. & DEVELOP. LAB, TEX. INSTRUMENTS INC, 66- Vis. indust. assoc. prof, electronic sci. ctr, South. Methodist Univ, 69- Am. Phys. Soc; Am. Inst. Mining, Metall. & Petrol. Eng. Defects in solids; elastic constants; electromigration; resistivity; structure of metal films; metallization studies related to integrated circuits. Address: Semiconductor Research & Development Lab, Texas Instruments Inc, P.O. Box 5012, Mail Stop 72, Dallas, TX 75222.

GHAUSI, MOHAMMED SHUAIB, b. Kabul, Afghanistan, Feb. 16, 30; m. 61; c. 2. ELECTRICAL ENGINEERING. B.S, California, Berkeley, 56, M.S, 57, Ph.D.(elec. eng), 60. Asst. prof. ELEC. ENG, N.Y. UNIV, 60-62, assoc. prof, 62-66, PROF, 66- Inst. Elec. & Electronics Eng. Electronic circuits and network theory. Address: Dept. of Electrical Engineering, New York University, Bronx, NY 10453.

GHAZI, HASSAN SUBHI, b. Aleppo, Syria, Feb. 20, 32; m. 65; c. 2. MECHANICAL ENGINEERING. B.S, Purdue, 54; M.Sc, Ohio State, 56, Ph.D. (mech. eng), 62. Asst. prof. mech. eng, Akron, 62-65; eng. scientist, B.F. GOODRICH CO, 65-66, sr. eng. scientist, 66-70, SECT. LEADER, ENG. SCI. SECT, 70- Assoc. prof, Univ. Akron, 65-69. Am. Soc. Mech. Eng; Am. Soc. Eng. Educ. Non-uniform flows through pipe orifices; heat transfer. Address: B.F. Goodrich Co, 500 S. Main St, Akron, OH 44318.

GHEITH, MOHAMED A, b. Kom Hamada, Egypt, Feb. 11, 25; m. 52; c. 2. GEOLOGY, MINERALOGY. B.Sc, Cairo, 45; M.S, Minnesota, 50, Ph.D. (geol), 51. Demonstr. GEOL, Cairo, 45-46; lectr, Ain-Shams, Cairo, 52-57; BOSTON UNIV, 58-59, asst. prof, 59-61, assoc. prof, 61-69, PROF, 69-, CHMN. DEPT, 64- Fel, sch. adv. studies, Mass. Inst. Tech, 57-59. Consult, Bur. Mining & Commerce, Egypt, 54-57. AAAS; fel. Geol. Soc. Am; Am. Crystallog. Asn; Nat. Asn. Geol. Teachers; Mineral. Soc. Am; Geol. Soc. Egypt. Geochemistry of iron oxides and oxide hydrates; geochronology of Northeast Africa; crystallography, genesis, stability relations and synthesis of some phosphate minerals and silicates. Address: Dept. of Geology, Boston University, Boston, MA 02215.

GHELARDI, RAYMOND J, b. San Francisco, Calif, Aug. 12, 20; m. 43; c. 4. MARINE ECOLOGY. Rockefeller fel, Scripps Inst, California, 55, M.S, 56; Ph.D.(biol. oceanog), San Diego, 60. Res. asst. marine ecol, Scripps Inst, California, 56-59; Nat. Sci. Found. fel. terrestrial ecol, Oxford, 60-62; asst. res. zoologist marine ecol, Bodega Marine Lab, California, Berkeley, 62-65; SCIENTIST, BIOL. STA, FISHERIES RES. BD. CAN, 65- U.S.A, 43-46. Quantitative, experimental and field ecology dealing with summarizing characteristics of terrestrial, benthic and neritic, marine communities. Address: Biological Station, Fisheries Research Board of Canada, Nanaimo, B.C, Can.

GHENT, ARTHUR W, b. Toronto, Ont, Sept. 8, 27; m. 61; c. 3. ECOLOGY, BIOMETRY. B.Sc.F, Univ. Toronto, 50, M.A, 54; Ph.D.(zool), Univ. Chicago, 60. Res. off, forest insect lab, Can. Dept. Agr, 50-59; asst. prof. zool, Univ. Okla, 60-64; POP. BIOL, UNIV. ILL, URBANA, 64-65, assoc. prof, 65-69, PROF, 70- Soc. Study Evolution; Can. Entom. Soc. Insect ecology and behavior; forest ecology. Address: 287 Morrill Hall, University of Illinois, Urbana, IL 61801.

GHENT, EDWARD DALE, b. Little Rock, Ark, Oct. 4, 37; m. 62. GEOLOGY. B.S, Yale, 59; Woodrow Wilson fel. & Nat. Sci. Found. summer fels, California, Berkeley, 62-63, Ph.D.(geol), 64. Asst. prof. GEOL, San Jose State Col, 64; lectr, Victoria Univ. Wellington, 64-67; asst. prof, UNIV. CALGARY, 67-70, ASSOC. PROF, 70- AAAS; Geol. Soc. Am; Mineral. Soc. Am; Geol. Asn. Can; Geochem. Soc. Metamorphic petrology; geochemistry; electron microprobe analysis. Address: Dept. of Geology, University of Calgary, Calgary 44, Alta, Can.

GHENT, KENNETH S(MITH), b. Hamilton, Ont, June 29, 11; nat; m. 42; c. 3. MATHEMATICS. B.A, McMaster, 32; S.M, Chicago, 33, fel, 34-35, Ph.D. (math), 35. Instr. math, Oregon, 35-39, asst. prof, 39-42; physicist, 11th Naval Dist, U.S.N, 42-45; assoc. prof. MATH, UNIV. ORE, 47-60, PROF, 60- Am. Math. Soc; Math. Asn. Am. Algebra and number theory; sums of values of polynomials multiplied by constants. Address: Dept. of Mathematics, University of Oregon, Eugene, OR 97403.

GHENT, WILLIAM ROBERT, b. Hamilton, Ont, Apr. 25, 22; m; c. 4. SURGERY. M.D. C.M, Queen's (Ont), 47. Clin. asst. SURG, QUEEN'S UNIV. (ONT), 55-60, asst. prof, 60-67, assoc. prof, 67-71, PROF, 71-; CHIEF OF SURG, HOTEL DIEU HOSP, 57- Fel, Royal Col. Physicians & Surgeons Can, 54; dir. automotive crash res. unit, Queen's Univ.(Ont), 66. R.C.N.R, 50, Lt. Comdr.(ret). Fel. Am. Col. Surg; fel. Int. Col. Surg. Address: Dept. of Surgery, Hotel Dieu Hospital, Kingston, Ont, Can.

GHEORGHIU, PAUL, b. Rumania, June 27, 16; U.S. citizen; m. 46; c. 1. PHYSICS. B.S.E.E, Signal Corps Mil. Acad, 37; lic. es sc, Polytech. Sch, 40; dipl. life sci, Adv. Prof. Sch, 55; Rensselaer Polytech, 63. Asst. prof. physics & electronics, Signal Corps Mil. Acad, 42-43; ed, Asn. Free Press, 48-56; proj. engr. electronics, Manson Labs, 57-59; Bulova Res. & Develop. Electronics, Bulova Watch Co, 59-60; sr. systs. engr. res. & develop, Transitron Electronic Corp, 60-62; dir. bio-med. & electronic res, adv. res. ctr, Hi-G, Inc, Conn, 62-66; v.pres, Med. Electrosci, Inc, N.Y, 66-70; MGR. INDUST. CONTROLS DIV, OPTO MECHANISMS, INC, PLAINVIEW, 70- Secy, Joint Mil. Comt. Defense Res, 40-42; sr. staff scientist, Frequency Electronics; consult, Lorad Electronics; Math. Assocs. Inc. Rumanian Army, Capt. AAAS; sr. mem. Inst. Elec. & Electronics Eng; sr. mem. Instrument Soc. Am; Int. Fedn. Med. Electronics & Biol. Eng; N.Y. Acad. Sci; Int. Soc. Cybernet. Med. Metrology of standards and traceability; highly diversified and interdisciplinary activity, within company objectives, embracing medical electronics, electro-chemical and solid state switching techniques, with emphasis on pioneering new ways posed by demanding space and oceanographic technology; life sciences; bio-engineering; environmental technology; applied physics; communication in their design; production and marketing; management of advanced electronics. Address: 737 Boelsen Dr, Westbury, NY 11590.

GHER, RALPH, JR, b. Urbana, Ill, Mar. 30, 25; m. 47; c. 2. INORGANIC CHEMISTRY. A.B, Illinois, 48, M.S, 49, Ph.D.(chem), 52. Sr. chemist, MINN. MINING & MFG. CO, 52-53, tech. supvr, 53-57, prod. specialist, 57-65, SALES MGR, 65- U.S.N.R, 43-45. Am. Chem. Soc. Inorganic chemistry; rare earths; organo-phosphorous compounds. Address: 2424 Tanglewood Rd, Decatur, GA 30033.

GHERARDI, GHERARDO J(OSEPH), b. Lucca, Italy, July 1, 21; nat; m. 57; c. 4. PATHOLOGY. A.B, Princeton, 42; M.D, Columbia, 45. From instr. to asst. prof. PATH, col. med, State Univ. N.Y. Downstate Med. Ctr, 50-54; ASSOC. PROF, sch. med, Tufts Univ, 54-70; SCH. MED, BOSTON UNIV, 70-; PATHOLOGIST, FRAMINGHAM UNION HOSP, 70- Assoc. vis. pathologist, Kings County Hosp, 54; pathologist, Tufts-New Eng. Med. Ctr, 54-70. Med.C, 46-48, Capt. Am. Med. Asn; Col. Am. Path; N.Y. Acad. Sci. Human diagnostic pathology. Address: 25 Kenilworth Rd, Wellesley, MA 02181.

GHERING, WALTER L, b. Edinboro, Pa, Nov. 3, 30. PHYSICS, ACOUSTICS. B.S, U.S. Naval Acad, 56; B.S, Pa. State, 61, M.S, 63, Ph.D.(physics), 68. RES. PHYSICIST, BABCOCK & WILCOX RES. CTR, 68- U.S.N, 51-60, Res, 60-, Lt. Acoust. Soc. Am; Soc. Nondestructive Test. Ultrasonics; non-destructive testing and instrumentation. Address: 2460 S. Linden Ave, Alliance, OH 44601.

GHERZI, ERNEST, S.J, b. San Remo, Italy, Aug. 8, 86. METEOROLOGY, SEISMOLOGY. Ph.D, Jesuits Inst. Philos, France, 10. Dir. meteorol. & seismol, ZiKaWei Observ, Shanghai, China, 30-49; lectr, St. Louis, 54-56; DIR. GEOPHYS. RES, GEOPHYS. OBSERV, COL. JEAN DE BREBEUF, 56- Mem. Int. Comns. Marine, Synoptic Meteorol, Seismol. & Hydrol, 33-49; lectr, Loyola Univ.(La), 57-59; mem. Int. Comn. Global Atmospheric Elec. Off, Order of Crown of Italy; Portuguese Order of St. James; gold medal, Italian Navy Far East; gold olive, Br. Int. Merchant Marine. Asst. chaplain, Allied Forces, 16-18. Am. Meteorol. Soc; Can. Asn. Physicists; Pontifical Acad. Sci; Lisbon Acad. Sci; Italian Inst. Geophys. Dynamic and tropical meteorology; radiometeorology; ionosphere and weather. Address: Geophysics Observatory, Jean-de-Brebeuf College, 3200 Chemin Ste. Catherine, Montreal, 250, Que, Can.

GHIA, KIRTI N, b. Bombay, India. FLUID DYNAMICS, APPLIED MECHANICS. B.S, Gujarat Univ, India, 60; univ. scholar, Ill. Inst. Technol, 61-69, Aerospace Res. Labs. grant, 64-65, M.S, 65, NASA grant, 65-69, Ph.D.(mech. & aerospace eng), 69. Res. engr, Premier Automobiles Ltd, India, 60-61; res. asst, FLUID DYNAMICS, Ill. Inst. Technol, 61-62, instr, 62, asst, 62-69; ASST. PROF, UNIV. CINCINNATI, 69- Instr, Ill. Inst. Technol, summer 63; consult, Huyck Corp, 65-67. Am. Inst. Aeronaut. & Astronaut; Am. Soc. Mech. Eng; Am. Soc. Eng. Educ. Confined coaxial heterogeneous jet mixing phenomena; flow augmentation in coanda type nozzles; feasibility studies of constant volume combustion for gas turbine engines; numerical solutions of Navier-Stokes and boundary layer equations. Address: Dept. of Aerospace Engineering, University of Cincinnati, Cincinnati, OH 45221.

GHIDONI, ESTELLE, O.S.U, b. Yonkers, N.Y, Feb. 2, 11. BIOLOGY. B.S, Col. New Rochelle, 32; M.S, Cath. Univ. Am, 44, Ph.D.(biol), 48. Instr. BIOL, COL. NEW ROCHELLE, 43-50, assoc. prof, 50-65, PROF, 65- Coord. develop. marine biol. sta, Columbia Island, L.I, N.Y. AAAS; Am. Soc. Microbiol; Nat. Sci. Teachers Asn.(chmn, 57). Effect of thyroid inhibiting drugs on tail regeneration in amphibian tadpoles. Address: Dept. of Biology, College of New Rochelle, New Rochelle, NY 10801.

GHIDONI, JOHN JOSEPH, b. Yonkers, N.Y, Feb. 22, 31; m. 56; c. 6. PATHOLOGY. B.Sc, Fordham, 53; M.D, State Univ. N.Y, 57. Intern, Brooklyn Hosp, 57-58; resident path, Bronx Munic. Hosp. Ctr, N.Y, 58-62; instr, Albert Einstein Col. Med, 62-63; asst. prof, Baylor Col. Med, 65-69, dir. lab. exp. path, 66-69; PROF. PATH, UNIV. TEX. MED. SCH, SAN ANTONIO, 69- U.S. Pub. Health Serv. fel, Albert Einstein Col. Med, 61-62, spec. fel, 62-63; consult. path, Vet. Admin. Hosp, Houston, Tex, 67-69. U.S.A.F, 63-65, Capt. Electron Micros. Soc. Am; Int. Acad. Path; Radiation Res. Soc; Am. Soc. Exp. Path; Am. Soc. Cell Biol; Am. Asn. Path. & Bact; Am. Soc. Artificial Internal Organs. Amyloidosis; epithelial metaplasia; cell injury by proton particles; effects of isoproteronal on salivary gland; cardiovascular prostheses; cellular dedifferentiation and differentiation. Address: Dept. of Pathology, University of Texas Medical School, 7703 Floyd Curl Dr, San Antonio, TX 78229.

GHIONIS, CONSTANTINE A, b. Poros, Greece, Jan. 1, 23; m. 60; c. 2. PHYSICAL CHEMISTRY, TEXTILES. M.S, Athens Tech, 48; Ph.D.(chem), Stuttgart Tech, 58. MGR. TEXTILE RES. & DEVELOP, REEVES BROS, INC, 71- Greek Royal Navy, 47-49, Ens. Am. Chem. Soc; Am. Asn. Textile Chem. & Colorists; Brit. Soc. Dyers & Colourists. Dyeing and finishing of textile synthetic fibers. Address: Textile Research & Development, Reeves Bros, Inc, P.O. Box 1531, Spartanburg, SC 29301.

GHIORSO, ALBERT, b. Vallejo, Calif, July 15, 15; m. 42; c. 2. PHYSICS. B.S, California, 37; hon. Ph.D, Gustavus Adolphus Col, 66. Mem. staff, metall. lab, Chicago, 42-46; physicist, LAWRENCE RADIATION LAB, UNIV. CALIF, BERKELEY, 46-69, DIR, HEAVY ION LINEAR ACCELERATOR, DEPT. CHEM, 69- Am. Phys. Soc. Transuranium elements; nuclear properties of heavy element isotopes; fission counters; electronic apparatus for measurement of nuclear radiations; reactions induced by heavy ions; systematics of radioactive decay. Address: Heavy Ion Linear Accelerator, Dept. of Chemistry, 268 Bldg. 71, Lawrence Radiation Lab, University of California, Berkeley, CA 94720.

GHIRARDELLI, ROBERT G(EORGE), b. San Francisco, Calif, Nov. 12, 30; m. 57; c. 5. ORGANIC CHEMISTRY. B.S, San Francisco, 52; Nat. Sci. Found. fel, Calif. Inst. Tech, 52-53, Dow Chem. Co. fel, 54-55, Ph.D.(chem), 56. Asst, Calif. Inst. Tech, 56-57; Ga. Inst. Tech, 57-58; asst. prof. chem, Robert Col. Istanbul, 58-60; chief org. chem, br, U.S. ARMY RES. OFF, 60-67, ASSOC. DIR. CHEM. DIV, 67- Vis. asst. prof, Duke Univ, 62- AAAS; Am. Chem. Soc. Stereochemistry; small ring compounds; reaction mechanisms. Address: Duke Box CM, Chemistry Division, U.S. Army Research Office, Durham, NC 27706.

GHIRON, CAMILLO A, b. Turin, Italy, Nov. 11, 32; U.S. citizen; m. 59; c. 3. BIOPHYSICS. S.B, Mass. Inst. Tech, 54; Ph.D.(molecular biol); Utah, 64. Res. asst. neurosurg, sch. med, N.Y. Univ, 56-57; biophys, Brookhaven Nat. Lab, 57-60; res. assoc. chem, Minnesota, 63-64; asst. prof. physiol, SCH. MED, UNIV. MO-COLUMBIA, 64-66, PHYSIOL. & BIOCHEM, 66-68, ASSOC. PROF, 68-, res. assoc. biochem, 64-66. Partic, Atomic Energy Comn. training prog. radiation phys. chem, Minnesota, 63-64; Nat. Heart Inst. sr. fel, biol. div, Oak Ridge Nat. Lab, 71-72. Chem.C, Res, 57, 2nd Lt. AAAS; Radiation Res. Soc; Biophys. Soc; Am. Chem. Soc; Brit. Biochem. Soc. Radiation inactivation kinetics of enzymes; photodynamic action. Address: Dept. of Biochemistry, University of Missouri-Columbia School of Medicine, Columbia, MO 65201.

GHISELIN, JON BREWSTER, b. Salt Lake City, Utah, May 25, 35; m. 57; c. 3. ANIMAL ECOLOGY. B.S, Utah, 55, fel, 55-56, M.A, 56; Sigma Xi-Sci. Res. Soc. Am. grant-in-aid, Wisconsin, Madison, 56, Ph.D.(zool), 67. Asst. zool, Wisconsin, Madison, 56-58 & 60-62, curator mus, 58-60, instr, Fox Valley Campus, Menasha, 62-66, ASST. PROF. biol, The Citadel, 66-67; Lycoming Col, 67-70; BIOL. SCIS, POINT PARK COL, 70- Field asst. zool, Utah, summer, 56. U.S.A, 57, Res, 60-68, Capt. AAAS; Am. Inst. Biol. Sci; Ornith. Union; Am. Soc. Mammal; Animal Behav. Soc; Cooper Ornith. Soc; Ecol. Soc. Am; Wildlife Soc. Habitat selection and utilization by birds and mammals; faunas of mountains and deserts. Address: Dept. of Biological Sciences, Point Park College, 201 Wood St, Pittsburgh, PA 15222.

GHISELIN, MICHAEL T(ENANT), b. Salt Lake City, Utah, May 13, 39. ZOOLOGY. B.A, Utah, 60; fel, Harvard, 64-65; Ph.D.(biol), Stanford, 65. Fel. systs, Marine Biol. Lab, 65-67; ASST. PROF. ZOOL, UNIV. CALIF, BERKELEY, 67- Pfizer Prize, Hist. Sci. Soc, 70. AAAS; Soc. Syst. Zool; Am. Soc. Nat; Paleont. Soc; Soc. Study Evolution. Malacology; marine biology; evolutionary biology; systematic theory; history, methodology and philosophy of biology. Address: Dept. of Zoology, University of California, Berkeley, CA 94720.

GHISTA, DHANJOO NOSHIR, b. Bombay, India, Jan. 10, 40; m. 67; c. 2. BIOMEDICAL ENGINEERING, APPLIED MECHANICS. B.Eng, Bombay, 60; Ph.D.(struct. mech), Stanford, 64. Res. assoc. appl. mech, Nat. Acad. Sci-Nat. Res. Coun, 64-67; res. scientist, Ames Res. Center, NASA, 67-69; ASSOC. PROF. biomed. eng, WASH. UNIV, 69-70, MECH. ENG, 70- Biomed. Eng. Soc. Optimum structural theory; three dimensional stress concentration; theory of strength of inhomogeneous medium; mathematical modeling of the human left ventricle; dynamics of musculo-skeletal frameworks; blood flow in curved tubes; mechanical properties of bone in terms of its ultrastructure. Address: Dept. of Mechanical & Aerospace Engineering, Washington University, St. Louis, MO 63130.

GHOLSON, R(OBERT) K(ARL), b. McLeansboro, Ill, Feb. 13, 30; m. 52; c. 3. BIOCHEMISTRY. B.A, Chicago, 50; B.S, Illinois, 55, Nat. Sci. Found. fel, 57-58, Ph.D.(biochem), 58. Res. assoc. BIOCHEM, Okla. State, 58-59; med. sch, Michigan, 59-61; Kyoto, 61-62; OKLA. STATE UNIV, 62-66, assoc. prof, 66-69, PROF, 69- U.S.N, 50-54. Am. Soc. Biol. Chem; Am. Chem. Soc. Intermediary metabolism of tryptophan; biological hydroxylations; biosynthesis of pyridine nucleotides. Address: Dept. of Biochemistry, Oklahoma State University, Stillwater, OK 74074.

GHORMLEY, JOHN A(NDERSON), b. Sioux City, Iowa, Mar. 4, 17; m. 43; c. 2. CHEMISTRY. B.S, Washington (Seattle), 41, M.S, 43; Ph.D, Tennessee, 52. Asst, Manhattan Dist, Chicago, 43-45; chemist, Oak Ridge Nat. Lab, 45-57; GROUP LEADER, Parma Res. Lab, Union Carbide Corp, 57-64; OAK RIDGE NAT. LAB, 64- Am. Chem. Soc; Radiation Res. Soc. Chemical effects of ionizing radiation; luminescence of alkali halides; gamma-ray dosimetry; electrochemical conversion of nuclear energy. Address: Oak Ridge National Lab, P.O. Box X, Oak Ridge, TN 37831.

GHOSE, HIRENDRA M, b. Patna, India; U.S. citizen; m. 60; c. 2. PHYSICAL & INORGANIC CHEMISTRY. B.Sc, Bihar Nat. Col, Patna, 49; M.Sc, Sci. Col. Patna, 53; Ph.D.(phys. chem), Mont. State Col, 60. Demonstr. physics, Bihar Nat. Col, Patna, 49-51, teacher chem, 53-55; instr, Skidmore Col, 59-60; sr. res. scientist, Glidden Co, 60-67; res. supvr, Addressograph Multigraph Corp, 67-70; ASSOC. PROF. PHYS. SCI, CUYAHOGA COMMUNITY COL, 70- Vis. lectr, State Univ. N.Y. Col. Plattsburgh, 59-60; consult, Friends Psychiat. Res. Inst, Spring Grove Ment. Hosp, Baltimore, Md, 66-67; consult. environ, chem. & educ. areas. Am. Chem. Soc. Surface reactivity and chemical kinetics; absorption; colloid and radiochemistry; environmental science. Address: Dept. of Physical Sciences, Cuyahoga Community College, 2900 Community College Ave, Cleveland, OH 44115.

GHOSE, RABINDRA NATH, b. Howrah, India, Sept. 1, 25; U.S. citizen; m. 64; c. 1. ELECTRICAL ENGINEERING, PHYSICS. B.E.E, Calcutta, 46; dipl, Indian Inst. Sci, Bangalore, 48; M.S, Washington (Seattle), 50, fel, 51-52; fel, Illinois, 52-54, M.A. & Ph.D.(elec. eng), 54, E.E, 56. Instr. elec. eng, Jadavpur Univ, India, 46-49; tech. officer & chief tech. instr, Hq. West. Command Indian Signals, 49-51; mem. tech. staff, Radio Corp. Am, 54-56; Space Tech. Lab, 56-59; dir. res. & adv. develop, Space-Gen. Corp, 59-63; PRES. & CHMN. BD, AM. NUCLEONICS CORP, 63- Reviewer sci. proposals, Nat. Sci. Found, 62; session chmn, Int. Conf. Microwaves, Commun. & Info. Theory, 64. Fel. AAAS; fel. Inst. Elec. & Electronics Eng; Brit. Inst. Elec. Eng. Electromagnetic field theories; microwaves; nuclear science; antennas. Address: American Nucleonics Corp, 6036 Variel Ave, Woodland Hills, CA 91364.

GHOSH, ABHA P, b. Calcutta, India, July 4, 38; m. 65; c. 2. MEDICINAL & ORGANIC CHEMISTRY. B.Sc, Univ. Calcutta, 57, M.Sc, 60, Coun. Sci. Indust. Res. fel. & Ph.D.(med. chem), 65. Lectr. chem, Narasingha Dutta Col, India, 65-66; fel, Inst. Paper Chem, Wis, 66-67; ASST. PROF. CHEM, SHAW UNIV, 67- Synthesis of pyrimidine derivatives and their actions on some microorganisms, showing that some kinds of groups present in 2,4 positions of pyrimidine enhance their activity as antimetabolites, whereas some groups completely deactivate. Address: Dept. of Chemistry, Shaw University, Raleigh, NC 27602.

GHOSH, AMAL K(UMAR), b. Thaton, Burma, June 21, 31; m. 61; c. 3. SOLID STATE PHYSICS. B.S, Calcutta, 51, M.S, 54, Ph.D.(physics), 61. Res. assoc, Notre Dame, 58-60; resident res. assoc, Argonne Nat. Lab, 60-62, asst. physicist, 62-65; mem. sci. staff, Itek Corp, 66-70; RES. ASSOC, ESSO RES. & ENG. CO, 70- Am. Phys. Soc. Optical properties of solids; radiation effects; photoimaging and semiconductor devices. Address: Room 3006, Bldg. 1, Esso Research & Engineering Co, P.O. Box 51, Linden, NJ 07036.

GHOSH, ANIL CHANDRA, b. Kamargaon, India, Sept. 1, 36; m. 68; c. 1. ORGANIC & MEDICINAL CHEMISTRY. B.Sc, Gauhati Univ, India, 56, M.Sc, 58; Coun. Sci. & Indust. Res. fel, Poona, 60-63, Ph.D.(chem), 63; A.R.I.C, London, Eng, 66. Lectr. chem, J.B. Col, Assam, India, 59; Coun. Sci. & Indust. Res. sr. res. fel. org. chem, Nat. Chem. Lab, Poona, 64; fel. chem, Nebraska, Lincoln, 64-66; res. assoc, N.C. State, 66-67; Swiss Fed. Inst. Tech, 68-69; SR. RES. ASSOC. exp. therapeut, Roswell Park Mem. Inst, 69-71; SHEEHAN INST. RES, 71- Am. Chem. Soc; Indian Chem. Soc. Steroids; photochemistry; natural products; synthesis; new reactions. Address: Sheehan Institute for Research, 767 B Concord Ave, Cambridge, MA 02138.

GHOSH, BHASKAR KUMAR, b. Dibrugarh, India, Feb. 10, 36; m. 60; c. 3. MATHEMATICAL STATISTICS. B.Sc, Calcutta, 55; Ph.D.(statist), London, 59. Res. asst. statist, Univ. Col, London, 58-59; statistician, Atomic Power Construct, Ltd, Eng, 59-60; asst. lectr. statist. & math, Chelsea Col. Sci. & Tech, 60-61; asst. prof. MATH, LEHIGH UNIV, 61-63, assoc. prof, 63-68, PROF, 68- Consult, Pa. Power & Light Co, 62-63; Int. Tel. & Tel. Corp, 64; Beryllium Corp, 65. Inst. Math. Statist; Am. Statist. Asn; Economet. Soc; Royal Statist. Soc. Probability; sequential analysis; testing of hypotheses. Address: Dept. of Mathematics, Lehigh University, Bethlehem, PA 18015.

GHOSH, BIJAN KUMAR, b. Siliguri, India, Aug. 1, 35; m. 60; c. 1. CELL PHYSIOLOGY, ELECTRON MICROSCOPY. M.Sc, Univ. Calcutta, 57, Coun. Sci. & Indust. Res. India fel. & D.Sc.(physiol. & biochem), 63. Sr. sci. asst. biochem, Indian Inst. Exp. Med, Calcutta, 61-64; Med. Res. Coun. Can. fel. ELECTRON MICROS. & CELL PHYSIOL, Univ. West. Ont, 64-66; Waksman Merck fel, INST. MICROBIOL, RUTGERS UNIV, 66-67, ASST. RES. PROF, 67- Nat. Sci. Found grant, 70-72; Nat. Inst. Gen. Med. Sci. res. career develop. award, 70-75. Am. Soc. Microbiol; Can. Soc. Biochem; Electron Micros. Soc. Am; fel. Am. Inst. Chem. Structure of subcellular components and the correlation of ultrastructure to physiological function of cell; structure, function and differentiation of biological membrane; application of quantitative techniques of electron microscopy. Address: Institute of Microbiology, Rutgers University, New Brunswick, NJ 08903.

GHOSH, CHITTA RANJAN, b. Mulghar, E.Pakistan, Mar. 1, 36. IMMUNOLOGY, MICROBIOLOGY. B.V.S, Univ. Calcutta, 57; Ph.D.(microbiol), Univ. Ky, 69. Vet. surgeon, Govt. W.Bengal, India, 58-63; INSTR. OBSTET. & GYNEC, SCH. MED, TUFTS UNIV, 69-; IMMUNOLOGIST, ST. MARGARET'S HOSP, 69- Am. Soc. Microbiol. Immunology of spirochetes, mycoplasma and cancer; autoimmune diseases; in vitro interaction of lymphocytes and target cells; immunology related to pregnancy and newborns. Address: Dept. of Pathology, St. Margaret's Hospital, Boston, MA 02125.

GHOSH, KALYAN K, b. Calcutta, India, Feb. 28, 38; m. 65; c. 2. POLYMER & PHYSICAL CHEMISTRY. B.Sc, Univ. Calcutta, 58, M.Sc, 61, Coun. Sci. & Indust. Res. fels, 62-65, Ph.D.(polymer chem), 65. Lectr. appl. chem, Univ. Calcutta, 65-66; Inst. Paper Chem. fel, Wis, 66-67; asst. prof. chem, SHAW UNIV, 67-69, CHMN. NATURAL & PHYS. SCI, 69- Fulbright travel award, Inst. Int. Educ, 66. Am. Chem. Soc. Solution properties of polymers; cellulose chemistry; graft polymerization; carbohydrate reactions. Address: Dept. of Chemistry, Shaw University, Raleigh, NC 27602.

GHOSH, MRIGANKA M(OULI), b. Calcutta, India, Nov. 5, 35; m. 67; c. 1. WATER CHEMISTRY, ENVIRONMENTAL ENGINEERING. B.Tech, Indian Inst. Technol, Kharagpur, 58; M.S, Univ. Ill, Urbana, 62, Ph.D.(sanit. eng), 65. Jr. engr, Hindusthan Steel Ltd, India, 58-59, asst. engr, 59-60; grad. asst. CIVIL ENG, Univ. Ill, Urbana, 61-65, asst. prof, 65-66; reader, Jadavpur Univ, India, 66-68; asst. prof, UNIV. MAINE, ORONO, 68-71, ASSOC. PROF, 71- Consult, Calcutta Metrop. Planning Orgn, 66-68; Edward C. Jordan & Co, 69-70; city of Somersworth, 69-; city of Dover, 71- Am. Water Works Asn; Am. Soc. Civil Eng; Water Pollution Control Fedn; Am. Chem. Soc; Am. Asn. Prof. Sanit. Eng. Chemistry of iron and manganese in natural waters; cultural eutrophication of lakes; effect of mercury and cadmium on stream biota; role of yellow organic acids in natural waters; physical chemical parameters affecting the removal of collods by porous media. Address: Dept. of Civil Engineering, University of Maine, Orono, ME 04473.

GHOSH, SAKTI P, b. Calcutta, India, Feb. 6, 35. MATHEMATICAL STATISTICS, COMPUTER SCIENCE. B.Sc, Calcutta, 55, M.Sc, 57, fel, 58; Ph.D. (statist), California, Berkeley, 62. Statistician, State Statist. Bur, Govt. W.Bengal, India, 58-59; asst. statist, California, Berkeley, 59-62; MEM. RES. STAFF, T.J. Watson Res. Ctr, IBM CORP, 62-68, IBM RES. LAB, 68- Adj. asst. prof, N.Y. Univ, 64- Inst. Math. Statist; Am. Statist. Asn. Sampling theory; information retrieval theory; information sciences; computer language; coding theory. Address: IBM Research Lab, Monterey & Cottle Rd, San Jose, CA 95114.

GHOSH, SANJIB KUMAR, b. Calcutta, India, Sept. 9, 25; m. 51; c. 2. PHOTOGRAMMETRY, GEODESY. B.Sc, Calcutta, 45; Off. Training Sch, Surv. India, Dehradun, 46-48; UN fel, Int. Training Ctr Aerial Surv, Delft, Netherlands, 56-57, Photog. Engr, 57; Ph.D.(photogram), Ohio State, 64. Surveyor, Surv. India, 48-60; res. asst. photogram, OHIO STATE UNIV, 60, res. assoc, 61, instr. PHOTOGRAM. & GEOD, 62-64, asst. prof, 64-67, ASSOC. PROF, 67- Mem. panel experts photogram, UNESCO, 66- Am. Soc. Photogram.(Presidential Award, 71); Am. Cong. Surv. & Mapping; Int. Soc. Photogram; Geog. Soc. India; Brit. Photogram. Soc. Geometric and physical aspects of photogrammetry; orientation of photogrammetric models; aerial triangulation; photogrammetric calibration of different surfaces; evaluation of various photogrammetric techniques. Address: 1056 Medhurst Rd, Columbus, OH 43220.

GHOSH, SAROJ BANDHU, b. Calcutta, India, Jan. 1, 30; m. 65. BIOCHEMISTRY, PHYSICAL CHEMISTRY. B.Sc, Univ. Calcutta, 49, M.Sc, 51, Ph.D. (phys. chem), 65. Res. scholar phys. chem, Univ. Calcutta, 52-53, jr. sci. asst. chem. microbiol, Bose Inst, India, 53-58, fel, 58-61; res. assoc. polymer chem, Purdue Univ, 61-62; chem. pharmacol, Vanderbilt Univ, 62-65; Off. Indian Govt. Scientists' Pool res. grant phys. biochem. & chem. microbiol, Bose Inst, 65-68; res. assoc. enzyme chem, dept. med, med. sch, Rutgers Univ, 68-70; BIOCHEMIST, MENT. RETARDATION RES. LAB, MUSCATATUCK STATE HOSP, 70- Fel. Indian Chem. Soc. Ion exchange problems of silicate minerals and synthetic resins; isolation of antibiotics from soil microorganisms; systematic extraction procedures; phase behavior of polymers; metabolism of drugs; enzyme chemistry; nutritional effects on brain composition. Address: Mental Retardation Research Lab, Muscatatuck State Hospital, Butlerville, IN 47223.

GHOSH, SUBRATA, b. Faridpur, E.Pakistan, Apr. 19, 32; m. 59. METALLURGICAL ENGINEERING. B.E, Bengal Eng. Col, India, 53; J.N. Tata scholar, Birmingham, 55-58, dipl, 56, univ. scholar, 56-58, Ph.D.(indust. metall), 58. Res. asst. metall, Tata Iron & Steel Co, India, 54-55; vis. res. metallurgist, Austrian Alpine Mt. Soc, 58; res. metallurgist, Steel Co. Wales, S.Wales, 59-60; res. metallurigst & asst. to dir, August-Thyssen Hutte, A.G, W.Ger, 60-61; asst. prof. metall, Detroit, 61-63; sr. res. scientist, CHRYSLER CORP, 63-65, res. specialist metall. res, 65-68, RES. STAFF SCIENTIST, METALL. RES. DEPT, 68- Consult, res. coun, Univ. Detroit, 61-; U.S.rep, 33rd Int. Found. Cong, New Delhi, India, 66; vis. lectr, Oakland Univ. Am. Foundrymen's Soc; Am. Soc. Metals; Indian Inst. Metals; Brit. Iron & Steel Inst. Liquid structure and mechanisms of solidification of metals and alloys; fundamentals of alloy strengthening mechanisms; aluminum, iron and nickel base alloys; cast structure and property relationships; casting problems; research coordination in steel and other metallurgical industries; high temperature superalloys. Address: Metallurgical Research Dept. 9410 (418-19-30), Chrysler Corp, P.O. Box 1118, Detroit, MI 48231.

GHOSHAL, NANI GOPAL, b. Dacca, India, Dec. 1, 34; m. 71. COMPARATIVE ANATOMY, NEUROANATOMY. G.V.Sc, Bengal Vet. Col, Calcutta, 55; D.T.V.M, Royal (Dick) Sch. Vet. Studies, 61; Dr. Med. vet, Faculty Vet. Med, Hannover, 62; Ph.D.(neuroanat), Iowa State, 66. Vet. asst. surgeon, Civil Vet. Dept, Govt. W.Bengal, India, 55; demonstr. comp. vet. anat, Bengal Vet. Col, Calcutta, 55-56; res. asst, M.B. Govt. Col. Vet. Sci. & Animal Husb, Mhow, 56-59; pool scientist, Indian Coun. Agr. Res, New Delhi, 63; instr. VET. ANAT, IOWA STATE UNIV, 63-66, asst. prof, 67-70, ASSOC. PROF, 70- AAAS; Am. Asn. Vet. Anat; fel. Royal Zool. Soc. Scotland; World Asn. Vet. Anat. Comparative neurology and angiology. Address: Dept. of Veterinary Anatomy, College of Veterinary Medicine, Iowa State University, Ames, IA 50010.

GHOSHTAGORE, RATHINDRA NATH, b. Sribari, E.Pakistan, July 8, 37; m. 67; c. 1. MATERIALS SCIENCE, CERAMICS. B.S, Univ. Calcutta, 57, M.S, 60; Sc.D.(ceramics), Mass. Inst. Technol, 65. Sr. physicist, fundamental res. lab, Xerox Corp, N.Y, 65-66; mem. tech. staff, mat. & processes, Fairchild Res. & Develop. Lab, Calif, 66-67; SR. ENGR, WESTINGHOUSE RES. LABS, 68- Am. Ceramic Soc; Am. Phys. Soc; Electrochem. Soc. Insulators and semiconductors; chemical vapor deposition of thin solid films in amorphous, plycrystalline, epitaxial and glassy state; diffusion in semiconductors; fabrication of silicon devices. Address: Westinghouse Research Labs, Pittsburgh, PA 15235.

GHUMAN, GIAN S(INGH), b. Barchuhi, India, July 7, 29; m. 48; c. 3. SOIL CHEMISTRY, GEOCHEMISTRY. B.S, Punjab, India, 52, M.S, 55; Ph.D. (soil sci), California, Davis, 67. Res. asst. fertilizer exp, Dept. Agr, Punjab, India, 55-57; asst. prof. soil chem, Shri Karan Narinder Col. Agr, India, 57-62; assoc. prof. EARTH SCI, SAVANNAH STATE COL, 67-71, PROF, 71- AAAS; Am. Soc. Agron; Soil Sci. Soc. Am; Int. Soc. Soil Sci; Clay Minerals Soc. Effectiveness of fertilizers on different soils; availability of iron and manganese as affected by soil treatments; investigations on mineral manganocalcite; clay minerals and mineralization in surface and ground waters. Address: Dept. of Earth Sciences, Savannah State College, Savannah, GA 31404.

GHURYE, SUDHISH G, b. Bombay, India, Nov. 10, 24; m. 53. STATISTICS. M.Sc, Bombay, 47; Ph.D.(math. statist), North Carolina, 52. Asst. prof. math, Oregon, 53-54; reader statist, Lucknow, 54-56; asst. prof, Chicago, 56-58; assoc. prof. MATH, Northwestern, 59-61; Minnesota, 61-62; prof, Ind. Univ, Bloomington, 62-68, chmn. dept, 64-67; PROF, UNIV. ALTA, 68-, CHMN. DEPT, 71- Assoc. ed, Ann. Math. Statist, 70- Am. Math. Soc; Inst. Math. Statist. Probability theory; mathematical statistics. Address: Dept. of Mathematics, University of Alberta, Edmonton 7, Alta, Can.

GHYS, ROGER, b. Hollogne aux Pierres, Belgium, Aug. 18, 29; Can. citizen; m. 56; c. 4. RADIOBIOLOGY. B.Sc, Liége, 51, M.D, 54. Res. asst. cancer, Interuniv. Inst. Nuclear Sci, Belgium, 56-57; radiobiol, Nat. Found. Sci. Res, Belgium, 57-60; asst. prof. biochem, sch. med, Laval, 60-64; HEAD RADIATIONS LAB, INST. MICROBIOL. & HYG, Univ. Montreal, 64-69; HEAD RADIOISOTOPES & NUCLEAR MED. LAB, SACRED HEART HOSP, 69-; DIR, RADIO-MED. LAB, INC, 69- Voluntary asst, tumour clin, sch. med, Liège, 56-59; Dutch-Belgian Cult. Cmn. res. grant, Dutch Cancer Inst, 57; Brit. Coun. scholar, Royal Cancer Hosp, London, 57-58; Interuniv. Inst. Nuclear Sci, Belgium, res. grant, Chester Beatty Res. Inst, London, 59; Nat. Res. Coun. Can. fel, Laval, 59-60; Med. Res. Coun. Can. res. grant, Charles H. Best Inst, Toronto, 61-62; asst. dir, 14th Bilateral Sem, World Univ. Serv. Can, Pakistan, 63. Cert. radiother, Col. Physicians Belg, 59. Belg. Army, 54-56, Lt-Physician. Radiation Res. Soc; Am. Physiol. Soc; Can. Biochem. Soc; Royal Soc. Med; Brit. Inst. Radiol; Brit. Asn. Radiation Res; Asn. Fr. Speaking Physiol; Belg. Soc. Radiol. Applications of radioisotopes to medicine and biology; aspects of radiosensitivity in mammals and microorganisms; radiomodifying and radiomimetic agents. Address: Radioisotopes & Nuclear Medicine Lab, Sacred Heart Hospital, 5400 Ouest, Bd. Gouin, Montreal, Que, Can.

GIACCHETTI, ATHOS, b. Florence, Italy, Jan. 1, 21; U.S. citizen; m. 48; c. 2. SPECTROSCOPY. Dr.(physics), Florence, 47. Asst. prof. physics, Nat. Univ. of the South, Argentina, 48-53; head spectros. sect, Nat. Atomic Energy Comn, 53-58; assoc. prof. atomic spectros, La Plata, 58-60; Org. Am. States fel. & vis. prof, Purdue, 60-61; assoc. physicist, Argonne Nat. Lab, 61-71; SPECIALIST, DEPT. SCI. AFFAIRS, ORGN. AM. STATES, 71- Italian Air Force, 41-45. Am. Phys. Soc; N.Y. Acad. Sci. Atomic spectroscopy; spectrochemistry; standard wave lengths; term analysis. Address: Dept. of Scientific Affairs, Organization of American States, 1735 I St. N.W, Washington, DC 20006.

GIACCONI, RICCARDO, b. Genoa, Italy, Oct. 6, 31; nat; m. 57; c. 3. ASTROPHYSICS. Ph.D.(physics), Milan, 54. Asst. prof. physics, Milan, 54-56; Fulbright fel, Indiana, 56-58; res. assoc, Princeton, 58-59; sr. scientist, AM. SCI. & ENG, INC, 59-62, chief space physics div, 62-63, v.pres. space res. & syst. div, 63-68, sr. v.pres, 68-69, EXEC. V.PRES, 69-, MEM. BD. DIRS, 66- Lectr, int. sch. physics, Enrico Fermi Inst, Varenna, Italy, summer 65; mem. Woods Hole Astron. Study Group, Nat. Acad. Sci, 65-, mem. x-ray-gamma-ray panel astron. study; assoc, Harvard Col. Observ, 70-72; mem. x-ray-gamma-ray panel, NASA Astron. Missions Bd, 68-71; vis. comt, Asn. Univ. Res. Astron, 71. Rontgen Prize Astrophys, Physikalisch-Medizinische Gessellschaft, Ger, 71. Nat. Acad. Sci; Am. Acad. Arts & Sci; AAAS; Am. Astron. Soc.(Helen B. Warner Prize, 66); Italian Phys. Soc. (Como Prize, 67); Am. Phys. Soc; Int. Astron. Union. X-ray astronomy; fields and particles. Address: American Science & Engineering Inc, 11 Carleton St, Cambridge, MA 02142.

GIACHINO, M(ARCELLO) T(HOMAS), b. La Maddalena, Italy, Aug. 21, 08; nat; m. 38; c. 3. INDUSTRIAL CHEMISTRY. B.S, Sch. Mines, Massa Marittima, Italy, 29; Ph.D.(chem), Univ. Torino, 32; dipl, Milan, 33. From chemist to chief chemist, Ammonia Brambilla Co, Verres, Italy, 34-41; fel, Indust. Reconstruct. Inst, Rome, 41-42; asst. supt, Terni Corp, 42-44; self employed, 44-47; res. chemist, Commercial Solvents Corp, La, 48-52; chief chemist, chem. div, W.R. Grace & Co, 53-55, res. dir, 56-62, spec. proj. dept, res. div, 62-67, sr. res. assoc, 67-70; RETIRED. Am. Chem. Soc. Gasification; catalysis; high pressure technology; nitrogen fixation; urea chemistry. Address: 6419 Amherst Ave, Ellicott City, MD 21043.

GIACOBBE, THOMAS JOSEPH, b. Newark, N.J, June 25, 41; m. 65; c. 2. ORGANIC CHEMISTRY, BIOCHEMISTRY. B.A, Bowdoin Col, 63; univ. fel,

Univ. Vt, 63-64, Nat. Insts. Health fel, 65-66, Ph.D.(chem), 68. Nat. Insts. Health fel, Univ. Wis, Madison, 68-69; spec. assignments dept, DOW CHEM. CO, 69-71, RES. BIOL. CHEMIST, 71- Am. Chem. Soc. Bio-organic chemistry; new synthetic organic reactions; cancer chemotherapy; agricultural chemistry. Address: 1801 Airfield Lane, Midland, MI 48640.

GIACOLETTO, L(AWRENCE) J(OSEPH), b. Clinton, Ind, Nov. 14, 16; m. 41; c. 1. ELECTRONICS. B.S, Rose Polytech, 38; M.S, Iowa, 39; Ph.D.(electronics), Michigan, 52. Asst, Iowa, 38-39; elec. machinery, Michigan, 39-41; res. engr, labs. div, Radio Corp. of Am, N.J, 46-56; res. mgr, electronics dept, sci. lab, Ford Motor Co, 56-60; PROF. ELEC. ENG, MICH. STATE UNIV, 60- Sig.C, 41-46, Res, 46-56, Lt. Col. Fel. AAAS; fel. Inst. Elec. & Electronics Eng; Am. Phys. Soc. Theory, design and application of solid state devices; electronics; communications. Address: Dept. of Electrical Engineering, Michigan State University, East Lansing, MI 48823.

GIACOMELLI, FILIBERTO, b. Pisa, Italy, Nov. 18, 28; m. 58. EXPERIMENTAL PATHOLOGY. M.D, Pisa, 54; Tübingen, 61; Nat. Insts. Health fel, Columbia, 61-63. Asst. med. path, Pisa, 56-57; Rome, 57-63; gen. path, Univ. Pisa, 63-66; asst. prof. PATH, Indiana, Indianapolis, 66-67; assoc, Columbia, 67-68; ASST. PROF, N.Y. MED. COL, 68- Light and electron microscopy; cytochemistry of normal and abnormal tissues. Address: Dept. of Pathology, New York Medical College, Fifth Ave. at 106th St, New York, NY 10029.

GIACOMETTI, LUIGI, b. Gubbio, Italy, Jan. 21, 26; U.S. citizen; m. 55; c. 2. BIOLOGY. M.Sc, Brown Univ, 62, Ph.D.(biol), 64. Asst. scientist, Ore. Regional Primate Res. Ctr, 64-67, assoc. scientist, 67-69, SCI. DIR, ORE. ZOOL. RES. CTR, 69- AAAS; Am. Asn. Anat. Anatomy. Address: Oregon Zoology Research Center, 4055 S.W. Canyon Rd, Portland, OR 97221.

GIAEVER IVAR, b. Norway, Apr. 5, 29; nat; m. 52; c. 4. SOLID STATE PHYSICS, MECHANICAL ENGINEERING. Siv.Ing, Tech. Univ. Norway, 52, Ph.D.(physics), Rensselaer Polytech. Inst, 64. Mech. engr, Norweg. Patent Off, 53-54; GEN. ELEC. CO, Can, 54-56, N.Y, 56-58, PHYSICIST, RES. LAB, 58- Guggenheim fel, 69-70. Oliver E. Buckley prize, 65. Am. Phys. Soc; Inst. Elec. & Electronics Eng. Stress analysis; heat transfer; superconductivity; tunneling; field ion microscopy. Address: General Electric Co, P.O. Box 1088, Schenectady, NY 12301.

GIAM, CHOO-SENG, b. Singapore, Singapore, Apr. 2, 31; m. 56; c. 2. PHYSICAL ORGANIC & ANALYTICAL CHEMISTRY. B.Sc, Univ. Malaya, 54, Hons, 55; M.Sc, Saskatchewan, 61, Ph.D.(chem), 63. Govt. analyst, Chem. Dept, Govt. Singapore, 55-58; lectr. chem, Univ. Malaya, 58-59; res. chemist, Imp. Oil, Can, 63-64; res. assoc. CHEM, California, 65-66; ASSOC. PROF, TEX. A&M UNIV, 66- Analyst, Munic. Coun, Malaya, 58-59; fels, Nat. Res. Coun. Can, 63-64, Pa. State, 64-65. Am. Chem. Soc; sr. mem. Chem. Inst. Can; assoc. mem. Royal Inst. Chem. Chemistry of heterocycles, effects of structures of organic compounds on their reactivities; nucleophilic reactions and mechanisms of these reactions. Address: Dept. of Chemistry, Texas A&M University, College Station, TX 77843.

GIAMALVA, MIKE J, b. Independence, La, Oct. 21, 24; m. 52; c. 6. HORTICULTURE, PLANT PATHOLOGY. B.S, Southeastern La. Col, 49; M.S, La. State, Baton Rouge, 50, Ph.D.(hort. & plant path), 60. Asst. prof. hort, La. State, Baton Rouge, 50-58, assoc. prof. plant path, 60-65; prof. agron, Somali contract team, Wyoming, 65-67; assoc. prof. PLANT PATH, LA. STATE UNIV, BATON ROUGE, 67-71, PROF, 71-, HEAD DEPT. OUTFIELD SUGARS, 68- U.S.A.A.F, 43-46. Am. Phytopath. Soc; Am. Soc. Hort. Sci; Am. Soc. Agron. Diseases of horticulture crops; variety selection; disease resistance of sugarcane. Address: Dept. of Outfield Sugars, Agricultural Center, Louisiana State University, Baton Rouge, LA 70803.

GIAMATI, CHARLES C, JR, b. Akron, Ohio, Aug. 26, 27; m. 54; c. 2. NUCLEAR PHYSICS. A.B, Oberlin Col, 50; A.M, Michigan, 52; Ph.D.(physics), Case, 62. Aeronaut. res. scientist, LEWIS RES. CTR, Nat. Adv. Cmt. Aeronaut, 52-55, PHYSICIST, NASA, 55- Lectr, Fenn Col, 61-65; Oberlin Col, 65-66; Fulbright-Hayes lectr. grant, Istanbul Tech. Univ, 66-67; lectr, Cleveland State Univ, 67-70. U.S.A, 45-47. AAAS; Am. Phys. Soc. Cosmic ray physics, large volume liquid scintillation and cerenkov counters; scattering of protons and alpha particles from complex nuclei. Address: Lewis Research Center, NASA, Cleveland, OH 44135.

GIAMBALVO, V(ITO) A(LBERT), b. Brooklyn, N.Y, Sept. 11, 12; m. 40; c. 4. ORGANIC CHEMISTRY. B.S, City Col. New York, 35. Org. chemist, Dr. B.T. Brooks, N.Y, 35-36; res. lab, Interchem. Corp, 36-38; United Color & Pigment Co, N.J, 38-44; Calco Chem. Co, 44-50; SR. RES. CHEMIST, AM. CYANAMID CO, 50- Am. Chem. Soc. Phthalocyanine, azo, vat pigments and dyes; preparation and conditioning of pigments. Address: American Cyanamid Co, Bound Brook, NJ 08805.

GIAMBONI, LOUIS A, b. Oakland, Calif, Aug. 18, 18; m. 60. PHYSICS. B.A, California, Los Angeles, 40; M.A, Calif. Inst. Tech, 47, Ph.D.(physics), 50. Physicist, Rand Corp, 50-60; Planning Res. Corp, 60-65; PRES, ADAMS RES. CORP, 65- Am. Phys. Soc. Systems analysis; operations research. Address: 954 Bluegrass Way, Los Angeles, CA 90049.

GIAMEI, ANTHONY FRANCIS, b. Corning, N.Y, Oct. 14, 40; m. 62; c. 2. METALLURGY, MATERIALS SCIENCE. B.E, Yale, 62; W.P. Murphy fel, Northwestern, 62, Nat. Sci. Found. fel, 63, Cabell fel, 65, Ph.D.(mat. sci), 67. Res. assoc. alloy studies, adv. mat. res. & develop. lab, PRATT & WHITNEY AIRCRAFT DIV, UNITED AIRCRAFT, 66-68, sr. res. assoc, 68-69, GROUP LEADER, 69-71, ALLOY RES, MAT. ENG. & RES. LAB, 71- Summers, metallographer, Delco Appliance Div, Gen. Motors, 60, metall. asst, 61 & metallurgist, Gen. Motors Res. Labs, 62. Am. Soc. Metals; Am. Inst. Mining, Metall. & Petrol. Eng.(Outstanding Paper Award, 70). Phase transformation morphology and kinetics; quantitative phase analysis by x-ray diffraction; stacking faults in ordered lattices; temperature dependence of strength in intermetallics; influence of structural changes on strength; unidirectional solidification. Address: Materials Engineering & Research Lab, Pratt & Whitney Aircraft Division, United Aircraft, Middletown, CT 06457.

GIAMMARIA, J(OHN) J(OSEPH), b. Riverside, N.J, Apr. 30, 14; m. 39. ORGANIC CHEMISTRY. B.A, Pennsylvania, 36. Chemist petrol. res, Socony Mobil Oil Co, 37-42, proj. leader & chemist, 42-57, res. assoc. & chemist, 57-71; RETIRED. Am. Chem. Soc; Soc. Automotive Eng. Lubricant and fuel additives research; high temperature oxidation and combustion of petroleum hydrocarbons; development of aviation greases and synthetic industrial oils. Address: 43 N. Drexel St, Woodbury, NJ 08096.

GIAMMONA, SAMUEL T, b. Grand Rapids, Mich, Dec. 17, 30. PEDIATRICS. B.S, Mich. State, 51; M.D, Yale, 54. Jr. instr. pediat, Michigan, 58-59; asst. prof, med. center, Indiana, 62-65; assoc. prof, sch. med, Univ. Miami, 65-69, sci. dir. ment. retardation prog, 67-69; prof. PEDIAT, UNIV. CALIF, SAN DIEGO, 69-71, ADJ. PROF, 71-; CHMN. DEPT, CHILDREN'S HOSP, 71- U.S.A, 55-57, Capt. Am. Acad. Pediat; Am. Fedn. Clin. Res. Pulmonary physiology in infants and children. Address: Dept. of Pediatrics, Children's Hospital, 3700 California St, San Francisco, CA 94118.

GIANCOLA, DOMINIC J, b. Jersey City, N.J, July 30, 26; m. 52; c. 3. ORGANIC CHEMISTRY. B.S, Notre Dame, 49; M.S, Yale, 53, Ph.D.(org. chem), 55; LL.B, Fordham, 63. Res. chemist, Lederle Labs, Am. Cyanamid Co, 49-51; patent liaison, M.W. Kellogg Co. Div, Pullman Corp, 55-57; patent attorney, Union Carbide Corp, 57-62; dir. chem. develop, Richardson-Merrell Inc, 62-68; PRES, PRINCETON ORGANICS, 68- U.S.N, 44-46. Am. Chem. Soc. Chemistry of steroids. Address: Princeton Organics, Box 420, Princeton, NJ 08540.

GIANCOLA, JOHN ROBERT, b. Chicago, Ill, Sept. 25, 32; m. 56; c. 3. METALLURGICAL & CHEMICAL ENGINEERING. B.S, Mass. Inst. Tech, 54; M.S, Ohio State, 59; Ph.D.(metall), Arizona, 68. Sales eng. trainee, Dearborn Chem. Co, 52-53, lab. technician, 53, jr. engr, 54; U.S. AIR FORCE, 54-, proj. engr, high temperature mat. sect, Air Force Mat. Lab, 54-58, ceramics & graphite br, 58-59, chief stage II sect, space & missile systs. div, 59-62, proj. engr, 62-64, asst. chief motor develop. br, U.S. Air Force Rocket Propulsion Lab, 66-67, dep. chief solid rocket div, 67-69, chief liquid rocket div, Calif, 69-70, CHIEF, FUZES BR, U.S. AIR FORCE ARMAMENT LAB, FLA, 70- U.S. Air Force mem, solid subgroup, Interagency Chem. Rocket Propulsion Group, 66-70. U.S.A.F, 54-, Lt. Col, Air Force Commendation Medal, 64; Meritorious Service Medal, 70. Am. Soc. Metals; Am. Inst. Mining, Metall. & Petrol. Eng; Am. Ord. Asn. Fusing for conventional munitions; chemical rocket propulsion; materials selection and application; fabrication and forming of metals; corrosion of metals and alloys; carbon and graphite; management of research and development; system optimization. Address: Fuzes Branch, U.S. Air Force Armament Lab, 608 Camborne Ave, Ft. Walton Beach, FL 32548.

GIANCOLI, DOUGLAS C(HARLES), b. San Francisco, Calif, July 2, 38; m. 60; c. 3. BIOPHYSICS, PHYSICS. A.B, Univ. Calif, Berkeley, 60, Nat. Sci. Found. fel, 61-63, Ph.D.(physics), 66; Whitney fel, Mass. Inst. Technol, 60-61, M.S, 61. Res. asst. physics, Univ. Calif, Berkeley, 63-66, Nat. Insts. Health fel. molec. biol, 66-68; asst. prof. PHYSICS, CALIF. STATE POLYTECH. COL, KELLOG-VOORHIS, 69-71, ASSOC. PROF, 71- AAAS; Am. Asn. Physics Teachers. Pion-nucleon interactions; mutagenesis; physics and biophysics education; thermodynamics in molecular biology. Address: Dept. of Physics & Earth Science, California State Polytechnic College, Kellog-Voorhis, 3801 W. Temple Ave, Pomona, CA 91768.

GIANETTO, ROBERT, b. Montreal, Que, Aug. 7, 27; m. 52; c. 4. BIOCHEMISTRY. B.Sc, Univ. Montreal, 49, M.Sc, 51, Ph.D.(biochem), 53. Nat. Res. Coun. Can. fel, Cath. Univ. Louvain, 52-53; ASSOC. PROF. BIOCHEM, UNIV. MONTREAL, 53- AAAS; N.Y. Acad. Sci; Can. Biochem. Soc. Enzymology; lysosomes. Address: Dept. of Biochemistry, Faculty of Medicine, University of Montreal, Montreal, Que, Can.

GIANINO, PETER D(OMINIC), b. East Boston, Mass, May 8, 32; m. 54; c. 3. SOLID STATE PHYSICS. B.S, Boston Col, 53; M.S, Northeastern, 59. Physicist, Sylvania Elec. Prod. Div, Gen. Tel. & Electronics Corp, 55-58; Ewen-Knight Corp, 58-59; RES. PHYSICIST, AIR FORCE CAMBRIDGE RES. LABS, 59- Part time lectr, Northeast. Univ. Ord.C, 53-55, 1st Lt. Am. Phys. Soc; Am. Asn. Physics Teachers. Antenna pattern synthesis of linear arrays; missile systems; three-level solid state masers; magnetic anisotropy and resonance at low temperatures; secondary electron emission; laser windows. Address: Air Force Cambridge Research Lab, LQR, Hanscom Field, Bedford, MA 01731.

GIANNETTI, JOSEPH PAUL, b. Paterson, N.J, Aug. 16, 36; m. 61; c. 2. PETROLEUM CHEMISTRY. B.S, Rutgers, 58; M.S, Pa. State, 60. Chemist, GULF RES. & DEVELOP. CO, GULF OIL CORP, 60-65, res. chemist, 65-69, SR. RES. CHEMIST, 69- Am. Chem. Soc. Petroleum processing; heterogeneous and homogeneous catalysis for hydrocarbon reactions. Address: Gulf Research & Development Co, P.O. Drawer 2038, Pittsburgh, PA 15230.

GIANNINA, THOMAS, b. Bayonne, N.J, June 4, 38; m. 60; c. 3. REPRODUCTIVE PHYSIOLOGY. B.S, St. Peter's Col, 60; M.S, Rutgers, 64. Scientist, Sloan Kettering Inst. Cancer Res, 61-63; Warner Lambert Res. Inst, 64-68; ENDOCRINOLOGIST, CIBA-GEIGY PHARMACEUT. CO, SUMMIT, 68- AAAS; N.Y. Acad. Sci; Am. Physiol. Soc; Soc. Study Reproduction. Reproductive endocrinology; inflammation; mechanisms of action of steroidal and nonsteroidal compounds; hormonal; traumatic and enzymatic factors and mechanisms involved in uterine blastocyst implantation. Address: 4 Hall Ave, Suffern, NY 10901.

GIANNINI, GABRIEL M(ARIA), b. Rome, Italy, Oct. 21, 05; nat; m. 31; c. 2. PHYSICS. Dr.(physics), Rome, 29. Student engr, Radio Corp. of Am, Victor Mfg. Co, Camden, 30-31; res. engr, Curtis Inst. Music, Phila, 31-34; John D. Rockefeller, Jr. & Riverside Church, N.Y, 33-35; res. engr. & co-exec, Transducer Corp, 36-39; cost control engr, Vultee Aircraft Corp, Calif, 39-41; staff asst. coordinator, off. v.pres. in charge mfg, Lockheed Aircraft Corp, 41-43; pres, G.M. Giannini & Co, Inc, 44-57; dir. res. lab. & pres, Giannini Sci. Corp, 57-65, PRES, GIANNINI INST, 65- Instr, eve. sch, California, 41-43; pres. & chief engr, Autoflight Corp, 44-47; mem, Nat. Air Coun, 48- Acoust. Soc. Am; Am. Phys. Soc; Am. Soc. Mech. Eng;

Soc. Automotive Eng; Instrument Soc. Am; assoc. fel. Am. Inst. Aeronaut. & Astronaut; sr. mem. Inst. Elec. & Electronics Eng. Reaction power plants and automatic flight equipment; plasma technology. Address: Giannini Institute, 79811 Ave. 54, Indio, CA 92201.

GIANNINI, MARGARET JOAN, b. Camden, N.J, May 27, 21; m. 48; c. 4. PEDIATRICS. Boston, 39-40; Temple, 40-42; M.D, Hahnemann Med. Col, 45. Assoc. prof. PEDIAT, N.Y. MED. COL, 48-67, PROF, 67-, DIR. UNIV. AFFILIATED MENT. RETARDATION CTR, 50- Attend. pediatrician, Metrop. Med. Inst, 48-; consult, Bur. Handicapped Children, N.Y. City Health Dept, 60-; div. med. facilities, U.S. Pub. Health Serv, 64; mem. perinatal comt, Bronx County Med. Soc, 64; state wide planning comt. ment. retardation, N.Y. State Dept. Ment. Hyg, 64; bd. dirs, Avard Learning Ctr. Adv. Bd, ment. retardation sect, Headstart Proj, Massive Econ. Neighborhood Develop; adv. coun, Asn. Help Retarded Children; chmn, Int. Seminar Ment. Retardation; ment. retardation task force state wide planning vocational rehab. serv, N.Y. State Dept. Educ. Dipl, Am. Bd. Pediatrics, 50. Am. Med. Women's Asn; fel. Am. Acad. Pediat; Am. Med. Asn; Nat. Asn. Retarded Children; Asn. Univ. Affiliated Facilities. Mental retardation. Address: Mental Retardation Center, New York Medical College, 1249 Fifth Ave, New York, NY 10029.

GIANNONI, GIOVANNI, b. Torino, Italy, Feb. 28, 35. MOLECULAR BIOLOGY. Ph.D.(chem), Turin, 59. Res. fel. biochem, Turin, 59-60; vis. scientist, Oxford, 60-61; res. assoc. biophys, Mass. Inst. Tech, 61-66; mem. res. staff, Bell Tel. Labs, 66-68; ASSOC. PROF. CHEM, N.Y. UNIV, 68- Fulbright travel grant, 61. Structure and function of biological membranes. Address: Soc. SNAM Progetti, LBR, 00015 Monterotondo, Roma, Italy.

GIANNOTTI, RALPH ALFRED, b. Long Island City, N.Y, May 12, 42; m. 64; c. 3. ORGANIC CHEMISTRY. B.S, St. John's Univ, 63, M.S, 65, Nat. Insts. Health fel. & Ph.D.(org. chem), 69. Res. asst. org. chem, St. John's Univ, 64-69; res. assoc, Mass. Inst. Technol, 69-70; ASST. PROF. CHEM, STATE UNIV. N.Y. AGR. & TECH. COL. FARMINGDALE, 70- Nat. Sci. Found. summer fel, 67. Am. Chem. Soc; Coblentz Soc. Synthesis and characterization of polypeptides with known repeating sequence of amino acids; solid phase peptide synthesis; proteins. Address: Dept. of Chemistry, State University of New York Agricultural & Technical College at Farmingdale, Farmingdale, NY 11735.

GIANOLA, UMBERTO F(ERDINANDO), b. Birmingham, Eng, Oct. 29, 27; m. 52; c. 3. PHYSICS. B.Sc, Birmingham, Eng, 48, Ph.D, 51. Consult, Royal Aircraft Estab, Eng, 51; res. fel, Univ. B.C, 51-53; mem. tech. staff, BELL TEL. LABS, INC, 53-63, head solid state digital device dept, 63-69, ocean res. dept, 69-71, DIR. OCEAN SYSTS. STUDIES CTR, 71- Am. Phys. Soc; Sci. Res. Soc. Am; fel. Inst. Elec. & Electronics Eng. Electron optics; nuclear radiation detectors; solid state devices for memory, logic and communication systems; ocean acoustics and antisubmarine warfare surveillance systems. Address: Room 2B-105, Bell Telephone Labs, Inc, Whippany, NJ 07981.

GIANTURCO, MAURIZIO, b. Potenza, Italy, Dec. 2, 28; m. 54; c. 2. ORGANIC CHEMISTRY. Univ. fels, Rome, 48, 49, 50, Dr.Chem, 51. Instr. org. chem, Rome, 51-52; res. assoc, Illinois, 52-56; res. chemist, Tenco, Inc, 56-57, head fundamental res. sect, 57-66; asst. dir. res, COCA-COLA CO, 66-68, DIR. CORP. RES. DEPT, 68- Montecatini res. fel, 51-52; Fulbright fel, 52-53. Am. Chem. Soc; N.Y. Acad. Sci; Ital. Chem. Soc; The Chem. Soc; Inst. Food Technol. Organic natural products; infrared and mass spectrometry. Address: 5265 West Kingston Court, N.E, Atlanta, GA 30305.

GIARDINI, A(RMANDO) A(LFONZO), b. Salamanca, N.Y, June 5, 25; m. 50; c. 4. MINERALOGY. B.S, Michigan, 51, M.S, 53, Ph.D.(mineral), 56. Phys. scientist, electrotech. lab, U.S. Bur. Mines, Tenn, 52; res. engr, res. & develop. lab, Carborundum Co, N.Y, 53-55; res. assoc. & teaching fel. mineral, Michigan, 56-57; phys. scientist & proj. leader, res. prog, U.S. Army Signal Res. & Develop. Lab, 57-65; PROF. GEOL, UNIV. GA, 65- U.S.N. 43-46. AAAS; Mineral Soc. Am; Geochem. Soc; Am. Soc. Mech. Eng; Am. Geophys. Union. Geological and geophysical studies. Address: Dept. of Geology, University of Georgia, Athens, GA 30601.

GIAROLA, ATTILIO JOSE, b. Jundiai, Brazil, Oct. 26, 30; m. 55; c. 2. ELECTRICAL ENGINEERING. B.S, São Paulo, 54; M.S, Washington (Seattle), 59, Ph.D.(elec. eng), 63. Instr. elec. eng, Aeronaut. Inst. Tech, Brazil, 55-57, assoc. prof, 63-65; instr, Seattle, 57-60; Washington, 60-62; res. engr, Boeing Co, 62-63, res. scientist, 65-68; ASSOC. PROF. ELEC. ENG, TEX. A&M UNIV, 68- Vis. prof, São Paulo, 65. Chmn, Nat. Electronics Conf, Brazil, 64. Inst. Elec. & Electronics Eng. Solid-state and microwave devices; parametric devices; optical devices; traveling wave tubes; frequency selective limiters; elastic-, spin-, and magnetoelastic-delay lines; bioeffects of electromagnetic radiation. Address: Dept. of Electrical Engineering, Texas A&M University, College Station, TX 77843.

GIAROLI, JOHN NELLO, b. Memphis, Tenn, Feb. 14, 28; m. 58; c. 6. ORAL SURGERY. B.S, Memphis State, 50; D.D.S, Tennessee, 53. Intern ORAL SURG, Charity Hosp, New Orleans, La, 56-57; resident, Confederate Mem. Hosp, Shrevesport, 57-59; ASSOC. PROF, COL. DENT, UNIV. TENN, MEMPHIS, 60-· U.S.A, 53-55, Res, 55-59, 1st Lt. Am. Dent. Asn; Am. Soc. Dent. for Children; Am. Acad. Oral Med; Am. Soc. Advan. Gen. Anesthesia in Dent; Int. Dent. Fedn; Am. Soc. Oral Surg. Address: Dept. of Oral Surgery, University of Tennessee College of Dentistry, Memphis, TN 38101.

GIARRUSSO, FREDERICK F(RANK), b. Little Falls, N.Y, May 23, 36; m. 62. ORGANIC CHEMISTRY. B.S, Arizona State, 58; Stanford, 61-62; Ph.D.(chem), Michigan, 66. Jr. res. chemist, Merck & Co, Inc, 58-61; fel. natural prod, Calif. Inst. Tech, 65-66; res. chemist, Gen. Elec. Res. & Develop. Ctr, N.Y, 66-68; sr. res. scientist, SQUIBB INST. MED. RES, 68-71, SECT. HEAD CHEM. & BIOL. RES. ADMIN, 71- U.S.A.R, 59. AAAS; Am. Chem. Soc. Synthetic organic and natural product chemistry; steroids. Address: Squibb Institute for Medical Research, Georges Rd, New Brunswick, NJ 08903.

GIAUQUE, W(ILLIAM) F(RANCIS), b. Niagara Falls, Ont, Can, May 12, 95, U.S. citizen; m. 32; c. 2. PHYSICAL CHEMISTRY. B.S, California, Berkeley, 20, fel, 20-22, Ph.D.(phys. chem), 22, LL.D, 63; Sc.D, Columbia, 36. Instr. CHEM, CALIFORNIA, BERKELEY, 22-27, asst. prof, 27-30, assoc. prof, 30-34, prof, 34-62, emer. prof, 62, PROF, 62- Faculty res. hon. lectr, Univ. Calif, 48; Gilbert N. Lewis mem. lectr, 60. Cresson Medal, Franklin Inst, 37; Nobel Laureate, chem, 49. Nat. Acad. Sci; Am. Chem. Soc.(Gibbs Medal, 51, Lewis Award, 55); fel. Am. Phys. Soc; Am. Philos. Soc; Am. Acad. Arts & Sci; fel, Franklin Inst. Tests of the third law of thermodynamics; low temperature calorimetry; especially on condensed gases; cryogenic apparatus; conversion of ortho to para hydrogen; magnetic method for attaining temperatures below 1 degree centigrade absolute; free energy and entropy from spectroscopy; oxygen isotopes in earth's atmosphere; originated carbon thermometer for measurements in liquid helium range; high field magnet design; magnetothermodynamic measuring methods, apparatus and data to high magnetic fields and low temperatures basic calibration of magnetic thermometers, without heat introduction in range below 1°K. Address: Dept. of Chemistry, University of California, Berkeley, CA 94720.

GIBALA, RONALD, b. New Castle, Pa, Oct. 3, 38; m. 60; c. 4. METALLURGY. B.S, Carnegie Inst. Tech, 60; M.S, Illinois, 62, Ph.D.(metall. eng), 65. Asst. prof. METALL, CASE WEST. RESERVE UNIV, 64-69, ASSOC. PROF, 69- Nat. Sci. Found. res. grant, 66-71; Atomic Energy Comn. res. contract, 67-72; U.S. Air Force Off. Sci. Res. grant, 71- Alfred Noble Prize, Am. Soc. Civil Eng. 69. AAAS; Am. Soc. Metals; Am. Inst. Mining, Metall. & Petrol. Eng. Physical metallurgy; defects in solids; acoustics; internal friction; mechanical properties of solids. Address: Division of Metallurgy & Materials Science, School of Engineering, Case Western Reserve University, Cleveland, OH 44106.

GIBALDI, MILO, b. N.Y.C, Dec. 17, 38; m. 60; c. 1. PHARMACOLOGY. B.S, Columbia, 60, Ph.D.(pharmaceut), 63. Asst. prof. pharm, Columbia, 63-66; PHARMACEUT, STATE UNIV. N.Y. BUFFALO, 66-67, assoc. prof, 67-69, PROF, 69- Nat. Insts. Health res. grant, 67-70. AAAS; Am. Chem. Soc; Am. Pharmaceut. Asn; Acad. Pharmaceut. Sci; Am. Asn. Cols. Pharm. Drug absorption; physical-chemical and biological properties of bile salts; dissolution phenomena; pharmacokinetics. Address: Dept. of Pharmaceutics, State University of New York at Buffalo, Buffalo, NY 14214.

GIBB, JAMES WOOLLEY, b. Magrath, Alta, Apr. 19, 33; m. 56; c. 2. BIOCHEMICAL PHARMACOLOGY. B.S, Alberta, 58, fel, 59-61, M.S, 61; fel, Michigan, 61-65, Ph.D.(pharmacol), 65. Prof. serv. rep, Schering Corp, 58-59; res. assoc. PHARMACOL, Nat. Heart Inst, 65-67; asst. prof, UNIV. UTAH, 67-71, ASSOC. PROF, 71- AAAS; N.Y. Acad. Sci; Am. Soc. Pharmacol. & Exp. Therapeut; Int. Asn. Dent. Res. Mechanism of carbon tetrachloride-induced hepatotoxicity; biosynthesis of catecholamines; neurochemistry. Address: Dept. of Pharmacology, University of Utah, Salt Lake City, UT 84112.

GIBB, RICHARD A, b. Fraserburgh, Scotland, Feb. 16, 36; m. 60; c. 3. GEOPHYSICS, GEOLOGY. B.Sc, Aberdeen, 58; M.Sc, Birmingham, 59, Ph.D. (geol), 61. Geophysicist, Bur. Mineral Resources, Geol. & Geophys, Australia, 62-65; RES. SCIENTIST, EARTH PHYSICS BR, DEPT. ENERGY, MINES & RESOURCES, CAN, 65- Secy. subcomt. gravity, Assoc. Comt. Geod. & Geophys, Can, 67- Fel. Geol. Asn. Can; Europ. Asn. Explor. Geophys. Geological interpretation of gravity data. Address: Earth Physics Branch, Dept. of Energy, Mines & Resources, Ottawa, Ont. K1A 0E4, Can.

GIBB, THOMAS R(OBINSON) P(IRIE), JR, b. Belmont, Mass, Feb. 10, 16; m. 39; c. 2. INORGANIC CHEMISTRY. B.S, Bowdoin Col, 36; fel, Mass. Inst. Tech, 36-39, Ph.D.(org-metallic chem), 40. Instr, Mass. Inst. Tech, 40-43, asst. prof, 43-46; dir. chem. res, Metal Hydrides, Inc, 46-51; assoc. prof. chem. & dir. sponsored res, TUFTS UNIV, 52-58, PROF. CHEM, 58- Consult, lab, Chem. Warfare Serv, 44-46; vis. prof, Univ. Fla, 63; Nat. Sci. Found. fel, 63-64; hon. res. assoc, Univ. Col, Univ. London, 64; guest investr, Woods Hole Oceanog. Inst, 70. Fel. AAAS; fel. Am. Inst. Chem; Electrochem. Soc; Am. Chem. Soc. Instrumental analysis; inorganic hydrides; structural inorganic; trace-constituents of sea water. Address: Dept. of Chemistry, Tufts University, Medford, MA 02155.

GIBBARD, H. FRANK, JR, b. Norman, Okla, Dec. 27, 40; m. 57; c. 4. PHYSICAL CHEMISTRY. B.S, Oklahoma, 62; S.M, Mass. Inst. Tech, 64, NASA fel, 65-66, Ph.D.(phys. chem), 67. Res. assoc, Mass. Inst. Tech, 66-67; ASST. PROF. CHEM, SOUTH. ILL. UNIV, CARBONDALE, 67- AAAS; Am. Chem. Soc. Physical chemistry of solutions of electrolytes and nonelectrolytes; vapor liquid equilibria; ion exchange resins. Address: Dept. of Chemistry, Southern Illinois University, Carbondale, IL 62901.

GIBBINS, BETTY J(ANE), b. Canton, Ohio, May 7, 23. CHEMISTRY. B.A, Mt. Union Col, 45; Akron, 45-46; M.S, Ohio State, 47, res. fel, 51-53, Ph.D. (chem), 53. Asst, res. lab, Goodyear Tire & Rubber Co, 45-46; instr. CHEM, Col. of Wooster, 48-51; Franklin & Marshall Col, 53-58; assoc. prof, LAKE ERIE COL, 58-67, PROF, 67- AAAS; Am. Chem. Soc. Molecular additive compounds and phase diagrams. Address: Dept. of Chemistry, Lake Erie College, Painesville, OH 44077.

GIBBINS, SIDNEY GORE, b. Mt. Vernon, N.Y, Feb. 24, 26; m. 53; c. 3. INORGANIC CHEMISTRY. B.S, Calif. Inst. Tech, 49; Ph.D.(chem), Washington (Seattle), 55. Res. chemist, E.I. du Pont de Nemours & Co, N.Y, 55-57; Olin Mathieson Chem. Corp, Calif, 57-59; Nat. Eng. Sci. Co, 59-61; Aerospace Corp, 61-64; asst. prof. CHEM, New Mexico Highlands, 64-65; UNIV. VICTORIA (B.C), 65-69, ASSOC. PROF, 69- U.S.A, 44-46, Sgt. Am. Chem. Soc. Boron, silicon and transition metal hydrides; hydrogen peroxide; hydrazine; instrumental analysis; mass and infrared spectrometry; nuclear magnetic resonance; gas chromatography; high vacuum techniques. Address: 3536 Henderson Rd, Victoria, B.C, Can.

GIBBON, DONALD L, b. Talara, Peru, Feb. 26, 37; U.S. citizen; m. 59; c. 1. MINERALOGY, ELECTRON MICROSCOPY. B.A, Rice, 58, Ph.D.(geol), 64. Res. assoc. geochem, Pa. State Univ, 64-66, asst. prof. mineral, 66-69, SR. RES. SCIENTIST, FERRO CORP, 69- C.Eng, 58-60, 1st Lt. Mineral Soc. Am; Electron Micros. Soc. Am. Igneous and experimental petrology; electron diffraction and microscopy and their application to problems in the materials industry; light microscopy; light micrography and photography; development of materials for pollution control. Address: Ferro Corp, 7500 Pleasant Valley Rd, Independence, OH 44131.

GIBBON, GERST ALAN, b. Pittsburgh, Pa, Nov. 10, 39; m. 63; c. 1. INORGANIC CHEMISTRY. B.A, Albion Col, 61; M.S, Carnegie-Mellon Univ, 65, Ph.D.(chem), 68. ASST. PROF. CHEM, CHATHAM COL, 67- Am. Chem. Soc. Chemistry of the group IV hydrides. Address: Dept. of Chemistry, Chatham College, Woodland Rd, Pittsburgh, PA 15232.

GIBBON, NORMAN CHARLES, b. Buffalo, N.Y, June 16, 29; m. 60; c. 2. MECHANICAL ENGINEERING. B.S, Iowa State, 57. Engr, LINDE DIV, UNION CARBIDE CORP, 57-62, proj. engr, 62-64, sect. engr, 64-67, div. engr, 67-70, SUPVR, 70- U.S.A.F, 51-52, S/Sgt. Am. Soc. Mech. Eng. Thermal insulation; vacuum technology; heat transfer; cryogenic equipment development. Address: Union Carbide Corp, P.O. Box 44, Tonawanda, NY 14150.

GIBBONS, BARBARA H(OLLINGWORTH), b. Newark, Del, Jan. 17, 32; m. 61; c. 2. BIOCHEMISTRY. A.B, Mt. Holyoke Col, 53; U.S. Pub. Health Serv. fel, Harvard, 59-63, Ph.D.(biochem), 63. ASST. RESEARCHER CYTOL, UNIV. HAWAII, 67- Kinetics of the hydration of carbon dioxide and dehydration of carbonic acid; kinetic properties of human erythrocyte carbonic anhydrases B and C; chemistry of cell motility. Address: Pacific Biomedical Research Center, University of Hawaii, Honolulu, HI 96822.

GIBBONS, D(ONALD) F(RANK), b. Birmingham, Eng, July 23, 26; m. 50; c. 2. BIOMATERIALS. B.Sc, Birmingham, 47, fel, 48-50, Ph.D, 50. Res. fel, Chicago, 50-52; res. assoc, Royal Mil. Col, Can, 52-54; mem. tech. staff, Bell Tel. Labs, 54-62; PROF. metall, CASE WEST. RESERVE UNIV, 62-67, BIOMED. ENG, 68-, DIR. CTR. STUDY MAT, 62- AAAS; Am. Inst. Mining, Metall. & Petrol. Eng; Am. Phys. Soc; Am. Soc. Test & Mat; Am. Inst. Physics; N.Y. Acad. Sci. Biomaterials; improvement of present and development of new materials suitable for biological implantation, including encapsulation of microelectronic circuits and electrode materials; examination of ancient works of art. Address: Center for Study of Materials, Case Western Reserve University, Cleveland, OH 44106.

GIBBONS, H(ENRY) B(ENDEL), b. Boston, Mass, Mar. 11, 06; m. 30; c. 2. MECHANICAL ENGINEERING. B.S, Mass. Inst. Tech, 29. Aeronaut. engr, Goodyear Zeppelin Corp, 29-39; from chief of structs. to assoc. dir. res. ctr, Ling-Temco Vought, Inc, 39-70; RETIRED. Wright Bros. medal, Soc. Automotive Eng, 47. Acoustics; aerophysics; electronics; life sciences; materials sciences; nuclear sciences. Address: Ling-Temco-Vought Research Center, Box 6144, Dallas, TX 75222.

GIBBONS, I(AN) R(EAD), b. Hastings, Eng, Oct. 30, 31; m. 61; c. 2. MOLECULAR BIOLOGY. B.A, Cambridge, 54, Ph.D.(biophys), 57. Res. fel. biophys, Pennsylvania, 57-58; biol, Harvard, 58-62, lectr, 62-63, asst. prof, 64-67; assoc. prof, PAC. BIOMED. RES. CTR, UNIV. HAWAII, 67-69, PROF. BIOPHYS, 69- Am. Soc. Cell Biol; Soc. Gen. Physiol; Am. Soc. Biol. Chem; Biophys. Soc. Cell motility; molecular organization of subcellular organelles, especially cilia and flagella. Address: Pacific Biomedical Research Center, University of Hawaii, Honolulu, HI 96822.

GIBBONS, J. WHITFIELD, b. Montgomery, Ala, Oct. 5, 39; m. 63; c. 3. POPULATION ECOLOGY, HERPETOLOGY. B.S, Univ. Ala, 61, Nat. Defense Educ. Act fel, 61-63, M.S, 63; Ph.D.(zool), Mich. State Univ, 67. Nat. Insts. Health fel. ECOL, SAVANNAH RIVER ECOL. LAB, 67-68, RES. ASSOC, 68- Dir. Nat. Sci. Found. Undergrad. Res. Participation Proj, 69 & 70; adj. asst. prof, Wake Forest Univ, 71. Population dynamics and ecology of fish, amphibians and reptiles; reproductive ecology of reptiles; effects of thermal effluents on natural populations of animals. Address: Savannah River Ecology Lab, P.O. Drawer E, Aiken, SC 29801.

GIBBONS, JAMES F, b. Leavenworth, Kans, Sept. 19, 31; m. 54; c. 3. ELECTRICAL ENGINEERING. B.S, Northwestern, 53; Nat. Sci. Found. fel, Stanford, 53-55, M.S, 54, Nat. Acad. Sci. fel, 55-56, Ph.D.(elec. eng), 56. Fulbright fel, Cambridge, 56-57; asst. prof. ELEC. ENG, STANFORD UNIV, 57-60, assoc. prof, 60-64, PROF, 64- Mem. tech. staff, Bell Tel. Labs, Inc, 56; Nat. Sci. Found. sr. fel, 63-64; Fulbright lectr, 63-64; mem. grad. fel. panel, Nat. Sci. Found, 64-70, chmn. eng. fel. panel, 68-70; consult, Fairchild Camera & Instrument Co, 66-70; mem, bd. dirs, Avantek, Inc, 68-; comt. higher educ, Dept. Health, Educ. & Welfare, 69-71. Transistor circuits; solid state devices: ion implantation in semiconductors. Address: Dept. of Electrical Engineering, Stanford Electronics Labs, Stanford University, Stanford, CA 94305.

GIBBONS, JEAN DICKINSON, b. St. Petersburg, Fla, Mar. 14, 38; m. 58. MATHEMATICAL STATISTICS. A.B, Duke, 58, M.A, 59; South. Fels. Fund fel, Columbia, 60-61; Ph.D.(statist), Va. Polytech, 63. Asst. prof. math, Mercer Univ, 58-60; math. & statist, Univ. Cincinnati, 61-63; STATIST, Univ. Pa, 63-68, assoc. prof, 68-70; PROF, UNIV. ALA, TUSCALOOSA, 70- Inst. Math. Statist; Am. Statist. Asn. Performance of nonparametric tests based on ranks of observations. Address: Dept. of Statistics, Box J, University of Alabama, University, AL 35486.

GIBBONS, JOHN H(OWARD), b. Harrisonburg, Va, Jan. 15, 29; m. 55; c. 3. NUCLEAR PHYSICS. B.S, Randolph-Macon Col, 49; Ph.D.(physics), Duke, 54. Res. assoc. nuclear physics, Duke Univ, 53-54; PHYSICIST, OAK RIDGE NAT. LAB, 54-, DIR. OAK RIDGE NAT. LAB-NAT. SCI. FOUND. ENVIRON. PROG, 70-, group leader geophys, lab, 65-69, dir. environ. qual. study proj, 69-70. Mem. nuclear cross sect. adv. comt, Atomic Energy Comn, 69-70. Fel. AAAS; fel. Am. Phys. Soc. Nuclear cross sections; stellar nucleosynthesis; proton reaction analysis; power plant siting and environment; population problems; socio-technical problems and environmental quality; technology assessment. Address: Oak Ridge National Lab-National Science Foundation Environmental Program, Bldg. 3603, Oak Ridge National Lab, Oak Ridge, TN 37830.

GIBBONS, J(OHN) J(OSEPH), b. Chicago, Ill, Apr. 8, 06; m. 35; c. 3. PHYSICS. B.A, Illinois, 28, M.S, 30, Ph.D.(physics), 33. Asst. PHYSICS, Illinois, 34-35, instr, 35-37; PA. STATE UNIV, 37-39, asst. prof, 39-44, assoc. prof, 44-52, prof, 52-71, EMER. PROF, 71-, acting chmn. dept, 62-64. Mem. comn. III, Fr-Int. Sci. Radio Union. Am. Phys. Soc. Wave mechanics; electromagnetic wave propagation in ionosphere; electrodynamics of ionized media. Address: Dept. of Physics, 123 Osmond Lab, Pennsylvania State University, University Park, PA 16802.

GIBBONS, JOSEPH H(ARRISON), b. Turbeville, S.C, Sept. 4, 34; m. 56; c. 2. CHEMICAL ENGINEERING. B.S, South Carolina, 56; M.S, Pittsburgh, 58, Ph.D.(heat transfer), 61. Jr. engr, Westinghouse Elec. Corp, 56-57, assoc. engr, 57-61, engr, 61-62, sr. engr, 62-63; ASSOC. PROF. CHEM. ENG, UNIV. S.C, 63- Am. Inst. Chem. Eng; Am. Soc. Eng. Educ; Am. Chem. Soc. Heat transfer and fluid dynamics with application to oceanography. Address: Dept. of Chemical Engineering, University of South Carolina, Columbia SC 29208.

GIBBONS, LOREN K(ENNETH), b. Cheboygan, Mich, Dec. 13, 38; m. 61; c. 2. ORGANIC CHEMISTRY. A.B, Albion Col, 60; Nat. Insts. Health fel, Kansas, 63-64, Ph.D.(org. chem), 64. RES. CHEMIST, NIAGARA CHEM. DIV, FMC CORP, 64- Am. Chem. Soc. Synthesizing potential herbicides; sterically hindered hydrocarbons and Claisen-type rearrangements. Address: Niagara Chemical Division, FMC CORP, 100 Niagara St, Middleport, NY 14105.

GIBBONS, LOUIS C(HARLES), b. Lost Springs, Wyo, Aug. 8, 14; m. 40; c. 1. CHEMISTRY. B.S, Ohio (Athens), 36; M.S, Ohio State, 38; fel. & Ph.D.(org. chem), 40. Chemist, Nat. Adv. Comt. Aeronaut, Va, 41, head org. synthesis sect, Ohio, 42-45, chief fuels br, 45-50, assoc. chief fuels & combustion res. div, 50-55; res. chem. supvr, Ohio Oil Co, 55-61, assoc. res. dir, MARATHON OIL CO, Colo, 61-70, RES. ADV, OHIO, 70- AAAS; Am. Chem. Soc; Am. Inst. Chem. Eng. Synthesis and combustion of hydrocarbons; paraffinic hydrocarbons derived from tetrahydrofurfuryl alcohol; aircraft fuels; petroleum chemistry. Address: Marathon Oil Co, 539 S. Main St, Findlay, OH 45840.

GIBBONS, M. SERAPHIM, C.S.J, b. St. Paul, Minn, Feb. 5, 13. MATHEMATICS. B.A, Col. St. Catherine, 33; M.A, Minnesota, 43, Ph.D.(math), 51. From instr. to PROF. MATH, COL. ST. CATHERINE, 41- Math Asn. Am; Am. Asn. Physics Teachers. Address: Dept. of Mathematics, College of St. Catherine, St. Paul, MN 55105.

GIBBONS, MATHEW G(ERALD), b. Oakland, Calif, Jan. 21, 19. ATMOSPHERIC & NUCLEAR PHYSICS. B.S, St. Mary's Col.(Calif), 40; M.A, California, Berkeley, 45, Ph.D.(physics), 53. Instr. chem, St. Mary's Col. (Calif), 40-42, physics, 42-45, asst. prof. & dept. head, 45-56; res. physicist, U.S. NAVAL RADIOL. DEFENSE LAB, SAN FRANCISCO, 56-64, phys. sci. adminr, 64-69, SCI. ED. OPTICS & SPECTROS, 69- Optical Soc. Am; Am. Asn. Physics Teachers; Am. Meteorol. Soc. Nuclear magnetic resonance; atmospheric transmission of visible and near infrared radiation; nuclear reactor hazards; nuclear weapon effects. Address: 5524 Lawton Ave, Oakland, CA 94618.

GIBBONS, N(ORMAN) E(DWIN), b. Niagara Falls, Ont, Apr. 8, 06; m. 31; c. 2. BACTERIOLOGY. B.A, Queen's (Can), 27, M.A, 28, Nat. Res. Coun. Can. bursar, 28-29; Ph.D.(bact), Yale, 32. Demonstr, Queen's (Can), 27-28; asst. sci, Biol. Bd. Can, 32-37; asst. res. biologist, Nat. Res. Coun. Can, 37-41, assoc. res. biologist, 42-47, res. off, 47-59, asst. dir, div. biosci, 59-69; RETIRED. Secy-gen, Int. Asn. Microbiol. Socs, 62- Mem, Order of Brit. Empire. Brit. Soc. Gen. Microbiol; Can. Soc. Microbiol. (secy-treas, 51-55, pres. elect, 58-59, pres, 59-60; Award, 70); Royal Soc. Can.(hon. treas, 56-59); Brit. Soc. Appl. Bact. Food microbiology; halophilic and psychrophilic bacteria. Address: 64 Fuller St, Ottawa, Ont. K1Y 3R8, Can.

GIBBONS, RONALD J, b. New York, N.Y, Dec. 10, 32; m. 59; c. 3. MICROBIOLOGY, BACTERIAL PHYSIOLOGY. B.S, Wagner Col, 54; M.S, Maryland, 56, Ph.D.(microbiol), 58. Res. fel. bact, FORSYTH DENT. CTR, HARVARD, 58-59, res. assoc. microbiol, 59-61, assoc. bact, 61-64, asst. prof, 64-65, assoc. staff mem, 65-67, SR. STAFF MEM, 67- Am. Soc. Microbiol; Int. Asn. Dent. Res.(res. award, 67); Am. Dent. Asn; N.Y. Acad. Sci. Microbiological ecology; physiology and ecology of bacteria indigenous to mucous membranes of man; microbiology of mixed anaerobic infections, dental caries and periodontal disease; anaerobic metabolism. Address: Forsyth Dental Center, Harvard University, 140 The Fenway, Boston, MA 02115.

GIBBONS, WALTER J, b. Ithaca, N.Y, Oct. 25, 03; m. 32; c. 4. VETERINARY MEDICINE. D.V.M, Cornell, 25, M.S, 28. Vet. practice, N.Y, 25-26; instr. vet. med, Cornell, 26-36, asst. prof, 36-46; PROF. LARGE ANIMAL SURG. & MED, AUBURN UNIV, 47-55, MED. & INFECTIOUS DISEASES, 55- Borden Award, 62. Vet.C.Res, 25-30, 2nd Lt. Am. Vet. Med. Asn; Am. Asn. Vet. Clinicians; Int. Fertil. Asn. Infectious diseases of domestic animals; cattle disease, especially bovine infertility. Address: 156 McAdory Hall, Auburn University, Auburn, AL 36830.

GIBBS, ALAN GREGORY, b. Weaverville, Calif, Feb. 23, 39; m. 69. APPLIED MATHEMATICS. B.S, Stanford, 60, M.S, 61, Atomic Energy Comn. fel, 62-65, Ph.D.(nuclear eng), 65. SR. RES. SCIENTIST, THEORET. PHYSICS UNIT, PAC. NORTHWEST LABS, BATTELLE MEM. INST, 65- Lectr, Ctr. Grad. Study Hanford, Wash, 67-68; Battelle vis. prof, Washington (Seattle), 68-69. Mathematics of transport theory, neutron scattering theory, nuclear reactor theory; statistical mechanics; stochastic processes; atmospheric physics. Address: Pacific Northwest Labs, Battelle Memorial Institute, P.O. Box 999, Richland, WA 99352.

GIBBS, C(ARLIN) F(RARY), b. Coatsburg, Ill; m. 36; c. 1. ORGANIC CHEMISTRY. B.S, Knox Col, 30; M.S, Illinois, 32, Ph.D.(org. chem), 35. Res. chemist, West. Cartridge Co, Ill, 35-36; B.F. GOODRICH CO, 36-44, MGR. polymerization res, 44-60, RUBBER RES, RES. CTR, BRECKSVILLE, 60- Am. Chem. Soc. Synthesis and characteristics of synthetic rubbers. Address: 3069 Orchard Rd, Silver Lake, Cuyahoga Falls, OH 44224.

GIBBS, CARTER B, b. Hebron, N.H, Nov. 21, 25; m. 47; c. 2. FORESTRY. B.S, New Hampshire, 50, M.S, 56; Ph.D.(forestry), State Univ. N.Y, 69. Forester, Brown Col, 51-52; mgr. forester, N.H. State Forestry Dept, 52-56; forester, Bur. Land Mgt, 56-57; RES. FORESTER, South. Forest Exp. Sta, U.S. FOREST SERV, 57-59, NORTHEAST. FOREST EXP. STA, 59- U.S.A.F, 44-46, Res, 46-, Capt. Soc. Am. Foresters. Silviculture of hardwoods and spruce-fir. Address: 255 Washington St, Brewer, ME 04412.

GIBBS, CHARLES SHELBY, b. Errol, N.H, Nov. 28, 88. VETERINARY MEDICINE. B.S, Bates Col, 16; M.S, Yale, 20, Ph.D.(bact), 21; D.V.M, Mich. State Col, 30. Asst. bacteriologist, Storrs Exp. Sta, Connecticut, 18-21; prof. bact, Nanking, 21-27; res. prof. vet. sci, exp. sta, Massachusetts, 29-36; poultry pathologist, Lederle Labs, Am. Cyanamid Corp, N.Y, 36-40; dir, Wene Poultry Labs, 40-58, inspector in charge poultry meat, U.S. Dept. of Agr, N.J, 58-67; BACTERIOLOGIST, PIONEER LABS, 67- Med.C, U.S.A, 18. Am. Vet. Med. Asn; Poultry Sci. Asn. Fowl laryngotracheitis and pox vaccines; Newcastle disease and chick bronchitis vaccines; modification of complement fixation test for infectious abortion in cattle; factors that govern the production of diphtheria toxins in artificial culture media. Address: 923 N. Main St, Pleasantville, NJ 08232.

GIBBS, CLARENCE JOSEPH, JR, b. Wash, D.C, Dec. 10, 24. VIROLOGY. A.B, Catholic Univ, 50, M.S, 52, Ph.D, 62. Med. bacteriologist clin. path, div. vet. med, Walter Reed Army Inst. Res, 52-55; virologist, dept. hazardous opers, div. commun. diseases, 55-59; arbovirus sect, lab. trop. virol, Nat. Inst. Allergy & Infectious Diseases, 59-63, CHIEF LAB. SLOW, LATENT & TEMPERATE VIRUS INFECTIONS, NAT. INST. NEUROL. DISEASES & BLINDNESS, 63- Ad hoc mem. expert comt, Nat. Inst. Allergy & Infectious Diseases, 64-; assoc. prof. epidemiol, sch. pub. health & hyg, Johns Hopkins Univ, neurology, sch. med. Outstanding serv. award, Nat. Inst. Allergy & Infectious Diseases, 62; commendation awards, U.S. Navy, 63, 64, 68, 69, 70; Dept. of Health, Educ. & Welfare distinguished serv. award for studies on viruse diseases of nervous syst, 70; President's meritorious serv. medal, 70; Surgeon Gen. Navy cert. merit, 70. U.S.N.R, 43-46, Med. Serv.C.Res, 46-, Capt. Am. Soc. Trop. Med. & Hyg; Am. Soc. Microbiol; Wildlife Disease Asn; N.Y. Acad. Sci. Zoology, epidemiology and immunogenicity of arboviruses and isolation and characterization of viral etiologies for progressive degenerative diseases of the nervous systems of man and animals; pre-senile and senile dementics; aging process in man; behavioral changes in man and animals associated with infectious processes; oneogenic and tumor viruses; mechanisms of tolerancy; masking; persistence; temperatures; slow infections of viral itiology; immunopathological process involved in virous diseases of man and animals; disease patterns in primitive populations. Address: Room 5B20, Bldg. 36, National Institute of Neurological Diseases & Blindness, National Institutes of Health, Bethesda, MD 20014.

GIBBS, FINLEY P, b. Wash, D.C, Aug. 15, 40; m. 63; c. 3. PHYSIOLOGY, ANATOMY. A.B, Univ. Calif, Berkeley, 63; Ph.D.(physiol), Univ. Ore, 68. ASST. PROF. ANAT. & PHYSIOL, SCH. MED. & DENT, UNIV. ROCHESTER, 68- Am. Physiol. Soc. Neuroendocrinology; biological control mechanisms. Address: Dept. of Anatomy, University of Rochester School of Medicine & Dentistry, Rochester, NY 14627.

GIBBS, FREDERIC A(NDREWS), b. Baltimore, Md, Feb. 9, 03; m. 30; c. 2. NEUROLOGY. A.B, Yale, 25; M.D, Hopkins, 29; hon. degree, Montpellier, 65. Asst. neuropath, Harvard Med. Sch, 29-30, res. fel. neuropath, 33-34, physiol, 34-35, neurol, 35-37, instr, 37-44; Johnson Found. fel, Univ. Pa, 30-32; dir. electroencephalog. lab, neuropsychiat. inst, UNIV. ILL. COL. MED, 44-71, assoc. prof. psychiat, 44-51, prof. NEUROL, 51-71, EMER. PROF, 71- Asst. to vis. neurologist, Boston City Hosp, 38, jr. vis. neurologist, 39-43, res. assoc, 43-47; consult. electroencephalog, Children's Hosp, Boston, 43; res. assoc. & dir. neurophysiol, Boston Psychopath. Hosp, 43-47; sr. consult. neuropsychiatrist, St. Luke's Hosp, Chicago, 44-47, dir. electroencephalog. lab, 47-60. Mead Johnson Award, 38; Lasker Award, 51; St. Valentine Award, 71. Am. Physiol. Soc; assoc. Am. Neurol. Asn; Am. Acad. Neurol; Am. Acad. Cerebral Palsy; Am. Epilepsy Soc; Am. Med. Electroencephalog. Asn. Cerebral circulation; electroencephalography; epilepsy. Address: 1427 Astor St, Chicago, IL 60610.

GIBBS, GERALD V, b. Hanover, N.H, June 28, 29; m. 59; c. 3. MINERALOGY. B.A, New Hampshire, 55; M.S, Tennessee, 57; Southern Illinois, 58; Ph.D.(mineral), Pa. State, 62. Res. assoc. mineral, Chicago, 61-62; res. mineralogist, Linde Co, Union Carbide Corp, N.Y, 62-63; asst. prof. MINERAL, Pa. State Univ, 63-65, assoc. prof, 65-67; PROF, VA. POLYTECH. INST. & STATE UNIV, 67- Nat. Sci. Found. fel, 60-61, grants, 64-66, 67-74. U.S.N, 46-50. Mineral. Soc. Am; Am. Geophys. Union. Bonding and silicate mineralogy; crystallography. Address: Dept. of Geological Sciences, Virginia Polytechnic Institute & State University, Blacksburg, VA 24061.

GIBBS, GORDON E(VERETT), b. Cordova, Ill, Sept. 25, 11; m. 41; c. 4. PEDIATRICS. A.B, Redlands, 32; M.A, California, 35, Ph.D.(physiol), 39, M.D, 42. Intern, univ. hosp, California, 42-43, resident, 45-47; sr. fel. pediat, Nat. Res. Coun, California, 47-49, Illinois, 49-50; assoc. prof. pediat. res, Univ. Md, 50-54; PEDIAT, COL. MED, UNIV. NEBR, 54-56, prof, 56-66, RES. PROF, 66-, chmn. dept, 56-66. Med.C, 43-45, Res, 45-71, Col; Bronze Star Medal. Am. Pediat. Soc; Soc. Pediat. Res; Soc. Exp. Biol. & Med; Am. Diabetes Asn; Am. Thoracic Soc; Am. Acad. Pediat. Juvenile diabetes; experimental diabetes in monkeys; effect of diet, insulin and hypophysectomy on retinal and renal complications; cystic fibrosis of the pancreas; clinical management and research; lysosomal enzymes. Address: Dept. of Pediatrics, University of Nebraska College of Medicine, Omaha, NE 68105.

GIBBS, HAROLD C(UTHBERT), b. Barbados, B.W.I, Apr. 29, 28; m. 54; c. 4. PARASITOLOGY. B.Sc, McGill, 51, M.Sc, 56, Ph.D, 58; D.V.M, Ont. Vet. Col, 55. Pathologist, Can. Wildlife Serv, 57-58; hon. asst. prof. PARASITOL, MACDONALD COL, McGILL UNIV, 58-63, ASSOC. PROF, 63- Lectr, Univ. Ottawa, 57-58; res. off, animal path. labs, Can. Dept. Agr, 58-62; sr. parasitologist, Ayerst, McKenna & Harrison, 62-63. Am. Soc. Parasitol; Wildlife Diseases Asn; Am. Vet. Med. Asn. Helminthology. Address: Dept. of Animal Science, Macdonald College, McGill University, Quebec, Que, Can.

GIBBS, HAROLD JOSEPH, b. Yakima, Wash, May 8, 19; m. 45; c. 3. SOIL MECHANICS, CIVIL ENGINEERING. B.S, Idaho, 40; M.S, Missouri, 41. Engr. struct, bur. yards & docks, U.S. Navy, Wash, D.C, 41-42; soil mech, SOILS ENG. LAB, BUR. RECLAMATION, U.S. DEPT. INTERIOR, 46-53, head spec. invests. & res. sect, 53-63, CHIEF, SOILS ENG. BR, 63- U.S.A, 42-46, Capt. Am. Soc. Civil Eng.(Wellington Prize, 57). Soil mechanics testing, including settlement, shear, permeability, and pile foundations; studies involving effective stress, pore fluid pressure, and shear. Address: Division of Research, U.S. Bureau of Reclamation, Denver Federal Center, Denver, CO 80225.

GIBBS, HUGH H(ARPER), b. Can, Oct. 22, 30; m. 56; c. 1. ORGANIC CHEMISTRY. B.Sc, Queen's (Can), 52, M.Sc, 53; Cincinnati Chem. Co. fel, Illinois, 53, Dow Chem. Co. fel, 54-55, Ph.D.(chem), 56. Res. chemist, PLASTICS DEPT, E.I. DU PONT DE NEMOURS & CO, INC, 56-67, sr. res. chemist, 67-70, RES. ASSOC, 70- Am. Chem. Soc. Synthetic organic chemistry; mechanisms of organic reactions; synthesis and reactions of fluorocarbon compounds; polymer chemistry. Address: Plastics Dept, Experimental Station, E.I. du Pont de Nemours & Co, Inc, Wilmington, DE 19898.

GIBBS, HYATT McDONALD, b. Hendersonville, N.C, Aug. 6, 38; m. 60; c. 2. ATOMIC PHYSICS, OPTICS. B.S.(elec. eng) & B.S.(physics), N.C. State, 60; Nat. Sci. Found. fel, California, Berkeley, 60-64, Ph.D.(physics), 65. Acting asst. prof. physics, California, Berkeley, 65-67; MEM. TECH. STAFF, BELL TEL. LABS, 67- Am. Phys. Soc; Inst. Elec. & Electronics Eng. Alkali and ion spin exchange; beta-decay time-reversal symmetry; optical polarization and collisional depolarization of lead and thallium; self-induced transparency pulse breakup, peak amplification, pulse compression; coherent optics. Address: Room 1C307, Bell Telephone Labs, Murray Hill, NJ 07974.

GIBBS, JAMES A(LBERT), b. Montgomery, Ala, Oct. 1, 17; m. 43; c. 4. ORGANIC CHEMISTRY. A.B, Fisk, 38, M.A, 40; Rosenwald fel, Harvard, 44, fel, 46-47, M.A, 47. Asst. chem, Fisk, 40-41; U.S. Civil Serv, Wash, D.C, 42-43; instr. chem, Fisk, 43-44; asst. prof, Hampton Inst, 45-46; res. chemist physiol, med. sch, Tufts, 47-49; chemist, Tracerlab, Inc, 49-57; tech. dir. & treas, Volk Radiochem. Co, Ill, 58-60; mgr. chem. labs, PACKARD INSTRUMENT CO, INC, 60-67, MGR. CHEM. & SUPPLIES, 67- Am. Chem. Soc; Am. Inst. Chem; N.Y. Acad. Sci. Synthesis of isotopically labeled compounds, C^{14}, H^2, H^3, S^{35}, I^{131}, P^{32}; radioassay techniques and instrumentation. Address: Packard Instrument Co, Inc, 2200 Warrenville Rd, Downers Grove, IL 60515.

GIBBS, JULIAN H(OWARD), b. Greenfield, Mass, June 24, 24; m. 46; c. 4. PHYSICAL CHEMISTRY. B.A, Amherst Col, 47; M.A, Princeton, 49, Ph.D.(chem), 50; hon. Sc.D, Amherst Col, 71. Fulbright fel, Cambridge, 50-51; instr. phys. chem, Univ. Minn, 51-52; res. assoc, res. lab, Gen. Elec. Co, 52-55; res. specialist, Am. Viscose Corp, 55-56, group leader, 56-58, res. scientist, 58-60; assoc. prof. CHEM, BROWN UNIV, 60-63, PROF, 63-, CHMN. DEPT, 64- Consult, Am. Viscose Corp, 60-64; Arthur D. Little Corp, 60-64; Corning Glass Works, 64-66; Am. Cyanamid Co, 64-69; Guggenheim fel, 67-68; Fulbright sr. res. fel, 67-68. Am. Chem. Soc; fel. Am. Phys. Soc.(prize for high polymer physics, 67); fel. Am. Inst. Chem. Statistical mechanics; polymers; glass transition; biological macromolecules; liquid water and aqueous solutions. Address: Metcalf Lab, Dept. of Chemistry, Brown University, Providence, RI 02912.

GIBBS, MARTIN, b. Phila, Pa, Nov. 11, 22; m. 50; c. 5. BIOLOGY. B.S, Phila. Col. Pharm, 43; Ph.D.(plant physiol), Illinois, 47. Asst. chem, Illinois, 43-44, bot, 44-45, agron, 45-47; mem. dept. biol, Brookhaven Nat. Lab, 47-56; assoc. prof. biochem, Cornell, 56-60, PROF, 60-64; BIOL, BRANDEIS UNIV, 64-, CHMN. DEPT, 65- Vis. prof, Pennsylvania, 54; Queens, 58; vis. scientist, Res. Inst. Adv. Study, Md, 59 & 60; consult, Nat. Sci. Found, 61-64; Nat. Insts. Health, 64-; ed, Physiologie Vegetale, 68-; Sci. Res. Soc. Am-Sigma Xi nat. lectr, 69; consult, NATO Fel. Bd. Am. Soc. Plant Physiol.(ed. in chief, Jour, 63-, ed, annual rev, 67-); Am. Soc. Biol. Chem; Brit. Biochem. Soc. Photosynthesis; carbohydrate metabolism of higher plants and algae. Address: Dept. of Biology, Brandeis University, Waltham, MA 02154.

GIBBS, MARVIN E, b. St. Louis, Mo, Dec. 30, 34; m. 60; c. 1. CHEMICAL ENGINEERING. B.S, Washington (St. Louis), 56, Shell Oil Co. fel. & Ph.D.(chem. eng), 60. Sr. res. engr, MONSANTO CO, Mo, 60-66, res. specialist, 66-67, res. group leader, 67-70, MFG. SUPT, TEX, 70- Am. Inst. Chem. Eng. Process research, using special techniques, including mathematics and reaction kinetics, to provide all necessary information for large scale production. Address: Monsanto Co, Texas City, TX 77591.

GIBBS, NORMAN E(DGAR), b. Keyport, N.J, Nov. 27, 41; m. 67. COMPUTER SCIENCE. B.S, Ursinus Col, 64; M.S, Purdue Univ, 66, Ph.D.(comput. sci), 69. ASST. PROF. MATH. & ASST. DIR. COMPUT. CTR, COL. WILLIAM & MARY, 69- Asn. Comput. Mach. Graph theoretic algorithms; programming systems and languages; data structures. Address: Computer Center, College of William & Mary, Williamsburg, VA 23185.

GIBBS, PETER (GODBE), b. Salt Lake City, Utah, Dec. 7, 24; m. 53; c. 3. PHYSICS. B.S, Utah, 47, M.S, 49, Ph.D.(physics), 51. Res. assoc. physics, Illinois, 51-52, instr, 52-54; Fulbright lectr. theoret. physics, Univ. Ceylon, Colombo, 54-55; ASSOC. RES. PROF. CERAMIC ENG, UNIV. UTAH, 56-, PROF. PHYSICS, 62-, CHMN. DEPT, 68-, assoc. prof, 57-62, acting chmn. dept, 67-68. Fulbright lectr, Univ. São Paulo, 63; consult, Atomics Int. Div, N.Am. Aviation, Inc, 58-63; dept. sci. affairs, Orgn. Am. States, 63; Stanford Res. Inst, 65- Purdy Prize, Am. Ceramic Soc, 62. U.S.N.R, 43-50, Ens. Fel. AAAS; Am. Phys. Soc; Am. Asn. Physics Teachers. Solid state and theoretical physics. Address: Dept. of Physics, University of Utah, Salt Lake City, UT 84112.

GIBBS, R. DARNLEY, b. Ryde, Isle of Wight, Eng, June 30, 04; m. 61; c. 1. BOTANY. B.Sc, London, 25, Ph.D, 33; M.Sc, McGill, 26. Biochemist, Am. Rubber Producers, 26-27; demonstr. BOT, McGILL UNIV, 25-26, 27-29, lectr, 29-37, asst. prof, 37-44, assoc. prof, 44-55, prof, 55-65, MacDonald prof, 65-71, EMER. PROF, 71- AAAS; Bot. Soc. Am; Am. Soc. Plant Physiol; fel. Royal Soc. Can. Tree physiology; comparative chemistry of higher plants as applied to problems of taxonomy. Address: 32 Orchards Way, Southampton SO2IRE, England.

GIBBS, R(ICHARD) L(AIRD), b. Columbus, Ohio, June 19, 22; m. 43; c. 3. ELECTRONICS. B.E.E, Ohio State, 49. Installer tel. equip, West. Elec. Co, 41-42; lab. tech, electrodeposition, Battelle Mem. Inst, 45-48; res. assoc. antennas, antenna lab, Ohio State, 49-50; elec. engr, flight simulators, Wright-Patterson AFB, 50-51; RES. ENGR, BATTELLE MEM. INST, 51- U.S.A, 42-45. Instrument Soc. Am. Instrumentation. Address: 1268 Brookridge Dr, Columbus, OH 43220.

GIBBS, RICHARD LYNN, b. Buffalo, N.Y, May 12, 39; m. 59; c. 3. ATOMIC & PLASMA PHYSICS. B.A, Univ. of the South, 61; M.S, Clarkson Tech, 63, Ph.D.(physics), 66. Asst. prof. PHYSICS, LA. TECH UNIV, 66-70, ASSOC. PROF, 70- AAAS; Am. Phys. Soc; Am. Asn. Physics Teachers. Atomic and molecular structure calculations; mathematical physics; experimental plasma measurements. Address: Dept. of Physics, Louisiana Tech. University, Ruston, LA 71270.

GIBBS, ROBERT H(ENRY), JR, b. New London, Conn, July 30, 29; m. 63; c. 4. ICHTHYOLOGY, VERTEBRATE ZOOLOGY. A.B, Cornell, 51, Ph.D.(vert. zool), 55. Asst. prof. biol, N.Y. State Teachers Col, Plattsburg, 55-56; res. assoc. marine biol, Woods Hole Oceanog. Inst, 56-58; asst. prof, Boston, 58-62, assoc. prof, 62-63; assoc. curator, DIV. FISHES, U.S. NAT. MUS, SMITHSONIAN INST, 63-67, CURATOR, 67- AAAS; Marine Biol. Asn. U.K; Am. Soc. Ichthyol. & Herpet; Am. Soc. Limnol. & Oceanog; Soc. Syst. Zool; Am. Soc. Mammal; Soc. Study Evolution; Am. Ornith. Union. Systematic ichthyology; vertebrate biology; biological oceanography. Address: Division of Fishes, U.S. National Museum, Smithsonian Institution, Washington, DC 20560.

GIBBS, ROBERT J(OHN), b. N.Y.C, Aug. 14, 26; m. 52; c. 5. PHYSICAL CHEMISTRY. B.S, Fordham Univ, 48, M.S, 49, Atomic Energy Comn. fel, 50-52, Ph.D.(phys. org. chem), 52. Res. assoc. phys. chem, sch. med, Univ. Va, 52-54; mem. staff, Mass. Inst. Technol, 54-56; chemist, east. utilization res. & develop. div, U.S. Dept. Agr, 56-64; grants assoc, div. res. grants, U.S. PUB. HEALTH SERV, 64, asst. to extramural opers. & procedures officer, off. dir, NAT. INSTS. HEALTH, 64-69, opers. anal. off, 69-71, CHIEF GEN. RES. SUPPORT BR, DIV. RES. RESOURCES, 71- U.S.N, 44-46. Fel. AAAS; Am. Chem. Soc. Science administration; kinetics of protein denaturation; physical properties of proteins; structural proteins of muscle. Address: 4205 Howard Rd, Beltsville, MD 20705.

GIBBS, RONALD JOHN, b. Joliet, Ill, Dec. 26, 33; m. 62. GEOCHEMISTRY. B.S, Northwest. Univ.(Ill), 57, M.S, 60; Ph.D.(oceanog), Univ. Calif, San Diego, 65. Asst. prof. GEOL, Univ. N.Mex, 65-66; Univ. Calif, Los Angeles, 66-70; ASSOC. PROF, NORTHWEST. UNIV.(ILL), 70- AAAS; Geol. Soc. Am; Clay Minerals Soc. Sedimentology; developing quantitative clay mineralogy techniques; geochemistry of dissolved and suspended loads of the Amazon, Yukon and other large river systems; oceanic processes affecting discharged materials of river systems. Address: Dept. of Geological Sciences, Northwestern University, Evanston, IL 60201.

GIBBS, S(AMUEL) JULIAN, b. Amory, Miss, Apr. 1, 32; m. 58; c. 3. RADIATION BIOLOGY, DENTISTRY. D.D.S, Emory Univ, 56; Ph.D.(radiation biol), Univ. Rochester, 69. Private practice, Ala, 59-63; fel. radiation biol, Univ. Rochester, 63-68, ASST. PROF. radiol. & dent. res, 68-70; ANAT. & RADIOL, VANDERBILT UNIV, 70- Consult, Vet. Admin. Hosp, Nashville, Tenn, 70- Dent.C, U.S.A.F, 56-59, Capt. AAAS; Radiation Res. Soc; Int. Asn. Dent. Res; Am. Dent. Asn; Am. Acad. Dent. Radiol. Cytokinetics of normal and malignant mammalian tissues in vivo; relation to circadian rhythm; tumor and oral tissues radiobiology. Address: Division of Radiotherapy, Vanderbilt University Medical School, Nashville, TN 37203.

GIBBS, THOMAS W(ATSON), b. Alexandria, Va, Sept. 27, 32; m. 54; c. 3. METALLURGY, MATERIALS ENGINEERING. S.B, Mass. Inst. Technol, 54, S.M, 55, Sc.D.(metall), 64. Assoc. scientist, Avco Corp, 57-59, sr. scientist, 59-64, staff scientist, 64-65; res. metallurgist, E.I. DU PONT DE NEMOURS & CO, INC, 65-68, RES. SUPVR, 68- U.S.A.F, 55-57, 1st Lt. Am. Inst. Mining, Metall. & Petrol. Eng; Am. Phys. Soc. Mechanical properties; high temperature metallurgy; high intensity arcs; mechanical testing; materials engineering; fiber metallurgy; composite materials; semiconductor preparation and properties; dimensional stability; wear; foundry metallurgy. Address: 2527 Deepwood Dr, Wilmington, DE 19810.

GIBBS, WILLIAM E(UGENE), b. Akron, Ohio, Sept. 23, 30; m. 48; c. 5. PHYSICAL CHEMISTRY. B.S. & M.S, Akron, 54, Ph.D.(chem), 59. Res. chemist, inst. rubber res, Akron, 53-55; Goodyear Tire & Rubber Co, 55-58; Air Force Mat. Lab, 58-59, group leader, 59-62, chief polymer br, 62-66, dir, 66-70; V.PRES. & DIR. RES. & DEVELOP, FOSTER GRANT CO. INC, 70- Mem. comt. macromolecules, Nat. Acad. Sci. U.S.A.F.R, 58-60, Capt. AAAS; Am. Chem. Soc; Soc. Plastics Eng; Faraday Soc; Sci. Res. Soc. Am. Synthesis and properties of polymers; physical chemistry of polymers; mechanisms of polymerizations and degradation. Address: Research & Development Division, Foster Grant Co. Inc, Leominster, MA 01453.

GIBBS, WILLIAM ROYAL, b. Dublin, Tex, July 6, 34; m. 55. PHYSICS. B.S, Univ. Tex, 55, M.A, 57; Ph.D.(physics), Rice Univ, 61. Res. assoc. physics, Univ. Neuchatel, 61-62; MEM. RES. STAFF, LOS ALAMOS SCI. LAB, 62- Nuclear reaction mechanisms; pion-nucleus interactions. Address: 307 Potrillo, Los Alamos, NM 87544.

GIBBY, I(RVIN) W(ELCH), b. West Ogden, Utah, July 15, 17; m. 41; c. 4. MEDICAL MICROBIOLOGY. B.S, Brigham Young, 39; M.S, Cincinnati, 42, fel. & Ph.D.(med. bact), 45. Res. supvr. bact, William S. Merrell Co, Ohio,

45-47; med. bact, U.S. ARMY CHEM. CORPS, Ft. Detrick, Md, 47-51, acting chief biol. warfare div, Dugway Proving Ground, Utah, 51-52, chief, test design & anal. off, 52-54, sci. dir, long range planning off, 55-56, opers. res. analyst biol. sci, opers. res. group, 56-66, CHIEF BIOL. SCI. DIV, MUCOM OPERS. RES. GROUP, EDGEWOOD ARSENAL, 66- U.S. Dept. Army fel, med. col, Cornell Univ, 62-63. Am. Soc. Microbiol; Sci. Res. Soc. Am. Host parasite interactions; operational analyses of biological phenomena. Address: 2307 Bel Air Rd, Fallston, MD 21047.

GIBBY, ROBERT G, JR, Psychol, see Suppl. I to 11th ed, Soc. & Behav. Vols.

GIBEAULT, VICTOR ANDREW, b. Pawtucket, R.I, Oct. 21, 41; m. 65; c. 2. AGRONOMY. B.S, Univ. R.I, 63, M.S, 65; Fisons fel, Sports Turf Res. Inst, Yorkshire, Eng, 65-66; Ph.D.(farm crops), Ore. State Univ, 71. ASSOC. AGRICULTURIST TURFGRASS & LANDSCAPE HORT, AGR. EXTEN. SERV, UNIV. CALIF, RIVERSIDE, 69- Am. Soc. Agron. Adaptation of turfgrass species and varieties to various habitats; herbicide influence on growth and development of turfgrasses. Address: Dept. of Plant Sciences, College of Biological & Agricultural Sciences, 1145 Bachelor Hall, University of California, Riverside, CA 92502.

GIBIAN, MORTON J, b. N.Y.C, Mar. 15, 39; m. 61; c. 2. PHYSICAL ORGANIC CHEMISTRY, ENZYMOLOGY. A.B, Columbia Univ, 60, Nat. Sci. Found. fel, 63-64, Ph.D.(chem), 65; Mass. Inst. Technol, 60-61. Nat. Inst. Health fel. enzyme chem, Northwest. Univ.(Ill), 65-66; asst. prof. CHEM, UNIV. CALIF, RIVERSIDE, 66-70, ASSOC. PROF, 70- Am. Chem. Soc. Enzyme mechanisms; kinetics and the chemistry of model enzymatic reactions; free radicals and photochemistry. Address: Dept. of Chemistry, University of California, Riverside, CA 92502.

GIBIAN, THOMAS G(EORGE), b. Prague, Czech, Mar. 20, 22; nat; m. 49; c. 4. CHEMISTRY. B.Sc, North Carolina, 42; Ph.D.(chem), Carnegie Inst. Tech, 48. Petrol. res, Atlantic Ref. Co, 48-51; develop. engr, Dewey & Almy Chem. Div, W.R. GRACE & Co, 51-52, plant mgr, 53-56, gen. mgr, battery separator div, 56-57, v.pres, org. chem. div, 57-62, chem. group, 62-63, pres, res. div, 63-66, V.PRES. & TECH. GROUP EXEC, MD, 66- Lectr, Drexel Inst. Technol, 49-51. R.A.F, 42-46. Am. Chem. Soc; Am. Inst. Chem; Am. Inst. Chem. Eng; Indust. Res. Inst. Administration and management. Address: Washington Research Center, W.R. Grace & Co, Clarksville, MD 21029.

GIBILISCO, JOSEPH, b. Omaha, Nebr, Feb. 6, 24; m. 51; c. 3. DENTISTRY. D.D.S, Minnesota, 48, M.S.D, 51. Chmn, oper. dent, Creighton, 49-51; assoc. prof. dent. & anat, Alabama, 51-54; consult, dept. dent, MAYO CLIN, 56-62, CHMN. DEPT. DENT, 62- Consult, dent. study sect, Nat. Insts. Health; U.S. Air Force Sch. Aviation Med, 58. Dent.C, 54-56, Capt. AAAS; Am. Dent. Asn; Int. Asn. Dent. Res; fel. Am. Col. Dent; Am. Acad. Oral Med. Clinical dentistry, particularly oral diagnosis and management of complex pain problems. Address: Dept. of Dentistry, Mayo Clinic, 200 First St. S.W, Rochester, MN 55901.

GIBLER, JOHN W(ESLEY), b. Willow City, N.Dak, Nov. 10, 20; m. 47; c. 3. PLANT PATHOLOGY. B.S, Mont. State Col, 46; M.S, Minnesota, 50, Ph.D, 51. Asst, Minnesota, 47-51; assoc. plant pathologist, Rockefeller Found, Mex. & Colombia, 51-57, plant pathologist, 57-62, asst. local dir, 62-65, resident rep, Ecuador, 65-68, assoc. dir. wheat prog, Int. Maize & Wheat Improv. Ctr, Mex, 68-69; SPEC. ASST. TO PRES, MASSEY-FERGUSON LTD, 69- Mem. feasibility wheat study team, Rockefeller Found-UN Food & Agr. Orgn, 61; Tex. A & M agr. res. team, U.S. Agency Int. Develop, Quito, Ecuador, 62, head, mission to Bolivia, 71; mem. U.S. del, Cent. Treaty Orgn. Meetings, Istanbul, 67; head, UN Develop. Prog. team, Brazil, 68; mem, World Bank team, Spain, 69. Agr. medal of merit & citation, Pres. of Ecudor, 63. U.S.N, 43-45, Lt.(jg). Am. Phytopath Soc; Am. Soc. Agron. Administration of research and breeding of wheat, barley and oats. Address: c/o Massey-Ferguson Ltd, Cx. Postal 30240, São Paulo, Brazil.

GIBLETT, ELOISE R(OSALIE), b. Tacoma, Wash, Jan. 17, 21. HEMATOLOGY, IMMUNOGENETICS. B.S, Washington (Seattle), 42, M.S, 47, M.D, 51. U.S. Pub. Health Serv. fel. hemat, Washington (Seattle) & post grad. med. sch, London, 53-55; clin. assoc, SCH. MED, UNIV. WASH, 55-57, clin. instr, 57-58, clin. asst. prof, 58-61, clin. assoc. prof, 61-66, clin. prof. hemat, 66-67, RES. PROF, 67-; HEAD IMMUNOGENETICS & ASSOC. DIR, KING COUNTY CENT. BLOOD BANK, 55- U.S. Pub. Health Serv. trainee genetics, Case West. Reserve Univ, 60; mem, Nat. Blood Resources Comt. Am. Soc. Hemat; Int. Soc. Hemat; Am. Soc. Human Genetics; Am. Asn. Immunol; Am. Fedn. Clin. Res; Brit. Soc. Immunol. Erythrokinetics; genetic polymorphisms of all blood components; blood group antibodies. Address: King County Central Blood Bank, Terry & Madison, Seattle, WA 98104.

GIBLEY, CHARLES W, JR, b. Phila, Pa, Oct. 28, 34; m. 56; c. 4. ZOOLOGY. B.S, Villanova, 56; M.S, Iowa State, 59, Ph.D.(zool), 61. Lab. instr. biol, Villanova, 57; res. asst. zool, Iowa State, 57-61; asst. prof. biol, Villanova Univ, 61-65; asst. biologist & asst. prof, Univ. Tex. M.D. Anderson Hosp. & Tumor Inst, 65-67; PROF. ANAT, PA. COL. PODIATRIC MED, 70-, ACAD. DEAN, 67-, prof. histo-embryol, 63-70. Asst. prof, Ore. Inst. Marine Biol, summers 61 & 62. AAAS; Am. Soc. Zool; Soc. Develop. Biol; Histochem. Soc; Electron Micros. Soc. Am; Am. Soc. Cell Biol; Am. Inst. Biol. Sci; N.Y. Acad. Sci. Experimental embryology; histochemistry and developmental causes underlying the morphogenesis of embryonic and adult kidney in vertebrates. Address: Dept. of Anatomy, Pennsylvania College of Podiatric Medicine, 804 Pine St, Philadelphia, PA 19107.

GIBNEY, R(OBERT) B(ERNARD), b. Wilmington, Del, Aug. 30, 11; m. 38; c. 1. METALLURGY. B.S, Delaware, 32; Ph.D.(phys. chem), Northwestern, 36. Mem. tech. staff, Bell Tel. Labs, Am. Tel. & Tel. Co, N.J, 36-48; phys. chemist, LOS ALAMOS SCI. LAB, 48-52, GROUP LEADER METALL. RES, 52- With Office Sci. Res. & Develop, 44. Am. Soc. Metals; fel. Am. Inst. Chem. Electrochemistry; batteries; electrographic paper; semiconductor; physical chemistry; photovoltaic effect of sodium; deuterium abundance in cholesterol; metallurgy of uranium; refractory metals. Address: CMB-13, Los Alamos Scientific Lab, Los Alamos, NM 87544.

GIBOR, AHARON, b. Jaffa, Israel, Sept. 16, 25; nat; m. 50; c. 2. PHYSIOLOGY. B.A, California, 50, M.A, 52; Ph.D.(biol), Stanford, 56. Res. biologist, Alaska Dept. Fish & Game, 57-59; chief biol. sect, Resources Res, Inc, 59-60; res. assoc. PHYSIOL, Rockefeller Inst, 60-63, asst. prof, 64-66; assoc. prof, UNIV. CALIF, SANTA BARBARA, 66-68, PROF, 68- Am. Soc. Plant Physiol; Soc. Gen. Physiol; Soc. Develop. Biol. General and algal physiology. Address: Dept. of Biology, University of California, Santa Barbara, CA 93106.

GIBSON, AUDREY JANE, b. Paris, France, Oct. 5, 24; m. 51; c. 4. MICROBIOLOGY, BIOCHEMISTRY. B.A, Cambridge, 46; Ph.D.(biochem), London, 49. Commonwealth Fund fel. microbiol, Hopkins Marine Sta, Stanford, 49-50; res. assoc, agr. res. coun. unit microbiol, Sheffield, 50-51, 53-63; asst. prof. microbiol. & phys. biochem, Johnson Res. Found, Pa, 63-67; ASSOC. PROF. MICROBIOL, CORNELL UNIV, 67- Res. assoc, Univ. Ill, 61. Brit. Soc. Gen. Microbiol. Inorganic requirements of bacteria; hemepigments including catalase and cytochromes, especially photosynthetic bacteria; pathways of carbon assimilation; relationship of light-induced changes in cell components to photosynthetic growth. Address: Microbiology Section, Division of Biological Sciences, Cornell University, Ithaca, NY 14850.

GIBSON, AUGUSTUS, b. Montclair, N.J, Dec. 4, 08; m. 37; c. 4. MEDICINE. B.S, Rutgers, 30; M.D, Columbia, 34. Intern, Presby. Hosp, 34-36; resident, Hosp. Res. Chronic Disease, 36; Mountainside Hosp, 36-37; practicing physician, N.J, 37-41; assoc. med. dir, Merck & Co, Inc, 42-50, med. dir, 50-56; exec. dir. med. res, Merck, Sharp & Dohme Res. Labs, 56-60; v.pres. & dir. med. res, Winthrop Labs, 60-63; dir. med. res, SCHERING CORP, 63, dir. res. & develop, 64, V.PRES, 64-70, CORP. RES, 70- Asst. med, Columbia-Presby. Med. Ctr, 38- Dipl, Nat. Bd. Med. Exam. Am. Soc. Hemat; Am. Therapeut. Soc; fel. Am. Med. Asn; Am. Rheumatism Asn; Am. Heart Asn; World Med. Asn; fel. N.Y. Acad. Med; N.Y. Acad. Sci; fel. Int. Soc. Hemat. Clinical investigation of new drugs. Address: Corporate Research Division, Schering Corp, 60 Orange St, Bloomfield, NJ 07003.

GIBSON, BENJAMIN FRANKLIN, V, b. Madisonville, Tex, Sept. 3, 38; m. 68. NUCLEAR PHYSICS. B.A, Rice, 61; Woodrow Wilson fel, Stanford, 61-62, Nat. Sci. Found. fel, 61-65, Ph.D.(physics), 66. Fel, Lawrence Radiation Lab, California, 66-68; Nat. Res. Coun. res. assoc, Nat. Bur. Standards, D.C, 68-70; RES. ASSOC. DEPT. PHYSICS, BROOKLYN COL, 70- Consult. physicist, Lawrence Radiation Lab, California, 68- Am. Phys. Soc. Theoretical nuclear, hypernuclear and elementary particle physics; non-relativistic quantum mechanics. Address: Dept. of Physics, Brooklyn College, Brooklyn, NY 11210.

GIBSON, CARL H, b. Springfield, Ill, Sept. 26, 34; m. 58; c. 2. CHEMICAL ENGINEERING, FLUID MECHANICS. B.S, Wisconsin, 56, M.S, 57; Ph.D. (chem. eng), Stanford, 62. Chem. engr, Oak Ridge Nat. Lab, 57-58; Peace Corps teacher, Univ. Osmania, India, 62-64; asst. res. engr, UNIV. CALIF, SAN DIEGO, 65-66, asst. prof. OCEANOG, 66-71, ASSOC. PROF, 71- Am. Inst. Chem. Eng; Am. Phys. Soc. Fluid dynamics; turbulence; turbulent mixing of passive and reaction scalar properties; transport phenomena; nuclear reactor engineering; oceanography. Address: Dept. of Aerospace & Mechanical Engineering Sciences, University of California, San Diego, P.O. Box 109, La Jolla, CA 92037.

GIBSON, COLVIN L(EE), b. Detroit, Mich, Apr. 12, 18; m. 41; c. 3. PARASITOLOGY. A.B, Michigan, 40, fel. & A.M, 41, fel. & Ph.D.(zool), 51. Parasitologist, onchocerciasis res. proj, Pan-Am. Sanit. Bur. & U.S. Pub. Health Serv, 48-52, lab. trop. diseases, NAT. INSTS. HEALTH, 52-57, spec. asst. to chief, extramural progs. br, Nat. Inst. Allergy & Infectious Diseases, 57-61, chief, virus reagents prog, 61-62, res. reference br, 62-63, sci. commun. off, 63, chief res. grants br, 63-65, parasitol. & med. entom. br, 65-68, ASST. TO DIR, 68- U.S.N.R, 44-46, U.S.P.H.S, 48-, Sci. Dir. Am. Soc. Parasitol; Am. Soc. Trop. Med. & Hyg.(ed, Trop. Med. & Hyg. News, 66-). Filarial diseases, especially onchocerciasis; epidemiology of toxoplasmosis. Address: Office of the Director, National Institutes of Health, Bethesda, MD 20014.

GIBSON, COUNT DILLON, JR, b. Covington, Ga, July 10, 21; m; c. 3. MEDICINE. B.S, Emory, 42, M.D, 44. Asst. med, col. physicians & surg, Columbia, 50-51; asst. prof, Med. Col. Va, 51-56, assoc. prof, 56-57; prof. prev. med. & chmn. dept, med. sch, Tufts Univ, 58-69; PROF. COMMUNITY & PREV. MED, CHMN. DEPT. & ASSOC. DEAN COMMUNITY HEALTH PROGS, MED. CTR, STANFORD UNIV, 69- Med.C, 45-47, Capt. Am. Med. Asn; fel. Am. Col. Physicians; fel. Am. Pub. Health Asn. Infectious diseases; medical care. Address: Dept. of Community & Preventive Medicine, Stanford University Medical Center, Stanford, CA 94305.

GIBSON, DANIEL MORGAN, JR, b. Seguin, Tex, Aug. 1, 32; m. 52; c. 4. MECHANICAL ENGINEERING. B.S, Texas A&M, 53, M.S, 58; M.A, Princeton, 60, Nat. Sci. Found. fels, 60 & 61, Ph.D.(mech. eng), 62. Sr. res. engr, GEN. DYNAMICS/FT. WORTH, 61-64, proj. res. engr, 64-66, STAFF SCIENTIST, 66- Vis. assoc. prof, Tex. A&M Univ, 64, adj. prof, 64- U.S.A, 53-55, Res, 55-61, 1st Lt. Am. Soc. Mech. Eng; Am. Inst. Aeronaut. & Astronaut. Incompressible turbulent boundary layers; magnetohydrodynamics; holography. Address: 6220 Greenway Rd, Ft. Worth, TX 76116.

GIBSON, DAVID F(REDERIC), b. West Newton, Mass, Jan. 10, 42; m. 63; c. 2. INDUSTRIAL ENGINEERING. B.S.I.E, Purdue Univ, 63, M.S.I.E, 64, Nat. Sci. Found. trainee, 66-68, Ph.D.(indust. eng), 69. Indust. engr, Naval Ord. Plant, Ill, 63; res. asst, Purdue Univ, 63-64; proj. indust. engr. & chief methods & standards br, Sacramento Army Depot, 65-66; instr. indust. eng, Purdue Univ, 68-69; asst. prof. indust. & mgt. eng, Mont. State Univ, 69-71; DEAN SCH. SYSTS. SCI, ARK. POLYTECH. COL, 71- U.S.A, 64-66, 1st Lt. Am. Inst. Indust. Eng; Inst. Mgt. Sci; Am. Soc. Eng. Educ. Management systems analysis and design. Address: School of Systems Science, Arkansas Polytechnic College, Russellville, AR 72801.

GIBSON, DAVID M(ARK), b. Kokomo, Ind, Aug. 7, 23; m. 51; c. 5. BIOCHEMISTRY. A.B, Wabash Col, 44; M.D, Harvard, 48. Res. fel. BIOCHEM, Illinois, 50-53; enzyme inst, Wisconsin, 53-58, asst. prof, 55-58; assoc. prof, SCH. MED, IND. UNIV, 58-61, PROF, 61-, CHMN. DEPT, 67-, acting chmn, 65-67. Estab. investr, Am. Heart Asn, 57-62. AAAS; Am. Soc. Biol. Chem; Am. Chem. Soc; Soc. Exp. Biol. & Med; Am. Diabetes Asn; Am. Soc. Cell Biol; Brit. Biochem. Soc. Fatty acid synthesis, oxidation and activation; metabolic control mechanisms. Address: Dept. of Biochemistry, Indiana University School of Medicine, 1100 W. Michigan St, Indianapolis, IN 46202.

GIBSON, DON CARROL, b. Downington, Ohio, Sept. 21, 28; m. 52; c. 2. VETERINARY MEDICINE, EPIDEMIOLOGY. Ohio Univ, 49-51; D.V.M, Ohio State Univ, 57; M.P.H, Univ. Mich, Ann Arbor, 67. Dep. health comnr, Portsmouth Health Dept, 57-64, health comnr, 64-68; biol. scientist, Off. Prog. Planning & Eval, NAT. INST. CHILD HEALTH & HUMAN DEVELOP, 68-69; HEALTH SCIENTIST ADMINR, ADULT DEVELOP. & AGING BR, 69- Dipl, Am. Bd. Vet. Pub. Health, 70. Am. Vet. Med. Asn; Am. Asn. Lab. Animal Sci; Am. Pub. Health Asn. Aging research in mammalian model systems and the epidemiology of environmental influences on aging; development of defined laboratory animals for research in aging. Address: Adult Development & Aging Branch, National Institute of Child Health & Human Development, Bethesda, MD 20014.

GIBSON, DONALD H(ENDERSON), b. Harrodsburg, Ky, Dec. 27, 34; m. 55; c. 4. ELECTRONIC ENGINEERING, INFORMATION SCIENCE. B.S, Kentucky, 56. Assoc. engr, IBM Corp, 56-59, staff engr, 59-65, adv. engr, 65-70, SR. ENG. MGR, 70- Lectr, Fairleigh Dickinson Univ, 67; Tufts Univ, 68; Joint Comput. Conf, 68; Univ. Calif, Berkeley, 69; Univ. Santa Clara, 69; Univ. Mo, 70; Europ. Orgn. Nuclear Res, Italy, 70. Int. Bus. Mach. awards, 67 & 68. Storage hierarchy concepts for large computer systems; design, development and evaluation techniques for large computer systems. Address: Dept. B61, Bldg. 707, IBM Corp, P.O. Box 390, Poughkeepsie, NY 12601.

GIBSON, DOROTHY HINDS, b. Italy, Tex, July 19, 33. ORGANIC & ORGANOMETALLIC CHEMISTRY. B.A, Tex. Christian Univ, 54, M.A, 56; Ph.D. (chem), Univ. Tex, Austin, 65. Instr. CHEM, Tex. Christian Univ, 56-61; res. assoc, Univ. Tex, Austin, 64-65; Univ. Colo, 65-69; asst. prof, UNIV. LOUISVILLE, 69-71, ASSOC. PROF, 71- AAAS; Am. Chem. Soc. Synthesis and properties of iron carbonyl carbonium ion complexes; preparations and rearrangements of cyclic organic peroxides; ring opening reactions of cyclopropanols. Address: Dept. of Chemistry, University of Louisville, Louisville, KY 40208.

GIBSON, D(OUGLAS) (LORNE), b. Winnipeg, Man, Dec. 23, 14; m. 37; c. 2. DAIRYING, AGRICULTURAL BACTERIOLOGY. B.S.A, Manitoba, 35; M.Sc, Minnesota, 37, Ph.D.(dairy bact), 40; Nat. Res. Coun. Can. fel, Nat. Inst. Res. in Dairying, Eng, 39-40. Bacteriologist, Borden Co, Toronto, 37-38, dir. res, 40-43; assoc. prof. dairying, UNIV. SASK, 46-48, HEAD DEPT. DAIRY & FOOD SCI, 48- Mem, Order of the Brit. Empire, 46. Can. Army, 43-46. Agr. Inst. Can. Dairy bacteriology and processing. Address: Dept. of Dairy & Food Science, University of Saskatchewan, Saskatoon, Sask, Can.

GIBSON, EARL DOYLE, b. Putnam, Okla, July 20, 23; m. 57; c. 4. COMMUNICATIONS ENGINEERING. B.S.E.E, Okla. Inst. Technol, 49; Advan. Engr. Prog, Gen. Elec. Co, 51; M.S.E.E, Univ. Md, 60. Engr, Gen. Elec. Co, 49-51; U.S. Naval Ord. Lab, Md, 51-56; chief anal. sect, ACF Industs, Inc, 56-63; sr. staff engr, Aerospace Corp, Calif, 63-66; SR. SPECIALIST, AUTONETICS, 66- Inst. Elec. & Electronics Eng. Data communications; adaptive equalization; adaptive receivers. Address: Autonetics, Code HB14, 3370 Miraloma Ave, Anaheim, CA 92803.

GIBSON, EDWARD F, b. Colorado Springs, Colo, Apr. 2, 37; m. 63; c. 3. NUCLEAR PHYSICS. B.A, Univ. Colo, Boulder, 59, M.A, 64, Ph.D.(physics), 66. Physicist, cryogenic eng. div, Nat. Bur. Standards, 58-64; res. asst. nuclear physics, Univ. Colo, 64-66, res. assoc, 66; Univ. Ore, 66-68, scientist in residence, U.S. Naval Radiol. Defense Lab, 68-69; ASST. PROF. PHYSICS, SACRAMENTO STATE COL, 69- Assoc. West. Univs. fel, summer 71. Am. Phys. Soc. Nuclear spectroscopy; nuclear reactions; elastic and inelastic ^3He scattering; gamma-ray spectroscopy; nuclear life times; low temperature electrical and thermal conductivity. Address: Dept. of Physics, Sacramento State College, 6000 J St, Sacramento, CA 95819.

GIBSON, ELEANOR JACK, b. Peoria, Ill, Dec. 7, 10; m. 32; c. 2. PSYCHOLOGY. A.B, Smith Col, 31, A.M, 33; Ph.D.(psychol), Yale, 38. Asst. PSYCHOL, Smith Col, 31-33, instr, 33-40, asst. prof, 40-49; res. assoc, CORNELL UNIV, 49-66, PROF, 66- Mem, Inst. Adv. Study, 58-59; fel. Center for Adv. Study Behav. Sci, 63-64. Nat. Acad. Sci; Am. Psychol. Asn.(award, 68, G. Stanley Hall Award, 70); Soc. Exp. Psychol; Soc. Res. Child Develop. Psychology of learning; generalization and differentiation applied to verbal learning; general, laboratory, experimental, animal, comparative and developmental psychology; reading. Address: Dept. of Psychology, Cornell University, Ithaca, NY 14850.

GIBSON, FRANK C(URRY), b. West Homestead, Pa, Nov. 23, 16; m. 45; c. 2. PHYSICS. B.S, Pittsburgh, 38. Physicist, explosives res. sect, explosives & phys. sci. div, BUR. MINES, U.S. DEPT. INTERIOR, 45-50, electronic scientist & chief instrumentation unit, 50-54, supvry. physicist, phys. res. sect, explosives tech. div, 54-60, proj. coord, Explosives Res. Ctr, 60-68, CHIEF APPROVAL & TESTING, HEALTH & SAFETY TECH. SUPPORT CTR, 68- U.S.A, 42-44. Am. Phys. Soc; Coal Mining Inst. Am; Am. Inst. Aeronaut. & Astronaut; Inst. Elec. & Electronics Eng. Explosives and propellants dealing with the detonation parameters of temperature, pressure and propagation characteristics including deflagration to detonation in gaseous, solid and liquid systems; instrumentation; electrical, electronic, mechanical, diesel and respiratory equipment for metal and non-metal mines. Address: 915 Gibson Lane, Pittsburgh, PA 19236.

GIBSON, GEORGE, b. Yonkers, N.Y, Mar. 20, 09; m. 40; c. 2. CHEMISTRY. B.S, Polytech. Inst. Brooklyn, 32, fel, 33-34, M.S, 35, Ph.D.(inorg. chem), 42. Chemist, Chemco Photo Prod, Inc, N.Y, 32-33; asst. chem, Polytech. Inst. Brooklyn, 32-42; asst. prof. CHEM, Ill. Inst. Tech, 42-45, assoc. prof, 45-53, acting chmn. dept, 53, PROF, 53-60; BROOKLYN COL, 60-, CHMN. DEPT, 62- Teacher, pub. sch, N.Y, 34-36; anal. chemist, Charles Pfizer Co, N.Y, 36-37; res. chemist, E.I. du Pont de Nemours & Co, N.J, 37-42.

Am. Chem. Soc. Chemistry of uranium; nonaqueous solvents; chemistry of hydrazine; coordination compounds. Address: Dept. of Chemistry, Brooklyn College, Brooklyn NY 11210.

GIBSON, GEORGE G, b. Windsor, Ont, July 11, 31; m. 63; c. 2. PATHOLOGY, PARASITOLOGY. B.A, Univ. Toronto, 55, M.A, 57; Ph.D.(zool), Univ. B.C, 65. Asst. prof. biol, Notre Dame Univ,(B.C), 65-66; RES. SCIENTIST, CAN. WILDLIFE SERV, 66- Am. Soc. Parasitol; Wildlife Disease Asn; Am. Micros. Soc; Can. Soc. Zool. Spiruroid nematodes of birds; wildlife helminthology. Address: Canadian Wildlife Service, 6 Beechwood Ave, Ottawa, Ont. K1L 8B4, Can.

GIBSON, GEORGE WILLIAM, b. Los Angeles, Calif, Nov. 5, 21; m. 48; c. 4. METALLURGICAL ENGINEERING. B.S, Univ. Ariz, 43; Yale, 46; M.S, Univ. Idaho, 67. Metall. engr, Am. Smelting & Ref. Co, 46-55; smelter metallurgist, Braden Copper Co, 55-58; metall. engr, Atomic energy div, Phillips Petrol. Co, 58-61, group leader, 61-64, chief metall. develop. sect, 64-66; chief appl. metall. sect, Idaho Nuclear Corp, 66-71; METALLURGIST, SOUTH. PERU COPPER CO, 71- U.S.A.A.F, 43-46, 1st Lt. Am. Inst. Mining, Metall. & Petrol. Eng; Am. Soc. Metals; Am. Nuclear Soc. Extractive metallurgy; non-ferrous metallurgy; powder metallurgy; nuclear metallurgy; non-destructive testing; nuclear engineering. Address: Southern Peru Copper Co, Ilo, Peru, S.A.

GIBSON, GERALD W, b. Saluda Co, S.C, Oct. 27, 37; m. 68. ORGANIC CHEMISTRY. B.S, Wofford Col, 59; Ph.D.(chem), Tennessee, 63. Asst. prof. CHEM, COL. CHARLESTON, 65-68, ASSOC. PROF, 68- U.S.A, 63-65, 1st Lt. AAAS; Am. Chem. Soc. Organolithium compounds; chemical information retrieval; Wiswesser line notation. Address: Dept. of Chemistry, College of Charleston, 66 George St, Charleston, SC 29401.

GIBSON, GILBERT H, b. Newberg, Ore, Mar. 8, 02; m. 31; c. 1. PHYSICS. B.A, Walla Walla Col, 31; Columbia, 49-50; M.S, Oregon State, 50. Teacher, Laurelwood Acad, 31-41; Yakima Valley Acad, 43-46; prin, Greater N.Y. Acad, 46-50; teacher, Glendale Union Acad, 50-56; assoc. prof. math. Atlantic Union Col, 57-69, dir. audio-visual serv, 67-69; ASSOC. PROF. MATH, WALLA WALLA COL, 69- Math. Asn. Am. Optics. Address: 34 Tremont Dr, College Place, WA 99324.

GIBSON, GILBERT L(EWIS), b. Washington, D.C, June 16, 24. PHYSICS. B.A, Cornell, 46. PHYSICIST, Henry A. Gardner Lab, Inc, 46-57; photom. & colorimetry sect, Nat. Bur. Standards, 57-59; Henry A. Gardner Lab, Inc, 59-63; HUNTER ASSOCS. LAB, INC, 63- Inter-Soc. Color Coun. Design and development of appearance measurement instrumentation, reflectometry, glossimetry, colorimetry; calibration of standards for use with same; psychophysics; photocell behavior. Address: 4817 Cumberland Ave, Chevy Chase, MD 20015.

GIBSON, GORDON, b. McKeesport, Pa, Jan. 9, 26; m. 55; c. 4. THEORETICAL PHYSICS. B.S, Pittsburgh, 49, M.S, 52, Ph.D.(physics), 55. Instr. physics & res. asst, Pittsburgh, 50-55; sr. scientist, atomic power div, WESTINGHOUSE ELEC. CORP, 55-64, fel. scientist, astronuclear lab, 64-67, ADV. SCIENTIST, 67- Consult, Lawrence Radiation Lab, Univ. Calif, 55-64. U.S.N, 44-46. Am. Phys. Soc. Neutron cross sections; nuclear rocket reactor; plasma and reactor physics; controlled fusion. Address: 120 Lamar Rd, Pittsburgh, PA 15241.

GIBSON, HAROLD F(LOYD), b. Retrop, Okla, Feb. 24, 21; m. 41; c. 2. ENGINEERING PHYSICS. B.S, Oklahoma, 43, M.S, 48. Physicist, radiation lab, Nat. Bur. Standards, 48-53; HARRY DIAMOND LABS, 53-56, supvr. physicist, 56-62, supvr. res. & develop, 62-69, CHIEF APPL. PHYSICS BR, 69- Ord.C, 43-46, 1st Lt. AAAS; Am. Phys. Soc. Solid state physics; energy sources and conversion techniques; laser materials; applied infrared and laser technology. Address: 10705 Jamaica Dr, Silver Spring, MD 20902.

GIBSON, HAROLD J(AMES), b. Wixom, Mich, June 18, 09; m. 32; c. 3. MECHANICAL ENGINEERING. B.S, Michigan, 29, M.S, 30. Res. engr, ETHYL CORP, 30-44, res. coord, 44-47, res. supvr, 47-54, dir. prod. appln, 54-57, tech. dir, res. labs, 57-63, MGR. LABS, 63- AAAS; Soc. Automotive Eng; Am. Petrol. Inst. Mechanical and chemical research on automotive emissions and petroleum fuels, lubricants and additives. Address: Ethyl Corp, 1600 W. Eight Mile Rd, Ferndale, MI 48220.

GIBSON, HARRY W(ILLIAM), b. Syracuse, N.Y, May 2, 41; m. 62; c. 2. ORGANIC CHEMISTRY. B.S, Clarkson Tech, 62, Nat. Defense Educ. Act fel, 62-65, Ph.D.(chem), 66. Investr. chem. with Prof. Ernest L. Eliel, Univ. Notre Dame, 65-66; sr. chemist, res. & develop. lab, chem. div, Union Carbide Corp, 66, res. chemist, 66-69; SCIENTIST, RES. LABS, XEROX CORP, 69- Am. Chem. Soc. Chemistry of Reissert compounds, epoxides and formic acid; liquid crystals; mechanism studies; conformational analysis; metal hydride reductions. Address: Research Labs, Xerox Corp, 800 Phillips Rd, Webster, NY 14580.

GIBSON, HENRY CLAY, JR, b. Phila, Pa, Mar. 15, 22; m. 52; c. 3. ATOMIC PHYSICS. A.B, Princeton, 50. PRES, Radiation Res. Corp, Fla, 50-56; FRANKLIN GNO CORP, 56- Dir, John Dusenbery Co, Inc, N.J, 58- U.S.N.R, 41-45, Lt. AAAS; Am. Inst. Physics; Am. Phys. Soc; Am. Meteorol. Soc; Inst. Elec. & Electronics Eng; Am. Geophys. Union. Plasma chromatograph, a gaseous electrophoresis instrument for rapid chemical analysis. Address: Franklin GNO Corp, P.O. Box 3250, West Palm Beach, FL 33402.

GIBSON, JAMES (BENJAMIN), b. Ellensburg, Wash, June 9, 28; m. 68; c. 1. ASTRONOMY. A.B, California, Berkeley, 52. Physicist, Lawrence Radiation Lab, Univ. Calif, 53-57; math. analyst, missiles & space div, Lockheed Aircraft Corp, 57-58; asst, Lick Observ, Univ. Calif, 58-60; astronr, Flagstaff Sta, U.S. Naval Observ, Ariz, 60-61; res. asst. astron, Van Vleck Observ, Wesleyan Univ, 61-63, res. assoc, 64-67; res. asst, Observ, Yale, 68-71, PRIN. OBSERVER, YALE-COLUMBIA SOUTH. OBSERV, 71- Res. assoc, Inst. Advan. Study, 66-67; NASA res. grant for eclipse exped, 66-67; vis. astronr, Kitt Peak Nat. Observ, 66-67. Fel. AAAS; Am. Astron. Soc; fel. Royal Astron. Soc; Royal Astron. Soc. Can. Observational astronomy; astrometry; comet and minor planet positions; intermediate bandwidth photoelectric photometry; systematic errors of trigonometric parallaxes; spectroscopy and spectral classification; airborne optical instrumentation; variable stars in galactic and globular clusters. Address: Yale-Columbia Southern Observatory, El Leoncito-Barreal, Provincia de San Juan, Argentina.

GIBSON, JAMES DARRELL, b. South Bend, Ind, Apr. 8, 34; m; c. 3. MECHANICAL ENGINEERING. B.S, Purdue Univ, 57, M.S, 59; Ph.D, Univ. N.Mex, 68. Assoc. engr, Douglas Aircraft Co, summers 57-58; sr. engr, Gen. Dynamics Corp, 59-63; instr. MECH. ENG, Univ. N.Mex, 63-68; ASSOC. PROF, UNIV. WYO, 68- Staff mem, Sandia Corp, summer 67; NASA-Am. Soc. Eng. Educ. fel, Langley Res. Ctr, 69, asst. proj. mgr, fel. prog, summer 70, proj. dir. systs. design fel. prog, 71; vis. prof, Rose-Hulman Inst. Technol, 71. Am. Soc. Eng. Educ; Am. Inst. Aeronaut. & Astronaut; Am. Soc. Mech. Eng. Vibrations and acoustics; interdisciplinary design. Address: Dept. of Mechanical Engineering, College of Engineering, University of Wyoming, Laramie, WY 82070.

GIBSON, J(AMES) DONALD, b. Steubenville, Ohio, Mar. 29, 12; m. 41; c. 2. ORGANIC CHEMISTRY. B.S. & A.B, Wheaton Col.(Ill), 34; Ph.D.(org. chem), Ohio State, 38. Lab. asst, Wheaton Col.(Ill), 31-34; asst. inorg. chem, Ohio State, 35-36, org. chem, 36-38, res. chemist, pure hydrocarbon proj, Am. Petrol. Inst, 38; master chemist, Phillips Petrol. Co, 39-47; sr. res. chemist, Carbide & Carbon Chem. Corp, 47-52; supvr. org. chem, Ford Motor Co, 52-58; STAFF CHEMIST, RES. DIV, ALLEGANY BALLISTICS LAB, HERCULES POWDER CO, 58- AAAS; Am. Chem. Soc.(treas, 47). Chemistry of hydrocarbons; hydrogen fluoride alkylation of paraffins; catalysis of hydrocarbons; preparation and properties of fluorocarbons; resins, synthetic lubricants; solid propellants, and fiber glass-resin technology. Address: Research Division, Allegany Ballistics Lab, Hercules Powder Co, Box 210, Cumberland, MD 21501.

GIBSON, JAMES EDWIN, b. Des Moines, Iowa, Aug. 22, 41; m. 61; c. 2. PHARMACOLOGY, TOXICOLOGY. B.A, Drake Univ, 64; U.S. Pub. Health Serv. trainee, Univ. Iowa, 65-69, M.S, 67, Ph.D.(pharmacol), 69. Chemist, chem. labs, Iowa State Dept. Agr, 62-64; jr. res. scientist pharmacol, neuropharmacol. div, Abbott Labs, Ill, 64-65; ASST. PROF. PHARMACOL, MICH. STATE UNIV, 69- AAAS; Teratology Soc. Determination and description of drug or chemical induced teratogenicity, embryotoxicity and perinatal toxicity in mammals with particular emphasis on molecular mechanisms of action. Address: Dept. of Pharmacology, Michigan State University, East Lansing, MI 48823.

GIBSON, JAMES H, b. Morgantown, W.Va, May 3, 30; m; c. 2. ANALYTICAL CHEMISTRY. B.S, West Virginia, 52; Ph.D.(anal. chem), Cornell, 57. Chemist, Eastman Kodak Co, N.Y, 57-60; fel. & res. assoc, Cornell, 60-61; chief chem. div, U.S. Army Chem. Corp, Dugway Proving Grounds, Utah, 61-63; ASSOC. PROF. ANAL. CHEM, COLO. STATE UNIV, 63-, DIR. ADMIN. & SERV, NATURAL RESOURCE ECOL. LAB, 71- Consult, U.S. Army Chem. Corp, Dugway Proving Grounds, 63-65; Nat. Sci. Found. grants, 64-70. AAAS; Am. Chem. Soc; Soc. Appl. Spectros. Spectroscopy, including flame, emission, atomic absorption, absorption spectroscopy and gas chromatography. Address: Natural Resource Ecology Lab, Colorado State University, Ft. Collins, CO 80521.

GIBSON, JAMES J(EROME), b. McConnelsville, Ohio, Jan. 27, 04; m. 32; c. 2. PSYCHOLOGY. B.S, Princeton, 25, A.M, 26, Ph.D, 28. Instr, PSYCHOL, Smith Col, 28-29; asst. prof, 29-36, assoc. prof, 36-49; PROF, CORNELL UNIV, 49- Vis. prof, California, 54-55; Fulbright sr. res. scholar, Oxford, 55-56; mem, Inst. Adv. Study, 58-59; fel, Center Adv. Study Behav. Sci, 63-64. Consult, U.S. Air Force; U.S. Navy; Cornell Aeronaut. Lab. Warren medal, 52; Nat. Insts. Health award, 64. Psychol, prog, 42-46, U.S.A.A.F, 41-46, Lt. Col. Nat. Acad. Sci; AAAS; Optical Soc. Am; Soc. Exp. Psychol; Am. Psychol. Asn.(award, 64). Vision, psychophysics, sensory mechanisms and psychological theory; social, symbolic and esthetic perception; theory of knowledge; spatial perception and behavior; development of perception and perceptive learning. Address: Dept. of Psychology, Cornell University, Ithaca, NY 14850.

GIBSON, JAMES O(SCAR), b. Sioux Falls, S.Dak, Sept. 4, 21; m. 41; c. 4. CHEMICAL ENGINEERING. Colorado, 48. Chief chem. engr, uranium chem, S.W. Shattuck Chem. Co, 49-51; res. assoc, Climax Molybdenum Co, 51-52; chem. eng. supvr. nerve gas, Rocky Mt. Arsenal Chem. Corp, 52-54; v.pres. res. chem, Rocky Mt. Res, Inc, 54-57; chem. eng. consult. high energy fuels, Frontier Oil Co, 57-58; staff chem. engr, Vitro Labs, Div, Vitro Corp. Am, N.J, 58-66; sect. chief carbide mat, DONALD W. DOUGLAS LABS, WEST. DIV, McDONNELL DOUGLAS CORP, 66-70, NUCLEAR PROJ. ENGR, 70- U.S.A.A.F, 41-45, 1st Lt. Am. Inst. Chem. Eng; Am. Nuclear Soc; Am. Chem. Soc. High temperature technology including plasma-physics, plasma-chemistry synthesis, and metallurgy of high temperature materials of construction and high temperature nuclear fuels; plasma processing; ultra high temperature nuclear and isotope fuels. Address: Donald W. Douglas Labs, Western Division, McDonnell Douglas Corp, 2955 George Washington Way, Richland, WA 99352.

GIBSON, JAMES R(ANDOLPH), b. New Orleans, La, Sept. 4, 28; m. 52; c. 2. CHEMICAL ENGINEERING. B.S, Okla. State, 54, M.S, 55. Sr. res. chem. engr, Texaco, Inc, Tex, 55-59; res. engr, Boeing Co, Kans, 59-62; res. group leader, MONSANTO RES. CORP, 62-70, SR. RES. GROUP LEADER, 70- U.S.M.C, 46-47, 51-54, Res, 54-57, Capt. Soc. Aerospace Mat. & Process Eng. Fuel, lubricant and aircraft functional fluids and protective coatings; design and operation of pilot units; economic evaluation of petroleum processes; process design; pollution control systems for air, water and solid state areas. Address: Monsanto Research Corp, P.O. Box 8, Station B, Dayton, OH 45407.

GIBSON, JEAN, O.S.B, b. Columbia, Utah, Dec. 1, 30. SPACE PHYSICS. B.A, Col. St. Benedict, 56; M.S, Iowa, 66, NASA traineeship, 68-69, Ph.D.(physics), 69. X-ray technologist, St. Cloud Hosp, 56-58; teacher, St. Boniface High Sch, 58-63; ASST. PROF. PHYSICS, ST. JOHN'S UNIV.(MINN) & COL.

ST. BENEDICT, 69- Am. Geophys. Union; Am. Asn. Physics Teachers. Measurements of solar x-rays by means of satellites and comparing them with radio emission from the sun in order to learn more about the processes taking place on the sun that produce radiation. Address: Dept. of Physics, College of St. Benedict, St. Joseph, MN 56374.

GIBSON, JOHN E(GAN), b. Providence, R.I, June 11, 26; m. 50; c. 4. ELECTRICAL ENGINEERING. B.S, Rhode Island, 50; M.E, Yale, 52, Ph.D.(elec. eng), 56. Instr. elec. eng, Yale, 52-56, asst. prof, 56-57; assoc. prof. Purdue, 57-59, prof, 60-65, dir. control & info. syst. labs, 61-65; DEAN ENG, OAKLAND UNIV, 65- Consult, various aerospace & electronics firms; mem. subpanel res. & develop. goals in high speed ground transportation, Dept. Commerce, 66-67; adv, electronics res. ctr, NASA, Mass, 66-70. Control system components; nonlinear automatic control; large scale systems; transportation systems; urban system studies, long range planning and operations research. Address: School of Engineering, Oakland University, Rochester, MI 48063.

GIBSON, JOHN G(RAHAM), II, b. Utica, N.Y, June 11, 97; m. 43; c. 2. HEMATOLOGY. B.A, Amherst Col, 19; M.B.H, Harvard, 21, M.D, 32. Intern & res, Peter Bent Brigham Hosp, 32-35, assoc. med, 40-46, res. assoc. Harvard Med. Sch, 46-64; SR. INVESTR, Protein Found, 64-68, BLOOD RES. INST, INC, 68- Proctor fel, Harvard Med. Sch, 35-37, res. fel, 37-40, instr, 40-46; mem. staff, radioactivity center, Mass. Inst. Tech, 41- Consult, State Blood Prog, Mass, 45; expert, climatic res. lab, Qm. Corps, U.S. Army, 47; consult, Am. Red. Cross, 49; Fenwal Labs, 52- President's Cert. Merit, 48. U.S.A, 17-18, 2nd Lt. Am. Soc. Clin. Invest; Int. Soc. Hemat. Blood volume, shock, preservation and dyscrasia. Address: 110 Francis St, Boston, MA 02215.

GIBSON, JOHN PHILLIPS, b. Pittsburgh, Kans, Sept. 18, 30; m. 53; c. 2. PATHOLOGY, TOXICOLOGY. B.S, Kansas State, 53, D.V.M. & M.S, 59; Purdue, 60; Ph.D.(vet. path), Ohio State, 64. Instr. vet. bact, Purdue, 59-60; res. assoc. vet. path, Ohio State, 60-64; PATHOLOGIST TOXICOL, WILLIAM S. MERRELL CO, DIV. RICHARDSON-MERRELL, INC, 64- Adj. asst. prof, col. med, Cincinnati, 65- U.S.A, 53-55, 1st Lt. Am. Col. Vet. Path; Am. Vet. Med. Asn; Am. Asn. Lab. Animal Sci; Int. Acad. Path. Eperythrozoon suis infection in swine; development of the gnotobiotic dog; congenital ascariasis in dogs; experimental distemper in the gnotobiotic dog; toxicity testing of therapeutic agents. Address: Dept. of Pathology & Toxicology, William S. Merrell Co, 110 E. Amity, Cincinnati, OH 45215.

GIBSON, JOSEPH W(HITTON), JR, b. Norristown, Pa, Feb. 24, 22; m. 46; c. 3. CHEMICAL ENGINEERING. B.S, Worcester Polytech, 44; Princeton & Mass. Inst. Tech, 44-45. RES. chem. engr, fiber & dyeing, E.I. DU PONT DE NEMOURS & CO, INC, 46-51, clothing comfort, 51-52, 53-57, leatherlike prods, 52-53, end use textiles, 57-67, SR. RES. ENGR. TEXTILE RES, 67- U.S.N.R, 44-64, Res, 64-, Lt. Am. Chem. Soc; Fiber Soc; Sci. Res. Soc. Am; Am, Asn. Textile Chem. & Colorists. Preparation and evaluation of enduse textiles; clothing comfort with human subjects; dyeing of synthetic fibers. Address: 1215 Hillside Blvd, Carrcroft, Wilmington, DE 19803.

GIBSON, JOSEPH W(OODWARD), b. Carson, La, Dec. 24, 17; m. 42; c. 2. INORGANIC & ANALYTICAL CHEMISTRY. B.S, Ouachita Baptist Col, 39. Instr. org. chem, Ouachita Baptist Col, 38-39; teacher, pub. sch, Ark, 39-40; foreman, bleach dept, Am. Finishing Co, Tenn, 40; tech. rep, D.W. Haering & Co, Inc, Tenn, 40-42, asst. serv. dir, Ill, 46-49, supvr. anal. labs, Ill, 47-49; serv. dir. & supvr. anal. labs, Texas, 49-64; area tech. rep, WRIGHT CHEM. CORP, Kans. & Mo, 64-69, mgr, S.Tex. Dist, 69-71, MGR, SOUTHWEST DIST, 71- U.S.N.R, 42-45, Lt. Am. Chem. Soc; Nat. Asn. Corrosion Eng; fel. Am. Inst. Chem. Internal and external methods of water conditioning; control of scale, corrosion and microorganisms in industrial waters; water analysis. Address: 3906 Tidewater, Houston, TX 77045.

GIBSON, KATHLEEN R(ITA), b. Phila, Pa, Oct. 9, 42. PHYSICAL ANTHROPOLOGY, NEUROANATOMY. B.A, Univ. Mich, Ann Arbor, 63; Nat. Insts. Health grant, Univ. Calif, Berkeley, 64-70, Ph.D.(anthrop), 70. ASST. PROF. ANAT, UNIV. TEX. DENT. BR. HOUSTON, 70- Assoc, grad. sch. biomed. sci, Univ. Tex. Houston, 71- AAAS; Am. Anthrop. Asn; Am. Asn. Phys. Anthrop; Am. Soc. Zool. Comparative neurology; brain maturation. Address: Dept. of Anatomy, University of Texas Dental Branch, Houston, TX 77025.

GIBSON, KENNETH D(AVID), b. Kuala Lumpur, Malaya, May 9, 26; m. 52; c. 3. BIOCHEMISTRY. M.A, Cambridge, 50; Ph.D.(biochem), London, 56. Leverhulme res. fel, London, 56-59; vis. scientist, Nat. Insts. Health, 59-60; lectr. chem. path, St. Mary's Hosp, London, Eng, 60-65; vis. prof. chem, Cornell, 65-68; asst. mem. PHYSIOL. CHEM, ROCHE INST. MOLECULAR BIOL, 68-71, ASSOC. MEM, 71- R.N, 44-47. AAAS. Biosynthesis of porphyrins and chlorophyll; biosynthesis of choline; theoretical studies of polypeptide structure; biogenesis of bacterial membranes. Address: Roche Institute of Molecular Biology, Nutley, NJ 07110.

GIBSON, KENNETH E(DWARD), b. Zillah, Wash, Nov, 15, 05; m. 57; c. 2. ENTOMOLOGY. B.S, Whitman Col, 25; fel, State Col. Wash, 26-27, M.S, 28. Res. entomologist, entom. res. div, agr. res. serv, U.S. Dept. Agr, N.Y, 27-66; entomologist regional pulse improvement proj, U.S. Agency Int. Develop, 66-69, New Delhi Dept. State, Wash, D.C, 69; entomologist, entom. res. div, U.S. Dept. Agr, 69-70; RETIRED. U.S.A.A.F, 42-46. AAAS; Entom. Soc. Am. Insect control; insecticide residues on agricultural crops. Address: 1332 Evergreen Dr, Twin Falls, ID 83301.

GIBSON, LEE B, b. Chicago, Ill, Mar. 3, 26; m. 53; c. 1. MICROPALEONTOLOGY. B.A, Washington (St. Louis), 49, M.A, 52; Texas A&M, 51-52; Chicago, 52-53; Ph.D.(paleobot), Oklahoma, 61. Instr. geol, New Hampshire, 53-54; paleontologist, Creole Petrol. Corp, Venezuela, 54-57, sr. paleontologist, 57-59; sr. res. geologist, FIELD RES. LAB, MOBIL OIL CORP, 61-70, RES. ASSOC, 70- U.S.A.A.F, 44-46, Sgt. Am. Asn. Petrol. Geol; Soc. Econ. Paleont. & Mineral; Sci. Res. Soc. Am. Paleoecology; application of animal population characteristics to paleoenvironmental inter-

pretation in conjunction with the development of new biostatigraphic methodology. Address: Field Research Lab, Mobil Oil Corp, P.O. Box 900, Dallas, TX 75201.

GIBSON, MELVIN R(OY), b. St. Paul, Nebr, June 11, 20. PHARMACOGNOSY. B.S, Nebraska, 42, M.S, 47; Am. Found. Pharm. Ed. fel, Illinois, 47-49, Ph.D.(pharmacog), 49. Asst. prof. PHARMACOG, WASH. STATE UNIV, 49-52, assoc. prof, 52-55, PROF, 55- Ed, Am. J. Pharmaceut. Educ, 56-61; sr. vis. fel. sci, Orgn. Econ. Coop. & Develop, Netherlands & Sweden, 62; mem, U.S. Pharmacopeia Revision Comt, 71-75. U.S.A, 42-46, Capt. Fel. AAAS; Am. Pharmaceut. Asn; Soc. Econ. Bot; Am. Asn. Cols. Pharm; Am. Soc. Pharmacog.(v.pres, 63-64, pres, 64-65); Am. Pub. Health Asn; N.Y. Acad. Sci. Public health; enzyme-alkaloid relations in plants; sterile plant tissue culture; plant biosynthesis. Address: Washington State University College of Pharmacy, Pullman, WA 99163.

GIBSON, PETER MURRAY, b. Laurel Hill, N.C, Sept. 1, 39; m. 70. MATHEMATICS. B.S, N.C. State Univ, 61, Nat. Defense Educ. Act fel, 61-64, M.S, 63, Ford Found. fel, 65-66, Ph.D.(math), 66. Instr. MATH, N.C. State Univ, 66-67; asst. prof, UNIV. ALA, HUNTSVILLE, 67-69, ASSOC. PROF, 69- Am. Math. Soc; Math. Asn. Am. Combinatorial mathematics; linear algebra. Address: Dept. of Mathematics, University of Alabama, Huntsville, AL 35807.

GIBSON, PRYCE B(YRD), b. Vinemont, Ala, Oct. 18, 15; m. 47; c. 4. PLANT BREEDING. B.S.(ed), Ala. Polytech, 38, B.S.(agr), 40, M.S, 42; Ph.D.(genetics), Wisconsin, 50. Asst. prof. agron, Ala. Polytech, 46-47, assoc. prof. & assoc. plant breeder, 49-55; geneticist, crops res. div, AGR. RES. SERV, U.S. DEPT. AGR, 55-71, RES. AGRONOMIST, PLANT SCI. RES. DIV, 71- U.S.A, 42-46, Maj. AAAS; Am. Soc. Agron; Am. Genetic Asn. Genetics and breeding of white clover, Trifolium repens. Address: Dept. of Agronomy, Clemson University, Clemson, SC 29631.

GIBSON, Q(UENTIN) H(OWIESON), b. Aberdeen, Scotland, Dec. 9, 18; m. 51; c. 4. PHYSIOLOGY, BIOPHYSICAL CHEMISTRY. M.B, B.Ch, Queen's Univ. Belfast, 41, M.D, 44, Ph.D.(biochem), 47, D.Sc.(biochem), 51. Demonstr. physiol, Queen's Univ. Belfast, 41-46, lectr, 46-47; sch. med, Univ. Sheffield, 47-55, prof. biochem. & chmn. dept, 55-63; PROF. phys. biochem. & physiol, Johnson Res. Found, sch. med, Univ. Pa, 63-66; BIOCHEM, CORNELL UNIV, 66- Am. Soc. Biol. Chem; fel. Royal Soc; Brit. Physiol Soc; fel. Am. Acad. Arts & Sci. Etiology and biochemistry of idiopathic methemoglobinemia; hemoglobinometry; measurement of rapid reactions; mechanisms of enzyme reactions. Address: Dept. of Biochemistry & Molecular Biology, Wing Hall, Cornell University, Ithaca, NY 14850.

GIBSON, R(ALPH) E(DWARD), b. King's Lynn, Eng, Mar. 30, 01; nat; m. 27; c. 3. PHYSICAL CHEMISTRY. B.Sc, Edinburgh, 22, Carnegie scholar, 23-24, Ph.D.(chem), 24. Phys. chemist, geophys. lab, Carnegie Inst, 24-46; mem. staff, appl. physics lab, JOHNS HOPKINS UNIV, 46-47, PROF. BIOMED. ENG, SCH. MED. & EMER. DIR. APPL. PHYSICS LAB, 69-, acting dir, 47-48, dir, 48-69. Lectr, George Washington, 29-32, adj. prof, 32-45; v.chmn, sect. H, Nat. Defense Res. Cmt, Wash, D.C, 41-44; chmn, rocket propellant panel, Joint Chiefs of Staff, 43-45; dir. res, Allegany Ballistics Lab, 44-46. Hillebrand Prize, Chem. Soc. Wash, 39; President's Cert. of Merit, 48; Pub. Serv. Award, U.S. Navy, 58; Conrad Award, 60; Hon. Comdr. Most Excellent Order Brit. Empire, 66; Dept. Defense distinguished pub. serv. medal, 69. Am. Chem. Soc; Am. Geophys. Union; Am. Phys. Soc; fel. Am. Inst. Aeronaut. & Astronaut. Physical chemistry of solutions; properties of matter under high pressure; mechanism of Kolbe's electrosynthesis; rockets; guided missiles ordnance and space technology. Address: Applied Physics Lab, Johns Hopkins University, Silver Spring, MD 20910.

GIBSON, RICHARD C(USHING), b. Cambridge, Mass, Dec. 31, 19; m. 42; c. 4. INSTRUMENTATION. B.S, Mass. Inst. Tech, 42, M.S, 46, Sc.D.(instrumentation), 53. Radar & commun. off, U.S. Air Force, 42-45, asst. prof. elec. eng, Air Force Inst. Tech, 46-51, chief, missile guid, res. & develop. command, 53-56, deputy chief of staff, Missile Develop. Center, 56-58, dir. exp. vehicles & instrumentation, res. & develop. command, 59-60, prof. astronaut, Air Force Acad, 60-65, head dept, 60-62, v.comdr, nat. range div, 65-67; PROF. ELEC. ENG. & HEAD DEPT, UNIV. MAINE, ORONO, 67- Lectr, Univ. Conn, 60-66; dir, F.J. Seiler Res. Lab, 62-65; mem, U.S. Air Force Sci. Adv. Bd, 70- U.S.A.F, 42-67, Col.(Ret). AAAS; Am. Soc. Eng. Educ. Human response characteristics; missiles; range instrumentation inertial guidance; astronautics. Address: Dept. of Electrical Engineering, University of Maine, Orono, ME 04473.

GIBSON, ROBERT CAMERON, b. Paterson, N.J, June 3, 35; m. 58; c. 3. METALLURGY. B.S, Lehigh, 56; M.S, Stevens Inst. Tech. 66. Mill metallurgist, Crucible Steel Co. Am, 56-57, staff metallurgist, 57-62; res. metallurgist, Bayonne Lab, INT. NICKEL CO, INC, 62-64, PAUL D. MERICA RES. LAB, 64-67, SECT. SUPVR. RES, 67- Ord.C, U.S.A, 57, Res, 56-62, 1st Lt. Am. Soc. Metals (Marcus A. Grossmann Award, 68); Am. Inst. Mining, Metall. & Petrol. Eng; Sci. Res. Soc. Am. High temperature iron, nickel and cobalt base alloys; melting, casting and working of high temperature alloys; stainless steels; superplasticity. Address: Paul D. Merica Research Lab, International Nickel Co, Inc, Sterling Forest, Suffern, NY 10901.

GIBSON, R(OBERT) D(ESMOND), b. Utica, Kans, July 2, 22; m. 47; c. 3. PHARMACOLOGY. B.S, Kansas, 48, M.S, 50; fel, Purdue, 53-54, Ph.D. (pharmacol), 54. Asst. instr. PHARMACOL, Kansas, 48-50, instr, 50-51; assoc. prof, Southwest. State Col.(Okla), 54-57; UNIV. NEBR, LINCOLN, 57-61, PROF, 61-, CHMN. DEPT, 57-, DEAN COL. PHARM, 61- Fel, Am. Found. Pharmaceut. Educ, 52-54. U.S.N.R, 42-46, 51-52. AAAS; Am. Pharmaceut. Asn; N.Y. Acad. Sci. Developmental pharmacology and teratology. Address: College of Pharmacy, University of Nebraska, Lincoln, NE 68508.

GIBSON, ROBERT HARRY, b. Clover, S.C, Jan. 25, 38; m. 60; c. 2. ANALYTICAL CHEMISTRY. A.B, Erskine Col, 60; M.A, Columbia, 61, Ph.D. (chem), 65. ASSOC. PROF. CHEM, UNIV. N.C. CHARLOTTE, 65- Am. Chem. Soc. Electroanalytical chemistry; polarography; electrochemistry of organic compounds. Address: Dept. of Chemistry, University of North Carolina at Charlotte, UNCC Station, Charlotte, NC 28213.

GIBSON, ROBERT J(OHN), JR, b. Phila, Pa, Sept. 25, 21; m. 45; c. 4. PHYSICS, BIOLOGICAL SCIENCES. A.B, Pennsylvania, 43, M.S, 47. Res. eng, Brown Instrument Co. Div, Minneapolis-Honeywell Regulator Co, 47-49; res. physicist, FRANKLIN INST. RES. LABS, 49-57, sr. res. physicist, 57-63, SR. STAFF PHYSICIST, 63- Am. Phys. Soc. Application of philosophy, discipline and techniques of the mathematical and physical sciences to problems of experiment, measurement and instrumentation of the biological sciences. Address: Franklin Institute Research Labs, 20th & Parkway, Philadelphia, PA 19103.

GIBSON, ROBERT W, JR, b. Canova, S.Dak, Mar. 15, 23; m. 48; c. 3. CHEMISTRY. B.A, Yankton Col, 44. Sr. Technician, Maytag Co, 44-45; chemist, Battelle Mem. Inst, 45-48, librn, 48-51, asst. chief info. mgt. div, 51-62; head readers serv, Thomas J. Watson Res. Ctr, Int. Bus. Mach. Corp, 62-65; LIBRN, RES. LABS. LIBR, GEN. MOTORS TECH. CTR, 65- Chmn, Coun. Nat. Libr. Asn, 71-72. AAAS; Am. Chem. Soc; Am. Soc. Info. Sci; Spec. Libr. Asn.(pres, 69-70). Information handling techniques. Address: Research Labs. Library, General Motors Technical Center, General Motors Corp, Warren, MI 48090.

GIBSON, ROBERT W(ILDER), b. Greensburg, Kans, Dec. 19, 17. MATHEMATICS, ALGEBRA. A.B, Ft. Hays Kans. State Col, 38; A.M, Univ. Ill, Urbana, 39, Ph.D.(math), 43. Assoc. prof. math, Kans. State Col, 43; prof. physics, William Penn Col, 47-49; eng. aide, Kans. State Hwy. Dept, 58-59; asst. prof. math, Okla. State Univ, 59-65, ASSOC. PROF, 65-69; CIVIL ENG, AUBURN UNIV, 69- Int. winner, map colouring prog. competition, Comput. & Data Processing Soc. Can, 62. AAAS; Math. Asn. Am; Soc. Indust. & Appl. Math; Inst. Mgt. Sci. Mathematical programming; abstract algebra; the transportation problem of linear programming; six- and eight-bar linkage cognates; mathematical theory of flexagons. Address: Dept. of Civil Engineering, Auburn University, Auburn, AL 36830.

GIBSON, ROGER E(DWARD), b. Washington Co, Tenn, Nov. 20, 22; m. 48; c. 5. ORGANIC CHEMISTRY, PHARMACOLOGY. B.S, E.Tenn. State Col, 45; Ph.D.(chem. & math), Tennessee, 48. SR. CHEMIST, TENN. EASTMAN CO. DIV, EASTMAN KODAK CO, 51- Plastic additives; new polymers; polymerization techniques. Address: Bldg. 56, Tennessee Eastman Co, P.O. Box 511, Kingsport, TN 37662.

GIBSON, SAM T(HOMPSON), Covington, Ga, Jan. 1, 16; wid; c. 4. INTERNAL MEDICINE. B.S, Ga. Inst. Technol, 36; M.D, Emory, 40. Res. fel. med, Harvard Med. Sch, 41-42, spec. res. assoc, 43, Milton fel, 47-49; asst. med. dir, blood program, Am. Nat. Red Cross, 49-51, assoc. med. dir, 51-53, assoc. dir, 53-56, dir, 56-66, sr. med. off, 57-67; ASST. DIR, DIV. BIOL. STANDARDS, NAT. INSTS. HEALTH, 67- Assoc, sch. med, George Washington, 49-63, asst. clin. prof, 63-, univ. hosp, 49- Med. house off, Peter Bent Brigham Hosp, 40-41, asst. res, 46-47, asst, 47-49. Consult, Nat. Naval Med. Ctr, Md, 50-63; adv. blood transfusion servs, League Red Cross Socs, 55-66. Med.C, U.S.N, 41-46, Res, 46-, Capt. AAAS; Am. Soc. Hemat; Int. Soc. Hemat; Am. Med. Asn; Am. Fedn. Clin. Res. Int. Soc. Blood Transfusion. Effectiveness of serum albumin on kidney and liver function in disease; blood banking and plasma fractionation. Address: National Institutes of Health, Bldg. 29, Room 130, Bethesda, MD 20014.

GIBSON, THOMAS ALVIN, JR, b. Joplin, Mo, June 17, 19; m. 45; c. 5. PHYSICAL CHEMISTRY. B.S, The Citadel, 40; M.S, Virginia, 48; M.S, California, Berkeley, 50. Asst. prof. chem. & physics, N.Ga. Col, 62-64; RES. CHEMIST, LAWRENCE RADIATION LAB, LIVERMORE, 64- U.S.A, 41-62, Lt. Col. Am. Chem. Soc; Health Physics Soc. Bioradiology; laboratory research and nuclear weapons tests to determine weapons effects; nuclear radiation, residual radiation and fallout; industrial and engineering applications of nuclear explosions; radiation health physics. Address: 40 Mariposa Ct, Danville, CA 94526.

GIBSON, THOMAS CHOMETON, b. Burnley, Eng, Apr. 30, 21; U.S. citizen; m. 59; c. 3. INTERNAL MEDICINE, CARDIOLOGY. B.A, Cambridge, 42, M.A, 45, M.B,B.Ch, 46. House physician med, London Hosp, Eng, 46-47; resident physician, London & Bath Hosps, 53-55; private practice, 56-57; fel. cardiol, sch. med, North Carolina, 57-59, instr. MED, 59-61, asst. prof, 61-62; COL. MED, UNIV. VT, 62-66, ASSOC. PROF, 66- Chmn. subcmt. congestive heart failure, sect. on community serv, Nat. Conf. Cardiovasc. Diseases, 63-64; mem. adv. comt. clin. criteria for congestive heart failure, U.S. Pub. Health Serv. Heart Disease Control Prog, 64; attend. physician, Med. Ctr. Hosp, Vt, Burlington. R.A.F, 47-52, Squadron Leader. Am. Med. Asn; Am. Heart Asn; Am. Geriat. Soc; Asn. Teachers Prev. Med; fel. Am. Col. Physicians; fel. Am. Col. Cardiol. Clinical cardiology; phonocardiography; electrocardiography; vectorcardiography; cardiovascular epidemiology. Address: Dept. of Medicine, College of Medicine, University of Vermont, Burlington, VT 05401.

GIBSON, THOMAS GEORGE, b. Milwaukee, Wis, Aug. 10, 34; m. 56; c. 2. INVERTEBRATE PALEONTOLOGY, MARINE BIOLOGY. B.S, Wisconsin, 56, M.S, 59; Nat. Sci. Found. fel, Princeton, 60, Ph.D.(geol), 62. GEOLOGIST, Shell Oil Co, 57; U.S. GEOL. SURV, PALEONT. & STRATIG. BR, U.S. NAT. MUS, 62- U.S.A, 56-57, 1st Lt. Paleont. Soc; Marine Biol. Asn. U.K. Distribution and taxonomy of marine Mollusca and Foraminifera in the Tertiary deposits of the Atlantic Coastal Plain and the Recent of the Atlantic Shelf. Address: Room E504, U.S. Geological Survey, U.S. National Museum, Washington, DC 20240.

GIBSON, WALTER M(AXWELL), b. Enoch, Utah, Nov. 11, 30; m. 53; div; c. 3. NUCLEAR CHEMISTRY. B.S, Utah, 54; Ph.D.(nuclear chem), California, 56. MEM. TECH. STAFF, BELL TEL. LABS, 59- Res. collab, Brookhaven Nat. Labs, 60-; adj. prof, Rensselaer Polytech, 63-; Rutgers, 63- U.S.A.F, 54-59, Res, 59-, Capt. Am. Phys. Soc. Nuclear and solid state physics, principally nuclear fission mechanism studies; principles and application of solid state detectors and interaction of charged particles with crystalline and amorphous media. Address: Dept. 1131, Bell Telephone Labs, Murray Hill, NJ 07974.

GIBSON, W(ALTER) W(ILLIAM), b. Charleston, S.C, Feb. 24, 07; m. 35; c. 1. BIOLOGY. A.B, Morehouse Col, Atlanta, 30; M.S, Iowa, 34; Ph.D.(zool), Ohio State Univ, 44. Asst. prof. BIOL, LeMoyne-Owen Col, 34-35, assoc. prof, 35-38, prof. & chmn. dept, 39-48; head dept, Tex. South. Univ, 48-51; PROF. & CHMN. DIV. NATURAL SCI, LeMOYNE-OWEN COL, 51-54, 59-, acting pres, 54-59. Entom. Soc. Am. Taxonomy and ecology of Araneida; ecological study of the spiders of a river-terrace forest in western Tennessee. Address: Division of Natural Sciences, LeMoyne-Owen College, Memphis, TN 38126.

GIBSON, WILLIAM ANDREW, b. Middletown, Ohio, Apr. 22, 29; m. 56; c. 3. HISTOCHEMISTRY, CYTOCHEMISTRY. B.A, Ohio State, 51, M.A, 52, D.D.S, 56; M.D.S, Tufts, 61. INDEPENDENT INVESTR, HISTOCHEM. SECT, LAB. HISTOL. & PATH, NAT. INST. DENT. RES, 64- Dent.C, 56-64, Capt. AAAS; Am. Dent. Asn; Am. Inst. Biol. Sci; Am. Soc. Cell Biol; Int. Asn. Dent. Res. Role of bacteria and systemic factors in periodontal disease; salivary gland physiology; cell and tissue culture of oral tissues; collagenase in human tissues; histochemistry of oral tissues. Address: Histochemistry Section, Lab. of Histology & Pathology, National Institute of Dental Research, Bethesda, MD 20014.

GIBSON, WILLIAM ARTHUR, b. Morgantown, W.Va, Aug. 8, 33; m. 65; c. 2. NUCLEAR PHYSICS. A.B, West Virginia, 54; Ph.D.(physics), Rochester, 61. Physicist, neutron physics div, Oak Ridge Nat. Lab, 60-67; V.PRES, TENNECOMP, INC, 67- Secondary particles produced in interaction of high energy protons with complex nuclei. Address: Tennecomp, Inc, Box J, Oak Ridge, TN 37830.

GIBSON, WILLIAM C(ARLETON), b. Ottawa, Ont, Sept. 4, 13; m. 46; c. 3. NEUROLOGY. B.A, British Columbia, 33; M.Sc, McGill, 36, M.D, 41; Ph.D. (physiol), Oxford, 38. Res. fel, Montreal Neurol. Inst, 34-35; demonstr, lab. physiol, Oxford, 35-38; lectr. neuropath, Sydney, 48-49; Kinsmen prof. neurol. res, UNIV. B.C, 49-63, RES. PROF. PSYCHIAT. & PROF. HIST. MED. & SCI, 63- Vis. lectr, Univ. Calif, 49; Yale, 60; mem. adv. bd, Am. Muscular Dystrophy Asns. Med.C, R.C.A.F, 41-45. Fel. Royal Soc. Med. Neuropsychiatry; forensic medicine; history of medicine. Address: Dept. of History of Medicine & Science, University of British Columbia, Vancouver 8, B.C, Can.

GIBSON, WILLIAM MILES, b. Prince George, B.C, Oct. 8, 25; m. 51; c. 10. PEDIATRICS. B.A, New Brunswick, 46; M.D, McGill, 50; Dipl. Child Health, London, 56. Teaching fel. pediat, Western Reserve, 56-57, instr, 57-58, sr. instr, 58-59; instr, British Columbia, 59-61, asst. prof, 61-64; ASSOC. PROF. pediat, COL. MED, OHIO STATE UNIV, 65-70, PHYS. MED, 70-, DIR. NISONGER CTR. MENT. RETARDATION, 68- AAAS; Am. Cong. Rehab. Med; Am. Rheumatism Asn. Mental retardation; medical education. Address: McCampbell Hall, Ohio State University College of Medicine, Columbus, OH 43210.

GIBSON, WILLIAM RAYMOND, b. Murphysboro, Ill, Oct. 21, 23; m. 46; c. 2. PHARMACOLOGY. B.S, Butler, 48, M.S, 56. Pharmacologist, ELI LILLY & CO, 56-63, asst. head biol. qual. control, 63-65, HEAD TOXICITY DEPT, 65- Lectr, Butler Univ, 58-67. U.S.N, 42-46. Soc. Toxicol; Acad. Pharmaceut. Sci. Pharmacology of anesthetics, sedatives, antihistamines and anticholinergics; toxicology of drugs and agricultural chemicals. Address: Toxicity Dept, Toxicology Labs, Eli Lilly & Co, P.O. Box 708, Greenfield, IN 46140.

GIBSON, WILLIAM W(ALLACE), b. Phila, Pa, Sept. 26, 28; m. 51; c. 3. ENTOMOLOGY. B.S, Rhode Island, 51; M.S, Kansas State, 55, Ph.D.(entom), 57. Jr. asst. entom. & plant path, univ. exp. sta, Rhode Island, 52, asst. zool, 52-53; entom, Kansas State, 53-56; curator insect collection, Rockefeller Found. Mex. Agr. Prog, 56-58; entomologist, Assoc. Seed Growers, Inc, 58-61; temporary asst. prof. BIOL, Northeast La. State Col, 62; asst. prof, STEPHEN F. AUSTIN STATE UNIV, 62-67, assoc. prof, 67-68, PROF, 68- U.S.A, 46-48. AAAS; Entom. Soc. Am; Mex. Soc. Entom. Biological and ecological investigations of insects; taxonomy of scarab dung beetles, especially Phanaeus; building, maintaining and renovating insect collections. Address: Dept. of Biology, Stephen F. Austin State University, Nacogdoches, TX 75961.

GIDASPOW, DIMITRI, b. Ukraine, Russia, June 4, 34; m. 60; nat. CHEMICAL ENGINEERING. B.Ch.E, City Col. New York, 56; M.Ch.E, Polytech. Inst. Brooklyn, 59; Inst. Gas Tech. fel. & Ph.D.(surface combustion), Ill. Inst. Technol, 62. Lectr. chem. eng, ILL. INST. TECHNOL, 62-63, adj. asst. prof. gas technol. & chem. eng, INST. GAS TECHNOL, 63-67, ADJ. ASSOC. PROF. GAS TECHNOL, 67-, MEM. STAFF, CTR. APPL. MATH, 70- Am. Inst. Chem. Eng; Am. Chem. Soc. Heat and mass transfer; fuel cells; applied mathematics. Address: Institute of Gas Technology, 17 W. 34th St, Chicago, IL 60616.

GIDDENS, DON P(EYTON), b. Augusta, Ga, Oct. 24, 40; m. 57; c. 3. FLUID MECHANICS, GAS DYNAMICS. B.A.E, Ga. Inst. Tech, 63, Nat. Defense Educ. Act fel, 63-66, M.S.A.E, 65, Ph.D.(aerospace eng), 66. Assoc. aircraft engr, Lockheed-Ga. Co, 63; mem. tech. staff, Aerospace Corp, Calif, 65 & 66-67; asst. prof. gas dynamics, GA. INST. TECHNOL, 68-70, ASSOC. PROF. AEROSPACE ENG, 70- Am. Inst. Aeronaut. & Astronaut. Fluid mechanics of the cardiovascular system and the application to medical problems; rarefied gasdynamics. Address: School of Aerospace Engineering, Georgia Institute of Technology, Atlanta, GA 30332.

GIDDENS, J(OEL) E(DWIN), b. Eastman, Ga, Feb. 11, 17; m. 42; c. 3. SOILS. B.S, Georgia, 40, M.S, 42; Gen. Educ. Bd. fel, Rutgers, 48-50, Ph.D. (soils), 50. Asst, Georgia, 40-42; jr. chemist, South. Regional Res. Lab, U.S. Dept. Agr, 42-45; asst. agronomist, UNIV. GA, 46-48, 50-52, assoc. prof. AGRON, 52-59, PROF, 59- U.S.A, 45-46. Am. Soc. Agron; Soil Sci. Soc. Am; Am. Chem. Soc; Am. Soc. Microbiol. Soil microbiology and trace elements. Address: 315 Parkway Dr, Athens, GA 30601.

GIDDENS, WILLIAM ELLIS, JR, b. Dublin, Ga, Oct. 8, 37; m. 61; c. 1. VETERINARY PATHOLOGY. D.V.M, Iowa State, 61; Ph.D.(path), Mich. State, 68. Nat. Insts. Health fel. path, Mich. State, 65-67, res. instr, 67-68; ASST. PROF. EXP. ANIMAL MED. & PATH, REGIONAL PRIMATE RES. CTR, UNIV. WASH, 68- Vet.C, U.S.A, 61-64, Capt. Am. Col. Vet. Path;

Am. Vet. Med. Asn; Int. Acad. Path. Comparative pathology; respiratory diseases of animals and man; pulmonary anatomy. Address: Regional Primate Research Center, University of Washington, Seattle, WA 98125.

GIDDINGS, GLENN W(ARD), b. Wesley, Iowa, Oct. 15, 00; m. 26; c. 2. PHYSICS. A.B, Cornell Col, 23; A.M, Wisconsin, 25, Ph.D.(physics), 30. Instr. physics, Wisconsin, 26-30; asst. prof, DePauw, 30-32, assoc. prof, 32-38, prof, 38-42; mgr. res. personnel, res. lab, Gen. Elec. Co, 46-59, consult, ed. relations, 59-65; RETIRED. Asst. dean men, DePauw, 39-42; tech. aide to dir. radiation lab, Mass. Inst. Tech, 42-46. AAAS; Am. Inst. Physics; Am. Asn. Physics Teachers. Photoelectric effect in metal vapors; utilization of scientific and technical personnel. Address: 909-P Ronda Sevilla, Laguna Hills, CA 92653.

GIDDINGS, J(OHN) CALVIN, b. American Fork, Utah, Sept. 26, 30; m. 57; c. 2. PHYSICAL CHEMISTRY. B.S, Brigham Young Univ, 52; Ph.D.(chem), Univ. Utah, 54. Res. assoc, Univ. Wis, 55-56; UNIV. UTAH, 56-57, asst. prof. CHEM, 57-59, assoc. prof, 59-61, assoc. res. prof, 61-62, res. prof, 62-66, PROF, 66- Mem. adv. bd. anal. chem, U.S. Air Force Off. Sci. Res, 62-64, chem. res. eval. panel, 64-; Foster lectr, State Univ. N.Y. Buffalo, 71; ed, Separation Sci. AAAS; Am. Chem. Soc. Chromatography; non-equilibrium kinetics; diffusion; porous materials; snow physics; environmental science. Address: 904 Military Dr, Salt Lake City, UT 84108.

GIDDINGS, JOHN G, b. Richmond, Va, May 6, 31. CHEMICAL ENGINEERING. B.E, Vanderbilt, 57; Ph.D.(chem. eng), Rice, 63. ENGR, film dept, E.I. DU PONT DE NEMOURS & CO, INC, 63-64, PLASTIC DEPT, 64- U.S.A, 50-64. Viscosity of hydrocarbons; manufacture of plastic resins. Address: Plastic Dept, E.I. du Pont de Nemours & Co, Inc, P.O. Box 1089, Orange, TX 77631.

GIDDINGS, L(ORRAIN) E(UGENE) JR, b. Tacoma, Wash, Oct. 23, 29; c. 3. PHYSICAL CHEMISTRY, SPECTROSCOPY. B.A, Vanderbilt, 51, M.A, 55, Ph.D.(phys. chem), 60. Res. chemist textile applns, Rohm & Haas Co, Pa, 53-55; forensic chemist, lab. criminal invest, U.S. Army, Japan, 55-57; proprietor, Giddings Assocs, Tenn, 57-62; fel. atomic & molecular spectros, Naval Res. Labs, Wash, 62-63; Peace Corps vol. prof. chem, Univ. Chuquisaca, Bolivia, 63-65; res. spectroscopist, U.S. Naval Res. Lab, Wash, D.C, 66-67; contract Fulbright prof. phys. chem, Univ. Chuquisaca, Bolivia, 67-69; SUPVR. PHYS. SCI. SECT, LUNAR RECEIVING LAB, MANNED SPACECRAFT CTR, NASA, HOUSTON, 69- Molecular spectroscopy; education and chemical industrial development in underdeveloped countries; chemical problems at high altitudes. Address: 110 Webster Villa-85, Webster, TX 77598.

GIDDINGS, S(YDNEY) A(RTHUR), b. Mildura, Australia, Sept. 5, 29; m. 54; c. 3. INORGANIC CHEMISTRY. B.Sc, Melbourne, Australia, 52; Socony Mobil Oil Co. fel. & Ph.D.(chem), Ohio State, 59. Chemist thermosetting resins, Imperial Chem. Industs, Australia, 51-53; tech. officer soil chem, Commonwealth Sci. & Indust. Res. Orgn, Australia, 53-56; res. chemist, inorg. polymers, Stamford Res. Labs, Am. Cyanamid Co, 59-64, sr. res. chemist, 64-66; group leader, FORMICA CORP, 66-71, MGR. TECH. SERV SIERRA PLANT, 71- Royal Australian Chem. Inst. Complex chemistry; chemistry of phosphates; platinum group chemistry; organo-metallics; photochromism. Address: P.O. Box 519, Rocklin, CA 95677.

GIDDINGS, WILLIAM P(AUL), b. Indianapolis, Ind, May 7, 33; m. 61; c. 2. PHYSICAL ORGANIC CHEMISTRY. B.A, DePauw, 54; Nat. Heart Inst. fel, Harvard, 55-59, M.A, 56, Ph.D.(phys. org. chem), 59. Res. instr. CHEM, Washington (Seattle), 59-60; asst. prof, Albion Col, 60-62; asst. prof, PAC. LUTHERAN UNIV, 62-65, assoc. prof, 65-70, PROF, 70-, CHMN. DEPT, 66- Summers, res. assoc, Mich, State, 61, vis. asst. prof, Washington (Seattle), 62 & 64; Nat. Sci. Found. res. grant, 64-66. Am. Chem. Soc. Nature of carbonium ion intermediates in solvolysis reactions, especially non-classical ions and dicarbonium ions. Address: Dept. of Chemistry, Pacific Lutheran University, Tacoma, WA 98447.

GIDEON, DONALD N(ASON), b. Fairmont, Minn, Apr. 26, 20; m. 46; c. 8. PHYSICS. A.B, St. Olaf Col, 41; Ph.D.(physics), Ohio State, 48. Instr. physics, Notre Dame, 47-49; asst. prof, Creighton, 49-53; prin. physicist, electronic physics div, BATTELLE MEM. INST, 53-54, appl. mech. div, 54-63, SR. RES. PHYSICIST, ADVAN. MECH. GROUP, 64- Am. Phys. Soc. Mechanical properties of materials, impact, instrumentation. Address: Advanced Mechanics Group, Battelle Memorial Institute, Columbus, OH 43201.

GIDEZ, LEWIS I(RWIN), b. Boston, Mass, Jan. 27, 27; m. 55; c. 5. BIOCHEMISTRY. B.S, Iowa State Col, 48; Ph.D.(biochem), Harvard, 53. Asst. med. biochemist, med. dept, Brookhaven Nat. Lab, 52-58; asst. prof. BIOCHEM, ALBERT EINSTEIN COL. MED, 58-69, ASSOC. PROF, 69- Estab. investr, Am. Heart Asn, 58-63; career scientist, Health Res. Coun, N.Y, 64-70; exec. ed, J. Lipid Res, 70- U.S.N.R, 45-47, Lt. Comdr. Am. Chem. Soc; Am. Soc. Biol. Chem. Chemistry and metabolism of lipides and lipoproteins; regulation of pancreatic enzymes. Address: 41 Demarest Ave, Demarest, NJ 07627.

GIDLEY, J(OHN) L(YNN), b. Lytle, Tex, Dec. 30, 24; m. 51; c. 7. CHEMICAL & PETROLEUM ENGINEERING. B.S, Texas, 50, univ. fel, 50-52, Dow Chem. Co. fel, 51-52, M.S, 52, Ethyl Corp. fel, 52-53, Union Carbide Corp. fel, 53-54, Ph.D.(chem. eng), 55. Sr. res. engr, prod. res. div, Humble Oil & Ref. Co, 54-63; new uses adv, Standard Oil Co.(N.J), 63-64, res. specialist, prod. res. div, Esso Prod. Res. Co, 64-68; hq. supv. engr, HUMBLE OIL & REFINING CO, 68-69, TECH. ADV. 69- U.S.A.F, 43-45, Res, 45-56, 1st Lt. Am. Chem. Soc; Am. Inst. Chem. Eng; Am. Inst. Mining, Metall. & Petrol. Eng. Well stimulation methods; sand control; cementing. Address: Humble Oil & Refining Co, P.O. Box 2180, Houston, TX 77001.

GIDLEY, PHILIP TUCKER, b. Danvers, Mass, July 22, 12; m. 33. CHEMISTRY. A.B, Brown, 34; Boston, 56-57; D.Sc, Calif. Inst. Tech, 59. Instr, Northeastern, 32; from supvr. to tech. mgr, Acushnet Process Co, 33-42; CONSULT. TECHNOLOGIST, STANDARD OIL CO.(N.J), 42-; PRES, GIDLEY RES. INST, INC, 44- Indust. chem. consult, 42- Civilian with Nat. Defense Res. Comt; U.S.A, 44. AAAS; Am. Soc. Test. & Mat; Soc. Advan. Mgt; Soc. Rheol; Economet. Soc; Am. Soc. Eng. Educ; fel. Am. Inst. Chem; fel. Royal Econ. Soc. Rubber product formation; industrial machine design; rubber chemical development. Address: P.O. Box 12, Fairhaven, MA 02719.

GIDLUND, ERICK, b. Seattle, Wash, Nov. 14, 30; m. 67; c. 2. CIVIL ENGINEERING, FLUID MECHANICS. B.S, Washington (Seattle), 59, Ph.D.(fluid mech), 63. Eng. trainee, eng. dept, City of Seattle, 58-59, civil engr, summers, 60-61; teaching asst. fluid mech, Washington (Seattle), 62; hydraul. engr, Corps Engrs, U.S. Army, 63; asst. prof. FLUID MECH. & HYDROL, N.Y. UNIV, 63-70, ASSOC. PROF, 70- U.S.A, 51-53. AAAS; Am. Water Resources Asn; Am. Soc. Civil Eng; Am. Geophys. Union; Water Pollution Control Fedn. Various areas of water phenomena, particularly the interaction between waves and structures; dispersion of contaminants in estuaries. Address: Dept. of Civil Engineering, New York University, University Heights, Bronx, NY 10453.

GIDWANI, JOANNA N, b. Detroit, Mich, June 5, 27; m. 51; c. 2. ZOOLOGY, ANATOMY. B.A, Oberlin Col, 48; M.A, Wellesley Col, 50; Ph.D.(anat), Ohio State, 60. Asst. comp. anat, Wellesley Col, 48-50; anat, Ohio State, 51-55, asst. instr, 57-60, instr, 60-61; ASST. PROF. BIOL, OHIO NORTH. UNIV, 64- Comparative anatomy and histology. Address: Dept. of Biology, Ohio Northern University, Ada, OH 45810.

GIEBISCH, GERHARD H(ANS), b. Vienna, Austria, Jan. 17, 27; m. 52; c. 2. PHYSIOLOGY. M.D, Univ. Vienna, Austria, 51. Asst. prof. pharmacol, med. sch, Univ. Vienna, 51-52, 56-57; PHYSIOL, med. col, Cornell, 53-56, 57-60, assoc. prof, 60-65, prof, 65-68; prof, SCH. MED, YALE, 68-70, STERLING PROF. PHYSIOL, 70-, CHMN. DEPT, 68- Estab. investr, Am. Heart Asn, 57-; mem, physiol. study sect, Nat. Insts. Health, 64; Nat. Insts. Health career award, 65-68. Harvey Soc; Am. Physiol. Soc; Biophys. Soc; Am. Soc. Nephrology; Ger. Nephrology Soc. Electrolyte metabolism; renal physiology, particularly studies on single nephrons, employing methods of micropuncture. Address: Dept. of Physiology, School of Medicine, Yale University, 333 Cedar St, New Haven, CT 06510.

GIEDT, W(ALVIN) R(OLAND), b. Eureka, S.Dak, Aug. 17, 05; m. 32; c. 2. EPIDEMIOLOGY, MICROBIOLOGY. B.S, South Dakota, 33; M.D, Chicago, 37; M.P.H, Hopkins, 41. Lab. instr. path, sch med, South Dakota, 33-35, asst. prof, 39-40; dir. labs, S.Dak. State Dept. Health, 41-43; chief div. epidemiol, Wash. State Dept. Health, 43-60, div. labs, 60-71; RETIRED. Mem. Int. Conf. Diseases in Nature Commun. to Man. Dipl, Am. Bd. Pub. Health & Prev. Med. U.S.P.H.S.R, Med. Dir.(ret). Fel. Am. Pub. Health Asn; Am. Med. Asn; fel. N.Y. Acad. Sci; Asn. State & Territorial Pub. Health Lab. Dirs. Arbovirus encephalitis; hospital infection control; sero-immunology; plague in campestral rodents. Address: 5717 N.E. 57th St, Seattle, WA 98105.

GIEDT, W(ARREN) H(ARDING), b. Leola, S.Dak, Nov. 1, 20; m. 50. MECHANICAL ENGINEERING. B.A.S, California, 44, M.S, 46, Ph.D.(mech. eng), 50. Instr. MECH. ENG, Univ. Calif, Berkeley, 47-50, asst. prof, 50-56, assoc. prof, 56-61, PROF, 61-65; UNIV. CALIF, DAVIS, 65-, head dept, 65-69. Serv. engr, Babcock & Wilcox Co, 50; consult, Bechtel Corp, 51; proj. leader, Detroit Controls Corp, 52-56; consult, Am. Standard Corp, 56-65; Lawrence Radiation Lab, 60-; Boeing Co, 62-66; Fulbright prof, Tokyo, 63; consult, NASA, 64-67. Jennings Award, Am. Welding Soc, 70. U.S.A.F.R, 47-52, Capt. Am. Soc. Mech. Eng.(ed, J. Heat Transfer, 67-); Am. Inst. Aeronaut. & Astronaut; Am. Soc. Eng. Educ. Heat transfer; thermodynamics; metallurgy. Address: 2945 Garden Court, El Macero, CA 95618.

GIEL, BOHDAN GIELECINSKI, U.S. citizen. ENVIRONMENTAL & INTERNAL MEDICINE. B.S, Univ. Chicago, 36; M.B, Chicago Med. Sch, 40, M.D, 41. Med. dir, Elwood Ord. Plant, Ill, 42-45; U.S. PUB. HEALTH SERV, 45-, dir, Perry County Health Dept, Ky, 45-46, med. dir, Joliet Arsenal, Ill, 46-50, chief med. off, Army Ord. Command, 50-54, resident int. med, Univ. & Vet. Admin. Hosps, Med. Col. Ga, 54-56, asst. chief, U.S. Pub. Health Serv. Hosp, Staten Island, N.Y, 56-57, dep. chief hosp, New Orleans, La, 57-60, chief med. serv, hosp, Lexington, Ky, 60-62, chief environ. med, Fed. Aviation Agency, 61-62, med. adv. to chief div. air pollution, 62-65, chief, div. career develop, Off. Surgeon Gen, 65-66, med. adv, Bur. Disease Prevention & Environ. Control, 66-67, Consumer Protection & Environ. Health Serv, 67-68, Environ. Health Serv, 68-69, med. adv. to dir, Bur. Mines, 69-70, CHIEF, MED. SERV. BR. OFF. & MED. DISABILITY EVAL. BR, CHIEF MED. OFF, U.S. COAST GUARD, 70-, SR. MED. OFFICER, MIL. CLINS, 70- Mem, U.S-W.Ger. Panel on Pulmonary Diseases of Ger. Miners, 69; Cong. Comt. to Study Coal Workers Pneumoconiosis, Gt. Brit, 69; U.S.P.H.S, 45-, Med. Dir; U.S.C.G, 70-, Capt. Am. Med. Asn; fel. Am. Pub. Health Asn; fel. Am. Geriat. Soc; Asn. Mil. Surg. U.S. Industrial toxicology, especially the effect of air pollutants on respiratory diseases; coal workers pneumoconiosis, asbestosis, mesotheliomas, bysinosis, lung cancer in uranium miners and silicosis; lead poisoning and the effects of oxidants such as ozone, oxides of nitrogen and sulfur dioxide on respiratory epithelium. Address: Capitol Park Towers, 301 G St. S.W, Washington, DC 20024.

GIELISSE, PETER J(ACOB) M(ARIA), b. 'S-Hertogenbosch, Netherlands, Mar. 7, 34; U.S. citizen; m. 56; c. 2. MINERALOGY, CRYSTALLOGRAPHY. M.S, Boston Col, 59; Mershon Nat. Defense scholar, Ohio State, 60-61, Ph.D.(mineral), 61. Res. engr. physics, Comstock & Wescott, Inc, Mass, 57-59; Res. Found. fel, Ohio State, 59-61; res. physicist, Air Force Cambridge Res. Labs, Mass, 61-63; res. engr. solid state physics, metall. prod. dept, Gen. Elec. Co, Detroit, 63-68; PROF. MAT. ENG, UNIV. R.I, 68- Res. asst. geophys, Boston Col, 58-59, instr. geol. & geophys, 61-63. Royal Dutch Army, 55-56, Lt.(jg). Am. Geophys. Union; Am. Mineral. Soc. Thermochemical mineralogy; physical, structural and optical properties of materials; phase equilibria in multi-component systems; crystal synthesis; very high pressure-high temperature materials; semiconductor devices. Address: Dept. of Material Engineering, Crawford Hall, University of Rhode Island, Kingston, RI 02881.

GIER, DELTA W(ARREN), b. Hepler, Kans, Mar. 2, 21; m. 42; c. 1. ORGANIC CHEMISTRY. B.S, Kans. State Col, 47, M.S, 48; Ph.D.(chem), Kansas, 57. Chemist, Nat. Ref. Co, 41-42; prod. supt, Trojan Chem. Co, 42-44; prof. chem, Park Col, 48-59; assoc. dir, Ford Found. proj, Austin Col, 59-61; chmn. dept. chem, Kansas State Col. Pittsburg, 61-63; res. chemist prod. develop, Chemagro Corp, 63-66; chmn. dept. chem, St. Andrews Presby. Col, 66-68; DIR. SCI, LEA COL, 68- Consult, Spencer Chem. Co, 56-59. J.L. Zwingle award, 56-57. U.S.N.A.F, 44-46. Am. Chem. Soc; fel. Am. Inst. Chem. Acetylenics; heterocyclics; phosphorous. Address: Lea College, Albert Lea, MN 56007.

GIER, H(ERSCHEL) T(HOMAS), b. Hepler, Kans, May 11, 07; m. 32; c. 3. CYTOLOGY, EMBRYOLOGY. B.A, Kans. State Teachers Col, 31; Ph.D. (zool), Indiana, 36. Asst. zool, Indiana, 31-36; Nat. Res. Coun. fel, Harvard, 36-37; instr. ZOOL, Ohio, 37-41, asst. prof, 41-46, assoc. prof, 46-47; KANS. STATE UNIV, 47-60, PROF, 60- Fel. AAAS; Soc. Zool; Wildlife Soc; Ecol. Soc. Am; Am. Asn. Anat; Am. Ornith. Union. Intracellular symbions; growth rate of Periplaneta americana; taxonomy of amphibians; reproductive potential and population of mammals; canine reproduction; bovine reproduction; testicular development; ovarian structure; follicular cycle; steroid effects on ovarian function. Address: Division of Biology, Kansas State University, Manhattan, KS 66502.

GIER, L(ELAND) J(ACOB), b. Hepler, Kans, Mar. 10, 04; m. 34. PLANT ECOLOGY, TAXONOMY. B.Sc, Kans. State Teachers Col, 28, M.Sc, 31, A.B, 34; fel, Nebraska, 31-33, Ph.D.(plant ecol), Duke, 40. Teacher, pub. schs, Kans, 21-22, 23-27; head dept. sci, pub. sch, Kans, 28-30; prof. biol, Campbell Col, 34-41; prof. biol. & head dept. biol. & geol, William Jewell Col, 41-68; PROF. SCI, MO. SOUTH. COL, 68- Fel. AAAS; Am. Inst. Biol. Sci; Am. Bryol. Soc; Am. Soc. Plant Taxon; Torrey Bot. Club; Nat. Asn. Biol. Teachers; Brit. Bryol. Soc; Int. Asn. Plant Taxon; Asn. Trop. Biol. Local flora; genus Thuidium in South America; micro-environment. Address: Dept. of Science, 310 Reynolds Hall, Missouri Southern College, Joplin, MO 64801.

GIER, RONALD E, b. Bloomington, Ind, Jan. 8, 35; m. 58; c. 3. DENTISTRY. B.S, Kansas State, 56; D.D.S, Washington (St. Louis), 59; M.S.D, Indiana, 57. PROF. DENT. & ORAL DIAG. & CHMN. DEPT, UNIV. MO-KANSAS CITY, 67- Consult, Kansas City Vet. Admin. Hosp, 67- Dent.C, U.S.N, 59-61, Lt. Am. Dent. Asn; Int. Asn. Dent. Res; Am. Acad. Oral Path; Am. Acad. Oral Med. Diagnosis and treatment of disease of the dental pulp. Address: School of Dentistry, University of Missouri-Kansas City, 650 E. 25th, Kansas City, MO 64108.

GIER, THURMAN E(UGENE), b. Conrad, Iowa, Feb. 27, 24; m. 45; c. 4. CHEMISTRY. B.S. & M.S, Michigan, 48; Ph.D.(chem. eng), Rensselaer Polytech, 51. Asst, Michigan, 45-48; asst. chem. engr, Gen. Elec. Co, 48-49; RES. CHEMIST, E.I. DU PONT DE NEMOURS & CO, WILMINGTON, 51- Sig.C, U.S.A, 45-47. Solvent extraction mechanisms; high pressure; high temperature syntheses; inorganic synthesis. Address: Chadds Ford, PA 19317.

GIERASCH, PETER JAY, b. Wash, D.C, Dec. 19, 40; m. 64; c. 2. ATMOSPHERIC SCIENCES. B.A, Harvard, 62, Ph.D.(appl. math), 68. Res. assoc. atmospheric sci, Harvard, 68-69; MEM. STAFF, INST. GEOPHYS. FLUID DYNAMICS, FLA. STATE UNIV, 69- Am. Meteorol. Soc. Dynamics of planetary atmospheres. Address: Institute of Geophysical Fluid Dynamics, Florida State University, Tallahassee, FL 32306.

GIERE, FREDERIC A(RTHUR), b. Galesville, Wis, Dec. 10, 23; m. 55; c. 3. ENDOCRINOLOGY, PHYSIOLOGY. A.B, Luther Col, 47; M.S, Syracuse, 51; Ph.D.(physiol), New Mexico, 53. Instr. biol, Luther Col, 47-49; asst. zool, Syracuse, 49-51; physiol, New Mexico, 51-53, asst. prof, 53-55; assoc. prof, BIOL, Luther Col, 55-62; PROF, LAKE FOREST COL, 62-, CHMN. DEPT, 64- Lectr, South Dakota, 61; summers, res. assoc, New Mexico, 53, 55, 56, Upjohn Co, 54, Iowa, 58; consult. subcontractor, Argonne Nat. Lab, 67-, dir. summer inst. radiobiol, 68; U.S. Pub. Health Serv. fel, Inst. Work Physiol, Oslo, Norway, 68-69. U.S.N.R, 42-46. Fel. AAAS; Am. Soc. Zool; Am. Physiol. Soc; Soc. Exp. Biol. & Med; N.Y. Acad. Sci; Am. Inst. Biol. Sci; Nat. Asn. Biol. Teachers. Water and electrolyte metabolism; work physiology. Address: Dept. of Biology, Lake Forest College, Lake Forest, IL 60045.

GIERING, JOHN E(DGAR), b. Easton, Pa, Feb. 8, 29; m. 54; c. 3. PHARMACOLOGY, PHYSIOLOGY. B.S, Moravian Col, 51; M.S, Purdue, 53, Purdue Res. Found. fel, 55-56, Ph.D.(physiol), 57. Sr. res. scientist, Astra Pharmaceut. Prod, Inc, 56-65, head hemat. sect, 65-66; HEAD DEPT. DEVELOP. PHARMACOL, PHARMACEUT. DIV, PENNWALT CORP, 66- Mem. coun. thrombosis, Am. Heart Asn. AAAS; N.Y. Acad. Sci. Reproductive physiology; action of sex steroids on uterine enzymes and morphology; blood coagulation; pharmacology of fibrinolytic agents and platelet aggregation; drug screening and evaluation. Address: Pharmaceutical Division, Pennwalt Corp, 755 Jefferson Rd, Rochester, NY 14623.

GIESBRECHT, JOHN, b. Man, Can, Oct. 29, 22; m. 47; c. 3. PLANT BREEDING, GENETICS. B.S.A, Univ. Man, 48, M.Sc, 52; Ph.D.(plant genetics), Univ. Minn, St. Paul, 59. RES. SCIENTIST, RES. STA, CAN. DEPT. AGR, 52- Crop Sci. Soc. Am; Genetics Soc. Can; Agr. Inst. Can. Development of corn and soybean varieties adapted to Manitoba; development of corn adapted to do well at high populations; inheritance of economically important characters in corn. Address: Canadian Dept. of Agriculture Research Station, P.O. Box 3001, Morden, Man, Can.

GIESE, ARTHUR C(HARLES), b. Chicago, Ill, Dec. 19, 04; m. 28; c. 1. BIOLOGY. B.S, Chicago, 27; fel, California, 28-29; Ph.D.(biol), Stanford, 33. Asst, STANFORD UNIV, 29-30, acting instr. BIOL, 30-33, instr, 33-36, asst. prof, 36-41, assoc. prof, 41-47, PROF, 47- Rockefeller Found. fel, Princeton & Woods Hole, 39-40; Guggenheim fel, Calif. Inst. Tech. & Northwestern, 47-48; European Marine Biol. Stas, 59. Summers, instr, Marine Biol. Lab, Woods Hole, 42, 44, 46, vis. prof, Calif. Inst. Tech, 50. With Off. Sci. Res. & Develop, 43. AAAS; Soc. Protozool; Am. Soc. Zool; Soc. Gen. Physiol. Cell physiology; effect of ultraviolet light on cell respiration, division, permeability and variability; bioluminescence; conjugation; photodynamic action; comparative physiology of nutrition and reproduction of marine invertebrates. Address: Dept. of Biological Sciences, Stanford University, Stanford, CA 94305.

GIESE, CLAYTON, b. Minneapolis, Minn, July 19, 31; m. 64. PHYSICS. B.S, Minnesota, 53, Ph.D, 57. Instr. PHYSICS, Chicago, 57-59, asst. prof, 59-65; ASSOC. PROF, UNIV. MINN, MINNEAPOLIS, 65- Am. Phys. Soc. Precision mass doublet spectroscopy; molecular beams; chemical physics. Address: Dept. of Physics, University of Minnesota, Minneapolis, MN 55455.

GIESE, GRAHAM SHERWOOD, b. Newport News, Va, Oct. 13, 31; m. 58; c. 5. OCEANOGRAPHY. B.S, Trinity Col.(Conn), 53; M.S, Rhode Island, 64; Ph.D. (geophys. sci), Chicago, 66. Res. asst. coastal processes, Woods Hole Oceanog. Inst, 56-62, asst. scientist, 67; asst. prof. OCEANOG, UNIV. P.R, 67-70, ASSOC. PROF, 70- AAAS; Am. Geophys. Union. Tropical oceanography; coastal and near-shore oceanography. Address: Dept. of Marine Sciences, University of Puerto Rico, Mayagüez, PR 00708.

GIESE, JOHN H, b. Chicago, Ill, Mar. 10, 15; m. 46; c. 2. MATHEMATICS. B.S, Chicago, 36; Ph.D.(math), Princeton, 40. Instr. math, Princeton, 39-40, 41-42; Rutgers, 40-42; Purdue, 42-44; aerodynamicist, Bell Aircraft Corp, N.Y, 44-46; MATHEMATICIAN, BALLISTIC RES. LABS, 46-58, CHIEF comput. lab, 59-68, APPL. MATH. DIV, 68- Lectr, Mich, 54-55; prof, dept. math, statist. & comput. sci, Univ. Del, 63- Am. Math. Soc; Soc. Indust. & Appl. Math; Asn. Comput. Mach. Differential geometry; supersonic compressible flow; partial differential equations; numerical analysis. Address: Applied Mathematics Division, Ballistic Research Labs, Aberdeen Proving Ground, MD 21005.

GIESE, R(ONALD) L(AWRENCE), b. Milwaukee, Wis, June 28, 34; m. 54; c. 2. ENTOMOLOGY, ECOLOGY. B.S, Wis. State Col, Milwaukee, 56; M.S, Wisconsin, 58, Ph.D.(entom, plant ecol), 60. Asst. prof. ENTOM, PURDUE UNIV, 60-64, assoc. prof, 64-67, PROF, 67-, DIR. NATURAL RESOURCES & ENVIRON. SCI. PROG, 70- Mem. environ. qual, Nat. Task Force. Fel. AAAS; Ecol. Soc. Am; Human Ecol. Soc; Entom. Soc. Am; Entom. Soc. Can; Int. Biometeorol. Soc; Am. Inst. Biol. Sci; Netherlands Royal Zool. Soc; Int. Asn. Ecol; Permanent Comt. Int. Cong. Entomol. Population dynamics; animal and plant ecology; computer science; radiology; bioclimatology; symbioses; forest stand structure and species composition related to insect fauna; mycangia; periodicity. Address: Dept. of Entomology, Entomology Hall, Purdue University, Wast Lafayette, IN 47907.

GIESE, ROSSMAN F(REDERICK), JR, b. New York, N.Y, June 7, 36; m. 60; c. 3. CRYSTALLOGRAPHY. B.A, Columbia, 56, M.A, 59, Ph.D.(mineral), 62. Sr. physicist, Carborundum Co, 61-66; asst. prof. GEOL. SCI, STATE UNIV. N.Y. BUFFALO, 66-68, ASSOC. PROF, 68-, ACTING CHMN. DEPT, 70- Sr. cancer res. scientist, ctr. crystallog. res, Roswell Park Mem. Inst, 66-68. AAAS; Am. Crystallog. Asn; Mineral. Soc. Am. Crystal structure and chemistry of refractory materials, particularly borides. Crystal structure analysis of complex inorganic compounds; mineralogy and crystallography of sulphides; crystal structure and crystal chemistry of minerals. Address: Dept. of Geological Science, State University of New York at Buffalo, Buffalo, NY 14214.

GIESECKE, ADOLPH H, b. Oklahoma City, Okla, Apr. 19, 32; m. 54; c. 4. MEDICINE, ANESTHESIOLOGY. M.D, Texas, 57. Intern, William Beaumont Army Hosp, El Paso, Tex, 57-58; res. ANESTHESIOL, Parkland Mem. Hosp, Dallas, 60-63; asst. prof, SOUTHWEST. MED. SCH, UNIV. TEX, 63-66, assoc. prof, 66-69, PROF, 69- Attend. anesthesiologist, Parkland Mem. Hosp, Children's Med. Center & Vet. Admin. Hosp, Dallas, Tex, 63-; Presby. Hosp, 67-; Fulbright lectr. & guest prof, Johannes Gutenberg Univ, Ger, 70. Med.C, 57-60, Capt. Am. Med. Asn; Am. Soc. Anesthesiol; Int. Anesthesia Res. Soc. Anesthesia for trauma and for obstetrics. Address: Dept. of Anesthesiology, Southwestern Medical School, University of Texas, Dallas, TX 75235.

GIESEKE, JAMES ARNOLD, b. Granite City, Ill, Oct. 16, 36; m. 62; c. 3. CHEMICAL ENGINEERING. B.S, Illinois, 59; M.S, Washington (Seattle), 63, Ph.D.(chem. eng), 64. Res. chem. engr, BATTELLE MEM. INST, 63-67, sr. chem. engr, 67-70, ASSOC. FEL, COLUMBUS LABS, 70- AAAS; Air Pollution Control Asn; Am. Inst. Chem. Eng; Am. Chem. Soc. Mechanics and physics of aerosols; dust collection problems. Address: Battelle Memorial Institute, Columbus Labs, 505 King Ave, Columbus, OH 43201.

GIESEKING, J(OHN) E(LDON), b. Altamont, Ill, Oct. 1, 05; m. 36; c. 1. SOILS. B.S, Illinois, 26, M.S, 27, Ph.D.(soils), 34; Bonn, Germany, 29-30; Nat. Res. Council fel, Missouri, 33-34. Asst. soils, Illinois, 27-32; soil chem, Missouri, 32-33; asst. prof. SOIL PHYSICS, UNIV. ILL, URBANA, 34-43, assoc. prof, 43-46, PROF, 46- Lectr, Nebraska, 58. Consult. chemist, Filtrol Corp, Calif, 43-45. AAAS; Am. Soc. Agron; Am. Chem. Soc; Am. Soil Sci. Soc; Int. Soc. Soil Sci; fel. Am. Inst. Chem. Cation and anion exchange studies; mutual flocculation between positive and negative colloids; the use of x-rays for diffraction studies; electron microscopy; petroleum cracking catalysts; the use of radioactive potassium and phosphorus in cation and anion exchange and fixation studies. Address: Dept. of Agronomy, 416 Turner Hall, University of Illinois, Urbana, IL 61801.

GIESEL, JAMES THEODORE, b. Toledo, Ohio, Nov. 17, 41; m. 64; c. 1. POPULATION BIOLOGY, ECOLOGY. B.S, Mich. State Univ, 63; Ph.D. (biol), Univ. Ore, 68. Ford Found. fel. pop. biol, Univ. Chicago, 69-70; ASST. PROF. ZOOL, UNIV. FLA, 70- Ecol. Soc. Am; Genetics Soc. Am; Soc. Study Evolution. Analysis of the temporal aspects of interspecific competition; isozymic analysis of the genetics of natural populations; theoretical analysis of the effects of age distribution in populations with overlapping generations on effective number and selection. Address: Dept. of Zoology, University of Florida, Gainesville, FL 32601.

GIESELER, L(UTHER) PAUL, b. Mich, June 1, 17; m. 45; c. 3. PHYSICS. B.S, Denver, 37; M.S, Michigan, 40. Physicist, Naval Ord. Lab, Md, 41-54; sr. engr, Melpar, Inc. Div, Westinghouse Air Brake Co, Va, 54-58; physicist, Ceir, Inc, 58-66; MEM. TECH. STAFF, BELLCOMM, INC, 66- Inst. Elec. & Electronics Eng. Instrumentation; electronics; solid state devices; computer technology; space sciences; fluid flow; optics. Address: Bellcomm, Inc, 955 L'Enfant Plaza North, S.W, Washington, DC 20024.

GIESS, E(DWARD) A(UGUST), b. Mineola, N.Y, Sept. 12, 29; m. 53; c. 3. CERAMICS. B.S, State Univ. N.Y. Col. Ceramics, Alfred, 51, M.S, 52, Ph.D.(ceramics), 58. Ceramic engr, res. div, Nat. Lead Co, 52-55; RES. STAFF MEM. CRYSTAL CHEM, RES. DIV, IBM CORP, 58- AAAS; fel. Am. Inst. Chem; Am. Ceramic Soc; Am. Phys. Soc. Flux melt crystal growth; solid state reactions and sintering; electrooptic and magnetic materials. Address: Thomas J. Watson Research Center, IBM Corp, P. O. Box 218, Yorktown Heights, NY 10598.

GIESSE, R(OBERT) C(ARL), b. Cleveland, Ohio, Oct. 14, 17; m. 41; c. 2. CHEMICAL ENGINEERING. Ch.E, Cincinnati, 41. Chem. engr. res. & develop, Procter & Gamble Co, 41-45; sr. proj. engr, Vulcan-Cincinnati, Ohio, 45-53; tech. dir, MJB Co, 53-57; chief engr. res. & develop, Am. Mach. & Metals, Inc, 57-61; pres, Processes Res, Inc, 61-67; PRES. & CHMN. BD, P/E DEVELOP. CORP, 67- Chmn. bd, PEDCo. Environ. Specialists, Inc, 69; PEDCo. Comp. Serv, Inc, 70. AAAS; Am. Chem. Soc; Am. Oil Chemists' Soc; Am. Ord. Asn; Am. Inst. Chem. Eng. Chemical and metallurgical processing; equipment design; newer or undeveloped fields such as dialysis, ion exchange, ultrasonics and the application of these to processing operations; machine design; industrial engineering. Address: P/E Development Corp, Suite 14, Atkinson Square, Cincinnati, OH 45246.

GIESSEN, BILL C(ORMANN), b. Pittsburgh, Pa, June 8, 32; m. 60; c. 1. METALLURGY. Tübingen, 51-52; Frankfurt, 53; D.Sc.(metall), Göttingen, 58. Res. assoc. metall, Mass. Inst. Technol, 59-68; ASSOC. PROF. CHEM, NORTHEAST. UNIV, 68- Am. Inst. Mining, Metall. & Petrol. Eng. Physical metallurgy; x-ray crystallography; crystal chemistry of metallic equilibrium and non-equilibrium phases; phase diagrams. Address: Dept. of Chemistry, Northeastern University, Boston, MA 02115.

GIESY, DANIEL P(ERRY), b. Cambridge, Mass, Oct. 29, 38; m. 62; c. 3. MATHEMATICS. B.A. & M.A, Ohio State, 60; Woodrow Wilson fel, Wisconsin, 60-61, Nat. Sci. Found. fels, 60-63, Ph.D.(math), 64. Asst. prof. MATH, Univ. South. Calif, 64-69; vis. assoc. prof, WEST. MICH. UNIV, 69-70, ASSOC. PROF, 70- Am. Math. Soc; Math. Asn. Am. Convexity in normed linear spaces. Address: Dept. of Mathematics, Western Michigan University, Kalamazoo, MI 49001.

GIESY, ROBERT, b. Columbus, Ohio, July 16, 22; m. 50; c. 4. PLANT MORPHOLOGY. A.B, Ohio State, 46, B.Sc, 54, Ph.D.(plant morphol), 57. Fulbright scholar, Univ. Col. North Wales, 57-58; instr. BOT, OHIO STATE UNIV, 58-62, asst. prof, 62-66, ASSOC. PROF, 66- U.S.M.C, 43-46, 1st Lt. Bot. Soc. Am; Electron Micros. Soc. Am. Address: Dept. of Botany, Ohio State University, Columbus, OH 43210.

GIEVER, JOHN B(ERTRAM), b. Omaha, Nebr, Sept. 18, 19; m. 43; c. 3. MATHEMATICS. B.S, Creighton, 42; Catholic Univ, 42; Savage & Bolles fels. & Ph.D.(math), Mass. Inst. Tech, 48. Instr. math, Boston, 48-51, asst. prof, 51-52; mem. staff, instrumentation lab, Mass. Inst. Tech, 52-53; asst. prof. MATH, Univ. Okla, 53-57, assoc. prof, 57-59, PROF, N.MEX. STATE UNIV, 59- U.S.A.A.F, 42-45. Am. Math. Soc; Asn. Symbolic Logic; Math. Asn. Am. Algebraic topology. Address: Dept. of Mathematics, New Mexico State University, University Park, NM 88001.

GIEVER, PAUL M(ATHEW), b. Miller, S.Dak, Dec. 4, 12; m. 36; c. 4. INDUSTRIAL HEALTH. B.S, S.Dak. Sch. Mines & Tech, 36; M.P.H, Michigan, 59. Engr, Climax Molybdenum Co, 37-40, air engr, 40-42; hygienist, Calif. State Health Dept, 46; dir. indust. health, Mont. State Health Dept, 46-47; chief engr, Ore. State Accident Cmn, 47-51; field engr, U.S. Pub. Health Serv, 51-54; res. engr, Detroit Edison Co, 54-57; assoc. prof. indust. health, Univ. Mich, 57-70; PRIN. SCIENTIST, WALDEN RES. CORP, 70- Consult, tech. adv. bd. air pollution, Int. Joint Cmn. U.S. & Can. & div. air pollution, U.S. Pub. Health Serv, 63- Dipl, Am. Bd. Indust. Hyg. Med. Serv. C, 42-46, Capt. Am. Indust. Hyg. Asn; Air Pollution Control Asn; Am. Soc. Test. & Mat. Community air pollution studies; evaluation of specific pollutants; development of improved techniques in sampling through instrumental and laboratory research; mineral content of drinking water as a possible factor in heart disease. Address: Walden Research Corp, 359 Allston St, Cambridge, MA 02139.

GIFFEE, JOSEPH W(ALTER), b. Geneva, Nebr, Mar. 6, 21; m. 45; c. 5. BIOCHEMISTRY. B.S, Iowa State Col, 43; M.S, Iowa, 47, Ph.D.(biochem), 51. Res. chemist pituitary hormones, labs, Armour & Co, 50-53; protein chemist, Qm. Food & Container Inst, 53-55, asst. chief, radiation preserv. br, 55-56; CHIEF, div. protein chem, 57-64; FOOD CHEM. DIV, FOOD LAB, U.S. ARMY NATICK LABS, 64- U.S.N.R, 44-46, Lt.(jg). Am. Chem. Soc; Inst. Food Technol; N.Y. Acad. Sci. Food chemistry, stability of stored rations; quality of dehydrated foods; food flavor; collagen and protein chemistry; mechanisms of quality loss in food components; radiation effects on foods and food components. Address: Food Lab, U.S. Army Natick Labs, Natick, MA 01760.

GIFFELS, CARL A, b. Lansing, Mich, Feb. 11, 33; m. 66; c. 1. PHYSICS. B.S, Univ. Detroit, 54; M.S, Carnegie Inst. Technol, 56, Ph.D.(physics), 60. Mem. tech. staff defense studies, BELL TEL. LABS, 60-65, supvr. radar data anal, 65-68, DEPT. HEAD reentry physics, 68-71, INTERCONNECTION DESIGN, 71- Am. Inst. Aeronaut. & Astronaut; Sci. Res. Soc. Am. Development of interconnection techniques for electronic circuits. Address: Interconnection Design Dept, Bell Telephone Labs, Whippany, NJ 07981.

GIFFEN, ROBERT H(ENRY), b. Pottsville, Pa, Feb. 10, 22; m. 49; c. 3. CHEMICAL ENGINEERING. B.S, Newark Col. Eng, 43; M.S, Iowa State Col, 47, Ph.D.(chem. eng), 51. Control chemist, Gen. Chem. Co, N.J. & Ill, 43-44; chem. engr, Los Alamos. Sci. Lab, California, 46; jr. res. asst, inst. atomic res, Iowa State Col, 47-51; sr. engr, BETTIS ATOMIC POWER LAB, WESTINGHOUSE ELEC. CORP, 51-57, supvr. engr, 57-64, fel. engr. 64-66, supvr, 66-69, MGR, 69- Manhattan Dist. Proj, C.Eng, U.S.A, 44-46. Am. Inst. Chem. Eng. Development of methods to predict and control build-up of crud and radioactivity in pressurized water atomic reactor power plants. Address: Bettis Atomic Power Lab, Westinghouse Electric Corp, Box 79, West Mifflin, PA 15122.

GIFFEN, WILLIAM M(ARTIN), JR, b. Akron, Ohio, June 23, 33; m. 61. POLYMER CHEMISTRY. B.S, Akron, 55, Firestone Tire & Rubber fel, 55-56, M.S, 56, Phillips Petrol. fel, 60-61, Ph.D.(polymer chem), 61. Asst. proj. chemist, Amoco Chem. Corp, Ind, 61-62; sr. res. chemist, Gen. Tire & Rubber Co, 62-64; tech. dept, marbon chem. div, BORG-WARNER CORP, W.Va, 64-68, RES. ASSOC. DEVELOP. DIV, OHIO, 68- Am. Chem. Soc. Emulsion, graft, and alkylene oxide polymerizations; cationic and anionic solution polymerizations; vinyl polymerizations and copolymerizations; latex formulation; high impact resins. Address: 1812 Rockland Ave, Belpre, OH 45714.

GIFFIN, GYNITH C(OLLEEN), b. Eureka, Kans, Sept. 11, 31. INORGANIC CHEMISTRY. B.S, Wichita, 53, M.S, 55; Ph.D.(inorg. chem), Illinois, 58. Asst. prof. chem, North. Ill. Univ, 58-62; assoc. prof, SUSQUEHANNA UNIV, 62-65, chmn. div. natural sci. & math, 64-65, PROF. CHEM. & CHMN. DEPT, 65- AAAS; Am. Chem. Soc. Rare earth element chemistry; hydroxamic acids-metal complex ions. Address: Dept. of Chemistry, Susquehanna University, 301 S. Market St, Selinsgrove, PA 17870.

GIFFIN, WALTER C(HARLES), b. Walhonding, Ohio, Apr. 22, 36; m. 56; c. 2. INDUSTRIAL ENGINEERING. B.Indust.Eng. & M.Sc, Ohio State, 60, Ph.D. (mass transportation), 64. Res. engr, Gen. Motors Res. Labs, 60-61; res. assoc. opers. res, eng. exp. sta, OHIO STATE UNIV, 61-62, instr. INDUST. ENG, 62-64, asst. prof, 64-68, assoc. prof, 68-71, PROF, 71- Sr. res. engr, Gen. Motors Defense Res. Labs, summer 65; consult, Gen. Motors Corp, 65-; Battelle Mem. Inst, 65- Am. Inst. Indust. Eng; Am. Soc. Eng. Educ; Opers. Res. Soc. Am; Inst.Mgt. Sci. Air traffic control, inventory control and transportation systems; queueing phenomena. Address: Dept. of Industrial Engineering, Ohio State University, 1971 Neil Ave, Columbus, OH 43210.

GIFFORD, ALLAN T(HURSTON), b. Fall River, Mass, Sept. 6, 06; m. 34; c. 3. HYDRAULIC ENGINEERING. S.B, Mass. Inst. Tech, 27, M.S, 46. Field engr, Metrop. Dist. Water Supply Comn, Mass, 27-28, off. engr, 28-31, asst. to res. engr, 31-34, concrete technician, 34-35; assoc. sanit. engr, Tenn. Valley Authority, 35-37; instr. civil eng, Mass. Inst. Tech, 37-40, asst. prof. hydraul. eng, 40-44, assoc. prof, 44-53; asst. chief opers. div, Richland Opers. Off, U.S. Atomic Energy Comn, 53-56, dir, 56-58, process eng. & mfg. div, 58-61, prod. div, 61-66; PROF. CIVIL ENG. & HEAD DEPT, LOWELL TECHNOL. INST, 66-, CHMN. DIV. ENG. SCI, 68- U.S.A.A.F, 42-44. Am. Soc. Civil Eng; Am. Geophys. Union; Am. Soc. Eng. Educ. Meteorology; hydrology. Address: Division of Engineering Science, Lowell Technological Institute, Lowell, MA 01854.

GIFFORD, CAMERON E(DWARD), b. New Bedford, Mass, Sept. 23, 31; m. 52; c. 2. ECOLOGY, PHYSIOLOGY. B.A, Earlham Col, 55; M.A, Harvard, 59; Ph.D.(zool), Georgia, 64. ASSOC. PROF. BIOL. & CHMN. DEPT, EARLHAM COL, 61-, DIR. DAVID WORTH DENNIS BIOL. STA, 67- Int. Ornith. Cong. Avian physiology; homing behavior in bats; chlorophyll determinations in various marine algae; lipid determinations and migratory behavior in the bobolink. Address: David Worth Dennis Biology Station, Earlham College, Richmond, IN 47374.

GIFFORD, CHARLES A, b. Berkeley, Calif, June 22, 26; m. 55; c. 2. INVERTEBRATE PHYSIOLOGY, ECOLOGY. A.B, Hope Col, 50; M.S, Miami (Fla), 53; Ph.D.(physiol), Illinois, 58. Res. scientist marine biol, Texas, 56-57; instr. zool, Vermont, 57-59; asst. prof. marine biol, Miami (Fla), 59-62; BIOL, Alfred Univ, 62-68; ASSOC. PROF, UNIV. W.FLA, 68- Nat. Sci. Found. res. grant, 63-; Am. Physiol. Soc. summer fel, 58. AAAS; Ecol. Soc. Am; Am. Soc. Zool; Am. Inst. Biol. Sci. Physiology and ecology of estuarine and terrestrial crustaceans, especially blood regulation and respiration. Address: Dept. of Biology, University of West Florida, Pensacola, FL 32504.

GIFFORD, DAVID S(TEVENS), b. Glens Falls, N.Y, Nov. 14, 24; m. 51; c. 4. ORGANIC CHEMISTRY. A.B, Dartmouth Col, 49; New Hampshire, 49-50; Ph.D.(org. chem), Connecticut, 60. Res. chemist, Naugatuck Chem. Div, U.S. Rubber Co, 50-54; asst. col. instr. chem, Connecticut, 55-56, 57-59, asst, 56-57; res. asst, Purdue, 59-61; asst. ed. ORG. INDEXING, CHEM. ABSTRACTS SERV, OHIO STATE UNIV, 61-63, assoc. ed, 63-69, SR. ASSOC. INDEXER, 69- Summer lectr, Univ. Conn, 59. AAAS; Am. Chem. Soc. Nomenclature and indexing of terpenes and carbohydrates. Address: 110 Brevoort Rd, Columbus, OH 43214.

GIFFORD, ERNEST M(ILTON), JR, b. Riverside, Calif, Jan. 17, 20; m. 42; c. 1. BOTANY. A.B, California, 42, Ph.D.(bot), 49. Lab. asst, UNIV. CALIF, DAVIS, 47-49, instr. BOT, 49-51, asst. prof, 51-57, assoc. prof, 57-62, PROF, 62-, BOTANIST, AGR. EXP. STA, 62-, jr. botanist, 49-51, asst. botanist, 51-57, assoc. botanist, 57-62, chmn. dept. bot, 63-68, 70-71. Merck sr. res. fel, Harvard, 56-57; Nat. Sci. Found. res. grant, Univ. Calif, 58-; John Simon Guggenheim Mem. Found. fel, 66-67; Fulbright res. scholar, Nat. Ctr. Sci. Res, France, 66-67. U.S.A, 42-46, Col. AAAS; Bot. Soc. Am; Soc. Develop. Biol. Developmental anatomy of vascular plants; meristems. Address: Dept. of Botany, University of California, Davis, CA 95616.

GIFFORD, F(RANKLIN) A(NDREW), JR, b. Union City, N.J, May 7, 22; m; c. 2. METEOROLOGY. B.S, N.Y. Univ, 47; M.S, Pa. State, 54, Ph.D.(meteorol), 55. Meteorologist, N.W. Airlines, Inc, 45-50; res. meteorologist, U.S. Weather Bur, 50-66, DIR, ATMOSPHERIC TURBULENCE & DIFFUSION LAB, NAT. OCEANIC & ATMOSPHERIC ADMIN, 66- Mem. adv. comt. reactor safeguards, U.S. Atomic Energy Comn, 58-68. U.S.A.A.F, 43-45, Capt. Am. Meteorol. Soc; Am. Astron. Soc; Sci. Res. Soc. Am. Atmospheric turbulence and diffusion; air pollution; reactor hazards; meteorology of other planets. Address: Atmospheric Turbulence & Diffusion Lab, National Oceanic and Atmospheric Administration, P.O. Box E, Oak Ridge, TN 37830.

GIFFORD, GEORGE E(DWIN), b. Minneapolis, Minn, Dec. 6, 24; m. 56; c. 2. MICROBIOLOGY. B.A, Minnesota, 49, M.S, 53, Ph.D.(microbiol), 55. Asst. bact. & immunol, Minnesota, 50-54, instr, 55-56; asst. prof. microbiol, UNIV. FLA, 57-64, assoc. prof, 64-68, PROF. IMMUNOL. & MED. MICROBIOL, 68-, acting chmn. dept, 65-66. U.S. Pub. Health Serv. spec. fel, Nat. Inst. Med. Res, England, 62-63. U.S.N, 43-46. AAAS; Am. Soc. Microbiol; Soc. Gen. Bact; Am. Soc. Cell Biol; Soc. Exp. Biol. & Med; Tissue Culture Asn. Biochemical studies of factors influencing virus replication in mammalian cells; interferon production and action. Address: Dept. of Immunology & Medical Microbiology, University of Florida, Gainesville, FL 32601.

GIFFORD, HAROLD, b. Omaha, Nebr, Jan. 25, 06; m. 36; c. 3. OPHTHALMOLOGY. B.Sc, Nebraska, 30, M.D, 31. Instr. OPHTHAL, COL. MED, UNIV. NEBR, 34-37, asst. prof, 37-42, assoc. prof, 42-64, PROF, 64- Practicing physician. Am. Ophthal. Soc; fel. Am. Acad. Ophthal. & Otolaryngol. Clinical research. Address: Suite 400, West Dodge Medical Bldg, 8300 Dodge St, Omaha, NE 68114.

GIFFORD, R(AY) W(ALLACE), JR, b. Westerville, Ohio, Aug. 13, 23; m. 47; c. 3. MEDICINE. B.S, Otterbein Col, 44; M.D, Ohio State, 47; M.S, Minnesota, 52. Intern, Colo. Gen. Hosp, Denver, 47-48; res. physician internal med, univ. hosp, Ohio State, 48-49; fel, Mayo Found, Minnesota, 49-52, instr. med, 53-58, asst. prof, 58-61; mem. staff, DIV. MED, CLEVELAND CLIN. FOUND, 61-67, HEAD DEPT. HYPERTENSION & NEPHROLOGY, 67- Consult, Mayo Clin. & Affiliated Hosps, 53-61. U.S.N.R, 54-56, Lt. Comdr. AAAS; Am. Med. Asn; Am. Heart Asn; Am. Fedn. Clin. Res; fel. Am. Col. Physicians; fel. Am. Col. Cardiol; fel. Am. Soc. Internal Med; Am. Soc. Clin. Pharmacol. & Therapeut; fel. Am. Col. Chest Physicians. Peripheral vascular diseases; hypertension and renal disease. Address: Dept. of Hypertension & Nephrology, Cleveland Clinic Foundation, 2020 E. 93rd St, Cleveland, OH 44118.

GIFFORD, RICHARD O(LIVER), b. Wilmington, Del, July 11, 32; m. 58; c. 3. SOIL PHYSICS. B.S, Univ. Del, 54; M.S, Univ. Md, 56, Ph.D.(agron), 60. Asst. prof. soil physics & asst. soil res. physicist, UNIV. NEV, RENO, 59-64, assoc. prof. soil physics & assoc. soil res. physicist, 64-71, PROF. SOIL PHYSICS & SOIL PHYSICIST, 71- AAAS; Am. Soc. Agron; Am. Meteorol. Soc. Soil structure and microclimatology; bioclimatology. Address: Agricultural Experiment Station, University of Nevada, Reno, NV 89507.

GIFFORD, WILLIAM E(LLSWORTH), b. Cleveland, Ohio, June 20, 19; m. 45; c. 4. CRYOGENICS, THERMODYNAMICS. B.M.E, Cornell, 41; M.S, Catholic Univ, 50. Test engr, Pratt & Whitney Aircraft, 42-43; field engr, Sperry Gyroscope Co, 43-45; cryogenic engr, Nat. Bur. Standards, 45-51; nuclear engr, Atomic Energy Cmn, 51-53; chief process eng. sect, Cambridge Corp, 53-54; cryogenics & thermodyn. consult, Arthur D. Little, Inc, 54-61; PROF. THERMODYN, SYRACUSE UNIV, 61-; PRES, CRYOMECH, INC, JAMESVILLE, 65- Cryogenic consult, Mitre Lab; Gen. Elec. Co; Jet Propulsion Lab. Heat transfer; refrigeration; nuclear reactor theory and design. Address: Dept. of Mechanical Engineering, 139 Link Hall, Syracuse University, Syracuse, NY 13210.

GIGAS, GUNTER, b. Durrenburg, Ger, Aug. 2, 28; U.S. citizen; m. 54; c. 2. PHYSICS. B.S, Nevada, 50; M.Sc, Southern California, 58, Ph.D.(nuclear physics), 62. Group leader, high altitude lab, AiResearch Div, Garrett Corp, 51-60; instr, physics, Southern California, 60-62; res. scientist guid. & control systs, Litton Industs. Inc, 62, SUPVR. RADIATION EFFECTS GROUP, ATOMICS INT, 62- Instr, Moorpark Col; Maj. Max C. Fleischmann scholar; Rueben Tompson scholar. philos. Am. Phys. Soc; Sci. Res. Soc. Am. Radiant effects in materials and devices; nuclear structure; particle physics. Address: 1313 Ramona Dr, Camarillo, CA 93010.

GIGGARD, E(ARL) D(AVID), b. Westminister, Md, March 6, 28; m. 49; c. 3. FOOD TECHNOLOGY. B.S, Maryland, 49, M.S, 51, Ph.D.(food tech), 54. Asst. hort, Maryland, 49-52; quality control supvr, John H. Dulany & Son, Inc, Md, 52-54, prod. supt, 54-55; from packaging engr. to MGR. PACKAGING PERFORMANCE, CONTINENTAL CAN CO, INC, CHICAGO, 55- Development of new or improved consumer products, food and non-food; improved packages and packaging techniques. Address: 322 Hudson, Clarendon Hills, IL 60514.

GIGGER, RICHARD P(IERCE), b. Fitchburg, Mass, Nov. 29, 19; m. 43; c. 1. ORGANIC CHEMISTRY, BIOCHEMISTRY. B.S, Rhode Island, 41, M.S, 49; Ph.D.(chem), State Col. Wash, 53. Asst, Rhode Island, 47-49; State Col. Wash, 49-52; chemist, res. & develop, Alrose Chem. Co, 52-56; DIR. anal. chem, CIBA-GEIGY CHEM. CORP, 56-61, qual. control, 61-64, TECH. INFO, 64- U.S.A.A.F, 41-46, 1st Lt. Am. Chem. Soc; Am. Soc. Info. Sci. Pharmaceuticals; pesticides; dyestuffs; industrial organic chemicals; information storage and retrieval. Address: Technical Information, Ciba-Geigy Chemical Corp, Ardsley, NY 10502.

GIGLIOTTI, HELEN JEAN, b. Rochester, N.Y, July 27, 36. BIOCHEMISTRY. B.A, Vassar Col, 58; Ph.D.(biochem), Michigan, 63. Res. assoc. biochem, Scripps Clin. & Res. Found, 63-67; ASSOC. PROF. CHEM, FRESNO STATE COL, 67- Consult, Cent. Calif. Med. Labs. AAAS; Am. Chem. Soc; Am. Asn. Clin. Chem. Clinical chemistry methods; enzymology and metabolism of folic acid coenzymes. Address: Dept. of Chemistry, Fresno State College, Fresno, CA 93726.

GIGNOUX, DOMINIQUE, b. Grenoble, France, Feb. 8, 29; U.S. Citizen; m. 56; c. 2. ELECTRICAL ENGINEERING. Lic.ès sci, École Normale Supérieure, Paris, 51; M.A, Harvard, 53. Elec. engr, SAMES, France, 53-55, consult. elec. eng, 55-60; PRES. res, Cosmic, Inc, 60-68; COLUMBIA RES. CORP, 68- Assoc. fel. Am. Inst. Aeronaut. & Astronaut; Inst. Elec. & Electronics Eng. Electric propulsion of spacecraft; electrostatic generators; nuclear accelerators. Address: 2801 N. Glade St. N.W, Washington, DC 20016.

GIGUERE, JACQUES L(EOPOLD), b. Ste-Germaine, Que, Sept. 17, 21; m. 56; c. 2. ORGANIC & ANALYTICAL CHEMISTRY. B.A, Laval, 43, B.A.Sc, 48, D.Sc.(chem), 50. Nat. Res. Coun. fel, Prairie Regional Lab, Saskatoon, Sask, 50-51; anal. chemist, Dept. Mines, Prov. Que, 51-52; lignin, Lignosol Chem. Ltd, 52-61, chief chemist, 61-70; DIR. SURV. & LABS, QUE. WATER BD, PROV. GOVERNMENT QUE, 70- Chem. Inst. Can. Lignosulfonates and their uses; inorganic and applied chemistry. Address: 914 Paradis, Ste. Foy 10, Que, Can.

GIGUERE, JOSEPH CHARLES, b. Ottawa, Ont, Aug. 10, 39; m. 63; c. 2. ELECTRICAL ENGINEERING. B.Eng, McGill Univ, 60; M.Eng, N.S. Tech. Col, 65, Ph.D.(elec. eng), 69. Lectr. ELEC. ENG, N.S. Tech. Col, 65-69; ASSOC. PROF, SIR GEORGE WILLIAMS UNIV, 69- Consult, EMI Electronics Ltd, N.S, 65-69. R.C.A.F, 60-63, Flying Officer. Inst. Elec. & Electronics Eng. Electrical network theory. Address: Dept. of Electrical Engineering, Sir George Williams University, Montreal, Que, Can.

GIGUERE, PAUL A(NTOINE), b. Quebec, Que, Jan. 13, 10; m. 37. PHYSICAL CHEMISTRY. B.A, Laval Univ, 30, B.Sc, 34; Nat. Res. Coun. Can. scholar, McGill Univ, 35-37, Ph.D.(phys. chem), 37; hon. D.Sc, Univ. Sherbrooke, 70. Asst. res. chemist, Can. Industs, Ltd, 37-38; Prov. Govt. Que. fel. chem, Calif. Inst. Technol, 39-41; lectr. PHYS. CHEM, LAVAL UNIV, 41-43, asst. prof, 43-47, PROF, 47-, MEM. BD. DIRS, 69-, dir. dept. chem, 56-67. Guggenheim fel, Calif. Inst. Technol, 46-47. Fel. AAAS; fel. N.Y. Acad. Sci; fel. Chem. Inst. Can; fel. Royal Soc. Can; fel. Spectros. Soc. Can. Properties and molecular structure of hydrogen peroxide and related compounds; infrared and Raman spectroscopy. Address: Dept. of Chemistry, Laval University, Quebec 10, Que, Can.

GIKAS, PAUL WILLIAM, b. Lansing, Mich, July 23, 28; m. 52; c. 3. PATHOLOGY. B.A, Michigan, 50, M.D, 54. Instr. PATH, UNIV. MICH, ANN ARBOR, 60-63, asst. prof, 63-66, assoc. prof, 66-69, PROF, 69- Chief lab. serv, Vet. Admin. Hosp, Ann Arbor, 60-68; mem. adv. cmt. traffic safety, Dept. Health, Ed. & Welfare, 66-68; consult, Armed Forces Inst. Path. & U.S. Pub. Health Serv, 67-68, 71. Distinguished serv. award, Univ. Mich, 65. Med.C, U.S.A, 56-58, Capt. Am. Med. Asn; Am. Asn. Automotive Med; Soc. Cryobiol; Int. Acad. Path. Pathogenesis of injuries in highway accidents; long term preservation of blood by freezing. Address: 1335 E. Catherine, Ann Arbor, MI 48104.

GILARDI, GERALD L(ELAND), b. San Mateo, Calif, June 7, 32. MICROBIOLOGY. B.S, California, Berkeley, 55; M.S, Kansas State, 59; Ph.D. (microbiol), Maryland, 61. Instr. Microbiol, N.Y. Med. Col, 61-62; City Col. N.Y, 61-65; HEAD, DIV. MICROBIOL, HOSP. FOR JOINT DISEASES & MED. CTR, N.Y, 65- U.S.A, 55-57. Am. Soc. Microbiol; Am. Med. Asn; Mycol. Soc. Am; N.Y. Acad. Sci. Morphology, physiology, and taxonomy of nonfermentative bacilli and their relationship to infection in man. Address: Division of Microbiology, Dept. of Labs, Hospital for Joint Diseases & Medical Center, 1919 Madison Ave, New York, NY 10035.

GILARDI, RICHARD DEAN, b. Wisconsin Rapids, Wis, Feb. 23, 40; m. 60; c. 1. PHYSICAL CHEMISTRY. B.S, Mass. Inst. Tech, 61; Ph.D.(phys. chem), Maryland, 66. Chemist, Am. Instrument Co, Maryland, 62-63; res. asst, Maryland, 63-66; chemist, Inst. Defense Anal, Va, 66; res. assoc. x-ray diffraction, NAVAL RES. LAB, 66-68, RES. CHEMIST, 68- Consult, Inst. Defense Anal, 65-66. Am. Crystallog. Asn; Am. Chem. Soc; Sci. Res. Soc. Am. Techniques of diffraction analysis; molecular structure determination by x-ray or electron diffraction; correlation of molecular structure with biological activity; molecular spectroscopy. Address: Naval Research Lab, Code 6030, Washington, DC 20390.

GILBARG, DAVID, b. Brooklyn, N.Y, Sept. 17, 18; m. 41; c. 1. APPLIED MATHEMATICS. B.S, City Col, 38; N.Y. Univ, 38-39; Ph.D.(math), Indiana, 41. Asst. math, Indiana, 39-41; physicist, Nat. Bur. Standards, 41-42; chief, fluid dynamics test sect, Naval Ord. Lab, 42-45, theoret. mech. subdiv, 45-46; asst. prof. MATH, Indiana, 46-50, assoc. prof, 50-57; PROF, STANFORD UNIV, 57-, exec. head dept, 59-69. U.S.N, 44-45. Am. Math. Soc; Math. Asn. Am; German Soc. Appl. Math. & Mech. Fluid dynamics; partial differential equations. Address: Dept. of Mathematics, Stanford University, Stanford, CA 94305.

GILBERT, ALFRED R(ACHELS), b. Rocky Mt, N.C, Nov. 27, 22; m. 48. ORGANIC CHEMISTRY. B.S, Richmond, 42; M.A, Duke, 43, Ph.D.(org. chem), 49. Jr. chemist, Naval Res. Lab, 44-46; res. assoc, res. lab, GEN. ELEC. CO, 49-57, liaison scientist, 57-59, MGR. polymer reaction res, 59-69, ORG. CHEM. BR, RES. & DEVELOP. CTR, 69- U.S.N.R, 44-46. Am. Chem. Soc. Fluorination; silicones; organic sulfur compounds; synthetic polymers; polymer reinforcement. Address: General Electric Co, Research & Development Center, P.O. Box 8, Schenectady, NY 12301.

GILBERT, A(LLAN) H(ENRY), b. Liverpool, Eng, Oct. 20, 29; m. 54; c. 2. ORGANIC CHEMISTRY. B.Sc, Liverpool, 51, Ph.D.(org. chem), 54. Can. Res. fel, New Brunswick, 54-56; res. chemist, LEVER BROS. CO, EDGEWATER, 56-65, SECT. CHIEF DETERGENT SOLIDS SECT, 65- Am. Chem. Soc. Synthetic organic chemistry and natural product investigation; preparation of synthetic perfumes. Address: 200 Beechwood Rd, Oradell, NJ 07649.

GILBERT, ARTHUR C(HARLES), b. N.Y.C, Sept. 23, 26; m. 53; c. 2. AERONAUTICAL ENGINEERING. B.A.E, N.Y. Univ, 46, M.A.E, 47, fel, 53-56, Sc.D.(eng. sci), 56. Aeronaut. res. scientist, Nat. Adv. Comt, Aeronaut, Va, 47-48; asst. chief vibrations, Piasecki Helicopter Corp, Pa, 48-51; sr. vibrations engr, Repub. Aviation Corp, N.Y, 51-52; asst. proj. engr, Bulova Res. & Develop. Labs, Inc, 52-54; assoc. eng. scientist, col. eng, N.Y. Univ, 54-56; supvr. acoustics & vibrations unit, dynamics sect, N.Am. Aviation Corp, Calif, 56-58; asst. prog. dir, weather reconnaissance prog, syst. div, Bendix Aviation Corp, 58-59, outer space planning, 59-61; chief space systs, corp. systs. ctr, United Aircraft Corp, 61-63, mgr. adv. systs. planning, 63-66, mgr. gen. eng. & test opers, 66-67; chief tech. staff, Cent. Intel. Agency, 67-68; v.pres, Systs. Technol. Lab. Inc, 68-70; PRES. & OWNER, ARTHUR C. GILBERT CONSULT. ENGR, 70- Sci. adv. to chief naval opers, U.S. Navy, 70- Am. Soc. Mech. Eng; assoc. fel. Am. Inst. Aeronaut. & Astronaut. Systems analysis and design; structural dynamics; advanced technical planning; engineering management. Address: 4701 Willard Ave, Chevy Chase, MD 20015.

GILBERT, A(RTHUR) D(ONALD), b. Niagara Falls, N.Y, Aug. 12, 16; m. 41; c. 4. ORGANIC CHEMISTRY. A.B, Middlebury Col, 38; Nat. Defense Res.

Comt. fel, Cornell, 41-42, Ph.D.(org. chem), 42. Asst. instr, chem, Cornell, 39-41, lab. asst, E.I. DU PONT DE NEMOURS & CO, INC, 36, 37, 40, res. chemist, east. lab, 42-50, lab. sect. head, 50-52, tech. specialist, explosives dept, tech. div, 52-55, asst. dir, Burnside lab, 55-56, mgr, tech. div, for. rels. dept, 56-58, patent & licensing sect, int. dept, 58-60, asst. dir, East. Lab, 60-63, dir, explosives exp. sta. lab, 63-68, STAFF MGR. EXPLOSIVES DEPT, RES. & DEVELOP. DIV, 68- Am. Chem. Soc; Soc. Chem. Indust. Detonator research; organic polymer intermediate research; fundamental chemistry of organic reactions of nitric acid. Address: 1311 Chadwick Rd, Welshire, Wilmington, DE 19803.

GILBERT, BARRY JAY, b. Brooklyn, N.Y, Feb. 2, 43; m. 65; c. 2. PHYSICS. B.S, Polytech. Inst. Brooklyn, 63; M.S, Lehigh, 65, Ph.D.(physics), 68. ASST. PROF. PHYSICS, PROVIDENCE COL, 68- Am. Asn. Physics Teachers. Theoretical plasma physics. Address: Dept. of Physics, Providence College, Providence, RI 02918.

GILBERT, BRIAN E, b. Hollywood, Calif, Jan. 31, 42; m. 70. CELL BIOLOGY. A.B, Univ. Calif, Berkeley, 64; San Francisco State Col, 64-66; Ph.D. (med. microbiol. & immunol), Univ. Calif, Los Angeles, 70. RES. ASST. MICROBIOL, SCH. MED, NORTHWEST. UNIV, 70- Am. Soc. Microbiol. Role of cystine in the morphogenesis of Histoplasma capsulatum; regulation of protein synthesis at the translational level during mouse brain development. Address: Dept. of Microbiology, Northwestern University School of Medicine, 303 E. Chicago Ave, Chicago, IL 60611.

GILBERT, CARTER R(OWELL), b. Huntington, W.Va, May 23, 30; m. 58; c. 2. ICHTHYOLOGY. B.Sc, Ohio State, 51, M.Sc, 53; fel, Michigan, 54-58, Ph.D. (zool, ichthyol), 60. Asst. zool, Ohio State, 52; ichthyol, div. fishes, mus. zool, Michigan, 58-59; res. assoc, U.S. Nat. Mus, 59-61; ASST. CURATOR natural sci, FLA. STATE MUS, 61-69, ICHTHYOL, 69-; ASST. PROF. ZOOL, UNIV. FLA, 69- Am. Soc. Ichthyol. & Herpet. Eastern North American freshwater fishes; sharks; western Atlantic marine fishes. Address: Florida State Museum, Gainesville, FL 32603.

GILBERT, CHARLES M(ERWIN), b. Wash, D.C, May 22, 10. PHYSICAL GEOLOGY. A.B, Cornell, 33; Ph.D, California, 38. From instr. to assoc. prof. GEOL, UNIV. CALIF, BERKELEY, 38-58, PROF, 58- Geol. Soc. Am; Soc. Econ. Paleont. & Mineral; Am. Asn. Petrol. Geol; Am. Geophys. Union. Areal geology and sedimentary petrology. Address: Dept. of Geology, 301 Earth Sciences Bldg, University of California, Berkeley, CA 94720.

GILBERT, CHARLES R(USSELL), b. Leavenworth, Kans, Aug. 28, 08; m. ZOOLOGY. A.B, Kansas, 31, M.A, 34, Nat. Sci. Found. fel, 59-60. Chmn. dept. sci, Morristown Norm. & Indust. Col, 35; dept. biol, BLUEFIELD STATE COL, 36-56, PROF. BIOL. & CHMN. DIV. NATURAL SCI, 57-, consult. math. & sci. workshop, 56, consult. & coordinator, 58- AAAS. Organic chemistry; physiology; bacteriology. Address: Division of Natural Science, Bluefield State College, Bluefield, WV 24701.

GILBERT, DANIEL L(EE), b. Brooklyn, N.Y, July 2, 25; m. 64; c. 1. PHYSIOLOGY. A.B, Drew, 48; M.S, Iowa, 50; Ph.D.(physiol), Rochester, 55. Instr. physiol, sch. med. & dent, Rochester, 55-56; Albany Med. Col, 56-59, asst. prof, 59-60; Jefferson Med. Col, 60-62; assoc. prof, 62-63; physiologist, NAT. INSTS. HEALTH, 62-63, HEAD SECT. CELLULAR BIOPHYS, LAB BIOPHYS, NAT. INST. NEUROL DISEASES & STROKE, 63- Bowditch Lectr, Am. Physiol. Soc, 64; consult, grad. coun, George Wash. Univ, 65-70; mem. corp, Marine Biol. Lab, Woods Hole. U.S.A, 43-45. Fel. AAAS; Biophys. Soc; Am. Physiol. Soc; Am. Chem. Soc; Soc. Exp. Biol. & Med; Soc. Gen. Physiol. Oxygen poisoning; cell permeability. Address: Lab. of Biophysics, National Institute of Neurological Diseases & Stroke, Bethesda, MD 20014.

GILBERT, DAVID ERWIN, b. Fresno, Calif, June 23, 39; m. 60; c. 2. PHYSICS. A.B, Univ. Calif, Berkeley, 62; M.A, Univ. Ore, 64, Ph.D.(physics), 68. Teaching asst. PHYSICS, Univ. Ore, 62-65, res. asst, 65-68; ASSOC. PROF. & CHMN. DEPT, EAST. ORE. COL, 68- Res. assoc, Univ. Ore, 69- Am. Asn. Physics Teachers. Atomic spectroscopy—studies of the effects of foreign gas on atomic absorption lines, total line shape studies. Address: Dept. of Physics, Eastern Oregon College, La Grande, OR 97850.

GILBERT, DON DALE, b. Ponca City, Okla, June 5, 34; m. 63; c. 2. ANALYTICAL CHEMISTRY. B.S, California, Berkeley, 56; Shell Co. Found. fel, Minnesota, 58-59, Procter & Gamble Co. summer fel, 59, Ph.D.(anal. chem), 59. Res. chemist, anal. & phys. measurement div, Calif. Res. Corp, Standard Oil Co. Calif, 59-65; asst. prof. CHEM, NORTH. ARIZ. UNIV, 65-68, ASSOC. PROF, 68- Am. Chem. Soc. Digital computers in chemical instrumentation; colorimetry; trace analysis; electroanalytical chemistry. Address: Dept. of Chemistry, Northern Arizona University, Flagstaff, AZ 86001.

GILBERT, DOUGLAS L, b. La Veta, Colo, June 28, 25; m. 49; c. 2. ECOLOGY. B.S, Colorado State, 50, M.S, 51; Nat. Wildlife Fedn. fel, univ. fel, Schon-René fel. & Ph.D.(wildlife mgt), Michigan, 62. Res. biologist, Colo. Game & Fish Dept, 51-52, pub. rels. specialist, 53-55; instr. wildlife mgt, Colo. Agr. & Mech. Col, 52-53; asst. prof. forestry, Montana, 55-56; assoc. prof. major wildlife mgt. & chmn. dept, Colo. State Univ, 57-66, prof. wildlife biol. & chmn. dept, 66-69; prof. wildlife sci, Cornell Univ, 69-71; PROF. WILDLIFE BIOL. & ASST. DEAN COL. FORESTRY & NATURAL RESOURCES, COLO. STATE UNIV, 71- U.S.A.A.F, 43-46, S/Sgt. AAAS; Wildlife Soc; Am. Soc. Range Mgt; Wildlife Disease Asn. Natural resource ecology; public relations in natural resource management; wildlife management. Address: Office of the Dean, College of Forestry & Natural Resources, Colorado State University, Ft. Collins, CO 80521.

GILBERT, EDGAR N(ELSON), b. Woodhaven, N.Y, July 25, 23; m. 48; c. 3. MATHEMATICS. B.S, City Col, 43; fel, Mass. Inst. Technol, 46-48, Ph.D. (math), 48. Asst. physics, Illinois, 43; staff mem, radiation lab, Mass. Inst. Technol, 44-46; BELL TEL. LABS, 48-69, MEM. TECH. STAFF, 69- Civilian with Off. Sci. Res. & Develop, 44. Am. Math. Soc. Electromagnetic theory; differential equations; information theory; switching theory. Address: Bell Telephone Labs, Murray Hill, NJ 07971.

GILBERT, EDWARD E, b. N.Y.C, May 1, 25; m. 61; c. 5. ENTOMOLOGY. B.S. & M.S, Southern Methodist, 50; Kansas, 50-51; Ph.D, California, Berkeley, 61. Asst. prof. biol, State Univ. N.Y. Stony Brook, 58-65; prof, Northeast Mo. State Teachers Col, 65-69; HEAD DEPT. BIOL, W.GA. COL, 69- Nat. Sci. Found. fel, radioecol. inst, Oak Ridge Inst. Nuclear Studies, 63; Nat. Sci. Found. grant, 67-69. U.S.A.A.F, 43-46. AAAS; Ecol. Soc. Am; Am. Inst. Biol. Sci. Systematics and population ecology of Coleoptera, particularly Tribolium and Curculionidae. Address: Dept. of Biology, West Georgia College, Carrollton, GA 30117.

GILBERT, E(DWARD) O(TIS), b. Joliet, Ill, Mar. 29, 30; m. 54; c. 3. ENGINEERING. B.S.E, Michigan, 52, Phi Kappa Phi fel, 52-53, M.S.E, 53, Ph.D. (instrumentation eng), 57. Instr, aeronaut. eng, Michigan, 53-57, asst. prof, 57-60, assoc. prof, 60-64; v.pres. res. & eng, Appl. Dynamics, Inc, 63-69, SR. V.PRES. TECHNOL, APPL. DYNAMICS COMPUT. SYSTS, DIV. RELIANCE ELEC, 69- Mem. tech. staff, Space Tech. Labs, Inc, Calif, 59-60. AAAS; Inst. Elec. & Electronics Eng. Design and application of analog and hybrid computers; automatic control; space and flight mechanics; instrumentation engineering; industrial control computer design and application. Address: Applied Dynamics Computer Systems, Division of Reliance Electric, Box 1488, Ann Arbor, MI 48106.

GILBERT, ELIZABETH F, b. Boston, Mass, Feb. 14, 29. PLANT ECOLOGY & TAXONOMY. B.A, Wellesley Col, 51; M.A, Michigan, 55, Ph.D.(bot), 59. Teacher, Northfield Sch, 51-54; instr. bot, Oberlin Col, 59-61, asst. prof. biol, 61-65; assoc. prof, Haile Sellassie Univ, 65-68; tutor, St. John's Col.(Md), Santa Fe, N.Mex, 68-71; ASSOC. PROF. BOT, KIRKLAND COL, 71- Summers, vis. lectr, Univ. Mich, 59, 60 & 61; grant-in-aid, Oberlin Col, 62. AAAS; Ecol. Soc. Am; Int. Asn. Plant Taxon. Ecology and taxonomy of the flora of Ethiopia. Address: Kirkland College, Clinton, NY 13323.

GILBERT, ELMER G(RANT), b. Joliet, Ill, Mar. 29, 30. ENGINEERING. B.S.E, Michigan, 52, M.S.E, 53, Ph.D.(instrumentation eng), 57. Instr. AERONAUT. ENG, UNIV. MICH, ANN ARBOR, 53-57, asst. prof, 57-59, assoc. prof, 59-63, PROF, 63-, MEM. COMPUT, INFO. & CONTROL ENG. PROG, 71- Inst. Elec. & Electronics Eng; Soc. Indust. & Appl. Math. Automatic control; electronic computers. Address: Computer, Information, & Control Engineering Program, University of Michigan, Ann Arbor, MI 48104.

GILBERT, ELMER W(ILHELM), b. Brooklyn, N.Y, Apr. 27, 05; m. 33; c. 2. INTERNAL MEDICINE. B.S, Columbia Union Col, 29; M.D, Loma Linda, 31. Instr. med, sch. med, Loma Linda, 33-46, clin. asst. prof, 46-49, asst. prof, 49-64; STAFF PHYSICIAN, PORTERVILLE STATE HOSP, 64-, ASST. SUPT. GEN. MED. & SURG, 67- Res. physician, Los Angeles County Hosp, 32-35, jr. attend. physician, 38-49, sr. attend. physician, 49-67, emer. sr. attend. physician, 67-; sr. attend. physician, White Mem. Hosp, 39-64. U.S.A.R, 35-43, 43-65; A.U.S, 43-46, Col.(ret). Fel. Am. Col. Physicians. Kidney disease; black widow spider bites; primary bronchogenic carcinoma. Address: Porterville State Hospital, P.O. Box 2000, Porterville, CA 93257.

GILBERT, ENGEL L(EE) R(USSELL), b. Frostburg, Md, July 6, 09; m. 40. ENTOMOLOGY. B.S, Maryland, 32, Ph.D.(entomol), 50. Field aide & asst, bur. entom, U.S. Dept. Agr, 32-37; asst. prof. entom, exten. serv, Maryland, 42-51; entomologist, plant pest control div, U.S. Dept. Agr, 51, in charge pesticides regulation testing lab, agr. res. ctr, Md, 51-71; RETIRED. Med.C, 43-46, Comdr. Entom. Soc. Am. Chemical insect control; insect attractants and traps; biology of lice. Address: 2188 Pine Ridge Dr, Clearwater, FL 33515.

GILBERT, ENID MAY FISCHER, b. Sydney, Australia, May 31, 27; m. 54; c. 5. PATHOLOGY. M.B,B.S, Sydney, 50. Asst. prof. PATH, W.Va. Univ, 63-67, assoc. prof, 67-70; vis. assoc. prof, UNIV. WIS, MADISON, 70-71, PROF, 71- Am. Soc. Clin. Path; Col. Am. Path; Am. Asn. Path. & Bact; Int. Acad. Path. Pediatric pathology; teratology. Address: Dept. of Pathology, University of Wisconsin, Madison, WI 53715.

GILBERT, EUGENE CHARLES, b. Manchester, N.H, Nov. 16, 42; m. 65; c. 2. PHYSICAL ORGANIC CHEMISTRY. A.B, St. Anselm's Col, 65; Ph.D. (phys. org. chem), Univ. Notre Dame, 69. Res. assoc. org. chem, Johns Hopkins Univ, 69-70; GROUP LEADER BASIC RES, JOHN STUART RES. LABS, QUAKER OATS CO, 70- Am. Chem. Soc. Conformational analysis; hydrogen bonding; carbonium ions and pyrolytic techniques; pyrolytic studies; halogenations; general synthesis and polymer research. Address: Quaker Oats Co, 617 W. Main St, Barrington, IL 60010.

GILBERT, EVERETT E(DDY), b. Ithaca, N.Y, May 5, 14; m. 44; c. 2. ORGANIC CHEMISTRY. B.A, Yale, 35, Ph.D.(chem), 38. Res. chemist, Tide Water Assoc. Oil Co, 38-41; gen. chem. div, Allied Chem. Corp, 41-44, supvr. org. res, 44-62, res. assoc, indust. chem. div, 62-69; CHIEF SYNTHESIS SECT, EXPLOSIVES DIV, PICATINNY ARSENAL, 69- Organic and agricultural chemicals; organic and inorganic sulfur and fluorine compounds; surface-active agents; sulfonation; explosives. Address: 7 Frederick Pl, Route 12, Morristown, NJ 07960.

GILBERT, FRANCIS CHARLES, b. Richmond, Calif, May 7, 28; m. 50; c. 2. NUCLEAR PHYSICS. B.S, California, Berkeley, 50, M.S, 52, Ph.D.(physics), 54. Res. asst. physics, Lawrence Radiation Lab, Univ. Calif, Berkeley, 50-54, physicist, nuclear test prog, Livermore, 50-58, controlled thermonuclear res. prog, 59-61, leader nuclear emulsion group, 61-64, high altitude physics group, 61-67, test dir, 62-67, sci. dep. to joint task force eight, 67-69, leader res. & develop. group, 70-71; DEP. DIR. DIV. MIL. APPLN, ATOMIC ENERGY COMN, 71- Exchange physicist, Fontenay Nuclear Res. Ctr, France, 60-61. Sig.C.Res, 50-62, Capt. Am. Phys. Soc. Fundamental particle, high energy, space and plasma physics; controlled thermonuclear research; physics of nuclear explosions. Address: Division of Military Applications, Atomic Energy Commission, Washington, DC 20545.

GILBERT, F(RANCIS) E(VALO), b. Mattoon, Ill, June 8, 16; m. 42; c. 2. CHEMISTRY. B.S, Illinois, 39. Chemist, Cuneo Press, Ill, 39-41; Eversharp, Inc, 46; CHIEF CHEMIST & DIR. RES, SANFORD INK CO, 46-, V.PRES, 67- Biochemist, Gen. Hosp, Med. Dept, U.S.A, 42-46. Am. Chem.

Soc. Specialty inks, writing, stamping, marking; adhesives, dextrine, gum and rubber types; packaging of above items for retail distribution. Address: 429 N. Park, La Grange Park, IL 60525.

GILBERT, FRANK A(LBERT), b. Exeter, N.H, Mar. 22, 00; m. 29; c. 3. BOTANY. B.S, Mass. Col, 22; Austin fel, Harvard, 23-24, M.A, 25, Ph.D.(mycol), 27. Inspector, White Pine Blister Rust Surv, U.S. Dept. Agr, 22-23; asst. bot, Radcliffe Col, 24-26; asst. prof, Marshall Col, 27-29, prof. & head dept, 29-42; res. botanist, Battelle Mem. Inst, 45-47, asst. supvr. agr. sci. div, 48-52, consult, 53-59; PROF. BIOL. & HEAD DEPT, UNION COL. (KY), 59- Harvard bot. exped, Newfoundland & Labrador, 25. U.S.A, 17-19, 42-45, Lt. Col. Bot. Soc. Am; Am. Mycol. Soc. Mineral nutrition of plants; the value of copper in plant nutrition; physiology of the Myxomycetes; flora of southern West Virginia. Address: Dept. of Biology, Union College, Barbourville, KY 40906.

GILBERT, FRANKLIN ANDREW, b. Burlington, N.J, June 8, 19; m. 44; c. 3. HORTICULTURE. B.S, Rutgers, 42, M.S, 48, Ph.D, 52. Field agent hort, U.S. Dept. Agr, Md, 42; asst. exten. specialist pomol, Rutgers Univ, 44-46, instr. & res. assoc, 46-50; asst. prof. HORT, UNIV. WIS, MADISON, 50-56, assoc. prof, 56-59, PROF, 59-, HORTICULTURIST; UNIV. EXP. FARMS, PENINSULA BR. EXP. STA, 69- U.S.A.A.F, 42-44. Am. Soc. Hort. Sci. Trees; small fruit. Address: Peninsula Branch Experiment Station, University of Wisconsin, Sturgeon Bay, WI 54235.

GILBERT, FREDERICK EMERSON, JR, b. Birmingham, Ala, June 1, 41; m. 62; c. 2. PATHOLOGY, CLINICAL CHEMISTRY. B.S, Birmingham South. Col, 63; M.S, Univ. Ala, 65, M.D, 68. Res. assoc. biochem, Mem. Inst. Path, 65-71; CHIEF CYTOPATH, CTR. DISEASE CONTROL, 71- South. Med. Asn. res. fel, 69-70; mem, Ad Hoc Adv. Comt. Cytol, 71- Med. Col. Ala. Res. Award, 68. U.S.P.H.S, 71-73, Surg. Am. Chem. Soc; Am. Asn. Clin. Chem; Am. Soc. Clin. Path; Col. Am. Path; Am. Soc. Hist. Med. Multiphasic screening to study the diseased codon; inorganic pyrophosphatase and its role in nucleotide metabolism. Address: Center for Disease Control, Bldg. 1, L255, Atlanta, GA 30333.

GILBERT, GARETH E, b. Fall River, Mass, Sept. 30, 21; m. 49; c. 2. BOTANY. B.Sc, Ohio State, 48, M.Sc, 49, Ph.D.(plant ecol), 53. Instr. BOT, OHIO STATE UNIV, 52-56, asst. prof, 56-61, ASSOC. PROF, 61- U.S.N, 42-46. Ecol. Soc. Am; Am. Chem. Soc. Plant ecology. Address: Dept. of Botany, Ohio State University, Columbus, OH 43210.

GILBERT, GEORGE LEWIS, b. Abington, Mass, Sept. 10, 33; m. 62; c. 3. INORGANIC CHEMISTRY. B.S, Antioch Col, 58; Du Pont fel, Mich. State, 61-62, Ph.D.(inorg. chem), 63. Res. chemist, Lawrence Radiation Lab, California, 63-64; asst. prof. CHEM, DENISON UNIV, 64-69, ASSOC. PROF. & CHMN. DEPT, 69-, SCI. COORD, 70-, acting chmn. dept. chem, 67-68. AAAS; Am. Crystallog. Asn; Am. Chem. Soc; The Chem. Soc. Reactions of noble gas compounds; coordination compounds and their structures. Address: Dept. of Chemistry, Denison University, Granville, OH 43023.

GILBERT, HARRIET S, b. Phila, Pa, June 22, 30; m. 57; c. 3. HEMATOLOGY. A.B, Bryn Mawr Col, 51; M.D, Columbia, 55. Intern, MT. SINAI HOSP, 55-56, asst. res. internal med, 56-58, clin. asst. hemat, 58-63, asst. attend. hematologist, 63-66, fel, 58-61, res. asst, 61-63, res. assoc, 63-64, asst. prof. med, MT. SINAI SCH. MED, 66-69, ASSOC. PROF. CLIN. MED, 69- Am. Cancer Soc. fel, 59-61, Sophie Abramson Silber mem. grant cancer res, 65-66. Consult, Elmhurst Hosp, New York, 64- Dipl, Nat. Bd. Med. Exam, 56; Am. Bd. Internal Med, 65. Am. Med. Asn; Am. Soc. Hemat; Am. Fedn. Clin. Res; Am. Col. Physicians; Hematology, especially myeloproliferative diseases; biochemical changes, including histamine and serotonin metabolism; clinical problems, particularly surgical and neurological complications; chemotherapy in control of myeloproliferative disease. Address: Dept. of Hematology, Mt. Sinai Hospital & School of Medicine, 100th St. & Fifth Ave, New York, NY 10029.

GILBERT, IRA H, b. N.Y.C, Oct. 21, 38; m. 66. ASTROPHYSICS. B.S, Polytech. Inst. Brooklyn, 59; hon. Woodrow Wilson fel, Harvard, 59, Nat. Sci. Found. fel, 59-61, A.M, 60, Ph.D.(physics), 65. Res. assoc. ASTROPHYS, BRANDEIS UNIV, 64-65, instr, 65-66, ASST. PROF, 66- AAAS; Am. Phys. Soc. Statistical stellar dynamics; cosmology. Address: Dept. of Astrophysics, Brandeis University, Waltham, MA 02154.

GILBERT, IRWIN H(ELLINGS), b. Frostburg, Md, July 6, 09; m. 38; c. 1. ENTOMOLOGY. B.S, Maryland, 32; fel, Ohio State, 40-42, M.Sc, 41. Pest control, Wash, D.C, 32-35; hort. inspector, State Dept. Agr, N.Y, 36-38; asst. exten. entomologist, Ohio State, 40-42, 46; ENTOMOLOGIST, INSECTS AFFECTING MAN BR, ENTOM. RES. DIV, AGR. RES. SERV, U.S. DEPT. AGR, 46-; PROF. ENTOM, UNIV. FLA, 63- Specialist, with U.S. Army, 51-53, 65, 67; consult, WHO, 58, 62, 63, 67, 69. Sanit.C, 42-46, Med. Serv. C. Res, 47-63, Lt. Col.(ret). Entom. Soc. Am; Can. Entom. Soc. Repellents for parasitic insects; human body louse control; household insect control. Address: 218 N.W. 30th St, Gainesville, FL 32601.

GILBERT, JAMES ALAN LONGMORE, b. Grantown-on-Spey, Scotland, Jan. 28, 18; m. 44; c. 4. INTERNAL MEDICINE. M.B, Ch.B, Edinburgh, 41, M.D, 47. Assoc. prof. MED, UNIV. ALTA, 57-63, PROF, 63-; DIR. CLIN. TEACHING UNIT, ROYAL ALEXANDRA HOSP, EDMONTON, ALTA, 70- Fel, Royal Col. Physicians, 47; fel, Royal Col. Physicians Edinburgh, 47; fel, Royal Col. Physicians & Surgeons Can, 50, exam. internal med, 57; fel, Royal Col. Physicians, London, 65. R.C.A.M.C, 43-45. Fel. Am. Col. Physicians; Can. Diabetic Asn; Can. Soc. Clin. Invest; fel. Royal Soc. Arts; Am. Gastroenterol. Asn; Can. Asn. Gastroenterol.(pres, 70); Int. Asn. Res. Med. Educ. (pres. elect). Pre-diabetic syndromes; physiological basis of the dumping syndrome following partial gastrectomy for peptic ulcer. Address: Room 1244, Royal Alexandra Hospital, Edmonton, Alta, Can.

GILBERT, JAMES BRYSON, b. Newark, Del, Mar. 17, 22; m. 54; c. 5. MOLECULAR BIOLOGY. B.S, Haverford Col, 43; M.D, Jefferson Med. Col, 46. Intern, Jefferson Hosp, 46-47; sr. asst. to sr. surgeon, Nat. Cancer Inst, 48-56; Hite fel, Texas, 56-58, Am. Heart Asn. estab. investr, Biochem. Inst. Tex, 58-63; asst. prof. biochem, W.Va. Univ, 63-70; Nat. Insts. Health spec. fel, UNIV. WIS, MADISON, 70-71, LECTR. PATH. & GEN. MED. SCI, 71- With radiation lab, Univ. Calif, 51-52. U.S.C.G, 47-48. Am. Soc. Biol. Chem; Genetics Soc. Am. Cell cycle; control mechanisms. Address: Molecular Biology Lab, University of Wisconsin, Madison, WI 53706.

GILBERT, J(AMES) C(ARL), b. Oswego, N.Y, June 12, 09; m. 40; c. 3. AGRICULTURE, VEGETABLE CROPS. A.B, Pomona Col, 31; M.A, Southern California, 34; Ph.D.(genetics), Hawaii, 59. Teacher private sch, Hawaii, 35-47; jr. olericulturist, agr. exp. sta, UNIV. HAWAII, 48-54, asst. olericulturist, 54-59, assoc. olericulturist & head veg. crops. dept, 59-61, assoc. horticulturist, 61-65, HORTICULTURIST, 65-, head dept. hort, 61-66. Am. Soc. Hort. Sci. Genetics and breeding of vegetable corps; vegetable type soybeans resistant to root knot nematodes and tobacco mosaic virus in tomatoes; heat tolerant cauliflower; edible podded peas; mosaic resistant cucumbers. Address: Room 109, Plant Science Bldg, University of Hawaii, 3190 Maile Way, Honolulu, HI 96822.

GILBERT, J(AMES) FREEMAN, b. Vincennes, Ind, Aug. 9, 31; m. 59; c. 3. GEOPHYSICS. B.S, Mass. Inst. Tech, 53, Nat. Sci. Found. fel, 55-56, Ph.D. (geophys), 56. Nat. Sci. Found. fel, Cambridge, 56; res. assoc, Mass. Inst. Tech, 56-57; asst. prof, inst. geophys, California, Los Angeles, 57-59, assoc. prof, 60; sr. res. geophysicist, Tex. Inst, Inc, 60-61; PROF. GEOPHYS, INST. GEOPHYS. & PLANETARY PHYSICS, UNIV. CALIF, SAN DIEGO, 61- Guggenheim fel, Cambridge, 64-65. Am. Phys. Soc; Am. Math. Soc; Am. Geophys. Union; Seismol. Soc. Am; Am. Acoust. Soc; Am. Acad. Arts & Sci; N.Y. Acad. Sci. Elastodynamics; seismology; communication theory; diffraction theory; normal mode theory; inverse problem of seismology. Address: Institute of Geophysics and Planetary Physics, University of California, San Diego, La Jolla, CA 92037.

GILBERT, JIMMIE D(ALE), b. Quitman, La, July 12, 34; m. 53; c. 4. ALGEBRA. B.S, La. Polytech, 56; fel, Auburn, 56-57, M.S, 57, Nat. Sci. Found. fel, 59-60, summer fel. & Ph.D.(math), 60. Instr. MATH, Auburn, 57-58; from asst. prof. to assoc. prof, LA. TECH UNIV, 58-68, PROF, 68- Am. Math. Soc; Math. Asn. Am. Group theory. Address: Dept. of Mathematics, Louisiana Tech University, Ruston, LA 71271.

GILBERT, JOEL STERLING, b. Wichita, Kans, Aug. 29, 35; m. 59; c. 3. MECHANICAL ENGINEERING. B.S, Oklahoma, 58, Ph.D.(mech. eng), 65; M.S, Okla. State, 60. Assoc. engr, Tex. Instruments, Inc, 58-59; res. asst. fluid contamination, Okla. State, 59-60; systs. engr, Sandia Labs, 60-61; instr. mech. eng, Oklahoma, 61-62, res. asst. radiant heat transfer, 64-65; asst. prof. mech. eng, Univ. Fla, 65-70; STAFF MEM, THEORET. DESIGN DIV, LOS ALAMOS SCI. LAB, 70-, vis. staff mem, summer 69. Staff engr, Sandia Labs, summers 67 & 68; consult, Sandia Labs. & Martin Marietta Corp, Fla, 68-69. Am. Soc. Mech. Eng; Am. Inst. Aeronaut. & Astronaut; Am. Soc. Eng. Educ; Nat. Soc. Prof. Eng. Thermodynamics; heat transfer; fluid mechanics; electromagnetic propagation. Address: Theoretical Design Division, Los Alamos Scientific Lab, P.O. Box 1663, Los Alamos, NM 87544.

GILBERT, JOHN B(ARRY), b. Hull, Eng, Jan. 21, 37; m. 59; c. 2. PHYSICAL CHEMISTRY. B.Sc, Univ. Hull, 57, Ph.D.(chem), 60. Res. fel. photochem, Univ. Alta, 60-62; RES. CHEMIST, RES. DEPT, IMP. OIL ENTERPRISES LTD, 62- Chem. Inst. Can. Petroleum refining, particularly refining processes for the manufacture of lubricating oils; catalytic processes, especially catalytic hydrogenation and hydrocracking; catalytic theory and reactor design theory. Address: Research Dept, Imperial Oil Enterprises Ltd, P.O. Box 3022, Sarnia, Ont, Can.

GILBERT, JOHN CARL, b. Laramie, Wyo, Jan. 30, 39; m. 65. ORGANIC CHEMISTRY. B.S, Wyoming, 61; Nat. Sci. Found. fel, Yale, 61-65, M.S, 62, Ph.D.(chem), 66. Asst. prof. CHEM, UNIV. TEX. AUSTIN, 65-71, ASSOC. PROF, 71- Am. Chem. Soc. Thermal and photochemical isomerization of hydrocarbons; chemistry of phosphoranes; organometallics. Address: Dept. of Chemistry, University of Texas at Austin, Austin, TX 78712.

GILBERT, JOHN JOUETT, b. Southampton, N.Y, July 18, 37; m. 59; c. 1. BIOLOGY. B.A, Williams Col, 59; Ph.D.(biol), Yale, 63. Nat. Insts. Health fel, Washington (Seattle), 63-64; asst. prof. BIOL, Princeton, 64-67; DARTMOUTH COL, 67-69, ASSOC. PROF, 69- AAAS; Am. Soc. Zool; Am. Soc. Limnol. & Oceanog; Ecol. Soc. Am; Brit. Ecol. Soc; Int. Asn. Theoret. & Appl. Limnol. Biology of rotifers; ecology; fresh-water and invertebrate biology; sexuality and form-change in ploimate rotifers. Address: Dept. of Biological Sciences, Dartmouth College, Hanover, NH 03755.

GILBERT, JOHN PARKER, b. Brooklyn, N.Y, Apr. 30, 26; c. 2. COMPUTER SCIENCE, STATISTICS. B.S, St. John's Col.(Md), 48; M.S, Univ. Chicago, 53, Ph.D, 62. Biostatistician, div. oncol, Chicago Med. Sch, 53-57; statist. consult, Ctr. Advan. Study Behav. Sci, 57-65; L.L. Thurstone distinguished fel, psychomet. lab, Univ. N.C, 65-66; STAFF STATISTICIAN, COMPUT. CTR, HARVARD, 66- Mem. comt. anesthesia, Nat. Acad. Sci, 65; anal. adv. comt, Nat. Assessment of Educ. Progress, 71- U.S.N.R, 44-46. Fel. AAAS; fel. Am. Statist. Soc; Inst. Math. Statist; Psychomet. Soc; Asn. Comput. Mach. Analysis of large files of medical data. Address: Harvard University Computing Center, 8 Mt. Auburn St, Cambridge, MA 02138.

GILBERT, JOHN RALPH, JR, b. Line Lexington, Pa, Feb. 15, 33; m. 53; c. 3. MATHEMATICS. B.S, Calif. State Polytech. Col, 57, M.A, 59; summer, Nat. Sci. Found. grant, Okla. State, 59; Nat. Sci. Found. grant, California, Los Angeles, 64. Instr. math, Calif. State Polytech. Col, 57-60; res. engr. comput, Lockheed Missile & Space Corp, 60-62; asst. prof. math, Calif. State Polytech. Col, 62-65; sr. systs. engr, Lockheed Missile & Space Co, 65; supvr. comput. methods group, Vandenberg Air Force Base, 65-67; mgr, WTR tech. data serv, 67-68; ASST. PROF. MATH, MISS. STATE UNIV, 68- U.S.N, 52-54, Res, 54-, Lt. Math. Asn. Am; Am. Statist. Asn. Application of statistics in industry. Address: Dept. of Mathematics, Mississippi State University, State College, MS 39762.

GILBERT, JOSEPH W(EST), JR, b. Ft. Valley, Ga, Aug. 8, 24; m. 48. SURGERY. M.D, Emory, 48. Intern surg, Bowman Gray Sch. Med, Wake Forest Col, 48-49, asst. res, 49-50, 52-54, res, 54-55; fel, surg. res, Children's Med. Ctr, Boston, Mass, 55-56; dep. chief clin. surg, Nat. Heart Inst, Nat. Insts. Health, 56-68; MEM. STAFF, VET. ADMIN. HOSP, ATLANTA, GA, 68- Guest investr, thoracic clin, Karolinska Inst, 65-66. Dipl, Am. Bd. Surg, 56; Am. Bd. Thoracic Surg, 57. U.S.N.R, 50-52. Cardiovascular and thoracic surgery. Address: Veterans Administration Hospital, Box 29457, Atlanta, GA 30329.

GILBERT, LAWRENCE I(RWIN), b. New York, N.Y, Jan. 24, 29; m. 52; c. 3. ZOOLOGY. B.S, Long Island, 50; M.S, N.Y. Univ, 55; Ph.D.(zool), Cornell, 58. Asst. prof. BIOL. SCI, NORTHWEST. UNIV.(ILL), 58-62, assoc. prof, 62-65, PROF, 65- Nat. Sci. Found. sr. fel, Berne, 64-65; vis. scientist, Am. Physiol. Soc, 63- U.S.N, 52-55, Lt.(jg). Soc. Exp. Biol. & Med; Am. Soc. Cell Biol; Soc. Gen. Physiol; Entom. Soc. Am. Invertebrate endocrinology; biochemical effect of insect hormones; insect physiology; lipid metabolism and transport in insects; endocrine gland ultrastructure; sterols and terpenes in insects. Address: Dept. of Biological Sciences, Northwestern University, Evanston, IL 60201.

GILBERT, MARGARET L(OIS), b. Wakefield, R.I, June 9, 28. BOTANY, ECOLOGY. B.S, Rhode Island, 49; Ph.D.(bot), Wisconsin, 53. Asst. prof. biol, Northwest. State Col.(La), 53-54; from asst. prof. to assoc. prof, FLA. SOUTH. COL, 54-61, PROF. BIOL. & CHMN. DEPT. BIOL. SCI. & DIV. NATURAL SCI, 61- Bot. Soc. Am; Ecol. Soc. Am. Plant ecology. Address: Dept. of Biological Sciences, Florida Southern College, Lakeland, FL 33802.

GILBERT, MARGARET S(HEA), b. Canton, Ohio, Feb. 25, 08; m. BIOLOGY. B.A, Oberlin Col, 30; M.A, Wellesley Col, 32; Ph.D.(embryol), Cornell, 35. Lectr. BIOL, Lawrence, 47-59, assoc. prof, 59-62, prof, 62-67; resident lectr, col. optom, PAC. UNIV, 68-70, PROF. OCULAR ANAT, 70- Embryology; anatomy; histology. Address: College of Optometry, Pacific University, Forest Grove, OR 97116.

GILBERT, MURRAY CHARLES, b. Lawton, Okla, Jan. 21, 36; m. 58; c. 4. GEOLOGY, PETROLOGY. B.S, Oklahoma, 58, Nat. Sci. Found. fel, 60, M.S, 61; Nat. Sci. Found. fel, California, Los Angeles, 61-64, Ph.D.(geol), 65. Asst. res. geologist, California, Los Angeles, 65; fel, Carnegie Inst. Geophys. Lab, 65-68; ASST. PROF. PETROL, VA. POLYTECH INST. & STATE UNIV, 68- Am. Geophys. Union; Geol. Soc. Am; Mineral. Soc. Am; Mineral Soc. Gt. Brit. & Ireland. Experimental mineralogy and petrology; amphiboles; aluminum silicate polymorphs; fayalite; sodic pyroxenes; field petrology; layered mafic rocks, Wichita Mountains, Oklahoma; Franciscan and Sanbagawa metamorphic belts. Address: Dept. of Geological Sciences, Virginia Polytechnic Institute & State University, Blacksburg, VA 24061.

GILBERT, MYRON B, b. Rochester, N.Y, Sept. 3, 21; m. 45; c. 3. COMPUTER SCIENCE. A.B, Cornell, 47; Mass. Inst. Tech, 48-49. Meteorologist, Pan Am. Grace Airways, 49-57; chief, systs. & applns. br, geophys. res. directorate, 57-60, chief, eval. div, Air Force Cambridge Res. Labs, 60-67, dir. environ. consult. serv, 67-69; MGR. TECH. COMMUN, HONEYWELL INFO. SYSTS, 69- U.S.A.A.F, 43-47, 1st Lt. Am. Meteorol. Soc; Am. Geophys. Union; Am. Inst. Aeronaut. & Astronaut; Am. Mgt. Asn. Evaluation and dissemination of scientific and technical information; computer design and development. Address: 65 Walnut St, Wellesley Hills, MA 02181.

GILBERT, NATHAN, b. New York, N.Y, Sept. 27, 13; m. 40; c. 2. PHYSICAL CHEMISTRY. B.S, California, 36; Ph.D.(phys. chem), Wisconsin, 42. Lab. asst, Shell Develop. Co, Calif, 35-39; res. assoc, Wisconsin, 39-42; assoc. chemist & proj. leader, Tenn. Valley Auth, 42-53; assoc. prof. CHEM. ENG, UNIV. CINCINNATI, 53-59, PROF, 59- Vis. lectr, Nat. Sci. Found. Conf. Systs. Eng, Washington (St. Louis), June 60; Orgn. Europ. Econ. Coop. sr. vis. fel. & vis. res. fel, Manchester Col. Sci. & Tech, Eng, 61-62; vis. prof, Okla. State Univ, 69. Res. partic, reactor exp. eng. div, Oak Ridge Nat. Labs, summer 56. Consult, Hilton-Davis Chem. Co, 59- Am. Inst. Chem. Eng; Am. Soc. Eng. Educ. Process control and dynamics; process simulation and optimization; optimal control theory; air pollution problems; economic evaluation of processes; chemical reactor design. Address: Dept. of Chemical & Nuclear Engineering, University of Cincinnati, Cincinnati, OH 45221.

GILBERT, NORMAN S(UTCLIFFE), b. Butte, Mont, July 8, 29; m. 48; c. 2. INTERNAL MEDICINE. B.S, La. State, 39, M.D, 43. Asst. internal med, SCH. MED, LA. STATE UNIV, NEW ORLEANS, 46-48, instr. med. & pharmacol, 50-51, asst. prof. MED, 51-58, assoc. prof, 58-65, PROF, 65-, ASSOC. DEAN, 64- Trainee, Ga. Warm Springs Found, 58-59; mem. staff, grad. sch, Minnesota, 61; La. State vis. prof. & chief party, sch. med, Univ. Costa Rica, 63-64. Dipl. Am. Bd. Internal Med, 53. Med.C, 44-46, Capt. Am. Med. Asn. Drug investigation; rehabilitation. Address: School of Medicine, Louisiana State University in New Orleans, 1542 Tulane Ave, New Orleans, LA 70112.

GILBERT, NORRIS W, b. Moline, Mich, Apr. 23, 12; m. 40; c. 2. AGRONOMY, BOTANY. B.S, Arizona, 39; M.S, Iowa State Col, 41. Jr. agronomist, U.S. Soil Conserv. Serv, 41-42; jr. investr, U.S. Civil Serv. Comn, 42-43; asst. agronomist, agr. res. admin, U.S. Dept. Agr, 43-45, div. west. irrig. agr, 45-47; exten. agronomist, Univ. Arizona, 47-50; res. agronomist, crops res. div, U.S. Dept. Agr, 50-66; adv. field crops, U.S. Agency Int. Develop. contract, Fed. Univ. Ceará, for Univ. Ariz, 66-70; ASST. PROF. AGR. & IRRIGATION ENG. & ASSOC. AGRONOMIST, U.S. AGENCY INT. DEVELOP. RES. CONTRACT, SUVALE BRAZIL, FOR UTAH STATE UNIV, 71- Am. Soc. Agron; Crop Sci. Soc. Am. Development of canaigre as a tannin-bearing cultivated crop and safflower as an oilseed crop. Address: U.S. Agency International Development, Rio, ENRN, APO New York 09676.

GILBERT, PAUL W(ILNER), b. Rochester, N.Y, Feb. 14, 16; m. 41; c. 2. MATHEMATICS. A.B, Rochester, 36, A.M, 37; Ph.D.(math), Duke, 40. Instr. MATH, Texas Tech. Col, 40-42; U.S. Mil. Acad, 45-46; SYRACUSE UNIV, 46-48, asst. prof, 48-54, assoc. prof, 54-67, PROF, 67- U.S.A.A.F, 43-46, U.S.A.R, Lt. Col.(ret). Am. Math. Soc; Math. Asn. Am. Topology; numerical analysis. Address: 540 Buckingham Ave, Syracuse, NY 13210.

GILBERT, PERRY W(EBSTER), b. North Branford, Conn, Dec. 1, 12; m. 38; c. 8. MARINE BIOLOGY, VERTEBRATE MORPHOLOGY. A.B, Dartmouth Col, 34; Cramer fel, Cornell, 36-37, Ph.D.(zool), 40. Instr. zool, Dartmouth Col, 34-36; asst, CORNELL UNIV, 37-40, instr, 40-43, asst. prof, 43-46, assoc. prof, 46-52, PROF, 52-68, NEUROBIOL. & BEHAV, 68-; EXEC. DIR, MOTE MARINE LAB, 68- Instr, Marine Biol. Lab, Woods Hole, 41; Carnegie fel, 49-50; Guggenheim fel, 57, 64; chmn. shark res. panel, Am. Inst. Biol. Sci, 58-; consult. comt. polar res, Nat. Acad. Sci, 59- AAAS; Am. Soc. Zool; Am. Soc. Ichthyol. & Herpet; Am. Soc. Mammal; Soc. Study Evolution; Am. Asn. Anat; Am. Ornith. Union. Morphology of birds, fish and mammals; development of vertebrate eyeball musculature; structural and functional adaptations of aquatic birds; biology of elasmobranch fishes. Address: Mote Marine Lab, 9501 Blind Pass Rd, Sarasota, FL 33581.

GILBERT, RAYMOND A(RTHUR), b. Mattoon, Ill, Apr. 19, 19; m. 45; c. 3. THEORETICAL PHYSICS. B.Sc, Ohio State Univ, 50, M.Sc, 52; hon. D.Sc, Univ. Albuquerque, 67. U.S. Air Force, 41-70, physicist, Lawrence Radiation Lab, Univ. Calif, 52-55, Air Force Spec. Weapons Ctr, 55-56, dep. dir. res, 56-57, dir, 58, dep. comdr. sci, Air Force Off. Sci. Res, 59-60, dep. chief staff, plans & opers. res. div, 60, chief staff, Off. Aerospace Res, 60-61, mil. asst. to dir. defense res. & eng, 61-63, dir, Air Force Weapons Lab, 63-66, v.comdr. res. & technol. div, 66-67, dir. labs. hq, Air Force Systs. Command, 67-70; DEP. TO EXEC. SECY, NAT. AERONAUT. & SPACE COUN, 70- Distinguished mgt. award, Air Force Asn, 70; distinguished serv. award, U.S. Air Force, 70. U.S.A.F, 41-70, Brig. Gen.(Ret). AAAS; Sci. Res. Soc. Am; Am. Inst. Aeronaut. & Astronaut; Inst. Elec. & Electronics Eng; Am. Ord. Asn. Management of research and development programs. Address: National Aeronautics & Space Council, Executive Office of the President, Washington, DC 20502.

GILBERT, RICHARD C(ARL), b. Ft. Wayne, Ind, Sept. 15, 27; m. 56; c. 3. MATHEMATICS. A.B, Harvard, 51; fel, California, Los Angeles, 51-53, Ph.D.(math), 58. Asst, California, Los Angeles, 53-55, acting instr. MATH, Riverside, 55-57, acting asst. prof, 57-58, asst. prof, 58-63; assoc. prof, CALIF. STATE COL. FULLERTON, 63-67, PROF, 67- Vis. asst. prof, Univ. Chicago, 61-62; vis. assoc. prof, math. res. ctr, Univ. Wis, 62-63. U.S.A, 45-46. Am. Math. Soc; Math. Asn. Am; Am. Sci. Affiliation. Spectral theory of linear operators. Address: Dept. of Mathematics, California State College at Fullerton, 800 N. State College Blvd, Fullerton, CA 92631.

GILBERT, R(ICHARD) D(EAN), b. Winnipeg, Man, Mar. 14, 20; nat; m. 44; c. 1. ORGANIC CHEMISTRY. B.Sc, Manitoba, 42, M.Sc, 43; Ph.D, Notre Dame, 50. Jr. res. chemist, Polymer Corp, 46-47, res. chemist, 50-51; Ky. Synthetic Rubber Corp, 51-55; group leader, chem. div, U.S. Rubber Co, 55-60, sect. mgr. synthetic rubber & latex, 60-66; assoc. prof. TEXTILE CHEM, N.C. STATE UNIV, 66-68, PROF, 68- Am. Chem. Soc; N.Y. Acad. Sci. High polymers. Address: 713 Dartmouth Rd, Raleigh, NC 27609.

GILBERT, RICHARD E(ARLE), b. Brooklyn, N.Y, Jan. 24, 33; m. 57; c. 5. CHEMICAL ENGINEERING. B.S, Worcester Polytech, 54; Ph.D.(chem eng), Princeton, 59. Asst. prof. CHEM. ENG, UNIV. NEBR, 58-63, assoc. prof, 63-69, PROF, 69- Am. Chem. Soc; Am. Inst. Chem. Eng; Am. Soc. Eng. Educ. Address: Dept. of Chemical Engineering, University of Nebraska, Lincoln, NE 68508.

GILBERT, RICHARD G(ENE), b. Holdenville, Okla, Dec. 3, 35; m. 59; c. 2. SOIL MICROBIOLOGY, PLANT PATHOLOGY. B.S, Colorado State, 61, M.S, 63, Ph.D.(plant path), 64. Res. scientist, soils lab, U.S. DEPT. AGR, Md, 64-71, RES. MICROBIOLOGIST, U.S. WATER CONSERV. LAB, SOIL & WATER CONSERV. RES. DIV, AGR. RES. SERV, ARIZ, 71- U.S.A, 54-57, Res, 57-62. Am. Phytopath. Soc; Soil Sci. Soc. Am; Am. Soc. Agron. Environmental ecology; water microbiology; soil biochemistry; nitrogen transformations in soil; eutrophication. Address: U.S. Water Conservation Lab, Soil & Water Conservation Research Division, Agriculture Research Service, U.S. Dept. of Agriculture, 4331 E. Broadway, Phoenix, AZ 85040.

GILBERT, RICHARD L(APHAM), JR, b. Schenectady, N.Y, Oct. 5, 16; m. 39; c. 3; m. 55; c. 1. CHEMISTRY. B.Chem, Cornell, 38. Chem. microscropist, Am. Cyanamid Co, 38-44, res. chemist, 44-48; Lion Oil Co, 48-50; res. chemist, AM. CYANAMID CO, 50-55, GROUP LEADER process develop, 55-62, PHOSPHORUS & NITROGEN RES, 62- Am. Chem. Soc; Am. Inst. Chem. Eng. Product and process development; fertilizers; phosphate and nitrogen feed supplements. Address: Agricultural Division, American Cyanamid Co, P.O. Box 400, Princeton, NJ 08540.

GILBERT, ROBERT A(RTHUR), b. Chicago, Ill, May 8, 23; m. 46; c. 4. PHYSICAL & INORGANIC CHEMISTRY. A.B, Wabash Col, 45; univ. fel, Ohio State, 47-48, Abbott Labs. fel, 48-49, Ph.D.(chem), 53. Prin. chemist, Battelle Mem. Inst, 49-56; RES. CHEMIST, OAK RIDGE NAT. LAB, 56- Mem. calorimetry Conf. Thermodynamics of solubility of metastable crystalline beryllium hydroxide; preparation of rare metals; preparation and properties of rare metal halides; calorimetry; fused salt thermodynamics. Address: 113 Cumberland View Dr, Oak Ridge, TN 37830.

GILBERT, R(OBERT) J(AMES), b. Morristown, Tenn, Dec. 14, 23; m. 47; c. 5. MECHANICAL ENGINEERING. B.S, Tennessee, 48. Engr, nylon tech, E.I. DU PONT DE NEMOURS & CO, INC, 49-52, res. engr, Dacron tech, 52-53, group supvr. tech. & process, 53-56, res. supvr. Dacron res, 56-57, tech. supvr, 57-62, sr. supvr. SPUNBONDED RES. & DEVELOP, 62-69, PROD. PLANNING SUPVR, 69- U.S.A.A.F, 42-46, 1st Lt. Am. Inst. Chem. Eng. Polymer gear meter pumps; spinning and drawing of nylon continuous filament yarn; polymerization; spinning and drawing of Dacron; staple and continuous filament yarn; processes for spunbonded webs. Address: 802 Nella Dr, Goodlettsville, TN 37072.

GILBERT, ROBERT L, b. Chicago, Ill, Jan. 28, 31; m. 55; c. 2. SOLID STATE PHYSICS. B.S, Ill. Inst. Tech, 55, M.S, 58, Ph.D.(physics), 67. Physicist, Admiral Corp, 55-57; proj. physicist, Nuclear-Chicago Corp, 58-62; asst. prof. PHYSICS, NORTHEAST. ILL. UNIV, 66-69, ASSOC. PROF, 69-, CHMN. DEPT, 70- Consult, solid state div, Oak Ridge Nat. Lab, 66, fel, 67-68. U.S.N.A.F.R, 49-57. Am. Inst. Physics. Theory of in alkali-halides. Address: Dept. of Physics, Northeastern Illinois University, Bryn Mawr at St. Louis Ave, Chicago, IL 60625.

GILBERT, R(OBERT) P(ERTSCH), b. New York, N.Y, Jan. 8, 32; m. 55; c. 1. MATHEMATICS. B.S, Brooklyn Col, 52; M.S.(math), & M.S.(physics), Carnegie Inst. Tech, 55, Ph.D.(math), 58. Instr. MATH, Pittsburgh, 57-59, asst. prof, 59-60; Mich. State, 60-61; Maryland, 61-64, res. assoc. prof, 64-65; PROF, Georgetown Univ, 65-66; IND. UNIV, BLOOMINGTON, 66- Ed-in-chief, Applicable Anal. Am. Math. Soc; Soc. Indust. & Appl. Math. (ed, J. Math. Anal). Classical analysis; functions of several complex variables; partial differential equations; complex analysis; numerical analysis. Address: Dept. of Mathematics, Indiana University, Bloomington, IN 47401.

GILBERT, ROBERT PETTIBONE, b. Chicago, Ill, Sept. 29, 17; m. 43; c. 6. INTERNAL MEDICINE. B.A, Haverford Col, 38; M.D, Northwestern, 43. Resident & fel, Univ. Hosp, Stanford, 46-48; clin. asst, instr. & assoc. med, med. sch, Northwest. Univ, 50-55, asst. prof, 55-59, assoc. prof, 59-65; ASSOC. PROF. MED. & ASSOC. DEAN, JEFFERSON MED. COL, THOMAS JEFFERSON UNIV, 65- Markle scholar, 52-57; res. assoc, Univ. Minn, 56-57; sr. staff physician, Vet. Admin. Res. Hosp, 54-56; dir. educ. & res, Evanston Hosp, 57. U.S.N, 43-46. Soc. Exp. Biol. & Med; Am. Physiol. Soc; Am. Med. Asn; Am. Heart Asn; Am. Fedn. Clin. Res. Myocardial infarction; cardiogenic shock; bacteremic shock; microcirculation; administration. Address: Jefferson Medical College, 1025 Walnut St, Philadelphia, PA 19107.

GILBERT, RONALD E, b. Altus, Okla, Jan. 7, 29; m. 48; c. 2. ORGANIC CHEMISTRY. B.S, Bethany-Nazarene Col, 50; Ph.D.(chem), Texas, 62. Res. chemist, Dow Chem. Co, 52-55, sr. res. chemist, 58-62; res. chemist, Spencer Chem. Div, GULF OIL CORP, MERRIAM, 62-71, SECT. SUPVR, PLASTICS DIV, 71- Am. Chem. Soc. Reactions of chlorinated hydrocarbons; oxidation of hydrocarbons. Address: 9642 Beverly, Overland Park, KS 66207.

GILBERT, SEYMOUR GEORGE, b. Orange, N.J, Mar. 24, 14; m. 39; c. 4. PACKAGING SCIENCE. B.S, Rutgers, 35, M.S, 38, Ph.D.(plant physiol), 41. Asst. bot, Rutgers, 36-39, plant physiol, 39-41, res. assoc. pomol, 41-42; assoc. plant physiologist, field lab, tung invest, U.S. Dept. Agr, 42-51; sr. chemist in charge malt res. sect, Pabst Brewing Co, 51-58; lab. mgr. & staff asst. to res. & develop. dir, Milprint, Inc, 58-60, res. mgr, 60-63, corporate tech. dir, 63-65; PROF. PACKAGING SCI, RUTGERS UNIV, 65- Instr, Univ. Fla, 46-51. Am. Chem. Soc. Packaging; enzyme technology; plant biochemistry. Address: 76 N. Ross Hall Blvd, Piscataway, NJ 08854.

GILBERT, THEODORE W(ILLIAM), JR, b. Attleboro, Mass, Nov. 4, 29. ANALYTICAL CHEMISTRY. B.S, Mass. Inst. Tech, 51; Ph.D.(chem), Minnesota, 56. Res. chemist, Oak Ridge Nat. Lab, 56-57; asst. prof. chem, Pa. State Univ, 57-60; ASSOC. PROF. ANAL. CHEM, UNIV. CINCINNATI, 60- Mem. staff, Brookhaven Nat. Lab, 66-67. Am. Chem. Soc. Spectrophotometric methods of analysis; trace analysis; analytical solvent extraction. Address: Dept. of Chemistry, University of Cincinnati, Cincinnati, OH 45221.

GILBERT, T(HOMAS) L(EWIS), b. Topeka, Kans, Nov. 24, 22; m. 46; c. 3. THEORETICAL PHYSICS. B.S, Calif. Inst. Tech, 44, M.S, 49; Ph.D.(theoret. physics), Ill. Inst. Tech, 56. Asst, Armour Res. Found, 44-46, asst. physicist, 47-49, assoc. physicist, 49-56, res. physicist, 56; asst. physicist, ARGONNE NAT. LAB, 56-58, ASSOC. PHYSICIST, 58- Am. Phys. Soc. Electronic structure of atoms, molecules and solids; interatomic forces. Address: Argonne National Lab, 223 M113, Argonne, IL 60439.

GILBERT, WALTER, b. Boston, Mass, Mar. 21, 32; m. 53; c. 2. MOLECULAR BIOLOGY. B.A, Harvard, 53, Nat. Sci. Found. fel, 53-57, M.A, 54; Ph.D.(math), Cambridge, 57. Nat. Sci. Found. fel. physics, HARVARD, 57-58, lectr. & res. fel, 58-59, asst. prof, 59-64, assoc. prof. biophys, 64-69, PROF. MOLECULAR BIOL, 69- Am. Phys. Soc; Am. Soc. Biol. Chem. Quantum field theory and elementary particles; protein synthesis; biophysics. Address: Biological Labs, Harvard University, Cambridge, MA 02138.

GILBERT, WALTER W(ILSON), b. Johnson City, Tenn, July 10, 22; m. 50; c. 2. ORGANIC CHEMISTRY. B.S, Ga. Inst. Tech, 44, M.S, 47; Ph.D. (chem), Wisconsin, 50. Jr. chem. engr, Tenn. Eastman Corp, 44; res. chemist, CENT. RES. DEPT, EXP. STA, E.I. DU PONT DE NEMOURS & CO, 50-63, supvr. mat. res, 63-67, res. mgr, develop. dept, 67-70, MGR. CHEM. RES. SECT, ELECTROCHEM. DEPT, 70- U.S.N.R, 44-46, Lt.(jg). Am. Chem. Soc. Reactions under high pressure; catalysis; inorganic crystal growth; tropolone; magnetic materials; compositions for hybrid circuits, industrial chemicals. Address: Route 2, Box 351, Berkeley Ridge, Hockessin, DE 19707.

GILBERT, WILLIAM BEST, b. Berea, Ky, Feb. 13, 21; m. 48; c. 2. AGRONOMY. B.S, Berea Col, 42; M.S, Kentucky, 52; Ph.D.(physiol, ecol), N.C. State, 56. Teacher, pub. schs, Ky, 45-50; asst, Kentucky, 50-52; N.C. STATE UNIV, 52-55, asst. prof. TURF MGT, 58-63, ASSOC. PROF, 63- Consult, Univ. N.C. mission, Peru, 55-58. U.S.A, 42-46, Capt. Am. Soc. Agron. Address: Dept. of Crop Science, North Carolina State University, Raleigh, NC 27607.

GILBERT, W(ILLIAM) D(OUGLAS), b. Kingston, Ont, Feb. 13, 10; m. 40; c. 3. MECHANICAL ENGINEERING. B.Sc, Queen's (Ont), 32; S.M, Mass. Inst. Technol, 35. Lectr. MECH. ENG, QUEEN'S UNIV.(ONT), 46-49, asst. prof, 49-51, assoc. prof, 51-59, PROF, 59-, head dept, 59-69. Summers, H.G. Acres & Co. Consult. Engrs, 49-55; civilian atomic power dept, Can. Gen. Elec. Co, 56-59; mem, Atomic Energy of Can. Ltd, Ont, 69-70. Can. Army, 39-45. Two phase fluid flow; thermodynamics. Address: Dept. of Mechanical Engineering, Queen's University, Kingston, Ont, Can.

GILBERT, W(ILLIAM) I(RWIN), b. Phila, Pa, Mar. 6, 15; m. 46; c. 2. ORGANIC CHEMISTRY. B.S, Pa. State Col, 36; A.M, Princeton, 38, Ph.D. (org. chem), 39. Instr. chem, West. Md. Col, 39-40; res. chemist, GULF RES. & DEVELOP. CO, 40-45, asst. head sect, new processes, 45-52, head petrochem. sect, 52-55, asst. dir. process div, 55-61, dir. petrochems. div, 61-68, mgr. Kansas City Lab, 68-71, DIR. PETROCHEMS. DIV, 71- AAAS; Am. Chem. Soc. Petroleum refining; petrochemicals. Address: Gulf Research & Development Co, Box 2038, Pittsburgh, PA 15230.

GILBERT, WILLIAM J(AMES), b. Shelton, Wash, Feb. 10, 16; m. 42; c. 4. BOTANY. B.S, Washington (Seattle), 38; M.S, Michigan, 39, Ph.D.(bot), 42. Asst. bot, Michigan, 38-40, fel, 40-42; res. biologist, Commerical Solvents Corp, Ind, 43-46; asst. prof. BIOL, ALBION COL, 46-48, assoc. prof, 48-57, PROF, 57-, ASSOC. ACAD. DEAN, 71-, chmn. dept. biol, 57-71, chmn. div. sci. & math, 62-65, dir. summer hon. col, 64. Coord, prog. marine biol, Great Lakes Col. Asn, 67-70. AAAS; Phycol. Soc. Am; Am. Inst. Biol. Sci; Int. Phycol. Soc. Morphology and taxonomy of cryptograms. Address: Dept. of Biology, Albion College, Albion, MI 49224.

GILBERT, W(ILLIAM) S(PENCER), b. New York, N.Y, May 25, 27; m. 56; c. 2. NUCLEAR PHYSICS. A.B, California, 48, Ph.D.(physics), 52. Physicist, radiation lab, California, 49-52; res. engr, atomic energy res. dept, N.Am. Aviation, Inc, 52-54; PHYSICIST, LAWRENCE RADIATION LAB, UNIV. CALIF, BERKELEY, 54- U.S.N.R, 45-46. Am. Phys. Soc; Am. Nuclear Soc. Accelerator design; radioactivity problems; shielding; experimental areas; superconductivity; cryogenics; superconducting magnets. Address: Lawrence Radiation Lab, University of California, Berkeley, CA 94720.

GILBERT, W(ILLIAM) W(AYNE), b. Greeley, Colo, Nov. 6, 09; m. 34, 50; c. 2. MECHANICAL ENGINEERING. B.S, Colorado, 31; M.S, Michigan, 32, Sc.D, 35. Faculty res. proj, Michigan, 32-34, instr. metal processing, 34-38, asst. prof, 38-42, assoc. prof, 42-50, prof. prod. eng, 50-54; consult, GEN. ELEC. CO, 54-55, MGR. MACHINING DEVELOP, 55-, surplus machine tool & equip. prog, 55-59. Dir. Civilian Pilot Training, 40. Metal cutting res, War Prod. Bd. Am. Soc. Eng. Educ; fel. Am. Soc. Mech. Eng; fel. Am. Soc. Metals; Soc. Mfg. Eng. Machinability of metals; teaching production engineering. Address: Room 143, Machining Development Lab, Bldg. 69, General Electric Co, Schenectady, NY 12305.

GILBERTSEN, VICTOR A(DOLPH), b. Winona, Minn, Nov. 4, 24; m. 48. SURGERY, CANCER. B.A, Hamline, 48; B.S, Minnesota, Minneapolis, 50, M.B, 52, M.D, 53, M.S, 57. Instr. surg, med. sch, UNIV. MINN, MINNEAPOLIS, 58-60, ASST. PROF. SURG, 60-71, GRAD. SCH, 61-, ASSOC. PROF, HEALTH SCI. CTR, 71-, DIR. CANCER DETECTION CTR, 60- Dipl, Am. Bd. Surg. U.S.A, 43-45. AAAS; Am. Col. Surg; Asn. Acad. Surg; Int. Union Against Cancer; Accademia Tiberina; Am. Med. Asn; Asn. Am. Med. Cols. Cancer detection, control and treatment; medical education. Address: Dept. of Surgery, University Health Sciences Center, University of Minnesota, 412 Union St. S.E, Minneapolis, MN 55455.

GILBERTSON, DONALD EDMUND, b. Whitehall, Wis, Oct. 22, 34; m. 57; c. 2. PARASITOLOGY, MEDICAL MALACOLOGY. B.S, Wis. State, 59; M.S, S.Dak. State, 62; Ph.D.(zool), Cincinnati, 66. Asst. zool, S.Dak. State, 60-62; Cincinnati, 62-65; res. fel. med. parasitol, sch. pub. health, Harvard, 66-68; ASST. PROF. ZOOL, UNIV. MINN, MINNEAPOLIS, 68- C.Eng, U.S.A, 53-55. AAAS; Am. Soc. Trop. Med. & Hyg; Am. Soc. Parasitol. Host parasite relationships; protein and nucleic acid metabolism of mollusks; control of disease bearing snails; biochemistry of mollusk body fluids. Address: Dept. of Zoology, College of Biological Sciences, University of Minnesota, Minneapolis, MN 55455.

GILBERTSON, JOHN R, b. Bemidji, Minn, Oct. 17, 29; m. 53; c. 3. BIOCHEMISTRY. B.A, Minnesota, 51, M.S, 55, Ph.D.(physiol), 60. Instr. physiol, Minnseota, 58-60; Nat. Insts. Health res. fel, Harvard Med. Sch, 60-62, res. assoc. BIOCHEM, 62-63; asst. prof, UNIV. PITTSBURGH, 63-68, assoc. res. prof, 68-69, ASSOC. PROF, 69- Nat. Insts. Health career develop. award, 66-71. U.S.N, 51-53. AAAS; Am. Chem. Soc; Int. Asn. Dent. Res. Lipid chemistry and biochemistry; cardiovascular physiology and physiology of exercise. Address: Dept. of Physiology & Pharmacology, School of Dental Medicine, University of Pittsburgh, Pittsburgh, PA 15213.

GILBERTSON, L(YLE) I(THIEL), b. Beloit, Wis, July 10, 03; m. 30; c. 3. INORGANIC CHEMISTRY. A.B, Augustana Col.(S.Dak), 25; A.M, Wisconsin, 26; Am. Silver Producers fel, Indiana, 37-38, Ph.D.(inorg. chem), 40. Asst. chem, Augustana Col.(S.Dak), 24-25; instr, Carleton Col, 26-27; State Col. Wash, 27-37, asst. prof, 38-42, 46; res. supvr. div. war res, Columbia, 42-45, res. supvr. & div. dir. s.a.m. labs, Carbide & Carbon Chem. Corp, 45-46; supvr. inorg. chem. res, Air Reduction Sales Co, 46-48, coord, Air Reduction Co, Inc, 48-49, admin. mgr, res. & eng. dept, 49-51, Murray Hill Labs, 51-53, dir, 53-58, admin. dir, cent. res. labs, 58-63; res. mgt. consult, Gilbertson Assocs, Inc, N.J, 62-65, pres, 64-65; HEAD DEPT. CHEM, S.DAK. SCH. MINES & TECHNOL, 65-69, PROF, 69- Civilian with Off. Sci. Res. & Develop, 44. Am. Chem. Soc; fel. N.Y. Acad. Sci; Electrochem. Soc.(treas, 55-61, v.pres, 61-64, pres, 64-65); fel. Am. Inst. Chem. Inorganic industrial chemicals; industrial gases; laboratory administration. Address: 1215 St. Andrew St, Rapid City, SD 57701.

GILBERTSON, ROBERT L(EE), b. Hamilton, Mont, Jan. 15, 25; m. 48; c. 2. MYCOLOGY, FOREST PATHOLOGY. B.A, Univ. Mont, 49; M.S, Washington (Seattle), 51; Ph.D.(mycol), State Univ. N.Y, 54. Asst, State Univ. N.Y. Col. Forestry, Syracuse, 51-54; asst. prof. forestry, Idaho, 54-59; asst. prof. forest bot, State Univ. N.Y. Col. Forestry, Syracuse, 59-61, assoc. prof, 61-67; PROF. PLANT PATH, UNIV. ARIZ, 67- Vis. assoc. prof, biol. sta, Univ. Mont, 64, 66; Univ. Minn, 70; consult, U.S. Forest Serv, 57- U.S.A, 43-46. Mycol. Soc. Am; Soc. Am. Foresters. Taxonomy of woodrotting fungi of North America. Address: Dept. of Plant Pathology, University of Arizona, Tucson, AZ 85721.

GILBERTSON, TERRY JOEL, b. La Crosse, Wis, May 18, 39; m. 67; c. 1. BIOCHEMISTRY, ORGANIC CHEMISTRY. B.S, Wis. State Univ, La Crosse, 62; Ph.D.(org. chem), Univ. Minn, Minneapolis, 67. Trainee BIOCHEM, Univ. Minn, St. Paul, 67-68; ASST. PROF, S.DAK. STATE UNIV, 68- Am. Chem. Soc. Biosynthesis of natural products; mechanisms and models of enzyme action. Address: Dept. of Pharmacy, South Dakota State University, Brookings, SD 57006.

GILBOE, DANIEL PIERRE, b. Amboy, Ill, Dec. 29, 34; m. 61. BIOCHEMISTRY. B.Sc, Wisconsin, Madison, 56, M.Sc, 59; Ph.D.(biochem), Minnesota, 67. Chemist, Minn. Mining & Mfg. Co, 56; res. chemist, Archer-Daniels-Midland Co, Minn, 60-63; res. assoc, Dept. Dairy Sci, Illinois, Urbana, 67-

68; RES. BIOCHEMIST, VET. ADMIN. HOSP, 68- AAAS; Am. Chem. Soc. Nutrition of parenteral infusion; amino acid metabolism; metabolic regulation in mammals and bacteria; reaction of chemotherapeutic antibiotics and DNA; enzymes of glycogen synthesis; degradation and regulation. Address: Veterans Administration Hospital, 54th St. & 48th Ave. S, Minneapolis, MN 55417.

GILBOE, DAVID D(OUGHERTY), b. Richland Center, Wis, July 13, 29; m. 51; c. 2. BIOCHEMISTRY, PHYSIOLOGY. B.A, Miami (Ohio), 51; M.S, Wisconsin, 55, Ph.D.(biochem), 58. Res. asst. biochem, UNIV. WIS, MADISON, 55-58, instr. physiol. chem. & surg, 58-61, asst. prof, 61-65, PHYSIOL. & SURG, 65-67, ASSOC. PROF, 67- Fulbright lectr. Univ. Chile, 70. U.S.N, 51-54, Res, 54-, Comdr. AAAS; Am. Chem. Soc; Am. Physiol. Soc; Am. Inst. Chem; N.Y. Acad. Sci. Biochemistry of brain function; transport of metabolites and intermediary metabolism of carbohydrates and amino acids in the central nervous system. Address: Dept. of Surgery, University Hospitals, University of Wisconsin, Madison, WI 53706.

GILBREATH, SIDNEY GORDON, III, b. Atlanta, Ga, Aug. 11, 31; m. 57; c. 3. INDUSTRIAL ENGINEERING. B.S, Tennessee, 58, M.S, 62; Nat. Sci. Found. trainee, Ga. Inst. Tech, 66-67, Ph.D.(indust. eng), 67. Indust. engr, Robertshaw Corp, 59-60; sales engr, Wallace & Tiernan Inc, 60-61; civil engr, Tenn. Valley Auth, 61-62; instr. INDUST. ENG, Ga. Inst. Tech, 62-66; asst. prof, Va. Polytech. Inst, 67-68; assoc. prof, TENN. TECHNOL. UNIV, 68-70, PROF, 70-, CHMN. DEPT, 69- U.S.N, 51-54. Am. Soc. Qual. Control; Am. Inst. Indust. Eng; Am. Soc. Eng. Educ. Statistical sampling; methods engineering; engineering economy. Address: Dept. of Industrial Engineering, Box 5011, Tennessee Technological University, Cookeville, TN 38501.

GILBREATH, WILLIAM P(OLLOCK), b. Portland, Ore, Nov. 10, 36; m. 65; c. 2. INORGANIC CHEMISTRY. B.A, Reed Col, 58; Ph.D.(inorg. chem), Univ. Wash, 62. RES. SCIENTIST, AMES RES. CTR, NASA, 62- Gen. partner, Oceanic Discoveries, Hawaii, 68. Am. Chem. Soc; The Chem. Soc; Am. Vacuum Soc. Gas-surface interactions particularly adsorption, desorption, electron desorption, high temperature oxidation, surface diffusion and catalysis studies. Address: Ames Research Center, NASA, Moffett Field, CA 94035.

GILBRECH, DONALD ALBERT, b. Holly Grove, Ark, Apr. 12, 27; m. 49; c. 2. ENGINEERING MECHANICS. B.S.I.E, Arkansas, 53, M.S, 54; Southern Fellowships Fund grant, Purdue, 56-58, Ph.D.(mech. eng), 58. Instr. ENG. MECH, UNIV. ARK, FAYETTEVILLE, 53-55, asst. prof, 55-56, assoc. prof, 58-63, PROF, 63- U.S.A.A.F, 45-46, C.Eng, 46-47, Res, 47-55, 2nd Lt. Am. Soc. Mech. Eng. Fluid mechanics, especially instrumentation, acoustics, pulsating flow, and gas dynamics; experimental stress analysis; engineering science. Address: Dept. of Engineering Science, University of Arkansas, Fayetteville, AR 72701.

GILBY, ANTHONY CHRISTOPHER, b. Sale, Eng, Feb. 26, 37; c. 1. PHYSICAL CHEMISTRY, SPECTROSCOPY. B.Sc, London, 58, Ph.D.(spectros), 62. Res. fel, sch. molecular spectros, Minnesota, Minneapolis, 62-64; sr. res. fel. far infrared spectros, Nat. Phys. Lab, Teddington, Eng, 65-66, magnetic circular dichroism, 66-68; DIR. RES, WILKS SCI. CORP, 68-, V.PRES, 70-, dir. eng. anal. instrumentation, 68-70. Consult, Wilks Sci. Corp, 64. Optical Soc. Am. High-resolution electronic spectroscopy; determination of infrared optical constants using attenuated total reflection; construction of high-resolution infrared spectrometer; far infrared spectroscopy with Michelson interferrometer; magnetic circular dichroism; design and development of infrared analyzers and accessories. Address: Wilks Scientific Corp, 140 Water St, South Norwalk, CT 06856.

GILCHRIST, BRUCE, b. Pontefract, Eng, Aug. 4, 30; nat; m. 54; c. 3. COMPUTER SCIENCES. B.Sc, London, 50, Ph.D.(meteorol), 52. Vis. meteorologist, Inst. Adv. Study, 52-54, mem. staff, 54-56; asst. prof. math. & dir. comput. center, Syracuse, 56-59; mgr. programming & comput, res. center, Int. Bus. Mach, 59-61, dir, systs. eng. prog, corporate staff, 61-63; planning, Serv. Bur. Corp, 63-65; mgr. sci. opers, IBM Data Processing Div, 65-68; EXEC. DIR, AM. FEDN. INFO. PROCESSING SOCS, INC, 68- Consult, U.S. Weather Bur, 55-59; U.S. Office Educ, 71-; mem. panel weather & river serv, Nat. Acad. Sci/Nat. Acad. Eng. comt. adv. Environ. Sci. Serv. Admin, 68-69; panel nat. progs. comput. sci. & eng. bd, Nat. Acad. Sci, 68-69. AAAS; Asn. Comput. Mach.(secy, 60-62, v.pres, 62-64); Am. Math. Soc; Am. Meteorol. Soc; Soc. Indust. & Appl. Math; Inst. Elec. & Electronics Eng; Royal Meteorol. Soc; Am. Fedn. Info. Processing Soc. (pres, 66-68). Methods and applications of high speed computation; manpower and regulatory aspects of the computer industry. Address: 67 Cross Ridge Rd, Chappaqua, NY 10514.

GILCHRIST, RALPH E(DWARD), b. Milwaukee, Wis, Dec. 17, 26; m. 55; c. 3. PETROLEUM ENGINEERING. B.A, Denver, 47; B.S, Texas, 50, fel, 50-51, M.S, 51; Gulf Oil Corp. fel, Pa. State, 55-56, Ph.D.(petrol. & natural gas eng), 58. Res. engr. petrol. prod. res, Texaco, Inc, 51-52; res. assoc. petrol. & natural gas eng, Pa. State, 54-57; asst. proj. engr. petrol. prod. res, Sinclair Res. Labs, Inc, 57-59; res. engr, Phillips Petrol. Co, 59-66; sr. res. engr, prod. dept, TENNECO OIL CO, 66-69, DIR. PROD. RES, 69- Lectr, Univ. Tulsa, 59-60. U.S.A; U.S.A.F, Res, Capt.(Ret). Am. Inst. Mining, Metall. & Petrol. Eng; Am. Petrol. Inst; Am. Soc. Oceanog. Research on drilling, production, reservoir engineering, oil & gas recovery, ocean sciences and engineering, and energy resources. Address: Tenneco Oil Co, Box 2511, Houston, TX 77001.

GILDART, LEE WILLIAM, b. Albion, Mich, Oct. 24, 10; m. 41; c. 4. PHYSICS. B.S, Michigan, 36, M.S, 38; Ph.D, Northwestern, 50. Asst, Dow Chem. Co, 39-41; Michigan, 42-43; res. physicist, Beckman Instruments, 44; instr, Northwestern, 45-49; asst. prof. PHYSICS, N.C. State Col, 50-53; assoc. prof, Univ. Ky, 54-65; PROF, FAIRLEIGH DICKINSON UNIV, 65-, CHMN. DEPT, 70- Estab. solid state physics, Inst. Technol, Bandung, Indonesia, 60-63. Am. Phys. Soc. Solid state physics; group V and VI compounds; invention of stibnite crystal switch; quasi-metals; orbital overlap shifting. Address: Dept. of Physics, Fairleigh Dickinson University, Teaneck, NJ 07666.

GILDE, HANS-GEORG, b. Ger, July 8, 33; U.S. citizen; m. 57; c. 2. ORGANIC CHEMISTRY. B.S, Albright Col, 57; Ph.D.(org. chem), Ohio, 61; summers, Case, 62 & 63. Instr. chem, Ohio, 60-61; asst. prof. org. chem, MARIETTA COL, 61-64, assoc. prof, 64-70, PROF. CHEM, 70- Am. Chem. Soc; The Chem. Soc. Electrolytic generation of free radicals. Address: 134 Warner St, Marietta, OH 45750.

GIL de LAMADRID, JESÚS, b. San Juan, P.R, Aug. 20, 26; m. 50; c. 3. MATHEMATICS. B.S, Chicago, 48, M.S, 49; fel, Michigan, 53-55, Ph.D. (math), 55. Instr. MATH, Ohio State Univ, 55-57; asst. prof, UNIV. MINN, MINNEAPOLIS, 57-64, assoc. prof, 64-67, PROF, 67- Res. assoc. & lectr, Yale Univ, 61-62; vis. prof, Univ. Rennes, 71-72. Am. Math. Soc. Functional analysis. Address: School of Mathematics, University of Minnesota, Minneapolis, MN 55455.

GILDEN, RAYMOND V(ICTOR), b. Chicago, Ill, Aug. 4, 35; m. 57; c. 3. IMMUNOLOGY, GENETICS. A.B, California, Los Angeles, 57, U.S. Pub. Health Serv, fel. & M.A, 59, Ph.D.(zool), 62. U.S. Pub. Health Serv. fel, Calif. Inst. Tech, 62-63; assoc. mem, Wistar Inst, Pennsylvania, 63-65; V.PRES, RES. DIV, FLOW LABS, INC, 65- Tumor viruses. Address: Research Division, Flow Labs, Inc, 1710 Chapman Ave, Rockville, MD 20852.

GILDENHORN, HYMAN L, b. Cleveland, Ohio, May 27, 21; m. 55. MEDICINE, RADIOLOGY. B.S, Ohio State, 43, M.S, 47; M.D, Cornell, 51. Intern med, Michael Reese Hosp, Chicago, Ill, 51-52; resident radiol, 52-55; assoc. radiologist, CITY OF HOPE MED. CTR, 56-57, DIR, DEPT. DIAG. RADIOL, 57- Asst. clin. prof, Univ. South. Calif, 69- Dipl, Am. Bd. Radiol, 56. U.S.N, 44-46. Am. Med. Asn; Radiol. Soc. N.Am; Int. Col. Radiol. Physical factors related to diagnostic roentgenology; clinical research in diagnostic roentgenology; synergism of irradiation and cholesterol diet in production of arteriosclerotic lesions in animals. Address: Dept. of Diagnostic Roentgenolgy, City of Hope Medical Center, 1500 E. Duarte Rd, Duarte, CA 91010.

GILDER, HELENA, b. New York, N.Y, Nov. 11, 13; m. 48; c. 4. BIOCHEMISTRY. A.B, Vassar Col, 35; M.D, Cornell, 40. Asst. path, col. physicians & surgeons, Columbia, 35-36; vis. investr, Scripps Metab. Clin, 38-39; med. intern, Mary Imogene Bassett Hosp, Cooperstown, N.Y, 40-41; Mary Putnam Jacobi fel, Rockefeller Inst. Hosp, 41-42, asst. res, 42-45, Commonwealth fel, 42-45, Rockefeller fel, 44-45, vis. investr, 45-46; res. assoc. biochem, MED. COL, CORNELL UNIV, 46-53, ASST. PROF. BIOCHEM, 53-, ASSOC. PROF. SURG, 64-, asst. prof, 53-64. Career scientist, Health Res. Coun, 61-67. AAAS; Am. Chem. Soc; Harvey Soc; N.Y. Acad. Sci; Am. Med. Women's Asn. Metabolism of tumor tissue; water and electrolyte metabolism; gastric physiology; biochemistry of injury. Address: F702 Cornell University Medical College, 1300 York Ave, New York, NY 10021.

GILDERSLEEVE, BENJAMIN, b. Damascus, Va, June 7, 07; m. 44; c. 3. GEOLOGY. B.S, Virginia, 30, M.S, 31; Ph.D.(geol), Hopkins, 39. Field asst, Va. Geol. Surv, 30-33; jr. geologist, U.S. Geol. Surv, 34; asst. geologist, Tenn. Valley Authority, 34-38, assoc. geologist, 38-43, geologist, 43-49, chief regional minerals sect, 49-51; geologist, U.S. GEOL. SURV, 51-71, GEOLOGIST IN CHARGE, 71- AAAS; fel. Geol. Soc. Am. Geological mapping; geology of dam sites; economic geology; mineral resources. Address: U.S. Geological Survey, P.O. Box 1176, Bowling Green, KY 42101.

GILDERSLEEVE, RICHARD E, b. Flushing, N.Y, Aug. 17, 14; m. 48; c. 2. ELECTRICAL ENGINEERING. B.E.E, Rensselaer Polytech, 48; Ph.D. (elec. eng), Syracuse, 58. Eng. asst, Consol. Edison Co, 34-41; instr. ELEC. ENG, SYRACUSE UNIV, 48-58, asst. prof, 58-66, ASSOC. PROF, 66- Sig.C, 41-46, Capt. Inst. Elec. & Electronics Eng. Microwave antennas. Address: Dept. of Electrical and Computer Engineering, Syracuse University, Syracuse, NY 13210.

GILDSETH, WAYNE, b. Sioux Falls, S.Dak, July 10, 35; m. 60; c. 2. PHYSICAL CHEMISTRY. B.A, Augustana Col.(S.Dak), 57; Göttingen, 57-58; Ph.D. (phys. chem), Iowa State, 64. MEM. FACULTY CHEM, Pacific Lutheran Univ, 64-66; AUGUSTANA COL.(S.Dak), 66- Am. Chem. Soc. Electrolytic solution chemistry; ionic complexes; fused salt chemistry. Address: Dept. of Chemistry, Augustana College, Sioux Falls, SD 57102.

GILE, LELAND HENRY, b. Alfred, Maine, Feb. 23, 20; m. 47. SOIL GENESIS, SOIL CLASSIFICATION. B.S, Maine, 53; M.S, Wisconsin, 54. Conserv. aide, SOIL CONSERV. SERV, U.S. DEPT. AGR, 46-50, soil scientist, 55-57, RES. SOIL SCIENTIST, 57- U.S.A.A.F, 42-45, Sgt. AAAS; Soil Sci. Soc. Am. Soil genesis and classification. Address: Soil Conservation Service, U.S. Dept. of Agriculture, P.O. Box 3129, University Park, NM 88001.

GILES, EUGENE, b. Salt Lake City, Utah, June 30, 33; m. 64; c. 2. PHYSICAL ANTHROPOLOGY. A.B, Harvard, 55, A.M, 60, Ph.D.(anthrop), 66; M.A, California, Berkeley, 56. Instr. ANTHROP, Illinois, Urbana, 64-66; asst. prof, Harvard, 66-70; ASSOC. PROF, UNIV. ILL, URBANA-CHAMPAIGN, 70- Nat. Sci. Found. fel. demog, Australian Nat. Univ, 67-68. U.S.A, 56-58. Fel. Am. Anthrop. Asn; Am. Asn. Phys. Anthrop. Analysis of morphological variation in crania; demography, physical variation and genetic structure of noncosmopolitan human populations. Address: Dept. of Anthropology, University of Illinois, Urbana-Champaign, Urbana, IL 61801.

GILES, F(REDERICK) H(ARVEY), JR, b. Chicago, Ill, March 22, 27; m. 56; c. 3. PHYSICS. B.S, Wheaton Col.(Ill), 47; Ph.D, Illinois, 55. Instr. PHYSICS, Bowling Green State Univ, 54-57; ASSOC. PROF, UNIV. S.C, 57- Fulbright lectr, Baghdad, 65-66, vis. lectr, Univ. Tex. exchange prof. prog, 66-67. U.S.N, 45-46. Fel. AAAS; fel. Am. Sci. Affiliation; Am. Phys. Soc; Biophys. Soc; Electrochem. Soc; Am. Asn. Physics Teachers. Chemical physics, especially surface activity during electrolysis; biological physics. Address: Dept. of Physics, University of South Carolina, Columbia, SC 29208.

GILES, JESSE A(LBION), III, b. New Kensington, Pa, June 2, 31; m. 53; c. 3. ORGANIC CHEMISTRY. B.S, North Carolina, 53; Naval fel, Alabama, 53-

54, M.S, 55. Res. chemist, R.J. Reynolds Tobacco Co, 54-67, SECT. HEAD RES. DEPT, R.J. REYNOLDS INDUSTS, 67- Am. Chem. Soc.(abstractor, Chem. Abstr, 55-66). Chemistry of plant natural products; diterpenes; aliphatic sulfur and boron compounds; radiocarbon and tritium tracer techniques. Address: Research Dept, R.J. Reynolds Industries, Winston-Salem, NC 27101.

GILES, JOAN P(OTT), b. New York, N.Y, Oct. 19, 19; m. 42; c. 3. MEDICINE. A.B, Vassar Col, 40; Vassar Col. fel. & M.D, N.Y. Univ, 43. Intern, Staten Island Hosp, N.Y, 44; clinic physician, child health sta, City Dept. Health, N.Y, 46-49; private practice, 46-56; asst. prof. PEDIAT, SCH. MED, N.Y. UNIV, 58-62, RES. ASSOC. PROF, 62-, res. fel, 53-54. Res. grant, Army Epidemiol. Bd, 56-; clin. dir, Planned Parenthood Asn, Staten Island, N.Y, 46-52; Health Res. Coun, New York, career scientist, 63-69. Am. Epidemiol. Soc. Pediatric virology; infectious hepatitis; measles; poliomyelitis; polio and measles vaccine trials; natural history and prevention of infectious hepatitis; natural history and prevention of rubella. Address: Dept. of Pediatrics, Post Graduate School of Medicine, New York University, 5501 First Ave, New York, NY 10016.

GILES, JOHN CRUTCHLOW, b. London, Eng, Jan. 15, 34; m. 56; c. 2. PHYSICS. B.Sc, Sheffield, 55; Ph.D.(physics), Exeter, 58. Nat. Res. Coun. Can. fel, British Columbia, 58-60, instr. PHYSICS, 60-62, asst. prof, 62-63; lectr, Aberdeen, 63-64; asst. prof, CALIF. STATE COL, HAYWOOD, 64-65, assoc. prof, 65-70, PROF, 70- Am. Asn. Physics Teachers. Solid state physics; semiconducting substances; optical and transport properties. Address: Dept. of Physics, California State College, Hayward, CA 94542.

GILES, LeROY W(ILLIAM), b. Rochester, N.Y, Aug. 19, 14; m. 34; c. 6. WILDLIFE MANAGEMENT. B.S, Arkansas, 37; M.S, Iowa State, 37-41. Wildlife technician, State Game & Fish Comn, Ark, 41-44; asst. refuge mgr, Sabine Refuge, U.S. FISH & WILDLIFE SERV, La, 45-49, Stillwater Wildlife Mgt. Area, 49-51, refuge mgr, 51-53, WILDLIFE MGT. BIOLOGIST, 53-55, Tule Lake N.W. Refuge, 56-57, RIVER BASIN STUDIES, 58- U.S.N, 45. Wildlife in water resource development. Address: Bureau of Sport Fisheries & Wildlife, P.O. Box 1306, Albuquerque, NM 87103.

GILES, NORMAN H(ENRY), b. Atlanta, Ga, Aug. 6, 15; m. 39, 69; c. 2. GENETICS. A.B, Emory, 37; M.A, Harvard, 38, Ph.D.(biol), 40. Parker fel, Harvard, 40-41; instr. bot, YALE, 41-45, asst. prof, 45-46, assoc. prof, 46-51, prof, 51-61, EUGENE HIGGINS PROF. GENETICS, 61- Prin. biologist, Oak Ridge Nat. Lab, 47-50; Fulbright & Guggenheim fels, Univ. Genetics Inst, Copenhagen, 59-60; Guggenheim fel, dept. genetics, Australian Nat. Univ, 66. Consult. biol, Oak Ridge Nat. Lab, 51-64; Brookhaven Nat. Lab, 56-64; genetics study sect, Nat. Insts. Health, 60-64, mem. genetics training comt, 66-70, res. career award comt. Nat. Acad. Sci; AAAS; fel. Am. Acad. Arts & Sci; Am. Soc. Nat; Genetics Soc. Am.(treas, 54-56, v.pres, 69, pres, 70); Bot. Soc. Am; assoc. Am. Ornith. Union. Genetics and cytology. Address: Dept. of Biology, Yale University, New Haven, CT 06520.

GILES, PETER C(OBB), b. Albany, Calif, Nov. 21, 29; m. 52; c. 3. PHYSICS. B.S, California, 52, M.S, 53, Ph.D.(physics), 58. SR. PHYSICIST, LAWRENCE RADIATION LAB, UNIV. CALIF, 58- Am. Phys. Soc. Nuclear physics; application of computers and numerical techniques to physical problems. Address: Lawrence Radiation Lab, University of California, P.O. Box 808, L-81, Livermore, CA 94551.

GILES, RALPH E, b. Rahway, N.J, Mar. 26, 41; m. 63; c. 4. PHARMACOLOGY, BIOCHEMISTRY. B.S, Fordham, 62; Ph.D.(pharmacol), Minnesota, 66. Asst. prof. pharmacol, Fordham, 66-68; SCIENTIST RESPIRATORY PHARMACOL, WARNER-LAMBERT RES. INST, 68- N.Y. Acad. Sci. Catecholamine metabolism; importance of catechol-o-methyl-transferase; uterine-inhibitory drugs; experimental production of emphysema; bronchodilators; respiratory pharmacology. Address: Warner-Lambert Research Institute, 170 Tabor Rd, Morris Plains, NJ 07950.

GILES, RICHARD A(LDEN), b. Cummington, Mass, Dec. 12, 17; m. 41; c. 3. BOTANY. B.S, Mass. State Col, 39; M.S, Mich. State Col, 41, Ph.D.(bot), 55. Plant mgr, Ashfield Div, Stanley Works, 41-47; asst. prof. BOT. & BIOL, EAST. MICH. UNIV, 47-54, assoc. prof, 54-57, PROF, 57-, HEAD DEPT. BIOL, 66- AAAS; Bot. Soc. Am; Am. Inst. Biol. Sci. Cytological and morphological studies of populations of trillium. Address: 118 Linden Place, Ypsilanti, MI 48197.

GILES, ROBERT H, JR, b. Lynchburg, Va, May 25, 33; m. 56; c. 2. ECOLOGY, WILDLIFE MANAGEMENT. B.S, Va. Polytech, 55, M.S, 58; Ph.D.(wildlife mgt), Ohio State, 64. Dist. biologist, Va. Comn. Game & Inland Fisheries, 58-60; asst. prof, wildlife mgt, Univ. Idaho, 63-67; ASSOC. PROF. FORESTRY, VA. POLYTECH. INST. & STATE UNIV, 67- U.S.A.R, 55-65, 1st Lt. Wildlife Soc. Conservation education evaluation; insecticide-ecology; forest ecology; computer simulation of ecological systems. Address: Dept. of Forestry, Virginia Polytechnic Institute & State University, Blacksburg, VA 24061.

GILES, ROBIN, b. London, Eng, Jan. 30, 26; m. 54; c. 3. MATHEMATICAL PHYSICS. B.Sc, Glasgow, 46, D.Sc.(foundations of thermodyn), 66. Asst. lectr. physics, Glasgow, 46-49, lectr, 49-64, sr. lectr, 64-66; assoc. prof. MATH, QUEEN'S UNIV.(ONT), 66-69, PROF, 69- Carnegie fel. physics, Inst. Theoret. Physics, Copenhagen, Denmark, 54-55; res. assoc. math, Tulane, 63-64. Kelvin Medal, Glasgow Univ, 68. London Math. Soc; Am. Math. Soc; Can. Math. Cong. Foundations of physics, especially thermodynamics and quantum mechanics. Address: Dept. of Mathematics, Queen's University, Kingston, Ont, Can.

GILES, WALDRON, b. Jersey City, N.J, Feb. 17, 32; m. 58; c. 1. PHYSICAL CHEMISTRY. B.S, Rutgers, 54; M.S, N.Y. Univ, 62, Ph.D, 63. Asst. res. scientist, N.Y. Univ, 58-63; sr. res. scientist, Bristol-Myers Prod. Div, N.J, 63-64; SUPV. ENGR. & PHYS. CHEMIST, VALLEY FORGE SPACE TECHNOL. CTR, GEN. ELEC. CO, 64- U.S.A. AAAS; Am. Chem. Soc; Am. Phys. Soc. Thermodynamics; non-aqueous reaction equilibria; rheology; kinetics solid state physics; shock propagation in polymers; computer applications to chemical and physical phenomona. Address: 1001 Townsend Circle, Wayne, PA 19087.

GILES, WILLIAM L(INCOLN), b. Oklahoma City, Okla, July 5, 11; m. 46; c. 3. BOTANY. B.S.A, Arkansas, 34, M.S, 35, L.L.D, 67; Ph.D.(bot), Missouri, 49. Nursery mgr, soil conserv. serv, U.S. Dept. Agr, Kans, 35-39, Beltsville, Md, 39-46; asst. instr, Missouri, 46-49; assoc. agronomist, Miss. State, 49-51; supt, delta br, exp. sta, 51-61; v.pres, DIV. AGR. & FORESTRY, MISS. STATE UNIV, 61-66, PRES, 66- Mem. cotton insects panel, Off. Sci. & Tech, 63-64. U.S.A, 42-46. Fel. AAAS; Am. Soc. Agron. Plant morphology; forage crops improvement. Address: Division of Agriculture & Forestry, Mississippi State University, State College, MS 39762.

GILETTI, BRUNO J(OHN), b. New York, N.Y, Dec. 6, 29; m. 53; c. 2. GEOCHEMISTRY. A.B, Columbia, 51, B.S, 52, fel, 53-54, M.A, 54, Ph.D.(geol), 57. Res. fel, Lamont Geol. Observ, Columbia, 57-58; dept. geol. & mineral, Oxford, 58-60; asst. prof. GEOL, BROWN UNIV, 60-62; assoc. prof, 62-67, PROF, 67- Am. Geol. Soc; Geochem. Soc; Am. Geophys. Union; Am. Chem. Soc. Absolute age determination of geological materials by isotopic analysis; distribution and abundance of radioactive and stable nuclides in the earth and their significance in geology and oceanography. Address: Dept. of Geological Sciences, Brown University, Providence, RI 02912.

GILFEATHER, FRANK L, b. Great Falls, Mont, Sept. 29, 42; m; c. 2. MATHEMATICS. B.A, Univ. Mont, 64, M.A, 66; Nat. Sci. Found. traineeship & Ph.D.(math), Univ. Calif, Irvine, 69. Assoc, Off. Naval Res, 69-70; ASST. PROF. MATH, UNIV. HAWAII, 70- Am. Math. Soc. Operator theory on Hilbert spaces. Address: Dept. of Mathematics, University of Hawaii, Honolulu, HI 96822.

GILFERT, JAMES C(LARE), b. Tamaqua, Pa, June 21, 27; m. 49; c. 3. ELECTRICAL ENGINEERING. B.S, Antioch Col, 50; Kettering Found. fel, Ohio State Univ, 50-51, M.Sc, 51, Ph.D.(physics), 57. Res. assoc, antenna lab, Ohio State Univ, 53-56, instr. ELEC. ENG, 57-58, asst. prof, 58-63, assoc. prof, 63-67; OHIO UNIV, 67-69, PROF. & CHMN. DEPT, 69- Sr. tech. specialist, N.Am. Aviation, Inc, 61-67; Am. Coun. Educ. fel, 71-72. U.S.N.R, 45-46. Inst. Elec. & Electronics Eng. Communications, electronic circuitry. Address: Dept. of Electrical Engineering, Ohio University, Athens, OH 45701.

GILFILLAN, ROBERT FREDERICK, b. Roanoke, Va, Oct. 30, 23; m. 51; c. 3. MICROBIOLOGY. B.A, Tennessee, 49, M.S, 50, Ph.D.(microbiol, biochem), 56. Asst. bact, Tennessee, 49-50, 54-55; bact. metab, Minnesota, 50-53; microbiologist, U.S. Dept. of Defense, Gen. Mills, Minn, 53-54; res. assoc. biol, Oak Ridge Nat. Lab, Tenn, 55-56; asst. prof. bact. & virol, Med. Col. S.C, 56-59; obstet. & gynec, med. sch, Tufts, 59-61; chief virol. unit, Found. Res. Nerv. Syst, 61-64; ASST. PROF. OBSTET. & GYNEC, TUFTS UNIV, 69-; CHIEF VIROLOGIST, ST. MARGARET'S HOSP, BOSTON, 64-, microbiologist, 59-61. Soc. Am. Bact. fel, sch. med, Yale, 57; res. assoc, sch. med, Univ. Boston, 61-64. U.S.A, 43-46. AAAS; Am. Soc. Microbiol. Virology; experimental pathology. Address: Dept. of Microbiology, Tufts University, Medford, MA 02155.

GILFOIL, THOMAS M(ARY), b. Springfield, Mass, Oct. 16, 22; m. 49; c. 4. PHYSIOLOGY. B.S, Hampden Col. Pharm, 52; M.S, Univ. Kansas City, 54; Ph.D.(physiol), Wisconsin, 58. Asst. pharmacol, Univ. Kansas City, 52-54; sch. med, Wisconsin, 55-58; instr. physiol, sch. med, West Virginia, 58-59; trainee neuropharmacol, res. labs, Vet. Admin, Pa, 59-60; res. assoc, Sterling-Winthrop Res. Inst, 60-63, res. biologist, 63-66; pharmacologist, div. pharmacol. & toxicol, Food & Drug Admin, 67-69; ASST. PROF. PSYCHIAT. & NEUROPHARMACOL, MED. SCH, UNIV. MO-ST. LOUIS, 69- U.S.A, 43-46. Am. Soc. Pharmacol. & Exp. Therapeut. Respiratory and circulatory reflexes; neuropharmacology; analgesics; inflammatory hyperesthesia. Address: University of Missouri Medical School, Missouri Institute of Psychiatry, St. Louis, MO 63139.

GILFORD, DOROTHY MORROW, b. Ottumwa, Iowa, Feb. 19, 19; m. 50. STATISTICS. B.S, Washington (Seattle), 40, fel, 40-42, M.S, 42; fel, Bryn Mawr Col, 43; Carnegie fel, Columbia, 44. Instr. math, Seattle Col, 42; lectr. statist, Bryn Mawr Col, 44-45; asst. prof, George Washington, 45-48; biometrician, Civil Aeronaut. Admin, 48-51; sampling expert, Fed. Trade Comn, 51-55; head, math. statist. br, OFF. NAVAL RES, 55-58, logistics & statist. br, 59-61, DIR, MATH. SCI. DIV, 62-, consult, 46-48. Res. assoc, North Carolina, 47-48; lectr, George Washington, 48-50; mem. adv. panel. math. sci, Nat. Sci. Found, 58-59; Inst. Math. Statist. rep. Conf. Bd. Math. Socs. Fed. Woman's award, 65. Fel. AAAS; Math. Soc; Soc. Indust. & Appl. Math; fel. Inst. Math. Statist; fel. Am. Statist. Asn; Inst. Mgt. Sci; fel. Royal Statist. Soc; Int. Statist. Inst. Multivariate statistical analysis; aviation biometry; sample survey methods; research administration. Address: Mathematical Sciences Division, Office of Naval Research, Washington, DC 20360.

GILFORD, LEON, b. Warsaw, Poland, Feb. 14, 17; nat; m. 50. MATHEMATICAL STATISTICS. A.B, Brooklyn Col, 39; A.M, George Washington, 49. Math. statistician, U.S. Bur. Census, 46-55, chief opers. res. & qual. control br, 55-60; sr. scientist, OPERS. RES, INC, 60-69, PRIN. SCIENTIST, 69- U.S.A, 42-46, Capt. Fel. AAAS; fel. Am. Statist. Asn; Inst. Math. Statist; Opers. Res. Soc. Am; Royal Statist. Soc; Inst. Mgt. Sci; Int. Asn. Statist. in Phys. Sci. Operations research; stochastic processes; mathematical models of military and space systems. Address: 6602 Rivercrest Ct, Washington, DC 20016.

GILFRICH, JOHN V(ALENTINE), b. Springfield, Mass, Sept. 14, 27; m. 54; c. 5. PHYSICAL & ANALYTICAL CHEMISTRY. B.A, Am. Int. Col, 49; George Washington, 54-56. Anal. chemist, Nat. Bur. Standards, 48-50, phys. chemist, 50-52; anal. chemist, U.S. Naval Ord. Lab, 52-60, phys. chemist, 60-66; res. chemist, NAVAL RES. LAB, 66-71, HEAD SPECTROCHEM. ANAL. SECT, X-RAY OPTICS BR, 71- U.S.A.A.F, 46-47. Am. Chem. Soc; fel. Am. Inst. Chem; Am. Crystallog. Asn; Sci. Res. Soc. Am; Electron Probe Anal. Soc. Am. General analytical chemistry and wet analysis, including application of x-ray diffraction and spectroscopy to analytical problems; application and study of x-ray physics. Address: Code 6681, Naval Research Lab, Washington, DC 20390.

GILGAN, MICHAEL WILSON, b. Burns Lake, B.C, Feb. 26, 38; m. 60; c. 2. BIOCHEMISTRY. B.Sc, British Columbia, 59, M.A, 62; Ph.D.(biochem), Wisconsin, 65. SR. SCIENTIST, HALIFAX LAB, FISHERIES RES. BD. CAN, 65- Am. Chem. Soc. Brain and smooth muscle phosphorylases; toxins of the mold Fusarium tricinctum; biochemistry and physiology of molt and sex hormones of crustaceans. Address: Fisheries Research Board, P.O. Box 429, Halifax, N.S, Can.

GILGORE, SHELDON G, b. Philadelphia, Pa, Feb. 13, 32; m. 56; c. 3. INTERNAL MEDICINE, ENDOCRINOLOGY. B.S, Villanova, 52; M.D, Jefferson Med. Col, 56. Intern med, hosp, Jefferson Med. Col, 56-57, res. internal med, 57-59, Nat. Insts. Health fel. endocrinol. & metab. disease, 59-61, instr. med, col, 61-63, assoc, 63; assoc. dir. clin. res, med. res. labs, Chas. Pfizer & Co, Inc, 63-65, dir. clin. pharmacol, 65-66, dir. dept. clin. res, 66-69, V.PRES. & MED. DIR, PFIZER PHARMACEUT, 69- Res. grants, Nat. Fund Med. Educ, 61-62, Nat. Sci. Found, 62-63. Nat. Guard, 57-, Capt. Am. Diabetes Asn; Am. Fedn. Clin. Res; assoc. fel. Am. Soc. Clin. Pharmacol. & Therapeut; N.Y. Acad. Sci. Carbohydrate metabolism in diabetes mellitus; lipid metabolism in diabetes mellitus and atherosclerosis; metabolic regulation of thyroid gland function. Address: Pfizer Pharmaceuticals, 235 E. 42nd St, New York, NY 10017.

GILGUT, C(ONSTANTINE) J(OSEPH), b. Athol, Mass, Mar. 11, 09; m. 33; c. 2. PLANT PATHOLOGY, HORTICULTURE. B.S, Mass. State Col, 31, M.S, 34; A.M, Harvard, 37, Ph.D.(biol), 42. Instr. bot, Mass. State Col, 31-34, exten. plant pathologist, 38-40, asst. plant path, hort. field sta. exp. sta, 34-38, 40-42, asst. res. prof. nurseryculture, 42-47; UNIV. MASS, 47-52, PROF. PLANT PATH, 52- Prof, Bunda Col. Agr, Univ. Malawi. Am. Phytopath. Soc. Diseases of fruit, vegetables, field crops and ornamentals; seed treatments; fungicides; canker of blue spruce and dogwood; apple scab control; strawberry virus; mycology. Address: Dept. of Plant Pathology, Fernald Hall, University of Massachusetts, Amherst, MA 01002.

GILHAM, PETER THOMAS, b. Sydney, Australia, Nov. 12, 30; m. 56; c. 3. ORGANIC CHEMISTRY, BIOCHEMISTRY. B.Sc, Sydney, 51, M.Sc, 53; Ph.D.(org. chem), New South Wales, 56. B.C. Res. Coun. fel, British Columbia, 56-58; Imp. Chem. Indust. res. fel. org. chem, Imp. Col, London, 58-59; lectr, Adelaide, 59-60; asst. prof, enzyme inst, Wisconsin, 60-62; assoc. prof. BIOL. SCI, PURDUE UNIV, 62-69, PROF, 69- Mem. subcomt. biol. chem, div. chem. & chem. technol, Nat. Acad. Sci-Nat. Res. Coun, 64-66. Am. Chem. Soc; Am. Soc. Biol. Chem. Stereo chemistry; nucleic acid structure and synthesis. Address: Dept. of Biological Sciences, Purdue University, Lafayette, IN 47907.

GILINSKY, VICTOR, b. Warsaw, Poland, May 28, 34; U.S. citizen; m. 64; c. 1. THEORETICAL PHYSICS. B.Eng.Phys, Cornell, 56; Nat. Sci. Found. fel. & Ph.D.(theoret. physics), Calif. Inst. Tech, 61. Mem. tech. staff, Aerospace Corp, 61; PHYS. SCIENTIST, RAND CORP, 61- Am. Phys. Soc; Inst. Strategic Studies. Many-body aspects of plasma physics; electromagnetic waves in the atmosphere; nuclear power technology; arms control; science and technology policy. Address: Rand Corp, 1700 Main St, Santa Monica, CA 90406.

GILINSON, PHILIP J(ULIUS), JR, b. Lowell, Mass, July 28, 14; m. 43; c. 2. ELECTRICAL ENGINEERING. B.S, Mass. Inst. Tech, 36, M.S, 52. Engr, Heinze Elec. Co, Mass, 36-38; Pacific Mills, Inc, 38-40; Doelcam Corp, 46-47; ELECTROMAGNETICS, INSTRUMENTATION LAB, MASS. INST. TECH, 47-54, asst. dir, 54-62; DEPUTY ASSOC. DIR, 62- U.S.A.A.F, 41-46, Lt. Col. Development and design of electromagentic devices in aeronautics and astronautics, particularly in the field of inertial guidance instrumentation systems; development of new precision measurement techniques in electromechanics; development of viscometer used in polymer chemistry and blood rheology research. Address: 8 Fuller Rd, Chelmsford, MA 01824.

GILJE, JOHN, b. Elkader, Iowa, Feb. 24, 39; m. 70. INORGANIC CHEMISTRY. B.Chem, Minnesota, 61; NASA trainee & Ph.D.(inorg. chem), Michigan, 65. Asst. prof. CHEM, UNIV. HAWAII, 65-69, ASSOC. PROF, 69- Am. Chem. Soc. Phosphorus, nitrogen and boron chemistry. Address: Dept. of Chemistry, University of Hawaii, Honolulu, HI 96822.

GILKERSON, W(ILLIAM) R(ICHARD), b. Greenville, S.C, June 5, 26; m. 56; c. 3. PHYSICAL CHEMISTRY. B.S, South Carolina, 49; Atomic Energy Cmn. fel, Kansas, 51-53, Ph.D.(chem), 53. Res. fel. CHEM, South Carolina, 53; Calif. Inst. Technol, 53-54; UNIV. S.C, 54-55, asst. prof, 55-59, assoc. prof, 59-66, PROF, 66- U.S.N, 44-46. Am. Chem. Soc. Conductance and dielectric properties of electrolytes in solution; ion pairing. Address: Dept. of Chemistry, University of South Carolina, Columbia, SC 29208.

GILKESON, (MURRAY) MACK, (JR), b. Augusta, Kans, Feb. 8, 22; m. 44; c. 4. CHEMICAL & METALLURGICAL ENGINEERING. B.E, Southern California, 44; M.S.(chem. eng), Kansas State Col, 47; Mich. Gas Asn. fel, 48; M.S.E, Michigan, 51, Ph.D.(chem. eng), 52. Cost acct, El Dorado Foundry, Inc, 46; asst. eng. res. inst, Michigan, 49-51; asst. prof. chem. eng, Tulane, 52-53, assoc. prof, 53-61; ENG, HARVEY MUDD COL, 61-64, PROF, 64- U.S.N.R, 43-46. Am. Chem. Soc; Am. Inst. Chem. Eng; Am. Soc. Eng. Educ. Reaction kinetics and mass transfer in contact catalysis; metal failures and corrosion; air pollution; overseas development. Address: Dept. of Engineering, Harvey Mudd College, Claremont, CA 91711.

GILKESON, RAYMOND A(LLEN), b. Sutherland, Nebr, Mar. 29, 21; m. 45; c. 3. SOIL SCIENCE. B.Sc, Nebraska, 49; M.Sc, Washington State, 51. Soil scientist, Soil Conserv. Serv, 51-53; from asst. soil scientist & asst. prof. soils to ASSOC. SOIL SCIENTIST & ASSOC. PROF. SOILS, WASH. STATE UNIV, 53- U.S.C.G.R, 42-45. Soil Sci. Soc. Am. Soil survey and classification; methods of soil survey of forest and range lands; airphoto interpretation. Address: 405 Johnson Hall, Washington State University, Pullman, WA 99163.

GILKEY, H(ERBERT) J(AMES), b. Montesano, Wash, Jan. 2, 90; m. 23; c. 2. CIVIL ENGINEERING, MECHANICS. B.S, Oregon State, 11; S.B, Mass. Inst. Tech, 16; B.S, Harvard, 16; M.S, Illinois, 23; hon. Sc.D, Buena Vista Col,

39. Asst. surveyor to Ore. state engr, 11; surveyor, U.S. Geol. Surv, 11-12; asst. construct. engr, State of Oregon, 13-14; asst. engr, track elevation, Pa. R.R, Ill, 16-17; struct. engr, A.R, Lord, Chicago, 19-20; asst. theoret. & appl. mech, Illinois, 21, instr, 22-23; from asst. prof. to prof. civil eng, Colorado, 23-31; PROF. THEORET. & APPL. MECH, IOWA STATE UNIV, 31-, head dept, 31-55. Testing engr, State Hwy. Dept, Colo, 23-31. Consult, Hoover Dam, U.S. Bur. Reclamation. Mem. Am. Relief Admin, Paris, 19; Hwy. Res. Bd, Nat. Acad. Sci-Nat. Res. Coun, 31-, joint comt. on specifications for concrete & reinforced concrete, 32-40. C.Eng, 17-19, Capt. Am. Soc. Civil Eng; hon. mem. Am. Soc. Test. & Mat; hon. mem. Am. Concrete Inst.(Wasson medal, 39, v.pres, 47, pres, 49, Turner gold medal, 59); Am. Soc. Eng. Educ.(v.pres, 43); Soc. Am. Mil. Eng. Concrete aggregates, curing and bond with steel; cement additions; properties and mechanics of engineering materials. Address: 212 Marston Hall, Iowa State University, Ames, IA 50010.

GILKEY, JOHN W(OODBURY), b. Ann Arbor, Mich, July 4, 16; m. 40; c. 4. CHEMISTRY. B.S, Antioch Col, 39; M.S, Michigan, 42. Chemist, Bryant Paper Co, Mich, 39-41; Dow Chem. Co, 42-47; DOW CORNING CORP, 47-54, res. supvr, 54-65, asst. to dir. develop, 65-70, STAFF MGR, RES. DEPT, 70- Am. Chem. Soc. Synthesis of organosilicon compounds and polymers; applications of organosilicon compounds to textiles, leather and as lubricants; synthesis and applications of organosilicon fluids. Address: Research Dept, Dow Corning Corp, Midland, MI 48640.

GILKEY, RUSSELL, b. Hopkinsville, Ky, Nov. 19, 20; m. 44; c. 2. ORGANIC CHEMISTRY. B.S, Kentucky, 43; Ph.D.(chem), Illinois, 49. Res. chemist, B.F. Goodrich Co, 43-45; sr. res. chemist, TENN. EASTMAN CO, 49-67, RES. ASSOC, 67- U.S.N.R, 45-46. Am. Chem. Soc. Polymers. Address: 1704 Springfield Ave, Kingsport, TN 37664.

GILL, ARTHUR, b. Haifa, Israel, Apr. 18, 30; U.S. citizen; m. 52; c. 2. ELECTRICAL ENGINEERING, COMPUTER SCIENCE. S.B, Mass. Inst. Tech, 55, S.M, 56; Ph.D.(elec. eng), California, Berkeley, 59. Res. engr, Raytheon Co, Mass, 56-57; asst. prof. elec. eng, UNIV. CALIF, BERKELEY, 59-64, assoc. prof, 64-70, PROF. ELEC. ENG. & COMPUT. SCI, 70-, RES. ENGR, ELECTRONICS RES. LAB, 57- Mem. adv. prog. develop. group, Bendix Aviation Corp, 58-60; consult, Kanput Indo-Am. Prog, U.S. Agency Int. Develop, 62-63; guest lectr, Int. Summer Sch. Automata Theory, Italy, 64; Guggenheim fel, 65-66. Inst. Elec. & Electronics Eng; Asn. Comput. Mach; Soc. Indust. & Appl. Math. Pattern recognition; automata theory; coding theory; computer organization and programming. Address: Dept. of Electrical Engineering & Computer Sciences, University of California, Berkeley, CA 94720.

GILL, A(TTICUS) J(AMES), b. Okmulgee, Okla, June 8, 14; c. 3. PATHOLOGY. M.D, Duke, 38. Intern PATH, Duke Hosp, 38-39, asst. resident, 40-41; resident, St. Paul Hosp, Texas, 39-40; instr, Univ. Tenn, 41-42, asst. prof, 42-43; UNIV. TEX.(SOUTHWEST) MED. SCH. DALLAS, 43-47, assoc. prof, 47-50, PROF, 50-, assoc. dean, 50-51, asst. dean bldg. & develop, 52-55, dean med. sch, 55-67. Fel. Am. Soc. Clin. Path; fel. Am. Med. Asn; fel. Col. Am. Path; Am. Col. Physicians. Histopathology; local eosinophilia in malignant neoplasms. Address: 7103 Lakewood Blvd, Dallas, TX 75214.

GILL, BENNINGTON P(EARSON), b. N.Y.C, Feb. 27, 98; m. 38; c. 5. MATHEMATICS. A.B. & B.S, City Col. New York, 17; A.M, Columbia, 18, Ph.D, 30. From asst. to assoc. prof, MATH, CITY COL. NEW YORK, 17-38, prof, 48-65, EMER. PROF, 65- Computer, Aberdeen Proving Grounds, 18. AAAS; Math. Asn. Am; Am. Math. Soc.(treas, 38-48). Approximation to algebraic functions by means of rational functions. Address: 53 Ross Ave, Demarest, NJ 07627.

GILL, C(HARLES) BURROUGHS, b. Sudbury, Ont, Apr. 8, 21; m. 55; c. 2. METALLURGICAL ENGINEERING. B.A.Sc, Toronto, 45; M.S, Mo. Sch. Mines, 47, Ph.D.(metall), 52. Res. metallurgist, Mo. Sch. Mines, 52-55; tech. supt, Deloro Smelting & Ref. Co, 55-57; PROF. METALL. ENG, LAFAYETTE COL, 57- Am. Soc. Metals; Am. Inst. Mining, Metall. & Petrol. Eng; Can. Inst. Min. & Metall. Extractive metallurgy and corrosion. Address: Dept. of Metallurgical Engineering, Lafayette College, Easton, PA 18042.

GILL, CLIFFORD C(RESSEY), b. Cape Town, S.Africa, Oct. 7, 21. PLANT PATHOLOGY. B.Sc, Cape Town, 42; Ph.D.(plant path), California, Berkeley, 64. Chem. analyst, Fuel Res. Inst, S.Africa, 45; control chem. analyst, Petersen, Ltd, 46-48; tech. adv, Kodak, Ltd, 48-56; control engr, Ont. Paper Co, Can, 56-57; anal. chemist, Gooch, Ltd, Calif, 57-58; RES. OFF, CAN. DEPT. AGR. RES. STA, 64- S.African Armoured Corps, 44-45. Am. Phytopath. Soc; Can. Phytopath. Soc; Bot. Soc. S.Africa; S.African Asn. Adv. Sci. Virus diseases of cereal crops. Address: Research Station, Canada Dept. of Agriculture, 25 Dafoe Rd, Winnipeg 19, Man, Can.

GILL, DENZELL L(EIGH), b. Leesville, La, Nov. 15, 09; m. 37; c. 2. PLANT PATHOLOGY. B.S, La. State, 31; fel, Cornell, 31-35, Ph.D.(plant path), 35. Instr. hort, col. agr, La. State, 35-37, asst. prof, 37-41; agent, U.S. DEPT. AGR, La, 41-42, assoc. pathologist, Ala, 46-50, pathologist, Ga, 50-68, RES. PLANT PATHOLOGIST, 68- U.S.A, 42-45, Maj. Am. Phytopath. Soc; Am. Soc. Hort. Sci. Azalea diseases; flower blight; camelia diseases; geranium cutting rots; cyclamen diseases; diseases of ornamental plants; lilies. Address: Experimental Station, U.S. Dept. of Agriculture, Tifton, GA 31794.

GILL, EUGENE, b. Jarhoriv, Ukraine, Feb. 15, 20; U.S. citizen; m. 45; c. 1. VETERINARY MEDICINE & PATHOLOGY. Vet. Dipl, Univ. Leipzig, 45; D.V.M, Univ. Munich, 51; M.S, Univ. Del, 56. Proj. leader respiratory diseases of poultry, Animal Disease & Parasite Res. Div. Agr. Res. Serv, U.S. Dept. Health, Educ. & Welfare, 60-67; asst. to dir, Vet. Sci. Res. Div, AGR. RES. SERV, U.S. DEPT. AGR, 67-70, ASST. TO DEP. ADMINR, 70- Consult, comt. on use of drugs in medicated feeds, Nat. Res. Coun, 67; task force on poultry res, U.S. Dept. Agr, 68; nat. conf. on food protection, Food & Drug Admin-Am. Pub. Health Asn, 70. Veterinary infectious diseases, microbiology and antibiotics. Address: Agricultural Research Service, U.S. Dept. of Agriculture, Washington, DC 20250.

GILL, GERALD C(LIFFORD), b. Mt. Elgin, Ont, Can, Apr. 5, 11; U.S. citizen; m. 40; c. 2. METEOROLOGY. B.A, Western Onterio, 34, M.A, 36. Instrument specialist, meteorol. div, Dept. Transport, Can, 36-46, chief radiosonde opers, 46-49; meteorol. engr, Mass. Inst. Tech, 49-55; assoc. res. engr. & lectr. meteorol. instruments, UNIV. MICH, ANN ARBOR, 55-59, assoc. prof. METEOROL, 59-64, PROF, 64- Consult, R.M. Young Co, 64-; White Sands Missile Range, 65-; NASA, 66-68; Nat. Oceanic & Atmospheric Agency, 67-; Detroit Edison, 68-; Nat. Res. Coun, 68- Am. Meteorol. Soc; Instrument Soc. Am; Am. Geophys. Union. Meteorological instruments; low pressure hydrogen generator; anemometer bi-directional vane; UVW anemometer; sensitive helicoid anemometers; sensitive UV water meters for use in Great Lakes. Address: Dept. of Meteorology & Oceanography, East Engineering Bldg, University of Michigan, Ann Arbor, MI 48103.

GILL, GORDON D(REW), b. Ishpeming, Mich, Feb. 24, 28; m. 51; c. 3. ENTOMOLOGY. B.A, North. Mich. Col, 50; M.A, Michigan, 51; Ph.D.(entom), Washington State, 59. Asst. zool, Washington State, 54-57; from asst. prof. to PROF. BIOL, NORTH. MICH. UNIV, 57-, head dept, 62-65. Med. entomologist, Arctic Aeromed. Lab, Ladd Air Force Base, Alaska, 52-54. U.S.A.F, 51-54, Res, 54-65, Capt. AAAS; Entom. Soc. Am; Wildlife Disease Asn. Taxonomy of the Heleomyzidae. Address: Dept. of Biology, Northern Michigan University, Marquette, MI 49855.

GILL, GURCHARAN S, b. Moga, Punjab, India, Mar. 26, 35; U.S. citizen; m. 58; c. 4. MATHEMATICS. B.S, Brigham Young, 58; M.S, Utah, 60, fel. & Ph.D.(math), 65. Asst. prof. MATH, BRIGHAM YOUNG UNIV, 65-67, ASSOC. PROF, 67- Am. Math. Soc; Math. Asn. Am. Functional analysis; topology. Address: Dept. of Mathematics, 310 M.S.C.B, Brigham Young University, Provo, UT 84601.

GILL, HARMOHINDAR SINGH, b. Ferozpur, India, Apr. 7, 33; m. 59; c. 2. PLANT PATHOLOGY, MYCOLOGY. B.Sc, Punjab, India, 53, M.Sc, 55; Ph.D.(plant path), Illinois, Urbana, 65. Res. asst. mycol, Indian Agr. Res. Inst, 56-61; exp. off. plant path, Dept. Agr, Tanzania, 61-62; res. assoc, Illinois, Urbana, 65-67; PLANT PATHOLOGIST-NEMATOLOGIST, RIVERSIDE COUNTY DEPT. AGR, 67- Am. Phytopath. Soc. General plant pathology especially diagnostic investigations of phytopathogenic organisms and nematodes; regulatory and extension. Address: Agriculture Commissioner's Office, Room 19, 4080 Lemon St, Riverside, CA 92501.

GILL, JACK M(ORRIS), b. Lufkin, Tex, Mar. 25, 36; m. 58; c. 2. ORGANIC CHEMISTRY. B.S, Lamar State Col, 58; Nat. Sci. Found. fels, Indiana, summer 59, 60, Nat. Insts. Health fels, 61-63, Ph.D.(org. chem), 63. Sr. res. chemist, Monsanto Co, Mo, 62-64; asst. dir. res, Wilkens Instrument & Res, Inc, Calif, 65-66; dir. res. & eng, Varian Aerograph, Calif, 66-69; mgr, autolab div, VIDAR CORP, 69-70, V.PRES, 71- Summer chemist, prod. div, Sun Oil Co, Tex, 58; Monsanto Chem. Co, 60. Am. Chem. Soc; Am. Oil Chem. Soc. Am. Mgt. Asn; Am. Soc. Test. & Mat. Organic and biochemistry; analytical and instrumental chemistry; chromatography; lab automation; computer science and electronic data systems. Address: Vidar Autolab, 77 Ortega Ave, Mountain View, CA 94040.

GILL, J(AMES) E(DWARD), b. Nelson, B.C, Jan. 16, 01; m. 25; c. 2. GEOLOGY. B.Sc, McGill, 21; fel, Princeton, 23-24, Procter fel, 24-25, Ph.D. (geol), 25. Asst. geol, Princeton, 22-23; instr, Rochester, 25-28, asst. prof, 28-29; McGILL UNIV, 29-39, assoc. prof, 39-49, prof, 40-57, Dawson Prof, 57-69, chmn. dept. GEOL. SCI, 59-66, EMER PROF, 69- Mining & field geologist, 18-23; asst. geologist, Geol. Surv. Can, 24; consult. geologist, 25-; sr. exchange lectr, U.S.S.R, 61. Leonard Medal, Eng. Inst. Can, 43; Centennial Medal of Can, 68. AAAS; Soc. Econ. Geol; Geol. Soc. Am; Am. Geophys. Union; Geol. Asn. Can; Can. Inst. Mining & Metall.(Barlow Mem. Award, 39, Gold Medal, 64); Royal Soc. Can.(Miller Medal, 57); Mineral Asn. Can.(Logan Medal, 67). Structural and economic geology. Address: Dept. of Geological Sciences, 317 Frank Davison Adams Bldg, McGill University, Montreal, Que, Can.

GILL, J(AMES) E(DWARD), b. Berkeley, Calif, Apr. 12, 31; m. 64; c. 1. PHYSICS, BIOPHYSICS. A.B, California, Berkeley, 55; M.S, Stanford, 58, Ph.D.(physics), 63. Physicist, film dept, E.I. du Pont de Nemours & Co, 62-65; BIOPHYSICIST, BIOMED. DIV, LAWRENCE RADIATION LAB, UNIV. CALIF, 65- U.S.A, 53-55. Am. Phys. Soc; Biophys. Soc. Intra and inter molecular charge and energy transfer; molecular physics; dielectrics; magnetic resonance. Address: Biomedical Division, Lawrence Radiation Lab, University of California, P.O. Box 808, Livermore, CA 94550.

GILL, J(AMES) W(ALLACE), b. Phila, Pa, Oct. 1, 31; m. 54; c. 4. BIOCHEMISTRY. B.S, Lehigh, 53; M.S, Va. Polytech, 55, Ph.D.(biochem), 58. Poultry microbiologist, exp. sta, New Hampshire, 57-60; fel, inst. microbiol, Rutgers, 60-62; res. biochemist, Hercules Inc, 62-69; RES. MICROBIOLOGIST, WORTHINGTON BIOCHEM. CORP, 69- Am. Soc. Microbiol; Am. Chem. Soc; Soc. Indust. Microbiol. Microbial physiology and biochemistry; fermentations; enzyme production and application. Address: Worthington Biochemical Corp, Freehold, NJ 07728.

GILL, JOCELYN R(UTH), b. Flagstaff, Ariz, Oct. 29, 16. ASTRONOMY. A.B, Wellesley Col, 38; S.M, Chicago, 41; Ph.D.(astron), Yale, 59. Lab. asst. & instr. astron, Mt. Holyoke Col, 40-42; mem. staff, radiation lab, Mass. Inst. Tech, 42-45; from instr. to asst. prof. astron, Smith Col, 45-52; instr. exten, California, 47-48; asst. prof, Mt. Holyoke Col, 52-57; assoc. prof. math. & astron, Arizona State Col, 59-60; res. asst. astron, Yale, 60-61; staff scientist, astron. & astrophys, OFF. SPACE SCI. & APPLN, HQS, NASA, 61-63, chief in flight sci, manned space sci. prog. off, 63-66, staff scientist, MANNED FLIGHT EXP. OFF, 66-68, PROG. SCIENTIST, 68- Lectr, Wellesley Col, 60-61. AAAS; Am. Astron. Soc; Am. Asn. Variable Star Observers. Celestial mechanics; numerical analysis of satellite orbits; motion of Neptune's satellite, Triton. Address: 560 N St. S.W, Apt. N-105, Washington, DC 20024.

GILL, JOHN L(ESLIE), b. La Harpe, Ill, May 25, 35; m. 59; c. 2. STATISTICS. B.S, Illinois, 56; M.S, Iowa State, 61, Ph.D.(animal breeding), 63. Res. assoc. statist, Iowa State, 61-62; ASSOC. PROF, Va. Polytech, 63-64; DAIRY SCI, MICH. STATE UNIV, 65- Vis. fel. math, Univ. New South Wales, 71. Ord.C, 56-58, Sgt. Biomet. Soc. Statistical genetics; Monte Carlo studies of quantitative genetic theory; design and analysis of experiments in biological research. Address: Dept. of Dairy Science, Michigan State University, East Lansing, MI 48823.

GILL, JOSEPH W(HEATON), b. Port Clinton, Ohio, Apr. 12, 05; m. 30; c. 2. CHEMISTRY. B.A, Ohio State, 21, B.Cer.E, 29, Ph.D.(ceramic eng), 31. Res. supvr, U.S. Gypsum Co, 32-60, sr. scientist, res. lab, 60-70; RETIRED. Am. Ceramic Soc; Nat. Inst. Ceramic Eng. Crystallization of gypsum; wood fiber board and hard board; casein paint products; colloids of Ohio heavy clays. Address: 685 Van Buren Ave, Des Plaines, IL 60018.

GILL, MERTON, b. Chicago, Ill, July 26, 14. PSYCHOANALYSIS. M.D, Univ. Chicago, 38. Prof. PSYCHIAT, State Univ. N.Y. Downstate Med. Ctr, 63-68; fel, res. ctr. ment. health, N.Y. Univ, 68-71; PROF, UNIV. ILL. MED. CTR, 71- Am. Psychoanal. Asn.(Menninger Prize, 61); Am. Psychiat. Asn; Am. Psychol. Asn. Hypnosis. Address: Dept. of Psychiatry Medical Center, University of Illinois at the Medical Center, P.O. Box 6998, Chicago, IL 60680.

GILL, PHILIP STEPHEN, b. Barnsley, Eng, Dec. 21, 41; m. 64; c. 2. ANALYTICAL & PHYSICAL CHEMISTRY. B.Sc, Manchester, 63, M.Sc, 64, Ph.D.(chem), 66. Fel, Univ. Waterloo, 66-67; RES. CHEMIST, E.I. DU PONT DE NEMOURS & CO, INC, 67- Am. Chem. Soc. Electron spin resonance of radical ions in solution; pyrolysis; gas chromatography; mass spectroscopic analysis; thermal analysis; laboratory automation. Address: E.I. du Pont de Nemours & Co, Inc, Box 1217, Parkersburg, WV 26101.

GILL, PIARA SINGH, b. Bassuwal, India, Feb. 15, 40; m. 67; c. 1. PHYSICAL CHEMISTRY, RADIATION CHEMISTRY. B.Sc, Panjab Univ, India, 61, M.Sc, 62; M.S, Kans. State Univ, 65, Ph.D.(chem), 67. Fel. CHEM, Univ. Houston, 67-68; res. assoc, Wright-Patterson AFB, Ohio, 68-69; ASST. PROF, TUSKEGEE INST, 69- Chemical reactions induced by radiation, specifically the collisional energy transfer from excited ions to neutral molecules; mass-spectrometric studies of ion-molecule reactions. Address: Dept. of Chemistry, Tuskegee Institute, AL 36088.

GILL, ROBERT A(NTHONY), b. Darlington, Eng, Apr. 29, 28; m. 57; c. 3. PHYSICAL CHEMISTRY. B.Sc, Durham, 49, Ph.D.(chem), 53. Sr. sci. off. anal. chem, Royal Naval Sci. Serv, Eng, 53-57; Atomic Energy Res. Estab, Eng, 57-58; sr. phys. chemist, ROHM AND HAAS CO, 58-64, group leader, 64-67, HEAD PAPER CHEM. LAB, 67- Am. Chem. Soc; Fiber Soc; Tech. Asn. Pulp & Paper Indust. Physical chemistry of polymers, adhesives, elastomers and textile fibers. Address: Rohm and Haas Co, Norristown & McKean Rds, Springhouse, PA 19477.

GILL, ROBERT F, JR, b. Rehoboth Beach, Del, Aug. 1, 13; m. 39; c. 1. PHYSICAL CHEMISTRY, CHEMICAL ENGINEERING. B.A, Hawaii, 38. Chemist-in-charge crime lab, Honolulu Police Dept, 38-41; res. chemist, Pac. Chem. & Fertilizer Co, 41-47; phys. chemist res. & develop, Dole Pineapple Co, 47-51; from chief chemist to tech. dir. new prod. & process develop, Res. Labs. Colo, Inc, 52-55; tech. dir. & v.pres, St. Eloi Corp, 55-58; staff phys. chemist, Union Thermoelec. Corp. Div, Comptometer Corp, 58-59, electrowriter div, Victor-Comptometer Corp, 59-61; dir, electronic enclosure div, Scully-Anthony Corp, 61-63; res. specialist, res. & develop. ctr, Cannon Elec. Co. Div, Int. Tel. & Tel. Corp, 63-65; consult. phys. chemist & chem. engr, 65-66; mat. & processes engr, info. sci. ctr, Collins Radio Co, 66-67; MEM. STAFF, BISSETT-BERMAN CORP, SANTA MONICA, 67- AAAS; Am. Chem. Soc; fel. Am. Inst. Chem. Surface and colloidal chemistry; process development of new or special materials. Address: 2839 Serang Pl, Costa Mesa, CA 92626.

GILL, ROBERT WAGER, b. Waterbury, Conn, Jan. 19, 40; m. 71. ECOLOGY. B.A, Oberlin Col, 61; M.S, Michigan, 63, Rackham fel, 65-66, Ph.D. (zool), 67. ASST. PROF. biol, UNIV. CALIF, RIVERSIDE, 67-71, BIOL. & STATIST, 71- AAAS; Ecol. Soc. Am; Brit. Ecol. Soc. Population and community ecology; population genetics; theroetical ecology. Address: Dept. of Biology, University of California, Riverside, CA 92502.

GILL, STANLEY J(ENSEN), b. Salt Lake City, Utah, Aug. 21, 29; m. 52; c. 2. PHYSICAL CHEMISTRY. A.B, Harvard, 51; Gen. Elec. Co. fel, Illinois, 53, Ph.D.(phys. chem), 54. Asst. CHEM, Illinois, 51, 52; res. assoc, Cornell, 54; asst. prof, UNIV. COLO, BOULDER, 56-60, assoc. prof, 60-64, PROF, 64- Du Pont fel, 57; Nat. Sci. Found. sr. fel, 66-67. U.S.A, 54-56; U.S.P.H.S.R, 56- Am. Chem. Soc; Am. Phys. Soc; The Chem. Soc; Soc. Rheol. Physical chemistry of high polymers; application of physical techniques to study biological materials; new experimental methods; thermodynamic properties of solutions. Address: Dept. of Chemistry, University of Colorado, Boulder, CO 80302.

GILL, STEPHEN P(ASCHALL), b. Baltimore, Md, Nov. 13, 38; m. 61. PHYSICS. B.S, Mass. Inst. Tech, 60; M.A, Harvard, 61, Ph.D.(appl. physics), 64. Physicist, Stanford Res. Inst, 64-66, head high energy gas dynamics, 66-68; PHYSICS INT. CO, 68-70, MGR. SHOCK DYNAMICS DEPT, 70- Continuum dynamics; shock wave physics; applied mathematics. Address: 32 Flood Circle, Atherton, CA 94025.

GILL, T(HOMAS) H(ARVEY), b. Phila, Pa, Jan. 21, 91; m. 18. FORESTRY. B.A, Pennsylvania, 13; M.F, Yale, 15; hon. D.H.C, Univ. de los Andes, Venezuela, 53. Timber estimator, Kaul Lumber Co, 15; asst. forest supvr, U.S. Forest Serv, 22, in charge ed. activities, 22-25; spec. investr. reforestation work, United Fruit Co, Cuba, 25-26; secy, Charles Lathrop Pack Forestry Found, 26-52, EXEC. DIR, 52-60; INT. SOC. TROP. FORESTERS, 60-, forester & dir, 26-38. Forester, Trop. Plant Res. Found, 26, conductor forest surv, Caribbean region, 26-30; Oberlaender Trust fel, 36; forestry adv, Supreme comdr. Allied Powers, Japan, 51, For. Opers. Admin, Formosa, 52, 56, P.I, 59. Mem. adv. comt, Timber Conserv. Bd, 30-32; forestry comt, Interim Comn. Food & Agr, UN, 44, forestry standing comt, Food & Agr. Orgn, 46, chmn. subcomt. unexploited forests, 46-; mem. comt. nat. parks & chmn. int. comt. trop. forestry, Nat. Acad. Sci. Del, Int. Forestry Cong, Budapest, 36; Soc. Am. Foresters del, Am. Sci. Cong, 40; secy. forestry comt, Conf. Food & Agr, Can, 45, spec. adv, Copenhagen,

46, U.S. del, D.C, 48, chmn. & del, trop. land utilization, Ceylon, 51, Asia-Pac. Forestry Comn, Singapore, 52; World Forestry Cong, Helsinki, 49; Dehra Dun, India, 54; mem. orgn. comt, World Forestry Cong, Wash, 60; exec. dir, Int. Union Socs. Foresters, 66-70. Chevalier, Merite Agricole, France, 47; forestry medal, Mex. & Ger. U.S.A.A.F, 17-19, Capt. Fel. Am. Soc. Foresters (Schlich Medal, 54); hon. mem. Mex. Forestry Soc; hon. mem. Mex. Natural Hist. Soc; hon. mem. Japanese Forestry Soc; hon. mem. Philippine Soc. Foresters; Am. Forestry Asn.(Fernow Award, 67); Ger. Forestry Asn. Forest education; tropical forestry; tropical forests of the Caribbean; forest policy. Address: Apt. 841, International Society of Tropical Foresters, 1500 Massachusetts Ave. N.W, Washington, DC 20005.

GILL, THOMAS J(AMES), III, b. Malden, Mass, July 2, 32; m. 61; c. 2. PATHOLOGY, PHYSICAL CHEMISTRY. A.B, Harvard, 53, M.A, 57; M.D, Harvard Med. Sch, 57. Asst. path, Peter Bent Brigham Hosp, 57-58; med. intern, New York Hosp-Cornell Med. Ctr, 58-59; asst. path, Peter Bent Brigham Hosp, 59-62, assoc, 62-70, sr. assoc, 70-71; PROF. & CHMN. DEPT, SCH. MED, UNIV. PITTSBURGH & PATHOLOGIST-IN-CHIEF UNIV. HEALTH CTR. PITTSBURGH, 71- Jr. fel, Harvard Med. Sch, 59-62, assoc, 62-65, asst. prof, 65-70, assoc. prof, 70-71; Lederle medical faculty award, 62-65; Nat. Insts. Health res. career develop. award, 65-71; assoc. mem. comn. immunization, Armed Forces Epidemiological Bd, 66-70, mem, 70-; consult, Surgeon Gen, U.S.A, 70-; mem. sci. adv. bd, St. Jude Children's Res. Hosp. Dipl, Am. Bd. Path, 65- AAAS; Am. Chem. Soc; Am. Asn. Immunol; Am. Soc. Exp. Path; Am. Soc. Biol. Chem; Int. Acad. Path; Transplantation Soc; Am. Soc. Cell Biol; Am. Asn. Path. & Bact. Immunology; genetics; developmental biology; physical chemistry of biological macromolecules. Address: Dept. of Pathology, University of Pittsburgh School of Medicine, 3550 Terrace St, Pittsburgh, PA 15213.

GILL, WILLIAM D(ELAHAYE), b. Portugal, Jan. 18, 35; Can. citizen; m. 62; c. 3. MATERIALS SCIENCE. B.A.Sc, British Columbia, 60, M.A.Sc, 62; Ph.D.(mat. sci), Stanford, 69. RES. PHYSICIST, RES. DIV, IBM CORP, 62- Am. Phys. Soc. Transport properties in insulating solids; photoconductivity; photovoltaic effects in heterojunctions. Address: Research Division, IBM Corp, Monterey & Cottle Rds, San Jose, CA 95114.

GILL, WILLIAM L, b. Cohoes, N.Y, Aug. 10, 19; m. 44; c. 3. PHYSICS, METALLURGICAL ENGINEERING. B.Met.E, Rensselaer Polytech, 42; Chicago, 48-50; M.S, Vanderbilt, 59. Metallurgist, Adirondack Foundries & Steel Co, N.Y, 42-43; gas turbine div, Gen. Elec. Co, Mass, 46; nuclear engr, New Port News Shipbldg. & Dry Dock Co, Va, 55-58, health physicist, 58-61; br. chief radiation protection, crew systs. div, NASA MANNED SPACECRAFT CTR, 61-64, support develop, 64-67, MATHEMATICIAN, COMPUT. ANAL. DIV, 67- NASA consult, Nat. Acad. Man in Space Comt, 60-63. Dipl, Am. Bd. Health Physics, 60. U.S.N.R, 43-46, U.S.N, 46-55, Lt. Am. Soc. Test. & Mat. Radiation protection; materials development and testing. Address: NASA Manned Spacecraft Center, Houston, TX 77058.

GILL, WILLIAM N(ELSON), b. N.Y.C, Sept. 13, 28; m. 54; c. 4. CHEMICAL ENGINEERING. B.S, Syracuse Univ, 51, M.A, 55, Ph.D.(chem. eng), 60. Field engr, Am. Blower Corp, 51-55; res. assoc, Syracuse Univ, 55-57, instr. chem. eng, 57-60, asst. prof, 60-63, assoc. prof, 63-65; prof. & chmn. dept, Clarkson Col. Technol, 65-71; MEM. FACULTY ENG. & APPL. SCI, STATE UNIV. N.Y. BUFFALO, 71- Turbulence and transport phenomena; role of transport phenomena in chemical reactions; reverse osmosis studies. Address: Faculty of Engineering and Applied Science, State University of New York at Buffalo, Buffalo, NY 14214.

GILL, W(ILLIAM) R(OBERT), b. McDonald, Pa, July 21, 20; m. 47; c. 5. AGRONOMY. B.S, Pa. State, 42; M.S, Hawaii, 49; Ph.D.(agron, soils), Cornell, 55. Soil scientist, Pineapple Res. Inst, Hawaii, 49-50, asst, Cornell, 52-55; res. soil scientist, NAT. TILLAGE MACH. LAB, U.S. DEPT. AGR, 55-71, DIR, 71- Res. lectr, grad. faculty, Auburn Univ, 57-; U.S. exchange scientist, U.S.S.R, 70. U.S.A, 43-47, 51-53, Res, 47-, Col. Am. Soc. Agron; Soil Sci. Soc. Am; Int. Soil Sci. Soc; Am. Soc. Agr. Eng. Dynamic relations of soil-machine systems with emphasis on tillage and traction in agricultural soils as they influence the efficiency and production of crops and soil physical conditions. Address: National Tillage Machinery Lab, U.S. Dept. of Agriculture, Box 792, Auburn, AL 36830.

GILLAM, B(ASIL) E(ARLY), b. Wellsville, Mo, Oct. 24, 13; m. 39; c. 1. MATHEMATICS. A.B, Missouri, 35, M.A, 36, Ph.D.(math), 40. Instr. MATH, Missouri, 37-44; PROF. & HEAD DEPT, DRAKE UNIV, 44- Am. Math. Soc; Math. Asn. Am. Metric geometry; new set of postulates for Euclidean geometry. Address: College of Pharmacy, Drake University, Des Moines, IA 50311.

GILLAM, W(ILLIAM) SHERMAN, b. Chadron, Nebr, Aug. 3, 08; m. 35; c. 2. CHEMISTRY. A.B, DePauw, 30; M.Sc, Nebraska, 33, Ph.D.(chem), 38; grad, Fed. Exec. Inst, Va, 70. Instr, soils, Nebraska, 35-38; head dept. chem, Nebr. Wesleyan, 38-39; asst. prof. soil chem, Mich. State Col, 39-40; prof. agr. chem, Purdue, 40-45; sr. res. chemist, Midwest Res. Inst, 45-50, mgr. chem. res. div, 50-53, asst. dir. chem. sci, 53-54; chief div. res, OFF. SALINE WATER, U.S. DEPT. INTERIOR, 54-64, ASST. DIR. RES, 65- Distinguished Service Award, U.S. Dept. Interior, 70. Am. Chem. Soc. Basic and applied research relevant to desalination. Address: Office of Saline Water, U.S. Dept. of Interior, Washington, DC 20240.

GILLARY, HOWARD L, b. N.Y.C, Feb. 6, 40. NEUROPHYSIOLOGY. A.B, Oberlin Col, 61; Woodrow Wilson Found. fel, 61-62; U.S. Pub. Health Serv. fel, 62-65; Ph.D.(biol), Johns Hopkins Univ, 66. Nat. Acad. Sci-Nat. Res. Coun. res. assoc. biophys, Naval Med. Res. Inst, Md, 65-67; res. assoc. & U.S. Pub. Health Serv. fel. biol, Stanford Univ, 67-69; ASST. PROF. PHYSIOL, UNIV. HAWAII, 69- Am. Soc. Zool. Sensory physiology; quantitative electrophysiological studies on labellar taste receptors of the blowfly, eyes of a terrestrial gastropod, and neural control of behavior in the crayfish; photoreceptors in a marine gastropod. Address: Dept. of Physiology, University of Hawaii, Honolulu, HI 96822.

GILLASPIE, ATHEY G(RAVES), b. Bedford, Va, Apr. 16, 04; m. 36; c. 2. CHEMISTRY. B.S, Lynchburg Col, 28; Cornell, 28; M.S, Duke, 30, Ph.D. (chem), 33. Res. chemist, Neon Res. Corp, Conn, 34-35; res. assoc, Duke, 35-36; head dept. sci, Chowan Col, 36-37; res. chemist, Champion Paper & Fibre Co, N.C, 37-43, Hamilton Lab, 43-52, res. dept, 52-70; RETIRED. Am. Chem. Soc; Tech. Asn. Pulp & Paper Indust. Terpenes; chloramines; organo-mercurials; geometrical configuration of ald-chlorimines. Address: 210 N. Washington Blvd, Hamilton, OH 45013.

GILLASPIE, ATHEY GRAVES, JR, b. Asheville, N.C, July 30, 38; m. 65; c. 1. PLANT PATHOLOGY. B.A, Miami Univ, 60; M.S, Purdue Univ, 62, Ph.D.(plant path), 65. RES. PLANT PATHOLOGIST, SUGARCANE FIELD STA, U.S. DEPT. AGR, 65- Am. Phytopath. Soc. Viruses of sugarcane, especially purification and characterization of these viruses. Address: Sugarcane Field Station, U.S. Dept. of Agriculture, Box 470, Houma, LA 70360.

GILLASPY, JAMES E(DWARD), b. Bartlett, Tex, Oct. 15, 17; m. 48; c. 2. ENTOMOLOGY. B.S, Agr. & Mech. Col, Tex, 40; Ohio State, 41; Texas, 52-54; Ph.D.(entom), California, 54. Inspector-entomologist, U.S. War Dept, Camp Shelby, Miss, 41-42; entomologist, bur. entom. & plant quarantine, U.S. Dept. Agr, 46-48; asst, California, 49-51; Texas, 53; salesman insecticides, Calif. Spray Chem. Corp, Standard Oil Co. Calif, Idaho, 54-55; res. grasshopper ecol, Univ. Idaho, 55, instr. life sci, San Bernardino Valley Union Jr. Col, 56-57; chem, Mt. San Antonio Jr. Col, 57-58; teacher, pub. sch, Calif, 59; asst. prof. natural sci. & math, Tex. Lutheran Col, 59-60; biol, Sul Ross State Col, 60-61; res. assoc, Harvard Mus. Comp. Zool, 61-63; asst. prof. BIOL, Mankato State Col, 63-66; ASSOC. PROF, TEX. A&I UNIV, 66- Sanit.C, 42-46, 1st Lt. AAAS; Ecol. Soc. Am; Am. Entom. Soc. Biology and taxonomy of aculeate Hymenoptera; organic evolution; animal behavior; economic entomology. Address: Dept. of Biology, Box 2198, Texas A&I University, Kingsville, TX 78363.

GILLCHRIEST, WILLIAM CLARENCE, b. Golden, Colo, Mar. 4, 28. BIOCHEMISTRY, MOLECULAR BIOLOGY. B.S, Denver, 50; Wisconsin, 54-58. Asst. biochem, Wisconsin, 54-58; res. assoc. & instr, Stanford, 58-60; res. scientist, U.S. Naval Missile Ctr, 60-62; sr. res. scientist, life sci. dept, Lockheed-Calif, 62-68; dir. res. & develop, Int. Tech. Develop, Inc, 68-71; CORP. DIR, U.S. MINERALS, INC, 71- U.S. Pub. Health Serv. fel, Stanford Univ, 58-60; res. scientist, City of Hope, 64. U.S.A.F, 53, Capt. Am. Chem. Soc; Biophys. Soc; fel. Am. Inst. Chem. Role of metal ions in molecular genetics and genetic products; genetic code in relation to co-factor incorporation into proteins; control of protein and polynucleotide synthesis; basic chemistry of aging, cellular and subcellular, in relation to proteins and polynucleotides; ${}^{10}_{5}B$ thermal neutron capture therapy for cancer. Address: 11790 Bellagio Rd, Los Angeles, CA 90049.

GILLE, JOHN C(HARLES), b. Akron, Ohio, Oct. 12, 34; m. 63; c. 2. METEOROLOGY, PHYSICS. B.S, Yale, 56; Mellon fel, Cambridge, 56-58, B.A, 58, M.A, 66; Nat. Sci. Found. fel, Mass. Inst. Tech, 58-60, Ph.D.(geophys), 64. Res. asst. METEOROL, Harvard, 60-64; asst. prof, FLA. STATE UNIV, 64-68, ASSOC. PROF, 68- Consult, Honeywell, Inc, 64-; vis. scientist, Nat. Ctr. Atmospheric Res, Colo, summer 67, 70; consult, IBM Corp, 67-68; meteorol. subcomt, NASA, 69-; vis. prof. astrophys, Univ. Colo, 70; consult, Barnes Eng, 71-; mem. steering comt, U.S. Radiation Working Group; prin. investr, Nimbus F Limb Radiance Inversion Exp. AAAS; Am. Geophys. Union; Am. Meteorol. Soc. Inversion of radiation measurements; radiative interactions with fluid dynamics in the laboratory and atmosphere; calculation and measurement of atmospheric infrared and visible radiation; upper atmosphere phenomena; planetary atmospheres; scattering. Address: Dept. of Meteorology, Florida State University, Tallahassee, FL 32306.

GILLEAN, MARFRED ELWOOD, b. Cooper, Tex, Oct. 28, 21. ELECTRICAL ENGINEERING. B.S, Washington (St. Louis), 50. Supvry, elec. engr, U.S. Naval Ord. Lab, Md, 46-59; ASSOC. MGR, MINUTEMAN RE-ENTRY SYSTS, TRW SYSTS, REDONDO BEACH, 59- Naval civilian serv. award, 54, 57. U.S.A, 43-46. Inst. Elec. & Electronics Eng. Design and development of re-entry systems for ballistic missiles; electrical system design and arming and fuzing design for ballistic and guided missile systems; development of instrumentation for determining missile system performance. Address: 113 South Ave, Redlands, CA 92373.

GILLELAND, MARTHA JANE, b. Monroe, La, Sept. 9, 40. BIOCHEMISTRY. B.S, La. Polytech. Inst, 62; Ph.D.(org. chem, biochem), La. State Univ, Baton Rouge, 68. Res. assoc. BIOCHEM, Edsel B. Ford Inst. Med. Res, Mich, 68-70; FEL, NORTHWEST. UNIV.(ILL), 70- AAAS; Am. Chem. Soc. Mechanism of enzyme action, especially mechanism of action of dehydrogenases and proteases. Address: Dept. of Chemistry, Northwestern University, Evanston, IL 60201.

GILLEN, ALICE KENYON, b. Rochester, N.Y, June 5, 36; m. GENETICS. A.B, Cornell Univ, 58; Ph.D.(genetics), Univ. Rochester, 64. Asst. prof. zool, Univ. Ga, 64-68; copy ed, Genetics, 68-71; RES. ASSOC. SCIENTIST, GENETICS FOUND, UNIV. TEX. AUSTIN, 71- Genetics Soc. Am. Population genetics; cytogenetics. Address: Genetics Foundation, University of Texas, Austin, TX 78712.

GILLEN, H(OWARD) W(ILLIAM), b. Chicago, Ill, Nov. 25, 23; m. 48; c. 4. NEUROLOGY, NEUROPHYSIOLOGY. B.S, Illinois, 47, M.D, 49. Intern, Charity Hosp, New Orleans, La, 49-50, res. neurol, 50-53; asst. proj. off, U.S. Naval Med. Res. Lab, Conn, 54-56; clin. clerk, Nat. Hosp, London, Eng, 56-57; asst. prof. psychiat. & chief div. neurol, sch. med, Mississippi, 57-59; asst. prof. neurol, sch. med, State Univ. N.Y, Buffalo, 59-65; assoc. prof. NEUROL, MED. CTR, UNIV. IND, INDIANAPOLIS, 65-69, PROF, 69-, DIR. CLIN. NEUROCHEM. LAB, 65- Asst, sch. med, Tulane, 50-52, instr, 52-53; res. training fel, Nat. Inst. Neurol. Diseases & Blindness, 52-53, spec. clin. fel, 56-57; attend. neurol, Vet. Admin. Hosp, Jackson, Miss, 57-59; consult. neurologist, Miss. State Hosp, 57-59; assoc. attend. neurologist, E.J. Meyer Mem. Hosp, Buffalo, N.Y, 59-64, attend, 64-65; consult, Craig Colony & Hosp, Sonyea, N.Y, 60-65; attend. neurologist, Vet. Admin. Hosp, Indianapolis, Ind, 65-; consult. neurologist & neurochemist, New Castle State Hosp, 66-; consult, Cornell Aeronaut. Lab, 66-; attend. neurologist, Marion County Gen. Hosp, Ind, 66-, acting head & dir. dept. neurol, 68-; dir. off. med. educ, 68-; consult. to dir, Armed Forces Radiobiol. Res. Inst,

68-70. U.S.N.R, 42-48, 53-, Capt. AAAS; Am. Med. Asn; Am. Acad. Neurol; Am. Epilepsy Soc; Asn. Res. Nerv. & Ment. Disease; Asn. Am. Med. Cols; Am. Chem. Soc; Am. Asn. Hist. Med; N.Y. Acad. Sci; Soc. Clin. Neurol.(pres. elect, 62-63, pres, 63-64); Marine Technol. Soc; Am. Ord. Asn; Philos. Sci. Asn; Royal Soc. Med; Brit. Soc. Philos. Sci. Mathematical theories of nervous system function; effects of environmental changes on function of nervous system; epilepsy theory; biochemical aspects of neuropathology; language disorders. Address: 960 Locke St, Indianapolis, IN 46202.

GILLEN, RAYMOND D(ANIEL), b. Tacoma, Wash, Feb. 2, 23; m. 58; c. 3. PHYSICAL CHEMISTRY, CHEMICAL ENGINEERING. B.S, Univ. Wash, 45; B.S.Ch.E, 46; M.S, Univ. Wis, Madison, 53; M.S.E, Univ. Pa, 65; Ph.D. (phys. chem), Temple Univ, 70. Chemist, St. Regis Paper Co, (Wash), 46-52; engr, Radio Corp. Am, N.J, 53-58; assoc. scientist, LEEDS & NORTHRUP CO, 59-60, RES. SCIENTIST, 60- Abstractor, Chem. Abstr. Serv, 60- Am. Chem. Soc; Tech. Asn. Pulp & Paper Indust; Am. Inst. Chem. Engrs. Crystal field theory; ferrospinels; electrochemistry; gas chromatography; analytical instrumentation; solid state conductors. Address: 26 Dickerson Rd, North Wales, PA 19454.

GILLENWATER, JAY YOUNG, b. Kingsport, Tenn, July 27, 33; m. 55; c. 3. UROLOGY. B.S, Tennessee, 54, M.D, 57; Pennsylvania, 62-65. Instr. histol. & gross anat, sch. med, Tennessee, 56; int. med, sch. med, Louisville, 60-62; asst. prof. UROL, SCH. MED, UNIV. VA, 65-67, PROF. & CHMN. DEPT, 67- Lectr, sch. med, Louisville, 61-62; U.S. Pub. Health Serv. fel. renal & cardiovasc. diseases, grad. hosp, Pennsylvania, 64-65; Nat. Insts. Health urol. training grant, 65-69, study grants, 66-68 & 66-71. Med. Res. Lab, U.S.A, 60-62, Res, 62-66, Capt. AAAS; Am. Physiol. Soc; Am. Fedn. Clin. Res; Am. Col. Surg; Am. Med. Asn. Renal physiology. Address: Dept. of Urology, University of Virginia School of Medicine, Charlottesville, VA 22901.

GILLEO, M(ATHIAS) ALTEN, b. East Grand Rapids, Mich, May 16, 22; div. ELECTROPHYSICS. B.S, Michigan, 44; S.M, Mass. Inst. Tech, 48, Ph.D. (electrophysics), 52. Elec. engr, bur. ships, U.S. Dept. Navy, 44-45, optics div, naval res. lab, 45-46; asst, insulation res. lab, Mass. Inst. Tech, 46-52; mem. tech. staff phys. res, Bell Tel. Labs, 52-58; staff scientist, Lockheed Aircraft Corp, 58-61; mem. tech. staff, Amelco Semiconductor Div, Teledyne, Inc, 61-64; physics group leader, Monsanto Co, 64-65, scientist & chmn. explor. phys. res, 65-67, scientist, new enterprise div, electronics enterprise, 67-69; MGR. OPTICAL PROCESSES DEPT, MAT. RES. CTR, ALLIED CHEM. CORP, 69- Affiliate prof, dept. elec. eng, Wash. Univ, 67-69. Am. Phys. Soc; Am. Crystallog. Asn; Inst. Elec. & Electronics Eng; N.Y. Acad. Sci. Plasma physics; physics of solids; magnetism and magnetic materials; x-ray crystallography; optical properties of insulators and semiconductors; photoconductivity; spectrophotometry; radiometry; photoelectric emission; semiconductor recombination radiation. Address: Optical Processes Dept, Materials Research Center, Allied Chemical Corp, P.O. Box 1021R, Morristown, NJ 07960.

GILLER, E(DWARD) B(ONFOY), b. Jacksonville, Ill, July 8, 18; m. 43; c. 5. CHEMICAL ENGINEERING. B.S, Illinois, 40, M.S, 48, Ph.D.(chem. eng), 50. Jr. engr, petrol. ref, Sinclair Oil Co, 40-41; U.S. AIR FORCE, 41-, chief radiation br, armed forces spec. weapons proj, 50-54, dir. res, spec. weapons ctr, 54-59, spec. asst. to comdr, off. aerospace res, 59-64, dir. sci. & tech, hq, 64-67; dir. mil. appln, U.S. ATOMIC ENERGY COMN, WASH. D.C, 67, ASST. GEN. MGR. MIL. APPLN, 67- U.S.A.F, 41-, Maj. Gen. AAAS; Am. Chem. Soc; fel. Am. Inst. Chem; Am. Inst. Chem. Eng. Low temperature viscosity of hydrocarbons; heat transfer; gaseous thermal diffusion; atmospheric transmission optics; effects of high intensity radiant energy; nuclear weapons effects; high energy particle physics; government research. Address: 723 Lawton St, McLean, VA 22101.

GILLER, FREDERICK B(ERNARD), b. Phila, Pa, Dec. 2, 37; m. 62; c. 2. PHARMACOLOGY. B.A, Temple, 58; M.Sc, Phila. Col. Pharm, 62, Ph.D. (pharmacol), 65. Asst. prof. pharmacol, Phila. Col. Pharm. & Sci, 65-67; tech. dir, Int. Info. Inc, 67-69, V.PRES. & EXEC. DIR, INFO. INTERSCI. INC, 69- Lectr, Phila. Col. Podiatry, 66-67, assoc. prof, 67-; Longwood Found. grant, Longwood Gardens, Pa, 66-68. AAAS; Am. Pharmaceut. Asn; Am. Soc. Microbiol; Am. Chem. Soc. Respiratory physiology and pharmacology; autonomic nerve physiology; ganglionic transmission toxicology. Address: Information Interscience Inc, 2101 Walnut St, Philadelphia, PA 19103.

GILLERMAN, ELLIOT, b. St. Louis, Mo, July 21, 13; m. 51; c. 2. GEOLOGY. A.B, Washington (St. Louis), 34, M.S, 37; California, 34-35; Ph.D.(geol), Texas, 57. Jr. topog. engr, U.S. Coast & Geod. Surv, 43-44; geologist, U.S. Geol. Surv, 44-53; instr. GEOL, Univ. Tex, 53-57; assoc. prof, UNIV. KANS, 57-68, PROF, 68-, DIR, NORTH COL, 67- Fulbright fel. & vis. prof, Nat. Univ. Eng, Peru, 64-65. AAAS; fel. Geol. Soc. Am; Soc. Econ. Geol; fel. Mineral. Soc. Am; Am. Inst. Mining, Metall. & Petrol. Eng. Geology of fluorspar deposits in southwestern United States; structural factors in mineral deposits; mineral resources in New Mexico; gemstones. Address: Dept. of Geology, University of Kansas, Lawrence, KS 66044.

GILLERY, FRANK HOWARD, b. Leeds, Eng, Sept. 15, 29; U.S. citizen; m. 54; c. 3. PHYSICS. B.Sc, Leeds, 51, Ph.D.(physics), 56. Res. assoc. ceramics, Pa. State, 53-57, asst. prof, 57-58; res. physicist, Pittsburgh Plate Glass Co, 58-60, group leader, 60-62, sr. res. assoc, 62-64, scientist, 64-69, SR. SCIENTIST, PPG INDUSTS, INC, 69- Am. Ceramic Soc; Am. Vacuum Soc. Vacuum and pyrolytic, conductive and optical coatings; glass; x-ray crystallography; ceramics. Address: PPG Industries, Inc, Box 11472, Pittsburgh, PA 15238.

GILLES, DONALD B, b. Toronto, Ont, Oct. 15, 28; m. 56; c. 2. MATHEMATICS, COMPUTER SCIENCE. B.A, Toronto, 50; Illinois, 50-51; Ph.D, Princeton, 53. Mathematician, Nat. Res. Develop. Corp, 53-55; res. asst. prof. appl. math, UNIV. ILL, URBANA, 56-59, assoc. prof, 59-63, PROF. appl. math. & comput. sci, 63-69, COMPUT. SCI, 69- Am. Math. Soc; Soc. Indust. & Appl. Math; Asn. Comput. Mach. Applied mathematics; numerical analysis; digital computer planning and design; programming; game theory. Address: Dept. of Computer Science, University of Illinois at Urbana, Urbana, IL 61801.

GILLES, FLOYD H(ARRY), b. Elgin, Ill, Oct. 18, 30; m. 52; c. 5. NEUROPATHOLOGY, NEUROLOGY. B.A, Chicago, 51, B.S. & M.D, 55. Intern, univ. hosp, Hopkins, 55-56, asst. neurol, sch. med, 56-59; instr. clin. neurol, sch. med, Georgetown Univ, 59-61; NEUROPATHOLOGIST, CHILDREN'S HOSP. MED. CTR, HARVARD MED. SCH, 62-, ASSOC. PROF. NEUROPATH, 71-, instr. clin. neurol, 62-69, asst. prof. neuropath, 69-71. Asst. resident, Baltimore City Hosps, 56-58; hosp, Johns Hopkins Univ, 58-59; Nat. Insts. Neurol. Diseases & Blindness spec. fel. neuropath, Cent. Anatomic Lab, Md, 61-62; neurol. consult, 61-62; mem. path. task force, perinatal res. br, Nat. Inst. Neurol. Diseases & Stroke, 70. Dipl, Am. Bd. Psychiat. & Neurol, 62. U.S.N, 59-61, Lt. Comdr. Am. Asn. Neuropath.(asst. secy-treas, 70). Pediatric neuropathology; reaction of fetal brain to insult. Address: Dept. of Neuropathology, Children's Hospital Medical Center, Harvard Medical School, 300 Longwood Ave, Boston, MA 02115.

GILLES, KENNETH A(LBERT), b. Minneapolis, Minn, Mar. 6, 22; m. 44; c. 2. BIOCHEMISTRY. B.S, Minnesota, 44, U.S. Dept. Agr. fel, 51-52, Ph.D.(biochem), 52. Chem. engr. food process develop, Pillsbury Mills, Inc, 46-49; instr. agr. biochem, Minnesota, 49-51; proj. leader cereal biochem, Gen. Mills, Inc, 52-60, basic milling res, 60-61; prof. & chmn. dept. cereal technol, N.DAK. STATE UNIV, 61-70, PROF. CEREAL CHEM. & V.PRES. AGR, 69- Ed, Cereal Chem, 61-68. U.S.N.R, 42-46, Res, 49-52. AAAS; Am. Chem. Soc; Am. Asn. Cereal Chem.(pres, 71-72); Inst. Food Technol. Cereal pentosans; amylolytic enzymes; lipids; synthetic condiments and food technology; wheat, semolina and flour quality and utilization. Address: Office of Vice President of Agriculture, North Dakota State University, Fargo, ND 58102.

GILLES, PAUL W(ILSON), b. Kansas City, Kans, Jan. 13, 21; m. 44; c. 3. PHYSICAL CHEMISTRY. A.B, Kansas, 43; Summerfield scholar; E.I du Pont de Nemours & Co. fel. & Ph.D.(phys. chem), California, 47. Asst. CHEM, California, 43-44, Manhattan Proj, 44-47; asst. prof, UNIV. KANS, 47-52, assoc. prof, 52-58, prof, 58-63, UNIV. DISTINGUISHED PROF, 63- AAAS; Am. Chem. Soc; Am. Phys. Soc. High temperature chemistry; thermodynamics; vaporization processes; vapor pressures; properties of refractory borides, carbides and oxides; dissociation energies and stabilities of high temperature gases; x-ray crystallography; mass spectrometry; high molecular weight of boron sulfides. Address: Dept. of Chemistry, University of Kansas, Lawrence, KS 66044.

GILLESPIE, ARTHUR SAMUEL, JR, b. Peiking, China, Nov. 21, 31; U.S. citizen; m. 53; c. 3. PHYSICAL & ANALYTICAL CHEMISTRY. B.S, Wake Forest, 53; M.A, Duke, 55. Staff mem. battery lab, Sania Corp, 55-56; res. engr, phys. chem. dept, Aluminum Co. Am, 56-61; res. chemist, measurements & controls lab, Res. Triangle Inst, 61-66; sr. chemist, Tex. Gulf Sulphur Co, 66-67; RES. CHEMIST, LITHIUM CORP. AM, BESSEMER CITY, 67- Am. Chem. Soc; fel. Am. Inst. Chem. Nuclear chemistry and radiochemistry; instrumentation design and development; water resources; water and air pollution control methods and administration; aluminum and alkali metals chemistry. Address: 618 Hillcrest Ave, Gastonia, NC 28052.

GILLESPIE, BRUCE G(RAHAM), b. Minneapolis, Minn, July 3, 10; m. 38; c. 2. CHEMICAL ENGINEERING, ORGANIC CHEMISTRY. B.Ch.E, Minnesota, 33, M.S, 36, Ph.D.(org. chem), 37. Engr. process res, opres. & ref. additives, Esso Res. & Eng. Co, 37-71; CONSULT, PETROL. REF. & REF. ADDITIVES, 71- Fel. AAAS; Am. Chem. Soc; fel. Am. Inst. Chem; N.Y. Acad. Sci. Organic chemical rearrangements; isotopic exchange reactions and separations; commercial production of petroleum fuels and lubricants; petroleum refining; refining additives. Address: 210 Elizabeth Ave, Cranford, NJ 07016.

GILLESPIE, CLAUDE MILTON, b. Huntsville, Ala, Dec. 13, 32; c. 2. NUCLEAR PHYSICS. B.S, Ga. Inst. Technol, 55; Ph.D.(physics), Ohio State Univ, 66. MEM. STAFF NUCLEAR WEAPON DESIGN, LOS ALAMOS SCI. LAB, 66- U.S.A.F, 55-65, Capt. Am. Phys. Soc; Am. Geophys. Union. Beta and gamma ray spectroscopy; phenomenology and hydrodynamics of explosions; theoretical and experimental nuclear weapon effects; design and testing of nuclear weapons; weapon system analysis. Address: Los Alamos Scientific Lab, Box 1663, Los Alamos, NM 87544.

GILLESPIE, COLIN J, b. Adelaide, Australia, May 11, 41; m. 63; c. 1. PHYSICS, BIOPHYSICS. B.Sc, Melbourne, 62; Ph.D.(physics), Monash Univ, Australia, 67. Nat. Res. Coun. Can. fel, WHITESHELL NUCLEAR RES. ESTAB, ATOMIC ENERGY CAN. LTD, 67-70, MEM. STAFF MED. BIOPHYS. BR, 70- AAAS; Biophys. Soc. Low temperature physics; superconductivity; solid state physics; nerve and membrane properties. Address: Medical Biophysics Branch, Whiteshell Nuclear Research Establishment, Atomic Energy of Canada Ltd, Pinawa, Man. R0E 1L0, Can.

GILLESPIE, DANIEL C(URTIS), b. Shamokin, Pa, Sept. 22, 22; m. 50; c. 3. CHEMICAL ENGINEERING, MANAGEMENT. B.S, Pa. State Col, 43; Polytech. Inst. Brooklyn, 44; Ohio State, 45; Eastman Kodak fel. & M.S.E, Michigan, 48. Develop. engr, Tide Water Assoc. Oil Co, N.J, 43-44; jr. scientist, Manhattan proj, Los Alamos, 44-46; chem. engr, DORR-OLIVER, INC, 48-54, sales engr, 54-57, mgr. develop. coord, 58-60, sales mgr. food & pharmaceut. div, 60-65, process equip. div, 65-67, mkt. dir. indust. process systs, 67-70, V.PRES. GLOBAL PROCESS EQUIP. DIV, 70- U.S.A, 42-45. Inst. Food Technol; Am. Soc. Sugar Beet Technol; Am. Inst. Chem. Eng. Pressure drops of fluidized solids in one-inch pipe; heat transfer coefficient of immiscible liquid condensation on finned tubing; current trends in continuous causticizing. Address: Dorr-Oliver, Inc, 77 Havemeyer Lane, Stamford, CT 06904.

GILLESPIE, DAVID H, b. Stoneham, Mass, Jan. 22, 40; m. 65; c. 1. GENETICS, BIOCHEMISTRY. B.S, Tufts, 61; Pub. Health Serv. fel, Illinois, 62-66, Ph.D.(microbiol), 66. Res. asst. genetics, Brookhaven Nat. Labs, 61-62; ASST. PROF. BIOL, BRANDEIS UNIV, 66- Staff mem. course on ribonucleic & desoxyribonucleic acid hybridization, Int. Lab, Italy, 66- Study of temperature-sensitive and drug resistant mutants in haploid and diploid bacteria to determine rules for their study in higher cell lines. Address: Dept. of Biology, Brandeis University, Waltham, MA 02154.

GILLESPIE, G(EORGE) RICHARD, b. Shamokin, Pa, Mar. 7, 26. CHEMICAL ENGINEERING. B.S, Pa. State Col, 49; M.S, Illinois, 51, Ph.D.(chem. eng), 53. Res. engr, east, lab, E.I. du Pont de Nemours & Co, 53-58, supvr. process develop, Repauno Process Lab, 58-64, asst. to prod. mgr, explosives dept, 64-67, asst. mgr. bus. anal, 67-68; admin. asst. to v.pres. eng. & res, ENGELHARD MINERALS & CHEMS, 68-69, mgr. planning, INDUSTS. DIV, 69-71, GROUP V.PRES. RES. & DEVELOP. & PLANNING, 71- Am. Inst. Chem. Eng. Aerosols; formation and measurement; reaction kinetics; heterogeneous catalysis. Address: Engelhard Minerals & Chemicals Corp, Engelhard Industries Division, 430 Mountain Ave, Murray Hill, NJ 07974.

GILLESPIE, GERALD J, b. Jeannette, Pa, Nov. 20, 26; m; c. 4. ORGANIC CHEMISTRY, MATHEMATICS. B.S, Georgetown, 49. Chemist, Swift & Co, 50-51; RES. DEPT, KOPPERS CO, INC, 51-67, RES. SCIENTIST, 67- U.S.A.A.F, 44-45. Am. Chem. Soc; Soc. Plastics Eng; Fedn. Socs. Paint Technol; fel. Am. Inst. Chem. Development and evaluation of epoxy resin, polyester resin, and thermoset polymer systems for application in coatings, adhesives, castings, laminates and glass reinforced industrial shapes; development of process equipment. Address: 211 N. First St, Jeannette, PA 15644.

GILLESPIE, HAZEL B(EATRICE), b. Woodmont, Conn, Mar. 4, 03. BACTERIOLOGY. B.S, Purdue, 27; Ph.D.(bact), Yale, 37. Dir. dairy lab, Brock-Hall Dairy, Conn, 27-29; asst. bact, Yale, 29-35; instr, Albertus Magnus Col, 36-40, dir. pub. health lab, 38-40; instr. BACT, N.J. Col. Women, RUTGERS UNIV, 40-43, asst. prof, 43-48, assoc. prof, 48-53, prof, 53-55, DOUGLASS COL, 55-68, chmn. dept, 55-68, RESEARCHER & EMER. PROF, 68- Am. Soc. Microbiol; Am. Acad. Microbiol; Am. Pub. Health Asn. Bacterial variation; serological and physiological effects of intestinal bacteria on their host; lactobacilli. Address: 31 Baldwin St, New Brunswick, NJ 08901.

GILLESPIE, J(AMES) H(OWARD), b. Bethlehem, Pa, Nov. 26, 17; m. 41; c. 3. VETERINARY SCIENCE, VIROLOGY. V.M.D, Pennsylvania, 39. Instr. poultry diseases & asst. poultry pathologist, New Hampshire, 40; asst. prof. poultry diseases, N.Y. STATE VET. COL, CORNELL UNIV, 46-48, bact, 48-50, assoc. prof. VET. BACT, 50-56, PROF, 56-, asst. dir. lab. diseases of dogs, 51-61. Exec. secy, adv. comt. foot & mouth disease, Nat. Acad. Sci, 61-; mem. comt. animal virus characterization & v.chmn. bd. comparative virol, WHO. U.S. Pub. Health Serv. fels, State Vet. Res. Inst, Amsterdam; Univ. Calif, Berkeley, 60-61. Vet.C, U.S.A, 40-45. AAAS; Am. Soc. Microbiol; Am. Vet. Med. Asn.(Gaines Award); Poultry Sci. Asn; Conf. Res. Workers Animal Diseases. Animal virology and bacteriology. Address: Dept. of Pathology & Bacteriology, New York State Veterinary College, Cornell University, Ithaca, NY 14850.

GILLESPIE, JAMES P(ITTARD), b. Peking, China, Nov. 21, 31; U.S. citizen; m. 57; c. 3. BIOLOGY, SCIENCE EDUCATION. B.S, Wake Forest Univ, 53; M.S, Univ. Tenn, 55; grant, Iowa State Univ, summer 59; Ph.D.(educ), George Peabody Col, 70. Asst. prof. biol, Athens Col, 57-58; teacher, jr. high sch, Del, 58-60; instr. sci, MARSHALL UNIV, 61-63, asst. prof. BIOL, 63-70, ASSOC. PROF, 70- Vis. lectr, George Peabody Col, summers 65 & 66, partic, faculty develop. inst. educ, 67-68; consult, Cabell County Bd. Educ, 66-67; spec. educ. nature training prog, Marshall Univ, summer 71. Am. Fern Soc; Nat. Sci. Teachers Asn. Floristics of local plants, ferns of West Virginia, Hypericaceae of Tennessee, Tennessee Heuchera, cytology of grasses, ferns and Salsola; science concept development and communication of science concepts in young children. Address: Dept. of Biology, Marshall University, Huntington, WV 25701.

GILLESPIE, JERRY RAY, b. Lincoln, Nebr, Jan. 25, 37. PHYSIOLOGY, PATHOLOGY. B.S. & D.V.M, Okla. State Univ, 61; Ph.D.(comp. path), Univ. Calif, Davis, 65. Asst. anat, Okla. State Univ, 57-61, supvr. animal care, univ. dairy barn, 60-61; gen. practitioner, Gothenburg Animal Hosp, Nebr, 61-62; asst. specialist anat, sch. vet. med, Univ. Calif, Davis, 62-65; fel, Cardiovasc. Res. Inst, San Francisco, 65-66; asst. prof. clin. sci, SCH. VET. MED, UNIV. CALIF, DAVIS, 66-68, assoc. prof, 68-71, ASSOC. PROF. PHYSIOL. & ASST. DEAN STUD. SERV, 71-, ASSOC. PROF. PHYSIOL, SCH. MED, 69- AAAS; Am. Physiol. Soc; Am. Vet. Med. Asn; Am. Col. Cardiol; Am. Soc. Anesthesiol. Investigations of respiratory mechanics in healthy animals and subjects with chronic respiratory diseases. Address: Office of Assistant Dean-Student Services, School of Veterinary Medicine, University of California, Davis, CA 95616.

GILLESPIE, J(ESSE) SAMUEL, JR, b. Lynchburg, Va, Dec. 20, 21; m. 50; c. 4. ORGANIC CHEMISTRY. B.S, Va. Mil. Inst, 43; Tenn. Eastman Corp. fel, Virginia, 48-49, Ph.D.(chem), 49. Asst. prof. chem, Richmond, 49-51; sr. chemist, Va-Carolina Chem. Corp, 51-53, group leader, 53-54, asst. div. mgr, 54-56, mgr. org. & agr. chems, 56-58; partner, Cox & Gillespie Chemists & Chem. Engrs, 58-62; sr. chemist, VA. INST. SCI. RES, 62-68, acting dir, 68-69, DIR, 69- Chem. Warfare Serv, 43-46, Lt. Mechanisms of organic reactions; synthetic organic chemistry; medicinal chemistry. Address: Virginia Institute for Scientific Research, 6300 River Rd, Richmond, VA 23229.

GILLESPIE, JOHN, b. Buffalo, N.Y, Oct. 30, 36. THEORETICAL PHYSICS. B.S, Rochester, 58; Ph.D.(theoret. physics), California, Berkeley, 63. Physicist, Lawrence Radiation Lab, California, 63; res. scientist, Columbia, 63-64, res. assoc, 64-65; Stanford Linear Accelerator Ctr, 65-67; mem. staff, theoret. physics ctr, Polytech. Sch, Paris, 67-68; res. physicist, Atomic Energy Comn, Saclay, France, 68-69; ASSOC. PROF. PHYSICS, BOSTON UNIV, 69- Asst. prof, Univ. Calif, Santa Cruz, 65-66. AAAS; Am. Phys. Soc. Elementary particles; scattering theory; nuclear theory. Address: Dept. of Physics, Boston University, Boston, MA 02215.

GILLESPIE, PAUL ALBERT, b. Rochester, N.Y, July 10, 43. MICROBIOLOGY, LIMNOLOGY. B.S, S.Dak. State Univ, 65, M.S, 67; Fed. Water Quality Admin. fel. & Ph.D.(microbiol), Ore. State Univ, 70. Nat. Sci. Found. fel, Ore. State Univ, 70-71; RES. MICROBIOLOGIST, CAWTHRON INST, 71- Am. Soc. Microbiol; Am. Soc. Limnol. & Oceanog. Marine and fresh-water microbial ecology; heterotrophic activity as it relates to the process of eutrophication. Address: Cawthron Institute, Box 175, Nelson, N.Z.

GILLESPIE, ROBERT H(OWARD), b. Richmond, Ind, Jan. 31, 16; m. 44; c. 3. ORGANIC CHEMISTRY. B.S, Indiana, 38; Illinois, 38-39; Ph.D.(org. chem), Wisconsin, 44. Asst, Nat. Defense Res. Cmt. projs, Wisconsin & Kendall Mills, 40-44, textile chemist, res. dept, Kendall Mills, 44-55, res. chemist, Theodore Clark Lab, 55-59; res. assoc, Inst. Paper Chem, 59-60; chemist, FOREST PROD. LAB, FOREST SERV, U.S. DEPT. AGR, 60-66, SUPVRY. CHEMIST, 66- Fel. AAAS; Am. Chem. Soc; fel. Am. Inst. Chem; Fiber Soc; Am. Soc. Test. & Mat; Forest Prod. Res. Soc. Organic synthesis; textile development; cellulose chemistry; pressure-sensitive adhesives; rubbers, resins and plastics; non-woven fabrics; chemistry of wood; wood adhesives. Address: Forest Products Lab, U.S. Forest Service, Madison, WI 53706.

GILLESPIE, ROBERT L, b. Mt. Carroll, Ill, Aug. 6, 16; m. 45; c. 1. VETERINARY MEDICINE. D.V.M, Iowa State, 51. VETERINARIAN, private practice, 51-63; animal health div, U.S. Dept. Agr, 63-67; DIV. TOXICOL, BUR. FOOD & DRUG ADMIN, U.S. DEPT. HEALTH, EDUC. & WELFARE, 67- U.S.A, 42-45. Toxicological evaluation of veterinary drugs for safety in the target animal and for potential hazards of residues remaining in food producing animals or their products. Address: 5125 Rondel Pl, Columbia, MD 21043.

GILLESPIE, R(ONALD) J(AMES), b. London, Eng, Aug. 21, 24; m. 50; c. 2. INORGANIC & PHYSICAL CHEMISTRY. B.Sc, London, 45, Ph.D, 49, D.Sc, 57; Commonwealth Fund fel, Brown, 53-54. Lectr. CHEM, Univ. Col, London, 49-58; assoc. prof, McMASTER UNIV, 58-60, PROF, 60- Am. Chem. Soc; Chem. Inst. Can; Faraday Soc; fel. Royal Inst. Chem; fel. Royal Soc. Can; The Chem. Soc.(Harrison mem. prize, 53). Inorganic and physical chemistry of nonaqueous solvents; structural inorganic chemistry; fluorine chemistry. Address: Dept. of Chemistry, McMaster University, Hamilton, Ont, Can.

GILLESPIE, R(USSELL) W(ILLIAM) H(EADY), b. Woodmont, Conn, Apr. 20, 05; m. 41; c. 2. BACTERIOLOGY. B.S, Purdue, 31; Ph.D.(bact), Yale, 35. Bacteriologist, Brock-Hall Dairy Co, Conn, 28-29; fel. bact, Yale, 35-37; from instr. to asst. prof, South Dakota, 37-42; instr, div. bact, U.S. Army Med. Sch, Wash, D.C, 42-46, instr. & chief diagnostic sect, div. bact, 46-48; ASSOC. PROF. VET. MICROBIOL. & ASSOC. BACTERIOLOGIST, COL. VET. MED, WASH. STATE UNIV, 48- Fulbright res. travel grant, Pan Am Zoonoses Ctr, Argentina, 65. U.S.A, 42-46, Maj. AAAS; Am. Soc. Microbiol; Wildlife Disease Asn; Am. Pub. Health Asn. Oxidation reduction potentials of bacterial cultures; serological typing of Clostridium perfringens; leptospirosis. Address: Dept. of Veterinary Microbiology, College of Veterinary Medicine, Washington State University, Pullman, WA 99163.

GILLESPIE, TERRY JAMES, b. Vancouver, B.C, Jan. 5, 41; m. 66; c. 1. METEOROLOGY. B.Sc, British Columbia, 62; M.A, Toronto, 63; Ph.D. (meteorol), Guelph, 68. Meteorologist, Can. Govt. Serv, 63-66; ASST. PROF. METEOROL, UNIV. GUELPH, 68- Consult, Ont. Dept. Univ. Affairs, 69- Am. Meteorol. Soc; fel. Royal Meteorol. Soc. Meteorology as applied to agriculture. Address: Dept. of Soil Science, University of Guelph, Guelph, Ont, Can.

GILLESPIE, THOMAS, b. Winnipeg, Man, Apr. 16, 24; m. 45; c. 2. PHYSICAL CHEMISTRY. B.Sc, Manitoba, 45; M.Sc, Alberta, 47; Ph.D.(phys. chem), London, 55, D.Sc, London, 63. Instr. physics, Alberta, 46-48; with physics & meteorol. sect, Suffield Exp. Sta, Can, 48-51, 55-56; physics sect, chem. defense exp. estab, Ministry Supply, Eng, 51-53; with phys. res. lab, Dow Chem. Co, 57-68; head wood protection sect, forest prod. lab, Dept. Forestry & Rural Develop, Can, 68-69; ASST. DEAN, SAGINAW VALLEY COL, 69-, adj. prof, 64-69. Consult, Dow Chem. Co. R.C.N, 43-45. Am. Chem. Soc; Sci. Res. Soc. Am; Soc. Rheol. Statistical physics; colloid chemistry; physics; aerosols; emulsions; adhesion; capillarity; polymers; rheology. Address: Saginaw Valley College, 2220 Pierce Rd, University Center, MI 48710.

GILLESPIE, WALTER L(EE), b. Hamilton, Ohio, Jan. 6, 30; m. 53; c. 2. ZOOLOGY. A.B, Miami (Ohio), 52, M.A, 54; summer, Washington (Seattle), 55; Ph.D.(zool), Illinois, 60. Asst. prof. zool, Butler, 59-60; instr. biol, Wells Col, 60-62, asst. prof, 62-65, assoc. prof, 65-67; ASSOC. PROG. DIR, TEACHER EDUC. SECT, NAT. SCI. FOUND, 67- AAAS; Ecol. Soc. Am; Am. Soc. Zool; Am. Ornith. Union; Arctic Inst. N.Am; Am. Soc. Mammal. Bird populations of the subarctic. Address: Teacher Education Section, National Science Foundation, Washington, DC 20550.

GILLESPIE, WILLIAM H(ARRY), b. Webster Springs, W.Va, Jan. 8, 31; m. 50; c. 5. FORESTRY, FOREST PATHOLOGY. B.S, West Virginia, 52, M.S, 54. Forest biologist, plant pest control div, W.VA. DEPT. AGR, 56-66, asst. dir, 66-67, dir, 67-69, EXEC. ASST. TO CMNR, 69- Instr, West Virginia, 58-, continuing ed. div, 66- Soc. Am. Foresters; Bot. Soc. Am; Int. Asn. Plant Taxon; Nat. Asn. Geol. Teachers; Am. Inst. Biol. Sci; Soil Conserv. Soc. Am. Paleobotany; economic botany of the Appalachian area, particularly edible and poisonous plants; paleobotany of eastern United States, especially compression floras and microfloristic studies; control of forest tree diseases. Address: West Virginia Dept. of Agriculture, Charleston, WV 25305.

GILLETT, GEORGE W(ILLSON), b. Hopewell, N.Y, May 30, 17; m. 43; c. 1. BOTANY. B.S, Iowa State, 40; Ph.D, California, 54. Asst. prof. bot, Mich. State, 56-62; Fulbright lectr, Turku, 62-63; assoc. prof. & dir, Harold L. Lyon Arboretum, Univ. Hawaii, 63-67; PROF. BOT. & DIR. BOTANIC GARDENS, UNIV. CALIF, RIVERSIDE, 67- U.S.A.A.F, 40-45, Maj. Bot. Soc. Am; Am. Soc. Plant Taxon. Experimental taxonomy of vascular plants; flora of the Hawaiian Islands and the Pacific. Address: Dept. of Biology, University of California, Riverside, CA 92502.

GILLETT, JAMES WARREN, b. Kansas City, Kans, Sept. 18, 33; m. 58, 70; c. 3. BIOCHEMISTRY. B.S, Kansas, 55; Nat. Sci. Found. fel, California,

Berkeley, 57-58, Ph.D.(biochem), 62. Res. specialist entom. & parasitol, California, Berkeley, 62, chemist, 62-64; asst. prof. AGR. CHEM, ORE. STATE UNIV, 64-70, ASSOC. PROF, 70- Mem, Int. Cong. Pesticide Chem, Int. Union Pure & Appl. Chem, Tel Aviv, 71; co-invest, U.S. Pub. Health Serv. grant. AAAS; Am. Chem. Soc; N.Y. Acad. Sci. Biochemical effects and transformation of insecticides; environmental toxicology. Address: Dept. of Agricultural Chemistry, Oregon State University, Corvallis, OR 97331.

GILLETT, J(OHN) M(ONTAGUE), b. Ottawa, Ont, Nov. 26, 18; m. 56; c. 2. PLANT TAXONOMY. B.A, Queen's (Ont), 49; Ph.D.(plant taxon), Washington (St. Louis), 52. BOTANIST, CAN. DEPT. AGR, 49- Herbarium asst, Mo. Bot. Gardens, 49-51. R.C.A.F, 40-45. Am. Soc. Plant Taxon; Int. Asn. Plant Taxon; Can. Bot. Asn. Trifolium; leguminosae; flora of Canada. Address: Plant Research Institute, Research Branch, Central Experimental Farm, Canada Dept. of Agriculture, Ottawa, Ont, Can. K1A 0C6.

GILLETT, LAWRENCE B, b. Montreal, Que, Aug. 22, 31; m. 61. GEOLOGY. B.S, McGill, 53, M.S, 56; M.A, Princeton, 56, Ph.D.(geol), 62. Asst. prof. GEOL, North Dakota, 59-62; ASSOC. PROF, STATE UNIV. N.Y. COL. PLATTSBURGH, 62- Summer consult, mining co, 59- Am. Geophys. Union; Nat. Asn. Geol. Teachers. Structures of diabase dikes; petrology of anorthosites, granites and syenites; base metal exploration in Ontario and British Columbia; glacial geomorphology. Address: Dept. of Physics & Earth Sciences, State University of New York College at Plattsburgh, Plattsburgh, NY 12901.

GILLETTE, D. DALE, b. Proctor, Minn, Dec. 17, 27; m. 49; c. 2. ANIMAL & VETERINARY PHYSIOLOGY. D.V.M, Iowa State, 53; Ph.D.(animal physiol), California, Davis, 62. Gen. practice vet. med, S.Dak, 53-54; meat inspector, State of Calif, 54-55; herd vet. & instr, Calif. State Polytech. Col, 55-58; asst. prof. VET. PHYSIOL, IOWA STATE UNIV, 61-65, ASSOC. PROF, 65- U.S.A.A.F, 46-47. Parturition in cattle and dogs; antibody absorption in puppies; computer data analysis. Address: Dept. of Veterinary Physiology & Pharmacology, Iowa State University, Ames, IA 50010.

GILLETTE, DALE ALAN, b. Lincoln, Nebr, Mar. 24, 43; m. 68. ATMOSPHERIC SCIENCES. B.S, Univ. Mich, 65, M.S, 66, Ph.D.(meteorol), 70. SCIENTIST, NAT. CTR. ATMOSPHERIC RES, 70- Size distribution and chemical composition of aerosols distant from anthropogenic sources; field and model studies of particulate lead. Address: 2895 Regis Dr, Boulder, CO 80303.

GILLETTE, DEAN, b. Chicago, Ill, Aug. 11, 25; m. 49; c. 1. MATHEMATICS. B.S, Oregon State Col, 48; A.M, California, 50, Ph.D.(math), 53. Asst. math, California, 50-53; mem. tech. staff, BELL TEL. LABS, 56-62, dir. mil. anal. ctr, 62-66, exec. dir. transmission systs. eng. div, 66-71, EXEC. DIR. SYSTS. RES, 71- U.S.N.R, 44-46. AAAS; Am. Math. Soc; Soc. Indust. & Appl. Math. Systems analysis; operations research. Address: Bell Telephone Labs, Murray Hill, NJ 07974.

GILLETTE, E(DWARD) L(eROY), b. Coffeyville, Kans, May 21, 32; m. 56; c. 4. RADIOLOGY, RADIATION BIOLOGY. B.S. & D.V.M, Kansas State, 56; M.S, Colo. State, 61, Ph.D.(physiol, radiation biol), 65. Instr. RADIOL, COLO. STATE UNIV, 59-65, asst. prof, 65-67, ASSOC. PROF, 67- Advan. fel, sect. exp. radiother, Univ. Tex, M.D. Anderson Hosp. & Tumor Inst, 68-69. Vet.C, 56-58, 1st Lt. Am. Vet. Med. Asn; Soc. Nuclear Med; Radiation Res. Soc; Am. Vet. Radiol. Soc; Radiol. Soc. N.Am; assoc. Am. Soc. Therapeut. Radiol. Veterinary radiation therapy and nuclear medicine; experimental radiotherapy. Address: Dept. of Radiology & Radiation Biology, Colorado State University, Ft. Collins, CO 80521.

GILLETTE, FRANK N(EWTON), b. La Harpe, Ill, July 16, 14; m. 42; c. 2. PHYSICS. B.S, Bradley Polytech, 38; fel, Illinois, 40-41, Ph.D.(physics), 42. Asst. physics, Illinois, 38-42; mem. staff, radiation lab, Mass. Inst. Tech, 42-45; from group leader eng. div. to head, apparatus develop. sect, GPL Div, Gen. Precision Aerospace, 46-51, head, prod. develop. dept, 51-58; indust. prod. eng. div, 58-61, assoc. dir. eng, 61-65, dir. res. & adv. develop, 65-69; DIR. TECHNOL, DEFENSE & SPACE SYSTS. GROUP, SINGER CO, 69- Fel. Soc. Motion Picture & TV Eng. Neutron absorption and velocity measurement; radar indicator design; improvements on design and application of multivibrator circuits; training devices; motion picture and television equipment; airborne Doppler navigation systems; magnetic resonance; optical image correlation; laser diffraction. Address: Singer Co, 30 Rockefeller Plaza, New York, NY 10020.

GILLETTE, JAMES R(OBERT), b. Hammond, Ind, Feb. 9, 28; m. 53; c. 2. BIOCHEMISTRY. A.B, Cornell Col, 47; M.S, Iowa, 49, Ph.D.(biochem), 54. Asst. prof. biol. & chem, Jamestown Col, 49-51; biochemist, DRUG ENZYME INTERACTION, NAT. HEART INST, NAT. INSTS. HEALTH, 54-58, HEAD SECT, 58-, ACTING CHIEF, 71-, deputy chief, 67-71. Claude Bernard vis. prof, Univ. Montreal, 71. Roland T. Lakey Hon. Lect. Award, 67. AAAS; Am. Soc. Biol. Chem; Am. Chem. Soc; Am. Soc. Pharmacol; N.Y. Acad. Sci. Metabolism of drugs and other foreign compounds. Address: Lab. of Chemical Pharmacology, National Heart & Lung Institute, National Institutes of Health, Bethesda, MD 20014.

GILLETTE, NORMAN J(OHN), b. Cicero, N.Y, Mar. 17, 11; m. 37; c. 3. PALEOBOTANY. A.B, Syracuse, 32, scholar, 32-34, M.A, 33; fel, Chicago, 34-35, Ph.D.(paleobot), 37. Asst. BOT, Chicago, 35-37; asst. prof, Idaho, 37-47; Syracuse, 47-53, assoc. prof, 53-64; PROF, STATE UNIV. N.Y. COL. OSWEGO, 64- AAAS; Bot. Soc. Am; Int. Soc. Plant Morphol. Morphology of fossil plants; Tertiary flora of Idaho; tropical botany of Jamaica. Address: Dept. of Botany-Physiology, State University of New York College at Oswego, Oswego, NY 13126.

GILLETTE, P(HILIP) ROGER, b. Mt. Vernon, Iowa, May 12, 17; m. 47; c. 2. PHYSICS. B.A, Cornell Col, 37; B.S, Illinois, 38, M.S, 39, Ph.D.(physics), 42. Mem. staff, radiation lab, Mass. Inst. Tech, 42-45; proj. engr, Sperry Gyroscope Co, N.Y, 45-48; physicist, Gen. Elec. Co, 48-50; sr. res. engr, STANFORD RES. INST, 50-57, SR. PHYSICIST, 57- Civilian with Off. Sci. Res. & Develop; U.S.A; U.S.A.A.F; U.S.N, 41-46. Am. Phys. Soc; Inst. Elec. & Electronics Eng. Molecular absorption and fluorescence spectroscopy; characteristics and design of pulseforming networks and pulse transformers; design of nuclear reactors; weapon systems operations analysis. Address: Stanford Research Institute, 1611 N. Kent St, Arlington, VA 22209.

GILLETTE, ROBERT K(ENT), b. Moscow, Idaho, Aug. 28, 42; m. 66; c. 1. ANALYTICAL CHEMISTRY. B.S, Clarkson Tech, 64; Ph.D.(anal. chem), Iowa State, 68. Sr. res. chemist, Mound Lab, Monsanto Res. Corp, Ohio, 68-71; ANAL. CHEMIST, TECH. CTR, OWENS-ILL, INC, 71- Am. Chem. Soc. Analytical chemistry methods development for glass analysis. Address: Owens-Illinois Technical Center, 1700 N. Westwood Ave, Toledo, OH 43651.

GILLETTE, R(OGER) H(ENRY), b. Orange, Mass, May 14, 11; m. 41. PHYSICAL CHEMISTRY. B.A, Wisconsin, 33, fel, 33-36, M.A, 34, Ph.D.(phys. chem), 36. Instr. chem. & jr. chemist, exp. sta, California, 36-37; instr. chem, Michigan, 37-40, asst. prof, 40-44; physicist, lab, Linde Air Prods. Co, 44-46, head physics & anal. div, 46-48, asst. to supt. lab, 48-51; dep. U.S. Forces, Austria, ed. consult, 51-52; dir-gen, Europ. Res. Assocs, S.A, Union Carbide Corp, Belg, 52-67, BUS. DIR. EAST. EUROPE, 67-70; CABOT EUROPE, CABOT CORP, 70- AAAS; Am. Chem. Soc; Optical Soc. Am. Infrared spectroscopy; mass spectroscopy; electron diffraction; x-ray diffraction; molecular structural theory; industrial instrumentation; fundamental properties of gaseous discharges. Address: Cabot Europe, 104 Ave. Charles de Gaulle, 92 Neuilly-sur-Seine, France.

GILLETTE, ROY (JAMES), b. Elkhorn, Wis, Aug. 29, 17; m. 40; c. 3. ZOOLOGY. A.B, Wayne State, 38; Ph.D.(zool), Washington (St. Louis), 43. Asst. zool, Washington (St. Louis), 38-43, instr, 43-44; Hopkins, 44-47; asst. prof, natural sci, Univ. Chicago, 47-53; HISTOL, UNIV. ILL, CHICAGO, 53-57, assoc. prof, 57-64, PROF, 64-, HEAD DEPT, 70- Rockefeller asst, Wash. Univ, 40-41; res. assoc, Off. Sci. Res. & Develop, Edgewood Arsenal, Md, 45; fel, Ctr. Advan. Study Theol. & Sci, Meadville Theol. Sch, Univ. Chicago, 68-69. Am. Soc. Zool; Am. Asn. Anat; Soc. Develop. Biol; Int. Asn. Dent. Res. Vertebrate embryology and histology; experimental morphology of epithelium, skeletal tissues and teeth. Address: Dept. of Histology, College of Dentistry, University of Illinois, P.O. Box 6998, Chicago, IL 60680.

GILLETTE, TEDFORD A, b. Burley, Idaho, Aug. 18, 35; m. 60; c. 5. FOOD SCIENCE, BIOCHEMISTRY. B.S, Univ. Idaho, 60, M.S, 62; Ph.D.(food sci), Mich. State Univ, 66. Res. assoc. biochem, Mich. State Univ, 66-68; ASST. PROF. FOOD & ANIMAL SCI, UTAH STATE UNIV, 69- Inst. Food Technol; Am. Soc. Animal Sci. Body composition; enzyme purification and characterization; meat processing. Address: Dept. of Food Science, Utah State University, Logan, UT 84321.

GILLHAM, JOHN K, b. London, Eng, Aug. 7, 30; m. 61; c. 2. POLYMER & ORGANIC CHEMISTRY. B.A, Cambridge, 53, hon. M.A, 57; Ph.D.(chem), McGill, 59. Res. chemist, Stamford Labs, Am. Cyanamid Co, 58-65; ASSOC. PROF. CHEM. ENG, PRINCETON, 65- Vis. res. chemist, plastics prog, Princeton, 64-65. Am. Chem. Soc. Synthesis, fabrication and evaluation of thermosetting composite structures; thermomechanical and thermal analysis of polymers. Address: Dept. of Chemical Engineering, Princeton University, Princeton, NJ 08540.

GILLHAM, NICHOLAS WRIGHT, b. N.Y.C, May 14, 32; m. 56. GENETICS. A.B, Harvard, 54, A.M, 55, U.S. Pub. Health Serv. fel, 58-62, Ph.D.(biol), 62. U.S. Pub. Health Serv. fel, Yale, 62-63; instr. biol, Harvard, 63-65, asst. prof, 65-68; ASSOC. PROF. ZOOL, DUKE UNIV, 68- U.S.A.F, 55-58, Res, 58-, 1st Lt. AAAS; Genetics Soc. Am; Am. Soc. Nat. Microbial genetics, particularly cytoplasmic inheritance in the unicellular green algae, Chlamydomonas. Address: Dept. of Zoology, Duke University, Durham, NC 27706.

GILLHAM, ROBERT A, JR, b. Pendleton, Ore, Mar. 30, 43; m. 70. ORGANIC CHEMISTRY. B.S, San Jose State Col, 65; Nat. Sci. Found. fel, Calif. Inst. Technol, 65-69, Ph.D.(org. chem), 69; med, Univ. Wash, 71- Res. chemist, U.S. Air Force Acad, 69-71. Am. Chem. Soc. U.S.A.F, 69-, Capt. Natural products synthesis; metallocene chemistry. Address: 4551 46th Ave. N.E, Seattle, WA 98105.

GILLIAM, JAMES WENDELL, b. Chicota, Tex, July 18, 38; m. 58; c. 3. SOIL CHEMISTRY. B.S, Okla. State, 60; M.S, Miss. State, 63, Ph.D.(soil chem), 65. Asst. prof. SOIL CHEM, N.C. STATE UNIV, 65-69, ASSOC. PROF, 69- Am. Soc. Agron; Soil Sci. Soc. Am. Fertilizer reactions in soils; uptake of nutrients by plants and plant analysis; cation exchange reactions of soil organic matter; contribution of fertilizers to contamination of surface waters. Address: Dept. of Soil Science, North Carolina State University, Raleigh, NC 27607.

GILLIAM, O(TIS) R(ANDOLPH), b. Waverly, Va, Sept. 19, 24; m. 53; c. 3. PHYSICS. B.S, Randolph-Macon Col, 43; Ph.D.(physics), Duke, 50. Instr. PHYSICS, UNIV. CONN, 50-51, 53-55, asst. prof, 56-62, assoc. prof, 62-67, PROF, 67- Consult, Am. Optical Co, 66-67; Brookhaven Nat. Lab; Picatinny Arsenal. U.S.N.R, 43-46, 51-53. Am. Phys. Soc; Am. Asn. Physics Teachers. Determination of the structure of matter by microwave methods, paramagnetism and radiation damage. Address: Dept. of Physics, University of Connecticut, Storrs, CT 06268.

GILLIAM, W(ILLIAM) F(ARR), b. Union, S.C, Aug. 13, 13. INORGANIC CHEMISTRY. B.S, The Citadel, 34; Ph.D.(inorg. chem), Cornell, 39. Asst. chem, Cornell, 34-39; res. assoc. res. lab, GEN. ELEC. CO, 39-56, specialist, tech. info, 56-65, MGR. TECH. INFO. OPER, SILICONE PROD. DEPT, 65- U.S.A. Am. Chem. Soc; N.Y. Acad. Sci. Chemistry of metallo-organic compounds of aluminum, gallium, indium and silicon. Address: Silicone Products Dept, General Electric Co, Waterford, NY 12188.

GILLICH, WILLIAM JOHN, b. Washington, D.C, Jan. 8, 35; m. 59; c. 2. MECHANICS. B.E.S, Hopkins, 57, M.S, 60, Ph.D.(mech), 64. Jr. instr. mech. eng, Hopkins, 57-59, instr, 59-60, res. asst, 61-64; res. physicist, TERMINAL BALLISTICS LAB, U.S. ARMY BALLISTIC RES. LABS, ABERDEEN PROVING GROUND, 64-71, supv. res. physicist & chief wave propagation & mat. sect, SOLID MECH. BR, 71, ACTING CHIEF, 71- Jr. engr, Martin

Co, summer 56; res. asst, John Hopkins Univ, summers 57-64, Dr. univ, 64-; instr, ballistic inst, Univ. Del. Exten, 69-70: Ord.C, 63-64, Res, 64-69, Capt. Soc. Natural Philos; Am. Soc. Mech. Eng; Soc. Exp. Stress Anal. Plastic and elastic wave propagation; dynamic continuum mechanics; shock wave reflections; Moire technology. Address: Wave Propagation & Material Section, Solid Mechanics Branch, Terminal Ballistic Lab, U.S. Army Ballistic Research Labs, Aberdeen Proving Ground, MD 21005.

GILLIES, ALASTAIR J, b. Halifax, Eng, Oct. 7, 24; U.S. citizen; m. 52; c. 4. ANESTHESIOLOGY, PHARMACOLOGY. B.Sc, Edinburgh, 47, M.B, Ch.B, 48. Res. house surgeon & res. anesthetist, Royal Infirmary, Edinburgh, 48-49; asst. res. anesthesiol, Mass. Gen. Hosp, 52; fel, Mayo Found, 53; asst. anesthetist, Strong Mem. Hosp, 54-55; asst. prof. ANESTHESIOL, sch. med, Yale, 55-59; PROF, MED. CTR, UNIV. ROCHESTER, 59-; ANESTHETIST-IN-CHIEF, STRONG MEM. HOSP, 59- Anesthesiologist, Grace New Haven Community Hosp, 55-59; consult, bur. heart disease, N.Y. State Dept. Health. R.A.F, 49-51, Squadron Leader. Am. Soc. Anesthesiol; Asn. Univ. Anesthetists; N.Y. Acad. Sci; Pan-Am. Med. Asn; Int. Anesthesia Res. Soc; Brit. Med. Asn. Address: Dept. of Anesthesiology, University of Rochester Medical Center, 260 Crittenden Blvd, Rochester, NY 14642.

GILLIES, A(RCHIBALD), b. Scotland, Oct. 30, 06; m. 35; c. 3. PHYSICAL CHEMISTRY. B.Sc, Alberta, 39, M.Sc, 40; Ph.D.(phys. chem), McGill, 42. Lectr. org. chem, Alberta, 39-40; demonstr. phys. chem, McGill, 40-42; res. chemist, explosives lab, Nat. Res. Coun. Can, 42-44; res. labs, Dom. Rubber Co, 44-63; sr. scientist, 63-68; sect. mgr, Uniroyal Res. Labs, 68-71; RETIRED. Fel. Chem. Inst. Can. Phase phenomena; chemical kinetics; agricultural chemicals; herbicides; insecticides; rubber technology; pollution studies. Address: 137 Westmount Rd, Guelph, Ont, Can.

GILLIES, DANIEL McGILVARY, b. Muang Prae, Siam, June 5, 12; nat; m. 45; c. 3. CHEMISTRY. B.S, Col. Wooster, 33; Ph.D.(phys. chem), Pennsylvania, 46. Asst. phys. chem, Pennsylvania, 40-42; res. chemist, Manhattan Dist. Proj, S.A.M. Labs, Columbia, 43-45; chief chemist, Chandler plant, 45-46; res. chemist, Tonawanda Labs, Linde Co, UNION CARBIDE CORP, 46-53, res. supvr, 53-55, asst. mgr, 55-57, asst. res. dir. & mgr, Speedway Res. Lab, 57-62, dir. res. Union Carbide Metals Co, 62-68, mgr. develop, gas prod. develop. lab, N.J, 68-70, MEM. STAFF, LINDE DIV, 70- Am. Chem. Soc. Crystal chemistry; ceramics; powder metallurgy; high temperature processes; general inorganic and physical chemistry. Address: Linde Division, Union Carbide Corp, Tarrytown Technical Center, Tarrytown, NY 10591.

GILLIES, DONALD B(RUCE), b. Toronto, Ont, Oct. 15, 28; m. 56; c. 2. MATHEMATICS. B.A, Toronto, 50; Illinois, 50-51; Ph.D.(math), Princeton, 53. Mathematician, Nat. Res. Develop. Corp, Eng, 53-55; res. asst. prof. APPL. MATH, UNIV. ILL, URBANA, 56-59, res. assoc. prof, 59-63, res. prof, 63-66, PROF, 66- Vis. prof, Stanford Univ, 63-64. Am. Math. Soc; Asn. Comput. Mach. Applied mathematics; numerical analysis; digital computer design; programming; game theory. Address: Dept. of Computer Science, University of Illinois at Urbana, Urbana, IL 61801.

GILLIES, GEORGE A(LEXANDER), b. Edmonton, Alta, July 29, 28; m. 55; c. 3. ORGANIC CHEMISTRY. B.Sc, Alberta, 49; Ph.D.(chem), California, 53. RES. CHEMIST, E.I. du Pont de Nemours & Co, 53-60; SHELL DEVELOP. CO, 60- Am. Chem. Soc; Sci. Res. Soc. Am. Separation of naturally occurring mixtures of fatty acids; synthetic polymers; chromatography; ion exchange; textile chemistry; detergents; polyolefin fibers; block polymers. Address: 2735 Hilgard Ave, Berkeley, CA 94709.

GILLIES, R(OBERT) A(RTHUR), b. Cass City, Mich, Jan. 9, 26; m. 50; c. 4. BACTERIOLOGY. B.S, Mich. State Normal Col, 50; M.S, Michigan, 52, Ph.D.(bact), 55. Instr. bact, Michigan, 55; res. assoc. food tech, Illinois, 55-56; sr. res. chemist & bacteriologist, Calif. Packing Corp, 56-67, mgr. admin. serv. & microbiol, DEL MONTE CORP, 67-69, MGR. RES. STAFF SERV, 69- U.S.A.A.F, 44-45. Am. Soc. Microbiol; Inst. Food Technol. Radiation preservation of foods; improvement of existing food products and processes; development of new food products; processes and packages. Address: 205 N. Wiget Lane, Walnut Creek, CA 94598.

GILLIESON, A. H. C. P, b. Vancouver, B.C, May 5, 10; m. 45; c. 2. ANALYTICAL CHEMISTRY. B.Sc, Edinburgh, 31, Carnegie scholar, 32-34, Ph.D.(chemother), 34. Chemist, Brit. War Dept, 34-39, chem. inspection dept, Ministry of Supply, 39-44, Tuballoys, Dept. Sci. & Indust. Res, Can, 44-46, prin. sci. off, Atomic Energy Res. Estab, Eng, 46-54, sr. prin. sci. off, U.K. Atomic Energy Auth, 54-59; SR. SCI. OFF, MINERAL SCI. DIV, MINES BR, FED. DEPT. MINES & TECH. SURV, OTTAWA, 59- Res. chemist, Calico Printers Asn, fall 34; comt. mem, Brit. Inst. Physics. Fel, Chem. Inst. Can; Spectros. Soc. Can.(pres, 64-65). Organic chemistry; biochemistry; bacteriology; chemotherapy; explosives; radiochemistry; emission and x-ray fluorescence; analysis including radioactive materials; nuclear safety; cosmology. Address: Mineral Sciences Division, Federal Dept. of Mines & Technical Surveys, 555 Booth St, Ottawa 4, Ont, Can.

GILLIGAN, WILLIAM H, b. Scranton, Pa, Apr. 16, 27; m. 54; c. 1. ORGANIC CHEMISTRY. B.S, Scranton, 50; M.S, Drexel Inst, 55; Ph.D.(org. chem), Georgetown, 65. RES. CHEMIST, Qm.C, U.S. Army, 51-54; Wyeth Inc, Pa, 54-56; Hazelton Power & Light Co, 57-59; Naval Ord. Sta, Md, 60-67, NAVAL ORD. LABS, WHITE OAK, MD, 67- U.S.N, 45-46. Am. Chem. Soc. Nitrogen, fluorine, carbohydrate and analytical chemistry. Address: 11600 Hickory Dr, Washington, DC 20022.

GILLILAN, JAMES HORACE, b. Kansas City, Mo, Dec. 21, 32; m. 70. MATHEMATICS. B.A, Missouri, 54, M.S, 55; Ph.D.(math), Illinois, 61. Instr. MATH, Univ. Mich, 61-63; ASST. PROF, UNIV. MO-KANSAS CITY, 66- U.S.A, 55-57, 1st Lt. Am. Math. Soc. Functional analysis. Address: Dept. of Mathematics, University of Missouri-Kansas City, Kansas City, MO 64110.

GILLILAN, LOIS A(DELL), b. Mapleton, Utah, June 15, 11. ANATOMY, PHYSIOLOGY. B.A, Mt. Holyoke Col, 35, Wooley fel, 38-39; A.M. Vassar Col, 37; Aberdeen, 39; Cent. Inst. Brain Res, Amsterdam, 39; univ. fel. &

Braun fel, Michigan, 39-40, Ph.D.(anat), 40; M.D, Pittsburgh, 47. Asst. physiol, Vassar Col, 35-38; vol. asst. neuroanat, Michigan, 39-42, asst. physiol, 41, Gelston fel, 41-42; instr. anat, Pittsburgh, 42-45; mem. med. staff, health serv, Illinois, 48-49; assoc. prof. ANAT, grad. sch. med, Univ. Pa, 49-60; MED. CTR, UNIV. KY, 60-63, PROF, 63- Am. Asn. Anat; Am. Neurol. Asn; Am. Asn. Neuropath; assoc. Am. Acad. Neurol. Physiology of lung lymphatics; thalamus and midbrain of mammals; autonomic nervous system; blood supply of the central nervous system. Address: Dept. of Anatomy, College of Medicine, University of Kentucky, Lexington, KY 40506.

GILLILAND, BOBBY EUGENE, b. Epps, La, Aug. 6, 36; m. 59; c. 1. ELECTRICAL ENGINEERING. B.S, La. Polytech, 58; Ga-Pac. Corp. fel, Arkansas, 63-64, M.S, 64, Instrument Soc. Am-Found. Instrumentation & Ed. Res. fel, 65-66, Ph.D.(electronics, instrumentation), 68. Res. asst. electronics & instrumentation, Arkansas, Little Rock, 62-67; asst. prof. ELEC. ENG, CLEMSON UNIV, 67-69, ASSOC. PROF, 69- Med.Serv.C, U.S.A, 59-62, Capt. Inst. Elec. & Electronics Eng; Am. Soc. Eng. Educ; Simulation Coun; Nat. Soc. Prof. Eng. Instrumentation; direct digital control; modeling and simulation of physical and physiological systems; optimal estimation; direct digital control of waste treatment plants; remote sensing of water pollutants; biomedical instrumentation and telemetry. Address: Dept. of Electrical & Computer Engineering, Clemson University, Clemson, SC 29631.

GILLILAND, DENNIS CRIPPEN, b. Warren, Pa, July 23, 38; m. 57; c. 3. STATISTICS, MATHEMATICS. B.A, Kent State, 59; fel, Case Western Reserve, 60-61; M.S, Mich. State, 63, Ph.D.(statist), 66. Develop. engr, Goodyear Aerospace Corp, 59-66; asst. prof. STATIST. & PROBABILITY, MICH. STATE UNIV, 66-69, ASSOC. PROF, 69- Lectr, Univ. Calif, Berkeley, 66-67. Inst. Math. Statist; Am. Statist. Asn; Math. Asn. Am. Coverage problems; decision theory; linear statistical models. Address: Dept. of Statistics & Probability, Michigan State University, East Lansing, MI 48823.

GILLILAND, E(DWIN) R(ICHARD), b. El Reno, Okla, July 10, 09; m. 38; c. 1. CHEMICAL ENGINEERING. B.S, Illinois, 30; M.S, Pa. State Col, 31; Sc.D. (chem. eng), Mass. Inst. Tech, 33; hon. D.Eng, Northeast. Univ, 48. Instr. CHEM. ENG, MASS. INST. TECHNOL, 34-36, asst. prof, 36-39, assoc. prof, 39-44, prof, 44-69, WARREN K. LEWIS PROF, 69-, dep. dean eng, 45-46, head dept. chem. eng, 61-69. Asst. rubber dir. in charge res. & develop, War Prod. Bd, 42-44; dep. chief div, 11, Nat. Defense Res. Comt, 44-45; mem, President's Sci. Adv. Comt, 61-65; consult, Off. Sci. & Technol, 65- Nat. Acad. Sci; Nat. Acad. Eng; AAAS; Am. Chem. Soc.(Baekeland Award, 44, indust. & eng. chem. award, 59); fel. Am. Inst. Chem. Eng.(prof. progress award, 50, William H. Walker Award, 54, Warren K. Lewis Award, 65, Founders Award, 71); Soc. Chem. Indust; Am. Inst. Chemists; Am. Acad. Arts & Sci; Am. Soc. Eng. Educ. Distillation; mass transfer; unit operations of chemical engineering; applied chemistry. Address: Dept. of Chemical Engineering, Massachusetts Institute of Technology, Cambridge, MA 02139.

GILLILAND, FLOYD RAY, JR, b. Cotter, Ark, Dec. 18, 39; m. 62; c. 1. ENTOMOLOGY, ZOOLOGY. B.S, Ark. Polytech. Col, 62; M.S, Arkansas, 64; Ph.D.(entom), Miss. State, 67. Asst. prof. ENTOM, AUBURN UNIV, 67-71, ASSOC. PROF, 71- AAAS; Entom. Soc. Am. Basic and applied studies of cotton insects, especially methods of biological control of cotton insects. Address: Dept. of Zoology & Entomology, Auburn University, Auburn, AL 36830.

GILLILAND, HAROLD EUGENE, b. Duncan, Okla, Sept. 9, 37. CHEMICAL ENGINEERING, PHYSICAL CHEMISTRY. S.B, Mass. Inst. Tech, 59, Sloan Found. fel. & S.M, 61, Nat. Sci. Found. fel. & Ph.D.(chem. eng), 65; Fulbright fel, Bristol, 59-60. Res. scientist, CONTINENTAL OIL CO, 64-67, RES. GROUP SUPVR, 67- Am. Inst. Mining, Metall. & Petrol. Eng. Heterogeneous catalysis; thermal methods of recovering hydrocarbon resources; petroleum recovery processes. Address: Continental Oil Co, P.O. Drawer 1267, Ponca City, OK 74601.

GILLILAND, JOE E(DWARD), b. Alhambra, Calif, Dec. 4, 27; m. 52; c. 2. CHEMICAL ENGINEERING. B.S, Tex. Tech. Col, 49; M.S, Okla. State, 60. Chem. engr, Tex. Brine Corp, 49-51; chem. engr, OZARK-MAHONING CO, 51-57, pilot plant supvr, 57-63, SUPT, SPEC. CHEM. DEPT, 63- Inst. Chem. Eng. Inorganic fluorine compounds; crystallization. Address: Special Chemicals Dept, Ozark-Mahoning Co, 1870 S. Boulder, Tulsa, OK 74119.

GILLILAND, JOHN L(AWRENCE), JR, b. Clearfield, Pa, Oct. 4, 10; m. 35; c. 3. CHEMICAL ENGINEERING. B.S, Colorado, 33. Jr. chem. engr, U.S. Bur. Reclamation, 33-34, chem. engr, 34-51; gen. chemist, IDEAL CEMENT CO, 51-64, dir. qual. control, 64-67, TECH. DIR, 67- Mem. nat. adv. comt. control tech, Nat. Air Pollution Control Admin. Am. Chem. Soc; Air Pollution Control Asn; Am. Soc. Test & Mat.(award of merit); Am. Concrete Inst; Am. Acad. Environ. Eng. Air pollution control; quality control of Portland cement manufacture; environmental controls. Address: Ideal Cement Co, 821 17th St, Denver, CO 80202.

GILLILAND, MAXWELL C(AMPBELL), b. Alhambra, Calif, Dec. 27, 25; m. 50; c. 3. ENGINEERING, APPLIED MATHEMATICS. B.S, California, Los Angeles, 54, Standard Oil Co. Calif. fel, 54-56, Ph.D.(eng), 56. Supt. commun. sect, U.S. Civil Serv, Guam, 48-49; res. engr, Lockheed Aircraft Corp, 49-53; sr. engr, Comput. Eng. Assocs, 56-57; chief comput. programming, pilotless aircraft div, Boeing Airplane Co, 57-59; mgr. adv. study progs, Berkeley Div, Beckman Instruments, Inc, 59-60, res. dir, 60-63, mgr. comput. opers, 63-65; PRES, COMPUT. RES, INC, 65- Consult. & lectr, Univ. Calif, Los Angeles, 56-57, 59-60. U.S.N, 43-46. Soc. Indust. & Appl. Math; Math. Asn. Am; Inst. Elec. & Electronics Eng. Analog, digital and hybrid simulation. Address: Computer Research, Inc, 7442 N. Figueroa St, Los Angeles, CA 90041.

GILLILAND, STANLEY E(UGENE), b. Minco, Okla, June 24, 40; m. 60; c. 3. FOOD MICROBIOLOGY. B.S, Okla. State Univ, 62, M.S, 63; Inst. Environ. Health Studies fel, N.C. State Univ, 63-65, Ph.D.(food sci), 66. ASST. PROF. FOOD SCI, N.C. STATE UNIV, 65- Am. Soc. Microbiol; Inst. Food Technol; Am. Dairy Sci. Asn. Nutrition of lactic starter cultures; growth of high population bacterial starter cultures; antagonisms of starter cultures toward food-borne pathogens; factors which limit the growth and action of starter cultures; microbial inactivation by electrohydraulic shock. Address: Dept. of Food Science, North Carolina State University, Raleigh, NC 27607.

GILLILAND, WILLIAM N(ATHAN), b. Portsmouth, Ohio, May 23, 19; m. 44; c. 2. GEOLOGY. B.A, Ohio State, 41, fel, 47-48, Ph.D.(geol), 48. Asst. geol, Ohio State, 41-42, 46-47; geologist, U.S. Geol. Surv, 48-49; asst. prof, Utah field sta, Ohio State, 49-50; from instr. to asst. prof. geol, Nebraska, 49-50, assoc. prof, 51-58, prof, 58-65, chmn. dept, 51-64; PROF. GEOL, RUTGERS UNIV, 65-, dean Newark Col. Arts & Sci, 65-68. Geologist, Tenn. Valley Authority, 42; consult, Calif. Co, 51-53; Shell Oil Co, 55; Creole Petrol. Corp, 56-57. U.S.A.A.F, 42-46, Lt. Fel. Geol. Soc. Am; Am. Asn. Petrol. Geol; Am. Inst. Prof. Geol. Stratigraphy; structural geology; petroleum geology. Address: Dept. of Geology, Rutgers University, Newark, NJ 07102.

GILLIN, JAMES, b. Floral Park, N.Y, Sept. 16, 25; m. 49; c. 2. CHEMICAL ENGINEERING. B.Ch.E, Cornell, 47, S.C. Johnson & Son Co. fel, 47-49, Ph.D.(chem. eng), 51. Sr. engr, chem. eng. process develop, MERCK & CO, INC, 49-52, group leader, 52-56, sect. mgr, pilot plant, 56-59, mgr, 59-62, dir, 62-64, chem. eng. res. & develop, 64-69, EXEC. DIR, new drug develop, 69-70, PLANNING & ADMIN, MERCK, SHARP & DOHME RES. LABS, 70- AAAS; Am. Chem. Soc; Am. Inst. Chem. Eng; N.Y. Acad. Sci; fel. Am. Inst. Chem. Ion exchange; vapor phase catalytic oxidation. Address: 13 Carol Rd, Westfield, NJ 07090.

GILLINGHAM, J. T, b. Anyox, B.C, June 3, 22; m. 47; c. 3. SOILS & PLANT NUTRITION. B.S.A, British Columbia, 44; M.Sc, McGill, 46; Ph.D.(soils), Clemson, 63. Lectr. soils, British Columbia, 48-50; biochemist, Royal Jubilee Hosp, Victoria, B.C, 50-59; res. off. soils & plant nutrit, Can. Dept. Agr, 63-67; asst. chemist, DEPT. AGR. CHEM. SERV, CLEMSON UNIV, 67-70, ASSOC. CHEMIST, 70- Agr. Inst. Can; Can. Soc. Soil Sci. Soil fertility and chemistry. Address: Dept. of Agricultural Chemical Services, Clemson University, Clemson, SC 29631.

GILLINGHAM, JAMES M(ORRIS), b. Gallipolis, Ohio, Mar. 29, 24; m. 48; c. 2. PHARMACEUTICAL CHEMISTRY. B.A, Denison, 49; Northwestern, 50. Asst. res. chemist, Parke, Davis & Co, 50-55; asst. sci. dir, Warren Teed Prods, 55-59; prod. mgr, Diamond Labs, 59-60, dir. pharmaceut. prods. develop, 60-61; v.pres. Vale Chem. Co, 61-70; MGR. PHARMACEUT. PROD, ANIMAL HEALTH DIV, AM. HOECHST CORP, 70- U.S.A.A.F, 43-45. Am. Chem. Soc; Am. Pharmaceut. Asn; Am. Inst. Chem; N.Y. Acad. Sci; Am. Soc. Qual Control. Research and products development in pharmaceutical and analytical chemistry; production and processing of veterinary and human pharmaceutical products. Address: Animal Health Division, American Hoechst Corp, 1721 Baltimore Ave, Kansas City, MO 64108.

GILLINGHAM, ROBERT J, b. Galvin, Wash, Oct. 29, 23. SOLID STATE PHYSICS, ELECTRONICS. M.A, Gonzaga Univ, 49; M.S, La. State Univ, 60, Ph.D.(physics), 63. ASST. PROF. PHYSICS, GONZAGA UNIV, 62- Head dept. sci. & dir. seismol. observ, Mt. St. Michael's Sem, 62-67; partic, Nat. Sci. Found. col. teacher res. participation prog, La. State Univ, summer 63. Am. Phys. Soc; Am. Asn. Physics Teachers; Seismol. Soc. Am. Electronic instrumentation. Address: Dept. of Physics, Gonzaga University, Spokane, WA 99202.

GILLIOM, RICHARD D, b. Bluffton, Ind, June 25, 34; m. 58; c. 3. ORGANIC CHEMISTRY. B.S, Southwest. at Memphis, 56; Sun Oil fel, Mass. Inst. Tech, 59-60, Nat. Sci. Found. fel, summer 59, Ph.D.(org. chem), 60. Res. chemist, Esso Res. Labs, Humble Oil & Ref. Co, 60-61; asst. prof. CHEM, SOUTHWEST. AT MEMPHIS, 61-64, assoc. prof, 64-71, PROF, 71- Fulbright lectr, Univ. Skoplje, 68-69. Am. Chem. Soc. Free radical reactions; effects of structure upon reactivity. Address: Dept. of Chemistry, Southwestern at Memphis, Memphis, TN 38112.

GILLIS, BERNARD T(HOMAS), b. Pierre, S.Dak, Mar. 7, 31; m. 53; c. 3. ORGANIC CHEMISTRY. B.S, Loras Col, 52; Ethyl Corp. fels, Wayne State, 52-55, Parke, Davis & Co. fel, 55-56, Ph.D.(org. chem), 56. Asst. org. chem, Wayne State, 52-53; fel, Mass. Inst. Tech, 56-57; asst. prof. chem, Duquesne Univ, 57-60, assoc. prof, 60-64, prof, 64-70, assoc. chmn. dept, 65-68, dean grad. sch, 68-70; ACAD. V.PRES. & PROVOST, IND. UNIV. PA, 70- AAAS; Am. Chem. Soc; fel. Am. Inst. Chem; The Chem. Soc. Organic synthesis; structure elucidation of natural products; divinyl ethers; oxidation of hydrazides and hydrazones; azo dienophiles; educational administration. Address: Office of the Academic Vice President, Indiana University of Pennsylvania, Indiana, PA 15701.

GILLIS, CATHERINE JOSEPHINE, S.N.D. de N, b. Antigonish, N.S, Apr. 12, 00; U.S. citizen. MATHEMATICAL STATISTICS. A.B, Emmanuel Col. (Mass), 42; A.M, Boston, 46, Ph.D.(math. statist), 59. Teacher parochial schs, Mass, 22-42; instr. MATH, EMMANUEL COL.(MASS), 42-50, asst. prof, 50-59, assoc. prof, 59-61, PROF, 61-, chmn. dept, 60-66. Math. Asn. Am; Inst. Math. Statist. Theory of range; non-parametric statistical inference. Address: Dept. of Mathematics, Emmanuel College, 400 The Fenway, Boston, MA 02115.

GILLIS, C(HARLES) N(ORMAN), b. Glasgow, Scotland, Feb. 3, 33; U.S. citizen; m. 60; c. 2. PHARMACOLOGY. B.Sc, Glasgow Univ, 54, Ph.D.(pharmacol), 57. Asst. lectr. exp. pharmacol, Glasgow Univ, 54-57; asst. prof. pharmacol, Univ. Alta, 57-61; Yale, 61-66, assoc. prof, 66-68; head cardiovasc. pharmacol, Squibb Inst. Med. Res, 68-69; ASSOC. PROF. ANESTHESIOL. & PHARMACOL, YALE SCH. MED, 69- Estab. investr, Am. Heart Asn, 64-68; vis. assoc. prof, med. sch, Rutgers Univ, 68-69. Am. Soc. Pharmacol. & Exp. Therapeut; Pharmacol. Soc. Can. Cardiopulmonary and autonomic pharmacology; neuropharmacology. Address: Dept. of Pharmacology, Yale University School of Medicine, New Haven, CT 06510.

GILLIS, H(UGH) A(NDREW), b. Sydney, N.S, Aug. 11, 35. PHYSICAL CHEMISTRY. B.Sc, St. Francis Xavier, 54; fel, Notre Dame, 54-55, Atomic Energy Cmn. fel, 55-57, Ph.D.(chem), 57. Gen. Elec. Co. res. fel. phys. chem, Leeds, 57-59; asst. prof. chem, St. Francis Xavier, 59-62; asst. prof, Case West. Reserve Univ, 62-67; ASSOC. RES. OFF, PHYSICS DIV, NAT. RES. COUNC. CAN, 67- Summer fel, Mellon Inst, 60. AAAS; Am. Chem. Soc; Chem. Inst. Can. Radiation chemistry. Address: Physics Division, National Research Council of Canada, Montreal Rd, Ottawa 7, Ont, Can.

GILLIS, JAMES E, JR, b. Lewiston, Maine, Apr. 22, 20; m; c. 1. GEOLOGY, GEOPHYSICS. B.S, Cath. Univ. Am, 41; M.S.B.A, George Wash. Univ, 66; grad, Indust. Col. Armed Forces, 66. Tech. secy, comt. geophys. sci, Joint Res. & Develop. Bd, U.S. Dept. Army, 46-47; secy, comt. Geophys. & geog, Res. & Develop. Bd, U.S. Dept. Defense, 47-49, res. analyst, planning div, 49-51, panel dir, 51-52; chief, coordination br, snow, ice & permafrost res. estab, Corps Eng, U.S. DEPT. ARMY, 52-53, acting dir, 53-58, adminstr, 58-59, phys. sci. adminstr. in charge res. satellite geod. & mapping, eng. res. & develop. labs, Ft. Belvoir, 59-60, chief, intel. div, U.S. Army Engr. Geod. Intel. & Mapping Res. & Develop. Agency, 60-67, assoc. dir. mapping & geog. sci. lab, U.S. Army Eng. Topog. Labs, 67-69, TECH. DIR, DIRECTORATE ADVAN. SYSTS, U.S. ARMY TOPOG. COMMAND, CORPS ENGRS, 69- Consult, NASA; Nat. Acad. Sci-Nat. Res. Coun. del, Int. Geophys. Year, Moscow, Russia, 59. Chem.C, U.S.A.A.F, 42-46. Geol. Soc. Am; Am. Geog. Soc; Soc. Am. Mil. Eng; Am. Soc. Photogram; Soc. Photog. Sci. & Eng; Am. Geophys. Union; Optical Soc. Am; Glaciol. Soc. Field and laboratory research and development programs in the physical sciences; satellite geodesy; mapping satellites; optical and electronic tracking techniques and equipment; methods, techniques and systems for collection and processing of military geographic intelligence. Address: Directorate of Advanced Systems, U.S. Army Topographic Command, Corps of Engineers, Washington, DC 20315.

GILLIS, M(ARVIN) B(OB), b. Soperton, Ga, Apr. 5, 20; m. 46; c. 3. BIOCHEMISTRY. B.S.A, Univ. Ga, 40; fel. & Ph.D.(nutrit), Cornell Univ, 47. Asst, Univ. Ga, 39-40; Cornell Univ, 40-42; supvr. nutrit. res, INT. MINERALS & CHEM. CORP, 47-51, supvr. biol. res, 51-54, mgr. res. org. & biol. sci, 54-56, assoc. dir. res, 56-57, dir, 57-64, animal health & nutrit, 64-66, div. v.pres, 66-69, Europe, 69-70, CORP. V.PRES, BUS. DEVELOP, 70- Res. assoc, Cornell Univ, 47-51; mem. bd. gov, Agr. Res. Inst, 57-70, secy, 58-60, v.pres, 60-62, pres, 62-63, 68-69; mem. agr. bd, Nat. Acad. Sci-Nat. Res. Coun, 61-66; dir. Animal Health Inst, 66-69; citizens adv. bd, Lake Forest Col. Poultry Sci. Res. Prize, 48. U.S.A.A.F, 42-45. Am. Chem. Soc; Am. Soc. Animal Sci; Poultry Sci. Asn; Am. Inst. Nutrit; Am. Inst. Chem. Role of pantothenic acid in reproduction; phosphorus in nutrition and metabolism; mineral metabolism; methylating compounds; effect of fertility on nutritional value of plants; fertilizer requirements of soils and crops; chemistry of amino acids; mineral processing; inorganic compounds of phosphorus and potassium; microbiology. Address: International Minerals & Chemical Corp, P.O. Box 192, Libertyville, IL 60048.

GILLIS, M(URLIN) F(ERN), b. Santa Cruz, Calif, Apr. 26, 35; m. 71; c. 3. VETERINARY MEDICINE, PHYSICS. B.S, Univ. Wash. 56; fels, Calif. Inst. Technol, 56-59, M.S, 59; D.V.M, Wash. State Univ, 63. Res. scientist, BIOL. DEPT, PAC. NORTHWEST LAB, BATTELLE MEM. INST, 66-68, SR. RES. SCIENTIST, 68- Mem. Coun. on thrombosis, Am. Heart Asn, 71- AAAS; Am. Vet. Med. Asn; Am. Heart Asn; Math. Asn. Am. Experimental surgery; bioengineering; biomaterials; implantology; fertility control; hyperbaric medicine. Address: 331 Bldg, 300 Area, Battelle Memorial Institute, Pacific Northwest Lab, P.O. Box 999, Richland, WA 99352.

GILLIS, PETER PAUL, b. Newport, R.I, Dec. 23, 30; m. 53; c. 4. SOLID MECHANICS, MATERIALS SCIENCE. Sc.B, Brown, 53, Sc.M, 61, Ph.D.(eng), 64. Prod. engr, Fram Corp, R.I, 56-57; develop. engr, Lessona Corp, 57-58; instr. mach. design, R.I. Sch. Design, 58-59; res. asst. eng, Brown Univ, 59-64; asst. prof. eng. mech, UNIV. KY, 64-68, ASSOC. PROF. MAT. SCI, 68- Consult, Spindletop Res. Inc, Ky, 64-66; Lawrence Radiation Lab, 65-; Sandia Corp, N.Mex, 67; Los Alamos Sci. Lab, 68-; Fulbright-Hays res. scholar, Physics & Eng. Lab, Dept. Sci. & Indust. Res, N.Z, 70-71; consult. div. compliance, Atomic Energy Comn, 70-; vis. scientist, State Univ. N.Y. Col. Forestry, Syracuse, 71. U.S.N, 53-56, Res, 56-, Lt. AAAS; Am. Inst. Mining, Metall. & Petrol. Eng; Am. Soc. Metals; Am. Phys. Soc; Am. Soc. Mech. Eng; Soc. Rheol; Soc. Wood Sci. & Technol. Flow and fracture properties of materials, particularly relations between these characteristics and the microstructure of the material in terms of the concepts of crystal physics. Address: Dept. of Metallurgical Engineering & Materials Science, University of Kentucky, Lexington, KY 40506.

GILLIS, RICHARD A, b. Rochester, N.Y, Mar. 20, 38; m. 60; c. 1. PHARMACOLOGY. B.A, Miami Univ, 60; Ph.D.(pharmacol), McGill Univ, 65. Res. fel. PHARMACOL, Harvard Med. Sch, 65-66, instr, 67; SCH. MED, GEORGETOWN UNIV, 67-69, ASST. PROF, 69- AAAS; Am. Soc. Pharmacol. & Exp. Therapeut. Cardiovascular and autonomic nervous system pharmacology. Address: Dept. of Pharmacology, Georgetown University School of Medicine, 3900 Reservoir Rd. N.W, Washington, DC 20007.

GILLIS, ROBERT E(DWARD), b. Manchester, N.H, May 16, 17; m. 42; c. 2. MICROBIOLOGY. Alabama, 37-39; City Col. New York, 40-42; D.D.S, Western Reserve, 48, Ph.D.(microbiol), 58. Asst. dent. surgeon, U.S. Pub. Health Serv, 48-49, fel. microbiol, Western Reserve, 49-51, instr, 51-57, res. coord, sch. dent, 56-57; from assoc. prof. to PROF. MICROBIOL. & ENDODONTICS & MEM. EXEC. FACULTY, COL. MED. & DENT. N.J, NEWARK, 57-, COORD. RES, 65- Med.C, U.S.A, 43-44. Am. Soc. Microbiol; Int. Asn. Dent. Res. Bacterial metabolism; carbohydrate metabolisms of oral microorganisms. Address: College of Medicine & Dentistry of New Jersey at Newark, 100 Bergen St, Newark, NJ 07103.

GILLIS, WILLIAM T(HOMAS), (JR), b. Perth Amboy, N.J, June 22, 33. PLANT TAXONOMY & ECOLOGY. B.A, Rutgers Univ, 55; M.S, Mich. State Univ, 57, Ph.D, 70. Admissions counsr, Mich. State Univ, 59-60, asst. instr. bot, 60-62, instr. natural sci, 62-68, planetarium lectr, 64-68; PLANT TAXONOMIST, FAIRCHILD TROP. GARDEN, UNIV. MIAMI, 68- Phytochem. Soc. N.Am; Am. Soc. Plant Taxon; Ecol. Soc. Am; Arctic Inst. N.Am; Int. Asn. Plant Taxon; Glaciol. Soc. Taxonomy of tropical vascular plants; taxonomy of Anacardiaceae; arctic ecology; phytogeography; flora of the Bahama Islands; poisonous plants of the West Indies. Address: Fairchild Tropical Garden, 10901 Old Cutler Rd, Miami, FL 33156.

GILLMAN, DAVID, b. N.Y.C, Sept. 6, 38. MATHEMATICS. B.S, Wisconsin, 58, M.S, 59, Ph.D.(math), 62. Res. instr. MATH, Cornell, 62; mem. Inst. Advan. Study, 62-64; asst. prof, UNIV. CALIF, LOS ANGELES, 64-69, ASSOC. PROF, 69- Topology. Address: Dept. of Mathematics, University of California, Los Angeles, CA 90024.

GILLMAN, HYMAN DAVID, b. Brooklyn, N.Y, Dec. 21, 41; m. 67; c. 1. INORGANIC & PHYSICAL CHEMISTRY. B.S, L.I. Univ, 63; Nat. Defense Educ. Act fel, Tufts Univ, 65-67, Du Pont fel, 67-68, Ph.D.(inorg. chem), 68. Fel, Tufts Univ, 68; SR. RES. CHEMIST, PENNWALT CHEM. CORP, 68- Am. Chem. Soc; The Chem. Soc. Preparation and study of coordination compounds; synthesis of high temperature coordination polymers with inorganic backbones. Address: Pennwalt Chemical Corp, 900 First Ave, King of Prussia, PA 19406.

GILLMAN, LEONARD, b. Cleveland, Ohio, Jan. 8, 17; m. 38; c. 2. MATHEMATICS. B.S, Columbia, 41, Carnegie Corp. fel, 42-43; M.A, 45, Ph.D. (math), 53. Asst. MATH, Columbia, 41-42, lectr, 43; assoc, Tufts Col, 43-45; mem. staff, opers. evaluation group, Mass. Inst. Tech, 45-51; instr, Purdue, 52-53, asst. prof, 53-56, assoc. prof, 56-60; PROF. & CHMN. DEPT, Rochester, 60-69; UNIV. TEX, AUSTIN, 69- Guggenheim Mem. fel, 58-59; mem. Inst. Advan. Study, 58-60; Nat. Sci. Found. sr. fel, 59-60; Math. Asn. Am. vis. lectr, 61-69; mem. comt. on regional develop, Nat. Acad. Sci-Nat. Res. Coun, 63-65, chmn, 65-66, mem. U.S. Comn. on Math. Instr, 65-66, chmn, 66-69, U.S. del, Int. Comn. Math. Instr, 66-69, mem. comt. sources & forms of support, 68-71, organizing comt, first int. cong. math. educ, 69; math. ed, W.W. Norton Co, 67- AAAS; Am. Math. Soc.(assoc. secy, 69-71); Math. Asn. Am. Theory of sets; topology; rings of continuous functions. Address: Dept. of Mathematics, University of Texas at Austin, Austin, TX 78712.

GILLMOR, R(OBERT) N(ILES), b. Marion, Iowa, Dec. 25, 06; m. 30; c. 2. METALLURGICAL ENGINEERING. B.S, S.Dak. Sch. Mines & Tech, 28. Develop. engr. process metall, Int. Smelting Co, 28-31; consult. & develop. engr. phys. metall, GEN. ELEC. CO, 31-42, MGR. works lab, 42-45, mat. & process lab, 45-55, div. lab, 55-69, MAT. & PROCESS LAB, 69- Am. Soc. Metals. Physical metallurgy in both ferrous and nonferrous metallurgy, especially austenitic, ferritic and martensitic stainless steels and their passive characteristics in various environmental media. Address: Materials & Process Lab, General Electric Co, Electronics Park, Syracuse, NY 13201.

GILLMORE, DONALD W(OOD), b. Lorain, Ohio, June 24, 19; m. 44; c. 3. FUEL TECHNOLOGY. B.A, Williams Col, 41; Anthracite fel, Pa. State, 51-53, Ph.D.(fuel tech), 54. Asst, titanium div, Nat. Lead Co, 41-43; res. assoc, Inst. Gas Tech, 43-44; sr. chemist, Butadiene Div, Koppers Co, Inc, 44-45; res. chemist, Houdry Process Corp, 45-48; asst. & assoc. fuel tech. div, Pa. State, 48-51; supvr. carbon res, Pittsburgh Coke & Chem. Co, 53-59; mgr. tech. br, electro minerals div, Carborundum Co, Niagara Falls, 60-67, plant mgr, 67-70; RES. SUPVR, U.S. BUR. MINES, 70- Am. Chem. Soc. Fuel and coal technology; physical chemistry; activated carbon; electron microscopy; Fischer-Tropsch synthesis; abrasives; electric furnacing; refractories; coal gasification, fluid-bed combustion and gasification; fly ash utilization; strip mine and coal refuse reclamation; coal preparation. Address: U.S. Bureau of Mines, P.O. Box 880, Morgantown, WV 26505.

GILLOOLY, RICHARD PETER, b. Boston, Mass, Sept. 12, 20; m. 45; c. 10. AERONAUTICAL ENGINEERING. B.S, Mass. Inst. Tech, 42, M.S, 46. Design engr, McDONNELL DOUGLAS ASTRONAUT. CO, 46-54, chief control dynamics, 54-59, sr. develop. engr. on F4B & F4C, 59-61, chief guid. & control, 61-64, Gemini Lab. develop. mgr, 64-65, eng. prog. mgr, advan. design, 65-68, syst. eng. & integration mgr, airlock module, SKYLAB PROG, 68-69, eng. mgr, 69, DEP. DIR, AIRLOCK MODULE, 69- U.S.A.F, 42-45, 1st Lt. Am. Inst. Aeronaut. & Astronaut. Automatic control of missiles and aircraft. Address: McDonnell Douglas Astronautics Co, Box 516, St. Louis, MO 63166.

GILLOTT, DONALD H, b. Connellsville, Pa, Aug. 25, 31; m. 70; c. 3. ELECTRICAL ENGINEERING. B.S, Pittsburgh, 56, M.S, 59, Ph.D.(elec. eng), 63. Jr. engr, Latrobe Steel Co, 54-56; instr. ELEC. ENG, Pittsburgh, 56-59, asst. prof, 60-66, assoc. prof, 66-68; PROF. & CHMN. DEPT, SACRAMENTO STATE COL, 68- Nat. Sci. Found. grant, 64-, travel grant, Europe, 66; design engr, Latrobe Steel Co, 56-58; consult, power supply div, Int. Bus. Mach. Corp, 59-63; Nat. Acad. Sci, 63- Am. Soc. Eng. Educ; sr. mem. Inst. Elec. & Electronics Eng. Flux penetration in magnetic materials, including effects of saturation and hysteresis. Address: Dept. of Electrical Engineering, Sacramento State College, 6000 J St, Sacramento, CA 95819.

GILLOW, EDWARD WILLIAM, b. Scranton, Pa, Apr. 14, 39; m. 62; c. 3. PHYSICAL & INORGANIC CHEMISTRY. B.S, Pa. State, 60; Ph.D.(phys. chem), State Univ. N.Y. Buffalo, 66. Fel. chem, Texas, Austin, 66-68; res. chemist, PIGMENTS DEPT, exp. sta. lab, E.I. DU PONT DE NEMOURS & CO, INC, 68-70, TECH. SERV. CHEMIST, CHESTNUT RUN LAB, 70- Am. Chem. Soc. Chemical kinetics; mechanisms of inorganic reactions; coordination complex, metall organic and inorganic synthesis; solution chemistry with nonaqueous solvents; chromatography of inorganic materials; surface chemistry of metals and metal oxides. Address: 1811 Bybrook Rd, Fairfax, Wilmington, DE 19803.

GILLULY, JAMES, b. Seattle, Wash, June 24, 96; m. 25; c. 2. GEOLOGY. B.S, Washington (Seattle), 20; Hopkins, 22; Ph.D.(geol), Yale, 26; hon. D.Sc, Princeton, 59. Jr. geologist, Nat. Ref. Co, 21; geol. aide, U.S. Geol. Surv, 21-23, asst. geologist, 23-25, assoc. geologist, 25-29, geologist, 29-36, sr. geologist, 36-42, prin. geologist, 43-50, res. geologist, 50-54, chief, gen. geol. br, 54-57, fuels br, 57-59, res. geologist, 59-66; RETIRED. Prof, California, Los Angeles, 38-50, faculty res. lectr, 48; Bownocker lectr, Ohio State, 51; part-time prof, Univ. Calif, Santa Cruz, 68. Ed, 'Monograph World Copper Resources.' Mem. div. geol. & geog, Nat. Res. Coun, 31-34, 51-54, chmn, 62-63. Mem. Int. Geol. Cong, 33, U.S. del, Denmark, 60, India, 64. With Off. Chief Eng, Southwest Pacific area, U.S.A, 44-45; U.S.N, 17-19; Distinguished Serv. Medal, U.S. Dept. Interior, 59. Nat. Acad. Sci; fel. Geol. Soc. Am.(1st v.pres, 47, pres, 48, Penrose Medal, 58); fel. Mineral. Soc. Am; Soc. Econ. Geol; Soc. Econ. Paleont. & Mineral; Seismol. Soc. Am; Am. Asn. Petrol. Geol; Am. Geophys. Union (Bucher Medal, 69); fel. Am. Acad. Arts & Sci; for. mem. Geol. Soc. London (Wm. Smith lectr, 62). Structural geology, especially thrust faults; economic geology of copper; petrology, especially metamorphism and rock alteration; stratigraphy. Address: 975 Estes St, Lakewood, CO 80215.

GILMAN, ALBERT F, III, b. Chicago, Ill, June 25, 31; m. 64. MATHEMATICS. B.S, Northwestern, 52; M.A, Montana, 58; M.A, Indiana, 62, Ph.D. (math), 63. Instr. math, Bowdoin Col, 63-64, asst. prof, 64-66; assoc. prof. math. & chmn. div. sci. & math, Col. of the Virgin Islands, 66-69; PROF. MATH. & ASST. V.PRES. ACAD. AFFAIRS, WEST. CAROLINA UNIV, 69-, DIR. COMPUT. CTR, 70- U.S.A, 54-56. Am. Math. Soc. Noncommutative schemes; economic models; psephology; politicometrics. Address: Western Carolina University, Cullowhee, NC 28723.

GILMAN, ALFRED, b. Bridgeport, Conn, Feb. 5, 08; m. 34; c. 2. PHARMACOLOGY. B.S, Yale, 28, Ph.D.(biochem), 31. Cox fel, sch. med, Yale, 31-32, Calco Chem. Co. res. fel. pharmacol. & toxicol, 32-35, asst, 35-36, asst. prof. PHARMACOL, 36-43; assoc. prof, col. physicians & surg, Columbia, 46-48, prof, 48-56; PROF. & CHMN. DEPT, ALBERT EINSTEIN COL. MED, 56-, assoc. dean grad. educ, 64-69. Mem. sci. & educ. coun, Am. Found. Allergic Diseases; div. med. sci, Nat. Res. Coun, 62-71; drug res. bd, Nat. Acad. Sci-Nat. Res. Coun, 64-; panel chem. & health, President's Sci. Adv. Comt, 70-; chmn. drug res. bd, Nat. Acad. Sci-Nat. Res. Coun, 71-72. With Off. Sci. Res. & Develop; U.S. Pub. Health Serv, 44; Sanit.C, 43-46, Maj. Nat. Acad. Sci; Soc. Pharmacol; Am. Physiol. Soc; Soc. Exp. Biol. & Med; Harvey Soc; hon. fel. Am. Acad. Allergy; fel. N.Y. Acad. Sci; fel. Am. Acad. Arts & Sci. Renal physiology; salt and water metabolism; pharmacodynamics. Address: Dept. of Pharmacology, Albert Einstein College of Medicine, Bronx, NY 10461.

GILMAN, DONALD L(AWRENCE), b. Hartford, Conn, Oct. 15, 31; m. 61; c. 3. METEOROLOGY. A.B, Harvard, 52; Nat. Sci. Found. fel, Mass. Inst. Tech, 53-55, M.S, 54, Ph.D.(meteorol), 57. Mem. res. staff, meteorol. dept, Mass. Inst. Tech, 55-58; res. meteorologist, extended forecast div, NAT. WEATHER SERV, NAT. OCEANIC & ATMOSPHERIC ADMIN, 58-64, chief develop. & testing sect, 64-71, CHIEF, LONG RANGE PREDICTION GROUP, NAT. METEOROL. CTR, 71- AAAS; Am. Meteorol. Soc; Am. Geophys. Union. Objective techniques of extended and long range forecasting; forecast verification; meteorological statistics. Address: National Meteorological Center, National Weather Service, National Oceanic & Atmospheric Agency, Washington, DC 20233.

GILMAN, EDWARD N(IMROD), b. Webster City, Iowa, Sept. 9, 10. MICROBIOLOGY, BIOCHEMISTRY. B.A, Iowa, 34; M.Sc, Iowa State Col, 38; Ph.D, Illinois, 50. Bacteriologist, Ill. State Dept. Health, 40-50; asst. prof. microbiol. & clin. path, med. ctr, Alabama, 50-55; VIROLOGIST & BIOCHEMIST, VIRUS-RICKETTSIAE DIV, U.S. ARMY BIOL. LAB, 55- Sanit.C, U.S.A, 42-46. AAAS; Am. Chem. Soc; Am. Soc. Microbiol; N.Y. Acad. Sci. Microbial metabolism; purification of viruses and rickettsiae and their products; clinical chemistry and pathology; immunology. Address: Virus-Rickettsiae Division, U.S. Army Biological Lab, Ft. Detrick, Frederick, MD 21701.

GILMAN, FREDERICK JOSEPH, b. Lansing, Mich, Oct. 9, 40; m. 67; c. 1. THEORETICAL PHYSICS. B.S, Mich. State, 62; Ph.D.(physics), Princeton, 65. Nat. Sci. Found. res. fel, Calif. Inst. Technol, 65-66, res. fel. THEORET. PHYSICS, 65-67; res. assoc, STANFORD LINEAR ACCELERATOR CTR, 67-69, ASSOC. PROF, 69- Am. Phys. Soc. Theoretical elementary particle physics; theoretical high energy physics. Address: Stanford Linear Accelerator Center, Stanford University, Stanford, CA 94305.

GILMAN, HENRY, b. Boston, Mass, May 9, 93; m. 29; c. 2. CHEMISTRY. B.S, Harvard, 15, M.S, 17, Ph.D.(chem), 18. Asst. chem, Harvard, 14-17, instr, 18-19; assoc, Illinois, 19; asst. prof. ORG. CHEM, IOWA STATE UNIV, 19-20, assoc. prof, 20-23, PROF, 23- Ed, Org. Synthesis; Org. Chem. U.S. Acad. Sci. off. del. & lectr, Soviet Union. Civilian with Manhattan Dist; Off. Sci. Res. & Develop; Nat. Defense Res. Comt; Joint Res. & Develop. Bd; U.S. Army, 44; proj. dir, Chem. Corps, U.S. Air Force; mem. int. org. comt. & lectr, Int. Organometallic Conf, Moscow, U.S.S.R, 71. Midwest gold medal; Frederick Stanley Kipping Award; First Firestone Int. Lect. Award; distinguished prof. sci. & humanities, 62. C.W.S, 17-19. Nat. Acad. Sci; AAAS (v.pres); Am. Chem. Soc; hon. fel. The Chem. Soc. Organometallic compounds; furans; physiological action and chemical constitution; polynuclear heterocycles; long-chained aliphatic compounds; organo silicon chemistry. Address: Dept. of Chemistry, Iowa State University, Ames, IA 50010.

GILMAN, JOHN J(OSEPH), b. St. Paul, Minn, Dec. 22, 25; m. 50; c. 3. PHYSICS, METALLURGY. M.S, Ill. Inst. Tech, 48; Campbell fel, Columbia, 48-50, Ph.D.(metall), 52. Res. engr. metall, Crucible Steel Co, 48-52; res. assoc, Gen. Elec. Co, 52-60; prof. eng, Brown Univ, 60-63; physics & metall, Univ. Ill, Urbana-Champaign, 63-68; DIR. MAT. RES. CTR, ALLIED CHEM. CORP, 68- Adj. prof, Columbia Univ, 68-; Campbell lectr, Am. Soc. Metals, 66; consult, Lawrence Radiation Lab; mem. mat. res. coun, adv. res. proj. agency, Dept. Defense, 68- U.S.N.R, 43-48. Am. Soc. Metals; Am. Inst. Mining, Metall. & Petrol. Eng.(Mathewson medal, 59); Am. Phys. Soc. Mechanical behavior of solids; solid state physics. Address: Allied Chemical Corp, Park Ave. & Columbia Rd, Morristown, NJ 07960.

GILMAN, JOHN RICHARD, JR, b. Malden, Mass, July 6, 25; m. 60; c. 2. ASTROPHYSICS. A.B, Harvard, 46. Mem. sales staff, John H. Breck, Inc, 47-48, dir. publicity, 49-53, asst. adv. mgr, 50-53, dir. new prod, mkt. res, 55-58, tech. dir, 56-62; dir. new prod, Acco Labs, Am. Cyanamid Corp, 63; exec. v.pres. & treas, AUGUST SAUTER AM, INC, N.Y.C, 64, NEW PROD. RES. CONSULT, 64-, PRES. & DIR, 65- U.S.N, 43-46. Soc. Appl. Spectros; Soc. Photog. Sci. & Eng; Soc. Cosmetic Chem; Am. Pharmaceut. Asn; N.Y. Acad. Sci. Problems related to creativity in research; direction of research and development efforts. Address: 395 Neck Rd, Tiverton Four Corners, RI 02878.

GILMAN, LAUREN C(UNDIFF), b. Bozeman, Mont, Nov. 24, 14. BIOLOGY. A.B, Baker, 36; univ. scholar, Hopkins, 36-37, Ph.D.(genetics), 40. Asst.

biol, Hopkins, 37-39, Brooks Fund res. grant, 40-41; asst. prof. ZOOL, South Dakota, 46-47; ASSOC. PROF, UNIV. MIAMI, 47- A.U.S, 41-46, Capt. Fel. AAAS; Soc. Protozool; N.Y. Acad. Sci; Am. Inst. Biol. Sci; Am. Genetic Asn; Am. Micros. Soc; Am. Soc. Zool. Occurrence distribution and interrelationship of mating types, inheritance of mating type and factors involved in the mating reaction of Paramecium caudatum. Address: Dept. of Biology, University of Miami, Coral Gables, FL 33124.

GILMAN, LUCIUS, b. Belvidere, Ill, Aug. 30, 10; m. 35. ORGANIC CHEMISTRY. B.Sc, Illinois, 33; Ph.D.(org. chem), McGill, 36. Res. chemist, E.I. du Pont de Nemours & Co, Del, 35-42; res. supvr. ord. dept, U.S. Army, Picatinny Arsenal, 42-56; tech. consult, mat. adv. bd, Nat. Res. Coun, 56-57; mgr. plastics & polymer res, Boston Lab, Monsanto Res. Corp, 57-65; RETIRED. Civilian with U.S.A, 44. Fel. Am. Chem. Soc. Properties of plastics; plastics applications for military uses; synthesis of polymers; organic chemical synthesis. Address: Turnpike Rd, Francestown, NH 03043.

GILMAN, NORMAN WASHBURN, b. Augusta, Maine, June 6, 38; m. 58; c. 2. ORGANIC CHEMISTRY. B.A, Occidental Col, 63; M.A, Princeton, 65, Nat. Insts. Health fel, 65-67, Ph.D.(org. chem), 67. Nat. Insts. Health fel, Harvard, 67-68; SR. RES. CHEMIST, HOFFMANN-LA ROCHE, INC, 68- U.S.M.C, 56-59. AAAS; Am. Chem. Soc. Optical activity as a tool for the study of organic reaction mechanisms; synthesis of natural products; heterocyclic chemistry for application to medicinal chemistry. Address: 5 Normandy Dr, Wayne, NJ 07470.

GILMAN, PAUL BREWSTER, JR, b. Havana, Cuba, Nov. 21, 29; U.S. citizen; m. 52; c. 4. PHYSICAL CHEMISTRY. B.S, Massachusetts, 51; M.S, Northeastern, 54; Ph.D.(phys. chem), Rutgers, 58. Res. chemist APPL. PHOTOG, EASTMAN KODAK CO, 57-60, sr. res. chemist, 60-62, res. assoc, 62-70, SR. RES. ASSOC, 70- Am. Chem. Soc; Soc. Photog. Sci. & Eng. Photochemistry; photographic science; spectral sensitization; luminescence; photothermographic materials. Address: Research Labs, B-59, Eastman Kodak Co, Kodak Park, Rochester, NY 14650.

GILMAN, PETER A, b. Hartford, Conn, May 28, 41; m. 66. FLUID DYNAMICS, HYDRODYNAMICS. B.A, Harvard Col, 62; Ford Found. fel, Mass. Inst. Tech, 62-64, S.M, 64, NASA trainee, 64-66, Ph.D.(meteorol), 66. Asst. prof. astro-geophys, Univ. Colo, Boulder, 66-70; MEM. STAFF, NAT. CTR. ATMOSPHERIC RES, 70-, CHMN. ADVAN. STUDY PROG, 71- Lectr, Univ. Colo, Boulder, 70- AAAS; Am. Meteorol. Soc; Am. Astron. Soc; Am. Geophys. Union. Geophysical fluid dynamics; magneto hydrodynamics; solar hydromagnetic dynamo theory; solar differential rotation theory; hydromagnetic boundary layers. Address: National Center for Atmospheric Research, Boulder, CO 80302.

GILMAN, RICHARD ATWOOD, b. Concord, N.H, Jan. 22, 35; m. 58; c. 1. GEOLOGY. A.B, Dartmouth Col, 57; M.S, Illinois, 59, Nat. Sci. Found. summer fel, 60, Ph.D.(geol), 61. Instr. phys. sci, Illinois, 61-63; asst. prof. GEOL, STATE UNIV. N.Y. COL. FREDONIA, 63-67, ASSOC. PROF, 67- Consult, Maine Geol. Surv, 62-; res. found. grant-in-aid, State Univ. N.Y. Col. Fredonia, 63; Nat. Sci. Found. fel, 71-72. AAAS; Geol. Soc. Am; Nat. Asn. Geol. Teachers. Structural analysis of igneous and metamorphic rocks. Address: Dept. of Geology, State University of New York College at Fredonia, Fredonia, NY 14063.

GILMAN, ROBERT E(DWARD), b. Concord, N.H, Jan. 19, 32; m. 54; c. 2. ORGANIC CHEMISTRY. A.B, Dartmouth Col, 54; Eli Lilly fel, Michigan, 56-57, M.S, 57, U.S. Pub. Health Serv. fel, 57-59, Ph.D.(chem), 59. Res. chemist, W.R. Grace & Co, 58-60; Nat. Res. Coun. Can. fel, 60-62; vis. asst. prof, Williams Col, 62-64; asst. prof. CHEM, ROCHESTER INST. TECHNOL, 64-68, ASSOC. PROF, 69- Nat. Sci. Found. sci. faculty fel, Univ. Calif, Los Angeles, 70-71. Am. Chem. Soc. Natural products; stereochemistry; reaction mechanisms. Address: Dept. of Chemistry, Rochester Institute of Technology, Rochester, NY 14623.

GILMAN, ROBERT HUGH, b. Utica, N.Y, July 28, 42; m. 69. MATHEMATICS. A.B, Princeton, 64; Nat. Sci. Found. fel. & Ph.D.(group theory), Columbia Univ, 69. ASST. PROF. MATH, STEVENS INST. TECHNOL, 69- Vis. mem, Courant Inst. Math. Sci, N.Y. Univ, 71-72. Am. Math. Soc. Finite groups; group theory. Address: Dept. of Mathematics, Stevens Institute of Technology, Hoboken, NJ 07030.

GILMAN, SID, b. Los Angeles, Calif, Oct. 19, 32; m. 62; c. 2. CLINICAL NEUROLOGY, NEUROPHYSIOLOGY. B.A, Univ. Calif, Los Angeles, 54, M.D, 57. Intern, Univ. Calif. Hosp, Los Angeles, 57-58; res. assoc, Nat. Insts. Health, 58-60; resident, neurol. unit, Boston City Hosp, Mass, 60-63; res. fel, Harvard Med. Sch. at Boston City Hosp, 62-65, instr. NEUROL, Harvard Med. Sch, 65-66, assoc, 66-68; asst. prof, COL. PHYSICIANS & SURGEONS, COLUMBIA UNIV, 68-70, ASSOC. PROF, 70- Ambrose & Gladys Bowyer Found. fel. med, 57-58. U.S.P.H.S, 58-60, Sr. Asst. Surg. AAAS; Am. Acad. Neurol; Am. Neurol. Asn; Asn. Res. Nerv. & Ment. Disease; Harvey Soc; Am. Physiol. Soc. Disorders of movement and behavior in humans and animals with lesions of the central nervous system; neurophysiological basis of hypotonia, spasticity and rigidity; neural transmitter substances. Address: Dept. of Neurology, College of Physicians & Surgeons, Columbia University, 630 W. 168th St, New York, NY 10032.

GILMARTIN, AMY JEAN, b. Red Bluff, Calif, Oct. 15, 32; m. 54; c. 4. SYSTEMATIC BIOLOGY. B.A, Pomona Col, 54; summer, Stanford, 54; M.Sc, Hawaii, 56, Am. Asn. Univ. Women fel, 67-68, Ph.D.(bot), 68; British Colombia, 57-58. Res. asst. bot, Hawaii Agr. Exp. Sta, 54-56; herbarium asst, British Colombia, 56-58, lab. instr. biol, 57-59; prof, Guayaquil, 62-64; asst. prof, Monterey Peninsula Col, 68-69; res. assoc, Flora N.Am. Proj, Smithsonian Inst, 69-71; PROF. BIOL. MONTEREY PENINSULA COL, 71- Mem. staff, Ecuadorian Inst. Natural Sci. & Acad. Natural & Chem. Sci, Ecuador, 64; Am. Philos. Soc. grant, 68-69. Consult, herbarium develop, Guayaquil, 62-64. AAAS; Int. Asn. Plant Taxon; Soc. Syst. Zool; Bot. Soc. Am; Soc. Study Evolution; Am. Soc. Plant Taxon; Asn. Trop. Biol. Tropical botany and the utilization of electronic data processors to facilitate systematic analyses; classical taxonomic work on the plant family Bromeliaceae. Address: Dept. of Biology, Monterey Peninsula College, Monterey, CA 93940.

GILMARTIN, MALVERN, b. Los Angeles, Calif, Nov. 14, 26; m. 54; c. 4. BIOLOGICAL OCEANOGRAPHY. B.A, Pomona Col, 54; M.S, Hawaii, 56; Ph.D.(oceanog), British Columbia, 60. Asst. marine bot, Hawaii, 54-56; BIOL. OCEANOG, British Columbia, 56-60; sr. scientist, Inter-Am. Trop. Tuna Comn, 60-65; assoc. prof, Univ. Hawaii, 65-67; prof, Hopkins Marine Sta, Stanford Univ, 67-69; prog. dir, Nat. Sci. Found, 69-70; PROF, HOPKINS MARINE STA, STANFORD UNIV, 70-, DIR. OCEANOG, 67-69, 70- Consult, Nat. Fishing Inst, Ecuador, 61-64; Empresa Puertos de Colombia, 63; coord, Inter-Am. El Nino proj, 62-64; mem. adv. bd, R/V Alpha Helix, 71-; biol. oceanog. panel Nat. Sci. Found, 70- U.S.N, 44-47, 50-53, Lt. AAAS; Am. Soc. Limnol. & Oceanog; Asn. Trop. Biol; Am. Inst. Biol. Sci; Phycol. Soc. Am; Int. Phycol. Soc. Primary production and plankton ecology; taxonomy and biology of dinoflagellates; taxonomy and ecology of deep water benthic algae. Address: Hopkins Marine Station, Pacific Grove, CA 93950.

GILMER, GEORGE HUDSON, b. Hampden-Sydney, Va, Sept. 3, 37. SOLID STATE PHYSICS. B.S, Davidson Col, 58; Du Pont fels, Virginia, 58-60, 61-62, U.S. Rubber Co. fel, 60-61, Ph.D.(physics), 62. Res. assoc, Cornell, 62-64; asst. prof. PHYSICS, WASHINGTON & LEE UNIV, 64-70, ASSOC. PROF, 70- Vis, Delft Technol. Univ, 70-71. Am. Phys. Soc. Crystal growth theory; grain boundary diffusion; critical point phenomena. Address: Dept. of Physics, Washington & Lee University, Lexington, VA 24450.

GILMER, ROBERT M(cCULLOUGH), b. Lawrence, Kans, Dec. 10, 20; m. 55. PHYTOPATHOLOGY. B.S, Wisconsin, 47, M.S, 48, Ph.D.(phytopath), 50. Asst. prof. PLANT PATH, N.Y. EXP. STA, CORNELL UNIV, 50-53, assoc. prof, 53-59, PROF, 59-, HEAD DEPT, 69- U.S.A.A.F, 43-46. Am. Phytopath. Soc. Virology of deciduous fruit trees. Address: New York State Agricultural Experiment Station, Geneva, NY 14456.

GILMER, ROBERT WILLIAM, JR, b. Pontotoc, Miss, July 3, 38; m. 63. ALGEBRA. B.S, Miss. State, 58; M.S, La. State, 60, Ph.D.(math), 61. Res. instr. MATH, La. State Univ, 61-62; vis. lectr, Univ. Wis, 62-63; asst. prof, FLA. STATE UNIV, 63-65, assoc. prof, 65-68, PROF, 68- Res. assoc, Off. Naval Res, 62-63; vis. prof, Miss. State Univ, summer, 62; Alfred P. Sloan Found. fel, 65-67; assoc. ed, Am. Math. Monthly, 71- Am. Math. Soc; Math. Asn. Am. Commutative ring theory. Address: Dept. of Mathematics, Florida State University, Tallahassee, FL 32306.

GILMER, THO(MA)S E(DWARD), b. Draper, Va, Nov. 6, 01; m. 23; c. 5. PHYSICS. B.S, Hampden-Sydney Col, 23; M.S, Virginia, 26, Ph.D.(physics), 37; Cornell, 31, 33, 34, 36; hon. D.Sc, Med. Col. Va, 62. Instr. math. & sci, Greenbrier Mil. Sch, W.Va, 23-25, 26-27; assoc. prof. math, HAMPDEN-SYDNEY COL, 27-34, prof. PHYSICS, 34-71, EMER. PROF, 71-, pres, 60-63. Instr, U.S. Army Univ.(France), 45-46; acting asst. prof, N.C. State Col, 46; vis. fel, Princeton, 63-64. Am. Phys. Soc; Am. Asn. Physics Teachers. Electro-optics; the effect on the eye of short flashes of light. Address: Box 203, Hampden-Sydney, VA 23943.

GILMER, T(HOMAS) E(DWARD), JR, b. Draper, Va, Mar. 4, 25; m. 51; c. 5. PHYSICS. B.S, Hampden-Sydney Col, 48; M.S, North Carolina, 53, Ph.D. (physics), 56. Instr. math, Ky. Mil. Inst, 48-50; asst, Duke, 53; North Carolina, 53-54; sr. scientist, Exp, Inc, Va, 55-56, head, solid state physics lab, 57-58; assoc. prof. PHYSICS, VA. POLYTECH. INST. & STATE UNIV, 58-62, PROF, 62-, ASSOC. DEAN COL. ARTS & SCI, 69-, acting head dept, 59-60. U.S.A, 43-45. Am. Phys. Soc. Neutron spectra and cross-sections; ionizing energy loss; magnetic resonance; semiconductors; infrared absorption in solids. Address: College of Arts & Sciences, Virginia Polytechnic Institute & State University, Blacksburg, VA 24061.

GILMER, WALTER SCOTT, JR, b. Roanoke, Va, Sept. 16, 20; m. 46; c. 3. PATHOLOGY. A.B, Washington & Lee, 42; M.D, Med. Col. Va, 45. Instr. PATH, Virginia, 51-52; Tennessee, 52-53, asst. prof, 53-59, assoc. prof, 59-62; lectr, Univ. N.C, 62-65; ASSOC. PROF, SCH. MED, UNIV. MISS, 65- Mem. staff, Cape Fear Valley Hosp, 64-65. Am. Asn. Path. & Bact; Int. Acad. Path; Orthop. Res. Soc; Am. Soc. Cytol. Bone physiology and pathology, including neoplastic disease, metabolic disease and fibrogenesis. Address: Dept. of Pathology, University of Mississippi School of Medicine, Jackson, MS 39216.

GILMONT, ERNEST RICH, b. Newton, Mass, July 1, 29; m. 65. ORGANIC CHEMISTRY. A.B, Middlebury Col, 51, M.Sc, 52; Ph.D.(org. chem), Mass. Inst. Technol, 56. Sr. res. chemist, FMC Corp, N.J, 56-58, group leader, 58-61; dir. res, U.S. Peroxygen Corp, Calif, 62-63; sr. scientist, MILL-MASTER ONYX CORP, 63-68, DIR. RES. & DEVELOP, A. GROSS & CO. DIV, NEWARK, N.J, 68- AAAS; Am. Chem. Soc; fel. Am. Inst. Chem.(pres-elect, 71-73, pres, 73-75); Am. Oil Chemists' Soc; The Chem. Soc. Fatty acids; hydrogenation; organic peroxides; polymerization catalysis; halogenation. Address: 165 W. 66th St, New York, NY 10023.

GILMONT, PAUL L(INCOLN), b. Brookline, Mass, Feb. 12, 14; m. 41; c. 2. CHEMISTRY. B.S, Mass. Inst. Tech, 35, Ph.D.(inorg. chem), 40. Res. chemist, Rayonier, Inc, 46-50; head pulp & paper res, Crosett Co, 50-56; supvr, Olin Mathieson Chem. Corp, 56-61; tech. dir, Calcasieu Paper, Wilco Co, 61-64; HEAD, PULP & PAPER RES, AM. POTASH & CHEM. CORP, 64- U.S.A, 40-46. Am. Chem. Soc; Tech. Asn. Pulp & Paper Indust. Wood pulping; bleaching; papermaking; by-products; specialties. Address: 8322 Carob St, Cypress, CA 90630.

GILMONT, ROGER, b. N.Y.C, Dec. 30, 16; m. 41; c. 1. CHEMICAL ENGINEERING. B.Ch.E, Cooper Union, 39; M.Ch.E, Polytech. Inst. Brooklyn, 43, Dr.Ch.E, 47. Draftsman, U.S. Coast & Geod. Surv, Wash, D.C, 40-41; jr. chem. engr, QM Corps, U.S. War Dept, 41; jr. materials engr, Nat. Bur. Standards, 41-42, jr. phys. chemist, 42-43; teacher chem. eng, City Col, 43-44; phys. chemist, Gen. Foods Corp, N.J, 44-47; tech. dir, Emil Greiner Co, 47-55, PRES, Manostat Corp, 55-61; ROGER GILMONT INSTRUMENTS, INC, 61-; ADJ. PROF. CHEM. ENG, POLYTECH. INST. BROOKLYN, 51-

AAAS; Am. Chem. Soc; Am. Technion Soc; Instrument. Soc. Am; Am. Inst. Chem; Am. Inst. Chem. Eng. Thermodynamics; instrument design; food spoilage; correlation of vapor liquid equilibria. Address: Roger Gilmont Instruments, Inc, 161 Great Neck Rd, Great Neck, NY 11021.

GILMORE, ALVAN R(AY), b. Pensacola, Fla, Nov. 6, 21; m. 43; c. 2. FORESTRY. B.S.F, Florida, 49; M.F. Duke, 50, Nat. Sci. Found. fel, 55-56, D.F, 61. Instr. FORESTRY, Florida, 50-52; asst. prof, Ala. Polytech. Inst. 53-58; assoc. prof, UNIV. ILL, URBANA, 58-68, PROF, 68- U.S.N, 40-46. Forest tree physiology; forest soils; forest ecology. Address: 1610 Chevy Chase, Champaign, IL 61820.

GILMORE, ARTHUR EDWIN, b. Pike, Calif, July 16, 08; m. 56. POMOLOGY. A.B, Stanford, 33, M.A, 34. Analyst pomol, col. agr, Univ. Calif, Davis, 35-42, prin. lab. technician, 42-46, assoc, exp. sta, 46-48, asst. specialist, 49, assoc. specialist, 50-59, specialist, 59-71; RETIRED. U.S.A, 42-46. Am. Soc. Hort. Sci. Action of liquid ammonia on carbohydrates; peach replant problem; phytotoxins and embryo culture of the peach. Address: 659 Sunset Court, Davis, CA 95616.

GILMORE, CHARLEY E, b. Los Angeles, Calif, May 10, 27; m. 51. VETERINARY PATHOLOGY. B.S, California, Davis, 57, D.V.M, 59. Intern vet. med, ANGELL MEM. ANIMAL HOSP, 59-60, resident path, 60-61, res. assoc. 61-65, assoc. pathologist, 65-67, DIR. PATH, 67- Res. fel, Harvard Med. Sch, 62-65, instr, 65-68, res. assoc, 68-69, asst. clin. prof, 70-; Mass. Inst. Tech, 65- Dipl, Am. Col. Vet. Path, 64. Am. Vet. Med. Asn; Int. Acad. Path. Veterinary and comparative pathology; hematologic diseases of animals. Address: 180 Longwood Ave, Boston, MA 02115.

GILMORE, CLAUDE RAYMOND, b. Seabrook, N.H, Aug. 12, 35; m. 55; c. 2. INVERTEBRATE ZOOLOGY, ECOLOGY. B.A, New Hampshire, 58, Nat. Defense Ed. Act fel, 61, M.S, 63, Ph.D.(zool), 66; Nat. Sci. Found. fel, Washington (Seattle), summer 63. Teacher, high sch, N.H, 58-61; asst. prof. BIOL, NASSON COL, 65-68, ASSOC. PROF, 68- Mem, Int. Oceanog. Found. U.S.N.R, 53-61. AAAS; Marine Biol. Asn. U.K. Systematics and ecology of marine polychaetous annelids. Address: Dept. of Biology, Nasson College, Springvale, ME 04083.

GILMORE, EARL C, b. Whitney, Tex, Sept. 7, 30; m. 54; c. 3. GENETICS. B.S, Texas A&M, 52, M.S, 57; Ph.D.(genetics), Minnesota, 67. Instr. agron, Texas A&M, 57-59; res. agronomist, U.S. Dept. Agr, 59-65; Dekalb Agr. Asn, Inc, 65-66; asst. prof. PLANT BREEDING, TEX. A&M UNIV, 66-70, ASSOC. PROF, 70- U.S.A, 52-54, 1st Lt. Am. Soc. Agron; Crop Sci. Soc. Am. Development of hybrid wheat, breeding wheat and flax; quantitative genetics of agronomic crops. Address: Dept. of Soil & Crop Science, Texas A&M University, College Station, TX 77843.

GILMORE, EARL H(OWARD), b. Turkey, Tex, July 9, 23; m. 46; c. 2. MATHEMATICS. B.S, Texas Tech. Col, 43, M.S, 47; du Pont fel, California, 49-50, Ph.D.(chem), 51. Phys. chemist, U.S. Naval Ord. Test Sta, 50-53; asst. prof. chem, Okla. State, 53-57, assoc. prof, 57-58; asst. prof. math, Tex. Tech. Col, 58-61, assoc. prof, 61-68; RES. CHEMIST, HELIUM RES. CTR, U.S. BUR. MINES, 68- Res. assoc, res. found, Okla. State Univ, 53-57. U.S.N.R, 43-45. Am. Chem. Soc; Am. Phys. Soc; Math. Asn. Am. Photoelectric photometry; energy level systems for excited molecule species. Address: Helium Research Center, U.S. Bureau of Mines, P.O. Box 10085, Amarillo, TX 79106.

GILMORE, ELEANOR L(A VERNE), b. Newark, N.J, July 25, 21. MEDICAL BACTERIOLOGY. B.S, Mich. State, 43, M.S, 44. Serologist Rh blood factors, Ortho Res. Found. Div, Johnson & Johnson, 44-45; chief bacteriologist prod. controls, Centaur Div, Sterling Drug, Inc, 45; res. bacteriologist problems in human fertility, Ortho Res. Found, 45-49; asst. polio, Wisconsin, 49-50, vet. bact, 50-52; chief bacteriologist rheumatic fever, City Health Dept, Madison, Wis, 52; MED. MICROBIOLOGIST DENT. BACT, DEPT. ORAL BIOL, U.S. ARMY INST. DENT. RES, WALTER REED ARMY MED. CTR, WASH, D.C, 52-, CHIEF BIOPHYS, SECT. & LECTR. MICROBIOL, 66- Registered, Nat. Registry Microbiol. Am. Soc. Microbiol; N.Y. Acad. Sci. Physiology of bacteria; pleuropneumonia like organisms. Address: Division of Oral Biology, Dept. of Biophysics, U.S. Army Institute of Dental Research, Walter Reed Army Medical Center, Washington, DC 20012.

GILMORE, FORREST R(ICHARD), b. Cisco, Texas, Aug. 25, 22; m. 51; c. 3. PHYSICS. B.S, Calif. Inst. Tech, 44, Ph.D.(physics), 51. Res. analyst, Douglas Aircraft Co, 44-45; instr. applied mech. & res. engr, Calif. Inst. Tech, 50-53; physicist, Rand Corp, 53-71; SR. STAFF SCIENTIST, R&D ASSOCS, 71- Am. Phys. Soc; Am. Geophys. Union. Hydrodynamics; shock waves; thermodynamics; radiation; atomic and molecular physics; nuclear weapons effects. Address: 341 Las Casas Ave, Pacific Palisades, CA 90272.

GILMORE, HERBERT C(LARENCE), b. Kennerdell, Pa, July 2, 21; m. 53; c. 3. DAIRY SCIENCE. B.S, Pa. State Col, 41; M.Sc, Massachusetts, 62. Assoc. prof. DAIRY SCI. EXTEN, PA. STATE UNIV, 45-66, PROF, 66- Am. Dairy Sci. Asn. Dairy records programs as conducted by U.S. Dept. of Agriculture and land grant colleges in cooperation with the breed organizations; dairy extension; records. Address: Dept. of Dairy Science Extension, 9 Borland Lab, Pennsylvania State University, University Park, PA 16801.

GILMORE, HUGH R(ICHMOND), JR, b. Emlenton, Pa, Sept. 21, 97; m. 24; c. 2. PATHOLOGY. M.D, Pennsylvania, 21. Intern, Lankenau Hosp, Phila, 22-24; private practice, 24-26; dispensary physician, U.S. Dept. Army, Wash, D.C, 27-31, chief pediat. serv, Gorgas Hosp, C.Z, 31-35, pathologist, 40-41, acting curator, Army Med. Mus, Wash, D.C, 36-37, instr, Army Med. Sch, 37-38, bacteriologist, Walter Reed Army Hosp, Wash, D.C, 38-39, commanding officer, Sixth Serv. Command Lab, 41-42, prev. med. officer, N.Africa & Italy, 42-45, commanding officer, Second Army Area Med. Lab, 46-49, chief path. & allied sci. div, Office Surg. Gen, Wash, D.C, 49-53, curator, med. mus, Armed Forces Inst. Path, 53-56; CHIEF CANCER CONTROL SECT, STATE DEPT. HEALTH, PA, 56- Med.C, 26-56, Col; Legion of Merit, 44; Bronze Star Medal, 45; Order of the Crown of Italy, 45. Am. Soc. Microbiol; Am. Asn. Path. & Bact; Am. Soc. Clin. Path; fel. Am. Med.

Asn; Asn. Mil. Surg. U.S; fel. Am. Col. Physicians; fel. Am. Col. Path; Int. Acad. Path. Public health; cancer control. Address: Pennsylvania Dept. of Health, Box 90, Harrisburg, PA 17120.

GILMORE, HUGH RICHMOND, III, b. Pittsburgh, Pa, Feb. 4, 26; m. 50; c. 5. MEDICINE, CARDIOLOGY. A.B, Swarthmore Col, 47; M.D, Pennsylvania, 50. Intern med, Hosp. Good Samaritan, Los Angeles, Calif, 50-51; res, med. center, Colorado, 51-52; fel, sch. med, Pennsylvania, 54-55; cardiol, Phila. Gen. Hosp, 55-56; Jackson Mem. Hosp, Miami, 56-57; instr. MED, SCH. MED. UNIV. MIAMI, 57-60, asst. prof, 60-63, ASSOC. PROF, 63- Consult, Vet. Admin. Hosp, Coral Gables, 57- U.S.N, 52-54, Lt.(jg). Am. Heart Asn. Address: 1150 N.W. 14th St, Miami, FL 33156.

GILMORE, JAMES E(UGENE), b. Tokay, N.Mex, July 13, 27; m. 53; c. 2. ENTOMOLOGY. B.S, New Mexico State, 50; M.S, Oregon State, 57. County office mgr. prod. & marketing admin, U.S. Dept. Agr, 50-54; asst. pests of pome & stone fruits, Oregon State, 55-57; entomologist, ENTOM. RES. DIV, AGR. RES. SERV, U.S. DEPT. AGR, citrus insect invests, Whittier & Riverside, Calif, 57-64, entomologist & asst. to chief, fruit & veg. insects res. br, 64-69, ASST. TO DIR, 69- U.S.N, 45-46. Entom. Soc. Am. Biology and control of insects and mites attacking citrus and deciduous fruits; insect and mite pathogens for biological control; resistance of mites to chemicals. Address: Entomology Research Division, Room 114 North Bldg, Plant Industry Station, Agricultural Research Service, U.S. Dept. of Agriculture, Beltsville, MD 20705.

GILMORE, JOHN (HAMILTON), b. Mt. Vernon, Ill, Apr. 21, 07; m. 34; c. 2. MEDICINE. B.S, Illinois, 30, M.D, 32. Assoc. RADIOL, MED. SCH, NORTHWEST. UNIV, 38-53, ASST. PROF, 53-; DIR. DEPT. RADIOL, WEST SUBURBAN HOSP, 61- Radiologist, Ill. Masonic Hosp, 35-61; med. dept, Peoples Gas Co, 41-; Ill. Eye & Ear Infirmary, 35-46; Evangelical Deaconess Hosp, 37-41; St. Vincent's Infant & Maternity Hosp, 38-42. Dipl, Am. Bd. Radiol. Med.C, 42-46, Lt. Col. Radiol. Soc. N.Am.(v.pres, 51, pres. elect, 68, pres, 69); Am. Roentgen Ray Soc; Am. Med. Asn; fel. Am. Col. Radiol. Horticulture; irradiation mutations. Address: Dept. of Radiology, West Suburban Hospital, 518 N. Austin Blvd, Oak Park, IL 60302.

GILMORE, JOHN T, b. Oakes, N.Dak, Sept. 1, 31; m. 59; c. 2. NUCLEAR CHEMISTRY. B.S, N.Dak. State Univ, 53; Fulbright fel, Univ. Cologne, 53-54; Ph.D.(nuclear chem), Univ. Calif, Berkeley, 60. From res. chemist to SR. RES. CHEMIST, CHEVRON RES. CO, STANDARD OIL CO. CALIF, 60- U.S.A.F, 54-56, 1st Lt. Am. Chem. Soc. X-ray and microprobe analysis; scanning electron microscopy; activation analysis. Address: Chevron Research Co, 576 Standard Ave, Richmond, CA 94804.

GILMORE, JOSEPH P(ATRICK), b. Brooklyn, N.Y, Sept. 30, 28; m. 50; c. 3. PHYSIOLOGY. B.S, St. John's (N.Y), 51; M.S, 52; Ph.D.(physiol), George Washington, 62. Asst. zool. & physiol, St. John's (N.Y), 50-52; physiologist, Naval Med. Field Res. Lab, Camp Lejeune, 52-55, head dept. physiol, 55-58; physiologist, lab. cardiovasc. physiol, Nat. Heart Inst, 58-64, dep. chief, 64-66; assoc. prof. physiol, med. sch, Univ. Va, 66-68, prof, 68-70; PROF. PHYSIOL. & BIOPHYS. & CHMN. DEPT, COL. MED, UNIV. NEBR, OMAHA, 70- Assoc, George Wash. Univ, 62-66; career development award, Nat. Insts. Health, 67; mem. study sect. cardio B, Nat. Insts. Health, 68-72. Am. Physiol. Soc; Am. Heart Asn; Am. Soc. Nephrology; Am. Soc. Pharmacol. & Exp. Therapeut. Hemorrhagic shock; burns; cardiovascular physiology and pharmacology; cardiodynamics; renal physiology. Address: Dept. of Physiology & Biophysics, College of Medicine, University of Nebraska, Omaha, NE 68105.

GILMORE, MAURICE EUGENE, b. N.Y.C, Jan. 2, 38; m. 64; c. 2. MATHEMATICS. A.B, Georgetown, 59; B.S, Syracuse, 61; Ph.D.(math), California, Berkeley, 67. Teaching asst. MATH, Syracuse, 59-61; asst, California, Berkeley, 61-66; instr, NORTHEAST. UNIV, 66-68, asst. prof, 68-71, ASSOC. PROF, 71- Prof. State Tech. Univ, Chile, 68-69. Am. Math. Soc; Math. Asn. Am. Algebraic topology; vector fields; homotopy groups; obstruction theory; differential topology; infinite dimensional manifolds; homotopy theory. Address: Dept. of Mathematics, Northeastern University, Boston, MA 02115.

GILMORE, PAUL C(ARL), b. Can, Dec. 5, 25; nat; m. 54; c. 2. MATHEMATICS. B.A, British Columbia, 49; M.A, Cambridge, 51; Ph.D.(math), Amsterdam, 53. Univ. res. assoc. math. & Nat. Res. Coun. Can. res. fel, Toronto, 53-55; asst. prof, Pa. State, 55-58; STAFF MATHEMATICIAN, THOMAS J. WATSON RES. CTR, IBM CORP, 58-, mgr. combinatorial math, 64-67. Vis. prof, Univ. B.C, 71-72. R.C.A.F, 43-46. Am. Math. Soc; Asn. Symbolic Logic; Opers. Res. Soc. Am.(Lanchester Prize, 64); Soc. Indust. & Appl. Math; Can. Math. Cong. Combinatorial mathematics; operations research; mathematical logic. Address: Thomas J. Watson Research Center, IBM Corp, Yorktown Heights, NY 10598.

GILMORE, RAYMOND MAURICE, b. Ithaca, N.Y, Jan. 1, 07; m. 40; c. 3. ZOOLOGY, ANTHROPOLOGY. A.B, California, 30, M.A, 33; Gibbs fel, Harvard, 34-35; Ph.D.(zool), Cornell, 42. Field zoologist, mus. vert. zool, California, 26-33; int. health div, Rockefeller Found, 35-40; assoc. entomologist, Off. Coord. Inter-Am. Affairs, 42-44; assoc. curator mammals, U.S. Nat. Mus, Smithsonian Inst, 44-46; biologist whale invests, U.S. Fish & Wildlife Serv, 46-58; RES. ASSOC. MARINE MAMMALS, NATURAL HIST. MUS, 58- Instr, exten. div, Univ. Calif, 59-60; asst. prof, U.S. Int. Univ, 63-65, assoc. prof, 65-66; vis. prof, Univ. Ga, 67, 68; Nat. Sci. Found. grant marine mammals south. oceans, 69-71. Am. Soc. Mammal. Marine mammals; arctic and antarctic mammals; South American mammals; public health; ethnozoology. Address: Natural History Museum, P.O. Box 1390, San Diego, CA 92112.

GILMORE, ROBERT, b. N.Y.C, June 10, 41. PHYSICS, MATHEMATICS. B.S.(math), B.S.(physics) & Woodrow Wilson & Nat. Sci. Found. fels, Mass. Inst. Technol, 62, Ph.D.(physics), 67. Instr. PHYSICS, MASS. INST. TECHNOL, 67-70, ASST. PROF, 70- Vis. prof, Ala. A&M Univ, 70-71; inst. theoret. physics, Univ. Frankfurt, summer 71. Applications of lie group theory as a unifying mechanism in all branches of modern physics. Address: Dept. of Physics, Massachusetts Institute of Technology, Cambridge, MA 02139.

GILMORE, ROBERT C(AMPBELL), b. Phila, Pa, May 15, 30; m. 61; c. 2. FORESTRY. B.S, Pa. State, 52; M. Wood Tech, N.C. State, 61. Woodlands mgr, Nittany Timberlands, Pa, 52; res. forester, Southeast. forest exp. sta, U.S. Forest Serv, N.C, 55-56; lab. supt. wood tech, SCH. FORESTRY, N.C, STATE UNIV, 57-69, ASST. PROF. WOOD & PAPER SCI, 69- U.S.A, 52-54. Soc. Wood Sci. & Technol; Forest Prod. Res. Soc. Wood technology. Address: School of Forestry, North Carolina State University, Raleigh, NC 27607.

GILMORE, SHIRLEY ANN, b. Connellsville, Pa, Jan. 1, 35. ANATOMY. B.A, Thiel Col, 57; Michigan, summer 56; U.S. Pub. Health Serv. fel, & Ph.D. (anat), Cincinnati, 61. U.S. Pub. Health Serv. res. fel, Uppsala, 61-62; instr. ANAT, MED. CTR, UNIV. ARK, LITTLE ROCK, 62-63, asst. prof, 63-67, ASSOC. PROF, 67- Mem. panel postdoctoral fels, Nat. Sci. Found, 71- AAAS; Am. Asn. Anat; Am. Inst. Biol. Sci; Am. Asn. Hist. Med; Soc. Exp. Biol. & Med. Radiation effects on maturing nervous system; normal maturation of nervous system; regenerative and reparative capacities of immature spinal cord. Address: Dept. of Anatomy, Medical Center, University of Arkansas, Little Rock, AR 72201.

GILMORE, THOMAS H(AROLD), b. Mass, Mar. 20, 24; m. 58. MEDICINE, PSYCHIATRY. Randolph-Macon Col, 43; Temple, 44; M.D, Rochester, 49. Intern med, Albany Hosp, N.Y, 49-50; staff psychiatrist, VET. ADMIN. HOSP, Albany, 50-56, chief psychiat. serv, 56-69; STAFF PSYCHIATRIST, BAY PINES, FLA, 69- Resident, Framingham Vet. Admin. Hosp, Boston, Mass, 50-53; assoc. prof, Albany Med. Col, 56-69. U.S.A, 43-46. Fel. Am. Psychiat. Asn. Clinical psychiatry and psychopharmacology. Address: Veterans Administration Hospital, Bay Pines, FL 33504.

GILMORE, W(ILLIAM) FRANKLIN, b. Bailey, Miss, Mar. 26, 35; m. 63; c. 2. MEDICINAL CHEMISTRY. B.S, Va. Mil. Inst, 57; Ph.D.(org. chem), Mass. Inst. Tech, 61. Chemist antiradiation drugs, Walter Reed Army Inst. Res, 62-63; res. assoc. peptides, inst. molecular biophys, Fla. State, 63-64; assoc. chemist. org. synthesis, Midwest Res. Inst, 64-65, sr. chemist, 65-67; asst. prof. pharmaceut. chem, SCH. PHARM, UNIV. MISS, 67-68, assoc. prof, 68-71, PROF. MED. CHEM. & CHMN. DEPT, 71-, chmn. dept. pharmaceut. chem, 69-71. Summers, chemist, Solvay Process Div, Allied Chem. Corp, 61, St. Francis Hosp, Colorado Springs, Colo, 63; mem. pharmacol. & toxicol. training comt, Nat. Inst. Gen. Med. Sci, 67-70. U.S.M.C.R, 53-55; U.S.A.R, 57-65, Capt. AAAS; Am. Chem. Soc.(Howe Award, 56); Acad. Pharmaceut. Sci; Am. Pharmaceut. Asn; Am. Asn. Cols. Pharm. Organic synthesis; mechanism of Favorskii rearrangement; synthesis of radioprotective compounds; synthesis of polypeptides. Address: Dept. of Medicinal Chemistry, University of Mississippi School of Pharmacy, University, MS 38677.

GILMOUR, C(AMPBELL) M(ORRISON), b. Scotland, July 2, 16; nat; m. 43; c. 3. MICROBIOLOGY. B.S.A, British Columbia, 41, M.S.A, 45; Ph.D. (bact), Wisconsin, 49. Assoc. prof. bact, Okla. Agr. & Mech. Col, 49-51; Ore. State Univ, 51-59, prof, 59-67; dir. ctr. environ. biol, Univ. Utah, 67-70, HEAD DEPT. BACT, UNIV. IDAHO, 70- Study-lecturship, Rockefeller Found; consult. water pollution. R.C.A.F, 42-43. Am. Soc. Microbiol. Classification and metabolism of soil microorganisms. Address: Dept. of Bacteriology, University of Idaho, Moscow, ID 83843.

GILMOUR, ERNEST HENRY, b. Adin, Calif, Aug. 17, 36; m. 57; c. 3. GEOLOGY, PALEONTOLOGY. B.S, Southern California, 60, summer, Nat. Sci. Found. fel, 60; Nat. Defense Ed. Act fel, Montana, 61-64, M.S, 64, Ph.D. (geol), 67. Eng. geologist, Calif. Dept. Water Resources, 56-61; geologist, Mont. Bur. Mines & Geol, summer 62; Cominco Am, Inc, 63; instr, Montana, 64; geologist, U.S. Geol. Surv, 64-65; asst. prof. mineral fuels & geologist, Mont. Bur. Mines & Geol, 65-67; ASSOC. PROF. GEOL, EAST. WASH. STATE COL, 67- Teaching asst, Southern California, 60-61, fel, foraminiferal ecol, summer 67. Mem. staff, Goudkoff & Hughes, Calif, 67; Mont. Bur. Mines & Geol, summer 68. Geol. Soc. Am; Am. Asn. Petrol. Geol; Am. Inst. Prof. Geol; Paleont. Soc; Soc. Vert. Paleont; Soc. Econ. & Paleont. & Mineral; Int. Bryozool. Asn. Carbonate petrology, paleontology and paleoecology; Paleozoic Bryozoa, Coelenterata, Protozoa and Brachiopoda; stratigraphic problems dealing with stratabound ore deposits. Address: Dept. of Geology, Eastern Washington State College, Cheney, WA 99004.

GILMOUR, H(UGH) S(TEWART) A(LLEN), b. Alta, Can, April 25, 26; m. 51; c. 2. PHYSICAL CHEMISTRY. B.A, British Columbia, 49; Ph.D.(chem), Utah, 53. Fel. chem, Illinois, 53-55; res. chemist, RES. LAB, EASTMAN KODAK CO, 55-68, RES. ASSOC, 68- Can. Army, 44-45. Am. Chem. Soc. Electron exchange reactions; photosynthesis; photochemistry; color photographic systems. Address: Research Lab, Eastman Kodak Co, Rochester, NY 14650.

GILMOUR, MARION VIRGINIA, b. New Hope, Pa, May 24, 36; m. 69. BIOCHEMISTRY. B.S, Wilmington Col, 58; Ph.D.(biochem), Rutgers, 65. Asst. bacteriologist, Parke-Davis Pharmaceut. Co, Mich, 58-59; fel, Royal N. Shore Hosp, Sydney Australia, 65-66; Johnson Res. Found, Univ. Pennsylvania, 66; Royal N. Shore Hosp, 66-67; ASST. PROF. BIOCHEM, MED. SCH, UNIV. LOUISVILLE, 67-; RES. ASSOC. CHEM. DEPT, YALE, 70- Characterization and mechanism of action of enzymes, particularly the mechanism of cytochrome oxidase. Address: Sterling Chemistry Lab, Yale University, 225 Prospect St, New Haven, CT 06520.

GILMOUR, THOMAS HENRY JOHNSTONE, b. Dunoon, Scotland, Sept. 27, 36; m. 62; c. 2. INVERTEBRATE ZOOLOGY. B.Sc, Glasgow, 60, Ph.D.(zool), 63. Asst. lectr. zool, Univ. Exeter, 63-64; asst. prof. INVERT. ZOOL, UNIV; SASK, 64-69, ASSOC. PROF, 69- AAAS; Marine Biol. Asn. U.K. Functional morphology of invertebrates. Address: Dept. of Biology, University of Saskatchewan, Saskatoon, Saskatchewan, Can.

GILOTRA, SUSHIL K, b. Lahore, India, Jan. 5, 32; m. 66; c. 2. ENTOMOLOGY, PARASITOLOGY. B.Sc, Panjab, 54, M.Sc, 56, scholar, 59-62; Sc.D, Hopkins, 64. Fel. entom, sch. hyg. & pub. health, Hopkins, 64-65, res. assoc, bionomics of mosquitoes, 65-68; biologist, Old Dominion Col. Res. Area, Montpelier, Va, 68-69; entom. & parasitol. sect. head, Gulf S. Res. Inst, 69-71; ENTOMOLOGIST, LA. STATE UNIV, NEW ORLEANS, 71- AAAS; Entom. Soc. Am; Am. Mosquito Control Asn. Transmission of disease agents by arthropods; genetics of insect vectors; control of insect vectors; ecology, biology and physiology of mosquitoes; mosquito and tick-borne zoonoses. Address: Dept. of Biological Sciences, Louisiana State University in New Orleans, Lake Front, New Orleans, LA 70122.

GILOW, HELMUTH M(ARTIN), b. Cedarburg, Wis, Sept. 11, 33. ORGANIC CHEMISTRY. B.A, Wartburg Col, 55; M.S, Iowa, 57, Ph.D, 59. Assoc. prof. CHEM, SOUTHWEST. AT MEMPHIS, 59-69, PROF, 69- Am. Chem. Soc. Pyrimidine and purine type derivatives; reactions and properties of beta diketones; substituent effects of positive poles in aromatic substitution. Address: Dept. of Chemistry, Southwestern at Memphis, Memphis, TN 38112.

GILPATRICK, J(OHN) D(ANIEL), b. Rumford, Maine, Feb. 24, 24; m. 46; c. 8. PLANT PATHOLOGY. B.Sc, McGill, 46; M.Sc, Alberta, 48; Ph.D, California, 61. Asst. plant pathologist, Dom. Lab. Plant Path, Edmonton, 47-48, St. Catherines, 50-52; asst. prof. bot, Ont. Agr. Col, Guelph, 48-50; plant pathologist, Shell Develop. Co, 52-56; asst. plant path, N.Mex. Col. Agr. & Mech, 56-57; prin. lab. technician, California, 57-61; sr. res. plant pathologist, Squibb Inst. Med. Res, N.J, 61-62; field res. rep, Chemagro Corp, 62-68; ASST. PROF. PLANT PATH, N.Y. STATE AGR. EXP. STA, CORNELL UNIV, 68- Am. Phytopath. Soc; Entom. Soc. Am. Root diseases; pesticides. Address: Dept. of Plant Pathology, New York State Agricultural Experiment Station, Cornell University, Geneva, NY 14456.

GILPIN, ROBERT H(ARRY), b. Thomas, W.Va, May 21, 19. MICROBIOLOGY. B.S, Maryland, 50; M.S, Fla. State, 53; Nat. Sci. Found. fel, Illinois, 53-55. Asst, Tennessee, 50-51; Fla. State, 51-53; asst. mycol, dept. bot, Illinois, 55; instr, Pensacola Jr. Col, 56-57; asst. prof. BIOL, Col. William & Mary, Norfolk Div, 57-61; FROSTBURG STATE COL, 61-68, ASSOC. PROF, 68- U.S.A, 43-45. Bot. Soc. Am; Mycol. Soc. Am. Physiology of the fungi; phycomycetes and ascomycetes of the fungi. Address: Dept. of Biology, Frostburg State College, Frostburg, MD 21532.

GILPIN, ROBERT RIDGEWAY, b. Viking, Alta, Nov. 6; m. 68. MECHANICAL ENGINEERING. B.Sc, Univ. Alta, 64; M.S, Calif. Inst. Technol, 65, Ph.D.(eng. sci), 68. Nat. Res. Coun. Can. fel, Univ. Toronto, 68-69 & York Univ. 69-70; ASST. PROF. MECH. ENG, UNIV. ALTA, 70- Heat transfer in ice formation and melting problems; energy balance of the earth's surface. Address: Dept. of Mechanical Engineering, University of Alberta, Edmonton, Alta, Can.

GILPIN, SHERMAN F, JR, b. Phila, Pa, June 29, 03; m. 37. NEUROLOGY. B.S, Pennsylvania, 26, M.D, 29. Clin. prof. neurol, SCH. MED, TEMPLE UNIV, 36-57, PROF. NEUROL. & CHMN. DEPT, 57- Attend. neurologist, Phila. Gen. Hosp, 36-; head dept. neuropsychiat, Methodist Hosp, 40-56; dir. dept. neuropsychiat, Germantown Hosp, 56-63; consult, Vet. Admin. Hosp; Shriner's Hosp. Crippled Children. Am. Psychiat. Asn; Am. Acad. Neurol. Clinical study of drug therapy of cerebral vascular disease. Address: 3701 N. Broad St, Philadelphia, PA 19140.

GILREATH, ESMARCH SENN, b. North Wilkesboro, N.C, Sept. 21, 04; m. 36. CHEMISTRY. A.B, North Carolina, 26, M.A, 27; fel, 29-31, Ph.D.(chem), 45. Lab. asst. chem, North Carolina, 26-27, instr, 42-44; Ga. Inst. Tech, 27-29; teacher, pub. sch, N.C, 33-35, 37-42; res. chemist, Am. Enka Corp, N.C, 45-46; asst. prof. ANAL. CHEM, WASH. & LEE UNIV, 46-52, assoc. prof, 52-55, PROF, 55-, head dept, 55-70. AAAS; Am. Chem. Soc; The Chem. Soc; Soc. Chem. Indust. Analytical chemistry; a semi-micro scheme of qualitative analysis for the cations without the use of hydrogen sulfide. Address: Dept. of Chemistry, Washington & Lee University, Lexington, VA 24450.

GILROY, JAMES J(OSEPH), b. Scranton, Pa, June 5, 26; m. 58; c. 2. BACTERIOLOGY. B.S, Scranton, 49; M.S, Catholic Univ, 51; Ph.D.(bact), Maryland, 58. Clin. bacteriologist, Children's Hosp, Wash, D.C, 52-53; bacteriologist, Army Chem. Center, Fort Detrick, Md, 53-54; asst. BACT, Maryland, 54-57; asst. & assoc. prof, Colorado State, 57-64; ASSOC. PROF, BOSTON COL, 64-, asst. chmn. dept, 67-69, chmn, 69-70. U.S.A.A.F, 44-45. Am. Soc. Microbiol. Bacterial metabolism; nutritional requirements for growth of rumen bacteria; nutritional requirements for toxin production by Clostridium perfringens; induction of fermentation enzymes in bacteria. Address: Dept. of Biology, Boston College, Chestnut Hill, MA 02167.

GILRUTH, ROBERT R(OWE), b. Nashwauk, Minn, Oct. 8, 13; m. 37; c. 1. AERONAUTICAL ENGINEERING. B.S, Minnesota, 35, fel, 36, M.S, 36; hon. D.Sc, Minnesota, 62, George Washington, 62, Ind. Inst. Tech, 62; D.Eng, Mich. Technol. Univ, 63; LL.D, N.Mex. State Univ, 70. Nat. Adv. Cmt. Aeronaut, 37-43, asst. chief flight res. div, 43-45, chief pilotless aircraft res. div, 45-51, asst. dir, Langley Res. Ctr, 51-58, dir. proj. Mercury, Space Task Group, NASA, 58-61, Manned Spacecraft Ctr, 61-72, DIR. KEY PERSONNEL DEVELOP, NASA, 72- Dir. Dynamic Develop, Inc, 55. Consult, Res. & Develop. Bd, 46-58. Mem. Sci. Adv. Bd, U.S. Air Force, 51-57, ballistic missile defense comt, 55. Louis Hill space transportation award, 62, NASA distinguished serv. medal, 62, 69; medal of honor, New York, 62; Goddard Mem. Trophy, 62; President's award for distinguished fed. civil serv, 62; U.S. Chamber Commerce, great living American award, 62; Spirit of St. Louis medal, Am. Soc. Mech. Eng, 65; Americanism award, China-Burma-India Vet. Asn, 65; Guggenheim Int. Astronautics award, Inst. Aeronaut. Sci, 66; Space Flight award, Am. Astronaut. Soc, 67; Rockefeller Pub. Serv. award, 69; James Watts Int. Medal. 71. Hon. fel, Am. Inst. Aeronaut. & Astronaut.(Reed award, 50); Nat. Acad. Eng; hon. fel. Royal Aeronaut. Soc. Airplane stability and structures; hydrofoil craft; aerodynamics; rocket propulsion; manned space flight; high temperature facilities. Address: Manned Spacecraft Center, NASA, Houston, TX 77058.

GILSDORF, ROBERT T(HOMAS), b. Ft. Lee, N.J, Nov. 29, 24; m. 56; c. 2. ORGANIC CHEMISTRY. B.S, Fordham, 47, M.S, 49, Ph.D.(org. chem), 52. Sr. chemist, J.T. Baker Chem. Co, 51-53; Colgate-Palmolive Co, 53-57; E.I. DU PONT DE NEMOURS & CO, INC, 57-63, SUPVR, 63- U.S.A, 44-46. Am. Chem. Soc; Am. Asn. Textile Chem. & Colorists. Organometallics; dyes and dye intermediates. Address: Chambers Works, E.I. du Pont de Nemours & Co, Inc, Deepwater, NJ 08023.

GILSON, ALBERT J(ACK), b. Lawrence, N.Y, Oct. 28, 28; m. 54; c. 2. NUCLEAR MEDICINE. B.A, Miami (Fla), 50; M.D, Cornell, 57. Intern, Jackson Mem. Hosp, 57-58; res. radiol, sch. med, Miami (Fla), 58-61, radiologist, sch. med, Emory, 61-62, asst. prof. radiol, 62-63, dir. div. nuclear med, 61-63; asst. prof. RADIOL, SCH. MED, UNIV. MIAMI, 64-67, assoc. prof, 67-70, PROF, 70-, DIR. DIV. NUCLEAR MED, 64- Dir. div. nuclear med, Mt. Sinai Med. Ctr, Miami Beach, Fla, 68-, Anna & Louis Hand cyclotron complex, 71- Dipl, Am. Bd. Radiol, 63. Soc. Nuclear Med; Aerospace Med. Asn; Am. Col. Radiol. Applications of radioactive isotopes in clinical and therapeutic medicine; utilization of monochromatic x-rays for bone densitometry; medical electronics. Address: Dept. of Radiology, School of Medicine, University of Miami, 1700 N.W. Tenth Ave, Miami, FL 33136.

GILSON, BRUCE ROBERT, b. N.Y.C, Sept. 9, 42. THEORETICAL CHEMISTRY. B.S, City Col. New York, 62; Nat. Sci. Found. fel. & M.S, Yale, 64; NASA traineeship & Ph.D.(phys. chem), Univ. Va, 69. Res. chemist, Franklin Inst, Pa, 65; res. assoc. CHEM, Univ. Va, 65-66; fel, RUTGERS UNIV, 69-71, ASST. INSTR, 70- AAAS; Am. Chem. Soc. Molecular-orbital theory. Address: 5210 Broadway, Bronx, NY 10463.

GILSON, IAN T, b. London, Eng, May 23, 36; m. 66; c. 2. POLYMER & ORGANIC CHEMISTRY. A.R.I.C, London, 59; A.R.I.C, Liverpool Col. Tech, Eng, 60; Ph.D.(chem), Southampton, 63; M.B.A, Univ. Chicago, 71. Nat. Sci. Found. res. assoc. with Dr. H. H. Sisler, Univ. Florida, 63-64; asst. prof. org. chem, Rollins Col, 64-65; res. chemist, exp. sta, E.I. du Pont de Nemours & Co, Del, 65-67; CHEMIST, NALCO CHEM. CO, 67- Am. Chem. Soc; Royal Inst. Chem; The Chem. Soc. Inorganic polymers; Polymer kinetics and characterization; organometallic chemistry; organic electrochemistry. Address: Nalco Chemical Co, 6216 W. 66th Place, Chicago, IL 60638.

GILSTEIN, JACOB B(URRILL), b. N.Y, Feb. 5, 23; m. 50; c. 5. PHYSICS. B.S, City Col, 43; M.S, N.Y. Univ, 50, Ph.D, 58. Physicist, pilotless aircraft instrumentation, Nat. Adv. Comt. Aeronaut, 46-47; res. assoc. combustion, rocket propulsion, detonation, res. div, N.Y. Univ, 47-56; physicist, missiles & space vehicles dept, Gen. Elec. Corp, Pa, 56-59, systs. appl, defense systs. dept, 59-61, systs. engr, missile & space div, 61-66, mgr. aerospace physics lab, reentry systs. dept, 66-68, aerospace physics & systs. anal, 68; DEP. BALLISTIC MISSILE DEFENSE, OFF. ASST. SECY. ARMY & DIR, ARMY ADVAN. BALLISTIC MISSILE DEFENSE AGENCY, 68- Sig.C, U.S.A, 43-46. Am. Phys. Soc; assoc. fel. Am. Inst. Aeronaut. & Astronaut. Instrumentation; combustion studies of jets and rockets; boundary layer theory; detonation in solid explosives; hypersonic aerodynamics; plasma physics; vulnerability and hardening; penetration aids; strategic defense systems. Address: 11712 Farmland Dr, Rockville, MD 20852.

GILTINAN, DAVID ANTHONY, b. Jamestown, N.Y, Dec. 7, 36; m. 67; c. 2. PHYSICS. B.S, Case Inst. Tech, 59, M.S, 63, Ph.D.(physics), Case Inst. Tech, 68. Coun, Dean Students Off, Case Inst. Tech, 67-68; assoc. prof. PHYSICS, EDINBORO STATE COL, 68-69, PROF. & HEAD DEPT, 69- Am. Phys. Soc; Am. Asn. Physics Teachers. Theoretical and nuclear physics; elementary particle reactions; phenomenological computer analysis. Address: Dept. of Physics, Edinboro State College, Edinboro, PA 16412.

GILTZ, M(AURICE) L(EROY), b. Massillon, Ohio, Sept. 24, 10; m. 45; c. 1. BIOLOGY, ZOOLOGY. B.Sc, Capital Univ, 37; M.S, Ohio State, 42, Ph.D, 54. Teacher, high schs, Ohio, 37-43; asst. instr. zool, OHIO STATE UNIV, 46-50, instr, 50-53, asst. prof, 54-59, assoc. prof, 60-68, PROF, col. biol. sci, 68-69, acad. faculty zool, 69-70, ORNITH, 70- Ecologist, Ohio Agr. Exp. Sta, 56- U.S.N.R, 43-46, Res, 46-52, Lt. AAAS. Ecological study of birds responsible for the destruction of crops, especially the life history and ethology of the red-winged blackbird. Address: Dept. of Zoology, Ohio State University, 1827 Neil Ave, Columbus, OH 43210.

GILVARG, CHARLES, b. N.Y.C, June 13, 25; m. 49; c. 4. BIOCHEMISTRY. B.Ch.E, Cooper Union, 48; Ph.D.(biochem), Chicago, 51. Nat. Found. Infantile Paralysis fel, 52-54; instr. biochem, sch. med, N.Y. Univ, 54-55, asst. prof, 55-60, assoc. prof, 60-63, prof, 63-64; chem, PRINCETON, 64-70, CHMN. DEPT. BIOCHEM. SCI, FRICK CHEM. LAB, 70- Cancer res. scholar, 55-58; U.S. Pub. Health Serv. sr. res. fel, 58-61, career res. develop. award, 61-64, consult, 62-; ed, Jour. Biol. Chem, 65-70. Sig.C, 43-46, Sgt. AAAS; Am. Soc. Biol. Chem; Am. Chem. Soc.(Paul-Lewis award, 62); Harvey Soc. Intermediary metabolism, particularly in microorganisms. Address: Dept. of Biochemical Sciences, Frick Chemistry Lab, Princeton University, Princeton, NJ 08540.

GILVARRY, JOHN J(AMES), b. Manchester, Eng, July 15, 17; nat. PHYSICS. B.S, City Col. New York, 40; M.A. & Ph.D.(physics), Princeton, 43. Res. physicist, Off. Sci. Res. & Develop. Proj, Princeton, 42-43, instr. physics, 43; res. physicist, Naval Ord. Lab, Wash, D.C, 43-46; N.Am. Aviation, Inc, Calif, 46-48; Douglas Aircraft Co, 48-49; Rand Corp, 49-56; res. labs, Allis-Chalmers Mfg. Co, Wis, 56-61, consult; res. physicist, Gen. Dynamics/Convair, 61, Gen. Dynamics/Astronautics, 61-64; Nat. Acad. Sci-Nat. Res. Coun. sr. resident res. assoc, space sci. div, theoret. studies br, Ames Res. Ctr, NASA, 64-67; RESIDENT CONSULT, PHYS. SCI. DEPT, RAND CORP, 68- Consult, inst. plasma physics, Stanford Univ; Inst. Defense Anal, Wash, D.C; res. div, Plas-Tech Equip. Corp, Mass; Benson-Lehner Corp, Calif. Fel. AAAS; fel. Am. Phys. Soc; Am. Math. Soc; Am. Astron. Soc; Math. Asn. Am; Am. Asn. Physics Teachers; Am. Geophys. Union; fel. Brit. Inst. Physics; Inst. Fundamental Studies Asn; Europ. Phys. Soc; Italian Soc. Physics. Nuclear and atomic physics; solid state physics; electronics; astronomy; astrophysics; geophysics; gravitational physics. Address: Physical Sciences Dept, Rand Corp, 1700 Main St, Santa Monica, CA 90406.

GILWOOD, MARTIN E(MANUEL), b. Warsaw, Poland, Dec. 12, 15; nat; m. 41; c. 4. CHEMICAL ENGINEERING. Ch.E, Rensselaer Polytech, 36. Res. chem. engr, Permutit Co. Div, Sybron Corp, 36-45, asst. mgr. res, 46-49, mgr. chem. res, 49-51, dir. res, 51-60, dir. develop, Ionac Chem. Co. Div, 60-62; CONSULT. ENGR, MARTIN GILWOOD ASSOCS, 62-; PRES, ENG. CHEM. SERV, INC, 68-; Acti Chem. Prod. Co, Inc, 63-68. Am. Chem. Soc; Am. Water Works Asn; Am. Inst. Chem. Eng; N.Y. Acad. Sci; Water Pollution Control Fedn. Industrial water purification; waste water treatment; air pollution control; waste water and heat recovery processes; ion exchange resins and processes. Address: Martin Gilwood Associates, 40 Fulton St, New Brunswick, NJ 08902.

GIMARC, BENJAMIN M, b. Nogales, Ariz, Dec. 5, 34; m. 59. PHYSICAL CHEMISTRY. B.A, Rice, 56; Ph.D.(phys. chem), Northwestern, 63. Instr. chem, Northwestern, 61-62; res. assoc, Hopkins, 62-63, U.S. Pub. Health Serv. fel. & lectr. CHEM, 63-64; asst. prof, Ga. Inst. Technol, 64-66; UNIV. S.C, 66-71, ASSOC. PROF, 71- U.S.N, 56-58, Lt.(jg). Am. Chem. Soc; Am. Phys. Soc. Quantum mechanical calculation of electronic properties of small atoms and molecules. Address: Dept. of Chemistry, University of South Carolina, Columbia, SC 29208.

GIMBREDE, LOUIS de A(GRAMONTE), b. Brooklyn, N.Y, Oct. 27, 09; m. 48; c. 1. GEOLOGY. A.B, Cornell, 39; M.A, Texas, 51; Ph.D.(geol), La. State, 61. Micropaleontologist, Shell Oil Co, 39-47; asst. geol, Texas, 49-51, bot, 51-52; asst. prof. GEOL, Agr. & Mech. Col, Tex, 52-54; asst, La. State Univ, 54-55; asst. prof, UNIV. SOUTHWEST. LA, 55-65, ASSOC. PROF, 65- Asst, La. State Univ, 57. Geol. Soc. Am; Soc. Econ. Paleont. & Mineral; Am. Asn. Petrol. Geol. Foraminifera; eocene and upper cretaceous. Address: Dept. of Geology, University of Southwestern Louisiana, P.O. Box 534, Lafayette, LA 70501.

GIMELLI, SALVATORE P(AUL), b. New York, N.Y, Feb. 22, 19; m. 44; c. 1. PHARMACEUTICAL CHEMISTRY. B.S, St. John's (N.Y), 41; M.S, Fordham, 47; Ph.D, Rutgers Univ, 66. Chemist, Philco Corp, 42-45; asst. chem, Fordham, 45-47; instr, Lafayette Col, 47-50; res. chemist pharmaceut, Reed & Carnrick, 50-54; from asst. prof. CHEM. to assoc. prof, FAIRLEIGH DICKINSON UNIV, 54-70, PROF, 70- Am. Chem. Soc. Synthetic medicinal products. Address: Dept. of Chemistry, Fairleigh Dickinson University, Teaneck Campus, Teaneck, NJ 07666.

GIMLETT, JAMES I, b. Salt Lake City, Utah, Dec. 10, 29; m. 54; c. 5. OPTICS, GEOPHYSICS. B.S, Stanford, 50, M.S, 52, Shell fel, 52-54, M.S, 61, Ph.D, 65. From geophysicist to chief geophysicist, Hycon Aerial Surv, Inc, 55-58; asst. prof. geophys, Nevada, 58-63; sr. res. scientist, ACTRON INDUSTS, INC, 63-66, MGR. OPTICS ENG, 66- Air Force Off. Sci. Res. grant geophys, 62-63. Am. Soc. Photogram; Soc. Explor. Geophys; Asn. Comput. Mach; European Asn. Explor. Geophys. Exploration geophysics; photogrammetry; image evaluation; optical design, fabrication and test. Address: Optics Engineering, Actron Industries, Inc, 700 Royal Oaks Dr, Monrovia, CA 91016.

GIMPLE, GLENN E(DWARD), b. Lovewell, Kans, Sept. 15, 40; m. 62; c. 2. INORGANIC CHEMISTRY. B.A. & Am. Chem. Soc. Petrol. Res. Found. fel, Kans. State Teachers Col, 62; Ph.D.(chem), Univ. Kans, 69. Asst. prof. CHEM, KANS. STATE TEACHERS COL, 65-71, ASSOC. PROF, 71- Am. Chem. Soc. Coordination compounds; use of substituted 2,2′-bipyrimidines as ligands in complexes of transition metals; kinetics and mechanisms of inorganic reactions; electron transfer reactions. Address: Dept. of Chemistry, Kansas State Teachers College, 1200 Commercial, Emporia, KS 66801.

GIN, THON T(OO), b. Washington, D.C, July 3, 25; m. 55; c. 3. MINERALOGY, GEOLOGY. B.S, Utah, 49, M.S, 50, Ph.D.(geol), 53. Sr. geologist, Columbia Mining Co, 53-61; mineralogist, U.S. STEEL CORP, 61-65, SR. GEOLOGIST, 65- U.S.A.A.F, 43-45, 2nd Lt. Geol. Soc. Am; Am. Inst. Min, Metall. & Petrol. Eng. Economic geology, petrology and mineralogy; ore beneficiation. Address: 2240 E. 7150 S, Salt Lake City, UT 84121.

GIN, W(INSTON), b. San Francisco, Calif, Aug. 24, 28. ENGINEERING PHYSICS. B.A, Arizona, 50, B.S, 51; Hughes co-op. fel, California, Los Angeles, 53-55, M.A, 55, M.S, 59. Mem. tech. staff, Hughes Aircraft Co, 53-57; res. engr, JET PROPULSION LAB, CALIF. INST. TECHNOL, 57-59, res. group supvr, 59-61, asst. sect. chief, SOLID PROPELLANT ENG. SECT, 61-63, SECT. CHIEF, 63- U.S.M.C, 52-53. Am. Inst. Aeronaut. & Astronaut. Rocket propulsion; gasdynamics; pyrotechnics. Address: Jet Propulsion Lab, California Institute of Technology, 4800 Oak Grove Dr, Pasadena, CA 91103.

GINDHART, PATRICIA S, b. Phila, Pa, Dec. 14, 40; m. 68; c. 1. PHYSICAL ANTHROPOLOGY, GENETICS. B.A, Univ. Pa, 62; Nat. Insts. Health fel, Univ. Tex, Austin, 68-71, Ph.D.(phys. anthrop), 71. Lab. asst. virol, Children's Hosp. Phila, 62-63; Nat. Drug Co, 63-65; genetics, Inst. Cancer Res, 65-66; res. asst. human growth, Fels Res. Inst, 66-67; CONSULT, HEALTH & EXAM. SURV, DIV. HEALTH EXAM. STATIST, NAT. CTR. HEALTH STATIST, 71- AAAS; Am. Asn. Phys. Anthrop; Brit. Soc. Study Human Biol; Soc. Res. Child Develop. Human biology; human growth; human genetics evolution. Address: 4916 S. 23rd St, Arlington, VA 22206.

GINDLER, JAMES E(DWARD), b. Highland, Ill, Jan. 4, 25; m. 49; c. 4. PHYSICAL CHEMISTRY. B.S, East. Ill. State Col, 50; M.S, Illinois, 51, fels. & Ph.D.(chem), 54. ASSOC. CHEMIST, ARGONNE NAT. LAB, 53- Vis. chemist, Nuclear Res. Ctr, Karlsruhe, 64-66. U.S.A, 43-46. Sci. Res. Soc. Am. Heavy element chemistry and nuclear properties; charge particle excitation functions; fission process; photonuclear reactions. Address: Argonne National Lab, 9700 S. Cass Ave, Argonne, IL 60439.

GINDSBERG, JOSEPH, b. Leipzig, Ger, Sept. 3, 20; U.S. citizen; m. 49; c. 3. PHYSICS. B.S, City Col. New York, 44; N.Y. Univ, 46-48; M.S, Northeastern, 61. Physicist, radio receiving tube div, Raytheon Mfg. Co, Mass, 48-49; asst. physics, N.Y. Univ, 49-50; electronics engr, Loral Electronics Corp, N.Y, 50-51, proj. engr, 51-55; sr. engr, missile systs. div, Raytheon Co, 55-59, prin. engr, 59-61; group leader, LFE Electronics Div, Lab. Electronics, Inc, 61-63, mgr. microwave tech. lab, 63-65; prin. engr, missile systs. div, Raytheon Co, Mass, 65-70; SR. STAFF ENGR, ELJIM LTD. DIV, KMS INDUSTS, INC, 70- U.S.N, 44-46. Sr. mem. Inst. Elec. & Electronics Eng. Generation and processing of microwave signals, particularly for airborne radar; microwave slot antennas; parametric amplification; modulation theory; noise theory and measurement; microwave spectroscopy and nuclear magnetic resonance; circuit design. Address: Eljim Ltd, P.O. Box 1201, Holon, Israel.

GINELL, ROBERT, b. N.Y.C, Apr. 27, 12; m. 44; c. 2. CHEMISTRY. B.S, Polytech. Inst. Brooklyn, 36, M.S, 40, Ph.D.(chem), 43. Asst. CHEM, Polytech. Inst. Brooklyn, 37-43; res. assoc, Nat. Defense Res. Cmt. Proj, North Carolina, 43-45; asst. prof, N.J. State Teachers Col, Jersey City, 45; BROOKLYN COL, 46-57, assoc. prof, 57-61, PROF, 61- Vis. prof, Utah, 60-61; exec. officer, Ph.D. chem. prog, City Univ. N.Y. Syst, 62-65. Fel. AAAS; Am. Chem. Soc; Am. Phys. Soc; fel. Am. Inst. Chem; fel. N.Y. Acad. Sci.(Morrison prize, 53). Theoretical chemistry; association theory; sorption; virial coefficients; theory of liquids and solids; thermonuclear reactions. Address: 848 McKenna Ave, Baldwin, NY 11510.

GINELL, WILLIAM S(EAMAN), b. New York, N.Y, Aug. 24, 23; m. 46; c. 3. PHYSICAL & INORGANIC CHEMISTRY. B.S, Polytech. Inst. Brooklyn, 43; Ph.D.(chem), Wisconsin, 49. Asst. chem, substitute alloy mat. labs, Columbia, 43-44; Wisconsin, 46-49; assoc. chemist, Brookhaven Nat. Lab, 49-53, chemist, 53-58; sr. res. specialist, Atomics Int. Div, N.Am. Aviation, Inc, 58-61; head inorg. chem. sect, Aerospace Corp, 61-63; prin. scientist, Douglas Aircraft Co, Calif, 63-67; SECT. CHIEF, McDONNELL DOUGLAS ASTRONAUT. CO, HUNTINGTON BEACH, 67- C.Eng, U.S.A, 44-46. Fel. AAAS; Am. Chem. Soc; Am. Nuclear Soc; N.Y. Acad. Sci; Am. Phys. Soc. Photochemistry; thermodynamics of high temperature reactions; nuclear reactor chemistry; crystal growth; liquid metal chemistry; nuclear radiation damage; semiconductors; infrared materials. Address: 16856 Escalon Dr, Encino, CA 91316.

GINER-SOROLLA, A(LFREDO), b. Vinaroz, Spain, Sept. 23, 19; m. 64; c. 1. ORGANIC CHEMISTRY, BIOCHEMISTRY. M.S, Madrid, 47, Dr. Pharm, 54; Ph.D, Cornell, 58. Asst. tuberc. study, Andreu Labs, Barcelona, 47-52; sci. adv, Spanish Div, Farbwerke Hoechst, 52-54; res. fel, Sloan-Kettering Inst, 54-57, res. assoc, 57-60; vis. scientist, univ. chem. lab, Cambridge Univ, 60-63; assoc, SLOAN-KETTERING INST. CANCER RES, 63-67, ASSOC. MEM, 67-, ASST. PROF. BIOCHEM, SLOAN-KETTERING DIV, MED. COL, CORNELL UNIV, 65- Asst, sch. pharm, Barcelona, 51-54. Synthesis of new purine and pyrimidine antometabolites; desoxyribonucleic acid biochemistry. Address: Sloan-Kettering Institute for Cancer Research, Section 7203, 145 Boston Post Rd, Rye, NY 10580.

GINGER, LEONARD G(EORGE), b. Chicago, Ill, Oct. 1, 18; m. 43; c. 6. ORGANIC CHEMISTRY. B.S, Northwestern, 39; M.S, Chicago, 41; Nat. Tuberc. Asn. fel, Yale, 41-43, Ph.D.(org. chem), 43. Jr. chemist, Merck & Co, N.J, 40-41; assoc. chemist, metall. lab, Manhattan proj, Chicago, 44; Pittsburgh Plate Glass fel, Northwestern, 44, Baxter Labs. fel, 45-49; assoc. chemist, Office Sci. Res. & Develop, 46; asst. sci. dir, BAXTER LABS, INC, 49-53, dir. org. chem. res, 53-57, res, 57-59, v.pres. RES. & DEVELOP, 59-69, SR. V.PRES, 69- AAAS; Am. Chem. Soc; N.Y. Acad. Sci. Bacterial chemistry; pyrogens; organic synthesis; micro-analytical methods; chemistry of tubercle bacillus; pharmaceuticals; parenteral nutrition; biomedical engineering; medical electronics; blood preservation; microbial enzymes. Address: Baxter Labs, Inc, 6301 Lincoln Ave, Morton Grove, IL 60053.

GINGER, ROGER D, b. Chicago, Ill, Aug. 22, 29; m. 53; c. 5. ORGANIC CHEMISTRY. Ph.B, Chicago, 48, M.S, 52; Ph.D.(chem), Ill. Inst. Technol, 57. SECT. HEAD, KENDALL CO, 55- Am. Chem. Soc. Mechanism of hydrolysis of carboxylic acid derivatives; determination of formation of intermediates based on isotopic tracer studies; lipid metabolism; drug and medical device design; sterilization technology; kinetic isotope effects. Address: 206 Berry Pkwy, Park Ridge, IL 60068.

GINGERICH, KARL A(NDREAS), b. Lahr, Ger, Oct. 8, 27. INORGANIC & PHYSICAL CHEMISTRY. Dipl, Freiburg, 54, Dr.rer.Nat, 57. Asst, Freiburg, 53-57; res. assoc, Illinois, 57-58; asst. prof. chem, Pa. State, 58-64; sr. chemist, Bettelle Mem. Inst, 64-68; PROF. CHEM, TEX. A&M UNIV, 68- Am. Chem. Soc; Am. Ceramic Soc; Soc. Ger. Chem. High temperature and solid state chemistry of transition metal oxides and phosphides; mass spectrometric investigation of incongruent vaporization processes; crystal chemistry; high temperature and high pressure transformations; vapor pressure measurements and derived thermodynamic properties. Address: Dept. of Chemistry, Texas A&M University, College Station, TX 77843.

GINGERICH, OWEN (JAY), b. Washington, Iowa, Mar. 24, 30; m. 54; c. 3. ASTRONOMY. B.A, Goshen Col, 51; M.A, Harvard, 53, Ph.D.(astron), 62. Dir, observ, American Univ, Beirut, 55-58, instr. astron, univ, 55-57, asst. prof, 57-58; lectr. astron, Wellesley Col, 58-59; ASTROPHYSICIST, SMITHSONIAN ASTROPHYS. OBSERV, 61-; assoc. prof. ASTRON. & HIST. SCI, HARVARD, 68-69, PROF, 69-, lectr, 60-69. Joint organizer, Harvard-Smithsonian Steller Atmosphere Confs, 64, 65, 68; astron. consult, Proj. Physics, Harvard, 64-69; dir, cent. telegram bur, Int. Astron. Union, 65-68, assoc. dir, Cent. Bur. Astron. Telegrams, 68-, pres, comn. on hist. of astron, 71-; mem. Copernicus Comt. & Kepler Comt, Int. Union Hist. & Philos. Sci; Sigma Xi nat. lectr, 71; George Darwin lectr, Royal Astron. Soc, 71. AAAS; Hist. Sci. Soc; Am. Astron. Soc; Am. Asn. Variable Star Observers; Royal Astron. Soc; Int. Astron. Union. Model stellar atmospheres; history of astronomy; applications of computers to history of astronomy. Address: Smithsonian Astrophysical Observatory, Cambridge, MA 02138.

GINGERY, ROY EVANS, b. Lodi, Ohio, June 3, 42; m. 64; c. 2. BIOCHEMISTRY, PLANT PATHOLOGY. B.S, Carnegie-Mellon Univ, 64; M.S, Wisconsin, 67, Ph.D.(biochem), 68. Asst. prof. PLANT PATH, Ohio Agr. Res. & Develop. Center, OHIO STATE UNIV, 68-69, RES. CHEMIST, U.S. DEPT. AGR. & OHIO AGR. RES. & DEVELOP. CTR, 69- Am. Phytopath. Soc. Nucleic acid metabolism in virus infected plants; biochemical mechanisms of disease resistance in plants. Address: Agricultural Research Service, U.S. Dept. of Agriculture, Ohio Agricultural Research & Development Center, Wooster, OH 44691.

GINGLES, TOMMY, b. Little Rock, Ark, Nov. 22, 14; m. 35; c. 1. SANITARY ENGINEERING. B.S, Agr. & Mech. Col, Tex, 55; U.S. Pub. Health Serv. fel, Missouri, 58, M.S, 59. Instr. civil eng, Agr. & Mech. Col, Tex, 56; assoc. prof. sanit. eng, Univ. Miss, 57-64; dir. sanit. eng, Dornblatt & Assocs. Consult. Engrs, 64-66; ASSOC. PROF. CIVIL ENG, Gulf Coast Technol. Inst, 66-69; MISS. STATE UNIV, 69- Consult, Int. Paper Co, 64. C.Eng, U.S.A, 42-45. Am. Soc. Civil Eng; Nat. Soc. Prof. Eng; Water Pollution Control Fedn; Am. Pub. Health Asn. Physical, chemical and biological aspects of sanitary engineering. Address: Dept. of Civil Engineering, Mississippi State University, State College, MS 39962.

GINGOLD, JAMES LEHMAN, b. Meadville, Pa, Oct. 21, 30; m. 54; c. 3. MICROBIOLOGY. B.S, Allegheny Col, 52; Syracuse, 53; U.S. Pub. Health Serv. fel, Pittsburgh, 60-65, Ph.D, 65. Res. asst. physiol, Harvard Med. Sch, 55-56; lab. instr. biol, Pittsburgh, 56-57, asst. MICROBIOL, sch. med, 57-64; SCIENTIST, WARNER-LAMBERT RES. INST, 65- Med.Serv.C, 53-55. Am. Soc. Microbiol. Medical microbiology; mammalian cell biology; immunology; delayed hypersensitivity. Address: Warner-Lambert Research Institute, Tabor Rd, Morris Plains, NJ 07950.

GINGOLD, KURT, b. Vienna, Austria, Aug. 7, 29; nat; m. 57; c. 2. CHEMISTRY. B.S, Tulane, 50; fel, Harvard, 50-52, M.A, 52, Procter & Gamble fel, 52-53, Ph.D.(chem), 53. Lit. chemist, Ethyl Corp, Mich, 53-54; RES. INFO. SCIENTIST, AM. CYANAMID CO, 56- V. pres, Int. Fedn. Translators, 63-66, mem. coun, 66- U.S.A, 54-56. Am. Chem. Soc; Am. Translators Asn. (pres, 63-65). Scientific literature; technical writing, editing and translation; organometallic and inorganic chemistry. Address: American Cyanamid Co, 1937 W. Main St, Stamford, CT 06904.

GINGRAS, B(ERNARD) A(RTHUR), b. Montreal, Que, Jan. 23, 27; m. 52; c. 4. ORGANIC CHEMISTRY. B.Sc, Montreal, 48, M.Sc, 49, Que. Res. Bd. bursaries, 48-50, Ph.D, 52; D.Phil, Oxford, 54. Lectr. org. chem, Montreal, 51-52; overseas fel, Nat. Res. Coun. Can, Oxford, 52; Merck & Co, Inc, 53; from assoc. res. off. to sr. res. off, div. appl. chem, NAT. RES. COUN. CAN, 54-67, assoc. awards off, 67-70, DIR. OFF. GRANTS & SCHOLAR, 70- Fel. Chem. Inst. Can; Prof. Inst. Pub. Serv. Can; Fr-Can. Asn. Advan. Sci. Textiles; fungicides for prevention of deterioration of fibers by microorganisms; photochemical degradation of cellulose; coordination chemistry. Address: Office of Grants & Scholarships, National Research Council of Canada, Montreal Rd, Ottawa, Ont. K1A 0R6, Can.

GINGRASS, RUEDI PETER, b. Milwaukee, Wis, May 10, 32; m. 58; c. 5. PLASTIC SURGERY. A.B, Michigan, 54, M.D, 58; M.S, Marquette, 63. Nat. Insts. Health head & neck cancer trainee, Duke Univ. Med. Center, 63-66; asst. prof. plastic surg. & exec. dir, sch. med, Marquette Univ, 67-71, ASSOC. PROF. PLASTIC SURG. & CHMN. DEPT, MED. COL. WIS, 71- Am. Soc. Plastic & Reconstructive Surg; Am. Cleft Palate Asn; Soc. Head & Neck Surg. Wound healing and wound infection; skin grafting. Address: 8700 W. Wisconsin Ave, Milwaukee, WI 53226.

GINGRICH, JOE R(AY), b. Wakefield, Kans, Dec. 12, 21; m. 46; c. 2. AGRONOMY, SOIL PHYSICS. B.S, Kans. State Col, 49, M.S, 52; Ph.D. (agron), Illinois, 55. Asst. soil fertility, Kans. State Col, 50-52; soil physics, Illinois, 52-55; asst. prof. agron, Vermont, 55-58; Okla. State, 58-64; agronomist, agr. div, Olin Mathieson Chem. Co, 64-66; soils adv. fertilizers, U.S. Agency Int. Develop, Vietnam, 66-68, soils adv, UNIV. ILL-U.S. AGENCY INT. DEVELOP. CONTRACT TEAM, UTTAR PRADESH AGR. UNIV, INDIA, 68-70, ADV. SOIL & WATER MGT, 71- U.S.N.R, 42-45. Water, air, temperature and compaction in soils and their effect on plant growth. Address: University of Illinois-U.S. Agency International Development, Uttar Pradesh Agricultural University, Pant Nagar Distt. Nainital, U.P, India.

GINGRICH, NEWELL S(HIFFER), b. Orwigsburg, Pa, Jan. 29, 06; m. 28; c. 2. PHYSICS. A.B, N.Cent. Col, 26; scholar, Lafayette Col, 26-27, M.A, 27; fel, Chicago, 28-30, Ph.D.(physics), 30. Lab. instr. PHYSICS, Lafayette Col, 26-27, instr, 27-28; asst. prof, Mt. Allison, 30-31; instr, Mass. Inst. Tech, 31-36; asst. prof, UNIV. MO-COLUMBIA, 36-39, assoc. prof, 39-43, PROF, 43- Grants-in-aid, Am. Asn. Adv. Sci; Rumford Fund, Am. Acad. Sci, Elizabeth Thompson Sci. Fund, Res. Corp; Nat. Sci. Found. fel, 59-60; res. assoc, Argonne Nat. Lab, summers 56-58. Physicist, Naval Ord. Lab, 41-43; tech. aide, liaison off, Office Sci. Res. & Develop, Wash, D.C, 43-44; Oak Ridge Nat. Lab, 52-53. AAAS; fel. Am. Phys. Soc; Am. Asn. Physics Teachers; Am. Crystallog. Asn. Compton effect in x-rays; circuits used with Geiger counter work; diffraction of x-rays by elements in liquid state; cosmic rays; atomic distribution in liquids; magnetic structure in crystals; neutron diffraction. Address: Dept. of Physics, University of Missouri-Columbia, Columbia, MO 65201.

GINGRICH, RICHARD EARL, b. Hamilton, Ohio, Nov. 23, 31; m. 54; c. 5. MEDICAL ENTOMOLOGY. B.S, Miami (Ohio), 53; Florida, 57-58; M.A, Ohio State, 58, Nat. Insts. Health grant, 58-61, Ph.D.(entom), 61. MED. RES. ENTOMOLOGIST, LIVESTOCK INSECTS INVESTS. LAB, ENTOM. RES. DIV, U.S. DEPT. AGR, 61- Consult. res. proj, Int. Regional Orgn. Farm Sanit, 64- U.S.A, 53-56. Entom. Soc. Am; N.Y. Acad. Sci; Soc. Invert. Path; Int. Comt. Biol. Control. Insect pathology; immunological relationships between vertebrate hosts and their insect parasites. Address: Livestock Insects Investigations Lab, Entomology Research Division, U.S. Dept. of Agriculture, Box 232, Kerrville, TX 78028.

GINI, DONALD, b. Managua, Nicaragua, Aug. 29, 33; U.S. citizen; m. 60; c. 2. PHYSICAL ORGANIC CHEMISTRY. B.S, St. Lawrence, 55; Ph.D.(phys. org. chem), Colorado, 61. Lab. technician, Eastman Kodak Co, 55-56; res. assoc, eng. exp. sta, Colorado, 59-62; sr. chemist, Minn. Mining & Mfg. Co, 62-66; RES. CHEMIST, ARAPAHOE CHEM. DIV, SYNTEX CORP, 66- Am. Chem. Soc. Terpenes and all aspects of urethanes, foams, elastomers, adhesives and fibers; fluorine chemistry of fluor-cyclobutanes and cyclobutenes; catalytic conversion of ortho and para-hydrogen; process development of steroids, fine organic chemicals and organometallics. Address: Arapahoe Chemicals Division, Syntex Corp, 2855 Walnut St, Boulder, CO 80302.

GINIVAN, F(RANCIS) J(OSEPH), b. Lowell, Mass, Feb. 1, 22. MATHEMATICS. B.Sc, St. Francis Xavier (Can), 44; M.Sc, Notre Dame, 50, fel, 49-51, Ph.D.(math), 52. Assoc. prof. MATH, ST. FRANCIS XAVIER UNIV, 52-70, PROF, 70- Am. Math. Soc; Math. Asn. Am; Can. Math. Cong. Topological groups. Address: Dept. of Mathematics, St. Francis Xavier University, Antigonish, N.S, Can.

GINKEL, WILLIAM LOUIS, b. Rochester, N.Y, Aug. 14, 20; m. 45; c. 2. CHEMICAL ENGINEERING. B.S. & B.A, Rochester, 42. Indust. engr, Eastman Kodak Co, 44-47; prod. engr, U.S. ATOMIC ENERGY COMN, 47-52, tech. servs. dir, 52-60, asst. tech. mgr, 60-63, dep. mgr, IDAHO OPERS. OFF, 63-64, MGR, 64- Administration and management of nuclear engineering development and testing programs for government agency. Address: U.S. Atomic Energy Commission, P.O. Box 2108, Idaho Falls, ID 83401.

GINN, H. EARL, b. Tylertown, Miss, July 7, 31; m; c. 2. INTERNAL MEDICINE. B.S, Baylor, 53; M.D, Emory, 57. Intern, med. center, Oklahoma, 57-58, res. internal med, 58-60; U.S. Pub. Health Serv. fel. renal & electrolyte physiol. & instr. med, New York Hosp, med. center, Cornell, 60-61; instr. med. & physiol, med. center, Oklahoma, 62, asst. prof. med, physiol. & urol, 62-65; asst. prof. MED, SCH. MED, VANDERBILT UNIV, 65-66, ASSOC. PROF, 66-, UROL, 65-; BIOMED. ENGR, SCH. ENG, 70- Nat. Insts. Health career res. develop. award, med. center, Oklahoma, 64-65, univ. hosp, Vanderbilt, 65- Clin. investr, Vet. Admin. Hosp, med. center, Oklahoma, 61-64, chief renal & electrolyte sect, Okla. City Vet. Admin. Hosp. & chief kidney sect, med. center, Univ. Oklahoma, 63-65; chief nephrology div, Vet. Admin. Hosp, Nashville, & chief renal dialysis units, Vanderbilt Univ. Hosp, 65- Gen. consult, Kidney Disease Control Prog, 67-68. Mem. coun. circulation, Am. Heart Asn; Mt. Desert Island Biol. Lab, Inc. U.S.M.C.R, 50-51. Am. Chem. Soc; Am. Physiol. Soc; Am. Soc. Artificial Internal Organs; Am. Soc. Nephrology; Harvey Soc. Renal transplantation; dynamics of hemodialysis; biochemistry of uremia. Address: School of Medicine, Vanderbilt University Medical Center, Nashville, TN 37203.

GINN, MARTIN E, b. New York, N.Y, Sept. 26, 29; m. 48; c. 4. PHYSICAL & ANALYTICAL CHEMISTRY. B.A, N.Y. Univ, 52, M.S, 54. Res. technician detergent chem, Colgate-Palmolive Co, 50-52; asst. res. div, N.Y. Univ, 52-54; res. chemist, res. & eng. div, Monsanto Chem. Co, 54-62; res. sect. head, prod. eval, Armour Grocery Prod. Co, 62-65, lab. & res. serv. mgr, 65-69, sr. tech. adv, Armour & Co, 69-71; DIR. RES. & DEVELOP, MASURY-COLUMBIA DIV, ALBERTO-CULVER CO, 71- Am. Chem. Soc; Am. Oil Chem. Soc. Surfactant or detergent research, especially physicochemical studies of mechanisms and development of analytical methods; development of cleaners and floor finishes. Address: Masury-Columbia Division, Alberto-Culver Co, 1502 N. 25th Ave, Melrose Park, IL 60160.

GINN, ROBERT FORD, b. Alamosa, Colo, Aug. 13, 31. CHEMICAL ENGINEERING, MATHEMATICS. B.S, Univ. Colo, Boulder, 53; M.S, Inst. Paper Chem, Lawrence Univ, 57; Nat. Sci. Found. fel, Univ. Del, 62-63, M.Ch.E, 64, Ph.D.(chem. eng), 68. Chem. engr, Albert E. Reed Paper Group, Eng, 57-58; res. engr, Nat. Vulcanized Fibre Co, Del, 59-60; Westvaco Corp, Md, 65-69; sr. scientist, Am. Can Co, Wis, 69-71; RES. FEL, INST. PAPER CHEM, 71- U.S.A, 54-56. Am. Chem. Soc; Tech. Asn. Pulp & Paper Indust; Soc. Rheol; Brit. Soc. Rheol. Application of the science of rheology to paper and board coating processes. Address: Box 318, Route 2, Hortonville, WI 54944.

GINNINGS, GERALD KEITH, b. Greensboro, N.C, Sept. 16, 28; m. 58; c. 3. MATHEMATICS, STATISTICS. B.A, Elon Col, 50; North Carolina, Greensboro, 52; M.A, Appalachian State Teachers Col, 62; Ed.D.(math, ed), Auburn, 66. Teacher electronics, H.L. Yoh Co. Commun, Ft. Sill, Okla, 59; field engr. Inter-Continental Ballistic Missile Launching Sites, Radio Corp. Am. Serv. Co, N.J, 59-61; design engr, Martin Co, Colo, 61; asst. prof. MATH, Berry Col, 62-65; assoc. prof, EAST TENN. STATE UNIV, 66-68, PROF, 68- Sig.C, U.S.A, 46-47. Modern and traditional algebra; breeching the barrier in communications which exists between the applied mathematics areas and the pure areas. Address: Dept. of Mathematics, East Tennessee State University, Box 2326, Johnson City, TN 37601.

GINNINGS, P(AUL) R(OLL), b. Shreveport, La, June 16, 23; m. 47; c. 2. CHEMICAL ENGINEERING. B.S, N.C. State Col, 48. Jr. chemist, viscose control lab, Indust. Rayon Corp, 48-49, jr. chem. engr, prod. supt. staff, 49-52; res. engr, tire cords & fabrics, RES. DIV, GOODYEAR TIRE & RUBBER CO, 52-53, chem. engr. de-icing res, 53-55, group leader ice-guard res, 55-62, new prod. res, 62-65, SECT. HEAD mat. eng. res, 65-68, FLEXIBLE FILMS & SHEETING, 68- U.S.A, 43-45. Am. Chem. Soc; Soc. Plastics Eng; Am. Inst. Chem. Vicose preparation and spinning, textiles as related to tire cords; conductive rubber; de-icing; rain erosion resistance of aircraft materials at high speeds; adhesives; structural laminates for aircraft ice-guards; rubber compounding; plastics processing; acoustical rubbers. Address: New Products Dept, Research Division, Goodyear Tire & Rubber Co, 142 Goodyear Blvd, Akron, OH 44316.

GINOCCHIO, JOSEPH NATALE, b. Summit, N.J, Dec. 25, 36; m. 64; c. 2. THEORETICAL NUCLEAR PHYSICS. B.S, Lehigh, 58; Union Carbide fel, Rochester, 62, Ph.D.(physics), 64. Res. assoc. NUCLEAR PHYSICS, Rutgers, 64-66; Mass. Inst. Tech, 66-68; ASST. PROF, YALE, 68- Am. Phys. Soc. Study of nuclear structure with shell model; random phase approximation applied to nuclear bound and scattering states; group theory as used in nuclear physics; four nucleon correlations in nuclei. Address: Dept. of Physics, Yale University, New Haven, CT 06520.

GINOS, JAMES Z(ISSIS), b. Hillsboro, Ill, Feb. 1, 23; m. 47; c. 2. ORGANIC CHEMISTRY. B.A, Columbia Col, 54; M.S, Stevens Inst. Tech, 57, Ph.D. (org. chem), 64. Chemist, Colgate-Palmolive Co, N.J, 52-57; chief chemist, Diamond Alkali, N.J, 57-58; chemist, Nopco Chem. Co, 59-64; asst. scientist, BROOKHAVEN NAT. LABS, 64-68, res. collab, 68-70, ASSOC. SCIENTIST, 70- Asst. instr, Newark Col. Eng, 59-60; res. asst. prof, Mt. Sinai Sch. Med, 68-70. Interne, Greece & Germany, 43-45. Am. Chem. Soc. Synthesis of peptides with biological activity; surfactants; pharmaceuticals; explosives; kinetic studies of reactions; evaluation and development of textile and agricultural chemicals. Address: Medical Dept, Brookhaven National Labs, Upton, L.I, NY 11973.

GINOZA, HERBERT S, b. Honolulu, Hawaii, Oct. 3, 24; m. 52; c. 2. BIOCHEMISTRY, MICROBIOLOGY. B.S, Nebraska, 50, M.A, 52. Biochemist, Thayer Vet. Admin. Hosp, 52-53; bacteriologist, U.S. Army Chem. Corp, Ft. Detrick, Md, 53-62; BIOCHEMIST, AMES RES. CTR, NASA, 62- U.S.A, 43-45, S/Sgt. Am. Soc. Microbiol. Sodium-intake and elevation of blood pressure; biosynthesis of pantothenic acid; genetics of bacterial L-forms; physical, chemical and biological nature of bacterial episomes; genetics of thermophilic bacteria. Address: NASA-Ames Research Center, Mountain View, CA 94035.

GINSBERG, ALVIN P(AUL), b. Brooklyn, N.Y, Jan. 7, 32. INORGANIC CHEMISTRY. A.B, N.Y. Univ, 54; Higgens fel, Columbia, 54-55, A.M, 55, Monsanto fel, 57-58, Ph.D.(chem), 59. Instr. chem, Brown, 59-60; MEM. TECH. STAFF, BELL TEL. LABS, 60- AAAS; Am. Chem. Soc; Am. Phys. Soc; The Chem. Soc. Preparation, spectroscopic and magnetic properties of transition metal compounds; applications of valence theory; hydride complexes. Address: Bell Telephone Labs, Murray Hill, NJ 07974.

GINSBERG, BERNARD, b. Marlin, Texas, Jan. 30, 03; m. 38; c. 1. PHYSICAL CHEMISTRY. S.B, Chicago, 26, fel, 27-28, Ph.D.(chem), 29. Asst. phys. chem, Chicago, 28-29; phys. chemist, chem. eng. econ, Standard Oil Co.(Ind), 29-66; RETIRED. Fel. AAAS; Am. Inst. Chem. Eng; Am. Chem. Soc. Petroleum refining. Address: 5242 Hyde Park Blvd, Chicago, IL 60615.

GINSBERG, DAVID M(ARK), b. Okeechobee, Fla, Jan. 18, 30; m. 59; c. 3. RADIATION BIOLOGY. B.S, La. State, 50; M.S, Tennessee, 60, Ph.D.(radiation biol), 63. Lab. chief, Environ. Health Lab, U.S. Army, 57-58, Walter Reed Army Inst. Res, 60, nuclear med. lab. off, 60-63, chief cellular biophys, 64-67, chief dept. biophys, div. nuclear med, 67-68, dep. dir. div, 68-70; chief med. isotopes br, Letterman Army Inst. Res, 70-71; RADIOBIOL. CONSULT, 71- Surgeon Gen. of Army liaison rep, subcomt. sanit. eng, Nat. Res. Coun, 57-58; mem. biophys-biophys. chem. study sect, Nat. Insts. Health, 68-70; partic, workshops on chem. radioprotective agents, U.S. Atomic Energy Comn, 69-70. U.S.A, 51-71, Lt. Col.(Ret). AAAS; Biophys. Soc; Radiation Res. Soc; Am. Soc. Microbiol; N.Y. Acad. Sci. Cellular injury and repair; nucleic acid synthesis in bacteria; bacterial physiology; human whole body burdens of radioisotopes; chemical radioprotectants. Address: 19C Golf's Edge, Century Village, West Palm Beach, FL 33401.

GINSBERG, DONALD M(AURICE), b. Chicago, Ill, Nov. 19, 33; m. 57; c. 2. PHYSICS. B.A, Chicago, 52, B.S, 55, M.S, 56; Nat. Sci. Found. fel, California, 55-59, Ph.D.(physics), 60. Res. assoc. PHYSICS, UNIV. ILL, URBANA-CHAMPAIGN, 59-60, asst. prof, 60-63, assoc. prof, 64-66, PROF, 66- Alfred P. Sloan res. fel, 60-64, Nat. Sci. Found. fel, 66-67. Am. Phys. Soc. Superconductivity. Address: Dept. of Physics, University of Illinois, Urbana-Champaign, Urbana, IL 61801.

GINSBERG, EDWARD S, b. N.Y.C, Oct. 4, 38; m. 61; c. 3. HIGH ENERGY PHYSICS. A.B. & Sc.B, Brown, 59; M.S, Stanford, 61, Ph.D.(physics), 65. Res. assoc. PHYSICS, Pennsylvania, 64-66; asst. prof, UNIV. MASS, BOSTON, 66-71, ASSOC. PROF, 71- Nat. Sci. Found. res. grant, 67- Am. Phys. Soc; Math. Asn. Am. High energy theoretical physics; weak and electromagnetic interactions; radiative convections. Address: Dept. of Physics, University of Massachusetts, 100 Arlington St, Boston, MA 02116.

GINSBERG, FELIX ELIAS, b. N.Y.C, Feb. 1, 32; m. 54; c. 2. APPLIED MATHEMATICS, SYSTEMS ANALYSIS. B.S, Polytech. Inst. Brooklyn, 55, M.S, 57; Ph.D.(math), N.Y. Univ, 62. Instr. math, Polytech. Inst. Brooklyn, 55-60; mathematician, Yorktown Heights Res. Ctr, Int. Bus. Mach. Corp, 62; asst. prof. eng. sci, Pratt Inst, 62-64; staff mem, Inst. Defense Anal, Va, 64-66; mgr. urban anal. lab, Riverside Res. Inst-Electronics Res. Labs, Columbia Univ, 64-70; MEM. STAFF, OFF. EMERGENCY PREPAREDNESS, EXEC. OFF. PRESIDENT, 70- Mathematician, Repub. Aviation Corp, N.Y, summer 57; res. asst, Courant Inst. Math. Sci, N.Y. Univ, 57-62; mathematician, Grumman Aircraft Corp, summer 58; consult, Sanders Assocs, Inc, 62-63. Math. Asn. Am; Soc. Indust. & Appl. Math. Mathematical physics; numerical analysis; hydrodynamics. Address: 11719 Lovejoy St, Silver Spring, MD 20902.

GINSBERG, HAROLD S(AMUEL), b. Daytona Beach, Fla, May 27, 17; m. 49; c. 4. VIROLOGY, MICROBIOLOGY. A.B, Duke, 37; M.D, Tulane, 41. Res, Mallory Inst. Path, Boston City Hosp, 41, asst, 42, intern, 4th med. serv, Harvard, 42-43, asst. res, Thorndike Mem. Lab, 43; asst. physician, hosp. & asst, Rockefeller Inst, 46-49, res. physician hosp. & assoc. inst, 49-51; assoc. prof. prev. med. & asst. prof. med, sch. med, Western Reserve, 51-60; PROF. MICROBIOL. & CHMN. DEPT, UNIV. PA, 60- Consult, Nat. Inst. Allergy & Infectious Diseases, Nat. Insts. Health, 58-; surgeon gen, U.S. Pub. Health Serv; NASA, 69- Mem. comn. acute respiratory diseases, Armed Forces Epidemiol. Bd. 59-; adv. bd, Am. Cancer Soc, 70- Ed, Jour. Bact; Jour. Virol; Jour. Exp. Med; Jour. Infectious Diseases. Med.C, 43-46, Maj. Am. Acad. Microbiol.(v.pres, 70-71, pres, 71-72); Am. Soc. Clin. Invest; Asn. Am. Physicians; Harvey Soc; Am. Asn. Immunol; Am. Soc. Biol. Chem; Am. Soc. Microbiol; Soc. Exp. Biol. & Med. Biochemistry of viral infections. Address: Dept. of Microbiology, School of Medicine, University of Pennsylvania, Philadelphia, PA 19104.

GINSBERG, HELEN F(LORENCE), b. N.Y.C, Jan. 14, 22. INFORMATION SCIENCE. A.B, Hunter Col, 42; Upjohn fel, Ohio State, 44-47, Ph.D.(chem), 47. Res. chemist, Naugatuck Chem. Div, U.S. Rubber Co, 47-48; sr. res. chemist, med. div, Schering Corp, 48-55, tech. documentalist, res. servs, 55-59, mgr. tech. document. dept, 59-62; asst. dir. sect. coord, Sterling-Winthrop Res. Inst, 62-65; coord, dent. res. info. ctr, Coun. Dent. Res, Am. Dent. Asn, 65-68; RES. INFO. SPECIALIST, ABBOTT LABS, 68- AAAS; Am. Chem. Soc; Am. Soc. Info. Sci; fel. Am. Inst. Chem. Organic syntheses; organic medicinal agents; radiopaque media; scientific documentation; machine processing of technical data. Address: Abbott Labs, North Chicago, IL 60064.

GINSBERG, JONATHAN I, b. Brooklyn, N.Y, Mar. 18, 41; m. 63; c. 2. MATHEMATICS. B.A, Yeshiva Univ, 61, Nat. Defense Educ. Act fel, 62-65, M.A, 64, Nat. Sci. Found. fels, 65-68, Ph.D.(math), 69. Instr. MATH, YESHIVA COL, 68-69, ASST. PROF, 69- Completeness theorems in various Banach spaces and algebras. Address: Dept. of Mathematics, Yeshiva College, Washington Heights, New York, NY 10033.

GINSBERG, MURRY B(ENJAMIN), b. New York, N.Y, Oct. 26, 28; m. 55; c. 2. ELECTRONIC ENGINEERING. B.E.E, City Col. New York, 49; M.S, Maryland, 58. ELECTRONICS ENGR, Bur. Ships, U.S. Navy Dept, 50-57; SYSTS. ANAL. OFF, HARRY DIAMOND LABS, DEPT. ARMY, 57- Inst. Elec. & Electronics Eng. Systems analysis and engineering of electronic weapon systems; radar and information theory. Address: 4419 36th St. N.W, Washington, DC 20008.

GINSBERG, S(TEWART) T(HEODORE), b. St. Paul, Minn, Apr. 18, 06; m. 30; c. 3. PSYCHIATRY. B.S. & B.M, Minnesota, 32, M.D. 33. Psychiatrist, Vet. Admin, Ind. 36-48; mem. teaching staff PSYCHIAT, sch. med, Ind. Univ. 48-53, assoc. clin. prof, 56-57, assoc. prof, 57-61, prof, 61-66; CLIN. PROF, EMORY UNIV, 66-; SUPT, GA. MENT. HEALTH INST, 71-; hosp. dir, Vet. Admin. Hosp, Lyons, N.J, 66-71; comnr. ment. health, State of Ind, 57-66. Chief prof. serv, Vet. Admin. Hosp, Marion, 48-53, mgr, Pa, 53-55, chief, psychiat. div, Wash, D.C, 55-57. Consult, community serv. comt, Nat. Inst. Ment. Health, Nat. Insts. Health, sub-comt, Inserv. Training of Ment. Health Training Comt, 63. Asst. exam, Am. Bd. Psychiat. & Neurol. Med.C, 34-36, 44-46; Med. Dept. Res, 46-66, Col.(ret). Am. Med. Asn; fel. Am. Psychiat. Asn; hon. fel. Am. Col. Dent. Clinical dentistry; utilization of community resources in psychiatric treatment; better utilization of personnel in the mental health specialties to overcome manpower shortages. Address: Georgia Mental Health Institute, 1256 Briarcliff Rd, N.E, Atlanta, GA 30306.

GINSBURG, BENSON E(ARL), b. Detroit, Mich, July 16, 18; m. 41; c. 3. GENETICS. B.S, Wayne State Univ, 39, M.S, 41; Sheldon fel. & Ph.D.(zool), Univ. Chicago, 43. Instr. zool. & physiol, Univ. Chicago, 43-44, res. assoc. pharmacol, 44-46, asst. prof. biol. sci, 46-49, assoc. prof. natural sci, 49-54, prof, 54-59, chmn. dept, 50-57, assoc. dean univ, 57-59, prof. biol. & head sect, 59-63, William Rainey Harper prof, 63-69; PROF. BIOBEHAV. SCI. & CHMN. DEPT, UNIV. CONN, 69- Sci. assoc, Jackson Lab; fel, Ctr. Advan. Study Behav. Sci, 57-58; consult. ed, Encycl. Britannica Films, 59-; mem. adv. comt. animal resources, Nat. Insts. Health, 65-; mem. panel behav. biol, Nat. Acad. Sci-Nat. Res. Coun, 66-67. With Off. Sci. Res. & Develop, 44; Nat. Defense Res, Comt, 44-46. AAAS; Genetics Soc. Am; Am. Soc. Nat; Biomet. Soc; Ecol. Soc. Am; Am. Soc. Human Genetics; Am. Genetic Asn. Gene action in mammalian nervous system; inheritance of emotionality; biological education; zoology. Address: Dept. of Biobehavioral Sciences, University of Connecticut, Box U-154, Storrs, CT 06268.

GINSBURG, CARL, b. N.Y.C, July 13, 36; m. 58. INORGANIC CHEMISTRY. B.S, Rensselaer Polytech, 57; Ph.D.(chem), Ohio, 64. ASST. PROF. CHEM, UTICA COL, SYRACUSE UNIV, 62- Am. Chem. Soc; Brit. Chem. Soc. Chemistry of metal chelate and coordination compounds. Address: Dept. of Chemistry, Utica College of Syracuse University, Utica, NY 13502.

GINSBURG, DAVID, b. N.Y.C, Sept. 5, 20; m. 40; c. 2. CHEMISTRY. B.S, City Col, 41; M.A, Columbia, 42; Ph.D.(org. chem), N.Y. Univ, 47. Prod. chemist, U.S. Rubber Co, Pa, 42-43; res. group leader, N.Y. Quinine & Chem. Works, Brooklyn, 43-48; res. chemist, Daniel Sieff Res. Inst, Weizmann Inst. Sci, 48-50, sr. res. chemist, 50-54; PROF. CHEM, ISRAEL INST. TECHNOL, 54-, v.pres. res, 59-60, acting pres, 61-62. Chmn, Israel Coun. Res. & Develop, 61-63; mem. bur, Int. Union Pure & Appl. Chem, 63-69; vis. prof, Brandeis Univ, 61 & 68; Univ. Zurich, 61; N.Y. Univ, 63-64; Boston Univ, 67; McGill Univ, 70; Royal Soc. vis. prof, Oxford, 70-71, vis. fel, Mertol Col, 70- Fel, U.S. Pub. Health Serv. & Harvard Corp, Harvard, 52-53; Lipsky fel, Oxford, 53; Guggenheim fel, Harvard, 60-61. Weizmann Prize, 54; Rothschild Prize, 65. Am. Chem. Soc; The Chem. Soc; Swiss Chem. Soc; Israel Chem. Soc.(pres, 55-57, 66-67). Natural products; stereochemistry of alicyclic systems; nonbenzenoid aromatic hydrocarbons; carcinogenic substances. Address: Israel Institute of Technology, Haifa, Israel.

GINSBURG, HERBERT, b. Schenectady, N.Y, May 2, 28; m. 51; c. 3. STATISTICS. B.A, State Univ. N.Y, 50, M.A, 51; North Carolina; M.S, N.C. State Col, 54. Eng. statistician, WESTINGHOUSE ELEC. CORP, 54-61, sr. res. statistician, res. labs, 61-63, FEL. STATISTICIAN, BETTIS ATOMIC POWER LAB, 63- Adj. mem. grad. faculty, Univ. Pittsburgh, 62- U.S.N, 45-46. Am. Statist. Asn; Royal Statist. Soc. Experimental design; empirical model building; teaching. Address: 103 Braddock Rd, Pittsburgh, PA 15221.

GINSBURG, ISADORE WILCHER, b. Chester, Pa, Sept. 3, 05; m. 43; c. 2. CLINICAL MEDICINE. A.B, Washington & Lee, 29; M.D, Temple, 34, M.Sc, 39. Instr. med, SCH. MED, TEMPLE UNIV, 39-42, asst. prof, 46-47, assoc. prof, 47-55, clin. prof, 55-57, PROF. CLIN. MED, 57- Consult, Veterans Admin. Hosp, Phila, 54-; Phoenixville Hosp, 40- Dipl, Am. Bd. Internal Med. Med.C, 42-46, Lt. Col. AAAS; Am. Med. Asn; Am. Heart Asn; Am. Med. Cols; fel. Am. Col. Physicians; Am. Fedn. Clin. Res. Clinical investigation in internal medicine. Address: Dept. of Clinical Medicine, Temple University School of Medicine, Philadelphia, PA 19151.

GINSBURG, JACK M(ARTIN), b. Phila, Pa, May 31, 28; m. 55; c. 1. PHYSIOLOGY. B.A, Pennsylvania, 49; Atomic Energy Comn. fel, Tulane, 51-53, Ph.D.(physiol), 53. Lab. asst. physiol, Tulane, 50-53; res. participant, biol. div, Oak Ridge Nat. Lab, 53-54; instr. pharmacol, Tulane, 54-55; PHYSIOL, Cincinnati, 57-59; asst. prof, col. med, Univ. Rochester, 59-68; ASSOC. PROF, MED. COL. GA, 68- Radiobiologist, Med.Res. Lab, U.S.A, 55-57, 1st Lt. AAAS. Biological transport; body fluid; electrolytes. Address: Dept. of Physiology, Medical College of Georgia, Augusta, GA 30902.

GINSBURG, MERRILL STUART, b. Chicago, Ill, July 20, 35. GEOPHYSICS. B.S, Mass. Inst. Tech, 59, M.S, 60; Ph.D.(geophys), Utah, 63. Sr. geophys. engr, geophys. serv. ctr, MOBIL OIL CORP, 63-65, sr. geophys. interpreter, 65-70, ASSOC. GEOPHYSICIST, EXPLOR. DEVELOP. DEPT. EXPLOR. SERVS. CTR, 71- Am. Geophys. Union; Soc. Explor. Geophys; European Asn. Explor. Geophys. Gravity and magnetics; applied mathematics. Address: Exploration Services Center, Mobil Oil Corp, Box 900, Dallas, TX 75221.

GINSBURG, MICHAEL, b. N.Y.C, Jan. 4, 35; m. 60; c. 2. MATHEMATICS. Ph.D.(math), Mass. Inst. Technol, 61. Asst. prof. MATH, Columbia Univ,

64-66; ASSOC. PROF, RUTGERS UNIV, 66- Topology; differential geometry; analysis; physics. Address: Dept. of Mathematics, Rutgers University, New Brunswick, NJ 08903.

GINSBURG, NATHAN, b. Casey, Ill, Aug. 25, 10; m. 42; c. 1. PHYSICS. B.A, Ohio State, 31, M.A, 32; Ph.D.(physics), Michigan, 35. Eng. res. fel, Michigan, 35-36; Johnston scholar, Hopkins, 36-38, asst, 38-41, instr. eng. sci. & mgt. defense training course in spectros, 41-42; asst. prof. PHYSICS, Texas, 42-46; SYRACUSE UNIV, 46-48, assoc. prof, 48-52, PROF, 52-, CHMN. DEPT, 65- Asst, Carnegie Institution, 41-42. Fel. Am. Phys. Soc; fel. Optical Soc. Am. Infrared and ultraviolet spectroscopy; molecular structure; atomic energy levels and Zeeman effect; intensities in molecular spectrum of hydrogen; determination of steroids; lattice vibrations. Address: Dept. of Physics, Syracuse University, Syracuse, NY 13210.

GINSBURG, R(OBERT) N(ATHAN), b. Wichita Falls, Tex, Apr. 26, 25; m. 56. GEOLOGY. A.B, Illinois, 48; M.A, Chicago, 50, Ph.D.(geol), 53. Asst. marine, geol, marine lab, Miami (Fla), 50-54; res. geologist, Shell Develop. Co, 54-60, res. assoc. geol, 60-65; PROF. geol. & oceanog, Johns Hopkins Univ, 65-70; SEDIMENTOL, COMPARATIVE SEDIMENTOL. LAB, UNIV. MIAMI, 70- C.Eng, 43-46, Sgt. Fel. Geol. Soc. Am; Soc. Econ. Paleont. & Mineral; Am. Asn. Petrol. Geol. Recent sediments; coral reefs; ancient and modern algal structures; carbonate geochemistry; marine geology. Address: School of Marine & Atmospheric Science University of Miami, Comparative Sedimentology Lab, Fisher Island Station, Miami, FL 33139.

GINSBURG, SARA, b. Leningrad, Russia, Apr. 21, 08; U.S. citizen. ORGANIC CHEMISTRY. B.S, Berlin, 31, Ph.D.(org. & biol. chem), 34. Res. chemist, UCLAF, Paris, France, 37-39; Lab. Dr. Coirre, Paris, 39-40; Soc. Esp. Prod. Quim, Madrid, Spain, 42-45; Soc. Zeltia, Madrid, 45-46; Publicker Industs, Inc, Pa, 46-47 & 51-52; Physicians Drug & Supply Co, 47-50; RES. ASSOC. & ASST. PROF. ORG. SYNTHESIS & BIOCHEM. PREP, COL. PHYSICIANS & SURGEONS, COLUMBIA UNIV, 53- Am. Chem. Soc. Design and synthesis of biologically active organic compounds. Address: Dept. of Neurology, Columbia University, College of Physicians & Surgeons, 630 W. 168th St, New York, NY 10032.

GINSBURG, SEYMOUR, b. Brooklyn, N.Y, Dec. 12, 27; m. 54; c. 2. COMPUTER SCIENCE. B.S, City Col. New York, 48; M.S, Michigan, 49, Ph.D. (math), 53. Asst. prof. math, Miami (Fla), 51-55; mathematician, Nat. Cash Register Co, 56-59; head systs. synthesis & orgn. sect, Hughes Res. Labs. & sr. mathematician, Syst. Develop. Corp, 59-71; PROF. COMPUTER SCI. & ELEC. ENG, UNIV. SOUTH. CALIF, 71- U.S.A, 46-47. Am. Math. Soc; Math. Asn. Am; Asn. Comput. Mach; Inst. Elec. & Electronics Eng. Set theory; real variable; switching theory; automata and formal language theory. Address: 14031 Margate St, Van Nuys, CA 91401.

GINSBURG, V(ICTOR), b. Singapore, Mar. 22, 30; nat; m. 55; c. 2. BIOCHEMISTRY. B.A, Univ. Calif, 52, Ph.D, 55. CHIEF BIOCHEM. SECT, NAT. INST. ARTHRITIS & METAB. DISEASES, NAT. INSTS. HEALTH, 56- Fel, Nat. Found. 58-59. Am. Chem. Soc; Am. Soc. Biol. Chem. Carbohydrate biochemistry. Address: National Institute of Arthritis & Medabolic Diseases, National Institutes of Health, Bethesda, MD 20014.

GINSBURGH, IRWIN, b. Brooklyn, N.Y, Apr. 15, 26; m. 46; c. 4. PHYSICS. B.S, City Col. New York, 47; fel, Rutgers, 50-51, Ph.D.(physics), 51. Asst, Rutgers, 47-50; res. physicist, AM. OIL CO, STANDARD OIL CO. IND, 51-57, sr. proj. physicist, 57-61, sr. res. supvr, 61-66; RES. ASSOC, 66- Indust. Res. 100 Award, Indust. Res. Mag, 68, 69, 71. U.S.N.R, 44-46. Am. Phys. Soc; Combustion Inst. Nuclear magnetic resonance; acoustics; industrial physics; shock tubes and detonations; instrumentation; analog computers; static electricity; automation; explosions. Address: 8925 Nashville, Morton Grove, IL 60053.

GINSKI, JOHN MARTIN, b. Chicago, Ill, May 26, 26; m. 56; c. 3. PHYSIOLOGY. B.S, Loyola (Ill), 49, M.S, 53, Ph.D.(physiol), 56; Atomic Energy Cmn. fel, Argonne Nat. Lab, 54-55. Res. assoc. pharmacol, Chicago, 55-56; physiol. & pharmacol, col. med, Saskatchewan, 57; instr, col. med, Nebraska, 57-59, asst. prof, 59-60; asst. prof, med. units, UNIV. TENN, 60-67, ASSOC. PROF. PHYSIOL. & BIOPHYS, COL. BASIC MED. SCI, 67- Vis. prof, Valle, Colombia, 63-64. Med.C, U.S.A, 45-46. AAAS; Am. Physiol. Soc; Soc. Exp. Biol. & Med. Electrolyte exchange across cellular membranes and the correlation of these mechanisms with physiological activity of the cells. Address: Division of Clinical Physiology, College of Basic Medical Sciences, University of Tennessee, 800 Madison, Memphis, TN 38103.

GINSLER, V(ICTOR) W(ILLIAM), b. N.Y.C, Mar. 21, 17; m. 42; c. 4. BIOCHEMISTRY. A.B, Kentucky, 39; Ohio State, 41-42. Res. chemist, Trojan Powder Co, Pa, 42-45; res. chemist & tech. serv. supvr. plastics & resins, Allied Chem. Corp, Ohio, 45-58; tech. dir. protective coatings, Rust-Oleum Corp, 58-62; MGR, COATING RESINS DEPT, FREEMAN CHEM. CORP, 62- Am. Soc. Test. & Mat; Am. Chem. Soc. Testing and evaluation of resins, plastics, protective coatings; corrosion resistance. Address: Freeman Chemical Corp, 222 E. Main St, Port Washington, WI 53074.

GINTER, MARSHALL L, b. Chico, Calif, Aug. 24, 35; m. 57; c. 2. PHYSICAL CHEMISTRY, MOLECULAR PHYSICS. B.S, Chico State Col, 58; Ph.D. (phys. chem), Vanderbilt, 61. Res. assoc. phys. chem, Vanderbilt, 59-60, dir. spectros. lab, 61-62; res. assoc. physics, Chicago, 62-66; asst. prof. MOLECULAR PHYSICS, UNIV. MD, COLLEGE PARK, 66-69, ASSOC. PROF, 69- Am. Phys. Soc; Am. Chem. Soc. Atomic and molecular structure; high resolution electronic spectroscopy; electronic structure of small molecules; atomic and molecular Rydberg states; molecular complexes in the gaseous phase; radiative and nonradiative energy transfer processes in the gaseous phase. Address: Institute for Molecular Physics, University of Maryland, College Park, MD 20740.

GINTHER, ROBERT J, b. Lewiston, Maine, July 19, 17; m. 43; c. 3. CHEMISTRY. B.S, Northeastern, 40. Chemist, Sylvania Elec. Prods, Inc, 40-46; chemist & head res. group, struct. & compos. luminescent mat, U.S. NAVAL RES. LAB, 46-69, HEAD, CENT. MAT. RES. ACTIVITY, 69- Am.

Phys. Soc; Electrochem. Soc; Sci. Res. Soc. Am. Luminescence of inorganic crystals and glasses. Address: U.S. Naval Research Lab, Washington, DC 20390.

GINTIS, DANIEL, b. Phila, Pa, Sept. 30, 23; m. 53; c. 2. PHYSICAL CHEMISTRY. A.B, Temple, 48; M.S, Purdue, 50, fel, 50-52, Ph.D.(phys. chem), 52. Chemist, east. regional res. lab, U.S. Dept. Agr, 48; instr. phys. chem, Purdue, 48-50; res. chemist, E.I. DU PONT DE NEMOURS & CO, 52-57, sr. res. chemist, 57-58, res. assoc, 58-59, res. supvr, 59-65, RES. FEL, 65- U.S.A.A.F, 43-45, Lt. Am. Asn. Textile Chem. & Colorists; Am. Chem. Soc; Fiber Soc. New textile products; fiber coatings; optical brighteners. Address: 1212 Dorcas Terr, Kinston, NC 28501.

GINZBARG, ARTHUR S(AMUEL), b. Warsaw, Poland, Sept. 4, 19; nat; m. 48; c. 1. THEORETICAL PHYSICS. B.A, Brooklyn Col, 42; M.S, Purdue, 45, Ph.D.(physics), 49. Asst, Minnesota, 42; from asst. to instr. physics, Purdue, 42-49; physicist, SHELL DEVELOP. CO, SHELL OIL CO, 49-59, from mgr, dept. physics & mech. to SR. RES. ASSOC, 59- Sci. Res. Soc. Am. Electromagnetic theory; solid state physics; numerical analysis and computing; geophysics. Address: Shell Development Co, P.O. Box 481, Houston, TX 77001.

GINZEL, K(ARL) H(EINZ), b. Reichenberg, Czech, June 1, 21; U.S. citizen; m. 58; c. 2. PHARMACOLOGY. M.D, Vienna, 48. Res. asst. pharmacol, Vienna, 48-53; sr. sci. off, biol. sect, Glaxo Labs, Eng, 54-55; sr. res. fel. neuropsychol. & pharmacol, Birmingham, 55-57; sr. lectr. neuro-pharmacol, inst. neurol, Nat. Hosp. Nervous Diseases, London, 57-60; head neuropharmacol. sect, Riker Labs, Calif, 60-70; PROF. PHARMACOL, SCH. MED, UNIV. ARK, LITTLE ROCK, 71- WHO res. fel. pharmacol, Oxford, 52-53; res. assoc. anatomist, Univ. Calif, Los Angeles, 69-71. Am. Soc. Pharmacol. & Exp. Therapeut; Brit. Physiol. Soc; Ger. Pharmacol. Soc. Pharmacology of neuromuscular and ganglionic transmission; introduction to clinical use of succinylcholine; central muscle relaxant agents; respiratory stimulant vanillic acid diethylamide; psychotomimetic drugs; 5-hydroxytryptamine; autonomic and cardiovascular pharmacology; neuropharmacology. Address: Dept. of Pharmacology, University of Arkansas School of Medicine, Little Rock, AR 72201.

GINZTON, EDWARD L(EONARD), b. Ekaterinoslavsk, Russia, Dec. 27, 15; U.S. citizen; m. 39; c. 4. PHYSICS. B.S, California, 36, M.S, 37; E.E, Stanford, 38, Ph.D, 40. Res. engr, Sperry Gyroscope Co, N.Y, 40-46; asst. prof. appl. physics & elec. eng, Stanford Univ, 46-47; MEM. BD. DIRS, VARIAN ASSOCS, 48-, pres, 64-68. Assoc. prof. elec. eng, Stanford Univ, 47-50, prof, 51-68, dir. microwave lab, 49-59, dir. Proj. M, 57-60; expert consult. develop. bd, Nat. Mil. Estab, 47-50; co-chmn, Stanford Mid-Peninsula Urban Coalition, 68- Nat. Acad. Sci; fel. Inst. Elec. & Electronics Eng.(Liebmann Mem. Prize, 58, Medal of Honor, 69); Nat. Acad. Eng. Microwave tube and measurements; linear electron accelerators; circuits. Address: Varian Associates, 611 Hansen Way, Palo Alto, CA 94303.

GIOIA, ANTHONY A(LFRED), b. Torrington, Conn, Apr. 7, 34; div; c. 3. MATHEMATICS. B.A, Connecticut, 55; M.A, Missouri, 61, Ph.D.(math), 64. Instr. MATH, Univ. Mo, 59-64; asst. prof, Tex. Technol. Col, 64-66; ASSOC. PROF, WEST. MICH. UNIV, 66- U.S.A.F, 56-59, Res, 59-, Maj. Am. Math. Soc; Math. Asn. Am. Theory of numbers; identities for multiplicative arithmetical functions. Address: Dept. of Mathematics, Western Michigan University, Kalamazoo, MI 49001.

GIOLLI, ROLAND A, b. San Vito, Italy, Feb. 22, 34; U.S. citizen; m. 63; c. 3. ANATOMY, HISTOCHEMISTRY. A.B, California, Davis, 56, Nat. Sci. Found. summer fel, Berkeley, 59, Ph.D.(anat), 60. Asst. anat, California, Berkeley, 57-59, res. anatomist, sch. optom, 60-63, Ment. Health Training Prog. fel, dept. anat. & brain res. inst, univ, Los Angeles, 63-64; asst. prof. anat, COL. MED, UNIV. CALIF, IRVINE, 64-70, ASSOC. PROF. HUMAN MORPHOL. & PSYCHOBIOL, 70- Am. Asn. Anat; Soc. Neurosci. Visual system; mechanisms of heavy metal impregnation of nervous tissue. Address: Dept. of Anatomy, College of Medicine, University of California, Irvine, CA 92664.

GION, EDMUND, b. Altheimer, Ark, Sept. 27, 29; m. 60; c. 2. PHYSICS. B.A, Reed Col, 59; M.S, Lehigh, 61, Ph.D.(physics), 65. RES. PHYSICIST, BALLISTIC RES. LABS, ABERDEEN PROVING GROUND, 65- U.S.A, 51-53. Am. Phys. Soc. Expansion tube flow; radiation; nonequilibrium flow phenomena. Address: EBL Ballistic Research Labs, Aberdeen Proving Ground, Aberdeen, MD 21005.

GIORDANO, ANTHONY B(RUNO), b. New York, N.Y, Feb. 1, 15; m. 39; c. 1. ELECTRICAL ENGINEERING. B.E.E, Polytech. Inst. Brooklyn, 37, fel, 37-39, M.E.E, 39, D.E.E, 46. Instr. ELEC. ENG, POLYTECH. INST. BROOKLYN, 39-45, asst. prof, 45-51, assoc. prof, 51-53, PROF, 53-, DEAN GRAD. STUDIES, 64-, assoc. dean grad. sch, 57-59, dean, 59-64. Asst, Off. Sci. Res. & Develop. Proj, 42-45; sr. res. assoc, Microwave Res. Inst, 45-49, res. supvr, 49-; v.chmn. res. comt, Eng. Found, 71- Wisdom award of honor, Wisdom Soc. AAAS; Am. Soc. Eng. Educ; fel. Inst. Elec. & Electronics Eng. Address: Dept. of Electrical Engineering, Polytechnic Institute of Brooklyn, 333 Jay St, Brooklyn, NY 11201.

GIORDANO, PAUL MICHAEL, b. Providence, R.I, Apr. 4, 36; m. 59; c. 3. SOIL CHEMISTRY, PLANT NUTRITION. B.S, Rhode Island, 59, M.S, 61; Ph.D.(soil chem), Connecticut, 64. Res. asst. micronutrients & soil chem, Univ. Connecticut, 60-64; RES. CHEMIST, TENN. VALLEY AUTHORITY, 64- Mem. micronutrient cmt, Coun. Fertilizer Appln, 68. U.S.A.R, 55-62. Soil Sci. Soc. Am. Plant-soil-fertilizer relationships, especially those pertaining to micronutrient reactions. Address: Tennessee Valley Authority, Muscle Shoals, AL 35660.

GIORDMAINE, J(OSEPH) A(NTHONY), b. Toronto, Ont, Can, Apr. 10, 33; m. 58; c. 3. PHYSICS. B.A, Toronto, 55; A.M, Columbia, 57, Esso Res. Ed. Found. fel, 58-59, Ph.D.(physics), 60. Instr. physics, Columbia, 59-61; mem. tech. staff, BELL TEL. LABS, INC, 61-71, DIR. CHEM. PHYSICS RES, 71- Consult, Fairchild Camera & Instrument Corp, 61; lectr, exten, Univ. Calif, 64-68; vis. prof, Munich Tech, 66; mem, comt. basic res. adv. Army Res. Off, Nat. Res. Coun, 67-, panel atomic, molecular & electronics physics, physics surv. comt, 70- Fel. Am. Phys. Soc; sr. mem. Inst. Elec. & Electronics Eng; Am. Astron. Soc; Optical Soc. Am. Molecular beams; paramagnetic resonance and relaxation; masers and lasers; nonlinear optical effects; optical properties of solids; radio astronomy. Address: Bell Telephone Labs, Inc, Murray Hill, NJ 07974.

GIORGI, A(NGELO) L(OUIS), b. Syracuse, N.Y, July 18, 17; m. 46; c. 2. RADIOCHEMISTRY. B.S, Syracuse, 39; M.S, New Mexico, 54, Ph.D, 57. Chemist, electrochem, Gen. Motors Corp, 40-42; jr. chemist, phys. chem, U.S. Bur. Mines, 42-44; asst. chemist, electrochem, Naval Res. Lab, 44-46; MEM. STAFF RADIOCHEM, LOS ALAMOS SCI. LAB, 46- Am. Chem. Soc; Electrochem. Soc. Superconductivity; study of superconducting properties of refractory carbides and nitrides. Address: 151 El Gancho, Los Alamos, NM 87544.

GIORGIO, ANTHONY JOSEPH, b. Hartford, Conn, Feb. 8, 30; m. 61; c. 3. HEMATOLOGY, BIOCHEMISTRY. A.B, Boston, 52, M.D, 57; M.S.P.H, Columbia Univ, 53. Instr. med, Univ. Utah, 62-66; ASST. PROF. pediat, N.Y. Med. Col, 67-70; MED, SCH. MED, UNIV. PITTSBURGH, 70- Nat. Insts. Health fel. biochem, Univ. Utah, 64-66; Nat. Insts. Health res. grant, 69- Med.C, U.S.N.R, 59-61, Res, 62-66, Lt. Comdr. Am. Inst. Nutrit; Am. Soc. Clin. Nutrit; Am. Soc. Microbiol; Am. Fedn. Clin. Res. Nutritional anemias; vitamin B_{12} metabolism; clinical laboratory methodology. Address: University of Pittsburgh School of Medicine, 931 Scaife Hall, Pittsburgh, PA 15213.

GIORI, CLAUDIO, b. Milano, Italy, June 2, 38; U.S. citizen; m. 63; c. 2. POLYMER & ORGANIC CHEMISTRY. Doctorate (polymer chem), Univ. Milano, 62. RES. SCIENTIST, E.N.I. Res. Labs, 63-65; fibers div, Allied Chem. Corp, 65-68; I.I.T. RES. INST, 68- AAAS; Am. Chem. Soc; Soc. Aerospace Mat. & Process Eng. Synthesis of high temperature resistant polymers; kinetics and mechanisms of polymerization; stereospecific polymerization; thermal degradation and stabilization of polymers; polymers for reverse osmosis processes; effect of radiation on polymers. Address: 1541 Meadow Lane, Glenview, IL 60025.

GIOUMOUSIS, GEORGE, b. New York, N.Y, Mar. 2, 29. PHYSICS. B.S, Polytech. Inst. Brooklyn, 51; M.S, Wisconsin, 54, Ph.D.(theoret. chem), 55. Physicist, Evans Signal Labs, 51; chemist, Shell Develop. Co, 56-64; RES. SCIENTIST, LOCKHEED PALO ALTO RES. LABS, 64- Am. Phys. Soc. Kinetic theory of gases; molecular scattering theory; ion-molecule reactions; detailed balance. Address: Materials Sciences Lab, Lockheed Palo Alto Research Labs, Palo Alto, CA 94304.

GIOVACCHINI, R(UBERT) PETER, b. Fresno, Calif, June 2, 28; m. 49; c. 3. MEDICAL SCIENCE. B.S, Creighton, 48, M.Sc, 54; Ph.D, Nebraska, 58. Instr. anat, col. med, Nebraska, 57-58; res. histopathologist, Toni Co, Ill, 58-59, asst. med. dir, 60-64; dir. med. eval, Gillette Med. Res. Inst, Wash, D.C, 64-67; V.PRES. & DIR. MED. EVAL DIV, GILLETTE CO. RES. INST, MD, 67- Assoc. anesthesia dept, Bishop Clarkson Mem. Hosp, 57-58. Soc. Toxicol; Am. Acad. Dermat. Toxicological and clinical evaluation of foods, drugs, chemicals and cosmetics. Address: Medical Evaluation Division, Gillette Co. Research Institute, 1413 Research Blvd, Rockville, MD 20850.

GIOVANELLA, BEPPINO C, b. Merano, Italy, June 12, 32; m. 71. CANCER. Laurea (biol), Univ. Rome, 56, Libera Docenza (gen. path), 62. Asst. cancer res, Regina Elena Inst, Rome, 56-60; Nat. Insts. Health fel, McArdle Lab, Univ. Wis, Madison, 60-62, res. assoc, 62-70; LAB. DIR, CANCER RES. LAB, ST. JOSEPH'S HOSP, 70-; CLIN. ASST. PROF. ONCOL, COL. MED, BAYLOR UNIV, 71- Am. Asn. Cancer Res. Radiobiology of tumors; skin carcinogenesis; effects of supranormal temperatures on normal and neoplastic cells; chemotherapy of malignant tumors; immunobiology of neoplastic cells; chemotherapy of malignant tumors; immunobiology of neoplastic diseases. Address: Cancer Research Lab, St. Joseph's Hospital, Houston, TX 77002.

GIOVINETTO, MARIO BARTOLOME, b. La Plata, Arg, May 5, 33; m. 66; c. 1. CLIMATOLOGY, GLACIOLOGY. M.S, Wisconsin, Madison, 66, Ph.D. (geog), 68. Res. asst. glaciol, Ohio State, summer 59, 59-61; res. assoc. geol, Michigan, 59; proj. asst. glaciol, Wisconsin, Madison, 61-67, acting instr. CLIMAT, 67-68; asst. prof, UNIV. CALIF, BERKELEY, 68-69, ASSOC. PROF, 69- Mem, Nat. Res. Coun, 71-74. Am. Meteorol. Soc; Am. Geophys. Union; Asn. Am. Geog; Am. Water Resources Asn; Glaciol. Soc. Arctic and Antarctic glaciology; physical climatology of glaciers and its implications on paleoclimates; precipitation phenomena in arid and semi-arid lands. Address: Dept. of Geography, University of California, Berkeley, CA 94720.

GIPPIN, MORRIS, b. N.Y.C, Apr. 4, 08; m. 44; c. 1. ORGANIC CHEMISTRY. A.B, Univ. N.C, 35; M.A, Brooklyn Col, 38; Ph.D.(chem), West. Reserve Univ, 51. Sr. res. chemist, POLYMERS, FIRESTONE TIRE & RUBBER CO, 51-69, SR. RES. SCIENTIST, 69- Sanit.C, 42-46, Capt. Am. Chem. Soc. High polymers, elastomers; polymerization catalyst systems. Address: 2810 Chamberlain Rd, Akron, OH 44313.

GIPSON, MACK, JR, b. Trenton, S.C, Sept. 15, 31; m. 56; c. 4. GEOLOGY. B.A, Paine Col, 53; M.S, Chicago, 61, J. Elmer Thomas fels, 61-63, Rollins D. Salisbury & Off. Naval Res. fels. & Ph.D.(geol), 63. Assoc. prof. GEOL, VA. STATE COL, 64-67, PROF, 67-, HEAD DEPT, 64- U.S.A, 54-56. Am. Geophys. Union; Nat. Asn. Geol. Teachers; Geol. Soc. Am. Petrofabrics of recent and ancient fine-grained sediments; sediment transport; sedimentation. Address: Dept. of Geology, Box D, Virginia State College, Petersburg, VA 23803.

GIPSON, ROBERT MALONE, b. Odessa, Tex, Apr. 9, 39; m. 61; c. 1. ORGANIC CHEMISTRY. B.S, Abilene Christian Col, 61; Rosalie B. Hite Found. fel, Texas, 62-65, M.A, 63, Ph.D.(org. chem), 65. RES. CHEMIST, AUSTIN LABS, JEFFERSON CHEM. CO, 65- Am. Chem. Soc. Metabolite analogs; medium ring organic compounds; organometallic chemistry. Address: 416 Brady Lane, Austin, TX 78746.

GIPSTEIN, EDWARD, b. Hartford, Conn, Oct. 20, 25; m. 51; c. 2. POLYMER & ORGANIC CHEMISTRY. B.S, Univ. Conn, 49; M.A, St. Joseph Col.

(Conn), 64. Chemist, Landers, Frary & Clark, 52-55; sr. res. chemist, Olin Mathieson Chem. Corp, 55-65; RES. STAFF MEM, RES. DIV, IBM CORP, 65- U.S.A, 44-46. Am. Chem. Soc; Sci. Res. Soc. Am. Organoboranes; polysulfides; polysulfones; cellulose derivative; vinyl polymers and monomers. Address: Research Division, IBM Corp, Bldg. 028, Monterey & Cottle Rd, San Jose, CA 95114.

GIRAITIS, ALBERT P(HILIP), b. Scranton, Pa, Sept. 20, 10; m. 35; c. 2. CHEMISTRY. A.B, Washington Col, 34; Ph.D.(org. chem), Clark, 38. Res. chemist, Standard Oil Co, N.J, 38-41, La. Div, 41-45; Kendall Ref. Co, Pa, 45-47; ETHYL CORP, 47-54, acting asst. dir, chem. res. & develop, 54-55, spec. assignment, admin. & staff, 55-56, asst. dir. chem. res. & develop, 56-66, assoc. dir. RES. PLANNING, 66-67, DIR, 67- Am. Chem. Soc. Organic chemistry; chemicals from petroleum; refining of white oil; certain reactions of diazomethane with cyclic ketones; synthesis of ethyl chloride; organometallic chemistry. Address: Ethyl Corp, P.O. Box 341, Baton Rouge, LA 70821.

GIRALA, ANTHONY SEVERINO, b. Monterrey, Mex, Feb. 11, 19; nat; m. 46; c. 4. MECHANICAL ENGINEERING. B.S, Houston, 54. Instrument maker, Naval Ord. Lab, 41-43, 44-46; Schlumberger Well Serv. Corp, 46-52; design engr, F.H. Maloney Co, 52-54, develop. engr, 54-59, v.pres. mech. res, 58-60; sr. res. engr, Welex Div, Halliburton Co, 60-61, asst. prod. mgr, 61-62; spec. proj. engr, plastics & rubber div, Wyatt Industs, Inc, chief tooling engr, 62-64; sr. res. engr, Proj. Mohole, sci. sect, Brown & Root, Inc, Tex, 64-67; SR. DESIGN ENGR, MANNED SPACECRAFT CTR, NASA, 67- Consult. engr. U.S.N.R, 44-45, Res, 46-58. Am. Soc. Test. & Mat; Nat. Soc. Prof. Eng; Inst. Elec. & Electronics Eng. Electromechanical systems employed in high pressure and high temperature environment; hydraulic systems and instrumentation for down-hole applications; applications of rubber and plastics; developed and patented a zero gravity urine receptacle for the Apollo Command Module; mechanisms to be employed in lunar environment. Address: 1210 Elliston St, Houston, TX 77023.

GIRARD, ARTHUR E(DWARD), b. Thompsonville, Conn, Apr. 26, 37; m. 60; c. 4. MICROBIOLOGY, ELECTRON MICROSCOPY. B.A, Univ. Conn, 58, M.S, 61, Ph.D.(microbiol), 69. Asst. bact, Univ. Conn, 58-61; Merck Inst. Therapeut. Res, N.J, 63-65; MICROBIOL, UNIV. CONN, 65-68, instr, HEALTH CTR, 68-70, ASST. PROF, 70- Chem.C, U.S.A, 61-62, 1st Lt. AAAS; Brit. Soc. Gen. Microbiol; Am. Soc. Microbiol. Microbial ultrastructure; chemical composition and taxonomy; oral microbiology; ecology of the oral cavity; microbiological factors associated with periodontal disease. Address: 12 Hartford Ave, Enfield, CT 06082.

GIRARD, DENNIS M(ICHAEL), b. Detroit, Mich, July 26, 39; m. 62; c. 3. MATHEMATICS. B.S, Univ. Detroit, 61, M.A, 62; Ph.D.(math), Ohio State Univ, 68. Aerospace engr, Lewis Res. Ctr, NASA, 62-63; asst. prof. math, Ohio State Univ, 68-69; ASST. PROF. ECOSYST. ANAL, UNIV. WIS, GREEN BAY, 69- AAAS; Am. Math. Soc; Soc. Indust. & Appl. Math; Math. Asn. Am. Complex analysis; asymptotic analysis, combinatorics; computer simulation of biological systems, mathematical ecology. Address: College of Environmental Sciences, University of Wisconsin-Green Bay, Green Bay, WI 54301.

GIRARD, FRANCIS H(ENRY), b. Chicago, Ill, Dec. 28, 35; m. 58; c. 3. BIOCHEMISTRY, ORGANIC CHEMISTRY. B.S, DePaul, 57, Nat. Sci. Found. fel. & M.S, 59; Ph.D.(chem), Northwestern, 64. Instr. chem, sch. nursing, Evanston Hosp, fall, 60; res. chemist, TONI CO. DIV. GILLETTE CO, 64-67, sr. res. chemist, 67-69, res. supvr. chem, 69-71, ASST. DIR. RES, 71- Am. Chem. Soc; Soc. Cosmetic Chem. Guanidine chemistry; phosphoramidic acid chemistry; intermediary metabolism; cosmetic chemistry, particularly chemistry and physics of hair; polymer chemistry. Address: 2108 N. Kennicott Dr, Arlington Heights, IL 60004.

GIRARD, K(ENNETH) F(RANCIS), b. Cohoes, N.Y, Sept. 20, 24; m. 53; c. 3. BACTERIOLOGY, IMMUNOLOGY. B.S, Siena Col, 48; M.Sc, McGill, 50, Ph.D.(bact), 52. Mgr. ed. serv, Lederle Labs, Am. Cyanamid Co, 52-54; asst. prof. bact. & immunol, med. sch, Dalhousie, 54-56; McGill, 56-58; sch. med, Tufts, 59-62; tech. dir, clin. labs, Boston Dispensary, New Eng. Med. Ctr, 59-61; ASST. DIR, DIV. OF DIAG. LABS, MASS. DEPT. PUB. HEALTH, 61- Res. assoc, sch. pub. health, Harvard, 62-; lectr, Simmons Col, 64-70. Med.C, U.S.A, 43-46. AAAS; Am. Soc. Microbiol; Am. Soc. Exp. Path; Am. Pub. Health Asn; Am. Asn. Clin. Chem. Listeriosis; rabies; syphilis serology. Address: Diagnostic Labs, Massachusetts State Dept. of Public Health, 281 South St, Jamaica Plain, MA 02130.

GIRARD, LOUIS J(OSEPH), b. Spokane, Wash, Mar. 29, 19; m. 45, 67; c. 7. OPHTHALMOLOGY. B.A, Rice Inst, 41; M.D, Texas, 44. Coordinator, grad. course ophthal, post-grad. med. sch, N.Y. Univ, 48-49, instr. OPHTHAL, 51-53; clin. asst. prof, post-grad. med. sch, Texas, 53; clin. assoc. prof, BAYLOR COL. MED, 53-56, assoc. chmn. dept, 56-58, PROF, 58-, chmn. dept, 58-70. Lectr, post-grad. med. sch, Texas, 59; exec. dir, Eyes Tex. Sight Found, 60. Bond award, 50. Consult, Ophthal. Found, Inc, 51-53; Southside Hosp, New York, 51-53; Montgomery County Hosp, Conroe, Tex, 55; Tex. Children's Hosp, 57; Vet. Admin. Hosp, Houston, 58- Chief, eye, ear, nose & throat sect, Regional Sta. Hosp, Ft. Belvoir, Va, Med.C, 45-47, Capt. Asn. Res. Vision & Ophthal; fel. Am. Col. Surg; Am. Acad. Ophthal. & Otolaryngol; Pan-Am. Asn. Ophthal. Ophthalmic surgery. Address: 1700 Holcombe Blvd, Houston, TX 77025.

GIRARD, ROLAND THOMAS, b. Lodi, N.J, Nov. 20, 14; m. 41; c. 3. CERAMICS. B.S, Rutgers, 37. CERAMIC ENGR, Works Lab, GEN. ELEC. CO, 37-55, ADV. TECHNOL. LAB, RES. & DEVELOP. CTR, 55- Am. Ceramic Soc; Am. Foundrymen's Soc; Am. Soc. Test. & Mat. Materials processing and application in refractories; coating for metals, cements, and insulations; conducting coatings. Address: Research & Development Center, General Electric Co, P.O. Box 8, Schenectady, NY 12301.

GIRARD, THEODORE ALSDORF, b. Fall River, Mass, Apr. 22, 21; m. 45; c. 2. ORGANIC CHEMISTRY. B.S, Massachusetts, 42; fel, N.Y. Univ, 42-43, M.S, 46. Analyst, Gen. Foods, Inc, 43-45; org. res. chemist, Heyden Chem. Corp, 45-52, group leader org. synthesis, 52-58, asst. dir. res. & develop, nuodex div, Tenneco Chem. Inc, 58-61, mgr. res, 61-66; V.PRES. res. & develop, MICH. CHEM, CORP, 66-68, MKT, 68- Mem, Textile Res. Inst. Am. Chem. Soc; Soc. Plastics Eng; Am. Inst. Chem; Soc. Indust. Microbiol. Pesticides; agricultural chemicals; fine chemicals; process development; organic synthesis; synthetic lubricants; plasticizers; stabilizers; driers; metal soap. Address: Michigan Chemical Corp, 351 E. Ohio St, Chicago, IL 60611.

GIRARDEAU, MARVIN D(ENHAM), JR, b. Lakewood, Ohio, Oct. 3, 30; m. 56; c. 3. THEORETICAL PHYSICS. B.S, Case, 52; M.S, Illinois, 54; Ph.D. (physics), Syracuse, 58. Nat. Sci. Found. fel. physics, Inst. Adv. Study, Princeton, 58-59; res. assoc, Brandeis, 59-60; mem. staff, Boeing Sci. Res. Labs, Wash, 60-61; res. assoc, Enrico Fermi Inst. Nuclear Studies, Chicago, 61-63; assoc. prof. PHYSICS, INST. THEORETICAL SCI, UNIV. ORE, 63-67, PROF, 67-, RES. ASSOC, 63-, dir, 67-69. Summers, aeronaut. res. scientist, Lewis Lab, Nat. Adv. Comt. Aeronaut, Ohio, 54, 56. Am. Phys. Soc. Quantum-mechanical many-body problems; statistical mechanics. Address: Institute of Theoretical Science, University of Oregon, Eugene, OR 97403.

GIRARDI, ANTHONY J(OSEPH), b. Philadelphia, Pa, Mar. 19, 26; m. 58; c. 2. MICROBIOLOGY. B.S, Pa. State, 49; Nat. Insts. Health fel, Pennsylvania, 50-52, Ph.D.(med. microbiol), 52. Instr. prev. med, sch. med, Yale, 52-53; virol, Pennsylvania, 53-56; chief res, Microbiol. Res. Found, 56-59; res. assoc, Merck Inst. Therapeut. Res, 59-63; WISTAR INST, 63-70, ASSOC. MEM, 70- Nat. Insts. Health res. fel, sch. med, Yale, 52-53, Nat. Cancer Inst. grant, 57- Res. assoc, Children's Hosp, Phila, 53-56. Consult, Microbiol. Assocs, Inc, 53-56. U.S.A, 43-46. Tissue Culture Asn; N.Y. Acad. Sci; Am. Asn. Cancer Res; Am. Asn. Immunol. Virology; cancer virus; tumor immunology. Address: Wistar Institute of Anatomy & Biology, 36th & Spruce Sts, Philadelphia, PA 19104.

GIRARDI, DANIEL J(AMES), b. Sault Ste. Marie, Can, Oct. 30, 15; nat. METALLURGICAL ENGINEERING. B.S.E, Wayne, 36; M.S.E, Michigan, 38, Ph.D.(metall. eng), 41. Res. engr, Michigan, 37-39; instr. metall. eng, Wisconsin, 41-43; metallurgist, Dow Chem. Co, Mich, 43-44; chief metallurgist, Manhattan Proj, Garfield Div, Houdaille-Hershey Corp, 44-46; metallurgist, TIMKEN CO, 46-57, mgr. metall. res. & process control, 57-64, DIR, METALL STEEL OPERS, 64- Am. Soc. Metals; Am. Inst. Min, Metall. & Petrol. Eng; Brit. Iron & Steel Inst. Physical and process metallurgy of steel. Address: Timken Co, Canton, OH 44706.

GIRARDOT, PETER R(AYMOND), b. Detroit, Mich, Aug. 15, 22; m. 53; c. 7. INORGANIC CHEMISTRY. B.S, Detroit, 44; fel, Michigan, 47-50, M.S, 48, Allied Chem. & Dye fel, 51, Ph.D.(chem), 52. Group leader, metall. lab, Chicago, 44-45; jr. physicist, ram-jet instrumentation, applied physics lab, Hopkins, 45; instr. chem, Michigan, 50-51; asst. inorg. chem, Eng. Res. Inst, 51-52; proj. leader, phys. & inorg. chem, Bjorksten Res. Labs, Inc, 52-55; sr. res. supvr, explor. inorg. chem. div, Pittsburgh Plate Glass Co, 55-66; PROF. CHEM. & DEAN SCI, UNIV. TEX, ARLINGTON, 66- U.S.N, 45-46. Am. Chem. Soc; Am. Phys. Soc. Inorganic chlorinations; halides, subhalides and polyhalides; extractive metallurgy; high temperature reactions; heavy industrial chemicals; Mössbauer spectroscopy. Address: Dept. of Chemistry, University of Texas at Arlington, Arlington, TX 76010.

GIRAUDI, CARLO, b. Turin, Italy, Mar. 28, 26; U.S. citizen; m. 50; c. 2. CHEMICAL ENGINEERING. D.Sc.(chem. eng), Milan Polytech, 49. Chem. engr, Ultra Chem. Works Div, Witco, 50-57, plant engr, 57-58, tech. dir. & v.pres, 58-61, v.pres. RES. DEVELOP. & ENG, WITCO CHEM. CO, 61-70, GROUP V.PRES, 70- Am. Chem. Soc; Am. Inst. Chem. Eng; Am. Inst. Chem; N.Y. Acad. Sci. Organic chemistry. Address: Witco Chemical Co, 277 Park Ave, New York, NY 10017.

GIRERD, R(ENÉ) J(EAN), b. Le Creusot, France, Mar. 1, 20; m. 49; c. 1. PATHOLOGY. M.D, Lyon, France, 53, Ph.D, 60. Asst, Montreal, 52-53; biochemist, F.W. Horner Ltd, 53-54; instr. med, Southern California, 54-55; biologist, Nepera Chem. Co, 55-57; sr. scientist, Warner-Lambert Res. Inst, 57-62; path. res, N.Y. Med. Col, 62-63; path. res, Albert Einstein Col. Med, 63-65; asst. prof. path, N.Y. Med. Col, 66-67; pathologist, Morristown Mem. Hosp, 67-68; LAB. DIR, DOVER GEN. HOSP, N.J, 69- French Air Force, 38-46. Am. Physiol. Soc. Pathology. Address: Jardine St, Dover, NJ 07801.

GIRI, NARAYAN C, b. India, May 1, 28; m. 62. MATHEMATICAL STATISTICS. B.Sc, Midnapore Col, 51; M.Sc, Calcutta, 53; Oregon, 58-59; Ph.D. (math. statist), Stanford, 61. Statist. asst, Jute Agr. Res. Inst, India, 53-55; res. investr. biomet, Indian Coun. Agr. Res, 55-58; asst. prof. MATH, Arizona, 61-62; asst. prof, Cornell, 62-64; assoc. prof, UNIV. MONTREAL, 64-70, PROF, 70- Grants, U.S. Off. Naval Res, 61-63, Nat. Sci. Cong. Asn. Biometry; design of experiments; sample survey; mathematics. Address: Dept. of Mathematics, University of Montreal, Montreal, Que, Can.

GIRIFALCO, LOUIS A(NTHONY), b. Brooklyn, N.Y, July 3, 28; m. 50; c. 8. SOLID STATE PHYSICS, METALLURGY. B.S, Rutgers, 50; M.S, Cincinnati, 52, Ph.D.(phys. chem), 54. Res. chemist, E.I. du Pont de Nemours & Co, 54-55; solid state physicist, NASA, 55-59, head, solid state physics sect, Lewis Res. Ctr, Ohio, 59-61; assoc. prof. metall. eng, UNIV. PA, 61-65, PROF. METALL. & MAT. SCI, 65-, dir. lab. res. struct. of matter, 67-69. Pres, Cara Corp, 69-70. AAAS; Am. Phys. Soc; Am. Inst. Mining, Metall. & Petrol. Eng. Surface chemistry; diffusion in solids; statistical mechanics of solids; lattice vibrations; imperfections in metals; cohesion in metals. Address: School of Metallurgy & Materials Science, University of Pennsylvania, Philadelphia, PA 19104.

GIRIJA VALLABHAN, CHIYYARATH VELAYUDHAN, Civil Eng, Eng. Mech, see VALLABHAN, C. V. GIRIJA.

GIRLING, F(RANK), b. Mt. Brydges, Ont, Jan. 28, 15; m. 39; c. 3. BIOPHYSICS. B.Sc, Western Ontario, 48, fel, 48-51, Ph.D.(biophysics), 51. Sci. serv. off, Defence Res. Med. Labs, 51-67; SR. SCIENTIST, ONT. SCI. CTR, 67- With Royal Aircraft Estab, Inst. Aviation Med, 55-56. Can. Army, 35-45. Am. Physiol. Soc; Can. Physiol. Soc. Environmental physiology; nervous system; population mechanics. Address: Ontario Science Centre, 770 Don Mills Rd, Don Mills, Ont, Can.

GIRLING, ROWLAND LEA, b. Lynchburg, Va, Oct. 19, 42; m. 67; c. 1. PHYSICAL & INORGANIC CHEMISTRY, BIOCHEMISTRY. B.S, North Carolina, 65; NASA trainee, South Carolina, 65-68, Petrol. Res. fel, 68-69, Ph.D. (chem), 69. RES. ASSOC. CRYSTALLOG, UNIV. PITTSBURGH, 69- Am. Chem. Soc; Am. Crystallog. Asn. Carbohydrate chemistry; sulfur biochemistry; transition metal complexes. Address: Dept. of Crystallography, University of Pittsburgh, Pittsburgh, PA 15213.

GIROLAMI, GUIDO, b. Sherman Island, Calif, Jan. 23, 24; m. 55; c. 3. BOTANY. A.B, California, 48, Ph.D.(bot), 52. Assoc. bot, California, 51-52; asst, res. found, N.Y. Univ, 52-54; asst. prof. bot, Hawaii, 54-57; plant mgr, Campbell Soup Co, 57-62; dir. tech. serv, Di Giorgio Corp, San Francisco, 63-67; tech. dir, Ralston Purina Int, RALSTON PURINA CO, 67-68, asst. to dir. new venture mgt, 68-69, V.PRES, RES. & DEVELOP. & PROD. DIR, CHECKERBOARD FOODS DIV, 69- U.S.N, 43-46, Ens. Bot. Soc. Am; Inst. Food Technol; N.Y. Acad. Sci. Relation of phyllotaxis to primary vascular organization; leaf histogenesis; pathological plant anatomy. Address: Ralston Purina Co, Checkerboard Square, St. Louis, MO 63199.

GIROLAMI, R(OLAND) L(OUIS), b. Milwaukee, Wis, Sept. 19, 24; m. 49. BACTERIOLOGY. B.S, Wisconsin, 50, M.S, 52, Ph.D.(bact), 55. Asst. bact, Wisconsin, 51-55; res. assoc, Oak Ridge Nat. Lab, 55-56; res. microbiologist, res. div, Nat. Dairy Prod. Corp, 56-57; ABBOTT LABS, 57-69, DIR. QUAL. ASSURANCE, ABBOTT SCI. PROD. DIV, 69- U.S.N, 43-46. Am. Soc. Microbiol. Fermentation microbiology; microbial genetics and physiology. Address: Quality Assurance Dept, Abbott Scientific Products Division, 820 Mission St, South Pasadena, CA 91030.

GIROTTI, ALBERT WILLIAM, b. Springfield, Mass, Aug. 9, 37; m. 69. BIOCHEMISTRY. S.B, Mass. Inst. Tech, 59; M.S. & Ph.D.(protein chem), Massachusetts, 65. Res. assoc. interaction of metal ions with proteins, med. col, Cornell Univ, 65-68; ASST. PROF. BIOCHEM, MED. COL. WIS, 68- Nat. Sci. Found. grant, 71-73. Am. Chem. Soc. Interaction of porphyrins and metalloporphyrins with proteins; interaction of metal ions with proteins. Address: Dept. of Biochemistry, Medical College of Wisconsin, 561 N. 15th St, Milwaukee, WI 53233.

GIROUARD, R(ONALD) M(AURICE), b. Sudbury, Ont, Mar. 22, 36; m. 67; c. 2. HORTICULTURE, PLANT PHYSIOLOGY. B.S.A, Univ. Toronto, 60; M.Sc, Ohio State Univ, 62; Ph.D.(hort), Purdue Univ, 67. RES. SCIENTIST, LAURENTIAN FOREST RES. CTR, CAN. FORESTRY SERV, 66- Mem, Comt. Forest Tree Breeding Can, 70- AAAS; Am. Soc. Hort. Sci; Can. Soc. Plant Physiol; Int. Plant Propagators Soc. Vegetative propagation of forest trees; anatomy and physiology of adventitious root formation in stem cuttings. Address: Laurentian Forest Research Centre, Canadian Forestry Service, P.O. Box 3800, Ste. Foy, Que. 10, Can.

GIROUARD, R(USTUM) E(RNEST), JR, b. Kaplan, La, Mar. 21, 40; m. 62; c. 2. ANIMAL NUTRITION & PHYSIOLOGY. B.S, La. State, 62, M.S, 64, Ph.D.(animal nutrit), 68. Res. asst. nutrit, La. State, 62-63, instr. dairy nutrit. physiol, 64-65, res. asst. animal nutrit, 65-67; sect. mgr. dairy res, Allied Mills, Inc, 67-69; OWNER-MGR, DAIRY-RICE CORP, 69- AAAS; Am. Dairy Sci. Asn; Am. Soc. Animal Sci. Nutritional requirements of dairy cattle; complete rations; digestibility of roughage; chemical treatment of roughages; ration effects on milk production; surfactants and bloat in cattle. Address: Dairy-Rice Corp, Route 1, Box 94A, Kaplan, LA 70548.

GIROUX, G(UY), b. Levis, Que, July 13, 26; m. 62; c. 2. PHYSICS. B.A. & B.Ph, Laval, 45, B.S, 50, M.S, 53, D.Sc,(physics), 55. Defence serv. sci. officer, Can. Res. & Develop. Estab, Can, 55-63; Defence Res. Bd, Liaison Off, Mass, 63-66; sci. consult, Can. Res. & Develop. Estab, 66-67, SECT. HEAD. OPTICAL & INFRARED SURVEILLANCE, DEFENCE RES. ESTAB, VALCARTIER, 67- Can. Asn. Physicists. Study of semiconductors used as photodetectors; infrared physics; nuclear physics; beta-rays spectroscopy; use of Fourier analysis in optics and noise problems; reentry physics; lasers; optical and infrared surveillance equipment and systems; optical & infrared counter-surveillance. Address: 699 Rue Dalquier, Ste-Foy, Quebec 10, Que, Can.

GIROUX, ROGER N(ICEPHORE), b. North Lancaster, Ont, July 31, 27; m. 60; c. 3. DAIRY SCIENCE. L.S.A, Montreal, 51, Agr. Res. Coun. Que. scholar, 51-52; Aluminum Lab. Res. Kingston, Toronto, 52-54, M.S.A, 54; Agr. Res. Coun. Que. scholar & U.S. Steel Corp. grant, Wisconsin, 54-57, Ph.D.(dairy, biochem), 57. Asst, Wisconsin, 54-57; prof. dairy chem. & concentrated milks, Prov. Que. Dairy Sch, 57-62; head dept. dairy tech, Inst. Agr. Tech, 62-63; ASST. TECH. DIR. & CHIEF CONTROL & RESEARCHES, COOP. AGRICOLE DE GRANBY, 63- Chief off. lab. anal. dairy prod. & dairy prod. substitutes, 61-63. Res. consult, Can. Dairy & Ice Cream J, 58; collab, Le Que. Laitier, 59. Am. Dairy Sci. Asn; Can. Inst. Food Tech; Agr. Inst. Can. Dairy technology; hygiene; biochemistry; new processes for making fluid sterile concentrated milk with a fresh milk flavor. Address: Cooperative Agricole de Granby, C.P. 219, Granby, Que, Can.

GIROUX, VINCENT A(RTHUR), b. Los Angeles, Calif, Nov. 26, 21; m. 40; c. 8. ELECTRICAL ENGINEERING. B.S, California, Los Angeles, 49; M.S.E.E, Southern California, 56. Eng. asst, South. Calif. Edison Co, 49-51; eng. assoc, Los Angeles Dept. Water & Power, 51-57; asst. prof. ENG, CALIF. STATE COL, LOS ANGELES, 57-61, assoc. prof, 61-66, PROF, 66- Lectr, Univ. South. Calif, 60- U.S.N, 42-45. Inst. Elec. & Electronics Eng; Am. Soc. Eng. Educ. Power system analysis and economics; interruption of large magnitude currents. Address: School of Engineering, California State College, 5151 State College Dr, Los Angeles, CA 90032.

GIROUX, YVES M(ARIE), b. Quebec, Que, June 15, 35; m. 58; c. 3. STRUCTURAL ENGINEERING. B.A, Laval Univ, 55, B.A.S, 59; M.S, Mass. Inst. Technol, 60, Ford Found. fel, 62-66, D.Sc.(struct. eng), 66. Asst. CIVIL ENG, LAVAL UNIV, 60-62, asst. prof, 64-68, ASSOC. PROF, 68-, HEAD DEPT, 67- Eng. Inst. Can; Am. Soc. Civil Eng; Am. Soc. Eng. Educ; Int. Asn. Shell Struct. Numerical analysis of structures; connections for steel structures. Address: Dept. of Civil Engineering, Faculty of Science, Laval University, Quebec 10, Que, Can.

GIRVAN, ROBERT F, b. Odebolt, Iowa, Jan. 7, 38; m. 58; c. 4. SOLID STATE PHYSICS. B.S, Iowa State, 60, M.S, 64, Ph.D.(physics), 66. Assoc. PHYSICS, Iowa State, 66; fel, Florida, 66-68; ASST. PROF, BOSTON COL, 68- AAAS; Am. Phys. Soc; Solar Energy Soc. Electronic structure of solids. Address: Dept. of Physics, Boston College, Chestnut Hill, MA 02167.

GIRVIN, EB C(ARL), b. Georgetown, Texas, Dec. 27, 17; m. 44; c. 3. GENETICS. B.A, Texas, 40, M.A, 41, Ph.D, 48. Prof. biol. & zool, Millsaps Col, 48-53; PROF. BIOL. & HEAD DEPT, SOUTHWEST. UNIV.(TEX), 53-, chmn. div. natural & appl. sci, 67-70. Mem, Tex. State Bd. Examiners Basic Sci, 60- U.S.N.R, 41-45, Lt. Comdr. AAAS. Address: Dept. of Biology, Southwestern University, Georgetown, TX 78626.

GISH, DUANE T, b. White City, Kans, Feb. 17, 21; m. 46; c. 4. BIOCHEMISTRY. B.S, California, Los Angeles, 49; Ph.D, California, 53. U.S. Pub. Health Serv. fel, Nat. Insts. Health, 52-53; Lilly fel. nat. sci, med. col, Cornell, 53-55, asst. prof, 56; asst. res. biochemist, virus lab, California, Berkeley, 56-60; RES. ASSOC, UPJOHN CO, 60- U.S.A, 40-46. Am. Chem. Soc. Protein and polypeptide isolation; structure determination and synthesis; synthesis of nucleosides and nucleotides. Address: Upjohn Co, 7244-25-3, Kalamazoo, MI 49001.

GISHLER, PAUL ERNEST, b. Golden Lake, Ont, July 30, 04; m. 40; c. 2. PHYSICAL CHEMISTRY. B.S, Alberta, 29, M.S, 31; Ph.D.(chem), McGill, 35. Res. chemist, Nat. Res. Coun. Can, 36-55; DIR. RES, Can. Chem. Co. Ltd, 55-63, CHEMCELL LTD, 63- Brit. Inst. Chem. Eng; fel. Royal Soc. Can; fel. Chem. Inst. Can. Pyrolysis of Alberta natural gas; the system calcium oxide-sulfur dioxide-water; roasting of sulphide ores; heat transfer and fluidized solids; oil recovery from Alberta oil sands; petrochemicals. Address: 10946-84th Ave, Edmonton, Alta, Can.

GISIN, BALTHASAR F(RIEDRICH), b. Basel, Switz, Jan. 16, 40. ORGANIC CHEMISTRY, PHYSIOLOGY. Ph.D.(org. chem), Univ. Basel, 67. Res. assoc. PHYSIOL, MED. CTR, DUKE UNIV, 67-69, ASST. PROF, 69- Guest investr, Rockefeller Univ, 67-69, vis. asst. prof, 69- Am. Chem. Soc; Am. Physiol. Soc; Swiss Chem. Soc. Peptide chemistry; ion complexing agents; organic catalysts; specificity in organic reactions; chemistry and physical chemistry of membranes; transport phenomena on membranes; enzymatic reactions. Address: Rockefeller University, 66th St. & York Ave, New York, NY 10021.

GISLASON, ERIC ARNI, b. Oak Park, Ill, Sept. 9, 40; m. 62. PHYSICAL CHEMISTRY. A.B, Oberlin Col, 62; Nat. Sci. Found. fel, Harvard, 62-66, Ph.D.(chem. physics), 67. Nat. Center Air Pollution Control spec. fel. CHEM, Univ. Calif, Berkeley, 67-69; ASST. PROF, UNIV. ILL, CHICAGO CIRCLE, 69- Am. Phys. Soc; Am. Chem. Soc. Molecular beam studies of chemical reactions and intermolecular potentials. Address: Dept. of Chemistry, University of Illinois at Chicago Circle, Chicago, IL 60680.

GISLASON, G(ERHARD) JOHN, b. Grand Forks, N.Dak, Sept. 16, 18; m; c. 2. UROLOGY. B.A, North Dakota, 39, B.S, 40; M.D, Pennsylvania, 42. Asst. instr. surg, sch. med, Pennsylvania, 44-48; asst. prof. UROL, HAHNEMANN MED. COL, 48-57, assoc. prof, 57-71, CLIN. PROF, 71-, head sect, 64-69. Assoc, grad. sch. med, Univ. Pa, 54-; chief urol, Abington Mem. Hosp, 66- Med.C, U.S.A, 44-46. Am. Med. Asn; Am. Urol. Asn; Am. Col. Surg; N.Y. Acad. Sci. Clinical problems in urinary tract disease. Address: 1245 Highland Ave, Abington, PA 19001.

GISLER, DONALD BARTLETT, b. Springfield, Mass, Feb. 28, 29; m. 50; c. 2. LABORATORY ANIMAL MEDICINE, TOXICOLOGY. B.S, Ohio State, 51, D.V.M, 55. Assoc. prof. lab. animal med, col. vet. med, Ohio State, 66-69; V.PRES, ARLINGTON RES. LABS. INC, 69- Vet. med. adv, proj. Little Joe, Mercury Space Prog, 58-62; consult. lab. animal med, Vet. Admin, D.C, 61; Cox Heart Inst, 62-68. Mem. adv. cmt. postdoctoral training, Nat. Acad. Sci-Nat. Res. Coun, 67-68. Dir. lab. animal med, U.S.A.F, 55-66, Res, 66-; Maj; Commendation Medal, 61. Indust. Vet. Asn; Am. Soc. Lab. Animal Practitioners (ed, 66-69); Int. Primatol. Soc; Asn. Lab. Animal Sci. Laboratory animal facilities design and construction. Address: Arlington Research Labs. Inc, Box 161, Plain City, OH 43064.

GISSEN, AARON J, b. N.Y.C, May 11, 17; m. 46; c. 3. ANESTHESIOLOGY, PHYSIOLOGY. B.S, Johns Hopkins Univ, 36; M.D, N.Y. Univ, 40. Assoc. prof. ANESTHESIOL, col. physicians & surgeons, Columbia Univ, 70-71; PROF, SCH. MED, HARVARD, 71-; DIR. DEPT. ANESTHESIOL, MASS. EYE & EAR INFIRMARY, 71- Assoc. attend, dept. anesthesiol, Presby. Hosp, N.Y.C, 70-71. Asn. Univ. Anesthetists; Am. Soc. Pharmacol. & Exp. Therapeut; Am. Physiol. Soc; Am. Soc. Anesthesiol; Am. Col. Anesthesiol. Physiology and pharmacology of clinical anesthesia; basic physiology of excitable membranes, processes of neuro-muscular transmission; effect of various clinically used drugs on above. Address: Dept. of Anesthesiology, Massachusetts Eye & Ear Infirmary, 243 Charles St, Boston, MA 02114.

GISSER, DAVID G, b. Kingston, N.Y, Dec. 6, 22; m. 51; c. 1. ELECTRICAL ENGINEERING. B.E.E, Rensselaer Polytech, 43, M.E.E, 52, Dr.Eng.(elec. eng), 65. Instr. ELEC. ENG, RENSSELAER POLYTECH INST, 47-53, asst. prof, 53-65, ASSOC. PROF, 65- U.S.N.R, 44-46. Inst. Elec. & Electronics Eng; Am. Soc. Eng. Educ; Instrument Soc. Am. Instrumentation for research and measurement, especially nuclear, electronic circuits, devices, instruments and communications systems. Address: Dept. of Electrical Engineering, Rensselaer Polytechnic Institute, Troy, NY 12181.

GISSER, H(ENRY), b. New York, N.Y, Apr. 16, 15; m. 38; c. 2. PHYSICAL ORGANIC CHEMISTRY. B.S, City Col. New York, 36; M.A, Columbia, 37; Ph.D.(chem), Temple, 52. CHEMIST, PITMAN-DUNN RES. LABS, FRANKFORD ARSENAL, 39-48, head org. chem. br, 48-58, DIR. CHEM. RES. LAB, 58- Mem. Artil. Trop. Test. Mission, Ord. Corp, 45; mem. group hydraul. fluids, panel lubricants, Res. & Develop. Bd, 51-53; panel lubricants & hydraul. fluids, Off. Asst. Secy. Defense Res. & Eng, 54-; v.chmn, Gordon Res. Conf. Friction, Lubrication & Wear, 66, chmn, 68; adj. assoc. prof, Temple Univ, 67-69. U.S. Army res. & develop. achievement award, 70. Fel. AAAS; Am. Soc. Lubrication Eng; Am. Chem. Soc; Sci. Res. Soc. Am; N.Y. Acad. Sci. Autoxidation of organic fluids; oxidation inhibitors; resins; low and high temperature fluids; lubricants; fluorine compounds; polymer, surface and radiation chemistry; friction and wear. Address: Chemical Research Lab, Pitman-Dunn Research Labs, Frankford Arsenal, Philadelphia, PA 19137.

GIST, GEORGE R(EINECKER), b. Brooke Co, W.Va, Sept. 8, 19; m. 47. AGRONOMY. B.Sc, West Virginia, 42, M.S, 47; Ph.D.(agron), Purdue, 56. Instr. & assoc. county exten. agent, OHIO STATE UNIV, 47-51, asst. prof, AGRON, 51-57, assoc. prof, 57-61, PROF, 61-, ASST. DIR. ADMIN, OHIO COOP. EXTEN. SERV, 70- U.S. Agency Int. Develop. mission, India, 61-63, chief party, Ohio State Univ. col. agr. faculty team in India, 67-70; adv. univ. admin, Univ. Udaipur. U.S.A, 42-45. Am. Soc. Agron. Forage crop production and crop physiology. Address: Ohio State University, 2120 Fyffe Rd, Columbus, OH 43210.

GIST, LEWIS A(LEXANDER), JR, b. Richmond, Va, Nov. 17, 21; m. 48; c. 2. ORGANIC CHEMISTRY. B.S, Va. Union, 47; M.S, Howard, 49; Gen. Ed. Bd. fel, Iowa State, 52-54, Nat. Med. Fels, Inc, fel, 54-55, Ph.D.(chem), 56. Asst. chem, Howard, 47-49, asst. instr, 49; res. asst, George Washington Carver Found, Tuskegee Inst, 49-52, res. assoc. & asst. prof, 56; assoc. prof. & head dept, Va. Union, 56-58; prof. & chmn. dept, Va. State Col, 58-64; ASSOC. PROG. DIR, SUMMER STUDY PROG. & COORD. FOR. ACTIVITIES, NAT. SCI. FOUND, 64- U.S.A, 42-46. Am. Chem. Soc; Am. Inst. Chem; Nat. Inst. Sci.(v.pres, 58-62, pres, 62-63). Chemistry of organometallic compounds of lithium, sodium, magnesium, tin and lead; chemistry of dienes, diketones and heterocyclic compounds. Address: Summer Study Program, National Science Foundation, Washington, DC 20550.

GISVOLD, OLE, b. Stanley, Wis, Sept. 24, 04; m. 29; c. 3. PHARMACEUTICAL CHEMISTRY. B.S, Wisconsin, 30, M.S, 32, Lloyd fel, 33-34, Ph.D, 34. Jr. chemist, Forest Prods. Lab, U.S. Forest Serv, 34-35; instr, col. pharm, Minnesota, 35-38, asst. prof, 38-40; PROF. PHARM, Ohio State, 40-41; UNIV. MINN, MINNEAPOLIS, 41- Ebert medal, 41, 53. Am. Chem. Soc; Am. Pharmaceut. Soc. Phytochemistry; synthesis of medicinal drugs; isolation of a naturally occurring antioxidant nordihydroguaiaretic acid; phytosterols and their sugar ethers; cardiac glycosides; organic and medicinal chemistry. Address: College of Pharmacy, University of Minnesota, Minneapolis, MN 55455.

GITHENS, JOHN H(ORACE), b. Woodbury, N.J, Jan. 2, 22; m. 45; c. 2. PEDIATRICS. B.A, Swarthmore Col, 44; M.D, Temple, 45. Instr. PEDIAT, Colorado, 51-52, asst. prof, 52-57, assoc. prof, 57-60; prof. & chmn. dept, col. med, Kentucky, 60-63; PROF. & ASSOC. DEAN, SCH. MED, UNIV. COLO, DENVER, 64- Mem. consult. staff, Denver Childrens Hosp. & Fitzsimmons Army Hosp. Dipl, Am. Bd. Pediat, 52. U.S.N.R, 46-48. Am. Med. Asn; Am. Acad. Pediat; Am. Fedn. Clin. Res; Soc. Pediat. Res; Am. Pediat. Soc. Pediatric hematology; medical education. Address: School of Medicine, University of Colorado Medical Center, Denver, CO 80220.

GITHENS, SHERWOOD, JR, b. Phila, Pa, Oct. 31, 08; m. 39; c. 4. PHYSICS. A.B, Bucknell, 31; fel, North Carolina, 31-36, M.A, 33, Ph.D.(physics), 36; Princeton, 33-34. Instr. physics, Wake Forest Col, 36-37, asst. prof, 37-41; instr. aircraft elec. systs, Air Corps Tech. Sch, Chanute Field, Ill, 41; asst. chief instr, Sheppard Field, Texas, 41-42; lectr. electronics, Harvard, 42-46; physicist, appl. physics lab, Hopkins, 46-49; prof. physics & chmn. dept, Baylor, 49-52; chief physics & electronics br, U.S. Army res. off, 52-55, dir. phys. sci. div, 55-57, internal res. div, 57-59, dep. chief scientist, 59-62; PROF. SCI. ED, DUKE UNIV, 62- Spec. lectr, N.C. State, 54-56; Duke, 58-59. Summer lectr, Baylor, 57. With Office of Sci. Res. & Develop, 45. Am. Phys. Soc; Am. Asn. Physics Teachers; Nat. Sci. Teachers Asn. Radio-frequency measurement apparatus; gaseous electronics; dissemination of scientific information; research administration; science teaching in public schools. Address: Dept. of Education, Duke University, Durham, NC 27708.

GITLIN, DAVID, b. Bronx, N.Y, Aug. 7, 21; m. 44; c. 2. PEDIATRICS. B.S, City Col. New York, 42; M.D, N.Y. Univ, 47. Res. fel. PEDIAT, Harvard Med. Sch, 50-52, instr, 52-54, assoc, 54-57, asst. prof, 57-63; PROF, SCH. MED, PITTSBURGH, 63- Res. collab, Brookhaven Nat. Lab, 54-65; Guggenheim fel, 58-59; mem. human embryol. & develop. study sect, Nat. Insts. Health, 60-64, res. career & fel. prog. comt, 64-68. Am. Soc. Clin. Invest; Soc. Pediat. Res; Am. Acad. Pediat.(E. Mead Johnson res. award, 56, Borden Res. Award, 63); Am. Pediat. Soc; Am. Asn. Immunol; hon. mem. Mex. Nat. Acad. Med. Metabolism of plasma proteins; immunity and hypersensitivity; biochemical genetics. Address: Children's Hospital of Pittsburgh, Pittsburgh, PA 15213.

GITLITZ, MELVIN HYMAN, b. Montreal, Que, Feb. 28, 40; m. 64; c. 2. INORGANIC & ORGANOMETALLIC CHEMISTRY. B.Sc, McGill, 61; Ontario fels, Western Ontario, 63-65, Ph.D.(chem), 65. SR. RES. CHEMIST, CORP. RES. LAB, M&T CHEM. INC, AM. CAN CO, RAHWAY, 65- AAAS; Am. Chem. Soc; Am. Inst. Chem. Dialkylamides and dithiocarbamates of transition metals; organometallic chemistry of the group IV A elements; grignard reagents. Address: 16 Maida Rd, Edison, NJ 08817.

GITMAN, LEO, b. N.Y.C, Sept. 3, 12; m. 36; c. 2. MEDICINE. B.A, Columbia, 33; M.D, Royal Col. Med. & Surg, Scotland, 39. Stewart Mem. res. fel. endocrinol, sch. med, Pittsburgh, 42; asst, res. unit, Metropolitan Hosp, N.Y, 46; Lakeside fel. exp. therapeut, Brookdale Hosp. Ctr, 48, attend. dept. med, 60-66, dir, dept. community health, 66-71; chief, geront. sect, 64-71, dir. multiphasic health screening ctr, 68-71; CONSULT, 71- Med. dir. & dir. res. div, Hebrew Home & Hosp. for Aged, Brooklyn, 54-60. Dipl, Am. Bd. Internal Med. Med.C, U.S.A, 42-46. Endocrine Soc; Geront. Soc; fel. Am. Col. Physicians. Public health; gerontology. Address: 1165 E. 17th St, Brooklyn, NY 11230.

GITTENS, E(DMUND) DONALD, b. Brooklyn, N.Y, Sept. 21, 13; m. 39; c. 2. ENGINEERING MECHANICS. B.S, Mass. Inst. Technol, 35; Harvard, 63. Sr. proj. engr, Arma Corp, 35-48, dept. head, 48-51, chief engr, 51-55, v.pres. & chief engr, ARMA DIV, AMBAC INDUSTS, INC, 55-57, v.pres. & div. mgr, 57-62; v.pres. govt. opers, 62-64, exec. v.pres, 64-67, GROUP V.PRES, 67- Naval Ord. Develop. award, 45. Am. Ord. Asn; Am. Inst. Aeronaut. & Astronaut; Inst. Elec. & Electronics Eng; Am. Inst. Navig; Am. Soc. Naval Eng; Am. Mgt. Asn; Nat. Security Indust. Asn. Electronic and electromechanical systems, components and automotive equipment. Address: AMBAC Industries, Inc, Executive Offices, One Old Country Rd, Carle Place, NY 11514.

GITTERMAN, C(HARLES) O(SCAR), b. Prince Albert, Sask, Apr. 14, 23; nat; m. 52; c. 2. MICROBIOLOGY. B.S.A, British Columbia, 44; M.S, Wisconsin, 49, Ph.D.(bacter), 51. Agr. scientist, bacter, Dom. Exp. Sta, Can. Dept. Agr, Summerland, B.C, 44-47; asst, Wisconsin, 47-51; MICROBIOLOGIST, MERCK & CO, INC, 51-70, MERCK SHARP & DOHME RES. LABS, 70- Am. Soc. Microbiol; Am. Asn. Cancer Res; Tissue Cult. Asn; N.Y. Acad. Sci. Mold physiology; bacteriophage; viruses; cancer research. Address: Merck Sharp & Dohme Research Labs, Lincoln Ave, Rahway, NJ 07065.

GITTES, HYMAN R(APHAEL), b. Newark, N.J, Mar. 30, 15; m. 42; c. 5. BIOCHEMISTRY. B.A, N.Y. Univ, 37. Asst. dir, Indust. Biol. Labs, Inc, Phila, 63-67; SCI. RES. OFF, U.S. FOOD & DRUG ADMIN, 67- U.S.A, 42-63, Lt. Col.(ret). AAAS; Health Physics Soc; Soc. Toxicol. Toxicology; nuclear radiation; industrial, food & cosmetic safety. Address: 13835 Blair Stone Lane, Wheaton, MD 20906.

GITTES, RUBEN FOSTER, b. Majorca, Spain, Aug. 4, 34; U.S. citizen; m. 55; c. 3. GENITO-URINARY SURGERY, ENDOCRINOLOGY. A.B, Harvard, 56, M.D, 60. Clin. assoc. surg, Nat. Cancer Inst, 63-65; clin. asst. urol, Mass. Gen. Hosp, 66-67; asst. prof. SURG. & UROL, California, Los Angeles, 68-69; assoc. prof, UNIV. CALIF, SAN DIEGO, 69-71, PROF, 71- Vis. asst, inst. urol, Hosp. de Santa Cruz y San Pablo, Barcelona, Spain, 67; mem. surg. training cmt, Nat. Insts. Health, 69- U.S.P.H.S, 63-65, Lt. Comdr. AAAS; Asn. Acad. Surg; Soc. Univ. Urol; Soc. Univ. Surg; fel. Am. Col. Surg. Experimental hyperparathyroidism; thyrocalcitonin and urinary calcium homeostasis; control of gonadal development; renal transplantation. Address: University Hospital, 225 W. Dickinson St, San Diego, CA 92103.

GITTINS, ARTHUR RICHARD, b. Edmonton, Alta, Can, May 26, 26; m. 49; c. 2. ENTOMOLOGY. B.Sc, Alberta, 52; fel, Idaho, 53-55, M.S, 55; Ph.D, Mont. State Col, 63. Entomologist, City of Edmonton, Alta, Can, 49-52; instr. ENTOM, UNIV. IDAHO, 55-58, asst. prof, 58-63, assoc. prof, 63-68, PROF. & HEAD DEPT, 69- Can. Army, 44-45. Am. Entom. Soc; Soc. Syst. Zool; Entom. Soc. Am; Entom. Soc. Can; fel. Royal Entom. Soc. London. Systematic entomology; insect anatomy and physiology. Address: Dept. of Entomology, University of Idaho, Moscow, ID 83843.

GITTINS, JOHN, b. Eng, Aug. 12, 32; Can. citizen; m. 58; c. 3. GEOLOGY. B.Sc, McMaster, 55, M.Sc, 56; Ph.D.(petrol), Cambridge, 59. Vis. res. assoc, geochem, Pa. State, 59-60, asst. prof. mineral, 60-61; ASSOC. PROF. GEOL, UNIV. TORONTO, 61- AAAS; Geol. Asn. Can; Mineral. Asn. Can; Brit. Geol. Soc; Mineral. Soc. Gt. Brit. & Ireland. Igneous and metamorphic petrology; phase equilibrium; experimental mineralogy and petrology; carbonatites and alkaline rocks. Address: Dept. of Geology, University of Toronto, Toronto 5, Ont, Can.

GITTLEMAN, ARTHUR P, b. Brooklyn, N.Y, Oct. 7, 41; m. 66. MATHEMATICS. A.B, California, Los Angeles, 62, M.A, 65, Ph.D.(math), 69. Tech. aide math, E.H. Plesset Assocs, 62; asst, California, Los Angeles, 62-65, inst. geophys, 65-66; asst. prof. MATH, CALIF. STATE COL. LONG BEACH, 66-70, ASSOC. PROF, 70- Math. Asn. Am; Am. Math. Soc. Calculus of variations and optimal control theory. Address: Dept. of Mathematics, California State College, Long Beach, CA 90801.

GITTLEMAN, JONATHAN, b. Newark, N.J, Feb. 5, 26; m. 47; c. 3. PHYSICS. B.S, Rutgers, 48, fel, 50-51, Ph.D.(physics), 52. Instr. physics, Rutgers, 51-52; RES. PHYSICIST. magnetism, Franklin Inst, 53-55; RES. LABS, RCA CORP, 55- U.S.A, 43-46. Sci. Res. Soc. Am. Superconductivity; cryogenics; ferromagnetism; infrared photoconductivity. Address: Research Labs, RCA Corp, Princeton, NJ 08540.

GITTLER, FRANZ LUDWIG, b. Breslau, Germany, Mar. 12, 24; U.S. citizen; m. 51; c. 4. PHYSICAL CHEMISTRY. B.A, Syracuse, 48; M.A, Buffalo, 50; Ph.D.(phys. chem), Pa. State, 54. Sr. chemist, Sylvania Elec. Prod, Inc, 54-57; scientist, Linde Lab, Union Carbide Corp, 57-58; MEM. RES. STAFF, BELL TEL. LABS, 58- Chem.C, 44-46, 2nd Lt. Am. Chem. Soc; Electrochem. Soc; Inst. Elec. & Electronics Eng. Statistical thermodynamics and thermodynamic properties of substances; chemistry and physics of semiconductor materials, processing and devices. Address: Bell Telephone Labs, 555 Union Blvd, Allentown, PA 18103.

GITTLESON, STEPHEN MARK, b. Washington, D.C, July 6, 38; m. 63. CELL PHYSIOLOGY, PROTOZOOLOGY. B.S, Tulane, 60, M.S, 62; Ph.D. (zool), California, Los Angeles, 66. Res. scholar, California, Los Angeles, 66; asst. prof. zool, Univ. Ky, 66-70; RES. ASSOC, STEVENS INST. TECHNOL, 71- Summer partic, NASA colloquium on theoret. biol. & biophys, Colo. State Univ, 65; partic. exec. ed. training prog, Rockefeller Univ, 70-71; Nat. Insts. Health, Heart & Lung Inst, Stevens Inst. Technol, 71- AAAS; Soc. Protozool; Instrument Soc. Am; Soc. Am. Nat; Am. Micros. Soc. Cellular effects of narcotic gases; antagonism between carbon dioxide and sodium bicarbonate; motile behavior of individual and aggregate swimming Protozoa; ecology of underground water Protozoa; biophysical chemistry of biopolymers. Address: Dept. of Chemistry & Chemical Engineering, Stevens Institute of Technology, Hoboken, NJ 07030.

GITZENDANNER, F(RED) A(NDREAS), b. Brooklyn, N.Y, March 4, 13; m. 36; c. 3. ENGINEERING. M.E, Stevens Inst. Tech, 34; M.Bus.Admin, Chicago, 52. Instr. econ. eng, Stevens Inst. Tech, 34-36; admin. asst, Dorr Co, Inc, 36-39; sales engr, Hammond Iron Works, 39-42; gen. mgr, Gilchrist Construct. Co, Inc, 45-46; assoc. dir. eng. res. dept, Standard Oil Co,(Ind), 46-60; asst. dir. res. & develop. dept, AM. OIL CO, 60-66, mgr. tech. & sci. comput. div, 66-68, MGR. INFO. SERV. & COMPUT. SCI. DEPT, 68- Proprietor, Gitzendanner Co, 45-46. Ord.C, 42-45, Lt. Col. Am. Soc. Eng. Educ; Inst. Mgt. Scis; Opers. Res. Soc. Am; Asn. Comput. Mach; Am. Petrol. Inst. Economics of engineering; risk analysis; applications of statistical techniques; operations research and computer applications. Address: American Oil Co, 910 S. Michigan Ave, Chicago, IL 60605.

GITZENDANNER, L. G, b. N.Y.C, Mar. 27, 19; m. 43; c. 4. MECHANICAL & ELECTRICAL ENGINEERING. B.S, Lehigh, 41. Develop. engr, elec. mech, GEN. ELEC. CO, 41-46, mgr. invest. sect, gen. eng. lab, 46-47, design sect, 47-50, mech. develop, 50-55, mech. equip. eng, 55-61, consult. engr. mech. eng, adv. tech. labs, 61-67, MGR. DISC DESIGN ENG, HONEYWELL INFO. SYSTS. INC, 67- C.A. Coffin award, 46. Inst. Elec. & Electronics Eng; Am. Soc. Mech. Eng; Nat. Soc. Prof. Eng. Electromechanical development engineering; automation; remotely operated tools for nuclear work; underwater sound; mechanical design. Address: Honeywell Information Systems Inc, 4000 W. Expressway, Oklahoma City, OK 73122.

GIUDICI, TULLIO ANDREA, b. Arcisate, Italy, Aug. 12, 35; U.S. citizen; m. 61. BIOCHEMISTRY, ORGANIC CHEMISTRY. B.S, Southern California, 59, Ph.D.(biochem), 67. Res. chemist, Furane Plastics, Inc, 59-61; Pasadena Found. Med. Res, 61-63; Nat. Insts. Health fel. CHEM, California, Santa Barbara, 67-70; ASST. PROF, TEX. A&M UNIV, 70- AAAS; Am. Chem. Soc. Chemistry of carbohydrates, nucleic acids and peptides; metabolism of sugars; identification and synthesis of biologically active compounds; new synthetic methods; mechanism of organic reactions and model enzyme studies; development of analytical procedures. Address: Dept. of Chemistry, Texas A&M University, College Station, TX 77843.

GIUFFRE, JOSEPH, b. Naples, Italy, July 26, 20; U.S. citizen; m. 52; c. 2. ELECTRICAL ENGINEERING, APPLIED PHYSICS. D.Sc.(electromech. eng), Pisa, 51. Proj. engr, elec. eng. dept, Arabian-Am. Oil Co, N.Y, 51-53; Bechtel Eng. Corp, Calif, 53-57; staff scientist, Douglas Aircraft Co, 57-60; mem. tech. staff, ground systs. group, Hughes Aircraft Co. 60-62; dept. head hydro eng. & marine systs, Astropower Inc, 62-64, HEAD UNDERSEA SYSTS. & TECHNOL, DOUGLAS AIRCRAFT CO, 64- Marine Technol. Soc. Undersea systems and oceanographic instrumentation; detection problems in antisubmarine warfare; propagation phenomena; signal processing by correlation methods; noise and dynamics of deep water ocean waves. Address: 3538 Kallen Ave, Long Beach, CA 90808.

GIUFFRIDA, ROBERT EUGENE, b. N.Y.C, Aug. 23, 28; m. 55; c. 2. ORGANIC CHEMISTRY. B.S, Columbia, 52. Chemist, U.S. Testing Co, 54-55; Ciba Pharmaceut. Prod, 55-60; RES. DIR, Org. Prod. Inc, 60-64; ELAN CHEM. CO, 64- U.S.A, 52-54. AAAS; Am. Chem. Soc; Am. Inst. Chem; N.Y. Acad. Sci. Synthetic organic chemistry. Address: Elan Chemical Co, 268 Doremus Ave, Newark, NJ 07105.

GIULIANELLI, JAMES LOUIS, b. Aug. 7, 40; U.S. citizen; m. 66; c. 1. PHYSICAL CHEMISTRY. B.S, Univ. Mass, Amherst, 62; Wis. Alumni Res. Found. & Nat. Sci. Found. res. grants & Ph.D.(chem), Univ. Wis, Madison, 69. Chemist, Johns-Manville Basic & Appl. Res. Ctr, 62; teaching asst. CHEM, Univ. Wis, 62-64, res. fel, 64-69; Robert Welch fel, Univ. Tex, Austin, 69-71; PROF, UNIV. OF THE ANDES, VENEZUELA, 71- Am. Chem. Soc. Mechanisms of radiative and radiationless transitions in molecules as deduced from emitted fluorescence and phosphorescence radiation; laser photochemistry; chemical effects of nuclear transformations; chemistry of sulfur atoms. Address: Faculty of Science, Dept. of Chemistry, University of the Andes, Merida, Venezuela.

GIULIANO, ROBERT W, b. Newark, N.J, Dec. 12, 35; m. 63; c. 2. CIVIL ENGINEERING. B.S, U.S. Mil. Acad, 58; M.S.E, Princeton, 62, M.A, 63, Ph.D.(civil eng), 66. Instr. math, U.S. Mil. Acad, 63-64, asst. prof, 64-66, staff off. mil. intel, U.S. Mil. Assistance Comd, Viet Nam, 66-67, asst. prof. ed. res, U.S. Mil. Acad, 67-70, assoc. prof. mech, 70-71; FEL, INST. COURT MGT, LAW SCH, UNIV. DENVER, 71- U.S.A, 58-71, Maj.(Ret). Am. Math. Soc; Soc. Am. Mil. Eng. Engineering mechanics; applied mathematics; structural design; soil mechanics. Address: 81 Harrison St, Garden City, NY 11530.

GIULIANO, VINCENT E, b. Detroit, Mich, Nov. 17, 29; m. 54; c. 5. APPLIED MATHEMATICS. A.B, Michigan, 52, fel, 52-53, M.S, 56; fel. & Ph.D.(appl. math), Harvard, 59. Staff mathematician, Gen. Motors Res. Center, 53-54; res. assoc. appl. math, comput. lab, Wayne State, 56; Harvard, 57-59; mem. sr. prfnl. staff opers. res, ARTHUR D. LITTLE, INC, 59-71, SR. STAFF MEM, 71-; ADJ. PROF, STATE UNIV. N.Y. BUFFALO, 71-, prof. & dean, sch. info. & libr. studies, 67-71. Res. fel, math. ling. & Gordon McKay vis. lectr, Harvard, 60-63, spec. lectr, summer, 64; lectr, NATO Adv. Study Inst, 63. U.S.A, 54-55. AAAS; sr. mem. Opers. Res. Soc. Am; Inst. Elec. & Electronics Eng; Asn. Comput. Mach; Am. Soc. Info. Sci; Asn. Comput. Ling. Information processing research; studies concerning diverse aspects of processing; storage retrieval and use of scientific, biomedical and natural-language information; visual and language pattern-processing problems; evaluatory studies of information systems. Address: 33 Hancock St, Lexington, MA 02173.

GIUS, JOHN A(RMES), b. Fairbanks, Alaska, June 2, 08; m. 36; c. 1. SURGERY. B.A, Oregon, 31, M.D, 34; D.Sc.(med), Columbia, 39. From instr. to assoc. prof. SURG, med. sch, Oregon, 39-52; assoc. prof, UNIV. IOWA, 52-53, PROF, 53- Med.C, U.S.N.R, 44-46. Soc. Univ. Surg; Am. Col. Surg. Venous circulation; bilary tract diseases. Address: University Hospital, Iowa City, IA 52240.

GIVEEN, SAMUEL M(ERRITT), b. Brunswick, Maine, Mar. 24, 20; m. 49; c. 2. MATHEMATICS. A.B, Bowdoin Col, 42; M.A, Harvard, 51. Instr. MATH, Maine, 46-49; NORTHEAST. UNIV, 51-54, asst. prof, 54-61, ASSOC. PROF, 61- U.S.A.A.F, 42-46, 1st Lt. Queuing theory and other mathematical techniques applied to complex systems. Address: 526 United Realty Bldg, Northeastern University, Boston, MA 02115.

GIVEN, PETER H(ERVEY), b. Swansea, Wales, Jan. 29, 18; m. 44; c. 1. ORGANIC CHEMISTRY, GEOCHEMISTRY. B.A, Oxford, 40, M.A, 43, D.Phil. (chem), 44. Sci. off, Brit. Coal Utilization Res. Asn, 44-60, head org. chem. sect, 50-60; assoc. prof. FUEL SCI, PA. STATE, UNIV, 61-62, PROF, 62-, head dept, 65-69. Am. Chem. Soc; Geochem. Soc; The Chem. Soc. Chemical aspects of coal utilization; catalytic chemistry; organic electrochemistry; nature and character of aromatic systems; organic geochemistry of coal. Address: Fuel Science Section, Material Sciences Dept, Pennsylvania State University, University Park, PA 16802.

GIVEN, ROBERT R, b. Los Angeles, Calif, July 20, 32; m. 59; c. 3. MARINE ECOLOGY. A.B, Chico State Col, 53; M.S, Univ. South. Calif, 63, Ph.D. (biol), 70. Diver-biologist marine zool, Pomona Col, 57-59; marine biologist, Southern California, 59-61, 62-63; diver-biologist, Calif. Dept. Fish & Game, 63-65; staff biologist, SANTA CATALINA MARINE LAB, UNIV. SOUTH. CALIF, 65-69, ASST. DIR, 69- Med.C, U.S.A, 53-55. Soc. Syst. Zool. Marine invertebrate ecology and taxonomy; ecology, taxonomy and distribution of southern California marine epifaunal invertebrates; taxonomy and distribution of World Cumacea. Address: Box 651, Avalon, Catalina Island, CA 90704.

GIVENS, EDWIN N, b. St. Louis, Mo, Dec. 8, 35; m. 57; c. 2. ORGANIC CHEMISTRY. Oak Ridge Inst. Nuclear Studies fel, Delaware, 62-64, M.S, 63, Ph.D.(org. chem), 65. Chemist, Reardon Paint Co, 58-59; SR. RES. CHEMIST, PAULSBORO LAB, MOBIL OIL CORP, 64- U.S.A, 59-60. Am. Chem. Soc. Chlorinations of bivalent sulphur compounds; heterogeneous catalysis. Address: Paulsboro Lab, Mobil Oil Corp, Paulsboro, NJ 08066.

GIVENS, JAMES ROBERT, b. Huntsville, Ala, Aug. 6, 30. REPRODUCTIVE ENDOCRINOLOGY. B.S, David Lipscomb Col, 52; M.S, Vanderbilt Univ, 53; M.D, Univ. Tenn, Memphis, 56. Internship, Memphis Hosps, 56-57, residency internal med, 59-61; U.S. Pub. Health Serv. fel. & instr. MED, Tufts Univ, 61-62; Vanderbilt Univ, 62-64; instr, UNIV. TENN, MEMPHIS, 64-65, asst. prof, 65-68, ASSOC. PROF, 68-, OBSTET. & GYNEC, 70-, DIR. DIV. REPRODUCTIVE MED, 70-, CO-DIR. CLIN. RES. CTR, 71-, asst. dir, 65-69, dep. chief, 70-71. U.S.P.H.S.R, 57-59, Surg. AAAS; Endocrine Soc; Am. Fedn. Clin. Res; Am. Fertil. Soc; Am. Col. Physicians; Am. Med. Asn. Understanding the inheritance and characterization of the pathophysiology of polycystic ovaries. Address: 951 Court Ave, Memphis, TN 38103.

GIVENS, M(ILES) PARKER, b. Richmond, Va, June 9, 16; m. 41; c. 3. EXPERIMENTAL PHYSICS. B.S, Richmond, 37; Ph.D.(exp. physics), Cornell, 42. Asst. physics, Cornell, 37-42; instr, Pa. State Col, 42-46, in charge electronic design, acoustic lab, Nat. Defense Res. Cmt, 44-46; physicist, applied physics lab, Hopkins, 46-47; asst. prof. OPTICS, UNIV. ROCHESTER, 47-53, assoc. prof, 53-57, PROF, 57- With U.S.A; U.S.N, 44. Fel. Optical Soc. Am; Am. Asn. Physics Teachers. Optical properties of metals; soft x-ray spectroscopy of metals; thyratron discharge phenomena; sound propagation; vacuum tube amplifier design; diffraction phenomena; halography. Address: Institute of Optics, University of Rochester, Rochester, NY 14627.

GIVENS, RICHARD SPENCER, b. Buffalo, N.Y, May 19, 40; m. 66; c. 2. ORGANIC CHEMISTRY. B.S, Marietta Col, 62; Nat. Insts. Health fel. & Ph.D. (org. chem), Wisconsin, 67. Nat. Insts. Health fel. org. chem, Iowa State, 66-67; ASST. PROF. CHEM, UNIV. KANS, 67- Am. Chem. Soc; Brit. Chem. Soc; N.Y. Acad. Sci. Photochemistry of beta, gamma-unsaturated ketones; photochemical syntheses; photooxidation; non-conjugated olefins. Address: Dept. of Chemistry, University of Kansas, Lawrence, KS 66044.

GIVENS, (JAMES) WALLACE, (JR), b. Alberene, Va, Dec. 14, 10; m. 37, 70; c. 3. MATHEMATICS. B.S, Lynchburg Col, 28, hon. D.Sc, 65; Kentucky, 28-29; du Pont fel, Virginia, 30-32, M.S, 31; J.S.K. fel, Princeton, 33-35, Ph.D.(math), 36; Inst. Adv. Study, Princeton, 35-37. Instr. math, Princeton, 35-36; Cornell, 37-41; Northwestern, 41-42, asst. prof, 42-46; assoc. prof, Ill. Inst. Tech, 46-47; prof, Univ. Tenn, 47-56; prof. & chmn. dept, Wayne State Univ, 56-60; consult, APPL. MATH. DIV, ARGONNE NAT. LAB, 60-62, SR. MATHEMATICIAN, 62-, assoc. dir, 62-64, dir, 64-70. Asst, Inst. Advan. Study, 35-37, mem, 55; consult, Oak Ridge Nat. Lab, 51-62; sr. scientist, N.Y. Univ, 53-55; consult, Space Technol. Labs; Thompson-Ramo-Wooldridge, Inc, 57-59; prof. math, Northwest. Univ, 60- AAAS; Am. Math. Soc; Soc. Indust. & Appl. Math; Math. Asn. Am; Asn. Comput. Mach. Digital computation of algebraic problems, especially Eigenvalues; Von Neumann geometry; spinors. Address: Applied Mathematics Division, Argonne National Lab, Argonne, IL 60439.

GIVENS, WILLIAM G(EARY), JR, b. Camden, Ark, Sept. 10, 32; m. 58. PHYSICAL CHEMISTRY. B.A, Rice Inst, 54; Ph.D, Wisconsin, 59. Res. chemist, Jersey Prod. Res. Co, 59; asst. prof. chem, Norwich, 59-61; exten. div, Wisconsin, 61-62; res. chemist, Gen. Dynamics/Astronaut, 62-64; Rocketdyne Div, N.Am. Aviation, Inc, 64-66; MEM. FACULTY DEPT. CHEM, GROSSMONT COL, 66- Am. Chem. Soc. Surface chemistry. Address: Dept. of Chemistry, Grossmont College, El Cajon, CA 92020.

GIVENS, WYATT WENDELL, b. Forestburg, Tex, Aug. 1, 32; m. 57; c. 2. NUCLEAR PHYSICS, MATHEMATICS. B.A, North Texas State, 56, M.A, 57; M.A, Rice, 60, Ph.D.(nuclear physics), 63. Res. asst, FIELD RES. LAB, Socony Mobil Oil Co, Inc, 57-58, sr. res. technologist, 62-71, RES. ASSOC, MOBIL RES. & DEVELOP. CORP, 71- U.S.N, 49-53. AAAS; Am. Phys. Soc; Sci. Res. Soc. Am. Basic and applied nuclear physics, especially oil well logging and oil exploration. Address: Mobil Research & Development Corp, Field Research Lab, P.O. Box 900, Dallas, TX 75221.

GIVIDEN, GEORGE MASSIE, JR, b. Lexington, Ky, Apr. 3, 29; m. 51; c. 5. OPERATIONS RESEARCH, EXPERIMENTAL PSYCHOLOGY. B.S, U.S. Mil. Acad, 51; M.A, Vanderbilt Univ, 57. Instr. statist. & psychol, U.S. Mil. Acad, 57-60; mem. faculty human factors eng, N.Y. Univ, 60-62; mgr. eng. res. dept, Tri-State Parachute Co, 62-65; chief proj. scientist, Stanford Res. Inst, 65-66; mgr. opers. anal. dept, Litton Sci. Support Lab, LITTON SYSTS, INC, 66-68, MGR. APPL. TECHNOL. LAB, MELLONICS DIV, 68- Consult, Fed. Aviation Agency, 63; U.S. Army Med. Corps, 64; Data Dynamics, Inc, 64; Tri-State Parachute Co, 65-66; Advan. Res. Projs. Agency, Dept. Defense, 70. U.S.M.C, 45-47; U.S.A, 51-60. Opers. Res. Soc. Am; Am. Psychol. Asn; Am. Statist. Asn. Operational field testing and evaluation; experimental design; information systems; weapons systems analysis. Address: 1388 Manor Rd, Monterey, CA 93940.

GIVIN, HOMER HOLT, JR, b. Napfor, Ky, Apr. 7, 20; m. 51; c. 2. PHYSICS, MANAGEMENT SCIENCE. B.S, Kentucky, 49, M.S, 51, Ph.D.(physics), 54. Instr. physics, Kentucky, 51-52, res. assoc, 52-54; appl. mathematician, IBM CORP, 54-56, tech. sales rep, 56-58, mgr. res. sales & contracts, 58-59, West. Data Processing Ctr, 59-62, univ. prog, 62-63, DIR. SYSTS. RES.

& DEVELOP. CTR, 63- Res. assoc, Southern California, 59; res. fel, California, Los Angeles, 59-62, vis. scholar, 63- Sig.C, U.S.A, 42-47. Am. Phys. Soc; Asn. Comput. Mach; Inst. Mgt. Sci. Design and application of information processing systems. Address: 1930 Century Park W, Los Angeles, CA 90067.

GIVLER, ROBERT L, b. Mason City, Iowa, May 8, 31; m. 56; c. 1. MEDICINE, PATHOLOGY. M.D, Iowa, 56. Intern, King Co. Hosps, Seattle, Wash, 56-57; instr. PATH, UNIV. IOWA, 57-58, asst, 58-61, assoc, 61, asst. prof, 63-71, ASSOC. PROF, 71- Med.C, 61-63, Res, 63-, Capt. Col. Am. Path; Am. Soc. Clin. Path; Int. Acad. Path. Leukemia; lymphoma. Address: Dept. of Pathology, Medical Labs, College of Medicine, University of Iowa, Iowa City, IA 52240.

GIVNER, MORRIS, LINCOLN, b. Montreal, Que, Sept. 11, 32; m. 62; c. 2. BIOCHEMISTRY. B.Sc, McGill, 54, M.Sc, 56, Salmon Found. fel, 57-59, Ph.D.(biochem), 59. Salmon Found. fel, Southwest Found. Res, Tex, 59-60; res. biochemist, AYERST RES. LABS, 62-69, HEAD, BIOCHEM. ENDOCRINOL, 69- Endocrine Soc; Can. Biochem. Soc; Can. Inst. Chem. Control of cholesterol, progesterone, androgen, and estrogen biosynthesis. Address: Ayerst Research Labs, P.O. Box 6115, Montreal, Que, Can.

GIVONE, DONALD DANIEL, b. Paterson, N.J, July 10, 36. ELECTRICAL ENGINEERING. B.S.E.E, Rensselaer Polytech, 58; M.S, Cornell, 61, Ph.D. (elec. eng), 63. ASSOC. PROF. ELEC. ENG, STATE UNIV. N.Y. BUFFALO, 63- Inst. Elec. & Electronics Eng; Asn. Comput. Mach. Switching circuit theory and logic design; computer technology. Address: Dept. of Electrical Engineering, State University of New York at Buffalo, Buffalo, NY 14214.

GIZA, CHESTER A(NTHONY), b. Three Rivers, Mass, May 18, 30; m. 61; c. 2. ORGANIC CHEMISTRY. B.S, Massachusetts, Amherst, 55, M.S, 58; Ph.D.(org. chem), Notre Dame, 68. Asst. chem, Massachusetts, Amherst, 54-57; lab. asst, E.I. du Pont de Nemours & Co, summers 56 & 57; chemist, Union Carbide Res. Inst, N.Y, 59-63; asst. chem, Notre Dame, 63-67; asst. prof. ORG. CHEM, WHEELING COL, 67-70, ASSOC. PROF, 70- AAAS; Am. Chem. Soc; The Chem. Soc. Synthesis and evaluation of biologically active organic compounds, with special attention to stereochemical aspects of structure. Address: Dept. of Chemistry, Wheeling College, Wheeling, WV 26003.

GIZA, YUEH-HUA CHEN, b. Taipei, Taiwan, China, Mar. 18, 29; m. 61. ORGANIC CHEMISTRY. B.Sc, Taiwan, 52; M.S, Tufts, 55; Ph.D, Massachusetts, 59. Asst. chem, Yale, 58-61; res. assoc, Inst. Muscle Disease, N.Y, 61-63; CHEM, Notre Dame, 64-68; ASST. PROF, WHEELING COL, 68- Am. Chem. Soc. Polymerization of sulfur containing organic compound; thermal stable polymers; metabolism of amino acids in plants. Address: 113 Alice Ave, Wheeling, WV 26003.

GIZIS, EVANGELOS JOHN, b. Tinos, Greece, Apr. 1, 34; m. 67; c. 1. BIOCHEMISTRY, FOOD SCIENCE. B.S, Athens; Ph.D.(food sci. & biochem), Oregon State, 63. Fel. food sci, Mich. State, 64-65; fel. enzymes & pectins, Mellon Inst, 65-66; biochemist, L.I. Jewish Hosp, Queens Hosp. Ctr. Affiliation, Jamaica, N.Y, 66-70; ASSOC. PROF. NATURAL SCI, CITY UNIV. NEW YORK, 70-; RES. CHEMIST, VET. ADMIN. HOSP, BROOKLYN, N.Y, 70- Res. collab, med. dept, Brookhaven Nat. Lab, 66-70. Soc. Exp. Biol. & Med; Am. Chem. Soc; Inst. Food Technol; N.Y. Acad. Sci; Am. Inst. Nutrit. Pectinolytic enzymes and pectins; vitamin B_{12} binders in milk, in normal human and pernicious anemia serum; chromatographic techniques. Address: Apt. 2-E, 87-50 167th St, Jamaica, NY 11432.

GJERSTAD, GUNNAR, b. Haugesund, Norway, May 30, 21; m. 53; c. 1. PHARMACY, BIOCHEMISTRY. B.S, Oslo, 45, M.S, 46; Fulbright & Smith-Mundt grants, Purdue, 51, univ. fel, 51-53, Ph.D, 54. Mgr. drugstore, Norway, 47; lectr, Oslo, 48-51; from asst. prof. to ASSOC. PROF. PHARM, UNIV. TEX, AUSTIN, 53- Edwin L. Newcomb Mem. Awards, 59 & 62. Norweg. Army, 48, 1st Lt. AAAS; Am. Chem. Soc; Am. Pharmaceut. Asn; Am. Soc. Pharmacog. Biosynthesis of medicinals. Address: College of Pharmacy, University of Texas at Austin, Austin, TX 78712.

GJESSING, ERLAND CHENEY, b. Quebec, Que, Can, June 29, 11; m. 39. CHEMISTRY. B.S, Copenhagen, 36; M.S, Mich. State Col, 38; Ph.D.(biochem), Cornell, 42. Rockefeller res. assoc, Cornell, 43; res. chemist, Pennsylvania, 44; asst. prof. biochem, Virginia, 45-50; res. assoc, dept. phys. chem, Harvard Med. Sch, 50-51; sr. scientist, Cancer Res. Inst, Deaconess Hosp, Mass, 51-54; ASSOC. PROF. BIOCHEM, COL. MED, UNIV. VT, 54- Civilian with Off. Sci. Res. & Develop; C.W.S, U.S.A, 44. Am. Chem. Soc; Am. Soc. Biol. Chem. Oxidizing enzymes; electrophoresis of proteins; isolation and purification of plasma and tissue proteins; microbiological growth factors; esterases; proteolytic enzymes. Address: Dept. of Biochemistry, University of Vermont College of Medicine, Burlington, VT 05401.

GJOSTEIN, NORMAN A, b. Chicago, Ill, May 26, 31; m. 59; c. 2. MATERIALS SCIENCE. B.S, Ill. Inst. Technol, 53, Standard Oil fel, 53-54, M.S, 54; Alcoa fel, Carnegie-Mellon Univ, 55-57, Ph.D.(metall eng), 58. Res. engr, Thompson-Ramo-Wooldridge, Inc, 58-60; sr. res. scientist, FORD MOTOR CO, 60-61, prin. res. scientist assoc, 61-64, staff scientist, 64-69, PRIN. RES. SCIENTIST, 69- Physics and chemistry of surfaces and interfaces; low energy electron diffraction; auger spectroscopy; materials properties and behavior. Address: Scientific Lab, Ford Motor Company, Dearborn, MI 48121.

GJULLIN, C(LAUDE) M(ELVIN), b. Little Falls, Minn, May 16, 03; m. 37. ENTOMOLOGY. B.S, Mont. State Col, 30; M.S, Oregon State Col, 37. Agent, bur. entomol. & plant quarantine, U.S. DEPT. AGR, 30-41, ENTOMOLOGIST, 42, in charge Portland Sta, 43-46, Corvallis, 46-53, ENTOMOL. RES. BR, AGR. RES. SERV, 53-69, FRESNO, CALIF, 69- With Office Sci. Res. & Develop, 44. AAAS; Entom. Soc. Am; Am. Mosquito Control Asn. Mosquito ecology and taxonomy; insecticides on mosquitoes and blackflies; mosquito repellants; attractants; chemosterilants. Address: U.S. Dept. of Agriculture, Agricultural Research Service, Entomology Research Division, 5544 Air Terminal Dr, Fresno, CA 93727.

GLABERSON, WILLIAM I, b. Chicago, Ill, Nov. 8, 44; m. 66; c. 1. PHYSICS. B.S, Chicago, 64, Ph.D.(physics), 69. ASST. PROF. PHYSICS, RUTGERS UNIV, 68- Alfred P. Sloan Found. fel, 71, 72. Am. Phys. Soc. Low temperature physics; superfluidity; hydrodynamics. Address: Dept. of Physics, Rutgers University, New Brunswick, NJ 08903.

GLADDEN, J(AMES) K(ELLY), b. Anniston, Ala, Sept. 14, 13; m. 44; c. 1. PHYSICAL CHEMISTRY. B.S, Howard Col, 42; M.S, Ga. Inst. Technol, 44; Ph.D.(chem), Northwestern, 52. Anal. chemist, Repub. Steel Co, 43; assoc. prof. CHEM, Ga. Inst. Technol, 51-59; PROF, TEX. A&M UNIV, 59- Res. assoc, eng. exp. sta, Ga. Inst. Technol, 58-59. U.S.N.R, 44-46. Am. Chem. Soc. Diffusion in supersaturated solutions as rate processes. Address: Dept. of Chemistry, Texas A&M University, College Station, TX 77843.

GLADDING, EDWARD K(ARCHER), b. Newport, R.I, July 4, 14; m. 54. CHEMISTRY. B.S, Worcester Polytech, 36; M.S, Mass. Inst. Tech, 37, Ph.D.(chem), 42. Du pont fel. cellulose chem, Mass. Inst. Tech, 42-43; CHEMIST, Magnolia Petrol. Co, 43-45; E.I. DU PONT DE NEMOURS & CO, INC, 45- With Off. Sci. Res. & Develop, 44. AAAS; Am. Chem. Soc. Elastomers. Address: E.I. du Pont de Nemours & Co, Inc, Elastomer Chemicals Dept, Experiment Station, Bldg. 353, Wilmington, DE 19898.

GLADDING, ELINOR H(ARTNELL), b. Cheltenham, Md, June 5, 12; m. 54. CHEMISTRY. A.B, Lynchburg Col, 32; B.S, George Peabody Col, 33; M.A, Hopkins, 45, Ph.D.(chem), 48. Asst. librarian, tech. library, Chem. Warfare Serv, Edgewood Arsenal, 38-42; sr. chemist, surv. antimalarial drugs, Hopkins, 43-46; PATENT CHEMIST, org. chem. dept, E.I. DU PONT DE NEMOURS & CO, INC, 48-58, ELASTOMER CHEMS. DEPT, 58- Civilian with Office Sci. Res. & Develop, 44. Am. Chem. Soc. Polarography; polarographic study of oximes; organic nomenclature and classification. Address: 2401 Pennsylvania Ave, Apt. 305, Wilmington, DE 19806.

GLADDING, JANE B, b. Richmond, Va, Jan. 1, 09; m. 31; c. 2. INORGANIC CHEMISTRY. A.B, Smith Col, 29; M.S, Richmond, 55. Technician, tissue culture, Rockefeller Inst, 29-35; abstr, tech. lit, Va-Carolina Chem. Corp, 47; mem. faculty chem, VA. COMMONWEALTH UNIV, 47-70, dean of women, 59-70, ASSOC. DEAN STUDENT LIFE & ASSOC. PROF. CHEM, 70- Am. Chem. Soc. Inorganic and physical aspects of chelation. Address: 1613 Park Ave, Richmond, VA 23220.

GLADE, RICHARD W(ILLIAM), b. Hammond, Ind, Sept. 27, 28; m. 51; c. 2. EMBRYOLOGY. B.A, Col. of Wooster, 50; M.S, Illinois, 52, univ. fel, 52-53, Nat. Sci. Found. fel, 53-55, Ph.D.(zool), 55. Asst. prof. biol, American Univ. Beirut, 55-58; ZOOL, UNIV. VT, 58-64, assoc. prof, 64-70, PROF, 70-, CHMN. DEPT, 64- Summers, asst, Illinois, 52-53, 55. Res. grants, Nat. Insts. Health, 59-60 & 64-66, Nat. Sci. Found, 59-62 & 68-70. Am. Soc. Zool; Soc. Develop. Biol. Experimental embryology and regeneration. Address: Dept. of Zoology, University of Vermont, Burlington, VT 05401.

GLADFELTER, BRUCE G, b. Phila, Pa, June 15, 36; m. 64; c. 2. GEOGRAPHY. A.B, Trinity Col.(Conn), 58; M.S.S, Syracuse, 60; M.A, Wisconsin, Madison, 66; univ. fel, Chicago, 67 & 69, Nat. Defense Ed. Act fel, 68, Nat. Sci. Found. grant, 67-70, Ph.D.(geog), 70. Teacher, high sch, Pa, 60-64; ASST. PROF. GEOG, UNIV. ILL, CHICAGO CIRCLE, 69- AAAS; Asn. Am. Geog. Geomorphology; Pleistocene; arid lands; physical geography. Address: Dept. of Geography, University of Illinois at Chicago Circle, Chicago, IL 60680.

GLADFELTER, W(ILBERT) E(UGENE), b. York, Pa, April 29, 28; m. 52; c. 3. PHYSIOLOGY. A.B, Gettysburg Col, 52; Nat. Sci. Found. fel, Pennsylvania, 56-58, Nat. Insts. Health fel, 58-59, Ph.D.(physiol), 60. Asst. instr. PHYSIOL, UNIV. PA, 54-56, 58-59; instr, W.VA. UNIV, 59-61, asst. prof, 61-69, ASSOC. PROF, 69- U.S.N, 46-48. AAAS; Am. Physiol. Soc; Animal Behav. Soc; N.Y. Acad. Sci. Neurophysiology; metabolism and energy exchange. Address: Dept. of Physiology & Biophysics, West Virginia University, Morgantown, WV 26506.

GLADING, BEN, b. Wash, D.C, May 21, 10; m. 34; c. 3. WILDLIFE MANAGEMENT. A.B, Michigan, 32; M.S, Kans. State Col, 33; California, 33-36. Jr. res. biologist, U.S. Forest Serv, 36-40; from jr. to sr. game biologist, Calif. Dept. Fish & Game, 40-57, asst. chief, bur. game conserv, 57-59, chief, br. game mgt, 59-69, regional mgr, 69-71; ECOL. CONSULT, 71- Pres, Point Reyes Bird Observ, 70- Wildlife Soc.(v.pres, 64-65, pres. elect, 65-66, pres, 66-67): Address: 1413 El Tejon Way, Sacramento, CA 95825.

GLADING, RALPH E(DMOND), b. Lorain, Ohio, Mar. 16, 12; m. 39; c. 2. CHEMISTRY. A.B, Oberlin Col, 36; M.S, Lawrence Col, 38, Ph.D.(cellulose, paper chem), 40. RES. CHEMIST, W.Va. Pulp & Paper Co, Md, 40-44, A.B. Dick Co, 44-62, WEYERHAEUSER CO, 62- Am. Tech. Asn. Pulp & Paper Indust. Ultraviolet absorption spectrum of lignin; preparation of high alpha pulp from oak wood; manufacture of papers from non-wood fibers; paper plates for offset lithography; coating of paperboard. Address: 12 Scenic View Pl, Longview, WA 98632.

GLADMAN, CHARLES H(ERMAN), b. Harrison County, Ohio, May 24, 17; m. 47; c. 1. MATHEMATICS. B.S, Ohio State, 38; M.A, 48. Instr. MATH, UNIV. TEX, EL PASO, 48-51, asst. prof, 51-57, ASSOC. PROF, 57- Mathematician, Schellenger Res. Labs, 58-60. U.S.A, 41-45. AAAS; Math. Asn. Am; Soc. Indust. & Appl. Math. Mathematical analysis. Address: Dept. of Mathematics, University of Texas at El Paso, El Paso, TX 79999.

GLADNER, JULES A, b. Brooklyn, N.Y, July 18, 22; m. 46; c. 3. BIOCHEMISTRY. B.S, Delaware, 48, M.S, 49; U.S. Pub. Health Serv. fel, Washington (Seattle), 50-53, Ph.D.(biochem), 53. Fel, Nat. Found. Infantile Paralysis & res. assoc. biochem, Mass. Inst, Tech, 53-54, fel, Am. Cancer Soc, 54; BIOCHEMIST, Naval Med. Res. Inst, 54-55; NAT. INSTS. HEALTH, 55- U.S.A, 43-46. Am. Chem. Soc; Am. Soc. Biol. Chem. Protein and enzyme biochemistry; sequency analysis; molecular aspects of enzyme activity as pertains to zymogen activation and blood clotting enzymes; organic synthesis. Address: National Institutes of Health, Bethesda, MD 20014.

GLADNEY, HENRY M, b. Prague, Czech, Feb. 8, 38; Can. citizen. COMPUTER SYSTEMS. B.A, Toronto, 60; M.A, Princeton, 62, Porter Ogden Jacobus fel, 62-63, Ph.D.(chem), 63. Res. staff mem, IBM CORP, 63-68, tech. adv. to v.pres. & chief scientist, 68-70, MGR. RES. COMPUT. FACILITY, SAN JOSE RES. LAB, 70- Am. Chem. Soc; Am. Phys. Soc. Laboratory automation, time sharing systems. Address: IBM Corp, Monterey & Cottle Rds, San Jose, CA 95114.

GLADNEY, WILLIAM J(ESS), b. Magnolia, Ark, Sept. 8, 40; m. 63; c. 1. ENTOMOLOGY, ACAROLOGY. B.S, South. State Col, 62; M.S, Arkansas, 64; Ph.D.(entom), Va. Polytech, 67. RES. ENTOMOLOGIST, U.S. DEPT. AGR, 67- Entom. Soc. Am; Am. Mosquito Control Asn. Biology and control of the brown recluse spider, Loxosceles reclusa and mosquitoes and ticks affecting man and livestock. Address: P.O. Box 232, U.S. Dept. Agriculture, Kerrville, TX 78028.

GLADROW, E(LROY) M(ERLE), b. Cleveland, Ohio, Sept. 2, 15; m. 47; c. 2. PHYSICAL CHEMISTRY. B.S, Heidelberg Col, 38; Ph.D.(chem), Iowa State Col, 48. Res. assoc. chemist, Nat. Defense Res. Cmt, Manhattan proj, Atomic Energy Comn, 42-47; res. chemist, Standard Oil Develop. Co, 47-58, Esso Standard Oil Co, 58-63, res. assoc, ESSO RES. & ENG. CO, 63-70, SR. RES. ASSOC, 70- Hydrocarbon catalysis; cracking, reforming, hydrocracking, hydrodesulfurization, isomerization, fuel cell; separation and preparation of pure rare earths; uranium fission products chemistry; radiation chemistry. Address: Esso Research & Engineering Co, P.O. Box 2226, Baton Rouge, LA 78821.

GLADSTONE, ARTHUR A, b. Burlington, Vt, July 7, 07; m. 39; c. 5. SURGERY. B.S, Vermont, 28, M.D, 31. Intern, Maine Gen. Hosp, 31-32; fel. SURG, Pennsylvania, 36-37; resident, Mt. Sinai Hosp, N.Y, 37-39; instr, COL. MED, UNIV. VT, 39-43, asst. prof, 43-49, assoc. prof, 50-67, CLIN. PROF, 67-, HEAD DIV. COLO-PROCTOL, 43- Chief surg, De Goesbriand Mem. Hosp, 43-; attend. surgeon, Med. Ctr. Hosp. Vt; consult surgeon, Fanny Allen Hosp; Porter Hosp; Vt. State Hosp; Capley Hosp. Dipl, Am. Bd. Surg. Soc. Surg. Alimentary Tract; Am. Proctol. Soc; fel. Am. Col. Surg. Colo-proctology; physiology of liver and biliary tract. Address: Dept. of Surgery, University of Vermont College of Medicine, Burlington, VT 05401.

GLADSTONE, GARY L(EONARD), b. N.Y.C, Nov. 28, 43. SOLID STATE PHYSICS. B.S, State Univ. N.Y. Stony Brook, 65; M.S, Univ. Pa, 66, Ph.D. (physics), 70. RES. STAFF PHYS. SCI, THOMAS J. WATSON RES. CTR, IBM CORP, 70- Am. Phys. Soc. Magnetic impurity problem, particularly local magnetic moment formation in metals; formation of and physical properties of liquid crystaline phase of matter. Address: Dept. of Physical Sciences, Thomas J. Watson Research Center, IBM Corp, P.O. Box 218, Yorktown Heights, NY 10598.

GLADSTONE, HAROLD M(AURICE), b. Brooklyn, N.Y, Jan. 23, 32; m. 59; c. 2. ORGANIC CHEMISTRY. B.S, Rensselaer Polytech, 52; Chas. Pfizer fel, Adelphi, 54-55, univ. fel, 55-56, M.S, 56; fel, Polytech. Inst. Brooklyn, 57-61, Ph.D.(org. chem), 61. Res. chemist, Armstrong Cork Co, 56-57; instr, eve, Adelphi, 58-60; res. chemist, Esso Res. & Eng. Co, 61-62; proj. mgr, Quantum Inc, 62-63, dir. lab, 63-65; mem. tech. staff, Bell Tel. Labs, 65-69; ASST. PROF. CHEM, MIDDLESEX COUNTY COL, 69-, CHMN. DEPT, 71-, asst. chmn, 70-71. U.S.N, 52-54, Lt.(jg). Am. Chem. Soc. Organic synthesis; reaction mechanisms; organic semiconductors; monomers; polymers; metallization of plastics; composite materials; photochemistry. Address: Dept. of Chemistry, Middlesex County College, Edison, NJ 08817.

GLADSTONE, MARTELL M(AURICE), b. Russia, Dec. 17, 12, U.S. citizen; m. 36; c. 1. CHEMISTRY. B.S, Chicago, 33, M.S, 35, Ph.D.(org. chem), 36. Res. Corp. fel. chem, Chicago, 36-40; res. chemist, Emulsol Corp, 40-59; asst. tech. dir, WITCO CHEM. CO, 59-64, TECH. DIR. ORG. CHEM. DIV, 64- U.S.A, 42-46. Am. Chem. Soc; fel. Am. Inst. Chem. Peroxide effect in olefine addition reactions; ergot alkaloids; oxytocic drugs synthetic surface-active agents. Address: Organic Chemistry Division, Witco Chemical Co, 400 N. Michigan Ave, Chicago, IL 60611.

GLADSTONE, MATTHEW T(HEODORE), b. Manchester, N.H, Apr. 25, 19; m. 46; c. 3. CHEMISTRY. B.S, Chicago, 40, Ph.D.(org. chem), 48. Lab. asst. chem, Chicago, 41-42, 46-47; res. assoc, Gen. Elec. Co, 47-50; abrasives div, tech. dept, Behr-Manning Corp, 51-54, group leader, 54-64, ASST. DIR. RES, COATED ABRASIVES DIV, NORTON CO, 64- U.S.A, 43-46, Chem.C.Res, 46-64, Lt. Col. AAAS; Am. Chem. Soc. Alkyd and phenolic resins; plastics; free radical reactions; reactions of free radicals in solution; decomposition of acetyl peroxide in acids, nitroalkanes and halogenated esters; fluorocarbon polymers; abrasives, epoxy resins; cloth finishing; polyurethanes. Address: Coated Abrasives Division, Norton Co, Troy, NY 12181.

GLADSTONE, ROBERT JAY, b. New York, N.Y, Feb. 20, 41; m. 66; c. 2. OPERATIONS RESEARCH, APPLIED MATHEMATICS. S.B, Mass. Inst. Tech, 62, Nat. Sci. Found. fel, 62-66, S.M. & E.E, 63, Ph.D.(elec. eng), 67. Staff appointee, div. sponsored res, Mass. Inst. Tech, summer 65; PROF. ASST. TO ASSOC. DIR, DIV. RES. EPIDEMIOL. & COMMUN. SCI, WHO, 67- Applied probability; health planning. Address: World Health Organization, Ave. Appia, Geneva, Switz.

GLADSTONE, WILLIAM T(URNBULL), b. Syracuse, N.Y, May 5, 31; m. 56; c. 2. FOREST GENETICS, WOOD SCIENCE. B.S, State Univ. N.Y. Col. Forestry, Syracuse Univ, 53; M.F, Yale, 65; St. Regis Paper Co. fel, N.C. State Univ, 65-66, Nat. Sci. Found. fel, 66-68, Ph.D.(forest genetics, wood sci), 69. Asst. pulp mill supt, Union Bag Camp Paper Corp, Va, 53-63; ASST. PROF. FOREST GENETICS, STATE UNIV. N.Y. COL. FORESTRY, SYRACUSE UNIV, 68- U.S.A. Eng.C, 53-55. Tech. Asn. Pulp & Paper Indust; Forest Prod. Res. Soc.(Wood Award, 69). Variability and heritability of wood properties; relationships between wood fiber properties and products manufactured from wood; environmental influences on wood properties. Address: Dept. of Silviculture, State University of New York College of Forestry, Syracuse University, Syracuse, NY 13210.

GLAENZER, RICHARD H, b. St. Louis, Mo, Nov. 29, 33; m. 63; c. 2. ELECTRICAL ENGINEERING, PHYSICS. B.S, Washington(St. Louis), 60, M.S, 64, Ph.D.(elec. eng), Carnegie-Mellon Univ, 68. Engr, McDONNELL DOUGLAS CORP, ST. LOUIS, 60-62, res. assoc, 62-64, RES. SCIENTIST, 67- U.S.A, 54-56. Am. Phys. Soc; Inst. Elec. & Electronics Eng. Integrated and hybrid circuits; photodetectors; infrared to visible image conversion; electrical behavior of defects in semiconductor materials and devices. Address: 12739 Asherton Dr, Bridgeton, MO 63044.

GLAESER, HANS HELLMUT, b. Chemnitz, Germany, June 30, 34; nat; m. 62. INORGANIC CHEMISTRY. B.S, Karlsruhe Tech, 55, M.S, 58, Dr. rer. nat, 61. Instr. inorg. & anal. chem, Karlsruhe Tech, 61-62; res. assoc. phys. inorg. chem, Wash. State Univ, 62-66; from res. chemist to SR. RES. CHEMIST, PIGMENTS DEPT, E.I. DU PONT DE NEMOURS & CO, INC, 66- Preparative inorganic and solid state chemistry; chemical kinetics; reaction mechanisms of inorganic exchange reactions. Address: Experimental Station, Pigments Dept, E.I. du Pont de Nemours & Co, Inc, Wilmington, DE 19898.

GLAESER, JOHN DOUGLAS, b. Abington, Pa, July 5, 34. GEOLOGY. B.S, Franklin & Marshall Col, 56; M.S, Miami (Ohio), 58; Ph.D.(geol), Northwest. Univ, 64. GEOLOGIST, TOPOG. & GEOL. SURV, PA, 61- Geol. Soc. Am; Am. Asn. Petrol. Geol; Soc. Econ. Paleont. & Mineral; Int. Asn. Sedimentol. Stratigraphy and sedimentation of the Triassic Newark-Gettysburg Basin; Upper Devonian rocks in northeastern Pennsylvania; sedimentology and modern analogues of eastern Triassic basins and Catskill delta; economic use of sedimentology of terrigenous clastics. Address: Topographic & Geological Survey, Dept. of Environmental Resources, Harrisburg, PA 17120.

GLAESER, ROBERT M, b. Kenosha, Wis, July 20, 37; m. 60; c. 3. BIOPHYSICS. B.S, Wisconsin, Madison, 59; Ph.D.(biophys), California, Berkeley, 64. Nat. Sci. Found. fel, math. inst, Oxford, 63-64; Nat. Insts. Health traineeship biophys, Chicago, 64-65; lectr. med. physics, UNIV. CALIF, BERKELEY, 65-66, asst. prof. BIOPHYS, 66-71, ASSOC. PROF, 71- AAAS; Biophys. Soc; Electron Micros. Soc. Am. Molecular composition and molecular organization of animal-cell surfaces; functional aspects of cell-surface structure and cell contacts; electron optics and the interpretation of electron microscopic images. Address: Division of Medical Physics, University of California, Berkeley, CA 94720.

GLAESER, WILLIAM A(LFRED), b. Utica, N.Y, Aug. 25, 23; m. 51; c. 3. MECHANICAL & METALLURGICAL ENGINEERING. B.M.E, Cornell, 49; M.S, Ohio State, 59. Develop. engr, Clark Bros, Inc, N.Y, 49-51; prin. engr, BATTELLE MEM. INST, 51-57, proj. leader, 57-59, asst. chief, eng. mech. div, 59-64, assoc. chief, exp. physics div, 64-69, FEL. LUBRICATION MECH, DIV. MECH. & SYSTS. ENG. DEPT, 69- C.Eng, U.S.A, 42-45. Bearings lubrication and wear phenomena, especially as concerned with unusual environments; metallurgical aspects of wear and friction. Address: Battelle Memorial Institute, 505 King Ave, Columbus, OH 43201.

GLAGOV, SEYMOUR, b. N.Y.C, Aug. 8, 25; m. 46; c. 1. PATHOLOGY. B.A, Brooklyn Col, 46; M.D, Geneva, 53. Instr. PATH, UNIV. CHICAGO, 58-61, asst. prof, 61-66, assoc. prof, 66-70, PROF, 70- Res. fel, Am. Heart Asn, 58-60, estab. investr, 62- Dipl, Am. Bd. Path, 60. Experimental pathology; physiopathology and biology of blood vessels; diseases of the liver; human pathology. Address: Dept. of Pathology, University of Chicago, 59th St. & Ellis Ave, Chicago, IL 60637.

GLAHN, HARRY ROBERT, b. Shelbyville, Mo, July 28, 28; m. 49; c. 2. METEOROLOGY. B.S. & B.S.Ed, Northeast Mo. State Teachers Col, 53; Okla. Agr. & Mech. Col, 53-54; Missouri, summer 57; scholar. & M.S, Mass. Inst. Tech, 58; American Univ, 60-61; U.S. Weather Bur. fel. & Ph.D.(meteorol), Pa. State, 63. Elem. teacher, Duncan Sch, Mo, 47-51; res. meteorologist, U.S. Weather Bur, 58-64, SUPVRY. RES. METEOROLOGIST, 64-67, TECH. DEVELOP. LAB, NAT. WEATHER SERV, 67- Res. meteorologist, Mass. Inst. Technol, summer, 58. U.S.A.F, 53-57, Res, 57-, Maj. Am. Meteorol. Soc. Application of statistics to meteorology. Address: Techniques Development Lab, National Weather Service, 8060 13th St, Silver Spring, MD 20910.

GLAID, ANDREW J(OSEPH), III, b. Pittsburgh, Pa, July 14, 23; m. 53; c. 5. BIOCHEMISTRY. B.S, Duquesne, 49, M.S, 50; Ph.D.(biochem), Duke, 55. Asst. prof. CHEM, DUQUESNE UNIV, 54-57, assoc. prof, 57-61, PROF, 61- Am. Chem. Soc. Kinetics of enzymatic reactions; stereochemistry of biologically active compounds. Address: Dept. of Chemistry, Duquesne University, Pittsburgh, PA 15219.

GLAMKOWSKI, EDWARD J(OSEPH), b. Brooklyn, N.Y, May 20, 36; m. 63; c. 2. ORGANIC CHEMISTRY. B.S, Fordham Univ, 58; Kettering fel, Ohio State Univ, 62, Ph.D.(chem), 63. Sr. res. chemist, Merck, Sharp & Dohme Res. Labs, Rahway, 63-71; RES. ASSOC, HOECHST PHARMACEUT. CO, SOMERVILLE, 71- Am. Chem. Soc; Brit. Chem. Soc. Steroids; penicillins; indole compounds; anti-inflammatory and central nervous system agents. Address: 7 Owens Dr, Warren, NJ 07060.

GLANTZ, PAUL J(OSEPH), b. Pittsburgh, Pa, Jan. 31, 21; m. 42; c. 6. BACTERIOLOGY. B.S, Pittsburgh, 43; M.S, Pa. State, 48, Ph.D.(bacter), 58. Instr. VET. RES, PA. STATE UNIV, 44-59, asst. prof, 59-66, ASSOC. PROF, 66- U.S. Pub. Health Serv. res. grant, 60-69; assoc. prof, Can. Med. Res. Coun, 68-69. AAAS; Am. Soc. Microbiol; N.Y. Acad. Sci. Infectious disease; enteric bacteriology; serology of E. coli pathogens. Address: Dept. of Veterinary Science, 105 Animal Industries Bldg, Pennsylvania State University, University Park, PA 16802.

GLANTZ, RAYMON M, b. Brooklyn, N.Y, July 1, 41; m. 64. NEUROPHYSIOLOGY. B.A, Brooklyn Col, 63; M.S, Syracuse, 64, Ph.D.(physiol. psychol), 66. Instr. physiol, sch. med, N.Y. Univ, 66-67; res. fel. neurophysiol, Calif. Inst. Tech, 67-69; ASST. PROF. BIOL, RICE UNIV, 69- Grass Found. fel. neurophysiol, Woods Hole Marine Biol. Lab, 67; vis. res. assoc, med. faculty, Rotterdam, summer, 70- AAAS; Am. Soc. Zool. Visual photoreceptors, transduction, coding, adaption; information processing in the invertebrate central nervous system; axon physiology; amoeboid movement and protoplasmic steaming. Address: Dept. of Biology, Rice University, Houston, TX 77001.

GLANVILLE, JAMES OLIVER, b. London, Eng, July 24, 41; m. 65; c. 2. INORGANIC & ANALYTICAL CHEMISTRY. B.Sc. & A.R.C.S, Univ. London, 62; Ph.D.(chem), Univ. Md, 67. Res. chemist, res. & develop. dept, inorg. div, FMC Corp, 68-69; ASSOC. PROF. CHEM, VA. WEST. COMMUNITY COL, 69- Am. Chem. Soc; Am. Inst. Chem. Address: 2624 Avenel Ave. S.W, Roanoke, VA 24015.

GLANZ, FILSON H, b. Los Angeles, Calif, Aug. 7, 34; m. 67; c. 1. ELECTRICAL ENGINEERING. B.S, Stanford, 56, M.S, 57, Ph.D.(elec. eng), 65. Engr, Librascope, Inc, 57-59; Stanford Res. Inst, 61-63; from asst. prof. to ASSOC. PROF, ELEC. ENG, UNIV. N.HAMP, 65- Inst. Elec. & Electronics Eng. Adaptive pattern recognition; information theory; underwater acoustics. Address: Dept. of Electrical Engineering, Kingsbury Hall, University of New Hampshire, Durham, NH 03824.

GLARUM, SIVERT HERTH, b. Providence, R.I, June 6, 33; m. 59; c. 2. PHYSICAL CHEMISTRY. B.A, Kalamazoo Col, 55; Ph.D.(chem), Brown, 60. MEM. TECH. STAFF, BELL TEL. LABS, 59- Am. Chem. Soc; Am. Phys. Soc. Dielectrics; solid state; paramagnetic resonance. Address: Bell Telephone Labs, Murray Hill, NJ 07971.

GLARUM, SIVERT N, b. Elberta, Mich, Apr. 11, 08; m. 32; c. 2. PHYSICAL CHEMISTRY. A.B, Kalamazoo Col, 29; Jesse Metcalf fel, Brown, 31-32, Ph.D.(chem), 33. Asst. chem, Brown, 30-31; res. assoc, Am. Asn. Textile Chem. & Colorists, 33-37; res. chemist, Rohm & Haas Co, Pa, 37-46; Ciba Prod. Corp, 46-62, chief chemist, Ciba Co, Inc, 52-59; asst. div. head, South. Res. Inst, 59-64, sr. res. adv, 64-71; RETIRED. With Off. Sci. Res. & Develop, 44. Am. Chem. Soc; Am. Asn. Textile Chem. & Colorists; Am. Inst. Chem. Research and development in the physical sciences. Address: 3165 College Terrace Ct, Traverse City, MI 49684.

GLASCOCK, HOMER H(OPSON), JR, b. Hannibal, Mo, Apr. 10, 29; m. 58; c. 3. PHYSICS. B.S, Missouri, 51, M.S, 56, Ph.D.(solid state physics), 61. RES. PHYSICIST, GEN. ELEC. CO, 60- U.S.A, 51-53, Res, 53-60. Am. Phys. Soc. Solid state and surface physics; physical electronics. Address: General Electric Co, P.O. Box 8, Schenectady, NY 12301.

GLASEBROOK, ARTHUR L(AWRENCE), b. Chicago, Ill, Oct. 22, 09; m. 45; c. 2. PHYSICAL CHEMISTRY. B.S, Michigan, 32; Ph.D.(chem), Hopkins, 34. Res. chemist, Gen. Motors Corp, Mich, 34-42; res. ctr, Hercules Powder Co, 42-44, mgr, gen. res. div, 44-51, high pressure res. div, 51-54, asst. to dir. res, 54-61, OVERSEAS TECH. MGR, HERCULES INC, 61- Am. Chem. Soc. High pressure reactions; distillation; catalysis; petrochemicals. Address: New Enterprise Dept, Hercules Inc, Hercules Tower, Wilmington, DE 19899.

GLASEL, JAY A(RTHUR), b. N.Y.C, Apr. 30, 34; m. 62. PHYSICAL CHEMISTRY, BIOCHEMISTRY. B.S, Calif. Inst. Technol, 55; Standard Oil Found. fel, Univ. Chicago, 55-59, Ph.D.(chem. physics), 59. Nat. Sci. Found. res. fels. chem. physics, Univ. Calif, San Diego, 60-61 & phys. chem, Imp. Col, Univ. London, 61-62; asst. prof. BIOCHEM, Col. Physicians & Surgeons, Columbia Univ, 64-70; ASSOC. PROF, UNIV. CONN. HEALTH CTR, 70- Sr. vis. scientist, Oxford, 70-71. U.S.A.F, 62-64, 1st Lt. Am. Phys. Soc; Biophys. Soc; Am. Chem. Soc. Physical biochemistry on structure and dynamics of macromolecules and interaction of solvent with macromolecular structure; nuclear magnetic resonance spectroscopy. Address: Dept. of Biochemistry, University of Connecticut Health Center, Farmington, CT 06032.

GLASER, ALAN ARTHUR, b. Pittsburgh, Pa, July 13, 33. MECHANICAL ENGINEERING. B.S, Carnegie Inst. Tech, 56, M.S, 59; Ph.D.(mech. eng), Pittsburgh, 65. Assoc. aeronaut. engr, Martin Co, Md, 56-57; res. asst. mech. eng, Carnegie Inst. Tech, 58-59; instr. & res. asst, Univ. Pittsburgh, 59-65, asst. prof, 65-70; CONSULT. MECH. ENGR, 71- Consult, Elliott Co, Pa, 65; Westinghouse Elec. Corp, 66; Ford Motor Co, Mich, 68; Vet. Admin. Hosp, Pittsburgh, Pa, 68-70. Sig.C, 57-58, 1st Lt. AAAS; Am. Soc. Eng. Educ; Am. Soc. Mech. Eng; Nat. Soc. Prof. Eng; Soc. Automotive Eng. Vibrations of elastic bodies; mechanical properties of skin, bone and tendon; mechanical characteristics of healing wounds in the skin; math modeling of human body and automotive structures for crash protection. Address: 27 Kingston Ave, Crafton, Pittsburgh, PA 15205.

GLASER, ARNOLD H(ENRY), b. Mt. Vernon, Wash, May 25, 19. METEOROLOGY. B.S, Washington (Seattle), 40, M.S, 41; Swope fel, Mass. Inst. Tech, 49-50, Sc.D.(meteorol), 52; Fulbright scholar, Imp. Col. London, 50-51, dipl, 51. Meteorologist, Pan. Am. Grace Airways, 42-43; instr. meteorol, Tech. Inst. Aviation, Brazil, 46-48; res. assoc, Mass. Inst. Tech, 48-49; Wisconsin, 52; assoc. prof, Agr. & Mech. Col. Texas, 53-56; res. assoc, Harvard, 57; chief proj. scientist, geophys. div, Allied Res. Assocs, Inc, 57-63; pres. & tech. dir, Aracon Geophys. Co, 63-66; v.pres, Allied Res. Assocs, Inc, Mass, 66-69; MEM. STAFF, NAT. OCEANIC & ATMOSPHERIC ADMIN, 69- U.S.A.A.F, 44-45. Am. Meteorol. Soc; Am. Geophys. Union; Royal Meteorol. Soc. Physical meteorology; satellite meteorology. Address: National Oceanic & Atmospheric Administration, Rockville, MD 20852.

GLASER, CHARLES, b. Raritan, N.J, Apr. 12, 15. BIOCHEMISTRY. B.S, Rutgers, 37, Ph.D.(biochem), 41. Lab. asst. physiol, Rutgers, 38-41; res. biochemist, Nixon Nitration Works, N.J, 41-43; asst, Squibb Inst. Med. Res, 42-45, res. assoc, E.R. Squibb & Sons, 45-46, biochemist & develop. chemist, 46-47, res. assoc. pharmacol, SQUIBB INST. MED. RES, 47-48, biochem. develop, 48-62, RES. SCIENTIST BIOL. PROD, 62- Am. Chem. Soc. Blood proteins; insulin; fibrinolysis; urokinase; bone chemistry. Address: 59 Thompson, Raritan, NJ 08869.

GLASER, DONALD A(RTHUR), b. Cleveland, Ohio, Sept. 21, 26; div; c. 2. PHYSICS, MOLECULAR BIOLOGY. B.S, Case, 46, D.Sc, 59; Ph.D.(physics), Calif. Inst. Tech, 50. Instr. PHYSICS, Michigan, 49-53, asst. prof, 53-55, assoc. prof, 55-57, prof, 57-59; vis. prof, UNIV. CALIF, BERKELEY, 59-60, PROF, 60- Vis. prof, Mass. Inst. Technol, 61-62. Charles Vernon Boys Prize, Brit. Inst. Physics & Phys. Soc, 58; Nobel Prize, 60. Nat. Acad. Sci; fel. Am. Phys. Soc.(prize, 59). Nuclear physics; cosmic rays; evolution. Address: Dept. of Physics & Molecular Biology, 229 MBVL, University of California, Berkeley, CA 94720.

GLASER, EDMUND M, b. New York, N.Y, Oct. 17, 27; m. 59; c. 3. COMPUTER SCIENCE, PHYSIOLOGY. B.E.E, Cooper Union, 49; M.S.E, Hopkins, 54, D.Eng, 60. Electromech. engr. control systs, Glenn L. Martin Co, 50-52; res. assoc, radiation lab, Hopkins, 52-60, fel. physiol, SCH. MED, 60-62; ASSOC. PROF, UNIV. MD, 62-70, PHYSIOL. & COMPUT. SCI, 70- Consult, Hoover Electronics, 58-59; Electronic Commun, Inc, 60-62; Westinghouse Elec. Corp, 62-63; Hopkins, 62-64. U.S.A, 46-47. AAAS; Soc. Neurosci; Inst. Elec. & Electronics Eng; Biophys. Soc; Acoust. Soc. Am. Sensory neurophysiology, especially auditive, and its relationship to information theory; biological control systems; application of computers to the neurosciences; biomedical engineering. Address: Dept. of Physiology, University of Maryland School of Medicine, Baltimore, MD 21201.

GLASER, EDWARD L(EWIS), b. Evanston, Ill, Oct. 7, 29; m. 50; c. 2. ELECTRICAL ENGINEERING. A.B, Dartmouth Col, 51. Mathematician & engr, Int. Bus. Mach. Corp, 51-55; consult. to dir. eng, Electrodata Div, Burroughs Corp, 55-56, mgr. systs. dept, res. div, 56-63; res. assoc, Mass. Inst. Technol, 63-67; CHMN. COMPUT. & INFO. SCI. DEPT, HEAD COMPUT. ENG. DIV. & DIR. ANDREW R. JENNINGS COMPUT. CTR, CASE WEST. RESERVE UNIV, 67- Fel. & sr. mem. Inst. Elec. & Electronics Eng. Information and computing sciences; architecture computing; design of computer systems; industrial management. Address: Andrew R. Jennings Computing Center, Case Western Reserve University, 10900 Euclid Ave, 215 Crawford Hall, Cleveland, OH 44106.

GLASER, FREDERIC M, b. Toledo, Ohio, Dec. 7, 35; m. 61; c. 1. PHYSICS, PHYSICAL CHEMISTRY. B.S, Purdue, 57; Kettering, McPherson & Nat. Sci. Found. fels. & Ph.D.(phys. chem), Ohio State, 63. Summer res. asst, Am. Cyanamid Co, 56-59; Nat. Sci. Found. fel. & res. assoc. physics, Chicago, 63-64; asst. prof, Bowling Green State Univ, 64-66; mem. staff, Houston Opers, TRW Systs. Inc, 66-69; ASSOC. PROF. PHYSICS, PAN AM. UNIV, 69- AAAS; Am. Phys. Soc; Am. Chem. Soc; Am. Math. Soc; Soc. Indust. & Appl. Math. Theoretical solid state physics; magnetic properties of metals and alloys; bonding theory of small molecules and ultraviolet spectra. Address: Dept. of Physical Sciences, Pan American University, Edinburg, TX 78539.

GLASER, GILBERT H(ERBERT), b. New York, N.Y, Nov. 10, 20; m. 46; c. 2. NEUROLOGY. A.B, Columbia, 40, M.D, 43, Sc.D.(med), 51; hon. M.A, Yale, 63. Intern, Mt. Sinai Hosp, N.Y, 43-44; asst. res. neurol, Neurol. Inst, 44-45, chief res, 45-46, asst, Columbia, 48-50, instr, 50-51, assoc, 51-52; asst. prof. NEUROL, SCH. MED, YALE, 52-55, assoc. prof, 55-63, PROF, 63-, CHMN. DEPT, 71-, head sect, 52-71. Resident psychiat, N.Y. Psychiat. Inst, 48-49, sr. res. scientist, 49-50; consult. to surg. gen, neurol. res. training grant comt, U.S. Pub. Health Serv, 56-60, mem. neurol. res. progs. grant comt, 68-72; vis. prof. neurol, Hosp. for Sick Children & Univ. Col, London, 65-66; mem. neuropharmacol. adv. comt. Food & Drug Admin, Dept. Health, Educ. & Welfare, 70-72. Med.C, 46-48, Capt. Am. Electroencephalog. Soc; Am. Epilepsy Soc.(ed, Epilepsia, pres, 63); Am. Neurol. Asn; Asn. Res. Nerv. & Ment. Disease; Am. Med. Asn; Am. Acad. Neurol.(pres. elect). Clinical neurology and neurophysiology; electroencephalography; epilepsy; neuromuscular disorders; metabolic disorders of the nervous system; developmental neurology. Address: Dept. of Neurology, Yale University School of Medicine, 333 Cedar St, New Haven, CT 06510.

GLASER, HAROLD, b. Kurseni, Lithuania, Aug. 28, 24; U.S. citizen; m. 45; c. 3. THEORETICAL PHYSICS. B.S, Roosevelt, 48; M.S, Northwestern, 49, Ph.D.(physics), 53. Instr, Roosevelt, 49-51; sr. physicist, appl. physics lab, Hopkins, 52-54; head theoret. anal. sect, syst. anal. br, Naval Res. Lab, 54-57, physicist, Off. Naval Res, 57-64, head nuclear physics br, 64-66; dep. chief solar physics, Off. Space Sci. & Applns, NASA, 66-67, chief, 67-70; PROGS. OFF, NAT. BUR. STANDARDS, 70- Lectr, Univ. Md, spring 56; res. assoc, Univ. South. Calif, 59; spec. asst. to asst. dir, div. math, physics & eng, Nat. Sci. Found, summer 62. Dept. Navy meritorious civilian serv. award, 65. U.S.A, 43-46. Int. Astron. Union; Am. Phys. Soc; Am. Geophys. Union; Am. Astron. Soc; Sci. Res. Soc. Am. Electromagnetic propagation; noise theory; radio astronomy; solar physics. Address: 312 Chartwell Dr, Silver Spring, MD 20904.

GLASER, H(ERMAN), b. Brooklyn, N.Y, Nov. 11, 23; m. 55; c. 1. PHYSICS. B.A, Brooklyn Col, 43; North Carolina, 43-44; Ph.D.(physics), Hopkins, 50. Instr. physics, North Carolina, 43-44; physicist, Naval Ord. Lab, 44-45; jr. instr. PHYSICS, Hopkins, 45-49; assoc. prof, Texas Tech. Col, 50-53; asst. prof. HOFSTRA UNIV, 53-60, assoc. prof, 60-69, PROF, 69- Am. Phys. Soc; Am. Asn. Physics Teachers. X-ray spectroscopy; low energy nuclear physics. Address: Dept. of Physics, Hofstra University, Hempstead, NY 11550.

GLASER, KURT, b. Vienna, Austria, Feb. 16, 15; nat; m. 46; c. 4. CHILD PSYCHIATRY. Vienna, 33-38; M.D, Lausanne, 39; M.Sc, Illinois, 48. Instr. pediat, col. med, Illinois, 45-50; asst. chief physician, med. sch, Hebrew Univ, Israel, 50-54; asst. prof. PEDIAT, SCH. MED, UNIV. MD, 54-62, ASSOC. PROF, 62-, ASST. CLIN. PROF. PSYCHIAT, 65-; CLIN. DIR, ROSEWOOD STATE HOSP, OWINGS MILLS, 61- Clin. instr. psychiat, sch. med, Maryland, 54-65. Consult, depts. pediat. & psychiat, Sinai Hosp. & Cent. Eval. Clin. Children, Univ. Md. Allen award, col. med, Illinois, 49. Fel. Am. Acad. Pediat; fel. Am. Psychiat. Asn; Am. Asn. Ment. Deficiency; Am. Acad. Ment. Retardation. Pediatric psychiatry; growth and development of premature infants; cellular composition of the bone marrow in normal infants and children; problems of child psychiatry, school phobia, learning disorders, suicide in children and adolescents, parental attitudes and teaching aspects; mental retardation. Address: 6114 Baltimore Ave, Baltimore, MD 21215.

GLASER, LESLIE, b. DeKalb, Ill, Sept. 4, 37; m. 58; c. 4. MATHEMATICS. B.A, DePauw, 59; M.S, Wisconsin, 61, Nat. Sci. Found. fel, 62-64, Ph.D. (topol), 64. Asst. prof. MATH, Rice Univ, 64-68; assoc. prof, UNIV. UTAH, 68-71, PROF, 71- Vis. mem, Inst. Adv. Study, 69-70; Sloan fel, 69-71.

Math. Asn. Am; Am. Math. Soc. Point set topology; combinatorial topology. Address: Dept. of Mathematics, University of Utah, Salt Lake City, UT 84112.

GLASER, LUIS, b. Vienna, Austria, Mar. 30, 32; U.S. citizen; m. 61; c. 2. BIOCHEMISTRY. B.A, Toronto, 53; Ph.D.(biochem), Washington (St. Louis), 56. Instr. BIOCHEM, SCH. MED, WASH. UNIV, 56-59, asst. prof, 59-63, assoc. prof, 63-67, PROF, 67- Am. Soc. Biol. Chem. Mechanisms of sugar synthesis; enzymatic synthesis of polysaccharides; bacterial cell wall components. Address: Dept. of Biological Chemistry, School of Medicine, Washington University, St. Louis, MO 63110.

GLASER, M(ILTON) A(RTHUR), b. New York, N.Y, Sept. 4, 12; m. 37; c. 3. ORGANIC CHEMISTRY. B.S, Tufts, 34. Engr, Mass, 31-32, 34-36; chief chemist & dir. res, Standard Varnish Works, 36-45; v.pres. & tech. dir, MIDLAND DIV, DEXTER CORP, 45-64, exec. v.pres. RES. & DEVELOP, 64-70, DIV. V.PRES, 70- Lectr, N.Dak. State Univ, Ill. Inst. Technol. & Univ. Mo. Pres, Fedn. Socs. Paint Tech, 56-57; v.pres. & trustee, Paint Res. Inst, 58, pres, 65-66; titular mem. org. coating sect, Int. Union Pure & Appl. Chem, 67- Heckel award, 63. Am. Chem. Soc; Am. Oil Chemists' Soc; Am. Inst. Chem. Eng; Am. Soc. Test. & Mat; Soc. Rheol; Am. Technion Soc; Nat. Asn. Corrosion Eng; fel. Am. Inst. Chem; Inst. Food Technol. Organic coatings including alkyd, silicone and phenolic polymers; high-temperature resistant coatings; corrosion resistant coatings for container linings; specialty coatings for severe exposure environments. Address: Midland Division, Dexter Corp, One E. Water St, Waukegan, IL 60085.

GLASER, MYRON B(ARNARD), b. N.Y.C, Dec. 31, 27; m. 59. ELECTRICAL ENGINEERING. B.E.E, City Col. New York, 50; M.Eng, Yale, 51. Assoc. proj. engr, Sperry Gyroscope Co, 51-53, proj. engr, 53-57, sr. engr, 57-58, prin, engr, Sperry Phoenix Co, 58-62; SR. RES. ENGR, STANFORD RES. INST, 62- Alternate del, Radio Tech. Cmn. Aeronaut, 64, partic. spec. comt. 117, 68- U.S.N. Inst. Elec. & Electronics Eng. Navigation and air traffic control systems; radar data processing and aircraft automatic flight control systems; all-weather landing systems and instrumentation; man-machine interactions; human operator workload. Address: Stanford Research Institute, Menlo Park, CA 94025.

GLASER, PAUL F, b. New York, N.Y, Apr. 17, 26; m. 47; c. 2. ELECTRICAL ENGINEERING. B.E.E, N.Y. Univ, 49, M.E.E, 53. Electronic engr, Am. Chronoscope Corp, 49-52, chief engr, 52-55; chief electronics engr, electronic prod. div, Gruen Watch Co, 55-56, dir. eng, 56-58; proj. engr, Thor control & elec. systs, TRW SYSTS. GROUP, 58, proj. engr, Explorer VI & Pioneer V, 58-60, systs. engr, Able V, 60, asst. prog. dir, orbiting geophys. observ. design & develop, 60-63, dir, space power & support systs. lab, 63-66, mgr. electronic hardware opers, 66-68, asst. gen. mgr. projs, ELECTRONICS SYSTS. DIV, 69-71, V.PRES. & GEN. MGR, 71- Lectr, Univ. Calif, Los Angeles, 61-63. U.S.N, 44-46. Am. Inst. Elec. & Electronics Eng. Space power; space communications and telemetry; data processing; radar; flight control systems; analog and digital computers; servo and control systems; ultrasonics; automated checkout systems; aircraft and missile instrumentation. Address: TRW Systems Group, TRW, Inc, 1 Space Park, Redondo Beach, CA 90278.

GLASER, PETER E(DWARD), b. Czech, Sept. 5, 23; nat; m. 55; c. 3. MECHANICAL ENGINEERING. Dipl, Leeds Col. Tech, England, 43, Charles Univ, Prague, 47; M.S, Columbia, 51, Quincy W. Boese & Eugene Higgins fel. & Ph.D, 55. Head design dept, Werner Textile Consults, 49-53; sr. res. engr, ARTHUR D. LITTLE, INC, 55-61, group leader, 61-66, SECT. HEAD ENG, SCI, 66- Mem. mat. adv. bd, Nat. Acad. Sci, 58, mem. study group solar energy, 71; mem. U.S. comt, Int. Inst. Refrig, 59, v.pres, comn. 2, 68- AAAS; Am. Soc. Mech. Eng; Am. Soc. Heat, Refrig. & Air-Conditioning Eng; Am. Soc. Test. & Mat; Solar Energy Soc.(pres, 68-70, dir, 70-); Soc. Automotive Eng. Thermal insulation developments for extreme temperatures; design of solar furnace and arc imaging furnace; high temperature research with imagining furnaces; development of instrumentation and experimental techniques for thermal properties measurements; plasma devices; lunar surface research; large scale uses of solar energy; technology transfer. Address: 62 Turning Mill Rd, Lexington, MA 02173.

GLASER, ROBERT, b. Brooklyn, N.Y, Mar. 17, 42; m. 62; c. 2. ORGANIC & BIO-ORGANIC CHEMISTRY. B.A, Univ. Pa, 63; Nat. Defense Educ. Act fel, Rutgers Univ, 66-69, Ph.D.(org. chem), 70. Develop. chemist, indust. adhesives div, PPG Industs. Inc, 63-66; res. assoc. org. chem, Princeton, 69-70, x-ray crystallog, 70-71; SR. LECTR. ORG. CHEM, UNIV. OF THE NEGEV, ISRAEL, 71- Nat. Insts. Health res. fel, 69-71. Am. Chem. Soc; The Chem. Soc. Interactions of polyamines with nucleic acids; organic synthesis of polycyclic molecules; crystal and molecular structure determination of organic molecules. Address: Dept. of Chemistry, University of the Negev, Beersheba, Israel.

GLASER, ROBERT J(OY), b. St. Louis, Mo, Sept. 11, 18; m. 49; c. 3. MEDICINE. S.B, Harvard, 40, M.D, 43. Intern med, Barnes Hosp, St. Louis, Mo, 44; resident, Peter Bent Brigham Hosp, Boston, Mass, 44-45; Barnes Hosp, St. Louis, Mo, 45-47; Nat. Res. Coun. fel, med. sch, Wash. Univ, 47-49, instr, 49-50, from asst. prof. to assoc. prof, 50-57, asst. & assoc. dean, 53-57, chief div. immunol, 54-57; prof. & dean, Univ. Colo, 57-63, v.pres. acad. affairs, 59-63; prof. social med, Harvard Med. Sch, 63-65; prof. med, dean sch. med. & v.pres. med. affairs, Stanford Univ, 65-70; V.PRES, HARKNESS-COMMONWEALTH FOUND, 70- Asst. med, Wash. Univ, 45-47; asst. physician, Barnes Hosp, St. Louis, Mo, 49-57; chief rheumatic fever clin, Wash. Univ. Clins, 49-57; vis. physician, Unit I Med. Serv, St. Louis City Hosp, 50, chief serv, 50-53; attend. physician, Colo. Gen. Hosp, 57-63; pres, Affiliated Hosps. Ctr, Inc, Boston, Mass, 63-65; chief of staff & attend. physician, Stanford Univ. Hosp, 65-70. Consult, State of Mo. Crippled Children's Serv, 49-55; div. of serv. for crippled children, Univ. Ill, 50-57; Vet. Admin. Hosps, Denver, & Grand Junction, Colo. & Albuquerque, N.Mex, 57-63; Fitzsimons Army Hosp, Denver, Colo, 57-63; Lowry AFB Hosp, 57-63; Nat. Health Res. Facilities Adv. Coun, 58-61; Vet. Admin, Mass, 63-65; Harvard Med. Servs, Boston City Hosp, 63-65; Peter Bent Brigham Hosp, Boston, 63-65. Mem. sci. adv. coun, Rheumatic Fever Res. Inst, 56-59; grad. training grant comt, Nat. Inst. Allergy & Infectious Diseases, 58-61; Nat. Health Res. Facilities Adv. Coun, 61-65; adv. coun, Nat. Inst. Dent. Res, 65-69; mem. adv. comt. higher educ, Dept. Health Educ. & Welfare, 67-68, ad hoc adv. comt, 67-68, nat. adv. ment. health coun, 70-; mem, Inst. Med, Nat. Acad. Sci, 71-; mem. exec. comt, Kaiser Found. Hosps. & Health Plan, Inc, 68-; Commonwealth Fund, 69-, Hewlett-Packard, 70-, Kaiser Family Found, 70-; bd. of visitors, sch. med, Univ. Pittsburgh, 68-; comt. med. affairs, Yale, 69-; bd. dirs, Inst. Educ. Mgt, 70-; exec. comt, inst. med, Nat. Acad. Sci, 70- Alpha Omega Alpha lectr, Univ. Alta, 63; Boston Univ, 63; Univ. Colo, 64; Univ. W.Va, 64; Univ. Louisville, 65; Univ. Cincinnati, 66; Univ. Calif, San Francisco, 67; N.Y. Med. Col, 69; Univ. Ind, 70; Lowell lectr, Mass. Gen. Hosp, 65. Dipl, Am. Bd. Internal Med, 51. Fel. AAAS; Am. Acad. Arts & Sci; Am. Soc. Clin. Invest; Asn. Am. Physicians; Am. Clin. & Climat. Asn; Am. Fedn. Clin. Res.(secy, 52-53, v.chmn, 53-54, chmn, 54-55); Am. Soc. Microbiol; Soc. Exp. Biol. & Med; Am. Soc. Exp. Path; fel. Am. Col. Physicians; Am. Med. Asn; Infectious Diseases Soc. Am; Am. Heart Asn; Asn. Am. Med. Cols.(asst. secy, 56-60, v.pres, 63-64, pres-elec, 67-68). Experimental streptococcal infections; rheumatic fever. Address: Harkness Commonwealth Foundation, 1 E. 75th St, New York, NY 10021.

GLASER, WARREN, b. N.Y.C, Apr. 8, 28; m. 61; c. 1. MEDICINE, PHYSIOLOGY. A.B, Columbia, 46, M.D, 50. Res. exp. med, Oak Ridge Inst. Nuclear Studies, 55-56; instr. MED, STATE UNIV. N.Y. DOWNSTATE MED. CTR, 56-57, asst. prof, 57-63, ASSOC. PROF, 63- Consult, med. div, Oak Ridge Inst. Nuclear Studies. Med.C, 51-53, Res, 53-, Comdr. Soc. Nuclear Med; assoc. Am. Col. Physicians; Harvey Soc; Am. Fedn. Clin. Res; fel. N.Y. Acad. Sci; fel. N.Y. Acad. Med. Renal physiology; electrolyte metabolism; magnesium ion distribution in the body. Address: Dept. of Medicine, State University of New York Downstate Medical Center, 450 Clarkson Ave, Brooklyn, NY 11203.

GLASFORD, GLENN M(ILTON), b. Arcola, Tex, Nov. 4, 18; m. 48; c. 2. ELECTRICAL ENGINEERING. B.S, Texas, 40; M.S, Iowa State Col, 42. Mem. staff, radiation lab, Mass. Inst. Tech, 42-45; head, adv. develop. group, TV transmitter dept, Allen B. DuMont Labs, 45-47; instr. ELEC. ENG, SYRACUSE UNIV, 47-48, asst. prof, 49-51, assoc. prof, 52-56, PROF, 56- Consult, Gen. Elec. Co, 48-53; Int. Bus. Mach. Corp, 57-59. Fel. AAAS; fel. Inst. Elec. & Electronics Eng; Soc. Motion Picture & TV Eng. Electronics; applications of electron tube and transistor circuits; television; radar. Address: Dept. of Electrical & Computer Engineering, Syracuse University, Syracuse, NY 13210.

GLASGOW, A(UGUSTUS) R(OSSELL), JR, b. Wash, D.C, Oct. 19, 11; m; c. 3. PHYSICAL CHEMISTRY. B.S, George Washington, 35; M.S, Maryland, 39; D.Sc.(phys. chem), Univ. Brussels, Belgium, 57. Res. assoc, Am. Petrol. Inst, Nat. Bur. Standards, 30-45, phys. chemist, sect. thermochem. & hydrocarbons, 45-50, pure substances, 50-63, anal. & purification, 63-65; CHIEF, PESTICIDES REFERENCE STANDARDS SECT, Food & Drug Admin, 65-70; ENVIRON. PROTECTION AGENCY, 70- With Int. Bur. Physico-Chem. Standards, Brussels, 56-57. AAAS; Am. Chem. Soc. Development of phase exchange processes; adsorption; crystallization, single crystals, distillation and extraction for preparing organic and inorganic compounds in high purity; separation of complex mixtures; cryoscopic purities; phase analysis; polymorphism; thermal analysis, pure crystalline polymorphs by phase separations at high temperatures; purification and purity of pesticides. Address: Environmental Protection Agency, Pesticides Reference Standards Section, Room 5156, S. Agricultural Bldg, Washington, DC 20250.

GLASGOW, D(ALE) W(ILLIAM), b. Sandyville, Iowa, Jan. 29, 25; m. 53; c. 2. NUCLEAR PHYSICS, MATHEMATICS. B.A, Simpson Col, 49; M.S, Oregon State, 56, univ. fels, 53-61, Ph.D.(nuclear physics), 61. Physicist, Gen. Elec. Co, 49-53; sr. physicist, Hanford Labs, Gen. Elec. Co, 61-65; Pac. Northwest Lab, Battelle Mem. Inst, 65, sr. res. scientist, 65-69; Ohio State Univ. vis. res. assoc, AEROSPACE RES. LAB, WRIGHT PATTERSON AFB, 69-71; SR. NUCLEAR PHYSICIST, ADENA CORP, 71- Summers, physicist, Los Alamos Sci. Lab, 55-57. U.S.M.C, 44-46. Am. Phys. Soc; Am. Asn. Physics Teachers. Beta and gamma ray spectroscopy; fast neutron physics; fast pulse techniques and time of flight techniques; particle accelerators; environmental science; nuclear reactors. Address: Adena Corp, Aerospace Research Lab, Wright Patterson Air Force Base, OH 45433.

GLASGOW, D(AVID) GERALD, b. Apple Creek, Ohio, Aug. 25, 36; m. 58; c. 3. POLYMER CHEMISTRY. A.B, Col. Wooster, 58; Ph.D.(org. chem), Cincinnati, 63. Sr. res. chemist, org. sect, MONSANTO RES. CORP, 62-67, polymer synthesis sect, 67-68, RES. GROUP LEADER, 68- Am. Chem. Soc; Soc. Aerospace Mat. & Process Eng. Polymer synthesis; polyurethanes; polyesters; polyamides; adhesives. Address: Monsanto Research Corp, 1515 Nicholas Rd, Dayton, OH 45418.

GLASGOW, JOHN CHARLES, b. Nashville, Tenn, Dec. 14, 32; m. 58; c. 3. APPLIED MECHANICS, STRUCTURAL DYNAMICS. B.S, Notre Dame, 54; M.S, St. Louis, 60. Struct. engr, McDonnell Aircraft Corp, Mo, 54-56, aero loads engr, 56-57, dynamics engr, 57-61; sr. engr, dynamics, N.Am. Aviation Inc, Ohio, 61-63; head dynamics sect, LEWIS RES. CTR, NASA, CLEVELAND, 63-68, RES. ENGR, SHORT TAKEOFFS & LANDING PROPULSION BR, 68- Instr, Washington (St. Louis), 59-61. Am. Inst. Aeronaut. & Astronaut. Structural mechanics; dynamic environments; testing of short takeoffs and landing propulsion and lifting systems. Address: 5862 Gareau Dr, North Olmsted, OH 44070.

GLASGOW, LESLIE L(LOYD), b. Portland, Ind, Mar. 29, 14; m. 42; c. 3. WILDLIFE MANAGEMENT. B.S, Purdue, 42; M.A, Maine, 48; Ph.D.(game mgt), Agr. & Mech. Col, Tex, 58. Frmo instr. to asst. prof. GAME MGT, LA. STATE UNIV, BATON ROUGE, 48-58, assoc. prof, 58-63, PROF, 63-, ASST. DIR. SCH. FORESTRY & WILDLIFE MGT, 71- Consult. wildlife, 55-; dir. La. Wildlife & Fish Comn, 67-69; asst. secy, Fish, Wildlife Parks & Marine Resources, U.S. Dept. Interior, 69-70. U.S.A.A.F, 43-46. Wildlife Soc. Game management. Address: School of Forestry & Wildlife Management, Louisiana State University, Baton Rouge, LA 70803.

GLASGOW, LOWELL A(LAN), b. Cincinnati, Ohio, Aug. 28, 32; m. 56; c. 3. VIROLOGY & IMMUNOLOGY, PEDIATRICS. B.A, Univ. Rochester, 54, fels, 55-56, 57-58, M.S. & M.D. 58. Wyeth pediat. fel, sch. med, Univ. Rochester, 59-61, chief resident instr. pediat, 62-63, instr. pediat. & microbiol, 63-64, asst. prof. microbiol. & sr. instr. pediat, 64-65, asst. prof. microbiol. & pediat, 65-67, assoc. prof. microbiol, asst. prof. pediat. & assoc. pediatrician, 67-68, assoc. prof. microbiol. & pediat. & sr. assoc. pediatrician, 68-70; PROF. MICROBIOL. & CHMN. DEPT. & PROF. PEDIAT, MED. CTR. UNIV. UTAH, 70- Res. assoc, Nat. Inst. Allergy & Infectious Disease, 60-62; U.S. Pub. Health Serv. spec. fel, 63-64; Mead Johnson pediat. res. grant, 63-64; assoc. dir. clin. microbiol. labs, Strong Mem. Hosp. & Monroe County Health Dept, 64-70; consult, Nat. Insts. Health on Antiviral Substance Prog, 69; Int. Cong. Virol, 69; partic, Int. Symp. Interferon, Lyon, France, 69, Louvain, Belg, 71; Int. Cong. Pediat, 69; exam, Univ. Lagos, 70; Townsend Found. pediat. res. award, 70; partic, U.S.-Soviet Health Exchange Prog. Antiviral Substances, Russia, 71. Dipl, Am. Bd. Pediat. U.S.P.H.S, 60-62, Sr. Asst. Surg. Am. Asn. Immunol; Am. Soc. Microbiol; Soc. Pediat. Res; Am. Acad. Pediat; Infectious Diseases Soc. Am; Am. Soc. Pediat. Host resistance to viral infections; interferon; development of antiviral substances; study of animal model systems and factors which modify host-virus relationships; the role of toxins in staphylococcal disease. Address: Dept. of Microbiology, 5C128 Medical Center, University of Utah, Salt Lake City, UT 84112.

GLASHAUSSER, CHARLES MICHAEL, b. Newark, N.J, Dec. 7, 39; m. 65; c. 1. NUCLEAR PHYSICS. B.S, Boston Col, 61; Nat. Sci. Found. & Woodrow Wilson fels, Princeton, 61, Ph.D.(physics), 66. Physicist, Saclay Nuclear Res. Ctr, France, 65-67; Lawrence Radiation Lab, Univ. Calif, Berkeley, 67-69; ASST. PROF. PHYSICS, RUTGERS UNIV, 69-. Am. Phys. Soc. Spin dependence in inelastic scattering and transfer reactions; polarization phenomena in nuclear reactions; nuclear structure information from reactions of polarized and unpolarized particles. Address: Dept. of Physics, Rutgers The State University, New Brunswick, NJ 08903.

GLASHOW, SHELDON L(EE), b. New York, N.Y, Dec. 5, 32. PHYSICS. A.B, Cornell, 54; M.A, Harvard, 55, Nat. Sci. Found, fel, 55-58, Ph.D.(physics), 59. Nat. Sci. Found. fel, Inst. Theoret. Physics, Copenhagen, 58-60; res. fel. PHYSICS, Calif. Inst. Technol, 60; asst. prof, Stanford Univ, 61; Univ. Calif, Berkeley, 61-64, assoc. prof, 64-66; LYMAN LAB, HARVARD, 66-67, PROF, 67- Sloan fel, 62-66; consult, Brookhaven Nat. Lab, 67-; vis. scientist, Europ. Orgn. Nuclear Res. Geneva, Switz, 68; vis. prof, Univ. Aix Marseille, 71. Elementary particles. Address: Lyman Lab, Harvard University, Cambridge, MA 02138.

GLASKY, ALVIN J(ERALD), b. Chicago, Ill, June 16, 33; m. 57; c. 4. BIOCHEMISTRY. B.S, Illinois, 54, univ. fel, 56-57, U.S. Pub. Health Serv. fel, 57-58, Ph.D.(biochem), 58. Asst. biochem, Illinois, 54-56; Nat. Sci. Found. fel, biochem. inst, Lund, 58-59 & Wenner-Grens Inst, Univ. Stockholm, 59; dir. biochem. res. labs, Michael Reese Hosp, Chicago, Ill, 59-62; group leader drug enzym, dept. pharmacol, Abbott Labs, 62-66; dir. res, Int. Chem. Nuclear Corp, 66-68; PRES, NEWPORT PHARMACEUT. INT, INC, 68- Asst. prof, col. med, Univ. Ill, 59-68; assoc. prof, Chicago Med. Sch, 68- AAAS; Am. Chem. Soc; Am. Soc. Microbiol; N.Y. Acad. Sci. Mechanisms of drug action; biochemical pharmacology; viral chemotherapy; nucleic acid metabolism; biochemistry of learning and memory. Address: Newport Pharmaceuticals International, Inc, 1590 Monrovia Ave, Newport Beach, CA 92660.

GLASNER, MOSES, b. Cluj, Rumania, June 29, 42; U.S. citizen. MATHEMATICS. B.A, California, Los Angeles, 63, M.A, 65, Ph.D.(math), 66. Acting asst. prof. MATH, California, Los Angeles, 66-67; ASST. PROF, CALIF. INST. TECHNOL, 67- Am. Math. Soc; Math. Asn. Am. Global aspects of potential theory. Address: Dept. of Mathematics, California Institute of Technology, 1201 E. California Blvd, Pasadena, CA 91109.

GLASOE, ALF M(ELIUS), b. Spokane, Wash, Oct. 26, 09; m. 33; c. 3. PHYSICAL CHEMISTRY. B.A, St. Olaf Col, 30; fel, N.Y. Univ, 30-34, M.Sc, 32, Ph.D.(chem), 35. Res. chemist, Muralo Co, N.Y, 34-35; sect. supvr, photog. tech. div, Eastman Kodak Co, 35-71; RETIRED. Am. Chem. Soc; Soc. Motion Picture & TV Eng. Photographic processing technology; study of color changes in cobaltous chloride solutions. Address: 340 Oakridge Dr, Rochester, NY 14617.

GLASOE, PAUL K(IRKWOLD), b. Northfield, Minn, Nov. 22, 13; m. 35; c. 3. CHEMISTRY. A.B, St. Olaf Col, 34; fel, Wisconsin, 37, Ph.D.(inorg. chem), 38. Asst. chem, Wisconsin, 34-38, instr. gen. chem, 38; Illinois, 38-40; res. chemist, Eastman Kodak Co, 40-47; assoc. prof. CHEM, Wittenberg Col, 47-49, PROF, 49-51; Carthage Col, 51-52; WITTENBERG UNIV, 52-, chmn. dept, 60-68. Nat. Sci. Found. faculty fel, Cornell Univ, 58-59 & King's Col, Univ. London, 68-69. Am. Chem. Soc. Colloids; chemical analysis of photographic developers; non-aqueous solvents; acidity in heavy water. Address: Dept. of Chemistry, Wittenberg University, Springfield, OH 45501.

GLASS, ALASTAIR MALCOLM, b. Harrogate, Eng, Aug. 2, 40; m. 64; c. 2. SOLID STATE PHYSICS. B.Sc, London, 61; Can. Commonwealth scholar, British Columbia, 61-64, Ph.D.(solid state physics), 64. Atomic Energy Res. Estab. res. fel. solid state physics, Kings Col, Univ. London, 64-67; MEM. TECH. STAFF, BELL TEL. LABS, 67- Stress-optical properties of germanium; optical properties of defects in magnesium oxide; optical and electrical measurements on ferroelectrics. Address: Bell Telephone Labs, Murray Hill, NJ 07974.

GLASS, ALEXANDER J(ACOB), b. Pittsfield Twp, N.Y, Jan. 4, 33; m. 59; c. 3. ATOMIC PHYSICS. B.S, Rensselaer Polytech, 54; M.S, Yale, 55, Stirling fel, 61-62, Ph.D.(physics), 63. Res. staff mem. PHYSICS, Res. Inst. Adv. Study, Md, 57-58; res. assoc, Yale, 63-64; res. staff mem, Inst. Defense Anal, 64-66; chief laser physics br, Naval Res. Lab, 66-68; PROF. ELEC. ENG, WAYNE STATE UNIV, 68-, CHMN. DEPT, 70-, MEM. RES. INST. ENG. SCI, 68- U.S.A, 54-57, Res, 57-62, Capt. AAAS; Am. Phys. Soc. Non-linear optics; computer applications to atomic calculations; numerical analysis; laser physics. Address: Dept. of Electrical Engineering, College of Engineering, Wayne State University, Detroit, MI 48202.

GLASS, ARTHUR W(ARREN), b. Flint, Mich, Mar. 14, 21; m. 50; c. 4. GENETICS. A.B, Gustavus Adolphus Col, 43; M.A, Minnesota, 48, Ph.D. 54. Assoc. prof. BIOL, GUSTAVUS ADOLPHUS COL, 50-59, PROF, 59-, HEAD DEPT, 50- Marine C, 44-46, 1st Lt. Am. Soc. Human Genetics; Soc. Study Evolution. Population genetics. Address: Dept. of Biology, Gustavus Adolphus College, St. Peter, MN 56082.

GLASS, BILLY PRICE, b. Memphis, Tenn, Sept. 9, 40; m. 66; c. 2. MARINE GEOLOGY. B.S, Tennessee, 63; Ford Found. fel, Columbia, 63-64, Ph.D.(marine geol), 68. Res. asst. marine geol, Lamont Geol. Observ, 65-67; res. scientist, Goddard Space Flight Ctr, U.S. Army Corps Engrs, 68-70, Nat. Res. Coun. resident res. assoc, 70; ASST. PROF. GEOL, UNIV. DEL, 71- Prin. investr. Apollo 12 & 14 lunar samples. Nininger Meteorite Award, 66-67. C.Eng, U.S.A.R, 68-, Capt. AAAS; Am. Geophys. Union; Meteoritical Soc; Soc. Econ. Paleont. & Mineral. Correlation and dating of marine sediments with paleomagnetics; microtektites; lunar geology. Address: 387 Hobart Dr, Newark, DE 19711.

GLASS, BRYAN P(ETTIGREW), b. Mandeville, La, Aug. 21, 19; m. 46; c. 2. MAMMALOGY. A.B, Baylor, 40; M.S, Agr. & Mech. Col Tex, 46; Ph.D, Okla. Agr. & Mech. Col, 52. Asst. ZOOL, Agr. & Mech. Col. Tex, 40-42, 45-46; asst. prof, OKLA. STATE UNIV, 46-52, assoc. prof, 53-61, PROF, 61-, DIR. MUS, 66- U.S.A.A.F, 42-45. Am. Soc. Ichthyol. & Herpet; Am. Soc. Mammal.(exec. secy-treas). Systematics of Oklahoma rodents; ecology of muskrats in Oklahoma; biology; taxonomy; migration of bats; Ethiopian mammals. Address: Oklahoma State University Museum, Stillwater, OK 74074.

GLASS, CARTER M, b. Marshall, Tex, Feb. 18, 35; m. 58; c. 2. AUTOMATIC CONTROL SYSTEMS, COMPUTER SCIENCE. B.S, U.S. Naval Acad, 57; M.S, U.S. Air Force Inst. Technol, 62; Ph.D.(elec. eng), Univ. Denver, 68. U.S. AIR FORCE, 58-, maintenance off. guided missiles, Eglin AFB, Fla, 58-60; instr. math, U.S. Air Force Acad, 62-65, asst. prof, 65-66, elec. eng, 66-67, assoc. prof, 68-69; prof. avionics eng. & head dept, Pakistan Air Force Col. Aeronaut. Eng, 69-71; ASSOC. PROF. ELEC. ENG, U.S. AIR FORCE ACAD, 71- Prof. engr, State of Colo, 66- U.S.A.F, 58-, Maj; Commendation Medal, 69. Sr. mem. Inst. Elec. & Electronics Eng. Analysis and synthesis of linear time varying systems; analysis of electrical circuits using digital and analog computers. Address: 1394 Shrider Rd, Colorado Springs, CO 80907.

GLASS, C(OY) M(ONTGOMERY), b. Sparrows Point, Md, Oct. 9, 28; m. 53; c. 4. METALLURGY. B.E, Hopkins, 49, M.A, 51, Ph.D, 55, Dr. Univ, 60. Asst. group dir. electrochem, Catalyst Res. Corp, 50-53; asst. prof. metall, Air Force Inst. Tech, 54-56; group leader, BALLISTIC RES. LAB, ABERDEEN PROVING GROUND, 56-63, chief solid mech. br, 63-68, CHIEF MAT. APPLN. GROUP, 69- Lectr, Johns Hopkins Univ, 59-68, vis. lectr, 68-69, chief mat. appln. group, 69- U.S.A.F.R, 54-56, Capt. AAAS; Am. Soc. Metals; Am. Inst. Mining, Metall. & Petrol. Eng. Schaped charge research; hypervelocity impact phenomena; physical metallurgy with emphasis on the high velocity deformation of metals. Address: Materials Application Group, Ballistics Research Lab, Aberdeen Proving Ground, MD 21005.

GLASS, CURTIS A, b. Sandusky, Ill, Nov. 17, 18; m. 42. ORGANIC & PHYSICAL CHEMISTRY. B.S, Bradley, 52; Illinois, Urbana, 65-66. Technician chem, NORTH. REGIONAL LAB, U.S. DEPT. AGR, 49-52, CHEMIST, 52- Am. Chem. Soc; Am. Oil Chemist's Soc; Soc. Appl. Spectros. Infrared and nuclear magnetic resonance spectroscopy applied to structural problems in lipids and carbohydrates. Address: Northern Regional Lab, U.S. Department of Agriculture, 1815 N. University Ave, Peoria, IL 61604.

GLASS, D(OUGLAS) G(ORDON), b. Hamilton, Ont, June 13, 23. ANALYTICAL CHEMISTRY. B.Sc, McMaster, 45. Chemist, Can. Packers Ltd, 45-48; tech. asst, CONNAUGHT MED. RES. LABS, Toronto, 48-51, sr. res. asst, 51-62, res. assoc, WILLOWDALE, 62-71, RES. MEM, 71- Fel. AAAS; Am. Chem. Soc; Spectros. Soc. Can; Can. Biochem. Soc; Chem. Inst. Can; N.Y. Acad. Sci. Heparin, penicillin; microbial enzymes; applications of infrared spectroscopy; chemical analytical methods. Address: 1260 King St. E, Hamilton 24, Ont, Can.

GLASS, DUDLEY B(REWER), b. Shawnee, Okla, Apr. 19, 12; m. 45; c. 2. ORGANIC CHEMISTRY. A.B, Georgetown Col, 35; univ. fel, Illinois, 38-39, Ph.D.(org. chem), 39. Asst. chem, Illinois, 35-38; res. chemist, EASTMAN KODAK CO, 39-46, group leader, 46-50, supvr, 50-58, sci. personnel asst, 58-61, MGR. sci. recruitment, 61-65, DOCTORAL RECRUITMENT, 65- Fel. AAAS; Am. Chem. Soc; Soc. Photog. Sci. & Eng. Organic chemistry of color photography; optical activity; polymerization and synthetic chemistry; personnel. Address: Eastman Kodak Co, 343 State St, Rochester, NY 14650.

GLASS, EDWARD H(ADLEY), b. Waltham, Mass, Feb. 19, 17; m. 42; c. 2. ENTOMOLOGY. B.S, Mass. State Col, 38; fel, Va. Polytech, 38-40, M.S, 40; Ph.D.(entomol), Ohio State, 43. Asst. entomologist, exp. sta, Va. Polytech, 40-41; entomologist, Am. Cyanamid Co, N.Y, 43-48; assoc. prof. ENTOMOL, N.Y. STATE AGR. EXP. STA, 48-55, PROF, 55-, HEAD DEPT, 69- Vis. prof, Univ. Philippines, 66-67. Fel. AAAS; Entom. Soc. Am. Biology and control of apple orchard insect pests; insect photoperiodism; tropical rice insects and their control; use of sex pheromones for insect detection and control. Address: Dept. of Entomology, New York State Agricultural Experiment Station, Geneva, NY 14456.

GLASS, EDWARD M(AURICE), b. Providence, R.I, Mar. 25, 17; m. 66; c. 1. CHEMISTRY. B.S, Rhode Island, 39; fel, Va. Polytech, 39-40, M.S, 40. Prof. asst, soils conserv. serv, U.S. Dept. Agr, 40-41; aircraft maintenance supvr, air mat. command, U.S. Air Force, 41-45, mem. tech. staff, mat. lab, 45-57, tech. dir, 57-62, spec. asst. to asst. secy. Air Force, res. & develop, 62-63; spec. asst. to dep. dir. res. & tech, off. dir, DEFENSE RES. & ENG, OFF. SECY. DEFENSE, 63-65, ASST. DIR. LAB. MGT, 65- Mem. mat. adv. bd, Nat. Acad. Sci, 57-62; comt. on mat, NASA, 60-62. U.S.A.A.F, 45-46. AAAS; Am. Soc. Lubrication Eng; N.Y. Acad. Sci; Sci. Res. Soc. Am; Am. Soc. Test. & Mat; Soc. Automotive Eng; Soc. Aerospace Mat. & Process Eng. Aeronautical and aerospace materials. Address: P.O. Box 1463, Silver Spring, MD 20902.

GLASS, GEORGE, b. Vienna, Austria, June 15, 36; U.S. citizen; m. 64; c. 2. HIGH ENERGY PHYSICS. S.B, Mass. Inst. Tech, 59, Ph.D.(physics), 64. Mem. res. staff PHYSICS, Mass. Inst. Technol, 64-65; res. assoc, Northeast. Univ, 65-66; ASST. PROF, UNIV. WASH, 66- Am. Phys. Soc; Am. Asn. Physics Teachers. High energy nuclear physics; particles; electronics; light. Address: 138 N.E. 53rd St, Seattle, WA 98105.

GLASS, GEORGE B. JERZY, b. Warsaw, Poland, Jan. 9, 03; nat; m. 33; c. 2. GASTROENTEROLOGY. M.D, Univ. Warsaw, 27. Intern, Hosp. Wolski, Warsaw, 27-28, resident, 28-29; fel, Krankenhaus am Urban, Berlin, Ger, 30-31; med. div, Allgemeines Hosp, Univ. Vienna, 31-32; Hosp. Hotel Dieu, Paris, France, 32-33; asst. physician, Hosp. Child Jesus, 33-38; asst. clin. prof. med, NEW YORK MED. COL, METROP. MED. CTR, 48-51, assoc. clin. prof, 51-54, assoc. prof, 54-62, PROF. MED. & DIR. GASTROENTEROL. LAB, 62-, chief sect. gastroenterol, 61-69. Assoc. physician, Metrop. Hosp, N.Y.C, 50-61, vis. physician, 62-; Bird S. Coler Mem. Hosp, 52-; assoc. attend. physician, Flower & Fifth Ave. Hosps, 54-61, attend. physician, 62-; assoc. clinician, Sloan-Kettering Inst, 60-66; assoc. vis. physician, James Ewing Hosp, 61-66; consult. gastroenterol, N.Y. Infirmary, 67-; assoc. consult, Mem. Hosp. Dipl, Am. Bd. Internal Med. Polish Army, 42-45. Asn. Am. Physicians; Am. Fedn. Clin. Res; Am. Physiol. Soc; Am. Gastroenterol. Asn; Soc. Exp. Biol. & Med; Int. Soc. Internal Med; Int. Soc. Hemat; Am. Col. Physicians; Am. Inst. Nutrit; Am. Soc. Hemat. Physiology and biochemistry of the stomach; intrinsic factor and vitamin B_{12} metabolism; chemistry and biological significance of large molecular substances in gastric juice; immunology of atrophic gastritis and pernicious anemia. Address: 60 Sutton Pl. S, New York, NY 10022.

GLASS, GRAHAM PERCY, b. Birmingham, Eng, July 21, 38; m. 65. PHYSICAL CHEMISTRY. B.Sc, Birmingham, 59; Ph.D.(chem), Cambridge, 63. Fel. CHEM, Harvard, 63-65; lectr, Essex, 65-67; ASST. PROF, RICE UNIV, 67- Am. Phys. Soc; Am. Chem. Soc. Reaction kinetics; shock tube chemistry. Address: Dept. of Chemistry, Rice University, Houston, TX 77001.

GLASS, HERBERT D(AVID), b. New York, N.Y, Oct. 14, 15; m. 44; c. 2. MINERALOGY. B.A, N.Y. Univ, 37; M.A, Columbia, 47, Ph.D.(geol), 51. GEOLOGIST, STATE GEOL. SURV, ILL, 48- U.S.A, 41-45, Capt. Mineral Soc. Am; Geol. Soc. Am; Mineral. Soc. Gt. Brit. & Ireland. Clay mineralogy and its application to stratigraphic correlation, interpretation and classification. Address: Illinois State Geological Survey, Urbana, IL 61801.

GLASS, H(IRAM) BENTLEY, b. Laichowfu, Shantung, China, Jan. 17, 06; m. 34; c. 2. GENETICS. A.B, Baylor, 26, fel, 28-29, M.A, 29, LL.D, 58; Ph.D.(genetics), Texas, 32; hon. Sc.D, Washington Col.(Md), 57; Sc.D, Western Reserve, 62. Teacher, pub. sch, Tex, 26-28; fel. genetics, Nat. Res. Coun, Univ. Oslo, Kaiser-Wilhelm Inst. & Missouri, 32-34; instr. zool, Stephens Col, 34-38; asst. prof. biol, Goucher Col, 38-42, assoc. prof, 42-46, prof, 46-48; assoc. prof, Hopkins, 48-52, prof, 52-65; DISTINGUISHED PROF. BIOL. & ACAD. V.PRES, STATE UNIV. N.Y. STONY BROOK, 65- Res. assoc, Teachers Col, Columbia, 36-37; Baltimore Rh Blood Typing Lab, 47-52; lectr, Davis Washington Mitchel, Tulane, 58; Stoneburner, Virginia Med. Col, 63; John Calvin McNair, North Carolina, 63. Consult, U.S. Dept. State, Ger, 50-51. Asst. ed, Quart. Rev. Biol, 44-48, assoc. ed, 49-57, ed, 58-; biol. ed, Houghton Mifflin Co, 46-; mem. ed. bd, Sci. & Sci. Monthly, 48-58, acting ed, 53; ed, McCollum-Pratt Symposia, 49-; dir. surv. biol. abstracting, Biol. Abstracts, 52-54, mem. bd. trustees, 54-60, pres, 58-60; ed, Surv. Biol. Progress, 54-62. Mem. governing bd, Inst. Biol. Sci, 51-53, pres, 54-56, chmn, biol. sci. curriculum study, 59-; mem. bd. sch. comnrs, Baltimore, Md, 54-58; adv. comt. biol. & med, Atomic Energy Comn, 55-63; chmn, 62-63; comt. genetic effects of atomic radiation, Nat. Acad. Sci, 55-64; democratic adv. coun. comt. sci. & tech, 59-60; Continuing Comt. Conf. Sci. & World Affairs, 58-64; Governor's Adv. Comt. Nuclear Energy, Md, 59- Del, Int. Union Biol. Scis, 53, 55. Nat. Acad. Sci; AAAS.(v.pres. & chmn. sect. F, 56, mem. bd. dirs, 59-66); Genetics Soc. Am.(v.pres, 60); Am. Soc. Zool; Am. Soc. Nat.(secy, 50-53, pres, 65); Am. Eugenics Soc; Hist. Sci. Soc; Am. Asn. Phys. Anthrop; Soc. Study Evolution; Am. Soc. Human Genetics; Am. Genetic Asn; Am. Asn. Univ. Prof.(pres, 58-60); Coun. Biol. Ed.(chmn, 57-59); Am. Acad. Arts & Sci; Am. Philos. Soc. Genetics of Drosophila; human genetics; history of genetics; suppressor genes; Rh Blood types. Address: State University of New York at Stony Brook, Stony Brook, NY 21218.

GLASS, HOWARD G(EORGE), b. Chicago, Ill, May 25, 09; m. 42; c. 2. PHARMACOLOGY. B.S, Illinois, 32; M.S, Northwestern, 35; Ph.D.(pharmacol), Chicago, 42; M.D, Marquette, 49. Chemist, Bauer & Black, Ill, 35-38; res. assoc, toxicity lab, Off. Sci. Res. & Develop, Chicago, 41-44; instr. pharmacol, sch. med, Oklahoma, 44-46; Marquette, 46-48; pharmacologist, Armour Labs, Ill, 49-53; Miles-Ames Res. Lab, Ind, 53-62; ASST. DIR, AM. MED. ASN, 62- Soc. Pharmacol. & Exp. Therapeut; Soc. Exp. Biol. & Med. Anoxia; respiratory physiology; toxicology of drugs; sedatives; clinical pharmacology of enzymes; antihypertensives; diuretics; antineoplastic agents. Address: Dept. of Drugs, American Medical Association, 535 N. Dearborn St, Chicago, IL 60610.

GLASS, I(RVINE) I(SRAEL), b. Poland, Feb. 23, 18; nat. Can; m. 42; c. 3. AEROSPACE ENGINEERING. B.A.Sc, Toronto, 47, M.A.Sc, 48, Ph.D.(aerophysics), 50; Imp. Col, London, 57-58. Aeronaut. engr, Canadair Ltd, Que, 46; Can. Car & Foundry, 47; A.V. Roe, Ont, 48; instr. aeronaut. eng, UNIV. TORONTO, 48-49, res. assoc. AEROPHYSICS, inst. aerophysics, 50-54, asst. prof, 54-56, assoc. prof, 56-60, PROF, INST. FOR AEROSPACE STUDIES, 60-, ASST. DIR, 68-, chmn. dept. aerospace eng. sci, grad. studies, 61-66. Aerodynamicist, Can. Armament Res. & Develop. Estab, Que, 52; lectr, U.S.S.R. Acad. Sci, Moscow Univ, summer 61; mem. assoc. comt, space res, Nat. Res. Coun. Can, 62-65, standing subcomt. on high speed flow, 67-, assoc. comt. aerodynamics, 68-71; res. adv. comt. on fluid mech, NASA, 65-70; consult, Am. & Can. indust. R.C.A.F, 42-45, Flight Lt. Fel. AAAS; Am. Phys. Soc; assoc. fel. Am. Inst. Aeronaut. & Astronaut; fel. Can. Aeronaut. & Space Inst. Hypersonic gasdynamics; aerophysics; shock-wave phenomena; sonic boom. Address: Institute for Aerospace Studies, University of Toronto, Toronto 5, Ont, Can.

GLASS, JAMES CLIFFORD, b. Los Angeles, Calif, Sept. 20, 37; m. 59; c. 3. NUCLEAR PHYSICS. B.A, California, Berkeley, 60; M.S, San Fernando Valley State Col, 65; Nat. Defense Ed. Act fel, Nevada, 65-68, Ph.D.(physics), 68. Assoc. physicist, Proj. Sherwood, Lawrence Radiation Lab, California, 60-61; physicist, Rocketdyne, N.Am. Aviation, Inc, 61-64; asst. prof. PHYSICS, N.DAK. STATE UNIV, 68-70, ASSOC. PROF, 70- Consult, Electro-Optical Systs, Inc, Xerox Corp, 64, sr. physicist, summer 64. Am. Asn. Physics Teachers; Am. Phys. Soc. Plasma propulsion; low energy nuclear physics especially in gamma ray spectroscopy; measurement of internal fields of materials by gamma-gamma directional correlations. Address: Dept. of Physics, North Dakota State University, Fargo, ND 58102.

GLASS, JOHN R(ICHARD), b. Lancaster, Pa, Aug. 31, 17; m. 40; c. 2. ANALYTICAL CHEMISTRY. B.S, Elizabethtown Col, 38; Polytech. Inst. Brooklyn, 39-44. Res. chemist water purification, Wallace & Tiernan Co, 39-45; sr. res. chemist, ANAL. RES, MOBIL OIL CORP, 45-61, RES. ASSOC, 61- John D. Goodell award, Am. Water Works Asn, 43. Am. Chem. Soc. Colorimetric and trace metal analysis; analytical instruments. Address: Research Lab, Mobil Oil Corp, Paulsboro, NJ 08066.

GLASS, J(OSEPH) EDWARD, b. Castleberry, Ala, Sept. 18, 37; m. 57; c. 3. PHYSICAL ORGANIC CHEMISTRY. B.S, La. State Univ, 59; Ph.D.(org. chem), Purdue Univ, 64. Res. chemist, UNION CARBIDE CORP, 64-66, proj. scientist, 66-69, RES. SCIENTIST, 69- Am. Chem. Soc. Polymer chemistry with emphasis on free radical kinetics and surface and colloidal properties of aqueous dispersions. Address: Union Carbide Corp, P.O. Box 8361, South Charleston, WV 25303.

GLASS, KING I(RWIN), b. Sweetwater, Tex, Mar. 11, 17; m. 44; c. 3. CHEMICAL ENGINEERING. B.S, Tex. Tech. Col, 39, M.S, 41; fel, Texas, 41-45, Ph.D.(chem. eng), 45. Apprentice engr, Phillips Petrol. Co, Okla, 41; res. chem. engr, bur. indust. chem, Tex, 45-47; assoc. engr, Elliot Co, Pa, 47-48; group leader, Lion Oil Co. Div, Monsanto Chem. Co, 49-57, SR. GROUP LEADER, MONSANTO CO, 57- Am. Chem. Soc; Am. Inst. Chem. Eng. Development of carbon black; electric discharge production of acetylene from methane; products from acetylene; olefin processing; chemical process development; pilot planting; cost estimation. Address: Monsanto Co, 800 N. Lindbergh Blvd, St. Louis, MO 63166.

GLASS, LAUREL E(LLEN), b. Selma, Calif, Oct. 1, 23. DEVELOPMENTAL BIOLOGY, ANATOMY. B.A, California, 51; Nat. Sci. Found. fel, Duke, 56-57, Ph.D.(exp. embryol), 58. Asst. zool, Duke, 53-56; res. assoc, path. res. lab, Vet. Admin. Hosp, Durham, N.C, 57-58; instr. ANAT, Duke, 58; SCH. MED, UNIV. CALIF, SAN FRANCISCO, 58-61, asst. prof, 61-66, ASSOC. PROF, 66- Am. Asn. Anat; Am. Soc. Cell Biol; Am. Soc. Zool; Soc. Develop. Biol; N.Y. Acad. Sci; Soc. Study Reproduction. Synthesis of biologically specific molecules during mammalian oogenesis and early development; macromolecular transfer between maternal body and oocyte or embryo; effects of x-irradiation on mammalian oogenesis and development. Address: Dept. of Anatomy, School of Medicine, University of California, San Francisco, CA 94122.

GLASS, NEEL W(ARREN), b. The Dalles, Ore, May 24, 24; m. 48; c. 2. NUCLEAR PHYSICS. B.S, Washington (Seattle), 48; M.A, California, Los Angeles, 50, Ph.D.(physics), 54. Physicist reactor tech, Hanford works div, Gen. Elec. Co, 48-49; res. engr. missiles, Hughes Aircraft Co, 51; mem. staff, LOS ALAMOS SCI. LAB, UNIV. CALIF, 54-57, alternate group leader, 57-63, GROUP LEADER, 63- U.S.A.A.F, 42-45. Am. Phys. Soc; Am. Geophys. Union. Low energy experimental nuclear physics among the lighter elements; photomultiplier and image intensifier development; nuclear weapons and testing. Address: 143 Monte Rey Dr. S, Los Alamos, NM 87544.

GLASS, PEGGY WELLS, b. Louisville, Ky. ANALYTICAL CHEMISTRY. B.S, Southwest Tex. State Univ, 62; Ph.D.(chem), Univ. Tex. Austin, 69. Chemist, Tracor Inc, 62-63; LAB. DIR. WATER QUAL, FORREST & COTTON INC, 62- Am. Chem. Soc; Water Pollution Control Fedn. Analytical methods for platinum metals; water quality evaluation and treatment methods. Address; 3607 Manor Rd, Austin, TX 78723.

GLASS, RICHARD STEVEN, b. N.Y.C, Mar. 5, 43; m. 70. ORGANIC CHEMISTRY. B.A, N.Y. Univ, 63; Ph.D.(chem), Harvard, 67. Nat. Insts. Health fel, Stanford Univ, 66-67; sr. res. chemist org. chem, Hoffmann La Roche, Inc, 67-70; ASST. PROF. CHEM, UNIV. ARIZ, 70- Am. Chem. Soc; The Chem. Soc. Total synthesis of natural products; synthetic methods; organosulfur chemistry; biorganic mechanisms. Address: Dept. of Chemistry, University of Arizona, Tucson, AZ 85721.

GLASS, ROBERT J(OHN), b. Pittsburgh, Pa, Aug. 3, 29; m. 53; c. 3. MECHANICAL & AEROSPACE ENGINEERING, MATHEMATICS. B.S, Yale, 52; Point Park Col, 54; George Washington, 57-60; Ford Found. fel, Maryland, 62-64, Ph.D.(mech. & aerospace eng, math), 66. Develop. engr, Homestead Industs, Inc, 52-53, asst. chief engr, 53-55; mem. faculty eng, U.S. Naval Acad, 57-60; Maryland, 60-66; Massachusetts, 66-67; PROF. MECH. ENG. & ASST. DEAN ENG, OHIO NORTH. UNIV, 67- Consult, Naval Ord. Lab, Md, 60-62, Naval Res. Lab, D.C, 66-67; aerospace div, Westinghouse Elec. Corp, 67-68. Mem, Creative Ed. Found. U.S.N, 55-60, Lt. AAAS; Soc. Indust. & Appl. Math; Soc. Gen. Systs. Res; Am. Soc. Mech. Eng. Dynamical system response; fast-breeder nuclear reactor response; physics of fluids; aeroelasticity; hydroelasticity; nonlinear differential equations; systems analysis and decision theory; research in creative thinking education. Address: 501 N. Main St, Ada, OH 45810.

GLASS, ROBERT LORING, b. Cambridge, Mass, June 15, 21; m. 44; c. 3. EPIDEMIOLOGY, DENTISTRY. S.B, Harvard, 43, M.P.H, 59, Dr.P.H, 64; D.M.D, Tufts, 46. Instr. clin. dent, Tufts, 46-49, asst. prof, 49-57, assoc. prof. dent, 57-60, prof, 60-64, pub. health, 60-61; ASSOC. PROF. DENT, HARVARD SCH. DENT. MED. & STAFF MEM, FORSYTH DENT. CENTER, 64- Consult, Vet. Admin, 48-49, 67-; indust. consult, 57-; consult, eng. sch, Dartmouth Col, 65-66; Mass. Dept. Pub. Health, 67-; Nat. Inst. Dent. Res. Dent.C, 53-55, Capt. Fel. AAAS; fel. Am. Pub. Health Asn; Am.

Statist. Asn; Int. Asn. Dent. Res. Epidemiology; preventive dentistry; oral diagnosis; statistics; clinical research. Address: 140 The Fenway, Boston, MA 02115.

GLASS, ROBERT L(OUIS), b. Chicago, Ill, May 15, 23; m. 46; c. 4. BIOCHEMISTRY. B.S, Illinois, 50; M.S, Minnesota, 54, Ph.D.(agr. biochem), 56. Instr, AGR. BIOCHEM, UNIV. MINN, ST. PAUL, 56, asst. prof, 56-61, ASSOC. PROF, 61- U.S.N, 42-45. Am. Chem. Soc. Lipid chemistry and biochemistry. Address: Dept. of Biochemistry, University of Minnesota, St. Paul, MN 55101.

GLASS, WERNER, b. Berlin, Ger, May 27, 27; U.S. citizen; m. 52; c. 3. CHEMICAL ENGINEERING. B.Ch.E, Syracuse Univ, 50; S.M, Mass. Inst. Technol, 51, Sc.D.(chem. eng), 56. Res. engr, Esso Res. & Eng. Co, Standard Oil Co.(N.J), 56-58, group head, 58-59, sr. engr, 59-63; asst. dir. res, Ionics, Inc, 63-64, dep. dir. res, 64-67; sr. engr, Esso RES. & ENG. CO, STANDARD OIL CO.(N.J), 67-68, eng. assoc, 68-71, SR. STAFF ADV, 71- Am. Inst. Chem. Eng. Fluidization; petroleum processing; electrodialysis; water and air pollution control. Address: Esso Research & Engineering Co, Standard Oil Co.(N.J), P.O. Box 215, Linden, NJ 07036.

GLASS, WILLIAM A, b. Winfield, Kans, Dec. 9, 31; m. 56; c. 2. RADIOLOGICAL PHYSICS. B.A, Southwest. Col, 53; M.A. & M.S, Kansas, 58, Nat. Sci. Found. fel, 62-63. Asst. prof. physics, Kans. State Teachers Col, 58-62; sr. res. scientist, radiol. physics, Pac. Northwest Labs, Battelle Mem. Inst, 63-69; RES. COLLAB, BROOKHAVEN NAT. LAB, 69- Clin. lectr, Washington (Seattle), 64-69. Mil. Intel, U.S.A, 53-56. AAAS; Am. Phys. Soc; Radiation Res. Soc. Interaction of charged particles in matter; radiation dosimetry; microdosimetry; ionization phenomena. Address: Brookhaven National Lab, 17 Cornell Ave, Upton, NY 11973.

GLASSBRENNER, CHARLES J, b. Albany, N.Y, Apr. 9, 28; m. 59; c. 3. PHYSICS. B.S, St. Bernardine of Siena Col, 50, M.S, 56; Ph.D.(physics), Univ. Conn, 63. Elec. engr, N.Y. State Architects Off, 51-55; physicist, Watervliet Arsenal, N.Y, 56-57; asst. physics, Univ. Conn, 57-60; physicist, res. lab. & Knolls Atomic Power Lab, Gen. Elec. Co, 60-64; sr. physicist, Controls for Radiation, Inc, Mass, 64-66; Ion Physics Corp, 66-67; ASSOC. PROF. PHYSICS, WORCESTER STATE COL, 67- Am. Phys. Soc. NASA-Am. Soc. Eng. Educ. summer faculty fel, NASA-Elec. Res. Ctr, Mass, 68 & 69; staff appointment, Lincoln Lab, Mass. Inst. Technol, summers 70 & 71. Radiation effects on solids; solid state physics; thermal conductivity; mechanical strength of solids; thermodynamics. Address: Dept. of Physics, Worcester State College, Worcester, MA 01602.

GLASSBROOK, C(LARENCE) I, b. Portland, Ore, Dec. 15, 13; m. 37; c. 1. PHYSICAL CHEMISTRY. B.S, Stanford, 35, M.S, 36. Asst. supt, Am. Bitumuls & Asphalt Co, 37-41; supvr, Westvaco Chlorine Prod. Co, 41-44; phys. chemist, res. lab, Socony Mobil Oil Co, 44-49; instrument specialist, Stanford Res. Inst, 49-56; develop. assoc, ETHYL CORP, 56-67, SR. DEVELOP. ASSOC, 67- Sr. mem. Instrument Soc. Am. Analytical instruments for plant use. Address: Ethyl Corp, P.O. Box 341, Baton Rouge, LA 70821.

GLASSER, ARTHUR C(HARLES), b. Pittsburgh, Pa, June 19, 21; m. 44; c. 3. PHARMACEUTICAL CHEMISTRY. B.S, Duquesne, 49; Ph.D.(pharm), Ohio State, 53. Asst. PHARMACEUT. CHEM, OHIO STATE, 50-51; assoc. prof, Kentucky, 53-59, prof. & head dept, 59-70, acting dean, col. pharm, 64-67, asst. dean admin, 67-70; DEAN COL. PHARM, UNIV. CINCINNATI, 70- U.S.N, 42-45. Am. Chem. Soc; Am. Pharmaceut. Asn. Plant chemistry; drug analysis. Address: 661 Allencrest Ct, Cincinnati, OH 45231.

GLASSER, JAY H(OWARD), b. New Haven, Conn, May 6, 35; m. 57; c. 4. BIOSTATISTICS. B.S, Connecticut, 57; M.Sc, Columbia, 60; Ph.D.(exp. statist), N.C. State, 67. Asst. statistician, New York Dept. Health, 58-59; instr. BIOSTATIST, SCH. PUB. HEALTH, North Carolina, 64-67, asst. prof, 67-69; ASSOC. PROF, UNIV. TEX, HOUSTON, 69- Am. Statist. Asn; Biomet. Soc. Stochastic models in the health sciences. Address: School of Public Health, University of Texas at Houston, P.O. Box 20186, Astrodome Station, Houston, TX 77025.

GLASSER, JULIAN, b. Chicago, Ill, May 23, 12; m. 42; c. 2. PHYSICAL CHEMISTRY. B.S, Illinois, 33, fel. & M.S, 35; fel. & Ph.D.(phys. chem), Pa. State, 39. Asst, Illinois, 34; Pa. State, 35-38; res. engr, Battelle Mem. Inst, 38-42; chief chemist & chief metallurgist, aluminum div, Olin Industs, Inc, Wash, 42-45; dir. res, Gen. Abrasive Co, N.Y, 45-47; supvr. & res. engr, Armour Res. Found, Ill, 47-53; tech. dir, Cramet, Inc, Tenn, 53-58; consult, 58-60; PRES, CHEM. & METALL. RES, INC, 60- Vis. prof, Vanderbilt, 58-59. Consult. to head metall. br, Navy Dept, Off. Naval Res, D.C, 52-53; consult. & staff metallurgist, mat. adv. bd, Nat. Res. Coun, 51-53, 58-61. Am. Chem. Soc; Am. Soc. Metals; Electrochem. Soc; Am. Inst. Mining, Metall. & Petrol. Eng; Am. Ceramics Soc; Am. Soc. Nondestructive Test. Extractive metallurgy; refractory metals; light metals; high temperature materials; vacuum and high temperature metallurgy; electrothermics; electrochemistry; electrometallurgy. Address: Chemical & Metallurgical Research, Inc, Professional Bldg, Chattanooga, TN 37402.

GLASSER, L(EO) G(EORGE), b. Wilkes-Barre, Pa, July 20, 16; m. 41; c. 3. ASTROPHYSICS, PHYSICS. A.B, Cornell, 38, M.A, 40; Nat. Univ. Panama, 41-42. Asst, Eastman Kodak Co, N.Y, 38; Nat. Geog. Soc, Cornell, 38-40; physicist, U.S. Navy Bur. Ord, Wash, D.C, 40-44; sr. physicist, Tenn. Eastman Corp, Oak Ridge, 44-45; res. engr. & supvr, eng. res. lab, E.I. DU PONT DE NEMOURS & CO, 45-55, res. mgr, 56-59, elec. res, mech. develop. lab, 59-60, asst. dir. eng. res. lab, 60-63, dir. eng. physics lab, 63-70, MGR. DIV. PROGS, 70- Dir, Mt. Cuba Astron. Observ. AAAS; Optical Soc. Am; Sci. Res. Soc. Am; Am. Astron. Soc. Development and application of colorimetric instruments and optical and other analytical instruments for process control; light measurement; refractometry; ultraviolet and infrared spectrophotometry. Address: Engineering Research & Development Division, Engineering Dept, E.I. du Pont de Nemours & Co, Wilmington, DE 19898.

GLASSER, M. LAWRENCE, b. Crookston, Minn, Oct. 5, 33; m. 56; c. 4. SOLID STATE PHYSICS, MATHEMATICS. B.A, Chicago, 53, fel. & M.S, 55; Wisconsin, 55-56; M.S, Miami (Fla), 57; Ph.D.(physics), Carnegie Inst. Tech, 62. Instr. physics, Miami (Fla), 57-58; sr. physicist, Battelle Mem. Inst, 62-64; asst. prof. physics, Univ. Wis, 64-66; sr. physicist, BATTELLE MEM. INST, 66-67, STAFF SCIENTIST, 67-, consult, 64. Am. Phys. Soc; Math. Asn. Am; Soc. Indust. & Appl. Math. Theoretical solid state physics; classical mathematical analysis. Address: Battelle Memorial Institute, 505 King Ave, Columbus, OH 43201.

GLASSER, RALPH F(REDERICK), b. Kitchener, Ont, Mar. 8, 20; U.S. citizen; m. 51; c. 1. ORGANIC CHEMISTRY, TOXICOLOGY. B.S.A, Univ. Toronto, 43; Ph.D.(insecticidal chem. & toxicol), Cornell Univ, 56. Chemist & bacteriologist, Hendry Connell Res. Found, 46-50; res. chemist, Can. Dept. Agr, 50-52; asst. entom, Cornell Univ, 52-56; tech. rep, AGR. CHEM. DIV, Shell Chem. Co, 56-60, sr. tech. salesman, 60-61, sales supvr, 61-63, sr. technologist, sales develop. dept, 63-64, coord. & spec. asst. to gen. mgr. legis. matters, 64-65, div. resp, 65-66, mgr. tech. coord. & registr, 66-68, mgr. pesticide regulation dept, 68-69, HEAD REGULATORY AFFAIRS DIV, SHELL INT. CHEM. CO, LTD, 69- R.C.A.M.C, 43-46, S/Sgt. Am. Chem. Soc; fel. Am. Inst. Chem. Pesticide legislation and regulation; chemistry and toxicology of pesticides and other chemicals; ecology; environmental and food residues. Address: Shell International Chemical Co, Ltd, Shell Centre, London SE1 7PGP, England.

GLASSER, RICHARD L(EE), b. Baltimore, Md, March 26, 27; m. 50; c. 3. NEUROBIOLOGY. A.B, Hopkins, 49; John F.B. Weaver fel, Maryland, 53-57, Ph.D.(physiol), 57. Instr. PHYSIOL, SCH. MED, UNIV. N.C, CHAPEL HILL, 57-59, asst. prof, 59-65, ASSOC. PROF, 65- Vis. asst. prof, sch. med, Duke, 59-61. U.S.N, 45-46. AAAS; Am. Physiol. Soc. Neurophysiology; neural control of respiration; neural control of cardiovascular activity; neural control of sweat gland activity; memory consolidation mechanisms. Address: Dept. of Physiology, University of North Carolina School of Medicine, Chapel Hill, NC 27514.

GLASSER, R(OBERT) G(ENE), b. Chicago, Ill, Apr. 14, 29; m. 52; c. 4. PHYSICS. A.B, Chicago, 48, B.S, 50, M.S, 52, Ph.D.(physics), 54. Asst, Chicago, 52-54, res. assoc, 54-55; physicist, U.S. Naval Res. Lab, 55-65; assoc. prof. physics, UNIV. MD, COLLEGE PARK, 65-68, PROF. PHYSICS & COMPUT. SCI, 68-, lectr, 58-65. Lectr, Am. Univ, 57. AAAS; Am. Phys. Soc; Fedn. Am. Sci; Asn. Comput. Mach. Elementary particle physics; mathematical physics; computers. Address: Dept. of Physics, University of Maryland, College Park, MD 20742.

GLASSER, S(TANLEY) R(ICHARD), b. New York, N.Y, Dec. 2, 26; m. 50; c. 2. REPRODUCTIVE & DEVELOPMENTAL BIOLOGY, ENDOCRINOLOGY. A.B, Cornell, 48; fel, Rutgers, 48-52, Ph.D.(zool), 52. Res. assoc. endocrinol, Brookhaven Nat. Lab, 51; assoc. radiation biol, sch. med. & dent, Rochester, 52-53, jr. scientist, 53-54, scientist, 54-62, instr, 54-57, asst. prof, 57-62, chief exp. endocrinol. sect, atomic energy proj, 54-62; ASSOC. RES. PROF. OBSTET. & GYNEC, SCH. MED, VANDERBILT UNIV, 62- Lectr, Am. Inst. Biol. Sci-Med. Ed. Nat. Defense, 59. Vis. asst. prof, Ill. Wesleyan, 58; vis. prof, Baylor, 59. U.S.N.A.F, 45-46. N.Y. Acad. Sci; Am. Soc. Zool; Radiation Res. Soc; Brit. Soc. Endocrinol; Endocrine Soc; Am. Physiol. Soc; Brit. Soc. Study Fertil; Soc. Study Reproduction. Biochemistry of reproduction; implantation, decidualization, placentation; mechanism of progesterone action; role of endocrines in development; nucleic acid and protein synthesis; hormone-chromatin interactions. Address: Center for Population Research, Dept. of Obstetrics & Gynecology, Vanderbilt University School of Medicine, Nashville, TN 37203.

GLASSGOLD, ALFRED E(MANUEL), b. Philadelphia, Pa, July 20, 29; m. 53; c. 2. THEORETICAL PHYSICS. B.A, Pennsylvania, 50; Ph.D.(physics), Mass. Inst. Tech, 54. Physicist, Oak Ridge Nat. Lab, 54-55; lectr. theoret. physics, Minnesota, 55-57; res. physicist, California, 57-63; assoc. prof. PHYSICS, N.Y. UNIV, 63-65, PROF, 65-, HEAD DEPT, 69- AAAS; Am. Phys. Soc. Statistical mechanics, atomic and nuclear structure. Address: Dept. of Physics, New York University, Four Washington Pl, New York, NY 10003.

GLASSICK, CHARLES E(TZWEILER), b. Columbia, Pa, Apr. 6, 31; m. 52; c. 5. ORGANIC CHEMISTRY. B.S, Franklin & Marshall Col, 53; Harvard fel. & M.A, Princeton, 55, Gen. Elec. Co. fel. & Ph.D.(chem), 57. Res. chemist, Rohm & Haas Co, 57-62; assoc. prof. chem, Adrian Col, 62-67; Am. Coun. Educ. fel. acad. admin, Fresno State Col, 67-68; v.pres, Great Lakes Cols. Asn, 68-69; assoc. dean ALBION COL, 69-71, V.PRES. ACAD. AFFAIRS, 71- Instr, Temple Univ, 58-62. Am. Chem. Soc. Synthesis of polycyclic aromatics and carcinogenics; plant growth regulatory chemicals and alkaloids. Address: Albion College, Albion, MI 49224.

GLASSMAN, EDWARD, b. New York, N.Y, Mar. 18, 29; m. 56; c. 4. NEUROBIOLOGY, GENETICS. A.B, N.Y. Univ, 49, M.S, 51; Ph.D.(biol), Hopkins, 55. Am. Cancer Soc. fel. cancer res, Calif. Inst. Tech, 55-57; res. assoc. biochem, City of Hope Med. Res. Ctr, 57-58; Nat. Insts. Health fel, Inst. Animal Genetics, Edinburgh, Scotland & Zool. Inst, Zurich, 57-58; res. assoc. genetics, City of Hope Med. Res. Ctr, 59-60; asst. prof, SCH. MED, UNIV. N.C, CHAPEL HILL, 60-63, assoc. prof, 63-67, PROF. BIOCHEM. & GENETICS, 67-, DIR. DIV. CHEM. NEUROBIOL, 71-, dir. neurobiol. prog, 65. Nat. Insts. Health career develop. award, 63; Guggenheim Mem. Found. fel. & vis. prof, sch. med, Stanford Univ, 68-69. AAAS; Genetics Soc. Am; Am. Chem. Soc; Am. Soc. Cell Biol; Am. Soc. Biol. Chem. Chemistry and mental processes. Address: Dept. of Biochemistry, School of Medicine, University of North Carolina at Chapel Hill, Chapel Hill, NC 27515.

GLASSMAN, HAROLD N(ELSON), b. Waterbury, Conn, Sept. 25, 12. BIOCHEMISTRY. A.B, Pennsylvania, 33, M.S, 36, Ph.D.(chem), Georgetown, 49. Asst. physiol, Pennsylvania & Marine Biol. Lab, Woods Hole, 35-38; biochem, Wistar Inst, Phila, 38-39; biochemist, CHEM. CORPS, U.S. ARMY, Camp Detrick, 44-56, ASST. SCI. DIR, FORT DETRICK, 56- Mem, Gov. Sci. Resources Adv. Bd, Md. U.S.A, 42-46. AAAS; Am. Chem. Soc; Am. Soc. Microbiol; Sci. Res. Soc. Am; Am. Acad. Microbiol; N.Y. Acad. Sci; Am. Pub. Health Asn. Surface active agents; erythrocyte permeability; toxins; spray drying; experimental airborne infection; toxoids; vaccines; pathogenesis of infectious disease; epidemiology; planning, coordination, and evaluation of largescale research and development programs. Address: U.S. Army Biological Defense Research Center, Frederick, MD 21701.

GLASSMAN, IRVIN, b. Baltimore, Md, Sept. 19, 23; m. 51; c. 3. ENGINEERING. B.E, Hopkins, 43, Dr.Eng. 50. Asst. chem. eng. res, substitute alloy mat. labs, Columbia, 43-46; res. assoc. AERONAUT. ENG, PRINCETON, 50-55, asst. prof, 55-59, assoc. prof, 59-64, PROF, 64- Nat. Sci. Found. sr. fel. & vis. prof, Univ. Naples, 66-67; chmn, propulsion & energetics panel, Adv. Group Aerospace Res. & Develop, NATO, 66-; ed, Combustion Sci. & Technol, 68-; mem. comt. on motor vehicle emissions, Nat. Res. Coun. AAAS; Am. Chem. Soc; Am. Inst. Aeronaut. & Astronaut; Am. Soc. Eng. Educ; Combustion Inst. Combustion processes in rockets and jet propulsion engines; kinetics of propellant systems; combustion of metals; environemtnal and fire research. Address: Guggenheim Labs, Princeton University, Princeton, NJ 08540.

GLASSMAN, JEROME M(ARTIN), b. Phila, Pa, Mar. 2, 19; m. 52; c. 3. PHARMACOLOGY. A.B, Pennsylvania, 39, M.A, 42; U.S. Pub. Health Serv. assistantship, Yale, 49-50, Ph.D.(pharmacol, pub. health), 50. Statistician, bur. census, U.S. Dept. Commerce, Wash, D.C, 40-43; hematologist, div. pharmacol, Food & Drug Admin, 43-45; instr. microanat. & physiol, Essex Col. Med. & Surg, 45-46; res. assoc, biol. div, Schering Corp, 46; instr. biol. sci, Hunter Col, 46-47; asst. lab. appl. physiol, Yale, 50-51; sr. res. pharmacologist, Wyeth Inst, 51-59, head dept. pharmacodynamics, 59-62; dir. div. pharmacol, USV Pharmaceut. Corp, N.Y, 62-68, biol. res, 68-70; DIR. CLIN. RES. & PHARMACOL, WAMPOLE LABS. DIV, DENVER CHEM. MFG. CO, 70- Asst. prof, N.Y. Med. Col, 63- Cert, Off. Sci. Res. & Develop, 45. AAAS; Biomet. Soc; Am. Soc. Pharmacol. & Exp. Therapeut; Soc. Exp. Biol. & Med; Am. Pub. Health Asn; N.Y. Acad. Sci; Soc. Toxicol; Am. Heart Asn; Am. Soc. Clin. Pharmacol. & Therapeut. Nature of fibrillae of cells; toxicology of dichloro-diphenyl-trichloroethane; toxicology of benzidine and its congeners; pharmacology and toxicology of N,N'-dibenzylethylene diamine dipenicillin G and other penicillin salts; adsorbents and anticholinergic drugs; pharmacology of hyaluronidase; cardiotonicity and cardiotoxicity of sympathomimetic amines; inflammation; bioassay; analgesic agents; psychopharmacologic agents; local anesthetics; anticoagulants. Address: Wampole Labs. Div, Denver Chemical Manufacturing Co, 35 Commerce Rd, Stamford, CT 06904.

GLASSMAN, ROBERT BRUCE, Physiol. Psychol, see 12th ed, Soc. & Behav. Vols.

GLASSMAN, SIDNEY F(REDERICK), b. Chicago, Ill, July 30, 19; m. 50; c. 2. PLANT TAXONOMY. B.S, Illinois, 42, M.A, 47; Ph.D.(bot), Oklahoma, 50. Asst. botanist, Chicago Natural Hist. Mus, 51; instr. bot, Wyoming, 51-52; asst. prof. BIOL. SCI, UNIV. ILL, CHICAGO CIRCLE, 52-59, assoc. prof, 59-63, PROF, 63-, CURATOR HERBARIUM, 55-, res. fel, 57. Fel, Nat. Res. Coun, Caroline Islands, 49; instr, Wilson Jr. Col, 53; summer, fel, Johnson Wax Co, Cuba, 58. U.S.N, 43-46. Am. Soc. Plant Taxon; Int. Asn. Plant Taxon. Revision of index of American palms and genus Copernicia; grass flora of Chicago region and revision of genus Syagrus. Address: Dept. of Biological Sciences, University of Illinois at Chicago Circle, Box 4348, Chicago, IL 60680.

GLASSNER, ALVIN, b. N.Y.C, Nov. 20, 13; m. 40; c. 3. PHYSICAL CHEMISTRY. B.S, City Col. of N.Y, 35; Ph.D.(phys. chem), Columbia, 40. Asst. Columbia, 40-41; Fed. Tel. & Radio Mfg. Co, N.J, 41-42; instr. chem, Brooklyn Col, 42; Trinity Col.(Conn), 46-49; chemist, Reaction Motors, N.J, 49-51; ASSOC. CHEMIST, ARGONNE NAT. LAB, 51- Sig.C, 42-46, Res. Chemist. AAAS; Am. Chem. Soc; Am. Phys. Soc. Electrode reactions; kinetics of heterogeneous reactions; polarographic analysis; rates of solution of metals in acids as a function of overvoltage; thermodynamics. Address: 206 Fir St, Park Forest,IL 60466.

GLASSON, T(HEODORE) J(AMES) E(DWARD), b. Boundbrook, N.J, Apr. 14, 22; m. 49; c. 3. CHEMICAL ENGINEERING. B.E, Yale, 43; M.S, Mass. Inst. Tech, 47. Chem. engr, pilot plant div, KNOLLS ATOMIC POWER LAB, GEN. ELEC. CO, 48-50, supvr. remote testing radioactive mat, 50-52, mgr. irradiations lab, 52-62, prod, W. Milton site, 62-64, qual. control, 64-67, auxiliary opers, 67-70, MGR. NUCLEAR CORE OPERS, 70- U.S.N, 43-46. Am. Nuclear Soc. Development activities; nuclear power. Address: Knolls Atomic Power Lab, General Electric Co, P.O. Box 1072, Schenectady, NY 12301.

GLASSTONE, SAMUEL, b. London, England, Mar. 5, 97; nat; m. 29; ATOMIC ENERGY. B.Sc, London, 16, M.Sc, 20, Ph.D.(phys. chem), 22, D.Sc, 26. Lectr. phys. chem, London, 19-21; Univ. Col. of Southwest, 21-28; Univ. Sheffield, 28-39; res. assoc. chem, Princeton, 39-41, sci. ed, univ. press, 41-42; prof. chem, Oklahoma, 42-43; consult. electrochem, Zenith Radio Corp, Ill, 43-46; prof. chem, Boston Col, 47-48; CONSULT. ATOMIC ENERGY CMN, 48-; LOS ALAMOS SCI. LAB, 52- Worcester Reed Warner medal, Am. Soc. Mech. Eng, 59. AAAS; The Chem. Soc; Am. Nuclear Soc. (Arthur Holly Compton Award, 68). Physical chemistry; electrochemistry; atomic energy; space science. Address: 103 Wiltshire Dr, Oak Ridge, TN 37830.

GLATHART, J(USTIN) L(EON), b. Findlay, Ohio, Mar. 25, 03; m. 31, 58. PHYSICS. B.S, Case, 25; M.S, Michigan, 31; Ph.D.(physics), Chicago, 39. Instr. physics, Williams Col, 25-29, 31-35; Michigan, 29-31; asst, Chicago, 35-38; prof. & head dept, Shurtleff Col, 38-43; vis. prof, Kenyon Col. 43-44; res.physicist, Preston Labs, Pa, 44-47; prof. PHYSICS, ALBION COL, 47-71, chmn.dept, 47-62, acting chmn, 64-65; EMER. PROF, 71- AAAS; Am. Phys. Soc; Am.Asn. Physics Teachers. Ferromagnetic permeability; fracture velocity in glass; mortality of glassware in service. Address: 418 Darrow St, Albion, MI 49224.

GLATZ, ALFRED CHRISTIAN, b. New Rochelle, N.Y, Dec. 25, 30; m. 55; c. 2. PHYSICAL CHEMISTRY. B.S, Muhlenburg Col, 53; fel. Polytech. Inst. Brooklyn, 55-57, Atomic Energy Comn. grant, 59-60, Ph.D.(phys. chem), 61. Res. chemist, Curtiss-Wright Corp, 57-58; proj. engr, Kearfott Co, Inc, 58-59; sr. phys. chemist, Carrier Res. & Develop, Co, 60-66; gen. phys. scientist, NASA-Electronics. Res. Ctr, 66-70; CHIEF SCIENTIST, VOLAND CORP, 70- Consult, Kearfott Co, Inc, 59-60. Wesley Mitman math prize, 53. Am. Chem. Soc; Inst. Elec. & Electronics Eng. Solid-state chemistry; phase equilibria; differential thermal analysis; x-ray dif-

fraction; computer determination of crystal structures; physical properties of materials; electrolyte solution theory; instrumentation. Address: 111 Palmer's Hill Rd, Stamford, CT 06902.

GLATZER, LOUIS, b. N.Y.C, Aug. 7, 40; m. 65; c. 1. BIOLOGY, GENETICS. A.B, Dartmouth Col, 63; Nat. Insts. Health fel. & M.S, N.C. State Univ, 65; Nat. Insts. Health trainee & Ph.D.(zool, biochem), Univ. Tex, Austin, 70. NAT. INST. GEN. MED. SCI. FEL, OAK RIDGE NAT. LAB, 70- Genetics Soc. Am; Am. Soc. Microbiol. Plasmid genetics; evolutionary relationships of nuclear and cytoplasmic genetic systems; molecular biology of recombination; homologies between related and unrelated DNA'S; studies on complex enzyme systems and aggregates. Address: Biology Division, Oak Ridge National Lab, P.O. Box Y, Oak Ridge, TN 37830.

GLAUBER, ROY J(AY), b. New York, N.Y, Sept. 1, 25; m. 60; c. 2. PHYSICS. B.S, Harvard, 46, fel, 46-49, M.S, 47, Ph.D.(physics), 49. Asst. theoret. physics, Los Alamos Sci. Lab, 44-46; Atomic Energy Comn. fel, Inst. Advan. Study, 49-50, mem, 49-51, Jewett fel, 50-51; lectr, THEORET. PHYSICS, Calif. Inst. Tech, 51-52; res. fel, HARVARD, 52-53, lectr, 53-54, asst. prof, 54-56, assoc. prof, 56-62, PROF, 62- Atomic Energy Comn. fel, Swiss Fed. Inst. Tech, 50; Fulbright lectr, Grenoble, France, 54; Guggenheim Mem. Found. fel, 59; U.S.-Soviet exchange lectr, Leningrad, 64; summers, guest lectr, Colorado, 58, 61, Washington (Seattle), 60, Brandeis, 61, California, Berkeley, 63, Sch. Theoret. Physics, France, 64, Inst. Sci. Studies, Cargese, Corsica, 67, Scottish univs, 69, McGill Univ, 69, Inst. Theoret. Physics, Herceg-Novi, Yugoslavia, 69, Cracow Sch. Theoret. Physics, Zakopane, Poland, 70, Ger. Electron Synchrotron Lab, Hamburg, Ger, 70; Nat. Sci. Found. sr. fel, 66-67; consult, radiation lab, Univ. Calif; Bell. Tel. Labs, Am. Tel. & Tel. Co; Lewis Res. Ctr, NASA, Ohio. Am. Phys. Soc; Am. Acad. Arts & Sci. Nuclear physics; particle diffraction and diffusion problems; elementary particle theory and high energy physics; quantum optics; statistical mechanics. Address: Lyman Lab. of Physics, Harvard University, Cambridge, MA 02138.

GLAUBERMAN, GEORGE ISAAC, b. New York, N.Y, Mar. 3, 41; m. 65; c. 2. MATHEMATICS. B.S, Polytech. Inst. Brooklyn, 61; M.A, Harvard, 62; Ph.D. (math), Wisconsin, 65. Asst. prof. MATH, Wisconsin, 65; instr, UNIV. CHICAGO, 65-66, asst. prof, 66-67, assoc. prof, 67-70, PROF, 70- Sloan Found. res. fel, 67-69; Nat. Sci. Found. fel, 71-72. Am. Math. Soc; Math. Asn. Am. Algebra, principally the theory of finite groups. Address: Dept. of Mathematics, University of Chicago, Chicago, IL 60637.

GLAUBERMAN, MARVIN H(OWARD), b. New York, N.Y, Sept. 8, 25; m. 49. PHYSICS, ELECTRONICS. B.S, Purdue, 47; M.S, Pa. State, 49. Instrumentation engr, U.S. Naval Proving Ground, 47-48; asst. proj. engr. guided missiles, Sperry Gyroscope Co, 49-51; from proj. engr. to mgr. syst. eng. lab, LFE Comput. Prod. Div, Lab. for Electronics, Inc, 51-58; from leader syst. projs. to mgr. defense planning, Radio Corp. Am, Pa, 51-68, dir. instructional systs, RCA CORP, Calif, 68-70, CHIEF ENGR, CONSUMER ELECTRONICS, 70- U.S.N.R, 44-46. Ground controlled approach radar; symbol recognition; guided missiles; digital computers; aerospace communications; major program management; product market planning; general management; television and audio products. Address: 9550 Copley Dr, Indianapolis, IN 46240.

GLAUBMAN, MICHAEL J(UDA), b. Baltimore, Md, Dec. 31, 24; m; c. 4. PARTICLE & NUCLEAR PHYSICS. B.S, Hebrew Univ, 47; M.A, Illinois, 50; Ph.D.(physics), 53. Asst. physics, Illinois, 49-53; Princeton, 53-55; res. assoc, Columbia, 55-56; sr. res. physicist, Atomics Int. Div, N.Am. Aviation, Inc, 56-59; asst. prof. PHYSICS, NORTHEAST. UNIV, 59-61, assoc. prof, 61-70, PROF. & CHMN. DEPT, 70- Am. Phys. Soc. Experimental nuclear structure; high energy experimental physics, especially K meson decay and boson resonances. Address: Dept. of Physics, Northeastern University, Boston, MA 02173.

GLAUDE, VITAL M. M, b. Guadeloupe, French W. Indies, Nov. 27, 25; m. 56; c. 4. PLASMA PHYSICS. L.Sc, Sorbonne, 51; Advan. Sch. Elec. Eng, Paris, 54; Ph.D.(elec. eng), Carnegie Mellon Univ, 67. Asst. prof. PHYSICS, UNIV. MONTREAL, 66-69, ASSOC. PROF, 69- Am. Phys. Soc. Physics of magnetoplasmas; effects of collisions and microturbulences on plasma wave echos; instabilities and turbulences in magnetoplasmas. Address: Dept. of Physics, University of Montreal, C.P. 6128, Montreal 101, Que, Can.

GLAUDEMANS, CORNELIS PIET JOHAN, b. Semarang, Dutch E. Indies, Apr. 16, 32; U.S. citizen; m. 56; c. 6. ORGANIC CHEMISTRY. B.Sc, Utrecht, 54; Ph.D.(org. chem), McGill, 58. Res. chemist, Am. Viscose Corp, 58-62; vis. scientist, Nat. Inst. Arthritis & Metab. Diseases, 62-65; CHEMIST, NAT. INSTS. HEALTH, 66- U.S. Pub. Health Serv. career develop. award & asst. prof, sch. med, Yale, 65-66. The Chem. Soc. Chemistry of naturally occurring and synthetic carbohydrates. Address: National Institutes of Health, Room 204, Bldg. 4, Bethesda, MD 20014.

GLAUSER, ELINOR M(IKELBERG), b. Phila, Pa, Aug. 24, 31; m. 52; c. 3. PHARMACOLOGY & PHYSIOLOGY. B.A, Pennsylvania, 52; Nat. Polio Found. fel, Woman's Med. Col.of Pa, 55, M.D, 57. Fel. physiol, Trudeau Soc, sch. med, Pennsylvania, 58-59; Kate Hurdmead fel, exp. med, Cambridge, 59-60; fel. med, Harvard Med. Sch, 60-61; assoc. res. dept, med, Woman's Med. Col. Pa, 61-63; instr. PHARM. & MED, SCH. MED, TEMPLE UNIV, 63-66, asst. prof, 66-70, ASSOC. PROF, 70- Nat. Insts. Health fel, 61-63; Am. Thoracic Soc. fel, 63-64. AAAS; Am. Thoracic Soc; Am. Chem. Soc; Am. Med. Asn; N.Y. Acad. Med. Pulmonary physiology, especially pulmonary alveolar-capillary gas diffusion and pulmonary blood flow in man. Address: 630 Richards Rd, Wayne, PA 19087.

GLAUSER, STANLEY C(HARLES), b. Phila, Pa, June 19, 31; m. 52; c. 3. BIOPHYSICAL CHEMISTRY. B.A, Pennsylvania, 51, M.S. & M.D, 55, U.S. Pub. Health Serv. fel, 56-57, Ph.D.(phys. chem), 59. Asst. phys. chem, sch. med, Pennsylvania, 52-54; res. assoc, Nat. Insts. Health, 57-59; Nat. Sci. Found. res. fel. molecular biol, Med. Res. Coun. Unit, Cavendish Lab, Cambridge, 59-60; res. assoc. biol, Mass. Inst. Tech, 60-61; asst. prof. molecular biol. & physiol, sch. med, Pennsylvania, 61-65; assoc. prof. MOLECULAR PHARMACOL, SCH. MED, TEMPLE UNIV, 65-68, PROF, 68- Instr, U.S. Dept. Agr. Grad. Sch, 58-59. U.S.P.H.S, 57-59, Sr. Asst. Surgeon.

AAAS; Am. Chem. Soc; Biophys. Soc; Am. Med. Asn; N.Y. Acad. Sci; Am. Physiol. Soc; Am. Soc. Pharmacol. & Exp. Therapeut; The Chem. Soc; Faraday Soc. Molecular biology; physical chemistry of hemoproteins and other porphyrin-like compounds of biological interest; thermodynamics; kinetics; genetics. Address: 630 Richards Rd, Wayne, PA 19087.

GLAUZ, ROBERT D(ORAN), b. Detroit, Mich, Aug. 13, 27; m. 53; c. 3. APPLIED MATHEMATICS. B.S.E, Michigan, 48, M.S, 49; Ph.D.(appl. math), Brown, 53. Instr. math, Mont. State Col, 49-50; asst, Brown, 51-53; mem. staff, Los Alamos Sci. Lab, Calif, 53-57; eng. anal. specialist, aircraft gas turbine div, Gen. Elec. Corp, 57-58; tech. specialist, Aerojet-Gen. Corp. Div, Gen. Tire & Rubber Co, 58-66, mgr. eng. anal. & prog, 66-68; PROF. MATH, UNIV. CALIF, DAVIS, 68- U.S.N.A.F, 45-47. Am. Math. Soc; Math. Asn. Am; Soc. Indust. & Appl. Math; Asn. Comput. Mach. Plasticity; shock waves; viscoelasticity; numerical analysis. Address: 3363 Club House Dr, El Macero, CA 95618.

GLAUZ, WILLIAM DONALD, b. Grand Rapids, Mich, Oct. 26, 33; m. 56; c. 4. ENGINEERING SCIENCES. B.S, Mich. State, 56; M.S, Purdue, 59, Ph.D.(eng. sci), 64. Instr, Purdue, 56-63; assoc. analyst, MIDWEST RES. INST, 63-64, sr. analyst, 64-66, prin. analyst, 66-69, head anal. & appl. math, 69-71, MGR. HWY. & TRAFFIC SYSTS. ENG, 71- Consult, Midwest Appl. Sci. Corp, 59-63; lectr, Univ. Mo, Kansas City, 64-69; comt. mem, Hwy. Res. Bd, Nat. Acad. Sci-Nat. Res. Coun. Am. Inst. Aeronaut. & Astronaut. Research management; highway safety; traffic analysis; simulation; digital computation; mechanics; applied mathematics; aerodynamics. Address: Midwest Research Institute, 425 Volker Blvd, Kansas City, MO 64110.

GLAVE, WILLIAM R(OGER), b. Chicago, Ill, May 2, 40. MEDICINAL & ORGANIC CHEMISTRY. B.A, Augustana Col, 62; North. Ill. Univ, 63-65; Ph.D.(med. chem), State Univ. N.Y. Buffalo, 70. Res. chemist, org. synthesis, Salsbury's Labs, Iowa, 62-63; RES. ASSOC. CHEM, Pomona Col, 69-71; MICROBIOL. ASSOCS, INC, 71- Am. Chem. Soc. Synthesis and evaluation of purine analogs related to adenosine as possible active-site directed reversible inhibitors of adenosine deaminase; correlation of biological activity with structure using a multiparameter approach and regression analysis. Address: Microbiological Associates, Inc, 4733 Bethesda Ave, Bethesda, MD 20014.

GLAVIANO, VINCENT V(ALENTINO), b. Frankfurt, N.Y, July 19, 20; m. 45; c. 2. PHYSIOLOGY. B.S, City Col. New York, 50; Ph.D.(physiol), Columbia, 54. Asst. physiol, col. physicians & surg, Columbia, 51-53, instr, 53-54, N.Y. Heart Res. fel. med, 54-56; asst. prof. PHYSIOL, col. med, Illinois, 56-60; assoc. prof, Stritch Sch. Med. & Grad. Sch, Loyola Univ.(Ill), 60-64, prof, 64-70; PROF. & CHMN. DEPT, CHICAGO MED. SCH, UNIV. HEALTH SCI, 70- U.S.A.A.F, 42-45. AAAS; Am. Physiol. Soc; Soc. Exp. Biol. & Med; Harvey Soc; N.Y. Acad. Sci; Am. Heart Asn. Cardiovascular physiology; catecholamines; cardiac metabolism; electrolytes and shock. Address: Dept. of Physiology & Biophysics, Chicago Medical School, University of Health Sciences, 2020 W. Ogden Ave, Chicago, IL 60612.

GLAVIS, F(RANK) J(OHNSON), b. Warrenton, Va, Oct. 13, 13; m. 40; c. 1. CHEMISTRY. A.B, Dartmouth Col, 35; Ph.D.(org. chem), Illinois, 38. Instr. org. chem, Illinois, 36-37; RES. CHEMIST, ROHM AND HAAS, 38- Am. Chem. Soc. Monomers and polymers; synthetic lubricants; additives for petroleum products; preparation of water-soluble polymers; hydrophilic solutions containing polymers; polysulfones from sulfur dioxide, olefins and acetylenes. Address: 187 Rydal Rd, Rydal, PA 19046.

GLAWE, LLOYD N(EIL), b. Des Moines, Iowa, Aug. 21, 32. INVERTEBRATE PALEONTOLOGY. B.S, Illinois, 54; M.S, La. State, 60, Pan-Am. Petrol. Found. fel, 61-63, Ph.D.(paleont), 66. Asst. prof. GEOL, NORTHEAST LA. UNIV, 64-67, ASSOC. PROF, 67- Summers, res. investr, Pan-Am. Petrol. Corp, 60, La. Geol. Surv, 61. U.S.A, 54-56. AAAS; Soc. Econ. Paleont. & Mineral. Classification and distribution of Gulf Coast Tertiary Pectinidae. Address: Dept. of Geology, Northeast Louisiana University, Monroe, LA 71201.

GLAZE, F(RANCIS) W(ARNER), JR, b. Waterbury, Conn, Apr. 22, 20; m. 68; c. 4. CHEMICAL ENGINEERING. B.S, Maryland, 41. Tech. invest. patents, E.I. DU PONT DE NEMOURS & CO, 46-49, supvr. personnel, 49-51, dyeing, textile res. lab, 51-53, weaving, 53-55, sr. res. engr. patents, 55-66, staff asst, for. patents, 66-68, info. serv. supvr, fabrics & finishes dept, 68-71, SERV. SUPVR, RES. & DEVELOP. LAB, 71- U.S.A, 41-46, Maj. Am. Chem. Soc; Am. Inst. Chem; Am. Soc. Info. Sci. Technical problems relating to selecting, filing, prosecuting and utilizing foreign patents in the field of synthetic textile fibers; information retrieval and systems development to include patent and economic data. Address: Marshall Lab, E.I. du Pont de Nemours & Co, P.O. Box 3886, Philadelphia, PA 19146.

GLAZE, ROBERT P, b. Birmingham, Ala, Apr. 14, 33; m. 58; c. 2. BIOCHEMISTRY. B.S, Univ. of the South, 55; Nat. Heart Inst. fel, Rochester, 55-58, U.S. Pub. Health Serv. fel, 58-61, Ph.D.(biochem), 61. Fel. physiol. chem, sch. med, Hopkins, 61-64; ASST. PROF. BIOCHEM, MED. CTR, UNIV. ALA, BIRMINGHAM, 64-, COORD. RES. GRANTS, 67-, ASSOC. DEAN SPEC. PROGS, SCHS. OF MED. & DENT, 69-, asst. dean, 67-69. U.S. Pub. Health Serv. fel, 62-63 & trainee, 62-64; Nat. Sci. Found. res. grant, 66-68. AAAS; Am. Chem. Soc. Mitochondrial electron transport; oxidative phosphorylation; phosphate transfer enzymes; uremia. Address: Coordinator of Research Grants, University of Alabama, 1919 Seventh Ave, S, Birmingham, AL 35233.

GLAZE, WILLIAM H, b. Sherman, Tex, Nov. 21, 34; m. 56; c. 2. PHYSICAL CHEMISTRY. B.S, Southwestern (Tex), 56; M.S, Wisconsin, 58, Ph.D.(chem), 61. Robert A. Welch fel, Rice, 60-61; asst. prof. CHEM, N. TEX. STATE UNIV, 61-63, assoc. prof, 63-65, PROF, 65- Robert A. Welch res. grant organometallic compounds, 63- Nat. Sci. Found. undergrad. equip. fel. consult, 64 & res. grant organometallic photochem, 69-71. Am. Chem. Soc. Chemistry of organometallic compounds, beryllium and lithium; infrared spectroscopy; nuclear magnetic resonance; reaction kinetics and mechanisms. Address: Dept. of Chemistry, North Texas State University, Denton, TX 76203.

GLAZENER, EDWARD W(ALKER), b. Raleigh, N.C, Feb. 3, 22; m. 47; c. 2. POULTRY HUSBANDRY. B.S, N.C. State Col, 43; M.S, Maryland, 45, Ph.D.(poultry genetics), 49. Poultry supvr, Green Pastures, N.C, 39-41; asst. county agent, exten. serv, N.C. State Col, 44-46; asst. prof. poultry husb, Univ. Md, 46; assoc. prof. POULTRY GENETICS, N.C. STATE UNIV, 46-49, PROF, 49-, DIR. ACAD. AFFAIRS, SCH. AGR. & LIFE SCI, 70-, head dept. poultry sci, 55-60, dir. instr, sch. agr. & life sci, 60-70, acting dean, 70-71. Mem, U.S. Dept. Agr. regional poultry breeding proj, Georgia. Fel. AAAS; Am. Genetic Asn; Poultry Sci. Asn. Genetics and endocrinology of poultry; thyroid activity as related to strain differences in growing chickens. Address: 111 Patterson Hall, School of Agriculture & Life Science, North Carolina State University, Raleigh, NC 27607.

GLAZENER, W(ILLIAM) C(ALEB), b. Georgetown, Tex, Nov. 9, 04; m. 29; c. 1. WILDLIFE MANAGEMENT. B.S, Texas Col. Arts & Indust, 29; M.S, Agr. & Mech. Col, Texas, 43. Teacher, pub. schs, Tex, 27-31, prin, 31-36, supt, 36-38; biologist, Tex. Game & Fish Cmn, 40-45, dir. div. wildlife restoration, 46-55; ASST. DIR, WELDER WILDLIFE FOUND, 55- Am. Soc. Range Mgt; Am. Soc. Mammal; Wildlife Soc.(secy, 51-53, v.pres, 53-54). Range management; ecology; conservation education. Address: Welder Wildlife Foundation, P.O. Drawer 1400, Sinton, TX 78387.

GLAZER, HAROLD, b. Phila, Pa, Apr. 29, 29; m. 55. MATHEMATICAL STATISTICS. A.B, Boston, 49, A.M, 50, Ph.D.(math), 63. Surv. statistician, QM Bd, Ft. Lee, 51-53; appl. mathematician, Harvard Observ, 53-55; sr. engr, missiles lab, Sylvania Elec. Prods, Inc, 55-58; airborne electronics div, Raytheon Mfg. Co, 58-61, mgr. comput. syst. & anal, Raytheon Airborne Opers, 61; mem. tech. staff, systs. anal, Mitre Corp, 61-68; MGR. ANAL. SYSTS. GROUP, VIATRON COMPUT. SYSTS. CORP, 68- Consult, 55-57. AAAS; Asn. Comput. Mach; Inst. Mgt. Sci; Am. Statist. Asn; Opers. Res. Soc. Am; Inst. Math. Statist. System analysis, applications and methodology; management systems development. Address: Viatron Computer Systems Corp, Route 62, Bedford, MA 01730.

GLAZIER, ELLIS R(OBERT), b. Allentown, Pa, Aug. 23, 29; m. 54; c. 2. ORGANIC CHEMISTRY. B.A, Cornell, 51; Du Pont fel, Rochester, 55-56, Ph.D.(org. chem), 56. Sloan fel. chem, Illinois, 56-57; sr. chemist, Mead Johnson & Co, 57-60; scientist, Worcester Found. Exp. Biol, 60-63; sr. appln. engr, Gen. Elec. Co, 63-64; tech. planner & mgr. tech. personnel, Philco Res. Labs, 64-65; mgr. mkt, Aerojet-Gen. Corp, 65; sr. appln. engr, Northrop Space Labs, Calif, 65-67; dir. clin. prod, CALBIOCHEM, INC, 67-69, MGR. OPERS, 69- Lectr, eve. col, Clark, 61-62; consult, Moleculon Res. Corp, Mass, 62-63. U.S.A.F, 51-53, Res, 53-59; U.S.A.R, 62-65, Capt. Structure and synthesis of natural organic materials; aerospace and defense; life sciences; chemical and biological warfare; enzymatic reactions for clinical diagnosis. Address: Calbiochem, Inc, 10933 N. Torrey Pines Rd, La Jolla, CA 92037.

GLAZIER, LYNN R(ODNEY), b. Leverett, Mass, May 18, 14; m. 36; c. 2. FOOD TECHNOLOGY. B.S, Massachusetts, 36, M.S, 41. Sanit. inspector, Berkshire County Health Dist, Mass, 36-40; dairy engr, Pfaudler Co, N.Y, 41-43, sales engr, 43-47, asst. mgr. dairy equipment sales, 47-50; sales rep, Manton-Gaulin Mfg. Co, Mass, 50-51; asst. prof. DAIRY MFG, UNIV. CONN, 51-62, ASSOC. PROF, 62- Nat. Sci. Found. fel, 62. Flavor studies. Address: Dept. of Dairy Manufacturing, University of Connecticut, Box U-40, Storrs, CT 06268.

GLAZIER, ROBERT H(ENRY), b. Amherst, Mass, Oct. 1, 26. ORGANIC CHEMISTRY. A.B, Amherst Col, 48; M.S, New Hampshire, 50; Ph.D.(chem), Kansas, 52. Prof. CHEM. & chmn. dept, Alderson-Broaddus Col, 52-54; Nebr. Wesleyan, 54-61; vis. prof, Kalamazoo Col, 61-62; assoc. prof, Washburn Univ, 62-70, PROF, 70- Address: Dept. of Chemistry, Washburn University, Topeka, KS 66621.

GLAZKO, ANTHONY J(OACHIM), b. San Francisco, Calif, Aug. 15, 14; m. 59; c. 3. BIOCHEMISTRY. A.B, California, 35, Ph.D.(biochem), 39. Asst. biochem, California, 36-39; res. assoc, Michigan, 39-41; asst. prof. biochem, sch. med, Emory, 46-47; LAB. DIR. CHEM. PHARMACOL, PARKE, DAVIS & CO, 47- Med.C, U.S.N, 41-46. Am. Physiol. Soc; Soc. Exp. Biol. & Med; Am. Chem. Soc; Am. Soc. Pharmacol. & Exp. Therapeut; N.Y. Acad. Sci; Am. Fedn. Clin. Res; Am. Soc. Clin. Pharmacol. & Therapeut; Int. Soc. Biochem. Pharmacol; Int. Leprosy Asn. Drug metabolism; species differences in metabolism; radioisotopes; analytical procedures. Address: Research Lab, Parke, Davis & Co, Ann Arbor, MI 48106.

GLEASON, ANDREW M(ATTEI), b. Fresno, Calif, Nov. 4, 21; m. 59; c. 3. MATHEMATICS. B.S, Yale, 42; soc. fel, Harvard, 46-50, hon. A.M, 53. Asst. prof. math, HARVARD, 50-53, assoc. prof, 53-57, prof, 57-69, HOLLIS PROF. MATHEMATICKS & NATURAL PHILOS, 69- Cleveland Prize, 52. U.S.N, 42-46, 50-52, Comdr. Nat. Acad. Sci; Am. Math. Soc.(v.pres, 62-63); Math. Asn. Am; Am. Acad. Arts & Sci; Math. Soc. Fr. Topological groups; Banach algebras. Address: Dept. of Mathematics, Harvard University, 2 Divinity Ave, Cambridge, MA 02138.

GLEASON, C(LARENCE) H(ENRY), b. Montreal, Que, May 19, 22; m. 50; c. 3. ORGANIC CHEMISTRY. B.Sc, McGill, 44, Nat. Res. Coun. Can. studentship, 45-47, Ph.D.(chem), 47. Lectr, McGill, 44-45; res. chemist, Charles E. Frosst & Co, 47-62, chief res. chemist, 62-69, EXEC. ASST. TO DIR. RES, MERCK FROSST LABS, 69- Lectr, Sir George Williams Col, 47-48; dir, Belair Chem. Ltd, Can, 64-65. Fel. Chem. Inst. Can; Am. Chem. Soc. Novel and improved medicinal agents. Address: 7514 Mountbatten Rd, Montreal 269, Que, Can.

GLEASON, E(DWARD) H(INSDALE), JR, b. North Adams, Mass, May 20, 27; m. 50; c. 4. ORGANIC CHEMISTRY. B.S, Northeastern, 53; Ph.D.(chem), State Univ. N.Y, 59. Res. chemist, Am. Cyanamid Co, 53-56; res. chemist, KOPPERS CO, INC, 59-67, MGR. LATICES RES, 67- U.S.A.A.F, 45-46. Am. Chem. Soc; fel. Am. Inst. Chem. Polymer chemistry; vinyl polymerization; copolymerization; emulsion polymerization. Address: Koppers Research Center, Koppers Co, Inc, 440 College Park Dr, Monroeville, PA 15146.

GLEASON, FRANK HOWES, b. Boston, Mass, Nov. 5, 38; m. 61; c. 2. MICROBIOLOGY, PLANT PHYSIOLOGY. B.S, Trinity Col.(Conn), 61; Ph.D.(bot), California, Berkeley, 67. Nat. Insts. Health fel. biochem, California, Berkeley, 67-68; ASST. PROF. BIOL, COLO. COL, 68- Milheim Found. res. grant, 69-70; Nat. Insts. Health res. grant, 69-71; res. fel, Australian Nat. Univ, 71-72. Am. Soc. Microbiol; Am. Soc. Plant Physiol; Bot. Soc. Am; Mycol. Soc. Am. Physiology and biochemistry of fungi; dehydrogenase enzymes in fungi; nutrition of lower fungi; respiratory electron transport in fungi; microbial metabolism; comparative biochemistry. Address: Dept. of Biology, Colorado College, Colorado Springs, CO 80903.

GLEASON, GALE R, JR, b. Battle Creek, Mich, Oct. 8, 27; m. 49; c. 4. BIOLOGY. B.S, Central Michigan, 50; M.S, Mich. State, 51, Ph.D.(fisheries, wildlife), 61. Nursery inspector entom, Mich. Dept. Agr, 53-54; instr. BIOL, Cent. Mich. Univ, 54-58, asst. prof, 58-62, assoc. prof, 62-65; PROF. & CHMN. DEPT, LAKE SUPERIOR STATE COL, 65-, CHMN. DIV. NATURAL SCI, 68- Atomic Energy Cmn. res. fel, 55-57. U.S.N.R, 45-46. Am. Soc. Limnol. & Oceanog. Benthic ecology, especially sediment analysis. Address: Division of Natural Sciences, Lake Superior State College, Sault Ste. Marie, MI 49783.

GLEASON, GEOFFREY I(RVING), b. Los Angeles, Calif, Apr. 23, 23; m. 50; c. 2. RADIOCHEMISTRY. B.Ch.E, Southern California, 47. Asst, Am. Potash & Chem. Co, 48-49; res. assoc, Abbott Labs, 49-52, mgr, Oak Ridge Div, 52-58, res. scientist, 58-64, RES. SCIENTIST, OAK RIDGE INST. NUCLEAR STUDIES, 64- U.S.N.R, 43-46. Am. Chem. Soc; Soc. Nuclear Med. Radiochemical separations; analytical chemistry; radiation measurement. Address: 127 Cumberland View Dr, Oak Ridge, TN 37830.

GLEASON, JAMES GORDON, b. Hammondsport, N.Y, Mar. 24, 15; m. 40; c. 1. MECHANICAL ENGINEERING. B.S, Ala. Polytech, 38; M.S, Arkansas, 54. Asst. instr, Ala. Polytech, 37-38, lab. technician & instr, 38-40; instr. mech. eng, UNIV. ARK, FAYETTEVILLE, 40-43, asst. prof, 43-45, assoc. prof. mech. eng. & head aeronaut. div, 45-54, PROF. MECH. & AERONAUT. ENG, 54- Summers, res. engr, Boeing Airplane Co, 51, 52, 55-60; Pratt & Whitney Aircraft, 61-65, 66, 67; Beech Aircraft, 68, 69; plant. eng, Forrest Park Canning Co. Am. Soc. Eng. Educ; Am. Soc. Mech. Eng; Soc. Automotive Eng; Nat. Soc. Prof. Eng. Theory of aeronautics; internal combustion engines; aircraft engines; flight training ground school; thermodynamics; refrigeration; machine design; compressible fluid flow. Address: Mechanical Engineering Bldg, University of Arkansas, Fayetteville, AR 72701.

GLEASON, LARRY N(EIL), b. Independence, Ore, June 3, 39; m. 63; c. 2. PARASITOLOGY. A.B, Chico State Col, 64; M.S.P.H, Univ. N.C, Chapel Hill, 65, Ph.D.(parasitol, zool), 69. Res. assoc. pharmacol, sch. med, Univ. Fla, 69-70; ASST. PROF. BIOL. & PARASITOL, WEST. KY. UNIV, 70- U.S.M.C.R, 57-59. Am. Soc. Parasitol. Taxonomy, life history, ecology and host-parasite relationship of trematodes and cestodes. Address: Dept. of Biology, Western Kentucky University, Bowling Green, KY 42101.

GLEASON, RAY EDWARD, b. Burlington, Vt, Dec. 17, 31; m. 64; c. 2. BIOSTATISTICS, GENETICS. B.Sc, Vermont, 54; M.S, Massachusetts, 60; Ph.D.(genetics, statist), Texas A&M, 63. Geneticist, Nedlar Farms, Inc, N.H, 54-58; trainee, div. math. biol, Harvard Med. Sch. & Peter Bent Brigham Hosp, 63-65; res. fel, ELLIOTT P. JOSLIN RES. LAB, HARVARD MED. SCH, 65-67, res. assoc, 69-70, PRIN. ASSOC. MED, MED. SCH, 70-, SR. INVESTR, RES. LAB, 70- Am. Sci. Affiliation; Am. Statist. Asn; Am. Genetic Asn; Biomet. Soc. Studies of the inheritance of diabetes mellitus in mice and humans; statistical analysis of data from diabetes research, and the influence of diet on blood glucose and serum insulin levels. Address: Elliott P. Joslin Research Lab, Harvard Medical School, 170 Pilgrim Rd, Boston, MA 02215.

GLEASON, ROBERT WILLARD, b. Santiago, Chile, Feb. 9, 32; U.S. citizen; m. 58; c. 3. ORGANIC CHEMISTRY. B.A, Middlebury Col, 54, M.S, 56; Ph.D.(org. chem), Mass. Inst. Tech, 60. Instr. CHEM, MIDDLEBURY COL, 60-63, asst. prof, 63-67, ASSOC. PROF, 67-, CHMN. DEPT, 70-, acting chmn. dept, 69-70. Vis. faculty res. assoc, Univ. Colo, 67-68. Am. Chem. Soc; The Chem. Soc. Peroxidation of olefins; oxidation of 1,1-disubstituted hydrazines; reductions of N-nitrosamines. Address: Dept. of Chemistry, Middlebury College, Middlebury, VT 05753.

GLEAVES, EARL WILLIAM, b. Miami, Okla, Apr. 3, 30; m. 50; c. 3. ANIMAL NUTRITION. B.S, Okla. State, 53, M.S, 61, Ralston Purina fel, 62, Ph.D.(animal nutrit), 65. Instr. poultry nutrit, Okla. State, 63-64; ASSOC. PROF. POULTRY EXTEN. & NUTRIT, UNIV. NEBR, LINCOLN, 64- Poultry Sci. Asn. Interrelationships of nutrition and physiology in the domestic fowl. Address: Dept. of Poultry Science, University of Nebraska, Lincoln, NE 68503.

GLEDHILL, BARTON L, b. Philadelphia, Pa, Sept. 29, 36; m. 59; c. 2. VETERINARY REPRODUCTION, CYTOCHEMISTRY. B.S, Pa. State, 58; V.M.D, Pennsylvania, 61; F.R.V.C.S, Royal Vet. Col. Sweden, 62, Ph.D.(vet. reproduction), 66. Am. Vet. Med. Res. Trust res. fel, 61-64; Nat. Insts. Health fel, 64-66; asst. prof. REPRODUCTION, SCH. VET. MED. UNIV. PA, 66-70, ASSOC. PROF, 70- Docent, Royal Vet. Col. Sweden, 66-; Nat. Insts. Health spec. fel, 68-70. Am. Vet. Med. Asn; Soc. Study Reproduction; N.Y. Acad. Sci; Brit. Soc. Study Fertility. Quantitative cytochemistry of male gametogenesis and fertilization; clinical investigation of male infertility; structure of male gametes. Address: University of Pennsylvania School of Veterinary Medicine, New Bolton Center, Kennett Square, PA 19348.

GLEDHILL, ROBERT H(AMOR), b. South Kingstown, R.I, Feb. 2, 31; m. 54; c. 3. POULTRY NUTRITION, BIOCHEMISTRY. B.S, Rhode Island, 52, M.S, 54; Ph.D.(poultry nutrit), Purdue, 57. Nutritionist, Archer-Daniels-Midland Co, 57-60; res. assoc, Corn Prod. Co, 60-61; res. nutritionist, Hales & Hunter Co, Ill, 61-66; POULTRY RES. SPECIALIST, CENT. SOYA CO, INC, 66- Poultry Sci. Asn; World Poultry Sci. Asn. Nutritional research on broilers, roasters, replacement birds, layers, breeders, turkeys and ducks. Address: Central Soya Co, Inc, 1230 N. Second St, Decatur, IN 46733.

GLEDHILL, R(ONALD) J(AMES), b. Cleveland, Ohio, Nov. 23, 14; m. 42; c. 4. CHEMISTRY. B.A, Ohio State, 39; Ph.D.(phys. chem), Minnesota, 46. Asst. chem, Minnesota, 39-43; res. chemist, EASTMAN KODAK CO, 46-67, RES. ASSOC, 67- Assoc. mem. Am. Chem. Soc. Color and constitution of dyes; color photography research; particle-size measurement; technical information retrieval systems. Address: Eastman Kodak Co, Kodak Park, Rochester, NY 14604.

GLEDHILL, WILLIAM EMERSON, b. Baltimore, Md, Aug. 1, 41; m. 65; c. 2. MICROBIOLOGY, BIOCHEMISTRY. B.A, Univ. Del, 63, M.S, 66; Nat. Defense Educ. Act. fel, Pa. State Univ, 67-69, Ph.D.(microbiol, biochem), 69. RES. MICROBIOLOGIST, TENNECO CHEM, INC, 69- AAAS; Am. Soc. Microbiol. Microbial physiology and ecology; industrial application of new types of microorganisms. Address: Tenneco Chemicals, Inc, Piscataway, NJ 08854.

GLEEKMAN, LEWIS W(OLFE), b. Lynn, Mass, June 10, 20; m. 45; c. 3. CHEMICAL ENGINEERING. B.Ch.E, Cooper Union, 42; Sheaffer Pen Co, fel, Iowa, 46-48, M.S, 47, Ph.D.(chem. eng), 48. Chem. engr, Mathieson Alkali Co, 42-43; metallurgist, Sam Tour & Co, 43-45; instr, Iowa, 46-47; asst. prof. chem. eng, Delaware, 48-52; res. engr, Sherritt Gordon Mines Ltd, 52-54; head, mat. eng. sect, eng. dept, Wyandotte Chem. Corp, 53-68; CONSULT. MAT. ENGR, MAT. & CORROSION ENG. SERV, 68- Tech. specialist, tech. detachment, Mil. Dist. Wash, 45-46; adj. prof, Wayne State Univ; UNESCO consult, Univ. Buenos Aires. Am. Soc. Eng. Educ; Am. Soc. Metals; Nat. Asn. Corrosion Eng; Am. Inst. Chem. Eng; Tech. Asn. Pulp & Paper Indust; Soc. Plastics Indust; Am. Technion Soc; Am. Soc. Test. & Mat; Nat. Soc. Prof. Eng. Mechanism of stress corrosion; economical materials of construction; fabrication of metals; analysis of material failures; corrosion of titanium; uses of titanium; expert witness investigation and testimony in materials science and engineering. Address: 25677 Friar Lane, Southfield, MI 48075.

GLEESON, AUSTIN M, b. Phila, Pa, Apr. 5, 38; m. 60; c. 2. ELEMENTARY PARTICLE PHYSICS. B.Sc, Drexel Inst, 60; M.Sc, Pennsylvania, 63, Ph.D.(physics), 65. Comput. designer, Radio Corp. Am, 56-58, 60-62; tech. rep, Burroughs Corp, 58-59; instr. PHYSICS, Drexel Inst, 59-60, 62-63; res. asst, Univ. Pennsylvania, 63-65; res. assoc, Syracuse Univ, 65-67, asst. prof, 67-69; UNIV. TEX. AUSTIN, 69-71, ASSOC. PROF, 71- Am. Inst. Physics. Strong interaction elementary particle phenomenology. Address: Dept. of Physics, University of Texas at Austin, Austin, TX 78712.

GLEESON, G(EORGE) W(ALTER), b. Granite, Ore, Mar. 1, 05; m. 29; c. 2. CHEMICAL ENGINEERING. B.S, Ore. State Col, 28, fel, 28-29, M.S, 34, Ch.E, 36. Instr. mech. & mat, ORE. STATE UNIV, 29-32, asst. prof. CHEM. ENG, 32-36, assoc. prof. in charge dept, 36-37, prof, 38-70, head dept, 38-44, acting dean eng, 44-45, dean eng, 45-70, EMER. PROF. & EMER. DEAN ENG, 70- Consult, 28- Coord, Army Spec. Training Prog. AAAS; Am. Chem. Soc; Am. Soc. Eng. Educ; Nat. Soc. Prof. Eng; Am. Inst. Chem. Eng. Design concrete mixes; oil gas production; mineral dressing; river pollution. Address: School of Engineering, Oregon State University, Corvallis, OR 97331.

GLEESON, THOMAS A(LEXANDER), b. New York, N.Y, Aug. 11, 20; m. 42; c. 2. METEOROLOGY. B.S, Harvard, 46; M.S, N.Y. Univ, 47, Ph.D.(meteorol), 50. Asst, N.Y. Univ, 47-49; from asst. prof. to assoc. prof. METEOROL, FLA. STATE UNIV, 49-59, PROF, 59- U.S.A.A.F, 42-45. AAAS; Am. Meteorol. Soc; Am. Geophys. Union. General meteorology and climatology; probability and statistical relations in meteorology. Address: Dept. of Meteorology, Florida State University, Tallahassee, FL 32306.

GLEGG, R(ONALD) E(DWARD), b. Kingston, Jamaica, Jan. 10, 21; U.S. citizen; m. 54; c. 3. CHEMISTRY. Ph.D.(chem), McGill, 46. Asst. prof. org. chem, New Brunswick, 46-48; Lowell Textile Inst, 48-50; chemist, histochem, McGill, 50-55; asst. prof, exp. sta, Cornell, 55-56; asst. dir, cellulose technol. div, EASTMAN KODAK CO, 56-65, asst. dir. polymer technol. div, 65-71, ASST. MGR. MFG. SERV. ORGN, 71- Consult, U.S. Pub. Health Serv, 50; lectr, Sir George Williams Col, 51-53; assoc. lectr, Univ. Rochester, 64. Am. Chem. Soc; Tech. Asn. Pulp & Paper Indust. Cellulose chemistry; plastics. Address: Manufacturing Services Organization, Eastman Kodak Co, Kodak Park Works, Rochester, NY 14650.

GLEGHORN, G(EORGE) J(AY), (JR), b. San Francisco, Calif, May 27, 27; m. 48; c. 3. ELECTRICAL ENGINEERING, APPLIED MATHEMATICS. B.S, Colorado, 47; M.S, Calif. Inst. Technol, 48, Ph.D.(elec. eng), 55. Mem. tech. staff, TRW Space Tech. Labs, 54-59, head launch opers, Pioneer I & V, Explorer VI Satellites, 59-60, head controls dept, 58-60, prog. dir, Able 5 Lunar Probe Satellite, 60-61, prog. dir, orbit. geophys. observ, 61-65, asst. dir. opers, space systs. prog. mgt, TRW SYSTS. GROUP, TRW, INC, 65-66, mgr. spacecraft opers, SPACE VEHICLES DIV, 66-70, MGR. DEFENSE SPACE SYSTS. OPERS, 70- U.S.N.R, 44-46, 51-53, Lt. Sr. mem. Am. Inst. Aeronaut. & Astronaut; Inst. Elec. & Electronics Eng; Sci. Res. Soc. Am. Control system and digital computer analysis and engineering; spacecraft and ballistic missile system engineering. Address: Space Vehicles Division, TRW Systems, 1 Space Park, Redondo Beach, CA 90278.

GLEICH, GERALD J, b. Escanaba, Mich, May 14, 31; m. 55; c. 3. IMMUNOLOGY, INTERNAL MEDICINE. B.A, Michigan, 53, M.D, 56. Intern, Phila. Gen. Hosp, Pa, 56-57; resident internal med, Jackson Mem. Hosp, Miami, Fla, 59-61; trainee allergy & immunol, med. ctr, Rochester, 61-63, instr. MED. & MICROBIOL, sch. med. & dent, 63-64; MAYO GRAD. SCH. MED, UNIV. MINN, 65-68, ASST. PROF, 68- Consult, Methodist Hosp. & St. Mary's Hosp, Rochester, Minn, 65-; Nat. Insts. Health res. grant, 66-69; Nat. Inst. Allergy & Infectious Disease grant, 70-71; mem, Arthritis Found. Dipl, Am. Bd. Allergy, 65. U.S.A.F, 57-59, Capt. Am. Acad. Allergy; Am. Fedn. Clin. Res; fel. Am. Col. Physicians. Antibody formation; hypersensitivity; immunoglobulins. Address: 200 First St. S.W, Rochester, MN 55901.

GLEICHAUF, PAUL H(ARRY), b. Brno, Czech, Aug. 27, 16; U.S. citizen; m. 51; c. 2. PHYSICS. Ph.D, Masaryk Univ, Brno, 39. Develop. engr, radio prod, Electrum Radio Co, 39-40; elec. components, Always Elec. Co,

45-46; res. engr, res. labs, Westinghouse Elec. Corp, 46-52; consult. engr, electronics lab, Gen. Elec. Co, 52-62; mgr. monochrome cathode ray res. & develop. & spec. monochrome cathode ray tube prod, Rauland Corp, Ill, 62-67; mgr. electronic tube eng, Stromberg Carlson Corp, Calif, 67-70, STAFF SCIENTIST, STROMBERG DATAGRAPHIX, INC, 70- Am. Phys. Soc; sr. mem. Inst. Elec. & Electronics Eng. Electron tube development; electron optics; high voltage arcs in vacuum; gas discharges; electroluminescent displays. Address: Stromberg DatagraphiX, Inc, P.O. Box 2449, San Diego, CA 92112.

GLEICHER, GERALD JAY, b. Brooklyn, N.Y, Jan. 31, 39; m. 66; c. 2. ORGANIC CHEMISTRY. B.S, Brooklyn Col, 59; M.S, Michigan, 61, Ph.D. (chem), 63. Instr. CHEM, Michigan, 63; res. assoc, Texas, 64-65; Princeton, 65-66; asst. prof, ORE. STATE UNIV, 66-70, ASSOC. PROF, 70- Am. Chem. Soc; The Chem. Soc. Free radical reaction mechanisms; quantum chemistry; linear free energy relationships; steric effects. Address: Dept. of Chemistry, Oregon State University, Corvallis, OR 97331.

GLEIM, C(LYDE) E(DGAR), b. Wheelersburg, Ohio, July 22, 13; m. 49; c. 3. ORGANIC CHEMISTRY. B.S, Ohio, 35; M.S, Ohio State, 38; Ph.D.(org. chem), Pa. State, 41. Asst. inorg. chem, Ohio, 35; asst. shift chemist, Sharple Solvents Co, Mich, 35-36, res. chemist, 36; asst. Ohio State, 37-38; Pa. State, 39-41; res. chemist, GOODYEAR TIRE & RUBBER CO, 41-50, sr. res. chemist, 50-58, HEAD PLASTICS POLYMERIZATION SECT, 58-65, polymer characterization & specialty polymers sect, 65-67, INFO. ANAL, POLYESTER DIV, FIBER TECH. CTR, 67- Instr, night col, Univ. Akron, 48-50. Am. Chem. Soc. Amyl naphthalenes and amines; pure hydrocarbons; urethans and derivatives; vinyl, allyl, urea-formaldehyde and phenolformaldehyde resins and rubber adhesives; molding and laminating resins; high molecular weight addition and condensation polymers. Address: Polyester Division, Fiber Technical Center, Goodyear Tire & Rubber Co, 142 Goodyear Bldg, Akron, OH 44316.

GLEIM, JAMES K(ILMER), b. Hummelstown, Pa, Apr. 18, 26. ASTRONOMY. A.B, Indiana, 50; M.A, Georgetown, 57; Ph.D.(astron), Pennsylvania, 65. Astronomer, U.S. Naval Observ, 51-59; Goddard Space Flight Ctr, NASA, 59-60; part-time res. engr, res. labs, Franklin Inst, Pa, 60-65; res. engr. physics & astron, off. space sci. & appln, NASA, D.C, 65-70; ASST. PROF. ASTRON, UNIV. FLA, 70- U.S.N, 44-46. Am. Astron. Soc. Positional astrometry; photometry. Address: Dept. of Astronomy, University of Florida, Gainesville, FL 32603.

GLEIM, PAUL STANLEY, b. Wheelersburg, Ohio, Dec. 20, 23; m. 50; c. 2. PHYSICAL CHEMISTRY. B.S, Ohio, 49. Chemist, res. div, Armco Steel Corp, 51-57; engr, semiconductor components div, TEX. INSTRUMENTS INC, 57-59, group leader, Germanium develop. dept, 59-62, semiconductor res. & develop. lab, 62-69, MGR. ADVAN. PROD, CHEM. MAT. DIV, 69- U.S.A, 43-46, T/Sgt. AAAS; Electrochem. Soc. Semiconductor crystal growth; vapor phase deposition of semiconductors and insulators; processing of semiconductors, especially technology of cutting, lapping, mechanical and chemical polishing; semiconductor fabrication; engineering and manufacturing of advanced silicon materials systems for integrated circuits. Address: MS 158, Chemical Materials Division, Texas Instruments, Inc, P.O. Box 5012, Dallas, TX 75222.

GLEIM, WILLIAM KARL THEODORE, b. Berlin, Ger, Sept. 25, 06; m. 38; c. 3. ORGANIC CHEMISTRY. B.S, Munich Tech. Univ, 30, M.S, 32, Dr.Eng, 36. Fel, Biochem. Inst, Sweden, 36-37; res. fel, med. sch, Tufts Univ, 37-41; mem. staff, A.D. Little, Inc, 41-42; Carnation Co, 42-43; ASST. DIR. RES, CORP. RES. CTR, UNIVERSAL OIL PROD. CO, 45- U.S.A, 43-45. AAAS; Am. Chem. Soc; Geochem. Soc. Process and catalyst research in the petroleum refining and petrochemical fields; residual oil and coal conversion; lubricating oils; sulfur removal and sweetening; oxidation inhibitors. Address: Universal Oil Products Co, 30 Algonquin Rd, Des Plaines, IL 60016.

GLEISER, CHESTER A(LEXANDER), b. Camden, N.J, Feb. 27, 19; m. 49; c. 2. VETERINARY & COMPARATIVE PATHOLOGY. V.M.D, Pennsylvania, 40; M.Sc, Ohio State, 41; M.P.H, Hopkins, 48. Chief vet. path. sect, Armed Forces Inst. Path, 50-53, dir. div. vet. med, Walter Reed Army Inst. Res, 53-56, pathologist & asst. chief animal assessment br, med. unit, Ft. Detrick, Md, 56-62; vet. adv, Ministry Agr, Repub. Panama, 62-65; PROF. VET. PATH, COL. VET. MED, TEX. A&M UNIV, 65- Mem. comts. med. & agr, Nat. Acad. Sci. U.S.A, 42-45, Col; Bronze Star Medal. Am. Soc. Exp. Path; Am. Vet. Med. Asn; Am. Col. Vet. Path; Int. Acad. Path. Experimental pathology in the realm of infectious diseases. Address: Dept. of Veterinary Pathology, College of Veterinary Medicine, Texas A&M University, College Station, TX 77843.

GLEISSNER, GENE H(EIDEN), b. Brooklyn, N.Y, Feb. 1, 28. MATHEMATICS. A.B, Columbia, 47, M.A, 48. Lectr, math, Columbia, 48-50; dep. head programming & coding br, U.S. Naval Weapons Lab, 50-54, head comput. div, 55-63, asst. dir. comput, comput. & anal. lab, 63-70; MEM. FACULTY, DEPT. COMPUT. SCI, STANFORD UNIV, 70- Assoc. tech. dir. appl. math. & head appl. math. lab, David Taylor Model Basin, D.C, 65-70. U.S.N.R, 55-58, Lt.(jg). Fel. AAAS; Math. Asn. Am; Am. Math. Soc; Soc. Indust. & Appl. Math; Asn. Comput. Mach. Applications, development, and programming of digital systems. Address: Dept. of Computer Science, Stanford University, Stanford, CA 94305.

GLEIT, CHESTER E(UGENE), b. New York, N.Y, Apr. 26, 33; m. 56; c. 4. ANALYTICAL & PHYSICAL CHEMISTRY. A.B, Chicago, 52, M.S, 55; Union Carbide Chem. Co. fel, Mass. Inst. Tech, 57-58, Ph.D.(chem), 58. Sr. scientist adv. develop. & planning, Bettis Atomic Power Lab, Westinghouse Elec. Corp, 58-61; head, adv. res. & develop. dept, Tracerlab. Div, Lab. for Electronics, Calif, 61-64; ASSOC. PROF. CHEM, N.C. STATE, 64- Mem. tech. adv. comt, Found. Med. Tech. AAAS; Am. Chem. Soc; Am. Asn. Contamination Control; Am. Micros. Soc. Chemistry of excited gases; microparticle analysis; behavior of elements at trace levels; radiochemistry. Address: 1428 Dixie Trail, Raleigh, NC 27607.

GLEITER, M(ELVIN) E(ARL), b. Alma, Wis, June 9, 26; m. 55; c. 2. BIOCHEMISTRY. B.A, Wartburg Col, 51; M.S, Purdue, 56, Du Pont fel, 56-57, Ph.D.(biochem), 58. Asst. biochem, Purdue Univ, 51-52, 54-56, 57-58; sr. res. biochemist, Monsanto Co, 58-64; WIS. STATE UNIV-EAU CLAIRE, 64-67, ASSOC. PROF, BIOCHEM, 67- Chem.C, U.S.A, 52-54. Am. Chem. Soc; Am. Soc. Plant Physiol. Effects of pesticides on environment; biological effects and metabolism of DDT; air and water pollution analysis, plant growth effects. Address: Dept. of Chemistry, Wisconsin State University-Eau Claire, Eau Claire, WI 54701.

GLEITMAN, HENRY, b. Leipzig, Ger, Jan. 4, 25; U.S. citizen; m. 58; c. 2. PSYCHOLOGY. B.S, City Col. New York, 46; Ph.D.(psychol), California, Berkeley, 49. Asst. prof. PSYCHOL, Swarthmore Col, 49-56, assoc. prof, 57-63; prof, Cornell, 63-64; PROF, UNIV. PA, 64-, chmn. dept, 64-71. Am. Psychol. Asn. Animal and human learning and forgetting; experimental aesthetics. Address: Dept. of Psychology, 106 College Hall, University of Pennsylvania, Philadelphia, PA 19104.

GLEN, G(ERALD) L(EONARD), b. Glen Lyon, Pa, July 8, 35; m. 57; c. 5. PHYSICAL CHEMISTRY. B.S, The Citadel, 57; Ph.D.(x-ray crystallog), Cornell Univ, 62. Res. chemist, Atlantic Refining Co, 62-66; sr. scientist, OWENS-ILL. TECH. CTR, 66-70, CHIEF, PHYSICS & CHEM. SECT, 70- Consult, Picatinny Arsenal, 63-70. U.S.A, 62-63, 1st Lt. Am. Chem. Soc; Am. Ceramic Soc; Am. Crystallog. Asn. Use of molecular orbital theory as interpretive tool for x-ray spectroscopy. Address: Owens-Illinois Technical Center, 1700 N. Westwood Ave, Toledo, OH 43607.

GLEN, ROBERT, b. Scotland, June 20, 05; m. 31; c. 2. ENTOMOLOGY. B.Sc, Saskatchewan, 29, M.Sc, 31; Dorr fel, Minnesota, 31-32, Shevlin fel, 32-33, Ph.D.(entomol), 40, hon. LL.D, 59, hon. D.Sc, 60. Jr. & asst. entomologist, Dom. Entom. Lab, Sask, 28-35, in charge wireworm invests, 35-45; res. coord. entom. div, CAN. DEPT. AGR, 45-50, chief, 50-57, assoc. dir. sci. serv, 57-59, dir-gen, res. br, 59-62, asst. dep. minister res, 62-68, SECY, COMMONWEALTH SCI. COMT. & SCI. ADV. TO COMMONWEALTH SECY-GEN, 68- Outstanding achievement award, Univ. Minn, 60; mem, Sci. Coun. Can, 66-68; Order of Can. Medal of Serv, 67. For. assoc. Nat. Acad. Sci; Entom. Soc. Am.(pres, 62, cert. merit, 64); Royal Soc. Can; Entom. Soc. Can.(pres, 57-58, outstanding achievement award, 64); Prof. Inst. Pub. Serv. Can; fel. Agr. Inst. Can; hon. mem. Can. Seed Growers Asn. Morphology and taxonomy of elaterid larvae; control of wireworms; research administration. Address: Commonwealth Scientific Committee, Africa House, Kingsway, London WC23 6BD, England.

GLEN, W(ILLIAM) L(AWRENCE), b. Gourock, Scotland, May 2, 11; nat; m. 44; c. 3. ORGANIC CHEMISTRY. B.Sc, Glasgow, 35, Ph.D.(org. chem), 38; Royal Tech. Col, Glasgow, 35; D.Phil.(org. chem), Oxford, 42. Asst. & demonstr, org. chem, Royal Tech. Col, Glasgow, 35-38; res. worker, Med. Res. Coun, Eng, 38-41; sci. off, Ministry Supply, 41-42; chief res. chemist & asst. works mgr, J.F. MacFarlan & Co, Edinburgh, 42-46; chemist, AYERST, MCKENNA & HARRISON, LTD, MONTREAL, 47-57, ASSOC. DIR. RES, 58- Fel. Royal Inst. Chem; fel. Can. Inst. Chem. Synthetic organic chemistry; organic nitrogen compounds; chemotherapy; antimalarials; alkaloids; steroids; pharmaceuticals. Address: P.O. Box 6115, Montreal, Que, Can.

GLENDE, ERIC A, JR, b. Fergus Falls, Minn, Nov. 12, 38; m. 69; c. 1. BIOCHEMISTRY. B.A, Concordia Col.(Moorhead, Minn), 60; M.S, North Dakota, 62, Ph.D.(biochem), 66. Res. assoc. path, SCH. MED, CASE WEST. RESERVE UNIV, 66-67, PHYSIOL, 67-68, ASST. PROF, 68- AAAS. Toxic and nutritional liver injury. Address: Dept. of Physiology, Case Western Reserve University School of Medicine, Cleveland, OH 44106.

GLENDENIN, LAWRENCE ELGIN, b. Bay City, Mich, Nov. 8, 18; m. 45; c. 3. NUCLEAR CHEMISTRY. S.B, Chicago, 41; Ph.D.(chem), Mass. Inst. Tech, 49. Chemist, metall. lab, Chicago, 42-43; Oak Ridge Nat. Lab, Tenn, 43-46; res. assoc, Mass. Inst. Tech, 46-49; assoc. chemist, ARGONNE NAT. LAB, 49-58, SR. CHEMIST, 58- Sci. exchange, Atomic Energy Res. Estab, Harwell, England, 58-59. Consult, Brookhaven Nat. Lab, 48-49; biophys. lab, Harvard Med. Sch, 47-49. Radiochemist, Bikini resurvey exped, 47. Am. Phys. Soc; Sci. Res. Soc. Am. Radioactivity, nuclear fission; analytical chemistry. Address: Argonne National Lab, 9700 S. Cass Ave, Argonne, IL 60439.

GLENDENING, BLAINE LOGAN, b. Bethany, Mo, July 15, 07; m. 30; c. 2. ANALYTICAL CHEMISTRY. A.B, Kans. State Col. Pittsburg, 32, M.S, 36; Ph.D.(rubidium nutrit), Kansas State, 53. Teacher, rural sch, Kans, 26-28; prin, high sch, Okla, 30-36; teacher, Kans, 36-37, 45-47; supt, Okla, 37-43; chemist, Phillips Petrol. Co, Kansas City Refinery, 43-45; instr. chem, Kansas State, 47-53; PRIN. CHEMIST, KANS. STATE DEPT. HEALTH, 53- Mem, Conf. State & Prov. Pub. Health Lab. Dirs. Dipl, Am. Bd. Clin. Chem, 64. AAAS; Am. Chem. Soc; Am. Acad. Forensic Sci. Toxicology; blood alcohol analysis; food and drug analysis. Address: Division of Labs, Kansas State Dept. of Health, 4000 E. Tenth, Topeka, KS 66607.

GLENDENING, MARY (ELIZA)BETH, b. Monument, Colo, Jan. 10, 14. BIOCHEMISTRY. A.B, West. State Col. Colo, 35; M.S, Denver, 37; fel, Colorado, 37-43, Ph.D.(biochem), 43. Asst, Denver, 35-37; res. assoc, Wayne, 43-44; MED. CTR, UNIV. CALIF, SAN FRANCISCO, 44-46, res. fel. obstet. & gynec, 47-52, asst. res. biochemist, 52-58, ASSOC. RES. BIOCHEMIST, 58- Civilian with Off. Sci. Res. & Develop, 44. AAAS; Am. Chem. Soc; Soc. Exp. Biol. & Med. Endocrinology; turnover of acid soluble phosphates in tissues; enzymes of placenta and of the blood coagulation. Address: 60 Redwood Ave, Corte Madera, CA 94925.

GLENDENING, NORMAN W(ILLARD), b. Chicago, Ill, Nov. 1, 13; m. 40; c. 2. ORGANIC & PHYSICAL CHEMISTRY. B.A, St. Olaf Col, 36; M.S, N.Dak. State, 40. Asst, Wisconsin, 37-38; asst. tech. dir, Albron Pigments Div, Aluminum Co. Am, 40-46; res. assoc. alkyd resins, Miner Labs, Ill, 47-48; formulator, appliance finishes res. & develop, Midwest Indust. Div, Glidden Co, 48-53, group leader, 53-62, sect. supvr, 62-64, qual. control dir, 64-67, MGR. QUAL. CONTROL, MIDWEST INDUST. DEPT, GLIDDEN-DURKEE DIV, SCM CORP, 67- AAAS; Am. Chem. Soc; Fedn. Socs. Paint Technol. Volatile by-products of air-dried linseed oil films; organic finishing systems; protective coatings. Address: Quality Control Dept, Midwest Industrial Dept, Glidden-Durkee Division, SCM Corp, 1855 N. LeClaire Ave, Chicago, IL 60639.

GLENDENNING, NORMAN KEITH, b. Galt, Can, Jan. 17, 31; m. 63; c. 2. THEORETICAL NUCLEAR PHYSICS. B.Sc, McMaster Univ, 54, M.Sc, 55; Ph.D.(physics), Ind. Univ, 59. Physicist, LAWRENCE RADIATION LAB, UNIV. CALIF, BERKELEY, 58-63, sr. staff mem, nuclear chem. div, 63-67, GROUP LEADER, NUCLEAR THEORY DIV, 67- Physicist, Lab. Nuclear Physics, Orsay, France, 62-63; Saclay Nuclear Res. Ctr, 62-63; mem, Int. Conf. Nuclear Struct, Kingston, Ont, 60, Padua, Italy, 62, Gatlinberg, Tenn, 66, Dubna, Russia, 68, Montreal, Que, 69; lectr, Radium Inst, Orsay, France, 62-63, vis. prof. summer 67; lectr. Enrico Fermi Sch. Physics, Italy, summer 67; vis. prof, Inst. Theoret. Physics, Frankfurt, Ger, summer 69. Fel. Am. Phys. Soc. Theoretical research in the field of direct nuclear reactions; two-nucleon transfer reactions; microscopic theory of inelastic scattering; nuclear structure. Address: Lawrence Radiation Lab, University of California, Berkeley, CA 94704.

GLENISTER, BRIAN F(REDERICK), b. Albany, Australia, Sept. 28, 28; nat; m. 56; c. 3. GEOLOGY. B.Sc, Western Australia, 49; M.Sc, Melbourne, 53; Fulbright & Smith-Mundt scholar, Iowa, 54-55, univ. fel, 55-56, Ph.D.(geol), 56. Asst, Univ. Melbourne, Australia, 50-54; Iowa, 54-56; sr. lectr. GEOL, Western Australia, 56-59; asst. prof, UNIV. IOWA, 59-62, assoc. prof, 62-66, PROF, 66-, CHMN. DEPT, 68- AAAS; Paleont. Soc; Soc. Econ. Paleont. & Mineral; Geol. Soc. Am; Brit. Paleont. Asn; Ger. Paleont. Soc; Royal Soc. West. Australia. Fossil cephalopods and conodonts, biostratigraphy. Address: Dept. of Geology, University of Iowa, Iowa City, IA 52240.

GLENISTER, PAUL ROBSON, b. Chicago, Ill, June 18, 18. BIOLOGY. B.Ed, Chicago Teachers Col, 39; S.M, Chicago, 41, Ph.D.(bot), 43. Teacher biol. & bot, Wilson Jr. Col, 43-50; RESEARCHER, J.E. SIEBEL SONS' CO, 50- AAAS; Am. Soc. Plant Physiol; Am. Soc. Brewing Chem. Brewing and fermentation. Address: 6432 S. California Ave, Chicago, IL 60629.

GLENN, ALFRED HILL, b. Yonkers, N.Y, June 3, 21; m. 47. METEOROLOGY. B.S, Wisconsin, 42; M.S, N.Y. Univ, 43; California, Los Angeles, 43; Tulane, 50. Jr. engr, Holway & Cochrane, Tulsa, 39-41; mem. staff, Chicago Bridge & Iron Co, 42; meteorologist, Air Weather Serv, Wash, D.C, 45-47; CONSULT. METEOROLOGIST & PRES, A.H. GLENN & ASSOCS, 47- Panel mem. oceanog, Res. & Develop. Bd, 47-48, mem. subcmt. on oceanog, joint meteorol. cmt; consult, Am. Meteorol. Soc. U.S.A.A.F, 43-45, Capt; Air Medal, 45. Nat. Acad. Sci; AAAS; Am. Meteorol. Soc.(Award for Appl. Meteorol, 62); Am. Soc. Limnol. & Oceanog; fel. Am. Soc. Civil Eng; Am. Geophys. Union; Soc. Petrol. Eng; fel. Royal Meteorol. Soc. Engineering meteorology and oceanography; hurricane and severe storm forecasting; decision theory applications in meteorological-oceanographic forecasting. Address: A.H. Glen & Associates, New Orleans Lakefront Airport, P.O. Box 26337, New Orleans, LA 70126.

GLENN, BERTIS L(AMON), b. Duncan, Okla, Sept. 9, 22; m. 54. VETERINARY & COMPARATIVE PATHOLOGY. D.V.M, Okla. State, 52, M.S, 61; Ph.D.(comp. path), Oklahoma, 63. Asst. prof. VET. PATH, OKLA. STATE UNIV, 53-64, assoc. prof, 64-67, PROF, 67- Nat. Sci. Found. sci. faculty fel, 61-62; Nat. Insts. Health Spec. fel, 62-63. Dipl, Am. Col. Vet. Path. U.S.A, 43-46, Res, 46-53, 2nd Lt. AAAS; Am. Vet. Med. Asn; N.Y. Acad. Sci. Photosensitivity diseases; liver function; congenital porphyria; genital diseases of the dog caused by hormonal disturbances; cytogenetics of domestic animals. Address: Dept. of Veterinary Pathology, College of Veterinary Medicine, Oklahoma State University, Stillwater, OK 74074.

GLENN, DAN MILLARD, b. Asheville, N.C, Dec. 3, 31; m. 55; c. 3. ORGANIC CHEMISTRY. B.S, Davidson Col, 53; M.S, Tennessee, 55, Nat. Insts. Health fel, 55-57, Ph.D.(chem), 57. Res. chemist, MARSHALL RES. LAB, E.I. DU PONT DE NEMOURS & CO, INC, 57-61, res. supvr, 61-65, res. mgr, 65-67, asst. mgr. refinish sales, 67-69, RES. MGR, 69- Am. Chem. Soc. Organic synthesis; polymer chemistry. Address: Marshall Research Lab, E.I. du Pont de Nemours & Co, Inc, 3500 Grays Ferry Ave, Philadelphia, PA 19146.

GLENN, EDWIN E(LWOOD), JR, b. Shreveport, La, June 4, 20; m. 46; c. 1. PHYSICAL CHEMISTRY. B.S, La. State Univ, 41; M.S, Univ. Tex, 48, Ph.D. (chem), 51. SR. RES. TECHNOLOGIST, Socony Mobil Oil Co, Inc, 50-68, MOBIL OIL CORP, 68- C.Eng, 41-46, Res, 45-52, Capt. Am. Chem. Soc. Corrosion of steel in air-free systems; fluid flow through porous media. Address: 6065 Ranchero Lane, Dallas, TX 75211.

GLENN, E(LDRIDGE) MYLES, b. Montgomery, W.Va, June 30, 20; m. 45; c. 2. PHYSIOLOGY. B.S, American Univ, 51; univ. fel, Utah, 51-52; univ. & Am. Arthritis & Rheumatism Found. fels, Western Reserve, 52-56, Ph.D, 56. Technician ENDOCRINOL. & STEROIDS, Nat. Insts. Health, 46-50; res. assoc, UPJOHN CO, 56-63, SR. RES. SCIENTIST, 63- Guest investr, Rockefeller Inst, 59; mem, Am. Arthritis Found. AAAS; Endocrine Soc; N.Y. Acad. Sci; Soc. Exp. Biol. & Med. Adrenocortical steroid physiology and mechanism of action of steroids; experimental arthritis and other connective tissue diseases. Address: Upjohn Co, Henrietta St, Kalamazoo, MI 49001.

GLENN, GEORGE R(EMBERT), b. Anderson, S.C, Sept. 2, 23; m. 44; c. 3. CIVIL ENGINEERING. B.C.E, Clemson, 43, M.S.C.E, 57; B.D, South. Baptist Theol. Sem, 55; Ph.D, Iowa State, 63. Field engr, Daniel Construct. Co, 46-47; resident engr, J.E. Sirrine Co, 48-50; consult. engr, 50-51; instr. eng, speed sci. sch, Louisville, 51-55; prof. eng. & head dept, Bluefield Col, 55-57; Wingate Col, 57-58; asst. prof. appl. sci, Southern Illinois, 58-64; PROF. CIVIL & ENVIRON. ENG, RUTGERS UNIV, 64-, asst. dean col. eng, 64-69, assoc. dean, 69-70. Res. consult, Inst. Indust. Res, Ky, summer 52; design engr, 54, 56, 58; with Nat. Sci. Found. res. participation prog, Iowa State Univ, 60, Ford Found. grant, 61-63; res. civil engr, U.S. Naval Civil Eng. Lab, Calif, 64; pres, Am. Field Serv, N.J; lime-pozzolan stabilization comn, soils & geol. div, Hwy. Res. Bd. C.Eng, 43-46, Res, 46-50; Nat. Guard, 50-51, 1st Lt. Am. Soc. Civil Eng; Am. Soc. Eng. Educ. Foundations; investigation and evaluation of soil properties; physico-chemical phenomena in soil stabilization; effect of soil properties upon use as an engineering material in foundations; structures. Address: Dept. of Civil Engineering, Rutgers University, New Brunswick, NJ 08903.

GLENN, HARRY D(ALE), b. Pittsburgh, Pa, Oct. 15, 19; m. 46; c. 2. ORGANIC CHEMISTRY. B.S, Westminster Col, 41, hon. LL.D, 66; Ph.D. (chem), Purdue, 49. Sr. chemist, chem. div, U.S. Rubber Co, 48-50, group leader, 50-55, mgr. reclaimed rubber res. & develop, 55-57, asst. to dir. res. & develop, 57-58, mgr. res. serv, 58-59, asst. to div. prod. mgr, 59-61, factory mgr, Baton Rouge Plant, 61-62, prod. mgr, 62-64, v.pres. & gen. mgr, 64-69, PRES, UNIROYAL LTD, 69- Am. Chem. Soc; Mfg. Chem. Asn; Soc. Plastics Indust. Rubber and agricultural chemicals; synthetic and reclaimed rubber; plastics. Address: 19 Oakland Ave, Montreal 217, Que, Can.

GLENN, HOWARD JAMES, b. Sioux Falls, S.Dak, May 23, 20; m. 43; c. 3. CHEMISTRY. B.A, St. Olaf Col, 41; M.S, Wisconsin, 44, du Pont fel, 47-48, Ph.D.(chem), 48. Asst. chem, St. Olaf Col, 41-42; Wisconsin, 42-44, Alumni Res. Found. asst, 46-47; res. chemist, Abbott Labs, 48-56, tech. assoc, radiopharmaceut. div, 56-62, head radioisotope res. & develop, new prod. div, 62-66; specialist nuclear med, dept. clin. develop, 66-70; ASSOC. PROF. CHEM. & ASSOC. CHEMIST, UNIV. TEX. M.D. ANDERSON HOSP. & TUMOR RES. INST, 70- Dainabot lectr, Japan, 67. U.S.N, 44-45. Assoc. Am. Chem. Soc; Soc. Nuclear Med; Am. Inst. Chem; N.Y. Acad. Sci; Europ. Thyroid Asn. Pharmaceuticals; formation of cyclic ketones by the inverse Friedel-Crafts reaction; studies related to the Mills-Nixon effect; analgesics; antivirus; radioisotopes; radiopharmaceuticals; radiobiologicals. Address: Dept. of Medicine, University of Texas M.D. Anderson Hospital & Tumor Research Institute, Texas Medical Center, Houston, TX 77025.

GLENN, JAMES FRANCIS, b. Lexington, Ky, May 10, 28; m. 48; c. 4. UROLOGY. B.A, Rochester, 50; Kentucky; M.D, Duke, 53. Intern gen. surg, Peter Bent Brigham Hosp, Boston, Mass, 52-54; resident urol. surg, med. ctr, Duke, 56-59, asst. urol, sch. med, 56-58, instr, 58-59; asst. prof, Yale, 59-61; assoc. prof, Bowman Gray Sch. Med, 61-63; PROF. UROL. & CHIEF UROL. SURG, MED. CTR, DUKE UNIV, 63- Asst. surgeon, Grace-New Haven Hosp, 59-61; attend. urol, N.C. Baptist Hosp, 61-63; consult, Vet. Admin. Hosp, Durham, 63-; Watts Hosp, 64-; Lincoln Hosp, 65- Med.C.Res, 53-55, Capt. Am. Col. Surg; Am. Urol. Asn; Soc. Pediat. Urol; Int. Soc. Urol; Am. Asn. Genito-Urinary Surg; Soc. Univ. Urol.(pres). Adrenal surgery; pediatric urology; genitourinary malignancies. Address: Dept. of Urology, Duke University Medical Center, Durham, NC 27706.

GLENN, JOHN CALLAWAY, b. Birmingham, Ala, Aug. 7, 32; m. 53; c. 4. ANIMAL SCIENCE, REPRODUCTIVE PHYSIOLOGY. B.S, Auburn, 53; M.S, Miss. State, 54; Ph.D.(animal breeding & physiol), Okla. State, 59. Instr. animal sci, Midwestern, 55-57; asst. prof, Imp. Ethiopian Col, 59-61; reproductive physiol, La. State Univ, 61-66; dir. sch. animal sci, Univ. Oriente, Venezuela, 66-68; assoc. prof. animal sci. & coord. int. prog, Univ. Fla, 68-71; EXEC. V.PRES, INT. SCI. CORP, 71- Summers, fel. biophys. & instrumentation inst, Baylor Univ, 64, consult, Ford Found, Venezuela, 64 & 65; hon. prof, Univ. Oriente, Venezuela, 68. AAAS; Am. Soc. Animal Sci. Livestock production in tropical environments; relationship between thyroid function, reproduction and adaptation; factors influencing reproductive efficiency in livestock. Address: International Scientific Corp, 1464 Seabord Dr, Baton Rouge, LA 70810.

GLENN, JOHN F(RANKLIN), b. Phila, Pa, May 4, 15; m. 43; c. 2. ORGANIC CHEMISTRY. B.S, Pennsylvania, 37; M.S, Delaware, 56, Ph.D.(chem), 60. Res. chemist, L.D. Caulk Co, 37-41, 46-58, asst. res. dir, 58-60, dir. res, 60-63, v.pres. res, Del, 63-68; DIR. CENT. RES. LAB, DENTSPLY INT, INC, 68- Mem, Franklin Inst; mem. comn. dent. mat, Int. Dent. Fedn. U.S.A, 41-46, Res, 46-63, Lt. Col. AAAS; Am. Chem. Soc; Int. Asn. Dent. Res. Physical organic chemistry; dental materials. Address: Dentsply International, Inc, 550 W. College Ave, York, PA 17404.

GLENN, JOSEPH LEONARD, b. Albany, N.Y, Jan. 20, 25; m. 50; c. 4. BIOCHEMISTRY. B.S, St. Lawrence, 50; M.S, Syracuse, 52, Ph.D, 54. Nat. Heart Inst. fel, Enzyme Inst, Wisconsin, 54-56; asst. prof. BIOCHEM, ALBANY MED. COL, 56-61, assoc. prof, 61-66, PROF, 66- Lederle Med. Faculty award, 58-61; U.S. Pub. Health Serv. res. career develop. award, 62- U.S.N, 43-46. Am. Soc. Biol. Chem. Cellular metabolism; enzymology. Address: Dept. of Biochemistry, Albany Medical College, Albany, NY 12208.

GLENN, MARLDON WELDON, b. Duncan, Okla, May 29, 19; m. 49; c. 4. VETERINARY PATHOLOGY. D.V.M, Okla. State, 51; Wyoming, 54-59; Am. Vet. Med. Asn. fel, Colo. State, 59-61, Nat. Insts. Health fel, 61-62, Ph.D. (animal path), 62. Asst. prof. vet. sci, Wyoming, 53-57, assoc. prof, 57-62, prof, 62-64; vet. path, Ga. Coastal Plain Exp. Sta, Univ. Georgia, 64-65; exten. vet, S.Dak. State Univ, 65-66; PATHOLOGIST, PATH. & TOXICOL. SECT, AGR. PROD. DIV, UPJOHN CO, KALAMAZOO, 66- Med.C, U.S.A, 42-46. Am. Vet. Med. Asn. Selenium toxicosis; urolithiasis in sheep and cattle. Address: 10830 Four Mile Road, Route 3, Plainwell, MI 49080.

GLENN, RICHARD A(LLEN), b. Brooklyn, N.Y, Mar. 16, 25; m. 47; c. 4. CIVIL ENGINEERING. B.S, Purdue, 49; Swope fel, Washington (St. Louis), 51-52, Ph.D.(geol), 53. Geologist & geophysicist, Standard Oil Co, Calif, 53-61; instr. eng, VENTURA COL, 61-67, DEAN INSTR, 67- U.S.A.A.F, 43-46, 2nd Lt. AAAS; Geol. Soc. Am; Am. Soc. Civil Eng; Am. Asn. Petrol. Geol. Geology and its relationship to the location of economic mineral deposits and to engineering; seismology. Address: 1880 Rice Rd, Ojai, CA 93023.

GLENN, RICHARD A(LVIN), b. McKinney, Tex, Feb. 4, 15; m. 38; c. 1. ORGANIC CHEMISTRY. B.A, N.Tex. State Teachers Col, 36; M.A, Texas, 39, Ph.D.(org. chem), 41. Res. chemist, Pittsburgh Coke & Chem. Co, 41-46; coal res. lab, Carnegie Inst. Tech, 46-54; fel, Mellon Inst, 54-55; mgr. chem. div, BITUMINOUS COAL RES, INC, 55-71, ASST. DIR. RES, 71- Mem. comt. chem. coal, Nat. Res. Coun, 58-62; chmn, Gordon Res. Conf. on Coal, 61. Am. Inst. Chem. Eng; Am. Chem. Soc; Am. Soc. Test. & Mat. Isolation of nitrogen compounds from petroleum distillates; coal tar bases; activated carbon from coal; chemistry of coal hydrogenation products; atmospheric contaminants from coal combustion; control of sulfur oxides in flue gases; nature, occurrence and removal of sulfur from coal; analysis and testing of coal; coking properties of coal; chemical, metallurgical and other process uses of coal; gasification of coal; non-fuel uses of coal. Address: Bituminous Coal Research, Inc, 350 Hochberg Rd, Monroeville, PA 15146.

GLENN, ROLLIN COPPER, U.S. citizen, Nov. 25, 27; m. 53; c. 3. SOILS. B.S, Va. Polytech. Inst. & State Univ, 55, M.S, 57; Ph.D.(soils), Univ. Wis, 59. Asst. prof. AGRON, MISS. STATE UNIV, 59-61, assoc. prof, 62-66, PROF, 66- U.S.A, 46-51, M/Sgt. Am. Soc. Agron; Soil Sci. Soc. Am; Soil Conserv. Soc. Am; Clay Minerals Soc; Int. Soc. Soil Sci. Soil chemistry and mineralogy; soil conservation, genesis and morphology; turf soils. Address: Dept. of Agronomy, Mississippi State University, P.O. Drawer NY, State College, MS 39762.

GLENN, THOMAS M, b. Detroit, Mich, July 20, 40; m. 62; c. 3. PHARMACOLOGY, PHYSIOLOGY. A.B, Rockhurst Col, 62; univ. fel. & M.S, Univ. Mo-Kansas City, 65, Nat. Inst. Ment. Health fel. & Ph.D.(pharmacol), 68. Assoc. prof. pharmacol, N.Dak. State Univ, 66-68; Fla. A&M Univ, 68-69; vis. assoc. prof, Univ. Miss, summer 69; Nat. Heart & Lung Inst. fel. physiol, sch. med, Univ. Va, 69-71; ASST. PROF. PHARMACOL, MED. COL. PA, 71- AAAS. Biochemistry; cardiovascular pharmacology, especially pathogenesis of circulatory shock and the therapeutics of shock, special emphasis on toxic factors in shock and the role of lysosomes and lysosomal enzymes in circulatory shock. Address: Dept. of Pharmacology, Medical College of Pennsylvania, 3300 Henry Ave, Philadelphia, PA 19129.

GLENN, WILLIAM A(LEXANDER), b. Can, Jan. 25, 22; m. 43; c. 2. STATISTICS. B.A, New Brunswick, 48; M.S, Va. Polytech, 58, Ph.D.(statist), 59. Asst. prof. math, Mt. Allison, 49-56; statist, Va. Polytech, 57-59, assoc. prof, 59-60; STATISTICIAN. RES. TRIANGLE INST, 60- R.C.A.F, 41-45. Am. Statist. Asn; Inst. Math. Statist; Biomet. Soc. Statistical design of experiments and paired comparisons; applications to the physical behavioral sciences; statistical aspects of the reliability of components and systems. Address: Research Triangle Institute, P.O. Box 12194, Research Triangle Park, NC 27709.

GLENN, W(ILLIAM) E(LLIS), b. Atlanta, Ga, May 12, 26; m. 49; c. 2. ELECTRONICS. B.E, Ga. Inst. Tech, 46; M.S, California, 49, Ph.D.(elec. eng), 52. Asst. electronics, radiation lab, California, 47-52; physicist, res. lab, Gen. Elec. Co, 52-67; DIR. APPL. PHYSICS DEPT, CBS LABS, COLUMBIA BROADCASTING SYST, INC, 67- U.S.N.R, 46-47, Res, 47-, Lt.(jg). Fel. Soc. Motion Picture & TV Eng. Pulse analysis for radiation energy spectrum determination; time-of-flight mass spectrograph; electro-mechanical transducers; color television reproducers; thermoplastic recording. Address: CBS Labs, High Ridge Rd, Stamford, CT 06905.

GLENN, WILLIAM G(RANT), b. Lansdowne, Pa, Dec. 21, 16; m. 39. ZOOLOGY. B.Sc, Trinity (Tex), 48, M.A, 52; M.Sc, Rutgers, 55, Ph.D.(zool), 56; U.S. Air Force fel, Sch. Aviation Med, 55-56. Asst. biol, genetics, Rutgers, 48, 53-55; instr. biol, Trinity (Tex), 49; teacher, pub. sch, Tex, 49-53; head, immunol. sect, U.S. Air Force Sch. Aviation Med, 56-63, chief immunobiol. unit, U.S. Air Force Sch. Aerospace Med, 63-69, sr. res. immunologist, 69-70; DIR. AUTOMATED BIOSYSTS. CTR. & CHIEF, IMMUNOL. SERV, CYBERTEK, INC, 70- Dipl, Am. Bd. Microbiol, 65. U.S.C.G, 42-46. AAAS; Am. Asn. Immunol; fel. Am. Acad. Microbiol; Am. Soc. Microbiol. Immunochemistry; antigen-antibody diffusion; plasma proteins; comparative serology; biomedical instrumentation. Address: Automated Biosystems Center, Cybertek, Inc, 146 W. Goodnight Ave, Aransas Pass, TX 78336.

GLENN, WILLIAM H(ENRY), JR, b. Philadelphia, Pa, Dec. 22, 37; m. 66; c. 2. PHYSICS. S.B. & M.S, Mass. Inst. Tech, 60, Ph.D.(physics), 66. Instr. physics, Southeast. Mass. Tech. Inst, 65; sr. res. scientist, UNITED AIRCRAFT RES. LABS, 66-68, PRIN. SCIENTIST, 68- Lectr, Hartford Grad. Ctr, Rensselaer Polytech, 68. Am. Phys. Soc; Inst. Elec. & Electronics Eng. Quantum and nonlinear optics; laser and plasma physics. Address: United Aircraft Research Labs, 400 Main St, East Hartford, CT 06108.

GLENN, WILLIAM W(ALLACE) L(UMPKIN), b. Asheville, N.C, Aug. 12, 14; m. 43; c. 2. SURGERY. B.S, South Carolina, 34; M.D, Jefferson Med. Col, 38; hon. M.A, Yale, 61. Intern, Pa. Hosp, 38-40; surg, Mass. Gen. Hosp, 40-41; 45-46; asst. physiol, sch. pub. health, Harvard, 41-43; assoc. surg, Jefferson Med. Col, 46-48; from instr. to PROF. SURG, SCH. MED, YALE, 48-, CHIEF CARDIOTHORACIC SURG, 68- Pres, Am. Heart Asn, 70-71. U.S.A, 41-46. Cardiovascular physiology and surgery; physiology of the lymphatics; medical education; cardiothoracic surgery. Address: Dept. of Surgery, Yale University School of Medicine, 333 Cedar, New Haven, CT 06510.

GLENNAN, T(HOMAS) KEITH, b. Enderlin, N.Dak, Sept. 8, 05; m. 31; c. 4. ELECTRICAL ENGINEERING. B.S, Yale, 27, hon. M.A, 61; hon. D.Sc, Clarkson Technol, 47, Oberlin Col, 50, John Carroll, 54, Akron, 59, Toledo, 61, Muhlenberg Col, 61, Columbia, 61, Southern California, 64, Lehigh Univ, 66; hon. D.E, Fenn Col, 53, Stevens Inst. Technol, 54, Case, 60; hon. LL.D, Western Reserve, 60, Tulane, 60, Miami (Ohio), 60; Cleveland State Univ, 67. Mem. staff, Elec. Res. Prod, Inc, N.Y, 27-35; opers. mgr, Paramount Pictures, Inc, Calif, 35-39, studio mgr, 39-41; exec, Vega Airplane Corp, 61; studio mgr, Samuel Goldwyn Studios, 41-42; dir. U.S. Navy underwater sound lab, div. war res, Columbia, 42-45; exec, Ansco Corp, 45-47; pres, CASE WEST. RESERVE UNIV, 47-66, EMER. PRES, 66- Comnr, Atomic Energy Comn, 50-52; first adminr, NASA, 58-61; trustee, Rand Corp, 62-; Case West. Reserve Univ, 70-; pres, Assoc. Univs, Inc, 65-68; asst. to chmn, Urban Coalition, 68-69; U.S. ambassador, Int. Atomic Energy Agency, 70-; alumni fel, Yale Corp, 62-68; dir, Repub. Steel Corp; Standard Oil Co.(Ohio); Air Prod. & Chem, Inc; Avco Corp. Medal for merit, U.S. Govt; distinguished serv. medal, NASA, 67. Nat. Acad. Eng; fel. Am. Acad. Arts & Sci; Benjamin Franklin fel. Royal Soc. Arts. Academic and research administration. Address: 11483 Waterview, Reston, VA 22070.

GLENNE, BARD, b. Oslo, Norway, May 2, 35; m. 67; c. 1. CIVIL & ENVIRONMENTAL ENGINEERING. B.S, Washington State, 57; M.S, Mass. Inst. Tech, 59; Ph.D.(civil eng), California, Berkeley, 66. Res. engr, Norwegian Inst. Water Res, 60-61; Swiss Fed. Inst. Tech, 62-63; Asst. prof. civil eng, Nevada, 63-64; res. assoc, California, Berkeley, 64-66; hydraul. engr, Nor-

consult A. S, Oslo, Norway, 66-68; asst. prof. CIVIL ENG, Ore. State Univ, 68-70; ASSOC. PROF, UNIV. UTAH, 70- Am. Geophys. Union; Am. Soc. Civil Eng; Int. Asn. Hydraul. Res; Norweg. Soc. Prof. Eng. Utilization and management of fresh and salt water resources. Address: Dept. of Civil Engineering, University of Utah, Salt Lake City, UT 84112.

GLENNER, GEORGE G(EIGER), b. Brooklyn, N.Y, Sept. 17, 27; m 54; c. 2. PATHOLOGY. A.B, Hopkins, 49, M.D, 53. Res. path, Mallory Inst. Path, Boston City Hosp, 54-55; res. pathologist, sect. histochem, path. lab, Nat. Insts. Health, 55-57; asst. pathologist, hosp, Hopkins, 57-58; chief, sect. histochem, path. lab, NAT. INST. ARTHRITIS & METAB. DISEASES, 59-70, CHIEF SECT. MOLECULAR PATH. LAB. EXP. PATH, 71- Asst, sch. med, Hopkins, 57-58; guest instr, sch. med, Kansas, 60, 61, 64, 65; assoc. prof, sch. med, Georgetown, 65- Dipl, Am. Bd. Path, 58. U.S.P.H.S, 55-, Med. Dir. Am. Soc. Exp. Path; Am. Asn. Path. & Bact; Histochem. Soc. Disturbances of protein metabolism; pathology of endocrine tumors; histochemistry and biochemistry of amino acids and proteolytic enzymes; histochemical enzyme kinetics; nature and pathogenesis of amyloidosis. Address: Section on Molecular Pathology, Lab. Experimental Pathology, National Institute of Arthritis & Metabolic Diseases, National Institutes of Health, Bethesda, MD 20014.

GLENNON, ALLAN N(EWTON), b. Omaha, Nebr, Dec. 9, 23; m. 49; c. 8. APPLIED PHYSICS, ELECTRONICS. B.S, U.S. Naval Acad, 45; B.S, U.S. Naval Postgrad. Sch, 52; M.S, Univ. Calif, Los Angeles, 53; cert, Armed Forces Staff Col, 59. Engr-scientist, Tracor, Inc, 65-69; pres, Image Assoc, Inc, 69-70; COMMUN. CONSULT, 70-; ENGR-SCIENTIST, TRACOR, INC, 71- U.S.N, 45-65, Lt. Comdr. Advanced sonar systems; underwater acoustics. Address: 3914 Sierra Dr, Austin, TX 78731.

GLESER, GOLDINE, b. St. Louis, Mo, June 15, 15; m. 36; c. 3. PSYCHOLOGY. A.B, Washington (St. Louis), 35, M.S, 36, Ph.D.(psychol), 50. Res. asst. neuropsychiat. & anat, Washington (St. Louis), 50-51, neuropsychiat, 52, instr. med. psychol, 52-53, res. assoc. neuropsychiat, 53-54; asst. prof. PSYCHOL, DEPT. PSYCHIAT, COL. MED, UNIV. CINCINNATI & CINCINNATI GEN. HOSP, 56-58, assoc. prof, 58-64, PROF, 64-, DIR. PSYCHOL. DIV, 67- Res. asst. prof, Illinois, 57-58, res. assoc. prof. ed, 58-63; fel. grad. sch, Univ. Cincinnati, 71. Consult, Off. Naval Res. & Univ. Illinois, 51-55; Bliss Res. Lab, Washington (St. Louis), 54-56; mem. adv. comt, clin. drug eval, psychopharmacol. serv. ctr, Nat. Inst. Ment. Health, 60-61. AAAS; Am. Psychol. Asn; Am. Statist. Asn; Psychomet. Soc; Am. Col. Neuropsychopharmacol; Soc. Multivariate Exp. Psychol. Psychometric theory; development of measures of personality and affect; effect of psychopharmacologic drugs. Address: Dept. of Psychiatry, University of Cincinnati College of Medicine, Cincinnati General Hospital, Cincinnati, OH 45229.

GLESER, LEON JAY, b. St. Louis, Mo, Dec. 17, 39; m. 69. MATHEMATICAL STATISTICS. B.S, Chicago, 60; M.S, Stanford, 62, Nat. Sci. Found. fel, 60-63, Ph.D.(statist), 63. Asst. prof. math. statist, Columbia, 63-65; JOHNS HOPKINS UNIV, 65-69, ASSOC. PROF. STATIST. & BIOSTATIST, 69- Vis. fel, Educ. Testing Serv, 71-72. AAAS; Am. Statist. Asn; Inst. Math. Statist. Statistical inference; multivariate statistical analysis; large sample theory; sociometrics; psychometrics; biometrics. Address: Dept. of Statistics, Johns Hopkins University, Baltimore, MD 21218.

GLESS, ELMER E, b. Rogers, Nebr, Feb. 3, 28; m. 62; c. 2. BIOLOGY, ACAROLOGY. B.A.Ed, Arizona State, 55; M.S, Iowa State, 57, Ph.D.(acarology), 68. Med. entomologist, U.S. Dept. Agr, Tex, 58-59; William Cooper & Nephews, Inc, 59-62; instr. biol, Northern Illinois, 62-64; field entomologist, Bernice P. Bishop Mus, Hawaii, 65-67; res. assoc, Iowa State, 67-68; asst. prof. biol, MONT. COL. MINERAL SCI. & TECHNOL, 68-70, ASSOC. PROF. BIOL. SCI. & HEAD DEPT, 70- U.S.N, 46-48. Am. Entom. Soc. Prostigmatid mite biology and taxonomy. Address: Dept. of Biological Sciences, Montana College of Mineral Science & Technology, Butte, MT 59701.

GLESS, GEORGE E, b. Schuyler, Nebr, Jan. 15, 17; m. 40; c. 2. ELECTRICAL ENGINEERING. B.S, Colorado, 40, M.S, 48; Nat. Sci. Found. fel, Iowa State, 61-62, Ph.D.(elec. eng), 63. Student engr, Commonwealth Edison Co, Ill, 40-41, electronic & control engr, 41-46; instr. ELEC. ENG, UNIV. COLO, BOULDER, 46-48, asst. prof, 48-56, assoc. prof, 56-64, PROF, 64-, in charge hybrid comput. facility, 66-69. Consult, sidewinder missile proj, Naval Ord. Test Sta, Calif, summer 59; partic, NASA summer inst, Houston & Rice Univs, summer 69. Am. Soc. Eng. Educ; Inst. Elec. & Electronics Eng. Computers and control systems; power system stability. Address: Dept. of Electrical Engineering, University of Colorado, Boulder, CO 80302.

GLESSNER, ALFRED JOSEPH, b. Chester, Pa, Jan. 19, 43; m. 66. CHEMICAL ENGINEERING. B.Ch.E, Villanova Univ, 64; Nat. Defense Educ. Act fel, Univ. Pa, 64-67, M.S, 67, Nat. Sci. Found grant, 67-69, Ph.D.(chem. eng), 69. RES. ENGR, RES. & DEVELOP, SUN OIL CO, 69- Am. Inst. Chem. Eng; Am. Chem. Soc. Physical adsorption; thermodynamics; statistical mechanics; molecular sieves; separation processes; solid-liquid phase equilibrium; petroleum refining processes; catalytic reforming; catalytic cracking. Address: Research & Development, Sun Oil Co, P.O. Box 426, Marcus Hook, PA 19061.

GLEW, DAVID N(EVILLE), b. Stamford, Eng, Sept. 27, 28; m. 52; c. 4. PHYSICAL CHEMISTRY. B.A, Cambridge, 49, British Celanese fel, 50-52, Ph.D.(phys. chem), 52. Fel, Nat. Res. Coun. Can, Ottawa, 52-54; Atomic Energy Cmn. contract, with Prof. J.H. Hildebrand, California, 54-55; sr. lectr. chem. & in charge dept, Univ. Natal, Durban, S.Africa, 55-57; res. chemist, DOW CHEM. CAN, LTD, 57-61, assoc. scientist, 61-67, SCIENTIST, 67- Faraday Soc; fel. Chem. Inst. Can. Water and aqueous solution structure, properties and H-bonding; reaction kinetics; thermodynamics and phase equilibria of aqueous systems. Address: Dow Chemical of Canada, Ltd, Sarnia, Ont, Can.

GLEW, DONALD H(ENRY), JR, b. Washington, D.C, Sept. 18, 24; m. 48; c. 3. SURGERY. B.S, Yale, 45; M.D, George Washington, 48. Intern, Walter Reed Gen. Hosp, 48-49, asst. resident surg, 49-50; chief surg. & prof. serv, Mobil Army Surg. Hosp, 50-53; chief surg, U.S. Army Dispensary, Pentagon, 53-54; jr. resident, Walter Reed Gen. Hosp, 54-55, sr. resident, 55-

56, chief resident, 56-57, clin. investr, Walter Reed Army Inst. Res, 57-58; chief surg, U.S. Army Hosp, Md, 58-61; surg. res. br, U.S. Army Res. & Develop. Command, Off. Surgeon Gen, 61-65; ASSOC. PROF. SURG. & DIR. SURG. RES. LABS, GEORGE WASHINGTON UNIV, 65- Teaching fel. surg, Walter Reed Gen. Hosp, 57-58; attending univ. staff mem, George Washington Univ. Hosp, 65-; prin. investr, U.S. Pub. Health Serv. grant, 67- Consult, Surgeon Gen, U.S. Army Res. & Develop, 65-; Fairfax Hosp, 67- Ed, Mil. Med, 65-67. Army mem, surg. study sect, U.S. Pub. Health Serv. Adv. Groups, Nat. Insts. Health, 61-65; interdept. comt, Nat. Blood Prog, 61-65; mem, Defense Atomic Support Agency Thermal & Blast Subpanels, 61-65; adv. comt, Surgeon Gen, 61-65; Army liaison mem. comt. shock & subcomt. transfusion probs, div. med. sci, Nat. Acad. Sci-Nat. Res. Coun, 61-65; mem, Brit-Am. Working Group Lasers, 63-65; ad hoc comn. artificial implantable heart, Nat. Heart Inst, 65- Dipl, Am. Bd. Surg, 58. Med.C, U.S.A, 42-46, 48-65, Lt. Col. AAAS; Am. Med. Asn; Asn. Mil. Surg. U.S; Am. Col. Surg; N.Y. Acad. Sci. Shock; trauma; gastrointestinal surgery; resuscitation; biological effects of lasers; small vessel surgery; plasma volume expanders. Address: George Washington University Medical Center, 2150 Pennsylvania Ave, N.W, Washington, DC 20037.

GLEWWE, CARL W(ILLIAM), b. St. Paul, Minn, May 1, 27; m. 53; c. 3. ELECTRICAL ENGINEERING, COMPUTER SCIENCES. B.S, Univ. Minn, 50, M.S, 55, Ph.D.(elec. eng), 58. Instr. elec. eng, Univ. Minn, 53-58; syst. design engr. DIGITAL COMPUT, UNIVAC DIV, SPERRY RAND CORP, 58-61, mgr, 61-69, GROUP MGR, 69- Sr. engr, Gen. Mills, Inc, 57-58. U.S.N, 45-46, 51-53. Computer design. Address: Defense Systems Division, Univac Division, Sperry Rand Corp, P.O. Box 3525, St. Paul, MN 55101.

GLEYSTEEN, LELAND F(REDERIC), b. Alton, Iowa, Oct. 4, 11; m. 35; c. 4. CHEMISTRY. A.B, Grinnell Col, 32; univ. fel, Brown, Ph.D.(phys. chem), 36. Instr. chem, Brown, 36-37; res. assoc, Textile Found, Brown, 37-38, Nat. Bur. Standards, 38-41, U.S. Cane Sugar Refiners res. proj, 41-45; sr. res. chemist, Phillips Petrol. Co, Tex, 45-46; RES. CHEMIST, Owens-Ill. Glass Co, 46-52; ATLAS CHEM. INDUSTS, INC, WILMINGTON, DEL, 52- Am. Chem. Soc; Am. Inst. Chem. Adsorption; conductance of solutions of electrolytes; physical chemistry of textile materials; physical and chemical nature of activated carbons. Address: 409 Locust Lane N, West Chester, PA 19380.

GLEYZAL, ANDRE, b. New Orleans, La, Nov. 23, 08. MATHEMATICS. B.A, Ohio State, 31, M.A, 33, Ph.D.(math), 36; Princeton, 36-37. Instr. physics, Boston Col, 37-38; prof. math, St. Michael's Col, 38-41; MATHEMATICIAN, U.S. Dept. Navy, 41-51; Nat. Bur. Standards, 51-53; U.S. NAVAL ORD. LAB, 53- Am. Math. Soc. General flow of metals; vibration of ships; general vibration problems; shock wave theory; linear programming; non-steady viscous flow of fluids; aerodynamical trajectories; tensor analysis; relativity, unified field theory, absolute Newtonian calculus; analytic space, time, matter. Address: U.S. Naval Ordnance Lab, Silver Spring, MD 20910.

GLEZEN, WILLIAM PAUL, b. Oblong, Ill, Mar. 15, 31; m. 53; c. 2. MEDICINE, INFECTIOUS DISEASES. B.S, Purdue, 53; B.S, Illinois, 54, M.D, 56. Instr. pediat, sch. med, North Carolina, 61-62; epidemiologist, Kansas City Field Sta, Commun. Disease Ctr, U.S. Pub. Health Serv, 62-64, chief respiratory & enteric virus disease unit, 64-65; asst. prof. PEDIAT, SCH. MED, UNIV. N.C, CHAPEL HILL, 65-69, ASSOC. PROF, 69- Instr, sch. med, Kansas, 63-65. U.S.P.H.S, 57-65, Comdr. Epidemiology and etiology of acute respiratory disease; epidemiology of mycobacterial infections. Address: Dept. of Pediatrics, School of Medicine, University of North Carolina at Chapel Hill, Chapel Hill, NC 27514.

GLICK, ARNOLD J, b. Brooklyn, N.Y, Nov. 7, 31; m. 53; c. 3. PHYSICS. B.A, Brooklyn Col, 55; Ph.D.(physics), Maryland, 61. Nat. Sci. Found. fel, Weizmann Inst, 59-61; asst. prof. PHYSICS, UNIV. MD, COLLEGE PARK, 61-67, ASSOC. PROF, 67- Nat. Sci. Found. fel, Univ. Paris, Orsay & Ctr. for Nuclear Study, Saclay, France, 67-68. U.S.A, 52-54. Am. Phys. Soc. Quantum mechanical many body problem; quantum mechanics of solids; superconductivity. Address: 9321 St. Andrews Pl, College Park, MD 20740.

GLICK, BRUCE, b. Pittsburgh, Pa, May 5, 27; m. 50; c. 3. PHYSIOLOGY, GENETICS. B.Sc, Rutgers, 51; M.Sc, Massachusetts, 53; Ph.D.(genetics & physiol), Ohio State, 55. Asst, Massachusetts, 51-52; Ohio State, 52-55; asst. & assoc. prof. POULTRY PHYSIOL. & ANIMAL GENETICS, MISS. STATE UNIV, 55-59, PROF, 59- U.S.A, 45-47. Fel. AAAS; Am. Physiol. Soc; Am. Asn. Immunol; Wilson Ornith. Soc; Poultry Sci. Asn; Am. Ornith. Union. Physiology of lymphatic tissue in the bird, especially bursa of Fabricius; stress picture in the chicken; immunology. Address: Dept. of Poultry Physiology & Animal Genetics, Mississippi State University, P.O. Box 5188, State College, MS 39762.

GLICK, C(HARLES) F(REY), b. Allentown, Pa, Apr. 21, 17; m. 46; c. 1. CHEMISTRY. B.S, Lehigh, 38, fel, 38-40, M.S, 40; univ. fel, Mass. Inst. Tech, 40-43, Du Pont fel, 42-43, Ph.D.(phys. chem), 43. Res. chemist, E.I. du Pont de Nemours & Co, N.J, 43-46; supvr. phys. res. lab, Barrett div, Allied Chem. & Dye Corp, 46-53; asst. head physics lab, Rohm & Haas Co, 53-56, res. technologist, 56-59; SECT. SUPVR, PHYSICS & ANAL. CHEM. DIV, U.S. STEEL CORP, 59- Am. Chem. Soc. Chemical physics; instrumental methods of organic and inorganic analysis. Address: M.S, 15, Applied Research Lab, U.S. Steel Corp, Monroeville, PA 15146.

GLICK, DAVID, b. Homestead, Pa, May 3, 08; m. 29, 41, 45; c. 4. HISTOCHEMISTRY. B.S, Pittsburgh, 29, Ph.D.(biochem), 32; summer, Columbia, 30. Asst. chem, Pittsburgh, 29-32; Hernsheim fel. chem, Mt. Sinai Hosp, N.Y, 32-34; chief chemist, Mt. Zion Hosp, San Francisco, 34-36; Rockefeller fel, Carlsberg Lab, Denmark, 36-37; chief chemist, Newark Beth Israel Hosp, 37-42; head vitamin & enzyme res, Russell-Miller Milling Co, Minn, 43-46; assoc. prof. physiol. chem, Minnesota, 46-50, PROF, 50-61; HISTOCHEM. & HEAD DIV, MED. SCH, STANFORD UNIV, 61- Vis. res. chemist, Carlsberg Lab, Denmark, 33; fel, Commonwealth Fund, Carlsberg Lab, Denmark, Inst. Cell Res, Stockholm, 49, 58-59, Zool. Sta, Naples, 59; career award, U.S. Pub. Health Serv, 62-; Macfarlane vis. prof, Glasgow, 70-71. Consult, toxicity lab, Chicago, 45-46; Vet. Admin. Hosp, Minneapolis, 46-47, Ft. Detrick, 57-67, Palo Alto, 61- Mem. cytochem. panel, comt. growth, Nat. Res. Coun, 51-55. Dipl, Am. Bd. Clin. Chem, 53. Ed, Methods of Biochem. Anal, 53- War chemist, Off. Sci. Res. & Develop, 42-43. AAAS; Am. Chem. Soc; Soc. Exp. Biol. & Med; Am. Soc. Biol. Chem; Histochem. Soc.(v.pres, 50, 69; pres, 51, 70); Am. Soc. Cell Biol; fel. Royal Micros. Soc; Int. Soc. Cell Biol; for. mem. Royal Danish Acad. Histochemistry quantitative techniques and applications. Address: Dept. of Pathology, Division of Histochemistry, R226, Stanford Medical Center, Palo Alto, CA 94305

GLICK, DAVID M, b. San Francisco, Calif, Jan. 4, 36; m. 61; c. 3. BIOCHEMISTRY, ENZYMOLOGY. B.A, Oberlin Col, 57; Ph.D.(biochem), Western Reserve, 62. Res. assoc. BIOCHEM, Weizmann Inst, 62-63; King's Col, London, 63; State Univ. N.Y. Buffalo, 64; Brookhaven Nat. Lab, 64-66; ASST. PROF, MED. COL. WIS, 66- Fel, Arthritis & Rheumatism Found, 62-64. AAAS; Am. Chem. Soc; Am. Soc. Biol. Chem; Brit. Biochem. Soc. Mechanism of enzyme action studied through kinetics, thermodynamics, and solute effects. Address: Dept. of Biochemistry, Medical College of Wisconsin, 561 N. 15th St, Milwaukee, WI 53233.

GLICK, FORREST I(RVING), b. Glasgow, Mont, May 24, 34; m. 58, 64; c. 3. PHYSICS. B.A, St. Olaf Col, 56; M.S, Minnesota, 59, Ph.D.(physics), 66. Instr. PHYSICS, Minnesota, 63-64; asst. prof, MANKATO STATE COL, 64-66, assoc. prof, 66-71, PROF, 71- Am. Phys. Soc; Am. Asn. Physics Teachers. Liquid helium; low temperature physics. Address: Dept. of Physics, Mankato State College, Mankato, MN 56001.

GLICK, F(RANCIS) J(AMES), b. Columbus, Ind, Oct. 9, 16; m. 55; c. 4. ORGANIC CHEMISTRY. A.B, DePauw, 39; fel. & Ph.D.(biochem), Illinois, 43. Asst. biochem, Illinois, 39-41; head chemist, Off. Sci. Res. & Develop. proj, med. sch, Illinois, 42-43; sr. chemist, Nat. Aniline Div, Allied Chem. & Dye Corp, 43-50; instr, Albion Col, 51; asst. prof, MacMurray Col, 51-54; CHEM, UNIV. MINN, DULUTH, 54-61, ASSOC. PROF, 61- Am. Chem. Soc. Laboratory preparation of pharmaceutical chemicals; chemistry of brain lipids; biochemical analytic chemistry; industrial research and development; organic chemistry. Address: Dept. of Chemistry, University of Minnesota, Duluth, MN 55812.

GLICK, GERALD, b. Brooklyn, N.Y, Apr. 3, 34; m. 63; c. 4. INTERNAL MEDICINE, CARDIOLOGY. A.B, Cornell, 55, M.D, 58. Intern med, sch. med, Rochester & Strong Mem. Hosp, 58-59, res, 59-60; U.S. Pub. Health Serv. fel. cardiol, 60-62; sr. investr, cardiol br, Nat. Heart Inst, 62-68; assoc. prof. pharmacol. & med. & dir. div. clin. cardiovasc. pharmacol, Baylor Col. Med, 68-71; DIR. CARDIOVASC. INST, MICHAEL REESE HOSP. & MED. CTR, 71- Am. Heart Asn. estab. investr, 63-69; attend physician, Nat. Heart Inst, 63-69; hon. med. asst, Postgrad. Med. Sch. & Hammersmith Hosp, London, Eng, 64-65; chief electrocardiographer, Nat. Insts. Health, 66-68. Dipl, Am. Bd. Internal Med, 66; Am. Bd. Cardiovasc. Disease, 68. U.S.P.H.S, 66-68, Sr. Surg. AAAS; fel. Am. Col. Physicians; Am. Physiol. Soc; Am. Fedn. Clin. Res; Am. Med. Asn; Am. Soc. Clin. Invest; Am. Soc. Pharmacol. Clinical cardiology and investigations relating to the autonomic nervous control of the cardiovascular system and the determinants of ventricular function. Address: Cardiovascular Institute, Michael Reese Hospital & Medical Center, Chicago, IL 60616.

GLICK, J. LESLIE, b. N.Y.C, Mar. 2, 40; m. 61; c. 2. MOLECULAR BIOLOGY. A.B, Columbia, 61, U.S. Pub. Health fel, 62-64, Ph.D.(zool), 64. U.S. Pub. Health Serv. vis. res, fel. biochem, Princeton, 64-65; sr. cancer res. scientist, Roswell Park Mem. Inst, 65-67, assoc. cancer res. scientist, 67-69; EXEC. V.PRES, ASSOC. BIOMEDIC SYSTS, INC, 69- Asst. res. prof, Roswell Park Div, State Univ. N.Y. Buffao, 67-68, assoc. res. prof. & acting chmn, 68-70. Am. Asn. Cancer Res; Am. Physiol. Soc; N.Y. Acad. Sci. Genetic transformation of mammalian cells. Address: Associated Biomedic Systems, Inc, 872 Main St, Buffalo, NY 14202.

GLICK, JOHN HENRY, JR, b. Cumberland, Md, June 16, 24; m. 54; c. 5. CLINICAL CHEMISTRY. A.B, Catholic Univ, 49; Ph.D.(biochem), St. Louis, 56. From instr. to asst. prof. biochem, Col. Med. & Dent. N.J. Newark, 56-66; BIOCHEM. IN PATH, MED. CTR, UNIV. KANS, 66-70, ASSOC. PROF, 70- U.S.A.A.F, 43-45. AAAS. Lipoproteins; patient test data analysis. Address: Dept. of Biochemistry in Pathology, University of Kansas Medical Center, Kansas City, KS 66103.

GLICK, LAVERNE A(LTON), b. Glasgow, Mont, Nov. 20, 31; m. 58; c. 1. ORGANIC CHEMISTRY. B.A, St. Olaf Col, 54; M.S, Purdue Univ, 58; Ph.D.(org. chem), Fla. State Univ, 63. Chemist, Monsanto Chem. Co, summers 55 & 56; SR. RES. CHEMIST, MOBIL CHEM. CO, METUCHEN, 62- Am. Chem. Soc. Synthetic organic chemistry; organic stereochemistry and agricultural chemicals. Address: 12 Lahiere Ave, Edison, NJ 08817.

GLICK, MILTON D(ON), b. Memphis, Tenn, July 30, 37; m. 65; c. 1. PHYSICAL & INORGANIC CHEMISTRY. A.B, Augustana Col.(Ill), 59; Ph.D.(phys. chem), Wisconsin, 65. Fel. x-ray crystallog, Cornell, 64-66; asst. prof. CHEM, WAYNE STATE UNIV, 66-70, ASSOC. PROF, 70- Am. Chem. Soc; Am. Crystallog Asn; The Chem. Soc. X-ray crystallographic studies on compounds of chemical and biological interest; structure and magnetism of rare earth complexes; computer applications in chemistry. Address: Dept. of Chemistry, Wayne State University, Detroit, MI 48202.

GLICK, PHILLIP RAY, b. Columbus, Ohio, June 17, 40; m. 62; c. 2. VETERINARY SURGERY, LABORATORY ANIMAL MEDICINE. D.V.M, Ohio State, 64; Illinois, 67-68. Vet, Quakertown Vet. Clin, 64-67; resident investr, lab. animal med, Hines Vet. Admin. Hosp, 67-68; sr. vet. biochem. res, cent. res. labs, Minn. Mining & Mfg. Co, 68-71; MGR. PROD. DEVELOP. & PROF. SERV, PITMAN-MOORE CO, 71- Mem. staff, Argonne Nat. Labs. & Shedd Aquarium, 67-68; vis. instr, col. vet. med, Univ. Minn, St. Paul. AAAS; Am. Asn. Lab. Animal Sci; Am. Vet. Med. Asn; Am. Soc. Lab. Animal Practitioners; Indust. Vet. Asn. Care and management of laboratory animals; areas of advanced surgery and healing and repair mechanisms. Address: Pitman-Moore Co, P.O. Box 344, Washington Crossing, NJ 08560.

GLICK, RICHARD E(DWIN), b. Chicago, Ill, Apr. 7, 27; m. 47; c. 4. PHYSICAL CHEMISTRY. B.S, Illinois, 51; Ph.D.(chem), California, Los Angeles, 54. Res. chemist, Brookhaven Nat. Lab, 54-55; Milton fel, Harvard, 55-56; asst. prof. CHEM, Pa. State, 56-59; FLA. STATE UNIV, 59-61, assoc. prof, 61-66, PROF, 66- Vis. scientist, Peymeinade, France, 70-71. U.S.N, 45-46. AAAS; Am. Chem. Soc; The Chem. Soc. Electron and heavy particle impact phenomena; radio frequency spectroscopy; chemical kinetics. Address: Dept. of Chemistry, Florida State University, Tallahassee, FL 32306.

GLICK, ROBERT L, b. Ashland, Ky, Jan. 26, 34; m. 58; c. 2. MECHANICAL ENGINEERING. B.S.M.E, Purdue Univ, 55, M.S.M.E, 59, Ph.D.(mech. eng), 66. Prin. engr, Huntsville Div, Thiokol Chem. Corp, Ala, 63-66; tech. specialist, Cummins Engine Co, Inc, Ind, 66-69; ASSOC. PROF. MECH. ENG, UNIV. KANS, 69- Am. Inst. Aeronaut. & Astronaut; Am. Soc. Eng. Educ. Internal ballistics of solid propellant rockets, thrust modulation and combustion of solid propellants; swirl and heat rejection in diesel engines; temperature measurement in nonsteady nonisothermal flows; turbulent entrance region flow; surface vehicle drag reduction. Address: Dept. of Mechanical Engineering, University of Kansas, Lawrence, KS 66044.

GLICK, SAMUEL SHIPLEY, b. Baltimore, Md, Dec. 18, 00; m. 27; c. 2. PEDIATRICS. A.B, Hopkins, 20; M.D, Maryland, 25. Intern, univ. hosp, Maryland, 25-26; res, Sydenham Hosp. Contagious Diseases, Baltimore, 26-27; St. Vincent's Infant Home, 27-28; health off, Dept. Health, Baltimore, 28-41; asst. prof. PEDIAT, MED. SCH, UNIV. MD, BALTIMORE CITY, 48-58, assoc. prof, 58-71; EMER. PROF, 71- V.pres, Aaron Brown Med. Educ. Found. Practicing pediatrician, 28- Med.C, State Guard, Capt. Fel. Am. Acad. Pediat. Nutritional diseases; study of child health services in Maryland; teaching medical students. Address: 3737 Clarks Lane, Baltimore, MD 21215.

GLICK, ZVI, b. Tel-Aviv, Israel, Nov. 20, 34; m. 65; c. 2. NUTRITION, BIOCHEMISTRY. B.Sc, Hebrew Univ, Israel, 59; M.S, California, Davis, 62, Ph.D.(nutrit), California, Berkeley, 67. Res. nutritionist, California, Berkeley, 65-67; res. fel. NUTRIT, HARVARD, 67-69, RES. ASSOC, 69- Consult, pioneering res. labs, U.S. Army, Natick, 68-69. Israeli Navy, 52-55. Inst. Food Technol. Biosynthesis of carotenoids; mechanism of toxicity of tannic acid and related phenolics to rats; mechanism of the regulation of food intake. Address: Dept. of Nutrition, Harvard University, 665 Huntington Ave, Boston, MA 02115.

GLICKER, SOL, b. N.Y.C, Aug. 19, 28; m. 59; c. 2. CHEMICAL KINETICS. B.S, City Col. New York, 52; Ph.D.(phys. chem), Polytech. Inst. Brooklyn, 65. CHEMIST, GODDARD SPACE FLIGHT CTR, NASA, GREENBELT, 62- U.S.A, 52-54, Sgt. Am. Chem. Soc. Gas phase chemical kinetics, particularly thermal and photochemical. Address: 12621 Milburn Lane, Bowie, MD 20715.

GLICKFELD, BARNETT W, b. New York, N.Y, Sept. 29, 39; m. 60. MATHEMATICS. B.A, Cornell, 59; Woodrow Wilson fel, Columbia, 59-60, M.A, 60, Nat. Sci. Found. fel, 60-64, Ph.D.(math), 64. Benjamin Pierce Instr. MATH, Harvard, 64-67; ASST. PROF, UNIV. WASH, 67- Vis. asst. prof, Rockefeller Univ. Analytic function theory in Banach algebras; functional analysis. Address: Dept. of Mathematics, University of Washington, Seattle, WA 98105.

GLICKMAN, IRVING, b. N.Y.C, Jan. 17, 14; m. 54; c. 2. ORAL PATHOLOGY. B.S, Brooklyn Col, 33; D.M.D, Tufts Col, 38. Instr. oper. dent, SCH. DENT. MED, TUFTS UNIV, 38-43, asst. prof. oral path, 43-47, assoc. prof, 47-48; prof. oral path. & periodont. & chmn. dept, 48-60, RES. PROF. ORAL PATH, PROF. PERIODONT. & CHMN. DEPT, 60-, dir. div. grad. & post-grad. studies, 50-60. Lectr, Unitarian med-dent. teaching mission, Europe, 46; consult, Boston Dispensary, 46-; Forsyth Dent. Ctr, 46-; Armed Forces Inst. Path, 55-; Vet. Admin. Hosp, Boston, 59-; mem, Army Med. Serv. Adv. Comt. Prev. Dent, 61-; consult, U.S. Naval Hosp, Chelsea, 64-; periodontist, Boston City Hosp, 64-; vis. prof, Harvard, 71-72. Chaim Award, 45; Samuel Charles Miller Mem. Award, 65. AAAS; Am. Acad. Oral Path; Am. Acad. Periodont; Am. Acad. Oral Med; Am. Dent. Asn; Int. Asn. Dent. Res; Int. Acad. Oral Path; hon. mem. Chilean Periodont. Soc; Arg. Periodont. Soc; All India Dent. Soc. Histopathology of periodontal disease. Address: Dept. of Periodontology, Tufts University School of Dental Medicine, 136 Harrison Ave, Boston, MA 02111.

GLICKMAN, SAMUEL ARTHUR, b. New York, N.Y, June 21, 18; m. 43; c. 3. ORGANIC CHEMISTRY. A.B, Brooklyn Col, 39; M.A, Columbia, 41, Ph.D. (org. chem), 44. Asst. chem, Nat. Defense Res. Comt. contract, Columbia, 41-42, asst, univ, 42-44; sr. org. res. chemist, GAF Corp, 44-54, res. fel, 54-60, asst. prog. mgr. acetylene derivatives, 60-68; SR. SCIENTIST, reaction motors div, THIOKOL. CHEM. CORP, 68-71, CHEM. DIV, 71- Am. Chem. Soc. Synthetic organic research; dyestuff organic research; acetylene reactions; vinyl and condensation polymerization; dyestuffs and intermediates; fluorochemistry; free radical reactions. Address: 173 Tiffany Lane, Willingboro, NJ 08046.

GLICKMAN, STEPHEN E, b. N.Y.C, Jan. 17, 33; m. 64. PHYSIOLOGICAL PSYCHOLOGY. B.S, Brooklyn Col, 54; Ph.D.(psychol), McGill, 59. Instr. PSYCHOL, New Mexico, 58; asst. prof, Northwestern, 58-65; assoc. prof, Univ. Mich, Ann Arbor, 65-68; PROF, UNIV. CALIF, BERKELEY, 68-, Miller res. fel, 62-64. Fel, sch. med, Washington (Seattle), summer 59. AAAS; Am. Psychol. Asn; Can. Psychol. Asn. Physiology of learning and motivation; comparative study of behavior. Address: Dept. of Psychology, Tolman Hall, University of California, Berkeley, CA 94720.

GLICKMAN, WALTER A, b. N.Y.C, Sept. 8, 38. PHYSICS. B.A, Alfred, 59; M.S, Pa. State, 62, Ph.D.(physics), 64. Asst. prof. PHYSICS, L.I. UNIV, 64-70, ASSOC. PROF, 70- Molecular spectroscopy. Address: Dept. of Physics, Long Island University, Brooklyn Center, Brooklyn, NY 11201.

GLICKSBERG, I. L, b. Long Beach, Calif, Apr. 1, 25; m. 50. MATHEMATICS. B.A, California, Los Angeles, 45, Ph.D.(math), 51. Asst. mathematician, Rand Corp, 50-55; asst. prof. MATH, Notre Dame, 55-58, assoc. prof, 58-62; PROF, UNIV. WASH, 62- Res. assoc, Princeton, 51-52. U.S.A.A.F, 45-46. Am. Math. Soc. Functional analysis. Address: Dept. of Mathematics, University of Washington, Seattle, WA 98105.

GLICKSMAN, ARVIN S(IGMUND), b. N.Y.C, Mar. 14, 24; m. 56; c. 5. MEDICINE, BIOLOGY. M.B, Chicago Med. Sch, 48, M.D, 49. Intern, Kings County Hosp, Brooklyn, 48-50; fel. med. scis, Atomic Energy Comn, dept. biochem, Duke, 50-52; resident, Mem. Ctr. for Cancer & Allied Diseases, 52-54; res. fel, Sloan Kettering Inst. Cancer Res, 54-55, asst, radiobiol. sect, 55-60, assoc, 60-65; assoc. dir. dept. radiation ther, Michael Reese Hosp. & Med. Ctr, Chicago, Ill, 65-67; assoc. prof. radiol, MT. SINAI SCH. MED, 67-70, PROF. RADIOTHER. & DIR. RADIOTHER. RES. UNIT, 70-; DEP. DIR. RADIOTHER. CTR, MT. SINAI HOSP, 67- Guest physician, Brookhaven Nat. Lab, 50-52; asst. attend. physician & med. consult, Mem. Ctr. Cancer & Allied Diseases, 55-; asst. attend. physician, Kings County Hosp, 55-60; James Ewing Hosp, 58-61, asst. vis. radiotherapist, 64-; Dillon fel, Royal Marsden Hosp, London, 61-62; Nat. Insts Health res. career develop. award, Royal Marsden Hosp. & Inst. Cancer Res, London, 62-64; asst. attend. radiotherapist, Mem. Hosp, 64- AAAS; Radiation Res. Soc; Am. Asn. Cancer Res; N.Y. Acad. Med; N.Y. Acad. Sci; Am. Radium Soc; Am. Soc. Therapeut. Radiol; Asn. Univ. Radiol; Brit. Inst. Radiol. Radiobiology; radiation therapy; oncology; internal medicine. Address: Radiotherapy Center, Mt. Sinai School of Medicine, 100th St. & Fifth Ave, New York, NY 10029.

GLICKSMAN, LEON ROBERT, b. Chicago, Ill, May 12, 38; m. 69; c. 2. THERMODYNAMICS, HEAT TRANSFER. B.S, Mass. Inst. Tech, 59, Ph.D. (mech. eng), 64; M.S, Stanford, 60. Instr. MECH. ENG, MASS. INST. TECHNOL, 62-64, asst. prof, 64-70, ASSOC. PROF, 70- Ford fel, 66-68. U.S.A, 64-66, Capt. Am. Soc. Mech. Eng.(Robert T. Knapp Award & Melville Medal, 69). Power plants; glass forming; radiation heat transfer. Address: Room 7-040, Massachusetts Institute of Technology, Cambridge, MA 02139.

GLICKSMAN, MARTIN, b. New York, N.Y, Mar. 4, 23; m. 48; c. 2. ORGANIC CHEMISTRY, SCIENCE EDUCATION. B.S, City Col. New York, 43; M.S, N.Y. Univ, 48, M.A, 52. Res. chemist, Foster D. Snell, Inc, N.Y, 46; Hema Drug Co, 47-50; prod. chemist, A.J. Cosmetto Labs, 50-54; SR. RES. SPECIALIST, CORP. RES. DEPT, GEN. FOODS CORP, TARRYTOWN, 54- Med.C, U.S.A, 43-46, Sgt. Am. Chem. Soc; Inst. Food Technol; Soc. Cosmetic Chem. Hydrocolloids and food product development. Address: 229 Valley Rd, Valley Cottage, NY 10989.

GLICKSMAN, MARTIN E, b. N.Y.C, Apr. 4, 37; m. 66. PHYSICAL METALLURGY. B.Met.E, Rensselaer Polytech, 57, Allegheny Ludlum fel, 57-60, Ph.D.(phys. metall), 61. Nat. Acad. Sci-Nat. Res. Coun. fel, NAVAL RES. LAB, 61-63, res. metallurgist, 63-66, acting br. head metal physics, 66-69, HEAD TRANSFORMATION & KINETICS BR, 69- Arthur S. Flemming award, 69. AAAS; Am. Inst. Mining, Metall. & Petrol. Eng; Am. Soc. Metals (Grossmann Award, 71); Sci. Res. Soc. Am.(award, 67). Solidification and crystal growth of metals and alloys; surface energy studies; defects in metals; thermodynamics of stressed systems; interfacial phenomena in metals; metallurgy of superconductors; lattice vacancies. Address: Code 6350, Naval Research Lab, Washington, DC 20390.

GLICKSMAN, M(AURICE), b. Toronto, Ont, Oct. 16, 28; nat; m. 49; c. 3. PHYSICS. S.M, Chicago, 52, Ph.D.(physics), 54. Researcher nuclear physics, Atomic Energy Proj, Chalk River, Can, 49-50; instr. physics, Roosevelt, 53-54; res. assoc, Inst. Nuclear Studies, Ill, 54; mem. tech. staff, RCA Labs, N.J, 54-62, head plasma physics, 61-63, dir. res, Tokyo Lab, 63-67, head gen. res, 67-69; UNIV. PROF. & PROF. ENG, BROWN UNIV, 69- Chmn, comt. mat. for radiation detection devices, Nat. Res. Coun-Nat. Mat. Adv. Bd, 71- Fel. Am. Phys. Soc; Phys. Soc. Japan. Nuclear properties; pi-meson scattering; semiconductor alloys; band structure; semiconductor transport properties; galvanomagnetic effects; hot electrons; plasmas in solids; gaseous plasmas; semiconductor luminescence. Address: Division of Engineering, Brown University, Providence, RI 02912.

GLICKSMAN, R(ICHARD), b. N.Y.C, Oct. 3, 24; m. 53; c. 2. PHYSICAL CHEMISTRY, SOLID STATE PHYSICS. B.S, N.Y. Univ, 48, M.S, 49, fel, 51-53, Ph.D.(chem), 54. Asst, Atomic Energy Cmn. contract, N.Y. Univ, 52-53; res. chemist, labs div, Radio Corp. Am, 53-59, eng. leader, electrochem. res. & develop, semiconductor & mat. div, 59, vacuum deposition & chem. thin film resistor labs, 59-60, MGR. adv. comput. devices, 60-63, adv. devices, electronic components & devices div, 63-68, OPTOELECTRONIC PROD. ENG, SOLID STATE DIV, RCA CORP, 68- U.S.A, 43-46, 1st Lt. Am. Chem. Soc; Electrochem. Soc; Inst. Elec. Electronics Eng. Semiconductor devices; integrated circuits; optoelectronic devices. Address: Solid State Division, RCA Corp, Sommerville, NJ 08876.

GLICKSTEIN, JOSEPH, b. N.Y.C, Aug. 31, 17; m. 41; c. 1. ANALYTICAL CHEMISTRY. B.S, Mich. State Col, 38; fel, N.Y. Univ, 46-51, Ph.D.(chem), 51. Asst. gastric chem. res, Mt. Sinai Hosp, N.Y, 38-40; City Dept. Hosps, New York, 40-42; res. engr, Bolsey Res. & Develop. Corp, 51-; proj. engr, Electro-Phys, Labs, Conn, 52-55; PROF. CHEM, Adelphi, 55-63; BROOKLYN COL, 63- Res. Collab, Brookhaven Nat. Lab, 58-62. U.S.A, 42-46. AAAS; Am. Chem. Soc; Electrochem. Soc; Inst. Elec. & Electronics Eng. Instrumentation; electrochemical studies, including polarography; spectrophotometry. Address: Dept. of Chemistry, Brooklyn College, Brooklyn, NY 11210.

GLICKSTEIN, MITCHELL, b. Boston, Mass, July 13, 31; m. 55; c. 2. PHYSIOLOGICAL PSYCHOLOGY. B.A, Chicago, 51, Ph.D.(psychol), 58. U.S. Pub. Health Serv. fel. biol, Calif. Inst. Tech, 58-59, univ. fel, 60-; res. assoc, sch. med, Stanford Univ, 60-61; assoc. prof. physiol. & biophysics, sch. med, Univ. Wash, 61-66, biol. struct, 66-67; PSYCHOL, BROWN UNIV, 67-70, PROF, 70- AAAS; Am. Psychol. Asn; Am. Physiol. Soc; Am. Asn. Anat. Brain mechanics in learning; anatomy of central visual pathways. Address: Walter S. Hunter Lab. of Psychology, Brown University, Providence, RI 02912.

GLICKSTEIN, STANLEY S, b. Brooklyn, N.Y, Nov. 12, 33; m. 57; c. 4. NUCLEAR PHYSICS. B.E.E, Polytech. Inst. Brooklyn, 55; M.S, Pa. State,

59, Ph.D.(physics), 61. Res. assoc. physics, Princeton, 61-63, instr, 63-64; SR. SCIENTIST, RD&A PHYSICS, BETTIS ATOMIC POWER LAB, WESTINGHOUSE ELEC. CORP, 64- Am. Phys. Soc. Reactor physics; low energy nuclear physics. Address: Bettis Atomic Power Lab, Westinghouse Electric Corp, Pittsburgh, PA 15122.

GLIDDEN, HARLEY F(REMONT), b. Lincoln, Nebr, Nov. 29, 05; m; c. 1. GENERAL SCIENCE. B.S, Buena Vista Col, 29; Iowa State, 36; M.A, Iowa, 34; Ph.D.(sci. ed), Nebraska, 54. Teacher, pub. sch, Iowa, 29-31, prin. & teacher, 31-35; instr. chem, Sheldon Jr. Col, 35-39; asst. prof. & supvr, natural sci, teachers col, Nebraska, 39-40; dean, Osceola Jr. Col, 40-41; Fairbury Jr. Col, Nebr, 41-42; asst. prof. sci. & supvr. lab. sch, UNIV. NORTH. COLO, 42-43, PROF. SCI, 46-, ASSOC. DEAN COL. ARTS & SCI, 66-, chmn. div, 55-66. U.S.N.R, 44-46. AAAS; Nat. Sci. Teachers Asn; Nat. Asn. Res. Sci. Teaching. Conservation education; training science teachers. Address: College of Arts & Sciences, University of Northern Colorado, Greeley, CO 80631.

GLIDDEN, KENNETH E(UGENE), b. South Berwick, Maine, Dec. 22, 06; m. 29; c. 5. CHEMISTRY. B.S, New Hampshire, 29, Ph.D.(phys. chem), Hopkins, 32. Asst, Brown Co, N.H, 29-30, res. chemist, 34-47; Brown Co. fel, Hopkins, 32-33; instr, Conn. State Col, 33-34; chief pulping sect, Inst. Paper Chem, Lawrence Col, 47-48; dir. res, Celon Co, 48-52, v.pres, 52-56, exec. v.pres, 56-59, plant mgr, Celon Div, Thatcher Glass Mfg. Co, Inc, 59-61, dir. res. & prod. develop, 61-63; DIR. RES, BURGESS CELLULOSE CO, 63- Instr, New Hampshire, 43, 44; sch. dept, Berlin, N.H, 47. Tech. Asn. Pulp & Paper Indust; fel. Am. Inst. Chem; Am. Chem. Soc; Soc. Plastics Eng. Cellulose esters; pulping and paper making; pretreatment of wood pulp sheets for viscose process; stereotype dry mats. Address: 1141 Hillcrest Dr, Freeport, IL 61032.

GLIDDEN, R(ICHARD) M(ILLS), b. Irvington, N.J, Nov. 3, 24; m. 52; c. 3. RUBBER CHEMISTRY. B.S, Rutgers, 50. TECH. DIR, AMES RUBBER CORP, 50-, V.PRES, 65- U.S.A, 43-46. Am. Chem. Soc. Development and manufacture of rubber compounds. Address: 39 Summit Trail, Sparta, NJ 07871.

GLIDEWELL, MARVIN E(LMER), b. Plainfield, Ind, Aug. 2, 16; m. 41; c. 4. CHEMISTRY. A.B, Indiana, 41. Res. & develop. chemist, MAGNAVOX CO, 41-50, prod. control chem, 50-53, in charge prod. control lab, 53-56, dir. special servs, group, 56-58, chief finish chemist, govt. & indust. prods. div, 58-70, DIR. MAT. EVAL. & PROCESSES LABS, 70-, mem. bd. dirs, credit union, 60-70. Am. Chem. Soc.(treas, 49, secy, 50). Production; engineering and design problems concerning adhesives, insulation materials, solders and tapes; specification finishes; environment testing; alchemical symbols. Address: The Magnavox Co, 2131 Coliseum Dr, South, Ft. Wayne, IN 46803.

GLIEDMAN, MARVIN, b. New York, N.Y, Aug. 3, 29; m. 54; c. 2. SURGERY. B.A, Syracuse, 50; M.D, State Univ, N.Y, 54. Asst. instr. SURG, State Univ. N.Y. Downstate Med. Ctr, 59-60, asst. prof, 60-64, assoc. prof, 64-66; PROF, ALBERT EINSTEIN COL. MED, 67-; CHIEF DEPT. SURG, MONTEFIORE HOSP. & MED. CTR, 67- Asst. attend. surgeon, Kings County Hosp, Brooklyn, 60-; Markle scholar acad. med, 64-69. Dudley Mem. Medal, 54; Linder Surg. Prize, 54. Off. in charge cardiopulmonary & surg. res. labs, U.S. Naval Hosp, St. Albans, U.S.N.R, 56-58, Lt. Am. Soc. Nephrol; Am. Surg. Asn; N.Y. Acad. Sci; Am. Col. Surg; Int. Cardiovasc. Soc; Transplantation Soc; Soc. Vascular Surg; Soc. Surg. Alimentary Tract; Int. Soc. Surg; Am. Gastroenterol. Asn; Am. Med. Asn; Am. Soc. Artificial Internal Organs; Soc. Univ. Surg; Asn. Acad. Surg. Gastrointestinal surgery and physiology with emphasis on the liver, particularly with regard to problems of cirrhosis and transplantation. Address: Dept. of Surgery, Montefiore Hospital & Medical Center, 111 E. 210th St, Bronx, NY 10467.

GLIMCHER, MELVIN J(ACOB), b. Brookline, Mass, June 2, 25. ORTHOPEDIC SURGERY, BIOPHYSICS. B.S.(gen. sci) & B.S.(mech. eng), Purdue, 46; M.D, Harvard Med. Sch, 50. Res. fel, HARVARD MED. SCH, 56, asst. prof. ORTHOP. SURG, 59-61, assoc. prof, 61-65, PROF, 65-; CHIEF ORTHOP. SERV, MASS. GEN. HOSP, 66- Res. fel. biol, Mass. Inst. Tech. & fel, sch. adv. studies, 56-59. U.S.M.C, 43-45, Med.C. Res, 46-, Lt.(jg). Electron Micros. Soc. Am; Orthop. Res. Soc; Biophys. Soc; Am. Acad. Arts & Sci. Biological mineralization. Address: Orthopedic Services, Massachusetts General Hospital, Boston, MA 02114.

GLIME, JANICE M(ILDRED), b. Cumberland, Md, Jan. 27, 41. ECOLOGY, BOTANY. B.S, Frostburg State Col, 62; M.S, W.Va. Univ, 64; Ph.D.(bot), 68. Asst. instr. plant taxon, Mich. State Univ, summers 66 & 67, plant morphol, 68, vis. asst. prof. bot, summer 70; instr. BIOL, PLYMOUTH STATE COL, 68-69, asst. prof, 69-70, ASST. PROF, 70- Partic, systs. ecol. inst, Nat. Sci. Found, summer 71. Ecol. Soc. Am; Am. Soc. Limnol. & Oceanog; Am. Bryol. & Lichenological Soc; Am. Inst. Biol. Sci; Am. Soc. Nat. Ecology of streams, especially bryophytes and insects; systems ecology. Address: Dept. of Natural Science, Boyd Hall, Plymouth State College, Plymouth, NH 03264.

GLIMM, JAMES G(ILBERT), b. Peoria, Ill, Mar. 24, 34; m. 57; c. 1. MATHEMATICS. A.B, Columbia, 56, A.M, 57, fel, 58, Ph.D.(math), 59. Nat. Sci. Found. fel, 59-60; asst. prof. MATH, Mass. Inst. Technol, 60-63, assoc. prof, 63-69; PROF, COURANT INST, N.Y. UNIV, 69- Guggenheim fels, 63-64, 65-66. Non-linear differential equations; functional analysis; operators on Hilbert space; mathematical physics; quantum field theory. Address: Courant Institute of Mathematical Sciences, New York University, 251 Mercer St, New York, NY 10012.

GLIMP, HUDSON A, b. Burnet, Tex, Nov. 22, 37; m. 61; c. 2. ANIMAL NUTRITION. B.S, Texas A&M, 60, M.S, 61; Ph.D.(animal nutrit), Okla. State, 64. Asst. prof. sheep exten, Kentucky, 64-66, sheep nutrit. res, 66-67; NUTRIT. INVEST. LEADER, U.S. MEAT ANIMAL RES. CTR, AGR. RES. SERV, DEPT. AGR, 67-; ASSOC. PROF, GRAD. FACULTY, UNIV. NEBR, LINCOLN, 69- Am. Soc. Animal Sci. Nutrition of the young ruminant; nutrition-genotype interactions in cattle and sheep; factors affecting nutrient utilization in ruminants. Address: U.S. Meat Animal Research Center, P.O. Box 166, Clay Center, NE 68933.

GLINOS, A(NDRÉ) D(IMITRI), b. Athens, Greece, Oct. 18, 19; nat; m. 59. CELL PHYSIOLOGY. Univ. fel, Nat. Univ. Athens, 37-41, M.D, 41. Resident physician med, Evangelismos Hosp, 42-45; res. assoc, div. cell biol, cancer inst, Univ. Paris, 45-46; res. fel. med, C.P. Huntington Mem. Labs, Harvard & Mass. Gen. Hosp, Boston, 46-48; res. assoc, div. cell physiol, Univ. Hosp, Hopkins, 48-53; CHIEF, growth physiol. sect, WALTER REED ARMY INST. RES, 53-61, DEPT. CELLULAR PHYSIOL, 61-; RES. PROF. ZOOL, UNIV. MD, COLLEGE PARK, 64- Govt. France fel, Paris, 45; Ella Lyman Cabot Trust fel, Harvard, 46; U.S. Pub. Health Serv. fel, Hopkins, 49; res. collab, Brookhaven Nat. Lab, 64-66; chief biomed. sci. br, U.S. Army Res. & Develop. Group, Europe, 66-69. Am. Physiol. Soc; Am. Asn. Cancer Res; Tissue Culture Asn; Am. Soc. Cell Biol; Int. Soc. Cell Biol. Carcinogenesis; regeneration; tissue culture; cellular ageing; cellular effects of radiation; control of cell growth and differentiation; general concepts and methodology of biomedical research. Address: Dept. of Cellular Physiology, Walter Reed Army Institute of Research, Washington, DC 20012.

GLINSKI, GEORGE S(TANISLAUS), b. St. Petersburg, Russia, Mar. 11, 12; nat. Can; m. 43; c. 6. ELECTRICAL ENGINEERING. Dipl. Ing, Warsaw Tech. Univ, Poland, 37; Grenoble, France, 41-42. Develop. engr, State Tel. & Radio Mfg. Co, Warsaw, Poland, 36-39; North. Elec. Co, Que, 42-48; dir. develop, Comput. Devices of Can, Ont, 48-54; mgr, Electro Data, Burroughs, 54-58; PROF. ELEC. ENG, UNIV. OTTAWA, 58-, CHMN. DEPT, 59-, V.DEAN, PURE & APPL. SCI, 66-, assoc. v. dean, 64-66. Lectr, McGill, 52-59. Fel. AAAS; Opers. Res. Soc. Am; Indust. Math. Soc; Soc. Indust. & Appl. Math; Asn. Comput. Mach; Asn. Symbolic Logic; fel. Inst. Elec. & Electronics Eng; Can. Opers. Res. Soc; Eng. Inst. Can; assoc. fel. Can. Aeronaut. & Space Inst. Nonlinear circuits; digital learning networks; general feedback systems. Address: Dept. of Electrical Engineering, University of Ottawa, Ottawa 2, Ont, Can.

GLINSKI, RONALD P, b. Windsor, Ont, Aug. 4, 41. ORGANIC CHEMISTRY, BIOCHEMISTRY. B.S, Univ. Windsor, 63; Nat. Insts. Health & Nat. Sci. Found. fels. & Ph.D.(org. chem), Wayne State Univ, 67. Sr. res. chemist ORG. BIOCHEM, ASH STEVENS INC, 66, RES. SUPVR, 68- Am. Chem. Soc; Chem. Inst. Can. Organic synthesis; carbohydrates; nucleotides; natural products; kinetics; enzymology; process development. Address: 4829 Williamson, Dearborn, MI 48126.

GLITZ, DOHN GEORGE, b. Buffalo, N.Y, Sept. 28, 36. BIOCHEMISTRY. B.S, Illinois, 58; M.S, Wisconsin, 60; Ph.D.(biochem), California, Berkeley, 63. Chemist, Swift & Co. Res. Labs, 58; fel, enzyme inst, Wisconsin, 63-64; U.S. Pub. Health Serv. fel, virus res. unit, Cambridge, 64-66; fel, virus lab, Univ. Calif, Berkeley, 66-67; asst. prof. BIOCHEM, MED. SCH, UNIV. CALIF, LOS ANGELES, 67-71, ASSOC. PROF, 71- Nucleic acid biochemistry, including physical and chemical properties; nucleic acid enzymology. Address: Dept. of Biological Chemistry, Medical School, University of California, Los Angeles, CA 90024.

GLOBE, SAMUEL, b. Brooklyn, N.Y, Mar. 16, 16; m. 40; c. 3. APPLIED PHYSICS. B.S, Brooklyn Col, 35; A.M, Michigan, 36; M.S, Harvard, 46, Ph.D.(appl. physics), 59. Teacher, pub. schs, N.Y, 38-42; physicist, U.S. Naval Shipyard, N.Y, 42-43, U.S. Naval Ord. Lab, 46-51, chief rockets & guided missiles br, 51-53, projectiles & bombs br, 53-55; sr. res. engr. Chicago Midway Labs, 55-56; prin. scientist, res. & adv. develop. div, Avco Corp, 56-58, assoc. chief physics sect, 58-59, asst. for. res. to v.pres, 59-62; assoc. mgr. eng. physics dept, BATTELLE MEM. INST, 62-67, mgr. dept. systs. & electronics, COLUMBUS LABS, 67-70, ASST. DIR, 70- Lectr, Maryland, 48-49; instr, Mass. Inst. Tech, 50-55. U.S.N.R, 43-46, Lt. Am. Phys. Soc; Inst. Elec. & Electronics Eng. Underwater acoustics; piezoelectricity; electromagnetic theory; magnetohydrodynamics; research management. Address: Battelle Memorial Institute, Columbus Labs, 505 King Ave, Columbus, OH 43201.

GLOBENSKY, YVON RAOUL, b. Montreal, Que, Feb. 6, 37; m. 59; c. 2. GEOLOGY, PALEONTOLOGY. B.Sc, Montreal, 59; Kansas, 59-61; M.Sc, New Brunswick, 62, Ph.D.(geol), 65. ASST. DIR. GEOL, GEOL. EXPLOR. SERV, QUE. DEPT. NATURAL RESOURCES, 64- AAAS; fel. Geol. Soc. Am; fel. Geol. Asn. Can; Paleont. Soc; Soc. Econ. Paleont. & Mineral. Geology of the St. Lawrence Lowlands with special interests in micropaleontology and specifically in conodonts. Address: Quebec Dept. of Natural Resources, 1620 Blvd de l'Entente, Quebec 6, Que, Can.

GLOBUS, ALBERT, b. N.Y.C, Oct. 13, 31; m. 51; c. 3. NEUROANATOMY, NEUROPHYSIOLOGY. B.A, Northwestern, 51, M.D, 55. Intern, Orange County Hosp, 55-56; private practice, Calif, 58-63; U.S. Pub. Health Serv. fel. neuroanat, California, Los Angeles, 63-67; guest scientist, Max Planck Inst, 67-68; ASST. PROF. HUMAN MORPHOL, PSYCHOBIOL. & PSYCHIAT, COL. MED, UNIV. CALIF, IRVINE, 68- Med.C, U.S.A, 56-58, Surg. Am. Med. Asn; Am. Asn. Anat; Soc. Gen. Systs. Res; Pan-Am. Asn. Anat. Golgi analysis of cortical anatomy; intracellular physiology of spinal motoneurons; iontophoresis of radioactive amino acids in spinal motoneurons; neurology. Address: Curricula of Human Morphology, College of Medicine, University of California, Irvine, CA 92664.

GLOCK, WALDO S(UMNER), b. Vinton, Iowa, Aug. 20, 97; m. 24; c. 1. ECOLOGY, GEOLOGY. B.A, Iowa, 20; Ph.D.(paleoclimat, geol), Yale, 25. Asst, Iowa, 20-22; Yale, 22-23, instr. hist. geol, 24; geol. & physiog, Ohio State, 24-31; res. assoc. & mem. staff, div. plant biol, Carnegie Institution, 31-38; instr. geol, Texas Tech. Col, 38-40, asst. prof, 40, assoc. prof, 41-42, 45-48; prof. geol. & dir. tree-ring res. lab, Macalester Col, 48-66; vis. prof, Univ. N.C, 66-67; VIS. FACULTY RES. ASSOC, INST. ARCTIC & ALPINE RES, UNIV. COLO, BOULDER, 67- Lectr, Univ. Minn, 50. Jr. geologist, U.S. Geol. Surv, 20-36; mem, Geol. Surv, Ohio, 25. Mem. natural hist. exped, Univ. Iowa, Fiji & New Zealand, 22. U.S.A, 17-19; U.S.A.A.F, 42-45, Res, 45-47, Maj. AAAS; fel. Geol. Soc. Am; Am. Geophys. Union; Am. Forestry Asn; Int. Soc. Biometeorol. Physiography of drainage systems; climatic indicators and cycles; tree-ring dating; anatomy and ecology of tree growth. Address: Institute of Arctic & Alpine Research, University of Colorado, Boulder, CO 80302.

GLOCKER, EDWIN M(ERRIAM), b. Phila, Pa, May 29, 10; m. 33; c. 2. CHEMISTRY. B.S, Hopkins, 51. Chemist, LaMotte Chem. Prod. Co, 27-43; asst. res. chemist, Davison Chem. Co, 43-44, res. chemist, 44-49, group leader, 49-51, staff asst. to v.pres. res. & develop, 51-54, mgr. res. statist. dept, RES. DIV, W.R. GRACE & CO, 54-63, mgr. math, 63-69, DEVELOP. ASSOC, 69- Am. Chem. Soc; Am. Soc. Qual. Control; Am. Inst. Chem. Eng. Sulfonephthalein indicators; monosodium glutamate; phosphates; fluorides; process development; application of statistical methods in research and production; operation of industrial processes at optimum conditions; computer applications. Address: 14697 Roxbury Rd, Glenelg, MD 21737.

GLOCKLIN, VERA C(HARLOTTE), b. Edmonton, Alta, Oct. 16, 26; U.S. citizen. PHYSIOLOGY, BIOCHEMISTRY. B.A, Toronto, 48; M.Sc, McGill, 50; Jr. Sterling & Boies fels. & Ph.D.(endocrinol), Yale, 59. Res. technician pharmacol, Western Reserve, 50-51, res. asst. ophthal, 51-53; cancer res. lab, Florida, 53-55; res. assoc, ophthalmic biochem, Univ. Chicago, 59-66; PHARMACOLOGIST, FOOD & DRUG ADMIN, DEPT. HEALTH, EDUC. & WELFARE, 66- U.S. Pub. Health Serv. med. res. grant, Inst. Neurol. Diseases & Blindness, 62-66; summer res. asst, dept. biol, Brookhaven Nat. Lab, 56; abstractor, Chem. Abstr, 55-60. Neuropharmacology; comparative biochemistry; cellular physiology; endocrinology. Address: 2000 S. Eads St, Apt. 1105, Arlington, VA 22202.

GLOCKNER, PETER G, b. Moragy, Hungary, Jan. 26, 29; nat; m. 55; c. 1. APPLIED MECHANICS, STRUCTURAL ENGINEERING. B.Eng, McGill, 55; fel, Mass. Inst. Tech, 55-56, M.Sc, 56; Ph.D.(civil eng), Michigan, 64. Struct. design engr, C.C. Parker, Whittaker & Co, Ltd, Alta, 56-58; asst. prof. appl. mech, Univ. Alberta, 58-62, assoc. prof, 62-68; PROF. CIVIL ENG, UNIV. CALGARY, 68- Am. Soc. Civil Eng; Eng. Inst. Can; Int. Asn. Shell Structures; Int. Asn. Bridge & Struct. Eng. Fundamentals of continuum mechanics and solid mechanics and their application to linear and nonlinear plate and shell theory and the static and dynamic linear and nonlinear response of plates and shells. Address: Dept. of Civil Engineering, University of Calgary, Calgary, Alta, Can.

GLOCKNER, PETER WILHELM, b. Bielefeld, Ger, June 19, 38; m. 65; c. 2. PETROLEUM & ORGANOMETALLIC CHEMISTRY. Dr.rer.nat.(chem), Univ. Munich, 64. Chemist, Shell Develop. Co, 65-70, ENGR, SHELL OIL CO, SAN FRANCISCO, 70- Soc. German Chem; Am. Chem. Soc; Soc. Automotive Eng. Metalorganic and catalytic chemistry; processes and products development of gasoline additives; exhaust emissions; pollution control. Address: 3094 Sweetbrier Circle, Lafayette, CA 94549.

GLOECKLER, GEORGE, b. Odessa, Russia, Aug. 10, 37; U.S. citizen; m. 58. PHYSICS. S.B, Chicago, 60, S.M, 61, NASA traineeship, 62-65, Ph.D.(physics), 65. Res. assoc. cosmic ray physics, Univ. Chicago, 65-66, Enrico Fermi fel, 66-67; ASST. PROF. PHYSICS, UNIV. MD, COLLEGE PARK, 67- Co-recipient, NASA res. grant, 68-; Sloan res. fel, 69-71. Am. Phys. Soc; Am. Astron. Soc; Am. Geophys. Union. Cosmic rays; investigation of charged particle radiation from the galaxy and the sun using balloon-borne and satellite instrumentation. Address: Dept. of Physics & Astronomy, University of Maryland, College Park, MD 20742.

GLOEGE, G(EORGE) H(ERMAN), b. Helena, Mont, Dec. 7, 04; m. 27; c. 4. CHEMISTRY. B.A, Intermountain Union Col, 26; Columbia Univ, 26-27; M.S, Univ. Wis, 31; D.Ed, Mont. State Col, 60; Univ. Colo, summers 36-39, 48, 50, 52, 54-55. Teacher, pub. sch, Mont, 27-28; prof. chem, Intermountain Union Col, 28-36; Billings Polytech. Inst, 36-39; dean, Custer County Jr. Col, 39-42, prin, 42-46; asst. prof. CHEM, EAST. MONT. COL, 46-47, assoc. prof, 47-48, PROF, 48-, chmn. dept. phys. sci, 66-71. Nat. Sci. Teachers Asn. Detection of carnuba wax in beeswax; science education, especially college general chemistry laboratory. Address: Dept. of Physical Sciences, Eastern Montana College, Billings, MT 59101.

GLOERSEN, P(ER), b. Washington, Pa, Dec. 19, 27; m. 53; c. 3. PHYSICS. M.A, Hopkins, 52, Ph.D.(physics), 56. PHYSICIST, Gen. Elec. Space Sci. Lab, 56-70; GODDARD SPACE FLIGHT CTR, NASA, 70- U.S.A, 52-54. Am. Phys. Soc; Am. Inst. Aeronaut. & Astronaut; N.Y. Acad. Sci. Plasma physics; physical properties of radiating shock waves in gases; high resolution molecular spectroscopy in the ultraviolet, visible and infrared; instrumentation; electric propulsion; remote sensing in the microwave regime. Address: NASA Goddard Space Flight Center, Code 652, Greenbelt, MD 20771.

GLOGAU, RICHARD C(LYDE), b. Denver, Colo, Nov. 20, 16; m. 40; c. 3. CHEMICAL ENGINEERING. B.Ch.E, Denver, 39. Chemist, Louviers works, E.I. du Pont de Nemours & Co, Inc, 40, chief chemist, 41, area supvr, 42, res. chem. engr, east. lab, 43-48, tech. asst, tech. div, 48-52, asst. mgr, du Pont works, 52-53, dir, Repauno Process Lab, 53-60, prod. mgr, explosives dept, 60-67; v.pres, ENGELHARD MINERAL & CHEM. CORP, 67-69, SR. V.PRES, DIR. & MEM. EXEC. COMT, 69-, PRES, ENGELHARD INDUSTS, 70- V.pres, Engelhard Industs, 67-69, exec. v.pres, 69-70; dir. indust, Engelhard S.p.A, Rome, dir, Engelhard Indust, Ltd, London, Engelhard Indust. Can, Ltd, Nippon Engelhard Ltd, Japan; dir, Amersil, Inc, 69-; dir, S.W. Shattuck Chem. Co, Inc, Colo, 70; chmn. & dir, Super-Cut, Inc. & Subsidiaries, Ill, 70; dir, Engelhard Indust. Proprietary Ltd, Australia, 71; dir, Baker Hakkin, K.K, Japan, 71. Am. Chem. Soc. Surface chemistry of explosive compositions; decomposition reactions of ammonium nitrate; synthesis of sodium nitrate; reaction of explosive compositions. Address: Engelhard Industries, 430 Mountain Ave, Murray Hill, NJ 07974.

GLOGE, DETLEF CHRISTOPH, b. Breslau, Ger, Feb. 2, 36; m. 69. COMMUNICATIONS. Dipl. Ing, Brunswick Tech. Univ, 61, Dr. Ing.(optical waveguides), 64. Asst. prof. electronics, Brunswick Tech. Univ, 64-65; MEM. TECH. STAFF. OPTICAL COMMUN. RES, BELL TEL. LABS, 65- Inst. Elec. & Electronics Eng. Optical communication systems; waveguides. Address: Bell Telephone Labs, HOH L115, Box 400, Holmdel, NJ 07733.

GLOGOVSKY, ROBERT L, b. North Chicago, Ill, May 29, 36; m. 61; c. 4. PHYSICAL CHEMISTRY, BIOCHEMISTRY. B.S, Northern Illinois, 59; Ph.D. (phys. chem), Colorado, 65. Kettering Found. intern CHEM, Kalamazoo Col, 64-65; asst. prof, ELMHURST COL, 65-70, ASSOC. PROF, 70-, CHMN. DEPT, 71- AAAS; Am. Chem. Soc. High pressure studies on macromolecules; hydrogen bonding in biological polymers. Address: Dept. of Chemistry, Elmhurst College, Elmhurst, IL 60126.

GLOGOW, ELI, Pub. Health Admin, see Suppl. I to 11th ed, Soc. & Behav. Vols.

GLOMB, WALTER L, b. Glen Ridge, N.J, Feb. 7, 25; m. 48; c. 6. COMMUNICATIONS, SPACE TECHNOLOGY. B.S, Columbia Univ, 46, M.S, 48. Engr, Paramount Motion Pictures, 46-50; from sr. engr. to V.PRES. & DIR. ADVAN. DEVELOP, ITT DEFENSE COMMUN. DIV, 50- Fel. Inst. Elec. & Electronics Eng; Am. Inst. Aeronaut. & Astronaut. Radio communication at microwave frequencies via line of sight; tropospheric scatter and satellite communication systems including transmission, switching and system organization. Address: ITT Defense Communications Division, 492 River Rd, Nutley, NJ 07110.

GLOMSET, JOHN A, b. Des Moines, Iowa, Nov. 2, 28; m. 54; c. 2. BIOCHEMISTRY, PHYSIOLOGY. Kand, Uppsala, 53, M.D, 60. Docent med. chem, Uppsala, 60; res. asst. prof. MED, UNIV. WASH, 60-64, res. assoc. prof, 64-71, RES. PROF, 71-, MEM. STAFF, REGIONAL PRIMATE CTR, 64- Am. Physiol. Soc. Lipoprotein metabolism. Address: Dept. of Medicine, University of Washington, Seattle, WA 98105.

GLOMSKI, CHESTER ANTHONY, b. Detroit, Mich, June 8, 28; m. 66; c. 2. ANATOMY, HEMATOLOGY. B.S, Detroit Inst. Tech, 51; M.S, Wayne State, 53; Ph.D.(anat), Minnesota, 61; M.D, Mississippi, 65. Teaching asst. anat, sch. med, Minnesota, 55-61; intern med, St. Paul-Ramsey Hosp, St. Paul, Minn, 65-66; ASST. PROF. ANAT, SCH. MED, STATE UNIV. N.Y. BUFFALO, 66- Consult. hemat, Cornell Aeronaut. Lab. Am. Asn. Anat; Pan. Am. Asn. Anat. Experimental hypersplenism; hematopoisesis; erythrocyte kinetics studies by neutron activation analysis; blood dyscrasias; mercury sequestration in tissues. Address: Dept. of Anatomy, School of Medicine, State University of New York at Buffalo, Buffalo, NY 14214.

GLOOR, PIERRE, b. Basel, Switz, Apr. 5, 23; Can. citizen; m. 54; c. 2. NEUROPHYSIOLOGY. M.D, Univ. Basel, 49; Ph.D.(neurophysiol), McGill Univ, 57. Lectr. electroencephalog, MONTREAL NEUROL. INST, McGILL UNIV, 55-57, asst. prof. exp. neurol, 57-62, assoc. prof. CLIN. NEUROPHYSIOL, 62-68, PROF, 68-, ELECTROENCEPHALOGRAPHER & CHIEF LAB, MONTREAL NEUROL. HOSP, 61-, assoc. electroencephalographer, 55-61. Electroencephalographer, Jewish Gen. Hosp, Montreal, 56-61; del, Int. Fedn. Soc. Electroencephalog. & Clin. Neurophysiol, 61-69; physician in charge electroencephalog, Royal Victoria Hosp, Montreal, 62- Robert Bing Prize, Swiss Acad. Med. Sci, 62. Swiss Army, 42-45. Can. Soc. Electroencephalog.(secy, 62-63, pres, 64-65); Can. Physiol. Soc; Can. Neurol. Soc; Can. Med. Asn; Am. Electroencephalog. Soc; Am. Physiol. Soc; Am. Epilepsy Soc; Int. Brain Res. Orgn. Neurophysiology of limbic system and hypothalamus; experimental and clinical electroencephalographic studies on epilepsy; physiological basis and history of electroencephalography. Address: Montreal Neurological Institute, 3801 University St, Montreal 112, Que, Can.

GLOOR, RICHARD DETMORE, b. Louisville, Ky, Mar. 3, 29; m. 54; c. 2. ELECTRICAL ENGINEERING. B.E.E, Louisville, 51; M.S.E.E, Mass. Inst. Tech, 55. Proj. engr. guidance, TRW Space Tech. Labs, 55-59, spacecraft, 60, dept. mgr. space power & support systs, 61-63, assoc. dir, TRW SYSTS. GROUP, 63-65, proj. mgr, 66-68, ASST. MGR. defense space systs. oper, space vehicles div, 69-70, DEFENSE SPACE SYSTS. DIV, 71- U.S.N, 51-54, Lt.(jg). Sci. Res. Soc. Am; Am. Inst. Aeronaut. & Astronaut. Automatic control, military communications and electronics; data processing; ballistic missiles and satellite guidance; electrical power, ground support systems and spacecraft systems management. Address: TRW Systems Group, 1 Space Park, Redondo Beach, CA 90278.

GLOOR, W(ALTER) E(RVIN), b. Cleveland, Ohio, Nov. 9, 07; m. 34. CHEMISTRY. B.S, Case, 29, Ch.E, 34. Res. chemist, HERCULES INC, N.J, 29-31, exp. sta, Del, 31-36, N.J, 36-44, plastics supvr, 44-46, new prod. develop, DEL, 46-64, supvr. prod. develop, 64-70, NEW PROD. MGR, DEVELOP. DIV, POLYMERS DEPT, 70- With U.S.A. Fel. AAAS; Am. Chem. Soc; fel. Am. Inst. Chem; N.Y. Acad. Sci. Cellulose products; technology; plastics and new uses; new additives for plastics; better molding compounds from polyolefins; fire retardancy. Address: Hercules Inc, Wilmington, DE 19899.

GLOOR, WALTER THOMAS, JR, b. Norfolk, Nebr, Sept. 26, 24; m. 48; c. 6. PHARMACY. B.S, Nebraska, 50; Ph.D.(pharmacog), Washington (Seattle), 55. Instr. pharm, col. pharm, Nebraska, 50-52; sr. scientist pharmaceut. chem, Smith Kline & French Labs, 55-56, unit head, invest. prod. lab. mfg. unit, 56-68; ASSOC. PROF. PHARM, col. pharm, Univ. R.I, 68-71; SCH. PHARM, W.VA. UNIV, 71- U.S.A, 43-46. Am. Chem. Soc; Am. Pharmaceut. Asn; Soc. Econ. Bot; N.Y. Acad. Sci. Alkaloid biosynthesis in fungi; problems in manufacture of parenterals, tablets and other pharmaceutical forms. Address: School of Pharmacy, West Virginia University, Morgantown, WV 26506.

GLOOSCHENKO, WALTER ARTHUR, b. Berkeley, Calif, Sept. 9, 38; m. 67. BIOLOGICAL OCEANOGRAPHY. B.S, California, Berkeley, 60, Davis, 62; Ph.D.(oceanog), Oregon State, 67. Soil scientist, U.S. Bur. Reclamation, 61-62; teacher, high sch, Calif. 62-64; asst. prof. oceanog, Fla. State Univ, 67-70; RES. SCIENTIST, FISHERIES RES. BD. CAN, 70- Chief scientist, P. R. Nuclear Ctr, summer 68. Nat. Guard 56-61. AAAS; Am. Soc. Limnol. & Oceanog; Phycol. Soc. Am; Int. Phycol. Soc; Int. Asn. Gt. Lakes Res; Int. Asn. Theoret. & Appl. Limnol. Chemical factors influencing marine and freshwater primary production by phytoplankton; phytoplankton physiological ecology; biological limnology. Address: Fisheries Research Board, Canada Centre for Inland Waters, Box 5050, Burlington, Ont, Can.

GLORIG, ARAM, b. Manchester, Eng, June 8, 06; nat; m. 44; c. 2. OTOLOGY. M.D, Loma Linda, 38. Intern, Mem. Assoc. Hosp, New London, Conn,

37-38; asst, path. lab, Los Angeles County Hosp, 38-39; res, Willard Parker Hosp, N.Y, 39-40; assoc. otolaryngol, Emory, 41-42, asst. prof, 46-47; chief audiol. & speech correction, phys. med. & rehab. div, dept. med. & surg, Vet. Admin, Wash, D.C, 47-53; assoc. prof. ear, nose & throat, Southern California, 53-64; CLIN. PROF. OTOLARYNGOL, UNIV. TEX. MED. SCH, DALLAS, 64-; DIR, CALLIER HEARING & SPEECH CTR, 64- Dir. audiol. & speech correction center, Walter Reed Army Hosp, 47-52; instr, Maryland, 48-53; lectr, Episcopal Eye, Ear & Throat Hosp, 49-53; clin. instr, George Washington, 51-53; assoc. prof, Loma Linda, 54-64; asst. prof, California, Los Angeles, 55-64; consult. to Surgeon Gen, U.S. Army; Off. Voc. Rehab, Wash, D.C; Civil Aeronaut. Admin; Vet. Admin. Dipl, Am. Bd. Otolaryngol, 47. Asst. chief ear, nose & throat, Lawson Gen. Hosp, Ga, 42, 49th Sta. Hosp, Iceland, 42-43, Eng, 43-45, U.S.A, 42-45. Fel. Acoust. Soc. Am; Am. Otol. Soc; fel. Am. Speech & Hearing Asn; fel. Am. Med. Asn; fel. Am. Acad. Ophthal. & Otolaryngol. Audiology; psychoacoustics. Address: Callier Hearing & Speech Center, 1966 Inwood Rd, Dallas, TX 75235.

GLOSKEY, CARL ROBERT, b. N.J, Nov. 26, 23; m. 47; c. 1. CHEMISTRY, CHEMICAL ENGINEERING. B.A, Rutgers Univ, 54; Sloan fel, Mass. Inst. Technol, 58-59, M.S, 59. Res. engr. & mgr. process develop, Metal & Thermit Corp, 52-60, gen. mgr. & v.pres, M&T CHEM, INC, AM. CAN CO, 61-69, GROUP V.PRES. & GEN. MGR. INT. DIV, 70- U.S.A.A.F, 43-45. Am. Chem. Soc; Am. Ceramic Soc; Am. Inst. Chem. Eng; Refractories Inst. Organometallic chemistry; international industrial chemistry; process engineering; chemicals based on tin, antimony, magnesium, phosphorus, for plastics, agriculture, biological use; water resource control. Address: M&T Chemicals, Inc, American Can Co, American Lane, Greenwich, CT 06830.

GLOTFELTY, JAMES SAMUEL, b. Batavia, Iowa, June 15, 05; m. 23; c. 1. HOSPITAL ADMINISTRATION, NEUROPSYCHIATRY. M.D, Iowa, 34. Intern, San Diego County Gen. Hosp, 34-35; res, U.S. Pub. Health Serv, Ky, 35-36; practicing physician, Iowa, 36-37; med. off, hosp. serv, Vet. Admin, 37-44, chief neuropsychiat. div, area off, St. Louis, 48-50, hosp. mgr, Lebanon, Pa, 50-55, Durham, N.C, 55-59, med. dir, Vet. Admin. Ctr, 59-61, dir, Vet. Admin. Hosps, Long Beach, 61-62, Oakland & Martinez, 62-64, area med. dir, San Francisco, 64-66, hosp. dir, Vet. Admin. Hosp, Long Beach, 66-70; RETIRED. Assoc. prof. psychiat. & asst. prof. hosp. admin, sch. med, Duke, 55-59; clin. prof. psychiat. & human behav, Univ. Calif-Calif. Col. Med, 66-70. Med.C, 42-46, Lt. Col. Fel. Am. Psychiat. Asn; fel. Am. Col. Physicians; assoc. mem. Am. Acad. Neurol. Clinical psychiatry and neurology; mental hygiene. Address: 5573 Oleta St, Long Beach, CA 90815.

GLOTH, RICHARD E(DWARD), b. Springfield, Mass, Aug. 25, 41; m. 66; c. 2. ORGANIC & ORGANOMETALLIC CHEMISTRY. B.A, Univ. Mass, Amherst, 63, M.S. & Petrol. Res. Fund summer fel, 69, Ph.D.(org. chem), 70. SR. RES. CHEMIST, HYDROCARBON SECT, GOODYEAR TIRE & RUBBER CO, 69- Del, Int. Cong. Pure & Appl. Chem, summer 71. Am. Chem. Soc. Synthesis and reactions of arene-chromium and arene-tungsten tricarbonyls; synthesis of organometallic catalysts; homogeneous and heterogeneous catalysis; rubber antitoxidants. Address: Research Division, Dept. 455B, Goodyear Tire & Rubber Co, 142 Goodyear Blvd, Akron, OH 44316.

GLOTZER, H(ERMAN) L(EONARD), b. Brooklyn, N.Y, June 24, 24; m. 45; c. 2. CHEMICAL ENGINEERING. B.S, Iowa, 47, M.S, 48; Ph.D, Syracuse, 52. Develop. engr. solid rocket engines, Aerojet Gen. Corp, 51-52, asst. sr. engr, 52-53; res. engr, org. chem. dept, E.I. DU PONT DE NEMOURS & CO, 53-56, res. supvr, 56-63, div. head, 63-66, chief supvr, Chamber Works, 66-68, supt. dye mfg, 69-71, SUPT. LIQUID WASTE TREATMENT, 71- U.S.A, 43-45. Am. Chem. Soc; Am. Inst. Chem. Eng. Organic flourine chemicals; intermediates; pigment finishing, sorption processes; solid rocket engines; radiation effects; chemical process economics; benzenoid chemicals and dyes; industrial waste treatment. Address: E.I. du Pont de Nemours & Co, Deepwater, NJ 19803.

GLOVER, ALAN M(ARSH), b. Rochester, N.Y, Sept. 26, 09; m. 49; c. 3. PHYSICS. B.A, Rochester, 30, M.A, 32; fel, 34-35, Ph.D.(physics), 34; Cornell, 33. Physicist, Inst. Paper Chem, Lawrence Col, 35-36; engr, res. & develop, lab, radiotron div, RCA CORP, N.J, 36-43, engr. in charge spec. purpose tube dept, 41-43, Victor Div, 43-50, prod. admin, 50-53, mgr. controls & standards, cathoderay & power tube div, 53-54, gen. mgr, semiconductor div, 55-56, semiconductor & mat. div, 56-58, v.pres, 58-63, div. v.pres. tech. progs, 63-70, TECH. ADV, 70- Mem. trustees coun, Univ. Rochester, 64-71; trustee, Wilkes Col, 70- AAAS; Am. Phys. Soc; Inst. Elec. & Electronics Eng. Electron physics; photoelectricity; secondary emission; anomalous dispersion; gaseous conduction; photoelectric surfaces and devices. Address: 30 Oak Hill Rd, Chatham, NJ 07928.

GLOVER, A(LLEN) DONALD, b. Kirksville, Mo, Jan. 6, 38; m. 63; c. 1. ORGANIC CHEMISTRY. A.B, Culver-Stockton Col, 60; Iowa State, 60-61; Ph.D.(chem, Carnegie Inst. Tech, 65. Res. fel. CHEM, Calif. Inst. Tech, 65-66; ASST. PROF, BRADLEY UNIV, 66- Am. Chem. Soc; The Chem. Soc. Structure elucidation of the products formed by photodimerizations; photochemical cycloaddition reactions of conjugated keto steroids. Address: Dept. of Chemistry, Bradley University, Peoria, IL 61606.

GLOVER, B(ENJAMIN) H(OWELL), b. Chicago, Ill, Apr. 29, 16; m. 40; c. 2. PSYCHIATRY. B.S, Northwestern, 37, M.S, 39, M.D, 43. Instr. biol, Allegheny Col, 40-42; asst. prof. PSYCHIAT, UNIV. WIS, MADISON, 47-58, ASSOC. PROF, 58- Consult, Vet. Hosp, Madison; Nat. Insts. Ment. Health grant teaching psychiat. to physicians, Wis. Dipl, Am. Bd. Psychiat, 52. Med.C, 43-47, Lt. Comdr. Fel. Am. Psychiat. Asn; Pan-Am. Med. Asn. Methods of electroshock therapy; psychotherapy; continuing medical education. Address: 3706 Spring Trail, Madison, WI 53711.

GLOVER, CHARLES RAY, b. Mountainair, N.Mex, Oct. 4, 39; m. 67. PLANT BREEDING. B.S, N.Mex. State Univ, 63, M.S, 67; Ph.D.(crop sci), Okla. State Univ, 71. Soil scientist, Soil Conserv. Serv, U.S. Dept. Agr, 63-65; AGRONOMIST, TAYLOR-EVANS SEED CO. DIV, DIAMOND SHAMROCK CORP, 70- Am. Soc. Agron; Crop Sci. Soc. Am. Development and improvement of grain sorghum, forage sorghum, corn and sorghum-sudangrass hybrids; small grains research. Address: Taylor-Evans Seed Co, Box 480, Tulia, TX 79088.

GLOVER, CLYDE A(LBERT), b. Birmingham, Ala, Oct. 27, 13; m. 44; c. 2. ANALYTICAL CHEMISTRY. B.S, Auburn, 35, M.S, 37; Ph.D.(anal. chem), North Carolina, 47. Res. chemist, TENN. EASTMAN CO, 47-51, sr. res. chemist, 51-71, RES. ASSOC, 71- U.S.A.R, 35-41; U.S.A.F, 41-45, Res, 45-62. AAAS; Am. Chem. Soc. Ebulliometry and ebulliometric molecular weight determination; thermal methods of analysis; trace metal analysis; polarography; anhydrous titrations and Ph measurements. Address: Research Labs, Tennessee Eastman Co, Kingston, TN 37662.

GLOVER, DAVID V(AL), b. Farmington, Utah, May 18, 32; m. 54; c. 6. GENETICS, CYTOGENETICS. B.S, Utah State, 54, M.S, 59; Ph.D.(genetics), California, 62. Asst. agron, Utah State, 57-59; GENETICS & PLANT BREEDING, California, 59-62; asst. prof, PURDUE UNIV, 62-65, ASSOC. PROF, 65- U.S.A.F, 55-57, Res, 59-, Capt. AAAS; Am. Genetic Asn; Am. Soc. Agron; Crop Sci. Soc. Am. Genetics and cytogenetics of crop plants; autotetraploid inheritance in alfalfa; breeding and physiology of alfalfa; genetics and biochemistry of maize endosperm gene interactions; chemical mutagenesis in plant genetics and breeding. Address: Dept. of Agronomy, Purdue University, West Lafayette, IN 47907.

GLOVER, DELBERT CLARKE, b. Savannah, Ga, June 30, 39; m. 68; c. 1. ORGANIC CHEMISTRY. B.S, Fisk, 61; Kansas, 61-62; Ph.D.(chem), Massachusetts, 66. Res. chemist, PLASTICS DEPT, E.I. DU PONT DE NEMOURS & CO, INC, 66-69, TECH. REP, 69- Am. Chem. Soc; Sci. Res. Soc. Am. Synthesis and reactions of Reissert compounds. Address: 623 Saddle Ridge Rd, Orange, CT 06477.

GLOVER, EARL ROBERT, b. Woodstock, Minn, Nov. 18, 15; m. 42; c. 2. AGRICULTURAL MARKETING & EDUCATION. B.S, Tex. Tech. Col, 39; M.S, Texas A&M, 41. With U.S. DEPT. AGR, 41-50, asst. to asst. adminstr. mkt. res, prod. & mkt. admin, 50-54, asst. to dir, agr. mkt. serv, 54-56, asst. to dep. adminstr. mkt. res. & statist, 56-57, asst. to dir. mkt. res, 57-58, asst. dept. adminstr, 58-64, AGR. RES. SERV, 64-66, acting dep. adminstr, 66-67, dep. adminr, 67-70, ASST. DEP. ADMINR. MKT. & NUTRIT, 70- Am. Mkt. Asn; Am. Agr. Econ. Asn; Am. Soc. Pub. Admin. Transportation; marketing facilities; food wholesaling and retailing; efficient handling of agricultural products during marketing; protecting and maintaining quality in agricultural products; objective methods for identifying and measuring quality; new and improved uses for agricultural products. Address: Office of Administrator, Agricultural Research Service, U.S. Dept. of Agriculture, Washington, DC 20250.

GLOVER, EVERETT D, b. Worcester, Mass, Feb. 1, 17; m. 40; c. 1. GEOCHEMISTRY. A.B, Clark, 41; M.S, Wisconsin, 52. Chemist, Wyman-Gordon Co, Mass, 42; res. chemist, Mem. Found. Neuro-Endocrine Res, Worcester State Hosp, 42-44; instr. math, Wisconsin, Milwaukee, 46-47; phys. sci, Custer County Jr. Col, 47-49; res. chemist, Nalco Chem. Co, 52-55; sr. res. technologist, Mobil Oil Co, 55-66; LECTR. GEOL, UNIV. WIS, MADISON, 66- Sig.C, U.S.A, 44-46, T/Sgt. AAAS; Geochem. Soc; Clay Minerals Soc; Electron Probe Anal. Soc. Am. Sedimentary geochemistry; x-ray and chemical mechanisms in geology. Address: Dept. of Geology & Geophysics, University of Wisconsin, Madison, WI 53706.

GLOVER, FRANCIS N(ICHOLAS), b. Brooklyn, N.Y, Jan. 11, 25. PHYSICS. A.B, Sacred Heart Col, P.I, 49, M.A, 50; Ph.D, St. Louis, 55. Instr. physics, Ateneo de Manila, 50-51; asst, St. Louis, 53-55; res. assoc, Woodstock Col.(Md), 55-59; ionosphere res. sect, Manila Observ, 59-65; ASST. PROF. PHYSICS, ATENEO DE MANILA UNIV, 65- Summer guest, Cent. Radio Propagation Lab, Boulder, Colo, 58-59. U.S.N.R, 43. Am. Phys. Soc; Inst. Elec. & Electronics Eng. Radio propagation; physics of the ionosphere. Address: Dept. of Physics, Ateneo de Manila University, P.O. Box 154, Manila, Philippines.

GLOVER, FRED A(RTHUR), b. San Francisco, Calif, May 18, 18; m. 41; c. 2. WILDLIFE MANAGEMENT. B.S, Ore. State Col, 41; fel, Pa. State Col, 41-42, M.S, 42; fel, Iowa State Col, 47-49, Ph.D.(zool), 49; cert. pub. admin, U.S. Dept. Agr. Grad. Sch. Field technician, State Conserv. Cmn, W.Va, 46-47; assoc. prof. & head dept. wildlife mgt, Humbolt State Col, 50-53; Atlantic flyway biologist, U.S. FISH & WILDLIFE SERV, 53-54, asst. chief sect. survs. & invests, 54-59, tech. asst, mgt. & enforcement br, 59-61, chief, sect. surveys and banding, 61-63, LEADER, COLO. COOP. WILDLIFE RES. UNIT, WILDLIFE RES. DIV, 63- Res. biologist, Wildlife Mgt. Inst, 51; Calif. Redwood Asn, 52-53. U.S.A.A.F, 42-46, 1st Lt. Wildlife Soc; Am. Soc. Mammal; Cooper Ornith. Soc; Wilson Ornith. Soc; Am. Ornith. Union; Ecol. Soc. Am. Waterfowl; wildlife population dynamics; economic status of wildlife. Address: Room 103, Cooperative Units Bldg, Colorado State University, Ft. Collins, CO 80521.

GLOVER, GEORGE IRVIN, b. Oakland, Calif, Mar. 8, 40; m. 59; c. 2. ORGANIC & PROTEIN CHEMISTRY. B.S, California, Berkeley, 62, Nat. Insts. Health fel, 63-66, Ph.D.(org. chem), 66. Sr. res. chemist, Air Prod. & Chem, Inc, 66-67; res. collab. protein chem. & enzyme, Brookhaven Nat. Lab, 67-70; ASST. PROF. CHEM, TEX. A&M UNIV, 70- Nat. Insts. Health fel, 67-69; asst. vis. scientist, Brookhaven Nat. Lab, 69-70. Am. Chem. Soc. Irreversible enzyme inhibitors; purification kinetics and active site histidine of bovine thrombin; synthesis of potential pesticides; synthesis of cyclic peptide for cyclolization studies. Address: Dept. of Chemistry, Texas A&M University, College Station, TX 77840.

GLOVER, ISRAEL E(VERETT), b. Oxford, N.C, Feb. 13, 13; m. 40; c. 1. MATHEMATICS. B.S, J.C. Smith Univ, 35; M.A, Michigan, 37, Gen. Ed. Bd. fel, 39-40; John Hay Whitney fel, Okla. State, 53-54, Ph.D.(math), 59. Flutter engr, Bell Aircraft Corp, 44-46; aeronaut. res. engr, Wright Patterson Air Force Base, 46-48; assoc. prof. math, Langston, 48-55; prof. & head dept, Prairie View Agr. & Mech. Col, 55-62; Fla. Agr. & Mech, 62-67; vis. prof, Teachers Col, Columbia, 67-68; prof. & head dept, Albany State Col, 68-69; PROF, Norfolk State Col, 69-71; MATH, D.C. TEACHERS COL, 71- Vis. scientist, Tex. Acad. Sci, 59-62 & Fla. Acad. Sci, 64-67; panelist,

Nat. Sci. Found, 61-69; dir-coord, Minn. Math. & Sci. Teaching Proj, Tallahassee Ctr, 63-67; dir. phys. sci. for non scientists proj, Fla. Agr. & Mech, 66-67; vis. lectr, Mu Alpha Theta. Summers, fel. hist. math, Univ. Mich, 62, consult, math, Gujarat Univ, India, 69. AAAS; N.Y. Acad. Sci; Am. Math. Soc; Math. Asn. Am. Analytic functions; topology. Address: 5468 Sandpiper Lane, Norfolk, VA 23502.

GLOVER, JOHN RICHARD, b. Steubenville, Ohio, Mar. 28, 37; m. 60; c. 1. FLUID MECHANICS. B.S.E.E, Iowa, 60, M.S, 61, Ph.D.(fluid mech), 65. Res. asst. instrumentation, INST. HYDRAUL. RES, UNIV. IOWA, 60-61, res. assoc, 61-65, ASST. PROF. MECH. & HYDRAUL, UNIV. & RES. ENGR, INST, 65- Electronic instrumentation, acquisition and reduction of unsteady-flow variables by analog and digital techniques. Address: Dept. of Mechanics & Hydraulics, University of Iowa, Ames, IA 52240.

GLOVER, KENNETH MERLE, b. Hamilton, Ohio, Oct. 11, 28; m. 49; c. 2. ATMOSPHERIC PHYSICS, ELECTRONICS. A.B, Miami (Ohio), 58, M.S, 60. Res. engr, corp. res. labs, P.R. Mallory & Co, 60-62; RES. PHYSICIST, AIR FORCE CAMBRIDGE RES. LABS, OFF. AEROSPACE RES, U.S. AIR FORCE, BEDFORD, 62- Instr, Ind. Cent. Col, 61-62. U.S.A.F, 51-55, S/Sgt. Inst. Elec. & Electronics Eng; Am. Meteorol. Soc; Sci. Res. Soc. Am. Radar backscatter cross-sections of dielectric spheres; backscatter from the clear atmosphere; radar observations of the tropopause; radar observations of insects; remote sensing of clear air turbulence. Address: 3 Captain Brown's Lane, Acton, MA 01720.

GLOVER, LEON C(ONRAD), JR, b. Exeter, N.H, July 5, 35; m. 63; c. 3. ORGANIC & POLYMER CHEMISTRY. B.S, Notre Dame, 57; Ph.D.(org. chem), Stanford, 62. Chemist, Shell Develop. Co, Calif, 62-64; STAFF CHEMIST, RAYCHEM CORP, 64- Am. Chem. Soc; Brit. Chem. Soc. Organic peroxides; vanadium catalyzed olefin polymerizations; lithium catalyzed living polymer systems; high temperature polymer synthesis and evaluation; polymer characterization. Address: Raychem Corp, 300 Constitution Dr, Menlo Park, CA 94025.

GLOVER, LYNN, III, b. Wash, D.C, Nov. 29, 28; m. 50. REGIONAL GEOLOGY. B.S, Va. Polytech. Inst. & State Univ, 52, M.S, 53; Ph.D.(geol), Princeton, 67. Geologist, U.S. Geol. Surv, 53-70; PROF. GEOL, VA. POLYTECH. INST. & STATE UNIV, 70- Fel. Geol. Soc. Am; Am. Asn. Petrol. Geol; Soc. Econ. Paleont. & Mineral; Am. Geophys. Union. Geology of the Caribbean and of the Appalachians. Address: Dept. of Geological Sciences, Virginia Polytechnic Institute & State University, Blacksburg, VA 24061.

GLOVER, ROBERT E(LLSWORTH), b. Ord, Nebr, Jan. 22, 96; m. 25; c. 3. ENGINEERING. B.S, Nebraska, 21, C.E, 36; M.S, Colorado, 50. Field surv, U.S. Reclamation Serv, Mont, 17-21; engr, Nebr. Capitol Cmn, 21-22; instr. civil eng, Mont. State Col, 22-23; from instrumentman to gen. engr, U.S. Bur. Reclamation, 23-54; Boeing Airplane Co, 55; hydraul. engr, U.S. Geol. Surv, 56-60; gen. engr, U.S. Bur. Reclamation, 60-66; PROF. CIVIL ENG, COLO. STATE UNIV, 66- Distinguished serv. award, U.S. Dept. Interior. U.S.A, 18-19. Am. Soc. Civil Eng; Am. Concrete Inst. Trial load method for design or arch dams; transient heat flow; applied mathematics; ground water hydraulics. Address: 1936 S. Lincoln St, Denver, CO 80210.

GLOVER, R(OLAND) L(EIGH), b. Peterborough, Ont, Can, Dec. 19, 11; nat; m. 37. ELECTROCHEMISTRY. B.A.Sc, Toronto, 34, M.A.Sc, 35. Asst, Toronto, 34-35; lab. technician, Nat. Carbon Co, Div. UNION CARBIDE CORP, Ont, 35-39, develop. engr, Ohio, 39-44, head prod. & process develop, 44-45, asst. supt. in charge eng. & lab, 45-48, supt, Ont, 49-50, factory mgr, 51-54, asst. dir. res, Ohio, 54-56, asst. to v.pres. & gen. mgr. N.Y, 56-59, gen. mgr. TECH, UNION CARBIDE CONSUMER PROD. CO. DIV, 59-62, V.PRES, 62- AAAS; Electrochem. Soc; Chem. Inst. Can. Research and development administration of chemical and electrochemical consumer products. Address: Consumer Products Division, Union Carbide Corp, 270 Park Ave, New York, NY 10017.

GLOVER, ROLFE E(LDRIDGE), III, b. Wilmington, Del, Sept. 6, 24; m. 57; c. 3. SOLID STATE PHYSICS. B.A, Bowdoin Col, 48; B.S, Mass. Inst. Tech, 48; Ph.D.(physics), Göttingen, 53. Fel, Nat. Sci. Found, California, 55-57; asst. prof. PHYSICS, Univ. N.C, 57-61; assoc. prof, UNIV. MD, COLLEGE PARK, 61-66, PROF, 66- Alfred P. Sloan res. fel, 58-62. U.S.A.A.F, 46-47. Fel. Am. Phys. Soc; Am. Asn. Physics Teachers. Superconductivity; phase transitions; amorphous materials; thin films; chemical reactions at low temperatures. Address: Dept. of Physics & Astronomy, Univeristy of Maryland, College Park, MD 20742.

GLOVER, ROY ANDREW, b. Cleveland, Ohio, Apr. 7, 41; m. 63; c. 3. NEUROANATOMY, HISTOLOGY. B.S, Calvin Col, 63; M.Sc, Ohio State, 65, Nat. Insts. Health fel, 66-68, Ph.D.(anat), 68. Instr. ANAT. UNIV. MICH, ANN ARBOR, 68-70, ASST. PROF, 70- Neurochemical and morphological interrelationship between the neural elements located within peripheral ganglia during various stages of the axon reaction. Address: Dept. of Anatomy, 4771 Medical Sciences Bldg, University of Michigan, Ann Arbor, MI 48104.

GLOVER, SANDRA JEAN, b. Mansfield, La, Jan. 19, 39. ENTOMOLOGY. B.S, Northwest. State Univ, 61; M.Ed, Georgia, 65, Ph.D.(entom), 68. Teacher, high sch, La, 61-64; asst. prof. biol, Miss. State Col. Women, 68; aquatic biologist, Fed. Water Pollution Control Admin, summer 68; res. fel. entom, Univ. Ga, 68-69; ASST. PROF. BIOL, APPALACHIAN STATE UNIV, 69- Partic, Nat. Sci. Found. summer inst, Univ. Mont, 64, acad. year inst, Univ. Ga, 64-65 & fel, 68-69. AAAS; Entom. Soc. Am; Am. Inst. Biol. Sci. Insect physiology and behavior. Address: Dept. of Biology, Appalachian State University, Boone, NC 28607.

GLOWER, DONALD D(UANE), b. Shelby, Ohio, July 29, 26; m. 53; c. 4. MECHANICAL ENGINEERING. B.S, U.S. Merchant Marine Acad, 46; Antioch Col, 53; M.Sc, Iowa State, 58, Ph.D, 60. Asst. engr. officer, Grace Lines Inc, 47-49; res. engr, Battelle Mem. Inst, 53-54; asst. prof, col. eng, Iowa State, 54-58, nuclear eng, 60-61; fel, Nat. Sci. Found, 59-60; mem. res. staff, Sandia Corp, 61-63; head radiation effects dept, Gen. Motors Corp, 63-64; PROF. & CHMN. nuclear eng, OHIO STATE UNIV, 64-68, MECH. ENG, 68- Mem, Ohio Atomic Energy Bd. U.S. Merchant Marine Acad. award, 61- AAAS; Am. Nuclear Soc; Am. Phys. Soc; Am. Soc. Eng. Educ; Am. Soc. Mech. Eng; Inst. Elec. & Electronics Eng. Energy conversion. Address: 2338 Kensington Dr, Columbus, OH 43221.

GLOYD, HOWARD K(AY), b. De Soto, Kans, Feb. 12, 02; m. 25, 47; c. 2. ZOOLOGY. B.Sc, Ottawa, 24, hon. D.Sc, 42; M.S, Kans. State Col, 29; Ph.D. (zool), Michigan, 37. Instr. biol, Ottawa, 24-27; zool, Kans. State Col, 27-29; Michigan, 29-36; dir, Chicago Acad. Sci, 36-58; lectr. ZOOL, UNIV. ARIZ, 58-59, res. assoc, 59-62, LECTR, 62- Consult, State Natural Hist. Surv, Ill, 40-47. AAAS; Am. Soc. Ichthyol. & Herpet.(v.pres, 39); Soc. Syst. Zool; Cooper Ornith. Soc; Am. Ornith. Union; Soc. Study Amphibians & Reptiles. Systematics and zoogeography of crotalid snakes. Address: Dept. of Biological Sciences, University of Arizona, Tucson, AZ 85721.

GLOYD, LEONORA K(ATHERINE), b. Larned, Kans, Aug. 29, 02; div; c. 2. ENTOMOLOGY. B.Sc, Kans. State Univ, 24, M.S, 25; summers, Univ. Mich, 24, 27. Asst, div. insects, mus. zool, Univ. Mich, Ann Arbor, 29-37; hon. curator insects, mus, Chicago Acad. Sci, 38-47; lab. asst, ILL. STATE NATURAL HIST. SURV, 47-56, asst. taxonomist, 56-65, assoc. taxonomist, 65-66, EMER. ASSOC. PROF. SCIENTIST, 67- Asst. curator insects, mus. zool, Univ. Mich, Ann Arbor, summer 54, Nat. Sci. Found. res. grant & res. assoc, 65-68, vis. res. assoc, 68- Soc. Syst. Zool. Life history, taxonomy and phylogeny of Odonata; monograph of the genus Argia. Address: Division of Insects, Museum of Zoology, University of Michigan, Ann Arbor, MI 48104.

GLOYER, STEWART EDWARD, b. Milwaukee, Wis, May 23, 42; m. 67; c. 1. ORGANIC CHEMISTRY. B.S, Rochester, 64; M.S, Michigan, 66, Ph.D.(chem), 69. Asst. org. chem, Michigan, 64-69; RES. CHEMIST, KRAFTCO CORP, 69- Am. Chem. Soc. Organic nitrogen chemistry; catalysis organic reactions. Address: 801 Waukegan Rd, Glenview, IL 60025.

GLOYER, STEWART WAYNE, b. Milwaukee, Wis, May 22, 10; m. 39; c. 3. CHEMISTRY. B.S, Beloit Col, 32; Ph.D.(chem), Wisconsin, 39. Res. chemist, Pittsburgh Plate Glass Co, 39-44, group leader, 44-52, asst. dir. res, 52-58, assoc. dir. res. & develop, 58-65, div. dir, coatings develop, 65-68, DIV. TECH. DIR. INDUST. PROD, PPG INDUSTS, INC, 68- Am. Chem. Soc; Forest Prod. Res. Soc; fel. Am. Inst. Chem; Fedn. Socs. Paint Technol. Protective and industrial coatings; resins, automotive finishes; electrocoating; ultra violet and radiation coatings; coil and container coatings. Address: PPG Industries, Inc, Coatings Resins Division, One Gateway Center, Pittsburgh, PA 15222.

GLOYNA, EARNEST F(REDERICK), b. Vernon, Tex, June 30, 21; m. 46; c. 2. SANITARY ENGINEERING. B.S, Texas Tech. Col, 46; M.S, Texas, 49; Dr. Eng.(sanit. eng, water resources), Hopkins, 53. Instrumentman, State Hwy. Dept, Tex, 46; office engr, Magnolia Petrol. Co, Tex, 46-47; res. partic, Oak Ridge Nat. Lab, 50; res. staff asst, Johns Hopkins Univ, 51-52; prof. eng, UNIV. TEX, AUSTIN, 52-70, DEAN ENG. & JOE J. KING PROF. ENG, 70-, DIR. CTR. RES. WATER RESOURCES, 52-, lectr, post-grad. sch. med, 56-60. Guest engr, Brookhaven Nat. Lab, 52; consult, various industs, cities & govt. agencies, including U.S. Air Force, U.S. Army, U.S. Senate, World Health Org. C.Eng, 42-45, Lt. Col. Nat. Acad. Eng; Am. Soc. Civil Eng; Acad. Environ. Eng; Nat. Soc. Prof. Eng; Am. Soc. Eng. Educ; Am. Water Works Asn; Water Pollution Control Fedn. Water and wastewater treatment. Address: Taylor Hall 167, University of Texas at Austin, Austin, TX 78712.

GLUCK, JEREMY V(ICTOR), b. Cleveland, Ohio, June 3, 27; m. 53; c. 3. METALLURGICAL ENGINEERING. B.S.E.(chem. eng) & B.S.E.(metall. eng), Michigan, 49, M.S.E, 50, Ph.D, 65. Asst, high temp. metall. res. inst, UNIV. MICH, 50-53, res. assoc, 53-59, assoc. res. engr, 59-65, RES. ASSOC, 65-; RES. METALLURGIST, TECUMSEH PROD. RES. LABS, 65- Res. engr, Conductron Corp, 62. Am. Inst. Min, Metall. & Petrol. Eng; Am. Soc. Metals. Physical metallurgy; metallurgical thermodynamics; welding; deep drawing; creep and high temperature metallurgy; solid state materials. Address: Tecumseh Products Co. Research Lab, 3869 Research Park Dr, Ann Arbor, MI 48104.

GLUCK, LOUIS, b. Newark, N.J, June 18, 24; m. 47; c. 4. BIOCHEMISTRY, PEDIATRICS. B.Sc, Rutgers, 48; M.D, Chicago, 52. Intern med, univ. clin, Chicago, 53; res. & fel. pediat, Columbia-Presby. Med. Center, 56-59; instr, sch. med, Stanford, 59-60; asst. prof, sch. med, Yale, 60-64, assoc. prof. PEDIAT, 64-68, PROF, sch. med, Univ. Miami, 68-69; SCH. MED, UNIV. CALIF, SAN DIEGO, 69- Mem. perinatal. rev. comt, Am. Col. Obstet. & Gynec; ed-in-chief, Current Probs. Pediat. Dipl, Am. Bd. Pediat, 63. U.S.A, 43-46, S/Sgt. AAAS; Am. Inst. Biol. Sci; Soc. Study Reproduction; Perinatal Res. Soc; Am. Pediat. Soc; Soc. Pediat. Res; Am. Thoracic Soc; Am. Acad. Pediat; Am. Inst. Chem. Developmental biochemistry; perinatal mortality studies. Address: Dept. of Pediatrics, School of Medicine, University of California, San Diego, P.O. Box 109, La Jolla, CA 92037.

GLUCK, PETER, b. Velky Berezny, Czech, Mar. 25, 22; m. 56. CHEMICAL ENGINEERING. B.Ch.E, City Col. New York, 56; Ohio State, 57-59. PRIN. CHEM. ENGR, BATTELLE MEM. INST, 56- Abstractor, Chem. Abstr. Serv. Czech. Army, U.S.S.R. Forces. Am. Inst. Chem. Eng; Am. Chem. Soc. Wear studies using radioisotope techniques; intrinsic radiotracer studies in unit operations on site production of tracers and their utilization in chemical processes; activation studies using a rabbit system in conjunction with a two megawath research reactor. Address: 1815 Kenwick Rd, Columbus, OH 43210.

GLUCK, RAFAEL, b. Berlin, Ger, May 19, 31; U.S. citizen; m. 58; c. 3. SOLID MECHANICS. B.S, California, Berkeley, 55; M.S, Purdue, 56, Saginaw Gear fel. & Ph.D.(appl. mech), 63; Stevens Inst. Tech, 59-60. Sr. develop. engr, develop. lab, U.S. Rubber Co, Ind, 56-58, mech. engr, res. ctr, N.J, 58-60; eng. fel. appl. mech, Purdue, 60-61, res. asst, 61-62; vis. lectr. theoret. mech, Israel Inst. Tech, 62-63; proj. engr, TRW SYSTS, 64-69, HEAD ANAL. DYNAMICS SECT, APPL. MECH. LAB, 69- Lectr, California, Los Angeles, 65- Israel Army, 48-50. Am. Inst. Aeronaut. & Astronaut. Dynamics of spacecraft; passive attitude control, spin, magnetic and gravity gradient stabilization; metal fatigue; stress analysis and biomechanics. Address: 23218 S. Carlow Rd, Torrance, CA 90505.

GLUCKSTEIN, FRITZ PAUL, b. Berlin, Ger, Jan. 24, 27; U.S. citizen; m. 55; c. 1. VETERINARY MEDICINE. B.S, Minnesota, 53, D.V.M, 55; Iowa State, 58-59. Vet. meat inspector, U.S. Dept. Agr, 55-56, asst. vet. pathologist, 58-59, vet. analyst, 59-63; chief microbiol. br, sci. info. exchange, Smithsonian Inst, 63-66; COORD. VET. AFFAIRS, NAT. LIBR. MED, U.S. PUB. HEALTH SERV, 66- Dipl, Am. Bd. Vet. Pub. Health, 66. Vet.C, 56-58, Res, 58-65, Capt. Am. Vet. Med. Asn; Am. Pub. Health Asn; U.S. Animal Health Asn; Royal Soc. Health. Foreign animal diseases; veterinary public health; analysis and retrieval of scientific information. Address: 5603 Oak Pl, Bethesda, MD 20034.

GLUCKSTEIN, MARTIN E(DWIN), b. Brooklyn, N.Y, May 19, 28; m. 51; c. 5. CHEMICAL ENGINEERING. B.S.E, Michigan, 50, M.S.E, 51, Ph.D, 57. Asst, eng. res. inst, Michigan, 51, res. assoc, 52-56, assoc. res. engr, 56; chem. engr, ETHYL CORP, 56-63, res. assoc, 63-64, RES. SUPVR, 64- Instr, Wayne State Univ, 57-62. AAAS; Am. Ord. Asn; Am. Chem. Soc; Am. Inst. Chem. Eng; Combustion Inst. Combustion; rate and transport processes; air pollution measurement and control; research management. Address: Ethyl Corp, 1600 W. 8 Mile Rd, Ferndale, MI 48220.

GLUCKSTERN, ROBERT LEONARD, b. Atlantic City, N.J, July 31, 24; m. 48; c. 3. PHYSICS. B.E.E, City Col. New York, 44; DuPont fels. & Ph.D.(physics), Mass. Inst. Tech, 48. Atomic Energy Cmn. fel. physics, California, Berkeley, 48-49 & Cornell, 49-50; res. assoc, Yale, 50-51, asst. prof, 51-57, assoc. prof, 57-64; prof. & head dept, UNIV. MASS, AMHERST, 64-69, assoc. provost, 69-71, V.CHANCELLOR ACAD. AFFAIRS & PROVOST, 71- Yale faculty fel, European Orgn. Nuclear Res, Switz, 61-62. Consult, Lawrence Radiation Lab, Livermore, 58-61; Brookhaven Nat. Lab, 63-; Los Alamos Sci. Lab, 64-; Nat. Accelerator Lab, 68-70; vis. prof, Univ. Tokyo, 70. U.S.N, 46-48. Am. Phys. Soc. Theoretical, nuclear and elementary particle physics; accelerator theory. Address: Whitmore Administration Bldg, University of Massachusetts, Amherst, MA 01002.

GLUDE, JOHN B(RYCE), b. Manette, Wash, Aug. 2, 18; m. 40; c. 3. MARINE BIOLOGY. B.S, Univ. Wash, 39, M.P.A, 69. Shellfish biologist, State Dept. Fisheries, Wash, 40-41, supvry. shellfish biologist, 45-48; assoc. naval architect, Todd Pac. Shipyard, 41-45; chief clam invests, U.S. FISH & WILDLIFE SERV, 48-58, shellfisheries br, BUR. COMMERCIAL FISHERIES, 58-62, dep. regional dir, 62-70, ASSOC. REGIONAL DIR, NAT. MARINE FISHERIES SERV, SEATTLE, 70- Am. Fisheries Soc; Ecol. Soc. Am; Nat. Shellfisheries Asn.(pres, 64-65); fel. Am. Inst. Fishery Res. Biol. Biology and ecology of marine shellfish, especially oysters and clams; administration of fisheries research and development programs. Address: 2703 W. McGraw St, Seattle, WA 98199.

GLUECK, ALAN ROBERT, b. Cleveland, Ohio, June 8, 33; m. 62; c. 4. CHEMICAL ENGINEERING. B.S, Mass. Inst. Tech, 55, Ch.E, 59; Union Carbide fel, Princeton, 55-56, M.S.E, 56; Ph.D.(chem. eng), Cambridge, 66. Aeronaut. res. engr, Lewis Res. Center, NASA, Ohio, 56-60; sr. engr, Dynatech Corp, Mass, 59-60; mgr. chem. eng, 60-62; supvr. math, Fitzwilliam Col, Univ. Cambridge, 63-64; assoc. specialist chem. eng, California, Berkeley, 65-66; prin. engr, Electronic Assocs, Inc, 66-67, staff engr. & proj. mgr, 67-70; dir. res, CHEM. TECHNOL. CORP, 70-71, PRES, 71- Fel. Am. Inst. Chem; N.Y. Acad. Sci; Am. Chem. Soc; Inst. Elec. & Electronics Eng; Am. Inst. Chem. Eng. Polymers and composite materials; instrumentation; process control; microwave power applications; computer languages and simulation; numerical analysis; molten salt reaction technology; kinetics; thermodynamics; fluid dynamics; desalination; ion exchange, air pollution; biotechnology. Address: 78 Pennington Lawrenceville Rd, Lawrenceville, NJ 08648.

GLUECK, BERNARD C(HARLES), b. Baltimore, Md, Aug. 26, 14; m. 36; c. 2. PSYCHIATRY. A.B, Columbia, 34, C.P.M, 51; M.D, Harvard Med. Sch, 38. Instr. PSYCHIAT, col. physicians & surgeons, Columbia Univ, 47-55, asst. psychoanalyst, psychoanal. clin, 51-55; assoc. prof, Univ. Minn, 55-59, prof, 59-60; DIR. RES, INST. LIVING, 60- Lectr, sch. med, Yale, 65- Med.C, U.S.A.A.F, 42-46. Am. Psychosom. Soc; fel. Am. Psychiat. Asn; Am. Psychopath. Asn.(treas, 52-64, v.pres, 64-65, pres, 66-67); Asn. Psychoanal. Med; fel. Acad. Psychoanal; Am. Col. Neuropsychopharmacol. Psychoanalysis; computers; behavioral science. Address: Institute of Living, Box 1929, Hartford, CT 06101.

GLUECK, HELEN IGLAUER, b. Cincinnati, Ohio, Feb. 4, 07; m. 31; c. 1. MEDICINE. B.A, Wisconsin, 29; M.D, Cincinnati, 34. Asst. prof. MED, COL. MED, UNIV. CINCINNATI, 50-59, assoc. prof, 59-67, PROF, 67- Dir. coagulation lab, Cincinnati Gen. Hosp, 56-, student health ctr, 49-59. Am. Soc. Hemat; Am. Fedn. Clin. Res; fel. Am. Col. Physicians; Int. Soc. Hemat. Blood coagulation. Address: Dept. of Medicine, University of Cincinnati College of Medicine, Cincinnati, OH 45219.

GLUECKSOHN-WAELSCH, SALOME, b. Ger, Oct. 6, 07; nat; m. 43; c. 2. EMBRYOLOGY, GENETICS. Ph.D, Freiburg, 32. Res. assoc. & lectr. zool, Columbia, 36-55; assoc. prof. anat, ALBERT EINSTEIN COL. MED, 55-58, PROF. GENETICS, 58- Am. Soc. Zool; Genetics Soc. Am; Am. Soc. Human Genetics; Am. Asn. Anat; Soc. Develop. Biol. Developmental genetics; role of genes in mammalian differentiation. Address: Dept. of Genetics, Albert Einstein College of Medicine, New York, NY 10461.

GLUNTZ, MARTIN L(UCIUS), b. Harrisburg, Pa, Feb. 11, 31; m. 53; c. 5. ORGANIC CHEMISTRY. B.S, Lebanon Valley Col, 53; M.S, Univ. Del, 57, Ph.D.(org. chem), 60. Develop. chemist, Am. Cyanamid Co, N.J, 60-63; plant chemist, Tenneco Colors Div, Tenneco Chem, Inc, Pa, 63-66, mgr. res, 66-68, plant mgr, S.C, 68-69; CHIEF PROD. DEVELOP. TECHNOLOGIST, HERSHEY FOODS CORP, 69- U.S.A, 53-55. Am. Chem. Soc. Dyes and dye intermediates; food technology. Address: 114 Sand Rd, Glenn Acres, Hershey, PA 17033.

GLUNZ, PAUL R, b. Milwaukee, Wis, July 17, 29; m. 57; c. 4. PATHOLOGY. B.S, Marquette, 54, M.D, 57. Intern, St. Mary's Hosp, Duluth, Minn, 57-58, res. path, 58-59, Milwaukee, Wis, 59-61; St. Joseph's Hosp, Marshfield, 61-62; asst. pathologist, ARMED FORCES INST. PATH, 62-63, acting chief hepatic & pediat. br, 63-65, PATHOLOGIST, CLIN. PATH. LAB, 65- Mem. panel liver path, Nat. Halothane Study, 63-; ad. hoc comt. chlordane residue tolerance, Nat. Acad. Sci-Nat. Res. Coun, 64-65; health planning coun. bd, S.Cent. Wis, 70-; Wis. State Bd. Health & Soc. Serv. & Gov. Health Task Force to Estab. Health Policy for Wis, 71-; pathologist, Watertown & Hartford Mem. Hosps, Wis. U.S.N, 47-50. Col. Am. Path; Am. Soc. Clin. Path. General anatomic and clinical pathology. Address: Consultant Physicians in Pathology, S.C, 130 Warren St, Beaver Dam, WI 53916.

GLUSHIEN, ARTHUR S(AMUEL), b. Brooklyn, N.Y, July 15, 11; m. 38; c. 1. CARDIOLOGY, INTERNAL MEDICINE. B.Sc, N.Y. Univ, 30, M.D, 36. Physician, U.S. Vet. Admin, 39-44, chief cardiol. sect, hosp, Aspinwall, 44-54, chief med. serv, hosp, Pittsburgh, 55-59; private practice, 59-64; CHIEF CARDIOL. SECT, VET. ADMIN. HOSP, EAST ORANGE, N.J, 64-, ASST. CHIEF, MED. SERV, 66-; ASSOC. PROF. MED, N.J. COL. MED, 66- Dipl, Am. Bd. Internal Med, 47. Med.C, 44-46, Maj. Am. Med. Asn; Am. Heart Asn; fel. Am. Col. Physicians; fel. Am. Col. Cardiol. Cardiovascular disease. Address: Veterans Administration Hospital, East Orange, NJ 07019.

GLUSKER, DONALD L(EONARD), b. Chicago, Ill, Oct. 6, 30; m. 55; c. 3. PHYSICAL & ORGANIC CHEMISTRY. B.S, California, 51; Rhodes scholar. & Ph.D.(chem), Oxford, 54. Res. fel. phys. org. chem. Nat. Sci. Found, Calif. Inst. Tech, 54-56; sr. chemist, ROHM & HAAS CO, 56-61, lab. head, 61-68, RES. SUPVR, 68- Am. Chem. Soc. Polymer chemistry; mechanisms of organic reactions. Address: Rohm & Haas Co, 5000 Richmond St, Philadelphia, PA 19137.

GLUSKER, JENNY P(ICKWORTH), b. Birmingham, Eng, June 28, 31; m. 55; c. 3. PHYSICAL CHEMISTRY. B.A, Oxford, 53, M.A. & D.Phil.(chem), 57. Res. fel, X-RAY CRYSTALLOG, Calif. Inst. Tech, 55-56; res. assoc, INST. CANCER RES, 56-67, asst. mem, 67, ASSOC. MEM, 67- Assoc. prof, Univ. Pa, 69- AAAS; Am. Crystallog. Asn; Am. Chem. Soc. X-ray crystallography; infrared spectroscopy; molecular structures in general; physical biochemistry. Address: Institute for Cancer Research, 7701 Burholme Ave, Philadelphia, PA 19111.

GLUSKOTER, HAROLD J(AY), b. Chicago, Ill, May 8, 35; m. 57; c. 3. GEOLOGY. B.S, Illinois, 56; M.S, Iowa, 58; Nat. Sci. Found. fel, California, Berkeley, 59-61, Ph.D.(petrol), 62. Asst. geologist, COAL SECT, ILL. STATE GEOL. SURV, 62-65, assoc. geologist, 65-70, GEOLOGIST, 70- Am. Asn. Petrol. Geol; Geol. Soc. Am; Am. Inst. Mining, Metall. & Petrol. Eng; Soc. Econ. Paleont. & Mineral. Geology of the Franciscan Formation, California, mineral matter in coal; inorganic chemistry of coal. Address: Illinois State Geological Survey, Natural Resources Building, Urbana, IL 61801.

GLUSMAN, MURRAY, b. N.Y.C, Dec. 31, 14; m. 49; c. 2. NEUROPSYCHIATRY. B.S, N.Y. Univ, 34, M.D, 38. Asst. neurol, COL. PHYSICIANS & SURGEONS COLUMBIA UNIV, 49-50, from asst. PSYCHIAT. to asst. clin. prof, 50-66, ASSOC. CLIN. PROF, 66-; CHIEF PSYCHIAT. RES. BEHAV. PHYSIOL, N.Y. STATE PSYCHIAT. INST, 66- Med.C, 41-45, Capt. AAAS; Am. Psychosom. Soc; Am. Med. Asn; Asn. Res. Nerv. & Ment. Diseases; Am. Psychiat. Asn. Manifestations of nutritional deficiency; quantitative estimation of gamma globulin in spinal fluid; electrical excitability of human cerebral cortex. Address: 50 E. 72nd St, New York, NY 10021.

GLUYAS, R(ICHARD) E(DWIN), b. Glendive, Mont, Aug. 6, 21; m. 49; c. 3. PHYSICAL CHEMISTRY. B.S, Mont. State Col, 43; M.S, Wisconsin, 44; Ph.D.(chem), Ohio State, 52. Chemist rocket propellants, Nat. Defense Res. Coun, Wisconsin, 44; Manhattan proj, Tenn. Eastman Corp, 44-46; asst. crystal structure, Ohio State, 46-52, res. assoc. x-ray crystallog, res. found, 52-56; res. chemist, silver iodide battery, Nat. Carbon Co, Union Carbide Corp, 56-57, tantalum capacitors, Kemet Co, 57-64; HEAD NUCLEAR MAT. SECT, LEWIS RES. CTR, NASA, 64- AAAS. Materials for nuclear power systems; structure, properties and reactions of solids; determination of crystal structure by x-ray diffraction. Address: Lewis Research Center, NASA, 21000 Brookpark Rd, Cleveland, OH 44135.

GLUYAS, T(HOMAS) M, JR, b. Phila, Pa, June 6, 13; m. 37; c. 3. ELECTRICAL ENGINEERING. B.S, Pa. State, 35. Engr, Philco Radio & TV Corp, 36-38; chief TV engr, Midland Broadcasting Co, 38-41; engr, Radio Corp. Am, 41-45, eng. leader, 45-50, ENG. MGR, 50-71, BROADCAST SYSTS. & COMMUN. SYSTS. DIV, RCA CORP, 71- Fel. Inst. Elec. & Electronics Eng. Engineering management of development and design of military radar and commercial broadcasting equipment. Address: RCA Corp, 15-4, Front & Cooper Sts, Camden, NJ 08102.

GLYDE, HENRY R(USSELL), b. Calgary, Alta, Oct. 31, 37; m. 64; c. 2. SOLID STATE & THEORETICAL PHYSICS. B.S, Univ. Alta, 60; Rhodes scholar, Oxford, 60, NATO-Nat. Res. Coun. Can. fel, 63, Ph.D.(physics), 64. Ciba Found. fel, Univ. Brussels, 64-65; res. fel. physics, Univ. Sussex, 65-69; PHYSICIST, ATOMIC ENERGY CAN. LTD, 69- Vis. scientist, div. chem, Nat. Res. Coun. Can, Ottawa, summer 68. Am. Phys. Soc; Can. Asn. Physicists. Mass spectrometry; diffusion in solids; interatomic potential functions; solidified inert gases; lattice dynamics; solid helium. Address: Atomic Energy of Canada Ltd, Chalk River Nuclear Labs, Chalk River, Ont, Can.

GLYMPH, E(AKIN) M(ILTON), b. Pomaria, S.C, Sept. 6, 15; m. 44; c. 3. BIOCHEMISTRY. B.S, Clemson Col, 36; Ph.D.(biophys. chem), Iowa State Col, 41. Res. chemist, Firestone Plantations Co, W.Africa, 41-46, FIRESTONE TIRE & RUBBER CO, 46-48, head latex group, res. lab, 48-66, MGR. NATURAL RUBBER RES. & DEVELOP, 66- With Firestone Rubber Reserve, 44. AAAS; Am. Inst. Chem; Am. Chem. Soc. Polarography; industrial fermentations; synthetic and hevea rubber latexes; latex preparations and applications. Address: 2691 Oak Park Blvd, Cuyahoga Falls, OH 44221.

GLYMPH, LOUIS MARETT, b. Fair Play, S.C, July 31, 11; m. 42; c. 4. AGRICULTURAL ENGINEERING. B.S, Clemson Col, 33. Agr. engr, soil conserv. serv, U.S. DEPT. AGR, 34-48, hydraul. engr, 48-55, SOIL & WATER CONSERV. RES. DIV, AGR. RES. SERV, 55-61, ASST. DIR. WATER-

SHED ENG, 61- Engr, Mo. River Basin Survey Cmn, 52; staff agr. engr, Kans. Water Resources Fact Finding & Res. Cmn, 54; consult, Govt. Turkey, 64. AAAS; Am. Geophys. Union; Am. Soc. Agr. Eng; Soil Conserv. Soc. Am. Fluvial sedimentation; agricultural hydrology. Address: 713 Milestone Dr, Silver Spring, MD 20904.

GLYNN, EMMETT P, b. Chicago, Ill, Mar. 8, 13; m. 40; c. 3. CHEMISTRY. B.S, Chicago, 37. Anal. chemist, control labs, Armour & Co, 37-40, develop. dept. asst, 40-51, group leader, detergent formulation, 51-61; dir. tech. serv, Hodag Chem. Corp, 61-63; MGR. PROD. DEVELOP, LIQUID CARBONIC DIV, GEN. DYNAMICS CORP, 63- Am. Chem. Soc. Organic reaction, particularly esterification; chemical processing; drying, evaporation, crystallization techniques; surface active chemistry application, particularly detergency; application of industrial gas technology. Address: Liquid Carbonic Division, General Dynamics Corp, 4400 W. 45th St, Chicago, IL 60632.

GLYNN, JOHN JOSEPH, b. Albany, N.Y, Mar. 13, 36; m. 57; c. 4. ORGANIC CHEMISTRY. B.S, Siena Col, 62; Ph.D.(org. chem), Rensselaer Polytech, 66. Instr. chem, Siena Col, 62-66; org-anal. chemist, chem, & dyestuff div, GAF CORP, 66-71, AZOIC AREA PROD. MGR, CHEM. DIV, 71- U.S.A, 55-58, Res, 58-62. Chem. Soc; Asn. Textile Chem. & Colorists. Synthesis of monomers and the subsequent polymers, including the investigation and development of a heterogeneous hydrogenation system; production of brighteners, ultraviolet absorbers, dyestuffs and their intermediates. Address: 1 New Castle Rd, R.D. 1, Waterford, NY 12188.

GLYNN, PETER W, b. Coronado, Calif, Apr. 20, 33; m. 60; c. 2. MARINE ECOLOGY. B.S, South Dakota, 55; M.S, Stanford, 60, Ph.D.(biol), 63. Asst. prof. marine ecol, Univ. P.R, Mayagüez, 60-67; ZOOLOGIST, SMITHSONIAN TROP. RES. INST, 67- Nat. Sci. Found. res. grant, 63-66. Ecol. Soc. Am; Sigma Xi (secy-treas, 60). Structure and function of littoral marine communities. Address: Smithsonian Tropical Research Institute, P.O. Box 2072, Balboa, CZ.

GLYNN, WILLIAM ALLEN, b. Nowata, Okla, Jan. 21, 35; m. 53; c. 2. MATHEMATICS. B.S, Northeast. State Col, 60; M.S, Okla. State Univ, 62, Nat. Sci. Found. Fel, 62-64, Ph.D.(math), 65. Asst. prof. MATH, West. Ill. Univ, 65-68; ASSOC. PROF. & CHMN. DEPT, VA. COMMONWEALTH UNIV, 68- Am. Math. Soc; Math. Asn. Am. Topology. Address: Department of Mathematics, Virginia Commonwealth University, 901 W. Franklin St, Richmond, VA 23220.

GMITTER, G(EORGE) T(HOMAS), b. Yonkers, N.Y, June 21, 20; m. 53; c. 2. ORGANIC CHEMISTRY. B.S, Manhattan Col, 42; fel, Notre Dame, 46-49, M.S, 47, Ph.D.(chem), 50; M.B.A, Univ. Akron, 68. Prod. shift supvr, Hercules Powder Co, 42-45; res. & develop. chemist, Velsicol Corp, 49-50; sect. leader, resin res. & develop, Armour & Co, 51-54; head condensation polymer res, GEN. TIRE & RUBBER CO, 55-62, mgr. plastics res, 62-64, plastics & org. chem. res, 64-68, TECH. DIR. CHEM. DIV, 68- Am. Chem. Soc; Soc. Plastics Eng. Acetylenes; thiophene alcohols; epoxides; diisocyanate polymers; vinyls; reinforced plastics; cellular plastics. Address: 3043 Stanley Rd, Akron, OH 44313.

GNAEDINGER, JOHN P(HILLIP), b. Oak Park, Ill, Jan. 11, 26; m. 56; c. 2. CIVIL ENGINEERING. B.C.E, Cornell, 46; M.S, Northwestern, 47. Structural designer, Shaw Metz & Dolio, Ill, 46-49; PRES, SOIL TESTING SERV, INC, 48- Pres, Ill. Eng. Coun, 62; mem, Spec. Adv. Comt. Struct. Response to Sonic Boom, Nat. Acad. Sci-Nat. Acad. Eng-Nat. Res. Coun, 64; chmn, Fed. Construct. Coun, 68-69; Bldg. Res. Adv. Bd, 69-71; spec. adv. comts, Soil Compaction for Fed. Housing Auth. & Slab-on-Ground Construct. Am. Soc. Test. & Mat; Am. Soc. Civil Eng; Nat. Soc. Prof. Eng. Soil mechanics and foundation engineering, chemical stabilization of soils; design foundations and superstructures of buildings. Address: Soil Testing Services, Inc, 111 Pfingsten Rd, Northbrook, IL 60062.

GNAEDINGER, RICHARD H, b. Pocahontas, Ill, Sept. 15, 30. FOOD SCIENCE, ANIMAL HUSBANDRY. B.S, Southern Illinois, 58; M.S, Mich. State, 60, Ph.D.(food sci), 62. Food technologist, bur. commercial fisheries, U.S. Fish & Wildlife Serv, 62-63, chemist, 63-68; asst. dir. pet foods nutrit. res, Ralston Purina Co, 68-70. Summer res. assoc, Mich. State Univ, 62. U.S.A, 51-53. Am. Asn. Lab. Animal Sci. Animal and pet nutrition; animal production; utilization of agricultural products; laboratory animal care. Address: 12817 Mariners Point Ct, St. Louis, MO 63141.

GNAEDINGER, ROBERT J(OSEPH), JR, b. Oak Park, Ill, Nov. 6, 23; m. 46; c. 4. PHYSICAL & SOLID STATE CHEMISTRY. B.S, Chicago, 45, Gustavus Swift fel, 48-49, M.S, 50, Atomic Energy Comn. fel, 50-51, Ph.D.(chem), 51. Res. assoc. physics, Illinois, 51-54; mem. tech. staff semiconductors, Bell Tel. Labs, Inc, 54-59; sr. solid state chemist, semiconductor prod. div, Motorola, Inc, 59-62; chief engr, Am. Micro Devices, Inc, 62-63; dir. device develop, CTS of Can, Ltd, 64-66; consult. scientist, United Aircraft Res. Labs, 66-68; consult, 68-69; PRES, ENVIRON. TEST ASSOCS, INC, 69- Am. Chem. Soc; Am. Phys. Soc; Electrochem. Soc; Inst. Elec. & Electronics Eng. Color center phenomena; imperfections in solids; semiconductors; physics and chemistry of surfaces; high vacuum techniques; sonic and chemical testing of environment; pollution problems; geophysical engineering studies. Address: Environmental Test Associates, Inc, 111 Pfingsten Rd, Northbrook, IL 60062.

GNAGY, RICHARD M(ACARTHUR), b. Tacoma, Wash, Nov. 21, 25. CHEMICAL ENGINEERING. B.S, Washington State, 49; M.S, Michigan, 55. Chem. engr, div. indust. res, Washington State, 50-54; technologist, Shell Chem. Co, 55-56; process engr, C.F. Braun & Co, 56-58; chem. engr, Aerojet-Gen. Corp. Div, Gen. Tire & Rubber Co, 58-69; CHIEF PROCESS ENGR, AM. WEST. DIV, BIGELOW LIPTAK CORP, 70- Specialist, Forest Prod. Lab, Univ. Calif, 71- U.S.A, 44-46. Am. Chem. Soc; Am. Inst. Chem. Eng. Air pollution, primarily fluoride pollution; extractive distillation of C₄ hydrocarbons; development work with nitrogen fluoride compounds; plant design of facilities for production of boron hydrides; nitro compounds; petrochemical plants. Address: P.O. Box 2304, Pleasant Hill, CA 94523.

GNANADESIKAN, MRUDULLA, b. Bombay, India, July 25, 40; m. 65; c. 2. MATHEMATICAL STATISTICS. B.A, Bombay, 60, M.A, 62; Ph.D.(math. statist), Purdue, 66. Assoc. mem. tech. staff, BELL TEL. LABS, MURRAY HILL, 65-66, mem. tech. staff, 66-67, CONSULT, STATIST. MODELS & METHODS DEPT, 67- Am. Statist. Asn; Inst. Math. Statist. Ranking and selection procedures; multivariate analysis; multiple decision theory; data analytic methods. Address: 23 Lisa Dr, Chatham, NJ 07928.

GNANADESIKAN, R(AMANATHAN), b. Madras, India, Nov. 2, 32; m. 65; c. 2. MATHEMATICAL STATISTICS. B.Sc, Madras, 52, M.A, 53; Indian Statist. Inst, Calcutta, 52-53; Ph.D.(math. statist), North Carolina, 57. Asst. math. statist, North Carolina, 54-57; sr. res. statistician, Procter & Gamble Co, 57-59; mem. tech. staff, BELL TEL. LABS, 59-68, HEAD STATIST. & DATA ANAL, RES. DEPT, 68- Consult, Cincinnati Bd. Ed, 57-59; lectr, univ. & consult, sch. med, Cincinnati, 58-59; adj. assoc. prof, Courant Inst. Math. Sci, N.Y. Univ, 61-63; adv, U.S. Bur. Census, 67-69; vis. prof, Imp. Col. Sci. & Technol, London, 69; parttime vis. prof, Princeton, 71. AAAS; Biomet. Soc; Am. Statist. Asn; Inst. Math. Statist; Math. Asn. Am; Royal Statist. Soc; Int. Asn. Statist. Phys. Sci. Multivariate analysis, especially in the fields of the analysis and design of experiments and related areas of data analysis and theoretical statistics. Address: Bell Telephone Labs, Mountain Ave, Murray Hill, NJ 07974.

GNAU, DONALD V(AUGHN), b. York, Pa, May 25, 16; m. 58; c. 2. PHYSICS. B.S, Pa. State Col, 39. Sales engr, Standard Elec. Time Co, 40-41; physicist, Simplex Wire & Cable Co, 41-43; res. physicist, CORNELL AERONAUT. LAB, 46-56, prin. physicist, 56-60, sect. head, 60-64, br. head, 64-70, ASST. DEPT. HEAD, 70- U.S.N.R, 43-46, Res, 46-, Lt. Inst. Elec. & Electronics Eng. Electronic computers and systems. Address: 824 E. Fillmore Ave, East Aurora, NY 14052.

GNEWUCH, CHARLES THOMAS, b. Fond du Lac, Wis, Sept. 26, 38. ORGANIC CHEMISTRY. B.S, Georgetown, 60; M.S, Iowa State, 63; Ph.D.(org. chem), Indiana, 66. Asst. prof. org. chem, Marquette, 66-69; RES. ASSOC. PHARMACOL, MED. COL. WIS, 69- Res. grant, Marquette Univ, 67-68. Am. Chem. Soc; The Chem. Soc. Indole alkaloids synthesis, based on biogenetic theory; synthesis of pentalene; medicinal chemistry including syntheses of B-adrenergic blocking agents; hemicholinium analogs; lipids. Address: Dept. of Pharmacology, Medical College of Wisconsin, Milwaukee, WI 53233.

GNIRK, PAUL FARRELL, b. Burke, S.Dak, May 16, 37; m. 57; c. 2. MECHANICAL & MINING ENGINEERING. B.S, S.Dak. Sch. Mines & Technol, 59; fel, Univ. Minn, 59-63, Ph.D.(rock mech), 66. Asst. prof. mining eng, S.Dak. Sch. Mines & Technol, 63-65; res. assoc, Rice Univ, 65-67; ASSOC. PROF. MECH. ENG, S.DAK. SCH. MINES & TECHNOL, 67- Mech. engr. & consult, Shell Develop. Co. & Shell Oil Co, Tex, summers 61-67; consult, S.Dak. Dept. Hwys, 68- AAAS; Am. Soc. Eng. Educ; Am. Geophys. Union; Am. Inst. Min, Metall. & Petrol. Eng; Am. Soc. Mech. Eng. Mechanics of rock failure in drilling; stability of underground openings; mechanical behavior of rock and metals in high-pressure, temperature environments; transient wave propagation; temperature distribution in flowing fluid columns & aniostropic materials; fluidics; pile driving mechanics. Address: Dept. of Mechanical Engineering, South Dakota School of Mines & Technology, Rapid City, SD 57701.

GO, MATEO LIAN POA, b. Amoy, China, Sept. 17, 18; m. 52; c. 3. STRUCTURAL ENGINEERING. B.C.E, Cornell, 42, McGraw fel, 43-46, Ph.D. (struct. & transportation eng, soil mech), 46; S.M.C.E, Mass. Inst. Tech, 43. Construct. engr, Mahony-Troast Construct. Co, N.J, 42, 46-47; mgr. Mateo L.P. Go Construct. Co, P.I, 47-53, tech. consult, Go Occo & Co, 53-54, br. mgr, 54-56; asst. prof. ENG, Syracuse Univ, 57-59; assoc. prof, UNIV. HAWAII, 59-63, PROF, 63-, DIR. PROF. ADV. SERV. CTR, 67-, CHMN. DEPT. CIVIL ENG, 69- Spec. lectr, Cebu Inst. Technol. Philippines, 47-50; pres, Eng. Assocs, 71. Am. Soc. Civil Eng; Am. Soc. Eng. Educ; Am. Concrete Inst. Airport engineering; space technology; structural mechanics; reinforced concrete; transportation and construction engineering. Address: Dept. of Civil Engineering, University of Hawaii, 2565 The Mall, Honolulu, HI 96822.

GO, VAY LIANG W(ONG), b. Ozamis City, Philippines, Aug. 29, 38; m. 63; c. 2. GASTROENTEROLOGY, INTERNAL MEDICINE. M.D, Univ. Santo Tomas, Manila, 63. Intern med, Northwest. Hosp, Minneapolis, 64, resident int. med, Mayo Grad. Sch. Med, Univ. Minn, 65-66, trainee, GASTROENTEROL, 67-69; res. assoc, MAYO CLIN, 69-71, CONSULT, 71- Fel, Banting & Best Dept. Med. Res, Univ. Toronto, 69-71. Donald C. Balfour Award, Mayo Found, 69. Am. Fedn. Clin. Res. Secretion and mechanism of action of gastrointestinal hormones; pancreatic exocrine function. Address: Gastroenterology Unit, Mayo Clinic, Rochester, MN 55901.

GOAD, WALTER B(ENSON), JR, b. Marlowe, Ga, Sept. 5, 25; m. 52; c. 3. PHYSICS. B.S, Union Col, 45; Ph.D.(physics), Duke, 54. MEM. STAFF, T-DIV, LOS ALAMOS SCI. LAB, 50- Sr. fel. biophys, Univ. Colo, 64-65, vis. prof, 66-; vis. scientist, Med. Res. Coun. Lab. Molecular Biol, Cambridge, Eng, 70-71. U.S.N.R, 45-46, Res, 46-, Lt.(jg). AAAS; Am. Phys. Soc; Biophys. Soc; N.Y. Acad. Sci. Theory of cosmic ray showers; neutron diffusion theory; theoretical molecular physics; biophysics. Address: Box 1663, Los Alamos, NM 87544.

GOATES, J(AMES) REX, b. Lehi, Utah, Aug. 14, 20; m. 48; c. 3. PHYSICAL CHEMISTRY. B.S, Brigham Young, 42; Ph.D.(phys. & soil chem), Wisconsin, 47. Asst. prof. CHEM, BRIGHAM YOUNG UNIV, 47-52, assoc. prof, 52-54, PROF, 54-, chmn. dept, 65-68. U.S.A, 43-45. Thermodynamic properties of metallic sulfides; thermodynamics and mechanisms of adsorption; thermodynamics of solutions. Address: Dept. of Chemistry, Brigham Young University, Provo, UT 84601.

GOATES, WALLACE A(LBERT), b. Lehi, Utah, Aug. 20, 07; m. 31; c. 3. AUDIOLOGY, SPEECH PATHOLOGY. B.A, Utah, 29; Yale, 31; fel, Iowa, 34-35, M.A, 35, fel, 36-37, Ph.D, 37; summers, Northwestern, 48, 55; Utah, 50-55. Asst. prof. speech & dir, speech clinic, Utah State, 35-37; dir. speech sci. lab, UNIV. UTAH, 37-43, PROF. speech 46-65, SPEECH PATH.

& AUDIOL, 65-, CLIN. LECTR. SURG, COL. MED, 50-, VIS. SURGEON, UNIV. HOSP. MED. CTR, 70-, dir, speech & hearing center, univ, 46-57, lectr. anat, col. med, 49-55, psychiat, 54-62, dir. inst. spec. ed, univ, 54. Summer guest lectr, Iowa, 38-42; consult, Vet. Admin. Hosp, Ft. Douglas, 54-; rehab. ctr, St. Marks Hosp, 59-; communicative disorders, Salt Lake Community Nursing Serv, 70-; private practice, 57-; ed. bull, Speech Pathologists & Audiologists Private Practice, 65-; dir, Utah Speech & Hearing Ctr, 68- U.S.N.R, 43-46, Res, 46-63, Lt. Comdr. AAAS; Am. Speech & Hearing Asn; Asn. Am. Med. Cols. Organic and psychologic disorders of speech and hearing. Address: 70 S. Ninth East St, Suite 3-A, Salt Lake City, UT 84102.

GOATLEY, JAMES L(EON), b. Tell City, Ind, Feb. 3, 32; m. 61; c. 4. BIOCHEMISTRY. B.S, Purdue Univ, 53, M.S, 58, Ph.D.(biochem), 62. Res. asst. biochem, Purdue Univ, 55-60; instr. NATURAL SCI, MICH. STATE UNIV, 60-63, asst. prof, 63-66, assoc. prof, 66-70, PROF, JUSTIN MORRILL COL, 70- Nat. Sci. Found. res. grants, 62-66. U.S.A, 53-55. AAAS; Am. Chem. Soc. Biochemistry of polysaccharides; science and culture. Address: Justin Morrill College, Michigan State University, East Lansing, MI 48823.

GOAZ, PAUL W(ILLIAM), b. Lafayette, Ind, Apr. 13, 22; m. 48; c. 2. DENTISTRY. D.D.S, Loyola (Ill), 50; M.S, Chicago, 53; B.S, Okla. State, 59. Intern, Zoller Mem. Clin, Chicago, 50-51, asst. dent. surg, 51-53; clin. asst. dent. surg, sch. med, Oklahoma, 53-54, instr, 54-59, asst. prof, 59-70; ASSOC. PROF. ORAL DIAG. & V.CHMN. DEPT, SCH. DENT, LOYOLA UNIV. CHICAGO, MAYWOOD, 70- Head dent. sect. & res. fel, Okla. Med. Res. Found, 53-62; private practice. U.S.N, 42-46, Res, 46- AAAS; Am. Dent. Asn; fel. Am. Col. Dent; Am. Asn. Phys. Anthrop; Int. Asn. Dent. Res. Salivary, bacterial growth factors; clinical testing of potential aticariogenic agents; dental morphology and anthropology. Address: 3916 Gilbert Ave, Western Springs, IL 60558.

GOBBLE, JAMES L(AWRENCE), b. Lafayette, Ind, July 6, 17; m. 39; c. 2. ANIMAL HUSBANDRY. B.S, Purdue, 39; M.S, Illinois, 42; Ph.D.(animal prod), Pa. State, 55. Asst. farm mgr, Croydon Farms, Ky, 39-40; asst. ANIMAL HUSB, Illinois, 40-42; instr, PA. STATE UNIV, 46-55, asst. prof, 55-60, ASSOC. PROF, 60- Consult, Maharashtra Agr. Univ, India, U.S. Agency Int. Develop, 69. U.S.N, 42-45. Am. Soc. Animal Sci. Swine nutrition and management; livestock feeds and feeding. Address: Dept. of Animal Science, Pennsylvania State University, University Park, PA 16802.

GOBEIL, RICHARD J(OHN), b. St. Paul, Minn, Feb. 11, 18; m. 44; c. 5. ORGANIC CHEMISTRY. B.S, Col. of St. Thomas, 40; M.S, Nebraska, 42, Ph.D. (chem), 44. From res. chemist to admin. asst. to lab. dir, E.I. DU PONT DE NEMOURS & CO, INC, 44-66, ADMINSTR, COST & PROCESS STUDIES, 66- Am. Chem. Soc. Derivatives of benzo(h)quinoline; hydrocarbon oxidation; synthetic organic chemistry; polymer intermediates and agricultural chemicals. Address: Experimental Station, E.I. du Pont de Nemours & Co, Wilmington, DE 19803.

GOBEL, STEPHEN, b. New York, N.Y, Dec. 27, 38; m. 61; c. 1. CYTOLOGY, NEUROBIOLOGY. D.D.S, N.Y. Univ, 63. Fel. cytol, col. dent, N.Y. Univ, 63-66; DENT. SURGEON, NAT. INST. DENT. RES, 66- N.Y. Univ. Founders' Day award, 63. Electron microscopical studies of the main sensory trigeminal nucleus, the object of these studies is to define the synaptic connections of the trigeminal nerve and the cells of this nucleus and to explain the complex integrative interactions of different axonal pathways in this nucleus at the fine structural level. Address: National Institute of Dental Research, Bldg. 30, Room 207, 9000 Rockville Pike, Bethesda, MD 20014.

GOBELI, G(ARTH) W(ILLIAM), b. Wellington, Kans, Feb. 22, 30; m. 54; c. 2. SOLID STATE PHYSICS. B.A, Rice Inst, 52; M.S, Illinois, 54, Int. Bus. Machines Corp. fel, Purdue, 55-57; Ph.D.(physics), 58. Asst. prof. physics, Purdue, 58-59; mem. tech. staff, Bell Tel. Labs, 59-68; MGR. LASER PHYSICS RES. DEPT, SANDIA CORP, 68- Am. Phys. Soc. Semiconductor surface studies; irradiation effects in semiconductors; high energy pulsed lasers; high energy density interactions with materials. Address: Research Dept, Sandia Corp, P.O. Box 5800, Albuquerque, NM 87115.

GOBERDHAN, CECIL K, b. Fyrish, Brit. Guiana, July 8, 26; nat. CHEMISTRY. B.S, Hartwick Col, 48; M.S, State Univ. N.Y, 51; Ph.D.(chem), Missouri, 54. Sect. chief new prod. develop, flexible packaging div, Continental Can Co, Inc, 54-58; assoc. res. chemist, radiation lab, Michigan, 58-61; proj. engr, Bendix Systs. Div, 61-63; res. specialist, Columbus Div, N.Am. Aviation, Inc, 63-69; Battelle Mem. Inst, 69-70; TECH. CONSULT, 70- Lectr, plastic progs. for indust, N.Y. Univ. AAAS; Soc. Aerospace Mat. & Process Eng; Am. Chem. Soc. Fiberglass reinforced plastics; structural and advanced composites; protective coatings; laminating resins and adhesives; matrix-reinforcement interface; coupling agents; failure mechanisms; micro and macromechanics. Address: Goberdhan & Associates, Consultants, 4879 Calvin Dr, Columbus, OH 43227.

GOBLE, A(LFRED) T(HEODORE), b. River Falls, Wis, Jan. 24, 09; m. 35; c. 3. PHYSICS. B.A, Wisconsin, 29, Ph.D.(physics), 33. Asst. PHYSICS, Wisconsin, 29-33, Univ. Alumni Res. Found. res. assoc, 33-34; instr, Tulsa, 34-35, asst. prof, 35-37; Alfred, 37-43, assoc. prof, 43-46; lectr, UNION COL.(N.Y), 45-46, assoc. prof, 46-54, PROF, 54-, chmn. dept, 66-71. Vis. asst. prof, Princeton, 42-43; res. assoc, Harvard, 44-45; mem. tech. staff, Space Tech. Lab, 58-59. Consult, Standard Rolling Mills, Inc, 49-54; Revere Copper & Brass, Inc, 54-; Thompson-Ramo-Wooldridge Corp, 55-58; Space Tech. Lab, 59-60; Aerospace Corp, 60-64. With Nat. Defense Res. Comt, 44. Am. Phys. Soc; Optical Soc. Am; Am. Asn. Physics Teachers. Theoretical spectroscopy; intensities in platinum-like spectra; recombination spectra of potassium; cosmic rays; high resolution spectroscopy; isotope shifts. Address: Dept. of Physics, Union College, Schenectady, NY 12308.

GOBLE, DAVID FRANKLIN, b. Pincher Creek, Alta, July 31, 40; m. 62; c. 1. THEORETICAL PHYSICS. Nat. Res. Coun. Can. bursary and B.Sc, Alberta, 62, M.Sc, 63; Imp. Oil Can. fel, Toronto, 63-65, Nat. Res. Coun. Can. scholar, 65, Ph.D.(theoret. physics), 67. ASST. PROF. THEORET. PHYSICS, DALHOUSIE UNIV, 68- NATO res. fel, inst. pure & appl. phys. sci, California, San Diego, 67-68. Am. Asn. Physics Teachers; Can. Asn. Physicists. Development of a microscopic theory of liquid helium four using many-body techniques; explanation of finite size effects in liquid helium four. Address: Dept. of Physics, Dalhousie University, Halifax, N.S, Can.

GOBLE, FRANS C(LEON), b. Chicago, Ill, July 11, 13. MICROBIOLOGY, PATHOLOGY. B.S, Battle Creek Col, 33; M.S, Michigan, 34, Sc.D. (zool), 39; fel, Rice Inst, 34-35. Asst, Michigan, 34, tech. asst. histol, 35-38; pathologist, bur. game, State Conserv. Dept, N.Y, 38-45; pathologist & parasitologist, Sterling-Winthrop Res. Inst, 45-51; head lab. path, Abbott Labs, 51-52; biol. consult, St. Thomas, Virgin Islands, 52-53; dir. parasitol, CIBA Pharmaceut. Co, 54-60, chemother, 61-68; DIR. BIOL, SMITH, MILLER & PATCH, INC, 69- Mem, 4th, 6th, 7th & 8th Int. Cong. Trop. Med. & Malaria; 1st Int. Cong. Chagas Disease, adv. group res, Pan-Am. Health Orgn, 62, consult. & chmn. chemother. res. group, 63-; mem. exp. adv. panel, parasitic diseases, WHO, 64- A.U.S, 43. Am. Soc. Parasitol; Soc. Protozool; Soc. Exp. Biol. & Med; Am. Soc. Trop. Med. & Hyg; Am. Asn. Vet. Parasitol; Am. Asn. Path. & Bact; Am. Asn. Lab. Animal Sci; Soc. Toxicol; Am. Asn. Contamination Control; Am. Soc. Microbiol; Reticuloendothelial Soc; Soc. Indust. Microbiol; N.Y. Acad. Sci; Royal Soc. Trop. Med. & Hyg; World Asn. Adv. Vet. Parasitol; Int. Col. Trop. Med. Pathology and chemotherapy of experimental infectious diseases; taxonomy of Metastrongyloidea; histology and hematology in subacute and chronic toxicity studies on synthetic organic compounds and antibiotics; reticuloendothelial blockade, anti-metabolites; immunity. Address: Smith, Miller & Patch, Inc, 401 Joyce Kilmer Ave, New Brunswick, NJ 08902.

GOBLE, GEORGE G, b. Eagle, Idaho, Sept. 11, 29; m. 53; c. 2. STRUCTURAL ENGINEERING. B.S, Idaho, 51; M.S, Washington (Seattle), 57, Ph.D. (struct), 61; Fulbright fel, Stuttgart Tech, 57-58. PROF. STRUCT, CASE WEST. RESERVE UNIV, 61- Vis. prof, California, Berkeley, 68- Lincoln prof. struct. design award, 66. U.S.A.F, 51-53, Res, 53-61, Capt. Am. Soc. Civil Eng.(Collingwood award, 65); Am. Concrete Inst; Soc. Exp. Stress Anal. Behavior of civil engineering structures; design of structures; optimum design of structures using mathematical programming; dynamic pile behavior. Address: 18908 Lomond Blvd, Cleveland, OH 44122.

GOBLE, ROBERT LLOYD, b. North Hornell, N.Y, June 10, 40; m. 62. THEORETICAL PHYSICS. B.A, Swarthmore Col, 62; Nat. Sci. Found. fel, Wisconsin, 62-63, Ph.D.(physics), 67. Res. asst, Wisconsin, 63-66; res. staff physicist, Yale, 66-67, instr. PHYSICS, 67-69; RES. ASSOC, UNIV. MINN, MINNEAPOLIS, 69- Am. Phys. Soc. Quantum field theories; interaction of elementary particles. Address: Dept. of Physics, University of Minnesota, Minneapolis, MN 55455.

GOBLICK, THOMAS J(OHN), JR, b. Old Forge, Pa, Mar. 30, 35; m. 59; c. 4. INFORMATION THEORY, COMMUNICATION TECHNOLOGY. B.S, Bucknell, 56; S.M, Mass. Inst. Technol, 58, Ph.D.(elec. eng), 62; Imp. Col, London, 58-59. STAFF MEM, LINCOLN LAB, MASS. INST. TECHNOL, 62- Lectr, Mass. Inst. Technol, 63-; vis. assoc. prof, Washington (St. Louis), 67-68. Consult, res. div, Monsanto Corp, Mo, 68. Mem. navigation adv. subcomt, NASA, 67-70. AAAS; Inst. Elec. & Electronic Eng. Theoretical and practical aspect of coding data for efficient and reliable transmission over noisy channels; experimental and analytical study of stimulus coding in the auditory system of vertebrates; advanced air traffic control techniques. Address: 51 Vaille Ave, Lexington, MA 02173.

GOBLIRSCH, R(ICHARD) P(AUL), b. Minneapolis, Minn, Jan. 1, 30; m. 52; c. 3. MATHEMATICS. B.A, Col. St. Thomas, 51; Alumni Res. Found. asst, Wisconsin, 51-53, M.A, 52, Ph.D, 56. Asst. MATH, Wisconsin, 53-56; instr, Virginia, 56-59; asst. prof, Rochester, 59-63; vis. asst. prof, Colorado, 63-64; ASSOC. PROF, COL. ST. THOMAS, 64- Am. Math. Soc; Math. Asn. Am. Euclidean topology; real variables. Address: Dept. of Mathematics, College of St. Thomas, St. Paul, MN 55101.

GOBRAN, RAMSIS, b. Sinbellawin, Egypt, Feb. 20, 32; U.S. citizen; m. 60; c. 3. ORGANIC CHEMISTRY. B.Sc, Alexandria, 52; Yale, 52-53; M.S, Southern California, 57, Parke, Davis Co. fel, 58-59, Ph.D.(chem), 59. Goodyear Rubber Co. fel, 59; res. polymer chemist, MINN. MINING & MFG. CO, 59-67, RES. SPECIALIST, 67- Am. Chem. Soc. Polymer, photographic and organic heterocyclic chemistry. Address: Minnesota Mining & Manufacturing Co, 3M Center, P.O. Box 33221, St. Paul, MN 55133.

GOBRAN, RIAD H(ILMY), b. Egypt, Feb. 8, 28; U.S. citizen; m. 54; c. 2. POLYMER CHEMISTRY. B.Sc, Alexandria, 48; Ph.D.(chem), Polytech. Inst. Brooklyn, 54. Sr. chemist, Thiokol Chem. Corp, 53-54, group leader, 54-55; Egyptian Nat. Res. Coun, 55-56; supvr, THIOKOL CHEM. CORP, 56-60, res. mgr, 60-66, mgr. RES. & DEVELOP, 66-67, DIR, 67- Am. Chem. Soc. Thermodynamics and solution properties of polymers; mechanical properties of elastomers and thermoplastics; condensation polymerization and urethane chemistry; free radical polymerizations and kinetics; ionic polymerizations; sulfur chemistry; fluorocarbons. Address: Thiokol Chemical Corp, 780 N. Clinton Ave, Trenton, NJ 08607.

GOCHENAUR, SALLY E(LIZABETH), b. Cleveland, Ohio, Mar. 30, 32. MYCOLOGY. B.S, Univ. Cincinnati, 58, M.S, 60; Ph.D.(bot), Univ. Wis, 64. Asst. prof. microbiol, ADELPHI UNIV, 64-70, ASSOC. PROF. BIOL, 70- Res. assoc, Univ. Wis, 64-; res. collab, Brookhaven Nat. Lab, 68-69. Bot. Soc. Am; Mycol. Soc. Am; Brit. Mycol. Soc; Ecol. Soc. Am. Fungal physiology; taxonomy and ecology of soil fungi. Address: Dept. of Biology, Adelphi University, Garden City, NY 11530.

GOCHENOUR, WILLIAM S(YLVA), JR, b. East St. Louis, Ill, July 18, 16; m. 40; c. 1. VETERINARY MEDICINE. V.M.D, Pennsylvania, 37. Lab. veterinarian, bur. animal indust, U.S. Dept. Agr, 37-38; res. vet, Pitman Moore Co. Div, Allied Labs, Inc, 39; U.S. ARMY, 39-, chief vet. bact, Med. Serv. Grad. Sch, Walter Reed Army Med. Ctr, 49-53, animal standards & liaison br, Off. Surgeon Gen, 53-54, animal assessment br, med. unit, Ft. Detrick, 54-63, DEP. DIR, WALTER REED ARMY INST. RES, WALTER REED ARMY MED. CTR, D.C, 63- Dipl, Am. Bd. Pub. Vet. Health; Am. Bd. Microbiol. Med.C, U.S.A, 39-, Col. Fel. AAAS; Soc. Exp. Biol. & Med;

Am. Pub. Health Asn; Am. Vet. Med. Asn; Asn. Mil. Surg; U.S; Am. Asn. Immunol; Conf. Pub. Health Vets; N.Y. Acad. Sci; Royal Soc. Health. Infectious diseases, especially respiratory diseases and the zoonoses. Address: Walter Reed Army Institute of Research, Walter Reed Army Medical Center, Washington, DC 20012.

GOCHMAN, NATHAN, b. Brooklyn, N.Y, Nov. 11, 33; m. 55; c. 2. BIOCHEMISTRY. B.S, Brooklyn Col, 55; Ph.D.(chem), Northwestern, 58. Supvr, bioanal. lab, G.D. Searle & Co, 58-62; dir. clin. chem, Technicon Instruments Corp, 62-66, res. lab. dir, 66-68; CLIN. CHEMIST, CLIN. CTR, NAT. INSTS. HEALTH, 68- AAAS; Am. Chem. Soc. Enzymology; analytical biochemistry; drug metabolism; development of methods and instruments for biochemical determinations with emphasis on automation. Address: 8548 Atwell Rd, Potomac, MD 20854.

GOCHNAUER, THOMAS A(LEXANDER), b. Appleton, Wis, July 29, 19; m. 50; c. 3. BACTERIOLOGY. Ph.D.(bact), Wisconsin, 50- Res. assoc. entom. & econ. zool, Minnesota, 49-61; chief apicult. sect, entom. res. inst, CAN. DEPT. AGR, 61-70, RES. SCIENTIST, ENTOM. SECT, OTTAWA RES. STA, 70- U.S.A, 42-45, Res, 45-48. AAAS; Am. Soc. Microbiol; N.Y. Acad. Sci; Can. Soc. Microbiol. Honeybee diseases and control; antibiotics; phages; effects of gamma radiation. Address: Entomology Section, Ottawa Research Station, Canada Dept. Agriculture, Ottawa, Ont. K1A 0C6, Can.

GODAR, EDITH M(ARIE), b. Chicago, Ill, June 19, 21. ORGANIC & ANALYTICAL CHEMISTRY. B.S, Rosary Col, 42; Ill. Inst. Technol; M.S, Loyola (Ill), 56, Ph.D.(org. chem), 59. Res. chemist, res. div, Am. Can. Co, 43-56; instr. chem, Loyola (Ill), 59-68; ASSOC. PROF, MARY MANSE COL, 68-, CHMN. DEPT. SCI. & MATH, 71- Instr, Rosary Col, 53-54; sr. res. chemist, Int. Minerals & Chem. Corp, 59-68; fel, Univ. Detroit, 68. Am. Chem. Soc; Soc. Appl. Spectros. Synthetic organic chemistry; instrumental methods of analysis. Address: Dept. of Chemistry, Mary Manse College, Toledo, OH 43620.

GODARD, HUGH P(HILLIPS), b. Montreal, Que, Oct. 19, 14; m. 38; c. 1. CHEMICAL ENGINEERING. B.A.Sc, British Columbia, 36, M.A.Sc, 37; Ph.D.(indust. & cellulose chem), McGill, 41. Chief chemist, chems. & explosives, Inspection Bd, U.K. & Can, 41-45; head, chem. div, Aluminium Labs, Ltd, 45-66, DEP. DIR. KINGSTON LAB, ALCAN INT. LTD. RES. CTR, KINGSTON, 66- Nat. Asn. Corrosion Eng.(pres, 59-60, Frank Newman Speller award, 63); Chem. Inst. Can. Corrosion of aluminum and its prevention. Address: Box 519, R.R. 3, Bath, Ont, Can.

GODBEE, H(ERSCHEL) W(ILLCOX), b. Hinesville, Ga, Mar. 4, 28; m. 52; c. 3. CHEMICAL ENGINEERING. B.Ch.E, Ga. Inst. Technol, 52, Ph.D.(chem. eng), 64. RES. ENGR, OAK RIDGE NAT. LAB, 58- Ord.C, 52-54, 1st Lt. Heat transfer, especially measurement of thermo-physical properties; safe economical treatment of radioactive wastes. Address: 104 Willow Lane, Oak Ridge, TN 37830.

GODBEY, JOHN KIRBY, b. Cisco, Tex, Nov. 14, 21; m. 43; c. 3. ELECTRONIC ENGINEERING. B.S, South. Methodist Univ, 44; fel, Univ. Tex, 46-47, M.S, 47. Res. technologist, Field Res. Labs, Magnolia Petrol. Co, 47-55; sr. res. technologist, Mobil Oil Corp, 55-68, SR. RES. ENGR, MOBIL RES. & DEVELOP. CORP, 68- U.S.N.R, 44-46, Lt.(jg). Inst. Elec. & Electronics Eng; Am. Inst. Min, Metall. & Petrol. Eng. Electrical prospecting methods; exploration and production well surveying; drilling methods and instrumentation; automatic control; borehole measurements. Address: 3990 Davila Dr, Dallas, TX 75220.

GODBEY, WILLIAM GIVENS, b. Georgetown, Tex, Sept. 24, 19; m. 53; c. 1. PHYSICAL & NUCLEAR CHEMISTRY. B.S.(chem) & B.S.(ed), Southwestern, 40; M.S, Missouri, 58, Ph.D.(agr. chem), 60. Anal. dir, Agr. Consult. Labs, 45-53; res. found. labs, Colo. Sch. Mines, 53-54; chief chemist, Am. Smelting & Ref. Co, 54-55; instr. agr. chem, Missouri, 55-60, asst. prof, 60-62; PROF. CHEM, Southwest Mo. State Col, 62-65; ALASKA METHODIST UNIV, 65- Nat. Insts. Health res. grant molecular studies on casein, 60-62. Agr. consult, Tex. Exp. Sta, Dow Chem. Co, Rio Grande Valley Cities & Texsun Citrus Growers, 45-51. U.S.A.A.F, 40-45, Capt. AAAS; fel. Am. Inst. Chem; Am. Chem. Soc. Molecular structure of biochemical macromolecules using electrophoresis, ultra centrifugation and wide and small angle x-ray scattering techniques. Address: Dept. of Chemistry, Alaska Methodist University, Anchorage, AK 99504.

GODBOLE, SADASHIVA SHANKAR, b. Indore, India, Sept. 7, 39; m. 62; c. 1. ELECTRICAL ENGINEERING. B.E, Victoria Jubilee Tech. Inst, India, 58; M.S, Va. Polytech. Inst. & State Univ, 69, Ph.D.(elec. eng), 71. Technician, Hindustan Elec. Co, India, 58; sect. engr, Heavy Elec. Ltd, 59-67; mem. tech. staff, Bell Tel. Labs, N.J, summer 69; SR. RES. ENGR, BABCOCK & WILCOX CO, 71- Automatic control; computer applications. Address: Lynchburg Research Center, Babcock & Wilcox Co, Lynchburg, VA 24505.

GODBOUT, EUGENE, b. St. Néreé, Bellechasse, Que, Aug. 11, 07; m. 32; c. 3. FIELD CROPS. B.A, Laval, 28, B.S.A, 32. Res. off. field husb, exp. sta, Ste. Anne de la Pocatiere, 32-54, herbices & spec. crops, 54-70; RETIRED. Herbicides; evaluation of special crops and soil fertility. Address: 1302 1ere Rue, La Pocatiere, Que, Can.

GODDARD, ALTON R, b. Big Spring, Tex, Feb. 5, 32; m. 54; c. 3. COMPUTER SCIENCE, MATHEMATICS. B.A, Howard Payne Col, 54; M.S, N.Tex. State Univ, 61; Ph.D.(educ), Tex. A&M Univ, 69. Assoc. prof. math, Tarleton State Col, 57-67; asst. prof, Tex. A&M Univ, 67-69; HEAD, DEPT. COMPUT. SCI, E.TEX. STATE UNIV, 67- U.S.N.R, 52-72, Lt. Comdr. Asn. Comput. Mach; Am. Math. Soc. Mathematics education. Address: Dept. of Computer Science, East Texas State University, Commerce, TX 75428.

GODDARD, DAVID R(OCKWELL), b. Carmel, Calif, Jan. 3, 08; m. 33, 52; c. 2. BOTANY, PLANT PHYSIOLOGY. A.B, California, 29, M.A, 30, fels, 30-33, Ph.D.(bot), 33; LL.D, Univ. Pa, 70. Nat. Res. Coun. fel, Rockefeller Inst, 33-35; instr. bot, Rochester, 35-38, asst. prof. & acting chmn. dept, 38-41, assoc. prof, 41-45, prof. 45-46; UNIV. PA, 46-57, Kuemmerle prof, 58-64, dir. div. biol, 57-61, chmn. dept. bot, 52-57, provost, 61-70, PROF. SCI. & PUB. POLICY, 71- Guggenheim fels, Chicago & Cambridge; chmn. dept. bot, Rochester, 41-46. Nat. Acad. Sci; Am. Bot. Soc.(award); Am. Soc. Plant Physiol.(Hales Medal, 48, ed-in-chief, Plant Physiol, 53-58, pres, 58); Soc. Gen. Physiol.(pres, 48); Am. Philos. Soc; Soc. Develop. Biol.(pres, 53); Am. Soc. Biol. Chem; Am. Acad. Arts & Sci. Plant respiration; respiratory enzymes; growth. Address: Fels Center of Government, University of Pennsylvania, 39th & Walnut St, Philadelphia, PA 19104.

GODDARD, EARL G(ASCOIGNE), b. Mesilla Park, N.Mex, Nov. 10, 17; m. 47; c. 2. ELECTRONIC SYSTEMS ENGINEERING. B.S, N.Mex. State Univ, 39; A.M. & E.E, Stanford Univ, 47. Instr. elec. eng, Rice Univ, 41-43; asst. microwave res, Off. Res. & Inventions proj, Stanford Univ, 46-47; asst. prof. elec. eng, Duke Univ, 47-48; electronics, U.S. Naval Post-Grad. Sch, Calif, 48-53, assoc. prof, 53-55; sr. res. engr, Stanford Res. Inst, 55-60, sr. proj. engr. radiation, 60-61; mgr. field eng. training, microwave tube group, Varian Assocs, 61-63; mgr. eng, Delcon Div, Hewlett-Packard, 64-65; electronic systs. engr, Dalmo Victor Div, Textron, 65-67; staff systs. engr, appl. technol. div, Itek, 67-69; SR. SCIENTIST, DALMO VICTOR DIV, TEXTRON, 69- U.S.N, 43-46, Res, 46-68, Lt. Comdr.(Ret). Sci. Res. Soc. Am; Inst. Elec. & Electronics Eng; Nat. Soc. Prof. Eng. Sonic measurements and instrumentation; data processing; programmed instruction. Address: 2522 Webster St, Palo Alto, CA 94301.

GODDARD, EDWIN N(EWELL), b. Oshkosh, Wis, Oct. 22, 04; m. 28; c. 3. STRUCTURAL GEOLOGY. A.B, Michigan, 27, M.S, 28, Ph.D.(econ. geol), 36. Instr. geol, Michigan, 28-30; jr. geologist, U.S. Geol. Surv, 30-34, asst. geologist, 34-39, assoc. geologist, 39-43, geologist, 43-45, from sr. geologist to prin. geologist & geol. map ed, 45-49; PROF. GEOL. & DIR. GEOL. FIELD WORK, UNIV. MICH, ANN ARBOR, 49-, chmn. dept, 52-56. Chmn. panel fel. prog, Nat. Sci. Found, 54-60; mem. field geol. team, Proj. Apollo, NASA. AAAS; fel. Am. Mineral. Soc; Soc. Econ. Geol; fel. Geol. Soc. Am; Geochem. Soc; Seismol. Soc. Am; Asn. Petrol. Geol; Am. Geophys. Union; Geol. Soc. France; Royal Netherlands Geol. & Min. Soc. Structure of the Sangre de Cristo Range, Colorado. Address: Dept. of Geology, University of Michigan, Ann Arbor, MI 48104.

GODDARD, E(RROL) D(ESMOND), b. Queenstown, S.Africa, Jan. 3, 26; m. 54; c. 2. PHYSICAL & COLLOID CHEMISTRY. B.Sc, Rhodes, S.Africa, 44, Beit fel, 46-47, M.Sc, 48; Ballot fel, Cambridge, 48-51, Ph.D.(chem), 51. Res. chemist, res. dept, Unilever, Eng, 51-54; res. fel, Nat. Res. Coun. Can, 54-56; res. chemist, cent. res. lab, Can. Industs, Ltd, Que, 56-59; SECT. CHIEF, LEVER BROS. CO, 60- S.African Army, 44-45. Am. Chem. Soc; Am. Oil Chem. Soc; Faraday Soc. Surface chemistry. Address: Research Center, Lever Brothers Co, 45 River Rd, Edgewater, NJ 07020.

GODDARD, JOE DEAN, b. Buncombe, Ill, July 13, 36; m. 57; c. 5. CHEMICAL ENGINEERING. B.S, Illinois, 57; Nat. Sci. Found. fel, California, 59, Ph.D.(chem. eng), 61. Res. engr, French Inst. Petrol, 62-63; asst. prof. CHEM. ENG, UNIV. MICH, ANN ARBOR, 63-68, ASSOC. PROF, 68- NATO fel, 61-63; Nat. Sci. Found. sr. fel, Univ. Cambridge, U.K, 70-71. Am. Inst. Chem. Eng. Applied mathematics; heat and mass transfer; rheology of non-Newtonian fluids; fluid mechanics. Address: Dept. of Chemical Engineering, University of Michigan, Ann Arbor, MI 48104.

GODDARD, JOHN B(URNHAM), b. New Haven, Conn, Nov. 7, 42; m. 68. INORGANIC CHEMISTRY. B.S, Mass. Inst. Technol, 64; Nat. Insts. Health fel, Northwest. Univ, 66-68, Ph.D.(inorg. chem), 69. Teaching asst. chem, Northwest. Univ, 65-68; RES. CHEMIST, MINING & METALS DIV, UNION CARBIDE CORP, 68- Am. Chem. Soc; Metall. Soc. Transition metal chemistry; nonferrous hydrometallurgy. Address: Research & Development Dept, Union Carbide Corp, P.O. Box 579, Niagara Falls, NY 14302.

GODDARD, MURRAY COWDERY, b. Cleveland, Ohio, May 14, 24; m. 46; c. 3. COLOR PHYSICS. S.B, Mass. Inst. Tech, 48; M.S, Case, 50; Rochester, 52-53. Photog. engr, color tech. div, EASTMAN KODAK CO, 50-64, sr. physicist, RES. LABS, 64-65, RES. ASSOC. image struct. & comput. appln, 65-68, COMPUTER-BASED LEARNING SYSTS, 68- U.S.A, 43-46. Am. Phys. Soc; Soc. Photog. Sci. & Eng; Soc. Motion Picture & TV Eng; Inst. Elec. & Electronics Eng; Optical Soc. Am. Image structure; computer applications; colorimetry; exposure determination; electronics; individualized learning systems for education and training. Address: Research Labs, Bldg. 81, Eastman Kodak Co, Rochester, NY 14650.

GODDARD, RAY E(VERETT), b. Lakeland, Fla, Sept. 28, 22; m. 43; c. 4. FOREST GENETICS. B.S.F, Florida, 47, M.S.F, 48; Ph.D.(genetics), Agr. & Mech. Col, Texas, 60. Silviculturalist, Texas Forest Serv, 48-59; asst. prof. FOREST GENETICS & asst. geneticist, AGR. EXP. STA, UNIV. FLA, 59-64, ASSOC. PROF. & ASSOC. GENETICIST, 64- U.S.A, 43-46. Soc. Am. Foresters; Am. Genetic Asn. Physiology, genetics and breeding of forest trees. Address: School of Forestry, University of Florida, Gainesville, FL 32601.

GODDARD, STEPHEN, b. Ogden, Utah, Jan. 5, 37; m. 66. ORNITHOLOGY, ECOLOGY. B.S, Utah State, 60, M.S, 62; Phillips Petrol. Co. fel. & Ph.D.(ecol. of blackbirds), 67. Res. asst. zool, Okla. State, 63-66; asst. prof. BIOL, WIS. STATE UNIV-RIVER FALLS, 66-70, ASSOC. PROF, 70- Wildlife Soc; Wilson Ornith. Soc; Am. Ornith. Union; Am. Soc. Mammal. Ecology and management of game and nongame bird populations. Address: Dept. of Biology, Wisconsin State University-River Falls, River Falls, WI 54022.

GODDARD, WILLIAM ANDREW, III, b. El Centro, Calif, Mar. 29, 37; m. 57; c. 4. THEORETICAL CHEMISTRY. B.S, Univ. Calif, Los Angeles, 60, Nat. Sci. Found. fels, 60-61, 62-64, Shell fel, 61-62; Ph.D.(eng. sci), Calif. Inst. Technol, 64. Noyes res. fel. chem, CALIF. INST. TECHNOL, 64-66, Noyes res. instr, 66, asst. prof. THEORET. CHEM, 67-71, ASSOC. PROF, 71- Alfred P. Sloan res. fel, 67-69. Am. Phys. Soc. Electronic wave functions and properties of molecules, atoms, and solids by ab-initio methods. Address: Arthur Amos Noyes Lab. of Chemical Physics, California Institute of Technology, 1201 E. California Blvd, Pasadena, CA 91109.

GODDARD, WILLIAM B(ELL), b. Oklahoma City, Okla, Feb. 18, 24; m. 49; c. 4. OBSTETRICS, GYNECOLOGY. A.B, Princeton, 44; M.D, Pennsylvania, 47. Res. OBSTET. & GYNECOL, univ. hosps, Iowa, 48-51, assoc, 53-

54, asst. prof, 54-59, assoc. prof, 59-61; dir, Denver Gen. Hosp, 61-66; CLIN. ASSOC. PROF. SCH. MED, UNIV. COLO, 66- Private practice. Med.C, 51-53, Capt. Am. Col. Obstet. & Gynec; Am. Col. Surg. Analgesic drugs in obstetrics; fetal monitoring. Address: 2020 Wadsworth, Lakewood, CO 80215.

GODDIN, AVERY H(OWE), b. Elkins, W.Va, Dec. 14, 09; m. 35. ELECTRICAL ENGINEERING. B.S, West Virginia, 31, M.S, 32. Entomologist, Ohio Agr. Exp. Sta, 32-36; Del. Agr. Exp. Sta, 36-37; E.I. DU PONT DE NEMOURS & CO, WILMINGTON, 37-55, plant pathologist, 55-59, ENTOMOLOGIST, 59- Entom. Soc. Am. Commercial entomology; agricultural plant pests. Address: 109 Briar Lane, Newark, DE 19711.

GODDIN, C(LIFTON) S(YLVANUS), (JR), b. Richmond, Va, July 23, 14. CHEMICAL ENGINEERING. B.S, Michigan, 36, M.S, 37, Ph.D, 65. Chem. engr, res. dept, Standard Oil Co.(Ind), 37-41; RES. ASSOC, RES. CTR, AMOCO PROD. CO, 46- U.S.N.R, 41-, Comdr. Am. Chem. Soc; Am. Inst. Chem. Eng; Am. Inst. Mining, Metall. & Petrol. Eng. Petroleum refining; petrochemicals; substitute fuels; thermodynamics. Address: Research Center, Amoco Production Co, Box 591, Tulsa, OK 74102.

GODDU, R(OBERT) F(ENNO), b. Winchester, Mass, Oct. 5, 25; m. 49; c. 3. ANALYTICAL CHEMISTRY. A.B, Harvard, 48; Procter & Gamble fel, Mass. Inst. Tech, 50-51, Ph.D.(anal. chem), 51. Res. chemist, HERCULES RES. CTR, 51-60, sr. res. chemist, 60-61, res. supvr, 61-67, MGR. fiber & film res. div, 67-69, MAT. SCI. DIV, 69- U.S.A, 43-45. AAAS; Am. Chem. Soc; Sci. Res. Soc. Am. Organic analysis; near-infrared and infrared spectrophotometry; spectrophotometric methods; photometric titrations; polymer chemistry processes and fabrication; polymer characterization. Address: Hercules Research Center, Wilmington, DE 19899.

GODEFROI, ERIK F(RED), b. Amsterdam, Netherlands, Oct. 14, 26; nat. ORGANIC CHEMISTRY. B.A, Columbia, 47; Ph.D.(org. chem), Colorado, 52. Sr. technician, Sloan Kettering Inst, 47-48; asst, Atomic Energy Comn, Colorado, 49-52; assoc. res. chemist, Parke, Davis & Co, 52-57, sr. res. chemist, 57-62; Janssen Pharmaceutica, Belgium, 62-69; ASSOC. PROF. ORG. CHEM, EINDHOVEN UNIV. TECHNOL, 69- Am. Chem. Soc; Royal Netherlands Chem. Soc. Heterocyclic chemistry; synthetic drugs affecting the central nervous system; organic synthesis. Address: Dept. of Organic Chemistry, Eindhoven University of Technology, Eindhoven, The Netherlands.

GÖDEL, KURT, b. Bruenn, Czech, Apr. 28, 06; nat; m. 38. MATHEMATICAL LOGIC. Ph.D.(math), Univ. Vienna, 30; hon. D.Litt, Yale, 51; hon.D.Sc, Harvard, 52, Amherst Col, 67. Privat-docent, Univ. Vienna, 33-38; mem, INST. ADVAN. STUDY, 33, 35, 38-53, PROF. MATH, 53- Einstein Award, 51. Nat. Acad. Sci; Am. Math. Soc; Asn. Symbolic Logic; Am. Acad. Arts & Sci; for. mem. Royal Soc; hon. mem. London Math. Soc; Am. Philos Soc. Foundations of mathematics; exact philosophy; mathematical logic. Address: School of Mathematics, Institute for Advanced Study, Princeton, NJ 08540.

GODENNE, GHISLAINE D, b. Brussels, Belg, June 2, 24. PSYCHIATRY. B.S, Univ. Louvain, 48, Fulbright fel, 51-52, M.D, 52; Baltimore Psychoanal. Inst, 62. Intern & resident, Providence Hosp, Wash, D.C, 52-54; ASSOC. PROF. psychiat, JOHNS HOPKINS UNIV, 55-68, asst. prof. ment. hyg, 62-68, pediat, 63-68, PSYCHIAT, MENT. HYG. & PEDIAT, 68-, DIR. ADOLESCENT SERV, JOHNS HOPKINS HOSP, 63-, intern & resident, 58-62. Fel, Mayo Clin, 54-57; Parke, Davis & Co. res. invest. grant, 57-58; consult, Baltimore City Hosps, 59-; Dept. Ment. Health, 64-; Nat. Inst. Ment. Health gen. practitioner grant, 61-63, career teaching award, 63-65. Fel. Am. Psychiat. Asn; Am. Psychosom. Asn; Am. Pub. Health Asn; fel. Am. Orthopsychiat. Soc; Soc. Adolescent Psychiat. Pediatrics. Address: Johns Hopkins Hospital, Baltimore, MD 21205.

GODER, HAROLD A(RTHUR), b. North Cape, Wis, July 3, 24; m. 57; c. 3. PLANT ECOLOGY. B.S, Wisconsin, 50, M.S, 51, Ph.D, 55. Assoc. prof. BIOL, Wis. State Col, 55-70; PROF, KEENE STATE COL, 70- U.S.A.A.F, 43-45. Ecol. Soc. Am; Nat. Asn. Biol. Teachers. Phytosociological study of Tsuga Canadensis at the termination of its range in Wisconsin. Address: Dept. of Biology, Keene State College, Keene, NH 03431.

GODFREY, ANDREW ELLIOTT, b. Phila, Pa, May 31, 40; m. 68. GEOMORPHOLOGY. A.B, Franklin & Marshall Col, 64; Nat. Defense Educ. Act fel, Johns Hopkins Univ, 64-67, Ph.D.(geog), 69. ASST. PROF. GEOL, VANDERBILT UNIV, 68- Summers, Nat. Sci. Comt. grant, Vanderbilt Univ, 69, geologist, U.S. Forest Serv, Utah, 71. AAAS; Geol. Soc. Am; Am. Quaternary Asn. Climatic and geologic factors of pediment formation; geochemistry of small streams and its relationship to processes of erosion; environmental factors in planning recreational land use. Address: Dept. of Geology, Box 14, Station B, Vanderbilt University, Nashville, TN 37203.

GODFREY, CHARLES S, b. San Francisco, Calif, Aug. 12, 18; m. 45, 63; c. 5. PHYSICS. B.S. & M.S, Mass. Inst. Tech, 41; Ph.D.(physics), California, 53. From physicist to div. leader PHYSICS, Lawrence Radiation Lab, California, 53-62; CHIEF SCIENTIST & V.PRES, PHYSICS INT. CO, 62- U.S.A.A.F, 42-46, Capt. Continuum mechanics and explosive phenomena. Address: Physics International Co, 2700 Merced St, San Leandro, CA 94577.

GODFREY, CURTIS L(OVEING), b. Naples, Tex, Dec. 2, 16; m. 41; c. 1. SOIL SCIENCE. B.S, Texas A&M, 39, M.S, 48; Ph.D, Iowa State, 51. Asst, Texas A&M, 47-48; Iowa State, 48-51; assoc. state chemist, AGR. EXP. STA, TEX. A&M UNIV, 51-56, assoc. prof. AGRON, 54-67, PROF, 67-, IN CHARGE SOIL SURV, 54- U.S.N.R, 42-46. Fel. AAAS; Am. Soc. Agron; Soil Sci. Soc. Am; Soil Conserv. Soc. Am.(commendation award, 69); Brit. Soc. Soil Sci; Int. Soc. Soil Sci. Soil genesis; morphology and classification; soil fertility and chemistry; soil and water resources. Address: Dept. of Soil & Crop Sciences, Texas A&M University, College Station, TX 77843.

GODFREY, DOUGLAS, b. Magrath, Alta, Can, July 12, 18; nat; m. 47; c. 2. CHEMICAL ENGINEERING. B.Sc, Utah, 42. Aeronaut. res. scientist, Lewis res. lab, Nat. Aeronaut. & Space Admin, 44-55; SR. RES. ENGR, CHEVRON RES. CO, STANDARD OIL CO. CALIF, 55- Lectr, exten. div, California. U.S.A.A.F, 43-44. Am. Soc. Lubrication Eng.(Alfred E. Hunt Mem. award, 57). Tribology-fundamentals of lubrication. Address: Chevron Research Co, P.O. Box 1627, Richmond, CA 94802.

GODFREY, EDWARD F(RELAUT), b. Littleton, N.H, Apr. 18, 24; m. 48; c. 1. GENETICS. B.S, New Hampshire, 49; M.S, Ohio State, 50, fel, 52, Ph.D. (genetics), 53. Assoc. prof, Tennessee, 53; res. geneticist, Mount Hope Farm, Mass, 53-58; J.J. Warren, Inc, 58-63; assoc. prof, Univ. Md, 63-69, exten. prof. poultry sci, 69-71; RETIRED. U.S.N, 43-46. Am. Inst. Biol. Sci; Poultry Sci. Asn; Am. Genetic Asn. Population genetics of mice, poultry and quail; poultry endocrinology. Address: 14800 Harold Rd, Silver Spring, MD 20904.

GODFREY, GEORGE F(RELAUT), b. Hingham, Mass, June 11, 20; m. 45; c. 2. POULTRY HUSBANDRY. B.S, New Hampshire, 41; M.S, Ohio State, 46, Ph.D, 49. Asst. poultry sci, Ohio State, 41-42, instr, 46-48; asst. prof. poultry husb, Okla. Agr. & Mech. Col, 48-49, assoc. prof. & poultry geneticist, exp. sta, 49-55, prof, 55; GENETICIST, V.PRES, HONEGGER FARMS CO, INC, 55- Co-op agent, U.S. Dept. Agr, 49-55. U.S.A, 42-46. AAAS; Genetics Soc. Am; Am. Genetic Asn; Poultry Sci. Asn. Genetics and breeding of poultry. Address: Honegger Farms Co, Inc, Forrest, IL 61741.

GODFREY, HENRY PHILIP, b. Poughkeepsie, N.Y, Aug. 7, 41. IMMUNOLOGY. A.B, Harvard, 61, M.D, 65. Intern med, Barnes Hosp, St. Louis, Mo, 65-66; surgeon, Div. Biol. Standards, Nat. Insts. Health, 66-70; Moseley traveling fel. from Harvard & hon. res. fel, Univ. Birmingham, 70-72; ASST. SCIENTIST, INST. EXP. IMMUNOLOGY, UNIV. COPENHAGEN, 72- U.S.P.H.S, 66-70, Surg. AAAS; Am. Soc. Microbiol; N.Y. Acad. Sci; Brit. Soc. Immunol. Cellular and biochemical bases of the induction of the immune response and its elicitation by antigenic materials, especially as related to disease processes. Address: Institute for Experimental Immunology University of Copenhagen, Nørre Allé 71, 2100 Copenhagen Ø, Denmark.

GODFREY, JOHN C(ARL), b. Cornelius, Ore, Mar. 11, 29; m. 54; c. 3. ORGANIC CHEMISTRY. B.A, Pomona Col, 51; Nat. Sci. Found. & E.I. du Pont fels, Rochester, 51-54, Ph.D.(org. chem), 54. Res. chemist, Shell Develop. Co, 54-55; Smith Kline & French fel. org. chem, Rutgers, 55-57, instr. chem, 57-59; res. chemist & group leader pharmaceut. chem, BRISTOL LABS DIV, BRISTOL-MYERS CO, 59-65, DIR. BIOCHEM. RES, 65- Summer res. chemist, Am. Cyanamid Co, 57. Consult, Will Corp, N.Y, 59- Am. Chem. Soc. Natural products; synthesis of penicillins; organic synthesis; analytical chemistry; design of molecular models and stereomodels; semisynthetic antibiotics. Address: Bristol Labs, P.O. Box 657, Syracuse, NY 13201.

GODFREY, JOHN D(ERRICK), b. Chesterfield, Eng, Apr. 12, 29; nat; m. 56; c. 3. PETROLOGY, GEOLOGY. B.Sc, Nottingham, 50; M.S, Chicago, 54, Ph.D, 62. Lectr, geol, Alberta, 54-56; ASSOC. RES. OFFICER, RES. COUN. ALTA, 56- External adv, Univ. Ceylon, 66-67. Igneous and metamorphic petrology, especially Precambrian and geochemical studies; isotope geology, particularly hydrogendeuterium. Address: Research Council of Alberta, 87th Ave. & 114th St, Edmonton, Alta, Can.

GODFREY, K(ENNETH) L(EROY), b. Providence, R.I, Feb. 27, 13; m. 43; c. 4. ORGANIC CHEMISTRY. Sc.B, Brown, 34, M.S, 36. Anal. chemist ORG. CHEM, MONSANTO CO, 36-40, res. chemist, 40-50; res. group leader, 50-55, RES. SECT. LEADER, 55- Am. Chem. Soc. Oil additives; agricultural chemicals; organophosphorus chemicals; mycobacteriostats. Address: 48 Orchard Lane, Kirkwood, MO 63122.

GODFREY, NORMAN B(ELL), b. Washington, D.C, June 16, 18; m. 44; c. 3. ORGANIC CHEMISTRY. B.S, California, 46; Ph.D.(chem), Rice Inst, 49. RES. CHEMIST, Visco Prods. Co, 49-52; Celanese Corp. Am, 53; JEFFERSON CHEM. CO, 54- U.S.A, 41-45. Am. Chem. Soc. Epoxy resin curing systems. Address: Jefferson Chemical Co, Inc, Box 4128, Austin, TX 78765.

GODFREY, PAUL R(USSELL), b. Ventnor, N.J, Nov. 26, 14; m. 40; c. 5. BIOCHEMISTRY. A.B, William Jewell Col, 38; M.S, Purdue, 40, Ph.D. (biochem), 52. Asst. prof. chem, Ouachita Col, 41-42; Furman, 42-43; asst. chemist, Purdue, 43-46; PROF. CHEM, La. Col, 46-70; TUSCULUM COL, 70- Summers, vis. prof, William Jewell Col, 59, res. partic, Oak Ridge Inst. Nuclear Studies, 60 & 61, res. assoc, 63, res. asst, sch. med, Tulane Univ, 64, res. partic, Case Inst. Technol, 65, vis. prof, Northwest. State Col. (La), 66, res. chemist, south. forest & range exp. sta, U.S. Forest Serv, 67. AAAS; Am. Chem. Soc. Analytical methods and nutritional studies of fluorine and iodine; lipid metabolism. Address: Dept. of Chemistry, Tusculum College, Greeneville, TN 37743.

GODFREY, ROBERT KENNETH, b. Bloomsbury, N.J, Aug. 29, 11; m. 46; c. 2. BOTANY. A.B, Maryville Col, 36; M.S, N.C. State Col, 38; M.A, Harvard, 40; Ph.D, Duke, 52. Asst. to curator, Gray Herbarium, Harvard, 39-40; supt. gardens, Orton Plantation, N.C, 40-41, 46-47; asst. prof. bot, N.C. State Col, 47-54; assoc. prof, FLA. STATE UNIV, 54-59, prof. & curator of herbarium, 59-62, prof. & acting head, 62-63, PROF. BIOL. SCI. & CHMN. DEPT, CURATOR OF HERBARIUM, 62- Plant explorer, plant introd. sect, U.S. Dept. Agr, Turkey & Union of S.Africa, 52-53; head, sect. environ. & syst. biol, Nat. Sci. Found, 66-67. U.S.N.R, 41-45. Am. Soc. Plant Taxon; Int. Asn. Plant Taxon General flora of southeastern United States. Address: Dept. of Biological Science, Florida State University, Tallahassee, FL 32306.

GODFREY, THOMAS N(IGEL) K(ING), b. Madison, Wis, Dec. 11, 27; m. 50; c. 1. PHYSICS. B.S, Mass. Inst. Tech, 50; Nat. Sci. Found. fel, Princeton, 52-54, Ph.D.(physics), 54. STAFF MEM, LOS ALAMOS SCI. LAB, 54- U.S.A, 46-47. AAAS; Cosmic rays; elementary particles; nuclear weapons. Address: 156 Tunyo, Los Alamos, NM 87544.

GODFREY, W(ILLIAM) EARL, b. Wolfville, N.S, Mar. 18, 10; m. 46; c. 1. ORNITHOLOGY. B.Sc, Acadia Univ, 34, hon. D.Sc, 69. Res. assoc. ORNITH, Cleveland Mus. Natural Hist, 40-57; CURATOR, NAT. MUS. CAN, 47-, HEAD VERT. ZOOL. SECT, 68- Fel. Am. Ornith. Union. Distribution, taxonomy and ecology of North American birds. Address: Vertebrate Zoology Section, National Museum of Natural Sciences, National Museums of Canada, Ottawa, Ont. K1A 0M8, Can.

GODIN, CLAUDE, b. Quebec City, Que, Mar. 12, 26; m. 53; c. 5. BIOCHEMISTRY. B.A, Laval, 46, B.Sc.A, 50, D.Sc.(chem), 53. Res. fel, Nat. Res. Coun, Can, Nat. Inst. Med. Res, England, 53-55; asst. prof. biol, Ottawa, 56-61, ASSOC. PROF, 61-70; BIOCHEM, LAVAL UNIV, 70- France-Can. exchange fel, Inst. Molecular Path, Paris, France, 67-68. Am. Chem. Soc; Can. Biochem. Soc; Chem. Inst. Can. Chemistry and biochemistry of proteins and amino acids. Address: Dept. of Biochemistry, Faculty of Sciences, Laval University, Quebec 10, Que, Can.

GODIN, GABRIEL, b. Montreal, Que, Oct. 11, 29. PHYSICAL OCEANOGRAPHY. B.A, Univ. Montreal, 48; B.Sc, McGill Univ, 52, M.Sc, 53, M.A, Univ. Toronto, 59; Ph.D.(phys. oceanog), Univ. Liverpool, 64. Teacher math, Royal Mil. Col.(Que), 55-56; physics, Laval Univ, 56-57; meteorologist, FED. GOVT, Toronto, Ont, 58-59, PHYS. OCEANOGR, MARINE SCI. BR, OTTAWA, ONT, 59- Centennial medal, Secy. State, 67. Tides & tidal power; analysis; modification of tides. Address: c/o Marine Sciences Branch, 615 Booth St, Ottawa, Ont, Can.

GODINO, CHARLES F, b. Brooklyn, N.Y, Mar. 31, 34; m. 56.. MATHEMATICS. B.A, St. Peter's Col.(N.J), 55; M.S, Notre Dame, 58, Ph.D.(math), 62. Instr. MATH, Notre Dame, 62; Joseph Fels Ritt instr, Columbia, 62-65; ASST. PROF, BROOKLYN COL, 65- Am. Math. Soc. Group theory; group representation theory; number theory. Address: Dept. of Mathematics, Brooklyn College, Brooklyn, NY 11210.

GODLEY, W(ILLIE) CECIL, b. Miley, S.C, Oct. 3, 22; m. 44; c. 3. GENETICS. B.S, Clemson Col, 43; M.S, N.C. State Col, 49, Ph.D, 55. Instr. animal husb, CLEMSON UNIV, 46, asst. prof, 47, assoc. prof, 52-57, PROF. ANIMAL SCI, 57-, animal husbandman & geneticist, 57-64, assoc. animal husbandman, 54-57. U.S.A, 43-46, Col. Am.Soc. Animal Sci; Am. Genetic Asn. Animal breeding. Address: 103 Lewis Rd, Clemson, SC 29631.

GODLOVE, TERRY F(RANCIS), b. Baltimore, Md, June 23, 27; m. 52; c. 2. PHYSICS. B.S, Lafayette Col, 50; M.S, Yale, 51, Ph.D.(physics), 55. PHYSICIST, NUCLEAR SCI. DIV, NAVAL RES. LAB, 55- U.S.N, 45-46. Am. Phys. Soc; Sci. Res. Soc. Am. Nuclear physics; particle accelerators; electronics. Address: Nuclear Sciences Division, Naval Research Lab, Washington, DC 20390.

GODMAN, GABRIEL C, b. Albany, N.Y, Jan. 24, 21. CELL BIOLOGY, PATHOLOGY. A.B, N.Y. Univ, 41, M.D, 44. House officer med, Bellevue Hosp, New York, 44-45; asst. path, Yale, 48-50; fel. path, Mt. Sinai Hosp. Sch. Med, 50-52; res. assoc. surg. path, COL. PHYSICIANS & SURGEONS, COLUMBIA, 52-54, asst. prof, 54-58, assoc. prof. MICROBIOL, 58-68, PROF, 68-, PATH, 69- Vis. investr. cell biol, Rockefeller Inst, 57-60; Nat. Insts. Health grant, 64-68, consult. study sect, 64-68. U.S.A.A.F, 44-47, Capt. Am. Asn. Path. & Bact; Am. Soc. Exp. Path; Am. Soc. Cell Biol; Harvey Soc; Int. Soc. Cell Biol. Electron microscopy; cellular pathology; virology; cell-virus relationships and cytopathic effects; cytochemistry; nuclear nucleoproteins; cytodifferentiation; regeneration; connective tissue. Address: Dept. of Pathology & Microbiology, College of Physicians & Surgeons, Columbia University, 630 W. 168th St, New York, NY 10032.

GODMAN, RICHARD M, b. Outram, Sask, Aug. 12, 22; U.S. citizen; m. 47; c. 1. FOREST MANAGEMENT. B.S, Michigan, 43, M.F, 64. Res. forester, northeast. forest exp. sta, U.S. FOREST SERV, 46-48, Alaska Forest Res. Center, 48-53, SILVICULTURIST, N.CENT. FOREST EXP. STA, 53- U.S.N, 44-46. Soc. Am. Foresters. Silvics, silviculture and management of forest species and types. Address: Institute of Forest Genetics, North Central Forest Experiment Station, Star Route 2, Rhinelander, WI 54501.

GODSCHALK, W(ILHELM), b. Rotterdam, Netherlands, Apr. 17, 32; m. 55. BIOCHEMISTRY, BIOPHYSICS. Ph.D.(biochem), Leiden, 64. Pub. health off, Pub. Health Serv, Netherlands, 56-65; res. assoc. physics & instr. biochem, UNIV. VA, 65-68, ASST. PROF. BIOCHEM, 68- Asst, Univ. Leiden, 61-64, res. assoc, 64-65. Am. Chem. Soc; Biophys. Soc. Structure and physico-chemical properties of viruses, proteins and nucleoproteins; association of protein subunits to large functional structures; development of new ultracentrifugal techniques; polarographic studies of proteins. Address: Dept. of Biochemistry, University of Virginia School of Medicine, Charlottesville, VA 22904.

GODSHALL, FREDRIC ALLEN, b. Pottstown, Pa, Sept. 4, 34; m. 59; c. 3. METEOROLOGY. B.S, Ursinus Col, 56; Mass. Inst. Technol, 56-57; M.S, N.Y. Univ, 58; Pa. State, 64-65. Meteorologist, Proj. Mercury, 61-66; Argonne Nat. Lab, 66; PROJ. SCIENTIST, ENVIRON. DATA SERV, ENVIRON. SCI. SERV. ADMIN, 66- U.S.N.R, Lt. Comdr. Application of satellite data in meteorology. Address: 1036 Pinecrest Dr, Annapolis, MD 21403.

GODSHALL, H(ERBERT) LYNN, b. Reading, Pa, Dec. 15, 40; m. 64; c. 1. ORGANIC CHEMISTRY. B.S, Lehigh Univ, 62; M.S, Yale, 63; Nat. Inst. Ment. Health fel. & Ph.D.(org. chem), Univ. Va, 68. SR. RES. CHEMIST, PENNWALT CORP, 68- Am. Chem. Soc. Chemistry of organic fluorine compounds; organic synthesis. Address: Organic Research Dept, Pennwalt Corp, 900 First Ave, King of Prussia, PA 19406.

GODSON, GODFREY NIGEL, b. London, Eng, June 20, 36; m. 69. MOLECULAR BIOLOGY. Ph.D.(biochem), Univ. London, 62. Staff biochem, Chester Beatty Cancer Res. Inst, London, 60-64; fel. molecular biol, California Inst. Technol, 64-67; res. fel, med. sch, Yale, 67-68; staff biochem, Med. Res. Coun, Nat. Inst. Med. Res, London, 68-69; ASST. PROF. MOLECULAR BIOL, RADIOBIOL. LABS, MED. SCH, YALE, 69- Replication of small RNA bacteriophages; regulation of protein synthesis in the small single strand DNA virus ϕX174; synthesis of DNA in Eschericia coli and role of the cell membrane in this process. Address: Radiobiology Labs, Yale University School of Medicine, 333 Cedar St, New Haven, CT 06510.

GODSON, W(ARREN) L(EHMAN), b. Victoria, B.C, May 4, 20; m. 42; wid; m. 67; c. 5. METEOROLOGY. B.A, British Columbia, 39, M.A, 41, Toronto, 44, Ph.D.(phys. meteorol), 48. Asst, METEOROL. SERV. CAN, 42-43, gen. res. & lectr, 43-51, supvr, res. unit, 51-54, SUPT, ATMOSPHERIC RES. SECT, 54- Special lectr, Toronto, 48-60; consult, Arctic meteorol. res. group, McGill Univ, 55-62; liaison off, Int. Union Geodesy & Geophys-World Meteorol. Orgn, 60- Patterson Medal, 68. Fel. Am. Meteorol. Soc; Can. Asn. Physicists; Royal Meteorol. Soc.(pres, Can. br, 57-59, Darton prize, 61, Buchan prize, 64); fel. Royal Soc. Can; Can. Meteorol. Soc; Int. Asn. Meteorol. & Atmospheric Physics (secy, 60-). Precipitation physics and induced precipitation; atmospheric infrared radiation; atmospheric ozone; numerical weather prediction; stratospheric fields of wind and temperature in the Arctic; atmospheric thermodynamics; long-period atmospheric oscillations. Address: 47 Winsdale Rd, Etobicoke, Ont, Can.

GODT, HENRY C(HARLES), JR, b. Ft. Smith, Ark, July 26, 25; m. 50; c. 1. ORGANIC CHEMISTRY. B.S, Michigan, 50, M.S, 51, Ph.D.(pharmaceut. chem), 54. Res. chemist, MONSANTO CO, 53-58, res. group leader, org. div, 58-70, TECHNOL. APPRAISAL MGR, 70- U.S.A, 43-46. Am. Chem. Soc; Am. Pharmaceut. Asn. Organic chemical synthesis and process development; medicinal chemistry; agricultural chemicals; petroleum additives. Address: 12410 Ballas Meadows Dr, St. Louis, MO 63131.

GODWIN, FRANCIS (WOOD), Indust. Develop, Res. Orgn, see 12th ed, Soc. & Behav. Vols.

GODWIN, JOHN T(HOMAS), b. Social Circle, Ga, Dec. 2, 17; m. 48; c. 3. PATHOLOGY. B.S, Emory, 38, M.D, 41. Res. path, Touro Infirmary, New Orleans, La, 41-42, 47-48; Am. Cancer Soc. fel, Mem. Hosp, 48-50; pathologist & lectr, Ochsner Found. Hosp. & sch. med, Tulane, 50-51; head div. path. & pathologist, hosp, Brookhaven Nat. Lab, 51-55; clin. asst. prof. path, EMORY UNIV, 55-58, assoc. prof. DENTAL PATH, SCH. DENT, 58-60, PROF, 60-; HEAD, BIOMED. REACTOR RES. PROJ. & SPECIAL RES. SCIENTIST, GA. INST. TECHNOL, 58- Preceptor, sr. med. students, Mem. Hosp, 49-50, asst. attend. pathologist, 51-55; asst, radioautographic div, physics dept, Sloan-Kettering Inst, 49-50, div. path, 54-55; asst. vis. pathologist, James Ewing Hosp, 51-55; pathologist & dir. labs, St. Joseph's Infirmary, Atlanta, 55-; res. collab, Brookhaven Nat. Lab, 55-; mem. vis. staff, Grady Hosp, Atlanta, 58-; adj. clin. prof, allied health sci. sch. & med. dir, med. technol. prog, Ga. State Univ, 71- Consult, Grady Clay Mem. Eye Clinic, 58- Mem, Governor's Sci. & Tech. Comn; Radiation Control Comt, State of Ga. Dipl, Am. Bd. Path, 49. U.S.N, 42-47, Res, 47-, Comdr. Am. Cancer Soc.(abstract ed, Jour, 54-55); Soc. Exp. Biol. & Med; fel. Am. Soc. Clin. Path.(silver medal, 52, gold medal, 53); Am. Thyroid Asn; Am. Med. Asn; Am. Asn. Path. & Bact; fel. Col. Am. Path; N.Y. Acad. Sci; Soc. Head & Neck Surg. Pathology and natural history of human neoplasms; human and animal carcinogenesis, particularly by ionizing radiations; thyroid physiology; radiology; diagnosis and treatment of human cancer. Address: 265 Ivy St. N.E, Atlanta, GA 30303.

GODWIN, RICHARD P, b. Clifton, N.J, Mar. 21, 22; m. 47; c. 4. MECHANICAL ENGINEERING. B.E, Yale, 45. Chief metallurgist, New Brit. Mach. Co, 46-50; phys. scientist, Atomic Energy Comn, Wash, 50-53, chief oper. div, Calif, 53-56, asst. dir. reactor develop, Wash, 56-61; mgr. sci. develop. dept, BECHTEL CORP, 61-65, asst. to pres, 65-67, mgr. corp. planning & develop, 67-71, V.PRES. & MGR. DIV. OPERS, HYDRO DIV, 71- Dir. research & develop, U.S. Maritime Admin, Wash, D.C, 58-61; mem, U.S. mission, Safety of Life at Sea Convention, 60; President's Adv. Cmt. Saline Water Conversion, 62-64. U.S.N, 42-46, Lt.(jg). Am. Nuclear Soc; Soc. Naval Archit. & Marine Eng. Reactor engineering; nuclear reactor development; nuclear ship design and construction; saline water conversion. Address: 130 Highland Ave, San Rafael, CA 94901.

GODWIN, ROBERT O(WEN), b. Dothan, Ala, July 31, 35; m. 57; c. 2. ELECTRICAL ENGINEERING. B.E.E, Ga. Inst. Tech, 58; Hughes fel, Southern California, 59-60, M.S, 60. Mem. tech. staff, Hughes Aircraft Co, 58-61; sr. res. engr, AUTONETICS DIV, N.AM. ROCKWELL CORP, 62-64, proj. engr, 64-66, group scientist, 66-69, MGR, 69- U.S.A, 61-62, Res, 62-, 1st Lt. Inst. Elec. & Electronics Eng; Nat. Soc. Prof. Eng. Laser research and development; range finders, illuminators and other applications; optical detection and signal processing; electronic design. Address: 5582 Chalon Rd, Yorba Linda, CA 92686.

GODYCKI, L(UDWIG) EDWARD, b. Bethlehem, Pa, Dec. 21, 21; m. 46; c. 3. PHYSICAL CHEMISTRY. B.S, Lehigh, 43, M.S, 47; Ph.D.(chem), Iowa State Col, 51. Asst. Lehigh, 46-48; Iowa State Col, 48-51; res. chemist, Houdry Process Corp, 51-52; asst. prof. chem, St. Louis, 52-56; assoc. chemist, res. lab, Int. Bus. Mach. Corp, N.Y, 56-64; mgr. mat, Bourns, Inc, 64-67; CONSULT, SEEC SERV, 67- Ord. Dept, U.S.A, 43-46, Capt. AAAS; Am. Chem. Soc; Am. Phys. Soc; Am. Crystallog. Asn. X-ray crystallography; surface chemistry and physics; semiconductor chemistry; electrochemistry. Address: 1060 Granada Ave, San Marino, CA 91108.

GODZESKI, C(ARL) W(ILLIAM), b. Champaign, Ill, July 17, 26; m. 49, 63; c. 2. MICROBIOLOGY. B.S, Illinois, 49; Atomic Energy Cmn. fel. & Ph.D.(bact), Pa. State Col, 53. Pathogenic bacteriologist, Pitman-Moore Co, 53-54; res. microbiologist, ELI LILLY & CO, 54-58, sr. res. microbiologist, 58-65, res. assoc, 65-69, CHIEF MICROBIOL, IMMUNOL. SERV, CLIN. RES. DIV, 69- U.S.N.R, 44-46. Am. Soc. Microbiol. Bacterial L forms and mycoplasma; penicillin and cephalosporin antibiotics; microbial ultrastructure. Address: 6236 Colebrook Dr, Indianapolis, IN 46220.

GOE, DON R(ICHARD), b. Baker, Mont, Mar. 23, 23; m. 51; c. 2. PHYSIOLOGY. B.A, Pacific Union Col, 45; M.A, Walla Walla Col, 50; Ph.D, Southern California, 58. Asst. zool, Southern California, 52-54; res. assoc. physiol, sch. trop. & prev. med, Loma Linda, 54-56, asst. instr, sch. med, 56-58, instr, 58-60; asst. prof. biol, Walla Walla Col, 60-61; DIR. PULMONARY PHYSIOL. RES, VET. ADMIN. HOSP, 61-, consult, 60-61. Med.C, U.S.N, 46-48. Physiology of exercise; biotoxicology. Address: Pulmonary Physiology Research, Veterans Administration Hospital, Walla Walla, WA 99362.

GOE, GERALD L(EE), b. Kansas City, Mo, Aug. 17, 42; m. 67; c. 1. ORGANIC CHEMISTRY. B.S, Univ. Mo-Columbia, 63; Nat. Sci. Found. fel, Mass. Inst. Technol, 64-66, Nat. Insts. Health fel, 66-67, Ph.D.(org. chem), 67. Nat. Insts. Health fel, Iowa State Univ, 67-69; ASST. PROF. CHEM, UNIV. NOTRE DAME, 69- Am. Chem. Soc. Organic photochemistry; photochemical and thermal cyclo-additions and rearrangements; theory, mechanism and synthetic applications. Address: Dept. of Chemistry, University of Notre Dame, Notre Dame, IN 46556.

GOEBEL, CARL JEROME, b. Milwaukee, Wis, Sept. 24, 29; m. 54; c. 5. ENVIRONMENTAL SCIENCES, RANGE MANAGEMENT. B.S, Univ. Idaho, 55; Ph.D.(range mgt), Utah State Univ, 60; Charles Bullard nat. award, Harvard, 62-63, M.P.A, 64. Range conservationist, U.S. Forest Serv, 58-59; asst. prof. forestry, Iowa State Univ, 59-63; range conservationist, U.S. Forest Serv, 63-68; ASSOC. PROF. FORESTRY & RANGE MGT, WASH. STATE UNIV, 68-, CHMN. DEPT. ENVIRON. SCI, 71- Med.C, U.S.N, 47-51. Soc. Am. Foresters; Soc. Range Mgt. Competition between the native bluebunch wheatgrass; introduced perennials by the annual wheatgrass and other less desirable annuals. Address: Forest & Range Management Dept, Washington State University, Pullman, WA 99163.

GOEBEL, CHARLES GALE, b. Indianapolis, Ind, Nov. 19, 17; m. 45; c. 3. ORGANIC CHEMISTRY. A.B, Indiana, 39; M.S, Purdue, 41, Ph.D.(org. chem), 44. Sr. chemist, EMERY INDUSTS, INC, 43-52, mgr. lab, 52-59, res. dir, 59-66, corp. tech. dir, 66-69, V.PRES. RES. & DEVELOP, 69- Am. Chem. Soc; Am. Oil. Chemists' Soc. Fatty acids and derivatives; plasticizers; synthetic lubricants, resins; plastics and detergents. Address: Emery Industries, Inc, 4900 Estes Ave, Cincinnati, OH 45232.

GOEBEL, CHARLES J(AMES), b. Chicago, Ill, Dec. 16, 30; m. 51; c. 2. THEORETICAL PHYSICS. Ph.B, Chicago, 49, Ph.D.(physics), 56. Res. assoc, Lawrence Radiation Lab, California, 54-56; asst. prof, Rochester, 56-59, assoc. prof. physics & astron, 59-61, assoc. prof. PHYSICS, UNIV. WIS, MADISON, 61-64, PROF, 64- Alfred E. Sloan res. fel. quantum field theory, 59-61. Fel. Am. Phys. Soc. Quantum field theory, especially meson scattering; general relativity. Address: Dept. of Physics, University of Wisconsin, Madison, WI 53706.

GOEBEL, CHARLES VINCENT, JR, b. Teaneck, N.J, Apr. 8, 36; m. 60; c. 3. POLYMER & PHYSICAL ORGANIC CHEMISTRY. B.S, Calif. Inst. Tech, 57; Nat. Sci. Found. fel, Harvard, 57-58, M.A, 60, Nat. Insts. Health fel, 60-62, Ph.D.(chem), 63. Chemist, Chevron Res. Corp, Standard Oil Co. Calif, 62-64; Reichhold Chem, 64-65; GROUP LEADER POLYMER CHEM, POLYMER CORP, 65- Am. Chem. Soc; The Chem. Soc. Kinetics and mechanisms of anionic polymerizations; polymer analytical chemistry and synthesis of monomers. Address: Polymer Corp, 501 Crescent Ave, Reading, PA 19603.

GOEBEL, EDWIN D(eWAYNE), b. Moline, Ill, Dec. 10, 23; m. 50; c. 2. ENVIRONMENTAL GEOLOGY. A.B, Augustana Col, 46; fel, Univ. Iowa, 50, M.S, 51; Ph.D.(micropaleont, econ. geol), Univ. Kans, 66. Asst. geol, Univ. Iowa, 50-51; geologist, State Geol. Surv, Kans, 51, div. head, 51-66, chief admin. serv, 66-67, sr. geologist, 67-71; PROF. GEOL, UNIV. MO-KANSAS CITY, 71- Summer asst, Amerada Petrol. Corp, 49; Mo. Geol. Surv, 50. U.S.A, 43-46. Am. Asn. Petrol. Geol; Geol. Soc. Am. Petroleum geology; subsurface stratigraphy; structural geology; micropaleontology. Address: Dept. of Geology, University of Missouri at Kansas City, Kansas City, MO 64110.

GOEBEL, HAROLD L, b. South Bend, Ind, June 25, 10; m. 39; c. 3. PHYSICAL CHEMISTRY. B.S, Notre Dame, 35, M.S, 36, Ph.D.(phys. chem), 38. EXEC. DEVELOP. CHEMIST, U.S. RUBBER CO, 38- Rubber technology; latex foam development and processing; polyurethane technology involving spreading and casting applications. Address: U.S. Rubber Co, Mishawaka, IN 46628.

GOEBEL, J(ACK) B(RUCE), b. Wallowa, Ore, Aug. 22, 32; m. 52; c. 3. MATHEMATICS. B.A, Oregon, 54, M.A, 56; Ph.D.(math), Oregon State, 62. Instr. math, Oregon State, 60-61; mathematician, Gen. Elec. Co, 61-63, sr. mathematician, 63-65; res. assoc. appl. math, Pac. Northwest Lab, Battelle Mem. Inst, 65-67; PROF. MATH. & HEAD DEPT, MONT. COL. MINERAL SCI. & TECHNOL, 67-, CHMN. GRAD. SCH, 69- Summers, staff mem, Mass. Inst. Technol, 56, Sandia Corp, 57. Am. Math. Soc; Soc. Indust. & Appl. Math; Math. Asn. Am. Abstract algebra; applied mathematics. Address: Dept. of Mathematics, Montana College of Mineral Science & Technology, Butte, MT 59701.

GOEBEL, M(AX) T(HEODORE), b. Compton, Ill, Oct. 28, 06; m. 32; c. 2. CHEMISTRY. A.B, Illinois, 28, Ph.D.(org. chem), 34. Res. chemist, Commercial Solvents Corp, Ind, 28-30; asst. chem, Illinois, 30-32; res. chemist, exp. sta, E.I. du Pont de Nemours & Co, Inc, 34-38, res. group leader, 38-41, asst. dir, exp. lab, Ohio, 41-44, dir, 44-48, asst. dir, res. div, indust. & biochem. dept, 48-50, dir, 50-70; RETIRED. Am. Chem. Soc. Animal nutrition; plant nutrients; herbicides; fungicides; regulation of plant growth; industrial chemicals. Address: Route 1, Chadds Ford, PA 19317.

GOEBEL, WALTHER F(REDERICK), b. Palo Alto, Calif, Dec. 24, 99; m. 30; c. 2. BIOCHEMISTRY. A.B, Illinois, 20, A.M, 21, Ph.D.(org. chem), 23; Friedrich Maximilian Univ, 23-24; hon.D.Sc, Middlebury Col, 59. Asst. CHEM. IMMUNOL, HOSP, ROCKEFELLER UNIV, 24-27, assoc, 27-34, assoc. mem, 34-44, MEM, 44-, PROF, 57- With Off. Sci. Res. & Develop. Nat. Acad. Sci; Am. Chem. Soc; Am. Soc. Biol. Chem; Am. Soc. Microbiol; Harvey Soc; Am. Asn. Immunol. Bacterial antigens; bacterial polysaccharides; synthetic carbohydrate protein antigens; blood group specific substances; antigens of dysentery bacilli; glucuronic acid; structure of polysaccharides; heterophile antigens; bacteriophage and viral receptors; colicines. Address: Rockefeller University, New York, NY 10021.

GOECKNER, N(ORBERT) A(NTHONY), b. Chicago, Ill, Sept. 30, 30; m. 54; c. 7. ORGANIC CHEMISTRY. B.S, Illinois, 54; U.S. Dept. Agr. fel, Iowa, 55-58, M.S, 57, Ph.D.(chem), 59; Swiss Fed. Inst. Tech, 58-59. Chemist gas chromatography sect, Standard Oil Co.(Ind), 59-61; asst. prof. CHEM, WEST. ILL. UNIV, 61-67, ASSOC. PROF, 67- Atomic Energy Comn. faculty fel, summers, 66, 68. U.S.N.R, 49-58. Am. Chem. Soc. Gas chromatography. Address: Dept. of Chemistry, Western Illinois University, Macomb, IL 61455.

GOEDEKE, A(RTHUR) DONALD, b. Washington, Mo, Sept. 10, 34; m. 56; c. 3. SPACE PHYSICS. B.S, Rockhurst Col, 56; Iowa, 56-59; summer, Mass. Inst. Tech, 60. Asst. math, Rockhurst Col, 55-56; physics, Iowa, 56-59, astron, 56-57; staff specialist space radiation, McDONNELL DOUGLAS ASTRONAUT. CO, 59-60, group head space environ, 60-61, group leader space physics, 61-62, sect. chief space physics & thermodyn, 62-63, dep. chief scientist, adv. space res. dept, 63-64, CHIEF SCIENTIST, SPACE SCI. DEPT, 64-, SPACE STA. PROG, 70- Lectr, eng. & sci. exten, Univ. Calif, Los Angeles, 63. U.S. del. & partic, Comt. Space Res. Int. Space Sci. Symp; Nice, 60, D.C, 63, Warsaw, 63, Buenos Aires, 65, Prague, 69, Seattle, 71. Mem. U.S. Antarctic Res. Prog. summer party, 61-62; space & atmospheric physics comt, Am. Inst. Aeronaut. & Astronaut, 63-66; partic. long range planning Antarctic res. aeronomy, Nat. Acad. Sci, 65; mem. working group IV, comt. space res, Int. Coun. Sci. Unions; group III, Int. Union Comt. Space & Terrestrial Physics. Cong. Antarctic medal, 68. AAAS; Am. Geophys. Union; Am. Phys. Soc; Am. Astronaut. Soc; assoc. fel. Am. Inst. Aeronaut. & Astronaut. Solar-terrestrial relationships; solar flare properties; nature and properties of solar cosmic radiation; ionosphere absorption in polar regions; rocket and satellite radiation experiments; geophysics; space radiation; planetary sciences; earth ecology; remote sensing. Address: 1406 Seacrest Dr, Corona del Mar, CA 92625.

GOEDEN, RICHARD D(EAN), b. Neillsville, Wis, May 20, 35; m. 62; c. 1. ENTOMOLOGY, BOTANY. B.S, Wisconsin, 62, M.S, 63, Ph.D.(entom), 65. Asst. entomologist, UNIV. CALIF, RIVERSIDE, 65-69, ASST. PROF. BIOL. CONTROL & LECTR, 69- U.S.A.F, 54-57. Mycol. Soc. Am; Entom. Soc. Am; Entom. Soc. Can. Biological control of weeds; population dynamics of phytophagous insects and weedy plants. Address: Division of Biological Control, University of California, Riverside, CA 92502.

GOEDERTIER, KUEI-LING LI, b. Hopei, China, Nov. 19, 25; m. 59; c. 1. PHYSICS. M.Sc, Cath. Univ. Peking, China, 47; Ph.D.(physics), Louvain, 58. Res. assoc. PHYSICS, North Carolina, 58-59; instr, Douglass Col, Rutgers, 59-60; GEORGIAN COURT COL, 60-63, asst. prof, 63-66, assoc. prof, 66-70, PROF, 70- Am. Asn. Physics Teachers. Microwave spectroscopy; molecular parameters by spectroscopic methods in optical and microwave region; x-ray analysis. Address: Dept. of Physics, Georgian Court College, Lakewood, NJ 08701.

GOEDERTIER, PETER V, b. Antwerp, Belgium, Nov. 15, 12; U.S. citizen; m. 59; c. 1. MATHEMATICS, PHYSICS. B.A, Louvain, 39, M.A, 41, lic. theol, 45; Harvard, 47-48. Prof. math. & statist, Adv. Inst. Commerce, Antwerp, 45-52; asst. prof. math. & physics, Philos. Col, Louvain, 50-53, assoc. prof, univ. & mem. res. staff, nuclear physics ctr, 53-58; res. asst. physics, Duke Univ, 58-59; MEM. RES. STAFF, RCA LABS, RCA CORP, 59- Gas and solid state masers and lasers; light scanning and modulation processing. Address: RCA Labs, RCA Corp, Princeton, NJ 08540.

GOEDICKE, THOMAS R. EUGENE, b. Prague, Czech, Feb. 21, 21; U.S. citizen. GEOPHYSICS, OCEANOGRAPHY. B.Sc, McGill, 45; M.S, N.C. State Col, 38; D.Sc, Polytech. Univ, Ger, 55. Geophysicist, Koulomzine & Co, 45-46; mine mgr, Claverny Gold Mines & Wendell Gold Mines, 46-47; Du Reine Mines, Ltd, 46; party chief, Sherwin Kelly Geophys. Servs, 48-49; consult. geophys, Associated Petrol. Developers, 50; asst. prof. geophys, econ. geol. & mineral, Agr. & Mech. Col. Texas, 51-54; geophysicist, Offshore Explor. Group, 55-57, res. asst. prof, marine lab, Miami (Fla), 59-64; dir, Inner Space Res. Found, 64-68; ASSOC. PROF. GEOL, AM. UNIV. BEIRUT, 68- Consult, Big M Marine Serv. Soc. Explor. Geophys; Am. Inst. Mining, Metall. & Petrol. Eng; Am. Geophys. Union; fel. Soc. Geol. France; Europ. Asn. Explor. Geophys. Economic geology of molybdenite deposits; resistivity methods of geophysical prospecting to location of nickel and to ground water; geophysical methods to exploration of the continental shelves; tectonics and petrography of Alps and Appalachians; world offshore oil provinces; under-water sound measurements and sound spectrum analysis; repetitive explosive under-water sound source; geophysical measurements and substructure of Bahamas. Address: Dept. of Geology, American University of Beirut, Beirut, Lebanon.

GOEDICKE, VICTOR (ALFRED), b. Holt, Wyo, Sept. 25, 12; m. 37. ASTRONOMY, MATHEMATICS. A.B, Michigan, 35, Rackham fel, 35-39, M.S, 36, Ph.D.(astron), 38; Cambridge, 38-39. Instr. astron, Wesleyan, 39-40; lectr, Brown, 40; instr, Yale, 40-44, asst. prof, 44-46; assoc. prof. MATH. & ASTRON, OHIO UNIV, 46-53, PROF, 53- Prof, U.S. Army Univ.(Italy), 45. AAAS; Am. Astron. Soc. Astronomical spectroscopy; astronomical photometry; spectrum of VV cephei; theory of statistics. Address: Dept. of Mathematics, Ohio University, Athens, OH 45701.

GOEDKEN, VIRGIL LINUS, b. Independence, Iowa, Nov. 29, 40; m. 66; c. 2. INORGANIC CHEMISTRY. B.S, Upper Iowa Col, 63; Ph.D.(chem), Fla. State Univ, 68. Fel. CHEM, Ohio State Univ, 68-70; ASST. PROF, UNIV. CHICAGO, 70- Am. Chem. Soc. Inorganic transition metal chemistry; reactions of coordinated ligands; correlation of stability and reaction rates with electronic structure; solid state studies via x-ray crystallography. Address: Dept. of Chemistry, University of Chicago, Chicago, IL 60637.

GOEHLER, BRIGITTE H(ANNA), b. Radebeul, Germany, July 24, 26; U.S. citizen. BACTERIOLOGY. M.S, Wayne State, 60, Ph.D.(bact), 64. Biologist, Inst. Tobacco Res, Germany, 51-52; German Acad. Agr. Sci, Berlin, 52-55; instr. biol, Wayne State, 60-62, asst. prof, 64-65; Nat. Insts. Health fel, 65-67; asst. prof. BIOL, CALIF. STATE POLYTECH. COL, 67-70, ASSOC. PROF, 70- Am. Soc. Microbiol. Bacterial physiology; molecular biology. Address: Dept. of Biological Sciences, California State Polytechnic College, Pomona, CA 91766.

GOEHRING, HARRY H(UBERT), b. Loyal Wis, Feb. 10, 08; m; c. 3. ZOOLOGY. B.E, Milwaukee State Teachers Col, 29; Ph.M, Wisconsin, 32; Ed.D, North Dakota, 55. Teacher, pub. sch, Wis, 29-31, N.Dak, 32-43; phys. & biol, N.Dak. State Teachers Col, 43-46; from assoc. prof. to prof. biol, St. Cloud State Col, 46-71; RETIRED. Nat. Sci. Found. vis. scientist lectr. Am. Soc. Mammal; Am. Inst. Biol. Sci; Nat. Sci. Teachers Asn. Bat banding; mortality in hibernating populations; bird banding, especially swift banding. Address: Dept. of Biology, St. Cloud State College, St. Cloud, MN 56301.

GOEHRING, J(OHN) BROWN, b. Pittsburgh, Pa, Apr. 24, 35; m. 60; c. 2. INORGANIC & ANALYTICAL CHEMISTRY. B.S, Davidson Col, 56; fel, North Carolina, 57-58, Nat. Sci. Found. fel, 59-60, Ph.D.(chem), 62. E.I. du Pont Co, asst. CHEM, North Carolina, 58-59, instr, 60-63; asst. prof,

WASHINGTON & LEE UNIV, 63-66, assoc. prof, 66-70, PROF, 70- Nat. Sci. Found. sci. faculty fel, Univ. Calif, Los Angeles, 69-70. AAAS; Am. Chem. Soc; Brit. Chem. Soc. Properties of inorganic electrolytes, experimentation in educational media. Address: Dept. of Chemistry, Washington & Lee University, Lexington, VA 24450.

GOEL, AMRIT LAL, b. Meerut, India, Mar. 4, 38; m. 67. APPLIED STATISTICS, OPERATIONS RESEARCH. B.Sc, Agra Univ, 57; B.Eng, Univ. Roorkee, 61; M.S, Univ. Wis, Madison, 63, Ph.D.(mech. eng), 68. Asst. mech. engr, Dept. Atomic Energy, India, 61-62; lectr. eng, Univ. Wis, Milwaukee, 67-68; asst. prof. INDUST. ENG, SYRACUSE UNIV, 68-71, ASSOC. PROF, 71- Fel, Rome Air Develop. Ctr, Griffiss A.F.B, 70-71; Nat. Sci. Found. res. grants, 69-71 & 70-71. Consult, res. grants data mgt. systs, U.S. Air Force, 69-, reliability & maintainability, 70- Am. Statist. Asn; assoc. mem. Opers. Res. Soc. Am; Asn. Comput. Mach; Am. Soc. Eng. Educ; Am. Soc. Qual. Control; fel. Royal Statist. Soc. Data management systems, especially optimal file design; optimal control chart procedures with emphasis on cusum charts; use of computers in education; modeling time series. Address: 427 Link Hall, Dept. of Industrial Engineering, Syracuse University, Syracuse, NY 13210.

GOEL, KAILASH C(HANDRA), b. Tasing, India, July, 12, 37; m. 62; c. 1. ENVIRONMENTAL SCIENCES. B.S, Banaras Hindu Univ, 59; M.Eng, Univ. Roorkee, 60; Ph.D.(water pollution control), Okla. State Univ, 68. Asst. engr, pub. health eng, State of Uttar, Pradesh, India, 60-64; sanit. engr, water & air resources comn, State of Del, 68, dir. labs, 68-69; DIR, ENVIRON. SCI. LAB, EDWARD H. RICHARDSON ASSOCS, INC, 69- Exten. prof, Univ. Del, 70-71. Dipl, Intersoc. Bd. Environ. Eng. Am. Soc. Civil Eng; Nat. Soc. Prof. Eng; Water Pollution Control Fedn; Am. Water Works Asn; assoc. mem. Am. Chem. Soc. Biological treatment of waste waters. Address: Environmental Sciences Lab, Edward H. Richardson Associates, Inc, P.O. Box 935, Dover, DE 19901.

GOEL, NARENDRA SWARUP, b. Muzaffarnagar, India, June 12, 41; m. 67; c. 2. BIOPHYSICS, CHEMICAL PHYSICS. B.Sc, Agra, 57; M.Sc, Delhi, 59; M.Sc, Poona, 62; Ph.D.(physics), Maryland, 65. Tech. & res. asst. physics, Indian Inst. Tech, Bombay, 59-62; asst, Maryland, 62-65, jr. instr, 64, res. assoc. biophys, inst. fluid dynamics & appl. math, 65-66; asst. prof. physics, UNIV. ROCHESTER, 66-71, ASSOC, RADIATION BIOL, BIOPHYS. & BIOMATH, 71-, fel, summer 67. Consult, Inst. Defense Anal, Va, 63-68; Jacobs scholar, Marine Biol. Lab, Mass, summer 66; consult, Ctr. Theoret. Biol, N.Y, 66-; Xerox Corp, summer 71. Biophys. Soc. Astrophysics; solid state physics; statistical mechanics; molecular biophysics; chemical kinetics; surface chemistry; membranology; ecology; neurophysiology. Address: Dept. of Radiation Biology & Biophysics, University of Rochester, Rochester, NY 14627.

GOEL, OM PRAKASH, b. Delhi, India, Sept. 25, 43; m. 68; c. 1. ORGANIC & MEDICINAL CHEMISTRY. B.Sc, Univ. Delhi, 62; Am. Petrol. Inst-Gulf Oil Co. fel, Carnegie-Mellon Univ, 63-65, M.S, 65, Nat. Sci. Found. fel, 65-66, Ph.D.(org. chem), 66. Assoc. res. chemist, PARKE, DAVIS & CO, 66-68, RES. CHEMIST, 68- Am. Chem. Soc. Fischer indole synthesis; reaction mechanisms; synthesis of potential new chemotherapeutic agents; process research. Address: 1525 Cherboneau Pl, Detroit, MI 48207.

GOEL, RAM GAPAL, b. Vrandaban, India, Oct. 2, 34; m. 53; c. 5. INORGANIC CHEMISTRY. B.Sc, Lucknow, 52, M.Sc, 55; Ph.D.(chem), British Columbia, 65. Lectr. CHEM, D.A.V. Col, Lucknow, 55-56; St. John's Col, Agra, 56-57; Roorkee, 57-62; res. assoc, Purdue, 65-66; ASST. PROF, St. Francis Xavier (Can), 66-67; UNIV. GUELPH, 67- Nat. Res. Coun. Can. res. grants, 66-71; dept. univ. affairs, Prov. Ont. res. grants, 68, 69, 71. Am. Chem. Soc; Chem. Inst. Can; fel. The Chem. Soc. Organometallic and coordination chemistry; inorganic fluorine chemistry; synthetic and structural studies. Address: Dept. of Chemistry, University of Guelph, Guelph, Ont, Can.

GOELL, JAMES E(MANUEL), b. N.Y.C, Oct. 13, 39; m. 60; c. 2. ELECTRICAL ENGINEERING, COMMUNICATION SCIENCES. B.E.E, Cornell, 62, M.S, 63, Ph.D.(elec. eng), 65. Coop. student elec. eng, Philco Corp, 59-61; MEM. TECH. STAFF, BELL TEL. LABS, 65- Inst. Elec. & Electronics Eng. Ferrites, millimeter waves; periodic structures; microwave tubes and circuits; optics; integrated optical circuits. Address: Bell Telephone Labs, Crawford Hill, Holmdel, NJ 07733.

GOELLNER, KARL E(UGENE), b. Port Gibson, N.Y, Sept. 18, 11; m. 34; c. 4. ZOOLOGY. B.S, Michigan, 33, M.S, 38, Ph.D.(zool), 43. From asst. to assoc. prof. BIOL, Luther Col, 46-49; COE COL, 49-56, PROF, 56- U.S.A.A.F, 43-45. AAAS; Am. Inst. Biol. Sci. Natural history and relationships of North American crayfishes; vertebrate natural history. Address: Dept. of Biology, Coe College, Cedar Rapids, IA 52402.

GOENS, DUANE N, b. Greenville, Ohio, July 27, 29; m. 53; c. 3. PHYSICAL CHEMISTRY, ELECTROCHEMISTRY. B.S, Wilmington Col.(Ohio), 51; M.S, Miami (Ohio), 52. Res. chemist, Diamond Alkali Co, 54-59; Am. Potash & Chem. Co, 59-61, sr. res. chemist, 61-65, res. proj. chemist, 65-67, head electrochem. sect, res. dept, 67-69; mgr. electrochem. sect, Kerr-McGee Tech. Div, Kerr-McGee Corp, 69-71; SR. RES. ENGR, HAZEN RES. INC, 71- Qm.C, U.S.A, 52-54. Am. Chem. Soc; Electrochem. Soc; Am. Inst. Mining, Metall. & Petrol. Eng. High temperature chlorination; electrode processes and reaction mechanisms; design and development of industrial electrolytic cells; electrolytic oxidations and reductions; electro-organics; electrometallurgy. Address: Hazen Research Inc, 4601 Indiana St, Golden, CO 80401.

GOEPFERT, GEORGE J(OSEPH), b. N.Y.C, Aug. 2, 15; m. 43. ORGANIC CHEMISTRY. A.B, Fordham, 37, M.S, 39, Ph.D.(chem), 42. Instr. org. chem, Fordham, 38-42; supv. develop. engr, Carborundum Co, 42-51; tech. dir, Speer Carbon Co, 51-54; dir. chem. & abrasives res. dept, CINCINNATI MILLING MACHINE CO, 54-62, MGR. CIMASTRA DIV, 62- Soc. Plastics Eng.(v.pres, 48, pres, 49). Fermentation; new and modified plastics of thermoplastic and thermosetting types; application of plastics and rubber to bonded and coated abrasive articles; carbon and graphite technology. Address: 5661 Wayside Ave, Cincinnati, OH 45230.

GOEPFERT, JOHN McDONNELL, b. N.Y.C, Feb. 11, 40; m. 62; c. 2. MICROBIOLOGY, FOOD BACTERIOLOGY. B.Sc, Cornell, 62, M.Sc, 64, Ph.D.(microbiol), 66. Asst. prof. BACT, FOOD RES. INST, UNIV. WIS, MADISON, 66-71, ASSOC. PROF, 71- Am. Soc. Microbiol; Inst. Food Technol; Brit. Soc. Appl. Bact. Detection of salmonella in foods; influence of environmental conditions on the behavior of salmonellae in laboratory media and food materials; bacillus cereus food poisoning. Address: Food Research Institute, University of Wisconsin, 2115 Herrick Dr, Madison, WI 53706.

GOEPP, ROBERT AUGUST, b. Chicago, Ill, Nov. 3, 30; m. 60; c. 3. DENTISTRY, PATHOLOGY. B.S, Loyola Univ.(Ill), 54, D.D.S, 57; M.S, Univ. Chicago, 61, Ph.D, 67. Instr. dent. & path, UNIV. HOSPS. & CLINS, UNIV. CHICAGO, 61-64, asst. prof. oral path, Zoller Mem. Dent. Clin. & dept. path, 64-70, ASSOC. PROF. ORAL PATH, PRITZKER SCH. MED, 70- Consult, Chicago Bd. Health, 63-64. Dipl, Am. Bd. Oral Path, 63- AAAS; Am. Dent. Asn; fel. Am. Acad. Oral Path; fel. Am. Acad. Dent. Radiol; N.Y. Acad. Sci; Int. Asn. Dent. Res; Radiation Res. Soc. Caries; oral pathology; dental radiology; radiation biology. Address: Dept. of Oral Pathology, Pritzker School of Medicine, University of Chicago Hospitals & Clinics, 5801 Ellis Ave, Chicago, IL 60637.

GOERING, CARROLL EUGENE, b. Platte Center, Nebr, June 8, 34; m. 60; c. 3. AGRICULTURAL ENGINEERING. B.S, Nebraska, 59; M.S, Iowa State, 62, Ph.D.(agr. eng, eng. mech), 65. Design engr, Int. Harvester Co, 59-61; asst. AGR. ENG, Iowa State Univ, 61-62, res. assoc, 62-65; asst. prof, UNIV. MO-COLUMBIA, 65-69, ASSOC. PROF, 69- U.S.A, 54-56. Am. Soc. Agr. Eng; Am. Soc. Eng. Educ. Research on precise equipment for agricultural pest control. Address: Dept. of Agricultural Engineering, University of Missouri-Columbia, Columbia, MO 65201.

GOERING, HARLAN L(OWELL), b. McPherson, Kans, July 13, 21; m. 44; c. 1. ORGANIC CHEMISTRY. A.B, Bethel Col, 43; Ph.D.(chem), Colorado, 48. Res. assoc, California, Los Angeles, 48-50; instr. CHEM, UNIV. WIS, MADISON, 50-52, asst. prof, 52-56, assoc. prof, 56-59, PROF, 59- Vis. prof, Harvard, 63. Am. Chem. Soc; The Chem. Soc. Mechanisms of organic reactions. Address: Dept. of Chemistry, University of Wisconsin, Madison, WI 53706.

GOERING, HARVEY L(LOYD), b. Moundridge, Kans, Apr. 19, 22; m. 42; c. 3. PHYSICAL CHEMISTRY. A.B, Bethel Col.(Kans), 46; Standard Oil Co. Ind. fel, Ohio State, 49-50, Ph.D.(chem), 50. Asst. chem, Ohio State, 47-49; prin. chemist, BATTELLE MEM. INST, 50-53, asst. chief, PHYS. CHEM. DIV, 53-54, chief, 54-60, ASST. MGR, CHEM. & CHEM. ENG. DEPT, 60- Am. Chem. Soc; Electrochem. Soc. Kinetics of hydrolysis of sterically-hindered esters; oil additives; wood preservatives; semiconductors; solid state chemistry. Address: Chemistry & Chemical Engineering Dept, Physical Chemistry Division, Battelle Memorial Institute, 505 King Ave, Columbus, OH 43201.

GOERING, JOHN JAMES, b. Clifton, Kans, June 2, 34; m. 56; c. 2. MARINE ECOLOGY. B.S, Bethel Col.(Kans), 56; M.S, Wisconsin, 60, Ph.D.(zool), 62. Asst. prof. MARINE SCI, INST. MARINE SCI, UNIV. ALASKA, 62-66, assoc. prof, 66-68, PROF, 68- Nat. Sci. Found. res. grant, 64-71. U.S.A.R, 56-62, Sgt. AAAS; Am. Soc. Limnol. & Oceanog. Nitrogen cycle in lakes and the sea; silicon cycle in the sea. Address: Institute of Marine Science, University of Alaska, College, AK 99701.

GOERING, KENNETH JUSTIN, b. San Francisco, Calif, Dec. 26, 13; m. 36; c. 3. CHEMISTRY. B.S, Mont. State Col, 36; M.S, Calif. Inst. Tech, 39; Ph.D.(biophys. chem), Iowa State Col, 41. Asst. chemist, exp. sta, Mont. State Col, 36-37; asst. org. chem, Calif. Inst. Tech, 37-38; Iowa State Col, 38-41; res. chemist, Anheuser-Busch Inc, Mo, 41-42; instr. chem, Iowa State Col, 42-43; chemist, Nebraska, 43-44; asst. chemist, Farm Crops Processing Corp, Nebr, 44-45; v.pres. & gen. mgr, Mold Bran Co. & Enzymes, Inc, 45-49; asst. prof. CHEM, MONT. STATE UNIV, 49-56, assoc. prof, 57-60, PROF, 60-, DEAN COL. GRAD. STUDIES, 67-, asst. dean grad. div, 64-67. Plant mgr, Agr. Prods. Corp, Iowa, 48-49. Civilian with Off. Sci. Res. & Develop, 44. Am. Chem. Soc; Am. Asn. Cereal Chem. Concentration and fractionation of enzymes and protein purification; isolation and study of properties of new starch sources. Address: College of Graduate Studies, Montana State University, Bozeman, MT 59715.

GOERING, ORVILLE, b. Moundridge, Kans, Nov. 6, 29; m. 53; c. 2. APPLIED MATHEMATICS, COMPUTER SCIENCE. A.B, Bethel Col.(Kans), 52; M.S, Iowa State, 54, Ph.D.(appl. math), 60. Instr. math, Iowa State Col, 58-60; systs. analyst, Int. Bus. Mach. Corp, 60-63; asst. prof. math. & appl. sci, Southern Illinois, 63-69; PRES, INTECH OF ST. LOUIS, INC, 69- Am. Math. Soc; Math. Asn. Am. Mathematical and numerical analysis. Address: Intech of St. Louis, Inc, 9953 Lewis & Clark Blvd, St. Louis, MO 63136.

GOERINGER, GERALD C(ONRAD), b. Phila, Pa, Jan. 2, 33; m. 57; c. 2. CELL BIOLOGY. A.B, Pennsylvania, 55; U.S. Pub. Health Serv. fel, Northwestern, 57-59, Ph.D.(embryol), 59. Life Ins. Med. Res. Fund fel, 59-62; res. fel. immunol, Stockholm, 62-63; asst. prof. biol, San Diego State Col, 63-66; ANAT, SCH. MED, GEORGETOWN UNIV, 66-70, ASSOC. PROF, 70- AAAS; Am. Asn. Anat; Am. Soc. Zool; Am. Inst. Biol. Sci. Developmental biology; hormonal effects during skin differentiation; organ culture techniques; cellular reaggregation and differentiation; antigens of subcellular fractions; metaplastic effects of ribonucleic acid; characteristics of cell types from mammalian oviduct. Address: Dept. of Anatomy, Georgetown University School of Medicine, 3900 Reservoir Rd. N.W, Washington, DC 20007.

GOERKE, L(ENOR) S(TEPHEN), b. Hitchcock, Okla, Jan. 22, 12; m; c. 2. PREVENTIVE MEDICINE, PUBLIC HEALTH. B.S, Southeast. State Col, 31; B.S. & M.D, Oklahoma, 36; M.S.P.H, California, 38. Intern, Good Samaritan Hosp, Portland, Ore, 36-37; county health off, Ore, 38-39, Calif, 40; clin. assoc. prof. prev. med. & pub. health, Col. Med. Evangelists, 47-50; assoc. clin. prof. infectious diseases, UNIV. CALIF, LOS ANGELES, 50-54, prev. med, 51-54, PROF. PREV. MED. & PUB. HEALTH, SCH. MED, 54-, CHMN. DEPT, 56-, PROF. PUB. HEALTH, SCH. PUB. HEALTH, 54-, DEAN SCH,

60-, assoc. dean, 56-60. Dir, med. bur. & dist. servs, Los Angeles City Health Dept, 46-54; assoc. clin. prof. prev. med, Southern California, 51-54. Consult, special proj. comt, State Dept. Pub. Health, 57- Mem, Calif. State Bd. of Health, 54-; pub. health res. study sect, Nat. Insts. Health, 57- Surgeon, France & Ger, Med.C, 40-46, Col. Am. Pub. Health Asn. Infectious diseases; public health practice and administration. Address: School of Public Health, University of California, Los Angeles, CA 90024.

GOERNER, GORDON L(AVERNE), b. Loveland, Colo, Feb. 27, 12; m. 35; c. 2. ORGANIC CHEMISTRY. A.B, Colorado, 34, Ph.D.(org. chem), 39. Asst. chem, Colorado, 34-39; assoc. prof, Culver-Stockton Col, 39-40; interim instr, Billings Polytech, 40-41; Defiance Col, 41-42; instr, Mich. State, 42-46, asst. prof, 46-60, assoc. prof, 60-61; HEAD CHEM. ISOLATION, RECOVERY & PURIFICATION UNIT, ANTIBIOTIC & FERMENTATION SECT, MICH. DEPT. PUB. HEALTH, 61- Am. Chem. Soc. Organic synthesis; unsaturated esters; alkyl benzenes; halogenated compounds; reaction of some azomethines of anthranilic acid and negatively substituted aliphatic aldehydes with acetic anhydride; alkylation of nitriles and ketones; nitrogen mustards; isolation, pruification and structure of anticancer and antibiotic substances produced by molds; chromatography of peptides. Address: Antibiotic & Fermentation Section, Michigan Dept. of Public Health, Lansing, MI 48914.

GOERNER, JOSEPH KOFAHL, b. Houston, Tex, Mar. 20, 25; m. 46; c. 5. CHEMICAL ENGINEERING. B.S, Rice, 45. Res. chem. engr, JEFFERSON CHEM. CO, INC, 46-52, supvr. process develop. div, 52-56, asst. to gen. mgr. res. & develop, 56-58, mkt. mgr. specialty prod, 58-61, mgr. prod. mkt, 61-66, asst. gen. mgr. mkt, 66-67, GEN. MGR. RES. & DEVELOP, 67- U.S.N.R, 45-46, Ens. Am. Chem. Soc; Am. Inst. Chem. Eng. Process development for production of derivatives of ethylene, propylene and related olefins. Address: 343 Wilchester, Houston, TX 77024.

GOERTEMILLER, CLARENCE C, JR, b. Big Stone Gap, Va, Feb. 19, 28; wid. DEVELOPMENTAL & CELL BIOLOGY. B.S, Maryland, 51; Ed.B, R.I. Col, 59; U.S. Pub. Health Serv. trainee & Sc.M, Brown, 62, Ph.D.(biol), 64. Res. fel. biol, Harvard Med. Sch, 64-65; asst. prof. ZOOL, UNIV. R.I, 65-70, ASSOC. PROF, 70-, summer faculty res. fel, 67. Summers, trainee, Brown Univ, 64, res. assoc, 66. U.S.N, 45-46. AAAS; Am. Soc. Zool; Am. Soc. Cell Biol. Development of secretory competence in salt-secreting epithelia. Address: Dept. of Zoology, University of Rhode Island, Kingston, RI 02881.

GOERTZ, ADALBERT, b. Langenau, Ger, Dec. 3, 28; m. 58; c. 4. MOLECULAR PHYSICS. B.S, Univ. Frankfurt, 54, M.S, 58; Nat. Insts. Health grant, Univ. Colo, Boulder, 66-68, Ph.D.(physics), 68. Physicist, Nat. Bur. Standards, Colo, 60-67; ASST. PROF. PHYSICS, PA. STATE UNIV, 68- German Phys. Soc. Microwave spectra of gases. Address: Dept. of Physics, College of Science, Pennsylvania State University, Mont Alto, PA 17237.

GOERTZ, GRAYCE E(DITH), b. Carnduff, Sask, July 9, 19; U.S. citizen. FOOD SCIENCE. B.S, Kans. State Univ, 41, M.S, 47, Ph.D.(food sci), 52. Instr. pub. sch, Kans, 41-44; pub. sch. & jr. col, 44-46; asst, Kans. State Univ, 46-47, 49-52, instr. foods, 47-48; Univ. Ill, 48-49; asst. prof, Ore. State Univ, 52-55; prof, Kans. State Univ, 55-65; PROF. & HEAD DEPT. FOOD SCI. & INST. ADMIN, UNIV. TENN, KNOXVILLE, 65- Inst. Food Technol; Poultry Sci. Asn; Am. Meat Sci. Asn; Am. Dietetic Asn; Am. Home Econ. Asn; Heat effects on proteins including pigments. Address: Home Economics 229, Dept. of Food Science & Institution Administration, University of Tennessee, 1215 Cumberland Ave, Knoxville, TN 37916.

GOERTZ, JOHN WILLIAM, b. Hackensack, N.J, Aug. 25, 29; m. 53; c. 3. VERTEBRATE ZOOLOGY, ANIMAL ECOLOGY. B.S, Oregon State, 57, M.S, 59; Okla. Wildlife Res. Unit fel. & Nat. Wildlife Fedn. fel, Okla. State, 59-60, Nat. Insts. Health fel, 60-62, Ph.D.(zool), 62. Asst. prof. ZOOL, LA. TECH. UNIV, 62-66, assoc. prof, 66-68, PROF, 68- U.S.N, 48-52. Am. Soc. Mammal; Wildlife Soc; Am. Ornith. Union; Ecol. Soc. Am. Population dynamics, biology, habitats, parasites, distribution, reproductive rates in rodent ecology; distribution and biology in mammalogy; nesting behavior in ornithology. Address: Dept. of Zoology, Louisiana Tech University, Ruston, LA 71270.

GOERTZEL, GERALD, b. Aug. 18, 19; m. 41; c. 3. PHYSICS. M.E. & M.S, Stevens Inst. Tech, 40; fel, N.Y. Univ, 46, Ph.D.(physics), 47. Asst. physics, N.Y. Univ, 40-41, instr. aeronaut. eng, 42-44; res. engr, Repub. Aviation Corp, N.Y, 41-42; physicist, Kellex Corp, 44-45; Clinton Lab, Oak Ridge, 46-48; Nuclear Develop. Corp. Am, 48-53, dir, sci. div, 53-55, tech. dir, 56-59; v.pres, Sage Instruments, Inc, N.Y, 60-63; SR. ENGR, ADVAN. SYSTS. DEVELOP. DIV, IBM CORP, 64- Lectr, Tennessee, 48; asst. prof, N.Y. Univ, 48-50, assoc. prof, 50-55. Fel. AAAS; fel. Am. Phys. Soc; fel. N.Y. Acad. Sci; Inst. Elec. & Electronics Eng; Instrument Soc. Am. Mass spectroscopy; theoretical physics; angular correlation of gamma rays; internal conversion; nuclear reactor theory; digital computing machines; data handling; physiological modelling; medical electronics; numerical analysis. Address: 7 Sparrow Circle, White Plains, NY 10605.

GOERTZEN, JACK O(LIVER), b. Rainier, Ore, Apr, 28, 24; m. 46, 64; c. 4. BIOLOGY, SOILS. B.A, Lewis & Clark Col, 50; M.S, Oregon State, 54. Res. asst. soils, Oregon State, 53-54; SALINITY LAB, U.S. DEPT. AGR, 54-59, soils chemist, 59-61, INSTR. ANAL. CHEM, 61- Pa. State Univ. consult. salinity, U.S. Agency Int. Develop, Maharashtra State, India, 70. U.S.A.A.F, 43-46. Am. Soc. Agron; Soil Sci. Soc. Am. Ion equilibria, surface area measurement and exchange equilibria in soils. Address: U.S. Salinity Lab, U.S. Dept. of Agriculture, P.O. Box 672, Riverside, CA 92502.

GOERZ, DAVID JONATHAN, JR, b. Los Angeles, Calif, Sept. 25, 34; m. 62; c. 2. PHYSICS. A.B, California, Los Angeles, 56; M.S, Stanford, 57. Res. asst. microwave physics, W.W. Hansen Lab, Stanford, 56, 58, res. assoc, 58-62; pres. & tech. dir, Vactite, Inc, 62-63; sr. engr, BECHTEL CORP, 63-64, supv. engr, 64-66, sr. supv. engr, 66-68, res. mgr, 68-71, MGR. BUS. DEVELOP-TECH, 71- Summer mem. tech. staff, Hughes Aircraft Co, 56-57. Consult, Hughes Aircraft Co, 59; Phys. Electronics Lab, 60; mem. bd. gov, Int. Microwave Power Inst, 68-, chmn, 70-71; gen. chmn, Microwave Power Conf, The Hague, 69. Inst. Elec. & Electronics Eng; Am. Vacuum Soc; Cryogenic Soc. Am. Accelerator physics; microwave theory and applications; ultra high vacuum; cryogenics; industrial process development and environmental research. Address: Business Development Dept, Bechtel Corp, 50 Beale St, San Francisco, CA 94105.

GOES, GUNTHER (WALTER), b. Stuttgart, Ger, Aug. 27, 21; m. 60. MATHEMATICS. M.A, Stuttgart Tech, 52, Ph.D.(math), 58. Res. fel. MATH, Ger. Res. Coun, 58-59; res. assoc, Northwestern, 59-60; asst. prof, De Paul, 60-61; res. fel, Western Ontario, 61-63; asst. prof, Kansas, 63-64; ASSOC. PROF, ILL. INST. TECHNOL, 64- Nat. Sci. Found. fel, 59-60, res. grants, 65 & 66-67; Can. Res. Coun. fel, 60-62; vis. prof, Univ. Stuttgart, 71. Am. Math. Soc; Ger. Math. Soc. Fourier series and sequence spaces; Banach algebras and harmonic analysis. Address: Dept. of Mathematics, Illinois Institute of Technology, Chicago, IL 60616.

GOETCHIUS, DONALD R(ALPH), b. New York, N.Y, Oct. 10, 11; m. 38; c. 4. CHEMISTRY. B.S, Alfred, 33. Ceramic engr, Ohio Brass Co, 33-37; chief chemist, U.S. Glass Co, 37-38; from group leader to asst. dir. enamel develop, FERRO CORP, 38-49, sales engr, 49-52, asst. mgr. ceramic sales, 52-56, mgr, 56-66, gen. mgr, frit & glaze div, 66-68, V.PRES. & GEN. MGR, FRIT DIV, 68- Civilian with Off. Sci. Res. & Develop, 44. Assoc. Am. Ceramic Soc; Nat. Inst. Ceramic Eng. Compositions of porcelain enamels; enamel compositions. Address: Ferro Corp, 4150 E. 56th St, Cleveland, OH 44105.

GOETCHIUS, GEORGE RICHARD, b. Ithaca, N.Y, March 1, 14; m. 40; c. 4. BACTERIOLOGY. B.S, Cornell, 35, M.S, 36. Asst. bact, State Dept. Health, N.Y, 36-42; res. bacteriologist, Winthrop Chem. Co, 42-46; chief bacteriologist, Rohm & Haas Co, 46-54; admin. asst. prod. develop, AYERST LABS, 54-58, chmn. new prod. SCREENING, 58-62, DIR. PROJ. COORD, 63- AAAS; Am. Soc. Microbiol; Soc. Indust. Microbiol; N.Y. Acad. Sci. Serology of syphilis; tissue culture; antiserum production; chemotherapy of infectious diseases; industrial disinfection. Address: Ayerst Labs, 685 Third Ave, New York, NY 10017.

GOETHERT, B(ERNHARD) H(ERMANN), b. Hannover, Ger, Oct. 20, 07; nat; m. 35; c. 4. AERODYNAMICS. B.S, Hannover Tech, 30; M.S, Danzig Tech, 34; Dr.Eng.(aeronaut. eng), Tech. Univ, Berlin, 38. Asst, Aeronaut. Inst, Danzig, 30-34; proj. engr, Res. Inst. Stress Anal, Berlin, 34-36; sci. staff engr, Gen. Res. Inst. Aerodyn, 36-39; chief dept. high speed aerodyn, Res. Inst. Aerodyn, 39-45; consult. & sect. chief, Wright Air Develop. Ctr, Wright Field, 45-52; chief, propulsion wind tunnel, Aro, Inc, Tullahoma, 52-56, engine test facility, 56-59, dir. eng, 59-63, res. v.pres. & chief scientist, 64; PROF. & DIR, UNIV. TENN. SPACE INST, TULLAHOMA, 64- Consult. rep, Ger. Res. Inst. Aeronaut, 58-59, aerospace res. & test facilities, 59-; mem. fluid dynamics panel, NATO-Adv. Group Aeronaut. Res. & Develop, 60-, interpanel space info. group, Adv. Group Aeronaut. Res. & Develop, 62, chmn, 63-; prof. Aachen Tech, 61; mem. res. adv. comt. fluid mech, NASA, 63-; chief scientist, Air Force Systs. Command, Andrews AFB, D.C, 64-; consult, Nat. Acad. Sci, 66- Scroll of appreciation, U.S. Air Force, 59. Fel. Am. Inst. Aeronaut. & Astronaut; Soc. Eng. Sci. High speed aerodynamics; jet propulsion; development of test equipment for aerodynamics; aerodynamic and propulsion tests; evaluation and management of technical test facilities; evaluation of systems. Address: 1703 Sycamore Circle, Manchester, TN 37325.

GOETINCK, PAUL F(IRMIN), b. Bruges, Belgium, June 17, 33; U.S. citizen; m. 58; c. 2. GENETICS. B.S, California, Davis, 56, Ph.D.(genetics), 63. Trainee biochem, California, Los Angeles, 62-64; asst. prof. ANIMAL GENETICS, UNIV. CONN, 64-68, ASSOC. PROF, 68- Nat. Insts. Health res. career develop. award, 68- Sig.C, U.S.A, 56-58, Sgt. AAAS; Am. Genetic Asn; Soc. Develop. Biol. Developmental genetics; embryology; protein biochemistry. Address: Dept. of Animal Genetics, University of Connecticut, Storrs, CT 06268.

GOETSCH, DENNIS D(ONALD), b. Brewster, Kans, Dec. 6, 24; m. 53; c. 3. ANIMAL PHYSIOLOGY. B.S, Kansas State, 52, D.V.M, 52, M.S, 55; Ph.D, Okla. State, 61. Instr. physiol, Kansas State, 52-55, asst. prof, 55-56; tech. dir, Specified, Inc, Ind, 56-57; asst. prof. physiol, Okla. State Univ, 57-61, assoc. prof, 61-63, prof, 63-69; PROF. PHYSIOL. & PHARMACOL. & HEAD DEPT, SCH. VET. MED, UNIV. GA, 69- Nat. Sci. Found. fel, 59-60. U.S.N, 54-55; Vet.C, U.S.A, 55-, Lt. Am. Soc. Vet. Physiol. & Pharmacol; Am. Soc. Animal Sci; Am. Vet. Med. Asn; Am. Physiol. Soc. Carbohydrate and energy metabolism, especially of the ruminant; ketosis of the ruminant animal. Address: Dept. of Physiology & Pharmacology, University of Georgia School of Veterinary Medicine, Athens, GA 30601.

GOETSCH, GERALD D, b. Colby, Kans, Apr. 6, 23; m. 47; c. 3. ANIMAL PHYSIOLOGY. D.V.M, Kansas State, 45; M.S, Purdue, 55, Ph.D.(animal physiol), 57. Asst. state veterinarian, Ill. State Dept. Agr, 45-46; private practice, Ill, 46-47; asst. prof. VET. PHYSIOL, Missouri, 47; Okla. State, 48-52; instr, SCH. VET. MED, PURDUE UNIV, 52-57, asst. prof, 57-58, assoc. prof, 58-59, PROF. & HEAD DEPT, 59- Mem. N.Cent. Regional Cmt. Ruminant Bloat, 54-62; coun. biol. & therapeut. agents, Am. Vet. Med. Asn, 62- Am. Vet. Med. Asn; Am. Soc. Vet. Physiol. & Pharmacol.(pres, 64); Conf. Res. Workers Animal Diseases. Metabolic diseases of animals; ruminant bloat; ketosis of sheep; gastric ulcers of swine. Address: Dept. of Veterinary Physiology, Purdue University School of Veterinary Medicine, West Lafayette, IN 47907.

GOETSCHEL, CHARLES THOMAS, b. Chicago, Ill, Sept. 21, 35; m. 58; c. 2. ORGANIC & INORGANIC CHEMISTRY. B.A, Northwestern, 57; Ph.D.(org. chem), Michigan, 62. Atomic Energy Comn. res. fel. catalysis, Northwest. Univ, 62-64; CHEMIST, Shell Develop. Co, 64-70; CTR. TECHNOL, KAISER ALUMINUM & CHEM. CORP, PLEASANTON, 70- Mem. Int. Cong Catalysis. U.S.N.A.F.R. Am. Chem. Soc. Application of organic chemistry to catalysis; inorganic radiation chemistry; inorganic fluorine chemistry; inert gas chemistry and high energy inorganic oxidizers. Address: 161 Rock Oak Court, Walnut Creek, CA 94598.

GOETTE, ROBERT L(OUIS), b. Gainesville, Fla, May 12, 29; m. 53; c. 3. ORGANIC CHEMISTRY. B.S, Florida, 49, fel, 49-52, M.S, 50, Ph.D.(org. chem), 53. Asst. Florida, 52-53; res. chemist, May Plant, E.I. du Pont de

Nemours & Co, Inc, 53-59; CHMN. DEPT. CHEM, TAEJON PRESBY. COL, 60- AAAS; Am. Chem. Soc; Korean Chem. Soc. Preparation of certain amines; quaternary ammonium halides and polymers from these quaternaires; ion exchange resins of the polyquaternary ammonium type; science education. Address: Dept. of Chemistry, Taejon Presbyterian College, 133 Ojung Dong, Taejon, Korea.

GOETTELMAN, ROBERT C(LEMENT), b. Grand Junction, Colo, May 26, 29; m. 51; c. 4. PHYSICS. B.A, Colorado, 53; Southern California, 54-55; Stanford, 56-57. Physicist cryogenics, Nat. Bur. Standards, 51-53; physicist atmospheric physics, Stanford Res. Inst, 54-60, Poulter Res. Labs, 60-69; sr. scientist, CONTROL DATA CORP, 69-70, PRIN. SCIENTIST, CONTROL DATA FRANCE, 70- Am. Phys. Soc; Sci. Res. Soc. Am. Magneto-optical data recording and processing; acousto-optical interactions applied to laser beam modulation and deflection; magneto-optical interactions using coherent light sources and magnetic thin films. Address: Control Data Corp, Beam Addressable Memory Group, 7801 Computer Ave, Minneapolis, MN 55435.

GOETTLER, LLOYD ARNOLD, b. Rockville Centre, N.Y, July 5, 39; m. 61; c. 4. CHEMICAL ENGINEERING. B.Ch.E, Cornell, 62; Ph.D.(chem. eng), Delaware, 67. SR. RES. ENGR, MONSANTO CO, 66- AAAS; Am. Inst. Chem. Eng; N.Y. Acad. Sci; Sci. Res. Soc. Am. Diffusion with simultaneous chemical reaction; diffusion and growth kinetics in crystallization, especially from the vapor; processing of polymeric materials filled with reinforcing fibers. Address: 12691 Markaire Dr, St. Louis, MO 63141.

GOETTSCH, ROBERT WAYNE, b. Atlantic, Iowa, Sept. 27, 27; m. 58; c. 3. PHARMACEUTICAL CHEMISTRY. B.S, Colorado, 51; univ. fel, Iowa, 51-53, M.S, 53, Am. Found. Pharmaceut. Ed. fel, 55-57, Ph.D.(pharmaceut. chem), 57; fel, Minnesota, 54-55. Instr. pharm, Colorado, 53-54; asst. prof. pharm. & pharmaceut. chem, Kansas, 57-60; pharmaceut. chem, Northeast La. State Col, 60-61; assoc. prof. pharmaceut, Tennessee, 61-65; PHARM, IDAHO STATE UNIV, 65-68, PROF, 68- Res. grant, Burroughs Wellcome & Co.(U.S.A), Inc, 62-63; consult, Palmer Chem. & Equip. Co, Inc, 62-65. Med.C, U.S.A, 46-47. AAAS; Am. Pharmaceut. Asn; Am. Chem. Soc; Acad. Pharmaceut. Sci. Applications of physical-chemical principles to pharmaceutical systems; interaction of drugs with macromolecules; drug degradation and stabilization; analytical methods for drugs and drug mixtures; pharmacy. Address: Dept. of Pharmacy, Idaho State University College of Pharmacy, Pocatello, ID 83201.

GOETZ, ABRAHAM, b. Grybów, Poland, Apr. 8, 26; nat; m. 55; c. 2. MATHEMATICS. Univ. Alma-Ata, U.S.S.R, 45-46; M.S, Wroclaw, 49; Ph.D.(math), Math. Inst, Polish Acad. Sci, 57. Asst. MATH, Wroclaw, 48-53, adj, 53-58, lectr, 58-64; Math. Inst, Polish Acad. Sci, 53-62; vis. assoc. prof, UNIV. NOTRE DAME, 62, ASSOC. PROF, 65- Am. Math. Soc; Polish Math. Soc. Topological and Lie groups; differential geometry; universal algebras. Address: Dept. of Mathematics, University of Notre Dame, Notre Dame, IN 46557.

GOETZ, CATHERINE G(ERTRUDE), b. Natchez, Miss, Sept. 28, 17; m. 58. PATHOLOGY. B.S, Loyola (La), 39; M.S, Tulane, 44; M.D, La. State, 50. From instr. to assoc. prof. med. tech, Loyola (La), 40-50; fel, path. dept, sch. med, La. State, 52-54, vis. asst. prof, 54-58; ASSOC. PROF. PATH, SCH. MED, UNIV. MISS, 59- Dipl, Am. Bd. Path, 55. Surgical and clinical pathology. Address: Dept. of Pathology, University of Mississippi School of Medicine, Jackson, MS 39216.

GOETZ, CHARLES A(LBERT), b. Lockwood, Mo, Jan. 7, 08; m. 34; c. 2. ANALYTICAL CHEMISTRY. B.S, Illinois, 32, M.S, 34, fel, 34-38, Ph.D.(chem), 38. Asst. agron, Illinois, 33-34, chem, 34-38; chief chemist, Cardox Corp, Ill, 38-39, dir. res, 39-43; v.pres. in charge res, 43-46; dir. eng. & develop, Brunswick Corp, 47-48; assoc. prof. CHEM, IOWA STATE UNIV, 48-50, PROF, 50-, SR. CHEMIST, INST. ATOMIC RES, 65-, chief metall. div, 50-62, chem. div, 50-65, head dept, univ, 50-65. Am. Chem. Soc; Electrochem. Soc. Carbon dioxide manufacture, storage, transportation and use as fire extinguishing agent; electrochemistry of chlorate and perchlorate manufacture; hard rubber molded products; wood technology; chemical burning powders; oxidation; reduction reactions; complexometric methods and perchloric acid applications. Address: Dept. of Chemistry, Iowa State University, Ames, IA 50010.

GOETZ, FREDERICK C(HARLES), b. Fond du Lac, Wis, June 22; m. 60; c. 4. INTERNAL MEDICINE. B.S, Harvard, 43, M.D, 46. Instr, MED. SCH, UNIV. MINN, MINNEAPOLIS, 55-56, asst. prof. MED, 56-62, assoc. prof, 62-68, PROF, 68- Med. C, U.S.A, 48-50. Endocrine Soc; Am. Diabetes Asn; Soc. Exp. Biol. & Med; Am. Fedn. Clin. Res. Diabetes mellitus in the human being, especially complications of diabetes and mechanisms of insulin secretion; endocrinology. Address: University of Minnesota Medical School, 412 Union St. S.E, Minneapolis, MN 55455.

GOETZ, HAROLD, b. Halliday, N.Dak, Dec. 20, 32; m. 60; c. 2. PLANT & RANGE ECOLOGY. B.S, N.Dak. State, 60, M.S, 63; Fulbright fel, Hohenheim Agr. Univ, 60-61; Ph.D.(range sci), Utah State, 68. Range conservationist, Bur. Indian Affairs, Nebr, 63; ASST. PROF. BOT, N.DAK. STATE UNIV, 63-69, ASSOC. PROF, 69-, CHMN. DIV. NATURAL SCI, 70- Mem, Great Plains Res. Coun. Comt, 66-; Great Plains Range & Livestock Adv. Comt, 66-; U.S. Govt. consult, 67- U.S.A, 53-55. Am. Soc. Range Mgt. (secy-treas, 65-); Am. Inst. Biol. Sci; Am. Forestry Asn; Ecol. Soc. Am. Rangeland ecology; effects of nitrogen fertilizer on the botanical composition of range sites as related to water use, phenological development, soil chemical and physical changes and other factors of the individual plant species. Address: 2405 Ninth St. N, Fargo, ND 58102.

GOETZ, J(OHN) A(RTHUR), JR, b. Oakland, Calif, Dec. 28, 18; m. 43; c. 4. ELECTRICAL ENGINEERING, ELECTRONICS. B.S.E.E, Nevada, 42. Asst. elec. engr, instrument develop, Ames Labs, Nat. Adv. Cmt. Aeronaut, 42-45; commercial engr, Nat. Union Elec. Corp, 45-47; chief engr, Electronic Enterprises, Inc, 47-48; prod. eng. mgr, Kip Electronics Corp, N.Y, 48-49; mem. electronics lab. staff, Int. Bus Mach. Corp, N.Y, 49-50, coord. electron tubes, electron tube res. labs, 50-51, proj. engr. & mgr, tube & diode anal. labs, 51-53, mgr. dept, elec. labs, 53-55, develop. engr. & mgr. dept, 55-56, sr. engr. & mgr. dept, 56, mgr, component eng. & tech. servs. div, Calif, 56-58, mgr. tech. planning staff, fed. syst. div, Owego Eng. Labs, 59-62; mgr. component & mat. eng, fed. systs. div, space guid. ctr, Owego, 62-67, mem. sr. eng. staff, qual. assurance supv, 67-68, SR. ENGR. FIELD PERFORMANCE PREDICTION & TRACKING, PROD. ASSURANCE, COMPONENTS DIV, E. FISHKILL FACILITY, IBM CORP, HOPEWELL JUNCTION, 68- Mem. U.S. Nat. Comt, Int. Electrotech. Comn. Am. Soc. Test. & Mat; Am. Statist. Asn; Inst. Elec. & Electronics Eng. Data processing and peripheral control systems equipment for advanced guidance missions compatible with environmental requirements on strategic missiles, space probes, reconnaissance satellites and manned high altitude vehicles; reliability; microminiaturization; nuclear tolerance; electrical and electronic components; international standards. Address: 11C, Scenic Apts, Wappingers Falls, NY 12590.

GOETZ, KENNETH L(EE), b. Java, S.Dak, Jan. 7, 32; m. 62; c. 1. PHYSIOLOGY. B.S, Univ. Wis, 58, Ph.D.(physiol), 63; M.D, Univ. Kans, 67. Instr. physiol, med. ctr, Univ. Kans, 63-65, asst. prof, 65-68; med. intern, ST. LUKE'S HOSP, 69, DIR. EXP. MED, 70- Lectr, dept. physiol, med. ctr, Univ. Kans; consult, Midwest Res. Inst. U.S.A.F, 51-55, S/Sgt. AAAS; Am. Physiol. Soc; Am. Heart Asn. Cardiovascular physiology; physiologic effects of changes in atrial pressures; regulation of body fluid volume. Address: Division of Experimental Medicine, St. Luke's Hospital, Kansas City, MO 64111.

GOETZ, RICHARD W, b. Cincinnati, Ohio, July 29, 36; m. 60; c. 4. ORGANIC CHEMISTRY. Chem.E, Cincinnati, 59, Standard Oil Ohio fel, 59-61, Nat. Sci. Found. fel, 61-63, Ph.D.(org. chem), 63. RES. CHEMIST, Monsanto Co, 63-64; U.S. INDUST. CHEM. CO. DIV, NAT. DISTILLERS & CHEM. CORP, 64- Am. Chem. Soc. Homogeneous and heterogeneous catalysis of organic reactions by transition metal compounds. Address: U.S. Industrial Chemical Co. Division, National Distillers & Chemical Corp, 1275 Section Rd, Cincinnati, OH 45237.

GOETZ, ROBERT H(ANS), b. Frankfort-on-Main, Ger, Apr. 17, 10; U.S. citizen; m. 37; c. 4. MEDICINE. M.D, Univ. Frankfort, 35; M.D, Switzerland, 36; M.B,Ch.B, Cape Town, 44. Assoc. prof. surg. & chief dept. surg. res, Cape Town, 45-47; assoc. prof. surg. & dir. surg. res, ALBERT EINSTEIN COL. MED, 57-63, PROF. SURG, 64-, CHIEF VASCULAR SURG, EINSTEIN COL. HOSP, 68- Arriss & Gale lectr, Royal Col. Surg, Eng, 49; Carnegie traveling fel, 55; chief dept. vascular diseases, Groote Schuur Hosp, Univ. Cape Town, 45-52, vascular invest. serv, 52-57; attend. surg, Bronx Munic. Hosp. Ctr, 58-; assoc. attend. surgeon, Lebanon Hosp, 58- Am. Med. Asn; fel. Am. Col. Cardiol; fel. Am. Col. Chest Physicians; fel. Am. Col. Surg; Soc. Circulation Res; Royal Soc. S.Africa; Int. Cardiovasc. Soc; Brit. Physiol. Soc. Hemodynamics as applied to cardiovascular diseases; vascular surgery. Address: Dept. of Surgery, Albert Einstein College of Medicine, Eastchester Rd. & Morris Park Ave, New York, NY 10461.

GOETZ, RUDOLPH W, b. Worcester, Mass, Dec. 24, 42; m. 66; c. 2. ORGANIC & ANALYTICAL CHEMISTRY. B.S, Mass. Inst. Technol, 64; fel. & Ph.d.(chem), Boston Col, 69. ASST. PROF. CHEM, CURRY COL, 68- Consult, Tim Hennigan Eng, 70- Am. Chem. Soc. Restricted rotation in acyclic aliphatic compounds by nuclear magnetic resonance; reaction rates of ortho substituted bezoic acids; stability constants for metal chelates; water treatment; pollution abatement; polycyclic polyalkene synthesis. Address: 96 Woodlawn Circle, Marshfield, MA 02050.

GOETZ, WILLIAM H(ARNER), b. Ann Arbor, Mich, Sept. 29, 14; m. 38; c. 3. HIGHWAY ENGINEERING, MATERIALS. B.S, Michigan, 36; M.S, Purdue, 42. Lab. technician, State Hwy. Dept, Mich, 36-38; res. chemist, PURDUE UNIV, 38-45, asst. prof. HWY. ENG, 45-49, assoc. prof, 49-56, PROF, 56-, ASST. HEAD SCH. CIVIL ENG, 68- Consult, K.E. McConnaughay, Inc, 48-; Corps Engrs, U.S. Army, 52-; div. chmn. hwy. res. bd, Nat. Acad. Sci-Nat. Res. Coun, 60-; consult, Nat. Co-op, Hwy. Res. Prog, 62- Roy W. Crum distinguished serv. award, Hwy. Res. Bd, 61. Am. Soc. Eng. Educ; Nat. Soc. Prof. Eng; Asn. Asphalt Paving Technol.(pres, 58); Am. Soc. Test. & Mat. Bituminous materials and pavements; bituminous mixture design; asphalt emulsions. Address: School of Civil Engineering, Civil Engineering Bldg, Purdue University, Lafayette, IN 47907.

GOETZE, GERHARD W, b. Niederdunzebach, Ger, June 19, 30. ELECTRONIC PHYSICS. B.S, Marburg, 54, M.S, 55, Ph.D.(physics), 58. Instr, Marburg, 56-58; researcher, WESTINGHOUSE ELEC. CORP, 59-64, mgr. appl. res, electronic tube div, 64-66, opers. mgr, 66-70, DIR. ELECTRONIC COMPONENTS, EUROPE, 70- Adj. prof, Univ. R.I; civilian consult, working group on spec. devices, Dept. Defense. Sr. mem. Inst. Elec. & Electronics Eng; Am. Phys. Soc; Ger. Phys. Soc. Secondary electron emission; low light level imaging and detection; image tubes; storage tubes; TV pickup tubes; photomultipliers. Address: Westinghouse Electric International GmbH, D-6000 Frankfurt/Main, Lindenstrasse, Germany.

GOETZE, NORMAN RICHARD, b. Hillsboro, Ore, Feb. 26, 30; m. 54; c. 3. AGRONOMY. B.S, Ore. State Col, 52, M.S, 55; Ph.D.(agron), Purdue Univ, 60. FARM CROPS SPECIALIST, ORE. STATE UNIV, 59- Weed Sci. Soc. Am; Am. Soc. Agron; Crop Sci. Soc. Am. Weed control; forage crops; turfgrass; seed production; cereals. Address: Dept. of Farm Crops, Oregon State University, Corvallis, OR 97331.

GOETZEL, CLAUS G(UENTHER), b. Ger, July 14, 13; nat; m. 38; c. 2. METALLURGY. Dipl, Tech. Hochsch, Berlin, Ger, 35; Ph.D, Columbia, 39. Head res. lab, Charles Hardy, Inc, 37-39; tech. dir. & works mgr, Am. Electro Metal Corp, 40-47; v.pres. & dir. res, Sintercast Corp. Am, 47-57; sr. res. scientist, N.Y. Univ, 57-60; CONSULT. SCIENTIST, RES. LAB, LOCKHEED AIRCRAFT CORP, PALO ALTO, 61- Adj. prof, N.Y. Univ, 44-60; chmn. program cmt, Int. Powder Metall. Conf, 60-; lectr, Stanford Univ, 61- Distinguished serv. award, Metal Powder Industs. Fedn, 69. AAAS; Am. Soc. Metals; Am. Inst. Mining, Metall. & Petrol. Eng; Am. Inst. Aeronaut. & Astronaut; Brit. Inst. Metals. Metals technology; high temperature materials; powder metallurgy; dispersion alloys; metal-nonmetal composites; nuclear reactor components; wear and corrosion-resistant parts; tools and dies. Address: 250 Cervantes Rd, Portola Valley, CA 94025.

GOFF, F(REDERICK) GLENN, b. West. Branch, Mich, Oct. 26, 37; m. 56; c. 6. BOTANY. B.S, Central Michigan, 62; M.S, Wisconsin, Madison, 64,

Nat. Sci. Found. fel, 64-66, Ph.D.(bot), 66. Botanist, arboretum, Wisconsin, Madison, 62-64, vis. asst. prof. bot, 66, res. assoc, 67; asst. prof. biol, Central Michigan, 66-67; forestry & bot, Univ. Mo-Columbia, 67-70; ECOLOGIST, OAK RIDGE NAT. LAB, 70- Fel. AAAS; Ecol. Soc. Am; Human Ecol. Soc; Brit. Ecol. Soc. Plant and forest ecology; quantitative and systems ecology; regional ecology. Address: Ecological Sciences Division, Oak Ridge National Lab, Oak Ridge, TN 37830.

GOFF, GERALD K, b. Apache, Okla, June 26, 25; m. 51; c. 2. MATHEMATICS. B.A, Phillips, 50, M.Ed, 53; Nat. Sci. Found. fel, Okla. State, 56-57, Ed.D.(math), 62. Instr, pub. schs, Okla, 50-53, prin, 53-56; asst. prof. MATH, Southwest. State Col.(Okla), 57-62, assoc. prof, 62-65; OKLA. STATE UNIV, 65-70, PROF, 70-, adj. prof, 62-64. High sch. lectr, Math. Asn. Am, 62-64; consult, sch. math. study group, Stanford Univ, 63-; Fulbright lectr, Uruguay, summer 68; vis. prof, Univ. Carabobo, Valencia, Venezuela, 70. U.S.N, 43-46. Math. Asn. Am. Number theory; prime and composite numbers. Address: Dept. of Mathematics, Oklahoma State University, Stillwater, OK 74074.

GOFF, JAMES FRANKLIN, b. Louisville, Ky, Aug. 1, 28; m. 59; c. 1. SOLID STATE PHYSICS. B.S, Mass. Inst. Technol, 50; M.S, Purdue Univ, 53, Ph.D.(physics), 62. RES. PHYSICIST, U.S. NAVAL ORD. LAB, 61- Chem.C, 53-55. Am. Phys. Soc. Thermal and electrical transport at low temperatures in semi-conductors; transition metal alloys and disordered solids. Address: 3405 34th Pl. N.W, Washington, DC 20016.

GOFF, JAMES W(INTHROP), b. Portland, Mich, Oct. 4, 20; m. 42; c. 5. WOOD TECHNOLOGY, APPLIED MECHANICS. B.S, Mich. State, 51, M.S, 52, Ph.D.(wood. tech), 57. Instr. forest prod, MICH. STATE UNIV, 52-57, asst. prof. PACKAGING, 57-59, assoc. prof, 59-60, PROF, 60-, DIR. SCH. PACKAGING, 66- Mem. faculty, logistics ed. & res. proj, U.S. Air Force & Ohio State Univ, 56-57; consult, Boeing Airplane Co, 59; Sandia Corp, 61-62; N.Am. Aviation, Inc, 62-64; Norton Co, 64; Commercial Carpet Co, 66; mem. sect. cmt. S2 mech. shock & vibration, U.S. Am. Standards Inst, 67. C.Eng, U.S.A, 43-45. Am. Soc. Test. & Mat; Packaging Inst. Shock and vibration environments experienced by goods during distribution; fragility of articles; materials used to protect items in distribution; design of protective system for goods. Address: School of Packaging, Michigan State University, East Lansing, MI 48823.

GOFF, JOHN A(LONZO), b. Colorado City, Colo, Oct. 19, 99; m. 33; c. 2. MECHANICAL ENGINEERING. B.S, Illinois, 21, M.S, 24, Ph.D.(mech. eng), 27. Asst. mech. eng, Illinois, 21-23, instr, 23-25, assoc, 25-27, assoc. prof. thermodyn, 30-35, prof, 35-38; mech. eng, UNIV. PA, 38-70, Whitney prof. dynamical eng, dir. dept. mech. eng. & dean Towne Sci. Sch, 38-50, dir. thermodyn. res. lab, 45-50, EMER. PROF. MECH. ENG, 70- Geophysicist, Sun Oil Co, Texas, 27-28; engr, Linde Air Prods. Co, N.Y, 28-29; res. engr, Westinghouse Res. Lab, Pa, 29-30, consult, 30-40. With Nat. Defense Res. Comt; Off. Prod. Res. & Develop. U.S.A, 43-45. Fel. Am. Soc. Mech. Eng; Am. Math. Soc. Thermodyanmics; properties of gases and gas mixtures; thermodynamic properties of moist air. Address: 623 Righters Mill Road, Narberth, PA 19072.

GOFF, KENNETH W(ADE), b. Salem, W.Va, June 14, 28; m. 50; c. 3. ELECTRICAL ENGINEERING. B.S, West Virginia, 50; S.M, Mass. Inst. Tech, 52, Acoust. Mat. Asn. fel, 52-53, Sc.D.(elec. eng), 54. Consult. engr, Bolt Beranek & Newman, Inc, 54-56; proj. mgr, Gruen Precision Labs, 56-57; from sr. scientist to head syst. anal. sect, LEEDS & NORTHRUP CO, 57-68, tech. mgr, digital equip. div, 68-69, SYSTS. DEVELOP. MGR, TECH. CTR, 69- Instrument Soc. Am; Inst. Elec. & Electronics Eng. Analysis of control systems; techniques for applying analog and digital computers to the control of industrial processes; hardware and software development for digital computer systems. Address: Technical Center, Leeds & Northrup Co, Dickerson Rd, North Wales, PA 19454.

GOFF, LOYAL G(LENN), b. Iowa, Aug. 18, 15; m. 39; c. 2. PHYSIOLOGY. B.S, Maryland, 52. Res. assoc. zool, Maryland, 48-52; physiologist, Nat. Insts. Health, 52-56; proj. off. physiol, Off. Naval Res, 56-60, asst. head physiol. br, 60-61; staff assoc, div. inst. prog, Nat. Sci. Found, 61-64, sr. staff assoc, 64-66; PROG. SCIENTIST, NASA, 66-70, VIKING 75 LANDER SCI, 70- Consult panel underwater swimmers, Nat. Acad. Sci-Nat. Res. Coun, 52-58. U.S.N, 42-45. Biophys. Soc. Environmental physiology; energy and heat cost of exercise; respiration. Address: NASA Headquarters, Code SL, Washington, DC 20546.

GOFF, RICHARD A(LLEN), b. Bucklin, Kans, Jan. 17, 13; m. 41; c. 2. ZOOLOGY. B.S, Kans. State Teachers Col, 37; M.S, Oklahoma, 39; Ph.D. (zool), California, 48. Asst. zool, Oklahoma, 37-39; teacher, pub. schs, Kans, 39-42; asst. ZOOL, California, 45-47; instr, UNIV. OKLA, 47-49, asst. prof, 49-53, assoc. prof, 53-62, PROF, 62-, chmn. dept, 58-62. Res. partic, Oak Ridge Nat. Lab, 58-59, summers, 55 & 56. AAAS; Am. Soc. Zool; Am. Inst. Biol. Sci. Experimental avian embryology; histochemistry of x-radiation response in limb buds. Address: Dept. of Zoology, University of Oklahoma, 730 Van Vliet Oval, Norman, OK 73069.

GOFF, SIDNEY, b. Newark, N.J, Aug. 18, 20; m. 43; c. 3. BIOLOGICAL CHEMISTRY. B.Sc, Rutgers, 42, fel, 46-49, Ph.D.(biochem), 49. Sr. phase instr. electronics, U.S. Dept. Air Force, 42-43; sr. biochemist, White Labs, Inc, 49-57, dir. agr. res, 57-59; animal nutrit, Am. Sci. Labs, Inc, 59-62; animal toxicol, Leberco Labs, 62-64; PROD. MGR. FEED ADDITIVES & NUTRIT, ANIMAL HEALTH DIV, E.R. SQUIBB & SONS, INC, 64- U.S.A.A.F, 43-46. AAAS; Am. Chem. Soc; Poultry Sci. Asn; World Poultry Sci. Asn; N.Y. Acad. Sci; Am. Inst. Chem; Am. Inst. Biol. Sci. Vitamin deficiencies and hematology; avian endocrinology; mineral metabolism; metabolism of analgesics; animal nutrition and nutritional interrelationships; wound healing; heavy metal toxicology. Address: Box 4, R.D. 2, River Rd, New Hope, PA 18938.

GOFF, STILLMAN R, b. Vermillion Co, Ind, Mar. 4, 10; m. 36; c. 4. CHEMISTRY. B.S, Illinois, 33. Res. chemist, Wilson & Co, 34-43; res. chemist & group leader, Raymond Labs, 43-48; asst. res. dir, Toni Co, 48-53, res. dir, 54-57, coord. prod. develop, 57-67; tech. dir, Colton Co. Div, GILLETTE CO, 67-70, CONSULT, 71- Am. Chem. Soc; Am. Oil Chem. Soc; Soc. Cosmetic Chem; N.Y. Acad. Sci; Am. Inst. Chem. Surface active agents; emulsions; cosmetics; collagen and keratin research; foods; surgical sutures. Address: 10638 Saratoga Circle, Sun City, AZ 85351.

GOFFINET, EDWARD P(ETER), JR, b. Louisville, Ky, Nov. 15, 30; m. 53; c. 2. CHEMICAL ENGINEERING. B.S, Notre Dame, 52. Res. engr, E.I. DU PONT DE NEMOURS & CO, INC, 52-62, RES. DIV. HEAD, ELASTOMER CHEM. DEPT, EXP. STA, 63- U.S.A, 52-54. Applied reaction kinetics; high temperature reactor research; mathematical engineering applications; hydrocarbon elastomer processes. Address: 2403 Annwood Dr, Wilmington, DE 19803.

GOFFMAN, MARTIN, b. Phila, Pa, June 22, 40; m. 65; c. 2. PHYSICAL CHEMISTRY, ELECTROCHEMISTRY. A.B, Temple, 61, M.A, 63, Atomic Energy Comn. fel, 63-65, Ph.D.(chem), 65. RES. CHEMIST, ELECTROCHEM, CENT. RES. LAB, AM. SMELTING & REF. CO, 65- AAAS; Am. Chem. Soc; Electrochem. Soc; Am. Soc. Metals; Sci. Res. Soc. Am. Transition metal complexes in fused salts; electrolytic processes and electrochemical kinetics; electrolytic refining of metals. Address: Central Research Lab, American Smelting & Refining Co, South Plainfield, NJ 07080.

GOFMAN, JOHN W(ILLIAM), b. Cleveland, Ohio, Sept. 21, 18; m. 40; c. 1. PHYSICAL CHEMISTRY. A.B, Oberlin Col, 39; Western Reserve, 39-40; Ph.D.(chem), California, 43, M.D, 46. Res. assoc. chem, UNIV. CALIF, 43-44, intern. med, dept. med, univ. hosp, 46-47, asst. prof. MED. PHYSICS, DONNER LAB. MED. PHYSICS, BERKELEY, 47-51, assoc. prof, 51-54, PROF, 54-, DIR. BIOL. & MED, LAWRENCE RADIATION LAB. & ASSOC. DIR, LAB, 63-; CLIN. INSTR. MED, MED. SCH, SAN FRANCISCO, 47- With Atomic Energy Comn; Off. Sci. Res. & Develop, 44. Hist. Sci. Soc; assoc. mem. Am. Med. Asn. Nuclear chemistry; nuclear physics; tracer research; macromolecule chemistry; cancer; atheromatosis. Address: Division of Medical Physics, Donner Lab, University of California, Berkeley, CA 94720.

GOFORTH, JOHN LAWRENCE, b. Beeville, Tex, June 24, 97; m. 30; c. 1. PATHOLOGY. B.A, Univ. Tex, 18; M.D, Johns Hopkins Univ, 23. Dir. DEPT. PATH, ST. PAUL HOSP, 26-60, CONSULT, 60-; CLIN. PROF. PATH, UNIV. TEX. MED. SCH, DALLAS, 55-, assoc. clin. prof, 48-55. Chmn, Adv. Health Bd, Dallas, 35-53; private practice. U.S.A, 18-19. Am. Soc. Clin. Path.(pres, 57); Am. Asn. Path. & Bact; Am. Med. Asn; Col. Am. Path; Am. Col. Physicians; Int. Acad. Path. Neoplasia. Address: 3744 W. Bay Circle, Dallas, TX 75218.

GOFORTH, W. REID, b. Wentzville, Mo, Feb. 13, 32; m. 63; c. 2. ZOOLOGY. B.S, Missouri, 54, M.A, 63, Nat. Wildlife Inst. fels, 63-64 & summers, 65-66, Ph.D.(zool), 68. Teacher & prin, high schs, Mo, 54-61; instr. zool, Missouri, 63-64; assoc. prof, Iowa Wesleyan Col, 64-69; LEADER, MO. COOP. WILDLIFE RES. UNIT, U.S. BUR. SPORT FISHERIES & WILDLIFE, UNIV. MO-COLUMBIA, 69- Wildlife Soc; Nat. Sci. Teachers Asn; Nat. Audubon Soc. Reproduction of Mustelidae; color aversion in Columbiform birds; hierarchy patterns and their effect on dove reproduction. Address: Missouri Cooperative Wildlife Research Unit, Room 111, Stephens Hall, University of Missouri-Columbia, Columbia, MO 65201.

GOGAN, NIALL J(OSEPH), b. Dublin, Ireland, Feb. 26, 41; m. 64; c. 3. INORGANIC CHEMISTRY. B.Sc, Nat. Univ. Ireland, 62, Ph.D.(inorg. chem), 65. Res. assoc. CHEM, Chicago, 65-67; Asst. Prof, MEM. UNIV. NEWF, 67-71, ASSOC. PROF, 71- Nat. Res. Coun. Can. operating grant, 68-, spec. equip. grant, 69. Am. Chem. Soc; sr. mem. Chem. Inst. Can; Brit. Chem. Soc. Organometallic chemistry; metal carbonyls; metalloporphyrins; electron spin resonance spectroscopy; reaction kinetics; oxidation reduction reactions; metal chelates. Address: Dept. of Chemistry, Memorial University of Newfoundland, St. Johns, Newf, Can.

GOGARTY, W(ILLIAM) B(ARNEY), b. Provo, Utah, Apr. 23, 30; m. 51; c. 5. CHEMICAL ENGINEERING. B.S, Utah, 53, Ph.D.(chem. eng), 60. Jr. engr, Shell Chem. Corp, 52; sr. res. scientist, MARATHON OIL CO, 59-67, MGR, PROD. TECHNOL. DEPT, DENVER RES. CTR, 67- Adj. assoc. prof, dept. chem. eng. & metall, Univ. Denver. Proj. engr, engr. agency, Chem.C, 53-55, Res, 55-59, Capt. Soc. Petrol. Eng; Am. Inst. Chem. Eng. Miscible phase displacement of oil as a means of secondary recovery. Address: Production Technology Dept, Denver Research Center, Marathon Oil Co, 7400 S. Broadway, Littleton, CO 80122.

GOGER, PAULINE ROHM, b. Connellsville, Pa, Jan. 22, 13; m. 42. INTERNAL MEDICINE. A.B, Oberlin Col, 34; M.A, Wellesley Col, 36; Ph.D.(zool), Pennsylvania, 42; M.D, N.Y. Univ, 50. Asst. histol. & embryol, Wellesley Col, 34-37; teacher, Punahoe Acad, Hawaii, 37-38; biol. & chem, Stevens Sch, Phila, 39-41; instr. biol, Simmons Col, 41-43; zool, N.J. Col. Women, Rutgers, 43-46, asst. prof, 46-50; from. intern to res. med, Bellevue Hosp, 50-53; instr. & asst. clin. vis. physician, N.Y. Univ-Bellevue Med. Ctr, 53; asst. INTERNAL MED, HUNTERDON MED. CTR, 53-57, assoc, 57-60, ASST. DIR, 60- Blood enzymes. Address: P.O. Box M, Stanton, NJ 08885.

GOGERTY, JOHN H(ARRY), b. Laramie, Wyo, Mar. 9, 33; m. 56; c. 5. PHARMACOLOGY. B.S, Wyoming, 54; M.S, Washington (Seattle), 57, Ph.D. (pharmacol), 59. Asst. pharmacol, sch. med, Washington (Seattle), 54-58; asst. prof, Oklahoma, 58-63, dir. poison info. ctr, 60-61; neuropharmacologist, SANDOZ, INC, 63-68, head PHARMACOL. SECT, 68-71, DIR, 71- AAAS; Am. Soc. Pharmacol. & Exp. Therapeut; Am. Soc. Pharmacol. & Chemother; N.Y. Acad. Sci. Neuropharmacology; neurophysiological and enzymological aspects of neuropharmacology; neuroendocrinology; behavioral pharmacology; neuropharmacology of sleep. Address: Pharmacology Section, Sandoz, Inc, Hanover, NJ 07961.

GOGGANS, JAMES F, b. Tifton, Ga, Oct. 30, 20; m. 50; c. 2. FORESTRY, GENETICS. B.S, Georgia, 42; M.F, Duke, 47; Ph.D.(forest genetics), N.C. State, 62. Asst. prof. forestry, AUBURN UNIV, 47-52, assoc. prof, 52-63, PROF. FOREST GENETICS, 63- C.Eng, 42-46, Capt. Soc. Am. Foresters. Tree breeding and genetics of forest trees; variation in anatomy of wood cells. Address: 100 Kuderna Acres, Auburn, AL 36830.

GOGGIN, WILLIAM C(HARLES), b. Alma, Mich, Aug. 26, 11; m. 39; c. 2. PLASTICS CHEMISTRY. B.S, Alma Col, 33, hon. D.Sc, 54; B.S, Michigan, 35, M.S, 36. Student, Dow Chem. Co, 36-37, engr, phys. res. lab, 37-39, salesman, spec. prod. div, 39-41, asst. mgr, plastics sales div, 41-42, mgr, 42-43, plastics develop. div, 43-47, plastics tech. serv, 47-59, gen. mgr. plastics dept, 59-67, pres. & dir, DOW CORNING CORP, 67-71, CHMN. & PRES, 71- Tech. consult, Qm.C, Ger, 45. Am. Chem. Soc; Soc. Plastics Indust; Mfg. Chem. Asn. Application research and development in field of plastics; administration. Address: Dow Corning Corp, Midland, MI 48640.

GOGGINS, JOHN FRANCIS, b. Flint, Mich, Oct. 26, 33; m. 60; c. 2. HISTOCHEMISTRY. Notre Dame, 51-54; D.D.S, Marquette, 58, M.S, 65. Private practice, 60-63; U.S. Pub. Health Serv. training grant, Marquette, 63-65; instr. oral path, sch. dent, 64-65; U.S. Pub. Health Serv. fel, NAT. INST. DENT. RES, 65-66, INVESTR, HISTOCHEM. SECT, EXP. PATH. BR, 66- U.S.A.F, 58-60, Capt; U.S.P.H.S, 66-, Dent. Dir. AAAS; Am. Dent. Asn; Int. Asn. Dent. Res; Histochem. Soc. Histochemistry and chemistry of connective tissues, bones and teeth. Address: Experimental Pathology Branch, Histochemistry Section, National Institute of Dental Research, Bethesda, MD 20014.

GOGLIA, GENNARO LOUIS, b. Hoboken, N.J, Jan. 15, 21; m. 42; c. 2. THERMODYNAMICS. B.S, Illinois, 42; M.S, Ohio State, 50; Ph.D.(mech. eng), Michigan, 59. Jr. engr, Rochester Ord. Dist, 42-45; develop. engr. refrig, Gen. Elec. Co, 45-47; instr. eng. ed, Ohio State, 47-51; asst. prof. mech. eng, Detroit, 51-59; assoc. prof, N.C. State Col, 59-62; prof. & head dept, Maine, 62-64; prof. eng, OLD DOM. UNIV, 64-65, PROF. THERMAL ENG, 65-, ASST. DEAN SCH. ENG, 70-, chmn. dept. thermal eng, 65-70. Tech, writer, cent. heading dept, Detroit Edison Co, 51-54; consult, Overhead Heaters Inc, 52-55; Du Pont summer res. fel, 61; co-dir. NASA summer faculty progs, NASA-Langley Res. Ctr, 68- Am. Soc. Mech. Eng; Am. Soc. Eng. Educ. Heat transfer; supersaturation phenomena; fluids. Address: School of Engineering, Old Dominion University, Norfolk, VA 23508.

GOGLIA, M(ARIO) J(OSEPH), b. Hoboken, N.J, Mar. 30, 16; m. 40; c. 2. MECHANICAL ENGINEERING. M.E, Stevens Inst. Tech, 37, M.S, 41; Ph.D. (thermodyn), Purdue, 48. Instr. mech. eng, Stevens Inst. Tech, 37-38; asst. prof, Illinois, 38-46; appln. engr, Repub. Flowmeters, 46-47; assoc. prof. mech. eng, Purdue, 47-48; prof, Ga. Inst. Tech, 48-58; dean, col. eng, Notre Dame, 58-60; regents prof. mech. eng. & assoc. dean faculties, Ga. Inst. Technol, 60-66, dean grad. div, 61-66; V.CHANCELLOR RES, REGENTS, UNIV. SYST. GA, 66- Asst, munitions develop. lab, Univ. Ill, 45-46; mem. adv. panel sci. & eng, Nat. Sci. Found; consult, Nat. Acad. Sci-Nat. Res. Coun; Nat. Sci. Found; Atomic Energy Comn; U.S. Off. Educ; South. Asn. Cols. & Schs. Civilian with Nat. Defense Res. Comt, 44. AAAS; Am. Soc. Mech. Eng; Am. Soc. Eng. Educ. Thermodynamics, heat transfer; fluid mechanics. Address: University System of Georgia, 244 Washington St. S.W, Atlanta, GA 30334.

GOGOLEWSKI, RAYMOND PAUL, b. Waterbury, Conn, Jan. 25, 41; m. 64; c. 1. THEORETICAL & APPLIED MECHANICS. B.S, Rensselaer Polytech. Inst, 62, univ. fel, 62-64, M.A.E, 64; Nat. Defense Educ. Act fel, Cornell Univ, 67-70, univ. fel, 69-70, Ph.D.(theoret. & appl. mech), 70. Proj. engr, Arnold Eng. Develop. Ctr, Sverdrup & Parcels, Inc, 64-65; anal. res. engr, United Aircraft Res. Labs, 65-67; ASST. PROF. ENG. MECH, N.C. STATE UNIV, 70- Am. Inst. Aeronaut. & Astronaut; Inst. Elec. & Electronics Eng; Soc. Indust. & Appl. Math. Theory of dynamical systems; optimal control and control systems; space mechanics; trajectory and mission analysis. Address: 1317 Westfield Ave, Raleigh, NC 27607.

GOGOS, COSTAS G, b. Athens, Greece, June 30, 38; m. 65. CHEMICAL ENGINEERING. B.S.Ch.E, Princeton, 61, M.S, 62, M.A, 64, Ph.D.(mech. eng), 66. Asst. prof. CHEM. ENG, STEVENS INST. TECHNOL, 64-70, ASSOC. PROF, 70- Am. Chem. Soc; Soc. Plastics Eng; Soc. Rheol. Physical properties of high polymers in particular rheological properties; rheological aspects of polymer processing; kinetics and morphology of deformed polymer crystals. Address: 7 Luxoro Pl, Fairview, NJ 07022.

GOGUEN, JOSEPH A, JR, b. Pittsfield, Mass, June 28, 41; m; c. 2. INFORMATION SCIENCES, MATHEMATICS. B.A, Harvard, 63; M.A, Univ. Calif, Berkeley, 66, Ph.D.(math), 68. Tutor, bur. study coun, Harvard, 61-62; teaching asst. math, Univ. Calif, Berkeley, 63-65, instr, 68; ASST. PROF. INFO. SCI, UNIV. CHICAGO, 68- Summers, prog. & digital design technician, Gen. Elec. Co, 59 & 60; res. asst. psychol, Univ. Pa, 61; jr. scientist, applied res. labs, Sylvania Electronic Systs, 62 & 63, consult, 63; Krohn-Rhodes Res. Inst, 66 & 67; IBM fel, T.J. Watson Res. Lab, N.Y, 71-72. Am. Math. Soc; Math. Asn. Am; Asn. Comput. Mach. Systems theory; minimal realization; generalizations of automata; category theory; logic; information; applications to electronics, fuzzy sets, computability, heuristics, music, control theory and philosophy. Address: Committee on Information Sciences, University of Chicago, Chicago, IL 60637.

GOH, KONG-OO, b. Fukien, China, Sept. 11, 29; U.S. citizen; m. 55; c. 4. HEMATOLOGY, CYTOGENETICS. A.B, Union Col.(Ky), 52; M.D, Louisville, 56. Intern, Highland Park Gen. Hosp, 56-57; med. res, Henry Ford Hosp, 57-59; spec. fel. & vis. res. fel, Mem. Sloan-Kettering Cancer Ctr, 59-60; trainee hemat, med. ctr, Rochester, 60-61, instr. med, sch. med. & dent, 61-64, sr. instr. med. & instr. obstet. & gynec, 64; sr. clinician & chief cytogenetics, Oak Ridge Inst. Nuclear Studies, Tenn, 64-69; ASSOC. PROF. MED, SCH. MED, UNIV. ROCHESTER, 69-, ANAT, SCH. MED. & DENT, 70-; CHIEF MED. ONCOL, MONROE COMMUNITY HOSP, 69- Asst. physician, Strong Mem. Hosp, 60-64, sr. assoc. physician, 69-; asst. physician, Rochester Munic. Hosp, 60-64; consult, Vet. Admin. Hosp, Batavia, N.Y, 64; consult. internist, Canandaigua, N.Y, 70- Am. Fedn. Clin. Res; Am. Soc. Hemat. Internal medicine. Address: Monroe Community Hospital, 435 E. Henrietta Rd, Rochester, NY 14620.

GOHEEN, A(USTIN) C(LEMENT), b. Bellingham, Wash, Apr. 22, 17; m. 42; c. 5. PLANT PATHOLOGY. B.S, Washington (Seattle), 47; Ph.D.(plant path), Washington State, 53. Observer, U.S. Weather Bur, 38-46; asst. dept. plant path, Washington State, 47-50; agent, N.J. Agr. Exp. Sta, U.S. DEPT. AGR, 50-53, plant pathologist, plant indust. sta, 53-55, U.S. Hort. Field Sta, 55-56, UNIV. CALIF, DAVIS, ASSOC, EXP. STA, 56-, SR. PLANT PATHOLOGIST, 59- Asst. res. specialist, agr. exp. sta, Rutgers, 50-53. U.S.A.A.F, 46-47. Am. Phytopath. Soc. Virus diseases of grapes. Address: Dept. of Plant Pathology, University of California, Davis, CA 95616.

GOHEEN, DAVID W(ADE), b. Bellingham, Wash, June 23, 20; m. 43; c. 2. ORGANIC CHEMISTRY. B.S, Washington (Seattle), 42, fel, 46-48, Atomic Energy Cmn. fel, 48-50, Ph.D.(chem), 51. Res. chemist org. chem, eng. res. inst, Michigan, 51-52; chief chem. res. sect, cent. res. dept, CROWN ZELLERBACH CORP, 52-55, res. specialist chem. prod. div, 55-67, SR. RES. CHEMIST, CENT. RES. DIV, 67- U.S.A.A.F, 42-46, 1st Lt. Am. Chem. Soc. Natural products; wood extractives; lingin; cellulose. Address: P.O. Box 826, Camas, WA 98607.

GOHEEN, GILBERT E(ARL), b. Barry, Ill, May 8, 12; m. 39; c. 3. ORGANIC CHEMISTRY. B.S, Illinois, 34; M.S, Iowa, 35, Ph.D.(org. chem), 38. Asst. org. chem, Iowa, 34-38; res. chemist, exp. div, Sun Oil Co, 38-42; chemist, process develop, Gen. Aniline Works, 42-44, mgr. N.Y. process develop. dept, 44-49, asst. to dir. res. assoc. dir. cent. lab, Gen. Aniline & Film Corp, 49-52; dir. res. & develop, J.T. Baker Chem. Co, 52-54; ASST. DIR. SOUTH. MKT. & NUTRIT. RES. DIV, AGR. RES. SERV, U.S. DEPT. AGR, 55- AAAS; Am. Chem. Soc; Am. Asn. Textile Chem. & Colorists. Preparation and analysis of haloamines and their reaction with ketenes; pyrrolidines; conversion of naphthenic acids to naphthene hydrocarbons; synthesis of multicyclopentyl hydrocarbons and color formers; technical information and indexing; dyes; detergents; reagents; utilization of farm crops. Address: Southern Regional Research Lab, Agricultural Research Service, U.S. Dept. of Agriculture, 1100 Robert E. Lee Blvd, New Orleans, LA 70124.

GOHEEN, HARRY EARL, b. Bellingham, Wash, July 19, 15; m. 40; c. 3. MATHEMATICS. A.B, Stanford, 36, A.M, 38, Ph.D.(math), 40; fel, Reed Col, 39-40. Instr. math, Wisconsin, 40-42, mathematician, Off. Naval Res, Mass, 46-47; asst. prof. math, Delaware, 47-48; Syracuse, 48-51; elec. eng, Moore Sch, Pennsylvania, 51-52; assoc. prof. MATH, Iowa State Col, 52-55; ORE. STATE UNIV, 55-59, PROF, 59- Vis. mem, Dublin Inst. Advan. Studies, 67. U.S.N, 42-45. Am. Math. Soc; Asn. Comput. Mach; Math. Asn. Am. Permutation groups; abstract finite groups; numerical analysis; computation of special functions; heat equation; programming; automata theory; mathematical biology; foundations of geometry. Address: Dept. of Mathematics, Oregon State University, Corvallis, OR 97331.

GOHLKE, ARTHUR FREDERICK, b. Vernon, Tex, May 21, 31; m. 55; c. 2. PLANT PHYSIOLOGY, SOILS. B.S, Tex. Tech. Col, 53, M.S, 58; Ph.D.(soil fertil), Purdue, 62. Chemist, Agr. Chem. Inc, Tex, 53-56; part-time instr. agron, Tex. Tech. Col, 57-58; instr, Purdue, 59-61; fel. plant biochem, Mich. State, 61-62; soil scientist, High Plains Res. Found, 63-64, asst. dir. & sr. soil scientist, 64-66; staff agronomist, Tenn. Corp, 66, asst. chief agronomist, 66-68, sr. res. assoc, 68-70, AGRON. RES. MGR. CHEM. & METALS GROUP, RES. & DEVELOP, CITIES SERV. CO, 70- Am. Soc. Agron; Soil Sci. Soc. Am; Crop Sci. Soc. Am; Am. Soc. Plant Physiol. Inorganic nutrients, their source role, rate, placement, microclimate and growth regulators on plant growth and biochemical processes. Address: Research & Development, Cities Service Co, Drawer 8, Cranbury, NJ 08512.

GOIN, COLEMAN J(ETT), b. Gainesville, Fla, Feb. 25, 11; m. 40; c. 2. HERPETOLOGY. B.S, Florida, 39, M.S, 41, fel, 41-42, Ph.D.(biol), 46. Asst. instr, BIOL. SCIS, UNIV. FLA, 42-45, instr, 45-47, asst. prof, 47-51, assoc. prof, 51-56, prof, 56-71, EMER. PROF, 71-; MEM. STAFF, MUS. NORTH. ARIZ, 71- Grant, Am. Acad. Sci. Am. Soc. Ichthyol. & Herpet. (v.pres, 42-46, treas, 52-57, pres. elect, 65, pres, 66); Soc. Study Evolution. Taxonomy, ecology and genetics of Amphibia. Address: Museum of Northern Arizona, Flagstaff, AZ 86001.

GOINES, WILLIAM H, b. Denver, Colo, Feb. 17, 12; m. 44; c. 3. CIVIL ENGINEERING. B.S, Texas, 36. HYDRAULIC ENGR, U.S. GEOL. SURV, Tex, 35-52, Miss, 52-55, TEX, 55- Am. Geophys. Union. Hydraulic investigations leading to development and use of surface water; hydraulic engineering; hydrology. Address: U.S. Geological Survey, 300 E. Eighth St, Austin, TX 78701.

GOING, DORA HENLEY, b. West Point, Miss, June 14, 16; m. 54. MEDICAL BACTERIOLOGY. B.S, Birmingham-South. Col, 37, Temple, 39; M.S, Michigan, 51, Ph.D.(bact), 53. Instr. bact. & med. tech, Alabama, 47-52, asst. prof, 52-57; MICROBIOL, DENT. BR, UNIV. TEX, HOUSTON, 57-61, assoc. prof, 61-65, PROF, 65- AAAS; Am. Soc. Microbiol. Infection and resistance; microbiology of oral cavity. Address: Dept. of Pathology & Microbiology, Dental Branch, University of Texas at Houston, P.O. Box 20068, Houston, TX 77025.

GOING, LOUIS H(ENRY), b. Parma, Mo, Oct. 13, 26; m. 49; c. 3. CHEMICAL ENGINEERING. B.S, Purdue, 47, M.S, 49. Proj. engr, process develop, PROCTER & GAMBLE CO, 49-51, group leader, 51-56, food prod. res, 56, sect. head, fats & oils process develop, 56-57, 58-64, explor. process develop. in foods, 57-58, indust. foods develop, 64-67, head new prod. develop, food prod. div, 67-70, MGR. PROCESS, PACKAGING DEVELOP. & TECH. SERV, INDUST. CHEM. DIV, 70- U.S.N, 45-46. AAAS; Oil Chem. Soc; fel. Am. Inst. Chem. Product, process and packaging development; factory technical service, industrial and agricultural chemicals; industrial, commercial and institutional cleaning and sanitizing products. Address: Ivorydale Technical Center, Procter & Gamble Co, Cincinnati, OH 45217.

GOING, ROBERT ERNEST, b. Parma, Mo, Apr. 15, 28; m. 54; c. 5. DENTISTRY, HISTOLOGY. A.B, Valparaiso, 48; B.S, Illinois, Chicago, 51, D.D.S, 53, M.S, 58. Intern, Fitzsimons Army Hosp, Denver, Colo, 53-54; U.S. Pub. Health Serv. fel, col. dent, Illinois, Chicago, 57-59; sch. med, Colorado, 59-60; asst. prof. oper. dent, Northwestern, 64-66; clin. investr, dent. res, Hines Vet. Admin. Hosp, Ill, 66; Ft. Miley Vet. Admin. Hosp. & dent. health ctr, U.S. Pub. Health Serv, 66-69; ASSOC. PROF. BIOMAT. & CHMN. DIV, COL. DENT, UNIV. FLA, 69- Consult, Hines Vet. Admin. Hosp, 64-66; consult. & mem. deans comt, Gainesville Vet. Admin. Hosp. Dent.C, 53-56, Capt. Am. Dent. Asn; Int. Asn. Dent. Res; fel. Am. Col. Dent. Dental materials; failures related to materials used in restorative dentistry; glass-ceramic dental restorations; microleakage. Address: Division of Biomaterials, University of Florida College of Dentistry, Gainesville, FL 32601.

GOINS, R(OBERT) R(ALPH), b. Fairland, Okla, Nov. 22, 16; m. 45; c. 2. CHEMICAL ENGINEERING. B.S, Okla. State, 40. Chemist, Tygart Valley Glass Co, 40-42; jr. engr. RES. & DEVELOP, PHILLIPS PETROL. CO, 42-45, group leader, 45-52, staff engr, 52-60, sect. mgr, planning & correlation br, 60-63, tech. asst. mech. develop. br, 63-70, RES. ENGR, 70- Am. Inst. Chem. Eng. Pebble heater heat exchanger; thermal cracking of light hydrocarbons; catalytic dehydrogenation; high polymers; materials handling and solids blending. Address: Research & Development Dept, Phillips Petroleum Co, Bartlesville, OK 74004.

GOINS, TRUMAN, b. Peason, La, Nov. 14, 20; m. 43; c. 1. CIVIL ENGINEERING. B.S, La. State, 50; M.S, Ohio State, 54. Asst. prof. agr. eng, Ohio Agr. Exp. Sta, 50-58; agr. eng. adv, U.S. Oper. Mission, Honduras, 58-61, U.S. Agency Int. Develop, Ecuador, 61-63, regional dir, 62, agr. adv, 63; res. agr. engr, agr. res. serv, U.S. Dept. Agr, Va, 63-66; water resources engr, U.S. Agency Int. Develop, Laos, 66-67, Wash, D.C, 67-68; CIVIL ENGR. & PROG. OFF, DEPT. HOUSING & URBAN DEVELOP, 68- U.S.C.G, 39-46, Res, 46-, Comdr. Am. Soc. Agr. Eng; Am. Soc. Civil Eng; Nat. Soc. Prof. Eng. Agricultural drainage and irrigation; soil and water conservation; crop tillage and rotation practices; farm building materials; land use and development; water resources planning and development; community planning and management. Address: 11610 Hickory Dr, Oxon Hill, MD 20022.

GOISHI, WATARU, b. Florin, Calif, Feb. 6, 28; m. 52; c. 2. RADIOCHEMISTRY. B.S, California, Berkeley, 50; U.S. Atomic Energy Comn. fels, Chicago, 51-53, Ph.D.(radiochem), 54. RADIOCHEMIST, Chicago, 53-54; LAWRENCE RADIATION LAB, UNIV. CALIF, 54-62, GROUP LEADER, NUCLEAR WEAPONS DIAG, 63- AAAS; Am. Chem. Soc. Fast neutron reactions and measurements; kinetics and mechanisms of inorganic reactions. Address: 5266 Kathy Way, Livermore, CA 94550.

GOJMERAC, W(ALTER) L(OUIS), b. Rib Lake, Wis, Apr. 8, 25; m. 55; c. 5. ENTOMOLOGY. B.S, Wisconsin, 49, Ph.D.(entom), 55; Charles O'Hara scholar, Marine Biol. Lab, Woods Hole, 52; M.S, Marquette, 53. Teacher, pub. sch, 49-51; asst. prof. entom. & asst. entomologist, N.Dak. Agr. Col, 55-57; res. entomologist, Calif. Spray Chem. Corp, Standard Oil Co. Calif, 57-65; ASSOC. PROF. ENTOM. & EXTEN. ENTOMOLOGIST, UNIV. WIS, MADISON, 65- Cert, Am. Registry Cert, Entom. U.S.M.C, 42-45. Fel. AAAS; Entom. Soc. Am. Research on control of insects affecting man and animals. Address: Dept. of Entomology, University of Wisconsin, Madison, WI 53706.

GOKCEN, NEV A(LTAN), b. Turkey, Sept. 21, 21; nat; m. 46; c. 3. THERMODYNAMICS. B.S, Pittsburgh, 42, M.S, 45; Sc.D.(metall), Mass. Inst. Tech, 51. Instr. metall, Lafayette Col, 43-44; Robert Col, 45-47; asst, Mass. Inst. Tech, 47-51, res. assoc, 51; assoc. prof, Michigan Tech, 51-56; Pennsylvania, 56-61; HEAD CHEM. THERMODYN. SECT, AEROSPACE CORP, 61-, elected trustees' roll, 69. Am. Chem. Soc; Am. Soc. Metals; Am. Inst. Mining, Metall. & Petrol. Eng. Physical chemistry of metals and alloys; high temperature chemistry; thermodynamics of solutions. Address: Chemical Thermodynamics Section, Aerospace Corp, Los Angeles, CA 90045.

GOKEN, GAROLD LEE, b. Decatur, Ill, Aug. 6, 37; m. 58; c. 3. POLYMER & ORGANIC CHEMISTRY. B.A, Millikin, 59; Nat. Defense Ed. Act fel. & Ph.D.(chem, pharmaceut. chem), Utah, 62. Sr. chemist, tape res. lab, Minn. Mining & Mfg. Co, 62-65, supvr, pioneering res. group, 65-69, res. supvr, INDUST. SPEC. PROD. DEPT, 3M CO, 69-71, RES. MGR, 71- Am. Chem. Soc. Synthetic polymer chemistry of adhesives and related materials; materials design and fabrication. Address: Industrial Special Products Dept, Bldg. 230, 3M Co, 3M Center, St. Paul, MN 55101.

GOKHALE, DATTAPRABHAKAR V, b. Poona, India, Mar. 18, 36; m. 61; c. 2. STATISTICS. B.Sc, Univ. Poona, 55, M.Sc, 57; U.S. State Dept. Fulbright traveling fel, 63; Ph.D.(statist), Univ. Calif, Berkeley, 66. Lectr. statist, Univ. Poona, 59-69, assoc. prof, 69-70; ASST. PROF. STATIST. & ASST. STATISTICIAN, UNIV. CALIF, RIVERSIDE, 70- Asst. prof, Univ. Calif, Berkeley, 66. Nonparametric tests for bivariate and multivariate independence; statistical inference; nonparametric statistical methods. Address: Dept. of Statistics, University of California, Riverside, CA 92502.

GOKHALE, NARAYAN R(AMCHANDRA), b. Bombay, India, Nov. 28, 24; U.S. citizen; m. 53; c. 2. ATMOSPHERIC PHYSICS. B.Sc, Bombay, 46 & 47; M.Sc, 50, Ph.D.(physics), 58. Fel. physics, McGill, 59-60; asst. prof, Windsor, 60-61; assoc. prof. ATMOSPHERIC SCI, STATE UNIV. N.Y. ALBANY, 61-62, PROF, 62-, RES. SCIENTIST, ATMOSPHERIC SCI. RES. CTR, 67-, res. assoc, 61-67, chmn. dept. earth & atmospheric sci, 63-68. Am. Meteorol. Soc; Am. Geophys. Union; Royal Meteorol. Soc. Cloud and precipitation physics. Address: Dept. of Atmospheric Science, State University of New York at Albany, Albany, NY 12203.

GOKHALE, SUDARSHAN D, b. Bombay, India, Oct. 17, 26; m. 56; c. 2. INORGANIC & PHYSICAL CHEMISTRY. B.Sc, Banaras Hindu Univ, 47; M.Sc, Univ. Bombay, 51; Dr.rer.nat, Univ. Tübingen, 54. Jr. res. asst, assay dept, India Govt. Mint, 51-52; res. asst. chem. div, Atomic Energy Estab, India, 56-58, jr. res. off, 59-64, sci. off, 64-65; metallurgist, Denison Mines Ltd, Can, 65-67; res. chemist, BASF WYANDOTTE CORP, 67-70, SR. RES. CHEMIST, 70- Res. chemist, Lawrence Res. Lab, Univ. Calif, 62-64. AAAS; Am. Chem. Soc. Preparative inorganic chemistry; hydrometallurgy; process and plant improvement; determination of properties; pilot plant; synthetic inorganic chemistry; pollution control. Address: Research Bldg, BASF Wyandotte Corp, 1419 Biddle Ave, Wyandotte, MI 48192.

GOKSEL, MEHMET ADNAN, b. Ankara, Turkey, May 27, 24; m. 60; c. 3. CHEMICAL ENGINEERING, EXTRACTIVE METALLURGY. M.Sc, Istanbul Univ, 49, D.Sc.(chem. eng), 51; Dr.rer.nat.habil.(chem. eng), Karlsruhe Tech. Univ, 56. Res. asst. indust. chem, Istanbul Univ, 49-52; res. fel,

Karlsruhe Tech. Univ, 52-55; sci. mil. adv, Turkish Gen. Staff, 55-57; docent indust. chem, Istanbul Univ, 57-60; Fulbright res. fel. extractive metall, Mich. Technol. Univ, 60-62; docent indust. chem, Istanbul Univ, 62-63, prof, 63-65; ASSOC. PROF. chem. eng, MICH. TECHNOL. UNIV, 65-67, EXTRACTIVE METALL, 65- Alexander von Humbolt fel, Karlsruhe Tech. Univ, 52-53; fel, Istanbul Univ, 53-55; consult, Emayetas Co, Turkey, 63-65. Turkish Army Res, 56-57, Lt. Am. Chem. Soc; Am. Inst. Min, Metall. & Petrol. Eng; Inst. Briquetting & Agglomeration. Agglomeration; pollution; building materials; chemical processes. Address: Institute of Mineral Research, Michigan Technological University, Houghton, MI 49931.

GOLAB, TOMASZ, b. Dynow, Poland, Oct. 18, 22; m. 58; c. 2. ORGANIC & ANALYTICAL CHEMISTRY. Silesian Polytech, 45-48; Ph.D.(org. chem), Basel, 60. Res. assoc. to Prof. Tadeus Reichstein, Basel, 60; scientist, Worcester Found. Exp. Biol, Mass, 60-62; SR. AGR. BIOCHEMIST, GREENFIELD LABS, ELI LILLY & CO, 62- Polish Underground Army, 41-45, 2nd Lt. AAAS; Am. Chem. Soc; N.Y. Acad. Sci; Swiss Chem. Soc. Cardiac glycosides and cardenolides, isolation and structure determination of Apocannoside, Cynocannoside, Pachygenin and Pachygenol; synthesis of new sugar; metabolism of 19-Nor-steroids in human and animals; pesticides metabolism; development of isotope and chromatographic techniques for steroids, antibiotics and pesticides. Address: 8116 Goldenrod Ct, Indianapolis, IN 46219.

GOLAND, ALLEN N(ATHAN), b. Chicago, Ill, Apr. 26, 30; m. 59; c. 2. PHYSICS. B.S, Roosevelt, 51; fel, Northwestern, 54-55, Ph.D.(physics), 56. Res. assoc. physics, BROOKHAVEN NAT. LAB, 56-58, solid state physicist, ord. mat. res. off, 58-63, assoc. physicist, 63-67, PHYSICIST, 68- Ed, Thin Films, 68-71; vis. prof, State Univ. N.Y. Stony Brook, 70; dir, NATO Advan. Study Inst, 71; vis. res. consult, Univ. São Paulo, 71. AAAS; fel. Am. Phys. Soc. Defects in solids; radiation effects; x-ray and neutron scattering; applications of particle accelerators to solid-state physics research. Address: Brookhaven National Lab, 510 B, Upton, NY 11973.

GOLAND, LEONARD, b. Brooklyn, N.Y, May 22, 23; m. 50; c. 2. AERONAUTICAL ENGINEERING. B.S, Cornell, 44, M.A.E, 48; Ph.D.(mech. eng), Pennsylvania, 62. Instr. mech. eng, Cornell, 46-48, res. engr, aeronaut. lab, 48-51; head eng. anal. sect, Reaction Motors, Inc, 51-52; lectr, grad. sch. aeronaut. eng. & chief proj. engr, Forrestal Res. Ctr, Princeton, 52-56; v.pres. eng, Kellett Aircraft Corp, Pa, 56-62; PRES, DYNASCI. CORP, 62- U.S.A, 43-46, 1st Lt. Am. Helicopter Soc; assoc. fel. Am. Inst. Aeronaut. & Astronaut.(Inst. Aeronaut. Sci. award, 47); assoc. fel. Royal Aeronaut. Soc; Helicopter Asn. Gt. Brit. Applied mechanics; aerodynamics; vibrations; aeroelectricity; dynamics. Address: Dynasciences Corp, Township Line Rd, Blue Bell, PA 19422.

GOLAND, MARTIN, b. New York, N.Y, July 12, 19; m. 48; c. 3. MECHANICS. M.E, Cornell, 40; LL.D, St. Mary's Univ. San Antonio, 68. Instr. mech. eng, Cornell, 40-42; sect. head appl. mech, res. lab, Curtiss Wright Co, N.Y, 42-46; chmn, eng. mech. div, Midwest Res. Inst, 46-50, dir. eng. sci, 50-55; v.pres. res, SOUTHWEST RES. INST, 55-57, v.pres. & dir, 57-59, PRES, 59- Mem. adv. comt, Harry Diamond Labs, 55-; adv. panel comt. sci. & astronaut, House of Rep, 59-; mem. nat. inventors coun, Dept. Commerce, 65-66, state tech. serv. eval. comt, 67-68; defense sci. bd. task force on in-house labs, Dept. Defense, 65-66; sci. adv. panel, Dept. Army, 65-; chmn, U.S. Army Weapons Command Adv. Group, 66-, mem. missile adv. group; sci. adv. comt, Bell Aerospace Co, 67-70; consult. Nat. Coun. Marine Resources & Eng. Develop, 67-71; mem. res. & technol. adv. comt. aeronaut, NASA, 67-70; mat. adv. bd, Nat. Res. Coun, 69-; adv. coun, sch. eng, George Wash. Univ, 70-; tech. adv. comt, Whirlpool Corp, 70-; sci. adv. comt, Gen. Motors, 71-; chmn. lab. adv. bd. undersea warfare, Dept. Navy, 71- Fel. AAAS; Nat. Acad. Eng; Eng. Joint Coun.(bd. dirs); hon. mem, Am. Soc. Mech. Eng; fel. Am. Inst. Aeronaut. & Astronaut.(pres, 71); Sci. Res. Soc. Am; Am. Ord. Asn. Applied mechanics; applied mathematics and engineering analysis; structures; aerodynamics; fluid flow; aircraft dynamics; vibration and impact problems; engineering analysis; operations research; industrial economics techniques. Address: Southwest Research Institute, 8500 Culebra Rd, San Antonio, TX 78284.

GOLAND, PHILIP PAKIER, b. Cincinnati, Ohio, Jan. 18, 09. PATHOLOGY. B.S, Cincinnati, 31, M.D, 35; M.S, Pennsylvania, 44. Intern, Harlem Hosp, N.Y, 35-37; asst. res. neurosurg, Jewish Hosp, Brooklyn, N.Y, 43-44; res. Univ. Hosp, Pennsylvania, 44-46; fel. res. surg. & neurosurg, Pennsylvania, 46-49; instr. path, col. med, Howard, 51-53, asst. prof, 53-56; res. assoc. & asst. pathologist, St. Joseph Hosp, 58-60; RES. ASSOC, COL. DENT, UNIV. ILL. MED. CTR, 61- Guest investr, Wistar Inst, Pa, 45-49. Dipl, Am. Bd. Path, 59. AAAS; Col. Am. Path. Chemotherapeutic dyes; selective staining; cross-linking agents; experimental oncology; experimental pathology. Address: Staff Apts, Apt. 809, University of Illinois, 809 S. Marshfield Ave, Chicago, IL 60612.

GOLARZ-DE BOURNE, MARIA NELLY, b. Montevideo, Uruguay, Jan. 21, 34; nat; m. 64. MICROSCOPIC ANATOMY, HISTOCHEMISTRY. B.A, Univ. of the Republic, Uruguay, 54; Ph.D.(anat), Emory, 63. Res. assoc. anat. micros, Univ. of the Republic, Uruguay, 55-58, asst. to prof. exp. biol, 58; asst. anat, med. sch, EMORY UNIV, 58-59, res. assoc, 60-63, histochem, YERKES PRIMATE RES. CTR, 63-66, ASST. HISTOCHEMIST, 66- Res. scientist, Colonial Res. Inst, 64-66; co-prin. investr, NASA grant, 67- Histochem. Soc; Am. Asn. Anat; Int. Primatol. Soc; Geront. Soc. Golgi apparatus; histochemistry of muscle diseases; space pathology. Address: Yerkes Primate Research Center, Emroy University, Atlanta, GA 30322.

GOLAY, MARCEL J(ULES) E(DOUARD), b. Neuchâtel, Switz, May 3, 02; nat; m; c. 4. PHYSICS. B.Sc, Neuchâtel, 20; Lic.E.E, Fed. Inst. Tech, Zurich, 24; Ph.D.(physics), Chicago, 31. Engr, Bell Tel. Labs, 24-28; Automatic Elec. Co, 30-31; from assoc. physicist to chief scientist, Signal Corps Labs, 31-55; SR. SCIENTIST, PERKIN-ELMER CORP, CONN, 55- Inst. Radio Eng, Diamond award, 51, Am. Chem. Soc, Sargent award, 60, Instrument Soc. Am, distinguished accomplishment award, 61. Am. Phys. Soc; Optical Soc. Am; Inst. Elec. & Electronics Eng. Acoustics; infrared; communications; nuclear magnetic resonance; gas chromatography. Address: Clair-Azur, 1095 Lutry, Switz.

GOLAY, MICHAEL W, U.S. citizen. NUCLEAR ENGINEERING. B.M.E, Univ. Fla, 64; U.S. Atomic Energy Comn. & Ford Found. fels. & Ph.D.(nuclear eng), Cornell Univ, 69. Res. assoc. NUCLEAR ENG, Rensselaer Polytech. Inst, 69-71; ASST. PROF, MASS. INST. TECHNOL, 71- Am. Nuclear Soc. Nuclear reactor physics; fluid mechanics; reactor engineering. Address: Dept. of Nuclear Engineering, Massachusetts Institute of Technology, Cambridge, MA 02139.

GOLBEN, MICHAEL, b. Rochester, N.Y, Nov. 22, 13; m. 43; c. 6. PHYSICAL CHEMISTRY. B.Chem, Cornell, 36, Ch.E, 37; Ph.D.(phys. chem), Kentucky, 49. Asst. dept. head, Am. Viscose Corp, 39-46, viscose res. chemist, 49-52, tech. supt, 52-54, group leader, pulp eval. lab, 54-58; assoc. tech. dir, Gould Nat. Batteries, Inc, 58-60; supvr. res. & develop. indust. finishing, MINN. MINING & MFG. CO, 60-68, IMAGING & ANAL. RES. PHOTO PROD, 69- Am. Chem. Soc; Electrochem. Soc. Viscose and rayon technology; thermodynamics of non-aqueous solutions; energy conversion; surfactant technology; mechanical plating; non-silver imaging. Address: 1381 Kohlman Ave, St. Paul, MN 55109.

GOLBER, DAVID (LAWRENCE), b. Pine Bluff, Ark, Oct. 23, 44. TOPOLOGY. B.S, Univ. Chicago, 64, Nat. Sci. Found. fel, 64-68, M.S, 65, Ph.D, 69. ASST. PROF. MATH, UNIV. CALIF, SAN DIEGO, 69- Am. Math. Soc. Topological transformation groups, especially cohomology theory of torus actions; cohomology manifolds; algebraic topology. Address: Dept. of Mathematics, University of California, San Diego, P.O. Box 109, La Jolla, CA 92037.

GOLBERG, LEON, b. Limassol, Cyprus, Aug. 22, 15; m. 44; c. 3. TOXICOLOGY, EXPERIMENTAL PATHOLOGY. M.Sc, Witwatersrand, 36, D.Sc.(biochem), 46; D.Phil.(org. chem), Oxford, 39; M.A, Cambridge, 48, M.B, B.Ch, 51. Jr. lectr. math, Witwatersrand, 36, lectr. chem, 39-40; res. biochemist, S.African Inst. Med. Res, 40-46; sr. lectr. chem. path, Manchester, 51-55; med. res. dir, Benger Labs, Ltd, 55-61; dir, Brit. Indust. Biol. Res. Asn, 61-67; RES. PROF. PATH, ALBANY MED. COL. & SCI. DIR, INST. EXP. PATH. & TOXICOL, 67- Milroy lectr, Royal Col. Physicians, London, 67- Consult. & chmn, report on comts, World Health Orgn, 64- Mem. steering comt, Trop. Prod. Inst, London, 63-66; task force on res. planning in environ. health sci, Nat. Inst. Environ. Health Sci, 68-69; drug res. bd. comt. on probs. of drug safety, Nat. Acad. Sci, 68-, food protection comt, Nat. Acad. Sci-Nat. Res. Coun, 69-; chmn. subcomt. on effects of pesticides on man, Secy. Health, Ed. & Welfare Comn. on Pesticides & Their Relationship to Environ. Health & panel mem, White House Conf. Food, Nutrit. & Health, 69; mem. hazardous mat. adv. comt, Environ. Protection Agency. Am. Chem. Soc; Soc. Toxicol; fel. Royal Inst. Chem; fel. Royal Col. Path. Development of improved methods of safety evaluation of drugs, food additives and other environmental chemicals; mechanisms and interrelationships of toxic action of environmental chemicals. Address: Institute of Experimental Pathology & Toxicology, Albany Medical College, Albany, NY 12208.

GOLBEY, ROBERT (BRUCE), b. New York, N.Y, July 15, 22; m. 48; c. 1. CHEMOTHERAPY. B.S, Bethany Col, 43; M.D, N.Y. Univ, 49. Res. fel, DIV. CLIN. CHEMOTHERAPY, SLOAN-KETTERING INST, 54, res. assoc, 55-57, asst, 57-60, ASSOC. MEM, 60-; CLIN. ASSOC. PROF. CLIN. MED, COL. MED, CORNELL UNIV, 70-, instr, 57-61, asst. prof, 61-70. Spec. fel. med, Mem. Ctr. & James Ewing Hosp, 54-57, clin. asst, Hosp, 57-59, asst. vis. physician, 59-62, assoc. vis. physician, 62-; clin. asst. physician, dept. med, Mem. Hosp, 57-60, asst. attend. physician, 60-62, assoc. attend. physician, 62-71, attending physician, 71-; consult, St. Joseph's Hosp, 60-; Stamford Hosp, 65- Med.C, U.S.A, 51-52, Res, 52-, Lt. Col. AAAS; Am. Asn. Cancer Res; Am. Soc. Clin. Oncol; Am. Med. Asn; James Ewing Soc; Harvey Soc; N.Y. Acad. Sci. Cancer chemotherapy; biology of malignant tumors and its relationship to clinical course and effective therapy. Address: Sloan-Kettering Institute, 444 E. 68th St, New York, NY 10021.

GOLCHERT, NORBERT WILLIAM, b. Chicago, Ill, July 12, 35; m. 58; c. 4. NUCLEAR CHEMISTRY, RADIOCHEMISTRY. B.S, Illinois, 58; M.S, Ill. Inst. Tech, 65, Ph.D.(chem), 69. Asst. in chem, ARGONNE NAT. LAB, 58-66, ASST. CHEMIST, 66- Am. Chem. Soc; Sci. Res. Soc. Am. Measurement of cross sections of nuclear reactions; radiochemical separation procedures; particularly the radioanalytical chemistry of technetium. Address: Argonne National Lab, 9700 S. Cass Ave, Argonne, IL 60439.

GOLD, ALBERT, b. Phila, Pa, July 2, 35; m. 60; c. 1. SOLID STATE PHYSICS. B.S, Lehigh, 56; Eastman-Kodak fel. & Ph.D.(physics), Rochester, 60. Res. assoc. physics, Illinois, 60-62; asst. prof. optics, Univ. Rochester, 62-65, assoc. prof, 65-69, assoc. dean col. eng. & appl. sci, 67-69; SPEC. ASST. TO PRES, ROCKEFELLER UNIV, 69-, DIR. POSTDOCTORAL AFFAIRS, 70- Consult, Argonne Nat. Lab, 60-69; United Aircraft Corp, 63-64; Eastman Kodak Co, 64-69. Am. Phys. Soc. Theory of optical properties of solids; theory of interaction of intense optical radiation with matter. Address: Rockefeller University, 66th St. & York Ave, New York, NY 10021.

GOLD, ALLEN, b. Montreal, Que, Dec. 19, 18; m. 42; c. 5. MEDICINE, ENDOCRINOLOGY. B.Sc, McGill, 40, M.D, C.M, 42, M.Sc, 48. Lectr. MED, McGILL UNIV, 49-70, ASSOC. PROF, 70-; SCI. DIR, HORMONE ASSAY LAB, 61- Assoc. physician, Montreal Gen. Hosp, 51-; consult. endocrinol. & metab, Queen Mary Vet. Hosp, 51-; endocrinol, Reddy Mem. Hosp. & Lachine Gen. Hosp. Fel, Royal Physicians & Surgeons Can, 49. R.C.A.M.C, 43-45, 46-, Capt. Endocrine Soc; Am. Diabetes Asn; fel. Am. Col. Physicians; Am. Thyroid Asn; Soc. Nuclear Med; Can. Soc. Clin. Invest; Can. Med. Asn. Clinical endocrinology, especially thyroid gland; development of new thyroid diagnostic tests. Address: Montreal General Hospital, Montreal 109, Que, Can.

GOLD, ALLEN M(ORTON), b. Chicago, Ill, May 25, 30; m. 52; c. 2. BIOCHEMISTRY. B.A, Chicago, 50, M.S, 52; Ph.D.(org. chem), Harvard, 55. Nat. Insts. Health fel, Swiss Fed. Inst. Tech, 55-56; staff scientist org. chem, Worcester Found. Exp. Biol, 56-58; vis. fel. BIOCHEM, COL. PHYSICIANS & SURGEONS, COLUMBIA UNIV, 58-62, asst. prof, 62-68, ASSOC. PROF, 68- Nat. Insts. Health res. career develop. award, 62-72. AAAS; Am. Chem. Soc; Am. Soc. Biol. Chem; Harvey Soc. Mechanism of enzyme action and chemistry of proteins. Address: Dept. of Biochemistry, College of Physicians & Surgeons, Columbia University, 630 W. 168th St, New York, NY 10032.

GOLD, A(LMA) HERBERT, b. Salt Lake City, Utah, Oct. 10, 11; m. 40; c. 2. PLANT PATHOLOGY. B.A, Utah, 38, M.A, 39; Ph.D.(plant physiol), California, 50. Asst. specialist, PLANT PATH, agr. exp. sta, UNIV. CALIF, BERKELEY, 48-51, instr, 51-53, lectr, 53-58, ASSOC. PROF, 59-, ASST. PLANT PATHOLOGIST, EXP. STA, 53-, jr. plant pathologist, 51-53. Fulbright fel, 57-58. Civilian with U.S.N, 42-45. Am. Phytopath. Soc. Morphology and serology; plant viruses; ecology of plant virus diseases. Address: Dept. of Plant Pathology, College of Agricultural Science, University of California, 108 Hilgard Hall, Berkeley, CA 94720.

GOLD, ALVIN H, b. Tyler, Tex, May 26, 32; m. 59; c. 1. BIOCHEMISTRY. B.A, Texas, 58, M.A, 61; fel, St. Louis, 61-64, Ph.D.(biochem, pharmacol), 65. Res. assoc. biol, State Univ. N.Y. Buffalo, 64-66; asst. prof. biochem, Bowman Gray Sch. Med, 66-68; PHARMACOL, SCH. MED, ST. LOUIS UNIV, 68-71, ASSOC. PROF, 71- U.S. Nat. Acad. Sci-East. Europ. res. fel, 71. AAAS; Am. Chem. Soc; Am. Soc. Biol. Chem; Am. Soc. Pharmacol. & Exp. Therapeut; Brit. Biochem. Soc. Hormone-medicated metabolic control systems; active site characterization of sulfhydryl-requiring enzymes. Address: Dept. of Pharmacology, St. Louis University School of Medicine, 1402 S. Grand St, St. Louis, MO 63104.

GOLD, ANDREW V(ICK), b. Inveresk, Scotland, Mar. 20, 34; m. 58; c. 3. PHYSICS. B.Sc, Edinburgh, 55; Carnegie scholar & Ph.D.(physics), Cambridge, 58. Fel. low-temperature & solid state physics, Nat. Res. Coun. Can, 58-60; res. assoc, Iowa State Univ, 60-61, asst. prof, 61-63, assoc. prof, 63-66, PROF, 66-68; PHYSICS, UNIV. B.C, 68- Sloan res. fel, 64-67. Fel. Am. Phys. Soc. Electronic and transport properties of metals; de Haas-van Alphen effect; ferromagnetism. Address: Dept. of Physics, University of British Columbia, Vancouver 8, B.C, Can.

GOLD, ARCHIE, b. Phila, Pa, June 15, 26; m. 55; c. 2. PHYSICS, SYSTEMS ENGINEERING. B.S, Drexel Inst. Technol, 48, M.S, 54; Univ. Pa, 56-57; Temple Univ, 59-66. Aeronaut. engr, Naval Air Develop. Ctr, Pa, 49-54; staff scientist & mgr, Radio Corp. Am, N.J, 54-66; chief missile phenomenology br, Advan. Res. Projs. Agency, Off. Secy. Defense, Wash, D.C, 66-68; DEP. DIR, ADVAN. BALLISTIC MISSILE DEFENSE AGENCY, U.S. ARMY, 68- Mem, ballistic missile early warning syst. ad hoc design comt, Radio Corp. Am, 61, ionization & Propagation panel, Defense Atomic Support Agency, 61-63, proj. scientist, fishbowl series, 62-63, mem, Air Force Minuteman ad hoc comt. reentry vehicles, 63; panel 272, Nat. Bur. Standards, Nat. Acad. Sci-Nat. Res. Coun, 67-; chmn, joint adv. comt, strategic panel, Advan. Ballistic Missile Defense Agency, U.S. Army Lincoln Lab, 68-69; mem, tripartite coop. prog, Advan. Res. Projs. Agency & Advan. Ballistic Missile Defense Agency, 68- Outstanding performance cert, Advan. Ballistic Missile Defense Agency, U.S. Army, 68, Dept. Army commendation, 71. U.S.N, 44-46. Sr. mem. AAAS; sr. mem. Am. Inst. Aeronaut. & Astronaut. sr. mem. Inst. Elec. & Electronics Eng. Reentry physics; electromagnetic propagation and scattering from hypersonic reentry vehicle or nuclear event produced plasma; ballistic missile defense system synthesis, evaluation, research and development; research and development management. Address: Office, Chief of Research & Development, U.S. Army Advanced Ballistic Missile Defense Agency, 11th Floor, Commonwealth Bldg, 1320 Wilson Blvd, Arlington, VA 22209.

GOLD, ARMAND J(OEL), b. Baltimore, Md, June 7, 26; m. 52; c. 2. ENVIRONMENTAL PHYSIOLOGY. A.B, West. Md. Col, 49; M.S, Maryland, 51, Ph.D.(physiol), 55. Asst. zool, Maryland, 50-52; physiologist, Chem. Corp. Med. Labs, U.S. Army, 52-55; asst. prof. physiol. res, sch. med, Maryland, 56-59; sr. develop. engr, Goodyear Aircraft Corp, 59-60; physiologist, missile & space vehicle dept, Gen. Elec. Co, 60-63; staff scientist, res. dept, Martin Co, 63-65; head dept. environ. physiol, Negev Inst. for Arid Zone Res, Beersheba, Israel, 65-67; ASSOC. PROF. PHYSIOL, HOWARD UNIV. COL, MED, 68- U.S.N, 44-46. AAAS; Am. Physiol. Soc; Aerospace Med. Asn. Acceleration stress; weightlessness; oxygen toxicity impact; hypoxia; heat stress. Address: Dept. of Physiology, Howard University College of Medicine, Washington, DC 20001.

GOLD, BERNARD, b. Brooklyn, N.Y, Mar. 31, 23; m. 45; c. 3. SPEECH COMMUNICATION, COMPUTER SCIENCE. B.E.E, City Col. New York, 44; Ph.D.(elec. eng), Polytech. Inst. Brooklyn, 49. Mem. staff radar, Avion Instrument Corp, 48-50; noise theory, Hughes Aircraft Co, 50-53; MEM. STAFF speech & comput, LINCOLN LAB, MASS. INST. TECHNOL, 53-69, COMMUN. DEPT, 69-, vis. prof, inst, 65-66. Fulbright fel. to Italy, 54-55. AAAS; Acoust. Soc. Am; sr. mem. Inst. Elec. & Electronics Eng. Noise theory; radar; pattern recognition; speech bandwidth compression; theory and design of computers. Address: Lincoln Lab, Massachusetts Institute of Technology, Lexington, MA 02173.

GOLD, DANIEL H(OWARD), b. New York, N.Y, Jan. 8, 29; m. 52; c. 2. PHYSICAL & ORGANIC CHEMISTRY. B.S, Brooklyn Col, 50; Dept. Interior fel, Polytech. Inst. Brooklyn, 53-54, Nat. Inst. Health fel, 54-56, Ph.D.(chem), 57. Chemist, Jewish Hosp, Brooklyn, 50-51; Sylvania Elec. Prod, Inc, N.Y, 51-53; sr. chemist, Am. Cyanamid Co, N.J, 56-62; sr. process res. specialist, Lummus Co, 62-67; GEN. SUPT. RUBBER CHEM. DEPT, AM. CYANAMID CO, BOUND BROOK, 67- Am. Chem. Soc. Organic process development; statistical experimental design and analysis; chromatography; complexation; metal ion-polyelectrolyte interactions. Address: 928 Field Ave, Plainfield, NJ 07060.

GOLD, DAVID P(ERCY), b. Durban, Natal, S.Africa, June 22, 33; Can. citizen; m. 59; c. 4. GEOLOGY, PETROLOGY. B.Sc, Natal, 53, Hons, 54, M.Sc, 58, Gregory fel, McGill, 59-60, Leroy fel, 60-61, Ph.D.(geochem), 63. Geol. asst. mineral explor, Union Corp. Ltd, S.Africa, 55-56; lectr. geol, Loyola Col.(Can), 62-64; res. assoc. geol. & geochem, PA. STATE UNIV, 64-68, ASSOC. PROF. GEOL, 68-, Wilson teaching award, 70. Nat. Res. Coun. Can. grant, 63-64; res. assoc, spec. proj, NASA grants, 64-71; Nat. Sci. Found. res. grants, 65-70; distinguished lectr, Am. Geol. Inst, 70; mem. postdoctoral fel. comt, Nat. Acad. Sci, 71; planetology comt, Int. Geol. Cong, 72.

Barlow Mem. Medal, Can. Inst. Mining & Metal. Eng, 67. Geol. Soc. Am; Mineral Asn. Can; Geol. Soc. S.Africa; Geol. Asn. Can; Meteoritical Soc. Structural geology; geophysical exploration and mining geology in Southern Africa; petrology and geochemistry of carbonatites and alkaline rocks; geological mapping in Northern Quebec; structural analysis in Canadian Appalachians, and around volcanic and impact craters. Address: Dept. of Geology & Geophysics, 310 Deike Bldg, Pennsylvania State University, University Park, PA 16802.

GOLD, EDWARD, b. New York, N.Y. Nov. 25, 41; m. 63; c. 2. PHYSICAL METALLURGY. B.S, Polytech. Inst. Brooklyn, 63; Campbell fel. & M.S, Columbia, 65, Sc.D, 67. Sr. scientist PHYS. METALL, appl. res. lab, AERONUTRONIC DIV, PHILCO-FORD CORP, 67-68, PRIN. SCIENTIST, ADVAN. DEVELOP. OPER, 68- Am. Inst. Mining, Metall. & Petrol. Eng. Field ion microscope study of short-range order in platinum base alloys; thermomechanical processing of aluminum alloys and superalloy development; physical metallurgy and mechanical properties of beryllium. Address: Room 204, Bldg. 2, Aeronutronic Division, Advanced Development Operation, Philco-Ford Corp, Newport Beach, CA 92663.

GOLD, ELI, b. New Haven, Conn, July 20, 20; m. 43; c. 2. VIROLOGY, PEDIATRICS. B.S, Connecticut, 42; M.D, Western Reserve, 50. Intern & res. pediat, Boston Children's Med. Ctr, 50-53; res, Cleveland City Hosp, 53-54; from instr. to asst. prof. prev. med. & pediat, SCH. MED, CASE WEST. RESERVE UNIV, 54-65, assoc. prof. PEDIAT, 65-69, PROF, 69- Microbiologist, Conn. State Dept. Health, summer 42; U.S. Pub. Health Serv. spec. res. fel, Inst. Virol, Scotland, 61-62, career develop. award, 64-70. Dipl. Am. Bd. Pediat. Med.C, 42-45, T/Sgt. Soc. Pediat. Res. Synthesis of herpes simplex particle; characteristics of meningococcus; virulence factors, expecially immunity. Address: Cleveland Metropolitan General Hospital, 3395 Scranton Rd, Cleveland, OH 44109.

GOLD, ELIJAH H(ERMAN), b. New York, N.Y, May 22, 36; m. 62; c. 2. ORGANIC CHEMISTRY. B.S, City Col, New York, 57; M.S, Yale, 58, Nat. Insts. Health fel. & Ph.D.(org. chem), 63. Fel, Columbia, 62-64; Nat. Insts. Health fel, Israel Inst. Tech, 64-66; sr. res. chemist, SCHERING CORP, 66-69, prin. chemist, 69-70, SECT. LEADER, MED. CHEM. DEPT, 70- Am. Chem. Soc. Mechanistic and synthetic organic chemistry; organic photochemistry; small ring heterocycles and medicinal chemistry. Address: Medicinal Chemistry Dept, Schering Corp, 60 Orange St, Bloomfield, NJ 07003.

GOLD, GEORGE, b. Budapest, Hungary, Sept. 5, 12; U.S. citizen; m. 48; c. 4. PATHOLOGY. M.D, Zurich, 38. From intern to res. path, Fordham Hosp, 41-43, asst. pathologist, 43-44; fel. & asst, New York City Cancer Inst, 47-48; chief lab, regional off, Vet. Admin, 52; dir, Willowbrook State Sch, 52-60; Craig Colony & Hosp, 60-63; LAB. DIR, BRONX STATE HOSP, 63-; ASST. CLIN. PROF, COL. PHYSICIANS & SURGEONS, COLUMBIA UNIV, 70-, res. assoc, 67-70. Med.C, 44-46, Res, 46-52, Capt. Am. Asn. Neuropath. Pathologic alterations in the central nervous system with special emphasis on toxic effects and degenerative changes. Address: Bronx State Hospital, 1500 Waters Pl, Bronx, NY 10461.

GOLD, GERALD, b. Pittsburgh, Pa, Aug. 8, 27; m. 54; c. 3. PHARMACY. B.Sc, Univ. Pittsburgh, 51, M.Sc, 58, Ph.D.(pharm), 61. RES. PHARMACIST, MILES HOME PROD, MILES LABS, INC, 61- Med.C, U.S.A, 51-53. Am. Pharmaceut. Asn. Emulsions; tablets; aerosols. Address: Miles Labs, Inc, 1127 Myrtle St, Elkhart, IN 46514.

GOLD, G(USTAVE) LENNARD, b. New York, N.Y, June 28, 28; m. 52; c. 3. INTERNAL MEDICINE. B.S, Purdue, 48; M.D, Virginia, 52. Fel, U.S. Pub. Health Serv, 53-54; clin. assoc, Nat. Cancer Inst, Nat. Insts. Health, 54-56, head solid tumor chemotherapy, 57-58; resident med, Peter Bent Brigham Hosp, Boston, Mass, 56-57; asst. dir. cancer chemother, sch. med, Georgetown Univ, 58-61, assoc. dir, 61-69; private practice, 69- Consult, Nat. Cancer Inst, Nat. Insts. Health, Md; Wash. Hosp. Ctr, Wash. D.C; Morris Cafritz Mem. Hosp. U.S.A.R, 48-51; U.S.P.H.S, 54-, Sr. Asst. Surg. Am. Asn. Cancer Res; Am. Fedn. Clin. Res; fel. Am. Col. Physicians. Medical oncology; chemotherapy of malignant diseases. Address: 9801 Georgia Ave, Silver Spring, MD 20902.

GOLD, HARRIS, b. N.Y.C, Mar. 20, 36; m. 60; c. 2. AERONAUTICS. B.M.E, Polytech. Inst. Brooklyn, 58; Boese fel. & M.S, Columbia, 59; Del Mar fel, Calif. Inst. Tech, 60, Boeing Aircraft fel, 61, Rand Corp, fel, 62-63, Ph.D. (aeronaut), 63. Asst. aeronaut, Calif. Inst. Tech, 59-63; sr. staff scientist, AVCO SYSTS. DIV, AVCO CORP, 63-66, mgr, aerophys. dept, 66-68, sr. consult. scientist, 68-70, PRIN. STAFF SCIENTIST, 70- Consult. E.H. Plesset Assocs, Inc, Calif, 61-62. Am. Inst. Aeronaut. & Astronaut. Laminar stability and laminar-turbulent transition of wake flows; jet flow fields; liquid film coating; ion exchange. Address: 18 Peachtree Rd, Lexington, MA 02173.

GOLD, HARVEY J(OSEPH), b. Southampton, N.Y, Oct. 20, 32; m. 51; c. 2. THEORETICAL BIOCHEMISTRY. B.S, Miami (Fla), 54; M.S, Wisconsin, 56, Ph.D.(food tech, biochem), 58. Asst, Wisconsin, 54-58; res. biochemist, U.S. Dept. Agr, 58-63; fel. BIOMATH, N.C. STATE UNIV, 63-65, ASSOC. PROF, 65- AAAS; Am. Chem. Soc; Math. Asn. Am; Am. Inst. Chem; Biophys. Soc; Int. Soc. Quantum Biol; N.Y. Acad. Sci. Theory of biochemical systems and enzyme catalysis. Address: Biomathematics Program, Dept. of Statistics, North Carolina State University, Raleigh, NC 27607.

GOLD, JAY J(OSEPH), b. New York, N.Y, Feb. 17, 23; m. 50; c. 2. INTERNAL MEDICINE, ENDOCRINOLOGY. A.B, N.Y. Univ, 46; M.D, State Univ, N.Y, 50. Intern, Brooklyn Jewish Hosp, 50-51, res. internal med, 51-52; fel. endocrinol, col. physicians & surg, Columbia, 52-54; res. internal med, Bronx Vet. Admin. Hosp, 54-55; ASSOC. PROF. MED, sch. med, Univ. Chicago, 56-65; MED. SCH, NORTHWEST. UNIV.(ILL), 65- Attend. endocrinol, Westside Vet. Admin. Hosp, 59-; staff consult, Highland Park Community Hosp; Skokie Valley Community Hosp; Lutheran Gen. Hosp. U.S.A, 43-46. Endocrine Soc; Soc. Study Reproduction; Am. Fedn. Clin. Res. Chemistry and physiology of pituitary, adrenal, gonads, hirsutism and infertility. Address: 9701 Kenton, Skokie, IL 60076.

GOLD, JEROME A, b. Brooklyn, N.Y, Feb. 8, 28; m. 49; c. 2. INTERNAL MEDICINE, INFECTIOUS DISEASES. B.S, Long Island, 47; M.D, Chicago Med. Sch, 53. Chief chest & infectious disease serv, U.S. Naval Hosp, Bethesda, Md, 57-59; asst. dir. med, Jewish Hosp, Brooklyn, N.Y, 59-60; asst. prof, State Univ. N.Y. Downstate Med. Ctr, 60-61; Chicago Med. Sch, 61-62; DIR. CLIN. RES. INFECTIOUS DISEASE, SMITH KLINE & FRENCH LABS, 62-; CLIN. ASSOC. PROF. MED, MED. COL. PA, 70-, clin. asst. prof, 63-70. Asst. vis. physician, Kings County Hosp, Brooklyn, 57-61; asst. attend. physician, Phila. Gen. Hosp, 63-; consult, U.S. Naval Hosps, Phila. & Bethesda, 63-; vis. assoc. prof, Univ. Pa. Sch. Med, 70-, assoc. physician, Presby-Univ. Pa. Hosp. U.S.N, 57-59, Lt. Comdr. AAAS; Am. Med. Asn; Am. Thoracic Soc; Am. Soc. Microbiol; N.Y. Acad. Sci; Am. Fedn. Clin. Res; Am. Soc. Trop. Med. & Hyg; Int. Union Against Tuberc. Pulmonary and infectious diseases, especially tuberculosis; antimicrobial chemotherapy. Address: Smith Kline & French Labs, 1500 Spring Garden St, Philadelphia, PA 19001.

GOLD, KENNETH, b. Jersey City, N.J, July 21, 32; m. 56; c. 4. MARINE BIOLOGY, PROTOZOOLOGY. B.A, N.Y. Univ, 53, M.S, 59, Nat. Insts. Health fels, 60, 61, Ph.D.(fishery biol), 62. Res. asst, Haskins Labs, 56-58; res. fels, New York Aquarium & Haskins Labs, 60-61; res. assoc. marine microbiol, Lamont Geol. Observ, Columbia, 63-65; RES. ECOLOGIST & HEAD DEPT. MARINE CHEM. & POLLUTION, OSBORN LABS. MARINE SCI, NEW YORK AQUARIUM, 65- U.S. Pub. Health Serv. fel, environ. radiation lab, inst. indust. med, N.Y. Univ, 62-63; U.S. Atomic Energy contract, microbiol. assays of seawater using radioisotopes, 63-69, role of planktonic protozoa in marine food chain, 69-; adj. asst. prof, Fordham Univ, 66-67. U.S.A.F, 53-55, 1st Lt. AAAS; Soc. Protozool; Am. Soc. Limnol. & Oceanog; Phycol. Soc. Am; Ecol. Soc. Am. Marine microbiology; nutrition and ecology of marine plankton; microbiological assays; radiation biology. Address: Osborn Labs. of Marine Sciences, New York Aquarium, Brooklyn, NY 11224.

GOLD, LEONARD MORTON, b. Phila, Pa, Feb. 23, 40; m. 62; c. 3. SOLID MECHANICS, DYNAMICS. B.S.M.E, Drexel Inst. Technol, 62, univ. assistantships, 62 & 66, M.S.M.E, 64, Ph.D.(appl. mech), 69. Res. mgr, Lawrence Div, C.G.S. Sci. Corp, 69; MECH. ENGR, MECH. & STRUCTURES GROUP, MAT. ENG. DIV, PITMAN-DUNN RES. LAB, U.S. ARMY FRANKFORD ARSENAL, 69- C.Eng, U.S.A, 64-66, Capt. Am. Soc. Mech. Eng; Soc. Exp. Stress Anal. Unstable material behavior of commercially pure aluminum; solid mechanics stress analysis and finite element techniques; x-ray residual stress analysis. Address: 1976 Green Tree Rd, Cherry Hill, NJ 08034.

GOLD, L(EWIS) PETER, b. Brockton, Mass, May 21, 35; m. 65. PHYSICAL CHEMISTRY. A.B, Harvard, 57, Nat. Sci. Found. fels, 57-61, A.M, 59, Ph.D.(chem), 62. Res. physicist, Columbia, 61-62, res. assoc. physics, 62-65; asst. prof. CHEM, PA. STATE UNIV, 65-70, ASSOC. PROF, 70- AAAS; Am. Phys. Soc. Microwave spectroscopy and molecular structure. Address: Dept. of Chemistry, Whitmore Lab, Pennsylvania State University, University Park, PA 16802.

GOLD, MARTIN. BIOCHEMISTRY, PHYSIOLOGY. B.Sc, Phila. Col. Pharm, 54; M.S, Hahnemann Med. Col, 56, Ph.D.(biochem), 59. Res. assoc. physiol, Hahnemann Med. Col, 59-64, res. asst. prof, 64-67; res. assoc, geront. res. inst, Phila. Geriat. Ctr, 67-70; DIR. CLIN. BIOCHEM, DEPT. LAB. MED, NAZARETH HOSP, 70- Nat. Inst. Arthritis & Metab. Diseases grant, 64-67; S.Cent. Pa. Health Asn. grant, 67-68. AAAS; Am. Inst. Chem; Am. Chem. Soc; Am. Physiol. Soc; Am. Asn. Clin. Chem. Glycolytic enzymes; proteinases; lipid metabolism, specifically free fatty acid and glyceride metabolism. Address: Dept. of Lab. Medicine, Nazareth Hospital, Philadelphia, PA 19152.

GOLD, MARTIN I, b. Phila, Pa, Nov. 22, 28; m. 51; c. 3. MEDICINE, ANESTHESIOLOGY. B.A, Pennsylvania, 50; M.D, State Univ. N.Y, 54. Res, grad. hosp, Pennsylvania, 54-57; from instr. to PROF. ANESTHESIOL, SCH. MED, UNIV. MD, 59- Nat. Insts. Health fel, 61-67 & spec. res. fel, 67-68; vis. prof, Royal Postgrad. Med. Sch, London, Eng, 67-68. U.S.N.R, 57-59, Lt. Am. Soc. Anesthesiol; Am. Soc. Pharmacol. & Exp. Therapeut; Asn. Univ. Anesthetists; Sci. Res. Soc. Am; Int. Anesthesia Res. Soc. Pulmonary physiology as related to mechanics and gases during anesthesia. Address: Dept. of Anesthesiology, University of Maryland Medical School, Baltimore, MD 21201.

GOLD, MARVIN, b. Toronto, Ont, Feb. 2, 36; m. 58; c. 5. BIOCHEMISTRY. B.A, Toronto, 57, Ph.D.(biophys), 62. Jane Coffin Childs fel, 62-63; asst. prof. develop. biol, Albert Einstein Col. Med, 65-67; ASSOC. PROF. med. biophys, UNIV. TORONTO, 67-69, MED. CELL BIOL, 69- Nucleic acids of bacteria and bacteriophage; genetics; enzymology. Address: Dept. of Medical Cell Biology, 4th Floor, Medical Sciences Bldg, Faculty of Medicine, University of Toronto, Toronto 181, Ont, Can.

GOLD, MARVIN B, b. New York, N.Y, June 23, 33; m. 62; c. 1. INORGANIC CHEMISTRY. B.Sc, Ohio State, 58; Ph.D.(chem), California, Berkeley, 62. Res. chemist, California, Berkeley, 63; asst. prof. INORG. CHEM, CHICO STATE COL, 63-67, assoc. prof, 67-71, PROF, 71-, CHMN. DEPT. CHEM, 70- U.S.A, 54-56. Am. Chem. Soc. Coordination chemistry; non-aqueous solvents. Address: Dept. of Chemistry, Chico State College, Chico, CA 95926.

GOLD, MARVIN H(AROLD), b. Buffalo, N.Y, June 23, 15; m. 40; c. 2. ORGANIC CHEMISTRY. A.B, California, Los Angeles, 37; Ph.D.(org. chem), Illinois, 40. Anna Fuller Fund fel, cancer res, Northwestern, 40-42; res. chemist, Visking Corp, Ill, 42-45, head org. chemist, 45-48; develop. chemist, AEROJET SOLID PROPULSION CO. DIV, GEN. TIRE & RUBBER CO, 48-50, sr. chemist, 50-51, prin. chemist, 51-56, assoc. dir, chem. dept, 56-58, asst. mgr, chem. div, 58-59, assoc. dir. in charge SACRAMENTO CHEM. OPERS, 59-60, mgr. propellant chem. div, 60-62, SR. SCIENTIST, 62- Spec. lectr, Brit. Govt. Personnel, Eng, 55. Meritorious pub. serv. citation, Secy. Navy, 63. Am. Chem. Soc; Am. Inst. Aeronaut. & Astronaut; Am. Ord. Asn; Sci. Res. Soc. Am. Polynuclear hydrocarbons; aliphatic nitro chemistry; solid propellants; high polymers; polymerization; cellulose;

vapor phase reactions at elevated temperatures. Address: Aerojet Solid Propulsion Co, Box 13400, Sacramento, CA 95813.

GOLD, NORMAN I(RVING), b. Chicago, Ill, Nov. 21, 21; m. 45; c. 3. BIOCHEMISTRY. B.S, Chicago, 43; M.S, Mass. Inst. Tech, 47, Ph.D.(biochem), 50. Res. biochemist, Mass. Gen. Hosp, 50; Peter Bent Brigham Hosp, 50-58; ASSOC. BIOCHEM, HARVARD MED. SCH, 53-, CHILDREN'S HOSP. MED. CTR, BOSTON, 58- Med.C, U.S.A, 43-46. Steroid hormone metabolism; endocrinology. Address: 15 Sycamore Rd, Newton, MA 02159.

GOLD, RAYMOND, b. New York, N.Y, Oct. 3, 27; m. 51; c. 4. PHYSICS. B.A, N.Y. Univ, 51, M.S, 54; Ph.D, Ill. Inst. Tech, 58. Physicist, Columbia, 52-54; group leader, Gen. Elec. Co, 54-55; res. physicist, Armour Res. Found, Ill. Inst. Tech, 55-58; prof. & head nuclear sci. & eng. dept, Lowell Tech. Inst, 58-62; MEM. STAFF, ARGONNE NAT. LAB, 62- Consult, U.S. Naval Radiol. Defense Lab, 59-60; Tech. Opers. Inc, 60-62; Avco Corp, 61-62. U.S.N, 45-48, 51-52. AAAS; Am. Phys. Soc; Am. Nuclear Soc; Am. Soc. Eng. Educ. Experimental nuclear physics; applied mathematics; cosmic rays and environmental radiation measurements. Address: 6402 Bradley Dr, Downers Grove, IL 60515.

GOLD, RICHARD F(RANK), b. Seattle, Wash, Sept. 14, 41; m. 66. INORGANIC CHEMISTRY. B.S, Trinity Col.(Conn), 63; Ph.D.(inorg. chem), Purdue Univ, 68. Res. asst, Purdue Univ, 66-68; sr. res. scientist, Battelle-Northwest, 68-69; RES. SCIENTIST, EAST. RES. CTR, STAUFFER CHEM. CO, 69- Am. Chem. Soc. Covalently bonded inorganic compounds; radiochemistry; heterogeneous catalysis; inorganic silicates. Address: Apt. C-4, 35 S. Broadway, Irvington, NY 10533.

GOLD, RICHARD R(OBERT), b. Chicago, Ill, Mar. 27, 30; m. 52; c. 3. PHYSICS, APPLIED MATHEMATICS. B.S, Illinois, 51, univ. fel. & M.S, 55, Ph.D.(gas dynamics, math), 56. Mem. tech. staff gas dynamics, McDonnell Aircraft Corp, 51-52 & summer, 55; inst. math, U.S. Armed Forces Inst, 52-54; mem. tech. staff aerodyn, Hughes Aircraft Co, 56-59, staff physicist, 59-61; head magnetogas dynamics sect, lab. div, Aerospace Corp, 61-64; mgr. aerospace physics res. dept, space systs. div, Hughes Aircraft Co, 64-68; PROF. MECH. ENG, CALIF. STATE COL, LONG BEACH, 68- Lectr. mech. eng. dept, Southern California, 57-58; phys. sci. exten, California, Los Angeles, 57-62. U.S.A.R, 52-54, 1st Lt. Assoc. fel. Am. Inst. Aeronaut. & Astronaut; Am. Phys. Soc. Electromagnetic wave propagation through plasmas; magnetohydrodynamics; fluid dynamics. Address: Dept. of Mechanical Engineering, California State College at Long Beach, Long Beach, CA 90801.

GOLD, ROBERT, b. Phila, Pa, Mar. 29, 42; m. 68. MATHEMATICS. B.A, Swarthmore Col, 64; Ph.D.(math), Mass. Inst. Tech, 68. Chief mathematician, S.Ross & Co, summer 68; ASST. PROF. MATH, OHIO STATE UNIV, 68- AAAS; Am. Math. Soc. Algebraic number theory; gamma extensions; structure of ideal class groups; imaginary quadratic fields; cyclotomic fields. Address: Dept. of Mathematics, College of Mathematics & Physical Sciences, Ohio State University, 231 W. 18th Ave, Columbus, OH 43210.

GOLD, ROBERT D, b. Brooklyn, N.Y, June 21, 31; m. 56; c. 3. ELECTRICAL ENGINEERING. B.E.E, City Col. New York, 53; M.S, Cornell, 57. Mem. tech. staff, res. labs, Radio Corp. Am, 57-61, eng. leader semiconductor electronics, N.J, 61-70; OPERS. MGR, MICROELECTRONICS DIV, LAMBDA ELECTRONICS CORP, 70- Sig.C, U.S.A, 53-55. Int. Soc. Hybrid Microelectronics; sr. mem. Inst. Elec. & Electronics Eng. Microwave semiconductor devices; tunnel and varactor diodes; high power transistors; semiconductor impact ionization; hybrid microelectronics; vacuum technology. Address: 21 Glenrich Dr, St. James, NY 11780.

GOLD, R(OBERT) M(URRAY), b. New York, N.Y, Jan. 29, 23; m. 48; c. 2. PHYSICAL CHEMISTRY. B.S, City Col. New York, 43; M.S, N.Y. Univ, 47, Ph.D.(chem), 54. Res. chemist, Manhattan Proj, 43-45; plant supt, Kings Electronics Co, 45-47; sr. res. assoc, Keuffel & Esser Co, 47-67; DIR. RES, ULANO PROD. CO, 67- AAAS; Am. Chem. Soc; Am. Electroplaters Soc; Nat. Microfilm Asn; Soc. Photog. Sci. & Eng; N.Y. Acad. Sci. Photographic chemistry; electrochemistry; thermography; photoconductivity. Address: Ulano Products Co, 610 Dean St, Brooklyn, NY 11238.

GOLD, THOMAS, b. Vienna, Austria, May 22, 20; nat; m. 47; c. 3. ASTRONOMY. B.A, Cambridge, 42, M.A, 46, Sc.D, 69; hon. M.A, Harvard, 57. Exp. off. radar res. & develop, British Admiralty, 42-46; res. grant, Cavendish Lab, Cambridge, 46-47, fel, Trinity Col, 47-51, demonstr. physics, 49-52, res. grant, Med. Res. Coun, zool. lab, 47-49; sr. prin. sci. off, Royal Greenwich Observ, 52-56; prof. astron, Harvard, 57-58, Robert Wheeler Willson prof. appl. astron, 58-59; prof. ASTRON, CORNELL UNIV, 59-71, JOHN L. WETHERILL PROF, 71-, DIR, CTR. FOR RADIOPHYSICS & SPACE RES, 59- Nat. Acad. Sci; fel. Royal Soc; fel. Am. Astron. Soc; Am. Geophys. Union; fel. Am. Acad. Arts & Sci; Int. Acad. Astronaut; Royal Astron. Soc. Cosmology; geophysics; radio astronomy; magnetohydrodynamics. Address: Dept. of Astronomy, Space Sciences Bldg, Cornell University, Ithaca, NY 14850.

GOLD, WILLIAM, b. Buffalo, N.Y, Jan. 2, 23; m. 52; c. 4. MICROBIOLOGY. B.S, Cornell, 43; M.S, Wisconsin, 48, Ph.D.(bact), 50. Instr. bact. & bact. physiol, 50; fel, Rutgers, 50-51; res. assoc, E.R. Squibb & Sons, 51-57; microbiologist, Bzura, Inc, 57-63; supvr. biol. res, Beech Nut Lifesavers, Inc, 63-67; ASST. PROF. MICROBIOL, COL. DENT, N.Y. UNIV, 67- Am. Chem. Soc; Am. Soc. Microbiol; N.Y. Acad. Sci. Biochemistry of microbial processes; dental research. Address: Dept. of Microbiology, New York University College of Dentistry, New York, NY 10010.

GOLDAK, GEORGE R, b. Prince Albert, Sask, Dec. 12, 36; m. 61; c. 3. CRYSTALLOGRAPHY. B.Eng, Saskatchewan, 58, M.Sc, 60, Ph.D.(geol), 67. RES. ASSOC. METALL. CRYSTALLOG, Alberta, 60-63; UNIV. SASK, 66- Theoretical crystal-structure analysis; x-ray diffraction topography of crystal imperfections. Address: Dept. of Electrical Engineering, University of Saskatchewan, Saskatoon, Sask, Can.

GOLDAN, PAUL D(AVID), b. Reno, Nev, Nov. 25, 33; m. 59; c. 3. PLASMA PHYSICS. B.S, Mass. Inst. Tech, 55; Fulbright grant, Heidelberg, 55-56; M.S, Illinois, 58, Ph.D.(plasma physics), 64. Physicist & Nat. Res. Coun. res. grant, Boulder Lab, Nat. Bur. Standards, 64-65; prof. physics, Dartmouth Col, 65-66; PHYSICIST, AERONOMY LAB, NAT. OCEANOG. & ATMOSPHERIC ADMIN, 66- Am. Phys. Soc. Use of microwave diagnostic techniques in plasma physics; electron beam measurement of quiescent and turbulent plasmas. Address: 444-0000, Aeronomy Lab, National Oceanographic & Atmospheric Administration, Boulder, CO 80302.

GOLDBAUM, GEORGE C, b. Mexico City, Mex, May 31, 22; U.S. citizen. AERONAUTICS, ASTRONAUTICS. B.S, Texas, 46, M.S, 53. Res. engr, defense res. lab, Texas, 51-56, spec. lectr, 54-56; group engr. aeronaut. & astronaut. sect, missile & space systs. div, Douglas Aircraft Co, Inc, 56-58, supvr, 58-61, chief, 61-62, adv. progs. mgr. advan. medium launch systs, 62-64, dir, 64-66, prog. integration for manned orbital lab. prog, 66-68, advan. missions off, manned orbiting lab, McDONNELL DOUGLAS ASTRONAUT. CO, 68-70, MGR. PROG. INTEGRATION, ADVAN. SENSOR SYSTS, ADVAN. SYSTS. & TECHNOL, 70- U.S.A, 40-41, S/Sgt. Am. Astronaut. Soc. Advance space systems design; total requirements for future systems and subsystems; system management. Address: Advance Sensor Systems, Advance Systems & Technology, McDonnell Douglas Astronautics Co, 5301 Bolsa Ave, Huntington Beach, CA 92647.

GOLDBERG, AARON, b. Brooklyn, N.Y, Nov. 4, 17. VETERINARY PARASITOLOGY. A.B, Brooklyn Col, 39; M.S, De Paul, 54; Ph.D.(bot), George Washington, 62. Res. clerk, census of agr, U.S. Bur. Census, 40-41; vet. parasitologist, zool. div, bur. animal indust, U.S. Dept. Agr, Md, 47-51, parasitologist in charge, zool. lab, Ill, 51-53, vet. parasitologist, VET. SCI. RES. DIV, NAT. ANIMAL PARASITE LAB, 53-71, ZOOLOGIST, 71- U.S.A, 41-45, Sgt. Am. Soc. Parasitol; Soc. Syst. Zool; Am. Soc. Plant Taxon; N.Y. Acad. Sci. Population dynamics within the host and on pasture; pathogenicity and morphology of gastrointestinal nematodes of cattle; phylogeny and taxonomy of angiosperms at family level and above. Address: National Animal Parasite Lab, Agricultural Research Center, Beltsville, MD 20705.

GOLDBERG, AARON S(OLOMON), b. N.Y.C, Aug. 28, 10; m. 49; c. 1. ORGANIC CHEMISTRY, BIOCHEMISTRY. B.S, City Col. New York, 38; Sc.D. (chemother), Paris, 51. Res. chemist biochem, N.Y. Hosp, 34-39; dir, Richard M. Koster Res. Lab, 39-41; chemist, Pasteur Inst, Paris, 47-51; assoc. chemist, Mt. Sinai Hosp, 51; HEAD DEPT. CHEM, Bronx Hosp, New York, 53-65; HOSP. JOINT DISEASES, 65- Lab. off. & chief, lab. serv, Army Hosps, Eng, France & Ger, Sanit.C, 43-46. AAAS; Am. Chem. Soc; Am. Asn. Clin. Chem. Chemotherapeutic effects of pyrimidine derivatives; mechanisms of detoxication of local anesthetics; clinical chemistry; analytical techniques. Address: Chemistry Lab, Hospital for Joint Diseases, New York, NY 10035.

GOLDBERG, ABRAHAM, b. N.Y.C, May 13, 33; m. 64; c. 1. PHYSICS. B.A, N.Y. Univ, 55; Nat. Sci. Found. fel, Stanford, 55-58, Ph.D.(physics), 60. Nat. Sci. Found. fel, 60-62; asst. prof. physics, Washington (Seattle), 62-64; PHYSICIST, LAWRENCE RADIATION LAB, UNIV. CALIF, 64- Am. Phys. Soc. Theoretical nuclear and high energy physics; numerical methods allied with computers. Address: Lawrence Radiation Lab, P.O. Box 808, Livermore, CA 94550.

GOLDBERG, ALAN HERBERT, b. Boston, Mass, Nov. 29, 31; m. 58; c. 2. ANESTHESIOLOGY, CARDIOVASCULAR PHYSIOLOGY. A.B, Brown, 53; M.D, Boston, 57; Ph.D.(physiol), Georgetown, 65. Intern surg, Univ. Hosp, Boston, Mass, 57-58; res. anesthesia, Mass. Gen. Hosp, 58-60; trainee cardiovasc. physiol, sch. med, Georgetown, 62-63, clin. instr. anesthesia & lectr. pharmacol, 63-65; asst. prof. anesthesiol, sch. med, Boston Univ. & asst. anesthesiologist, univ. hosp, 65-69, assoc. prof. & assoc. anesthesiologist, 69-70, lectr. physiol, 70; ASSOC. PROF. ANESTHESIA, HARVARD MED. SCH, 70- Nat. Heart Inst. fel, 62-65, D.C. Gen. Hosp, 63-64; res. fel, sch. med, Georgetown Univ, 64-65; Nat. Insts. Health career develop. award, 66-70; consult, Chelsea Naval Hosp, 69-; supv. physician, resucitation serv, cardiovasc. unit & dir. anesthesia res. & assoc. vis. physician, Boston City Hosp, 70- Dipl, Nat. Bd. Med. Exam, 58; Am. Bd. Anesthesiol, 63. U.S.P.H.S, 60-62, Sr. Asst. Surg. AAAS; Am. Physiol. Soc; Am. Soc. Pharmacol. & Exp. Therapeut; Cardiac Muscle Soc; Asn. Univ. Anesthetists; Am. Fedn. Clin. Res; Am. Soc. Anesthesiol; Int. Anesthesia Res. Soc; fel. Am. Col. Anesthesiol. Myocardial contractility; renal physiology and blood flow; vascular resistance. Address: Anesthesia Research Lab, Boston City Hospital, 818 Harrison Ave, Boston, MA 02118.

GOLDBERG, ALAN MARVIN, b. New York, N.Y, Nov. 20, 39; m. 60; c. 2. PHARMACOLOGY. B.S, Long Island, 61; Wisconsin, 61-62; Ph.D, Minnesota, 66. Res. asst, Wisconsin, 61-62; Minnesota, 62-66; res. fel, Inst. Psychiat, Indiana, 66-67, asst. prof. pharmacol, 67-69; ENVIRON. MED, JOHNS HOPKINS UNIV, 69-71, ASSOC. PROF, 71- Consult, New Castle State Hosp; spec. consult. sect. epilepsy, Nat. Inst. Neurol. Diseases & Stroke. Ind. Neurol. Soc. award, 67. AAAS; Am. Soc. Pharmacol. & Exp. Therapeut; Soc. Neurosci; Am. Soc. Neurochem; N.Y. Acad. Sci. Acetylcholine metabolism; drug action on the central nervous system; neurotransmitters and experimental epilepsy. Address: Dept. of Environmental Medicine, Johns Hopkins University School of Hygiene, Baltimore, MD 21205.

GOLDBERG, A(LBERT) I(SAAC), b. N.Y.C, Oct. 23, 15; m. 40; c. 3. CHEMISTRY. B.A, Brooklyn Col, 37, M.A, 43; George Washington, 41-42; Ph.D. (org. chem), Polytech. Inst. Brooklyn, 47. Jr. chemist, Holabird Ord. Depot, U.S. War Dept, Md, 41-43; chemist, U.S. Indust. Chem, N.J, 43-44; res. assoc, Polytech. Inst. Brooklyn, 44-47; res. chemist, Nat. Starch Prods, 48-51, supvr. polymer res, 51-55, MEM. TECH. STAFF, NAT. STARCH & CHEM. CO, 55- AAAS; Am. Chem. Soc; N.Y. Acad. Sci. Polymerization of vinyl monomers; protective coatings; adhesives. Address: 47 West End Ave, Summit, NJ 07901.

GOLDBERG, ALFRED, b. Montreal, Que, Can, Oct. 2, 23; nat; m. 50; c. 3. PHYSICAL METALLURGY. B.Eng, McGill, 46; M.S, Carnegie Inst. Tech, 47; Ph.D.(metall), California, 55. Res. engr. phys. metall, California, 47-53; asst. prof. metall, U.S. Naval Postgrad. Sch, 53-59, assoc. prof, 59-64; SR. SCIENTIST, LAWRENCE LIVERMORE LAB, 64- Am. Soc. Metals; Metall. Soc. Calorimetry of alloys; deformation of metals; phase transformations. Address: Metallurgy Division, Dept. of Chemistry, Bldg. 332, Lawrence Livermore Lab, Box 808, Livermore, CA 94550.

GOLDBERG, ALFRED L, b. Providence, R.I, Sept. 3, 42; m. 70. PHYSIOLOGY, BIOCHEMISTRY. A.B, Harvard, 63, Nat. Insts. Health fel, 65-66, Ph.D.(physiol), 68; Churchill fel, Cambridge, 63-64. Instr. PHYSIOL, HARVARD MED. SCH, 68-69, asst. prof, 69-71, ASSOC. PROF, 71- Nat. Res. Coun-Air Force Off. Sci. Res. fel, 68-69; Med. Found, Inc, fel, 69-71; Wise & Helen Burroughs lectr, Univ. Iowa, 70. AAAS; Am. Physiol. Soc. Regulation of growth and protein metabolism in mammalian tissues; mechanisms of muscle hypertrophy and atrophy; neuromuscular function; mechanisms of intracellular protein turnover; amino acid metabolism; hormonal effects on muscle. Address: Dept. of Physiology, Harvard Medical School, Boston, MA 02115.

GOLDBERG, ARTHUR FRANK, b. N.Y.C, July 6, 28; m. 62; c. 2. HEMATOLOGY, HISTOCHEMISTRY. A.B, Syracuse, 48; N.Y. Univ, 48-49; M.D, Lausanne, 54. Res. assoc. path, Albert Einstein Col. Med, 60; res. asst. hemat, Mt. Sinai Hosp, New York, 61-62; INSTR. CLIN. MED, SCH. MED, N.Y. UNIV, 62- Nat. Insts. Health res. grant, 61-67, Dipl, Am. Bd. Internal Med, 63. U.S.N.R, 57-58, Lt. Am. Soc. Hemat; Am. Med. Asn; Am. Soc. Clin. Oncol; Am. Fedn. Clin. Res; Am. Soc. Internal Med. Cytochemistry of cellular organelles in blood cells; blood forming tissues in benign and malignant states; associated cellular changes in malignancy; chemotherapy of malignant tumors. Address: 950 Park Ave, New York, NY 10028.

GOLDBERG, ARTHUR H, b. N.Y.C, Jan. 21, 35; m. 62; c. 2. PHARMACY. B.S, Columbia Univ, 56, M.S, 65; Nat. Insts. Health fel. & Ph.D.(pharmacy), Univ. Mich, 68. Res. chemist, Lion Pharmaceut, Inc, 60-61; Shulton, Inc, 61-63; ASST. PROF, PHARM, COLUMBIA UNIV, 68- U.S.A.F, 1st Lt. AAAS; Am. Pharmaceut. Asn; Acad. Pharmaceut. Sci. Drug transport and availability; diffusional aspects of dissolution. Address: Dept. of Pharmacy, Columbia University, 115 W. 68th St, New York, NY 10023.

GOLDBERG, BENJAMIN, b. Baltimore, Md, Jan. 22, 14; m. 43. HISTOCHEMISTRY. M.A, Hopkins, 39, Ph.D.(bot), 48. Antibiotics analyst, Food & Drug Admin, D.C, 46; biologist, med. div, Chem. Corps, Army Chem. Center, Md, 46-49; INSTR. prev. med, SCH. MED, JOHNS HOPKINS UNIV, 49-51, GYNEC-OBSTET, 51- Sanit.C, U.S.A, 40-45, Lt. Histochem. Soc. Enzyme histochemistry. Address: Dept. of Gynecology-Obstetrics, 202 Pathology Bldg, Johns Hopkins Hospital, Baltimore, MD 21205.

GOLDBERG, BENJAMIN, b. New York, N.Y, Apr. 14, 15; m. 38; c. 3. PHYSICS. B.S, City Col, 36. Physicist, eng. res. & develop. labs, U.S. ARMY, 41-46, chief reflector res. lab, 47-49, proj. engr. infrared, 50-51, chief, illum. sect, 51-52, far infrared sect, 52-53, night vision equip. br, 54-58, mine detection br, 58-62, barrier and intrusion detection div, 63-65, warfare vision div, 65, dep. dir, NIGHT VISION LAB, 65-68, DIR, 68- Except. civilain serv. award, U.S. Army, 45, meritorious civilian serv. awards, 69 & 70. AAAS; Optical Soc. Am; Sci. Res. Soc. Am. Infrared; illumination; reflector optics; mine detection; intrusion detection; image intensification. Address: 8717 Sundale Dr, Silver Spring, MD 20910.

GOLDBERG, BURTON D(AVID), b. Milwaukee, Wis, Jan. 6, 27. PATHOLOGY. B.S, Northwestern, 48, M.D, 50. Intern, Cincinnati Gen. Hosp, 51-52; instr. PATH, sch. med, Boston, 53-55; Tufts, 54-55; teaching fel, Harvard Med. Sch, 56-57; asst. prof, SCH. MED, N.Y. UNIV, 57-59, ASSOC. PROF, 60- Res, Mallory inst. path, Boston City Hosp, 52-55; res. fel, Nat. Found. Infantile Paralysis, 55-57; res. assoc, Mass. Inst. Tech, 56-57; asst. pathologist, Bellevue Hosp, 57-59. Dipl, Am. Bd. Path, 56. U.S.N.R, 45-46. Am. Soc. Exp. Path. Electron microscopy; cell biology. Address: Dept. of Pathology, New York University, 550 First Ave, New York, NY 10016.

GOLDBERG, COLMAN, b. Detroit, Mich, July 8, 24; m. 49; c. 3. PHYSICS. B.S, Wayne State, 48; M.S, Northwestern, 49, fel, 50-51, Ph.D.(physics), 51. Res. physicist, res. labs, Westinghouse Elec. Corp, 51-58, sect. mgr, 58-64; mem. tech. staff, Bell Tel. Labs, 64-66; PROF. ELEC. ENG, NORTHWEST. UNIV, 66- U.S.A.A.F, 43-46. AAAS; Am. Phys. Soc; Inst. Elec. & Electronics Eng. Semiconductor devices; physics of semiconductors. Address: Dept. of Electrical Engineering, Technological Institute, Northwestern University, Evanston, IL 60201.

GOLDBERG, DAVID C, b. Dallas, Tex, June 27, 21; m. 43; c. 3. METALLURGY, MATERIALS SCIENCE. B.S, Antioch Col, 43; Ohio State, 43-44; Stevens Inst. Tech, 46-47. Engr, Battelle Mem. Inst, 41-44; Saunders Mach. & Tool, 46-47; sr. engr, Hamilton Watch Co, 47-51; supvr. metall, aviation gas turbine div, WESTINGHOUSE ELEC. CORP, 51-54, mgr, 54-60, adv. engr, 60-61, dir. space mat, 61-62, mgr. struct. mat. & processes, ASTRONUCLEAR LAB, 62-66, MGR. MAT. DEPT, 66- Mem. comt. toxicity of beryllium, Mat. Adv. Bd-Nat. Acad. Sci, 53-54, refractory metal sheet rolling panel C, 64-66, chmn. tubing comt, 66-67, mem. comt. tech. aspects of strategic mat, 67-71; mem. res. adv. comt, mat, NASA, 62-71, chmn, 67-70; mem. NATO Summer Support Eval. Conf. Refractory Metals, 67. U.S.A.A.F, 44-45. Am. Inst. Aeronaut. & Astronaut; Am. Soc. Metals; Am. Soc. Test. & Mat; Sci. Res. Soc. Am; Am. Ord. Asn. Development and application of titanium, super alloys and refractory metals to advanced propulsion and power generating apparatus. Address: 2355 Willowbrook Rd, Upper St. Clair, PA 15241.

GOLDBERG, DAVID E(LLIOTT), b. Scranton, Pa, July 26, 32; m. 59; c. 2. INORGANIC CHEMISTRY. B.S, George Washington, 54; Ph.D.(inorg. chem), Pa. State, 59. Instr. CHEM, Pa. State Univ, 58-59; BROOKLYN COL, 59-62, assoc. prof, 66-70, PROF, 70-, DEP. CHMN. DEPT, 63- F.G. Cottrell grant, 60-61; City Univ. New York grant, 64-65; Nat. Inst. Gen. Med. spec. fel, Univ. Sussex, 66-67. Am. Chem. Soc; The Chem. Soc. Stability and bonding in coordination compounds; solvent extraction of heavy metal ions by coordination. Address: Dept. of Chemistry, Brooklyn College, Brooklyn, NY 11210.

GOLDBERG, EDWARD B, b. Bronx, N.Y, July 19, 35; m. 62; c. 2. BIOLOGY. B.A, Columbia, 56; univ. fel, Hopkins, 57-58, Nat. Insts. Health fel, 58-59, Ph.D.(biol), 61; Nat. Insts. Health fel, Calif. Inst. Tech, summer 59, Vanderbilt, 59-61, Nat. Sci. Found. fel, 61. Jr. instr. biol, Hopkins, 56-57; guest investr. bacteriophage genetics, Carnegie Inst, 61-63, fel, Genetics Res. Unit, 63-65; asst. prof. microbiol, SCH. MED. & DENT, TUFTS UNIV, 65-69, ASSOC. PROF. MOLECULAR BIOL. & MICROBIOL, 69- Fel, Nat. Found. Med. Res, 61-63; vis. prof, Hadassah Med. Sch-Hebrew Univ, 69-70. AAAS; Am. Soc. Biol. Chem. Mechanisms of control of DNA penetration recombination and transcription of bacteriophage. Address: Dept. of Molecular Biology and Microbiology, School of Medicine & Dentistry, Tufts University, 136 Harrison Ave, Boston, MA 02111.

GOLDBERG, EDWARD D, b. Sacramento, Calif, Aug. 2, 21; m. 45; c. 2. GEOCHEMISTRY. B.S, Univ. Calif, 42; Ph.D.(chem), Univ. Chicago, 49. Asst. prof. CHEM, SCRIPPS INST. OCEANOG, UNIV. CALIF, SAN DIEGO, 49-55, assoc. prof, 55-60, PROF, 60- Guggenheim fel, Berne, 61; NATO Fel, Univ. Brussels, 70. U.S.N.R, 42-46, Lt. AAAS; Geochem. Soc; Am. Geophys. Union. Geochemistry of marine waters; marine sedimentation; meteoritics; radiochemistry; atmospheric and marine pollution. Address: Scripps Institution of Oceanography, La Jolla, CA 92037.

GOLDBERG, EDWIN A(LLEN), b. Dallas, Tex, Sept. 13, 16; m. 42; c. 2. ELECTRONICS. B.S, Texas, 38, M.S, 40. Seismic engr, Magnolia Petrol. Co, 38-39; asst. elec. eng, Texas, 39-40; engr, res. dept, RCA CORP, 40-42, mem. tech. staff, res. labs, 42-57, MGR. missile & weapon systs, defense electronic prods. div, spec. systs. develop. dept, 57-58, eng. & admin, ASTRO-ELECTRONICS DIV, 58, design, 58-59, space vehicle systems, 59-62, spacecraft design & test, 62-64, spacecraft tests, 64-65, SPEC. PROJS, 65- Ord. Dept, U.S.A, 45. Inst. Elec. & Electronics Eng. Electronic analog computer components and systems; color television systems; satellite and space electronics systems. Address: Electro-Mechanical Design, Space Power & Sr. Technical Staff, RCA Astro-Electronics Division, P.O. Box 800, Princeton, NJ 08540.

GOLDBERG, ERWIN, b. Waterbury, Conn, Jan. 14, 30; m. 51; c. 3. ZOOLOGY, PHYSIOLOGY. B.A, State Univ. N.Y, 51; M.S, Iowa, 53, U.S. Pub. Health Serv. fel, 54-56, Ph.D.(zool, biochem), 56. Res. assoc. zool, Iowa, 56-58; asst. prof. biol, West Virginia, 58-61; zool, N.Dak. State, 61-63; BIOL, NORTHWEST. UNIV.(ILL), 63-66, ASSOC. PROF, 66- AAAS; Soc. Develop. Biol; Am. Soc. Biol. Chem; Am. Soc. Zool. Physiology and biochemistry of mammalian germ cells; reproductive physiology; developmental biology. Address: Dept. of Biological Sciences, Northwestern University, Evanston, IL 60201.

GOLDBERG, ESTELLE M(AXINE), b. Las Vegas, Nev, Apr. 19, 34; m. 54; c. 2. MATHEMATICS. B.A, California, Los Angeles, 53; M.A, Columbia, 59, Ph.D.(math), 65. Asst. prof. MATH, SAN FRANCISCO STATE COL, 62-66, ASSOC. PROF, 66- Am. Math. Soc; Math. Asn. Am. Algebra; homological algebra. Address: Dept. of Mathematics, San Francisco State College, San Francisco, CA 94132.

GOLDBERG, E(UGENE), b. Chicago, Ill, May 29, 27; m; c. 2. NUCLEAR PHYSICS. B.S, Ill. Inst. Tech, 48, M.S, 50; Atomic Energy Comn. fel, Wisconsin, 51-53, Ph.D.(physics), 53. Asst. physics, Ill. Inst. Tech, 48-50; Alumni Res. Found. asst, Wisconsin, 50-51; sr. physicist, Livermore Proj, LAWRENCE RADIATION LAB, UNIV. CALIF, 53-65, EXP. PHYSICS DIV. LEADER, 65- U.S.N.R, 45-46. Am. Phys. Soc; Am. Nuclear Soc. Experimental nuclear physics; interaction of charged particles with light nuclei: using Van de Graaff generator; thermonuclear weapon development; neutronic design of epithermal homogeneous reactors; experimental studies of heavy ion interactions. Address: 5454 Greenridge Rd, Castro Valley, CA 94546.

GOLDBERG, EUGENE P, b. Southampton, N.Y, Nov. 11, 28; m. 50; c. 3. ORGANIC CHEMISTRY. B.S, Miami (Fla), 50; Cottrell fel. & M.S, Ohio (Athens), 51; fel, Brown, 52-53, Ph.D.(chem), 53. Asst, Ohio (Athens), 51; Brown, 52; res. & develop. chemist, chem. develop. dept, Gen. Elec. Co, 53-57, specialist prod. develop, 57, supvr. dielec. adv. develop, capacitor dept, 57-60; mgr. polymer chem, res. ctr, Borg-Warner Corp, 60-64, assoc. dir, head chem. res. dept, 64-66; MGR. CHEM. RES. LAB, ROCHESTER RES. CTR, XEROX CORP, 66- AAAS; Am. Chem. Soc. Diels-Alder reactions; heterocyclics; hydrocarbon oxidation; polymer science; condensation polymerization; polycarbonates; polysulfonates; block copolymers; dielectric fluids and polymers; surface chemistry; electrostatic processes and materials; enzyme chemistry; liquid crystals; organic photoconductors. Address: 124 Roby Dr, Rochester, NY 14618.

GOLDBERG, GERALD, b. Phila, Pa, June 27, 33; div; c. 2. POLYMER & ORGANIC CHEMISTRY. B.A, Temple, 54, M.A, 60. Chemist, Publiker Industs, 54; Quaker Chem. Prod. Corp, 54-59; sr. chemist, Foster Grant Co, 60-64; group leader adhesives & coatings, Marbon Div, BORG-WARNER CORP, 64-68, DEVELOP. SPECIALIST PLASTICS & POLYMERS, DEVELOP. DIV, 68- Am. Chem. Soc. Emulsion and suspension polymerization; synthesis and application of textile treating agents; adhesives and coatings development; applications of additives in polymeric materials; fire retardants. Address: 404 37th St, Vienna, WV 26101.

GOLDBERG, GERSHON M(ORTON), b. Paterson, N.J, April 5, 24; m. 51; c. 3. ORGANIC CHEMISTRY. B.S, Pa. State Col, 44, M.S, 47, Ph.D.(org. chem), 49. Fel, Northeastern, 49-50; RES. CHEMIST, petrol, Daugherty ref. div, L. Sonnenborn Sons, Inc, 50-54; TECH. OPERS. INC, 54- AAAS; Am. Chem. Soc; Soc. Photog. Sci. & Eng; Royal Photog. Soc. Gt. Brit. Solubility of quaternary ammonium compounds; organosilicon compounds; petroleum sulfonates; photographic chemistry; sensitizing dyes; thin films; unconventional photographic systems. Address: 31 Grand View Rd, Arlington, MA 02174.

GOLDBERG, HAROLD, b. Milwaukee, Wis, Jan. 31, 14; m. 36; c. 2. ELECTRICAL ENGINEERING, BIOPHYSICS. B.S, Wisconsin, 35, M.S, 36, fel, 35-37, Ph.D.(elec. eng), 37, fel, 38-41, Ph.D.(physiol), 41. Asst. math, Wisconsin, 37-38, fel. physiol, 38-41; sr. res. engr, Stromberg-Carlson Co, N.Y, 41-45; prin. res. engr, radio div, Bendix Aviation Corp, Md, 45-47; chief eng, electronics div, Nat. Bur. Standards, 47-54; v.pres, Emerson Radio & Phonograph Corp, 54-61; exec. v.pres. & dir, Emertron, Inc, 61-

63; v.pres. res. & eng, Raytheon Co, 63-64; v.pres. & gen. mgr. mil. electronics div, Ling-Temco-Vought, Inc, 64-65; v.pres. & dir, LTV Electrosysts, Inc. & gen. mgr. Garland Div, 65-69; EXEC. V.PRES. & DIR, RIKER-MAXSON CORP, 69- Chmn. fuze panel, guided missiles comt, res. & develop. bd, U.S. Dept. Defense. Award, U.S. Dept. Commerce, 53. Am. Phys. Soc; Am. Ord. Asn; Am. Mgt. Asn; fel. Inst. Elec. & Electronics Eng. Electronics and biophysics; research and aerospace general management. Address: 5190 Linnean Terr. N.W, Washington, DC 20008.

GOLDBERG, HAROLD D(ORIAN), b. N.Y.C, Oct. 1, 13. PHYSICS. B.S, City Col, 33; Columbia, 33-36. Teacher, pub. schs, N.Y, 35-42; res. scientist, Columbia Univ, 42-68; ASST. CLIN. PROF. MED. PHYSICS, ALBERT EINSTEIN COL. MED, 68- Spec. instr, Albert Einstein Col. Med, 58-68. With Off. Sci. Res. & Develop; Nat. Defense Res. Comt; Atomic Energy Comn; U.S.A; U.S.N; U.S.A.F; Nat. Insts. Health. AAAS; Am. Phys. Soc; Inst. Elec. & Electronics Eng. Biomedical, electronic, nuclear, and oceanographic instrumentation; electromagnetic induction transducer. Address: Albert Einstein College of Medicine, Yeshiva University, 1300 Morris Park Ave, Bronx, NY 10461.

GOLDBERG, HARRY, b. Phila, Pa, May 19, 18; m. 46; c. 2. MEDICINE. A.B, Pennsylvania, 39; M.D, L.I. Col. Med, 44. Intern, Mt. Sinai Hosp, Albert Einstein Med. Ctr, 44-45; res. path, Metrop. Hosp, N.Y, 45-46, 48; internal med, Mt. Sinai Hosp, Pa, 48-49; fel. cardiovasc. diseases, Michael Reese Hosp, Ill, 50; asst. prof. physiol, Hahnemann Med. Col, 51-53, med, 53-60; DIR, CARDIOVASC. DEPT, ALBERT EINSTEIN MED. CTR, 60-; PROF. MED, SCH. MED, TEMPLE UNIV, 66- Dir, cardiopulmonary lab, Hahnemann Med. Col, 51-60. Dipl, Am. Bd. Internal Med, 53. Med.C, 46-48, Capt. AAAS; Am. Physiol. Soc; Am. Heart Asn; fel. Am. Col. Physicians; fel. Am. Col. Chest Physicians; Am. Fedn. Clin. Res; N.Y. Acad. Sci; Fedn. Am. Socs. Exp. Biol. Clinical cardiovascular research; cardiology. Address: Cardiovascular Dept, Albert Einstein Medical Center, York & Tabor Rds, Philadelphia, PA 19141.

GOLDBERG, HENRY, b. Brussels, Belgium, Nov. 22, 31; U.S. citizen; m. 56; c. 2. PHYSICS. B.S, City Col. New York, 54; Ph.D.(physics), Maryland, 59. Solid state physicist, Nat. Bur. Standards, 56-59; res. assoc. PHYSICS, radiation lab, Hopkins, 59-60; lectr, STATE UNIV. N.Y. BUFFALO, 60-61, ASST. PROF, 61- Nat. Sci. Found. grant, 61-64. AAAS; Am. Phys. Soc; Am. Asn. Physics Teachers. Crystal field theory; solid state theory; magnetically confined plasmas. Address: Dept. of Physics, State University of New York at Buffalo, Buffalo, NY 14214.

GOLDBERG, HENRY P(ETER), b. N.Y.C, Dec. 14, 10; m. 42; c. 4. CARDIOLOGY. A.B, Johns Hopkins Univ, 32, M.D, 36. Asst. PEDIAT, Johns Hopkins Univ, 39-41; res. fel, MED. COL, CORNELL UNIV, 46-48, asst. prof, 50-60, assoc. prof, 60-71, PROF, 71-; DIR. PEDIAT, NORTH SHORE HOSP, 69- Asst. prof, Yale, 52-53; pediatric cardiologist, Queens Med. Ctr, 57-64; St. Vincents Med. Ctr, 63-68; consult, St. Albans Naval Hosp, 48-63; Phelps Mem. Hosp, Tarrytown, N.Y, 58-; Good Samaritan Hosp, N.Y, 59-; St. Vincents Med. Ctr, 68-; Booth Mem. Hosp, Queens, N.Y, 70-; Meadowbrook Hosp. Med.C, 44-46, Lt. Comdr. Harvey Soc; N.Y. Acad. Sci; Am. Acad. Pediat. Heart disease. Address: 440 E. 63rd St, New York, NY 10021.

GOLDBERG, HERBERT S(AM), b. N.Y.C, July 23, 26; m. 48; c. 2. MICROBIOLOGY. B.S, St. John's (N.Y), 48; M.A, Missouri, 50; fel. & Ph.D.(bact), Ohio State, 53. Asst. bact, Ohio State, 50-53; asst. prof. MICROBIOL, SCH. MED, UNIV. MO-COLUMBIA, 53-57, assoc. prof, 57-61, PROF, 61-, ASSOC. DEAN, 71-, asst. to dean, 66-67, asst. dean, 67-71. Wellcome Trust traveling fel, 60-64; vis. scientist, Cambridge, 60; vis. prof, Southern Illinois, 61; consult, World Health Orgn, 62-67, 67-72. Med.C, U.S.N, 44-46. AAAS; Am. Soc. Microbiol; N.Y. Acad. Sci; Soc. Appl. Bact; Brit. Soc. Gen. Microbiol; French Soc. Microbiol. Nitrofurans in chemotherapy; antibiotic assay techniques; nontherapeutic uses of antibiotics; chemotherapy of Leptospiroses; bacteroides identification; research administration. Address: School of Medicine, University of Missouri-Columbia, Columbia, MO 65201.

GOLDBERG, HOWARD S, b. Chicago, Ill, Mar. 26, 36; m. 64; c. 2. PARTICLE PHYSICS. B.S.E.E, Michigan, Ann Arbor, 58; Ph.D.(physics), California, Berkeley, 64. Asst. prof. PHYSICS, Tuskegee Inst, 64-66; UNIV. ILL, CHICAGO CIRCLE, 66-70, ASSOC. PROF, 70- Am. Phys. Soc. Strong and weak interactions in elementary particle high energy physics. Address: Dept. of Physics, University of Illinois at Chicago Circle, Box 4348, Chicago, IL 60680.

GOLDBERG, HYMAN, b. Montreal, Que, Can, May 21, 39; m. 65; c. 1. PHYSICS. B.Sc, McGill, 59; Woodrow Wilson fel, Mass. Inst. Tech, 59-60, Int. Bus. Mach. fel, 62-63, Ph.D.(physics), 63. Instr. PHYSICS, Brandeis, 63-64, res. assoc, 64; Nat. Res. Coun. Can. overseas fel, Theoret. Physics Lab, Orsay, France, 64-65; instr. & res. assoc, Cornell Univ, 65-67; asst. prof, NORTHEAST. UNIV, 67-69, ASSOC. PROF, 69- Res. staff mem, Mass. Inst. Technol, 63-64. Am. Phys. Soc. Elementary particle physics. Address: Dept. of Physics, Northeastern University, Boston, MA 02115.

GOLDBERG, IRVING H(YMAN), b. Hartford, Conn, Sept. 2, 26; m. 56; c. 2. MEDICINE, PHARMACOLOGY. B.S, Trinity Col.(Conn), 49; M.D, Yale, 53; fel, Rockefeller Inst, 57-60, Ph.D.(biochem), 60; hon. A.M, Harvard, 64. Intern med, Columbia-Presby. Med. Center, N.Y, 53-54, asst. res, 54-56, chief res, 56-57; asst. prof. med. & biochem, Chicago, 60-64, assoc. prof, 64; med, HARVARD MED. SCH, 64-68, prof, 68-72, chmn. div. med. sci, 68-70, GUSTAVUS ADOLPHUS PFEIFFER PROF. PHARMACOL. & CHMN. DEPT, 72- Instr, Col. Physicians & Surgeons, Columbia Univ, 56-57; mem, B.C. Res. Coun. Can, 59; chief endocrinol. metab. unit, Beth Israel Hosp, Boston, 64-68, physician, 64-; Guggenheim Mem. Found. fel, Univ. Oxford, 70-71. Faculty res. assoc. award, Am. Cancer Soc, 60-71. U.S.N, 45-46. Am. Soc. Biol. Chem; Am. Soc. Clin. Invest; Endocrine Soc; Asn. Am. Physicians; Am. Chem. Soc. Biosynthesis of nucleic acids and protein; protein hormone synthesis, especially thyroglobulin; endocrinology; mechanism of action of antibiotics affecting nucleic acid synthesis and function; protein synthesis. Address: Dept. of Pharmacology, Harvard Medical School, Boston, MA 02115.

GOLDBERG, IRWIN, b. New York, N.Y, Dec. 22, 30; m. 55; c. 1. THEORETICAL PHYSICS. B.S, Syracuse, 51, Ph.D, 56; scholar, Rochester, 51-54, M.S, 54. Asst, Rochester, 51-54; Syracuse, 54-56, res. assoc, 56; physicist, Brookhaven Nat. Lab, 57-59; asst. prof. PHYSICS, Michigan, 59-61; N.Y. Univ, 61-62; ASSOC. PROF, Rutgers, 62-64; Clarkson Col. Technol, 64-67; DREXEL UNIV, 67- Consult, United Aircraft Corp, 61-62; Space Sci, Inc, 65- Am. Phys. Soc; Fedn. Am. Sci. Quantum field theory; theories of elementary particles; general theory of relativity; quantum electrodynamics. Address: Dept. of Physics, Drexel University, Philadelphia, PA 19104.

GOLDBERG, IVAN D, b. Phila, Pa, May 13, 34; m. 61; c. 3. MICROBIAL GENETICS. A.B, Pennsylvania, 56; Ph.D.(microbiol), Illinois, 61. Fel. microbial genetics, inst. microbiol, Rutgers, 61-62; Oregon State, 62-63; Army Biol. Labs, Ft. Detrick, 63-64, microbial geneticist, 64-71; ASSOC. PROF. MICROBIOL, MED. CTR, UNIV. KANS, 71- Am. Soc. Microbiol. Microbial genetics including transformation and transduction; bacteriophages and lysogeny. Address: 39th & Rainbow Blvd, Kansas City, KS 66103.

GOLDBERG, JACOB, b. San Francisco, Calif, June 4, 26; m. 48; c. 4. ELECTRONIC ENGINEERING. B.S, Univ. Calif, 50; M.S, Stanford Univ, 54; Weizmann Inst, 58. GROUP MGR, STANFORD RES. INST, 51- U.S.N, 44-46. Inst. Elec. & Electronics Eng; Asn. Comput. Mach. Computers; logical design of digital computers; software engineering. Address: 3373 Cowper St, Palo Alta, CA 94306.

GOLDBERG, JANICE BETTY, Psychol, Educ, see Suppl. I to 11th ed, Soc. & Behav. Vols.

GOLDBERG, JAY M, b. Chicago, Ill, Nov. 9, 35; m. 59; c. 4. NEUROPHYSIOLOGY, NEUROANATOMY. A.B. & S.B, Univ. Chicago, 56, Ph.D. (psychol), 60. Nat. Sci. Found. fel, 60-62; Nat. Inst. Health trainee, 62-63; asst. prof. PHYSIOL, UNIV. CHICAGO, 63-68, ASSOC. PROF, 68- AAAS; Acoustical Soc. Am; Am. Asn. Anat; Psychonomic Soc. Behavior of single neurons in brain; auditory neurophysiology; tracing of anatomical pathways; vestibular neurophysiology. Address: Dept. of Physiology, University of Chicago, 951 E. 58th St, Chicago, IL 60637.

GOLDBERG, JERALD M(ELVIN), b. Dallas, Tex, Oct. 1, 28. GEOLOGY, GEOGRAPHY. B.S, Southern Methodist, 48, M.S, 49. Geologist, TexFel Petrol. Corp, 49-50, 52-56; dist. geologist, William J. Carey Co, 56-57; geologist, Bluebonnet Oil Corp, 57-61; U.S. Geol. Surv, 61-62 & 65, geol. consult, U.S. Army Hq, Europe, 62-65; prog. scientist, NASA, 65-69; ASST. CHIEF OFF. PROG. & BUDGET, GEOL. DIV, U.S. GEOL. SURV, 69- U.S.A, 50-52, Sgt. Geol. Soc. Am. Program formulation and administration of geologic programs; development of techniques for the application of geologic data to environmental problems and land-use planning. Address: U.S. Geological Survey, Room 4214, GSA Bldg, Washington, DC 20242.

GOLDBERG, JOHN EDWARD, b. Seattle, Wash, Sept. 29, 09; m. 44; c. 1. MECHANICS, STRUCTURAL ENGINEERING. B.S, Northwestern, 30, fel, 30-31, C.E, 31; Ph.D.(mech), Ill. Inst. Tech, 55. Engr, City of Chicago, 32-42; struct. engr, Waco Aircraft Co, Ohio, 42-43; Consol. Vultee Aircraft Co, Calif, 43-47; asst. prof. mech. & assoc. dir. fundamental mech. res, Ill. Inst. Tech, 47-50; assoc. prof. struct. eng, Purdue, 50-53, 54-55; design specialist, Convair div, Gen. Dynamics Corp, Calif, 53-54; PROF. STRUCT. ENG, PURDUE UNIV, 56-, ACAD. HEAD, 65- Instr. eve. sch, Univ. Calif, 44-47. Mem. column res. coun, ship res. comt, Nat. Acad. Sci. Am. Soc. Civil Eng; Am. Soc. Eng. Educ; Int. Asn. Bridge & Struct. Eng. Structural dynamics; structural analysis; failure of structures; elastic stability; shell theory; thermal stresses; nuclear reactors; missiles; aircraft; ships; engines. Address: School of Civil Engineering, Purdue University, Lafayette, IN 47907.

GOLDBERG, JOSEPH, b. New York, N.Y, Apr. 30, 23; m. 45; c. 4. MECHANICAL & AERONAUTICAL ENGINEERING. B.A.E, N.Y. Univ, 44; M.S.E, Princeton, 59. Aerodynamicist, Chance-Vought Aircraft, 44; flight test engr, Wright Field Air Develop. Center, 44-46; aerodynamicist, Fairchild Aircraft, 46-47; sr. aerodynamicist, Glenn L. Martin Co, 47-49; aerodyn. design specialist, Naval Air Develop. Center, 49-52; res. assoc. flight dynamics, Princeton, 52-60; asst. prof. aeronaut. eng, Illinois, 60-61; ASSOC. PROF. MECH. ENG, Drexel Inst, 61-65; VILLANOVA UNIV, 65- Consult, Curtiss-Wright Corp, Boeing Vertol Div. & Aeronaut. Res. Assocs. Princeton, 52-60; Thiokol Chem. Corp. & Piasecki Aircraft, 61- U.S.A.A.F, 44-46. AAAS; Am. Inst. Aeronaut. & Astronaut; Am. Soc. Eng. Educ; Am. Soc. Mech. Eng. Flight dynamics of missiles and fixed-wing and rotary wing aircraft; automatic controls; systems dynamics. Address: Dept. of Mechanical Engineering, Villanova University, Villanova, PA 19085.

GOLDBERG, JOSEPH L(OUIS), b. N.Y.C, Sept. 11, 09. ORGANIC CHEMISTRY. B.S, City Col, 30; A.M, Columbia, 33, Ph.D.(biochem), 47. Microanalyst, Rockefeller Inst, 34-37; instr. CHEM, CITY COL. NEW YORK, 41-51, ASST. PROF, 51- Civilian with Office Sci. Res. & Develop, 44. Am. Chem. Soc. Quantitative organic microanalysis; amino acids and proteins; isolation of antibiotics. Address: Dept. of Chemistry, City College of New York, New York, NY 10031.

GOLDBERG, JOSHUA N(ORMAN), b. Rochester, N.Y, May 30, 25; m. 49; c. 2. PHYSICS. A.B, Rochester, 47, M.S, Syracuse, 50, Ph.D.(physics), 52. Physicist, Armour Res. Found, Ill. Inst. Tech, 52-56; gen. physics br, aeronaut. res. lab, U.S. Air Force, 56-63; PROF. PHYSICS, SYRACUSE UNIV, 63- Instr, grad. ctr, Ohio State, 58-59; Nat. Sci. Found. sr. fel, King's Col, London, 60-61; adj. assoc. prof, Cincinnati, 62-63; vis. prof, Technion, Haifa, 71. U.S.N.R, 44-46. AAAS; Am. Phys. Soc. General relativity; cosmology; theoretical physics in general. Address: Dept. of Physics, College of Liberal Arts, Syracuse University, Syracuse, NY 13210.

GOLDBERG, JULIUS, b. Birmingham, Ala, Oct. 13, 21; m. 54; c. 3. MICROBIOLOGY, PUBLIC HEALTH. B.S, Kentucky, 46, M.S.P.H, 47, Ph.D.(bact), 51; fel, Louisville, 50; Dr.P.H.(epidemiol), Univ. Mich, 67. Res. assoc. prev. med, col. med, Tennessee, 48-50; from instr. to asst. prof. bact. & dir. virus diagnostic lab, med. col, Univ. S.C, 51-54; asst. prof. microbiol. & pub. health, Chicago Med. Sch, 54-57, assoc. prof, 57-64, PROF, 64-

67; PREV. MED. & PUB. HEALTH, STRITCH SCH. MED, LOYOLA UNIV. CHICAGO, 67- Sr. Fulbright res. scholar, Univ. W.Indies, 60-61; venereal disease consult, Chicago Bd. Health, 62- Med.Dept, U.S.A, 42-46. Soc. Exp. Biol. & Med; Asn. Teachers Prev. Med; N.Y. Acad. Sci. Medical microbiology; granuloma inguinale; allergic encephalitis; venereal diseases; environmental health effects; epidemiology. Address: Dept. of Preventive Medicine, Loyola University Medical Center, 2160 S. First Ave, Maywood, IL 60153.

GOLDBERG, KARL, b. Brooklyn, N.Y, Mar. 15, 29; m. 53. MATHEMATICS. B.S, Mass. Inst. Tech, 49; M.A, Columbia, 50; Nat. Sci. Found. fel, American Univ, 56-57, Ph.D.(math), 57. MATHEMATICIAN, NAT. BUR. STANDARDS, 51-56, 57- Math. Asn. Am; fel. N.Y. Acad. Sci. Combinatorial analysis; matrix theory; formal power series; number theory. Address: National Bureau of Standards, Gaithersburg, MD 20760.

GOLDBERG, LAWRENCE SPENCER, b. St. Louis, Mo, June 11, 40; m. 69; c. 1. SOLID STATE PHYSICS. B.S, Washington (St. Louis), 61; Ph.D.(physics), Cornell, 66. Res. asst. solid state physics, Phys. Inst, Frankfurt, 66-67; RES. PHYSICIST, OPTICAL SCI. DIV, QUANTUM OPTICS BR, NAVAL RES. LAB, 67- AAAS; Am. Phys. Soc; Sci. Res. Soc. Am. Color center research; optical and electron spin resonance; nonlinear optics and laser physics. Address: Code 6510 Naval Research Lab, Washington, DC 20390.

GOLDBERG, LEO, b. Brooklyn, N.Y, Jan. 26, 13; m. 43; c. 3. ASTROPHYSICS. B.S, Harvard, 34, A.M, 37, Agassiz fel, 37-38, Ph.D.(astrophys), 38; hon. Sc.D, Univ. Mass, 70. Asst. astron, Harvard, 34-37, spec. res. fel, 38-41, res. assoc, 41; asst. & res. assoc, McMath-Hulbert Observ, Univ. Mich, 41-46, asst. prof, 45-46, assoc. prof, 46-48, prof, 48-60, chmn. dept. astron. & dir. observ, 46-60; HIGGINS PROF. ASTRON, HARVARD, 60-; DIR, KITT PEAK NAT. OBSERV, 71- Mem. U.S. nat. comt, Int. Astron. Union, 56-66, chmn, 56-61, v.pres, 58-64, chmn. U.S. del, Gen. Assembly, 58 & 61; chmn. org. comt, Assoc. Univ. for Res. in Astron, Inc, 56-57, mem. bd. dir, 66-71; bd. trustees, Assoc. Univs, Inc, 57-66; mem. space sci. bd, Nat. Acad. Sci, 58-64, bd. dir, Benjamin Apthorp Gould Fund, 59-69; mem, U.S. Air Force Sci. Adv. Bd, 59-62; ed, Ann. Rev. Astron. & Astrophys, 61-; mem. solar phys. subcomt, NASA, 62-65, sci. & tech. adv. comt. manned space flight, 64-70, chmn, Astron Missions Bd, 67-70; mem. defense sci. bd, Dept. Defense, 62-64; staff mem, Smithsonian Astrophys. Observ, 60-66; chmn. dept. astron, Harvard, 66-71; dir, Harvard Col. Observ, 66-71. Naval Ord. Develop. award, 46. Nat. Acad. Sci; Am. Astron. Soc.(v.pres, 59-61, pres, 64-66); Am. Philos. Soc; Am. Acad. Arts & Sci; for. assoc. Royal Astron. Soc; Royal Belgian Soc. Sci; Int. Acad. Astronaut; Optical Soc. Am. Astrophysics and solar physics. Address: Kitt Peak National Observatory, P.O. Box 4130, Tucson, AZ 85717.

GOLDBERG, LEON I(SADORE), b. Charleston, S.C, Sept. 26, 26; m. 58; c. 2. PHARMACOLOGY, INTERNAL MEDICINE. B.S, Med. Col. S.C, 46, M.S, 51, Ph.D.(pharmacol), 52; M.D, Harvard Med. Sch, 56. Asst. pharmacol, Med. Col. S.C, 49-52, res. assoc, 52-54; res. fel. anesthesiol, Mass. Gen. Hosp, 54-56, intern internal med, 56-57, asst. res, 57-58; clin. assoc. cardiol, Nat. Heart Inst, 58-61; assoc. prof. pharmacol. & internal med, SCH. MED, EMORY UNIV, 61-66, PROF. PHARMACOL, 66-, INTERNAL MED, 67-, DIR. CLIN. PHARMACOL. PROG, 61- U.S.P.H.S, 58, Sr. Asst. Surg. Am. Soc. Pharmacol. & Exp. Therapeut; Soc. Exp. Biol. & Med; Am. Fedn. Clin. Res; Am. Soc. Clin. Invest. Pharmacology of cardiovascular drugs; clinical pharmacology; physiology of hypothermia and hyperthermia; pharmacology of monoamine oxidase inhibitors; pharmacology of dopamine. Address: Clinical Pharmacology Program, School of Medicine, Emory University, Atlanta, GA 30303.

GOLDBERG, LEON J(OSEPH), b. Concord, N.H, Feb. 28, 05; m. 56. ELECTRICAL ENGINEERING. B.S, Mass. Inst. Tech, 26, M.S, 27. Engr. indust. control, Gen. Elec. Co, 27-56, adv. elec. tech, 56-65, res. & develop. ctr, 65-70; RETIRED. Sr. mem. Inst. Elec. & Electronics Eng. Design and application of circuit interrupters, arcing and solid state types; circuit protective devices; electrical system protection. Address: 927 St. David's Lane, Schenectady, NY 12309.

GOLDBERG, LEON PHILIP, b. Bronx, N.Y, Sept. 20, 23; m. 53; c. 4. PHYSICS. B.S, City Col. N.Y, 47; M.S, N.Y. Univ, 50. Instr. physics, Queens Col.(N.Y), 47-49; physicist, Picatinny Arsenal, 49-51; mem. sci. staff Hudson Lab, Columbia, 52-54; instr. physics, City Col. New York, 54-57; mem. res. staff, plasma physics lab, Princeton, 57-62, mem. prof. staff, 62-68; ASSOC. PROF. PHYSICS, GLASSBORO STATE COL, 68- Instr, Univ. Col, Rutgers, 57-68. Am. Asn. Physics Teachers. High energy radiation; underwater sound propagation; plasma physics; computation. Address: 14 Agate Rd, East Brunswick, NJ 08816.

GOLDBERG, LEONARD STEPHEN, b. Charleston, S.C, Mar. 19, 36. IMMUNOHEMATOLOGY. M.D, Med. Col. S.C, 59. Fel. hemat, med. ctr, California, Los Angeles, 65-67; immunohemat, med. ctr, California, San Francisco, 67-68; asst. prof. MED, MED. CTR, UNIV. CALIF, LOS ANGELES, 68-71, ASSOC. PROF, 71- Clin. investr, Vet. Admin, 68-71. Dipl, Am. Bd. Internal Med, 67. U.S.A.F, 61-63, Capt. Hematologic diseases associated with or caused by immune mechanisms. Address: Dept. of Medicine, University of California Medical Center, Los Angeles, CA 90024.

GOLDBERG, LOUIS J, b. Middletown, N.Y, July 20, 36; m. 63. NEUROPHYSIOLOGY, NEUROANATOMY. B.A, Brooklyn Col, 56; D.D.S, N.Y. Univ, 60; Ph.D.(anat), Univ. Calif, Los Angeles, 68. Nat. Inst. Dent. Res. fels, N.Y. Univ, 61-62, SCH. DENT, UNIV. CALIF, LOS ANGELES, 64-68, ASST. PROF. ORAL BIOL, 68-, ANAT, SCH. MED, 69- Nat. Insts. Health career develop. award, 68. Dent.C, U.S.A, 62-64, Capt. Neurophysiological studies in oral pharyngeal reflexes. Address: Dept. of Anatomy, University of California Center for the Health Sciences, Los Angeles, CA 90024.

GOLDBERG, MARK A(RTHUR), b. N.Y.C, Sept. 4, 34; m. 69; c. 1. PHARMACOLOGY, NEUROLOGY. S.B, Columbus Univ, 55; fel, Univ. Chicago, 55-57, U.S. Pub. Health Serv. fel, 57-59, Ph.D.(pharmacol), 59, Wilder fel, 59-62, M.D, 62. Res. assoc. & instr. pharmacol, Univ. Chicago, 59-62; intern, Bronx Munic. Hosp, N.Y, 62-63; resident neurol, Presby. Hosp, 63-66; mem. staff, U.S. Army Med. Res. Lab, Md, 66-67; asst. prof. neurol, Col. Physicians & Surgeons, Columbia Univ, 68-71; CHIEF DIV. NEUROL, HARBOR GEN. HOSP. & ASST. PROF. NEUROL. & PHARMACOL, UNIV. CALIF, LOS ANGELES, 71- U.S. Pub. Health Serv. fel, 64-66. Med.C, U.S.A, 66-68, Capt. Am. Acad. Neurol; Am. Soc. Neurochem. Neuropharmacology; neurology. Address: 1000 W. Carson St, Torrance, CA 90509.

GOLDBERG, MARTIN, b. Phila, Pa, Sept. 15, 30; m. 51; c. 3. NEPHROLOGY. B.A, Temple Univ, 51, M.D, 55. Rotating Intern, Phila. Gen. Hosp, 55-56; asst. resident, internal med, Cleveland Clin. Hosp, 56-57; resident, Phila. Gen. Hosp, 57-58; sr. resident, 58-59; asst. prof. MED, chem. sect, SCH. MED, UNIV. PA, 59-63, assoc. prof, 63-67, RENAL-ELECTROLYTE SECT, 67-70, PROF, 70-, CHIEF SECT, 66- Fel. med, chem. sect, sch. med, Univ. Pa, 59-61; mem. staff, med. clin, Hosp. of Univ. Pa, 59-61, clin. investr, gen. clin. res. ctr, 61-, mem. attending staff, hosp, 62-; asst. attending physician, pulmonary disease serv, Phila. Gen. Hosp, 60-; Nat. Insts. Health res. grant, 65-; training grant, 69-; Hoechst Found. res. award, 66-; Lederle Fund res. award, 66-; John Hartford Found. res. grant, 70-; mem. gen. med. study sect, Nat. Insts. Health; mem. coun. on kidney in cardiovascular disease, Am. Heart Asn. Phila. Gen. Hosp. res. prize, 59; Nat. Insts. Health res. career develop. award, 62. AAAS; Am. Soc. Clin. Invest; fel. Am. Col. Physicians; Am. Physiol. Soc; Am. Fedn. Clin. Res; Am. Soc. Clin. Pharmacol. & Therapeut; Am. Soc. Nephrology; Int. Soc. Nephrology; Am. Heart Asn. Renal physiology and pathophysiology; renal pharmacology; action of diuretics; regulation of sodium excretion; renal regulation of calcium and phosphate transport; action of parathyroid hormone on the kidney. Address: Renal-Electrolyte Section, Dept. of Medicine, Hospital of the University of Pennsylvania, 3400 Spruce St, Philadelphia, PA 19104.

GOLDBERG, MARTIN A, b. N.Y.C, Sept. 19, 29; m. 51; c. 2. APPLIED MECHANICS. B.A.E, N.Y. Univ, 51; M.S, Buffalo, 55; Ph.D.(appl. mech), Rensselaer Polytech, 58. Struct. engr, Bell Aircraft Corp, 53-55; instr. appl. mech, Rensselaer Polytech, 55-58; res. engr, Grumman Aircraft Corp, 58-62; specialist engr, Repub. Aviation Corp, 62-64; assoc. prof. APPL. MECH, POLYTECH. INST. BROOKLYN, 64-70, PROF, 70- C.Eng, 51-53, Lt. Assoc. mem. Am. Soc. Mech. Eng; Soc. Eng. Sci; assoc. mem. Soc. Naval Archit. & Marine Eng. Solid mechanics; applied elasticity, plates, shells and elastic stability; heat conduction. Address: 208 Violet St, Massapequa Park, NY 11762.

GOLDBERG, MARVIN, b. New York, N.Y, Sept. 14, 39; m. 61; c. 2. HIGH ENERGY PHYSICS. B.S, City Col. New York, 60; Ph.D.(physics), Syracuse, 65. Res. asst. PHYSICS, SYRACUSE UNIV, 60-65, res. assoc, 65-66, asst. prof, 66-69, ASSOC. PROF, 69- Am. Phys. Soc. Experimental study of elementary particles and their interactions, especially classification of these particles and measurement of their quantum numbers. Address: Dept. of Physics, Syracuse University, Syracuse, NY 13210.

GOLDBERG, MARVIN C(HARLES), b. Denver, Colo, June 10, 33; m. 54; c. 5. PHYSICAL CHEMISTRY. B.A, Colorado, 55; M.S, Denver, 68; Ph.D.(chem), 69. Assayer, Colo. Assaying Co, 57-58; RES. CHEMIST, sch. med, Colorado, 58-60; U.S. GEOL. SURVEY, 60- U.S.A, 55, 57, Res, 57-63. AAAS; Am. Chem. Soc; Can. Asn. Appl. Spectros. Field of water quality; interactions of organic solutes with hydrologic environment. Address: Geological Survey, U.S. Dept. of Interior, Denver Federal Center, Bldg. 15, Room 120, Denver, CO 80225.

GOLDBERG, MELVIN A(RTHUR), b. Chicago, Ill, Aug. 29, 13; m. 38; c. 3. ORGANIC CHEMISTRY. B.S, Illinois, 34; Lilly & univ. fels, Chicago, 34-37, Ph.D.(org. chem), 37. Tech. dir, D.B. Lesser & Co, Chicago, 38-40; res. chemist, Acme Cosmetic Co, 40-41; dir. res, Cereals Res, Inc, 41-42; res. chemist, Lady Esther Ltd, 42-45, chief chemist, 45-46; res. chemist, Pepsodent div, LEVER BROTHERS CO, 46-48, chief supvr. prods. res, 48-52, sect. chief, prod. improv. & develop, 52-63, TECH. SERV. MGR, 63- Am. Chem. Soc. Soaps and detergents; synthesis of antimalarial drugs; cosmetics; biphenyl derivatives of hydrazine. Address: Research & Development Division, Lever Brothers Co, 45 River Rd, Edgewater, NJ 07020.

GOLDBERG, MELVIN LEONARD, b. Chester, Pa, June 19, 32; m. 54; c. 2. BIOCHEMISTRY, PATHOLOGY. B.A, Calif. Inst. Tech, 54; M.A, Illinois, Urbana, 55; Nat. Insts. Health fel, N.Y. Univ, 57-62, Ph.D.(biochem), 62; M.D, Univ. Calif, San Francisco, 66. Intern PATH, SCH. MED, UNIV. CALIF, SAN FRANCISCO, 66-67, asst. res. pathologist, 67-69, ASST. PROF. IN RESIDENCE, 69- Res. grants, Nat. Insts. Health & Univ. Calif. Cancer Res. Coord. Comt, 68-74; career develop. award, Nat. Insts. Health, 71-76. U.S.A.F, 55-57, Res, 57-68, Capt. AAAS; Am. Soc. Exp. Path. Mechanism of action of enzymes; mode of action and control of mammalian ribonucleic acid polymerase; study on control of mammalian gene activity. Address: Dept. of Pathology, School of Medicine, University of California, San Francisco, CA 94122.

GOLDBERG, MERRILL B, b. Minneapolis, Minn, June 14, 43. MATHEMATICAL ANALYSIS. B.A, Univ. Minn, Minneapolis, 64; Woodrow Wilson fel, Univ. Calif, San Diego, 64-65, Nat. Sci. Found. fel, 64-68, M.A, 65, Ph.D. (math), 69. Specialist MATH, San Diego City Schs, 68-69; ASST. PROF, UNIV. COLO, BOULDER, 69- Am. Math. Soc. Martingale theory; Ergodic theory; abstracting L_p spaces; Orlicz spaces. Address: Dept. of Mathematics, University of Colorado, Boulder, CO 80302.

GOLDBERG, MILTON I(RVING), b. N.Y.C, Aug. 22, 11; m. 50; c. 3. PHYSICS. B.S, City Col. New York, 32; M.A, Columbia, 34. Teacher, schs, N.Y, 35-42; res. scientist spec. govt. projs, Columbia, 42-69; ASST. PROF. PHYSICS, WESTCHESTER COMMUNITY COL, 70- Asst. clin. prof, Albert Einstein Col. Med, 70-, spec. instr, 58-69. With Off. Sci. Res. & Develop; Nat. Defense Comt; Atomic Energy Comn; U.S. Army; U.S. Navy; U.S. Air Force; Nat. Insts. Health. AAAS; Am. Phys. Soc; Inst. Elec. & Electronics Eng; Am. Asn. Physics Teachers. Biomedical, electronic, nuclear and oceanographic instrumentation; electromagnetic induction transducer. Address: R.F.D. 1, Box 289, Barrett Rd, Katonah, NY 10536.

GOLDBERG, MORRIS (H), b. New Haven, Conn, Dec. 24, 20; m. 43; c. 4. BIOCHEMISTRY. B.S, Connecticut, 44, Ph.D.(chem), 51. Res. chemist, Heyden Chem. Corp, 45; Nat. Heart Inst. fel, Wisconsin, 51-52; fel, Harvard, 52-53; res. chemist, Brown Co, 53-54; asst, sch. med, Yale, 54-55; res. chemist, nuclear fuel div, Olin Mathieson Chem. Corp, 56-62; CLIN. CHEMIST, NORWALK HOSP, 63- U.S.A, 46-47. Am. Chem. Soc; fel. Am. Asn. Clin. Chem. Enzymes; steroids; microanalysis; biochemistry of mental disease. Address: 11 Quaker Lane, Trumbull, CT 06611.

GOLDBERG, MORTON EDWARD, b. Phila, Pa, July 11, 32; m. 54; c. 3. PHARMACOLOGY. B.S, Phila. Col. Pharm, 54, M.S, 55, D.Sc.(pharmacol), 58. Sr. res. pharmacologist, Abbott Labs, 58-60; res. fel, Mellon Inst, 60-63, sr. fel, 64; staff pharmacologist, Hazleton Labs, Inc, 64-65; sr. pharmacologist, Union Carbide Corp, 65-67, asst. dir. pharmacol, 67-68, dir, 68-69; HEAD GEN. PHARMACOL. SECT, WARNER LAMBERT RES. INST, 69- AAAS; N.Y. Acad. Sci; Am. Pharmaceut. Asn; Am. Soc. Pharmacol. & Exp. Therapeut; Soc. Toxicol; Soc. Exp. Biol. & Med; Int. Soc. Biochem. Pharmacol. Central nervous system and behavioral pharmacology; neuropharmacology; neurochemistry. Address: General Pharmacology Section, Warner Lambert Research Institute, Tabor Rd, Morris Plains, NJ 07950.

GOLDBERG, MORTON F(ALK), b. Lawrence, Mass, June 8, 37; m. 68. MEDICINE, OPHTHALMOLOGY. A.B, Harvard, 58, M.D, 62. Intern med, Peter Bent Brigham Hosp, 62-63; resident & fel. ophthal, Johns Hopkins Hosp, 63-67; asst. prof, med. sch, Yale, 67-69; fel. genetics, Johns Hopkins Univ. & Hosp, 69; PROF. OPHTHAL. & HEAD DEPT, COL. MED, UNIV. ILL. & OPHTHALMOLOGIST-IN-CHIEF, UNIV. HOSP. & EYE & EAR INFIRMARY, 70- Prog. dir, Nat. Eye Inst. training grants, 70; consult, Vet. Admin. Hosp, Chicago, 70- Dipl, Am. Bd. Ophthal, 68. U.S.P.H.S, 67-69, Surg. Asn. Res. Vision & Ophthal; Am. Acad. Ophthal. & Otolaryngol. Retinopathies; ocular genetics; diabetes mellitus; sickle cell retinopathy; ocular trauma; laser photocoagulation; retinal surgery. Address: Dept. of Ophthalmology, College of Medicine, University of Illinois Eye & Ear Infirmary, 1855 W. Taylor St, Chicago, IL 60680.

GOLDBERG, NELSON D, b. Cleveland, Ohio, June 22, 31; m. 58; c. 2. PHARMACOLOGY, BIOCHEMISTRY. B.S, Toledo, 53; Ph.D.(pharmacol), Wisconsin, 63. Nat. Insts. Health fel, Washington (St. Louis), 62-64; instr. PHARMACOL, MED. SCH, UNIV. MINN, MINNEAPOLIS, 64-65, asst. prof, 64-68, ASSOC. PROF, 68- U.S.A, 55-57. Am. Soc. Pharmacol. & Exp. Therapeut; Am. Soc. Neurochem; Am. Soc. Biol. Chem. Mechanisms of hormonal and metabolic regulation of glycogenolysis, glycogenesis, glycolysis, gluconeogenesis and Krebs cycle; roles of 3'5' adenylate and guanylate in cell function. Address: 105 Millard Hall, University of Minnesota, Minneapolis, MN 55455.

GOLDBERG, NEWTON N(ATHANIEL), b. New York, N.Y, Dec. 7, 25; m. 48; c. 3. PHYSICAL & ORGANIC CHEMISTRY. B.S, Bucknell, 48, M.S, 49; Ph.D.(org. chem), Pittsburgh, 53. Res. chemist, WESTINGHOUSE ELEC. CORP, 53-66; sr. chemist, 66-69, tech. dir, INDUST. PLASTICS DIV, 69-70, MGR, 70- U.S.A, 44-46. AAAS; Am. Chem. Soc; Fedn. Socs. Paint Technol. Synthetic organic chemistry; nitrogen heterocycles; organometallics; dielectric properties of phenolic resins; polymerizations; epoxide and polyamide resins; mesomorphic materials, liquid crystals; fluidized bed coatings. Address: Industrial Plastics Division, Chemical Products Plant, Westinghouse Electric Corp, Manor, PA 15665.

GOLDBERG, NORMAN, b. Phila, Pa, Aug. 5, 21; m. 63; c. 3. PHYSICS. B.S, Pa. State Teachers Col.(West Chester), 43; M.S, Pennsylvania, 48, Ph.D.(physics), 54. Res. assoc, Washington (St. Louis), 54-56; asst. prof. physics, Pennsylvania, 56-59; PHYSICIST, UNIVAC DIV, SPERRY RAND CORP, 59- U.S.A, 43-46. Am. Phys. Soc; Inst. Elec. & Electronics Eng; Optical Soc. Am. Nuclear Physics; magnetism; thin films; magnetooptics. Address: Univac, P.O. Box 500, Blue Bell, PA 19422.

GOLDBERG, P(AUL), b. Brooklyn, N.Y, May 29, 29; m. 51; c. 2. PHYSICAL CHEMISTRY. B.S, Brooklyn Col, 50; M.S, Yale, 51, Gen. Elec. Co. fel, 52-53, Ph.D.(chem), 53. Sr. engr. res. labs, Sylvania Elec. Prods, Inc, 53-58, eng. specialist, 58-60, Gen. Tel. & Electronics Lab, Inc, 60-64, prog. mgr, 64-67; dir. eng, Veritron West, Inc, 67-69; MGR. PHYS. CHEM. LAB, POLAROID CORP, CAMBRIDGE, 69- Nat. Cancer Inst. spec. fel, Hebrew Univ. Jerusalem, 62-63. Consult, Chem. Corps, U.S.A, 57-62. AAAS; Soc. Photog. Sci. & Eng. Physical chemistry of synthetic polyelectrolytes; luminescence of zinc sulfide; electroluminescence; energy storage and conversion; electrochemistry; stabilization of free radicals; photographic science and technology. Address: 12 Crocker Circle, West Newton, MA 02165.

GOLDBERG, PHILIP A, b. Scranton, Pa, Dec. 25, 22; m. 47; c. 2. PHYSICS, PHYSICAL SCIENCE. B.A, Reed Col, 44; M.A, California, Berkeley, 47, fel, Los Angeles, 49-53, Ph.D, 53. Instr. physics & group leader, solid state devices res. proj, Oregon, 47-49, asst. prof. & supvr. semiconductors lab, 53-56; group leader, phys. res. staff, Boeing Airplane Co, 56-57, sr. staff scientist & head geo-astrophys. lab, sci. res. labs, 58-59, phys. scientist, electronics & aero-astronaut. depts, 59-61; planetary sci. dept, Rand Corp, 61-63; consult. phys. scientist, 63-67; mem. staff, Plasma Res. Lab, Columbia Univ, 67-69; ASST. PROF. APPL. MATH, RICHMOND COL, 69- AAAS; Am. Phys. Soc; Inst. Elec. & Electronics Eng; Am. Geophys. Union. Semiconductors; ionized gases; upper atmosphere physics. Address: Dept. of Applied Mathematics, Richmond College, 130 Stuyvesant Place, Staten Island, NY 10301.

GOLDBERG, RICHARD, b. Philadelphia, Pa, May 22, 24; m. 47; c. 2. MATHEMATICS. B.A, Swarthmore Col, 48; Rockefeller Found. fel, N.Y. Univ, 48-51, Inst. Math. Sci. fel, 51-54, Ph.D.(math), 54. Lab. asst. physics, Barfol Res. Found, 44-45; res. assoc. math, inst. math. sci, N.Y. Univ, 54-55; mathematician PROGRAMMING RES, THOMAS J. WATSON RES. LAB, IBM CORP, 55-61, RES, STAFF MEM, 61- Am. Math. Soc; Asn. Symbolic Logic; Asn. Comput. Mach. Programming research; mechanical theorem proving; mathematical logic. Address: 311 W. 78th St, New York, NY 10024.

GOLDBERG, RICHARD A(RAN), b. Boston, Mass, Jan. 6, 36; m. 65; c. 1. PHYSICS. B.S, Rensselaer Polytech, 57; Eastman Kodak fel, Pa. State, 60-61, Ph.D.(physics), 63. Nat. Acad. Sci-Nat. Res. Coun. resident res. assoc, GODDARD SPACE FLIGHT CTR, NASA, 63-64, PHYSICIST, 64- Mem. comn. 3, U.S. Nat. Comt, Int. Sci. Radio Union. AAAS; Am. Phys. Soc; Am. Geophys. Union; Soc. Terrestrial Magnetism & Elec. Japan. Ionospheric motions; geophysical phenomena relating to ionospheric disturbances; sounding rocket studies of ionospheric composition and density with mass spectrometry, in-situ probes, radio propagation techniques, airglow measurements; mesospheric aeronomy. Address: Code 625, Lab. for Planetary Atmospheres, NASA Goddard Space Flight Center, Greenbelt, MD 20771.

GOLDBERG, RICHARD J(AY), b. Des Moines, Iowa, July 22, 23; m. 46; c. 2. PHYSICAL CHEMISTRY. B.S, Northwestern, 45, M.S, 47; Ph.D.(chem), Calif. Inst. Tech, 52. Supvr. anal. chem, Tenn. Eastman Corp, 44-46; proj. assoc. phys. chem, Wisconsin, 51-53; mem. staff. phys. chem, Technicolor Corp. Am, 53-59, mem. res. staff, 59-61, dir. res. & develop, 61-69, v. v.pres, 63-69; V.PRES. ENG, HOUSTON FEARLESS CORP, 69- U.S.A, 43-46. Am. Chem. Soc; Soc. Motion Picture & TV Eng; Soc. Photo-Optical Instrument. Eng; Soc. Photog. Sci. & Eng. Light scattering; antibody-antigen reactions; ultracentrifuge; gelatin; color photography; photographic chemistry; dye transfer process; color reproduction. Address: Houston Fearless Corp, 11801 W. Olympic Blvd, Los Angeles, CA 90064.

GOLDBERG, RICHARD R(OBINSON), b. Chicago, Ill, Sept. 6, 31; m. 53; c. 4. MATHEMATICS. B.S, Northwestern, 51; A.M, Harvard, 52, Ph.D.(math), 56. Instr. MATH, Northwestern, 57-58, asst. prof, 58-61, assoc. prof, 61-67, PROF, 67-68; UNIV. IOWA, 68-, CHMN. DEPT, 70- Am. Math. Soc. Fourier analysis; integral transforms. Address: Dept. of Mathematics, University of Iowa, Iowa City, IA 52240.

GOLDBERG, ROBERT C, b. Sacramento, Calif, Nov. 1, 24; m. 50; c. 2. MEDICINE, PHYSIOLOGY. B.A, California, Berkeley, 48, M.A, 49, Ph.D.(physiol), 51; M.D, Harvard, 55. Res. asst. physiol, California, Berkeley, 49-51; asst. sch. med, Harvard, 57-58; teaching fel, sch. med, Tufts, 57-58; assoc. res. physiol, California, Berkeley, 58-64; ASSOC. CLIN. PROF, SCH. MED, UNIV. CALIF, SAN FRANCISCO, 64- Borden Award, 55. U.S.A, 42-46. AAAS; Endocrine Soc; Am. Pub. Health Asn; Am. Med. Asn; Am. Fedn. Clin. Res; fel. Am. Col. Physicians; Am. Thyroid Asn. Thyroid metabolism; thyroid pituitary reactions; radiation carcinogenesis; diabetes; methods of medical practice. Address: 2930 Summit St, Oakland, CA 94609.

GOLDBERG, ROBERT J(ACK), b. Denver, Colo, May 22, 14; m. 40; c. 3. GENETICS. A.B, Illinois, 37; Ph.D.(biol), Ill. Inst. Tech, 54. Instr. biol, Chicago City Jr. Col, 41-54; assoc, Chicago Teachers Col, 54-59, prof, 59-64, dean grad. studies, 62-64; PROF. BIOL, V.PRES. ACAD. AFFAIRS & DEAN FACULTY, NORTHEAST. ILL. UNIV, 64- U.S.N.R, 42-46, Lt. Genetics Soc. Am; Soc. Study Evolution; Soc. Syst. Zool. Taxonomy and speciation of Gastrotrichia. Address: Dept. of Biology, Northeastern Illinois University, 5500 N. St. Louis Ave, Chicago, IL 60625.

GOLDBERG, ROBERT NATHAN, b. Stamford, Conn, Dec. 11, 43; m. 67. PHYSICAL CHEMISTRY. B.A, Hopkins, 65; Ph.D.(chem), Carnegie-Mellon Univ, 68. Asst, Carnegie-Mellon Univ, 65-68, fel. electrolyte solutions, Mellon Inst, 68-69; CHEMIST, NAT. BUR. STANDARDS, 69- Am. Chem. Soc. Chemical thermodynamics and its applications to biochemistry, electrolyte solutions and isotope effects: microcalorimetry; solution calorimetry. Address: Room A303, Physics Bldg, National Bureau of Standards, Washington, DC 20234.

GOLDBERG, SAMUEL, b. New York, N.Y, Mar. 14, 25; m. 53; c. 1. MATHEMATICS. B.S, City Col, 44; Ph.D.(math), Cornell, 50. Instr. MATH, Lehigh, 50-52, asst. prof, 52-53; OBERLIN COL, 53-55, assoc. prof, 55-61, PROF, 61- Vis. assoc. prof, grad. sch. bus. admin, Harvard, 59-60. U.S.A, 44-46. Am. Math. Soc; Math. Asn. Am; Opers. Res. Soc. Am; Am. Statist. Asn. Mathematical theory of probability; mathematical statistics; mathematical models in the social sciences. Address: Dept. of Mathematics, Oberlin College, Oberlin, OH 44074.

GOLDBERG, SAMUEL I, b. Toronto, Ont, Aug. 15, 23; nat; m. 51; c. 3. MATHEMATICS. B.A, Toronto, 48, M.A, 49, Nat. Res. Coun. Can. scholar, 50-51, Ph.D, 51. Demonstr. physics, Toronto, 48-50, reader, 49-50; sci. off, Defence Res. Bd, Ottawa, 51-52; asst. prof. MATH, Lehigh, 52-55; assoc. prof, Wayne State, 55-61, vis. assoc. prof, UNIV. ILL, URBANA, 60-61, assoc. prof, 61-65, PROF, 65- Air Force Off. Sci. Res. grant, 56-64; res. fel, Harvard, 59-60; consult, Avco Corp, 63-66; Nat. Sci. Found. grant, 64-; vis. prof, Univ. Calif, Berkeley, 66-67, Univ. Toronto, 68; ed-at-large, Marcel Dekker, Inc, 69- Can. Army, 43-46. Am. Math. Soc. Differential geometry; topology; algebra. Address: Dept. of Mathematics, University of Illinois, Urbana, IL 61801.

GOLDBERG, SEYMOUR, b. Boston, Mass, July 12, 27; m. 48; c. 2. ELECTRICAL ENGINEERING, ELECTRONICS. B.S, Northeastern, 48; M.S, Mass. Inst. Tech, 49. Asst, Mass. Inst. Tech, 48-49; engr. res. & develop, Sylvania Elec. Prod, Inc, 49-51; engr. & dir. tube res. & develop, Edgerton, Germehausen & Grier, Inc, 51-64, dir. component res. & develop, 64-65, staff scientist, EG&G, INC, 65-71, DIV. STAFF ENGR, 71- U.S.M.C, 45-46. Sr. mem. Inst. Elec. & Electronics Eng; Soc. Explor. Geophys. Gas discharges and vacuum tube technology; hydrogen thyratrons; electron optics and wide band width transient instrumentation and electron devices; marine seismic exploration and semiconductor detectors. Address: 46 Turning Mill Rd, Lexington, MA 02173.

GOLDBERG, SEYMOUR, b. Brooklyn, N.Y, Mar. 24, 28; m. 52; c. 1. MATHEMATICS. A.B, Hunter Col, 50; M.A, Ohio State, 52; Ph.D.(math), California, Los Angeles, 58. Asst. math, Ohio State, 50-52; math. analyst, Lockheed Aircraft Corp, 52-54; asst. math, California, Los Angeles, 54-58; Brown fel, Hebrew Univ, Israel, 58-59; asst. prof. MATH, New Mexico State, 59-62; assoc. prof, UNIV. MD, 62-67, PROF, 67- Summers, res. mathematician & scientist, 55-58. U.S.A, 45-47. Am. Math. Soc. Functional analysis, particularly theory of linear operators on a normed linear space. Address: Dept. of Mathematics, University of Maryland, College Park, MD 20742.

GOLDBERG, SHELDON S(UMNER), b. Springfield, Mass, Aug. 19, 28; m. 54; c. 3. BACTERIOLOGY, MEDICINE. A.B, Syracuse, 48; M.S, Massachusetts, 51; Fulbright scholar. & Ph.D.(bact), Kansas State, 54; M.D, Tufts, 60.

Bacteriologist, biol. warfare div, U.S. Army Chem. Corps, 54-56; Waksman-Merck res. fel, Rutgers, 56; Nat. Found. Infantile Paralysis res. fel, med. sch, Tufts, 57-60; intern, St. Joseph's Hosp, Syracuse, N.Y, 60-61; res, St. Christopher's Hosp. Children & Phila. Gen. Hosp, Hosp. Med. Ctr, Temple, 61-65, res. fel, 65-66; private practice, 66- Res. fel, L.I. Biol. Lab, 56; mem. staff, Mercy Hosp, Wesson Mem. Hosp. & Springfield Hosp; consult, Belchertown State Hosp. Am. Soc. Microbiol; Brit. Soc. Gen. Microbiol; Int. Broncho-Esophagol. Soc; Pan Am. Asn. Oto-Rhino-Laryngol. & Broncho-Esophagol; Israel Med. Asn. Soil microbiology; bacteriophage; microbial genetics; infectious diseases; diseases of ear, nose and throat. Address: 120 Maple St, Springfield, MA 01103.

GOLDBERG, STANLEY, b. Cleveland, Ohio, Aug. 4, 34; m. 57; c. 3. PHYSICS, HISTORY OF PHYSICS. B.S, Antioch Col, 60; A.M.T, Harvard, 61, Ph.D.(educ), 69. ASSOC. PROF. HIST. OF SCI, HAMPSHIRE COL, 65- Sr. lectr, Sci. Educ. Ctr, Univ. Zambia, 68-70. U.S.N.R, 52-54. Am. Asn. Physics Teachers. History of physics of the 19th and 20th century, especially electrodynamics; science education for non-scientists in high school and college. Address: School of Natural Sciences, Hampshire College, Amherst, MA 01002.

GOLDBERG, STANLEY IRWIN, b. New York, N.Y, Apr. 12, 30; m. 56; c. 3. ORGANIC CHEMISTRY. B.S, Maryland, 53; Ph.D, Indiana, 58. Res. assoc. & instr. CHEM, Illinois, 59-60; asst. prof, Univ. S.C, 60-65, assoc. prof, 65-71; PROF, LA. STATE UNIV, NEW ORLEANS, 71- Vis. prof, Univ. Bristol, 69-70. Matheson, Coleman & Bell Award, 71. U.S.A.F, 57-59. Am. Chem. Soc; Brit. Chem. Soc. Organic chemistry of ferrocene; lupin alkaloids; asymmetric selection and general structural and stereochemical studies. Address: Dept. of Chemistry, Louisiana State University in New Orleans, New Orleans, LA 70122.

GOLDBERG, STEPHEN ROBERT, b. N.Y.C, Mar. 4, 41. ZOOLOGY. B.A, Boston Univ, 62; M.S, Univ. Ariz, 65, Ph.D.(zool), 70. ASST. PROF. BIOL, WHITTIER COL, 70- AAAS; Am. Inst. Biol. Sci; Am. Soc. Ichthyol. & Herpet; Soc. Study Amphibians & Reptiles. Herpetology; ecology; vertebrate reproductive cycles; comparative vertebrate histology; comparative endocrinology. Address: Dept. of Biology, Whittier College, Whittier, CA 90608.

GOLDBERG, WILLIAM, b. Toledo, Ohio, Nov. 26, 35; m. 56; c. 4. CONTINUUM MECHANICS, ENGINEERING MECHANICS. B.S, Toledo, 57; M.S, Purdue, 61, Ph.D.(eng. mech), 67. Chief instr. missile tracking radar, U.S. Army Air Defense Sch, 59, res. & develop. off. mech, U.S. Army Ballistic Res. Labs, Aberdeen Proving Ground, 61-64; U.S. AIR FORCE, 64-, asst. prof. mech, U.S. Air Force Inst. Technol, 67-70, assoc. prof, 70-71, PROG. MGR. LASER WINDOW GROUP, PHYSICS DIV, AIR FORCE MAT. LAB, 71- Instr, Univ. Del, 62-64. U.S.A, 57-64; U.S.A.F, 64-, Maj. Soc. Rheol; Soc. Exp. Stress Anal; Am. Soc. Mech. Eng; Am. Inst. Aeronaut. & Astronaut. Nonlinear theory of viscoelasticity; impact mechanics; dynamic plasticity. Address: Laser Window Group, Physics Division, Air Force Materials Lab, Wright-Patterson Air Force Base, OH 45433.

GOLDBERGER, MARVIN L(EONARD), b. Chicago, Ill, Oct. 22, 22; m. 45; c. 2. THEORETICAL PHYSICS. B.S, Carnegie Inst. Tech, 43; Ph.D.(physics), Chicago, 48. Physicist, radiation lab, California, 48-49; res. assoc. PHYSICS, Mass. Inst. Tech, 49-50; asst. prof, Chicago, 50-53, assoc. prof, 53-57; Higgins prof, Palmer Phys. Lab, PRINCETON, 57-70, CHMN. DEPT, 70- Higgins vis. assoc. prof, 53-54; mem. President's Sci. Adv. Comt, 65-69. Dannie Heineman Prize, 61. U.S.A, 43-46. Nat. Acad. Sci; Am. Phys. Soc; Am. Acad. Arts & Sci; Fedn. Am. Sci. High energy nuclear physics; meson physics. Address: Joseph Henry Labs, Jadwin Hall, Princeton University, Princeton, NJ 08540.

GOLDBERGER, MICHAEL ERIC, b. N.Y.C, Oct. 21, 35; m. 59, div. EXPERIMENTAL NEUROLOGY. B.A, Brooklyn Col, 58; M.S, Emory, 62; Ph.D.(anat), Pennsylvania, 64. U.S. Pub. Health Serv. fel, 66-67; ASST. PROF. NEUROANAT, UNIV. CHICAGO, 67- U.S. Pub. Health Serv. gen. res. support fel, 67-69, career develop. award, 68-73; Pa. Plan for Develop. Scientists in Med. Res. fel, 67-68; Nat. Sci. Found. res. grant psychobiol, 68-70. AAAS; Am. Asn. Anat. Restitution of function in monkeys following lesions of the motor systems; methods if increasing restitution through training and secondary lesions; anatomical and physiological analysis of motor function. Address: Dept. of Anatomy, University of Chicago, Chicago, IL 60637.

GOLDBERGER, ROBERT F(RANK), b. N.Y.C, June 2, 33; m. 58; c. 3. BIOCHEMISTRY. A.B, Harvard, 54; M.D, N.Y. Univ, 58. Intern, Mt. Sinai Hosp, N.Y, 58-59; trainee, Inst. Enzyme Res, Univ. Wis, 59-61; vis. scientist, Weizmann Inst, 63; med. off. & biochemist, LAB. CHEM. BIOL, NAT. INST. ARTHRITIS & METAB. DISEASES, 63-66, CHIEF, BIOSYNTHESIS & CONTROL SECT, 66-, acting chief, 69-70. U.S.P.H.S, 61-63, Sr. Asst. Surg. Am. Soc. Microbiol; Biophys. Soc; Am. Fedn. Clin. Res; Am. Soc. Biol. Chem. Protein chemistry; biochemical genetics and evolution; biological regulatory mechanisms; enzyme induction and repression. Address: Lab. of Chemical Biology, National Institute of Arthritis & Metabolic Diseases, Bldg. 10, 9N-317, National Institutes of Health, Bethesda, MD 20014.

GOLDBERGER, W(ILLIAM) M(ORGAN), b. Perth Amboy, N.J, Dec. 26, 28; m. 56; c. 4. CHEMICAL ENGINEERING. B.Ch.E, Ga. Inst. Tech, 50; fels, Polytech. Inst. Brooklyn, 54-56, 57-59, M.S, 56, Ph.D.(chem. eng), 61. Res. engr, appl. res. labs, U.S. Steel Corp, 56-57; instr. chem. eng, Stevens Inst. Tech, 59-60; sr. chem. engr, BATTELLE MEM. INST, 60-65, CHIEF, DIV. MINERALS & METALL. PROCESSING, BATTELLE-COLUMBUS LABS, 65- U.S.N, 52-54. Am. Inst. Chem. Eng; Am. Inst. Min, Metall. & Petrol. Eng. High and ultra-high temperature chemical process development; development of new processing for separating and purifying chemical compounds; application of fluidized solids systems in chemical processing; assessment of mineral resources and recovery mineral values from deposits and ores. Address: Division of Minerals & Metallurgical Processing, Battelle-Columbus Labs, 505 King Ave, Columbus, OH 43201.

GOLDBLATT, HARRY, b. Muscatine, Iowa, Mar. 14, 91; m. 29; c. 2. PATHOLOGY. B.A, McGill, 12, M.D, 16; hon. D.Sc, Case West. Reserve Univ, 66. Res. surg, Royal Victoria Hosp, 16-17; pathologist in charge, Lakeside Hosp, Ohio, 19-21; Beit fel, Lister Inst. Prev. Med, London, 21-24, res. exp. path, 21-23, exp. physiol, univ. col, 23-24; asst. prof. path, sch. med, Western Reserve, 24-27, assoc. prof, 27-35, prof. exp. path, 35-46, assoc. dir, inst. path, 29-46; prof. path, sch. med, Southern California, 46-53; DIR. LOUIS D. BEAUMONT MEM. RES. LABS, MT. SINAI HOSP, 53-; EMER. PROF. EXP. PATH, SCH. MED, CASE WEST. RESERVE UNIV, 61-, prof, 55-61. Dir, inst. med. res, Cedars of Lebanon Hosp, 46-53; Mickle fel, Toronto, 48. Phillips award, Am. Col. Physicians, 36; Eisenman award, Ohio, 44. Med.C, 17-19, Lt. Soc. Exp. Biol; Am. Soc. Clin. Path.(Ward-Burdick Award, 39); Am. Soc. Exp. Path; Am. Asn. Path. & Bact; Am. Med. Asn; Am. Asn. Physicians; N.Y. Acad. Med.(Ferdinand C. Valentine award, 64); Brit. Physiol. Soc; Path. Soc. Gt. Brit. & Ireland. Experimental rickets; vitamins; light; experimental peritonitis; experimental hypertension; experimental cancer. Address: Louis D. Beaumont Mem. Labs, Mt. Sinai Hospital, 1800 E. 105th St, Cleveland, OH 44106.

GOLDBLATT, L(EO) A(RTHUR), b. Corona, N.Y, Nov. 20, 03. ORGANIC CHEMISTRY. B.A, Clark, 25, M.A, 26; Ph.D.(chem), Pittsburgh, 30. Asst. chem, Clark, 25-26; Pittsburgh, 26-29, instr, 29-40; from asst. chemist to chemist in charge fundamental sect, naval stores res. div, bur. agr. & indust. chem, U.S. DEPT. AGR, 40-52, oil chem. sect, oilseed div, South. regional res. lab, 52-58, head oilseed invests, west. utilization res. & develop. div, AGR. RES. SERV, 59-63, CHIEF, OILSEED CROPS LAB, south. utilization res. & develop. div, 63-70, SOUTH. MKT. & NUTRIT. RES. DIV, 70- Glycerine res. award, 58. AAAS; Inst. Food Technol; Am. Chem. Soc; Am. Oil Chem. Soc. Naval stores, turpentine; resin and fatty acids; terpene derivatives; insecticides; tung oil; castor oil; oilseed meals; cottonseed; peanuts; proteins; aflatoxins; mycotoxins. Address: Southern Regional Research Lab, U.S. Dept. of Agriculture, P.O. Box 19687, New Orleans, LA 70119.

GOLDBLITH, SAMUEL A(BRAHAM), b. Lawrence, Mass, May 5, 19; m. 41; c. 2. FOOD SCIENCE. S.B, Mass. Inst. Technol, 40, S.M, 47, Ph.D, 49. Mem. staff, Arthur D. Little, Inc, 40-41; res. assoc, FOOD SCI, MASS. INST. TECHNOL, 49-52, asst. prof, 52-55, assoc. prof. & exec. off. dept, 55-59, PROF, 59-, DEP. DEPT. HEAD, 67-, exec. off. dept, 61-67, acting head, 59-61. Tech. aide, comt. radiation preservation food, Nat. Acad. Sci-Nat. Res. Coun, 53-56, mem. comt. radiation preservation food, 59-63, 71-73, chmn, 63-71, mem. ad hoc subcomt. high level dosimetry, 56-59, ad hoc subcomt. radionuclides in foods, food protection comt, 60-61, comt. nutrit, 60-62, gen. comt. foods, 63-71, U.S. adv. comt. foot-and-mouth disease, 62-71, gen. comt. Dept. Defense Food Prog, 70-, chmn. task group feeding study protocol, 70-; Am. Inst. Biol. Sci. adv. comt. radiation pasteurization of foods to Atomic Energy Comn, 60-62, 65-70; Nat. Pub. Health Serv. comt, Surgeon Gen, U.S, 61; off. U.S. Atomic Energy Comn. team to Japan, conf. on radioisotopes, 61, 64, 66 & 67; mem. sci. adv. coun, Refrig. Res. Found, 70-73. U.S.A, 41-46, Capt. Radiation Res. Soc; Am. Chem. Soc; Am. Nuclear Soc; fel. Inst. Food Technol.(Monsanto Award, 53, Babcock-Hart Award, 69, Nicholas Appert Award, 70); Am. Soc. Microbiol; Int. Inst. Refrig. Radiation preservation of foods; freeze dehydration of foods; microwaves and their application in food processing; food processing. Address: Dept. of Nutrition & Food Science, Massachusetts Institute of Technology, 77 Massachusetts Ave, Cambridge, MA 02139.

GOLDBLOOM, DAVID E(LLIS), b. London, Eng, 1933; U.S. citizen. NUTRITION, BIOCHEMISTRY. B.A, Cambridge, 55, M.A, 61; Ph.D.(nutrit), Univ. Calif, Berkeley, 68. Res. asst. biochem, Unilever Food Res. Labs, Eng, 58-60; asst. mkt. res, F.W. Berk Chem. Co. London, 61; chemist qual. control, Watney's Brewery, 61-62; ASST. PROF. NUTRIT, FRESNO STATE COL, 68- R.A.F, 56-58. Comparative biochemistry of heme proteins. Address: Dept. of Home Economics, Fresno State College, Fresno, CA 93710.

GOLDBLOOM, RICHARD B, b. Montreal, Que, Dec. 16, 24; m. 46; c. 3. MEDICINE. B.Sc, McGill Univ, 45, M.D, C.M, 49. Asst. prof. PEDIAT, faculty med, McGill Univ, 62-67; PROF. & HEAD DEPT, DALHOUSIE UNIV, 67-; PHYSICIAN-IN-CHIEF, IZAAK WALTON KILLAM HOSP. FOR CHILDREN, 67- Assoc. physician, Montreal Children's Hosp, 62-67; chmn. med. adv. bd, Can. Cystic Fibrosis Found, 69-; mem, Med. Res. Coun. Can, 70-; dir, Atlantic Res. Ctr. Ment. Retardation. Fel, Royal Col. Physicians & Surgeons Can, 55; Lederle med. faculty award, 62. Soc. Pediat. Res; Am. Acad. Pediat; Can. Paediat. Soc; Am. Pediat. Soc; Nutrit. Soc. Can; Soc. Clin. Invest. Address: Dept. of Pediatrics, Dalhousie University, Halifax, N.S, Can.

GOLDBLUM, K(ENNETH) B(ERNARD), b. Minneapolis, Minn, Feb. 4, 12; m. 36; c. 2. CHEMICAL ENGINEERING. B.Ch.E, Univ. Minn, 33, M.S, 35, Ph.D.(chem. eng), 39. Chemist, State Testing Mill, Minneapolis, 33-39; engr, chem. develop, polycarbonate res. & develop. sect, chem. mat. dept, GEN. ELEC. CO, 40-60, specialist, prod. develop, 60-62, mgr. eval. & testing, 62-66, specialist prod. eval, 66-70, CONSULT, CHEM. DEVELOP. OPER, 70- AAAS; Am. Chem. Soc; hon. mem. Am. Soc. Test. & Mat; Soc. Plastics. Eng. Physical testing and evaluation in chemical development; polyimide resins; polyester resins; oxygen index flammability method; torsional pendulum. Address: General Electric Co, 1 Plastics Ave, Bldg. 108, Pittsfield, MA 01201.

GOLDBURG, ARNOLD, b. N.Y.C, Aug. 11, 27; m. 58; c. 3. FLUID PHYSICS. B.S.E, Princeton, 48, Ph.D.(aerospace eng), 60; M.S, Mass. Inst. Tech, 51, Eng, 52. Asst. dir. Proj. SQUID, Princeton Univ-Off. Naval Res, 58-60; prin. res. scientist, Avco-Everett Res. Lab, 60-66; head flight sci. lab, BOEING SCI. RES. LABS, 66-70, CHIEF SCIENTIST, SUPERSONIC TRANSPORT PROG, 70- Mem. res. & tech. adv. subcomt, fluid mech, NASA, 69-70. U.S.N, 45-46. Am. Phys. Soc; Am. Inst. Aeronaut. & Astronaut; Am. Geophys. Union; Am. Astronaut. Soc. Aerothermochemistry of combustion; boundary layer fluid mechanics; reentry heat transfer; flow fields of hypersonic bodies; clear air turbulence; sonic boom; magneto-hydrodynamics; electroaerodynamics. Address: Flight Sciences Lab, Boeing Scientific Research Labs, P.O. Box 3981, Seattle, WA 98124.

GOLDBURG, WALTER (ISAAC), b. N.Y.C, Sept. 27, 27; m. 56; c. 2. SOLID STATE PHYSICS. B.A, Cornell, 51; fel. & Ph.D, Duke, 54. Res. physicist, Carnegie Inst. Tech, 54, 56, instr. PHYSICS, 56-59; asst. prof, Pa. State, 59-61, assoc. prof, 61-63; UNIV. PITTSBURGH, 63-66, PROF, 66- U.S.A, 45-46. Am. Phys. Soc. Low energy nuclear physics; nuclear magnetic resonance; critical phenomona. Address: Dept. of Physics, University of Pittsburgh, Pittsburgh, PA 15213.

GOLDE, HELLMUT, b. Berlin, Ger, Feb. 6, 30; nat; m. 57; c. 3. ELECTRICAL ENGINEERING, COMPUTER SCIENCE. Dipl. Ing, Munich Tech. Univ, 53; M.S, Stanford Univ, 55, Ph.D.(elec. eng), 59. Asst. microwave studies, Stanford Univ, 53-55, 56-59, res. assoc, 59; asst. prof. elec. eng, UNIV. WASH, 60-64, assoc. prof, 64-69, PROF. ELEC. ENG. & COMPUT. SCI, 69- Inst. Elec. & Electronics Eng; Asn. Comput. Mach. Digital computers. Address: Dept. of Electrical Engineering & Computer Science Group, University of Washington, Seattle, WA 98105.

GOLDEN, ABNER, b. New York, N.Y, July 22, 18; m. 43; c. 3. PATHOLOGY. A.B, Columbia, 39; M.D, Harvard, 42. Instr. PATH, Emory, 48-50, asst. prof, 50-52, assoc. prof, 52-55, PROF, 55-61; GEORGETOWN UNIV, 61-, CHMN. DEPT, 62-, pathologist, Univ. Hosp, 50- Med.C, 44-46, Capt. Radiation Res. Soc; Am. Med. Asn; Am.Asn. Path. & Bact; Am. Col. Path; Am. Fedn. Clin. Res; Am. Soc. Exp. Path. Endocrine pathology; renal disease. Address: Dept. of Pathology, Georgetown University, Washington, DC 20007.

GOLDEN, ALFRED, b. N.Y.C, Aug. 4, 08. PATHOLOGY. B.S, Wisconsin, 30, M.S, 34; M.D, Washington (St. Louis), 37. Res. assoc. bacter. & immunol, Wisconsin, 31-35; sch. med, Washington (St. Louis), 36-38; res. path, Western Reserve & Allied Serv, 38-40; assoc. prof, col. med, Tennessee, 46-50; sch. med, Buffalo, 50-55; col. med, Wayne State, 55-56; DIR. LABS, JENNINGS MEM. HOSP, DETROIT, 55-; ALEXANDER BLAIN MEM. HOSP, 55- Consult. pathologist, Washington Sanitarium, D.C, 41-45; Buffalo Eye Bank & Res. Soc, 50-55; Mem. Hosp, Niagara Falls, N.Y, 51-54; chief lab. serv, Vet. Admin. Hosp, 49-55, consult. pathologist, Detroit, 55-56. Pathologist & exec. off, Armed Forces Inst. Path. & lectr, Army med. sch, div. trop. med, 41-45, med. off. in charge trop. diseases, trop. disease invest. unit, Off. Inter-Am. Affairs, 45-46, Med.C, 40-46, Lt. Col. Fel. Am. Soc. Clin. Path; Am. Soc. Exp. Path; Am. Asn. Path. & Bact; fel. Am. Col. Physicians; fel. Col. Am. Path. Pathology of diseases of the lungs and infectious and tropical diseases; experimental tumor pathology. Address: 26764 York Rd, Huntington Woods, MI 48070.

GOLDEN, A(LVA) MORGAN, b. Milledgeville, Ga, July 13, 20; m. 57; c. 1. NEMATOLOGY. B.S.A, Georgia, 50, M.S.A, 51; Ph.D.(plant path. & nematol), Maryland, 56. Asst. plant path, Georgia, 50-51; plant pathologist fungicide develop, Vanderbilt Co, N.Y, 51; asst. nematologist PLANT NEMATOL, U.S. DEPT. AGR, Md, 52-55, assoc. nematologist, 55-56, NEMATOLOGIST, Calif, 56-59, NEMATOL. INVESTS, AGR. RES. SERV, CROPS RES. DIV, PLANT INDUST. STA, 59- U.S.A, 41-45. AAAS; Soc. Nematol; Am. Phytopath. Soc; Soc. Syst. Zool; Am. Soc. Sugar Beet Technol; Soc. Europ. Nematol; Can. Soc. Zool; Orgn. Trop. Am. Nematol. Plant nematology, with emphasis on taxonomy of plant parasitic nematodes. Address: Nematology Investigations, U.S. Dept. of Agriculture, Agricultural Research Service, Crops Research Division, Plant Industry Station, Beltsville, MD 20705.

GOLDEN, BEN ROY, b. Bainbridge, Ga, Nov. 19, 37; m. 64; c. 4. GENETICS. B.S, Mid. Tenn. State Univ, 58; M.A, George Peabody Col, 60; U.S. Pub. Health Serv. trainee, Brown Univ, 67-70, Ph.D.(genetics), 71. Teacher, high sch, Ill, 58-66; partic. Nat. Sci. Found. acad. year inst, Brown Univ, 66-67; ASST. PROF. GENETICS DEVELOP, SKIDMORE COL, 70- Partic. Nat. Sci. Found. summer inst, Stephen Col, 65. AAAS. Analysis of the meiotic behavior of x-ray induced chromosome aberrations in an attempt to determine the mechanisms of pairing and disjunction in the spermatocytes of the Drosophila male. Address: Dept. of Biology, Skidmore College, Saratoga Springs, NY 12866.

GOLDEN, DAVID E, b. N.Y.C, May 27, 32; m. 62; c. 2. PHYSICS, SPECTROSCOPY. B.A, N.Y. Univ, 54, Ph.D.(physics), 61. Asst. physics, N.Y. Univ, 54-59, instr, 59-60, asst. prof, 60-61; Adelphi Univ, 61-62; eng. specialist gaseous electronics, Gen. Tel. & Electronics Labs, Inc, Calif, 62-63; res. scientist phys. electronics, Lockheed Palo Alto Res. Labs, 63-65, staff scientist, 65-67; prof. PHYSICS, Univ. Bari, 67-70; ASSOC. PROF, UNIV. NEBR, LINCOLN, 70- Instr. physics, City Col. New York, 56-58; N.Y. Univ, 58-59, res. assoc, 60-61; consult, Autometric Corp, N.Y, 61-62; sr. scientist, Sylvania Elec. Prod, Mass, 69-70; consult, Advan. Res. Instrument Systs, Inc, Tex, 70- Am. Phys. Soc. Electron scattering from atoms and molecules; electron spectroscopy; resonances in electron scattering; ion-molecule reactions; gaseous electronics; plasma physics; residual gas analyzers. Address: Behlen Lab. of Physics, University of Nebraska, Lincoln, NE 68508.

GOLDEN, DAVID MARK, b. New York, N.Y, July 18, 35; m. 63; c. 3. PHYSICAL CHEMISTRY. A.B, Cornell, 56; Ph.D.(phys. chem), Minnesota, 61. Phys. chemist, STANFORD RES. INST, 63-70, SR. PHYS. CHEMIST, 70- Ord.C, 61-63, Capt. Am. Chem. Soc; Am. Phys. Soc. Chemical kinetics and thermochemistry; molecular spectroscopy. Address: Stanford Research Institute, Menlo Park, CA 94025.

GOLDEN, GERALD SEYMOUR, b. Hartford, Conn, June 18, 33; m. 55; c. 3. ANALYTICAL CHEMISTRY. S.B, Mass. Inst. Tech, 54; Ph.D.(chem), Rensselaer Polytech, 57. Anal. res. chemist radiochem, nuclear div, Combustion Eng, Inc, 57-61, supvr. chem. sect, 61-62; head, anal. chem. lab, UNITED AIRCRAFT CORP, 62-65, CHIEF, ANAL. & RADIOISOTOPE LABS, 65- Am. Chem. Soc; Sci. Res. Soc. Am. Solvent extraction mechanisms; analysis of trace elements in materials; general analytical and radiochemistry. Address: Research Labs, United Aircraft Corp, East Hartford, CT 06108.

GOLDEN, JOHN O(RVILLE), b. Nashville, Tenn, Jan. 8, 37; m. 58; c. 4. CHEMICAL ENGINEERING. B.E, Vanderbilt, 59, M.S, 60; Ph.D.(chem. eng), Iowa State, 64. Res. asst. chem. eng, Vanderbilt, 59-60; Iowa State, 60-64; res. scientist assoc. thermodyn, Huntsville Res. & Eng. Ctr, Lockheed Missiles & Space Co, 64-67; asst. prof. CHEM. & PETROL. REF. ENG, COLO. SCH. MINES, 67-70, ASSOC. PROF, 70- Consult, Lockheed Missiles & Space Co, 67; NASA-Am. Soc. Eng. Educ. summer faculty fel, 68; consult, Samsonite Corp, 68-70; Martin Marietta, 71. Am. Inst. Chem. Eng. Thermodynamics; fluid mechanics; solvent extraction; mass and heat transfer; phase change processes. Address: Dept. of Chemical & Petroleum Refining Engineering, Colorado School of Mines, Golden, CO 80401.

GOLDEN, KELLY PAUL, b. Detroit, Mich, Oct. 12, 43; m. 64. ELECTRICAL ENGINEERING, MATERIALS SCIENCE. B.S. & M.S, Mich. State Univ, 65, Ph.D.(elec. eng), 71. Comput. operator, Mich. State Univ, 65-66, teaching asst. elec. eng, 66-67; consult, OKEMOS RES. LAB, OWENS-ILL. INC, 67-71, ELEC. ENGR, 71- AAAS; Inst. Elec. & Electronics Eng. Electronic circuit design; instrumentation; solid state science; electrical properties of materials and devices; computer science; hardware and software. Address: 286 Durand St, East Lansing, MI 48823.

GOLDEN, LARON E, b. Arkadelphia, Ark, Apr. 20, 20; m. 41; c. 4. SOIL FERTILITY, PLANT NUTRITION. B.S, Arkansas, 49; M.S, La. State, 51, Ph.D.(agron), 59. Instr. agron. & hort, South. State Col, 49-53; asst. prof. AGRON, Houston, 53-58; LA. STATE UNIV, BATON ROUGE, 58-70, ASSOC. PROF, 70- Checchi & Co-Agency Int. Develop, consult, Repub. Guinea, W.Africa, 64; Bahamas Sugar Proj. consult, Owens-Ill. Inc, 65-67. U.S.A, 41-45, Res. 46-, Col. Am. Soc. Agron; Am. Soc. Sugar Cane Technol; Int. Soc. Sugar Cane Technol. Sugar cane nutrition; tropical crops. Address: Dept. of Agronomy, Louisiana State University, Baton Rouge, LA 70803.

GOLDEN, RICHARD LESLIE, b. Baltimore, Md, Apr. 9, 30; m. 54; c. 4. CHEMICAL ENGINEERING. B.E, Hopkins, 51; Textile Res. Inst. fel. & Ph.D.(chem. eng), Princeton, 54; Pennsylvania, 57-58. Res. chem. engr, Socony Mobil Oil Co, 54-55, sr. res. chem. engr, 55-59; res. engr, Sci. Design Co, 59-60, sect. head, 60-64, acting asst. dir. proj. res, 64-66; asst. dir. eng. res, HALCON INT. INC, 66-70, ASST. V.PRES. DEVELOP, 70- Am. Inst. Chem. Eng. Chemical process research and development; catalysis and reaction kinetics; transport phenomena. Address: Halcon International Inc, 2 Park Ave, New York, NY 10016.

GOLDEN, ROBERT K, b. Brooklyn, N.Y, Feb. 16, 25. PHYSICS, MATHEMATICS. B.S, Pa. State, 47; M.S, Pennsylvania, 49, Ph.D.(physics), 55; fel, California, Los Angeles, 50-51. Instr. physics, Pennsylvania, 49-50, res. assoc, 53-55; physicist, Eckert-Mauchly Div, Remington Rand Corp, 51-53; consult. physicist, N.Y, 55-57; staff engr, Int. Bus. Mach. Corp, 57-62; res. dir, Computronics Inc, 62-64; dir, N.Y. Off, Data Systs. Analysts, Inc, N.J, 64-65; pres, Compunet, Inc, 65-69; v.pres. & dir, Comput. Profile Group Ltd, 69-70; PRES. & DIR, DWYGOFAX, INC, 71- Mem. adj. faculty, grad. dept. elec. eng, Polytech. Inst. Brooklyn, 61-68; lectr. comput. sci, City Col. N.Y, 66-67. A.U.S, 44-46. Am. Phys. Soc; Inst. Elec. & Electronics Eng; Asn. Comput. Mach. Digital computer man-machine information systems and control systems; nuclear physics. Address: Box 3673, Grand Central Station, New York, NY 10017.

GOLDEN, SIDNEY, b. Boston, Mass, June 23, 17; m. 41; c. 2. CHEMISTRY. B.S, City Col. New York, 38; Purdue, 40-42; Nat. Res. fel, Harvard, 46-48, Ph.D.(phys. chem), 48. Asst. chem, Purdue, 41-42; res. assoc, Nat. Defense Res. Comt, George Washington, 42-46; phys. chemist, Hydrocarbon Res, Inc, 48-51; asst. prof. CHEM, BRANDEIS UNIV, 51-53, assoc. prof, 53-59, PROF, 59- Fulbright sr. scholar, 59-60; Guggenheim fel, 59-60; lectr, Polytech. Inst. Brooklyn, 49-50; res. assoc, Mass. Inst. Technol, 52; vis. prof, Univ. Calif, Berkeley, 63; Hebrew Univ. Jerusalem, 67-68. Consult, Nat. Bur. Standards, 57-64; Presidential Cert. of Merit, 48. Am. Chem. Soc; fel. Am. Phys. Soc; fel. Am. Inst. Chem; Faraday Soc; fel. Am. Acad. Arts & Sci. Theoretical chemical kinetics; quantum mechanics; free radicals; ionic solvation; metal-ammonia solution. Address: Dept. of Chemistry, Brandeis University, Waltham, MA 02154.

GOLDEN, STANLEY A, b. Brooklyn, N.Y, Mar. 29, 27; m. 58. CHEMICAL & SPACE PHYSICS. Ph.B. & B.S, Chicago, 50; Ph.D.(phys. chem), Iowa State, 59. Res. assoc. radiochem, Argonne Cancer Res. Hosp, Univ. Chicago, 50-54; sr. physicist, Rocketdyne Div, N.Am. Aviation, Inc, Canoga Park, 59-62, prin. scientist, 62-65, proj. scientist, 65-68; ASSOC. SCIENTIST, AEROJET GEN. CORP, 68- Vis. asst. prof, Southern California, 61-63. Consult, Ballistic Missile Res. Adv. Coun, 61-; referee, Nat. Res. Coun-Nat. Acad. Sci, 64- U.S.A, 45-46. AAAS; Am. Phys. Soc; Combustion Inst; Am. Inst. Aeronaut. & Astronaut; Optical Soc. Am. Theoretical molecular spectroscopy; radiative non-equilibrium theory; radiative transport theory; chemiluminescence; spectral line shape theory; plasma physics; rocket exhaust and reentry plasma phenomenology. Address: Aerojet General Corp, Bldg. 160, Dept. 4611, 1100 W. Hollyvale, Azusa, CA 91702.

GOLDEN, W(ALTER) R(ICHARD) C(HAIM), b. New Milford, Conn, Nov. 11, 13; m. 46; c. 2. CLINICAL CHEMISTRY. B.S, Yale, 35, Ph.D.(physiol. chem), 40; Milbank fel, Cornell, 39-41. Lab. asst, med. sch, Yale, 36-39; res. biochemist, dept. pub. health, med. col, Cornell, 41-42; biochemist, Norwalk Gen. Hosp, Conn, 46; Stamford Hosp, 46-70; RETIRED. Dipl, Am. Bd. Clin. Chem. Sanit.C, 42-46, Capt. AAAS; Am. Chem. Soc; Am. Asn. Clin. Chem. Avian carbohydrate metabolism; evaluation of nutritional status; clinical chemistry. Address: 722 Rockrimmon Rd, Stamford, CT 06903.

GOLDENBAUM, GEORGE C(HARLES), b. N.Y.C, Aug. 11, 36; m. 61; c. 3. PLASMA PHYSICS. B.S, Muhlenberg Col, 57; Ph.D.(physics), Maryland, 66. Physicist, Nat. Bur. Standards, 58-61; res. assoc. plasma physics, Maryland, 66-69; RES. PHYSICIST, U.S. NAVAL RES. LAB, 69- Vis. scientist, Culham Lab, Eng, 66-67. Am. Phys. Soc. Dynamics of low density plasmas; collision free shock waves in plasmas; plasma turbulence; interaction of radiation with plasmas. Address: U.S. Naval Research Lab, Code 7720, Washington, DC 20390.

GOLDENBERG, G(ERALD) J, b. Brandon, Man, Nov. 27, 33; m. 59; c. 4. INTERNAL MEDICINE, ONCOLOGY. M.D. Manitoba, 57; London, 63-64; Ph.D. (morphol, hemat, biochem), Minnesota, 65. Lectr. INTERNAL MED, UNIV. MANITOBA, 64-66, asst. prof, 66-70, ASSOC. PROF. 70- Res. asst. Man. Cancer Found, 64-; clin. res. assoc, Nat. Cancer Inst. Can, 67- Consult. Winnipeg Children's Hosp, 67- Can. Soc. Clin. Invest; Am. Asn. Cancer Res; Am. Soc. Exp. Path. Cancer chemotherapy; mechanism of action of alkylating agents; tumor immunology; membrane transport. Address: Faculty of Medicine, University of Manitoba, 700 Bannatyne Ave. Winnipeg 3, Man. Can.

GOLDENBERG, H(AROLD) MARK, b. Toronto, Ont, Can, June 1, 35; U.S. citizen; m. 58; c. 3. PHYSICS. B.S, Calif. Inst. Tech, 56; Int. Bus. Mach. Corp. fel, Harvard, 56-57, A.M, 57, Nat. Sci. Found. fel, 58-60, Ph.D. (physics), 60. Nat. Sci. Found. fel, Heidelberg, 61-62; instr. PHYSICS,

Palmer Phys. Lab, Princeton, 62-64, asst. prof, 64-67; ASSOC. PROF, HASBROUCK LAB, UNIV. MASS, AMHERST, 67- Am. Phys. Soc; Am. Asn. Physics Teachers. Atomic beam and nuclear spectroscopy; gravitational and relativity research; cosmology. Address: Dept. of Physics, University of Massachusetts, Amherst, MA 01002.

GOLDENBERG, HARRY, b. Brooklyn, N.Y, Dec. 11, 22; m. 47; c. 1. BIO-CHEMISTRY. B.S, City Col. N.Y, 44; fel, Polytech. Inst. Brooklyn, 46-47, Nat. Inst. Health fel, 47-49, Ph.D.(chem), 50. Res. chemist, Kellex Corp, 44; sr. res. chemist, Jewish Hosp, Brooklyn, 50-52; instr. biochem, Brooklyn Col, 51-53; chief chemist & dir. labs, Hillside Hosp, 53-64; chief, RES. DIV, BIOSCI. LABS, 65-67, SR. RES. SCIENTIST, 67- U.S.A, 44-46. Fel. AAAS; Soc. Exp. Biol. & Chem; Am. Chem. Soc; N.Y. Acad. Sci; Am. Asn. Clin. Chem. Specificity, kinetics and methods of enzymes; drug metabolism; psychopharmacology; endocrinology; calcification; analytical biochemistry; thin layer and gas chromatography. Address: Bio-Science Labs, 7600 Tyrone Ave, Van Nuys, CA 91405.

GOLDENBERG, IRA STOVIN, b. Bridgeport, Conn, Feb. 23, 25; m. 52; c. 4. MEDICINE. B.A, Michigan, 47; M.D, Boston, 51. Instr. SURG, SCH. MED, YALE, 56-58, asst. prof, 58-64, assoc. prof, 64-68, PROF, 68-, ATTEND. SURGEON, MED. CTR, 60- Attend. surgeon, Vet. Admin. Hosp, West Haven. Dipl, Am. Bd. Surg. U.S.A, 43-46. AAAS; Endocrine Soc; Soc. Univ. Surg; Am. Fedn. Clin. Res; N.Y. Acad. Sci. Oncology and general surgery; endocrinology. Address: Dept. of Surgery, School of Medicine, Yale University, New Haven, CT 06510.

GOLDENBERG, MARTIN I(RWIN), b. Jersey City, N.J, May 10, 33; m. 54; c. 2. MEDICAL BACTERIOLOGY, LABORATORY MEDICINE. B.S, Rutgers, 54; M.S, Yale, 57, Ph.D.(med. microbiol), 60. Microbiologist, State Dept. Health, Hawaii, 60-61; scientist, Commun. Disease Ctr, U.S. Pub. Health Serv, San Francisco, 61-68, Fort Collins, Colo, 68-70; LAB. DIR, U.S. MED. CTR, 70- Assoc. mem. grad. faculty, Colo. State Univ, 68-70. Chem.C, 54-56, 1st Lt. Fel. AAAS; fel. Am. Pub. Health Asn; Am. Soc. Med. Technol. Administration of clinical laboratory. Address: 2920 Rocklyn Rd, Springfield, MO 65804.

GOLDENBERG, MARVIN M, b. N.Y.C, July 7, 35; m. 57; c. 2. PHARMACOLOGY, PHYSIOLOGY. B.S, Long Island, 57; M.S, Temple, 59; Ph.D. (pharmacol), Woman's Med. Col. Pa, 65. Sr. res. scientist, EATON LABS, NORWICH PHARMACAL CO, 65-70, SR. RES. SCIENTIST II, 70- N.Y. Acad. Sci; Sci. Res. Soc. Am. Autonomic nervous system pharmacology in relation to the gastrointestinal area; toxicology with regard to the antidotal effectiveness of agents against cyanide. Address: Eaton Labs, Norwich Pharmacal Co, Norwich, NY 13815.

GOLDENBERG, NEAL, b. Brooklyn, N.Y, Apr. 29, 35; m. 57; c. 3. PHYSICAL CHEMISTRY. B.S, City Col. New York, 56; M.S, Arkansas, 58, Am. Oil Co. fel. & Ph.D.(phys. chem), 61. Instr. chem, Arkansas, 61; sr. res. chemist, Mound Lab, Monsanto Res. Corp, 61-65, in charge plutonium isotope fuels group, snap prog, 65-67; asst. prof. chem, Fairleigh Dickinson Univ, 67-69; TECH. COORD, SPACE NUCLEAR SYSTS. DIV, U.S. ATOMIC ENERGY COMN, 69- Am. Chem. Soc. Physical properties of electrolytic solutions in mixed solvents; thermodynamics of liquid metals at high temperatures; high temperature electrochemistry; space electric nuclear power systems. Address: 8504 Postoak Rd, Potomac, MD 20854.

GOLDENBERG, SEYMOUR, b. Phila, Pa, Apr. 4, 13. MEDICINE. A.B, Temple, 35; M.D, Eclectic Med. Col, 39. Assoc. attend. anesthesiologist, Post-Grad. Hosp, N.Y. Univ, 47-50, assoc. prof. anesthesiol, post-grad. med. sch, 50-64; ATTEND. ANESTHESIOLOGIST, DOCTOR'S HOSP, 64- Attend. anesthesiologist, Rochester Gen. Hosp, 50; asst. attend. anesthesiologist, Bellevue Hosp, 50-; assoc. attend. anesthesiologist, univ. hosp, N.Y. Univ, 50- Consult, Wyckoff Heights Hosp, 50; St. Barnabas Hosp, 51- Anesthesiologist, Beaumont Gen. Hosp. & 127th Evacuation Hosp, Med.C, 44-46, Capt. Am. Soc. Anesthesiol; N.Y. Acad. Sci. Anesthesiology. Address: 971 California Rd, Eastchester, NY 10709.

GOLDENBURG, E(DWIN) H(AROLD), b. Chicago, Ill, April 12, 20; m. 48; c. 3. ORGANIC CHEMISTRY. B.S, Illinois, 47. Sr. res. chemist, NALCO CHEM. CO, 56-61, GROUP LEADER, 62- U.S.A, 42-45. Am. Chem. Soc. Applied organic chemistry. Address: Nalco Chemical Co, 6216 W. 66th Pl, Chicago, IL 60638.

GOLDENSOHN, ELI S(AMUEL), b. New York, N.Y, June 25, 15; m. 40; c. 3. NEUROLOGY. A.B, George Washington, 37, M.D, 40. Instr. med. sch, Colorado, 45-48, asst. prof. physiol, 49-53, attend. staff, 51-53, dir. epilepsy serv, 53; asst. prof. NEUROL, col. physicians & surgeons, Columbia, Univ, 53-61, assoc. prof, 61-63; PROF, sch. med, Univ. Pa, 63-67; COL. PHYSICIANS & SURGEONS, COLUMBIA UNIV, 67- Consult, Vet. Admin. Hosp, Bronx, 59-61. Med.C, U.S.A, 41-45. Am. Electroencephalog. Soc. (pres, 71); Am. Neurol. Asn; Am. Epilepsy Soc.(pres, 68); Am. Acad. Neurol. Brain physiology; electrical activity of the brain; convulsive disorders. Address: Columbia University Neurological Institute, 710 W. 168th St, New York, NY 10032.

GOLDENSON, JEROME, b. Greensburg, Pa, July 23, 12. CHEMISTRY. B.S, Carnegie Inst. Tech, 34, 36-40; Pittsburgh, 34-35; Hopkins, 41-44. Res. chemist, Nat. Alloy Steel Co, Pa, 35-37; Am. Gas & Elec. Corp, W.Va, 37-38; Acme Protection Equip. Co, Pa, 38-39; design engr, E.W. Voss Mach. Co, 39-40; phys. chemist, chem. ctr, U.S. Army, 40-55, chief colloid br, physicochem. res. div, chem. res. & develop. labs, 55-71; CHEM. CONSULT, 71- Mining Adv. Bd, Carnegie Inst. Tech. Superior Performance award, U.S. Dept. Army, 58. Am. Chem. Soc; Coblentz Soc; Sci. Res. Soc. Am; Am. Ord. Asn. Infrared spectroscopy; organic phosphorus compounds; aluminum soaps; aerosols; colloid chemistry; alloy steels; chemical analytical methods of traces of gases in air. Address: 7233 Park Heights Ave, Baltimore, MD 21208.

GOLDENTHAL, EDWIN I(RA), b. Plainfield, N.J, Feb. 2, 30; m. 70; c. 3. PHARMACOLOGY. B.S, George Washington, 52, M.S, 53, Ph.D.(pharmacol), 56. Chemist, Geol. Surv, U.S. Dept. Interior, 51-53; pharmacologist, Food & Drug Admin, Dept. Health, Educ. & Welfare, 56-63, chief, drug rev. br, div. toxicol. eval, 63-66, dep. dir, off. new drugs, 66-70; dir. safety eval, INT. RES. & DEVELOP. CORP, MATTAWAN, 70-71, ASST. DIR. RES, 71-

U.S.N.R, 48-53. Soc. Toxicol; Am. Soc. Pharmacol. & Exp. Therapeut; Europ. Soc. Study Drug Toxicity. Toxicology; drug metabolism. Address: 5182 Whippoorwill Dr, Kalamazoo, MI 49002.

GOLDER, RICHARD H(ARRY), b. Phila, Pa, July 6, 22; m. 57. BIOCHEMISTRY. B.S, Wisconsin, 44; Ph.D.(biochem), Temple, 57. Chemist, Barret Div, Allied Chem. & Dye Corp, 44-45, Phila. Rust-Proof Co, 45-46; tech. asst, Gen. Chem. Co, 47-49; asst, Inst. Cancer Res, 49-56; fel, Johnson Found, Pennsylvania, 56-59; physiol-chem. inst, Marburg, 59-60; chem, Pennsylvania, 60-64; ASSOC. PROF. BIOCHEM, SCH. DENT, TEMPLE UNIV, 64- U.S.A, 46-47. AAAS; Am. Chem. Soc. Controlling factors in glucose catabolism; nucleic acid changes following drug administration. Address: Dept. of Biochemistry, Temple University School of Dentistry, 3223 N. Broad St, Philadelphia, PA 19140.

GOLDEY, J(AMES) M(EARNS), b. Wilmington, Del, July 3, 26; m. 51; c. 2. PHYSICS. B.S, Delaware, 50; indust. fel. & Ph.D.(physics), Mass. Inst. Tech, 55. Mem. tech. staff, BELL TEL. LABS, 54-59, engr. transistor develop, 59-61, head silicon transistor and integrated circuit dept, 61-66, device technol dept, 66-69, DIR. MAT. & PROCESS TECHNOL. LAB, 69- U.S.A, 44-46, 1st Lt. Am. Phys. Soc; Inst. Elec. & Electronics Eng. Semiconductor physics; semiconductor device physics. Address: Bell Telephone Labs, 555 Union Blvd, Allentown, PA 18103.

GOLDFARB, A(BRAHAM) ROBERT, b. Phila, Pa, Jan. 11, 08; m. 29; c. 1. CHEMISTRY. B.S, City Col. New York, 28; M.S, Chicago, 31; Ph.D.(org. chem), N.Y. Univ, 35. Asst. synthesis organicals, Mt. Sinai Hosp, New York, 28-29; synthesis polypeptides, Ortho Sprague Found, Chicago, 30-32; chief chemist, Jewish Hosp, Brooklyn, 34-36; L.R. Bruce, Inc, Conn, 36-44; sr. chemist, Pyridium Corp, N.Y, 44-45; Celanese Corp, Md, 45-46, Velsicol Co, Ill, 46-47; instr. biochem. & phys. chem, Chicago Med. Sch, 47-48, assoc, 48-52, asst. prof, 52-59, assoc. prof, 59-62; ASSOC. PROF. PHYSIOL. CHEM, SCH. MED, WAYNE STATE UNIV, 62-; DIR. BIOCHEM. RES, SINAI HOSP. DETROIT, 62- Consult, Nat. Insts. Health. Parker Award, 57. AAAS; Am. Chem. Soc; Am. Soc. Biol. Chem. Synthetic organic chemistry; biochemistry; immunochemistry; physical chemistry; structure proteins; x-ray study of crystal structure beta methyl glucoside; derivatives of choline and beta methyl choline. Address: 19541 Cranbrook Dr, Detroit, MI 48221.

GOLDFARB, ALVIN F, b. May 16, 23; U.S. citizen; m. 48; c. 4. GYNECOLOGY, ENDOCRINOLOGY. B.A, Vanderbilt, 43, M.D, 47. Rotating intern, Metrop. Hosp, New York, 47-48, res. OBSTET. & GYNEC, 48-49, 50; fel, Jefferson Med. Col, 49-50; instr, New York Med. Col, 53-63; assoc, THOMAS JEFFERSON UNIV, 58-63, asst. prof, 63-68, ASSOC. PROF, 68- Nat. Cancer Inst. trainee, New York Med. Col, 53-55; mem, Psycho Endocrine Res. Coun. Gt. Brit. Dipl, Am. Bd. Obstet. & Gynec. Fel. Am. Col. Obstet. & Gynec; Am. Med. Asn; Am. Fertil. Soc; Endocrine Soc; Am. Soc. Cytol; Acad. Psychosom. Med; N.Y. Acad. Sci; Int. Fertil. Asn. Human reproduction; gynecological endocrinology. Address: 829 Spruce St, Philadelphia, PA 19107.

GOLDFARB, IVAN JOEL, b. N.Y.C, Apr. 10, 32; m. 53; c. 3. PHYSICAL & POLYMER CHEMISTRY. B.S, Univ. Ky, 53; Houdry fel, Univ. Cincinnati, 54-55, M.S, 55, Nat. Sci. Found. fel, 56-58, Ph.D.(phys. chem), 59. Res. chemist, polymer sect, AIR FORCE MAT. LAB, WRIGHT-PATTERSON AIR FORCE BASE, 58-60, GROUP LEADER POLYMER DEGRADATION, POLYMER BR, 60- U.S.A.F, 58-60, Res, 60-, Capt. Am. Chem. Soc; Sci. Res. Soc. Am. Mechanisms of thermal degradation of polymers; thermogravimetric analysis; kinetics of polymer decomposition; vapor phase osmometry. Address: 6506 Cheri Lynne Dr, Dayton, OH 45415.

GOLDFARB, SHELDON, b. New York, N.Y, Feb. 5, 29; m. 54; c. 3. ANALYTICAL CHEMISTRY. B.S, City Col. New York, 49. Chemist, Greenpoint Hosp, N.Y, 50-52; chief chemist, Panray Corp, N.J, 52-63; qual. control mgr, Baxter Lab, Inc, Mass, 63-64; chief chemist, Beecham Prod. Inc, Clifton, 64-67; DIR. QUAL. CONTROL, Chemway Corp, N.J, 67-70; KETCHUM LABS, INC, AMITYVILLE, N.Y, 70- AAAS; Am. Chem. Soc; Soc. Cosmetic Chem; N.Y. Acad. Sci; fel. Am. Inst. Chem; Am. Soc. Qual Control. Quality control and analytical methods as applied to pharmaceutical industry; hair dyes and related cosmetic products; analytical and quality control of toiletries and cosmetics; packaging control, design and development. Address: 126 Windham Rd, Hillsdale, NJ 07642.

GOLDFARB, THEODORE D, b. New York, N.Y, May 6, 35; m. 55; c. 3. PHYSICAL CHEMISTRY. A.B, Cornell, 56; Texaco fel, California, 57-59, Ph.D.(chem), 59. Asst, California, 56-57; asst. prof. CHEM, STATE UNIV. N.Y. STONY BROOK, 59-67, ASSOC. PROF, 67- AAAS; Am. Phys. Soc; Am. Chem. Soc. Molecular structure and spectroscopy; applications of spectroscopic techniques to the study of silicon and germanium analogues of small organic molecules; vibrational spectroscopy; photochemistry of polyenes; matrix-isolation studies of reaction intermediates. Address: Dept. of Chemistry, State University of New York at Stony Brook, Stony Brook, NY 11790.

GOLDFEDER, ANNA, b. Poland, July 25, 97; nat. EXPERIMENTAL PATHOLOGY. D.Sc, Prague, 23; fel, Vienna, 28-29; Masaryk Univ, 24-29. Asst. path, Masaryk Univ, 23-25, res. assoc, dept. physiol, 25-28, in charge lab. cancer res, 28-31; res. fel. cancer, Lenox Hill Hosp, New York, 31-33; res. worker biol. chem, Harvard Med. Col, 33; bacter. & immunol, col. physicians & surg, Columbia, 34; res. fel, CANCER DIV, DEPT. HOSPS, NEW YORK, 34, in charge div, 34-50, from sr. biologist to PRIN. RES. SCIENTIST & DIR. CANCER & RADIOBIOL. RES. LAB, 50- From res. assoc. to prof, N.Y. Univ, 34- AAAS; Soc. Exp. Biol. & Med; Radiol. Soc. N.Am. (award, 48); Radiation Res. Soc; Am. Asn. Cancer Res; fel. N.Y. Acad. Med; fel. N.Y. Acad. Sci; Am. Soc. Cell Biol. Relationship between radiation, viral and chemical carcinogenesis and inherent or genetic biological properties of a specific inbred strain of mice. Address: Cancer and Radiobiological Research Lab, 99 Ft. Washington Ave, New York, NY 10032.

GOLDFIELD, MARTIN, b. N.Y.C, Mar. 18, 21; m. 55; c. 2. MICROBIOLOGY. A.B, Louisville, 42; M.D, Boston, 50. Intern, Presby. Hosp, Chicago, 50-51; asst. med, sch. med, Boston, 51-52; fel. pediat, Harvard, 52-54; from instr. to asst. prof. div. infectious diseases, dept. med, Tulane, 54-56, asst. prof, div. epidemiol, 56-58; asst. dir, labs, STATE DEPT. HEALTH, N.J, 58-63, dir, 63-70, ASST. COMNR, 71- Asst. res, Mass. Mem. Hosp, 51-52, res, 52-53; asst, Boston Univ, 52-54; res. fel, Nat. Found. Infantile Paralysis, 53-54; asst. vis. physician, Charity Hosp, New Orleans, La, 54-58; assoc. prof, N.J. Col. Med. & Dent, 58-, vis. prof, 68-; sch. vet. med, Univ. Pa, 71- U.S.A, 42-45. Conf. State & Prov. Pub. Health Lab. Dirs; Am. Pub. Health Asn.(award, 61); Asn. Teachers Prev. Med; Am. Soc. Trop. Med. & Hyg; Asn. State & Territorial Pub. Health Lab. Dirs; Am. Med. Asn; Am. Soc. Microbiol; N.Y. Acad. Sci; Infectious Diseases Soc. Am. Basic virologic investigation and epidemiologic studies. Address: New Jersey State Dept. of Health, State House, Box 1540, Trenton, NJ 08625.

GOLDFIEN, ALAN, b. Brooklyn, N.Y, Apr. 16, 23; m. 50; c. 6. MEDICINE. A.B, California, 46, M.D, 50. Asst. meteorol, N.Y. Univ, 43-44; res. fel. med, Harvard, 53-56; RES. ASSOC. PHYSIOL, UNIV. CALIF, SAN FRANCISCO, 56-, MEM, CARDIOVASC. RES. INST, 58-, PROF. MED. & DIR. DIV. REPRODUCTIVE MED. & ENDOCRINOL, 67-, assoc. prof. med, 61-67, asst. prof, 58-61. Res. fel, Nat. Cancer Inst, Nat. Insts. Health, 53-55, Nat. Inst. Arthritis & Metab. Disease, 56-57; Gianini fel. med. sci, California, 57-58. Asst, Peter Bent Brigham Hosp, Mass, 53-56. Bennett prize, 58. U.S.N.R, 44-45. AAAS; Am. Physiol. Soc; Endocrine Soc; Am. Fedn. Clin. Res; Am. Soc. Clin. Invest. Adrenal medullary secretion; nervous control of intermediary metabolism; physiology of reproduction; medical complications of pregnancy. Address: Dept. of Obstetrics & Gynecology, University of California Medical Center, San Francisco, CA 94122.

GOLDFINE, HOWARD, b. Brooklyn, N.Y, May 29, 32; m. 63; c. 2. BIOCHEMISTRY, MICROBIOLOGY. B.S, City Col. N.Y, 53; U.S. Pub. Health Serv. fel, Univ. Chicago, 55-57, Ph.D.(biochem), 57. U.S. Pub. Health Serv. res. fel, 58-60; res. fel, dept. chem, Harvard, 59-62; instr. bact. & immunol, Harvard Med. Sch, 62-63, assoc, 63-66, asst. prof, 66-68; ASSOC. PROF. MICROBIOL, SCH. MED, UNIV. PA, 68- Am. Cancer Soc. scholar, 60-63; tutor biochem. sci, Harvard, 60-67, Nat. Inst. Allergy & Infectious Diseases, res. career develop. award, 65-68; mem. physiol. chem. study sect, div. res. grants, Nat. Insts. Health, 69- AAAS; Am. Soc. Biol. Chem; Am. Soc. Microbiol; Fedn. Am. Sci. Microbial metabolism; lipid chemisrty and metabolism; cell membrane structure and function. Address: Dept. of Microbiology, School of Medicine, University of Pennsylvania, Philadelphia, PA 19104.

GOLDFINGER, GEORGE, b. Budapest, Hungary, Dec. 24, 11; nat; m. 34. PHYSICAL CHEMISTRY. Dr.Chem, Paris, 37. Nitrogen prod. chemist, S.A.R. Chem. & Eng. Prods, Rumania, 37-38; tech. adv, Zarnesti Cellulose Factory, 39-40; res. collab, forest prods. lab, U.S. Forest Serv, 40-41; res. fel, Polytech. Inst. Brooklyn, 41-43, 45, res. chemist, G.L. Cabot, Inc, Mass, 43-45; assoc. prof. chem, Buffalo, 45-51, prof, 51-56; sci. adv, Armour Res. Found, Ill. Inst. Technol, 56-57; sr. res. assoc, Naugatuck Chem. Div, U.S. Rubber Co, 57-67; assoc. prof. TEXTILE CHEM, N.C. STATE UNIV, 67-69, PROF, 69- UNESCO Tech. Asst. Prog, India, 53-54. Am. Chem. Soc; fel. N.Y. Acad. Sci. Kinetics of polymerization; mechanism of oxidation of cellulose; properties of carbon black and carbon black rubber systems; color science. Address: Dept. of Textile Chemistry, North Carolina State University, Raleigh, NC 27607.

GOLDFISCHER, L(ESTER) I(RVING), b. N.Y.C, Jan. 27, 24; m. 44; c. 3. ELECTRICAL ENGINEERING. B.S.E.E, Purdue, 48; M.E.E, Polytech. Inst. Brooklyn, 52. Engr, RCA Labs, Inc, 48-49; proj. engr, Sperry Gyroscope Co, 48-51; Radio Receptor Co, Inc, 51-52; PRIN. ENGR, GPL DIV. SINGER-GEN. PRECISION, INC, 52- Sig.C, U.S.A, 43-46. Optical Soc. Am. Optical correlation applied to navigation. Address: GPL Division, Singer-General Precision, Inc, 63 Bedford Rd, Pleasantville, NY 10570.

GOLDFISCHER, SIDNEY L, b. N.Y.C, Dec. 28, 26; m. 54; c. 4. PATHOLOGY, CYTOCHEMISTRY. B.S, Columbia Univ, 58; M.D, N.Y. Univ, 61. U.S. Pub. Health Serv. spec. fel, 63-65; asst. prof. PATH, ALBERT EINSTEIN COL. MED, 65-71, ASSOC. PROF, 71- Lectr, Nat. Sci. Found. course histochem, Vanderbilt Univ, 67, 69, 70, 71; attend. pathologist, Bronx Munic. Hosp. Ctr, 71- AAAS; Histochem. Soc; Am. Soc. Cell Biol; Int. Acad. Path; Am. Soc. Exp. Path; French Soc. Electron Micros. Development of cytochemical staining procedures for light and electron microscopy; application of these procedures which permit a synthesis of functional and morphological studies to problems in physiology and pathology at the subcellular level. Address: Dept. of Pathology, Albert Einstein College of Medicine, Yeshiva University, 1300 Morris Park Ave, Bronx, NY 10461.

GOLDFRANK, MAX, b. Glen Ridge, N.J, Jan. 16, 11; m. 34; c. 2. CHEMICAL ENGINEERING. A.B, Columbia, 31, B.S, 32, Ch.E, 33. Chemist, STEIN, HALL & CO, INC, 34-44, asst. mgr. lab, N.Y, 44-45, chief chemist, starch & allied res. lab, 45-46, adhesive lab, 46-47; exec. asst. to tech. dir, 47-50, mgr. labs, N.Y, 50-54, mgr. develop, starch & allied prods, 54-70, MGR. PATENTS & REGULATORY COMPLIANCE, 70- Am. Chem. Soc; Am. Soc. Test. & Mat; Am. Asn. Cereal Chem; Inst. Food Technol. Starches; dextrines; adhesives; carbohydrate gums; food additives. Address: Stein Hall & Co, 605 Third Ave, New York, NY 10016.

GOLDHABER, ALFRED SCHARFF, b. Urbana, Ill, July 4, 40; m. 69. THEORETICAL PHYSICS. A.B, Harvard, 61; Nat. Sci. Found. fel, Princeton, 61-64, Ph.D.(physics), 64. Miller fel. PHYSICS, Univ. Calif, Berkeley, 64-66, lectr, 66-67; ASST. PROF, STATE UNIV. N.Y. STONY BROOK, 67- Vis. staff mem, Los Alamos Sci. Lab, 64-; U.S-U.S.S.R. Acad. Sci. exchange vis, 70; Nat. Sci. Found. sr. fel, Europ. Orgn. Nuclear Res, 71. Am. Phys. Soc. High energy theory; weak interactions; optical models; electrodynamics; nuclear physics; classical limits. Address: Dept. of Physics, State University of New York at Stony Brook, Stony Brook, NY 11790.

GOLDHABER, GERSON, b. Chemnitz, Ger, Feb. 20, 24; nat; m. 69; c. 2. NUCLEAR PHYSICS. M.Sc, Hebrew Univ, 47; Ph.D, Wisconsin, 50. Asst. PHYSICS, Hebrew Univ, 47; Wisconsin, 48-50; instr, Columbia, 50-53; acting asst. prof, UNIV. CALIF, BERKELEY, 53-54, asst. prof, 54-58, assoc. prof, 58-64, PROF, 64-, asst. res. prof, Miller Inst. Basic Res, 57-58. Ford Found. fel, Europ. Orgn. Nuclear Res, 60-61; group leader, Lawrence Berkeley Lab, Berkeley, 62-; vis. prof, Inst. Madras, India, 65; Ford Found consult, Latin Am. Sch. Physics, Caracas, Venezuela, 66; lectr, Second Hawaii Topical Conf. Particle Physics, 67. Fel. Am. Phys. Soc. Nuclear emulsion and bubble chamber techniques; meson and antiproton interactions; high energy and elementary particle physics. Address: Dept. of Physics, Lawrence Berkeley Lab, University of California, Berkeley, CA 94720.

GOLDHABER, GERTRUDE SCHARFF, b. Mannheim, Germany, July 14, 11; nat; m. 39; c. 2. PHYSICS. Ph.D.(physics), Munich, 35. Res. assoc. physics, Imp. Col, London, 35-39; res. physicist, Illinois, 39-48, special res. asst. prof. physics, 48-50; consult, BROOKHAVEN NAT. LAB, N.Y, 48-50, assoc. physicist, 50-58, physicist, 58-62, SR. PHYSICIST, 62- Consult, Argonne Nat. Lab, 46-50; Los Alamos Sci. Lab, 53-; chmn, panel on evaluation of nuclear data compilations, Nat. Acad. Sci-Nat. Res. Coun, 69- Fel. Am. Phys. Soc. Ferromagnetism; photoneutrons; spontaneous fission neutrons; identity of beta-rays with atomic electrons; nuclear structure; K-forbiddenness; odd-odd nuclei; variable moment of inertia law; parity violation in electromagnetic transitions. Address: Dept. of Physics, Brookhaven National Lab, Upton, NY 11973.

GOLDHABER, J(ACOB) K(OPEL), b. Brooklyn, N.Y, Apr. 12, 24; m. 51; c. 3. MATHEMATICS. B.A, Brooklyn Col, 44; M.A, Harvard, 45; Ph.D.(math), Wisconsin, 50. Instr. MATH, Connecticut, 50-53; Cornell, 53-55; asst. prof, Washington (St. Louis), 55-58, assoc. prof, 58-60; res. assoc. prof, UNIV. MD, 60-61, PROF, 61-, HEAD DEPT, 68- Nat. Sci. Found. sci. faculty fel, 66-67. AAAS; Am. Math. Soc; Math. Asn. Am. Algebra. Address: Dept. of Mathematics, University of Maryland, College Park, MD 20742.

GOLDHABER, MAURICE, b. Lemberg, Austria, April 18, 11; nat; m. 39; c. 2. PHYSICS. Ph.D.(physics), Cambridge, 36. Bye fel, Magdalene Col, Cambridge, 36-38; asst. prof. physics, Illinois, 38-43, assoc. prof, 43-45, prof, 45-50; sr. scientist, BROOKHAVEN NAT. LAB, 50-60, chmn. dept. physics, 60-61, DIR, 61- Morris Loeb lectr, Harvard, 55; consult, labs, Atomic Energy Comn; mem. nuclear sci. comt, Nat. Res. Coun; bd. gov, Weizmann Inst. Sci; adj. prof, State Univ. N.Y. Stony Brook, 67-; mem. bd. gov, Tel Aviv Univ. Tom W. Bonner Prize, 71. Nat. Acad. Sci; fel. Am. Phys. Soc; fel. Am. Acad. Arts & Sci. Neutron physics; radioactivity; nuclear isomers, photoelectric effect and models; fundamental particles. Address: Brookhaven National Lab, Upton, NY 11973.

GOLDHABER, MICHAEL H(ENRY), b. Urbana, Ill, Sept. 9, 42. ELEMENTARY PARTICLE THEORETICAL PHYSICS. A.B, Harvard, 63; Ph.D.(physics), Stanford, 68. Res. assoc. high energy physics, Rockefeller Univ, 68-70; ASST. PROF. PHYSICS, UNIV. ARIZ, 70- Am. Phys. Soc; Fedn. Am. Sci. Large radius proton electromagnetic structure; asymptotic proton form factors; strong interactions. Address: Dept. of Physics, University of Arizona, Tucson, AZ 85721.

GOLDHABER, PAUL, b. N.Y.C, Mar. 16, 24; m. 49; c. 2. DENTISTRY. D.D.S, N.Y. Univ, 48; B.S, City Col. New York & cert, Columbia, 54; hon. M.A, Harvard, 62. Asst. ophthal. res, Harvard Med. Sch, 48-50; asst. dent, sch. dent. & oral surg, Columbia, 50-; res. fel. dent. med, HARVARD SCH. DENT. MED, 54-55, res. assoc. oral path, 55-56; assoc, 56-59, asst. prof, 59-62, assoc. prof. PERIODONT, 62-66, PROF, 66-, DEAN, SCH. DENT. MED, 68-, dir. postdoctoral studies, 62-68. Vol. tissue-cult. technician, Sloan-Kettering Inst. Cancer Res, 46-48; asst. ophthal. res, Mass. Eye & Ear Infirmary, 48-50; vis. res. fel, Sloan-Kettering Inst. Cancer Res, 54-55, res. fel, 55-56; sr. res. fel, U.S. Pub. Health Serv, 56-61, res. career develop. award, 61-66; dent. consult, Fulbright Med. Sci. Comt, 65- Dipl, Am. Bd. Periodont, 54. U.S.A, 43-44, Dent.C, 52-53, 1st Lt. Fel. AAAS; Tissue Cult. Asn; Am. Asn. Cancer Res; Am. Acad. Periodont; Am. Soc. Cell Biol; fel. N.Y. Acad. Sci; Int. Asn. Dent. Res. Periodontal disease; oral carcinogenesis; bone transplantation; bone resorption and formation in tissue culture. Address: Harvard School of Dental Medicine, 188 Longwood Ave, Boston, MA 02115.

GOLDHAGEN, SAMUEL, b. Philadelphia, Pa, Sept. 29, 22; m. 54; c. 1. PHYSICAL CHEMISTRY. B.S, Maryland, 44, M.S, 49; Ohio State & Syracuse, 45-46. Phys. chemist, U.S. Army Corps Engrs, 49-51; head thermochem. sect, U.S. Naval Ord. Sta, 51-55; develop. chemist, Aerojet-Gen. Corp, 55-57, tech. specialist, 57-61, prin. chemist, 61-66, sr. chem. specialist, 66-70; CONSULT, 70-; V.PRES, SIERRA TECHNOL. CORP, 71- U.S.A, 44-46. Am. Chem. Soc; Am. Inst. Aeronaut. & Astronaut; Am. Ord. Asn. Solid and liquid propellants for rockets, guns, gas generators and commercial devices; composite and conventional explosives for industrial and military use; polymers and filled polymers. Address: 4330 Vassar Way, Sacramento, CA 95841.

GOLDHAMMER, PAUL, b. Portland, Ore, Nov. 10, 29. NUCLEAR PHYSICS. B.A, Reed Col, 52; Ph.D.(physics), Washington (St. Louis), 56. Asst. prof. PHYSICS, Delaware, 56-57; Nebraska, 57-61, assoc. prof, 61-64, PROF, 63-64; UNIV. KANS, 64- Fel. Am. Phys. Soc. Theoretical nuclear physics. Address: Dept. of Physics, University of Kansas, Lawrence, KS 66044.

GOLDHEIM, S(AMUEL) L(EWIS), b. Baltimore, Md, Aug. 4, 10; m. 34; c. 2. CHEMISTRY. Chemist, Calvert Distilling Co, 33-34; Oldetyme Distillers, Ind, 34-35, plant mgr, 35-40; Schenley Distilling Co, 40-41; dir. quality control, United Distillers, 45-48; consult, 48-53; dir, Am. Biochem. Lab, Inc, 53-64; PRES, ABCO LAB, INC, 65- Instr, Johns Hopkins Univ, 33; teacher, pub. schs, Md, 33-35. U.S.A, 41-45, Maj. AAAS; N.Y. Acad. Sci; Am. Chem. Soc; Am. Soc. Qual. Control; Inst. Food Technol. Fermentation; paperboard testing. Address: 2219 Rogene Dr, Apt. 203, Baltimore, MD 21209.

GOLDHIRSH, JULIUS, b. Phila, Pa, Oct. 2, 35; m. 60; c. 2. ELECTRICAL ENGINEERING. B.S, Drexel Inst, 58; M.S, Rutgers, 60; Ph.D,(elec. eng), Pennsylvania, 64. Asst. instr. elec. eng, Rutgers, 58-59, res. asst. plasmas, 59-60; instr. ELEC. ENG, Univ. Pa, 60-65, asst. prof, 65-71; ASSOC. PROF, HOLON UNIV. TECHNOL, ISRAEL, 71- Consult, Raytheon Co, Mass, 63-68. Inst. Elec. & Electronics Eng. Antenna and microwave analysis; radio wave propagation; numerical analysis of electromagnetic field problems. Address: Holon University of Technology, 52 Golomb St, P.O. Box 305, Holon, Israel.

GOLDHOFF, ROBERT M(AURICE), b. Cincinnati, Ohio, Sept. 3, 20; m. 53; c. 2. METALLURGY. Ch.E, Cincinnati, 43, M.S, 50; Ph.D.(metall), Ohio

State, 55. Asst, Int. Nickel Co, 40-41; Wright Aeronaut. Corp, 42; foundry metallurgist, Dayton Malleable Iron Co, 46-49; phys. metallurgist, Battelle Mem. Inst, 50-53; SUPVR. METALL. RES, GEN. ELEC. CO, 55- Ord.C, U.S.A, 43-46. Am. Soc. Metals; Am. Soc. Test. & Mat; Am. Soc. Mech. Eng. Development and use of materials particularly alloy steel in the power generating industry; steam turbine generators. Address: Materials & Processes Lab, General Electric Co, 1 River Rd, Schenectady, NY 12305.

GOLDHOR, SUSAN, b. Brooklyn, N.Y, Mar. 24, 39. DEVELOPMENTAL BIOLOGY. A.B, Columbia, 60; Woodrow Wilson fel, Yale, 60-62, M.S, 62, Nat. Insts. Health fel, 65-67, Ph.D.(biol), 67. Am. Cancer Soc. res. fel, dept. biol. sci, Stanford, 67-68, Nat. Insts. Health res. fel, 68-69; ASST. PROF. DEVELOP. BIOL, BIOL. INST, HACETTEPE UNIV, TURKEY, 69- Fedn. Am. Sci. Membranes in early embryonic development and differentiation, mitochondrial differentiation; membranes in cancer; membrane components, especially structural protein. Address: Biology Institute, Hacettepe University, Ankara, Turkey.

GOLDIAMOND, ISRAEL, b. Ukraine, Russia, Nov. 1, 19; nat; m. 46; c. 3. EXPERIMENTAL PSYCHOLOGY. B.A, Brooklyn Col, 42; Indiana, 44; California, 46; Ph.D.(exp. psychol), Chicago, 55. Admin. asst, Inst. Design, Ill, 47-48; dir, K.A.M. Nursery Sch, 48-49; asst. psychol, Chicago, 49-54, res. assoc, 54-55; asst. prof, Southern Illinois, 55-59, assoc. prof, 59-60; prof, Arizona State, 60-63; exec. dir, Inst. Behav. Res, 63-68; PROF. PSYCHIAT. & PSYCHOL, UNIV. CHICAGO, 68- Dir. perception & conditioning lab, Southern Illinois, 55-59; Nat. Sci. Found. res. grants, 56-59; consult, Anna State Hosp, 56-60; prin. investr, U.S. Dept. Health, Ed. & Welfare, 57-59; Ill. Psychiat. Training & Res. Authority, 57-60; Cambridge Res. Center, U.S. Air Force, 59-; Nat. Inst. Ment. Health Career develop. award, 63-68; lectr, Wash. Sch. Psychiat, 63-68; assoc. prof, sch. med, Johns Hopkins Univ, 66-67, prof, 67-68. U.S.A, 42-45, Sgt. AAAS; Optical Soc. Am; Ecol. Soc. Am; Am. Psychol. Asn. Experimental analysis and application of conditions of behavioral control; signal detection, perception and psychophysics; operant conditioning of monitoring, recognition and verbal behaviors; experimental psychopathology and controlled alteration; training devices. Address: Dept. of Psychiatry, University of Chicago, 950 E. 59th St, Chicago, IL 60637.

GOLDICH, S(AMUEL) S(TEPHEN), b. Grand Forks, N.Dak, Jan. 17, 09. GEOLOGY. A.B, Univ. Minn, 29, Ph.D.(geol), 36; A.M, Univ. Syracuse, 30. Asst. geol, Mo. Sch. Mines, 30-32; fel, Wash. Univ, 32-34; asst. & chemist, rock anal. lab, Univ. Minn, 34-36; instr. geol, Agr. & Mech. Col, Tex, 36-37, asst. prof, 38-40, assoc. prof, 40-41; geologist, U.S. Geol. Surv, 42-45, 47-48 & 59-60, chief, br. isotope geol, 60-64; assoc. prof. geol, Univ. Minn, 48-49, prof, 49-50; prof. geol. & geochem. & dir. mineral. constitution labs, Pa. State Univ, 64-68; PROF. GEOL, NORTH. ILL. UNIV, 68- Assoc. prof. & acting prof, Agr. & Mech. Col, Tex, 45-46; geologists, bur. econ. geol, Tex, 46-48. AAAS; fel. Am. Geophys. Union; fel. Geol. Soc. Am; fel. Mineral. Soc. Am; Am. Chem. Soc; Am. Asn. Petrol. Geol; Geochem. Soc; Soc. Econ. Paleont. & Mineral; Mineral. Asn. Can. Areal geology in Trans-Pecos, Texas; origin of laterite and bauxite; petrology; geochemistry; geochronology. Address: Dept. of Geology, Northern Illinois University, De Kalb, IL 60115.

GOLDIE, HARRY, b. Brooklyn, N.Y, May 3, 27; m. 53; c. 2. MICROWAVE & PLASMA PHYSICS. B.E.E, City Col. New York, 60; M.S, Polytech. Inst. Brooklyn, 63. Sr. res. asst. plasma electrophys. & microwaves, microwave res. inst, Polytech. Inst. Brooklyn, 60-63; sr. engr. & group leader res. on plasmas & microwaves, MICROWAVE TECH. LAB, WESTINGHOUSE ELEC. CORP, 63-69, FEL. ENGR, 69- U.S.N, 51-52. Inst. Elec. & Electronics Eng. Research into microwave interactions with weakly-ionized plasmas; development of microwave control devices for eventual use in radar systems. Address: 3706 Allenswood Court, Randallstown, MD 21133.

GOLDIE, MARK, b. Hartford, Conn, Aug. 31, 26; m. 52; div; c. 2; m. 63; c. 1. EMBRYOLOGY. B.S, Connecticut, 50, Nat. Cancer Inst. fel, 55-57, Ph.D. (zool), 57; M.A, Columbia, 53. Res. assoc, Inst. Living, Conn, 57-58; instr. biol, Brown, 58-59; asst. prof. zool, La. State, 59-60; physiol, Col. Osteop. Med. & Surg, 60-63, assoc. prof, 63-64; ASST. PROF. BIOL, LOYOLA UNIV. CHICAGO, 64- U.S.A, 45-46, 50-51. Am. Soc. Zool. Teratology; embryonic nutrition; physiology of phenocopies. Address: Dept. of Biological Sciences, Loyola University of Chicago, 6525 N. Sheridan Rd, Chicago, IL 60626.

GOLDIN, ABRAHAM, b. New York, N.Y, Nov. 10, 11; m. 42; c. 2. PHARMACOLOGY. B.S, Brooklyn Col, 33; M.A, Columbia, 35, Ph.D.(zool), 42. Lab. asst. bact. & physiol, Brooklyn Col, 33-38, instr. zool, 45-46; lab. instr. biol, Queens Col.(N.Y), 38-42; biologist & chief, biol. sect, med. div, U.S. Army Chem. Center, 46-49; biologist & chief, biol. sect, med. div, U.S. Army Chem. Center, 46-49; biologist, NAT. CANCER INST, 48-58, pharmacologist, 58-63, chief drug eval. br, cancer chemother. nat. serv. ctr, 63-65, ASSOC. CHIEF LAB. RES. CHEMOTHER, DRUG RES. & DEVELOP, 66- Asst, Johns Hopkins Univ, 47-48, res. assoc, 54-; vis. prof, grad. sch. biochem, Brandeis Univ, 57-68. U.S.A, 42-45. AAAS; Assoc. Soc. Exp. Biol. & Med; assoc. Am. Asn. Cancer Res; Am. Soc. Microbiol; Am. Asn. Lab. Animal Sci; assoc. N.Y. Acad. Sci; affilliate, Royal Soc. Med; cor. mem. Italian Cancer Soc; Int. Soc. Chemother. Cancer research; chemical pharmacology; physiology. Address: National Cancer Institute, Bldg. 37, Room 5E24, Bethesda, MD 20014.

GOLDIN, ABRAHAM S(AMUEL), b. Brooklyn, N.Y, Apr. 22, 17; m. 45; c. 3. CHEMISTRY. A.B, Columbia, 37, A.M, 41; Ph.D, Tennessee, 51. Control chemist, East. Wine Corp, N.Y, 41; prod. chemist, Mutual Chem. Co, N.J, 42; res. asst, s.a.m. labs, Columbia, 42-45; tech. engr. & chemist, Carbide & Carbon Chems. Corp, 45-50; radiochemist, U.S. Pub. Health Serv, 51-60; chem. dir, Nat. Lead Co, Inc, 60-61; assoc. prof, N.Y. Univ, 61-62; dep. officer in charge, Northeast. Radiol. Health Lab, 62-68; ASSOC. PROF. SCH. PUB. HEALTH, HARVARD, 68- U.S.A, 42-46. AAAS; Am. Chem. Soc; Health Phys. Soc; Am. Inst. Chem; Am. Pub. Health Asn. Radioactive waste treatment; measurement of radioactivity in environment, including air, water, food; application of radioactive tracers; radiation safety in use of nuclear energy. Address: 15 Carriage Lane, Winchester, MA 01890.

GOLDIN, HERBERT HAROLD, b. Sommerville, N.J, Feb. 11, 37; m. 59; c. 2. GENETICS. B.A, Hartwick Col, 60; M.A, State Univ. N.Y. Buffalo, 63, fel. & Ph.D.(biol), 66. Nat. Insts. Health fel, 66-67; ASST. PROF. BIOL, UNIV. TOLEDO, 67- Am. Soc. Zool; Am. Genetics Asn; Inst. Biol. Sci. Genetic control of cellular metabolism in Drosophila. Address: Dept. of Biology, University of Toledo, Toledo, OH 43606.

GOLDIN, MILTON, b. N.Y.C, July 26, 17; m. 51; c. 3. BACTERIOLOGY. B.S, Brooklyn Col, 38; M.S, Univ. Ill, 48; Ph.D, Chicago Med. Sch, 70. Bacteriologists, U.S. Pub. Health Serv, 41-42; chief bacteriologists, Hektoen Inst, Cook County Hosp, 46-48; DIR. MICROBIOL. DEPT, MT. SINAI HOSP. MED. CTR, 48-, BACTERIOLOGIST, MED. RES. FOUND, 48- Assoc. prof, Chicago Med. Sch, 49- Sanit.C, 42-46, Capt. Am. Soc. Microbiol. Factors determining virulence of infectious organisms; immunological studies in collagen diseases; mycotic infections in humans. Address: Dept. of Pathology, Mt. Sinai Hospital Medical Center, 2755 W. 15th St, Chicago, IL 60608.

GOLDING, BRAGE, b. Chicago, Ill, Apr. 28, 20; m. 41; c. 3. CHEMICAL ENGINEERING. B.S, Purdue Univ, 41, Ph.D.(chem. eng), 48. Asst. dir. res, Lilly Varnish Co, 48-57, dir, 57-59; prof. chem. eng. & head sch, Purdue Univ, 59-66, res. assoc, 48-57, vis. prof, 57-59; v.pres, Wright State Campus, Miami Univ-Ohio State Univ, 66, PRES, WRIGHT STATE UNIV, 66- Indust. consult, 59- U.S.A, 41-46, Res, 46-53, Maj. Fel. AAAS; Am. Chem. Soc; Soc. Plastics Eng; Am. Soc. Test. & Mat; Am. Inst. Chem. Eng. Surface coatings technology; polymer technology and research; organic technology. Address: Wright State University, Colonel Glenn Highway, Dayton, OH 45431.

GOLDING, D(AVID) R.V, b. Chicago, Ill. CHEMISTRY. A.B, Harvard, 41; Sheldon Traveling fel, 41; Ph.D.(chem), Calif. Inst. Tech, 44. Fel. chem, Calif. Inst. Tech, 41-43, asst, Comt. Med. Res. proj, 43-45; res. chemist, E.I. du Pont de Nemours & Co, 45-59; supvr. solid rocket propellants fuels, Rocketdyne Div, N.Am. Aviation, Inc, 59-67; DIR. CHEM. PROCESS RES, DOLE DIV, CASTLE & COOKE, 67- Mem, Gov. Task Force on Pearl Harbor; Hawaii Waste Adv. Comn. Am. Chem. Soc; Sci. Res. Soc. Am. Industrial organic chemical development work; industrial research and development of textile fibers; solid propellant combustion characteristics. Address: 46 498 Haiku Plantation Dr, Kaneohe, HI 96744.

GOLDINGS, HERBERT JEREMY, b. Boston, Mass, May 28, 29; m. 55; c. 3. PSYCHIATRY. A.B, Harvard, 50, M.D, 54; grad, Boston Psychoanal. Soc. Inst, 65. Intern med, Boston City Hosp, 54-55; teaching fel, HARVARD MED. SCH, 55-57, res. fel. psychiat, 57-58, asst. psychiat, 60-65, instr. psychiat, 65-69, ASST. CLIN. PROF. PSYCHIAT, 69-, SR. PHYSICIAN, CHILD PSYCHIAT. SERV, MASS. MENT. HEALTH CTR, 61-, ASSOC. DIR. CHILD PSYCHIAT, 65-, res. psychiat, 55-58, fel, 57-58 & 60-61. Mem. faculty, Boston Psychoanal. Soc. & Inst, 68- Consult, div. legal med, Mass, 57-58; 5040th U.S. Air Force Hosp, Alaska, 58-60; Parents Asn. Retarded Children, Alaska, 58-60. Asst. examiner, Am. Bd. Psychiat. & Neurol, 64- Dipl, Am. Bd. Psychiat. & Neurol, 61, cert. child psychiat, 64. Med.C, U.S.A.R, 58-61, Capt. Am. Psychiat. Asn; Am. Med. Asn; fel. Am. Acad. Child Psychiat; Am. Psychoanal. Asn; Int. Psychoanal. Asn. Child psychiatry; psychoanalysis; medical education. Address: 65 Sterling St, West Newton, MA 02165.

GOLDISH, DOROTHY M(AY) (BOWMAN), b. N.J, May 6, 34; m. 58; c. 2. ORGANIC CHEMISTRY. B.S, Stanford, 55; Richards fel, California, 56-57, McEnerney fel, 57-58, Ph.D.(chem), 58. Asst. prof. CHEM, CALIF. STATE COL. LONG BEACH, 58-70, ASSOC. PROF, 70- Am. Chem. Soc. Heterocyclic chemistry; natural products. Address: Dept. of Chemistry, California State College, Long Beach, CA 90801.

GOLDISH, ELIHU, b. Marietta, Ohio, Oct. 18, 28; m. 58; c. 2. PHYSICAL CHEMISTRY. B.Sc, Marietta Col, 49; Ph.D.(chem), Calif. Inst. Technol, 56. Fel, Ohio State Univ, 56-57; res. fel. chem, Univ. South. Calif, 58-60; RES. CHEMIST, RES. CTR, UNION OIL CO. CALIF, 60- Fel, Univ. Calif, Los Angeles, 66. Am. Crystallog. Asn. Molecular structure investigations by x-ray and electron diffraction. Address: Research Center, Union Oil Co. California, Brea, CA 92621.

GOLDKAMP, ARTHUR H(ARVEY), b. Cincinnati, Ohio, Aug. 8, 29; m. 52; c. 8. CHEMISTRY. B.S, Univ. Notre Dame, 51; M.S, Loyola Univ. Chicago, 53; Gen. Elec. Co. fel, Univ. Ill, Urbana, 55-56, Ph.D.(org. chem), 56. Lab. asst, Univ. Notre Dame, 50-51; res. asst, Loyola Univ. Chicago, 51-53; sr. res. investr, G.D. Searle & Co, 56-69; Nat. Insts. Health trainee clin. chem, Univ. Wash, 69-71. AAAS; Am. Chem. Soc; The Chem. Soc; Am. Asn. Clin. Chem; N.Y. Acad. Sci. Pharmaceutical chemistry; medical biochemistry; amino acids; peptide synthesis; steroids; nitrogen heterocycles; benzene derivatives; body constituents. Address: 12162 S.E. 14th St, Bellevue, WA 98005.

GOLDLUST, MARVIN B(ERTRAM), b. Brooklyn, N.Y, Apr. 27, 42; m. 63; c. 1. IMMUNOLOGY. B.S, City Col. New York, 62; Ph.D.(biochem) & Nat. Inst. Gen. Med. Sci. fel, Brandeis Univ, 67. RES. INVESTR. IMMUNOL, SQUIBB INST. MED. RES, 70- Univ. fels, sch. med, Johns Hopkins Univ, 66-68, Nat. Inst. Allergy & Infectious Diseases fel, 68-69, Pub. Health Serv. training grant, 69-71. Effects of clostridial proteinase(s) on complement; mechanism of reaction of sixth component of complement; anti-inflammatory drug evaluation. Address: Dept. of Biochemical Pharmacology, Squibb Institute for Medical Research, New Brunswick, NJ 08903.

GOLDMACHER, JOEL E, b. Brooklyn, N.Y, May 5, 37; m. 68; c. 4. ORGANIC CHEMISTRY. B.S, City Col. N.Y, 59; Nat. Insts. Health fel, Purdue Univ, 61-63, Ph.D.(chem), 63. Mem. tech. staff, RCA Corp, 63-69; prog. mgr. reprography res, St. Regis Tech. Ctr, 69-70; DIR. RES. & DEVELOP, OPTEL CORP, 70- Two IR-100 awards, Indust. Res. Mag. Am. Chem. Soc; Am. Inst. Chem. Liquid crystals; organic dyes; photoconductors. Address: Optel Corp, Box 2215, Princeton, NJ 08691.

GOLDMAN, AARON SAMPSON, b. Red Lion, Pa, Feb. 8, 32. STATISTICS. Nat. Sci. Found. fel. & Ph.D, Okla. State, 61. Math. statistician, Los Alamos Sci. Lab, 60-69; ASSOC. PROF. MATH, UNIV. NEV, LAS VEGAS, 69-

U.S.A.F, 54-56, 1st Lt. Am. Statist. Asn. Sample size determination in experimental work; particle size statistics. Address: Dept. of Mathematics, University of Nevada, Las Vegas, NV 89109.

GOLDMAN, ALAN J(OSEPH), b. N.Y.C, Mar. 2, 32; m. 55; c. 1. MATHEMATICS. B.A, Brooklyn Col, 52; Nat. Sci. Found. fel, Princeton, 52-54, M.A, 54, Ph.D.(math), 56. Instr. math, Princeton, 55-56; mathematician, NAT. BUR. STANDARDS, 56-61, CHIEF OPERS. RES. SECT, 61-, DEP. CHIEF APPL. MATH. DIV, 68- Lectr, American Univ, 56-57; Catholic Univ, 57-63. U.S. Dept. Commerce silver medal, 67. Am. Math. Soc; Soc. Indust. & Appl. Math; Math. Asn. Am; Opers. Res. Soc. Am. Theory of games; linear and non-linear programming; operations research; transport systems and cost-effectiveness analysis. Address: 4822 Chevy Chase Dr, Apt. 203, Chevy Chase, MD 20015.

GOLDMAN, ALEX, b. N.Y.C, Apr. 3, 21; m. 44; c. 3. MAGNETISM, PHYSICAL CHEMISTRY. B.S, City Col. New York, 50; Polytech. Inst. Brooklyn, 50-52; A.M, Columbia, 53, Socony Vacuum fel, 54-55, Ph.D.(phys. chem), 55. Res. chemist, Endo Prod, Inc, 50-51; asst. chem, Columbia, 51-54; mat. engr, Westinghouse Elec. Corp, 55-60, sr. res. scientist, 60-66; mgr. electronic ceramic res, MAGNETICS, INC, 66-69, RES. DIR, 69- U.S.N, 44-46. Am. Chem. Soc. Research and development of magnetic materials; magneto optic effects; microwave ferrites; crystal growth; diffusion; adsorption; electronic ceramic research. Address: Magnetics, Inc, Butler, PA 16001.

GOLDMAN, ALFRED, b. St. Louis, Mo, Oct. 6, 95; m. 36; c. 3. MEDICINE. B.A, Wash. Univ, 16, M.D, 20, M.S, 22. Res. path, SCH. MED, WASH. UNIV, 20-21, intern, 21-22, res. med, 22-24, instr, 24-43, asst. prof, 43-50, assoc. prof, 50-71, EMER. PROF. CLIN. MED, 71-, chief chest clin, 35-71. Consult, Barnes Hosp, 43-; Koch Hosp, 43-; Homer Phillips Hosp, 43-; U.S. Pub. Health Serv, 48-; Vet. Admin, 50- U.S.A, 17-18. Am. Col. Physicians; Am. Col. Chest Physicians(pres, 64-65). Diseases of the chest; tuberculosis; pleural effusions; hyperventilation syndrome; arteriovenous fistula of the lungs. Address: 8631 Delmar St, St. Louis, MO 63124.

GOLDMAN, ARMOND SAMUEL, b. San Angelo, Tex, May 26, 30; m. 50; c. 5. PEDIATRICS, IMMUNOLOGY. M.D, Univ. Tex, 53. Instr. pediat, UNIV. TEX. MED. BR, GALVESTON, 58-59, asst. prof. 59-66, ASSOC. PROF, 66-, DIR. DIV. IMMUNOL-ALLERGY, 59-, CO-DIR. POISON CONTROL CTR, 67-, dir, 58-67. Prin. investr. Nat. Inst. Health res. grants, 64-67 & 68-71; asst. chief staff and chief pediat. div, Shriner's Burns Inst, Galveston, 67- Dipl, Am. Bd. Pediat, 60. U.S.A, 55-57. Reticuloendothelial Soc; Soc. Pediat. Res. Am. Acad. Pediat. Immunologic functions of human colostral cells; etiology of primary immunologic defects; effect of burns upon the activation of macrophages; epidemiology of burn injuries. Address: Dept. of Pediatrics, University of Texas Medical Branch, Galveston, TX 77550.

GOLDMAN, CHARLES C, b. Cincinnati, Ohio, Aug. 14, 18; m. 42; c. 2. MATHEMATICS. M.A, Cincinnati, 42, Ph.D.(math), 49. Instr. math, Cincinnati, 46-49; Purdue, 49-50; mathematician, Wright Air Develop. Ctr, U.S. Air Force, 50-60; res. assoc, NAT. CASH REGISTER CO, 60-62, sr. staff analyst, 62-69, MGR. EDUC. PROD, 69- U.S.A.A.F, 42-46, Res, 46-53. Am. Math. Soc; Inst. Elec. & Electronics Eng. Systems synthesis and analysis; navigation and control; information processing; pattern recognition and self organizing systems. Address: National Cash Register Co, S. Main & K Sts, Dayton, OH 45409.

GOLDMAN, CHARLES L(EWIS), b. Malden, Mass, Dec. 10, 28; m. 51. BACTERIOLOGY. B.S, Providence Col, 50; scholar, Tufts, 51-52, M.S, 52; fel, Massachusetts, 53-56, Ph.D, 57. Res. instr, dept. vet. sci, Massachusetts, 56-57, asst. prof, 57-59; chief microbiologist, Food & Drug Res. Labs, Inc, 59; sr. chemist, res. ctr, Gen. Foods Corp, N.Y, 59-61; microbiologist, AVON PROD, INC, 61-67, sect. head res. div, 67-70, MGR, MICROBIOL. DEPT, 70- AAAS; Am. Soc. Microbiol; Soc. Cosmetic Chem; Am. Pub. Health Asn; Soc. Indust. Microbiol; N.Y. Acad. Sci. Industrial and sanitary microbiology; microbiology of integument. Address: 10 Canterbury Lane, Suffern, NY 10901.

GOLDMAN, CHARLES R(EMINGTON), b. Urbana, Ill, Nov. 9, 30; m. 53; c. 4. ZOOLOGY, LIMNOLOGY. B.S, Illinois, 52, M.S, 55; fel, Michigan, 57-58, Ph.D.(fisheries), 59. Asst. aquatic biol, State Natural Hist. Surv, Ill, 54-55; asst. fisheries, Michigan, 55-57; biologist fisheries res, U.S. Fish & Wildlife Serv, Alaska, 57-58; instr. ZOOL, UNIV. CALIF, DAVIS, 58-60, asst. prof, 60-63, assoc. prof, 63-66, PROF, 66-, dir. inst. ecol, 66-69. Biologist, eng. res. inst, Univ. Mich, 56-57; Nat. Sci. Found. sr. fel, 64; Guggenheim fel, 65; mem. sci. & technol. adv. coun, Calif. State Assembly, 70-73. Consult, fisheries res. inst, Univ. Wash, 61; div. natural resources, Humbolt State Col, 62; Eng-Sci, Inc, Calif, 62-63; attorney gen, State of Minn, 70; Environ. Protection Agency, 71- Antarctic serv. medal, 68. U.S.A.F, 52-54, Res, 54-, Capt. Fel. AAAS; Am. Soc. Limnol. & Oceanog; Ecol. Soc. Am; Int. Asn. Theoret. & Appl. Limnol. Aquatic biology-limnology; biological productivity and limiting factors; field work on African, Alaskan, Antarctic, Argentine, California, Lapland, Italian and New Zealand lakes. Address: Division of Environmental Studies, University of California, Davis, CA 95616.

GOLDMAN, DAVID E(LIOT), b. Boston, Mass, Aug. 11, 10; m. 38; c. 1. BIOPHYSICS, PHYSIOLOGY. A.B, Harvard, 31, 37-38; Ph.D.(physiol), Columbia, 43. Lab. asst. physiol, Mass. Dept. Ment. Health Cmn, Boston, 31-36; instr, physiol, col. physicians & surgeons, Columbia, 40-41, asst. surg, 42-43, res. assoc. physics, Nat. Defense Res. Cmt, univ, 43-44; mem. staff, Naval Med. Res. Inst, 44-47, head biophys. div, 47-55, sci. liaison officer, Off. Naval Res, London, 55-57, head biophys. div, Naval Med. Res. Inst, 57-67; PROF. PHYSIOL. & BIOPHYS, MED. COL. PA, 67-, DIR. GRAD. PROG, 70- Mem. comt. on hearing & bioacoust, Nat. Res. Coun, 53-, mem. coun, 70-; biophys. study sect, Nat. Insts. Health, 58-64, physiol. training grant comt, 70- U.S.N, 44-69, Capt.(Ret). AAAS; Am. Phys. Soc; Acoust. Soc. Am; Biophys. Soc; Am. Physiol. Soc. Electrical and mechanical phenomena in cells and tissues; theoretical biology; shock-vibration-bioacoustics; physical factors in health and safety. Address: Dept. of Physiology & Biophysics, Medical College of Pennsylvania, 3300 Henry Ave, Philadelphia, PA 19129.

GOLDMAN, DAVID T(OBIAS), b. Brooklyn, N.Y, Jan. 25, 33; m. 57; c. 4. THEORETICAL PHYSICS. A.B, Brooklyn Col, 52; Atomic Energy Comn. fel, Vanderbilt, 53-54, M.S, 54; Ph.D.(physics), Maryland, 58. Physicist, Evans Sig. Lab, 52-53; asst. physics, Maryland, 54-58; res. assoc, Pennsylvania, 58-59; theoret. physicist, Knolls Atomic Power Lab, Atomic Energy Comn, 59-63, supv. physicist, 63-65; chief theoret. physics, reactor radiations div, NAT. BUR. STANDARDS, 65-69, PROG. LEADER, STANDARD NUCLEAR REFERENCE DATA, 65-, PROG. ANALYST, SCI. & TECHNOL. PROG, 70- Physicist, Naval Res. Lab, 56; Oak Ridge Nat. Lab, 57-58; adj. assoc. prof, Rensselaer Polytech. Inst, 60-65; sci. policy analyst, Bur. Budget, 69-70; sci. fel, Dept. Commerce 69-70. Fel. Am. Phys. Soc; Am. Nuclear Soc. Theoretical nuclear physics; nuclear reactions and structure; reactor physics; effect of chemical binding. Address: National Bureau of Standards, Washington, DC 20234.

GOLDMAN, DEXTER S(TANLEY), b. Boston, Mass, June 17, 25; m. 64; c. 5. BIOLOGICAL CHEMISTRY. B.S, Univ. Calif, Los Angeles, 48; Ph.D.(comp. biochem), Univ. Calif, 51. Asst, Univ. Calif, 48-51; trainee, heart inst, Univ. Wis, 51-53, asst. prof, enzyme inst, 54-59, clin. assoc. prof, 59-71; chief biochemist, Vet. Admin. Hosp, 53-71; PROF. & DIR, INST. BIOL, HAIFA UNIV, 71- Vis. res. prof, div. biochem, Scripps Clin. & Res. Found, Univ. Calif, La Jolla, 63; vis. prof, Hebrew Univ, Israel, 68-69. U.S.N, 44-46. AAAS; Am. Chem. Soc; Am. Soc. Biol. Chem; Am. Soc. Cell Biol; Am. Thoracic Soc; Am. Acad. Microbiol; Am. Soc. Microbiol. Physiology and enzyme systems of the tubercle bacillus; enzymatic basis of disease and chemotherapy. Address: Institute for Biology, Haifa University, Haifa, Israel.

GOLDMAN, ERNEST HAROLD, b. Lynn, Mass, Oct. 4, 22; m. 48; c. 2. COMPUTER ENGINEERING. B.S, U.S. Coast Guard Acad, 43; M.S, Harvard, 49, Sc.D.(elec. eng), 52. Instr. physics, Bridgeport, 47-48; develop. engr, eng. lab, Int. Bus Mach. Corp, 51-52, sr. engr, 52-55, mgr. comput. test planning & testing, 55-57, res. mgr. exp. systs, T.J. Watson Res. Ctr, 57-61, res. dir, 61-64, mgr, E. FISHKILL LAB, 64-70, MGR. COMPONENT INDUST. EVAL, IBM CORP, 70- Bowdoin prize, Harvard, 50. U.S.C.G, 43-47, Lt. AAAS; sr. mem. Inst. Elec. & Electronics Eng; Asn. Comput. Mach. Computer technology; computer applications; electronic systems and circuits; business modelling; information retrieval and management systems. Address: East Fishkill Lab, IBM Corp, Hopewell Junction, NY 12533.

GOLDMAN, HAROLD, b. Chicago, Ill, March 29, 27; m. 53; c. 2. NEUROPHYSIOLOGY. M.S, Chicago, 53; Ph.D.(physiol), Illinois, 57. Instr. psychiat, COL. MED, OHIO STATE UNIV, 57-58, asst. prof, 58-66, pharmacol, 64-66, ASSOC. PROF. PSYCHIAT. & PHARMACOL, 66-; RES. NEUROENDOCRINOLOGIST, RES. DIV, COLUMBUS PSYCHIAT. INST, 57- U.S.N, 45-46. Biophys. Soc; N.Y. Acad. Sci; Am. Physiol. Soc. Interregulation of nervous and endocrine systems; metabolism of nervous tissue; small organ blood flow; neurohumors; regional cerebral blood flow; biologic bases of sociopathy. Address: Dept. of Psychiatry, College of Medicine, Ohio State University, Columbus, OH 43210.

GOLDMAN, HENRY M(AURICE), b. Boston, Mass, Dec. 6, 11; m. 36; c. 2. ORAL PATHOLOGY, PERIODONTOLOGY. Brown Univ, 29-31; D.M.D, Harvard, 35. Fel. oral path, Harvard, 35-37, instr, 37-46; prof. periodont. & chmn. dept, grad. sch. med, Univ. Pa, 52-58; PROF. STOMATOL, SCH. MED, BOSTON UNIV, 58-, DEAN, SCH. GRAD. DENT, 62-, chmn. dept. stomatol, 58-64. Head, Riesman Dent. Clin, Beth Israel Hosp, 48-; vis. lectr, Columbia Univ, 51-58; chief stomatol. serv, Boston Univ. Hosp, 58-; consult, Dent. & Oral Registry, Armed Forces Inst. Path, 47-54; mem. subcomt. periodontia, Nat. Res. Coun, 48-50; ad hoc comt. periodont, Nat. Inst. Dent. Res, 58-59, consult, 57-65, consult to dir, 70-; mem. Ivory Cross Exped, 48; assoc. dir, Boston Univ. Med. Ctr, 70- Dipl, Am. Bd. Periodont, dipl, Am. Bd. Oral Path, pres, 55-56; dipl, Am. Bd. Oral Med; Presidential Citation, 45; Hinman Award, 51, 67; Gold medal award, 69; Gies Award, 70. Dent.C, U.S.A, 43-45. AAAS; fel. Am. Col. Dent; fel. Am. Acad. Oral Path. (pres, 51-52); Am. Acad. Periodont.(ed, Periodontol, 68-); fel. Am. Pub. Health Asn; N.Y. Acad. Sci; Int. Asn. Dent. Res; fel. Int. Col. Dent. Oral medicine. Address: 176 Grant Ave, Newton Center, MA 02159.

GOLDMAN, IRA BERNARD, b. Baltimore, Md, Apr. 11, 39; m. 63; c. 2. CHEMICAL ENGINEERING, FLUID DYNAMICS. B.S, Maryland, 61, Ph.D. (chem), 65. Res. engr, Esso Res. & Eng. Co, 65-69; SR. ENGR, WEST. ELEC. CO, INC, AM. TEL. & TEL. CO, Md, 69-71, ENG. RES. CTR, 71- AAAS; Am. Chem. Soc; Am. Inst. Chem. Eng; Am. Soc. Lubrication Eng. Basic studies in friction, lubrication and wear research; mass transport and fluid rheology studies; substrates and materials for interconnects and printed wiring boards; electrochemistry; plating. Address: Western Electric Co, Inc. Engineering Research Center, P.O. Box 900, Dept. 20A32, Princeton, NJ 08540.

GOLDMAN, IRVING MAURICE, b. Washington, D.C, Aug. 27, 31; m. 52; c. 2. ORGANIC CHEMISTRY. A.B, Cornell, 53; Nat. Insts. Health fel, Mass. Inst. Tech, 55-57, Ph.D.(org. chem), 57. Res. chemist, Procter & Gamble Co, 57-58; Firmenich, Inc. res. assoc. flavor chem, Mass. Inst. Tech, 58-60; res. chemist, CHAS. PFIZER & CO, INC, 60-67, proj. leader, 67-71, MGR, 71- Am. Chem. Soc. Photochemistry; natural products; perfumes and flavors; medicinal chemistry; heterocyclic chemistry. Address: Charles Pfizer & Co, Inc, Groton, CT 06357.

GOLDMAN, I(RWIN), b. Jersey City, N.J, Apr. 7, 23; m. 49; c. 2. CHEMICAL ENGINEERING. B.Ch.E, Cooper Union, 44; M.Ch.E, Polytech. Inst. Brooklyn, 52. Chem. engr, Foster Wheeler Corp, 44; engr, Sylvania Elec. Prods, Inc, 46-50, sr. engr, 50-52, asst. to mgr. physics lab, 52-55, mgr. tech. planning, 55-57, assoc. dir. res, chem-metall. lab, 57-58, assoc. dir. admin, 58-63; DIR. PLANNING, MERCK SHARP & DOHME INT, N.J, 63-70, MANAGING DIR, BELG, 70- Spec. lectr, Polytech. Inst. Brooklyn, 53-56; lectr, Hofstra Col, 54-55, adj. asst. prof, 55-59, adj. assoc. prof, 59- Mem. cmt, materials adv. bd, div. eng. & indust. res, Nat. Acad. Sci-Nat. Res. Coun. U.S.N, 44-46. Am. Chem. Soc; Electrochem. Soc; Sci. Res. Soc. Am; sr. mem. Inst. Elec. & Electronics Eng; Inst. Mgt. Sci. Electrochemistry; selenium rectifiers; color television; research administration; corporate planning. Address: 43 Avenue de L'Observatoire, Brussels, Belgium 1180.

GOLDMAN, ISRAEL DAVID, b. Jersey City, N.J, Nov. 17, 36; m. 64; c. 3. BIOPHYSICS. B.A, N.Y. Univ, 58; M.D, Univ. Chicago, 62. Fel, biophys. lab, Harvard Med. Sch, 65-66; ASST. PROF. MED. & PHARMACOL, SCH. MED, UNIV. N.C, 69- Dir, Nat. Cancer Inst. res. grant, 70; co-dir, Nat. Inst. Environ. Health Sci. grant, 70; Pharmaceut. Mfrs. Asn. Found. faculty develop. award, 71. U.S.P.H.S, 66-69, Sr. Asst. Surg. AAAS; Fedn. Am. Soc. Exp. Biol; Biophys. Soc; Am. Soc. Pharmacol. & Exp. Therapeut. Transport characteristics of the folic acid compounds in normal and malignant mammalian tissues; mechanisms of membrane transport. Address: Dept. of Medicine, University of North Carolina School of Medicine, Chapel Hill, NC 27514.

GOLDMAN, JACK L(ESLIE), b. Chicago, Ill, Nov. 20, 35. PHYSICAL CHEMISTRY. B.A. & B.S, Chicago, 58; M.S, Loyola (Ill), 61, Ph.D.(chem), 66. Instr. chem, Mundelein Col, 63-65; res. phys. chemist, Velsicol Chem. Corp, 66-67; MEM. FACULTY NATURAL SCI. & CHEM, SHIMER COL, 67-, CHMN. NATURAL SCI, 70- AAAS; Am. Chem. Soc; fel. Am. Inst. Chem; Am. Asn. Physics Teachers; N.Y. Acad. Sci; Am. Phys. Soc. Conceptual development of quantum mechanics; methodology of science, especially the interrelations between biological and physical sciences; integrative principles in the sciences and humanities. Address: Dept. of Natural Sciences & Chemistry, Shimer College, Mt. Carroll, IL 61053.

GOLDMAN, JACOB E, b. N.Y.C, July 18, 21; m. 43; c. 3. PHYSICS. A.B, Yeshiva, 40, hon. LL.D, 61; du Pont fel, Pennsylvania, 41, Tyndall fel, 42, M.A. & Ph.D.(physics), 43. Asst. physics, Pennsylvania, 41-42, asst. instr, 43, res. assoc, Nat. Defense Res. Comt. proj, 43; res. physicist, res. labs, Westinghouse Elec. Corp, 43-50; lectr, Carnegie Inst. Technol, 50, asst. prof, 51-55; mgr. physics dept, sci. lab, Ford Motor Co, 55-60, assoc. dir, 60-62, dir, 62-68; from group v.pres. to SR. V.PRES. RES. & DEVELOP, XEROX CORP, 68- Westinghouse lectr, grad. sch, Pittsburgh, 45-50; group leader, Westinghouse Elec. Corp, 46-50; head lab, magnetics res, Carnegie Inst. Technol, 53-55; Edwin Webster prof, Mass. Inst. Technol, 59. Consult, Oak Ridge Nat. Lab; Brookhaven Nat. Lab; Naval Ord. Lab; U.S. Steel Corp; Allis-Chalmers Mfg. Co. Chmn. sci. adv. comt, Detroit Inst. Cancer Res; gen. chmn, Nat. Conf. Magnetism & Magnetic Mat, 56-58; chmn. panel mat. res. & mem. solid state adv. panel, Nat. Acad. Sci; mem. adv. panel, select comt. govt. res, U.S. House Rep; adv. comt. solid state, off. sci. res, U.S. Air Force. Fel. Am. Phys. Soc; Am. Asn. Physics Teachers; Inst. Elec. & Electronics Eng. Solid state physics; semiconductors; physics of metals; ferromagnetism; magnetic materials; magnetostriction phenomena; low temperature properties of metals; administration of research. Address: Xerox Corp, Stamford, CT 06904.

GOLDMAN, JAMES ALLAN, b. Chicago, Ill, Nov. 20, 35; ANALYTICAL CHEMISTRY. B.S. & B.A, Chicago, 58; Ph.D.(chem), Northwestern, 63. Instr. CHEM, Northwestern, 61-62; ASST. PROF, POLYTECH. INST. BROOKLYN, 62- AAAS; Am. Chem. Soc; Am. Asn. Physics Teachers; N.Y. Acad. Sci; Am. Inst. Chem. Potential precipitate-impregnated membrane electrodes; science education; philosophy and contemporary sociology of science; science, technology and society interactions between science and the humanities. Address: Dept. of Chemistry, Polytechnic Institute of Brooklyn, 333 Jay St, Brooklyn, NY 11201.

GOLDMAN, JAY, b. Norfolk, Va, Apr. 15, 30; m. 59. INDUSTRIAL ENGINEERING. B.S, Duke, 50; M.S, Mich. State, 51; D.Sc.(indust. eng), Washington (St. Louis), 55. Lectr. indust. mgt, Washington (St. Louis), 52-55, indust. eng, 55-56, asst. prof, 56-63, acting chmn. human & orgn. factor area, 63; prof. INDUST. ENG, N.C. State, 64-68; PROF. & CHMN. DEPT, UNIV. MO-COLUMBIA, 68- Consult, Off. Naval Res, Ill; Artcraft Venetian Blind Mfg. Co, Mo; Goffre Carbon Co, Argentina; Boeing Airplane Co, Wash; Dr. LeGear Med. Co, Mo; Shampaine Industs; McDonnell Aircraft Corp; Banner Hardware Co; Beltx Corp; Mead Johnson & Co, Ind; med. center, Duke, U.S. Pub. Health Serv. D.C; mem. health care systs. study sect, Nat. Ctr. Health Serv. Res. & Develop, Dept. Health, Educ. & Welfare; adv. panels for grad. progs, N.C. State Univ. & Rensselaer Polytech. Inst. Am. Soc. Eng. Educ; Am. Inst. Indust. Eng; Opers. Res. Soc. Am; Am. Soc. Heat, Refrig. & Air-Conditioning Eng; Am. Col. Radiol. Administrative organization and system design for health care delivery; design of man-machine work systems; measurement of human performance; human factors engineering. Address: Dept. of Industrial Engineering, University of Missouri-Columbia, Columbia, MO 65201.

GOLDMAN, JOSEPH L, b. San Francisco, Calif, Aug. 25, 32; m. 55; c. 2. METEOROLOGY. B.S, Texas A&M, 58, M.S, 60; Chicago, 60-63; Ph.D, Univ. Okla, 71. Mathematician, W.Coast Res. Co, Calif, 55-56; meteorologist, Gulf Consult, Tex, 56-58; res. scientist, Texas A&M Res. Found, 58-60; res. asst. meteorol, Chicago, 60-62, meteorologist, 62-65; prin. investr, Nat. Eng. Sci. Co, Tex, 65-66; ASSOC. DIR, INST. STORM RES, 66-; ASSOC. PROF. PHYSICS. & METEOROL, UNIV. ST. THOMAS (TEX), 68- U.S.A.F, 51-55. AAAS; Am. Meteorol. Soc; Marine Technol. Soc; Am. Geophys. Union; N.Y. Acad. Sci; Royal Meteorol. Soc. Severe weather phenomena—effective forecasting and control through physical-hydrodynamic principles, effects on ocean environment and ecological, sociological and induced behavioristic aspects; urban pollution control; meteorological engineering. Address: Institute for Storm Research, 3812 Montrose Blvd, Houston, TX 77006.

GOLDMAN, KENNETH M(ARVIN), b. Pittsburgh, Pa, Dec. 8, 22; m. 51; c. 3. METALLURGICAL ENGINEERING. B.S, Carnegie Inst. Tech, 43, Office Naval Res. fel, 49-51, D.Sc.(metall), 52. Student engr, Nat. Tube Co, Pa, 43-44; jr. scientist, Manhattan Dist, Los Alamos, N.Mex, 44-46; asst, Carnegie Inst. Tech, 46-49; sr. scientist, METALL, BETTIS ATOMIC POWER LAB, WESTINGHOUSE ELEC. CORP, 51-55, supvr, 55-59, SECT. MGR, 59- C.Eng, U.S.A, 44-46. Am. Soc. Metals; Am. Inst. Mining, Metall. & Petrol. Eng.(Hunt award, 52); British Inst. Metals. Physical chemistry of steelmaking; radioactive tracers applied to metallurgy; fissionable materials; metallurgy of zirconium and uranium. Address: Bettis Atomic Power Lab, Westinghouse Electric Corp, P.O. Box 79, West Mifflin, PA 15122.

GOLDMAN, LAWRENCE, b. Boston, Mass, May 6, 36. BIOPHYSICS. B.S, Tufts, 58; Nat. Sci. Found. fel, California, Los Angeles, 58-59, Nat. Insts. Health fel, 60-64, Ph.D.(neurophysiol), 64. Nat. Insts. Health fel, col. physicians & surgeons, Columbia, 64-65; asst. prof. zool, UNIV. MD, 65-67, PHYSIOL, SCH. MED, 67-70, ASSOC. PROF, 70- Vis. scientist, lab. biophys, Nat. Insts. Health, 66-; NATO sr. fel, Queen Mary Col, London, 70. AAAS; Biophys. Soc; Soc. Gen. Physiol; Am. Physiol. Soc; Soc. Neurosci. Membrane biophysics; theory of excitable membranes; impulse initiation and propagation; membrane transport and selectivity. Address: Dept. of Physiology, University of Maryland School of Medicine, Baltimore, MD 21201.

GOLDMAN, LEON, b. San Francisco, Calif, Feb. 14, 04; m. 31; c. 3. SURGERY. A.B, California, 26, M.D, 30; M.S, Northwestern, 39. Intern SURG, univ. hosp, California, 29-30, asst. resident, sch. med, 30-33, resident & instr, 33-35; instr. & exec. officer, San Francisco Hosp, 35-37; asst. prof, SCH. MED, UNIV. CALIF, SAN FRANCISCO, 37-43, assoc. prof, 43-49, PROF, 49-, chmn. dept. & assoc. dean, sch. med, 56-63. Consult, Shriners Hosp. Crippled Children, San Francisco; Vet. Admin. Hosp, Ft. Miley; univ. surg. serv, San Francisco Gen. Hosp; surg. serv, U.S. Naval Hosp, Oakland, 59. Dipl, Am. Bd. Surg, 49. AAAS; Soc. Univ. Surg; Am. Col. Gastroenterol; Am. Thyroid Asn; Am. Surg. Asn; Am. Col. Surg.(1st v.pres, 62). Breast; biliary and gastrointestinal tract; parathyroid and thyroid. Address: Dept. of Surgery, University of California Medical Center, U-112, San Francisco, CA 94122.

GOLDMAN, LEON, b. Cincinnati, Ohio, Dec. 7, 05; m. 36; c. 3. DERMATOLOGY. B.S, Cincinnati, 27, M.D, 30; Zurich, 32-33. From asst. to PROF. DERMAT, COL. MED, UNIV. CINCINNATI, 35- Dir, Laser Labs. Med. Center, Univ. Cincinnati & Children's Hosp. Res. Found; consult. dermatologist, 35-; Markle fel, 44; consult, Bur. Occup. Safety & Health; Environ. Protection Agency. With Off. Sci. Res. & Develop; Off. Civilian Defense, 44. Soc. Invest. Dermat; Am. Dermat. Asn; Am. Soc. Trop. Med. & Hyg; Am. Asn. Hist. Med; fel. Am. Acad. Dermat; fel. Royal Soc. Trop. Med. & Hyg; Swedish Dermat. Soc. Clinical and tropical dermatology; syphilology; history of medicine; laser technology; biomedical laser; laser art; laser music. Address: Dept. of Dermatology, University of Cincinnati College of Medicine, Cincinnati, OH 45229.

GOLDMAN, LEON, b. Washington, D.C, Oct. 9, 18; m. 46; c. 2. ORGANIC CHEMISTRY. B.S, Maryland, 39, fel, 40-41, M.S, 41, Ph.D.(chem), 44. Asst, Maryland, 41-43; Cooper Union, 43-46; Rockefeller Inst. Med. Res, 46; SR. RES. SCIENTIST, LEDERLE LABS. DIV, AM. CYANAMID CO, 46- Asst, Cooper Union, 46-48. Cyanamid Award. Am. Soc. Biol. Chem; Am. Chem. Soc; Brit. Chem. Soc. Synthesis of antimalarial drugs; chemotherapy; chemistry of antibiotics; countercurrent distribution; synthesis of pharmacologically active compounds; chemistry of nucleosides and alkaloids; cardiovascular agents. Address: Lederle Labs Division, American Cyanamid Co, Pearl River, NY 10965.

GOLDMAN, LEONARD M(ANUEL), b. N.Y.C, Mar. 22, 25; m. 52; c. 3. PHYSICS. A.B, Cornell, 45; M.Sc, McGill, 48; Ph.D, Rochester, 52. Asst. PHYSICS, McGill, 47-48; Rochester, 48-52; RES. ASSOC, Princeton, 52-56; RES. & DEVELOP. CTR, GEN. ELEC. CO, 56- U.S.N.R, 44-46, Ens. Fel. Am. Phys. Soc. High temperature plasma physics; low energy nuclear physics. Address: General Electric Research & Development Center, P.O. Box 8, Schenectady, NY 12301.

GOLDMAN, MALCOLM, b. Brooklyn, N.Y, July 18, 29; m. 66. MATHEMATICS. B.A, Minnesota, 49, M.A, 51; Ph.D.(math), Chicago, 55. Mem. tech. staff, Bell Tel. Labs, Inc, 54-55; instr. MATH, Michigan, 55-60; vis. asst. prof, Reed Col, 60-62; ASSOC. PROF, N.Y. UNIV, 62- Am. Math. Soc. Probability theory; functional analysis. Address: Dept. of Mathematics, New York University, University Heights, Bronx, NY 10453.

GOLDMAN, MANUEL, b. Montreal, Que, May 19, 32; U.S. citizen; m. 69; c. 1. MICROBIAL PHYSIOLOGY, METABOLISM. B.S, Roosevelt, 53; S.M, Chicago, 55; Ph.D.(microbiol), Michigan, 62. Fel, inst. sci. tech, Michigan, 61-62; asst. prof. biol. & microbiol, Wayne State, 62-64; microbiologist, Stanford Res. Inst, 64-67; ASST. PROF. BIOL. SCI, UNIV. ILL, CHICAGO CIRCLE, 67- AAAS; Soc. Indust. Microbiol; Am. Soc. Microbiol; Am. Chem. Soc. Metabolism and physiology of sporeforming bacteria; environmental modification of cellular metabolism and development; mode of action of psychopharmacological drugs. Address: Dept. of Biological Sciences, University of Illinois at Chicago Circle, Chicago, IL 60680.

GOLDMAN, MARTIN, b. Brooklyn, N.Y, Oct. 9, 26; m. 48; c. 4. ORGANIC CHEMISTRY. B.S, Polytech. Inst. Brooklyn, 49; Mills fel, Rochester, 51-52, Ph.D.(org. chem), 53. Asst, Rochester, 49-51; res. chemist, color photog, Eastman Kodak Co, 53-59, res. assoc, 59-63, novel photog. processes, 63-67; chemist, Israeli Govt, 67-69; DIR. QUAL. CONTROL, BERKEY PATHE HUMPHRIES, ISRAEL, LTD, 69- Sig.C, U.S.A, 44-46. Am. Chem. Soc. Chemistry of the perinaphthenes; reaction of arylglyoxals with malonic acid; investigation of the preparation and properties of new types of couplers for color photography. Address: 78 Bayit Vegan St, Jerusalem, Israel.

GOLDMAN, MARTIN EDWARD, b. Brooklyn, N.Y, June 14, 42; m. 69. TOPOLOGY. B.A, Harpur Col, 63; M.A, Yale, 65, Nat. Sci. Found. fel. & Ph.D.(math), 67. G.C. Evans instr. MATH, Rice Univ, 67-69; ASST. PROF, CITY COL. NEW YORK, 69- Am. Math. Soc; Math. Asn. Am. Topology of two and three dimensional manifolds. Address: Dept. of Mathematics, City College, City University of New York, New York, NY 10031.

GOLDMAN, MARVIN, b. N.Y.C, May 2, 28; m. 53; c. 2. RADIATION BIOLOGY. A.B, Adelphi Col, 49; M.S, Maryland, 51; Atomic Energy Comn. fel, Rochester, 53, Ph.D.(radiation biol), 57. Asst, Maryland, 50-51; biologist, phys. biol. lab, Nat. Insts. Health, 51-52; res. assoc, Rochester, 53-57, jr. scientist, Atomic Energy Proj, sch. med. & dent, 57-58; assoc. res. radiation biologist, SCH. VET. MED, UNIV. CALIF, DAVIS, 58-64, RES. RADIATION BIOLOGIST & LECTR. PHYSIOL. SCI, 64-, ADJ. PROF. RADIOBIOL, SCH. MED, 69- Mem. comt. 31, Nat. Coun. Radiation Protection. AAAS; Orthop. Res. Soc; Soc. Exp. Hemat; Radiation Res. Soc; Health Phys. Soc; Soc. Appl. Spectros. Biologic effects of radiations; radiation aging; isotope toxicity and metabolism; radiation dosimetry; bone physiology and kinetics; trace mineral metabolism; in vivo isotope detection; health physics; nuclear medicine. Address: Radiobiology Lab, University of California, Davis, CA 95616.

GOLDMAN, MAX, b. Newtown, Conn, Nov. 28, 20; m. 58; c. 2. ENDOCRINOLOGY, BIOLOGY. B.A, N.Y. Univ, 48; M.A, Missouri-Columbia, 53; Ph.D.(endocrinol), California, Berkeley, 64. Asst. prof. BIOL, Long Island, 64-68; ASSOC. PROF, UNIV. S.DAK, 68- Participant, Spec. training div, multi-track summer inst, Oak Ridge Assoc. Univs, summer 69. AAAS; Am. Inst. Biol. Sci; N.Y. Acad. Sci. Thyroid gland—influence of testosterone, ovarian hormones, melatonin, DDT, mercury, lead poisoning; dimethyl sulfoxide and thyroid function; thyroid function and age. Address: Dept. of Biology, University of South Dakota, Vermillion, SD 57069.

GOLDMAN, MAX, b. Brooklyn, N.Y, March 15, 24; m. 52; c. 3. CHEMICAL ENGINEERING. B.Ch.E, City Col, 49; M.S.Ch.E, Carnegie Inst. Tech, 50, Standard Oil Co.(Ind), fel, 53, Am. Cyanamid Co. fel. & Ph.D.(chem. eng), 54. RES. ENGR, Radio Corp. Am, 50-51; film dept, Yerkes Lab, E.I. du Pont de Nemours & Co, 54-70; RES. ASSOC, RENSSELAER RES. CORP, 70- U.S.A.A.F, 42-45. Kinetics and thermodynamics; extrusion and orientation of plastic films; polymerization and coating of plastics films. Address: Rensselaer Research Corp, 1125 Peoples Ave, Troy, NY 12180.

GOLDMAN, MORRIS, b. Brooklyn, N.Y, May 2, 19; m. 41; c. 4. PARASITOLOGY. A.B, Brooklyn Col, 39; M.S, Columbia Univ, 49; U.S. Pub. Health Serv. fel, 50-51; Sc.D.(parasitol), Johns Hopkins Univ, 53. PARASITOLOGIST, U.S. Pub. Health Serv, 42, Commun. Disease Ctr, Atlanta, Ga, 46-61, Nat. Insts. Health, Bethesda, Md, 61-66; Bionetics Res. Labs, Kensington, 66-69; KIMRON VET. INST, BET DAGON, ISRAEL, 70- Kimble Award, 62. U.S.A, 42-46. Am. Soc. Parasitol; Am. Soc. Trop. Med. & Hyg; Soc. Protozool. Biology and immunology of protozoans of medical and veterinary importance; immunofluorescence; microfluorimetry. Address: Parasitology Dept, Kimron Veterinary Institute, Bet Dagon, Israel.

GOLDMAN, MORTON, b. Woonsocket, R.I, Dec. 14, 20. AEROSPACE ENGINEERING. B.S, Rhode Island, 42. Prod. engr, Pa. Ord. Works, U.S. Rubber Co, 42-43; ballistics engr, George Washington, 43-46; proj. engr, Allegany Ballistics Lab, Hercules Powder Co, 46-48; prog. mgr. shipbd. guided missile prog, appl. physics lab, Hopkins, 48-57; field sta. engr, Ramo-Wooldridge Corp, 57-59, propulsion mgr. ballistic missile & space prog, space tech. lab, Thompson-Ramo-Wooldridge Corp, Calif, 59-61; SPEC. ASST. TO V.PRES, DIR. PROPULSION & SYSTS. ENG. DIR. SPACE LAUNCH VEHICLES, AEROSPACE CORP, 61- Inst. Aeronaut. & Astronaut. Chemical propulsion; systems engineering and technical direction of complete rocket booster systems used in the national space programs; high energy chemical propulsion sub-systems. Address: Aerospace Corp, P.O. Box 95085, Los Angeles, CA 90045.

GOLDMAN, MORTON I(RWIN), b. N.Y.C, Nov. 29, 26; m. 50; c. 2. NUCLEAR & CIVIL ENGINEERING. B.S, N.Y. UNIV, 48; M.S, Mass. Inst. Technol, 50 & 58, Sc.D.(nuclear eng), 60. Training & res. asst, sanit. eng. res. lab, N.Y. Univ, 48-49; res. asst. radiation, radioactivity res. lab, Mass. Inst. Technol, 49-50; lectr. radiation safety & waste disposal, U.S. Pub. Health Serv, 50-54, chief waste disposal, soils & eng. sect, 54-56, proj. leader, radioactive waste disposal proj, Mass. Inst. Technol, 56-59; consult. nuclear installations, div. radiol. health, U.S. Pub. Health Serv, 59-61; V.PRES. & GEN. MGR. ENVIRON. SAFEGUARDS DIV, NUS CORP, 61- Secy. reactor safeguards comt, U.S. Pub. Health Serv-Mass. Inst. Technol, 56-59; U.S. rep. & chmn, panel mgt. radioactive wastes at nuclear power plants, Int. Atomic Energy Agency, Vienna, 68. Dipl, Inter-Soc. Bd. Environ. Eng. AAAS; Am. Soc. Civil Eng; Am. Nuclear Soc; Am. Acad. Environ. Eng; Air Pollution Control Asn. Site selection; waste disposal; environmental aspects of power generating facilities; radiochemistry; environmental surveillance and meteorological programs; aerospace nuclear safety. Address: Environmental Safeguards Division, NUS Corp, 4 Research Place, Rockville, MD 20850.

GOLDMAN, NORMAN L, b. New York, N.Y, Aug. 11, 33. CHEMISTRY. B.S, City Col. New York, 54; M.A, Harvard, 56; Nat. Insts. Health fel. & Ph.D. (org. chem), Columbia, 59. Nat. Sci. Found. fel, Imp. Col, London, 59-60; Nat. Insts. Health fel, Columbia, 61; asst. prof. CHEM, QUEENS COL. (N.Y), 61-68, ASSOC. PROF, 69- Am. Chem. Soc. Synthetic organic chemistry. Address: Dept. of Chemistry, Queens College, Flushing, NY 11367.

GOLDMAN, OSCAR, b. Brooklyn, N.Y, Feb. 2, 25; m. 49. MATHEMATICS. B.S, City Col. New York, 44; A.M, Princeton, 46, Ph.D.(math), 48. Peirce instr. MATH, Harvard, 48-51; asst. prof, Brandeis, 51-55, assoc. prof. & chmn. dept, 55-60, PROF, 61-62; UNIV. PA, 62-, chmn. dept, 63-67. Nat. Sci. Found. faculty fel, 60-61; mem, Inst. Adv. Study, 60-62; vis. scholar, Univ. Calif, Berkeley, 67-68. Am. Math. Soc; Math. Asn. Am; Math. Soc. Japan. Algebra and algebraic number theory. Address: Dept. of Mathematics, University of Pennsylvania, Philadelphia, PA 19104.

GOLDMAN, PETER, b. N.Y.C, May 23, 29; m. 59; c. 2. BIOCHEMISTRY, PHARMACOLOGY. B.Eng.Phys, Cornell, 52; M.A, Harvard, 53; M.D, Hopkins, 57. Res. assoc. biochem, Nat. Heart Inst, 59-63; SR. INVESTR. BIOCHEM. PHARMACOL, NAT. INSTS. HEALTH, NAT. INST. ARTHRITIS & METAB. DISEASES, 63- Nat. Insts. Health fel, 59-60. U.S.P.H.S, 60-63, Res, 63-, Sr. Surg. Am. Soc. Biol. Chem; Am. Chem. Soc; Am. Soc. Pharmacol. & Exp. Therapeut. Fatty acid synthesis; biological importance of the carbon-fluorine bond; structure function relationships of biologically active compounds; clinical pharmacology and toxicology. Address: National Institute of Arthritis & Metabolic Diseases, National Institutes of Health, Bethesda, MD 20014.

GOLDMAN, RALPH, b. N.Y.C, June 11, 19; m. 41; c. 3. INTERNAL MEDICINE, A.B, California, 39, M.D, 42. Chief metab. sect. & renal clinic, U.S. Vet. Admin. Hosp, Los Angeles, 49-55, chief med. serv, Sepulveda, 55-58; assoc. prof. MED, SCH. MED, UNIV. CALIF, LOS ANGELES, 59-64, PROF, 64- Mem, Nat. Kidney Disease Found. Dipl, Am. Bd. Internal Med, 50; Willard O. Thompson Award, Am. Geriat. Soc, 70. U.S.N.R, 44-46, Lt. AAAS; Soc. Exp. Biol. & Med; Am. Med. Asn; fel. Am. Col. Physicians; Fedn. Clin. Res. Metabolic and renal diseases; clinical and physiological problems related to renal disease, especially renal failure; geriatrics. Address: Dept. of Medicine, University of California School of Medicine, Los Angeles, CA 90024.

GOLDMAN, RALPH F(REDERICK), b. Boston, Mass, Mar. 3, 28; m. 56; c. 2. PHYSIOLOGY. A.B, Denver, 50; A.M, Boston, 51, U.S. Pub. Health Serv. fel, 52-55, Ph.D.(physiol), 55; S.M, Northeastern, 62. Res. fel, U.S. Pub. Health Serv, 55; physiologist, U.S. Qm. Res. & Eng. Command, 56-62; DIR, MIL. ERGONOMICS LAB, U.S. ARMY RES. INST. ENVIRON. MED, 62- Vis. assoc. prof, State Univ. N.Y. Buffalo, 64-65; adj. assoc. prof, Boston Univ, 69- Biophys. Soc; Am. Physiol. Soc; Sci. Res. Soc. Am; Inst. Elec. & Electronics Eng; Am. Soc. Heating, Refrig. & Air-Conditioning Eng; Brit. Ergonomics Res. Soc. Environmental physiology; human heat, cold and work stresses; clothing; heat transfer; body composition. Address: U.S. Army Research Institute of Environmental Medicine, Natick, MA 01760.

GOLDMAN, ROBERT B(ARNETT), b. Phila, Pa, June 21, 27; m. 47; c. 3. PHYSICS. B.A, Temple, 48, fel, 49-51, M.A, 50, Ph.D, 52. Asst, Villanova Col, 49-50; Temple, 50-51; physicist, Philco Corp, 51-62, mem. corporate eng. & res. staff, 62-68, dir. advan. technol, electronics group, Philco-Ford Corp, 68-69; TECH. DIR. GOVT. & INDUST. DIV, URBANA OPERS, MAGNAVOX CO, 69- Lectr, Temple, 54- U.S.N.R, 45-46. Acoustical Soc. Am. Acoustics-propagation; transducers; noise control; communications; information theory; control systems; transmission and reception of electromagnetic energy for detection; surveillance; guidance. Address: Government & Industrial Division, Urbana Operations, Magnavox Co, 1505 E. Main St, Urbana, IL 61801.

GOLDMAN, ROBERT D(AVID), b. Port Chester, N.Y, July 23, 39; m. 65; c. 2. CELL BIOLOGY. B.A, Univ. Vt, 61, M.S, 63; Ph.D.(biol), Princeton, 67. Am. Cancer Soc. fel, dept. histochem, Royal Postgrad Med. Sch, London & Med. Res. Coun. Gt. Brit. Exp. Virus Res. Unit, Glasgow, 67-69; ASST. PROF. BIOL, CASE WEST. RESERVE UNIV, 69- Biophys. Soc; Soc. Develop. Biol; Am. Soc. Cell Biol. Ultrastructural basis for normal and abnormal cell motility. Address: Dept. of Biology, Case Western Reserve University, Cleveland, OH 44106.

GOLDMAN, SAUL, b. Montreal, Que, Dec. 3, 43; m. 67. PHYSICAL & ANALYTICAL CHEMISTRY. B.Sc, McGill Univ, 64, Nat. Res. Coun. Can. scholar. & Ph.D.(anal. chem), 69. Res. assoc. solution chem, UNIV. FLA, 69, NAT. RES. COUN. CAN. FEL, 70- D.W. Ambridge Award, McGill Univ, 70. Solvent extraction; ion association; hydration; solvation; thermodynamics of ion transfer; isopiestic studies; electrostatic interactions; calorimetry; electromotive force studies; solubility; nonelectrostatic interactions. Address: Dept. of Chemistry, University of Florida, Gainesville, FL 32601.

GOLDMAN, STANFORD, b. Cincinnati, Ohio, Nov. 14, 07; m. 35; c. 3. ELECTRICAL ENGINEERING. A.B, Cincinnati, 26, A.M, 28; Ph.D.(physics), Harvard, 33. Sound engr, Photophone, Inc, Radio Corp. Am, N.Y, 30-31; sr. engr, Gen. Elec. Co, Conn, 35-46; res. assoc. ELEC. ENG, Mass. Inst. Tech, 46-49; PROF, SYRACUSE UNIV, 49- Vis. Makay prof, California, Berkeley, 62; vis. prof, Univ. Calif, San Diego, 70. Consult. physicist, Electronics Res. Lab, U.S. Air Force, 46-54; Gen. Elec. Co, 54-; Eng. & Res. Develop. Lab, U.S. Army, 58-; summers, consult, Electronics Lab, U.S. Navy, 57; Proj. Mich, 58. AAAS; Am. Phys. Soc; Biophys. Soc; fel. Inst. Elec. & Electronics Eng; N.Y. Acad. Sci. Mathematical biology; noise and inforamtion theory. Address: Dept. of Electrical Engineering, Syracuse University, Syracuse, NY 13210.

GOLDMAN, STEPHEN L, b. New York, N.Y, Sept. 18, 42. GENETICS. B.S, Brooklyn Col, 63; M.S, Missouri-Columbia, 67, Ph.D.(genetics), 68. Res. asst. GENETICS, Univ. Mo-Columbia, 64-68; Nat. Insts. Health fel, Univ. Tex, Dallas, 69-71; ASST. PROF, UNIV. TOLEDO, 71- AAAS; Genetics Soc. Am; Am. Inst. Biol. Sci. Genetic recombination in maize and gene conversion in Schizosaccharromyces pombe. Address: Dept. of Biology, University of Toledo, Toledo, OH 43606.

GOLDMANN, KURT, b. Eschwege, Ger, Sept. 8, 21; nat; m. 55; c. 3. MECHANICAL ENGINEERING. B.S, Pa. State Col, 42; M.S, Mass. Inst. Tech, 46. Chief analyst, free piston mach, Lima-Hamilton Corp, 46-49; sr. engr, nuclear energy aircraft, Nuclear Engine Propulsion Aircraft Proj, Fairchild Eng. & Aircraft Co, 49-50; res. engr, Carrier Corp, 51; mgr, MCR primary systs. dept, nuclear reactors, United Nuclear Corp, 51-71, MGR. LIQUID METAL SYSTS. DEPT, GULF UNITED NUCLEAR FUELS CO, 71- U.S.A.A.F, 42-45. Am. Soc. Mech. Eng; Am. Nuclear Soc. Thermodynamics; fluid flow and heat transfer; liquid metal technology; free piston; gas turbine and nuclear power plants. Address: 62 Holbrooke Rd, White Plains, NY 10605.

GOLDMANN, MORTON A(ARON), b. Chicago, Ill, July 11, 24; m. 51; c. 4. INTERNAL MEDICINE, CARDIOLOGY. B.S, Illinois, 43, M.D, 46. Assoc. prof. MED, COOK COUNTY GRAD. SCH. MED, 53-62, PROF, 62-, ASSOC. PROF. MED, UNIV. ILL. COL. MED, 70-, asst. prof, 61-70. Attend. physician, Louis A. Weiss Mem. Hosp, 52-; assoc. attend. physician, Cook County Hosp, 52-62, attend. physician, 62-; Ill. Res. Hosp, 53-; clin. asst. prof, col. med, Illinois, 61-70, clin. assoc. prof, 70-; attend. physician, Lutheran Gen. Hosp, 59-, chief of med, 65-67, bd. trustees, 70-; attending physician & head cardiol. lab, Skokie Valley Community Hosp, pres. med. staff, 68-70. Dipl, Am. Bd. Internal Med. U.S.A, 43-49, Capt. AAAS; Int. Soc. Internal Med; Am. Med. Asn; Am. Heart Asn; fel. Am. Col. Cardiol; fel. Am. Col. Physicians. Cardiology. Address: 9555 Gross Point Rd, Skokie, IL 60076.

GOLDMARK, PETER CARL, b. Budapest, Hungary, Dec. 2, 06; nat; m. 39; c. 4. PHYSICS. B.Sc, Vienna Tech, 30, Ph.D.(physics), 31; hon. Ph.D.(sci), Fairfield Univ, 69, Polytech. Inst. Brooklyn, 70. TV engr, Pye Radio, Ltd, Eng, 31-33; consult. engr, New York, 33-36; chief TV engr, Columbia Broadcasting System, Inc, 36-44, dir. eng. res. & develop. dept, 44-51, v.pres, in charge CBS Labs, Conn, 51-54, pres. & dir. res, 54-71; SCIENTIST, GOLDMARK COMMUN. CORP, 72- Group leader, radio res. labs, Harvard, 42-45; vis. prof, sch. med, Pennsylvania. Mem, Conn. Res. Adv. Comt. Medal, TV Broadcasters Asn, 54; Vladimir K. Zworykin TV prize, 61; Nat. Urban Serv. Award, 68; Elliott Cresson Medal, Franklin Inst, 69. With Off. Sci. Res. & Develop; U.S.N, 44. Fel. Soc. Motion Picture & TV Eng.(David Sarnoff Gold Medal Award, 69, Progress Medal, 70); Am. Phys. Soc; fel. Inst. Elec. & Electronics Eng.(Liebmann Mem. Prize, 45, achievement award, 60). Television; recording; radiobroadcasting and reception. Address: c/o Kinney National Service, Inc, 10 Rockefeller Plaza, New York, NY 10020.

GOLDNER, ANDREW M, b. Zurich, Switz, June 14, 34; U.S. citizen; m. 70. PHYSIOLOGY. B.S, Oberlin Col, 56; M.A, Stanford Univ, 57, U.S. Pub. Health Serv. fel, 61-62; U.S. Pub. Health Serv. fels, George Wash. Univ, 62-66, Ph.D.(physiol), 66. Instr. physiol. sci, Menlo Col, Calif, 59-61; lectr. biol, Montgomery Jr. Col, Md, 65-66; U.S. Pub. Health Serv. fel. biophys, Harvard Med. Sch, 66-67; U.S. Pub. Health Serv. fel. physiol, sch. med, Yale, 67-69, res. assoc, 69-70; ASST. PROF. HUMAN PHYSIOL, SCH. MED, UNIV. CALIF, DAVIS, 70- Consult, biol. commun. proj, George Wash. Univ, 66-69; lectr, South. Conn. State Col, 68-69; S.Cent. Community Col, 69-70. AAAS; Am. Physiol. Soc; Biophys. Soc; Biomed. Eng. Soc. Membrane phenomena; intestinal permeability—relationship between nutrients and electrolyte transport; effects of hormones and divalent cations on epithelial permeability. Address: Dept. of Human Physiology, School of Medicine, University of California, Davis, CA 95616.

GOLDNER, H(ERMAN), b. Wilkes-Barre, Pa, Aug. 20, 28; m. 55. MICROBIOLOGY. B.S, King's Col, 50; M.S, Catholic Univ, 52; Ph.D.(med. microbiol), Pennsylvania, 57. Lectr. bact, King's Col, 52; asst. cancer immunol, Wistar Inst, 55-57; res. immunologist, Biochem. Res. Found, 57-59; res. assoc, Merck Inst. Therapeut. Res, Div. Merck & Co, Inc, 59-63; asst. mem, S.Jersey Med. Res. Found, 63-65; assoc. mem, RES. LABS, ALBERT EINSTEIN MED. CTR, 65-70, ADMIN. OFF. RES, NORTH. DIV, 71- Leukemia scholar, Leukemia Soc, 67-70. Med.Serv.C, U.S.A, 52-54, Res, 54-, Lt. Col. Am. Soc. Microbiol; Am. Asn. Immunol; Soc. Exp. Biol. & Med; N.Y. Acad. Sci. Enteric bacteriology; immunohematology; tissue immunology; virus and tissue culture. Address: Korman Research Labs, Albert Einstein Medical Center, York & Tabor Rds, Philadelphia, PA 19141.

GOLDNER, J(OSEPH) LEONARD, b. Omaha, Nebr, Nov. 18, 18; m; c. 2. ORTHOPEDIC SURGERY. A.B, Minnesota, 39; B.Sc.Med. & M.D, Univ. Nebr, 43. Resident orthop, med. ctr, DUKE UNIV, 46-50, assoc, 50, asst. prof. ORTHOP. SURG, 51-53, assoc. prof, 53-56, PROF, MED. CTR, 56-, CHIEF ORTHOP-AMPUTEE CLINS, 55-, CHMN. DIV. ORTHOP. SURG, 68- Res, Ga. Warm Springs Found, 47-48; fel, amputee training sch, Univ. Calif, Los Angeles, 55; exchange fel, Am. & Brit. Orthop. Asn, Eng, 55; mem. appl. physiol. study sect, Nat. Insts. Health, 63-67; attend. orthop. surgeon, Vet. Admin. Hosp, Durham, N.C; Watts Hosp; N.C. Cerebral Palsy Hosp; consult, McCain Tuberc. Sanatorium, N.C; Army Hosp, Ft. Bragg. Vis. prof, Children's Hosp, Australia, 66; Univ. Calif, Los Angeles, 67; Harvard, 68; Univ. N.Mex, 71; crippled children's div, State Bd. Health, Vt, 71. Gibson Mem. lectr, Winnipeg, Can, 69; Hoke-Kite lectr, 71. Dipl, Am. Bd. Orthop. Surg, 52. Med.C, U.S.N, 44-46. Am. Soc. Surg. of Hand (pres, 69-70); Am. Med. Asn; Am. Orthop. Asn; Can. Orthop. Asn; Am. Acad. Orthop. Surg; Am. Acad. Cerebral Palsy. Tendon healing; hand reconstruction; amputee problems; fat embolism. Address: Division of Orthopedic Surgery, Duke University Medical Center, Box 3706, Durham, NC 27710.

GOLDNER, KARL J(OHN), b. Minneapolis, Minn, Nov. 20, 09; m. 37; c. 3. PHARMACOGNOSY. B.S, Minnesota, 30, M.S, 32, Ph.D.(pharmaceut. chem), 38. Instr. PHARM, Wisconsin, 37-40; asst. prof, UNIV. TENN, MEMPHIS, 40-42, assoc. prof, 42-47, PROF, 47- Am. Pharmaceut. Asn; Am. Soc. Pharmacog. Phytochemistry; biosynthesis. Address: Dept. of Molecular & Quantum Biology, University of Tennessee, Memphis, TN 38103.

GOLDNER, MARTIN G(ERHARD), b. Berlin, Ger, July 1, 02; nat; m. 32; c. 1. INTERNAL MEDICINE. M.D, Frankfurt Am. Main, Germany, 26. Asst, Univ. Clinic Charite, Berlin, Germany, 27-33; dir, Sanitorium Metab. Diseases, Baden, 34-38; instr. med, sch. med, Chicago, 40-43, asst. prof, 43-47; clin. asst. prof, med. center, Colorado, 47-50; PROF, MED, STATE UNIV. N.Y. DOWNSTATE MED. CTR, 50-, asst. dean, 63-71; dir. med, Jewish Hosp. Med. Ctr, 60-71, Jewish Chronic Disease Hosp, 52-60. Attend. physician, Billings Hosp, Univ. Chicago, 40-47; chief, metab. sect. & dir, res. lab, Veterans Admin. Hosp, Ft. Logan, Colo, 47-50, chief med. serv, Brooklyn, 50-52; hon. prof, Univ. Puebla. Dipl, Am. Bd. Internal Med. Med.C, 44-46, Capt. AAAS; Soc. Exp. Biol. & Med; Endocrine Soc; Am. Med. Asn; fel. Am. Diabetes Asn; fel. Am. Col. Physicians; fel. N.Y. Acad. Med; Ger. Diabetes Asn. Endocrinology; metabolism. Address: Jewish Hospital & Medical Center, 555 Prospect Place, Brooklyn, NY 11238.

GOLDNER, RONALD B, b. N.Y.C, Mar. 24, 35; m. 59; c. 1. ELECTRICAL ENGINEERING, SOLID STATE PHYSICS. S.B. & S.M, Mass. Inst. Technol, 57, E.E, 59; Ph.D.(elec. eng), Purdue, 62. Asst, Mass. Inst. Technol, 57-59, res. assoc, lab. insulation res, 59; instr. ELEC. ENG, Purdue, 59-62; asst. prof, Mass. Inst. Technol, 62-64; TUFTS UNIV, 64-69, ASSOC. PROF, 69- Ford Found. fel. eng, 62-64. Consult, 63- Sig.C, 59, 1st Lt. Am. Phys. Soc; Inst. Elec. & Electronics Eng. Superconductivity; photoconductivity; electroluminescence; thermal conductivity of solids; acoustic and microwave properties of solids; electron-phonon interactions. Address: Dept. of Electrical Engineering, Tufts University, Medford, MA 02155.

GOLDREICH, PETER, b. N.Y.C, July 14, 39; m. 60; c. 2. ASTROPHYSICS. B.Eng.Phys, Cornell, 60, Andrew D. White & Nat. Sci. Found. fels. & Ph.D. (physics), 63. Instr. astron, Cornell, 63; Nat. Acad. Sci-Nat. Res. Coun. fel, Cambridge, 63-64; asst. prof. astron. & geophys, Univ. Calif, Los Angeles, 64-66; assoc. prof. ASTRON. & PLANETARY SCI, CALIF. INST. TECHNOL, 66-69, PROF, 69- Theoretical study of solar system; galactic structure and cosmology. Address: 2827 N. Holliston Ave, Altadena, CA 91001.

GOLDRICK, RICHARD M(ORGAN), b. Alliance, Ohio, Mar. 10, 12; m. 40. ORGANIC CHEMISTRY. B.S, Mt. Union Col, 34; M.S, Syracuse, 36; fel, Purdue, 37, 38-40, Ph.D.(org. chem), 40. Lab. asst. gen. & org. chem, Mt. Union Col, 32-34; gen. chem, Syracuse, 34-36, private res, 36; lab. asst. gen. chem, Purdue, 36-38; res. chemist, plastics dept, E.I. du Pont de Nemours & Co, 40-51; res. mgr. plastics dept, Irvington Varnish & Insulator Div, MINN. MINING & MFG. CO, 51-56, sr. res. chemist, elec. prod. lab, 56-68, CHEMIST SPECIALIST, DIELECTRICS MAT. & SYSTS. LAB, 68- Am. Chem. Soc; Soc. Plastics Eng. Organic fluorides; thermoplastics and acrylic polymers; thermoplastic extrusion; vinyl polymerization; synthesis; pressure sensitive adhesives. Address: 2685 Brookview Dr, St. Paul, MN 55119.

GOLDRING, IRENE P, b. New York, N.Y; m. 49; c. 1. EXPERIMENTAL ZOOLOGY, CELL PHYSIOLOGY. A.B, Hunter Col, 38; M.S, N.Y. Univ, 48, fel, 48-50, Ph.D.(cellular physiol), 53. Clin. technician clin. path, Molnar Labs, N.Y, 38-41; res. technician path. chem, Post-Grad. Hosp, New York, 41-43; path. & physiol, sch. med, N.Y. Univ, 43-46; jr. res. assoc. radiation biol. & cellular physiol, Brookhaven Nat. Lab, 50-53; from res. assoc. to ASST. PROF. cellular physiol, ALBERT EINSTEIN COL. MED, 59-69, SURG, 69-; ASSOC. PROF. BIOL, STERN COL, YESHIVA UNIV, 69- Lectr, N.Y. Univ, assoc, arts degree prog, sch. continuing educ. AAAS; Am. Soc. Zool; Am. Soc. Cell Biol; Tissue Cult. Asn; N.Y. Acad. Sci. Central nervous system—experimental morphology, radiation effects; effects of smoke and noxious gases on single cells in vitro; tissue culture of normal and malignant cells and organs; biological effect of air pollutants on animals; tissue culture aspects of wound healing; experimental emphysema in animals. Address: Dept. of Biology, Stern College, Yeshiva Univ, 249 Lexington Ave, New York, NY 10016.

GOLDRING, LIONEL S(OLOMON), b. Los Angeles, Calif, Oct. 24, 22; m. 49; c. 1. PHYSICAL CHEMISTRY. B.A, California, Los Angeles, 43; Atomic Energy Cmn. fel, Mass. Inst. Tech, 49-50, Ph.D.(phys. chem), 50. Jr. chemist, Oak Ridge Nat. Lab, 43-46; res. assoc, Mass. Inst. Tech, 46, asst, 46-49; res. chemist, Brookhaven Nat. Lab, 50-52; head radiochem. group, Nuclear Develop. Corp. Am, 53-57, mem. adv. proj. group, 58-60; sr. res. chemist, Am. Mach. & Foundry Co, Inc, 60-64, sr. tech. specialist, 64-66, sr. res. specialist, res. dept, 66-67, lab. mgr, 67-70, MGR. CHEM. & PHYS. RES, AMF, INC, 70- Consult, Brookhaven Nat. Lab, 47-49. AAAS; Am. Chem. Soc; Am. Nuclear Soc; Am. Mgt. Asn; Indust. Res. Inst. Polymer and plastics science and engineering; inorganic chemistry; nuclear science; air and water pollution. Address: Central Technical Staff, AMF, Inc, 689 Hope St, Stamford, CT 06907.

GOLDRING, SIDNEY, b. Kremnitz, Poland, Apr. 2, 23; nat; m. 45; c. 2. NEUROSURGERY. M.D, Washington, 47. Instr. neurosurg, SCH. MED, Wash. Univ, 56-58, asst. prof, 58-61, assoc. prof, 61-64; PROF, Univ. Pittsburgh, 64-66; NEUROL. SURG, WASH. UNIV, 66- Instr, Univ. Med. Unit to Thailand, 52-53; sr. staff, Presby. Univ. Hosp, 64-; Children's Hosp, 64-; consult, Vet. Admin. Hosp, 64-; Eye & Ear Hosp, 64-; U.S. Pub. Health Serv. div. res. grants. U.S.P.H.S, 52-53; U.S.A, 53-55, Capt. Am. Physiol. Soc. Electrophysiological studies in animal and human cerebral cortex, employing direct current amplifiers and non-polarizable recording electrodes for correlation of slow electrical changes with various physiological and pathological states; microelectrode and computer techniques in study of experimental epilepsy. Address: Dept. of Neurological Surgery, Washington University School of Medicine, St. Louis, MO 63110.

GOLDSACK, DOUGLAS E, b. London, Ont, July 17, 39; m. 64; c. 2. BIOPHYSICAL CHEMISTRY. B.Sc, Western Ontario, 61; Mass. Inst. Technol, 61-62; Ph.D.(chem), Wisconsin, 66. Res. assoc. biophys. chem, Wisconsin, 66-67; res. scientist, Vancouver Lab, Fisheries Res. Bd. Can, 67-68; ASST. PROF. BIOPHYS. CHEM, LAURENTIAN UNIV, 68- Physical chemistry of proteins. Address: Dept. of Chemistry, Laurentian University, Sudbury, Ont, Can.

GOLDSBERRY, RONALD EUGENE, b. Wilmington, Del, Sept. 12, 42; m. 65; c. 2. ORGANOMETALLIC & POLYMER CHEMISTRY. B.S, Cent. State Univ, 64; Dow Chem. fel, Mich. State Univ, summer 68, Ph.D.(inorg. chem), 69. Instr. chem, Mich. State Univ, 64-69; RES. SCIENTIST, AMES RES. CTR, NASA, 69- Prof, Nairobi Col, Calif, 69-; asst. prof, San Jose State Col, 70- U.S.A, 69-71, Capt. AAAS; Am. Chem. Soc. Photochemistry of macromolecules; organo-silicon chemistry; spectroscopy. Address: 3784 Pruneridge Ave, Santa Clara, CA 95051.

GOLDSBERRY, STEVE, b. Helena, Ark, Jan. 13, 27; m. 58; c. 3. ANATOMY, EMBRYOLOGY. B.S, Ark. Agr, Mech. & Nor. Col, 53; M.S, Mich. State, 55, Ph.D.(anat), 65; Michigan, 58; Minnesota, 59. Assoc. prof. biol, Miles Col, 55-56; histologist, Mich. State, 56-57; asst. prof. VET. ANAT, TUSKEGEE INST, 57-66, ASSOC. PROF, 66- U.S.A, 46-49, Res, 49-52. AAAS; Am. Soc. Med. Technol; Am. Asn. Vet. Anat. Histology; histochemistry; cytology. Address: Dept. of Veterinary Anatomy, School of Veterinary Medicine, Tuskegee Institute, AL 36088.

GOLDSBOROUGH, JOHN P(AUL), b. Newark, N.J, May 19, 34; m. 56; c. 2. PHYSICS. B.S, Lehigh, 56; Nat. Sci. Found. fel, Stanford, 57-60, Ph.D. (physics), 61. Res. staff mem, Int. Bus. Mach. Corp, 60-66; DIR. RES, SPECTRA-PHYSICS INC, 66- Am. Phys. Soc. Lasers; magnetic resonance; photoconductivity; low temperature physics. Address: Spectra-Physics Inc, 1250 W. Middlefield Rd, Mountain View, CA 94040.

GOLDSBY, A(RTHUR) R(AYMOND), b. Flora, Ill, Nov. 20, 04; m. 34; c. 1. ORGANIC CHEMISTRY. A.B, Ill. Col, 28; M.S, Northwestern, 30, Am. Petrol. Inst. jr. fel, 30-31, Ph.D.(org. chem), 32; Columbia, 40-41, 46-47, 54. Asst. chem, Northwestern, 28-30, 31-32; chemist, Nat. Aluminate Corp, Ill, 32-33; res. chemist, Nat. Aniline & Chem. Co, N.Y, 33-36; dir. explor. res. gasoline, Tex. Co, 36-40, tech. adv, Texaco Develop. Corp, 40-55; dir. res, Stratford Eng. Corp, Mo, 55-57; tech. adv, TEXACO INC, 57-62, TECH. ASSOC, 62- Am. Chem. Soc; Am. Inst. Chem; Am. Inst. Chem. Eng. Reactions of furan and furfural; pyrolysis of olefins and paraffins; synthetic organic detergents; aviation gasoline; alkylation; isomerization; catalytic cracking; fuel composition in relation to engine performance; recovery of sulfuric acid licensing. Address: Texaco, Inc, 135 E. 42nd St, New York, NY 10017.

GOLDSCHMID, OTTO, b. Vienna, Austria, May 1, 10; nat; m. 42; c. 2. PHYSICAL CHEMISTRY. Dipl. Ing, Univ. Stuttgart, 34; Univ. Vienna, 36-38; Ph.D.(chem), Univ. Calif, 40. RES. SUPVR, OLYMPIC RES. DIV, ITT RAYONIER, INC, 39- Am. Chem. Soc. Viscosity of suspensions and solutions; absorption spectra of organic compounds; composition and structure of cellulose fibers; lignin chemistry. Address: 726 S. Ninth St, Shelton, WA 98584.

GOLDSCHMIDT, ALFRED, b. Zurich, Switzerland, Feb. 23, 14; nat; m. 38; c. 2. ORGANIC CHEMISTRY. Dipl. Ing, Fed. Inst. Tech, Zurich, 37. Prod. asst. veg. oil ref, Italy, 37-38; RES. CHEMIST, synthetic drying oils, Switzerland, 38-41; by-prods. corn ref. Clinton Foods, Inc, 41-44; CHEM. LUBE OILS, CHEVRON RES. CO, STANDARD OIL CO. CALIF, 45- AAAS; Am. Chem. Soc; Swiss Chem. Soc. Vegetable oils, edible and drying; chemicals from corn; organic halides; polymers, lube oil additives. Address: 911 Galvin Dr, El Cerrito, CA 94530.

GOLDSCHMIDT, BERNARD M(ORTON), b. N.Y.C, Feb. 7, 36; m. 65; c. 2. ORGANIC CHEMISTRY. B.S, City Col. New York, 57; Ph.D.(chem), Wisconsin, 62. Fel. chem, State Univ. N.Y. Stony Brook, 62-63; ENVIRON. MED, MED. CTR, N.Y. UNIV, 63-64, res. assoc. scientist, 65-70, ASST. PROF, 70- Assoc. prof, Adelphi Univ; private consult. Synthesis of natural products; kinetics of organic reactions; chemical carcinogenesis. Address: Dept. of Environmental Medicine, New York University Medical Center, 550 First Ave, New York, NY 10016.

GOLDSCHMIDT, ERIC N(ATHAN), b. Berlin, Germany, Nov. 25, 27; nat; m. 54; c. 3. ORGANIC CHEMISTRY. B.S, Brooklyn Col, 50; Thayer scholar, Harvard, 50-51, A.M, 51, Joseph Eveleth scholar, 51-52, Nat. Insts. Health fel, 52-53, Ph.D.(org. chem), 55; Nat. Insts. Health fel, Columbia, 53-54. Lectr. chem, Brooklyn Col, 50; scientist, Warner-Chilcott Labs, 56-57; sr. scientist, Warner Lambert Res. Inst, 57-62, sr. lit. chemist, 62-67; res. specialist, Off. Eng. Res. & lectr, dept. chem, Univ. Pa, 67-68; asst. to dir. res, ENDO LABS, INC, 68-70, ASST. TO V.PRES. RES, 70- Lectr, Brooklyn Col, 50, 69; Hofstra Univ, 69- U.S.A, 46-47, Chem.C, 54-56. AAAS; fel. Am. Inst. Chem; N.Y. Acad. Sci; The Chem. Soc. Antimetabolites; biosynthesis inhibitors; nitrogen heterocycles; chemotherapeutic agents; new synthetic methods; information storage and retrieval; research administration. Address: Endo Labs, Inc, 1000 Stewart Ave, Garden City, NY 11530.

GOLDSCHMIDT, E(UGENE) P(HILIP), b. N.Y.C, Apr. 9, 24; m. 49; c. 2. MICROBIAL GENETICS. B.S, Col. William & Mary, 44; M.S, Michigan, 45; Atomic Energy Comn. fel, Purdue, 50-52, Ph.D.(bact), 52. Bacteriologist, Lederle Labs Div, Am. Cyanamid Corp, 47-48; asst. physiol, Purdue, 49; Nat. Insts. Health fel, Western Reserve, 52-54; asst. prof. bact, Georgia, 54-55; sect. chief, med. microbiol. div, Ft. Detrick, Md, 55-61; spec. lectr. microbiol, Texas, 61-63, assoc. biologist, div. molecular biol, M.D. Anderson Hosp. & Tumor Inst, 63-66; ASSOC. PROF. BIOL. & BIOPHYS, UNIV. HOUSTON, 66- Am. Soc. Microbiol; Brit. Soc. Gen. Microbiol. Genetics and physiology of microorganisms. Address: Dept. of Biology & Biophysics, University of Houston, 3801 Cullen Blvd, Houston, TX 77004.

GOLDSCHMIDT, LEONTINE, b. Arad, Austria, Mar. 9, 13; nat. PSYCHOBIOLOGY. Ph.M, Vienna, 35, Ph.D.(pharmacog), 37. Instr, inst. pharmacog, Vienna, 35-37; asst. biochem, sch. med, Boston, 42-45; biologist, dept. hemat, U.S. Naval Radiol. Defense Lab, Calif, 47-50; tech. translator, U.S. Dept. Army, N.Y, 51; chemist, Argus Chem. Lab, 52-54; CHIEF DEPT. BIOCHEM, CREEDMOOR INST. PSYCHOBIOL. STUDIES, STATE DEPT. MENT. HYG, N.Y, 54- Lectr, sch. psychiat, N.Y. Univ. Dipl, Nat. Registry Clin. Chem. Fel. AAAS; N.Y. Acad. Sci; Am. Asn. Clin. Chem; Am. Chem. Soc. Biochemistry of mental disease; clinical chemistry; radiobiology. Address: Creedmore Institute, P.O. Box 40, St. 60, Queens Village, NY 11427.

GOLDSCHMIDT, MILLICENT, b. Erie, Pa, June 11, 26; m. 49; c. 2. MICROBIOLOGY. B.A, Case West. Reserve Univ, 47; Brystol-Myers Co. fel, Purdue Univ, 48-49, E.R. Squibb & Co. fel, 49-50, M.S, 50, Purdue Res. Found. fel, 51-52, Ph.D.(microbiol), 52. Asst. zool, Purdue Univ, 51-52; res. assoc, dept. biochem, sch. med, Case West. Reserve Univ, 53; biophys, res. labs, George Washington Univ, 56-59; instr. chem, Hood Col, 59-60; asst. prof. med, in bact, from sch. med, Univ. Md, to med. unit, U.S. Army, Ft. Detrick, 60-61; Nat. Insts. Health fel. microbiol, Univ. Tex, 61-63; res. microbiologist, col. med, Baylor Univ, 63-67; asst. prof. microbiol. & asst. microbiologist, dept. path, Univ. Tex. M.D. Anderson Hosp. & Tumor Inst, 67-71, assoc. microbiologist, depts. clin. path. & med, 70-71; ASSOC. PROF. MICROBIOL, UNIV. TEX. GRAD. SCH. BIOMED. SCI, HOUSTON, 70- Mem. faculty, sch. blood banking, Univ. Tex. M.D. Anderson Hosp. & Tumor Inst, 70-, consult, dept. clin. path. Am. Soc. Microbiol. Instrumentation; medical, biochemical and biophysical aspects of microbiology. Address: University of Texas Graduate School of Biomedical Sciences at Houston, Texas Medical Center, 109 Herman Professional Bldg, Houston, TX 77025.

GOLDSCHMIDT, VICTOR W, b. Montevideo, Uruguay, Apr. 20, 36; U.S. citizen, m. 58; c. 3. FLUID MECHANICS. B.S, Syracuse, 57, Ph.D.(eng), 65; M.S, Pennsylvania, 60. Appl. engr, control valve div, Honeywell, Inc, 57-59, develop. engr, 59-60; instr. mech. eng, Syracuse, 60-64; asst. prof. civil eng, PURDUE UNIV, 64-68, ASSOC. PROF, 68, MECH. ENG, 68- Am. Soc. Mech. Eng; Am. Soc. Civil Eng.(Freeman Fund Award, 71); Am. Soc. Eng. Educ. Incompressible fluid mechanics; fundamental studies in turbulence, particularily related to its dispersion of scalar contaminants, interaction with acoustics and measurements of properties characterizing turbulence; international engineering educational programs. Address: School of Mechanical Engineering, Purdue University, Lafayette, IN 47907.

GOLDSCHMIEDT, HENRY, b. Vienna, Austria, Apr. 9, 05; U.S. citizen. BIOCHEMISTRY, INDUSTRIAL CHEMISTRY. Ph.D.(chem), Vienna, 27. Biochemist, State Sero Therapeut. Inst, Austria, 27-38; DIR. RES, MEM. CO, INC, 45- Soc. Promoting Int. Sci. Rels; Am. Chem. Soc. Skin respiration; development of cosmetic products. Address: 310 Riverside Dr, New York, NY 10025.

GOLDSHMID, JHUDA, b. Tel-Aviv, Israel, Oct. 26, 31; m. 59; c. 3. SANITARY ENGINEERING. B.Sc, Israel Inst. Technol, 54; Union Carbide Corp. fel, Case Inst. Technol, 60-61, Ph.D.(chem. eng), 61. Res. scientist, res. div, American Standard, Inc, 61-63; water qual. engr, Mekoroth Water Co, 63-66, dir. water qual. control, 66-70; SR. ENGR, AMBIENT PURIFICATION TECHNOL, INC, 70- Mem, Nat. Comt. Water Qual. Res, Israel, 68-70. Am. Inst. Chem. Eng; Am. Chem. Soc; Am. Water Works Asn; Int. Asn. Water Pollution Res; Asn. Archit. & Eng. Israel. Taste and odor in surface water supplies; recharge of surface water and of treated sewage effluent; general limnology; wet scrubber technology. Address: Ambient Purification Technology, Inc, P.O. Box 71, Riverside, CA 92502.

GOLDSMITH, ALFRED N(ORTON), b. N.Y.C, Sept. 15, 87; m. 30. RADIO & ELECTRONICS ENGINEERING. B.S, City Col. New York, 07, fel, 07-10; Ph.D, Columbia Univ, 11; hon. Sc.D, Lawrence Col, 35. Tutor physics, City Col, 10-11, instr, 11-15, asst. prof, 15-19; dir. res. dept, RCA CORP, 19-22, chief broadcast engr, 22-23, v.pres. & gen. engr, 27-33, consult, engr, 33-62, HON. V.PRES. & SR. TECH. CONSULT, 62-, MEM. BD, DIRS, COMMUN, INC, 59- Consult. radio engr, 14-; assoc. prof, City Col. New York, 19-23; chmn. bd. consult. engrs, Nat. Broadcasting Co; chmn. panels, 2, 11 & 11-A, Nat. TV Syst. Comt, 40, 50-54; mem, Int. Comt. Wireless Tel; hon. mem, Int. TV Comt, 59-; mem, coun. on med. TV, Inst. Advan. Med. Commun, 60- Mod. Pioneer Award, Nat. Asn. Mfrs, 40, Harris Medal, 42; award, Radio Corp. Am. Labs, 50- AAAS; Am. Phys. Soc; Acoust. Soc. Am; assoc. fel. Am. Astronaut. Soc; Am. Inst. Aeronaut. & Astronaut; Soc. Motion Picture & TV Eng.(pres, 32, progress award); hon. fel. Int. Col. Surg; fel. Inst. Elec. & Electronics Eng.(ed, Proc, Inst. Radio Eng, 12-54, emer. ed, 54-, secy, 18, pres, 27); fel. Brit. Inst. Elec. Eng; hon. mem. Australian Inst. Radio & Electronics Eng; Benjamin Franklin fel. Royal Soc. Arts. Motion picture engineering; radio telegraphy and telephony; photophysics; trasmission of canal rays through thin partitions; precision measurements in radio engineering; electrical musical instruments; sound motion pictures; radio television; color television; tri-dimensional motion pictures and television systems. Address: 424 Madison Ave, New York, NY 10017.

GOLDSMITH, ARTHUR, b. Chicago, Ill, May 20, 15; m. 41; c. 1. ELECTRICAL ENGINEERING. B.S, Armour Inst. Tech, 37, M.S, 40; Ph.D.(elec. eng), Ill. Inst. Tech, 44; M.B.A, Stanford, 60. Asst. elec. eng, Ill. Inst. Tech, 37-41; asst. electronics officer, U.S. Atlantic Fleet Serv. Force, 42-45; sr. engr, Motorola, Inc, 45-47; officer-in-charge, Naval Res. Training Center, Ill, 47-48; reserve electronics prog. officer, 12th Naval Dist, 48-51, 54-57; exec. officer, Naval Commun. Sta, Port Lyautey, French Morocco, 51-52; supt. port engr. & electronics officer, Mil. Sea Transportation Serv, Pac, 53-54; exec. officer, Naval Commun. Sta, Alaska, 57-58; res. asst, grad. sch. bus, Stanford, 58-60; dir. eng, Wilcox Elec. Co, 60-62; chief engr, mil. commun, Motorola, Inc, 62-64; dep. dir, Commun. & Systs, Inc, 64-68; CHIEF TECH. DIV, OFF. TELECOMMUN, OFF. SECY. TRANSPORTATION, 68- U.S.N.R, 41-45, 47-58, Res, 45-47, 58-, Capt. Am. Soc. Eng. Educ; Inst. Elec. & Electronics Eng. Design, development and application of communication and electronic systems to transportation; application of satellite systems for communication and navigation; engineering management; management of the radio frequency spectrum. Address: Office of Telecommunications, U.S. Dept. of Transportation, 400 Seventh St. S.W, Washington, DC 20590.

GOLDSMITH, C. THOMAS, b. Flushing, N.Y, Jan. 12, 30; m. 55; c. 3. EXPERIMENTAL PSYCHOLOGY. A.B, Fordham, 51, M.A, 53, Ph.D.(exp. psychol), 59. Asst, Fordham, 52-54; eng. psychologist, Picatinny Arsenal, U.S. Army, 55-56, chief human factors, 56-58; human factors specialist, Grumman Aircraft Eng. Corp, 58-62, mem. tech. staff, Fairchild Camera & Instrument Corp, 62-68; PRES, DISPLAY SCI, INC, 68- Am. Psychol. Asn; Human Factors Soc. System Engineering; analysis complex man-machine systems; engineering psychology. Address: Display Sciences, Inc, 3 Industrial Ave, Upper Saddle River, NJ 07458.

GOLDSMITH, CARL, b. Newburyport, Mass, Feb. 22, 31; m. 59; c. 2. INTERNAL MEDICINE, NEPHROLOGY. A.B, Harvard, 52; M.D, Univ. Va, 56. Nat. Inst. Arthritis & Metab. Diseases clin. trainee, southwest. med. sch, Univ. Tex, 59-61; instr. med, Med. Col. Va, 61-62; instr. internal med, med. sch, Georgetown Univ, 62-64, asst. prof, 64-69; ASSOC. PROF. MED, SCH. MED, UNIV. MIAMI, 69-; CHIEF RENAL SECT, JACKSON MEM. HOSP, 70- Markle Found. scholar med, 62-67; consult, U.S. Soldiers' Home Hosp, D.C, 64-65; res. career develop. award, Nat. Inst. Arthritis & Metab. Diseases, 66-70. AAAS; fel. Am. Col. Physicians; Am. Fedn. Clin. Res; Am. Soc. Nephrology; N.Y. Acad. Sci. Renal physiology; disorders of kidney function; fluid and electrolyte imbalance; aspects of potassium deficiency in the human; some aspects of renal-tubular handling of potassium. Address: Dept. of Medicine, School of Medicine, University of Miami, Miami, FL 33152.

GOLDSMITH, CHARLES HARRY, b. Flin Flon, Man, Aug. 27, 39; m. 66; c. 2. APPLIED STATISTICS, BIOSTATISTICS. B.Sc, Univ. Man, 61, M.Sc, 63; Ph.D.(exp. statist), N.C. State Univ, 69. Lectr. statist, Carleton Univ. (Ont), 63-65; res. assoc. biostatist, Univ. N.C. Chapel Hill, 65-69; ASST. PROF. BIOSTATIST. & APPL. MATH, McMASTER UNIV, 69- Consult, dept. hwys. & educ, Man. Prov. Govt, 63; abstractor, Exec. Sci. Inst, 67-71; adv, med. commun. comt, Mohawk Col. (Ont), 70-71. Shewell Award, Am. Soc. Qual. Control, 68, Frank J. Wilcoxon Award, 70. Am. Statist. Asn; Biomet. Soc; Royal Statist. Soc; Soc. Epidemiol. Res. Variance component designs; experimental designs; regression analysis; data analysis; computer applications of statistical methods; epidemiology. Address: Faculties of Science, Engineering and Medicine, McMaster University, Hamilton, Ont, Can.

GOLDSMITH, DALE P(RESTON) J(OEL), b. Catasauqua, Pa, Oct. 30, 16. BIOCHEMISTRY. B.S, Lehigh, 38; M.A, Harvard, 40; Ph.D.(org. chem), Pa. State Col, 42; M.S, Rochester, 57.. Chemist, Nat. Aniline & Chem. Co, N.Y, 37; res. labs, Socony-Vacuum Oil Co, N.J, 38-39; instr. org. chem, Pa. State Col, 40-42, Parke, Davis & Co. fel, 42-43; sr. res. chemist, Merck & Co, Inc, 43-55; instr. physiol, sch. med, Rochester, 57-63, asst. prof, 63-64; ASSOC. PROF. BIOCHEM, COL. MED, UNIV. NEBR, OMAHA, 64- Mem, Int. Union Pure & Appl. Chem. AAAS; Am. Chem. Soc; Am. Physiol. Soc; N.Y. Acad. Sci; fel. Am. Inst. Chem; Am. Oil Chem. Soc. Mucosal regeneration; atherosclerosis; medicinal chemicals; gastrointestinal biochemistry; lipid metabolism. Address: Dept. of Biochemistry, College of Medicine, University of Nebraska, 42nd & Dewey Ave, Omaha, NE 68105.

GOLDSMITH, DAVID JONATHAN, b. Flushing, N.Y, Aug. 25, 31; m. 59; c. 2. ORGANIC CHEMISTRY. B.S, Michigan, 52, M.S, 53; Ph.D.(chem), Columbia, 58. Res. fel, Harvard, 57-59; asst. prof. CHEM, Wayne State, 59-63; EMORY UNIV, 63-68, ASSOC. PROF, 68- Vis. prof, Univ. Strasbourg, 71-

72. Am. Chem. Soc. Chemistry of natural products. Address: Dept. of Chemistry, College of Arts & Sciences, Emory University, Atlanta, GA 30332.

GOLDSMITH, DONALD L(EON), b. Phila, Pa, Aug. 12, 37; m. 63; c. 2. MATHEMATICS. B.A, Univ. Pa, 59, M.A, 60, Ph.D.(math), 64. Asst. prof. MATH, Fordham Univ, 64-68; ASSOC. PROF, WEST. MICH. UNIV, 68-, faculty res. fel, summer 70. Nat. Sci. Found. res. grant, 66-68; vis. mem, Courant Inst. Math. Sci, N.Y. Univ, 68-69. Am. Math. Soc; Math. Asn. Am. Number theory. Address: Dept. of Mathematics, Western Michigan University, Kalamazoo, MI 49001.

GOLDSMITH, EDWARD I, b. Far Rockaway, N.Y, Nov. 13, 27; m. 52; c. 4. SURGERY. A.B, Cornell Univ, 47, M.D, 50. Fel. surg. res, Harvard Med. Sch, 51-52; asst. SURG, sch. med, Univ. Colo, 57-58; instr, MED. COL, CORNELL UNIV, 58-60, clin. asst. prof, 60-66, CLIN. ASSOC. PROF, 66-Sr. res. fel, N.Y. Hosp, 59-62; asst. attend. surgeon, 59-64, assoc. attend. surgeon, 64- Presidential Merit Medal of Philippines for contributions to control of schistosomiasis, 68; dipl, Am. Bd. Surg; Trumpeldor Medal, State Israel, 71. Med.C, U.S.A.R, 52-54, 1st Lt. Fel. Am. Col. Surg; Am. Soc. Artificial Internal Organs; Int. Primatol. Soc; Transplantation Soc; Am. Soc. Trop. Med. & Hyg; Royal Soc. Trop. Med. & Hyg. Cardiovascular surgery; organ transplantation; use of primates in medical research; schistosomiasis; extracorporeal hemofiltration. Address: New York Hospital-Cornell Medical Center, 525 E. 68th St, New York, NY 10021.

GOLDSMITH, E(LI) D(AVID), b. New York, N.Y, Apr. 10, 07; m. 40; c. 1. ZOOLOGY. B.S, City Col. New York, 26; A.M, Harvard, 28, Austin fel, 33-34, Ph.D.(biol), 34; M.S, N.Y. Univ, 31. Asst. zool, Harvard, 28-29, 31-33; lab. instr. comp. anat, N.Y. Univ, 29-31; instr. biol. & chem, City Col. New York, 34-45; asst. prof. anat, COL. DENT, N.Y. UNIV, 45-48, assoc. prof. HISTOL, 48-51, PROF, 51-, RES. COORD, 48- Harvard grant, Marine Biol. Lab, Woods Hole, 32; Bermuda Biol. Sta, 34; Commonwealth Fund. grant, 44; Thompson Fund grant, 44, 46; U.S. Pub. Health Serv. grant, 47-; Am. Cancer Soc. grant, 51-55; biomed. res. coord, Off. Naval Research, U.S. Dept. Navy, N.Y, 51-53; acting dir, off. res. serv, N.Y. Univ, 63-64. Consult. to surgeon gen, U.S. Pub. Health Serv; consult to dir, Nat. Inst. Dent. Res; sci. consult, Osborn Labs. Marine Sci. Mem. corp, Bermuda Biol. Sta; mem, selection panel sr. res. fels, Nat. Insts. Health; dent. prog. proj. comt, Nat. Inst. Dent. Res. Alumni res. award gold medal, Columbia Dent. Alumni, 61. Fel. AAAS; fel. Am. Col. Dent; Am. Soc. Nat; Soc. Exp. Biol. & Med; Sci. Res. Soc. Am; Am. Soc. Zool; Soc. Develop. Biol; Endocrine Soc; Am. Physiol. Soc; Am. Micros. Soc; Am. Chem. Soc; fel. Geront. Soc; Harvey Soc; Entom. Soc. Am; Am. Asn. Anat; Am. Asn. Cancer Res; fel. N.Y. Acad. Sci; fel. N.Y. Acad. Med; hon. mem. Am. Acad. Oral Med; Int. Asn. Dent. Res. Regeneration effect of chemicals and endocrines; carcinogenesis; anti-vitamin; vitamin endocrinology relation ship; goitrogenic drugs; radioactive iodine; blood depressors; dental histology; antimetabolites; nucleic acid metabolism in Drosophila; chemosterilants and controlled insect populations; teratology. Address: Dept. of Histology, College of Dentistry, New York University, New York, NY 10010.

GOLDSMITH, G(EORGE) J(ASON), b. Newburyport, Mass, Mar. 29, 23; m. 45; c. 4. PHYSICS. B.S, Univ. Vt, 44; M.S, Purdue Univ, 48, Ph.D.(physics), 55. Instr. physics, Purdue Univ, 48-55; physicist, labs, RCA Corp, 55-68; ASSOC. PROF. PHYSICS, BOSTON COL, 68- U.S.N, 44-46. AAAS; Am. Phys. Soc. Ferroelectricity; photoconductivity in insulators; solid state and nuclear physics; science-society. Address: Dept. of Physics, Boston College, Chestnut Hill, MA 02215.

GOLDSMITH, GRACE A(RABELL), b. St. Paul, Minn, Apr. 8, 04. MEDICINE. B.S, Wisconsin, 25; M.D, Tulane, 32; M.S, Minnesota, 36; hon. D.M.S, Woman's Med. Col. Pa, 62. Intern, Touro Infirmary, New Orleans, La, 32-33; fel. internal med, Mayo Clin, 33-36; instr. MED, SCH. MED, TULANE UNIV. LA, 36-39, asst. prof, 39-43, assoc. prof, 43-49, PROF, 49-, DEAN SCH. PUB. HEALTH & TROP. MED, 67- Mem, Nutrit. Surv, Newf, 44 & 48; sci. adv. comt, Nutrit. Found, 48-64; food & nutrit. bd, Nat. Res. Coun, 48-69, chmn, 58-68; mem. biochem. & nutrit. study sect, U.S. Pub. Health Serv, 49-51, nutrit. study sect, 59-63, gastroenterol. & nutrit. training comt, 66-70; food nutrit. adv. comt, U.S. Dept. Agr, 51-63, chmn, 54-56; mem, Gordon Res. Conf. Vitamins & Metab, 54; consult, inst. nutrit, Pan-Am. Sanit. Bur, Cent. Am. & Panama, 54; mem. sci. adv. comt, Nat. Vitamin Found, 55-58; orgn. prog. comt, Int. Nutrit. Cong, 60, U.S. del, Scotland, 63; mem. sci. adv. comt, Food & Agr. Orgn. for Conf. Marine Resources World Nutrit, 61; adv. comt. & bd, Fedn. Am. Socs. Exp. Biol, 62-65; sci. adv. comt, Spec. Dairy Indust. Bd, 62-66; consult, La. State Bd. Health, 62-67; trustee, Am. Freedom from Hunger Found, 63-67; mem. corp. vis. comt, dept. nutrit. & food sci, Mass. Inst. Technol, 64-65; panel on world food supply, President's Sci. Adv. Comt, 66-67; comt. etiology & epidemiol. of anemias, Int. Union Nutrit. Sci, 67-; chmn. iron comt, food & nutrit. bd. Nat. Acad. Sci-Nat. Res. Coun, 69-; consult, nutrit. prog, La. State Dept. Health, 69-; mem, Study Comn. Dietetics, 70; nat. adv. arthritis & metab. diseases coun, Nat. Insts. Health, 70-; consult. physician, Charity Hosp, La; Touro Infirmary, New Orleans. Award, Univ. Minn, 64; dipl, Am. Bd. Internal Med; dipl, Am. Bd. Nutrit. AAAS; Soc. Exp. Biol. & Med; Am. Soc. Clin. Invest; fel. Am. Pub. Health Asn; fel. Am. Med. Asn.(Goldberger Award, 65); Am. Diabetes Asn; Asn. Am. Physicians; fel. Am. Col. Physicians; Am. Inst. Nutrit.(Osborn & Mendel Award, 59, pres, 63-64); hon. mem. Am. Dietetic Asn; Am. Soc. Clin. Nutrit.(pres-elect, 71); fel. N.Y. Acad. Sci; Int. Soc. Hemat. Nutrition; interrelationships of niacin and tryptophan; vitamins of the B-complex and macrocytic anemia; clinical and laboratory tests for evaluation of nutritional status; lipid metabolism in man. Address: School of Public Health & Tropical Medicine, Tulane University of Louisiana, 1430 Tulane Ave, New Orleans, LA 70112.

GOLDSMITH, HARRY L, b. Nürnberg, Germany, May 11, 28; Can. citizen; m. 58; c. 2. PHYSICAL CHEMISTRY. B.A, Oxford, 50, B.Sc, 51; Defence Res. Bd. fel, Royal Mil. Col.(Ont), 57-58; Ph.D.(chem), McGill, 61. Tech. officer phys. chem, dyestuffs div, Imp. Chem. Industs, Ltd, Eng, 50-56; fel. suspension rheology, McGILL UNIV, 61-64, Med. Res. Coun. Can. scholar blood rheology, 64-67, asst. prof. EXP. MED, 66-70, ASSOC. PROF, 70-; MED. RES. COUN. CAN. RES. ASSOC. BLOOD RHEOLOGY, 67- Am. Physiol. Soc; Can. Soc. Clin. Invest; Int. Soc. Biorheol; European Soc. Microcirc. Solution kinetics; lyophopic colloids; flow of suspensions of model rigid and deformable particles through tubes; flow behavior of human red blood cells and platelets in artificial tubes. Address: McGill University Medical Clinic, Montreal General Hospital, 1650 Cedar Ave, Montreal 109, Que, Can.

GOLDSMITH, HENRY, b. Berlin, Ger, Jan. 17, 23; nat; m. 52; c. 4. CHEMICAL ENGINEERING. B.E, Hopkins, 45, M.S, 47, D.Eng, 48. Asst, Hopkins, 45-48; res. consult, John Crerar Libr, 48; proj. engr, govt. res. labs, Ohio, 49; secy-treas, Nybalt Metal Co, 50-63; dir. res. & develop. & chmn. new prod. develop, Catalyst Res. Corp, 63-69, dir. res. & develop, Electronic Aids, Inc, 66-69; pres, Fedder Software Corp, 69-71; ADMINR. SALES & PROD, POLAND BROS. DIV, APL CORP, 71- Civilian with Atomic Energy Comn, Off. Sci. Res. & Develop, 48. AAAS; Am. Chem. Soc; Am. Inst. Chem. Eng. Petroleum; rubber; metallurgy; high pressure synthesis. Address: Poland Brothers Division, APL Corp, 1300 S. Race St, Baltimore, MD 21230.

GOLDSMITH, HENRY A(RNOLD), b. Berlin, Germany, Dec. 17, 10; nat; m. 41; c. 2. PHYSICAL CHEMISTRY. Dipl, Berlin, 32; Ph.D.(chem), Univ. Genoa, Italy, 34; dipl, Univ. Pavia, Italy, 35. From chemist to chief chemist, Glyco Prods. Co, Inc, N.Y, 35-44; chemist coatings, Standard Varnish Works, Inc, 44-46; chief chemist cleaning compounds, Phipps Prods, Inc, Mass, 47-48; chemist specialties, Pioneer Prods. Co, Inc, N.J, 48; org. chem, Colgate-Palmolive-Peet Co, 48-50; chief chemist detergents, Theobald Industs, 50-54; metal cleaners, Solventol Chem. Prod. Co, Mich, 54-58; from group leader to mgr. surface prep, Turco Prod. Div, Purex Corp, Calif, 58-64; sr. scientist, U.S. Borax Res. Corp, Anaheim, 65-67; RES. CHEMIST, PUREX CORP, 68- Am. Chem. Soc; Am. Oil Chem. Soc. Organic chemistry and applications in the fields of fat derivatives, detergents, surfactants, emulsifiers and resins. Address: Purex Corp, 24600 S. Main St, Wilmington, CA 90744.

GOLDSMITH, JEWETT, b. Baltimore, Md, Apr. 1, 19; m. 56; c. 3. PSYCHIATRY. A.B, Hopkins, 38; M.D, Maryland, 42. Intern, Kings County Hosp, Brooklyn, 42-43; Vet. Admin. res. psychiat, hosp, Duke, 46-48, instr. med. sch, 48-49, assoc, 50-54, asst. prof, 54-59; asst. prof. PSYCHIAT, MED. SCH, NORTHWEST. UNIV, 59-64, ASSOC. PROF, 64-; DIR. INPATIENT SERV, ILL. STATE PSYCHIAT. INST, 70-, dir. northwest. serv, 59-70. With ment. hyg. clin, Vet. Admin, 49-50; dir. psychiat. out-patient clin, hosp, Duke Univ, 50-56; psychiat. attend, Vet. Admin. Hosp, Durham, 54-56, ward physician, 56-59; consult, Family Serv. Agency, 54-59. Dipl, Am. Bd. Psychiat. & Neurol, 48. Med.C, U.S.N.R, 43-46, Lt. AAAS; Am. Psychiat. Asn; Am. Med. Cols; Am. Med. Asn. Psychiatric treatment and education. Address: Illinois State Psychiatric Institute, 1601 W. Taylor St, Chicago, IL 60612.

GOLDSMITH, JOHN ROTHCHILD, b. Portland, Ore, Jan. 5, 22; m. 47; c. 4. PUBLIC HEALTH. B.A, Reed Col, 42; M.D, Harvard, 45, M.P.H, 57. Res. fel. prev. med, Harvard Med. Sch, 55-57; head air pollution med. studies, Calif. State Dept. Pub. Health, 57-65; epidemiologist, WHO, Switz, 64-66; HEAD ENVIRON. EPIDEMIOL. UNIT, CALIF. STATE DEPT. PUB. HEALTH, 66- Temporary consult, WHO, 63; spec. consult, div. air pollution & Surgeon General's Adv. Cmt. Smoking & Health, U.S. Pub. Health Serv; regents lectr, Univ. Calif, Irvine. U.S.N.R, 46-48. AAAS; fel. Am. Pub. Health Asn; Am. Fedn. Clin. Res; Am. Thoracic Soc; N.Y. Acad. Sci; Royal Soc. Health; Int. Epidemiol. Asn. Environmental epidemiology; air quality standard setting; internal medicine. Address: Environmental Epidemiology Unit, California State Dept. of Public Health, 2151 Berkeley Way, Berkeley, CA 94704.

GOLDSMITH, JOSEPH, b. Waynesburg, Pa, Mar. 13, 15. PHYSICS, OPTOMETRY. B.S, Waynesburg Col, 37; D.Optom, Pa. State Col. Optom, 40. Practicing optometrist, Pa, 40-42; electronic engr, Raytheon Mfg. Co, Mass, 42-45; Am. Phenolic Corp, Ill, 45-47; prof. physics, Waynesburg Col, 47-50; electronic staff engr, Martin Co, Md, 50-59, develop. missiles & electronic systs, Orlando Div, 59-62, res. div, 62-67, SR. STAFF ENGR, ORLANDO DIV, MARTIN MARIETTA CORP, 67- Radar and microwave development; guided missiles; bomber defense; countermeasures, plasma sheath and esaki diode development; lasers and laser systems; high power pulsed gas lasers. Address: 171 Dommerich Dr, Maitland, FL 32751.

GOLDSMITH, JULIAN R(OYCE), b. Chicago, Ill, Feb. 26, 18; m. 40; c. 3. GEOLOGY, GEOCHEMISTRY. S.B, Chicago, 40, Ph.D.(geol), 47. Asst. petrol, Chicago, 41-42; res. chemist, Corning Glass Works, 42-46; asst. petrol, UNIV. CHICAGO, 46-47, res. assoc. GEOCHEM, 47-51, asst. prof, 51-55, assoc. prof, 55-58, prof, 58-69, CHARLES E. MERRIAM DISTINGUISHED SERV. PROF, 69-, ASSOC. DEAN PHYS. SCI. DIV, 60-, chmn. dept. geophys. sci, 63-71, assoc. chmn, 61-62, acting dean phys. sci. div, 62. Co-ed, J. Geol, 57-62; mem. earth sci. panel, Nat. Sci. Found, 58-61, chmn, 60-61, mem, Nat. Sci. Bd, 64-70; consult, Lawrence Radiation Lab, Univ. Calif; U.S. Geol. Surv; consult. ed, Encycl. Britannica; McGraw-Hill Encycl. Sci. & Technol. AAAS; fel. Geol. Soc. Am; Mineral. Soc. Am. (award, 55, v.pres, 68-69, pres, 70-71); Am. Acad. Arts & Sci; Am. Chem. Soc; Am. Crystallog. Asn; Geochem. Soc.(v.pres, 55); Am. Ceramic Soc; Am. Geophys. Union; Mineral Soc. Gt. Brit. & Ireland. Phase equilibria and crystal chemistry of silicates and carbonates. Address: Dept. of Geophysical Sciences, University of Chicago, Chicago, IL 60637.

GOLDSMITH, LEONARD J, b. London, Eng, Aug. 19, 33; U.S. citizen; m. 58; c. 2. NEUROPSYCHOLOGY. B.S, Roosevelt Univ, 58; M.S, Ill. Inst. Technol, 61; Ph.D, Univ. Ill, 65. Asst. prof. psychol, York Univ, 65-70; CHIEF PSYCHOLOGIST, TORONTO GEN. HOSP, 70- AAAS; Am. Psychol. Asn; Can. Psychol. Asn. Psychopharmacology; measurement. Address: Dept. of Psychiatry, Toronto General Hosptial, Toronto, Ont, Can.

GOLDSMITH, LOUIS, b. Toronto, Ont, Can, Feb. 11, 29; m. 52; c. 3. BIOCHEMICAL ENGINEERING. B.A.Sc, Toronto, 51, M.A.Sc, 52, Ph.D.(immunochem, biochem), 55. Asst, Connaught Med. Res. Labs, Toronto, 53-55, sr. res. asst, 55-56; res. chemist, Dawe's Fermentation Prods. Inc, Mich, 56-59; asst. to mgr, fine chems. div, Dawe's Labs, Inc, 59-60, dir. tech. opers, 60-62, mgr. chem. opers, 62-63, dir. res. & develop, 63-66, mgr. fine chem. div, 66-69, V.PRES. & GEN. MGR, DAWE'S FERMENTATION

PROD. INC. 69- Am. Chem. Soc. Fermentation chemicals, enzymes, antibiotics, vitamins and insulin. Address: Dawe's Fermentation Products, Inc, 4800 S. Richmond St. Chicago, IL 60632.

GOLDSMITH, MARGARET TOWELL, b. Rushford, N.Y. April 24, 00; m; c. 1. BACTERIOLOGY. B.S. Columbia, 37; fel. Maryland, 40-41, M.S. 43, Ph.D. (bact). 44. Instr. bact. Maryland. 41-45; bacteriologist, U.S. Dept. Agr, 46-59; scientist adminstr. Nat. Insts. Health, 59-63, exec. secy. cardiovasc. study sect. 63-70; RETIRED. Mem. staff. div. res. grants. Off. Sci. Res. & Develop. 43-44. AAAS; Am. Soc. Microbiol; Am. Acad. Microbiol; Brit. Soc. Gen. Microbiol. Essential growth substances for certain actinomyces; disinfecting properties of quaternary ammonium compounds; proteolytic enzymes of actinomycetes; enzyme inhibitors; grants administration. Address: 108 Devon Court, Silver Spring, MD 20910.

GOLDSMITH, MARK, b. New York, N.Y, July 14, 21. CHEMISTRY. A.B, Harvard, 43; Ph.D.(chem), Chicago, 48. Chemist, metall. lab, Chicago, 43-44; assoc. chemist, Argonne Nat. Lab, 48-52; fel, dept. physics & astron, Ohio State, 52-55; FEL. SCIENTIST, BETTIS ATOMIC POWER LAB, WESTINGHOUSE ELEC. CORP, 55- Fel, Nat. Ctr. Sci. Res, France, 55-56. Neutron physics. Address: Bettis Atomic Power Lab, Westinghouse Electric Corp, P.O. Box 79, West Mifflin, PA 15122.

GOLDSMITH, MARTIN, b. Los Angeles, Calif, Nov. 21, 29; m. 61; c. 3. MECHANICAL ENGINEERING. B.S, California, Berkeley, 51; M.S, Calif. Inst. Tech, 52, Ph.D.(mech. eng), 55. Engr, Rand Corp, 55-61; GROUP DIR. SPEC. PROJS, AEROSPACE CORP, 61- Vis. assoc, environ. qual. lab, Calif. Inst. Technol, 71-72. Am. Inst. Aeronaut. & Astronaut. Combustion; rocket propulsion; space booster systems; ballistic missile systems; hardened facilities; electric powerplant siting. Address: Aerospace Corp, 1111 Mill St, San Bernardino, CA 92408.

GOLDSMITH, MARY HELEN M(ARTIN), b. Boston, Mass, May 2, 33; m. 55; c. 2. BIOLOGY, PLANT PHYSIOLOGY. B.A, Cornell, 55; Nat. Sci. Found. fel, Radcliffe Col, 55-57, A.M, 56, E.A. Colton fel, 58-59, Ph.D.(biol), 60. Nat. Cancer Inst. fel, Harvard, 59-60; King's Col, London, 60-61; RES. ASSOC. BIOL, YALE, 61-, LECTR, 63-64, 66- Am. Soc. Plant Physiol; Soc. Gen. Physiol; Scand. Soc. Plant Physiol. Transport and metabolism of auxin; tropisms; control of extension growth; bioelectric potentials of plant cells. Address: Dept. of Biology, Yale University, New Haven, CT 06520.

GOLDSMITH, NORRIS W(HITNEY), b. Wyandanch, N.Y, Sept. 6, 03; m. 30; c. 2. PHYSICS. A.B, Cornell Univ, 24, Ph.D.(physics), 32; Albany State Teachers Col, 34-35. Asst. biophys. res. & radium technician, Mem. Hosp, N.Y, 24-25; State Inst. Malignant Disease, N.Y, 25-26; asst. & instr. physics, Cornell Univ, 26-31; asst. prof. physics & elec. eng, Washington & Lee Univ, 31-33; prin. pub. sch, N.Y, 34-41; physicist, Cheney Bros, Conn, 43-47; assoc. prof. physics, Adelphi Col, 47-52; physicist, Ford Instrument Co, Long Island City, 52-55; prof. physics, State Univ. N.Y. Col. Oswego, 57-71; RETIRED. Design of high-speed parachutes; development of parachute test devices; tension operated stopmotion for yarn winder. Address: 150 W. Seventh St, Oswego, NY 13126.

GOLDSMITH, RALPH S(AMUEL), b. Baltimore, Md, Feb. 23, 31; m. 53; c. 3. MEDICINE, ENDOCRINOLOGY. B.S, Franklin & Marshall Col, 50; fel, Maryland, 53, M.D, 54. Intern, Walter Reed Army Hosp, 54-55, res. physician, internal med, 56-58, student investr, metab, Inst. Res, 58-59; chief, metab. br, U.S. Army Surg. Res. Unit, 59-63; instr. MED, Harvard Med. Sch, 63-64, assoc, 64-68, asst. prof, 68, res. assoc, Thorndike Mem. Lab, 63-68; asst. prof, MAYO GRAD. SCH. MED, UNIV. MINN, 68-71, ASSOC. PROF, 71-, DIR, CLIN. STUDY UNIT, MAYO CLIN. & FOUND, 68-, CONSULT, DIV. ENDOCRINOL, CLIN, 68- Civilian Scientist, U.S. Army, 62-63; asst. physician, second & fourth med. servs, Boston City Hosp, 64- Consult, U.S. Army Res. Inst. Environ. Med, 63- Med.C, 54-62, Maj. AAAS; Endocrine Soc; Am. Fedn. Clin. Res; Am. Col. Physicians; N.Y. Acad. Sci; Orthop. Res. Soc. Calcium and phosphorous metabolism; parathyroid hormone; calcitonin; bone diseases. Address: Mayo Clinic & Foundation, Rochester, MN 55901.

GOLDSMITH, RICHARD, b. Salem, Mass, Sept. 30, 18; m. 55; c. 3. GEOLOGY. A.B, Maine, 40; Ph.D.(geol), Univ. Wash, 52. Geologist, U.S. GEOL. SURV, 52-69, CHIEF, BR. ATLANTIC ENVIRON. GEOL, AGR. RES. CTR, 69- U.S.A, 42-46. AAAS; Geol. Soc. Am; N.Y. Acad. Sci. Igneous and metamorphic petrology; areal geology; geomorphology and glacial geology; economic geology. Address: U.S. Geological Survey, Agriculture Research Center, Bldg. 420, Beltsville, MD 20705.

GOLDSMITH, RICHARD E, b. Cincinnati, Ohio, Oct. 25, 21; m. 44; c. 3. MEDICINE. Michigan, 39-42; M.D, Cincinnati, 45. Intern, Kings County Hosp, 45-46; fel, Cincinnati Gen. Hosp, 47, res, 47-49; fel, Mass. Gen. Hosp, Boston, 49-51; instr. MED, COL. MED, UNIV. CINCINNATI, 52-56, asst. prof, 56-61, assoc. clin. prof, 61-64, assoc. prof, 64-70, PROF, 70-; SR. INVESTR, METAB. LAB, CINCINNATI GEN. HOSP, 51- Dir. radioisotope lab, Cincinnati Vet. Admin. Hosp, 53-63. U.S.A, 46-47, Capt. Am. Fedn. Clin. Res; Am. Thyroid Asn; Endocrine Soc. Address: Dept. of Medicine, University of Cincinnati College of Medicine, Cincinnati, OH 45221.

GOLDSMITH, ROBERT LANDAU, b. Herrin, Ill, Sept. 26, 40; m. 66. CHEMICAL ENGINEERING. S.B, Mass. Inst. Technol, 62, Sun Oil, Esso Res. & Eng. & Sci. Design fels. & Ph.D.(chem. eng), 66. Nat. Sci. Found. fel, Inst. Catalysis Res, Lyon, France, 66-67; res. engr, ABCOR, INC, CAMBRIDGE, 67-70, PROG. MGR, 70- Am. Chem. Soc; Am. Inst. Chem. Eng. Membrane polymeric research; process development and equipment design for liquid and gas separations and waste treatment, primarily involving reverse osmosis; ultrafiltration and permeation; fundamental and applied catalysis. Address: 220 Belmont St, Watertown, MA 02172.

GOLDSMITH, TIMOTHY H(ENSHAW), b. N.Y.C, May 1, 32; m. 55; c. 2. BIOLOGY. B.A, Cornell, 54; univ. fel, Harvard, 54-56, U.S. Pub. Health Serv. fel, 56-58, Ph.D.(biol), 58. Jr. fel, Soc. of Fellows, Harvard, 58-61; instr, Marine Biol. Lab, Woods Hole, 59-61; asst. prof. BIOL, YALE, 61-63, assoc. prof, 63-70, PROF, 70-, CHMN. DEPT, 71- Guggenheim fel, 67-68; corp. mem, Marine Biol. Lab. AAAS; Am. Soc. Zool; Soc. Gen. Physiol; Biophys. Soc; Am. Physiol. Soc; Asn. Res. Vision & Ophthal. Neurophysiology and biochemistry of light sensitive systems, particularly color vision of arthropods. Address: Dept. of Biology, Yale University, New Haven, CT 06520.

GOLDSMITH, WERNER, b. Düsseldorf, Germany, May 23, 24; nat; c. 2. APPLIED MECHANICS. B.S, Texas, 44, M.S, 45. Pittsburgh, 45-46; Pennsylvania, 46-47; Ph.D.(mech. eng), California, Berkeley, 49. Tutor appl. math, Texas, 44-45; mech. engr, Westinghouse Elec. Corp, 45-47; instr. eng. design, UNIV. CALIF, BERKELEY, 47-49, asst. prof, 49-55, assoc. prof. eng. mech, 55-60, PROF. APPL. MECH, 60- Guggenheim fel, 53-54, Instr, Pittsburgh & Pennsylvania, 45-47; consult, Naval Ord. Test Sta, 51-; Waterways Exp. Sta, 51-52; Los Alamos Sci. Lab, 53-54; Stanford Res. Inst, 54-59; Lawrence Radiation Lab, California, 57-59; Sandia Corp, 64-68; Bur. Mines, 65-; consult & chmn, head injury construct. comt, Nat. Inst. Neurol. Diseases & Stroke, Nat. Insts. Health, 66-70; private consult, 53- Secy, U.S. Nat. Cong. Appl. Mech, 62. Am. Soc. Mech. Eng; Soc. Exp. Stress Anal. Impact and collisions; wave propagation; biomechanics; head injury; experimental stress analysis; material properties; dynamics; rock mechanics; continuum mechanics. Address: Division of Applied Mechanics, 6129 Etcheverry Hall, University of California, Berkeley, CA 94720.

GOLDSTEIN, ABRAHAM, b. Brooklyn, N.Y, March 14, 13; m; c. 1. DENTISTRY. B.S, Brooklyn Col, 34; D.D.S, N.Y. Univ, 38. Instr. periodont, col. dent. N.Y. Univ, 38-48, asst. prof, 48-61, assoc. prof, 61-68; DIR. DENT. HYG. PROG, PHOENIX COL, 68- Dir. dent. asst. prog, Maricopa Tech. Col. & dent. auxiliary prog, Maricopa County Jr. Col. Dist, 68- AAAS; fel. Am. Acad. Oral Med.(pres, 61-62); fel. Am. Col. Dent; Am. Acad. Periodont; Sci. Res. Soc. Am; Am. Dent. Asn; N.Y. Acad. Sci. Periodontal disease; oral medicine. Address: 5646 N. 12th St, Phoenix, AZ 85014.

GOLDSTEIN, ABRAHAM M. B, b. Iasi, Romania, Aug. 10, 11; U.S. citizen; m. 47; c. 1. UROLOGY, HISTOLOGY. Dr. Med. & Surg, Univ. Iasi, 36. Instr. histol, Univ. Iasi, 32-36; prof, Onesco Col, Bucharest, 41-44; sec. physician, Caritas Hosp, 44-48; primary physician, Oncol. Inst, 50-60; asst, Allgemeines Hosp, Hamburg, Ger, 60-61; instr. anat, hist. & path, Univ. South. Calif, 61-62; ASSOC. PROF. HISTOL, Calif. Col. Med, 62-68; SCH. MED, UNIV. SOUTH. CALIF, 69-, ADJ. PROF. UROL, 70- Asst. prof, sch. med, Univ. Bucharest, 49-54; consult, Los Angeles County Gen. Hosp, 63-; Ger. Govt. fel, 64; Nat. Insts. Health res. grant, 64-; Nat. Acad. Sci. travel awards, Europ, 68 & 70. Romanian Army, 36. Am. Asn. Anat; fel. Royal Soc. Health; N.Y. Acad. Sci. Microscopic three dimensional architecture of tissues and organs; regeneration mechanism of urinary bladder; changes in the urinary tract following extensive subtotal cystectomy; tumors of the urogenital systems; mechanism of regeneration of the urothelium; function of the straight segments of the nephron under normal and increased intratubular pressure. Address: Dept. of Urology, University of Southern California School of Medicine, 1200 N. State St, Los Angeles, CA 90033.

GOLDSTEIN, A(LAN) JAY, b. Phila, Pa, June 26, 27; m. 52; c. 3. MATHEMATICS. B.S, Pa. State, 48, M.A, 51; Ph.D.(math), Mass. Inst. Technol, 55. Asst. prof. math, Polytech. Inst. Brooklyn, 54-57; MEM. TECH. STAFF, BELL TEL. LABS, MURRAY HILL, 57- U.S.N, 45-46. Am. Math. Soc; Soc. Indust. & Appl. Math. Topology; communication theory; switching theory; computers. Address: Bell Telephone Labs, Room 2C 469, Murray Hill, NJ 07974.

GOLDSTEIN, ALBERT, b. Brooklyn, N.Y, Feb. 20, 28; m. 52; c. 4. ORGANIC CHEMISTRY. B.Sc, Rutgers, 51; Ph.D.(org. chem), Cornell, 54. Res. chemist, cent. res. labs, Gen. Foods Corp, 54-55; Catalin Corp. Am, 55-59; chief chemist, Chemirad Corp, 59-65; sr. scientist, Devro, Johnson & Johnson, 65-69; dir. res, Hydron Labs, Nat. Patent Develop. Corp, New Brunswick, 69-71; CHEM. CONSULT, GOLDSTEIN ASSOCS, 71- U.S.A, 46-48. Am. Chem. Soc; Inst. Food Technol; Am. Asn. Textile Chem. & Colorists. Process and product development, especially flame retardants, organic and inorganic coatings, ethylenimine chemistry, food packaging and acrylic resins. Address: 87 Glenwood Dr, New Shrewsbury, NJ 07724.

GOLDSTEIN, ALBERT, b. New York, N.Y, May 26, 38; m. 68. SOLID STATE PHYSICS. B.S, City Col. New York, 60; Ph.D.(physics), Mass. Inst. Tech, 65. Staff mem. physics, nat. magnet lab, Mass. Inst. Tech, 65; res. assoc, École Normale Supérieure, Paris, 65-67; STAFF MEM, T.J. WATSON RES. CTR, IBM CORP, 67- Am. Phys. Soc; Am. Inst. Physics. Resonant Raman effect; Fermi surface studies; transparent ferroelectronics. Address: 444 E. 84th St, New York, NY 10028.

GOLDSTEIN, ALLAN L, b. Bronx, N.Y, Nov. 8, 37; m. 61; c. 2. BIOCHEMISTRY. B.S, Wagner Col, 59; M.S, Rutgers, 61, Ph.D.(physiol, biochem), 64. Teaching asst. zool, Rutgers, 59-61, asst. instr. physiol, 61-63, instr, 63-64; U.S. Pub. Health Serv. res. fel. BIOCHEM, Albert Einstein Col. Med, 64-66, instr, 66-67, asst. prof, 67-71, assoc. prof, 71-72; PROF. & DIR. DIV, UNIV. TEX. MED. BR, GALVESTON, 72- Health Res. Coun. City New York career scientist award, 67- AAAS; Am. Asn. Immunol; Endocrine Soc; Am. Soc. Biol. Chem. Isolation, purification, mechanism of action and biological role of thymic humoral factors; lymphoid tissue biochemistry; hormonal control of metabolic processes. Address: Division of Biochemistry, University of Texas Medical Branch, Galveston, TX 77550.

GOLDSTEIN, ALLEN A, b. Baltimore, Md, Jan. 7, 25; m. 49; c. 4. APPLIED MATHEMATICS. B.A, St. John's Col.(Md), 47; M.A, Georgetown Univ, 52, Ph.D, 54. Engr. & physicist, Kellex Corp, 48-51; physicist, math. comput, appl. math. lab, Nat. Bur. Standards, 51-54; res. assoc. astron, observ, Georgetown Univ, 54-55; design specialist, Convair Div, Gen. Dynamics Corp, 55-60; res. assoc. elec. eng, Mass. Inst. Technol, 60-63; assoc. prof. MATH, Univ. Tex, 63-64; UNIV. WASH, 64-65, PROF, 65- Am. Math. Soc. Application of functional analysis to numerical analysis and applied mathematics. Address: Dept. of Mathematics, University of Washington, Seattle, WA 98105.

GOLDSTEIN, A(LLEN) M(ARK), b. Brooklyn, N.Y, Oct. 1, 19; m. 42; c. 2. INORGANIC CHEMISTRY. B.S, Mass. Inst. Tech, 47. Chemist gas kinetics,

Mass. Inst. Tech, 47-48; group leader radiochem, Tracerlab, Inc, 48-51; tech. dir. radiochem, Isotopes Specialties Co, 52-56, gen. mgr, 56-59; PRES, U.S. Nuclear Corp, 59-64; TECH. ASSOCS, 65- Chief radiol. servs, mutual aid region one, State of Calif, 54-; consult, Los Angeles Health Dept, 59- Sig.C, U.S.A, 42-46. AAAS; Am. Chem. Soc; Am. Nuclear Soc. Radiochemistry; radiation and photochemistry; radiological hazard evaluation and protection. Address: 12328 Magnolia Blvd, North Hollywood, CA 91607.

GOLDSTEIN, A(RTHUR) M(URRAY), b. N.Y.C, Mar. 13, 22; m. 50; c. 3. AGRICULTURAL CHEMISTRY. B.S, City Col. New York, 43; M.S, Ohio State, 47. Chemist, natural gums lab, STEIN HALL & CO, INC, 47-51, chief chemist, 51-56, paper lab, 56-58, dir. N.Y. LABS, 58-60, dir. res, 60-71; TECH. DIR, 71- Sig.C, U.S.A, 42-46. Am. Chem. Soc; Tech. Asn. Pulp & Paper Indust; Inst. Food Technol; Am. Asn. Textile Chem. & Colorists. Natural hydrocolloids, including guar gum; cellulose chemistry; pulp and paper technology; food technology; starch chemistry; adhesives; resins; synthetic water soluble polymers. Address: 3 Glenwood Rd, Plainview, NY 11803.

GOLDSTEIN, AUGUST, JR, b. Shreveport, La, Dec. 3, 20; m. 45; c. 3. GEOLOGY. B.S, La. State, 40, M.S, 42; Colo. Sch. Mines, 46; Ph.D.(geol), Colorado, 48. Geologist, Remvo Superior Vermiculite Co, Colo, 45-46; Winter-Weiss Co, 46-47; asst. geol, Colorado, 47-48; res. geologist, Stanolind Oil & Gas Co, 48-57; chief geologist, Bell Oil & Gas Co, 57-63, mgr. explor, 63-65; GEN. MGR, LUBELL OIL CO, 65- Instr, Denver exten, Univ. Colo, 48. U.S.A.A.F, 42-46, Res, 46-65, Lt. Col.(ret). Fel. Geol. Soc. Am; Soc. Econ. Paleont. & Mineral; Am. Asn. Petrol. Geol.(distinguished serv. award, 71). Sedimentary petrography; petroleum geology. Address: Lubell Oil Co, 1033 Mayo Bldg, Tulsa, OK 74103.

GOLDSTEIN, AVRAM, b. N.Y.C, July 3, 19; m. 47; c. 4. PHARMACOLOGY. A.B, Harvard, 40, M.D, 43. Intern, Mt. Sinai Hosp, N.Y, 44; instr. pharmacol, Harvard, 47-49, assoc, 49-51, asst. prof. pharmacol. & tutor biochem. sci, 52-55; PROF. PHARMACOL, STANFORD UNIV, 55-, chmn. dept, 55-70. Moseley traveling fel, Harvard, 49-50; asst. Bern, 51-52. Ed, Molecular Pharmacol, 65-68. Med.C, 44-46, Capt. Am. Soc. Pharmacol. & Exp. Therapeut; Am. Soc. Biol. Chem; Genetics Soc. Am. Mechanism of drug action; narcotics; narcotic addiction; methadone treatment. Address: Dept. of Pharmacology, Stanford Medical Center, Stanford University, Palo Alto, CA 94305.

GOLDSTEIN, B(ERNARD), b. New York, N.Y, Sept. 22, 27; m. 55; c. 2. PHYSICS. B.A, Brooklyn Col, 49; M.S, Polytech. Inst. Brooklyn, 51, Ph.D. (physics), 55. Asst. PHYSICS, Polytech. Inst. Brooklyn, 49-55; MEM. RES. STAFF, DAVID SARNOFF RES. CTR, RCA CORP, 55- Vis. scientist, Ecole Normale Supérieure, Univ. Paris, 68-69. U.S.N, 46-48, Am. Phys. Soc. Solid state physics; inorganic luminescent materials; phosphors; diffusion in solids; compound semiconductors; electron paramagnetic resonance. Address: David Sarnoff Research Center, RCA Corp, Princeton, NJ 08540.

GOLDSTEIN, BERNARD, b. San Francisco, Calif, Oct. 21, 35; m. 61; c. 1. PHYSIOLOGY, MORPHOLOGY. B.A, San Francisco State Col, 62, M.A, 64; Nat.Insts.Health fel, California, Davis, 67-68, Ph.D.(functional morphol), 68. Instr. zool, San Francisco State Col, summers, 64 & 65; lectr, California, Davis, spring 67; asst.prof. BIOL, SAN FRANCISCO STATE COL, 68-71, ASSOC. PROF, 71- Nat.Sci.Found. instnl.grant, 69. U.S.A, 57-59, Res, 59-62. AAAS; Am. Soc. Zool; Cooper Ornith. Soc. Burrowing mechanisms of fossorial mammals; population dynamics; biological properties of bone; ecological physiology of vertebrates; biology of man. Address: Dept. of Physiology & Behavioral Biology, San Francisco State College, 1600 Holloway, San Francisco, CA 94132.

GOLDSTEIN, BURTON J, Psychiat, see Suppl. I to 11th ed, Soc. & Behav. Vols.

GOLDSTEIN, BYRON (BERNARD), b. N.Y.C, Nov. 24, 39. BIOPHYSICS. B.S, City Col. New York, 61; Cornell Univ, 61-63, N.Y. State teaching fel, 61, Nat. Sci. Found. summer fels, 64 & 65; Ph.D.(plasma physics), N.Y. Univ, 67. Instr. PHYSICS, N.Y. Univ, 67-68; lectr, Queens Col.(N.Y), 68; ASSOC. PROF, FAIRLEIGH DICKINSON UNIV, 68- Nat. Insts. Health fel, chem, Univ. Calif, San Diego, 69-70. AAAS; Biophys. Soc; Am. Phys. Soc; Am. Asn. Physics Teachers. Physics and physical chemistry of biopolymers; theory of chain molecule entanglements; applications of statistical mechanics to macromolecules. Address: Dept. of Physics, Fairleigh Dickinson University, Teaneck, NJ 07666.

GOLDSTEIN, DAVID, b. New Orleans, La, Sept. 20, 08; m. 39; c. 2. ENVIRONMENTAL MEDICINE. B.A, Cornell, 28; M.D, N.Y. Univ, 33, fel, 37, Med.Sc.D, 40. Assoc. prof. ENVIRON. MED, MED. CTR, N.Y. UNIV, 51-55, PROF, 55-, ASSOC. DIR. INST. & DEPT, 70-, acting chmn. dept, 66-67. Med. dir, New York Times, 46- Dipl, Am. Bd. Internal Med, 43; Am. Bd. Prev. Med, 55. Med.C, 43-46, Maj. Am. Med. Asn; fel. Indust. Med. Asn; fel. Am. Col. Physicians; fel. N.Y. Acad. Med; fel. Am. Acad. Occup. Med. Occupational medicine. Address: Dept. of Environmental Medicine, New York University Medical Center, 550 First Ave, New York, NY 10016.

GOLDSTEIN, DORA B(ENEDICT), b. Milton, Mass, Apr. 25, 22; m. 47; c. 4. PHARMACOLOGY. M.D, Harvard Med. Sch, 49. Fel. bacter, Harvard Med. Sch, 53-55; res. assoc. PHARMACOL, SCH. MED, STANFORD UNIV, 55-70, SR. SCIENTIST, 70- Am. Soc. Biol. Chem; Am. Soc. Pharmacol. & Exp. Therapeut. Induction of cholinesterase synthesis in bacteria; effects of amino acid starvation in bacteria; biochemical effects of barbiturates; alcohol; drug dependence. Address: Dept. of Pharmacology, Stanford University School of Medicine, Stanford, CA 94305.

GOLDSTEIN, E. BRUCE, b. Washington, D.C, Mar. 31, 41; m. 66. PSYCHOLOGY, BIOPHYSICS. B.S, Tufts, 63; Sc.M, Brown, 65, U.S. Pub. Health Serv. fel, 65-67, Ph.D.(psychol), 68. Res. asst. psychol, Brown, 63-65; U.S. Pub. Health Serv. res. fel, Harvard, 67-69; ASST. PROF. PSYCHOL. & PHARMACOL, UNIV. PITTSBURGH, 69- Psychonomic Soc; Asn. Res. Vision & Ophthal. Visual physiology; photochemistry and electrophysiology of vision. Address: Dept. of Psychology, University of Pittsburgh, Pittsburgh, PA 15213.

GOLDSTEIN, EDWARD, b. Stanislawow, Poland, Jan. 28, 23; U.S. citizen; m. 59; c. 3. TELEPHONE ENGINEERING. B.E.E, Minnesota, 49; Stevens Inst. Tech, 54-58. Mem. staff, Bell Tel. Labs, Inc, 49-65; eng. dir. equip. & bldg, Am. Tel. & Tel. Co, 66-70; V.PRES, NEW YORK TEL. CO, 70- Mem, v.chmn. & now chmn, sci. adv. group to electronics command, U.S. Army, 64- Sig.C, U.S.A, 44-47, 50-52, Res, 48-69, Lt. Col. Inst. Elec. & Electronics Eng. Telephone communications, particularly switching. Address: Breezy Point, Little Silver, NJ 07739.

GOLDSTEIN, ELI, b. Russia, May 21, 97; nat; m. 24; c. 2. MEDICINE. M.D, L.I. Col. Med, 22; fel, City Hosp, N.Y, 24-25; B.S, Columbia, 26; Univ. Vienna, 26. Assoc. attend. physician, Fifth Ave. Hosp, 26-38; Sydenham Hosp, 39-40; assoc. prof. med, N.Y. MED. COL, 56-61, PROF. CLIN. MED, 61- Assoc. attend. physician, Flower-Fifth Ave. Hosp, 49-61, attending physician, 61-; dir. med, Hebrew Home for Aged, 50-; assoc. vis. physician, Metropolitan Hosp, 53-58, vis. physician, 58-; assoc. vis. physician, Bird S. Coler Mem. Hosp, 53-58, vis. physician, 58- Dipl, Am. Bd. Internal Med, 37. AAAS; Am. Geriatrics Soc; Am. Med. Asn; fel. Am. Col. Physicians; fel. N.Y. Acad. Med. Cardiology; hematology; geriatrics. Address: 150 E. 94th St, New York, NY 10028.

GOLDSTEIN, ERNST M(ORITZ), b. Berlin, Ger, Apr. 23, 07; nat; m. 34; c. 2. ORGANIC CHEMISTRY. Dipl. Ing, Tech. Univ, Ger, 28, Ph.D.(chem), 30. Chemist, Inst. Gas Anal, Ger, 28-36; res. chemist, Turkish Govt, 36-38; Showa Steel Works, China, 40-43; prof. inorg. chem, Mukden Med. Col, China, 46-47; res. chemist, Reduction & Ref. Co, N.J, 49-52; group leader, Nickel Processing Corp, U.S. Govt, 54-57; sr. res. chemist, Metal & Thermit Corp, 57-61; proj. metallurgist, Shieldalloy Corp, 61-62; sr. res. scientist, Martin-Marietta Corp, Colo, 62-69; ASSOC. PROF. ENG. MECH. & MAT. SCI, FLA. TECHNOL. UNIV, 69- Mem. faculty, Valencia Jr. Col, 68; McCoy Air Base, 68. Am. Chem. Soc; Am. Soc. Metals; N.Y. Acad. Sci; Am. Soc. Eng. Educ. Hypervelocity materials; refractory metals; graphites; ceramics; composites. Address: 3118 Dellwood Dr, Orlando, FL 32806.

GOLDSTEIN, FRED B(ERNARD), b. Phila, Pa, Dec. 11, 24; m. 45; c. 3. BIOCHEMISTRY. B.Sc, Phila. Col. Pharm, 51; Ph.D.(biochem), McGill, 55. ASSOC. RES. SCIENTIST, N.Y. STATE DEPT. MENT. HYG, 55- Lectr, Letchworth Village, 57- U.S.A, 43-45. AAAS; Am. Asn. Ment. Deficiency; Am. Acad. Ment. Retardation; Am. Chem. Soc; Brit. Biochem. Soc. Biochemical aspects of mental retardation with reference to intermediary metabolism and neurochemistry. Address: New York State Dept. of Mental Hygiene, Letchworth Village, Thiells, NY 10984.

GOLDSTEIN, FREDERICK J, b. Phila, Pa, Jan. 12, 42; m. 67; c. 1. NEUROPHARMACOLOGY. B.Sc, Phila. Col. Pharm, 63, M.Sc, 65, Nat. Sci. Found. trainee, summer 67, Ph.D.(pharmacol), 68. Asst. PHARMACOL, PHILA. COL. PHARM, 64-67, instr, 67-68, ASST. PROF, 68-, CHMN, CONTINUING EDUC. PROG. FOR PHARMACISTS, 69- Instr, sch. nursing, Misericordia Hosp, 65-67; lectr-consult, teacher workshops on drug abuse, Temple Univ, 70-; consult, Vick Chem. Co, 70-; del, Greater Phila. Coun. Narcotics & Dangerous Drug Abuse, Inc, 70- AAAS; Am. Pharmaceut. Asn; Acad. Pharmaceut. Sci; Am. Asn. Cols. Pharm. Effects of tricyclic antidepressants upon catecholamine-induced inhibibion of peripheral sympathetic ganglionic transmission; effects of phenobarbital-induced increases in catabolic enzyme activity upon action of antihypertensive drugs. Address: Dept. of Pharmacology, Philadelphia College of Pharmacy, 43rd St. & Kingsessing Ave, Philadelphia, PA 19104.

GOLDSTEIN, GERALD, b. New York, N.Y, Oct. 20, 22; m. 53; c. 3. MICROBIOLOGY, MEDICINE. B.S, Moravian Col, 48; M.D, Pennsylvania, 52. Intern, Univ. Va. Hosp, 52-53; res. internal med, Vet. Admin. Hosp, Dallas, Tex, 53-54, Martinsburg, W.Va, 54-56; instr. microbiol, SCH. MED, UNIV. VA, 57-59, asst. prof. microbiol. & instr. med, 59-63, ASSOC. PROF. MICROBIOL, 63-, INTERNAL MED, 69-, U.S. PUB. HEALTH SERV. SR. RES. FEL, 59-, Damon Runyon Cancer Res. fel, 56-58, asst. prof. med, 63-69. U.S.A, 42-45. Immunology with respect to infectious diseases and tumors. Address: Dept. of Microbiology, University of Virginia, Charlottesville, VA 22903.

GOLDSTEIN, GERALD, b. N.Y.C, Apr. 23, 30; m. 51; c. 4. ANALYTICAL CHEMISTRY. B.A, Brooklyn Col, 51; M.S, Tennessee, 59, Ph.D.(chem), 65. Anal. chemist, Ledoux & Co, 52-53; Lucius Pitkin, Inc, 53-56; chemist, OAK RIDGE NAT. LAB, 56-66, GROUP LEADER, ANAL. CHEM. DIV, 66- AAAS; Am. Chem. Soc; Sci. Res. Soc. Am; fel. Am. Inst. Chem; N.Y. Acad. Sci. Analytical biochemistry. Address: Analytical Division, Oak Ridge National Lab, Oak Ridge, TN 37830.

GOLDSTEIN, GIDEON, b. Kaunas, Lithuania, Jan. 21, 37; m. 65; c. 2. IMMUNOLOGY, INTERNAL MEDICINE. M.B, B.S, Univ. Melbourne, 59, M.D, 63, Ph.D.(immunopath), 67. Resident med. & path, Royal Melbourne Hosp, 61-64; pathologist, Walter & Eliza Hall Inst, 64-66; vis. scientist, lab. immunol, Nat. Inst. Allergy & Infectious Diseases, 67-68; RES. ASSOC. PROF. PATH, SCH. MED. & POST-GRAD. MED. SCH, N.Y. UNIV, 68- Mem. med. adv. bd, Myasthenia Gravis Found, 71. Am. Asn. Immunol; Am. Rheumatism Asn; Am. Soc. Exp. Path; Am. Asn. Path. & Bact. Immunopathology; experimental models of myasthenia gravis; isolation of thymic hormones; pathogenesis of rheumatic fever and rheumatoid arthritis. Address: Dept. of Pathology, New York University School of Medicine & Post-Graduate Medical School, 400 E. 34th St, New York, NY 10016.

GOLDSTEIN, GILBERT, b. Brooklyn, N.Y, Apr. 23, 14; m. 51; c. 1. BIOCHEMISTRY. B.S, Brooklyn Col, 34; M.S, Inst. Polytech. Brooklyn, 41, fel, 41-42, Ph.D.(chem), 51. Chemist, Dextran Corp, 50-52; asst. clin. biochemist, Mem. Hosp. & asst, Sloan Kettering Inst, 52-57; assoc. chemist, Mt. Sinai Hosp, 57-66, RES. BIOCHEMIST, BETH ISRAEL MED. CTR, 66- U.S.A, 42-46. AAAS; Am. Chem. Soc. Enzymes; proteins. Address: 1245 Park Ave, New York, NY 10028.

GOLDSTEIN, GORDON D(AVID), b. Rochester, N.Y, April 7, 17; m. 42; c. 2. ELECTRONIC ENGINEERING. B.E.E, Clarkson Tech, 40. Inspector equip, radio navig. systems, U.S. Sig. Corps, 41-44; develop. engr. instrumentation, Wash. Inst. Tech, Inc, 44-50; chief engr. computer, U.S. Bur. Census,

50-51; electronic scientist, U.S. Naval Ord. Lab, DEPT. NAVY, 51, head, res. & develop. br, applied math. lab, David Taylor Model Basin, 52-56, ELECTRONIC ENGR. & ED. DIGITAL COMPUT. NEWSLETTER, INFO. SYSTS, OFF. NAVAL RES, 56- Treas, spring joint comput. conf, Am. Fedn. Info. Processing Socs, 71; mem. subcomt. travel grants comput. sci, div. math. sci, Nat. Acad. Sci. AAAS; Asn. Comput. Mach; Inst. Elec. & Electronics Eng. Research administration information systems; computers and their applications. Address: 9520 Saybrook Ave, Silver Spring, MD 20901.

GOLDSTEIN, HANS L, b. Aachen, Ger, June 27, 15; m. 45; c. 2. PHYSICS, ELECTRICAL ENGINEERING. Ph.D.(physics), Frankfurt, 47. Engr. develop, Elektrotechnische Versuchwerkstaette, Ger, 41-46, 49-51; res. assoc, inst. appl. physics, Frankfurt, 46-47; res. asst, Max Planck Inst. Biophys, Frankfurt A.M, 47-49; Pennsylvania, 51-52; MEM. TECH. STAFF DEVELOP. RES, BELL TEL. LABS, 52- Vis. instr. physics, Drew, 64- Inst. Elec. & Electronics Eng; Am. Phys. Soc. Power supplies; magnetic amplifiers; microwave properties of organic materials; microwave ferrites. Address: Bell Telephone Labs, Radar Research Dept, Whippany, NJ 07981.

GOLDSTEIN, HAROLD WILLIAM, b. Jersey City, N.J, Aug. 23, 31; m. 59; c. 2. PHYSICAL CHEMISTRY. B.S, Univ. Ala, 53, M.S, 55; Monsanto Chem. Co. fel, Ohio State Univ, 59, Ph.D.(phys. chem), 60. Staff mem, res. inst, Union Carbide Corp, 60-63; sr. res. scientist, Martin Co, Martin-Marietta Corp, Fla, 63-65; MGR. SPACE EXP. & APPLN, SPACE SCI. LAB, GEN. ELEC. CO, 65- Am. Chem. Soc; Am. Inst. Aeronaut. & Astronaut. High temperature thermodynamics; mass spectrometry; ablation kinetics; material properties; space experiments; spacecraft contamination; air pollution. Address: Space Science Lab, General Electric Co, P.O. Box 8555, Philadelphia, PA 19101.

GOLDSTEIN, HERBERT, b. N.Y.C, June 26, 22. PHYSICS. B.S, City Col. New York, 40; Columbia, 40-41; fel, Mass. Inst. Technol, 41-43, Ph.D. (physics), 43. Tutor physics, City Col. New York, 40-41; mem. staff, radiation lab, Mass. Inst. Technol, 42-46, fel, Atomic Energy Comn, 49-50; instr. physics, Harvard, 46-49; sr. physicist, Nuclear Develop. Corp. Am, 50-61; PROF. NUCLEAR ENG. SCI, COLUMBIA UNIV, 61- Vis. assoc. prof, Brandeis, 52-53. With Off. Sci. Res. & Develop, 44. Am. Phys. Soc. Electromagnetic theory; radio wave propagation; theory of nuclear forces; neutron cross sections; radiation shielding; nuclear reactors. Address: Columbia University, 520 W. 120th St, New York, NY 10027.

GOLDSTEIN, HERBERT J, b. New York, N.Y, Sept. 20, 23; m. 47; c. 4. ORGANIC & POLYMER CHEMISTRY. A.B, N.Y. Univ, 46, Ph.D.(chem), 52. Res. chemist, Jackson Lab, E.I. du Pont de Nemours & Co, 52-56; sr. res. scientist, TEXUS RES. CTR, TEX-U.S. CHEM. CO, 56-64, mgr. org. res. sect, 64-69, MGR. POLYMERIZATION SECT, 69- U.S.A, 43-45. Am. Chem. Soc. Nitrogen heterocycles; urethane chemistry; dyes; polymerization; olefin chemistry; instrumental analysis. Address: Texus Research Center, P.O. Box 98, Parsippany, NJ 07054.

GOLDSTEIN, HERMAN B(ERNARD), b. Providence, R.I, June 19, 17; m. 42; c. 2. TEXTILE & PAPER CHEMISTRY. A.B, Brown Univ, 40. Dir. res, Providence Textile Chem. Co, 40-44; tech. mgr, Warwick Chem. Div, SUN CHEM. CORP, 45-52, mgr. prod. & res, textile chem. dept, 53-63, res. mgr, Chem. Prod. Div, 63-67; GEN. MGR, CHEM. DIV, 68- Adv, U.S. Dept. Agr, 65-68. Am. Asn. Textile Chem. & Colorists; Tech. Asn. Pulp & Paper Industs; Am. Chem. Soc; Am. Soc. Test. & Mat; Am. Inst. Chem. Chemical specialties, auxiliaries, and processing aids for textile, paper, and related industries including water and oil repellents, soil release agents, permanent press resins, softeners, dyehouse chemicals, paper sizes and coating insolubilizers as applicable in United States, Europe and Far East. Address: Chemicals Division, Sun Chemical Corp, P.O. Box 70, Chester, SC 29706.

GOLDSTEIN, HYMAN, b. N.Y.C, Jan. 14, 09; m. 39; c. 3. BIOSTATISTICS. A.B, Columbia, 30, A.M, 31, Ph.D.(psychol), 34. Psychologist, State Correction Dept, N.Y, 36-39, statistician, bur. cancer control, State Health Dept, 39-43, sr. statistician, 44-50; chief hosp. reports & records unit, current reports sect, biomet. br, Nat. Inst. Ment. Health, 50-52, sect, 52-57, chief biomet. br, Nat. Inst. Neurol. Diseases & Blindness, 57-67, assoc. dir. div. res, children's bur, U.S. Dept. Health, Educ. & Welfare, 67-69, acting assoc. dir. div. res, maternal & child health serv, Health Serv. & Ment. Health Admin, 69-70; RES. BIOSTATISTICIAN, DIV. MATERNAL & CHILD HEALTH, SCH. PUB. HEALTH, UNIV. CALIF, BERKELEY, 70- Adj. prof, dept. obstet. & gynec, sch. med, Univ. Calif, San Francisco, 70- Consult, Am. Found. for Blind, N.Y, 67-; United Cerebral Palsy, 70-; Ford Found, 71- Am. Statist. Asn; Am. Pub. Health Asn. Etiological studies of neurological and sensory organ diseases; blindness statistics; maternal and child health research. Address: 1930 Vine St, Berkeley, CA 94709.

GOLDSTEIN, IRVING, b. Worcester, Mass, Dec. 19, 20; m. 55; c. 2. ELECTRICAL ENGINEERING. B.S.E.E, Worcester Polytech, 47; Mass. Inst. Tech, 47-48. Engr, equip. div, RAYTHEON CO, 47-54; sr. engr, missile systs. div, 54-55, sect. head microwave systs, 55-56, br. mgr, 56-58, dept. mgr. solid state physics, missile & space div, 58-64, lab. mgr. electro-optics, space & info. systs. div, 64-69, MGR. OPTICAL SYSTS. DEPT, MISSILE SYSTS. DIV, 69- Inst. Elec. & Electronics Eng. Optical maser systems; microwave solid state field; infrared and laser missile guidance systems; electro optics fusing; laser Doppler radar systems for the remote sensing of clear air turbulence, trailing vortices and winds. Address: Optical Systems Dept, Missile Systems Division, Raytheon Co, Box 918, Bedford, MA 01730.

GOLDSTEIN, IRVING S(OLOMON), b. Bronx, N.Y, Aug. 20, 21; m. 45; c. 3. WOOD & PAPER CHEMISTRY. B.S, Rensselaer Polytech, 41; M.S, Ill. Inst. Tech, 44; fel, Harvard, 46-48, Ph.D.(org. chem), 48. Asst. chem, Ill. Inst. Tech, 41-42; res. chemist, N.Am. Rayon Corp, 48-51; sr. chemist, res. dept. Koppers Co, Inc, 51-53, leader, wood preserving group, 53-55, mgr. wood chem, 55-63; sr. res. chemist, Nalco Chem. Co, 63-66; mgr. paper res, corp. res. & develop. dept, Continental Can Co, 66-68; PROF. forest sci, Tex. A&M Univ, 68-71; WOOD & PAPER SCI. & HEAD DEPT, N.C. STATE UNIV, 71- U.S.N.R, 42-46, Lt. AAAS; Am. Chem. Soc; Forest Prod. Res. Soc; Soc. Wood Sci. & Technol; Tech. Asn. Pulp & Paper Indust. Wood, cellulose and lignin chemistry; pulp chemistry; chemical utilization of wood. Address: Dept. of Wood & Paper Science, School of Forest Resources, North Carolina State University, Raleigh, NC 27607.

GOLDSTEIN, IRWIN JOSEPH, b. Newark, N.J, Sept. 8, 29; m. 59; c. 1. BIOCHEMISTRY. B.A, Syracuse, 51; Ph.D.(biochem), Minnesota, 56. Fel, Minnesota, 56-59; Guggenheim fel, Lister Inst. Prev. Med, London, Eng, 59-60; Nat. Insts. Health gen. med. sci. fel, Swedish Forest Prod. Res. Lab, 60-61; asst. prof. BIOCHEM, State Univ. N.Y. Buffalo, 61-65; ASSOC. PROF, UNIV. MICH, 65- Am. Heart Asn. estab. investr, 63-68. AAAS; Am. Chem. Soc; Am. Soc. Biol. Chem; Brit. Biochem. Soc; Brit. Chem. Soc. Chemical synthesis, modification and structure of carbohydrates; immunochemistry; chemical studies on the nature and mechanism of action of phytohemagglutinins. Address: Dept. of Biological Chemistry, University of Michigan, Ann Arbor, MI 48104.

GOLDSTEIN, JACK, b. Phila, Pa, June 24, 30. BIOCHEMISTRY. B.S, Brooklyn Col. Pharm, 52; M.N.S, Cornell, 57, Ph.D.(biochem), 59. Asst. biochem, Cornell, 55-57; res. chemist, U.S. Plant, Soil & Nutrit. Lab, 57-59; vis. investr, biochem, Rockefeller Inst, 59-61, res. assoc, 61-64, asst. prof, 64-65; ASSOC. PROF. BIOCHEM, MED. COL, CORNELL UNIV, 65-; INVESTR, NEW YORK BLOOD CTR, 65- Med.C, 53-54, Res, 54- Am. Soc. Biol. Chem; Am. Chem. Soc. Ribonucleic acids; protein structure and biosynthesis. Address: New York Blood Center, 310 E. 67th St, New York, NY 10021.

GOLDSTEIN, JACK S(TANLEY), b. N.Y.C, May 10, 25; m. 48; c. 3. PHYSICS. B.S, City Col, 47; M.S, Oklahoma, 48; Ph.D.(physics), Cornell, 53. Res. physicist, Cornell Aeronaut. Lab, 48-50; asst, Cornell, 50-52; mem, Inst. Adv. Study, 52-53; res. assoc, Mass. Inst. Technol, 53-54; sr. physicist, Baird-Atomic, Inc, Mass, 54-57; asst. prof. physics, BRANDEIS UNIV, 57-60, assoc. prof, 60-66, PROF. ASTROPHYS, 66-, DIR. ASTROPHYS. INST, 64-, vis. asst. prof, 56-57; chmn. dept. physics, 67-69. Fulbright scholar, Israel, 60-61, Fulbright scholar & Guggenheim fel, Univ. Rome, 66-67. U.S.N.R, 43-45, Lt.(jg). Am. Phys. Soc; Am. Astron. Soc. Quantum mechanics; field theory; nuclear physics; astrophysics. Address: Dept. of Physics, Brandeis University, Waltham, MA 02154.

GOLDSTEIN, J(ACOB) H(ERMAN), b. Atlanta, Ga, Dec. 18, 15; m. 53. PHYSICAL CHEMISTRY. A.B, Emory, 43, M.S, 45; Nat. Res. Council fel, Harvard, 46-49, M.S, 47, Ph.D.(chem), 49. Asst. prof. CHEM, EMORY UNIV, 49-51, assoc. prof, 51-57, prof, 57-60, CANDLER PROF, 60- Am. Chem. Soc; Am. Phys. Soc. Nuclear magnetic resonance spectroscopy, including biological applications; computer applications in chemistry; quantum theory. Address: Dept. of Chemistry, Emory University, Atlanta, GA 30322.

GOLDSTEIN, JEROME A, b. Pittsburgh, Pa, Aug. 5, 41; m. 64; c. 2. MATHEMATICAL ANALYSIS. B.S, Carnegie Inst. Tech, 63, M.S, 64, Ph.D.(math), 67. NASA trainee MATH, Carnegie Inst. Tech, 63-66, lectr, 66-67; mem, Inst. Adv. Study, 67-68; asst. prof, TULANE UNIV, LA, 68-71, ASSOC. PROF, 71- Sigma Xi faculty res. award, Tulane Univ, 70-71. Am. Math. Soc; Math. Asn. Am; Inst. Math. Statist; Soc. Indust. & Appl. Math. Mathematical analysis; probability; functional analysis; partial differential equations; stochastic equations. Address: Dept. of Mathematics, Tulane University, New Orleans, LA 70118.

GOLDSTEIN, JOSEPH I, b. Syracuse, N.Y, Jan. 6, 39; m. 63; c. 2. METALLURGY, MATERIALS SCIENCE. B.S, Mass. Inst. Technol, 60, M.S. & Sc.D. (metall), 62. Metallurgist, Smithsonian Astrophys. Observ, 63-64; aerospace technologist, Goddard Space Flight Ctr, NASA, 64-68; ASSOC. PROF. METALL. & MAT. SCI, LEHIGH UNIV, 68- Lectr, Univ. Md, 66-67. Electron Probe Anal. Soc. Am; Am. Inst. Min, Metall. & Petrol. Eng; Am. Soc. Metals; Am. Geophys. Union; Meteoritical Soc; Int. Metallog. Soc. Solid state kinetics; meteorites; lunar samples; phase equilibria. Address: Dept. of Metallurgy & Materials Science, Lehigh University, Bethlehem, PA 18015.

GOLDSTEIN, J(ULIAN) RICHARD, b. Rochester, N.Y, July 25, 11; m. 65; c. 3. MECHANICAL & AERONAUTICAL ENGINEERING. B.S, Rochester, 32; fel, Calif. Inst. Tech, 33-34, M.S, 34. Res. engr, Douglas Aircraft Co, Inc, 34-43, chief, Douglas Res. Labs, 43-46; assoc. dir, project Rand, 46-48; V.PRES, RAND CORP, 48-, MEM-TRUSTEE & MEM. EXEC. COMT. & FINANCE COMT, 51- Mem-trustee, Syst. Develop. Corp, 57-62; chmn. exec. comt, 57-61. Administration of research in all fields of the physical and social sciences. Address: The Rand Corp, 1700 Main St, Santa Monica, CA 90406.

GOLDSTEIN, JULIUS L, b. Brooklyn, N.Y, July 9, 35; m. 62; c. 3. ELECTRICAL ENGINEERING. B.E.E, Cooper Union, 57; M.E.E, Polytech. Inst. Brooklyn, 60; Nat. Insts. Health fel, Rochester, 61-65, Ph.D.(elec. eng), 66. Staff engr, Polytech. Res. & Develop, N.Y, 57-60; lectr, Rochester, 60-61; fel, hearing res, lab. psychophys, Harvard, 66-68; asst. prof. ELEC. ENG, MASS. INST. TECHNOL, 68-71, ASSOC. PROF, 71- Lectr, Polytech. Inst. Brooklyn, 59-60; summers, Nat. Sci. Found. fel, 61 & 63; Nat. Sci. Found. fel, Inst. Perception Res, Eindhoven, Netherlands, 65-66. AAAS; Inst. Elec. & Electronics Eng; Acoustical Soc. Am. Electronics circuits; systems analysis; auditory psychology and physiology. Address: Dept. of Electrical Engineering, 20 B-221, Massachusetts Institute of Technology, 77 Massachusetts Ave, Cambridge, MA 02139.

GOLDSTEIN, LADISLAS, b. Dombrad, Hungary, Feb. 6, 06; nat; m. 33. PHYSICS. B.S, Col. City Nagyvarad, 24; M.S, Paris, 28, fel, 29-34, D.Sc. (nuclear physics), 37. Asst, inst. radium, Paris, 34-37, res. assoc. & Nat. Ctr. Res. France fel, 37-40; res. assoc, Inst. Atomic Physics, Lyon, 40-41; dir. labs, Can. Radium & Uranium Corp, N.Y, 42-44; researcher, Admiralty Res. Labs, Eng, 44-45; res. physicist, Fed. Telecommun. Labs, 45-51; PROF. ELEC. ENG, UNIV. ILL, URBANA-CHAMPAIGN, 51- With U.S.A.F, 44. AAAS; Am. Phys. Soc. Nuclear physics; use of gas discharge phenomena in microwave physics; microwave propagation through media containing free electrons; infrared radiation detection; application of ionizing radiations of radioactive substances. Address: Dept. of Electrical Engineering, Bldg. 607-E. Healy, University of Illinois, Urbana-Champaign, Urbana, IL 61820.

GOLDSTEIN, LARRY JOEL, b. Phila, Pa, Dec. 4, 44; m. 67; c. 2. MATHEMATICS. B.A. & M.A, Univ. Pa, 65; Woodrow Wilson fel, Princeton, 65, Nat. Sci. Found. fel, 65-67, M.A. & Ph.D.(math), 67. Josiah Willard Gibbs instr. MATH, Yale, 67-69; ASSOC. PROF, UNIV. MD, COLLEGE PARK, 69- Summer res. partic, conf. on algebraic groups, Bowdoin Col, 68 & Am. Math. Soc. Conf. on Number Theory, State Univ. N.Y. Stony Brook, 69; Nat. Sci. Found. res. grants, 69-72. Am. Math. Soc; Math. Asn. Am. Effective techniques for computation of class numbers of algebraic number fields. Address: Dept. of Mathematics, University of Maryland, College Park, MD 20742.

GOLDSTEIN, LEON, b. Malden, Mass, Feb. 6, 33; m. 58; c. 3. PHYSIOLOGY. B.S, Northeast. Univ, 54; Gillette fel, Boston, 55-57, Ciba fel, 57-58, Ph.D. (pharmacol), 58. Res. fel. zool, Dartmouth Col, 58-59, instr, 59-60; res. assoc, Cancer Res. Inst, New England Deaconess Hosp, 60-62; assoc. PHYSIOL, Harvard Med. Sch, 62-64, asst. prof, 64-68; ASSOC. PROF. MED. SCI, BROWN UNIV, 68- Nat. Insts. Health res. career develop. award, 63; lectr, Harvard Med. Sch, 68-69. Am. Chem. Soc; Am. Soc. Zool; Soc. Gen. Physiol; Am. Physiol. Soc. Kidney; comparative physiology; marine biology. Address: Division of Biological & Medical Sciences, Brown University, Providence, RI 02912.

GOLDSTEIN, LEONIDE, b. Paris, France, Apr. 2, 14; m. 48; c. 3. NEUROPHARMACOLOGY. Lic. es Sci, Paris, 41, D.Sc, 51; B.A, Amherst Col, 45. Asst, Inst. Biol, France, 39-40; biol, Amherst Col, 42-45; instr. genetics, Paris, 45-50, asst. prof, Sorbonne, 50-58; vis. assoc. prof. pharmacol, Emory, 58-61; RES. SCIENTIST, BUR. RES. NEUROL. & PSYCHIAT, N.J. NEUROPSYCHIAT. INST, 61- Vis. sr. fel, Princeton. French Army, 39-40; Free French Forces, 42-45. Am. Soc. Pharmacol. & Exp. Therapeut; Am. Col. Neuropsychopharmacol; Am. Statist. Asn; Am. Electroencephalog. Soc; Biomet. Soc; Soc. Biol. Psychiat; Asn. Psychophysiol. Study Sleep; French Genetic Soc; French Physiol. Asn. Statistical studies on living systems; effects of drugs on central nervous systems; electrophysiological studies on the action of drugs on the brain. Address: Section of Neuropharmacology, Bureau of Research Neurology & Psychiatry, New Jersey Neuro-Psychiatric Institute, Box 1000, Princeton, NJ 08540.

GOLDSTEIN, LESTER, b. Brooklyn, N.Y, June 28, 24; m. 64; c. 1. BIOLOGY. B.A, Brooklyn Col, 48; Harrison fel, Pennsylvania, 51, U.S. Pub. Health Serv. fel, 52, Ph.D, 53. Lectr. biol, Queens Col.(N.Y), 50; asst. instr. zool, Pennsylvania, 50-51; U.S. Pub. Health Serv. fel, California, Berkeley, 53-55, asst. res. physiologist, med. ctr, California, San Francisco, 55-59; assoc. prof. zool, Univ. Pa, 59-64, PROF. BIOL, 64-67; inst. develop. biol, UNIV. COLO, BOULDER, 67-68, DEPT. MOLECULAR, CELLULAR & DEVELOP. BIOL, 68- Damon Runyon Mem. Fund fel, 55-56; summer, Lalor Found. fel, Haverford Col, 59. U.S.A, 43-46. Am. Soc. Cell Biol; Int. Soc. Cell Biol. Cell biology; interrelationships of nucleus and cytoplasm. Address: Dept. of Molecular, Cellular & Developmental Biology, University of Colorado, Boulder, CO 80302.

GOLDSTEIN, LEWIS C(HARLES), b. Paterson, N.J, Dec. 31, 17. CYTOLOGY. B.S, Richmond, 38, M.S, 40; Ph.D.(biol), Virginia, 47. Instr. zool, Virginia, 46-47; asst. prof. biol, Sampson Col, 47-49; Champlain Col, 49-53; Massachusetts, 53-54; Smith Col, 54-55; prof. & head dept, VA. COMMONWEALTH UNIV, 55-71, ASST. DEAN ARTS & SCI, 69- U.S.N, 42-46. AAAS; Am. Soc. Zool; Am. Inst. Biol. Sci; N.Y. Acad. Sci. Histology of the oyster; nematocysts of hydra; oogenesis of hamster. Address: Virginia Commonwealth University, 901 W. Franklin St, Richmond, VA 23220.

GOLDSTEIN, LOUIS, b. Dombrad, Hungary, Mar. 25, 04; nat; m. 33; c. 1. PHYSICS. Testimonium Maturitatis, Col. City Nagyvarad, 22; lic. es S, Paris, 26, D.Sc.(theoret. physics), 32. Researcher, Inst. Henry Poincare, Paris, 28-32, res. assoc, 32-39; independent researcher, N.Y. Univ, 39-41; instr. physics, City Col, 41-44; mem. staff, wave propagation group, Office Sci. Res. & Develop. contract, Columbia, 44-46; physicist, Fed. Telecommunications Lab, Int. Tel. & Tel, N.Y, 46; MEM. STAFF, LOS ALAMOS SCI. LAB, 46- Fel. Am. Phys. Soc. Theory of atoms; atomic nuclei, statistical mechanics; low temperature physics. Address: Los Alamos Scientific Lab, P.O. Box 1663, Los Alamos, NM 87544.

GOLDSTEIN, LOUIS A(RNOLD), b. Spring Valley, N.Y, Apr. 15, 07; m. 35; c. 2. SURGERY. B.S, Alfred, 28; M.D, Rochester, 32. Instr. ORTHOP. SURG, SCH. MED. & DENT, UNIV. ROCHESTER, 37-41, asst. prof, 51-54, assoc. prof, 54-67, clin. prof, MED. CTR, 67-69, PROF. & CHMN. DIV, 69- Private practice. Consult, Batavia Veterans Admin. Hosp, N.Y; Genesee Hosp, N.Y; Monroe County Tuberc. Sanitorium, N.Y. Med.C, 42-46, Lt. Col. Am. Med. Asn; Am. Orthop. Asn; Am. Acad. Orthop. Surg; Am. Col. Surg. Scoliosis. Address: Division of Orthopaedic Surgery, Medical Center, University of Rochester, 260 Crittenden Blvd, Rochester, NY 14620.

GOLDSTEIN, MARTIN, b. N.Y.C, Nov. 18, 19; m. 54; c. 3. PHYSICAL CHEMISTRY. B.S, City Col. New York, 40; Ph.D.(chem), Columbia, 50. U.S. Pub. Health Serv. fel, Brooklyn Polytech. Inst, 50-51; fel, Harvard, 51-53; fel, Mellon Inst, 53-58; vis. scientist, Nat. Phys. Lab. Israel, 58-60; staff scientist, chem. dept, sci. lab, Ford Motor Co, 60-65; vis. assoc. prof. ceramics, Mass. Inst. Tech, 64-65; PROF. CHEM, BELFER GRAD. SCH. SCI, YESHIVA UNIV, 65- Chmn, Gordon Res. Conf. on Glass, 65; vis. prof, Univ. Ill, 67-68. Am. Ceramic Soc.(Forrest & Meyer Awards, 65); fel. Am. Phys. Soc. Glass state; glass transition; kinetics of phase transitions, light scattering. Address: Dept. of Chemistry, Belfer Graduate School of Science, Yeshiva University, New York, NY 10033.

GOLDSTEIN, MARVIN E, b. Cambridge, Mass, Oct. 11, 38; m. 65; c. 1. FLUID MECHANICS, APPLIED MATHEMATICS. M.S, Northeastern, 61; B.S, Mass. Inst. Tech, 62; Ph.D.(mech. eng), Michigan, 65. Res. assoc. FLUID MECH, Mass. Inst. Tech, 65-67; AEROSPACE ENGR, ADV. RES. INST, NASA-LEWIS RES. CTR, 67- Am. Phys. Soc. Fluid mechanics; heat transfer; mathematics; geophysics. Address: Advanced Research Institute, NASA-Lewis Research Center, Cleveland, OH 44135.

GOLDSTEIN, MARVIN S(HERWOOD), b. Newark, N.J, Feb. 13, 34; m. 66; c. 3. PHYSICAL CHEMISTRY. B.S, N.Y. State Col. Teachers, Albany, 56; Columbia, 56-57; Nat. Sci. Found. fel, Rensselaer Polytech, 59, Ph.D.(phys. chem), 60. Res. engr, Allison Div, Gen. Motors Corp, 59-60; res. chemist, org. chem. div, AM. CYANAMID CO, 60-69, GROUP LEADER, REF. CATALYST RES, STAMFORD RES. LABS, 69- Lectr, Univ. Conn, 62-63. Am. Chem. Soc; Catalysis Soc. Catalysis; surface chemistry; kinetics and thermodynamics of oxidation and combustion; high energy fuels; boron hydrides. Address: Stamford Research Labs, American Cyanamid Co, 1937 W. Main St, Stamford, CT 06904.

GOLDSTEIN, M(AURICE) S(ABIN), b. Montreal, Que, Can, Jan. 10, 24; nat; m. 57; c. 3. ENDOCRINOLOGY. B.Sc, McGill, 43, M.D, 47. U.S. Pub. Health Serv. fel, 49-51; asst. dir. DEPT. METAB. & ENDOCRINE RES, MED. RES. INST, MICHAEL REESE HOSP, 51-57, DIR, 57- Asst, med. sch, Tufts, 50-51; prof. lectr, Chicago, 52- AAAS; Am. Physiol. Soc; Endocrine Soc; Am. Diabetes Asn; N.Y. Acad. Sci; Soc. Exp. Biol. & Med. Mechanism of action of hormones, insulin, adrenal cortex and adrenalins, thyroxine. Address: Dept. of Metabolic & Endocrine Research, Michael Reese Hospital, 29th & Ellis Ave, Chicago, IL 60616.

GOLDSTEIN, MAX, b. N.Y.C, Jan. 4, 20; m. 46. MATHEMATICS. B.A, Brooklyn Col, 40; M.S, N.Y. Univ, 62. Asst. head. numerical anal. group, theoret. physics div, Nat. Res. Coun. Can, 43-46; alternate group leader, Los Alamos Sci. Lab, 46-57; sr. res. scientist, ATOMIC ENERGY COMN. COMPUT. & APPL. MATH. CTR, N.Y. UNIV, 57-66, ASSOC. DIR, 66-, PROF. COMPUT. SCI, COURANT INST. MATH. SCI, 67-, ASSOC. CHMN. DEPT, 70-, adj. assoc. prof. math, 63-66, adj. prof, 66-67. Am. Math. Soc; Asn. Comput. Mach. Numerical mathematical analysis; general purpose automatic digital calculating machines. Address: Courant Institute, New York University, 251 Mercer St, New York, NY 10012.

GOLDSTEIN, MAXWELL K(ARL), b. Baltimore, Md, Jan. 15, 09; m. 39; c. 2. ELECTRONICS. B.E, Hopkins, 30, Dr.Eng, 33. Head dept. electronics, Molded Insulation Co, Pa, 34-35; radio proj. engr, U.S. Sig. Corps-Aircraft Radio Lab, Wright Field, 35-37; radio design airway engr, Civil Aeronaut. Authority, D.C, 37-39; head, direction finder sect, Naval Res. Lab, 39-43, systs. eng. sect, 43-46, electronics air navig. sect, 46-48; electronics res. scientist, Air Navig. Develop. Bd, 49-51; v.pres, BALCO RES. LAB, 51-54, PRES, 54-, PRES, BALCO ELECTRONICS, 65- Naval rep, Nat. Defense Res. Cmt; Res. & Develop. Bd, 44-46; electronics consult. & head progs. res. div, Off. Naval Res, 48-49. Award, Wash. Acad. Sci, 48; distinguished civilian serv. award, U.S. Dept. Navy. Inst. Elec. & Electronics Eng. Electronic air navigation systems; precision and ultra stable capacitors; linear and controlled temperature coefficient capacitors; temperature immune high stability capacitors and resistor capacitor networks; time delay and programming mechanisms; automation systems for product performance evaluation and control. Address: 32 Rosemont Terr, West Orange, NJ 07052.

GOLDSTEIN, MELVIN E, b. Glen Ridge, N.J, July 27, 36. BOTANY, PHYCOLOGY. B.A, Indiana, 58; Nat. Insts. Health fel. & Ph.D.(bot), 63. ASST. PROF. BOT, McGILL UNIV, 63- Bot. Soc. Am; Am. Phycol. Soc; Am. Soc. Protozool; Int. Phycol. Soc. Speciation, sexuality, cytology and genetics of the colonial green flagellate Eudorina; taxonomy, morphology and ecology of the marine algae of Barbados. Address: Dept. of Botany, Stewart Biology Bldg, McGill University, Montreal 2, Que, Can.

GOLDSTEIN, MELVIN J(OSEPH), b. N.Y.C, Dec. 28, 33; m. 55; c. 3. ORGANIC CHEMISTRY. B.A, Columbia, 54; Nat. Sci. Found. fel, Yale, 54-58, Ph.D.(chem), 58. Fel, Nat. Sci. Found, Harvard, 58-59; instr. CHEM, CORNELL UNIV, 59-61, asst. prof, 61-66, ASSOC. PROF, 66- NATO sr. sci. fel, 68. Am. Chem. Soc; Brit. Chem. Soc; fel. N.Y. Acad. Sci; Swiss Chem. Soc. Organic reaction mechanisms; applications of kinetic isotope effects. Address: Dept. of Chemistry, Cornell University, Ithaca, NY 14850.

GOLDSTEIN, MELVIN MYRON, b. Chicago, Ill, Apr. 9, 35; m. 65; c. 2. ANALYTICAL CHEMISTRY. B.A, Northwestern, 56; Ethyl Corp. fel, Illinois, 56-60, M.S, 59, Ph.D.(anal. chem), 60. Res. chemist, Visking Co, Union Carbide Corp, 60-61; Toni Co. Div, Gillette Co, 61-69; SR. RES. CHEMIST, ARMOUR-DIAL INC. DIV, GREYHOUND CORP, 69- Am. Chem. Soc. X-ray diffraction; gas, liquid, ion-exchange and thin-layer chromatography; visible, ultraviolet and infrared absorption spectroscopy; trace analysis in body fluids; methods development, especially for the analysis of cosmetics, surfactants and germicides. Address: 1512 W. Touhy Ave, Chicago, IL 60626.

GOLDSTEIN, MENEK, b. Kolmya, Poland, Apr. 8, 24. BIOCHEMISTRY. Ph.D, Berne, 55. Res. instr. biochem, Berne, 54-56; mem. res. staff, Worcester Found. Exp. Biol, 56-57; instr. neurochem, MED. CTR, N.Y. UNIV, 58-59, asst. prof. biochem, 60-63, assoc. prof, 63-69, PROF. NEUROCHEM, 69- Am. Chem. Soc; Am. Soc. Biol. Chem. Neurochemistry; metabolism and biosynthesis of biogenic amines; role of hormones in the central nervous system; mode of action of hormones and enzymes in vivo; steroid hormones. Address: Dept. of Psychiatry, New York University Medical Center, 550 First Ave, New York, NY 10016.

GOLDSTEIN, MILTON NORMAN, b. Cleveland, Ohio, Jan. 15, 25; m. 52; c. 2. ZOOLOGY. B.S, Western Reserve, 46, M.S, 47, Ph.D.(zool), 52. U.S. Pub. Health Serv. fel. path, Western Reserve, 52-54; investr. cancer res, Roswell Park Mem. Inst, 54-55, sr. cancer res. scientist, 55-62; cell biol labs, St. Jude Children's Res. Hosp, Memphis, Tenn, 62-66; ASSOC. PROF. ANAT, SCH. MED, WASH. UNIV, 66- Tissue Cult. Asn; Am. Asn. Anat; Am. Asn. Cancer Res; Am. Soc. Cell Biol. Cytology; differentiation of cells in vitro; histochemistry; electron microscopy applied to cells growing in tissue culture. Address: Dept. of Anatomy, Washington University School of Medicine, St. Louis, MO 63130.

GOLDSTEIN, MOISE H(ERBERT), JR, b. New Orleans, La, Dec. 26, 26; m. 70; c. 4. BIOPHYSICS, ELECTRICAL ENGINEERING. B.S, Tulane, 49; S.M, Mass. Inst. Tech, 51, Sc.D, 57. Asst. elec. eng, Mass. Inst. Tech, 49-51, defense staff, 52-55; mem. staff, Texas Co, 51-52; instr. elec. eng, Mass Inst. Tech, 55-56, asst. prof, 56-61, assoc. prof, 61-63; BIOMED. ENG, JOHNS HOPKINS UNIV, 63-67, PROF, 67- Nat. Sci. Found. fel, Pisa, 59-60; vis. lectr, Mass. Inst. Technol, 63-64; Guggenheim Found. fel, 70-71; consult, Bell Tel. Labs. Fel. Acoustical Soc. Am; Inst. Elec. & Electronics Eng; Soc. Neurosci; Biomed. Eng. Soc; Soc. Gen. Physiol. Sensory neurophysiology; neural coding of acoustic signals and its role in animal communication. Address: Johns Hopkins University Medical School, 503 Taylor Research Bldg, 720 Rutland Ave, Baltimore, MD 21205.

GOLDSTEIN, MURRAY, b. N.Y.C, Oct. 13, 25; m. 57; c. 2. MEDICAL ADMINISTRATION. B.A, N.Y. Univ, 47; D.O, Still Col. Osteop. & Surg, 50; M.P.H, California, 59; hon. D.Sc, Kirksville Col. Osteop. & Surg, 67. Intern, Still Osteop. Hosp, Des Moines, Iowa, 50-51, res, 51-53; asst. chief, grants & training br, Nat. Heart Inst, NAT. INSTS. HEALTH, 53-59, res. grants rev. br, 59-60, assoc. dir. extramural prog, NAT. INST. NEUROL. DISEASES & STROKE, 60-70, DIR. EXTRAMURAL PROG, 70- Vis. scientist, Mayo Grad. Sch. Med, Univ. Minn, 67-68. U.S.A, 43-45, U.S.P.H.S, 53. AAAS; Am. Osteop. Asn; Am. Pub. Health Asn; Am. Heart Asn. Cardiovascular diseases; cerebrovascular diseases; public health; epidemiology. Address: National Institute of Neurological Diseases & Stroke, Bethesda, MD 20014.

GOLDSTEIN, MYRON, b. Los Angeles, Calif, July 5, 35. MATHEMATICS. B.S, California, Los Angeles, 57, M.A, 60, Ph.D.(math), 63. Instr. MATH, California, Los Angeles, 63; prof, Ariz. State Univ, 63-68; ASSOC. PROF, ORE. STATE UNIV, 68- Math. Asn. Am; Am. Math. Soc. Riemann surfaces. Address: Dept. of Mathematics, Oregon State University, Corvallis, OR 97331.

GOLDSTEIN, NORMAN P(HILIP), b. Brooklyn, N.Y, Mar. 31, 21; m. 43; c. 3. BIOCHEMISTRY, NEUROLOGY. B.S, N.Y. Univ, 41; M.A, George Washington, 42, M.D, 46. Intern, Mt. Sinai Hosp, N.Y, 46-47; instr. biochem, George Washington, 47-49; fel. med, Mayo Clin, 49-50, psychiat, 50-53, asst. to staff neurol, 53; chief, sect. clin. biochem, Nat. Inst. Ment. Health, Nat. Insts. Health, 53-55; instr. NEUROL, MAYO CLIN. & MAYO GRAD. SCH. MED, UNIV. MINN, 55-60, asst. prof, 60-64, assoc. prof, 64-67, PROF, 67-, HEAD SECT, 66-, CONSULT, 55- Assoc, sch. med, George Wash. Univ, 53-55, prof. lectr, 67- U.S.A, 42-45. AAAS; Am. Neurol. Asn; Am. Med. Asn; Am. Psychiat. Asn; Asn. Res. Nerv. & Ment. Disease; Am. Acad. Neurol. Experimental allergic meningoencephalomyelitis; cerebrospinal fluid electrophoresis; Wilson's disease; cerebral edema; multiple sclerosis. Address: Mayo Clinic, Rochester, MN 55901.

GOLDSTEIN, NORMAN P(HILLIP), b. Montreal, Que, Aug. 11, 40. NUCLEAR PHYSICS. B.Sc, McGill, 61, M.Sc, 63, Ph.D.(nuclear physics), 67. SR. PHYSICIST, WESTINGHOUSE RES. LAB, WESTINGHOUSE ELEC. CORP, 67- Am. Phys. Soc. Short lifetime measurements with a fast-slow coincidence system; nuclear scattering from low atomic weight nuclei at 100 million electron volts; radiation damage studies; neutron detectors for fast breeder reactors; design of radiation monitors. Address: Westinghouse Research Labs, Westinghouse Electric Corp, Pittsburgh, PA 15235.

GOLDSTEIN, PAUL, b. Paris, France, Aug. 25, 36; U.S. citizen; m. 62. PHYSICAL CHEMISTRY, CRYSTALLOGRAPHY. B.S, Brooklyn Col, 58; Nat. Sci. Found. fel, Princeton, 58-60, Willard Mackay fel, 60-61, Ph.D. (phys. chem), 63. Fel. crystallog, Univ. Calif, Los Angeles, 63-64; sr. physicist, Philips Labs. Div, N.Am. Philips Co, Inc, N.Y, 64-68; SCIENTIST, XEROX CORP, WEBSTER, 68- Am. Crystallog. Asn. Determination of crystal structures of organic and inorganic compounds by single crystal x-ray diffraction; crystallographic computing and programming. Address: 78 Greenvale Dr, Rochester, NY 14618.

GOLDSTEIN, RAYMOND, b. Dec. 15, 31. PHYSICS. B.S, City Col. New York, 53; M.S, Lehigh, 57, Ph.D.(physics), 62. Staff scientist physics, Boeing Sci. Res. Labs, 62-67; SR. SCIENTIST, JET PROPULSION LAB, 67- U.S.A, 54-56. Am. Phys. Soc; Am. Asn. Physics Teachers. Shock waves; condensation; magnetohydrodynamics; gaseous conduction; photoionization; electric propulsion. Address: Jet Propulsion Lab, 4800 Oak Grove Dr, M.S. 122-123, Pasadena, CA 91103.

GOLDSTEIN, R(ICHARD) J(AY), b. N.Y.C, Mar. 27, 28; m. 63; c. 3. MECHANICAL ENGINEERING. B.M.E, Cornell, 48; M.S, Minnesota, 50, fel, 50-51, M.S.E, 51, Minneapolis-Honeywell fel, 56-57, Ph.D, 59. Instr, Minnesota, 48-50; develop. engr, Oak Ridge Nat. Lab, 51-54; sr. res. engr, Lockheed Aircraft Corp, 56; instr, Minnesota, 57-59; asst. prof. eng, Brown, 59-61; assoc. prof. MECH. ENG, UNIV. MINN, MINNEAPOLIS, 61-65, PROF, 65- Fel, Nat. Ctr. Sci. Res, France, 60-61; Nat. Sci. Found. sr. fel, Cambridge, Eng, 71-72. U.S.A, 54-55, 1st Lt. Am. Soc. Mech. Eng; Am. Phys. Soc. Heat transfer; thermodynamics; fluid mechanics. Address: 520 Janalyn Circle, Golden Valley, MN 55416.

GOLDSTEIN, ROBERT, b. N.Y.C, Aug. 6, 12; m. 41; c. 2. MEDICINE. A.B, Princeton, 33; M.D, Harvard, 37. Asst. MED, Harvard Med. Sch, 46-51, instr, 51-54, clin. assoc, 54-58; asst. prof, med. sch, Tufts, 57-61; assoc. prof, N.Y. MED. COL, 61-65, PROF, 65-, CHMN. DEPT, 71- Asst. med. sch, Tufts, 46-50, instr, 50-51; estab. investr, Am. Heart Asn, 58- Dipl, Am. Bd. Internal Med, 49. Med.C, 41-46, Res, 46-54, Comdr. AAAS; Am. Soc. Hemat; Am. Heart Asn; Am. Physiol. Soc; Int. Soc. Hemat. Internal medicine, especially hematology; blood coagulation. Address: Dept. of Medicine, New York Medical College, 1249 Fifth Ave, New York, NY 10029.

GOLDSTEIN, ROBERT, b. Wilkes-Barre, Pa, Sept. 7, 24; m. 48; c. 2. AUDIOLOGY, PSYCHOPHYSIOLOGY. B.S, Pa. State, 48; Ph.D.(audiol), Washington (St. Louis), 52. Res. assoc, Cent. Inst. Deaf, 53-57; dir. div. audiol. & speech path, Jewish Hosp. St. Louis, Mo, 58-67; PROF. COMMUN. DISORDERS, UNIV. WIS, MADISON, 67- Asst. prof, Washington (St. Louis), 53-60, assoc. prof. 64-67. U.S.A, 43-46. AAAS; Acoust. Soc. Am; fel. Am. Speech & Hearing Asn.(pres, 71-72); Alexander Graham Bell Asn. for Deaf. Electrophysiologic tests of hearing; nature of auditory disorders in children; central auditory function. Address: Elm Dr. C, Madison, WI 53706.

GOLDSTEIN, ROBERT JAY, b. N.Y.C, Aug. 27, 37; m. 63. PARASITOLOGY. B.S, Brooklyn Col, 60; M.S, Fla. State Univ, 63; Ph.D.(microbiol), Univ. Tex, 67. ASST. PROF. BIOL, EMORY UNIV, 67- Am. Soc. Parasitol. Systematics and taxonomy of elasmobranch cestodes; histochemistry of flatworms; marine parasitology; diseases of freshwater fishes; behavior of cichlids and killifishes. Address: Dept. of Biology, Emory University, Atlanta, GA 30322.

GOLDSTEIN, RUBIN, b. New York, N.Y, Mar. 29, 33; m. 56; c. 3. THEORETICAL PHYSICS, APPLIED MATHEMATICS. A.B, Princeton, 55; A.M, Harvard, 56, Ph.D.(physics), 60. Res. assoc. appl. physics & instr. math, Harvard, 60; asst. prof. nuclear eng, California, Berkeley, 60-65; physicist, dept. appl. sci, Brookhaven Nat. Lab, 65-71; CONSULT. STAFF PHYSICIST, NUCLEAR POWER DEPT, COMBUSTION ENG, INC, 71- Summers, staff physicist, Atomics Int. Div, N.Am. Aviation, Inc, Calif, 56, 59, 61, Lincoln Lab, Mass. Inst. Tech, 57, Lawrence Radiation Lab, California, 62, 63, Vallecitos Atomic Lab, Gen. Elec. Co, 64; consult, Gen. Elec. Co, 62-65; adj. prof, Columbia Univ, 70. Am. Phys. Soc. Theoretical reactor physics; resonance absorption theory; nuclear physics; analytic approximation techniques; transport theory; variational and iterative methods. Address: Dept. 492-12, Combustion Engineering, Inc, Windsor, CT 06095.

GOLDSTEIN, SAMUEL J(OSEPH, JR), b. Indianapolis, Ind, June 23, 25; m. 56; c. 3. RADIO ASTRONOMY. B.S, Purdue, 48; M.S, Stanford, 54, Ph.D.(elec. eng), 58. Res. engr, jet propulsion lab, Calif. Inst. Tech, 51-53; acting instr. elec. eng, Stanford, 55; res. asst. ASTRON, Harvard, 55-58, res. assoc, 58-61, lectr, 61-65; ASSOC. PROF, UNIV. VA, 65- Consult, jet propulsion lab, Calif. Inst. Tech, 60-62; vis. res. off, astrophys. br, Nat. Res. Coun. Can, 70-71. Sig.C, U.S.A, 43-46. Inst. Elec. & Electronics Eng; Am. Astron. Soc; Int. Astron. Union. Galactic structure. Address: Leander McCormick Observatory, University of Virginia, Charlottesville, VA 22903.

GOLDSTEIN, SIDNEY, b. Utica, N.Y, Oct. 18, 30; m. 56; c. 2. CARDIOLOGY. B.A, Cornell Univ, 52, M.D, 56. Intern, N.Y. Hosp-Cornell Med. Ctr, 56-57, resident, 59-61, N.Y. Heart Assoc. res. fel, 61-62; dir. cardio-pulmonary lab, Rochester Gen. Hosp, 62; asst. prof. MED, UNIV. ROCHESTER, 66-69, ASSOC. PROF, 69- Mem. coun. clin. cardiol, Am. Heart Asn. Med.C, U.S.A, 57-59, Capt. Am. Fedn. Clin. Res; fel. Am. Col. Physicians; fel. Am. Col. Cardiol. Cardiac physiology. Address: 1425 Portland Ave, Rochester, NY 14621.

GOLDSTEIN, SIDNEY, b. Phila, Pa, Mar. 27, 32; m. 55; c. 3. PHARMACOLOGY. B.Sc, Phila. Col. Pharm, 54, M.Sc, 55, D.Sc, 58. Sr. res. pharmacologist, Eaton Labs, Norwich Pharmacol. Co, 58-59; Lederle Labs, Am. Cyanamid Co, 59-61; Nat. Drug. Co, 61-64, dir. pharmacol, 64-67, prod. develop, 67-70; SECT. HEAD ANTI-INFLAMMATORY & RESPIRATORY SECTS. & CLIN. MONITOR-MED. RES. DEPT, WILLIAM S. MERRELL CO, 70- Lectr, Phila. Col. Pharm, 67-70. AAAS; Am. Pharmaceut. Asn; Am. Soc. Pharmacol. & Exp. Therapeut; Soc. Exp. Biol. & Med. Respiratory research; tropical steroids and anti-infectives. Address: William S. Merrell Co, 110 E. Amity Rd, Reading, OH 45215.

GOLDSTEIN, SOLOMON, b. N.Y.C, May 2, 29; m. 54. BOTANY, MYCOLOGY. B.A, City Col. New York, 52; M.S, Michigan, 53, fel, 55-58, Ph.D.(bot), 59. Instr. bot, Michigan, 58-59; asst. prof. biol, State Univ. N.Y. Stony Brook, 59-60; res. assoc. microbiol, Yale, 60-64; dep. chmn. grad. div, BROOKLYN COL, 64-69, PROF. BIOL, 69- Med.C, U.S.A, 53-55. Bot. Soc. Am; Mycol. Soc. Am; Am. Soc. Microbiol; Am. Soc. Protozool; Brit. Soc. Gen. Microbiol. Physiology and morphology of marine phycomycetes. Address: Dept. of Biology, Brooklyn College, Brooklyn, NY 11210.

GOLDSTEIN, STANLEY P(HILIP), b. Brooklyn, N.Y, Feb. 3, 23; m. 48; c. 2. ASTRONAUTICAL ENGINEERING. B.S, Oklahoma, 49; M.S, N.Y. Univ, 56; Ph.D.(astronaut), Polytech. Inst. Brooklyn, 69. Develop. engr, Vapor Recovery Systs, Co, 50-52; proj. engr, Aldison Res. Labs, 52-54; assoc. prof. ENG. SCI, HOFSTRA UNIV, 54-67, PROF, 67-, CHMN. DEPT, 54-, DIR. ACAD. COMPUT. CTR, 71- U.S.A.F, 42-46, 1st Lt. Am. Soc. Eng. Educ; Asn. Comput. Mach. Compressible flow; free convection heat transfer; computer science. Address: Dept. of Engineering Science, Hofstra University, Hempstead, NY 11218.

GOLDSTEIN, STUART FREDERICK, b. Beloit, Wis, Sept. 11, 39. CELL PHYSIOLOGY. B.A, Univ. Minn, 62; Ph.D.(cell biol), Calif. Inst. Technol, 68. Med. Res. Coun. Gt. Brit. grant, Queen Elizabeth Col, London, 68-69; U.S. Pub. Health Serv. grant, Univ. Calif, Berkeley, 69-71; ASST. PROF. ZOOL, UNIV. MINN, MINNEAPOLIS, 71- Am. Soc. Cell Biol. Flagellar and ciliary motility. Address: Dept. of Zoology, University of Minnesota, Minneapolis, MN 55455.

GOLDSTEIN, THEODORE P(HILIP), b. Baltimore, Md, Feb. 23, 28; m. 68. ORGANIC CHEMISTRY, BIOCHEMISTRY. B.A, Hopkins, 51, M.A, 58, Ph.D. (chem), 61. Chemist, U.S. Army Chem. Corps, 52-55; Sinai Hosp. Baltimore, 55-56; res. chemist, Cent. Res. Lab, Socony Mobil Oil Co, Inc, 61-63, SR. RES. CHEMIST, MOBIL RES. & DEVELOP. CORP, 63- U.S.N, 56-58. AAAS; Am. Chem. Soc. Histochemistry; catalysis. Address: Mobil Research & Development Corp, Box 1025, Princeton, NJ 08540.

GOLDSTICK, THOMAS KARL, b. Toronto, Ont, Aug. 21, 34; m. 63. BIOMEDICAL & CHEMICAL ENGINEERING. B.S, Mass. Inst. Tech, 57, M.S, 59; Jane Lewis fel, California, Berkeley, 61-63, Ph.D.(eng. sci), 66. Res. engr, iron ore res, Jones & Laughlin Steel Corp, 59-61; asst. res. engr. mech. eng. & surg, California, Berkeley & San Francisco, 66-67; asst. prof. CHEM. ENG, NORTHWEST. UNIV, 67-71, ASSOC. PROF, 71- Nat. Insts. Health spec. res. fel, Univ. Calif, San Diego, 71-72. Biomed. Eng. Soc; Am. Chem. Soc; Am. Inst. Chem. Eng; Microcirc. Soc. Mass transport in biological systems, applying traditional engineering techniques to living systems; oxygen transport in the microcirculation. Address: Dept. of Chemical Engineering, Northwestern University, Evanston, IL 60201.

GOLDSTINE, HERMAN H(EINE), b. Chicago, Ill, Sept. 13, 13; m. 41, 66; c. 2. MATHEMATICS. B.S, Chicago, 33, M.S, 34, Ph.D.(math), 36. Asst. math, Chicago, 36-39; instr, Michigan, 39-45, asst. prof, 45-48; asst. proj. dir, electronic comput. proj, INST. ADVAN. STUDY, 46-50, MEM. SCH. MATH, 50-; IBM FEL, THOMAS J. WATSON RES. CTR, IBM CORP, 69-, consult. to dir. res, 67-69, dir. sci. develop, data processing div, 65-67, math. sci, res. ctr, 58-65. Instr, Univ. Chicago, 37-39; vis. prof, Yeshiva Univ, 59-64. Consult, Army Math. Steering Comt; mem, survey panel comput, Conf. Bd. Math. Sci; bd. trustees, adv. coun, dept. math, Princeton. Ord. Dept, 42-46, Lt. Col. Am. Math. Soc; Math. Asn. Am. Abstract spaces; calculus of variations; applied mathematics; electronic computers; numerical analysis. Address: IBM Corp, Thomas J. Watson Research Center, Yorktown Heights, NY 10598.

GOLDSTON, EUGENE F(RIZZELLE), b. Goldston, N.C, Nov. 3, 05; m. 30; c. 2. SOILS. B.S, N.C. State Col, 29. Res. asst. prof. soil sci, N.C. State Univ, 29-66; ASST. PROF. AGRON, VA. POLYTECH. INST. & STATE UNIV, 66- Am. Soc. Agron; Soil Sci. Soc. Am; Soil Conserv. Soc. Am; Int. Soc. Soil Sci. Soil research and survey. Address: Box 504, 18 E. Market St, Leesburg, VA 20075.

GOLDSWORTHY, PATRICK D(ONOVAN), b. Co. Wexford, Ireland, Apr. 20, 19; nat; m. 42; c. 1. BIOCHEMISTRY. A.B, California, 41, M.A, 47, Ph.D.(biochem), 52. Asst. biochem, sch. med, California, 47-50, res. assoc. neurol, 50-52; med, SCH. MED, UNIV. WASH, 52-56, res. instr, 56-57, res. asst. prof. med. & lectr. biochem, 57-69; RES. ASSOC. PROF. MED, 69- Med.C, 41-42; U.S.A.A.F, 42-45, Res, 45-53, Capt. Am. Soc. Biol. Chem. Synthesis and metabolism of proteins and amino acids. Address: Dept. of Medicine, BB 512 University Hospital, SK-30, University of Washington, Seattle, WA 98195.

GOLDTHORPE, FRED C, b. Chicago, Ill, Dec. 24, 25; m. 50; c. 6. ANATOMY. B.S, Utah, 51, M.A, 52, Ph.D.(anat), 67. Teacher, pub. sch, 52-53; assoc. dir. training dept, J.B. Roerig & Co, 53-54; dir. med. & sales training, Riker Labs. Inc, Rexall Drug & Chem. Co, 54-64; ASSOC. PROF. BIOL. SCI, UNIV. UTAH, 64- Prof. theol, Salt Lake Inst. Relig, 64- U.S.A.A.F, 43-45. Use of tritiated thymidine-glycine in determinations of bone growth; use of various adrenal cortical steroids in treatment of secondary shock following thermal burns. Address: 201 Biological Sciences Bldg, University of Utah, Salt Lake City, UT 84112.

GOLDTHWAIT, CHARLES F(RANCIS), b. Cummington, Mass, Apr. 23, 86; m. 13; c. 2. CHEMISTRY. B.S, Worcester Polytech, 09; hon. D.Sc, N.C. State Univ, 65. Chief chemist, S. Slater & Sons, Inc, Mass, 09-16; chemist in charge lab. & dyeing, Klearflax Linen Looms, Inc, Minn, 16-23, supt. cotton mercerizing & dyeing, Md, 23-24; head test, Heminway Silk Co, Conn, 24-25; sr. indust. fel, Mellon Inst, 25-39, 40-41; consult, P. McGraw Wool Co, Pa, 39-40; sr. cotton technologist, South. regional res. lab, bur. agr. & indust. chem, U.S. Dept. Agr, 41-50, head cotton chem. processing sect, agr. res. serv, 51-56; vis. prof. chem, sch. textiles, N.C. State Univ, 57-61, consult, 61-67; RETIRED. Mem, Textile Res. Inst. Am. Chem. Soc; Am. Asn. Textile Chem. & Colorists (Olney Medal, 62); Brit. Textile Inst; Brit. Soc. Dyers & Colourists. Application of chemistry and physics to the development and manufacture of textiles. Address: 2112 Ridge Rd, Raleigh, NC 27607.

GOLDTHWAIT, DAVID A(TWATER), b. Providence, R.I, Nov. 7, 21; m. 49; c. 4. BIOCHEMISTRY. Harvard, 39-42; M.D, Columbia, 45. Asst. prof. biochem. & med, CASE WEST. RESERVE UNIV, 51-57, assoc. prof, 57-68, PROF. BIOCHEM, 68- Med.C, U.S.A, 46-48. Am. Soc. Biol. Chem; Am. Soc. Clin. Invest. Nucleic acids; metabolism; cancer. Address: 7 Pepper Ridge Rd, Cleveland, OH 44124.

GOLDTHWAIT, R(ICHARD) G(RAHAM), b. Duluth, Minn, Feb. 9, 19; m. 49; c. 2. CHEMICAL ENGINEERING. B.S, Pa. State, 40. Asst, Pa. State, 40-41; buyer, Westinghouse Elec. Corp, 41-43; proj. leader & chem. engr, GULF RES. & DEVELOP. CO, 43-49, asst. group leader, 49-53, group leader, 53-56, asst. sect. head, 56-60, sect. supvr, 60-65, staff engr, 65-66, TECH. CONSULT, 66-, GULF RES. LAB, NETHERLANDS, 69- Am. Chem. Soc; Am. Inst. Chem. Eng. Pilot plant work in petroleum refining and related fields; catalytic reforming; thermal and catlytic cracking; isomerization; distillation; hydrogenative processes; correlation development; process control. Address: Gulf Research Lab, P.O. Box 7045, Rotterdam, The Netherlands.

GOLDTHWAIT, RICHARD P(ARKER), b. Hanover, N.H, June 6, 11; m. 37; c. 4. GEOLOGY. A.B, Dartmouth Col, 33; M.A, Harvard, 37, fel, 38-39, Ph.D.(geol), 39. Instr. geol, Dartmouth Col, 34-35; asst, Harvard, 36-38; instr, Brown, 39-40, asst. prof, 41-42; tech. consult, Air Transportation Command, U.S. Air Force, 42-43, mat. engr, Air Materiel Command, 43-46; assoc. prof. GEOL, OHIO STATE UNIV, 46-48, PROF, 48-, dir. inst. polar studies, 60-65, chmn. dept. geol, 65-69. Fulbright res. scholar, N.Z, 57; NATO sr. fel, 69; mem. cmt. Alaskan earthquake, Nat. Acad. Sci. AAAS; fel. Geol. Soc. Am; fel. Am. Geog. Soc; Am. Geophys. Union; fel. Arctic Inst. N.Am; Glaciol. Soc. Glacial geology of western Ohio and central New Hampshire; glacier studies in Alaska, the Alps, Baffin Island, Greenland; river floodplain studies in New Hampshire and Ohio; reconnaissance geomorphology of northeast Tibet, central Baffin Island, New Zealand, Antarctica; international geophysical year glaciology data reduction. Address: Dept. of Geology, Ohio State University, 125 S. Oval Dr, Columbus, OH 43210.

GOLDTHWAITE, DUNCAN, b. N.Y.C, Mar. 31, 27; m. 56; c. 4. PETROLEUM GEOLOGY. B.A, Oberlin Col, 50; M.A, Harvard, 52. Geologist, S.Dak. State Geol. Surv, summer, 50; fuels br, U.S. Geol. Surv, summer, 51; CHEVRON OIL CO, N.Dak. & S.Dak, 52-54, geophysicist, Miss. & N. La, 54-57, dist. geologist, N. La, 57-58, Mich. & Appalachians, 58-64, SR. STAFF GEOLOGIST, S. LA. & ATLANTIC COAST PHOSPHATES, 64- U.S.N, 45-46. Fel. Geol. Soc. Am; Am. Asn. Petrol. Geol. Structure and stratigraphy as related to petroleum in Michigan, Appalachians, and Gulf Coast; phosphate investigations. Address: Chevron Oil Co, 1111 Tulane Ave, New Orleans, LA 70112.

GOLDTHWAITE, W(ILLIAM) H(ARLOW), b. Middlebury, Vt, May 21, 21; m. 52; c. 3. PHYSICS. A.B, Middlebury Col, 49; M.S, New Hampshire, 51. Asst. physics, New Hampshire, 49-51; prin. physicist, eng. physics, BATTELLE MEM. INST, 51-55, proj. leader, 55-56, asst. div. chief, 56-57, div. chief, 57-65, assoc. mgr. PHYSICS DEPT, 65-69, MGR, 69- U.S.N.R, 44-46. Am. Nuclear Soc. Engineering physics; friction, wear and lubrication; nuclear energy; reactor engineering; thermophysical properties. Address: Dept. of Physics, Battelle Memorial Institute, 505 King Ave, Columbus, OH 43201.

GOLDWASSER, EDWIN L(EO), b. N.Y.C, Mar. 9, 19; m. 40; c. 5. PHYSICS. B.A, Harvard, 40; Westinghouse fel, California, Berkeley, 49-50, Ph.D. (physics), 50. Physicist, degaussing ships, bur. ord, Dept. Navy, 41-43, sr. physicist, Navy Yard, Mare Island, 43-45; asst. physics, California, Berkeley, 46-49, res. assoc, 50-51; Univ. Ill, Urbana, 51-53, asst. prof, 53-56, assoc. prof, 56-59, prof, 59-67; DEP. DIR, NAT. ACCELERATOR LAB, 67- Consult, Phys. Sci. Study Comt, 56-61; Fulbright & Guggenheim fels, Univ. Rome, 57-58; consult, Argonne Nat. Lab, 60-62; v.chmn. div. phys. sci, Nat. Res. Coun, 61-66, chmn, 66-68; mem, panel high energy accelerator physics, gen. adv. comt, Atomic Energy Comn. & President's Sci. Adv. Comt, 62-63; physics surv. comt, Nat. Acad. Sci, 63-65, site selection comt, 65-66; sci. adv. comn, State of Ill, 67- Fel. Am. Phys. Soc; Fedn. Am. Sci. Elementary particle physics; cosmic rays; electron and photon interactions; ion physics. Address: National Accelerator Lab, P.O. Box 500, Batavia, IL 60510.

GOLDWASSER, EUGENE, b. N.Y.C, Oct. 14, 22; m. 49; c. 3. BIOCHEMISTRY. S.B, Chicago, 43, Ph.D.(biochem), 50. Am. Cancer Soc. fel, Copenhagen, 50-52; res. assoc. BIOCHEM. ARGONNE CANCER RES. HOSP, UNIV. CHICAGO, 52-56, assoc. prof, 56-59, assoc. prof, 59-63, PROF, 63- Guggenheim fel, dept. biochem, Oxford, 66-67. AAAS; Am. Soc. Biol. Chem; Biochem. Soc; Tissue Cult. Asn; Int. Soc. Develop. Biol. Biochemistry of nucleic acids; biochemistry of erythropoiesis. Address: Dept. of Biochemistry, Argonne Cancer Research Hospital, University of Chicago, 950 E. 59th St, Box 420, Chicago, IL 60637.

GOLDWASSER, SEYMORE, b. Paterson, N.J, May 22, 15; m. 37; c. 3. PHYSICAL CHEMISTRY. B.A, Amherst Col, 35; Ph.D.(phys. chem), Princeton, 39. Tech. asst. to R.A. Beebe, Amherst Col, 35-36; res. chemist, M.W. Kellogg Co, N.J, 39-46; phys. chemist, LEVER BROS, 46-49, chief supvr. anal. res, 49-51, sect. chief PHYS. SPECTROS. RES, 51-56, SR. SCIENTIST, 56- Adj. assoc. prof, Fairleigh-Dickinson Univ, 66- Am. Chem. Soc; Am. Oil Chem. Soc; Optical Soc. Am; Am. Asn. Textile Chem. & Colorists; Am. Soc. Test. & Mat; Inter Soc. Color Coun. Surface, soap and phosphate chemistry; color measurement and specification. Address: Lever Brothers, 45 River Rd, Edgewater, NJ 07020.

GOLDWATER, LEONARD J(OHN), b. New York, N.Y, Jan. 15, 03; m. 53. MEDICINE. A.B, Michigan, 24; M.D, N.Y. Univ, 28, Sc.D.(internal med), 37; M.S, Columbia, 41. Intern & resident physician, Bellevue Hosp, N.Y, 29-32; instr. med, col. med, N.Y. Univ, 32-36, instr. & asst. prof. prev. med, 38-41; prof. indust. hyg, SCH. PUB. HEALTH, COLUMBIA UNIV, 46-52, OCCUP. MED, 52-69, EMER. PROF, 69-; VIS. PROF. ENVIRON. SCI, UNIV. N.C, CHAPEL HILL, 69-; PROF. COMMUNITY HEALTH SCI, DUKE UNIV, 69-, vis. scholar, 68-69. Harben Lectr, Royal Inst. Pub. Health & Hyg, 64; praelector, St. Andrews, 66. Sr. indust. hyg. physician, State Dept. Labor, N.Y, 36-38, consult. div. indust. hyg; off. voc. rehab, U.S. dept. Health, Ed. & Welfare, 52-60; Atomic Energy Cmn, 48-49. Mem. expert adv. panel soc. & occup. health, WHO; Nat. Air Pollution Res. & Develop. Adv. Coun, 70- Dipl, Am. Bd. Internal Med; dipl, Am. Bd. Prev. Med. U.S.N.R, 41-46, Comdr. Fel. Am. Med. Asn; fel. Am. Pub. Health Asn; Am. Indust. Hyg. Asn; fel. Am. Indust. Med. Asn; fel. Am. Acad. Occup. Med.(pres, 59); Am. Conf. Govt. Indust. Hygienists; fel. N.Y. Acad. Med. Occupational medicine; industrial toxicology. Address: Route 3, Box 197, Chapel Hill, NC 27514.

GOLDWATER, WILLIAM H(ENRY), b. Plattsburgh, N.Y, Apr. 4, 21; m. 48; c. 2. BIOCHEMISTRY. A.B, Columbia, 41, Gies fel. & Ph.D.(biochem), 47. Res. technician, Mt. Sinai Hosp, N.Y, 41-42; asst, Columbia, 42-43, div. war res, 43-45, med. sch, 46-47, res. chemist, Mt. Sinai Hosp, 47-48; res. assoc, sch. med, Tulane, 48-49, assoc, 49-51, asst. prof. biochem. & med, 51; radiol. biochemist, U.S. Naval Radiol. Defense Lab, 52-59; biochemist, div. res. grants, NAT. INSTS. HEALTH, 59-62, chief, spec. res. projs, Nat. Heart Inst, 62-69, assoc. dir. extramural progs, Nat. Inst. Environ. Health Sci, 69-70, SPEC. ASST. TO ASSOC. DIR. EXTRAMURAL RES. & TRAINING, 70- Fel, coun. epidemiol, Am. Heart Asn; mem. res. & develop. study group, Comn. Govt. Procurement, 71- With Off. Sci. Res. & Develop, 43-45. Fel. AAAS; Am. Chem. Soc; Am. Asn. Clin. Chem; fel. Am. Col. Cardiol; Am. Pub. Health Asn; N.Y. Acad. Sci. Metabolism and nutrition; cardiovascular research; metabolism, nutrition, cardiovascular and environmental health research; science administration and policy. Address: Bldg 1, Room 238, National Institutes of Health, Bethesda, MD 20014.

GOLDWEIN, MANFRED I(SAAC), b. Bochum, Ger, Apr. 19, 24; U.S. citizen; m. 49; c. 3. INTERNAL MEDICINE, HEMATOLOGY. B.S, Univ. Del, 50; M.D, Univ. Vt, 54. Asst. instr. MED, UNIV. PA, 55-58, instr, 58-60, assoc, 60-62, ASST. PROF, 62- U.S.A, 42-45. Am. Col. Physicians; Am. Soc. Hemat. Clinical hematology; vitamin B_{12} metabolism; ineffective erythropoiesis. Address: Hospital of the University of Pennsylvania, 3400 Spruce St, Philadelphia, PA 19104.

GOLDWHITE, HAROLD, b. London, Eng, Dec. 25, 31; m. 58; c. 4. INORGANIC CHEMISTRY. B.A, Cambridge, 53, Ph.D.(chem), 56. Res. assoc. CHEM, Cornell, 56-58; lectr, Manchester, 58-62; asst. prof, CALIF. STATE COL. LOS ANGELES, 62-64, assoc. prof, 64-67, PROF, 67- Am. Chem. Soc; The Chem. Soc. Chemistry of compounds containing phosphorus; fluorine chemistry; organometallic chemistry. Address: Dept. of Chemistry, California State College at Los Angeles, Los Angeles, CA 90032.

GOLDWIRE, HENRY CRAWFORD, JR, b. Carlsbad, N.Mex, Jan. 24, 42; m. ASTROPHYSICS. B.A, Rice, 63, NASA fel, 66, Ph.D.(space sci), 67. Res. Asst. astrophys, Rice, 67; res. fel, Calif. Inst. Tech, 67-68; ASST. PROF. SPACE SCI, RICE UNIV, 68- Mem. staff, Ling-Temco-Vought, Inc, summers 61-64. Award, Sigma Xi, 67. Am. Astron. Soc; Am. Phys. Soc; Int. Astron. Union. Radio astronomy; search for spectral lines; conditions of astrophysical plasmas. Address: Dept. of Space Science, Rice University, Houston, TX 77001.

GOLDWYN, ROGER M(ARTIN), b. Tulsa, Okla, Dec. 18, 36; m. 64; c. 2. APPLIED MATHEMATICS, ENGINEERING. B.A, Rice, 58, Schlumberger Found. fel, 58-59, B.S, 59, Nat. Sci. Found. fel, 59-60, M.S, 60; Nat. Sci. Found. fels, Harvard, 60-62, A.M, 61, Shell Found. fel, 62-63, Ph.D.(appl. math), 64. Asst. prof. elec. eng, Rice Univ, 64-66; mem. res. staff, THOMAS J. WATSON RES. CTR, Int. Bus. Mach. Corp, 67-70, MGR. BIOMED. DATA PROCESSING, IBM CORP, 71- Nat. Sci. Found. grant, 64-66; consult, guid. & control div, Manned Spacecraft Ctr, NASA, Vet. Admin. Hosp, Houston & Esso Prod. Res. Lab, 64-66; asst. clin. prof, Albert Einstein Col. Med. & lectr, dept. elec. eng, Univ. Conn, 69- Sci. Res. Soc. Am;

Inst. Elec. & Electronics Eng. Stability problems in control theory; wave propagation; multivariate data analysis; biomedical data analysis. Address: Thomas J. Watson Research Center, IBM Corp, P.O. Box 218, Yorktown Heights, NY 10598.

GOLDZIEHER, JOSEPH W(ILLIAM), b. Budapest, Hungary, Sept. 21, 19; nat; m; c. 1. ENDOCRINOLOGY. A.B, Harvard, 40; M.D, N.Y. Univ, 43. Intern, Bellevue Hosp, 43-44; asst. res. & res. path, New York Hosp, 44-46; res. endocrinol, univ. hosp, Duke, 46-47; dir. res, St. Clare's Hosp, 48-53; mem. sr. staff & chief endocrine lab, SOUTHWEST FOUND. RES. & EDUC, 54-58, chmn. dept. endocrinol, 58-66, DIV. DIR. CLIN. SCI, 66- Attend. physician, hosps, 47-53; mem. res. unit, Metrop. Hosp, 49-53; res. assoc, N.Y. Med. Col, 49-53; res. prof, Trinity Univ.(Tex), 56-70; consult, Brooke Army Med. Ctr; Lackland Air Force Hosp. Dipl, Am. Bd. Clin. Chem. Endocrine Soc; Geront. Soc; assoc. fel. Am. Col. Obstet. & Gynec; Am. Fertil. Soc; Am. Asn. Clin. Chem; N.Y. Acad. Sci; fel. Am. Soc. Clin. Pharmacol. & Chemother; hon. mem. Mex. Soc. Endocrinol. & Metab. Steroid chemistry; reproductive physiology and disease; fertility control; hormonal contraceptives. Address: 515 Medical Professional Bldg, San Antonio, TX 78212.

GOLEMAN, D(ENZIL) LYLE, b. Coles Co, Ill, Jan. 3, 24; m. 52; c. 3. ECONOMIC ENTOMOLOGY. B.S, East. Ill. State Col, 49; M.S, Iowa State Col, 51, Ph.D.(entom), 54. Assoc. agr. exp. sta. & agr. exten. serv, Iowa State Col, 51-54; asst. exten. entomologist, Ohio State, 54-56, exten. entomologist, 56-59; entomologist, Am. Cyanamid Co, 59-65; EXTEN. SPECIALIST AGR. CHEM, OHIO STATE UNIV, 65-, CHMN. DEPT. ENTOM, 68- Ord. Dept, U.S.A, 46-47. AAAS; Entom. Soc. Am. Management of insect pests; use of insecticides including benefits and risks. Address: Dept. of Entomology, College of Biological Sciences, Ohio State University, 1735 Neil Ave, Columbus, OH 43210.

GOLEMBA, FRANK J(OHN), b. Hamilton, Ont, Dec. 3, 43; m. 67. POLYMER CHEMISTRY, PHOTOCHEMISTRY. B.Sc, Univ. Toronto, 65, Nat. Res. Coun. Can. scholar, 65-70, Paints Res. Inst. fel, 66-69, M.Sc, 67, Ph.D. (polymer chem), 70. RES. SCIENTIST, FIBERGLAS CAN. LTD, 70- Soc. Plastics Eng; Am. Chem. Soc; Chem. Inst. Can. Polymer synthesis, structure and properties, reinforced polymers, polymer photochemistry, chemistry of the matrix reinforcement interface. Address: Fiberglas Canada Ltd, P.O. Box 3005, Sarnia, Ont, Can.

GOLES, GORDON G(EORGE), b. Chicago, Ill, Mar. 6, 34; m. 63; c. 2. GEOCHEMISTRY. A.B, Harvard, 56; Ph.D.(chem), Univ. Chicago, 61. Asst. res. chemist, Univ. Calif, San Diego, 61-62, asst. prof. chem, 62-67; ASSOC. PROF. CHEM. & GEOL, UNIV. ORE, 67-, DIR, CTR. VOLCANOLOGY, 71-, staff mem, 67-71. AAAS; Geochem. Soc; Geochem. Soc. Japan. Meteoritics, especially as it bears on the history of the solar system; trace-element geochemistry; activation analysis; archaeology; lunar sample analyses. Address: Dept. of Geology, University of Oregon, Eugene, OR 97403.

GOLESTANEH, A(HMAD) A(LI), b. Esfahan, Iran, June 2, 20; nat; m. 51; c. 3. THEORETICAL PHYSICS. M.Sc, Teheran, 42; Ph.D.(physics of metals), Manchester, 52; Columbia, 61-64. Chief tech. off, Iranian State Rwys, 42-47, chief engr, 52-54; sr. res. off, Brit. Welding Res. Asn, 55-57; res. assoc, Gen. Elec. Co, Pa, 57-59; asst. prof. physics, Utica Col, 59-60; Polytech. Inst. Brooklyn, 61-64; res. worker, Columbia Univ, 64-66; assoc. prof. PHYSICS, MT. UNION COL, 66-70, PROF, 70- Instr, Univ. Tehran, 42-46, 53-54; Behrend Ctr, Pa. State Univ, 59; Fordham Univ, 63; consult, gen. eng. lab, Gen. Elec. Co, N.Y, 60; Nat. Found. grants. Am. Phys. Soc. Theory of elementary particles; field theory; nuclear physics. Address: Dept. of Physics & Astronomy, Mount Union College, Alliance, OH 44601.

GOLIBER, E(DWARD) W(ILLIAM), b. Buffalo, N.Y, Nov. 21, 20; m. 52; c. 4. CHEMISTRY. B.S, Canisius Col, 43; Ph.D.(chem), Mass. Inst. Technol, 48. Lab. technician, Nat. Aniline Div, Allied Chem. & Dye Corp, N.Y, 41-42; res. chemist, Linde Air Prod. Co, N.Y, 43-46; sr. res. chemist, Carboloy Dept, GEN. ELEC. CO, 48-58, consult. engr, METALL. PROD. DEPT, 58-60, MGR. HARD METALS RES, 60- Am. Chem. Soc; Am. Ceramic Soc; Am. Inst. Mining, Metall. & Petrol. Eng. Cemented carbides; powder metallurgy; oxides; refractory materials; inorganic chemistry. Address: Metallurgical Products Dept, General Electric Co, Roosevelt Park, P.O. Box 237, Detroit, MI 48232.

GOLIBERSUCH, DAVID C(LARENCE), b. Buffalo, N.Y, Jan. 20, 42; m. 68; c. 1. PHYSICS. B.S, Rensselaer Polytech. Inst, 63; NASA fel, Univ. Pa, 64-67, M.S, 65, Ph.D.(physics), 69. Physicist, Harry Diamond Lab, Wash, D.C, summer 63; Nat. Sci. Found. fel. physics, Imp. Col. Sci. & Technol, Univ. London, 69-70; PHYSICIST, GEN. ELEC. RES. & DEVELOP. CTR, 70- Am. Phys. Soc; Biophys. Soc. Solid state physics; magnetism; biophysics; membranes; fluctuation phenomena. Address: Physical Sciences Branch, General Electric Research & Development Center, Box 8, Schenectady, NY 12301.

GOLIGHTLY, DANOLD WAYNE, b. Cape Girardeau, Mo, Apr. 12, 41; m. 69. ANALYTICAL SPECTROCHEMISTRY. A.B, Southeast Mo. State Col, 62; M.S, Iowa State Univ, 65, Ph.D.(chem), 67. Res. chemist, mat. res. lab, Univ. Ill, Urbana, 67-69; res. assoc, Ctr. Nuclear Studies, Grenoble, France, 69-70; res. assoc, Ames Lab, Iowa State Univ, 70-71; RES. CHEMIST, SPECTROCHEM. SECT, ANAL. CHEM. DIV, NAT. BUR. STANDARDS, 71- Am. Chem. Soc; Soc. Appl. Spectros; Am. Soc. Test. & Mat. Analytical chemistry; instrumental analysis, particularly optical atomic emission and atomic adsorption spectrometry; solids spark source mass spectrometry; isotope dilution methods. Address: Spectrochemistry Section, Analytical Chemistry Division, National Bureau of Standards, Washington, DC 20234.

GOLIGHTLY, JOHN PAUL, b. Toronto, Ont, Mar. 6, 40; m. 65; c. 2. GEOLOGY, CRYSTALLOGRAPHY. B.Sc, McGill, 61, Ph.D.(geol), 68; Queen's (Ont), 61-63. Crystallographer, Norton Res. Corp. Can. Ltd, 67-70; RES. GEOLOGIST, INT. NICKEL CO, 70- Am. Crystallog. Asn. Geochemistry of amphibolites; crystal structure of dawsonite; crystal field spectra of iron in minerals; crystal structure and physics of silicon carbide; geochemistry and mineralogy of nickeliferous laterites. Address: Exploration Research Dept, Sheridan Park Lab, International Nickel Co, Toronto, Ont, Can.

GOLIK, RAYMOND JOHN, b. Chicago, Ill, Mar. 25, 32; m. 58; c. 3. FLUID DYNAMICS. B.S.M.E, Illinois, 53, M.S, 59, Ph.D.(mech. eng), 62. Design engr, Diamond Nat. Corp, 55-56; tech. engr, jet engine dept, Gen. Elec. Co, 56-58; instr. thermodyn, Illinois, 59-62; mem. tech. staff fluid mech, TRW SYSTS, 62-65, sect. head fluid dynamics res, 65-68, MGR. REENTRY PHYSICS DEPT, 68- U.S.A, 53-55, 1st Lt. Reentry physics, study of phenomena associated with the dynamics, thermodynamics, fluid mechanics and chemistry of flow fields surrounding bodies at hypersonic speeds during atmospheric entry. Address: 112 17th St, Manhattan Beach, CA 90266.

GOLIKE, RALPH C(ROSBY), b. West Alton, Mo, Jan. 11, 27; m. 52; c. 5. PHYSICAL CHEMISTRY. B.S, Missouri, 50, M.A, 52; Ph.D.(chem), Minnesota, 55. Asst. chem, Missouri, 49-51; Minnesota, 51-54; res. chemist, E.I. DU PONT DE NEMOURS & CO, INC, 54-62, staff scientist, 62-69, RES. SUPVR, FILM RES. LAB, EXP. STA, 69- U.S.A, 45-46. Am. Phys. Soc; Am. Chem. Soc. Physical chemistry of high polymers; infrared and nuclear resonance spectroscopy. Address: 2 Berrywood Ct, Woodbine, Wilmington, DE 19810.

GOLIN, STUART, b. Chicago, Ill, Jan. 15, 38; m. 71. SOLID STATE PHYSICS, COMPUTER SCIENCE. M.Sc, Chicago, 59, Nat. Sci. Found. fel, 59-63, Ph.D.(physics), 63; Carnegie-Mellon Univ, 69-70. Res. assoc. physics, Chicago, 63-64; Nat. Sci. Found. fel, Nuclear Res. Ctr, Saclay, France, 64-65; asst. prof. metall. eng, Univ. Ill, 65-66; physics, Univ. Pittsburgh, 66-69; MEM. TECH. STAFF, COMPUT. CTR, RCA LABS, 70- Am. Phys. Soc; Asn. Comput. Mach. Theoretical solid state physics; band structure calculations; computer systems; resource allocation and pricing. Address: Computer Center, RCA Labs, Princeton, NJ 08540.

GOLINKIN, HERBERT S(HELDON), b. Chicago, Ill, May 24, 40; m. 61; c. 2. PHYSICAL ORGANIC & POLYMER CHEMISTRY. A.B, Johns Hopkins Univ, 61; Nat. Res. Coun. Can. scholar, Univ. Alta, Calgary, 61-63 & stud, 64-66, univ. scholar, summer 63, Ph.D.(phys. org. chem), 66. Fel. phys. org. chem, div. pure chem, Nat. Res. Coun. Can, 66-68; asst. prof. chem, Univ. Minn, 68-70; RES. CHEMIST, RES. & DEVELOP. DEPT, AMOCO CHEM. CORP, 70- Petrol. Res. Fund grant, 68-70. Am. Chem. Soc; Chem. Inst. Can. Aqueous solutions; reaction kinetics; reaction mechanisms; piezochemistry; effects of external fields on chemical reactions; condensation polymers. Address: Amoco Chemicals Corp, Standard Oil Technical Center, P.O. Box 400, Naperville, IL 60540.

GOLL, DARREL E(UGENE), b. Garner, Iowa, Apr. 19, 36; m. 58; c. 3. MOLECULAR BIOLOGY, BIOCHEMISTRY. B.S, Iowa State, 57, M.S, 59; Nat. Insts. Health fel. & Ph.D.(biochem), Wisconsin, 62. Asst. prof. BIOCHEM, IOWA STATE UNIV, 62-65, assoc. prof, 65-70, PROF, 70- U.S. Pub. Health Serv. res. grant, 64-67, 69-; Nat. Insts. Health Spec. fel, Univ. Calif, Los Angeles, 66-67; Samuel Cate Prescott Res. Award, Inst. Food Technol. AAAS; Am. Chem. Soc. Chemistry of muscle proteins; muscle contraction; connective tissue protein; chemistry of gerontological changes; protein structure; nucleic acid and protein biosynthesis. Address: Muscle Biology Group, Iowa State University, Ames, IA 50010.

GOLL, R(OBERT) J(OHN), b. Milwaukee, Wis, Jan. 14, 26. PHYSICAL CHEMISTRY. B.S, Beloit Col, 47, Northwestern, 48; Ph.D.(chem), Wisconsin, 60. Res. chemist, cent. res. dept, E.I. du Pont de Nemours & Co, Inc, Del, 59-69; ASSOC. PROF. PHYSICS, MIAMI-DADE JR. COL, 69-, CHMN. DEPT, 70- U.S.N.R, 43-46; U.S.A, 50-52. Molecular structure; science education. Address: Dept. of Physics, Miami-Dade Junior College, 11380 N.W. 27th Ave, Miami, FL 33167.

GOLLAN, FRANK, b. Brno, Czech, July 1, 09; nat; m. 36; c. 2. MEDICINE. M.D, Prague, 34; Paris & Zurich, 36. Clin. asst, Prague, 36-38; res. assoc. exp. path, Western Reserve, 41-45; asst. prof. physiol, Minnesota, 46-48; prof, fels. res. inst, Antioch Col, 48-52, asst. dir, radioisotope unit, Thayer Vet. Admin. Hosp, 52-55, dir. res, 55-60; CHIEF RADIOISOTOPE SERV, VET. ADMIN. HOSP, 60- U.S.P.H.S, 44-46, Surg. AAAS; Am. Physiol. Soc; Am. Med. Asn; N.Y. Acad. Sci. Cardiovascular physiology. Address: Radioisotope Service, Veterans Administration Hospital, 1201 N.W. 16th St, Miami, FL 33125.

GOLLER, EDWIN JOHN, b. Lawrence, Mass, Jan. 28, 40. ORGANIC CHEMISTRY. B.S, Merrimack Col, 61; univ. assistantship & M.S, Northeast. Univ, 64; Nat. Defense Educ. Act fel & Ph.D.(org. chem), Univ. N.H, 69. Instr. CHEM, Merrimack Col, 63-66; ASST. PROF, VA. MIL. INST, 69- Am. Chem. Soc. Mechanistic organometallic chemistry; stereochemistry; organic synthesis. Address: 306 N. Main St, Lexington, VA 24450.

GOLLEY, FRANK B(ENJAMIN), b. Chicago, Ill, Sept. 24, 30; m. 53; c. 3. ECOLOGY. B.S, Purdue, 52; Wash. Wildlife Res. fel, Washington State, 52-54, M.S, 54; Ph.D.(zool), Mich. State, 58. Asst. prof. zool, North Carolina, 59; prof. biol, N.C. Col, 59; instr. zool, UNIV. GA, 59-62, asst. prof, 62-64, assoc. prof. zool. & dir. Savannah River Ecol. Lab, 64-68, PROF. ZOOL. & EXEC. DIR. INST. ECOL, 68- Mem, Orgn. Trop. Studies. AAAS; Ecol. Soc. Am; Am. Soc. Mammal; Int. Soc. Trop. Ecol; Int. Asn. Ecol. Ecosystem and tropical ecology; energy flow; mineral cycling; mammalogy. Address: Institute of Ecology, The Rockhouse, University of Georgia, Athens, GA 30601.

GOLLMAR, DOROTHY MAY, b. Big Bend, Wis, May 4, 27; m. 62. MATHEMATICS. B.S, Wisconsin, 49, M.A, 51; Nat. Sci. Found. summer fels, Colorado, 52, Oregon, 54, Wisconsin, 55 & Michigan, 56. Teacher, pub. sch, Wis, 49-50; Ill, 50-51; instr. MATH, Monticello Col, 51-54; from asst. prof. to ASSOC. PROF, State Univ. N.Y. Col. Cortland, 54-62; WIS. STATE UNIV-WHITEWATER, 62- AAAS; Am. Math. Soc; Math. Asn. Am. Address: Dept. of Mathematics, Wisconsin State University-Whitewater, Whitewater, WI 53190.

GOLLNICK, PHILIP D, b. Amherst, Wis, Nov. 22, 34; m. 56; c. 3. EXERCISE PHYSIOLOGY. B.S, Wis. State Univ, 56; M.S, Wash. State Univ, 58, Ph.D.(phys. educ, biochem. & physiol), 60. Asst. prof. physiol, Springfield Col, 60-61; Nat. Heart Inst. fel, WASH. STATE UNIV, 61-63, asst. prof. PHYS. EDUC, 63-66, assoc. prof, 66-71, PROF, 71- AAAS; Am. Physiol.

Soc; N.Y. Acad. Sci. Adaptations in function and structure in response to exercise stress; control mechanisms for the mobilization of substrates during exercise. Address: Dept. of Physical Education, Washington State University, Pullman, WA 99163.

GOLLOB, FRED, b. N.Y.C, Oct. 7, 27; m. 51; c. 3. PHYSICAL CHEMISTRY. B.A, Columbia, 50, M.A, 51, Ph.D, 54. Res. chemist, Marshall & Newburgh labs, E.I. du Pont de Nemours & Co, 53-58; group leader, cent. res. lab, Air Reduction Co, Inc, 58-62; DIR, GOLLOB ANAL. SERV, INC, 62- U.S.N, 46-48. AAAS; Instrument Soc; Am. Asn. Consult. Chem. & Chem. Eng; Am. Chem. Soc; Soc. Appl. Spectros. Gas analysis. Address: Gollob Analytic Service, Inc, 47 Industrial Rd, Berkeley Heights, NJ 07922.

GOLLONG, PAUL B(ERNHARD) W(ERNER), b. Berlin, Ger, May 24, 16; nat; m. 44. MECHANICAL & INDUSTRIAL ENGINEERING. B.S, Cincinnati, 41. Signaling systs. engr, Holtzer-Cabot Co, Ill, 41-42; res. engr, Celotex Corp, Ill, 42-43; proj. engr, Armstrong Cork Co, Pa, 43-46; consult. engr, Griffenhagen & Assoc, Ill, 47-50, prin. assoc, 50-51; res. engr, IIT Res. Inst, 51-52, chief Asia & Far East Opers, 52-54, dir. int. div, 54-61; int. adminr, Boeing Co, Wash, 61-33; sr. adv, UN, 63-66, proj. mgr. Israel, 66-69, SR. SCI. AFFAIRS OFF, 70- Dir, Appl. Tech. Ltd, U.K; mem, Int. Exec. Adv. Coun. AAAS; Nat. Soc. Prof. Eng; Am. Inst. Indust. Eng; Opers. Res. Soc. Am; Soc. Int. Develop; Asia Soc. Planning and development of research facilities in Peru, Thailand, Colombia, Israel, Sudan, Mexico, Burma, Afghanistan, Philippines and Venezuela; industrialization of native agricultural products; techno-economic studies on natural resources; advancement of national research programs in underdeveloped countries. Address: United Nations, New York, NY 10017.

GOLLUB, SEYMOUR, b. Phila, Pa, Feb. 21, 25; m. 50; c. 2. MEDICINE, PHYSIOLOGY. B.A, Pennsylvania, 47; Ph.D.(physiol), Jefferson Med. Col, 54; M.D, Hahneman Med. Col, 58. Res. asst. path, Mt. Sinai Hosp, Phila, Pa, 49-50; res. assoc, Albert Einstein Med. Ctr, 50-53, assoc. dir. res. surg, south. div, 55-63, dir, Mandell Lab, 56-63; DIR. HEMAT, ST. BARNABAS HOSP, 63- Private & Govt. res. grants physiol. & hemat, 55-; dir. coagulation lab, Hahnemann Hosp, 56-63, assoc. res. surg, Med. Col, 58-60; dir. res. lab, Hillman Med. Ctr, 57-63. Consult, Roswell Park Mem. Hosp, Buffalo, N.Y, 57-59; mem. comn. plasma, Nat. Res. Coun, 68-71. Int. Soc. Hemat; Am. Soc. Hemat; Microcirculatory Soc; Am. Soc. Exp. Path. Hematology, coagulation, surgery circulation; enzymology. Address: St. Barnabas Hospital, 183rd St. & Third Ave, Bronx, NY 10457.

GOLOD, WILLIAM H, b. N.Y.C, June 28, 33; m. 61; c. 1. PHARMACY, PHYSICAL PHARMACY. B.S, Fordham, 54; M.S, St. Louis Col. Pharm, 55; Ph.D.(pharm), Purdue, 58. Asst. prof. PHARM, MED. UNIV. S.C, 58-64, assoc. prof, 64-67, PROF, 67-, dean sch. pharm, 65-67, asst. dean, 63-65. AAAS; Am. Chem. Soc; Am. Pharmaceut. Asn; Am. Soc. Hosp. Pharmacists; Am. Hosp. Asn. Effects of surface area on drug absorption and activity; use of carbowaxes and synthetic gums as tablet coatings in place of sugar. Address: School of Pharmacy, Medical University of South Carolina, 80 Barre St, Charleston, SC 29401.

GOLOMB, FREDERICK M, b. N.Y.C, Dec. 18, 24; m. 54; c. 2. SURGERY. B.S, Yale, 45; M.D, Rochester, 49. Asst. prof. CLIN. SURG, SCH. MED, N.Y. UNIV, 56-70, ASSOC. PROF, 70-, DIR. CANCER CHEMOTHER. SERV, MED. CTR, 67-, TUMOR SERV, UNIV. HOSP, 70- Secy. N.Y. Cancer Soc, 69-71. Dipl, Am. Bd. Surg. U.S.A, 53-54, Capt. Am. Med. Asn; Am. Asn. Cancer Res; fel. Am. Col. Surg; Am. Soc. Clin. Oncol; Soc. Head & Neck Surg; Soc. Surg. Alimentary Tract; Pan-Am. Med. Asn. General surgery; cancer surgery and chemotherapy; regional techniques for administration of cancer chemotherapeutic agents; tissue culture techniques for drug selection; techniques of reconstructive surgery following radical exenterations; tumor immunology. Address: Dept. of Clinical Surgery, New York University School of Medicine, 550 First Ave, New York, NY 10021.

GOLOMB, MICHAEL, b. Munich, Ger, May 3, 09; nat; m. 39; c. 2. MATHEMATICS. Univ. Würzburg, 28-30; Ph.D.(math), Univ. Berlin, 33. Res. assoc. elec. eng, Cornell Univ, 39-42, instr. math, 40-42; Purdue Univ, 42-44; res. engr. & chief, anal. sect, Franklin Inst, 44-46; assoc. prof. MATH, PURDUE UNIV, 46-50, PROF, 50- Vis. prof, math. res. ctr, Univ. Wis, 56-57, 58, 67 & 70. With Off. Sci. Res. & Develop, U.S.N, 44. Fel. AAAS; Am. Math. Soc; Soc. Indust. & Appl. Math; Math. Asn. Am; Soc. Natural Philos. Integral and functional equations; ordinary and partial differential equations; theory of approximation; functional analysis. Address: 1407 Woodland Ave, West Lafayette, IN 47906.

GOLOMB, SOLOMON WOLF, b. Baltimore, Md, May 31, 32; m. 56; c. 2. MATHEMATICS. A.B, Hopkins, 51; A.M, Harvard, 53, Ph.D.(math), 57; Fulbright scholar, Oslo, 55-56. Sr. res. engr, commun, jet propulsion lab, Calif. Inst. Tech, 56-58; res. group supvr, 58-60, asst. sect. chief, 60-63; assoc. prof. MATH. & ELEC. ENG, UNIV. SOUTH. CALIF, 62-64, PROF, 64- Consult, aerospace & electronics indust, 54-; res. fel. inst. commun. sci, Mass. Inst. Technol, 59; vis. prof, Calif. Inst. Technol, 71-72; mem. comn. VI, Int. Sci. Radio Union, 60- Am. Math. Soc; Math. Asn. Am; Soc. Indust. & Appl. Math; Inst. Elec. & Electronics Eng. Information and communication theory; application of combinatorial mathematics to coding and switching theory; genetic coding; probability; prime number theory. Address: Dept. of Mathematic & Electrical Engineering, Olin Hall 330-C, University of Southern California, University Park, Los Angeles, CA 90007.

GOLOMSKI, WILLIAM A(RTHUR), b. Custer, Wis, Oct. 14, 24; m. 60. APPLIED MATHEMATICS, STATISTICS. B.S, Wis. State Col, 48; M.S, Marquette, 50; M.S.E.M, Milwaukee Sch. Eng, 69. Instr. math, St. Louis, 52-53; asst. prof. Marquette, 53-57; staff asst, oper. div, Oscar Mayer & Co, 57-58, mgr. oper. res, 58-59; v.pres, H.J. Mayer & Sons Co, 59-61; mem. staff, Jos. Schlitz Brewing Co, 61-64, asst. to exec. v.pres, 64-67; V.PRES, JOHN MORRELL & CO, 67- Mgt. consult, 50-58; lectr, Univ. Wis, 58, mem. adv. coun, sch. educ, 58-64; consult, U.S. Bur. Census, 60; mem. Comn. on Prod. Qual, 67-70. U.S.A.A.F, 43-46. Fel. AAAS; fel. Am. Soc. Qual. Control.(v.pres, 64-66, pres, 66-67, testimonial award, 70); fel. N.Y. Acad. Sci; Opers. Res. Soc. Am; Am. Statist. Asn; Inst. Mgt. Sci; Inst. Math. Statist. Industrial operations research; marketing; management science; mathematical programming; applied mathematics and statistics in quality, nutrition and financial growth. Address: 80 Indian Hill Rd, Winnetka, IL 60093.

GOLOSKIE, RAYMOND, b. Providence, R.I, Oct. 30, 30; m. 54; c. 2. NUCLEAR PHYSICS. Sc.B, Brown, 53; M.A, Harvard, 55, Ph.D.(physics), 61. Instr. PHYSICS, Colgate, 59-62; ASST. PROF, WORCESTER POLYTECH. INST, 62- Experiments in nuclear scattering and nuclear reactions at energies below 2 million electron volts and at energies near 100 million electron volts. Address: Dept. of Physics, Worcester Polytechnic Institute, Worcester, MA 01609.

GOLOWICH, EUGENE, b. Mt. Vernon, N.Y, July 21, 39; m. 61; c. 2. PHYSICS. B.S, Rensselaer Polytech, 61; Ph.D.(physics), Cornell, 65. Instr. PHYSICS, Cornell, 65; res. assoc. Carnegie-Mellon Univ, 65-67; asst. prof, UNIV. MASS, AMHERST, 67-70, ASSOC. PROF, 70- AAAS; Am. Phys. Soc. Theoretical physics; high energy physics. Address: Dept. of Physics, University of Massachusetts, Amherst, MA 01002.

GOLTON, WILLIAM C(HARLES), b. Chicago, Ill, Mar. 27, 36; m. 64. ANALYTICAL CHEMISTRY. B.S, Univ. Ky; M.S, Univ. Iowa, 59, Ph.D.(anal. chem), 62. Res. chemist, FABRICS & FINISHES DEPT, MARSHALL LAB, E.I. DU PONT DE NEMOURS & CO, INC, 62-68, STAFF CHEMIST, 68- Am. Chem. Soc. Chemical electroanalysis; product development and quality control; consumer products; organic coatings and related products; acid-base theory; equilibria in nonaqueous solvents; absorption spectroscopy; particle characterization. Address: Fabrics & Finishes Dept, Marshall Lab, E.I. du Pont de Nemours & Co, Inc, P.O. Box 3886, Philadelphia, PA 19146.

GOLTZ, ROBERT W, b. St. Paul, Minn, Sept. 21, 23; m. 45; c. 2. DERMATOLOGY, HISTOPATHOLOGY. B.S, Minnesota, Minneapolis, 43, M.B, 44, M.D, 45. Clin. instr. DERMAT, Minnesota, Minneapolis, 51-58, clin. asst. prof, 58-61, clin. assoc. prof, 61-65; prof. & dir. div, med. ctr, Univ. Colo, Denver, 65-71; PROF. & CHMN. DEPT, MED. SCH, UNIV. MINN, MINNEAPOLIS, 71- Res. grants, Am. Cancer Soc, 58-59; U.S. Pub. Health Serv, 59-66; grad. sch, Minnesota, Minneapolis, 62-64. A.U.S, 46-48, Capt. Am. Dermat. Asn; Am. Acad. Dermat; Soc. Invest. Dermat; Histochem. Soc; Am. Soc. Dermatopath. Venereology; dermatopathology; histochemistry. Address: C394 Mayo Memorial Bldg, University of Minnesota, Minneapolis, MN 55455.

GOLUB, A(BRAHAM), b. Brooklyn, N.Y, May 16, 21; m. 50; c. 2. MATHEMATICAL STATISTICS. B.A, Brooklyn Col, 41, fel, 41-42; M.A, Delaware, 49; George Wash. Univ, 52-55. Sect. chief, surveillance br, ballistic res. labs, Aberdeen Proving Ground, 46-50, asst. chief, 50-55, chief, artillery weapon systs. br, 55-62, assoc. tech. dir, ballistic res. labs, 62-64; dep. spec. asst. opers. res, Off. Asst. Secy. Army, DEPT. ARMY, 64-67, asst. dep. undersecy. army, 67-69, SCIENTIFIC ADV. TO ASST. CHIEF OF STAFF FOR FORCE DEVELOP, WASH, D.C, 69- Instr, Univ. Del, 50-51. Res. & develop. tech. achievement award, 62; exceptional civilian serv. award, 69. U.S.A, 43-46, Sgt. Opers. Res. Soc. Am; Am. Math. Soc; Inst. Math. Statist; Am. Ord. Asn. Weapons systems analysis; operations research; ordnance; statistical estimation; acceptance sampling; experimental design; analysis of variance. Address: 5375 Duke St, Alexandria, VA 22304.

GOLUB, ALLYN LLOYD, b. Brooklyn, N.Y, June 28, 40. DEVELOPMENTAL BIOLOGY. B.A, Univ. Hartford, 62; M.S, Univ. Miami, 66, Ph.D.(biol), 69. Investr, BIOL. DIV, OAK RIDGE NAT. LAB, 69-71, NAT. INSTS. HEALTH FEL, 71- Developmental biology and biochemistry of Artemia salina. Address: 224 N. Purdue, Apt. 308, Oak Ridge, TN 37830.

GOLUB, EDWARD S, b. Chicago, Ill, Oct. 6, 34; m. 59; c. 2. IMMUNOLOGY, CELL BIOLOGY. B.S, Roosevelt Univ, 56; M.S, Miami Univ, 59; Ph.D.(bacteriol), Univ. N.C, 64. Res. fel. immunol, Duke Univ, 64-65; Scripps Clin. & Res. Found, 65-68; ASST. PROF. BIOL. SCI, PURDUE UNIV, 68- U.S. Pub. Health Serv. career develop. award, 68; Merck Found. faculty develop. award, 69. AAAS; Am. Asn. Immunol; Am. Soc. Exp. Path. Mechanism of hypertensity reactions; induction of immunologic tolerance; cell interactions in the immune response; functional ontogeny of immunity. Address: Dept. of Biological Sciences, Purdue University, Lafayette, IN 47907.

GOLUB, ELLIS ECKSTEIN, b. N.Y.C, Nov. 1, 42; m. 64; c. 2. BIOCHEMISTRY. B.A, Brandeis, 63; Ph.D.(biochem), Tufts, 69. Nat. Insts. Health res. fel. BIOL, CALIF. INST. TECHNOL, 69-71, RES. FEL, JET PROPULSION LAB, 71- AAAS; Am. Chem. Soc; N.Y. Acad. Sci. Antibiotic biosynthesis; enzymology; differentiation. Address: Division of Biology, California Institute of Technology, Pasadena, CA 91109.

GOLUB, GENE H, b. Chicago, Ill, Feb. 29, 32. MATHEMATICS. B.S, Illinois, 53, M.A, 54, Ph.D.(math), 59. Nat. Sci. Found. fel, math. lab, Cambridge, 59-60; mem. staff, Lawrence Radiation Lab, California, 60-61; mem. tech. staff, Space Tech. Labs, Inc, Thompson Ramo Wooldridge, Inc, 61-62; vis. asst. prof. COMPUT, SCI, STANFORD UNIV, 62-64, asst. prof, 64-66, assoc. prof, 66-70, PROF, 70- Soc. Indust. & Appl. Math. Numerical analysis. Address: Dept. of Computer Science, Stanford University, Stanford, CA 94305.

GOLUB, M(ORTON) A(LLAN), b. Montreal, Que, June 11, 25; nat; m. 54; c. 2. PHYSICAL & POLYMER CHEMISTRY. B.Sc, McGill, 44; M.Sc, New Brunswick, 47; du Pont fel, Missouri, 48-49, Ph.D.(chem), 51. Explosive analyst, Defense Indust, Ltd, Que, 44-45; teacher, private sch, Montreal, 45-46; demonstr. physics, New Brunswick, 46-47; asst. chem, Missouri, 47-48, instr. math, 49-51; res. chemist, B.F. Goodrich Chem. Co, 51-54, res. ctr, 54-60; sr. polymer chemist, Stanford Res. Inst, 60-68; Nat. Res. Coun-NASA sr. resident res. assoc, AMES RES. CTR, NASA, 68-70, RES. SCIENTIST, 70- Instr, Foothill Col, 63-68. AAAS; Am. Chem. Soc. Reactions and characterization of high polymers; photochemistry; radiation chemistry; elastomers. Address: Ames Research Center, NASA, Moffett Field, CA 94035.

GOLUB, ORVILLE J(OSEPH), b. St. Louis, Mo, Aug. 24, 15; m. 41; c. 5. BACTERIOLOGY. B.S, Washington (Seattle), 36, M.S, 38; Ph.D.(microbiol), California, 44. Res. worker, special proj. div, U.S. Dept. Navy, 46-47; acting chief virus br, chem. corps, U.S. War Dept, Md, 47-48; assoc, BIO-SCI. LABS, 48-67, EXEC. V.PRES, 67- U.S.N, 41-46. AAAS; Am. Soc.

Microbiol; Endocrine Soc; Am. Asn. Immunol. Immunology; anaphylaxis; bacterial and virus infectious diseases; experimental respiratory infection; influenza; endocrinology laboratory methods. Address: Bio-Science Labs, 7600 Tyrone Ave, Van Nuys, CA 91405.

GOLUB, SAMUEL J(OSEPH), b. Middleboro, Mass, July 25, 15; m. 40; c. 2. BIOLOGY, TEXTILE TECHNOLOGY. B.S, Massachusetts, 38, fel, 38-40, M.S, 40; Ph.D.(biol), Harvard, 46. Inspector biol. mat, dept. ord, U.S. Navy, 42; asst. prof. bot, Massachusetts, 46-47, assoc. prof, 47; bot. ed, G. & C. Merriam Co, 47-49; lectr. biol, Brandeis, 49-50, asst. prof, 50-56; sr. res. assoc, Fabric Res. Labs, Inc, 57-59; assoc. dir, ACH Fiber Serv, Inc, 59-63; ASST. DIR. BIOL. SCI, FABRIC RES. LABS, INC, 63- AAAS; Bot. Soc. Am; Am. Soc. Plant Physiol; Mycol. Soc. Am; Soc. Indust. Microbiol; Am. Soc. Test. & Mat; Am. Asn. Textile Chem. & Colorists; Fiber Soc; fel. Am. Inst. Chem. Plant morphology and pathology; developmental morphology; textile fiber analysis. Address: Fabric Research Labs, Inc, 1000 Providence Hwy, Dedham, MA 02026.

GOLUB, STEPHEN, b. Brooklyn, N.Y, Jan. 7, 43; m. 63; c. 2. PHYSICAL CHEMISTRY, PHYSICS. B.S, Columbia, 63, N.Y. State Regents fel, 63-65, M.A, 64, Ph.D.(chem), 68. Nat. Acad. Sci-Nat. Res. Coun. res. assoc. & physicist, electron physics sect, Atomic Physics Div, Nat. Bur. Standards, 67-69; MEM. STAFF, ESSO RES. CTR, 69- Am. Phys. Soc. Atomic and molecular physics; chemical physics; molecular moments and polarizabilities; electro optical effects; negative ion photodetachment; electron affinities; chemisorption. Address: Esso Research Center, P.O. Box 45, Linden, NJ 07036.

GOLUBA, RAYMOND WILLIAM, b. Streator, Ill, Oct. 5, 39; m. 61; c. 2. MECHANICAL ENGINEERING. B.S, Illinois, 61, M.S, 62; Ph.D.(mech. eng), Wisconsin, 68. Engr. ARO, Inc, Arnold Air Force Sta, Tenn, 62-63; instr. thermodyn, Wisconsin, Madison, 63-64; ENGR, DEPT. MECH. ENG, LAWRENCE LIVERMORE LAB, 68- Am. Soc. Mech. Eng. Heat transfer in oscillating flows; heat transfer from capillary wetted surfaces with applications toward heat pipes. Address: Dept. of Mechanical Engineering, Lawrence Livermore Lab, Livermore, CA 94550.

GOLUBIC, STEPHAN, b. Zagreb, Yugoslavia, May 4, 34; m. 66; c. 2. ECOLOGY, PHYCOLOGY. Dipl. biol, Zagreb, 56, Ph.D.(biol. sci), 63. Res. asst, inst. exp. biol, Yugoslavia Acad. Sci, Zagreb, 56-59; Inst. Marine Biol, Rovinj, 59-63; Alexander von Humdoldt Found. fel, inst. limnol, Univ. Freiburg, 63-65; res. assoc. geol, Princeton, 65-66; instr. BIOL, Yale, 66-68, asst. prof, 68-69; ASSOC. PROF, Paterson State Col, 69-70; BOSTON UNIV, 70- Nat. Sci. Found. res. grant, 67-69, 70-71. Yugoslav Army, 61-62. AAAS; Phycol. Soc. Am; Int. Phycol. Soc; Int. Asn. Theoret. & Appl. Limnol. Phycology, ecology and taxonomy of Cyanophyta; limnology; marine biology; ecology of carbonate deposition and dissolution; water pollution. Address: Dept. of Biology, Boston University, 2 Cummington St, Boston, MA 02215.

GOLUBJATNIKOV, RJURIK, b. Kuressaare, Estonia, June 19, 31; U.S. citizen. MICROBIOLOGY, EPIDEMIOLOGY. B.A, Millikin, 54; M.P.H, Michigan, 58, Ph.D.(epidemiol. sci), 64. Asst. prof. prev. med. & dir. vaccine eval. prog. lab, State Univ. N.Y. Buffalo, 64-67; ASST. PROF. PREV. MED. & CHIEF IMMUNOL. SECT, STATE LAB. HYG, UNIV. WIS, MADISON, 67- Assoc. investr, U.S. Pub. Health Serv. res. grant, 64-68; prin. investr, Huixquilucan Serum Surv. grant, 67-68; adv, Inst. Nutrit. Cent. Am. & Panama, 68; Ecol. Studies Mycoplasma grant, 68-69. U.S.A, 54-56. AAAS; Am. Pub. Health Asn; Am. Soc. Microbiol; Asn. Teachers Prev. Med; Archaeol. Inst. Am. Immunology, including primary and secondary antibody responses and immunologic memory; infectious disease epidemiology; serological epidemiology; vaccine studies. Address: State Lab. of Hygiene, University of Wisconsin Medical Center, Madison, WI 53706.

GOLUBOVIC, ALEKSANDAR, b. Moribor, Yugoslavia, Feb. 19, 20; m. 60; c. 1. CHEMISTRY. Dipl, Zagreb, 43, Ph.D.(chem), 60. Res. chemist, Inst. Indust. Res, Zagreb, 45-56; res. assoc. CHEM, Mass. Inst. Tech, 56-62; sr. scientist, Tyco Labs, Mass, 62-64; RES. SCIENTIST, AIR FORCE CAMBRIDGE RES. LABS, 64- Am. Chem. Soc. Organic semiconductors and photoconductors; organic peroxides and bioperoxides. Address: Air Force Cambridge Research Labs, Laurence G. Hanscom Field, Bedford, MA 01730.

GOLUBOW, JULIUS, b. N.Y.C, June 2, 29; m. 58; c. 3. BIOCHEMISTRY. B.S, City Col. New York, 52; M.S, Purdue, 55; U.S. Health Serv. trainee, Pittsburgh, 58-59, Ph.D.(biochem), 60. Asst, Purdue, 53-55; Pittsburgh, 55-59; res. assoc. biochem, med. col, Cornell Univ, 59-61, instr, 61-63, asst. prof, 63-68; ASSOC. PROF. BIOL. SCI, LEHMAN COL, 68- Asst, Sloan-Kettering Inst. Cancer Res, summer 55. AAAS; Am. Chem. Soc; Harvey Soc; Brit. Biochem. Soc; N.Y. Acad. Sci. Enzymology; mineral metabolism. Address: Dept. of Biological Sciences, Herbert H. Lehman College, Bedford Park Blvd. W, Bronx, NY 10468.

GOLUEKE, CLARENCE GEORGE, b. Menominee, Mich, Sept. 28, 17; m. 48; c. 1. ENVIRONMENTAL SCIENCES. B.A, St. Louis Univ, 39; M.A, Univ. Ill, 41; Ph.D.(mycol), Univ. Calif, 53. Instr. gen. sci, Nazareth Col, 45-46; asst. bot, Univ. Ill, 48; UNIV. CALIF. BERKELEY, 48-51, LECTR. & RES. BIOLOGIST, SANIT. ENG. RES. LAB, 51- Consult, N.Am. Rockwell Corp; Calif. State Depts. Water Resources & Pub. Health; solid wastes mgt. off, Environ. Protection Agency. Los Angeles Pub. Health Found. Award; Arthur M. Wellington Prize, Am. Soc. Civil Eng, 66. Am. Acad. Polit. & Soc. Sci; Am. Pub. Health Asn. Environmental health sciences; waste treatment and reclamation; closed environmental systems. Address: 2691 McMorrow Rd, San Pablo, CA 94806.

GOLUMBIC, CALVIN, b. Lock Haven, Pa, Nov. 8, 12; m. 46; c. 1. BIOCHEMISTRY. B.S, Pa. State Col, 34; scholar, Rutgers, 34-35, M.S, 25, Ph.D.(org. chem), 37. Res. assoc. antioxygens, Iowa, 37-42; chemist, Rockefeller Inst, 42-45; asst. res. prof. chem, Pittsburgh, 45-47; chemist, Bur. Mines, 47-53; naval stores res. sect, AGR. RES. SERV, U.S. DEPT. AGR, 53-54, head, quality evaluation sect, biol. scis. br, marketing res. div, 54-60, chief field crops & animal prods. br, 60-67, asst. dir. mkt. qual. div, Md, 67-68, asst. dep. adminr. to ADMINR, 68- Civilian with Nat. Defense

Res. Comt, 42-45. Am. Chem. Soc; Soc. Exp. Biol. & Med; N.Y. Acad. Sci; Inst. Food Technol. Antioxidants and autooxidation of fats; vitamin E; nitrogen mustards; countercurrent distribution; coal, food and agricultural chemistry; synthetic liquid fuels; terpenes. Address: U.S. Dept. of Agriculture, Room 320 Administration Bldg, Washington, DC 20250.

GOLUMBIC, NORMA, b. Brooklyn, N.Y, Apr. 30, 16; m. 46; c. 1. ORGANIC CHEMISTRY. B.A, Brooklyn Col, 36; M.S, Iowa, 38. Chemist, Bur. Mines, 42-50; sci. writer, agr. res. serv, U.S. Dept. Agr, 55; Nat. Cancer Inst, 56-58, head, res. & prog. reports sect, 58-69, asst. chief, res. info. br, 65-69; INFO. OFF, DIV. NURSING, NAT. INSTS. HEALTH, 69- AAAS; Am. Chem. Soc; fel. Am. Inst. Chem. Synthetic liquid fuels; coal chemistry; catalysis; cancer research literature; medical writing. Address: Division of Nursing, National Institutes of Health, Bethesda, MD 20014.

GOMAN, E(DWARD) G(ORDON), b. Aberdeen, Wash, July 27, 20; m. 43; c. 3. MATHEMATICS. B.S, Oregon State Col, 43, fel, 46-47, M.S, 47; California, Los Angeles, 50. Instr. MATH, UNIV. PUGET SOUND, 47-48, asst. prof, 48-57, assoc. prof, 57-64, PROF, 65-, CHMN. DEPT, 48- U.S.N.R, 43-46. Am. Math. Soc; Math. Asn. Am. Vector products in higher dimensional space. Address: 11910 86th Ave. E, Puyallup, WA 98371.

GOMATOS, PETER J(OHN), b. Cambridge, Mass, Feb. 13, 29. BIOCHEMISTRY, ANIMAL VIROLOGY. S.B, Mass. Inst. Technol, 50; M.D, Hopkins, 54; Ph.D.(virol), Rockefeller Inst, 63. Med. asst. resident, Boston City Hosp, 57-58; sr. med. resident, Mass. Gen. Hosp, 58-59; guest investr, Rockefeller Inst, 63-64; ASSOC. MEM, SLOAN-KETTERING INST, 64- Vis. investr, Max Planck Inst. Virus Res, 64; Inst. Virol, Univ. Glasgow, 64-65. U.S.N.R, 55-57, Res, 57-, Comdr. Am. Chem. Soc; Harvey Soc; Am. Asn. Immunol; Am. Col. Physicians. Study of physical-chemical characteristics of viruses; effects of viruses on cells; neoplastic potential of various viruses. Address: Sloan Kettering Institute, 410 E. 68th St, New York, NY 10021.

GOMBA, FRANK J(OSEPH), b. Perth Amboy, N.J, Dec. 19, 30; m. 55; c. 1. INORGANIC CHEMISTRY. A.B, Montclair State Col, 52, A.M, 54. Teacher, pub. sch, N.J, 52-57; asst. prof. CHEM, U.S. NAVAL ACAD, 57-63, ASSOC. PROF, 63- Summers, Harvard, 54, Nat. Sci. Found. Inst, Mich. State, 57, Mont. State Col, 59. Am. Chem. Soc. Chemical education; inorganic mechanisms; polarography of chromium complexes. Address: Dept. of Chemistry, Division of Mathematics & Science, U.S. Naval Academy, Annapolis, MD 21402.

GOMBERG, HENRY J(ACOB), b. N.Y.C, Apr. 16, 18; m. 67; c. 5. NUCLEAR ENGINEERING. B.S.E, Univ. Mich, 41, M.S.E, 43, Ph.D.(elec. eng), 51; hon. D.Sc, Albion Col, 68. Asst. dir, Mem. Phoenix Proj, Univ. Mich, 52-59, dir, 59-61, prof. nuclear eng. & chmn. dept, 58-61; prof. physics & dep. dir, P.R. Nuclear Ctr, Univ. P.R, 61-66, dir, 66-71; PRES, KMS FUSION INC, 71- Res. proj. dir. new high resolution methods of radiation detection, Atomic Energy Comn, 50-58; lectr, Oak Ridge Inst. Nuclear Studies, 51-53; Carnegie prof, Univ. Hawaii, 61; consult, Atomic Energy Comn; Lockheed Aircraft Corp; Argonne Nat. Lab; chmn. comt. res. reactors, Nat. Acad. Sci-Nat. Res. Coun; mem. comt. radiation effects, div. phys. sci, Nat. Res. Coun. U.S.N.R, 44-45, Ens. Fel. Am. Nuclear Soc; Am. Phys. Soc; Am. Soc. Eng. Educ; Inst. Elec. & Electronics Eng; High resolution detection of radiation; effect of radiation on matter; biological effects of radiation; reactor safety and accident analysis; reactor site selection; nuclear energy; development of nuclear fusion for power and other peaceful purposes. Address: KMS Fusion Inc, 3941 Research Park Dr, Ann Arbor, MI 48104.

GOMER, R(OBERT), b. Vienna, Austria, Mar. 24, 24; nat; m. 55; c. 2. PHYSICAL CHEMISTRY. B.A, Pomona Col, 44; Ph.D.(chem), Rochester, 49. Atomic Energy Cmn. fel. CHEM, Harvard, 49-50; instr, JAMES FRANCK INST. & UNIV. CHICAGO, 50-51, asst. prof, 51-54, assoc. prof, 54-58, PROF, 58- Sloan fel, 58-61; Bourke lectr, Eng, 59; Guggenheim fel, 69-70. U.S.A, 44-46. Am. Chem. Soc. Reaction kinetics of gaseous systems; surface chemistry and physics; field and ion emission. Address: James Franck Institute, 5640 Ellis Ave, Chicago, IL 60637.

GOMES, ALERCIO (MOREIRA), b. Espirito Santo, Brazil, Mar. 12, 15; m. 44; c. 2. ASTRONOMY. M.S, Brazil, 42, dipl, 49; Sc.Dr.(astron), Naval Acad, Brazil, 53. Prof. astron, Naval Acad, Brazil, 53; prin. astronr, Nat. Observ, 55; prof. astron, Brazil, 58; prof. celestial mech. Inst. Mil. Eng. Exercito & dir. hydrographic off, Brazilian Navy, 65-71; PROF. ASTROPHYS, FED. UNIV. FLUMINENSE, 71- Res. fel, Mt. Wilson & Palomar Observs, 59, 60 & 61; Guggenheim Found. res. fel, 60, 61 & 64; vis. prof, Bonn, 62; vis. astronr, U.S. Naval Observ, 64. Mem, Super-Nova Int. Res. Prog, Palomar Observ, 60-61. Int. Astron. Union; Am. Astron. Soc; Royal Astron. Soc; Astron. Soc. Japan. Statistical astronomy; intergalactic obscuration; cosmology. Address: Rua Ipiranga, Number 25, Apt. 401, Rio de Janeiro ZC-01, Brazil.

GOMES, WAYNE REGINALD, b. Modesto, Calif, Nov. 15, 38; m. 64; c. 2. ENDOCRINOLOGY, REPRODUCTIVE PHYSIOLOGY. B.S, Calif. State Polytech. Col, 60; M.S, Washington State, 62; Ph.D.(endocrine physiol), Purdue, 65. Asst. prof. DAIRY SCI, OHIO STATE UNIV, 65-69, ASSOC. PROF, ANIMAL REPRODUCTION CTR, 69- Res. award, Ohio Sigma Xi, 70. AAAS; Am. Dairy Sci. Asn; Am. Soc. Animal Sci; N.Y. Acad. Sci; Soc. Study Reproduction; Am. Physiol. Soc; Brit. Soc. Study Fertil; Endocrine Soc. Nature and levels of the sex steroids involved in reproductive processes. Address: Dept. of Dairy Science, Animal Reproduction Center, Ohio State University, Columbus, OH 43210.

GOMEZ, ILDEFONSO LUIS, b. Cardenas, Cuba, Jan. 23, 28; m. 54; c. 6. ORGANIC CHEMISTRY. D.Sc,(chem), Havana, 52. Anal. chemist, Cia Rayonera Cuba, 51-52, res. chemist, 52-56; tech. supvr, Plinex S.A, 56-58, tech. supt, 58-61; sr. res. chemist, MONSANTO CO, 61-67, res. specialist, 67-68, specialist tech. dept, plastic prod. & resins div, 68-70, SPECIALIST PACKAGING DIV, BLOOMFIELD, CONN, 70- Consult, Ministry Commerce, Cuba, 58-60; vis. lectr, Univ. Havana, 59-60. Am. Chem. Soc; Soc. Plastics Eng. High tenacity rayon; compounding and processing polyvinyl chloride resins; stabilization to light of rigid polyvinyl chloride; polyurethane foam; epoxy resins; drying and blending highly hygroscopic thermoplastics; rheology and processing of polymeric compositions based on acrylonitrile with low permeability to gases. Address: 223 Franklin Rd, Longmeadow, MA 01106.

GOMEZ, MANUEL, b. Pueblo, Colo, Sept. 26, 21; m. 49; c. 2. FUEL TECHNOLOGY. B.S, Univ. Denver, 47, M.S, 49. Chemist, coal br, U.S. BUR. MINES, DEPT. INTERIOR, 48-56, technologist, coal tech. br, 56-59, chem. engr, Denver Coal Res. Lab, 59-63, CHEM. RES. ENGR, 63-66, DIV. MINE SYSTS. ENG, 66- Med.C, 43-46, Sgt. Am. Chem. Soc; Soc. Min. Eng; Am. Inst. Min, Metall. & Petrol. Eng. Coal technology and coal tar chemistry. Address: Division Mine Systems Engineering, U.S. Bureau of Mines, Denver Federal Center, Bldg. 20, Denver, CO 80225.

GOMEZ-IBANEZ, JOSE D(ANIEL), b. Sarrion, Spain, Oct. 9, 11; nat; m. 39; c. 3. CHEMISTRY. Lic. Ciencias, Madrid, 33; fel, Univ. Int. de Santander, 33; A.M, Oberlin Col, 38; Ph.D.(phys. chem), Cornell, 45. Instr. CHEM, WESLEYAN UNIV, 42-46, asst. prof, 45-51, assoc. prof, 51-55, PROF, 55- Lectr, Hartford Col, 44-48; vis. prof, chem. inst, Univ. São Paulo, 71- AAAS; Am. Chem. Soc; Faraday Soc; Hist. Sci. Soc. Thermodynamics of solutions; determination of activity coefficients by the cryoscopic method; large molecules. Address: Hall-Atwater Lab. of Chemistry, Wesleyan University, Middletown, CT 06457.

GOMEZPLATA, ALBERT, b. Colombia, S.Am, July 2, 30; nat. CHEMICAL ENGINEERING. B.Sc, Polytech. Inst. Brooklyn, 52; M.Sc, Rensselaer Polytech. Inst, 54, Ph.D.(chem. eng), 59. Process engr, gen. chem. div, Del. Works, 52-53; asst. prof. CHEM. ENG, UNIV. MD, COLLEGE PARK, 58-62, assoc. prof, 62-68, PROF, 68- Year in indust. prof, E.I. du Pont de Nemours & Co, Inc, 65-66; vis. prof, Univ. P.R, 70-71; consult, div. air qual. control, State of Md. Fel. Am. Inst. Chem; Am. Inst. Chem. Eng; Am. Soc. Eng. Educ; N.Y. Acad. Sci. Kinetics; heterogeneous flow systems; fluidized beds. Address: Dept. of Chemical Engineering, University of Maryland, College Park, MD 20740.

GOMM, FRED BRYANT, b. Afton, Wyo, June 26, 28; m. 53; c. 4. RANGE MANAGEMENT. B.S, Utah State, 50, fel, 53-55, M.S, 56. Instr. pub. sch, Idaho, 50-51; range scientist, PLANT SCI. RES. DIV, AGR. RES. SERV, U.S. DEPT. AGR, Ariz. & Mont, 55-71, RES. AGRONOMIST, SQUAW BUTTE EXP. STA, 71- U.S.A, 51-52, Sgt. Am. Soc. Range Mgt. Range improvement and artificial reseeding of range lands; improvement of flood-irrigated meadows. Address: Squaw Butte Experiment Station, Plant Science Research Division, Agricultural Research Service, U.S. Dept. of Agriculture, Burns, OR 97720.

GOMMEL, WILLIAM R(AYMOND), b. Indianapolis, Ind, Aug. 16, 24; m. 43; c. 3. METEOROLOGY. A.B, California, Los Angeles, 51, M.A, 52, 58-60; George Washington, 57-58. Prod. draftsman, Atkins Saw Div, Borg-Warner Corp, Ind, 40-42; asst. sta. weather off, U.S. Air Force, 44-50, weather cent. anal. supvr, Ger, 52-53, chief tech. info. & ed, Hqs. 2nd Weather Wing, 53-55, tech. pubs. br, sci. servs, Hqs. Air Weather Serv, 55-56, asst. to dir, Sci. Serv, 56-58, staff meteorologist, ballistic missile div, 60-61, space systs. div, 62-63, staff scientist, directorate sci. & tech, Hqs, 64-65; asst. prof. math, IND. CENT. COL, 65-69, ASSOC. PROF. MATH. & EARTH SCI, 69-, CHMN. DEPT. EARTH SCI, 66- Part-time instr, dept. geosci, Purdue Univ. U.S.A.F, 43-65, Lt. Col.(Ret); Commendation Medal, 65. AAAS; Am. Geophys. Union; Am. Meteorol. Soc. Interaction between sea and atmosphere; climatic change; synoptic meteorology; cloud physics; upper atmosphere; satellites; instrumentation. Address: 2301 Lawrence Ave, Indianapolis, IN 46227.

GOMOLL, ALLEN W, b. Chicago, Ill, July 10, 33; m. 55; c. 2. PHARMACOLOGY. B.S, Univ. Ill, 55, M.S, 58, U.S. Pub. Health Serv. fel, 58-61, Ph.D.(pharmacol), 61. Instr. pharmacol, col. med, Univ. Ill, 61-62, asst. prof, 62-66; sr. scientist and group leader, MEAD JOHNSON RES. CTR, 66-67, group leader CARDIOVASC. PHARMACOL, 67-69, sect. leader, 69-70, PRIN. INVESTR, 70- AAAS; N.Y. Acad. Sci; Am. Heart Asn; Am. Soc. Pharmacol. & Exp. Therapeut; Soc. Exp. Biol. & Med. Cardiovascular pharmacology; effects of drugs on adrenal cortical hormone biosynthesis. Address: Pharmacology Dept, Mead Johnson Research Center, 2404 Pennsylvania Ave, Evansville, IN 47721.

GOMORY, RALPH E, b. Brooklyn, N.Y, May 7, 29. MATHEMATICS. B.A, Williams Col, 50, Cambridge, 50-51; Ph.D.(math), Princeton, 54. Asst. prof. math. & Higgins lectr, Princeton, 57-59; mgr. mgt. sci. & combinatorial studies, T.J. WATSON RES. CTR, IBM CORP, 59-64, IBM fel, 64-65, dir. math. sci. dept, 65-70, mem. corp. tech. comt, 70, DIR. RES, 70- Mem. adv. panel, appl. math. div, Nat. Bur. Standards, 64-68; Mayor's Opers. Res. Coun. City of N.Y, 66-70, v.chmn, 69-70; consult, Nat. Sci. Found, 67-69; mem. comt. appln. math, div. math. sci, Nat. Res. Coun, 67-70, chmn, 69-70, mem-at-large, 69-; Andrew D. White prof-at-large, Cornell Univ, 70-; adj. prof, Courant Inst, N.Y. Univ, 70-; mem. vis. comt. Sloan Sch. Mgt, Mass. Inst. Technol, 71-74; coun. grad. sch. business, Univ. Chicago, 71-74. U.S.N, 54-57, Lt.(jg). Am. Math. Soc; Inst. Mgt. Sci; Opers. Res. Soc. Am.(Lancaster Prize, 64); Soc. Indust. & Appl. Math. Linear and integer programming; network flow theory; nonlinear differential equations. Address: IBM T.J. Watson Research Center, Box 218, Yorktown Heights, NY 10598.

GOMPERTZ, MICHAEL L, b. New Haven, Conn, Dec. 10, 12; m. 41; c. 2. INTERNAL MEDICINE, GASTROENTEROLOGY. B.A, Yale, 33; M.D, Columbia, 37. Asst. chief GASTROENTEROL, VET. ADMIN. HOSP, MEMPHIS, 53-55, CHIEF, 55-; PROF. MED, COL. MED, UNIV. TENN, MEMPHIS, 68-, instr, 55-58, asst. prof, 58-66, assoc. prof, 66-68. U.S.A.A.F, 43-46, Capt. Fel. Am. Col. Physicians; Am. Gastroenterol. Asn. Clinical research in liver disease and peptic ulcer disease. Address: Veterans Administration Hospital, 1030 Jefferson Ave, Memphis, TN 38104.

GOMPF, THOMAS E(DWARD), b. Elizabeth, N.J, Apr. 4, 25; m. 50; c. 1. ORGANIC CHEMISTRY. A.B, Hopkins, 48, M.A, 49, Ph.D.(org. chem), 52. Res. chemist, cent. res. lab, Gen. Aniline & Film Corp, 52; EASTMAN KODAK CO, 52-57, sr. res. chemist, 57-59, RES. ASSOC, 60- Lectr, Rochester, 57-58. U.S.A, 44-46. Am. Chem. Soc. Couplers for photographic color film; organic chemistry related to color photography; photographic emulsion technology. Address: Research Labs, Eastman Kodak Co, 343 State St, Rochester, NY 14650.

GONA, AMOS G, b. Nandyal, India, July 16, 33; U.S. citizen; m. 62; c. 2. ENDOCRINOLOGY, ELECTRON MICROSCOPY. B.Sc, Andhra, India, 54; M.A, City Col. New York, 65; Nat. Insts. Health fel. & Ph.D.(anat), Albert Einstein Col. Med, 67. Lectr. demonstr. zool, Andhra Christian Col, India, 54-55; Rangoon, 55-57; sci. master, Anglo-Chinese Sch, Malaysia, 57-60; sr. biol. master, Opoku Ware Sch, Ghana, 60-63; Nat. Insts. Health fel. ANAT, Albert Einstein Col. Med, 68; ASST. PROF, COL. MED. & DENT. N.J, NEWARK, 68- Am. Asn. Anat; Am. Soc. Zool; Soc. Develop. Biol; N.Y. Acad. Sci. Endocrines and neuroendocrines in amphibian metamorphosis; ultrastructural studies on hormone action. Address: Dept. of Anatomy, College of Medicine & Dentistry of New Jersey at Newark, Newark, NJ 07303.

GONANO, JOHN ROLAND, b. Winchester, Va, Jan. 21, 39; m. 59; c. 2. LOW TEMPERATURE PHYSICS. B.S, West Virginia, 60; Ph.D.(physics), Duke, 67. Fel. thermal expansion magnetic mat, dept. physics, Florida, 66-68; RES. PHYSICIST, Nat. Bur. Standards, 68-71; U.S. ARMY MOBILITY EQUIP. RES. & DEVELOP. CTR, 71- U.S.A.F, 61-62. Investigation of magnetic interactions by means of specific heat, nuclear magnetic resonance and thermal expansion measurements; low temperature thermometry; application of physical principles to land mine detection. Address: U.S. Army Mobility Equipment Research & Development Center, SMEFB-XR, Ft. Belvoir, VA 22060.

GONCZ, JOHN H(ENRY), b. Somerville, Mass, Feb. 9, 33; m. 64; c. 2. PHYSICS. S.B, Mass. Inst. Tech, 54, M.S, 59. Engr, Edgerton, Germeshausen & Grier, Inc, 54-55, sci. exec, 57-68; res. scientist, div. land res, Commonwealth Sci. & Indust. Res. Org, Canberra, Australia, 68-70; RES. SCHOLAR, DEPT. ENG. PHYSICS, AUSTRALIAN NAT. UNIV, 70- Sig.C, 55-57, 1st. Lt. Am. Phys. Soc. Physics and application of xenon flashtubes; gaseous discharge devices; triggered spark gaps; optical systems for illumination and signaling; seismology; digital signal processing. Address: c/o 1527 16th St. N, St. Petersburg, FL 33704.

GONDA, THOMAS ANDREW, Psychiat, see 12th ed, Soc. & Behav. Vols.

GONET, FRANK, b. New Bedford, Mass, Nov. 8, 10; m. 42; c. 2. PHYSICAL CHEMISTRY. Boston; Warsaw, Poland. Chem. specialist, U.S. TARIFF COMN, 41-59, CHIEF, CHEM. DIV, 59- AAAS; Am. Chem. Soc; Am. Asn. Textile Chem. & Colorists; Am. Inst. Chem; N.Y. Acad. Sci. Chemical market research and international trade. Address: 4007 N. Woodstock St, Arlington, VA 22207.

GONG, JOSEPH KWOCK, b. San Francisco, Calif, Dec. 13, 25; m. 66; c. 2. PHYSIOLOGY, RADIATION BIOLOGY. A.B, California, Berkeley, 51, M.A, 59, Ph.D.(physiol), 63. Jr. investr. radiobiol, U.S. Naval Radiol. Defense Lab, 51-54, sr. investr, 55-63; res. assoc. surg, med. col, Cornell, 63-64; asst. prof. ORAL BIOL, STATE UNIV. N.Y. BUFFALO, 64-68, ASSOC. PROF, 68- Sr. radiobiologist, Marshall Island Resurv. Exped, Atomic Energy Comn, 55 & 56; dep. proj. off, Oper. Hardtack, U.S. Naval Radiol. Defense Lab, 58; lectr. & consult, Oak Ridge Inst. Nuclear Studies, 67; partic, meeting of investrs. pop. biol. of altitude, WHO-Pan.Am. Health Orgn. Invest. Biol. Pop, 67. U.S.A.A.F, 44-46. AAAS; Radiation Res. Soc; Health Physics Soc. X-ray effects on bone growth; fission-product contamination and decontamination; fallout inhalation; radio-contamination of marine animals; high altitude and x-ray effects on bone and marrow, vascular volume and hematology; quantitative skeletal biology; leukemia. Address: Dept. of Oral Biology, State University of New York at Buffalo, Buffalo, NY 14214.

GONGWER, CALVIN ANDREW, b. Portland, Ore, June 25, 15; m. 40; c. 3. MECHANICAL & AERONAUTICAL ENGINEERING. B.S, Columbia, 37; M.S, Calif. Inst. Tech, 39. Asst, hydraul. mach. lab, Calif. Inst. Tech, 37-39; mem. res. labs. div, Gen. Motors Corp, Mich, 39-41; mem. sci. staff, U.S. Navy Underwater Sound Lab, Conn, 41-45; supvr. underwater develop, Aerojet-Gen. Corp, 45-51, mgr. underwater engine div, 51-58, dir, aerojet systs. div, 58-59, mgr. anti-submarine warfare div, 59-65, sr. scientist, 65-66; PRES. INNERSPACE CORP, 66- Pres, Lunar Space Corp, Calif, 63-66; consult, Aerojet. Gen. Corp, 66-67. Am. Soc. Mech. Eng; Am. Inst. Aeronaut. & Astronaut. Hydrodynamics, especially design of underwater high-speed propulsion systems and bodies; underwater jet propulsion. Address: Innerspace Corp, 19017 E. Leadora Ave, Glendora, CA 91740.

GONICK, E(LY), b. Detroit, Mich, May 24, 25; m. 52; c. 2. INORGANIC CHEMISTRY. A.B, DREW UNIV, 48; Syracuse Univ, 48-49; Ph.D.(inorg. chem), Pa. State Col, 51. Res. chemist, E.I. DU PONT DE NEMOURS & CO, WILMINGTON, 51-55, tech. supvr, 55-58, asst. lab. dir, 58-62, tech. sect. mgr, 62-64, asst. dir. res, 65-70, MGR, INORG. FIBERS DIV, PIGMENTS DEPT, 70- U.S.N.R, 43-46, Res, 46-54, Lt.(jg). Am. Chem. Soc; Optical Soc. Am. Coordination compounds; polymers; pigments; surface chemistry; fiber reinforcement of plastics. Address: R.D, 2, Unami Trail, Newark, DE 19711.

GONICK, EMANUEL, b. Omaha, Nebr, Jan. 24, 08; m. 41; c. 1. PHYSICAL & COLLOID CHEMISTRY. B.A, California, 30, M.S, 41; Ph.D.(chem), Stanford, 45. Instr. CHEM, San Mateo Jr. Col, 41-43; lectr, Stanford, 43-44, Bristol-Myers Co. fel. & res. assoc, 45-46; assoc. prof, Chico State Col, 46-47; asst. prof, San Francisco State Col, 47-49; assoc. prof, West. State Col. of Colo, 49-51; PROF, PHOENIX COL, 51- AAAS; Am. Chem. Soc. Colloidal electrolytes; complex ions: gas membrane osmometry; hindered free radicals. Address: Dept. of Chemistry, Phoenix College, Phoenix, AZ 85013.

GONICK, HARVEY C, b. Apr. 10, 30; U.S. citizen; m. 67; c. 2. NEPHROLOGY. B.S, Univ. Calif, Los Angeles, 51; Nat. Heart Inst. fel, Univ. Calif, San Francisco, 54, Charles Nelson fel. & Kaiser Found. fel, 54-55, M.D, 55. Intern int. med, Peter Bent Brigham Hosp, Boston, Mass, 55-56; asst. med, sch. med, Boston Univ, 56-57; resident int. med. & fel. nephrol, Wadsworth Vet. Admin. Hosp, Los Angeles, Calif, 59-61; asst. MED, SCH. MED, UNIV. CALIF, LOS ANGELES, 60-61, instr, 61-64, asst. prof, 64-69, ASSOC.

PROF, 69- Nat. Heart Inst. fel. nephrol, Mass. Mem. Hosp, Boston, 56-57; clin. investr, Wadsworth Vet. Admin. Hosp, Los Angeles, Calif, 61; mem, Nat. Kidney Found, 63-, traveling fel, 63; chmn. sci. adv. coun, S.Calif. Kidney Found, 64-70; mem. coun. circulation, Am. Heart Asn, 64-; mem. renal dialysis & transplantation adv. comt, Calif. State Dept. Public Health, 69-71; mem. ad hoc steering comt, Kidney Disease Planning Proj, Calif. Regional Med. Prog, 70, area rep, 71. Med.C, U.S.A.F, 57-59, Capt. AAAS; fel. Am. Col. Physicians; Am. Fedn. Clin. Res; Am. Med. Asn; Pan Am. Med. Asn; Am. Heart Asn; Am. Soc. Nephrol; Soc. Exp. Biol. & Med. Renal pathophysiology; acid-base metabolism; effects of transport inhibitors on renal tubular function. Address: Dept. of Medicine, University of California at Los Angeles School of Medicine, Los Angeles, CA 90024.

GONOR, JEFFERSON JOHN, b. Lafayette, La, Nov. 8, 32; m; c. 1. INVERTEBRATE ZOOLOGY, MARINE BIOLOGY. B.S, Southwestern Louisiana, 53; fel, Tulane, 53-54; univ. fel, Washington (Seattle), 55-59, Nat. Sci. Found. fel, 61, summer fels, 58, 59, Ph.D.(invert. zool), 64. Acting instr. zool, Washington (Seattle), 59, 60; vis. asst. prof. biol, Univ. of the Pacific, 60, 62; ASST. PROF. marine sci, Alaska, 62-64; BIOL. OCEANOG, ORE. STATE UNIV, 65- Res. participant, Orgn. Trop. Studies, 64; mem. resident staff, Newport Marine Lab, Ore, 65- AAAS; Soc. Syst. Zool; Ecol. Soc. Am. Systematics of opisthobranch gastropods; molluscan functional anatomy; neurosecretion in barnacles; reproduction in marine invertebrates; biological oceanography. Address: Oregon State University, Marine Science Center, Newport, OR 97365.

GONSALVES, LENINE M, b. New Bedford, Mass, Nov. 23, 27; m. 52; c. 4. ELECTRICAL ENGINEERING. B.S, U.S. Naval Acad, 52; Brown, 54-55; summer, Boston, 59; M.S.E.E, Northeastern, 60. Proj. engr, res. dept, Aerovox Corp, 52-53; instr. ELEC. ENG, SOUTHEAST. MASS. UNIV, 53-56, assoc. prof, 56-57, PROF. & CHMN. DEPT, 57- Consult, eng. & res. sect, Aerovox Corp, 57, 61-62; prof. & chmn. dept. elec. eng, Col. Petrol. & Mineral, Dharan, Saudi Arabia, 69-71. U.S.A.F, 46-48; U.S.N, 48-52. Nat. Soc. Prof. Eng; Am. Soc. Eng. Educ; Inst. Elec. & Electronics Eng. Circuit theory; oceanographic instrumentation. Address: Dept. of Electrical Engineering, Southeastern Massachusetts University, North Dartmouth, MA 02747.

GONSALVES, NEIL IGNATIUS, b. Georgetown, Brit. Guiana, Feb. 1, 38; U.S. citizen; m. 61; c. 2. GENETICS. B.S, Georgetown Univ, 59; U.S. Pub. Health. Serv. trainee, Brown Univ, 63-65, NASA trainee, 65-68, Ph.D. (biol), 69. ASST. PROF. GENETICS, Lowell State Col, 68-69; R.I. COL, 69- Am. Soc. Zool; Genetics Soc. Am; Soc. Invest. Dermat. Radiation biology of mammalian skin; mechanisms of wound healing in mammalian skin. Address: 281 River Ave, Providence, RI 02908.

GONSHERY, MARVIN E, b. Phila, Pa, June 9, 25; m. 57; c. 3. OPTICS. A.B, Temple Univ, 47, M.A, 50. Instr. physics, Temple Univ, 48-50; physicist, fire control exp. lab, FRANKFORD ARSENAL, 50-63, SR. PHYSICIST & PROJ. LEADER, FIRE CONTROL EXPLOR. DEVELOP. LABS, 63- Commendation, U.S. Dept. of Army, 62 & 66. Optical Soc. Am; Sci. Res. Soc. Am. Photometric and radiometric measurements; application of radioluminescent sources to optical fire control equipment; effects of nuclear radiation on optical materials and components. Address: 14 Silvertop Lane, Cherry Hill, NJ 08034.

GONSHOR, HARRY, b. Montreal, Que, Sept. 26, 28; U.S. citizen; m. 62. MATHEMATICS. B.Sc, McGill, 48, fel, 48-49, M.Sc, 49; fels, Harvard, 49-53, Ph.D.(math), 53. Vis. instr. MATH, Southern California, 53-54; asst. prof, Miami (Fla), 54-55; Pa. State, 55-57; from asst. prof. to ASSOC. PROF, RUTGERS UNIV, 57- Am. Math. Soc; Can. Math. Cong. Functional analysis; algebra. Address: Dept. of Mathematics, Rutgers The State University, Brunswick, NJ 08903.

GONTER, C(LARA) ELLEN, b. Dover, Ohio, Feb. 28, 22. ANALYTICAL CHEMISTRY. B.S, Carnegie Inst. Tech, 52. Sci. aide, Chem. Warfare Serv, 42-45; technician, Pittsburgh Coke & Chem. Co, 46-48, chemist, anal. res, 48-55, asst. supt, anal. servs, 55-59, anal. res, 59-64, supvr, USS Chem. Div, U.S. Steel Corp, 64-69; LAB. SUPVR, ANAL. SERV. LAB, NUS CORP, 69- AAAS; Am. Chem. Soc; Am. Inst. Chem; Am. Soc. Test. & Mat; Am. Pub. Health Asn. Wet and instrumental chemistry. Address: Cyrus William Rice Division, Analytical Service Lab, NUS Corp, 15 Noble Ave, Pittsburgh, PA 15205.

GONYEA, LORRAINE M, Med. Technol, Hemat, see STEWART, LORRAINE M.

GONZALES, CIRIACO Q, b. Socorro, N.Mex, Oct. 22, 33; m. 58; c. 4. ENTOMOLOGY, ECOLOGY. B.S, N.Mex. State Univ, 54; M.S, Univ. Ariz, 58; Ph.D.(entom), Univ. Calif, Berkeley, 62. Asst. res. entomologist, Univ. Calif, Berkeley, 61-63; ASSOC. PROF. BIOL, COL. SANTA FE, 63- Med.C, U.S.A, 54-56. AAAS; Entom. Soc. Am; Am. Inst. Biol. Sci. Insect ecology and behavior; association of insect species with rabbit brush; desert or arid land ecology. Address: Dept. of Biology, College of Santa Fe, Santa Fe, NM 87501.

GONZALES, DOUGLAS EATON, b. Oak Park, Ill, Mar. 3, 37; m. 58. SPACE & RADIATION PHYSICS. A.B, Ripon Col, 59; Ph.D.(theoret. physics), Univ. Calif, Berkeley, 66. Student aide, reactor eng. dept, Argonne Nat. Lab, 58; mathematician & comput. programmer, comput. dept, Lawrence Radiation Lab, 59, res. physicist, Proj. Sherwood, 60-67; space disturbances lab, Dept. Commerce, Colo, 67-68, ionospheric prediction group, 68-70; RES. PHYSICIST & INSTR, Brazilian Space Comn, São José dos Campos, 70-71; INST. PHYSICS, CATH. UNIV. RIO DE JANEIRO, 71- Theoretical space and plasma physics research, particularly cometary processes and structure, collisionless plasma shock waves, ionospheric and magnetosphere dynamics; experimental detection and analysis of natural radiation in the environment. Address: Institute of Physics, Catholic University of Rio de Janeiro, Brazil.

GONZALES, ELWOOD J(OHN), b. New Orleans, La, Oct. 19, 27; m. 63; c. 4. INORGANIC CHEMISTRY. B.S, Loyola (La), 53; Res. Corp. fel, Tulane, 54-55, M.S, 55, Am. Cyanamid Co. fel, 55-56, Ph.D.(chem), 58. Res. chemist cellulose chem, SOUTH. MKT. & NUTRIT. RES. DIV, AGR. RES. SERV, U.S. DEPT. AGR, NEW ORLEANS, 57-63, RES. CHEMIST PHYS. CHEM. INVESTS, 63- AAAS; Am. Chem. Soc; Sci. Res. Soc. Am; Am. Asn. Textile Chem. & Colorists; Am. Inst. Chem. Kinetics and mechanisms of cellulose reactions; modification of cotton cellulose. Address: 2137 Graham Dr, Gretna, LA 70053.

GONZALES, FEDERICO, b. San Antonio, Tex, July 16, 21; m. 45; c. 7. CELL BIOLOGY, BIOPHYSICS. B.S, St. Louis, 48, M.S, 51, Ph.D.(biophys), 54. Sr. res. fel. biol, Univ. Texas M.D. Anderson Hosp. & Tumor Inst, 53-54, res. assoc, 54-55, instr. anat, dent. br, Texas, 55-57, asst. prof, 57-61; col. med, Baylor, 57-63, exp. biol, 61-63; ASSOC. PROF. ANAT, SCHS. DENT. & MED, NORTHWEST. UNIV, 63- U.S. Pub. Health Serv. sr. res. fel, 58-62, career develop. award, 62-63. U.S.A.A.F, 43-45, 1st Lt. AAAS; Am. Soc. Cell Biol; Am. Physiol. Soc; Am. Asn. Anat; Tissue Cult. Asn; Soc. Exp. Biol. & Med. Differentiation in tissue culture; survival of frozen tissues; ultrastructure of bone and other hard tissues; ultrastructure of heart. Address: Dept. of Anatomy, Northwestern University, 303 E. Chicago, IL 60611.

GONZALES, SERGE, b. Boston, Mass, Feb. 23, 36; m. 68; c. 1. GEOLOGY. A.B, Duke, 58; M.S, Miami (Ohio), 60; Ph.D.(stratig, paleont), Cornell, 63. Assoc, Miami (Ohio), 59-60; asst, Cornell, 60-63; petrol. geologist, Humble Oil & Ref. Co, La, 63-66; asst. prof. GEOL, Miami Univ, 66-71; ASST. PROF. & DEPT. REP, INST. AREA & COMMUNITY DEVELOP, UNIV. GA, 71- Staff consult, Earth Sci. Labs, Ohio, 67-69. Am. Inst. Prof. Geol; Geol. Soc. Am; Am. Asn. Petrol. Geol; Nat. Asn. Geol. Teachers. Geological sciences; stratigraphy; mineral resources; environmental and engineering geology. Address: Dept. of Geology, University of Georgia, Athens, GA 30601.

GONZALEZ, ELSA LUCILA, b. Buenos Aires, Argentina, Oct. 1, 25. BIOCHEMISTRY, ENZYMOLOGY. E.R. Squibb & Sons fel, Buenos Aires, 49-50, Lic en quimica, 50, Ph.D.(chem), 51; La Plata, 50-51; Marine Biol. Lab, Woods Hole, 53. Asst. microbiol, Buenos Aires, 49-50, biochem, 51-52; fel. zool, Columbia, 52-53; res. assoc. med, Chicago, 53-56; dermat, Illinois, 56-57; enzyme chem, Wisconsin, Madison, 57-58, path, 58-59; dermat, Michigan, 59-60; res. fel, Mass. Gen. Hosp, 60; Med. Res. Coun. Eng. fel, Birmingham, 60-61; instr. chem, Ladycliff Col, 62-63 & 64-66; Reed Col, 63-64; sr. res. investr, G.D. Searle & Co, Ill, 66-67; asst. prof. biochem, Ill. Col, Podiatric Med, 68-70; VIS. SCIENTIST, WELLCOME INST. HIST. MED, 70- Teaching asst, St. Mary's Col.(Ind), 56; St. Mary's Hosp, Madison, Wis, 58-59; sci. info. specialist, John Crerar Libr, Ill, 66-67; Lowry-Cocroft Abstracts, Inc, 66- Am. Chem. Soc; N.Y. Acad. Sci; Argentine Chem. Soc; Brit. Fedn. Univ. Women. Crystals in biology; microbiology. Address: 32 Dorset Square, London, W.W.1, England.

GONZALEZ, GUILLERMO, b. Havana, Cuba, June 25, 44; U.S. citizen. ELECTRICAL ENGINEERING. B.S.E.E, Univ. Miami, 65, M.S.E.E, 66; Ph.D.(elec. eng), Univ. Ariz, 69. Sr. engr, Bell Aerosysts. Co, Ariz, 67-69; ASST. PROF. ELEC. ENG, UNIV. MIAMI, 69- Nat. Sci. Found. grants, 69-70 & 71-72. Inst. Elec. & Electronics Eng. Electromagnetic wave propagation in different media; electromagnetic aspects of optics and advanced boundary value problems. Address: 658 Bird Rd, Coral Gables, FL 33146.

GONZALEZ, I. ERNEST, b. Mexico City, Mex, July 31, 22; U.S. citizen; m. 44; c. 4. MEDICINE, HISTOCHEMISTRY. B.S, Brigham Young, 48, M.S, 50; fel, Ohio State, 50-51; fel, Oklahoma, 51-54, Ph.D.(anat), 54, M.D, 58. Am. Heart Asn. res. fel, Okla. Med. Res. Found, 55-58; resident PATH, Med. Col. Ala, 59-61; ASST. CLIN. PROF, SCH. MED, UNIV. CALIF, SAN FRANCISCO, 61- Res. grants, Am. Heart Asn, 60-63, Calif. Heart Asn, 63-64, Nat. Insts. Health, 63-66. Consult, San Francisco Gen. Hosp, 62-; Stanford Res. Inst, 64; NASA, 64- Mem. coun. arteriosclerosis, Am. Heart Asn, 58-; pathologist, French Hosp, San Francisco, 65-67, dir. labs, 67- U.S.A, 44-46, S/Sgt. Am. Soc. Exp. Path; Histochem. Soc. Comparative and experimental atherosclerosis; histochemistry of adrenal gland; diagnostic enzymology. Address: French Hospital, 4131 Geary Blvd, San Francisco, CA 94118.

GONZALEZ, LUIS L, b. Edinburg, Tex, June 7, 28; m; c. 4. SURGERY. B.A, Texas, 49, M.D, 53; D.Sci.(surg), Cincinnati, 54. Instr. SURG, COL. MED, CINCINNATI, 59-63, asst. prof, 63-69, ASSOC. PROF, 69-, ASST. CHIEF SURG. SERV, VET. ADMIN. HOSP, 65-, chief, 61-65. Asst. attend. surgeon, Cincinnati Gen. Hosp, 61-; attend. surgeon, Christian R. Holmes Hosp, 64-; assoc. attend. surgeon, Christ Hosp, 64- U.S.M.C, 46-48. Am. Col. Surg; Int. Cardiovasc. Soc. Cardiovascular research; thoracic surgery. Address: Dept. of Surgery, University of Cincinnati College of Medicine, Cincinnati, OH 45220.

GONZALEZ, M(ARIA) D(OLORES) PEREZ, b. São Paulo, Brazil, Oct. 26, 23; m. 49; c. 2. ANIMAL & COMPARATIVE PHYSIOLOGY. B.S, São Paulo, 44, Lic.Sc, 45, D.Sc, 49. ASST. PROF. faculty of philos, sci. & letters, UNIV. SAO PAULO, 45-70, GEN. PHYSIOL, BIOSCI. INST, 70- AAAS; Brazilian Soc. Advan. Sci. Function of hemoglobins in invertebrates; respiratory metabolism of invertebrates; relation to growth and environmental factors to respiration; influence of several inhibitors upon respiration; metabolism of insect muscles; neurosecretion of invertebrates. Address: Dept. of General Physiology, Biosciences Institute, University of São Paulo, Caixa Postal 2926, São Paulo, Brazil.

GONZALEZ, MARIO O(CTAVIO), b. Matanzas, Cuba, Sept. 14, 13; m. 37; c. 3. MATHEMATICS. D.Sc.(physics, math), Havana, 38; Mass. Inst. Tech, 39; Princeton, 40-41. Assoc. prof. MATH, Havana, 40-44, PROF, 44-60; UNIV. ALA, TUSCALOOSA, 61- Guggenheim Mem. Found. fel. math, 39-40. Am. Math. Soc; Math. Asn. Am; Arg. Math. Union; cor. mem. Lima Acad. Exact, Phys. & Natural Sci. Differential equations; operational calculus; theory of functions. Address: Dept. of Mathematics, University of Alabama in Tuscaloosa, Box 1056, University, AL 35486.

GONZALEZ, MOLINA CARLOS, b. San Sebastian, P.R, June 28, 23; m. 55; c. 4. PLANT BREEDING. B.S.A, Univ. P.R, Mayagüez, 50; M.S, Iowa State Univ, 57, Ph.D.(plant breeding), 64. PLANT BREEDER SUGARCANE, EXP. STA, UNIV. P.R, MAYAGÜEZ, 54-, PROF. AGRON, UNIV, 69- Am. Soc.

Agron; Int. Soc. Sugar Cane Technol. Breeding, evaluation and selection of sugarcane varieties of desirable agronomic characteristics, resistant to main local diseases, suitable to mechanical harvesting, and with adaptation to the variable ecological conditions prevailing in the island. Address: Dept. of Agronomy, University of Puerto Rico, Mayagüez, PR 00709.

GONZALEZ, OSCAR D(AVID), b. El Paso, Tex, Oct. 21, 22. PHYSICAL CHEMISTRY. B.S, Tex. Col. Mines & Metall, 43; fel, Ohio State, 46-51, Ph.D.(chem), 51. Res. assoc, Ohio State, 52; res. chemist, Franklin Inst, 53-54, sr. res. chemist, 54-55; asst. prof, Loyola(Ill), 55-57; PHYS. CHEMIST, E.C. BAIN LAB, U.S. STEEL RES. CTR, 57- U.S.N.R, 44-46. AAAS; Am. Chem. Soc. Surface chemistry; aqueous systems; adsorption of electrolytes on ionic solids. Address: E.C. Bain Lab, U.S. Steel Research Center, Monroeville, PA 15146.

GONZALEZ, PAULA, S.C, b. Albuquerque, N.Mex, Oct 25, 32. CELL BIOLOGY, SCIENCE EDUCATION. A.B, Col. Mt. St. Joseph, 52; M.S, Cath. Univ. Am, 61, U.S. Pub. Health Serv. fel, 61-65, Ph.D.(cell physiol), 66. Instr. anat, physiol. & chem, Regina Sch. Nursing, N.Mex, 52-54; teacher, Seton High Sch, Ohio, 55-60; ASST. PROF. BIOL. & CHMN. DEPT, COL. MT. ST. JOSEPH, 65- Am. Inst. Biol. Sci; Nat. Sci. Teachers Asn; Nat. Asn. Biol. Teachers. Nucleolar changes during the cell cycle; course and curriculum development for undergraduate core curriculum in biology for majors. Address: Dept. of Biology, College of Mt. Saint Joseph-on-the-Ohio, Mt. St. Joseph, OH 45051.

GONZALEZ, RAUL A(LBERTO), b. Talca, Chile, Feb. 8, 33; U.S. citizen; m. 58; c. 3. CHEMICAL ENGINEERING. B.S, Santa Maria Univ. Chile, 57; M.Sc, Univ. Va, 60, D.Sc.(chem. eng), 62. Res. engr, Santa Maria Univ. Chile, 57-58; prof. chem. eng, Cath. Univ. Chile, 62; res. engr, Jackson Lab, E.I. DU PONT DE NEMOURS & CO, INC, N.J, 62-69, SR. RES. ENGR, PERMASEP PROD, WILMINGTON, 69- Reaction kinetics; reverse osmosis; process evaluation and design. Address: 206 Dallas Ave, Newark, DE 19711.

GONZALEZ, REGINALD N(URSE), b. N.Y.C, July 25, 17; m. 40, 58; c. 7. ORGANIC & POLYMER CHEMISTRY. B.Sc, McGill Univ, 41; M.Sc, Univ. Del, 49, Ph.D.(org. chem), 57. Metall. asst, Dom. Bridge Co, Que, 41-42; chemist process develop, Mallinckrodt Chem. Works, 42-44; res. chem. engr, gen. chem. div, Allied Chem. Corp, 44-50, res. mgr. plastics div, 62-65; res. chemist, plastics div, Monsanto Co, 51-58; group leader plastics res, Dewey & Almy Chem. Div, W.R. Grace & Co, 58-62; asst. dir. plastics res, Reichhold Chem, Inc, 65-66, assoc. dir, 66-67; TECH. DIR. & EXEC. SECY, SCI. RES. COUN, JAMAICA, 67- Monsanto acad. leave award, 55-56; chmn, Commonwealth Sci. Comt, 68-71; mem. adv. comt, Trop. Prod. Inst, 69- Am. Chem. Soc; N.Y. Acad. Sci; The Chem. Soc; Jamaican Asn. Scientists (secy, 67-69, pres, 69-71). Process development for organic chemicals; radical initiation of vinyl polymerization; mechanisms and kinetics of organic reactions; emulsion polymer systems; polymer characterization. Address: Scientific Research Council, P.O. Box 502, Kingston, Jamaica.

GONZALEZ, RICHARD D, b. N.Y.C, Apr. 11, 32; m. 62; c. 1. PHYSICAL CHEMISTRY. B.Ch.E, Rensselaer Polytech, 61; M.A, Hopkins, 63, Ph.D. (chem), 65. ASST. PROF. CHEM, UNIV. R.I, 65- U.S.A.F, 53-57, S/Sgt. Am. Chem. Soc. Surface chemistry; heterogeneous catalysis. Address: Dept. of Chemistry, University of Rhode Island, Kingston, RI 02881.

GONZALEZ-ANGULO, AMADOR, b. Tijuana, Mex, May 29, 33; m. 58; c. 2. NEUROPATHOLOGY. B.S, Univ. Sonora, 51; M.D, Nat. Univ. Mexico, 58. Instr. PATH, col. med, Baylor Univ, 61-63; ASST. PROF, MED. SCH, NAT. UNIV. MEXICO, 66-; CHIEF ELECTRONIC MICROS. SECT, DIV. PATH, DEPT. SCI. RES, NAT. MED. CTR, 66- Consult, Methodist Hosp, Houston, Tex, 62-63; Ben Taub Gen. Hosp, 62-63; Biomed. Inst, Nat. Univ. Mexico, 67-68. Dipl, Am. Bd. Path, 63. Electron Micros. Soc. Am; Am. Asn. Anat; Am. Soc. Clin. Path; Mex. Asn. Path.(pres, 69); Am. Soc. Cell Biol; Latin Am. Soc. Anat. Path. Cell organelle pathology as seen with the electron microscope; survey of central nervous system diseases in Mexico; experimental neuropathology with the electron microscope. Address: Dept. Science Research, National Medical Center, Apartado 73-032, Mexico 73, D.F.

GONZALEZ-BONORINO, FELIX, b. Buenos Aires, Arg, Aug. 17, 18; m. 44; c. 3. GEOLOGY. Geol. Sci.D, Buenos Aires, 42. Geologist, Nat. Geol. Serv, Arg, 41-49, chief, 53-54; Guggenheim res. fel, 54-55; vis. prof, Mo. Sch. Mines, 55-57; PROF. GEOL, BUENOS AIRES, 57-69; UNIV. CHILE, 69- Mem. sci. adv. bd, UNESCO, 58-61; exec. comt, Nat. Res. Coun, Arg, 58-65; higher ed. adv, Inter-Am. Develop. Bank, D.C, 61-62; v.pres, Int. Union Geol. Sci, 64-68; pres, Nat. Inst. Mining Geol, Arg, 64- Fel. Geol. Soc. Am; fel. Am. Mineral. Soc. Sedimentology; clay mineralogy; regional geology; petrology. Address: Dept. of Geology, University of Chile, Casilla 13518, P.O. Box 15, Santiago, Chile.

GONZALEZ DE ALVAREZ, GENOVEVA, b. Mayagüez, P.R, Oct. 21, 26; m. 51; c. 2. ORGANIC CHEMISTRY. B.S, Univ. P.R, Rio Piedras, 47; M.A, Radcliffe Col, 50; M.S. & Ph.D.(chem), Univ. Madrid, 66. Asst. instr. CHEM, Univ. P.R, Río Piedras, 46-47, instr, 47-51; UNIV. P.R, MAYAGÜEZ, 51-54, asst. prof, 54-58, assoc. prof, 58-68, PROF, 68- AAAS; Am. Chem. Soc. Alkaloids of Retama sphaerocarpa Boiss; synthesis of potential hypotensive agents. Address: 202 Méndez Vigo St. W, Mayagüez, PR 00708.

GONZALEZ-FERNANDEZ, JOSE M(ARIA), b. Buenos Aires, Arg, Nov. 10, 22; U.S. citizen; m. 57; c. 2. MATHEMATICS, PHYSIOLOGY. M.D, Buenos Aires, 47; M.Sc, Northwestern, 54, Ph.D.(math), 58. Instr. math, Washington (Seattle), 57-58; res. assoc. physiol, Mayo Clin, 58-59; temporary mem. staff math, Courant Inst. Math. Sci, N.Y. Univ, 59-60; mem. staff, math. res. ctr, Wisconsin, 60-62; RES. MATHEMATICIAN, NAT. INSTS. HEALTH, 62- Am. Math. Soc. Integrability theorems in trigonometric series; tauberian theorems; integral equations; transport and consumption of oxygen in blood capillary-tissue systems. Address: National Institutes of Health, Bethesda, MD 20014.

GONZALEZ-VELASCO, ENRIQUE A(LBERTO), b. Madrid, Spain, July 28, 40; m. 71. MATHEMATICS. Telecommun. engr, Sch. Telecommun. Eng, Spain, 64; Sc.M, Brown, 66, Ph.D.(appl. math), 69. ASST. PROF. MATH, BOSTON COL, 68- Ordinary differential equations; dynamical systems. Address: Dept. of Mathematics, Boston College, Chestnut Hill, MA 02167.

GONZALO, JULIO ANTONIO, b. Donalbay, Spain, Apr. 27, 36. SOLID STATE PHYSICS. Lic. physics, Madrid, 59, Ph.D.(physics), 62. Res. assoc. solid state physics, P.R. NUCLEAR CTR, 62-65, assoc. scientist, 65-69, SR. SCIENTIST, 69- Vis. res. collab, Brookhaven Nat. Lab, 63-64. Spanish Army, 58-61, Lt. Am. Phys. Soc. Dielectric and thermal properties of ferroelectric crystals; determination of magnetic structure by neutron diffraction; radiation effects in ferroelectric materials. Address: Puerto Rico Nuclear Center, College Station, Mayaguez, PR 00708.

GONZENBACH, CARLOS TIRZO, b. Quito, Ecuador, Mar. 20, 15; U.S. citizen; m. 21; c. 6. POLYMER CHEMISTRY. B.S, Cent. Univ. Ecuador, 40; M.S, Univ. Fla, 44; Ph.D.(plant path), Cornell Univ, 49. Sect. rep. trade, Pennsalt Int. Corp, 50-53; chemist, Pa. Indust. Chem. Corp, 53-62; GROUP LEADER HYDROCARBON POLYMERS, SCHENECTADY CHEM, INC, 62- Am. Chem. Soc. Thermoplastic resins; tackifiers; pressure sensitive adhesives; hot melt adhesives. Address: 109 Glenhill Dr, Scotia, NY 12302.

GOOCHEE, HERMAN FRANCIS, b. Emporium, Pa, Oct. 13, 21; m. 49; c. 3. INORGANIC CHEMISTRY. B.S, St. Vincent Col, 43; N.C. State, 44-45; Minnesota, 45-46; Maryland, 47-49; M.S, Tennessee, 57. Lab. engr, Stupakoff Ceramic & Mfg. Co, 43-45; engr, Speer Carbon Co, 46-52; supvr. process eng, Union Carbide Nuclear Co, Tenn, 52-57; consult. & supvr. cent. eng, Speer Carbon Co. Div, Air Reduction Co, Inc, 57-60, dir. process eng, 60-61, dir. develop. & tech. serv, 61-67, dir. MFG. CARBON & GRAPHITE, AIRCO SPEER, 67-70, V.PRES, 70- U.S.A, 45-46, TS/Sgt. AAAS; Am. Ceramic Soc; Am. Chem. Soc. Technical management; ceramic research; carbon and graphite development; utilities operations; nuclear engineering and operations; combustion engineering and furnace design; technical supervision and planning. Address: 301 Russ Lane, St. Mary's, PA 15857.

GOOD, A. L, b. Marysville, Pa, Jan. 8, 21; m. 43; c. 4. VETERINARY PHYSIOLOGY. V.M.D, Pennsylvania, 43; M.S, Kansas State, 50; Ph.D.(vet. physiol), Minnesota, 56. Asst. prof. PHYSIOL, col. vet. med, Kansas State, 46-51; instr, COL. VET. MED, UNIV. MINN, ST. PAUL, 51-56, assoc. prof, 56-61, PROF, 61- Vet.C, 41-46, Maj. AAAS; Am. Vet. Med. Asn; Am. Physiol. Soc. Cardiovascular physiology of large domestic animals; temperature regulation in animals; effects of anesthetics in large domestic animals. Address: College of Veterinary Medicine, University of Minnesota, St. Paul, MN 55101.

GOOD, ARMIN E, b. Kendallville, Ind, Oct. 21, 23; m. 51; c. 2. MEDICINE. M.D, Harvard, 47. Asst. prof. MED, UNIV. MICH, ANN ARBOR, 62-66, ASSOC. PROF, 66- U.S.A, 43-46, 49-51, Capt. Clinical research in rheumatology. Address: Dept. of Internal Medicine, University of Michigan, Ann Arbor, MI 48104.

GOOD, BILL J(EWEL), b. Alma, Ark, May 1, 24; m. 52; c. 2. PHYSICS. B.S, Ark. State Teachers Col, 50; M.S, Univ. Ark, 52; Ph.D.(physics), La. State Univ, 57. Instr. PHYSICS, Univ. Ark, 52-54; asst, LA. STATE UNIV, 54-57, res. assoc, 57-58, ASSOC. PROF, 58-, DEAN COL. SCI, 66- U.S.C.G, 42-45. Am. Phys. Soc. Low temperature physics; hydrodynamics of liquid helium; theoretical aspects of superfluids and superconductivity. Address: College of Sciences, Louisiana State University in New Orleans, Lake Front, New Orleans, LA 70122.

GOOD, C(LARENCE) ALLEN, b. St. Joseph, Mo, Sept. 20, 07; m. 30; c. 4. RADIOLOGY. A.B, Williams Col, 29; M.D, Washington (St. Louis), 33; Mayo Found. fel, Minnesota, 35-38; M.S, 38. Asst. radiol, sch. med, Washington (St. Louis), 35; instr. RADIOL, MAYO GRAD. SCH. MED, UNIV. MINN, 39-45, asst. prof, 45-50, assoc. prof, 50-57, PROF, 57-; SR. CONSULT, MAYO CLIN, 67-, mem. roentgenol. sect, 39-58, head sect, 58-67. Hickey Mem. Lectr, 61; Carman Mem. Lectr, 61; Caldwell Lectr, 62; Gordon Richards Mem. Lectr, 65; secy, Am. Bd. Radiol, 69- Am. Roentgen Ray Soc.(secy, 57-66, pres, 67-68); Radiol. Soc. N.Am; fel. Am. Med. Asn; fel. Am. Col. Radiol. Diagnostic radiology; influence of extrabiliary disease of function of gallbladder. Address: Mayo Clinic, Rochester, MN 55901.

GOOD, DON L, b. Van Wert, Ohio, Oct. 8, 21; m. 47; c. 3. ANIMAL SCIENCE. B.S, Ohio State, 47; M.S, Kansas State, 50; Ph.D.(animal sci), Minnesota, 56. Instr. ANIMAL SCI, KANS. STATE UNIV, 47-49, asst. prof, 49-53, assoc. prof, 53-61, PROF, 61-, HEAD DEPT. ANIMAL SCI. & INDUST, 66- Mem. res. cmt, Am. Hereford Asn, 63-; U.S. Agency Int. Develop. consult, Ahmadu Bello Univ, Zaria, Nigeria, 68 & 69; consult, Govt. Turkey, 71. Col. Agr. Centennial Award, Ohio State Univ, 70. U.S.A, 43-46, S/Sgt. Am. Soc. Animal Sci. Production and relationship of live animal evaluation to carcass characteristics and economical production traits in beef cattle. Address: Dept. of Animal Science & Industry, Kansas State University, Manhattan, KS 66502.

GOOD, E(RNEST) E(UGENE), b. Van Wert, Ohio, Jan. 7, 13; m. 40; c. 3. ZOOLOGY. B.Sc, Ohio State, 40, M.Sc, 47, Ph.D.(zool), 52. Proj. biologist, soil conserv. serv, U.S. Dept. Agr, 35-40, asst. agr. aide, 40-41; proj. leader, Ind. Dept. Conserv, 41-42; farmer, 42-48; instr. ZOOL, OHIO STATE UNIV, 48-53, asst. prof, 53-59, assoc. prof, 59-70, PROF, UNIV. DEPT. & SCH. NATURAL RESOURCES, 70- Collab, U.S. Fish & Wildlife Serv, Dept. Interior, 49- Wildlife Soc; Am. Soc. Mammal; Wilson Ornith. Soc; Am. Ornith Union. Animal ecology and behavior; ecology. Address: School of Natural Resources, Ohio State University, Columbus, OH 43210.

GOOD, FREDERICK H(OPKINS), b. Holdredge, Nebr, May 11, 11; m. 35; c. 2. SURGERY. A.B, Colo. State Col, 33; B.S, Nebraska, 36; M.D, Colorado, 38. Teaching fel. biochem, Colo. State Col, 31-33; ASSOC. CLIN. PROF. SURG, SCH. MED, UNIV. COLO, 33- Chief of staff, Mercy Hosp; mem. surg. staff, Children's Hosp; St. Joseph's Hosp; Gen. Rose Mem. Hosp; St. Anthony's Hosp; active surg. staff, hosps; sr. attend. surgeon, Colo. Gen. Hosp; Denver Gen. Hosp. Distinguished serv. award, hosps, Univ. Colorado, 63. Am. Med. Asn; Am. Asn. Med. Cols; Am. Col. Surg; N.Y. Acad. Sci; Int. Col. Surg. Colloid chemistry; biochemistry. Address: 9300 E. Center Ave, Denver, CO 80231.

GOOD, GEORGE M(ERLIN), b. Welfords Wharf, Va, Oct. 25, 18; m. 41; c. 4. CHEMISTRY. B.S, Heidelberg Col, 40; California, 40-42. Asst. zool, California, 40-42; jr. chemist, Shell Develop. Co, 42-45, chemist, 45-52, res. supvr, 52-55, tech. asst. to pres, N.Y, 55-57, res. supvr, Calif, 57-60, sr. engr, SHELL OIL CO, 60-61, spec. engr, N.Y, 61-65, mgr. prod. appln. dept, Shell Chem. Co, 65-69, STAFF BUYER PURCHASING, CHEM. & PROCESS MAT, 69- With Koninklyke-Shell-Lab, Amsterdam, 52-53. Am. Chem. Soc. Petroleum refining research; catalytic and thermal cracking of pure hydrocarbons; experimental embryology of invertebrates and amphibians; development of applications for petroleum products. Address: 4906 Clift Haven, Houston, TX 77018.

GOOD, H(AROLD) M(ARQUIS), b. Brantford, Ont, Jan. 16, 20; m. 45; c. 4. PLANT PATHOLOGY. B.A, Univ. Toronto, 43, Ph.D, 47. Lectr. bot, Univ. Toronto, 47-49; asst. prof. BIOL, QUEEN'S UNIV.(ONT), 49-55, assoc. prof, 55-64, PROF, 64-, ASSOC. HEAD DEPT, 70- Can. Phytopath. Soc; Can. Bot. Asn; Brit. Mycol. Soc. Pathology of wood destroying fungi; physiology of fungus spores. Address: Dept. of Biology, Queen's University. Kingston, Ont. Can.

GOOD, IRVING JOHN, b. London, Eng, Dec. 9, 16. MATHEMATICS, STATISTICS. B.A, Cambridge, 38, Ph.D.(math), 41, M.A, 43, Sc.D.(math, statist), 63; D.Sc, Oxford, 64. Civil servant, For. Off, 41-45, govt. commun. hq, 48-59; lectr. math. & electronic comput, Manchester, 45-48; spec. merit dep. chief sci. off, Admiralty Res. Lab, 59-62; consult. math, statist. & electronic comput, commun. res. div, Inst. Defense Anal, 62-64; sr. res. fel, Trinity Col, Oxford & Atlas Comput. Lab, Sci. Res. Coun, 64-67; res. prof. STATIST, VA. POLYTECH. INST. & STATE UNIV, 67-69, PROF, 69-, MEM. ADV. BD, 70- Mem. commun. theory comt, Ministry Supply, Gt. Brit, 53-59; vis. res. assoc. prof, Princeton, 55; lectr, sixth summer res. inst, Univ. Melbourne, 66; distinguished mem, Crypto-Math. Inst, 67; mem. adv. bd, Ctr. Study Pub. Choice, Va. Fel. Inst. Math. Statist; Math. Asn. Am; London Math. Soc; Mind Asn; Royal Statist. Soc; Brit. Soc. Philos. Sci; Brit. Asn. Advan. Sci; Int. Statist. Inst; Am. Math. Soc; Am. Statist. Asn; Biomet. Soc; U.K. Brain Res. Asn. Mathematical analysis; cryptology; computers; mathematical statistics; foundations of statistical and scientific inference; machine intelligence; scientific speculation; information theory. Address: Dept. of Statistics, Virginia Polytechnic Institute & State University, Blacksburg, VA 24061.

GOOD, JOHN M(AXWELL), b. St. Louis, Mo, Mar. 15, 24; m. 49; c. 2. GEOLOGY. A.B, Washington (St. Louis), 47, M.S, 48. Geologist & geophysicist, Standard Oil Co, Tex, 48-50; asst. park naturalist, Nat. Park Serv, Dept. Interior, 55-56, park naturalist, 56-57, geologist, 58-59, prin. naturalist, geol, 59-60, asst. chief park naturalist, 61-62, chief park naturalist, Wyo, 63-68; SUPT, ACADIA NAT. PARK, 68- Geol. Soc. Am. Geomorphology and glacial geology. Address: P.O. Box 428, Bar Harbor, ME 04609.

GOOD, MARY L(OWE), b. Grapevine, Tex, June 20, 31; m. 52; c. 2. INORGANIC CHEMISTRY, RADIOCHEMISTRY. B.S, Ark. State Teachers Col, 50; M.S, Arkansas, 53, Ph.D.(inorg. chem, radiochem), 55. Instr. CHEM, LA. STATE UNIV, NEW ORLEANS, 54-56, asst. prof, 56-58, assoc. prof, 58-63, PROF, 63- Mem. bd. dirs, Oak Ridge Assoc. Univ, 71- Am. Chem. Soc; Am. Nuclear Soc. Extraction of inorganic complexes from aqueous media by certain alkyl ammonium compounds; solution studies of the actinides; Mössbauer studies of iron, tin, ruthenium and europium compounds; far infrared studies of coordination compounds; new preparative methods for inorganic complexes. Address: Dept. of Chemistry, Louisiana State University in New Orleans, Lakefront, New Orleans, LA 70122.

GOOD, MYRON L(INDSAY), b. Buffalo, N.Y, Oct. 25, 23; m. 50; c. 3. PHYSICS. B.A, Buffalo, 43; Ph.D.(physics), Duke, 51. Physicist, radiation lab, California, 51-59; assoc. prof. PHYSICS, Univ. Wis, 60-62, PROF, 62-67; STATE UNIV. N.Y. STONY BROOK, 67- U.S.A.A.F, 43-45. Am. Phys. Soc. Beta decay; high energy physics. Address: Dept. of Physics, State University of New York at Stony Brook, Stony Brook, NY 11790.

GOOD, NEWELL E(MANUEL), b. Bellevue, Ohio, Dec. 31, 05; m. 33, 58. MEDICAL ENTOMOLOGY. A.B, Heidelberg Col.(Ohio), 27; M.S, George Washington, 29, Ph.D.(zool), 35. Jr. biol. aide, bur. animal indust, U.S. Dept. Agr, 27-29, jr. entomologist, bur. entomol. & plant quarantine, 29-31, asst. entomologist, 31-38; assoc. entomologist, U.S. Pub. Health Serv, 38-43, from asst. sanitarian to scientist, 43-53; pub. health entomologist, Phila. Dept. Pub. Health, 53-68; SR. MED. ENTOMOLOGIST, N.Y. STATE DEPT. HEALTH, 68- Med. entomologist, UNNRA mission to China, 46-47. AAAS; Am. Soc. Trop. Med. & Hygiene; Entom. Soc. Am; Sci. Res. Soc. Am; Am. Mosquito Control Asn. Invertebrate vector and arbovirus investigations and control; taxonomy, distribution, ecology and control of mosquitoes and ectoparasites. Address: New York State Dept. of Health, 901 N. Broadway, White Plains, NY 10603.

GOOD, NORMAN E(VERETT), b. Brantford, Ont, May 20, 17; m. 52; c. 6. PLANT PHYSIOLOGY. B.A, Toronto, 48; Ph.D.(biochem), Calif. Inst. Tech, 51. Res. fel. photosynthesis, Minnesota, 51-52; Agr. Res. Coun, Gt. Brit. res. fel, Cambridge, 52-54; plant physiologist, sci. serv, Can. Dept. Agr, 54-57; res. fel. photosynthesis, Univ. Minn, 57-58; plant physiologist, sci. serv, Can. Dept. Agr, 58-62; assoc. prof. BOT. & PLANT PATH, MICH. STATE UNIV, 62-66, PROF, 66- Photosynthesis, especially chloroplast reactions; metabolism of growth substances and aromatic acids in general; amino acid metabolism. Address: Dept. of Botany, Michigan State University, East Lansing, MI 48823.

GOOD, PEARL, b. Wilno, Poland, Aug. 15, 29; U.S. citizen; m. 53; c. 3. ORGANIC CHEMISTRY. D.Sc,(org. chem), 51. Chemist. enzym, Sloan Kettering Inst. Cancer Res, Cornell, 51-52; qual. anal, E.F. Drew & Co, N.Y, 52-53; plastics res, Ideal Toy Co, N.Y, 53-54; clin. biochem, St. Lukes Hosp, N.Y, 54-55; RES. ASSOC. PLANT LIPIDS, POMONA COL, 63- Lipids of plants and microorganisms, their separation and characterization. Address: Dept. of Chemistry, Pomona College, Claremont, CA 91711.

GOOD, PHILLIP I, b. Montreal, Que, Dec. 26, 37; m; c. 2. CELL CULTURE, MATHEMATICAL STATISTICS. A.B, California, Berkeley, 58, Ph.D.(math. statist), 65. Analyst, Info. Res. Assocs, Inc, 66-67; co-dir, Inst. Human Encounter, Calif, 68-70; Nat. Insts. Health collab, Jet Propulsion Lab, 70-71. Traineeship cell cult, Wistar Inst, 68-69. Tissue Cult. Asn; Biomet. Soc. Aging; tissue homoestasis; stochastic processes. Address: 1158 Monticito, Los Angeles, CA 90031.

GOOD, RALPH E(DWARD), b. Chicago, Ill, Feb. 24, 37; m. 62. PLANT ECOLOGY. B.S, Illinois, 60, M.S, 61; Ph.D.(ecol), Rutgers, 65. Res. assoc. forestry, Illinois, 61; teaching asst. biol, Rutgers, 64; lectr, Queens Col.(N.Y), 65-66, asst. prof, 66-67; BOT, RUTGERS UNIV, 67-71, ASSOC. PROF, 71- Summer res. fel. biol, Minnesota, 65. AAAS; Ecol. Soc. Am; Am. Inst. Biol. Sci. Salt marsh ecology and productivity; light reflectance from vegetation; tree seedling survival under natural and artificial conditions; life histories of pine barrens species. Address: Dept. of Biology, Rutgers, The State University, Camden, NJ 08102.

GOOD, RICHARD A(LBERT), b. Ashland, Ohio, Sept. 24, 17; m. 46; c. 3. MATHEMATICS. A.B, Ashland Col, 39; Alumni Res. Found. scholar, Wisconsin, 39-41, M.A, 40, Ph.D.(algebra), 45. Asst. MATH, Wisconsin, 41-43, acting instr, 43-45; asst. prof, UNIV. MD, 45-54, assoc. prof, 54-60, PROF, 60- Nat. Sci. Found. res. partic. award, summer 63. AAAS; Soc. Indust. & Appl. Math; Am. Math. Soc; Math. Asn. Am. Semigroups; matrices; games; linear programing. Address: Dept. of Mathematics, University of Maryland, College Park, MD 20742.

GOOD, ROBERT A(LAN), b. Crosby, Minn, May 21, 22; m. 46; c. 5. PEDIATRICS. B.A, Minnesota, 44, M.B, 46, M.D. & Ph.D.(anat), 47; hon. Dr, Univ. Uppsala, 64. Asst. anat, MED. SCH, UNIV. MINN, MINNEAPOLIS, 44-45, res. fel. poliomyelitis, 47-48, Whitney fel. rheumatic fever, 48-49, instr. pediat, 50-51, asst. prof, 51-53, assoc. prof, 53-54, Am. Legion heart res. prof, 54-60, prof. MICROBIOL. & PEDIAT, 60-69, REGENTS PROF, 69-, PROF. PATH. & CHMN. DEPT, 70- Markle Found. scholar med. sci, 50-55. Vis. investr, Rockefeller Inst, 49-50, asst. physician, hosp, 49-50. Howard Taylor Ricketts Award, Univ. Chicago, Am. Acad. Achievement golden plate award, Gairdner Found. Award, Borden Award, Asn. Am. Med. Cols, City of Hope Award & Albert Lasker Award, 70. Nat. Acad. Sci; Am. Asn. Anat; Am. Soc. Exp. Path; Am. Asn. Immunol; Am. Soc. Clin. Invest.(past pres). Natural and acquired resistance to gram-negative endotoxins, agammaglobulinemias and hypergammaglobulinemias; rheumatic fever; acute-phase reactions, immunology and hypersensitivity reactions; immunopathology. Address: Dept. of Pediatrics, University of Minnesota Medical School, Minneapolis, MN 55455.

GOOD, ROBERT C(AMPBELL), b. Erwin, Tenn, Aug. 23, 26; m. 51; c. 2. BACTERIOLOGY. B.A, Tennessee, 49, M.S, 50; Ph.D.(med. microbiol), Northwestern, 54. Res. bacteriologist, Bauer & Black Div, Kendal Co, 50-51; sr. res. microbiologist, Int. Minerals & Chem. Corp, 54-59; sr. res. asst. exp. tuberc, Christ Hosp. Inst. Med. Res, 59-60, res. assoc, 60-63; assoc. res. bacteriologist, nat. ctr. primate biol, Univ. Calif, Davis, 63-69; mem. staff microbiol, life sci. ctr, TRW HAZLETON LABS, 69-71, SR. PROJ. MGR, 71- U.S.A, 45-46. AAAS; Am. Soc. Microbiol; Am. Thoracic Soc. Mycobacteria; chemotherapy; virulence; enteric pathogens, amino acid fermentations. Address: Toxicology-Biosciences Lab, TRW Hazleton Labs, 9200 Leesburg Turnpike, Vienna, VA 22180.

GOOD, ROBERT D(AVIS), b. Ashland, Ohio, Apr. 23, 11; m. 45. CHEMICAL ENGINEERING. B.S, Carnegie Inst. Technol, 32. Chem. res. engr, Manhattan dist, N.Y, 43-45; tech. adv. plant opers, Tenn, 45-46, chem. engr, Houdaille-Hershey Corp, Mich, 46-47, supt. electroplating, Ill, 47; proj. engr, chem. plants div, BLAW-KNOX CO, 47-66, ASST. MGR. FOOD PROCESSING DEPT, 66- C.Eng, U.S.A, 42-46. Architecture; engineering; construction; project engineering in fats, oils, petrochemical and dyestuffs technology; minerals refining; technical management. Address: Blaw-Knox Chemical Plants, Inc, 1 Oliver Plaza, Pittsburgh, PA 15222.

GOOD, ROBERT H(OWARD), b. Ann Arbor, Mich, Aug. 26, 31; m. 64; c. 1. HIGH ENERGY PHYSICS. A.B, Michigan, 53; Ph.D.(physics), California, Berkeley, 61. Physicist, Saclay Nuclear Res. Ctr, France, 61-62; Univ. Calif, San Diego, 62-66; PROF. PHYSICS, CALIF. STATE COL, HAYWARD, 66- Experimental high energy nuclear physics. Address: Dept. of Physics, California State College at Hayward, 25800 Hillary St, Hayward, CA 94542.

GOOD, ROBERT J(AMES), b. Lincoln, Nebr, Aug. 13, 20; m. 46; c. 2. CHEMISTRY. B.A, Amherst Col, 42; M.S, California, 43; Allied Chem. & Dye Co. fel, Michigan, 48-49, Ph.D.(chem), 50. Asst. chem, California, 42-43; teaching fel, Michigan, 46-48; chemist, Dow Chem. Co, Calif, 43-44; Am. Cyanamid & Chem. Co, Calif, 44-46; res. chemist, Monsanto Chem. Co, Ala, 49-53; asst. prof. appl. sci, Cincinnati, 53-56; sr. staff scientist, Convair Sci. Res. Lab, Gen. Dynamics Corp, 57-64; PROF. CHEM. ENG, STATE UNIV. N.Y. BUFFALO, 64- Am. Chem. Soc; Faraday Soc; Nat. Asn. Corrosion Eng. Surface chemistry and physics; thermodynamics; interfacial tension; adhesion; wetting; heat of immersion; embrittlement of metals by liquid metals; intermolecular forces; rheology; solubility of nonelectrolytes; solvent-swelling of polymers; gas-diffusion through polymers; surface phenomena in polymers; surface phenomena at zero gravity; dielectrics; electron diffraction of solids; fracture; materials science; biophysics. Address: Dept. of Chemical Engineering, State University of New York at Buffalo, Acheson Hall, Chemistry Rd, Buffalo, NY 14214.

GOOD, R(OLAND) H(AMILTON), JR, b. Toronto, Ont, Oct. 22, 23; nat; m. 44; c. 3. THEORETICAL PHYSICS. B.M.E, Lawrence Inst. Tech, 44; M.A.E, Chrysler Inst. Eng, 46; fel, Michigan, 47-49, M.S, 48, Rackham fel, 49-51, Ph.D.(physics), 51. Engr, Chrysler Corp, 42-47; instr. PHYSICS, California, 51-53; asst. prof, Pa. State, 53-56; assoc. prof, IOWA STATE UNIV, 56-59, prof, 59-70, DISTINGUISHED PROF, 70- Vis. assoc. prof, Univ. Colo, 58; mem, Inst. Advan. Study, 60-61; Nat. Sci. Found. sr. fel, 60-61; vis. prof, Inst. Math. Sci, Madras, India, 68; guest, Stanford Linear Accelerator Ctr, 68-69. Fel. Am. Phys. Soc. Elementary particles; solid state. Address: Dept. of Physics, Iowa State University, Ames, IA 50010.

GOOD, THOMAS A(RNOLD), b. Atwater, Minn, Feb. 8, 25; m. 68; c. 1. PEDIATRICS. B.A. & B.S, Minnesota, 48, M.B, 51, M.D, 52. Intern pediat, hosp, Minnesota, 51-52, asst. res, 52-53; chief res. & res. instr, Utah, 53-56, asst. res. prof, 56-58; asst. prof, sch. med, Maryland, 58-63, assoc.

prof, 63-66, chief pediat. metab. clin, 60-66; assoc. prof. PEDIAT, MED. COL. WIS, 66-71, PROF, 71-, DIR. PEDIAT. RES, 70- Arthritis & Rheumatism Found. fel, Univ. Utah, 54-57; assoc. pediatrician, Salt Lake Gen. Hosp, 55-58; consult, Md. Univ. Hosp, 60-66; dir. poison control ctr, Univ. Md, 61-65; dir. pediat. metab. endocrine & renal serv, Milwaukee County Gen. Hosp. & Milwaukee Child Hosp. AAAS; Endocrine Soc; Am. Rheumatism Asn; N.Y. Acad. Sci; Soc. Pediat. Res; Am. Acad. Pediat. Steroid 6, salicylate and adrenal cortical metabolism; infectious diseases; rheumatoid arthritis; rheumatic fever and related diseases; cancer research; enzyme chemistry; biology and chemistry of proteins and mucopolysaccharides. Address: Dept. of Pediatrics, Medical College of Wisconsin, 1700 W. Wisconsin Ave, Milwaukee, WI 53233.

GOOD, WALTER A(MOS), b. Hillsdale, Mich, Apr. 25, 16; m. 42; c. 2. PHYSICS. A.B, Kalamazoo Col, 37; M.S, Iowa, 39, Ph.D.(physics), 41. Asst. physics, Iowa, 37-41; PHYSICIST, nat. defense res. comt, dept. terrestrial magnetism, Carnegie Institution, 41-42; APPL. PHYSICS LAB, JOHNS HOPKINS UNIV, 42-68, MEM. PRIN. PROF. STAFF, 68- Pres. comt. int. aeromodels, Int. Astronaut. Fedn, 65-66. Am. Phys. Soc; Soc. Automotive Eng. Rigidity modulus of beta-brass single crystals; computers; electric and hydraulic servomechanisms; proximity fuse; electrogyrotachometer; missile control systems. Address: Applied Physics Lab, Johns Hopkins University, Silver Spring, MD 20910.

GOOD, WILFRED M(ANLY), b. Hope, Kans, Oct. 13, 13; m. 41; c. 3. PHYSICS. A.B, Kansas, 36, M.A, 38; Ph.D, Mass. Inst. Technol, 44. PHYSICIST, OAK RIDGE NAT. LAB, 46-, dir. high voltage lab, 57-63. With Off. Sci. Res. & Develop, 44. Fel. Am. Phys. Soc. Nuclear reactions among the very light nuclei; neutron physics. Address: 113 Taylor Rd, Oak Ridge, TN 37830.

GOOD, WILLIAM B(RENEMAN), b. Middletown, Pa, Nov. 19, 20; m. 51; c. 2. PHYSICS. B.S, North Carolina, 48, M.S, 50; fel, Alabama, 54-56, Ph.D. (physics), 57. Physicist, Rohm & Haas Co, Redstone Arsenal, Ala, 50-54; assoc. prof. PHYSICS, Baylor, 56-57; asst. prof, N.MEX. STATE UNIV, 57-61, assoc. prof, 61-66, PROF, 66-, HEAD DEPT. 71- U.S.M.C, 42-45, Sgt. Fel. AAAS; Am. Phys. Soc; Am. Asn. Physics Teachers; Am. Geophys. Union. Upper atmosphere; condensation and nucleation phenomena; properties of supercooled liquids; physics of fluids. Address: Dept. of Physics, Box 3D, New Mexico State University, Las Cruces, NM 88001.

GOODALE, FAIRFIELD, JR, b. Boston, Mass, May 4, 23; m. 45; c. 5. PATHOLOGY. A.B, Western Reserve, 46, M.D, 50. Intern, Mt. Auburn Hosp, 50-51; res. path, Mass. Gen. Hosp, 51-54, chief res, 54-55; U.S. Pub. Health Serv. res. fel, St. Mary's Hosp, London, Eng, 55-56; Radcliffe Infirmary, Dept. Regius Prof, Oxford, 56-57; asst. prof, Dartmouth Med. Sch, 58-60; assoc. prof, Albany Med. Col, 60-63; PROF. PATH. & CHMN. DEPT, MED. COL. VA, 63- Am. Cancer Soc. res. fel, Harvard Med. Sch, 54-55, asst, 57-58; Mass. Gen. Hosp, 57-58; assoc. dir. labs, Mary Hitchcock Mem. Hosp. & Clin, 58-60. U.S.A.A.F, 42-45, 2nd Lt. Am. Soc. Clin. Path; Am. Soc. Path. & Bact; Am. Soc. Exp. Path; Am. Med. Asn; fel. Col. Am. Path; Soc. Exp. Biol. & Med; Int. Acad. Path. Pathogenesis of fever; pulmonary hypertension; experimental atherosclerosis. Address: Dept. of Pathology, Medical College of Virginia, Richmond, VA 23231.

GOODALE, G(ORDON) M(URRAY), b. Anderson, S.C, Oct. 22, 24; m. 46; c. 3. ORGANIC CHEMISTRY. B.S.(chem) & B.S.(chem. eng), Clemson Col, 45; M.A, N.C. Univ, 47, Ph.D.(chem), 53. Asst. prof. chem, Presby. Col.(S.C), 48-50; res. chemist, process develop. lab, Carbide & Carbon Chem. Co, 52-55, group leader, develop. dept, Union Carbide Corp, 55-63, mgr. mkt. develop, new prod, chem. div, N.Y, 63-66, mkt. mgr. org. chem, Union Carbide Belg, 66-67, textile chem, chem. & plastics develop. div, N.Y, 67-71; MGR. OPER, VALCHEM DIV, UNITED MERCHANTS, 71- Am. Chem. Soc; Tech. Asn. Pulp & Paper Indust; Am. Asn. Textile Chem. & Colorist. Plasticizers; oil additives; synthetic lubes; vinyl ethers; silicates; process and product development; paper and textile chemistry. Address: Valchem Division, United Merchants, Langley, SC 29834.

GOODALE, M(INOTT) R, b. Hartford, Conn, May 21, 23; m. 46; c. 4. MECHANICAL ENGINEERING. B.M.E, Rensselaer Polytech, 49. Mech. engr, elec. boat div, Gen. Dynamics Corp, 49-51; abrasive engr, Bay State Abrasive Prod. Co, 51-52; mech. engr, Wallingford Steel Co. Div, Allegheny Ludlum Steel Corp, 52-54; Hamilton Standard Div, United Aircraft Corp, 54-56, sr. equip. engr, 56-59, asst. proj. engr, mil. prod, 59-62; proj. engr, east. industs. div, Lab. Electronics, Inc, 62-65; sr. proj. engr, Hamilton Standard Div, United Aircraft Corp, 65-68; chief engr, MIL. PROD, EAST. INDUSTS. DIV, LFE CORP, 68, dir. eng, 68-70, PROD. MGR, AEROSPACE SYSTS, 70- U.S.N.A.F, 43-45. Design and development of custom designed liquid cooling, air conditioning, and refrigeration systems for use by the military for cooling ground based and airborn electronics. Address: 185 Preston Dr, Meriden, CT 06450.

GOODALL, DAVID WILLIAM, b. Edmonton, Eng, Apr. 4, 14; m. 49; c. 4. BOTANY, STATISTICS. B.Sc, London, 35, Beit fel, 37-39, Ph.D.(plant physiol) & dipl, Imp. Col, 41; D.Sc.(bot), Melbourne, 53. Res. asst, res. inst. plant physiol, Imp. Col, London, 39-42, sci. off, 42-46; plant physiologist, W.African Cacao Res. Inst, Ghana, 46-48; sr. lectr. bot, Melbourne, 48-52; Univ. Col. Gold Coast, 52-53, reader, 53-54; prof. agr. bot, Reading, 54-56; dir. Tobacco Res. Inst, Commonwealth Sci. & Indust. Res. Orgn, Australia, 56-61, sr. prin. res. scientist, div. math. statist, Perth, 61-67; prof. biol. sci, Univ. Calif, Irvine, 66-69; PROF. BOT. & RANGE SCI. & DIR. INT. BIOL. PROG. DESERT BIOME, UTAH STATE UNIV, 69- Ecol. Soc. Am; Am. Soc. Range Mgt; Brit. Soc. Exp. Biol; Brit. Asn. Appl. Biol; Brit. Ecol. Soc; Brit. Inst. Biol; Statist. Soc. Australia; Int. Soc. Trop. Ecol; Int. Soc. Biometeorol; Int. Soc. Plant Geog. & Ecol. Physiology of plant growth and nutrition; application of statistics and computer methods in plant ecology and taxonomy. Address: Ecology Center, Utah State University, Logan, UT 84321.

GOODALL, FORREST R, b. Houlton, Maine, June 14, 31; m. 63; c. 2. CELLULAR PHYSIOLOGY, DEVELOPMENTAL BIOLOGY. A.B, Colby Col, 56; M.S, Illinois, Urbana, 60, fel, 60-61, Ph.D.(physiol, biochem), 63. Res. asst. endocrinol, Sterling Drug Co, N.Y, 57-58; instr. physiol, Illinois, Urbana, 61-62; res. fel. cytol, Dartmouth Med. Sch, 62-66; asst. prof. biol, South. Methodist Univ, 66-69; DIR. DIV. CYTOCHEM. & CELL BIOL, DEPT. PATH, BAYLOR UNIV, 69- U.S. Pub. Health Serv. fel, 62-65; Lalor Found. fel, 65-66; Am. Heart Asn. grant-in-aid, 65-70. U.S.N, 50-54. AAAS; Am. Inst. Biol. Sci; Am. Soc. Zool; Am. Soc. Cell Biol. Contractile protein synthesis; control of spermatogenesis; hormonal control of lysosomal activity; hormonal effects at the cellular level; embryonic induction mechanisms. Address: Dept. of Pathology, Baylor University Medical Center, Dallas, TX 75246.

GOODALL, McCHESNEY, b. Staunton, Va, Nov. 10, 16; m. 53; c. 4. PHYSIOLOGY. M.D, Med. Col. Va, 47; Ph.D, Karolinska Inst. Sweden, 51. Res. internal med, McGuire Hosp, Richmond, Va, 51-53; asst. prof. physiol, sch. med, Yale, 53-55; prof, Duke, 55-58; asst. dir. res, Mem. Res. Ctr. & Hosp, Tennessee, 58-61, med. dir, 61-64; PROF. physiol. & surg. res, UNIV. TEX. MED. BR. GALVESTON, 68-70, PHARMACOL, PHYSIOL. & SURG, 70-, dir. res, Shriners Burns Inst, 64-68. Estab. investr, Am. Heart Asn, 54-59; mem, White House Conf. Aging, 70- U.S.N.A.F, 41-46, Lt. Discoverer of L-dopa and dopamine in mammalian tissue; biosynthesis and metabolism of L-dopa, dopamine, adrenaline-noradrenaline; sympathetic nervous system; cardiovascular research. Address: Dept. of Pharmacology University of Texas Medical Branch, Galveston, TX 77550.

GOODALL, MARCUS CAMPBELL, b. London, Eng, Mar. 3, 14; m. 60; c. 2. BIOPHYSICS. Draftsman designer aerodyn, Luton Aircraft Ltd, 36-37; develop. engr. electronics, Pye Radio Ltd, 37-42; exp. off. microwave eng, Brit. Admiralty, 42-45; sr. engr. electron physics, Marconi Ltd, 45-49; mem. math. physics, Inst. Adv. Study, 49-50; physicist, Standard Tel. Ltd, Eng, 50-51; res. fel, muscle biophys, Inst. Muscle Res, 51-53; lectr, Michigan, 53-56; res. assoc, Mass. Inst. Tech, 56-59; cognitive systs, Cornell, 59-60; staff mem. neurophysiol. & epistemology, Mass. Inst. Tech, 60-65; sr. res. assoc. physics, Boston Univ, 65-70; ASSOC. PROF. PHYSIOL. & BIOPHYS, MED. CTR, UNIV. ALA, BIRMINGHAM, 70- Assoc. mem. biomed. res. inst, Am. Med. Asn, 66-70. Soc. Gen. Systs. Res; Am. Math. Soc; Biophys. Soc; London Math. Soc; Royal Geog. Soc. Foundations of relativistic quantum mechanics; theories of epigenesis; biological control mechanisms; membrane biophysics and biochemistry. Address: Dept. of Physiology & Biophysics, Medical Center, University of Alabama in Birmingham, Birmingham, AL 35233.

GOODCHILD, CHAUNCEY G(EORGE), b. New Castle, Pa, June 18, 12; m. 34; c. 3. ZOOLOGY. B.S, Westminster Col.(Pa), 33, hon. LL.D, 61; Sandham fel, N.Y. Univ, 40-41, Ph.D.(parasitol), 41. Instr. BIOL, Westminister Col.(Pa), 34-35, instr. & acting head dept, 35-36; asst, N.Y. Univ, 36-40; instr, City Col, 40-41; assoc. prof, Southwest Mo. State Col, 41-46, prof, 46-52; assoc. prof, EMORY UNIV, 52-57, PROF, 57-, chmn. dept, 57-64. Instr, Marine Biol. Lab, Woods Hole, 43-52, corp. mem. AAAS; Am. Micros. Soc; Am. Soc. Parasitol; Am. Soc. Zool; Am. Soc. Trop. Med. & Hyg. Biology of helminth parasites. Address: Dept. of Biology, Emory University, Atlanta, GA 30322.

GOODDING, JOHN A(LAN), b. Lincoln, Nebr, Mar. 11, 22; m. 45; c. 2. AGRONOMY. B.S, Nebraska, 47; M.S, Kansas State, 50; Ph.D, Washington State, 57. Instr, Kansas State, 48-51; Washington State, 53-55; asst. prof. agron. & asst. agronomist, Nebraska, 55-61; assoc. prof. AGRON, UNIV. MINN, ST. PAUL, 61-68, PROF, 68-, ASST. DEAN COL. AGR, 70-, asst. dir. resident instr, 61-70. U.S.A, 43-46, Res, 46-51, 1st Lt. Range management; seed technology; miscellaneous legumes. Address: Office of the Dean, 277 Coffey Hall, University of Minnesota College of Agriculture, St. Paul, MN 55101.

GOODE, HARRY D(ONALD), b. Newark, N.J, May 31, 12; m. 46. GEOLOGY. B.S, Arizona, 51; Ph.D.(geol), Colorado, 59. Switchman, N.Y. Tel. Co, 30-48; geol. field asst, U.S. Geol. Surv, 49-52, geologist, 52-59, asst. dist. geologist, 59-62; assoc. prof. GEOL, UNIV. UTAH, 62-68, PROF, 68- Lectr West. Elec. Co, 47. Superior performance award, U.S. Geol. Surv, 61. Sig.C, 42-46, Capt. Fel. AAAS; fel. Geol. Soc. Am; Am. Asn. Petrol. Geol; Am. Quaternary Asn. Ground water geology, especially springs in bedrock; geomorphology; Quaternary geology, especially deposits of Lake Bonneville. Address: Dept. of Geological & Geophysical Sciences, University of Utah, Salt Lake City, UT 84112.

GOODE, HENRY P(HILLIP), b. Lenexa, Kans, Jan. 1, 09; m. 32; c. 2. INDUSTRIAL ENGINEERING. B.S, Kansas, 30, M.S, 34. Indust. engr, West. Elec. Co, Ill, 30-32; chief inspector, Am. Can Co, Mo, 35-41; assoc. prof. mech. eng, Stanford, 41-52; PROF. INDUST. ENG. & OPERS. RES, Southern Methodist, 52-57; CORNELL UNIV, 57- Am. Soc. Qual. Control; Am. Soc. Eng. Educ; Am. Inst. Indust. Eng. Production engineering; industrial statistics. Address: Dept. of Operations Research, Cornell University, Ithaca, NY 14850.

GOODE, JULIA PRATT, b. Carnesville, Ga, Feb. 26, 29. ANALYTICAL CHEMISTRY. B.A, Agnes Scott Col, 50; M.S, Emory, 52. Chemist, Ga. Dept. Pub. Health, 52-53; asst. to dir. agr. res, Tenn. Corp, 53-56; chmn. dept. sci, Fulton County Bd. Ed, 56-66; assoc. prof. chem, Baptist Col. at Charleston, 66-69; ASST. PROF. MED. TECHNOL, MED. UNIV. S.C, 69- Am. Chem. Soc. Quantitative techniques in paper chromatography. Address: Deptl of Clinical Pathology, Medical University of South Carolina, 80 Barre St, Charleston, SC 29401.

GOODE, LEMUEL, b. Saulsville, W.Va, Jan. 2, 21; m. 47; c. 2. PHYSIOLOGY. B.S, W.Va. Univ, 42, M.S, 46; N.C. State Col; Ph.D, Univ. Fla, 61. Asst. county agent, N.C. STATE UNIV, 46-47, instr. ANIMAL SCI, 47-48, asst. prof, 48-60, assoc. prof, 60-65, PROF, 65- South. Fels. Fund. faculty fel. U.S.A, 42-45. Am. Soc. Animal Sci; Soc. Study Reproduction; Brit. Soc. Study Fertility. Physiology of reproduction; effects of nutrition; environment and hormones on ovarian activity and reproductive rate; animal genetics and pasture utilization. Address: Dept. of Animal Science, North Carolina State University, Raleigh, NC 27607.

GOODE, M(ELVYN) DENNIS, b. New Albany, Ind, Feb. 18, 40; m. 68. CELL BIOLOGY, BIOPHYSICS. B.S, Univ. Kans, 63; Ph.D.(cell biol), Iowa State Univ, 67. Asst. biomed. res, Argonne Nat. Labs, 63; res. assoc. anat, Univ.

Pa, 67-68; ASST. PROF. ZOOL, UNIV. MD, COLLEGE PARK, 68- Vis. investr, Univ. Tex. M.D. Anderson Hosp. & Tumor Inst, 69; res. grants, Univ. Md. gen. res. bd, 69-70, biomed. sci. comt, 70-71 & Am. Cancer Soc, 70-72. AAAS; Am. Soc. Cell Biol. Isolation and characterization of the mitotic apparatus; kinetics of microtubule formation; ultrastructure of developing muscle; relationship between myosin synthesis and DNA synthesis; microtubule protein synthesis during mammalian cell cycle. Address: Dept. of Zoology, University of Maryland, College Park, MD 20742.

GOODE, M(ONROE) J(ACK), b. Whitney, Ala, Feb. 15, 28; m. 50; c. 3. PLANT PATHOLOGY. B.S, Miss. State Col, 52, M.S, 54; Ph.D.(plant path), N.C. State Col, 57. Asst. prof. PLANT PATH, UNIV. ARK, FAYETTEVILLE, 57-61, assoc. prof, 61-66, PROF, 66- U.S.A, 46-49. AAAS; Am. Phytopath. Soc. Diseases of vegetable crops; physiology of disease resistance. Address: Dept. of Plant Pathology, University of Arkansas, Fayetteville, AR 72701.

GOODE, ROBERT P, b. N.Y.C, Sept. 12, 36. BIOLOGY. B.A, N.Y. Univ, 57; Cornell, 57-58; M.A, Columbia, 60, Nat. Sci. Found. fel, 60-61, Nat. Insts. Health fels, 61-63, Ph.D.(exp. embryol), 64. ASST. PROF. embryol. & histol, Otterbein Col, 63-64; EMBRYOL, CITY COL. NEW YORK, 64- Am. Soc. Zool; Soc. Develop. Biol. Regeneration of limbs in amphibia, particularly of adults in several species of Anurans under natural conditions; induction of regeneration in amphibians and mammals. Address: Dept. of Biology, City College of New York, Convent Ave. at 138th St, New York, NY 10031.

GOODE, WILLIAM E(DWARD), b. Denton, Tex, July 20, 23; m. 45; c. 3. ORGANIC CHEMISTRY. B.S, N.Tex. State Col, 46, M.S, 47; Eli Lilly fel, Illinois, 49-50, Ph.D.(org. chem), 50. Instr, Ill. Inst. Tech, 50-51; CHEMIST, Off. Synthetic Rubber, 51-52; ROHM AND HAAS CO, 52-, ASST. DIR. RES, 70-, lab. head, 57-63, res. supvr, 63-70. U.S.A.F, 42-45, Capt; Distinguished Flying Cross. Am. Chem. Soc. Polymerization mechanisms; properties and structures of polymers; agricultural pesticides. Address: Rohm and Haas Co, Norristown & McKean Rds, Spring House, PA 19477.

GOODELL, BERTRAM C, b. Southbridge, Mass, 1911; m. 41; c. 2. FORESTRY. B.S, Massachusetts, 33; M.F, Harvard, 37; M.S, Hopkins, 57; Ph.D, Colorado State, 63. Prin. hydrologist, Rocky Mt. Forest & Range Exp. Sta, U.S. Forest Serv, 45-69; PROF. FORESTRY, UNIV. B.C, 69- Collab, col. forestry & range mgt, Colorado State, 58- Am. Soc. Foresters. Hydrology; hydraulics; climatology; ecology. Address: Faculty of Forestry, University of British Columbia, Vancouver, B.C, Can.

GOODELL, H(ORACE) G(RANT), b. Decatur, Ill, Oct. 12, 25; m. 56; c. 2. GEOLOGY. B.S, South. Methodist Univ, 54; Ph.D, Northwest. Univ, 58. From asst. prof. to prof. geol, Fla. State Univ, 57-70; PROF. ENVIRON. SCI, UNIV. VA, CHARLOTTESVILLE, 70- U.S.N.A.F, 43-49, 50-51, Res, 51-, Capt. Geol. Soc. Am; Soc. Econ. Paleont. & Mineral; Geochem. Soc; Am. Asn. Petrol. Geol. Sedimentary petrology; lithostratigraphy; geochemistry; marine geology. Address: Dept. of Environmental Sciences, University of Virginia, Charlottesville, VA 22901.

GOODELL, JOHN D(eWITTE), b. Omaha, Nebr, Sept. 20, 09; m. 43; c. 5. ELECTRONICS. Ph.D.(deductive sci), Univ. Lodz, 56. Consult. engr, electronics, acoustics, 31-41; Detroit signal lab, Signal Corps, U.S. Army, 41-43; pres. & dir. eng. electronics, audio & computers, Minn. Electronics Corp, 46-57; mgr. prod. develop, Columbia Broadcasting Syst. Labs, 57-60, pres. Robodyne Div, 60-61, automation div, 61-62; corp. tech. dir, U.S. Industs, Inc, 62-63; PRES, GOODELL MOTION PICTURES, 63- Pres, Inst. Appl. Logic, 50-; pres. & dir. eng, Int. Sci. Industs. Corp, 53-57. Ed. jour, Computing Systs, 50- U.S.N.R, 43-46. Logical foundations of computing machinery; special computing devices; magnetic structures; electronic circuitry; electrophysiology, special sensing systems-electrical, biological and mechanical; learning theory; teaching machines and systems. Address: Goodell Motion Pictures, 355 Kenneth St, St. Paul, MN 55105.

GOODELL, WARREN F(RANKLIN), JR, b. Champaign, Ill, May 10, 24; m. 46; c. 2. PHYSICS. B.S, Illinois, 44; A.M, Columbia, 47, Ph.D.(physics), 51. Mem. staff, radiation lab, Mass. Inst. Technol, 44-46; assoc. dir. particle physics, Nevis Cyclotron Lab, COLUMBIA UNIV, 51-64, res. admin, off. projs. & grants, 64-67, V.PRES. ADMIN, 67- Am. Phys. Soc. Experimental high energy particle physics; electronic instrumentation; academic research administration; contract and grant administration. Address: 211 Low Memorial Library, Columbia University, New York, NY 10027.

GOODENOUGH, DAVID G(EORGE), b. Victoria, B.C, Nov. 12, 42; m. 65. ASTRONOMY. Walter Helm fel, Univ. Toronto, 64-65, Prov. Ont. fels, 65-68, M.Sc, 67, Rheinhart fel, 68, Nat. Res. Coun. Can. fel, 68-69, Ph.D.(astron), 69. Fel, Univ. Victoria (B.C), 69-70; ASST. PROF. ASTRON, WHEATON COL.(MASS), 70- Am. Astron. Soc; Royal Astron. Soc. Can. Photometry of star clusters; abundance analyses of strong-cyanogen stars. Address: Dept. of Physics & Astronomy, Wheaton College, Norton, MA 02766.

GOODENOUGH, JOHN B(ANNISTER), b. Jena, Ger, July 25, 22; U.S. citizen; m. 51. PHYSICS. A.B, Yale, 43; Ph.D.(physics), Chicago, 52; hon. Dr., Univ. Bordeaux, 67. Res. engr, Westinghouse Elec. Corp, 51-52; RES. PHYSICIST, LINCOLN LAB, MASS. INST. TECHNOL, 52- Fel, Neurosci. Res. Prog, 61-, mem. exec. comt, div. solid state physics, 65-68; bd. mem, Univ. Without Walls, Roxbury, Mass, 71- U.S.A.F, 42-48, Res, 48-53. AAAS; Soc. Neurosci; fel. Am. Phys. Soc; Phys. Soc. Japan. Theory of solids; transition metal compounds; magnetism; brain function. Address: Lincoln Lab, Massachusetts Institute of Technology, P.O. Box 73, Lexington, MA 02173.

GOODENOUGH, ROBERT D(UANE), b. Dunkirk, N.Y, Dec. 4, 23; m. 48; c. 4. INORGANIC CHEMISTRY. B.S, Purdue, 49. Anal. res. chemist, DOW CHEM. CO, 58-62, group leader inorg. res, 62-67, mgr. patent develop. plastics, 67-69, PATENT ADMINSTR, DESIGNED PROD. DEPT, 69- U.S.A, 43-46. Am. Chem. Soc; Sci. Res. Soc. Am. Inorganic development of products and processes for natural brines and nonferrous ores. Address: Patent Administration, Dow Chemical Co, 2040 Dow Center, Midland, MI 48640.

GOODENOUGH, URSULA WILTSHIRE, b. Queens Village, N.Y, Mar. 16, 43; m. 69; c. 1. CELL BIOLOGY, GENETICS. B.A, Columbia Univ, 63, Nat. Insts. Health fel. & M.A, 65; Nat. Insts. Health fel. & Ph.D.(biol), Harvard, 69. Nat. Insts. Health fel, biol. labs, HARVARD, 69-71, ASST. PROF. BIOL, 71- Am. Soc. Cell Biol; Genetics Soc. Am. Cell biology and genetics of gametic differentiation in Chlamydomonas reinhardi; membrane structure; organelle genetics. Address: Biological Labs, Harvard University, Cambridge, MA 02138.

GOODER, HARRY, b. Castleford, Eng, May 7, 28; m. 54; c. 2. BIOCHEMISTRY, GENETICS. B.Sc, Leeds, 49, Ph.D.(biochem), 52. Res. fel. bact, Harvard Med. Sch, 52-54, teaching fel, 54-55; mem. sci. staff, Cent. Pub. Health Lab, Med. Res. Coun, Eng, 55-61; asst. prof. BACT. & IMMUNOL, SCH. MED, UNIV. N.C, CHAPEL HILL, 61-63, assoc. prof, 63-68, PROF, 68- Am. Soc. Microbiol; Brit. Soc. Gen. Microbiol; Brit. Soc. Immunol; fel. Royal Inst. Chem. Bacterial structure and chemistry, specifically cell walls and L forms; bacterial physiology, specifically exotoxins; bacterial genetics; medical bacteriology. Address: Dept. of Bacteriology & Immunology, University of North Carolina School of Medicine, Chapel Hill, NC 27514.

GOODEVE, ALLAN McCOY, b. Toronto, Ont, Aug. 12, 23; m. 59. PHARMACOGNOSY. Ph.B, Toronto, 48, M.Sc, 56; B.S.P, Saskatchewan, 50; Ph.D.(pharmacog), Purdue, 60. ASST. PROF. PHARMACOG, North Carolina, 59-60; UNIV. B.C, 60- R.C.A.F, 43-46. AAAS; Am. Soc. Pharmacog; Am. Chem. Soc; Am. Pharmaceut. Asn; Am. Inst. Hist. Pharm; Can. Pharmaceut. Asn; Can. Acad. Hist. Pharm; Asn. Faculties Pharm. Can. Alkaloid biosynthesis—ergot alkaloids; solanaceous alkaloids. Address: Faculty of Pharmaceutical Sciences, University of British Columbia, Vancouver 8, B.C, Can.

GOODFELLOW, ELSIE F, b. Westcliff, Essex, Eng, Apr. 30, 24; m. 46. NEUROANATOMY, HISTOLOGY. B.Sc, London, 54, Ph.D.(neurophysiol), 60. Demonstr. zool. & bot, Mid. Essex Tech. Col, Eng, 53-55; res. asst. pharmacol, May & Baker Pharmaceut. Co, 55-56; res. assoc. neurophysiol, SCH. MED, CREIGHTON UNIV, 56-60, asst. prof. NEUROANAT, 60-64, ASSOC. PROF, 64- Instr, Southend Munic. Col, Eng, 54-55. AAAS; Am. Asn. Anat; Am. Physiol. Soc. Investigation of behavioral mechanisms of central nervous system, especially functions of the rhinencephalon and neuro-endocrine relationships. Address: Dept. of Neuroanatomy, Creighton University School of Medicine, 637 N. 27th St, Omaha, NE 68131.

GOODFELLOW, ROBERT DAVID, b. Oak Park, Ill, Sept. 29, 37; m. 62; c. 2. BIOCHEMISTRY, CELL PHYSIOLOGY. B.A, N.Cent. Col.(Ill), 59; M.S, Northwestern, 61, Ph.D.(biochem), 65. Trainee develop. physiol, Northwestern, 62-64, instr. biol. sci, 64-65, asst. prof, 65; Milstead fel. chem. enzym, Milstead Lab. Chem. Enzym, Shell Res. Ltd, Eng, 65-66; ASST. PROF. BIOL, UNIV. NOTRE DAME, 66- AAAS; Am. Soc. Zool; Entom. Soc. Am; Brit. Biochem. Soc; Royal Entom. Soc. London. Metabolism of insect development; control of cholesterol utilization in eukaryotic cells; modes of action of insect hormones; organization and function of subcellular organelles; controls of polyisoprenoid biosynthesis in invertebrates. Address: Dept. of Biology, University of Notre Dame, Notre Dame, IN 46556.

GOODFRIEND, LEWIS S(TONE), b. New York, N.Y, May 21, 23; m. 61; c. 4. ACOUSTICS. M.E, Stevens Inst. Tech, 47; M.E.E, Polytech. Inst. Brooklyn, 52. Res. engr, Stevens Inst. Tech, 47-49; chief engr, Audio Facilities Corp, 50; chief elec. engr, Audio Instrument Co, Inc, 51-53; CONSULT. ENGR. ACOUST, GOODFRIEND-ASSOCS, 53- Ed, Sound & Vibration Mag, 66-71; v.pres, mgt. div, Zurr Environ. Engrs; group v.pres. noise pollution control group, Zurh Industs Inc. U.S.M.C, 43-45. Fel. Acoust. Soc. Am.(ed, Noise Control, 54-58); fel. Audio Eng. Soc.(ed, jour, 52-54); sr. mem. Inst. Elec. & Electronics Eng; Am. Soc. Test & Mat; Am. Indust. Hyg. Asn. Architectural acoustics; industrial noise control; community noise and responses to it; aviation and aerospace acoustics; acoustical instruments and speech communication, including sound reinforcing systems. Address: Goodfriend-Associates, 7 Saddle Rd, Cedar Knolls, NJ 07927.

GOODFRIEND, PAUL LOUIS, b. Dallas, Tex, Aug. 10, 30; m. 53; c. 2. PHYSICAL CHEMISTRY. B.S, Virginia, 52; univ. fel, Ga. Inst. Tech, 54-55, Nat. Sci. Found. fel, 55-56, Ph.D.(chem), 57. Fel. chem, Rochester, 56-58; asst. prof, Col. William & Mary, 58-61; res. chemist, Texaco Exp, Inc, 61-66; assoc. prof. CHEM, UNIV. MAINE, ORONO, 66-70, PROF, 70- Am. Chem. Soc. Molecular spectroscopy and quantum mechanics; excited states of free radicals; kinetics. Address: Dept. of Chemistry, University of Maine at Orono, Orono, ME 04473.

GOODFRIEND, THEODORE L, b. Phila, Pa, Sept. 30, 31; m. 64. INTERNAL MEDICINE, BIOCHEMISTRY. A.B, Swarthmore Col, 53; M.D, Pennsylvania, 57. Intern, Univ. Hosps. Cleveland, 57-58; asst. res. med, Barnes Hosp, Washington (St. Louis), 60-62; Helen Hay Whitney res. fel. biochem, Brandeis, 62-65; ASST. PROF. MED. & PHARMACOL, UNIV. WIS, MADISON, 65- Consult, Arthur D. Little, Inc, Mass, 64- U.S.P.H.S.R, 58-60, Sr. Asst. Surg. Am. Soc. Pharmacol. Enzyme synthesis in tissue culture; antibodies to small polypeptides; kinins. Address: Dept. of Pharmacology, University of Wisconsin School of Medicine, Madison, WI 53706.

GOODGAL, SOL H(OWARD), b. Baltimore, Md, July 25, 21; m. 46; c. 2. GENETICS, BIOCHEMISTRY. B.S, Maryland, 42; Nat. Res. Coun. fel, Hopkins, 49-50, Ph.D.(biol), 50. Res. assoc. inst. co-op. res, Hopkins, 50-52, biochem, 52-58, asst. prof. & dir. sch. hyg. & pub. health, 58-61; assoc. prof. MICROBIOL, SCH. MED, UNIV. PA, 61-66, PROF, 66- Fel, Pasteur Inst, 59-60. U.S.A, 42-46. AAAS; Genetics Soc. Am; Am. Soc. Microbiol; Am. Soc. Nat; Am. Soc. Biol. Chem. Transformation of bacteria; bacteriophage; role of nucleic acid in genetic determination; radiation effects on genetics of microorganisms. Address: Dept. of Microbiology, University of Pennsylvania School of Medicine, Philadelphia, PA 19104.

GOODGAME, THOMAS H, b. Camden, Ark, May 23, 21; m. 46; c. 1. ENVIRONMENTAL SCIENCES, CHEMICAL ENGINEERING. B.S, La. Tech Univ, 42; M.S, La. State Univ, Baton Rouge, 47; Arthur D. Little fel, Mass. Inst. Technol, 50, Standard Oil fel, 51, Humble Oil fel, 52, D.S.(chem. eng), 53. Engr, Jones Mills Works, Aluminum Co. Am, 42-43; asst. prof. mech. &

chem. eng, La. Tech Univ, 47-49; group leader res. & develop. & sr. chem. engr, Cabot Corp, 53-55; head res. & develop, Tex. Butadiene & Chem. Corp, 55-57; assoc. prof. chem. eng, Ga. Inst. Technol, 57-59; sr. proj. engr, Cabot Corp, 59-62, gen. mgr. chem. plant, Cabot Titania Corp, 63-64; sr. res. engr, WHIRLPOOL CORP, 64-67, mgr. eng. res, 67-70, DIR. ENVIRON. CONTROL, 70- Consult. engr, 47-49, 57-59; fel, Atomic Energy Comn. Summer Inst. Nuclear Eng, 58; part time prof, Mich. State Univ, 65- Dipl, Environ. Eng. Intersoc. Bd, 70. U.S.N, 43-46, Res, 46-, Capt. AAAS; Inst. Environ. Sci; Am. Asn. Cost Eng; Am. Soc. Eng. Educ; Solar Energy Soc; Am. Soc. Heat, Refrig. & Air-Conditioning Eng; Am. Chem. Soc; Nat. Soc. Prof. Eng; Sci. Res. Soc. Am; Am. Inst. Chem. Eng. Mass transfer between phases; inorganic chemicals and pigments; production and processes; engineering economy; convective heat transfer; radiative heat transfer; solvent extractation; distillation; air; water; noise; pollution control; solid waste management. Address: Whirlpool Corp. Research & Engineering Center, Monte Rd, Benton Harbor, MI 49022.

GOODGE, WILLIAM R(USSELL), b. Seattle, Wash, Apr. 26, 28; m. 57; c. 2. ANATOMY, VERTEBRATE ZOOLOGY. B.S, Washington (Seattle), 49, Ph.D. (zool), 57; M.A, Michigan, 50. Asst. zool, Washington (Seattle), 53-55, acting instr, 55-57; instr. gross & neurol. anat, sch. med, W.Va. Univ, 57-61, asst. prof, 61-64; ANAT, SCH. MED, UNIV. MO-COLUMBIA, 64-70, ASSOC. PROF, 70- Med. Serv.C, U.S.A, 50-52. AAAS; Am. Asn. Anat; Cooper Ornith. Soc; Am. Ornith. Union. Vertebrate functional anatomy, musculature, sense organs and glands; histology and histochemistry. Address: Dept. of Anatomy, University of Missouri-Columbia School of Medicine, Columbia, MO 65201.

GOODGOLD, JOSEPH, b. N.Y.C, Mar. 21, 20; m. 42; c. 2. MEDICINE. B.A, Brooklyn Col, 41; M.D, Middlesex Univ, 45. DIR. ELECTRODIAG. DEPT, INST. REHAB. MED, MED. CTR, N.Y. UNIV, 56-, DIR. RES. & EDUC, DEPT. REHAB. MED, 70-, PROF. REHAB. MED, SCH. MED, 63-, lectr, sch. educ, 56, assoc. prof. phys. med. & rehab, sch. med, 58-63. Consult, City Law Dept, N.Y, 55; div. voc. rehab, State Educ. Dept, 59; Brookdale Hosp. Ctr, Brooklyn, 64-; attend, Bellevue Hosp, 65; consult, Manhattan Vet. Admin. Hosp, 69. Chief dept. phys. med. & rehab, Ft. Campbell Hosp, Ky, 52-53, Med.C, 50-53, Capt. Am. Med. Asn; Am. Asn. Electromyog. & Electrodiag; Am. Rheumatism Asn; Am. Cong. Rehab. Med; N.Y. Acad. Sci. Electrophysiology. Address: Institute of Rehabilitation Medicine, Medical Center, New York University, 550 First Ave, New York, NY 10016.

GOODHART, F(RANK) WILLIAM, b. Centre Hall, Pa, Oct. 4, 32; m. 57. PHARMACY. B.S, Temple Univ, 54, M.S, 56; Am. Found. Pharmaceut. Educ. fel, Purdue Univ, 57-59, Ph.D.(pharm), 59. Asst, Wyeth, Ind, 54; Temple Univ, 54-55, mfg. pharm. trainee, Merck Sharp & Dohme, Inc, 55-56; asst, Purdue Univ, 56-57; sr. res. pharmacist, E.R. Squibb & Sons Div, Olin Mathieson Chem. Co, 59-63; sr. scientist, WARNER-LAMBERT RES. INST, 63-69, SR. RES. ASSOC, 69- Formulation of medicinal products, particularly solid dosage forms; process development; biopharmaceutics. Address: 22 Pepperidge Rd, Morristown, NJ 07960.

GOODHART, ROBERT STANLEY, b. Altoona, Pa, July 19, 09; m. 35; c. 2. MEDICINE. B.S, Lafayette Col, 30; M.D, N.Y. Univ, 34, Wyckoff fel, 39-41, D.Med.Sc, 40; Rockefeller Found. fel, Oxford, 38-39. Intern, Brooklyn Hosp, N.Y, 34-36; res. physician, psychiat. div, Bellevue Hosp, 36-39; instr. med, col. med, N.Y. Univ, 39-42, asst. prof, 42-47, asst. dean, 39-40; sci. dir, Nat. Vitamin Found, Inc, 46-67, pres, 62-67; EXEC. SECY. COMT. MED. EDUC, N.Y. ACAD MED, 67- Res. fel, Milbank Mem. Fund, 41-42; mem. comt. nutrit. indust, food & nutrit. bd, Nat. Res. Coun, 41-49, v.chmn, 42-46, chmn, 46-49; chief indust. feeding prog. div, War Food Admin, 43-46; physician in charge, Wash. Heights Nutrit. Clin, City Health Dept, N.Y, 48-68; lectr, Columbia Univ, 50-; chmn. adv. comt, emergency food authority, Off. Civil Defense, N.Y, 50-; mem. comt. nutrit, adv. bd. qm. res. & develop, Nat. Acad. Sci-Nat. Res. Coun, 60-62, adj. prof, Mt. Sinai Med. Sch, City Univ. New York, 69- U.S.P.H.S, 42-46, Surg. Am. Soc. Clin. Invest; fel. Geront. Soc; Harvey Soc; fel. Am. Pub. Health Asn; fel. Am. Med. Asn; Am. Inst. Nutrit; fel. N.Y. Acad. Sci; fel. N.Y. Acad. Med. Nutritional disturbances and related disorders in man. Address: New York Academy of Medicine, 2 E. 103rd St, New York, NY 10029.

GOODHEART, CLARENCE F(RANCIS), b. Porterville, Calif, Jan. 24, 16; m. 41; c. 2. ELECTRICAL ENGINEERING. B.S, Calif. Inst. Technol, 36; M.S, Ohio State, 38. Asst. elec. eng, Ohio State, 36-38; instr, Agr. & Mech. Col, Texas, 38-42; proj. engr. & sect. head, Naval Ord. Lab, 42-47; PROF. ELEC. ENG, UNION COL.(N.Y), 47-, chmn. dept, 47-69. Am. Soc. Eng. Educ; Inst. Elec. & Electronics Eng. Electrical engineering education; underwater ordnance, particularly in magnetic devices. Address: Dept. of Electrical Engineering, Union College, Schenectady, NY 12308.

GOODHEART, CLYDE R(AYMOND), b. Erie, Pa, June 9, 31; m. 53; c. 3. BIOLOGY, MEDICINE. B.S, Northwestern, 53, M.S. & M.D, 57. Res. fel. animal virol. & cell. biol, Calif. Inst. Tech, 58-61; asst. prof, pediat, sch. med, Univ. South. Calif, 61-64, assoc. prof, 65; assoc. mem. staff, inst. biomed. res, Am. Med. Asn-Educ. & Res. Found, Ill, 65-69, mem. staff, 69-70; SR. MICROBIOLOGIST, RUSH-PRESBY-ST. LUKE'S MED. CTR, CHICAGO, 70-; PRES. BIOLABS, INC, 70- AAAS; Am. Soc. Microbiol; Am. Soc. Cell Biol; Biophys. Soc. Experimental embryology; respiratory physiology; tissue culture; autoradiography; animal virology and viral oncology. Address: BioLabs, Inc, Box 32, Prairie View, IL 60069.

GOODHUE, CHARLES THOMAS, b. Ames, Iowa, Apr. 30, 32; m. 53; c. 3. BIOCHEMISTRY. B.S, Illinois, 54; Chas. Pfizer & Co. fel, California, 58-59, Ph.D.(biochem), 61. Res. biochemist, Distillation Prod. Industs, 61-65; RES. MICROBIOLOGIST, EASTMAN KODAK CO, 65. U.S.N, 54-57, Res, 57-, Lt. Am. Chem. Soc; Am. Soc. Microbiol. Biochemistry of microorganisms. Address: Research Labs, Eastman Kodak Co, Rochester, NY 14650.

GOODIN, J(OE) R(AY), b. Claude, Tex, July 28, 34. PLANT PHYSIOLOGY, DEVELOPMENTAL BIOLOGY. B.S, Tex. Tech Univ, 55; M.S, Mich. State Univ, 58; Ph.D.(plant physiol), Univ. Calif, Los Angeles, 63. Asst. prof. PLANT PHYSIOL, Univ. Calif, Riverside, 63-70; ASSOC. PROF, TEX. TECH UNIV, 70- U.S.A.F, 55-57, Capt. Soc. Sigma Xi (secy-treas, 66-68); Soc. Develop. Biol; Bot. Soc. Am; Am. Soc. Plant Physiol; Am. Soc. Range Mgt.(secy-treas, 65-67). Salinity and drought tolerance; environmental stress; physiological aging and juvenility in plants. Address: Dept. of Biology, Texas Tech University, Lubbock, TX 79409.

GOODING, ANSEL M(ILLER), b. Seymour, Iowa, July 12, 24; m. 47; c. 3. GEOLOGY. A.B, Augustana Col, 49; M.S, Iowa, 51, Nat. Sci. Found. grant, 55-56, Ph.D.(geol), 57. Instr. GEOL, EARLHAM COL, 51-55, asst. prof, 55-59, assoc. prof, 59-62, PROF. & HEAD DEPT, 62- Summers, field asst, U.S. Geol. Surv, 48, geologist, Mo. Geol. Surv, 50, 52; Nat. Sci. Found. grants, 57-59, 60-63, 64-67. U.S.N, 44-46. AAAS; Geol. Soc. Am; Nat. Asn. Geol. Teachers. Geomorphology; Pleistocene geology. Address: Dept. of Geology, Earlham College, Richmond, IN 47374.

GOODING, C(HESTER) M(ARTIN) (BRIGGS), b. Ypsilanti, Mich, Oct. 30, 08; m. 34; c. 2. ORGANIC CHEMISTRY. A.B, Eastern Michigan, 30; fel, Michigan, 30-34, M.S, 32, Ph.D.(org. chem), 34; Columbia Univ, 47. Chief res. chemist, BEST FOODS DIV, Corn Prod. Co, 34-63, ASST. DIR. RES. FATS & OILS, RES. CTR, CPC INT. INC, 63- Adv. fats & oils comt, U.S. Del. Codex Alimentarius, 64-; mem. bd. dir, Res. & Develop. Assocs; patent agent. Am. Chem. Soc; Am. Oil Chemists' Soc; Soc. Chem. Indust; The Chem. Soc; Inst. Food Technol; Asn. Res. Dirs. Fats and oils technology; food products; preservations; antioxidants. Address: Best Foods Research Center, CPC International Inc, Box 1534, 1120 Commerce Ave, Union, NJ 07083.

GOODING, GUY V, JR, b. Kinston, N.C, Mar. 16, 31; m. 51; c. 5. PHYTOPATHOLOGY. B.S, N.C. State Col, 54, M.S, 58; Ph.D.(plant path), California, Davis, 62. Plant pathologist, U.S. Forest Serv, 62-65; asst. prof. PLANT PATH, N.C. STATE UNIV, 65-67, ASSOC. PROF, 67- U.S.A, 53-55, 1st Lt. Am. Phytopath. Soc. Plant virology; general phytopathology. Address: Dept. of Plant Pathology, North Carolina State University, Raleigh, NC 27607.

GOODING, RONALD HARRY, b. Edmonton, Alta, Oct. 18, 36; m. 59; c. 1. ENTOMOLOGY, BIOCHEMISTRY. B.Sc, Alberta, 57; M.A, Rice Inst, 60; Sc.D.(pathobiol), Hopkins, 64. Asst. entom, Can. Dept. Agr, Lethbridge, summers 56-58; res. assoc. biochem, Vanderbilt, 64-66; asst. prof. ENTOM, UNIV. ALTA, 66-70, ASSOC. PROF, 70- Oper. grants, Univ. Alta. Gen. Res. Fund, 67-68, Nat. Res. Coun. Can, Can. Dept. Agr. & Alta. Agr. Res. Trust, 67-, Defense Res. Bd. Can, 69- R.C.A.F, 52-54. AAAS; Entom. Soc. Can; Can. Soc. Zool. Insect biochemistry; medical entomology. Address: Dept. of Entomology, University of Alberta, Edmonton, Alta, Can.

GOODING, TERENCE J, b. Risca Mon, Eng, Mar. 27, 34; m. 55; c. 3. PLASMA & NUCLEAR PHYSICS. B.Sc, Wales, 55; Fulbright scholar, Minnesota, 55-58, Ph.D.(physics), 58. Res. asst. physics, Minnesota, 55-58; fel, UK Atomic Energy Authority, Eng, 58-60; physicist, Lawrence Radiation Lab, Calif, 60-61; sr. staff scientist, Gen. Dynamics/Astronaut, 61-65; pres, Maxwell Labs, Inc, 65-70; PRES, INTERTEK INDUSTS, 70- Am. Phys. Soc, Am. Inst. Aeronaut. & Astronaut. Space physics. Address: 9244 Balboa Ave, San Diego, CA 92123.

GOODINGS, DAVID A(MBERY), b. Toronto, Ont, July 8, 35; m. 60; c. 3. SOLID STATE PHYSICS. B.A, Univ. Toronto, 57; Grainger stud. from King's Col, Cambridge, 57-59, Nat. Res. Coun. Can. fel, 59-60, Ph.D. (physics), 61. Res. assoc. theoret. physics, Atomic Energy Res. Establish, Harwell, 60-61; PHYSICS, Univ. Pittsburgh, 61-64; lectr, Univ. Sussex, 64-68; asst. prof, Am. Univ. Beirut, 68-69; ASSOC. PROF, McMASTER UNIV, 69- Vis. lectr, Brit. Ministry Overseas Develop. prog, Univ. Ife, Nigeria, 66. Am. Phys. Soc; Can. Asn. Physicists. Atomic hyperfine structure; transport properties of ferromagnetic metals; magnetic properties of rare earth metals; x-ray emission in metals; Wannier functions in copper; molecular crystals. Address: Dept. of Physics, McMaster University, Hamilton, Ont, Can.

GOODINGS, J(OHN) M(ARTIN), b. Toronto, Ont, Feb. 18, 37; m. 61; c. 2. PHYSICAL CHEMISTRY. B.A, Univ. Toronto, 58; Ont. Res. Found. fel, Cambridge, 58-61, Ph.D.(phys. chem), 61. Asst. prof. CHEM, McGill Univ, 61-65; ASSOC. PROF, YORK UNIV.(ONT), 65- Thornton res. fel, Thornton Res. Ctr, Eng. Chem. Inst. Can. Chemical physics of ionized and neutral gases; electron collisions; negative ions; plasma diagnostics; mass spectrometry of plasmas. Address: Dept. of Chemistry, York University, Toronto, Ont, Can.

GOODISMAN, JERRY, b. Brooklyn, N.Y, Mar. 22, 39; m. 63; c. 2. CHEMICAL PHYSICS. A.B, Columbia Col, 59; A.M, Harvard, 60, Woodrow Wilson fel, Gen. Elec. fel. & U.S. Rubber fel, Ph.D.(chem), 63. Instr. phys. chem, Univ. Ill, Urbana, 63-65, asst. prof. CHEM, 65-69; ASSOC. PROF, SYRACUSE UNIV, 69- Am. Phys. Soc. Electronic wavefunctions of small molecules; Hartree-Fock wavefunctions; quantum statistical theories. Address: Dept. of Chemistry, Syracuse University, Syracuse, NY 13216.

GOODJOHN, ALBERT J, b. Calgary, Alta, Feb. 18, 28; m. 51; c. 6. NUCLEAR PHYSICS. B.Sc, Univ. Alta, 50, M.Sc, 51; Ph.D.(physics), Queen's Univ. (Ont), 56. Design specialist, Canadair Div, Gen. Dynamics Corp, 56-59; staff mem. theoret. physics, GULF GEN. ATOMIC INC, 59-61, div. head, 61-63, proj. mgr. advan. concepts, 63-66, asst. dept. chmn. reactor physics, 64-66, assoc. div. mgr, 66-70, MGR. NUCLEAR MKT, 70- Fel. Am. Nuclear Soc. Experimental and theoretical reactor and nuclear physics. Address: Gulf General Atomic Inc, P.O. Box 608, San Diego, CA 92112.

GOODKIN, JEROME, b. New York, N.Y, Mar. 22, 29; m. 52; c. 2. PHYSICAL CHEMISTRY, ELECTROCHEMISTRY. B.A, N.Y. Univ, 52, M.S, 54; Monsanto fel, Rensselaer Polytech, 57-58, Ph.D.(phys. chem), 59. Res. asst. phys. chem, N.Y. Univ, 52-54; asst. Rensselaer Polytech, 54, 56-58; sect. coord, Catalyst Res. Corp, 58-61; res. chem, res. div, FMC Corp, 62-63; sr. res. scientist, Yardney Elec. Corp, 63-68; PROF. CHEM, TRENTON STATE COL, 68- Adj. prof, Mercer County Community Col, 63-68. U.S.A, 54-56. Am. Chem. Soc; Electrochem. Soc. Molten salt chemistry; constitution of solution and electrochemical phenomena; corrosion of steel; electrode processes; batteries. Address: 22 Camelia Ct, Trenton, NJ 08638.

GOODKIND, JOHN M, b. N.Y.C, Aug. 27, 34; m. 63; c. 2. PHYSICS. A.B, Amherst Col, 56; Ph.D.(physics), Duke, 60. Res. asst. PHYSICS, Stanford, 60-62; asst. prof, UNIV. CALIF, SAN DIEGO, 62-67, ASSOC. PROF, 67- Sloan Found. fel, 62-66; Nat. Sci. Found. res. grant, 62- Am. Phys. Soc. Low temperature physics; liquid and solid helium three; nuclear adiabatic demagnetization; superconductivity; geophysics; gravimetry. Address: Dept. of Physics, University of California, San Diego, P.O. Box 109, La Jolla, CA 92037.

GOODKIND, M(ORTON) JAY, b. New York, N.Y, Apr. 29, 28; m. 54; c. 2. INTERNAL MEDICINE. A.B, Princeton, 49; M.D, Columbia, 53. Instr. internal med, sch. med, Yale, 58-62, asst. prof, 62-64; MED, SCH. MED, UNIV. PA, 64-70, ASSOC. PROF, 70-; DIR. CORONARY CARE UNIT, PHILA. GEN. HOSP, 71- Advan. fel, Am. Heart Asn, 59-61, grants-in-aid, 59-61, 61-67, estab. investr, 61-66; U.S. Pub. Health Serv. grant-in-aid, Nat. Heart Inst, 61-67; consult, Vet. Admin. Hosp, Phila. & Alson Army Hosp, Ft. Dix, N.J. U.S.P.H.S, 56-, Res, 54-56, Surg. Am. Fedn. Clin. Res; Am. Physiol. Soc; Am. Col. Physicians. Effects of thyroid hormone on myocardial metabolism of norepinephrine and on myocardial contractility and hemodynamics; cardiovascular hemodynamics; renal function in congestive heart failure; cardiology. Address: Philadelphia General Hospital, 34th St. & Civic Center Blvd, Philadelphia, PA 19104.

GOODKIND, RICHARD JERRY, b. Brooklyn, N.Y, Oct. 5, 37; m. 60; c. 1. PROSTHODONTICS. Columbia Col, 55-58; D.M.D, Tufts Univ, 62; M.S, Univ. Mich, 64. ASSOC. PROF. DENT. & DIR. GRAD. RESTORATIVE DENT, SCH. DENT, UNIV. MINN, MINNEAPOLIS, 66- Consult. & mem. prosthodontic staff, Univ. Minn. Hosp, 68- Dipl, Am. Bd. Prosthodont, 67. U.S.A.F, 62-64, Capt. Am. Prosthodont. Soc; Am. Col. Prosthodontists. Complete and removable prosthodontics. Address: Dept. of Dentistry, University of Minnesota Medical Center, Minneapolis, MN 55455.

GOODLETT, V(ERNON) WILSON, b. Greenville, S.C, May 16, 34; m. 56; c. 2. PHYSICAL CHEMISTRY. B.S, Wofford Col, 56; U.S. Steel Co. fel, Vanderbilt, 57-59, Ph.D.(chem), 59. Res. chemist, TENN. EASTMAN CO, 59-62, sr. res. chemist, 62-67, res. assoc, 67-70, HEAD PHYS. & ANAL. CHEM. RES. DIV, 70- U.S.A.R, 60-, 2nd Lt. Am. Chem. Soc. Molecular structure; nuclear magnetic resonance spectrometry; visible, ultra-violet and infrared spectroscopy. Address: Bldg. 150, Tennessee Eastman Co, P.O. Box 511, Kingsport, TN 37664.

GOODLEY, G(EORGE) RICHARD, b. New Brunswick, N.J, July 22, 32; m. 55; c. 3. PHYSICAL INORGANIC CHEMISTRY. B.S, Delaware, 54, M.S, 58. Chemist, pigments dept, E.I. DU PONT DE NEMOURS & CO, INC, 54-65, res. chemist, TEXTILE FIBERS DEPT, 65-67, SR. RES. CHEMIST, TECH. SECT, 67- Am. Chem. Soc. Distillation; surface chemistry of pigments; x-ray and infrared spectroscopy; electron microscopy; kinetics of crystal growth; pigment-polymer interactions. Address: Textile Fibers Dept, E.I. du Pont de Nemours & Co, Inc, Kinston, NC 28501.

GOODLIN, ROBERT C(LAIR), b. Eugene, Ore, June 27, 26; m. 51; c. 4. MEDICINE, GENETICS. A.B, Stanford, 49; M.D, Oregon, 53; Dight Inst. Human Genetics, 58-61. Res. obstet, univ. hosp, Minnesota, 54-58, instr. OBSTET. & GYNEC, med. col, 58-61; asst. prof, SCH. MED, STANFORD UNIV, 61-66, ASSOC. PROF, 66- U.S.N, 44-46. Am. Soc. Human Genetics; Soc. Gynec. Invest; Perinatal Res. Soc. Fetal physiology, congenital malformations. Address: Dept. of Gynecology & Obstetrics, Stanford University School of Medicine, Stanford, CA 94305.

GOODLOE, PAUL M(ILLER), II, b. Berea, Ky, May 21, 11; m. 35; c. 3. CHEMISTRY. B.S, East. Ky. State Teachers Col, 32; fel, Tennessee, 32-33; Ph.D.(chem), Hopkins, 36. Asst. org. chem, Hopkins, 34-35; res. chemist, Socony-Vacuum Oil Co, Inc, N.J, 36-43, supvr, N.Y, 43-46; mem. staff tech. sales, Brown Co, N.H, 46-53, asst. dir. res, 53-55, dir. control, 55-57, asst. tech. dir, 57-58, dir. res. & develop, 58-60, gen. mgr, chem. prod. div, 60-62; pres, Kenrich Petrochem, Inc, N.J, 62-65; consult. & exec. v.pres, Vensearch Corp, Tex, 65-68; PRES, ASSOC. CHEM. INDUSTS, INC, 68-; V.PRES, NOLAN CO, MD, 68-; MGR. SPEC. PROJS, WHITE CHEM. CORP, N.J, 68- Am. Chem. Soc; Am. Inst. Chem; Am. Inst. Chem. Eng; Tech. Asn. Pulp & Paper Indust. Rubber and plastics compounding; plasticizers and fillers; cellulose products; emulsions; detergents; production of specialty chemicals; research administration; market development; mergers and acquisitions. Address: Associated Chemical Industries, Inc, P.O. Box 689, East Orange, NJ 07019.

GOODMAN, ABRAHAM H(ARRISON), b. St. Louis, Mo, June 20, 10; m. 40; c. 2. CHEMICAL ENGINEERING, FOOD TECHNOLOGY. B.S, Rose Polytech. Inst, 32; M.S, Purdue Univ, 33. Asst. dir. res, Am. Maize Prods. Co, 33-43; Doughnut Corp. Am, 43-58, RES. DIR, FOOD PROCESS & DEVELOP, D.C.A. FOOD INDUSTS, 59- AAAS; Am. Chem. Soc; Am. Oil Chem. Soc; Inst. Food Technol; Am. Asn. Cereal Chem. Basic studies in food technology. Address: 18 Florence St, Great Neck, NY 11023.

GOODMAN, ADOLPH W(INKLER), b. San Antonio, Tex, July 20, 15; m. 47; c. 4. MATHEMATICS. B.Sc, Cincinnati, 39, M.A, 41; Pennsylvania, 41-43; Syracuse, 43-44; Ph.D.(math), Columbia, 47. Prin. eng. draftsman, U.S. Navy Yard, Pa, 41-43; instr. math, Syracuse, 43-44; sr. stress engr, Repub. Aviation Corp, N.Y, 44-46; instr. MATH, Rutgers, 47-49; assoc. prof, Univ. Ky, 49-55, PROF, 55-64; UNIV. S.FLA, 64- Mem, Inst. Advan. Study, 56-57. Am. Math. Soc; Math. Asn. Am. Theory of functions of a complex variable; conformal mapping; polynomials; graph theory; number theory. Address: Dept. of Mathematics, University of South Florida, Tampa, FL 33620.

GOODMAN, ALAN LAWRENCE, b. Miami Beach, Fla, July 27, 38; m. 64; c. 2. ORGANIC & POLYMER CHEMISTRY. B.S, Delaware, 59; Nat. Sci. Found. fel, Stanford, 59, summer, Du Pont fel, 62, Allied Chem. Corp. fel, 62, Ph.D.(org. chem), 64. Res. fel, Brandeis, 63-64; sr. res. chemist, plastics div, Allied Chem. Corp, 64-66; RES. CHEMIST, ELASTOMER CHEM. DEPT, E.I. DU PONT DE NEMOURS & CO, INC, 66- Am. Chem. Soc. Relations of structure to spectra; photochemistry; mechanisms of reactions; polymer properties and synthesis. Address: 2637 Majestic Dr, Brandywood, Wilmington, DE 19810.

GOODMAN, ALBERT, b. Brooklyn, N.Y, Apr. 11, 25; m. 47, 65; c. 3. PHYSICS. B.S, City Col. New York, 45; M.S, Univ. N.Mex, 55, Ph.D, 61. Radar engr, Hazeltine Electronics Corp, 45-46; jr. physicist, Los Alamos Sci. Lab, 46-49, mem. staff, nuclear physics res, 56-60; appl. physics res, SANDIA CORP, 49-56, STAFF MEM, SOLID STATE RES. WEAPON SYSTS. HIGH ALTITUDE ROCKET & SATELLITE INSTRUMENTATION, 60- Mem, New Mexico vis. scientist prog. Am. Phys. Soc. Nuclear physics; weapon systems. Address: P.O. Box 11282, Albuquerque, NM 87112.

GOODMAN, A(LBERT), b. New York, N.Y, Jan. 22, 27; m. 48; c. 3. CHEMISTRY. B.S, City Col, 46; M.S, N.Y. Univ, 51; Ph.D.(chem), Polytech. Inst. Brooklyn, 56. Instr. biol, City Col, 47-51; res. chemist, Dextran Corp, 51-55; E.I. DU PONT DE NEMOURS & CO, INC, 55-66, res. supvr, 66-69, SUPVR. PLANT TECHNOL, NYLON DIV, 69- U.S.A.A.F, 45-47. AAAS; Am. Chem. Soc; Sci. Res. Soc. Am. Structure-property relationships in fibers; polymer physics and rheology; polymer chemistry; enzymatic polymerization of carbohydrates; ionic polymerization of vinyl compounds and block copolymers; stereoregular polymerizations; kinetics of polymerizations; fiber-fabric structural relationships; electrical properties of fibers and fabrics. Address: 1334 Root Trail, Martinsville, VA 24112.

GOODMAN, ALLAN C(OOPER), Audiol, Speech Path, see 12th ed, Soc. & Behav. Vols.

GOODMAN, A(LVIN) M(ALCOLM), b. Phila, Pa, July 8, 30; m. 66; c. 1. ELECTRICAL ENGINEERING, SOLID STATE PHYSICS. B.S, Drexel Inst, 52; Munn fel, Princeton, 53-54, Nat. Sci. Found. fel, 54-55, M.A, 55, Inst. Bus. Mach. Corp. fel, 55-56, Ph.D.(elec. eng), 58. Asst. elec. eng, Princeton, 56-57; asst. prof, Case, 57-59; MEM. TECH. STAFF ELECTRONIC RES. LAB, DAVID SARNOFF RES. CTR, RCA CORP, 59- Am. Phys. Soc. Inst. Elec. & Electronics Eng. Metal-semiconductor contacts; photoconductivity and photovoltaic effects; semiconductor physics and devices; insulator physics and chemistry. Address: Electronic Research Lab, David Sarnoff Research Center, RCA Labs, Princeton, NJ 08540.

GOODMAN, ARNOLD F(RANK), b. Raleigh, N.C, Feb. 10, 33; m. 56; c. 3. COMPUTER SYSTEMS, STATISTICS. B.S, N.C. State Col, 54; Purdue, 54-55; M.S, Stanford, 59, Ph.D.(statist), 61. Math. statistician, nat. adv. comt, flight res. center, NASA, 55-57; res. specialist, Autonetics Div, N.Am. Rockwell Corp, 61-63, sr. tech. specialist, 63-64, tech. staff to mgr. comput. & simulation ctr, space div, 64-66, tech. adv. to div. dir. comput. & data systs, 66-67; SR. TECH. STAFF, INFO. SYSTS, McDONNELL DOUGLAS ASTRONAUT. CO, HUNTINGTON BEACH, 67- Lectr. eng, ext. div, Univ. Calif, 62-64; assoc. prof. opers. res. & statist, Calif. State Col, Long Beach, 65-66; mem. Comn. Nat. Info. Syst. Math, 68-69; co-founder & v.pres, Info. Ctr. South. Calif. Libr, 70-; expert consult, NASA, 70- U.S.A.F, 55-57, Res, 57-, Capt. Am. Statist. Asn; Asn. Comput. Mach; Inst. Math. Statist. Computer and information system planning, review, user interaction, measurement and effectiveness evaluation; system analysis; mathematical modeling; statistical analysis; statistics and probability in secondary mathematics; solving problems with mathematics. Address: 18231 Hillcrest Circle, Villa Park, CA 92667.

GOODMAN, BERNARD, b. Phila, Pa, June 14, 23; m. 51; c. 3. THEORETICAL & SOLID STATE PHYSICS. A.B, Pennsylvania, 43, Ph.D.(physics), 55. Res. stress analyst, Int. Harvester Co, 47-52; res. assoc. PHYSICS, Missouri, 52-54, asst. prof, 54-57, assoc. prof, 58-63, PROF, 64; UNIV. CINCINNATI, 65- Guggenheim fel, 62; guest prof, inst. theoret. physics, Univ. Uppsala, 62; Gothenburg 71. Fel. Am. Phys. Soc. Lattice dynamics; electron correlations and many-body theory; disordered systems. Address: Dept. of Physics, University of Cincinnati, Cincinnati, OH 45221.

GOODMAN, BILLY L(EE), b. Pauls Valley, Okla, Jan. 21, 30; m. 51; c. 5. POULTRY SCIENCE. B.S, Okla. State, 51, M.S, 53; Ph.D, Ohio State, 59. Asst. POULTRY, Okla. State, 51-52, instr, 52-55; Ohio State, 55-58; PROF, SOUTH. ILL. UNIV, CARBONDALE, 58- Poultry Sci. Asn. Poultry genetics and breeding. Address: Dept. of Animal Industries, Southern Illinois University, Carbondale, IL 62901.

GOODMAN, CHARLES D(AVID), b. N.Y.C, May 9, 28; m. 52; c. 2. PHYSICS. A.B, Clark Univ, 49; Ph.D, Univ. Rochester, 55. Physicist, OAK RIDGE NAT. LAB, 55-62, SR. PHYSICIST, 62- Vis. scientist, Weizmann Inst. Sci, 66. Fel. Am. Phys. Soc. Experimental nuclear physics, especially medium-energy nuclear physics relating to reaction mechanisms and nuclear structure; automatic data handling; cyclotrons. Address: Oak Ridge National Lab, Oak Ridge, TN 37830.

GOODMAN, CLARK (DROUILLARD), b. Memphis, Tenn, Sept. 9, 09; m. 33; c. 2; m. 70. NUCLEAR PHYSICS. B.S, Calif. Inst. Technol, 32; Ph.D.(physics), Mass. Inst. Technol, 40. Res. chemist, Union Oil Co, 32-33; res. chemist & sales engr, Kelco Co, 33-36; asst. physics, Mass. Inst. Technol, 36-40, res. assoc, 40-42, asst. prof, 42-47, assoc. prof, 47-58; dir. res. & v.pres, Schlumberger Ltd, 58-62; v.pres, Houston Res. Inst, 62-68; PROF. PHYSICS, UNIV. HOUSTON, 65-, chmn. dept, 65-69. Secy. comt. standards of radioactivity, Nat. Res. Coun, 38-46; tech. aide, div. 17, Nat. Defense Res. Comt, 45-46; sr. physicist, Clinton Labs, Oak Ridge, 46; Fulbright lectr, Osaka Univ, 54-55; asst. dir, div. reactor develop, Atomic Energy Comn, 55-59, mem. licensing & regulations panel; mem. bd. dirs, Simmonds Precision Prod. Co, 68-; lunar & planetary missions bd, NASA; chmn. comt. radioactive waste disposal, Nat. Acad. Sci, 67-70. Consult, Manhattan Dist, 43-46; Joint Cong. Comt. Atomic Energy, 61-62; Adv. Res. Proj. Agency, 61-66; NASA, 65-; Atomic Safety & Licensing Bd, 66- Fel. Am. Phys. Soc; fel. Geol. Soc. Am; Am. Asn. Petrol. Geol. Experimental nuclear physics; radioactivity of terrestrial materials; nuclear engineering; geophysics; medium energy physics. Address: Dept. of Physics, University of Houston, Houston, TX 77004.

GOODMAN, DAVID M(ARSHALL), b. New York, N.Y, Jan. 13, 23; m. 44; c. 3. ELECTRICAL ENGINEERING, ELECTRONICS. B.E.E, City Col, 43; M.E.E, N.Y. Univ, 51. Proj. engr, Sperry Gyroscope Co, 46-49; asst. tech. res. dir, airborne combat info. ctr, N.Y. UNIV, 49-51, proj. dir, 51-56, SR. RES. SCIENTIST & DIR, PROJ. SETE, NAT. TEST EQUIP. INFO. CTR, SCH.

ENG. & SCI, 56- U.S.N, 45-46. Inst. Elec. & Electronics Eng; Am. Inst. Aeronaut. & Astronaut; Instrument Soc. Am. Automatic telephone answering sets with remote control; color television display devices and systems; non-linear and sweep frequency measuring devices; long life and high power vacuum tubes; automatic test systems with pattern recognition displays. Address: 3843 Debra Court, Seaford, NY 11783.

GOODMAN, D(eWITT) S(TETTEN), b. New York, N.Y, July 18, 30; m. 57; c. 2. MEDICINE, BIOCHEMISTRY. A.B, Harvard, 51, M.D, 55. Intern med, Presby. Hosp, N.Y, 55-56, asst. res, 58-59; investr, Nat. Heart Inst, Nat. Insts. Health, 56-58 & 60-62; res. fel, Helen Hay Whitney Found, Hammersmith Hosp, London, Eng, 59-60; asst. prof. MED, COLUMBIA UNIV, 62-67, assoc. prof, 67-69, PROF, 69- Career scientist, Health Res. Coun. of City of New York, 64-; mem. metab. study sect, Nat. Insts. Health, 66-70; v.chmn, Gordon Res. Conf. Lipid Metab, 67, chmn, 68; mem. coun. arteriosclerosis, Am. Heart Asn, mem. exec. comn, 69-, mem. adv. coun. res, 70- S.J. Meltzer Award, Soc. Exp. Biol. & Med, 63. AAAS; Asn. Am. Physicians; Am. Soc. Clin. Invest.(ed, J. Clin. Invest, 70-72); Am. Soc. Biol. Chem; Endocrine Soc; Harvey Soc; Am. Oil Chemists' Soc. Lipid and lipoprotein metabolism; cholesterol and cholesteryl ester turnover and metabolism; vitamin A and carotenoids; vitamin A transport; vitamin D transport and metabolism; lipid-protein and ion-protein interactions; hyperlipidemia and arteriosclerosis. Address: Dept. of Medicine, College of Physicians & Surgeons, Columbia University, New York, NY 10032.

GOODMAN, DONALD C(HARLES), b. Chicago, Ill, Nov. 24, 27; m. 68; c. 6. NEUROANATOMY, COMPARATIVE NEUROLOGY. B.S, Univ. Ill, 49, M.S, 50, fel, 53-54, Ph.D.(zool), 54. Instr. ANAT, sch. med, Univ. Pa, 54-56, fel, inst. neurol. sci, 54-55; instr. Univ. Mich, 56; asst. prof, Univ. Fla, 56-59, assoc. prof, 59-63, prof, 63-68, chmn. dept, 65-68; PROF. & CHMN. DEPT, UPSTATE MED. CTR, STATE UNIV. N.Y, 68- Nat. Inst. Neurol. Diseases & Stroke res. grant, 58-; mem. study sect, neurol. B, Nat. Insts. Health, 68-71, anat. training prog, 71-75. Res. award, Soc. Sigma Xi, 62. U.S.A, 46-48. AAAS; Am. Asn. Anat. Neuromorphological plasticity of central nervous system and its relationship to recovery of brain function; comparative neurology of cerebellum and basal ganglia and of brain structure of reptiles. Address: Dept. of Anatomy, Upstate Medical Center, State University of New York, Syracuse, NY 13210.

GOODMAN, ELI I, b. Bronx, N.Y, June 26, 29; m. 51; c. 3. CHEMICAL ENGINEERING. B.S, Mass. Inst. Tech, 50, M.S, 51. Jr. chem. engr, Brookhaven Nat. Lab, 51-53, assoc. chem. engr, 53-55; sr. chem. engr, Nuclear Sci. & Eng. Corp, Pa, 55-59; sr. engr, Westinghouse Elec. Corp, 59-65; opers. analyst, U.S. ATOMIC ENERGY COMN, 65-67, chief plans & forecast br, 67-70, ASST. SCI. REP, TOKYO, 70- Am. Nuclear Soc; Am. Inst. Chem. Eng. Nuclear power reactors; applications of radioactivity; international aspects of nuclear energy. Address: U.S. Atomic Energy Commission, American Embassy, APO San Francisco 96503.

GOODMAN, FRED, b. New York, N.Y, Nov. 13, 28; m. 53; c. 2. GENETICS, MOLECULAR BIOLOGY. A.B, Brooklyn Col, 49, M.A, 52; Nat. Insts. Health fel, Columbia, 56-58, Ph.D.(zool), 58. Lect. asst. biol, Brooklyn Col, 49-50, substitute instr, 50-52; res. asst. biochem, Columbia, 52-54, lectr. zool, 54-56, res. worker biochem, 58-60; asst. prof. BIOL, STERN COL. WOMEN, YESHIVA UNIV, 60-64, assoc. prof, 64-67, PROF, 67- Nat. Insts. Health grants, 61-67, 67-70; vis. assoc. prof, Univ. Calif, Los Angeles, 66; vis. prof, Bar-Ilan Univ, Israel, 68-69. AAAS; Am. Soc. Microbiol; N.Y. Acad. Sci. Nucleic acid and protein synthesis; radiation biology; metabolic events in bacteriophage-infected cells. Address: Dept. of Biology, Stern College for Women, Yeshiva University, 253 Lexington Ave, New York, NY 10016.

GOODMAN, GARY, b. Mount Vernon, N.Y, Apr. 16, 38. ASTRONOMY. B.Sc, Calif. Inst. Tech, 60; M.S, Illinois, Urbana, 63, Ph.D.(astron), 69. Teaching asst. astron, Illinois, Urbana, 60-68; Nat. Res. Coun. res. assoc, Ames Res. Ctr, NASA, 69-71; VISTA VOLUNTEER, 71- Consult, Magnavox, 69; summers, scientist, Avco-Everett Res. Lab, 62, 63 & 64, sr. res. engr, Lockheed Missiles & Space Co, 67. Am. Astron Soc. Planetary atmospheres; construction of theoretical model atmospheres; molecular spectroscopy. Address: P.O. Box 79, Brooklyn, IA 52211.

GOODMAN, GEORGE J(ONES), b. Evanston, Wyo, Nov. 5, 04; m. 48; c. 1. BOTANY. A.B, Wyoming, 29; Lackland fel, Washington (St. Louis), 29-33, M.S, 30, Ph.D.(plant taxon), 33. Herbarium asst, Mo. Bot. Garden, 31-33; from instr. BOT. to asst. prof, Oklahoma, 33-36; from asst. prof. to assoc. prof, Iowa State Col, 36-45; FROM PROF. TO REGENTS PROF. & CURATOR HERBARIUM, UNIV. OKLA, 45- With soil conserv. serv, U.S. Dept. Agr, Kans. & Tex, 34; field study, Iowa State Col, south. Mex. & Guatemala, 44. AAAS; Am. Soc. Plant Taxon; Bot. Soc. Am; Soc. Study Evolution; Torrey Bot. Club. Plant taxonomy, especially of Eriogoneae and plains flora. Address: Dept. of Botany & Microbiology, University of Oklahoma, Norman, OK 73069.

GOODMAN, G(ERALD) M, b. Kansas City, Mo, July 2, 21; m. 47; c. 4. CHEMICAL ENGINEERING. B.S, Illinois, 47. Chem. engr, tech. serv, res. dept, Standard Oil Co.(Ind), 47-52, group leader, 52-61; group leader planning & scheduling div, MFG. DEPT, AM. OIL CO, 61-67, head cost engr, 67- C.Eng, 41-45, Capt. Am. Inst. Chem. Eng. Address: American Oil Co, 910 S. Michigan, Chicago, IL 60680.

GOODMAN, GILBERT, b. Bayonne, N.J, Feb. 27, 21; m. 53; c. 2. CERAMICS, MATERIALS SCIENCE. B.Sc, Rutgers, 41; Sc.D.(ceramics), Mass. Inst. Tech, 49. Mem. tech. staff, Bell Tel. Labs, N.J, 44-46; res. assoc, res. lab, Gen. Elec. Co, 48-58, specialist measurements, budgets & facilities, 58-60, res. assoc, 60-64; res. dir, Vitramon, Inc, 64-67; MGR. mat. res. dept, corp. res. group, GLOBE-UNION, INC, 67-70, CORP. APPL. RES. GROUP, 70- Part-time assoc. prof, col. eng, Marquette Univ, 70-71. U.S.A, 42-45. Electrochem. Soc; Am. Phys. Soc; Am. Ceramic Soc. Electrochemistry; batteries; electronic materials; components. Address: 8934 N. Lake Dr, Milwaukee, WI 53217.

GOODMAN, GORDON L(OUIS), b. Chicago, Ill, Aug. 19, 33; m. 62; c. 2. INFORMATION SCIENCE. A.B, Harvard, 55, Ph.D, 59. Chemist, Argonne Nat. Lab, 59-71; HEAD, COMMUNAISSANCE, 70- Lectr, Harvard, summer 60; vis. prof, Cornell Univ, 64; prof, South. Ill. Univ, 70. AAAS; Asn. Comput. Mach; fel. Am. Phys. Soc. Social, legal, economic and technical aspects of information technology. Address: Communaissance, Box 422, Downers Grove, IL 60515.

GOODMAN, HAROLD O(RBECK), b. Minneapolis, Minn, Sept. 8, 24; m. 43; c. 4. GENETICS. B.A, Minnesota, 48; M.A, 50, Nat. Insts. Health fel, 52-54, Ph.D, 53. Fel. med. genetics, Bowman Gray Sch. Med, 53-54; instr. zool, Mich. State Col, 54-56, asst. prof, 56-58; PREV. MED. & GENETICS, BOWMAN GRAY SCH. MED, 58-60, assoc. prof, 60-70, PROF, 70- U.S.A, 43-46. Am. Soc. Human Genetics; Am. Genetic Asn; Brit. Eugenics Soc. Genetics of dental caries; salivary components; atherosclerosis; mongolism. Address: Dept. of Preventive Medicine & Genetics, Bowman Gray School of Medicine, Wake Forest University, Winston-Salem, NC 27103.

GOODMAN, HAROLD S(TANLEY), b. Kansas City, Mo, June 10, 26; m. 52; c. 3. MICROBIOLOGY. A.B, Kansas, 49; fel, Wayne State, 50-52, M.S, 52; Ph.D, Michigan, 54. Asst. virol, Kansas, 48-49; bact, Michigan, 52-54; path, Pittsburgh, 54-55; res. assoc. immunol, Mt. Sinai Med. Res. Found, 55-59; med, obstet. & gynec, Chicago, 59-64; mem. staff, Michael Reese Res. Found, 64-68; ASSOC. PROF. obstet. & gynec, UNIV. ILL. MED. CTR, 68-69, MICROBIOL, 69- U.S.N, 44-46. Am. Asn. Immunol. Immunology and immunohematology. Address: Dept. of Microbiology, University of Illinois at the Medical Center, Chicago, IL 60680.

GOODMAN, H(ENRY) G(AINES), JR, b. Richmond, Va, Aug. 26, 04; m. 43. ORGANIC CHEMISTRY. B.S, Va. Polytech, 27, M.S, 28; Ph.D.(org. chem), Pittsburgh, 38. Indust. water consult. & analyst, Froehling & Robertson, Inc, Va, 28-29; plant chemist, Curtin Howe Corp, 29-30; res. chemist, Sylvania Indust. Corp, Va, 30-33; res. chemist & indust. fel, Mellon Inst, 34-59; group leader & tech. serv. mgr. textile chem. res. & develop. dept, chem. div, Union Carbide Corp, 59-67; tech. dir, C.H. Patrick & Co, Inc, 67-70; CONSULT. ORG. SYNTHESIS & TEXTILE CHEM, 70- Lectr, Univ. Pittsburgh, 47- Sci. Res. Soc. Am; Am. Chem. Soc; fel. Am. Inst. Chem. Organic synthesis; textiles; pharmaceutical chemistry; solvents; protective coatings; Friedel-Crafts reactions on metadiphenylbenzene. Address: 107 W. Avondale Dr, Greenville, SC 29609.

GOODMAN, HENRY H(ARRIS), JR, b. San Marcos, Tex, Nov. 4, 18; m. 44; c. 4. CHEMISTRY. B.S, Southwest Tex. Teachers Col, 38; Ph.D.(org. chem), Texas, 50. Teacher, pub. sch, Tex, 38-41; res. chemist, E.I. DU PONT DE NEMOURS & CO, INC, 50-55, PLASTICS CONSULT, DETROIT, 55- U.S.N, 41-46, Res, 46-, Lt. Comdr. Am. Chem. Soc; Soc. Plastics Eng; Soc. Automotive Eng. Polymer chemistry. Address: 1425 Lakewood Rd, Bloomfield Hills, MI 48013.

GOODMAN, H(ENRY) MAURICE, b. Glen Cove, N.Y, May 4, 34; m. 61; c. 3. PHYSIOLOGY, ENDOCRINOLOGY. A.B, Brandeis Univ, 56; Andelot fel. & A.M, Harvard, 57, U.S. Pub. Health Serv. fel. & Ph.D.(physiol), 60. Jr. fel, Harvard, 60-62; teaching fel. med, Tufts Univ, 61-62; instr. PHYSIOL, Harvard Med. Sch, 62-63, assoc, 63-66, asst. prof, 66-69, assoc. prof, 69-70; PROF. & CHMN. DEPT, UNIV. MASS. MED. SCH, 70- U.S. Pub. Health Serv. career develop. award, 66- Am. Physiol. Soc; Am. Soc. Zool; Endocrine Soc. Physiological actions of growth hormone; endocrine regulation of metabolism; physiology of adipose tissue. Address: Dept. of Physiology, University of Massachusetts Medical School, 419 Belmont St, Worchester, MA 01604.

GOODMAN, HOWARD C(HARLES), b. Rochester, N.Y, July 18, 20; m. 42; c. 3. IMMUNOLOGY. A.B, Harvard, 41; M.D, Hopkins, 44. Intern & asst. res. med. serv, Peter Bent Brigham Hosp, Boston, 44-45, 47-48; res. med. serv, Sawtelle Vet. Admin. Hosp, Los Angeles, 48-49; res. assoc, inst. med. res, Cedars of Lebanon Hosp, 49-53; res. assoc, Nat. Heart Inst, 53-60, head clin. allergy sect, Nat. Inst. Allergy & Infectious Diseases, 60-63; CHIEF IMMUNOL. UNIT, WHO, 63- Asst. med. unit, St. Mary's Hosp, London, 51-52; Howard Hughes med. res. fel, 51-53; clin. assoc. prof, med. sch, Southern California, 52-53. Med.C, 45-47, Capt. AAAS; Soc. Exp. Biol. & Med; Am. Physiol. Soc; Am. Fedn. Clin. Res; Am. Asn. Immunol. Internal medicine; basic and clinical immunology. Address: World Health Organization, Geneva, Switz.

GOODMAN, IRVING, b. Denver, Colo, May 22, 17; m. 43; c. 4. BIOCHEMISTRY. B.A, Colorado, 39, M.A, 41, Ph.D.(chem), 44. Asst. chem, Colorado, 39-43; instr, 43-47, asst. prof, 47-49; sr. res. chemist, Wellcome Res. Labs. Div, Burroughs, Wellcome & Co, Inc, 52-59; ASST. PROF. BIOCHEM, COL. PHYSICIANS & SURGEONS, COLUMBIA UNIV, 59- Guggenheim fel, Cambridge & Brussels, 49-51; res. assoc, Paris, 51-52. With Off. Sci. Res. & Develop, 44. Fel. AAAS; Am. Chem. Soc; Am. Soc. Biol. Chem; The Chem. Soc; N.Y. Acad. Sci. Nucleic acid derivatives and homologues; amino acids and peptides; carbohydrates; mechanisms of drug action; bivalent sulfur compounds; metabolic inhibitors. Address: Dept. of Biochemistry, College of Physicians & Surgeons, Columbia University, 630 W. 168th St, New York, NY 10032.

GOODMAN, IRVING J, b. Detroit, Mich, Jan. 9, 33; m. 60; c. 4. PSYCHOLOGY, NEUROBIOLOGY. B.S, Wayne State, 58; Ph.D.(brain-behavior), Rochester, 68. Asst. prof. psychol-psychiat, W.VA. UNIV, 66-71, ASSOC. PROF. PSYCHOL, 71- Consult, Vet. Admin. Hosp, 68- U.S.N, 55-57. Am. Psychol. Asn; Asn. Psychophysiol. Study Sleep; Animal Behav. Soc. Brain-behavior relationships. Address: Dept. of Psychology, West Virginia University, Morgantown, WV 26506.

GOODMAN, J(ACK) J(OSEPH), b. Free City of Danzig, June 22, 27; nat; m. 52; c. 4. ORGANIC CHEMISTRY. B.S, Rutgers, 50; Dupont fel, Iowa State, 54-55, Ph.D.(org. chem), 55. Res. supvr. RES. & DEVELOP, Toni Co, Ill, 55-62; dir, Noxzema Chem. Co, 63-67, v.pres, Noxell Corp, 67-68; CORP. V.PRES, CHESEBOROUGH-PONDS, INC, 68- U.S.A.A.F, 45-46. Am. Chem. Soc. Organometallic and sulfur chemistry; varied organic synthesis; cosmetic formulations. Address: Research Division, Cheseborough-Ponds, Inc, 485 Lexington Ave, New York, NY 10017.

GOODMAN, JAMES M(ARION), b. Henryetta, Okla, July 23, 29; m. 53; c. 2. GEOGRAPHY. B.A, Oklahoma, 52; M.S, Northwestern, 53, Ph.D.(geog), 63. ASSOC. PROF. geog. & geol, West. Ky. State Col, 56-64; GEOG, Wis. State Univ-Oshkosh, 64-66; Ore. Col. Educ, 66-67; UNIV. OKLA, 67- Dir, Nat. Defense Ed. Act Inst. Adv. Study Geog, 65. U.S.A.F, 54-56, 1st Lt. AAAS; Asn. Am. Geog. Karst landscapes of Kentucky penny royal; physical geography and earth science in secondary education. Address: Dept. of Geography, University of Oklahoma, Norman, OK 73069.

GOODMAN, JAMES R, b. Riverton, Wyo, May 23, 33; m. 53; c. 2. STRUCTURAL & CIVIL ENGINEERING. B.S, Univ, Wyo, 55; M.S, Colo. State Univ, 61; Nat. Lumber Mfrs. fel, Univ. Calif, Berkeley, 63, Nat. Sci. Found. fel, 64, Ph.D.(struct. eng), 67. Bridge designer, Wyo. State Hwy. Dept, 55-57; instr. CIVIL ENG, COLO. STATE UNIV, 57-61, asst. prof, 61-67, ASSOC. PROF, 67- Summers, field tech, U.S. Geol. Surv, 51 & 52, city engr, Riverton Wyo, 53, field engr, Bishop & Spurlock, 54, comput. prog. develop, Wyo. State Hwy. Dept, 59 & 60. Am. Soc. Civil Eng; Am. Soc. Eng. Educ; Forest Prod. Res. Soc. Research in properties of wood and wood engineering; application of computers to engineered structures. Address: Dept. of Civil Engineering, Colorado State University, Fort Collins, CO 80521.

GOODMAN, JAY I(RWIN), b. Brooklyn, N.Y, Apr. 4, 43; m. 65; c. 1. PHARMACOLOGY, ONCOLOGY. B.S, L.I. Univ, 65; Nat. Insts. Health fel, Univ. Mich, 65-69, Ph.D.(pharmacol), 69. Nat. Cancer Inst. res. fel, McArdle Lab. Cancer Res, Univ. Wis, Madison, 69-71; ASST. PROF. PHARMACOL, MICH. STATE UNIV, 71- Am. Chem. Soc. Chemical carcinogenesis; toxicology; biochemical pharmacology. Address: Dept. of Pharmacology, Michigan State University, East Lansing, MI 48823.

GOODMAN, JEROME, b. Brooklyn, N.Y, Apr. 2, 26. PHYSICAL CHEMISTRY. B.S, Polytech. Inst. Brooklyn, 49, Ph.D.(chem), 61; Fulbright fel, Paris, 57-59. Dir. res, Radiation Res. Corp, 55-59; sr. scientist, Radiation Appln. Inc, 59-60; dir. chem. res, chem. lab, Nuclear Res. Assocs, Inc, 60-71; SR. ANALYST, EDWARDS & HANLY, 71- Sr. instr, Polytech. Inst. Brooklyn, 64-65; consult, chem. eng. res. div, N.Y. Univ, 63-64. U.S.A.A.F, 44-45. AAAS; Am. Chem. Soc. Radiation and polymer chemistry; photochemistry. Address: 35 Pond Rd, Great Neck, NY 11024.

GOODMAN, JOAN WRIGHT (MRS. CHARLES D), b. El Paso, Tex, May 14, 25; m. 52; c. 2. PHYSIOLOGY. B.A, Columbia, 45; fel, Rochester, 47-51, Ph.D.(physiol), 52. Chemist, Tidewater Assoc. Oil Co, 45; asst. chem, Manhattan proj, Rochester, 45-46, technician electromyog, dept. orthop, 46-47, jr. scientist cell physiol, div. radiation biol, Univ. Atomic Energy Proj, 53-54; res. assoc. biol, Mass. Inst. Technol, 56; SR. RES. BIOLOGIST, DIV. BIOL, OAK RIDGE NAT. LAB, 57- Lectr, grad. sch. biomed. sci, Univ. Tenn, 69- Am. Physiol. Soc; Radiation Res. Soc; Am. Asn. Immunol; Transplantation Soc; Int. Soc. Hemat; Soc. Exp. Biol. & Med; Am. Soc. Hemat; Exp. Hemat. Soc. Mammalian physiology; transplantation; immunogenetics; hemopoiesis. Address: Division of Biology, Oak Ridge National Lab, Oak Ridge, TN 37830.

GOODMAN, JOEL W(ARREN), b. New York, N.Y, Feb. 2, 33; m. 64. MICROBIOLOGY. B.A, Brooklyn Col, 53; Ph.D.(microbiol), Columbia, 59. Fel, Nat. Inst. Med. Res, London, 59-60; asst. prof. MICROBIOL, SCH. MED, UNIV. CALIF, SAN FRANCISCO, 60-65, assoc. prof, 65-70, PROF, 70- AAAS; Am. Asn. Immunol. Immunochemistry of proteins; basic structural studies of proteins and antiproteins; mechanism of immune induction. Address: Dept. of Microbiology, University of California, San Francisco, CA 94122.

GOODMAN, JOHN D(AVID), b. Fairfield, Iowa, Apr. 8, 20; m. 48; c. 2. PARASITOLOGY. B.S, Parsons Col, 42; M.A, Michigan, 47, fel, 49-51, Ph.D. (zool), 51. Mem. faculty, Mercer Univ, 48-49; Univ. Redlands, 51-66; vis. prof, faculty agr, Makerere Univ. Col, Uganda, 66-71; PROF. BIOL, ANDERSON COL, 71- Fulbright scholar, Uganda, E.Africa, 58-59. Sanit.C, U.S.A, 42-45. Am. Soc. Parasitol; Am. Micros. Soc; Am. Soc. Ichthyol. & Herpet; Soc. Syst. Zool; Wilson Ornith. Soc; Wildlife Disease Asn; Am. Ornith. Union. Trematode life histories and systematics; parasites of reptiles and amphibians relating to their geographic distribution and evolution; natural history studies of vertebrates; American deserts, especially the desert bighorn sheep; ecology of tropical diseases; schistosomiasis. Address: Dept. of Biology, Anderson College, Anderson, IN 46011.

GOODMAN, JOHN MOTT, b. Modesto, Calif, Aug. 22, 39; m. 60; c. 2. SOLID STATE PHYSICS. B.A, Swarthmore Col, 60; Danforth fel, Nat. Sci. Found. fel. & Ph.D.(physics), Cornell, 67. Instr. PHYSICS, Harvey Mudd Col, 65-67, asst. prof, 67-71; VIS. ASST. PROF, CLAREMONT MEN'S COL, PITZER COL. & SCRIPPS COL, 71- Instr, Cornell Univ, summers 61 & 63; consult, Sci. Am, Sept. 67 & 68 issues; Charles Eamse, 69- Am. Phys. Soc; Am. Asn. Physics Teachers (spec. merit award, apparatus competition, 69). Teaching and history of physics; relationships between science and the arts; experimental techniques and instrumentation; uses of computer in education; electronic properties of solids, especially metals at cryogenic temperatures; superconductivity. Address: Joint Science Dept, Claremont Colleges, Claremont, CA 91711.

GOODMAN, J(OSEPH) J(ACOB), b. Montreal, Que, Feb. 3, 21; nat; m. 48; c. 3. PLANT PATHOLOGY, MICROBIOLOGY. B.S, Saskatchewan, 44; M.S, Alberta, 47; Ph.D, Minnesota, 51. Plant breeder, Agr. Exp. Sta, Swift Current, Sask, 44-45; asst. plant sci, Alberta, 45-47, plant pathol, Minnesota, 47-51; MICROBIOLOGIST, LEDERLE LABS, AM. CYANAMID CO, 51- Am. Soc. Microbiol; Soc. Indust. Biol. Physiology of bacteria and fungi in relation to the production of metabolic products such as antibiotics, enzymes, organic acids and vitamins. Address: Lederle Labs, American Cyanamid Co, Pearl River, NY 10965.

GOODMAN, JOSEPH R(OBERT), b. Tacoma, Wash, Oct. 13, 11; m. 42; c. 4. BIOCHEMISTRY. B.S, Washington (Seattle), 35, Ph.D.(chem), 41. Asst. supt, Steinhart Aquarium, Calif. Acad. Sci, 41-42; teacher chem. & math, war relocation authority, Utah, 43-44; res. biochemist, sch. med, Southern California, 46-47; chem. oceanogr, Philippine Rehab. Prog, U.S. Dept. Interior, Manila, 47-48; chief biochemist, Brentwood Vet. Admin. Hosp, Los Angeles, 48-50, head physiol. chem. res, VET. ADMIN. HOSP, Long Beach, 50-61, CHIEF RES, SAN FRANCISCO, 61- Consult, Orange County Hosp, 57-61. AAAS; Am. Chem. Soc; Soc. Exp. Biol. & Med; Electron. Micros. Soc; Am. Asn. Clin. Chem. Medical biochemistry; electron microscopy; oceanography. Address: General Medical Research, (151), Veterans Administration Hospital, 42nd Ave. & Clement St, San Francisco, CA 94121.

GOODMAN, JOSEPH W(ILFRED), b. Boston, Mass, Feb. 8, 36; m. 62; c. 1. OPTICS. A.B, Harvard, 58; M.S, Stanford, 60, Ph.D.(elec. eng), 63. Res. asst. electronic countermeasures, Stanford Electronics Labs, 58-62; fel. info. theory, Norweg. Defence Res. Estab, 62-63; res. assoc. optical systs, Stanford Electronics Labs, 63-65, res. engr, 66-67; asst. prof. ELEC. ENG, STANFORD UNIV, 67-69, ASSOC. PROF, 69- Optical Soc. Am. traveling lectr, 68-69. Frederick Emmons Terman Award, Am. Soc. Eng. Educ, 71. AAAS; fel. Optical Soc. Am; Inst. Elec. & Electronics Eng. Application of Fourier methods to the analysis and synthesis of optical systems; statistical problems in optics; theory of partial coherence; holography; optical processing of information; digital image processing. Address: Dept. of Electrical Engineering, Stanford University, Stanford, CA 94305.

GOODMAN, L(AWRENCE) E(UGENE), b. New York, N.Y, Mar. 12, 20; m. 51; c. 3. MECHANICS. A.B, Columbia, 39, B.S, 40, Nat. Res. Coun. fel, 46-47, Ph.D.(appl. mech), 49; M.S, Illinois, 42. Electro-mech. engr, appl. physics lab, Hopkins, 43-44, 46; instr. civil eng, sch. eng, Columbia, 47-48; from res. asst. prof. to res. assoc. prof, Illinois, 49-53; prof. mech, UNIV. MINN, MINNEAPOLIS, 54-65, PROF. CIVIL ENG, 65-, head dept, 65-71. Nat. Sci. Found. sr. fel, 62-63. U.S.N.R, 45-46, Res, 46-54, Lt.(jg). Fel. Am. Soc. Civil Eng; fel. Am. Soc. Mech. Eng. Stress analysis; photoelasticity; gyroscopic instruments; applied mechanics; vibration of structures. Address: 1589 Vincent St, St. Paul, MN 55108.

GOODMAN, LEON, b. Livingston, Mont, Dec. 16, 20; m. 56; c. 2. ORGANIC CHEMISTRY. B.S, Univ. Calif, Berkeley, 41; Ph.D.(chem), Univ. Calif, Los Angeles, 50. Res. asst. explosives chem, Off. Sci. Univ. & Develop, 42-45; res. chemist, Los Alamos Sci. Lab, 50-55; chemist, Stanford Res. Inst, 55-61, chmn. dept. bioorg. chem, 61-70; PROF. CHEM. & CHMN. DEPT, UNIV. R.I, 70- Res. assoc, Univ. South. Calif, 53-54; mem. med. chem. study sect, Nat. Insts. Health, 70-73. U.S.N, 45-46. Am. Chem. Soc; The Chem. Soc; N.Y. Acad. Sci. Cancer chemotherapy; nucleoside chemistry; carbohydrate chemistry; nitrogen heterocyclic chemistry; silicon chemistry; organic chemistry of high explosives; organic sulfur chemistry. Address: Dept. of Chemistry, University of Rhode Island, Kingston, RI 02881.

GOODMAN, LEON JUDIAS, b. New York, N.Y, Sept. 5, 30; m. 51; c. 2. ELECTRICAL ENGINEERING, PHYSICS. B.S, Cooper Union, 59; Columbia, 59-60. Detail draftsman, North. Elec. Co. Ltd, Que, Can, 50, jr. toolmaker, 50-51; draftsman, W. Green Elec. Co, 51-52; engineer's asst, Wright Aeronaut. Corp, 52-55; design draftsman, Walter Motor Truck Co, 55-56; indust. hygienist, health & safety lab, Atomic Energy Cmn, 56-58; res. scientist, radiol res. lab, Columbia Univ, 58-67; PROJ. MGR, BROOKHAVEN NAT. LAB, 67- Assoc. assigned to radiol. physics, Columbia Univ, 67- Inst. Elec. & Electronics Eng; Health Physics Soc; Radiation Res. Soc. Design and development of instrumentation, systems and experiments for neutron dosimetry in connection with radiobiological research into the effects of radiation on living systems. Address: Brookhaven National Lab, 17 Cornell Ave, Upton, NY 11973.

GOODMAN, LEONARD S(EYMOUR), b. Los Angeles, Calif, Dec. 28, 21; m. 44; c. 3. NUCLEAR PHYSICS. B.A, California, Los Angeles, 43; Ph.D. (physics), Chicago, 52. Jr. physicist, U.S. Naval Ord. Lab, 44-46; assoc. physicist, ARGONNE NAT. LAB, 47-60, SR. PHYSICIST, 60- Guggenheim fel, 60-61. U.S.N.R, 44-45. Fel. Am. Phys. Soc. Atomic beams; physics of diagnostic x-rays. Address: Bldg. 203, Argonne National Lab, Argonne, IL 60439.

GOODMAN, LESTER, b. Cleveland, Ohio, June 18, 27; m. 51; c. 4. BIOENGINEERING. B.S, Case, 56, M.S, 59, Ph.D.(mech. eng), 62. Owner, Goodman Salvage Co, 49-59; asst. mech. eng, Case, 56-57, instr, 57-62, asst. prof. eng, 62-64, assoc. prof, 64-, asst. dir, Systs. Res. Ctr, 61-65; CHIEF BIOMED. ENG. & INSTRUMENTATION, NAT. INSTS. HEALTH, 65- Mem. bioinstrumentation adv. coun, Am. Inst. Biol. Sci; sci. adv. bd, U.S. Air Force; pres, Alliance Eng. in Med. & Biol. U.S.N.R, 45-46. AAAS; Am. Soc. Mech. Eng; Inst. Elec. & Electronics Eng; Biophys. Soc; N.Y. Acad. Sci; Asn. Advan. Med. Instrumentation; Biomed. Eng. Soc; Nat. Soc. Prof. Eng; Soc. Advan. Med. Systs. Systems engineering; automatic control systems; computers; information sciences; physiological systems analysis, especially homeostasis; health care systems. Address: Biomedical Engineering & Instrumentation, National Institutes of Health, Bethesda, MD 20014.

GOODMAN, LIONEL, b. Brooklyn, N.Y, Apr. 23, 27; m. 50. PHYSICAL CHEMISTRY. M.S, Cornell, 51; Ph.D.(chem. physics), Iowa State Col, 54. Teaching fel. phys. chem, Cornell, 48-50; asst, Iowa State Col, 50-53; fel, Fla. State, 54-55; asst. prof. CHEM, Pa. State, 55-60, assoc. prof, 60-66; PROF, RUTGERS UNIV, 66- Nat. Sci. Found. sr. fel, 61-62; vis. prof, Sorbonne, 64; Guggenheim fel, 65. U.S.N.R, 45-46. Am. Chem. Soc; Am. Phys. Soc; Faraday Soc. Quantum chemistry; theoretical and experimental molecular spectroscopy. Address: Dept. of Chemistry, Rutgers, The State University, New Brunswick, NJ 08903.

GOODMAN, LOUIS E, b. Baltimore, Md, Mar. 7, 13; m. 42; c. 2. SURGERY, ONCOLOGY. A.B, Hopkins, 34; M.D, Maryland, 38. Intern surg, Sinai Hosp, Baltimore, 38-39; Grace New Haven Community Hosp, Conn, 39-41; from asst. res. to res. surg, Franklin Square Hosp, 41-43; INSTR. SURG, SCH. MED, UNIV. MD, BALTIMORE, 46-; from instr. to ASST. PROF, SCH. MED, JOHNS HOPKINS UNIV, 50-; HEAD TUMOR CLIN, SINAI HOSP, 57- Sr. attend. surgeon, Sinai & Franklin Square Hosps, Baltimore, 45- Am. Asn. Cancer Res; Am. Med. Asn. Cancer research as applied to experimental chemotherapy; new drugs; new techniques of administration; surgery as applied to cancer. Address: 225 Medical Arts Bldg, Baltimore, MD 21201.

GOODMAN, LOUIS P, b. N.Y.C, Aug. 20, 38; m. 65; c. 1. FOOD SCIENCE, HORTICULTURE. B.S, Rutgers Univ, 61; Nat. Insts. Health fels, Mich. State Univ, 61-68, M.S, 63, Ph.D.(food sci), 68. Res. asst, fruits & veg. lab, Mich. State Univ, 61-63, fats & oils lab, 63-68; RES. CHEMIST, KRAFTCO CORP, GLENVIEW, 68- Air Nat. Guard, 63-69, S/Sgt. Inst. Food Technol; Am. Oil Chem. Soc. Pomology; sonication studies on the hydrolysis of triglycerides and egg phospholipids by lipolytic enzymes; shortenings; emulsifier systems; simulated dairy products. Address: 47 Valley Rd, Highland Park, IL 60035.

GOODMAN, L(OUIS) S(ANFORD), b. Portland, Ore, Aug. 27, 06; m. 33; c. 2. PHARMACOLOGY. B.A, Reed Col, 28; M.D. & M.A, Oregon, 32; hon. D.Sc, Univ. Man, 65, Univ. Utah, 69. Asst. psychol, Reed Col, 27-29; neurol. & pharmacol, sch. med, Oregon, 29-32; house off. med, Hopkins Hosp, 32-33; Nat. Res. Coun. fel, sch. med, Yale, 34, instr. pharmacol. & toxicol, 35-37, asst. prof, 37-43; prof. pharmacol. & physiol. & chmn. dept, col. med, Vermont, 43-44; PROF. PHARMACOL. & CHMN. DEPT, COL. MED, UNIV. UTAH, 44- Mem. pharmacol. study sect, U.S. Pub. Health Serv, 48-52, pharmacol. & exp. therapeut. study sect, 54; res. cmt. sci. coun, Am. Heart Asn, 53-55; med. bd, Myasthenia Gravis Found, 53-58; Nat. Adv. Neurol. Diseases & Blindness Coun, 54-58; pharmacol. test cmt, Nat. Bd. Med. Exam, 55-59; sr. postdoctoral fel. eval. cmt, Nat. Sci. Found; pharmacol. test cmt, Nat. Bd. Med. Exam, 55-59; adv. coun, Life Inst. Med. Res. Fund, 56-59; sci. bd, Nat. Neurol. Res. Found, 57-64; res. grants cmt, Univ. Utah, 57-64, grad. coun, 57-69; chmn. pharmacol. training cmt, Nat. Insts. Health, 58-61, mem. cmt. res. career awards, div. gen. med. sci, 62, nat. adv. ment. health coun, 62-66, nat. adv. coun, health res. facilities, 66-70; adv. cmt. psychopharmacol. serv. ctr, Nat. Inst. Ment. Health, 58-62; panel neuropharmacol, Int. Brain Res. Orgn, 60. Mem. Depts. State & Health, Ed. & Welfare neurol. sci. mission to U.S.S.R, 58; U.S. rep, Int. Union Physiol. Sci, 63-66. Nat. Acad. Sci; AAAS; Am. Soc. Pharmacol. & Exp. Therapeut.(ed. in chief, Pharmacol. Rev, 49-53, pres, 59-60); Soc. Exp. Biol. & Med; Am. Acad. Neurol; hon. mem. Acad. Anesthesiol; hon. mem. Am. Soc. Anesthesiol; fel. Am. Col. Neuropsychopharmacol; fel. N.Y. Acad. Sci. Anticonvulsant and sympatholytic drugs; pharmacodynamics. Address: Dept. of Pharmacology, University of Utah College of Medicine, Salt Lake City, UT 84112.

GOODMAN, MAJOR M, b. Des Moines, Ia, Sept. 13, 38; m. 70; c. 2. GENETICS, EVOLUTIONARY BIOLOGY. B.S, Iowa State Univ, 60; Nat. Sci. Found. fel, N.C. State Univ, 61-65, M.S, 63, Ph.D.(genetics), 65. Nat. Sci. Found. fel, inst. genetics, advan. sch. agr, Univ. São Paulo, 65-67; vis. asst. prof. statist, N.C. STATE UNIV, 67-68, asst. prof. STATIST. & GENETICS, 68-70, ASSOC. PROF, 70- Del, Int. Genetics Cong, Tokyo, 67; mem, Maize germ plasm resources comt, Rockefeller Found, 70- Crop Sci. Soc. Am; Genetics Soc. Am; Soc. Study Evol; Soc. Econ. Bot; Soc. Syst. Zool; Am. Soc. Nat; Int. Asn. Plant Taxon. Evolution of cultivated plants; numerical taxonomy; history and evolution of maize; applied multivariate statistics. Address: Dept. of Statistics, North Carolina State University, Raleigh, NC 27607.

GOODMAN, MILTON, b. Minneapolis, Minn, May 7, 21. CHEMICAL ENGINEERING. B.S, Minnesota, 43, M.S, 49. Engr, Houdaille Hershey Corp, 43-45; instr. math. & mech, Minnesota, 46-49; math. & eng, West Coast Univ, 49-54; engr, missiles & space div, Lockheed Aircraft Corp, 54-58; mem. tech. staff, propulsion & power dept, Hughes Aircraft Co, 58-62; SR. ENGR. SCIENTIST, PROPULSION DEPT, McDONNELL DOUGLAS ASTRONAUT. CO, 62- Assoc. fel. Am. Inst. Aeronaut. & Astronaut. Electric, nuclear and chemical advance propulsion for spacecraft and missiles; nuclear and solar space power; heat transfer; fluid dynamics. Address: McDonnell Douglas Astronautics Co, 5301 Bolsa Ave, Huntington Beach, CA 92647.

GOODMAN, M(ORRIS), b. Milwaukee, Wis, Jan. 12, 25; m. 46; c. 3. IMMUNOLOGY. B.S, Univ. Wis, 48, M.S, 49, Alumni Res. Found. fel. & Ph.D. (zool), 51. U.S. Pub. Health Serv. res. fel, Calif. Inst. Technol, 51-52; res. assoc, med. col, Univ. Ill, 52-54; Detroit Inst. Cancer Res, 54-58; res. assoc. & assoc, Lafayette Clin, COL. MED, WAYNE STATE UNIV, 58-60, res. assoc. prof, 60-66, PROF. ANAT, 66- Dir. res, Plymouth State Home & Training Sch, 66; mem. adv. panel syst. biol, div. biol. & med. sci, Nat. Sci. Found, 69-72. U.S.A.A.F, 43-45. Am. Asn. Immunol; Am. Soc. Zool; Am. Acad. Neurol; Am. Asn. Phys. Anthrop; Soc. Develop. Biol; Am. Asn. Ment. Deficiency; Int. Primatol. Soc. Physical chemistry of avian and mammalian antibody-antigen systems; serological detection of tissue specificities; immunological analyses of serum proteins; molecular evolution of primates. Address: 24211 Oneida St, Oak Park, MI 48237.

GOODMAN, MURRAY, b. N.Y.C, July 6, 28; m. 51; c. 3. ORGANIC CHEMISTRY. B.S, Brooklyn Col, 49; Ph.D.(org. chem), Univ. Calif, 53. Res. assoc. org. chem, Mass. Inst. Technol, 52-55; fel, Am. Cancer Soc, Nat. Res. Coun, Cambridge, 55-56; asst. prof. chem, Polytech. Inst. Brooklyn, 56-60, assoc. prof, 60-64, prof, 64-71, dir. polymer res. inst, 67-71; PROF. CHEM, UNIV. CALIF, SAN DIEGO, 71- Ed, Biopolymers, 63- AAAS; Am. Chem. Soc; The Chem. Soc. Stereochemistry; biopolymer model systems; stereoregular synthetic polymers; peptide chemistry. Address: 9760 Blackgold Rd, La Jolla, CA 92037.

GOODMAN, NICOLAS D(ANIELS), b. Berlin, Ger, June 23, 40; U.S. citizen; m. 62. MATHEMATICAL LOGIC. A.B, Harvard, 61; M.S, Stanford, 63, Ph.D.(math), 68. Instr. MATH, Illinois, Chicago, 65-66; ASST. PROF, Santa Clara, 68-69; STATE UNIV. N.Y. BUFFALO, 69- Asn. Symbolic Logic; Am. Math. Soc. Mathematical intuitionism, particularly the theory of constructions; proof theory. Address: Dept. of Mathematics, State University of New York at Buffalo, 4246 Ridge Lea Rd, Amherst, NY 14226.

GOODMAN, NORMAN L, b. Milburn, Okla, Sept. 29, 31; m. 57; c. 3. MICROBIOLOGY, BIOCHEMISTRY. B.S, Southeast. State Col, 54; M.S, Oklahoma, 60, Nat. Insts. Health fel, 61, Ph.D.(microbiol), 65. Teacher, pub. sch, Okla, 56-57; microbiologist, oper. res, tuberc. br, communicable disease ctr, U.S. Pub. Health Serv, 63-68; asst. prof. microbiol. & dir. diag. bact. labs, Med. Univ. S.C, 68-70; ASSOC. PROF. COMMUNITY MED, MED. MYCOL. PROG, COL. MED, UNIV. KY, 70- U.S.A, 54-56. AAAS; Am. Soc. Microbiol; Bot. Soc. Am. Environmental study of pathogenic fungi and epidemiology of histoplasmosis. Address: Dept. of Community Medicine, Medical Mycology Program, College of Medicine, University of Kentucky, Lexington, KY 40506.

GOODMAN, PHILIP, b. New York, N.Y, Mar. 28, 25; m. 50; c. 3. PHYSICAL CHEMISTRY. A.B, N.Y. Univ, 43; M.S, Chicago, 48; Ph.D.(chem), Ohio State, 52. Res. chemist, rheol. polymers, Nat. Bur. Standards, 52-53; phys. chemist polymers, Naval Powder Factory, 53-56; res. physicist, Corning Glass Works, 56-60; Allied Res. Assocs, 60-63; HEAD CHEM. DEPT, PANAMETRICS, INC, 63- U.S.A, 43-46. AAAS; Am. Phys. Soc; Am. Chem. Soc; fel. Am. Inst. Chem. Solid state; high temperature materials; instrumentation; rheology of polymers and polymeric solutions, glasses and ceramics; meteorology and atmospheric composition. Address: 18 Holmes Rd, Lexington, MA 02173.

GOODMAN, RALPH R(AYMOND), b. Detroit, Mich, March 18, 27; m. 50; c. 3. THEORETICAL PHYSICS. B.S.E, Univ. Mich, 50 & 51, M.S, 52; U.S. Pub. Health Serv. fel, 52-53, Ph.D.(physics), 58. Instr. physics, Univ. Mich, 56; physicist, U.S. Navy Electronics Lab, 58-59; asst. prof. physics, Colo. State Univ, 59-64, assoc. prof, 64-66, prof, 66-68; ASSOC. DIR. RES, U.S. NAVAL RES. LAB, 68- Sr. scientist, antisubmarine warfare ctr, Supreme Allied Comdr, Atlantic, Italy, 61-63. U.S.A, 44-46. Am. Phys. Soc. Theoretical solid state semiconductors; elastic shell theory; acoustics. Address: Code 8000, U.S. Naval Research Lab, Washington, DC 20390.

GOODMAN, RICHARD E, b. New York, N.Y, Dec. 25, 35; m. 57; c. 3. CIVIL & GEOLOGICAL ENGINEERING. B.A, Cornell, 55, M.S, 58; Ford fel. & Ph.D.(geol. eng), California, 63. Eng. aide, U.S. Corps Engrs, 55-56; geol. engr, Hunting Tech. Serv. & Photronix Inc, 58; Geotech. & Resources, 58-59; asst. prof. GEOL. ENG, UNIV. CALIF, BERKELEY, 62-68, ASSOC. PROF, 68- Grants, Petrol. Res. Found, 64-66; Nat. Sci. Found, 64-66, 68-71. AAAS; Geol. Soc. Am; Am. Inst. Mining, Metall. & Petrol. Eng; Asn. Eng. Geol; Am. Soc. Civil Eng; Int. Soc. Rock Mech. Applications of geological data in civil engineering design; dams, underground works; behavior of rocks under load; physical and mathematical model studies of jointed rock masses. Address: Dept. of Civil Engineering, 472 Davis Hall, University of California, Berkeley, CA 94720.

GOODMAN, RICHARD E, b. Los Angeles, Calif, Jan. 28, 38. MOLECULAR BIOLOGY, MICROBIAL PHYSIOLOGY. B.A, Univ. Calif, Los Angeles, 60, U.S. Pub. Health Serv. fel, 62-65, Ph.D.(microbiol), 65. U.S. Pub. Health Serv. fel. microbiol, sch. med, Univ. Wash, 65-67; asst. prof. BIOL, CALIF. STATE COL, SAN BERNARDINO, 67-70, ASSOC. PROF, 70- AAAS; Am. Soc. Microbiol. Delayed lactose fermentation by Enterobacteriaceae; physiology of streptomycin-dependent bacteria; biochemical genetics of eye pigment formation in flour beetles. Address: Dept. of Biology, California State College at San Bernardino, 5500 State College Pkwy, San Bernardino, CA 92407.

GOODMAN, ROBERT M(ENDEL), b. Phila, Pa, Nov. 21, 20; m. 49; c. 3. ELECTRICAL ENGINEERING. B.S, Pennsylvania, 43. Design engr, Hazeltine Electronics Corp, 43-47; res. assoc, group supvr. & instr. Pennsylvania, 47-51; co-founder, v.pres, treas. & admin. dir, Am. Electronic Labs, Inc, 51-59; LAB. MGR. BIODYNAMICS, LABS. RES. & DEVELOP, FRANKLIN INST, 59- Adj. prof, dept. obstet. & gynec, div. reprod. biol, Hahnemann Med. Col, 70- Sci. Res. Soc. Am; Inst. Elec. & Electronics Eng; Instrument Soc. Am; Biophys. Soc. Instrumentation for the life sciences; implementation of effort, administration and technical prosecution. Address: Labs. for Research & Development, Franklin Institute, 20th & Race Sts, Philadelphia, PA 19103.

GOODMAN, ROBERT N(ORMAN), b. Yonkers, N.Y, Dec. 15, 21; m. 49; c. 3. PLANT PATHOLOGY. B.S, New Hampshire, 48, M.S, 50; Ph.D.(hort), Missouri, 52. Asst. hort, Univ. N.H, 48-50; UNIV. MO-COLUMBIA, 50-52, asst. prof, 52-55, assoc. prof, 55-61, prof, 61-68, PROF. PLANT PATH. & CHMN. DEPT, 68- Guggenheim fel, Swiss Fed. Inst. Technol, 58-59; Nat. Insts. Health spec. fel, Astbury Dept. Biophys, Univ. Leeds, 65-66. Lalor Found. Award, 59. U.S.A.A.F, 42-45, Res, 45-, Lt. Col. Am. Soc. Hort. Sci; Am. Phytopath. Soc. Control of bacterial pathogens with antibiotics and antibacterial substances; adsorption and translocation of organic antimicrobial substances by foliage; bacterial toxins; ultrastructural changes in plants caused by bacteria. Address: 605 Crestland Ave, Columbia, MO 65201.

GOODMAN, ROE WILLIAM, b. Pasadena, Calif, Jan. 9, 38; m. 61; c. 1. PURE MATHEMATICS. B.S, Fla. South. Col, 58; Woodrow Wilson fel, Mass. Inst. Technol, 58, Nat. Sci. Found. fel, 59-61, Ph.D.(math), 63. Instr. MATH, Mass. Inst. Technol, 62-63; Nat. Acad. Sci-Nat. Res. Coun. fel, Harvard, 63-64; lectr, Mass. Inst. Technol, 64-66, asst. prof, 66-71; ASSOC. PROF, RUTGERS UNIV, 71- Vis. mem, Inst. Adv. Study, 68-69. Am. Math. Soc; Math. Asn; Am. Functional analysis and operator theory; representations of Lie groups and harmonic analysis; quantum field theory. Address: Dept. of Mathematics, Rutgers, The State University, New Brunswick, NJ 08903.

GOODMAN, RONALD KEITH, b. Yuma, Ariz, Oct. 31, 29; m. 59; c. 4. PHYSICS. B.S, Wheaton Col, 53, M.S, San Jose State Col, 67. Engr, Fargo Co, Calif, 57-58, chief engr, 58-61; res. operator, LAWRENCE LIVERMORE LAB, UNIV. CALIF, 61-66, PHYSICIST, 66- U.S.N, 54-56. Am. Phys. Soc; Am. Vacuum Soc. Ultra-high vacuum and related surface physics; plasma physics in controlled thermonuclear research. Address: L-386, Lawrence Livermore Lab, University of California, Box 808, Livermore, CA 94550.

GOODMAN, SEYMOUR, b. N.Y.C, Nov. 12, 33. PHYSICAL CHEMISTRY, COMPUTER SCIENCE. B.S, City Col. New York, 54; M.S, Chicago, 54; Ph.D.(chem), Columbia, 62. Instr. chem, QUEENS COL.(N.Y), 62-64, asst. prof. CHEM, 65-69, ASSOC. PROF, 69-, DIR. COMPUT. CTR, 65- Nat. Sci. Found. grant, 65-67. AAAS; Am. Chem. Soc; Am. Phys. Soc; Asn. Comput. Mach. Electron spin resonance spectroscopy; molecular orbital theory; photochemistry; general computer pattern recognition; information retrieval. Address: Dept. of Chemistry, Queens College, Flushing, NY 11367.

GOODMAN, THEODORE R(OBERT), b. Brooklyn, N.Y, Mar. 21, 25; m. 56. AERODYNAMICS, APPLIED MATHEMATICS. B.A.E, Rensselaer Polytech, 45; M.A.E, Calif. Inst. Tech, 46; Ph.D.(aeronaut. eng), Cornell, 54. From jr. aerodynamicist to assoc. aerodynamicist, Cornell Aeronaut. Lab, 46-51, prin. engr, 53-55; Allied Res. Assocs, Inc, 56-61; V.PRES, OCEANICS, INC, 62- Assoc. fel. Am. Inst. Aeronaut. & Astronaut; Am. Soc. Mech. Eng. Hydrodynamics; theoretical aerodynamics; fluid mechanics; boundary layer and wing theory; heat transfer; aeroelasticity; ballistics; system identification. Address: 21 Chapel Pl, Great Neck, NY 11021.

GOODMAN, TINE, b. Leeuwarden, Netherlands, Sept. 11, 37; m. 61; c. 1. ELECTRON MICROSCOPY, TOXICOLOGY. B.Sc, McMaster Univ, 61, univ. fel. & M.Sc, 63; Nat. Res. Coun. Can. & Ontario fels. & Ph.D.(histol, embryol), Univ. Ottawa, 67. RES. SCIENTIST CELL TOXICOL, FOOD & DRUG DIRECTORATE, NAT. HEALTH & WELFARE, 66- AAAS; Electron Micros. Soc. Am; Can. Soc. Cell Biology; Can. Asn. Res. Toxicol. Action of food additives and drugs on cell organelles of animal tissues. Address: Pharmacology Division Research Labs, Food & Drug Directorate, Dept. Health & Welfare, Ottawa, Ont. K1A 0L2, Can.

GOODMAN, VICTOR H(ERKE), b. Kansas City, Mo, Nov. 11, 18; m. 43. BOTANY. B.A, Missouri, 47; Ph.D.(plant physiol), Cornell, 51. Asst. bot, Cornell, 47-51; assoc. plant physiologist, agr. exp. sta, Miss. State Col, 51-53; asst. prof. BOT, UNIV. CALIF, RIVERSIDE, 54-59, ASSOC. PROF, 59- U.S.A.A.F, 42-46, 1st Lt. Bot. Soc. Am; Phycol. Soc. Am. Physiological anatomy of plants; terrestrial algae. Address: Dept. of Biology, University of California, Riverside, CA 92502.

GOODNER, CHARLES J(OSEPH), b. Seattle, Wash, Aug. 19, 29; m. 51; c. 3. ENDOCRINOLOGY. B.A, Reed Col, 51; M.D, Utah, 55. Asst. Prof. MED, King County Hosp, UNIV. WASH, 62-67, ASSOC. PROF, HARBORVIEW MED. CTR, 67- Endocrine Soc; Am. Diabetes Asn; Am. Fedn. Clin. Res; Am. Soc. Clin. Invest. Address: Dept. of Medicine, Harborview Medical Center, University of Washington, 325 Ninth Ave, Seattle, WA 98124.

GOODNER, DWIGHT B(ENJAMIN), b. What Cheer, Iowa, Aug. 15, 13; m. 36. MATHEMATICS. B.A, William Penn Col, 34; T. Wistar Brown fel, Haverford Col, 34-35, M.A, 35; fel, Illinois, 48-49, Ph.D.(math), 49. Instr. MATH, S.Dak. State Col, 37-42, asst. prof, 42-46; FLA. STATE UNIV, 49-51, assoc. prof, 51-54, PROF, 54-, MEM, CONSULT. BUR. COMT. UNDERGRAD. PROG. MATH, 62-, asst. dean, grad. sch, 53-55, assoc. dean, 55-58. Mem. comt. exam, Educ. Test. Serv, N.J, 65-; consult, U.S. Agency Int. Develop, India, summers 66 & 67; mem, Comt. Undergrad. Prog. Math, 67-71. U.S.N.R, 42-46, Res, 46-, Lt. Comdr. Am. Math. Soc; Math. Asn. Am; London Math. Soc; Edinburgh Math. Soc; Indian Math. Soc. Linear spaces; non-Euclidean geometry. Address: Dept. of Mathematics, Florida State University, Tallahassee, FL 32306.

GOODNER, JOHN T(ETARD), b. Denver, Colo, Oct. 29, 12; m. 42; c. 1. MEDICINE. A.B, Columbia, 35, M.D, 40. Asst, surg. bact. lab, col. physicians & surg, Columbia, 36-40; surg. intern 4th surg. div, Bellevue Hosp, 41-42; surg. res, St. John's Episcopal Hosp, Brooklyn, 46-49; fel. surg, Mem. Hosp, N.Y, 49-52, spec. fel. thoracic surg, 52-56; assoc. attend. surgeon, Manhattan Eye, Ear & Throat Hosp, 56-61; CLIN. INSTR. SURG, MED. COL, CORNELL UNIV, 61-; ASSOC. ATTEND. SURGEON, MEM. HOSP, 66- Trainee, Nat. Cancer Inst, Nat. Insts. Health, 51; res. fel, Sloan Kettering Inst, 52-53; asst, Sloan Kettering Div, Cornell Univ, 53-54; asst. attend. surgeon, tumor serv, Manhattan Eye, Ear & Throat Hosp, 53-56, attend. surgeon, 61-; asst. vis. thoracic surgeon, Kings County Hosp. Ctr, 53-58, assoc. vis. thoracic surg, 58-64; jr. asst. attend. surgeon, thoracic serv, Methodist Hosp, 54-56; clin. asst. surgeon, thoracic serv, mem. ctr. & dept. prev. med, Mem. Hosp, 56-58, asst. attend. surgeon, 58-66; consult. gen. surgeon, clin. reconstruct. plastic surg, 56-, attend. gen. surgeon & chief tumor clinic, 64-; clin. asst. vis. surgeon, James Ewing Hosp, 57-58, asst. vis. surgeon, thoracic serv, 58-66, assoc. vis. surgeon, 66-69; assoc. attend. surgeon, Misericordia Hosp, 58-62; Lawrence Hosp, Bronxville, 60-67, attend. surg, 67-; consult, St. Francis Hosp, Poughkeepsie, N.Y. Dipl, Am. Bd. Surg, 50; dipl, Am. Bd. Thoracic Surg, 58. Med.C, 42-46, Maj. AAAS; N.Y. Acad. Sci; Royal Soc. Health; fel. Am. Geriat. Soc; Am. Radium Soc; Am. Med. Asn; fel. Am. Col. Surg; James Ewing Soc; Soc. Head & Neck Surg; Pan-Am. Med. Asn. Cancer of esophagus and lung. Address: Memorial Hospital, 444 E. 68th St, New York, NY 10021.

GOODNIGHT, CLARENCE J(AMES), b. Gillespie, Ill, May 30, 14; m. 40; c. 2. ZOOLOGY. A.B, Illinois, 36, A.M, 37, Ph.D.(zool), 39. Asst. zool, Illinois, 36-40, Monsanto Chem. Co. fel, 39-40; tutor biol, Brooklyn Col, 40-42; instr. zool, Illinois, 42-44; biol, N.J. State Teachers Col, Jersey City, 44-46; asst. prof. zool, Purdue, 46-48, assoc. prof, 48-55, prof, 55-65; PROF. BIOL. & HEAD DEPT, WEST. MICH. UNIV, 65- Res. assoc, Am. Mus. Natural Hist, 50-; consult. biol. abstr. AAAS; Ecol. Soc. Am; Am. Soc. Zool; Soc. Syst. Zool; Am. Micros. Soc.(pres, 71); Am. Soc. Limnol. & Oceanog; Entom. Soc. Am; Nat. Asn. Biol. Teachers; Nat. Sci. Teachers Asn. Toxicity of poisons to aquatic organisms; physiology of oligochaetes; taxonomy, ecology and physiology of arachnids; physiological ecology and radioecology. Address: Dept. of Biology, Western Michigan University, Kalamazoo, MI 49001.

GOODNIGHT, MARIE L(OUISE), b. Blue Island, Ill, Aug. 27, 16; m. 40; c. 2. BIOLOGY. B.S, Kans State Col, 38; M.S, Illinois, 39. Lab. asst. hormone mfg, Hosp. Liquids, Inc, Chicago, 39; instr. zool, Illinois, 42-44; biol, Purdue, 46-65; mem. staff, West. Mich. Univ, 65-70; free-lance writer, 70- Habits of the Myriapoda; taxonomy and distribution of the Phalangida. Address: Dept. of Biology, Western Michigan University, Kalamazoo, MI 49001.

GOODRICH, ARTHUR L(EONARD), b. Marshall, Colo, May 31, 05; m. 29; c. 3. EMBRYOLOGY, MORPHOLOGY. B.S, Col. of Idaho, 28; fel, Idaho, 28, M.S, 29; Ph.D.(invert. morphol), Cornell, 38; Kans. State Col. Instr. ZOOL, KANS. STATE UNIV, 29-38, asst. prof, 38-42, assoc. prof, 42-47, prof, 48-70, EMER. PROF, 70-, instr, army specialized training program. Res. fel, Calif. Inst. Technol, 54. Ornithology; compiling and publishing in biology; fate of entoderm in embryogeny of terrestrial isopods; invertebrate embryology. Address: Dept. of Zoology, Kansas State University, Manhattan, KS 66502.

GOODRICH, CECILIE A(NN), b. Denver, Colo, Apr. 27, 41. PHYSIOLOGY. B.S, Univ. Mich, 62; Woodrow Wilson fel, Harvard, 62-63, Nat. Insts. Health fel, 63-67, Ph.D.(physiol), 67. Fel. physiol, lab. neuropharmacol, Nat. Inst. Med. Res, Eng, 67-68; res. fel. anat, Harvard Med. Sch, 68-71; ASST. PROF. BIOL, CLEVELAND STATE UNIV, 71- Nat. Insts. Health fels, 67-71, res. grant, 69-72. Assoc. mem. Am. Physiol. Soc; Am. Soc. Zool. Cerebrospinal fluid; temperature regulation; hibernation; control of respiration. Address: Dept. of Biology, Cleveland State University, Cleveland, OH 44115.

GOODRICH, CHARLES WILLIAM, b. Keokuk, Iowa, Dec. 21, 35; m. 61; c. 4. ORGANIC CHEMISTRY. B.A, Augustana Col.(Ill), 58; M.S, Iowa, 61, Ph.D.(org. chem), 63. SR. RES. CHEMIST, Lycra Tech. Sect, E.I. DU PONT DE NEMOURS & CO, INC, 62-64, Benger Lab, 64-65, LYCRA TECH. SECT, 65- Am. Chem. Soc. Polyurea-urethane chemistry. Address: 417 Shore Rd, Waynesboro, VA 22980.

GOODRICH, DAVID R, b. New York, N.Y, Jan. 31, 36; m. 61; c. 1. CHEMICAL ENGINEERING. B.S, Rensselaer Polytech. Inst, 57; M.S, Polytech. Inst. Brooklyn, 71. Engr, Procter & Gamble Co, 57-60, group leader process develop, 60-62; res. engr, cent. res. div, Am. Cyanamid Co, 63-66, group leader contract res, 66-68; SR. PROCESS ENGR, LOCTITE CORP, 68- U.S.A, 59. Am. Chem. Soc. Natural fats and oils process technology; advanced rocket propellant oxidizers; direct hydrocarbon fuel cell batteries; catalytic combustion of hydrocarbons. Address: 336 Tremont St, Newington, CT 06111.

GOODRICH, D(ONALD) WELLS, Psychiat, see 12th ed, Soc. & Behav. Vols.

GOODRICH, F(RANK) C(HAUNCEY), b. Peking, China, Apr. 4, 24; m. 46; c. 2. PHYSICAL CHEMISTRY. A.B, Williams Col.(Mass), 47; Westinghouse fel. & Ph.D.(chem), Columbia, 52. Res. chemist, Calif. Res. Corp, Standard Oil Co. Calif, 52-59, sr. res. chemist, 59-65; assoc. prof. CHEM, CLARKSON COL. TECHNOL, 65-68, PROF, 68- Exten.lectr, Univ. Calif, 56-65. U.S.A.F, 42-45. AAAS; Am. Chem. Soc. Thermodynamics and statistical mechanics; colloid chemistry; hydrodynamics. Address: Dept. of Chemistry, Clarkson College of Technology, Potsdam, NY 13676.

GOODRICH, JACK K, b. Hardeman Co, Tenn, Sept. 7, 29; m. 56; c. 4. RADIOLOGY. M.D, Tennessee, 53. Fel. radiol, Alton Ochsner Med. Found, 57-60; instr, med. center, Mississippi, 60-61, asst. prof. radiol. & nuclear med, 61-65, assoc. prof, 65-66; RADIOL, NUCLEAR MED. DIV, MED. CTR, DUKE UNIV, 66-71; PROF, 71- Consult. adv. comt. radiopharmaceut, Food & Drug Admin; mem. adv. panel, U.S. Pharmacopeia. Med.C, 53-56, Res, 56-64, Capt. Fel. Am. Col. Radiol; Soc. Nuclear Med; Am. Med. Asn; Radiol. Soc. N.Am; Am. Soc. Hosp. Pharmacists. Nuclear instrument design; clinical application of low energy nuclides for scanning; nuclear medicine technology training program. Address: Division of Nuclear Medicine, Duke University Medical Center, Box 3223, Durham, NC 27710.

GOODRICH, JUDSON E(ARL), b. Seneca, Kans, Aug. 14, 22; m. 51; c. 3. ORGANIC CHEMISTRY. A.B, Kansas, 47, M.A, 48; Ph.D.(chem), California, 51. Asst. instr, Kansas, 47-48; California, 48-51; assoc. res. chemist, Calif. Res. Corp, STANDARD OIL CO. CALIF, 51-54, res. chemist, 54-60, sr. res. chemist, 60-64, RES. ASSOC, CHEVRON RES. CO, 64- U.S.N.R, 42-46, Lt. Am. Chem. Soc. Positive halogen salts; desulfurization of thioamides; cyclic ketals of diketones; fuel oil stability; lubricating grease gelling agents; cationic polymerization; stabilization of polyolefins. Address: 42 Oxford Dr, San Rafael, CA 94903.

GOODRICH, MAX, b. Calhoun, Mo, Dec. 11, 05; m. 29; c. 2. PHYSICS. B.A, Westminster Col.(Mo), 27; Ph.D.(physics), Minnesota, 36. Instr. math, Salt Lake Collegiate Inst, 27-29; asst. instr. PHYSICS, Minnesota, 29-36; instr, LA. STATE UNIV, 36-39, asst. prof, 39-44, assoc. prof, 44-50, PROF, 50-, DEAN, GRAD. SCH, 61- Physicist, war res. lab, Texas, 45; sr. physicist, Oak Ridge Nat. Lab, 49-50; chief, grad. acad. prog. br, U.S. Off. Educ, 68-69; mem. comput. comt, South. Regional Educ. Bd, 68-72. Fel. AAAS; fel. Am. Phys. Soc; Am. Asn. Physics Teachers. Electron impact phenomena; dry disc rectifiers; electron diffraction; electron scattering in helium; spectrometry of beta- and gamma-rays. Address: Graduate School, Louisiana State University, Baton Rouge, LA 70803.

GOODRICH, MICHAEL A(LAN), b. New York, N.Y, Apr. 24, 33; m. 55; c. 3. ENTOMOLOGY. B.S, Bucknell, 55; M.Ed, Pa. State, 61, Ph.D.(entom), 64. Asst. zool. & entom, Pa. State, 61-64, instr. entom, 63; assoc. prof. ZOOL, EAST. ILL. UNIV, 64-71, PROF, 71- Entom. Soc. Am; Entom. Soc. Can; Soc. Syst. Zool; Animal Behav. Soc. Taxonomy of beetles of the subfamily Cetoniinae; reptile behavior; animal behavior. Address: Dept. of Zoology, Eastern Illinois University, Charleston, IL 61920.

GOODRICH, RICHARD DOUGLAS, b. New Richmond, Wis, July 2, 36; m. 56; c. 2. ANIMAL NUTRITION. B.S, Wis. State, River Falls, 58; M.S, S.Dak. State, 62; Ph.D.(animal nutrit), Okla. State, 65. PROF. ANIMAL SCI, UNIV. MINN, ST. PAUL, 65- Am. Soc. Animal Sci. Ruminant and mineral nutrition; forage evaluation; characterization of silage fermentation; adaptation to and utilization of nonprotein nitrogen by ruminants. Address: Dept. of Animal Science, University of Minnesota, St. Paul, MN 55101.

GOODRICH, ROBERT BRUCE, b. Portland, Conn, June 19, 14; m. 37; c. 2. CHEMISTRY. B.A, Wesleyan, 36, M.A, 38; Tennessee, 46-47. Asst. phys. chem, Wesleyan, 36-37; res. chemist, Dewey & Almy Chem. Co, Mass, 37-39; chemist, State Hy. Dept, Conn, 39-43; res. chemist, SAM Labs, Columbia, 43-46; sr. chemist, Oak Ridge Nat. Lab, 46-48; chemist, alternate sect. chief, Nat. Bur. Standards, 48-53; asst. div. chief, Diamond Ord. Fuze Labs, 53-55, chief power supply br, 55-63; CONSULT, U.S. GOVT, 63- Batteries; military power sources; electrodeposition; metal surface treatments; thermoplastics; material testing methods; environmental technology. Address: 3905 Huntington St, N.W, Washington, DC 20015.

GOODRICH, ROBERT KENT, b. Lapoint, Utah, July 5, 41; m. 65; c. 1. MATHEMATICS. B.A, Utah, 63, Nat. Sci. Found. fel. & Ph.D.(math), 66. ASSOC. PROF. MATH, UNIV. COLO, BOULDER, 66- Am. Math. Soc. Functional analysis. Address: Dept. of Mathematics, University of Colorado, Boulder, CO 80302.

GOODRICH, ROBERT STUART, JR, b. Wilmington, Del, June 16, 34; m. 57; c. 3. MATERIALS SCIENCE. B.M.E, Delaware, 56; M.Met.E, Washington (St. Louis), 60; Atomic Energy Comn. fel, Rensselaer Polytech, 62-63, Ph.D.(mat. sci), 63. Engr, Delco Prod. Div, Gen. Motors Corp, Ohio, 56-57; res. fel, Lawrence Radiation Lab, California, 63-64; sr. res. eng, Graham Res. Lab, Jones & Laughlin Steel Corp, Pa, 64-66; asst. prof. MAT. SCI, VANDERBILT UNIV, 66-70, ASSOC. PROF, 70- Assoc. dir, eng. mat. prog, Eng. Div, Nat. Sci. Found, 69-70. U.S.A.F.R, 57. AAAS; Am. Inst. Min, Metall. & Petrol. Eng; Am. Soc. Metals; Am. Soc. Eng. Educ. Microstructures of metals and materials and the relationship between microstructure and mechanical properties; electron and field ion microscopy; x-ray diffraction techniques. Address: School of Engineering, Vanderbilt University, Box 1723, Station B, Nashville, TN 37203.

GOODRICH, ROY GORDON, b. Dallas, Tex, Sept. 17, 38; m. 59; c. 3. SOLID STATE PHYSICS. B.S, La. Polytech, 60; Southern Mississippi, 60-61; M.A, California, Riverside, 63, Ph.D.(physics), 65. Instr. PHYSICS, Univ. South. Miss, 60-61; asst. prof, LA. STATE UNIV, BATON ROUGE, 65-67, ASSOC. PROF, 67- Am. Phys. Soc. Electron spin resonance and Fermi surface of metals. Address: Dept. of Physics & Astronomy, Louisiana State University, Baton Rouge, LA 70803.

GOODRICK, RICHARD EDWARD, b. Verdun, Que, Can, Feb. 19, 41; U.S. citizen; m. 66. MATHEMATICS. B.S, Washington (Seattle), 61; M.S, Wisconsin, 64, Ph.D.(math), 66. Asst. prof. MATH, Utah, 66-69; CALIF. STATE COL, HAYWARD, 69-71, ASSOC. PROF, 71- Vis. fel, Univ. Warwick, 68-69. Am. Math. Soc. Piece wise linear topology. Address: Dept. of Mathematics, California State College at Hayward, 25800 Hillary St, Hayward, CA 94542.

GOODRIDGE, ALAN G, b. Peabody, Mass, Apr. 2, 37; m. 60; c. 2. BIOCHEMISTRY. B.S, Tufts, 58; M.S, Michigan, 63, Ph.D.(zool), 64. Nat. Inst. Arthritis & Metab. Diseases res. fel, Harvard Med. Sch, 64-67; mem. staff physiol, med. ctr, Univ. Kans, 67-68; ASSOC. PROF. MED. SCI, UNIV. TORONTO, 68- U.S.N, 58-61, Lt.(jg). AAAS; Am. Inst. Biol. Sci; Brit. Biochem. Soc; Can. Biochem. Soc; Am. Physiol. Soc; Am. Soc. Biol. Chem. Regulation of lipid metabolism; regulation of enzyme concentration in Eukaryotes. Address: C.H. Best Institute, University of Toronto, 112 College St, Toronto, Ont, Can.

GOODROW, MARVIN H(ENRY), b. San Fernando, Calif, Sept. 27, 30; m. 60; c. 2. ORGANIC & INORGANIC CHEMISTRY. B.A, Pomona Col, 52; Ph.D, California, Los Angeles, 56. Asst, California, Los Angeles, 52-56; fel, Michigan, 56-58, instr. chem, 58-59; res. proj. chemist, Am. Potash & Chem. Corp, 59-63; mem. tech. staff, TRW Space Tech. Labs, 63-64; res. chemist, agr. res. div, Shell Develop. Co, 64-68; INSTR. CHEM, MODESTO JR. COL, 68- Mich. Mem. Phoenix Proj. fel, 56-58; Nat. Sci. Found. summer fels, 68, 69 & 71. Terpenes; molecular rearrangements; phosphorus-boron polymers; organometallic compounds; agricultural chemicals. Address: 1216 Mt. Vernon Dr, Modesto, CA 95350.

GOODSELL, ELIZABETH, b. Chicago, Ill, Jan. 26, 27; wid; c. 2. PHARMACOLOGY. B.S, St. Xavier Col, 45; M.S, Illinois, 47, Ph.D.(pharmacol), 61. Instr. sci, St. Xavier Col, 47-48; res. asst. pharmacol, ABBOTT LABS, 48-53, chem, 56-57, SR. PHARMACOLOGIST, 60- General pharmacology, including blood coagulation, enzyme induction, antidiabetic drugs, and general screening procedures; enzymology; biogenic amines and cyclic amp. Address: Abbott Labs, North Chicago, IL 60064.

GOODSON, JAMES BROWN, JR, b. Sandersville, Ga, July 10, 15; m. 37; c. 1. SANITARY ENGINEERING. B.S, Florida, 37, Ph.D.(chem), 50. Chemist, Int. Paper Co, S.C, 37-41; proj. engr, Sheppard T. Powell & Assocs, Md, 50-63; proj. engr, BLACK, CROW & EIDSNESS, INC, 63-68, V.PRES, 68- Chem.C, 41-46, Lt. Col. Am. Inst. Chem. Eng; Am. Chem. Soc; Am. Water Works Asn; Water Pollution Control Fedn. Water and waste water treatment; pulp and paper manufacturing process. Address: 700 S.E. Third St, Gainesville, FL 32601.

GOODSON, JO MAX, b. Lubbock, Tex, Mar. 18, 39; m. 69; c. 1. PHARMACOLOGY, DENTAL RESEARCH. B.S, Tex. Tech Univ, 62; D.D.S, Univ. Texas, 62; M.S, Univ. Rochester, 69, Ph.D.(pharmacol), 70. ASSOC. PROF. PHARMACOL, UNIV. CALIF, SAN FRANCISCO, 70- Effects of prostaglandins on bone metabolism and relationship to periodontal disease; chromatographic methodology, and analysis of human jaw movements. Address: Division of Oral Biology, School of Dentistry, University of California, San Francisco, CA 94122.

GOODSON, LESLIE ALAN, b. London, Eng, Apr. 11, 33; m. 60. ORGANIC CHEMISTRY. B.Sc, London, 57, Ph.D.(chem), 61; A.R.I.C, Royal Inst. Chem, 58; A.W.P, Woolwich Polytech, 61. Control chemist, Prince Regent Tar Co, 55-57; res. chemist, Shell Chem. Co, 60-63, info. off, 63-64; editing, CHEM. ABSTRACTS SERV, OHIO STATE UNIV, 64-69, MEM. ED. PLANNING & DEVELOP, 69- Am. Chem. Soc; The Chem. Soc; Royal Inst. Chem; Soc. Chem. Indust. Chemical literature; allenes; acetylenes; aluminum alkyls; polyalkylene glycols. Address: Chemical Abstracts Service, Ohio State University, Columbus, OH 43210.

GOODSON, L(OUIE) AUBREY, JR, b. Providence, N.C, Dec. 20, 22; m. 45; c. 4. TEXTILES. B.S, N.C. State Col, 43; L.L.B, Georgetown, 51. Res. chemist, Dan River Mills, Inc, 46-48, asst. dir. res, 51-53; patent searcher, Fisher & Christen, 48-51, patent lawyer & partner, Fisher, Christen & Goodson, 53-59; V.PRES. & DIR. RES, DAN RIVER, INC, 59- U.S.A, 43-46. Am. Chem. Soc; Am. Asn. Textile Chem. & Colorists; Am. Asn. Textile Technol. Textile chemistry. Address: Dan River, Inc, 2291 Memorial Dr, Danville, VA 24541.

GOODSON, LOUIS H(OFFMAN), b. Liberty, Mo, Apr. 5, 13; m. 40; c. 3. ORGANIC CHEMISTRY. A.B, Missouri, 35; M.A, Harvard, 38, Ph.D.(org. chem), 40. Org. res. chemist, Maltbie Labs, 40-44; asst. lab. dir, George A. Breon & Co, 44-47; sr. res. chemist, MIDWEST RES. INST, 48-55, head biochem. sect, 55-63, prin. biochemist, 64-69, SR. ADV. BIOL, 69- AAAS; N.Y. Acad. Sci; Am. Chem. Soc; Sci. Res. Soc. Am. Organic syntheses of chemotherapeutic agents; biochemistry; use of enzymes in detection of chemical and biological materials. Address: 5740 Cherry St, Kansas City, MO 64110.

GOODSON, RAYMOND EUGENE, b. Canton, N.C, Apr. 22, 35; m. 57; c. 2. SYSTEMS & CONTROL ENGINEERING. A.B, Duke, 57, B.S.M.E, 59; M.S.M.E, Purdue, 61, Fier fel, 61, Ph.D.(fluids, automatic control), 63. Asst. prof. MECH. ENG, PURDUE UNIV, 63-65, assoc. prof, 65-70, PROF, 70- Consult, Duncan Meter Co, 63-64; LeTourneau Westinghouse Co, 65-66; consult. engr, Corning Glass Works, 66-; consult, W.Va. Pulp & Paper Co, 67-; TRW Systs. Group, 68-; Westinghouse Elec. Co, Inc, 69-; Columbus Dispatch, 70-; res. grants, Nat. Sci. Found, NASA & Off. Naval Res; mem, Simulation Coun. Am. Soc. Mech. Eng; Instrument Soc. Am; Inst. Elec. & Electronics Eng. Modeling and simulation of physical systems; computers and computation; instrumentation; fluid line dynamics; vibrations and dynamics. Address: Automatic Control Center, School of Mechanical Engineering, Purdue University, Lafayette, IN 47907.

GOODSPEED, EDWIN W(ILLIAM), b. Marcellus, Mich, Dec. 5, 03; m. 27; c. 1. CHEMISTRY. A.B, Western Michigan, 27; M.S, Michigan, 31, Ph.D. (chem), 34. Instr, pub. schs, Mich, 27-31; lab. asst, Michigan, 32-34; res. chemist, Parker Rust Proof Div, Hooker Chem. Corp, 35-45, asst. res. dir, 45, asst. to pres, 46, advert. dept, 47, sect. leader & specification writer, res. dept, 48-68; RETIRED. Am. Chem. Soc. Quantitative separation of calcium and barium; development of various analytical methods; corrosion-resistant and paint holding coatings; coatings on metals as an aid in cold forming; deep drawing lubricants. Address: 10288 Cedar Island Rd, Union Lake, MI 48085.

GOODSPEED, F(REDERICK) M(AYNARD) (COGSWELL), b. St. John, N.B, Sept. 14, 14; m. 46; c. 2. MATHEMATICS. B.Sc, Manitoba, 35, fel, Toronto, 35-36, fel, 36-37, M.A, 36; Imp. Order Daughters Empire fel, Cambridge, 37-39, Ph.D.(math), Cambridge, 42. Exp. off, Projectile Develop. Estab, 40-46; Can. Armament Res. Estab, 46-47; asst. prof. MATH, Queen's (Ont), 47-50; assoc. prof, Univ. B.C, 50-59; LAVAL UNIV, 59-64, PROF, 64- Can. Math. Cong. Analysis; armaments. Address: Dept. of Mathematics, Laval University, Quebec, Que, Can.

GOODSPEED, NEIL CALVIN, b. Clear Lake, Wis, Dec. 12, 22; m. 54; c. 4. INORGANIC & ANALYTICAL CHEMISTRY. B.S, Wis. State Col, River Falls, 46; M.S, Iowa, 52, Ph.D.(inorg. chem), 56. RES. SUPVR. INORG. CHEM, energy div, Olin Mathieson Chem. Corp, 55-60; CHEM. DIV, PPG INDUSTS, INC, 60- U.S.M.C, 44-46, 1st Lt. Am. Chem. Soc. High energy fuels and oxidizers; pigments. Address: Chemical Division, PPG Industries, Inc, Barberton, OH 44203.

GOODSPEED, ROBERT MARSHALL, b. Somerville, Mass, Feb. 11, 38; m. 63; c. 2. MINERALOGY, PETROLOGY. B.S, Tufts, 60; M.S, Maine, 62; Ph.D. (geol. & geochem), Rutgers, 68. ASST. PROF. GEOL, SUSQUEHANNA UNIV, 66-, CHMN. DEPT. GEOL. SCI, 69-; SCI. DIV, 70- AAAS; Mineral. Soc. Am; Geol. Soc. Am. Coexisting feldspars and other minerals of granulitic rocks in Pre-Cambrian terrains such as the New Jersey highlands; geochemistry of soils-bedrock-water in local watershed for environmental geology. Address: Dept. of Geological Sciences, Susquehanna University, Selinsgrove, PA 17870.

GOODSTEIN, DAVID LOUIS, b. New York, N.Y, Apr. 5, 39; m. 60; c. 2. PHYSICS. B.S, Brooklyn Col, 60; Ford Found. fel, Washington (Seattle), 61, NASA fel, 63-65, Ph.D.(physics), 65. Asst. PHYSICS, Washington (Seattle), 60-61, res. instr, 65-66; res. fel, Calif. Inst. Tech, 66-67; Nat. Sci. Found. fel, Univ. Rome, 67-68; asst. prof, CALIF. INST. TECHNOL, 68-71, ASSOC. PROF, 71-, Sloane fel, 69-71. Am. Acad. Arts & Sci. Thermal properties of helium and other gases in thin films. Address: Dept. of Physics, California Institute of Technology, Pasadena, CA 91109.

GOODSTEIN, MADELINE P, b. New York, N.Y, Oct. 23, 20; m. 47; c. 3. SCIENCE EDUCATION, CHEMISTRY. B.A, Brooklyn Col, 41; M.S, Polytech. Inst. Brooklyn, 48; Ed.D.(chem), Columbia, 68. Chemist, Trubek Labs, 41-47, consult, 48; ASST. PROF. CHEM, CENT. CONN. STATE COL, 68- Am. Chem. Soc; Nat. Asn. Res. Sci. Teaching. Oxidation-reduction concept; science education for non-scientist. Address: Dept. of Chemistry, Central Connecticut State College, New Britain, CT 06525.

GOODSTEIN, ROBERT, b. Brooklyn, N.Y, June 16, 26; m. 51; c. 3. ENGINEERING MECHANICS. B.S, Mass. Inst. Tech, 46; M.S, Ohio State, 49, Ph.D.(eng. mech), 57. Instr. theoret. & appl. mech, Iowa State Col, 49-53; res. engr, Boeing Co, 53-55; from instr. to asst. prof. eng. mech, Ohio State, 55-58; from res. specialist to sr. group engr, BOEING CO, 58-69, GUID. & CONTROL TECH. MGR, 69- Lectr, Univ. Wash, 63-71. U.S.A, 46-47. Aerospace Indust. Asn. Am. Inertial navigation components and systems; dynamics and vibrations. Address: Electronics Technology Dept, Boeing Co, P.O. Box 3985, Seattle, WA 98004.

GOODWILL, ROBERT, b. Ridgeway, Pa, Dec. 13, 36; m. 65; c. 2. QUANTITATIVE & POPULATION GENETICS. B.S, State Univ. N.Y. Col. Fredonia, 63; Ph.D.(genetics), Univ. Minn, 69. ASST. PROF. biol, Bemidji State Col, 68-69; ANIMAL SCI, UNIV. KY, 69- U.S.N, 55-59. AAAS; Genetics Soc. Am; Am. Genetic Asn; Am. Inst. Biol. Sci; Environ. Mutagen Soc. Effects of population structure on selection using Tribolium castaneum; biochemical investigations of quantitatively inherited characters. Address: Dept. of Animal Science, Agricultural Science Center, Room 222, University of Kentucky, Lexington, KY 40506.

GOODWIN, BRUCE EDWARD, b. Morristown, N.J, June 27, 33. MATHEMATICS. B.S, Rensselaer Polytech, 59, M.S, 61, Ph.D.(math), 63. Res. fel. inst. fluid dynamics & appl. math, Maryland, 63-64; asst. prof. MATH, UNIV.

DEL, 64-69, ASSOC. PROF, 69- Am. Math. Soc; Math. Asn. Am; Soc. Indust. & Appl. Math. Theory and application of integral equations, groups, rings, and fields; Hamilton's principle and its consequences. Address: Dept. of Mathematics, University of Delaware, Newark, DE 19711.

GOODWIN, BRUCE K, b. Providence, R.I, Oct. 14, 31; m. 56; c. 3. GEOLOGY. A.B, Univ. Pa, 53; M.S, Lehigh Univ, 57, Ph.D.(geol), 59. Instr. GEOL, Univ. Pa, 59-63; asst. prof, COL. WILLIAM & MARY, 63-66, assoc. prof, 66-71, PROF, 71- Geologist, Vt. Geol. Surv, summers 56-60; Pa. Topog. & Geol. Surv, 61-63; Va. Div. Mineral Resources, 65-71. U.S.A, 53-55. AAAS; fel. Geol. Soc. Am; Nat. Asn. Geol. Teachers. Geology of the eastern piedmont of North America, particularly the role of the piedmont in the development of the Appalachian Mountain system; igneous and metamorphic geology; structural geology. Address: Dept. of Geology, College of William & Mary, Williamsburg, VA 23185.

GOODWIN, DuWAYNE LEROY, b. Blackfoot, Idaho, May 19, 19; m. 44; c. 5. BOTANY. B.S, Idaho, 42; M.S, Wisconsin, 46; Minnesota, 46-47; Ph.D.(bot), Wash. State Col, 56. Asst. bot, Wisconsin, 45-46; Minnesota, 46-47; asst. prof, Idaho State Col, 47-49; range mgt, Nevada, 54-55; Utah State, 55-64; UN RANGE MGT. EXPERT, Pakistan Forest Inst, Peshawar, 64-67; RANGE & PASTURE IMPROV. PROJ, FOOD & AGR. ORGN, 67- With Nat. Reactor Testing Sta, 57-58. U.S.A.A.F, 42-45, Capt. Am. Soc. Range Mgt; Brit. Ecol. Soc. Field characters of seedings of range plants; vegetational history of Snake River plains; life history of Artemisia tridentata; wild land management of arid zones; wild land resources. Address: Food & Agricultural Organization, Box 1555, Tehran, Iran.

GOODWIN, ERNEST BARTLETT, b. Providence, R.I, Oct. 1, 09; m. 39, 53; c. 6. ELECTRONICS. B.S, R.I. State Col, 32; M.A, Boston, 39; Bowdoin Col, 42; Mass. Inst. Technol, 42. Eng, inspector, Providence Eng. Co, 33-34; teacher, pub. sch, R.I, 35-41; instr. electronics, R.I. State Col, 46-51, asst. prof. ELEC. ENG, UNIV. R.I, 51-58, ASSOC. PROF. & ASST. TO DEAN ENG, 58- U.S.N.R, 42-45, Res, 45-63, Capt. Radar. Address: Dept. of Electrical Engineering, University of Rhode Island, Wakefield, RI 02881.

GOODWIN, FRANCIS EUGENE, b. Hastings, Nebr, Sept. 7, 27; m. 49; c. 3. APPLIED PHYSICS. M.S, California, Los Angeles, 57. Sr. staff engr, quantum electronics, HUGHES RES. LABS, 57-71, HEAD OPTICAL COMMUN. & RADAR SECT, 71- U.S.A, 53-55, Sgt. Inst. Elec. & Electronics Eng; Am. Phys. Soc. Wideband laser communication; continuous wave laser radar. Address: Hughes Research Lab, 3011 Malibu Canyon Rd, Malibu, CA 90265.

GOODWIN, FREDERICK K(ERN), b. Seattle, Wash, May 29, 31; m. 55. MATHEMATICS, PHYSICS. B.A, Grinnell Col, 53; Drake; San Jose State Col. Aeronaut. res. scientist, NASA, Calif, 56-59; head numerical anal. sect, Vidya Div, Itek Corp, 59-66; RES. ENGR, NIELSEN ENG. & RES. INC, MOUNTAIN VIEW, 66- U.S.A, 53-55. Am. Inst. Aeronaut. & Astronaut. Numerical analysis; aerodynamics. Address: 483 Distel Dr, Los Altos, CA 94022.

GOODWIN, GLEN, b. Phonex, Can, Nov. 24, 18; U.S. citizen; m. 44. ASTRONAUTICS. B.S, Univ. Wash, 42. Engr, Lewis Res. Ctr, NASA, 43-45, aeronaut. res. scientist, AMES RES. CTR, 46-58, chief heat transfer res. br, 59-62, thermo & gas dynamics div, 63-68, DIR, ASTRONAUT, 69- Del, Int. Cong. Aeronaut. Sci, Zurich, Switz, 60. Assoc. fel. Am. Inst. Aeronaut. & Astronaut; Am. Geophys. Union. Aerodynamic heating; reentry trajectory analysis; heat protection systems; influence of chemistry on flow fields. Address: NASA/Ames Research Center, Moffett Field, CA 94035.

GOODWIN, HARRY A, b. Littleton, N.H, July 12, 15; m. 43; c. 5. WILDLIFE ECOLOGY. B.A, St. Anselm's Col, 39; M.S, Univ. Maine, Orono, 42. Regional supvr. river basin studies, Bur. Sport Fisheries & Wildlife, U.S. Dept. Interior, 50-53, supvr. Mo. River Basin studies, 53-60, asst. dir, Northwest Region, 60-66, chief, Off. Int. Activities/Endangered Species, 66-71; WILDLIFE ECOLOGIST, INT. UNION CONSERV. NATURE & NATURAL RESOURCES, UNESCO, 71-, mem, survival serv. comn. U.S. del, Intergovt. Conf. Experts on the Sci. Basis for Rational Use & Conserv. Resources of Biosphere, UNESCO, Paris, 68; U.S. rep, sci. exchange progs, Romania, Yugoslavia; mem, U.S./Japan Panel on Nat. Parks & Comparable Reserves; Asian/Pacific Forestry Comn. AAAS; Am. Fisheries Soc; Wildlife Soc. Limnology; life history of Atlantic salmon; ecological studies of effects of water resource projects on fish and wildlife resources. Address: Residence de la Côtezo, 1110 Morges, Switz.

GOODWIN, HARRY B(RIMHALL), b. Albany, N.Y, Nov. 5, 15; m. 37; c. 4. METALLURGY. B.S, Mass. Inst. Tech, 37. Trainee metallurgist, Bethlehem Steel Co, 37-39; res. metallurgist, Crown Cork & Seal Co, 40-41; self-employed, 46-47; res. metallurgist, Appl. Physics Lab, 48-49; res. engr, BATTELLE MEM. INST, 49-51, asst. div. chief, 51-52, consult. metallurgist, 52-59, asst. mgr, dept. metall, 59-62, dept. metall. & physics, 63-64, asst. to dir, COLUMBUS LABS, 64-69, ASST. DIR, 69- U.S.A, 41-46, Ord.C.Res, 46-, Col. Am. Soc. Metals; Am. Inst. Mining, Metall. & Petrol. Eng; Soc. Res. Adminr. Metallurgy of molybdenum and chromium; development of high temperature alloys; preparation of high purity metals, iron, chromium and molybdenum; improved methods of iron smelting; titanium alloys; research administration; management information systems; storage retrieval and analysis of technical information with emphasis on machine methods. Address: Columbus Labs, Battelle Memorial Institute, 505 King Ave, Columbus, OH 43201.

GOODWIN, JAMES G(RANVILLE), b. Pittsburgh, Pa, Sept. 30, 29; m. 60; c. 2. METALLURGY. B.S, Pa. State, 51; Carnegie Inst. Tech, 51-56; M.S, Pittsburgh, 65. Jr. engr, BETTIS ATOMIC POWER LAB, WESTINGHOUSE ELEC. CORP, 51-53, assoc. engr, 53-55, engr, 55-58, sr. engr, 58-64, fel. engr, 64-67, supvr. core mat, 67-70, MGR. ADV. PROCESS DEVELOP, 70- Am. Soc. Metals; Am. Inst. Min, Metall. & Petrol. Eng. Metallurgy of zirconium alloys, hafnium and nuclear materials; mechanical, corrosion and physical property studies; melting and fabrication of reactive and nuclear metals; development of nuclear components and assemblies. Address: Westinghouse Electric Corp, Bettis Atomic Lab, P.O. Box 79, West Mifflin, PA 15122.

GOODWIN, JAMES THOMAS, b. Dyersburg, Tenn, Nov. 25, 38; m. 65; c. 2. AQUATIC ENTOMOLOGY. B.S, Memphis State, 64; M.S, Tennessee, Knoxville, 65, Ph.D.(entom), 67. Asst. prof. BIOL, MEMPHIS STATE UNIV, 67-71, ASSOC. PROF, 71- U.S.A.F, 56-60, Res, 60-62. Entom. Soc. Am. Taxonomy and distribution of Tabanidae, Megaloptera and Odonata, especially immature stages. Address: Dept. of Biology, Memphis State University, Memphis, TN 38111.

GOODWIN, JESSE FRANCIS, b. Greenville, S.C, Feb. 7, 29; m. 59; c. 2. CLINICAL BIOCHEMISTRY. B.S, Xavier (La), 51; M.S, Wayne State, 53, Ph.D.(chem), 57. Res. assoc, col. med, Wayne State & spec. instr, col. pharm, 58-59; clin. biochemist, Wayne County Gen. Hosp, Eloise, Mich, 58-62; DIR. CORE LAB, GEN. CLIN. RES. CTR, WAYNE STATE UNIV, 63-, ASST. PROF. PEDIAT, COL. MED, 70-, biochem, 66-70, instr, 64-66. Biochemist, dept. labs, Children's Hosp, Detroit. AAAS; Am. Chem. Soc; Am. Asn. Clin. Chem; fel. Am. Inst. Chem; N.Y. Acad. Sci. Methodology in clinical chemistry procedures; metabolism of muco-polysaccharides, chelates and gold; methodology in carbohydrate, protein, drug and trace metal estimation. Address: Wayne State University College of Medicine & Children's Hospital of Michigan, 3901 Beaubien St, Detroit, MI 48201.

GOODWIN, JOHN M(ILTON), b. Corsicana, Tex, Oct. 6, 12; m. 34; c. 1. ELECTRICAL ENGINEERING. B.S, Agr. & Mech. Col, Tex, 33, M.S, 37. Asst. operator & shooter, Humble Oil & Refining Co, Tex, 33; asst, Agr. & Mech. Col, Tex, 36-37; assoc. prof. elec. eng. & mech. drawing, UNIV. TEX, ARLINGTON, 37-41, 46-51, prof. eng, 51-59, ASSOC. PROF. ELEC. ENG, 59- Summers, engr, Tex. Elec. Serv. Co. U.S.A.A.F, 41-46. Address: Dept. of Electrical Engineering, University of Texas at Arlington, Arlington, TX 76010.

GOODWIN, JOHN T(HOMAS), JR, b. San Diego, Calif, May 28, 14; m. 38; c. 5. ORGANIC CHEMISTRY. B.S, Okla. Agr. & Mech. Col, 36; Tulsa, 37-39; Ph.D.(org. chem), Pittsburgh, 48. Chemist, Mid-Continent Petrol. Corp, 36-39; asst. org. chem, Pittsburgh, 39-40; res. chemist, Gulf Res. & Develop. Co, Pa, 40-41; fel, Mellon Inst, 41-43, indust. fel, 46, sr. fel, 46-49; group leader, Dow Corning Corp, 49-51, chemist, Gen. Elec. Co, 51-54; mgr. chem. res, Midwest Res. Inst, 54-57; tech. dir, Corn Industs. Res. Found, Inc, D.C, 57-65; DIR. CHEM. & CHEM. ENG, SOUTHWEST RES. INST, 65- U.S.N, 43-46. AAAS; Am. Chem. Soc; fel. N.Y. Acad. Sci. Microencapsulation; membrane technology; radiation polymerization; organosilicon chemistry; carbohydrates. Address: Southwest Research Institute, 8500 Culebra Rd, San Antonio, TX 78284.

GOODWIN, JONATHAN H(ALL), b. Atlanta, Ga, July 15, 44. GEOCHEMISTRY, SEDIMENTARY PETROLOGY. A.B, Amherst Col, 66; Nat. Defense Educ. Act. fel, Univ. Wyo, 66-69, Nat. Sci. Found. fel, 69-70, Ph.D.(geol), 71. ASST. PROF. GEOL, UNIV. UTAH, 70- Partic, Nat. Sci. Found. Student Seminar, N.Mex, 67. Geol. Soc. Am; Soc. Econ. Paleont. & Mineral; Mineral Soc. Am. Geochemistry of diagenesis in sedimentary rocks; alteration and formation of zeolites in tuffaceous rocks; paleolimnology and geochemistry of ancient saline lakes; carbonate petrology; analysis of depositional environments. Address: Dept. of Geology, 711 Mines Bldg, University of Utah, Salt Lake City, UT 84112.

GOODWIN, KENNETH, b. N.Y.C, Sept. 30, 20; m. 47; c. 1. GENETICS. B.S, Cornell, 48; M.S, 50, Ph.D.(animal genetics), 52. Asst. animal genetics, Cornell, 48-52; geneticist, Kimber Farms, Inc, Calif, 52-64; Heisdorf & Nelson Farms, Inc, 64-66; PROF. POULTRY SCI. & HEAD DEPT, PA. STATE UNIV, 66- U.S.A.A.F, 42-45. AAAS; Genetics Soc. Am; Am. Genetic Asn; Poultry Sci. Asn. Genetics of poultry; improvement of economic characters; genetics and disease resistance. Address: Dept. of Poultry Science, Pennsylvania State University, 214 Animal Industries Bldg, University Park, PA 16802.

GOODWIN, LESTER K(EPNER), b. Casper, Wyo, July 2, 28; m. 58; c. 1. NUCLEAR PHYSICS. B.S, Calif. Inst. Tech, 50; M.A, California, Berkeley, 57, Ph.D.(physics), 60. Physicist, Los Alamos Sci. Lab, 51-53, 56; Lawrence Radiation Lab, California, 60; Aeronutronic Div, Ford Motor Co, 60-63, sect. supvr. Aeronutronic Div, Philco Corp, 63-69; SR. SCIENTIST, KMS TECHNOL. CTR, 69- Summers, tech. asst, Naval Ord. Test Sta, Calif, 48, 49, res. asst, Los Alamos Sci. Lab, 50. U.S.A, 53-56. AAAS; Am. Phys. Soc. Laser effects; nuclear weapons effects; neutron, gamma and meson cross-section measurements; aerosol research; nuclear weapon testing; rf ion-source development. Address: KMS Technology Center, KMS Industries, Inc, 3848 Campus Dr, Newport Beach, CA 92660.

GOODWIN, MELVIN H(ARRIS), JR, b. Thomasville, Ga, Jan. 9, 17; m. 42; c. 2. EPIDEMIOLOGY, PARASITOLOGY. B.S, Georgia, 41, M.S, 51; Ph.D. (parasitol), Emory, 55. Asst, rabies lab, State Dept. Health, Ga, 38-39, malaria control biologist, 42-43; mem. staff, entom. div, communicable disease center, U.S. Pub. Health Serv, 44-46, chief library & reports div, 47-48, malaria invests. sect, 49-53, asst. chief invests, tech. br, 53-57, chief, Phoenix field sta, 57-66; dir, div. prev. med. serv, Ariz. State Health Dept, 66-69; DIR, ARIZ. HEALTH PLANNING AUTH, 69- Biologist in charge malaria res. sta, Emory Univ, 39-42, dir, 44-57, assoc. sch. med. 48-57. Sci. Res. Soc. Am; Am. Soc. Trop. Med. & Hyg. Health planning; ecology of enteric diseases, malaria and other infectious diseases. Address: Arizona Health Planning Authority, 2980 Grand Ave, Phoenix, AZ 85017.

GOODWIN, PAUL ALLEN, b. Piermont, N.H, Nov. 30, 19; m. 46; c. 2. ORGANIC CHEMISTRY. B.S, Trinity Col.(Conn), 40, M.S, 42. Develop. chemist, Gen. Elec. Co, 42-50, sect. head, new prod. develop. lab, 50-54, mkt. positions, 54-62, MGR. res. & develop, insulating mat. dept, 62-69; MKT. & APPLN. DEVELOP, LOCTITE CORP, 69- Am. Chem. Soc. Electrical insulation; silicones; synthetic resins and plastics; adhesives. Address: Loctite Corp, Newington, CT 06111.

GOODWIN, PAUL N(EWCOMB), b. Evanston, Ill, Nov. 3, 26; m. 51; c. 2. RADIOLOGICAL PHYSICS. B.S, Harvard, 48; M.A, Hopkins, 56; Ph.D.(med. physics), London, 59. Physicist, U.S. Pub. Health Serv. Hosp, Baltimore, 49-56; U.S. Pub. Health Serv. Hosp, Royal Cancer Hosp, London, Eng, 56-59; radiol. dept, Hopkins Hosp, 59-66, ASST. PROF. RADIOL, sch. med. & sch.

hyg. & Pub. Health, Johns Hopkins Univ, 62-66; COL. PHYSICIANS & SURGEONS, COLUMBIA-PRESBY. MED. CTR, COLUMBIA UNIV, 66- Dipl, Am. Bd. Radiol. & Am. Bd. Health Physics. Health Physics Soc; Am. Asn. Physicists in Med; Soc. Nuclear Med; Radiol. Soc. N.Am; Am. Col. Radiol. Radiological physics; medical application of radiation and radioactive isotopes; radiation dosimetry and protection; calorimetric measurement of x-rays; spectral measurement of high energy x-rays. Address: Dept. of Radiology, Columbia-Presbyterian Medical Center, New York, NY 10032.

GOODWIN, PETER W(ARREN), b. Wilmington, Del, Apr. 12, 36; m. 58; c. 2. GEOLOGY. A.B, Dartmouth Col, 58; M.S, Iowa, 61, Ph.D.(geol), 64. Instr. GEOL, TEMPLE UNIV, 63-64, asst. prof, 64-69, ASSOC. PROF, 69- AAAS; Geol. Soc. Am; Paleont. Soc; Nat. Asn. Geol. Teachers. Early Ordovician conodonts; Ordovician stratigraphy. Address: Dept. of Geology, Temple University, Philadelphia, PA 19122.

GOODWIN, RALPH A(BIJAH), b. Chariton, Iowa, Jan. 1, 13; m. 39; c. 2. PHYSICS. A.B, Simpson Col, 35; fel, Iowa State Col, 35-39, M.S, 37, Ph.D. (physics), 39; Hopkins, 45-46. Instr. physics, N.Dak. Col, 39-41; asst. prof, Ft. Hays Kans. State Col, 41; instr. ELEC. ENG, U.S. NAVAL ACAD, 41-47, assoc. prof, 47-50, PROF, 50- U.S.N, 42-45. Am. Phys. Soc; Am. Asn. Physics Teachers. Quantitative spectroscopy; evaporation of metals; counters. Address: Dept. of Science, U.S. Naval Academy, Annapolis, MD 21402.

GOODWIN, RICHARD H(ALE), b. Brookline, Mass, Dec. 14, 10; m. 36; c. 2. BOTANY. A.B, Harvard, 33, M.A, 34, univ. scholar, 34-35, Harvard fel, 35-37; Ph.D.(biol), 37; fel, Atkins Inst. Arnold Arboretum, Cuba, 35. Am-Scandinavian Found. fel, Copenhagen, 37-38; instr. BOT, Rochester, 38-41, asst. prof, 41-44; PROF, CONN. COL, 44-, dir. arboretum, 44-65. Cmnr, Conn. Geol. & Natural Hist. Surv, 45-; pres, Conserv. & Res. Found, 53-; Nature Conservancy, 56-58, 64-66, Mem. biol. coun, Nat. Res. Coun, 53-57; bd. dirs, Am. Inst. Biol. Sci, 62-71. AAAS; Bot. Soc. Am; Am. Soc. Plant Physiol; Soc. Study Develop. & Growth (secy, 49-53); Am. Soc. Plant Taxon; Soc. Study Evolution; Am. Soc. Nat; Torrey Bot. Club; fel. Am. Acad. Arts & Sci. Effect of light on growth of plants; physiology of growth; plant hormones; fluorescent substances on plants; morphogenesis of roots; bioecology of natural areas. Address: Dept. of Botany, Connecticut College, New London, CT 06320.

GOODWIN, R(OBERT) A(RCHER), JR, b. Kuling, China, Aug. 3, 14; U.S. citizen; m. 44; c. 3. INTERNAL MEDICINE. B.S, Virginia, 36; M.D, Hopkins, 40. Asst. res. physician, Thorndike Mem. Lab, Boston City Hosp, 41-42; asst. res. & res. physician, hosp, VANDERBILT UNIV, 46-47, instr. CLIN. MED, SCH. MED, 47-51, asst. prof, 51-56, ASSOC. PROF, 56- Chief pulmonary disease serv, Vet. Admin. Hosp, 47- Med.C, 42-46, Maj. Am. Thoracic Soc; fel. Am. Col. Physicians. Infectious diseases; pulmonary diseases. Address: Veterans Administration Hospital, Nashville, TN 37203.

GOODWIN, ROBERT D(ANIELS), b. N.Y.C, Aug. 20, 15; m. 40; c. 2. PHYSICAL CHEMISTRY. B.S, North Carolina, 40; Hopkins, 40-42; Loomis fel. & Ph.D.(phys. chem), Yale, 44. Res. chemist, Off. Sci. Res. & Develop, 41-42; instr. quant. anal, Yale, 44; res. chemist, Allied Chem. & Dye Corp, 44-48; sr. technologist, Socony-Vacuum Labs, 48-52; Forrestal Res. Ctr, Princeton, 52-53; Air Reduction Labs, N.J, 53-56; PHYS. CHEMIST, NAT. BUR. STANDARDS, 56- Nat. Bur. Standards gold medal award. AAAS; Am. Chem. Soc. Catalysis; Reppe and oxo chemistry; compressibility and calorimetry of cryogenic fluids; thermodynamic properties of fluid hydrogen. Address: Cryogenic Engineering Lab, National Bureau of Standards, Boulder, CO 80302.

GOODWIN, ROBERT E(ARLE), b. Rensselaer, N.Y, May 16, 26; m. 54; c. 2. VERTEBRATE ZOOLOGY. B.S, Hartwick Col, 51; M.S, Cornell, 53, Ph.D. (vert. zool), 60. Instr. comp. anat, COLGATE UNIV, 59-67, ASSOC. PROF. ZOOL, 67- U.S.N, 44-46. Am. Soc. Mammal; Am. Soc. Ichthyol. & Herpet; Am. Ornith. Union. Ecology, behavior, and toxonomy of vertebrates, particularly birds and mammals. Address: Dept. of Biology, Colgate University, Hamilton, NY 13346.

GOODWIN, R(OBERT) J(ENNINGS), b. Jane Lew, W.Va, Apr. 12, 23; m. 44; c. 4. PETROLEUM ENGINEERING. B.S.E.M, West Virginia, 48; M.S, Agr. & Mech. Col, Texas, 55. Field prod. engr, Ohio Oil Co, La, 48-52; res. technologist, Tex. Petrol. Res. Comt, Agr. & Mech. Col, Tex, 52-55; res. eng, prod. eng. div, GULF RES. & DEVELOP. CO, 55-57, sect. head well completion, 57-60, sect. supvr. drilling res, 60-67, dir. prod. div, 67-70, TECH. CONSULT, 70- U.S.A, 43-45. Am. Inst. Mining, Metall. & Petrol. Eng. Petroleum production engineering; particularly design of technically and economically feasible drilling and production systems for unusual environments, such as deep water, Arctic. Address: Gulf Research & Development Co, P.O. Drawer 2038, Pittsburgh, PA 15230.

GOODWIN, SIDNEY S, b. Corbin, Ky, May 3, 06; m. 28; c. 2. GEOLOGY, MINING, B.S, Kentucky, 28, Cincinnati, 28-30. Geologist, N.J. ZINC CO, Va, 30-37, resident geologist, 37-42, mine foreman, 42-44, asst. mgr, 44-45, local mgr, 45-47, asst. to mines mgr, N.Y, 47-48, mgr. mines, 48-53, v.pres. explor. & mining, 53-71, CONSULT, 71- Fel. Geol. Soc. Am; Soc. Econ. Geol; Geochem. Soc; Am. Inst. Mining, Metall. & Petrol. Eng; Mining & Metall. Soc. Am. Mining geology. Address: 11 Arch St, Ogdensburg, NJ 07439.

GOODWIN, TOMMY LEE, b. Little Rock, Ark, Apr. 6, 36; m. 59; c. 2. FOOD TECHNOLOGY. B.S.A, Arkansas, 58, M.S, 60; Ph.D.(food tech), Purdue, 62. Asst. prof. poultry prod. tech, Nebraska, 62-64; UNIV. ARK, FAYETTEVILLE, 64-66, assoc. prof, ANIMAL SCI, 66-71, PROF, 71- U.S.N.R, 54-62. Inst. Food Technol; Poultry Sci. Asn. Factors affecting quality and tenderness of poultry meat and improving quality of eggs. Address: Dept. of Animal Sciences, University of Arkansas, Fayetteville, AR 72701.

GOODWIN, WILLARD E, b. Los Angeles, Calif, July 24, 15; m. 42; c. 3. UROLOGY. A.B, California, 37; M.D, Hopkins, 41. Intern, Hopkins Hosp, 41-42, pathologist, 42, asst. res, James Buchanan Brady Urol. Inst, 46-48, res, 48-49, instr. urol, med. sch, univ, 48-50, asst. prof, 50-51; assoc. prof. SURG, SCH. MED, UNIV. CALIF, LOS ANGELES, 51-53, PROF, 53-, PROF. SURG. UROL, 70-, chief div. urol, 51-71. Nat. Res. Coun. fel, 47-48; consult. urol. sect, Wadsworth Vet. Admin. Hosp, Los Angeles; consult, Los Angeles County Harbor Gen. Hosp, Torrance; St. Francis Hosp, Lynwood; mem. consult. staff, Hollywood Presby. & Mt. Sinai Hosps, Los Angeles; hon. consult. staff, Santa Monica Hosp; courtesy staff, St. John's Hosp, Santa Monica; Hosp. Good Samaritan, Los Angeles; vis. staff, Cedars of Lebanon Hosp. Dipl, Am. Bd. Urol, 51. Med. Dept, 42-46, Maj. Am. Col. Surg; Am. Med. Asn; Am. Urol. Asn; Am. Asn. Hist. Med; Soc. Univ. Surg; Am. Asn. Genito-Urinary Surg; Clin. Soc. Genito-Urinary Surg; Am. Surg. Asn; hon. mem. Urol. Soc. Australasia; Int. Soc. Urol; Brit. Asn. Virol. Surg; German Soc. Virol. Genitourinary surgery. Address: Division of Urology, University of California School of Medicine, Los Angeles, CA 90024.

GOODWIN, WILLIAM J(ENNINGS), b. Bybee, Va, Apr. 30, 25; m. 47; c. 2. MEDICAL ENTOMOLOGY. B.S, Okla. State, 50; M.S, Cornell, 51, Ph.D, 53. Assoc. prof. entom, Clemson Col, 53-57; vector control adv, Int. Co-op. Admin, Tripoli, Libya, 57-58, malaria adv, 59-61; Agency Int. Develop, Port-au-Prince, Haiti, 61-63; scientist administr, Nat. Inst. Health, 64-65; ord, Bur. State Serv, U.S. Pub. Health Serv, 65-67; CHIEF, REGIONAL PRIMATE RES. CTR, NAT. INSTS. HEALTH, 67- U.S.A, 43-46, Res, 46-52, 55-57, U.S.P.H.S, 57-, Capt. AAAS; Entom. Soc. Am; Am. Soc. Trop. Med. & Hyg; Am. Mosquito Control Asn; Am. Pub. Health Asn; Int. Primatol. Soc. Medical and veterinary entomology; malaria eradication; science administration; public health. Address: 4513 Edgefield Rd, Kensington, MD 20795.

GOODWIN, WILLIAM M(cCULLOUGH), b. Sardis, Ohio, Sept. 8, 99; m. 27; c. 2. DENTISTRY. D.D.S, Western Reserve, 22. Private practice, 22-42; asst. chief dent. div, U.S. vet. admin, Columbus, Ohio, 46-49, prfnl. div, Wash, D.C, 49-53, dir. dent. res. & educ. serv, 53-67; RETIRED. Mem. dent. study sect, U.S. Pub. Health Serv, 53-67. Dent.C, U.S.A, 42-46. AAAS; Am. Dental Asn; Asn. Mil. Surg. U.S; fel. Am. Col. Dent. Dental research administration. Address: 12500 Davan Dr, Silver Spring, MD 20904.

GOODWINE, JAMES K, JR, b. Evanston, Ill, Mar. 9, 30; m. 59; c. 2. MECHANICAL & AUTOMOTIVE ENGINEERING. B.S, Purdue, 52, M.S, 56, Nat. Sci. Found. summer fel, 59, Ph.D.(mech. eng), 60. Res. asst. mech. eng, Purdue, 56-57, instr, 57-59; res. engr. petrol. prod, Chevron Res. Co, 59-67; staff engr, eng. dept, UNITED AIR LINES, 67-70, MGR. POWER PLANT ENG, SAN FRANCISCO, 70- U.S.A, 52-54. AAAS; Soc. Automotive Eng. Petroleum products, especially jet fuels and gasolines; fundamentals of combustion, including computer simulation of engine cycles; smog; turbine engine maintenance. Address: 8 Elkin Ct, San Rafael, CA 94901.

GOODWYN, JACK R(AY), b. Center, Tex, June 28, 34; m. 55; c. 3. PHYSICAL CHEMISTRY. B.A, Baylor Univ, 56, Ph.D.(phys. chem), 60. Chemist, TEX. EASTMAN CO, 60-65, SR. CHEMIST, PLASTICS LAB, 65- Chemist, Dow Chem. Co, summer 56. Am. Chem. Soc; Soc. Plastics Eng. Molecular structure of high polymers. Address: Plastics Lab, Texas Eastman Co, P.O. Box 7444, Longview, TX 75601.

GOODWYN, L. WAYNE, b. Kingsville, Tex, Apr. 21, 41; m. 64; c. 2. PURE MATHEMATICS. B.S, Univ. Md, 64, Nat. Sci. Found. fel, 66-68, Ph.D. (math), 68. ASST. PROF. MATH, UNIV. KY, 68- Am. Math. Soc. Topological dynamics, specifically in topological entropy. Address: Dept. of Mathematics, University of Kentucky, Lexington, KY 40506.

GOODY, RICHARD (MEAD), b. Eng, June 19, 21; nat; m; c. 1. PHYSICS. B.A, Cambridge, 42, Ph.D.(physics), 49; hon. A.M, Harvard, 58. Sci. off, Ministry Aircraft Prod, Eng, 42-46; fel, St. John's Col, Cambridge, 50-53; reader, Imp. Col, London, 53-58; Abbott Lawrence Rotch prof. dynamic meteorol. & dir. Blue Hill Meteorol. Observ, HARVARD, 58-68, MALLINKRODT PROF. PLANETARY PHYSICS, 68-, DIR. CTR. EARTH & PLANETARY PHYSICS, 71- Nat. Acad. Sci; Am. Meteorol. Soc; Am. Acad. Arts & Sci; Am. Phys. Soc; Am. Astron. Soc; Royal Meteorol. Soc.(Buchan Prize, 58); Brit. Inst. Physics & Phys. Soc; Am. Geophys. Union. Physics and dynamics of the atmospheres of the earth and other planets; infrared spectroscopy. Address: Division of Engineering & Applied Physics, Pierce Hall 939, Harvard University, Cambridge, MA 02138.

GOODYEAR, WILLIAM FREDERICK, JR, b. Camden, N.J, Aug. 13, 29; m. 53; c. 2. ORGANIC & PHYSICAL CHEMISTRY. B.S, Rutgers, 57, Nat. Sci. Found. fel, 57-59, Ph.D.(org. chem), 59. Res. chemist, ARMSTRONG CORK CO, 59-63, res. supvr, 63-69, RES. MGR, 69- U.S.N.R, 47-51; U.S.A, 51-53, Sgt. AAAS; Am. Chem. Soc; Soc. Plastics. Eng. Reaction kinetics; organophosphorus-organic peroxide reaction mechanisms; filled plastics. Address: 2905 Brookfield Rd, Lancaster, PA 17601.

GOODYER, ALLAN V(ICTOR), b. New York, N.Y, Nov. 21, 18; m. 46; c. 3. CARDIOVASCULAR DISEASES. B.S, Yale, 39, M.D, 42. Intern, New Haven Hosp, 42-43, asst. res. med, 46-47; fel, YALE, 47-48, instr. internal med, 48-50, asst. prof. MED, 50-56, assoc. prof, 56-66, PROF, 66- Markle Found. scholar, 49-54; estab. investr, Am. Heart Asn, 54-59. Am. Soc. Clin. Invest; Am. Fedn. Clin. Res; Asn. Univ. Cardiol; Am. Col. Cardiol; Asn. Am. Physicians. Cardiovascular physiology and disease. Address: 789 Howard Ave, New Haven, CT 06519.

GOOGIN, J(OHN) M(ELVIN), b. Lewiston, Maine, May 2, 22; m. 49; c. 4. PHYSICAL CHEMISTRY. B.S, Bates Col, 44, hon. D.Sc, 68; Ph.D.(chem), Univ. Tenn, 53. Sr. scientist, develop. div, Y-12 Plant, Union Carbide Nuclear Co, 53-68, SR. STAFF CONSULT. PROD. OPERS, NUCLEAR DIV, UNION CARBIDE CORP, 68- Ernest Orlando Lawrence Mem. Award with citation in chem. & metall, Atomic Energy Comn, 67. AAAS; Am. Chem. Soc; Sci. Res. Soc. Am; Am. Soc. Metals. Separation of isotopes; separation and purification of metals by solvent extraction and ion exchange; high temperature technology; metallurgy, ceramics and chemistry of nuclear materials. Address: Nuclear Division, Union Carbide Corp, P.O. Box Y, Oak Ridge, TN 37830.

GOOLSBY, CHARLES M(ARTEL), b. Quitman, Ga, July 21, 20; m. 55; c. 6. CELL BIOLOGY. B.Sc, Nebraska, 48, M.Sc, 51; Marine Biol. Labs, Woods

Hole, 54; Ph.D.(zool, endocrinol), Harvard, 55. Asst. physiol. & pub. health, Nebraska, 48-51; endocrinol, Harvard, 51-54; prof. BIOL, Tenn. Agr. & Ind. State, 54-58; from asst. prof. to assoc. prof, NORTHEAST. UNIV, 58-65, PROF, 65- Summer prof, Nat. Sci. Found. Inst. Teachers, N.C. Col. Durham, 59; res. assoc, Blood Res. Inst, Jamaica Plain, Mass, 61-69; sr. prog. assoc, Inst. Serv. to Educ, Newton, 68-70; Wash, D.C, 70-71. U.S.A, 42-46, Res, 46-57, 1st Lt. AAAS; Endocrinology; influence of other steroids on the action of estrogens and androgens in the growth; histochemistry and biochemistry of responding organs; biophysics and biochemistry of cells; curriculum development and consulting in biological education. Address: 360 Huntington Ave, Boston, MA 02115.

GOON, DAVID JAMES WONG, b. LaCrosse, Wis, Jan. 15, 42. PHYSICAL ORGANIC CHEMISTRY. B.Ch, Univ. Minn, Minneapolis, 64; M.S, Univ. Ill, Urbana, 66, U.S. Pub. Health trainee & Ph.D.(org. chem), 68. Fel. CHEM, Univ. Ill, Chicago Circle, 68-69, instr, 68-70; TEACHING FEL, UNIV. GUELPH, 70- Am. Chem. Soc. Solvolysis; kinetics and mechanism; organic photochemistry; oxidation. Address: 1827 Hewitt Ave, St. Paul, MN 55104.

GOON, EDWARD J(AMES), b. Portland, Maine, Aug. 8, 25; m. 52; c. 4. PHYSICAL CHEMISTRY. A.B, Bowdoin Col, 50; S.B, Mass. Inst. Tech, 50; Ph.D.(chem), Rensselaer Polytech, 53. Asst. chem, Rensselaer Polytech, 50-52, res. assoc, 52-53; Tufts Col, 53-59; proj. mgr, NAT. RES. CORP, 59-63, sr. chemist, 63-69, PROG. MGR, RES. & DEVELOP, 69- AAAS; Am. Chem. Soc; Electrochem. Soc. Development of tantalum powder for electrolytic capacitor applications; development of methods for preparation of sintered tantalum anodes for capacitors. Address: 1499 Great Plain Ave, Needham, MA 02192.

GOONEWARDENE, HILARY FELIX, b. Colombo, Ceylon, Apr. 9, 25; U.S. citizen; m. 63; c. 3. ENTOMOLOGY, PLANT PATHOLOGY. B.Sc, Sydney, 53; B.Agr. Sc, New Zealand, 57; M.S, Rutgers, 60, Ph.D.(entom, plant path), 61. Res. off, Cmn. Sci. & Indust. Res. Org, Australia, 52-53; crop protection off, Coconut Res. Inst, Ceylon, 56-58; res. asst. entom, Rutgers, 58-61, agr. chem, 61; tech. dir. pesticides, coatings & resins div, Pittsburgh Plate Glass Co, 61-63; head pesticides res. & develop, Smith Kline & French Labs, Inc, 63-64; RES. ENTOMOLOGIST, AGR. RES. SERV, U.S. DEPT. AGR, 64- Agr. res. grants adminstr. for several cols, univs. & industs, 61-64; consult. AAAS; Entom. Soc. Am. Development of mass rearing techniques; artificial diets; investigations into aspects of sex attraction for Japanese beetles. Address: Entomology Research Division, U.S. Dept. of Agriculture, Ohio Agricultural Research and Development Center, Wooster, OH 44691.

GOOR, RONALD STEPHEN, b. Washington, D.C, May 31, 40; m. 67. BIOCHEMISTRY, MOLECULAR BIOLOGY. B.A, Swarthmore Col, 62; Chicago, 62-63; Ph.D.(biochem), Harvard, 67. Nat. Insts. Health fel, 67-69; staff fel. biol. viruses, Nat. Inst. Allergy & Infectious Diseases, 69-70; SPEC. ASST. TO DIR, NATIONAL MUS. NATURAL HIST, SMITHSONIAN INST, 70- AAAS; Am. Chem. Soc; Am. Soc. Biol. Chem; N.Y. Acad. Sci. Mode of action of diphtheria toxin; mammalian protein synthesis; biochemistry of oncogenic viruses. Address: 9200 Burley Dr, Bethesda, MD 20034.

GOORLEY, JOHN T(HEODORE), b. Galion, Ohio, Mar. 12, 07; m. 35; c. 4. PHARMACEUTICAL CHEMISTRY. B.S, Ohio State, 30; M.S, Purdue, 32, Ph.D.(pharm), 34. Chief analyst, Burroughs Wellcome Co, N.Y, 33-38; dir. res, Lex Labs, Cuba, 39-42; Ben Venue Labs, Ohio, 46-48; Johnson & Johnson, Argentina, 48-50; owner, Goorley Labs, 50-55; assoc. prof. pharmaceut. chem, Ohio Northern, 56-57; v.pres. & gen. mgr, Inland Alkaloid Co, Ind, 57-58; assoc. prof. pharmaceut. chem, NORTHEAST LA. UNIV, 48-67, PROF. PHARMACOG, 67- Fulbright Hays prof, Honduras, 66-67. Sanit.C, 42-45, Res, 45-63, Lt. Col. AAAS; Am. Chem. Soc; Am. Pharmaceut. Asn; N.Y. Acad. Sci. Pharmaceutical and medicinal chemistry. Address: College of Pharmacy, Northeast Louisiana University, Monroe, LA 71201.

GOORVITCH, DAVID, b. San Pedro, Calif, July 16, 41; m. 66. ATOMIC PHYSICS. B.A, California, Berkeley, 63, Ph.D.(physics), 67. PHYSICIST, AMES RES. CTR, 67- Am. Phys. Soc; Optical Soc. Am. Isotope shift and hyperfine structure of radioactive elements; spectroscopy of highly stripped elements; accurate wavelength determinations of thorium transitions. Address: Ames Research Center, Moffett Field, CA 94035.

GOOS, ROGER D(ELMON), b. Beaman, Iowa, Oct. 29, 24; m. 46; c. 2. MYCOLOGY. B.A, Iowa, 50, M.S, 55, Ph.D, 58. Teacher, pub. sch, Iowa, 51-53; asst. bot, Iowa, 53-58; mycologist, cent. res. labs, United Fruit Co, Mass, 58-62; scientist, Nat. Insts. Health, 62-64; curator fungi, Am. Type Culture Collection, 64-68; assoc. researcher BOT, Univ. Hawaii, 68-69, vis. assoc. prof, 69-70; ASSOC. PROF, UNIV. R.I, 70-, CHMN. DEPT, 71- A.U.S, 44-46, Res, 46-52. AAAS; Mycol. Soc. Am; Bot. Soc. Am; Am. Phytopath. Soc; Asn. Trop. Biol; Brit. Mycol. Soc. Soil mycology; classification and life histories of the fungi imperfecti and ascomycetes; tropical fungi; diseases of the banana plant. Address: Dept. of Botany, University of Rhode Island, Kingston, RI 02881.

GOOSEY, MALCOLM H(AYES), JR, b. Big Timber, Mont, Nov. 22, 27; m. 48; c. 4. ENGINEERING PHYSICS. B.S, Mont. State Col, 52. Physicist, SAVANNAH RIVER LAB, E.I. DU PONT DE NEMOURS & CO, INC, 52-63, RES. SUPVR. ELECTRONICS, 63- C.Eng, 46-48, Sgt. Instrument Soc. Am. Eddy current non-destructive testing; nuclear reactor instrumentation; low-level switching; data acquisition systems. Address: Bldg. 773-A, Savannah River Lab, E.I. du Pont de Nemours & Co, Inc, Aiken, SC 29802.

GOOSSENS, JOHN CHARLES, b. Chicago, Ill, Aug. 19, 28; m. 56; c. 3. ORGANIC CHEMISTRY. B.S, Notre Dame, 50; Off. Naval Res. fel, Maryland, 51-54, Ph.D.(org. chem), 57. Asst, Wayne State, 50-51; chemist, Standard Oil Co, Ind, 55-60; RES. CHEMIST, silicone prod. dept, GEN. ELEC. CO, 60-71, PLASTICS DEPT, PITTSFIELD, 71- Am. Chem. Soc. Polymers; lubrication; organometallics. Address: 45 Grange Hall Rd, Dalton, MA 01226.

GOOSSENS, PIERRE J, b. Brussels, Belg, Mar. 17, 39; m. 63; c. 2. METALLOGENY, ECONOMIC GEOLOGY. Lic. Geol. & Mineral, Cath. Univ. Louvain, 62, hon. D.S, 65. Assoc. expert. mineral explor, UN Develop. Prog, 65-68, expert, 68-70; asst. prof. geol, Univ. South. Miss, 70-71; ASSOC. PROF. ECON. GEOL, MICH. TECHNOL. UNIV, 71- AAAS; Geol. Soc. Belgium; Swiss Soc. Mineral. & Petrog; Soc. Geol. Appl. Mineral Deposits; Soc. Econ. Geol; Soc. Explor. Geochem; Am. Inst. Mining, Metall. & Petrol. Eng. Chemical zonality of garnets and metamorphic processes; metallogeny of the Andean cordillera; plate tectonic, especially geotectonic, and mineral deposits; continental drift. Address: Dept. of Geology, Michigan Technological University, Houghton, MI 49931.

GOOTMAN, PHYLLIS M(YRNA) A(DLER), b. N.Y.C, June 8, 38; m. 58; c. 2. NEUROPHYSIOLOGY. B.A, Columbia Univ, 59; U.S. Pub. Health Serv. grants, Albert Einstein Col. Med, 60-62 & 64-65, Nat. Insts. Health fel, 65-67, Ph.D.(physiol), 67. Res. assoc. PHYSIOL, sch. med, Univ. Wash, 63; instr, ALBERT EINSTEIN COL. MED, 68-70, ASST. PROF, 70-; Nat. Insts. Health fels, 68-69 & 70-71. AAAS; Am. Physiol. Soc; Biophys. Soc; Soc. Neurosci. Central nervous system regulation of cardiovascular function; interrelations between vasomotor and central respiratory centers. Address: Dept. of Physiology, Albert Einstein College of Medicine, 1300 Morris Park Ave, New York, NY 10461.

GOPALAKRISHNAN, A, b. Trivandrum, India, Aug. 4, 37; m. 67; c. 1. NUCLEAR ENGINEERING. B.Sc, Univ. Kerala, 58; M.S, Univ. Calif, Berkeley, 67, Ph.D.(nuclear eng), 69. Jr. res. off, Indian Atomic Energy Comn, Bombay, 59-61; res. asst. nuclear eng, Univ. Calif, Berkeley, 61-63, mgr. reactor heat transients proj, 63-66; sr. engr, Cetec Corp, Calif, 66-68; jr. specialist, off. res. serv, Univ. Calif, Berkeley, 68-69; MEM. STAFF, ARGONNE NAT. LAB, U.S. ATOMIC ENERGY COMN, 69- Avittom Thirunal gold medal, Univ. Kerala, 58. Am. Nuclear Soc; Am. Soc. Mech. Eng; Brit. Nuclear Energy Soc. Design and safety of nuclear reactors; thermal-hydraulic and safety analysis of liquid metal fast breeder reactors; heat transfer and fluid mechanic model studies and experimentation. Address: EBR-II Project, Argonne National Lab, Argonne, IL 60439.

GOPLEN, B(ERNARD) P(ETER), b. Griffin, Sask, March 6, 30; m. 56; c. 4. GENETICS, PLANT BREEDING. B.S.A, Saskatchewan, 52, M.Sc, 55, Hantleman & Sask. Res. Council scholars, 55, 58, Ph.D.(genetics), 58; Myers scholar, California, 57-58. Asst. agron, California, 55-57; AGROSTOLOGIST, RES. STA, CAN. DEPT. AGR, 58- Agr. Inst. Can. Bloat research in legumes; developing low fraction I protein alfalfa. Address: Canada Dept. of Agriculture Research Station, University Campus, Saskatoon, Sask, Can.

GOPLERUD, CLIFFORD P, b. Osage, Iowa, Dec. 6, 24; m. 47; c. 4. OBSTETRICS, GYNECOLOGY. Carlton Col, 42-43; Washington & Lee, 43-44; M.D, Iowa, 48. Intern med, Cincinnati Gen. Hosp, Ohio, 48-49; asst. resident OBSTET. & GYNEC, Grady Mem. Hosp, 49-50, 51-52, resident, 52-53; asst. prof, UNIV. IOWA HOSPS, 58-61, assoc. prof, 61-66, PROF, 66- Med. C, 43-46, 48-56, Lt. Col. Am. Med. Asn; Am. Col. Obstet. & Gynec; Asn. Profs. Gynec. & Obstet. Erythroblastosis; aminocentesis; diabetes in pregnancy; infectious problems in obstetric patients. Address: Dept. of Obstetrics & Gynecology, University of Iowa Hospitals, Iowa City, IA 52240.

GORA, EDWIN K(ARL), b. Bielsko, Poland, Oct. 22, 11; nat; m. 45; c. 5. THEORETICAL PHYSICS. Ph.M, Jagellonian Univ, Poland, 34; Sc.D, Leipzig, Germany, 43. Lectr. physics, St. Xavier's Col, India, 35-37; asst. theoret. physics, Lwow, Poland, 37-38; Warsaw, 38-39; asst. physics, Munich, 44-45, lectr, 45-47, asst. theoret. physics,47-48; asst. prof. PHYSICS, Col. Steubenville, 48-49; PROVIDENCE COL, 49-52, assoc. prof, 52-55, PROF, 55-, CHMN. DEPT, 68- Vis. prof, Rhode Island, 62-63; consult, U.S. Army Missile Command, 63- Am. Phys. Soc; Europ. Phys. Soc. Classical and quantum theory of radiation; molecular spectroscopy. Address: Dept. of Physics, Providence College, Providence, RI 02908.

GORA, THADDEUS A, JR, b. Elizabeth, N.J, Nov. 16, 41; m. 66. SOLID STATE PHYSICS. B.S, Rensselaer Polytech, 63; U.S. Steel fel, Delaware, 65-66, Ph.D.(solid state physics), 68. Res. fel, Delaware, summer, 68; PHYSICIST, FELTMAN RES. LABS, PICATINNY ARSENAL, 68- U.S.A, 68-70, Capt. Am. Phys. Soc. Band structure of psuedo-stable solids; x-ray photoelectron spectroscopy; graded band structure in heterogeneous materials. Address: 410 Morris Ave, Mountain Lakes, NJ 07046.

GORADIA, CHANDRA P, b. Rajula, India, Aug. 6, 39; m. 69. ELECTRICAL ENGINEERING, PHYSICS. B.Sc, Univ. Bombay, 60, M.Sc, 62; M.E.E, Univ. Okla, 64, Ph.D.(elec. eng), 68. Asst. res. scientist, biophys. res. lab, Tulsa Div, Avco Corp, 64-65; asst. prof. ELEC. ENG, CLEVELAND STATE UNIV, 67-71, ASSOC. PROF, 71- AAAS; Inst. Elec. & Electronic Eng. Semiconductor surfaces; surface barrier nuclear radiation detectors. Address: Dept. of Electrical Engineering, Cleveland State University, 1983 E. 24th St, Cleveland, OH 44115.

GORAN, MORRIS, b. Chicago, Ill, Sept. 4, 16; m. 51; c. 2. CHEMISTRY. B.S, Chicago, 36, M.S, 39, Ph.D.(sci. ed), 57. Chemist, Dearborn Chem. Co, Ill, 41-43; instr. physics, Indiana, 43-44; assoc. prof. chem, ROOSEVELT UNIV, 46-58, PROF. PHYS. SCI, 58-, CHMN. DEPT, 46- Lectr, George Williams Col, 51-53. Res. chemist, Manhattan proj, Oak Ridge, Tenn. C.Eng, U.S.A, 44-46. AAAS; Am. Chem. Soc; Am. Phys. Soc; Hist. Sci. Soc; Am. Inst. Chem; Am. Asn. Physics Teachers. Natural science history and methods; science education. Address: Dept. of Physical Science, Roosevelt University, Chicago, IL 60605.

GORAN, ROBERT CHARLES, b. St. Louis, Mo, Feb. 7, 17; m. 47; c. 2. AERONAUTICAL ENGINEERING. B.S, Washington (St. Louis), 37. Chem. engr, titanium div, Nat. Lead Co, 37-40; Fraser-Brace Eng. Co, 41-43; sr. supvr, Trojan Powder Co, 43-44; stress anal. eng, Consol-Vultee Aircraft Corp, 44-45; stress engr, McDONNELL AIRCRAFT CO, 45-51, sr. engr. & supvr. struct. design & anal, 51-55, engr. & supvr. proj. strength, 55-60, chief strength engr. & dept. head, 60-70, DIR. STRUCT. TECHNOL, 70- Mem. res. adv. comt, space vehicle struct, NASA, 64-67, aircraft struct, 69-71; mem. indust. adv. group, U.S. Air Force Aircraft Struct. Integrity Prog, 68- Structural design, analysis and development of aerospace vehicles. Address: Dept. 230, Bldg. 1, L.3, McDonnell Aircraft Co, P.O. Box 516, St. Louis, MO 63166.

GORANSON, E(DWIN) A(LEXANDER), b. New Westminister, B.C, Nov. 12, 04; m. 35; c. 3. MINING GEOLOGY. B.A.Sc, British Columbia, 28; scholar, Harvard, 28, A.M, 30, traveling scholar, 32, Ph.D.(geol), 33. Asst. to Prof. E.S. Larsen, Harvard, 29, instr. mining geol, 30-33; geologist, Labrador Explor. Co, 33; geologist & engr, Base Metals Mining Corp, 33-37; geologist, E. Malartic Mines, Ltd, Can, 37-43; J.P. Norrie, Ltd, 43-45; consult. geologist, 45-49; geologist, N.J. Zinc Explors, Ltd, 49-50, N.J. Zinc Explor. Co.(Can) Ltd, 50-70; CONSULT. GEOLOGIST, 70- Geol. Soc. Am; fel. Soc. Econ. Geol; Am. Inst. Min, Metall. & Petrol. Eng; fel. Geol. Soc. Can; Can. Inst. Min. & Metall. Address: 66 Billings Ave, Ottawa, Ont. K1H 5K7, Can.

GORANSON, RICHARD BRUCE, b. Malden, Mass, Feb. 9, 37; m. 58. BIOMEDICAL & NUCLEAR ENGINEERING. B.A, California, Riverside, 58; Nat. Defense Ed. Act fel, Arizona, 63-66, M.S, 68. Microwave physicist, U.S. Naval Ord. Lab, Calif, 58-60; res. assoc, Lunar & Planetary Lab, Arizona, 61-62; nuclear engr, Idaho div, Argonne Nat. Lab, summer 63; Hanford opers, Gen. Elec. Co, summer 64; Pac. Northwest Labs, Battelle Mem. Inst, summer 65; PROJ. ENGR, ENG, DONALD W. DOUGLAS LABS, McDONNELL DOUGLAS CORP, 66- Am. Nuclear Soc; Am. Soc. Artificial Internal Organs. Managing development of small radioisotope heat sources for terrestial and aerospace applications. Address: Donald W. Douglas Labs, 2955 George Washington Way, Richland, WA 99352.

GORBATSEVICH, SERGE N, b. Poland, Mar. 15, 22; U.S. citizen; div. PULP & PAPER TECHNOLOGY. B.S, State Univ. N.Y. Col. Forestry, Syracuse, 54, M.S, 55. Res. chemist, Consol. Water Power & Paper Co, Wis, 55-56; instr. pulp & paper tech, STATE UNIV. N.Y. COL. FORESTRY, SYRACUSE, 56-61, asst. prof, 62-65, ASSOC. PROF, PAPER SCI. & ENG, 65- Tech. Asn. Pulp & Paper Indust. Pulping; bleaching; paper properties. Address: Dept. of Paper Science & Engineering, State University of New York College of Forestry at Syracuse University, Syracuse, NY 13210.

GORBATY, MARTIN L(EO), b. N.Y.C, Nov. 17, 42; m. 68; c. 1. ORGANIC CHEMISTRY. B.S, City Univ. New York, 64; Ph.D.(org. chem), Purdue Univ, 69. RES. CHEMIST, Esso Agr. Prod. Lab, 69-70, CORP. RES. LAB, ESSO RES. & ENG. CO, 70- Am. Chem. Soc. Synthesis of new elastomeric materials by cationic polymerization. Address: Corporate Research Lab, Esso Research & Engineering Co, P.O. Box 45, Linden, NJ 07036.

GORBET, DANIEL WAYNE, b. Corpus Christi, Tex, Oct. 16, 42; m. 62; c. 2. AGRONOMY, PLANT BREEDING & GENETICS. B.S, Tex. A&I Univ, 65; M.S, Okla. State Univ, 68, Ph.D.(crop sci), 71. ASST. PROF. AGRON, AGR. RES. CTR, UNIV. FLA, 70- Am. Soc. Agron; Crop Sci. Soc. Am. Sorghum breeding and genetics; breeding, genetics and management of peanuts. Address: Agricultural Research Center, University of Florida, P.O. Box 878, Marianna, FL 32446.

GORBMAN, AUBREY, b. Detroit, Mich, Dec. 13, 14; m. 38; c. 4. ZOOLOGY. A.B, Wayne, 35, M.S, 36; Ph.D.(zool), California, 40. Asst. zool, California, 36-40, res. assoc, inst. exp. biol, 40-41; instr. biol, Wayne, 41-44; Childs fel, Yale, 44-46; asst. prof. ZOOL, Barnard Col, Columbia, 46-49, assoc. prof, 49-54, prof, 54-63, exec. officer dept, univ, 52-55, col, 57-60; PROF. UNIV. WASH, 63-, chmn. dept, 63-66. Fulbright scholar, Col. of France, 51-52; res. collab, Brookhaven Nat. Lab, 52-60; Guggenheim fel, Hawaii, 55-56; vis. prof, Nagoya, 56; U.S. Pub. Health Serv. fel. & vis. prof, Tokyo, 60; ed-in-chief, Gen. & Comparative Endocrinol, 60- Am. Soc. Nat; Soc. Exp. Biol. & Med; Am. Soc. Ichthyol. & Herpet; Am. Soc. Zool; Endocrine Soc; Am. Asn. Anat; fel. N.Y. Acad. Sci. Comparative endocrinology; actions of hormones on nervous system. Address: Dept. of Zoology, University of Washington, Seattle, WA 98105.

GORBUNOFF, MARINA J, b. Moscow, Russia, May 25, 27; U.S. citizen; m. 53; c. 1. ORGANIC CHEMISTRY. B.S, Syracuse, 51; M.S, Yale, 54, Ph.D.(chem), 56. Res. fel. org. chem, Bryn Mawr Col, 56-57; Pennsylvania, 57-59; res. chemist, East. Regional Res. Lab, Agr. Res. Serv, U.S. Dept. Agr, 61-67, SR. RES. ASSOC. BIOCHEM, BRANDEIS UNIV, 67- Am. Chem. Soc. Structure of proteins; chemical modification of active groups on proteins; synthetic organic chemistry. Address: Graduate Dept. of Biochemistry, Brandeis University, 415 South St, Waltham, MA 02154.

GORBY, CHARLES K, b. Phila, Pa, Mar. 24, 27; m. 59; c. 2. EXPERIMENTAL MEDICINE, PHARMACOLOGY. B.Sc, Phila. Col. Pharm, 51, M.Sc, 52; Ph.D.(pharmacol), Jefferson Med. Col, 56, M.D, 59. Intern, Fitzgerald Mercy Hosp, Darby, Pa, 59-60; chief drug & narcotic control, Pa. Dept. Health, 61-62; clin. pharmacol. dir, Squibb Inst. Med. Res, 62-66; res. asst. prof. med, Hahnemann Med. Col, 63-67; ASST. PROF. CLIN. MED, THOMAS JEFFERSON SCH. MED, 67- Lectr, sch. nursing, Fitzgerald Mercy Hosp, 60-; Phila. Col. Pharm, 63-; clin. pharmacologist & dir. psychopharmacol, res. unit, Haverford State Hosp, Pa, 66-; asst. in med, Lankenau Hosp, Phila, 69-; assoc, Franklin Inst, 70; Smithsonian Inst, 70; mem. bd. health, Haverford Township, 71. U.S.N, 45-46. AAAS; Am. Therapeut. Soc; Am. Med. Asn; Am. Pharmaceut. Asn. Autonomic nervous system; psychotropic drug areas; clinical pharmacology and therapeutics. Address: 138 Brookline Blvd, Havertown, PA 19083.

GORDAN, GILBERT S(AUL), b. San Francisco, Calif, July 8, 16; m. 41, 65. MEDICINE. A.B, California, 37, M.D, 41, Nat. Inst. Health fel, 47, Ph.D.(endocrinol), 47. Intern, univ. hosp, UNIV. CALIF, SAN FRANCISCO, 40-41, asst. resident med, MED. SCH, 41-42, clin. instr, 45-47, instr. med. & pharmacol, 48-49, asst. prof, 49-54, assoc. prof. MED, 54-63, PROF, 63-, CHIEF ENDOCRINE CLINICS, 56- Commonwealth fel, Harvard Med. Sch, 47-48; commonwealth fund fel, Col. Physicians & Surgeons, Columbia Univ, 62-63; Strangeways lab, Cambridge; Guggenheim fel. & vis. prof, Univ. Makerere, Univ. Athens, Hebrew Univ; William Beaumont vis. prof, sch. med, Wash. Univ, 70. Consult, Cancer Chemother. Nat. Serv. Ctr, U.S. Pub. Health Serv, 57-59, chmn, coop. breast cancer group, 56-59, mem. & spec. consult, hormone evaluation joint comt. clin. & endocrinol. panels, 57-59; consult, manned orbiting lab. proj, U.S. Air Force, Aerospace Corp, 64- Ed, Year Book Endocrinol, 51-63. Med.C, 42-45, Maj. Am. Soc. Clin. Invest; Endocrine Soc; Soc. Exp. Biol. & Med; fel. Am. Col. Physicians; Am. Fedn. Clin. Res; hon. mem. Royal Soc. Med; Asn. Am. Physicians; Israel Med. Asn. Clinical and experimental endocrinology; calcium metabolism; bone physiology; parathyroid function; anabolic steroids. Address: Dept. of Medicine, University of California, San Francisco, CA 94122.

GORDEE, R(OBERT) S(TOUFFER), b. Chicago, Ill, June 12, 32; m. 61; c. 1. MICROBIOLOGY. B.S, Mich. State, 54; M.S, Purdue, 59, Purdue Res. Found. & Todd-Beechnut fel. & Ph.D.(mycol, biochem), 61. Fisheries biologist, Great Lakes Fishery Invest, U.S. Fish & Wildlife Serv, 54; res. scientist, biophys-res. div, Lockheed-Calif. Co, 61-64; sr. microbiologist, Biol-Pharmacol. res. div, LILLY RES. LABS, 64-70, res. scientist, biol. res. div, 70-71, HEAD DEPT. EXP. CHEMOTHER, 71- Summer vis. scholar, Univ. Mich, 62. Med.Serv.C, U.S.A, 55-57. AAAS; Am. Soc. Microbiol; Am. Inst. Biol. Sci; N.Y. Acad. Sci. Antimicrobial agents; fungal chemotherapy. Address: Dept. M-787, Lilly Research Labs, Indianapolis, IN 46206.

GORDEN, BERNER J, b. Detroit, Mich, Jan. 22, 39; m. 62; c. 2. ORGANIC CHEMISTRY. B.A, Luther Col.(Iowa), 61; M.S, Wayne State, 64, Ph.D.(org. chem), 65. Asst. prof. CHEM, Muskingum Col, 65-67; SAGINAW VALLEY COL, 67-71, ASSOC. PROF, 71-, CHMN. DEPT, 69- Am. Chem. Soc; Am. Inst. Chem. Conformational analysis; organic synthesis; mechanisms and reagents in organic reactions. Address: Dept. of Chemistry, Saginaw Valley College, 2250 Pierce Rd, University Center, MI 48710.

GORDEN, ROBERT WAYNE, b. LaPorte Co, Ind, Aug. 22, 32; m. 54; c. 4. MICROBIOLOGY, ECOLOGY. B.S, Manchester Col, 57; M.S, Georgia, 62, Nat. Sci. Found. fel, 62-67, Nat. Insts. Health Found. fel. & Ph.D.(microbiol), 67. Teacher-coach, high sch, Ind, 57-61; instr. biol, Manchester Col, 62-64; asst. prof. microbiol, Tex. Tech. Univ, 67-70; ASSOC. PROF. BIOL, SOUTH. COLO. STATE COL, 70- Atomic Energy Comn. res. partic, Oak Ridge Nat. Labs, summer, 69. AAAS; Ecol. Soc. Am; Am. Inst. Biol. Sci; Am. Soc. Microbiol. Ecology of microorganisms of lakes and aquatics; microcosms. Address: Dept. of Biology, Southern Colorado State College, Pueblo, CO 81004.

GORDEUK, STEPHEN, JR, b. Dayton, Ohio, Aug. 20, 16; m. 46; c. 6. POULTRY PATHOLOGY. B.S, Rutgers, 40, M.S, 42; V.M.D, Univ. Pa, 45. Asst. prof. animal path. res, PA. STATE UNIV, 45-47, ASSOC. PROF, 47-53, VET. SCI, 53- U.S. Animal Health Asn; Conf. Res. Workers Animal Diseases. Poultry disease diagnosis. Address: Wiley Lab, Dept. of Veterinary Science, Pennsylvania State University, University Park, PA 16802.

GORDH, GEORGE RUDOLPH, JR, b. Macon, Ga, May 12, 44; m. 68. TOPOLOGY. B.A, Guilford Col, 66; Nat. Sci. Found. traineeship, Univ. Calif, Riverside, 66-70, community teaching fel, 70, univ. assistanceship & Ph.D.(topology), 71. FEL. MATH, UNIV. KY, 71-72. Math. Asn. Am; Am. Math. Soc. Continua theory; structure of compact Hansdorff spaces and continua; irreducible continua; hereditarily unicoherent continua; hereditarily decomposable continua; quasi-ordered and totally ordered spaces; upper semi-continuous decompositions; fixed point theory; monotone inverse limit systems. Address: Dept. of Mathematics, University of Kentucky, Lexington, KY 40506.

GORDON, ADRIENNE SUE, b. Chicago, Ill, Mar. 28, 40. BIOCHEMISTRY. B.A, Northwest. Univ, 62; Ph.D.(chem), Mass. Inst. Technol, 66. Res. fel, Harvard Med. Sch, Mass. Gen. Hosp, Boston, 66-70; RES. ASSOC. BIOCHEM, ROCHE INST. MOLECULAR BIOL, NUTLEY, 70- Am. Chem. Soc. Structure and function of cell membranes. Address: 8200 Boulevard E, North Bergen, NJ 07047.

GORDON, ALBERT Mc(CAGUE), b. Tanta, Egypt, Sept. 23, 34; U.S. citizen; m. 60; c. 2. BIOPHYSICS. B.S, Univ. Rochester, 56; Ph.D.(solid state physics), Cornell Univ, 61. Nat. Found. fel, Univ. Col, Univ. London, 60-62; fel. biophys, UNIV. WASH, 62-64, instr. PHYSIOL. & BIOPHYS, 64-65, asst. prof, 65-70, ASSOC. PROF, 70- AAAS; Biophys. Soc; Am. Physiol. Soc. Mechanical properties of muscle and the contractile mechanism; electrical properties of biological membranes; excitation-contraction coupling in muscle. Address: Dept. of Physiology & Biophysics, University of Washington, Seattle, WA 98105.

GORDON, ALBERT RAYE, b. McKeesport, Pa, Sept. 22, 39; m. 65; c. 2. CELL BIOLOGY, ELECTRON MICROSCOPY. B.A, Western Reserve, 61, M.A, 67, Ph.D.(biol), Case Western Reserve, 68. Fel. biol, Case Western Reserve, 67-68; ASST. PROF, Knox Col.(Ill), 68-69; LIFE SCI, SOUTHWEST MO. STATE COL, 69- AAAS; Am. Soc. Cell Biol; Electron Micros. Soc. Am; Am. Soc. Plant Physiol; Am. Inst. Biol. Sci; Bot. Soc. Am. Significance and functions of multiple enzyme systems; cellular and ultrastructural localization of peroxidas isoenzymes and their relationship to plant tissue differentiation and function. Address: Dept. of Life Sciences, Southwest Missouri State College, Springfield, MO 65802.

GORDON, ALBERT S(AUL), b. Brooklyn, N.Y, Aug. 8, 10; m. 35; c. 1. PHYSIOLOGY. B.S, City Col. New York, 30; M.S, N.Y. Univ, 31, Ph.D.(physiol), 34. Asst. instr. BIOL, WASH. SQ. COL, N.Y. UNIV, 31-36, instr, 36-44, asst. prof, 44-47, assoc. prof, 47-54, PROF, 54- Instr, Newark Inst. Arts & Sci, 34-35; fel, Dazian Found. Med. Res, 49-51; sci. adv, New Eng. Inst. Med. Res, 59- Mem. study sect. hemat, Nat. Insts. Health, 58-62, 65-65, erythropoietin comt, Nat. Heart Inst, 64-71; grants, Am. Cancer Soc, Damon Runyon Mem. Fund Cancer Res, Nat. Sci. Found, Commonwealth Fund, U.S. Air Force & Nat. Insts. Health. AAAS; Am. Soc. Zool; Am. Physiol. Soc; Soc. Exp. Biol. & Med; Endocrine Soc; Harvey Soc; Soc. Study Blood; Soc. Hemat; Reticuloendothelial Soc.(pres, 61-64, ed-in-chief, Jour, 64-); Am. Asn. Anat; fel. N.Y. Acad. Sci.(Morrison prize, 48 & 66); Am. Soc. Nephrol; Int. Soc. Hemat; Royal Soc. Med. Red and white blood cell formation release and destruction; physiology of reticuloendothelial system; endocrine interrelations; humoral regulation of hematopoiesis. Address: Dept. of Biology, Washington Square College, New York University, Washington Square, New York, NY 10003.

GORDON, ALEXANDER L(EWIS), b. N.Y.C, Sept. 17, 15; m. 45; c. 2. INDUSTRIAL CHEMISTRY, CHEMICAL ENGINEERING. B.S, Worcester Polytech. Inst, 36, M.S, 37. Chemist, Vellumoid Co, 38-43, chief chemist, 43-60, res. mgr, 60-64, prod. develop. mgr, 64-65, Vellumoid Div, Fed-Mogul Corp, 65-70, MGR. RES. & DEVELOP, VELLUMOID PLANT, NAT. SEAL DIV, 70- Am. Chem. Soc; Am. Soc. Test. & Mat; Soc. Automotive Eng. Product and application development; engineering data preparation; technical service. Address: 18 Chippewa Rd, Worcester, MA 01602.

GORDON, ALVIN S, b. New York, N.Y, Oct. 25, 14; m. 42. PHYSICAL CHEMISTRY. B.S, Polytech. Inst. Brooklyn, 37; fel, N.Y. Univ, 37-41, Ph.D.(phys. chem), 41. Asst. phys. chemist, Boyce Thompson Inst, 41-42; res. assoc, Nat. Defense Res. Cmt, Carnegie Inst. Tech, 42-45; PHYS. CHEMIST, U.S. Bur. Mines, 45-51; NAVAL WEAPONS CTR, 51-, sci. liaison off, Off. Naval Res, London, Eng, 57-59. Vis. sr. res. scientist, Princeton, 64-65. Am. Chem. Soc; fel. Am. Phys. Soc. Kinetics and mechanism of reactions. Address: Code 6059, Naval Weapons Center, China Lake, CA 93555.

GORDON, ANNETTE WATERS, b. Sylvania, Ga, Aug. 9, 37; m. 62; c. 1. ORGANIC CHEMISTRY, BIOCHEMISTRY. B.S, Duke, 59; Nat. Defense Ed. Act fel. & Ph.D.(org. chem), Vanderbilt, 68. Asst. prof. CHEM, MURRAY STATE UNIV, 62-68, ASSOC. PROF, 68- Am. Chem. Soc. Stereochemistry. Address: Dept. of Chemistry, Murray State University, Murray, KY 42071.

GORDON, ARCHER S(AMUEL), b. Aurora, Ill, Jan. 8, 21; m. 51; c. 3. CARDIOVASCULAR SURGERY, PHYSIOLOGY. B.A, N.Cent. Col, 42; B.S, Illinois, 44, M.D, 45, fel, 49-52, M.S, 50, Ph.D.(physiol), 52. Res. assoc, dept. clin. sci, col. med, Illinois, 52-58; mem. staff, dept. surg, sch. med, Southern California & Los Angeles County Gen. Hosp, 59-64; chief cardiovasc. surg. & res, Lovelace Clin. & Found, 64-68; instr. surg, sch. med, Univ. South. Calif, 68-70; DIR. MED. RES, STATHAM INSTRUMENTS, INC, 68- Mem. attend. staff, Presby. Hosp, Ill, 57-58; assoc, Cook County Hosp, 57-58; Hosp. of Good Samaritan, Los Angeles, 59- Consult, Chem. Corps Med. Labs. & Am. Inst. Elec. Eng, 50-58; Nat. Res. Coun, 51, 57-58. U.S.A.A.F, 46-48, Capt. Am. Physiol. Soc; Soc. Exp. Biol. & Med; Am. Col. Chest Physicians; Am. Med. Asn. Respiratory physiology and resuscitation; cardiovascular physiology and surgery. Address: Statham Instruments, Inc, 2230 Statham Blvd, Oxnard, CA 93030.

GORDON, ARNOLD J, b. Boston, Mass, Dec. 13, 37; m. 64; c. 2. ORGANIC CHEMISTRY. B.Sc, Northeastern, 60; univ. fel, N.Y. Univ, 60-62, M.S, 62, Nat. Sci. Found. fel, 63-64, Ph.D.(org. chem), 64. Instr. gen. & org. chem, N.Y. Univ, 64; res. chemist, U.S. Army Edgewood Arsenal, 65-66; asst. prof. chem, Catholic Univ. Am, 66-71; ASSOC. DIR. SCI. SERV, PFIZER INC, 71- Res. grants, Catholic Univ, 67; Res. Corp, Am. Chem. Soc. Petrol. Res. Fund & Nat. Sci. Found, 67-71; manuscript referee, J. Org. Chem, 67-; Chem. Rev, 68; Am. Chem. Soc-Du Pont small grants award, 68. Chem.C, U.S.A, 64-66, Capt. AAAS; Am. Chem. Soc; N.Y. Acad. Sci; Am. Inst. Chem; Sigma Xi (pres, 70-71). Chemistry and biochemistry of drugs; stereochemistry of di-coordinated oxygen; synthesis and properties of imides and other nitrogen compounds; chemical education. Address: Pfizer Inc, 235 E. 42nd St, New York, NY 10017.

GORDON, ARNOLD L, b. N.Y.C, Feb. 4, 40; m. 70. PHYSICAL OCEANOGRAPHY. B.A, Hunter Col, 61; Ph.D.(oceanog), Columbia Univ, 65. Res. asst. OCEANOG, LAMONT-DOHERTY GEOL. OBSERV, COLUMBIA UNIV, 61-65, RES. ASSOC, 65-, ASSOC. PROF, 71-, asst. prof, 66-71. Ford Found. fel, 61-65, Nat. Sci. Found. res. grant, 65- AAAS; Am. Geophys. Union. Circulation of the Caribbean Sea; physical oceanographic investigations in the Antarctic ocean area. Address: Lamont-Doherty Geological Observatory, Columbia University, Palisades, NY 10964.

GORDON, ARTHUR LEONARD, b. Winnipeg, Man, Aug. 15, 21; U.S. citizen; m. 49; c. 6. AGRICULTURAL BIOCHEMISTRY. B.S, Minnesota, 48, Ph.D. (agr. biochem), 52. Res. chemist, A.E. Staley Mfg. Co, Ill, 52-56; Seaplant Corp, Mass, 56-59; Marine Colloids, Inc, Maine, 59-60; SR. SCIENTIST, Nat. Dairy Prod. Corp, 60-71, KRAFTCO, INC, 71- Sanit.C, 42-45, S/Sgt. Am. Chem. Soc; Am. Asn. Cereal Chem; Inst. Food Technol. Polysaccharides, particularly of seaweed origin; industrial gums and their applications; proteins, nutrition and applications thereof. Address: Kraftco, Inc, 801 Waukegan Rd, Glenview, IL 60025.

GORDON, BARRY M(AXWELL), b. Chicago, Ill, Jan. 26, 30; m. 58; c. 2. PHYSICAL CHEMISTRY. B.S, California, Los Angeles, 51; Phillips Petrol. Co. fel, Washington (St. Louis), 53-55, Ph.D.(chem), 55. Res. assoc. chem, Brookhaven Nat. Lab, 55-57; asst. prof, State Univ. N.Y. Stony Brook, 57-63; ASSOC. CHEMIST, BROOKHAVEN NAT. LAB, 63- Am. Chem. Soc. Kinetic studies of oxidation-reduction reactions; nuclear reactions; radiochemistry. Address: Brookhaven National Lab, Upton, NY 11973.

GORDON, BENJAMIN EDWARD, b. New York, N.Y, May 8, 16; m. 40; c. 3. ANALYTICAL CHEMISTRY, RADIO CHEMISTRY. B.S, Illinois, 40, M.S, 42. Res. chemist, Shell Oil Co, 42-54; sr. technologist radiochem, 54-57, group leader radiochem. & radiation chem, 57-61, SUPVR. RADIOCHEM, Shell Develop. Co 61-71; KONINKLIJKE SHELL LABS, 71- Am. Chem. Soc. Radiochemistry as applied to analytical chemistry; gas chromatography; product and process research; reaction mechanism; kinetics; activation analysis; instrumentation; applying nuclear techniques to problems in environmental conservation. Address: Koninklijke Shell Labs, Badhuisweg 3, Amsterdam, Holland.

GORDON, BENJAMIN S(OLOMON), b. N.Y.C, Nov. 21, 06; m. 31; c. 2. PATHOLOGY. B.S, City Col, 27; M.D, St. Louis, 31. Chief lab. serv, Vet. Admin. Hosp, Bronx, 48-67; assoc. prof. path, Albert Einstein Col. Med, Yeshiva, 54-67; DIR. LABS, HILLCREST GEN. HOSP, FLUSHING, 67- Consult, Jewish Chronic Disease Hosp, 50-; med. mus. technol, Vet. Admin. Hosp, Bronx, 67- Med.C, 42-46, Capt. Am. Soc. Clin. Path; Am. Med. Asn; Am. Asn. Path. & Bact; Am. Col. Physicians; Col. Am. Path; Int. Acad. Path. Pathologic anatomy; cardiac and gastrointestinal pathology; anatomic museums. Address: 162-54 12 Rd, Whitestone, NY 11357.

GORDON, BERNARD L(UDWIG), b. Westerly, R.I, Nov. 6, 31; m. 59; c. 2. MARINE BIOLOGY, OCEANOGRAPHY. B.Sc, Univ. R.I, 55, M.Sc, 58. Instr. biol, R.I. Col, 56-60; teaching fel, Boston Univ, 60-61; instr. natural sci, NORTHEAST. UNIV, 61-65, asst. prof. EARTH SCI, 65-68, ASSOC. PROF, 69- Consult, Mass. State Dept. Educ, 63; Quincy Marine Sci. Prog, Mass, 65-; mem. bd. dirs, South. New Eng. Marine Sci. Asn, 65-; Littauer Found. grant, 66; consult, Wally Sea Prod. Co, 67-; oceanog. educ. ctr, Woods Hole Oceanog. Inst, Bur. Commercial Fisheries & Marine Biol. Lab, 68- AAAS; Nat. Asn. Biol. Teachers; Am. Fisheries Soc; Am. Soc. Limnol. & Oceanog; Marine Technol. Soc; Nat. Oceanog. Asn; Am. Soc. Ichthyol. & Herpet; Am.

Soc. Oceanog; Nat. Asn. Res. Sci. Teaching; Am. Littoral Soc. Marine ichthyology; parasitology; oceanography; marine sciences; fish surveys; life history studies; history of sciences. Address: Dept. of Earth Science, Northeastern University, Boston, MA 02115.

GORDON, BURGESS LEE, b. Spokane, Wash, Apr. 10, 92; m. 42; c. 1. MEDICINE. A.B, Gonzaga, 12; M.D, Jefferson Med. Col, 19; hon. LL.D, Gonzaga, 53; hon. M.Sc, Women's Med. Col, 57. Teaching fel, Harvard Med. Sch, 22-25; instr. med, Jefferson Med. Col, 26-27, demonstr, 27-29, assoc, 29-30, asst. prof, 30-33, assoc. prof, 34-35, clin. prof, 45-51, Mullen prof. med. & pres, Woman's Med. Col, 51-57; dir. med. ed, Lovelace Found, 57-60; assoc. ed, jour, AM. MED. ASN, 60-64, DIR. OFF. CURRENT MED, 64- Dir, Barton Mem. & White Haven Div, col. hosp, Jefferson Med. Col, 46-51, vis. prof, 62-; consult, Lovelace Found, 60- Dipl. Am. Bd. Internal Med, 37. U.S.A, 17-19, Med.C, 42-46. Am. Soc. Clin. Invest; Am. Thoracic Soc; Am. Med. Asn; Asn. Am. Physicians; Am. Col. Physicians. Cardiovascular and pulmonary diseases; physiology of respiration; instruments for medical study and treatment. Address: 1550 Lake Shore Dr, Chicago, IL 60610.

GORDON, CHARLES F(RANCIS), b. Philadelphia, Pa, Dec. 8, 22; m. 46; c. 4. ANALYTICAL CHEMISTRY. B.A, La Salle Col, 48. Chemist, Kessler Chem. Co, 48-49; east. region res. bur, U.S. Dept. Agr, 49-51; sect. chief gen. chems, U.S. Army Qm. Corps Res. Labs, 51-54; sr. chemist & group leader agr. & food additive residues, ROHM AND HAAS CO, 54-68, registr. and petitions coord, 68, PROD. REGISTR. MGR, AGR. & SANIT. CHEM. DEPT, 68- U.S.A.A.F, 43-45, Lt. Am. Chem. Soc. Micro analytical chemistry; development and application of procedures for the removal and identification of pesticides and other chemical residues in biological systems. Address: Agricultural & Sanitary Chemicals Dept, Rohm and Haas Co, Independence Mall West, Philadelphia, PA 19105.

GORDON, CHARLES N, b. Buffalo, N.Y, Apr. 13, 35. ELECTRON MICROSCOPY. B.A, N.Y. Univ, 64; U.S. Pub. Health Serv. grant, 64-69, Ph.D. (biochem), 69. Res. asst. BIOCHEM, Merck & Co, N.J, 58-64; ASST. PROF, UNIV. CALIF, IRVINE, 69- Electron Micros. Soc. Am. Electron microscopy of biological macromolecules. Address: Dept. of Biochemistry, University of California, Irvine, CA 92664.

GORDON, C(HESTER) D(UNCAN), b. Ankerton, Alta, Oct. 13, 20; nat; m. 50; c. 3. ORGANIC CHEMISTRY. B.Sc, Alberta, 49; Ph.D.(org. chem), Notre Dame, 52. Res. chemist, Calif. Res. Corp. Div, Standard Oil Co. Calif, 52-60, sr. res. chemist, CHEVRON RES. CO, 60-66, SR. RES. ASSOC, 66- R.C.A.F, 41-45. Am. Chem. Soc; Can. Inst. Chem. Organic synthesis; vinyl polymerizations; nitrogen chemistry. Address: Chevron Research Co, 576 Standard Ave, Richmond, CA 94802.

GORDON, C(HESTER) H(ENRY), b. Rochester, Pa, Apr. 5, 20; m. 45; c. 2. MATHEMATICS. B.S, Bethany Col.(W.Va), 41; S.M, Mass. Inst. Tech, 46, Ph.D.(math), 50. Asst. math, Mass. Inst. Tech, 41-42, res. assoc, 42-46, instr, 46-47; asst. prof, Williams Col, 48-51; res. specialist, Boeing Airplane Co, 51-54; partner, Huff & Gordon, Consults, 54-55; assoc. dir. systs. eng. div, Planning Res. Corp, Calif, 55-66; independent consult, 66-67; V.PRES, SCI. & TECHNOL. ASSOCS, INC, 67- Oper. Res. Soc. Am. Systems analysis; management sciences. Address: Science & Technology Associates, Inc, 10884 Santa Monica Blvd, Los Angeles, CA 90025.

GORDON, CLARENCE C(ONRAD), b. Seattle, Wash, July 26, 28; m. 53; c. 3. BOTANY, MYCOLOGY. B.S, Washington (Seattle), 56; Ph.D.(plant path), Washington State, 60. Asst. prof. BOT, UNIV. MONT, 60-65, assoc. prof, 65-70, PROF, 70- U.S. Forest Serv. co-op. grant, 60-65; Nat. Sci. Found. grant, 64-66. U.S.A, Sgt. Ontogeny; morphology and cytology of parasitic fungi; phanerogams occurring in the coniferous forest of North America. Address: Dept. of Botany, University of Montana, Missoula, MT 59801.

GORDON, C(LEMENT) D(AVIS), b. Glen Gardner, N.J, Mar. 13, 09; m. 35; c. 4. POULTRY BREEDING. B.S, Rutgers, 30; M.S, Kans. State Col, 31; Ph.D.(animal breeding), Wisconsin, 38. Asst. prof, Ala. Polytech, 36-37, assoc. prof, 37-39; asst. poultry husbandman, poultry sect, bur. animal indust, U.S. Dept. Agr, Md, 39-42, assoc. poultry husbandman, field sta, Fla, 42-43, animal husbandman in charge sta, 43-48, poultry coordinator, Nat. Poultry Improve. Plan, Md, 48; poultry inspector, State Livestock Bd, Fla, 48-55; Head Dept. Poultry Husbandry, R.I, 56-57; geneticist, Nat. Poultry Improv. Plan, Agr. res. serv, U.S. Dept. Agr, 57-60; poultry expert, Food & Agr. Orgn, UN Mex. & Venezuela, 60-62; res. geneticist, Southeast Poultry Res. Lab, Agr. Res. Serv, U.S. Dept. Agr, 63-65, in charge Southwest Poultry Exp. Sta, Ariz, 65-67, Southeast Poultry Res. Lab, Ga, 67-69; RETIRED. Poultry Sci. Asn. Meat and egg quality; breeding for acclimatization to subtropical conditions; breeding chickens for resistance to respiratory disease related to broiler condemnations. Address: Rio Panuco 63, Apt. 501, Colonia Cuauhtemoc, Mexico 5, D.F.

GORDON, CLIFFORD M(ARK), b. Plymouth, N.H, Mar. 6, 28; m. 52; c. 3. NUCLEAR PHYSICS. B.S, Bates Col, 52; M.A, Wesleyan Univ, 54. PHYSICIST, Nucleonics Div, NAVAL RES. LAB, 54-66, OCEAN SCI. DIV, 66- U.S.A.A.F, 46-48. Am. Phys. Soc; Sci. Res. Soc. Am; Am. Geophys. Union. Ocean current measurement; radioactivation analysis. Address: Ocean Science Division, Naval Research Lab, Washington, DC 20390.

GORDON, COURTNEY PARKS, b. Bridgeport, Conn, Dec. 3, 39; m. 64; c. 1. ASTRONOMY. A.B, Vassar Col, 61; M.A, Univ. Mich, 63, Nat. Sci. Found. trainee, 66-67, Ph.D.(astron), 67. Res. assoc. radio astron, Nat. Radio Astron. Observ, Va, 67-69, asst. scientist, 69-70; ASST. PROF. ASTRON, HAMPSHIRE COL, 70- Am. Astron. Soc. Spectroscopy of carbon stars; galactic neutral hydrogen; pulsars. Address: School of Natural Science & Mathematics, Hampshire College, Amherst, MA 01002.

GORDON, DANIEL I(SRAEL), b. Norwich, Conn, Aug. 12, 20; m. 43; c. 3. PHYSICS, ELECTRICAL ENGINEERING. B.E, Yale, 42, M.Eng, 47; Maryland, 45-62. Elec. engr, U.S. NAVAL ORD. LAB, 42-64, RES. PHYSICIST, 64- Guest scientist, Israel Inst. Technol, 68-69; Weizmann Inst. Sci, 68-69. Awards of merit, U.S. Dept. Navy, 61, 70; superior accomplishment awards, 64, 65, 66, 67, 70. U.S.N, 44-45. Am. Phys. Soc; sr. mem. Inst. Elec. &

Electronics Eng; Am. Soc. Test. & Mat. Magnetic materials research and development; magnetic measurements and properties; effects of electrons and nuclear particles on magnetic materials; applications in special magnetic devices such as magnetometers. Address: U.S. Naval Ordnance Lab, White Oak, Silver Spring, MD 20910.

GORDON, DAVID A(LBERT), b. New Jersey, Mar. 31, 23; m. 46; c. 4. ORGANIC & POLYMER CHEMISTRY. B.S, Illinois, 48; Ph.D.(chem), Ga. Inst. Technol, 52. From chemist to group leader plastics, plastic additives & synthetic fibers, Dow Chem. Co, 52-63; tech. develop. mgr, Geigy Indust. Chem, 63-66, dir. appln. res, Geigy Res. Div, 66-68, ASSOC. RES. DIR. PLASTICS & ADDITIVES DIV, CIBA-GEIGY CORP, 68- U.S.A, 43-45. Am. Chem. Soc; Soc. Plastics Eng; Am. Soc. Test. & Mat. Polymers; monomers; plastics; plastic additives, screeners, antioxidants, antistatic agents, plasticizers, dye receptors. Address: Plastics & Additives Division, Ciba-Geigy Corp, Ardsley, NY 10502.

GORDON, DAVID B(UDDY), b. Chicago, Ill, Dec. 17, 18; m. 48; c. 3. PHYSIOLOGY. B.S, Chicago, 45; M.S, Southern California, 49, Ph.D.(physiol), 51. Instr. physiol, Southern California, 51-55, Am. Heart Asn. fel, 55-56; asst. prof, Miami (Fla), 57-72, Am. Heart Asn. adv. fel, 62-64; asst. chief, PHYSIOL. RES. LAB, VET. ADMIN. HOSP, SAN FRANCISCO, 64-66, CHIEF, 66-; LECTR. PHYSIOL, UNIV. CALIF, SAN FRANCISCO, 64- Med.C, U.S.A, 45-48. AAAS; Am. Physiol. Soc; Am. Heart Asn. Cardiovascular physiology; hypertension; endocrine function of kidneys. Address: 65 Blossom Dr, San Rafael, CA 94901.

GORDON, DERCK A(LEXANDER), b. Buffalo, N.Y, Jan. 13, 32. PHYSICAL CHEMISTRY. B.A, Buffalo, 53; Ph.D, Calif. Inst. Tech, 58. Sr. res. engr, Jet Propulsion Lab, Calif. Inst. Tech, 58-59; chemist, Stanford Res. Inst, 59-62; mem. tech. staff, TRW Systs. Inc, 62-67; V.PRES, W. KENSINGTON ENG, 70- Am. Chem. Soc; Am. Inst. Aeronaut. & Astronaut; Am. Vacuum Soc. Solid rocket propellants; electric spacecraft propulsion; vacuum technology and mass spectroscopy. Address: West Kensington Engineering, 411 Glendale Blvd, Los Angeles, CA 90026.

GORDON, DONALD, b. Indianapolis, Ind, June 5, 39; m. 62; c. 1. BOTANY, PLANT TAXONOMY. B.A, Hanover Col, 61; M.A, Indiana, 64, Ph.D.(bot), 66. Asst. prof. BIOL, New Mexico State, 66-68; MANKATO STATE COL, 58-70, ASSOC. PROF, 70- Nat. Sci. Found. res. grant, 68-70. AAAS; Bot. Soc. Am; Am. Soc. Plant Taxon; Int. Soc. Plant Taxon. A revision of the genus Gleditsia; biosystematics of Maurandya and related genera. Address: Dept. of Biology, Mankato State College, Box 69, Mankato, MN 56001.

GORDON, D(ONALD) H(ARVEY), b. La Junta, Colo, Dec. 4, 13; m. 40; c. 3. CHEMICAL & METALLURGICAL ENGINEERING. B.S, Univ. Wis, 36, M.S, 39, Ph.D.(chem. eng), 42. Instr. chem. eng, Univ. Wis, 36-42; res. engr, acetate res. sect, rayon technol. div, E.I. du Pont de Nemours & Co, 42-45, res. group leader, 45-48, res. supvr, 48-51; pres. & gen. mgr, Indust. Mach. Works, Inc, 51-56; V.PRES. & MGR. ENG, VA. METALCRAFTERS, INC, 56- AAAS; Am. Chem. Soc; Am. Soc. Metals; Am. Foundrymen's Soc; Am. Inst. Chem. Eng. Green sand casting of cast iron, brass and aluminum. Address: Virginia Metalcrafters, Inc, 1010 E. Main St, Waynesboro, VA 22980.

GORDON, DONALD THEILE, b. Cincinnati, Ohio, June 10, 35; m. 61; c. 3. PLANT PATHOLOGY, VIROLOGY. B.S, Univ. Cincinnati, 60; Alumni Res. Found. fel, Univ. Wis, 60-63, Nat. Insts. Health fel, 64-65, Ph.D.(plant path), 66. ASSOC. PROF. PLANT PATH, OHIO STATE UNIV. & OHIO AGR. RES. & DEVELOP. CENTER, WOOSTER, 66- AAAS; Am. Phytopath. Soc. Isolation, characterization and identification of plant viruses, especially those of corn, small grains, bean and soybean. Address: Dept. of Plant Pathology, Ohio Agricultural Research & Development Center, Wooster, OH 44691.

GORDON, DONOVAN, b. Beloit, Wis, Aug. 15, 34; m. 63; c. 2. VETERINARY MEDICINE & PATHOLOGY. D.V.M, Iowa State, 59; M.S. & Ph.D.(vet. path), Wisconsin, 67. Vet, Pines Meadow Vet. Clin, 61-63; pathologist, ABBOTT LABS, 68-71, HEAD PATH. SECT, INDUST. BIO-TEST LABS, 71- Vet.C, U.S.A, 59-61, 1st Lt. Am. Vet. Med. Asn; Am. Col. Vet. Path. Viral oncology; chemical carcinogens. Address: 1250 McDaniels Ave, Highland Park, IL 60035.

GORDON, DOUGLAS LITTLETON, b. Baton Rouge, La, Mar. 15, 24; m. 47; 61; c. 4. MEDICINE. La. State Univ, 41-43, M.D, Tulane Univ, 46. Intern, Charity Hosp, New Orleans, La, 46-47; fel. internal med, Ochsner Clin, 47-49; instr. MED, sch. med, Tulane Univ, 49-51, 53-57; clin. asst. prof, SCH. MED, LA. STATE UNIV, 57-62, clin. assoc. prof, 62-67, CLIN. PROF, 67- Clin. assoc, endocrinol. res. lab, mem. staff, sect. endocrinol, clin. & mem. vis. staff, hosp, Alton Oschner Med. Found, 49-51, 53-57; asst. vis. physician, Tulane Univ, Charity Hosp, 51, vis. physician, 53-57; mem. vis. staff, Baton Rouge Gen. & Our Lady of the Lake Hosps, 54-; private practice, 54-; dep. coroner, East Baton Rouge Parish, 55-71; vis. physician, La. State Univ, 57-61, sr. vis. prof, Charity Hosp, 61-; mem. staff, sect. med, Baton Rouge Clin, 59- Dipl, Am. Bd. Internal Med, 53. U.S.N, 43-46; Med.C, 51-53, Capt. AAAS; Endocrine Soc; Am. Med. Asn; Aerospace Med. Asn; Fedn. Clin. Res; fel. Am. Col. Physicians; Am. Diabetes Asn; N.Y. Acad. Sci. Internal medicine and endocrinology. Address: 134 N. 19th St, Baton Rouge, LA 70806.

GORDON, EDGAR S(TILLWELL), b. Chicago, Ill, Nov. 6, 06; m. 36; c. 3. BIOCHEMISTRY, MEDICINE. B.A, Wisconsin, 27, M.A, 29; M.D, Harvard, 32. Intern, Chicago, 33-34; res, Mass. Gen. Hosp, 34; Wis. Gen. Hosp, 35-36; fel. adrenal physiol, MED. SCH, UNIV. WIS, MADISON, 36-37, instr. biochem, 37-40, asst. prof. MED, 40-42, assoc. prof, 46-53, PROF, 53-, CHIEF STAFF, MED. CTR, 70- Lectr, Am. Med. Asn, 68 & 71; consult, U.S. Atomic Energy Comn; Oak Ridge Inst. Nuclear Studies; NASA; Nat. Insts. Health. Dipl, Am. Bd. Internal Med; Am. Bd. Nutrit. Asn. Am. Physicians; Am. Col. Physicians; Am. Diabetes Asn; Am. Soc. Clin. Nutrit; Am. Clin. & Climat. Asn; Endocrine Soc; Am. Soc. Clin. Invest; Am. Med. Asn; Am. Inst. Nutrit; N.Y. Acad. Sci. Metabolism; endocrinology; nutrition; adrenal and pituitary hormones; lipid metabolism; electrolyte metabolism. Address: Dept. of Medicine, University of Wisconsin, 1300 University Ave, Madison, WI 53706.

GORDON, EDWARD, b. Fallsburgh, N.Y, July 12, 23; m. 46; c. 2. MATHEMATICS, BUSINESS ECONOMICS. B.Ch.E, City Col. New York, 43; M.A, Southern California, 54; M.B.E, Claremont Grad. Sch. & Univ. Ctr, 65, Ph.D.(econ-bus. econ), 70. Res. chem. engr. process develop, refinery res. lab, Shell Oil Co, Tex, 43-51; sr. res. engr. liquid rockets propellants, jet propulsion lab, Calif. Inst. Tech, 51-55; computer analyst & supvr. eng. anal. sect, res. lab, United Gas Corp, 55-62; TECH. SPECIALIST, systs. anal. div, rocket engine opers-nuclear, AEROJET GEN. CORP. DIV, GEN. TIRE & RUBBER CO, 62-65, SYSTS. ENG, AEROJET ELECTROSYSTS. CO, 65- Lectr, Claremont Grad. Sch & Univ. Ctr, 70- U.S.N, 44-46, Lt.(jg). Asn. Comput. Mach. Computer use and applications; industry simulation; thermodynamic behavior of fluids; theory of the firm; mathematical economics; corporate finance; econometrics; economic theory of decision making; systems analysis; data acquisition and analysis; business economics. Address: 974 Ottawa Dr, Claremont, CA 91711.

GORDON, EDWARD E(MANUEL), b. N.Y.C, Mar. 6, 07; m. 55; c. 3. MEDICINE. A.B, Harvard, 28; M.D, Tufts, 33. Asst. prof. clin. phys. med. & rehabil, col. med, N.Y. Univ, 50-52; assoc. prof. rehabil. med, col. physicians & surgeons, Columbia, 52-55; assoc. clin. prof. PHYS. MED. & REHAB, COL. MED, UNIV. ILL, 55-64, clin. prof, 64-68, PROF, 68-; DIR. DEPT. PHYS. MED, MICHAEL REESE HOSP. & MED. CTR, 55- Dir. dept. phys. med, Roosevelt Hosp, N.Y, 50-52; med. dir, Inst. Crippled & Disabled, N.Y, 52-55. Mem. adv. bd, Nat. Found. Med.C, 43-46, Maj. Am. Thoracic Soc; Am. Med. Asn; Am. Heart Asn. Rehabilitation; muscle metabolism; work metabolism and tolerance; electromyography. Address: Dept. of Physical Medicine & Rehabilitation, University of Illinois College of Medicine, Chicago, IL 60680.

GORDON, EDWIN E(ARL), b. Chicago, Ill, Jan. 9, 27; m. 56; c. 2. MEDICINE. M.S. & M.D, Northwest. Univ, 52. Fel. biochem, Harvard, 53-55, instr. MED, 56-57; fel, U.S. Pub. Health Serv, post grad. med. sch, Univ. London, 57-58; assoc, Albert Einstein Col. Med, 58-61, asst. prof. med, 61-67; ASSOC. PROF, SCH. MED, N.Y. UNIV, 67-, DIR. DIABETES & METAB. DIV, 71- Career scientist award, Health Res. Coun. City of N.Y, 61-77. U.S.N, 45-46. Am. Soc. Clin. Invest; Am. Physiol. Soc; Fedn. Clin. Res; Harvey Soc; Brit. Med. Res. Soc. Clinical investigations; effect of hormones on intermediary metabolism. Address: New York University School of Medicine, 550 First Ave, New York, NY 10016.

GORDON, ELLIS D(AVIS), b. Johnson Co, Kans, Aug. 6, 13; m. 37; c. 3. GEOLOGY. A.B, Kansas, 43; M.Sc, Nebraska, 49. Chief party, test drill unit, Kans. Geol. Surv, 39-42; geologist, Kans. State Hwy. Cmn, 42-44; geologist & ground water hydrologist, Nebr. Geol. Surv, 44-49; geologist, ground water br, U.S. GEOL. SURV, N.Dak, 49-51, mineral deposits br, Colo, 51-52, ground water br, Wash, D.C, 52-54, N.Mex, 54-58, dist. geologist, WATER RESOURCES DIV, Wyo, 58-67, STAFF HYDROLOGIST, REGIONAL HQ. STAFF, COLO, 67- Am. Asn. Petrol. Geol; Am. Geophys. Union; Am Inst. Prof. Geol; Geol. Soc. Am. Ground water hydrology; subsurface research in ground water; stratigraphy; mineral deposits. Address: Bldg. 25, Water Resources Division, U.S. Geological Survey, Denver Federal Center, Lakewood, CO 80225.

GORDON, EMANUEL, b. Malden, Mass, Mar. 24, 19; m. 48; c. 2. METALLURGY. B.S, Northeastern, 41; Carnegie Inst. Tech, 42-43. Metallurgist, Carnegie-Ill. Steel Corp, 41-44; head reduction metall, Manhattan Proj, Mass. Inst. Tech, 44-49; chief metallurgist, Reeves Instrument Corp, 49-51; engr, Singmaster & Breyer, 51-52; chief metall. engr, Metal Hydrides, Inc, 52-55; supvry. metallurgist, Combustion Eng, 55-56; tech. mgr, nuclear fuel div, Olin Mathieson Chem. Corp, Conn, 56-62; mgr, New Haven Res. Labs, United Nuclear Corp, 62-66; EXEC. ASST. W.R. GRACE & CO, 66- Mem. Oper. Crossroads, atomic bomb tests, Bikini, 47. Manhattan Dist. Spec. Award, 45. Am. Soc. Metals; Am. Inst. Mining, Metall. & Petrol. Eng; Am. Nuclear Soc. Metallurgy and ceramics; nuclear materials; fuel alloys and elements; control materials; moderators; refractory metals. Address: 90 Brooklawn Circle, New Haven, CT 06515.

GORDON, E(UGENE) I(RVING), b. New York, N.Y, Sept. 14, 30; m. 56; c. 2. PHYSICS. B.S, City Col. New York, 52; Gen. Dynamics Corp. fel, Mass. Inst. Tech, 55, Radio Corp. Am. fel, 56, Ph.D.(physics), 57. Mem. staff, Mass. Inst. Tech, 57; tech. staff, BELL TEL. LABS, INC, 57-64, head optical device dept, 64-68, DIR. ELECTROOPTICAL DEVICE LAB, 68- Am. Phys. Soc; fel. Inst. Elec. & Electronics Eng. Properties of ionized media; microwave tubes; optical masers; coherent light techniques; image and display devices. Address: Electrooptical Device Lab, Room 2A-330, Bell Telephone Labs, Inc, 600 Mountain Ave, Murray Hill, NJ 07974.

GORDON, F(RANCIS) B(YRON), b. Fairbury, Ill, Mar. 15, 05; m. 30; c. 4. MICROBIOLOGY. B.S, Ill. Wesleyan, 27; Ph.D, Chicago, 36, M.D, 37. Instr. bact, Chicago, 36-39, asst. prof, 39-43, assoc. prof, 43-47, prof, 47-48; div. chief, Army Biol. Labs, Ft. Detrick, 48-54; head div. virol, NAVAL MED. RES. INST, 54-62, DIR. DEPT. MICROBIOL, 62- Rockefeller Found. fel, Nat. Inst. Med. Res, London, 38-39; lectr, Maryland, 51-53, vis. prof, 58-60; spec. lectr, George Washington, 51- Consult, Secy. War, 42-45. Managing ed, J. Infectious Diseases, 41-48, adv. ed, 48- Mem. microbiol. panel, Off. Naval Res, 51-54, 65- AAAS; Am. Soc. Microbiol; Soc. Exp. Biol. & Med; Am. Asn. Immunol. Poliomyelitis; arboviruses; psittacosis; trachoma. Address: Dept. of Microbiology, Naval Medical Research Institute, Bethesda, MD 20014.

GORDON, GARY D(ONALD), b. Elkins, W.Va, May 28, 28; m. 56; c. 5. PHYSICS. B.A, Wesleyan, 50; M.A, Harvard, 51, Ph.D.(physics), 54. Instr. physics, Harvard, 54; res. physicist, biol. warfare labs, U.S. Army, 55-56; mem. staff, Opers. Res, Inc, 57-58; sr. engr. astro-electronics div, RCA Corp, N.J, 59-64, adminstr. course develop, current concepts sci. & eng. prog, prod. eng, 65-68; MEM. TECH. STAFF, COMSAT LABS, CLARKSBURG, 69- Am. Phys. Soc; Am. Asn. Physics Teachers; Am. Inst. Aeronaut. & Astronaut. Piezoelectricity; cosmic rays; aerosols; operations research; space and plasma physics; spacecraft thermal design; Fortran programming. Address: 400 Center St, Washington Grove, MD 20880.

GORDON, GEORGE S(ELBIE), b. Pittsfield, Mass, Apr. 28, 19; m. 46; c. 2. PHYSICAL & INORGANIC CHEMISTRY. A.B, Princeton, 41; Ph.D.(chem),

Northwestern, 49. Chemist, Tenn. Eastman Corp, 41-42; develop. engr, Gen. Elec. Co, 48-51; v.pres. & dir. res. & develop, Titanium Zirconium Co, Inc, 51-55; dir. res, U.S. Potash Co, 55-56; assoc. dir. chem. res, U.S. Borax Res. Corp, 56-58; dir. chem. res. & v.pres, Armour Res. Found, Ill. Inst. Tech, 59-64; CHIEF, textile & apparel tech. ctr, NAT. BUR. STANDARDS, 64-66, off. eng. standards & anal, 66-67, OFF. INDUST. SERV, 67- AAAS; Am. Chem. Soc. Catalysis; mechanism of catalytic alkylation reactions; semiconductors; chemistry of zirconium compounds. Address: 4845 Broad Brook Dr, Bethesda, MD 20014.

GORDON, GERALD A(RTHUR), b. Chicago, Ill, Mar. 5, 34; m. 67; c. 2. POLYMER CHEMISTRY, PHYSICS. B.S, Purdue, 56; M.S, Mass. Inst. Tech, 57, fels, Procter & Gamble Co, 57, Humble Oil & Refining Co, 57-58, Kimberly-Clark Corp, 58-59, Sc.D.(chem. eng), 61. Res. chemist, Munising Div, Kimberly-Clark Corp, 61-63; sr. res. chemist, CONTINENTAL CAN CO, 63-70, SR. RES. SCIENTIST, 70- Lectr, dept. chem, Roosevelt Univ; adj. prof, dept. mat. eng, Univ. Ill, Chicago Circle. AAAS; Am. Chem. Soc. Permeability of polymers; structure of highly cross-linked polymers; polymer morphology. Address: Materials Research Dept, Research & Development Division, Continental Can Co, 7622 S. Racine, Chicago, IL 60620.

GORDON, GERALD BERNARD, b. Harrisburg, Pa, June 4, 34; m. 56; c. 4. PATHOLOGY. B.S, Franklin & Marshall Col, 56; M.D, Yale, 59. Rotating intern, Univ. Hosps, Cleveland, Ohio, 59-60; resident, PATH, Yale-New Haven Med. Ctr, 60-63; res. fel, sch. med, Yale, 63-64, instr, 64; asst. pathologist, Armed Forces Inst. Pathol, Wash, D.C, 64-66; asst. prof, Rutgers Med. Sch, 66-68, ASSOC. PROF, 68-70; STATE UNIV. N.Y. UPSTATE MED. CTR, 70- Nat. Sci. Found. summer fel, med. sch, Yale, 57-58; U.S. Pub. Health Serv. trainee. & fel, 61-64; consult, Vet. Admin. Hosp, Lyons, N.J. & Muhlenberg Hosp, Plainfield, 66-70; U.S. Pub. Health Serv. grant, 67-; assoc. attending pathologist, State Univ. Hosp, Syracuse, N.Y, 70-; attending pathologist, Vet. Admin. Hosp, 71- Mosby Award, Yale Sch. Med, 59. U.S.A, 64-66, Capt. Int. Acad. Path; Am. Asn. Path. & Bact; Am. Soc. Exp. Path. Experimental cellular pathology utilizing electron microscopy, tissue culture, histochemistry and biochemistry; studies in phagocytosis, intracellular digestion, lipid metabolism and accumulation; muscular diseases. Address: Dept. of Pathology, State University of New York Upstate Medical Center, 766 Irving Ave, Syracuse, NY 13210.

GORDON, GERALD M, b. Detroit, Mich, May 24, 31; m. 53; c. 2. METALLURGY. B.S, Wayne State, 56; Inco fel. & Ph.D.(metall), Ohio State, 59. Sr. metallurgist, Stanford Res. Inst, 59-63; VALLECITOS NUCLEAR CTR, GEN. ELEC. CO, 63-69, MGR, METALL. DEVELOP, 69- Intel.C, U.S.A, 51-54. Am. Inst. Min, Metall. & Petrol. Eng; Am. Soc. Metals. Physical metallurgy of nuclear reactor materials; stress corrosion and electrochemistry of stainless steels and zirconium alloys; oxidation mechanism in high temperature alloys; thermal shock behavior of brittle materials. Address: General Electric Co, Vallecitos Nuclear Center, P.O. Box 846, Pleasanton, CA 94566.

GORDON, GILBERT, b. Ill, Nov. 11, 33; m. 57; c. 2. INORGANIC CHEMISTRY. B.S, Bradley, 55; Dupont fel, Mich. State, 58-59, Ph.D.(inorg. chem), 59. Asst, Mich. State, 55-58; res. assoc, Chicago, 59-60; asst. prof. CHEM, Univ. Md, 60-64, assoc. prof, 64-67, PROF, 67; UNIV. IOWA, 67- Summer fel, Nat. Sci. Found, 59; consult, Nat. Bur. Standards, 60-; Japan Soc. Promotion Sci. vis. prof, fall 69. Am. Chem. Soc. Magnetic and optical properties of inorganic compounds; electron transfer processes; coordination chemistry; equilibria in aqueous solutions; mechanisms of inorganic reactions. Address: Dept. of Chemistry, University of Iowa, Iowa City, IA 52240.

GORDON, HAROLD THOMAS, b. Holyoke, Mass, Nov. 21, 18; m. 55; c. 3. BIOCHEMISTRY. B.S, Mass. State Col, 39; M.A, Harvard, 40, fel, 40-42, 46-47, Ph.D.(biol), 47. Asst, Off. Sci. Res. & Develop. proj, Harvard Med. Sch, 42-45, res. assoc. insecticides, univ, 45-46; asst. insect toxicologist, UNIV. CALIF, BERKELEY, 47-50, assoc. insect toxicologist, 50-58, insect toxicologist, 58-63, INSECT BIOCHEMIST, 63- Am. Chem. Soc; Entom. Soc. Am; N.Y. Acad. Sci; Brit. Biochem. Soc. Insect growth, nutrition, reproduction and toxicology; ultramicroanalysis. Address: Dept. of Entomology, University of California, Berkeley, CA 94720.

GORDON, HARRY H(ASKIN), b. Brooklyn, N.Y, Aug. 4, 06; m. 35, 48; c. 2. PEDIATRICS. A.B, Cornell, 26, M.D, 29; hon. D.Sc, Yeshiva Univ, 71. Intern & assoc. res. path, Montefiore Hosp, New York, 29-30; intern & asst. pediat, Yale, 30-32; from asst. to asst. prof, med. col, Cornell, 32-46; prof. & head dept, sch. med, Colorado, 46-52; assoc. prof, sch. med, Hopkins, 52-62; PROF. PEDIAT, ALBERT EINSTEIN COL. MED, 62-, DIR. RES. MENT. RETARDATION & HUMAN DEVELOP, ROSE FITZGERALD KENNEDY CTR, 62-; assoc. dean, Col, 66-67, dean, 67-70. Specialist & sr. specialist, maternal & child health res, U.S. Children's Bur, med. col, Cornell, 37-42. Attend. pediatrician, N.Y. Hosp, 32-46; pediatrician-in-chief, Colo. Gen. Hosp, 46-51; Sinai Hosp, Baltimore, Md, 52-62; vis. pediatrician, Bronx Munic. Hosp. Ctr, 62- Consult, U.S. Pub. Health Serv, 48-53, 55-58, 59-; surgeon gen, U.S. Dept. Army, 47-62. Mem. food & nutrit. bd, Nat. Res. Coun, 55-59, adv. coun, 70- Borden award, Am. Acad. Pediat, 44; Grover F. Powers Award, Nat. Asn. Retarded Children, 63. Med.C, 42-46, Lt. Col. AAAS; fel. Am. Pediat. Soc.(pres, 66-67); fel. Soc. Pediat. Res.(v.pres, 50, pres, 51); fel. Am. Soc. Clin. Invest; fel. Soc. Exp. Biol. & Med. Metabolism of premature infants; therapy of malaria; tocopherol nutrition; human developmental biology; mental retardation. Address: Dept. of Pediatrics, Albert Einstein College of Medicine, 1300 Morris Park Ave, Bronx, NY 10461.

GORDON, H(ARRY) W(ILLIAM), b. New York, N.Y, Mar. 31, 24; m. 50; c. 1. BIOCHEMISTRY, ENZYMOLOGY. B.S, Long Island, 48; fel, Georgetown, 50-52, M.S, 51, Ph.D.(biochem), 52. Biochemist & instr, N.Y. Univ-Bellevue Med. Ctr, 52-55; enzymologist & res. assoc. biochem, Colgate-Palmolive Co, 55-57; asst. dir. res. & develop, Block Drug Co, 57-59; dir. exp. res. lab, St. Barnabas Med. Ctr, 59-62, consult. dir. exp. res, 62; dir. RES. & PROD. DEVELOP, JULIUS SCHMID, INC, 62-68, V.PRES, 68- U.S.A, 43-46. Fel. AAAS; Am. Chem. Soc; Electron. Micros. Soc. Am; N.Y. Acad. Sci. Physiology; pharmacology; toxicology. Address: Julius Schmid, Inc, 423 W. 55th St, New York, NY 10019.

GORDON, HAYDEN S(AMUEL), b. Whitebird, Idaho, June 18, 10; div. MECHANICAL ENGINEERING. B.S, California, 37, state scholar & M.S, 38, Ph.D, 50. Res. engr, Shell Oil Co, Calif, 37; asst. mech. eng, California, 37-38; asst. prof. physics, San Bernardino Jr. Col, 38-39; instr. & jr. engr, California, 39-42; sr. engr. & asst. chief develop, Ryan Aeronaut. Co, Calif, 42-45; sr. engr, Lawrence Radiation Lab, California, 45-55, nuclear propulsion div. leader, 55-57, chief engr, 57-64; MEM. STAFF, W.M. BROBECK & ASSOC, 65- Consult, 65-; dir, Eng. Develop. Corp, Calif; dir. & chmn, Berkeley Sci. Capital Corp. Civilian with Atomic Energy Comn, 44. AAAS; Am. Soc. Mech. Eng. Evaporation of water from quiet surfaces; heat transfer by free convection from small diameter wires. Address: 17 Culver Ct, Orinda, CA 94563.

GORDON, HELMUT A(LBERT), b. Malinska, Austria, May 5, 08; nat; m. 42; c. 2. PHYSIOLOGY, PHARMACOLOGY. M.D, Pázmány Peter Univ, Budapest, 32, Dr. Habil, 44; Italian State scholar, Rome, 29. Asst. prof. physiol, col. med, Univ. Budapest, 32-37, adjunctus, 38-44, privatdocent, 44; res. assoc. biol, N.Y. Univ, 37-38; asst. res. prof, Lobound Labs, Univ. Notre Dame, 46-52, assoc. res. prof, 52-62; PROF. PHARMACOL, COL. MED, UNIV. KY, 62- Eszterhazy fel, 37; Rockefeller fel, N.Y. Univ, 38. Am. Physiol. Soc; Geront. Soc; fel. N.Y. Acad. Sci.(A. Cressy Morrison award, 66). Effects of microbial flora on cardiovascular, digestive and defensive systems; aging phenomena; germ-free life studies. Address: Dept. of Pharmacology, College of Medicine, University of Kentucky, Lexington, KY 40506.

GORDON, HOWARD R, b. Plattsburg, N.Y, May 21, 40; m. 64. OPTICS, SPECTROSCOPY. B.S, Clarkson Tech, 61; M.S, Pa. State, 63, Ph.D.(physics), 65. Asst. prof. physics, Col. William & Mary, 65-67; PHYSICS & MARINE SCI, UNIV. MIAMI, 67-70, ASSOC. PROF, 70- Optical Soc. Am. Oceanography; infrared spectroscopy and lasers; molecular force constants; light scattering; underwater optics; radiation transfer. Address: Dept. of Physics, University of Miami, Coral Gables, FL 33124.

GORDON, HUGH, b. New York, N.Y, Nov. 23, 30. MATHEMATICS. A.B, Columbia, 51, Higgins fel, 51-52, A.M, 52, Ph.D.(math), 58. Asst. MATH, Columbia, 52-53, lectr, 53-58; Peirce instr, Harvard, 58-61; asst. prof, Univ. Pa, 61-66; assoc. prof, STATE UNIV. N.Y. ALBANY, 66-69, PROF, 69- Am. Math. Soc. Abstract analysis. Address: Dept. of Mathematics, State University of New York at Albany, 1400 Washington Ave, Albany, NY 12203.

GORDON, HYMIE, b. Cape Town, S.Africa, Sept. 20, 26. MEDICAL GENETICS, INTERNAL MEDICINE. B.Sc, Cape Town, 46, M.B, Ch.B, 50, S.African Coun. Sci. & Indust. Res. bursar, 56-58, M.D, 58. Intern med, Groote Schuur Hosp, Cape Town, 51-52, registr, 55-58; Addington Hosp, Durban, 52-55; Frank Forman res. fel, Postgrad. Med. Sch, London, 58-59; asst. physician, Johns Hopkins Hosp, Baltimore, Md, 59-61; sr. lectr. & consult. med, Cape Town, 61-69; CONSULT. GENETICS & MED, MAYO CLIN, 69- Eli Lilly fel, 59-60; vis. prof, Mayo Found, 67. Fel, Royal Col. Physicians, Edinburgh, 66. AAAS; Am. Soc. Human Genetics; Brit. Genetical Soc; fel. Brit. Interplanetary Soc; fel. Royal Soc. Med; Brit. Soc. Study Human Biol. Clinical cardiology; nutrition and heart disease; clinical biochemical and population genetics; genetics counseling. Address: Section of Medical Genetics, Mayo Clinic, 200 First St. S.W, Rochester, MN 55901.

GORDON, IRVING, b. Cleveland, Ohio, June 20, 14; m. 39; c. 3. MICROBIOLOGY. M.D, Michigan, 37. Intern & res, L.I. Col. Med, 37-39; jr. med. bacteriologist, N.Y. State Dept. Health, 39-40; fel, Rockefeller Found, 41; from instr. to assoc. path. & bact, Albany Med. Col, 42-43, 46-48, assoc. prof. med. & bact, 48-55; PROF. MICROBIOL. & CHMN. DEPT, SCH. MED, UNIV. SOUTH. CALIF, 55-; SR. ATTEND. PHYSICIAN, LOS ANGELES COUNTY GEN. HOSP, 56-, assoc. dean, univ, 63-66. Volunteer asst, Trudeau Sanatorium, N.Y, 42; from sr. med. bacteriologist to prin. med. bacteriologist, div. labs. & res, State Dept. Health, N.Y, 46-53, asst. dir, 53-55; sr. lectr, Univ. Sheffield, England, 54; Holme lectr, med. sch, London, 54. Consult, U.S. Pub. Health Serv, 51-55, 56-57, 66- Chem. Corps, U.S. Army, 56-, virus lab, Calif. State Dept. Pub. Health, 56-64. Bacteriologist & immunologist, comn. acute respiratory diseases, Epidemiol. Bd, U.S. Army, 43-46; assoc. mem. comn. enteric infections, Armed Forces Epidemiol. Bd, 53-59, comn. viral infections, Armed Forces Epidemiol. Bd, 53-; mem. bact. test comt, Nat. Bd. Med. Exam, 56-59; allergy & infectious disease training grant comt, Nat. Insts. Health, 62-66; comt. etiology of cancer, Am. Cancer Soc, 60-63, comt. personnel in res, 64-; spec. adv. comt, prophylaxis of poliomyelitis, Calif. State Dept. Pub. Health, 60-63. Dipl, Am. Bd. Path, Am. Bd. Microbiol; Nat. Bd. Med. Exam. AAAS; Am. Soc. Clin. Invest; Am. Soc. Microbiol; Soc. Exp. Biol. & Med; Harvey Soc; Am. Asn. Immunol; Am. Fedn. Clin. Res; fel. Col. Am. Path; Am. Acad. Microbiol. Virology; immunology; host-parasite relationships. Address: Dept. of Microbiology, University of Southern California School of Medicine, 2025 Zonal Ave, Los Angeles, CA 90033.

GORDON, IRVING, b. St. Paul, Minn, Jan. 29, 22; m. 52; c. 2. ORGANIC CHEMISTRY. B.Chem, Univ. Minn, 43, Ph.D.(org. chem), 50. Fel. amino acids & peptides, Univ. Pittsburgh, 50-51; res. chemist, org. & inorg. phosphorus chem, Oldbury Electro-Chem. Co, 51-56; Hooker Electro-Chem. Co, 56-64, sr. chemist, HOOKER CHEM. CORP. DIV, OCCIDENTAL PETROL. CORP, 64-69, SUPVR. TECH. INFO. CTR, HOOKER RES. CTR, 69- U.S.N.R, 43-46. Electrochemistry; polymer chemistry; chemical patents; statistics; information science; computer science and programming; chemical information center design. Address: 1334 Garrett Ave, Niagara Falls, NY 14305.

GORDON, I(RWIN), b. N.Y.C, Nov. 27, 24; m. 48; c. 2. CERAMICS. B.S, Rutgers, 48, M.S, 51, Ph.D.(ceramics), 52. Asst, Rutgers Univ, 48-52; MEM. TECH. STAFF, RCA LABS, 52- C.Eng, U.S.A, 43-46. Am. Ceramic Soc. Single crystals; ferrites. Address: 658 Rosedale Rd, Princeton, NJ 08540.

GORDON, JACQUELINE IRENE, b. Hanford, Calif, Dec. 26, 26; m. 51; c. 3. ATMOSPHERIC OPTICS. B.A, California, Los Angeles, 49. Asst. engr. & head visibility br, VISIBILITY LAB, SCRIPPS INST. OCEANOG, 56-65, assoc. develop. engr. & head geophys. br, 65-66, CONSULT, 66- Optical

Soc. Am. Visual detection predictions; luminous directional reflectance of man made objects, natural terrains, and sea surface; beam transmittance, path radiance and contrast transmittance of the atmosphere. Address: 2941 Ashwood Dr, Corvallis, OR 97330.

GORDON, J(AMES) P(OWER), b. N.Y.C, Mar. 20, 28. PHYSICS. B.S, Mass. Inst. Technol, 49; M.A, Columbia, 51, Ph.D.(physics), 55. Asst. physics, Columbia, 53-55; mem. tech. staff electronics res, BELL TEL. LABS, INC, 55-59, HEAD QUANTUM ELECTRONICS RES. DEPT, 59- Fel. Am. Phys. Soc; sr. mem. Inst. Elec. & Electronics Eng. Quantum electronics; interaction of electromagnetic waves with matter; communication theory. Address: Bell Telephone Labs, Inc, Holmdel, NJ 07733.

GORDON, JOAN, b. Pine Island, Minn, Feb. 8, 23. FOODS, NUTRITION. B.S, Minnesota, 45, M.S, 47, Ph.D.(home econ), 53. Asst. home econ, Minnesota, 45-47, instr, 47-53; asst. prof, Iowa State Col, 53-54; Minnesota, 54-55, assoc. prof, 55-60; PROF. foods & nutrit. Pa. State Univ, 60-67; FOODS, UNIV. MINN, ST. PAUL, 67- AAAS; Am. Home Econ. Asn; Am. Dietetic Asn; Inst. Food Technol; Am. Chem. Soc; Am. Inst. Nutrit; Am. Pub. Health Asn. Vitamins; food quality. Address: College of Home Economics, 253 McNeal Hall, University of Minnesota, St. Paul, MN 55101.

GORDON, JOEL E(THAN), b. Denver, Colo, May 9, 30; m. 56; c. 2. PHYSICS. A.B, Harvard, 52; Rotary Int. fel, Cambridge, 52-53; Ph.D. (physics), Univ. Calif. Berkeley, 58. Asst. prof, PHYSICS, AMHERST COL, 57-63, assoc. prof, 63-68, PROF, 68- Attached staff, atomic energy res. estab, Harwell, Eng, 64-65; spec. staff mem, Rockefeller Found, 68-69; vis. prof, Univ. Valle, Colombia, 68-69. Am. Phys. Soc; Am. Asn. Physics Teachers. Low temperature and solid state physics. Address: Dept. of Physics, Amherst College, Amherst, MA 01002.

GORDON, JOHN C, b. Nampa, Idaho, June 10, 39; m. 64; c. 1. PLANT PHYSIOLOGY, SILVICULTURE. B.S, Iowa State, 61, Ph.D.(plant physiol, silviculture), 66; Fulbright fel, Helsinki, 61-62. Instr. forestry, Iowa State, 65-66; res. plant physiologist, pioneering res. proj, n.cent. forest exp. sta, U.S. Forest Serv, 66-70; ASSOC. PROF. FORESTRY, IOWA STATE UNIV, 70- Am. Soc. Plant Physiol; Soc. Am. Foresters. Photosynthesis and translocation in trees; carbohydrate metabolism; cell wall formation. Address: 220 Northbrook Circle, Ames, IA 50010.

GORDON, JOHN E(DWARD), b. Columbus, Ohio, Aug. 5, 31; m. 56; c. 2. ORGANIC & PHYSICAL CHEMISTRY. B.Sc, Ohio State, 53; Nat. Sci. Found. fel, California, 53-56, Ph.D.(chem), 56. Instr. chem, Brown, 56-58; fel, Mellon Inst, 58-65; from asst. to assoc. scientist, Woods Hole Oceanog. Inst, 65-68; assoc. prof. CHEM, KENT STATE UNIV, 68-70, PROF, 70- Am. Chem. Soc; The Chem. Soc. Organic electrolytes. Address: Dept. of Chemistry, Kent State University, Kent, OH 44242.

GORDON, JOHN E(VERETT), b. Austin, Minn, June 18, 90; m. 21; c. 2. EPIDEMIOLOGY. S.B, Chicago, 16, Ph.D.(bact), 21, M.D, Rush Med. Col, 26; hon. A.M, Harvard, 43. Instr. bact, Chicago, 19-21; assoc. prof, Western Ontario, 21-25; asst. supt, Munic. Contagious Disease Hosp, Chicago, 25-27; med. dir, Herman Kiefer Hosp, Detroit, 27-33; field dir. int. health div, Rockefeller Found, N.Y, 33-38; prof. PREV. MED. & EPIDEMIOL, SCH. PUB. HEALTH, HARVARD, 38-58, EMER. PROF, 58-; SR. LECTR. EPIDEMIOL, MASS. INST. TECHNOL, 64- Epidemiologist, City Health Dept, Detroit, 27-33; clin. lectr, Michigan, 31; dir, Am. Red Cross-Harvard Field Hosp, Eng, 40-42. Consult. to Surgeon Gen, U.S. Army; U.S. Pub. Health Serv; U.S. Dept. Navy; WHO; Pan-Am. Health Orgn. Mem, Order Pub. Health, France; Order Brit. Empire; Liberty Cross, Norway. U.S.A, 17-19, 42-46, Col; Distinguished Serv. Medal; Legion of Merit; Bronze Star; Army Commendation Medal; Croix de Guerre with Palm Leaves. Ecol. Soc. Am; Am. Soc. Trop. Med. & Hyg; Am. Epidemiol. Soc; Am. Pub. Health Asn; fel. Am. Med. Asn; Asn. Mil. Surg. U.S; Am. Col. Physicians; hon. fel. Royal Sanit. Inst; fel. Royal Col. Physicians; fel. Royal Soc. Med; hon. mem. Peru Public Health Soc; hon. mem. South African Nutrit. Soc; hon. mem. Romanian Soc. Biol. Synergism of nutrition and infection; acute diarrheal disease; epidemiology of nutritional deficiency diseases. Address: Dept. of Nutrition & Food Science, Massachusetts Institute of Technology, Cambridge, MA 02139.

GORDON, JOHN P(ETERSEN), b. Port Washington, N.Y, Aug. 29, 28; m. 56; c. 4. ELECTRICAL ENGINEERING. B.S, Va. Polytech, 53, M.S, 59; Illinois. Test engr, Appalachian Elec. Power Co, 53-55; assoc. prof. ELEC. ENG, Va. Polytech, 55-65; instr, UNIV. ILL, URBANA, 65-69, ASST. PROF, 69- U.S.N, 46-48. Am. Soc. Eng. Educ; Inst. Elec. & Electronics Eng. Analysis and synthesis of circuits; electromagnetic fields. Address: Dept. of Electrical Engineering, University of Illinois at Urbana-Champaign, Urbana, IL 61801.

GORDON, JOHN S(TEVENS), b. Mt. Kisco, N.Y, Sept. 7, 31. CHEMICAL ENGINEERING. B.Ch.E, Cornell, 53; M.S, Ohio State, 56. Process develop. technologist, Socony-Mobil Labs, 53-54; proj. engr, liquid rocket fuels, Wright-Patterson Air Force Base, 54-57; unit supvr, propellant liaison & thermochem, reaction motors div, Thiokol Chem. Corp, N.J, 57-62; mgr, phys. chem. tech, Astrosyst. Int, Inc, 62-67; CHEM. ENGR, ATLANTIC RES. CORP, 67- Summer, process develop. technologist, Socony-Mobil Labs, 52. U.S.A, 54-56, 1st Lt. Am. Chem. Soc; Am. Inst. Aeronaut. & Astronaut; Am. Inst. Chem. Eng; Combustion Inst. Thermochemical calculations and propellant properties; high temperature thermodynamic, radiative and electromagnetic properties of gases. Address: Atlantic Research Corp, Shirley Highway, Alexandria, VA 22314.

GORDON, JOSEPH GROVER, II, b. Nashville, Tenn, Dec. 25, 45. INORGANIC CHEMISTRY, DYNAMICS. A.B, Harvard, 66; Nat. Sci. Found. fel, Mass. Inst. Technol, 67-70, Ph.D.(chem), 70. ASST. PROF. CHEM, CALIF. INST. TECHNOL, 70- AAAS; Am. Chem. Soc; The Chem. Soc. Chemical dynamics; mechanisms of electron transfer reactions; photoelectrochemistry. Address: Gates Lab, 131-30, California Institute of Technology, Pasadena, CA 91109.

GORDON, JOSEPH R, b. Boston, Mass, May 17, 24; m. 47; c. 3. ORGANIC & POLYMER CHEMISTRY. B.A, Amherst Col, 44; Standard Oil Calif. fel, Illinois, 47-48, Ph.D.(chem), 49. Res. chemist, Johnson & Johnson, N.J, 49-51; Kolker Chem, 51-52; Gen. Chem. Div, Allied Chem. Corp, 52-59, res. supvr, 59-63, mgr. polymer res, 63-64; dir. develop. res, LUBRIZOL CORP, 64-70, ADMIN. ASST, RES. & DEVELOP, 70- Sig.C, U.S.A, 44-46. Am. Chem. Soc. Address: Lubrizol Corp, Box 3057, Euclid Station, Cleveland, OH 44117.

GORDON, JULIAN, b. Chingford, Essex, Eng, Feb. 10, 36; m. 61; c. 1. MOLECULAR BIOLOGY, BIOCHEMISTRY. B.Sc, London, 57, Med. Res. Coun. Brit. scholar, 57-61, NATO fel, 61-63, Ph.D.(biophys), 63. Res. asst, Biochem. Inst, Uppsala, 63-65; res. assoc, Rockefeller Univ, 65-68, asst. prof. molecular biol, 68-72; SR. INVESTR, FRIEDRICH MIESCHER INST, BASEL, SWITZ, 72- Mechanism of function and biosynthesis of the protein synthetic machinery in the cell, including mechanism of action of the polypeptide chain elongation factors and studies of their biosynthesis. Address: Friedrich Miescher Institute, CH 4002, Basel, Switz.

GORDON, KENNETH LLEWELLYN, b. Taylorville, Ill, June 7, 99. ZOOLOGY. A.B, Colo. Col, 24; A.M, Missouri, 25; Ph.D, Cornell, 36. From asst. prof. to prof. ZOOL, ORE. STATE UNIV, 27-67, EMER. PROF, 67- Am. Soc. Mammal; Wilderness Soc. Ornithology; conservation of wildlife; ecology; zoogeography. Address: Dept. of Zoology, Oregon State University, Corvallis, OR 97331.

GORDON, KENNETH M(ILTON), b. Beardstown, Ill, Nov. 30, 11; m. 43; c. 3. ORGANIC CHEMISTRY. A.B, Illinois, 38; Pabst fel, Northwestern, 38-42, Ph.D.(chem), 42. Res. chemist, Corn Prods. Ref. Co, 42-44; Corn Prod. Ref. Co. fel, Mellon Inst, 44-46; assoc. prof. chem, Col. of William & Mary, 46-53; fel, Firestone Tire & Rubber Co, Chicago, 54-55; PROF. CHEM, BIRMINGHAM-SOUTH. COL, 55-, CHMN. DEPT, 62- Am. Chem. Soc. Specificity of enzyme reactions; organic qualitative analysis. Address: Dept. of Chemistry, Birmingham-Southern College, Birmingham, AL 35204.

GORDON, KURTISS J(AY), b. N.Y.C, July 20, 40; m. 64; c. 1. ASTRONOMY. B.S, Antioch Col, 64; M.A, Univ. Mich, 66, Ph.D.(astron), 69. Jr. res. assoc, Nat. Radio Astron. Observ, Va, 67-69, res. assoc, 69-70; ASST. PROF. ASTRON, HAMPSHIRE COL, 70- Am. Astron. Soc; Royal Astron. Soc. Kinematics of spiral galaxies; properties of galactic neutral hydrogen; pulsars. Address: Five-College Astronomy Dept, Hampshire College, Amherst, MA 01002.

GORDON, L(EON) B(ARRAS), b. Cleveland, Ohio, Jan. 17, 17; m. 49; c. 2. ORGANIC CHEMISTRY. B.A, Texas, 41, M.A, 46, Ph.D.(chem), 49. Chemist, Lucidol Corp, 41-43; instr. chem, Texas, 44-48; res. chemist, Pan Am. Ref. Corp, 48-55; sr. chemist, Pan Am. Petrol. Corp, 55-60; SR. PROJ. CHEMIST, AM. OIL CO, 60- Am. Chem. Soc. Utilization drip oils; hydrocarbon resins and polymers; elastomers; oxidation hydrocarbons; ozonolysis; reactions allylic chlorides; pesticides. Address: Research Dept, American Oil Co, Box 431, Whiting, IN 46394.

GORDON, LEON L(EWIS), b. Forest City, N.C, Nov. 17, 26; m. 53; c. 2. STATISTICAL DESIGN, BIOMETRY. B.S, North Carolina, 48; M.S, Rutgers, 57. Anal. chemist, Wallace & Tiernan, Inc, N.J, 50-51; control chemist, Ethicon, Inc, 51-54, res. chemist 54-56, res. statistician, 56-63, mgr. statist, 63-69; DIR. STATIST, WALLACE PHARMACEUT, CARTER WALLACE, INC, 69- U.S.N.R, 45-46. Am. Statist. Asn; Am. Chem. Soc; Am. Soc. Qual. Control; Biomet. Soc. Statistical consultation in research and clinical studies of pharmaceuticals and related products; process and product development, improvement and approval; development and interpretation of physical, chemical and biological methods. Address: Carter-Wallace, Inc, Half Acre Rd, Cranbury, NJ 08512.

GORDON, LOUIS I(RWIN), b. Los Angeles, Calif, Aug. 17, 28; m. 51; c. 3. CHEMICAL OCEANOGRAPHY. B.S, Univ. Calif, Los Angeles, 51, M.S, San Diego, 53; Ore. State Univ, 66-69. Asst. geochem, Scripps Inst. Oceanog, Univ. Calif, 58, res. chemist, 58-62, asst. specialist marine chem, San Diego, 62-64, assoc. specialist, 64-66; INSTR. OCEANOG, ORE STATE UNIV, 69- Chem.C, U.S.A, 53-55. AAAS; Am. Geophys. Union; Am. Soc. Limnol. & Oceanog. Chemical oceanography; dissolved gases; nutrients; carbon; analytical chemistry; stable isotopes in oceanography; atmospheric and biological exchange processes, coastal processes. Address: Dept. of Oceanography, Oregon State University, Corvallis, OR 97331.

GORDON, LYLE J, b. Rupert, Idaho, Aug. 19, 26; m. 46; c. 3. CHEMICAL ENGINEERING. B.S, Washington (Seattle), 48, M.S; 50, Ph.D.(chem. eng), 62. Proj. engr, SCOTT PAPER CO, 53-55, develop. engr, 55-57, develop. mgr, 57-59, RES. & DEVELOP. MGR. PULPING, 59- U.S.N.R, Lt.(jg). Am. Inst. Chem. Eng; Tech. Asn. Pulp & Paper Indust.(Shibley award, 56). Liquid-solid fluidization; sulfite and high yield pulping. Address: West Coast Division, Scott Paper Co, Everett, WA 98201.

GORDON, MALCOLM S(TEPHEN), b. Brooklyn, N.Y, Nov. 13, 33; m. 59; c. 1. COMPARATIVE PHYSIOLOGY, MARINE BIOLOGY. B.A, Cornell, 54; Nat. Sci. Found. fel, Yale, 54-57, Ph.D.(zool), 58; Fulbright fel, Cambridge, 57-58. Asst. oceanog, Cornell, 51-53; instr. ZOOL, UNIV. CALIF, LOS ANGELES, 58-60, asst. prof, 60-65, assoc. prof, 65-68, PROF, 68-, DIR. INST. EVOLUTIONARY ENVIRON. BIOL, 70- Guggenheim fel, 61-62; Nat. Acad. Sci. exchange vis, USSR, 65; asst. dir. res, Nat. Fisheries Ctr. & Aquarium, Dept. of Interior, D.C, 68-69; vis. prof, Chinese Univ, Hong Kong, 71-72. Fel. AAAS; Am. Soc. Ichthyol. & Herpetol; Am. Soc. Zool; Soc. Exp. Biol. & Med; Am. Physiol. Soc. Comparative vertebrate physiology with emphasis on fishes and amphibians; mechanisms of osmoregulation and salinity adaptation; adaptation to low temperatures and high hydrostatic pressures; ecological physiology. Address: Dept. of Zoology, University of California, Los Angeles, CA 90024.

GORDON, MALCOLM WOFSY, b. Stamford, Conn, Dec. 2, 17; m. 46; c. 3. BIOCHEMISTRY. B.S, City Col, 40; Hite Cancer Found. fel, Texas, 47-48, M.A, 47, Ph.D.(biochem), 48. Asst. biochem, Texas, 46-47, res. assoc, 48; Merck fel, Calif. Inst. Tech, 48-50; dept. physiol. chem, Wisconsin, 50-53;

res. assoc. Inst. Living, 53-56; dir, Biochem. Res. Labs, 56-58; mem. grad. faculty, UNIV. CONN, 58-70, PROF. BIOBEHAV. SCI, 70-; DIR. RES, ABRAHAM RIBICOFF RES. LABS, 68- Vis. prof, Trinity Col.(Conn), 57-58; summer, dir. prog. biochem, Nat. Sci. Found, Loomis Sch, 62-64; adj. prof, Univ. Hartford, 63- U.S.A, 42-45. AAAS; Am. Chem. Soc; Am. Biochem. Soc; Am. Physiol. Soc; Am. Soc. Biol. Chem; Brit. Biochem. Soc. Neurochemistry. Address: Abraham Ribicoff Research Center, Norwich Hospital, Box 508, Norwich, CT 06360.

GORDON, MANUEL J(OE), b. Cleveland, Ohio, July 3, 22; m. 43; c. 2. ZOOLOGY. B.Sc, Ohio State, 49; M.A, California, 52, Ph.D.(zool), 55. Res. fel. zool, California, 55-57; asst. prof. res, dairy dept, Mich. State, 57-61; MGR. APPLN, RES. DEPT, SPINCO DIV, BECKMAN INSTRUMENTS, INC, 61- U.S.A.A.F, 42-46, Sgt. AAAS; Soc. Human Genetics; Genetics Soc. Am; Soc. Sci. Study Sex; Am. Genetic Asn; Am. Inst. Biol. Sci; N.Y. Acad. Sci. Physico-chemical biology; reproductive physiology; genetics. Address: 3640 Evergreen Dr, Palo Alto, CA 94303.

GORDON, MARK A, b. Springfield, Mass, Oct. 13, 37; m. 61; c. 2. RADIO ASTRONOMY. B.A, Yale, 59; Ph.D.(astro-geophys), Colorado, 66. Scientist, Arctic Inst. N.Am, 59-61; mem. staff astron, Lincoln Lab, Mass. Inst. Technol, 66-69; ASST. SCIENTIST, NAT. RADIO ASTRON. OBSERV, 69- Am. Astron. Soc; Royal Astron. Soc. Jupiter and nebular radio emission; interstellar medium. Address: 1621 Rugby Ave, Charlottesville, VA 22901.

GORDON, MARSHALL, b. Paducah, Ky, Sept. 1, 37; m. 62; c. 1. PHYSICAL ORGANIC CHEMISTRY. B.A, Murray State Col, 59; Ph.D.(chem), Vanderbilt, 63. Asst. prof. CHEM, MURRAY STATE COL, 63-65, ASSOC. PROF, 65-68, PROF, 68- Petrol. Res. Corp. res. grant, 65-67; summer res. chemist, E.I. du Pont de Nemours & Co, 61. Am. Chem. Soc. Mechanism of electrophilic substitution in π-deficient N-heterocyclic compounds; chemistry of organometallic compounds. Address: Box 397, University Station, Murray, KY 42071.

GORDON, MARTIN J(AY), b. New York, N.Y, Nov. 1, 29; m. 56; c. 3. ORGANIC CHEMISTRY. B.S, Miami (Fla), 50; Naval Res. fel, Alabama, 51-55, M.S, 52, Ph.D, 60. Res. chemist, film dept, E.I. DU PONT DE NEMOURS & CO, 58-60, group leader, 60-61, develop. supvr, 61-66, GROUP SUPVR, TEXTILE FIBERS DEPT, 66- U.S.A, 55-57. Am. Chem. Soc. Synthetic organic and polymer chemistry. Address: 1808 Glen Oaks Terrace, Chattanooga, TN 37412.

GORDON, MAXWELL, b. U.S.S.R, Feb. 13, 21; nat; m. 49; c. 2. ORGANIC CHEMISTRY. A.B, & B.S, Phila. Col. Pharm, 41; M.S, Pennsylvania, 46, Nat. Insts. Health fel, 46-48, Ph.D.(org. chem), 48; dipl, Imp. Col, London, 51. Anal. chemist, U.S. Naval Med. Supply Depot, N.Y, 41-42; instr. org. chem, Phila. Col. Pharm, 46-47; res. fel, radiation lab, California, 49-50; Swiss Tech. Inst, Zurich, 48-49; Imp. Col, London, 50-51; res. assoc, radioisotope lab, Squibb Inst. Med. Res, 51-55; sr. scientist, Smith Kline & French Labs, 55-57, head phys. sci. sect, 57-68, assoc. dir. res. activities, 68-70; DIR. RES. PLANNING, BRISTOL LABS, 70- Chmn. bd, Omni Res, Inc, Mayaguez, P.R, 70- U.S.N.R, 41-45, Res, 45-, Capt. AAAS; Am. Chem. Soc; N.Y. Acad. Sci; The Chem. Soc; Swiss Chem. Soc; Soc. Ger. Chem; Austrian Chem. Soc; Pharmaceut. Soc. Japan. Chemical kinetics; azulenes; heterocycles; cancer; radioactive tracers; antibiotic biosynthesis; medicinal chemistry; scientific documentation; research planning; bio-electronics. Address: 513 Standish Dr, Syracuse, NY 13224.

GORDON, MICHAEL DAVID, b. Detroit, Mich, Nov. 20, 42; m. 69. PHYSICAL & THEORETICAL CHEMISTRY. B.S, Univ. Mich, Ann Arbor, 64; M.S, Univ. Ill, Urbana, 65, Procter & Gamble Co. fel, 65-66, Minn. Mining & Mfg. Co. fel, 66-67, Firestone Tire & Rubber Co. fel, 67-68, Ph.D.(phys. chem), 69. Fel, Univ. Ill, Urbana, 69; RES. CHEMIST, ORG. CHEM. DEPT, E.I. DU PONT DE NEMOURS & CO, INC, 69- Am. Chem. Soc; Am. Phys. Soc. Calculation of physical properties of small molecules via theoretical methods; development of theoretical methods for the calculation of physical properties of dye molecules; mathematical modeling of photosensitive systems. Address: Organic Chemicals Dept, Jackson Lab, E.I. du Pont de Nemours & Co, Inc, P.O. Box 525, Wilmington, DE 19899.

GORDON, MILLARD F(REEMAN), b. Eastvale, Pa, Sept. 3, 21; m. 43; c. 2. ELECTRICAL ENGINEERING. B.S, Carnegie Inst. Tech, 42, M.S, 47, D.Sc, 48. Assoc. prof. eng, Brown, 50-54; head penetrations systs. dept, Thompson-Ramo-Wooldridge, Inc, 54-60; sr. staff adv, Bissett-Berman Corp, 60-67; CHIEF SCIENTIST RADAR, HUGHES AIRCRAFT CO, CULVER CITY, 67- Sig.C, 43-46, Capt. Inst. Elec. & Electronics Eng. Research, development and management. Address: 19451 Vintage St, Northridge, CA 91324.

GORDON, MILTON, b. N.Y.C, May 28, 29; m. 52; c. 3. MICROBIOLOGY. A.B, Univ. Calif, Los Angeles, 50; M.S, George Wash. Univ, 55, Ph.D, 62. Microbiologist, U.S. Army Biol. Labs, 51-70; HEALTH SCIENTIST ADMINSTR, DIV. RES. GRANTS, NAT. INSTS. HEALTH, 70- Chem.C, U.S.A, 51-53. AAAS; Am. Soc. Microbiol; Sci. Res. Soc. Am. Immunology; medical bacteriology. Address: Division of Research Grants, National Institutes of Health, Bethesda, MD 20014.

GORDON, MILTON ANDREW, b. Chicago, Ill, May 25, 35; m. 62; c. 2. MATHEMATICS, STATISTICS. B.S, Xavier Univ. La, 57; M.A, Univ. Detroit, 60; Nat. Sci. Found. grant, Ill. Inst. Technol, 64, Ph.D.(math), 68. Mathematician, labs. appl. sci, Univ. Chicago, 59-62, instr. math, LOYOLA UNIV. CHICAGO, 66-68, asst. prof, 68-71, DIR. AFRO-AM. STUDIES PROG, 71- Math. Asn. Am; Am. Math. Soc. General algebraic systems and statistics, especially as they relate to the social and behavioral sciences; curriculum for Afro-American Studies Program. Address: Loyola University of Chicago, 6525 N. Sheridan Rd, Chicago, IL 60626.

GORDON, MILTON P(AUL), b. St. Paul, Minn, Feb. 8, 30; m. 55; c. 4. BIOCHEMISTRY. B.A, Minnesota, 50; Upjohn Co. fel, Illinois, 50-51, Ph.D. (biochem), 53. Asst. Illinois, 52-53; res. fel, Nat. Cancer Inst, Sloan-Kettering Inst, 53-55, asst, 55-57; asst. res. biochemist, virus lab, California, 57-59; asst. prof. BIOCHEM, UNIV. WASH, 59-61, assoc. prof, 61-66, PROF, 66- Vis. res. chemist, Princeton, 66-67. AAAS; Am. Chem. Soc.(ed, Biochemistry, 61-); Am. Phytopath. Soc; Am. Soc. Plant Physiol; Am. Soc. Biol. Chem; Biophys. Soc. Biological effects of the incorporation of analogues into nucleic acids; structure of the ribonucleic acid of tobacco mosaic virus; methyl purines; photochemistry of nucleic acids. Address: 8255 45th Ave. N.E, Seattle, WA 98115.

GORDON, MORRIS A(ARON), b. Waterbury, Conn, April 3, 20; div; c. 3. MYCOLOGY, MICROBIOLOGY. B.S, City Col, 40; M.S, Chicago, 42; fel. & Ph.D.(bot, mycol), Duke, 49. Mycologist, Communicable Disease Center, U.S. Pub. Health Serv, 49-53, head, airborne pathogens lab, 53-54; res. specialist, chem. corps training command, Ft. McClellan, Ala, 54-55; asst. prof. microbiol. & mycol, Med. Col, S.C, 55-57, assoc. prof, 57-59, sr. res. scientist, DIV. LABS. & RES, N.Y. STATE DEPT. HEALTH, 59-61, assoc. res. scientist, 61-68, PRIN. RES. SCIENTIST, 68-; ASSOC. PROF. MICROBIOL, ALBANY MED. COL, 64-, assoc, 60-64. Instr, med. sch, Emory, 49-54; La. State Univ. Inter-Am. fel, Cent. Am, 59. Consult, grant comts, Nat. Insts. Health, 59-; mem, bact. & mycol. study sect, Nat. Insts. Health, 71- U.S.A, 42-46. Mycol. Soc. Am; fel. Am. Acad. Microbiol; Am. Soc. Microbiol; Sci. Res. Soc. Am; N.Y. Acad. Sci; Int. Soc. Human & Animal Mycol; Med. Mycol. Soc. Americas. Medical mycology. Address: 538 Myrtle Ave, Albany, NY 12208.

GORDON, M(ORTON) M(AURICE), b. Atlantic City, N.J, Nov. 8, 24; m. 50; c. 2. PHYSICS. B.S, Chicago, 46; Ph.D.(physics), Washington(St. Louis), 50. Instr. PHYSICS, Florida, 50-52, asst. prof, 52-54, assoc. prof, 54-57, prof, 57-59; assoc. prof, MICH. STATE UNIV, 59-62, PROF, 62- Physicist, Oak Ridge Nat. Lab, 57-58. Am. Phys. Soc; Am. Asn. Physics Teachers. Atomic and nuclear scattering theory; accelerator theory. Address: Dept. of Physics, Michigan State University, East Lansing, MI 48823.

GORDON, MOSES, b. Tremont, Pa, May 4, 09; m. 39; c. 2. CHEMICAL ENGINEERING. B.Ch.E, Minnesota, 29; fel, North Dakota, 29-31, M.S, 32; Hormel fel, Minnesota, 38-39, Ph.D.(chem. eng), 41. Instr. chem. eng, North Dakota, 31-35; asst, Minnesota, 35-38; chem. engr, petrol. refinery, Standard Oil Co. Ind, 39-42, chem. engr, 46-69; DIR. PLACEMENT, ST. JOSEPH'S CALUMET COL, 69- Consult. U.S.A, 42-46. Am. Inst. Chem. Eng. Power requirements for agitation; heat transmission in a jacketed kettle; heat transfer and power consumption in an agitated kettle; jet and diesel fuels; home heating oils. Address: P.O. Box 388, Whiting, IN 46394.

GORDON, MYRA, b. Mt. Vernon, N.Y, Dec. 12, 39. ORGANIC CHEMISTRY. A.B, Mt. Holyoke Col, 60; Nat. Sci. Found. coop. fels, Pittsburgh, 61-64, Ph.D.(chem), 65. ASST. PROF. CHEM, Tulane, 66-70; UNIV. WEST. ONT, 70- Am. Chem. Soc; The Chem. Soc. Organophosphorus chemistry; intermolecular interactions; molecular spectroscopy, particularly nuclear magnetic resonance spectroscopy. Address: Dept. of Chemistry, University of Western Ontario, London, Ont, Can.

GORDON, N. L, b. Elizabeth, N.J, June 9, 24; m. 49; c. 1. MATHEMATICS. B.A, Rutgers, 51. Mathematician, U.S. Govt, Ft. Monmouth, N.J, 56-59; DIR, SYSTS. & PROG. RES, COMPUT. CTR, DAVID SARNOFF RES. CTR, RCA LABS, 59- U.S.M.C, 43-45. Asn. Comput. Mach; Soc. Indust. & Appl. Math; Am. Math. Soc. Scientific computing; problem solving; numerical analysis; computer languages. Address: RCA Labs, David Sarnoff Research Center, Systems & Programming Research, Princeton, NJ 08540.

GORDON, N(ATHAN), b. New York, N.Y, Sept. 12, 17; m. 44; c. 2. CHEMISTRY. B.A, Brooklyn Col, 38; M.S, Georgetown, 48, Ph.D.(biochem), 52. Chemist, U.S. Food & Drug Admin, 46-48; U.S. Dept. Agr, 48-52; intel. res. specialist, U.S. Army Chem. Corps, 52-55, dir. tech. opers, Intel. Agency, 55-62, chief atomic, biol. & chem. div, U.S. Army For. Sci. & Tech. Ctr, D.C, 62-67, CHIEF, CHEM. BR, U.S. ARMY SCI. & LIAISON ADV. GROUP, 67- Lectr, Montgomery Jr. Col, 64-69. U.S.A, 43-46, Res, 57-70, Lt. Col. (Ret). AAAS; Am. Inst. Chem; Am. Chem. Soc. Coal tar colors; pesticides; chemical warfare agents; drugs; foodstuffs; natural products; animal behavior. Address: 1121 University Blvd. W, Silver Spring, MD 20902.

GORDON, NEIL E, JR, b. Baltimore, Md, Apr. 20, 20; m. 41; c. 2. CHEMISTRY. A.B, Cent. Col.(Mo), 40; M.S, Polytech. Inst. Brooklyn, 45. Phys. chemist, res. labs, Int. Nickel Co, Ltd, 41-43, anal. chemist, 43-45, chief spectrographer, 45-50; supvr, instrumental sect, anal. chem, Bettis Field, WESTINGHOUSE ELEC. CORP, 50-55, mgr. tech. serv. labs. & site coordinator, waltz mill site, atomic power div, 55-67, mgr. spectrochem. anal, BETTIS ATOMIC LAB, WEST MIFFLIN, 67-69, MGR. RADIOCHEM, 69- Am. Chem. Soc; Am. Soc. Test. & Mat; Am. Nuclear Soc; Am. Soc. Metals; Soc. Appl. Spectros. Industrial and nuclear materials management. Address: Stanton Dr, R.D. 1, New Stanton, PA 15672.

GORDON, P(AUL), b. Hartford, Conn, Jan. 1, 18; m. 41; c. 2. PHYSICAL METALLURGY. S.B. & S.M, Mass. Inst. Tech, 40, Sc.D.(metall), 49. Asst. steel metall, Mass. Inst. Tech, 40-43, group leader, Manhattan Proj. & Atomic Energy Comn, 43-48, res. assoc. metall. of uranium, 48-49; asst. prof. metall, Ill. Inst. Tech, 49-50; Inst. Study of Metals, Chicago, 50-54; PROF. METALL, ILL. INST. TECHNOL, 54-, CHMN. DEPT, 66- AAAS; Am. Soc. Eng. Educ; Am. Soc. Metals; Am. Inst. Mining, Metall. & Petrol. Eng. Transformations in metals; recrystallization; grain growth; order-disorder phenomena; precipitation; metal failures; surface reactions. Address: 3300 S. Federal St, Chicago, IL 60616.

GORDON, PAUL, b. Warren, Pa, May 3, 33; m. 63; c. 3. APPLIED MATHEMATICS, FLUID DYNAMICS. B.S, Pennsylvania, 55, M.A. & M.S, 58, Ph.D.(math), 67. Teacher, high sch, N.J, 55-56; programmer, Gen. Elec. Co, 56-60, math. analyst, 60-66, mgr. sci. prog. & appl. math, 66-70; ASSOC. PROF. MATH, DREXEL UNIV, 70- Soc. Indust. & Appl. Math; Am. Math. Soc; Math. Asn. Am. Numerical analysis. Address: Dept. of Mathematics, Drexel University, Philadelphia, PA 19104.

GORDON, PAUL G(ENE), b. Denver, Colo, Oct. 2, 28; m. 51; c. 2. INORGANIC & ORGANIC CHEMISTRY. B.S, Denver, 50; M.S, Illinois, 51, Ph.D. (chem), 54. Asst, Illinois, 51-53; MGR, CHEM. SALES CO, 54- Am. Chem. Soc. Synthesis of ammono-and hydrazino-carbonic acid derivatives and evaluation of compounds as sources of nitrogen and biological activity towards plants, insects and microorganisms. Address: 7103 E. Ohio Dr, Denver, CO 80222.

GORDON, PHILIP N(EWTON), b. Boston, Mass, April 21, 19; m. 44; c. 3. ORGANIC CHEMISTRY. B.S, Polytech. Inst. Brooklyn, 42; M.S, Minnesota, 50. Jr. anal. chemist, Tenn. Valley Authority, 42-43; res. org. chemist, PFIZER, INC, 50-67, RESIDUE CHEMIST, 67- U.S.N.R, 43-, Lt. AAAS; Am. Chem. Soc; Am. Microchem. Soc. Antibiotics; trace analysis. Address: Landing Rd, Old Lyme, CT 06371.

GORDON, RICHARD EDWARDS, b. N.Y.C, July 15, 22; m. 59; c. 4. PSYCHIATRY, PSYCHOLOGY. B.S, Yale, 43; M.D, Univ. Mich, 45; M.A, Columbia Univ, 56, Ph.D.(social psychol), 61. Dir. ment. health res. unit, Englewood Hosp, 53-60; prof. psychol. & psychiat, Wagner Col, 60-67; ASSOC. PROF. PSYCHIAT. & MED. DIR. COMPUT. & BEHAV. SCI. DIV. & MULTIPHASE HEALTH TESTING CTR, UNIV. FLA, 67- Dir. psychiat, Res. & Guid. Assocs, 61-; mem, N.J. Ment. Health Comn, 57-61; dir, Sigma Sci. Corp, 71- Dipl, Am. Bd. Neurol. & Psychiat. Med.C, 51-53, Capt. AAAS; Am. Med. Asn; Am. Psychiat. Asn; Am. Psychol. Asn. Social and preventive psychiatry. Address: Dept. of Psychiatry, University of Florida, Gainesville, FL 32601.

GORDON, RICHARD F, JR, b. Seattle, Wash, Oct. 5, 29; m; c. 6. ASTRONAUTICAL ENGINEERING, CHEMISTRY. B.S, Washington (Seattle), 51. U.S. NAVY, 51-, selected as astronaut, NASA, 63, pilot for backup crew, Gemini VIII, 66, pilot, Gemini XI, 66, backup command module pilot, Apollo IX, command module pilot, Apollo XII, 69, adv. to Apollo XIII mission, 69-70, BACKUP SPACECRAFT COMDR, APOLLO XV, 70- Navy Distinguished Flying Crosses; exceptional serv. medal, NASA; Navy Astronaut. Wings; Navy Distinguished Serv. medal, Inst. Navig. award, 69; Godfrey L. Cabot award, 70; Rear Admiral William S. Parsons award, 70. U.S.N, 51-, Capt. Soc. Exp. Test Pilots. Address: Manned Spacecraft Center, NASA, Houston, TX 77058.

GORDON, RICHARD LEE, b. Lewiston, Idaho, Nov. 6, 35; m. 59; c. 3. PHYSICS. B.S, Washington State, 58, Ph.D.(physics), 66. Physicist, Lawrence Radiation Lab, California, 58-61; SR. RES. SCIENTIST SOLID STATE PHYSICS, PAC. NORTHWEST LABS, BATTELLE MEM. INST, 65-, lectr. physics, Joint Ctr. Grad. Study, 68- Shock hydrodynamics; surface physics; stimulated Brillouin scattering; solid state physics. Address: Pacific Northwest Labs, Battelle Memorial Institute, P.O. Box 999, Richland, WA 99352.

GORDON, RICHARD S(EYMOUR), b. New York, N.Y, June 28, 25; m. 51; c. 5. BIOCHEMISTRY, NUTRITION. A.B, Rochester, 47; Am. Cancer Soc. fel, Sloan-Kettering Inst. Cancer Res, 47-48; Sloan-Kettering fel, Harvard, 48-49, univ. fels, 50-52; A.M, 54; Ph.D.(biochem), Mass. Inst. Tech, 54. Asst. to Prof. Fieser, Harvard, 50-51; res. assoc, Mass. Inst. Tech, 52-55; res. chemist, Merrimac Div, MONSANTO CO, 51-54, res. biochemist, org. chem. div, 54-55, scientist physiol. nutrit, 55-57, sr. group leader physiol. nutrit. & biochem, 57-60, asst. dir. res, 60; dir. res, agr. div, 60-63, cent. res. dept, 63-67, gen. mgr, new enterprise div, 67-71, v.pres, 69-71, CHIEF SCIENTIST, 71- Consult, 49-51. Mem. agr. bd, Nat. Acad. Sci. U.S.A, 43-46, Res, 46-49; U.S.P.H.S.R, 49-57. AAAS; Am. Chem. Soc; Am. Soc. Microbiol; Animal Nutrit. Res. Coun; Poultry Sci. Asn; N.Y. Acad. Sci; Brit. Chem. Soc. Physiological nutrition; growth limiting biosynthetic reactions; amino acid and vitamin A and E metabolism and nutritional requirements; energy metabolism; microbial physiology and genetics; nutrition and diseases interrelationships; poultry and animal nutrition. Address: Monsanto Co, 800 N. Lindbergh Blvd, St. Louis, MO 63166.

GORDON, R(OBERT), b. New York, N.Y, June 23, 17; m. 41; c. 2. NUCLEAR ENGINEERING. B.S.M.E, Cooper Union, 40; M.S, California, Berkeley, 57, Ph.D.(nuclear eng), 62. Engr, power plant lab, air mat. command, Wright Field, Ohio, 40-42, 45; Consol. Vultee Aircraft Corp, 43; asst. chief engr, adv. liquid propulsion dept, Aerojet-Gen. Corp, Gen. Tire & Rubber Co, 45-51, liquid engine div, 51-56; supv. rep, Aerojet-Gen. Nucleonics, 57-58, tech. staff mem, 59-61, sci. adv. to v.pres. & gen. mgr, 61, v.pres. & tech. dir, 61-65, mgr. snap 8 div, Aerojet-Gen. Corp, Von Karmen Ctr, 65-68, mech. systs. opers, 68-70; PRES, STRUCT. COMPOSITES INDUSTS, INC, 71- Mem. tech. adv. comt. space power, NASA/Off. Advan. Res. & Technol, chmn. subcomt. dynamic power systs. U.S.A.A.F, 43-45, 1st Lt. Am. Nuclear Soc; Am. Inst. Aeronaut. & Astronaut; Soc. Aerospace Mat. & Process Eng. Nuclear reactor technology; propulsion; rocketry; power conversion; systems analysis; research and research management; advanced composite materials and structures. Address: Structural Composites Industries, Inc, 6344 N. Irwindale Ave, Azusa, CA 91702.

GORDON, ROBERT B(OYD), b. East Orange, N.J, Dec. 25, 29; m. 52; c. 2. ENGINEERING, GEOPHYSICS. B.S, Yale, 52, Gen. Elec. Co. Coffin fel, 53-54, D.Eng.(metall), 55. Asst. prof. metall, Columbia, 55-57; YALE, 57-60, assoc. prof. eng. & appl. sci, 60-68, PROF. appl. sci. & geol, 68-69, GEOPHYS. & APPL. SCI, 69- Consult, Nat. Acad. Sci, 57-59. Am. Phys. Soc; Geol. Soc. Asn; Am. Inst. Mining, Metall. & Petrol. Eng; Am. Geophys. Union. Applied science; solid state science of earth materials. Address: Dept. of Geology & Geophysics, Yale University, Box 2161 Yale Station, New Haven, CT 06520.

GORDON, ROBERT DIXON, b. Toronto, Ont, Dec. 15, 36; m. 60; c. 2. PHYSICAL CHEMISTRY. B.Sc, McMaster Univ, 59, Imp. Oil grad. fel, 59-62, M.Sc, 61; Nat. Res. Coun. Can. scholar, Univ. London, 62-64, Ph.D.(phys. chem), 64. Lectr. CHEM, Univ. Ibadan, 64-66; asst. prof, QUEEN'S UNIV. (ONT), 66-71, ASSOC. PROF, 71- Ultraviolet spectroscopy of gaseous molecules and of molecular crystals. Address: Dept. of Chemistry, Queen's University, Kingston, Ont, Can.

GORDON, ROBERT E(DWARD), b. New York, N.Y, June 25, 25; m. 48; c. 2. ECOLOGY. A.B, Emory, 49; M.S, Georgia, 50; Carnegie fel, Tulane, 52-54, Ph.D, 56. Curator mus, Highlands Biol. Sta, 49-50; asst. prof. BIOL, Northeast. La. State Col, 54-58; UNIV. NOTRE DAME, 58-63, assoc. prof, 63-66, PROF, 66-, V.PRES. ADVAN. STUDY, 71-, head dept. biol, 64-67, assoc. dean sci, 67-71. Ed, Am. Midland Naturalist, 58-64; sect. ed, Biol. Abstr, 63; mem. gov. bd, Am. Inst. Biol. Sci, 69-, exec. comt, 71-; mem. U.S. nat. comt, Int. Fedn. Doc. & Int. Union Biol. Sci, 70- AAAS; Animal Behav. Soc; Am. Soc. Zool; Ecol. Soc. Am; Am. Soc. Ichthyol. & Herpet; Coun. Biol. Ed. (exec. secy, 63-). Scientific communication; ecology, systematics and behavior of cold-blooded vertebrates. Address: University of Notre Dame, Notre Dame, IN 46556.

GORDON, ROBERT J(ULIAN), b. Seattle, Wash, July 31, 23; m. 48; c. 2. ORGANIC CHEMISTRY. B.S, California, Los Angeles, 47, Ph.D.(chem), 52. Technologist petrol. res. Shell Oil Co, 52-58, sr. technologist, 58-59, group leader, 59-61, res. supvr, Shell Develop. Co, 61-64; supvry. physicist, vehicle pollution lab, Calif. State Dept. Health, 64-68; ASST. PROF. PATH, SCH. MED, UNIV. SOUTH. CALIF, 68- U.S.A.A.F, 42-45, 2nd Lt. AAAS; Am. Chem. Soc. Reaction mechanisms in Grignard alkylations, aromatic sulfonation, preflame combustion reactions and photochemical air pollution; mass spectrometry; infrared spectrophotometry; environmental carcinogens. Address: 2 Silver Eagle Rd, Rolling Hills Estates, CA 90274.

GORDON, ROBERT SIRKOSKY, JR, b. New York, N.Y, Mar. 26, 26; m. 51; c. 4. PHYSIOLOGY. A.B. & M.D, Harvard, 49. Res. med, Presby. Hosp, New York, N.Y, 49-53; clin. assoc, Nat. Heart Inst, 53-54, investr, 54-64, CLIN. DIR, NAT. INST. ARTHRITIS & METAB. DISEASES, 64- Chief sect. clin. res, Pakistan-SEATO Cholera Res. Lab, 61-64. Am. Physiol. Soc; Am. Soc. Clin. Invest; Am. Fedn. Clin. Res; Asn. Am. Physicians. Physiology of plasma proteins and lipids; gastroenterology. Address: National Institute of Arthritis & Metabolic Diseases, Bethesda, MD 20014.

GORDON, RODERICK ANGUS, b. Watrous, Sask, Aug. 2, 11; m. 39; c. 3. ANESTHESIA. B.Sc, Saskatchewan, 34; M.D, Toronto, 37; dipl. anesthesia, Royal Col. Physicians & Surgeons, Eng, 40. From anesthetist to sr. anesthetist, TORONTO GEN. HOSP, 45-61, ANESTHETIST-IN-CHIEF, 61-; PROF. ANESTHESIA, UNIV. TORONTO, 61- Consult, Dir. Gen. Med. Serv, Can. Army, 51-54; Can. Forces Med. Coun, 56-65; Hosp. Sick Children, Sunnybrook, Wellesley & Princess Margaret Hosp. & Women's Col. Hosp, Toronto, 61- Fel, Royal Col. Physicians, Can, 53, Royal Col. Surgeons, Eng, 64. R.C.A.M.C, 39-45, Res, 45-52, Col. Soc. Anesthesiol; Acad. Anesthesiol.(pres, 62-63); Can. Med. Asn; Can. Anaesthetists Soc.(secy-treas, 46-61, pres, 63-64). Anesthesiology. Address: 92 Golfdale Rd, Toronto 12, Ont, Can.

GORDON, ROGER PAUL, b. New York, N.Y, Jan. 5, 36. PHYSICAL CHEMISTRY. B.S, Pennsylvania, 57; Ph.D.(phys. chem), New York Univ, 64. Res. assoc. transport processes, Kansas, 63-66; asst. prof. CHEM, UPSALA COL, 65-69, ASSOC. PROF, 69- Fel. Am. Inst. Chem. Metal-ammonia solutions; theoretical and experimental study of irreversible and transport processes. Address: Dept. of Chemistry, Upsala College, East Orange, NJ 07019.

GORDON, RONALD CLAIRE, b. Gettysburg, S.Dak, Jan. 28, 36; m. 60. BACTERIOLOGY. B.Sc, S.Dak. State, 61, M.Sc, 62; Ph.D.(microbiol), McGill, 67. RES. MICROBIOLOGIST, ALASKA WATER LAB, ENVIRON. PROTECTION AGENCY, 67- Jr. bacteriologist, S.Dak. State Pub. Health Serv, summer 60. U.S.M.C, 56-57; U.S.N, 57-58. AAAS; Am. Soc. Microbiol; Can. Soc. Microbiol; Arctic Inst. N.Am; Water Pollution Control Fedn; Am. Inst. Biol. Sci. Physiology and biochemistry of microorganisms; ecology of microorganisms in marine and fresh water environments. Address: Alaska Water Lab, College, AK 99701.

GORDON, RONALD J(EFFERY), b. Baltimore, Md. Aug. 11, 44; m. 67; c. 2. CHEMICAL ENGINEERING. B.S, Univ. Md, 65; M.S, Princeton, 67, Ph.D. (chem. eng), 69. ASST. PROF. CHEM. ENG, UNIV. FLA, 69- Am. Inst. Chem. Eng; Am. Chem. Soc; Soc. Rheol. Polymer rheology, turbulent drag reduction, hemorheology. Address: 2000 S.W. 16th St, Apt. 72, Gainesville, FL 32601.

GORDON, RONALD STANTON, b. Oakland, Calif, Sept. 29, 37; m. 63. CERAMIC & CHEMICAL ENGINEERING. B.S, California, Berkeley, 59, M.S, 61; Sc.D.(ceramics), Mass. Inst. Tech, 64. Res. asst. cement & concrete, California, Berkeley, 56-61; ceramics, Mass. Inst. Tech, 61-64; asst. prof. ceramic eng, UNIV. UTAH, 64-69, ASSOC. PROF. MAT. SCI. & ENG, 69- Mem. staff, lighting res. lab, Gen. Elec. Co, Ohio, 71-; Nat. Sci. Found. res. initiation grant, 65-67; Atomic Energy Comn. res. grant, 66- Nat. Guard, 56-61. AAAS; Am. Ceramic Soc; Nat. Inst. Ceramic Eng; Electrochem. Soc; Metall. Soc. Solid state studies in ceramic materials; raction kinetics; thermodynamics of solids; cement chemistry; mechanical behavior of ceramics at elevated temperatures; solid state electrochemistry. Address: Division of Materials Science & Engineering, University of Utah, Salt Lake City, UT 84112.

GORDON, RONNIE DREW, b. Waxahachie, Tex, Sept. 25, 41; m. 65; c. 2. ORGANIC CHEMISTRY. B.S, Texas, Arlington, 63; Ph.D.(org. chem), Texas, Austin, 68. Fel, Texas, Austin, 67-68; RES. CHEMIST, Continental Oil Co, Okla, 68-71; LONE STAR GAS CO, 71- Am. Chem. Soc. Electron spin resonance spectroscopy; mechanisms of radical addition reactions. Address: Lone Star Gas Co, 2601 Logan St, Dallas, TX 75215.

GORDON, RUTH E(VELYN), b. Richmondville, N.Y. BACTERIOLOGY. A.B, Cornell, 32, M.S, 33, Ph.D.(bacter), 34. Instr, N.Y. Vet. Col, Cornell, 34-37; asst. bacteriologist, div. soil microbiol, U.S. Dept. Agr, 38-42, bacteriologist, 50-51; asst. bacteriologist, Army Med. Center, 43-44; bacteriologist, Am. Type Culture Collection, 44-47, curator, 47-50; assoc. res. specialist, N.J. Agr. Exp. Sta, 51-54; assoc. prof. INST. MICROBIOL, RUTGERS UNIV, 54-71, PROF. MICROBIOL, 71- AAAS; Am. Soc. Microbiol; Am. Acad. Microbiol; Brit. Soc. Gen. Microbiol; Can. Soc. Microbiol. Taxonomy of aerobic, sporeforming bacteria; mycobacteria; nocardiae; streptomycetes. Address: Institute of Microbiology, Rutgers University, New Brunswick, NJ 08903.

GORDON, SAMUEL, b. New York, N.Y, Feb. 7, 17; m. 44; c. 3. BIOCHEMISTRY. B.A, N.Y. Univ, 40, M.S, 49; Abbott Labs. fel, Cornell, 50-51, Pub. Health Serv. fel, 51-53, Ph.D.(biochem), 53. Chemist, Lederle Labs, 46-

49; asst. biochem, med. col, Cornell, 49-53; GROUP LEADER, LEDERLE LABS, AM. CYANAMID CO, 53- U.S.N.R, 44-46. AAAS; Am. Chem. Soc; N.Y. Acad. Sci; N.Y. Acad. Med. Posterior pituitary hormones; enzymes; lipid metabolism; toxicology and safety evaluation. Address: 393 Blauvelt Rd, Pearl River, NY 10965.

GORDON, SAMUEL M(ORRIS), b. Boston, Mass, Sept. 27, 98; m. 23; c. 2. CHEMISTRY. B.S, Tufts Col, 22; M.S, Iowa, 23; Wrigley fel, Wisconsin, 24-26, Ph.D.(biochem), 26. Asst. chem, Iowa, 22-23; chemist, Portland Cement Asn, Ill, 23-24; Nat. Res. Coun. fel. biol, Wisconsin, 26-28; chief, bur. chem, Am. Dent. Asn, Ill, 28-38; dir. res. & v.pres, Endo Labs, Inc, N.Y, 38-59; assoc. exp. sta, Univ. Calif, Berkeley, 59-67; RES. BIOCHEMIST, INST. CHEM. BIOL, UNIV. SAN FRANCISCO, 66- Consult, drug admin, Health Dept, N.Y, 30; ed, Dent. Sci. & Dent. Art; Accepted Dent. Remedies. Med.C, 17-19; U.S.A, 42-44, Lt. Col. Fel. AAAS; Am. Chem. Soc; Harvey Soc; Soc. Exp. Biol. & Med; affil. fel. Am. Med. Asn; fel. Am. Med. Writers' Asn; fel. Am. Col. Angiol; fel. Am. Inst. Chem; fel. N.Y. Acad. Sci. Medicinal chemistry. Address: 2270 Sloat Blvd, San Francisco, CA 94116.

GORDON, S(AMUEL) ROBERT, b. Alton, Ill, Feb. 19, 43. MATHEMATICS. B.S, Calif. Inst. Technol, 64; Nat. Sci. Found. fel, Yale, 64-68, M.A, 66, Ph.D.(math), 69. Acting instr. MATH, Yale, 68-69; asst. prof. in residence, Univ. Calif, Los Angeles, 69-70; ASST. PROF, UNIV. CALIF, RIVERSIDE, 70- Am. Math. Soc. Jordan algebras and Lie algebras and the connections between them, especially the use of techniques from algebraic groups to study the automorphism groups and Lie algebras of Jordan algebras. Address: Dept. of Mathematics, University of California, Riverside, CA 92502.

GORDON, S(AUL), b. Bronx, N.Y, Nov. 29, 25; m. 46; c. 4. ANALYTICAL CHEMISTRY. B.A, Ohio State, 46; M.S, Kentucky, 49, Ph.D.(chem), 51. Chemist, Picatinny Arsenal, 51-52, group leader, 52-55, chief basic chem. res. unit, 55-59, staff chemist specialist, pyrotech. lab, 59-61; asst. prof. chem, Florham-Madison Campus, Fairleigh Dickinson, 60-62, assoc. prof, 62-66, prof, 66-67, chmn. dept, 63-67, dir. annual thermoanal. insts, 62-67; PRES, CTR. PROF. ADVAN, DIV. TECHNOL. ADVAN. CTRS, INC, 67- Govt. & indust. consult. AAAS; Am. Chem. Soc; Instrument Soc. Am; fel. Am. Inst. Chem; Am. Soc. Training & Develop; Inst. Food Technol. Thermoanalytical techniques and instrumentation; differential thermal analysis; thermogravimetry. Address: 29 Division St, P.O. Box 997, Somerville, NJ 08876.

GORDON, SHEFFIELD, b. Chicago, Ill, Feb. 10, 16; m. 64. PHYSICAL CHEMISTRY. S.B, Chicago, 37; Ph.D.(phys. chem), Notre Dame, 53. Chemist, Alton R.R. Co, 38-41; asst, Chicago, 41-42; res. assoc, metall. lab, 42-46; Notre Dame, 46-49; ASSOC. CHEMIST, ARGONNE NAT. LAB, 50- For. collab, Saclay Nuclear Res. Ctr, France, 65. AAAS; Am. Phys. Soc; Am. Chem. Soc; Faraday Soc; Radiation Res. Soc. Radiation chemistry; photochemistry; surface chemistry. Address: Argonne National Lab, Bldg. 200, A 157, 9700 Cass Ave, Argonne, IL 60439.

GORDON, SHELDON P, b. N.Y.C, July 11, 42; m. 65. MATHEMATICS. B.S, Polytech. Inst. Brooklyn, 63; M.Sc, McGill Univ, 65, Ph.D.(math), 69. Lectr. MATH, McGill Univ, 63-68; ASST. PROF, QUEENS COL.(N.Y.), 68- Stability theory for differential equations and for difference equations. Address: Dept. of Mathematics, Queens College, Flushing, NY 11367.

GORDON, SOLON A(LBERT), b. Phila, Pa, Jan. 29, 16; m. 40. BOTANY. B.S, Pa. State Col, 38; Newcombe fel, Michigan, 40-43, M.S, 41, Ph.D. (plant physiol), 44. Asst, Michigan, 39-40; chemist, bur. plant indust, U.S. Dept. Agr, 43-44; head chemist, Inst. Trop. Agr, P.R, 44-47; prof. biol, col. agr, Puerto Rico, 47-48; SR. BIOLOGIST, DIV. BIOL. MED. RES, ARGONNE NAT. LAB, 48- Consult, Off. Space Sci. & Applns, NASA; mem. comt. on photobiol. & comt. on life sci, Space Sci. Bd, Nat. Acad. Sci-Nat. Res. Coun; secy-gen, 5th Int. Cong. Photobiol. Fel. AAAS; Am. Soc. Plant Physiol; Am. Bot. Soc; Am. Soc. Gen. Physiol; Radiation Res. Soc; Scandinavian Soc. Plant Physiol; Japanese Soc. Plant Physiol. Phytohormone biochemistry and physiology; radiation biology. Address: Argonne National Lab, Argonne, IL 60439.

GORDON, STANLEY H(OWARD), b. Malden, Mass, June 22, 25; m. 58. ELECTRONIC ENGINEERING. B.S, Northeastern, 47. Electronic engr, Melpar, Inc. Div, Westinghouse Air Brake Co, Va, 47-49; electronic scientist, Diamond Ord. Fuze Lab, Wash, D.C, 49-59; SR. ENGR, APPL. PHYSICS LAB, JOHNS HOPKINS UNIV, 59- Consult, Israel Inst. Tech, 64-65. U.S.C.G.R, 43-45. Inst. Elec. & Electronics Eng. Microelectronics; circuit and system design and analysis; system analysis, design and development of IR and laser systems. Address: 806 Orange Dr, Silver Spring, MD 20901.

GORDON, STUART ALBERT, b. Limerick, Sask, Aug. 4, 24; m. 49; c. 2. PHYSICS. B.A, Saskatchewan, 47, M.A, 48; Rochester, 50-52; Ph.D.(aerophysics), Toronto, 64. Res. officer atomic physics, Nat. Res. Coun. Can, 48-50; res. physicist, Consol. Vacuum Corp, 54-57; sr. scientist, aerophysics, Aerochem. Res. Lab, Inc, Pfaudler Permutit Inc, 61-65; res. scientist, Space Res. Inst, McGILL UNIV, 65-69, RES. DIR, 67-; RES. SCIENTIST, SPACE RES. CORP, 69- Am. Inst. Aeronaut. & Astronaut; Am. Phys. Soc; Am. Vacuum Soc. Fluid mechanics; low density gas dynamics; upper atmosphere physics; vacuum instrumentation; heat transfer. Address: Space Research Corp, 2055 Peel St, Montreal 2, Que, Can.

GORDON, THOMAS PASCOE, b. Pittsburgh, Pa, Aug. 11, 32; m. 58; c. 2. CHEMISTRY. A.B, Princeton, 54; M.S, Calif. Inst. Technol, 56, Ph.D. (chem), 59. Res. chemist org. chem, S.B, Penick & Co, N.Y, 59-61; dir. res, Fine Chem. Can, Ltd, 61-62; V.PRES, GORDON LUBRICATING CO. & SUBSIDIARIES, 62- Lectr, Pittsburgh, 64- AAAS; Am. Chem. Soc. Enzyme kinetics; physical chemistry of inorganic free radicals in aqueous solution; synthesis of pharmacologically active quinaoline-ones. Address: 1136 Cornell Rd, Pittsburgh, PA 15205.

GORDON, WILLIAM A(NTHONY), b. London, Eng, Feb. 25, 32; m. 57; c. 3. PALEONTOLOGY. B.Sc, London, 56, Ph.D.(geol), 60. Lectr. GEOL, Puerto Rico, 56-60, asst. prof, 60-62; Oberlin Col, 62-66; assoc. prof, UNIV. SASK, REGINA, 66-71, PROF, 71- Mem, Sask. Oil & Gas Conserv. Bd. Geol. Soc. Am; Paleont. Soc; Brit. Geol. Soc; Geol. Asn. Can; Can. Asn. Petrol. Geol. Biostratigraphy of Jurassic foraminifera; paleogeography of ancient life; paleoecology. Address: Dept. of Geology, University of Saskatchewan, Regina, Sask, Can.

GORDON, WILLIAM BERNARD, b. Washington, D.C, Nov. 16, 35; m. 61; c. 2. MATHEMATICS. B.S, George Washington, 59, M.S, 60; Ph.D.(math), Hopkins, 68. Mathematician, Naval Res. Lab, 60-62; asst. prof. math, Towson State Col, 66-68; instr, Hopkins, 68-69; MATHEMATICIAN, MATH. RES. CTR, NAVAL RES. LAB, 69- U.S.A, 54-56. AAAS; Am. Math. Soc. Global analysis; analysis on manifolds. Address: Math. Research Center, Naval Research Lab, Washington, DC 20390.

GORDON, WILLIAM E(DWIN), b. Paterson, N.J, Jan. 8, 18; m. 41; c. 2. RADIO ENGINEERING. B.A, N.J. State Teachers Col, 39, M.A, 42; M.S, N.Y. Univ, 46; Ph.D.(elec. eng), Cornell, 53. Teacher, pub. sch, N.J, 39-42; instr, N.Y. Univ, 44-45; assoc. dir. elec. eng, res. lab, Texas, 46-48; res. assoc, Cornell, 48-53, assoc. prof. elec. eng. 53-59, prof, 59-66, Walter R. Read prof. eng, 65-66; PROF. ELEC. ENG. & SPACE SCI. & DEAN ENG. & SCI, RICE UNIV, 66-, v.pres. univ, 69-72. Chmn. comt. sci. radio, Nat. Acad. Sci, 57-60; chmn. U.S. del, Int. Sci. Radio Union, 60, chmn, comn. II, 69-; dir. Arecibo Ionospheric Observ, P.R, 60-65; mem. adv. panel radio telescopes, Nat. Sci. Found, 60-66; trustee, Cornell Univ. Corp. Atmospheric Res, 65-66; chmn. bd. trustees, Upper Atmosphere Res. Corp, 71-; mem, Radio Propagation Comn; chmn, radio meteorol. comn, Int. Coun. Sci. Unions; consult, Gen. Elec. Co; Stromberg Carlson Co. Div, Gen. Dynamics Corp; Cornell Aeronaut. Lab; Lincoln Lab; Stavid Eng. Co. Balth. Vander Pol Award, 66. Civilian with Nat. Defense Res. Comt; U.S.A.A.F, 42-46, Capt. Nat. Acad. Sci; AAAS; Am. Meteorol. Soc; fel. Inst. Elec. & Electronics Eng; N.Y. Acad. Sci; Am. Geophys. Union; Int. Sci. Radio Union. Radio physics, meteorology and waves. Address: College of Science & Engineering, Rice University, P.O. Box 1892, Houston, TX 77001.

GORDON, WILLIAM EDWIN, b. Lumsden, Sask, Can, Mar. 31, 19; nat; m. 43; c. 3. PHYSICAL CHEMISTRY. B.A, Univ. Sask, 37, Hons, 38, M.A, 40; fel, Harvard, 40-43, Ph.D.(phys. chem), 43. Res. assoc. & group leader, Off. Sci. Res. & Develop. contract, Oceanog. Inst. Woods Hole, 43-46; asst. prof. chem, Univ. Mo, 46-50; group & sect. leader, res. & develop. div, Arthur D. Little, Inc, 50-61; mem. staff, Inst. Defense Anal, 61-62; Combustion & Explosives Res, Inc, 62-65; ASSOC. PROF. CHEM, PA. STATE UNIV, McKEESPORT, 66- Cert, Dept. Defense, 49. AAAS; Am. Chem. Soc; Am. Phys. Soc; Combustion Inst; fel. Am. Inst. Chem. Combustion and explosion phenomena; chemical process technology; physical and numerical analysis. Address: 1351 Terrace Dr, Pittsburgh, PA 15228.

GORDON, WILLIAM G(EORGE), b. N.Y.C, Jan. 31, 08; m. 44. BIOCHEMISTRY. A.B, Cornell, 27, M.A, 28; Ph.D.(physiol. chem), Yale, 33. Asst. physiol. chem, Yale, 29-33, Nat. Res. Council fel, 33-34, Coxe fel, 34-35; instr. biochem, Stanford, 35-39; Smith, Kline & French fel. agr. & biol. chem, Pa. State, 39-41; from assoc. chemist to SUPVRY. CHEMIST, EAST. REGIONAL RES. LAB, AGR. RES. SERV, U.S. DEPT. AGR, 41- Superior serv. award, U.S. Dept. Agr, 59. AAAS; Am. Chem. Soc.(Borden award, 58); Am. Soc. Biol. Chem. Protein chemistry; isolation and composition of milk proteins. Address: Eastern Regional Research Lab, Chestnut Hill Station, U.S. Dept. of Agriculture, Philadelphia, PA 19118.

GORDON, WILLIAM J(OHN), b. East McKeesport, Pa, Dec. 4, 39; m. 65. APPLIED MATHEMATICS. B.S, Pittsburgh, 61; Boeing Co. fel, Nat. Sci. Found. grant & Ph.D.(appl. math), Brown, 65. Reactor analyst, Westinghouse Elec. Corp. 60-61; res. mathematician, res. labs, Boeing Co, 62; res. asst. appl. math, Brown, 62-65; sr. res. mathematician, RES. LABS, GEN. MOTORS CORP, 65-71, ASST. HEAD DEPT. MATH, 71- Am. Math. Soc; Soc. Indust. & Appl. Math; Asn. Comput. Mach. Numerical analysis; optimization techniques; approximation theory. Address: Dept. of Mathematics, General Motors Research Labs, Warren, MI 48090.

GORDON, WILLIAM L(IVINGSTON), b. Tanta, Egypt, Jan. 17, 27; U.S. citizen; m. 49; c. 3. SOLID STATE PHYSICS. B.Sc, Muskingum Col, 48; M.Sc, Ohio State, 50, Gen. Elec. Co. Coffin fel, 52-53, Ph.D, 54. Instr. PHYSICS, Ohio State, 54-55; CASE WEST. RESERVE UNIV, 55-56, asst. prof, 56-61, assoc. prof, 61-67, PROF, 67- Am. Phys. Soc. Cryogenics; structure of liquid helium; Fermi surfaces in metals; transport properties in metals. Address: Dept. of Physics, Case Western Reserve University, Cleveland, OH 44106.

GORDUS, ADON A(LDEN), b. Chicago, Ill, Mar. 23, 32; m. 58. PHYSICAL CHEMISTRY. B.S, Ill. Inst. Tech, 52; Ph.D, Wisconsin, 56. Asst, UNIV. MICH, ANN ARBOR, 56-57, instr. CHEM, 57-60, asst. prof, 60-64, assoc. prof, 64-70, PROF, 70-, ASSOC. DIR. HONORS PROG, 64- AAAS; Am. Chem. Soc; Am. Phys. Soc. Neutron activation analysis of archaeological artifacts, ancient and medieval coins; environmental and forensic chemistry. Address: Dept. of Chemistry, University of Michigan, Ann Arbor, MI 48104.

GORDY, EDWIN, b. Phila, Pa, May 17, 25; m; c. 3. BIOMEDICAL ENGINEERING. Harvard, 42-44; M.D, Jefferson Med. Col, 48; D.Sc.(physiol. chem), Pennsylvania, 52. Intern, Jewish Hosp, Phila, 48-49; head, instrument design & develop. dept, Roswell Park Mem. Inst, 54-65; sr. scientist, instrument design & develop. lab, Worcester Found. Exp. Biol, 65-67; DIR. RES, LEXINGTON INSTRUMENTS CORP, 67- Consult, Biomed. Instrumentation, 71- Head, electronics lab, Walter Reed Army Inst. Res, Med.C, 52-54, Capt. Biophys. Soc; assoc. Inst. Elec. & Electronics Eng. Development of new research tools for use in biological research. Address: 17 Otis St, Newtonville, MA 02160.

GORDY, THOMAS D(ANIEL), b. High Point, N.C, Oct. 8, 15; m. 35; c. 4. ELECTRICAL ENGINEERING. B.S.E.E, North Carolina, 36; M.E.E, Rensselaer Polytech, 48, Ph.D.(elec. eng), 55. Test engr, GEN. ELEC. CO, 36-37, elec. engr, 37-41, develop. engr. magnetics, 41-53, statist. anal, 53-56, specialist opers. res. & synthesis, 56-60, administr. bus. res, 60-61, CONSULT. ENGR. LOGISTICS MGT, 61- Lectr, Williams Col.(Mass), 56-

57; adj. prof, Rensselaer Polytech, Inst, 57-65. Am. Statist. Asn; fel. Inst. Elec. Eng; Inst. Mgt. Sci. Research, development and application of oriented magnetic core steels; business operations, their integration and inter-relations; design of logistics systems. Address: General Electric Co, Ordnance Systems, 100 Plastics Ave, Pittsfield, MA 01201.

GORDY, WALTER, b. Lawrence, Miss, Apr. 20, 09; m. 35; c. 2. PHYSICS. B.A, Miss. Col, 32; M.A, North Carolina, 33, Ph.D.(physics), 35; hon. Dr, Lille, France, 55; hon. LL.D, Miss. Col, 59. Asst. physics, North Carolina, 32-33, 34-35; assoc. prof. math. & physics, Baylor Col, 35-41; fel. physics, Nat. Res. Coun, Calif. Inst. Tech, 41-42; mem. staff, radiation lab, Mass. Inst. Technol, 42-46; assoc. prof. PHYSICS, DUKE UNIV, 46-48, PROF, 48-, JAMES B. DUKE PROF, 58- Mem. adv. comt, Off. Ord. Res, U.S. Army, 53-57; Nat. Res. Coun, 54-57, 68-; Fulbright screening comt. physics, Assoc. Res. Coun, 55-56; vis. prof, Univ. Tex, 58; mem. Nat. Res. Coun. Panel for selection Nat. Sci. postdoctoral fels, 59-61, 64-66; physics adv. panel, Radio Standards Lab, Nat. Bur. Standards, 59-65. Sci. res. award, Oak Ridge Inst. Nat. Studies, 49. Nat. Acad. Sci; AAAS; Radiation Res. Soc; fel. Am. Phys. Soc. Infrared spectroscopy; hydrogen bonding; electron diffraction; electronegativities of the elements; microwave radar; millimeter and submillimeter waves; microwave and radiofrequency spectroscopy; nuclear moments; molecular structures; radiation damage. Address: Dept. of Physics, Duke University, Durham, NC 27706.

GORE, BRYAN FRANK, b. Berwyn, Ill, Dec. 3, 38; m. 63; c. 3. PARTICLE PHYSICS. B.Eng.Phys, Cornell, 61; M.S, Michigan, 64, Ph.D.(physics), 67. ASST. PROF. PHYSICS, Idaho, 67-68; CENT. WASH. STATE COL, 68- Faculty res. fel. physics, Idaho, summer 68; vis. scientist, ctr. theoret. physics, Univ. Md, College Park, 69-70; Stanford Linear Accelerator Ctr, summer, 71. Consult, Bunker Hill Co, Kellogg, Idaho, 67-68. Am. Phys. Soc; Am. Asn. Physics Teachers. S-matrix investigation of pion-pion scattering. Address: Dept. of Physics, Central Washington State College, Ellensburg, WA 98926.

GORE, DOROTHY J, b. Oklahoma City, Okla, May 1, 26. GEOLOGY, GEOGRAPHY. B.S, Principia Col, 48; M.S, Illinois, 52; Ph.D.(geol), Wisconsin, 63. Asst. geologist, Ill. State Geol. Surv, 48-52; asst. prof. geol, Principia Col, 52-65; EARTH SCI, SOUTH. ILL. UNIV, 65-69, ASSOC. PROF, 69- AAAS; Mineral. Soc. Am; Geol. Soc. Am; Nat. Asn. Geol. Teachers; Am. Inst. Mining, Metall. & Petrol. Eng. Petrology and mineralogy of granite and related rocks. Address: Dept. of Earth Sciences & Urban Regional Planning, Southern Illinois University, Edwardsville, IL 62025.

GORE, EDWARD MICHAEL, b. N.Y.C, Nov. 6, 20; m. 47; c. 3. PHARMACOLOGY, BIOCHEMISTRY. B.Sc, Fordham, 42, M.Sc, 50; M.A, Villanova Univ, 71. Chemist, med. col, Cornell, 48-49; biochem. sect, Rockefeller Inst, 49-50; BIOCHEMIST & GROUP LEADER TOXICOL, WYETH LABS. INC, 50- U.S.A, 42-45. AAAS; Am. Chem. Soc; N.Y. Acad. Sci; Brit. Biochem. Soc. Chemical pharmacology and drug metabolism; drug toxicity; antibiotics; analgesics; central nervous system; behavioral effects of drugs, psychopharmacology; excretion studies; blood and urine chemistry; steroid chemistry and endocrinology. Address: Dept. of Toxicology, Wyeth Labs. Inc, P.O. Box 861, Paoli, PA 19301.

GORE, IRA, b. New York, N.Y, Sept. 10, 13; m. 54; c. 1. PATHOLOGY. A.B, Cornell, 34, M.D, 37. From intern to res, 37-41; pathologist, Armed Forces Inst. Path, 46-50; col. med, Baylor, 50-51; Henry Ford Hosp, 51-52; col. med, Utah, 52-53; Mt. Sinai Hosp, Ill, 53-54; asst. clin. prof. PATH, sch. med, Harvard, 54-60; assoc. clin. prof, 60-62, assoc. nutrit. sch. pub. health, 54-62; PROF, SCH. MED, Boston, 62-68; UNIV. ALA, BIRMINGHAM, 68- Pathologist, Vet. Admin. Hosp, 54-62; lectr, Harvard Med. Sch, 62-68. Am. Soc. Clin. Path; Am. Med. Asn; Am. Asn. Path. & Bact; Col. Am. Path. Hemopoietic and cardiovascular diseases. Address: Dept. of Pathology, University of Alabama, 1919 Seventh Ave. S, Birmingham, AL 35233.

GORE, ROBERT C(UMMINS), b. Evansville, Ind, Aug. 18, 07; m. 36; c. 1. PHYSICAL CHEMISTRY. A.B, Evansville Col, 29; A.M, Indiana, 30, univ. fel, 30-31, Ph.D.(phys. chem), 33; Chicago, 41. Asst. chem, Indiana, 29-30, 31-33, instr, 33-36; Kentucky, 36-37; Illinois, 37-41, assoc, 41-42, special res. assoc, 42-43; group leader & res. physicist, Stamford res. labs, Am. Cyanamid Co, 43-59; consult. chemist & spectroscopist, 59-60; sr. spectroscopist, PERKIN-ELMER CORP, 60-71, CONSULT. CHEMIST-SPECTROSCOPIST, 71- Consult, biol. labs, Chem. Corps, U.S. Army, 52-54, Army Chem. Center, 54-60. Civilian with Off. Sci. Res. & Develop, 41-43. Am. Chem. Soc; Optical Soc. Am. Colloid chemistry; dielectric constants; infrared spectroscopy; sanitary chemistry; instrumental methods of analysis. Address: R.D. 2, South Salem, NY 10590.

GORE, W(ILBERT) L(EE), b. Meridian, Idaho, Jan. 25, 12; m. 35; c. 5. CHEMISTRY. B.S, Utah, 33, M.S, 35; hon. H.H.D, Westminster Col.(Utah), 71. Chem. engr, Am. Smelting & Ref. Co, Utah, 34-41; area process engr, Remington Arms Co, 42-43, supt. statist. eng, 43-45; sr. res. supvr, polychems. dept. E.I. du Pont de Nemours & Co, 46-58; PRES. W.L. GORE & ASSOCS, INC, 58- Dir, Samuel Moore Co. Am. Chem. Soc; Soc. Plastics Eng; Am. Statist. Asn. Plastics research; fabrication and use of plastics; statistical methods; design of experiments; operations research. Address: W.L. Gore & Associates, 555 Papermill Rd, Newark, DE 19711.

GORE, WILLIS C(ARROLL), b. Baltimore, Md, May 20, 26; m. 50; c. 3. ELECTRICAL ENGINEERING. B.E, Hopkins, 48, Dr.Eng, 52. Jr. instr. ELEC. ENG, JOHNS HOPKINS UNIV, 47-49, instr, 49-52, asst. prof, 52-58, ASSOC. PROF, 58- U.S.N.R, 44-46. Sr. mem. Inst. Elec. & Electronics Eng. Digital computers; information theory; algebraic coding theory. Address: 1302 Brook Meadow Dr, Baltimore, MD 21204.

GORECKI, DONNA, b. Chicago, Ill, Oct. 28, 31. CYTOLOGY, DEVELOPMENTAL BIOLOGY. B.S, Univ. Chicago, 59, M.S, 60; U.S. Pub. Health Serv. fel, Loyola Univ. Chicago, 64-67, Ph.D.(anat), 69. Res. asst, dept. biophys, Univ. Chicago, 60-61; dept. anat, Loyola Univ. Chicago, 62-64, res. assoc, 67-69; ASST. PROF. BIOL, Chicago City Col, 69 & 70; ROOSEVELT UNIV, 70- AAAS; Am. Inst. Biol. Sci; Am. Soc. Zool; Soc. Develop. Biol. Electron microscopy of the chloride cell of the fish gill; sex chromatin in the naturally occurring avian freemartin; the incidence of sex chromatin in the avian amnion. Address: P.O. Box 11685, Ft. Dearborn Station, Chicago, IL 60611.

GOREE, JAMES GLEASON, b. Birmingham, Ala, June 21, 35; m. 61; c. 2. ENGINEERING MECHANICS, APPLIED MATHEMATICS. B.S.M.E, Florida, 60; M.S.A.E, Washington (Seattle), 62; Ph.D.(eng. mech), Alabama, 66. Res. engr, Redstone Arsenal Res. Div, Rohm & Haas Co, 61-62; asst. prof. ENG. MECH, Kentucky, 62-63; CLEMSON UNIV, 66-68, ASSOC. PROF, 68- Consult, aerospace sci. lab, Lockheed-Ga. Co, 66-68. U.S.A, 53-55. Am. Soc. Mech. Eng. Three-dimensional elasticity; mathematical analysis of composite materials. Address: Dept. of Engineering Mechanics, Clemson University, Clemson, SC 29631.

GOREE, WILLIAM S(TROZIER), b. Birmingham, Ala, June 21, 35; m. 63; c. 1. LOW TEMPERATURE PHYSICS. B.S.M.E, Florida, 59, M.S.E, 60, Ph.D.(solid state physics), 64. Physicist, Stanford Res. Inst, 64-67, chmn. low temperature physics dept, 67-69, sr. physicist, 69; MGR. CRYOGENICS DIV, DEVELCO INC, 69- Co-chmn, Conf. Physics of Superconducting Devices, Charlottesville, Va, 67; chmn, Int. Conf. Fluctuations in Superconductors, Asilomar, Calif, 68; secy, Int. Conf. Sci. Superconductivity, Stanford Univ, 69. U.S.A, 52-54. Am. Phys. Soc. Development of superconducting devices as magnetometers and magnetic shields; measurements of the magnetic properties of biological molecules. Address: Develco Inc, 530 Logue Ave, Mountain View, CA 94040.

GORELICK, ARTHUR N(ATHANIEL), b. Philadelphia, Pa, Oct. 30, 14; m. 57; c. 3. VETERINARY MEDICINE. V.M.D, Pennsylvania, 37; M.S, Ohio State, 41. Vet. pathologist, Pa. Bur. Animal Indust, 37-39; jr. veterinarian, Bur. Animal Indust, U.S. Dept. Agr, 39; instr. bact, Ohio State, 39-41; proj. supvr. bact. res, Camp Detrick, Md, 46-51, br. chief, 51-52, dept. chief, med. bact. div, Ft. Detrick, 52-56, chief, 56-60, virus & rickettsia div, 60-69, dir. biol. sci. labs, 69-71; RETIRED. Dipl, Am. Bd. Microbiol. Vet.C. Res, 37-, Col. AAAS; Am. Soc. Microbiol; N.Y. Acad. Sci; Soc. Exp. Biol. & Med; Am. Vet. Med. Asn; Tissue Culture Asn; Am. Acad. Microbiol. Infectious diseases; research administration. Address: Route 5, Frederick, MD 21701.

GOREN, HOWARD JOSEPH, b. Bialocerkwe, U.S.S.R, Apr. 9, 41; Can. citizen; m. 65; c. 2. BIOCHEMISTRY, ENZYMOLOGY. B.S, Univ. Toronto, 64; fel, State Univ. N.Y. Buffalo, 67, Ph.D.(biochem, pharmacol), 69. Nat. Res. Coun. Can. fel, dept. biophys, Weizmann Inst. Sci, 68-70; ASST. PROF. MED. BIOCHEM, UNIV. CALGARY, 70- Univ. gen. res. fund grant, Univ. Calgary, 71-72. Can. Biochem. Soc. Synthesis of polypeptides, determination of their secondary and tertiary structure by physical methods and their application as enzyme models. Address: Faculty of Medicine, University of Calgary, Calgary 44, Alta, Can.

GOREN, MAYER B(EAR), b. Tomaszow, Poland, Mar. 19, 21; nat; m. 43; c. 2. ORGANIC CHEMISTRY. B.A, Rice, 42, fel, 42-43, M.A, 43; univ. fel, Harvard, 46-48, Du Pont fel, 48-49, Ph.D.(org. chem), 49. Jr. chemist, Shell Develop. Co, 43-44; asst. prof. chem, Northeastern, 49-51; sr. chemist, Kerr-McGee Oil Indust, Inc, 51-58, chief res. chemist, 58-63; ASST. PROF. MICROBIOL, SCH. MED, UNIV. COLO, DENVER, 67-; SR. RES. SCIENTIST, NAT. JEWISH HOSP. & RES. CTR, 63- U.S.N.R, 44-46, Lt.(jg). Am. Chem. Soc; Am. Soc. Microbiol. Lipids; surface chemistry of mycobacteria; microbiology and immunochemistry; polysaccharides; polyelectrolytes; ion exchange. Address: 125 Locust St, Denver, CO 80220.

GOREN, SIMON L, b. Baltimore, Md, Aug. 31, 36; m. 62; c. 1. CHEMICAL ENGINEERING. B.E.S, Johns Hopkins Univ, 58, Nat. Sci. Found. fels, 58-60, Martin Vanguard fel, 60-61, D.Eng.(chem. eng), 62. Engr, Esso Res. & Eng. Co, Standard Oil Co. N.J, 61-62; asst. prof. CHEM. ENG, UNIV. CALIF, BERKELEY, 62-67, assoc. prof, 67-71, PROF, 71- Hydrodynamics and mass transfer of oscillatory flow; particulate systems. Address: Dept. of Chemical Engineering, University of California, Berkeley, CA 94720.

GORENSTEIN, DAVID GEORGE, b. Chicago, Ill, Oct. 6, 45; m. 67. ORGANIC CHEMISTRY, BIOCHEMISTRY. S.B, Mass. Inst. Technol, 66, univ. fel, Harvard, 66-67, summer, Nat. Sci. Found. trainee, 67, A.M, 67, Nat. Insts. Health fel, 67-69, Ph.D.(chem), 69. ASST. PROF. CHEM, UNIV. ILL, CHICAGO CIRCLE, 69- Am. Chem. Soc. Petrol. Res. Fund grant, 70-73; Nat. Inst. Gen. Med. Sci. grant, 71-74; Res. Corp. grant, 71- Am. Chem. Soc. Pseudorotation in pentacovalent phosphoranes; application of nuclear magnetic resonance to enzymatic mechanisms; physical organic and bioorganic studies of biologically important phosphate esters. Address: Dept. of Chemistry, University of Illinois at Chicago Circle, Chicago, IL 60680.

GORENSTEIN, PAUL, b. New York, N.Y, Aug. 15, 34. ASTROPHYSICS, NUCLEAR PHYSICS. B.Eng. Phys, Cornell, 57; Atomic Energy Cmn. fel. & Ph.D.(physics), Mass. Inst. Tech, 62. Instr. physics, Mass. Inst. Tech, 62-63; Fulbright fel. & spec. consult, Nat. Cmt. Nuclear Energy, Italy, 63-65; sr. scientist, AM. SCI. & ENG, INC, 65-70, SR. STAFF SCIENTIST, 70- Am. Phys. Soc; Am. Astron. Soc. X-ray astronomy and planetology, especially using nuclear techniques; nuclear instrumentation and high energy nuclear physics. Address: 100 Memorial Dr, Cambridge, Mass. 02142.

GORENSTEIN, SAMUEL, b. N.Y.C; m. 48; c. 2. OPERATIONS RESEARCH, MATHEMATICS. M.S, N.Y. Univ, 58, NASA & IBM Corp. fels, 66, Ph.D.(opers. res), 68. Statistician, U.S. Govt, 42-43; cert. pub. acct, I.J. Drucker & Co, 45-49; controller, Am. Jewish Comt, 49-59; mathematician, Syst. Develop. Corp, 59-63; advan. systs. develop. div, IBM CORP, 63-66, mem. sci. staff, N.Y. Sci. Ctr, 68-70, MEM. RES. STAFF, T.J. WATSON RES. CTR, 70- Adj, Fairleigh Dickinson Univ, 63-64; adj. assoc. prof, N.Y. Univ, 69- U.S.A.F, 43-45, 2nd Lt. Am. Math. Soc; Am. Inst. Indust. Eng. Measurement and evaluation problems for computer systems; project management with resource constraints; statistical aspects of computer simulation; control models; queueing and reliability. Address: T.J. Watson Research Center, IBM Corp, P.O. Box 218, Yorktown Heights, NY 10598.

GORENZ, AUGUST M(ARK), b. Aurora, Ill, Apr. 25, 20. PLANT PATHOLOGY. B.E, Ill. State Norm. Univ, 40; M.S, Wisconsin, 42, Ph.D.(plant path), 48. Plant pathologist, U.S. Dept. Agr, 48-52; plant path. adv, Inst. Inter-Am. Affairs, Int. Coop. Admin, 52-61; hort. adv, U.S. AGENCY INT. DEVELOP, 61-66, PLANT PATH. ADV. & HEAD DIV, COCOA RES. INST. NIGERIA, 66- Sig.C, U.S.A, 42-46. AAAS; Am. Inst. Biol. Sci; Am. Phytopath. Soc; Bee Res. Asn. Tropical plant pathology and horticulture; apiculture. Address: IBADAN-ID, Dept. of State, Washington, DC 20521.

GORES, ROBERT J(AMES), b. Prairie du Chien, Wis, Aug. 1, 25; m. 50; c. 3. ORAL SURGERY. D.D.S, Marquette, 50; Mayo Found. fel, Minnesota, 52-55, M.S, 55. INSTR. ORAL SURG, SCH. DENT, UNIV. MINN, 56- Consult, Mayo Clin. & Hosps, 55- Dent.C, 49-52, Res, 52-, Capt. Am. Soc. Oral Surg; Am. Dent. Asn; Int. Asn. Dent. Res. Dental physiology as related to anesthesia and to oral surgical procedures. Address: University of Minnesota School of Dentistry, Rochester, MN 55901.

GORESKY, CARL A, b. Mundare, Alta, Aug. 25, 32; m. 55; c. 6. INTERNAL MEDICINE. B.Sc, McGill, 53, M.D, C.M, 55, Ph.D.(physiol), 65; fel, Hopkins, 58-59. Sessional lectr. physiol, McGILL UNIV, 63-64, asst. prof. MED, 64-66, ASSOC. PROF, 66-; ASST. DIR, UNIV. MED. CLIN, MONTREAL GEN. HOSP, 70- Fel, Royal Col. Physicians & Surgeons Can, 60, award, 63. Fel. Am. Col. Physicians. Physiology of transcapillary exchange; multiple indicator dilution techniques to investigate exchange of materials across the sinusoids of the liver; analysis of dilution curves. Address: University Medical Clinic, Montreal General Hospital, Room 1068, Montreal 109, Que, Can.

GORESLINE, HARRY E(DWARD), b. Gardner, Kans, Aug. 13, 98; m. 70; c. 2. FOOD TECHNOLOGY. B.S, Ore. State Col, 26; M.S, Iowa State Col, 28, Ph.D.(sanit. bact), 31. Jr. bacteriologist, eng. exp. sta, Iowa, 27-30; from assoc. bacteriologist to sr. bacteriologist, food res. div, bur. agr. chem. & eng, U.S. Dept. Agr, 30-43, food technologist, poultry br, prod. & mkt. admin, 43-52, dir. chem. & microbiol. div, 52-54, assoc. dir. res. food labs, 54-56, dep. sci. dir, Food & Container Inst. Armed Forces, 56-63; mem. staff, Joint Div. Atomic Energy in Food & Agr, Int. Atomic Energy Agency, Vienna, Austria, 63-69; CONSULT, 69- Lectr, Am. Univ, 32-34. Am. Chem. Soc; Am. Soc. Microbiol; fel. Am. Pub. Health Asn; fel. Inst. Food Technol. Food bacteriology and radiation technology; sanitation; quality control; fermentation; microbiology. Address: Kaasgraben Gasse 52/4/7, Vienna 1190, Austria.

GORETSKY, M. EDWARD, b. N.Y.C, July 3, 24; m. 53; c. 5. OPERATIONS ANALYSIS. B.A.E, N.Y. Univ, 51; M.S, Newark Col. Eng, 57; Ph.D. (bus. admin), Am. Univ, 68. Aerodynamicist, Curtiss Propeller Div, Curtiss-Wright Corp, 51-56, prod. appln. engr, Wright Aeronaut. Div, 56-57; res. analyst, Melpar, Inc, 57-58; cost engr, Anal. Serv, Inc, 58-65, chief, econ. anal. br, 65-68; HEAD cost & econ. anal. sect, TRW SYSTS, INC, 68-70, MGT. SYSTS. SECT, 70- U.S.N.R, 44-46. Opers. Res. Soc. Am. Management sciences including development of information systems, economic analysis, cost analysis, and operations analysis. Address: 8209 Marcy Ave, Springfield, VA 22152.

GORETTA, L(OUIS) A(LEXANDER), b. Portland, Ore, Aug. 2, 22; m. 51; c. 3. ORGANIC CHEMISTRY. B.S, Portland, 43; M.S, Notre Dame, 44, Ph.D.(chem), 51. Res. chemist, fats & oils, Armour & Co, 50-53; petrol, Standard Oil Co, 53-59; sr. chemist, NALCO CHEM. CO, 59-66, GROUP LEADER, 66- U.S.N.R, 44-46. Am. Chem. Soc; Sci. Res. Soc. Am; fel. Am. Inst. Chem. Hydrocarbons; industrial chemicals. Address: 321 Osage Lane, Naperville, IL 60540.

GORFEIN, DAVID SCHLANGER, Exp. Psychol, see Suppl. I to 11th ed, Soc. & Behav. Vols.

GORGES, HEINZ A(UGUST), b. Stettin, Ger, July 22, 13; U.S. citizen; m. 57. ENGINEERING. M.E, Dresden Tech, 38; Ph.D.(mech. eng), Hanover Tech, 46. Group leader supersonics, Aero Res. Estab, Ger, 40-45; scientist, Royal Aircraft Estab, Eng, 46-49; prin. sci. off, Weapons Res. Estab, S.Australia, 49-59; sci. asst. aeroballistics, Marshall Space Flight Ctr, NASA, Ala, 59-61; dir. adv. projs, Cook. Tech. Ctr, Ill, 61-62; sci. adv, IIT Res. Inst, 62-66; ASST. V.PRES. ENVIRON. & PHYS. SCI. DIV, TRACOR, INC, 66- Prof, Redstone Exten, Univ. Ala, 60-61. Assoc. fel. Am. Inst. Aeronaut. & Astronaut; Am. Geophys. Union; Am. Soc. Mech. Eng; Acoust. Soc. Am. Supersonics and hypersonics; aerodynamics of propulsion; environmental sciences; research management. Address: Environmental & Physical Sciences Division, Tracor Inc, 6500 Tracor Lane, Austin, TX 78721.

GORHAM, EVILLE, b. Halifax, N.S, Oct. 15, 25; m. 48; c. 4. PLANT ECOLOGY, LIMNOLOGY. B.Sc, Dalhousie, 45, M.Sc, 47; Royal Soc. Can. fel, State Forest Res. Inst, Stockholm, 50-51; Ph.D.(plant ecol), London, 51. Lectr. bot, Univ. Col, London, 50-54; ecologist, Brit. Freshwater Biol. Asn, 54-58; lectr. bot, Toronto, 58-59, asst. prof, 59-62; assoc. prof, Minnesota, 62-65; prof. bot. & head dept. biol, Alberta, Calgary, 65-66; PROF. BOT, UNIV. MINN, MINNEAPOLIS, 66-, head dept, 67-71. Ecol. Soc. Am; Am. Soc. Limnol. & Oceanog; Int. Asn. Limnol; Fedn. Am. Sci; Brit. Freshwater Biol. Asn. Chemical aspects of ecology, limnology and soil science. Address: Dept. of Botany, University of Minnesota, Minneapolis, MN 55455.

GORHAM, JOHN FRANCIS, b. Medford, Mass, Sept. 24, 21; m. 48; c. 2. CHEMICAL ENGINEERING. B.S, Maine, 50, M.S, 52. Jr. engr, Stamford Lab, Am. Cyanamid Co, 52-53; instr. CHEM. ENG, UNIV. MAINE, 53-56, asst. prof, 56-62, ASSOC. PROF, 62- U.S.A, 42-45. Am. Inst. Chem. Eng; Tech. Asn. Pulp & Paper Indust. Process dynamics and control; pulp and paper technology; electronic computer specialties. Address: Dept. of Chemical Engineering, University of Maine, Orono, ME 04473.

GORHAM, J(OHN) R(ICHARD), b. Puyallup, Wash, Dec. 19, 22; m. 44; c. 2. VETERINARY MEDICINE. B.S. & D.V.M, State Col. Wash, 46, M.S, 47; Ph.D, Wisconsin, 53. Asst. prof. path, State Col. Wash, 47-51; asst. virol, Wisconsin, 51-53; vet. in charge, fur animal disease sta, U.S. Dept. Agr, Wash. State Univ, 53-66, DIR, ENDOPARASITE VECTOR PIONEERING RES. LAB, ANIMAL DISEASE & PARASITE RES. DIV, AGR. RES. SERV, WASH, 66-, assoc. prof. path, 53-57. Dipl, Col. Lab. Animal Med. U.S.A, 42-44, Res, 49-, Maj. Am. Soc. Exp. Path; Am. Vet. Med. Asn; Am. Asn. Immunol. Virology and epizootiology; virus and rickettsial diseases of carnivores; endoparasitic transmission of viruses and Rickettsiae. Address: Animal Disease & Parasite Research Division, Agricultural Research Service, Pullman, WA 99163.

GORHAM, J(OHN) RICHARD, b. Montgomery Co, Ohio, July 27, 31; m. 52; c. 4. MEDICAL ENTOMOLOGY. A.B, Miami (Ohio), 53, M.S, 56; Ph.D. (entom), Ohio State, 60; dipl, Malaria Eradication Training Ctr, Jamaica, 61; Univ. Alaska, 70. Res. asst. invert. zool, Univ. N.Mex, 53; prev. med. technician, Army Health Nursing Serv, Walter Reed Army Med. Ctr, 54-55; grad. asst. zool, Miami Univ, 55-56, instr, 56-57; grad. asst, Ohio State Univ, 57, asst. instr, 58-60; consult. entomologist malaria eradication, Pan Am. Health Orgn, Paraguay, 61-63; res. assoc, Inst. Int. Med, Univ. Md, 63-64; Pakistan Med. Res. Ctr, 64-65; SR. SCIENTIST, vector borne disease training sect, Ctr. Disease Control, U.S. PUB. HEALTH SERV, Ga, 66-69, RES. ENTOMOLOGIST, ARCTIC HEALTH RES. CTR, ALASKA, 69- Res. assoc, Conserv. Found, N.Y, 58-59; aquatic entomologist, Maine Forest Serv, 58-59; U.S. Pub. Health Serv. trainee, sch. trop. med, Univ. P.R, 60-61; vis. lectr, Atlanta Baptist Col, 68-69; consult. entomologist, Alaska Air Command, 70-; lectr, Univ. Alaska, 71- U.S.P.H.S, 66-, Lt. Col. AAAS; Am. Inst. Biol. Sci; Am. Sci. Affiliation; Am. Mosquito Control Asn; Human Ecol. Soc; Int. Asn. Ecol; Royal Soc. Trop. Med. & Hyg; Am. Soc. Trop. Med. & Hyg; Entom. Soc. Am. Ecology and systematics of mosquitoes; ecology of Paraguay; arctic ecology; pest management; terrestrial and aquatic ecology; zoonoses; ecology of vector-borne diseases; malariology; arbovirology; ecology of pesticides; myrmecology; venomous arthropods. Address: Arctic Health Research Center, College, AK 99701.

GORHAM, PAUL R(AYMOND), b. Fredericton, N.B, Apr. 16, 18; m. 43; c. 3. PLANT PHYSIOLOGY. B.A, New Brunswick, 38; fel, Maine, 38-40, M.S, 40; fel, Calif. Inst. Tech, 40-43, Ph.D.(plant physiol), 43. Agr. asst. plant physiol, div. bot. & plant path, Dom. Dept. Agr, Ottawa, 43-45; jr. res. off, div. biosci, Nat. Res. Coun. Can, 45-46, asst. res. off. plant sci. invests, 46-51, assoc. res. off, plant physiol. sect, 51-57, sr. res. off, 57-65, prin. res. off, 65-69, head sect, 52-69; PROF. BOT, UNIV. ALTA, 69-, CHMN. DEPT, 71- Mem. Can. Comt, Int. Biol. Prog, chmn. prod. processes subcomt. AAAS; Am. Soc. Plant Physiol; Bot. Soc. Am; Am. Soc. Agron; Phycol. Soc. Am; Can. Biochem. Soc; Can. Soc. Plant Physiol.(pres, 58-59); Agr. Inst. Can; fel. Royal Soc. Can; Can. Bot. Asn; Int. Phycol. Soc; Int. Asn. Theoret. & Appl. Limnol. Physiology of blue-green algae; translocation; physiology of submerged aquatic macrophytes. Address: Dept. of Botany, University of Alberta, Edmonton, Alta, Can.

GORHAM, WILLIAM F(RANKLIN), b. Brandon, Vt, Aug. 13, 26; m. 53; c. 4. ORGANIC & POLYMER CHEMISTRY. A.B, Miami (Ohio), 48; Ph.D.(chem), Mass. Inst. Tech, 51. Sr. res. chemist, Bakelite Corp, 51-56, group leader, PLASTICS DIV, UNION CARBIDE CORP, 56-65, ASST. DIR. RES, 65- U.S.N.R, 44-46. Am. Chem. Soc. Synthetic organic chemistry. Address: Union Carbide Corp, 1 River Rd, Bound Brook, NJ 08805.

GORI, GIO BATTA, b. Tarcento, Italy, Feb. 23, 31; U.S. citizen; m. 58; c. 2. VIROLOGY, CELL PHYSIOLOGY. D.Biol.Sc.(bot), Camerino, 56. Assoc. microbiol, Ist. Superiore Sanità, Italy, 56-58; virol, Pittsburgh, 58-59; assoc. dir, Ist. Sclavo, Italy, 59-60; assoc. virol, Wistar Inst, Pennsylvania, 60-62; dir. qual. control & asst. to pres, Microbiol. Assocs. Inc, 62-63, dir. prod, 63-65; head, virol. & immunol. dept, Melpar Inc, 65-67; dir. biol. res. lab, Litton Systs. Inc, 67-68; ASSOC. SCI. DIR. PROG. ETIOLOGY, NAT. CANCER INST, NAT. INSTS. HEALTH, 68- AAAS; Soc. Indust. Microbiol; Am. Asn. Lab. Animal Sci; Am. Soc. Microbiol; Soc. Cryobiol. Algae; halophilic bacteria; virus epidemiology; production and control of polio vaccines; continuous cultivation of cells and viruses; cell transformation; normal and pathological cell metabolism; transplantation immunity; viral and chemical carcinogenesis; planning and management of research programs. Address: 6503 Pyle Rd, Bethesda, MD 20034.

GORIN, EVERETT, b. U.S.A, Dec. 16, 10; m. 50; c. 2. PHYSICAL CHEMISTRY. B.S, California, 31; Ph.D.(chem), Princeton, 34. Res. fel, Princeton, 38-39; res. supvr, Magnolia Petrol. Co, 39-46; res. assoc, Socony Vacuum Oil Co, 46-47; MGR. PROCESS RES, PITTSBURGH CONSOLIDATION COAL CO, 47- Am. Chem. Soc; Am. Inst. Chem. Catalysis; process development; reaction kinetics; quantum chemistry and photo chemistry; radiochemistry. Address: Consolidation Coal Co, Research Division, Library, PA 15129.

GORIN, GEORGE, b. Como, Italy, Aug. 19, 25; m. 52; c. 2. PHYSICAL CHEMISTRY. A.B, Brooklyn Col, 44; M.A, Princeton, 47, Thiokol Corp. fel, 47-48, Ph.D.(chem), 49. Asst, Princeton, 44; chemist, Heyden Chem. Corp, 45; res. assoc, Rutgers, 49-50; fel, Purdue, 51; asst. prof. CHEM, Oregon, 52-55; OKLA. STATE UNIV, 55-58, assoc. prof, 58-61, PROF, 62- Nat. Insts. Health career develop. award, 63- AAAS; Am. Chem. Soc; The Chem. Soc; Am. Soc. Biol. Chem. Structure of proteins and enzymes; kinetics and thermodynamics of biochemical reactions; radiation damage; sulfur compounds. Address: Dept. of Chemistry, Oklahoma State University, Stillwater, OK 74074.

GORIN, P(HILIP) A(LBERT) J(AMES), b. Bristol, Eng, Dec. 26, 31; m. 56; c. 3. CHEMISTRY. B.Sc, Bristol, England, 52, Ph.D.(carbohydrate chem), 56; Queen's (Can), 54-55. ASSOC. RES. OFF, PRAIRIE REGIONAL LAB, NAT. RES. COUN. CAN, 55- Fel. Chem. Inst. Can; Am. Chem. Soc. Carbohydrates, especially the structure of microbiological products and their properties. Address: Prairie Regional Lab, National Research Council, Saskatoon, Sask, Can.

GORING, D(AVID) A(RTHUR) I(NGHAM), b. Toronto, Ont, Nov. 26, 20; m. 48; c. 3. PHYSICAL CHEMISTRY. B.Sc, Univ. Col, London, 42; Nat. Res. Council Can. studentship, McGill, 48, fel, 48-49, Ph.D.(phys. chem), 49; Merck fel, Cambridge, 49-51, Ph.D.(phys. chem), 53. Asst. res. officer phys. chem, Atlantic regional lab, Nat. Res. Council Can, 51-55; scientist II, PULP & PAPER RES. INST, 55-60, res. group leader, 60-71, DIR. RES, 71- Res. assoc, McGill Univ, 56-68, sr. res. assoc, 68- R.A.F, 43-46, Flying Officer. Fel. Chem. Inst. Can; Can. Pulp & Paper Asn; fel. Royal Soc. Can; fel. Int. Acad. Wood Sci. Physical chemistry of cellulose, hemicellulose and lignin both in solution and in the solid state; hydrodynamic behavior of polymers and polyelectrolytes. Address: Pulp & Paper Research Institute of Canada, 570 St. John's Rd, Pointe Claire, Que, Can.

GORING, GEOFFREY E(DWARD), b. N.Y.C, Nov. 8, 20; m. 55; c. 3. CHEMICAL ENGINEERING, PHYSICS. B.E, Yale, 42; Sc.D.(chem. eng), Mass. Inst. Tech, 49; M.S, Fairleigh Dickinson, 62. Proj. leader, Pittsburgh Consol. Coal Co, Pa, 49-52; proj. scientist, Standard Oil Co. Ind, 52-54; proj. dir, Am. Messer Corp, N.Y, 54-56; tech. liaison, Argonne Nat. Lab, Ill, Union Carbide Corp, 56-69, sr. scientist, N.Y, 59-62; asst. div, dir, Atlantic Res. Corp, Va, 62-63; assoc. prof. ENG. SCI, TRINITY UNIV, 63-67, PROF, 67- C.Eng, 42-46, Capt. Am. Phys. Soc. Thermodynamics; applied mathematics; environmental science; materials science. Address: Dept. of Engineering Science, Trinity University, 715 Stadium Dr, San Antonio, TX 78212.

GORINI, LUIGI C(OSTANTINO), b. Milano, Italy, Nov. 13, 03; m. MICROBIAL GENETICS. Ph.D.(org. chem), Univ. Pavia, Italy, 25. Teacher & res, Sorbonne, Paris, 48-55; res. assoc, N.Y. Univ, 55-57; PROF. MICROBIOL. & MOLECULAR GENETICS, HARVARD MED. SCH, 58- Nat. Acad. Sci; AAAS; Am. Soc. Microbiol; Am. Soc. Biol. Chem; Am. Acad. Arts & Sci. Enzymology. Address: Dept. of Microbiology & Molecular Genetics, Harvard Medical School, 25 Shattuck St, Boston, MA 02115.

GORLIN, RICHARD, b. Jersey City, N.J, June 30, 26. MEDICINE. M.D, Harvard Med. Col, 48. Intern & med. house off, Peter Bent Brigham Hosp, 48-49, asst, 49-51, sr. asst. res, 51-52; Moseley traveling fel, St. Thomas's Hosp, London, Eng, 52-53; chief res. physician, PETER BENT BRIGHAM HOSP, 53-54, assoc, 57-60, sr. assoc, 60-66, physician, 66-69, CHIEF, CARDIOL, 69- Res. fel. med, Harvard Med. Sch, 49-51, teaching fel, 51-52, instr, 56-58, assoc, 58-61, asst. prof, 61-68, assoc. prof, 68-; Brower traveling scholar, Am. Col. Physicians, 60. Attend. physician, U.S. Vet. Hosp, Rutland, 58-; lectr, U.S. Naval Hosp, Chelsea, 59-; clin. asst, St. Thomas's Hosp, London, 60; consult, Nat. Heart & Lung Inst. Dipl, Am. Bd. Internal Med. Off. in charge cardiopulmonary function lab, hosp, Portsmouth, Va, Med.C, 54-56, Lt. Comdr. Am. Physiol. Soc; Am. Soc. Clin. Invest; Am. Heart Asn; Am. Fedn. Clin. Res; fel. Am. Col. Cardiol; Asn. Am. Physicians; fel. Am. Col. Physicians. Academic medicine; cardiac physiology. Address: Peter Bent Brigham Hospital, 721 Huntington Ave, Boston, MA 02115.

GORLIN, ROBERT J(AMES), b. Hudson, N.Y, Jan. 11, 23; m. 52; c. 2. ORAL PATHOLOGY. A.B, Columbia, 43; D.D.S, Washington (St. Louis), 47; M.S, Iowa, 56. Fels. path, Columbia, 47-50, instr. dent, 50-51; ORAL PATH, Iowa, 51-55; assoc. prof, UNIV. MINN, MINNEAPOLIS, 56-58, PROF. & CHMN. DIV, 68-, CONSULT, UNIV. HOSPS, 60-, DIR. HUMAN GENETICS CLIN, 71- Fulbright exchange prof. & Guggenheim fel, Royal Dent. Sch, Copenhagen, 61. Consult, U.S. Vet. Admin. Hosp, Minneapolis; Steadman's Med. Dictionary; Nat. Fedn. Birth Defects; Glenwood Hills Med. Ctr; Mt. Sinai Hosp; Hennepin County Gen. Hosp; WHO; Nat. Insts. Health; coun. dent. educ, Am. Dent. Asn; Armed Forces Inst. Path; Pediatrics; Jour. Dent. Res; Am. Jour. Disease Children; Jour. Pediat; Geriatrics; Acad. Oral Biol. Sci. Mem. bd. dirs, Group Health, Inc; Minn. Human Genetics League; dent. study sect, Nat. Insts. Health. Dipl, Am. Bd. Oral Path, 55, dir, 70-75. U.S.A, 43-44; U.S.N, 53-55. Am. Dent. Asn; Am. Acad. Oral Path.(secy-treas, 58-64, v.pres, 64-65, pres, 66-67); Am. Acad. Dermat; Int. Asn. Dent. Res; Int. Acad. Path; Int. Soc. Craniofacial Biol.(pres, 69-70). Pediatrics; relationships between oral and systemic disease; oral syndromes; human genetics. Address: Division of Oral Pathology, School of Dentistry, University of Minnesota, Minneapolis, MN 55455.

GORMAN, CHARLES DAVID, b. Springfield, Mo, June 23, 32; m. 60; c. 2. APPLIED MATHEMATICS. B.A, Missouri, 54, M.A, 55; Ph.D.(math), Yale, 58. Instr. math, Washington (Seattle), 58-59; asst. prof, Minnesota (Minneapolis), 59-60; temporary mem, Courant Inst. Math. Sci, N.Y. Univ, 60-61; asst. prof, WASH. UNIV, 61-64, ASSOC. PROF. appl. math, 64-66, ENG, 66- Consult, plasma physics lab, McDonnell Aircraft Corp, Mo, 62- Am. Math. Soc; Am. Phys. Soc; Soc. Indust. & Appl. Math. Differential equations; plasma physics. Address: School of Engineering, Washington University, St. Louis, MO 63130.

GORMAN, D(ONALD) H(ERBERT), b. Fredericton, N.B, May 6, 22; m. 44; c. 5. MINERALOGY. B.Sc, New Brunswick, 47; Beaverbrook scholar, Royal Sch. Mines, London, 48-49; Ph.D.(mineral), Toronto, 57. Lectr. MINERAL, UNIV. TORONTO, 52-58, asst. prof, 58-65, ASSOC. PROF, 65- Pres, Val Jon Explor. Co. Consult. R.C.N, 44-46, Sub. Lt. Mineral Soc; Mineral. Asn. Can.(treas, 56-58, pres, 63); Mineral. Soc. Am; Gt. Brit. & Ireland. Radioactive minerals; descriptive mineralogy. Address: Dept. of Mineralogy, University of Toronto, Toronto 5, Ont, Can.

GORMAN, JOE (JOSEPH B), b. San Francisco, Calif, Apr. 25, 18; m. 44, 68; c. 4. BIOLOGY. A.B, California, Los Angeles, 47; M.A, California, Berkeley, 51, Ph.D.(zool), 54. Chemist anal-develop, Richfield Oil Corp, Calif, 44-48; from instr. to asst. prof. sci. & chmn. dept, Col. of Holy Names (Calif), 48-54; instr, Bakersfield Col, 54-56; asst. prof, St. Louis, 56-60; asst. prof. & head sci. div, Missouri, St. Louis, 60-61; prof. & chmn. natural sci. div, Delta Col, Michigan, 61-62; prof. titulare, Central Inst. Biol, Concepcion, Chile, 62-64; prof. BIOL, La Verne Col, 64-69; ASSOC. PROF, UNIV. REDLANDS, 69- Am. Philos. Soc. grant, 58; res. assoc, Inst. Exp. Path, Jewish Hosp, St. Louis, Mo, 60-61. Summers, Nat. Sci. Found. grants, 56, 57, assoc. prof, Washington (St. Louis), 61, Ford-Col. Sci. Improv. Prog. grant, Mex, 69. AAAS; Animal Behavior Soc; Am. Soc. Ichthyol. & Herpet; Cooper Ornith. Soc; Ecol. Soc. Am; Soc. Syst. Zool; Brit. Herpet. Soc. Zoology; vertebratology; physiologic ecology, especially lower land vertebrates; herpetology; biosystematics. Address: Dept. of Biology, University of Redlands, Redlands, CA 92373.

GORMAN, J(OHN) R(ICHARD), b. Fairbank, Iowa, Nov. 11, 13; m. 46; c. 2. MATHEMATICS. A.A, Los Angeles City Col, 34; B.A, California, Los Angeles, 36, fel, 36-37, M.A, 38. Instr, Compton City Col, 39-41, 46-47; U.S. NAVAL ACAD, 47-48, asst. prof. MATH, 48-58, ASSOC. PROF, 58- U.S.N.R, 41-64, Comdr. Math. Asn. Am. Analysis. Address: 217 Norwood Rd, Wardour, Annapolis, MD 21401.

GORMAN, J(OSEPH) G(ERARD), b. Monessen, Pa, June 5, 26; m. 61; c. 2. EXPERIMENTAL PHYSICS. B.E.E, Virginia, 46, M.A, 48; Ph.D.(physics), Carnegie Inst. Tech, 54. Res. asst. atomic physics, Nat. Bur. Standards, D.C, 48-50; asst. to dir. nuclear physics, nuclear res. center, Carnegie Inst. Tech, 54-55; res. physicist, WESTINGHOUSE RES. LABS, 55-59, sr. res. physicist, 59-62, FEL. PHYSICIST, 62- Vis. res. assoc. plasma physics, Proj. Matterhorn, Princeton, 55-60, plasma physics lab, 60- U.S.N, 43-46, Res, 46-54, Lt.(jg). Am. Phys. Soc. Analysis of solids with the mass spectrometer; total cross sections for pions in hydrogen; Langmuir probes in highly magnetized plasmas; particle confinement in the stellarator. Address: Forrestal Research Center, P.O. Box 451, Princeton, NJ 08540.

GORMAN, MARVIN, b. Detroit, Mich, Sept. 24, 28; m. 53; c. 3. BIO-ORGANIC CHEMISTRY. B.S, Michigan, 50, Univ. fel, 50-52; Schering fel, Wayne State, 52-53, Pfizer fel, 53-54, Ph.D.(org. chem), 55. Res. fel, Israel Inst. Tech, 54-55; Wayne State, 56; org. chemist, RES. LABS, ELI LILLY & CO, 56-64, res. assoc, 64-69, RES. ADV, 69- AAAS; The Chem. Soc; Am. Chem. Soc; Am. Soc. Microbiol; N.Y. Acad. Sci. Natural products; isolation, characterization and structure determination, primarily of alkaloiks and antibiotics; chemistry of beta-lactam antibiotics; ionophoretic substances. Address: Research Labs, Eli Lilly & Co, 307 E. McCarty St, Indianapolis, IN 46206.

GORMAN, (CHARLES) MEL(VILLE), b. San Francisco, Calif, Nov. 18, 10; m. 37; c. 2. INORGANIC CHEMISTRY, HISTORY OF SCIENCE. B.S, San Francisco, 31; M.S, California, 39; Ph.D.(chem), Stanford, 46. Instr. CHEM, UNIV. SAN FRANCISCO, 31-39, asst. prof, 39-46, assoc. prof, 46-52, PROF, 52- Faculty fel, Ford Found, 54-55; Nat. Sci. Found, 59-60. Am. Chem. Soc; Hist. Sci. Soc; Soc. Hist. Tech. Transmission of scientific ideas from Europe to seventeenth and eighteenth century America; properties of thiocyanic acid and its salts. Address: Dept. of Chemistry, University of San Francisco, San Francisco, CA 94117.

GORMAN, W(ILLIAM) ALAN, b. Montreal, Que, Oct. 18, 25; m. 50; c. 3. GEOLOGY. B.Sc, McGill, 49, M.Sc, 52, Que. Dept. Mines scholar, 52-54, Ph.D, 56. Field geologist, Que. Dept. Mines, 51-56; asst. prof. GEOL. SCI, QUEEN'S UNIV. (ONT), 55-65, assoc. prof, 65-71, PROF, 71- Geologist, Steep Rock Iron Mines, 57-59; spec. lectr, Royal Mil. Col, Can, 59-64, 68-71. R.C.A.F, 43-46, Sgt. Geol. Soc. Am; fel. Geol. Asn. Can. Pleistocene geology; engineering geology; hydrogeochemistry. Address: 8 MacKenzie Cres, Kingston, Ont, Can.

GORMAN, WILLIAM G(EORGE), b. Hackensack, N.J, Aug. 6, 28; m. 50; c. 4. PHARMACY. B.S, Rutgers, 50; M.S, Ohio State, 54, Am. Found. Pharmaceut. Ed. fel, 55-57, Ph.D.(pharm), 57. Res. assoc. prod. develop, STERLING-WINTHROP RES. INST, 57-64, res. pharmacist & group leader, 64-68, sr. res. pharmacist, 68-70, SR. RES. ASSOC, 70- U.S.C.G, 51-53. Am. Pharmaceut. Asn; Am. Chem. Soc. Solvents; aerosols; sprays; pressure packaging; packaging. Address: 25 Old Troy Rd, East Greenbush, NY 12061.

GORMICAN, ANNETTE, b. Fond du Lac, Wis, Apr. 26, 24. NUTRITION. B.S, Col. St. Catherine, 46; M.S, Iowa, 47, Mary Swartz Rose fel, 63, Nat. Insts. Health & Am. Home Econ. Asn. fels, 64-65, Ph.D.(nutrit), 65. Chief dietitian, Mercy Hosp, Jackson, Mich, 48-50; clin. dietitian, diabetes clin, Univ. Minn, Minneapolis, 52-60, asst. prof. nutrit, 55-60; dir. dietetics, sch. med, Univ. Wis, Madison, 61-62; therapeut. dietitian, Univ. Iowa, 62-64; asst. prof. nutrit, col. med, Univ. Nebr, 65-66, asst. prof. nutrit, sch. nursing, dir. dietetic internship & assoc. dir. dept. dietetics, univ. hosps, 67-68; ASST. CLIN. PROF. MED. & DIR. DIETETIC INTERNSHIP, CTR. HEALTH SCI. & ASST. PROF. NUTRIT. SCI, COL. AGR. & LIFE SCI, UNIV. WIS, MADISON, 68- Instr, sch. home econ, Univ. Minn, St. Paul, 52-54; Allied Health Professions grants, 68-71. Lipid metabolism; trace elements in foods; mineral absorption; computer applications in nutrition. Address: University of Wisconsin Center for Health Sciences, Madison, WI 53706.

GORMLEY, WILLIAM T(HOMAS), b. Versailles, Ky, May 24, 15; m. 47; c. 5. ORGANIC CHEMISTRY. B.S, Kentucky, 37, M.S, 45; Ph.D.(chem), N.Y. Univ, 52. Chemist, State Testing Labs, Ky, 37-42; Cincinnati Ord. Dist, 42-43; instr. chem, Army Student Training Program, Kentucky, 43-44; chemist, Wm. S. Merrell Co, 44-46; instr. chem, Hunter Col, 46-52; res. chemist, E.I. du Pont de Nemours & Co, 52-53; fel, Mellon Inst, 53-60; RES. CHEMIST, KOPPERS CO, INC, MONROEVILLE, 61- Am. Chem. Soc. Mannich reaction; organic peroxides; synthetic lubricants; high polymers. Address: 406 W. Swissvale Ave, Pittsburgh, PA 15218.

GORMLY, JOHN BERNARD, Psychol, see Suppl. I to 11th ed, Soc. & Behav. Vols.

GORMSEN, SVEND T(HEODORE), b. Denmark, Feb. 24, 09; nat; m. 36; c. 2. MATHEMATICS. B.S, Ohio State, 35; M.S, Florida, 49, Ph.D.(math), 53. Teacher, pub. sch, N.Y, 35-40; Ohio, 40-43; instr. MATH, Syracuse, 46-47; asst. prof, Florida, 47-54; prof, Rollins Col, 54-56; VA. POLYTECH, 56-69, EMER. PROF, 69-; PROF. MATH, JACKSONVILLE UNIV, 69- U.S.N.R, 43-46, Res, Capt.(Ret). Math. Asn. Am; Am. Math. Soc. Algebraic geometry; involutions theory. Address: Dept. of Mathematics, Jacksonville University, Jacksonville, FL 32211.

GORN, SAUL, b. Boston, Mass, Nov. 10, 12; m. 43. COMPUTER & INFORMATION SCIENCES. B.A, Columbia, 31, Ph.D.(math), 42; exchange fel, Bordeaux, 31-32, dipl. d'etudes sup, 32. Asst, Columbia, 37; instr. math, Brooklyn Col, 38-42; staff mathematician, aircraft radiation lab, air material command, 46-51; math. adv, comput. lab, Aberdeen Proving Ground, 51-55; assoc. prof. ELEC. ENG, UNIV. PA, 55-64, PROF, 64- U.S.A.A.F, 42-46. Van Amringe prize, Columbia. AAAS; Am. Math. Soc; Soc. Indust. & Appl. Math; Asn. Comput. Mach. Foundations of geometry; lattice theory; mathematics of high speed computing; learning models; mechanical languages. Address: Moore School of Electrical Engineering, University of Pennsylvania, Philadelphia, PA 19104.

GORNALL, A(LLAN) G(ODFREY), b. River Hebert, N.S, Aug. 28, 14; m. 41; c. 4. BIOCHEMISTRY. B.A, Mount Allison, 36; fel, Toronto, 37-41, Ph.D. (path. chem), 41. Lectr, PATH. CHEM, UNIV. TORONTO, 46, asst. prof, 46-52, assoc. prof, 52-63, PROF, 63-, CHMN. DEPT, 66- Reeve Prize, 41;

Nuffield Fel, 49. Royal Can. Navy, 42-46, Lt. Comdr. Am. Chem. Soc; Endocrine Soc; Can. Physiol. Soc.(treas, 54-57); Can. Biochem. Soc; Can. Soc. Clin. Chem; Can. Soc. Clin. Invest; Can. Fedn. Biol. Soc.(hon. treas, 57-62); Brit. Biochem. Soc; Am. Physiol. Soc; fel. Royal Soc. Can. Urea synthesis; liver function; protein and steroid methodology; metabolic effects of hormones; aldosterone; electrolytes; hypertension; pregnancy toxemia; active site of carbonic anhydrase. Address: 135 Hanna Rd, Toronto 352, Ont, Can.

GORNICK, FRED, b. New York, N.Y, March 12, 29; m. 50; c. 2. PHYSICAL CHEMISTRY. B.S, City Col. New York, 51; Ph.D.(phys. chem), Pennsylvania, 59. Chemist, Allied Chem. & Dye Corp, 51-52; Rohm & Haas Co, 52-53; asst. instr. chem, Pennsylvania, 53-54, asst, 56-59; phys. chemist, Nat. Bur. Standards, 59-65; assoc. prof. mat. sci, Univ. Va, 65-67; CHEM, UNIV. MD, BALTIMORE COUNTY, 67-69, PROF. & CHMN. DEPT, 69- Nat. Res. Coun. fel, 59-60; lectr, Georgetown, 64-65; consult, Nat. Bur. Standards, 65- U.S.A, 54-56. AAAS; Am. Chem. Soc; Am. Phys. Soc. Physical chemistry of macromolecules; thermodynamics and kinetics of crystallization in high polymers; investigations of synthetic polypeptides. Address: Dept. of Chemistry, University of Maryland, Baltimore County, 5401 Wilkens Ave, Baltimore, MD 21228.

GORNOWSKI, EDWARD J(OHN), b. Wilmington, Del, Feb. 27, 18; m. c. 4. CHEMICAL ENGINEERING. B.Ch.E, Villanova Col, 38, Ph.D.(chem. eng), Pennsylvania, 43. Chem. engr, Pyrites Co, Del, 38-39; chem. engr, La. Div, STANDARD OIL CO.(N.J), 42-45, dept. to v.pres, Esso Res. & Eng. Co. Div, 45-64, mgr. chem. prod, Humble Oil & Ref. Co. Div, 64-65, dept. mgr. coord. & planning, 65-66, v.pres. opers, Esso Europe Inc, 66-69, EXEC. V.PRES. & DIR, ESSO RES. & ENG. CO, N.J, 69- Am. Chem. Soc; Am. Inst. Chem. Eng; Nat. Acad. Eng. Catalytic cracking and reforming, low temperature polymerization; coal gasification; pressure volume temperature relations of benzene; model II hydroformer. Address: Esso Research & Engineering Co, P.O. Box 111, Linden, NJ 07036.

GORODETZKY, CHARLES W, b. Boston, Mass, May 31, 37; m. 61; c. 4. PHARMACOLOGY, MEDICINE. B.S, Mass. Inst. Tech, 58; M.D, Boston, 62; Kentucky, 65-68. Intern med, Boston City Hosp, Mass, 62-63; med. off, pharmacol, ADDICTION RES. CTR, NAT. INST. MENT. HEALTH, 63-65, outside-serv. pharmacol, 65-68, CHIEF SECT. DRUG KINETICS & METAB, 68- Adj. Sr. Surg. AAAS; Am. Soc. Pharmacol. & Exp. Therapeut; Soc. Neurosci; Am. Soc. Clin. Pharmacol. & Therapeut; N.Y. Acad. Sci. Biochemical and clinical pharmacology, especially opioids, sedative-hypnotics and psychotomimetics. Address: National Institute of Mental Health Addiction Research Center, P.O. Box 2000, Lexington, KY 40507.

GOROG, ISTVAN, b. Budapest, Hungary, Mar. 13, 38; U.S. citizen. ELECTRICAL ENGINEERING, PHYSICS. B.Sc, California, Berkeley, 61, M.Sc, 62, Ph.D.(elec. eng), 64. Asst, California, Berkeley, 61-64; mem. tech. staff, RCA LABS, 64-70, HEAD OPTICAL ELECTRONICS RES. GROUP, 70- Nat. Sci. Found. fel, Italy, 68- Am. Phys. Soc. Lasers and quantum electronics; electro-optics; plasmas. Address: RCA Labs, Princeton, NJ 08540.

GOROVSKY, MARTIN A, b. Chicago, Ill, Apr. 26, 41; m. 67; c. 1. BIOLOGY, CELL BIOLOGY. A.B, Univ. Chicago, 63, U.S. Pub. Health Serv. fel, 63-68, Ph.D.(cell biol), 68. Nat. Sci. Found. fel, 68-70; ASST. PROF. BIOL, UNIV. ROCHESTER, 70- AAAS; Am. Soc. Cell Biol. Molecular biology; study of structure and function of eukaryotic nuclei. Address: Dept. of Biology, University of Rochester, Rochester, NY 14627.

GOROZDOS, RICHARD E(MMERICH), b. Chicago, Ill, May 20, 28; m. 54; c. 6. ELECTRICAL ENGINEERING. B.S, Illinois, 50, M.S, 51; Ph.D.(elec. eng), Maryland, 60. ELEC. ENGR, Naval Res. Lab, 51-54; Ballistic Res. Lab, 54-56; APPL. PHYSICS LAB, JOHNS HOPKINS UNIV, 56- U.S.A, 54-56. Tactical missile guidance and control systems; digital control systems; precision tracking; network synthesis. Address: 11204 Healy St, Silver Spring, MD 20902.

GORRES, BYRON THOMAS, b. Amery, Wis, Nov. 15, 36; m. 58; c. 4. PHYSICAL CHEMISTRY. B.S, Wis. State, River Falls, 60; Nat. Sci. Found. summer fel, Princeton, 61, M.A, 62, Nat. Insts. Health fel, 62-64, Ph.D.(phys. chem), 64. Res. technician, Minn. Mining & Mfg. Co, 56-60, chemist, 60, sr. chemist, 64-69, RES. SPECIALIST, 3M CO, 69- Am. Chem. Soc; Am. Crystallog. Asn. X-ray crystallography and automation of analytical methods with computers. Address: 3M Co, 2301, Hudson Rd, St. Paul, MN 55119.

GORRILL, ALBERT D(AVID) L(INCOLN), b. Bulyea, Sask, Jan. 28, 35; m. 57; c. 3. ANIMAL NUTRITION & PHYSIOLOGY. B.S.A, Univ. Sask, 58, Nat. Res. Coun. Can. bursary, 58-59, M.Sc, 60; Nat. Res. Coun. Can. scholar, Mich. State Univ, 64-66, Ph.D.(dairy nutrit), 66. Res. off. dairy nutrit. & mgt, CAN. DEPT. AGR, P.E.I, 60-63, RES. SCIENTIST, NUTRIT. SECT, N.B, 66- Can. Soc. Animal Prod.(secy, 69-72); Nutrit. Soc. Can; Agr. Inst. Can; Am. Dairy Sci. Asn. Calf and lamb nutrition and management; pancreatic enzyme secretion; abomasal and intestinal digestion and absorption; protein sources in milk replacers; early weaning of calves and lambs. Address: Canada Dept. of Agriculture, Nutrition Section, Research Station, Box 280, Fredericton, N.B, Can.

GORRILL, WILLIAM R(OY), b. Holbrook, Mass, Oct. 1, 21; m. 43; c. 4. SOILS. B.S, Northeastern, 48; M.S, Maine, 56. Instr. civil eng, UNIV. MAINE, ORONO, 48-51, eng. asst. soils eng, tech. exp. sta, 51-53, asst. engr, 53-55, soils engr, 55-57, assoc. prof. soil mech, 57-64, PROF. CIVIL ENG, 64-, soils engr, 57-59. Soils engr, Maine State Hwy. Cmn, 55-57. C.Eng, U.S.A.A.F, 42-45. Am. Soc. Civil Eng; Soc. Eng. Educ. Fundamental properties and behavior of various components in highway pavements; loan carrying capacity of foundation piles as influenced by soils and end bearing conditions; water flow through multilayered soils. Address: Dept. of Civil Engineering, University of Maine, Orono, ME 04473.

GORSIC, J(OSEPH), b. Ponova vas, Slovenia, Jan. 6, 24; nat; m. 66; c. 3. PLANT GENETICS. B.S, Illinois, 52; Ph.D, Chicago, 57. Instr. BIOL, Marquette, 57-59; ASSOC. PROF, ELMHURST COL, 59- Dipl. Ing, State Univ. Agr. & Forestry, Austria, 65. AAAS; Am. Genetic Asn. Comparative genetics in plants. Address: Dept. of Biology, Elmhurst College, Elmhurst, IL 60126.

GORSICA, HENRY J(AN), b. Brno, Czech, June 24, 07; nat; m. 31; c. 3. BIOCHEMISTRY. B.S, Wisconsin, 29, M.S, 31, Ph.D.(biochem), 34. Asst, Wisconsin, 31-35; res. chemist, Pabst Brewing Co, Wis, 35-43; dir. labs, Northwest. Yeast Co, Ill, 43-46; chief chemist & plant supt, Fearn Labs, Inc, 46-51, v.pres. in charge res. & prod, Fearn Foods, Inc, 51-54; dir. labs, B. Heller & Co, Ill, 55-66; ASST. PROF. CHEM, WIS. STATE UNIV, 66- Fel. AAAS; Am. Chem. Soc. Biochemistry of processed meat products; spices and spice extractives; flavorings; malting, brewing, fermentations and production of active dry yeast; production of soup bases and seasonings; chemistry of foods and nutrition. Address: Dept. of Chemistry, 229 Upham Hall, Wisconsin State University, Whitewater, WI 53190.

GORSICH, RICHARD DAVID, b. Helena, Mont, Mar. 25, 31; m. 60; c. 2. ORGANIC CHEMISTRY. B.S, Montana State Col, 53; Ph.D.(org. chem), Iowa State, 57. Res. chemist, ETHYL CORP, 57-68, APPL. RES. ASSOC, 68- Am. Chem. Soc. Organometallic chemistry; detergent and surfactant applications. Address: Ethyl Corp, P.O. Box 341, Baton Rouge, LA 70821.

GORSKI, JACK, b. Green Bay, Wis, Mar. 14, 31; m. 55; c. 2. ENDOCRINOLOGY, BIOCHEMISTRY. B.S, Wisconsin, 53; M.S, Washington State, 56, Ph.D.(animal sci), 58; U.S. Pub. Health Serv. fel, Utah, 57. U.S. Pub. Health Serv. fel, Wisconsin, 58-61; asst. prof. physiol. & biophys, UNIV. ILL, URBANA, 61-64, assoc. prof, 64-67, PROF, 67-69, PHYSIOL. & BIOCHEM, 69- Nat. Sci. Found. sr. fel, Princeton, 66-67. Am. Soc. Cell Biol; Am. Soc. Biol. Chem; Am. Physiol. Soc; Endocrine Soc. Molecular mechanisms of hormone action; estrogen control of the uterus; regulation of ovarian steroid synthesis; regulation of protein synthesis. Address: 524 Burrill Hall, University of Illinois, Urbana, IL 61801.

GORSKI, LEON JOHN, b. New Britain, Conn, Sept. 29, 38; m. 62; c. 2. ECOLOGY, BIOLOGY. B.S, Cent. Conn. State Col, 61; fel, Univ. Conn, 61-63, M.S, 63, Chapman grant, Nat. Sci. Found. grant & univ. grant, 63-69, Ph.D, 69. ASST. PROF. ECOL. & BIOL, CENT. CONN. STATE COL, 65- Am. Ornith. Union; Am. Inst. Biol. Sci; Soc. Syst. Zool. Systematics and ecology of sibling species of the Traill's flycatchers; significance of vocalizations as reproductive isolating mechanisms; tropical overwintering behavior of the two song forms of the Traill's flycatcher in Panama and Peru; multidisciplinary environmental education programs at college and state levels. Address: Dept. of Biological Sciences, Central Connecticut State College, New Britain, CT 06050.

GORSKI, ROBERT A(LEXANDER), b. Passaic, N.J, Nov. 24, 22; m. 44; c. 5. PHYSICAL CHEMISTRY. B.A, La Salle Col, 47; M.S, Pennsylvania, 49, Ph.D.(phys. chem), 51. Instr. algebra, trigonom. & calculus, La Salle Col, 46-48, phys. chem, 48-49; res. asst. thermodynam. res. lab, Pennsylvania, 49-51; res. chemist, org. phys. chem, Jackson Labs, E.I. DU PONT DE NEMOURS & CO, INC, 51-54, FREON PRODS. LAB, 54-67, TECH. ASSOC, 67- U.S.A, 43-46. Am. Chem. Soc. Interaction coefficients of binary gas mixtures; organic physical chemistry; development of technical and material compatibility data for fluorinated compounds for sales promotion. Address: 735 Harvard Lane, Newark, DE 19711.

GORSKI, ROGER A(NTHONY), b. Chicago, Ill, Dec. 30, 35; m. 59; c. 2. NEUROENDOCRINOLOGY. B.S, Illinois, 57, M.S, 59; Ph.D.(anat), California, Los Angeles, 62. Asst. prof. ANAT, SCH. MED, UNIV. CALIF, LOS ANGELES, 62-66, assoc. prof, 66-70, PROF, 70-, V.CHMN. GRAD. AFFAIRS, 67- AAAS; Am. Asn. Anat; Am. Physiol. Soc; Endocrine Soc; Int. Brain Res. Orgn; Soc. Neurosci; Soc. Study Reproduction; Int. Soc. Psychoneuroendocrinol. Sexual differentiation of hypothalamic control of reproduction; hypothalamic regulation of ovulation; effect of steroids on brain; electrical activity of hypothalamus; regulation of sexual behavior. Address: Dept. of Anatomy, University of California School of Medicine, Los Angeles, CA 90024.

GORSKI, THEODORE WILLIAM, b. Latrobe, Pa, Nov. 9, 24; m. 53; c. 6. BIOCHEMISTRY, MICROBIOLOGY. B.S, St. Vincent Col, 49; fel, St. Louis, 50-51, M.S, 52, Ph.D.(physiol, biochem), 56. Asst. exped. to Arctic, St. Louis Univ, 50-51, instr, 53-54; asst. prof, Duquesne, 54-55; cytologist, Mercy Hosp, Toledo, Ohio, 55-58; dir. res, Cancer Cytol. Res. Fund. Toledo, 56-65; PRES, SCI. ASSOCS, INC, 67- Adj. prof, Univ. Toledo, 59-67; dir. res, Path. Labs, 61-71. Dipl, Nat. Registry Clin. Chem. U.S.A, 43-45. AAAS; Am. Asn. Clin. Chem; Am. Soc. Microbiol. Sterility testing ethylene oxide and irradiated products; industrial and food microbiology, biochemistry, toxicology, pharmacology; ethylene oxide residues, pyrogens, safety. Address: 30335 Oregon Rd, Perrysburg, OH 43551.

GORSLINE, DONN S(HERRIN), b. Los Angeles, Calif, Dec. 15, 26. OCEANOGRAPHY. B.S, Mont. Sch. Mines, 50; M.S, Southern California 54, Calif. Res. Corp. fel, 56-57, Ph.D.(geol, oceanog), 58. Asst. oceanog, Allan Hancock Found, Southern California, 54-56, res. assoc. geol, 53-57; asst. prof. marine geol, oceanog. inst, Fla. State, 58-61, assoc. prof. & acting dir, 61-62; assoc. prof. GEOL, UNIV. SOUTH. CALIF, 62-66, PROF, 66-; RES. ASSOC, ALLAN HANCOCK FOUND, 62- Mem. adv. panel coastal geog, Nat. Acad. Sci-Nat. Res. Coun, 61; gen. chmn. & ed, Nat. Shallow Water & Coastal Res. Inst, 61-62; mem. planning group earth sci. curriculum prog, Am. Geol. Inst, 63; panel course content & sequence, Geol. Study Prog, 64-; adv. comn. ocean resources, Calif, 65-69; ed, Marine Geol, 67-70. U.S.N, 44-46, 50-52, Lt.(jg). Fel. AAAS; fel. Geol. Soc. Am; fel. Am. Geog. Soc; Am. Soc. Limnol. & Oceanog; Soc. Econ. Paleont. & Mineral.(ed, J. Sedimentary Petrol, 70-); Am. Asn. Petrol. Geol; Am. Asn. Quaternary Environ; Int. Asn. Sedimentol. Sedimentology; marine geology; coastal studies; shallow water oceanography; continental margin. Address: Dept. of Geological Sciences, University of Southern California, Los Angeles, CA 90007.

GORSLINE, GEORGE W(ILLIAM), b. Battle Creek, Mich, Dec. 19, 23; m. 47; c. 3. COMPUTER SCIENCE, GENETICS. B.S, Va. Polytech. Inst, 48; M.S, Pa. State Univ, 57, Ph.D.(agron), 59. Exten. county agent, Pa. State Univ, 48-56, instr. agron, 56-60, asst. prof, 60-65; dir, comput. ctr, Univ. Ohio, 65-67; assoc. prof. COMPUT. SCI, VA. POLYTECH. INST. & STATE UNIV,

67-70, PROF. & CHMN. DEPT, 70- C.Eng, U.S.A, 43-45. AAAS; Asn. Comput. Mach; Am. Agron. Soc; Crop Sci. Soc. Am. Education; non-numeric symbol manipulation; pseudo-random number generation; symbolic mathematics. Address: Dept. of Computer Science, Virginia Polytechnic Institute & State University, Blacksburg, VA 24061.

GORSON, ROBERT O, b. Philadelphia, Pa, July 16, 23; m. 46. RADIOLOGY, MEDICAL PHYSICS. B.A, Pennsylvania, 49, M.S, 52. Univ. health physicist, Pennsylvania, 49-51, res. fel. radiol. physics, sch. med, 51-52, instr, 52-53, assoc, 53-59, grad. sch. med, 55-59; assoc. prof. radiol, JEFFERSON MED. COL, 59-65, PROF. MED. PHYSICS, 65-, CHIEF DIV. MED. PHYSICS, COL. HOSP, 59- Vis. lectr, grad. sch. med, Pennsylvania, 59- Consult, Phila. Dept. Pub. Health, 57-; div. radiation health, U.S. Pub. Health Serv, 63- Chmn. subcomt. 3, Nat. Comt. Radiation Protection, 61-, mem. subcomt. 16, 63-; secy. comn. units, standards and protection, Am. Col. Radiol, 61-; mem. bd. dirs, Nat. Coun. Radiation Protection & Measurements, 64-; adv. comt. med. x-ray protection, U.S. Pub. Health Serv, 64-66. Dipl, Am. Bd. Radiol, 54; Am. Bd. Health Physics, 60, mem, 64-65, chmn, 65-67. U.S.N, 44-46, Res, 46-63, Lt. Health Phys. Soc; Am. Phys. Soc; Am. Asn. Physicists in Med; Am. Asn. Physics Teachers; Radiol. Soc. N.Am; Radiation Res. Soc; Am. Radium Soc; Soc. Nuclear Med; fel. Am. Col. Radiol. Radiation and health physics. Address: Division of Medical Physics, Jefferson Medical College Hospital, 10th & Sansom Sts, Philadelphia, PA 19107.

GORTATOWSKI, MELVIN J(EROME), b. Chicago, Ill, Oct. 30, 25. ORGANIC & BIOLOGICAL CHEMISTRY. B.S, Illinois, 50, Eastman Kodak Co. fel, 54-55, Ph.D.(chem), 55; M.S, Wash. State Col, 52. Asst. chem. res, div. fluorine chem, Ill. State Geol. Surv, 52-53; res. instr. & fel, lab. for study hereditary & metab. disorders, col. med, Utah, 56-58, res. assoc, dept. psychiat, 58-59, res. instr. biochem, 59-65; asst. prof. pediat, Univ. South. Calif, 65-71; CHIEF CHEM. SECT, UTAH STATE HEALTH DEPT. LAB, 71- Biochemist, Vet. Admin. Hosp, Salt Lake City, 59-65; assoc. investr, clin. res. ctr, Childrens Hosp, Los Angeles, 65-71. U.S.A, 44-46. Am. Chem. Soc. Metabolic disease associated with mental retardation including inherited disorders of amino acid, carbohydrate and fat metabolism; environmental chemistry, especially health hazards from drugs, pesticides, pollutants in air, water and food. Address: 4045 Foubert Ave, Salt Lake City, UT 84117.

GORTEN, RALPH J, b. Magdeburg, Germany, Apr. 7, 29; U.S. citizen; m. 62; c. 2. NUCLEAR MEDICINE. B.A, West. Md. Col, 51; M.D, Pennsylvania, 55. Intern, Univ. Maryland Hosp, 55-56, res. internal med, 56-58; Nat. Insts. Health res. fel. cardiol, sch. med, Duke, 58-59; internist & flight surgeon, consult. sect. & chief radioisotope sect, dept. internal med, U.S. Air Force Sch. Aerospace Med, 59-61; Nat. Insts. Health spec. res. fel. cardiovasc. physiol. & electronic instrumentation, sch. med, Washington (Seattle), 61-63; staff internist & chief radioisotope serv, depts. med. & physiol, sch. med, Duke Univ. & Vet. Admin. Hosp, 63-66, div. nuclear med, dept. radiol, Univ, 66-71; ASSOC. PROF. RADIOL. & MED. & DIR. NUCLEAR MED, SCH. MED, UNIV. TEX, GALVESTON, 71- U.S.A.F, 59-61. Am. Fedn. Clin. Res; Am. Heart Asn; Soc. Nuclear Med; Am. Med. Asn. Cardiovascular physiology, pharmacology and diseases; use of isotopes in clinical medicine and in study of cardiovascular system; use of digital computers in nuclear medicine. Address: Dept. of Radiology & Medicine, University of Texas Medical Branch, Galveston, TX 77550.

GORTHY, WILLIS C(HARLES), b. Buffalo, N.Y, Dec. 4, 34; m. 59; c. 3. CYTOLOGY, HISTOLOGY. A.B, Columbia, 56; M.S, N.Y. Univ, 61; Nat. Insts. Health fel, Princeton, 60-63, M.A, 63, Ph.D.(biol), 65. Res. aide, Sloan-Kettering Inst. Cancer Res, 57-60; Nat. Acad. Sci-Nat. Res. Coun. res. assoc, human nutrit. res. div, U.S. Dept. Agr, 64-66; ASST. PROF. ANAT, COLO. STATE UNIV, 66- Res. grants, Nat. Inst. Neurol. Diseases & Blindness & Nat. Eye Inst, U.S. Dept. Health, Educ. & Welfare, 68- Electron Micros. Soc. Am; Am. Asn. Vet. Anat; Asn. Res. Vision & Ophthal. Growth of animal tumors and tissue cultures; light and electron microscopical studies of mammalian eye; nutritional studies of rats, involving light and electron microscopy; morphological and histochemical studies of the lens; cell physiology. Address: Dept. of Anatomy, Colorado State University, Ft. Collins, CO 80521.

GORTLER, LEON B(ERNARD), b. Des Moines, Iowa, Jan. 30, 35; m. 60; c. 3. ORGANIC CHEMISTRY. A.B, B.S. & M.S, Chicago, 57; Ph.D.(chem), Harvard, 62. Fel, California, Berkeley, 61-62; instr. CHEM, BROOKLYN COL, 62-64, asst. prof, 64-68, ASSOC. PROF, 68- Am. Chem. Soc; The Chem. Soc. Synthesis and decomposition of peresters; study of reaction mechanisms; stereochemical studies of acyclic molecules. Address: Dept. of Chemistry, Brooklyn College, Brooklyn, NY 11210.

GORTNER, ROSS AIKEN, JR, b. Cold Spring Harbor, N.Y, June 2, 12; m. 38; c. 2. BIOCHEMISTRY. B.A, Minnesota, 33, M.S, 34; univ. fel, Michigan, 34-35, Ph.D.(biol. chem), 37. Asst. biol. chem, Michigan; 35-37; instr. BIOCHEM, WESLEYAN UNIV, 37-41, asst. prof, 41-46, assoc. prof, 46-48, PROF, 48-, DIR. SCI. CTR, 67-, ASSOC. DIR. SCI, GRAD. SUMMER SCH, 71- Assoc. exec. secy, food & nutrit. bd, Nat. Res. Coun, 43-44; Fulbright lectr, Copenhagen, 54-55; vis. investr, Max Planck Inst. Biochem, 61-62; mem. bd. control, Conn. Agr. Exp. Sta, 63-, secy, 67-; prog. dir. col. sci. curriculum improvement, Nat. Sci. Found, 66-67. U.S.N.R, 44-46, Lt. AAAS; Am. Chem. Soc; Am. Inst. Nutrit. Nutritional aspects of selenium poisoning; effects of diet on teeth; protein metabolism and nutrition; hematologic and chemical changes in vitamin E deficiency; human nutrition. Address: Shankin Lab. of Biology, Wesleyan University, Middletown, CT 06457.

GORTNER, WILLIS A(LWAY), b. Cold Spring Harbor, L.I, N.Y, Dec. 20, 13; m. 60; c. 4. BIOLOGICAL CHEMISTRY. A.B, Minnesota, 34; Ph.D.(biochem), Rochester, 40. Res. chemist, Gen. Mills, Inc, 34-37, 40-42; asst. biochem, Rochester, 37-40; asst. prof. biochem. & chem. eng, Cornell, 43-45, assoc. prof. biochem, 45-48; head chem. dept, Pineapple Res. Inst. Hawaii, 48-64; DIR. HUMAN NUTRIT. RES. DIV, AGR. RES. SERV, U.S. DEPT. AGR, 64- With U.S. Dept. Agr, 44; Bjorksten Res. Found, 53; Nat. Acad. Sci-Nat. Res. Coun, 57; Nat. Canners Asn, 61; California, 63. U.S.N, 47. AAAS; Am. Chem. Soc; Am. Soc. Biol. Chem; Inst. Food Tech; Am. Inst. Nutrit; Am. Soc. Clin. Nutrit. Food biochemistry; processing of foods such as dehydration and freezing; vitamins; fat rancidity and analysis; plant enzymes and growth regulators; fruit development and composition; human nutrition. Address: Human Nutrition Research Division, Agricultural Research Service, U.S. Dept. of Agriculture, Beltsville, MD 20705.

GORTON, BERT S(ORELLE), b. New Orleans, La, Oct. 28, 28; m. 63; c. 3. ORGANIC CHEMISTRY. B.S, Rice Inst, 49; M.S, Texas, 55, Nat. Sci. Found. fel, 56-57, Ph.D.(chem), 57. Phys. sci. aide, U.S. Dept. Agr, 49-50; res. chemist ELECTROCHEM. DEPT, E.I. DU PONT DE NEMOURS & CO, 57-68, STAFF SCIENTIST, 68- U.S.A, 50-52. Am. Chem. Soc. Polymers; developmental biochemistry; synthesis nitrogen heterocyclics; antimetabolites. Address: N. Union St, Kennett Square, PA 19348.

GORTON, H(ENRY) CLAY, b. Soda Springs, Idaho, Mar. 7, 23; m. 49; c. 5. SOLID STATE PHYSICS. B.A, Brigham Young, 52, M.A, 53. Sr. physicist, BATTELLE MEM. INST, 53-58, proj. leader, 58-62, ASSOC. CHIEF, ELECTRONIC MAT. & DEVICES DEPT, 62- U.S.A.A.F, 42-46. AAAS; sr. mem. Inst. Elec. & Electronics Eng. Investigation of the fundamental electronic properties of elemental and compound semiconductors. Address: Battelle Memorial Institute, 505 King Ave, Columbus, OH 43201.

GORTON, KENNETH A(RNOLD), b. Chelsea, Mich, March 19, 10; m. 41. GEOLOGY. B.A, Michigan, 33, Ph.D.(geol), 41. Geologist, Mich. Geol. Surv, 35-36; petrol. engr, 36-40; instr. geol, Purdue, 41-43; GEOLOGIST, Potash Co. of Am, N.Mex, 43-44; Gen. Petrol. Corp, 44-53; Mobil Oil Co. Div, Socony Mobil Oil Co, COLO, 53-67, MOBIL OIL CORP, ALASKA, 67- Am. Asn. Petrol. Geol. Petroleum exploration; structural geology. Address: Mobil Oil Corp, Pouch 7-003, Anchorage, AK 99501.

GORTON, ROBERT LESTER, b. Houston, Tex, Oct. 19, 31; m. 60; c. 4. MECHANICAL ENGINEERING. B.S, La. Polytech, 53; M.S, La. State, 60; Am. Oil Found. fel, Kansas State, 65-66, Ph.D.(mech. eng), 66. Engr, Schlumberger Well Surv. Corp, 55-58; assoc. MECH. ENG, La. State, 59-60; instr, KANS. STATE UNIV, 60-66, asst. prof, 66-69, ASSOC. PROF, 69-, ASST. HEAD DEPT, 66- Summer mem. staff, Pratt & Whitney Aircraft Co, 67; NASA faculty fel, 70. Am. Soc. Mech. Eng; Am. Soc. Eng. Educ. Porous body heat transfer; gas turbine blade cooling; environmental engineering. Address: Dept. of Mechanical Engineering, College of Engineering, Seaton Hall, Kansas State University, Manhattan, KS 66502.

GORTSEMA, FRANK P(ETER), b. Grand Rapids, Mich, Dec. 25, 33; m. 59. PHYSICAL & INORGANIC CHEMISTRY. A.B, Calvin Col, 55; Ethyl Corp. fel, Purdue, 58-59, Ph.D.(phys. chem), 60. SR. RES. CHEMIST, Parma Res. Center, UNION CARBIDE CORP, Ohio, 59-63, RES. INST, N.Y, 63- Am. Chem. Soc. Chemistry of ruthenium in solution; thermoelectric properties of rare earth nitrides and monosulfides; preparation and properties of reduced valency transition metal fluorides; platinum hexafluoride chemistry; fibrous ceramics. Address: Union Carbide Research Institute, P.O. Box 278, Tarrytown, NY 10591.

GORUM, ALVIN EUGENE, b. Denver, Colo, Oct. 14, 25; m. 46; c. 2. PHYSICAL METALLURGY. B.S, Arizona, 50, M.S, 55; Ph.D.(mat. sci), California, 59. Mill metallurgist, St. Anthony Mining & Develop. Co, 50-51; instr. phys. metall, Arizona, 51-54; mem. staff, Los Alamos Sci. Lab, 54-56; assoc. res. engr, California, 56-59; head mat. res. Rheem Semiconductor Corp, 59-61; dir. mat. sci. div, Stanford Res. Inst, 61-70; DIR. ARMY MAT. & MECH. RES. CTR, 70- Mem, Army Res. Coun, 71. U.S.A, 43-46. Fel. Am. Soc. Metals; Am. Ceramic Soc. Mechanical properties of materials; dislocation phenomena; electronic properties of materials; high temperature materials. Address: Army Materials & Mechanics Research Center, Watertown, MA 02172.

GORWITZ, KURT, b. Vienna, Austria, Apr. 16, 28; U.S. citizen; m. 51; c. 2. BIOSTATISTICS. B.B.A, City Col. New York, 50; M.S, Columbia, 55; M.P.A, Syracuse, 55; Sc.D.(ment. health), Hopkins, 66. Biostatistician, N.Y. State Dept. Health, 51-55; dir. vital statist, St. Louis Dept. Health, 55-58; DIR. statist, Md. State Dept. Ment. Hyg, 58-69; Md. State Dept. Health & Ment. Hyg, 69-70; MICH. CTR. HEALTH STATIST, 70- Nat. Inst. Ment. Health res. grant, 66-70. Consult, South. Regional Educ. Bd; sch. med, Johns Hopkins Univ. & Univ. Ark. & Del. State Dept. Ment. Health; Croatia, Yugoslavia Dept. Health; N.C. Dept. Health. Fel. AAAS; fel. Am. Pub. Health Asn. Development and maintenance of health data systems for administration, evaluation and planning; differential rates of morbidity, mortality as related to availability and use of health resources. Address: Michigan Center for Health Statistics, 3500 N. Logan St, Lansing, MI 48914.

GORZ, H(ERMAN) J(ACOB), b. Eagle River, Wis, Nov. 22, 20; m. 51; c. 2. GENETICS, PLANT BREEDING. B.S, Wisconsin, 42, M.S, 48, Ph.D.(agron. genetics), 51. Assoc. prof. agron. & assoc. agronomist, N.Dak. Agr. Col, 51-54; RES. GENETICIST, PLANT SCI. RES. DIV, AGR. RES. SERV, U.S. DEPT. AGR, 54- U.S.A, 45-46. Genetics Soc; Soc. Agron. Genetics and breeding of clover; genetics of coumarin biosynthesis; interspecific hybridization; insect resistance in clovers. Address: Dept. of Agronomy, University of Nebraska, Lincoln, NE 68503.

GORZYNSKI, EUGENE A(RTHUR), b. Buffalo, N.Y, Oct. 8, 19; m. 46; c. 3. BACTERIOLOGY. B.A, State Univ. N.Y. Buffalo, 49, M.A, 51; Ph.D.(microbiol), 68. Assoc. res. bacteriologist, Children's Hosp, 47-68; sr. cancer res. scientist, Springville Labs, Roswell Park Mem. Inst, 68-69; ASST. PROF. MICROBIOL, SCH. MED, STATE UNIV. N.Y. BUFFALO & ASST. DIR. PUB. HEALTH LABS, ERIE COUNTY LAB, 69- Med.C, 40-45, Res, 45-70, Col. Fel. AAAS; Am. Soc. Microbiol; fel. Am. Pub. Health Asn; Am. Asn. Immunol. Bacterial hemagglutination; antigenic analysis of various intestinal bacteria and staphylococci; antibiotics. Address: 31 Oakridge Dr, Hamburg, NY 14075.

GOSBEE, JOHN LLOYD, b. Charlottetown, P.E.I, Dec. 25, 41; m. 65; c. 1. PHYSIOLOGY, ENDOCRINOLOGY. B.Sc, Queen's Univ.(Ont), 65, M.Sc, 67, Ph.D.(physiol), 70. MED. RES. COUN. CAN. FEL, DIV. PHARMACOL. & THERAPEUT, FACULTY MED, UNIV. CALGARY, 70- Can. Physiol. Soc. Autoradiographic analysis of nucleic acid precursor uptake by adenohypophysis with altered adrenocorticotrophic hormone secretion; direct involvement of neurotransmitters with release of antidiuretic hormone and oxytocin. Address: Division of Pharmacology, University of Calgary, Calgary, Alta, Can.

GOSE, EARL E(UGENE), b. Aberdeen, Wash, Mar. 14, 34; m. 62. ENGINEERING. B.S, Carnegie Inst. Tech, 56; Nat. Sci. Found. fels, California, 56-59, Ph.D.(chem. eng), 60. Nat. Sci. Found. fel, Sorbonne, 60-61; fel, Mass. Inst. Tech, 61-62; asst. prof. eng, Case, 62-65; ASSOC. PROF. INFO. ENG, UNIV. ILL, CHICAGO CIRCLE, 65- Assoc. prof, dept. physiol, Univ. Ill. Med. Ctr; staff mem, Presby. St. Luke's Hosp, Chicago; prof, Rush Med. Col. Sig.C, 60, 1st Lt. AAAS; Am. Soc. Cybernet; Asn. Comput. Mach; Inst. Elec. & Electronics Eng; Instrument Soc. Am; Pattern Recognition Soc; Soc. Photo-Optical Instrument. Eng. Pattern recognition; natural and artificial intelligence; neurophysiology; biomedical engineering. Address: Dept. of Information Engineering, University of Illinois at Chicago Circle, Box 4348, Chicago, IL 60680.

GOSFIELD, EDWARD, JR, b. New York, N.Y, July 17, 18; m. 41; c. 3. INTERNAL MEDICINE, CARDIOLOGY. A.B, Pennsylvania, 39, M.S, 40, M.D, 44. Asst. instr. internal med, GRAD. SCH. MED, UNIV. PA, 50-52, instr, 52-54, assoc. 54-59, asst. prof, 59-63, ASSOC. PROF. CLIN. MED, 63- Consult, Wills Eye Hosp, 50-; chief hypertension clin, grad. hosp, Univ. Pa, 57-, assoc. physician, hosp, 59-; Presby-Univ. Pa. Med. Ctr, 71- Dipl, Am. Bd. Internal Med, 52. Med.C, 45-47, Capt. Am. Heart Asn; fel. Am. Col. Physicians; fel. Am. Col. Cardiol; N.Y. Acad. Med. Cardiovascular disease. Address: 2113 Spruce St, Philadelphia, PA 19103.

GOSHAW, ALFRED THOMAS, b. West Bend, Wis, Aug. 26, 37; m. 66; c. 2. ELEMENTARY PARTICLE PHYSICS. B.S, Wisconsin, Madison, 59, Nat. Sci. Found. fel, 59-60, M.S, 61; Ph.D.(physics), 66. Instr. physics, Princeton, 66-69; vis. scientist, nuclear physics apparatus div, EUROP. ORGN. NUCLEAR RES, 69-70, STAFF MEM, BUBBLE CHAMBER DIV, 70- Am. Phys. Soc. Studies of the K meson; elastic and inelastic deuteron-deuteron interactions at high energies; hyperon resonances. Address: TCL Division, European Organization for Nuclear Research, 1211 Geneva 23, Switz.

GOSHEN, CHARLES E(RNEST), b. Altoona, Pa, Sept. 2, 16; m. 40; c. 2. MEDICINE. A.B, Columbia, 38, M.D, 42; cert, N.Y. Med. Col, 52. Prof. assoc. div. med. sci, Nat. Res. Coun, 57-61; assoc. prof. PSYCHIAT, sch. med, W.Va. Univ, 61-67; ASSOC. PROF. & PROF. ENG. MGT, VANDERBILT UNIV, 67- Dipl, Am. Bd. Psychiat. & Neurol, 48. Med.C, U.S.A, 43-46. AAAS; Geront. Soc; Am. Med. Asn; fel. Am. Psychiat. Asn. Influence of maternal attitudes on etiology of mental retardation; characterological obstacles to economic growth; application of behavioral science knowledge and skill to other sciences; environmental requirements for therapy. Address: Center for Engineering Management Studies & Dept. of Psychiatry, Vanderbilt University, Station B, Box 1729, Nashville, TN 37203.

GOSHI, KEIICHI, b. Taikyu, Korea, Jan. 17, 27; U.S. citizen; m. 57; c. 1. MEDICINE. M.D, Kobe Med. Col, 49, Ph.D.(biochem), 61; fel, Hopkins, 59-62. Intern, Kobe Med. Col, 49-50, res. asst. biochem, 50-55; intern, St. Francis Hosp, Honolulu, Hawaii, 55-56, res, 57-58; Med. Col. Va, 56-57; Sinai Hosp, Baltimore, Md, 58-59; asst. prof. MED, Med. Col. Va, Va. Commonwealth Univ, 62-65; ASST. CLIN. PROF, SCH. MED, UNIV. HAWAII, 67- Private practice, 65- Am. Fedn. Clin. Res; Am. Acad. Allergy; Am. Soc. Microbiol. Host-response to staphylococcal infection. Address: 1010 S. King St, Honolulu, HI 96814.

GOSHORN, R(OLAND) H(ENRY), b. Ladoga, Ind, April 20, 07. ORGANIC CHEMISTRY. A.B, Manchester Col, 29; M.S, Illinois, 32; fel, Purdue, 36, Ph.D, 37. Asst. chem, Manchester Col, 28-29; Illinois, 29-30; Purdue, 34-36; RES. CHEMIST, Sharples Chem, Inc, 36-53; Pennsalt Chems. Co, 53-59, PENNWALT CORP, 69- Am. Chem. Soc. Preparation of alkyl bromides; effect of hydrogen ion concentration on antiseptic and bactericidal action of benzoic acid and inorganic salts; preparation of alpha-phenyl-alkanoic acids and their bactericidal and physical properties; catalytic production of amines, alkyl mercaptans and sulfides; aliphatic and heterocyclic sulfur chemicals. Address: 329 Skippack Pike, Ft. Washington, PA 19406.

GOSLIN, ROY N(ELSON), b. Lincoln, Nebr, Nov. 21, 04; m. 34; c. 2. PHYSICS, MATHEMATICS. B.A, Nebr. Wesleyan, 28; fel, Wyoming, 28-30, M.A, 30; Ohio State, 39-41; hon. D.Sc, Oglethorpe Univ, 71. Instr. physics, Ala. Polytech, 30-39, asst. prof, 40-44; res. physicist, Clinton Eng. Works & Tenn. Eastman Corp, Tenn, 44-46; PROF. PHYSICS & CHMN, DIV. SCI, OGLETHORPE UNIV, 46-, PROF. MATH, 65-, dir. admissions, 54-58. Consult, Carbide & Carbon Chem. Corp, 49-53; South. Res. Inst, Ala, 55-56; Oak Ridge Nat. Lab, 59- AAAS; Am. Phys. Soc; Am. Asn. Physics Teachers. Mass spectroscopy; electrical discharges; high voltage insulation; plasma physics. Address: Dept. of Physics, Oglethorpe University, 4484 Peachtree Rd. N.E, Atlanta, GA 30319.

GOSLINE, CARL A(NTHONY), b. Beloit, Wis, Feb. 11, 21; m. 41; c. 2. CHEMISTRY, BUSINESS MANAGEMENT. B.A, State Univ. Iowa, 41; Stanford Univ, 67-68. Field group supvr, Manhattan Proj, Univ. Chicago, 43-44; prod. supvr, Hanford Works, E.I. du Pont de Nemours & Co, Inc, 44-46, res. engr. & consult. mgr, eng. dept, 47-52, plant tech. mgr, Chambers Works, 53-56, dir. eng. test ctr, 57-62, mkt. mgr. new ventures, 62-66; exec. v.pres, Hexcel Corp, Calif, 66-67; corp. v.pres, Fibreboard Corp, 67-68; Univ. Patents, Inc, 69-70; PRES. & TREAS, MGA TECHNOL, INC, 71- Dir, Mol-En Corp, 69-70; pres, Fluid Jet Systs, Inc, 69-70; dir, Piranha, Inc, 71-; chmn. field testing comt, Nat. Acad. Sci-Nat. Res. Coun. for U.S. Army Mat. Command. Am. Soc. Mech. Eng; Am. Mkt. Asn; Am. Mgt. Asn. Pollution abatement; comparative testing appraisal of materials for maintenance and construction, plant equipment and mechanical components, packages, drums, cartons, boxes and containers; test engineering; field testing; venture appraisal, management; industrial market development; marketing, corporate planning and management; heat transfer; international technology transfer and licensing. Address: Apt. 3307, Lake Point Tower, 505 N. Lake Shore Dr, Chicago, IL 60611.

GOSLINE, WILLIAM (ALONZO), b. Toledo, Ohio, Dec. 20, 15; m; c. 2. ICHTHYOLOGY. B.S, Harvard, 38; Ph.D.(ichthyol), Stanford, 41. Jr. biol. aide, Pacific pilchard invest, fish & wildlife serv, U.S. Dept. Interior, 41; fisheries expert, Brazilian Govt, 43-45; asst. curator fishes, zool. mus, Michigan, 45-48; assoc. prof. ZOOL. & ENTOMOL, UNIV. HAWAII, 48-54, PROF, 54- Guggenheim fel, British Mus. Natural Hist, London, England & U.S. Nat. Mus, Wash, D.C, 58-59. British Army, 41-43. Am. Soc. Ichthyol. & Herpet; Am. Fisheries Soc; Soc. Study Evolution. Taxonomy of Central Pacific fishes; classification of modern teleostean fishes. Address: Dept. of Zoology, University of Hawaii, Honolulu, HI 96822.

GOSLING, J(OHN) R(ODERICK) G(WYNNE), b. Cleveland, Ohio, Mar. 8, 26; m. 46; c. 3. OBSTETRICS, GYNECOLOGY. M.D, Michigan, 50. Res. OBSTET. & GYNEC, MED. SCH, UNIV. MICH, ANN ARBOR, 50-53, instr, 55-59, asst. prof, 59-62, ASSOC. PROF, 62-, ASST. DEAN MED. SCH, 64-, consult, health serv, 56-59. Consult, Ypsilanti State Hosp, 56-59; Markle scholar, 60-; dir. dept. obstet. & gynec, Wayne County Gen. Hosp, 61-64. Dipl, Am. Bd. Obstet. & Gynec, 60. Med.C, 53-55, Capt. Am. Col. Obstet. & Gynec; Am. Col. Surg; N.Y. Acad. Med. Gynecologic pathology; carcinoma of the female reproductive tract; anatomy and pathology of the human placenta. Address: Dept. of Obstetrics & Gynecology, University of Michigan, Ann Arbor, MI 48104.

GOSLING, JOHN T(HOMAS), b. Akron, Ohio, July 10, 38; m. 63; c. 2. SPACE PHYSICS, ASTRONOMY. B.S, Ohio Univ, 60; Ph.D.(physics), Univ. Calif, Berkeley, 65. STAFF SCIENTIST, Los Alamos Sci. Lab, 65-67; HIGH ALTITUDE OBSERV, NAT. CTR. ATMOSPHERIC RES, 67- Mem, Inter-Union Comn. Solar-Terrestrial Physics, 68- AAAS; Am. Geophys. Union; Am. Astron. Soc. Solar wind and solar physics; solar-terrestrial relationships; upper atmosphere physics. Address: High Altitude Observatory, National Center for Atmospheric Research, Boulder, CO 80302.

GOSLING, JOHN WILLIAM, b. Lake Clear Junction, N.Y, July 7, 15; m. 39; c. 4. ORGANIC CHEMISTRY, MATHEMATICS. B.S, Hamilton Col, 36; Cornell, 37. Chemist, EASTMAN KODAK CO, 37-45, photog. technician, 45-59, SUPVR. PHOTOG. SERV, 59- Soc. Photog. Sci. & Eng. Photographic masking; applied photography; lithography. Address: Kodak Park Works, Eastman Kodak Co, Rochester, NY 14650.

GOSLING, KEITH, b. Surrey, Eng, Sept. 6, 35. INORGANIC & ORGANOMETALLIC CHEMISTRY. B.Sc, Manchester, 58, Ph.D.(chem), 62. Res. assoc. fluorocarbon phosphorus chem, Southern California, 62-65; res. fel. aluminum-nitrogen chem, Sussex, 65-67; ASST. PROF. CHEM, W.VA. UNIV, 67- Am. Chem. Soc; The Chem. Soc. Synthesis and study of the fluorides and fluorocarbon derivatives of group five elements and organoaluminum-nitrogen compounds. Address: Dept. of Chemistry, West Virginia University, Morgantown, WV 26506.

GOSLOW, GEORGE E, JR, b. Tacoma, Wash, May 16, 39; m. 60; c. 3. VERTEBRATE MORPHOLOGY. A.B, California, Los Angeles, 62, Nat. Insts. Health fel, Davis, 66-67, Ph.D.(zool), 67; M.A, Humboldt State Col, 65. Assoc. ZOOL, California, Davis, 65-66; ASST. PROF, NORTH. ARIZ. UNIV, 67- Am. Soc. Zool; Soc. Neurosci. Functional vertebrate morphology, especially bone-muscle systems as they relate to the control of locomotion; motor units and muscle proprioceptors. Address: Dept. of Biology, Northern Arizona University, Flagstaff, AZ 86001.

GOSMAN, ALBERT LOUIS, b. Detroit, Mich, May 27, 23; m. 46; c. 2. THERMODYNAMICS, MECHANICAL ENGINEERING. B.S, Univ. Mich, 50; M.S, Univ. Colo, Boulder, 55; Ford Found. grant, 63-64; Ph.D.(thermodyn), Univ. Iowa, 65. Instr. mech. eng, Colo. Sch. Mines, 50-53, asst. prof, 53-55; res. engr, Northrop Aircraft, Inc, Calif, 56-58; asst. prof. mech. eng, Colo. Sch. Mines, 58-62; instr. mech. eng, Univ. Iowa, 62-65; assoc. prof, Wayne State Univ, 65-67; prof. mech. eng. & head dept, WICHITA STATE UNIV, 67-71, ASSOC. DEAN COL. ENG, 71- Res. engr, cryogenics div, Nat. Bur. Standards, Colo, summers 59-69; panel del, Nat. Res. Coun-Nat. Bur. Standards Conf. Thermodyn, 69. C.Eng, U.S.A, 43-45, Sgt. Am. Soc. Mech. Eng; Am. Soc. Eng. Educ. Determination of thermodynamic properties of liquids and gases; equation of state for liquid and gaseous argon from triple point to 1000 atmospheres and 1000 degrees Kelvin. Address: College of Engineering, Wichita State University, Wichita, KS 67208.

GOSNELL, AUBREY BREWER, b. Provo, Ark, Sept. 1, 29; m. 48; c. 3. PHYSICAL ORGANIC CHEMISTRY & POLYMER CHEMISTRY. B.S, Henderson State Col, 51; M.S, Arkansas, 62; Duke, 62-63; Ph.D.(org. chem), N.C. State, 67. Teacher high sch, Mansfield, Ark, 49-51; tester, refinery lab, El Dorado Refinery, Am. Oil Co, Ark, 51-58, refinery operator, 58-60; res. chemist, Camile Dreyfus Lab, Res. Triangle Inst, 62-67; ASSOC. PROF. CHEM, HENDERSON STATE COL, 67- Consult. assoc, Adv. Tech. Consults. Corp, 69- Nat. Guard, 47-62. Am. Chem. Soc; fel. Am. Inst. Chem. Gas chromatographic analysis of chlorinated fatty acids; synthesis and characterization of branched polystyrenes; solution properties of branched polymers; synthesis and properties of well defined graft copolymers; anionic polymerization. Address: Dept. of Chemistry, Henderson State College, Arkadelphia, AR 71923.

GOSNELL, REX BEACH, b. Akron, Ohio, Oct. 25, 30; m. 53; c. 2. ORGANIC & POLYMER CHEMISTRY. A.B, Manchester Col, 53; M.S, Purdue, 55, Ph.D.(org. chem), 57. Develop. chemist, Union Carbide Chem. Co, 57-60; res. chemist, RES. & DEVELOP. DIV, WHITTAKER CORP, 60-61, res. specialist, 61-64, asst. dept. mgr, 64-66, dept. mgr, 66-69, GEN. MGR, 69- Am. Chem. Soc. Effect of molecular structure on performance of polymers. Address: Research & Development Division, Whittaker Corp, 3540 Aero Ct, San Diego, CA 92123.

GOSS, CHARLES M(AYO), b. Peoria, Ill, Feb. 16, 99; m. 28; c. 3. ANATOMY. A.B, Yale, 21, Goodrich scholar, 25-26, M.D, 26. Instr. ANAT, sch. med, Yale, 26-29; col. physicians & surg, Columbia, 29-31, asst. prof, 31-38; prof, sch. med, Alabama, 38-47; sch. med. La. State Univ, 47-66; VIS. PROF. SCH. MED, GEORGE WASH. UNIV, 66- Guggenheim fel, 56; prof. extraordinary, sch. med, Costa Rica, 61-62; mem. Int. Anat. Nomenclature Comt. Ed, Gray's Anat, 48, 54, 59, 66, 72. Parker prize, 26; distinguished alumnus award, Bradley, 56; Golden Apple award, Student Am. Med. Asn. Soc. Exp. Biol. & Med; Am. Asn. Anat.(pres, 64-65, managing ed, Anat. Record, 47-67); Am. Asn. Phys. Anthrop; Am. Asn. Hist. Med. Experimental embryology of mammalian heart; histology and tissue culture of muscle; gross anatomy of muscles and fasciae; reproductive physiology and embryology of monkey; history of medicine in Ancient Greece. Address: 7809 Moorland Lane, Bethesda, MD 20014.

GOSS, DAVID, b. Boston, Mass, July 20, 37; m. 70. NUCLEAR PHYSICS. B.S, Southwestern (Tex), 59; M.S, Mich. State, 61; Ph.D.(nuclear physics), Texas, 64. ASSOC. PROF. PHYSICS, NEBR. WESLEYAN UNIV, 64- Am. Phys. Soc; Am. Asn. Physics Teachers; Fedn. Am. Sci. Nuclear structure and computational physics. Address: Dept. of Physics, Nebraska Wesleyan University, Lincoln, NE 68504.

GOSS, DONALD A, b. Morristown, N.J, May 1, 34; m; c. 2. OBSTETRICS, GYNECOLOGY. A.B, Hamilton Col, 55; M.D, Harvard Med. Sch, 59. PROF. OBSTET. & GYNEC. & CHMN. DEPT, SCH. MED, VANDERBILT UNIV, 66- U.S.A.F, 65-66, Res, 67-, Maj. AAAS; Endocrine Soc; Am. Fertil. Soc; Int. Fertil. Asn. Immunoassay of gonadotrophins; ovulation suppression and induction. Address: Dept. of Obstetrics & Gynecology, Vanderbilt University School of Medicine, Nashville, TN 37203.

GOSS, JAMES A(RTHUR), b. Brigham City, Utah, May 19, 24; m. 47; c. 6. BOTANY. B.S, Utah State Agr. Col, 51; Ph.D.(bot), California, Los Angeles, 57. Jr. plant physiologist, regional salinity lab, U.S. Dept. Agr, 51-54; asst. bot, California, Los Angeles, 55, atomic energy, sch. med, 56; instr. BOT, KANS. STATE UNIV, 56-57, asst. prof, 57-67, ASSOC. PROF, 67- U.S.A, 43-45. Am. Soc. Plant Physiol; Bot. Soc. Am; Am. Inst. Biol. Sci; Am. Microchem. Soc. Address: Division of Biology, Kansas State University, Manhattan, KS 66502.

GOSS, JOHN R(AY), b. Winona, Minn, May 30, 23; m. 47; c. 4. AGRICULTURAL & MECHANICAL ENGINEERING. B.S, California, Los Angeles, 52, M.S, Davis, 55. Asst. specialist agr. eng, UNIV. CALIF, DAVIS, 53-57, assoc. specialist, 57-58, asst. prof. eng. & asst. agr. engr, 58-62, ASSOC. PROF. ENG. & ASSOC. AGR. ENGR, 62-, ACAD. ASST. TO CHANCELLOR, 63-, CHMN. DEPT. AGR. ENG, 68- U.S.M.C, 43-49, 1st Lt. Am. Soc. Agr. Eng. Combine harvester performance in legume, cereal and dry bean crops for seed and food; pneumatic conveying and forage harvesting machinery research; microclimatic factors, especially nocturnal and diurnal radiation. Address: Dept. of Agricultural Engineering, University of California, Davis, CA 95616.

GOSS, LEONARD J(OYCE), b. Manhattan, Kans, Feb. 27, 13; m. 39; c. 2. ANIMAL PATHOLOGY. D.V.M, Ohio State, 34, Ph.D.(path), Cornell, 38. Asst. poultry res, N.Y. State Vet. Col, Cornell, 34-38, instr. vet. path, 35-38; pathologist, exp. sta, Kentucky, 38-39; veterinarian, N.Y. Zool. Soc, 39-52, asst. dir, 52-58; DIR, CLEVELAND ZOOL. PARK, 58- Consult, Walter Reed Army Med. Center. Mem, sci. adv. comt, New Eng. Regional Primate Res. Ctr. Am. Soc. Mammal; Am. Asn. Path. & Bact; Am. Vet. Med. Asn; Am. Col. Vet. Path. Veterinary pathology; diseases of wild animals; incidence and classification of avian neoplasms. Address: Cleveland Zoological Park, P.O. Box 09040, Cleveland, OH 44109.

GOSS, LOUIS, b. Washington, D.C, May 1, 26; m. 53; c. 1. PHARMACEUTICAL CHEMISTRY. B.S, Butler, 54, M.S, 55, Ph.D.(pharm. chem), 57. Dir. res, Inland Alkaloid Co, 58; assoc. dir. res, Reed & Carnrick Co, 58; res. chemist, Whitehall Labs, N.J, 58-60; sr. res. chemist, Nat. Drug Co, N.J, 60-67; DIR. PHARMACEUT. DEVELOP, USV PHARMACEUT. CORP, 67- U.S.N.R, 44-46. AAAS; Am. Chem. Soc; Am. Pharmaceut. Asn. New medicinal drugs and new compounds in specialized fields of medicine. Address: 6 Boxwood Place, Port Chester, NY 10573.

GOSS, MEREDITH R, b. Seiling, Okla, July 11, 26; m. 49; c. 3. MATHEMATICS, STATISTICS. B.A, Duke, 49; M.S, Okla. State, 61. MGR. ENG. STATIST. SECT, RES. & DEVELOP. DEPT, PHILLIPS PETROL. CO, 61- Am. Statist. Asn; Inst. Math. Statist. Experimental design; data analysis. Address: Research & Development Dept, 222 Electro-Mechanics Lab, Phillips Petroleum Co, Bartlesville, OK 74003.

GOSS, RICHARD J(OHNSON), b. Marblehead, Mass, July 19, 25; m. 51; c. 2. BIOLOGY. A.B, Harvard, 48, A.M, 51, fel, 49-52, Ph.D.(biol), 52. Instr. BIOL, BROWN UNIV, 52-54, asst. prof, 54-58, assoc. prof, 58-64, PROF, 64- Fel, Carnegie Inst, 60; trustee, Mt. Desert Island Biol. Lab, 60-64. U.S.A, 43-45. AAAS; Soc. Develop. Biol; Am. Soc. Zool; Am. Asn. Anat; Int. Soc. Cell Biol. Regeneration and growth regulation. Address: Division of Biological & Medical Sciences, Brown University, Providence, RI 02912.

GOSS, ROBERT C(HARLES), b. Huntington, Ind, Mar. 31, 29; m. 50; c. 3. MICROBIOLOGY. B.S, Huntington Col, 51; M.S, Purdue, 53, Ph.D.(plant sci), 57. Asst. biol. & plant path, Purdue, 51-55, instr. zool. & chem, exten, 55-56; plant pathologist, United Fruit Co, Costa Rica, 56; instr. gen. sci. & math, Woodworth Sch, Mich, 57-58; asst. prof. MICROBIOL, Loyola (La), 58-64; assoc. prof, UNIV. NORTH. IOWA, 64-71, PROF, 71- Soc. Indust. Microbiol; Am. Phytopath. Soc; Nat. Asn. Biol. Teachers. Soil microbiology; plant pathogens, control and cancer. Address: Dept. of Biology, College of Natural Sciences, University of Northern Iowa, Cedar Falls, IA 50613.

GOSS, ROBERT N(ICHOLS), b. Des Moines, Iowa, Jan. 7, 21; m. 42; c. 3. MATHEMATICS. A.B, Drake, 42; M.S, Iowa State Col, 47, Ph.D.(applied math), 50. Instr. math, Iowa State Col, 46-50; Tulsa, 50-51; MATHEMATICIAN, U.S. NAVY ELECTRONICS LAB, 51-, HEAD MATH. DIV, 68- Lectr, California, Los Angeles, 51-54, 56- U.S.A.A.F, 43-46, 1st Lt. Am. Math. Soc; Soc. Indust. & Appl. Math; Math. Asn. Am; Asn. Comput. Mach; Math. Soc. France. Digital computer programming; partial differential equations; mathematical linguistics. Address: Naval Electronics Lab. Center, San Diego, CA 92152.

GOSS, ROY LEON, b. Weslaco, Tex, Jan. 29, 26; m. 52. AGRONOMY. B.S, Washington State, 50, B.Ed, 51, Ph.D, 60. Teacher, high sch, Wash, 51-53; soil conservationist, soil conserv. serv, U.S. Dept. Agr, 53-55; jr. agronomist, WEST. WASH. EXP. STA, WASH. STATE UNIV, 60-61, asst. agronomist, 61-66, AGRONOMIST, 66- U.S.N.R, 43-46. Am. Soc. Agron. Effect of fertility ratio and level on shoots, roots, quality, and diseases of turf grasses; control measures for crabgrass, annual bluegrass, and other turf weeds. Address: Western Washington Research & Extension Center, Puyallup, WA 98371.

GOSS, WILBUR H(UMMON), b. Tacoma, Wash, June 16, 11; m; c. 3. PHYSICS. B.S, Puget Sound, 32; Ph.D.(physics), Washington (Seattle), 39. Lectr. physics, British Columbia, 39-40; asst. prof, New Mexico State, 40-42; res. physicist, appl. physics lab, Johns Hopkins Univ, 42-61, asst. dir, 61-67; CONSULT, 67- Presidential cert. merit; distinguished pub. serv. award, U.S. Navy, 61; Potts Medal, Franklin Inst, 62. Fel. Am. Phys. Soc. Electron physics; combustion; ordnance development. Address: 1050 Monte Dr, Santa Barbara, CA 93110.

GOSS, WILLIAM A(LBERT), b. East Orange, N.J, Jan. 12, 32; m. 56; c. 4. MICROBIOLOGY. B.S, Rutgers, 54, fel, 54-58, Ph.D.(microbiol), 58. Asst. microbiol. chem, inst. microbiol, Rutgers, 58-59; res. assoc. chemother, Squibb Inst. Med. Res, N.J, 59-62; res. microbiologist & group leader, STERLING-WINTHROP RES. INST, 62-65, sect. head bact, 65-69, HEAD. DEPT. MICROBIOL, 69-, SR. RES. MICROBIOLOGIST, 69- AAAS; Am. Soc. Microbiol. Antibiotic fermentations and the production of biosynthetic antibiotics; chemotherapy of mycotic diseases, especially the dermatophytes; bacteriology of skin; topical antiseptics; mode of action of antimicrobial agents; development of bio-assay systems. Address: Sterling-Winthrop Research Institute, Renssalaer, NY 12144.

GOSS, WILLIAM D(AVID), b. Horton, Kans, June 4, 15; m. 42; c. 2. ANALYTICAL CHEMISTRY. B.S, Arizona, 40. Denver. Lab. clerk & chemist, Phelps Dodge Corp, 40-42; CHEMIST, U.S. Pub. Health Serv, 49-50; quality of water br, U.S. GEOL. SURV, 50-52, BR. ANAL. LABS, 52- U.S.A.A.F, 42-46, Lt. Col. Am. Chem. Soc. Fire assay. Address: 2461 Perry St, Denver, CO 80212.

GOSS, WILLIAM PAUL, b. Milford, Conn, May 23, 38; m. 63; c. 1. THERMAL SCIENCES, TRANSPORTATION. B.S.E, Connecticut, 61, M.S, 62, Ph.D.(thermal sci), 67. Res. asst. heat transfer, Connecticut, 61-62; sr. anal. engr, Pratt & Whitney Div, United Aircraft Corp, 62-64; instr. MECH. ENG, Univ. Conn, 64-67; asst. prof, Va. Polytech. Inst, 68-70; ASSOC. PROF, UNIV. MASS, AMHERST, 71- Consult, Mitre Corp, 67-71. AAAS; Am. Inst. Chem. Eng; Soc. Automotive Eng; Nat. Soc. Prof. Eng; Am. Soc. Eng. Educ; Am. Inst. Aeronaut. & Astronaut; Am. Soc. Mech. Eng. Aerodynamics of tube vehicle transportation systems; two phase flow; transportation system engineering. Address: Dept. of Mechanical & Aerospace Engineering, University of Massachusetts, Amherst, MA 01002.

GOSSARD, A(RTHUR) C(HARLES), b. Ottawa, Ill, June 18, 35. PHYSICS. B.A, Harvard, 56; Nat. Sci. Found. fel. & Ph.D.(physics), California, Berkeley, 60. MEM. TECH. STAFF, BELL TEL. LABS, 60- Nat. Sci. Found. fel, Saclay Nuclear Res. Ctr, France, 62-63. Am. Phys. Soc. Solid state physics, nuclear magnetic resonance; ferromagnetism; transition metals; superconductivity. Address: Bell Telephone Labs, Murray Hill, NJ 07974.

GOSSARD, EARL E(VERETT), b. Eureka, Calif, Jan. 8, 23; m. 48; c. 3. PHYSICAL OCEANOGRAPHY, RADIO METEOROLOGY. A.B, California, Los Angeles, 48, M.S, California, San Diego, 51, Ph.D, 56. From physicist to HEAD RADIO PHYSICS DIV, U.S. NAVY ELECTRONICS LAB, SAN DIEGO, 48- Mem, Int. Radio Sci. Union. U.S.A.A.F, 43-46, 1st Lt. Am. Meteorol. Soc; Am. Geophys. Union. Micrometeorology; lower ionosphere physics; internal gravity waves. Address: 563 Orchid Lane, Del Mar, CA 92014.

GOSSELIN, RICHARD P(ETTENGILL), b. Springfield, Mass, June 29, 21; m. 44; c. 2. MATHEMATICS. B.S, Chicago, 44, Ph.D, 51; M.A, Rochester, 48. Sr. mathematician, inst. air weapons res, Chicago, 51-52; prof. MATH. & head dept, Youngstown Col, 52-55; assoc. prof, UNIV. CONN, 55-61, PROF, 61- Summers, res. grant, Nat. Sci. Found, 57-58; res. contract, U.S. Air Force, 59-60. Consult, inst. air weapons res, Chicago. U.S.A.A.F, 42-46, Capt. Am. Math. Soc; Math. Asn. Am. Trigonometric series; trigonometric interpolating polynomials; localization theory and L^p Fourier series. Address: Dept. of Mathematics, University of Connecticut, Storrs, CT 06268.

GOSSELIN, ROBERT E(DMOND), b. Springfield, Mass, Sept. 2, 19; m. 48; c. 2. PHARMACOLOGY. A.B, Brown, 41; Ph.D.(mammalian physiol), Rochester, 45, M.D, 47; Yale, 47-48. Asst, Office Sci. Res. & Develop. contract, Rochester, 42-44; med. intern, Grace-New Haven Community Hosp, Conn, 47-48; instr. PHARMACOL, sch. med, Rochester, 48-54, asst. prof, 54-56; PROF. & CHMN. DEPT, DARTMOUTH MED. SCH, 56- Researcher, Atomic Energy Proj, 48-52, 54-56; mem, toxicol. study sect, U.S. Pub. Health Serv, 64-68; consult, Food & Drug Admin, 66-69. U.S.A, 44-46, Med.C, 52-54, Capt. AAAS; Soc. Exp. Biol. & Med; Am. Physiol. Soc; Soc. Pharmacol. & Exp. Therapeut; Soc. Toxicol. Polyphosphate metabolism; atropine metabolism; ultraphagocytosis of radiocolloids; physiology and pharmacology of cilia; drug receptor kinetics; microcirculatory function; clinical toxicology. Address: Dept. of Pharmacology & Toxicology, Dartmouth Medical School, Hanover, NH 03755.

GOSSELINK, JAMES G, b. Kodaikanal, India, Sept. 14, 31; U.S. citizen; m. 55; c. 3. PLANT PHYSIOLOGY. A.B, Oberlin Col, 53; Nat. Sci. Found. fel, Rutgers, 55-56, M.S, 58, Ph.D.(hort), 59. Res. horticulturist, new crops res. br, U.S. Dept. Agr, 59-61; asst. prof. biol, State Univ. N.Y. Binghamton, 61-64; plant physiol, LA. STATE UNIV, BATON ROUGE, 64-66, bot. & dir. sci. training progs, 66-68, ASSOC. PROF. BOT. & MARINE SCI, 68- U.S.A, 53-55. AAAS; Am. Soc. Plant Physiol; Am. Inst. Biol. Sci; Am. Soc. Limnol. & Oceanog; Ecol. Soc. Am. Plant nutrition, physiological and systems ecology. Address: Dept. of Botany, Louisiana State University, Baton Rouge, LA 70803.

GOSSER, LAWRENCE WAYNE, b. Seattle, Wash, Aug. 21, 38. PHYSICAL ORGANIC & ORGANOMETALLIC CHEMISTRY. B.S, Washington (Seattle), 60; U.S. Rubber Co. fel, California, Los Angeles, Ph.D.(chem), 64. Instr. chem, Cent. Ore. Col, 64-65; CHEMIST, CENT. RES. DEPT, E.I. DU PONT

DE NEMOURS & CO, INC, 65- Am. Chem. Soc. Organic reactions involving carbanions; homogeneo s catalysis; chemistry of organo-transition metal complexes. Address: 5-D Mary Ella Dr, Wilmington, DE 19805.

GOSSER, LEO A(NTHONY), b. Shelby, Ohio, May 30, 42; m. 65; c. 2. ANALYTICAL CHEMISTRY. B.S, St. Vincent Col, 64; Nat. Sci. Found. fel, Ohio State, summer 66, Ph.D.(chem), 69. Teaching asst. anal. chem, Ohio State, 64-66 & 69; res. assoc, 66-69; SCIENTIST, WARNER-LAMBERT RES. INST, MORRIS PLAINS, 69- Am. Chem. Soc. Determination of equilibrium constants in model non-enzymatic Schiff base systems; development of analytical methods for pharmaceutical products and their metabolites. Address: Lawrence Rd, Randolph Township, Dover, NJ 07801.

GOSSETT, C(HARLES) R(OBERT), b. Manila, P.I, Sept. 29, 29; m. 52; c. 4. NUCLEAR PHYSICS. B.S, Duke, 51; M.A, Rice, 53, Ph.D.(physics), 55. Physicist, nucleonics div, NAVAL RES. LAB, 55-58, supvry. physicist, radiation div, 58-66; RES. PHYSICIST, NUCLEAR SCI. DIV, 66- Am. Phys. Soc; Sci. Res. Soc. Am. Experimental nuclear physics; parameters of nuclear energy levels by the study of accelerator induced reactions. Address: Nuclear Sciences Division, Code 6611, Naval Research Lab, Washington, DC 20390.

GOSSETT, WILLIAM H, b. Des Moines, N.Mex, May 18, 30; m. 54; c. 2. ANIMAL NUTRITION & PHYSIOLOGY. B.S, N.Mex. State Univ, 52, M.S, 59; Ph.D.(animal nutrit), Purdue Univ, 62. Dep. inspector, N.Mex. State Dept. Agr, 57-58; asst. Purdue Univ, 59-62; res. technician, Conagra, Inc, Nebr, 62-63, dir. biol. res, 63-66, dir. res. & develop, 66-68, ruminant res. develop, 68-70; ANIMAL NUTRITIONIST, VIGORTONE PROD. CO, 70- U.S.A.F, 52-56, 1st Lt. Am. Soc. Animal Sci; Am. Dairy Sci. Asn; Poultry Sci. Asn. Growth of Hereford heifers; factors affecting urea utilization; commercial feeding trials with broilers, layers, swine, dairy and beef; product development in many areas of poultry, swine, dairy and beef. Address: Vigortone Products Co, P.O. Box 1230, Cedar Rapids, IA 52406.

GOSSICK, BEN R(OGER), b. Fairfield, Iowa, May 6, 14; m. 41; c. 4. PHYSICS. B.A, Pomona Col, 39; M.A, Columbia, 41; M.S. & Ph.D, Purdue, 54. Instr, U.S. Naval Training Sch, elec. eng. dept. Minnesota, 42-44; tech. writer, Minneapolis-Honeywell Regulator Co, 44-45; engr, Radio Corp. Am. Ind. & N.J, 45-47; Nuclear Eng. Propulsion Aircraft Proj, Oak Ridge, Tenn, 47-50; asst, Purdue, 50-52, instr, 52-54, asst. prof, 54-56; chief device res, semiconductor div, Motorola, Inc, Ariz, 56-57; PROF. PHYSICS, Arizona State, 57-63; Harpur Col, 63-66; UNIV. KY, 66-, CHMN. DEPT, 69- Fel. AAAS; fel. Am. Phys. Soc. Transient behavior of semiconductor rectifying barriers; radiation effects in semiconductors; metal-semiconductor boundary properties. Address: Dept. of Physics, University of Kentucky, Lexington, KY 40506.

GOSSLEE, DAVID G(ILBURT), b. Fargo, N.Dak, June 22, 22; m. 47; c. 3. STATISTICS, CLIMATOLOGY. B.S, Moorhead State Col, 47; M.S, Iowa State, 50; Ph.D, N.C. State Col, 56. Instr. math, N.Dak. State, 50-54, statistician, 54-58; assoc. prof. biomet, Connecticut, 58-61; BIOMETRICIAN, OAK RIDGE NAT. LAB, UNION CARBIDE CORP, 61- U.S.A, 43-46, 1st Lt. Am. Statist. Asn; Biomet. Soc. Biometrics; design and analysis of experiments; statistical research on methods of analyzing disproportionate data. Address: Oak Ridge National Lab, Union Carbide Corp, Box Y, Oak Ridge, TN 37830.

GOSTYN, ERNEST, b. Ger, June 12, 02; nat; m. 31; c. 1. ELECTRICAL ENGINEERING. M.S, Berlin Inst. Tech, 27. Develop. engr, Carl Lindstroem, Inc, Ger, 27-32; design engr, radio dept, Peerless Cabinet Corp, N.Y, 34; in charge res. & develop. & asst. chief engr, F.W. SICKLES DIV, GEN. INSTRUMENT CORP, 37-50, chief engr, 50-68, DIR. DEFLECTION & INDUST. COMPONENT ENG, 68- Sr. mem. Inst. Elec. & Electronics Eng. Design of radio and television circuits; components and equipment; design of electronic test equipment. Address: F. W. Sickles Division, General Instrument Corp, Chicopee, MA 01014.

GOSWAMI, AMIT, b. Faridpur, India, Nov. 4, 36; m. 60; c. 2. THEORETICAL PHYSICS. B.Sc, Presidency Col, Calcutta, India, 55, M.Sc, 60, D.Phil. (physics), 64. Instr, PHYSICS, Case Western Reserve Univ, 63-65, asst. prof, 65-67; ASSOC. PROF, UNIV. ORE, 68-, RES. ASSOC, INST. THEORET. SCI, 68- Am. Phys. Soc. Generalized pairing in light nuclei; bootstrap theory of vibrations; use of surface-delta-interaction in nuclear structure calculations; theory of fine structure of giant dipole resonance; gapless superconductivity in nuclei. Address: Dept. of Physics, University of Oregon, Eugene, OR 97403.

GOSWAMI, BHUVENESH C, b. Bannu, W.Pakistan, Oct. 13, 37; m. 68; c. 6. TEXTILE PHYSICS. B.Text, Delhi, 59; M.Text, Bombay, 63; Commonwealth scholar, Manchester, 63-66, Ph.D.(textile physics), 66. Sci. officer, Sri Ram Inst. Indust. Res, 66-67; vis. lectr. fiber & textile physics, Clemson, 67-68; STAFF SCIENTIST, TEXTILE RES. INST, 69- Am. Asn. Textile Chem. & Colorists; Am. Asn. Textile Tech; assoc. Brit. Textile Inst; Fiber Soc. Influence of physical and structural factors on flammability behavior of textiles; structural mechanics of yarns and fabrics. Address: Textile Research Institute, P.O. Box 625, Princeton, NJ 08540.

GOSWAMI, SANTOSH RANJAN, b. Mymensingh, India, Jan. 11, 35; m. 70. ENVIRONMENTAL & SANITARY ENGINEERING. B.Tech, Indian Inst. Technol, Kharagpur, 57; Can. Commonwealth scholar, McGill Univ, 60-62, M.Eng, 62; M.S, Univ. Ill, Urbana, 64; Ph.D.(bio-environ. eng), Okla. State Univ, 69. Eng. asst, Rourkela Steel Proj, India, 57-58; asst. engr, Durgapur Steel Proj, 58-60; part-time demonstr. munic. eng, McGill Univ, 60-62; res. asst. sanit. eng, Univ. Ill, Urbana, 62-64; asst. bioeng, Okla. State Univ, 64-69; ENGR, ENVIRON. PROTECTION AGENCY, STATE OF ILL, 69- Wat-Mull Found. grant, Honolulu, Hawaii, 69. Assoc. mem. Am. Soc. Civil Eng; Am. Water Works Asn; Soc. Civil Eng. France. Bio-environmental engineering; industrial waste treatment; hydrology; water supplies; water treatment plant design; sewer and waste water treatment. Address: Environmental Protection Agency, State of Illinois, 2200 Churchill Rd, Springfield, IL 62706.

GOSWITZ, FRANCIS ANDREW, b. St. Paul, Minn, Sept. 8, 31; m. 56; c. 3. NUCLEAR MEDICINE, HEMATOLOGY. B.S, Marquette, 53, M.D, 56. Intern, Univ. Iowa Hosps, 56-57, res. internal med, 57-58, 60, 61-63; fel. nuclear med, Oak Ridge Inst. Nuclear Studies, 60-61; hemat, med. center, Univ. Utah, 63-65; clinician INTERNAL MED. & coord. med. radioistope courses, spec. training div, OAK RIDGE ASSOC. UNIVS, 65-68, SR. CLINICIAN, MED. DIV, 68- Med.C, U.S.A, 58-60, Capt. Soc. Nuclear Med; Am. Med. Asn; Am. Soc. Hemat; N.Y. Acad. Sci. Internal medicine; effects of irradiation on hematopiesis; radioprotective cytologic agents; diagnostic applications of radioisotopes in medicine; biochemical and physiological characteristics of the erythrocyte and lymphocyte; cancer chemotherapy. Address: Medical Division, Oak Ridge Associated Universities, P.O. Box 117, Oak Ridge, TN 37830.

GOSWITZ, HELEN VODOPICK, b. Milwaukee, Wis, Apr. 29, 31; m. 56; c. 3. HEMATOLOGY, NUCLEAR MEDICINE. B.S, Marquette, 53, M.D, 56. Intern, Univ. Iowa Hosp, 56-57, res. internal med, 57-60, instr. internal med, 61-63; fel. nuclear med, Oak Ridge Inst. Nuclear Studies, 60-61; hemat, Utah, 63-65; CLINICIAN INTERNAL MED, OAK RIDGE ASSOC. UNIVS, 65- Soc. Nuclear Med; Am. Med. Asn; Am. Soc. Hemat. Internal medicine; granulocytokinetics; histocompatibility testing. Address: Oak Ridge Associated Universities, P.O. Box 117, Oak Ridge, TN 37830.

GOTAAS, HAROLD B(ENEDICT), b. Mellette, S.Dak, Sept. 3, 06; m. 31; c. 1. SANITARY ENGINEERING. B.S, South Dakota, 28, hon. Sc.D, 55; M.S, Iowa State Col, 30; S.M, Harvard, 37, Sc.D.(sanit. eng), 42; hon. D.Eng, Rose Polytech. Inst, 69. Engr, Am. Bridge Co, Pa, 30; bridge designer, State Hwy. Comn, Iowa, 31; chief designer Clinton Bridge Works, 31-32; asst. prof. civil eng, S.Dakota, 32-37; from asst. prof. to prof. sanit. eng, North Carolina, 37-42; chief engr, Inst. Inter-Am. Affairs, Wash, D.C, 42-44, dir. div. health & sanit, exec. v.pres. & pres, 45-46; prof. sanit. eng, California, 46-57; prof. CIVIL ENG, NORTHWEST. UNIV, 57-67, WALTER P. MURPHY PROF, 67-, EMER. DEAN TECHNOL. INST, 71-, dean, 57-71. City engr, Vermillion, S.Dak, 33-37; chmn, div. civil eng, California, 48-53, dir. sanit. eng. lab, 49-57; mem. eng. panel, Nat. Sci. Found, 60-63; Great Lakes Comn, 61. Spec. consult, sanit. study sect, U.S. Pub. Health Serv, 49-54; consult, World Health Orgn, 54-; nat. adv. health coun, U.S. Dept. Health, Educ. & Welfare, 56-60, dir, Eng. Col. Res. Coun, 58-61. Cross Boyaca, Colombia; Condor of the Andes, Bolivia; Order of Merit, Chile; Order of Honor & Merit, Haiti. U.S.A, 42-46, Col; Legion Merit. Nat. Acad. Eng; hon. mem. Am. Soc. Civil Eng.(Croes Medal, 58, Hering Medal, 58); Am. Soc. Eng. Educ; Nat. Soc. Prof. Eng; Am. Water Works Asn; fel. Am. Pub. Health Asn; Water Pollution Control Fedn.(Eddy Award, Allen Award); Inter-Am. Asn. Sanit. Eng.(pres, U.S. sect, 59-61); Am. Acad. Environ. Eng. Water treatment and purification; sewage and industrial waste treatment; air sanitation; municipal engineering. Address: Dept. of Civil Engineering, Northwestern University, Evanston, IL 60201.

GOTELLI, DAVID M, b. Stockton, Calif, Jan. 1, 43; m. 65; c. 1. BOTANY, MYCOLOGY. B.A, Univ. Calif, Berkeley, 64; Fed. Water Pollution Control Admin. fel, Univ. Wash, 67-69, Ph.D.(bot), 69. ASST. PROF. BIOL, STANISLAUS STATE COL, 70- Mycol. Soc. Am; Bot. Soc. Am. Ultrastructure and development of biflagellate fungi; culture and development of higher basidiomycetes. Address: Dept. of Biological Sciences, Stanislaus State College, 400 Monte Vista Ave, Turlock, CA 95380.

GOTH, ANDRES, b. Tolcsva, Hungary, May 6, 14; nat; m. 41; c. 2. PHARMACOLOGY. Lic.Med, Chile, 39. Intern, U.S. Marine Hosp, La, 39-40; asst. PHARMACOL, sch. med, Vanderbilt, 40-44; asst. prof, UNIV. TEX. (SOUTHWEST) MED. SCH, 44-46, assoc. prof, 46-50, PROF. & CHMN. DEPT, 50- AAAS; Am. Chem. Soc; Soc. Exp. Biol. & Med; Am. Soc. Pharmacol. & Exp. Therapeut; Am. Med. Asn. Penicillin and aspergillus antibiotics; antibacterial chemotherapy; bismuth aspergillic acid complex; histamine metabolism and hypersensitivity; carbohydrate metabolism and inflammation. Address: University of Texas (Southwestern) Medical School, 5323 Harry Hines Blvd, Dallas, TX 75235.

GOTH, ROBERT W, b. Phillips, Wis, May 10, 27; m. 54; c. 3. PLANT PATHOLOGY. B.S, Wis. State, Superior, 54; M.S, Minnesota, 57, Ph.D.(plant path), 61. Plant pathologist, CROPS RES. DIV, AGR. RES. SERV, U.S. DEPT. AGR, 61-68, RES. PLANT PATHOLOGIST POTATO INVEST, 68- U.S.A, 45-47, 50-52, Sgt. Am. Phytopath. Soc. Nature of resistance, mode of infection, and physical and chemical nature of the causal organisms of virus, fungal, and bacterial diseases of potatoes, beans, peas, and related legumes. Address: H.H. 13, Crops Research Division, Plant Industry Station, Agriculture Research Service, U.S. Dept. of Agriculture, Beltsville, MD 20705.

GOTHÁRD, NICHOLAS, b. Pécs, Hungary, Dec. 12, 33; U.S. citizen; m. 57; c. 2. AIR POLLUTION, PHYSICS. Budapest Tech, 52-56; S.M, Mass. Inst. Tech, 62; NASA fel, Cornell, 63-65, Ph.D.(space sci), 65. Develop. engr, Radio Commun. Equip, Can, 57-58; RCA Victor Co. Ltd, Que, 58-60; res. engr, Mass. Inst. Tech, 61-62; Dynatech Corp, Mass, 63; asst. prof. magnetohydrodyn. & ionospheric physics & mem, ionospheric res. lab, Pa. State, 65-66; asst. prof. elec. eng, Tex. A&M Univ, 66-68; V.PRES. & DIR. OPERS, FILTERON INT, INC, 68- Electromagnetic wave theory; magnetohydrodynamics and plasma physics; ionospheric physics; air pollution control. Address: Filteron International, Inc, 2322 Irving Blvd, Dallas, TX 75207.

GOTHELF, BERNARD, b. Chicago, Ill, May 8, 28; m. 58; c. 5. PHARMACOLOGY. B.S, Illinois, 50; M.S, Iowa, 52; Ph.D.(pharmacol), Loyola (Ill), 65. Asst. prof. PHARMACOL, Loyola (La), 63-64; instr, sch. med, Marquette, 64-66; asst. prof, dent. br, Univ. Tex, Houston, 66-69, RES. ASSOC, UNIV. TEX. MED. BR. GALVESTON, 70- Med.Serv.C, U.S.A, 52-54. AAAS. Neuropharmacology; neurochemistry; analysis and distribution of chlorpromazine in tissues. Address: Dept. of Pharmacology, University of Texas Medical Branch, Galveston, TX 77550.

GOTLIEB, C(ALVIN) C(ARL), b. Toronto, Ont, Mar. 27, 21; m. 49; c. 3. COMPUTER SCIENCE. B.A, Toronto, 42, M.A, 46, Ph.D.(physics), 47; hon. Dr. Math, Univ. Waterloo, 68. Asst. Nat. Res. Coun. Can, Toronto, 42-47; asst. prof. physics, UNIV. TORONTO, 48-58, assoc. prof, 58-60, prof, 60-

64, PROF. COMPUT. SCI, McLENNAN LAB, 64-, dir. inst. comput. sci, 62-70, head dept. comput. sci, univ, 64-67. Civilian sci. off, Nat. Res. Coun. Can, 42-47; mem, Admiralty Sig. Estab. & Ministry Supply, Eng, 43-44; consult, defense res. med. labs, Royal Can. Air Force, 46-56; Can. del, Int. Fedn. Info. Process. Socs, 59-65, v.chmn. prog. comt, Int. Fedn. Info. Processing Congress, 71; UN; Ottawa Dept. Commun. Fel. Royal Soc. Can; Asn. Comput. Mach.(ed-in-chief, Commun, 62-65, Jour, 66-68, ed, J. Asn. Comput. Mach, 69-, info. processing letters, 71-); Can. Info. Processing Soc.(v.pres, 58-59, pres, 59-60); fel. Brit. Comput. Soc. Computer systems and applications; scheduling problems; programming languages; business data processing; social implications of computers. Address: Dept. of Computer Science, McLennan Lab, University of Toronto, Toronto, Ont, Can.

GOTO, SHOSUKE, b. Seattle, Wash, June 9, 15. AGRICULTURE. B.Sc, Alberta, 41, M.Sc, 43; Ph.D, Minnesota, 53. Asst. plant path, Alberta, 39-43; Minnesota, 48-53; plant pathologist, Dugway Proving Ground, Utah, 53-54; Ft. Detrick, Md, 54-60; ASSOC. PLANT PATHOLOGIST, HAWAII AGR. EXP. STA, UNIV. HAWAII, 60-, ASST. DEAN, COL. TROP. AGR, 58-, ASSOC. PROF. PLANT PATH, 60-, asst. plant pathologist, 56-61, asst. dir, 59-62. U.S.A, 44-47, Lt. Col. AAAS; Am. Soc. Microbiol; Am. Phytopath. Soc. Diseases of tropical crops. Address: College of Tropical Agriculture, University of Hawaii, Honolulu, HI 96822.

GOTOFF, SAMUEL P, b. N.Y.C, Mar. 22, 33; m. 56; c. 3. IMMUNOLOGY. B.A, Amherst Col, 54; M.D, Univ. Rochester, 58. Instr. sch. med, Yale, 60-61; clin. instr. pediat, ABRAHAM LINCOLN SCH. MED, UNIV. ILL, 61-63, from asst. to assoc prof, 65-71, assoc. prof. microbiol, 68-71, PROF. PEDIAT. & MICROBIOL, 71- Attend. physician, Munic. Contagious Disease Hosp, 67. U.S.P.H.S, 61-63. AAAS; Am. Acad. Pediat; Soc. Pediat. Res; Am. Asn. Immunol; Am. Soc. Microbiol; Reticuloendothelial Soc; Am. Soc. Nephrol; Am. Pub. Health Asn; Infectious Diseases Soc. Am; Am. Soc. Pediat. Nephrology. Cell-mediated immunity; immune deficiency diseases; immunologic renal diseases. Address: Dept. of Pediatrics, Abraham Lincoln School of Medicine, University of Illinois, 840 S. Wood St, Chicago, IL 60612.

GOTOLSKI, WILLIAM H(ENRY), b. Newark, N.J, Sept. 6, 26; m. 51; c. 2. CIVIL ENGINEERING. B.S, Columbia, 46, M.S, 47; Ph.D.(civil eng), Pa. State, 59. Instr. CIVIL ENG, Ohio, 47-52; PA. STATE UNIV, 52-60, assoc. prof, 60-65, PROF, 65- Assoc. mem. Hwy. Res. Bd, Nat. Acad. Sci-Nat. Res. Coun. Am. Soc. Civil Eng; Am. Soc. Test. & Mat. Soil mechanics, foundations and earth structures; bituminous concrete. Address: Dept. of Civil Engineering, 212 Sacket Bldg, Pennsylvania State University, University Park, PA 16802.

GOTS, JOSEPH S(IMON), b. Phila, Pa, Oct. 12, 17; m. 42; c. 2. MICROBIOLOGY. A.B, Temple, 39; M.S, Pennsylvania, 41, Abbott fel, 47-48, Ph.D. (med. bact), 48. Bact. lab. aide, Pennsylvania, 39-41; special field agent Bang's diseases res, U.S. Dept. Agr, 41-42; instr. bact, SCH. MED, UNIV. PA, 48-49, assoc, 49-51, asst. prof. MICROBIOL, 51-55, assoc. prof, 55-63, PROF, 63- Vis. investr, Inst. Radium, Paris, 65-66; consult, Parke Davis & Co, Mich. Dipl, Am. Bd. Microbiol. Sanit.C, 42-46, Capt. AAAS; Am. Soc. Microbiol; Soc. Exp. Biol. & Med; Genetics Soc. Am; Am. Soc. Biol. Chem; Am. Asn. Cancer Res; Am. Acad. Microbiol; N.Y. Acad. Sci; Soc. Gen. Physiol; Brit. Soc. Gen. Microbiol. Mechanism of action of chemotherapeutics and of resistance to chemotherapeutics; bacterial metabolism; respiratory enzymes; biochemical mutations in bacteria; biosynthesis of purines and amino acids. Address: Dept. of Microbiology, University of Pennsylvania School of Medicine, Philadelphia, PA 19104.

GOTSCH, L(ENARD) P(AUL), b. Oak Park, Ill, Dec. 9, 13; m. 44; c. 1. PHYSICAL CHEMISTRY. B.A, Valparaiso, 36; M.S, Va. Polytech, 37; Ph.D. (phys. chem), Virginia, 40. Res. chemist, AM. CAN CO, 40-59, assoc. dir, res, 59-64, DIR, Princeton Lab, 64-68, TECH. LIAISON, 68- AAAS; Am. Chem. Soc; Am. Soc. Eng. Educ. Adsorption of gases on solids; food chemistry and technology; heat treatment of metals; metallurgy of tin plate; research administration. Address: 86 Leabrook Lane, Princeton, NJ 08540.

GOTSHALL, DANIEL WARREN, b. Springfield, Ill, Dec. 20, 29; m. 52. FISHERIES. B.S, Humboldt State Col, 57, M.S, 70. Fisheries biologist, marine resources opers, CALIF. DEPT. FISH & GAME, 57-59, marine biologist, 60-64, assoc. marine biologist, 64-70, SR. MARINE BIOLOGIST, MARINE RESOURCES REGION, LONG BEACH, 70- Mem. adv. bd. underwater parks & reserves, Calif. Dept. Parks & Recreation, 71. U.S.N, 52-54. Am. Fisheries Soc; Am. Littoral Soc; Nat. Shellfisheries Asn. Life history of blue rockfish; marine sport fishing; population dynamics of the ocean shrimp, Pandalus jordani and the market crab, Cancer magister; benthic ecology using scuba and underwater photography. Address: 2201 Garden Rd, Monterey, CA 93940.

GOTT, ALLAN D(ALE), b. Cleveland, Ohio, July 28, 23; m. 45; c. 1. INORGANIC CHEMISTRY. B.S, Univ. of the South, 48; M.S, Illinois, 49, Ph.D. (inorg. chem), 52. Res. chemist, inorg. res. dept, Mallinckrodt Chem. Works, 52-55; Va-Carolina Chem. Co, 55-57; MONSANTO CO, 57-60, purchasing agent, 60-64, RES. CHEMIST, INORG. RES. DEPT. & MGR. PURCHASING RES, 64- U.S.A.A.F, 43-46, 2nd Lt. Am. Chem. Soc; Sci. Res. Soc. Am. Stereo chemistry of inorganic coordination compounds. Address: Inorganic Research Dept, Monsanto Co, 800 N. Lindbergh, St. Louis, MO 63166.

GOTT, EUYEN, b. Kweilin, China, Jan. 2, 15; U.S. citizen; m. 48; c. 2. ELECTRICAL ENGINEERING. B.S, Nat. Kwangsi Univ, China, 38; A.M, Stanford, 45, Engr, 50; Dr.Eng, Hopkins, 59. Instr. elec. eng, Nat. Kwangsi Univ, China, 38-41; head design engr, Yee-Chong Mfg. Co, 41-44; develop. engr, Radio Corp. Am, 45-49; proj. engr, Sierra Electronics Corp, 50-53; res. assoc, radiation lab, Hopkins, 53-59; assoc. prof. elec. eng, Univ. Hawaii, 59-63, prof, 63-65; mem. tech. staff, Hughes Aricraft Co, 65-66, staff engr, 66-67; sr. tech. specialist, Autonetics Div, N.Am. Rockwell Corp, 67-69; vis. prof, Calif. State Col, Fullerton, 70-71; SR. RES. SCIENTIST, NORDEN DIV, UNITED AIRCRAFT CORP, 71- Inst. Elec. & Electronics Eng; Am. Soc. Eng. Educ. Detection of signal in noise; information

processing systems; circuit theory; computer-aided active network analysis and synthesis. Address: Dept. 541, Norden, Division of United Aircraft Corp, Norwalk, CT 06856.

GOTT, PRESTON F(RAZIER), b. Waxahachie, Texas, Nov. 21, 19; m. 42; c. 2. PHYSICS. B.S, Texas, 44, fel, 46-47, M.A, 47. Tutor, Texas, 44-46; from instr. to asst. prof, Hardin Col, 47-49; asst. prof. PHYSICS, TEX. TECH UNIV, 49-57, ASSOC. PROF, 57-, prin. investigator res. contract, 59-60. Summers, physicist, Aberdeen Proving Ground, 54, 55, 56, 58; engr, Arnold Eng. Develop. Ctr, 57; physicist, Land-Air Div, Dynalectron Corp, White Sands Missile Range & Holloman Air Force Base, N.Mexico, 61-64; consult, Land-Air Div, Dynalectron Corp, 63 & 65; sr. scientist, space instruments sect, jet propulsion lab, Calif. Inst. Technol, 65, 66, 67, 70; consult. summer contract with Duke Univ, signature & propagation lab, U.S. Army Ballistic Res. Labs, Aberdeen Proving Ground, Md, 68, 71. Fel. AAAS; Soc. Photo-Optical Instrument. Eng; Am. Phys. Soc; Optical Soc. Am; Photog. Soc. Am; Soc. Photog. Sci. & Eng; Am. Asn. Physics Teachers; Biol. Photog. Asn. Photography; modern physics; atmospheric optics; experimental optical design. Address: Dept. of Physics, Texas Tech University, Lubbock, TX 79409.

GOTT, VINCENT L(YNN), b. Wichita, Kans, Apr. 14, 27; m. 54; c. 2. CARDIOVASCULAR SURGERY. B.S, Wichita, 51; M.D, Yale, 53. Instr. SURG, med. sch, Minnesota, 59-60; asst. prof, sch. med, Wisconsin, 60-63, assoc. prof, 63-65; SCH. MED, JOHNS HOPKINS UNIV, 65-68, PROF, 68-, CHIEF CARDIAC SURG, JOHNS HOPKINS HOSP, 65- Markle scholar acad. med, 62-67. U.S.N, 45-46. Soc. Univ. Surg; fel. Am. Col. Surgery; Am. Soc. Artificial Internal Organs. Cardiovascular research, including myocardial metabolism, artificial heart valves; artificial pacemakers; coronary artery disease; intravascular clotting problems; clinical problems; clinical surgery of the heart and blood vessels. Address: Johns Hopkins Hospital, 608 Blalock Bldg, Baltimore, MD 21205.

GOTTENBERG, WILLIAM G, b. Plentywood, Mont, May 8, 32; m. 56; c. 2. ENGINEERING MECHANICS. B.S, Oregon State, 54; M.Eng, Yale, 55, Gulf Res. & Develop. Corp. fel, 56-58, D.Eng, 58. Mem. tech. staff, Space Tech. Labs, Thompson Ramo Wooldridge, Inc, 58-63; assoc. prof. eng. mech, UNIV. COLO, BOULDER, 63-71, PROF. MECH. ENG. & CHMN. DEPT, 71- Consult, TRW Space Tech. Labs, 63- Soc. Rheol; Soc. Eng. Sci. Non-steady combustion; dynamics of continuous systems; mechanical behavior of materials; experimental mechanics. Address: Dept. of Mechanical Engineering, University of Colorado, Boulder, CO 80302.

GOTTERER, GERALD S, b. New York, N.Y, Oct. 17, 33; m. 56; c. 2. BIOCHEMISTRY. A.B, Harvard, 55; M.D, Chicago, 58; Ph.D.(biochem), Hopkins, 64. Intern internal med, Grace-New Haven Community Hosp, 58-59; instr. PHYSIOL. CHEM, SCH. MED, JOHNS HOPKINS UNIV, 65-66, ASST. PROF, 66- U.S. Pub. Health Serv. fels, 59-64. Am. Chem. Soc; Am. Soc. Biol. Chem. Functional interactions of lipids and enzymes; active transport; mitochondrial biochemistry; biochemistry of intestinal mucosa. Address: Dept. of Physiological Chemistry, Johns Hopkins University School of Medicine, 725 N. Wolfe St, Baltimore, MD 21205.

GOTTESMAN, ELIHU, b. Brooklyn, N.Y, June 6, 19; m. 49; c. 3. PHARMACEUTICAL CHEMISTRY. B.A, Hopkins, 39; M.S, Fordham, 40; Brooklyn Col, 40-41; chemist, Food & Drug Res. Labs, Inc, 41-42; supvr. vitamin lab, ENDO LABS, INC, GARDEN CITY, 46-52, MGR. PARENTERAL PROD. DIV, 52- Ed, Int. Blue Book, 47-52. Sanit.C, 42-46, 1st Lt. AAAS; Am. Chem. Soc; Am. Pharmaceut. Asn; N.Y. Acad. Sci; Am. Asn. Contamination Control; Royal Soc. Health. Development of pharmaceutical equipment and procedures; and of pharmaceutical dosage forms; equipment and special building construction for pharmaceutical industry. Address: 148 Mead Court, Wantagh, NY 11793.

GOTTESMAN, MAX E(LLIOT), b. N.Y.C, Mar. 4, 35; m. 60; c. 2. MOLECULAR BIOLOGY. B.A, Swarthmore Col, 56; M.D, Yale, 60, Ph.D.(pharmacol), 65. U.S. Pub. Health Serv. fel, 60-64; Jane Coffin Child Fund fel, Rockefeller Univ, 64-66; med. off. res, Nat. Inst. Arthritis & Metab. Diseases, 66-71, HEAD SECT. BIOCHEM. GENETICS, NAT. CANCER INST, 71- U.S.P.H.S, 66-69, Comdr. Integration and excision of the bacteriophage lambda genome. Address: National Institutes of Health, Bethesda, MD 20014.

GOTTESMAN, ROY T(ULLY), b. Bayonne, N.J, March 6, 28; m. 54; c. 2. ORGANIC CHEMISTRY. B.S, Rutgers, 47, M.S, 50, Ph.D.(chem), 51; Minnesota, 47-48. Asst. chem, Minnesota, 47-48; Rutgers, 48-51; chemist res. & develop, Heyden Chem. Corp, 51-56, group leader, RES. & DEVELOP. DEPT, Heyden Div, Heyden Newport Chem. Corp, 56-61, supvr. org. res, 61-65; MGR, TENNECO CHEM, INC, 65-70, TECH. DEVELOP. INTERMEDIATES DIV, 70- Am. Chem. Soc; Weed Sci. Soc. Am. Synthetic organic chemistry; preparation and reactions of polyols; chemistry of salicylic acid; process development and improvement; agricultural chemicals; research administration; biocides, paint and plastics additives; polymers. Address: Research & Development Dept, Intermediates Division, Tenneco Chemicals, Inc, Turner Pl, P.O. Box 2, Piscataway, NJ 08854.

GOTTFRIED, BYRON S(TUART), b. Detroit, Mich, May 24, 34; m. 59; c. 3. CHEMICAL ENGINEERING, OPERATIONS RESEARCH. B.S, Purdue, 56; M.S, Michigan, 58; Ph.D.(chem. eng), Case Inst. Tech, 62. Assoc. engr, Lewis Res. Ctr, NASA, 59-62; Gulf Res. & Develop. Co, 62-65; asst. prof. mech. eng, Carnegie-Mellon Univ, 65-68; sect. supvr, econ. & comput. sci. div, Gulf Res. & Develop. Co, 68-70; ASSOC. PROF. INDUST. ENG, SYSTS. MGT. ENG. & OPERS. RES, UNIV. PITTSBURGH, 70- Consult, Lord Corp, 65-68; Westinghouse Elec. Corp, 66-68. Sig.C, U.S.A, 58, Res, 56-58 & 58-64, 1st Lt. Am. Inst. Chem. Eng; Soc. Petrol. Eng; Simulation Coun. Simulation and optimization of complex engineering systems; industrial applications of digital computers; boiling heat transfer; fluid flow in porous media. Address: Dept. of Industrial Engineering, Systems Management Engineering & Operations Research, University of Pittsburgh, Pittsburgh, PA 15213.

GOTTFRIED, DAVID, b. Brooklyn, N.Y, Nov. 24, 24; m. 55; c. 4. GEOCHEMISTRY, PETROLOGY. B.S, Brooklyn Col, 49; M.S, American Univ, 58. Lectr, Brooklyn Col, 50-52; GEOLOGIST, U.S. GEOL. SURV, 52- Asst. geol, N.Y. Univ, 50-51; summer, mem. staff, Iron Ore Co, Can, 51. U.S.N.R, 43-46. AAAS; Geochem. Soc; Mineral Soc. Am; Geol. Soc. Am. Distribution of minor elements in igneous complexes; age determinations of igneous using the radioactive accessory minerals. Address: 5201 Augusta St, Washington, DC 20016.

GOTTFRIED, EUGENE L(ESLIE), b. Passaic, N.J, Feb. 26, 29; m. 57. MEDICINE. A.B, Columbia, 50, M.D, 54. Intern, Presby. Hosp, New York, N.Y, 54-55, asst. res, 57-58; res, Bronx Munic. Hosp, Center, 58-59; asst. instr, MED, Albert Einstein Col. Med, 59-60, instr, 60-61, assoc, 61-65, asst. prof, 65-69; ASSOC. PROF, MED. COL, CORNELL UNIV. & DIR. LAB. CLIN. HEMAT. & ASSOC. ATTEND. PHYSICIAN, N.Y. HOSP, 69- Fel. med, Bronx Munic. Hosp. Ctr, 59-60, asst. vis. physician, 60-66, assoc. attend. physician, 66-69; asst. vis. physician, Lincoln Hosp, 63-69. Health Res. Coun. New York career scientist, 64- Dipl, Nat. Bd. Med. Exam; Am. Bd. Internal Med. Med.C.Res, 55-57, Lt. Comdr. AAAS; Am. Soc. Hemat; Am. Fedn. Clin. Res; Harvey Soc; fel. Am. Col. Physicians; fel. Int. Soc. Hemat. Internal medicine; hematology; plasmalogens; lipids of blood cells; hemolytic phosphatides. Address: New York Hospital-Cornell Medical Center, 525 E. 68th St, New York, NY 10021.

GOTTFRIED, J(ACOB) B(AER), b. Bedzin, Poland, Apr. 10, 07; nat; m. 35; c. 2. CHEMISTRY. B.S, Iowa State Col, 32. Anal. chemist, CORN PROD. CO, 33-36, protein res. chemist, 36-38, res. chem. engr, 38-44, res. group leader, 44-56, CHIEF CHEMIST, ARGO, 56- Am. Chem. Soc. Protein process development; carbohydrate research and dextrose and corn syrup process development and improvement; ion exchange. Address: 525 Hawthorne Pl, Chicago, IL 60657.

GOTTFRIED, KURT, b. Vienna, Austria, May 17, 29; m. 55; c. 2. THEORETICAL PHYSICS. B.Eng, McGill, 51, M.Sc, 53; Ph.D.(theoret. physics), Mass. Inst. Tech, 55. Asst. physics, Mass. Inst. Tech, 52-55; jr. fel, Soc. of Fels, Harvard, 55-58; res. fel, inst. theoret. physics, Copenhagen, 58-59; physics, Harvard, 59-60, asst. prof, 60-64; from assoc. prof. to PROF. PHYSICS, CORNELL UNIV, 64- Guggenheim fel, European Orgn. Nuclear Res, Geneva, 63-64, mem. staff, 70- Am. Phys. Soc. Theory of nuclear structure; quantum-mechanical many body problem; elementary particles. Address: Dept. of Physics, Cornell University, Ithaca, NY 14850.

GOTTFRIED, SIDNEY P(AUL), b. N.Y.C, Oct. 11, 12; m. 46; c. 1. ORGANIC CHEMISTRY. B.S, N.Y. Univ, 33, Ph.D.(org. chem), 41; A.M, Columbia, 35. Res. fel. org. chem. & biochem, Jewish Hosp, Brooklyn, 35-41, asst. chemist, 41-42; instr. blood chem, Hunter Col, 46-52; adj. asst. prof. CHEM, UNIV. BRIDGEPORT, 51-64, ADJ. ASSOC. PROF, 64-, CLIN. CHEMIST, BRIDGEPORT HOSP, 50- Assoc. chemist, Jewish Hosp, Brooklyn, 46-47; biochemist, U.S. Vet. Hosp, 47-50. Consult, Masonic Home & Hosp, Wallingford, Conn, 62- Sanit.C, 42-46, Capt. Fel. AAAS; Am. Chem. Soc; N.Y. Acad. Sci. Organic synthesis; clinical microchemistry; biochemistry of organic diseases, mental diseases, atherosclerosis. Address: 107 Bennett St, Fairfield, CT 06604.

GOTTHEIL, EDWARD, b. Montreal, Que, Aug. 6, 24; U.S. citizen; m. 51; c. 2. PSYCHIATRY, PSYCHOLOGY. B.A, Queen's (Ont), 46; M.A, McGill, 48; Ph.D.(psychol), Texas, 51, M.D, 55. Chief psychologist, Austin State Hosp, Tex, 50-51; intern, Roanoke Mem. Hosp, Va, 55-56; res. psychiat, Letterman Gen. Hosp, San Francisco, Calif, 56-59; post psychiatrist, Ft. Riley, Kans, 60-62; chief med. res. proj, West Point, N.Y, 62-64; assoc. prof. PSYCHIAT, JEFFERSON MED. COL, 64-69, PROF, 69- Consult, Friend's Hosp, Phila , 64-69; East. Pa. Psychiat. Inst, 64-69; Del. State Hosp, 64-; Coatesville Vet. Admin. Hosp, 67- U.S.A, 56-64, Maj. AAAS; Am. Psychol. Asn; Am. Psychiat. Asn; Am. Orthopsychiat. Asn. Small group interactions; psychiatric decision making; diagnosis; preventive social psychiatry; behavioral recording and data reduction; alcoholism; schizophrenia; medical education; emotional communication; sexual beliefs and behavior. Address: Dept. of Psychiatry, Jefferson Medical College, Philadelphia, PA 19107.

GOTTLEIB, ANATOL, b. Mendyk, U.S.S.R, June 10, 08; nat; m. 42; c. 3. INORGANIC CHEMISTRY. Dipl.Ing, Graz. Tech, 35, Dr.Tech.Sci, 47. Instr. anal. chem. & inorg. tech, Graz. Tech, 41-52; chemist, anal. labs, U.S. Steel Co, 52-53; instr. PHYS. SCI, UNIV. ILL, CHICAGO CIRCLE, 53-58, ASST. PROF, 58- Roumanian Army, 35-36, 40. Am. Chem. Soc. Analytical chemistry. Address: 6950 W. Imlay St, Chicago, IL 60631.

GOTTLIEB, A(BRAHAM) ARTHUR, b. Haifa, Palestine, Dec. 14, 37; U.S. citizen; m. 58; c. 2. BIOCHEMISTRY, IMMUNOLOGY. A.B, Columbia, 57; M.D, N.Y. Univ, 61. Med. house off, Peter Bent Brigham Hosp, 61-62, asst. res. physician, 62-63; clin. assoc, Nat. Insts. Health, 63-65; Nat. Inst. Gen. Med. Sci. spec. res. fel. chem, Harvard, 65-67, career develop. award med. sch, 67-69, asst. prof. med, summer 69; ASSOC. PROF. MICROBIOL, INST. MICROBIOL, RUTGERS UNIV, 69- U.S.P.H.S, 63-65, Surg. AAAS; Am. Asn. Immunol; Am. Chem. Soc; Am. Fedn. Clin. Res; Am. Soc. Biol. Chem; Am. Soc. Cell Biol; Reticuloendothelial Soc. Molecular biology of antibody production; antigen metabolism; DNA replication in lymphoid cells and myeloma tumors; hybridization of nucleic acids. Address: Institute of Microbiology, Rutgers, The State University, New Brunswick, NJ 08903.

GOTTLIEB, A(BRAHAM) M(ITCHELL), b. Chicago, Ill, Feb. 22, 09; m. 34; c. 2. MEDICINE, CARDIOLOGY. B.S, Illinois, 30, M.D, 33. Ward physician, med. serv, Vet. Admin. Hosp, Tuscaloosa, Ala, 38-39, Milwaukee, Wis, 39-40, sect. chief cardiol, 40-42; sect. chief cardiol, Vet. Admin. Hosp, Dearborn, 46; asst. prof. med, col. med, Wayne State Univ, 48-60; assoc. prof, Univ. Wis, Madison, 60-62, PROF, 62-68; CLIN. MED, STANFORD UNIV, 68-; DIR, VET. ADMIN. HOSP, 68- Chief prof. serv, Vet. Admin. Hosp, Dearborn, 46-60, attend. consult, 48-60, hosp. dir, Madison, Wis, 60-68. Dipl, Am. Bd. Internal Med, 48. Med.C, 42-45, Res, 45-71, Col.(Ret). Am. Med. Asn; Am. Heart Asn; fel. Am. Col. Physicians. Cardiovascular; pulmonary; sarcoidosis. Address: Veterans Administration Hospital, 3801 Miranda, Palo Alto, CA 94304.

GOTTLIEB, ARLAN J, b. N.Y.C, July 22, 33; m. 64; c. 2. INTERNAL MEDICINE, HEMATOLOGY. A.B, Columbia, 54, M.D, 58. Intern med, Mt. Sinai Hosp, New York, 58-59, asst. res, 59-61, chief res, 61-62; res. fel. molecular biol, lab. molecular biol, sect. chem. genetics, Nat. Inst. Arthritis & Metab. Diseases, 62-66, biophys, lab. chem, Nat. Inst. Neurol. Diseases & Blindness, 66-67; asst. prof. MED, sch. med, Univ. Pa, 67-71; ASSOC. PROF, STATE UNIV. N.Y. UPSTATE MED. CTR, 71-, CHIEF SECT. HEMAT, 71- Asst. clin. prof, sch. med, George Washington, 66-67; Nat. Inst. Arthritis & Metab. Diseases res. grant, 67-70. Attend, D.C. Gen. Hosp. George Washington Serv, 66-67; univ. hosp, Pennsylvania, 67-71; consult. & attend, Vet. Admin. Hosp, Pa, 67-71, hematologist & attend, N.Y, 71- Res. career develop. award, 68- U.S.P.H.S, 62-67, Sr. Surg. AAAS; Am. Fedn Clin. Res; N.Y Acad. Sci. Relationship between structure and function of biologically active genetically determined proteins in health and diseases. Address: Dept. of Medicine, State University of New York Upstate Medical Center, Syracuse, NY 13210.

GOTTLIEB, DANIEL HENRY, b. Hollywood, Calif, Dec. 7, 37; m. 65; c. 1. MATHEMATICS. B.A, California, Los Angeles, 59, M.A, 61, Ph.D.(math), 62. Instr. math, Illinois, 62-64; res. mathematician, Inst. Defense Anal, N.J, 64-67; ASSOC. PROF. MATH, PURDUE UNIV, 67- Am. Math. Soc. Algebraic topology. Address: Dept. of Mathematics, Purdue University, Lafayette, IN 47907.

GOTTLIEB, DAVID, b. N.Y.C, Oct. 5, 11; m. 37; c. 2. PLANT PATHOLOGY. B.S, City Col, 37; M.S, Iowa State Col, 40; Ph.D.(microbiol, plant path), Minnesota, 42. Fel, Minnesota, 43-44; Koppers fel, Delaware, 44-45; asst. prof. PLANT PATH, UNIV. ILL, URBANA-CHAMPAIGN, 46-51, assoc. prof, 51-53, PROF, 53- Medal, Univ. Pavia, 55. Am. Soc. Microbiol; Am. Phytopath. Soc; Soc. Indust. Microbiol; Mycol. Soc. Am; fel. Am. Acad. Microbiol. Antibiotics; physiology of fungi and plant parasitism; taxonomy and physiology of Actinomyces. Address: Dept. of Plant Pathology, University of Illinois, Urbana-Champaign, Urbana, IL 61801.

GOTTLIEB, FREDERICK JAY, b. New York, N.Y, June 17, 35; m. 58; c. 3. GENETICS, DEVELOPMENTAL BIOLOGY. B.A, Hofstra Col, 56; M.A, Wesleyan, 58; California, Davis, 58-59, Ph.D.(genetics), Berkeley, 62. Nat. Insts. Health trainee entom, California, Berkeley, 60, genetics, 60-62; instr. zool, UNIV. PITTSBURGH, 62-63, asst. prof. BIOL, 64-67, ASSOC. PROF, 67-, ASSOC. PROF. BIOL. & BIOSTATIST, GRAD. SCH. PUB. HEALTH, 71- Consult, Proj. Solo; Am. Cancer Soc. instnl. res. grants, 63-66; U.S. Pub. Health Serv. res. grant, 63-67; mem. exec. comt, comput. ctr, Univ. Pittsburgh, 69- AAAS; Soc. Develop. Biol; Genetics Soc. Am. Genetic control of development in Drosophila melanogaster and Ephestia kuhniella, with emphasis on the ultrastructural expression of pigmentation and female sterility mutants; genetic control of behavior in Drosophila. Address: Dept. of Biology, University of Pittsburgh, Pittsburgh, PA 15213.

GOTTLIEB, G. EUGENE, b. Venningen, Ger, Sept. 3, 33; U.S. citizen; m. 58; c. 3. INORGANIC CHEMISTRY. B.S, Rutgers Univ, 56, M.B.A, 64, Ph.D. (ceramics), 71; M.A, Temple, 58. Engr, Philco Corp, 58-60; MEM. TECH. STAFF, RCA LABS, DAVID SARNOFF RES. CTR, 60- Am. Chem. Soc; Electrochem. Soc; Inst. Elec. & Electronics Eng. Semiconductor materials; chemical transport and epitaxial growth; synthesis, crystal growth and evaluation of electronic materials. Address: RCA Labs, Princeton, NJ 08540.

GOTTLIEB, GERALD LANE, b. New York, N.Y, Feb. 6, 41; m. 68. ELECTRICAL ENGINEERING, PHYSIOLOGY. B.S, Mass. Inst. Tech, 62, M.S, 64; Nat. Insts. Health trainee, Univ. Ill. Med. Ctr, 66-69, Ph.D.(physiol), 70. Res. & develop. engr, aeronutronics div, Philco-Ford Corp, 64-66; INSTR. BIOENG, UNIV. ILL, CHICAGO CIRCLE, 67-; ASST. PROF. BIOMED. ENG, RUSH MED. COL, 70- Nat. Inst. Ment. Health fel, Univ. Ill. Med. Ctr, 69-70. N.Y. Acad. Sci; Inst. Elec. & Electronics Eng. Nervous control of human motor system; computer applications for research and clinical testing in a medical scientific environment. Address: Dept. of Biomedical Engineering, Presbyterian-St. Lukes Hospital, 1753 W. Congress Pkwy, Chicago, IL 60612.

GOTTLIEB, GILBERT, b. Brooklyn, N.Y, Oct. 22, 29; m. 61; c. 4. PSYCHOLOGY. A.B, Miami(Fla), 55, M.S, 56; U.S. Pub. Health Serv. fel, Duke, 57-58, Ph.D.(psychol), 60. Res. assoc. med. psychol, med. ctr, Duke, 58-59; mem. staff clin. psychol, N.C. DEPT. MENT. HEALTH, DOROTHEA DIX HOSP, RALEIGH, 59-61, RES. SCIENTIST BIOPSYCHOL, PSYCHOL. LAB, DIV. OF RES, 61- Asst. prof. psychol, N.C. State, 61-65, assoc. prof, 65-; ed. sect. on animal behav, Biol. Abstr, 65- U.S.A, 51-53, Sgt. AAAS; Psychonomic Soc; Animal Behav. Soc. Developmental and comparative psychology; behavioral embryology. Address: Box 7575, Raleigh, NC 27611.

GOTTLIEB, IRVIN M, b. Phila, Pa, July 15, 21. INORGANIC & ANALYTICAL CHEMISTRY. B.S, Pennsylvania, 43, M.S, 47, Ph.D.(chem), 53. Dep. chief textile finishes lab, Qm. Res. & Develop. Lab, Pa, 51-54; group leader, Textile Res. Inst, N.J, 55-58, PROF. CHEM, Trenton State Col, 58-61; PMC COLS, 61-, HEAD DEPT, 67- U.S.A, 44-46, Sgt. Fiber Soc; Am. Chem. Soc; The Chem. Soc; fel. Am. Inst. Chem. Flame and thermal protection; functional finishes for textiles. Addrdss: Dept. of Chemistry, PMC Colleges, Chester, PA 19131.

GOTTLIEB, JACQUES S(IMON), b. Trinidad, Colo, Feb. 2, 07; m. 34; c. 3. PSYCHIATRY. B.S, Harvard, 28, M.D, 33. Clin. asst. psychiat, Worcester State Hosp, 32-33, asst. internist, Mem. Found. Neuro-Endocrine Res, 33-34, assoc. internist, 35; asst. res. clin. neurol, Montefiore Hosp, New York, 34-35; intern, Worcester Hahnemann Hosp, 35-36; res, Psychopath. Hosp, Iowa, 36-37; assoc. clin. psychiat, col. med, Iowa, 37-40, asst. prof, 40-43, assoc. prof. 43-47, prof, 47-53; prof. psychiat. & chmn. dept, Miami, 53-55; DIR, LAFAYETTE CLIN, 55-; PROF. PSYCHIAT, COL. MED, WAYNE STATE UNIV, 55-, CHMN. DEPT, 61- Chief, out-patient dept, Psychopathic Hosp, Iowa City, 37-40, sr. physician, 40-43, asst. dir, 43-53; dir. inst, Jackson Mem. Hosp. Psychosonomic Soc; fel. Am. Med. Asn; fel. Am. Psychiat. Asn. Genetic, physiogenic, psychogenic and clinical studies. Address: Lafayette Clinic, 951 E. Lafayette, Detroit, MI 48207.

GOTTLIEB, JOAN EIGER, b. New York, N.Y, Aug. 12, 35; m. 57; c. 1. BOTANY. B.S, City Col, 55; M.A, Radcliffe Col, 57, Andersen fel. & Ph.D. (biol), 58. Asst. prof. biol, California Western, 58-59; instr. bot, Pittsburgh, 59-61, asst. prof, 61-62; TEACHER BIOL, CHURCHILL AREA SCHS, PITTSBURGH, 62- Bot. Soc. Am; Nat. Audubon Soc; Int. Soc. Plant Morphol. Plant morphogenesis, especially stelar and foliar development. Address: Churchill Area High School, 2550 Greensburg Pike, Pittsburgh, PA 15221.

GOTTLIEB, LEONARD S(OLOMON), b. Boston, Mass, May 26, 27; m; c. 3. PATHOLOGY. A.B, Bowdoin Col, 46; M.D, Tufts Univ, 50; M.P.H, Harvard School Pub. Health, 69. Instr. PATH, med. sch, Tufts Univ, 53-55, sr. instr, 57-58, asst. prof, 58-62, assoc. prof, 62-67, PROF, 67-71; SCH. MED, BOSTON UNIV, 71-; ASSOC. DIR, MALLORY INST. PATH, BOSTON CITY HOSP, 66-, assoc. pathologist, 60-66, asst. pathologist, 57-60. Instr, med. sch, Boston Univ, 53-61, lectr. path, 61-71; physician-in-chief, dept. clin. labs, Boston Dispensary, 57; vis. physician, Boston City Hosp, 57, res. assoc, 57-59, asst. physician, 58, assoc. vis. physician, 59; consult. & lectr, U.S. Naval Hosp, Chelsea, Mass, 57-58; lectr, Harvard Med. Sch, 63-; Univ. Mass, 71- Dipl, Nat. Bd. Med. Exam. Asst. chief path, U.S. Naval Hosp, Chelsea, Med.C, 55-57, 60-63, Lt. Comdr. AAAS; Am. Soc. Clin. Path; Soc. Exp. Biol. & Med; Am. Soc. Cell Biol; Int. Acad. Path; Am. Soc. Exp. Path; Am. Asn. Study Liver Disease; Am. Gastroenterol. Asn; Am. Pub. Health Asn; Am. Soc. Clin. Nutrit; Am. Inst. Nutrit. Gastrointestinal and liver diseases; electron microscopy in experimental pathology; nutritional pathology. Address: Mallory Institute of Pathology, Boston City Hospital, Boston, MA 02118.

GOTTLIEB, MELVIN B(URT), b. Chicago, Ill, May 25, 17; m. 48; c. 2. PHYSICS. B.S, Chicago, 40, Ph.D, 50. Res. assoc, Harvard, 43-45; instr. phys. sci, Chicago, 45-46, asst. physics, 46-50; asst. prof, Iowa, 50-54; assoc. dir, proj. Matterhorn, Princeton, 54-61, DIR. PLASMA PHYSICS LAB. & PROF. ASTROPHYS. SCI, PRINCETON, 61- Civilian with Off. Sci. Res. & Develop. Am. Phys. Soc. Cloud chamber studies of penetrating showers; rocket and balloon-borne studies of primary cosmic ray intensities; low momentum cut off in intensity of heavy nuclei in cosmic rays; plasma physics; controlled thermonuclear reactors. Address: Plasma Physics Lab, Princeton University, P.O. Box 451, Princeton, NJ 08540.

GOTTLIEB, MELVIN H(ARVEY), b. N.Y.C, May 2, 29; m. 60. PHYSICAL CHEMISTRY. B.S, Brooklyn Col, 49; Ph.D.(chem), Polytech. Inst. Brooklyn, 54. Chemist textile finishes, United Merchants & Mfrs, 49-50; scientist, Nat. Heart Inst, Nat. Insts. Health, 53-56; chemist, Interchem. Corp, 56-59; mem. tech. staff, Bell Tel. Labs, 59-65; RES. SCIENTIST, NAT. INST. ARTHRITIS & METAB. DISEASES, NAT. INSTS. HEALTH, 65- Am. Chem. Soc. Ion exchange; ion exchange membranes; surface chemistry; electrochemistry; lipid physical chemistry. Address: National Institute of Arthritis & Metabolic Diseases, National Institutes of Health, MHG Bldg. 2, Room 319, Bethesda, MD 20014.

GOTTLIEB, MILTON, b. New York, N.Y, July 2, 33; m. 57; c. 1. PHYSICS. B.S, City Col, 54; M.S, Pennsylvania, 56, Ph.D.(physics), 59. Res. assoc. physics, Gen. Atomic div. Gen. Dynamics Corp, 56-59; RES. PHYSICIST, RES. LABS, WESTINGHOUSE ELEC. CORP, 59- Am. Phys. Soc. Solid state physics. Address: Research Labs, Westinghouse Electric Corp, Pittsburgh, PA 15235.

GOTTLIEB, MORRIS J(OSEPH), b. New York, N.Y, Mar. 27, 12; m. 35; c. 3. MATHEMATICS. A.B, Missouri, 34; M.S, Washington (St. Louis), 35, Ph.D. (math), 37. Instr. math, St. Louis Freshman Col, 37-39; Washington (St. Louis), 40-42, asst. prof, 46-47; mem, Inst. Adv. Study, 47-49; asst. prof. math, Chicago, 49-58; V.PRES, Market Facts, Inc, 53-64; AUDITS & SURV, INC, 64- Teacher, pub. sch, Mo, 39-42. U.S.A.A.F, 42-45. Statistics; applications of mathematics to social sciences; marketing; orthogonal polynomials; calculus of variations; analysis; some polynomials orthogonal on a finite or enumerable set of points. Address: 363 E. 76th St, New York, NY 10021.

GOTTLIEB, OTTO RICHARD, b. Brno, Czech, Aug. 31, 20; m. 47; c. 3. ORGANIC CHEMISTRY. Indust. Chem, Rio de Janeiro, 45; D.Sc.(org. chem), Brasil, 66. Prod. chemist, Ornstein & Cia, Brazil, 46-54; res. assoc. natural prod. chem, inst. agr. chem, Ministry Agr. & Nat. Res. Coun, 55-58, res. head, 59-63; prof. org. chem. & coord, cent. inst. chem, Brasilia, 64-65; PROF. ORG. CHEM, FED. AGR. UNIV. RIO DE JANEIRO, 66- Res. fel. org. chem, Weizmann Inst. Sci, 60; prof. & adv. grad. org. chem, Univ. Minas Gerais, 62-; vis. prof, Univ. Sheffield, 64; prof. & coord. grad. org. chem, Fed. Univ. Pernambuco, 66-67; vis. prof, Univ. São Paulo, 68-; coord. phytochem, Nat. Res. Inst. Amazonia, 68- AAAS; Brazilian Acad. Sci; Brazilian Chem. Asn; Brit. Chem. Soc; Am. Chem. Soc; N.Y. Acad. Sci; Bot. Soc. Brazil; Brazilian Soc. Sci. Progress. Analytical chemistry; gasometric titrations; natural products chemistry; chemistry of Brazilian Lauraceae, Leguminosae, Guttiferae, Moraceae, Euphorbiaceae, Icacinaceae, Annonaceae, Myrtaceae and Myristicaceae; essential oils; plant chemosystematics and phylogeny. Address: Rua Cinco de Julho 323, Apt. 1001, Rio de Janeiro, ZC-07, Brasil.

GOTTLIEB, PETER, b. Cleveland, Ohio, Nov. 29, 35; m. 57; c. 2. STATISTICS. B.S, Calif. Inst. Tech, 56; Ph.D.(physics), Mass. Inst. Tech, 59. Mem. tech. staff PHYSICS, Hughes Res. Labs, Calif, 59-65; staff scientist, res. & systs. ctr, Gen. Precision Inc, 64-65, adv. tech. ctr, 65-66; MEM. TECH. STAFF, JET PROPULSION LAB, CALIF. INST. TECHNOL, 66- Part-time instr, exten. div, California, Los Angeles, 59-, part-time res. fel, San Diego, 62-64. Am. Statist. Asn. Statistical mechanics; communication theory; probability theory. Address: 246 S. Anita Ave, Los Angeles, CA 90049.

GOTTLIEB, SHELDON F, b. N.Y.C, Dec. 22, 32; m. 56; c. 4. PHYSIOLOGY, MICROBIOLOGY. B.A, Brooklyn Col, 53; M.S, Massachusetts, 56; Ph.D. (physiol), Texas, 59. Res. physiologist, res. labs, Linde Div, Union Carbide Corp, 59-64; asst. prof. physiol. & anesthesiol, Jefferson Med. Col, 64-68; ASSOC. PROF. DIV. BIOL. SCI, PURDUE UNIV, 68- Biologist, res. labs, Beth Israel Hosp, New York, N.Y, 64-66; consult, comt. high oxygen pressure equip, Am. Soc. Anesthesiol, 64- U.S.A, 54-56. AAAS; Am. Soc. Microbiol; Am. Physiol. Soc; Soc. Gen. Physiol; N.Y. Acad. Sci; Aerospace Med. Soc; Undersea Med. Soc. Physiological and biochemical effects of gaseous environments on living systems. Address: Biological Sciences Division, Purdue University, 2101 Colisum Blvd. E, Ft. Wayne, IN 46805.

GOTTLIEB, SIDNEY, b. N.Y.C, Aug. 3, 18; m. 42; c. 4. BIOCHEMISTRY. B.S, Wisconsin, 40, fel, Calif. Inst. Tech, 40-43, Ph.D.(bio-org. chem), 43. Asst. chemist, U.S. Dept. Agr, Md, 43-44, assoc. chemist, 44-46; res. assoc, Nat. Res. Council, Wash, D.C, 46-47; assoc. chemist, food & drug admin, Fed. Security Agency, 47-48; res. assoc, Maryland, 48-51; CONSULT, U.S. DEPT. DEFENSE, 51- Am. Chem. Soc. Chemical structure of soil organic matter; synthetic fungicide; fungicidal antibiotics; chemistry of lignin; synthetic estrogens; atropine; inhibitor in the Guayule rubber plant. Address: 1629 Beulah Rd, Vienna, VA 22180.

GOTTLING, JAMES GOE, b. Baltimore, Md, Dec. 11, 32; m. 56; c. 3. SOLID STATE ELECTRONICS. B.S, Lehigh, 53 & 54; S.M, Mass. Inst. Tech, 56, Gen. Dynamics Corp. fel, 56-57, Sc.D.(elec. eng), 60. Res. asst. ELEC. ENG, Mass. Inst. Tech, 54-56, 57-60, div. sponsored res, 60, asst. prof, 60-65; assoc. prof, OHIO STATE UNIV, 65-70, PROF, 70- Ford Found. fel, 61-63. Inst. Elec. & Electronics Eng. Active thin film electronic circuit devices; study of current through thin insulating films; application of thin magnetic films to digital computer memories. Address: Dept. of Electrical Engineering, Ohio State University, Columbus, OH 43210.

GOTTO, ANTONIO MARION, JR, b. Nashville, Tenn, Oct. 10, 35; m. 59; c. 3. BIOCHEMISTRY, METABOLISM. B.A, Vanderbilt, 57, M.D, 65; Rhodes scholar, Oxford, 57-59, Nat. Sci. Found. fel, 59-61, Ph.D.(biochem), 61. Res. assoc. biochem, Vanderbilt, 61-64, molecular biol, 64-65; intern, Mass. Gen. Hosp, 65-66, med. resident, 66-67; staff assoc, Nat. Heart Inst, Nat. Insts. Health, 67-69, head sect. molecular struct, molecular disease br, Nat. Heart & Lung Inst, 69-71; PROF. MED. & BIOCHEM. & CHIEF DIV. ARTERIOSCLEROSIS & LIPOPROTEIN RES, BAYLOR COL. MED. & THE METHODIST HOSP, HOUSTON, 71- Am. Cancer Soc. res. scholar, Vanderbilt Univ, 63-65; Borden med. stud. res. award, 65; fel. Coun. Arteriosclerosis, Am. Heart Asn; dir. specialized ctr. res. arteriosclerosis & lipid res. clin, Nat. Insts. Health, Houston. U.S.P.H.S, 65-67, Surg. Am. Soc. Clin. Invest; Am. Fedn. Clin. Res; Am. Heart Asn; Biophys. Soc; Am. Soc. Biol. Chem. Lipid metabolism; structure and function of the plasma lipoproteins. Address: Dept. of Medicine, Baylor College of Medicine, The Methodist Hospital, Houston, TX 77025.

GOTTSCHALK, ALEXANDER, b. Chicago, Ill, Mar. 23, 32; m. 60; c. 3. RADIOLOGY, NUCLEAR MEDICINE. B.A, Harvard, 54; M.D, Wash. Univ, 58; Res. assoc. RADIOL, Donner Lab, Lawrence Radiation Lab, Univ. Calif, Berkeley, 62-64; asst. prof, HOSPS, UNIV. CHICAGO, 64-66, assoc. prof, 66-68, PROF, 68-, CHIEF NUCLEAR MED. SECT, 64-; DIR. ARGONNE CANCER RES. HOSP, 67- Faculty res. assoc, Am. Cancer Soc, 65- Am. Col. Radiol; Radiol. Soc. N.Am; Asn. Univ. Radiol.(secy-treas, 68-69, pres. elect, 69-70); Soc. Nuclear Med; Am. Roentgen Ray Soc; Am. Thyroid Asn. Isotope development and clinical applications; instrumentation in nuclear medicine; image processing. Address: University of Chicago Hospitals & Clinics, 950 E. 59th St, Chicago, IL 60637.

GOTTSCHALK, BERNARD, b. Frankfurt, Ger, Jan. 6, 35; U.S. citizen; m. 61; c. 3. HIGH ENERGY PHYSICS. B.S, Rensselaer Polytech, 55; A.M, Harvard, 57, Ph.D, 62. Res. fel. PHYSICS, Harvard, 62-65; asst. prof, NORTHEAST. UNIV, 65-68, ASSOC. PROF, 68- Vis. scientist, Stanford Linear Accelerator Ctr, 71-72. Am. Phys. Soc. Medium-energy nuclear physics; experimental high energy physics. Address: Dept. of Physics, Northeastern University, Boston, MA 02115.

GOTTSCHALK, CARL W(ILLIAM), b. Salem, Va, April 28, 22; m. 47; c. 3. PHYSIOLOGY, INTERNAL MEDICINE. B.S, Roanoke Col, 42, Sc.D, 66; M.D, Virginia, 45. Intern med, Mass. Gen. Hosp, 45-46, asst. res. & res. med, 50-52; res. fel. physiol, Harvard Med. Sch, 48-50; fel. cardiol, N.C. Mem. Hosp, UNIV. N.C, CHAPEL HILL, 52-53, instr. med, SCH. MED, 53-55, asst. prof, 55-59, assoc. prof. MED. & PHYSIOL, 59-61, prof, 61-69, KENAN PROF, 69-, AM. HEART ASN. CAREER INVESTR, 61-, estab. investr, 57-61. Consult. to Surgeon Gen, 51; mem. physiol. study sect, Nat. Insts. Health, 61-65; Harvey lectr, 62; mem. res. career awards comt, Nat. Inst. Gen. Med. Sci, 65-69, physiol. test comt, Nat. Bd. Med. Exam, 66-70, physiol. training comt, 69-73; biol. & med. sci. adv. comn, Nat. Sci. Found, 67-69, v.chmn, 68, chmn, 69. Horsley mem. prize, Univ. Va, 56; Homer W. Smith award, N.Y. Heart Asn, 70. Med.C, 46-48, Capt. Am. Physiol. Soc; Am. Soc. Clin. Invest; Soc. Exp. Biol. & Med; Asn. Am. Physicians; Am. Fedn. Clin. Res; fel. Am. Col. Physicians; fel. Am. Acad. Arts & Sci. Renal physiology, utilizing micropuncture techniques. Address: Dept. of Medicine, School of Medicine, University of North Carolina, Chapel Hill, NC 27514.

GOTTSCHALK, CHARLES M(AX), b. Bochum, Ger, Feb. 2, 28; nat; m. 48; c. 2. PHYSICS. B.E.S, Fenn Col, 50; Pa. State, 50-51; George Washington, 55-56; M.S. in L.S, Catholic Univ, 66. Physicist, Pa. State, 50-51; res. analyst, Library of Cong, 51-54; physicist instrumentation, Nat. Bur. Standards, 54-56; phys. sci. administr. & head, reference sect, sci. & tech. div, Library of Cong, 56-62, chief, stack & reader div, 62, head, systs. identification anal. sect, 62-63; info systs. specialist, div. tech. info, U.S. Atomic Energy Cmn, 63-66, dir. libraries, 66-68, SR. OFF, INT. ATOMIC ENERGY AGENCY, 69- Res. analyst & consult, Arctic Inst. N.Am, 54-59; res. assoc, Ohio State, 58-59; exec. secy, panel educ. & training, Comt. Sch. & Tech. Info, 65-68; consult, Agr. Info. Syst, Food & Agr. Orgn, 71- U.S.A, 46-47; U.S.M.C.R, 47-49. AAAS; Am. Soc. Info. Sci; Am. Phys. Soc; Am. Nuclear Soc; Asn. Comput. Mach; Am. Soc. Metals. Information storage and retrieval; documentation; nuclear science literature; information science; federal government science policies and programs; scientific and technical library organization. Address: International Atomic Energy Agency, P.O. Box 645, A-1011 Vienna, Austria.

GOTTSCHALK, JOHN SIMISON, b. Berne, Ind, Sept. 27, 12; m. 37; c. 2. BIOLOGY. A.B, Earlham Col, 34; M.A, Indiana, 43; LL.D, Earlham Col, 66. Naturalist, State Dept. Conserv, Ind, 34-38, supt. fisheries, 38-41; sr. bacteriologist, Schenley Labs, 44-45; aquatic biologist, U.S. FISH & WILD-

LIFE SERV, 45-51, asst. chief br. fed. aid, 51-57, chief div. sport fisheries, 58-59, regional dir, 59-64, dir. bur. sport fisheries & wildlife, 64-70, ASST. TO DIR. NAT. MARINE FISHERIES SERV, 70- Wildlife Soc.(v.pres, 55); Am. Fisheries Soc.(v.pres, 41, 63, pres, 64). Limnology; fish population dynamics; wildlife management. Address: 4664 34th St. N, Arlington, VA 22207.

GOTTSCHALK, LOUIS A(UGUST), b. St. Louis, Mo, Aug. 26, 16; m. 44; c. 4. PSYCHIATRY, PSYCHOANALYSIS. A.B, Washington (St. Louis), 40, M.D, 43. Asst. neuropsychiat, sch. med, Washington (St. Louis), 44-46; instr. psychiat, Southwest. Med. Col, Texas, 47-48; res. assoc. & instr. electroencephalog. & clin. neurophysiol, Inst. Psychosom. & Psychiat. Res. & Training, Ill, 48-51; res. psychiatrist, Nat. Inst. Ment. Health, 51-53; res. prof. psychiat. & coord. res, med. col, Univ. Cincinnati, 53-67; PROF. PSYCHIAT. & HUMAN BEHAV. & CHMN. DEPT, COL. MED, UNIV. CALIF, IRVINE, 67- Asst. chief child psychiat. clin, Michael Reese Hosp, 50-51; training & supv. analyst, Chicago Inst. Psychoanal, 57-67; Nat. Inst. Ment. Health res. career award, 61-67. Dir. psychiat. serv. & residency training prog, Orange County Med. Ctr, Metrop. State Hosp, Fairview State Hosp. & Vet. Admin. Long Beach Hosp. Mem. clin. psychopharmacol. res. rev. comt, Nat. Inst. Ment. Health, 68-71; res. adv. comt, Calif. State Dept. Ment. Hyg, 68-71. U.S.P.H.S, 46-53, Comdr. AAAS; Am. Psychosom. Soc; fel. Am. Col. Neuropsychopharmacol; Am. Psychoanal. Asn; fel. Am. Psychiat. Asn.(Hofheimer Award, 55); Am. Asn. Res. Nerv. & Ment. Disease; fel. Am. Col. Psychiat; Int. Psychoanal. Asn. Psychophysiological relations; psychopharmacology; psychoanalytic process; psychotherapeutic interview; determinates in personality problems and medical illness of children; methods of assessing emotional variables more precisely and with some degree of quantification; outcome of psychotherapy. Address: Dept. of Psychiatry & Human Behavior, University of California College of Medicine, Irvine, CA 92664.

GOTTSCHALK, ROBERT NEAL, b. Milwaukee, Wis, Apr. 24, 28; m. 52; c. 4. CHEMICAL ENGINEERING. B.S, Wisconsin, 52. Chem. prod. engr, CHEM. PROD. DIV, ANSUL CO, 52-53, pilot plant engr, 53-60, sr. proj. engr, 60-65, eng. mgr, 65-69, mgr. chem. mfg. eng, 69-70, MGR. CHEM. ENVIRON. ENG, 70- Manager design, construct. and start-up of herbicide plant in Malaysia, 69. U.S.M.C, 46-48. Am. Chem. Soc. Design, development and production; process for nitrogen heterocyclics; glycol ethers; organic arsenic compounds. Address: Chemical Products Division, Ansul Co, Marinette, WI 54143.

GOTTSCHALK, W(ALTER) H(ELBIG), b. Lynchburg, Va, Nov. 3, 18; m. 52; c. 2. MATHEMATICS. B.S, Univ. Va, 39, M.A, 42, Ph.D.(math), 44; hon. M.A, Wesleyan Univ, 64. Instr. MATH, Univ. Pa, 44-47, asst. prof, 47-52, assoc. prof, 52-56, prof, 56-63, chmn. dept, 55-58; PROF, WESLEYAN UNIV, 63-, CHMN. DEPT, 64-69, 70-71. Mem, Inst. Advan. Study, 47-48; dele, Conf. Topological Dynamics, Huntsville, Ala, 61 & 62; Grenoble, France, 63; Ft. Collins, Colo, 66; Cleveland, 69. AAAS; Am. Math. Soc. (assoc. secy, 71-); Soc. Indust. & Appl. Math; Math. Asn. Am. Topological dynamics. Address: Dept. of Mathematics, Wesleyan University, Middletown, CT 06457.

GOTTSCHALL, (WALTER) CARL, b. Pittsburgh, Pa, Nov. 15, 38; m. 62; c. 3. RADIATION & INORGANIC CHEMISTRY. B.S, Calif. Inst. Tech, 60; univ. & Dupont fels, Nat. Insts. Health grant & Ph.D.(inorg. chem), Colorado, 64. Res. assoc. radiation chem, Argonne Nat. Lab, 64-66; asst. prof, CHEM, UNIV. DENVER, 66-71, ASSOC. PROF, 71- Am. Chem. Soc. Address: Dept. of Chemistry, University of Denver, University Park, Denver, CO 80210.

GOTTSCHALL, GERTRUDE Y(OUNKER), b. New York, N.Y. BIOCHEMISTRY, CELL PHYSIOLOGY. B.A, Barnard Col, Columbia, M.A, univ; Ph.D.(biochem), Cornell, 36. Asst. biochem, med. col, Cornell, 34-37; biochemist in charge nutrit. serv, U.S. Pub. Health Serv, 38-39; assoc. chemist, bur. chem. & eng, U.S. Dept. Agr, 39-42, sr. chemist, civilian food requirements br, 43-45; qm. corps, War Dept, 42-43, sr. biochemist, 45-46; asst. prof. chem, vet. session, Hunter Col, 46-48; res. assoc. biochem, col. physicians & surgeons, Columbia, 49-50; asst. prof, col. med, State Univ. N.Y, 52-54; from assoc. to asst. prof, col. physicians & surgeons, Columbia, 54-57; asst. prof, Rockefeller Inst, 57-63; res. assoc. hemat, Mt. Sinai Hosp, New York, 63-66, sr. res. assoc, 66-68; RES. ASSOC, LENOX HILL HOSP, 68- Instr, sch. nursing, N.Y. Hosp, 34-37, N.Y. Univ, 51; investr, Marine Biol. Lab, Mass, summers 35-37; instr. Hunter Col, 38; secy. comt. civilian nutrit, U.S. Dept. Agr, 43-44; liaison, U.S. Dept. Agr. & food & nutrit. bd, Nat. Res. Coun, 43-45; mem, Secy. Agr. Comt. Post War Planning, 45; asst. prof, Mt. Sinai Sch. Med, 66-68; corp, Marine Biol. Lab, Mass. AAAS; Am. Chem. Soc; fel. Am. Soc. Clin. Chem; N.Y. Acad. Sci. Cellular biochemistry; proteolytic and mucolytic enzymes; white blood cell and gastrointestinal enzymes; nutrition and metabolism; protein purification; blood gluthatione. Address: Lenox Hill Hospital, 100 E. 77th St, New York, NY 10021.

GOTTSCHANG, JACK L(OUIS), b. Woodland, Calif, Feb. 16, 23; m. 42; c. 4. MAMMALOGY, HERPETOLOGY. B.A, San Jose State Col, 47; Ph.D.(zool), Cornell Univ, 50. Asst. ZOOL, Cornell Univ, 47-50; asst. prof, UNIV. CINCINNATI, 50-58, assoc. prof, 58-70, PROF, 70- U.S.N.R, 43-46, Lt.(jg). AAAS; Am. Soc. Mammal; Am. Soc. Zool. Taxonomy; ecology; life history studies; small mammals. Address: Dept. of Zoology, University of Cincinnati, Cincinnati, OH 45221.

GOTTSCHLICH, CHAD F, b. Laura, Ohio, Feb. 26, 29; m. 50; c. 4. CHEMICAL ENGINEERING. Ch.E, Univ. Cincinnati, 51, Ph.D.(chem. eng), 61; M.S.E, Princeton, 53. Engr. petrol. ref, Standard Oil Co, Ohio, 52-54; instr. chem. eng, Univ. Cincinnati, 54-60; res. assoc. mech. eng, Northwest. Univ, 60-61, asst. prof, 61-63; Univ. Pa, 63-66; SECT. MGR. RES, SELAS CORP. AM, 66- Am. Inst. Chem. Eng; Am. Chem. Soc. Measurements of the properties of high temperature gases; industrial heating. Address: Research Dept, Selas Corp. of America, Dreshertown Rd. & Limekilenn Pike, Dresher, PA 19025.

GOTTSCHO, ALFRED M(ORTON), b. Brooklyn, N.Y, April 29, 19; m. 41; c. 3. CHEMICAL ENGINEERING, BIOCHEMISTRY. B.Ch.E, City Col, 40; M.S, Franklin & Marshall Col, 54. Tech. serv. engr, rubber & plastic printing plates, Mosstype Corp, N.J, 40-41; engr. fuel consumption study, U.S. Corps Engrs, 41-42; prod. supvr. explosives, Plumbrook Ord. Works, Ohio, 42-44; chem. engr. tobacco processing, RES LAB, GEN. CIGAR CO, LANCASTER, 46-57, asst. dir, develop, 57-68, DIR. RES. & DEVELOP. & ASST. V.PRES, 68- U.S.A, 44-46. AAAS; Am. Chem. Soc; Tech. Asn. Pulp & Paper Indust; Am. Soc. Test. & Mat; Soc. Chem. Indust. Alkaloids of tobacco and their changes during industrial processing; changes in nitrogenous constituents in cigar tobaccos; development of tobacco sheets. Address: 348 Landis Ave, Millersville, PA 17551.

GOTTSEGEN, ROBERT, b. New York, N.Y, June 21, 19; m. 52; c. 3. DENTISTRY. A.B, Michigan, 39; D.D.S, Columbia, 43, cert, 47. U.S. Pub. Health Serv. res. fel, Nat. Insts. Health, 48-50; asst. clin. prof. dent, COLUMBIA UNIV, 49-59, assoc. clin. prof, 59-69, PROF. DENT, CHMN. DEPT. PERIODONT. & DIR. POSTDOCTORAL DENT. EDUC, 69- Attend. dent, Presby. Hosp. Dipl, Am. Bd. Periodont. U.S.A, 43-46. AAAS; Am. Acad. Periodont.(pres, 70-71); Am. Acad. Oral Path; Int. Asn. Dent. Res; fel. Am. Col. Dent. Address: 931 Fifth Ave, New York, NY 10021.

GOTTSHALL, RUSSELL Y, b. Boyertown, Pa, Jan. 22, 07; m. 38; c. 2. BACTERIOLOGY. B.S, Albright Col, 28; M.S, Pittsburgh, 29, Ph.D. (bacter), 32. BACTERIOLOGIST, Wm. S. Merrell Co, 33-36; STATE DEPT. PUB. HEALTH, MICH, 36- Fel. AAAS; Am. Soc. Microbiol; Am. Asn. Immunol; fel. Am. Pub. Health Asn. Preparation of bacterial toxoids and vaccines and their antigenecity in human subjects. Address: State Dept. of Public Health, 3500 N. Logan St, Lansing, MI 48914.

GOTTSTEIN, WILLIAM J, b. Syracuse, N.Y, July 15, 29; m. 55; c. 3. ORGANIC CHEMISTRY. B.S, Le Moyne Col.(N.Y), 51. SR. RES. SCIENTIST, BRISTOL LABS, INC, SYRACUSE, 52- Am. Chem. Soc. Chemical alteration of natural products. Address: 116 Woodmancy Lane, Fayetteville, NY 13066.

GOTWALD, WILLIAM H(ARRISON), JR, b. Trenton, N.J, May 6, 39; m. 64. ENTOMOLOGY. B.S, Millersville State Col, 61; M.S, Pa. State Univ, 64; Ph.D.(entom), Cornell Univ, 68. Instr. zool, Pa. State Univ, Altoona, 63-65; ASST. PROF. BIOL, UTICA COL, 68- Nat. Sci. Found. grant, 70-73. AAAS; Am. Inst. Biol. Sci; Asn. Trop. Biol; Entom. Soc. Am; Soc. Syst. Zool. Phylogeny and systematics of the ants, especially the morphology and behavior of tropical ants belonging to the subfamilies Ponerinae and Dorylinae. Address: Dept. of Biology, Utica College, Burrstone Rd, Utica, NY 13502.

GOTWALS, ROBERT de HAVEN, b. Newark, Del, Jan. 27, 13; m. 36; c. 2. ENGINEERING. Drexel Inst. Civil engr, E.I. DU PONT DE NEMOURS & CO, 33-38, construct. engr, 38-39, maintenance construct. engr, 39-42, field engr, Atomic Energy Cmn, 42-44, Co, 44-50, process engr, 50-66, engr, air & water pollution abatement prog, 66-70, MFG. SUPVR, 70- Am. Inst. Chem. Eng. Radio amplifiers; maintenance; construction; civil engineering; chemical engineering; radio; designs of various types of complete chemical plants throughout United States, Mexico, Brazil, Japan and Europe. Address: 1211 Mayfield Rd, Mayfield, Wilmington, DE 19803.

GÖTZ, MANFRED, b. Hof, Ger, July 5, 30; m. 58; c. 3. ORGANIC CHEMISTRY. Dipl, Munich, 56, Dr. rer. nat, 58. Nat. Res. Coun. Can. fel. chem, New Brunswick, 58-61; chemist, Pharma Res. Ltd, Que, 61-69; DIR. DEPT. OF CHEM, AYERST RES. LABS, 69- Ger. Chem. Soc. Natural products; synthesis. Address: Ayerst Research Labs, 1025 Laurentian Blvd, P.O. Box 6115, Montreal 101, Que, Can.

GOU, PERNG-FEI, b. China, July 1, 36; m. 66; c. 1. APPLIED MECHANICS. B.S, Cheng Kung Univ, Taiwan, 57; M.S, Stanford, 62; D.Eng.S.(eng. mech), Columbia, 67. Asst. appl. mech, Columbia, 64-67; ASST. PROF, Stevens Inst. Tech, 67-68; MECH. ENG, POLYTECH. INST. BROOKLYN, 68- Nat. Sci. Found. res. grant, 69-70. Am. Soc. Mech. Eng. Elasticity: plasticity; stress waves in solids; dynamics; vibrations; materials science. Address: Dept. of Mechanical Engineering, Polytechnic Institute of Brooklyn, Brooklyn, NY 11201.

GOUBAU, G(EORG), b. Munich, Ger, Nov. 29, 06; nat; m. 42; c. 2. PHYSICS. M.S, Inst. Tech, Munich, 30, Dr. Ing, 31, Dr.Ing.Habil, 35. Asst. prof. physics, Inst. Tech, Munich, 31-35, assoc. prof, 35-39; prof. appl. physics & dir. dept, Jena, 39-45; PHYSICIST & CONSULT, U.S. ARMY ELECTRONIC COMMAND, FT. MONMOUTH, 47- Guest prof, Univ. Wis, 62; mem. U.S. nat. comt, Int. Sci. Radio Union, 59. AAAS; N.Y. Acad. Sci; fel. Inst. Elec. & Electronics Eng.(Diamond Mem. Award, Inst. Radio Eng, 57, Boljahn Award, 62). Ionsphere; electromagnetic theory; microwave circuits; wave guides; optical transmission. Address: 18 Stirrup Lane, Eaton Town, NJ 07724.

GOUCK, H(ARRY) (KYDD), b. Andover, Mass, June 21, 13; m. 40; c. 2. MEDICAL ENTOMOLOGY. B.S, New Hampshire, 36; M.S, Massachusetts, 37. Biol. aide, tick res, U.S. DEPT. AGR, Mass, 38-41, ENTOMOLOGIST, Ga, 42-45, mosquito res, Fla, 46-48, corn earworms res, 48-51, REPELLENT RES, AGR. RES. SERV, 51- Superior serv. award, U.S. Dept. Agr. Entom. Soc. Am. Insect repellent and attractants, especially mosquitos, ticks, mites and biting flies; reaction of repellents on skin and cloth. Address: P.O. Box 1268, Gainesville, FL 32601.

GOUD, PAUL A, b. The Hague, Netherlands, Sept. 2, 37; Can. citizen; m. 61; c. 3. COMMUNICATIONS. B.Sc, Alberta, 59; M.A.Sc, British Columbia, 61, Ph.D.(elec. eng), 64. Mem. sci. staff, res. & develop. labs, North. Elec. Co, Ont, 65-66; asst. prof. MICROWAVE COMMUN, UNIV. ALTA, 66-68, ASSOC. PROF, 68- Nat. Res. Coun. Can. res. grant, 66-; Dept. Commun. Can. res. grant, 71- Sr. mem. Inst. Elec. & Electronics Eng. Theory and design of electron beams; characterization of semiconductor microwave devices; microwave communications. Address: Dept. of Electrical Engineering, University of Alberta, Edmonton 7, Alta, Can.

GOUDARZI, GUS (HOSSEIN), b. Iran, Mar. 27, 18; nat; m. 44; c. 4. MINING & GEOLOGICAL ENGINEERING. B.S, Mont. Sch. Mines, 39, M.S, 41. Miner hard rock mining, Anaconda Copper Mining Co, 37-41, sampler, 41-42, mining engr, 42-46, geol. engr, 46-48, supvr. underground mining & develop, 48-50; econ. geologist mineral explor, Agency for Int. Develop, U.S. Geol. Surv, Ghana, 50-52, Arabia, 52-54, Libya, 54-57, chief party & tech. adv. minerals & ground water invest, 57-62, acting dir. dept. mines & geol, Libyan govt. 62-63, regional geol, Ky, 64-68, ECON. EXPLOR. GEOLOGIST, U.S. GEOL. SURV-U.S. AGENCY INT. DEVELOP, 68- U.S.N, 44-46, Res, 48-50. Geol. Soc. Am; Am. Inst. Mining, Metall. & Petrol. Eng. Mining methods; mapping and evaluation of mineral occurrences; mine examination, evaluation and development; regional geology. Address: American Consulate General, U.S. Geological Survey-U.S. Agency for International Development, Recife, Brazil, APO New York 09676.

GOUDEY, GORDON M(ELVIN), b. N.Y.C, June 20, 22; m. 52; c. 1. ENGINEERING GRAPHICS. B.Sc, Acadia, 43; M.A, N.Y. Univ, 54. Instr. math, Curtiss Wright Corp, 52-53; descriptive geom. & eng. drawing, Newark Col. Eng, 53-56; asst. prof, Fairleigh Dickinson, 56-64; ASSOC. PROF. MATH, UNIV. BALTIMORE, 64-, CHMN. DEPT, 68- U.S.A.A.F, 43-46, 2nd Lt. Am. Soc. Eng. Educ. Development of spatial concepts. Address: Dept. of Mathematics, University of Baltimore, Baltimore, MD 21201.

GOUDSMIT, ESTHER M(ARIANNE), b. Ann Arbor, Mich, July 29, 33. INVERTEBRATE EMBRYOLOGY, BIOCHEMISTRY. B.A, Univ. Mich, Ann Arbor, 55, M.S, 59, Ph.D.(zool), 64; U.S. Pub. Health Serv. trainee, Univ. London, 60-61. Res. asst. marine ecol, Woods Hole Oceanog. Inst, 59; U.S. Pub. Health Serv. fel. biochem, Nat. Inst. Arthritis & Metab. Diseases, Bethesda, Md, 64-66; res. assoc. pathobiol, sch. pub. health, Johns Hopkins Univ, 67-69; ASST. PROF. BIOL, BROOKLYN COL, 69- Zool. Soc. London; Am. Soc. Zool; Soc. Develop. Biol. Carbohydrate metabolism in snails; comparative biochemistry; intertidal faunal ecology. Address: Dept. of Biology, Brooklyn College, Brooklyn, NY 11210.

GOUDSMIT, SAMUEL A(BRAHAM), b. The Hague, Holland, July 11, 02; nat; m. 27; c. 1; m. 60. PHYSICS. Rockefeller fel, Tubingen, 26-27; Ph.D. (physics), Leiden, 27; hon. D.Sc, Case, 58. Asst, Amsterdam, 23-26; instr, Michigan, 27-28, assoc. prof, 28-32, prof, 32-46; Northwestern, 46-48; sr. scientist, Brookhaven Nat. Lab, 48-70, chmn. physics dept, 52-60; ED-IN-CHIEF, AM. PHYS. SOC, 51- Gugggnheim Found. fel, Rome & Paris, 38; vis. lectr, Harvard, 41; mem. staff radiation lab, Mass. Inst. Technol, 41-46; (intelligence), War Dept, 44-46; vis. prof, Rockefeller Inst, 57- Ed, Phys. Rev, 51-62, Phys. Rev. Letters, 58- Off. Order of Brit. Empire; Res. Corp. award; Max Planck Medal; Medal of Freedom. Nat. Acad. Sci; Am. Philos. Soc; fel. Am. Phys. Soc; Am. Nuclear Soc; correspondent Royal Netherlands Acad. Sci. Electron spin; atomic structure and spectra. Address: American Physical Society, Brookhaven National Lab, Upton, L.I, NY 11973.

GOUGH, BOBBY JOE, b. Trout, La, Mar. 13, 34; m. 56. BACTERIOLOGY, ZOOLOGY. B.A, La. Polytech, 57, M.S, 62; M.S, La. State, 63. Res. microbiologist, agr. res. ctr, U.S. Dept. Agr, 63-66; RES. BIOLOGIST, GULF SOUTH RES. INST, 66- Am. Soc. Mammal; Am. Soc. Microbiol. Comparative hematology of small mammals; nucleic acid studies in Anaplasma marginale; survival of Clostridium perfringens in fresh meat; biological effects of pesticides on natural fauna. Address: Gulf South Research Institute, P.O. Box 1177, New Iberia, LA 70560.

GOUGH, DENIS IAN, b. Port Elizabeth, S.Africa, June 20, 22; m. 45; c. 2. GEOPHYSICS. B.Sc, Rhodes Univ. Col, S.Africa, 43, M.Sc, 47; Ph.D.(geophys), Witwatersrand, 53. Res. officer geophys, S.African Nat. Phys. Res. Lab, 47-55, sr. res. officer, 55-58; lectr. physics, Univ. Col. Rhodesia & Nyasaland, 58-60, sr. lectr, 61-63; assoc. prof. geophys, Southwest Ctr. for Adv. Studies, Dallas, 64-66; PROF. UNIV. ALTA, 66-68, PHYSICS, 66- Mem, Nat. Comt. Geod. & Geophys, Cent. African Fedn, 60-63; subcomt. gravity, adv. comt. geophys. & geod, Nat. Res. Coun. Can, 67-, subcomt. geomag. & aeronomy, 67- S.African Corps.Sig, 43-45. Am. Geophys. Union; fel. Royal Astron. Soc; European Asn. Explor. Geophys. Studies of crustal structure through gravity and magnetic anomalies; studies of paleomagnetism, especially in relation to continental drift; study of upper mantle temperature distribution through electromagnetic induction. Address: Dept. of Physics, University of Alberta, Edmonton, Alta, Can.

GOUGH, FRANCIS J(ACOB), b. Grafton, W.Va, Apr. 9, 28; m. 50; c. 2. PLANT PATHOLOGY. B.S, West Virginia, 52, M.S, 54, Ph.D.(plant path), 57. Asst. plant path, West Virginia, 52-57; plant pathologist cereal rusts, U.D. DEPT. AGR, N.Dak, 57-67, RES. PLANT PATHOLOGIST, DEPT. PLANT SCIS, TEX. A&M UNIV, 67- U.S.A.F, 46-49. Am. Phytopath. Soc. Genetics of host-parasite relationships. Address: Dept. of Plant Sciences, Texas A&M University, College Station, TX 77843.

GOUGH, KENNETH HENRY, b. Dec. 20, 26; U.S. citizen; m. 54; c. 3. AUDIOLOGY, SPEECH SCIENCE. B.A, Sir George Williams, 55; M.A, State Univ. Iowa, 57; Ph.D.(audiol, speech sci), Purdue, 66. Sales engr, Williams E. Wilson Ltd, Que, 47-54; speech clinician, Hosp. Sch. for Severely Handicapped Children, State Univ. Iowa, 57-59; assoc. dir. speech & hearing, Vt. Asn. Crippled, 59-62; asst. prof. speech path, Purdue, 65-66; asst. prof. commun. disorders & chmn. dept, Massachusetts, 66-69; ASSOC. PROF. SPEECH PATHOL. & AUDIOL. & HEAD DIV, SCH. REHAB. MED, UNIV. ALTA, 69- Consult, Vet. Admin. Hosp, Northampton, Mass, 66-; hon. asst. clin. prof, dept. community med, faculty med. & sci. & res. assoc, med. staff, univ. hosp, Univ. Alta, 70- Am. Speech & Hearing Asn. Speech pathology. Address: Division of Speech Pathology & Audiology, School of Rehabilitation Medicine, E.A. Corbett Hall, University of Alberta, Edmonton, Alta, Can.

GOUGH, LILLIAN, b. Detroit, Mich, May 15, 18. MATHEMATICS. B.A, Buffalo, 39, M.A, 49, Ph.D.(math), 53. Instr. MATH, Buffalo, 46-53; asst. prof, Oswego State Teachers Col, 53-55; assoc. prof, WIS. STATE UNIV-RIVER FALLS; 55-58, PROF, 58-, CHMN. DEPT, 56- Math. Asn. Am. Topology. Address: 451 E. Union St, River Falls, WI 54022.

GOUGH, MICHAEL, b. Springfield, Mo, Feb. 4, 39; m. 64; c. 2. MICROBIOLOGY, GENETICS. B.A, Grinnell Col, 61; U.S. Pub. Health Serv. fel, Brown, 62-64, Ph.D.(biol), 66. Fel. microbial genetics, dept. human genetics, Michigan, 65-68; ASST. PROF. MICROBIOL, Baylor Col. Med, 68-72; STATE UNIV. N.Y. STONY BROOK, 7/72- U.S. Pub. Health Serv. trainee, 66-68; Nat. Sci. Found. res. grant, 69- U.S.A, 57. AAAS; Am. Soc. Microbiol. Interactions between bacteriophages and bacteria that are necessary to establish and maintain lysogeny. Address: Dept. of Microbiology, State University of New York at Stony Brook, Stony Brook, NY 11790.

GOUGH, PATRICIA M(ARIE), b. Eagle River, Wis, Jan. 13, 37. BIOCHEMISTRY, IMMUNOCHEMISTRY. B.S, Wisconsin, 58; M.S, Minnesota, 61, Ph.D.(biochem), 66. Res. asst. biochem, Minnesota, 58-61, bact, 61-65, res. assoc, 65-67; res. chemist, rabies invests. lab, Nat. Commun. Disease Ctr, 67-68; ASST. PROF. IMMUNOCHEM, VET. MED. RES. INST, IOWA STATE UNIV, 68- Am. Pub. Health Asn. Immunochemistry of infectious diseases; mechanisms of immune response to antigens isolated from bacteria and viruses. Address: Veterinary Medical Research Institute, Iowa State University, Ames, IA 50010.

GOUGH, ROBERT GEORGE, b. Kitchener, Ont, May 20, 39; U.S. citizen; m. 67. ORGANIC CHEMISTRY. B.Sc, Univ. Waterloo, 62; Ph.D.(chem), Pa. State Univ, 67. RES. ASSOC. CHEM, CINCINNATI MILACRON INC, 67- Am. Chem. Soc. Photochemistry; design of photostable compounds; photochemical syntheses using chemically generated electronically excited molecules; chemiluminescence, ultraviolet stabilizers and other additives for polymers; mechanisms in reaction of Grignard reagents. Address: Applied Sciences Research & Development, Cincinnati Milacron Inc, Cincinnati, OH 45209.

GOUGH, WILLIAM CABOT, b. Jersey City, N.J, Aug. 22, 30; m. 57; c. 2. POWER ENGINEERING. B.S.E, Princeton, 52, M.S.E, 55. Res. asst, Forrestal Res. Ctr, Princeton, 52-53; admin. engr, div. reactor develop, U.S. ATOMIC ENERGY COMN, 53-55, proj. off, 55-58, indust. info. off, div. tech. info, 58-60, ELEC. ENGR, DIV. RES, 60- Summers, mat. checker, elec. generating sta. construct, M.H. Treadwell, 50; draftsman, Gibbs & Hill, Inc, 51; jr. elec. engr, Am. Gas & Elec. Serv. Corp, 52; fel. sci. & pub. policy, Harvard, 66-67. Sustained superior performance award, U.S. Atomic Energy Comn, 66 & spec. achievement award for develop. fusion torch concept, 70; mem, Ctr. Study Democratic Insts, 70- U.S.N, 55-58, Lt.(jg). AAAS; Am. Nuclear Soc; World Future Soc. Electrical power generation by conventional, nuclear fission and controlled fusion systems; development of controlled fusion power, industrial applications of ultra-high temperature plasmas, fusion torch; closing of the materials cycle; environmental implications of energy use. Address: Division of Research, J-309, U.S. Atomic Energy Commission, Washington, DC 20545.

GOUGHNOUR, ROY R(OBERT), b. Canton, Ohio, May 10, 28; m. 68; c. 3. CIVIL ENGINEERING. B.S, Mich. State, 61, M.S, 65, Ph.D.(civil eng), 67. Engr, A.C. Aukermann Co, 58-64; ASSOC. PROF. eng, Northern Arizona, 67-68; CIVIL ENG, MICH. STATE UNIV, 68- Mechanical properties of frozen soil and ice. Address: Dept. of Civil Engineering, Michigan State University, East Lansing, MI 48823.

GOUGOUTAS, JACK ZANOS, b. Mansfield, Ohio, Feb. 22, 39; m. 63; c. 2. X-RAY CRYSTALLOGRAPHY, SOLID STATE CHEMISTRY. B.A, Harvard, 61, Ph.D.(chem), 64. Fel. CHEM, Harvard, 64-65, asst. prof, 65-69, ASSOC. PROF, 69-71; UNIV. MINN, MINNEAPOLIS, 71- Alfred P. Sloan fel, 67-69; consult, Eli Lilly Co, Inc, 67-69; E.R. Squibb & Sons, 67-; vis. prof, Iowa State Univ, summer 68. Am. Crystallog. Asn. X-ray diffraction studies of molecular structures; chemical reactions and phase transformations in organic solids. Address: Dept. of Chemistry, University of Minnesota, Minneapolis, MN 55455.

GOUIN, FRANCIS R, b. Laconia, N.H, June 3, 38; m. 62; c. 2. PLANT PHYSIOLOGY. Cert, Thompson Sch. Agr, 58; B.S, Univ. N.H, 62; M.S, Univ. Md, College Park, 65, Ph.D.(hort, bot), 69. Exten. specialist HORT, UNIV. MD, COLLEGE PARK, 65-69, ASST. PROF, 69- Am. Soc. Hort. Sci. Mineral nutrition of woody ornamental plants; winter hardiness of roots of container grown woody ornamental plants; chemical weed control in and around woody ornamental plants. Address: Dept. of Horticulture, University of Maryland, College Park, MD 20740.

GOUIN, PIERRE L(AURIER), S.J, b. Champlain, Can, Sept. 13, 17. GEOPHYSICS. B.A, Col. Jean-de-Brebeuf, Can, 43; L.Ph, Immaculate-Conception Univ, 44; M.Sc, Boston Col, 53. Dean faculty sci, HAILE SELASSIE UNIV, 54-57, DIR. GEOPHYS. OBSERV, 57-, PROF, 71- Haile Selassie Prize Trust Int. Award, 68. Inst. Elec. & Electronics Eng; fel. Royal Astron. Soc; Am. Geophys. Union. Seismology and gravimetry of Ethiopia, especially Agar and the Ethiopian Rift. Address: Geophysical Observatory, Haile Selassie University, P.O. Box 1176, Addis Ababa, Ethiopia.

GOUINLOCK, EDWARD V(ERNON), JR, b. Buffalo, N.Y, Jan. 14, 28. PHYSICAL & POLYMER CHEMISTRY. B.A, Williams Col, 50; Procter & Gamble Co. fel, Cornell, 53-54, Ph.D.(phys. chem), 55. Res. chemist, film dept, E.I. du Pont de Nemours & Co, N.Y, 54-55; polymer chem, HOOKER CHEM. CO, 57-64, sr. chemist, 64-70, GROUP LEADER, 70- Summers, lab. technician, Linde Div, Union Carbide Corp, 50-51. Chem.C, U.S.A, 55-57. Am. Chem. Soc. Physical properties and characterization of polymers; polymer configuration, processing, evaluation and synthesis. Address: 977 Delaware Ave, Buffalo, NY 14209.

GOULARD, BERNARD, b. Paris, France, May 9, 33; m. 59; c. 1. THEORETICAL & NUCLEAR PHYSICS. Lic, Nancy, 57; Dr.(nuclear physics), Grenoble, 60; Ph.D.(physics), Pennsylvania, 64. Fel. theoret. physics, Bartol Res. Found, 64-65; asst. prof. PHYSICS, LAVAL UNIV, 65-70, ASSOC. PROF, 70- Am. Phys. Soc. Weak interaction of muons and neutrinos with nuclei; electron scattering and isobaric properties of nuclei. Address: Dept. of Physics, Laval University, Quebec, Que, Can.

GOULD, A. LAWRENCE, b. Feb. 6, 41; U.S. citizen. STATISTICS. A.B, Case West. Reserve Univ, 62, Ph.D.(biomet, statist), 67; Iowa State Univ, 62-65. Statistician, Res. Triangle Inst, 67-69; SECT. HEAD CLIN. BIOSTATIST, DIV. MED. AFFAIRS, MERCK SHARPE & DOHME RES. LABS, 69- Am. Statist. Asn; Biomet. Soc. Statistical methodology pertinent to problems arising in reality, expecially in the biological and medical sciences. Address: Division of Medical Affairs, Merck Sharpe & Dohme Research Labs, West Point, PA 19486.

GOULD, ANNE BRIMLEY, b. Bangor, Maine, Jan. 30, 28. BIOLOGY, BIOCHEMISTRY. B.S, Maine, 50; M.S, Rutgers, 54; Ph.D, Brown, 61. RES. BIOCHEMIST, Vet. Admin. Hosp, 62-66; MT. SINAI HOSP. OF CLEVELAND, 66- Am. Soc. Nephrology. Biochemical and physiological properties of renin; hypertension; erythropoiesis. Address: 939 Aintree Park Dr, Mayfield Village, OH 44143.

GOULD, ARNOLD H(ENRY), b. Albany, N.Y, May 21, 16; m. 43; c. 4. DERMATOLOGY. B.S, Univ. Ark, 37, M.D, 42. Fel, GEORGETOWN UNIV, 43-45, instr. DERMAT. SYPHILOL, 47-51, clin. asst. prof, 51-64, CLIN. ASSOC. PROF, 64- Med. consult, D.C. Dept. Corrections, 56-70; chief dept. dermat, Georgetown Univ, med. div, D.C. Gen. Hosp. Dipl, Am. Bd. Dermat; vicennial medal, Georgetown Med. Sch, 67. Fel. Am. Acad. Dermat; Am. Venereal Disease Asn. Use of depilatories on facial hirsutism; estrogenic hormones in acne vulgaris; sodium sulfacetamide in seborrhea and seborrheic dermatitis. Address: University Medical Bldg, 2141 K St. N.W, Washington, DC 20037.

GOULD, AUSTIN J(UDSON), b. Stillwater, Okla, Dec. 12, 10; m. 34; c. 2. PHYSICAL CHEMISTRY. B.S, Okla. State, 31; Proctor fel, Princeton, 33-34, Ph.D.(phys. chem), 34. Chemist, Eastman Kodak Co, 34-37, asst. prod. supvr, 37-40, asst. supt, 40-50, supt, 50-52, asst. mgr. film mfg, 53-54, asst. to gen. mgr, 54-56, mgr, 56-59, v.pres, 59-71; RETIRED. Am. Chem. Soc. Adsorption; heavy hydrogen; reactions of cellulose; casting of films of cellulose esters; inter-relations of hydrogen and deuterium molecules. Address: Huntington Hills, Rochester, NY 14622.

GOULD, B(ERNARD) S(IDNEY), b. Boston, Mass, Oct. 15, 11; m. 38; c. 3. BIOCHEMISTRY. S.B, Mass. Inst. Tech, 32; Textile Found. traveling fel, London, 32-34, Ph.D.(biochem), 34. Instr. biol. & pub. health & res. assoc, MASS. INST. TECHNOL, 34-37, asst. prof. BIOCHEM, 37-43, assoc. prof, 43-69, PROF, 69- Comn. Relief Belg. Educ. Found. fel, Cath. Univ. Louvain, 37; consult, Gillette Co. With Off. Sci. Res. & Develop, 44. Am. Soc. Microbiol; Am. Soc. Biol. Chem; N.Y. Acad. Sci. Biochemistry of molds; pigments production; general metabolic processes; enzymology in deficiency conditions such as scurvy and B_1 deficiencies; mechanism of antibacterial agents; wound healing; collagen biosynthesis. Address: Dept. of Biology, Massachusetts Institute of Technology, 77 Massachusetts Ave, Cambridge, MA 02139.

GOULD, CHARLES J(AY, JR), b. Eaton, Ohio, Feb. 28, 12; m. 40; c. 2. PLANT PATHOLOGY. A.B, Marshall Col, 34; M.S, Iowa State Col, 37, Ph.D.(plant path), 42. Instr. bot, Iowa State Col, 37-41; asst. prof, Okla. Agr. & Mech. Col, 40; asst. plant pathologist, WEST. WASH. RES. & EXTEN. CTR, WASH. STATE UNIV, 41-43, res. plant pathologist, 43-46, assoc. plant pathologist, 46-52, PLANT PATHOLOGIST, 52- Fulbright scholar, Netherlands, 51; sabbatical leave, Europe, 67. Res. award, Soc. Am. Florists, 50. Am. Phytopath. Soc. Diseases of turf grasses, iris, tulips, narcissus, rhododendrons and other ornamental plants. Address: Western Washington Research & Extension Center, Washington State University, Puyallup, WA 98371.

GOULD, CHARLES W(EBSTER), b. Atlanta, Ga, Feb. 16, 15; m. 40; c. 3. ORGANIC CHEMISTRY. A.B, Oberlin Col, 36; fel, Rochester, 39-40, Ph.D. (org. chem), 40. Asst. chem, Rochester, 36-39; RES. CHEMIST, Pittsburgh Plate Glass Co, Ohio, 40-42; Marco Chem, Inc, Pa. & N.J, 42-44; HERCULES POWDER CO, 44- Am. Chem. Soc; Tech. Asn. Pulp & Paper Indust. Synthetic organic chemistry; amino alkane sulfonic acids; stereo chemistry of alicyclic compounds; polyester type thermosetting resins; polymerization; development of emulsifiers used for emulsion polymerization; synthetic rubber; polyethylene; wax emulsions; paper sizes. Address: 106 Hoiland Dr, Shipley Heights, Wilmington, DE 19803.

GOULD, C(LARK) W(EBSTER), b. Portland, Ore, May 21, 16; m. 42; c. 3. ORGANIC CHEMISTRY. B.S, Col. Puget Sound, 38; M.S, Calif. Inst. Tech, 40, Ph.D.(org. chem), 42. Res. fel. chem, Calif. Inst. Tech, 42-44; group leader org. characterization, Gen. Aniline & Film Corp, 44-50, res. assoc, 50-55; ANAL. CHEMIST, PHYS. CHEM. SECT, RES. & DEVELOP. CTR, GEN. ELEC. CO, 55- With Nat. Defense Res. Comt, 42-44. AAAS; Am. Microchem. Soc; Am. Chem. Soc. Walden inversion; qualitative and quantitative organic microanalysis; chromatographic adsorption; molecular and fractional distillation; functionality of polymers; countercurrent separation processes; differential scanning calorimetry of polymers. Address: 1932 Village Rd, Schenectady, NY 12309.

GOULD, DAVID H(UNTINGTON), b. N.Y.C, Nov. 23, 21; m. 45; c. 3. ORGANIC CHEMISTRY. B.S, Yale, 42, M.S, 44, Sheffield fel. & Ph.D.(org. chem), 45. Lab. asst, Yale, 42-44; res. chemist, Nopco Chem. Co, 44-48; res. assoc, Hickrill Chem. Res. Found, 48-49, sr. res. chemist, Schering Corp, 49-57, adminstr, extramural sci. res, 57-59; grant res, Colgate-Palmolive Co, 59-68, head tech. info. serv, 68-70; CLIN. RES. ASSOC, MERCK SHARP & DOHME RES. LABS, 70- Dir, N.Valley Consumers Coop, 54-58; exec. secy, Schering Found, div. Schering Corp, 58-59. Fel. AAAS; Am. Chem. Soc; Int. Asn. Dent. Res; N.Y. Acad. Sci; Am. Soc. Microbiol; fel. Am. Inst. Chem; Drug. Info. Asn. Natural products; sterols; vitamins; cortical and sex hormones; dental medicine; chemotherapeutics; chemical structure retrieval; medicinal chemistry; clinical research. Address: Medical Affairs International, Merck Sharp & Dohme Research Labs, Scott Ave, Rahway, NJ 07065.

GOULD, DON(ALD) B(OYD), b. Norman, Okla, Dec. 6, 06; m. 30; c. 2. GEOLOGY. B.S, Oklahoma, 28; M.S, Iowa, 30, Ph.D.(geol), 34. Instr. geol, Southwestern Col.(Kans), 28-29; asst. prof. geol. & geog, Cornell Col, 31-37; assoc. prof. geol, Colo. Col, 37-51, prof, 51-55; admin. geologist, Geophoto Serv, 55-63, res. geologist, 63-71, photogeologist, 51-52; RETIRED. Geologist, Darby Petrol. Co, 44; summers, Continental Oil Co, 46, 48, 49. Fel. Geol. Soc. Am; Am. Asn. Petrol. Geol. Structural geology of Colorado and Utah; stratigraphy of Paleozoic rocks of Colorado and Utah; regional geology of Canadian Arctic archipelago; tectonics of piercement domes of Queen Elizabeth Islands; photogeology. Address: 10195 W. 17th Pl, Lakewood, CO 80215.

GOULD, DOUGLAS J(AY), b. San Francisco, Calif, May 29, 23; m. 47; c. 3. MEDICAL ENTOMOLOGY. B.A, California, 44, Ph.D.(parasitol), 53. Asst. parasitol, California, 47-48, 50-51; parasitology, State Dept. Pub. Health, Calif, 48-50; entomologist, Walter Reed Army Inst. Res, 51-64; CHIEF, DEPT. ENTOM, SOUTHEAST ASIA TREATY ORGN. MED. RES. LAB, 64- Collab, U.S. Nat. Mus, 53-55. U.S.A, 44-46. Am. Soc. Trop. Med. & Hyg; Am. Mosquito Control Asn; Royal Soc. Trop. Med. & Hyg. Arthropod transmission of infectious diseases; microbiology of medically important arthropods; ecology of arthropod borne diseases. Address: Southeast Asia Treaty Organization Medical Research Lab, A.P.O. San Francisco, CA 96346.

GOULD, EDWIN, b. Newark, N.J, Nov. 21, 33; m. 68; c. 1. ECOLOGY, ANIMAL BEHAVIOR. B.S, Cornell, 55; Ph.D.(zool), Tulane, 62. Asst. Prof. MENT. HYG, LAB. COMP. BEHAVIOR, JOHNS HOPKINS UNIV, 62-67, assoc. prof, Nat. Insts. Health fel, Yale, 62-63; mem. expeds. to Madagascar. U.S.A. AAAS; Am. Ornith. Union; Am. Soc. Mammal; Am. Soc. Zool; Animal Behavior Soc; Am. Soc. Ichthyol. & Herpet. Echolocation and communication in the Insectivora and bats; homing orientation in turtles; rodent population dynamics; feeding efficiency in bats; comparative behavior. Address: Dept. of Mental Hygiene, Johns Hopkins University, 615 N. Wolfe St, Baltimore, MD 21205.

GOULD, EDWIN S(HELDON), b. Los Angeles, Calif, Aug. 19, 26; m. 52; c. 2. INORGANIC & ORGANIC CHEMISTRY. B.S, Calif. Inst. Tech, 46; Ph.D. (chem), California, Los Angeles, 50. Instr. chem, Polytech. Inst. Brooklyn, 50, asst. prof, 52-55, assoc. prof, 55-59; sr. inorg. chemist, Stanford Res. Inst, 59-66; PROF. CHEM, San Francisco State Col, 66-67; KENT STATE UNIV, 67- Nat. Sci. Found. sci. faculty fel, 57-58, sr. fel, Stanford Univ, 62-63; Nat. Insts. Health spec. fel, Univ. Calif, 63-64. Am. Chem. Soc; The Chem. Soc. Chelating agents; electron transfer reactions in solution; photosynthesis; organo-selenium compounds; reactions of alkyl borates; metallo-aromatics; x-ray crystallography; catalysis of oxidation by transition metals. Address: Dept. of Chemistry, Kent State University, Kent, OH 44240.

GOULD, ERNEST A(LVA), b. Basin, Wyo, Jan. 29, 13, m. 38; c. 3. SURGERY. B.S, Univ. Wyo, 35; M.D, George Wash. Univ, 39. Fel. surg, Lahey Clin, 46-48; clin. instr. SCH. MED, GEORGE WASH. UNIV, 48-61, assoc. clin. prof. SURG, 61-68, CLIN. PROF, 68-, ASSOC, UNIV. HOSP, 48-, chmn. dept. gen. surg, hosp ctr, 58-63, pres. med. staff, 63-68, chmn. dept. surg, 68-70. Dipl, Am. Bd. Surg. Med.C, 42-46, Maj. Am. Cancer Soc.(St. George Medal, 65); Am. Med. Asn; Am. Thyroid Asn; fel. Am. Col. Surg; Pan-Am. Med. Asn. Thyroid; stomach; breast; liver; cancer; biliary tract; surgery of malignant diseases. Address: Suite 304, 106 Irving St. N.W, Washington, DC 20010.

GOULD, ERNEST MORTON, JR, b. Northampton, Mass, Dec. 26, 18; m. 47. FOREST ECONOMICS. B.Sc, New Hampshire, 40; M.F, Harvard, 42, M.P.A, 48, M.A, 49, Ph.D.(econ), 51. Res. assoc, cmt. res. in social sci, Harvard, 48-50, from res. fel. to FOREST ECONOMIST, HARVARD FOREST, 50-, LECTR. BIOL, 65- Consult, U.S. Forest Serv, D.C, 60- C.Eng, 42-46, Capt. AAAS; Soc. Am. Foresters; Am. Econ. Asn; Am. Agr. Econ. Asn. Forest production; forest policy formation, especially coordinated use of natural resources for many products. Address: Harvard Forest, Harvard University, Petersham, MA 01366.

GOULD, FLOYD T(RAFFORD), b. New York, N.Y, June 16, 17; m. 56; c. 3. PHYSICAL CHEMISTRY. A.B, Brown, 40; Ph.D.(chem), Columbia, 56. Staff scientist, pupin cyclotron labs, Columbia, 53-58; physicist, Knolls Atomic Power Lab, 58-63; Lab. for Electronics, Inc, Mass, 63-67; STAFF SCIENTIST, HONEYWELL EDP, BILLERICA, 67- Staff scientist, chem. dept, Brookhaven Nat. Lab. Chem.C, U.S.A.R, 42-48, Maj. Am. Phys. Soc. Am. Chem. Soc. Very low energy neutron scattering. Address: 63 Wake Robin Rd, Sudbury, MA 01776.

GOULD, FRANK W(ALTON), b. Mayville, N.Dak, July 25, 13; m. 40; c. 3. BOTANY. B.A, North. Ill. State Teachers Col, 35; M.S, Wisconsin, 37; Ph.D.(bot), California, 41. Instr. biol, Dixie Jr. Col, 41-42; Compton Jr. Col, 42-44; asst. prof. bot, Arizona, 44-49; assoc. prof. range & forestry, TEX. A&M UNIV, 49-64, prof. RANGE SCI, 64-69, DISTINGUISHED PROF, 69-, CURATOR TRACY HERBARIUM, 49- With U.S. Forest Serv, 44; Food & Agr. Orgn, UN appointee, Mex, 52. AAAS; Am. Soc. Plant Taxon; Bot. Soc. Am; Am. Soc. Range Mgt. Plant taxonomy, especially cytotaxonomy; the tribes Andropogoneae and Chlorideae of the Gramineae. Address: Dept. of Range Science, Texas A&M University, College Station, TX 77843.

GOULD, GEORGE C, III, b. Buffalo, N.Y, Nov. 1, 32; m. 57; c. 2. METALLURGY. B.S, Antioch Col, 55; M.S, Ill. Inst. Tech, 57; Ph.D.(metall), Case 60. Instr. metall, Fenn Col, 57-59; MGR. PHYS. CHEM. UNIT, MAT. & PROCESSES LAB, GEN. ELEC. CO, 60- Am. Inst. Mining, Metall. & Petrol. Eng. Address: General Electric Co, 1 River Rd, Schenectady, NY 12305.

GOULD, GEORGE DOUGLAS, b. Berkeley, Calif, Dec. 20, 19; m. 45; c. 4. CHEMICAL ENGINEERING. B.S, California, 42; M.S, Mass. Inst. Tech, 47. Res. engr, Calif. Res. Corp, STANDARD OIL CO, CALIF, 47-57, supvry. res. engr, 57-59, staff engr, 59-65, SR. STAFF ENGR, CHEVRON RES. CO, 65- U.S.A, 42-46, Maj. Am. Inst. Chem. Eng. Petroleum process research with emphasis on oil shale evaluation and development plus related secondary recovery processes in oil field production; distillate hydrocracking; fuel oil desulfurization; catalytic reforming with bimetallic catalysts. Address: Chevron Research Co, 200 Bush St, San Francisco, CA 94120.

GOULD, GEORGE E(DWIN), b. Concordia, Kans, Apr. 22, 05; m. 29. ENTOMOLOGY. A.B, Kansas, 27, M.A, 29; Ph.D.(entomol), Purdue, 42. Asst. entomol, mus, Kansas, 27-28; asst. entomologist, Va. Truck Exp. Sta, 28-31; asst. entomologist, exp. sta, PURDUE UNIV, 31-38, assoc. entomologist, 38-44, asst. prof. ENTOMOL, 44-52, assoc. prof, 52-59, PROF, 59- Consult, W.B. McCloud & Co, Ill, 45, 46. AAAS; Entom. Soc. Am. Economic entomology; soil and vegetable insects. Address: Dept. of Entomology, Purdue University, Lafayette, IN 47907.

GOULD, G(ERALD) G(EZA), b. Budapest, Hungary, Nov. 17, 13; m. 41; c. 3. ELECTRICAL ENGINEERING. B.S, City Col, 35; M.S, Purdue, 36; Maryland. Elec. engr. develop. high voltage equip, Porcelain Prods, Inc, 36-40; signal syst, New York Subways, 40-42; proj. engr. frequency control, acoustics, U.S. Naval Ord. Lab, 46-51; chief engr. torpedo res. & develop, U.S. Navy Bur. Ord, 51-55, tech. dir, U.S. Naval Underwater Weapons Res. & Eng. Sta, 55-70, DEP. TECH. DIR, U.S. NAVAL UNDERWATER SYSTS. CTR, 70- Chmn, Undersea Warfare Res. & Develop. Planning Coun, 65-66; U.S. Navy Lab. Dirs. Coun, 67-69. Meritorious civilian serv. award, U.S. Navy, 56; superior accomplishment award, U.S. Naval Underwater Ord. Sta, 57, excellence in mgt. award, 65; excellence in tech. mgt. award, U.S. Naval Underwater Weapons Res. & Eng. Sta, 70. U.S.N.R, 42-70, Comdr. (Ret). Inst. Elec. & Electronics Eng; Nat. Soc. Prof. Eng; Acoust. Soc. Am. Management of research and development; underwater weapons systems; electrical generation; high voltage engineering. Address: U.S. Naval Underwater Systems Center, Newport, RI 02840.

GOULD, GORDON, b. N.Y.C, July 17, 20. PHYSICS. B.S, Union Col.(N.Y), 41; M.S, Yale, 42; M.S, Columbia Univ, 54. Lectr, Yale, 42-43; staff scientist, SAM Proj, Columbia Univ, 43-45, res. asst, univ, 55-58; res. scientist, Semon Bache Co, 45-47, consult, 47-54; staff scientist, TRG, Inc, Div. Control Data Corp, 58-67, asst. to pres. res. planning, 61-67; PROF. ELECTROPHYS, L.I. GRAD. CTR, POLYTECH. INST. BROOKLYN, 67- Summer engr, West. Elec. Co, 41; tutor, City Col. New York, 47-54; dir, Sphere, Inc, 71- Laser Indust. Asn.(pres, 71); Am. Phys. Soc; Optical Soc. Am. Gas physics; plasmas; thin films; molecular beams; lasers. Address: Long Island Graduate Center, Polytechnic Institute of Brooklyn, Route 110, Farmingdale, NY 11735.

GOULD, HARVEY A, b. Oakland, Calif, Sept. 4, 38. PHYSICS. Ph.D.(physics), California, Berkeley, 66. Nat. Res. Coun-Nat. Acad. Sci. res. fel, Nat. Bur. Standards, D.C, 66-67; asst. prof. PHYSICS, Univ. Mich, Ann Arbor, 67-71; ASSOC. PROF, CLARK UNIV, 71- Am. Phys. Soc. Many body theory; statistical mechanics. Address: Dept. of Physics, Clark University, Worcester, MA 01610.

GOULD, HENRY WADSWORTH, b. Portsmouth, Va, Aug. 26, 28; m. 69. MATHEMATICS. B.A, Virginia, 54, M.A, 56; North Carolina, 57-58. Instr. MATH, W.VA. UNIV, 58-61, asst. prof, 61-65, assoc. prof, 65-69, PROF, 69-, res. stipends, summers, 60 & 62. Consult, Sci. Serv, D.C, 59-60; Nat. Sci. Found. res. grant, 60- Sig.C, U.S.A, 51-52. Fel. AAAS; Am. Math. Soc; Math. Asn. Am; Soc. Indust. & Appl. Math; Ger. Math. Asn; Indian Nat. Acad. Sci; Polish Mat. Soc. Combinatorial analysis; theory of special functions; analytic and additive number theory; theory of binomial coefficient summations; history of mathematics. Address: Dept. of Mathematics, West Virginia University, Morgantown, WV 26506.

GOULD, HOWARD R(OSS), b. Adrian, W.Va, Nov. 10, 21; m. 48; c. 2. GEOLOGY. B.A, Minnesota, 43; California, 46-47; Ph.D.(geol), Southern California, 53. Training assoc, div. war res, California, 43-45, assoc. marine geologist, 46; asst. geol, Scripps Inst, California, 46-47, geologist, U.S. Geol. Surv, D.C, 47-54; asst. prof. oceanog, Washington (Seattle), 53-56; sr. geologist, geol. res. sect, Humble Oil & Ref. Co, 56-63, staff geologist, 63-64, chief, 64; mgr. stratig, & struct. geol. div, ESSO PROD. RES. CO, 64-66, mgr. stratig. geol. div, 66-67, RES. SCIENTIST, 67- Spec. consult, U.S. Navy. Civilian with Off. Sci. Res. & Develop, 44. AAAS; fel. Geol. Soc. Am; Soc. Econ. Paleont. & Mineral; Am. Asn. Petrol. Geol; Am. Geophys. Union. Sedimentation, especially in marine and lake environments; general geology of the sea floor; petroleum geology. Address: Esso Production Research Co, Box 2189, Houston, TX 77001.

GOULD, I(RA) A, (JR), b. Atchison, Kans, Sept. 28, 05; m. 29; c. 1. DAIRY INDUSTRY. B.S, West Virginia, 31; M.S, Mich. State Col, 33; fel, Wisconsin, 33-34, Ph.D.(dairy indust), 38. Asst. dairy, Mich. State Col, 31-33; instr. dairy mfg, 34-38, asst. prof, 38-42, assoc. prof, 42-44; prof, Univ. Md, 44-49; prof. dairy technol. & chmn. dept, Ohio State Univ, 49-70, CHIEF OF PARTY, OHIO STATE UNIV-U.S. AGENCY INT. DEVELOP. MISSION TO INDIA, 70- Asst, exp. sta, Mich. State Col, 34-42, assoc, 42-44; off. U.S. del, XIVth Int. Dairy Cong, Rome, 56, adv, XVth cong, London, 59, lectr, XVIth cong, Copenhagen, 62; consult, UNICEF, 60; Food & Agr. Orgn, 66. Fel. AAAS; Am. Chem. Soc.(Borden Award, 46); Am. Dairy Sci. Asn.(v.pres, 55, pres, 56, award of honor, 66); Inst. Food Technol; Am. Chem. Soc; Int. Asn. Milk, Food & Environ. Sanit. Biochemical and biophysical chemistry and microbiology of milk and dairy foods. Address: New Delhi (I.D), Dept. of State, Washington, DC 20521.

GOULD, JACK R(ICHARD), b. Brooklyn, N.Y, Feb. 28, 22; m. 45; c. 2. ORGANIC CHEMISTRY. B.A, Brooklyn Col, 43; M.S, Pa. State, 47, Dow Corning Corp. fel, 48-49, Ph.D.(org. chem), 49. Chemist res. & develop, Montrose Chem. Co, 43-45; asst. chem, Pa. State, 45-48; res. chemist petrochems, Houdry Process Corp, 49-51; proj. leader, Reaction Motors, Inc, Olin Mathieson Chem. Corp, 51-53, sect. head, chem. dept, 54-56; head org. chems. sect, Chauncey Res. Center, Stauffer Chem. Co, 56-63; dir. res, Metalsalts Corp, 63-64; mem. sr. staff contract res, res. & develop. dept, M.W. Kellogg Co, 64-69; SR. TECH. STAFF, COMT. AIR & WATER CONSERV, AM. PETROL. INST, 69- Am. Chem. Soc; N.Y. Acad. Sci; Sci. Res. Soc. Am; Air Pollution Control Asn. Organic and organometallic chemistry and industrial applications; boron hydrides and derivatives; nitrogen fluorides; high energy fuels and monopropellants; organic and organometallic biocides; air and water pollution control; oil spill control technology. Address: 6021 Neilwood Dr, Bethesda, MD 20852.

GOULD, LAURENCE McKINLEY, b. Lacota, Mich, Aug. 22, 96; m. 30. GEOLOGY. B.S, Michigan, 21, M.A, 23, Sc.D.(glacial geol), 25; hon. D.Sc, Polytech. Inst. Brooklyn, 31, Union Col, 58, Columbia, 59, Notre Dame, 60; LL.D, Coe Col, 45, Macalester Col, 46, Michigan, 54, Dartmouth Col, 59, N.Y. Univ, 59, Occidental Col, 61, Brandeis, 61, Col. Wooster, 62, Minnesota, 62, St. Olaf Col, 62, Harvard, 62, Kalamazoo Col, 63; L.H.D, Ripon Col, 51, Southwestern at Memphis, 53, Wayne State, 58, Carleton Col, 62; Litt.D, Chicago Med. Sch, 55. Instr. geol, Michigan, 21-26, asst. prof, 26-28; geologist, geographer & 2nd in command, Byrd Antarctic Exped, 28-30; assoc. prof. geol, Michigan, 30-32; prof. geol. & geog, Carleton Col, 32-62, pres, 45-62; PROF. GEOL, UNIV. ARIZ, 63- Asst. dir. & geologist, Univ. Mich. Greenland Exped, 26; geographer & topographer, Putnam Arctic Exped, 27. Mem. Nat. Sci. Bd, 53-62, chmn. comt. polar res, Nat. Acad. Sci, 58-; pres, Sci. Comt. Antarctic Res, 63-70; mem. U.S. nat. comt. & dir. U.S. antarctic prog, Int. Geophys. Year, 57-59. Cong. Gold Medal, 31; Gold Medal, Chicago Geog. Soc, 31; Cross of St. Olaf, Norway, 49; Explorers Club Medal, 59; U.S. Navy Distinguished Pub. Serv. Medal, 57. Ambulance Serv, U.S.A, 16-18; chief arctic sect, Arctic Desert & Tropic Info. Ctr, U.S.A.A.F, 42-44. AAAS (chmn. bd. dir, 65, pres, 64); fel. Geol. Soc. Am; Am. Geog. Soc.(David Livingston Gold Medal, 30). Geology and glaciology of Antarctica; Pleistocene geology of Upper Mississippi Valley; geology of Baffin Island; strategy and politics in the polar areas; Antarctica in world affairs; antarctic prospect, the polar regions and their relations to human affairs. Address: Dept. of Geosciences, University of Arizona, Tucson, AZ 85721.

GOULD, LAWRENCE, b. Boston, Mass, Nov. 28, 30; m. 53; c. 2. PHYSICS. S.B, Mass. Inst. Tech, 50; Ph.D.(physics), 54. Res. physicist, MICROWAVE ASSOCS, INC, 53-54, v.pres. & mgr, tube div, 56-64, exec. v.pres. & gen. mgr, 64-69, PRES, 69- U.S.A, 54-56. Am. Phys. Soc; sr. mem. Inst. Elec. & Electronics Eng. Gaseous and physical electronics; microwave devices; utilizing ionized media, ferrites and semiconductors. Address: 71 Sevland Rd, Newton, MA 02159.

GOULD, LAWRENCE A, b. Brooklyn, N.Y, Dec. 15, 30; m. 57; c. 2. INTERNAL MEDICINE, CARDIOLOGY. B.A, Brooklyn Col, 52; M.D, N.Y. Univ, 56. Clin. instr. med, N.Y. Med. Col, 62-65; asst. chief cardiol. serv, Bronx Vet. Admin. Hosp, N.Y, 65-67, chief cardiol. serv, 65-69; CHIEF CARDIAC CATHETERIZATION LAB, MISERICORDIA-FORDHAM HOSP, 69- Asst. prof, Albert Einstein Col. Med, 70- Dipl, Nat. Bd. Med. Exam, Am. Bd. Internal Med. & Am. Bd. Cardiovasc. Disease. Med.C, U.S.A, 57-59, Capt. Am. Heart Asn; fel. Am. Col. Physicians; fel. Am. Col. Cardiol; Am. Fedn. Clin. Res. Clinical research of the cardiovascular system; cardiac hemodynamic studies. Address: Misericordia-Fordham Hospital, 600 E. 233rd St, Bronx, NY 10466.

GOULD, LAWRENCE P(EABODY), b. Wash, D.C, Feb. 28, 07; m. 33; c. 3. CHEMISTRY. B.Ch, Cornell Univ, 29, Ph.D.(chem), 33. Chemist, Indust. Chem. Div, Allied Chem. Corp, 33-70; DIR. RES. & DEVELOP, ASPEN INDUSTS. INC, 70- AAAS; Am. Chem. Soc; fel. Am. Inst. Chem. The hydrols; heavy chemicals. Address: 608 Cumberland Ave, Syracuse, NY 13210.

GOULD, LEONARD A(BRAHAM), b. Brooklyn, N.Y, Nov. 20, 27; m. 59. ELECTRICAL ENGINEERING. S.B, Mass. Inst. Tech, 48, Sc.D.(elec. eng), 53. Asst. ELEC. ENG, MASS. INST. TECHNOL, 48-50, instr, 50-53, asst. prof, 53-60, assoc. prof, 60-68, PROF, 68-, ASSOC. DIR, ELECTRONIC SYSTS. LAB, 69- Fulbright res. fel, Tech. Univ. Denmark, 57; vis. prof, dept. appl. physics, Michelson Inst, Bergen, Norway, 68-69. Inst. Elec. & Electronics Eng; Am. Inst. Chem. Eng. Chemical process control; dynamic behavior and control of distributed systems; systems science. Address: 49 Forty Acres Dr, Wayland, MA 01778.

GOULD, MARTIN JAMES, b. Houston, Tex, Mar. 30, 15; m. 54; c. 1. PHYSICS, GEOPHYSICS. B.A, Rice, 35, M.A, 36, fel, 36-37; Ph.D.(appl. geophys), Calif. Inst. Tech, 41. Res. physicist, geophys. res. lab, Stanolind Oil & Gas Co, 39-40; assoc. physicist magnetics, Naval Ord. Lab, 41-42, assoc. engr. aircraft radar, 42-43, prin. engr. spec. weapons, 43-45; consult. geophys, 46-56; res. specialist, RCA Missile Test Ctr, 56-57; dir. res. nat. electronics lab, Thiokol Chem. Corp, 57-58; mem. tech. staff, space tech. labs, Thompson Ramo Wooldridge, Inc, 58-60; space physics lab, Aerospace Corp, 60-61; head electromagnetics res, NORTHROP SPACE LABS, HAWTHORNE, 61-62, chief space detection systs, electromagnetics syst. group, 62-65, SCIENTIST, 65- Inst. Elec. & Electronics Eng; Am. Inst. Aeronaut. & Astronaut; Soc. Explor. Geophys. Optical space tracking and communications systems; geophysical environmental noise problems in detection of radiating and illuminated target sources; earth resources remote sensing from satellites; offshore oil production underwater technology. Address: 7 Williamsburg Lane, Rolling Hills, CA 90274.

GOULD, M(AX) R(ANDALL), b. Beloit, Kans, Feb. 25, 24; m. 48; c. 4. CHEMISTRY. B.S, Kans. State Col, 50. Res. chemist, QUAKER OATS CO, 50-53, proj. leader, 53-57, group leader, 57-63, group mgr, food res, 63-68, mgr, 68-71, ASST. DIR. RES. & DEVELOP. CEREALS, 71- U.S.N, 43-46. Am. Asn. Cereal Chem; Inst. Food Tech. Product development. Address: Quaker Oats Co, 617 W. Main St, Barrington, IL 60010.

GOULD, M(ERLE) L(ESTER), b. Hitchcock, S.Dak, Mar. 10, 19; m. 42; c. 3. CHEMICAL ENGINEERING. B.Sc, Nebraska, 43. Chem. engr, process design, Shell Develop. Co, 43-51; chief develop. engr, Vulcan Copper & Supply Co, 51-53; res. chemist, ETHYL CORP, 53-54, supvr. process design & develop, 54-57, asst. dir. chem. res. & develop, 57-59, asst. dir. commercial develop, 59-63, dir, 63-64, trade rels, 64-66, GEN. MGR, INDUST. CHEM. DIV, 66- Am. Chem. Soc; Am. Inst. Chem. Eng. Development of petrochemical processes and markets. Address: Ethyl Corp, Ethyl Tower, 451 Florida, Baton Rouge, LA 70801.

GOULD, PHILLIP, b. New York, N.Y, Feb. 19, 40; m. 64; c. 2. MECHANICAL ENGINEERING. B.M.E, City Col. New York, 61; S.M, Mass. Inst. Tech, 63, Sc.D.(mech. eng), 65. Asst. prof. mech. eng, Mass. Inst. Tech, 65-67; MEM. SYSTS. EVAL. DIV, INST. FOR DEFENSE ANAL, 67- Fel. eng, Mass. Inst. Tech, 65-67. AAAS; Am. Inst. Aeronaut. & Astronaut; Am. Soc. Mech. Eng; Opers. Res. Soc. Am. Continuum mechanics; operations analysis. Address: Systems Evaluation Division, Institute for Defense Analyses, 400 Army-Navy Dr, Arlington, VA 22202.

GOULD, PHILLIP L, b. Chicago, Ill, May 24, 37; m. 61; c. 3. STRUCTURAL ENGINEERING, SOLID MECHANICS. B.S, Univ. Ill, Urbana, 59, univ. fel. & M.S, 60; NASA trainee, Northwest. Univ, 64, Ph.D.(civil eng), 66. Struct. designer, Skidmore, Owings & Merrill, Ill, 60-63; prin. struct. engr, Westenhoff & Novick, 63-64; asst. prof. CIVIL & ENVIRON. ENG, WASH. UNIV, 66-68, ASSOC. PROF, 68- Consult, design of shell roof struct, 66- Ord.C,

U.S.A, 59-60 & 63, 1st Lt. Am. Soc. Civil Eng; Am. Soc. Eng. Educ; Am. Acad. Mech; Int. Asn. Shell Struct. Analysis and design of multistory building frames, highway bridges, shell roof structures, and pressure vessels; development of computer-based numerical techniques for the analysis of thin shells and human hearts. Address: School of Engineering & Applied Science, Washington University, St. Louis, MO 63130.

GOULD, R(OBERT) GORDON, b. Chicago, Ill, June 24, 09; m. 39; c. 2. BIO-CHEMISTRY. B.S, Harvard, 30, Ph.D.(org. chem), 33. Instr. & tutor biochem. sci, Harvard, 31-34; fel. chem, Nat. Res. Coun, Columbia, 34-35; instr. biochem. & org. chem, Iowa, 35-36; asst. chem. pharmacol, Rockefeller Inst, 36-42; assoc. bact, Harvard Med. Sch, 42-43, biochem, 46-47; assoc. prof, col. med, Illinois & assoc. attend. biochemist, Presby. Hosp, 47-52; sect. leader biochem, Los Alamos Sci. Lab, California, 51-60; ASSOC. PROF. BIOCHEM. IN MED, SCH. MED, STANFORD UNIV, 60- Spec. res. fel, U.S. Pub. Health Serv, 56-57, 66-67. Consult, Argonne Nat. Lab, 47-51; U.S. Pub. Health Serv, 54-58, 61-65; Lilly Co, 53-55; Vets. Admin. Hosp, Stanford, 62-, varian, 70-; Calif. State Dept. Pub. Health, 67. Mem, coun. arteriosclerosis, Am. Heart Asn, pres, 57-58. Sanit.C, 43-46, Capt. Am. Soc. Biol. Chem; Soc. Exp. Biol. & Med; Royal Soc. Med. Sterol biosynthesis and metabolism; action of radiation on biosynthetic processes; mechanism of action of hormones; atherosclerosis. Address: Dept. of Medicine, School of Medicine, Stanford University, Palo Alto, CA 94304.

GOULD, ROBERT H(ENDERSON), b. Three Rivers, Mich, Feb. 4, 19; m. 43; c. 3. PHYSICS. B.A, Col. Wooster, 40; fel, La. State, 40-42, M.S, 42. Proj. engr, Sperry Gyroscope Co, N.Y, 42-46; asst. prof. physics & res. dept. head, Champlain Col, 46-53; physicist, adv. electronics ctr, Gen. Elec. Co, 53-60, adv. systs. engr, flight test opers, 60-64, proj. engr, reentry systs. dept, 64-65, mgr. MOL Segment Test Integration, 65-69, systs. engr, aerospace electronics dept, 69-70; ASST. DEAN TECHNOL, TOMPKINS-CORTLAND COMMUNITY COL, 70- Am. Phys. Soc; Sci. Res. Soc. Am. Academic administration; occupational curriculum development; management of research and development programs; undergraduate teaching. Address: 1 Berkshire Dr, Dryden, NY 13053.

GOULD, ROBERT JOSEPH, b. Providence, R.I, May 31, 35; m. 65. THEO-RETICAL PHYSICS, ASTROPHYSICS. B.S, Providence Col, 57; Ph.D.(theoret. physics), Cornell, 63. Res. physicist, UNIV. CALIF, SAN DIEGO, 63-64, asst. res. physicist, 64-65, asst. prof. PHYSICS, 65-68, ASSOC. PROF, 68- Sr. lectr, Univ. Sydney, 68-69. Am. Phys. Soc; Am. Astron. Soc. Theoretical astrophysics; atomic processes in low-density plasmas; high-energy phenomena in astrophysics. Address: Dept. of Physics, University of California at San Diego, P.O. Box 109, La Jolla, CA 92037.

GOULD, ROBERT K, b. Gloucester, Mass, Jan. 4, 29; m. 58; c. 1. PHYSICS. B.S, Maine, 51; M.S, Brown, 56, Ph.D.(physics), 61. Asst. prof. PHYSICS, Muskingum Col, 57-59; Lafayette Col, 60-64, assoc. prof, 64-68; PROF. & CHMN. DEPT, MIDDLEBURY COL, 68- Acoustical Soc. Am; Am. Asn. Physics Teachers. High intensity sound and interaction of sound and heat transfer in liquids. Address: Dept. of Physics, Middlebury College, Middlebury, VT 05753.

GOULD, ROBERT WILLIAM, b. Shanghai, China, Feb. 5, 34; U.S. citizen; m. 55; c. 4. METALLURGY. B.S, Florida, 55, M.S, 62, Ford fel. & Ph.D. (metall), 64; Pa. State, 55-57. Field engr, Am. Cyanamid Co, 57; res. engr, Kaiser Aluminum & Chem. Corp, 57-59; instr. METALL, UNIV. FLA, 59-62, asst. prof, 64-68, ASSOC. PROF, 68- X-ray diffraction; small angle x-ray scattering; precipitation in metallic and ceramic systems; fatigue; radiography; x-ray spectroscopy. Address: Dept. of Metallurgy & Materials Engineering, University of Florida, Gainesville, FL 32601.

GOULD, ROY W(ALTER), b. Los Angeles, Calif, Apr. 25, 27; m. 52; c. 2. ELECTRICAL ENGINEERING, PHYSICS. B.S, Calif. Inst. Technol, 49, Ph.D.(physics), 56; M.S, Stanford, 50. Res. engr. missile guid, jet propulsion lab, Calif. Inst. Technol, 51-52; electron tubes, Hughes Aircraft Co, 53-55; asst. prof. elec. eng, CALIF. INST. TECHNOL, 55-58, assoc. prof, ELEC. ENG. & PHYSICS, 58-62, PROF, 62- Nat. Sci. Found. sr. fel, 63-64; asst. dir. res, U.S. Atomic Energy Comn, D.C, 70- U.S.N, 45-46. Fel. Am. Phys. Soc; fel. Inst. Elec. & Electronics Eng; Nat. Acad. Eng. Electron and ion dynamics; plasma oscillation and wave phenomena; physics of ionized gases; electromagnetism; microwaves; plasma physics; controlled thermonuclear fusion. Address: U.S. Atomic Energy Commission, Washington, DC 20545.

GOULD, STEPHEN JAY, b. New York, N.Y, Sept. 10, 41; m. 65; c. 1. PALEONTOLOGY, EVOLUTIONARY BIOLOGY. A.B, Antioch Col, 63; Nat. Sci. Found. fel, Columbia, 63-67, Ph.D.(paleont), 67. Asst. prof. GEOL, Antioch Col, 66; HARVARD, 67-71, ASSOC. PROF, 71- Nat. Sci. Found. grant, 69-71. AAAS; Paleont. Soc; Soc. Study Evolution; Soc. Syst. Zool; Am. Soc. Nat; Brit. Palaeont. Asn. Evolutionary paleontology; quantitative studies of form, function and ontogeny in relation to phylogeny; evolution and speciation in land snails; systematic zoology; history and philosophy of geology and evolutionary biology. Address: Museum of Comparative Zoology, Harvard University, Cambridge, MA 02138.

GOULD, S(YDNEY) H(ENRY), b. Ilderton, Ont, Jan. 25, 09; m. 37; c. 3. MATHEMATICS. B.A, Toronto, 29; Ph.D.(classics), Yale, 33; M.A, Columbia, 38. Master Latin, Milton Acad, Mass, 30-31; Seymour fel. Acropolis inscriptions, Am. Sch. Classical Studies, Athens, 34; instr. classics, Yale, 34-35; from lectr. to asst. prof, Toronto, 35-43; res. off, Nat. Res. Coun. Can, 43-45; assoc. prof. classics, Toronto, 45-47; asst. prof. math, Purdue, 47-55; prof, Williams Col, 55-56; exec. ed, Math. Rev, 56-62; ED. TRANS, AM. MATH. SOC, 62- Vis. lectr, Kansas, 53; res. assoc, Brown, 56-59, vis. lectr, 59-60. Am. Math. Soc; Math. Asn. Am. Influence of mathematics on English literature; Eigenvalue theory; dialect of Archimedes; translation of Cardan and foreign mathematics. Address: American Mathematical Society, P.O. Box 6248, Providence, RI 02904.

GOULD, SYDNEY WARD, b. Sandusky, Ohio, Sept. 14, 95; m. 21; c. 2. TAX-ONOMY. B.S, U.S. Mil. Acad, 19, B.S, Mass. Inst. Tech, 21. Asst. secy. to v.pres, Lomas & Nettleton Co, Conn, 22-42, v.pres, 46-51; DIR. INT. PLANT INDEX FOR NEW YORK BOT. GARDEN & CONN. AGR. EXP. STA,

NEW HAVEN, 60- C.Eng, 18-22, 42-45, Col. AAAS; Am. Soc. Plant Taxon; Inst. Asn. Plant Taxon; Bot. Soc. Am. Data processing; computers in botany; preparation of geo-code for defining areas of earth by four letter symbols. Address: 5 Opening Hill Rd, Madison, CT 06443.

GOULD, THELMA B(ERNICE) C(LARK), b. Detroit, Mich, Feb. 8, 25. PHARMACOLOGY. B.S, Michigan, 47, M.S, 48, Ph.D.(pharmacol), 51. Asst. physiol, med. sch. Michigan, 47-48; pharmacol, California, 48-49; Michigan, 49-51, res. assoc, 52-53; Inst. Int. Ed. exchange fel, Switz, 51-52; res. assoc, Cancer Inst. Miami, 53-55; res. instr, PATH, SCH. MED, UNIV. MIAMI, 55-58, res. asst. prof, 58-62, RES. ASSOC. PROF, 62- Am. Soc. Exp. Path; Soc. Study Reproduction. Zinc and trace elements in reproductive endocrinology; cadmium carcinogenesis. Address: 1532 Siena Ave, Coral Gables, FL 33146.

GOULD, WALTER L(EONARD), b. Burlington, Wyo, Apr. 5, 23; m. 47; c. 3. AGRONOMY. B.S, Wyoming, 48, M.S, 57; Ph.D.(field crops), Oregon State, 64. Conservationist, soil conserv. serv, U.S. Dept. Agr, 48-56, agronomist, agr. res. serv, 64-66; instr. AGRON, N.MEX. STATE UNIV, 57-60, asst. prof, 66-69, ASSOC. PROF, 69- U.S.N, 43-46. Weed Sci. Soc. Am. Weed control in field and vegetable crops and on rangeland; control of brush on rangeland. Address: Dept. of Agronomy, New Mexico State University, Las Cruces, NM 88001.

GOULD, WALTER PHILLIP, b. North Adams, Mass, July 14, 25; m. 54; c. 2. FORESTRY, WILDLIFE MANAGEMENT. B.S, Massachusetts, 50; M.F, Yale, 51; Ph.D.(forest shrub ecol), Syracuse Univ, 66. Forester, Brown Co, 51-54; ASSOC. PROF. FOREST & WILDLIFE MGT. & CHMN. DEPT, UNIV. R.I, 54- Fel, Mem. Univ. Newf, 67-68. U.S.A.A.F, 43-46. Soc. Am. Foresters; Wildlife Soc. Effects of silvicultural practices on the ecology of forest wildlife species. Address: Dept. of Forest & Wildlife Management, University of Rhode Island, Kingston, RI 02881.

GOULD, WENDELL O(LIVER), b. Kalispel, Mont, July 5, 10; m. 36; c. 2. PHYSICS. B.S. & M.S, Wash. State, 30, fel, 34-36; fel, Calif. Inst. Technol, 36-40. Equip. engr, Bell Tel. Labs, Inc, 30-32; asst. chief engr, Mitchell Camera Corp, Calif, 40-44; tech. aide, Off. Sci. Res. & Develop, 44-47; sci. warfare adv, Res. & Develop. Bd, 47-52; proj. engr. & gen. mgr, Hydrofoil Corp, 52-54; consult, Nat. Res. Coun, 54-55; unit chief, Boeing Co, 55-70; V.PRES, TEMPS RES, INC, 70- AAAS; Optical Soc. Am. Objective and quantitative determination of graininess of photographic emulsions; growth of single crystals. Address: 5720 S. Morgan Place, Seattle, WA 98118.

GOULD, WILBUR A(LPHONSO), b. Colebrook, N.H, Aug. 7, 20; m. 44; c. 3. HORTICULTURE, FOOD TECHNOLOGY. B.S, New Hampshire, 42; M.S, Ohio State, 47, Ph.D.(hort, food tech), 49. Plant breeder, Ferry-Morse Seed Co, 42; food inspector, U.S. Dept. Agr, 43-44; instr. HORT, OHIO STATE UNIV, 47-49, asst. prof, 49-52, assoc. prof, 52-56, PROF. & HEAD DIV. FOOD PROCESSING, 56- Food consult, annual fine food expos, Germany, U.S. Dept. Agr, 59. U.S.N, 44-46. Fel. AAAS; Am. Soc. Hort. Sci; Inst. Food Tech. Quality evaluation and control in food processing especially plant efficiencies; new product development; food regulations and standards. Address: Division of Food Processing, Ohio State University, Columbus, OH 43085.

GOULD, WILLIAM ALLEN, b. Clearfield, Pa, Dec. 3, 41; m. 65; c. 2. MATH-EMATICS, COMPUTER SCIENCE. B.S, Elizabethtown Col, 63; M.A, Pa. State Univ, 66, Ed.D.(math), 71. Instr. math, SHIPPENSBURG STATE COL, 66-68, asst. prof, 68-69, assoc. prof, 69-70, ASST. DIR. COMPUT. CTR, 70- Math. Asn. Am. Solution preserving operators for three-dimensional second order partial differential equations; computer simulation of the academic course loadings. Address: Computer Center, Shippensburg State College, Shippensburg, PA 17257.

GOULD, WILLIAM E, b. Orange, N.J, May 7, 34. MATHEMATICS. B.A, Rutgers, 56, M.S, 58; M.A, Princeton, 64, Nat. Sci. Found. fel, 65-66, Ph.D. (math), 66. Instr. MATH, Rutgers, 61-62; Washington Col, 62-66; assoc. prof, Bradley, 66-69; ASSOC. PROF, CALIF. STATE. COL, DOMINGUEZ HILLS, 69- Math. Asn. Am; Asn. Symbolic Logic. Logic. Address: Dept. of Mathematics, California State College at Dominguez Hills, 1000 E. Victoria St, Dominguez Hills, CA 90246.

GOULD, WILLIAM ROBERT, III, b. Cincinnati, Ohio, Nov. 16, 31; m. 62; c. 2. ZOOLOGY. B.S, Colorado State, 54; M.S, Okla. State, 60, Ph.D.(zool), 62. Nat. Insts. Health fel, 62-63; prog. leader, Bur. Commercial Fisheries, U.S. Fish & Wildlife Serv, 63; ASST. LEADER MONT. COOP. FISHERY UNIT, MONT. STATE UNIV, 64- Med.C, U.S.A, 55-57, Res, 57-62. Am. Fisheries Soc; Am. Soc. Ichthyol. & Herpet. Biology and ecology of fishes; biology of aquatic insects. Address: Dept. of Zoology and Entomology, Montana State University, Bozeman, MT 59715.

GOULD-SOMERO, MEREDITH, b. Billings, Mont, Feb. 2, 40; m. 68. DE-VELOPMENTAL BIOLOGY. B.A, Mt. Holyoke Col, 61; Nat. Sci. Found. fel, Duke Univ, 61-62; U.S. Pub. Health Serv. fel, Stanford Univ, 62-66, Ph.D. (biol), 67. U.S. Pub. Health Serv. fel. biochem, Univ. Wash, 67-68; fel. zool, Univ. B.C, 68-70; RES. BIOLOGIST, UNIV. CALIF, SAN DIEGO, 70- Am. Soc. Zool; Soc. Develop. Biol. Biochemistry of marine invertebrate development; spermatogenesis; male sterility; germ cell and sex determination in Drosophila. Address: Dept. of Biology, University of California, San Diego, P.O. Box 109, La Jolla, CA 92037.

GOULDEN, CLYDE E(DWARD), b. Kansas City, Kans, Nov. 30, 36; m. 57; c. 2. ECOLOGY, LIMNOLOGY. B.S, Kans. State Teachers Col, 58, M.S, 59; Ph.D.(zool), Indiana, 62. Res. assoc. limnol, Yale, 62-64; lectr. BIOL, 63-64, asst. prof, 64-66; lectr, UNIV. PA, 66-67, ADJ. ASSOC. PROF, 70-; ASSOC. CURATOR, DEPT. LIMNOL, ACAD. NATURAL SCI, 66- Res. grants, Am. Philos. Soc. Penrose fund & Soc. Sigma Xi, 64; exchange scientist, cultural exchange prog, Acad. Sci, U.S.S.R-Nat. Acad. Sci, 66; Nat. Sci. Found, 67- AAAS; Am. Soc. Nat; Soc. Study Evolution; Ecol. Soc. Am. (ed, Aquatics, Ecol). Ecology and systematics of the Cladocera; paleolimnology; evolution of the aquatic community. Address: Dept. of Limnology, Academy of Natural Sciences, 19th & The Parkway, Philadelphia, PA 19103.

GOULDEN, C(YRIL) H(AROLD), b. Bridgend, Wales, June 2, 97; m. 29; c. 2. GENETICS, STATISTICS. B.S.A, Saskatchewan, 21, M.S.A, 23, hon. L.L.D, 54; Ph.D.(plant breeding), Minnesota, 25; hon. D.Sc, Manitoba, 64. Cerealist, Saskatchewan, 21-23; officer-in-charge, cereal breeding lab, Dom. Exp. Farms, Man, 25-48, chief cereal div, exp. farms serv, Can. Dept. Agr, 48-55, dir, 55-59, asst. dep. minister, res. br, 59-62; PROJ. OFFICER AGR, CAN. CORP. WORLD EXHIB. 67, MONTREAL, QUE, 65- Biomet. Soc.(pres, 58); fel. Am. Statist. Asn; fel. Royal Soc. Can; Agr. Inst. Can. (pres, 55-56); Prfnl. Inst. Can. Pub. Serv.(Gold medal, 53). Plant breeding; genetics; biometry. Address: 10 Kitimat Crescent, Ottawa, Ont. K2H 7G5, Can.

GOULDING, C(HARLES) E(DWIN), JR, b. Tampa, Fla, Nov. 23, 16; m. 50. ENGINEERING. B.S, Tampa, 39; M.S, Florida, 44, scholar, 44-46, Ph.D. (chem), 46. Asst. to plant supt, E. Mugge Co, 35-38; plant chemist, U.S. Phosphoric Co, 39-41; lab. instr. inorg. chem, Florida, 41-46; consult. engr. & consult. chemist, Instituto Nacional de Obras Sanitarias, 46-50; eng. consult, 47-51; tech. coordinator, Wyeth Int, Ltd, 51-54; proj. mgr. & engr. in charge, Bioquimica, S.A, 54-58; int. chem. process consult, 58-63; dir. naval nuclear training, N.Y. Shipbldg. Corp, 63-64; consult, domestic chem. & biol. process, 65-68; scholar, Moore Sch. Elec. Eng, Univ. Pa, 66-68; vis. lectr. sci, Univ. Chattanooga, 68-69; consult, environ. pollution, 69-71; ENVIRON. CONSULT, E.H. RICHARDSON ASSOCS, 71- AAAS; Am. Chem. Soc; Inst. Elec. & Electronics Eng; Am. Inst. Chem. Eng; Instrument Soc. Am; Am. Soc. Training & Develop; Venezuelan Col. Eng. Electrical and chemical characteristics and their interrelation in the water molecule. Address: E.H. Richardson Associates, P.O. Box 675, 153 E. Chestnut Hill Rd, Newark, DE 19711.

GOULDING, ROBERT LEE, JR, b. Daytona Beach, Fla, June 29, 20; m. 44; c. 3. ENTOMOLOGY. B.S, Florida, 46; M.S, Ohio State, 48, Ph.D.(entom), 55. Entomologist insects affecting man & animal, U.S. Dept. Agr, 48-49; Fla. State Bd. Health, 49-53; asst. prof. ENTOM, ORE. STATE UNIV, 55-63, assoc. prof, 63-70, PROF, 71-, RES. COORD, ENVIRON. HEALTH SCI. CTR, 68- U.S.A.A.F, 41-44, Sgt. Entom. Soc. Am; Mosquito Control Asn. Biology and control of arthropods affecting livestock and other animals. Address: Dept. of Entomology, Oregon State University, Corvallis, OR 97331.

GOULET, MARCEL, b. Quebec, Que, Nov. 7, 31; m. 59; c. 5. WOOD PHYSICS. B.A, Laval, 50, B.Sc, 54; D.Sc.(wood tech), Munich, 59. PROF. WOOD TECHNOL, LAVAL UNIV, 59- Forest Prod. Res. Soc; Soc. Wood Sci. & Tech. Wood-moisture and wood-temperature relationships. Address: Faculty of Forestry, Laval University, Quebec 10, Que, Can.

GOULET, NORMAND R(OBERT), b. New Bedford, Mass, Apr. 18, 30; m. 58; c. 1. VIROLOGY. B.S, Providence Col, 51; M.S, Michigan, 53, Ph.D.(epidemiol. sci), 58. Virologist, Nat. Drug Co, 58-59; assoc. virologist, Merck Sharp & Dohme Div, 59-61; MEM. STAFF, res. labs, Nat. Drug Co, 61-65; gen. res. support br, NAT. INSTS. HEALTH, 65-70, GEN. CLIN. RES. CTRS. BR, 70- Co-adj. instr, Rutgers Univ, 64-65; mem, Found. Adv. Educ. in Sci; Ctr. for Study Democratic Insts. AAAS; Tissue Cult. Asn; Am. Soc. Microbiol; Soc. Indust. Microbiol; Am. Pharmaceut. Asn; N.Y. Acad. Sci; World Future Soc. Biological sciences; immunology. Address: 7545 Spring Lake Dr, Bethesda, MD 20034.

GOULEY, ROMEO W(ORDEN), b. Salem, Ore, Jan. 10, 20; m. 44; c. 4. ORGANIC CHEMISTRY. B.A, Willamette, 40; M.S, Ore. State Col, 41; Ph.D. (chem), Northwestern, 44. Fel. chem, Pa. State Col, 44-45; supt. crop prod, Yakima Chief Ranches, Wash, 53-57; res. technologist, petrol, Shell Oil Co, 57-61; mem. staff, tech. sales, Evanstrom Co, 61-64; sect. head pilot plant, res. & develop. labs, KAISER ALUMINUM & CHEM. CORP, 64-66, tech. supt, 66-68, MGR. ENG. SERV, CTR. TECHNOL, 68- Am. Chem. Soc. Product development. Address: Center for Technology, Kaiser Aluminum & Chemical Corp, P.O. Box 870, Pleasanton, CA 94566.

GOULIAN, MEHRAN, b. Weehawken, N.J, Dec. 31, 29; m. 61; c. 3. HEMATOLOGY. A.B, Columbia, 50, M.D, 54. Intern, Barnes Hosp, St. Louis, Mo, 54-55; resident med, Mass. Gen. Hosp, Boston, 58-59, 61; fel. hemat, sch. med, Yale, 59-60; res. fel, Harvard Univ. & Mass. Gen. Hosp, 60, 62-63, instr, 63-65; fel. biochem, sch. med, Stanford, 65-67; assoc. prof. med. & biochem, Univ. Chicago, 67-70; PROF. MED, UNIV. CALIF, SAN DIEGO, 70- U.S.P.H.S, 55-57, Clin. Assoc. Biochemistry of nucleic acids. Address: Dept. of Medicine, University of California, San Diego, P.O. Box 109, La Jolla, CA 92037.

GOULIANOS, KONSTANTIN, b. Salonica, Greece, Nov. 9, 35; m. 63. HIGH ENERGY PHYSICS. Fulbright scholar, Columbia, 58, M.A, 60, Ph.D.(physics), 63. Res. assoc. PHYSICS, Columbia, 63-64; instr, Princeton, 64-67, asst. prof, 67-71; ASSOC. PROF, ROCKEFELLER UNIV, 71- High energy interactions; time reversal invariance. Address: Rockefeller University, New York, NY 10021.

GOULSON, HILTON T(HOMAS), b. Montevideo, Minn, May 4, 30; m. 54; c. 2. PARASITOLOGY. A.B, Luther Col,(Iowa), 52; M.S.P.H, North Carolina, 53, Ph.D.(parasitol), 57. Instr. PARASITOL, SCH. PUB. HEALTH, UNIV. N.C, CHAPEL HILL, 54-57, res. assoc, 57-59, asst. prof, 59-61, assoc. prof, 61-69, PROF, 69- Am. Soc. Trop. Med. & Hyg; Am. Soc. Parasitol; fel. Am. Pub. Health Asn. Medical parasitology; immunity studies and host-parasite relationships of nematode parasites. Address: Dept. of Parasitology & Lab. Practice, University of North Carolina, Chapel Hill, NC 27514.

GOUNARIS, ANNE DEMETRA, b. Boston, Mass, Oct. 24, 27. BIOCHEMISTRY. A.B, Boston, 55; Du Pont fel, Radcliffe Col, 57-58, Nat. Insts. Health fel, 58-59, Ph.D.(chem), 60. Nat. Insts. Health res. fels, Brookhaven Nat. Lab, 60-62; Nat. Insts. Health fel, Carlsberg Lab, Denmark, 62-63, Rast-Østed Found. fel, 63-64; res. assoc. enzyme action & protein structure, Rockefeller Inst, 64-66; asst. prof. biochem, VASSAR COL, 66-68, ASSOC. PROF, 68- Summers, res. assoc, Brookhaven Nat. Lab, 64; Nat. Insts. Health grant, 68-71. AAAS; Am. Chem. Soc; N.Y. Acad. Sci. Pyruvic acid dehydrogenase system of Escherichia coli; mechanism phospho gluco mutase; modification of subtilisin; thiamine pyrophosphate requiring enzymes; alpha-keto decarboxylase. Address: Dept. of Chemistry, Vassar College, Poughkeepsie, NY 12601.

GOURARY, BARRY S(HOLOM), b. Rostov, Russia, Feb. 10, 23; nat; m. 53; c. 2. THEORETICAL PHYSICS. A.M, Columbia, 50. Asst, radiation lab, Columbia, 47-50, lectr, math, 50-51; physicist, sound sect, Nat. Bur. Standards, 51; mem. sr. staff, appl. physics lab, Hopkins, 51-59, prin. staff, 59-60; fel. physicist, res. labs, Westinghouse Elec. Corp, 60, supvry. physicist, 61, mgr. luminescence sect, 61-62; sr. staff scientist, res. labs, United Aircraft Corp, 62-68; dir. electronic & optical technol, defense-space group, INT. TEL. & TEL. CORP, 68-70, tech. dir. electron tube div, 70, dir. technol, defense-space group, 70-71, MGT. CONSULT, 71- Fel. Am. Phys. Soc; Inst. Elec. & Electronics Eng; Am. Statist. Asn; N.Y. Acad. Sci; Am. Ord. Asn; Am. Mgt. Asn; Soc. Photog. Sci. & Eng; Optical Soc. Am. Solid state physics; electromagnetic theory; quantum mechanics; device theory; management science. Address: 187 Gates Ave, Montclair, NJ 07042.

GOURARY, MINA H(ASKIND), b. Gomel, Russia, Oct. 1, 23; nat; m. 53; c. 2. STATISTICS. B.A, Brooklyn Col, 46; M.A, Columbia, 49; M.B.A, Univ. Hartford, 68. Computist, logistics res. proj, George Washington, 50-54, res. assoc, 54-57, sr. res. scientist, 57-61; OPERS. RES. CONSULT, 61- Opers. Res. Soc. Am; Am. Statist. Asn. Inventory control theory; naval logistics; operations research; investment analysis and portfolio management. Address: 187 Gates Ave, Montclair, NJ 07042.

GOURAS, PETER, b. Brooklyn, N.Y, Apr. 15, 30; m. 59; c. 3. PHYSIOLOGY. A.B, Hopkins, 51, M.D, 55. Intern surg, Hopkins, 55-56; res. assoc. physiol, Nat. Insts. Health, 56-57; Nat. Found. fel, Cambridge, 58-59; assoc. physiol, med. sch, Pennsylvania, 59-60; res. assoc. ophthal. & physiol, NAT. INSTS. HEALTH, 60-68, chief sect. ophthal. physiol, Nat. Inst. Neurol. Diseases & Blindness, 68-71, HEAD SECT. PHYSIOL, LAB. VISION RES, NAT. EYE INST, 71- Mem. comt. vision res. & training, Nat. Eye Inst, 70-; comt. sensory prosthesis, Nat. Inst. Neurol. Diseases & Blindness, 70- AAAS; Optical Soc. Am; Am. Physiol. Soc; Int. Soc. Clin. Electroretinography; Asn. Res. Vision & Ophthal. Neurophysiology; retina; visual pathways; vision. Address: National Institutes of Health, Rm. 10D03, Bldg. 10, Bethesda, MD 20014.

GOUREVITCH, GEORGE, b. France, Apr. 6, 31; U.S. citizen; m. 56. PSYCHOLOGY. B.S, Columbia, 54, M.A, 56, Ph.D.(psychol), 63. Res. psychologist, sch. med, N.Y. Univ, 57-63, instr. otorhinolaryngol, 63-64; lectr. psychol, Queen's Col.(N.Y), 63-64; Nat. Insts. Health fel. physiol, Washington(Seattle), 64-66; Nat. Insts. Health spec. fel, Princeton, 66-68; ASSOC. PROF. PSYCHOL, HUNTER COL, 68- Acoustical Soc. Am; Am. Psychol. Asn; N.Y. Acad. Sci. Auditory animal psychophysics and neurophysiology. Address: Dept. of Psychology, Hunter College, 695 Park Ave, New York, NY 10021.

GOURISHANKAR, VEMBU, b. Simla, Punjab, India, Jan. 22, 29; m. 66; c. 2. ELECTRICAL ENGINEERING, APPLIED MATHEMATICS. B.E, Univ. Madras, 50; M.S, Univ. Ill, 58, Ph.D, 61. Asst. prof. ELEC. ENG, Univ. Ill, Urbana-Champaign, 61-65; assoc. prof, UNIV. ALBERTA, 65-70, PROF, 70- Inst. Elec. & Electronics Eng; Soc. Indust. & Appl. Math. Optimization and stability of control systems; transportation systems; process control systems. Address: Dept. of Electrical Engineering, University of Alberta, Edmonton, Alta, Can.

GOURLEY, D(ESMOND) R(OBERT) H(UGH), b. Port Arthur, Ont, Nov. 2, 22; m. 46; c. 5. PHARMACOLOGY. B.A, Univ. Toronto, 45, Ont. Res. Coun. scholar, 47-49, Ph.D.(cellular physiol), 49. Lab. instr. comp. anat, Univ. Toronto, 45-46, asst. cellular physiol, 46-47, demonstr, 47-49; asst. PHARMACOL, SCH. MED, UNIV. VA, 49-51, asst. prof, 51-53, assoc. prof, 53-62, PROF, 62-, chmn. dept, 67-68. Travel grants, Fedn. Am. Socs. Exp. Biol, Brussels, 56 & Int. Union Physiol. Soc, Buenos Aires, 59; A. von Humboldt Found. fel, Univ. Freiburg, 68-69. Am. Soc. Pharmacol. & Exp. Therapeut; Am. Physiol. Soc; Soc. Exp. Biol. & Med; Pharmacol. Soc. Can. Effects of insulin on isolated muscle tissue; active transport and phosphate metabolism in erythrocytes; effects of drugs at cell membranes; molecular mechanism of drug tolerance and dependence. Address: Dept. of Pharmacology, University of Virginia School of Medicine, Charlottesville, VA 22903.

GOURLEY, EUGENE VINCENT, b. Detroit, Mich, Nov. 15, 40; m. 62; c. 1. ZOOLOGY. B.A, Eastern Michigan, 62, M.S, 64; Ph.D.(turtle behav), Florida, 69. Interim instr. zool, Florida, 68-69; ASSOC. PROF. BIOL, RADFORD COL, 69- AAAS; Am. Soc. Zool; Animal Behav. Soc. Address: Dept. of Biology, Radford College, Radford, VA 24141.

GOURLEY, LLOYD E(UGENE), JR, b. Bergheim, Tex, Apr. 22, 23; m. 48. PHYSICS. B.S, Texas, 46, fel, 46-48, M.A, 48, fel, 58-59, Ph.D, 59. Asst. physicist, Atlantic Ref. Co, 48-51; res. physicist, N.Mex Inst. Min. & Tech, 51-56; assoc. prof. PHYSICS, AUSTIN COL, 59-66, PROF, 66- Summers, mem. staff, Los Alamos Sci. Lab, 57, 58. Am. Phys. Soc; Am. Asn. Physics Teachers. Properties of solids under high pressures. Address: Dept. of Physics, Austin College, Box 1309, Sherman, TX 75090.

GOURSE, J(EROME) A(LLEN), b. Bristol, VA, June 15, 29. ORGANIC CHEMISTRY. B.S, Va. Polytech. Inst, 50; M.S, Univ. Del, 51; Ph.D.(chem), Univ. Ill, 59. RES. CHEMIST, VELSICOL CHEM. CORP, 58- U.S.M.C, 51-53, Sgt. Am. Chem. Soc; fel. Am. Inst. Chem. Polymer chemistry. Address: Velsicol Chemical Corp, 330 E. Grand Ave, Chicago, IL 60611.

GOURZIS, JAMES THEOPHILE, b. Boston, Mass, Mar. 30, 28; m. 62; c. 2. PHARMACOLOGY. A.B, Harvard, 49; A.M, Boston, 51; Ph.D, Manitoba, 62; M.D, 63. Jr. pharmacologist, Ciba Pharm. Prod. Inc, 51-52; sr. pharmacologist, Riker Lab, Inc, 52-57; res. assoc. pharmacol. & therapeut, Manitoba, 57-62; lectr, 62-63; col. med, Univ. Cincinnati, 63-66; asst. dir. clin. invest, McNeil Labs Inc, 66-68, dir. clin. pharmacol, 68-70; DIR.

CLIN. PHARMACOL, SCHERING CORP, 70- Assoc. dir, Bethesda Med. Res. Ctr, 64-66. Am. Soc. Pharmacol. & Exp. Therapeut; Am. Fedn. Clin. Res; Am. Med. Asn; Soc. Exp. Biol. & Med; Can. Pharmacol. Soc; Am. Therapeut. Soc; Int. Anesthesia Res. Soc. Cardiovascular physiology and pharmacology; clinical pharmacology. Address: Dept. of Clinical Pharmacology, Schering Corp, 60 Orange St, Bloomfield, NJ 07003.

GOUSE, S. WILLIAM, JR, b. Utica, N.Y, Dec. 15, 31; m. 55; c. 2. MECHANICAL ENGINEERING. S.B. & S.M, Mass. Inst. Technol, 54, Visking Corp. fel, 54-55, Gen. Elec. Co. fel, 55-56, Sc.D.(mech. eng), 58. Instr. mech. eng, Mass. Inst. Technol, 56-57, asst. prof, 57-65, assoc. prof, 65-67; prof, Carnegie-Mellon Univ, 67-69; tech. asst. for civilian technol. to dir, Off. Sci. & Technol, Off. of President, 69-70; ASSOC. DEAN CARNEGIE INST. TECHNOL. & SCH. OF URBAN & PUB. AFFAIRS, CARNEGIE-MELLON UNIV, 71- AAAS; Am. Soc. Mech. Eng; Soc. Automotive Eng; Am. Soc. Heating, Refrig. & Air-Conditioning Eng; Am. Inst. Chem. Eng; Am. Soc. Eng. Educ; Am. Inst. Aeronaut. & Astronaut. Energy; transportation; housing; environment; heat transfer; engineering education; automotive propulsion. Address: 3037 Sturbridge Court, Allison Park, PA 15101.

GOUTERMAN, MARTIN (PAUL), b. Phila, Pa, Dec. 26, 31. CHEMICAL PHYSICS. B.A, Chicago, 51, Nat. Sci. Found. fel, 54-58, M.S, 55, Ph.D. (physics), 58. Res. fel. CHEM, Harvard, 58-59, instr, 59-61, asst. prof, 61-66; assoc. prof, UNIV. WASH, 66-68, PROF, 68- Am. Phys. Soc. Electronic spectra of porphyrins; vibronic coupling in molecules; radiationless transitions. Address: Dept. of Chemistry, University of Washington, Seattle, WA 98105.

GOUW, T(AN) H(OK), b. Djakarta, Indonesia, Jan. 17, 33; U.S. citizen; m. 60; c. 2. ANALYTICAL CHEMISTRY, CHEMICAL ENGINEERING. Chem. Ing, Delft Technol. Univ, 58, D.Sc, 62. Asst. chem. eng, Delft Technol. Univ, 58-62; assoc. res. chemist, Calif. Res. Corp, 62-63; res. chemist, CHEVRON RES. CO, 63-68, SR. RES. ENGR, 68- Mem. staff, letters & sci. exten, Univ. Calif, Berkeley. Am. Chem. Soc; Netherlands Royal Inst. Eng. Chromatography; analytical physico-chemical separation methods; instrumental methods of analysis. Address: Chevron Research Co, 576 Standard Ave, Richmond, CA 94802.

GOVAN, DUNCAN EBEN, b. Winnipeg, Man, Aug. 23, 23; m. 50; c. 6. UROLOGY. M.D, Univ. Man, 48; Ph.D.(surg), Univ. Chicago, 57. Fel. gynec, Winnipeg Clin, Man, 50-51; instr. urol, sch. med, Univ. Chicago, 53-54; private practice, Can, 54-61; asst. prof. SURG, SCH. MED, STANFORD UNIV, 61-64, assoc. prof, 64-70, PROF, 70- Surg. consult, Vet. Admin. Hosp, Palo Alto, Calif, 61-67; Santa Clara County Hosp, San Jose, 65-67. Fel, Royal Col. Surgeons, Can, 56. Fel. Am. Col. Surg. Neurophysiology of the urinary tract; pediatric urology; hydronephrosis and urinary infection. Address: Dept. of Surgery, Stanford Medical Center, Stanford, CA 94305.

GOVE, H(ARRY) E(DMUND), b. Niagara Falls, Ont, Can, May 22, 22; nat; m. 45; c. 2. PHYSICS. B.Sc, Queen's(Ont), 44; Ph.D.(physics), Mass. Inst. Tech, 50. Res. assoc, Mass. Inst. Tech, 50-52; assoc. res. officer, Atomic Energy Can, Ltd, 52-58, br. head nuclear physics, 56-63, sr. res. officer, 58-63; PROF. PHYSICS & DIR. NUCLEAR STRUCT. RES. LAB, UNIV. ROCHESTER, 63- R.C.N.V.R, 44-45, Lt. Am. Phys. Soc; Can. Asn. Physicists. Structure of nuclei and mechanisms of nuclear reactions principally employing particle accelerators. Address: 52 Poplar Dr, Rochester, NY 14625.

GOVE, JESSIE L(OUISE), b. Alameda, Calif, Aug. 26, 23. ANALYTICAL CHEMISTRY. B.S, New Hampshire, 48; Ph.D.(chem), Pa. State, 57. Chemist anal. develop, Rohm & Haas Co, 48-52; RES. CHEMIST, AM. CYANAMID CO, 57- AAAS; Am. Chem. Soc; Soc. Appl. Spectros. Infrared and nuclear magnetic resonance spectroscopy. Address: Apt. 2A, 3 Dartmouth Ave, Somerville, NJ 08876.

GOVE, N(ORWOOD) B(ABCOCK), b. N.Y.C, Oct. 23, 32; m. 59; c. 3. NUCLEAR PHYSICS. B.A, Harvard, 53; Gen. Elec. Co. fel, Illinois, 56-57, Ph.D.(physics), 58. PHYSICIST, MATH. DIV, OAK RIDGE NAT. LAB, 58- Consult, George Washington, 59-62. Am. Phys. Soc; Am. Soc. Info. Sci. Decay schemes of radioactive nuclei. Address: Mathematics Division, Oak Ridge National Lab, Oak Ridge, TN 37830.

GOVETT, GERALD JAMES, b. Barry, South Wales, July 30, 32; m. 68. GEOCHEMISTRY. B.Sc, Univ. Wales, 55; D.I.C. & Ph.D.(geol), Univ. London, 58. Assoc. res. off. & geochemist, Res. Coun. Alta, 58-65; UN tech. expert & vis. prof, Univ. Philippines, 65-66; vis. prof, Univ. N.B, 66-67; UN consult, Cyprus, 67-68; assoc. prof. GEOL, UNIV. N.B, 68-70, PROF, 70- Consult, Off. Econ. Coop. & Develop, Greece, 71. Brit. Inst. Mining & Metall. Exploration geochemistry, primary and secondary dispersion; geochemistry and genesis of mineral deposits, especially sulfides. Address: Dept. of Geology, University of New Brunswick, Fredericton, N.B, Can.

GOVIER, G(EORGE) W(HEELER), b. Nanton, Alta, June 15, 17; m. 40; c. 3. CHEMICAL ENGINEERING. B.A.Sc, Univ. B.C, 39; M.Sc, Univ. Alta, 45; Sc.D.(chem. eng), Univ. Mich, 49. Plant operator, Standard Oil Co, B.C, 39-40; from lectr. to asst. prof. chem. eng, Univ. Alta, 40-48, prof. chem. eng. & head dept. chem. & petrol. eng, 48-59, dean, faculty eng, 59-63; CHMN. ENERGY RESOURCES CONSERV. BD, 62-, mem, 48-59, dep. chmn, 59-62. Consult, 40-62; off. engr, Standard Oil Co, B.C, summer 41; design engr, Aluminum Co. Can, summer 42; spec. studies engr, Oil & Gas Conserv. Bd, Alta, summer 45; mem. permanent coun, World Petrol. Cong, 60-; part-time prof, Univ. Alta. & Univ. Calgary, 63-; mem. bd. dirs, Petrol. Recovery Res. Inst, 66-; mem, Alta. Univs. Comn, 68-71; chmn. comts, Univ. Calgary. Am. Inst. Chem. Eng; fel. Chem. Inst. Can.(R.S. Jane Mem. Award, 64); fel. Eng. Inst. Can; Can. Inst. Mining & Metall.(pres. elect, 65-66, pres, 66-67; Selwyn G. Blaylock Medal, 71). Pipeline flow of complex mixtures, especially non-Newtonians, gas-liquid, liquid-liquid and solid-liquid mixtures. Address: Energy Resources Conservation Board, 603 Sixth Ave. S.W, Calgary 42, Alta, Can.

GOVIER, JOHN P(EABODY), b. Bellefonte, Pa, Aug. 24, 13; m. 44; c. 3. PETROLEUM ENGINEERING. B.Sc, Pa. State, 34. Sr. res. chemist, Phillips Petrol. Co, 36-44; dist. reservoir engr, Creole Petrol. Corp, 44-52, dist. engr, 52-53, div. prod. engr, 53-57; assoc. prof. PETROL. ENG, UNIV. MO-ROLLA, 57-60, PROF, 60- AAAS; Am. Inst. Mining, Metall. & Petrol. Eng; Am. Soc. Eng. Educ. Multi-phase fluid flow through porous media; commercial synthesis of dodecyl mercaptans; petroleum reservoir model studies; mathematical techniques in unsteady-state fluid flow in petroleum reservoirs. Address: Dept. of Petroleum Engineering, University of Missouri-Rolla, Rolla, MO 65401.

GOVIER, WILLIAM C(HARLES), b. Nashville, Tenn, Apr. 6, 36; m. 59; c. 2. CLINICAL PHARMACOLOGY. B.A, Kalamazoo Col, 57; M.D, McGill, 61; Ph.D.(pharmacol), Univ. Miss, 65. Fel. PHARMACOL, med. ctr, Univ. Miss, 62-63, instr, 63-65, asst. prof, 65-66; Southwest. Med. Sch, Univ. Tex, 66-68; sr. surgeon, exp. therapeut. br, Nat. Heart Inst, U.S. Pub. Health Serv, 68-70; dir. res. systs. develop, Worley & Ringe, Inc, 70-71; MEM. STAFF, CLIN. PHARMACOL. DIV, CIBA PHARMACEUT. CO, 71- Fel, Oxford Univ, 65-66. Lederle med. faculty award, 67. AAAS; N.Y. Acad. Sci; Am. Soc. Pharmacol. & Exp. Therapeut; Soc. Exp. Biol. & Med. Cardiovascular; autonomic; peptides; tissue regeneration. Address: CIBA Pharmaceutical Co, Summit, NJ 07901.

GOVIER, WILLIAM M(ILLER), b. Defiance, Ohio, Mar. 26, 15; m. 33; c. 4. PHARMACOLOGY. A.B, Kalamazoo Col, 35; M.D, Vanderbilt, 39. Intern, U.S. Marine Hosp, New Orleans, La, 39-40; asst. pharmacol, sch. med, Vanderbilt, 40-43; asst. prof. pharmacol. & physiol, Bowman Gray Sch. Med, 43-44; pharmacologist, Sharp & Dohme, Inc, Pa, 44-47; Upjohn Co, 47-54; dir, dept. pharmacol, Schering Corp, 54-58; clin. invest, Warner-Lambert Res. Inst, 58-59; head, dept. pharmacol, McNeil Lab, Inc, 59-60; dir. biol. sci, Warner-Lambert Res. Inst, 60-63, v.pres. biol. res, 63-65, ethical drug res, 65-68; PRES, MEAD JOHNSON RES. CTR, 68- With Off. Sci. Res. & Develop; U.S. Pub. Health Serv, 40-43; v.pres, Warner-Chilcott Labs, 66-68. AAAS; Am. Chem. Soc; Am. Soc. Pharmacol. & Exp. Therapeut; Soc. Exp. Biol. & Med; N.Y. Acad. Sci; Am. Soc. Cell Biol; Pharmacol. Soc. Can; Am. Soc. Clin. Pharmacol. & Therapeut. Enzymatic mechanism of shock and of mechanism of action of sympathomimetic amines, vitamin E and digitoxin; isolation of coenzyme A; effect of barbiturates on acetylation; choline cycle in cardiac decompensation; plasma substitutes; serum heart disease; barbiturate anaesthetics; tranquilizers; serotonin metabolism; antihistamines; muscle relaxants. Address: Mead Johnson Research Center, 2404 Pennsylvania St, Evansville, IN 47721.

GOVINDARAJULU, ZAKKULA, b. Atmakur, India, May 15, 33; m. 61; c. 2. MATHEMATICS, STATISTICS. B.A, Madras, 52, M.A, 53; Ph.D.(math, statist), Minnesota, 61. Lectr. asst. math, Madras Christian Col, Madras, 52-54, res. asst. statist, univ, 53-56; lectr. asst. math. & statist, Govt. Arts Col, Madras, 54-56; asst. biostatist, Minnesota, 56-57, math, 57-60, instr, 60-61; asst. prof, Case, 61-64, assoc. prof, 64-68; PROF. STATIST, UNIV. KY, 68- Nat. Sci. Found. grant, 62-64, 68-69; U.S. Air Force grant & vis. assoc. prof, Univ. Calif, Berkeley, 64-65; U.S. Pub. Serv, Nat. Ctr. Health Statist, 70-71; vis. prof, Univ. Mich, Ann Arbor, 72. Fel. AAAS; Inst. Math. Statist; fel. Am. Statist. Asn; Math. Asn. Am; Int. Asn. Statist. in Phys. Sci; fel. Royal Statist. Soc. Statistical inference; probability theory; non-parametric statistical inference; biostatistics; statistics applied to physical and biological sciences. Address: Dept. of Statistics, University of Kentucky, Lexington, KY 40506.

GOVINDJEE, b. Allahabad, India, Oct. 24, 33; m. 57; c. 2. BIOPHYSICS, PLANT PHYSIOLOGY. B.S, Allahabad, 52, M.S, 54; Ph.D.(biophys), Illinois, Urbana, 60. Lectr. bot, Allahabad, 54-56; fel. physico-chem. biol, UNIV. ILL, URBANA, 56-59, res. asst. bot, 59-60, U.S. Pub. Health Serv. fel. biophys, 60-61, asst. prof. bot, 61-65, assoc. prof. BOT. & BIOPHYS, 65-69, PROF, 69- Vis. res. scientist, Res. Inst. Advan. Study, Baltimore, summer 62; Carnegie Inst. Dept. Plant Biol, summer 63; Nat. Ctr. Sci. Res. France, 68; Europ. Molecular Biol. Orgn. fel, Max-Volmer Inst. Phys. Chem, West Berlin, summer 68. Partic, Int. Biochem. Cong, Moscow, 61; Int. Biophys. Cong, Stockholm, 61; Int. Bot. Cong, Edinburgh, 64 & Seattle, 69; Int. Photobiol. Cong, Oxford, 64; Int. Conf. Photosynthesis, Freudenstadt, W.Ger, 68 & Stressa, Italy, 71; Int. Conf. Blue-Green Algae, Madras, India, 70. AAAS; Am. Soc. Plant Physiol; Biophys. Soc; Am. Inst. Biol. Sci. Photosynthetic mechanisms of green plants and the relation of chlorophyll fluorescence to photosynthesis. Address: Dept. of Botany, 297 Morrill Hall, University of Illinois, Urbana, IL 61801.

GOW, K. V, b. Ottawa, Ont, Aug. 29, 19; m. 61; c. 3. PHYSICAL METALLURGY, CERAMICS. B.A.Sc, Toronto, 43, Ph.D.(phys. metall), 51; M.Sc, Rutgers, 49; Nat. Res. Coun. Can. fel, Birmingham, 51-52, M.Sc, 52. Sr. sci. off. PHYS. METALL, Can. Dept. Mines & Tech. Surv, 55-62; assoc. prof, N.S. Tech. Col, 64-68, PROF, 68- Brit. Ceramic Soc; Can. Inst. Mining & Metall; Am. Inst. Mining, Metall. & Petrol. Eng. Growth of metal single crystals and bicrystals; deformation of metal crystals; structure and mechanical properties of electrodeposited metals and alloys. Address: Dept. of Metallurgy, Nova Scotia Technical College, Halifax, N.S, Can.

GOW, WILLIAM ALEXANDER, b. Toronto, Ont, Nov. 11, 20; m. 45; c. 2. METALLURGICAL ENGINEERING. B.A.Sc, Toronto, 43. Res. engr, radioactivity div, MINES BR, DEPT. ENERGY, MINES & RESOURCES, 46-53, sect. head, hydrometall. sect, EXTRACTION METALL. DIV, 53-70, ASST. CHIEF, 70- Nipissing fel, 46. R.C.E, 43-46. Can. Inst. Mining & Metall. Hydrometallurgical treatment of ores and concentrates; development of uranium ore treatment processes; application of leaching, ion exchange and solvent extraction methods to various metallic ores. Address: Extraction Metallurgy Division, Mines Branch, Dept. of Energy, Mines & Resources, Ottawa, Ont, Can.

GOWAN, ALASTAIR C(AMPBELL), b. Aberdeen, Scotland, Mar. 30, 35. PHYSICAL CHEMISTRY. B.Sc, Aberdeen, 56, Ph.D.(chem), 59. Res. fel. chem, British Columbia, 59-60; res. chemist, chem. develop. oper, GEN. ELEC. CO, 60-65, mgr. prod. develop, polymer prod. oper, 65-67, tech. mkt. polymer prod, 67-68, mgr. polymer prod. res. & develop, 68-71, MGR.

POLYESTER PROD. BUS, 71- Faraday Soc; Am. Chem. Soc; Brit. Chem. Soc. Polymer chemistry and physics. Address: General Electric Co, 1 Plastics Ave, Pittsfield, MA 01201.

GOWANS, CHARLES S(HIELDS), b. Salt Lake City, Utah, Sept. 17, 23; m. 50; c. 3. GENETICS, MICROBIOLOGY. A.B, Utah, 49; Henry Newell fel, Stanford, 54-55, Nat. Insts. Health fel, 55-56, Ph.D.(biol), 57; Nat. Insts. Health fel, Indiana, 56-57. Asst. biol, Stanford, 52-55; asst. prof. BOT, UNIV. MO-COLUMBIA, 57-63, assoc. prof, 63-68, PROF, 68- Lalor Found. award, Harvard, summer 58; vis. prof, dept. bot, Nat. Taiwan Univ, 65-66; spec. chair, Inst. Bot, Acad. Sinica, Nankang, Taiwan, 65-66. Med.C, U.S.A, 42-45. Genetics Soc. Am; Phycol. Soc. Am; Am. Soc. Microbiol. Genetics of algae, specifically biochemical genetics of Chlamydomonas. Address: Dept. of Botany, University of Missouri-Columbia, Columbia, MO 65201.

GOWANS, KENNETH D, b. Duncans Mills, Calif, Feb. 9, 17; m. 40; c. 3. SOIL SCIENCE. B.S, California, 43. Soil surveyor, California, Davis, 42-43; soil chemist citrus mgt, Limoneira Co, 46-52; assoc. specialist soil morphol, California, Davis, 52-62, assoc. agriculturist soil classification, Agr. Exten. Serv, 62-65; soil scientist, Harza Eng. Co, Int, Lahore, West Pakistan, 65-69; AGRICULTURALIST, UNIV. CALIF. AGR. EXT, 69- U.S.N, 43-45. Am. Soc. Agron; Soil Sci. Soc. Am; Soil Conserv. Soc. Am. Advising environmental landscape managers in the use of modified soils in urban areas and in the establishment and management of turfgrass; adaptive research in turfgrass culture and soil management. Address: University of California Agricultural Extension, 224 W. Winton Ave, Hayward, CA 94544.

GOWARD, G(EORGE) W(ILLIAM), b. Chicago, Ill, May 31, 27; m. 50; c. 5. ANALYTICAL CHEMISTRY. B.Sc, Alberta, 49, M.Sc, 51; McKay fel, Princeton, 53-54, Ph.D.(chem), 54. Sr. scientist, anal. chem, Bettis Atomic Power Lab, Westinghouse Elec. Corp, 55-56, supvry. scientist, 56-61; sr. res. assoc, adv. mat. res. & develop. lab, PRATT & WHITNEY AIRCRAFT DIV, UNITED AIRCRAFT CORP, 61-64, tech. supvr. oxidation & coatings, 64-70, SUPVR. COATINGS, MAT. ENG. & RES. LAB, 70- Am. Chem. Soc; Am. Soc. Test. & Mat. Development of high-temperature protection of gas turbine engine materials. Address: Materials Engineering & Research Lab, Pratt & Whitney Aircraft Division, United Aircraft Corp, East Hartford, CT 06108.

GOWDEY, C(HARLES) W(ILLIS), b. St. Thomas, Ont, Sept. 3, 20; m. 46; c. 4. PHARMACOLOGY. B.A, Western Ontario, 44, M.Sc, 46; D.Phil.(pharmacol), Oxford, 48. Demonstr. PHARMACOL, Oxford, 46-48; lectr, MED. SCH, UNIV. WEST. ONT, 48-49, asst. prof, 50-51, assoc. prof, 52-60, PROF. & HEAD DEPT, 60- Am. Soc. Pharmacol. & Exp. Therapeut; Can. Pharmacol. Soc; Can. Physiol. Soc. Tranquilizers; physiological responses to hypoxia, hyperoxia and decompression sickness; anti-inflammatory agents; cardiovascular pharmacology. Address: Health Sciences Centre, University of Western Ontario, London, Ont, Can.

GOWDY, KENNETH KING, b. Memphis, Tenn, June 25, 32; m. 52; c. 4. MECHANICAL ENGINEERING. B.S, Kansas State, 55, M.S, 61; Ph.D.(mech. eng), Okla. State, 65. Engr. trainee, Continental Pipeline, 55; instr. & asst. to dean, KANS. STATE UNIV, 57-62, asst. prof. MECH. ENG, 62-70, ASSOC. PROF, 70-, ASST. DEAN ENG, 65- U.S.A.F, 55-57, Capt. Am. Soc. Mech. Eng; Am. Soc. Eng. Educ. Automatic controls; systems analysis. Address: Dean's Office, Seaton Hall, Kansas State University, Manhattan, KS 66502.

GOWDY, SPENSER O, b. Phila, Pa, July 6, 41. MATHEMATICS. B.S, West Chester State Col, 63; M.A, Villanova Univ, 65; Ph.D.(math), Temple Univ, 71. Asst. MATH, Villanova Univ, 63-65; Instr, ST. JOSEPH'S COL.(PA), 65-68, ASST. PROF, 68- Math. Asn. Am. Group theory; small cancellation groups. Address: Dept. of Mathematics, St. Joseph's College, Philadelphia, PA 19131.

GOWE, R(OBB) S(HELTON), b, St. Boniface, Man, Oct. 9, 21; m; c. 3. GENETICS. B.S.A, Toronto, 45; M.S, Cornell, 47, Ph.D.(genetics & physiol), 49. Asst. genetics, dept. poultry, Cornell, 45-49; head, poultry breeding, poultry div, exp. farms serv, CAN. DEPT. AGR, 49-59, chief, genetics sect, ANIMAL RES. INST, 59-65, DIR, 65- Tom Newman mem. int. award. AAAS; Poultry Sci. Asn; Am. Genetic Asn; Genetics Soc. Am; World Poultry Sci. Asn; Genetics Soc. Can; Can. Soc. Animal Prod; Asn. Sci, Eng. & Technol. Community Can. Poultry genetics. Address: Animal Research Institute, Research Branch, Canada Dept. of Agriculture, Ottawa, Ont. Can. K1A 0C6.

GOWEN, F(REDERICK) A(RTHUR), b. Boston, Mass, July 8, 23; m. 53; c. 3. HORTICULTURE. B.S, New Hampshire, 49; Ph.D.(hort), Minnesota, 56. Asst. prof. hort, Nebraska, 56-60; pulse breeder, Int. Develop. serv, Nigeria, 60-62; Legume Agronomist, U.S. Agency Int. Develop, 63-65; hort. adv. & lectr, Agr. Res. Training Sta, Umudike, E.Nigeria, 66-67; teacher, high sch, N.H, 68-69; plant breeder, J. Harris Co, N.Y, 69-71; PLANT BREEDER & AGR. ADV, U.S. AGENCY INT. DEVELOP, PANAMA, 71- Lectr, Univ. Ife, Nigeria, 63- U.S.A, 46-47. Am. Soc. Hort. Sci; Genetics Soc. Am; Nigerian Agr. Soc. Culture and breeding of edible legumes; genetics and physiology of fruits and vegetables; human nutrition; rural development. Address: c/o Mrs. Arthur Gowen, Stratham, NH 03885.

GOWEN, GEORGE F, b. Philadelphia, Pa, Jan. 28, 23; m. 57; c. 4. SURGERY. B.A, Pennsylvania, 48; M.D, Jefferson Med. Col, 52. Asst. prof. SURG, sch. med, Yale, 57-61; Woman's Med. Col. Pa, 62-64; ASSOC. PROF, JEFFERSON MED. COL, 64-; DIR. SURG, MISERICORDIA HOSP, 64- Staff surgeon, Vet. Hosp, West Haven, Conn, 57-62; Nat. Insts. Health grant, 63-66. U.S.M.C, 43-46, 1st Lt. Am. Col. Surg; N.Y. Acad. Sci. Techniques of hypothermia; circulatory arrest under deep hyperthermia; circulatory assistance in hemorrhagic shock. Address: Dept. of Surgery, Misericordia Hospital, 54th & Cedar Ave, Philadelphia, PA 19143.

GOWEN, RICHARD J, b. New Brunswick, N.J, July 6, 35; m. 55; c. 4. ELECTRICAL & BIOMEDICAL ENGINEERING. B.S, Rutgers, 57; M.S, Iowa State, 61, Ph.D.(elec. eng), 62. U.S. AIR FORCE, 57-, ground electronics off, 57-59, asst. prof. elec. eng, U.S. AIR FORCE ACAD, 62-63, res. assoc. bioeng, 63-64, asst. prof. ELEC. ENG, 64-65, assoc. prof, 65-71, PROF, 71- DEP. HEAD DEPT, 69- Summers, res. engr, Radio Corp. Am. Labs, 57, Nat. Sci. Found. fel, 63. Mem. Nat. Comt. Eng. Tech. in Med. & Biol. U.S.A.F, 57-, Maj. Inst. Elec. & Electronics Eng. Physiological monitoring; biological simulation; computer design; semiconductor circuits. Address: Dept. of Electrical Engineering, U.S. Air Force Academy, CO 80840.

GOWER, BOBBY GENE, b. West Frankfort, Ill, Aug. 14, 37; m. 59. ORGANIC & POLYMER CHEMISTRY. B.A, Southern Illinois, 58, M.A, 60; Gen. Mills fel. & Ph.D.(org. chem), Minnesota, 63. RES. CHEMIST PETROCHEM, SINCLAIR RES. INC, HARVEY, 63- Am. Chem. Soc. Biosynthesis; radioactive tracer feedings to barley; low molecular weight polymers. Address: 407 Huron St, Park Forest, IL 60466.

GOWER, HOWARD D(ALE), b. Salem, Ore, Dec. 18, 27; m. 54; c. 2. GEOLOGY. B.S, Oregon, 52; M.A, California, 58. Geologist, U.S. GEOL. SURV, 52-71, CHIEF BR. PAC. ENVIRON. GEOL, 71- U.S.A, 46-47. Geol. Soc. Am; Am. Asn. Petrol. Geol. Geology of phosphates and mineral fuels; Tertiary stratigraphy and structural geology; coal resources. Address: 800 La Mesa Dr, Menlo Park, CA 94025.

GOWER, J(AMES) F(RANCIS) R(ODERICK), b. Beer, Eng, July 25, 40; m. 66; c. 1. RADIO ASTRONOMY. B.A, Cambridge, 62, Ph.D.(radio astron), 66. Fel. radio astron, Cambridge, 66-67; asst. prof, Univ. B.C, 67-71; CONSULT, MARINE SCI. BR, ENVIRON. CAN, 71- Am. Astron. Soc; fel. Royal Astron. Soc. Radio astronomy, especially extra galactic radio sources; remote sensing in oceanography. Address: Marine Sciences Branch, Environment Canada, 1230 Government St, Victoria, B.C, Can.

GOWGIEL, JOSEPH MICHAEL, b. Summit, Ill, May 19, 26; m. 57; c. 1. DENTISTRY, ANATOMY. D.D.S, Loyola (Ill), 50; Zoller Dent. Clin. fel, Chicago, 51-58, Ph.D, 58. Intern, Zoller Dent. Clin, Chicago, 50-51, instr. dent. surg, 58-60, asst. prof, 60-63; ASSOC. PROF. ANAT. SCH. DENT, LOYOLA UNIV. CHICAGO, 64-, CHMN. DEPT. 69- Fel. AAAS; Am. Asn. Anat; Int. Asn. Dent. Res. Normal histophysiology of the oral tissues, especially of tooth development and the adult peridontal ligament. Address: Dept. of Anatomy, School of Dentistry, Loyola University, 2160 S. First Ave, Maywood, IL 60153.

GOWING, DONALD P(ROCTOR), b. Medford, Mass, Aug. 27, 18; m. 47; c. 3. PLANT PHYSIOLOGY. A.B, Cornell Univ, 49, Ph.D, 52. PLANT PHYSIOLOGIST, Pineapple Res. Inst, 52-64; C. Brewer & Co, 64-65; HAWAIIAN AGRONOMICS CO. INT, 65- U.S.A, 39-46. AAAS; Am. Chem. Soc; Am. Soc. Hort. Sci; Bot. Soc. Am; Am. Soc. Plant Physiol; Weed Sci. Soc. Am. Herbicides; plant growth regulators; physiological diseases. Address: Hawaiian Agronomics Co. Int, P.O. Box 1769, Teheran, Iran.

GOY, ROBERT W(ILLIAM), b. Detroit, Mich, Jan. 25, 24; m. 48; c. 3. PSYCHOLOGY. B.S, Univ. Mich, 47; Ph.D, Univ. Chicago, 53. U.S. Pub. Health Serv. fel. anat. & psychol, Univ. Kans, 54-56, instr. anat, 56-59, asst. prof, 59-61, assoc. prof, 61-63; assoc. scientist, Ore. Regional Primate Res. Ctr, 63-65, chmn. dept. reprod. physiol. & behav, 65-71, sr. scientist, 67-71; DIR, WIS. REGIONAL PRIMATE RES. CTR, 71-, vis. scientist, 61-63. Assoc. prof, med. sch, Univ. Ore, 65-66, prof, 66-71; Univ. Wis, Madison, 71- U.S.A, 43-46. Am. Asn. Anat; Endocrine Soc; Animal Behav. Soc; Brit. Soc. Study Fertil. Comparative endocrinology of reproduction and reproductive behavior. Address: Wisconsin Regional Primate Research Center, 1223 Capitol Ct, Madison, WI 53706.

GOYAN, FRANK M(AYER), b. Placerville, Calif, June 22, 08. PHYSICAL CHEMISTRY. B.S, California, 30, fel, 30-31, M.S, 31, Ph.D.(chem), 37. Assoc, Calif. Col. Pharm, 31-32; instr, col. pharm, California, 32-42, asst. prof, 42-43; mem. sci. staff, war res, Columbia, 43; UNIV. CALIF, SAN FRANCISCO, 44-45, asst. prof. chem, SCH. PHARM, 45-48, assoc. prof, 48-54, PROF, 54-56, CHEM. & PHARMACEUT. CHEM, 56-, acting dean students, 63-65. Mem, U.S. Pharmacopeia Revision Comt, 50-60. Mem, Off. Sci. Res. & Develop, 43-45. AAAS; Am. Chem. Soc; Faraday Soc; Electrochem. Soc; Am. Pharmaceut. Asn. Thermoelectric instrumentation applied to determination of colligative and thermodynamic properties of solutions. Address: School of Pharmacy, University of California, San Francisco, CA 94122.

GOYAN, JERE E(DWIN), b. Oakland, Calif, Aug. 3, 30; m. 52; c. 3. PHARMACEUTICAL CHEMISTRY. B.S, Univ. Calif, San Francisco, 52, Ph.D.(pharmaceut. chem), 57. Asst. prof. PHARM, Univ. Mich, 56-61, assoc. prof, 61-63; UNIV. CALIF, SAN FRANCISCO, 63-65, PROF, 65-, DEAN SCH. PHARM, 67-, assoc. dean, 66-67, chmn. dept, 65-67. Consult, Appl. Mgt. Scis, Md, 71; mem. adv. comt, Nat. Formulary, 65-70, comt. specifications, 70-74; pharm. adv. comt, dept. prof. & voc. standards, State Calif, 67-69; construct. schs. pharm. rev. comt, div. physician manpower, bur. health manpower, Health Educ. & Welfare, U.S. Pub. Health Serv, Nat. Insts. Health, 67-69; mem. adv. group secondary sch. systs. vocational educ. prog. health workers, adult & vocational div, San Francisco Pub. Schs, 68-69; res. & educ. comt, Vet. Admin. Hosp, San Francisco, 68-, res. & educ. budget & evaluation subcomt, 68-70, chmn, 70-, mem. deans' comt, 68-; pharm. rev. comt, bur. health prof. educ. & manpower training, 69-71; vis. comt, col. pharm, Wayne State Univ, 70-71; Am. Pharmaceut. Asn. rep. on U.S. Adopted Names rev. bd, 70, 71; adv. comt. allied health prof. prog, dept. occup. prep. San Francisco Unified Sch. Dist, 70- Fel. AAAS; N.Y. Acad. Sci; Am. Pharmaceut. Asn; Acad. Pharmaceut. Sci; Am. Pub. Health Asn. Kinetics of drug degradation, properties of drugs in solution. Address: School of Pharmacy, University of California, San Francisco, CA 94122.

GOYCO DAUBON, JOSE A, b. Santurce, P.R, Oct. 14, 14; m. 39; c. 4. NUTRITION, BIOCHEMISTRY. B.S.Ph, Puerto Rico, 37; Guggenheim Mem. fel, Wisconsin, 43-44, M.S, 44. Lab. technician chem, agr. exp. sta, UNIV. P.R, SAN JUAN, 37-39, anal. chemist, 39-41, asst. chemist, sch. trop. med, 41-45, instr. chem, 45-47, assoc, 47-49, assoc. biochemist, sch. med, 49-52, res. assoc. biochem, 52-57, asst. prof, 57-65, assoc. prof, 65-68, PROF. BIOCHEM. & NUTRIT, 68- Am. Inst. Nutrit; Latin Am. Soc. Nutrit. Analytical cnemistry. Address: Dept. of Biochemistry, School of Medicine, University of Puerto Rico, San Juan, PR 00905.

GOYER, GERARD R, b. Montreal, Que, May 13, 38; m. 60; c. 2. PHARMACOLOGY. B.A, Univ. Montreal, 58, B.Pharm, 62, D.Ph.(pharmacol), Sorbonne, 65. Asst. prof. PHARMACOL, UNIV. MONTREAL, 65-69, PROF, 69-; SCI. DIR, NADEAU & DESBERGERS PHARMACEUT. LABS, 69- Del, Int. Cong. Pharmacol, Basel, Switz, 69; mem, Med. Res. Coun. Can, 70-; exec. mem, Can. Asn. Faculties Pharm, 70-; del, Symp. Biol. Aspects Electrochem, 71. AAAS; Fr-Can. Asn. Advan. Sci; N.Y. Acad. Sci; French Soc. Therapeut. & Pharmacodyn; Pharmacol. Soc. Can; Int. Pharmaceut. Fedn. Neuromuscular pharmacology, especially curarizing drugs, anticholinesterasic agents, reactivators of phosphorylated cholinesterases; absorption of drugs, particularly vitamins and hormones. Address: School of Pharmacy, University of Montreal, Montreal, Que, Can.

GOYER, GUY G(ASTON), b. Montreal, Que, Feb. 14, 22; m. 50; c. 4. PHYSICAL CHEMISTRY. B.A, Montreal, 43, B.Sc, 47, Ph.D.(phys. chem), 50. Res. assoc, cent. aerosol lab, Columbia, 50-52; sr. chemist, cloud physics proj, dept. meteorol, Chicago, 52-55; res. chemist, cent. res. lab, Can. Industs, Ltd, 55-58, explosives res. lab, McMasterville, 58-62; prog. scientist, NAT. CTR. ATMOSPHERIC RES, 62-70, SR. SCIENTIST, CTR. & DEP. DIR, NAT. HAIL RES. EXP, 70- Consult. Sci. Res. Soc. Am; Chem. Inst. Can; Am. Meteorol. Soc. Aerosols; cloud physics; hailstorms; weather modification. Address: National Hail Research Experiment, National Center for Atmospheric Research, P.O. Box 1470, Boulder, CO 80303.

GOYER, ROBERT A(NDREW), b. Hartford, Conn, June 2, 27; m. 55; c. 4. PATHOLOGY. B.S, Col. of Holy Cross, 50; M.D, St. Louis Univ, 55. Nat. Found. fel, sch. med, St. Louis Univ, 59-60, instr. PATH, 60-62, asst. prof, 62-65; SCH. MED, UNIV. N.C, CHAPEL HILL, 65-68, assoc. prof, 68-71, PROF, 71- Res. fel, metab. unit, Univ. Col. Hosp. Med. Sch, Univ. London, 61-62; clin. pathologist, Cardinal Glennon Mem. Hosp. Children, St. Louis, 62-63, dir. labs, 63-65. Dipl, Am. Bd. Path, 64. U.S.N, 45-47. AAAS; Am. Med. Asn; fel. Col. Am. Path; Soc. Exp. Biol. & Med; Am. Soc. Human Genetics; Am. Soc. Clin. Path; Am. Asn. Path. & Bact; Fedn. Am. Socs. Exp. Biol. Experimental pathology; kidney; heavy metal poisoning. Address: Dept. of Pathology, School of Medicine, University of North Carolina at Chapel Hill, Chapel Hill, NC 27514.

GOYER, ROBERT G, b. Montreal, Que, Can, May 13, 38; m. 60; c. 2. PHARMACOLOGY. B.A, Montreal, 58, B.Sc, 62; Ph.D.(pharmacol), Sorbonne, 65. From asst. prof. to ASSOC. PROF. PHARMACOL, FACULTY PHARMACOL, UNIV. MONTREAL, 65-; SCI. DIR, DESBERGERS & NADEAU PHARMACEUT. LABS, 71- Grants, Med. Res. Coun. Can, Med. Res. Coun. Que, Can. Found. Advan. Pharm, 66-; consult, Desbergers & Nadeau Pharmaceut. Labs. AAAS; N.Y. Acad. Sci; French-Can. Asn. Advan. Sci; French Soc. Therapeut. & Pharmacodyn; Pharm. Soc. Can. Anticholinesterasic agents and reactivators of phosphorylated acetylcholinesterases; neuromuscular agents versus acetylcholine synthesis, storage and liberation. Address: Faculty of Pharmacy, University of Montreal, C.P. 6128, Montreal 3, Que, Can.

GOYETTE, LEWIS E(DWARD), b. Kansas City, Mo, July 22, 24; m. 46; c. 3. BOTANY. A.B, Kansas, 47, Ph.D.(bot), 51. Res. botanist, agr. chem, res. dept, Va-Carolina Chem. Corp, 51-52, sr. biologist, 52-55, group leader, 55-57, sect. leader, 57-59, prod. mgr, chem. div, 59-64; V.PRES, DRAGON CHEM. CORP, 64- U.S.A, 42-46. Fungicides, relation of structure to activity; defoliants, herbicides and plant growth regulators. Address: 3806 Winding Way Rd. S.W, Roanoke, VA 24015.

GOYINGS, LLOYD SAMUEL, b. White Cloud, Mich, Dec. 26, 33; m. 54; c. 5. PATHOLOGY, BIOCHEMISTRY. B.S, Mich. State, 58, D.V.M, 60, Upjohn Co. grant, 60-61, M.S, 61, Ph.D.(path), 65. Instr. path, Mich. State, 61-65, asst. prof. path, surg. & med, 65-66; res. assoc. PLANT & ANIMAL PATH, UPJOHN CO, 66-70, RES. HEAD, 70- Am. Vet. Med. Asn; Conf. Res. Workers Animal Diseases; Am. Asn. Lab. Animal Sci. Canine dermatology; atypical mycobacteniosis in cattle, dogs, cats and chickens; canine hypothyroidism; causation of canine leukemia; canine cancer registry. Address: Dept. of Pathology & Toxicology, 9610 Agricultural Division, Upjohn Co, Kalamazoo, MI 49001.

GOZ, BARRY, b. Brooklyn, N.Y, Oct. 21, 37; m. 61; c. 1. PHARMACOLOGY, BIOCHEMISTRY. B.A, Columbia, 58; U.S. Pub. Health Serv. fel, State Univ. N.Y, 61-65, Ph.D.(pharmacol), 65. U.S. Pub. Health Serv. fel. PHARMACOL, SCH. MED, YALE, 65-67, ASST. PROF, 67- Am. Soc. Microbiol. Cellular and viral replication and control mechanisms; pyrimidine analogues and nucleic acid metabolism; antiviral agents. Address: Dept. of Pharmacology, Yale University, 333 Cedar St, New Haven, CT 06510.

GOZANI, TSAHI, b. Tel-Aviv, Israel, Nov. 25, 34; m. 58; c. 4. REACTOR & NUCLEAR PHYSICS. B.Sc, Israel Inst. Tech, 56, M.Sc, 58; D.Sc.(reactor physics), Swiss Fed. Inst. Tech, 62. Sr. scientist, Nuclear Res. Ctr, Negev, Israel, 62-65; res. assoc. nuclear eng, Rensselaer Polytech, 65-66; STAFF MEM, nuclear br, linear accelerator facility, Gulf Gen. Atomic Co, 66-71, RADIATION TECHNOL. DIV, GULF ENERGY & ENVIRON. SYSTS. CO, 71- Mem. Israeli sci. del, Geneva Conf. Peaceful Uses of Atomic Energy, 64; lectr, Argonne Nat. Lab. Asn. Midwest Univs, 68; vis. prof, Tel-Aviv Univ, 70-71; del, Int. Symposium on Safeguard Res. & Develop, Ger, 70. Am. Nuclear Soc; Phys. Soc. Israel. Low energy photofission; nondestructive methods for nuclear fuel assay; reactor kinetics; applied radiation. Address: Radiation Technology Division, Gulf Energy & Environmental Systems Co, P.O. Box 608, San Diego, CA 92112.

GRAAE, JOHAN E. A, b. Copenhagen, Denmark, July 1, 09; U.S. citizen; m. 41; c. 3. MECHANICAL & CHEMICAL ENGINEERING. M.Sc, Tech. Univ. Denmark, 35. Mech. engr, Burmeister & Wain, Denmark, 35-38; field engr, Vacuum Oil Co, Denmark, 38-40; develop. engr, F.L. Smith & Co, N.Y, 40-43; proj. engr, Lummus Co, 43-56; SR. MECH. ENGR, ARGONNE NAT. LAB, 56- Am. Inst. Chem. Eng; Am. Nuclear Soc; Sci. Res. Soc. Am. Design and development of processes and equipment for production of fissionable material; equipment and facilities for remote handling, reprocessing and refabrication of nuclear, radioactive fuel. Address: 315 N. Myrtle Ave, Elmhurst, IL 60126.

GRAB, E(UGENE) G(RANVILLE), JR, b. Nashville, Tenn, Apr. 17, 14; m. 45; c. 2. NUTRITION, FOODS. B.S, Pennsylvania, 34, M.S, 35. Chemist, Adams Apple Prod. Corp, Pa, 35-37, prod. mgr, 37-41; assoc. mkt. specialist, U.S. Dept. Agr, Ill, 41-45; food processing specialist, Tenn. Valley Auth, 45-48; in charge customer res, south. dist, HEEKIN CAN CO, DIAMOND INT, INC, 48-55, assoc. dir. res, 55-57, DIR. RES, 57-, V.PRES, 64- Am. Chem. Soc; Am. Soc. Biol. Chem; Master Brewers Asn. Am; Inst. Food Technol; Am. Inst. Chem. Eng; Am. Inst. Chem; Soc. Soft Drink Technol. Development of new or improvement of existing food products; determination of cause of food spoilage in tin, tin free steel and aluminum containers; evaluation quality of foodstuffs; calculation of heat processes; development of new lacquers, fluxes and plate types in the manufacture of tin cans. Address: Research Dept. Heekin Can Co, 8200 Broadwell Rd, Cincinnati, OH 45244.

GRABAU, WARREN E(DWARD), b. Albion, Mich, Aug. 31, 19; m. 43; c. 1. GEOMORPHOLOGY. B.S. & M.S, Mich. State, 50. Consult. geologist, Francis Eng. Co, 50-53; geologist, U.S. Geol. Surv, 53-56; SUPVRY. GEOLOGIST, U.S. ARMY CORPS ENG. WATERWAYS EXP. STA, 56- Dept. of Army res. & develop. achievement award, 70. U.S.A, 41-45. AAAS; Am. Inst. Biol. Sci. Quantitative geomorphology and vegetation physiognomy; terrain description and analysis by numerical means; operations analysis. Address: U.S. Army Corps of Engineers Waterways Experiment Station, P.O. Box 631, Vicksburg, MS 39180.

GRABBE, EUGENE M(UNTER), b. Johnstown, Pa, Dec, 4, 12; m; c. 4. PHYSICS. B.S, Duke, 35; M.S, Brown, 37; Ph.D.(physics), Yale, 40. Res. physicist, U.S. Rubber Co, 39-45; adv. new prod. develop, Homelite Corp, 45-48; assoc. head comput. systs. dept, res. & develop. labs, Hughes Aircraft Co, 48-54; sr. staff consult. automation, TRW Systs, 54-64; dir. int. comput. opers, Bunker-Ramo Corp, 64-66; mgr. technol. planning, TRW Systs, Calif, 66-71; MGR, HAWAII STATE CTR. SCI. POLICY & TECHNOL. ASSESSMENT, 71- V.pres. & dir. Compagnie Europeenne, D'Automatisme Electronique, France, 60-65; dep. managing dir, Int. Systs. Control, Ltd, Eng, 61-65; mem. trade mission automation, U.S. Dept. Commerce, Italy, 62, U.K, 64, East. Europe, 68. Asn. Comput. Mach; fel. Inst. Elec. & Electronics Eng. Digital computers; automatic control; computer control systems. Address: State Dept. of Planning & Economic Development, P.O. Box 2359, Honolulu, HI 96804.

GRABEL, ARVIN, b. New York, N.Y, Mar. 8, 35; m. 69. ELECTRONICS. B.E.E, N.Y. Univ, 56, M.E.E, 57, Sc.D.(elec. eng), 64. Instr. ELEC. ENG, N.Y. Univ, 57-63; asst. prof, NORTHEAST. UNIV, 64-67, ASSOC. PROF, 67- AAAS; Inst. Elec. & Electronics Eng.(ed, Circuit Theory Newsletter, 59-61); Am. Soc. Eng. Educ. Solid state circuits; active network synthesis. Address: Dept. of Electrical Engineering, Northeastern University, 360 Huntington Ave, Boston, MA 02115.

GRABEN, HENRY WILLINGHAM, b. Talladega, Ala, Nov. 9, 34; m. 61; c. 2. THEORETICAL PHYSICS. B.S, Birmingham-South. Col, 57; South. Fels. Fund fel, Tennessee, 57-60, M.S, 61, Nat. Sci. Found. fels, 61-62, summer, 61, Ph.D.(physics), 62. Physicist plasma physics, Oak Ridge Nat. Lab, 62-63; asst. prof. PHYSICS, CLEMSON UNIV, 63-67, ASSOC. PROF, 67- Am. Phys. Soc; Am. Asn. Physics Teachers. Theoretical study of intermolecular forces. Address: Dept. of Physics, Clemson University, Clemson, SC 29631.

GRABENSTEIN, DANIEL E(DWARD), b. New York, N.Y, May 1, 34; m. 61; c. 2. PHYSICS, MATHEMATICS. B.S, Queens Col.(N.Y), 56; M.S, Drexel Inst, 60. Engr, nuclear div, Martin-Marietta Corp, Md, 56-60, res. assoc, Rias Div, 60-67; supvr. physics sect, cent. res. dept, Riegel Paper Corp, 67-69; RES. SCIENTIST, AMP, INC, 69- Nat. Guard, 54-56, Sgt. Am. Phys. Soc. Electrical and optical properties of alkali halides; conductivity and photoconductivity; development of electrical contact materials. Address: AMP, Inc, 425 Prince St, Harrisburg, PA 17105.

GRABENSTETTER, ROBERT J(OHN), b. Rochester, N.Y, Aug. 6, 16; m. 41; c. 1. PHYSICAL CHEMISTRY. B.S, Rochester, 37, Ph.D.(phys. chem), 41. Lab. asst, Rochester, 37-39; instr. chem, Lafayette Col, 41; res. assoc, Nat. Defense Res. Comt. Princeton, 41-42; Northwestern, 42-45; Carnegie Tech, 45; RES. CHEMIST, PROCTER & GAMBLE CO, 45- AAAS; Am. Chem. Soc. Mechanism of detergency; photochemistry; adsorption and catalysis; photochemical decomposition of ethylene iodide; gem-diphosphonic acids; polynuclear complexes of calcium. Address: Miami Valley Labs, Procter & Gamble Co, P.O. Box 39175, Cincinnati, OH 45239.

GRABER, CHARLES D(AVID), b. Pomeroy, Ohio, Dec. 19, 17; m. 44; c. 3. BACTERIOLOGY. B.S, Ohio State, 39; M.S, Colorado, 54; Ph.D.(bact), Ohio State, 57. Bacteriologist & immunologist, surg. res. unit, Brooke Army Med. Ctr, 41-62; asst. prof. MICROBIOL, col. med, Baylor Univ, 62-66; ASSOC. PROF, MED. UNIV. S.C, 66- U.S.A, 57-62, Lt. Col. Soc. Exp. Biol. & Med; Am. Asn. Immunol. Burn infection immunology; effect of intestinal microflora on bile acid metabolism in atherosclerosis; selective depletion of lymphocytes to overcome rejection phenomenon by clone striping. Address: Dept. of Microbiology, Medical University of South Carolina, 80 Barre St, Charleston, SC 29401.

GRABER, GEORGE, b. N.Y.C, Nov. 24, 40; m. 65. ANIMAL NUTRITION. B.S, Rutgers Univ, 63, M.S, 67; Ph.D.(animal sci), Univ. Ill, Urbana, 71. ANIMAL HUSBANDMAN; DIV. NUTRIT. SCI, NON-RUMINANT BR, BUR. VET. MED, FOOD & DRUG ADMIN, 71- Dairy science award, Rutgers Univ, 63. Nat. Guard, 64-70, Sgt. Poultry Sci. Asn; Am. Soc. Animal Sci. Amino acid metabolism in chick and pig; vitamin-amino acid interrelation; swine metabolism studies. Address: Division of Nutritional Science, Bureau of Veterinary Medicine, Food & Drug Administration, Room 7B-18, 5600 Fisher Lane, Rockville, MD 20852.

GRABER, HARLAN DUANE, b. Newton, Kans, July 19, 35; m. 58; c. 3. NUCLEAR PHYSICS. B.S, Bethel Col.(Kans), 57; Ph.D.(physics), Kansas, 64. Asst. prof. PHYSICS, CORNELL COL, 62-65, ASSOC. PROF, 65- Am. Phys. Soc; Am. Asn. Physics Teachers. Low energy nuclear physics; gamma ray spectroscopy. Address: 612 Third Ave. S, Mt. Vernon, IA 52314.

GRABER, JEAN WEBER, b. Cedar Point, Kans, Sept. 12, 24; m. 45. ZOOLOGY. B.S, Washburn, 45; M.A, Michigan, 49; Nat. Sci. Found. fel, Oklahoma, 56, Ph.D.(zool), 58. Med. technician, Lattimore Labs, 45-48; Stormont-Vail Hosp, 52; asst. ANIMAL SCI, UNIV. ILL, URBANA-CHAMPAIGN, 59-60, res. assoc, 60-69, ASST. PROF, 69- Am. Ornith. Union. Ecology, taxonomy and physiology of birds. Address: 107 Animal Genetics Bldg, University of Illinois, Urbana-Champaign, Urbana, IL 61801.

GRABER, LELAND D, b. Marion, S.Dak, Nov. 5, 24; m. 55; c. 3. MATHEMATICS. B.S, Wheaton Col.(Ill), 48; M.A, Minnesota, 50; Ph.D.(math), Iowa State, 64. Res. engr, aeronaut. res. dept, Minneapolis-Honeywell Regulator Co, 51-53; instr. MATH, American Univ. Beirut, 53-59; Iowa State, 59-64; asst. prof. Fla. Presby. Col, 64-70; ASSOC. PROF, CENT. COL.(IOWA), 70- U.S.N.R, 43-46, Lt.(jg). Math. Asn. Am; Am. Math. Soc. Functional analysis, linear operators in banach spaces. Address: Dept. of Mathematics, Central College, Pella, IA 50219.

GRABER, RICHARD R(EX), b. Kingman Co, Kans, Aug. 25, 24; m. 45. ZOOLOGY. B.S, Washburn, 48; M.A, Michigan, 49; Ph.D, Oklahoma, 55. Asst. zool, Michigan, 48-50; mus. field collector, La. State, 51-52; asst, biol. surv, Oklahoma, 52-55; instr. biol, Southwest. Tex. State Teachers Col, 55-56; WILDLIFE SPECIALIST, ILL. NATURAL HIST. SURV, 56- U.S.N, 43-46. Cooper Ornith. Soc; Wilson Ornith. Soc. Evolution, migration and ecology of birds. Address: Illinois Natural History Survey, Natural Research Bldg, Urbana, IL 61801.

GRABER, ROBERT P(HILIP), b. Glen Ullin, N.Dak, Oct. 4, 18; m. 59; c. 2. ORGANIC CHEMISTRY. B.Chem, Minnesota, 41; Ph.D.(chem), Wisconsin, 49. Jr. chemist, Merck & Co, Inc, 41-46, sr. chemist, 49-56; proj. leader, res. labs, Gen. Mills, Inc, 57-58, sect. leader, 58; mem. res. staff, Searle Chem. Inc, Ill, 63, SCI. DIR, SEARLE DE MEX, S.A. DE C.V, 68- Am. Chem. Soc. Antibiotics; synthetic estrogens; steroids; natural products; fermentations. Address: Searle de Mexico, S.A. de C.V, Bulevar Toluca 13, Naucalpan, Edo. de Mexico, Mex.

GRABER, T(OURO) M(OR), b. St. Louis, Mo, May 27, 17; m. 41; c. 5. ORTHODONTICS. D.D.S, Washington (St. Louis), 40; M.S.D, Northwestern, 45, Ph.D, 50. Instr. orthod, Northwest. Univ.(Ill), 45-46, asst. prof, 46-53, assoc. prof, 53-69, dir. res. cleft lip & palate inst, 49-69; PROF. ORTHOD, RES. ASSOC. & HEAD DEPT, UNIV. CHICAGO, 69- Assoc. attend. orthodontist Children's Mem. Hosp, 58-62; spec. lectr, Univ. Mich, 59-; Grieve Mem. Lect, 64. Dipl, Am. Bd. Orthod, 54. U.S.A, 42-44, Capt. AAAS; Am. Asn. Orthod; Am. Dent. Asn; Int. Asn. Dent. Res. Maxillo-facial deformities; diagnosis of orthodontic therapy; cephalometric radiography in orthodontics; use of extraoral appliances in orthodontic therapy. Address: 2895 Sheridan Pl, Evanston, IL 60201.

GRABIEL, CHARLES E(DWARD), b. Alliance, Ohio, July 31, 27; m. 49; c. 4. ORGANIC CHEMISTRY. A.B, Col. of Wooster, 50; Ph.D.(chem), Brown, 54. Asst, Brown, 50-53; chemist DOW CHEM. CO, 54-65, MGR. CHEM. MKT. RES, 65- U.S.N.R, 45-46. Am. Chem. Soc. Vapor-liquid equilibrium; polynitroparaffins; polyelectrolytes. Address: Dow Chemical Co, Midland, MI 48640.

GRABILL, JAMES RODNEY, b. Unionville, Md, Apr. 24; m. 43. MEDICINE, PHARMACOLOGY. Georgetown, 46-48; American Univ, 47; M.D, Maryland, 52. Intern, Bon Secours Hosp, Baltimore, Md, 52-53; private practice, 53-65; assoc. dir. clin. res, Abbott Labs, Ill, 65-69; ASSOC. MED. DIR, LABS. DIV, SCHERING CORP, N.J, 69- Faculty mem. med, med. sch, Northwestern, 65- Consult, Md. Hosp. Serv, 60-65. U.S.N.R, 43-45. Am. Med. Asn. Types of agents-antineoplastic, cardiovascular, anti-inflammatory and learning and memory enhancers; psychopharmaceuticals and antibiotics. Address: Labs. Division, Schering Corp, Galloping Hill Rd, Kenilworth, NJ 07033.

GRABINER, SANDY, b. N.Y.C, Dec. 15, 39; m. 64; c. 1. MATHEMATICS. B.A, Rice Univ, 60; Nat. Sci. Found. fel, Harvard, 60-64, A.M, 61, Ph.D. (math), 67. Instr. MATH, Mass. Inst. Technol, 67-69; ASST. PROF, CLAREMONT GRAD. SCH, 69- Nat. Sci. Found. res. grant, 70-71. AAAS; Am. Math. Soc; Math. Asn. Am. Banach algebras and operators on Banach spaces; applications of formal power series to functional analysis. Address: Dept. of Mathematics, Claremont Graduate School, Claremont, CA 91711.

GRABLE, ALBERT E, b. San Bernardino, Calif, Mar. 10, 39; m. 62; c. 3. ENTOMOLOGY, BOTANY. B.A, La Sierra Col, 59; M.S, Univ. Minn, 62, Ph.D.(entom), 65. Instr. BIOL, WALLA WALLA COL, 63-65, asst. prof, 65-70, ASSOC. PROF, 70- Entom. Soc. Am; Bot. Soc. Am; Int. Bot. Cong. Biology of parasitic hymenoptera; taxonomy of flowering plants. Address: Dept. of Biology, Walla Walla College, College Place, WA 99324.

GRABLE, ALBERT R, b. Worland, Wyo, June 8, 32; m. 50; c. 3. SOIL SCIENCE. B.S, Wyoming, 56; M.S, Colorado State, 59, Ph.D.(soils), 63. Soil scientist, agr. res. serv, U.S. Dept. Agr, 56-67; res. invest. leader, North. Great Plains Res. Ctr, N.Dak, 67-69; V.PRES, CROWLEY LAND & DEVELOPMENT CO, 69- Am. Soc. Agron; Soil Sci. Soc. Am. Soil fertility and management; agricultural meteorology; soil aeration; pasture and meadow management. Address: Crowley Land & Development Co, Ordway, CO 81063.

GRABOIS, NEIL R, b. N.Y.C, Dec. 11, 35; m. 56; c. 2. ALGEBRA, NUMBER THEORY. B.A, Swarthmore Col, 57; M.A, Univ. Pa, 59, Ph.D.(math), 63. Asst. instr. MATH, Univ. Pa, 57-61; instr, Lafayette Col, 61-63; asst. prof, WILLIAMS COL, 63-68, ASSOC. PROF, 68-, DEAN, 70- Math. Asn. Am; Am. Math. Soc. Homological algebra; ring theory; algebraic number theory. Address: Dept. of Mathematics, Williams College, Williamstown, MA 01267.

GRABOWSKI, BERNARD F, b. Nanticoke, Pa, Feb. 23, 31; m. 67; c. 1. PHARMACEUTICAL CHEMISTRY. B.S, Temple, 52, M.S, 54; Ph.D.(pharmaceut. chem), Maryland, 58. Asst. PHARMACEUT. CHEM, Temple, 52-54; instr, Maryland, 54-57, U.S. Pub. Health fel, 57-58; asst. prof, Fordham Univ, 58-60, U.S. Pub. Health Serv. fel, 60-61; asst. prof, Ohio North. Univ, 61-63; UNIV. MO-KANSAS CITY, 63-65, assoc. prof, 65-69, PROF, 69- Mem, Gov. Adv. Coun. Alcoholism & Drug Abuse. AAAS; Am. Chem. Soc; Am. Pharmaceut. Asn; Am. Asn. Cols. Pharm; Am. Inst. Hist. Pharm; The Chem. Soc. Heterocycles; indoles; organic reaction mechanism; pharmaceutical analysis. Address: Dept. of Pharmaceutical Chemistry, School of Pharmacy, University of Missouri-Kansas City, 5100 Rockhill Rd, Kansas City, MO 64110.

GRABOWSKI, CASIMER T(HADDEUS), b. Cleveland, Ohio, Aug. 16, 27; m. 54; c. 1. ZOOLOGY, EMBRYOLOGY. B.S, Western Reserve, 50; Nat. Sci. Found. fel, Hopkins, 52-54, Ph.D.(zool), 54. Jr. instr. biol, Hopkins, 50-52; instr. anat, Univ. Pittsburgh, 54-58, asst. prof, 58-60; assoc. prof. ZOOL, UNIV. MIAMI, 60-67, PROF, 67- AAAS; Am. Soc. Zool; Teratology Soc; Soc. Develop. Biol; Int. Soc. Develop. Biol. Experimental embryology; teratology and embryonic physiology as related to normal and abnormal morphogenesis; effects of teratogenic agents on cardiovascular physiology of mammalian embryos. Address: Dept. of Biology, University of Miami, Coral Gables, FL 33124.

GRABOWSKI, Z(BIGNIEW) W(OJCIECH), b. Plock, Poland, June 22, 31; U.S. citizen; m. 65. NUCLEAR PHYSICS. M.S, Jagiellonian Univ, 54; Fil. lic, Univ. Uppsala, 61, Ph.D.(physics), 62. Teaching asst, Tech. Univ. Gliwice, Poland, 54-55; res. asst. nuclear physics, Nuclear Res. Inst, Poland, 55-58; Univ. Uppsala, 58-62; proj. mgr. physics of Aurora, Kiruna Geophys. Observ, Sweden, 62-63; res. assoc, PURDUE UNIV, 63-65, ASST. PROF. PHYSICS, 65- Physics of Aurora. Address: Dept. of Physics, Purdue University, Lafayette, IN 47907.

GRABOYES, HAROLD, b. Phila, Pa, Mar. 21, 31; m. 54; c. 3. ORGANIC CHEMISTRY. B.A, Temple, 52; M.S, Drexel Inst, 54; Ph.D, Pennsylvania, 57. Control chemist, Publicker Industs, 52-54, res. chemist, 54-57; sr. res. chemist org. chem, SMITH, KLINE & FRENCH LABS, 57-69, SR. INVESTR, 69- AAAS; Am. Chem. Soc. Organic synthesis, especially in the benzenoid, allycylic and heterocyclic fields. Address: Smith, Kline & French Labs, 1500 Spring Garden St, Philadelphia, PA 19104.

GRABSKE, ROBERT JEROLD, b. Independence, Mo, June 29, 36; m. 57; c. 1. BIOCHEMISTRY. B.S, Kansas, 59, M.S, 60, Ph.D.(comp. biochem. & physiol), 64. BIOCHEMIST, LAWRENCE LIVERMORE LAB, UNIV. CALIF, 64- Summer supvr. radiation dept, Marine Biol. Lab, Woods Hole, 60-63, 66. Am. Soc. Cell Biol. Radioactivity in natural water sources; developmental changes in the oxidative capacity of brain tissue; mineral accumulation by mitochondria; electron microscopy of chromatin. Address: Lawrence Livermore Lab, L-523 University of California, Livermore, CA 94551.

GRACA, JOSEPH G(EORGE), b. Minneapolis, Minn, Dec, 20, 13; m. 43; c. 3. PHARMACOLOGY. B.S, Col. of St. Thomas, 39; Ph.D.(pharmacol), Minnesota, 53. Asst. prof. chem. & pharmacol, Macalester Col, 51-53; vet. physiol. & pharmacol, Iowa State, 53-57, assoc. prof, 57-59; coord. dir, Pharmatox Labs, Inc, 59-71; VIS. PROF. VET. PHYSIOL. & PHARMACOL, UNIV. MINN, ST. PAUL, 71- Assoc, Ames Labs, Atomic Energy Comn, 54-59. U.S.A, 43-45. AAAS; Am. Inst. Chem. Neuropharmacology; age-drug relationships; rare earth toxicity. Address: Dept. of Veterinary Physiology & Pharmacology, University of Minnesota, St. Paul, MN 55101.

GRACE, CHARLES T(HERON), b. Boulder, Colo, Feb. 24, 14; m. 37. MECHANICAL ENGINEERING. B.S, Colorado, 36; Yale, 36-37; M.S, Illinois, 41. Student engr, Cooper-Bessemer Eng. Co, Ohio, 38; instr. MECH. ENG, Illinois, 38-42; asst. prof, Iowa State Col, 42-46; assoc. prof. UNIV. N.MEX, 46-49, PROF, 49-, ASST. DEAN ENG, 63-, chmn. dept. mech. eng, 53-63. Machine design consult. Am. Soc. Eng. Educ; Am. Soc. Mech. Eng. Machine design; dynamics. Address: 518 Aliso S.E, Albuquerque, NM 87108.

GRACE, DONALD W(AYNE), b. Pittsburgh, Pa, Nov. 7, 27; m. 47; c. 5. COMPUTER SCIENCE, NUMERICAL ANALYSIS. B.S, Carnegie Inst. Technol, 53, M.S, 54; M.S, Stanford Univ, 63, Ph.D.(computational anal), 65. Mathematician, Procter & Gamble Co, 54-70; ASSOC. PROF. COMPUT. SCI, OKLA. STATE UNIV, 70- C.Eng, U.S.A, 45-49, 1st Lt. Asn. Comput. Mach. Optimization methods, especially mathematical programming; graph theoretic methods in molecular structures. Address: Dept. of Computer Science, Oklahoma State University, Stillwater, OK 74074.

GRACE, EDWARD E(VERETT), b. Gulfport, Miss, Apr. 15, 27; m. 54; c. 3. MATHEMATICS. B.S, North Carolina, 51, univ. fel, 51-52, Nat. Sci. Found. fel, 52-55, Ph.D.(math), 56. Instr. MATH, North Carolina, 55-56; asst. prof, Emory, 56-62; vis. assoc. prof, Georgia, 62-63; PROF, ARIZONA STATE UNIV, 63- Nat. Sci. Found. faculty fel, Wisconsin, 61-62, summers, lectr, 58, res. assoc, 62. U.S.N.R, 45-46. Am. Math. Soc; Math. Asn. Am. Point set topology. Address: 1119 E. Broadmor Dr, Tempe, AZ 85281.

GRACE, HAROLD P(ADGET), b. Parsons, Kans, Apr. 19, 19; m. 42; c. 2. CHEMICAL ENGINEERING. B.S, Pennsylvania, 41. Field engr, eng. dept, E.I. DU PONT DE NEMOURS & CO, INC, 41-44, res. engr, ENG. RES. LAB, 46-52, res. proj. engr, 52-56, res. assoc, 56-71, RES. FEL, 71- Colburn award, Franklin Inst, 56. U.S.N.R, 44-46, Lt.(jg). Am. Chem. Soc; Am. Inst. Chem. Eng. Chemical engineering research and development involving particulate solids, particle mechanics, mechanical separations, particle size analysis, dispersion, mixing, size reduction, and flocculation. Address: 108 N. Concord Ave, Havertown, PA 19083.

GRACE, JOHN NELSON, b. Pittsburgh, Pa, May 27, 24; m. 43, 58; c. 4. ELECTRICAL ENGINEERING. B.S, Carnegie Inst. Tech, 49, Tau Beta Pi fel, 49-50, M.S, 50, Swope fel, 50-51, D.Sc.(elec. eng), 51. Engr, control res. & develop, Res. Labs, WESTINGHOUSE ELEC. CORP, 49, special prods. div, 50, sr. scientist instrumentation & control, BETTIS ATOMIC POWER LAB, WEST MIFFLIN, 50-54, supvr. reactor-plant kinetics, 54-55, MGR, adv. reactor develop, 55-57, reactor physics & kinetics, 57-65, CORE ENG. PHYSICS & KINETICS, 66- Lectr, Carnegie Inst. Technol; Univ. Pittsburgh. U.S.A.A.F; 43-46, 1st Lt. Fel. Am. Nuclear Soc; Inst. Elec. & Electronics Eng. Reactor-plant kinetics; reactor physics; core engineering. Address: 101 Jordom Dr, Bethel Park, PA 15102.

GRACE, JOHN ROSS, b. London, Ont, June 8, 43; m. 64; c. 2. CHEMICAL ENGINEERING. B.E.Sc, Western Ontario, 65; Athlone fel, Cambridge, 65-67, Nat. Res. Coun. Can. scholar, 67-68, Ph.D.(chem. eng), 68. ASSOC. PROF. CHEM. ENG, McGILL UNIV, 68- AAAS; Am. Inst. Chem. Eng; Chem. Inst. Can; Brit. Inst. Chem. Eng. Address: Dept. of Chemical Engineering, McConnell Engineering Bldg, McGill University, Montreal, Que, Can.

GRACE, NORMAN DAVID, b. Worcester, Mass, Sept. 23, 36; m. 60; c. 2. GASTROENTEROLOGY, INTERNAL MEDICINE. A.B, Brown, 58; M.D, Tufts, 62. Asst. clin. instr. MED, Albany Med. Col, 63-65; Nat. Inst. Arthritis & Metab. Diseases res. fel, SCH. MED, TUFTS UNIV, 65-67, instr, 67-69, ASST. PROF, 69- Clin. fel. gastroenterol, Albany Med. Col, 64-65. U.S.A.R, 63-69, Capt. AAAS; Am. Gastroenterol. Asn; Am. Asn. Study Liver Diseases; Am. Fedn. Clin. Res. Liver disease; portal hypertension; iron metabolism; hemochromatosis. Address: 48 Rosalie Rd, Needham, MA 02194.

GRACE, NORMAN S(INGERS), b. Naini Tal, U.P. India, Aug. 15, 06; m. 36; c. 3. PHYSICAL CHEMISTRY. B.Sc, Saskatchewan, 27, Nat. Res. Coun. Can. student, 29-30; Beit sci. fel, Imp. Col, London, 29-31, D.I.C. & Ph.D. (phys. chem), London, 31. Commonwealth Fund res. fel. & res. assoc. chem. & physics, Univ. Calif, 31-33; demonstr. physics, Univ. Toronto, 33-35; res. chemist, Gutta Percha & Rubber Ltd, Toronto, 35-37; Nat. Res. Coun. Can, 37-39; chief chemist, DUNLOP CAN. LTD, 40-45, tech. supt, 45-54, GEN. MGR. DUNLOP RES. CTR, 54- Mgr. tech. serv. div, Polymer Corp, 43-44. Mem. assoc. cmt. synthetic rubber res, Nat. Res. Coun. Am. Chem. Soc; Am. Soc. Test. & Mat; Chem. Inst. Can. Chemistry of rubber, resins and paints; phase rule of hydrated aluminates of calcium; polyiodides of the alkali metals; spectroscopy; hyperfine structure; nuclear studies; low temperature phenomena; colloid chemistry of rubber latex; rubber chemistry; physical testing; developed utilization and manufacture of synthetic rubbers. Address: Dunlop Research Center, Dunlop Canada Ltd, Sheridan Park, Ont, Can.

GRACE, OLIVER D(AVIES), b. Wash, D.C, Dec. 21, 14; m. 48; c. 2. VETERINARY SCIENCE. D.V.M, Colo. Agr. & Mech. Col, 40; M.S, Illinois, 51. Field veterinarian, bur. animal indust, U.S. Dept. Agr, 40-42, veterinarian in charge serol. lab, N.H, 42-46; food & drug admin, Dept. Health, Ed. & Welfare, Illinois, 46-53; head dept. vet. med, Baxter Labs, Inc, 53-55; assoc. prof. VET. SCI, UNIV. NEB, LINCOLN, 55-63, PROF, 63- Dipl, Am. Col. Vet. Microbiol. Am. Vet. Med. Asn; Am. Asn. Avian Path; Conf. Res. Workers Animal Diseases. Etiology, pathogenesis and pathology of the infectious diseases of large animals and poultry. Address: Dept. of Veterinary Science, University of Nebraska, Lincoln, NE 68503.

GRACE, RICHARD E(DWARD), b. Chicago, Ill, June 26, 30; m. 55; c. 2. METALLURGICAL ENGINEERING. B.S.Met.E, Purdue, 51; Jones & Laughlin Steel Corp. fel, Carnegie Inst. Technol, 52-54, Ph.D, 54. Asst. prof. METALL. ENG, PURDUE UNIV, 54-58, assoc. prof, 58-62, PROF, 62-, HEAD SCH, 65-, HEAD DIV. INTERDISCIPLINARY ENG. STUDIES, 70- Prin. res. investr, U.S. Atomic Energy Comn; consult, Midwest Industs; mem. eng. educ. & accreditation comt, Engrs. Coun. Prof. Develop. Am. Soc. Metals (Bradley Stoughton Award, 62); Am. Soc. Eng. Educ; Am. Inst. Mining, Metall. & Petrol. Eng. Metallurgical kinetics; diffusion and mass transport; high temperature oxidation; nonstoichiometric compounds. Address: 2204 Huron Rd, West Lafayette, IN 47906.

GRACE, ROBERT A(MBROSE), b. Milwaukee, Wis, Apr. 7, 13; m. 51; c. 3. MEDICAL PHYSIOLOGY. B.S, Marquette, 38, M.S, 43. Teacher, pub. sch, Fla, 41-42; counselor, voc. guid. ctr, Marquette, 46-51, instr. & res. assoc. med. physiol, sch. med, 52-63; asst. prof. mil. sci. & tactics, Wisconsin, 51-52; assoc. res. physiologist, life support dept, WHIRLPOOL CORP, 63-68, RES. PHYSIOLOGIST, LIFE SCI. DEPT, 68- U.S.A, 42-46, Capt. Sci. Res. Soc. Am. Physiology of stress; cardiovascular physiology; metabolism; nutrition and human factors in space ecologies; industrial hygiene; environmental comfort. Address: Research & Engineering Center, Whirlpool Corp, Monte Rd, Benton Harbor, MI 49022.

GRACE, ROBERT ARCHIBALD, b. London, Ont, Jan. 1, 38. HYDRODYNAMICS, WATER RESOURCES. B.E.Sc, Univ, West. Ont, 60; S.M, Mass. Inst. Technol, 62, Ph.D.(hydrodyn. & water resources), 66. Assoc. res. scientist, Hydronautics, Inc, Md, 61-63; engr, Electricité de France, Chatou, 63; asst. prof. FLUID MECH, UNIV. HAWAII, 66-69, ASSOC. PROF, 70- Am. Soc. Civil Eng; Marine Technol. Soc. Coastal engineering; ocean wave forces on structures; marine disposal of wastes; synthetic hydrologic time series. Address: Dept. of Civil Engineering, University of Hawaii, Honolulu, HI 96822.

GRACE, THOMAS MICHAEL, b. Beaver Dam, Wis, Oct. 3, 38; m. 63; c. 3. CHEMICAL ENGINEERING. B.S, Univ. Wis, Madison, 60; Ph.D, Univ. Minn, Minneapolis, 63. Aerospace technologist, Lewis Res. Ctr, NASA, 63-65; RES. ASSOC. & ASSOC. PROF. CHEM. ENG, INST. PAPER CHEM, 66-, CHMN. DEPT, 70- Air Pollution Control Asn. Chemical recovery technology; heat and mass transfer. Address: 1043 E. South River St, Appleton, WI 54911.

GRACELY, F(REDERICK) R(EICHMAN), b. Des Moines, Iowa, Sept. 22, 11; m. 49. ELECTRONICS. A.B, Drake, 33; B.S, Iowa State Col, 34, E.E, 44; M.A, American Univ, 53. Teacher, pub. sch, Iowa, 35-36; physicist-radio engr, Nat. Bur. Standards, Wash, D.C, 38-45; elec. engr, Fed. Communications Comn, 46-48; opers. analyst, U.S. Air Force, 51-60; SPACE & AERONAUT. SCIENTIST, NASA, 60- Nat. Bur. Standards & dept. terrestrial magnetism, Carnegie Institution Exped, Greenland, 41. Civilian with Office Sci. Res. & Develop, 44. Oper. Res. Soc. Am; Am. Soc. Info. Sci. Radio wave propagation; ionosphere research; operations and systems analysis. Address: 1734 P St. N.W, Washington, DC 20036.

GRACIA, ALBERT J(OSEPH), b. Cambridge, Mass, Oct. 11, 05; m. 29; c. 2. CHEMICAL ENGINEERING. B.S, Mass. Inst. Tech, 28. Chem. engr, Goodyear Tire & Rubber Co, 28-33, sect. head synthetic rubber, 33-41, mgr. chem. eng. div, 41-50, asst. to v.pres, 50-52, gen. mgr, Goodyear Atomic Corp, 52-56, mgr. res. & develop, 56-61, v.pres, 61-69; RETIRED. Civilian with Off. Rubber Reserve, 44; trustee, Defiance Col, 53. Am. Chem. Soc; Inst. Chem. Eng. Rubber coagulation improvements; organic accelerator developments; processing techniques for resins; monomer preparation. Address: 2414 Kensington Rd. Akron, OH 44313.

GRACIAS, CECILIO EUGENIO, b. Macao, Sept. 2, 28; m. 55; c. 2. ANALYTICAL CHEMISTRY, SPECTROSCOPY. Ch.Eng, Lisbon Tech, 54, M.Ch.Eng, 57; Portuguese Shell Oil Co. fel, 57-61; Minn. Mining & Mfg. Co. fel, 60-61; Ph.D.(chem), Minnesota, 62. Instr. anal. chem, inst. adv. tech, Lisbon Tech, 54-57, lectr, 56-57; asst. quant. anal, Minnesota, 59-60; res. chemist, E.I. du Pont de Nemours & Co, 61-64; asst. prof. chem, col. pharm, Univ. Ill, 64-67; GROUP LEADER ANAL, COATED ABRASIVE DIV, NORTON CO, 67- Asst, Nuclear Energy Ctrs, Portugal, 54-57; summers, Univ. Minn, 59, 60, 61. AAAS; Am. Chem. Soc; Soc. Appl. Spectros. Ionic and molecular interactions in non-aqueous media; applied spectroscopy; analytical instrumentation; microanalysis; electron and optical microscopy; polymer analysis; gas chromatography; electroanalysis; wet chemistry. Address: 4026 Buckingham Dr, Schenectady, NY 12304.

GRACIE, G(ORDON), b. Toronto, Ont, Sept. 11, 30; m. 58; c. 2. PHOTOGRAMMETRY. B.A.Sc, Toronto, 52; Int. Training Centre Aerial Surv, 55-57; Ph.D.(civil eng), Illinois, 63. Proj. engr. aerial surv, Photographic Surv. Corp, 52-55; instr. civil eng, Illinois, 57-63, asst. prof, 63-65, sr. scientist photogram, autometric opers, Raytheon Co, 65-71; PROF. GEOG, UNIV. TORONTO, 71- Am. Soc. Civil Eng; Am. Soc. Photogram; Am. Cong. Surv. & Mapping; Soc. Photo-Optical Instrumentation Eng; Can. Inst. Surv. Aerial surveying; photogrammetry; surveying; analytical photogrammetry; non-topographic photogrammetry; statistics. Address: Erindale College, University of Toronto, Clarkson, Ont, Can.

GRACY, ROBERT WAYNE, b. McKinney, Tex, Dec. 30, 41; m. 63. BIOCHEMISTRY. B.S, Calif. State Polytech. Col, 64; Nat. Defense Ed. Act fel, California, Riverside, 64-68, Ph.D.(biochem), 68. Chemist, Space Gen, El Monte, Calif, 63-64; Damon Runyon fel. molecular biol, Albert Einstein Col. Med, 68-70; ASST. PROF. BIOCHEM, N.TEX. STATE UNIV, 70- Lectr, Calif. State Polytech. Col, 63-64. AAAS; Am. Chem. Soc. Protein chemistry and enzymology; structure and function of enzymes and relation to catalytic mechanisms; physical, chemical and catalytic properties of enzymes, especially metalloproteins and metabolic diseases. Address: Dept. of Chemistry, North Texas State University, Denton, TX 76203.

GRAD, ARTHUR, b. Stryj, Austria, Jan. 31, 18; nat; m. 46; c. 2. MATHEMATICS. B.S, City Col. New York, 38; A.M, Columbia, 39; Ph.D.(math), Stanford, 48. Mathematician, U.S. Coast & Geod. Surv, 41-46; res. assoc. & acting instr. math, Stanford, 46-48; mathematician, Off. Naval Res, 48-53; comput. facility, Atomic Energy Cmn, N.Y. Univ, 53-54; head math. br, Off. Naval Res, 54-59; prog. dir. math. sci. & head math. sci. sect, Nat. Sci. Found, 59-63; assoc. dean grad. div, Stanford, 63-64; prof. math. & dean grad. sch, Ill. Inst. Technol, 64-71; PRES, POLYTECH. INST. BROOKLYN, 71- Lectr, Univ. Md, 49-53; mem. comt. expert exam, U.S. Civil Serv. Comn, 51-53; liaison rep, div. math, Nat. Acad. Sci-Nat. Res. Coun, 59-63, mem. comt. on travel grants, 60-63, liaison rep, comt. on use of electronic comput, 62-63, mem. comt. on sources & forms of support, div. math, 69-, chmn, 70- AAAS; Am. Math. Soc; Math. Asn. Am. Functions of a complex variable, conformal mapping; schlicht functions. Address: Polytechnic Institute of Brooklyn, 333 Jay St, Brooklyn, NY 11201.

GRAD, B(ERNARD), b. Montreal, Que, Feb. 4, 20; m. 48; c. 2. BIOLOGY. B.Sc, McGill, 44, Banting fel, 47-48, Nat. Cancer Inst. Can. fel, 48-49, Ph.D.(exp. morphol), 49. Asst. endocrinol, geront. & cancer, McGILL UNIV, 49-55, lectr, 55-61, asst. prof, 61-65, ASSOC. PROF, 65- Ed, Excerpta Medica, 58- Ciba Found. award, 55. Geront. Soc; Am. Asn. Cancer Res; Can. Physiol. Soc. Endocrinology of thyroid and adrenal and their role in aging; cancer and organic psychoses; etiology and pathogenesis of leukemia; biopoesis; biomagnetics; anti-stress compounds. Address: 4936 Kent Ave, Montreal 252, Que, Can.

GRAD, HAROLD, b. New York, N.Y, Jan. 14, 23; m. 49; c. 2. MATHEMATICS. B.E.E, Cooper Union, 43; M.S, N.Y. Univ, 45, Ph.D.(appl. math), 48. Asst. prof. MATH, N.Y. UNIV, 48-53, assoc. prof, 53-57, PROF, 57-, DIR. MAGNETO-FLUID DYNAMICS DIV, COURANT INST. MATH. SCI, 60- Mem. adv. comt. thermonuclear, Oak Ridge Nat. Lab, 64-67. Boris Pregel Award, N.Y. Acad. Sci, 70. Nat. Acad. Sci; fel. AAAS; fel. Am. Phys. Soc; Am. Math. Soc. Kinetic theory; statistical mechanics; gas dynamics; magnetohydrodynamics; plasma physics; controlled thermonuclear fusion. Address: Courant Institute of Mathematical Sciences, New York University, New York, NY 10012.

GRAD, PETER P(AUL), b. Vienna, Austria, Sept. 11, 21; nat; m. 42. CHEMICAL ENGINEERING. B.S, Polytech. Inst. Brooklyn, 49. Chemist, Reichhold Chems, Inc, N.Y, 42-43; chem. engr, Gar-Baker Labs, Inc, 43-44, 46-49; chief analyst, Borden Co, 49-52; chief chemist, Aerovox Corp, 52-56, tech. dir, 56-60; chief chem. engr, Rotron Mfg. Co, 60-70, MGR. MFG. ENG, ROTRON INC, 70- Mem. bd. trustees, New Bedford Inst. Tech. Chemist, Navy Med. Center, U.S.N, 44-46. Am. Mgt. Asn; Am. Chem. Soc; Electrochem. Soc; Soc. Plastic Eng; Inst. Elec. & Electronics Eng. Plastics; insulation; dielectrics; solid state electronic components; project engineering; technical management. Address: Manufacturing Engineering Dept, Rotron Inc, Woodstock, NY 12498.

GRADISHAR, FREDERICK J(OHN), b. Aurora, Minn, Feb. 9, 18; m. 44; c. 3. CHEMICAL ENGINEERING. B.Ch.E, Minnesota, 40; M.S, Kansas State, 41; Ph.D.(chem. eng), Va. Polytech, 48. Res. engr, Westvaco Chlorine Prod. Div, FMC Corp, W.Va, 41-42; eng. officer uranium processing, Naval Res. Lab, D.C. & Phila, 43-46, res. engr. fluorine processes, JACKSON LAB, E.I. DU PONT DE NEMOURS & CO, INC, 48-52, res. supvr, 52-56, head eng. div, 57-63, res. assoc, 63-70, RES. DIR. & HEAD, 70- U.S.N, 43-46, Lt.(jg). AAAS; Am. Inst. Chem. Eng; Am. Chem. Soc. Halogenation processes; electrochemistry; economic evaluations. Address: Jackson Lab, E.I. du Pont de Nemours & Co, Inc, P.O. Box 525, Wilmington, DE 19898.

GRADSTEN, MARCEL A(LDOUS), b. Brussels, Jan. 24, 08; nat; m. 49; c. 1. ORGANIC CHEMISTRY. Ph.D.(chem), Frankfurt, 32. Littauer Res. Found. fel. sulfonamides, N.Y. Univ, 42-43; RES. CHEMIST, rubber accelerators & plasticizers, J.M. Huber Corp, 44; textile chemicals, org. synthesis, Sun Chem. Corp, 45-49; bactericides, fungicides; insecticides, & agr. chem, Heyden Newport Chem. Corp, 50-62; Hogan Faximile Corp, 62-64; ARGUS CHEM. CORP, 65- AAAS; Am. Chem. Soc. Organic synthesis. Address: 48 Everett Rd, Demarest, NJ 07627.

GRADY, HAROLD JAMES, b. Excelsior Springs, Mo, May 3, 20; m. 44; c. 5. BIOCHEMISTRY. Ph.D.(biochem), St. Louis, 51. Asst. prof. biochem. & med, MED. CENTER, UNIV. KANS, 50-55, assoc. prof. BIOCHEM. IN PATH, 55-65, PROF, 65- Consult, Vet. Admin, General, Research & Baptist hosps, Kansas City. U.S.N.R, 44-46. AAAS; Am. Soc. Clin. Path; Am. Chem. Soc; Am. Asn. Clin. Chem. Steroid metabolism and clinical chemistry. Address: 3510 W. 73rd St, Prairie Village, KS 66208.

GRADY, HAROLD R(OY), b. Wooster, Ohio, Aug. 8, 22; m. 45; c. 3. PHYSICAL CHEMISTRY. A.B, Wooster Col, 43; Ph.D.(chem), Brown, 49. Res. chemist, Manhattan Proj, Oak Ridge, Tenn, 44-46; prof. chem. & head dept, Muskingum Col, 49-53, 54-55; cryog. engr, H.L. Johnston, Inc, 53-54; dir. chem. res, Vanadium Corp. Am, Ohio, 55-67; mgr. vanadium chem. res, FOOTE MINERAL CO, 67-71, GEN. MGR, LITHIUM BATTERY DEPT, 71- Am. Chem. Soc; Am. Phys. Soc; Electrochem. Soc. Infrared spectroscopy; vanadium compounds; analytical chemistry; metallurgy. Address: Foote Mineral Co, Route 100, Exton, PA 19341.

GRADY, HUGH G(ERARD), b. Phila, Pa, Aug. 4, 09; m. 34; c. 4. PATHOLOGY. A.B, St. Joseph's Col.(Pa), 30; M.D, Jefferson Med. Col, 34. Intern, Phila. Gen. Hosp, 34-36, res. pathologist, 36-37; instr. path, Jefferson Med. Col, 37-38; res. fel, Nat. Cancer Inst, Mass. & Md, 38-42; from asst. to assoc. prof. path, Jefferson Med. Col, 46-48; sci. dir, Am. Registry Path, 49-54; chief, path. div, Armed Forces Inst. Path, 54-56; PROF. PATH, COL. MED. & DENT. N.J, NEWARK, 57-, chmn. dept, 57-69. PATHOLOGIST, St. Mary's Hosp, 46-48. U.S.A, 42-46. Am. Asn. Path. & Bact; Am. Soc. Exp. Path; Am. Med. Asn. Tumors induced by hydrocarbons; ultraviolet; estrogens; azo dyes; histogenesis of lung tumors; pathology of genital tract and breast. Address: College of Medicine & Dentistry of New Jersey at Newark, 100 Bergen St, Newark, NJ 07103.

GRADY, JOSEPH E(DWARD), b. Plains, Pa, Apr. 1, 27; m. 54; c. 4. MICROBIOLOGY. B.S, Scranton, 48; M.S, Purdue, 51, Nat. Insts. Health fel, 57-58, Ph.D, 58. MICROBIOLOGIST, Lederle Labs. div, Am. Cyanamid Co, 51-54; UPJOHN CO, 58- U.S.N. 45-46. AAAS; Am. Soc. Microbiol; N.Y. Acad. Sci. Antibiotics, screening, in vitro and in vivo evaluation. Address: Upjohn Co, Kalamazoo, MI 49001.

GRADY, LEE TIMOTHY, b. Chicago, Ill, Mar. 21, 37; m. 64; c. 2. PHARMACEUTICAL ANALYSIS. B.S, Illinois, 59, Nat. Sci. Found. fels, 59-61, Ph.D. (org. chem), 63. Sr. res. pharmacologist, Merck Inst. Therapeut. Res, 65-68; SR. SUPVR. DRUG STANDARDS LAB, AM. PHARMACEUT. ASN. FOUND, 68- AAAS; Am. Chem. Soc; Acad. Pharmaceut. Sci. Physical organic chemistry; drug metabolism; medicinal chemistry; chromatography; analytical chemistry; drug assay. Address: Drug Standards Lab, American Pharmaceutical Association Foundation, 2215 Constitution Ave, N.W, Washington, DC 20037.

GRAEBEL, WILLIAM P(AUL), b. Manitowoc, Wis, July 15, 32; m. 54; c. 2. ENGINEERING MECHANICS. B.S, Wisconsin, 54, M.S, 55; Ph.D.(eng. mech), Michigan, 59. Mem. tech. staff, Bell Labs, Inc, 55-56; instr. ENG. MECH, UNIV. MICH, 56-59, asst. prof, 59-62, assoc. prof, 62-67, PROF, 67- Am. Phys. Soc; Soc. Indust. & Appl. Math; Am. Soc. Mech. Eng. Fluid mechanics. Address: Dept. of Engineering Mechanics, University of Michigan, Ann Arbor, MI 48104.

GRAEBERT, ERIC W, b. Laren, Holland, Jan. 20, 24; U.S. citizen; m. 46; c. 3. CHEMICAL ENGINEERING. B.S.Che.E, Pittsburgh, 49. Prod. mgr. alkali dept, PROCTER & GAMBLE CO, 49-50, distillation dept, 50-51, hydrogenation dept, 51-52, chem. engr, 52-54, prod. develop. engr, 54-56, tech. serv. engr, 56-60, mgr. tech. serv. dept, 61-71, HEAD DEPT. INDUST. FOOD PROD, ENGLAND, 71- Mem. res. comt, Nat. Peanut Coun, 66- Am. Asn. Cereal Chem. Detailed knowledge of the technology of foodstuffs from field to finished product, including edible fats, peanuts, flour, sugar, potatoes, starch, fruits, nuts and food flavors. Address: 7375 Drake Rd, Cincinnati, OH 45243.

GRAEBNER, JOHN E, b. Wilkinsburg, Pa, Dec. 19, 39. PHYSICS, MATHEMATICS. B.S, Valparaiso Univ, 61; Ph.D.(physics), Northwest. Univ, 68. Asst. reactor physics, Brookhaven Nat. Lab, summer 61; MEM. TECH. STAFF, BELL TEL. LABS, 67- Electronic structure of metals; low temperature techniques. Address: Bell Telephone Labs, Murray Hill, NJ 07974.

GRAEF, E(LBRIDGE) R(UHL), b. N.Y.C, Mar. 29, 20; m. 57; c. 4. CHEMICAL ENGINEERING. B.S, Princeton, 41, M.S, 42. Chem. engr, res. div, E.I. DU PONT DE NEMOURS & CO, INC, Del, 42-50, asst. tech. supt, Victoria Plant, Tex, 50-52, tech. supt, Sabine River Works, 52-53, asst. tech. mgr, Belle Works, 53-57, tech. mgr, 57-58, RES. MGR, INDUST. & BIOCHEM. RES. LAB, EXP. STA, 62- U.S.N, 44-46, Lt.(jg). Am. Chem. Soc; Am. Inst. Chem. Eng. Process development of industrial chemicals. Address: Industrial & Biochemicals Research Lab, Experimental Station, E.I. du Pont de Nemours & Co, Inc, Wilmington, DE 19898.

GRAEF, IRVING PHILIP, b. New York, N.Y, Mar. 21, 02; m. 31; c. 2. PATHOLOGY, INTERNAL MEDICINE. A.B, Cornell, 23, M.D, 26. Fel. med, col. med, N.Y. UNIV-BELLEVUE MED. CTR, 29-30, instr, 30-31, path, 31-34, asst. prof, 34-36, assoc. prof, 36-46, asst. prof. CLIN. MED, 46-48, ASSOC. PROF, POST-GRAD. MED. SCH, 48-, pathologist, polio res. proj, 46-52. Asst. pathologist, Bellevue Hosp, 31-34, pathologist, 41-46; assoc. attend. physician, 3rd N.Y. Univ. Med. Div, Goldwater Mem. Hosp, 46-50; attend. consult, U.S. Vet. Admin. Bronx Hosp, 46-50; assoc. vis. physician, 4th med. div, Bellevue Hosp, N.Y. Univ, 48-52, vis. physician, 52-; attend. physician, Lenox Hill Hosp, 55-66, dir. med, 66, consult. physician, 66-; attend. physician, Univ. Hosp, 61-; consult. physician, Monmouth Mem. Hosp. Mem, coun. arteriosclerosis, Am. Heart Asn. Dipl, Am. Bd. Path. With Nat. Defense Coun; consult to U.S. Secy. War. Med.C, 43-46, Lt. Col; Commendation ribbon with two stars. Soc. Exp. Biol. & Med.(secy-treas, 53-55); Am. Soc. Exp. Path; Endocrine Soc; Harvey Soc; Am. Heart Asn; Am. Asn. Path. & Bact; fel. Am. Diabetes Asn.(ed, Jour, 60-66); fel. Am. Col. Physicians; Am. Fedn. Clin. Res; fel. N.Y. Acad. Med; affiliate mem, Royal Soc. Internal Med; Int. Soc. Internal Med. Metabolic disorders; experimental lipid pneumonia; war gas research; effects of nitrogen and sulfur mustards gases; cardiovascular and renal diseases; arteriosclerosis. Address: 791 Park Ave, New York, NY 10021.

GRAEF, PHILIP E(DWIN), b. New York, N.Y, Oct. 29, 23; m. 49; c. 1. BIOLOGY. A.B, Emory & Henry Col, 47; M.A, George Peabody Col, 48; Ph.D.(biol), Virginia, 55. Asst. prof. chem, Bridgewater Col, 48-50; BIOL, E.Carolina Col, 55-57; PROF, COLUMBIA COL.(S.C), 57-, CHMN. DEPT. SCI, 71- Nat. Sci. Found. summer grant, 47. U.S.N. 43-46. Nat. Asn. Biol. Teachers; Am. Inst. Biol. Sci. Megasporogenesis, ovule development and megagametogenesis of flowering plants. Address: Dept. of Science, Columbia College, Columbia, SC 29203.

GRAEF, WALTER L, b. Staten Island, N.Y, Jan. 17, 38; m. 65; c. 1. ORGANIC & PHARMACEUTICAL CHEMISTRY. B.S, Albany Col. Pharm, Union (N.Y), 59; M.S, Wisconsin, 61, Nat. Insts. Health fel, 61-63, Ph.D. (pharmaceut. chem), 63. Res. chemist org. chem, dyes div, E.I. du Pont de Nemours & Co, 63-64; asst. prof. pharmaceut. chem, Fordham Univ, 64-66; asst. ed, CHEM. ABSTR. SERV, 66-71, MGR. ORG. INDEXING DEPT, 71- Am. Chem. Soc. Sterochemical requirements for ganglionic blockade; synthesis of short chain mono- and bis- quaternary ammonium compounds. Address: Chemical Abstracts Service, 2540 Olentangy River Rd, Columbus, OH 43210.

GRAEFF, DANIEL MACK, b. Gordon, Nebr, Jan. 17, 42; m. 63; c. 2. PHARMACOLOGY. B.S, Univ. Wyo, 65; Nat. Sci. Found. fel. & Ph.D.(pharmacol), Wash. State Univ, 70. ASST. PROF. PHARMACOL, DRAKE UNIV, 70- Cardiovascular pharmacology and molecular mechanisms of drug action. Address: Dept. of Pharmacology, Drake University, 28th & Forest, Des Moines, IA 50311.

GRAEME, MARY LEE, b. Valentines, Va, Aug. 20, 22; div. BIOLOGY. B.A, Richmond, 44; North Carolina, 44-45. Asst. endocrinol, spec. proj, North Carolina, 45-46; Michigan, 46-47; PHARMACOL, Ciba Pharmaceut. Co, N.J, 47-51; res. asst, Johnson & Johnson & Ethicon, Inc, N.J, 51-60; Ortho Pharmaceut. Co, N.J, 60-61; GROUP LEADER, Geigy Chem. Corp, 61-71; PHARMACOL. DEPT, CIBA-GEIGY CORP, 71- Am. Soc. Pharmacol. & Exp. Therapeut. Cardiovascular uterine physiology; arthritis in animals; general pharmacology. Address: Dept. of Pharmacology, Ciba-Geigy Corp, Ardsley, NY 10502.

GRAESSLE, OTTO E(DWARD), b. Elizabeth, N.J, Nov. 26, 16; m. 41; c. 7. CHEMOTHERAPY. B.A, N.Y. Univ, 43; Ph.D.(microbiol), Rutgers, 49. Res. assoc, MERCK INST, 47-49, asst. to dir, 49-57, RES. ASSOC, 57- Am. Soc. Microbiol; N.Y. Acad. Sci; Asn. Gnotobiotics. Pharmacological and chemotherapeutic properties of antibiotics; hormones and resistance to infection; bacterial endotoxins; reticuloendothelial system; non-specific resistance. Address: Merck Institute for Therapeutic Research, Rahway, NJ 07065.

GRAESSLEY, WILLIAM W(ALTER), b. Muskegon, Mich, Sept. 10, 33; m. 52; c. 3. CHEMICAL ENGINEERING. B.S. & B.S.E, Michigan, 56, Nat. Sci. Found. fel, 56-59, M.S.E, 57, Ph.D.(chem. eng), 60. Sr. chemist, Air Reduction Co, N.J, 59-63; asst. prof. CHEM. ENG. & MAT. SCI, NORTHWEST. UNIV.(ILL), 63-66, assoc. prof, 66-69, PROF, 69- Am. Chem. Soc; Am. Inst. Chem. Eng; Am. Phys. Soc; Soc. Rheol. High polymers, particularly flow properties and relationship between polymerization conditions and structure. Address: Dept. of Chemical Engineering, Northwestern University, Evanston, IL 60201.

GRAETZER, HANS G(UNTHER), b. Ger, Feb. 13, 30; U.S. citizen; m. 57; c. 4. PHYSICS. B.A, Oberlin Col, 52; M.S, Yale, 53, Ph.D.(physics), 56. Assoc. prof. PHYSICS, S.DAK. STATE UNIV, 56-70, PROF, 70- Nat. Sci. Found. fel, Univ. Colo, 63-64; summers, partic, Inst. Oak Ridge Nat. Lab, 57, res. assoc, Argonne Nat. Lab, 59, physicist, Naval Radiol. Defense Lab, 61, mem. staff, Smithsonian Inst, 70. Am. Asn. Physics Teachers; Fedn. Am. Sci; Am. Phys. Soc. Nuclear reactions; gamma ray spectroscopy; elastic proton scattering; history of science and technology. Address: Dept. of Physics, South Dakota State University, Brookings, SD 57007.

GRAETZER, REINHARD, b. Ger, Sept. 28, 33; U.S. citizen; m. 62; c. 2. NUCLEAR PHYSICS. A.B, Oberlin Col, 55; M.A, Wisconsin, 57, Ph.D.(physics), 62. Ford Found. fel, Inst. Theoret. Physics, Denmark, 62-64; res. assoc. & instr. PHYSICS, Wisconsin, 64-65; ASST. PROF, PA. STATE UNIV, 65- Vis. sr. res. assoc, Univ. Colo, Boulder, 71-72. Am. Phys. Soc. Experimental nuclear structure; coulomb excitation; multiple coulomb excitation; nuclear spectroscopy; internal conversion. Address: Dept. of Physics, Pennsylvania State University, University Park, PA 16802.

GRAEVE, ROLF E, b. Kassel, Ger, Nov. 1, 33; m. 61; c. 4. ORGANIC & MEDICINAL CHEMISTRY. M.S, Brunswick Tech, 59, Dr.rer.nat, 61; Tech. Univ, Berlin, 59-61. Asst. res. scientist & fel. org. chem, N.Y. Univ, 61-63; res. assoc. & fel, Hopkins, 63-64; GROUP LEADER MED. CHEM, Aldrich Chem. Co, 64-70; PHARM. CHEM. RES. DEPT, CHEMISCHE WERKE ALBERT, 70- Am. Chem. Soc; Soc. Ger. Chem. Synthetic organic and medicinal chemistry. Address: Pharmaceutical Chemistry Research Dept, Chemische Werke Albert, Albertstr. 10, 6202 Wiesbaden-Biebrich, Germany.

GRAF, CARL JOHN, b. Buffalo, N.Y, Nov. 20, 17; m. 46; c. 2. NEUROLOGY. Canisius Col, 35-37; M.D, Buffalo, 41. Fels. neuropath. & neurophysiol, Ill. Neuropsychiat. Inst, Univ. Illinois, 44-45; assoc. prof. NEUROL. SURG, MED. SCH, UNIV. IOWA, 67-68, PROF, 68- Consult, DeGraff Mem. Hosp,

Tonawanda, N.Y; Tri-County Mem. Hosp, Warsaw; Olean Gen. Hosp; Niagara Falls Mem. Hosp; Buffalo State Hosp; U.S. Pub. Health Serv. Outpatient Clin, Buffalo; Brooks Mem. Hosp, Dunkirk; Lake Shore Intercommunity Hosp, Silver Creek; Vet. Admin. Hosp, Iowa City, Iowa. Med.C, U.S.A.R, 56, Maj. Honor al Merito, U.S.S. Hope, Peru, 63. Neurosurg. Soc. Am. (v.pres, 53-54, pres, 60-61; Am. Acad. Neurol; Am. Col. Surg; Am. Med. Asn; Am. Asn. Neurol. Surg; Pan-Am. Med. Asn.(exec. secy, 59-60); Royal Med. Soc; Scandinavian Neurosurg. Soc; N.Y. Acad. Sci. Neurological surgery; origin and treatment of intracranial aneurysms; problems in pain with attention to aberrant pain pathways; treatment of carotid; cavernous fistula. Address: Dept. of Surgery, University Hospitals, University of Iowa School of Medicine, Iowa City, IA 52240.

GRAF, DOLORES IRMA, b. Mount Pleasant, Iowa, Mar. 22, 41. ECOLOGY, PLANT MORPHOLOGY. B.A, Iowa Wesleyan Col, 63; M.S, Iowa State, 65, summer honorarium, 68 & 69, Ph.D.(bot), 69; Colorado, summer 68. Instr. BIOL, IOWA WESLEYAN COL, 65-67, asst. prof, 67-69, ASSOC. PROF, 69- Distribution patterns of Eastern Red Cedar in Iowa. Address: Dept. of Biology, Iowa Wesleyan College, Mount Pleasant, IA 52641.

GRAF, DONALD L(EE), b. Howard Co, Iowa, Jan. 24, 25; div. GEOCHEMISTRY. Geol.E, Colo. Sch. Mines, 45; A.M Columbia, 47, Ph.D. (mineral), 50. Geologist, indust. minerals div, Ill. State Geol. Surv, 48-63, geochemist, chem. group, 63-65; prof. geol. & geophys, Univ. Minn, Minneapolis, 65-69; PROF. GEOL, UNIV. ILL, URBANA, 69- Res. fel. geophys, Harvard, 61-63. Fel. Am. Geophys. Union; fel. Geol. Soc. Am; fel. Mineral. Soc. Am.(award, 60). Sedimentary mineralogy and geochemistry. Address: Dept. of Geology, University of Illinois, Urbana, IL 61801.

GRAF, E(DWARD) R(AYMOND), b. Cullman, Ala, Sept. 26, 31; m. 61; c. 1. ELECTRICAL ENGINEERING. B.Sc, Auburn, 57, M.Sc, 58; Ph.D.(elec. eng), Stuttgart Tech, 63. Asst. prof. ELEC. ENG, Auburn, 58-59; asst. German Res. Found, 60-63; assoc. prof, AUBURN UNIV, 63-69, PROF, 69- Consult, U.S. Army Missile Command, Redstone Arsenal & George C. Marshall Space Flight Center, 63- U.S.A.F, 51-55. Asn. Ger. Eng. Electromagnetic field theory; antennas and propagation; laser. Address: Dept. of Electrical Engineering, Auburn University, Auburn, AL 36830.

GRAF, ERLEND H(AAKON), b. Oslo, Norway, Oct. 21, 39; U.S. citizen; m. 68. LOW TEMPERATURE PHYSICS. B.S, Mass. Inst. Tech, 61; Ph.D.(physics), Cornell, 68. ASST. PROF. PHYSICS, STATE UNIV. N.Y. STONY BROOK, 67- Am. Phys. Soc. Liquid and solid helium; solid hydrogen; nuclear magnetic resonance. Address: Dept. of Physics, State University of New York at Stony Brook, Stony Brook, NY 11790.

GRAF, G(OTTFRIED) C(HRISTIAN), b. Louisville, Ky, Jan. 23, 11; m. 38. PHYSIOLOGY. B.S, Mich. State, 34; M.S, Minnesota, 40, Ph.D.(physiol), 51. Teacher, pub. sch, Mich, 34-35; dairy supvr, Connecticut, 35-42, instr, 42-43, asst. prof. nutrit. & asst. dairy specialist, 43-45; assoc. prof. & assoc. dairy specialist, VA. POLYTECH. INST. & STATE UNIV, 45-50, assoc. prof. nutrit. & physiol, 50-52, PROF. DAIRY SCI, 52-, head dept, 52-64. AAAS; Am. Soc. Animal Sci; Am. Dairy Sci. Asn. Urea as a feed for dairy cattle; stress conditions in dairy cattle; comparative value of hard and commercially softened water for lactating dairy cattle; pasture evaluation; feed digestibility techniques; arsanilic acid in calf rations; physiology of lactation; role of hormones in milk secretion; ejection and plasma levels of oxytocin in cattle. Address: Dept. of Dairy Science, Virginia Polytechnic Institute & State University, Blacksburg, VA 24061.

GRAF, J(OHN) E(NOS), b. Banning, Calif, May 28, 89; m. 31. ENTOMOLOGY. A.B, Pomona Col, 10. Asst. entom, bur. entom, U.S. Dept. Agr, 11-15; entomologist, Ky. Tobacco Prod. Co, 16; asst. entom, bur. entom, U.S. Dept. Agr, 17-18, entomologist in charge field work, truck crop insect invests, Fla. & Ala, 18-23, entomologist in charge truck crop insects, 23-26, sr. & prin. entomologist, 26-31; asst. chief, bur. entom, 28-31; assoc. dir, U.S. Nat. Mus, 31-45, asst. secy, SMITHSONIAN INST, 45-58, FEL, 58- Mem. fed. hort. bd, U.S. Dept. Agr, 26-31. AAAS; Am. Med. Asn. Biology and control of truck crop insects. Address: 2035 Parkside Dr, Washington, DC 20012.

GRAF, LISELOTTE, b. Vienna, Austria, Sept. 5, 10; nat. PATHOLOGY, IMMUNOLOGY. M.D, Vienna, 37. Instr. path, med. sch, Columbia, 42-45; sr. pathologist, State Dept. Health, N.Y, 45-58; assoc, Sloan-Kettering Inst. Cancer Res, 58-65, head sect. immunol, 59-65; mem. staff, dept. path, Albert Einstein Col. Med, 65-68; RES. PATHOLOGIST, DEPT. NEUROSCI, N.Y. STATE PSYCHIAT. INST, 68- Dipl, Am. Bd. Path, 57. Am. Asn. Immunol. Experimental pathology. Address: 722 W. 168th St, New York, NY 10032.

GRAF, LLOYD H(ERBERT), b. Wis, Sept. 14, 19; m. 43; c. 6. BIOLOGICAL CHEMISTRY. B.S, Wisconsin, 41, M.S, 43, Ph.D.(biochem), 48. Biochemist, U.S. ARMY BIOL. LABS, 48-53, SUPVRY. BIOCHEMIST, PHYS. DEFENSE DIV, 53- U.S.N.R, 44-46. Sci. Res. Soc. Am. Microbial nutrition and physiology; analytical biochemistry. Address: 618 Wilson Pl, Frederick, MD 21701.

GRAF, PETER E(MIL), b. Baltimore, Md, Mar. 31, 30; m. 58; c. 3. PHYSICAL CHEMISTRY. B.S, Rochester, 51; Minn. Mining & Mfg. Co. fel, Wisconsin, 54-55, Ph.D.(phys. chem), 56. Res. chemist, Calif. Res. Corp, 56-66; SR. RES. CHEMIST, CHEVRON RES. CORP, 66- Am. Chem. Soc. Chemical kinetics; photochemistry; non-electrolyte solutions; colloid chemistry; emulsion theory and technology. Address: 253 Manzanita Dr, Orinda, CA 94563.

GRAF, WALTER H, b. Baden, Austria, Mar. 7, 36; m. 63. CIVIL ENGINEERING, HYDRAULICS. Dipl.Ing, Vienna, 59; Ph.D.(civil eng), California, Berkeley, 63. Tech. asst. eng, Austrian State Forest Dept, 56; Danube Hydropower Auth. & surveyor consult. bur, 57; engr, Finnish Waterways & Hwy. Dept, Helsinki, 58; design engr, Consult Off, Vienna, 59-60; teaching asst, California, Berkeley, 60-62; lectr. ext. serv, 61-63, res. asst, 62-63; asst. prof. CIVIL ENG, Cornell Univ, 63-68; ASSOC. PROF. & DIR. HYDRAUL. & SANIT. ENG. LAB, LEHIGH UNIV, 68- Top award, Bavarian

Acad. Sci, Ger, 67. Am. Soc. Civil Eng; Austrian Eng. Soc; Int. Asn. Hydraul. Res. River and fluvial hydraulics; sedimentation and pipes hydraulics. Address: Dept. of Civil Engineering, Lehigh University, Bethlehem, PA 18015.

GRAF, WILLIAM, b. Odessa, Russia, Jan. 29, 13; nat; m. 37; c. 2. ZOOLOGY. B.S, Oregon State Col, 38, M.A, 39, Ph.D.(zool), 43; Mich. State Col, 39-40. Lab. asst. zool, Ore. State Col, 36-37, asst, 37-39; Mich. State Col, 39-40; field biologist, Ore. State Game Cmn, 43; asst. prof, biol, Ariz. State Teachers Col, 46-47; from asst. prof. zool. to PROF. CONSERV, SAN JOSE STATE COL, 47- U.S.A, 42-45. Am. Soc. Mammal; Wildlife Soc; Ecol. Soc. Am; Ger. Mammal. Soc. Ecological and economic studies of mammals and birds; natural history of the Roosevelt elk; field zoology life histories and behavior management of mammals; New Zealand and Hawaii deer investigations. Address: 146 Pleasant Ridge Ave, San Jose, CA 95114.

GRAFF, ALAN R(OBERT), b. Chicago, Ill, June 1, 10; m. 40; c. 3. CHEMICAL ENGINEERING. B.Chem, Cornell, 32, Ch.E, 33. Indust. engr, indust. eng. div, E.I. du Pont de Nemours & Co, N.J, 33-35, design engr, Del, 35-38; chem. engr. & v.pres, Lake Erie Chem. Co, Ohio, 38-40; v.pres, Columbia Malting Co, 40-42, pres, 42-64; engr. consult. & entrepreneur, malting plant design & construct, Europe, Brit, Ireland, 64-68; dir. brewery servs, Lummus Co, Ill, 66-68; dir. qual. control & lab. dir, H.W. Rickel & Co, Mich, 68-71; CONSULT. ENGR, 71- Am. Chem. Soc; Am. Soc. Brewing Chem; Master Brewers Asn. Am; Am. Asn. Cereal Chem; Am. Inst. Chem. Eng; Am. Inst. Chem. Malting process; production of enzymes. Address; 201 E. Kirby St, Detroit, MI 48202.

GRAFF, DARRELL JAY, b. Cedar City, Utah, Sept. 8, 36; m. 62; c. 1. HELMINTHOLOGY. B.S, Utah State, 58, M.S, 60; Nat. Insts. Health fel. & Ph.D. (parasitol), California, Los Angeles, 63. Asst, zool, physiol, & parasitol. labs, Utah State, 57-60; Univ. Calif, Los Angeles, 60-62; nat. Sci. Found. fel, Rice Univ, 63-64, Nat. Insts. Health fel, 64-65; asst. prof. PHYSIOL, WEBER STATE COL, 65-70, ASSOC. PROF, 70- Part time res. asst, communicable disease ctr, U.S. Pub. Health Serv, 57-58; summer aid, insect control, Agr. Res. Serv, U.S. Dept. Agr, 59; partic, Int. Cong. Parasitol, Wash. D.C, 70; conf. on aging, Nat. Insts. Health, Univ. Calif, Riverside, 70; tech. writer, Allied Health Professions Projs, Univ. Calif, Los Angeles, 70; co-dir, Nat. Sci. Found. undergrad. res. proj. grant to Weber State Col, 70, partic, Nat. Sci. Found. Col. Sci. improvement proj. grant, 71-; consult, Albion Labs, Utah. Nat. Guard, 54-63, Sgt. Am. Soc. Parasitol. Carbohydrate and protein metabolism of parasites; active absorption of amino acids by tapeworms. Address: Dept. of Zoology, Weber State College, Ogden, UT 84403.

GRAFF, GEORGE STEPHEN, b. New York, N.Y, Mar. 16, 17; m. 42; c. 5. AERODYNAMICS. B.A, DeSales Col, 39; B.S, Detroit, 42. Draftsman, Continental Aviation & Eng. Corp, 40-42; aerodynamicist, McDonnell Aircraft Corp, 42-45, proj. aerodynamicist, 45-50, chief aerodynamicist, 50-54, chief aerodyn. engr, 54-57, mgr. aeromech, 57-60, asst. chief engr, 60-61, dir. syst. tech, 61-64, v.pres. eng. technol, 64-68, v.pres. eng, McDONNELL DOUGLAS CORP, 68-71, CORP. V.PRES, 71-, PRES, McDONNELL AIRCRAFT CO, 71-, mem. bd. dirs. & exec. v.pres, 70-71. Mem. subcomt. stability & control, Nat. Adv. Comt. Aeronaut, 51-56, aerodyn. stability & control, NASA, 56-58, missile & spacecraft aerodyn, 59-61, chmn. res. & technol. adv. subcomt. aircraft aerodyn, 67-68, mem. res. & technol. adv. comt. aeronaut, 67- Stability and control. Address: Dept. 002, McDonnell Aircraft Co, P.O. Box 516, St. Louis, MO 63166.

GRAFF, MORRIS M(ORSE), b. LaFayette, Ind, Mar. 3, 10; m. 39; c. 3. ENDOCRINOLOGY. B.A, N.Y. Univ, 39; M.Sc, Tulane, 46. Asst. biochem, Columbia, 29-42; asst. chemist, U.S. Dept. Agr, La, 42-44; assoc. chemist, 44-47; chemist, U.S. Army Chem. Ctr, Md, 47-49; res. med. br, endocrinol. serv, NAT. CANCER INST, NAT. INSTS. HEALTH, 49-56, endocrinol. sect. cancer chemother, NAT. SERV. CTR, 56-59, EXEC. SECY, ENDOCRINOL. STUDY SECT, 59- U.S.A.F.R, 49-, Lt. Col. Am. Chem. Soc; Endocrine Soc. Fats and sterols; food chemistry; rosin acids; naval stores; chromatography; rubber chemistry; cancer chemotherapy; biochemistry. Address: Division of Research Grants, National Institutes of Health, Bethesda, MD 20014.

GRAFF, ROBERT WILLIAM, b. Indianapolis, Ind, Nov. 28, 38; m. 60; c. 2. ELECTRICAL ENGINEERING, PLASMA PHYSICS. B.S.E.E, Purdue Univ, 60, M.S.E.E, 61, Ph.D.(elec. eng), 67. Technician, Airborne Instruments Lab, N.Y, summers 59 & 60; ASST PROF. ELEC. ENG, DREXEL UNIV, 66- Inst. Elec. & Electronics Eng; Int. Union Radio Sci. Radiation produced by electromagnetic sources in plasmas; diagnosis of air pollution by microwave spectroscopy; scattering of electromagnetic energy by plasma wakes. Address: Dept. of Electrical Engineering, Drexel University, Philadelphia, PA 19104.

GRAFF, SAMUEL, b. N.Y.C, July 25, 05; m. 32; c. 2. CHEMISTRY. B.S, Purdue, 27; Ph.D.(biochem), Columbia, 31. Physicist, Standard Chem. Co, 27-29; biochemist, COLUMBIA UNIV, 29-51, PROF. BIOCHEM, COL. PHYSICIANS & SURGEONS, 51- AAAS; Harvey Soc; Soc. Develop. Biol; Am. Cancer Soc; Am. Soc. Biol. Chem; Am. Asn. Cancer Res; Soc. Exp. Biol. & Med; Am. Soc. Cell Biol; Am. Chem. Soc; Brit. Biochem. Soc. Tissue and cell culture; development and automation of large scale cell culture systems. Address: Dept. of Biochemistry, College of Physicians & Surgeons, Columbia University, New York, NY 10032.

GRAFF, THOMAS D, b. Paoli, Pa, Feb. 10, 26; m. 49; c. 2. ANESTHESIOLOGY. A.B, Haverford Col, 49; M.D, Temple, 53. Intern, U.S. Pub. Health Serv. Hosp, 53-54; res. anesthesia, Detroit Receiving Hosp, 54-56; instr, sch. med, Maryland, 56; anesthesiologist, Hosp. Women of Md, Baltimore, 57; jr. asst. res. pediat, Baltimore City Hosps, 61-62; asst. prof. ANESTHESIA, SCH. MED, JOHNS HOPKINS UNIV, 62-64, ASSOC. PROF, 64- U.S.A, 44-46, Sgt. Am. Med. Asn; Am. Soc. Anesthesiol. Address: Dept. of Anesthesiology, School of Medicine, Johns Hopkins University, Baltimore, MD 21205.

GRAFF, WILLIAM (ARTHUR), b. Highland, Ill, Dec. 25, 23; m. 45; c. 2. CERAMICS. B.S, Illinois, 46, M.S, 47, Owens-Ill. Glass Co. fel, 47-49, Ph.D.(ceramics), 49. Asst. ceramics, Illinois, 46-47; res. glass technologist, glass tech. lab, GEN. ELEC. CO, 49-53, res. supvr. 53-66, MGR. GLASS RES. LAB, LAMP GLASS DEPT, 66- U.S.A, 43. Am. Chem. Soc; Am. Ceramic Soc; Brit. Soc. Glass Tech; Ger. Soc. Glass Tech. Formation, properties, structure, reactions and uses of glasses and semi-vitreous materials. Address: Lamp Glass Dept, Glass Research Lab, General Electric Co, 24400 Highland Rd, Richmond Heights, OH 44143.

GRAFF, WILLIAM J(OHN, JR), b. Marshall, Tex, May 10, 23; m. 44; c. 3. MECHANICAL ENGINEERING. B.S, Texas A&M, 47, M.S, 48; Ph.D.(mech. eng), Purdue, 51. Convair grant, Oak Ridge Sch. Reactor Tech, 52-53; instr. mech, Texas A&M, 46-48; mach. design, Purdue, 48-51; sr. propulsion engr, Gen. Dynamics/Convair, 51-54, nuclear group engr, 54-56; prof. mech. eng. & chmn. dept, Southern Methodist, 56-61; dean instr, Texas A&M, 61-65, acad. admin, 65-66; PROF. CIVIL ENG, UNIV. HOUSTON, 66- Partic, Scand. & Russian comp. educ. field study, 63; res. partic, Oak Ridge Nat. Lab, summer 59; NASA Manned Space Flight Ctr, Houston, summer, 68. Consult, Gen. Dynamics/Convair, 56-57; Tex. Instruments, Inc, 58-61. U.S.A.F, 42-45, Res, 45-55, 1st Lt. Am. Soc. Mech. Eng; Am. Soc. Eng. Educ; Am. Soc. Civil Eng; Am. Soc. Metals. University administration; automation of library procedures; nuclear science; heat transfer; structures; vibrations; properties of materials. Address: Dept. of Civil Engineering, University of Houston, Houston, TX 77004.

GRAFFIS, DON W(ARREN), b. Royal Center, Ind, Feb. 17, 28; m. 56; c. 3. AGRONOMY. B.S, Purdue, 50, M.A, 56; Ph.D.(agron), Illinois, 60. Voc. agr. instr, Van Buren Twp. Schs, Ind, 50; field rep, plant food div, Swift & Co, 52-53; voc. agr. instr, Noble Twp. Schs, Ind, 53-55; res. assoc. forage crops, Illinois, 58-60; exten. agronomist, Rutgers, 60-63; Ohio State, 63-66; EXTEN. & RES. AGRONOMIST, DEPT. AGRON, UNIV. ILL, URBANA, 66- U.S.A, 50-52, Sgt. Am. Soc. Agron; Crop Sci. Soc. Am. Production management of forage crops in humid regions. Address: Dept. of Agronomy, University of Illinois, Urbana, IL 61801.

GRAFFIUS, J(AMES) HERBERT, b. Pitcairn, Pa, June 8, 28; m. 67. BOTANY. B.S, Pittsburgh, 54, M.S, 58; Ph.D.(bot), Mich. State, 63. Asst. biol, Pittsburgh, 54-58; BOT, Mich. State Univ, 58-62; asst. prof, OHIO UNIV, 62-68, ASSOC. PROF, 68- Sig.C, U.S.A, 46-48. Phycol. Soc. Am; Int. Phycol. Soc; Am. Micros. Soc; Ecol. Soc. Am; Int. Asn. Plant Taxon; Soc. Protozool; Am. Soc. Limnol. & Oceanog. Phycology; taxonomy and ecology of fresh-water algae; bog algae; aquatic biology. Address: Dept. of Botany, Ohio University, Athens, OH 45701.

GRAFIUS, JOHN EDWARD, b. Rochester, N.Y, June 8, 16; m. 42; c. 2. GENETICS, PLANT BREEDING. B.S, Mich. State Col, 37; M.S, Iowa State Col, 38, Ph.D.(plant breeding), 43. Asst. agron, Iowa State Col, 37-41; from asst. prof. to prof, S.Dak. State Col, 41-52; assoc. prof. FARM CROPS, MICH. STATE UNIV, 52-54, PROF, 54- Am. Soc. Agron. Small grain breeding; biometry; plant pathology. Address: Dept. of Crop & Soil Sciences, Michigan State University, East Lansing, MI 48823.

GRAFIUS, MELBA A, b. Phila, Pa, Aug. 22, 20. BIOCHEMISTRY. B.S, Temple, 42; M.S, Maryland, 48; Ph.D.(biochem), Georgetown, 64. Chemist, U.S. Naval Eng. Exp. Sta, Md, 43-46; U.S. Bur. Mines, W.Va, 47-49; MED. SERV.C, 49-, chemist; Naval Med. Res. Inst, 49-53, biochemist, Naval Med. Field Res. Lab, 55-58, instr. biochem. & toxicol, Naval Med. Sch, 58-62, BIOCHEMIST, U.S. NAVAL MED. RES. INST, 62- Med.Serv.C, U.S.N, 49-, Comdr. AAAS; fel. Am. Inst. Chem; Am. Chem. Soc. Physico-chemical properties of acetylcholinesterase; function of biological components on electrogenic membranes. Address: Dept. of Environmental Biosciences, U.S. Naval Medical Research Institute, Bethesda, MD 20014.

GRAFSTEIN, BERNICE (MRS. HOWARD SHANET), b. Toronto, Ont, Can, Sept. 17, 29; m. 63; c. 1. PHYSIOLOGY. B.A, Toronto, 51; Ph.D.(physiol), McGill, 54. Asst. physiol, McGill, 51-54, lectr, 54-55; hon. res. asst. anat, Univ. Col. London, 55-57; asst. prof. PHYSIOL, McGill Univ, 57-62; Rockefeller Univ, 62-69; ASSOC. PROF, MED. COL, CORNELL UNIV, 69- Nat. Res. Coun. Can. fel, Univ. Col. London, 55-56; Grass Found. fel, Woods Hole Marine Biol. Lab, 61; trustee, Grass Found, 65-; adj. assoc. prof, Rockefeller Univ, 69- AAAS; Am. Physiol. Soc; Can. Physiol. Soc; Int. Brain Res. Orgn; Soc. Neurosci. Development of the nervous system; growth and regeneration of nervous tissue; electrical activity of the central nervous system. Address: Dept. of Physiology, Cornell University Medical College, New York, NY 10021.

GRAFSTEIN, DANIEL, b. N.Y.C, Dec. 24, 27; m. 47; c. 1. CHEMISTRY. B.S, City Col. New York, 48; M.S, Purdue, 49, Atomic Energy Comn. fel, 50-51, Ph.D.(chem), 51. Res. chemist, Westinghouse Elec. Corp, 51-56; reaction motors div, Thiokol Chem. Corp, 56-57, group leader, 57-58, unit supvr, adv. res. group, 59-61; sr. staff scientist, Aerospace Res. Center, Gen. Precision, Inc, 62-63, prin. staff scientist & mgr. chem. dept, 63-66, mgr, mat. dept, 66-69; MGR. CHEM. RES. PROG, GOVT. RES. LAB, ESSO RES. & ENG. CO, 69- AAAS; Am. Chem. Soc; Am. Phys. Soc; Electrochem. Soc; N.Y. Acad. Sci. Fluorine, boron and structural chemistry; organometallics; carboranes; photochemistry; photoconductivity; fluorescence; laser materials. Address: Government Research Lab, Esso Research & Engineering Co, P.O. Box 8, Linden, NJ 07036.

GRAFTON, BENJAMIN F(RANKLIN), b. Bernice, La, Jan. 4, 19; m. 43; c. 4. SOIL CHEMISTRY. B.S, La. Polytech, 47; M.S, La. State, 50. Instr. chem, La. Polytech, 47-48; agronomist, soil surv, State Agr. Exp. Sta, La, 50-52; ASSOC. PROF. AGRON, LA. TECH UNIV, 52- Asst, La. State Univ, 48-50. U.S.A, 41-45. Am. Soc. Agron; Soil Sci. Soc. Am. Soil fertility and classification. Address: Dept. of Agronomy, Box 4028, Louisiana Tech University, Ruston, LA 71270.

GRAFTON, ROBERT B(RUCE), b. Rochester, N.Y, May 15, 35; m. 67; c. 1. APPLIED MATHEMATICS. Sc.B, Brown, 58, Ph.D.(appl. math), 67. Engr, bur. ships, Atomic Energy Comn, 58-62; asst. prof. MATH, Missouri, Columbia, 67-71, summer res. fel, 68; ASST. PROF, TRINITY COL, 71- U.S.N, 58-62, Lt. Math. Asn. Am; Am. Math. Soc; Soc. Indust. & Appl. Math. Differential equations and numerical analysis. Address: Dept. of Mathematics, Trinity College, Hartford, CT 06106.

GRAFTON, THURMAN S(TANFORD), b. Chicago, Ill, Dec. 20, 23; m. 46; c. 4. LABORATORY ANIMAL MEDICINE. D.V.M, Mich. State, 47; Maryland, 50; New Mexico, 63-64. Instr. surg. & med, vet. col, Mich. State, 47-48; vet. lab. officer, Walter Reed Army Inst. Res, 48-50; asst. chief, dept. virus & rickettsial diseases, 406th Med. Gen. Lab, Japan, 50-52; assoc. prof. virol, Maryland, 52-53; course supvr. vet. serv, U.S. Air Force Sch. Aviation Med, 53-56; exec. officer clin. lab, 7520th Med. Clin. Lab, Eng, 56-60; chief vivarium br, 6571st Aeromed. Res. Lab, Holloman Air Force Base, N.Mex, 60-64; asst. chief nutrit. br, food div, U.S. Army Natick Labs, Mass, 64-66; PROF. LAB. ANIMAL SCI. & CHMN. DEPT, SCH. HEALTH REL. PROFESSIONS, RES. ASSOC. PROF. MICROBIOL, SCH. MED. & DIR. LAB ANIMAL FACILITIES, STATE UNIV. N.Y. BUFFALO, 66- Consult, Children's Buffalo Gen, Meyer Mem, Millard Filmore & Vet. Admin. Hosps, 66-; chmn. adv. coun. animal sci, State Univ. N.Y. Agr. & Tech. Col. Delhi, 66- U.S. Air Force rep, Int. Conf. Vet. Ed, London, 59. Dipl, Am. Col. Lab. Animal Med, 66, oral examiner, 66-68. Vet.C, U.S.A.F, 44-66, Lt. Col; Commendation Medal, 66. Am. Vet. Med. Asn; Asn. Gnotobiotics; Asn. Schs. Allied Health Professions; Conf. Pub. Health Vets; Am. Soc. Lab. Animal Practitioners (pres, 71-72); Am. Asn. Zoo Vets; Wildlife Disease Asn. Virus and rickettsial diseases of the Far East; improved support of the use of animals in biomedical research; diseases and treatment of aquatic animals; medical research management; education and utilization of animal technicians. Address: Dept. of Laboratory Animal Science, State University of New York at Buffalo, Buffalo, NY 14214.

GRAGE, THEODOR B, b. Münster, Ger, Mar. 24, 27; U.S. citizen; m. 53; c. 8. SURGERY. Münster, 46-51; M.D, Creighton, 55; M.S. & Ph.D.(surg), Minnesota, 63. Intern med, Creighton Mem. St. Joseph's Hosp, 55-56; fel. SURG, UNIV. MINN. HOSPS, 56-61, instr, 61-62, asst. prof, 63-69, ASSOC. PROF, 69- Am. Cancer Soc. adv. clin. fel, 62-65. Soc. Head & Neck Surg; Am. Col. Surg; Am. Asn. Clin. Oncol, Am. Asn. Cancer Res. Surgical treatment of malignant diseases and chemotherapy of solid tumors. Address: University of Minnesota, Health Sciences Center, Dept. of Surgery, Minneapolis, MN 55455.

GRAGG, WILLIAM BRYANT, JR, b. Bakersfield, Calif, Nov. 2, 36; m. 58; c. 3. MATHEMATICS. B.S, Univ. Denver, 57; M.S, Stanford Univ, 59; Ph.D. (math), Univ. Calif, Los Angeles, 64. Mathematician numerical anal, Bellcomm, Inc, 63-64; Oak Ridge Nat. Lab, 64-67; asst. prof. MATH, UNIV. CALIF, SAN DIEGO, 67-70, ASSOC. PROF, 70- Vis. asst. prof, Univ. Tenn, 65-67. Soc. Indust. & Appl. Math; Asn. Comput. Mach; Am. Math. Soc. Numerical analysis, especially quadrature, ordinary initial value problems, Padé table, continued fractions and matrices. Address: Dept. of Mathematics, University of California, San Diego, P.O. Box 109, La Jolla, CA 92037.

GRAH, RUDOLF F(ERDINAND), b. San Diego, Calif, Aug. 21, 15; m. 41; c. 6. FORESTRY. B.S, Oregon State Col, 39; M.S, California, 41; Schoen-Rene fel, Michigan, 53-54, Ph.D, 57. Field aide, plant disease invest, U.S. Dept. Agr, 36-39; field asst, U.S. Forest Serv, 41; asst, California, 39-43; forester, Rubber Develop. Corp, 43-46; exten. forester, UNIV. CALIF, BERKELEY, 46-55, PROF. FORESTRY, SCH. FORESTRY & FORESTER, EXP. STA, 55- Sr. res. fel, N.Z. Forest Res. Inst, 65-66. Soc. Am. Foresters; Forest Prod. Res. Soc. Relation of stocking to quality production; economics of techniques and systems; appraisals; analysis of management systems. Address: School of Forestry, University of California, Berkeley, CA 94720.

GRAHAM, ALAN K(EITH), b. Houston, Tex, May 5, 34; m. 60. PLANT MORPHOLOGY, PALEOBOTANY. B.A, Texas, 56, M.A, 58; Ph.D.(bot), Michigan, 62. Instr. bot, Michigan, 62-63; fel, evolutionary biol. prog, Harvard, 63-64; asst. prof. BOT, KENT STATE UNIV, 64-68, ASSOC. PROF, 68- Nat. Sci. Found. res. grants, 66-68, 69-71; vis. res. scientist, Univ. Amsterdam, 69-70; res. assoc, Nat. Univ. Mex, 71. AAAS; Bot. Soc. Am; Geol. Soc. Am; Int. Asn. Plant Taxon. Tertiary history of Latin American vegetation. Address: Dept. of Biological Sciences, Kent State University, Kent, OH 44240.

GRAHAM, A(LBERT) RONALD, b. Red Deer, Alta, Feb. 15, 17; m. 42; c. 1. MINERALOGY. B.A, Alberta, 37; B.Sc, Queen's (Ont), 40, M.Sc, 47; Ph.D. (mineral), Toronto, 50. Jr. engr, McKenzie Red Lake Gold Mines, Ont, 40-41; mines scientist mineral, Dept. Mines & Tech. Survs, 49-52; mineralogist, Dominion Gulf Co, Gulf Res. & Develop. Co, 52-55; FALCONBRIDGE NICKEL MINES LTD, 55-60, sr. mineralogist, 60-70, ASST. MGR, METALL. LABS, THORNHILL, 70- R.C.A.F, 43-45, Flight Lt. Fel. Mineral. Soc. Am; Mineral. Asn. Can; Can. Inst. Min. & Metall; Can. Asn. Appl. Spectros. Descriptive mineralogy; qualitative and quantitative x-ray diffraction and fluorescence analysis; development of mineralogical techniques for applications in mining, in geological exploration and in extractive metallurgy. Address: 18 George Henry Blvd, Willowdale, Ont, Can.

GRAHAM, ALOYSIUS, S. J, b. St. Mary's, Ont, July 27, 16. ORGANIC CHEMISTRY. B.A, Loyola Col.(Que), 37; M.A, Toronto, 43. Teacher, high sch, Can, 43-44; chem, Campion Col, 48-51; org. chem, LOYOLA COL. MONTREAL, 52-58, chmn. chem. dept, 58-69, assoc. dean sci, 63-68, DEAN, SCI, 68- Am. Chem. Soc; Chem. Inst. Can; Brit. Chem. Soc. Organic synthesis in the field of explosives; chemical education. Address: School of Science, Loyola College of Montreal, 7141 Sherbrooke St. W, Montreal 262, Que, Can.

GRAHAM, A(NGUS) F(REDERICK), b. Toronto, Ont, Mar. 28, 16; nat; m. 54; c. 3. MICROBIOLOGY. B.A.Sc, Toronto, 38, M.A.Sc, 39; Ph.D.(biochem), Edinburgh, 42, D.Sc.(microbiol), 52. Lectr. biochem, Edinburgh, 40-47; res. assoc. microbiol, Connaught Med. res. labs, Toronto, 47-58; prof, Univ. Pa, 58-70; mem. Wistar Inst, 58-70; CHMN, DEPT. BIOCHEM, MED. SCH, McGILL UNIV, 70- Eleanor Roosevelt Int. Cancer fel, 64; mem. study sect. on virology & rickettsiology, Nat. Insts. Health, 65-69. Am. Soc. Microbiol. Replication of mammalian viruses. Address: Dept. of Biochemistry, McGill University Medical School, Montreal, Can.

GRAHAM, A(RCHIBALD) R(OBERT), b. Inverness, Que, Aug. 25, 02; m. 41; c. 2. ENTOMOLOGY. B.S.A, McGill, 23, M.Sc, 26; Nat. Res. Coun. Can. bursar, Toronto, 27-28. Investr, CAN. DEPT. AGR, ONT, 23-48, administr. maintenance & serv, DOM. PARASITE LAB, 48-51, tech. off, 51-58, RES. OFF, 58- AAAS; Entom. Soc. Can. Biological control of forest insect pests and weeds; nutrition of insects. Address: 6 Eastwood Park Dr, Belleville, Ont, Can.

GRAHAM, ARTHUR H(UGHES), b. Phila, Pa, Nov. 18, 33; m. 60; c. 1. METALLURGY, ELECTROCHEMISTRY. B.S, Pa. State, 58, M.S, 60, Gen. Elec. Found. fel. & Ph.D.(metall), 63. Res. metallurgist, ENG. MAT. LAB, E.I. DU PONT DE NEMOURS & CO, 63-66, sr. res. metallurgist, 66-70, SR. RES. SPECIALIST, 70- Am. Soc. Metals; Electrochem. Soc. Address: Engineering Materials Lab, Experimental Station, E.I. du Pont de Nemours & Co, Wilmington, DE 19898.

GRAHAM, ARTHUR KENNETH, b. Philadelphia, Pa, Dec. 25, 96; m. 31; c. 1. ELECTROCHEMISTRY. B.S, Pennsylvania, 19, Ch.E, 24, M.S, 25, Ph.D. (electrochem), 27; Columbia, 21. Res. worker, Scovill Mfg. Co, Conn, 19-20; instr. chem, Pennsylvania, 21-26; chem. engr, Hanson Munning Co, N.J, 26-28; instr. chem. eng, Pennsylvania, 28-34, asst. prof, 34-37; owner-consult, A. Kenneth Graham & Assoc, 36-42; consult. & dep. chief conserv. div, War Prod. Bd, 42-43; dir. res, Manhattan Proj, Houdaile Hershey Corp, Ill, 43-44; consult, Graham, Savage & Assocs, Inc, 44-68; RETIRED. Ed-in-chief, Electroplating Eng. Handbook. U.S.M.C, 18. Hon. mem. Electrochem. Soc.(v.pres, 39); hon. mem. Am. Electroplaters Soc.(managing ed. & exec. secy, 45-51; gold medal awards; sci. achievement award, 60); Am. Soc. Test. & Mat.(Sam Tour Award, 61). Electrodeposition of metals and alloys; restoration of ancient bronze; electroplating; electroforming; metal finishing; plating waste treatment and water conservation; plating plant engineering. Address: 107 Foxcroft Square Apts, Jenkintown, PA 19046.

GRAHAM, ARTHUR R(ENFREE), b. London, Ont, Nov. 2, 19; m. 50; c. 4. PHYSIOLOGY. B.Sc, Western Ontario, 48, fel, 49-54, M.Sc, 51, Ph.D.(physiol), 54. Assoc. prof. zool, Memorial Univ, 54-57; PHYSIOL. SCI, ONT. VET. COL, UNIV. GUELPH, 57-71, PROF, 71- AAAS; N.Y. Acad. Sci; Can. Physiol. Soc. Physiology of central nervous system; ruminant digestive system. Address: Dept. of Biomedical Sciences, Ontario Veterinary College, University of Guelph, Guelph, Ont, Can.

GRAHAM, AUGUSTUS W(ASHINGTON), b. Oxford, N.C, Apr. 9, 25; m. 50; c. 4. INORGANIC CHEMISTRY. B.S, North Carolina, 49, Ph.D.(chem), 54. Sr. chemist, TEXTILE FIBERS DEPT, E.I. DU PONT DE NEMOURS & CO, 52-58, group supvr. process & prod. develop, 58-61, SUPVR. RES, 61- U.S.A, 43-47. Am. Chem. Soc. Light scattering properties of solutions of polyvalent cations; spinning, drawing and dyeing of synthetic fibers; industrial fibers applications research. Address: Textile Fibers Dept, E.I. du Pont de Nemours & Co, Wilmington, DE 19898.

GRAHAM, BENJAMIN F(RANKLIN), JR, b. East Milton, Mass, Sept. 24, 20; m. 47; c. 4. BOTANY, PLANT ECOLOGY. B.S, Maine, 43, M.S, 48; Ph.D. (bot), Duke, 59. Instr. bot, Maine, 48-51; Miami (Ohio), 54-56; res. assoc, Dartmouth Col, 57-59; assoc. prof. BIOL, GRINNELL COL, 59-68, PROF, 68- Vis. biologist, Brookhaven Nat. Lab, 65-66. U.S.A, 43-46, 51-52, Capt. Fel. AAAS; Am. Inst. Biol. Sci; Ecol. Soc. Am. Forest ecology; natural root grafts; palynology; radiation ecology. Address: Dept. of Biology, Grinnell College, Grinnell, IA 50112.

GRAHAM, BLANCHE D, b. Lincoln, Nebr, Apr. 29, 25; m. 51; c. 2. MICROBIOLOGY, GENETICS. B.A, Nebraska, 47; M.A, Detroit, 68. Res. asst. MICROBIOL, PARKE DAVIS & CO, 47-52 & 55-68, RES. ASST. SPECIALIST, DEPT. ANTIBIOTICS, 68- AAAS; Soc. Indust. Microbiol; Am. Soc. Microbiol; Genetics Soc. Am. Antibiotic screening and taxonomy of antibiotic producing microorganisms; induction of phage maturation in presumptive lysogenic Streptomycetes. Address: Dept. of Antibiotics, Parke Davis & Co, Detroit, MI 48232.

GRAHAM, B(OYNTON), b. Haverhill, Mass, Feb. 23, 12; m. 43; c. 4. CHEMISTRY. A.B, Clark, 34; Ph.D.(org. chem), N.Y. Univ, 37. Instr. chem, N.Y. Univ, 34-37; res. chemist, EXP. STA, E.I. DU PONT DE NEMOURS & CO, 37-70, RES. FEL, PHOTOPROD. DEPT, 70- With Off. Sci. Res. & Develop, 44. Am. Chem. Soc. Polymer preparation and evaluation. Address: Experimental Station, E.I. du Pont de Nemours & Co, Wilmington, DE 19898.

GRAHAM, BRUCE, b. Crete, Nebr, Dec. 26, 16; m. 37; c. 5. CHEMISTRY. B.S, Oregon State Col, 42, fel, 43-45, Off. Sci. Res. & Develop. fel, 45, Ph.D.(org. chem), 45. Asst. chem, Oregon State Col, 42-43; res. chemist, Eastman Kodak Co, 45-52, sr. org. chemist, Stanford Res. Inst, 52-54, head org. chemist, 54-56, mgr. org. chem. sect, 56-58, chmn. dept. biol. sci, 58-62, dir. life sci. div, 62-65; pres, Gulf South Res. Inst, 65-70; DIR, RES. & DEVELOP. INSTS. OF THE U.S, 70- Prof, Southwest. La. Univ, 66-70. AAAS; Am. Chem. Soc. Synthesis of antimalarial drugs; synthesis of organic, photographic chemicals; amino alcohols derived from pyrimidines; polymer chemistry; radiation chemistry; research administration; biological sciences. Address: Research & Development Institutions of the U.S, Suite 132, Box C, 1500 Massachusetts Ave. N.W, Washington, DC 20005.

GRAHAM, BRUCE D(OUGLAS), b. Roberts, Wis, Dec. 15, 15; m. 46; c. 3. PEDIATRICS. A.B, Alabama, 39; M.D, Vanderbilt, 42. Asst. prof. PEDIAT, univ. hosp, Michigan, 51-54, assoc. prof. & dir. pediat. labs, 54-59; PROF. & HEAD DEPT, faculty med, Univ. B.C, 59-64; COL. MED, OHIO STATE UNIV, 64-; MED. DIR, CHILDREN'S HOSP, 70-, chief staff, 64-70. Pediatrician-in-chief, Health Ctr. Children, Vancouver, B.C, 59-64; chief pediat, Children's Hosp, 61-64. Med.C, 43-46, Maj. AAAS; Soc. Pediat. Res; Am. Acad. Pediat; Am. Pediat. Soc; Am. Med. Asn. Acid base metabolism of premature infants, full term and sick children; oxygen tension study of newborn infants and sick children. Address: Children's Hospital, 561 S. 17th St, Columbus, OH 43205.

GRAHAM, CARL F(RANCIS), b. Limon, Colo, Jan. 2, 15; m. 41; c. 3. CHEMISTRY. Sc.B, Baker, 38; Kansas City, 38-39. Instr, Baker, 35-38; lab. head, Procter & Gamble Mfg. Co, 38-41; res. sect. head, J.B. Ford Co, 41-43; rev. supvr, Wyandotte Chem. Corp, 43-56, res. mgr, 56-57; dir. res. & develop, Turco Prods, Inc, Purex Corp, Ltd, 57-66, admin. asst. to v.pres. chem. res, indust. & inst. group, 64-66; mgr. res. & develop, AMWAY CORP, 67-70; MGR. INDUST. & GOVT, TECH. RELATIONS, 70- Civilian consult, Chem.C, U.S.A, 52-63. Am. Chem. Soc; Am. Soc. Test. & Mat; Am. Oil Chem. Soc; Am. Ord. Asn; fel. Am. Inst. Chem. Specialized detergents; heavy chemicals; glycols and other organics; products and raw material specifications; research management. Address: Amway Corp, 7575 E. Fulton Rd, Ada, MI 49301.

GRAHAM, CHARLES D(ANNE), JR, b. Phila, Pa, Oct. 15, 29; m. 52; c. 4. PHYSICAL METALLURGY. B.Met.E, Cornell, 52; Ph.D.(metall), Birmingham, England, 54. Res. metallurgist, res. & develop. ctr, Gen. Elec. Co, N.Y, 54-69; PROF. METALL. & MAT. SCI, UNIV. PA, 69- Guggenheim fel, inst. solid state physics, Univ. Tokyo, 61-62. Am. Phys. Soc; Am. Inst. Mining, Metall. & Petrol. Eng; Phys. Soc. Japan; Inst. Elec. & Electronics Eng. Magnetic materials; magnetic measurements; superconducting magnets. Address: School of Metallurgy & Materials Science, University of Pennsylvania, Philadelphia, PA 19104.

GRAHAM, CHARLES E(DWARD), b. St. Paul, Minn, Nov. 22, 19; m. 43; c. 3. GEOLOGY. B.S, State Col. Wash, 47, M.S, 49; Ph.D.(geol), Iowa, 54. Asst. geologist, State Bur. Mines & Geol, Mont, 49-50; asst. instr. GEOL, Univ. Iowa, 51-53; instr, DENISON UNIV, 53-54, asst. prof, 54-59, assoc. prof, 59-66, PROF, 66- U.S.A.A.F, 42-45, 1st Lt. Geol. Soc. Am; Nat. Asn. Geol. Teachers; Am. Geophys. Union. Structural and urban geology. Address: Dept. of Geology & Geography, Denison University, Granville, OH 43023.

GRAHAM, CHARLES LEE, b. White Lake, S.Dak, Aug. 12, 31; m. 58; c. 3. ENTOMOLOGY, PARASITOLOGY. B.S, North. State Col, 59; Nat. Defense Ed. Act fel. & M.S, Utah State, 62, Nat. Defense Ed. Act & Nat. Insts. Health fels. & Ph.D.(entom, parasitol), 64. RES. ENTOMOLOGIST, EPIPHYTOLOGY RES. LAB, PLANT SCI. DIV, AGR. RES; SERV, U.S. DEPT. AGR, 63- Instr, Frederick Community Col. U.S.A.F, 51-55. AAAS; Entom. Soc. Am; Am. Mosquito Control Asn; Sci. Res. Soc. Am. Insect flight; tissue culture; respiration and aging as well as the basic relationships between vector and host in insect borne plant viruses. Address: Epiphytology Research Lab, Plant Sciences Division, Agricultural Research Service, U.S. Dept. of Agriculture, Ft. Detrick, Frederick, MD 21701.

GRAHAM, CHARLES L(EROY), b. Monmouth, Ill, Sept. 13, 09; m. 34; c. 2. ANALYTICAL CHEMISTRY. B.S, Monmouth Col, 30; M.S, Illinois, 34. Anal. chemist, Am. Can Co, 30-33; food technologist, La Choy Food Prod, 34-35; anal. chemist, UPJOHN CO, 35-37; chief control chemist, 47-60; mgr. chem. control, 60-62; CONTROL TECH. ADV, 63- Mem, comt. revision, U.S. Pharmacopeia, 60-; Nat. Formulary Bd, 60- Am. Chem. Soc. Chemical analysis applied to product control in the pharmaceutical industry; assay procedures, particularly instrumental methods. Address: 328 S. Drake Rd, Kalamazoo, MI 49009.

GRAHAM, CHARLES RAYMOND, JR, b. Baltimore, Md, June 17, 40; m. 62; c. 3. ICHTHYOLOGY, PHYSIOLOGY. B.S, Loyola Col.(Md), 62; assistantship, Univ. Del, 62-64, M.S, 64, fel, 64-66, Ph.D.(icthyol, cytol), 67. Instr. BIOL, LOYOLA COL.(MD), 66-67, asst. prof, 67-71, ASSOC. PROF, 71- Summers, trainee, sch. med, Marquette Univ, 67 & 68, res. assoc, 69 & 70. Am. Soc. Zool. Morphology and physiology of chondrichthian reproductive systems; morphology and physiology of cellular membranes. Address: 6 Reservoir Rd, Pikesville, MD 21208.

GRAHAM, C(LYDE) BENJAMIN, b. Hannibal, Mo, Jan. 15, 31; m. 56; c. 1. RADIOLOGY. B.A, Univ. Ill, Urbana, 54; M.D, Univ. Wash, 58. Asst. radiol, SCH. MED, UNIV. WASH, 59-62; assoc, 62-63, instr, 63-65, asst. prof. RADIOL. & PEDIAT, 65-69, ASSOC. PROF, 69- Am. Cancer Soc. clin. fel, 60; James Picker Found. adv. fel. acad. radiol, 62-64 & scholar. radiol. res, 64-66. Dipl, Am. Bd. Radiol, 66. Am. Roentgen Ray Soc; Soc. Pediat. Radiol; Asn. Univ. Radiol; Am. Col. Radiol. Bone development; neonatal diagnostic roentgenology. Address: Dept. of Radiology, SS 230, University of Washington Hospital, Seattle, WA 98105.

GRAHAM, COLIN C, b. Jan. 16, 42; U.S. citizen. MATHEMATICS. B.A, Harvard, 64; Ph.D.(math), Mass. Inst. Technol, 68. ASST. PROF. MATH, NORTHWEST. UNIV, 68- Am. Math. Soc; Math. Asn. Am. Abstract harmonic analysis; uniform algebras. Address: Dept. of Mathematics, Northwestern University, 2033 Sheridan Rd, Evanston, IL 60201.

GRAHAM, DAVID E, b. New York, N.Y, July 29, 15; m. 41; c. 3. CHEMISTRY. B.S, N.Y. Univ, 36; M.S, Illinois, 37, Ph.D.(org. chem), 40. Consult, Williams Oil-O-Matic Heating Corp, Ill, 39-40; mem. staff, Nat. Defense Res. Comt. & Off. Sci. Res. & Develop. contracts, Illinois, 40-43; org. & chlorination chemist, Amecco Chems, Inc, N.Y, 43-44; process develop. chemist, Gen. Aniline Works, 44-56, sect. mgr. chems. & specialties, GAF CORP, 56-62, SR. TECH. ASSOC, 62- Am. Chem. Soc. Hydrogen bonding; catalysis; catalytic hydrogenation; chlorination; dyestuffs and intermediates; fine chemicals; isocyanates; surfactants; herbicides and hydrocarbons. Address: GAF Corp, Box 12, Linden, NJ 07036.

GRAHAM, DAVID T(REDWAY), b. Mason City, Iowa, June 20, 17; m. 41; c. 3. INTERNAL MEDICINE. B.A, Princeton, 38; M.A, Yale; M.D, Wash. Univ, 43. Commonwealth fel. MED, med. col, Cornell Univ, 48-51; asst. prof, Wash. Univ, 51-57; assoc. prof, SCH. MED, UNIV. WIS, MADISON, 57-63, PROF, 63-, CHMN. DEPT, 71- U.S.A, 45-47. Am. Psychosom. Soc; Am. Med. Asn; Am. Fedn. Clin. Res.(ed, Proc, 54-59); Soc. Psychophysiol. Res; Soc. Biol. Psychiat. Psychosomatic medicine. Address: University Hospitals, 1300 University Ave, Madison, WI 53706.

GRAHAM, DEAN M(cKINLEY), b. Santa Ana, Calif, May 9, 23; m. 47; c. 4. BIOPHYSICS. Ph.B, Wisconsin, 43; Ph.D.(biophys), California, 53. Bldg. contractor, Calif, 47-49; res. scientist, Atomic Energy Cmn, 49-53; sr. res. scientist, Upjohn Co, Mich, 53-57; prog. dir. pharm. res, Stanford Res. Inst, Calif, 57-58; dir. pharmaceut. res, White Labs, Inc, N.J, 58-60; v.pres, K-V Pharmacal Co, 60-61; PRES, D. GRAHAM LABS, 61- Consult, 57-58. U.S.N, 42-47, Lt. AAAS; Am. Chem. Soc; Am. Pharmaceut. Asn; Pharmaceut. Mfrs. Asn; N.Y. Acad. Sci. Atherosclerosis; physiology of digestive system; circulatory system; physiology and pharmacology of drug absorption; design of drug dosage forms. Address: D. Graham Labs, Inc, Hobart, NY 13788.

GRAHAM, DEE M(cDONALD), b. Dixon, Miss, Oct. 11, 27; m. 48; c. 7. DAIRY BACTERIOLOGY. B.Sc, Miss. State Col, 50; Judging fel. & M.Sc, Iowa State Col, 51, Nat. Insts. Health fel. & Ph.D.(dairy bact), 54. Res. assoc. dairy bact, Iowa Agr. Exp. Sta, 51-52; asst. prof. dairying, Clemson Col, 53-57, assoc. prof, 57-58; div. chief evaporated milk res, Pet Milk Co, 58-60, mgr. milk prod. develop, 61-65, assoc. dir. res, 65-68, tech. dir, grocery prod. div, 68-69; CHMN. DEPT. FOOD SCI. & NUTRIT, UNIV. MO-COLUMBIA, 69- Mem. food protect. comt. & comt. on rev. of food additives, Nat. Acad. Sci-Nat. Res. Coun. U.S.A, 46-48, Sgt. Am. Dairy Sci. Asn. Product development; flavor chemistry; organo-leptic analysis; milk manufacturing technology. Address: Dept. of Food Science & Nutrition, 1-74 Agriculture, University of Missouri-Columbia, Columbia, MO 65201.

GRAHAM, DONALD C. W, b. Thomasville, Ga, Jan. 11, 32; m. 53; c. 4. FOOD SCIENCE, NUTRITION. B.S, Ft. Valley State Col, 54; M.S, Tuskegee Inst, 58; Ph.D.(food sci), Cornell Univ, 71. Clerk, off. registrar, Ft. Valley, State Col, 54-56; res. asst. physiol, Tuskegee Inst, 58-61, instr. nutrit, 59-61; nutrit. & gen. sci, Alabama State Col, 61-65; res. technician nutrit, CORNELL UNIV, 65-68, ASST. PROF. FOOD SCI, 71- Mem, grad. faculty food sci. & technol. & faculty inst. food sci. & mkt, Cornell Univ, 71- AAAS; Inst. Food Technol. Effects of food processing on nutritional quality; nutritional value of fungal proteins and characterization of fungal proteins; unusual food fermentations, their characterization and nutritional evaluation. Address: Dept. of Food Science, Stocking Hall, Cornell University, Ithaca, NY 14850.

GRAHAM, DONALD I, JR, b. Chicago, Ill, Nov. 5, 12; m. 40; c. 2. CIVIL ENGINEERING. C.E, Northwestern, 37. Engr, Dravo Construct. Co, Pa, 33-34; State Hwy. Dept, Ill, 35-36; construct. engr, Sanit. Dist, City of Chicago, 36-37; asst. dist. supvr, safety & fire protection engr, Factory Ins. Asn, 37-41; safety & fire protection supvr, Hanford Eng. Works, E.I. du Pont de Nemours & Co, 41-45; dir. safety & conserv. servs, Moore & Wright Co, Mich, 45; safety dir. & chief safety sect, Nat. Bur. Standards, Wash, D.C, 46-48; safety dir. & res. engr, Ord. Res. & Develop. Div, Ft. Bliss, 48-50, coord. & tech. adv, fuels & field protective measures, Rocket & Guided Missile Agency, Redstone Arsenal, 50-60, tech. adv. human factors eng. res, Res. & Eng. Directorate, U. S. ARMY MISSILE COMMAND, 60-64, proj. engr. missiles, warheads & fuses, surface-to-air missile develop. proj. off. & chief, spec. warfare off, develop. div, res. & develop. directorate, REDSTONE ARSENAL, 64-70, SR. PROJ. ENGR, TERMINAL HOUSING DATA BANK, 70- Assoc. mem. panel fuels & oxidizers, res. & develop. bd, U.S. Dept. Army. Am. Soc. Safety Eng; Am. Inst. Aeronaut. & Astronaut; Am. Ord. Asn. Chemicals; high explosives; solid and liquid rocket propellants; guided missiles; project engineering. Address: 1800 Governors Dr, S.E, Huntsville AL 35801.

GRAHAM, (FRANK) DUNSTAN, b. Princeton, N.J, Aug. 17, 22; m. 44; c. 2. AERONAUTICAL ENGINEERING. B.S.E, Princeton, 43, M.S.E, 47. Aerodynamicist, Boeing Airplane Co, 47-48; flight res. engr, Cornell Aeronaut. Lab, 48-50; supvry. gen. engr, Wright Air Develop. Center, 50-55; chief engr. flight controls, Lear, Inc, 55-59; TECH. DIR, SYSTS. TECHNOL, INC, 59-; PROF. AERONAUT. ENG, PRINCETON, 66-, assoc. prof, 59-66. U.S.A, 43-46, 51-53, 1st Lt. Am. Inst. Aeronaut. & Astronaut; Inst. Elec. & Electronics Eng. Aeronautical instrumentation and automatic guidance and control; system engineering. Address: Dept. of Aerospace & Mechanical Sciences, Princeton University, Princeton, NJ 08540.

GRAHAM, EDMUND F, b. Mesilla Park, N.Mex, July 25, 24; m. 48; c. 6. PHYSIOLOGY, CRYOBIOLOGY. B.S, Utah State Univ, 49; M.S, S.Dak. State Col, 52; Ph.D.(physiol), Univ. Minn, 55. Asst. dairy biochem, S.Dak. State Col, 50-52; ANIMAL PHYSIOL, UNIV. MINN, ST. PAUL, 52-53, res. fel, 53-55, instr, 55-56, asst. prof, 56-59, assoc. prof, 58-61, PROF, 61- Am. Soc. Animal Sci; Am. Dairy Sci. Asn; Soc. Study Reproduction; Soc. Cryobiol; Brit. Soc. Study Fertil. Physiology and biochemistry of reproductive processes in animal industries; cryobiology and preservation of cells and tissue at low temperature. Address: Dept. of Animal Science, University of Minnesota, St. Paul, MN 55101.

GRAHAM, EDWARD UNDERWOOD, b. Washington, D.C, Sept. 27, 43; m. 67. ELECTRICAL ENGINEERING, INFORMATION SCIENCE. B.S, Mass. Inst. Tech, 64; M.S, Carnegie-Mellon Univ, 65, Ph.D.(systs. & commun. sci), 69. CONSULT. SYSTS. ENG. & INFO. PROCESSING, AUERBACH CORP, ARLINGTON, 68- Simulation Coun; Inst. Elec. & Electronics Eng; Pattern Recognition Soc. Optimization theory; automatic control; picture processing; systems sciences. Address: 2434 39th St. N.W, Washington, DC 20007.

GRAHAM, E(LLIS) R(AY), b. Fairview, Utah, May 12, 11; m. 45; c. 3. SOILS. B.S, Brigham Young, 33, M.S, 36; Ph.D.(soils), Missouri, 38. From instr. to PROF. SOILS, UNIV. MO-COLUMBIA, 38-, summer acting dean grad. sch, 65. Fulbright res. fel, Australia, 51; summers, with Oak Ridge Nat. Lab, 56-57; with Los Alamos Sci. Lab, Univ. Calif, 57-58; partic, UN Develop. Prog. proj, Univ. Chile, fall 68; vis. prof, Univ. Hawaii, spring 69. U.S.N, 42-45. Soil chemistry, mineralogy and plant nutrition; radiochemistry and waste disposal of fission products. Address: Dept. of Soils, University of Missouri-Columbia, Columbia, MO 65201.

GRAHAM, ERIC S(TANLEY), b. Kingston, Ont, Dec. 31, 21; m. 45; c. 2. ORGANIC CHEMISTRY. B.Sc, Queen's (Ont), 42, M.Sc, 46; Ph.D.(org. chem), Mass. Inst. Tech, 50. Prof. chem, Kenyon Col, 50-61, chmn. dept, 54-59; PRINCIPAL, ROYAL ROADS MIL. COL, 61- Faculty fel, Fund. Advan. Educ, Univ. Col, Univ. London, 54-55; Nat. Sci. Found. fel, Northwest. Univ, 57; chief reader, adv. placement prog, Col. Entrance Exam. Bd, 58-61; vis. scientist, Am. Chem. Soc. Vis. Scientist Prog, 58-64; mem. Chem. Bond Approach Group, 59-61; vis. prof, Univ. Dacca, 61; Univ. Redlands, 62, 63, 65; mem. bd. dirs, Serv. Admin. Col. & Univ, 66-68. Can. Army, 42-45. Chem. Inst. Can; Am. Chem. Soc; The Chem. Soc; Humanities Asn. Can. Chemistry education. Address: 3065 Uplands Rd, Victoria, BC, Can.

GRAHAM, FRANCES K(EESLER), b. U.S.A, Aug. 1, 18; m. 41; c. 3. PSYCHOLOGY. B.A, Pa. State, 38; Ph.D.(psychol), Yale, 42. Asst. & instr. med. psychol, Washington (St. Louis), 42-48, instr. & res. assoc, 53-57; instr. psychol, Barnard Col, Columbia, 48-51; res. assoc. med. psychol, UNIV. WIS, MADISON, 57-64, assoc. prof. PEDIAT, 64-68, PROF, 68-, PSYCHOL, 69- Psychologist & acting dir, St. Louis Psychiat. Clin, 42-44; res. scientist award, Nat. Inst. Ment. Health, 64-74, mem. staff exp. psychol. study sect, 70-74; Am. Psychol. Asn. rep, Nat. Res. Coun, 71-74; spec. consult, Nat. Inst. Neurol. Diseases & Blindness. AAAS; Soc. Psychophysiol. Res; Soc. Res. Child Develop; Am. Psychol. Asn. Developmental psychophysiology with special interest in attentional processes and the development of high-risk infants. Address: Dept. of Psychology, University Hospitals, Madison, WI 53706.

GRAHAM, GEORGE ALFRED CECIL, b. Ireland, Feb. 25, 39; m. 68. APPLIED MATHEMATICS, MECHANICS. B.A, Dublin, 61; M.S, Brown, 64; Ph.D.(math), Glasgow, 66. Asst. prof. MATH, N.C. State, 66-67; SIMON FRASER UNIV, 67-69, ASSOC. PROF, 69- Mathematical theories of elasticity and viscoelasticity. Address: Dept. of Mathematics, Simon Fraser University, Burnaby 2, B.C, Can.

GRAHAM, GEORGE G, b. Hackensack, N.J, Oct. 4, 23; m. 49; c. 6. PEDIATRICS, NUTRITION. A.B, Univ. Pa, 41, M.D, 45. Mem. staff pediat, Brit. Am. Hosp, Lima, Peru, 47-50, chief, 52-55; res. resident, Hosp. Univ. Pa, 51; resident, Baltimore City Hosps, Md, 55-57; mem. staff, Cleveland Clin, 57-59; dir. res, Brit. Am. Hosp, 60-65; ASSOC. PROF, SCH. MED, JOHNS HOPKINS UNIV, 65-, PROF. INT, HEALTH, SCH. HYG. & PUB. HEALTH, 68- Lectr, Mass. Inst. Technol, 62-65; vis. prof, Agrarian Univ, Peru, 62-65; assoc. chief pediat, Baltimore City Hosps, 65-; mem. comt. amino acids, food & nutrit. bd, Nat. Res. Coun, 66-; consult. nutrit, Nat. Insts. Health, 66-, mem. nutrit. study sect, 71-; consult. nutrit, Agency for Int. Develop, 69- Am. Inst. Nutrit; Am. Soc. Clin. Nutrit; Soc. Pediat. Res; Am. Pediat. Soc. Address: Dept. of International Health, Johns Hopkins University, 615 N. Wolfe St, Baltimore, MD 21205.

GRAHAM, GEORGE L(AURIN), b. Scribner, Nebr, Dec. 12, 02. HELMINTHOLOGY. A.B, Grand Island Col, 27; M.S, Kans. State Col, 30; Sc.D, Hopkins, 33. Asst. biol, Grand Island Col, 24-26; parasitol, Kans. State Col, 28-30, instr. zool. & parasitol, 30-31; asst. helminthol, sch. hygiene & pub. health, Hopkins, 31-33; fel. animal & plant path, Rockefeller Inst, 33-35, asst, 35-39, assoc, 39-47; ASSOC. PROF. PARASITOL, SCH. VET. MED, UNIV. PA, 47- Am. Soc. Parasitol; Am. Soc. Zool; Am. Micros. Soc; Am. Soc. Trop. Med. & Hyg. Resistance of chickens to nematodes resistance of rats to Nippostrongylus muris; parasite strains; effect of diet upon parasitism; migration of Ascaris; biology of Strongyloides. Address: School of Veterinary Medicine, University of Pennsylvania, Philadelphia, PA 19104.

GRAHAM, G(EORGE) T(HOMAS) E(MMERSON), b. Rosetown, Sask, Aug. 9, 17; nat; m. 42; c. 2. PHYSICAL ORGANIC CHEMISTRY. B.S, Saskatchewan, 39, M.S, 41; Ph.D.(chem), Chicago, 56. Res. chemist, Esso Res. & Eng. Co, N.J, 49-51; RES. SCIENTIST, UNIROYAL, INC, 51- Can. Army, 42-46, Capt. Polyurethane rubbers; patents. Address: Uniroyal, Inc, Wayne, NJ 07470.

GRAHAM, G(ORDON) A(LEXANDER) R(OBERT), b. Saskatoon, Sask, Mar. 19, 17; nat; m. 43; c. 1. PHYSICS. A.B, Saskatchewan, 38; McGill, 39-40; Cornell, 40-41; Du Pont fel, Rochester, 48-49, Ph.D.(physics), 49. Lab. instr. physics, Saskatchewan, 37-39; demonstr, McGill, 39-40; asst, Cornell, 40-41; jr. res. physicist, Nat. Res. Coun. Can, Halifax, 41-43, Montreal, 43-45; asst. res. physicist, Chalk River, 45-46; instr. physics, Rochester, 46-48; servo engr, missile guid, Bell Aircraft Corp, 49-51; prin. physicist, Cornell Aeronaut. Lab, 51-60, asst. head appl. physics dept, 60-61; staff scientist, Aerospace Corp, 61-63; sr. scientist, Hughes Aircraft Co, 63-67; chief scientist & dir. eng, Electronic Specialty Co, 67-68; MEM. SR. STAFF, RAND CORP, 68- AAAS; Am. Phys. Soc. Nuclear physics; atmospheric physics; guided missiles; reconnaissance systems; radar; defense against ballistic missiles and satellites; satellite inspection; electronic warfare; tactical warfare systems. Address: Rand Corp, 1700 Main St, Santa Monica, CA 90406.

GRAHAM, HAROLD L(aVERNE), b. Cleburne, Tex, July 16, 30; m. 52; c. 2. CHEMICAL ENGINEERING. B.E, Vanderbilt, 55, M.S, 58; Ph.D, Iowa State, 60. Gas field, reservoir engr, Phillips Petrol. Co, 55-56; instr. chem. eng, Vanderbilt, 56-58, asst. prof, 58-61, assoc. prof, 61-62; res. engr, Jersey Prod. Res. Co. Div, STANDARD OIL CO.(N.J), 62-64, sr. res. engr, Esso Prod. Res. Co. Div, 64-66, sr. res. specialist, 66-67, res. supvr, 67-71, TECH. ADV. DRILLING, HUMBLE OIL & REF. CO, 71- U.S.N, 50-54. Am. Inst. Chem. Eng; Am. Inst. Min, Metall. & Petrol. Eng. Fluid mechanics in continuous media. Address: Humble Oil & Refining Co, Room 1975, P.O. Box 2180, Houston, TX 77001.

GRAHAM, HAROLD N(ATHANIEL), b. N.Y.C, July 27, 21; m. 44; c. 5. ORGANIC CHEMISTRY. B.A, Cornell, 41; Ph.D.(org. chem), Chicago, 46. Res. chemist, THOMAS J. LIPTON, INC, 52-60, mgr. food res, 60-62, asst. dir. res, 62-67, DIR. FOOD RES, 67- Dir, Ceytea Ltd, Colombo, Ceylon, 66. AAAS; Am. Chem. Soc; fel. Am. Inst. Chem; Inst. Food Tech. Free radical chemistry; chemistry of natural products; biochemistry of plants and microorganisms; petroleum and synthetic rubber research; flavor chemistry; gas-liquid chromatography; food chemistry; food product development; plant proteins. Address: Thomas J. Lipton, Inc, 800 Sylvan Ave, Englewood Cliffs, NJ 07632.

GRAHAM, HARRY M(ORGAN), b. Whittier, Calif, June 18, 29. ENTOMOLOGY. B.S, California, 51, M.S, 53, Ph.D.(entomol), 59. ENTOMOLOGIST, U.S. DEPT. AGR, 58- U.S.A, 53-55. AAAS; Entom. Soc. Am. Insect ecology and economic entomology. Address: U.S. Dept. of Agriculture, P.O. Box 1033, Brownsville, TX 78520.

GRAHAM, HENRY COLLINS, b. Pittsburgh, Pa, Aug. 16, 34; m. 57; c. 3. CERAMIC ENGINEERING. B.S, Alfred, 56, M.S, 58; Ph.D.(ceramic eng), Ohio State, 65. Mem. staff crysallzable glasses, res. lab, Pittsburgh Plate Glass, Pa, 57-60; RES. PHYSICIST, AEROSPACE RES. LABS, WRIGHT PATTERSON AFB, 60- U.S.A, 56-57, Capt. Am. Ceramic Soc. Determining the defect structure of both metals and metal oxides by making measurements such as electrical conductivity and continuous weight change under various ambient conditions; behavior of materials in reactive atmospheres including the determination of the reaction mechanisms and the influence of the defect structure and the microstructural features on these mechanisms. Address: Aerospace Research Labs, LL, Bldg. 450, Wright Patterson AFB, OH 45433.

GRAHAM, HERBERT W(ILLIAM), b. New Brighton, Pa, Dec. 18, 05; m. 30; c. 2. OCEANOGRAPHY, BIOLOGY. B.S, Pittsburgh, 29; M.A, Stanford, 34, Ph.D.(biol), 38. Herbarium asst, Carnegie Mus, Pittsburgh, 24-28; asst. bot, Pittsburgh, 29; chemist & biologist, Carnegie Inst. Dept. Terrestrial Magnetism, 29-38; asst. prof. biol, Texas Christian, 38-39; assoc. prof. zool, Mills Col, 39-43, prof, 43-50; oceanogr, Philippine Fishery Prog, U.S. Fish & Wildlife Serv, 48-50, chief red tide lab, Sarasota, Fla, 50-51, N.Atlantic fishery invests, 51-57, dir. Bur. Commercial Fisheries Biol. Lab, 58-70; RETIRED. Lectr, Univ. N.H, 57. AAAS. Chemical oceanography; marine planktology; taxonomy of dinoflagellates; fishery biology. Address: 36 Wilson Rd, Woods Hole, MA 02543.

GRAHAM, HOWARD EDWARD, b. La Grande, Ore, Oct. 19, 17; m. 41; c. 3. METEOROLOGY. B.S, Oregon State, 41; U.S. Naval Acad, 44-45. Meteorologist, U.S. Weather Bur, Portland, Ore, 46-56, res. meteorologist, Nat. Hurricane Res. Proj, D.C, 56-59; METEOROLOGIST, NAT. FOREST ADMIN, U.S. FOREST SERV, 59- U.S.N, 42-46, Lt. Am. Meteorol. Soc. Fire whirlwinds; hurricane winds for engineering design of seawalls and other structures; applied meteorology in forest fire control work. Address: U.S. Forest Service, P.O. Box 3623, Portland, OR 97208.

GRAHAM, JACK B(ENNETT), b. Superior, Nebr, Oct. 16, 13; m. 41; c. 6. PHYSICAL GEOLOGY. A.B, York Col, 35; B.S, Nebraska, 37; M.S, Iowa, 40, Ph.D.(geol), 42. Asst. geol, Iowa, 38-42; jr. geologist, ground-water br, U.S. Geol. Surv, 42-43, asst. geologist, 43-45, assoc. geologist, 45-48, dist. geologist, 48-52, chief water utilization sect, tech. coord. br, 52-54; ground water geologist, Leggette & Brashears, 54-55, PARTNER, LEGGETTE, BRASHEARS & GRAHAM, 55- AAAS; Am. Inst. Prof. Geol.(v.pres, 67); Geol. Soc. Am; Am. Inst. Min, Metall. & Petrol. Eng. Ground water geology and hydrology; hydrogeology. Address: Leggette, Brashears & Graham, 551 Fifth Ave, New York, NY 10017.

GRAHAM, JACK RAYMOND, b. High Point, N.C, Sept. 15, 25; m. 48; c. 3. ORGANIC CHEMISTRY. A.B, North Carolina, 50, M.A, 52. Chemist, Westvaco Chem. Div, FMC CORP, 52-54, NIAGARA CHEM. DIV, 54-55, proj. leader, 55-58, group leader, 58-62, supvr, 62-63, MGR, 63- U.S.A, 43-45. Am. Chem. Soc. Synthesis, residue analysis, process development and formulation of organic chemicals for use as agricultural pesticides. Address: Niagara Chemical Division, FMC Corp, Middleport, NY 14105.

GRAHAM, JAMES CARL, b. Clarendon, Tex, May 20, 41; m. 64; c. 2. AGRONOMY, BOTANY. B.S, Tex. Tech. Col, 63; M.S, Wisconsin, 64, Ph.D. (agron), 66. Res. asst, Wisconsin, 63-66; sr. res. chemist, MONSANTO CO, 66-69, RES. SPECIALIST, 69- Am. Soc. Agron; Crop Sci. Soc. Am; Crop physiology, physiological aspects of yield of major field crops; practical aspects of stress physiology and plant growth regulation. Address: Monsanto Co, 800 N. Lindbergh Blvd, St. Louis, MO 63166.

GRAHAM, JAMES D(OUGLAS), b. Columbus, Ohio, Mar. 21, 41; m. 66; c. 2. DEVELOPMENTAL GENETICS, EXPERIMENTAL HEMATOLOGY. M.A, Kent State Univ, 67, Ph.D.(physiol), 69. Instr. BIOL, Kent State Univ, 67-69; ASST. PROF, BOWLING GREEN STATE UNIV, 69- Res. assoc, inst. med. res, Toledo Hosp, 69- Genetics Soc. Am; N.Y. Acad. Sci. Control of hemopoiesis; genetic mechanisms of developmental regulation; cellular bases of myelogenous leukemias. Address: Dept. of Biology, Bowling Green State University, Bowling Green, OH 43403.

GRAHAM, JAMES H, b. Boston, Mass, Dec. 16, 16; m. 44; c. 5. MEDICINE, PATHOLOGY. B.S, Tufts, 39, M.D, 43. PATHOLOGIST, ST. ELIZABETH'S HOSP, 49-; CLIN. PROF. PATH, SCH. MED, BOSTON UNIV, 67-, assoc. clin. prof, 55-67. Lectr, Harvard & Tufts, 55-; Boston Col, 63- Consult, U.S. Brighton Marine Hosp. & Lemuel Shattuck Hosp, 62- Dipl, Am. Bd. Path, 50. U.S.N.R, 44-46, Lt. Am. Asn. Path. & Bact; Am. Soc. Clin. Path. Histology. Address: St. Elizabeth's Hospital, 736 Cambridge St, Brighton, MA 14626.

GRAHAM, JAMES W, b. Copper Cliff, Ont, Jan. 17, 32; m. 55; c. 3. MATHEMATICS, COMPUTER SCIENCE. B.A, Univ. Toronto, 54, M.A, 55. Appl. sci. rep, Int. Bus. Mach. Corp, 55-59; asst. prof. MATH, UNIV. WATERLOO, 59-63, assoc. prof, 63-66, PROF, 66-, DIR. COMPUT; CTR, 61- Asn. Comput. Mach; Am. Math. Soc; Math. Asn. Am; Comput. Soc. Can.(pres, 65-66). Non-numeric computing including sorting; specialized computer languages; information retrieval. Address: Computing Center, University of Waterloo, Waterloo, Ont, Can.

GRAHAM, JOHN B(ORDEN), b. Goldsboro, N.C, Jan. 26, 18; m. 43; c. 3. PATHOLOGY. B.S, Davidson Col, 38; M.D, Cornell, 42. Intern PATH, N.Y. Hosp, 42-43; asst, Cornell Univ, 43-44; instr. UNIV. N.C, CHAPEL HILL, 46-49, asst. prof, 49-53, assoc. prof, 53-58, prof, 58-66, ALUMNI DISTINGUISHED PROF, 66-, DIR. GENETICS TRAINING PROG, 61-, COORD. INTERDEPARTAMENTAL GRAD. PROGS. BIOL, 68-, chmn. bd. pop. ctr, 64-67, assoc. dean med. sch, 68-70. Markle scholar, 49-54; mem. res. career award comt, U.S. Pub. Health Serv, 59-62, genetics training comt, 62-66, chmn, 67-71; mem. path. test comt, Nat. Bd. Med. Exam, 63-67; Int. Comt. Hemostasis & Thrombosis, 63-67; res. adv. comt, inst. behav. genetics, Univ. Colo, 67- Dipl, Am. Bd. Path, 61; O. Max Gardner Award, Univ. N.C, 68. Med.C, U.S.A, 44-46, Capt. AAAS; Am. Soc. Exp. Path; Soc. Exp. Biol. & Med; Am. Soc. Human Genetics (secy, 64-67, pres. elect, 71-); Am. Med. Asn; Int. Soc. Hemat; Am. Inst. Biol. Sci; Am. Asn. Path. & Bact. Physiology of blood coagulation; hemorrhagic diseases; human genetics; population control. Address: Dept. of Pathology, School of Medicine, University of North Carolina at Chapel Hill, Chapel Hill, NC 27514.

GRAHAM, JOHN D(AVID), b. New Haven, Conn, Mar. 21, 36; m. 64. PHYSICAL CHEMISTRY. B.S, Providence Col, 57; Monsanto Co. fel, Mich. State, 59-60, Nat. Sci. Found. summer fel, 60, Ph.D.(phys. chem), 61. Nat. Sci. Found. fel, Yale, 61-63; res. chemist, Union Carbide Corp, 64-65; asst. prof. CHEM, NORTH. ILL. UNIV, 65-68, ASSOC. PROF, 68- Am. Chem. Soc; Am. Phys. Soc. Molecular structure; nuclear magnetic resonance; quantum chemistry. Address: Dept. of Chemistry, Northern Illinois University, De Kalb, IL 60115.

GRAHAM, JOHN E(LWOOD), b. Kingston, Ont, Jan. 30, 33; m. 57. STATISTICS, MATHEMATICS. B.Sc, Carleton, 55; M.A, Queen's (Ont), 57; M.S, Iowa State, 60, Ph.D.(statist), 63. Statistician, Dominion Bur. Statist, 57-58, 63-65; asst, statist. lab, Iowa State, 58-63; asst. prof. MATH, CARLETON UNIV.(ONT), 65-70, ASSOC. PROF, 70- Am. Statist. Asn; Can. Agr. Econ. Soc. Sample survey methods and theory; teaching of statistics. Address: Dept. of Mathematics, Carleton University, Ottawa, Ont, Can.

GRAHAM, JOHN W(ILLIAM), JR, b. Dayton, Ohio, May 25, 15; m. 42; c. 4. CIVIL ENGINEERING. B.C.E, Ohio State, 39; C.E, Princeton, 40; D.Sc, Carnegie Inst. Tech, 50; L.H.D, St. Lawrence Univ, 68. Engr, fabricated steel construct. div, Bethlehem Steel Corp, Pa, 40-42, 45-46; from instr. to assoc. prof, Carnegie Inst. Technol, 46-55, asst. dean col. eng. & sci, 48-55, dean stud, 55-56; v.pres, Cooper Union, 56-59; dean col. eng. & appl. sci, Univ. Rochester, 59-66; PRES, CLARKSON COL. TECHNOL, 66- C.Eng, 42-46, Maj. Am. Soc. Eng. Educ; Am. Soc. Civil Eng; Nat. Soc. Prof. Eng. Properties and behavior under load of structures and structural materials. Address: Clarkson College of Technology, Potsdam, NY 13676.

GRAHAM, JOSEPH H, b. Richmond, Va, Sept. 23, 33; m. 58; c. 1. ORGANIC CHEMISTRY. B.S, Va. Union, 53; M.S, Howard, 56, Ph.D.(org. chem), 59. RES. CHEMIST, DIV. DRUG CHEM, FOOD & DRUG ADMIN, DEPT. HEALTH, EDUC. & WELFARE, WASH, D.C, 59- Am. Chem. Soc; Asn. Off. Anal. Chem. Preparation and properties of benzyl-o-nitrophenylglyoxals; development of analytical procedures for equine conjugated estrogens and synthetic estrogens in pharmaceuticals; gel filtration. Address: 7516 Greer Dr, Oxon Hill, MD 20022.

GRAHAM, J(OSEPH) H(ARRY), b. Anderson, S.C, Sept. 11, 21; m. 46; c. 2. PLANT PATHOLOGY. B.S, Clemson, 42; Ph.D.(plant path), N.C. State Col, 50. Asst. prof. plant path, Pa. State, 51-54, assoc. prof, 54-64, prof, 64-66; plant pathologist, U.S. Regional Pasture Res. Lab, 50-66; ASST. BR. CHIEF, VEG. & ORNAMENTALS RES. BR, U.S. DEPT. AGR, 66- U.S.N.R, 42-46, Lt. Comdr. AAAS; Am. Phytopath. Soc. Diseases of forage grasses, legumes and field crops; research administration; production of vegetables and ornamentals. Address: Plant Industry Station, Agricultural Research Service, U.S. Dept. of Agriculture, Beltsville, MD 20705.

GRAHAM, JOSEPH J(AMES), b. Ironwood, Mich, Dec. 30, 21; m. 43; c. 5. ZOOLOGY. B.S, Michigan, 48, M.A, 49; Ph.D.(zool), Toronto, 54. Sr. biologist, McMaster, 49; res. investr. ecol, Toronto, 50-52; assoc. biol. oceanogr, Narragansett Marine Lab, Rhode Island, 52-53, fishery biologist, 53-55; FISHERY RES. BIOLOGIST, Honolulu Biol. Lab, NAT. MARINE FISHERIES SERV, U.S. DEPT. COMMERCE, 55-60, BIOL. LAB, Tex, 60-61, MAINE, 61- Lectr, grad. sch, Univ. Maine. U.S.A, 42-45. Bionomics; ecology of fishes, especially larval fishes. Address: Biological Lab, National Marine Fisheries Service, U.S. Dept. of Commerce, West Boothbay Harbor, ME 04575.

GRAHAM, KENNETH, b. Sask, Sept. 3, 11; m. 68; c. 1. ENTOMOLOGY. B.A, British Columbia, 33; M.Sc, McGill, 37; Ph.D.(exp. biol, biochem), Toronto, 45. Field asst, Triangulation Surv, B.C, 30; insect pest investr, Can. Dept. Agr, 31-36, agr. asst, 37-40, agr. scientist, 40-48; PROF. FOREST ENTOM, UNIV. B.C, 48- Vis. prof, Univ. Calif, Berkeley, fall 67. Entom. Soc. Can. Forest insect ecology and behavior; forest entomology. Address: Faculty of Forestry, University of British Columbia, Vancouver 8, B.C, Can.

GRAHAM, LAURENCE DRELL, b. Chicago, Ill, Aug. 22, 41. PHYSICS. B.A, Oberlin Col, 62; M.S, Washington (Seattle), 63; Ph.D.(physics), Northwest. Univ.(Ill), 68. Res. assoc. PHYSICS, Univ. Ill, Urbana, 68-69; ASSOC. PROF, WHITTIER COL, 69- Address: Dept. of Physics, Whittier College, Whittier, CA 90608.

GRAHAM, LAURINE LaPLANCHE, b. N.Y.C, July 4, 38; m. 64; c. 1. PHYSICAL CHEMISTRY. B.S, Maryland, 59; Nat. Insts. Health fel, Mich. State, 61-63, Ph.D.(chem), 63. ASST. PROF. physics, W.Va. State Col, 64-65; CHEM, NORTH. ILL. UNIV, 65- Am. Chem. Soc. Nuclear magnetic resonance; energy barriers to internal rotation; molecular configurations; proton exchange; hydrogen bonding; proton-fluorine spin-spin coupling. Address: Dept. of Chemistry, Northern Illinois University, De Kalb, IL 60115.

GRAHAM, LE ROY CULLEN, b. Meeker, Colo, Dec. 14, 26; m. 49; c. 4. ELECTRICAL ENGINEERING, APPLIED MATHEMATICS. B.S, Colorado, 50; commun. develop. training prog, Bell Tel. Labs, 50-53; M.S, Stevens Inst. Tech, 56. Mem. tech. staff, Bell Tel. Labs, 50-56; sr. develop. engr, ARIZ. DIV, GOODYEAR AEROSPACE CORP, 56-67, eng. specialist, 57-60, SR. ENG. SPECIALIST, 60- U.S.N.R, 44-46. Inst. Elec. & Electronics Eng. Coherent radar system; synthesis of new systems and image analysis; development of telephone transmission lines. Address: Goodyear Aerospace Corp, Litchfield Park, AZ 85340.

GRAHAM, LEWIS T(EXADA), b. Alexandria, La, Oct. 2, 14; m. 39; c. 2. ENTOMOLOGY. B.S, Southwestern Louisiana, 36; fel, La. State, 36-38, M.S, 38; Ph.D.(entom), Iowa State, 47. Asst. zool. & entom, Iowa State, 38, instr, 38-39, asst. entom. & assoc. exten. entomologist, 39-42; asst. entomologist, Nebraska, 42-43; asst. prof. BIOL, UNIV. SOUTHWEST. LA, 46-49, assoc. prof, 49-52, PROF, 52-, DEAN COL. LIB. ARTS, 65-; head dept. biol, 54-65. Dir, Vermilion Bay Marine Lab, 58-64. U.S.N, 42-45, 51-52, Comdr. AAAS; Entom. Soc. Am; Am. Soc. Oceanog. Economic entomology; three-cornered alfalfa hopper; insect toxicology; biometrics. Address: Box 403, Southwestern Station, Lafayette, LA 70501.

GRAHAM, LEWIS T(EXADA), JR, b. Alexandria, La, Aug. 24, 40; m. 62; c. 2. BIOCHEMISTRY, NEUROBIOLOGY. B.S, Southwestern Louisiana, 62; Nat. Sci. Found. fel, Nat. Inst. Ment. Health fel. & Ph.D.(biochem), Indiana, 67. Res. biochemist, Vet. Admin. Hosp, Sepulveda, Calif, 67-69; ASST. PROF. PSYCHIAT. & BIOCHEM, INST. PSYCHIAT. RES, MED. CTR, IND. UNIV,

INDIANAPOLIS, 69- U.S.A.R, 57-65. Am. Soc. Neurochem; Soc. Neurosci; Int. Soc. Neurochem. Utilization of microtechniques in the identification of synaptic transmitters in nerve tissue. Address: Institute for Psychiatric Research, Indiana University Medical Center, 1100 W. Michigan St, Indianapolis, IN 46207.

GRAHAM, LOIS, b. Troy, N.Y, Apr. 4, 25. MECHANICAL ENGINEERING. B.M.E, Rensselaer Polytech, 45; M.S, Ill. Inst. Technol, 49, Ph.D, 59. Test engr, Carrier Corp, 45-46; asst. mech, ILL. INST. TECHNOL, 46-48, assoc. prof. & asst. dir. dept, 48-69, ASSOC. PROF. MECH. ENG, 69- Am. Soc. Mech. Eng; Am. Soc. Eng. Educ. Thermodynamics; heat transfer; combustion. Address: Dept. of Mechanical & Aerospace Engineering, Illinois Institute of Technology, 3300 S. Federal St, Chicago, IL 60616.

GRAHAM, LOUIS SPARKMAN, JR, b. Wash, D.C, Dec. 29, 20; m. 43; c. 2. PATHOLOGY. B.A, Virginia, 42, M.D, 45. Instr. path, Virginia, 52-53; asst. prof, Alabama, 54-55, assoc. prof, 55-56; ASSOC. PATHOLOGIST, Druid City Hosp, Tuscaloosa, Ala, 56-62; ST. THOMAS HOSP, 62- U.S.A, 46-48. Am. Soc. Clin. Path; Am. Med. Asn; Col. Am. Path. General clinical pathology. Address: St. Thomas Hospital, Nashville, TN 37203.

GRAHAM, MALCOLM, b. Penn, Nov, 26, 23; m. 52; c. 2. MATHEMATICS. B.S, N.J. State Col, Trenton, 46; M.S, Massachusetts, 48; Ed.D.(math, ed), Columbia, 54. Instr. math, Marion Inst, 48-49; assoc. prof, Longwood Col, 51-55; E.Carolina Col, 55-56; asst. prof, UNIV. NEV, 56-58, assoc. prof. math. & chmn. div. sci, math. & appl. sci, 59-64, PROF. MATH, 64-, chmn. dept, 65-66. U.S.A, 43-44. Math. Asn. Am; Am. Math. Soc. Applied science; general mathematics. Address: Dept. of Mathematics, University of Nevada, La Vegas, NV 89109.

GRAHAM, MARTIN H(AROLD), b. Jamaica, N.Y, July 12, 26; m. 49; c. 2. INSTRUMENTATION, COMPUTER SCIENCE. B.E.E, Polytech. Inst. Brooklyn, 47, D.E.E.(electronics), 52; M.Sc, Harvard, 48. Instr, Polytech. Inst. Brooklyn, 47-50; res. assoc, Brookhaven Nat. Lab. 50-52, electronic engr, 52-57; assoc. prof. elec. eng, Rice, 57-62, PROF, 62-66; COMPUT. SCI, UNIV. CALIF, BERKELEY, 66-, assoc. dir. comput. ctr, 66-69. Vis. prof, California, Berkeley, 64-65. Consult, Brookhaven Nat. Lab, 57-61; Univ. Chicago, 58-60; Shell Develop. Co, 58-60; Tex. Instruments, Inc, 58-; U.S. Atomic Energy Comn, 60-63; manned spacecraft ctr, NASA, 63-64. U.S.N.R, 44-46. Fel. Inst. Elec. & Electronics Eng. Digital computers; electronic instrumentation; medical electronics. Address: 3060 Buena Vista Way, Berkeley, CA 94708.

GRAHAM, O(WEN) H(UGH), b. Thorndale, Tex, Apr. 18, 17; m. 40; c. 4. MEDICAL & VETERINARY ENTOMOLOGY. B.S, Texas A&M, 38, M.S, 40, Ph.D.(animal parasitol), 62. Jr. entomologist, bur. entom. & plant quarantine, U.S. Dept. Agr, Tex, 39-41, Ariz, 41-42, entomologist, Tex, 42; Corps. Engrs, U.S. Army, C.Z, 50-56; entomologist & asst. sta. leader, livestock insects lab, ENTOM. RES. DIV, U.S. DEPT. AGR, 56-64, invest. leader, livestock insects invest, 64-70, RES. ENTOMOLOGIST, 70- Adv, U.S. del. livestock prod. in Ams, Food & Agr. Orgn, UN, Jamaica, 58; consult, Orgn. Int. Regional para Sanidad Agropecuaria, San Salvador. Sanit.C, 42-46; Med.Serv.C.Res, 46-, Lt. Col. AAAS; Ent. Soc. Am.(Geigy Recognition Award, 71); Am. Mosquito Control Asn; Mex. Soc. Entom. Use of animal systemic insecticides for control of hypoderma and dermatobia bots in livestock; arthropod transmission of animal diseases; control of Boophilus and other ticks. Address: Livestock Insects Lab, U.S. Dept. Agriculture, P.O. Box 232, Kerrville, TX 78028.

GRAHAM, PAUL F(RANKLIN), b. Dayton, Ohio, May 19, 18; m. 41; c. 4. ENGINEERING MECHANICS. B.C.E, Ohio State, 48, M.Sc, 52. Surveyor, F.J. Cellarius Eng. Co, Ohio, 39-40; instr. ENG. MECH, OHIO STATE UNIV, 48-53, asst. prof, 53-56, from assoc. prof. to PROF, 56- U.S.A, 41-46, Maj. Am. Soc. Eng. Educ; Soc. Exp. Stress Anal; Nat. Soc. Prof. Eng. Application of digital computers to solution of structural problems; structural plasticity; elastic stability; strength of materials. Address: Dept. of Engineering, Ohio State University, Columbus, OH 43210.

GRAHAM, PAUL R(OGER), b. Crystal City, Mo, June 26, 21; m. 47; c. 4. ORGANIC CHEMISTRY. B.S, St. Louis, 50. Anal. chemist, MONSANTO CO, 50-53, res. chemist, 53-62, res. group leader, 62-69, PROJ. MGR, 69- Liaison, Food & Drug Admin. Plasticizer and polymer chemistry, especially stabilization of polymers to light and heat; plasticizer application, especially vinyl dispersions, plasticizer evaluation and resin studies; synthesis and application of polymers for paper coating and saturation, especially emulsion polymerization and starch chemistry; development of new plasticizers and polymer modifiers with particular emphasis on nontoxic and permanent plasticizers for polyvinyl chloride. Address: Monsanto Co, 800 N. Lindbergh Blvd, St. Louis, MO 63166.

GRAHAM, PETER, b. Calcutta, India, Sept. 21, 29; m. 58. ECOLOGY, MEDICAL ENTOMOLOGY. B.Sc, Rhodes Univ, S.Africa, 53, Hons, 54, M.Sc, 56; Ph.D.(entom), Univ. Alta, 68. Entomologist, WHO, 58-62, acting sr. malaria adv. to Govt. of Sarawak, 61-62; entomologist, tsetse fly studies, Govt. of Botswana, 62-64; ASST. PROF. BIOL, Algoma Col, 67-68; Lindenwood Col, 68-69; THOMAS MORE COL, 69- Fel. Zool. Soc. London; fel. Royal Entom. Soc. London; Entom. Soc. South. Africa; Entom. Soc. Can; Entom. Soc. Am; Can. Soc. Zool; Am. Inst. Biol. Sci. The dynamics of mosquito population and especially the biases in methods in sampling for mosquito populations. Address: Dept. of Biology, Thomas More College, Covington, KY 41017.

GRAHAM, PETER JOSEPH, b. Laconia, N.H, Oct. 19, 21; m. 46; c. 1. ORGANIC CHEMISTRY. B.S, New Hampshire, 42; M.S, 44; Am. Viscose fel, Purdue, 46-47, Ph.D.(org. chem), 47. Res. chemist, res. found, Purdue, 44-46; exp. sta, E.I. DU PONT DE NEMOURS & CO, 47-56, res. supvr, fabrics & finishes dept, Marshall Lab, 56-61, res. mgr, 61-64, dir. exp. sta. lab, 64-69, tech. mgr, 69-70, PLANNING MGR, 70- AAAS; Am. Chem. Soc. Organic research; synthesis; polymers; finishes; coatings; adhesives. Address: 4006 Lakeview Dr, Greenville, DE 19807.

GRAHAM, RAYMOND, b. Clinton, Ind, July 1, 35. PHYSICAL CHEMISTRY, MOLECULAR SPECTROSCOPY. B.S, Ind. State Univ, Terre Haute, 62;

Nat. Defense Educ. Act fel, Mont. State Univ, 62-65, Ph.D.(chem), 70. ASST. PROF. CHEM, ROCKY MT. COL, 70- Nat. Sci. Found. res. partic, Wash. State Univ, summer 71. U.S.N, 54-58. Am. Chem. Soc. Absorption spectroscopy of forbidden transitions in organic molecules; luminescence spectra of transition metal complexes. Address: Dept. of Chemistry, Rocky Mountain College, Billings, MT 59102.

GRAHAM, R(ICHARD) C(HARLES) B(URWELL), b. Miami Beach, Fla, Apr. 17, 26; Can. citizen; m. 52; c. 4. PHARMACOLOGY. B.Sc, Western Ontario, 49, M.Sc, 51, Ph.D.(endocrinol, pharmacol), 55. Pharmacologist, food & drug labs, Dept. Nat. Health & Welfare, Can, 55-60; investr. med. sci, Inst. Exp. Med, Caracas, Venezuela, 60-62; pharmacologist, food & drug labs, DEPT. NAT. HEALTH & WELFARE, 62-66, asst. chief div. med. & pharmacol, FOOD & DRUG DIRECTORATE, 66-70, ASST. DIR. DRUG ADV. BUR, 70- Cairncross & Lawrence Prize, Ont, 55. Soc. Toxicol; Pharmacol. Soc. Can; Pan-Am. Med. Asn. Toxicology of pesticides and drugs; pharmacology of ataractic drugs; biological activity of plant products; endocrinology. Address: Drug Advisory Bureau, Food & Drug Directorate, Dept. of National Health & Welfare, Ottawa, Ont. K1A 0L2, Can.

GRAHAM, RICHARD H, b. Pittsburgh, Pa, May 25, 21; m. 46; c. 3. PHYSICS. B.S, Washington (Seattle), 48. Physicist, Allis-Chalmers Mfg. Co, Wis, 49-51; lead physicist exp. reactor physics, Calif, Res. & Develop. Co, 51-54; sect. chief reactor eng, U.S. Atomic Energy Cmn, Wash, D.C, 54-56; sect. head, Lockheed Aircraft Corp, 56-59; consult. prod. planning, atomic power equip. dept, Gen. Elec. Co, 59-66, mgr, uranium develop. oper, nuclear energy div, 66-67; develop. dir. nuclear fuels div, GULF OIL CORP, 67-68, coord. base progs, GULF GEN. ATOMIC INC, 68-71, MGR. PLANNING & ANAL, 71- Tech. secy, adv. comt. reactor safeguards & consult, U.S. Atomic Energy Comn, 57-59. U.S.A.A.F, 41-45. AAAS; Am. Nuclear Soc; Am. Phys. Soc. Nuclear fuel cycle optimization; nuclear reactor design; experimental physics, reactor kinetics and evaluation; medical physics; artificial kidney design. Address: Gulf Energy & Environmental Systems, P.O. Box 608, San Diego, CA 92112.

GRAHAM, ROBERT (CLARK), b. Harbor Springs, Mich, June 9, 06; m. 49; c. 8. OPTOMETRY. A.B, Mich. State, 31; B.Sc, Ohio State, 37. Spec. rep. ophthal. instruments, Bausch & Lomb Optical Co, 37-40; from west. mgr. to sales mgr, Univis Lens Co, 40-46; DIR. RES, Plastic Optics Co, 46-47; ARMORLITE LENS CO, INC, 47- Assoc. prof, Los Angeles Col. Optom, 48-68; spec. lectr, sch. med, Loma Linda, 50-; dir, Adv. Concepts Tech, Inc, 64- AAAS; Optical Soc. Am; Am. Ord. Asn; Am. Asn. Physics Teachers. Variable focus lenses; hard resin optics; contact lenses; prismatic effects of ophthalmic lenses; lens manufacturing. Address: 185 S. Euclid Ave, Pasadena, CA 91101.

GRAHAM, R(OBERT) A(LBERT), b. Dallas, Tex, Feb. 11, 31; m. 51; c. 3. PHYSICS. B.S, Texas, 54, M.S, 58. Res. engr, Southwest Res. Inst, 56-57; MEM. RES. STAFF, SANDIA LABS, 58- C.Eng, 54-56, 1st Lt. AAAS; Am. Phys. Soc. Solid mechanics; mechanical and physical properties of solids under shock wave loading conditions; shock wave mechanics; high pressure physics. Address: High Pressure Physics Research Division 5132, Sandia Labs, Albuquerque, NM 87115.

GRAHAM, ROBERT LESLIE, b. Saratoga, Iowa, Jan. 9, 26; m. 57; c. 1. INORGANIC & PHYSICAL CHEMISTRY. B.A, Mankato State Col, 52; M.S, Minnesota, 54; Ph.D.(inorg. chem), Virginia, 58. Res. chemist, Orlon Res. Dept, E.I. du Pont de Nemours & Co, 58-59; assoc. prof. CHEM, Va. Polytech, 59-63; MANKATO STATE COL, 63-70, PROF, 70-, CHMN. DEPT, 64- U.S.N, 44-46. Am. Chem. Soc. Thermochemistry of inorganic compounds by solution calorimetry. Address: Dept. of Chemistry, Mankato State College, Mankato, MN 56001.

GRAHAM, ROBERT L(OCKHART), b. Peterborough, Ont, Feb. 17, 21; m. 44; c. 3. PHYSICS. B.A, McMaster, 43, M.A, 45; Ph.D.(physics), London, 49, Dipl, Imp. Col, 49. Res. physicist, Nat. Res. Coun. Can, 43-46, asst. res. off, ATOMIC ENERGY CAN, LTD, 49-54, assoc. res. off, 54-61, SR. RES. OFF, NUCLEAR LABS, 62- Vis. physicist, Lawrence Radiation Lab, Univ. Calif, 62-63. Fel. Am. Phys. Soc; Can. Asn. Physicists. Low energy nuclear physics, chiefly beta and gamma ray spectroscopy and associated techniques; positron annihilation in liquids and solids. Address: Chalk River Nuclear Labs, Atomic Energy of Canada, Ltd, Chalk River, Ont, Can.

GRAHAM, ROBERT MONTROSE, b. St. Johns, Mich, Sept. 26, 29; m. 54; c. 2. COMPUTER SCIENCE. B.A, Michigan, 56, M.A, 57. Sr. programmer, comput. ctr, Univ. Michigan, 59-60, res. asst, 60-61, co-chmn. & lectr, summer conf. automatic prog, 61, 62 & 63, lectr. math, 61-62; res. assoc, 61-63; prog. coord, Comput. Ctr. & Proj. MAC, MASS. INST. TECHNOL, 63-66, div. sponsored res. staff, 66-67, lectr. COMPUT. SCI, 65-67, ASSOC. PROF, 67- Lectr, Univ. N.C, summer 60; consult, Socony Mobil Oil Co, 60-61; Pure Oil Co, summer 61; Gen. Motors Corp. Tech. Ctr, 61-63; lectr, Moore Sch. Eng, Univ, Pa, summer 65; consult, Honeywell, Inc, 68-; Hebrew Univ. Jerusalem, summer 69; underwater sound lab, U.S. Navy, 69; mem. bd. dirs, Intercomp, 69-71; consult, First Bus. Comput, 70-; vis. assoc. prof, Univ. Calif, Berkeley, 70- U.S.A, 52-55, Sgt. Am. Asn. Comput Mach. Computer science curriculum development; programming languages and language translation; computer operating and supervisory systems; time sharing and on-line interactive systems; software design and implementation tools; system performance analysis. Address: Project MAC, Massachusetts Institute of Technology, 545 Technology Sq, Cambridge, MA 02139.

GRAHAM, ROBERT P(ATTERSON), b. Seattle, Wash, Aug. 27, 13; m. 38; c. 1. CHEMICAL ENGINEERING. B.S, Washington (Seattle), 35, M.S, 36. Res. assoc, Battelle Mem. Inst, 36-39; chem. engr, Johns Manville Co, 39-42; WEST. REGIONAL RES. LAB, U.S. DEPT. AGR, 42-59, prin. chem. engr, 59-69, HEAD PROCESSING DEVELOP, 69- Am. Chem. Soc; Am. Inst. Chem. Eng. Process and equipment development; compression of dehydrated vegetables; pectin; agricultural wastes; drying of heat labile biological materials and organisms. Address: 7447 Terrace Dr, El Cerrito, CA 94530.

GRAHAM, ROBERT REAVIS, b. Hiawatha, Kans, Jan. 8, 25; m. 50; c. 3. ELECTRICAL ENGINEERING. B.S, Kansas, 49; Michigan, 55-57. Dept. head microwave eng, McDONNELL DOUGLAS ELECTRONICS CO, 61-64, dir. foliage progs, 64-65, v.pres. foliage progs, 65-66, v.pres. & group exec. mil. radar div, Mich, 66-68, v.pres. & gen. mgr, Ann Arbor div, 68-71, CORP. V.PRES, MO, 71- U.S.N.R, 43-46, Ens. Inst. Elec. & Electronics Eng. Electrooptical head up displays for military and commercial aircraft; optical pattern recognition devices; holograms. Address: McDonnell Douglas Electronics Co, 2600 N. Third St, St. Charles, MO 63301.

GRAHAM, ROGER K(ENNETH), b. N.Y.C, May 24, 29; m. 50; c. 2. CHEMISTRY. B.S, Mass. Inst. Technol, 50; Atomic Energy Comn. fel, Chicago, 51-53, Ph.D, 53. Res. chemist, ROHM AND HAAS CO, 53-60, HEAD LAB, 60- Am. Chem. Soc; The Chem. Soc. Graft and block copolymers; polymer chemistry; monomer and polymer synthesis modifiers for polyvinyl chloride. Address: Rohm and Haas Co, Box 219, Bristol, PA 19007.

GRAHAM, RONALD A(RTHUR), b. College Point, N.Y, Jan. 6, 24; m. 50; c. 3. CHEMICAL ENGINEERING. B.S, Columbia, 44. Glass technol. engr, Corning Glass Wcrks, 44-47; res. proj. engr, Wyandotte Chems. Corp, 47-50, sect. head eng, 50-53, asst. to dir. contract res, 53, mgr. dept, 54-57, dir, 57-61, asst. to v.pres, res, 61-64, mfg, 64-66; mgr. lab. facilities, CELANESE RES. CO, 66-68, DIR. ADMIN. & TECH. SUPPORT, 68- U.S.A.A.F, 45-47. Am. Chem. Soc; Am. Inst. Chem. Eng; fel. Am. Inst. Chem. Rocket propellant technology; glass technology; silicates; high temperature reactions; heat transfer; chemical process development; management of research and industrial chemicals manufacturing; engineering, facilities and financial management; administration and general management. Address: Celanese Research Co, Morris Ct, Box 1000, Summit, NJ 07901.

GRAHAM, RONALD LEWIS, b. Taft, Calif, Oct. 31, 35; m. 60; c. 2. MATHEMATICS. B.S, Alaska, 58; Nat. Sci. Found. & Woodrow Wilson fels, M.A, & Ph.D.(math), California, Berkeley, 62. HEAD DISCRETE MATH. SYSTS. DEPT, BELL TEL. LABS, 62- Mem, Signal Info. & Monitoring Serv. U.S.A.F, 55-59. Am. Math. Soc; Math. Asn. Am. Combinatorial, number, and graph theories; algorithms. Address: 2C-380, Bell Telephone Labs, Murray Hill, NJ 07974.

GRAHAM, R(ONALD) P(OWELL), b. Ottawa, Ont, Apr. 25, 15. ANALYTICAL CHEMISTRY. B.A, Queen's (Ont), 37, Nat. Res. Coun. Can. bursary, 37-38, M.A, 38; scholar, Columbia, 38-39, A.M, 40, Ph.D.(chem), 42. Asst. CHEM, Columbia, 39-42; lectr, McMASTER UNIV, 42-44, asst. prof, 44-48, assoc. prof, 48-53, PROF, 53-, DEAN SCI. STUDIES, 67-, chmn. dept, 52-58, dean sci, 62-68, Am. Chem. Soc; fel. Chem. Inst. Can.(chem. educ. award, 61, Fisher Sci. Lectr. Award, 70); Chem. Inst. Can; fel. Brit. Chem. Soc; Brit. Soc. Anal. Chem. Less-common metals. Address: Dept. of Chemistry, McMaster University, Hamilton, Ont, Can.

GRAHAM, SHIRL O(RBY), b. Lincoln, Nebr, Apr. 23, 18; m. 41; c. 3. PLANT PATHOLOGY. B.A, Nebraska, 41; Ph.D.(plant path), Washington State, 54. Asst. pathologist, State Dept. Agr, Wash, 48-50; asst. PLANT PATH, WASH. STATE UNIV, 50-54, asst. prof. & asst. plant pathologist, 54-61, assoc. prof. & assoc. plant pathologist, 61-67, PROF. & PLANT PATHOLOGIST, 67-, ACTING CHMN. DEPT, 70-, assoc. dean grad. sch, 69-70. Consult, div. grad. prof, U.S. Off. Educ, 69- U.S.A, 41-46, Capt. AAAS; Mycol. Soc. Am; Am. Phytopath. Soc; Am. Inst. Biol. Sci. Physiology and biochemistry of plant diseases; antibiotic isolation and characterization; biological control, axenic culture of obligate plant parasites. Address: Dept. of Plant Pathology, Washington State University, Pullman, WA 99163.

GRAHAM, SHIRLEY ANN, b. Flint, Mich, Mar. 20, 35; m. 60; c. 3. BOTANY, TAXONOMY. B.S, Mich. State, 57; Fulbright fel, Copenhagen, 57-58; M.A, Michigan, 59, Ph.D.(bot), 63. Botanist, Harvard, 63-64; asst. prof. bot, Univ. Akron, 65-66; RES. ASSOC. BIOL. SCI, KENT STATE UNIV, 67- Bot. Soc. Am; Am. Soc. Plant Taxon; Asn. Trop. Biol; Int. Asn. Plant Taxon. Taxonomic studies in family Lythraceae, especially genus Cuphea. Address: Dept. of Biological Sciences, Kent State University, Kent, OH 44240.

GRAHAM, STANLEY E(DWARD), b. Lottie, La, Mar. 23, 17; m. 44; c. 3. SURGERY. B.S, La. State Univ, 38, M.D, 43. Instr. surg, SCH. MED, UNIV. ALA, BIRMINGHAM, 49-53, asst. prof, 53-59, assoc. prof, 59-69, CLIN. ASSOC. PROF. NEUROSURG. & SURG, 69- Consult, Vet. Admin. Hosps, Tuskegee & Birmingham; Pickens County Hosps, Aliceville & Reform; State Crippled Children's Serv; State Voc. Rehab. Serv, Montgomery; Univ. Hosp; St. Vincent's Hosp; S. Highlands Infirmary; Highland Ave. Baptist Hosp; East End Mem. Hosp; chief neurosurg, Children's Hosp. Dipl, Am. Bd. Neurol. Surg. Am. Asn. Neurol. Surg; Am. Med. Asn; Cong. Neurol. Surg. Neurosurgery. Address: School of Medicine, University of Alabama in Birmingham, 1919 S. Seventh Ave, Birmingham, AL 35233.

GRAHAM, T(HOMAS) W(ILLIAM), b. Harperville, Miss, Aug. 19, 05; m. 34; c. 2. PATHOLOGY. B.S, La. State, 31; M.S, Minnesota, 31-35; plant pathologist, bur. plant indust, U.S. DEPT. AGR, N.J, 35-38, S.C, 40-43, bur. plant indust, soils & agr. eng, 43-53, SR. PATHOLOGIST, 59- Assoc. Am. Phytopath. Soc; Soc. Nematol. Breeding for disease resistance in tobacco; genetics of fungi; epidemiology of dutch elm disease; taxonomy, biology and control of plant parasitic nematodes. Address: Crops Research Division, U.S. Dept. Agriculture, Agricultural Research Service, Pee Dee Experimental Station, Florence, SC 29501.

GRAHAM, W(ALTER) DONALD, b. Ottawa, Ont, Can, June 2, 19; m. 42; c. 2. BIOCHEMISTRY. B.S.A, Ont. Agr. Col, 40; M.Sc, McGill, 42; Reuben Wells Leonard & univ. fels. & Ph.D.(biochem), Toronto, 45. Ont. Res. Found. res. fel. pharmaceut, Toronto, 45-47; biochemist nutrit. res, Wash. State Col, 48-49; chemist pharmacol. res, food & drug lab, Can. Dept. Nat. Health & Welfare, 49-58; dir, res, Midwest Med. Res. Found, 58-64; DIR. PROD. & PROCESS RES, FARMLAND INDUST, INC, 64- Mem. shock & plasma expander panel, Defence Res. Bd. Can, 56-58. AAAS; Am. Chem. Soc; Am. Soc. Pharmacol. & Exp. Therapeut; Poultry Sci. Asn. Feeds; fertilizers; agricultural chemicals; animal health products; paints; petroleum; batteries; chemical engineering; agricultural engineering; food technology. Address: 3315 N. Oak Trafficway, Kansas City, MO 64116.

GRAHAM, W(ALTER) EARL, b. Phila, Pa, June 17, 08; m. 34; c. 2. FOOD TECHNOLOGY. B.S, Pa. State Col, 30; Pennsylvania, 30-32. Chief chemist, food preservation, Francis H. Leggett & Co, N.J, 32-37; res. rep. canning tech, Crown Can Co, Mo, 37-40, dept. dir. metal container res, Crown can div, Crown Cork & Seal Co, 40, mgr. tech. serv, 42-57; east. mgr. aerosols, Clayton Corp, 57-61, v.pres, 61-69; CONSULT, EARL GRAHAM AEROSOLS, 69- AAAS; Inst. Food Technol. Aerosol packaging; food canning and preserving; metal can development. Address: St. Peters Rd, Star Route, Pottstown, PA 19464.

GRAHAM, WALTER J(AMES), b. Wilkes-Barre, Pa, Aug. 17, 24; m. 57. PHYSICS. B.S, Catholic Univ, 45. Electronic scientist, radio div, NAVAL RES. LAB, 45-49, radiation div, 49-51, ELECTRONIC SCIENTIST & SECT. HEAD ELECTRONICS DIV, ELECTRON TUBE RES. BR, 51- Am. Phys. Soc. Gas lasers; electron physics; inductively excited plasmas; sheath instabilities; plasma waves; atomic parameters in gas discharges; microwave systems; nuclear test instrumentation; special purpose electron tubes. Address: R.R. 1, Box 650, Accokeek, MD 20607.

GRAHAM, W(ALTER) ROBERT, b. Rifle, Colo, Feb. 15, 23; m. 45; c. 2. VETERINARY PATHOLOGY. D.V.M, Colo. State Univ, 50, M.S, 54. Asst. pathologist, diag. lab, Colo. State Univ, 50-54; RES. ASSOC. PATH, UPJOHN CO, 55-, MGR, ANIMAL REARING & PROCUREMENT UNIT, 68-, sect. head, 59-68. Dipl, Am. Col. Lab. Animal Med. Am. Vet. Med. Asn; Am. Col. Vet. Path; Am. Asn. Lab. Animal Sci. Diseases of laboratory animals; development of specific pathogen-free laboratory animal colonies; laboratory animal rearing and care. Address: Dept. of Animal Rearing & Procurement, Portage Rd. Bldg. 146, Upjohn Co, Kalamazoo, MI 49001.

GRAHAM, WALTER WAVERLY, JR, b. College Grove, Tenn, Dec. 1, 06; m. 31; c. 2. MATHEMATICS. B.A, Vanderbilt, 29, M.A, 30; Ph.D.(math), Peabody Col, 43. Instr. math, VANDERBILT UNIV, 30-39, asst. prof, 39-46, assoc. prof, APPL. MATH, 46-49, PROF, 49-, head dept, 51-68. U.S.N.R, 43-46, Lt. Am. Soc. Eng. Educ; Math. Asn. Am. Applications of mathematics in engineering theory and practice. Address: Dept. of Applied Mathematics, Vanderbilt University, Nashville, TN 37203.

GRAHAM, WALTER WAVERLY, III, b. Nashville, Tenn, Apr. 30, 33; m. 55; c. 2. NUCLEAR ENGINEERING. B.S, U.S. Naval Acad, 55; M.S, Vanderbilt, 60; Atomic Energy Cmn. spec. fel, Ga. Inst. Tech, 62-64, Ph.D.(nuclear eng), 65. Res. & develop. staff assoc, Gen. Atomic Div, Gen. Dynamics Corp, 60-62; asst. prof. NUCLEAR ENG, GA. INST. TECHNOL, 65-68, ASSOC. PROF, 68-, RES. SCIENTIST, NUCLEAR RES. CTR, 65-; V.PRES, TECH. ANAL. CORP, 70- Consult, comput. systs. U.S.N, 55-59, Res, 59-, Lt. Comdr. Am. Nuclear Soc. Heavy water reactor kinetics; space dependence of response; computer-aided nuclear experimentation; delayed neutron phenomena; design optimization; fission product control. Address: 4700 Jett Rd. N.W, Atlanta, GA 30327.

GRAHAM, WILLIAM A(RTHUR) G(ROVER), b. Rosetown, Sask, Aug. 23, 30; m. 51; c. 5. INORGANIC CHEMISTRY. B.A, Saskatchewan, 52, M.A, 53; Ph.D.(chem), Harvard, 56. Lectr. & res. assoc. chem, Southern California, 56-57; res. chemist & consult, Arthur D. Little, Inc, 57-62; assoc. prof. CHEM, UNIV. ALTA, 62-67, PROF, 67- Am. Chem. Soc; The Chem. Soc; Chem. Inst. Can. Organometallic and coordination compounds; metal hydrides and carbonyls. Address: Dept. of Chemistry, University of Alberta, Edmonton, Alta, Can.

GRAHAM, WILLIAM B(AGLEY), b. Eugene, Ore, Aug. 14, 20; m. 46; c. 2. PHYSICS. B.S, Mass. Inst. Tech, 42. Lab. asst. physics, Mass. Inst. Tech, 40-42; engr, Lockheed Aircraft, 42; engr, Fed. Tel. & Radio Labs, 42-43; res. engr, Sperry Gyroscope Co, 46-50; mem. res. staff, RAND CORP, 50-58, head proj. staff, 56-58, assoc. head eng. div, 59-60, head electronics dept, 60-68, HEAD ENG. SCI. DEPT, 68- Mem. ballistic missile defense cmt, U.S. Air Force Sci. Adv. Bd, 55-62, div. adv. groups, ballistic systs. div, 61-, space systs. div, 63-, electronic systs. div. & tactical air command task force, 64-; U.S. contingent, Tri-Partite Intercontinental Ballistic Missile Defense Conf, 56; sci. adv. comt. ballistic missiles, Secy. Defense, 57-61; anti-intercontinental ballistic missile panel, President's Sci. Adv. Comt, 61-; ballistic missile adv. comt, Adv. Res. Projs. Agency, Dept. Defense, 62-; dep. sci. dir, U.S. Air Force Proj. Forecast, 62-64; consult, off. dir, Defense Res. & Eng. Defense Sci. Bd, 67-69, Defense Sci. Bd, 71- Cert. of Commendation, U.S. Navy, 60; Commander's Award, Space & Missile Systs. Orgn, U.S. Air Force, 69. U.S.N.R, 43-46, Lt.(jg). AAAS. Radar system design and analyses; weapons systems analyses; intercontinental ballistic missile defense systems; tactical and strategic aircraft and missile systems; air defense systems; automatic radar target detector. Address: Engineering Science Dept, Rand Corp, 1700 Main St, Santa Monica, CA 90406.

GRAHAM, WILLIAM B(URDEN), b. Chicago, Ill, July 14, 11; m. 40; c. 4. RESEARCH ADMINISTRATION. S.B, Chicago, 32; J.D, 36. Patent lawyer & partner, Dawson & Ooms, 40-45; v.pres. & gen. mgr, BAXTER LABS, INC, 45-53, pres, 53-71, CHMN. & CHIEF EXEC. OFF, 71- General management; research management and administration. Address: Baxter Labs, Inc, 6301 Lincoln Ave, Morton Grove, IL 60053.

GRAHAM, WILLIAM DOYCE, JR, b. Clarendon, Tex, Feb. 22, 39; m. 62; c. 2. PLANT GENETICS & BREEDING. M.S, Purdue, 65, Ph.D.(genetics), 67. Asst. prof. PLANT GENETICS & BREEDING, CLEMSON UNIV, 66-71, ASSOC. PROF, 71- Am. Soc. Agron; Crop Sci. Soc. Am. Small grain genetics, including disease resistance; genetics of yield and variety development. Address: Dept. of Agronomy & Soils, Clemson University, Clemson, SC 29631.

GRAHAM, W(ILLIAM) H(ARDIN), b. Birmingham, Ala, April 27, 32; m. 56; c. 3. ORGANIC CHEMISTRY. B.S, La. State, 53, M.S, 55; Nat. Sci. Found. fel, Fla. State, 57-58, Ph.D.(chem), 58. Noyes res. fel. chem, Calif. Inst. Tech, 58-59; res. chemist, ROHM & HAAS CO, 59-69, head anal. team, Redstone Res. Div, 69-70, GROUP LEADER, synthetic chem. group, 70, PESTICIDE RESIDUES, BRISTOL RES. LABS, 70- Am. Chem. Soc. Organic reaction mechanisms; diazo, small-ring, nitrogen-fluorine compounds, diazirines, propellants, pesticide residues. Address: Rohm & Haas Co, Box 219, Bristol, PA 19007.

GRAHAM, WILLIAM JOSEPH, b. Cle Elum, Wash, Jan. 6, 32. BEHAVIORAL ECOLOGY. B.A, Whitman Col, 54; Washington (Seattle), 58-59; M.S, Michigan, 62, Ph.D.(zool), 68. Teacher, pub. schs, 56-58, 59-60; instr. zool, Michigan, summer 64 & 65, res. asst, 65-67; lectr. BIOL, City Col. New York, 67-68, ASST. PROF, 68-71; STATE UNIV. N.Y. COL. GENESEO, 71- U.S.A, 54-56. Am. Soc. Zool; Ecol. Soc. Am; Am. Soc. Mammal. Daily activity patterns and social interactions in small mammals; effects of behavior on numbers and densities of animals. Address: Dept. of Biology, State University of New York College at Geneseo, Geneseo, NY 14454.

GRAHAM, WILLIAM LEE, b. Crellin, Md, Dec. 18, 25; m. 55; c. 3. DENTISTRY. A.B, Marietta Col, 48; D.D.S, Univ. Md, 53. Instr. oral diag, sch. dent, Univ. Md, 55-56, assoc. prof, 57-59; oral diag. & roentgenol, SCH. DENT, W.VA. UNIV, 59-63, prof, 63-70, PROF. ORAL DIAG. & CHMN. DEPT, 70- Dent. consult, Garrett County Mem. Hosp, Oakland, Md, 61-; W.Va. Univ. Hosp, 62-; Vet. Admin. Hosp, Clarksburg, 70- Dipl, Am. Bd. Oral Med. U.S.N, 43-46. Am. Dent. Asn. Oral diagnosis; oral medicine. Address: Dept. of Oral Diagnosis, West Virginia University Medical Center, Morgantown, WV 26506.

GRAHAM, WILLIAM MUIR, b. Wainwright, Alta, June 30, 29; m. 55; c. 3. ECOLOGY, INSECT BEHAVIOR. B.Sc, Alberta, 53; British Columbia, 54-55; dipl, Imp. Col, London, 56; Ph.D.(insect behav), St. Andrews, 64. Res. asst, forest biol. lab, Can. Dept. Agr, summers, 49-55; stored prod. entomologist, Maize & Produce Bd, Govt. Kenya, 57-61; storage specialist, Trop. Stored Prod. Centre, Ministry of Overseas Develop, U.K. Govt, 64-67, head ecol. sect, 67-68; ASSOC. PROF. BIOL, LAKEHEAD UNIV, 68- Entom. Soc. Can. Forest and stored products entomology; general ecological problems. Address: Dept. of Biology, Lakehead University, Port Arthur, Ont, Can.

GRAHAM, WILLIAM RENDALL, b. Melbourne, Australia, Nov. 22, 38; m. 65. PHYSICS, MOLECULAR BIOPHYSICS. B.Sc, Melbourne, 59, M.Sc, 61; Exhib. 1851 overseas scholar, Oxford, 61-64, D.Phil.(exp. nuclear physics), 65. Res. staff molecular biophysicist, YALE, 65-68, ASST. PROF. MOLECULAR BIOPHYS, 68- Experimental nuclear physics; field ion microscopy of biological molecules; surface physics. Address: Dept. of Molecular Biophysics, Box 1937, Yale Station, New Haven, CT 06520.

GRAHAM, W(ILLIAM) R(ICHARD), JR, b. Guelph, Ont; nat; m. 34; c. 2. NUTRITION. B.S.A, Ont. Agr. Col, 29; M.S.A, Toronto, 31, Ph.D.(biochem), 33. Res. fel, Nat. Inst. Res. in Dairying, 33-35; Gen. Ed. Bd. & Nat. Res. Coun. fel, Missouri, 35-36; dir. res, Am. Dairies, Inc, Mo, 36-41; v.pres, Cerophyl Labs, Inc, 41-49; dir. res, QUAKER OATS CO, 49-69, SR. RES. FEL, 69- Pres, Can. subsidiary, Am. Dairies, Inc, Mo; mem. comt. int. nutrit. progs, Nat. Res. Coun. Can. Biochem. Soc; Am. Chem. Soc; hon. fel. Am. Soc. Animal Sci; Am. Dairy Sci. Asn; Poultry Sci. Asn; Am. Inst. Nutrit; Asn. Res. Dirs. Development and improvement of food and feed products; forage dehydration and inert gas storage; hormones in animal production; phosphatase test for identification of unpasteurized milk. Address: Quaker Oats Co, 617 W. Main St, Barrington, IL 60010.

GRAHN, DOUGLAS, b. Newark, N.J, Apr. 25, 23; m. 46; c. 3. GENETICS. B.S, Rutgers, 48; M.S, Iowa State, 50, Atomic Energy Comn. fel, 51-52, Ph.D.(genetics), 52. Asst. zool, Rutgers, 48; genetics, Iowa State Col, 48-51; assoc. scientist biol, Argonne Nat. Lab, 53-58; geneticist, U.S. Atomic Energy Comn, 58-61; assoc. biologist, DIV. BIOL. & MED. RES, ARGONNE NAT. LAB, 61-62, assoc. dir, 62-66, SR. BIOLOGIST, 66- Mem. radiation control adv. bd, Md. State Dept. Health, 60-61; panel on radiobiol, space sci. bd, Nat. Acad. Sci-Nat. Res. Coun, 62, space radiation study panel, 62-67, radiobiol. adv. panel, 67-71, chmn, 71-; consult, McDonnell Aircraft Corp, Mo, 63-65; off. manned space flight, NASA, 64-70; sci. prog. coord. for. exhibit prog, U.S. Atomic Energy Comn, 66-69; mem. comt. biol. sci, Ill. Bd. Higher Educ, 69-70. U.S.A, 43-45. AAAS; Genetics Soc. Am; Am. Soc. Human Genetics; Radiation Res. Soc; Am. Soc. Nat. Mammalian radiation genetics; x-chromosome genetics; external radiation toxicology and epidemiology. Address: Division of Biological & Medical Research, Argonne National Lab, Argonne, IL 60439.

GRAHN, EDGAR H(OWARD), b. Bremerton, Wash, Nov. 19, 19; m. 50. INORGANIC CHEMISTRY. B.S, Col. of Puget Sound, 41; M.S, Idaho, 48; fel, Illinois, 53, Ph.D.(chem), 55. Instr. CHEM, UNIV. IDAHO, 46-52, asst. prof, 52-57, assoc. prof, 57-62, PROF, 62-, ASSOC. DEAN GRAD. SCH, 71-, asst. dean, 65-71, exec. secy. res. coun, 61-71. Med.C, 43-46. Am. Chem. Soc. Coordination compounds and optical isomerism. Address: Office of the Dean, Graduate School, University of Idaho, Moscow, ID 83843.

GRAIFF, LEONARD B(ALDINE), b. Litchfield, Ill, Dec. 16, 33; m. 63. MECHANICAL ENGINEERING. B.Sc, Illinois, 55, Gardner-Denver fel, 55-56, M.Sc, 56; Shell Oil Co. fel, Purdue, 57-58, Ph.D.(combustion eng), 59. Res. engr. FUELS RES, Shell Oil Co, Ill, 59-62, Thornton Res. Centre, Shell Res. Ltd, Eng, 62-64, res. group leader, SHELL OIL CO, Ill, 64-69, TEX, 69-70, STAFF ENGR, 70- Soc. Automotive Eng.(Henry Ford Mem. Award & Arch T. Colwell Merit Award, 67); Combustion Inst. Combustion phenomena; petroleum fuels; antiknock mechanisms; automotive exhaust emissions. Address: 1418 Pirates Cove, Houston, TX 77058.

GRAIG, FRANK A, b. Vienna, Austria, Nov. 8, 14; U.S. citizen; div; c. 1. INTERNAL MEDICINE, ENDOCRINOLOGY. M.D, Univ. Budapest, 40. DIR. DIV. MED, GRASSLANDS HOSP, 66-; PROF. MED, NEW YORK MED. COL, 70- Res. fel, Metropolitan Hosp. Res. Unit, 48-51; prin. investr, Nat. Insts. Health grant, 65-; consult, United Hosp, Port Chester, N.Y, 70- AAAS; Endocrine Soc; fel. Am. Col. Physicians; Harvey Soc; Am. Thyroid Asn. Levels and regulations of CPK activity related to endocrine gland function; diagnosis, treatment and research aspects of muscle disease, both neurogenic and primary myopathies. Address: Division of Medicine, Grasslands Hospital, Valhalla, NY 10595.

GRAINGER, DAVID A, b. Sydney, Australia, Sept. 25, 34; m. 60; c. 5. RESTORATIVE DENTISTRY. B.D.S, Univ. Sydney, 56; D.D.S, Northwest. Univ, 57. Intern dent, Forsyth Dent. Ctr, Boston, 57-58, teaching fel, 58-59; instr. OPERATIVE DENT, dent. sch, Tufts Univ, 64-65, asst. prof, 65-68, assoc. prof, 68-69; PROF. & CHMN. DIV, COL. DENT, UNIV. FLA, 69- Asst, sch. dent. med, Harvard, 58-59; instr, Forsyth Sch. Dent. Hygienists, 58-59; consult, Vet. Admin. Hosp, Gainesville, Fla, 69-; dir. Space Coast Study Group, 70- Fel. Australian Col. Dent. Surg, 68. Am. Dent. Asn; Int. Asn. Dent. Res; Am. Acad. Gold Foil Opers; Australian Soc. Prosthodont; Australian Dent. Asn; Am. Asn. Dent. Schs. Television and cinematography related to learning processes in operative dentistry; caries measurement; fissure sealants; relationship of the periodontal col to restorative dentistry. Address: Division of Operative Dentistry, College of Dentistry, University of Florida, Gainesville, FL 32601.

GRAINGER, E(DWARD) H(ENRY), b. Moncton, N.B, July 24, 26; m. 61; c. 3. MARINE BIOLOGY. B.A, Mt. Allison, 47; M.Sc, McGill, 49, Ph.D.(zool), 53. Asst. scientist, east. arctic invests, FISHERIES RES. BD. CAN, 53-55, assoc. scientist, arctic unit, 55-61, SR. SCIENTIST, ARCTIC BIOL. STA, 61- Am. Soc. Limnol. & Oceanog; fel. Arctic Inst. N.Am. Arctic zooplankton; echinoderms. Address: Arctic Biological Station, Fisheries Research Board of Canada, P.O. Box 400, Ste. Anne de Bellevue, Que, Can.

GRAINGER, R(OBERT) BALL, b. Centerview, Mo, Mar. 3, 23; m. 47; c. 2. NUTRITION, BIOCHEMISTRY. B.S, Cent. Mo. State Col, 47; M.A, Missouri, 49, Ph.D.(physiol. chem), 54. Asst, Missouri, 47-52, instr, 52-53; asst. prof. animal nutrit, Kentucky, 53-58, assoc. prof, 58-60; res. chemist, Monsanto Co, St. Louis, 60-61, prod. develop, 61-63, res. group leader, 63-68; dir. res, Diamond A. Cattle Industs, 68-70; V.PRES, AGR. TECHNOL, INC, 70- U.S.N.R, 42-46. Am. Soc. Animal Sci; Poultry Sci. Asn; Am. Dairy Sci. Asn. Monogastric and ruminant intermediary metabolism. Address: 5102 Galley Rd, No. 315A, Colorado Springs, CO 80915.

GRAINGER, R(OBERT) M(OORE), b. Can, Feb. 27, 19; m. 43; c. 2. DENTISTRY, OPERATIONS RESEARCH. D.D.S, Toronto, 43, dipl, 50, M.Sc.D, 51. Prof. epidemiol. & statist. & chmn. div. dent. res, faculty dent, Univ. Toronto, 51-67; clin. dir. faculty dent, Univ. B.C, 67-68; assoc. dir. extra mural prog, Nat. Inst. Dent. Res, Md, 68-69; ASSOC. DIR, ASN. CAN. MED. COLS, 69- Consult, Ont. Govt, 51-59; mem. coun. dent. therapeut, Am. Dent. Asn; dent. study sect, Nat. Insts. Health; panel experts, WHO; assoc. dent. comt, Nat. Res. Coun. Can; grants adv. comt, Dept. Nat. Health & Welfare, Can; part-time sci. off, Can. Med. Res. Coun. Can. Centennial Medal. Can. Army, 42-45, Res, 45-, Capt. Biomet. Soc; Int. Asn. Dent. Res; Inst. Soc. Cranio-Facial Biol; Can. Dent. Asn; Can. Pub. Health Asn; Royal Col. Dent. Can. Epidemiology; statistical analysis in dental and education research; computer programming; studies on costs of medical education, availability of applicants and characteristics of medical students, staffing and curriculum in Canadian medical colleges; evaluation of health care delivery programs. Address: Association of Canadian Medical Colleges, 151 Slater St, Ottawa, Ont, Can.

GRAINGER, THOMAS H(UTCHESON), JR, b. Bethlehem, Pa, Dec. 14, 13; m. 41; c. 1. BACTERIOLOGY. B.A, Lehigh, 36, M.S, 38, Ph.D.(bact), 46; Pennsylvania, 38-41. Asst, Sharp & Dohme, Pa, 36-38; asst. instr, med. sch, Pennsylvania, 39-41; instr. bact, Lehigh, 46-47, asst. prof, 47-49, assoc. prof, 49-59; asst. dir. biol. labs, NAT. DRUG CO, 59-70, MRG, BIOL. SERV, 70- Lectr, inst. microbiol, Univ. Colo, 64. U.S.A, 42-46, Maj. Fel. AAAS; Am. Soc. Microbiol; Am. Forestry Asn; Pharmaceut. Mfg. Asn; Am. Inst. Biol. Sci; Am. Asn. Contamination Control; Wild Life Soc; Hist. Sci. Soc; Am. Med. Writers Asn; fel. Am. Pub. Health Asn; N.Y. Acad. Sci. General bacteriology; history of bacteriology. Address: Biological Services, National Drug Co, Swiftwater, PA 18370.

GRALLA, EDWARD JOSEPH, b. Wyoming Co, Pa, Mar. 14, 32; m. 59; c. 3. VETERINARY MEDICINE. Rutgers Univ, 55-57; V.M.D, Univ. Pa, 61. Vet. practitioner, 61-62; toxicologist, med. res. lab, Chas. Pfizer & Co, Inc, 62-69; ASST. PROF. LAB. ANIMAL SCI. & PHARMACOL, SCH. MED, YALE, 69- U.S.N, 51-55, Ens. Am. Vet. Med. Asn; Am. Asn. Lab. Animal Sci; Soc. Toxicol. Experimental toxicology; improving animal models for predicting adverse chemical effects in man; toxicology of anti-cancer agents. Address: 12 Ledgewood Dr, North Branford, CT 06471.

GRALOW, RAY C(ARL), b. Wausau, Wis, Oct. 27, 12; wid; c. 2; m. 62. PHYSICAL CHEMISTRY. B.S, Wisconsin, 34. With tech. serv, Corn Prods. Ref. Co, 34-39, new prods. dept, 39-43, chem. salesman, 43-48, sales mgr, chem. div, 48-53, dir. prod. develop, Corn Prods. Co, 53-63, asst. to v.pres. res, 63-66, tech. coord, Corn Prods. Int, 66-68, mem. develop. staff, Corn Prods. Co, 68-69; RETIRED. Am. Chem. Soc. Commercial Develop. Asn. Food product development. Address: 29 Sussex Rd, Tenafly, NJ 07670.

GRAM, MARY R(OSE), b. Maryville, Mo, Oct. 17, 24. NUTRITION. B.S, Northwest Mo. State Col, 45; M.S, Nebraska, 47; Ph.D.(nutrit), California, Berkeley, 57. Asst, Nebraska, 47-50, asst. prof. home econ, 50-52; asst, California, Berkeley, 52-56; asst. prof, Washington State, 56-59, assoc. prof, 59-64; PROF. NUTRIT. & HEAD DEPT, UNIV. TENN, KNOXVILLE, 64- AAAS; Am. Home Econ. Asn; Am. Dietetic Asn; Am. Inst. Nutrit; Inst. Food Technol; Am. Pub. Health Asn. Protein, mineral and fat metabolism; human nutrition. Address: Dept. of Nutrition, College of Home Economics, University of Tennessee, Knoxville, TN 37916.

GRAM, THEODORE EDWARD, b. Minneapolis, Minn, Sept. 26, 34; m. 59; c. 3. PHARMACOLOGY, BIOCHEMISTRY. B.S, Minnesota, 57, M.S, 62, Nat. Insts. Health fel, 63-64, Ph.D.(pharmacol, biochem), 64. Asst. pharmacol, Minnesota, 58-64; U.S. Pub. Health Serv. fel, Iowa, 65-67; res. assoc. chem. pharmacol, Nat. Inst. Gen. Med. Sci, Nat. Heart Inst, Md, 67-70; SUPVRY. PHARMACOLOGIST & HEAD SECT. ENZYME-FOR. CHEM. INTERACTION, PHARMACOL-TOXICOL. BR, NAT. INST. ENVIRON. HEALTH SCI, NAT. INSTS. HEALTH, 70- AAAS; Soc. Exp. Biol. & Med; Am. Soc. Pharmacol. & Exp. Therapeut; N.Y. Acad. Sci; Biochem. Soc. Hepatic microsomal structure and function; biochemistry and enzymology of microsomal drug metabolism and electron transport; cell biology. Address: Pharmacology-Toxicology Branch, National Institute of Environmental Health Sciences, National Institutes of Health, P.O. Box 12233, Research Triangle Park, NC 27709.

GRAMAS, JOHN VINCENT, b. Brooklyn, N.Y, Sept. 7, 39; m. 63. PHYSICAL ORGANIC CHEMISTRY, PHOTOCHEMISTRY. B.S, St. Francis Col.(Pa),

61; Ph.D.(org. chem), Pa. State, 65. Res. chemist, E.I. DU PONT DE NEMOURS & CO, 65-69, SR. RES. CHEMIST, PHOTO PRODS. DIV, 69- Am. Chem. Soc. Photopolymer research and development; silver halide coating quality. Address: 51 Devonshire Court, Middletown, NJ 07748.

GRAMERA, ROBERT EUGENE, b. Joliet, Ill, Feb. 6, 36; m. 57; c. 2. BIOCHEMISTRY, ORGANIC CHEMISTRY. B.S, Lewis Col, 57; M.S, Purdue, 61, Ph.D.(biochem), 63. State anal. control chemist, Purdue, 57-63; res. scientist, Moffett Tech. Ctr, Corn Prod. Co, 63-65, res. sect. head polymer res. & develop, 65-69; tech. supvr. appl. packaging, Crown Zellerbach Corp, Calif, 69-70, supvr. plant & customer trials, packaging res. & develop. lab, 70-71; DIR. TECH. DEVELOP. & SERV, GREAT WEST. SUGAR CO, 71- Am. Chem. Soc. Isolation, purification and structural investigation of polysaccharides; synthesis of polymerizable monosaccharide monomers; organic reaction mechanisms of carbohydrates; chemistry of urethane foams from carbohydrate based poloyols. Address: Great Western Sugar Co, P.O. Box 5308, Terminal Annex, Denver, CO 80217.

GRAMIAK, RAYMOND, b. Phila, Pa, Mar. 23, 24; m. 49; c. 4. MEDICINE, RADIOLOGY. Pennsylvania, 42-43; Delaware, 43-44; Princeton, 44-45; M.D, Rochester, 49. Fel. cinefluorography, Rochester, 52-53, res. radiol, 53-56, instr, 56-57; private practice, N.Y. 57-65; assoc. prof. RADIOL, UNIV. ROCHESTER, 65-67, PROF, 67- U.S.A, 43-46, Med.C, 49-52, Capt. Am. Col. Radiol; Radiol. Soc. N.Am. Diagnostic radiology; cardiac ultrasonics. Address: Dept. of Radiology, University of Rochester, 260 Crittenden Blvd, Rochester, NY 14620.

GRAMINSKI, EDMOND LEONARD, b. Dunkirk, N.Y, Oct. 14, 29; m. 56; c. 7. PHYSICAL ORGANIC CHEMISTRY, RHEOLOGY. B.S, Buffalo, 52, Ph.D. (chem), 56. Sr. res. chemist, Olin Mathieson Chem. Co, 55-60; Harris Res. Labs, Div. Gillette Razor Co, 60-64; PROJ. LEADER RHEOLOGY OF PAPER, NAT. BUR. STANDARDS, 64- Tech. Asn. Pulp & Paper Indust; fel. Am. Inst. Chem; Am. Chem. Soc. Determination of the factors essential to the durability and permanence of paper. Address: A369 Polymer Bldg, National Bureau of Standards, Washington, DC 20234.

GRAMLICH, JAMES VANDLE, b. Charleston, Ark, July 25, 39; m. 58; c. 2. BOTANY, PLANT PHYSIOLOGY. B.S, Arkansas, 61, Nat. Sci. Found. fel, 61-62, M.S, 62; Nat. Sci. Found. fel, Auburn, 62-64, Ph.D.(bot), 65. Instr. bot, Auburn, 64-65; sr. plant physiologist, ELI LILLY & CO, 65-69, HEAD PLANT SCI. RES, LILLY RES. CENTER, LTD, 69- Nat. Guard & Med.C. Res, 55-63, Sgt. Weed Sci. Soc. Am; Am. Soc. Agron. Absorption, translocation, metabolism and evaluation of herbicides; commercial development of herbicides, fungicides, insecticides and plant growth regulators. Address: 1 Beverley Close, Camberley, Surrey, Eng.

GRAMLING, L(EA) G(ENE), b. High Springs, Fla, Nov. 3, 08; m. 33; c. 1. PHARMACEUTICAL CHEMISTRY. Ph.G, Florida, 31, B.S, 35, scholar, 35-38, M.S, 36, Ph.D.(pharmacol), 38. Asst. prof. pharmacol. & pharmacog, George Washington, 38-43, acting dean col. pharm, 42-43; asst. prof. PHARMACEUT. CHEM, UNIV. FLA, 46-49, assoc. prof, 49-56, PROF, 56-, CHMN. DEPT, 59- Med.Admin.C, 43-46, 2nd Lt. Fel. AAAS; Am. Chem. Soc; Am. Pharmaceut. Asn.(Ebert Prize, 39). Biological assays; plant chemistry; derivatives of cumic acid; history of Florida pharmacy; isolation and identification of constituents of natural products using newer solvents. Address: Dept. of Pharmaceutical Chemistry, College of Pharmacy, University of Florida, Gainesville, FL 32601.

GRAMS, GARY WALLACE, b. Moline, Ill, June 13, 42; m. 64; c. 1. ORGANIC CHEMISTRY, BIOCHEMISTRY. B.S, Valparaiso Univ, 64; univ. fel, Northwest. Univ, 64-68, Ph.D.(org. chem), 68. CHEMIST, CEREAL PROPERTIES LAB, NORTH. MKT. & NUTRIT. RES. DIV, AGR. RES. SERV, U.S. DEPT. AGR, 68- Am. Chem. Soc. Approaches to the synthesis of ribonucleotides using organochemical methods; effects of processing on nutritional value of cereals and cereal products; analysis of lipid constituents of cereal grains. Address: 6407 N. Upland Terr, Peoria, IL 61614.

GRAMS, GERALD W(ILLIAM), b. Mankato, Minn, Dec. 7, 38; m. 62; c. 1. METEOROLOGY, LASERS. B.S, Mankato State Col, 60; Ford Found. fel, Mass. Inst. Technol, 61-64, Ph.D.(meteorol), 66. Teacher, high sch, Minn, 60-61; atmospheric physicist meteorol, Air Force Cambridge Res. Labs, summer 62; res. assoc. METEOROL. & LASER APPLNS, Mass. Inst. Technol, 66-67; aerospace technologist, electronics res. ctr, NASA, Cambridge, 67-70; SCIENTIST, NAT. CTR. ATMOSPHERIC RES, 70- Lectr, Northeast. Univ, 67-70; res. affiliate, res. lab. electronics, Mass. Inst. Technol, 67-70; mem. subpanel meteorol, earth surv. planning panel, NASA, Wash, D.C, 69-70. Am. Meteorol. Soc; Am. Geophys. Union; Optical Soc. Am. Meteorology and physics of the upper atmosphere; laser-atmospheric interactions; laser radar measurement techniques; stratospheric aerosols; noctilucent clouds; ozone photochemistry. Address: National Center for Atmospheric Research, Boulder, CO 80302.

GRANADOS, ROBERT R, b. El Centro, Calif, Sept. 24, 37; m. 65; c. 3. ENTOMOLOGY, VIROLOGY. B.S, California, Davis, 60; M.S, Wisconsin, 62, Ph.D.(entom, plant path), 65. Asst. entomologist, BOYCE THOMPSON INST, 64-69, ASSOC. VIROLOGIST, 69- Nat. Sci. Found. fel, 65-66. Am. Phytopath. Soc; Entom. Soc. Am; Electron Micros. Soc. Am; Soc. Invert. Path. Insect virology; mechanism of virus replication in insect cells; insect tissue culture. Address: Boyce Thompson Institute, 1086 N. Broadway, Yonkers, NY 10701.

GRANAHAN, LEON EDMUND, b. Boston, Mass, Oct. 24, 25; m. 52; c. 7. PHYSICAL & ORGANIC CHEMISTRY. B.S, Col. Holy Cross, 48, M.S, 49. Teaching fel. chem, Col. Holy Cross, 48-49; res. chemist, Belding-Corticelli Co, 49-51; GILLETTE CO, 51-60, asst. opers. mgr, 60-62, supv. toiletries, mfg. mgt, 62-64, asst. int. toiletries, 64-71, EXEC. ASST. TO V.PRES. OPERS. SERV, 71- U.S.N.A.F, 43-45. Am. Chem. Soc; Cosmetic, Toiletry & Fragrance Asn; Soc. Cosmetic Chemists. Industrial research and development; toiletry manufacture. Address: The Gillette Co, Prudential Towers, Boston, MA 02199.

GRANATA, WALTER H(AROLD), JR, b. N.Y.C, Dec. 2, 26; m. 47; c. 5. PETROLOGY, STRATIGRAPHY. B.A, Hamilton Col, 49; M.A, Missouri, 52; Ph.D.(geol), Wyoming, 60. Geologist, Sohio Petrol. Co, 52-60; staff geologist, Monsanto Chem. Co, 60-63; regional stratigrapher, Sinclair Oil & Gas Co, 64-65; asst. prof. GEOL, Wis. State, River Falls, 65-66; assoc. prof, INDIANA UNIV. PA, 66-70, PROF, 70- U.S.A.A.F, 44-45. Soc. Econ. Paleont. & Mineral; Am. Asn. Petrol. Geol. Cretaceous stratigraphy and structure of upper Gulf Coastal Plain; Cenozoic stratigraphy of South Louisiana; carbonate petrology and paleoenvironmental analysis of Paleozoic rocks in West Texas; Appalachian Basin studies. Address: Dept. of Geoscience, Indiana University of Pennsylvania, Indiana, PA 15701.

GRANATEK, ALPHONSE P(ETER), b. Hartford, Conn, Feb. 13, 20; m. 43; c. 2. CHEMISTRY. B.S, Trinity Col. (Conn), 42; M.S, Syracuse, 53. Chemist, U.S. Indust. Chem, Md, 42-44; Ernest Bischoff Pharmaceut. Co, Conn, 44-46; dir. prod. develop. labs, BRISTOL LABS, BRISTOL-MYERS CO, 46-67, DIR. PROD. DEVELOP. RES, 67- Am. Chem. Soc; Am. Pharmaceut Asn. Insecticides; resins; antacid resins; antibiotics; pharmacy; development of pharmaceuticals; medical biochemistry; physics; electronics. Address: Bristol Labs, Bristol-Myers Co, Thompson Rd, Syracuse, NY 13201.

GRANATEK, EDMUND S(TANLEY), b. Hartford, Conn, Mar. 27, 22; m. 52. PHARMACY, PHARMACEUTICAL CHEMISTRY. B.S, Connecticut, 50, M.S, 52. Pharmacist, Arthurs Drug Store, 48-52; sr. res. scientist, prod. develop, Bristol Labs, Inc, 52-66, DIR. PROD. DEVELOP. RES, BRISTOL-MYERS CO. INT. DIV, 66- Asst. instr, Univ. Conn, 50-52. Sig.C, 42-45, Sgt. Am. Pharmaceut. Asn. Pharmaceutical product development; antibiotics and chemotherapeutics; drug analysis; instruction. Address: Bristol-Myers Co. International Division, P.O. Box 1235, Syracuse, NY 13201.

GRANATH, LOUIS P(ETER), b. Spokane, Wash, July 26, 01; m. 31, 44, 53, 66; c. 3. PHYSICS. B.S, State Col. Wash, 23; fel, Minnesota, 23-26; Ph.D.(physics), N.Y. Univ, 31. Asst. physicist, Nat. Bur. Standards, 26-27; jr. physicist, Naval Res. Lab, 27-29; instr. physics, N.Y. Univ, 29-40; contract physicist, U.S. Navy Dept, 40-44; applied physics lab, Hopkins, 44-45; asst. prof. PHYSICS, Univ. Conn, 45-46; WORCESTER POLYTECH. INST, 46-49, assoc. prof, 49-70, EMER. PROF, 70-; ADMINR, MARY MILNER REST HOME, 69- AAAS; fel. Am. Phys. Soc. Spectroscopy; biophysics. Address: 16 Claflin St, Milford, MA 01757.

GRANATIR, WILLIAM, b. Phila, Pa, Apr. 1, 16; m. 41; c. 4. PSYCHIATRY. B.A, Univ. Pa, 36, M.D, Hahnemann Med. Col, 41. Intern, Mt. Sinai Hosp, Phila, Pa, 41-42; res. psychiat, St. Elizabeth Hosp, Wash, D.C, 46-48; dir, Wash. Inst. Ment. Hyg, 48-50; mem. faculty, Wash. Sch. Psychiat, 50-58; instr. psychiat, WASH. PSYCHOANAL. INST, 58-66, TRAINING & SUPV. ANALYST, 66- Private practice, 50-; consult, Jewish Social Serv. Agency, 51- U.S.A.A.F, 42-46, Capt. Fel. Am. Psychiat. Asn. Psychoanalysis. Address: Washington Psychoanalytic Institute, 4545 Connecticut Ave. N.W, Washington, DC 20008.

GRANATO, A(NDREW) V(INCENT), b. Cleveland, Ohio, May 9, 26; m. 56; c. 4. PHYSICS. B.S, Rensselaer Polytech, 48, M.S, 50; Ph.D.(applied math), Brown, 55. Res. assoc. appl. math, Brown, 53-57; res. asst. prof. PHYSICS, UNIV. ILL, URBANA, 57-59, assoc. prof, 61-64, PROF, 64- Guggenheim Found. fel, Germany, 59-60; vis. prof, Aachen Tech, 60-61. U.S.N.R, 44-46, Res, 46-60. Fel. Am. Phys. Soc; Acoust. Soc. Am. Ultrasonic wave propagation; dislocations in crystals; radiation damage. Address: Dept. of Physics, University of Illinois, Urbana, IL 61803.

GRANATSTEIN, V(ICTOR) L(AWRENCE), b. Toronto, Ont, Feb. 8, 35; m. 55; c. 2. PLASMA PHYSICS, ELECTROMAGNETICS. B.S. & Boese fel, Columbia, 60, M.S. & Doehla fel, 61, Ph.D.(eng, plasma physics), 63. Res. assoc. plasma waves, Columbia, 63-64; MEM. TECH. STAFF, BELL TEL. LABS, INC, 64- Vis. sr. lectr, dept. physics, Hebrew Univ. Jerusalem, 69-70. Inst. Elec. & Electronic Eng; Am. Phys. Soc. Turbulence of fluids and plasmas; electromagnetic propagation through random media; plasma waves; laser light interaction with contaminants in air and water; environmental physics. Address: Bell Telephone Labs, Whippany NJ, 07981.

GRANBERG, C(HARLES) BOYD, b. Wessington, S.Dak, May 6, 21; m. 55; c. 3. PHARMACY, PHARMACOLOGY. B.S, S.Dak. State Col, 42; M.S, Illinois, 47, Ph.D.(pharmacol), 50. Instr. PHARM, Illinois, 47-49; PROF, DRAKE UNIV, 50- Ed, Am. J. Pharmaceut. Ed, 61- U.S.A, 43-45. Gastro-intestinal x-ray contrast media; pharmocodynamics. Address: Dept. of Pharmacy, Drake University, Des Moines, IA 50311.

GRANBERRY, (EDGAR) HERMAN, b. Jacksonville, Ark, July 5, 18; m. 39; c. 3. MECHANICAL ENGINEERING, TRANSPORTATION. B.S, Texas Tech. Col, 40. Mech. engr, SKF Industs, 40-41; mech. res. engr, Physicist Res. Co, 41; time study engr, methods engr, asst. chief methods engr. & chief tool designer, Nat. Automatic Tool Co, 42-46; chief engr, Medley Mfg. Co, 46, head mech. dept, 46-64, mgr. eng. dept, res. & eng. div, West Point Mfg. Co, 64-65, mgr. eng. & serv. div, 65-68, transportation, telecommun. & eng, 68-71, DIR. TRANSPORTATION, WEST POINT PEPPERELL, INC, 71- Trustee & v.chmn, Gorgas Scholar. Found, Inc, 52-71. Am. Soc. Mech. Eng. Method and production engineering; management. Address: Transportation Center, West Point Pepperell, Inc, P.O. Box 71, West Point, GA 31833.

GRANBORG, BERTIL SVANTE MIKAEL, b. Stockholm, Sweden, Aug. 9, 23; U.S. citizen; m. 63; c. 1. ELECTRICAL ENGINEERING. M.S, Royal Inst. Tech, Sweden, 53; fel, Wisconsin, 58-60, Ph.D.(elec. eng, math), 61. Invest. engr, Swedish State Power Bd, 53-56; instr. elec. eng, Wisconsin, 56-60; res. engr, Gen. Elec. Co, 61-63; ASSOC. PROF. ELEC. ENG, UNIV. HAWAII, 64- Mem. staff, high tension lab, Royal Inst. Technol, Sweden, 51-52; high tension & short circuit labs, Electricité de France, 52; vis. teacher, Trade Sch. Math, Sweden, 54-55; staff scientist, strike avionic systs. div, Autonetics Div, N.Am. Rockwell Corp, summer 68; Nat. Res. Coun. sr. resident res. assoc. & vis. scientist, Manned Spacecraft Ctr, NASA, 70-71. Swedish Army, 44-45, 51. Inst. Elec. & Electronics Eng; Swed. Asn. Eng. & Architects. Automatic feedback control; industrial process control; steel mill and steam station automation; power production, distribution and control; high voltage test and protection; magnetic materials. Address: Dept. of Electrical Engineering, University of Hawaii, Honolulu, HI 96822.

GRANCIO, MICHAEL R, b. Brooklyn, N.Y, Apr. 24, 42; m. 67. CHEMICAL ENGINEERING, POLYMER CHEMISTRY. B.E, City Col. New York, 64, M.E, 66, Ph.D.(chem. eng), 69. Chem. engr, Interchem. Corp, 64; SR. RES. ENGR, POLYMERS & PETROCHEM. RES, MONSANTO CO, 68- Am. Chem. Soc; Am. Inst. Chem. Eng. Emulsion polymerization; solid state polymer rheology; polymer melt rheology. Address: Monsanto Co, 730 Worcester St, Indian Orchard, MA 01051.

GRAND, ARTHUR FREDERICK, b. Newark, N.J, Dec. 18, 41; m. 64; c. 2. PHYSICAL INORGANIC CHEMISTRY. B.S, Union Col.(N.Y), 63; M.S, Michigan, 64, Ph.D.(chem), 68. CHEMIST, FMC CORP, PRINCETON, 67- Am. Chem. Soc. Charge-transfer complexes and their spectra; industrial crystallization; copper and alloy pickling. Address: 28 Jeffery Lane, East Windsor, NJ 08520.

GRAND, NICHOLAS G(EORGE), b. Montreal, Que, Can, June 15, 16; nat; m. 36; c. 1. PATHOLOGY. A.B, Washington (St. Louis), 42; D.D.S, St. Louis, 51, M.S, 54. Asst, N.Y. Univ, 32-38; surg. res. asst, med. col, Cornell, 38-40; asst. & demonstr, Washington (St. Louis), 40-43; instr. PATH. & ORAL HISTOL, St. Louis, 51-55, asst. prof, 55-56; Marquette, 56-57; assoc. prof, COL. DENT, UNIV. ILL. COL. MED, 57-64, PROF, 64- Med.C, 43-46, Lt. Col. AAAS; Am. Soc. Microbiol; Soc. Exp. Biol. & Med; Am. Dent. Asn; Am. Acad. Oral Path; Int. Asn. Dent. Res. Cancer research; microbiology; tissue culture. Address: Dept. of Pathology, College of Dentistry, University of Illinois at the Medical Center, 808 S. Wood St, Chicago, IL 60612.

GRAND, PAUL SHELDON, b. N.Y.C, June 1, 41; m. 63; c. 2. ORGANIC CHEMISTRY. B.S, Queens Col.(N.Y), 63; Stanford Univ, 63-64; Univ. Mich, 64-65; Nat. Insts. Health trainee, Calif. Inst. Technol, 66, fel, 66-68, summer, Nat. Sci. Found. fel, 66, Ph.D.(chem), 69. Res. chemist, COLGATE-PALMOLIVE CO, 68-70, SR. RES. CHEMIST, 70- Am. Chem. Soc; Soc. Cosmetic Chem. Synthetic organic chemistry of natural products; detergency; microbiology; cationic resins. Address: Colgate-Palmolive Co, 909 River Rd, Piscataway, NJ 08854.

GRAND, STANLEY, b. Paterson, N.J, Jan. 5, 27; m. 47; c. 2. PHYSICAL CHEMISTRY. B.S, N.Y. Univ, 48; Ph.D.(phys. chem), Polytech. Inst. Brooklyn, 51. Res. chemist, phys. chem. dyes, Am. Cyanamid Co, 51-53; sect. leader anal. chem, mineral benefits lab, Columbia, 54-57; dir. res. & develop, Radiation Res. Corp, 57-64; head dept. chem. & physics, W.Orange Lab, Vitro Labs, 64-66; V.PRES, NUCLEAR RES. ASSOCS, INC, 66- U.S.N, 44-45. Am. Chem. Soc. High temperature materials and coatings; nuclear weapons effects, arcs and plasmas. Address: Nuclear Research Associates, Inc, 12 Nevada Dr, New Hyde Park, NJ 11040.

GRAND, THEODORE I, b. Newark, N.J, Feb. 10, 38. ANATOMY. B.A, Brown, 59; Nat. Insts. Health fel, California, Berkeley, 60-62, Ph.D.(anthrop), 64. Asst. scientist PHYS. ANTHROP, ORE. REGIONAL PRIMATE RES. CTR, 63-66, ASSOC. SCIENTIST, 67- Vis. asst. prof, Univ. Ore, 65. Am. Asn. Phys. Anthrop; Am. Soc. Mammal; Am. Soc. Zool. Comparative anatomy of musculo-skeletal system; primate anatomy and evolution; history of anatomy. Address: Oregon Regional Primate Research Center, 505 N.W. 185th St, Beaverton, OR 97005.

GRANDA, ALLEN M(ANUEL), b. Belvedere, Calif, Feb. 20, 29; m. 58; c. 3. PHYSIOLOGICAL PSYCHOLOGY. A.B, California, Los Angeles, 50; A.M, Southern California, 52; Ph.D, Brown, 59. Res. physiologist, Walter Reed Army Inst. Res, 58-65; assoc. prof. psychol, UNIV. DEL, 65-71, PROF. PHYSIOL. PSYCHOL, 71- Vis. prof, sch. med, Keio Univ, Japan, 71-72. U.S.N, 52-55, Lt.(jg). AAAS; Optical Soc. Am; Psychonomic Soc; Int. Soc. Clin. Electroretinography; Asn. Res. Vision & Ophthal. Vision; sensory processes; central neural processes. Address: Dept. of Psychology, University of Delaware, Newark, DE 19711.

GRANDAGE, ARNOLD HERBERT EDWARD, b. Springfield, Mass, Nov. 12, 18; m. 45; c. 2. STATISTICS. B.A, Lehigh, 42; Ph.D.(statist), N.C. State Col, 54. Assoc. prof. STATIST, N.C. STATE UNIV, 55-61, PROF, 61-, dir. comput. ctr, 56-61. Consult, Miller-Warden Assocs. Biomet. Soc. Industrial, physical science and highway construction applications of statistics; use of computers in statistics. Address: Dept. of Experimental Statistics, North Carolina State University, Raleigh, NC 27607.

GRANDCHAMP, YVON, b. Montreal, Que, Dec. 27, 27; m. 53; c. 3. MATHEMATICS. B.Sc, Univ. Montreal, 50, M.Sc, 51. ASSOC. PROF. MATH, UNIV. OTTAWA, 53- General mathematics. Address: 191 Marlborough, Ottawa, Ont. K1N 8G3, Can.

GRANDE, FRANCISCO, b. Colunga, Spain, June 29, 09; m. 41; c. 2. PHYSIOLOGY. M.D, Madrid, 32. Assoc. prof. physiol, med. sch, Madrid, 35-39, head dept. physiol, nat. inst. nutrit, 36-39; Inst. Med. Res, Spain, 40-53; assoc. prof. PHYSIOL. HYG, UNIV. MINN, MINNEAPOLIS, 54-59, PROF, 58- Prof, med. sch, Zarogoza, 50-53; dir, Jay Phillips Res. Lab, Mt. Sinai Hosp, Minneapolis, Minn, 66- AAAS; Am. Physiol. Soc; Soc. Exp. Biol. & Med; Am. Inst. Nutrit. Physiology of metabolism and nutrition, especially lipid metabolism. Address: Labs. of Physiological Hygiene, University of Minnesota, Minneapolis, MN 55455.

GRANDEL, EUGENE ROBERT, b. Chicago, Ill, Jan. 16, 33; m. 62; c. 2. DENTISTRY. B.S, Illinois, 56, D.D.S, 58, M.S, 62. Instr. ORAL PATH, Illinois, 61-63; asst. prof, SCH. DENT, LOYOLA UNIV. CHICAGO, MAYWOOD, 63-68, ASSOC. PROF, 68-, PEDODONTICS, 70- Am. Acad. Oral Path; Int. Asn. Dent. Res. Cytology; histochemistry; enzymatic cytology. Address: Dept. of Pedodontics, Loyola University School of Dentistry, 2160 S. First Ave, Maywood, IL 60153.

GRANDINE, JOSEPH D(ANIEL), II, b. Crandon, Wis, Mar. 5, 23; m. 44; c. 3. PHYSICAL CHEMISTRY, APPLIED MATHEMATICS. S.B, Harvard, 43; fel, Southern California, 46-49, Ph.D.(chem), 49. Res. chemist, Dewey & Almy Co, 43-46; E.I. du Pont de Nemours & Co, 49-60; pres, Kenett Comput. Consults, Inc, 57-62; v.pres, Data Processing, Inc, 62-63; dir. prod. planning, Adage, Inc, 63-68; pres, Problematics, Inc, 69-71; MEM. DEVELOP. STAFF, MILLIPORE CORP, 71- Am. Chem. Soc. Address: Millipore Corp, 336 Baker Ave, Concord, MA 01742.

GRANDINE, LESTER D(AVID), b. Laona, Wis, July 19, 25; m. 51; c. 2. PHYSICAL CHEMISTRY. B.S, Wisconsin, 48, Ph.D.(chem), 52. Res. chemist, textile fibers dept, pioneering res. lab, E.I. du Pont de Nemours & Co, Va, 52-57, sr. res. chemist, 57-59, indust. prods. res, Spruance Res. Lab, 59-61; sr. scientist, Philip Morris Res. Ctr, Va, 61-64; SR. RES. CHEMIST, E.I. DU PONT DE NEMOURS & CO, INC, 64- U.S.A, 43-46. Physical chemistry of high polymers including mechanical properties solubility; textile fibers; physical properties of aerosols. Address: 1610 Hardee Rd, Kinston, NC 28501.

GRANDSTAFF, JAMES O(KLEY), b. Reinersville, Ohio, Mar. 9, 07; m. 29. ANIMAL SCIENCE. B.S.C, Ohio State, 30; Mass. Inst. Technol, 39. Admin. asst, U.S. Dept. Agr, D.C, 30-31, asst. animal fiber technologist, bur. animal indust, 36-39, assoc. animal fiber technologist, 39-43; dir. southwest range and sheep breeding lab, U.S. Depts. Interior & Agr. in co-op. N.Mex. Agr. Exp. Sta, 43-52; sr. animal husbandman, off. exp. stas, U.S. DEPT. AGR, 52-56, asst. dir. animal sci. progs, state exp. stas. div, AGR. RES. SERV, 56-60, DIR. ANIMAL SCI. PROGS, CO-OP. STATE RES. SERV, 60- AAAS; Am. Soc. Animal Sci. Animal fiber technology; sheep husbandry and genetics; administration. Address: Co-operative State Research Service, U.S. Dept. of Agriculture, Washington, DC 20005.

GRANDTNER, MIROSLAV M(ARIAN), b. Liptovska-Teplicka, Slovak, Aug. 23, 28; Can. citizen; m. 62; c. 1. FORESTRY. Ing.F, Louvain, 55, Dr.Sc. (agron), 62; M.Sc, Laval, 59. Chief cartographer, Center Phytosociol. Mapping, Belgium, 56-57; asst. forest ecol, LAVAL UNIV, 57-58, asst. prof. BOT, 58-63, Assoc. prof, 63-67, PROF, 67- Summer asst. cartographer, Fed. Inst. Vegetation Mapping, Ger, 54. AAAS; Arctic Inst. N.Am; Am. Polar Soc; Int. Soc. Plant Geog. & Ecol; Can. Bot. Asn; Ecol. Soc. Am; Int. Asn. Ecol. Forest ecology and phytosociology; vegetation mapping. Address: Faculty of Forestry, Laval University, Quebec 10, Que, Can.

GRANDY, CHARLES CREED, b. Alamosa, Colo, Dec. 6, 28; m. 51; c. 6. MATHEMATICS, PHYSICS. B.S, Colorado State, 52; M.S, Northeastern, 62. Mem. tech. staff digital comput. applns, Lincoln Lab, Mass. Inst. Tech. 52-58, assoc. group leader air defense systs, 58; head dept. systs. test. & eval, MITRE CORP, 58-60, command & control systs, 60-62, assoc. tech. dir. systs. eng, 62-65, systs. planning, 65-67, tech. dir. Nat. Command & Control Systs. Div, 67-71, ASST. V.PRES. WASH. OPERS, 71- U.S.A, 46-48, S/Sgt. AAAS; Math. Asn. Am; Soc. Indust. & Appl. Math; Am. Mgt. Asn. Applications of digital computers to real time control problems; systems engineering in military command and control systems; operations research; statistical inference and experimental design. Address: Mitre Corp, 1820 Dolley Madison Blvd, McLean, VA 22101.

GRANDY, THOMAS B(OYDE), b. Garnish, Newf, Nov. 4, 38; m. 65; c. 2. COMPUTER SCIENCE, NUCLEAR PHYSICS. B.A, Mem. Univ. Newf, 59, B.Sc, 60, M.Sc, 63; Ph.D.(nuclear physics), Univ. Alta, 67. Fel. physics, Univ. Montreal, 67-68; res. assoc, Univ. Ky, 68-70; ASST. PROF. COMPUT. SCI, UNIV. WINDSOR, 70- Can. Info. Processing Soc; Can. Comput. Sci. Asn. Nuclear structure in low energy nuclear physics, especially neutron physics; application of audio response techniques to computer aided instruction. Address: Dept. of Computer Science, University of Windsor, Windsor 11, Ont, Can.

GRANDY, WALTER THOMAS, JR, b. Phila, Pa, June 1, 33; m. 55; c. 4. THEORETICAL PHYSICS. B.S, Colorado, 60, Ph.D.(physics), 64. Phys. sci. aide, Nat. Bur. Standards, Colo, 58-60, mathematician, 60-61, physicist, 61-63; asst. prof. PHYSICS, UNIV. WYO, 63-67, assoc. prof, 67-69, PROF, 69-, CHMN. DEPT, 71- Fulbright scholar, Brazil, 66-67. U.S.N, 53-57, Lt.(jg). Fel, AAAS; Brazilian Phys. Soc; Am. Asn. Physics Teachers; Am. Phys. Soc. Statistical mechanics; electrodynamics; general relativity; science education. Address: Dept. of Physics, University of Wyoming, Laramie, WY 82070.

GRANET, IRVING, b. N.Y.C, July 2, 24; m. 51; c. 3. MECHANICAL & NUCLEAR ENGINEERING. B.M.E, Cooper Union, 44; M.M.E, Polytech. Inst. Brooklyn, 48; scholar, Oak Ridge Sch. Reactor Tech, 55-56, dipl, 56. Proj. engr, res. dept, Foster Wheeler Corp, 47-53, sr. engr, nuclear energy dept, 53-55, dir, staff eng, 55-59; assoc. scientist plasma propulsion proj, Repub. Aviation Corp, 59-64, power conversion div, 64-70, PROJ. MGR, REPUB. AVIATION DIV, FAIRCHILD-HILLER CORP, 70- Instr, Polytech. Inst. Brooklyn, 51-52; adj. asst. prof, C.W. Post Col, Long Island, 59-; adj. assoc. prof, N.Y. Inst. Technol, 68- Consult, Tech. Specialties Corp, 54. U.S.A.A.F, 45-47. Am. Soc. Mech. Eng; Nat. Soc. Prof. Eng; N.Y. Acad. Sci; Am. Soc. Naval Eng. Physics; heat transfer and fluid mechanics; applied magnetohydrodynamics and space propulsion. Address: Republic Aviation Division, Fairchild-Hiller Corp, Farmingdale, NY 11735.

GRANETT, PHILIP, b. Bayonne, N.J, Apr. 4, 10; m. 39; c. 3. ECONOMIC ENTOMOLOGY. B.S, Rutgers, 33, M.S, 34, fel, 34-41, Ph.D.(entom), 41. Asst. entomologist, RUTGERS UNIV, 33-34, 41-46, assoc. res. specialist ENTOM, 46-56, RES. SPECIALIST, 56-, RES. PROF, 62- Civilian with Off. Sci. Res. & Develop, 41-44. AAAS; Entom. Soc. Am; Am. Mosquito Control Asn. Entomology; insecticides; insect repellents; economic zoology; control of problem birds. Address: Dept. of Entomology & Economic Zoology, College of Agriculture & Environmental Science, Rutgers, The State University, P.O. Box 231, New Brunswick, NJ 08903.

GRANEY, DANIEL O, b. Los Angeles, Calif, Oct. 29, 36; m. 60; c. 2. ANATOMY. A.B, California, Berkeley, 58, M.A, San Francisco, 62, Ph.D.(anat), 65. Res. fel. anat, Harvard Med. Sch, 64-66; instr; BIOL. STRUCT, SCH. MED, UNIV. WASH, 66-68, ASST. PROF, 68- Am. Asn. Anat; Am. Soc. Cell Biol. Fine structure of gastrointestinal absorption and secretion; bulk transport by capillary endothelia; uptake of ferritin and proteins by intestine of suckling animals. Address: Dept. of Biological Structure, University of Washington, Seattle, WA 98195.

GRANEY, MAURICE R, b. Indianapolis, Ind, Apr. 1, 07; m. 35; c. 3. ENGINEERING. B.S.I.E, Purdue, 35, M.S, 37, Ph.D.(indust. psychol), 42. Asst. engr, Mod. Housing Corp, Gen. Motors Corp, 27-29; engr. & consult, Ind. Gunite & Construct. Co, Am. Construct. Co. & E.J. Culbertson Co, 30-34; from instr. to asst. prof. eng, Purdue, 35-42, supvr. div. tech. insts, 43-48; assoc. prof. & head, 48-50, prof. indust. mgt. & head dept. & dir. indust. mgt. ed. servs, 52-56; supt. training dept, Inland Steel Co, 50-51; PROF. ENG. & DEAN SCH. ENG, UNIV. DAYTON, 56- Exam. & mem, ed. & accreditation comt. & chmn. subcomt. tech. insts, Engrs. Coun. Prfnl. Develop, 56-60; Inst. Certification Eng. Technicians, 62-64; lectr, U.S. Army Ord, Ill; consult, industs. & tech. schs. AAAS; Am. Soc. Eng. Educ; Nat. Soc. Prof. Eng. Industrial management; test construction; measurement of mechanical aptitude; executive and management development; engineering and technical institute education; organization and administration of higher education, especially technical education. Address: School of Engineering, University of Dayton, Dayton, OH 45409.

GRANGAARD, DONALD HAMMER, b. Douglas, N.Dak, Jan. 10, 12; m. 34; c. 1. ORGANIC CHEMISTRY. B.A, North Dakota, 33; M.S, Ohio State, 35, Ph.D.(chem), 37. Asst. chem, Ohio State, 33-37; res. assoc. cellulose chem, Mass. Inst. Tech, 37-39; res. chemist, KIMBERLY-CLARK CORP, 39-62, SR. RES. ASSOC, NEENAH, 62- Am. Chem. Soc; Soc. Chem. Indust. Lignin and cellulose chemistry. Address: 2403 N. Union St, Appleton, WI 54911.

GRANGER, CARL V, b. Brooklyn, N.Y, Nov. 26, 28; m. 51; c. 2. MEDICINE. A.B, Dartmouth Col, 48; M.D, N.Y. Univ, 52. Asst. chief phys. med, Letterman Gen. Hosp, 58-61; instr, sch. med, Yale, 61-63, asst. prof, 63-67, assoc. clin. prof, 67-68, assoc. dir. dept. phys. med, New Haven Hosp, 61-66, acting chief, 66-67; PROF. PHYS. & REHAB. MED. & CHMN. DEPT, SCH. MED, TUFTS, 68-; PHYSIATRIST IN CHIEF, NEW ENG. MED. CTR. HOSP, 68- Survey consult, Comn. Accreditation of Rehab. Facilities, 68; mem. expert med. comt, Am. Rehab. Found, 68; med. adv. bd, Nat. Multiple Sclerosis Soc, 69. Med.C, U.S.A. 54-61, Res, 61-69, Maj. Am. Asn. Electromyop. & Electrodiag.(pres, 68-69); Am. Cong. Rehab. Med; Am. Acad. Phys. Med. & Rehab. Electrodiagnosis; peripheral nerve disorders; braces and splints. Address: Rehabilitation Institute, New England Medical Center Hospitals, 185 Harrison Ave, Boston, MA 02111.

GRANGER, GALE A, b. San Pedro, Calif, June 18, 37; m. 60; c. 2. MICROBIOLOGY. B.S, Washington (Seattle), 62, M.S, 63, Nat. Insts. Health fel, 63-65, Ph.D.(microbiol), 65. Asst. prof. MICROBIOL, UNIV. CALIF, IRVINE, 67-71, ASSOC. PROF, 71- Nat. Insts. Health res. grants & career develop. award, 67-75. U.S.A, 59, Res, 59-65. Transplantation Soc; Am. Asn. Immunol; Reticuloendothelial Soc; N.Y. Acad. Sci. Immunology; cell biology especially in vitro studies of immune cell induced graft cell destruction; cellular and sub cellular mechanisms. Address: Dept. of Molecular Biology & Biochemistry, University of California, Irvine, CA 92664.

GRANGER, JOHN V(AN) N(UYS), b. Cedar Rapids, Iowa, Sept. 14, 18; m. 45; c. 3. PHYSICS. A.B, Cornell Col, 41; fel. & M.S, Harvard, 42, fel, 47-49, Ph.D.(physics), 48. Instr. math, Cornell Col, 41; res. assoc, Harvard, 42-47; head radio systs. lab, Stanford Res. Inst, 49-53, asst. dir. eng. div, 53-56; pres, Granger Assocs, 56-70, DEP. DIR. BUR. INT. SCI. & TECHNOL. AFFAIRS, U.S. DEPT. OF STATE, 71- Sci. Res. Soc. Am; fel. Inst. Elec. & Electronics Eng.(pres, 71); fel. Brit.Inst. Elec. Eng; fel. Electronics Inst. E.Africa. Antennas and propagation; communications systems; electrical noise. Address: Bureau of Internal Scientific & Technological Affairs, Room 7831, Dept. of State, Washington, DC 20520.

GRANGER, MAURICE ROY, b. Vancouver, B.C, Jan. 31, 37; m. 65; c. 1. PHYSICAL ORGANIC CHEMISTRY. B.Sc, British Columbia, 59, Nat. Res. Coun. Can. stud. & M.Sc, 61; Ph.D.(phys. org. chem), California, Berkeley, 65. Res. fel, Alberta, Calgary Campus, 64-65, Nat. Res. Coun. Can. fel, 65-66; asst. prof. chem, Univ. Calgary, 66-70; CHMN. DEPT. SCI, CARIBOO COL, 70- Am. Chem. Soc; Chem. Inst. Can; The Chem. Soc. Properties of strongly basic solutions; carbanions; organometallic compounds; hydrogen bonding and molecular complex formation. Address: Dept. of Chemistry, Cariboo College, P.O. Box 860, Kamloops, B.C, Can.

GRANGER, ROBERT A, II, b. Evanston, Ill, Aug. 7, 28; m. 51; c. 2. MATHEMATICAL PHYSICS, FLUID DYNAMICS. B.A, Pomona Col, 55; M.S, Drexel Inst. Technol, 59; Ford Found. fel, 63-65; Ph.D.(physics), Univ. Md, 70. Res. scientist aeroelasticity, Martin Co, Md, 55-60; PROF. ENG, U.S. NAVAL ACAD, 60- Consult, U.S. Naval Reserve Off. Candidate Sch, Md, 64-; Trident Eng. Assoc, Md, 65-; guest lectr, Royal Aircraft Estab, Eng, 68-69; Munich Tech. Univ, 68-69; consult, Bay-Tech Eng, Md, 69-70; guest lectr, Eugenides Found, 70-71; consult, Cadcom, Inc, Md, 70- Hon. mem. Inst. Mod. Physics, Greece. Applied and theoretical mathematical physics; boundary layer research; vortex dynamics; solutions of Navier-Stokes equations. Address: Dept. of Mechanical Engineering, U.S. Naval Academy, Annapolis, MD 21204.

GRANICK, S(AM), b. New York, N.Y, Feb. 16, 09; m. 38; c. 2. PLANT PHYSIOLOGY, BIOCHEMISTRY. B.S, Michigan, 31, M.S, 33, Newcombe fel, 34-38, Ph.D. (plant physiol), 38. Rockefeller fel, ROCKEFELLER UNIV, 38-39, asst, 39-46, assoc. prof. BIOCHEM, 46-64, PROF, 64- Nat. Acad. Sci; Am. Acad. Arts & Sci; Am. Soc. Nat.(v.pres, 63); Am. Soc. Biol. Chem; Soc. Develop. Biol.(pres, 66); Am. Chem. Soc; Am. Soc. Plant Physiol; Bot. Soc. Am. Biochemistry of iron and porphyrin metabolism; chlorophyll synthesis; chloroplasts; control mechanisms of heme and chlorophyll biosynthesis. Address: Dept. of Biochemistry, Rockefeller University, 66th St. & York Ave, New York, NY 10021.

GRANIK, GERALD, b. Newark, N.J, Sept. 20, 22. APPLIED MECHANICS, BIOMECHANICS. B.S, Newark Col. Eng, 50, M.S, 54; M.S, Stevens Inst. Technol, 58, Sc.D.(appl. mech), 65. Proj. engr. stress & vibration anal, Baldwin Lima Hamilton Co, Pa, 50-52; asst. instr. physics, NEWARK COL. ENG, 52-54, instr, 54-58, asst prof, 58-65, ASSOC. PROF. CIVIL & ENVIRON. ENG, 65- U.S.A, 42-44. Mechanical properties of diseased bones. Address: Dept. of Civil & Environmental Engineering, Newark College of Engineering, Newark, NJ 07102.

GRANITO, CHARLES EDWARD, b. Brooklyn, N.Y, Nov. 14, 37; m. 59; c. 3. INFORMATION SCIENCE. B.S, Miami (Fla), 60, M.S, 62. Chemist, indust. liaison off, U.S. Army Res. Labs, Edgewood Arsenal, Md, 62-66; T.R. Evans Res. Ctr, Diamond Shamrock Corp, 66-67, sr. res. chemist, 67-69; mgr. info. serv, INST. SCI. INFO, 69-70, DIR. CHEM. INFO. SERV, 70- Cert. of achievement, U.S. Dept. Army, 66. AAAS; Am. Chem. Soc; Chem. Notation Asn.(v.pres, 68, pres, 69); Sci. Res. Soc. Am; fel. Am. Inst. Chem; Drug. Info. Asn; Am. Soc. Info. Sci. Information retrieval; biochemistry; structure-activity studies; Wiswesser line notation; marketing; selective dissemination of information; substructure searching. Address: Institute for Scientific Information, 325 Chestnut St, Philadelphia, PA 19106.

GRANLUND, JOHN, b. Oakland, Calif, May 17, 24; m. 45; c. 4. ELECTRICAL ENGINEERING. S.B, Mass. Inst. Tech, 44, S.M, 47, Sc.D.(elec. eng), 50. Asst, lab. electronics, Mass. Inst. Tech, 46-52, mem. staff, Lincoln Lab, 52-56, asst. prof. elec. eng, 56-59; SR. SCIENTIST, ITT DEFENSE COMMUN, 59- Consult, Nat. Co, 54; Chu Assocs, 57; Carr Fastener Corp, 57; Newmont Explor, Ltd, 57; Fed. Telecommun. Labs, 57-59; Lincoln Lab, Mass. Inst. Tech, 58-59. U.S.N.R, 43-46. Inst. Elec. & Electronics Eng. Frequency modulation; multipath transmission; ionospheric scatter propagation; radar; antennas for scatter communication systems; diversity reception devices. Address: ITT Defense Communications, 492 River Rd, Nutley, NJ 07110.

GRANNEMANN, W(AYNE) W(ILLIS), b. New Haven, Mo, Oct. 11, 23; m. 47; c. 3. SOLID STATE PHYSICS, ELECTRICAL ENGINEERING. B.S, Texas, 47, fel, 48-49, M.A, 49, Ph.D.(physics), 53. Asst. prof. physics, Ark. Polytech. Col, 49-51; res. physicist, Defense Res. Lab, Tex, 52-53; Calif. Res. Corp, Standard Oil Co, Calif, 53-56; assoc. prof. ELEC. ENG, UNIV. N.MEX, 56-63, PROF, 63-, dir. eng. exp. sta, 59-63, bur. eng. res, 60-71. Consult, McAllister & Assocs, Inc; Sandia Corp. U.S.N, 44-46. Inst. Elec. & Electronics Eng. Semiconductors; solid state devices; waves in solids; physical electronics; seismic instrumentation; radiation effects on electronics. Address: Dept. of Electrical Engineering, University of New Mexico, Albuquerque, NM 87106.

GRANNIS, GEORGE F(RANKLIN), b. Syracuse, N.Y, May 10, 26; m. 49; c. 4. BIOCHEMISTRY. A.B, Michigan, 47, B.S, 48, M.S, 50; Ph.D.(physiol. chem), Temple, 61. Res. asst. biochem, Michigan, 49-51, univ. hosp, 51-52, Atomic Energy Cmn. Lab, 52-53; Fels. Inst. Med. Res, Temple, 53-56, instr. physiol. chem, sch. med, 56-61; res. assoc, Cardeza Found, Jefferson Med. Col, 61-65; cystic fibrosis res. inst. labs, sch. med, Temple Univ, 65-68, res. asst. prof. biochem, univ, 65-68; ASST. PROF. PATH, OHIO STATE UNIV, 68- U.S.N.R, 44-46, Lt.(jg). AAAS; Am. Chem. Soc; Am. Asn. Clin. Chem; fel. Am. Inst. Chem; Geront. Soc. Protein structure; chemistry of blood coagulation; clinical chemistry; gerontology. Address: Dept. of Pathology, Ohio State University, 410 W. Tenth Ave, Columbus, OH 43201.

GRANO, JOSEPH, JR, b. Arlington, Mass, May 15, 28; m. 51; c. 3. CHEMICAL ENGINEERING. B.S, Mass. Inst. Tech, 50; M.B.A, Am. Int. Col, 56. Res. engr, MONSANTO CO, 50-58, res. specialist, 58-63, RES. GROUP LEADER, 63- Chem.C, U.S.A, 50-52. Plastics, process and applications, thermosetting polymers, rigid vinyl, high density polyethylene and polypropylene resins. Address: Monsanto Company, 730 Worcester St, Indian Orchard, MA 01051.

GRANOFF, ALLAN, b. New Haven, Conn, June 26, 23; m; c. 4. VIROLOGY. B.S, Connecticut, 48; M.S, Pennsylvania, 49, Ph.D.(virol), 52. Asst. div. infectious diseases, Pub. Health Res. Inst. New York, 52-55, assoc, 55-62; assoc. prof. MICROBIOL, UNIV. TENN, MEMPHIS, 62-65, PROF, 65-; LAB. VIROL, ST. JUDE CHILDREN'S RES. HOSP, 65-, CHMN. VIROL. & IMMUNOL. LABS, 69-, biol, 65-69. Mem. virol. study sect, Nat. Insts. Health, 69-73. Dipl, Am. Bd. Med. Microbiol. U.S.A, 43-46. AAAS; Am. Soc. Microbiol; Soc. Exp. Biol. & Med; Am. Asn. Cancer Res; Am. Asn. Immunol. Multiplication and genetics of myxoviruses; tumor viruses. Address: St. Jude Children's Research Hospital, 332 N. Lauderdale, P.O. Box 318, Memphis, TN 38101.

GRANOFF, BARRY, b. Jersey City, N.J, June 30, 38; m. 67; c. 1. MATHEMATICS. B.S, Fairleigh Dickinson Univ, 60; fel, Courant Inst. Math. Sci, N.Y. Univ, 60-62, M.S, N.Y. Univ, 62, Nat. Sci. Found. fel, 62-65, Ph.D.(math), 65. Assoc. res. scientist, Courant Inst. Math. Sci, N.Y. Univ, 65-66; asst. prof. MATH, BOSTON UNIV, 66-70, ASSOC. PROF, 70- AAAS; Am. Math. Soc; Soc. Indust. & Appl. Math; Math. Asn. Am. Applied mathematics and analysis; partial and ordinary differential equations, asymptotic methods, methods of mathematical physics and electromagnetic theory. Address: Dept. of Mathematics, Boston University, 270 Bay State Rd, Boston, MA 02215.

GRANOFF, BARRY, b. Brooklyn, N.Y, Sept. 7, 40; m. 65; c. 2. PHYSICAL CHEMISTRY. B.S, City Col. New York, 62; M.A, Princeton, 64, Ph.D. (x-ray crystallog), 66. Res. chemist, E.I. du Pont de Nemours & Co, Inc, 66-69; TECH. STAFF MEM, SANDIA LABS, 69- Am. Chem. Soc; Am. Crystallog. Asn. Structure of carbon and graphite; graphitization kinetics and catalysis; structure-property correlations in carbon-carbon composites; heatshield materials. Address: Organization 5313, Sandia Labs, Box 5800, Albuquerque, NM 87112.

GRANQUIST, D(ONALD) P(AUL), b. Mt. Vernon, Wash, Dec. 31, 22; m. 45; c. 2. CHEMICAL ENGINEERING. B.S, Washington (Seattle), 44, M.S, 47, Ph.D, 57. Sr. engr, Gen. Elec. Co, 47-65; sr. res. scientist, APPL. MATH. DEPT, PAC. NORTHWEST LABS, BATTELLE MEM. INST, 65-70, SR. RES. ENGR, 70- Am. Chem. Soc; Am. Inst. Chem. Eng; Am. Nuclear Soc. Nuclear engineering; separations processes; reactor fuel cycle analysis; systems analysis; high-speed computers. Address: 1208 Van Giesen, Richland, WA 99352.

GRANQUIST, WILLIAM T(HOMAS), b. Warren, Pa, Dec. 27, 23; m. 48; c. 3. PHYSICAL & COLLOID CHEMISTRY. B.S, Case, 44; Ph.D.(phys. chem), Pittsburgh, 62. Asst. chem. eng, Case, 44; res. chemist, Floridin Co, 45-49, tech. dir, 49-54; sr. fel, MELLON INST, 54-69, ADV. FEL, CARNE-

GIE-MELLON UNIV, 69-; ASST. TECH. DIR, BAROID DIV, NL INDUST, INC, 69- AAAS; Am. Chem. Soc; fel. Am. Inst. Chem; Mineral. Soc. Am; Soc. Rheol; fel. N.Y. Acad. Sci; Am. Ceramic Soc; Clay Minerals Soc. Adsorption of gases on mineral surfaces; adsorption from solution; preparation of inorganic gel adsorbents and catalysts; hydrothermal synthesis of clay minerals; colloid chemistry of clay minerals. Address: 1505 Butlercrest, Houston, TX 77055.

GRANSTROM, MARVIN L(E ROY), b. Anaconda, Mont, Sept. 25, 20; m. 44; c. 3. SANITARY & CIVIL ENGINEERING. B.S, Morningside Col, 42; B.S, Iowa State Col, 43; M.S, Harvard, 47, Ph.D.(sanit. eng), 55. Instr. sanit. eng, Case, 47-49; assoc. prof, North Carolina, 49-58; PROF. CIVIL & ENVIRON. ENG, RUTGERS UNIV, 58- Consult, Nat. Univ. Eng, Peru, 55-57; mem, sanit. eng. subcmt, Nat. Acad. Sci-Nat. Res. Coun, 63-; consult, WHO, Peru, Chile, Arg, & Brazil, 66- U.S.M.C.R, 43-46, 1st Lt. Am. Soc. Civil Eng; Am. Chem. Soc; Am. Water Works Asn; Water Pollution Control Fedn; Am. Water Resources Asn. Ecology. Address: Dept. of Civil & Environmental Engineering, Rutgers, The State University, New Brunswick, NJ 08903.

GRANT, ALAN CARSON, b. Pictou, N.S, Can, Aug. 21, 33; m. 66; c. 2. MARINE GEOLOGY, GEOPHYSICS. B.A, Acadia, 55; B.Sc, Dalhousie, 63, Ph.D, 71; M.Sc, New Brunswick, 65. Computer, geophys-seismic crew, Socony Mobil Oil of Can, Ltd, 55-57, interpreter, 57-59, party chief, 59-61; sci. off, BEDFORD INST. OCEANOG, 65-71, RES. SCIENTIST, 71- Soc. Explor. Geophys; Geol. Asn. Can; Can. Soc. Explor. Geophys. Seismic profiling. Address: Bedford Institute of Oceanography, P.O. Box 1006, Dartmouth, N.S, Can.

GRANT, ANDREW DAVIDSON, b. Jersey City, N.J, Aug. 6, 32; m. 60; c. 1. CHEMICAL ENGINEERING. B.S, Newark Col. Eng, 60. Chemist, Maschmeijer Div, Shulton, Inc, 56-59, toiletries div, 59-60, pilot plant supvr, fine chem. div, 60; sr. develop. engr, Rock Hill Lab, chemetron chem. div, Chemetron Corp, 60-63, develop. mgr, Newport Plant, 63-65, mgr. process develop, Rock Hill Lab, 65-68, TECH. DIR. ORG. CHEM, S.B. PENICK & CO, 68- Assoc. Am. Inst. Chem. Eng. Process development in pharmaceuticals, fine chemicals, essential oils and aromatic chemicals. Address: 8 McKinley Ave, West Caldwell, NJ 07006.

GRANT, ARTHUR E, b. Freeport, Ill, Oct. 27, 23; m. 47; c. 3. PHYSICAL MEDICINE, REHABILITATION. DePaul, 41-43; Syracuse, 43; Chicago & Illinois, Urbana, 44-45; Loyola (Ill), 46-48; M.D, Western Reserve, 50. Intern, Fitzsimons Gen. Hosp, 50-51, resident phys. med. & rehab, Letterman Gen. Hosp, 51-54, staff physician, phys. med. serv, 54-55, Brooke Gen. Hosp, 55-57, chief, phys. med. serv, 60-66, Letterman Gen. Hosp, 66-67; PROF. PHYS. MED. & REHAB. & CHMN. DEPT, MED. SCH, UNIV. TEX, SAN ANTONIO, 67- U.S.A, 43-46, Med.C, 50-67, Lt. Col. Am. Cong. Rehab. Med; Am. Acad. Phys. Med. & Rehab; Am. Med. A'sn; Am. Geriat. Soc; Am. Asn. Electromyog. & Electrodiag. Clinical and research electromyography and electrodiagnosis; rehabilitation of neurologic disorders. Address: Dept. of Physical Medicine & Rehabilitation, University of Texas Medical School at San Antonio, 7703 Floyd Curl Dr, San Antonio, TX 78284.

GRANT, ARTHUR F(REDERICK), JR, b. Phila, Pa, Aug. 28, 21; m. 44; c. 4. CHEMICAL ENGINEERING. B.S, Pennsylvania, 46. Chem. engr, Carbide & Carbon Chem. Div, Union Carbide Corp, 46-48; sect. chief, jet propulsion lab, Calif. Inst. Tech, 49-58; assoc. dir, space tech labs, Thompson-Ramo-Wooldridge Inc, 58-67, ASST. GEN. MGR, power systs. div, 67-69, SCI. & TECH. DIV, TRW INC, 69- U.S.N.R, 43-46, Lt.(jg). Sci. Res. Soc. Am. Propulsion; chemistry; heat transfer; combustion; catalysts; hydraulics. Address: 1432 Via Cataluna, Palos Verdes Estates, CA 90275.

GRANT, BLAKE FRANCIS, b. Hugo, Okla, Sept. 22, 35; m. 57; c. 2. COMPARATIVE PHYSIOLOGY. B.Sc, Oklahoma, 59, M.Sc, 62, Ph.D.(zool), 67. Res. asst. comp. physiol, Oklahoma, 60-65, instr. hemat, 65; biologist, Bingham Lab, Yale, 65-67, instr. biol, 67; CHIEF BIOLOGIST, FISH-PESTICIDE RES. LAB, 67- U.S.M.C, 54-56. AAAS; Am. Soc. Zool. Physiology of fishes; fish endocrinology. Address: Fish-Pesticide Research Lab, Route 1, Columbia, MO 65201.

GRANT, BRUCE S, b. New York, N.Y, Apr. 17, 42; m. 64; c. 1. GENETICS. B.S, Bloomsburg State Col, 64; Nat. Insts. Health fel. & M.S, N.C. State, 66, Ph.D.(genetics), 68. ASST. PROF. BIOL, COL. WILLIAM & MARY, 68- Genetics Soc. Am; Soc. Study Evolution. Behavioral genetics as it pertains to questions of population genetics and evolution. Address: Dept. of Biology, College of William & Mary, Williamsburg, VA 23185.

GRANT, CLARENCE L(EWIS), b. Dover, N.H, July 8, 30; m. 52; c. 3. ANALYTICAL CHEMISTRY. B.S, New Hampshire, 51, M.S, 56; Ph.D.(soils, chem), Rutgers, 60. Instr, pub. sch, N.J, 51-52; res. asst. chem, New Hampshire, 52-53, instr, 53-55, res. assoc, 55-57, asst. prof, 57-58; asst. instr. soils & chem, Rutgers, 58-60, assoc. prof. soils, 60-61; res. assoc. prof. chem, eng. exp. sta, UNIV. N.H, 61-64, RES. PROF, CTR. INDUST. & INSTNL. DEVELOP, 64- Am. Chem. Soc; Soc. Appl Spectros.(pres. elect, 68, pres, 69); Am. Soc. Test. & Mat; fel. Am. Inst. Chem. Development of analytical methods for trace metals; distribution of trace metals in biological and geologic materials; analytical reference standards for biological materials; spectrochemistry; radio tracers; statistics in chemistry. Address: Center for Industrial & Institutional Development, University of New Hampshire, Durham, NH 03824.

GRANT, DALE W(ALTER), b. Woodland, Maine, Dec. 22, 23; m. 48; c. 3. MICROBIOLOGY. B.S, Colorado State, 52, M.S, 53; fel, Stanford, 58-59; Ph.D, Purdue Univ, 65. Res. microbiologist, Bioferm Corp, Calif, 53-57; head microbiol. res. unit, 57-61; res. asst. MICROBIOL, Purdue Univ, 61-65; asst. prof, COLO. STATE UNIV, 65-70, ASSOC. PROF, 70- AAAS; Am. Soc. Microbiol. Polypeptide biosynthesis; antibiotic biosynthesis; mycotoxins; microbial decomposition of agricultural wastes. Address: Dept. of Microbiology, Colorado State University, Ft. Collins, CO 80521.

GRANT, DARROLL L(EE), b. Tacoma, Wash, May 26, 41; m. 66; c. 2. MEAT & ANIMAL SCIENCE. B.S, Wash. State Univ, 64; M.S, Univ. Conn, 66; Ph.D.(food sci), Kans. State Univ, 70. ASST. PROF. ANIMAL SCI, TEX. A&I UNIV, 70- Am. Soc. Animal Sci; Am. Meat Sci. Asn. Mineral composition of bovine tissue as related to physiological maturity; methods to improve beef palatability; intensification of beef production in south Texas. Address: School of Agriculture, Texas A&I University, Kingsville, TX 78363.

GRANT, DAVID A(LEXANDER), b. Des Moines, Iowa, May 17, 16; m. 38; c. 3. EXPERIMENTAL PSYCHOLOGY. B.A, Iowa, 38; M.A, Wisconsin, 39; Ph.D, Stanford, 41. Instr. PSYCHOL, UNIV. WIS, MADISON, 41-48, prof, 48-67, CLARK L. HULL RES. PROF, 67-, CHMN. DEPT, 50-54, 70-. Summers, lectr, Northwestern, 48; Stanford, 49; Columbia, 53; California, Los Angeles, 55; Southern California, 55; Washington (Seattle), 61. Vis. prof, California, 59-60. Ed, J. Exp. Psychol, 63- Consult, U.S. Air Force, 54-58. Mem, Nat. Res. Coun, 56-58; exp. psychol. study sect, Nat. Insts. Health, 59-65. Social psychologist, res. br. morale servs. div, U.S. War Dept, 44. Psychomet. Soc; Am. Psychol. Asn.(secy-treas, 55-58, pres, exp. psychol, 61); Am. Statist. Asn; Soc. Exp. Psychol. Conditioning and learning; problem solving; experimental design and analysis. Address: Dept. of Psychology, University of Wisconsin, Madison, WI 53706.

GRANT, DAVID C(ARROLL), b. N.Y.C, Feb. 5, 38; m. 60; c. 2. ECOLOGY, INVERTEBRATE ZOOLOGY. B.A, Col. Wooster, 59; Nat. Sci. Found. fel, Yale, 59-60, Bur. Commercial Fisheries fels, 62-64, Ph.D.(biol), 65. Ford Found. fel, summer, 64; Nat. Sci. Found. res. assoc, 64-65; res. biologist, systs-ecol. prog, Marine Biol. Lab, Woods Hole, 65-68, asst. dir. systs-ecol. prog, 66-68; ASST. PROF. BIOL, DAVIDSON COL, 68- Mem. corp, Marine Biol. Lab, Woods Hole, 66-, spec. lectr. ecol, summer course, 66, 67 & 68. AAAS; Am. Soc. Limnol. & Oceanog; Am. Inst. Biol. Sci; Am. Soc. Zool; Ecol. Soc. Am. Marine biology; biological oceanography; niche diversification and community structure. Address: Dept. of Biology, Davidson College, Davidson, NC 28036.

GRANT, DAVID E(VANS), b. Milwaukee, Wis, Jan. 15, 24; m. 45; c. 2. PHYSICAL CHEMISTRY. B.A, Haverford Col, 45; Ph.D.(phys. chem), Wisconsin, 51. Res. chemist, HERCULES RES. CTR, 51-66, res. supvr, 66-71, RES. ASSOC, 71- U.S.N, 44-46. Am. Chem. Soc; Am. Inst. Physics; Soc. Plastics Eng. Relation of properties of thermoplastic polymers to their structure and composition. Address: 108 Banbury Dr, Wilmington, DE 19803.

GRANT, DAVID M(ORRIS), b. Salt Lake City, Utah, Mar. 24, 31; m. 53; c. 5. PHYSICAL CHEMISTRY. B.S, Utah, 54, Nat. Sci. Found. fel, 54-57, Ph.D.(chem), 57. Instr. CHEM, Illinois, 57-58; asst. prof, UTAH, 58-62, assoc. prof, 62-65, PROF, 65-, CHMN. DEPT, 62- Am. Chem. Soc; Am. Phys. Soc. High resolution nuclear magnetic resonance; carbon-13 magnetic resonance; molecular and electronic structure. Address: Dept. of Chemistry, University of Utah, Salt Lake City, UT 84112.

GRANT, DONALD R, b. Cut Knife, Sask, Aug. 4, 32; m. 55; c. 6. BIOCHEMISTRY, ORGANIC CHEMISTRY. B.S.A, Univ. Sask, 55; Ph.D, Wash. State Univ, 64. Chemist, Maple Leaf Milling Co, Toronto, 55-58; jr. chemist, Wash. State Univ, 58-63; asst. prof. ORG. & CEREAL CHEM, UNIV. SASK, SASKATOON, 63-68, ASSOC. PROF, 68- Chem. Inst. Can. Nitrogen metabolism of seed crops and separation and properties of seed proteins of agricultural crops, particularly wheat and peas. Address: Dept. of Chemistry & Chemical Engineering, University of Saskatchewan, Saskatoon, Sask, Can.

GRANT, D(OUGLAS) H(OPE), b. Glasgow, Scotland, Apr. 29, 34; m. 70; c. 3. PHYSICAL CHEMISTRY. B.Sc, Glasgow, 56, Gas Coun. scholar, 56-59, Ph.D.(polymer chem), 62. Res. fel. polymer chem, appl. chem. div, Nat. Res. Coun. Can, 59-61; NATO-Dept. Sci. & Indust. Res. fel. & res. asst. phys. chem, Bristol Univ, 61-62, Imp. Chem. Indust. res. fel, 62-64; asst. prof. CHEM, MT. ALLISON UNIV, 64-71, ASSOC. PROF, 71- Vis. lectr, Loughborough Univ. Technol, 71-72. Kinetics and mechanism of thermal decomposition reactions of synthetic polymers in solid state and in solution, by appropriate techniques; analytical chemistry. Address: Dept. of Chemistry, Mt. Allison University, Sackville, N.B, Can.

GRANT, DOUGLAS R(ODERICK), b. Toronto, Ont, Mar. 4, 39; m. 64; c. 2. ENVIRONMENTAL GEOLOGY. B.Sc, Dalhousie Univ, 60, univ. assistantship, 61-62, Defense Res. Bd. Can. scholar. & M.Sc, 63, Nat. Res. Coun. Can. assistantship, 64; univ. assistantship, Cornell Univ, 66-68, Ph.D.(sea-level changes), 70. Sci. off, GEOL. SURV. CAN, 68-69, RES. SCIENTIST, 70- Fel. Geol. Asn. Can. Sea-level changes; glacial history; environmental change; quaternary, surficial and applied geology. Address: Geological Survey of Canada, 601 Booth St, Ottawa, Ont. K1A 0E8, Can.

GRANT, EDWIN ALLEN, JR, b. Boston, Mass, Apr. 7, 30; m. 56; c. 3. ORGANIC CHEMISTRY. B.S, Northeastern, 52; Ph.D.(org. chem), Wisconsin, 57. Sr. chemist, DUPLICATING PRODS. DIV, MINN. MINING & MFG. CO, 57-59, develop. supvr, 59-62, res. supvr, 62-65, proj. supvr, 65-68, LAB. PROJ. MGR, 68- Am. Chem. Soc; Nat. Microfilm Asn. Photoconductive materials; thermography; photography; thermographic reactions and toners; synthesis of organic photosensitive materials. Address: 2542 Bittersweet Lane, St. Paul, MN 55109.

GRANT, ERNEST W(ALTER), b. Brockton, Mass, July 17, 18; m. 45; c. 2. PHARMACEUTICAL CHEMISTRY. B.S, Mass. Col. Pharm, 39, M.S, 48; fel, Purdue, 48-51, Ph.D.(pharmaceut. chem), 51. CHEMIST, ELI LILLY & CO, 51- C.W.S, 42-46, 1st Lt. Am. Chem. Soc. Analytical chemistry; alkaloids. Address: Eli Lilly & Co, 740 S. Alabama St, Indianapolis, IN 46206.

GRANT, EUGENE F(REDRICK), b. Baker, Ore, June 15, 17; m. 43; c. 2. ELECTRICAL ENGINEERING. B.S, Ore. State Col, 41, M.S, 42. Res. engr. res. lab, Westinghouse Elec. Corp, Pa, 42-45; proj. engr, Sperry Gyroscope Co, N.Y, 45-46; chief appl. math. br, electronic res. lab, Air Forces, U.S. Army, 46-51; sect. mgr. electronics, W.L. Maxson Corp, N.Y, 51-54; v.pres. eng, Nat. Co. Inc, Mass, 54-62; chief scientist, space systs. div, HUGHES AIRCRAFT CO, Culver City, 62-71, PROG. MGR, SPEC. PROGS. DIV, SPACE & COMMUN. GROUP, EL SEGUNDO, 71- Civilian with Off. Sci. Res. & Develop, 44. Sr. mem. Inst. Elec. & Electronics Eng; assoc.

fel. Am. Inst. Aeronaut. & Astronaut; N.Y. Acad. Sci. Space systems and technology; design of pulsed radar, doppler radar and digital and analogue computers; communication systems; atomic frequency standards. Address: 4748 N. La Villa Marina, Marina Del Rey, CA 90291.

GRANT, FREDERICK CYRIL, b. Boston, Mass, July 18, 25; m. 53. PHYSICS. B.S, Mass. Inst. Technol, 47; M.A, Col. William & Mary, 62; Ph.D. (physics), Va. Polytech, 67. Scientist, Nat. Adv. Comt. Aeronaut, 48-58; PHYSICIST, NASA, 58- Am. Phys. Soc. Theoretical and experimental supersonic aerodynamics; flight mechanics of entry into planetary atmospheres; plasma physics, especially Vlasov equations; tornado structure, dynamics. Address: 399 Stanton Rd, Newport News, VA 23606.

GRANT, FRED(ERICK) W(ARREN), JR, b. Milwaukee, Wis, June 26, 26; m. 58; c. 2. ORGANIC CHEMISTRY. B.S, Worcester Polytech, 50; Ph.D. (org. chem), Yale, 55. Res. chemist, Olin Mathieson Chem. Co, 54-57; E.I. du Pont de Nemours & Co, 57-58; asst. prof. org. chem, Hopkins, 58-59; chem, Hamilton Col, 59-66; sr. res. biochem, MARCY STATE HOSP, 66-71; ASSOC. RES. BIOCHEM, 71- U.S.N.R, 44-46. AAAS; Am. Chem. Soc; Soc. Biol. Psychiat. Natural products and steric effects; psychopharmacology. Address: Research Division, Marcy State Hospital, Marcy, NY 13403.

GRANT, GEORGE C, b. Medford, Mass, Aug. 13, 29; m. 52; c. 2. BIOLOGICAL OCEANOGRAPHY, FISHERY BIOLOGY. B.S, Massachusetts, 56; M.A, Col. William & Mary, 62; Nat. Defense Ed. Act fel, Rhode Island, 65-66, Ph.D. (biol. oceanog), 67. Fishery res. biologist, Bur. Commercial Fisheries, U.S. Fish & Wildlife Serv, N.C, 56-60; ASST. PROF. MARINE SCI, UNIV. VA, 67-; COL. WILLIAM & MARY, 68-; ASSOC. MARINE SCIENTIST, VA. INST. MARINE SCI, 67- U.S.A, 48-52. Am. Soc. Limnol. & Oceanog; Am. Soc. Ichthyol. & Herpet; Soc. Syst. Zool; Atlantic Estuarine Res. Soc. Distribution, ecology and morphometrics of North Atlantic Chaetognatha; general interest and graduate teaching in marine zooplankton; population dynamics and ecology of commercially important fisheries; early life history and population dynamics of marine fishes; marine zooplankton, specializing in the Chaetognatha; application of computer techniques to problems in taxonomy. Address: Virginia Institute of Marine Science, Gloucester Point, VA 23062.

GRANT, G(ORDON) A(LLISON), b. Yarmouth, N.S, Aug. 4, 04; m. 29; c. 1. BIOCHEMISTRY. B.Sc, Dalhousie, 27, M.Sc, 29; fel, Toronto, 30-32, Ph.D. (biochem), 32; Royal Soc. Can. fel, London, 33-34, Beit fel, Lister Inst, 34-37, Ph.D. (biochem), 37. Lectr. biochem, Dalhousie, 27-30; chief res. chemist, res. & biol. labs, Ayerst, McKenna & Harrison, Ltd, 37-47, dir. res, 48-57, dir. & v.pres. res. & develop, 57-69. Fel. AAAS; Am. Chem. Soc; Endocrine Soc. (v.pres); Can. Physiol. Soc; fel. Chem. Inst. Can; Brit. Biochem. Soc; Brit. Chem. Soc. Antibiotics; hormones; sterol hormones; alkaloids; vitamins. Address: 341 Morrison Ave, Mt. Royal 305, Que, Can.

GRANT, H(AROLD) L(AURIER), b. Guysborough, N.S, May 15, 27; m. 54; c. 2. PHYSICS. B.Sc, Acadia, 47; M.Sc, Western Ontario, 49; Ph.D. (physics), Cambridge, 57. Instr. physics, Brandon Col, 49-50; SCI. OFF, Pac. Naval Lab, 50-67, DEFENCE RES. ESTAB. PAC, 71- Can. Asn. Physicists. Fluid mechanics; acoustics. Address: Defence Research Establishment Pacific, Victoria, B.C, Can.

GRANT, HAROLD S(INCLAIR), b. Bangor, Ireland, Jan. 7, 05; nat; m. 28; c. 4. MATHEMATICS. A.B, Pennsylvania, 26, A.M, 27, Ph.D. (math), 33. Asst. instr, Pennsylvania, 27-29; instr, Buffalo, 29-30; MATH, RUTGERS UNIV, 30-35, asst. prof, 35-45; assoc. prof, 46-50, prof, 50-65, EMER. PROF, 65- Prof, Old Dom. Univ, 66-70, emer. prof, 70- Am. Math Soc; Math. Asn. Am. Number theory; algebraic number fields; real variable. Address: 9414 Hammett Pkwy, Norfolk, VA 23503.

GRANT, HOMER H(AMILTON), JR, b. Wenatchee, Wash, Feb. 12, 08; m. 33; c. 1. ENGINEERING. B.S, Washington (Seattle), 32, M.S, 33, E.E, 46; hon. D.Sc, Northrop Inst. Tech, 65. Res. engr. & chief div. res. & statist, Wash. State Pub. Utilities Comn, 34-39; statistician, Bonneville Power Admin, U.S. Dept. Interior, Ore, 40; transportation res. engr, Calif. State Pub. Utilities Comn, 40-43; transportation engr, asst. to v.pres. & gen. mgr, Key Syst. Transit Lines, 43-46; prof. gen. eng, Univ. South. Calif, 48-54, prof. indust. eng. & head dept, 54-67, acting head dept. gen. eng, 54-55, elec. eng, 59-62, acting dean sch, 59, assoc. dean 60-62; PRES, NORTHROP INST. TECHNOL, 67- Consult, Army Mgt. Eng. Training Agency & various corps. Am. Soc. Eng. Educ; Inst. Elec. & Electronics Eng; fel. Am. Inst. Indust. Eng; Nat. Soc. Prof. Eng. Applications of computers and statistics; econometrics; engineering education; technical administration; industrial engineering. Address: Northrop Institute of Technology, 1155 W. Arbor Vitae St, Inglewood, CA 90306.

GRANT, JAMES ALEXANDER, b. Inverness, Scotland, Oct. 3, 35; m. 64; c. 2. GEOLOGY. B.Sc, Aberdeen, 57; M.Sc, Queen's (Ont), 59; Ph.D. (geol), Calif. Inst. Technol, 64. Asst. prof. GEOL, UNIV. MINN, Minneapolis, 64-69, ASSOC. PROF, DULUTH, 69- Geologist, Minn. Geol. Surv, 64-; Nat. Sci. Found. grant, 66-68; summers, asst. geologist, Ont. Dept. Mines, 56-58, geologist, 59-62. Geol. Soc. Am; Am. Geophys. Union. Metamorphic petrology; field, petrologic and rubidium-strontium isotopic studies of the Grenville front and the Precambrian of southwestern Minnesota; phase equilibria in high-grade metamorphism. Address: Dept. of Geology, University of Minnesota, Duluth, MN 55812.

GRANT, JAMES J, JR, b. Teaneck, N.J, May 24, 35; m. 57; c. 4. THEORETICAL PHYSICS. B.S, Manhattan Col, 56; M.S, Rensselaer Polytech, 58; Nat. Sci. Found. fel, Fordham, 62-63, Ph.D. (physics), 64. Instr. PHYSICS, ST. PETER'S COL. (N.J), 58-61, asst. prof, 61-64, ASSOC. PROF, 64-, CHMN. DEPT, 63- Am. Asn. Physics Teachers. Atomic scattering theory; particle physics employing nuclear emulsion techniques. Address: Dept. of Physics, St. Peter's College, Kennedy Blvd, Jersey City, NJ 07306.

GRANT, JAMES N(EWITT), b. Garysburg, N.C, Oct. 1, 03; m. 30; c. 1. PHYSICS. A.B, Duke, 25; N.C. State Col, 28; U.S. Dept. Agr. Grad. Sch, 38-41. Teacher, pub. sch, N.C, 25-28, prin, 28-37; sci. aide, U.S. Dept. Agr, 37-38, cotton technologist, 38-42, south. regional res. lab, bur. agr. & indust. chem, fiber physics invests, 42-45, assoc. physicist, 45-46, acting physicist in charge, 46-47, physicist in charge, Agr. Res. Serv, 47-57, head, 58-70; RETIRED. Am. Phys. Soc; Fiber Soc; Sci. Res. Soc. Am. Fiber structure and physical behaviors of native and chemically modified cottons. Address: 237 Clifton Rd, Rocky Mount, NC 27801.

GRANT, JOHN GRAY, b. Brandon, Man, Can, Jan. 16, 99; nat; m. 25; c. 3. HYGIENE. B.A, McMaster, 19; M.D, Manitoba, 24. Asst. prof. HYG, IOWA STATE UNIV, 30-36, PROF, 36-, PHYSICIAN, STUDENT HEALTH SERV, 64-, dir. serv. & head dept, 36-64. Civilian with Atomic Energy Comn, 46. Fel. Am. Med. Asn. Nutritional status of college women as related to their dietary habits; anthropometric measurements, the formed elements of the blood, basal metabolism and dietary balances. Address: Iowa State University Hospital, Ames, IA 50010.

GRANT, LELAND F(AUNTLEROY), b. Etowah, Tenn, Oct. 30, 13; m. 39; c. 2. GEOLOGICAL ENGINEERING. B.S, Tennessee, 47. Geologic aide, Tenn. Valley Authority, 36-39, geologist, 39-57; secy. & geologist, Schmidt Eng. Co, Inc, 57-63, CHIEF GEOLOGIST, HENSLEY-SCHMIDT, INC, 63- Indust. consult; mem. U.S. Comt. Large Dams. Fel. Geol. Soc. Am; Am. Inst. Prof. Geol; Am. Soc. Civil Eng. Engineering geology; foundation investigation and treatment. Address: 1212 American National Bank Bldg, Chattanooga, TN 37402.

GRANT, L(EONIDAS) S(IMPSON), JR, b. Newbern, N.C, Feb. 25, 07. CHEMICAL ENGINEERING. B.S, Va. Polytech, 28. Plant student, Mathieson Alkali Works, Va, 29; anal. chemist, Hercules Powder Co, 29-41, supvr, essential mat. lab, Radford Ord. Works, 41-43; res. & develop. chemist, Personal Prod. Corp, 44-59, process engr, 60-66, textile engr, 67-70; RETIRED. AAAS; Am. Chem. Soc. Purification and utilization of cellulosic fibers; fiber testing; textile preparatory processing and absorbency characteristics of porous materials. Address: 13300 Harrowgate Rd, Chester, VA 23831.

GRANT, LOUIS R(USSELL), JR, b. Macon, Mo, July 9, 28; m. 55; c. 2. INORGANIC CHEMISTRY. B.S, Lincoln (Mo), 49; M.S, Howard, 55; Ph.D. (chem), Southern California, 61. Sr. res. engr, ROCKETDYNE DIV, N.Am. Aviation, Inc, 60-62, res. specialist, 62, prin. scientist, 62-63, res. specialist, 63-68, MEM. TECH. STAFF, N.AM. ROCKWELL CORP, 68- U.S.A, 50-52. Am. Chem. Soc; Brit. Chem. Soc. Synthesis and characterization of simple and complex metal hydrides, Lewis acidbase complexes, organometallic compounds of groups III and V elements and thermostable compounds; chemistry of explosives. Address: Advanced Programs Dept, Rocketdyne, D589-198, 6633 Canoga Ave, Canoga Park, CA 91304.

GRANT, M(ARSHALL) N(ELSON), b. Lethbridge, Alta, Mar. 28, 17; m. 45; c. 2. PLANT BREEDING. B.Sc, Alberta, 44, M.Sc, 46; fel, Wisconsin, 46-47, Ph.D, 49. Plant pathologist, CAN. DEPT. AGR, 49-51, spring wheat breeder, RES. STA, 51-60, WINTER WHEAT BREEDER, 60- Can. Soc. Agron. (pres, 54-55); Agr. Inst. Can. Breeding winterhardy winter wheats; investigating components of winterhardiness in cereals. Address: Plant Science Section, Research Station, Canada Dept. of Agriculture, Lethbridge, Alta, Can.

GRANT, MICHAEL P(ETER), b. Oshkosh, Wis, Feb. 26, 36; m. 61; c. 2. ELECTRICAL ENGINEERING. B.S, Purdue, 57, M.S, 58, Ph.D. (elec. eng), 64. Engr, Westinghouse Res. Labs, 53-57; instr. elec. eng, Purdue, 58-64; sr. engr, INDUST. NUCLEONICS CORP, 64-66, MGR. SYSTS. & CONTROL, 66- Inst. Elec. & Electronics Eng. Statistical communication theory and application to radar systems; control of industrial processes in real time employing digital computer systems. Address: Industrial Nucleonics Corp, 650 Ackerman Rd, Columbus, OH 43202.

GRANT, NICHOLAS J(OHN), b. South River, N.J, Oct. 21, 15; m. 63; c. 5. METALLURGY, MATERIALS SCIENCE. B.S, Carnegie Inst. Tech, 38; Sc.D. (metall), Mass. Inst. Technol, 44. Metall. engr, Bethlehem Steel Co, 38-40; asst, MASS. INST. TECHNOL, 41-42, instr. steel making, 42-43, asst. prof. METALL, 44-47, assoc. prof, 47-54, PROF, 54-, PROJ. SUPVR, 43-, DIR. CTR. MAT. SCI. & ENG, 68- Tech. dir, Invest. Castings Inst, distinguished serv. award, 56; tech. dir, Titanium Adv. Bd; pres, New Eng. Mat. Lab, Inc, 56-67; chmn. mat. adv. comt, NASA, 63-65. Merit award, Carnegie Inst. Technol, 64. Civilian with Atomic Energy Comn; Off. Sci. Res. & Develop; U.S.N; Nat. Adv. Comt. Aeronaut, 44-59; NASA, 59-68, 71- Am. Soc. Metals; Am. Inst. Mining, Metall. & Petrol. Eng; Brit. Inst. Metals; Am. Soc. Test. & Mat. Heat resistant materials; powder metallurgy; deformation and fracture; structure-property control. Address: Center for Materials Science & Engineering, Massachusetts Institute of Technology, Cambridge, MA 02139.

GRANT, NORMAN H(OWARD), b. Chicago, Ill, July 21, 27; m. 50; c. 2. BIOCHEMISTRY. S.B, Chicago, 47; M.S, Illinois, 48, Atomic Energy Comn. fel. & Ph.D. (chem), 50. Sr. res. biochemist, labs, Armour & Co, 50-56; sr. res. scientist biochem, Wyeth Inst. Med. Res, 56-67; ASST. MGR. BIOCHEM, WYETH LABS, 68- Am. Chem. Soc; Soc. Exp. Biol. & Med; Am. Soc. Biol. Chem; Biochem. Soc. Chemotherapy; proteins; RNA; aging; anti-infectious agents; inflammation; proteinases; connective tissue proteins; solid state reactions. Address: Wyeth Labs, Box 8299, Philadelphia, PA 19101.

GRANT, NORMAN K(ENNEDY), b. Edinburgh, Scotland, Dec. 28, 33; m. 66. STRUCTURAL GEOLOGY. B.Sc, Univ. Edinburgh, 57, studentship & Ph.D. (geol), 61. Asst. lectr. GEOL, Grant Inst. Geol, Univ. Edinburgh, 60-61; lectr, Univ. Ibadan, 61-67; res. asst, Oxford, 67-68; Univ. Leeds, 68-69; ASST. PROF, OBERLIN COL, 69- Fel. Geol. Soc. London. History of the Precambrian and early Paleozoic rocks of West Africa; rubidium-strontium geochronology; the isotopic composition of strontium in igneous rocks. Address: Dept. of Geology, Oberlin College, Oberlin, OH 44074.

GRANT, PAUL E(RNEST), b. Auburn, Maine, Jan. 19, 27. PHYSICS. B.S, Maine, 48; M.S, Brown, 50, Ph.D. (physics), 53. Proj. head, Air Force Cambridge Res. Center, 53; physicist & math. group leader, Army Chem. Corps,

54-55; asst. prof. physics, Stevens Inst. Tech, 55-56; sr. engr, Martin Co, 56-58; mem. tech. staff, Lincoln lab, Mass. Inst. Tech, 58-59; head sub-dept. adv. design, Mitre Corp, 59-63; mem. staff, Res. Anal. Corp, 63-70; PRES, POTOMAC LABS, 70- U.S.A, 53-55. Acoust. Soc. Am; Am. Phys. Soc; Optical Soc. Am; Opers. Res. Soc. Am. Acoustics; ultrasonics; nuclear and weapon physics; infrared technology; operations research and military systems engineering. Address: 8827 Tuckerman Lane, Potomac, MD 20854.

GRANT, PAUL MICHAEL, b. Poughkeepsie, N.Y, May 9, 35; m. 58; c. 3. SOLID STATE PHYSICS. B.S, Clarkson Tech, 60; A.M, Harvard, 61, Int. Bus. Mach. Corp. fel, 61-65, Ph.D.(physics), 65. STAFF MEM. SOLID STATE PHYSICS, RES. LAB, IBM CORP, 65- Am. Phys. Soc. Applications of computers to experimental physics and chemistry. Address: Research Lab, IBM Corp, Monterey & Cottle Rds, San Jose, CA 95114.

GRANT, PETER MALCOLM, b. Cleethorpes, Eng, Sept. 30, 33; m. 58. ORGANIC CHEMISTRY. B.Sc, Birmingham, 54, U.K. Atomic Energy Res. Estab. fel, 56-57, Ph.D.(org. chem), 57. U.K. Atomic Energy Res. Estab. fel, Birmingham, 57-58; plant mgr, gen. chem. div, Imp. Chem. Industs, Ltd, 58-59; res. chemist, textile fibers div, Du Pont of Can, Ltd, 59-61; distillation prod. industs. div, EASTMAN KODAK CO, 61-62, head chem. uses lab, 62-69, SR. RES. CHEMIST, 69- Am. Chem. Soc. Enzymic synthesis of carbohydrates; radiation of carbohydrates; fat soluble vitamins; food emulsifiers; polymers; coatings. Address: Tennessee Eastman Research Labs, Bldg. 150A, Kingsport, TN 37662.

GRANT, PETER RAYMOND, b. London, Eng, Oct. 26, 36; m. 62; c. 1. ZOOLOGY. B.A, Cambridge, 60; Ph.D.(zool), British Columbia, 64. Fel. ZOOL, Yale, 64-65; asst. prof, McGill Univ, 65-68, ASSOC. PROF, 68- Brit. Army, 55-57, 2nd Lt. AAAS; Soc. Study Evolution; Am. Ornith. Union; Ecol. Soc. Am; Animal Behav. Soc; Can. Soc. Zool. Evolutionary significance of interactions among animal species, approached through ecology, behavior, systematics and genetics. Address: Dept. of Biology, McGill University, Montreal, Que, Can.

GRANT, PHILIP, b. N.Y.C, Sept. 22, 24; m. 46; c. 3. EMBRYOLOGY. B.S, City Col. New York, 47; A.M, Columbia, 49, Ph.D.(zool), 52; Fulbright fel, Brussels, 50-51. Tutor & instr. biol, City Col. New York, 47-54; res. assoc. embryol, Inst. Cancer Res, 54-57; asst. prof. pathobiol, sch. hyg. & pub. health, Johns Hopkins Univ, 57-62; prog. dir. develop. biol, Nat. Sci. Found, 62-66; PROF. BIOL, UNIV. ORE, 66- U.S. Pub. Health Serv. fel, Columbia 52-54, sr. res. fel, 58. U.S.A, 43-46. AAAS; Am. Soc. Zool; Soc. Develop. Biol; Marine Biol. Asn; Am. Soc. Cell Biol; Int. Soc. Develop. Biol. Embryology; cancer and cell physiology. Address: Dept. of Biology, University of Oregon, Eugene, OR 97403.

GRANT, RALPH MAYNARD, b. Detroit, Mich, Mar. 27, 35; m. 58; c. 1. ENGINEERING PHYSICS. B.S, Michigan, 59, M.S, 61; Ph.D.(physics), Delft, 64. Res. engr, Holley Carburetor Co, 56-58; res. assoc. infrared optics, inst. sci. & tech, Michigan, 61-62; sr. scientist, nuclear reactor inst, Delft, 62-64; assoc. res. physicist, Michigan, 64-65, res. physicist & lectr. elec. eng, 65-66; pres, G.C. Optronics, Inc, 66-71, chmn. bd, 68-71; PRES, AM. SAFETY TIRE CO, 71- Am. Soc. Nondestructive Test.(achievement award, 70). Nuclear engineering; applied engineering physics; solid state physics; optical devices; holography; applications of interferometric holographic instruments; holographic nondestructive testing systems and machines. Address: 1000 Forest Rd, Ann Arbor, MI 48105.

GRANT, RICHARD E(VANS), b. St. Paul, Minn, June 18, 27; m. 58; c. 3. INVERTEBRATE PALEONTOLOGY. M.S, Minnesota, 53; Nat. Sci. Found. fel, Texas, 54-55, Shell Oil Co. fel, 55-56, Ph.D.(geol), 58. Instr. geol, Texas, 53-54; res. asst. invert. paleont, Smithsonian Inst, 57-61; GEOLOGIST, U.S. GEOL. SURV, 61- U.S.N.R, 45-46; U.S.A.R, 50-54, 2nd Lt. AAAS; fel. Geol. Soc. Am; Soc. Econ. Paleont. & Mineral; Am. Asn. Petrol. Geol; Paleont. Soc. Paleontology of Upper Cambrian trilobites and brachiopods; paleontology of Permian brachiopods. Address: E-316 Natural History Bldg, U.S. Geological Survey, Washington, DC 20242.

GRANT, ROBERT B(YRON), b. St. Louis, Mo, Jan. 15, 22; m. 48; c. 4. OPERATIONS & SYSTEMS ANALYSIS. B.S, Washington (St. Louis), 43, M.S, 48, Sc.D.(appl. mech), 51. Eng. off, Commun. Plant Eng. Agency, 44-46; lectr, appl. mech, Washington (St. Louis), 46-50; supvr. anal. mech. Southwest Res. Inst, 51-55; tech. consult. opers. res, Phillips Petrol. Co, 55-57, mgr. eng. & opers. anal. div, 57-64; dir. opers. res, Celanese Corp. Am, 64-65, dir. mgt. servs, 65-68; v.pres. electronic systs. ctr, New York Stock Exchange, 68-70; PRES, ALPHA-OMEGA ASSOCS, ST. LOUIS, 70- U.S.A, 43-46, Sig.C, Res, 46-53; Capt. Fel. AAAS; Sci. Res. Soc. Am; Opers. Res. Soc. Am; Asn. Comput. Mach; Inst. Mgt. Sci; Am. Mgt. Asn; Soc. Indust. & Appl. Math. Management sciences; decision theory; stochastic processes; systems design; dynamics; fluid and nonlinear mechanics; applied mathematics. Address: 6497 Epphingham Lane, Florissant, MO 63033.

GRANT, ROBERT CHARLES S, b. Dorrigo, Australia. PHYSICAL CHEMISTRY. B.Sc, Univ. N.S.W, 63, Commonwealth scholar, 63-66, Ph.D.(gas phase kinetics), 67. Res. assoc, Cath. Univ. Am, 66-67; Calif. State Col. Los Angeles, 67-68; sr. res. chemist, process instruments div, Beckman Instruments, Calif, Inc, 69-71; AIR POLLUTION CONTROL SPECIALIST, AIR RESOURCES BD, STATE OF CALIF, 71- Am. Chem. Soc; The Chem. Soc. Gas phase chemical kinetics; photochemistry; atmospheric chemistry and air pollution; hygrometry; waste water analysis; process analyzers. Address: 9228 Henley Way, Sacramento, CA 95826.

GRANT, RODERICK M, JR, b. Chicago, Ill, July 9, 35; m. 57; c. 3. SOLID STATE & MEDICAL PHYSICS. B.S, Denison, 57; M.S, Wisconsin, 59, Ph.D.(physics), 65. Teaching asst. PHYSICS, Wisconsin, 57-59, instr, Marathon County Center, 59-61, res. asst, univ, 61-65; asst. prof, DENISON UNIV, 65-70, ASSOC. PROF. & CHMN. DEPT, 70- AAAS; Am. Asn. Physics Teachers; Am. Asn. Physicists in Med; Am. Phys. Soc. Problems of medical physics; physics of thermoluminescence of lithium fluoride crystals, pure and doped with magnesium. Address: Dept. of Physics, Denison University, Granville, OH 43023.

GRANT, ROGER J(OHN), b. Tillsonburg, Ont, Feb. 5, 43; m. 64. PHYSICAL CHEMISTRY. A.B, Messiah Col, 64; Ph.D.(chem), Syracuse, 68. ASST. PROF. CHEM, MESSIAH COL, 68- AAAS; Am. Chem. Soc; Chem. Inst. Can. Density studies of liquid binary alloys in an effort to determine evidence for compound formation. Address: Dept. of Chemistry, Messiah College, Grantham, PA 17027.

GRANT, RONALD, b. London, Eng, May 25, 10. NEUROPHYSIOLOGY. B.Sc, London, 30; Brit. Ministry of Agr. scholar, Edinburgh, 30-33, Ph.D.(reproductive physiol), 33. Lectr. zool, Leeds, 33-35; Commonwealth Fund fel, Chicago, 35-36; Columbia, 36-37; lectr. physiol. & zool, McGill, 37-43, PHYSIOL, 43-45, asst. prof, 45-46; res. assoc, STANFORD UNIV, 47-49, asst. prof, 49-52, assoc. prof, 52-57, PROF, 57- Guggenheim fel, 55-56. AAAS; Am. Physiol. Soc; Arctic Inst. N.Am; fel. N.Y. Acad. Sci. Temperature regulation and physiology of fever; central autonomic and respiratory neurophysiology. Address: Dept. of Physiology, Stanford University, Stanford, CA 94305.

GRANT, RONALD W(ARREN), b. Cleveland, Ohio, Nov. 4, 37; m. 59; c. 3. NUCLEAR CHEMISTRY. B.S, Case, 59; Ph.D.(nuclear chem), California, Berkeley, 63. PROJ. MGR, SCI. CTR, N.AM. ROCKWELL CORP, 63- Mem. prog. comt, U.S. Conf. Magnetism & Magnetic Mat, 70; comt. mem, ad hoc adv. panel Mössbauer data, Nat. Res. Coun. AAAS; Am. Phys. Soc; Sci. Res. Soc. Am. Magnetic properties of materials; Mössbauer spectroscopy; synthesis and characterization of solid state materials. Address: Science Center, North American Rockwell Corp, 1049 Camino Dos Rios, Thousand Oaks, CA 91360.

GRANT, ROWLAND FREDERICK, b. Winnipeg, Man, Oct. 12, 29; m. 57. PHYSICAL CHEMISTRY. B.A, British Columbia, 52, M.Sc, 55, Ph.D.(chem), 60. Anal. chemist, Aluminium Labs, Que, 52-54; Nat. Res. Coun. Can. fel, 59-60; res. chemist, B.C. Res. Coun, 61; asst. prof. chem, Can. Joint Serv. Col, 61-66; head dept. chem. & chem. technol, Selkirk Col, 66-69, dean studies, 67-69; PRES, OKANAGAN COL, 69- Nuclear magnetic resonance studies of solids and liquids; dielectric studies of liquids; physical properties of fatty acids, soaps and related compounds. Address: Okanagan College, Box 550, Kelowna, B.C, Can.

GRANT, SHELDON KERRY, b. Cedar City, Utah, Apr. 29, 39; m. 60; c. 3. MINERALOGY, PETROLOGY. B.S, Utah, 61, Nat. Sci. Found. fels, 61-64, Ph.D.(geol. eng), 66. Asst. prof. geol. eng, UNIV. MO-ROLLA, 65-70, ASSOC. PROF. GEOL, 70- Am. Inst. Min, Metall. & Petrol. Eng; Mineral. Soc. Am. Paragenesis in hydrothermal ore deposits; ignimbrites and ore deposits; tectonic evolution in tertiary strain systems. Address: Dept. of Geology & Geophysics, University of Missouri-Rolla, Rolla, MO 65401.

GRANT, STANLEY CAMERON, b. Cedar Rapids, Iowa, Apr. 21, 31; m. 54; c. 3. ENVIRONMENTAL GEOLOGY, REMOTE SENSING. B.A, Coe Col, 53; Danforth fel. & M.A, Univ. Wyo, 55; Danforth fel, Petro-Nuclear Ltd. grant & Ph.D.(geol), Univ. Idaho, 71. Petrol. geologist, Calif. Co, Standard Oil of Calif, 55; chief geologist, Gas Hills Uranium Co, Am. Nuclear, 55-56; instr, Howard County Jr. Col, Big Spring, Tex, 61-62; ASST. PROF. aerospace study, Univ. Idaho, 66-69; GEOL, UNIV. NORTH. IOWA, 70- U.S.A.F, 56-69, Maj. AAAS; Geol. Soc. Am; Nat. Asn. Geol. Teachers; Am. Inst. Mining, Metall. & Petrol. Eng; Am. Soc. Photogram. Thirtyfive millimeter color oblique aerial photographic techniques in geologic reconnaissance; photographic remote sensing of the physical environment; land use studies and engineering geology of parts of northeast Iowa; recreation geography of the Wallace, Idaho area. Address: Dept. of Earth Science, College of Natural Sciences, University of Northern Iowa, Cedar Falls, IA 50613.

GRANT, U(LYSSES) J(ERRY), b. Rosedale, Okla, Dec. 31, 20; m. 42; c. 2. PLANT BREEDING, GENETICS. B.S, Okla. State Univ, 43, M.S, 48, Ph.D. (plant breeding), Cornell, 52. Asst. geneticist, ROCKEFELLER FOUND, 51-54, assoc. geneticist, 54-56, geneticist & asst. dir, Indian Agr. Prog, 57-59, acting dir, Colombian Agr. Prog, 59-60, DIR, 60-67, DIR. GEN, CENTRO INTERNACIONAL DE AGRICULTURA TROPICAL, 67- U.S.A, 43-46, Maj. AAAS; Am. Soc. Agron. Plant breeding and genetics of corn. Address: Centro Internacional de Agricultura Tropical, Apartado Aereo 67-13, Apartado Nacional 737, Cali, Valle, Colombia, S.Am.

GRANT, VERNE (EDWIN), b. San Francisco, Calif, Oct. 17, 17; m. 46, 60; c. 3. BOTANY, GENETICS. A.B, California, 40, Ph.D.(bot), 49. Asst. bot, California, 46-49; Nat. Res. Coun. fel, Carnegie Inst, 49-50; asst. prof. bot, Claremont Col, 51-53, assoc. prof, 53-57, prof, 57-67; biol, Inst. Life Sci, Tex. A&M Univ, 67-68; prof. biol. sci. & dir. Boyce Thompson Southwest. Arboretum, Univ. Ariz, Superior, 68-70; PROF. BOT, UNIV. TEX, AUSTIN, 70- Geneticist, Rancho Santa Ana Bot. Garden, 50-67; spec. lectr. Univ. Tex, spring 56. Phi Beta Kappa sci. award, 64. Translator, U.S. War Dept, 43-45. Nat. Acad. Sci; Am. Soc. Nat; Genetics Soc. Am; Soc. Study Evolution (v.pres, 66, pres, 68); Bot. Soc. Am.(certificate of merit, 71); Am. Soc. Plant Taxon; Int. Asn. Plant Taxon. Cytotaxonomy and phylogeny of Polemoniaceae; fertility relationships in annual Gilias; effects of pollinating animals on flower evolution; evolutionary theory; speciation in higher plants; population biology of cholla cacti. Address: Dept. of Botany, University of Texas, Austin, TX 78712.

GRANT, WALTER J, b. Hermon, Maine, July 24, 30; m; c. 2. SOIL SCIENCE. M.S, Maine, 57. Soil scientist, SOIL & WATER CONSERV, AGR. RES. SERV, U.S. DEPT. AGR, EXP. STA, UNIV. MAINE, ORONO, 57-70, COLLAB. AGRON, 70- U.S.A.F, 51-52; Nat. Guard, 47-55. Assoc. Am. Soc. Agron. Soil and water conservation. Address: U.S. Dept. Agriculture Experiment Station, U.S. Dept. of Agriculture, University of Maine at Orono, Orono, ME 04473.

GRANT, W(ALTER) MORTON, b. Lawrence, Mass, July 12, 15; m. 36; c. 3. OPHTHALMOLOGY. S.B, Harvard, 36, M.D, 40. Asst. ophthal. res, HARVARD MED. SCH, 41-42, instr, 42-46, assoc, 46-51, asst. prof, 51-55, assoc. prof, 55-67, PROF. OPHTHAL, 67- Dir. Glaucoma Consult. Serv, Mass. Eye & Ear Infirmary, 60-, Ophthalmic Res. Adminr, 71-; mem. study sect, Nat. Insts. Health, 60-63; chmn. adv. panel, Hazardous Substances Labeling Act, Fed. Drug. Admin, U.S. Dept. Health, Educ. & Welfare, 63-64;

mem. ophthal. panel, drug efficacy study, Nat. Res. Coun, 69. Consult, Medical Letter, 59; Nat. Coun. to Combat Blindness, 59-62; U.S. Pharmacopeia, 60; Nat. Adv. Neurol. Dis. Blindness Coun, 69-; Boston Childrens Med. Ctr, 70- N.E. Ophthal. Soc. Award, 50; Proctor Medal, 56; Knapp Medal, 61; Res. to Prevent Blindness Trustees' Award, 69. Civilian with Off. Sci. Res. & Develop, 42-46. Am. Chem. Soc; Am. Ophthal. Soc.(Howe Medal, 68); Am. Med. Asn. Physiology of aqueous humor; chemical injuries of eyes; toxicology of the eye; investigation and development of new drugs for treatment of glaucoma; development of colorimetric microchemical analytical methods; investigation of factors controlling outflow of aqueous humor from normal and glaucomatous eyes; clinical study of glaucoma. Address: 243 Charles St, Boston, MA 02114.

GRANT, WILLARD H, b. Springfield, Mass, Jan. 19, 23; m. 50; c. 4. GEOLOGY, CHEMISTRY. A.B, Emory Univ, 48, M.S, 49; Ph.D.(geol), Johns Hopkins Univ, 55. From assoc. prof. to PROF. GEOL, EMORY UNIV, 52-Sig.C, 43-46. AAAS; Geochem. Soc; Clay Minerals Soc. Chemistry and mineralogy of the weathering environment; structural petrology. Address: Dept. of Geology, Emory University, Atlanta, GA 30322.

GRANT, WILLIAM C(HASE), JR, b. Baltimore, Md, Aug. 24, 24; m. 47; c. 2. ZOOLOGY. A.B, Dartmouth Col, 49; Cramer fel, Yale, 49-50, Ph.D.(zool), 53. Asst. zool, Yale, 49-53; asst. prof, Gettysburg Col, 53-54; Col. William & Mary, 54-55; Dartmouth Col, 55-56; BIOL, WILLIAMS COL, 56-61, assoc. prof, 62-66, PROF, 66-, CHMN. DEPT, 62- Asst. dir, Nat. Sci. Found-Am. Soc. Zool. summer inst, 58, dir, 63; Nat. Insts. Health spec. fel, Oxford, 65-66; corp. mem, Mt. Desert Island Biol. Lab, secy; mem. bd. dirs, Chase Forests & Sanctuary; mem, consults. bur, Off. Biol. Educ, 68- U.S.A. Fel. AAAS; Ecol. Soc. Am; Am. Soc. Zool. Physiological ecology; endocrinology of lower vertebrates; invertebrate ecology in relation to pesticides. Address: Dept. of Biology, Williams College, Williamstown, MA 01267.

GRANT, W(ILLIAM) F(REDERICK), b. Hamilton, Ont, Oct. 20, 24; m. 49; c. 1. CYTOGENETICS. B.A, McMaster, 47, M.A, 49; Blandy fel, Virginia, 50-53, Ph.D.(biol), 53. Botanist, Colombo Plan, Dept. Agr, Malaya, 53-55; asst. prof. GENETICS, MACDONALD COL, McGILL UNIV, 55-61, assoc. prof, 61-67, PROF, 67- McGill del, Int. Cong. Genetics, Netherlands, 63; del, Int. Bot. Cong, Scotland, 64; vis. prof, Univ. Calif, Los Angeles, summer 64. Fel. AAAS; Am. Genetic Asn; Am. Soc. Plant Taxon; Bot. Soc. Am; Soc. Study Evolution.(v.pres. I, 72); Crop Sci. Soc. Am; Int. Asn. Plant Taxon; Can. Bot. Soc; Genetics Soc. Can.(secy, 69-72, ed, Bull, 69-); Am. Inst. Biol. Sci; Am. Soc. Cell Biol; Can. Soc. Cell Biol; Environ. Mutagen Soc; Int. Orgn. Biosyst; Phytochem. Soc. N.Am. Cytogenetics; chemosystematics; chemical mutagenesis; cytogenetic effects of pesticides; mutations in man by environmental agents. Address: Genetics Lab, Macdonald Campus of McGill University, Montreal, Que, Can.

GRANT, W(ILLIAM) W(ALLACE), b. Perth, Ont, Mar. 5, 16; m. 47; c. 6. MEDICINE, PEDIATRICS. B.A, Alberta, 38; M.D, Manitoba, 44; cert. pediat, Royal Col. Physicians & Surg, Can, 53, psychiat, 57. Teaching fel. pediat, Manitoba, 44-45; asst. physician, Psychopath. Hosp, Winnipeg, 45-47; supt, Children's Hosp, 47-50; res. fel. PEDIAT, Yale, 51-52; demonstr. & spec. lectr, UNIV. MAN, 52-54, asst. prof, 54-57, assoc. prof, 57-67, PROF, 67-, ACTING HEAD DEPT, 70-; DIR. CHILD DEVELOP. CLIN, CHILDREN'S HOSP, 64-, acting physician-in-chief, 70-71. Traveling bursary, Kellogg Found, 47; nat. health training grant, Govt. Can, 50-53; clin. fel, Yale, 50-51; res. fel, Commonwealth Found, 51; grant, Rockefeller Found, 53-55; consult, children's prog, Soc. Crippled Children & Adults, Man. Am. Acad. Pediat; Can. Pediat. Soc; Can. Med. Asn. Behavior development of preschool children; problems of the handicapped child; pediatric teaching. Address: Children's Hospital, 685 Bannatyne, Winnipeg 3, Man, Can.

GRANT, WILSON C(LARK), b. Bradley Beach, N.J, June 27, 15; m. 40; c. 3. PHYSIOLOGY. A.B, Wesleyan, 37, M.A, 38; Cancer Found. fel, Maryland, 40-42, Ph.D.(physiol), 42. Lab. asst, Wesleyan, 37-40; instr. histol, sch. med, Maryland, 41-42; from instr. to asst. prof. physiol, col. physicians & surgeons, Columbia, 46-52; head dept, physiol. res. div, Am. Cyanamid Co, 52-58; res. labs, Vet. Admin. Hosp, 58-63. PROF. PHYSIOL, SCH. MED, UNIV. MIAMI, 58- U.S.N.R, 42-46. Am. Physiol. Soc; Soc. Exp. Biol. & Med; Geront. Soc. Anoxia; erythropoiesis; cholesterol metabolism. Address: Dept. of Physiology, University of Miami School of Medicine, Coral Gables, FL 33134.

GRANTHAM, JARED JAMES, b. Dodge City, Kans, May 19, 36; m. 58; c. 4. MEDICINE, NEPHROLOGY. A.B, Baker, 58; M.D, Kansas, 62. Fel. nephrology, Nat. Heart Inst, 64-66, staff investr, 66-69; ASST. PROF. MED, SCH. MED, UNIV. KANS, 69-, HEAD, NEPHROLOGY SECT, 70- Kaw Valley Heart Asn. grant, 69-70; Nat. Inst. Arthritis & Metab. Diseases grant, 69-73. Am. Soc. Nephrology; Am. Physiol. Soc; Am. Fedn. Clin. Res. Fluid and electrolyte metabolism; nephrology; electrolyte transport; mechanism of action of antidiuretic hormone. Address: School of Medicine, University of Kansas, 39th & Rainbow, Kansas City, KS 66103.

GRANTHAM, LEROY F(RANCIS), b. Chadron, Nebr, Nov. 23, 29; m. 52; c. 6. INORGANIC & PHYSICAL CHEMISTRY. B.S, Chadron State Col, 51; M.S, Iowa State, 54; Dowell fel, Kansas State, 57-58, Ph.D.(chem), 59. Jr. chemist, Ames Lab, Iowa State, 54; chemist, Phosphate Develop. Works, 54-56; sr. chemist, ATOMICS INT, N.AM. AVIATION, INC, 59-63, res. specialist, 63-67, MEM. TECH. STAFF-V, 67- Chem.C, U.S.A, 54-56. Am. Chem. Soc; Sci. Res. Soc. Am. Isotopic and electron exchange; corrosion; fused salts; metal-salt melts; high temperature chemistry; hydrogen permeation; mass spectrometry; pollution control. Address: Dept. 741, Atomics International, P.O. Box 309, Canoga Park, CA 91304.

GRANTHAM, R. JACK, b. Mattoon, Ill, Mar. 15, 21; m. 53; c. 1. ORGANIC CHEMISTRY. B.Ed, Eastern Illinois, 42; Ph.D.(chem), Duke, 51. Chemist, Sinclair Res. Labs, Inc, 42-46; GROUP LEADER, sales develop, Eastman Chem. Prods, Inc, 50-57; res. & develop. div, W.R. Grace & Co, 57-58; COMMERCIAL PROD. DEVELOP, CALLERY CHEM. CO, 58- Am. Chem. Soc. Petroleum additives; antioxidants; plastic stabilizers; polymer sys-

tems; catalysis; textile finishing agents; detergents; paints; electrostatics; paper treating; end use research to find commercial markets for new chemicals; polyurethane foams. Address: Callery Chemical Co, Callery, PA 16024.

GRANTHAM, RODNEY ELLIOTT, b. Richmond, Va, May 20, 21; m. 43; c. 2. PHYSICS, ELECTRICAL ENGINEERING. B.S, Purdue, 42; M.S, George Washington, 51. Electronic scientist, Nat. Bur. Standards, 45-50; U.S. NAVAL ORD. LAB, 50-57, proj. mgr, 57-61, electronic engr, 61-62, phys. sci. adminr, 62-70, CHIEF, AIR & SURFACE EVAL. DEPT, 70- Mem. Seabed summer study, 64. Meritorious civilian serv. awards, 55, 60; cert. commendation, Secy. of Navy, 60. U.S.N.R, 42-45, Lt. Inst. Elec. & Electronics Eng; Am. Phys. Soc; Am. Asn. Physics Teachers. Waveguide-below-cutoff microwave standard attenuators; reflectionless waveguide terminations; electromagnetic Doppler-frequency system for miss distance measurements; telemetering of angular missile system using linearly-polarized electromagnetic waves; laser energy measurements; missile arming and fuzing systems. Address: Air & Surface Evaluation Dept, U.S. Naval Ordnance Lab, White Oak, Silver Spring, MD 20910.

GRANTZ, ARTHUR, b. N.Y.C, Nov. 9, 27; m. 51; c. 4. GEOLOGY. A.B, Cornell Univ, 49; M.S, Stanford Univ, 61, Ph.D.(geol), 66. Asst, Cornell Univ, 49; geologist, Alaska Geol. Br, U.S. GEOL. SURV, 49-66, chief, Br. Pac. Environ. Geol, 66-71, GEOLOGIST, BR. ALASKAN MINERAL RESOURCES & BR. PAC-ARCTIC MARINE GEOL, 71- AAAS; Geol. Soc. Am; Am. Asn. Petrol. Geol; Arctic Inst. N.Am. Structural geology and stratigraphy of Alaska; geologic structure of northern Alaska's continental shelves; active faults. Address: U.S. Geological Survey, 345 Middlefield Rd, Menlo Park, CA 94025.

GRANZOW, KENNETH DONALD, b. Oak Park, Ill, Mar. 26, 33; m. 52; c. 4. PHYSICS, ELECTRICAL ENGINEERING. B.S, Illinois, 58, M.S, 59; New Mexico, 59-63. Staff mem, Sandia Corp, 59-63; res. physicist, DIKEWOOD CORP, 63-66, sr. res. physicist, 66-68, LEADING SCIENTIST, 68- AAAS; Am. Phys. Soc. Electromagnetism; quantum field theory; atmospheric physics; gas discharges. Address: Dikewood Corp, 1009 Bradbury Dr. S.E, Albuquerque, NM 87106.

GRAPPEL, SARAH FAY, b. Brooklyn, N.Y, Jan. 11, 39. MICROBIOLOGY, IMMUNOCHEMISTRY. B.S, Brooklyn Col, 60; Ph.D.(microbiol), Rutgers, 65. Res. asst. cytol, Rockefeller Inst, 60; fel. DERMAT, SCH. MED, TEMPLE UNIV, 65, instr, 66-70, ASST. PROF, 70- AAAS; Am. Soc. Microbiol; Med. Mycol. Soc. Am; Reticuloendothelial Soc. Immunology of pathogenic fungi. Address: Skin & Cancer Hospital, 3322 N. Broad St, Philadelphia, PA 19140.

GRASLEY, MICHAEL H, b. Barberton, Ohio, Jan. 24, 37; m. 63. ORGANIC CHEMISTRY. B.S, Ohio, 58; M.S, Kentucky, 60; Ph.D.(org. chem), Florida, 63. Res. chemist, Shell Develop. Co, Calif, 63-67, SR. TECHNOLOGIST, SHELL CHEM. CO, N.Y, 67-69, CHEM. ECON. DEPT, 69- Am. Chem. Soc. Chemistry of small ring compounds; carbene chemistry; photochemistry. Address: Chemical Economics Dept, Shell Chemical Co, One Shell Plaza, Houston, TX 77001.

GRASS, ALBERT M(ELVIN), b. Quincy, Mass, Sept. 3, 10; m. 36; c. 2. ELECTRONICS. B.S, Mass. Inst. Tech, 34; hon. D.Sc, Drexel Inst, 63. PRES, GRASS INSTRUMENT CO, 35- Res. engr, Harvard Med. Sch, 35-43; staff mem, radiation lab, Mass. Inst. Tech, 41-45. With Off. Sci. Res. & Develop. AAAS; Biophys. Soc; Soc. Photo-Optical Instrument. Eng; Am. Electroencephalog. Soc; Inst. Elec. & Electronics Eng. Electro-medical instruments; radar range circuits; electroencephalograph devices; servomechanisms. Address: Grass Instrument Co, 101 Old Colony Ave, Quincy, MA 02169.

GRASSE, KENNETH M(ARK), b. Fond du Lac, Wis, Apr. 8, 20; m. 47; c. 6. CHEMICAL ENGINEERING. B.S.Ch.E, Ill. Inst. Tech, 42; M.S, Lawrence Col, 48. Res. chemist, Howard Paper Mills, Inc, 52-59, res. dir, 59-68; TECH. SERV. MGR. COMMUNICATIONS & PACKAGING PAPER DIV, ST. REGIS PAPER CO, 68- U.S.A.A.F, 42-45. Pulp and paper technology. Address: 2921 Red Oak Rd, Dayton, OH 45432.

GRASSELLI, JEANETTE G(ECSY), b. Cleveland, Ohio, Aug. 4, 28; m. 57. ORGANIC CHEMISTRY, SPECTROSCOPY. B.S, Ohio, 50; M.S, Western Reserve, 58. Chemist infrared spectros, STANDARD OIL CO, OHIO, 50-56, PROJ. LEADER ABSORPTION SPECTROS. GROUP, 56-, SUPVR. MOLECULAR SPECTROS, 70-, sr. res. chemist, 60-70. Am. Chem. Soc; Soc. Appl. Spectros.(pres, 70); Coblentz Soc. Molecular spectroscopy; infrared; nuclear magnetic resonance. Address: Standard Oil Co, 4440 Warrensville Center Rd, Cleveland, OH 44128.

GRASSELLI, ROBERT KARL, b. Celje, Yugoslavia, June 7, 30; nat; m. 57. PHYSICAL CHEMISTRY. A.B, Harvard, 52; M.S, Western Reserve, 55, Ph.D.(phys. chem), 59. Chemist, STANDARD OIL CO.(OHIO), 52-55, sr. chemist & proj. leader basic res, 55-59, tech. specialist, 60-62, sr. res. chemist, 62-65, res. assoc, 65-69, SR. RES. ASSOC, 69- Am. Chem. Soc; Catalysis Soc. Heterog. catalysis; reaction mechanisms; petrochemicals; membrane diffusion; thermal diffusion. Address: Standard Oil Co.(Ohio), 4440 Warrensville Center Rd, Cleveland, OH 44128.

GRASSETTI, DAVIDE R(ICCARDO), b. Padua, Italy, Aug. 24, 20; U.S. citizen; m. 52; c. 4. BIOCHEMISTRY, PHARMACOLOGY. B.S, Lausanne, 41, Ph.D. (chem), 45, Ch.E, Polytech. Sch, 45. Instr. pharmaceut. chem, Padua, 48-50; res. assoc. org. chem, Mass. Inst. Tech, 50-52; Yale, 52-54; res. chemist, Nopco Chem. Co, 54-56; assoc. res. chemist, sch. med, California, San Francisco, 57-62; proj. dir. cancer chemother, inst. chem. biol, Univ. San Francisco, 62-66; asst. dir. RES, AREQUIPA FOUND, SAN FRANCISCO, 66-67, DIR, 67- Lectr, med. ctr, California, San Francisco, 60-64. Am. Chem. Soc. Vitamin A; antibiotics; antimetabolites; organic fluoro compounds; narcotics; drugs at enzyme level; biological function of sulfhydryl groups; cell surfaces and cancer; prevention and mechanism of metastases. Address: 26 Northgate Ave, Berkeley, CA 94708.

GRASSHOFF, JURGEN MICHAEL, b. Berlin, W.Ger, May 7, 36; U.S. citizen; m. 63; c. 3. POLYMER & ORGANIC CHEMISTRY. M.S, Hannover Tech. Univ, 61; Ph.D.(org. chem), Swiss Fed. Inst. Technol, 65. Head, prod. develop. lab, Steding & Co, W.Ger, 61-62; sci. co-worker, Swiss Fed. Inst. Technol, 65; res. chemist, Pennsalt Chem. Corp, Pa, 65-67; SCIENTIST, POLAROID CORP, CAMBRIDGE, 67- Abstractor, Chem. Abstr. Serv, 68- Am. Chem. Soc. Aromatic diepoxides and diglycols; charge-transfer polymerization of vinylidene cyanide with electron-donating monomers; radical copolymerization of highly fluorinated monomers; swelling of water-soluble polymers; grafting of cellulose derivatives and polyvinyl alcohol. Address: 7 John Robinson Rd, Hudson, MA 01749.

GRASSI, RAYMOND CHARLES, b. Highland Park, Mich, Nov. 27, 18; m. 42. MECHANICAL ENGINEERING. B.S, California, 40, M.S, 44. Inspector, Nordstrom Valve Co, 40-41, tool design engr, 41-42; instr. mech. eng, UNIV. CALIF, BERKELEY, 42-44, 45-46, asst. prof, 46-52, from assoc. prof. to PROF. INDUST. ENG, 52-, OPER. RES, 70- Res. engr, Off. Sci. Res. & Develop. contract, 44, 45-46; Bur. Ships contract, 48-49, ed. supvr, 43-44, 46-; Off. Naval Res. contract, 49-50; Atomic Energy Comn, Oak Ridge, 50-52; Off. Ord. Res, U.S. Army, 54-; engr, Boeing Aircraft Co, Wash, 46. U.S.C.G, 44-45. Am. Soc. Mech. Eng; Am. Soc. Metals; Am. Soc. Eng. Educ. Welding; residual stresses; structure; copper brazing of steel; effect of combined stresses on materials; production processes involving metal working or forming; stress rupture tests of various metals subjected to liquid-metal environment. Address: Dept. of Mechanical Engineering, University of California, Berkeley, CA 94720.

GRASSL, EDWARD F(RANCIS), b. Wis, Jan. 19, 20; m. 46; c. 2. NUTRITION, BIOCHEMISTRY. B.S, Mich. State, 52, M.S, 53, Ph.D.(chem, nutrit), 56. Nutrit. consult, Mich. Dept. Conserv, 52-56; nutritionist & biochemist, mkt. develop, Commercial Solvents Corp, 56-59; dir. prod. support res, Hess & Clark Div, Vick Chem. Co, 59-62; gen. mgr, Pharmacia Fine Chems, Inc, 62-65; ADMIN. ASST. TO DIR. RES, S.B. PENICK & CO, 65- U.S.M.C, 41-46. Animal nutrition; industrial chemical development; dietary requirements of domestic and wild animals applicable to human needs; development of new chromatographic gel filters for water soluble biologicals. Address: S.B. Penick & Co, 215 Watchung Ave, Orange, NJ 07050.

GRASSLE, JOHN FREDERICK, b. Cleveland, Ohio, July 14, 39; m. 64. ECOLOGY. B.S, Yale, 61; Nat. Sci. Found. fel, Duke, 65, Ph.D.(zool), 67. Fulbright-Hays grant, Univ. Queensland, 67-69; ASST. SCIENTIST, WOODS HOLE OCEANOG. INST, 69- Am. Soc. Limnol. & Oceanog; Ecol. Soc. Am. Population biology of marine benthic organisms. Comparative studies of deep sea benthos and coral reef communities. Address: Woods Hole Oceanographic Institution, Woods Hole, MA 02543.

GRASSO, JOSEPH A(NTHONY), b. Cambridge, Mass, Sept. 17, 35; m. 63. ANATOMY, CYTOLOGY. B.S, Tufts, 57; Ph.D.(anat), Ohio State, 61. Instr. ANAT, Ohio State, 59-60, asst. prof, 61; U.S. Pub. Health Serv. fel, Chicago, 61-63; sr. instr, sch. med, Case West. Reserve Univ, 63-64, asst. prof, 64-70; ASSOC. PROF, SCH. MED, BOSTON UNIV, 70- Am. Soc. Cell Biol; Am. Soc. Zool; Soc. Develop. Biol. Morphologic and chemical development of erythrocytes. Address: Dept. of Anatomy, Boston University School of Medicine, Boston, MA 02118.

GRASSY, RICHARD G(EORGE), b. Fond du Lac, Wis, Mar. 26, 11; m. 35; c. 5. GEOLOGICAL ENGINEERING. B.S, Cincinnati, 33, Geol.E, 35. Test boring inspector, U.S. Corps Engrs, 34-36, assoc. geologist groundwater hydrol, 42-43; asst. geologist sedimentation, res. div, Soil Conserv. Serv, 36-42; tech. adv. WEAPON EFFECTS, off. naval intel, Dept. Navy, 46-49; tech. adv, PHYS. VULNERABILITY DIV, Dept. Air Force, 49-62, PHYS. SCI. ADMINR, DEFENSE INTELLIGENCE AGENCY, 62- Mem, U.S. Strategic Bombing Surv, 45-46. Air Force Meritorious Serv. Award, 55, 57. U.S.N, 43-46, Lt, Commendation Medal, 45. AAAS; Am. Geophys. Union; Geochem. Soc; Seismol. Soc. Am. Sedimentary petrology; groundwater hydrology; blast effects on structures; radiation effects. Address: 6001 25th Rd, North Arlington, VA 22207.

GRATCH, SERGE, b. Monte San Pietro, Italy, May 2, 21; nat; m. 51; c. 10. THERMODYNAMICS. B.S, Pennsylvania, 43, M.S, 45, Ph.D.(mech. eng), 50. Asst. instr. mech. eng, Pennsylvania, 43-44, instr, 44-47, assoc, 47-49, asst. prof, 49-51; sr. scientist res, Rohm & Haas Co, 51-59; assoc. prof. mech. eng, tech. inst, Northwestern, 59-61; supvr. appl. sci, FORD MOTOR CO, 61-62, mgr. chem. process & develop, appl. res. off, 62-69, ASST. DIR. ENG. SCI, SCI. RES. STAFF, 69- AAAS; Am. Chem. Soc; Am. Soc. Mech. Eng; Soc. Automotive Eng. Thermodynamic properties of moist air; intermolecular forces in gas mixtures; zero-pressure thermodynamic properties of gases from spectroscopic data; chemical kinetics; polymerization kinetics; viscoelasticity; pollution control. Address: Scientific Research Staff, Ford Motor Co, P.O. Box 2053, Dearborn, MI 48121.

GRATIAN, J(OSEPH) WARREN, b. Hartford, Conn, Sept. 5, 18; m. 43; c. 3. ELECTRICAL ENGINEERING. B.S, Illinois, 41; M.S, Rochester, 63. From jr. engr. to asst. elec. engr, Naval Ord. Lab, D.C, 41-43; from res. asst. to res. assoc. physics, Michigan, 43-45; elec. engr, res. div, Stromberg Carlson Co, 45-50, sr. engr, 50-56, asst. sect. head, electroacoustics lab, res. & develop. dept, Stromberg Carlson Div, Gen. Dynamics Corp, 56-58, sect. head, info. storage sect, appl. physics lab, 58-61, prin. engr, electronics div, 62, eng. staff specialist, 63-71; CONSULT, 71- Acoust. Soc. Am; Audio Eng. Soc; Inst. Elec. & Electronics Eng; Sci. Res. Soc. Am. Analog and digital magnetic recording; electronic circuits; electroacoustics; signal analysis; solid-state devices and digital information storage techniques. Address: 156 Willowbend Rd, Rochester, NY 14618.

GRATKOWSKI, HENRY J(OHN), b. Scranton, Pa, Nov. 19, 19; m. 46; c. 3. PLANT ECOLOGY. B.S, Oregon State, 50, Ph.D, 62; M.F, Yale, 51. RES. FORESTER, PAC. NORTHWEST FOREST & RANGE EXP. STA, U.S. FOREST SERV, 51- U.S.A, 42-46, Capt. Soc. Am. Foresters; Ecol. Soc. Am; Brit. Ecol. Soc. Forest management. Address: 22 Royal Oaks Dr, Roseburg, OR 97470.

GRATTAN, JEROME F(RANCIS), b. Southold, L.I. N.Y, Aug. 25, 12; m. 44; c. 6. BIOCHEMISTRY. B.S, Holy Cross Col, 35, fel, 35-36, M.S, 36; Boston, 36-38. Instr. chem, Holy Cross Col, 35-36; res. chemist, Boston Dispensary, 36-38; asst. biochem, Squibb Inst. Med. Res, 38-41; res. chemist, Int. Vitamin Corp, 41-43; res. biochemist, CARROLL DUNHAM SMITH PHARMACAL CO, 46-50, dir. RES, 51-58, V.PRES, 58-; ADMINR. INSTRUMENT DIV, SMITH, MILLER & PATCH, INC, 70-, dir. res, 60-63, v.pres, 63-70. U.S.N, 43-46, Lt. AAAS; Am. Chem. Soc; Pharmaceut. Mfrs. Asn; N.Y. Acad. Sci; fel. Am. Inst. Chem; Soc. Toxicol. Polythionates; depressants; relaxants; vitamins; hormones. Address: 12 Kerschner Lane, East Brunswick, NJ 08816.

GRATTIDGE, WALTER, b. Manchester, England, May 28, 24; nat; m. 49; c. 2. PHYSICS, PHYSICAL ELECTRONICS. B.Sc, Manchester, England, 44, Ph.D.(physics), 49. Res. assoc. physics, Missouri, 49-51; mem. staff, res. lab. electronics, Mass. Inst. Tech, 51-53; res. assoc. electron physics, res. lab, GEN. ELEC. CO, 53-56; liaison scientist, 56-59, specialist sci. rels, 59-66, specialist TECH. INFO, 66-68, MGR, 68- Trustee, Eng. Index, 71- Am. Soc. Info. Sci; Am. Phys. Soc; Brit. Inst. Physics & Phys. Soc. Electron emission; surface physics; new methods of electrical power generation; research administration; information systems; information search & retrieval; selective dissemination; libraries and information centers; technical communication and documentation. Address: Corporate Research & Development, General Electric Co, P.O. Box 8, Schenectady, NY 12301.

GRATZ, NORMAN G, b. Minneapolis, Minn, May 16, 25; m. 58; c. 1. MEDICAL ENTOMOLOGY. B.Sc, California, Berkeley, 48, M.Sc, 50; Charles Brown fel, Hebrew Univ, Israel, 50-52; WHO fel, 54; D.Sc.(zool), Geneva, 66. Dir. vector control, Ministry of Health, Israel, 53-58; proj. leader res. unit, WHO, Liberia, 58-61, Nigeria, 61-62, SCIENTIST/ENTOMOLOGIST, VECTOR BIOL. & CONTROL UNIT, SWITZ, 62- Guest lectr, Hebrew Univ, Israel, 55-58, vis. prof, dept. med. ecol, med. sch, 70. U.S.N, 43-45. Am. Mosquito Control Asn. The biology and control of arthropod vectors and rodent reservoirs of human disease. Address: Vector Biology & Control Unit, World Health Organization, Geneva, Switz.

GRATZEK, JOHN B, b. St. Paul, Minn, Jan. 23, 31; m. 57; c. 4. VIROLOGY. B.S, St. Mary's Col.(Minn), 52; D.V.M, Minnesota, 56; M.S, Wisconsin, 59, Ph.D.(virol), 61. Instr. vet. sci, Wisconsin, 56-61; assoc. prof. virol, Iowa State, 61-66; PROF. MICROBIOL. & PREV. MED. & HEAD DEPT, UNIV. GA, 66- Am. Vet. Med. Asn. Bovine virus diarrhea; infectious bovine rhinotracheitis; infectious enteritis of turkeys; fish diseases. Address: Dept. of Microbiology, University of Georgia College of Veterinary Medicine, Athens, GA 30601.

GRÄTZER, GEORGE (ANDREW), b. Budapest, Hungary, Aug. 2, 36; m. 61; c. 1. MATHEMATICS. Ph.D.(algebra), Eötvös Lóránd, Budapest, 60. Res. algebra, math. inst, Hungarian Acad. Sci, 59-63; vis. asst. prof. MATH, Pa. State, 63-64, assoc. prof, 64-66, PROF, 66-67; UNIV. MAN, 67-, vis. prof, 66-67. Can. Res. Coun. Can. fels, 61, grant, 67-; Nat. Sci. Found. grant, 65-67; ed-in-chief, Algebra Universalis; mem. math. grant comt, Nat. Res. Coun. Am. Math. Soc; Can. Math. Cnog. Lattice theory; universal algebra; applications of logic to lattices and algebras. Address: Dept. of Mathematics, University of Manitoba, Winnipeg 19, Man, Can.

GRATZER, LOUIS B(ERNARD), b. Tacoma, Wash, Nov. 15, 20; m. 46; c. 2. AERONAUTICAL ENGINEERING. B.S, Univ. Wash, 44, M.S, 51, Ph.D. (aeronaut, astronaut), 68. Res. assoc. & instr. aeronaut. eng, Univ. Wash, 44-53; aeronaut. engr. aerodyn, AIRPLANE DIV, BOEING CO, 53-58, group engr, 58-63, res. unit chief, 63-69, CHIEF ENGR. AERODYN. TECHNOL, 69- Am. Inst. Aeronaut. & Astronaut. Aerodynamic and fluid dynamic research and application to design and development of subsonic and supersonic civil transport and military aircraft. Address: 8026 S. 113th St, Seattle, WA 98178.

GRATZNER, HOWARD G, b. Phila, Pa, July 21, 34; m. 60. GENETICS. B.S, Pa. State, 56; A.M, Temple, 60; Ph.D.(genetics), Fla. State, 64. Res. asst. biochem, Albert Einstein Med. Center, 56-58; asst. prof. zool, South Florida, 64-67; Nat. Insts. Health spec. res. fel, Calif. Inst. Technol, 67-68; asst. prof. zool, Univ. Miami, 68-71; RES. SCIENTIST, PAPANICOLAOU CANCER RES. INST, 71- U.S.A.F.R, 57-63. AAAS; Genetics Soc. Am. Genetic control of protein synthesis; biochemical basis of morphogenesis; biological clock mechanisms. Address: Papanicolaou Cancer Research Institute, 1155 N.W. 14th St, Miami, FL 33136.

GRAU, ALBERT A, b. Zurich, Switz, Oct. 25, 18; U.S. citizen; m. 65; c. 1. MATHEMATICS, COMPUTER SCIENCE. B.S, Michigan, 40, M.S, 41, fel, 42-44, Ph.D.(math), 44. Instr. math, Michigan, 44, Rackham fel, Inst. Adv. Study, 44-45; instr. math, Drake, 45-46; asst. prof, Kentucky, 46-47, assoc. prof, Alabama, 47-48; Oklahoma, 48-56, prof, 56-57; sr. mathematician, Oak Ridge Nat. Lab, 56-63; PROF. MATH. & ENG. SCI, NORTHWEST. UNIV, 63-, COMPUT. SCI, 70- Lectr, George Wash. Univ, 47; Univ. Tenn, 57-60; consult, Oak Ridge Nat. Lab, 63-66; Argonne Nat. Lab, 67- Am. Math. Soc; Math. Asn. Am; Soc. Indust. & Appl. Math; Asn. Comput. Mach. Boolean algebra; numerical analysis; programming languages and compilers. Address: Dept. of Engineering Science, Technical Institute, Northwestern University, Evanston, IL 60201.

GRAU, C(HARLES) R(ICHARD), b. National City, Calif, Nov. 5, 20; m. 41; c. 4. POULTRY NUTRITION. B.S, California, 42, Ph.D.(animal nutrit), 46. Instr. AVIAN SCI, UNIV. CALIF, DAVIS, 46-48, asst. prof, 48-53, assoc. prof, 53-58, PROF, 58-, CHMN. DEPT, 69-, NUTRITIONIST, EXP. STA, 58- Soc. Develop. Biol; Teratol. Soc; Am. Soc. Cell Biol; Soc. Exp. Biol. & Med; Poultry Sci. Asn; Tissue Culture Asn; Am. Inst. Nutrit. Amino acid requirements and metabolism in the chick; protein concentrates as amino acid sources; amino acid requirements of laying hens; metabolism of phenylalanine and tyrosine in the chick and mouse; metabolism of gossypol in laying hens; energy needs and food intake; nutrition of chick embryos. Address: Dept. of Avian Sciences, University of California, Davis, CA 95616.

GRAUB, MILTON, b. Phila, Pa, Dec. 27, 19; m. 47; c. 1. PEDIATRICS. A.B, Temple, 40; M.D, Hahnemann Med. Col, 44. Res. PEDIAT, Phila Gen. Hosp, Pa, 48-50; asst. prof. HAHNEMANN MED. COL, 52-69, ASSOC. PROF, 69- Asst. chief pediat, Phila. Gen. Hosp, 50- Trustee, Nat. Cystic Fibrosis Res. Found, 55-, pres, 64-65. Mem. Nat. Health Coun, 65. Med.C, 46-48, Capt. Am. Acad. Pediat. Etiology, course and therapy of cystic fibrosis of the pancreas. Address: 5063 Woodbine Ave, Philadelphia, PA 19131.

GRAUBARD, MARK A(ARON), b. Plock, Poland, Jan. 5, 04; nat; m; c. 2. PHYSIOLOGY. B.S, City Col, 26; M.A, Columbia, 27, Ph.D.(genetics, zool), 30. Asst. zool, Columbia, 28-31; Nat. Res. Council fel, Manchester, England & London, 31-33; asst. genetics, Columbia, 33-34, res. assoc. biol. chem, 34-38; physiol, Clark, 38-41; nutrit. ed, food distribution admin, U.S. Dept. Agr, 42-46; asst. prof. NATURAL SCI, Chicago, 46-47; assoc. prof, UNIV. MINN, MINNEAPOLIS, 47-58, PROF. & CHMN. NAT. SCI. PROG, 59- AAAS; Am. Physiol. Soc; Genetics Soc. Am; Am. Soc. Zool; Hist. Sci. Soc; N.Y. Acad. Sci. Chemistry and physiology of the pigment reaction; oxidases and hormone metabolism; history of science. Address: Dept. of Natural Science, University of Minnesota, Minneapolis, MN 55455.

GRAUE, DENNIS JEROME, b. Minot, N.Dak, Sept. 12, 39; m. 59; c. 2. CHEMICAL ENGINEERING. B.S, Colorado, 61; Nat. Sci. Found. fel, Calif. Inst. Tech, 61-65, M.S, 62, Ph.D.(chem. eng), 65. Res. engr, Chevron Oil Field Res. Co, 65-69; ENGR, CHEVRON STANDARD LTD, ALTA, CAN, 69- Summers, res. engr, E.I. du Pont de Nemours & Co, 60, engr, 61, res. engr, Chevron Oil Field Res. Co, 62 & Calif. Inst. Tech. res. grant, 65. Am. Inst. Chem. Eng; Soc. Petrol. Eng. Fluid flow through porous media; oil reservoir behavior; diffusion; transport phenomena. Address: 316 Queens Court, Edmonton 73, Alta, Can.

GRAUE, LOUIS C(HARLES), b. Louisiana, Mo, Dec. 23, 23; m. 49; c. 2. MATHEMATICS. B.S, Chicago, 47, M.S, 48; Ph.D.(math), Indiana, 50. Asst. prof. MATH, Sacramento State Col, 50-56; assoc. prof, Coe Col, 56-59; from assoc. prof. to PROF, BOWLING GREEN STATE UNIV, 59-, CHMN. DEPT, 65- U.S.N.R, 45-46. Math. Asn. Am. Mathematics, algebra and differential geometry. Address: Dept. of Mathematics, Bowling Green State University, Bowling Green, OH 43402.

GRAUER, AMELIE L, b. Vienna, Austria, May 7, 99; U.S. citizen; m. 44. BIOCHEMISTRY. Ph.D.(chem), Vienna, 23. RES. CHEMIST, Polytech. Inst. Brooklyn, 50-52; N.Y. Med. Col, 52-57; Albert Einstein Col. Med, 57; ophthal, Col. Physicians & Surgeons, Columbia Univ, 58-66; res. chemist, dept. path, N.Y. Univ, 66-70; CONSULT. BIOCHEMIST, 70- Am. Chem. Soc. Enzymes; steroids; general chemistry and organic preparation; abstracts, bibliographies, technical translations and literature reaserch. Address: 720 West End Ave, Apt. 628, New York, NY 10025.

GRAUER, ROBERT C(OLEMAN), b. Pittsburgh, Pa, Aug. 3, 02; m. 46; c. 1. PATHOLOGY, ENDOCRINOLOGY. B.S, Pittsburgh, 25, M.D, 27. Intern, Mercy Hosp, 27-28; resident-in-path, Allegheny Gen. Hosp, 28-29; pathologist, SINGER RES. INST, 29-37, HEAD DEPT. RES. ENDOCRINOL. & METAB, 37-, DIR. INST, 49-, dir. res, 48-49. Instr, Pittsburgh, 30-35, 46-48, lectr, 35-53, asst. prof, 48-59; adj. prof, Pa. State, 65- Assoc, Allegheny Gen. Hosp, 37-49, attend. physician, 49-; endocrinologist, Pittsburgh Diag. Clin, 45-64; Elizabeth Steele Magee Hosp, 46-63; consult, Montefiore & Butler Mem. Hosps. Mem, Laurentian Hormone Conf, 45. AAAS; Endocrine Soc; Am. Soc. Exp. Path; Soc. Exp. Biol. & Med; Am. Med. Asn; Am. Asn. Path. & Bact; Am. Asn. Cancer Res; Am. Soc. Clin. Path; Am. Diabetes Asn; Am. Thyroid Asn; fel. Am. Col. Physicians; fel. Col. Am. Path. Experimental breast tumors; effect of steroids on breast cancer; vitamin D; fungus infections; bone dystrophies; sex hormone proportions; thyroid gland; blood iodine. Address: Singer Research Institute, North Ave, Pittsburgh, PA 15212.

GRAUMAN, JOSEPH URI, b. Hadera, Israel, Oct. 1, 41; U.S. citizen; m. 69. HIGH ENERGY PHYSICS. B.S, Stevens Inst. Technol, 63, M.S, 65, Ph.D. (physics), 69. Vis. asst. prof. PHYSICS, Stevens Inst. Technol, 69-70; ASST. PROF, JERSEY CITY STATE COL, 70- Res. assoc, Stevens Inst. Technol, 70- AAAS; Am. Phys. Soc; Am. Asn. Physics Teachers. High energy particle physics; instructional uses of the computer in physics. Address: Castle Point Station, Box S-1898, Hoboken, NJ 07030.

GRAUMANN, HUGO O(SWALT), b. Granite, Okla, May 31, 13; m. 35; c. 1. AGRONOMY. B.Sc, Okla. Agr. & Mech. Col, 38, M.Sc, 40; Ph.D.(agron), Nebraska, 50. Asst. agron, Okla. Agr. & Mech. Col, 38-40, instr, 40-41, asst. prof. & asst. agronomist, 41-46, assoc. prof, 46-47; agronomist, U.S. DEPT. AGR, 47-53, res. agronomist, forage & range res. br, AGR. RES. SERV, 53-58, chief, 58-64, assoc. dir, crops res. div, 64-70, DIR. PLANT SCI. RES. DIV, 70- Agronomist, Univ. Nebr, 47-53. AAAS; Am. Soc. Agron; Am. Genetic Asn; Crops Sci. Soc. Am. Forage crops; administration. Address: Plant Science Research Division, Agricultural Research Service, U.S. Dept. of Agriculture, Beltsville, MD 20705.

GRAUPE, DANIEL, b. Jerusalem, Israel, July 31, 34; m. 68; c. 1. CONTROL & SYSTEMS ENGINEERING. B.S.M.E, Israel Inst. Technol, 58, B.S.E.E, 59, Dipl. Ing, 60, Anna Frank Prize, 60-61; Ph.D.(elec. eng), Univ. Liverpool, 63. Engr. automatic control, Israel Govt. Industs, Tel Aviv, 59-60; lectr. elec. eng, Univ. Liverpool, 63-67; sr. lectr. mech. engr, Israel Inst. Technol, 67-70; ASSOC. PROF. ELEC. ENG, COLO. STATE UNIV, 70- Israeli Air Force, 52-55, Sgt. Assoc. fel. Brit. Inst. Math. & Appln; Brit. Inst. Elec. Eng. Problems of automatic control, specifically adaptive control and artificial intelligence problems; methods of identification and estimation of processes and signals; applications of same to industrial and medical systems. Address: Dept. of Electrical Engineering, Colorado State University, Ft. Collins, CO 80521.

GRAVA, JANIS (JOHN), b. Vecgulbene, Latvia, Jan. 24, 20; U.S. citizen; m. 42; c. 2. SOIL SCIENCE. M.S, Univ. Göttingen, 48, Ph.D.(agron), 50. Res. asst, SOIL SCI, Kansas State, 52-53, instr, 53-54; res. fel, UNIV. MINN, ST. PAUL, 54-57, asst. prof, 57-65, ASSOC. PROF, 65- Mem, Regional Soil Test Cmt, 55-, chmn, 58. Am. Soc. Agron; Soil Sci. Soc. Am; Int. Soc. Soil Sci. Crop production; soil fertility, chemical analyses and testing; grass seed production. Address: Dept. of Soil Science, University of Minnesota, St. Paul, MN 55101.

GRAVATT, CLAUDE C(ARRINGTON), JR, b. Washington, D.C, Dec. 12, 39; m. 64; c. 2. CHEMICAL PHYSICS. B.S, Richmond, 62; Nat. Sci. Found. fel, Duke, 64-65, Ph.D.(phys. chem), 66. Res. grant chem. physics, Cornell, 65-67; mem. tech. staff, Bell Tel. Labs, N.J, 67-69; RES. CHEM. PHYSICIST, NAT. BUR. STANDARDS, 69- Am. Phys. Soc; Am. Chem. Soc. Electromagnetic scattering investigations of critical phenomena, liquid crystals, liquids and solutions; electrical conductivity of solid state organic materials; air pollution analysis by light scattering. Address: Polymers Bldg, B-220, National Bureau of Standards, Washington, DC 20234.

GRAVE, THOMAS B(ROOKS), b. Richmond, Ind, Aug. 29, 98; m. 29; c. 3. CHEMISTRY. A.B, Hopkins, 19, Ph.D.(chem), 23. Hynson, Westcott & Dunning fel, Hopkins, 23-24, asst. med, 25-26; assoc. chemist, med. res. div, Edgewood Arsenal, Md, 26-27; asst. chem. pharmacol, Rockefeller Inst, 28-29; res. chemist, E.R. Squibb & Sons, N.Y, 31-34; consult, 35-41; assoc. chemist, Chem. Warfare Serv, 42-43; res. chemist, Evans Res. & Develop. Corp, 43-52; owner & dir, Brooks Labs, 53-70; RETIRED. C.W.S, U.S.A, 18; civilian with Office Sci. Res. & Develop; U.S.N, 47-51. Am. Chem. Soc. Medicinal and structural chemistry; catalytic hydrogenation; explosives; flame-proofing. Address: 594 Forest Ave, Rye, NY 10580.

GRAVEL, DENIS F(ERNAND), b. St. Lambert, Que, Nov. 24, 35. ORGANIC CHEMISTRY. B.Sc, Montreal, 58, Nat. Res. Coun. Can. fels, 59-62, M.S, 59, Ph.D.(org. chem), 62. Nat. Res. Coun. Can. fel. ORG. CHEM, Swiss Fed. Inst. Tech, 62-64; asst. prof, UNIV. MONTREAL, 64-67, ASSOC. PROF, 67- Chem. Inst. Can; Brit. Chem. Soc. Mechanism of ring enlargement reaction by nitrous acid deamination; organic photochemistry. Address: Dept. of Chemistry, University of Montreal, P.O. Box 6128, Montreal, Que, Can.

GRAVELL, MANETH, b. Tamagua, Pa, Aug. 15, 32; m. 63; c. 3. VIROLOGY. B.S, Muhlenberg Col, 59; M.S, Lehigh, 65, Ph.D.(biol), 66. Res. assoc. virus & tissue cult, Merck Inst. Ther. Res, 59-61; spec. technologist, St. Jude Children's Res. Hosp, 65-66; instr. microbiol, Hahnemann Med. Col, 66-67; res. assoc. VIROL, ST. JUDE CHILDREN'S RES. HOSP, 67-68, ASST. MEM, 68- From instr. to asst. prof, col. med, Tennessee, 67- U.S.A, 54-57. AAAS; Am. Soc. Microbiol. Cell and virus interactions. Address: St. Jude Children's Research Hospital, 332 N. Lauderdale, Memphis, TN 38101.

GRAVELLE, CLIFTON (ROY), b. Joplin, Mo, July 29, 27; m. 49; c. 3. VIROLOGY, MICROBIOLOGY. B.S, Oklahoma, 52, M.S, 56; M.P.H, Michigan, 63. VIROLOGIST, COMMUNICABLE DISEASE CTR, U.S. PUB. HEALTH SERV, 57- U.S.N.R, 47-49; U.S.A, 52-54; U.S.P.H.S, 57-, Capt. Am. Soc. Microbiol. Etiological studies of enteric and oncogenic virus diseases in humans. Address: U.S. Public Health Service, 2002 W. 39th St, Kansas City, KS 66103.

GRAVEN, STANLEY N, b. Greene, Iowa, May 20, 32; m. 54; c. 4. PEDIATRICS, BIOCHEMISTRY. B.S, Wartburg Col, 55; M.D, Iowa, 56; Wisconsin, 64-65. Intern med, Madigan Army Hosp, Tacoma, Wash, 56-57; res. pediat, Cincinnati Children's Hosp, Ohio, 57-58; Univ. Iowa Hosps, 58-60; chief pediat. serv, U.S. Air Force Hosp, Fairchild Air Force Base, Wash, 60-62, dir. newborn & premature serv, Wilford Hall, Lackland Air Force Base, Tex, 62-64; U.S. Pub. Health Serv. Fel. biochem. & pediat, UNIV. WIS, 64-66, asst. prof. PEDIAT, 66-70, ASSOC. PROF, 70-; DIR, WIS. NEONATAL CTR, 66- Consult, Lakeland Village, Wash, 60-62. Dipl, Am. Bd. Pediat, 61. U.S.A.F, 56-64, Capt. Am. Acad. Pediat. Neonatology; newborn and premature physiology and biochemistry. Address: 5813 Driftwood Ave, Madison, WI 53705.

GRAVEN, WENDELL M(AURICE), b. Holloway, Minnesota, Oct. 14, 26. PHYSICAL CHEMISTRY. B.S, Hamline, 48; Ph.D.(chem), California, 52. Asst, California, 48-51, assoc. chem, 51-52; res. assoc, Princeton, 52-54; asst. prof. chem, Oregon, 54-60; res. scientist, aeronutronic div, Philco Corp, 60-65; MEM. TECH. STAFF, AEROSPACE CORP, 65- Am. Chem. Soc. Chemical kinetics; complex ion equilibria; photochemistry; electrochemistry; catalysis; organometallics; pulsed radiation dosimetry. Address: Materials Sciences Lab, Aerospace Corp, El Segundo, CA 90245.

GRAVENOR, C(ONRAD) P(ERCIVAL), b. Renfrew, Ont, Dec. 19, 23; m. 48. GEOLOGY. B.A, Toronto, 49; M.S, Wisconsin, 50; Ph.D.(geol), Indiana, 52. Lectr. geol, Alberta, 52-54, asst. prof, 54-56; chief geologist, Res. Coun. Alta, 56-63, asst. dir. res, 63-65; dir. res, Peace River Mining & Smelting Ltd, 65-67, gen. mgr, Ont, 67-70; V.DEAN DIV. SCI. & MATH, UNIV. WINDSOR, 70- Can. Army, 43-46. Glacial geology; mineralogical investigations of soils. Address: Division of Science & Mathematics, University of Windsor, Windsor, Ont, Can.

GRAVENSTEIN, JOACHIM STEFAN, b. Berlin, Ger, Jan. 25, 25; nat; m. 49; c. 8. MEDICINE, ANESTHESIOLOGY. Dr. med, Univ. Bonn, 51; fel, Harvard, 52-55, M.D, 58. Intern, Surg. Univ. Hosp, Switz, 51; clin. fel. anesthesia, Mass. Gen. Hosp, 52-54; res. assoc, Harvard, 55-56; fel, Mass. Gen. Hosp, 54-58, assoc. anesthetist, 58; prof. surg. & chief anesthesia, col. med, Univ. Fla, 58-65, PROF. ANESTHESIOL. & CHMN. DEPT, 65-69; SCH. MED, CASE WEST. RESERVE UNIV, 69- Dipl, Am. Bd. Anesthesiol. Am. Soc. Anesthesiol; Am. Soc. Pharmacol. & Exp. Therapeut. Anesthetics and cardiovascular pharmacology. Address: University Hospitals, 2065 Adelbert Rd, Cleveland, OH 44106.

GRAVER, JACK EDWARD, b. Cincinnati, Ohio, Apr. 13, 35; m. 61; c. 3. MATHEMATICS. B.A, Miami Univ, 58; M.A, Ind. Univ, 61, Ph.D.(math), 64. Lectr. MATH, Ind. Univ, 64; res. instr, Dartmouth Col, 64-66; asst. prof, SYRACUSE UNIV, 66-70, ASSOC. PROF, 70- AAAS; Am. Math Soc; Math. Asn. Am; Soc. Indust. & Appl. Math. Topology; combinatorics; graph theory; systems of subsets of a finite set. Address: Dept. of Mathematics, Syracuse University, Syracuse, NY 13210.

GRAVER, RICHARD BYRD, b. Cambridge City, Ind, Apr. 5, 32; m. 52; c. 5. CHEMICAL ENGINEERING, POLYMER CHEMISTRY. B.S.Ch.E, Purdue Univ, 54; M.S.E, Univ. Mich, 55, Ph.D.(chem. eng), 58. Res. chemist resins, Archer Daniels Midland Co, 57-59, proj. leader, 59-61, group leader, 61-67; MGR. POLYMER RES, CELANESE COATINGS CO, 67- Am. Chem. Soc; Am. Oil Chem. Soc; Tech. Asn. Pulp & Paper Indust; Am. Asn. Textile Chem. & Colorists. Polymers for coatings. Address: 108 Dorsey Lane, Louisville, KY 40223.

GRAVES, ARTIS P, b. Hiawatha, W.Va, Sept. 23, 07; m. 40; c. 3. ZOOLOGY, EMBRYOLOGY. B.S, Bluefield State Col, 31; M.S, Iowa, 38, Ph.D.(zool), 43. Instr. BIOL, Morristown Col, 31-35; Shorter Col, 35-36, Morris Brown Col, 36-41, PROF. & CHMN. DEPT, 42-50; A&T STATE UNIV. N.C, 50- Nat. Sci. Found. sci. faculty fel, 59-60. Summers, Dir. Sci. Work Shop, 44, prof, Texas Southern, 50, assoc. dir, Nat. Sci. Found. Insts. for high sch. sci. teachers, 59-63 & dir, inst. for high sch. biol. teachers, 62-65. AAAS; Nat. Inst. Sci.(pres, 50-51); Nat. Asn. Biol. Teachers; Am. Soc. Zool; Soc. Exp. Biol. & Med. Early embryology of the golden hamster; Cricetus auratus waterhouse; parabiotic studies on certain anurians and urodelians of the southeastern region of the United States. Address: Dept. of Biology, A&T State University of North Carolina, Greensboro, NC 27411.

GRAVES, BRUCE BANNISTER, b. Lafayette, Ind, Dec. 7, 28; m. 53; c. 3. PHYSICAL CHEMISTRY, ELECTROCHEMISTRY. B.A, Swarthmore Col, 51; M.S, Louisville, 64, Ph.D.(chem), 67. Sci. glassworker, Purdue, 52-59; chemist, Radiochem, Inc, Ky, 60-62, chief chemist, 62-65, lab. mgr, 64-65; chemist, Corhart Refractories Co, Corning Glass Works, summer, 66; asst. prof. CHEM, Ky. South. Col, 66-67, assoc. prof. & acting head dept, 67-68; asst. prof, EAST. MICH. UNIV, 68-69, ASSOC. PROF, 69- Prin. investr, Nat. Sci. Found. grant, 69-73. AAAS; Electrochem. Soc; Am. Chem. Soc. Differential thermal analysis; differential scanning calorimetry; catalysis and transient processes in electrochemistry; glass surface chemistry; history of glassworking and science; carbon 14 and tritium dating; isotope substitutuions in spectrophotometry; photosensitivity; thermodynamics. Address: 1209 Roosevelt Blvd, Ypsilanti, MI 48197.

GRAVES, CHARLES C(ARLETON), b. New Haven, Conn, Nov. 28, 22; m. 49; c. 5. MECHANICAL ENGINEERING. B.E, Yale, 43, M.E, 47, D.Eng, 52. Aeronaut. res. scientist, Nat. Adv. Comt. Aeronaut, 48-53, asst. mgr. turbojet combustion sect, 53-56; proj. leader & leader reactor anal. group, Nuclear Develop. Corp. Am, 56-58, mgr. reactor anal. sect, 58-60; consult. engr, United Nuclear Corp, 60-65; PROF. NUCLEAR SCI. & ENG, CATH. UNIV. AM, 65- Lectr, City Col. New York, 60; adj. assoc. prof, grad. sch, Columbia, 60- U.S.A, 43-44; U.S.N, 44-46, Ens. Am. Nuclear Soc; Combustion Inst. Nuclear engineering; reactor physics; heat transfer; combustion. Address: Dept. of Nuclear Science & Engineering, Catholic University of America, Washington, DC 20017.

GRAVES, CHARLES NORMAN, b. Fitchburg, Mass, Feb. 6, 30; m. 63; c. 4. PHYSIOLOGY, BIOCHEMISTRY. B.S, Okla. State, 58; M.S, Illinois, Urbana, 59, Ph.D.(dairy sci), 62. Res. assoc. DAIRY SCI, UNIV. ILL, URBANA, 61-64, asst. prof, 64-68, ASSOC. PROF, 68- Res. fel, Johns Hopkins Univ, 68-69. U.S.A, 53-55, Sgt. AAAS; Am. Dairy Sci. Asn; Am. Soc. Animal Sci; Brit. Soc. Study Fertil. Metabolic pathways present in spermatozoa in the presence of various substrates and under different gaseous regimes; nucleic acid turnover in spermatozoa during in vitro storage; early embryonic development. Address: Dept. of Dairy Science, University of Illinois, Urbana, IL 61803.

GRAVES, CLAYBORN L(OWELL), b. Asbury, Mo, July 7, 15. MATHEMATICAL STATISTICS. B.S, Kans. State Col, 36; M.S, Southern California, 40, 40-51. Teacher, pub. schs, Calif, 36-42; voc. counselor, Veterans Admin, Los Angeles, 46-51; statistician, U.S. Air Force Materiel Command, 51-52; Los Angeles Ord. Dist, Pasadena, 52-54; MATH. STATISTICIAN, U.S. NAVAL FLEET MISSILE SYSTS. ANAL. & EVAL. GROUP ANNEX, NAVAL WEAPONS STA-SEAL BEACH, CORONA, 54- Teacher, exten. serv, California, Los Angeles, 54- Sig.C, U.S.A, 42-46. Sr. mem. Am. Soc. Qual. Control; Am. Statist. Asn. Statistical analysis of data relative to measurement reliability; quality control and reliability of missile components and systems. Address: 4800 Crescent Dr, Anaheim, CA 92806.

GRAVES, CLINTON H(ANNIBAL), JR, b. Ackerman, Miss, July 22, 27; m. 64. PLANT PATHOLOGY. B.S, Miss. State, 50; Ph.D.(phytopath), Wisconsin, 54. Asst. plant pathologist, Miss. Agr. Exp. Sta, 53-60, assoc. plant pathologist, 60-66; PROF. PLANT PATH, MISS. STATE UNIV, 66- Gen. Ed. Bd. scholar. U.S.N.R, 45-46. Am. Phytopath. Soc. Virology and diseases of fruit crops. Address: Drawer PG, Mississippi State University, State College, MS 39762.

GRAVES, DAVID J(AMES), b. Niagara Falls, N.Y, Feb. 25, 41; m. 66; c. 1. CHEMICAL & BIOMEDICAL ENGINEERING. B.S, Carnegie-Mellon Univ, 63; M.S, Mass. Inst. Technol, 65, U.S. Pub. Health Serv. trainee, 65-67, D.Sc.(chem. eng), 67. Develop. engr, Procter & Gamble Co, summer 63; res. engr, Mass. Inst. Technol, summer 64; ASST. PROF. CHEM. ENG, UNIV. PA, 69- Nat. Sci. Found. grant enzyme eng, Univ. Pa, 71- Med. Serv.C, U.S.A, 67-69, Capt. AAAS; Am. Chem. Soc; Am. Inst. Chem. Eng. Applied chemistry, particularly polymer, surface and enzyme chemistry; biomedical applications of chemical engineering. Address: School of Chemical Engineering, 311-A Towne Bldg, University of Pennsylvania, Philadelphia, PA 19104.

GRAVES, DONALD J, b. Evanston, Ill, Oct. 15, 33; m. 58; c. 5. BIOCHEMISTRY. B.S, Illinois, 55; Nat. Insts. Health fel, Washington (Seattle), 57-59, Ph.D.(biochem), 59. Nat. Insts. Health fel. enzym, Minnesota, 59-61; asst. prof. BIOCHEM, IOWA STATE UNIV, 61-65, assoc. prof, 65-68, PROF, 68- Nat. Insts. Health career develop. award, 65-69, 70- Am. Soc. Biol. Chem; Am. Chem. Soc. Mechanism of enzyme action; protein chemistry. Address: Dept. of Biochemistry & Biophysics, Iowa State University, Ames, IA 50010.

GRAVES, EDWIN E(UGENE), b. Struthers, Ohio, Dec. 26, 16; m. 41; c. 3. PHYSICAL SCIENCES. B.Sc, Ohio State, 39. Teacher, pub. sch, Ohio, 39-41; engr. physics, BATTELLE MEM. INST, 41-47, rep. patent licensing, Battelle Develop. Corp, 47-50, asst. chief. graphic arts res. div, 50-58, eng. physics dept, 58-62, sr. res. asst, dept. econ. & info. res, 63-66, exec. asst. to dir, COLUMBUS LABS, 66-70, ADMIN. MGR, SPONSOR & PROG. DEVELOP, 70- AAAS. Research administration and planning; business management; coordination of interdisciplinary research. Address: Columbus Labs, Battelle Memorial Institute, 505 King Ave, Columbus, OH 43201.

GRAVES, ELIZABETH R(IDDLE), b. Nashville, Tenn, Jan. 23, 16; m. 37; c. 3. PHYSICS. B.S, Chicago, 36, fel, 38-40, Ph.D.(physics), 40. Mem. staff, metall. lab, Chicago, 42-43; LOS ALAMOS SCI. LAB, UNIV. CALIF, 43-, GROUP LEADER, 50- Civilian with Office Sci. Res. & Develop, 44. Fel. Am. Phys. Soc. Nuclear physics; measurement of cross sections for the interaction of fast neutrons with materials. Address: Los Alamos Scientific Lab, Los Alamos, NM. (Deceased Jan. 6, 1972.)

GRAVES, GLEN A(TKINS), b. Monroe Co, Ind, Nov. 11, 27; m. 51; c. 3. NUCLEAR PHYSICS. A.B, Indiana, 48, M.S, 50, Atomic Energy Cmn. fel, 50-51, Ph.D.(physics), 53. Res. assoc, LOS ALAMOS SCI. LAB, 49, mem. staff, 52-67, ASST. GROUP LEADER, 67- Prof, New Mexico, 54-; summer guest lectr. for Nat. Sci. Found. Sponsored Adv. Subj. Matter Inst, Florida, 62; head physics sect, Int. Atomic Energy Agency, Austria, 69-70. Am. Phys. Soc; Am. Inst. Aeronaut. & Astronaut; Am. Nuclear Soc. Nuclear spectroscopy; beta and gamma emission; nuclear reactor physics; radiation problems of propulsion reactors. Address: Los Alamos Scientific Lab, P.O. Box 1663, Los Alamos, NM 87544.

GRAVES, GRANT O(STRANDER), b. Columbus, Ohio, Jan. 21, 05; m. 40; c. 3. MEDICINE, RADIOLOGY. A.B, Ohio State, 26, M.A, 29, M.D, 32. Asst. anat, Ohio State, 28-31, substitute intern, Starling-Loving Univ. Hosp, 31-32, asst. res. med, 33-34; intern med, univ. hosp, Duke, 32-33; instr. ANAT, COL. MED, OHIO STATE UNIV, 35-37, asst. prof, 37-44, assoc. prof, 44-60, PROF. & CHMN. DEPT, 61-, CHMN. CURRICULUM COMT, 63-, ASST. PROF. MED. & RADIOL, 48-, instr. med, 38-49, radiol, 47-48, v.chmn. dept. anat, 60-61. AAAS; fel. Am. Med. Asn; fel. Am. Col. Physicians. Medical education; early embryology of brain and Amblystoma; developmental anomalies of human brain; referred pain; clinical anatomy of eustachian tube. Address: Dept. of Anatomy, 4068 Medical Science Bldg, Ohio State University College of Medicine, 333 W. Tenth Ave, Columbus, OH 43210.

GRAVES, HANNON B, b. Independence, Va, Mar. 7, 43; m. 63; c. 2. GENETICS. B.S, Va. Polytech, 65, Ph.D.(genetics), 68. ASST. PROF. ETHOLOGY, PA. STATE UNIV, 68- AAAS; Genetics Soc. Am; Animal Behav. Soc; Poultry Sci. Asn. Behavior genetics; ecology; psychology. Address: Dept. of Poultry Science, Pennsylvania State University, University Park, PA 16802.

GRAVES, HAROLD E(DWARD), b. Beardsley, Minn, Feb. 20, 09; m. 35; c. 2. CHEMICAL ENGINEERING. B.S. & M.S, Minnesota, 32, Ph.D.(chem. eng), 35. Res. chemist, calco chem. div, Am. Cyanamid Co, 35-36; assoc. prof. chem. eng, Miss. State Col, 36-38; instr, Yale, 38-40; asst. prof, Worcester Polytech, 40-41, prof, 41-48; prof. & head dept, Rhode Island State Col, 48-52; chief chem. engr, Jackson & Church Co, 52-56; supvr. process eng. sect, DOW CHEM. CO, 56-64, chief process engr, MIDLAND DIV, 64-67, STAFF ASST, 67- Am. Chem. Soc; Nat. Soc. Prof. Eng; Am. Inst. Chem. Eng. Process design. Address: 43-5 Berkshire Ct, Midland, MI 48642.

GRAVES, HARVEY W(ILBUR), JR, b. Rochester, N.Y, June 18, 27; m. 60; c. 3. NUCLEAR ENGINEERING. B.A, Dartmouth, 50, M.S, 51; Pittsburgh, 53-57. Engr, Westinghouse Elec. Corp, 51-53, nuclear engr, 53-55, supvry. engr, 55-56, mgr, nuclear eng, 56-66, advan. reactor develop, 66-68; CONSULT. ENGR, 68-; LECTR, DEPT. NUCLEAR ENG, UNIV. MICH, 68- U.S.N, 45-46. Am. Nuclear Soc. Nuclear reactor physics and engineering; applied mathematics; nuclear fuel management; nuclear power. Address: 3125 Geddes Ave, Ann Arbor, MI 48104.

GRAVES, HOWARD B(RADLEY), JR, b. Yonkers, N.Y, June 21, 07; m. 43. GEOLOGY. B.S, Beloit Col, 29; Chicago, 29-32; M.S, Washington (St. Louis), 34, Ph.D.(geol), 36. Jr. geologist, Tex. Co, 36-41; anal. chemist, Chickasaw Ord. Works, 42-45; Int. Minerals & Chem. Corp, 46-62; CHEMIST, CITRUS EXP. STA, UNIV. FLA, 62- Structural geology; pre-Cambrian structure of Missouri. Address: 826 S. Ingraham Ave, Lakeland, FL 33801.

GRAVES, HOWARD K, b. Elgin, Ill, July 2, 28; m. 57; c. 4. MECHANICAL ENGINEERING. B.S, Mass. Inst. Tech, 50. Engr, Am. Colortype Co, 55-56; from asst. chief engr. to spec. proj. engr, Bell & Howell Co, 56-60; head new prod. res, Graflex, Inc, 60-62; proj. engr, develop. Booz-Allen Appl. Res, Inc, 62-65, eng. dir, 65-71; CONSULT, 71- U.S.A, 53-55. Development of new products; applied research in mechanics, electromechanics and optics. Address: 6633 Somerset Dr, Cleveland, OH 44141.

GRAVES, JERRY B(ROOK), b. Tylertown, Miss, Feb. 28, 35; m. 60; c. 1. ENTOMOLOGY. B.S, Mississippi State, 55, M.S, 58; Ph.D.(entom), La. State, 62. Res. assoc. ENTOM, LA. STATE UNIV, 61-63, asst. prof, 63-66, assoc. prof, 66-71, PROF, 71- U.S.A, 55-57, 1st Lt. Entom. Soc. Am. Control of cotton insects; insecticide resistance; insect toxicology; insecticide-wildlife relationships. Address: Dept. of Entomology, Louisiana State University, University Station, Baton Rouge, LA 70803.

GRAVES, J(OHN) H(ENRY), b. Pottstown, Pa, May 11, 24; m. 50; c. 4. VETERINARY MEDICINE. D.V.M, Cornell, 47. Res. veterinarian serol, Plum Island Animal Disease Lab, AGR. RES. SERV, U.S. DEPT. AGR, 56-57, Animal Virus Res. Inst, Eng, 57-58, prin. veterinarian immunol, Plum Island Animal Disease Lab, 58-63, vet. adv. animal disease control, U.S. Agency Int. Develop. & Nat. Acad. Sci, Arg, 63-64, PRIN. VETERINARIAN IMMUNOL, PLUM ISLAND ANIMAL DISEASE LAB, 64- AAAS; Am. Asn. Immunol. Immunology of domestic animals, especially to foot and mouth disease from vaccination of infection; types and characteristics of antibodies found after infection with this virus. Address: Plum Island Animal Disease Lab, Agricultural Research Service, U.S. Dept. of Agriculture, Box 848, Greenport, NY 11944.

GRAVES, JOHN L(OWELL), b. Chicago, Ill, Dec. 15, 28; m. 56; c. 2. BIOCHEMISTRY, QUANTUM CHEMISTRY. B.A, Oberlin Col, 50; Nat. Insts.

Health fel, Chicago, 51-54, Ph.D.(biophys), 56. Nat. Found. Infantile Paralysis fel, California, 56-57; res. fel. chem, Harvard, 57-58; instr. biochem, col. med, Florida, 58-60, asst. prof, 60-64; proj. assoc, theoret. chem. inst, Univ. Wis, 64-66; ASST. PROF. CHEM, UNIV. N.C, GREENSBORO, 66- Nat. Insts. Health fel, quantum theory group, Univ. Uppsala, 63-64. AAAS; Am. Phys. Soc; Am. Chem. Soc. Enzyme and protein chemistry; physical and theoretical chemistry. Address: Dept. of Chemistry, University of North Carolina, Greensboro, NC 27412.

GRAVES, LEON F(RANKLIN), b. Philadelphia, N.Y, Dec. 8, 14; m. 46; c. 2. METEOROLOGY. B.S, Cornell, 37, M.A, 40; M.S, Mass. Inst. Technol, 46. Lab. asst. meteorol, Cornell, 35-42; instr, Mass. Inst. Technol, 42-46; asst. prof. PHYSICS, UNIV. HOUSTON, 46-51, ASSOC. PROF, 51- Summers, sr. nuclear engr, Convair div, Gen. Dynamics Corp, Tex, 56-57; mem. tech. staff, Houston Off, Nat. Eng. Sci. Co, 61-65; lectr, Tex. A&M Univ, 65-66. AAAS; Am. Meteorol. Soc; Am. Oceanog. Soc; Am. Asn. Physics Teachers. General physics; physical meteorology and bio-meteorology. Address: 4380 Harvest Lane, Houston, TX 77004.

GRAVES, LEROY D, b. Kokomo, Ind, Mar. 12, 12; m. 34; c. 2. CIVIL ENGINEERING. B.S, Purdue, 33, M.S, 41. Field engr, State Dept. Conserv, Ind, 33-37; res. engr, joint hwy. res. proj, Purdue, 37-41; soils engr, Ohio River Div. Labs, Corps Engrs, 41-46; asst. prof. CIVIL ENG, UNIV. NOTRE DAME, 46-51, ASSOC. PROF, 51-, ASST. CHMN. DEPT, 68-, acting head dept, 60-61. Soil mech. consult, 46- Assoc, Hwy. Res. Bd, Nat. Acad. Sci-Nat. Res. Coun, 38-; mem, Int. Coun. Soil Mech. & Found. Eng, 48- Fel. Am. Soc. Civil Eng; Nat. Soc. Prof. Eng; Am. Soc. Eng. Educ. Soil mechanics and foundation engineering; highways and airports. Address: Dept. of Civil Engineering, University of Notre Dame, Box G, Notre Dame, IN 46556.

GRAVES, LYNN B(OYD), JR, b. Elgin, Ill, Oct. 5, 28; m. 53; c. 2. CELL PHYSIOLOGY, PROTOZOOLOGY. B.A, Ohio Wesleyan, 53; M.Sc, Ohio State, 57, Ph.D.(zool), 59. Meullhaupt scholar, Ohio State, 59-60; asst. prof. cell physiol, Montana State, 60-63; fel. math. biol. & biomed. data processing, sch. pub. health, Michigan, 63-65; assoc. prof. cell physiol, North. Ill. Univ, 65-70; FEL. BOT, UNIV. WIS, MADISON, 70- U.S.M.C, 46-50, Sgt. AAAS; Soc. Protozool; Am. Soc. Zool. Colony formation in the Volvocida; microbodies in algal flagellates; substrate uptake and utilization in Euglena. Address: Dept. of Botany, Birge Hall, University of Wisconsin, Madison, WI 53706.

GRAVES, QUINTIN B(RANSON), b. Fairview, Okla, Oct. 23; 05; m. 32; c. 2. CIVIL ENGINEERING. B.S, Kansas, 31; M.S, Iowa, 32. Asst. surv, Iowa, 31-33; instr. civil eng, Tennessee, 33-35; jr. engr, Tenn. Valley Authority, 35-37; from instr. to assoc. prof. CIVIL ENG, Texas, 37-46; assoc. prof, OKLA. STATE UNIV, 46-71, EMER. PROF, 71-; ENGR, C.H. GUERNSEY & CO, 71- Acting dir. div. sanit. eng, State Bd. Health, S.Dak, 45-46. Sr. sanit. engr, Pub. Health Serv. Res, 54- Am. Soc. Civil Eng.(Croes Medal, 40); Am. Soc. Eng. Educ; Am. Water Works Asn.(Fuller Award); Water Pollution Control Fedn.(Arthur Sidney Bedell award, 53). Biological and volume loading of trickling filters for sewage; currents and sedimentation basis for water treatment; electric heating of sludge digesters; delayed incubation of inoculated membrane filters; aerobic sludge digestion with domestic and synthetic wastes. Address: 607 N. Bellis, Stillwater, OK 74074.

GRAVES, ROBERT C(HARLES), b. Evanston, Ill, Oct. 24, 30; m. 56; c. 3. ZOOLOGY, ENTOMOLOGY. B.S, Northwestern, 52, M.S, 53, Ph.D.(biol. sci), 56. Asst. BIOL, Northwestern, 52-56; instr, Lake Forest Col, 56-57; prof, Flint Community Col, 57-66, assoc. prof, BOWLING GREEN STATE UNIV, 66-68, PROF, 68- Summers, asst, Marine Biol. Lab, Mass, 52-53; entomologist, Des Plaines Valley Mosquito Abatement Dist, Ill, 55-57; Highlands Biol. Sta, N.C, 62; vis. prof, Univ. Ark, 68. Entom. Soc. Am; Entom. Soc. Can. Ecology, systematics and distribution of Cicindelidae and Carabidae; fungus-inhabiting insects; Coleoptera. Address: Dept. of Biology, Bowling Green State University, Bowling Green, OH 43402.

GRAVES, ROBERT L(AWRENCE), b. Chicago, Ill, Sept. 1, 26; m. 51; c. 4. MATHEMATICS. B.A, Oberlin Col, 47; M.A, Harvard, 48, fel, 49-51, Ph.D. (math), 52. Sr. proj. supvr, Standard Oil Co.(Ind), 51-58; asst. prof. appl. math, UNIV. CHICAGO, 58-62, assoc. prof, 62-65, PROF, 65- U.S.N.R, 44-46, Ens. Am. Math. Soc; Opers. Res. Soc Am; Math. Asn. Am; Asn. Comput. Mach; Inst. Mgt. Sci. Operations research, especially linear programming; digital computers. Address: Graduate School of Business, University of Chicago, Chicago, IL 60637.

GRAVES, R(OY) W(ILLIAM), JR, b. Ada, Okla, Dec. 29, 15; m. 42; c. 3. GEOLOGY. B.S, Agr. & Mech. Col, Texas, 39; M.S, Mo. Sch. Mines, 41; Ph.D.(geol), Texas, 49. Lab. asst. mineral, Mo. Sch. Mines, 39-41; instr. geol, Texas, 46-48; res. geologist, Calif. Res. Corp, Standard Oil Co, Calif, 49-55; div. stratigrapher, Calif. Co, 55-57, area geologist, 57-61; sr. geologist, Monsanto Chem. Co, 61-63; ADJ. ASSOC. PROF. GEOL. & GEOLOGIST, INFO. SERV. DEPT, UNIV. TULSA, 63- Fel. Geol. Soc. Am; Am. Asn. Petrol. Geol; Geosci. Info. Soc; Am. Soc. Info. Sci; Asn. Earth Sci. Ed. Sedimentary petrology and paleoecology. Address: 6864 E. 57th St, Tulsa, OK 74145.

GRAVES, WAYNE H(AIGH), b. Des Moines, Iowa, Dec. 6, 25. PHYSICS, ELECTRICAL ENGINEERING. B.S, Iowa State, 50; M.S, Iowa, 58, Ph.D. (elec. eng), 61. Physicist, Eng. Res. Assoc, Minn, 50-51; staff engr. commun, Collins Radio Co, Iowa, 52-63; electronics, viron div, Geophys. Corp. Am, 64-66; ELECTRONICS RES. ENGR, N. STAR RES. & DEVELOP. INST, MINNEAPOLIS, 66- U.S.N.R, 44-46. AAAS; Soc. Indust. & Appl. Math; Inst. Elec. & Electronic Eng. Non-linear circuit theory and electromagnetic propagation. Address: 5010 Diane Dr, Minnetonka, MN 55343.

GRAVES, WILLIAM EARL, b. Conway, Mass, June 1, 41; m. 60; c. 3. ENDOCRINOLOGY, PHYSIOLOGY. B.S, Massachusetts, Amherst, 63; M.S, Wisconsin, Madison, 65, Ph.D.(endocrinol, reproductive physiol), 67. Asst. prof. VERT. PHYSIOL, STATE UNIV. N.Y. COL. FORESTRY, SYRACUSE UNIV, 67-71, ASSOC. PROF, 71- Consult, Nat. Sci. Found. summer res. prog. for undergrad, 68 & 69. AAAS. Feeding behavior in hibernators; neuroendocrine aspects of initiation of hibernation; reproduction in seasonal

breeders. Address: Dept. of Forest Zoology, State University of New York College of Forestry at Syracuse University, Syracuse, NY 13210.

GRAVES, W(ILLIAM) E(WING), b. Louisville, Ky, Mar. 17, 30. REACTOR PHYSICS. A.B, Univ. Louisville, 51; M.S, Ind. Univ, 53, Ph.D.(physics), 55. Physicist, SAVANNAH RIVER LAB, E.I. DU PONT DE NEMOURS & CO, INC, 55-61, RES. SUPVR. THEORET. PHYSICS DIV, 61- Am. Nuclear Soc. Experimental and theoretical physics of nuclear reactors. Address: Theoretical Physics Division, Savannah River Lab, E.I. du Pont de Nemours & Co, Inc, Aiken, SC 29801.

GRAVESON, ROBERT T(URNER), b. Buffalo, N.Y, Mar. 11, 24; m. 50; c. 5. ELECTRONIC ENGINEERING. B.S, Princeton, 47, M.S, 48. Asst. microwave res, Princeton, 47-48; from trainee to sr. engr. radiation instrumentation, N.Y. Opers. Off, U.S. ATOMIC ENERGY COMN, 48-52, proj. engr, health & safety lab, 52-55, chief, develop. br, 55-60, DIR, INSTRUMENTATION DIV, 60- U.S.N.R, 42-46, Res, 46-55, Lt.(jg). Inst. Elec. & Electronics Eng. Radiation detectors; gamma spectroscopy; transistor circuits; environmental instruments. Address: 60 Apple Lane, Briarcliff Manor, NY 10510.

GRAVETT, HOWARD L, b. Normal, Ill, Sept. 21, 11; m. 37. GENETICS. A.B, James Millikin, 33; M.A, Illinois, 34, Ph.D.(genetics), 39; Marine Biol. Lab, Woods Hole, 35, 40, 50. Asst. biol, Illinois, 33-35, asst. genetics, 35-37; asst. prof. BIOL, Elon Col, 37-39, assoc. prof, 39-42, prof, 42-46, head dept, 46; asst. prof. TEXAS A&M UNIV, 46-48, assoc. prof, 48-54, PROF, 54- U.S.A.A.F, 42-45, Capt. AAAS; Am. Inst. Biol. Sci; Am. Soc. Zool; Nat. Asn. Biol. Teachers. Genetics of Drosophila; embryology. Address: Dept. of Biology, Texas A&M University, College Station, TX 77840.

GRAVITT, JAMES C(LEVELAND), b. Bessemer, Ala, Feb. 29, 28; m. 49; c. 3. PHYSICS. B.S, N.Ga. Col, 52; M.S, Vanderbilt, 54, Ph.D.(physics), 58. Asst. prof. physics, Univ. Kansas City, 56-59; sr. engr, syst. eng, Midwest Res. Inst, 59-63; res. assoc. PHYSICS, Vanderbilt, 63-65; chmn. dept, Hartwick Col, 65-66; ASSOC. PROF, UNIV. MO-ST. LOUIS, 66- Consult, Midwest Res. Inst, 57-59. U.S.N, 45-49. Am. Asn. Physics Teachers. Absorption of sound in gases and liquids; thermal transpiration in gases; viscosity of gases. Address: 8001 Natural Bridge Rd, St. Louis, MO 63121.

GRAVLEY, W(ILTON), b. Carrollton, Tex, Nov. 2, 23; m. 46; c. 2. MECHANICAL ENGINEERING. B.S, Southern Methodist, 49, M.S, 61. Jr. engr, Allis Chalmers Mfg. Co, Wis, 49-52; res. technologist, Socony Mobil Oil Co, Inc, 53-59, sr. res. technologist, 59-64, eng. assoc, 64-67, SUPVR, MOBIL RES. & DEVELOP. CORP, 67- U.S.A.A.F, 42-46. Am. Soc. Mech. Eng; Sci. Res. Soc. Am. New methods, techniques or devices to reduce cost of drilling oil wells. Address: Mobil Research & Development Corp, P.O. Box 900, Dallas, TX 75221.

GRAY, ALAN, b. Brooklyn, N.Y, Oct. 11, 26; m. 51; c. 2. VIROLOGY. B.A, Pa. State, 48, M.S, 50; U.S. Pub. Health Serv. fel, Pennsylvania, 52-53, Ph.D.(pub. health, prev. med), 53. Asst, Pa. State, 49-50; fel, U.S. Pub. Health Serv, Pennsylvania, 53-55; chief virus dept, Microbiol. Assocs, D.C, 55-60; mgr. biol. develop, MERCK SHARP & DOHME, 60-63, bact. & viral vaccine prod, 63-70, DIR, BIOL. PROD, 70- Instr, Maryland, 58. Res. assoc, Children's Hosp, Phila, Pa, 53-55. Dipl, Am. Bd. Microbiol. U.S.N, 44-45. AAAS; Am. Soc. Microbiol; Tissue Cult. Asn; N.Y. Acad. Sci. Viral diagnosis; veterinary and human vaccines; viral tumors; blood products. Address: Merck, Sharpe & Dohme, West Point, PA 19486.

GRAY, ALFRED, b. Dallas, Tex, Oct. 22, 39; m. 64. GEOMETRY. B.A, Univ. Kans, 60, M.A, 61; Ph.D.(math), Univ. Calif, Los Angeles, 64. Instr. MATH, Univ. Calif, Berkeley, 64-65, asst. prof, 65-68; assoc. prof, UNIV. MD, COLLEGE PARK, 68-70, PROF, 70- Nat. Sci. Found. fel, Univ. Calif. Berkeley, 65-66; Univ. Md. faculty develop. fel, 69; partic, Int. Cong. Mathematicians, Moscow 66 & Nice 70; Oberwolfach Conf, 67 & 69. AAAS; Am. Math. Soc; Math. Asn. Am. Differential geometry; complex analysis. Address: Dept. of Mathematics, University of Maryland, College Park, MD 20742.

GRAY, ALLAN, JR, b. San Angelo, Tex, Aug. 27, 30; m. 54; c. 2. MATHEMATICS. B.S, New Mexico State, 52, M.S, 55, Ph.D.(math), 60. Instr. math, New Mexico State, 55-58; mathematician, White Sands Missile Range, 58-61; ASSOC. PROF. MATH, NORTH. ARIZ. UNIV, 61- U.S.A, 52-54, 2nd Lt. Am. Math. Soc; Math. Asn. Am. Monomial and permutation groups. Address: Dept. of Mathematics, Northern Arizona University, Flagstaff, AZ 86001.

GRAY, ALLAN P, b. New York, N.Y, May 14, 22; m. 47; c. 1. ORGANIC CHEMISTRY. A.B, Cornell, 43; A.M, Columbia, 47, Ph.D.(chem), 50. Jr. chemist, cent. labs, Gen. Foods Corp, 43-44; asst, Columbia, 47-50; fel, Chicago, 50-51; res. chemist, Irwin, Neisler & Co, 51-56, dir. chem. res, Neisler Labs, Inc, 56-66; Union Carbide Res. Inst, 66-69; ASSOC. PROF. PHARMACOL, COL. MED, UNIV. VT, 69- Synthesis and properties of nitrogen heterocycles; ammonium salts. alkaloids; hypotensive agents; muscle relaxants; analgesics; central agents; molecular mechanisms of synaptic neurotransmission. Address: Dept. of Pharmacology, Given Medical Bldg, University of Vermont, Burlington, VT 05401.

GRAY, ALLEN G(IBBS), b. Birmingham, Ala, July 28, 15; m. 48; c. 2. PHYSICAL CHEMISTRY, METALLURGY. B.S, Vanderbilt, 37, M.S, 38; Ph.D. (phys. chem), Wisconsin, 40. Lab. instr. chem, Vanderbilt, 37-38; instr, Wisconsin, 38-40; res. chemist, E.I. du Pont de Nemours & Co, 40-52; tech. ed, Steel, 52-57; ED, METAL PROGRESS, AM. SOC. METALS, 57-, DIR. PUBL, 61- Consult. & prog. dir, Manhattan Dist, 42-46; ed-in-chief, Modern Electroplating, 53; mem. comt. tech. aspects of critical & strategic mat, nat. mat. adv. bd, Nat. Acad. Sci, 68-69, chmn, 70; ed. series Monographs on Metall. in Nuclear Tech, Atomic Energy Comn, mem. adv. comt. indust. info. Am. Chem. Soc; Electrochem. Soc; Am. Soc. Test. & Mat; Am. Electroplaters Soc; Am. Soc. Metals (William Hunt Eisenman Medal, 67). Antioxidants; high speed tin plating and electroplating; organic coatings and dispersions; electropolishing; heat treatment; surface active agents; materials and corrosion; chemicals in metal working; ferrous and nonferrous metallurgy; coatings for uranium; chemistry of steelmaking; high temperature materials; vacuum melting; materials selection and process engineering for manufacturing. Address: American Society for Metals, Metals Park, OH 44073.

GRAY, ALMA M(ARCUS), b. Rotterdam, Netherlands, Oct. 1, 25; U.S. citizen; m. SOLID STATE PHYSICS. B.Sc, McGill, 48, M.Sc, 50; fel, Illinois, 50-51; Ph.D.(physics), Rensselaer Polytech, 64. Jr. engr, Nat. Res. Coun. Can, 49-50, res. asst. atomic physics, 53-54; solid state physics, McGill, 52-53; res. engr, Sprague Elec. Co, Mass, 54-59; PHYSICIST, WATERVLIET ARSENAL, U.S. DEPT. ARMY, 64- Am. Phys. Soc. Electronic energy band structure. Address: Research & Engineering Division, Watervliet Arsenal, Watervliet, NY 12189.

GRAY, ANDREW P, b. Bonner Springs, Kans, July 20, 16; m. 54; c. 1. VETERINARY MEDICINE, PATHOLOGY. B.S. & D.V.M, Kansas State, 53, Nat. Defense Ed. Act fel, 61-64, M.S, 63, Nat. Insts. Health fel, 64-66, Ph.D. (path), 66. Private practice vet. med, Ind, 53-61; ASSOC. PROF. VET. PATH. & VET. PATHOLOGIST, KANS. STATE UNIV, 66- U.S.A, 41-45, Corp. Am. Vet. Med. Asn; U.S. Animal Health Asn. Lungs, upper respiratory tract, eye and adnexa of domesticated animals. Address: 3011 Wayne Dr, Manhattan, KS 66502.

GRAY, A(UGUSTINE) H(EARD), JR, b. Long Beach, Calif, Aug. 18, 36; m. 59; c. 1. ENGINEERING, MATHEMATICS. S.M. & S.B, Mass. Inst. Technol, 59; Ph.D.(eng. sci), Calif. Inst. Technol, 64. Instr. physics, San Diego State Col, 59-60; instr. eng. sci. Calif. Inst. Technol, 64; asst. prof. ELEC. ENG, UNIV. CALIF, SANTA BARBARA, 64-69, ASSOC. PROF, 69- Consult, Delco Electronics; Gen. Motors; Culler-Harrison Labs. Inst. Elec. & Electronics Eng; Soc. Indust. & Appl. Math; Acoustical Soc. Am; Am. Soc. Mech. Eng. Applied mathematics; stochastic processes; applied mechanics; numerical analysis; signal processing. Address: 2726 Cuesta Rd, Santa Barbara, CA 93105.

GRAY, BRAYTON, b. Chicago, Ill, Dec. 19, 40; m. 61. MATHEMATICS. Ph.D.(math), Chicago, 65. Lectr. MATH, Manchester, 64-66; asst. prof, UNIV. ILL, CHICAGO CIRCLE, 66-69, ASSOC. PROF, 71- Lectr, Univ. Aarhus, Denmark, 69-70. Am. Math. Soc. Algebraic topology; homotopy groups of spheres; homotopy theory. Address: Dept. of Mathematics, University of Illinois at Chicago Circle, Chicago, IL 60680.

GRAY, CARL, b. Neodesha, Kans, Nov. 5, 20; m. 50; c. 4. SOIL CHEMISTRY. B.S, Kans. State Col, 43, M.S, 47; Ph.D.(soil chem. & fertility), Illinois, 53. Asst, Texas Res. Found, 47-52; asst. prof. soils, Florida, 52-54; prof. agr, Midwestern, 54-60, assoc. prof. chem, 60-66; EXTEN. SOIL CHEMIST, TEX. AGR. EXTEN. SERV, 66- U.S.A.A.F, 42-45. Am. Soc. Agron; Soil Sci. Soc. Am; Am. Chem. Soc; Int. Soil Sci. Soc. Fertility, salinity and physical problems of soils; soil testing. Address: Soil Testing Lab, Texas A&M University, College Station, TX 77843.

GRAY, CHARLES A(UGUSTUS), b. Washington, D.C, Oct. 15, 38; m. 65; c. 2. CHEMICAL ENGINEERING. B.Ch.E, Cornell, 61; Nat. Sci. Found. fel. & Ph.D.(chem. eng), Mass. Inst. Tech, 66. Instr. indust. chem, Mass. Inst. Technol, 63; res. engr, cent. res. ctr, FMC CORP, 65-69, engr, supvr, INORG. CHEM. DIV, 69-70, mgr. eng. res, 70-71, SUPT. TECH. DEPT, S.CHARLESTON PLANT, 71- Am. Inst. Chem. Eng; Am. Chem. Soc. Process development; reaction engineering; process modeling. Address: Inorganic Chemicals Division, FMC Corp, P.O. Box 8127, South Charleston, WV 25303.

GRAY, CLARKE T(HOMAS), b. Norwood, Ohio, May 7, 19; m. 42; c. 2. MICROBIOLOGY. B.S, East. Ky. State Col, 41; fel, Ohio State, 46-48, Ph.D. (bact), 49; hon. M.A, Dartmouth Col, 64. Instr. bact, Ohio State, 48-49; res. assoc. bact. & immunol, Harvard Med. Sch, 49-59; Guggenheim fel. biochem, cell metab. res. unit, Oxford, 59-60; assoc. prof, DARTMOUTH MED. SCH, 60-62, PROF. MICROBIOL, 62-, CHMN. DEPT, 66-, ADJ. PROF. BIOL, 71- AAAS; Am. Soc. Microbiol; N.Y. Acad. Sci; Am. Soc. Biol. Chem. Physiology of mycobacteria; oxidative phosphorylation; bacterial enzymes; biological formation of hydrogen; regulation of enzyme formation; aerobic and anaerobic electron transport. Address: Dept. of Microbiology, Dartmouth Medical School, Hanover, NH 03755.

GRAY, CLIFFTON H(ERSCHEL), JR, b. Riverside, Calif, Dec. 27, 25; m. 55; c. 1. GEOLOGY. B.A, California, Los Angeles, 49; M.A, Claremont Grad. Sch, 53. Asst. geol. sci, Pomona Col, 50-51; geologist, mineral deposits br, U.S. Geol. Surv, 51-54; jr. mining geologist, STATE DIV. MINES & GEOL, CALIF, 54-55, asst. mining geologist, 55-58, assoc. mining geologist, 58-70, SR. & DISTRICT GEOLOGIST, 70- U.S.A, 45-46, Sgt. Fel. AAAS; Geol. Soc. Am; Mineral. Soc. Am; Am. Asn. Petrol. Geol; Am. Inst. Prof. Geol; Am. Inst. Mining, Metall. & Petrol. Eng; Soc. Econ. Geol. Economic geology; nonmetallic industrial minerals, especially limestone and dolomite in California. Address: 4464 Edgewood Place, Riverside, CA 92506.

GRAY, DAVID MONTGOMERY, b. Charlottesville, Va, Dec. 27, 42; div; c. 2. ELECTROCHEMISTRY. B.S, Mississippi, 64, Ph.D.(chem), 68. Assoc. scientist, Lockheed-Ga. Co, Va, 68-70; MEM. STAFF CHEM, GEORGIA STATE UNIV, 70- AAAS; Am. Chem. Soc; Electrochem. Soc. Theoretical analysis of mixed potential generation at mixed or polyelectrodes in view of modern theories of current-overvoltage relations. Address: Dept. of Chemistry, School of Special Studies, Georgia State University, Atlanta, GA 30303.

GRAY, DEAN O(RLEY), b. Coles Co, Ill, Apr. 2, 13; m. 48; c. 2. MATHEMATICS. B.Ed, East. Ill. State Col, 36; M.B.A, Houston, 48; M.A, Rice Inst, 60. Teacher, pub. sch, Ill, 36-41; from instr. to ASSOC. PROF. MATH, UNIV. HOUSTON, 41- U.S.N, 42-46, 51-52, Lt. Comdr. Math. Asn. Am. Non linear programming; partial differential equations. Address: 7718 Broadview Blvd, Houston, TX 77017.

GRAY, DON N(ORMAN), b. Carlyle, Ill, July 28, 31; m. 59; c. 3. ORGANIC CHEMISTRY. B.S, Colorado State, 53; fel, Colorado, 55-56, scholars, 56-57, Ph.D.(org. chem), 56. Res. org. chemist, Dow Chem. Co, 56-57; res. chemist, Denver Res. Inst, Univ. Denver, 57-64, asst. prof. chem, 60-64; mem. staff, Martin Marietta Corp, Md, 64-66; sr. res. scientist, Owens-Ill, Res. Lab, Mich, 66-68, sect. head, OWENS-ILL. TECH. CTR, 68-70, MGR. MAT. STUDIES DEPT, C&TP DIV, 70- Instr, exten, Colorado, 57-64. AAAS; Am. Chem. Soc; Brit. Chem. Soc. Fluorine and polymer chemistry; photochemistry; explosives; high temperature polymers. Address: Owens-Illinois Technical Center, 1700 N. Westwood Ave, Toledo, OH 43607.

GRAY, DONALD, b. Milton, Pa, Apr. 4, 38; m. 70. MOLECULAR BIOPHYSICS. B.A, Susquehanna Univ, 60; Nat. Sci. Found. fel, Yale, 60-66, M.S, 63, Ph.D.(molecular biophys), 67. Nat. Inst. Gen. Med. Serv. fel, Univ. Calif, Berkeley, 67-69; ASST. PROF. BIOL, UNIV. TEX, DALLAS, 70- AAAS; Biophys. Soc. The circular dichroism of polynucleotides; the influence of sequence and configuration of polynucleotides on their optical properties. Address: Division of Biology, University of Texas at Dallas, Box 30365, Dallas, TX 75230.

GRAY, DONALD J(AMES), b. Spokane, Wash, Jan. 16, 08; m. 35; c. 2. ANATOMY. B.S, Washington (Seattle), 31, fel, 31-34, M.S, 33, Ph.D.(bacter), 37. Asst. ANAT, Washington (Seattle), 34-35, assoc, 35-37, instr, 37-39; asst. prof, STANFORD UNIV, 39-45, assoc. prof, 45-49, PROF, 49-, ACTING CHMN. DEPT, 61- Nat. Insts. Health sr. res. fel, U.S. Pub. Health Serv, 47-48, 59-60; guest prof, Wayne State, 59-60. AAAS; Am. Asn. Anat; Am. Asn. Phys. Anthrop. Gross and microscopic anatomy; developmental anatomy; physical anthropology; development and histogenesis of human joints. Address: Dept. of Anatomy, Stanford University, Stanford, CA 94305.

GRAY, DONALD M, b. Lynn, Mass, Oct. 4, 29; m. 67. PHYSICS. B.S, Massachusetts, 51; M.S, N.Y. Univ, 55; Ph.D.(physics), Rensselaer Polytech, 66. Engr. physics, Bendix Missiles, 55-58; RES. PHYSICIST, BAND STRUCT, WATERVLIET ARSENAL, 66- U.S.A, 52-54. Am. Phys. Soc. Band structure calculations; bond structure calculations including pressure effects. Address: Watervliet Arsenal, Bldg. 10, Watervliet, NY 12189.

GRAY, DONALD R, b. Akron, Ohio, Mar. 17, 42; m. 64; c. 2. INORGANIC CHEMISTRY. B.S, Mt. Union Col, 64; Nat. Insts. Health fel & Ph.D.(inorg. chem), Mich. State Univ. 71. Teacher, U.S. Peace Corps, 64-66; SR. RES. CHEMIST, EASTMAN KODAK CO, 70- Chemical fixation of molecular nitrogen; photographic applications of coordination chemistry. Address: Eastman Kodak Research Labs, Bldg. 59, 343 State St, Rochester, NY 14650.

GRAY, DWIGHT E(LDER), b. Knoxville, Ohio, July 6, 03; m. 31. PHYSICS. A.B, Muskingum Col, 25; M.S, Ohio State, 29, Ph.D.(physics), 32. Teacher, pub. sch, Ohio, 25-29; asst. physics, Ohio State, 29-32; from instr. to assoc. prof, Akron, 32-43; ed, underwater sound lab, Harvard, 43-45; supvr. tech. reports & liaison, appl. physics lab, Hopkins, 45-50; chief tech. info. div, Libr. of Cong, 50-55; prog. dir, publications, Nat. Sci. Found, 55-63; chief, sci-tech. div, Libr. of Cong, 63-65; CONSULT. & ED, 65- Dir. phys. abstract study, Am. Inst. Physics, 48-50, Wash. rep, 66-; tech. adv, Tech. Info. Br, Atomic Energy Cmn, 50. Summers, conductor, tech. report writing workshops, Pa. State, 55-58. AAAS; Am. Phys. Soc. Zeeman and Paschen-Back effect spectroscopy. Address: 1001 Spring St, Apt. 1105, Silver Spring, MD 20910.

GRAY, EARL E, b. Milliken, Colo, Jan. 30, 29; m. 49; c. 2. ELECTRICAL ENGINEERING. B.S.E.E, Colorado State, 55, M.E.E, 60; Mich. Col. Min. & Tech, 56-57; Nat. Sci. Found. fel, Denver, 65-66. Specialist ELEC. ENG, Gen. Elec. Co, 55-56; instr, Mich. Col. Min. & Tech, 56-57; asst. prof, Colorado State, 57-62; UNIV. IDAHO, 62-65, ASSOC. PROF, 66-, Nat. Sci. Found. sci. faculty fel, 69-70. Elec. engr, Nat. Bur. Standards, 61. Inst. Elec. & Electronics Eng; Am. Soc. Eng. Educ. Electronics; logic design; information theory. Address: Dept. of Electrical Engineering, University of Idaho, Moscow, ID 83843.

GRAY, EDWIN R, b. New Britain, Conn, May 30, 31; m. 59; c. 2. HUMAN ANATOMY, ELECTROMYOGRAPHY. B.S, Univ. Conn, 55; Voc. Rehab. fel, Univ. Vt, 63, M.Sc, 65; Voc. Rehab. fel, Queens Univ.(Ont), 65, Ph.D. (anat, electromyography), 67. Asst. prof. anat, Univ. Conn, 67-69; ASSOC. PROF. BIOMECH, PA. STATE UNIV, 69- Speaker, Second Int. Cong. Electromyographic Kinesiology. Med.C, U.S.A, 56-57. Am. Asn. Anat; Can. Asn. Anat; Am. Phys. Ther. Asn; Int. Soc. Electromyog. & Kinesiology. Electromyographic kinesiology; single motor unit research. Address: Biomechanics Lab, Pennsylvania State University, University Park, PA 16802.

GRAY, ELMER, b. Gray Hawk, Ky, Mar. 29, 34; m. 57; c. 1. PLANT BREEDING. B.S, Berea Col, 56; M.S, Kentucky, 58; Ph.D.(plant breeding), Cornell, 62. Asst. prof. agron, Tennessee, 62-68, assoc. prof, 68; WEST. KY. UNIV, 68-71, PROF. AGRON. & ASST. DEAN GRAD. COL, 71- Am. Soc. Agron; Crop Sci. Soc. Am. Developing improved varieties of forage crops for southeastern United States; plant science; genetics; statistics. Address: Dept. of Agriculture, Western Kentucky University, Bowling Green, KY 42102.

GRAY, E(RNEST) D(AVID), b. Winnipeg, Man, Can, Oct. 3, 30; m. 57; c. 1. BIOCHEMISTRY. B.Sc, Manitoba, 52; Ph.D.(physiol. chem), Minnesota, 58. Asst. physiol. chem, Minnesota, 52-58, instr, 58; asst. lectr. biochem, Glasgow, 58-59, res. fel, Imp. Chem. Industs, 59-60; res. assoc, Col. Physicians & Surgeons, Columbia, 60-62; asst. prof. PEDIAT. & BIOCHEM, UNIV. MINN, MINNEAPOLIS, 62-68, ASSOC. PROF, 68- AAAS; Brit. Biochem. Soc; Am. Soc. Biol. Chem; Am. Chem. Soc; Am. Soc. Microbiol. Nucleic acid; metabolism, nuclease action. Address: Dept. of Pediatrics, University of Minnesota, Minneapolis, MN 55455.

GRAY, ERNEST P(AUL), b. Vienna, Austria, March 12, 26; nat; m. 54; c. 2. THEORETICAL PHYSICS. A.B, Cornell, 47, fel, 46-49, Ph.D.(theoret. physics), 52. Asst. physics, Cornell, 49-52; sr. staff mem. & physicist, APPLIED PHYSICS LAB, JOHNS HOPKINS UNIV, 51-58, PRIN. STAFF MEM, 58-, CHIEF, THEORET. PLASMA PHYSICS STAFF, 66-, Parsons vis. prof, Univ, 68-69. Parsons fel, 57-58. U.S.A, 44-46. Am. Phys. Soc. Exchange currents in nuclei; problems in the propagation and scattering of 3cm-waves; atomic excitation, ionization and recombination; gas discharge and plasma physics; highly ionized plasmas; charged particle trajectories. Address: Applied Physics Lab, Johns Hopkins University, 8621 Georgia Ave, Silver Spring, MD 20910.

GRAY, FAITH HARRIET, b. Mt. Vernon, N.Y, Jan. 15, 40. ZOOLOGY. B.S, Chatham Col, 62; M.A, Mt. Holyoke Col, 64; Nat. Insts. Health fel. & Ph.D. (entom), Ohio State Univ, 68. Fel. physiol, Univ. Miami, 68-70; entom, Ohio

State Univ, 70-71; ASST. PROF. BIOL, WASHINGTON & LEE UNIV, 71- AAAS; Am. Inst. Biol. Sci; Am. Entom. Soc; Am. Soc. Zool; Geront. Soc. Insect physiology; comparative endocrinology; mechanisms of cellular aging. Address: Dept. of Biology, Washington & Lee University, Lexington, VA 24450.

GRAY, FENTON, b. Santa Clara, Utah, Aug. 12, 16; m. 38; c. 5. SOIL SCIENCE. B.S, Utah, 38; Utah State; Ph.D.(soils), Ohio State, 51. Soil surveyor, Utah Agr. Exp. Sta, 39-41; soil conserv. serv, U.S. Dept. Agr, 41-48; asst. SOILS, Ohio State, 48-51; asst. prof, OKLA. STATE UNIV, 51-53, assoc. prof, 53-59, PROF, 59- Sr. soil scientist & proj. leader, Food & Agr. Admin, UN, Brazil, 61-62; travel grant to N.Z, Australia & Orient, 68. U.S.A, 45-46. Fel. AAAS; Am. Soc. Agron; Soil Sci. Soc. Am; Soil Conserv. Soc. Am.(educ. award, Okla, 69); Clay Minerals Soc. Basic chemical, physical and mineralogical properties of Oklahoma soils with relationships to morphology, genesis, classification, soil and water conservation, productivity and good land use. Address: Dept. of Agronomy, Oklahoma State University, Stillwater, OK 74074.

GRAY, FRANK D(AVIS), JR, b. Marshall, Minn, Aug. 24, 16; m. 41. INTERNAL MEDICINE. B.S, Northwestern, 38; M.D, Columbia, 43. Intern & asst. res. med, Bellevue Hosp, 43-44; asst. surg, Hopkins, 46-47; asst. res. MED, Yale, 47-48, fel, 48-49, instr, 49-51, asst. prof, 51-57, assoc. prof, 57-68; PROF, JEFFERSON MED. COL, 68-; DIR. DIV. MED, LANKENAU HOSP, 68- Med.C, 44-46, Res, 46-, Col. AAAS; Am. Soc. Clin. Invest; Hist. Sci. Soc; Am. Med. Asn; Am. Heart Asn; fel. Am. Col. Physicians; fel. Am. Col. Chest Physicians; Am. Fedn. Clin. Res. Clinical physiology of heart and lungs; capillary circulation. Address: Lankenau Hospital, Philadelphia, PA 19151.

GRAY, F(REDERICK) W(ILLIAM), b. Wakefield, Mass, Oct. 4, 18; m. 49; c. 2. ORGANIC CHEMISTRY. B.S, Tufts Col, 41, M.S, 43; fel, Pa. State Col, 47-48, Ph.D.(chem), 49. Asst, Tufts, 41-43; res. chemist, cent. res. lab, Gen. Aniline & Film Co, 43-46; asst, Pa. State, 46-49; res. chemist, COLGATE-PALMOLIVE CO, PISCATAWAY, 49-63, res. assoc, 63-68, SR. RES. ASSOC, 68- AAAS; Am. Chem. Soc; fel. Am. Inst. Chem; The Chem. Soc; N.Y. Acad. Sci. Organic synthesis; dye intermediates; vinyl polymers; synthetic detergents; optical brighteners; chlorine and oxygen bleaches; development of household specialty product. Address: 14 Stockton Rd, Summit, NJ 07901.

GRAY, FRIEDA G(ERSH), b. Hartford, Conn, Nov. 30, 17; m. 41. MEDICINE. A.B, Hunter Col, 39; M.D, N.Y. Med. Col, 44. Asst. bact, col. physicians & surg, Columbia, 39-41; intern & asst. resident med, Bellevue Hosp, 44-46; asst. path, univ. & hosp, Hopkins, 46-47; res. fel. MED, sch. med, Yale, 47-49, instr, 49-53, asst. clin. prof, 53-59, assoc. clin. prof, 59-60, asst. prof, 60-66, ASSOC. PROF, 66-68; JEFFERSON MED. COL, 68-; DIR. DIV. AMBULATORY CARE, LANKENAU HOSP, 68- Supt. & chief med, Woodruff Hosp, 53-60; attend. physician & dir, med. clins, Yale-New Haven Hosp, 60-68. AAAS; Am. Med. Asn; Am. Heart Asn; Am. Rheumatism Asn; Am. Fedn. Clin. Res. Computerized medical and hospital information systems; rheumatic diseases; health care delivery. Address: Lankenau Hospital, Lancaster & City Line Aves, Philadelphia, PA 19151.

GRAY, GARNETT G, b. Holcomb, Mo, May 23, 35; m. 57. PHYSICS. A.B, Millikin, 56; M.S, Nebraska, 58, Ph.D.(physics), 65. Asst. prof. PHYSICS, TRINITY UNIV.(TEX), 62-66, ASSOC. PROF, 66- Am. Asn. Physics Teachers. Inelastic high energy collisions. Address: Dept. of Physics, Trinity University, San Antonio, TX 78212.

GRAY, GARY D, b. St. Louis, Mo, Aug. 6, 36; m. 59; c. 2. BIOCHEMISTRY, IMMUNOLOGY. A.B, Cent. Methodist Col, 59; M.S, Univ. Mo, 63, Ph.D. (biochem), 64. Res. scientist, UPJOHN CO, KALAMAZOO, 64-67, SR. RES. SCIENTIST, 67- Enzymology; immunology; immunosuppression; transplantation; hypersensitivity diseases. Address: 7931 E. T.S. Ave, Scotts, MI 49088.

GRAY, GARY RONALD, b. Coushatta, La, Dec. 4, 42; m. 67; c. 1. BIOCHEMISTRY. B.S, Ouachita Baptist Univ, 64; univ. assistantship, Univ. Iowa, 64-66, NASA traineeship, 66-67, M.S, 67, U.S. Pub. Health Serv. traineeship, 67-68, Ph.D.(biochem), 69. Fel. BIOCHEM, Univ. Iowa, 69; NAT. INSTS. HEALTH FEL, UNIV. CALIF, BERKELEY, 69- Am. Chem. Soc. Nuclear magnetic resonance studies of sugar phosphates; structural studies of bacterial lipopolysaccharides; carbohydrate chemistry and reaction mechanisms. Address: Dept. of Biochemistry, University of California, Berkeley, CA 94720.

GRAY, GEORGE A(LEXANDER), b. Armagh, Ireland, Apr. 16, 21; nat; m. 44; c. 2. CIVIL ENGINEERING. B.C.E, Clarkson Tech, 43; M.Eng, Yale, 48, Tau Beta Pi fel, 51, D.Eng, 59. Instr. math, Clarkson Tech, 46-47, asst. prof. CIVIL ENG, 48-51; Yale, 53-59; PROF, VA. POLYTECH. INST, 59- U.S.A, 43-46, Res, 46-53, Capt. AAAS; Am. Soc. Civil Eng; Am. Soc. Eng. Educ; Nat. Soc. Prof. Eng; Am. Concrete Inst; Int. Asn. Bridge & Struct. Eng. Structural engineering; structural mechanics. Address: Dept. of Civil Engineering, Virginia Polytechnic Institute, Blacksburg, VA 24061.

GRAY, GRACE W(ARNER), b. Chicago, Ill, Nov. 20, 24. PHARMACOLOGY. B.A, Mt. Holyoke Col, 45; Ph.D.(pharmacol), Michigan, 51. Jr. res. pharmacologist, William S. Merrell Co, 45-47; asst, Michigan, 47-51; sr. res. pharmacologist, William S. Merrell Co, 45-47; asst, Michigan, 47-51; sr. res. pharmacologist, Bristol Labs, 51-54; instr. pharmacol, sch. med. Marquette, 54-57, asst. prof, 57-63; U.S. Pub. Health Serv. trainee lipid metab, col. med, Tennessee, 63-64; asst. prof. PHARMACOL, Woman's Med. Col. Pa, 64-67; ASSOC. PROF, COL. VET. MED, UNIV. MINN, ST. PAUL, 67- AAAS; Am. Chem. Soc; Am. Soc. Pharmacol. & Exp. Therapeut. Autonomic and gastrointestinal pharmacology. Address: Dept. of Veterinary Physiology & Pharmacology, University of Minnesota College of Veterinary Medicine, St. Paul, MN 55101.

GRAY, HAMILTON, b. Gardiner, Maine, July 26, 10; m. 36, 66; c. 3. CIVIL ENGINEERING. B.A, Harvard, 33, M.S, 34, Sc.D.(soil mech), 38. Asst. civil eng, grad sch. eng, Harvard, 34-36; soils engr, Moran, Proctor, Freeman & Mueser, N.Y, 36-40; asst. prof. CIVIL ENG, N.Y. Univ, 40-45; prof, Maine, 45-55; PROF. OHIO STATE UNIV, 55-, chmn. dept, 55-71. Assoc. Hwy. Res. Bd, 38-; soils engr, State Hwy. Comn, Maine, 45-55. Consult. engr, 40- Am. Soc. Civil Eng.(Wellington Award, 58); Am. Soc. Test. & Mat. Structural properties of soils; structural analysis of foundations; frost action in soils; consolidation of fine-grained soils. Address: Dept. of Civil Engineering, Ohio State University, 2036 Neil Ave, Columbus, OH 43210.

GRAY, HARRY B, b. Woodburn, Ky, Nov. 14, 35; m. 57; c. 2. INORGANIC CHEMISTRY. B.S, West. Ky. State Col, 57; Nat. Sci. Found. fel. & Ph.D. (chem), Northwestern, 60. Nat. Sci. Found. fel. CHEM, Copenhagen, 60-61; asst. prof, Columbia Univ, 61-63, assoc. prof, 63-65, PROF, 65-66; GATES & CRELLIN LABS. CHEM, CALIF. INST. TECHNOL, 66- FMC Corp. lectr, Princeton, 64; affiliate, Rockefeller Inst, 64-; A.P. Sloan res. fel, 64-66. Consult, Union Carbide Chem. Co, 62-; W.A. Benjamin Co, 63- E.C. Franklin Mem. Award, 67; Fresenius Award & Shoemaker Award, 70. Nat. Acad. Sci; Am. Chem. Soc.(award pure chem, 70). Electronic structures of metal complexes; inorganic reaction mechanisms. Address: Gates & Crellin Labs. of Chemistry, California Institute of Technology, Pasadena, CA 91109.

GRAY, H(ARRY) J(OSHUA), b. St. Louis, Mo, June 24, 24; m. 49; c. 4. ELECTRICAL ENGINEERING. B.S, Pennsylvania, 44, M.S, 47, Ph.D, 53. Assoc. elec. eng, Moore Sch, Pennsylvania, 43-53, asst. prof, 53-54; proj. engr, Remington Rand Corp. & Univac, 54-55, staff engr, 55-57; assoc. prof. ELEC. ENG, MOORE SCH. ELEC. ENG, UNIV. PA, 57-64, PROF, 64- Consult, Philco Corp, 58-63; Int. Tel. & Tel. Corp, 59; Curtiss-Wright Electronics Div, 60; Xerox Corp, 66-67; Burroughs Corp, 67-70. U.S.N.R, 41-46, Res, 46-54, Ens. Inst. Elec. & Electronics Eng. Digital computer engineering and microelectronics; information sciences; cognitive modeling. Address: Moore School of Electrical Engineering, University of Pennsylvania, Philadelphia, PA 19104.

GRAY, HENRY E(MIL), b. Zalma, Mo, Dec. 2, 19; m. 47; c. 2. ENTOMOLOGY. B.S, Missouri, 43, A.M, 47; Ph.D, Illinois, 53. Asst, Missouri, 46-47; instr. biol. sci, Calif. Polytech. Col, 47-50; asst, Illinois, 50-53; res. entomologist, Niagra chem. div, Food Mach. & Chem. Corp, 53-56; entomologist, DOW CHEM. CO, 54-66, PROD. TECH. SPECIALIST, AGR-ORG. DEPT, 66- U.S.N.R, 43-46, Lt. Entom. Soc. Am; Am. Mosquito Control Asn. Insecticides; fumigants; carbohydrate components of honeydew. Address: Agriculture-Organics Dept, Dow Chemical Co, P.O. Box 1706, Midland, MI 48640.

GRAY, HENRY H(AMILTON), b. Terre Haute, Ind, Mar. 18, 22; m. 44; c. 2. GEOLOGY. B.S, Haverford Col, 43; M.S, Michigan, 46, Pa. State Col; Ph.D.(geol); Ohio State, 54. Geologist, U.S. Geol. Surv, 43-45; instr. geol, Kent State, 48-51, asst. prof, 51-53; coal geologist, IND. GEOL. SURV, 54-60, map ed, 55-61, HEAD STRATIGRAPHER, 60- Soc. Econ. Paleont. & Mineral; Am. Asn. Petrol. Geol. Stratigraphy; sedimentary petrology; geology and land use; geologic mapping. Address: 106 S. Glenwood West, Bloomington, IN 47401.

GRAY, HENRY L(UTHER), b. Tulsa, Okla, May 18, 36; m. 58; c. 2. MATHEMATICS, STATISTICS. B.S, Tex. Tech. Col, 59, M.S, 61; Ph.D.(math), Texas, 66. Res. engr, Tracor Inc, 63-65; asst. prof. math, Tex. Tech. Col, 65-66; sr. scientist supvr. math. tech, LTV Electrosysts. Inc, 66-67; assoc. prof. math, TEX. TECH UNIV, 67-70, PROF. MATH. & STATIST, 70-, CHMN. DEPT. MATH, 71- Consult, Tracor Inc, 65-66; LTV Electrosysts. Inc, 65-66; United Technol. Lab. Am. Statist. Asn. Statistics and numerical analysis; linear and non-linear estimation. Address: Dept. of Mathematics, Texas Technological University, Lubbock, TX 79409.

GRAY, H(UGH) W(ILLIAM), b. Broughton, Kans, Dec. 3, 12; m. 38; c. 4. CHEMISTRY. B.Sc, Nebraska, 36, Avery fel. & M.Sc, 37; Chem. Found. fel. & Ph.D.(org. chem), Illinois, 39. Chemist, E.I. DU PONT DE NEMOURS & CO, INC, 39-46, res. supvr, 46-53, lab. dir, 53-68, ASST. TO DIR, RES. & DEVELOP, 68- Am. Chem. Soc; Am. Inst. Chem. Condensation polymers; fibers; films and plastics; synthetic organic chemistry. Address: Film Dept, E.I. du Pont de Nemours & Co, Inc, Wilmington, DE 19898.

GRAY, IRVING, b. Boston, Mass, Apr. 27, 20; m. 47; c. 2. BIOCHEMISTRY, BIOPHYSICS. B.S, Va. Polytech, 41; Ph.D.(biochem), Mass. Inst. Technol, 48. Develop. electrochemist, Westinghouse Elec. & Mfg. Co, Pa, 41; res. biochemist, med. serv, U.S. Army, 48-52, head dept. biochem, Walter Reed Army Inst. Res, 52-56, sci. dir. res. & develop, qm. res. & eng. ctr. labs, 56-59, chief, phys. sci. div, med. unit, 59-64; PROF. BIOL, GEORGETOWN UNIV, 64- U.S.A, 41-64, Col. AAAS; Am. Physiol. Soc; Biophys. Soc; Soc. Exp. Biol. & Med; N.Y. Acad. Sci; Am. Soc. Zool. Biochemical response to stress; enzyme kinetics in temperature adaptation. Address: Dept. of Biology, Georgetown University, Washington, DC 20007.

GRAY, I(RVING) E(MERY), b. Providence, R.I, May 23, 97; m. 27; c. 3. ZOOLOGY. B.S, Massachusetts, 21; M.S, Wisconsin, 24, Ph.D.(ecol), 26. Instr. ZOOL, De Pauw, 21-22; asst, Wisconsin, 22-26; asst. prof, Tulane, 26-30; instr, DUKE UNIV, 30-31, asst. prof, 31-36, assoc. prof, 36-42, prof, 42-67, chmn. dept, 40-56; EMER. PROF, 67- Vis. prof, Univ. P.R, 65; N.C. Wesleyan, 68. Mem. corp, Marine Biol. Lab, Woods Hole, 29- U.S.A, 18-19. AAAS; Am. Soc. Zool; Soc. Syst. Zool; Am. Soc. Ichthyol. & Herpet; Ecol. Soc. Am; Am. Soc. Limnol. & Oceanog. Blood constituents of fishes; biology of fishes and amphibians; ecology of insects; gill areas of crabs and fishes; marine ecology. Address: 124 Pinecrest Rd, Durham, NC 27705.

GRAY, JACK E(LLSWORTH), b. Jackson, Mich, Jan. 24, 23; m. 48; c. 3. VETERINARY PATHOLOGY. D.V.M, Mich. State Col, 50, M.S, 51. Res. fel, Regional Poultry Res. Lab, 50-51; res. prof. vet. sci, Massachusetts, 51-54; VET. RES. PATHOLOGIST, UPJOHN CO, 54- Dipl, Am. Col. Lab. Animal Med. U.S.A, 43-46. AAAS; Soc. Toxicol; Am. Vet. Med. Asn; Am. Col. Vet. Path. Drug toxicity; pathology of experimental infections and kidney disease in laboratory animals; avian pathology. Address: Pathology & Toxicology Research Unit, Upjohn Co, 301 Henrietta St, Kalamazoo, MI 49001.

GRAY, JAMES ARTHUR, b. Spokane, Wash, Apr. 27, 12; m. 43; c. 3. ANIMAL HUSBANDRY. B.S, Wyoming, 32, M.S, 39. Asst. dept. wool, Wyoming, 38-40; from asst. prof. to assoc. prof. animal husb, TEX. A&M

UNIV, 40-49, ANIMAL HUSBANDMAN, AGR. EXTEN. SERV, 49- Am. Soc. Animal Sci. Lamb feeding investigations; wool technology research; determination of yield of raw wool from its density under pressure; production and marketing of sheep, Angora goats, wool and mohair. Address: B-11, County Courthouse, San Angelo, TX 76901.

GRAY, JAMES CLARKE, b. Schenectady, N.Y, Dec. 1, 02; m. 34; c. 1. ZOOLOGY. A.B, Syracuse, 25, M.A, 27; Ph.D.(zool), Chicago, 29. Asst. zool, Syracuse, 25-27; Chicago, 27-29; instr. biol, Western Reserve, 27-37, asst. prof, 37-43, assoc. prof, 43-60; PROF. SCI. & MATH. & CHMN. DIV, STATE UNIV. N.Y. COL. NEW PALTZ, 60- Asst. dean & acting dir. admissions, Western Reserve, 43-45, chmn. dept. biol, 57-60. AAAS; Am. Soc. Zool; Am. Micros. Soc. Embryology; vertebrates; experimental tissue culture. Address: Dept. of Biology, State University of New York College at New Paltz, New Paltz, NY 12561.

GRAY, JAMES F, S.M, b. St. Louis, Mo, Apr. 21, 22. MATHEMATICS. B.Sc, Dayton, 43; M.S, Northwestern, 49; Ph.D.(math), Notre Dame, 58. Teacher, private schs, Texas, 43-44, 52-54, Mo, 44-46, 50-52, Ill, 46-50; instr. MATH, Notre Dame, 54-58; asst. prof, St. Mary's San Antonio, 58-60, chmn. dept. & assoc. prof, 61-64, dir. comput. ctr, 62-64; SUPVR. SCHS, St. Louis Prov. Soc. Mary, 64-65; ST. LOUIS ARCHDIOCESAN SCH. BD, 65-, V.PRES, 66- Collab, Nat. Sci. Found. Inst. Math. Teachers, Cath. Univ. P.R. & Okla. State Univ; instr, St. Louis Prov. Soc. Mary, summers 53 & 54; consult, Tulsa Educ. Conf, 61 & 64; Piper prof, 61; v.chmn. bd. trustees, St. Mary's Univ. San Antonio, 68-; v.pres, Conf. Relig. Dirs. Educ, 69-; mem. comt. educ. & curricula, Conf. Bd. Math. Sci, 71- Am. Math. Soc; Math. Asn. Am. Algebra; field and valuation theory, especially as relating to number theory and generalized p-adic analysis. Address: St. Louis Province of Society of Mary, Marycliff, Glencoe, MO 63038.

GRAY, J(AMES) LORNE, b. Brandon, Man, Mar. 2, 13; m. 40; c. 1. MECHANICAL ENGINEERING. B.E, Saskatchewan, 35, M.Sc, 38, hon. LL.D, 61; hon. D.Sc, British Columbia, 61. Lectr. eng, Saskatchewan, 39; assoc. dir. gen, res. & develop. div, dept. reconstruct. & supply, Ont, 45-46; asst. to pres, Montreal Armature Works Ltd, 46-47; sci. asst. to pres, Nat. Res. Coun. Can, 47-49, chief admin, Chalk River Proj, 49-52; gen. mgr, ATOMIC ENERGY OF CAN. LTD, 52-54, v.pres. admin. & opers, 54-58, PRES, 58- Mem. Atomic Energy Control Bd, Can, 58- R.C.A.F, 39-45, Wing Comdr. Am. Nuclear Soc; Eng. Inst. Can. Development of civil uses of atomic energy; relations of government to industry, utilities, consulants and the public in the application of atomic energy developments. Address: Atomic Energy of Canada, Ltd, 275 Slater St, 20th Floor, Ottawa 4, Ont, Can.

GRAY, JANE, b. Omaha, Nebr, Apr. 19, 31. PALEONTOLOGY. B.A, Radcliffe Col, 51; Nat. Sci. Found. fel, Denmark Geol. Inst, 52-53, McEnerney fel, California, 53-55, Ph.D.(paleont), 58. Ed. asst, J. Sedimentary Petrol, Illinois, 51-52; instr. geol, Texas, 56-58; res. assoc. palynology, Arizona, 58-61; CURATOR PALEOBOT, UNIV. ORE, 62-, ASSOC. PROF. BIOL, 66- Summers, sci. aide, U.S. Geol. Surv, 49-51; palynologist, Shell Oil Co, Calif, 54-55. Bot. Soc. Am; Soc. Study Evolution; Int. Soc. Taxon. Pollen morphology; distribution, taxonomy and paleoecology of late Mesozoic and Cenozoic pollen and spores; Silurian bio stratigraphy. Address: Paleoecology Labs, Museum of Natural History, University of Oregon, Eugene, OR 97403.

GRAY, JOHN A(UGUSTUS), III, b. Waterbury, Conn, Aug. 13, 24; m. 52; c. 3. PHYSICAL CHEMISTRY. B.S, Yale, 45, Ph.D.(chem), 49. RES. CHEMIST, MIAMI VALLEY LABS, PROCTER & GAMBLE CO, 48- Fel. AAAS; Am. Chem. Soc; Int. Asn. Dent. Res. Physical chemical studies of detergents, solutions, dentifrices, tooth structure and caries mechanism. Address: 8764 Long Lane, Cincinnati, OH 45231.

GRAY, JOHN HENRY, III, b. N.Y.C, Dec. 13, 35; m. 59. NUCLEAR & INORGANIC CHEMISTRY. B.S, Haverford Col, 57; M.S, Carnegie Inst. Tech, 59, Ph.D.(nuclear chem), 62. Res. specialist nuclear & inorg. chem, Martin-Marietta Corp, 62-65, supvr. nuclear chem. sect, 65-68; NUCLEAR TECH. ENG, ALLIED CHEM. CORP, 68- Am. Chem. Soc; Am. Nuclear Soc. Terrestrial and space development of isotopic fuels; nuclear and inorganic physical and chemical property measurements; radiochemical analysis; nuclear instrumentation. Address: 25 Frederick Place, Morristown, NJ 07960.

GRAY, JOHN LEWIS, b. Falls Church, Va, July 4, 20; m. 42; c. 2. FOREST ECONOMICS & MANAGEMENT. B.S, Pa. State Univ, 41; M.F, Yale, 42; D.F.(forestry econ), Duke Univ, 69. From asst. prof. to prof. forestry, forestry exten, N.C. State Col, 45-63; from assoc. prof. to PROF. FORESTRY & DIR. SCH. FOREST RESOURCES & CONSERV, UNIV. FLA, 63- Chmn, South. Exten. Forestry Coun, 54-60; N.C. Forestry Coun, 55-56; mem. forestry res. adv. comt, U.S. Dept. Agr, 64-; U.S. rep, permanent comt, Int. Union Forestry Res. Orgn, 67- U.S.A.A.F, 42-44, 2nd Lt. Soc. Am. Foresters; Wildlife Soc. Farm and other small forest ownerships management; analysis of timber supply from small forest ownerships. Address: School of Forest Resources & Conservation, University of Florida, Gainesville, FL 32601.

GRAY, JOHN S(TEPHENS), b. Chicago, Ill, Aug. 11, 10; m. 35; c. 2. PHYSIOLOGY. B.S, Knox Col, 32; M.S, Northwestern, 34, Ph.D.(physiol), 36, M.D, 46. Instr. PHYSIOL, MED. SCH, NORTHWEST. UNIV, 36-39, asst. prof, 40-45, assoc. prof, 45-46, PROF, 46-, chmn. dept, 46-70. Res. physiologist, U.S. Air Force, Randolph Field, 42-46; Guggenheim fel, 62. AAAS; Am. Physiol. Soc; Soc. Exp. Biol. & Med. Gastrointestinal and respiratory physiology. Address: Dept. of Physiology, Medical School, Northwestern University, 303 E. Chicago Ave, Chicago, IL 60611.

GRAY, JOHN W(ALKER), b. St. Paul, Minn, Oct. 3, 31; m. 57. MATHEMATICS. B.A, Swarthmore Col, 53; Ph.D.(math), Stanford, 57. Mem. Inst. Adv. Study, 57-59; Ritt instr. MATH, Columbia, 59-62; asst. prof, UNIV. ILL, URBANA, 62-64, assoc. prof, 64-66, PROF, 66- Nat. Sci. Found. sr. fel, 66-67. AAAS; Am. Math. Soc. Category theory; sheaf theory and its geometrical applications. Address: Dept. of Mathematics, University of Illinois, Urbana, IL 61801.

GRAY, JOSEPH B(URNHAM), b. Annapolis, Md, Aug. 8, 15; m. 41; c. 4. CHEMICAL ENGINEERING. B.A, St. John's Col,(Md), 36; B.E, Hopkins, 38, Ph.D.(chem. eng), 41. Chem. engr, process design div, res. lab, Standard Oil Co, Ind, 41-43, group leader, 43-47; asst. prof. chem. eng, Syracuse, 47-50, assoc. prof, 50-51; res. eng, E.I. DU PONT DE NEMOURS & CO, INC, 51-60, CONSULT, 61- Am. Chem. Soc; Am. Inst. Chem. Eng. Fluid mechanics; agitation and mixing. Address: Engineering Dept, E.I. du Pont de Nemours & Co, Inc, Louviers Bldg, Wilmington, DE 19898.

GRAY, KENNETH BENJAMIN, JR, Mgt. Sci, see 12th ed, Soc. & Behav. Vols.

GRAY, KENNETH EUGENE, b. Herrin, Ill, Jan. 11, 30; m. 55; c. 3. PETROLEUM ENGINEERING. B.S, Tulsa, 56, M.S, 57; Ph.D.(petrol. eng), Texas, 63. Drilling engr, Calif. Co, 57-59; reservoir engr, Sohio Petrol. Co, 59-60; asst. prof. PETROL. ENG, UNIV. TEX, AUSTIN, 62-65, assoc. prof, 65-68, HALLIBURTON PROF, 68-, CHMN. DEPT, 66-, DIR. CTR. EARTH SCI, 68- Res. grants, petrol. res. fund, Am. Chem. Soc, 63-; Tex. Petrol. Res. Comt, 63-; Am. Petrol. Inst, 64-; Gulf Res. & Develop. Co, 64- Consult, res. dept, Continental Oil Co, 63-; mem, U.S. Nat. Comt. Rock Mech; ed. bd, Int. Jour. Rock Mech. U.S.A, 47-48, 50-51, Res, 51-57, M/Sgt. Fel. Am. Inst. Chem; N.Y. Acad. Sci; Am. Acad. Mech. Rock mechanics; properties and behavior of rocks under conditions of elevated temperature and pressure; reservoir transients; unsteady state reservoir pressure analysis. Address: Dept. of Petroleum Engineering, University of Texas at Austin, Austin, TX 78712.

GRAY, KENNETH R(USSELL), b. Vancouver, B.C, Can, Dec. 4, 09; nat; m. 50; c. 2. CHEMISTRY. B.A, British Columbia, 30, M.A, 31; Nat. Res. Council Can. bursar, McGill, 31-32, Ph.D.(cellulose chem), 34. Demonstr. chem, McGill, 32-34; chemist, Can. Indust, Ltd, 35; res. chemist, U.S. Rubber Co, 35-37; res. group leader, ITT RAYONIER, INC, 37-53, RES. SUPVR, 53- AAAS; Am. Chem. Soc; Am. Soc. Hort. Sci; Int. Soc. Hort. Sci; Int. Soc. Soil Sci. Cellulose chemistry; silvichemicals; lignin; bark products; plant mineral nutrition; drilling mud additives; concrete admixtures; chelates; water treatment. Address: 409 E. Harvard Ave, Shelton, WA 98584.

GRAY, LEWIS R(ICHARD), b. Madison, Wis, Feb. 14, 36; m. 58; c. 2. PLANT MORPHOLOGY, PALYNOLOGY. B.S, Miami (Fla), 59; M.S, Cincinnati, 61; Ph.D.(bot), Illinois, 65. Instr. BIOL, CHICAGO CITY COL, MAYFAIR CAMPUS, 65-67, asst. prof, 67-70, ASSOC. PROF, 70-, ACTING CHMN. DEPT, 71- Am. Asn. Stratig. Palynologists. Palynology of coals of Pennsylvania age. Address: 811 W. Hintz Rd, Arlington Heights, IL 60004.

GRAY, LINSLEY S(HEPARD), JR, b. Sandwich, Ill, Oct. 11, 29; m. 51; c. 4. ANALYTICAL CHEMISTRY. B.S, Beloit Col, 51; Ph.D.(chem), Iowa State, 58. Jr. chemist, Ames Lab, Iowa State, 51-52, asst, 52-58; chemist, E.I. du Pont de Nemours & Co, 58-59; ARMOUR & CO, 59-60, sr. res. chemist, 60-66, SECT. HEAD PHYS. CHEM. RES, 66- Am. Chem. Soc; Optical Soc. Am; Coblentz Soc; Soc. Appl. Spectros; Am. Oil Chem. Soc. Spectroscopy. Address: Research Lab, Armour Industrial Chemical Co, 8401 W. 47th St, McCook, IL 60529.

GRAY, LOUISE DILLON, Appl. Physics, see YOUNG, LOUISE GRAY.

GRAY, MARION C(AMERON), b. Ayr, Scotland, March 26, 02; nat. MATHEMATICS. Hon. M.A, Edinburgh, 22; Ph.D.(math), Bryn Mawr Col, 26. Instr. physics, Edinburgh, 26-27; asst. math, Imp. Col, London, 27-30; asst. engr, Am. Tel. & Tel. Co, 30-34; mem. tech. staff, Bell Tel. Labs, Inc, 34-67; RETIRED. AAAS; Am. Math. Soc; Math. Asn. Am; Inst. Elec. & Electronics Eng. Wave propagation over spherical earth; mathematical theory of antenna radiation; propagation of waves in loaded wave guides; numerical analysis. Address: 221 S. Harrison St, East Orange, NJ 07018.

GRAY, MARY JANE, b. Columbus, Ohio, June 13, 24; m. 63; c. 4. MEDICINE. B.A, Swarthmore Col, 45; M.D, Washington (St. Louis), 49; Med.Sc.D, Columbia, 53. Intern, Barnes Hosp, 49-50; asst. res, obstet. & gynecol, Presby. Hosp, 50-53, chief res, 56; Barnes Foster res. fel, Columbia, 53-54; Karolinska Inst, Sweden, 55; instr. OBSTET. & GYNECOL, col. physicians & surgeons, Columbia, 56-59, assoc, 59-60; asst. prof, COL. MED, UNIV. VT, 60-62, assoc. prof, 62-71, PROF, 71- Assoc. attend. physician, DeGoesbriand Mem. & Mary Fletcher Hosps; trainee, marriage coun. Phila, dept. psychiat, Univ. Pa, 70-71. Dipl, Am. Bd. Obstet. & Gynec. AAAS; Soc. Gynec. Invest; Am. Col. Obstet. & Gynec; Am. Radium Soc; Am. Fertil. Soc; Am. Med. Asn. Toxemia of pregnancy; electrolyte changes of menstrual cycle; gynecologic cancer; sex education; marriage counseling. Address: Dept. of Obstetrics & Gynecology, College of Medicine, University of Vermont, Given Medical Bldg, Burlington, VT 05401.

GRAY, MARY W(HEAT), b. Hastings, Nebr, Apr. 8, 39; m. 64. MATHEMATICS. A.B, Hastings Col, 59; Fulbright grant, Frankfurt, 59-60; Nat. Sci. Found. Inst. summer fel, Oregon, 62; Nat. Defense Ed. Act fel, Nat. Sci. Found. fel. & M.A, Kansas, 62, Ph.D.(math), 64. Asst. prof. MATH, Calif. State Col. Hayward, 65-68; assoc. prof, AM. UNIV, 68-71, PROF, 71- Summers, physicist, Nat. Bur. Standards, 59, 61 & 63, instr, California, Berkeley, 65. Translator, Am. Math. Soc, 64-66. AAAS; Am. Math. Soc; Math. Asn. Am; N.Y. Acad. Sci. Category theory; homological algebra; ring theory. Address: Dept. of Mathematics, American University, Massachusetts & Nebraska Aves. N.W, Washington, DC 20016.

GRAY, MICHAEL WILLIAM, b. Medicine Hat, Alta, July 18, 43; m. 68; c. 1. BIOCHEMISTRY. B.Sc, Univ. Alta, 64, Ph.D.(biochem), 68. Nat. Res. Coun. Can. fel. radiobiol, sch. med, Stanford Univ, 68-70; ASST. PROF. BIOCHEM, DALHOUSIE UNIV, 70- Med. Res. Coun. Can. res. grant, 70-72. Can. Biochem. Soc. Chemical structure and biological function of RNA; minor nucleoside components of tRNA; comparative studies of mitochondrial and cytoplasmic RNA in higher plants; significance of mitochondrial nucleic acids to mitochondrial function. Address: Dept. of Biochemistry, Dalhousie University, Halifax, N.S, Can.

GRAY, M(ILDRED) GENEVA, b. Cambridge, Mass, Oct. 19, 07. EXPERIMENTAL BIOLOGY. B.S, Boston, 28, M.A, 33, Ph.D.(pharmacol), 38; Radcliffe Col, 33-34; Mass. Inst. Tech, 30, 58; Harvard Med. Sch, 33-34; N.Y. Univ, 63. Asst, Mass. Gen. Hosp, 28-32; assoc. chemist, Commonwealth of Mass, 32-35; fel, Harvard Med. Sch, 36-39; instr. physiol, Brooklyn Col, 39-40; group leader, biol. lab, Arthur D. Little, Inc, 42-57; res. physiologist, thermal sect, pioneering res. div, U.S. Qm. Res. & Eng. Labs, 57-61, TOXICOL. safety off, U.S. Army Natick Labs, 60-70, sci. intel. off, 61-70; RES. FEL, MARINE PLANT TOXICOL, HARVARD, 70- Res. assoc, Harvard Med. Sch, 40-42. Fel. Am. Inst. Chem; Am. Chem. Soc; Am. Soc. Pharmacol. & Exp. Therapeut; Sci. Res. Soc. Am; Am. Indust. Hyg. Asn. Protection of individual soldier from thermal and nuclear radiation; industrial toxicology; pharmacology of topical applications; effect of drugs on behavior. Address: 4 Lake Rd. Terrace, Cochituate, MA 01778.

GRAY, NEWTON M(cLEAN), b. Vancouver, Wash, Jan. 25, 07; m. 42; c. 2. PHYSICS. B.A, Reed Col, 29; Ph.D, N.Y. Univ, 33. Asst. physics, N.Y. Univ, 29-33; tutor, City Col. New York, 33-37, instr, 37-46, asst. prof, 46-48; assoc. prof, Whitman Col, 48-49, prof, 49-57; res. engr, Boeing Co, 57-63; RETIRED. Hyperfine structure in atomic spectra; digital computer systems implementation. Address: 420 S.W. 129th St, Seattle, WA 98146.

GRAY, OSCAR SAMUEL, b. Evansville, Ind, Dec. 12, 18; m. 39; c. 4. BIOPHYSICS. Sci. dir, Gray-Schrier Med. Res. Found, 63-64; SCI. DIR. & PRES, GRAY RES. FOUND, INC, 64-; CHMN. BD. & PRES, GRAY INDUST, INC, 64- Consult, Sanders Med. Res. Lab, Univ. Miami, 58-61; Union Carbide Res. & Develop. Corp, 62-63; Ga. Beverages, Inc, 63-64. U.S.A, 44-46. AAAS; N.Y. Acad. Sci; Royal Soc. Health. Biophysics research and development emphasizing applied and novel use of energies; application of research to production in hematology; immunology and food processing. Address: 2300 W. Commercial Blvd, Ft. Lauderdale, FL 33309.

GRAY, OTIS P, b. Racine, Wis, Apr. 1, 10; m. 49; c. 1. ORGANIC CHEMISTRY. Ph.B, Wisconsin, 33; M.Econ, Vienna, 53, Dr. Chem. Econ, 56. Various positions chem. eng, 34-37; state chemist I, U.S. Dept. Agr, Wis, 37-40; indust. economist, U.S. Dept. Army, 46-50; consult. high temperature mat, 50-58; sr. appln. engr, GEN. ELEC. CO, 58-65, SR. REP. AEROSPACE & DEFENSE RES, 65- Chem.C, U.S.A.R, 35-58, Lt. Col. AAAS; Am. Chem. Soc. Synthetic and condensation organic chemistry; industrial chemistry; high temperature ceramic and graphitic materials; aerospace research. Address: 2207 Fordham Dr, Alexandria, VA 22307.

GRAY, PAUL, b. Vienna, Austria, Dec. 8, 30; U.S. citizen; m. 52; c. 1. SYSTEMS ENGINEERING, OPERATIONS RESEARCH. B.A, N.Y. Univ, 50; Minnesota, 50-51; M.A, Michigan, 54; M.S, Purdue, 62; Ph.D.(opers. res), Stanford Univ, 68. Asst. systs. eng, Willow Run Labs, Michigan, 51-52, asst. tech. ed, 52-55; nuclear engr, Convair/Gen. Dynamics, 55-58; proposal engr, Solar Aircraft Co, 58-60; instr. elec. eng, Purdue, 60-62; res. engr. SYSTS. ENG, STANFORD RES. INST, 62-64, SR. RES. ENGR, 65-69, 70-, prog. dir. transportation, 69-70. Consult, Cubic Corp, Calif, 61; lectr, Stanford Univ, 68-69, consult. assoc. prof, 69- Inst. Elec. & Electronics Eng; Inst. Mgt. Sci; Opers. Res. Soc. Am. Urban systems; transportation; public safety; air traffic control; mixed integer programming; site location; information and decision processes; numerical analysis and digital computation; capital budgeting. Address: Stanford Research Institute, Menlo Park, CA 94025.

GRAY, PAUL E, b. Newark, N.J, Feb. 7, 32; m. 55; c. 4. ELECTRICAL ENGINEERING. S.B, Mass. Inst. Tech, 54, Nat. Sci. Found. fel. & S.M, 55, Sc.D.(elec. eng), 60. Instr. ELEC. ENG, MASS. INST. TECHNOL, 57-60, asst. prof, 60-64, assoc. prof, 64-67, prof, 67-68, Class of 1922 prof, 68-71, CHANCELLOR, 71-, dean sch. eng, 70-71, assoc. provost, 69-70, asst. provost, 68-69, assoc. dean student affairs, 65-68. Ford Found. fel, 61-63. U.S.A, 55-57, 1st Lt. Inst. Elec. & Electronics Eng; fel. Am. Acad. Arts & Sci. Physical electronics and circuit characterization of semiconductor devices; electric and magnetic properties of high-field superconductors; solid-state energy conversion. Address: Massachusetts Institute of Technology, Office of the Chancellor, Room 3-208, 77 Massachusetts Ave, Cambridge, MA 02139.

GRAY, PETER, b. London, Eng, June 4, 08; nat; m. 33. ZOOLOGY. B.Sc, London, 29, Ph.D.(zool), 31, dipl, Imp. Col, London, 33. Asst. zool, Royal Col. Sci, 27-29; zoologist, Norwich Castle Mus. Eng, 29-31; lectr. embryol, Edinburgh, 31-37; Rockefeller Found. fel, Rochester, 38-39; assoc. prof. BIOL, UNIV. PITTSBURGH, 39-43, prof, 43-45, head dept, 45-64, ANDREY AVINOFF PROF, 64- Consult. ed, Pergamon Pub. Co. With Off. Sci. Res. & Develop; U.S. Maritime Comt, 44. U.S.A.A.F, 44. AAAS; Am. Soc. Zool; Am. Micros. Soc.(pres, 62-63); Am. Asn. Anat; Royal Micros. Soc. Amphibian embryology; Crustacean parasites; optical and electron microscopy; statistical procedures in biology; tropical deterioration. Address: Dept. of Biology, University of Pittsburgh, Pittsburgh, PA 15213.

GRAY, PETER R(YGAARD), b. Ishpeming, Mich, Nov. 7, 28; m. 51; c. 4. NUCLEAR CHEMISTRY. B.S, Mich. Col. Min, 50, M.S, 51; Ph.D.(chem), California, 56. CHEMIST, Argonne Nat. Lab, 50-51; E.I. du Pont de Nemours & Co, 51-52; Dow Chem. Co, 55-61; RADIATION LAB, PHILLIPS PETROL. CO, 61- Nuclear physics; activation analysis; spectroscopy. Address: Radiation Lab, Phillips Petroleum Co, Bartlesville, OK 74003.

GRAY, PETER V(ANCE), b. Oak Park, Ill, July 17, 28; m. 56; c. 3. SOLID STATE PHYSICS. B.S, Union Col, 58; Woodrow Wilson fel, Univ. Ill, 58, M.S, 59, Gen. Elec. fel, 59-61, Ph.D.(physics), 62. Res. assoc. elec. eng, Univ. Ill, 62-63; PHYSICIST, GEN. ELEC. CO, 63- U.S.N, 51-54. Am. Phys. Soc. Semiconductor surface physics. Address: General Electric Research & Development Center, P.O. Box 8, Schenectady, NY 12301.

GRAY, RALPH DONALD, JR, b. Akron Ohio, May 15, 38; m. 68. CHEMICAL ENGINEERING. B.S.Ch.E, Case Inst. Technol, 60; Nat. Defense Educ. Act. fel, Univ. Del, 60-63, M.Ch.E, 63, Ph.D.(chem. eng), 65. Engr. HYDROCARBON THERMODYN, ESSO RES. & ENG. CO, 64-67, res. engr, 67-71, SR. RES. ENGR, 71- Am. Inst. Chem. Eng; Am. Chem. Soc. Chemical engineering thermodynamics with emphasis on hydrocarbon thermodynamics, equation of state methods and computer calculation techniques. Address: Technology Dept, Esso Research & Engineering Co, Box 101, Florham Park, NJ 07932.

GRAY, RALPH J, b. Wheeling, W.Va, Oct. 28, 23; m. 49; c. 4. PETROGRAPHY, GEOLOGY. B.S, W.Va. Univ, 51, M.S, 52; Ohio State Univ, 55-56. Geol. asst, W.Va. Geol. & Econ. Surv, 50-51; cartog. photogram. aid, photogram. div, Army Map Serv, 51-52; geologist, fuels br, U.S. Geol. Surv, 52-57; SR. RES. ENGR, APPL. RES. LAB, U.S. STEEL CORP, 57- Geol. Soc. Am; Mineral. Soc. Am; Am. Asn. Stratig. Palynologists. Use of palynology in coal correlation; application of coal petrographic techniques to the prediction of coking properties of coal; use of microscopic techniques in raw materials utilization. Address: U.S. Steel Corp, Applied Research Lab, Monroeville, PA 15146.

GRAY, RAYMOND FRANCIS, b. Morrillton, Ark, Apr. 3, 26; m. 46; c. 2. MICROBIOLOGY. B.S, Missouri, 52, M.A, 54, Ph.D.(microbiol), 60. Asst. instr. MICROBIOL, sch. med, Missouri, 56-60; head dept, Clin. Labs, 60-69; V.PRES, LAB. EXP. BIOL, INT. BIO-RES, INC, 69- Lectr. bot, univ. col, Washington (St. Louis), 61- Consult, Lab. Exp. Biol, Mo, 60-; Pleasant View Tuberc. Sanitorium, Ill, 65- U.S.M.C, 43-45. Am. Soc. Microbiol; Am. Pub. Health Asn. Studies on various hemolysins of staphylococci and their inter-reactions with hemolysins from other organisms; classification of atypical Mycobacterium. Address: International Bio-Research, Inc, Lab. for Experimental Biology, 100 N. Euclid Ave, St. Louis, MO 63108.

GRAY, REED A(LDEN), b. Santa Clara, Utah, Jan. 12, 21; m. 51; c. 2. BIOCHEMISTRY. B.S, Utah, 43, fel, 42-44, M.S, 44; fel, Calif. Inst. Tech, 46-48, Ph.D.(biochem), 48. Assoc. biochemist, Pineapple Res. Inst, Hawaii, 48-53; plant physiologist, Merck & Co, N.J, 53-60; PLANT PHYSIOLOGIST & MGR. HERBICIDE RES. & BIOCHEM, AGR. RES. CTR, STAUFFER CHEM. CO, 60- Glycerine res. award, 55. Chem.C, U.S.A, 44-46. AAAS; Am. Chem. Soc; Bot. Soc. Am; Am. Soc. Plant Physiol; Weed Sci. Soc. Am; Am. Phytopath. Soc. Plant biochemistry; study of plant growth inhibitors and hormones; biochemistry of pineapple wilt; plant viruses; antibiotics and plant diseases; weed control; herbicides; metabolism of herbicides; behavior and persistence of herbicides in soils. Address: Agricultural Research Center, Stauffer Chemical Co, P.O. Box 760, Mountain View, CA 94040.

GRAY, RICHARD C, b. West Salem, Ohio, Nov. 17, 28; m. 53; c. 2. ANIMAL PHYSIOLOGY & BREEDING. B.S, Iowa State, 52; M.S, Missouri, 63, Nat. Insts. Health fel, 63-65, Ph.D.(animal physiol), 65. Asst. prof. ANIMAL SCI, WIS. STATE UNIV, RIVER FALLS, 65-71, PROF, 71-, CHMN. DEPT, 69- U.S.A.F, 46-49, S/Sgt. Am. Soc. Animal Sci. Endocrinology of the boar; freezing of boar semen; accelerated lambing. Address: Dept. of Animal Science, Wisconsin State University, River Falls, WI 54022.

GRAY, ROBERT C(OPPING), b. Holley, N.Y, May 26, 14; m. 46. SOIL FERTILITY. B.S, Cornell, 35; California, Berkeley, 46-47; M.S, Iowa State, 53; Ph.D.(agr. econ), Va. Polytech, 63. Teacher, pub. sch, N.Y, 35-41; soil scientist, U.S. Bur. Reclamation, 47-49; exten. spec. agron, Iowa State, 49-57; AGRICULTURALIST, TENN. VALLEY AUTHORITY, 57- U.S.A, 42-46, Maj. Am. Soc. Agron; Soil Sci. Soc. Am. Educational programs for introduction and use of new and improved fertilizer materials developed by Tennessee Valley Authority, including both technology and marketing. Address: 1801 Shenandoah Rd, Florence, AL 35630.

GRAY, ROBERT HOWARD, b. Meadville, Pa, Sept. 14, 37; m. 61; c. 2. CELL BIOLOGY. B.S.Ed, Ohio, 60, M.S, 62; Ph.D.(bot), Illinois, 67. Nat. Insts. Health fel, Univ. Wis, 67-69; ASST. PROF. ENVIRON. & INDUST. HEALTH & RES. ASSOC, UNIV. MICH, 69- Am. Soc. Cell Biol. Ultrastructural and biochemical effects of cells and tissues associated with exposure to drugs and pesticides and the molecular mechanisms involved. Address: Cellular Chemistry Lab, Dept. of Environmental & Industrial Health, 1535 School of Public Health, University of Michigan, Ann Arbor, MI 48104.

GRAY, ROBIN B(RYANT), b. Statesville, N.C, Dec. 4, 25; m. 49; c. 2. AEROSPACE ENGINEERING. B.A.E, Rensselaer Polytech, 46; M.S, Ga. Inst. Tech, 47; Ph.D.(aeronaut), Princeton, 57. Res. engr, Ga. Inst. Tech, 47-49; from asst. to res. assoc, Princeton, 49-56; assoc. prof. aeronaut. eng, GA. INST. TECHNOL, 56-61, PROF. AEROSPACE ENG, 61-, ASSOC. DIR, 67- U.S.N, 43-46. Am. Helicopter Soc; Am. Inst. Aeronaut. & Astronaut. Rotary wing and propeller aerodynamics. Address: School of Aerospace Engineering, Georgia Institute of Technology, Atlanta, GA 30332.

GRAY, ROLAND H, JR, b. Toledo, Ohio, Nov. 9, 28; m. 51; c. 8. CHEMICAL ENGINEERING. B.S, Northwest. Univ, 51. Proj. engr, Dow Chem. Co, Mich, 51-59; Mgr. process develop, Dewey & Almy Chem. Div, W.R. GRACE & CO, Mass, 59-62, asst. plant mgr, Ky, 62-64, mgr. tech. develop, WASH. RES. CTR, 64-66, dir. develop, 66-68, ceramics, 68-69, sugar, 69-70, DIR. DEVELOP, 70- Sr. exec, Mass. Inst. Technol, 67. Am. Inst. Chem. Eng; Sugar Indust. Tech; Am. Soc. Sugar Beet Technol. Commercial development; process and product development, new processes for new products and improving existing processes; processes for obtaining high purity metal oxides for high performance ceramic materials; new process for improving sugar cane refining. Address: Development Dept, Washington Research Center, W.R. Grace & Co, Clarksville, MD 21029.

GRAY, ROY C, JR, b. Flemingsburg, Ky, June 4, 28; m. 54; c. 3. ANIMAL SCIENCE, BIOLOGICAL SCIENCE. B.S, Kentucky, 56, M.S, 56; Ph.D.(animal sci), Auburn Univ, 64. Instr. animal sci, Auburn Univ, 57-64; asst. prof, Univ. Ky, 64-68, assoc. exten. prof. & faculty asst. to dean col. agr, 68-69; pres. & chief exec. off, Purebred Herds of Am. Inc, 70; PRES. & FOUNDER, MOD. CATTLE MGT, INC, 70- U.S.A, 50-53, Res, 61-62, Maj. Beef cattle, management, production, nutrition. Address: Route 5, Box 125, Nicholasville, KY 40356.

GRAY, SEYMOUR J(EROME), b. Rochester, N.Y, Nov. 30, 11; m. 35; c. 2. MEDICINE. B.A, Rochester, 33; M.D, Pennsylvania, 36; fel, Chicago, 37-39, Ph.D.(med), 45. Asst. res. & res. MED, Chicago, 37-39; asst, 39-41, instr, 41-44, asst. prof, 44; HARVARD MED. SCH, 46-58, ASSOC. CLIN. PROF, 58- Lectr, U.S. State Dept. Cultural Exchange Prog; vis. prof, Mass. Inst. Tech, 63- Consult, U.S. Naval Hosp, Chelsea, Mass, 46-; nat. adv. coun, gastrointestinal cancer cmt, U.S. Pub. Health Serv, 55-60; Bur. Latin Am, Agency Int. Develop, 62, mem. task force on Cent. Am. mobile med. unit prog, 62. Chmn. working group ed. in med. & related fields, bur. ed. & cultural affairs, U.S. Dept. State, 61; mem. ad hoc panel S.Am. health progs, President's Sci. Adv. Cmt, 61. Mem, Order Hipolito Unanue, Peru; Comdr, Order of Merit Bernardo O'Higgins, Chile. Hon. mem. faculty, Univ. Chile, 56; dipl, Am. Bd. Internal Med. Civilian with Off. Sci. Res. & Develop, 44; U.S.N, 44-46. AAAS; Am. Physiol. Soc; Am. Soc. Clin. Nutrit; Am. Fedn. Clin. Res; hon. mem. Argentine Acad. Surg; hon. mem. Peruvian Acad. Med; hon. mem. Argentine, Brazilian, Chilean, Uruguayan & Venezuelan Gastroenterol. Socs. Cancer; nutrition; intestinal absorption of nutrients. Address: Harvard Medical School, Boston, MA 02114.

GRAY, SIDNEY, b. N.Y.C, Mar. 13, 24; m. 46; c. 3. PHYSICS. B.Sc, N.Y. Univ, 46; Atomic Energy Cmn. fel, Rutgers, 49-51, Ph.D.(physics), 51. Gen. scientist, New Brunswick Lab, Atomic Energy Comn, 51; res. engr, RCA Labs, RCA CORP, 51-60, leader camera tube res, astro-electronics div, 60-66, group head, visible camera tube res, conversion devices lab, 66-68, MGR. APPL. PHYSICS, ADVAN. TECHNOL, DEFENSE ELECTRONICS PRODS, 68- U.S.A.F, 43-46, Res, 46-53, 1st Lt. Am. Phys. Soc; Optical Soc. Am; Am. Inst. Aeronaut. & Astronaut. Electronic image acquisition; television camera tubes; electron optics. Address: Defense Electronics Products, RCA Corp, Camden, NJ 08102.

GRAY, STEPHEN WOOD, b. Oakland, Calif, Apr. 27, 15; m. 38. ANATOMY. A.B, Lake Forest Col, 36; A.M, Illinois, 37, fel, 38-39, Ph.D.(zool), 39. Instr. physiol, Illinois, 39-42; PROF. ANAT, SCH. MED, EMORY UNIV, 46- U.S.A.A.F, 42-45, Capt. Am. Soc. Zool; Am. Physiol. Soc; Am. Asn. Anat. Effects of gravity on tissues; dynamics of growth; embryological defects; smooth muscle. Address: Dept. of Anatomy, Emory University School of Medicine, Atlanta, GA 30332.

GRAY, THEODORE FLINT, JR, b. Anniston, Ala, Feb. 25, 39; m. 60; c. 3. ORGANIC & POLYMER CHEMISTRY. B.A, Centre Col, 60; Ph.D.(org. & polymer chem), Florida, 64. Res. chemist, RES. LABS, TENN. EASTMAN CO, DIV. EASTMAN KODAK, 65-66, SR. RES. CHEMIST, 66- Am. Chem. Soc. Kinetics and stereochemistry of intra-intermolecular polymerization; polymer structure relation to glass transitions, melt rheology and mechanical properties; structure influence on polymer stability; relation of polymer and reinforcement variables to composite's properties. Address: Research Labs, Tennessee Eastman Co, Division of Eastman Kodak, Kingsport, TN 37660.

GRAY, THOMAS C(HARLES), b. Twin Falls, Idaho, June 2, 35; m. 56; c. 4. MOLECULAR GENETICS, METABOLISM. B.S, East. Mont. Col, 60; Ph.D. (biol), Vanderbilt Univ, 65. Fel. biol, West. Reserve Univ, 64-66, res. assoc, 66-67; asst. prof. zool, Mont. State Univ, 67-68; ASST. PROF. MICROBIOL, UNIV. KY, 68- U.S.A, 55-57. Am. Soc. Microbiol; Genetics Soc. Am. Molecular genetics of pneumococcus; in vivo and in vitro chemical mutagenesis; genetic fine-structure and genetic recombination;metabolic pathways. Address: Dept. of Microbiology, University of Kentucky, Lexington, KY 40506.

GRAY, THOMAS I(RA), JR, b. Blytheville, Ark, Dec. 4, 18; m. 43; c. 4. METEOROLOGY. B.S, Ark. State Col, 40; Weather Bur-Civil Aeronaut. Admin. scholar, Chicago, 40-41. Asst. observer meteorol, Little Rock Off, U.S. Weather Bur, 41, asst. analyst, five-day forecast sect, cent. off, 41-43, analyst, 43-44, analyst supvr, 44-45, supv. analyst & asst. forecaster, extended forecast sect, 45-57, supvr. Antarctic Weather Cent, U.S. Nat. Cmt, Int. Geophys. Year, 57-59; U.S. rep, Int. Antarctic Analysis Ctr, Sci. Cmt. Antarctic Res, Australia, 59-62; RES. METEOROLOGIST, METEOROL. SATELLITE LAB, NAT. ENVIRON. SATELLITE SERV, NAT. OCEANIC & ATMOSPHERIC ADMIN, 62- Meteorol. adv, U.S. mem, Spec. Cmt. Antarctic Res, Canberra, Australia, 59, Wellington, New Zealand, 61; mem. Civil Serv. Bd. Exam, 63- AAAS; Am. Meteorol. Soc; Am. Geophys. Union. World weather description and prediction using theory models and practice to determine discreet information from remote sensor data of meteorological satellites or other indirect systems. Address: Suite 300, Meteorological Satellite Lab, National Environmental Satellite Service, National Oceanic & Atmospheric Administration, 3737 Branch Ave. S.E, Washington, DC 20031.

GRAY, THOMAS J(AMES), b. Atherstone, Eng, July 28, 17; nat; m. 41; c. 3. PHYSICAL CHEMISTRY. B.Sc, & Ph.D.(chem), Bristol, 38. Lectr. chem, Bristol, 46-53; assoc. prof. phys. chem, State Univ. N.Y. Col. Ceramics, Alfred, 53-55, prof, 58-68, adminr, off. res, 64-68; DIR, ATLANTIC INDUST. RES. INST, NOVA SCOTIA TECH. COL, 68- Sig.C, Brit. Army, 39-46, Maj. Am. Chem. Soc; Am. Phys. Soc; fel. Am. Ceramic Soc; Faraday Soc; fel. Am. Inst. Chem; Can. Res. Mgt. Asn; Can. Ceramic Soc; Eng. Inst. Can. Catalysis; semiconductors; dielectric and magnetic properties of materials; high vacuum technique; high temperature materials; fuel cells; thermoelectric devices. Address: Atlantic Industrial Research Institute, Nova Scotia Technical College, P.O. Box 1000, Halifax, N.S, Can.

GRAY, TRUMAN S(TRETCHER), b. Spencer, Ind, May 3, 06; m. 31. ELECTRICAL ENGINEERING. B.S, Texas, 26, B.A, 27; Coffin fel, Mass. Inst. Tech, 28-30, M.S, 29, Sc.D.(elec. eng), 30. Asst. physics, Texas, 24-27; ELEC. ENG, MASS. INST. TECHNOL, 27-28, instr, 30-35, asst. prof, 35-42, assoc. prof, 42-60, prof, 60-71, EMER. PROF, 71- Am. Soc. Eng. Educ; fel. Inst. Elec. & Electronics Eng. Photoelectric integraph; gas tubes; electronic tube applications; nuclear instrumentation; applied electronics. Address: 22 Hayes Ave, Lexington, MA 02173.

GRAY, WALTER C(LARKE), b. Roanoke, Va, Oct. 4, 19; m. 54; c. 6. CHEMICAL ENGINEERING. B.S, Va. Polytech, 41, fel, 47-49, M.S, 49, Tenn. Eastman Co. fel, 49-50, fel, 51-52, Ph.D.(chem. eng), 52. Supvr. tech. dept, Radford Arsenal, Hercules Powder Co, 51-52; RES. ENGR, Carothers Res. Lab, exp. sta, E.I. DU PONT DE NEMOURS & CO, INC, Del, 52-54, DACRON RES. LAB, KINSTON, 54- U.S.A, 41-47, Lt. Col. Nat. Soc. Prof. Eng. Ultrasonics; polymers such as polyamides, polycaproamides and polyethylene terephthalate by continuous polymerization; propellants for guided missiles; miscellaneous design; development and fundamental research. Address: Route 1, Box 621, Greenville, NC 27834.

GRAY, WALTER SCOTT, JR, b. Denison, Tex, Dec. 19, 32; m. 62; c. 3. TAXONOMY, ECOLOGY. B.S, Southeast. State Col, 54; Univ. Okla, 50-51, 56-57; M.S, Univ. of the Pac, 69; Ph.D.(biol), George Washington Univ, 72. Biol. teacher, pub. schs, Tex. & Calif, 54-68; res. assoc. Antarctic Crustacea, NAT. MUS. NATURAL HIST, SMITHSONIAN INST, 69-71, RES. ASST. CRUSTACEA, 71-, res. assoc, 66-67. Nat. Sci. Found. fel, inst. teachers, Univ. Calif, Berkeley, summers, 59 & 62; res. assoc. & Nat. Sci. Found. res. fel, Univ. of the Pac, summer 64; res. assoc, Ore. State Univ, summer 68; Nat. Sci. Found-Smithsonian Inst. grant, 69-71. Consult, Smithsonian Oceanog. Sorting Ctr, 69-; Tex. Instruments, Inc, 71-; B-K Dynamics, 71-; Hazleton Labs, 71- AAAS; Am. Inst. Biol. Sci. Ecology and systematics of marine amphipods. Address: Division of Crustacea, National Museum of Natural History, Washington, DC 20560.

GRAY, WALTER S(TEVEN), b. Ponca City, Okla, Feb. 21, 38. NUCLEAR PHYSICS. B.S, Okla. State, 58, M.S, 60; NASA fel, Colorado, 63-64, Ph.D. (physics), 64. Res. assoc. nuclear physics, UNIV. MICH, 64-66, ASST. PROF. PHYSICS, 66- Summers, physicist, U.S. Naval Ordnance Lab, Md, 59, 60. Am. Phys. Soc. Nuclear spectroscopy and accelerator-induced nuclear reactions. Address: Dept. of Physics, 738 Physics-Astronomy Bldg, Cyclotron Lab, N. Campus, University of Michigan, Ann Arbor, MI 48105.

GRAY, WILLARD F(RANKLIN), b. Flint, Tex, Dec. 25, 13; m. 37; c. 2. ELECTRICAL ENGINEERING. B.S, Texas Tech. Col, 34; M.S, Agr. & Mech. Col, Texas, 40. Clerk, Tex. Power & Light Co, 34-35, asst. engr, 35-36, statistician, 35-37; instr. elec. eng, Texas Tech. Col, 37-39, asst. prof, 39-43, assoc. prof, 43-46; asst. prof. in charge elec. mach. lab, Mass. Inst. Technol, 46-47; assoc. prof. ELEC. ENG, UNIV. ALA, TUSCALOOSA, 47-49, PROF, 49-, ASSOC. ACAD. V.PRES. & DEAN ADMIN, 71-, head dept, 59-66, asst. v.pres. acad. affairs, 66-68, asst. v.pres. admin, 68-71. Am. Soc. Eng. Educ; Inst. Elec. & Electronics Eng; Nat. Soc. Prof. Eng; Nat. Coun. Eng. Exam. Networks; electrical apparatus and machinery. Address: Box 3625, University of Alabama, University, AL 35486.

GRAY, W(ILLIAM) D(AVID), b. Gilford, North Ireland, May 12, 16; nat; m. 44, c. 2. PHARMACOLOGY. B.A, Clark, 38; M.A, Toronto, 40; fel, 38-40, Columbia, 46-47; Utah, 47-48; Sterling-Winthrop fel, Yale, 48-49, Ph.D. (pharm), 50. Res. assoc, Ciba Pharmaceut. Prods, Inc, N.J, 40-42; Merck Inst. Therapeut. Res, 46-47; pharmacologist, LEDERLE LABS. DIV, AM. CYANAMID CO, 50-54, group leader, pharmacol, 54-56, head, dept. exp. pharmacol, 56-71, DIR, CENT. NERVOUS SYST. DISEASE THER. RES, 71- U.S.A.A.F, 42-46. Am. Soc. Pharmacol. & Exp. Therapeut. Neuropharmacology; general pharmacodynamic and behavioral actions of CNS agents; biochemical pharmacology of CNS agents; biogenic amines and anticonvulsant action of carbonic anhydrase inhibitors. Address: 31 Diane Dr, New City, NY 10956.

GRAY, WILLIAM D(UDLEY), b. Jeffersonville, Ind, Sept. 21, 12; m. 41; c. 3. MYCOLOGY. A.B, DePauw, 33; Nat. Res. Coun. fel, Wisconsin, 38; Ph.D. (bot), Pennsylvania, 38. Asst. bot, Pennsylvania, 34-38; instr. plant path, Swarthmore Col, 38; res. mycologist, Joseph E. Seagram & Sons, Inc, Ky, 39-40, from mycologist to dir. res, 42-44; instr. plant physiol. & path, Miami (Ohio), 40-42; biologist, Qm Depot, Ind, 44-46; assoc. prof. BOT, Iowa State Univ, 46-47; Ohio State Univ, 47-52, PROF, 52-64; South. Ill. Univ, 64-70; NORTH. ILL. UNIV, 70- Fulbright lectr, Univ. Col. Rhodesia & Nyasaland, 59; summer consult, Ctr. Adv. Studies, India, 64; consult, Wright-Patterson Air Force Base, 60- Bot. Soc. Am; Mycol. Soc. Am. Industrial mycology; physiology of fungi. Address: Dept. of Biological Sciences, Northern Illinois University, DeKalb, IL 60115.

GRAY, W(ILLIAM) M(acDONALD), b. Toronto, Ont, Oct. 3, 14; m. 45; c. 3. PHYSICS. B.A, Toronto, 35, Banting Inst. fel, 36-37, M.A, 37, Nat. Res. Coun. Can. scholars: 38-40, Res. Coun. Ont. scholars, 47-49, Ph.D.(physics), 49. Demonstr. physics, Western Ontario, 35-36; Toronto, 37-38, 46-47; lectr, Reading, 49-52; asst. res. off, Nat. Res. Coun. Can, Ottawa, 52-53; sci. off, MINES BR, Dept. Mines & Tech. Surv, 53-56, sr. sci. off, 56-65, RES. SCIENTIST, CAN. DEPT. ENERGY, MINES & RESOURCES, 65- R.C.N, 40-46, Lt. Comdr. Optical Soc. Am; Can. Asn. Physicists; Brit. Inst. Physics. & Phys. Soc. Spectroscopy; physics of rocks. Address: 348 Billings Ave, Ottawa, Ont. K1H 5L3, Can.

GRAY, WILLIAM MASON, b. Detroit, Mich, Oct. 9, 29; m. 54; c. 3. METEOROLOGY. B.A, George Washington, 52; M.S, Chicago, 59, Ph.D.(geophys. sci), 64. Res. asst. meteorol, Chicago, 57-60; asst. meteorologist, COLO. STATE UNIV, 61-64, asst. prof. ATMOSPHERIC SCI, 64-67, ASSOC. PROF, 67- Nat. Sci. Found. res. grant, Japan, 65-66. U.S.A.F, 53-57, Res, 57-71, Maj. Am. Meteorol. Soc. Atmospheric science; tropical meteorology and storms; cumulus convection; meteorological observations; tornadoes. Address: Dept. of Atmospheric Science, Colorado State University, Ft. Collins, CO 80521.

GRAY, WILLIAM ROBERT, b. London, Eng, Jan. 29, 37; m. 62; c. 2. MOLECULAR BIOLOGY. B.A, Cambridge, 60, M.A, & Ph.D.(protein chem), 64. Res. fel. BIOL, Calif. Inst. Technol, 64-66, sr. res. fel, 66-70; ASSOC. PROF, UNIV. UTAH, 70- AAAS; Protein structure, function, and evolution; antibodies, cell membranes, structural proteins; techniques for determining protein sequence; mass spectrometry. Address: Dept. of Biology, University of Utah, Salt Lake City, UT 84112.

GRAY, WILLIAM T(HURSTON, III), b. Cincinnati, Ohio, Sept. 6, 07; m. 38; c. 2. PHYSICS. B.S, Northwestern, 28, E.E, 29, Ph.D.(physics), 35. Elec. engr, Gen. Elec. Co, 29-32; res. physicist, Corning Glass Works, 35-48; Leeds & Northrup Co, 48-51, chief phys. div, res. dept, 51-58, sr. scientist, 58-61, staff scientist, 61-67, prin. scientist, 67-72; RETIRED. Optical Soc. Am; Am. Ceramic Soc; Inst. Elec. & Electronics Eng. Radiation phyrometry, visible and infrared; methods for calibration of temperature measuring instruments; accuracy of temperature measurements. Address: 521 Walnut St, Jenkintown, PA 19046.

GRAYBEAL, JACK DANIEL, b. Detroit, Mich, May 16, 30; m. 54; c. 3. PHYSICAL CHEMISTRY. B.S, West Virginia, 51; M.S, Wisconsin, 53, Ph.D. (phys. chem), 55. Mem. tech. staff, Bell Tel. Labs, 55-57; asst. prof. CHEM, W.Va. Univ, 57-62, assoc. prof, 62-68; VA. POLYTECH. INST. & STATE UNIV, 68-69, PROF, 69- AAAS; Am. Chem. Soc; Am. Phys. Soc.

Microwave spectroscopy; nuclear quadrupole resonance spectroscopy; molecular structure. Address: Dept. of Chemistry, Virginia Polytechnic Institute & State University, Blacksburg, VA 24061.

GRAYBEAL, WALTER THOMAS, b. Lansing, N.C, June 16, 18; m. 54; c. 2. EDUCATIONAL PSYCHOLOGY, MATHEMATICS. B.A, Appalachian State Teachers Col, 39; A.M, North Carolina, 48, Ph.D.(ed. psychol, math), 58. Teacher, pub. schs, N.C, 39-44; instr. math, North Carolina, 46-47; Oak Ridge Mil. Inst. N.C, 47-48; math. & physics, EMORY & HENRY COL, 48-49, asst. prof, 49-55, assoc. prof, 55-58, PROF. MATH, 58-, ASSOC. ACAD. DEAN, 71-, acting chmn. math. dept, 62-63, dir. admissions, 63-65, dir. instnl. studies, 65-69, registr, 65-71, asst. acad. dean, 69-71. U.S.N, 44-46. Math. Asn; Am; Am. Phys. Soc. Statistical research involving predictive factors relating to achievement and success in mathematics. Address: Dept. of Mathematics, Emory & Henry College, Emory, VA 24327.

GRAYBIEL, ASHTON, b. Port Huron, Mich, July 24, 02; m. 34; c. 2. MEDICINE. A.B, Southern California, 24, A.M, 25; M.D, Harvard Med. Sch, 30. Moseley traveling fel, Univ. Col. Hosp, London, 32-33; Dalton fel, Mass. Gen. Hosp, 33-34; INSTR. CARDIOL, SCH. AVIATION MED, U.S. DEPT. NAVY, 42-, RES. AVIATION PHYSIOL, 42-, SPEC. ASST. SCI. PROGS. & HEAD, PSYCHOPHYSIOL. DEPT, 70-, dir. res, 45-70. Instr, Harvard Med. Sch, 40-42; res. assoc, fatigue lab, Harvard, 36-42; lectr, med. col, Alabama, 58-68. With Nat. Res. Council, 44. Med.C, U.S.N, 42-45. Am. Med. Asn; Am. Heart Asn; Am. Physiol. Asn. Electrocardiography in practice; clinical electrocardiography; effect of acceleration on semicircular canals and otolith organs. Address: Psychophysiology Dept, Naval Aerospace Medical Research Lab, Naval Aerospace Medical Institute, Pensacola, FL 32512.

GRAYBILL, BRUCE M(YRON), b. Council Bluffs, Iowa, Oct. 2, 31; m. 52; c. 3. PHYSICAL ORGANIC CHEMISTRY. B.S, Iowa State, 55; Tenn. Eastman fel, Fla. State, 57-58, Ph.D.(chem), 59. Res. chemist, Rohm & Haas Co, 59-61; asst. prof. CHEM, GRACELAND COL, 61-66, assoc. prof, 66-70, PROF. & CHMN. DIV. SCI. & MATH, 70- Summers, Nat. Sci. Found. fels, Case Inst. Technol, 63, Ore. State Univ, 64, Univ. Tenn, 65, Univ. Calif, Riverside, 68; Atomic Energy Comn. faculty fel, P.R. Nuclear Ctr, 70. Am. Chem. Soc; Am. Inst. Chem.(sr. award, 54). Organic reaction mechanisms. Address: Dept. of Chemistry, Graceland College, Lamoni, IA 50140.

GRAYBILL, FRANKLIN A, b. Carson, Iowa, Sept. 23, 21; m. 47; c. 2. MATHEMATICAL STATISTICS. B.S, William Penn Col, 47; M.S, Okla. State, 49; Ph.D.(math. statist), Iowa State, 52. Prof. math. & sta. statistician, agr. exp. sta, Okla. State, 52-60; PROF. MATH. STATISTS. & DIR. STATISTS. LAB, COLO. STATE UNIV, 60- Consult, Standard Oil Co.(N.J), 54- U.S.A, 42-46. Biomet. Soc; fel. Am. Statist. Asn. Variance component analysis. Address: Statistical Lab, Colorado State Universtiy, Ft. Collins, CO 80521.

GRAYDON, W(ILLIAM) F(REDERICK), b. Toronto, Ont, June 27, 19; m. 45; c. 5. PHYSICAL CHEMISTRY. B.A.Sc, Toronto, 42, M.A.Sc, 45; Ph.D.(chem), Minnesota, 49. Asst. prof. CHEM. ENG, UNIV. TORONTO, 49-59, PROF, 59-, ASSOC. DEAN, FACULTY APPL. SCI, 66-, CHMN. DEPT. CHEM. ENG. & APPL. CHEM, 70- Am. Chem. Soc; Faraday Soc; Chem. Inst. Can; The Chem. Soc. Ion exchange; corrosion; process dynamics; applied physical chemistry. Address: Faculty of Applied Science, University of Toronto, Toronto 5, Ont, Can.

GRAYHACK, JOHN T(HOMAS), b. Kankakee, Ill, Aug. 21, 23; m. 50; c. 5. UROLOGY. B.S, Chicago, 45, M.D, 47. Instr. UROL, sch. med, Hopkins, 52-54; asst. prof, MED. SCH, NORTHWEST. UNIV.(ILL), 56-61, assoc. prof, 61-63, PROF. & CHMN. DEPT, 63- Fel, Am. Cancer Soc, 50-51; Runyon fel, 52-54. U.S.A.F, 54-56, Capt. AAAS; Am. Med. Asn; Am. Asn. Genito-Urinary Surg; Clin. Soc. Genito-Urinary Surg; Endocrine Soc. Factors in normal and abnormal prostatic growth; evaluation and treatment of diseases of genito-urinary tract. Address: Dept. of Urology, Northwestern University Medical School, 303 E. Chicago Ave, Chicago, IL 60611.

GRAYSON, EDWIN, b. Barrow-in-Furness, Eng, Sept. 7, 13; nat; m. 42. CHEMICAL ENGINEERING. Ch.E, Rensselaer Polytech, 35, M.S, 36. Group leader, TENN. EASTMAN CO, 36-46, res. chem. engr, res. labs, 46-50, sr. res. chem. engr, 50-66, CHEM. PROJ. ENGR, ENG. DIV, 66- Am. Inst. Chem. Eng; Nat. Soc. Prof. Eng. Design and construction of chemical equipment; supervision of research maintenance shop. Address: Tennessee Eastman Co, Kingsport, TN 37660.

GRAYSON, HERBERT G, b. New York, N.Y, Jan. 5, 26; m. 47; c. 3. CHEMICAL ENGINEERING. B.S, City Col. New York, 46; M.S, Polytech. Inst. Brooklyn, 52. Sr. develop. eng, eng. dept. Socony Mobil Oil Co, Inc, 47-64, PROD. PLANNER, PROD. DEPT, MOBIL OIL CORP, 64- Am. Inst. Chem. Eng. Properties of petroleum; vapor-liquid equilibria and enthalpy; unit operations; fluid flow; heat transfer; tray efficiency; properties of granular solids; air pollution; energy and technological forecasting. Address: Products Dept, Mobil Oil Corp, 150 E. 42nd St, New York, NY 10017.

GRAYSON, JAMES McD(ONALD), b. Bland, Va, Aug. 6, 13; m. 45; c. 4. ENTOMOLOGY. B.S, Va. Polytech, 35, M.S, 37; Gen. Ed. Bd. fel, Iowa State, 39-40, Ph.D.(entomol), 41. Lab. asst. ENTOMOL, VA. POLYTECH. INST. & STATE UNIV, 36-37, instr, 37-39, 40-42, asst. prof, 42-46, assoc. prof, 46-54, PROF. & HEAD DEPT, 54-, asst. entomologist, exp. sta, Holland, 44-46. Mem, Int. Cong. Plant Protection, Ger, 57, Austria, 67; Pan-Am. Sanit. Bur-WHO seminar, Panama City, 58; Int. Congs. Entom, Austria, 60 & Eng, 64. Entom. Soc. Am. Insect resistance to insecticides; insect physiology and toxicology. Address: Dept. of Entomology, Virginia Polytechnic Institute & State University, Blacksburg, VA 24061.

GRAYSON, J(OHN), b. Huddersfield, Eng, Jan. 4, 19; m. 61. PHYSIOLOGY. B.Sc, Victoria Univ. Manchester, 40, M.Sc, 41, M.B. & Ch.B, 43, M.D, 49, D.Sc.(physiol), 66. Res. asst. surg, Royal Victoria Infirmary, Eng, 47-49; lectr. PHYSIOL, Univ. Bristol, 49-55; prof. & chmn. dept, Univ. Ibadan, 55-67; vis. prof, Univ. Alta, 67-68; PROF, UNIV. TORONTO, 68- Mem. arctic panel, Defence & Civil Inst. Environ. Med, Can, 68- R.A.M.C, 44-47. Can. Physiol. Soc; Brit. Physiol. Soc; Europ. Soc. Microcirc; Can. Soc. Microcirc.(v.pres, 71). Control of blood flow in the peripheral tissues; responses of skin blood vessels to environmental change; role of gastro-intestinal and liver vessels in homeostasis; metabolic control of brain vessels; haemodynamics of heart blood vessels, especially as affected by acute occlusion and atheroma. Address: Dept. of Physiology & Medical Sciences, University of Toronto, Toronto, Ont, Can.

GRAYSON, JOHN F(RANCIS), b. Bay City, Mich, Mar. 23, 28; m. 51; c. 4. PALYNOLOGY. B.S, Univ. Mich, 51, fel, 52-54, M.S, 52, Ph.D.(bot), 56. Sr. res. palynologist, res. labs, Socony Mobil Oil Co, Tex, 54-62; res. group supvr, RES. CTR, Pan Am. Petrol. Corp, 61-68, RES. ASSOC, 68-71, AMOCO PROD. CO, 71- U.S.A, 45-47. AAAS; Am. Asn. Petrol. Geol; Am. Geol. Inst; Am. Asn. Stratig. Palynologists; Geol. Soc. Am; Bot. Soc. Am. Plant geography and ecology; stratigraphic geology; paleontology; paleobotany. Address: Research Center, Amoco Production Co, P.O. Box 591, Tulsa, OK 74102.

GRAYSON, LAWRENCE P(ETER), b. Brooklyn, N.Y, May 16, 37; m. 64; c. 4. ELECTRICAL ENGINEERING. B.E.E, Polytech. Inst. Brooklyn, 58, fels, 58-61, M.E.E, 59, Ph.D.(elec. eng), 62. Asst. prof. elec. eng, Johns Hopkins Univ, 62-67; Ford Found. res. eng, practice, Thomas J. Watson Res. Ctr, IBM Corp, 67-68; assoc. prof. elec. eng, Manhattan Col, 68-69; specialist comput. in educ, bur. res, U.S. OFF. EDUC, 69-70, DEP. DIR. DIV. EDUC. TECHNOL, BUR. LIBR. & EDUC. TECHNOL, 70- Summer res. engr, Grumman Aircraft Eng. Co, 62; consult, math. br, Frankford Arsenal, 62-66; mem, educ. systs. comt, Nat. Acad. Eng. Comn. on Educ, 68-; Nat. Comt. Full Develop. Instructional TV Fixed Serv, 69- U.S.A, 61-62, 1st Lt. Inst. Elec. & Electronics Eng; Am. Soc. Eng. Educ. Nonlinear oscillations; nonlinear and adaptive control systems; engineering education; educational technology; computers, satellites. Address: Division of Libraries & Educational Technology, U.S. Office of Education, Washington, DC 20202.

GRAYSON, MARTIN, b. New York, N.Y, Mar. 2, 28; m. 70. PHYSICAL & ORGANIC CHEMISTRY. B.A, N.Y. Univ, 48; Standard Oil (Ind) fel, Purdue, 49-50, Atomic Energy Cmn. fel, 50-52, Ph.D.(chem), 52. Res. chemist, nitrogen div, Allied Chem. Co, 52-56; MEM. STAFF, AM. CYANAMID CO, 56- Adj. assoc. prof, Univ. Bridgeport. AAAS; Am. Chem. Soc; Tech. Asn. Pulp & Paper Indust. Organophosphorus chemistry; catalysis; transition metal chemistry; kinetics; peroxide and oxidation chemistry; lignin and carbohydrates. Address: American Cyanamid Co, 1937 W. Main St, Stamford, CT 06904.

GRAYSON, MERRILL, b. N.Y.C, Apr. 19, 19. OPHTHALMOLOGY, SURGERY. B.A, N.Y. Univ. 38, M.D, 41. Asst. prof. OPHTHAL, med. center, Indiana, 57-60; assoc. prof. & chmn. dept, sch. med, Arkansas, 60-61; assoc. prof, MED. CTR, UNIV. IND, INDIANAPOLIS, 61-68, PROF, 68-, SURG. DIR. LIONS EYE BANK OF IND, 61- Med. bd. dirs, Eye Bank Asn. Am, 68- Dipl, Am. Bd. Ophthal, 55. Med.C, U.S.A.F, 54-56, Maj. Am. Acad. Ophthal. & Otolaryngol.(merit award, 71); Am. Med. Asn. Diseases and surgery of the cornea. Address: Dept. of Ophthalmology, Medical Center, Indiana University, 1100 W. Michigan St, Indianapolis, IN 46202.

GRAYSON, PHILLIP WARREN, b. Oklahoma City, Okla, Oct. 18, 40; m. 63; c. 1. ANALYTICAL CHEMISTRY. B.S, Lamar State Col, 63; NASA fel, Tex. Tech, Col, 63-67, M.S, 66, Welch Found. fel, 67-68, Ph.D.(anal. chem), 68. SR. RES. CHEMIST, ANAL. RES. & DEVELOP, MONSANTO CO, 68- Am. Chem. Soc. The chemistry of rhenium compounds in liquid ammonia; the 2-pyridylketoximes as analytical reagents for determining rhenium; the use of gel permeation chromatography for the seapration and analysis of small molecules and oligomers; heterogeneous catalysis. Address: Lab. AR-32, Monsanto Co, P.O. Box 1311, Texas City, TX 77590.

GRAYSON, WILLIAM C(URTIS), JR, b. Decatur, Miss, Nov. 17, 29; m. 51; div; c. 3. THEORETICAL PHYSICS. S.B, Chicago, 50; fel. & Ph.D.(physics), Duke, 55. Physicist, LAWRENCE RADIATION LAB, UNIV. CALIF, 54-58, group leader, theoret. div, 58-68, HEAD THEORET. PHYSICS DIV, 68- Am. Phys. Soc. Nuclear models; beta decay; neutron transport. Address: Lawrence Radiation Lab, University of California, P.O. Box 808, Livermore, CA 94551.

GRAYSON-SMITH, HUGH, b. Toronto, Ont, May 16, 00; m. 31; 55; c. 1. PHYSICS. B.A, Toronto, 21, M.A, 22, Ph.D.(spectros), 26. Demonstr. physics, Toronto, 24-27; meteorologist, Dom. Meteorol. Serv, 27-29; asst. prof. PHYSICS, British Columbia, 29-32; lectr, Toronto, 32-35, asst. prof, 35-38, assoc. prof, 38-49; prof. & head dept, UNIV. ALTA, 49-64, EMER. PROF, 64-; AUTHOR, 64- Mem. metrol. div, Nat. Res. Coun. Can, 40. Mem. Order of the British Empire. Am. Phys. Soc; Royal Soc. Can; Am. Asn. Physicists. Spectroscopy; meteorology; superconductivity; physical properties of liquid helium; low temperature calorimetry; oxygen equipment for aircraft; dielectrics and second-order transitions; textbooks of science for the non-specialist. Address: 3020 Oakdowne Rd, Victoria, B.C, Can.

GRAYSTON, J. THOMAS, b. Wichita, Kans, Sept. 6, 24; m. 47; c. 3. PREVENTIVE MEDICINE. B.S, Chicago, 47, M.D, 48, M.S, 52. Epidemiologist, Commun. Disease Ctr, U.S. Pub. Health Serv, 51-53; instr. med, Chicago, 53-55, asst. prof, 55-60, assoc. prof, 60; prof. prev. med. & chmn. dept, sch. med, UNIV. WASH, 60-70, PROF. EPIDEMIOL. & INT. HEALTH, 70-, V.PRES. HEALTH AFFAIRS, 71-, dean sch. pub. health & community med, 70-71. Chief div. microbiol. & epidemiol, Naval Med. Res. Unit, Taiwan, 57-60; assoc. mem, Cmn. Acute Respiratory Diseases, 61-65, mem, 65-; panel on biol. & med, Dept. Defense, 62-66; virol. & rickettsiology study sect, Nat. Insts. Health, 63-67, int. ctrs. comt, 67-71; expert comt. trachoma, WHO, 71- Dipl, Am. Bd. Internal Med, 57; Am. Bd. Prev. Med, 68. Am. Soc. Clin. Invest; Soc. Exp. Biol. & Med; fel. Am. Pub. Health Asn; Am. Fedn. Clin. Res; Am. Epidemiol. Soc; Int. Epidemiol. Soc; Am. Asn. Physicians; Infectious Diseases Soc. Am; Am. Col. Prev. Med. Epidemiology and prevention of infectious diseases; international health. Address: WJ 10, University of Washington, Seattle, WA 98195.

GRAYZEL, HAROLD G(REGORY), b. Kharkov, Russia, Apr. 30, 99; nat; m; c. 2. MEDICINE. B.S, City Col, 20; M.D, N.Y. Univ, 24. Intern, Sinai

Hosp, Md, 24-25, pediat. res, Jewish Hosp, N.Y, 25-27; intern, Willard Parker Hosp, 27; Bellevue Hosp, 27; from instr. to asst. prof. CLIN. PEDIAT, STATE UNIV. N.Y. DOWNSTATE MED. CTR, 30-37, 48-63, ASSOC. PROF, 63- Vis. pediatrician, dept. hosps, Neposint Beach Hosp, 27-42; from asst. to attend. pediatrician, Jewish Hosp, Brooklyn, 28-; dir. pediat, Jewish Chronic Disease Hosp, 61-; consult. pediatrician, Jewish Hosp. Brooklyn, 64- Private practice. Dipl, Am. Bd. Pediat, 36. U.S.A, 17-19. Fel. Am. Diabetes Asn; fel. Am. Med. Asn; fel. Am. Acad. Pediat. Diabetes; tuberculosis; carbohydrate metabolism; dietary production of amyloidosis in animals; specific nutritional factors and liver extract factors on production and treatment of amyloidosis; blood and urine pepsinogen studies in health and diseases. Address: Dept. of Pediatrics, State University of New York Downstate Medical Center, 450 Clarkson Ave, Brooklyn, NY 11203.

GRAZIADEI, PASQUALE P. C, b. Pavia, Italy, July 13, 21; m. 58; c. 4. NEUROANATOMY. M.D, Pavia, 47. Specialist internal med, inst. clin. med, Univ. Pavia, 47-49, asst. prof. anat, univ, 47-52; Genoa, 52-58, prof, 58-62; hon. res. assoc, Univ. Col, London, 62-66; vis. asst. prof. BIOL. SCI, FLA. STATE UNIV, 66-67, ASSOC. PROF, 67- Consult, Nutrit. Found, 68-70. Am. Asn. Anat; Am. Physiol. Soc. Comparative neuroanatomy; chemo-receptor systems; invertebrates' taste; vertebrate olfactory organs. Address: Dept. of Biological Science, Florida State University, Tallahassee, FL 32306.

GRAZIANO, F(RANCIS) D(OMINIC), b. Flushing, N.Y, Mar. 24, 33; m. 54; c. 5. PHYSICAL CHEMISTRY. B.S, Iona Col, 54; Atomic Energy Comn. fel, Buffalo, 55-57, M.A, 56, Union Carbide Corp. fel, 58, Ph.D.(chem), 60. Asst, Buffalo, 54-57; res. chemist, film dept, E.I. du Pont de Nemours & Co, 58-60; res. supvr. org. coatings, Nat. Steel Corp, 60-63; dir. metal decorating res, Midland Indust. Finishes Co, Inc, 63-66, V.PRES. & TECH. DIR, 66-69, MIDLAND DIV, DEXTER CORP, 69- Summers, chemist, Union Carbide Corp, N.Y, 56-57. AAAS; Am. Chem. Soc. Exchange reaction kinetics using isotopic tracers; inorganic complex ion chemistry; polyester and polyurethane chemistry; chemical conversion coatings for metal surfaces; container and weatherable coatings; silicone copolymer chemistry and coatings. Address: Midland Division, Dexter Corp, P.O. Box 620, Waudegan, IL 60085.

GRAZIANO, KENNETH DONALD, b. Dunkirk, N.Y, Apr. 10, 42; m. 69. IMMUNOBIOLOGY. B.A, Colgate Univ, 63; M.S, Syracuse Univ, 65; Ph.D.(biol), Johns Hopkins Univ, 70. NAT. INSTS. HEALTH FEL, SCH. MED, JOHNS HOPKINS UNIV, 69- AAAS; Am. Soc. Zool; Transplantation Soc. Differences of normal and malignant cell surface antigens and their relation to differences between embryonic and adult cell surfaces; control and prevention of malignant growth and spread. Address: Division of Oncology, Baltimore City Hospitals, Baltimore, MD 21224.

GRDINIC, MARCEL RUDOLPH, b. Sarajevo, Yugoslavia; m. 55. ORGANIC CHEMISTRY, CHEMICAL ENGINEERING. Masters D, Univ. Zagreb, 52, Ph.D.(org. chem), 59. Fel. chem, Univ. Ore, 61-63, asst. prof, 63-66; ORG. CHEM, UNIV. WIS, MARATHON CAMPUS, 66-68, ASSOC. PROF, 69- Croatian Chem. Soc; Am. Chem. Soc. Natural products; alkaloids; antiradiation compounds; organic structural chemistry; organic synthetic chemistry; reaction mechanisms. Address: Dept. of Chemistry, University of Wisconsin, Marathon Campus, Wausau, WI 54401.

GREAGER, O(SWALD) H(ERMAN), b. Hyattsville, Md, Aug. 23, 05; m. 26; c. 1. CHEMISTRY. B.S, Maryland, 25; M.S, Michigan, 27, Ph.D.(chem), 29. Chemist, E.I. du Pont de Nemours & Co, 29-42; tech. off, Manhattan eng. dist, 42-46; head separations div. tech. dept, Hanford Atomic Prod. Oper, Gen. Elec. Co, 47-48, asst. mgr, tech. sect, 48-51, mgr, tech. eng. dept, 51-54, pile tech. eng. dept, 54-56, res. & eng, irradiation processing dept, 56-65, consult. engr, atomic prod. div, 65-68, mgr. div. planning oper, 68-70; NUCLEAR CONSULT, 70- Chmn, Wash. State Thermal Power Plant Site Eval. Coun, 70- U.S.A, 42-46, Lt. Col. Fel. Am. Nuclear Soc; Am. Chem. Soc. Liquid-solid interfacial relationships; pigments and paints; cement and related building materials; nuclear technology. Address: P.O. Box 202, Richland, WA 99352.

GREANEY, F(RANK) J(AMES), b. Birmingham, Eng, Sept. 16, 97; m. 48. PLANT PATHOLOGY. B.S.A, Toronto, 22; M.S, Minnesota, 26, Ph.D.(plant path), 31. Plant disease investr, 20-23; asst. plant pathologist, Dom. Rust Res. Lab, Can. Dept. Agr, 23-26, plant pathologist, 26-37, agr. scientist, 37-46; dir, Line Elevators Farm Serv, Man, 46-67; RETIRED. AAAS; Am. Phytopath. Soc; Can. Phytopath. Soc; fel. Agr. Inst. Can. Root-rot diseases of cereals; seed-borne diseases of cereals; soil microbiology; agricultural administration and extension. Address: 3148 Village Green Dr, Sarasota, FL 33580.

GREANEY, T(HOMAS) J(OSEPH), JR, b. Houston, Tex, Sept. 28, 21; m. 44; c. 4. CHEMICAL ENGINEERING. B.S, Rice Inst, 43. Mem. tech. serv. div, Humble Oil & Ref. Co, 43-51, sect. head, 52-57, asst. head tech. div, 57-60, mgr. res. & develop, 60-61, hqs. 61-64; new prod. lines, Esso Chem. Co, Inc, New York, N.Y, 65-66; mgr. paramins & specialties div, Enjay Chem. Co, 66-70; SR. ADV, PARAMINS DEPT, ESSO CHEM. CO, NEW YORK, 70- Am. Chem. Soc; Am. Inst. Chem. Eng. Organic and physical chemistry catalysis; engineering; research administration. Address: 50 Tanglewood Dr, Summit, NJ 07901.

GREANEY, WILLIAM A, b. Memphis, Tenn, Jan. 10, 31; m. 54; c. 2. OPERATIONS RESEARCH. B.S.Ch.E, Tennessee, 52; M.S, Cornell, 59; Ph.D.(opers. res), Case, 65. Proj. engr, Wright Air Develop. Ctr, 53-55; nuclear engr, Internuclear Co, 57-61; asst. prof. indust. eng, State Univ. N.Y. Buffalo, 64-67; assoc. prof, Univ. Pittsburgh, 67-70; tech. assoc. econ. & comput. sci. div, Gulf Res. & Develop. Co, 70; MGR. ANAL. SERV, COMPUTATION & COMMUN. SERV. DEPT, GULF OIL CORP, 71- U.S.A.F, 53-55, 1st Lt. Opers. Res. Soc. Am; Inst. Mgt. Sci. Nuclear engineering. Address: Computation & Communication Services Dept, Gulf Oil Corp, P.O. Box 2038, Pittsburgh, PA 15230.

GREAR, JOHN W(ESLEY), JR, b. Wrigley, Tenn, Nov. 19, 37. BOTANY, TAXONOMY. B.S, Austin Peay State, 59; M.S, Vanderbilt, 63; Ph.D.(plant systs), Columbia, 68. Instr. biol, Austin Peay State, 62-64; ASST. PROF, La. State Univ, New Orleans, 68-70; BOT, UNIV. TORONTO, 70- Am. Inst. Biol. Sci; Can. Bot. Asn; Am. Soc. Plant Taxon. Revisionary and monographic studies of angiosperms, especially of the Leguminosae. Address: Dept. of Botany, University of Toronto, Toronto 181, Ont, Can.

GREATHOUSE, CHARLES ALFRED, b. Jackson, Tenn, Nov. 22, 31; m. 58; c. 3. TOPOLOGY. B.A, Union Univ, 58; univ. fel, Univ. Tex, Austin, 59-60, M.A, 60; Nat. Sci. Found. fel, Univ. Rochester, summer 62; Nat. Sci. Found. grant, Fla. State Univ, 62-63, Ph.D.(math), 63. Instr. MATH, Tex. A&M Univ, 60-61; asst. prof. & res. assoc, Univ. Tenn, Knoxville, 63-64; asst. prof, Vanderbilt Univ, 64-66; prof, Samford Univ, 66-70; PROF. & HEAD DEPT, LAMBUTH COL, 70- Co-dir, Nat. Sci. Found. summer inst. undergrad. res. math, Vanderbilt Univ, 65. U.S.A, 53-55. Am. Math. Soc. Embedding of topological and combinatorial manifolds in Euclidean spaces and equivalence classes of various types of embeddings. Address: Dept. of Mathematics, Lambuth College, Jackson, TN 38301.

GREATHOUSE, GLENN A(RTHUR), b. West Salem, Ill, Aug. 16, 03; m. 25; c. 2. NUCLEAR CHEMISTRY & ENGINEERING. B.Ed, Ill. State Norm. Univ, 27; M.S, Illinois, 29; fel, Duke, 30-31, Ph.D.(biochem, biophys), 31. Asst. prof. plant physiol, Maryland, 31-36; proj. leader, div. cotton, bur. plant indust, U.S. Dept. Agr, 36-43; dir, prev. deterioration of mat. proj, Nat. Defense Res. Comt. & George Washington Univ, 43-45; Nat. Acad. Sci-Nat. Res. Coun, 45-55; head prof. nuclear eng, Univ. Fla, 55-60; pres, Orlando Res, Inc, 55-64; Nuclear Res. Chem, Inc, 64-67; SPEC. TECH. CONSULT, MALLINCKRODT CHEM. WORKS, 67- Prof, grad. sch, U.S. Dept. Agr, 35-36, 40-43; interim prof, Univ. Fla, 51-55. Mem. U.S-Brit. Sci. Mission, Eng, Europe, Africa & Panama, 45; U.S. del, World Conf. Atoms for Peace, 58. Award, Nat. Defense Res. Comt; develop. award, U.S. Naval Bur. Ord; Brit. Govt. Freedom Medal. Mem. sci. comt, Off. Sci. Res. & Develop, 44-45; spec. consult, Off. Chief Ord, U.S. Dept. Army, 44-45, new develop. br, 45. AAAS; Am. Chem. Soc; Am. Nuclear Soc; Soc. Am. Mil. Eng; Nat. Asn. Corrosion Eng; fel. Am. Inst. Chem; Arctic Inst. N.Am. Radioactive C^{14} compounds; nuclear engineering administration and research. Address: P.O. Box 332, Ormond Beach, FL 32074.

GREATHOUSE, TERRENCE RAY, b. Hindsboro, Ill, Nov. 7, 32; m. 61; c. 2. ANIMAL NUTRITION. B.S, Illinois, Urbana, 55, M.S, 58; Ph.D.(animal nutrit), Kentucky, 64. Asst. prof. beef cattle res. & animal scientist, Univ. Ill, Urbana, 58-67; assoc. prof. BEEF CATTLE RES, MICH. STATE UNIV, 67-70, PROF, 70- U.S.M.C, 55-57, 1st Lt. Am. Soc. Animal Sci. Beef cattle research in feeding, breeding and management studies. Address: 2206 Butternut Dr, Okemos, MI 48864.

GREAVES, DONALD C(RITCHFIELD), b. Minot, N.Dak, June 26, 24; m. 54; c. 2. PSYCHIATRY. M.D, Washington (St. Louis), 49; B.S, Montana State, 59. Intern internal med, Salt Lake County Gen. Hosp, 49-50; asst. PSYCHIAT. med. col, Cornell, 51-53, instr, 53-55; assoc. prof, med. center, Oklahoma, 55-58; PROF. & HEAD DEPT, MED. CTR, UNIV. KANS, 58-, LECTR. HIST. MED, 69- Res. Payne Whitney Psychiat. Clin, N.Y. Hosp, 50-54, asst. attend. psychiatrist, 54-55; chief, in-patient servs, univ. hosps, Oklahoma, 55-58; consult. psychiatrist, Kansas City, Mo, 58-; Wadsworth, Kans, 58-; Topeka, 59. U.S.A, 43-44. AAAS; Am. Psychosom. Soc; Am. Med. Asn; fel. Am. Psychiat. Asn; Asn. Am. Med. Cols; N.Y. Acad. Sci. Psychopharmacology; medical education. Address: Dept. of Psychiatry, Medical Center, University of Kansas, Kansas City, KS 66103.

GREBENE, ALAN B, b. Istanbul, Turkey, Mar. 13, 39; m. 67; c. 1. ELECTRONICS. B.Sc, Robert Col, Istanbul, 61; M.Sc, Univ. Calif, Berkeley, 63; Ph.D.(elec. eng), Rensselaer Polytech. Inst, 68. Mem. tech. staff, Fairchild Semiconductor, 63-64; Sprague Elec. Co, 64-65; lectr. elec. eng, Rensselaer Polytech. Inst, 65-68; mgr. circuit res, Signetics Corp, 68-71; V.PRES. ENG, EXAR INTEGRATED SYSTS, INC, 71- Lectr, Univ. Santa Clara, 68-71. AAAS; Inst. Elec. & Electronics Eng; Am. Soc. Eng. Educ. Integrated circuits research and development. Address: Exar Integrated Systems, Inc, 733 N. Pastoria Ave, Sunnyvale, CA 94086.

GREBER, ISAAC, b. Poland, Sept. 20, 28; U.S. citizen; m. 53; c. 2. FLUID MECHANICS. B.M.E, City Col. New York, 50; M.S.A.E, Michigan, 52; overseas fel, Swed. Aeronaut. Inst, 56; Ph.D.(aerodyn), Mass. Inst. Tech, 59. Group leader theoret. aerodyn, United Aircraft Res. Labs, 52-54; sr. aerodyn. engr, Chance Vought Aircraft Corp, 54-55; assoc. prof. ENG, CASE WEST. RESERVE UNIV, 59-70, PROF, 70- Fulbright fel, appl. math. dept, Tel-Aviv, 66-67. AAAS; Am. Inst. Aeronaut. & Astronaut; Am. Soc. Eng. Educ. Fluid mechanics of jets; fluidic devices; radiation gas dynamics; viscous flows; gas dynamics. Address: Case Western Reserve University School of Engineering, Cleveland, OH 44106.

GREBNER, EUGENE E(RNEST), b. Pittsburgh, Pa, Feb. 6, 31; m. 55; c. 2. BIOCHEMISTRY, MICROBIOLOGY. A.B, Hiram Col, 52; M.S, Pittsburgh, 60, U.S. Pub. Health Serv. fel, 62-64, Ph.D.(biochem), 64. U.S. Pub. Health Serv. fel. biochem, Nat. Insts. Health, Md, 64-67; RES. BIOCHEMIST, ALBERT EINSTEIN MED. CTR, 67- U.S.A, 52-54, Sgt. AAAS. Glycoproteins & glycolipids. Address: Albert Einstein Medical Center, York & Tabor Rds, Philadelphia, PA 19141.

GRECCO, WILLIAM L, b. Brockway, Pa, Aug. 28, 24; m. 47; c. 9. CIVIL ENGINEERING, URBAN PLANNING. B.S, Pittsburgh, 47, M.S, 51; Ph.D.(transportation), Mich. State, 62. Instr. civil eng, Pittsburgh, 47-53, asst. prof, 53-56, assoc. prof, 56-61; res. asst, Mich. State, 61-62; assoc. prof, PURDUE UNIV, 62-67, PROF. URBAN PLANNING & ENG, 67- Consult, Dines & Grecco, 50-52; Found. Assocs, 52; Donald M. McNeil, 53-58; mem. info. syst. storage & retrieval comt, Hwy. Res. Bd, Nat. Acad. Sci-Nat. Res. Coun, 64; mem. bd. dir, Purdue Calument Found, 67-71. U.S.N, 44-46. Am. Soc. Civil Eng.(ed. jour, 68-71); Am. Soc. Eng. Educ; Inst. Traffic Eng; assoc. Am. Inst. Planners. Urban traffic forecasting by system engineering; recreational travel; synthetic travel patterns. Address: 406 New Civil Engineering Bldg, Purdue University, Lafayette, IN 47907.

GRECO, CLAUDE V(INCENT), b. Bronx, N.Y, Sept. 13, 30. ORGANIC CHEMISTRY. B.S, Manhattan Col, 52; M.S, New Mexico Highlands, 55; Ph.D.(chem), Fordham, 60. Asst. chem, Wellcome Res. Labs, 52-53; Fordham,

56-57; assoc. chemist, Midwest Res. Inst, 59-61; fel, State Univ. N.Y, 61-62; asst. prof. ORG. CHEM, ST. JOHN'S UNIV.(N.Y), 62-70, ASSOC. PROF, 70- AAAS; N.Y. Acad. Sci; The Chem. Soc; Am. Chem. Soc. Synthetic organic chemistry; substitution reactions; mesoionic compounds; condensed heterocyclic systems; chemotherapy. Address: Dept. of Chemistry, St. John's University, Jamaica, NY 11432.

GRECO, EDWARD C(ARL), b. Marsala, Italy, Nov. 2, 11; m. 38; c. 2. ENGINEERING, CORROSION. B.S, Northwest. State Univ, 34; hon. D.Sc, Centenary Col. Anal. chemist, United Gas Pipe Line Co, La, 38-42; explosives div, E.I. du Pont de Nemours & Co, Tenn, 43-44; sr. res. assoc, United Gas Corp, 44-67; dir. res. & planning, suppl. educ. ctr, NORTHWEST. STATE UNIV, 67-68, coord. sci. res, 68-69, dir, inst. sci. res, 69-70, COORD. SCI. & TECHNOL. & LECTR. CHEM, 70- Explosives chemist, Lone Star Ord. Plant, U.S. Army, Tex, 41-43; pres. cong. & chmn. permanent coun, 2nd Int. Cong. Metallic Corrosion, v.pres, 4th & 5th Int. Cong. Metallic Corrosion; head, sci. exchange group, USSR; v.chmn, Int. Corrosion Coun; ed, J. Mat. Protection; hon. ed, Corrosion Control Abstracts. Fel. AAAS; fel. Am. Inst. Chem; Nat. Asn. Corrosion Eng.(pres). Corrosion mechanism and engineering; natural gas; metals; mechanisms of hydrogen sulfide corrosion of steels; hydrogen sulfide cracking of high strength steels; corrosion science. Address: Northwestern State University, Natchitoches, LA 74157.

GRECO, SALVATORE J(OSEPH), b. Richmond, Calif, Jan. 25, 21; m. 46; c. 6. PHARMACY. B.S, Duquesne, 42; Ph.D.(pharm), Maryland, 48. Asst. prof. chem, Temple, 48-49; PHARM, George Washington, 49-52, assoc. prof, 52-56; assoc. prof. & asst. to dean, CREIGHTON UNIV, 56-58, PROF. & DEAN SCH. PHARM, 58- U.S.A, 43-46. Am. Pharmaceut. Asn; Am. Asn. Cols. Pharm. Product development of pharmaceuticals. Address: School of Pharmacy, Creighton University, Omaha, NE 68102.

GRECZ, NICHOLAS, b. Brest, Poland, Feb. 16, 22; U.S. citizen; m. 46; c. 2. MICROBIOLOGY. Dipl. agr, Munich, 49; B.A, Bradley, 51; M.S, Ill. Inst. Tech, 55, U.S. Pub. Health Serv. grant, 58-60, Ph.D.(microbiol), 60; Chicago, 56. Technician food res, Chicago, 51-58, proj. dir. antibiotics, 58-60; microbiologist food res, U.S. Army Qm. Food & Container Inst, Chicago, Ill, 60-62, head microbiol, 62-63; asst. prof. phys. microbiol, ILL. INST. TECHNOL, 63-65, ASSOC. PROF. MICROBIOL, 65- U.S. Pub. Health Serv. career develop. award & res. grant, 64-69; sci. consult, Continental Ins. Co, 64-71; mem. ad hoc comt, Nat. Adv. Bd. Mil. Personnel Supplies, Nat. Acad. Sci-Nat. Res. Coun, 69; sci. adv, Electro-Physics, Inc, 69; sci. consult, Dr. S. Gaymont Labs, 70-; Am. Hosp. Supply Co, 71-; proj. dir. res. grant, Food & Drug Admin, 71- Am. Soc. Microbiol; Inst. Food Technol; Biophys. Soc. Physical biology; food microbiology; biophysics; bacterial spores. Address: Dept. of Biology, Biophysics Lab, Illinois Institute of Technology, 3101 S. Dearborn St, Chicago, IL 60616.

GREDING, EDWARD J, JR, b. Mar. 30, 40; U.S. citizen; m. 61. ZOOLOGY, HERPETOLOGY. B.S, Texas, Arlington, 61; M.S, East Texas State, 62; Ph.D.(zool), Texas, Austin, 68. Instr. BIOL, Tarleton State Col, 62-65; asst. prof, Pan Am. Col, 68-71; PROF, UNIV. EL SALVADOR, 71- U.S.C.G, 58. AAAS; Soc. Syst. Zool; Am. Ecol. Soc; Soc. Study Evolution; Am. Inst. Biol. Sci; Am. Soc. Ichthyol. & Herpet; Soc. Study Amphibians & Reptiles. Ecology and evolution of frogs of the American tropics. Address: Dept. of Biology, University of El Salvador, San Salvador, El Salvador.

GREEAR, PHILIP FRENCH-CARSON, b. Troutdale, Va, Aug. 25, 18; m. 43; c. 5. PLANT TAXONOMY, PALEOBOTANY. B.S.A, Georgia, 49, M.S, 59, univ. fels, 60-61, 63-64, Ph.D.(bot-ecol), 67. Asst. prof. biol, SHORTER COL.(GA), 61-62, assoc. prof, 62-63, acting head DEPT. BIOL. & EARTH SCI, 64-67, HEAD DEPT, 67- Summer vis. lectr, Univ. Ga, 62, 63; Nat. Sci. Found. res. partic, 64; chmn. bd, Bio-acoust. Res. Inst, Ga; mem, Ga. Natural Areas Coun. & Ga. Natural Environ. Educ. Coun; mem. bd. & exec. comt, Ga. Conservancy. U.S.A.F, 42-53, Capt. Taxonomy of the Azalea group of Rhododendron; flora and vertebrate paleontology of northwest Georgia. Address: Dept. of Biology & Earth Sciences, Shorter College, Rome, GA 30161.

GREEBLER, PAUL, b. Buffalo, N.Y, Dec. 13, 22; m. 46; c. 3. PHYSICS, NUCLEAR ENGINEERING. B.S, Univ. Colo, Boulder, 44; M.S, Rutgers Univ, 52, Ph.D.(physics), 54. Sr. res. physicist, res. ctr, Johns-Manville Corp, N.J, 46-55; res. physicist, Knolls Atomic Power Lab, GEN. ELECTRIC CO, N.Y, 55-56, sr. reactor physicist, CALIF, 56-59, specialist nuclear reactors, 58-59, MGR. advan. reactor physics, 59-65, NUCLEAR ENG, BREEDER REACTOR DEVELOP. OPER, 65- U.S. Atomic Energy Comn. del. & reactor physics specialist, Conf. Fast Reactor Physics, Vienna, 61, Plutonium Recycle, Brussels, 62, U.S. Fast Reactor Team visit to U.K. & Euratom, 60, 67, U.S.S.R, 70; consult, nat. neutron cross sect. ctr, Brookhaven Nat. Lab, N.Y, 68-; fel, Am. Nuclear Soc, 71. 6 patent awards, Gen. Elec. Co, 60-70. Sig.C, U.S.A, 44-46, 1st Lt. Am. Nuclear Soc; Am. Phys. Soc. Reactor physics methods; nuclear magnetic resonance studies of hydrogen occlusion in metals; heat transfer mechanisms in thermal insulating materials. Address: Breeder Reactor Development Operation, General Electric Co, 310 DeGuigne Dr, Sunnyvale, CA 94086.

GREECHIE, RICHARD JOSEPH, b. Boston, Mass, Apr. 12, 41. MATHEMATICS. B.A, Boston Col, 62; Wayne State, 62-63; Nat. Sci. Found. summer fel, Florida, 63, Ph.D.(math), 66. Asst. prof. MATH, Massachusetts, Boston, 65-67; KANS. STATE UNIV, 67-70, ASSOC. PROF, 70-, DIR, CTR. MATH. FOUND. EMPIRICAL STUDIES, 70- AAAS; Am. Math. Soc; Math. Asn. Am; Soc. Indust. & Appl. Math. Orthomodular lattice theory; empirical logics ranging from the classical logics to the non-classical quantum-mechanical logics, especially the way in which the classical sub-logics interrelate in the non-classical logic. Address: Dept. of Mathematics, Kansas State University, Manhattan, KS 66502.

GREELEY, FREDERICK, b. Winnetka, Ill, Aug. 26, 19; m. 44; c. 4. BIOLOGY, WILDLIFE MANAGEMENT. B.A, Kenyon Col, 41; M.S, Wisconsin, 49, Ph.D.(zool, wildlife mgt), 54. Res. assoc. endocrine studies of pheasants, Wisconsin, 54-55; deer nutrit, New Hampshire, 55-56; proj. leader pheasant range anal. & nutrit, Ill. Natural Hist. Surv, 56-60; ASSOC. PROF. WILDLIFE BIOL, UNIV. MASS, AMHERST, 60- U.S.A, 41-45, 1st Lt. Wildlife Soc; Cooper Ornith. Soc; Wilson Ornith. Soc; Am. Ornith. Union; Am. Soc. Mammal. Avian ecology and physiology, especially endocrine responses to the environment; population dynamics; nutrition of wild species of birds and mammals. Address: Dept. of Forestry & Wildlife Management, University of Massachusetts, Amherst, MA 01002.

GREELEY, MELVIN G, b. Mountain View, Okla, June 11, 31; m. 59; c. 1. ANIMAL NUTRITION. B.S, Okla. State, 54, M.S, 57; Ph.D.(animal nutrit), Minnesota, 61. Asst. animal husb, Okla. State, 56-57; Minnesota, 57-61; asst. animal scientist, Rockefeller Found, 61-65; MGR. swine feed res, Quaker Oats Co, 65-69; swine res, Allied Mills, Inc, 69-71; PET FOOD NUTRIT, QUAKER OATS CO, 71- U.S.A, 54-56. Am. Soc. Animal Sci. Effect of energy and protein and their interrelationships on efficiency of swine production and quality of carcasses. Address: Quaker Oats Co, Barrington, IL 60010.

GREELEY, R(ICHARD) S(TILES), b. Framingham, Mass, Dec. 25, 27; m. 51; c. 2. PHYSICAL CHEMISTRY. B.S, Harvard, 49; M.S, Northwestern, 51; Ph.D, Tennessee, 59. Develop. engr, Oak Ridge Nat. Lab, 54-60; engr. adv. design, MITRE CORP, BEDFORD, 60-63, assoc. dept. head STRATEGIC SYSTS, 63-70, ASSOC. DIV. DIR, 70- U.S.N, 51-54, Res, 54-, Lt.(jg). Am. Chem. Soc; Am. Nuclear Soc. Electronic system design; electromagnetic propagation; nuclear burst effects sensing; high temperature aqueous electrochemistry. Address: 7017 Whittier Blvd, Bethesda, MD 20034.

GREEN, AGNES ANN, I.H.M, b. Alvin, Ill, Aug. 15, 12. CHEMISTRY. A.B, Immaculate Heart Col, 34, B.S, 38; M.S, Southern California, 42; Ph.D. (phys. chem), Stanford, 46. Teacher, high sch, Los Angeles, 34-41; asst. prof. CHEM, IMMACULATE HEART COL, 42-46, assoc. prof, 46-52, PROF, 52-, CHMN. DEPT, 48- Vis. prof, Brown Univ, 65-66. Am. Chem. Soc. Vapor-phase dissociation of complex compounds of boron; solubilization in solutions of colloidal electrolytes; paper chromatography; use of tracers in studies of stability of complexes; kinetics of inorganic reactions. Address: Dept. of Chemistry, Immaculate Heart College, Los Angeles, CA 90027.

GREEN, ALEX E(DWARD) S(AMUEL), b. N.Y.C, June 2, 19; m. 46; c. 5. PHYSICS. B.S, City Col. New York, 40; fel, Calif. Inst. Tech, 40-44, M.S, 41; Ph.D.(physics), Cincinnati, 48. Physicist & instr, Calif. Inst. Tech, 40-44; instr. physics & math, Newark Col. Eng, 45-46; asst. prof. physics, Cincinnati, 46-53; from assoc. prof. to prof. & acting head dept, Fla. State, 53-59, sci. dir, Tandem Van de Graaff Lab, 58-59; chief physics, Convair Div, Gen. Dynamics & mgr, space sci. lab, Astronaut. Div, 59-63; GRAD. RES. PROF. PHYSICS & AEROSPACE ENG, UNIV. FLA, 63- Lectr, exten. div, California, 60-63. Consult, Jet Propulsion Lab; Marshall Space Flight Ctr; Inst. Defense Anal; consult. & group leader theoret. div, Los Alamos Sci. Lab, 57-58. Medal of Freedom, 47. Civilian with U.S.A.A.F, 44-45. Fel. Am. Phys. Soc; Am. Asn. Physics Teachers; Optical Soc. Am; Am. Geophys. Union. Theoretical nuclear, atomic and atmospheric physics. Address: Dept. of Physics, University of Florida, Gainesville, FL 32601.

GREEN, B(ARRETT) K(ERFOOT), b. Dayton, Ohio, Sept. 11, 06; m. 41; c. 2. COLLOID & ORGANIC CHEMISTRY. B.S, Cornell, 28, 29-33. Res. chemist, Carborundum Co, N.Y, 28-29; chem. res. dept, NAT. CASH REGISTER CO, 33-44, foreman finishes dept, 44, chem. res, 44-53, dept. head fundamental res, 53-56, mgr. chem. res, 56-67, dir. cent. res. div, 67-68, asst. v.pres, 68-71, RES. CONSULT, 71- AAAS; Am. Chem. Soc; Inst. Elec. & Electronics Eng. Colloids; physical organic chemistry; microencapsulation; phototropy; liquid phase equilibria; coacervation; printing; information storage; paper coating. Address: National Cash Register Co, Main & K Sts, Dayton, OH 45409.

GREEN, BEN A(RTHUR), JR, b. Tuscaloosa, Ala, July 10, 30; m. 54, 69; c. 2. PHYSICS, BEHAVIOR MODIFICATION. B.S, Alabama, 49, M.S, 50; Ph.D, Hopkins, 56. Instr. physics, Baylor, 50-51; proj. engr, Bendix radio commun. div, Bendix Aviation Corp, 56-57; res. physicist, Union Carbide Corp, 57-61; asst. prof. physics, Case West. Reserve Univ, 61-67; staff physicist, Comn. on Col. Physics, Univ. Mich, 67-68; STAFF SCIENTIST, EDUC. RES. CTR, MASS. INST. TECHNOL, 68- Consult, psychiatric serv, Mass. Inst. Technol. AAAS; Am. Phys. Soc; Am. Asn. Physics Teachers; Asn. Advan. Behav. Ther. Design of instructional systems; behavior therapy. Address: Education Research Center, Massachusetts Institute of Technology, 20C-231, Cambridge, MA 02139.

GREEN, BEVERLEY R, b. Vancouver, B.C, Apr. 17, 38. BIOCHEMISTRY. B.Sc, British Columbia, 60; Nat. Res. Coun. scholar, 63-64; Ph.D.(biochem), Washington (Seattle), 65. NATO fel, Free Univ. Brussels, 66-67; ASST. PROF. BOT, UNIV. B.C, 67- AAAS; Can. Bot. Asn. Chloroplast DNA and size of chloroplast genome; morphogenesis in Acetabularia; DNA of mosses, ferns and fern-allies. Address: Dept. of Botany, University of British Columbia, Vancouver 8, B.C, Can.

GREEN, BRIAN, b. Liverpool, Eng, Feb. 21, 35; m. 62; c. 2. ORGANIC CHEMISTRY. B.Sc, Liverpool, 56, Ph.D.(org. chem), 59. Res. asst. org. chem, Maine, 59-61, res. assoc, 61-64; Alexander von Humboldt fel, Max Planck Inst. Biochem, Munich, Ger, 64-65; asst. prof. CHEM, UNIV. MAINE, 65-69, ASSOC. PROF, 69- Alexander von Humboldt fel. org. chem, Univ. Bonn, 71-72. Am. Chem. Soc; The Chem. Soc. Chemistry of natural products, especially terpenoids and steroids with emphasis on both synthetic and degradative aspects of the field. Address: 8 Franklin St, Stillwater, ME 04489.

GREEN, CARL E(DWIN), b. N.Y.C, Apr. 28, 06; m. 29, 56; c. 3. SANITARY ENGINEERING. A.B, Stanford, 28, C.E, 40. Sanit. engr, State Bd. Health, Oregon, 28-41; consult. engr, John W. Cunningham & Assocs, 41-51; CARL E. GREEN & ASSOCS, 51-66, CONSULT. ENGR. & PLANNER, 66- Lectr, med. sch, Oregon, 29-41; chmn, Interstate Tech. Adv. Cmt. Pollution of Columbia River, 41. Dipl, Environ. Eng. Intersoc. Bd. Fel. AAAS; fel. Am. Soc. Civil Eng.(2nd v.pres, 39, v.pres, 40, pres, 41); Am. Water Works Asn; Water Pollution Control Fedn.(dir. at large, 49-52; Arthur S. Bedell Award, 49); Nat. Soc. Prof. Eng; fel. Am. Pub. Health Asn; Consult. Eng. Coun. Shellfish sanitation; water supply treatment; sewage treatment; stream pollution; milk sanitation; camp sanitation; sanitary bacteriology; air pollution control. Address: Carl E. Green & Associates, 1730 S.W. Skyline Blvd, Portland, OR 97221.

GREEN, CECIL H(OWARD), b. Manchester, Eng, Aug. 6, 00; nat; m. 26. APPLIED GEOPHYSICS. S.B, & S.M, Mass. Inst. Tech, 24; hon. D.Eng, Colo. Sch. Mines, 53; hon. D.Sc, Sydney & Tulsa, 61, British Columbia, 64. Party chief, GEOPHYS. SERV, INC, 30-36, supvr, 36-42, v.pres, 42-51, pres, 51-56, chmn. bd, 56-61, HON. CHMN. BD, 61-; V.PRES. & MEM. BD, TEX. INSTRUMENTS, INC, 41-; PRES. ST. MARK'S SCH. TEX, 65- Mem. exec. comt, Grad. Res. Center Southwest, 60-; life mem. corp, Mass. Inst. Tech, 62, chmn. physicists vis. comt, 64-65; chmn. earth scientists vis. comt, Toronto, 63-; mem. adv. coun, Colo. Sch. Mines, 63; corp, Scripps Clin. & Res. Found, 64- Soc. Explor. Geophys. (pres, 46); Am. Soc. Eng. Educ; Am. Asn. Petrol. Geol; Am. Geophys. Union. Application of seismology to petroleum exploration. Address: 13500 N. Central Expressway, Dallas, TX 75222.

GREEN, CHARLES ALLAN, b. Cleveland, Ohio, Aug. 21, 31; m. 61; c. 2. MATHEMATICS. B.A. & B.S, Ohio, 54, M.S, 58; Ph.D.(math), Wisconsin, 64. Instr. MATH, Ohio, 58-59, 61-62, asst. prof, 64-65; UNIV. MAINE, 65-69, ASSOC. PROF, 69- U.S.A, 54-56, Res, 56-62, Capt. Math. Asn. Am; Am. Math. Soc. Measure theory, particularly finitely additive measures; lattices; Boolean rings and algebras. Address: Dept. of Mathematics, University of Maine, Orono, ME 04473.

GREEN, C(HARLES) DAVID, b. Olney, Ill, Sept. 1, 40; m. 61; c. 1. ORGANIC CHEMISTRY. B.A, Southern Illinois, 62; Illinois, 62-63; Ph.D.(org. chem), Arizona, 67. RES. CHEMIST, Celanese Chem. Co, 67-68, CELANESE COATINGS CO, 68- Am. Chem. Soc; Fedn. Socs. Paint Technol; Inter-Soc. Color. Coun. Bulk organic chemicals; surface coatings; color technology. Address: Technical Center, Research Dept, Celanese Coatings Co, P.O. Box 99038, Louisville, KY 40299.

GREEN, CHARLES E, b. San Diego, Calif, Mar. 27, 12; m. 37; c. 2. ACOUSTICS, ELECTRONIC ENGINEERING. A.B, Univ. Calif, Los Angeles, 36, E.B, 37, B.S, 42. Instr, pub. schs, San Diego, Calif, 37-46, counselor, 44-46; res. physicist, Navy Electronics Lab, 46-59, SUPVRY. PHYSICIST, 59-67; NAVAL UNDERSEA CTR, 67- Consult, systs. comd. transducer repair facilities, Navy Bur. Ships Publs, 67- Presidential Citation, 64. Acoust. Soc. Am. Underwater transducers; measurement and evaluation of sonar components and systems; automated electronic systems. Address: 3427 Florida St, San Diego, CA 92104.

GREEN, CHARLES E, JR, b. Chester, Mont, Jan. 23, 43; m. 66; c. 1. PLANT GENETICS & BIOCHEMISTRY. B.S, Mont. State Univ, 65, Nat. Insts. Health fel, 67, Ph.D.(genetics), 70. RES. SPECIALIST PLANT GENETICS, UNIV. MINN, MINNEAPOLIS, 70- Tissue Cult. Asn; Genetics Soc. Am. Development of zea maize tissue cultures to investigate maize genetics via haploid plants, cell fusions, transformations and other aspects of biochemistry. Address: Dept. of Agronomy & Plant Genetics, 311 Plant Sciences Bldg, University of Minnesota, Minneapolis, MN 55455.

GREEN, CHARLES F(RANCIS), b. Soldier, Kans, June 1, 91; c. 2. ELECTRICAL ENGINEERING, MATHEMATICS. A.B, Kansas, 14, A.M, 15; Colorado; Ph.D.(math. physics, astron), Illinois, 20; Chicago. Asst. math, Illinois, 15-17, instr, 19-23; exchange instr, Mass. Inst. Technol, 23; asst. prof, Illinois, 24-29; engr, aeronaut. & marine eng. dept, Gen. Elec. Co, 29-40, design engr. aeronaut. & marine eng, 40-45, consult. engr. & mgr. adv. develop, aeronaut. & ord. systs, 45-56; vis. prof. elec. eng, Cornell Univ, 56-69; RETIRED. Consult, Gen. Elec. Co, 24-29, upper atmosphere res. panel, 46-56, adv. electronics ctr, 56- U.S.A.A.F, 17-19, 1st Lt. Am. Inst. Aeronaut. & Astronaut; Soc. Indust. & Appl. Math; fel. Inst. Elec. & Electronics Eng; Nat. Soc. Prof. Eng. Astronautics; space sciences; aeronautical sciences; applied mathematics. Address: 819 Fairway Dr, Waynesboro, VA 22980.

GREEN, CHARLES R, b. Fredericksburg, Va, Aug. 15, 42; m. 64; c. 2. ORGANIC & ANALYTICAL CHEMISTRY. B.S, Univ. Va, 64, Nat. Defense Educ. Act fel, 64-67, Ph.D.(chem), 68. RES. CHEMIST, R.J. REYNOLDS INDUSTS, INC, 68- Am. Chem. Soc. Chemistry of smoke from tobacco and other materials. Address: R.J. Reynolds Industries, Inc, Winston-Salem, NC 27102.

GREEN, CLOID DARRYL, b. Sheldon, Iowa, May 26, 21; m. 42; c. 6. ANESTHESIOLOGY. B.S, Minnesota, 42, M.D, 45; M.S, Iowa, 57. Intern, Harper Hosp, Detroit, Mich, 45-46; resident path, 46-47; private practice, S.Dak, 48-55; resident, Vet. Admin. Hosp. & Univ. Hosp, Iowa City, 55-57; instr. anesthesiol, Univ. Iowa, 57; asst. prof. sch. med, Univ. Va, 60-63, assoc. prof, Univ. Hosp, 63-69; PROF. ANESTHESIA & CHMN. DEPT, FACULTY MED, MEM. UNIV. NEWF, 69- Nat. Insts. Health grant. U.S.A.F, 57-60, Lt. Col. Am. Med. Asn; Am. Soc. Anesthesiol. Metabolic effects of anesthetic agents; biopack design for space research. Address: Dept. of Anesthesia, Faculty of Medicine, Memorial University of Newfoundland, St. John's, Newfoundland, Can.

GREEN, DANIEL G, b. New York, N.Y, Sept. 3, 37; m. 57; c. 2. PHYSIOLOGICAL OPTICS. B.S.E.E, Illinois, 59; M.S. & Ph.D.(elec. eng), Northwestern, 64. Asst. elec. eng. & bioeng, Northwestern, 59-64; Nat. Sci. Found. fel, physiol, lab, Cambridge, 64-65; U.S. Pub. Health Serv. fel, Nobel Insts. Neurophysiol, Stockholm, Sweden, 65-66; asst. prof. physiol. optics, UNIV. MICH, ANN ARBOR, 66-70, ASSOC. PROF. PHYSIOL. OPTICS, PSYCHOL. & ELEC. ENG, 71- Instr. elec. engr, Northwest. Univ, summer 61. AAAS; Am. Physiol. Soc; Asn. Res. Vision & Ophthal; Optical Soc. Am; Soc. Neurosci; Am. Inst. Elec. & Electronics Eng. Bio-medical engineering and physiology of vision. Address: Dept. of Ophthalmology, Kresge Medical Research Bldg, University of Michigan, Ann Arbor, MI 48104.

GREEN, DANIEL THOMAS, b. Phila, Pa, June 8, 30; m. 60; c. 4. MATHEMATICS, PHYSICS. B.S, Niagara, 54; M.S, Catholic Univ, 58. Mathematician, U.S. NAVAL WEAPONS LAB, 58-63, supvry. mathematician, 63-64, head prog. systs. br, 64-67, head armament concepts anal. div, 67-70, HEAD COMPUT. FACILITIES DIV, 70- Asn. Comput. Mach; Opers. Res. Soc. Am. Computer programming in the targeting and deployment areas and systems programming. Address: Code KO, U.S. Naval Weapons Lab, Dahlgren, VA 22448.

GREEN, DAVID, b. Phila, Pa, Oct. 1, 34; m. 58; c. 3. HEMATOLOGY. A.B, Pennsylvania, 56; M.D, Jefferson Med. Col, 60. Fel. hemat, Jefferson Hosp, Phila, Pa, 63-64; consult. med, San Diego County Gen. Hosp, Calif, 65-66; U.S. Pub. Health Serv. spec. fel, Oxford, 66-67; ASST. PROF. INTERNAL MED, MED. SCH, NORTHWEST. UNIV, 67- Dipl, Am. Bd. Internal Med, 67. Blood coagulation, primarily the study of Factor VIII in congenital and acquired deficiency states and in hypercoaguable syndromes. Address: Northwestern University Medical School, 303 E. Chicago Ave, Chicago, IL 60611.

GREEN, DAVID E(ZRA), b. N.Y.C, Aug. 5, 10; m. 36; c. 2. CHEMISTRY. B.Sc, N.Y. Univ, 30, A.M, 32; Ph.D.(biochem), Cambridge, 34. Beit Mem. fel, Cambridge, 34-38, sr. Beit Mem. fel, 38-40; res. fel, Harvard, 40-41; res. assoc, Columbia, 41-45; asst. prof. BIOCHEM, 46-47, assoc. prof, 47-48; PROF, UNIV. WIS, MADISON, 48- Lewis lab. award, Am. Chem. Soc, 46. U.S.A, 44. Nat. Acad. Sci; Am. Soc. Biol. Chem; Harvey Soc; Am. Acad. Arts & Sci; N.Y. Acad. Sci; for. fel. Belgium Royal Soc. Sci. Energy transductions in membrane; systems; ultrastructure; biophysics. Address: Enzyme Institute, University of Wisconsin, Madison, WI 53706.

GREEN, D(AVID) F(RANCIS), b. Lake City, Colo, Jan. 1, 11; m. 36; c. 1. PHYSIOLOGICAL CHEMISTRY. B.S, Ch.E, Denver, 32, M.S, 33, fel, 33-34; fel, Rutgers, 34-38, Ph.D.(physiol), 38. Asst, Denver, 32-34; Rutgers, 34-38, fel, 38-39; mgr. vet. dept, Merck & Co, Inc, 39-51; nutritionist, Armour & Co, 51-52; nitrogen div, Allied Chem. & Dye Corp, 52-57; exec. dir. animal sci. res, Merck Sharp & Dohme res. labs, Merck & Co, Inc, 57-69; RETIRED. AAAS; Am. Chem. Soc; Am. Soc. Animal Sci; Am. Dairy Sci. Asn; U.S. Animal Health Asn; N.Y. Acad. Sci. Clinical research in nutrition; chemotherapy of diseases of domestic animals; ruminant nutrition. Address: 51 Washington Ave, Morristown, NJ 07960.

GREEN, DAVID H(ARRISON), b. Pittsfield, Mass, May 18, 31; m. 54. NUCLEAR PHYSICS. B.S, Union (N.Y), 51; M.S, Case, 55, Ph.D.(physics), 61. RADIO PHYSICIST, LAMP DIV, GEN. ELEC. CO, 60- Eve. lectr, John Carroll, 62- Summer physicist, Naval Ord. Lab, Md, 51. Am. Phys. Soc. Gamma ray scattering, gamma ray absorption coefficients, radioisotopes. Address: General Electric Co, Lamp Division, Nela Park, Cleveland, OH 44112.

GREEN, DAVID WILLIAM, b. Hudson, Mich, Nov. 19, 42; m. 67; c. 1. PHYSICAL CHEMISTRY. B.A, Albion Col, 64; Ph.D.(chem), Univ. Calif, Berkeley, 68. Lectr. chem, Univ. Calif, Berkeley, 68; res. assoc. physics, lab. molecular struct. & spectra, Univ. Chicago, 68-71; ASST. PROF. CHEM, ALBION COL, 71- Fel, Lawrence Radiation Lab, Univ. Calif, Berkeley, 68. AAAS; Am. Chem. Soc; Optical Soc. Am. Molecular electronic spectroscopy and structure; high resolution optical spectroscopy; high temperature chemistry; molecular hyperfine structure. Address: Dept. of Chemistry, Albion College, Albion, MI 49224.

GREEN, DETROY E(DWARD), b. Zalma, Mo, Mar. 26, 30; m. 51; c. 4. AGRONOMY. B.S, Missouri, 54, M.S, 61, Ph.D.(field crops), 65. Instr. voc. agr, high sch, Mo, 54-59; instr. field crops, Missouri, 61-64; asst. prof. AGRON, IOWA STATE UNIV, 64-67, ASSOC. PROF, 67- U.S.A, 51-53, Sgt. Am. Soc. Agron; Crop Sci. Soc. Am. Genetics, breeding, and physiology related to soybean seed quality. Address: Dept. of Agronomy, Iowa State University, Ames, IA 50010.

GREEN, DON WESLEY, b. Tulsa, Okla, July 8, 32; m. 54; c. 2. CHEMICAL & PETROLEUM ENGINEERING. B.S, Tulsa, 55; M.S, Oklahoma, 59, Nat. Sci. Found. fel, 59-61, Ph.D.(chem. eng), 63. Res. reservoir engr, Continental Oil Co, 62-64; asst. prof. CHEM. & PETROL. ENG, UNIV. KANS, 64-67, assoc. prof, 67-71, PROF, 71-, CHMN. DEPT, 70-, acting chmn. dept, 67-68. U.S.A.F, 55-57, 1st Lt. Am. Soc. Eng. Educ; Am. Inst. Chem. Eng; Am. Inst. Min, Metall. & Petrol. Eng. Fluid flow through porous media; dispersion of heat and mass in porous media; mathematical modeling of natural resource systems. Address: Dept. of Chemical Engineering, University of Kansas, Lawrence, KS 66045.

GREEN, DONALD E(UGENE), b. Napa, Calif, Nov. 25, 26; m. 51; c. 5. BIOCHEMICAL PHARMACOLOGY, ANALYTICAL CHEMISTRY. B.S, Univ. Calif, Berkeley, 48, M.S, Univ. Calif, San Francisco, 52, B.S, 55; Stanford, 48; Ph.D. (med. chem), Wash. State Univ, 62. Instr. pharmaceut. chem, Idaho State Univ, 55-57, 58-60; res. chemist, Varian Assocs, 62-64; mgr. dept. biophys, 64-66; sr. res. chemist, Synvar Res. Inst, 66-67; anal. instrument res, Varian Assocs, 67-70; RES. BIOCHEMIST, DRUG RES. LAB, VET. ADMIN. HOSP, 70-, RES. SCIENTIST, BIOCHEM. RES. LAB, MENLO PARK DIV, 71-, biochemist, 62-64. Res. fel, sch. pharm, Univ. Calif, San Francisco, 62; res. assoc, sch. med, Stanford Univ, 71- U.S.N.R, 44-46, 51-53. AAAS; Am. Chem. Soc; Am. Pharmaceut. Asn; Int. Asn. Forensic Toxicol. Chemical structure/pharmacological activity relationships of central nervous system drugs; mechanisms of drug actions; metabolism of cannabinoids and phenothiazine tranquilizers; development of gas chromatography/mass spectrometry interfaces and chemical vapor analysis microanalytical instrumentation. Address: Biochemical Research Lab, Menlo Park Division, Veterans Administration Hospital, Palo Alto, CA 94304.

GREEN, D(ONALD) M(acDONALD), b. Poughkeepsie, N.Y, Apr. 6, 30; m. 57; c. 3. GENETICS. A.B, Oberlin Col, 54; Ph.D, Rochester, 58. Res. assoc, biol. div, Oak Ridge Nat. Lab, 58-60; res. fel. chem. & tutor biochem. sci, Harvard, 60-64; assoc. prof. biol, Univ. Pittsburgh, 64-67; PROF. BIOCHEM, UNIV. N.H, 67- Microbial genetics; genetic structure of bacteria and viruses; mutagenesis. Address: Dept. of Biochemistry, University of New Hampshire, Durham, NH 03824.

GREEN, D(ONALD) WAYNE, b. Coldwater, Mich, June 19, 24; m; c. 2. PHYSICS. B.A, Kalamazoo Col, 49; Ph.D.(physics), Ohio State, 54. Assoc. prof. PHYSICS, KNOX COL.(ILL), 54-70, PROF, 70- U.S.A.A.F, 43-45. Am.

Phys. Soc; Am. Asn. Physics Teachers; Am. Nuclear Soc. Low energy particle accelerators; stopping power of various materials for protons. Address: 1668 Maple Ave, Galesburg, IL 61401.

GREEN, DUANE L(IONEL), b. Susquehanna, Pa, Apr. 17, 16. ORGANIC CHEMISTRY. B.S, Pa. State, 38, M.S, 42, Ph.D.(org. chem), 45. Chemist, Reilly Tar & Chem. Co, N.J. & Ind, 38-40; asst, Pa. State, 40-43; res. chemist, E.I. du Pont de Nemours & Co, Del, 43-46, 47-53; instr, Clarkson Tech, 46-47, assoc. prof, 53-54, head dept. chem. & chem. eng, 54-58; dept. engr, Abadan Inst. Tech, Iran, 58-59, sr. res. engr, pioneering labs, E.I. du Pont de Nemours & Co, 59-60; assoc. prof. chem, Rider Col, 60-61, chmn. dept. sci, 61-62; prof. CHEM, Monmouth Col.(N.J), 62-67, chmn. dept, 63-67; TEACHER, HINCKLEY SCH, 67-, HEAD SCI. DEPT, 69- Instr, Univ. Buffalo, 47-48. Am. Chem. Soc; Am. Inst. Chem. Eng. High polymer, addition and condensation type; molding powder formulations; viscose research; spinning of fibers; wet, dry and melt methods; thermal decomposition of alpha-substituted acids. Address: Hinckley School, Hinckley, ME 04944.

GREEN, EARL L(EROY), b. Meadville, Pa, Aug. 7, 13; m. 40. GENETICS. B.S, Allegheny Col, 35, hon. Sc.D, 60; Sc.M, Brown, 37, Ph.D.(genetics), 40. Keen fel, Chicago, 40-41; instr. zool, Ohio State, 41-43, assoc. prof, 46-55, prof, 55-56; DIR, JACKSON LAB, 56- Geneticist, div. biol. & med, U.S. Atomic Energy Comn, 53-55. Ed, Ohio Jour. Sci, 51-53. U.S.A.A.F, 43-46. Am. Genetics Soc; Am. Statist. Asn. Mouse genetics; radiation genetics. Address: Jackson Lab, Bar Harbor, ME 04609.

GREEN, EDWARD H, b. N.Y.C, Nov. 27, 06; m. 30; c. 1. ELECTRONICS. B.S, City Col. New York, 29; fel, Brooklyn Col, 29-30; A.M, Columbia, 31, Ph.D.(physics), 40. From tutor to PROF. PHYSICS, BROOKLYN COL, 30- With U.S.N, 46. Am. Phys. Soc. Specific heats of metals; vacuum tube circuits; circuitry; instrumentation; physical optics; absorption in iodine, barium and some compounds of barium. Address: Dept. of Physics, Brooklyn College, Brooklyn, NY 11210.

GREEN, EDWARD J(EWETT), b. Bakersfield, Calif, Oct. 31, 31. CHEMICAL OCEANOGRAPHY. A.B, Univ. Calif, Santa Barbara, 58; summer fel, Woods Hole Oceanog. Inst, 59; Ph.D.(geochem), Mass. Inst. Technol, 65. Res. chemist, div. sponsored res, Mass. Inst. Technol, summer 65; asst. prof. geochem, Carnegie Inst. Technol, 65-71; ASSOC. PROF. OCEANOG. & GEOL. SCI, UNIV. MAINE, 71- AAAS; Geochem. Soc; Soc. Econ. Paleont. & Mineral; Am. Geophys. Union; Am. Chem. Soc; The Chem. Soc. Mineral equilibria, especially thermodynamics of low temperature aqueous systems; marine geochemistry and cycle of atmospheric gases between earth, ocean and atmosphere; theoretical petrology and predictive models for silicate systems. Address: Dept. of Oceanography, Marine Lab, University of Maine, Walpole, ME 04551.

GREEN, ELIZABETH UFFORD, b. N.Y.C, Feb. 12, 08; m. 40. CYTOLOGY. A.B, Bryn Mawr Col, 29, scholar, 33-34, M.A, 34, fel, 34-35, 39-40, Ph.D.(cytol), 40. Asst, Rockefeller Inst, 30-33; demonstr. biol, Bryn Mawr Col, 35-38, 42-43, instr, 43-44; res. assoc, Inst. Cancer Res, 45-51, assoc. mem, 51-57; RES. ASSOC, DEPT. BIOL, HAVERFORD COL, 57- Instr, Rosemont Col, 41-42. AAAS; Soc. Develop. Biol; assoc. Am. Soc. Zool; Am. Asn. Cancer Res. Transplantable tumors in mice; crystalline inclusions; carcinogens on frog embryos; mitotic rates; ribonucleic acid, macronuclear structure and electron microscopy of immobilization antigens in paramecium. Address: Dept. of Biology, Haverford College, Haverford, PA 19041.

GREEN, ESTILL I(BBOTSON), b. St. Louis, Mo, Nov. 24, 95; m. 18; c. 1. ELECTRICAL ENGINEERING. A.B, Westminster Col.(Mo), 15, hon. Sc.D, 56; B.S, Harvard, 21. Prof. Greek, Westminster Col.(Mo), 16-17; commun. engr, Am. Tel. & Tel. Co, N.Y, 21-34, Bell Tel. Labs, 34-38, dir. transmission apparatus develop, 48-53, mil. commun. systs, 53-55, v.pres, 55-58, exec. v.pres, 59-60; consult. & dir, Xerox Corp. & United-Carr, Inc, 60-68; MGT. CONSULT, 68- Mem, Eng. Found. Bd, 54-59; trustee, Westminster Col.(Mo), 57-; chmn, conserv. comn, Millburn Township, N.J, 69-; trustee & former pres, Hartshorn Arboretum; consult. & dir, Scantlin Electronics, Inc, 68-; consult, Gillette Co, 67- U.S.A, 17-19. Fel. AAAS; fel. Acoust. Soc. Am; fel. Inst. Elec. & Electronics Eng.(dir, 59-63). Communication systems and apparatus; research and engineering management. Address: 95 Farley Rd, Short Hills, NJ 07078.

GREEN, EUGENE L, b. Minneapolis, Minn, Oct. 15, 27; m. 51, 69; c. 4. PHYSICS, OPTICS. B.S, Carnegie Inst. Tech, 47, M.S, 49; Ph.D.(physics), Temple, 65. Physicist, U.S. Army, Frankford Arsenal, Pa, 49-65; RES. PHYSICIST, NAVAL UNDERWATER SYSTS. CTR, NEW LONDON LAB, 65- AAAS; Optical Soc. Am. Optical information processing, properties of alloys, image analysis and instrumentation; laser development; acoustic array signal processing. Address: Naval Underwater Systems Center, New London Lab, New London, CT 06320.

GREEN, FARNO L(OUIS), b. Memphis, Tenn, Nov. 29, 19; m. 44; c. 2. PHYSICS. B.A, Miss. Col, 41; M.S, La. State, 49. Assoc. prof. physics & head dept, Wayland Baptist Col, 48-49; head dept, Howard Col, 49-51; physicist, Oak Ridge Nat. Lab, 51-55; sr. res. physicist & group leader nuclear physics, res. labs, Gen. Motors Corp, 56-63; v.pres. & gen. mgr, Viso Corp, 63-66; EXEC. ENGR, MFG. DEVELOP, TECH. CTR, GEN. MOTORS CORP, 66- Silver medal, Am. Roentgen Ray Soc, 62. U.S.A, 40-42; U.S.A.A.F, 42-45; Air Nat. Guard, 50-51, Maj. Am. Phys. Soc; Am. Nuclear Soc; Am. Soc. Nondestructive Test. Applied nuclear physics; industrial and medical applications of radioisotopes and nuclear techniques, accelerator and reactor production of radioisotopes; cyclotron design and theory; automotive manufacturing processes and systems; corporate operating systems. Address: General Motors Corp, Manufacturing Development, Technical Center, 12 Mile & Mound Rd, Warren, MI 48090.

GREEN, FLOYD J, b. Sharonville, Ohio, Dec. 11, 17; m. 41; c. 3. ORGANIC & ANALYTICAL CHEMISTRY. A.B, Maryville Col.(Tenn), 41; M.S, Cincinnati, 50; Ph.D, St. Thomas Inst, 69. Res. chemist bldg. mat, Phillip Carey Mfg, 41-46; chemist reagent chem, Matheson, Coleman & Bell Div, Matheson Co. Inc, 46-50, chief chemist, 50-54, TECH. DIR, MC&B MFG. CHEMISTS, WILL ROSS CO, INC, 54-, V.PRES, 68- Adj. asst. prof, St. Thomas Inst. U.S.N, 42-45. AAAS; fel. Am. Inst. Chem; Am. Chem. Soc; Am. Soc. Test. & Mat. Research in dyes, particularly oxazones; high purity organic reagents. Address: MC&B Manufacturing Chemists, Will Ross Co, Inc, 2909 Highland Ave, Cincinnati, OH 45212.

GREEN, FLOYD W(ILSON), b. Pilot Knob, Mo, July 27, 12; m. 40; c. 3. CHEMISTRY. A.B, DePauw, 38; Ph.D.(inorg. chem), Cornell, 42. Lab. asst, Cornell, 38-40, recitation asst, 40-42; res. chemist, COATINGS & SPECIALTY PROD. DEPT, IMP. DIV, HERCULES, INC, 42-56, res. supvr, 56-57, DIR. TECH. SERV, 57- Am. Chem. Soc. Fluocolumbates; chemical pigment colors. Address: 56 Garfield St, Glens Falls, NY 12801.

GREEN, F(RANCIS) E(ARL), b. Slaton, Tex, May 19, 25; m. 50; c. 2. GEOLOGY, ARCHAEOLOGY. B.S, Tex. Tech. Col, 50, M.S, 51, Ph.D.(geol), 54; Columbia, 54-55. Instr. geol, Tex. Tech. Col, 52-53; res. asst. vert. paleont, Am. Mus. Natural Hist, 54-55; geologist-stratigrapher, Tidewater Oil Co, 55-57; researcher geol. & paleont, Monahans Ecol. Proj, Tex. Tech Univ, 57-59, field rep. mus, 59-65, curator collections, 59-70, acting dir, 64-65, DIR, 65-70; INTERPRETIVE PLANNING, PARKS SERV, TEX. PARKS & WILD DEPT, 70- U.S.A, 43-46. Soc. Vertebrate Paleont; Soc. Am. Archaeol. Paleontology of late Quaternary time. Address: 6704 Notre Dame Dr, Austin, TX 78723.

GREEN, F(RANK) O(RVILLE), b. Toledo, Iowa, Nov. 2, 08; m. 35; c. 3. CHEMISTRY. B.S, Greenville Col, 31; fel, Northwestern, 35-37, M.S, 37, Abbott fel, 39, Ph.D.(org. chem), 39. Teacher, pub. sch, Ohio, 31-35; asst. instr, Northwestern, 37-39; prof. & dir. dept, Greenville Col, 39-41; res. chemist, Bauer & Black Co, Ill, 41-42; Swift & Co, 42-45; asst. prof. CHEM, WHEATON COL, 45-50, assoc. prof, 50-55, PROF, 55- Fulbright vis. lectr, Univ. Cairo & Ibrahim Univ, Egypt, 52-53; res. assoc, radiobiol. unit, Mt. Vernon Hosp, Eng, 57-58; chem. consult, Daubert Chem. Co, 60-66. Summers, res. assoc, Argonne Nat. Labs, 55-56, vis. prof, summer inst. high sch. chem. teachers, Colorado, 61, vis. instr, 65, reader, adv. placement exam. chem, Ed. Testing Serv, N.J, 61. 63, 64, 66, 67, 68; Nat. Sci. Found. res. participant biophys, Colorado, 62, vis. prof, Nat. Sci. Found. summer inst. high sch. & jr. high sch. sci. teachers, 63; Nat. Sci. Found-Atomic Energy Cmn. summer inst. radiation biol, Univ. Hawaii, 64; res. assoc, Ore. State Univ, 67, 68, 70; partic, Nat. Sci. Found. conf. elem. sci. teaching, Fla. State Univ, 69. Mem, Int. Cancer Cong, London, 58. Childs Mem. Fund award, 57. AAAS; Am. Chem. Soc; Am. Inst. Chem. Acylals; phenoxthins; biochemistry; organic chemistry. Address: Dept. of Chemistry, Wheaton College, Wheaton, IL 60187.

GREEN, GEORGE BENJAMIN, b. Lake City, Minn, Jan. 22, 06; m. 42. MEDICINE. A.B, South Dakota, 34, B.S, 36; M.D, Rush, Chicago, 38; dipl, Sch. Aviation Med, 42. Intern med, Bridgeport Hosp, Conn, 38-39; res. path, Fifth Ave. Hosp, N.Y, 39-40, ophthal, 40; med. corp, U.S. Air Force, 40-61, mem. staff, clinic, Ft. Slocum, N.Y, 40-42, squadron, group & fighter wing surgeon, European Theater, 43-45, from asst. chief to chief phys. standards, 46-49, staff officer, Armed Forces Med. Policy Council, Dept. Defense, 49-51, asst. air attache, France, Belgium & Switzerland, 51-54, chief, med. team, asst. chief of staff, Intel, Va, 54-61; MEM. STAFF, BUR. MED, FOOD & DRUG ADMIN, 61- Dipl, Am. Bd. Prev. Med, 53. Med.C, U.S.A.F, 40-61, Col, Bronze Star Medal; Commendation Ribbon; Medal Honor, French Air Force Med. Serv; hon flight surgeon, French Air Force; dipl. hon, Belg. Air Force. AAAS; Am. Astronaut. Soc; Am. Inst. Aeronaut. & Astronaut; Am. Med. Asn; Asn. Mil. Surg. U.S; fel. Aerospace Med. Asn; Am. Pub. Health Asn; fel. Am. Col. Prev. Med. Aerospace medicine; international advances in space medicine. Address: Bureau of Medicine, Food & Drug Administration, Washington, DC 20204.

GREEN, GEORGE G, b. Sayre, Okla, Mar. 21, 22; m. 46; c. 1. ANIMAL SCIENCE & NUTRITION. B.S, Okla. State, 50, M.S, 56; Ph.D.(nutrit), Texas A&M, 58. Asst. exten. agent agr, Okla. State Univ, 50-51, exten. agent, 51-52; farm mgr, 52-54; assoc. prof. animal sci, Va. Polytech, 58-63; exten. specialist livestock, Auburn, 63-64; ASSOC. PROF. ANIMAL SCI, VA. POLYTECH. INST, 64- Am. Soc. Animal Sci. Appetite and growth among ruminants. Address: 104 Agnew Hall, Virginia Polytechnic Institute, Blacksburg, VA 24061.

GREEN, GEORGE GARRET, b. Bound Brook, N.J, Oct. 23, 18; m. 43; c. 4. RADIOLOGY. B.S, Rutgers, 40; M.D, N.Y. Med. Col, 43. Attend. radiol, Fitkin Mem. Hosp, Neptune, N.J, 50-62, dir. radioisotopes, 59-62; assoc. prof. radiol, sch. med, W.Va. Univ, 63-69; private practice, St. Anthony's Hosp, Ill, 69- Consult, Allenwood Hosp. & Marlboro State Hosp, N.J, 56-62. Med.C, 45-47, Capt. Fel. Am. Col. Radiol; Radiol. Soc. N.Am. Address: Dept. of Radiology, St. Anthony's Hospital, 767 30th St, Rock Island, IL 61201.

GREEN, GERALD, b. N.Y.C, June 29, 41; m. 67. BIOLOGICAL CHEMISTRY. B.Sc, Brooklyn Col, 64; U.S. Pub. Health Serv. fel, Ind. Univ, Bloomington, 66-69, Ph.D.(biol. chem), 70. RES. ASSOC. CHEM, UNIV. CALIF, LOS ANGELES, 70- Am. Chem. Soc. Interaction of small molecules and organic solvents on DNA and synthetic polynucleotide macrostructure; immunoglobulin-hapten structural studies. Address: 1230 25th St, Santa Monica, CA 90404.

GREEN, G(ORDON) J(OHN), b. Winnipeg, Man, Sept. 15, 20; m. 51; c. 3. PLANT PATHOLOGY. B.S.A, Manitoba, 49; M.S, Wisconsin, 50, fel, 52, Ph.D.(plant path), 53. RES. SCIENTIST & PLANT PATHOLOGIST, RES. STA, CAN. DEPT. AGR, 53- R.C.A.F, 40-46. Am. Phytopath. Soc; Can. Phytopath. Soc; Agr. Inst. Can; Genetics Soc. Can. Diseases of cereal crops, particularly physiologic specialization in the stem rusts attacking cereals and grasses. Address: Research Station, Research Branch, Canada Agriculture, 25 Dafoe Rd, Winnipeg 19, Can.

GREEN, HANNAH O(PPENHEIMER), b. Dusseldorf, Ger, Oct. 14, 35; U.S. citizen; m. 66; c. 2. BIOCHEMISTRY. B.S, Carnegie-Mellon Univ, 57; M.S, Cornell, 60, Ph.D.(biochem), 64. Chemist, res. lab, Jones & Laughlin Steel Corp, Pa, 57-58; RES. ASSOC. BIOCHEM, dept. biochem. & biophys, Univ.

Hawaii, 64-66; dept. physiol. & pharmacol, DUKE UNIV, 69-70, DEPT. BIOCHEM, 70- Am. Chem. Soc. Enzymology, protein structure activity relationship; membranes. Address: 600-5 La Salle St, Apt. 9E, Durham, NC 27705.

GREEN, HAROLD D(AVID), b. Zanesville, Ohio, Aug. 11, 05; m. 34; c. 2. PHYSIOLOGY. B.S, Col. of Wooster, 27, hon. D.Sc, 57; M.D, Western Reserve, 31. Intern, J.D. Archbold Mem. Hosp, Ga, 31-32; Lakeside Hosp, Ohio, 32-33, asst. resident, 33; instr. physiol, sch. med, Western Reserve, 33-35, sr. instr, 36-37, asst. prof, 37-39, assoc. prof, 40-45; GORDON GRAY PROF. PHYSIOL. & CHMN. DEPT, BOWMAN GRAY SCH. MED, WAKE FOREST COL, 45-, ASSOC. PHARMACOL. & INTERNAL MED, 66- Instr, med. sch, Yale, 35-36; vis. asst. prof, col. med, Tennessee, 38; Commonwealth Fund fel. & guest, Mass. Inst. Tech, 39-40; Mellon lectr, Pittsburgh, 57. Biophys. Soc; Am. Physiol. Soc; Soc. Exp. Biol. & Med; Am. Soc. Pharmacol. & Exp. Therapeut; Am. Heart Asn; fel. Am. Col. Physicians; Col. Clin. Pharmacol. & Chemother. Measurement of coronary blood flow; electrical excitability of cerebral cortex; peripheral circulatory studies in normal and abnormal conditions; hormonal and autonomic nervous control of circulation in various vascular beds; autonomic blocking drugs; autoregulation in vascular beds; control of resistance and capacitance vessels. Address: Dept. of Physiology, Bowman Gray School of Medicine, Wake Forest College, Winston-Salem, NC 27103.

GREEN, HAROLD RUGBY, b. Hallettsville, Tex, Feb. 19, 26; m. 53. MATHEMATICS. B.A, Tex. Wesleyan Col, 46; M.A, Texas Christian, 48; Arkansas, 56; Alabama, 60; M.S, North Texas State, 61. Teacher pub. schs, Tex, 46-55; asst. prof. MATH, Arlington State Col, 55-59; McNeese State Col, 59-60; UNIV. TEX, ARLINGTON, 60-63, ASSOC. PROF, 63- Number theory. Address: Dept. of Mathematics, University of Texas at Arlington, Arlington, TX 76010.

GREEN, HARRY, b. Phila, Pa, Sept. 7, 17; m. 45; c. 2. BIOCHEMISTRY. A.B, Pennsylvania, 38, M.S, 39, Harrison fel, 40-41, Ph.D.(org. chem), 42. Sr. res. chemist, Lion Oil Ref. Co, Ark, 41-44; Whitemarsh Res. Labs, Pennsalt Mfg. Co, 44-47; res. assoc. physiol. chem, Pennsylvania, 47-52; chief biochem. res, Wills Eye Hosp, 52-58; sr. res. scientist, SMITH KLINE & FRENCH LABS, 58-64, head neurobiochem, 64-67, DIR. BIOCHEM. PHARMACEUT, 67-; ASST. PROF. BIOCHEM, GRAD. SCH. MED, UNIV. PA, 54- AAAS; Am. Chem. Soc; Am. Soc. Biol. Chem; Asn. Res. Vision & Ophthal; Asn. Res. Nerv. & Ment. Diseases; Am. Soc. Pharmacol. & Exp. Therapeut; Int. Soc. Biochem. Pharmacol; N.Y. Acad. Sci. Intermediary metabolism; ocular biochemistry and physiology; enzymology; corticosteroids; neurobiochemistry; drug metabolism. Address: Smith Kline & French Labs, 1500 Spring Garden St, Philadelphia, PA 19101.

GREEN, HARRY E(DWARD), b. Dagus Mines, Pa, Nov. 9, 12; m. 38; c. 4. CHEMISTRY. B.A, Carleton Col, 34; Minnesota, 37-42. Asst. chem, Carleton Col, 34-37; agr. biochem, univ. farm, Minnesota, 38-42; instr. chem, Univ. Kansas City, 42-43; res. chemist, proj. leader in org. chem. & mgr. res. supply dept, Dr. Salsbury's Labs, 43-50, mgr, chem. synthesis dept, 50-57, chem. prod. dept, 57-59, chem. process develop, 59-71, SCIENTIST, CHEM. DEVELOP. DEPT, SALSBURY LABS, 71- Am. Chem. Soc. Synthesis of organic chemicals, particularly arsenicals; chemicals, process development and production. Address: Salsbury Labs, Charles City, IA 50616.

GREEN, HARRY J(AMES), JR, b. St. Louis, Mo, Dec. 7, 11; m. 39; c. 2. CHEMICAL ENGINEERING. B.Ch.E, Ohio State, 32, Ph.D.(chem. eng), 43; M.S, Mass. Inst. Tech, 38. Instr. chem, Agr. & Tech. Col, N.C, 34-37, asst. prof, 38-41, prof, 43-44; sr. engr, materials eng. dept, Stromberg-Carlson Co, 44-59, supvr. mfg. res. & develop, PROD. ENG. DEPT, 59-67, prin. engr. microelectronics, electronics div, Gen. Dynamics, 67-70; SCIENTIST, RES. DEPT, XEROX CORP, 70- Am. Chem. Soc; Am. Soc. Metals. Materials engineering; metals; polymer applications; wire and insulation; telephone transmitter materials; electrical properties of plastics; microelectronic packaging of thick and thin film hybrid circuits; xerographic materials development. Address: 307 Greeley St, Rochester, NY 14609.

GREEN, HARRY WESTERN, II, b. Orange, N.J, Mar. 13, 40; m. 61; c. 3. GEOPHYSICS, STRUCTURAL GEOLOGY. A.B, Univ. Calif, Los Angeles, 63, Socony Mobil scholar, 63-64, NASA trainee, 64-67, M.S, 67, Ph.D.(geol), 68. Res. assoc, geol. & metall, Case West. Reserve Univ, 68-70; ASST. PROF. GEOL, UNIV. CALIF, DAVIS, 70- Nat. Sci. Found. res. grant, 69- AAAS; Am. Geophys. Union; Geol. Soc. Am; Electron Micros. Soc. Am. Experimental rock deformation at high temperature and pressure; elucidation of deformation mechanisms utilizing high voltage transmission electron microscopy; theoretical studies of deformation in the earth's interior; solid earth geophysics; experimental structural geology. Address: Dept. of Geology, University of California, Davis, CA 95616.

GREEN, HOWARD, b. Toronto, Ont, Sept. 10, 25; nat; m. 54. CELL BIOLOGY. M.D, Toronto, 47; M.S, Northwestern, 50. Instr. biochem, Chicago, 50-53; Nat. Insts. Health vis. scientist, Cornell, 54; instr. pharmacol, sch. med, N.Y. Univ, 55, asst. prof. path, 57-60, assoc. prof, 60-65, prof, 65-68, prof. cell biol. & chmn. dept, 68-70; PROF. BIOL, MASS. INST. TECHNOL, 70- Differentiation; genetics; cancer. Address: Dept. of Biology, Massachusetts Institute of Technology, Room 56-535, 77 Massachusetts Ave, Cambridge, MA 02139.

GREEN, HOWARD T(HACHER), b. Woonsocket, R.I, Mar. 15, 23; m. 47; c. 4. METALLURGY. B.E, Yale, 43; M.S, Pennsylvania, 49, Ph.D.(metall), 52. Metallurgist, Babcock & Wilcox Co, 51-54; GEN. ELEC. CO, 54-55, MGR. chem, metal powders & ingot prods, eng. sub-sect, 55-60, refractory metal prod, 60-68, METALL. ENG. OPER, 68- U.S.N, 43-46. Am. Soc. Metals; Am. Inst. Min, Metall. & Petrol. Eng. Refractory metals; powder metallurgy. Address: General Electric Co, 100 Woodlawn Ave, Pittsfield, MA 01201.

GREEN, IRVING J(OSEPH), b. Bayonne, N.J, Sept. 10, 23; m. 51; c. 3. VIROLOGY. A.B, California, 48; M.S, Wisconsin, 53; Ph.D, Univ. Calif, Los Angeles, 70. MED.SERV.C, U.S. NAVY, 50-, res. assoc. virol. & tissue culture, naval med. res. unit 4, Great Lakes, Ill, 51-66, California, 56-60, head, virol. & tissue culture dept, Naval Med. Res. Unit 2, Taiwan, 60-63, California, Los Angeles, 63-65, off. in charge, U.S. Naval Biol. Lab, Naval Supply Ctr, 65-69, RES. MICROBIOLOGIST, U.S. NAVAL MED. RES. UNIT ONE, UNIV. CALIF, BERKELEY, 69- Med. Dept, U.S.A, 43-46; Med. Serv.C, U.S.N, 50-, Capt. Tissue culture; studies on the effect of viruses in various tissue culture systems; preservation of mammalian cells by freezing; isolation of new influenza B virus strain in Taipei, Taiwan; demonstration of the double-stranded nature of the RNA genome of Colorado tick fever virus. Address: U.S. Naval Medical Research Unit One, Bldg. T-19, University California, Berkeley, Berkeley, CA 94720.

GREEN, JACK, b. Poughkeepsie, N.Y, June 19, 25; m. 52; c. 6. GEOCHEMISTRY, GEOLOGY. B.S, Va. Polytech, 50; N.Y. State Vet. scholar, Columbia, 51, Ph.D.(geol), 53. Geologist, U.S. Atomic Energy Comn, Utah, 51-52; California Co, N.Dak, 52-55; res. geologist, California Res. Corp, Standard Oil Co, Calif, 55-59; space sci. lab, space & info. systs. div, N.Am. Aviation, Inc, Calif, 59-65; Douglas Advan. Res. Labs, McDonnell Douglas Corp, 65-70; LECTR. GEOL, CALIF. STATE COL. LONG BEACH, 70- Adj. prof, Univ. South. Calif, 63-; invited lectr, Soviet Acad. Sci, NASA & various insts. & asns; consult, Univ. Hawaii; NASA; Nat. Geographic; Encycl. Britannica; Serendipity, Inc; McDonnell Douglas Corp; Inst. for Future; head working group volcanology as appl. to planetology, Int. Asn. Volcanology. Fel. AAAS; Geol. Soc. Am; fel. Am. Astronaut. Soc; Am. Geophys. Union; fel. Mineral Soc. Am; N.Y. Acad. Sci; Geochem. Soc; Am. Astron. Soc; Int. Union Geol. Sci; Int. Asn. Planetology (pres). Application of the geosciences to the study of terrestrial and extraterrestrial environments and processes; distribution of the chemical elements; oceanic resources. Address: 941 Via Nogales, Palos Verdes Estates, CA 90274.

GREEN, JACK PETER, b. N.Y.C, Oct. 4, 25; m. 58. PHARMACOLOGY. B.S, Pa. State, 47, M.S, 49; U.S. Pub. Health Serv. fel. & Ph.D.(pharmacol), Yale, 51, M.D, 57. Res. fel. with Prof. H. Dam, Polytech. Inst, Denmark, 53-55; asst. prof. PHARMACOL, Yale, 57-61, assoc. prof, 61-66; med. sch, Cornell Univ, 66-68, PROF. & CHMN. DEPT, MT. SINAI SCH. MED, 68- U.S. Pub. Health Serv. res. career prog. award, 58-66; Eleanor Roosevelt fel, 64-66; vis. scientist, Inst. Phys. Chem. Biol, Univ. Paris, 64-66; consult, chem/biol. info. handling rev. comt, div. of res. facilities & resources, Nat. Insts. Health, 66-68, mem, 68-70, preclin. psychopharmacol. res. rev. comt, Nat. Inst. Ment. Health, 69-; steering comt, exec. comt, Biochem. Pharmacol. Discussion Group, 66-70; prog. comt, Gordon Res. Conf. on Med. Chem, 67-68, 72. Claude Bernard Award, 66. AAAS; Am. Soc. Biol. Chem; Am. Chem. Soc; Harvey Soc; Am. Soc. Pharmacol. & Exp. Therapeut; N.Y. Acad. Med; Drug Info. Asn. Mechanism of action of drugs. Address: Dept. of Pharmacology, Mt. Sinai School of Medicine, 100th St. & Fifth Ave, New York, NY 10029.

GREEN, JAMES A(LBERT), b. Norman, Okla, Feb. 5, 24; m. 45; c. 3. PHYSIOLOGY. B.S, Abilene Christian Col, 52; M.A, Rice Inst, 54, Ph.D.(physiol, biochem), 56. Res. assoc. microbiol. & biochem, col. med, Baylor, 54-56, instr. biochem. & radiol, 56; physiologist, cellular res, U.S. Air Force Sch. Aerospace Med, 56-60; chief biochem. br, Civil Aeromed. Res. Inst, Okla, 60-63; supvr. biomed. requirements group, Apollo Eng, space & info. div, N.Am. Aviation, Inc, 63-65, bio-eng. requirements, Apollo Support Group, life sci. opers, space & systs. info. div, 65-67, mgr. biosci, life sci. opers, N.AM. ROCKWELL CORP, 67-69, PROG. MGR. ARTIFICIAL GRAVITY STUDIES, LIFE SCI, SPACE DIV, 69- Assoc. prof, med. sch, Univ. Okla, 60-63; prof. chem. & dir. life sci, Oklahoma City Univ, 61-63. U.S.M.C, 41-45. Soc. Exp. Biol; Am. Sci. Affiliation; Aerospace Med. Asn; Am. Inst. Aeronaut. & Astronaut. Endocrine and enzymic changes in relation to stress; energy metabolism and enzymic changes in response to hypoxia and exercise; bacterial biosynthesis; environmental physiology and biochemistry; reactions of normal human subjects to wide variety of stress situations as applicable to vehicular design requirements. Address: North American Rockwell Corp, Space Division, 12214 Lakewood Blvd, Downey, CA 90214.

GREEN, JAMES A(RNOLD), b. Hull, Ill, Jan. 21, 20; m. 42; c. 2. ANATOMY. B.A, Illinois, 41, Ph.D.(animal sci), 50. Asst. zool. & physiol, Illinois, 46-48; animal sci, 48-50; instr. ANAT, North Carolina, 50-53, asst. prof, 53-57; assoc. prof, Univ. Ill, 57-61; assoc. prof, SCH. MED, UNIV. MO-COLUMBIA, 61-65, PROF, 65- U.S.A, 41-46. Soc. Exp. Biol. & Med; Am. Asn. Anat; Endocrine Soc. Reproduction biology; electron microscopy. Address: Dept. of Anatomy, School of Medicine, University of Missouri-Columbia, Columbia, MO 65201.

GREEN, JAMES HENRY, b. Wash, D.C, Dec. 31, 03; m. 30. ANALYTICAL CHEMISTRY. B.S, Howard, 25, M.S, 27; Cornell, 36-37; Pennsylvania, 46 & 47. Head dept. sci, Kittrell Col, 27-29; chem, Agr. & Tech. Col. N.C, 29-30; PROF. CHEM, CLAFLIN COL, 30-, chmn. dept, 30-60. Vis. prof, Howard Univ, 44. Fel. AAAS; assoc. mem. Am. Chem. Soc; assoc. mem. Nat. Inst. Sci. General chemistry; indicators; polarography. Address: Dept. of Natural Science, Claflin College, Orangeburg, SC 29115.

GREEN, JAMES H(ENRY), b. Ipswich, Australia, Oct. 12, 22; m. 47; c. 3. PHYSICAL & NUCLEAR CHEMISTRY. B.Sc, Queensland, 45, M.Sc, 47; Ph.D.(chem), Cambridge, 50. Asst. prof. chem, Queensland, 47-48; res. off, Commonwealth Sci. & Indust. Res. Orgn, Melbourne, 50-54; res. fel. chem, Univ. Tech. Sydney, 54-55; lectr, New South Wales, 55-57, sr. lectr, 57-60, prof. nuclear & radiation chem, 60-66; DEAN GRAD. SCH, NEW ENG, INST, 66-, V.PRES. RES, 69- Consult, inst. dent. res, Dept. Agr. & Hunter Valley Res. Found, New South Wales, 57-66; head monitoring serv, ABC warfare, Civil Defense Orgn, 57-66; mem. radiation chem. cmt, Australian Inst. Nuclear Sci. & Eng, 60-66; therapeut. substances cmt, Australian Commonwealth Dept. Health, 64-66. Am. Chem. Soc; Reticuloendothelial Soc; Sci. Res. Soc. Am; The Chem. Soc; fel. Royal Australian Chem. Inst; Australian Radiation Soc. Radiation chemistry; stable and radioactive isotope tracers; positronium chemistry; isotope dating and geochemistry; mass spectrometry; chemical effects of nuclear transformations; gaseous ion reactions; radiochemistry. Address: New England Institute, Box 308, Ridgefield, CT 06877.

GREEN, JAMES W(ESTON), b. Elkins, W.Va, May 16, 13; m. 61; c. 2. PHYSIOLOGY. B.S, Davis-Elkins Col, 35; Pennsylvania, 40-41; M.A, Princeton, 47, Ph.D.(biol), 48. Instr. chem, Potomac State Col, 41-42; asst. biol, Princeton, 48-49; asst. prof. PHYSIOL, RUTGERS UNIV, 48-55, assoc. prof, 55-61, PROF, 61-, CHMN. DEPT, 66-, DIR. GRAD. PHYSIOL, 68- Ford fel, 53-54. U.S.A, 42-46. Am. Soc. Zool; Soc. Gen. Physiol.(secy, 59-61); Am. Physiol. Soc; N.Y. Acad. Sci. Cell permeability; cation regulation in cells and tissues; tissue cell membranes; membrane biochemistry; photo-oxidation in cells; red cell aging. Address: Dept. of Physiology, Rutgers, The State University, New Brunswick, NJ 08903.

GREEN, JAMES WILSON, b. Little Rock, Ark, Feb. 18, 06; m. 28; c. 2. ELECTRICAL ENGINEERING. B.S, U.S. Mil. Acad, 27; M.S, Yale, 28; California, 45-46; Ph.D.(elec. eng), Purdue, 50. Instr. radio & tel, sig. sch, U.S. Army, 28-31, dir. training lit, 40-42, off, radio dept, Philippines, 31-34, instr. elec, U.S. Mil. Acad, 34-38, commandant, radar sch, Sig.Corps, 42-44, chief sig. off, Armed Forces, West Pac, 44-46, prof. elec, U.S. Mil. Acad, 46-57; elec. eng, Univ. Ark, 57-70, assoc. dean col. eng, 60-61, admin. v.pres, univ, 62-70; RETIRED. U.S.A, 28-57, Brig. Gen.(Ret). Am. Soc. Eng. Educ; Inst. Elec. & Electronics Eng; Nat. Soc. Prof. Eng. Communications. Address: 804 Crest Dr, Fayetteville, AR 72701.

GREEN, JEROME J(OSEPH), b. Chicago, Ill, Oct. 10, 32; m. 58; c. 4. SOLID STATE PHYSICS. B.S, Northwestern, 54; Int. Bus. Machines Corp. fel, Harvard, 54-56, A.M, 55, Ph.D.(appl. physics), 59. Asst, Harvard, 57-59; mem. staff, RES. DIV. RAYTHEON, INC, 59-62, PRIN. RES. SCIENTIST, 62-, MGR. MAGNETIC GROUP, 70- Sr. mem. Inst. Elec. & Electronics Eng. Microwave physics; ferromagnetic resonance; magnetic circuits; phase shifters; magnetic memories. Address: 28 Winchester Dr, Lexington, MA 02173.

GREEN, JOHN A, b. Detroit, Mich, Feb. 6, 34; m. 56; c. 3. PHYSICS. B.S, Michigan, 56, M.S, 57, Ph.D.(nuclear physics), 62. Assoc. res. physicist, CONDUCTRON CORP, 61-63, HEAD DEPT. PROPAGATION ANAL, 63- Instrumentation in nuclear physics and radar; data reduction and data analysis procedures. Address: Dept. of Propagation Analysis, Conductron Corp, 3475 Plymouth Rd, Ann Arbor, MI 48107.

GREEN, JOHN C(HANDLER), b. West Hartford, Conn, Feb. 7, 32; m. 58; c. 2. GEOLOGY. A.B, Dartmouth Col, 53; Fulbright scholarship, Oslo, Norway; fels, Harvard, 54-56, M.A, 56, fels, 56-58, Ph.D, 60. Asst. prof. GEOL, UNIV. MINN, DULUTH, 58-64, assoc. prof, 64-68; PROF, 68-; GEOLOGIST, MINN. GEOL. SURV, 62- Col. consult, Earth Sci. Curriculum Proj, 64-65. AAAS; Geol. Soc. Am; Mineral Soc. Am; Norweg. Geol. Soc. Petrology of igneous and metamorphic rocks; geology of northern New England; Pre-Cambrian geology of Minnesota; volcanology. Address: Dept. of Geology, University of Minnesota, Duluth, MN 55812.

GREEN, JOHN GILBERT, b. Solway, Minn, Oct. 24, 28; m. 52; c. 3. PLANT PHYSIOLOGY. B.S, Moorhead State Col, 56; M.S, N.Dak. State, 58; Ph.D. (plant physiol), Iowa State, 61. Res. assoc. cell physiol, Oak Ridge Nat. Lab, 61-62, Nat. Insts. Health fel, 62-63, biologist, 63-64; develop. engr, tech. div, Union Carbide Nuclear Co, 64-66; biol. div, Oak Ridge Nat. Lab, 66-67; assoc. prof. agron. & anal. biochemist, tobacco & health progs, Univ. Ky, 67-71; ASSOC. PROF. BIOL. & CHMN. DEPT, AURORA COL, 71- Consult. multidisciplinary sci. & instrument develop. Chem.C, 51-53, Sgt. AAAS; Biomedical engineering; seed physiology; weed control; cryobiology. Address: Dept. of Biology, Aurora College, Aurora, IL 60507.

GREEN, JOHN H, b. Pittsburgh, Pa, Jan. 23, 29. MICROBIOLOGY, BIOCHEMISTRY. B.A, Rochester, 51; Indiana, 51-52; M.A, State Univ. N.Y. Col. Teachers, Albany, 55; Ph.D.(microbiol), Mich. State, 63. Instr. chem. & bact, State Univ. N.Y. Agr. & Tech. Inst. Alfred, 56-58; fel, Inst. Agr. & Indust. Microbiol, Univ. Mass, 63-64, Nat. Insts. Health res. assoc, 64-66; RES. MICROBIOLOGIST, U.S. NAT. MARINE FISHERIES SERV, NAT. OCEANIC & ATMOSPHERIC AGENCY, 66- Am. Soc. Microbiol; Inst. Food Tech. Microbial physiology. Address: U.S. National Marine Fisheries Service, National Oceanic & Atmospheric Agency, Regents Dr, College Park, MD 20740.

GREEN, JOHN I(RVING), b. Cedarhurst, N.Y, Mar. 25, 24; m. 60; c. 2. ECOLOGY, BOTANY. B.S, State Univ. N.Y. Col. Forestry, 49; M.S, Syracuse, 51; Nat. Wildlife Fedn. grant, Cornell Univ, Ph.D.(sci. educ), 61. Teacher, high sch, N.Y, 51-53; asst. prof. biol, bot. & zool, State Univ. N.Y. Brockport, 55-56; exten. biologist wildlife educ, wildlife div, Mines & Resources Dept, Prov. Newf, 58-60; asst. prof, N.J. State Sch. Conserv, 61-62; asst. prof. conserv, exten. div, Cornell Univ, 62-65; ECOL. & BOT, ST. LAWRENCE UNIV, 65-70, ASSOC. PROF, 70- Guest lectr, Mem. Univ, 59-60. U.S.M.C.R, 42-, Maj. Am. Wildlife Soc; Soc. Am. Foresters; Ecol. Soc. Am; Am. Nature Study Soc. Wildlife and sociological impact; development of techniques and methods for teaching conservation; wildlife ecology; waterfowl. Address: Dept. of Biology, St. Lawrence University, Canton, NY 13617.

GREEN, J(OHN) J(OSEPH), b. Portsmouth, Eng, Nov. 9, 05; m. 30; c. 2. PHYSICS, AERONAUTICS. B.Sc, London, 28, Busk studentship, 28-29, dipl, Imp. Col, 29, Beit fel, 29-30, Ph.D, 30. Jr. res. physicist, Nat. Res. Coun. Can, 30-35, asst. res. engr, 35-43; chief res. engr, test & develop. estab, Royal Can. Air Force, 43-45; chief res. aeronaut. engr, Air Transport Bd, 45-49; chief div, B, Defence Res. Bd. & sci. adv. to Chief Air Staff, Royal Can. Air Force, 49-55; defence res. mem. Can. Joint Staff & Defence Res. Attache, Can. Embassy, Wash, D.C, 55-59; chief supt, Can. Armament Res. & Develop. Estab, 59-63; dir. res, LITTON SYSTS. CAN. LTD, 63-69, govt. rels, 69-70, CONSULT, 71- Mem. bd. dirs, Leigh Insts. Ltd, 70-; v.chmn. consult. comt, Nat. Mus. Sci. & Technol; mem. assoc. comt. avionics, Nat. Res. Coun. Can; chmn. spec. study comt. aeronaut. res. & develop. in Can, Can. Sci. Coun. Mem. Order Brit. Empire, 43; King's commendation, 45. Int. Coun. Aeronaut. Sci; fel. Am. Inst. Aeronaut. & Astronaut; hon. fel. Can. Aeronaut. & Space Inst.(pres, 54-55, 62-63, ed-in-chief, jour); fel. Royal Aeronaut. Soc; Can. Res. Mgt. Asn. Electronics; inertial navigation. Address: Apt. 1006, 2400 Carling Ave, Ottawa, Ont. K2B 7H2, Can.

GREEN, JOHN M, b. Carlisle, Pa, Jan. 10, 40; m. 66; c. 1. MARINE BIOLOGY. B.Sc, Michigan, 61; M.Sc, Miami, 64; Ph.D.(ichthyol), British Columbia, 68. ASST. PROF. MARINE BIOL, MEMORIAL UNIV, 68- Am. Soc. Ichthyol. & Herpet; Marine Technol. Soc; Can. Soc. Zool. Behavioral ecology of littoral fishes, particularly with respect to the function of endogenous tidal and circadian activity rhythms in these fishes. Address: Dept. of Biology, Memorial University of Newfoundland, St. John's, Newf, Can.

GREEN, JOHN M(ELVIN), b. Cozad, Nebr, Jan. 30, 18; m. 41; c. 3. AGRONOMY. B.S, Iowa State Col, 41, Ph.D.(crop breeding), 47; M.S, Mont. State Col, 43. Agronomist, Miss. Agr. Exp. Sta, 47-48, geneticist, 48-49; agronomist, Okla. Agr. Exp. Sta, 49-58; res. farm dir, Anderson Clayton Co, Ltd, 58-60; RES. DIR, McNAIR SEED CO, 60- Am. Soc. Agron. Corn breeding methods; genetics of barley and cotton; breeding of corn, tobacco, cotton, small grains. Address: McNair Seed Co, Laurinburg, NC 28352.

GREEN, JOHN R(OOT), b. Alameda, Calif, Sept. 19, 20; m. 51; c. 3. PHYSICS. B.S, California, 41, Ph.D.(physics), 50. Asst. prof. PHYSICS, UNIV. N.MEX, 50-55, assoc. prof, 55-62, PROF, 62- Fulbright fel, Univ. Aleppo, 66-67. U.S.A.A.F, 42-46, Res, 46-52. Am. Phys. Soc. Cosmic radiation; design of cloud chambers; plastic crystals; phase transformations; dielectric properties. Address: Dept. of Physics, University of New Mexico, Albuquerque, NM 87106.

GREEN, JOHN W(ILLIAM), b. Garrett, Ind, Dec. 21, 35; m. 64. PHYSICAL CHEMISTRY. B.A, Miami (Ohio), 57; Du Pont fel, Wisconsin, 58, Nat. Sci. Found. fel, 59, Ph.D.(phys. chem), 62. Res. chemist, Calif. Res. Corp, STANDARD OIL CO. CALIF, 62-70, SR. RES. CHEMIST, CHEVRON RES. CO, 70- Am. Chem. Soc; Electron Micros. Soc. Am. High temperature thermodynamic studies; mass spectrometry; neutron activation analysis; radiotracer methods; optical and electron microscopy; x-ray diffraction. Address: Chevron Research Co, 576 Standard Ave, Richmond, CA 94802.

GREEN, JOHN W(ILLIE), b. Hearne, Tex, Mar. 8, 14; m. 38; c. 2. MATHEMATICS. B.A, Rice Inst, 35, M.A, 36; fel, California, 36-38, Ph.D.(math), 38. Asst. math, Rice Inst, 35-36; Peirce Inst, Harvard, 38-39; instr, Rochester, 39-41, asst. prof, 41-43; mathematician, ballistic res. lab, Aberdeen Proving Grounds, 43-45; asst. prof. MATH, UNIV. CALIF, LOS ANGELES, 45-48, assoc. prof, 48-54, PROF, 54- Mem, Inst. Adv. Study, 51; chmn, Conf. Bd. Math. Sci, 71-72. Am. Math. Soc.(assoc. secy, 47-55, secy, 57-67); Math. Asn. Am. Potential theory; theory of functions; convex bodies; harmonic functions. Address: Dept. of Mathematics, University of California, Los Angeles, CA 90024.

GREEN, JOHN W(ILSON), b. Seattle, Wash, Mar. 12, 12; m. 42. ORGANIC CHEMISTRY. B.S, Princeton, 33, Ph.D.(org. chem), 37; M.S, Pennsylvania, 34. Fel. carbohydrate chem, Rockefeller Found, Princeton, 37-38; asst. cellulose, INST. PAPER CHEM, LAWRENCE UNIV, 38-45, res. assoc, 45-67, CHMN. ORG. CHEM. SECT, 67- Am. Chem. Soc; The Chem. Soc. Cellulose and sugar chemistry. Address: Organic Chemistry Section, Institute of Paper Chemistry, Lawrence University, Appleton, WI 54911.

GREEN, JONATHAN P, b. N.Y.C, June 16, 35; m. 59; c. 1. ZOOLOGY, PHYSIOLOGY. B.S, Pa. State, 57; Nat. Sci. Found. summer fel, Minnesota, 59, Ph.D.(zool), 63; Nat. Insts. Health fel, 59-63. Nat. Insts. Health training grant pathobiol, Hopkins, 63 & fel, 63-64; asst. prof. biol, Brown Univ, 64-72; LECTR. PHYSIOL, SCH. BIOL. SCI, UNIV. MALAYA, 71- Mem, Marine Biol. Lab, Woods Hole, Mass, instr. invertebrate zool, 66-70. AAAS; Am. Soc. Zool. Physiological and morphological color changes in Crustacea; physiology and ultrastructure of the crustacean epidermis. Address: School of Biological Sciences, University of Malaya, Kuala Lumpur, Malaysia.

GREEN, JOSEPH, b. Brooklyn, N.Y, Oct. 5, 28; m. 51; c. 3. POLYMER CHEMISTRY. B.S, City Col. New York, 50; M.S, Kansas, 52. Chemist, U.S. Rubber Reclaiming Co, Inc, 51-55; Food Mach. & Mfg. Corp, Inc, 55-56; supvr. appl. chem. res. sect, Reaction Motors Div, Thiokol Chem. Corp, 56-66, MGR. synthesis & polymer chem. dept, 66-67; POLYMERIZATION RES, PETROCHEM. RES. GROUP, CITIES SERV. RES. CTR, CRANBURY, 67- Fel. Am. Inst. Chem; Am. Chem. Soc; Soc. Plastics Eng. Polymer chemistry, synthesis and evaluation; rubber chemistry and formulation; thermal stability and chemical resistance; flame retardancy; propellant chemistry; boron and nitroso polymers; carboranes; fluorocarbons; polyurethanes; polyesters; polypropylene; polyethylene; acrylonitrile butadiene styrene; butyl rubber. Address: 3 New Dover Rd, East Brunswick, NJ 08816.

GREEN, JOSEPH M(ATTHEW), b. New York, N.Y, Nov. 29, 26; m; c. 3. THEORETICAL PHYSICS. B.S, Calif. Inst. Tech, 49, Ph.D.(physics), 57; Chicago, 49-50. Asst. physics, Chicago, 49-50; math, Calif. Inst. Tech, 52-54, hydrodyn, hydrodyn. lab, 50-57; PHYSICIST, Rand Corp, 57-71; RES. & DEVELOP ASSOCS, 71- Summers, physicist, missile dynamics, div, Nat. Bur. Standards, 48-49. U.S.N, 45-46. Am. Phys. Soc. Interaction of radiation with matter; equation of state; nuclear physics; optical model calculations. Address: 24617 Eliat St, Woodland Hills, CA 91364.

GREEN, JULIUS, b. U.S, Aug. 24, 19; m. 46; c. 2. FOOD TECHNOLOGY. B.S, City Col. New York, 40; M.S, Polytech. Inst. Brooklyn, 46. Res. chemist & chief control chemist food processing, Am. Dietaids Co, 41-45; res. chemist, new prod. develop, Allied Food Indust, 45-47; proj. leader prod. & process develop, res. ctr, GEN. FOODS CORP, 47-54, sect. head, 54-59, lab. dir, prod. develop, 60-62, lab. mgr, food law serv, 62-63, Jello Div. Lab, 63-66, tech. res. dir, Gen. Foods Ltd, Eng, 66-69, DEVELOP. MGR, GEN. FOODS INT, 69- Am. Chem. Soc; Inst. Food Technol. Product and process development of nuts, popcorn, cereals, coffee and coffee substitutes; food preservation; flavor technology, chemistry application; gelatin and starch-base desserts. Address: 11 Meadowlark Dr, West Nyack, NY 10994.

GREEN, KEITH, b. Kent, Eng, Feb. 20, 40; m. 64; c. 1. HIGH ENERGY PARTICLE PHYSICS. B.Sc, London, 62; Ph.D.(physics), Bristol, 66. RES. ASSOC. PHYSICS, Bristol, 65-67; UNIV. WASH, 67- High energy physics. Address: Dept. of Physics, University of Washington, Seattle, WA 98105.

GREEN KEITH, b. Nuneaton, Eng, Aug. 16, 40; m. 64; c. 2. PHYSIOLOGY, BIOPHYSICS. B.Sc, Univ. Leicester, 61; Nuffield Found. fel, Univ. St. Andrews, 61-64, Ph.D.(physiol), 64. Nat. Insts. Health res. fel. OPHTHAL, SCH. MED, JOHNS HOPKINS UNIV, 64-66, instr, 66-67, asst. prof, 67-71, ASSOC. PROF, 71- Nat. Eye Inst. res. career develop. award, 70. AAAS; Am. Physiol. Soc; Biophys. Soc. Solute and solvent transfer across biological membranes; mechanisms underlying control of corneal thickness; mechanism of aqueous humor formation; hormonal effects on membrane transport. Address: 267 Woods Bldg, Wilmer Institute, Johns Hopkins University School of Medicine, Baltimore, MD 21205.

GREEN, LARRY J, b. Memphis, Tenn, Jan. 1, 31; m. 58; c. 2. ORTHODONTICS. B.S, Pittsburgh, 53, D.D.S, 56, M.S, 60; Nat. Inst. Dent. Res. fel, Iowa, 62-65, Ph.D.(anat. growth), 65. Asst. prof. ORTHOD, Pittsburgh, 60-62; SCH. DENT, STATE UNIV. N.Y. BUFFALO, 65-67, assoc. prof, 67-71, PROF, 71- Clin. practice, 60-62. Dent.C, 56-58, Capt. AAAS; Am. Dent. Asn; Am. Asn. Orthod; Int. Asn. Dent. Res; fel. Am. Col. Dent. Anatomic growth, especially facial. Address: Dept. of Orthodontics, School of Dentistry, State University of New York at Buffalo, 236 Capen Hall, Buffalo, NY 14214.

GREEN, L(ARRY) Q(UENTIN), b. Pa, Mar. 13, 22; m. 46; c. 3. ORGANIC CHEMISTRY. B.S, Maryland, 43, Ph.D.(chem), 49; M.S, Pa. State, 47. Chemist, E.I. DU PONT DE NEMOURS & CO, 48-56, supvr, 56-66, tech. supvr. org. chem. dept, DYES & CHEM. DIV, 66-68, MGR. NON-TEXTILE INDUSTS, 68- Am. Chem. Soc. Textile chemicals; fluorochemicals; organic titanates. Address: Dyes & Chemicals Division, E.I. du Pont de Nemours & Co, Wilmington, DE 19898.

GREEN, LAWRENCE, b. Gelenes, Hungary, May 3, 37; U.S. citizen; m. 63; c. 2. NUCLEAR PHYSICS. B.S, City Col. New York, 59; Atomic Energy Cmn. grant & Ph.D.(nuclear physics), Pa. State, 63. SR. SCIENTIST NEUTRON PHYSICS, BETTIS ATOMIC POWER LAB, WESTINGHOUSE ELEC. CORP, 64- Am. Nuclear Soc; Am. Phys. Soc. Low energy nuclear physics. Address: 151 Dutch Lane, Pittsburgh, PA 15236.

GREEN, LEON, JR, b. Austin, Tex, Aug. 13, 22; m. 51; c. 3. MECHANICAL ENGINEERING. B.S, Calif. Inst. Tech, 44, M.S, 47, Ph.D.(mech. eng), 50. Res. engr, chem. eng. dept. & jet propulsion lab, Calif. Inst. Tech, 44-49; atomic energy res. dept, N.Am. Aviation, Inc, 49-51; sr. engr, solid engine div, prin. engr, liquid engine div. & head appl. mech, space tech. div, Aero-jet-Gen. Corp. div, Gen. Tire & Rubber Co, 51-59; acting mgr. aerothermo-chem. & mats, & mgr. propulsion, Aeronutronic Div, Ford Motor Co, 59-62; chief scientist, Lockheed Propulsion Co, 62-64; sci. dir, res. & tech. div, Air Force Systs. Command, Bolling A.F.B, D.C, 64-67; asst. dir. planning, Wash. area, Lockheed Aircraft Corp, 67-70, dir, 70; EXEC. SECY, DEFENSE SCI. BD, OFF. DIR. DEFENSE RES. & ENG, 70- Consult, comt. solid propellant instability of combustion, Asst. Secy. Defense, 57-59. AAAS; Am. Soc. Mech. Eng; Am. Inst. Aeronaut. & Astronaut; Sci. Res. Soc. Am; Solar Energy Soc; World Future Soc. Rocket propulsion; heat transfer and fluid dynamics; combustion; high-temperature materials; research management; technology assessment. Address: Room 3D1040, The Pentagon, Washington, DC 20301.

GREEN, L(EON) W(ILLIAM), b. Passaic, N.J, Dec. 12, 25; m. 56; c. 2. MATHEMATICS. A.B, Harvard, 48; M.A, Yale, 49, Atomic Energy Comn. fel, 49-51, Ph.D.(math), 52. Instr. MATH, Princeton, 52-53; UNIV. MINN, MINNEAPOLIS, 53-54, asst. prof, 54-63, PROF, 63- U.S.A, 44. Am. Math. Soc. Differential geometry; topological dynamics. Address: Dept. of Mathematics, Inst. of Technology, University of Minnesota, Minneapolis, MN 55455.

GREEN, LISLE R(OYAL), b. Ogden, Utah, Nov. 18, 18; m. 46; c. 4. RANGE MANAGEMENT. B.S, Utah State, 41, M.S, 48. Ranch planner, soil conserv. serv, U.S. Dept. Agr, 46-47, range conservationist, U.S. Forest Serv, 48-54; asst. prof. range mgt, Calif. State Polytech. Col, 55-60; fuel-break proj. leader, FOREST FIRES RES, U.S. FOREST SERV, 60-70, SUPRVY. RANGE SCIENTIST, 70- Assoc. agr. exp. sta, Univ. Calif, Riverside, 64- U.S.A.F, 41-46, Res, 46-, Lt. Col. Soil Conserv. Soc. Am; Am. Soc. Range Mgt; Soc. Am. Foresters. Ecology and management of annual plant and chaparral covered land, including fertilization, revegetation, use of herbicides, prescribed fire and effects of fire and cultural practices. Address: Forest Fire Lab, P.O. Box 5007, Riverside, CA 92507.

GREEN, LONZO F(RANCIS), b. Weatherford, Okla, Dec. 24, 30. SOIL SCIENCE. B.S, Okla. Agr. & Mech. Col, 52; M.S, Ohio State Univ, 54, Ph.D. (soil biochem), 56. Asst. agron, Ohio Exp. Sta, 52-56; agriculturalist, Int. Mineral & Chem. Corp, 58-62; Sun Oil Co, Pa, 63-66; sr. res. agronomist, U.S. Steel Corp, 66-69; SR. SCIENTIST, AM. CAN CO, 70- Fel. Am. Potash. Asst. plant pathologist, Biol. Warfare Labs, Chem.C, U.S.A.R, 56-58. Am. Soc. Agron; Am. Chem. Soc; Am. Acad. Arts & Sci; N.Y. Acad. Sci. Plant nutrition; soil biochemistry; plant biochemistry. Address: 1417 Alpha Court, West Palm Beach, FL 33406.

GREEN, LOUIS C(RAIG), b. Macon, Ga, Feb. 2, 11; m. 40. ASTROPHYSICS. A.B, Princeton, 32, M.A, 33, Ph.D.(astron), 37. Instr. astron, exten. div, Rutgers, summers 31-33; math. & astron, Allegheny Col, 37-39, asst. prof, 39-41; instr. ASTRON, HAVERFORD COL, 41-42, asst. prof, 42-48, assoc. prof, 48-53, PROF, 53-, CHMN. DEPT, 42-, physics, 63-65, provost, 65-68, acting pres, summer 67. Vis. asst. prof, Swarthmore Col, 44; lectr, Bryn Mawr Col, 44-46; Guggenheim fel, 55-56; vis. prof, Max Planck Inst. Munich, 59; mem, Inst. Advan. Study, 62-63, 68-69. Fel. Am. Phys. Soc; Am. Astron. Soc. Far ultraviolet spectroscopy; atomic wave functions. Address: Dept. of Astronomy, Haverford College, Haverford, PA 19041.

GREEN, MARCUS HERBERT, b. Harrisburg, Pa, July 31, 05; m. 30; c. 2. BIOLOGY. B.S, Albright Col, 29; M.S, Pittsburgh, 35; hon. D.Sc, Lebanon Valley Col, 64. Teacher, pub. sch, Pa, 29; instr. biol. & chem, ALBRIGHT COL, 30-35, asst. prof, 35-37, BIOL, 37-48, assoc. prof, 48-62, prof, 62-66, HENRY-PFEIFFER CHAIR, 66- Am. Soc. Prof. Biol. Developmental anatomy of vertebrates; vertebrate embryology, especially the circulatory and nervous systems and dentition of mammals; development of a general science course for liberal art students; initiation of a new interdisciplinary program in science and religion. Address: 1138 Spring St, Reading, PA 19604.

GREEN, MARGARET, b. Shamrock, La, March 27, 17. MICROBIOLOGY. B.S, La. State, 37; M.S, Emory, 39; Ph.D, Wisconsin, 52. Med. bacteriologist, Charity Hosp, Shreveport, La, 40-42; instr. bacter, La. State, 42-47; asst, Wisconsin, 47-52; asst. prof. BACTER, UNIV. ALA, 62-55, assoc. prof, 55-64, PROF, 64-, CHMN. DEPT. MICROBIOL, 70-, acting head, 68-70. AAAS; Am. Chem. Soc; Am. Soc. Microbiol. Physiology of bacteria; nitrogen-fixation; arthrobacteriology; morphogenesis; iron bacteria. Address: College of Arts & Science, University of Alabama, Box H, University, AL 35486.

GREEN, MARGARET C(REIGHTON), b. Prince Albert, Sask, Jan. 11, 14; nat; m. 40. GENETICS. B.A, Conn. Col, 35; Sc.M, Brown, 37; Ph.D.(zool), Iowa, 40. Asst. biol, Brown, 35-37; Iowa, 37-40; zool, Ohio State, 41-43, instr, 46-47, res. assoc, 51-53, 55-56; biologist, Nat. Sci. Found, 53-55; staff scientist genetics, JACKSON LAB, 56-67, SR. STAFF SCIENTIST, 67- Am. Soc. Nat; Genetics Soc. Am. Mammalian developmental genetics. Address: Jackson Lab, Bar Harbor, ME 04609.

GREEN, MARK M, b. N.Y.C, Apr. 6, 37; m. 58; c. 1. ORGANIC CHEMISTRY. B.S, City Col. New York, 58; N.Y. Univ, 62-64; Nat. Insts. Health fel, Princeton, 64-65, Ph.D.(chem), 66. Nat. Insts. Health res. fel, CHEM, Stanford Univ, 66-67; ASST. PROF, UNIV. MICH, ANN ARBOR, 67- U.S.A, 59-60, Res, 59-65. AAAS; Am. Chem. Soc; The Chem. Soc. Organic stereochemistry; synthetic methods in organic chemistry; mechanistic mass spectroscopy. Address: Dept. of Chemistry, University of Michigan, Ann Arbor, MI 48104.

GREEN, MARY ELOISE, b. East Liberty, Ohio, June 10, 03. FOODS. B.S, Ohio State, 28, M.S, 33; fel, Iowa State Col, 47-49, Ph.D.(foods, nutrit), 49. Teacher, pub. schs, Ohio, 23-26, 28-37; instr. ed, Ohio Wesleyan, 37-39; FOODS & NUTRIT, OHIO STATE UNIV, 39-46, asst. prof, 46-55, assoc. prof, 55-68, PROF, 68- AAAS; Am. Home Econ. Asn; Am. Dietetic Asn; Inst. Food Technol; Am. Asn. Cereal Chem. Physical properties of meats, flour mixtures and starchy foods; food preservation. Address: School of Home Economics, Ohio State University, 1787 Neil Ave, Columbus, OH 43210.

GREEN, MAURICE, b. New York, N.Y, May 5, 26; m. 50; c. 3. BIOCHEMISTRY. B.S, Michigan, 49; M.S, Wisconsin, 52, Ph.D.(biochem), 54. Nat. Found. Infantile Paralysis res. fel, Pennsylvania, 54-55, instr. biochem. & Lalor fel, 55-56; asst. prof. MICROBIOL, SCH. MED, ST. LOUIS UNIV, 56-60, assoc. prof, 60-63, PROF, 63-, DIR. INST. MOLECULAR VIROL, 64- Sr. fel, U.S. Pub. Health Serv, 58-62, res. career award, 62- U.S.N, 44-46. AAAS; Am. Soc. Biol. Chem; Am. Chem. Soc; Am. Soc. Microbiol. Nucleic acids and viruses; metabolism of virus infected cells; molecular biology of viruses, nucleic acid and proteins; cell biochemistry. Address: Institute for Molecular Virology, St. Louis University School of Medicine, 3681 Park Ave, St. Louis, MO 63110.

GREEN, M(ELVILLE) S(AUL), b. Jamaica, N.Y, June 9, 22; m. 50; c. 2. THEORETICAL PHYSICS. B.A, Columbia, 44; M.A, Princeton, 47, Ph.D, 51. Instr. nat. sci, Chicago, 47-50, asst. prof, 50-51; res. assoc. theoret. physics, Maryland, 51-54; physicist, thermodyn. sect, Nat. Bur. Standards, 54-60, chief statist. physics sect, Wash, D.C, 60-68; PROF. PHYSICS, TEMPLE UNIV, 68- Fulbright res. grant & Guggenheim fel, Utrecht, Netherlands, 57-58. Fel. Am. Phys. Soc. Statistical mechanics of time dependent phenomena; critical phenomena. Address: Room A114, Dept. of Physics, Barton Hall, Temple University, Philadelphia, PA 19122.

GREEN, MELVIN H(OWARD), b. Pittsburgh, Pa, Feb. 21, 37; m. 65; c. 1. BIOCHEMISTRY, VIROLOGY. B.S, Pittsburgh, 58; Nat. Insts. Health & Nat. Sci. Found. fels. & Ph.D.(biochem), Illinois, 62. Nat. Insts. Health fel. virol, Calif. Inst. Technol, 62-63; asst. prof. BIOL, UNIV. CALIF, SAN DIEGO, 63-67, ASSOC. PROF, 67- Am. Cancer Soc. res. scholar, 70-71. AAAS. Regulation of genetic expression of lytic and temperate bacteriophages; replication of polyoma virus; development of DNA tumor viruses. Address: Dept. of Biology, University of California, San Diego, La Jolla, CA 92037.

GREEN, M(ELVIN) M(ARTIN), b. Minneapolis, Minn, Aug. 24, 16; m. 46. GENETICS. B.A, Minnesota, 38, M.A, 40, Ph.D.(zool), 42. Asst. prof. zool, Missouri, 46-50; GENETICS, UNIV. CALIF, DAVIS, 50-55, assoc. prof, 55-60, PROF, 60-, GENETICIST, EXP. STA, 69- Sanit.C, 42-46, Capt. Genetics Soc. Am; Am. Soc. Nat. Drosophila genetics; mutation; pseudoallelism. Address: Dept. of Genetics, University of California, Davis, CA 95616.

GREEN, MELVIN W(ILLIAM), b. Bluffs, Ill, Feb. 28, 10; m. 44; c. 2. PHARMACEUTICAL CHEMISTRY. B.S, Univ. Pittsburgh, 32, Ph.D.(chem), 37; hon. D.Sc, Phila. Col. Pharm. & Sci, 71. Asst, U.S. Pharmacopoeia, Mellon Inst, 36-38; asst. prof. chem, col. pharm, Cincinnati, 38-40; instr. pharmacol, sch. med, Georgetown, 40-42; chief chemist, Am. Pharmaceut. Asn, 42-47. dir. lab, 47-49; assoc. prof. pharmaceut. chem, sch. pharm, Wisconsin, 49-52; DIR. EDUC. RELS, AM. COUN. PHARMACEUT. EDUC, 52- Mem. Pan-Am. Pharmaceut. & Biochem. Fedn; consult, U.S. Agency Int. Develop, 68-; Pan-Am. Health Orgn, 70- Am. Chem. Soc; Am. Inst. Chem; Am. Soc. Hosp. Pharmacists; Am. Pharmaceut. Asn; N.Y. Acad. Sci; P.R. Acad. Arts & Sci. Standardization of drugs; mode of action of drugs; organic analytical reactions; pharmaceutical control and education. Address: American Council on Pharmaceutical Education, 77 W. Washington St, Chicago, IL 60602.

GREEN, MICHAEL E(NOCH), b. New York, N.Y, Nov. 5, 38. PHYSICAL CHEMISTRY. B.A, Cornell, 59; Nat. Sci. Found. fels, Yale, 60-63, M.S, 61, Ph.D.(phys. chem), 64. Res. assoc. exciton transport, Calif. Inst. Tech, 63-64; Peace Corps vis. lectr. chem, Middle East Tech, Ankara, 64-66; ASST. PROF. PHYS. CHEM, CITY COL. NEW YORK, 66- AAAS; Am. Chem. Soc; Am. Phys. Soc. Electronic properties of organic solids; electrical noise generated during ion transport across membranes; membrane transport. Address: Dept. of Chemistry, City College of New York, 140 St. & Convent Ave, New York, NY 10031.

GREEN, MICHAEL JOHN, b. Slough, Eng, Nov. 30, 42; m. 68; c. 2. ORGANIC CHEMISTRY. B.S, Sheffield, 64, Ph.D.(org. chem), 67. Res. assoc. org. chem, Ben May Lab. Cancer Res, Univ. Chicago, 67-69; Brookhaven Nat. Lab, 69-71; SR. SCIENTIST, NATURAL PROD. RES. DIV, SCHERING CORP, 71- Am. Chem. Soc; Brit. Chem. Soc. Steroid chemistry; synthesis and structure-activity relationships of biologically active organic compounds; chemical modification of proteins-hemoproteins. Address: Natural Products Research Division, Schering Corp, Bloomfield, NJ 07003.

GREEN, MILTON, b. Pueblo, Colo, Jan. 13, 12; m. 44; c. 2. PHYSICS. B.S, Wyoming, 35; M.A, California, 37, Ph.D.(physics), 41. Asst. physics, California, 36-39; jr. physicist, Nat. Bur. Standards, 42-43, asst. physicist, 43-45; physicist, res. & develop. labs, U.S. Army Signal Corps, Ft. Monmouth, 45-54, phys. scientist & group leader, 54-60; sr. staff scientist, res. labs, Burroughs Corp, Pa, 60-64; RES. PHYSICIST, U.S. NAVY UNDER WATER SOUND LAB, 64- Am. Phys. Soc; Inst. Elec. & Electronics Eng. Electrical conduction in solids, mainly semiconductors; transport phenomena; thermoelectricity; photoelectricity; photographic photometry; underwater optics. Address: 201 Gardner Ave, New London, CT 06320.

GREEN, MILTON, b. Boston, Mass, Apr. 30, 20; m. 54; c. 4. ORGANIC CHEMISTRY. B.S, Mass. Inst. Tech, 40, univ. fel, Columbia, 47-49, Lilly fel, 49-51, Ph.D.(chem), 51. Chemist, Atlantic Gelatin Co, 40-41; res. chemist, biochem. & proteins, Burroughs-Wellcome Co, 41-42; sulfa drugs, Hoffmann-La Roche, Inc, 42-43; pharmaceut. & amino acids, Wyeth Inst, 43-44; textile finishing, U.S. Finishing Corp, 46-47; sr. chemist & group leader photog. & org. chem, POLAROID CORP, 51-59, asst. mgr. org. res. div, 59-65, mgr. photog. chem. res, 65-68, ASST. DIR. CHEM. RES. & DEVELOP, 68- U.S.M.C, 44-46. Am. Chem. Soc. Chemistry of the photographic process; pharmaceuticals; proteins; amino acids; dyes. Address: 38 Winston Rd, Newton Center, MA 02159.

GREEN, MINO, b. New York, N.Y, Mar. 10, 27; m. 51; c. 2. PHYSICAL CHEMISTRY. B.Sc, Durham, 48, Ph.D.(chem), 51, D.Sc, 64. Res. fel. radio chem, Mass. Inst. Tech, 51, asst. group leader, solid state physics, Lincoln lab, 51-55; res. fel. phys. chem, Imp. Col, London, 55-56; div. chief solid state chem. & metall, Zenith Radio Corp, 56-60; assoc. dir. electrochem. lab, Univ. Pa, 60-62; MGR. & DIR. RES, ZENITH RADIO RES. CORP, U.K, LTD, 62- Vis. prof, Univ. Bradford, 67- Physics and chemistry of surfaces and solids. Address: Zenith Radio Research Corp, U.K, Ltd, 6 Dalston Gardens, Stanmore, Middlesex HA7 1BJ, England.

GREEN, MORRIS, b. Brooklyn, N.Y, Apr. 27, 31. RADIATION BIOLOGY. B.A, Brooklyn Col, 52; Atomic Energy Cmn. fel, Rochester, 52-54, Dazian Found. fel, 54-55, Ph.D.(radiation biol), 58. Coffin res. fel. radiation biol, Rochester, 58-64; asst. prof. BIOL. SCI, HUNTER COL, 64-70, ASSOC. PROF, 70-, asst. dir. grad. studies, 64-70. Am. Chem. Soc. Biological effects of radiation; blood and liver proteins and their functions; tracer chemistry; diabetes, action of insulin; amino acid and protein metabolism. Address: Dept. of Biological Sciences, Hunter College, 695 Park Ave, New York, NY 10021.

GREEN, MORTON, b. Brooklyn, N.Y, Oct. 25, 17; m. 46; c. 3. VERTEBRATE PALEONTOLOGY. A.B, Univ. Kans, 40, M.A, 42; Ph.D.(paleont), Univ. Calif, 54. CHMN. DEPT. BIOL, S.DAK. SCH. MINES & TECHNOL, 50-, ASSOC. DIR. MUS. GEOL, 68-, res. assoc, 50-61, curator vert. paleont, 62-68. Soc. Vert. Paleont; Geol. Soc. Am; Am. Soc. Mammal; Soc. Study Evolution. Paleontology; mammals. Address: Dept. of Biology, South Dakota School of Mines & Technology, Rapid City, SD 57701.

GREEN, NATHAN, b. Cleveland, Ohio, Nov. 27, 16; m. 40; c. 2. ORGANIC CHEMISTRY. B.S, George Washington, 44; Maryland, 45-46; Oak Ridge Inst. Nuclear Studies, 56; U.S. Dept. Agr. Grad. Sch, 62-70. Mat. engr. cement & concrete, Nat. Bur. Standards, 35-44; RES. CHEMIST, ENTOM. RES. DIV, U.S. DEPT. AGR, 44- Abstractor, Chem. Abstr, 64- U.S. Dept. Agr. Award, 68. Fel. AAAS; Am. Chem. Soc; Entom. Soc. Am. Synthesis of safe insecticides; insect attractants; radioactive labelled pesticides. Address: Pesticide Chemicals Research Branch, Agricultural Research Center, Beltsville, MD 20705.

GREEN, N(ORMAN) BAYARD, b. Bloomington, Md, Nov. 15, 05; m. 30; c. 1. HERPETOLOGY. B.S, Davis & Elkins Col, 26, Sc.D, 67; M.S, W.Va. Univ, 31; Ph.D, Ohio State Univ, 52. Instr. pub. sch, W.Va, 26-38; instr. MARSHALL UNIV, 38-45; asst. prof. ZOOL, 45-47, assoc. prof, 47-52, PROF, 52-, chmn. dept, 47-65, dean col. arts & sci, 68. Curator herpet. collections, W.Va. Biol. Surv. Am. Soc. Ichthyol. & Herpet; Soc. Study Amphibians & Reptiles. Distribution and life histories of West Virginia amphibia and reptiles. Address: Dept. of Zoology, Marshall University, Huntington, WV 25701.

GREEN, ORVILLE, b. Oak Park, Ill, Jan. 14, 26; m. 54; c. 3. PEDIATRICS, ENDOCRINOLOGY. A.B, Harvard, 49; M.D, Northwestern, 54. Clin. res. fel. pediat. med, univ. hosp, Hopkins, 57-60, Nat. Insts. Health res. fel, 58-60; asst. prof. pediat, col. med, Ohio State, 60-61, assoc. prof, 61-63, asst. prof. med, 60-63; assoc. prof. PEDIAT, MED. SCH, NORTHWEST. UNIV, 63-68, PROF, 68-; DIR. DIV. ENDOCRINOL, CHILDREN'S MEM. HOSP, 63- U.S.A, 44-46, Sgt. AAAS; Am. Endocrine Soc; Am. Fedn. Clin. Res; Am. Med. Asn; Royal Soc. Med. Pediatric endocrinology; growth, sexual development and disorders of children and adolescents; sex hormones metabolism and secretion. Address: Division of Endocrinology, Children's Memorial Hospital, 707 Fullerton Ave, Chicago, IL 60614.

GREEN, PAUL B(ARNETT), b. Phila, Pa, Feb. 15, 31; m. 57. BOTANY. B.A, Pennsylvania, 52; jr. fel, Harvard, 55; Ph.D, Princeton, 57. Asst. prof. BOT, Univ. Pa, 58-62, assoc. prof, 62-69, PROF, 69-70; STANFORD UNIV, 70- Soc. Develop. Biol; Bot. Soc. Am; Am. Soc. Plant Physiol. Plant development; growth of cell walls. Address: Dept. of Biology, Stanford University, Stanford, CA 94305.

GREEN, PAUL E(LIOT), JR, b. Durham, N.C, Jan. 14, 24; m. 48; c. 5. ELECTRONICS. A.B, North Carolina, 44; M.S, N.C. State Col, 48; Sc.D, Mass. Inst. Tech, 53. Staff mem. Lincoln Lab, 53-58, group leader, 58-69; HEAD COMMUN. SCI. DEPT, INT. BUS. MACH. RES. LAB, 69- U.S.N.R, 42-45. Fel. Am. Inst. Elec. & Electronics Eng. Communication theory applied to radar astronomy; seismology; design of computer-communication systems. Address: Roseholm Pl, R.F.D. 3, Mt. Kisco, NY 10549.

GREEN, PHILLIP JOSEPH II, b. July 12, 41; U.S. citizen; m. 60; c. 2. COSMIC RAY PHYSICS. B.S, Southwest. at Memphis, 63; Ph.D.(physics), La. State Univ, 67. ASST. PROF. PHYSICS, TEX. A&M UNIV, 67- Am. Phys. Soc; Am. Geophys. Union; Am. Inst. Phys. High energy cosmic ray research; muon intensity measurements and their implications. Address: Dept. of Physics, Texas A&M University, College Station, TX 77843.

GREEN, R(ALPH) E(LLIS), b. St. John's Newf, Feb. 8, 31; m. 52; c. 4. NUCLEAR & REACTOR PHYSICS. B.Sc, Dalhousie, 52, M.Sc, 54; Ph.D.(physics), McGill, 56. Res. off. reactor physics, ATOMIC ENERGY CAN. LTD, 56-67, accelerator physics, 67-70, HEAD REACTOR CONTROL BR, CHALK RIVER, 70- Can. Asn. Physicists. Angular correlation of positron annihilation radiation; positronium lifetimes; experimental studies of natural uranium, heavy water reactor lattices; high power continuous wave electron linear accelerators; reactor control and instrumentation systems. Address: 21 Frontenac Crescent, Deep River, Ont, Can.

GREEN, RALPH J, JR, b. Naylor, Mo, Aug. 17, 23; m. 44; c. 3. PLANT PATHOLOGY. B.S, Indiana State, 48; M.S, Purdue, 50, Ph.D, 54. Instr. PLANT PATH, Purdue, 51-53; Chicago, 53-55; asst. prof, PURDUE UNIV, 55-58, assoc. prof, 58-66, PROF, 66- U.S.A, 43-46. Am. Phytopath. Soc. Soilborne plant pathogens and soil microbiology. Address: Dept. of Botany & Plant Pathology, Purdue University, Lafayette, IN 47907.

GREEN, R(ALPH) V(ERNON), b. Litchfield, Ill, Feb. 11, 13; m. 39; c. 2. CHEMICAL ENGINEERING. B.S, Illinois, 35, M.S, 36; Delaware, 39. Tech. asst, exp. sta, Illinois, 33-34, instr. chem, univ, 35-36; chem. engr, INDUST. & BIOL. CHEM. DEPT, E.I. DU PONT DE NEMOURS & CO, INC, Del, 36-39, W.VA, 40-43, group leader, 43-45, asst. tech. supt, 45-52, tech. supt, 52-54, tech. specialist, 54-58, STAFF ENGR, 58- Am. Chem. Soc; Am. Inst. Chem. Eng; fel. Am. Inst. Chem. Synthesis gas generation and processing. Address: Industrial & Biological Chemicals Dept, E.I. du Pont de Nemours & Co, Inc, P.O. Box 635, Belle, WV 25015.

GREEN, RICHARD E, b. Seward, Nebr, Mar. 23, 31; m. 55; c. 4. SOIL PHYSICS. B.S, Colorado State, 53; M.S, Nebraska, 57; Ph.D.(soil mgt), Iowa State, 62. Instr. soil sci, Nebraska, 57-58; asst. agronomist, Maui Br, UNIV. HAWAII, 62-65, ASSOC. PROF. SOIL SCI, MANOA CAMPUS, 65- U.S.A, 53-55, 1st Lt. Am. Soc. Agron; Soil Sci. Soc. Am. Behavior of pesticides in soils and water; soil physics; water quality. Address: Dept. of Agronomy & Soil Science, University of Hawaii, Honolulu, HI 96822.

GREEN, RICHARD H, b. Baker, Mont, July 22, 36; m. 58; c. 2. MICROBIOLOGY. B.A, Whitman Col, 58; M.S, Washington State, 61, U.S. Pub. Health Serv. fel. & Ph.D.(microbiol), 65. Inst. Environ. Sci. asst. sanit. chemist, Washington State, 61-63; sr. engr, Boeing Co, Wash, 65-67; mem. tech. staff, JET PROPULSION LAB, CALIF. INST. TECHNOL, 67-68, SUPVR. PLANETARY QUARANTINE GROUP, 68- Am. Soc. Microbiol; Am. Inst. Aeronaut. & Astronaut; Am. Asn. Contamination Control. Environmental health, especially water pollution; space microbiology, including life detection, environmental simulation, planetary quarantine and spacecraft sterilization. Address: Jet Propulsion Lab 223-208, California Institute of Technology, 4800 Oak Grove Dr, Pasadena, CA 91103.

GREEN, RICHARD J(AMES), b. Newark, N.J, Apr. 15, 28; m. 57; c. 4. PHYSICS. B.S, Col. Holy Cross, 49; M.S, Fordham, 55; Rensselaer Polytech, 56-57; Temple, 58-60. Anal. engr. nuclear propulsion, Pratt & Whitney Aircraft Div, United Aircraft Corp, 55-57; sr. res. technologist, Socony-Mobil Oil Co, 57-61; tech. asst. to assoc. adminstr, NASA, 61-66, prog. engr, Lunar Surface Exp, 66-67, mgr, Apollo Lunar Surface Exp. Prog, 67-70; EXEC. ASST. TO ASST. DIR, NAT. SCI. FOUND, 70- Exceptional Sci. Achievement Medal, NASA, 69, Apollo Achievement Award, 69 & 70; Commendation Award, Atomic Energy Comn, 70. U.S.A.F, 50-54, 61-62, Res, 65-, Maj. AAAS; Am. Inst. Aeronaut. & Astronaut. Aerospace engineering; program management and administration; nuclear propulsion systems; radiation effects; advanced lubricants; lunar and planetary exploration. Address: 3304 Carpenter St. S.E, Washington, DC 20020.

GREEN, RICHARD LEE, b. Bakersfield, Calif, June 3, 38; m. 65; c. 2. PHYSICAL CHEMISTRY. B.S, Col. Pac, 60; M.A, Oregon, 63, Ph.D.(phys. chem), 65. RES. ENGR, BOEING CO, 65- Am. Chem. Soc. Thermal conductivity of gas mixtures, chemical kinetics, and thermodynamics; compatibility of liquid rocket propellants with materials; ultra sensitive analytical chemistry techniques; neutron activation. Address: 15441 Tenth Ave. S, Seattle, WA 98148.

GREEN, RICHARD STEDMAN, b. Somerville, Mass, Mar. 2, 14; m. 43; c. 3. SANITARY ENGINEERING. S.B, Harvard, 36, S.M, 37. Sr. sanit. eng. aid, Mass. Dept. Pub. Health, 37-38; supt. water purification, Panama Canal, 38-40; res. assoc. sch. med, Pennsylvania, 40-41; sanit. engr, U.S. PUB. HEALTH SERV, Md, Wash. & Maine, 41-42, dir. div. pub. health eng, dept. health, Alaska, 42-46, sanit. engr. dir, hq, Wash, D.C, 46-67, dir. off. environ. health, Indian Health Serv, Md, 67-71, ASST. SURG. GEN. & CHIEF ENG. OFF, WASH, D.C, 71- William B. Hatfield Award, Water Pollution Control Fedn, 70; dipl, Environ. Eng. Intersoc. Bd. Fel. Am. Soc. Civil Eng; fel. Am. Pub. Health Asn; Am. Water Works Asn. Water quality control. Address: U.S. Public Health Service, Washington, DC 20014.

GREEN, ROBERT, b. Newcastle-on-Tyne, Eng, July 27, 30; m. 57; c. 3. GEOLOGY. B.Sc, Durham, 51, Ph.D, 54. Fulbright travel scholar, Yale, 54, Schuchert res. fel, 54-55, asst. geol, 55-56; asst. res. off, RES. COUN, ALTA, 56-62, assoc. res. off, 62-65, head, geol. div, 59-65, CHIEF, EARTH SCI. BR, 65- Stratigraphy and micropaleontology. Address: Earth Science Branch, Research Council of Alberta, 87th Ave. & 114th St, Edmonton, Alta, Can.

GREEN, ROBERT A, b. Brooklyn, N.Y, May 13, 25; m. 51; c. 5. MEDICAL ADMINISTRATION, INTERNAL MEDICINE. B.S, Illinois, 46, M.D, 48. Chief tuberc. sect, Talihina Med. Ctr, Okla, 52-54; asst. chief PULMONARY DISEASE SECT, VET. ADMIN. HOSP, Bronx, N.Y, 54-58, CHIEF, ANN ARBOR, 58-; PROF. INTERNAL MED, MED. SCH, UNIV. MICH, ANN ARBOR, 70-, ASSOC. DEAN STUD. AFFAIRS, 68-, assoc. prof. internal med, 63-70. U.S.N.R, 42-44; U.S.P.H.S, 52-54, Sr. Asst. Surg. Am. Thoracic Soc. Pulmonary diseases; tuberculosis; unclassified mycobacterial disease; lung cancer. Address: Dept. of Internal Medicine, University of Michigan Medical School, Ann Arbor, MI 48104.

GREEN, ROBERT B(OYCE), b. Atlanta, Ga, Apr. 11, 25; m. 46; c. 2. METALLURGY. B.S.E, Princeton, 44; S.M, Mass. Inst. Tech, 47, Sc.D, 51. Jr. engr, Gates Rubber Co, 45; fel. & asst. mech. eng, Mass. Inst. Tech, 46-48, instr, 48-50, asst. prof, 50-52; assoc. prof. physics, Stevens Inst. Tech, 52-54; dir. phys. res, Engelhard Indust, Inc, 54-58; mat. mgr, semiconductor & mat. div, Radio Corp. Am, 59-62; div. mgr, process equip. div, Engelhard Indust, Inc, 62-65; mgr, mat. lab, cent. eng, Defense Electronic Prod, RCA CORP, N.J, 65-70, DOMESTIC LICENSING, N.Y, 70- AAAS; Am. Soc. Metals; Brit. Inst. Metall; Am. Inst. Mining, Metall. & Petrol. Eng; Brit. Inst. Metals. Flow and fracture of metals. Address: Domestic Licensing, RCA Corp, 1133 Ave. of the Americas, New York, NY 10036.

GREEN, ROBERT E(DWARD), JR, b. Clifton Forge, Va, Jan. 17, 32; m. 62; c. 2. METALLURGY, SOLID STATE PHYSICS. B.S, Col. William & Mary, 53; Sc.M, Brown, 56, Ph.D.(metal physics), 59. Physicist, underwater explosions res. div, Norfolk Naval Shipyard, 59; Fulbright grant metal physics, Aachen Tech. Univ, 59-60; asst. prof. MECH, JOHNS HOPKINS UNIV, 60-65, assoc. prof, 65-70, PROF. & CHMN. DEPT, 70- Ford Found. residency as sr. engr, Radio Corp. Am, Pa, 66-67. AAAS; Acoust. Soc. Am; Am. Phys Soc; Am. Inst. Mining, Metall. & Petrol. Eng; Soc. Natural Philos; Am. Soc. Metals. Recovery; recrystallization; elasticity; plasticity; crystal growth and orientation; x-ray diffraction; electrooptical systems; linear and nonlinear elastic wave propagation; light-sound interactions; ultrasonic attenuation; dislocation damping; fatigue. Address: Dept. of Mechanics, Johns Hopkins University, Baltimore, MD 21218.

GREEN, ROBERT E(UGENE), b. Pittsburg, Kans, June 18, 23; m. 44; c. 2. MATHEMATICS, ELECTRONICS. A.B, Kans. State Col, Pittsburg, 50, M.S, 52. Instr. math, Kans. State Col. Pittsburg, 52-53; engr, Mid-Continent Telecasting, Inc, 53-55; dir. dept. ed, Dage Div, Thompson-Products, Inc, 55-58; consult. to v.pres. electronics div, Thompson-Ramo Wooldridge, Inc, 58; asst. exec. dir, adv. bd. ed, Nat. Acad. Sci-Nat. Res. Coun, 58-61, asst. to exec. off, 61, EXEC. SECY. COMT. SCI. & PUB. POLICY, NAT. ACAD. SCI, 62- Sig.C, 42-46, Res, 50-62, Capt. AAAS; Math. Asn. Am. Foundations of mathematics; symbolic logic; antenna design; radio wave propagation. Address: National Academy of Sciences, 2101 Constitution Ave. N.W, Washington, DC 20418.

GREEN, ROBERT H(OLT), b. Charleston, S.C, Oct. 31, 11; m. 43; c. 3. MEDICINE. B.A, Univ. of the South, 33; North Carolina, 33-34; M.D, Hopkins, 38; hon. M.A, Yale, 67. Intern med, Strong Mem. Hosp, Univ. Rochester, 38-39; fel, univ. hosps, Western Reserve, 39-40, asst. resident, 40-41; fel. med. sci, Nat. Res. Coun, Rockefeller Inst, 41-42, 46-47; asst. prof. med, sch. med, Yale, 47-50, assoc. prof, 50-53, assoc. clin. prof, 53-57, assoc. prof, 57-60; sch. med, N.Y. Univ, 60-65, prof, 65-67; Yale, 67-69; prof. med. & dean sch. med, Med. Univ. S.C, 69-70; PROF. PATH. & MED, SCH. MED, YALE, 70- Asst. resident physician, hosp, Rockefeller Inst, 41-42; private practice, 53-57; assoc. sci. dir, health res. coun, City New York, 60-64; chief med. serv, Manhattan Vet. Admin. Hosp, New York; assoc. chief staff res, Vet. Admin. Hosp, West Haven, 67- Dipl, Am. Bd. Internal Med. Med.C, 42-46, Lt. Comdr. Am. Soc. Clin. Invest; Soc. Exp. Biol. & Med; Am. Asn. Immunol; Am. Med. Asn; Am. Fedn. Clin. Res. Internal medicine; infectious diseases; virology. Address: Veterans Administration Hospital, W. Spring St, West Haven, CT 06516.

GREEN, ROBERT JAMES, b. Effingham, Ill, Mar. 27, 41. ENGINEERING MECHANICS. B.S, Wash. Univ, 64; M.S, Univ. Calif, Berkeley, 65, Ph.D. (eng. sci), 68. ASST. PROF. MECH, UNIV. DENVER, 68- Res. engr, Sandia Labs, summer 70. Dynamic plasticity; shock waves in solids; energy absorption systems. Address: Division of Mechanics, University of Denver, Denver, CO 80210.

GREEN, R(OBERT) L(AMAR), b. Moultrie, Ga, Nov. 15, 14; m. 40; c. 1. AGRICULTURAL ENGINEERING. B.S.A.E, Georgia, 34; univ. fel, Iowa State, 38-39, M.S, 39; Gen. Ed. Bd. fel, Mich. State, 50-51, Ph.D.(agr. eng), 53. Terracing foreman & jr. agr. engr, soil conserv. serv, U.S. Dept. Agr, Ga, 34-38, conservationist, 39-41, 46-47; asst. prof. agr. eng, La. State, 47-50; agr. engr, U.S. Special Tech. & Econ. Mission Indonesia, 51-53; asst. prof. agr. eng, La. State Univ, 53-54; supt. & agr. engr, S.E. Tidewater exp. sta, soil & water conserv. res. div, agr. res. serv, U.S. Dept. Agr, 54-58; PROF. AGR. ENG. & HEAD DEPT, UNIV. MD, COLLEGE PARK, 58- State drainage engr, Md, 58-, chmn, Gov. Spec. Comt. Study Shore Erosion, 60-67, state dept. water resource comn, 64-; chmn, Gov. Adv. Comt. Resources Develop. & Conserv, 62-67; Water Sci. Adv. Bd, Md, 68- U.S.A, 41-46, Res, 46-, Col. Fel. Am. Soc. Agr. Eng; Am. Soc. Eng. Educ; Soil Conserv. Soc. Am. Drainage and irrigation; machinery; materials handling; crop processing; farm structures; agricultural waste management emphasizing land applications; water resources management. Address: Dept. of Agricultural Engineering, University of Maryland, College Park, MD 20742.

GREEN, ROBERT LEE, JR, b. Fairfield, Ala, Aug. 17, 21; div; c. 2. PSYCHIATRY. B.S, Alabama, 43; M.D, Hahnemann Med. Col, 46. Intern, Jeff-Hillman Hosp, Birmingham, Ala, 46-47; res. obstet. & gynec, Carraway Methodist, De Paul & St. Vincent's Hosps, 49-52; private practice, Ala, 52-53; staff. psychiatrist, Kennedy Vet. Admin. Hosp, Memphis, Tenn, 53, phys. med. & rehab. serv, 54-55, acting chief serv, 55-56; resident psychiatrist, VET. ADMIN. HOSP, DURHAM, 56-59, staff psychiatrist, 59-61, CHIEF DEPT. PSYCHIAT, 61- Resident psychiatrist, Duke, 56-59, instr. dept. psychiat, med. ctr, 59-60, asst. prof, 60-63, assoc. prof, 63-; lectr. serv. training prog, Cherry State Hosp, Goldsboro, 64-66. Clin. investr, Vet. Admin, 59-60, mem. cent. off. res. comt, 63-65. U.S.A.F, 47-49, Capt. Am. Med. Asn; Am. Psychiat. Asn; Soc. Psychophysiol. Res; Soc. Biol. Psychiat; Asn. Mil. Surg. U.S. Electroencephalography; psychophysiology; neurophysiology. Address: Dept. of Psychiatry, Veterans Administration Hospital, Durham, NC 27705.

GREEN, ROBERT (LESTER), b. Pittsburgh, Pa, Sept. 14, 15; m. 40; c. 2. CERAMICS. B.S, Pittsburgh, 37; Sc.D.(ceramics), Mass. Inst. Tech, 40. Asst, ceramics res. lab, Gen. Elec. Co, 39-47; DIR. RES. WHITEWARES, RES. & PROD. CONTROL, LENOX, INC, 47- Am. Ceramic Soc. Dielectrics; semiconductors; glass; properties of ceramic raw materials; glazes glass-body interaction and stresses. Address: Lenox, Inc, Tilton Road, Pomona, NJ 08240.

GREEN, ROBERT P(ATRICK), b. N.Y.C, Mar. 17, 25; m. 47; c. 4. PULP & PAPER TECHNOLOGY. B.S, Syracuse, 49; M.B.A, Miami (Ohio), 59. Res. chemist pulp res. & develop, Champion Papers, Inc, 49-54, pilot plant engr, 54-58, group leader, 58-59, mgr, 59-61; res. chemist, KIMBERLY-CLARK CORP, NEENAH, 61-62, mgr. pulp process controls, 62-71, SR. DEVELOP. ENGR, 71- U.S.A, 43-45, S/Sgt. Tech. Asn. Pulp & Paper Indust; Can. Pulp & Paper Asn. Pulping and bleaching, including wood and agricultural fibers; end use of pulp fibers; research management. Address: 47 Meadow Brook Ct, Appleton, WI 54911.

GREEN, ROBERT S(MITH), b. Lafayette, Ind, Dec. 17, 14; m. 38; c. 1. CIVIL ENGINEERING. B.S, Purdue, 36, M.S, 42. Detailer, Am. Bridge Co, 36; draftsman, Sinclair Ref. Co, 36-37; technician, Carnegie-Ill. Steel Corp, 37-38; instr. gen. eng, Purdue, 38-40; asst. struct. engr, spec. eng. div, Panama Canal, 40-41; engr, Blaw Knox Corp, Pa, 41-42; Weirton Steel Co, 42-47; asst. prof. indust. eng, OHIO STATE UNIV, 47, prof. welding eng. & chmn. dept, 48-54, PROF. CIVIL ENG, 70-, EXEC. DIR. ENG. EXP. STA, 54-, ASSOC. DEAN COL. ENG, 58- Consult, Nat. Cert. Pipe Welding Bur, N.Y, 48- U.S.N.R, 43-46, Lt.(jg). Nat. Soc. Prof. Eng; Am. Soc. Civil Eng; Am. Soc. Mech. Eng; Am. Soc. Metals; Am. Soc. Eng. Educ; Am. Soc. Test. & Mat; Am. Welding Soc. Indeterminate structures; metal joining; materials for high temperature service. Address: Office of the Dean, College of Engineering, Ohio State University, 2070 Neil Ave, Columbus, OH 43210.

GREEN, ROBERT WOOD, b. La Grange, Ill, Aug. 7, 22; m. 43; c. 2. PHYSICS. B.S, Morningside Col, 43; M.S, Iowa, 49; Nat. Sci. Found. fel, Iowa State, 58-59, Ph.D.(physics), 60. Assoc. prof. PHYSICS, Iowa Wesleyan Col, 49-50; instr, Morningside Col, 50-52, asst. prof, 52-55; instr, Iowa State, 55-56, res. assoc, 56-58; PROF, MORNINGSIDE COL, 60-, head dept, 60-70. U.S.N, 44-46, Lt.(jg). Am. Phys. Soc; Am. Asn. Physics Teachers. Ultrasonic properties of single crystals of silver and copper; electric and magnetic properties of rare earth metal crystals. Address: Dept. of Physics, Morningside College, Sioux City, IA 51106.

GREEN, ROGER H(ARRISON), b. N.Y.C, June 22, 39; m. 63; c. 1. ECOLOGY. B.S, Col. William & Mary, 61; Ph.D.(zool), Cornell Univ, 65. Fulbright fel, dept. zool, Univ. Queensland, 65-66; resident ecologist, syst-ecol. prog, Marine Biol. Lab, Woods Hole, 66-68; asst. prof. ZOOL, UNIV. MAN, 68-71, ASSOC. PROF, 71- Ecol. Soc. Am; Japanese Soc. Pop. Ecol. Ecology of marine and fresh-water populations and communities; statistical methods in ecological research; phenotypic and genotypic variability at the intraspecific level. Address: Dept. of Zoology, University of Manitoba, Winnipeg 19, Man, Can.

GREEN, ROY MONTAGUE, b. Oct. 25, 35; Brit. citizen; m. 61; c. 2. PHYSICS. B.Sc, Liverpool, 56; M.A, Toronto, 58, McKee-Gilchrist fel, 58-60, Ph.D.(gamma-ray spectrometry), 61. Res. off. health physics, Australian Atomic Energy Div, 61-64; mem. sci. staff, semiconductor lab, RES. LABS, RCA LTD, MONTREAL, 64-65, sr. mem. sci. staff, 65-68, DIR. OPTO-ELECTRONIC SYSTS. LAB. & DIR. RES. PROG. DEVELOP, 68- Lectr, Thomas More Inst. for Adult Ed, 65- Sr. mem. Inst. Elec. & Electronics Eng; Brit. Inst. Physics & Phys. Soc; Can. Asn. Physicists; fel. Australian Inst. Physics. Gamma-ray spectrometry; whole-body counters; semiconductor radiation detectors; lithium drifted germanium and silicon detectors; junction devices; gas lasers; laser communication systems. Address: 121 Rothbury Rd, Pointe Claire, Que, Can.

GREEN, RUPERT L, b. Clayton, N.Y, Nov. 21, 31; m. 58. CARDIOVASCULAR PHYSIOLOGY. B.S, Syracuse Univ, 58; Nat. Sci. Found. grant, Wayne State Univ, 64, Ph.D.(physiol, pharmacol), 68. Res. asst. cardiovasc. pharmacol, Sterling Winthrop Res. Inst, 58-63; res. assoc. physiol. & pharmacol, Wayne State Univ, 68-69; ASST. PROF. PHYSIOL, MED. UNIV. S.C, 69- U.S.N.A.F, 50-54. AAAS. Cardiovascular pharmacology. Address: Dept. of Physiology, Medical University of South Carolina, 80 Barre St, Charleston, SC 29401.

GREEN, SAUL, b. N.Y.C, Jan. 8, 25. BIOCHEMISTRY. B.S, City Col, 48; M.S, Iowa, 50, Ph.D.(biochem), 52. Instr. biochem, Virginia, 52-54; res. assoc, dept. med, med. col, Cornell, 54-59; asst. mem, SLOAN-KETTERING INST, 59-61, assoc, 61-67, ASSOC. MEM, 67-, ASSOC. PROF. BIOCHEM, SLOAN-KETTERING DIV. GRAD. SCH. MED. SCI, CORNELL UNIV, 67-, asst. prof, 62-67. Dir. clin. chem. lab, univ. hosp, Univ. Va, 52-54. Nat. Insts. Health res. career develop. award, 63. U.S.A, 44-46. Am. Chem. Soc; Am. Soc. Biol. Chem; Am. Asn. Cancer Res. Carbohydrate metabolism in ascites tumor cells; blood enzymes; NAD^+ and NAD^+ glycohydrolase in normal and tumor tissues, regulatory action of enzymes. Address: Division of Biological Chemistry, Sloan-Kettering Institute, 410 E. 68th St, New York, NY 10021.

GREEN, SIMON, b. Vienna, Austria, Mar. 15, 08; nat; m. MATHEMATICS. B.S, Fed. Col, Vienna, Austria, 27; M.S, Vienna, 31; Ph.D, Pittsburgh, 52. Prof. MATH, Fed. Gymnasium, Vienna, Austria, 31-37; assoc. prof, Lincoln, 48-51; prof, Smith Col, 52-54; assoc. prof, Tulsa, 54-58; South Carolina, 58-60; prof, Arizona State, 60-64; SR. ASSOC. PROF, CALIF. STATE POLYTECH. COL, 64- Res. assoc, Boeing Airplane Co, 55. 59. Consult, U.S. Navy Electronics Lab, San Diego, 63. Am. Math. Soc; Am. Asn. Physics Teachers; Math. Asn. Am; Can. Math. Soc. Vector analysis; algebra. Address: Dept. of Mathematics, California State Polytechnic College, Pomona, CA 91766.

GREEN, STANLEY J(OSEPH). b. New York, N.Y, Mar. 11, 20; m. 51; c. 3. CHEMICAL ENGINEERING. B.Ch.E. City Col. New York. 40; Maryland, 44-45; M.S. Drexel Inst. 53; Ph.D.(chem. eng). Univ. Pittsburgh. 68. Inspector. U.S. Corps Engr. N.Y, 41; concrete engr. Sci. Concrete Serv. Corp. 41-42; from jr. chem. engr. to assoc. chem. engr. U.S. Bur. Mines. Md. 42-45; chem. engr. Fercleve Corp. Oak Ridge. 45; Acme Coppersmithing & Machine Co. 45-54; sr. engr. heat transfer & hydraul. sect. BETTIS ATOMIC POWER LAB. WESTINGHOUSE ELEC. CORP. 54-59. MGR. THERMAL & HYDRAUL. ENG. SECT, 59- Chmn. coord. comt. Nat. Heat Transfer Conf. AAAS; Am. Chem. Soc; Am. Soc. Mech. Eng; Am. Inst. Chem. Eng. Phase rule chemistry applied to separation of compounds from solution by evaporation and crystallization; heterogeneous kinetics; production of alcohol from potatoes; batch solvent extraction of oil seeds; design chemical process equipment; liquid-vapor equilibrium; heat transfer and fluid flow research and design; single phase and two phase heat transfer and pressure drop. Address: 5423 Northumberland St, Pittsburgh, PA 15217.

GREEN, TERRY C, b. Abilene, Tex, Nov. 4, 35; m. 63; c. 2. ELECTRICAL ENGINEERING, APPLIED PHYSICS. B.S.E.E, Texas, 58; M.S, Trinity (Tex), 69. Design engr, Chance Vought Aircraft Co, Tex, 58; SR. RES. ENGR, DEPT. APPL. ELECTROMAGNETICS, SOUTHWEST RES. INST, 62-U.S.A.F, 58-62; Nat. Guard, 62-68, Capt. Inst. Elec. & Electronics Eng. Design of radio-direction finding antennas and techniques and application to radio position finding and propagation problems; applications of radio-direction finding techniques to current radio-astronomy research. Address: 14323 Clear Creek, San Antonio, TX 78232.

GREEN, THEODORE, III, b. Buffalo, N.Y, Mar. 7, 38; m. 65; c. 1. PHYSICAL OCEANOGRAPHY, ENGINEERING MECHANICS. A.B, Amherst Col, 59; M.S, Stanford, 61, Ph.D.(eng. mech), 65. Asst. prof. oceanog, Naval Postgrad. Sch, 65-69; ASSOC. PROF. METEOROL. & CIVIL ENG, UNIV. WIS, MADISON, 69- AAAS; Am. Geophys. Union; Am. Soc. Civil Eng. Convection; cavitating hydrofoils; small-scale air-sea interaction; lake circulations; water waves. Address: Depts. of Meteorology & Civil Engineering, University of Wisconsin, 1225 W. Dayton St, Madison, WI 53706.

GREEN, THEODORE JAMES, b. North Adams, Mass, Oct. 29, 35; m. 60; c. 2. MICROBIOLOGY, PHARMACOLOGY. B.S, Cornell, 57. Res. asst. cardiovasc. pharmacol, Sterling Winthrop Res. Inst, 57-66, assoc. res. biologist, 66-68; HEAD ANIMAL CARE & RES, WARREN TEED PHARMACEUT. RES. CTR, 68- Consult. biologist, Arlington Res, Ohio, 69-70. U.S.N.R, 52-60. Am. Asn. Lab. Animal Sci. Wildlife biology; animal health; cardiovascular and gastro-intestinal pharmacology; animal models for research; microbiology; endotoxin shock. Address: Warren Teed Pharmaceuticals, 582 W. Goodale St, Columbus, OH 43215.

GREEN, THOM HENNING, b. Steamboat Springs, Colo, Sept. 1, 15; m. 42; c. 2. PETROLEUM GEOLOGY. B.A, Colorado, 39; cert, California, Los Angeles, 43. Geophysicist, Shell Oil Co, 39-43, geologist, 46-48; dist. geologist, Sunray Oil Corp, 48-49, res. geologist, 49-51, div. geologist, 51-52; chief geologist, Fargo Oils, Ltd, 52-56; consult. geologist, 56-60; EXPLOR. MGR, WILCOX OPERATING CO, 60- U.S.A.A.F, 43-45, 1st Lt. Geol. Soc. Am; Soc. Explor. Geophys; Am. Asn. Petrol. Geol. Structural geology; petroleum reservoir fluid mechanics as related to migration and accumulation. Address: Suite 660, 2121 S. Columbia, Tulsa, OK 74114.

GREEN, THOMAS A(LLEN), b. Cleveland, Ohio, Mar. 21, 25; m. 49; c. 4. THEORETICAL PHYSICS. B.S, Case, 47; Sc.D.(physics), Geneva, 51. Asst, Geneva, 49-50; mem. theoret. staff, radiation lab, California, 51; assoc. physics, Columbia, 51-53; asst. prof, Wesleyan Univ, 53-58, assoc. prof, 58-64; mem. staff, lab, SANDIA CORP, 63-69, SUPVR. DIV. 5234, ATOMIC & MOLECULAR PROCESSES THEORY, 69- U.S.N.R, 44-46. AAAS; fel. Am. Phys. Soc; Am. Asn. Physics Teachers. Atomic collisions. Address: 700 Morningside Dr. S.E, Albuquerque, NM 87108.

GREEN, THOMAS M(YER), III, b. Seattle, Wash, June 23, 28; m. 52; c. 2. NUCLEAR PHYSICS. B.A, Dartmouth Col, 50, M.A, 55; Ph.D.(physics), California, 59. Asst, Dartmouth Col, 53-55; res. physicist metall, California, 56, asst, 57, radiation lab, 57-59; physicist, Boeing Co, 59-65; asst. prof. PHYSICS, SEATTLE UNIV, 65-69, ASSOC. PROF, 69- U.S.N, 50-53. Am. Astron. Soc; Am. Phys. Soc; Am. Asn. Physics Teachers. Atomic beams and nuclear moments; defects in solids; plasmas; astrophysics. Address: 3233 134th N.E, Bellevue, WA 98005.

GREEN, THOMAS W(HITE), JR, b. Biggs, Calif, June 19, 19; m. 42; c. 5. INTERNAL MEDICINE. B.S, La. State, 38; Ph.D, Ohio State, 42, M.D. 46. Consult, Chem. Corps, U.S. Army, 50-52; assoc. med. dir, Cutter Labs, 54-60; PRES, BERKELEY BIOL. LABS, 60- Div. chief, biol. labs, Army Chem. Corps, Ft. Detrick, Md, Med.C, 52-54, Capt. AAAS; Am. Soc. Microbiol; Am. Med. Asn; Am. Col. Physicians. Allergy; immunology; infectious disease. Address: Second & Hearst St, Berkeley, CA 94710.

GREEN, VERNON A(LBERT), b. McClain County, Okla, Apr. 13, 21; m. 49; c. 2. BIOCHEMICAL PHARMACOLOGY. B.S, Oklahoma, 49, M.S, 50; Ph.D.(pharmacol), Texas, 60. Instr. pharm, Oklahoma, 49-50; PHARMACOL, Texas, 50-51, asst. prof, 51-62; PROF, UNIV. MO, KANSAS CITY, 62-; TOXICOLOGIST, CHILDREN'S MERCY HOSP, 68- AAAS; Am. Pharmaceut. Asn; Am. Soc. Pharmacol. & Therapeut; Am. Acad. Clin. Toxicol. Pharmacodynamics; mechanisms of drug absorption and activity; cholinesterase activity in cellular permeability. Address: Dept. of Toxicology, Children's Mercy Hospital, 24th & Gillham Rd, Kansas City, MO 64108.

GREEN, VICTOR E(UGENE), JR, b. De Ridder, La, Sept. 3, 22; m. 45; c. 2. FIELD CROPS. B.S, La. State, 47, M.S, 48; fel, Purdue, 49-51, Ph.D.(soil sci), 51. Asst. agronomist, Agr. Exp. Sta, La, 47-49; Everglades Exp. Sta, UNIV. FLA, 51-56, assoc. agronomist, 56-65, AGRONOMIST, 65- Agr. adv, U.S. Agency Int. Develop-Univ. Fla. contract, Costa Rican Govt, 65-68; curriculum adv, Sch. Agr, Jamaica, West Indies, 70. U.S.A, 42-46, Res, 46-, Col. Am. Soc. Agron; Soil Sci. Soc. Am; Int. Soc. Soil Sci. Organic soils; tropical crops including rice, aloe, dioscorea, sugarcane and coffee; corn; sorghum; millets; rural development and crop campaigns in tropical areas. Address: Dept. of Agronomy, Rolfs Hall, University of Florida, Gainesville, FL 32601.

GREEN, WALTER L(UTHER), b. Roanoke Rapids, N.C, Mar. 13, 34; m. 56; c. 3. ELECTRICAL & SYSTEMS ENGINEERING. B.S, Auburn Univ, 57, M.S, 60; Nat. Sci. Found. & Ford Found. fels, Texas A&M Univ, 62-65, Ph.D. (elec. eng), 65. Instr. elec. eng, Auburn Univ, 58-61; staff engr, missile systs. proj. eng, Sandia Corp, N.Mex, 61-62; instr. elec. eng, Tex. A&M Univ, 62-65; assoc. prof, Miss. State Univ, 65-66; adv. engr, fed. systs. div, IBM Corp, Ala, 66-68; ASSOC. PROF. ELEC. ENG, UNIV. TENN, KNOXVILLE, 68- Mem. faculty, summer prog, NASA George C. Marshall Space Flight Ctr, Ala, 69 & 70; consult, nuclear div, Union Carbide Corp, Oak Ridge, Tenn, 69- Sig.C, U.S.A, 53-55. Inst. Elec. & Electronics Eng; Am. Soc. Eng. Educ. Control system theory and application, including guidance and control of space vehicles, multivariable and machine-tooling control systems. Address: Dept. of Electrical Engineering, University of Tennessee, Knoxville, TN 37916.

GREEN, WALTER P(ERRY), JR, b. Waterbury, Conn, June 12, 14; m. 41; c. 1. ORGANIC CHEMISTRY. S.B, Mass. Inst. Tech, 35, Ph.D.(org. chem), 40. Anal. chemist, Am. Brass Co, 35-37; org. chemist, Gulf Res. & Develop. Co, 40; chemist, Calco Div, Am. Cyanamid Co, 45-48; group leader wood chem, Masonite Corp, 48-59; CHIEF CHEMIST, INDUST. DYESTUFF CO, 59- Ord.C, 40-45, Capt. Fel. AAAS; Am. Chem. Soc. Fine chemicals. Address: 29 Riley Dr, East Providence, RI 02915.

GREEN, WALTER V(ERNEY), b. Schenectady, N.Y, Sept. 20, 29; m. 55; c. 3. PHYSICAL METALLURGY. B.S, Wisconsin, 52, M.S, 53, Ph.D.(metall. eng), 60. Asst. metall. eng, Wisconsin, 52-56; MEM. STAFF METALL, LOS ALAMOS SCI. LAB, UNIV. CALIF, 56- Vis. prof, Bariloche Atomic Ctr, Arg, 64-65. Summers, res. lab, Gen. Elec. Co, 52; res. lab, Westinghouse Elec. Corp, 53. Am. Soc. Metals; Am. Inst. Mining, Metall. & Petrol. Eng. High temperature strength, plasticity and fracture of metals, graphite and ceramics; hydrogen in iron; structure and properties of grain boundaries; dislocations; diffusion; radioactive tracer techniques; radiation damage. Address: Los Alamos Scientific Lab, P.O. Box 1663, Los Alamos, NM 87544.

GREEN, WILLARD W(YNN), b. Minneapolis, Minn, Nov. 17, 10; m. 40. ANIMAL BREEDING. B.S, Minnesota, 33, M.S, 34, Dorr fel, 35, Ph.D.(animal breeding), 39. Asst, Minnesota, 34-35, instr. ANIMAL HUSB, 37-42, asst. prof, 42-44, assoc. prof, 44-48, PROF, UNIV. MD, COLLEGE PARK, 48- Instr, Univ. Alaska, 35-37; vis. prof. & head dept, Univ. P.R, 47-48. AAAS; Am. Soc. Animal Sci; Am. Chem. Soc. Animal breeding-beef cattle; new techniques for selection of breeding stock; using body measurements of steers to estimate weights of carcass cuts; rate; efficiency of gain; growth breeding stock. Address: Dept. of Animal Science, University of Maryland, College Park, MD 20742.

GREEN, WILLIAM ASA, b. Bethlehem, Pa, Nov. 16, 09; m. 35; c. 1. BACTERIOLOGY, ZOOLOGY. B.S, Moravian Col, 31; M.S, Lehigh, 33, Ph.D.(bact), 50. Bacteriologist, Sharpe & Dohme Inc, 33-34; teacher, Bethlehem Sch. Dist, 35-45; prof. microbiol, Muhlenberg Col, 45-56; PROF. MICROBIOL. & HEAD DEPT. SCI, KUTZTOWN STATE COL, 57- U.S.N, 43-45, Res, 45-61, Lt. Comdr. Morphology of bacteria as observed under electron microscope. Address: Dept. of Science, Kutztown State College, Kutztown, PA 19530.

GREEN, WILLIAM B(INKLEY), b. Hagerstown, Md, Apr. 21, 28; m. 51; c. 3. PHYSICS, ELECTRICAL ENGINEERING. B.E.E, Hopkins, 50; S.M, Mass. Inst. Tech, 52, Ph.D.(physics), 55. Design engr. semiconductors, Westinghouse Elec. Corp, Youngwood, 55-58, supvry. engr, 58-60, prod. eng. mgr. thermoelec, 60-62, mfg. eng. mgr. semiconductors, 62-63, prod. mgr, 63-69; GEN. MGR. BURROUGHS CORP, West. Microcircuits Orgn, 69-70, RANCHO BERNARDO PLANT, 70- Adj. prof, Univ. Pittsburgh, 59-68. Am. Phys. Soc. Electrical breakdown of dielectric materials; design and development of semiconductor devices. Address: 16304 Martincoit Rd, Poway, CA 92064.

GREEN, WILLIAM DELAP, b. Boston, Mass, July 16, 36; m. 64; c. 4. ATMOSPHERIC CHEMISTRY & PHYSICS. B.S, Tufts, 58; M.S, Arizona, 62. Res. asst, Arizona, 58-64; res. chemist, Aerojet-Gen. Corp. Div, Gen. Tire & Rubber Co, 64-65; res. geologist, METEOROL. RES. INC, 65, res. scientist, 65-68, MGR. ENVIRON. CHEM, 68- Air Pollution Control Asn; Am. Meteorol. Soc; Am. Geophys. Union; Geochem. Soc. Radioactive age determinations; gas content of minerals; atmospheric nuclei; atmospheric chemistry; tracer materials; aerosol physics; air pollution; weather modification. Address: Meteorology Research Inc, 464 Woodbury Rd, Altadena, CA 91001.

GREEN, WILLIAM HARRIS, b. Gainesville, Fla, July 23, 43; m. 68. PHYSICAL CHEMISTRY. B.S, South Carolina, 63, Ph.D.(phys. chem), 67. Nat. Acad. Sci-Nat. Res. Coun. res. assoc, 67-68; RES. SCIENTIST, U.S. NAVAL RES. LAB, 68- AAAS; Am. Chem. Soc; Soc. Appl. Spectros; Coblentz Soc. Vibrational analysis of small molecules, especially ring compounds; ring-puckering vibration; basic molecular structure via mid-infrared, far-infrared and Raman spectroscopy; pseudorotation in five membered rings; chemical lasers; collisional energy transfer. Address: Code 6110, U.S. Naval Research Lab, Washington, DC 20390.

GREENAWALT, JOHN W, b. Oil City, Pa, June 23, 27; m. 50; c. 3. MICROBIOLOGY. B.S, Edinburo State Col, 50; M.S, Case West. Reserve Univ, 55; David M. Ross & Nat. Insts. Health fels. & Ph.D.(microbiol), Purdue Univ, 60. Nat. Insts. Health fel, Univ. Stockholm, 60-61; SCH. MED, JOHNS HOPKINS UNIV, 61-62, instr. BIOCHEM, 62-63, asst. prof, 63-68, ASSOC. PROF, 68- U.S.A, 45-47, S/Sgt. Electron Micros. Soc. Am; Am. Chem. Soc; Am. Soc. Microbiol; Am. Soc. Biol. Chem; Am. Soc. Cell Biol. Biochemical cytology; structure and function of biological membranes; mitochondrial biogenesis. Address: Dept. of Physiological Chemistry, Johns Hopkins University School of Medicine, 725 N. Wolfe St, Baltimore, MD 21205.

GREENAWAY, KEITH R(OGERS), b. Woodville, Ont, Apr. 8, 16; m. 44; c. 2. ELECTRONICS. Can. Electronics Inst, 35-39. Instr. electronics & navig, Royal Can. Air Force, 40-45, researcher, navig. projs, with U.S. Navy, 45-46, with U.S. Air Force, 46-48, arctic res, Defence Res. Bd, 48-54, lectr. navig, Strategic Air Comd, U.S. Air Force, 54-56, adminstr, hqs,

56-59, commanding off, cent. navig. sch, Royal Can. Air Force, 59-63, Royal Can. Air Force Sta. Clinton, 63-67, air adv. to chief of air staff, Royal Malaysian Air Force, 67-70; CONSULT, DEPT. INDIAN AFFAIRS & NORTH. DEVELOP, 70- Chmn, defense res. bd. comt. navig. res. Mc-Kee Trans-Can. trophy, 52; Massey medal, Royal Can. Geog. Soc, 60. R.C.A.F, 40-70, Brig. Gen.(Ret); Johan Mangku Negara, 70. Inst. Navig. (Thurlow award, 51); fel. Artic Inst; fel. Can. Aeronaut. & Space Inst; assoc. fel, Royal Meteorol. Soc.(pres. prize, Can. br, 50); fel. British Inst. Navig. Aerial navigation, especially polar navigation; arctic research. Address: 472 Wellesley Ave, Ottawa, Ont, K2A 1B4, Can.

GREENAWAY, WALTER THOMAS, b. Hanover, Pa, May 30, 12; m. 35; c. 1. CHEMISTRY, STATISTICS. B.S, Gettysburg Col, 34; cert, U.S. Dept. Agr. Grad. Sch, 64. Chemist, E.A. Siebel Co, Ill, 34-40, chief chemist, 40-42; Nat. Distillers Prod. Corp, 42-45; owner-operator, W.T. Greenaway Chem. & Microbiol. Lab, Pa, 45-50; chemist, Jordan Chem. Co, Ill, 50-52; grain technologist, grain div, U.S. DEPT. AGR, Md, 52-66, RES. CHEMIST, MKT. QUAL. RES. DIV, AGR. RES. SERV, 66- Mem, Int. Cereal Chem. Comt, alpha amylase activity & sedimentation test wheat qual, 64-66; food & nutrit. comt, Int. Biol. Prog, 66-67. Am. Asn. Cereal Chem. Fermentation of liquids by yeast and production of ethyl alcohol; fermentation of doughs and the baking of bread; development of simple, practical tests for the evaluation of wheat and other grain. Address: U.S. Grain Marketing Research Center, Market Quality Research Division, Agricultural Research Division, U.S. Dept. of Agriculture, 1515 College Ave, Manhattan, KS 66502.

GREENBANK, JOHN (THOMAS), b. Olathe, Colo, Apr. 2, 06. BIOLOGY. B.S, New Mexico, 35, M.S, 37; Ph.D.(zool), Michigan, 43. Fisheries technician, State Game & Fish Dept, N.Mex, 35-37; fisheries technician, Mich. Inst. Fish Res, 37-41, 42-43; fish biologist, State Dept. Conserv, La, 41-42; asst, univ. mus, Michigan, 42-43; fisheries biologist, conserv. dept, Wis, 44-50; consult. fishery biologist, 50-58; instr. math, Northeast Mo. State Teachers Col, 58-59; fishery biologist, Food & Agr. Orgn, UN, Buga, Colombia, 59-60; assoc. prof. biol, Northeast Mo. State Col, 61-62; free-lance writer, fish mgt, 62-67; CONSULT. & LECTR. NATURAL RESOURCES CONSERV, 67- Biologist, State Bd. Health, Wis, 38-39; lectr, Humbolt State Col, 65-66. Am. Fisheries Soc; Am. Soc. Limnol. & Oceanog. Freshwater fisheries management; fish population and life history; toxicity tolerance in fish; freshwater ecology. Address: 2060 N. 15th St, Grand Junction, CO 81501.

GREENBAUM, LEON J, JR, b. Baltimore, Md, Sept. 24, 23; m. 62; c. 2. PHYSIOLOGY. B.S, Loyola Col.(Md), 47; M.S, Maryland, 55, Nat. Insts. Ment. Health fel, 60-62, Ph.D.(physiol), 63. Res. asst. neurophysiol, Johns Hopkins Hosp, 47-49; physiologist, Off. Naval Res, 50-53; res. assoc. pharmacol, Inst. Study Analgesic-Sedative Drugs, 53-55; physiologist, U.S. Naval Med. Res. Inst, 57-60; res. assoc, Med. Col. Va, 60-64; PHYSIOLOGIST, U.S. Naval Med. Res. Inst, 64-70; NEUROL. DISORDERS PROG. PROJ, NAT. INST. NEUROL. DISEASES & STROKE, 70- Nat. Inst. Ment. Health fel, sch. med, Univ. Md, 62-64; guest scientist, Naval Med. Res. Inst, 70-Med.Serv.C, U.S.N, 42-45, 50-53 & 64-, Comdr. AAAS; Aerospace Med. Asn; Undersea Med. Soc. Neurophysiology of inert gas narcosis; cortical excitability; respiratory physiology of divers; hyperbaric pharmacology. Address: 16 Sussex Rd, Silver Spring, MD 20910.

GREENBAUM, LOWELL M(ARVIN), b. Brooklyn, N.Y, June 13, 28; m. 50; c. 3. PHARMACOLOGY, BIOCHEMISTRY. B.S, City Col. New York, 49; Charlton res. fel. & Ph.D.(physiol), Tufts Col, 53. Instr. physiol, sch. med, Tufts Col, 53-54; Am. Cancer Soc. res. fel. biochem, sch. med, Yale, 54-56; instr. PHARMACOL, col. med, State Univ. N.Y. Downstate Med. Ctr, 56-57, asst. prof, 58-64; COL. PHYSICIANS & SURGEONS, COLUMBIA UNIV, 64-69, assoc. prof, 69-71, PROF, 71- Vis. prof, Osaka Univ, 70. AAAS; Am. Soc. Biol. Chem; Am. Soc. Pharmacol. & Exp. Therapeut; Am. Chem. Soc; Harvey Soc; The Chem. Soc. Intracellular proteinases; pharmacologically active polypeptides; protein precursors of pharmacologically active polypeptides; inflammation and injury. Address: Dept. of Pharmacology, College of Physicians & Surgeons, Columbia University, 630 W. 168th St, New York, NY 10032.

GREENBAUM, MICHAEL ARNOLD, b. Montreal, Que, Oct. 5, 29; U.S. citizen; m. 59; c. 1. PHYSICAL & THEORETICAL CHEMISTRY. A.B, Chicago, 50; B.S, N.Y. Univ, 53, M.S, 54; Ph.D.(chem), Yale, 56. Org. res. chemist, Stanford Res. Inst, 57-58; head, theoret. anal. sect, Von Karman Res. Ctr, Aerojet Gen. Corp, 58-61; chem. dept, res. div, Maremont Corp, 61-67; SR. MEM. ADV. TECH. STAFF, MARQUARDT CO, 67-, DIR. MED. RES, 70- A.P. Sloan fel, Rutgers Univ, 56; fel, Univ. South. Calif, 56-58; dir. renal res. labs, Mt. Sinai Hosp, Los Angeles. Am. Chem. Soc; Am. Vacuum Soc; Combustion Inst; Brit. Chem. Soc; Am. Soc. Nephrology; Am. Soc. Artificial Internal Organs. Physical organic chemistry; tracer studies of reaction mechanisms; high temperature thermodynamics and thermochemistry of inorganic molecules; development of new artificial kidney systems and related equipment. Address: The Marquardt Co, 16555 Saticoy St, Van Nuys, CA 91409.

GREENBAUM, SHELDON B(ORIS), b. Brooklyn, N.Y, Apr. 15, 23; m. 48; c. 3. ORGANIC CHEMISTRY. B.S, City Col. New York, 44; Fulton fel, Tennessee, 45-46, M.S, 46; fel, Maryland, 51, Ph.D.(chem), 52. Res. chemist, Gordon-Lacey Chem. Prod. Co, 43-44; Pyridium Corp, 44; asst, Maryland, 46-50; res. assoc. & instr. med. chem, dept. pharmacol, sch. med, Western Reserve, 52-53; asst, Yale, 53-56; res. chemist, Hooker Chem. Corp, 56-66; DIR. ORG. RES. FINE CHEM, DIAMOND SHAMROCK CHEM. CO, N.J, 66- Am. Chem. Soc; Entom. Soc. Am. Chemistry of vitamin D; vitamin E; riboflavin; calcium pantothenate; animal health products; antibiotics; pesticides; pyrimidines; chemical patents. Address: Diamond Shamrock Chemical Co, First & Essex St, Harrison, NJ 07029.

GREENBAUM, WILLIAM H(ENRY), b. New York, N.Y, Feb. 29, 24; m. 44; c. 3. ELECTRICAL ENGINEERING. B.S.E.E, N.Y. Univ, 51, M.S.E.E, 53. Electronic engr, Sonotone Corp, 42-55; dir. eng, Otarian Listener Corp, N.Y, 55-63; hearing aid div, Zenith Radio Corp, 63-69, dir. med. electronics eng, 66-69; V.PRES. & DIR. ENG, UNILUX, INC, 69- Sig.C, 42-46, 1st Lt. Acoust. Soc. Am; Audio Eng. Soc; Inst. Elec. & Electronics Eng. Audio engineering; hearing aid design, development and manufacture; stroboscopy, video strobe; high speed machinery analysis. Address: Unilux, Inc, 48-20 70th St, Woodside, NY 11377.

GREENBERG, ALBERT J, b. New York, N.Y, Nov. 20, 12; m. 36; c. 2. CHEMICAL ENGINEERING. B.Ch.E, Cooper Union, 32, M.Ch.E, 33; Sc.D. (electro-biochem), Fordham, 34. Teacher, high sch, 35-38; dir, Jay Labs, 35-41; chief res. & develop, U.S. Army Ord, 41-46; PRES. & DIR, JAY LABS, 46-; PRES. & CONSULT, SCI. ASSOCS, 63- Mem, President's Conf. Tech. Res, 57-64; consult, Andover Sch. Syst, 58-; Gen. Elec. Corp. & Sylvania Info. Systs. Co, 66-; Thurston Aircraft Corp, 68-; pres. & dir, Thanatron, Inc, 71-; mem. Int. Oceanog. Found; Inst. Arctic & Antarctic Studies. AAAS; Am. Chem. Soc; Nat. Soc. Prof. Eng; N.Y. Acad. Sci. Ballistics; pyrotechnics; aerosols; whiteout; electro-biochemistry; plasma physics; specialized research into particulate measuring devices; psychological and physiological effects due to whiteout conditions; marine science and oceanography. Address: 123 North St, Andover, MA 01810.

GREENBERG, ARTHUR BERNARD, b. Brooklyn, N.Y, Mar. 28, 29; m. 51; c. 3. AERONAUTICAL ENGINEERING. B.S.M.E. & B.S.Aero.E, Purdue, 50, M.S, 52, Ph.D.(aeronaut. eng), 55. Sr. engr, Aerojet-Gen. Corp, 55-57; instr. mech. eng, Dayton, 57-58; mem. tech. staff, Space Tech. Labs, 58-60; head performance anal. dept, AEROSPACE CORP, 60-62, dir. propulsive vehicle systs, 62-63, asst. dir. group II study progs, 63-64, group dir. tech. anal. & planning, 64, asst. gen. mgr, syst. planning div, 64-69, ASSOC. TO V.PRES. CORP. PLANNING, 69- Am. Inst. Aeronaut. & Astronaut. Rocket propulsion; systems research and definition of advanced aerospace launch and reentry vehicles; propulsion devices; satellite systems. Address: Aerospace Corp, P.O. Box 95085, Los Angeles, CA 90045.

GREENBERG, BERNARD, b. N.Y.C, Apr. 24, 22; m. 49; c. 4. MEDICAL ENTOMOLOGY. B.A, Brooklyn Col, 44; M.A, Univ. Kans, 51, Ph.D, 54. Instr. ZOOL, col. pharm, UNIV. ILL, 54-55, asst. prof, 55-61, assoc. prof, 61-66, PROF, CHICAGO CIRCLE, 66- Vis. scientist, Istituto Superiore Sanità, Rome, 60-61, Fulbright Res. fel, 67-68; Inst. Pub. Health & Trop. Disease, Mex, 62-63. U.S.A.A.F, 44-46. Fel. AAAS; Entom. Soc. Am; Am. Soc. Trop. Med. & Hyg. Insect physiology; acarology; host-contaminant biology. Address: Dept. of Biological Sciences, University of Illinois at Chicago Circle, Box 4348, Chicago, IL 60680.

GREENBERG, BERNARD, b. Springfield, Mass, Oct. 5, 24; m. 49; c. 2. SYSTEMS ANALYSIS. A.B, Massachusetts, 48; M.A, George Washington, 54. Chief sci. intel. sect, U.S. Army Corp Engrs, D.C, 48-57; eval. specialist, Martin Co, Md, 57-58; weapons systs. anal. engr, missile systs. div, Repub. Aviation Corp, N.Y, 58-59; opers. analyst, weapons systs. lab, STANFORD RES. INST, 59-60, sr. opers. analyst, 60-62, prog. mgr. sea based systs, 62-65, sr. systs. analyst, systs. res. div, 65-67, prog. mgr, opers. res. dept, 67-70, SR. OPERS. ANALYST, SYSTS. ENG. DIV, 70-, asst. dir. regional security studies ctr, 68-70. U.S.A, 43-46. Opers. Res. Soc. Am; Sci. Res. Soc. Am. Scientific intelligence; weapons systems; systems requirements and evaluation analysis; criminal justice system studies; residential crimes analysis; innovative investigation procedure development; security systems research; police operations analysis. Address: Stanford Research Institute, Menlo Park, CA 94025.

GREENBERG, B(ERNARD) G(EORGE), b. N.Y.C, Oct. 4, 19; m. 46; c. 3. BIOSTATISTICS. B.S, City Col, 39; Ph.D.(exp. statist), N.C. State Col, 49. Statistician, State Dept. Health, N.Y, 40-41; asst. statistician, N.C. State Col, 46-49; PROF. BIOSTATIST. & HEAD DEPT, SCH. PUB. HEALTH, UNIV. N.C, CHAPEL HILL, 49- Summers, vis. prof, Va. Polytech. Inst, 54, Univ. Mich, 58 & 59, Univ. Minn, 60, Univ. Wash, 61 & Yale, 65. Consult, Nat. Insts. Health, 55- U.S.A, 41-46, Capt. Biomet. Soc.(pres, 71); fel. Am. Statist. Asn; fel. Am. Pub. Health Asn.(Bronfman Prize, 66); Inst. Math. Statist; Pop. Asn. Am; Royal Statist. Soc. Design of experiments; statistical methods of analysis in medical and public health research. Address: School of Public Health, University of North Carolina at Chapel Hill, Chapel Hill, NC 27514.

GREENBERG, CHARLES BERNARD, b. Elizabeth, N.J, Dec. 20, 39; m. 67; c. 1. CERAMIC ENGINEERING. B.S, Rutgers, 61; Edward Orton Jr. fel, Illinois, 61-62, M.S, 62, Lead Industs. Asn. fel, 62-65, Ph.D.(ceramic eng), 65. Sr. res. ceramist, GLASS RES. CTR, PPG INDUSTS, 65-69, RES. ASSOC, 69- Optical Soc. Am; Am. Ceramic Soc. Thin transparent films; glass lasers. Address: PPG Industries, Glass Research Center, Pittsburgh, PA 15238.

GREENBERG, CYRUS M(ARVIN), b. Phila, Pa, Nov. 28, 25; m. 59. PHYSIOLOGY, BIOCHEMISTRY. A.B, Temple, 50; A.M, Oregon, 52; Ph.D.(zool), Rutgers, 55. Asst. zool, Oregon, 51-52; Rutgers, 52-55, res. fel. endocrinol, 55-56; sr. res. scientist biochem, SMITH, KLINE & FRENCH LABS, 57-62, dir. sci. employ, 62-67, SCI. DIR. RES. & DEVELOP. AGREEMENTS & PROD. ACQUISITION & LICENSING, 67- U.S.N, 43-46. AAAS; Am. Soc. Zool; N.Y. Acad. Sci. Endocrinology. Address: Smith, Kline & French Lab, 1500 Spring Garden St, Philadelphia, PA 19101.

GREENBERG, DANIEL, b. New York, N.Y, Dec. 31, 27; m. 53; c. 2. PHYSICAL CHEMISTRY. B.S, Yale, 48; M.S, Chicago, 49; Atomic Energy Comn. fel, Columbia, 51-53, Ph.D.(chem), 54. Res. assoc. radiochem, Columbia, 54-55; res. scientist nuclear physics, Armour Res. Found, 55-57; proj. leader radiation chem. res, indust. reactor labs, U.S. INDUST. CHEM. CO, 58-68, sr. res. assoc, POLYMER SERV. LAB, 68-71, GROUP LEADER, PILOT PLANT, 71- AAAS; Am. Nuclear Soc; Am. Chem. Soc; Am. Phys. Soc. Nuclear and radiation chemistry; polymer chemistry; radiochemistry. Address: 2110 Bristol Rd, Champaign, IL 61820.

GREENBERG, DANIEL, b. Phila, Pa, Sept. 28, 34; m. 54; c. 2. HISTORY OF SCIENCE. M.A, Columbia, 56, Quincy Ward Boese fel, 57-58, univ. fel, 58-59, Ph.D.(physics), 60. Instr. physics, Barnard Col, Columbia Univ, 59-60, asst. prof, 60-63, assoc. prof. hist. of sci, Columbia Univ, 64-66; MEM. STAFF, SUDBURY VALLEY SCH, 68- Am. Phys. Soc; Am. Asn. Physics Teachers; Soc. Hist. Tech. Address: 171 Dutton Rd, Sudbury, MA 01776.

GREENBERG, DAVID B(ERNARD), b. Norfolk, Va, Nov. 2, 28; m. 52; c. 3. CHEMICAL ENGINEERING. B.S, Carnegie Inst. Tech, 52; M.S, Hopkins, 59; Ph.D, La. State, 64. Res. engr, Victor Div, Radio Corp. Am, 52-53; Nat. Distillers Prods. Corp, 53-55; Food Mach. & Chem. Corp, 55-56; asst, Hopkins, 56-58; asst. prof. chem, U.S. Naval Acad, 58-61; instr. CHEM. ENG, LA. STATE UNIV, BATON ROUGE, 61-64, res. fel, 64-65, asst. prof, 64-67, ASSOC. PROF, 67- U.S.N, 47-49, Res, 49-, Lt.(jg). Am. Chem. Soc; Am. Inst. Chem. Eng; Am. Soc. Eng. Educ; Simulation Coun. Heat, mass, momentum transfer; high vacuum distillation; reaction kinetics; laser irradiation studies on bioorganisms; hybrid computation. Address: Dept. of Chemical Engineering, Louisiana State University, Baton Rouge, LA 70803.

GREENBERG, DAVID M(ORRIS), b. Boston, Mass, Sept. 15, 95; m. 18; c. 2. BIOCHEMISTRY. A.B, California, 21, Ph.D.(biochem), 24. Instr. BIOCHEM, UNIV. CALIF, BERKELEY, 24-28, asst. prof, 28-31, assoc. prof, 31-41, prof, 41-63, chmn. dept, 46-63, EMER. PROF, 63-, RES. BIOCHEMIST ONCOL, MED. SCH, SAN FRANCISCO, 63- Guggenheim fel, Cambridge, 29-30. Mem. panel on isotopes, comt. on growth, Nat. Res. Coun, 46-48. With Atomic Energy Comn, 44. Fel. AAAS; Am. Chem. Soc; Am. Soc. Biol. Chem; Soc. Exp. Biol. & Med.(ed, 46-52); Am. Asn. Cancer Res; Am. Cancer Soc; Brit. Biochem. Soc. Metabolism of amino acids and proteins; isotopes in biology. Address: Dept. of Biochemistry, Cancer Research Institute, School of Medicine, University of California, San Francisco, CA 94122.

GREENBERG, ELLIOTT, b. N.Y.C, Mar. 14, 27; m. 51; c. 3. PHYSICAL & INORGANIC CHEMISTRY. B.S, City Col. New York, 47; M.S, Univ. Mich, 48, fel, 49-51, summer fel, 53, Ph.D.(chem), 55. Instr, Univ. Mich, 51-54; assoc. chemist, Argonne Nat. Lab, Ill, 54-69; ASSOC. PROF. CHEM, PRAIRIE STATE COL, 69- U.S.N, 45-46. Am. Chem. Soc; Sci. Res. Soc. Am. Fluorine bomb calorimetry; general chemistry. Address: 203 Berry St, Park Forest, IL 60466.

GREENBERG, G(OODWIN) ROBERT, b. Danube, Minn, June 23, 18; m. 42; c. 4. BIOCHEMISTRY. B.A, Minnesota, 41, M.S, 42, Ph.D, 44. Asst. physiol. chem, Minnesota, 42-44; res. fel. med, Utah, 44-46; sr. instr. BIOCHEM, Western Reserve, 46-48, asst. prof, 48-54, assoc. prof, 54-57; PROF, UNIV. MICH, ANN ARBOR, 57- Sr. fel. Nat. Sci. Found, Univ. Durham, Eng. Civilian with Chem. Warfare Serv, Utah, 44-45, Off. Sci. Res. & Develop, 45-46. Am. Soc. Biol. Chem. Nucleic acid metabolism; protein biosynthesis; bacteriophage metabolism; microbial genetics. Address: M5450 Medical Science Bldg, University of Michigan, Ann Arbor, MI 48104.

GREENBERG, HAROLD, b. New York, N.Y, Jan. 3, 28; m. 55; c. 3. OPERATIONS RESEARCH. B.A, Brooklyn Col, 49; M.S, N.Y. Univ, 58, Ph.D.(opers. res), 64. Physicist, Navy Dept, 49; sr. engr, Sylvania Elec. Corp, 51-55; mem. tech. staff, Ramo-Wooldridge Corp, 55-56; engr, Arma Corp, 56-58; res. analyst, Port of New York Auth, 58-60; mem. sr. proj, Radio Corp. Am, 60-61; assoc. prof. OPERS. RES, N.Y. Univ, 61-66; PROF, NAVAL POSTGRAD. SCH, 67- Vis. prof, Tel-Aviv Univ, 70- Mathematical programming; inventory analysis; traffic. Address: Dept. of Operations Research, Naval Postgraduate School, Monterey, CA 93940.

GREENBERG, HARRY, b. Montreal, Que, Mar. 28, 03; nat; m. 29. ORGANIC CHEMISTRY; B.Sc, McGill, 25, M.Sc, 27, Hunt fel, 28-29, Ph.D.(org. chem), 29. Res. chemist, U.S. Indust. Chems. Inc, 29-50, NAT. DISTILLERS PROD. CORP, 50-64, SR. RES. ASSOC, 64- Am. Chem. Soc. Organic chemistry involving solvents; pharmaceuticals, amino acids and dye intermediates; non-coutchouc constituents of the latex of Hevea Brasiliensis; amino acids in rubber latex; polyesters; polyamides; sebacic acid and derivatives; inorganic chemistry involving preparative metallurgy of zirconium, tantalum, columbium and hafnium; synthetic rubber; olefin catalysis. Address: National Distillers Products Corp, 1275 Section Rd, Cincinnati, OH 45237.

GREENBERG, HARVEY J, b. Phila, Pa, Oct. 16, 40; m. 66; c. 1. SYSTEMS ANALYSIS. B.S, Univ. Miami, 62; Ph.D.(opers. res), Johns Hopkins Univ, 68. Reliability engr, N.Am. Aviation Corp, 62-63; systs. engr, Martin Co, 63-64; Westinghouse Elec. Corp, 64-65; ASSOC. PROF. SYSTS. ENG, SOUTH. METHODIST UNIV, 68- Consult, Mobil Oil Corp, 68-70; Nat. Sci. Found. fel, 71. Soc. Indust. & Appl. Math; Opers. Res. Soc. Am; Math. Asn. Am; Inst. Mgt. Sci. Theoretical foundations of optimization and computer implementation; axiomatic foundations of problems and algorithms and the inherent topological structures; advances in education such as use of Gestalt psychology. Address: CS/OR Center, Southern Methodist University, Dallas, TX 75222.

GREENBERG, H(ERBERT) J(ULIUS), b. Chicago, Ill, Nov. 28, 21; m. 46; c. 3. APPLIED MATHEMATICS. B.S, Northwestern, 40, M.S, 41, fel, 41-42; fel, Brown, 42-43, Ph.D.(appl. math), 46. Asst, Brown, 43-45, res. assoc, 45-47, asst. prof. math, 47-49; Carnegie Inst. Tech, 49-51, assoc. prof, 51-56; assoc. dir. atomic energy comn. comput. & appl. math. ctr, N.Y. Univ, 56-58; mem. staff, res. div, Int. Bus. Mach. Corp, 58-65, asst. dir. math. sci, 60-65, dir, 65; PROF. MATH. & CHMN. DEPT, UNIV. DENVER, 65- Assoc. prof, inst. math. sci, N.Y. Univ, 56-68; head math. sci. div, Denver Res. Inst, 66- Mem. appl. math. group, Off. Sci. Res. & Develop, Brown Univ, 43-45. AAAS; Soc. Indust. & Appl. Math; Math. Asn. Am. Applied mechanics; numeral analysis; computing; mathematical education. Address: Dept. of Mathematics, University of Denver, Denver, CO 80210.

GREENBERG, HERMAN SAMUEL, b. Phila, Pa, Jan. 13, 39; m. 70. ORGANIC & MEDICINAL CHEMISTRY. A.B, Temple Univ, 60, A.M, 64; Ph.D. (org. chem), Univ. Pa, 69. Jr. medicinal chemist, Smith Kline & French Labs, 60-63; chemist, Polysci. Inc, 69-70; FEL. PHARMACOL, SCH. MED, UNIV. PA, 70- Am. Chem. Soc; The Chem. Soc. Bio-organic chemistry; biochemistry. Address: 6903 Oakland St, Philadelphia, PA 19149.

GREENBERG, HOWARD, b. New York, N.Y, Jan. 16, 28; m. 57. THEORETICAL PHYSICS. B.S, City Col. New York, 49; M.S, N.Y. Univ, 51, Ph.D. (physics), 57. Asst. PHYSICS, N.Y. Univ, 51-55; from instr. to ASST. PROF, CITY COL. NEW YORK, 55- Am. Phys. Soc; Am. Asn. Physics Teachers. Atomic physics; scattering of electrons by atoms. Address: Dept. of Physics, City College of New York, New York, NY 10031.

GREENBERG, IRWIN, b. New York, N.Y, Sept. 18, 35; m. 56; c. 2. OPERATIONS RESEARCH, APPLIED MATHEMATICS. B.I.E, N.Y. Univ, 56, Eng. Sc.D, 64; M.S, Northeastern, 60. Opers. analyst, Avco Res. & Adv. Develop. Div, 56-60; instr. INDUST. ENG, N.Y. UNIV, 61-64, asst. prof, 64-66, ASSOC. PROF, 67- Res. analyst, Port N.Y. Authority, 60-66; Fulbright travel grant & vis. res. scientist, Delft, 66-67. Opers. Res. Soc. Am; Inst. Mgt. Sci. Stochastic processes; queuing; applied probability; weapon systems analysis; theory of traffic flow; quality control; inventory models. Address: 9 Jackson Rd, Briarcliff Manor, New York, NY 10510.

GREENBERG, JACK S(AM), b. Warsaw, Poland, May 23, 27; m. 52; c. 2. PHYSICS. B.Eng, McGill, 50, M.Sc, 51; Ph.D.(physics), Mass. Inst. Technol, 55. Rutherford mem. fel, 55-56; instr. PHYSICS, YALE, 56-58, asst. prof, 58-64, ASSOC. PROF, 64-, dir. grad. studies, 67-69. Nat. Sci. Found. grant, 61-64; vis. scientist, Weizmann Inst. Sci, 69-70. Fel. Am. Phys. Soc. Nuclear and high energy physics. Address: Dept. of Physics, Yale University, New Haven, CT 06520.

GREENBERG, JAMES M, b. Chicago, Ill, July 30, 40. MATHEMATICS, CONTINUUM MECHANICS. B.C.E, Cornell, 63, Ph.D.(appl. math), 66. Fel, Mellon Inst, 66-67; asst. prof. MATH, Carnegie-Mellon Univ, 67-69; ASSOC. PROF, Case West. Reserve Univ, 69-71; STATE UNIV. N.Y. BUFFALO, 71- Am. Math. Soc; Soc. Natural Philos. Nonlinear conservation laws of viscous and hyperbolic type; free boundary problems for elliptic and parabolic partial differential equations. Address: Dept. of Mathematics, State University of New York at Buffalo, Amherst, NY 14226.

GREENBERG, JAY R, b. Davenport, Iowa, Aug. 23, 43. CELL & MOLECULAR BIOLOGY. B.S, Chicago, 64, Ph.D.(cell biol), 68. Nat. Insts. Health fel. MOLECULAR BIOL, INST. CANCER RES, 68-70, RES. ASSOC, 70- RNA synthesis in eukaryotes and its regulation. Address: Institute for Cancer Research, 7701 Burholme Ave, Philadelphia, PA 19111.

GREENBERG, JEROME H(ERBERT), b. Trenton, N.J, Sept. 1, 23; m. 45; c. 3. PREVENTIVE MEDICINE. M.D, Georgetown, 49; Army Med. Serv. Grad. Sch, 54-55. U.S. ARMY, 53-, chief dept. epidemiol, Walter Reed Army Inst. Res, 57-58, asst. chief, commun. disease br, prev. med. div, off. surgeon gen, 58-60, prev. med. adv, Korean Mil. Adv. Group, 60-62, chief prev. med. br, hq, fourth U.S. Army, Tex, 64-65, dir. dept. prev. med. and. field serv. sch, Brooke Army Med. Ctr, 65-69, assoc. commandant, Walter Reed Army Inst. Res. Med. Ctr, Wash, D.C, 69-70, chief prev. med, div, OFF. SURGEON GEN, DEPT. ARMY, 70-71, DIR. HEALTH ENVIRON, 71- Fel. trop. med, sch. trop. med, Calcutta, 59; inter-am. trop. med. prog, La. State, 64. Dipl, Am. Bd. Prev. Med, 58. U.S.A, 42-45, 49-52, 53-, Col. Am. Med. Asn; Am. Pub. Health Asn; Asn. Mil. Surg. U.S; Am. Col. Prev. Med; Am. Soc. Trop. Med. & Hyg. Epidemiology; immunology. Address: Office of the Surgeon General, Dept. of Army, Washington, DC 20314.

GREENBERG, J(EROME) MAYO, b. Baltimore, Md, Jan. 14, 22; m. 47; c. 4 THEORETICAL PHYSICS. Ph.D.(physics), Hopkins, 48. Physicist, Nat. Adv. Comt. Aeronaut, 44-46; instr. physics, exten. div, Virginia, 45-46; asst. prof, Delaware, 48-51; res. assoc, Inst. Fluid Dynamics & Appl. Math, Maryland, 51-52; asst. prof. physics, Rensselaer Polytech. Inst, 52-56, assoc. prof, 56-57, PROF, 57-70; ASTROPHYS, STATE UNIV. N.Y. ALBANY, 70-; SR. RES. ASSOC, DUDLEY OBSERV, 70- Orgn. Europ. Econ. Coop. sr. vis. fel, Univ. Leiden, 61; lectr, Enrico Fermi Int. Sch, Italy, summer 61; mem. sch. math, Inst. Advan. Study, Princeton, 65-66; dir. astron, Rensselaer Polytech. Inst, 67-70; vis. astronr, inst. astron, Univ. Hawaii, summer 68; prof. lab. astrophys, Univ. Leiden, 68-69; mem. comn. interstellar matter & planetary nebulae, Int. Astron. Union; mem. comn. six, Int. Radio and Sci. Union. U.S.A.A.F.R, 44-46. AAAS; Am. Astron. Soc; fel. Am. Phys. Soc. Theory of particle scattering and wave scattering; interstellar matter; astrophysics. Address: 2126 Union St, Schenectady, NY 12309.

GREENBERG, JOEL S, b. Brooklyn, N.Y, May 21, 31; m. 52; c. 3. ELECTRICAL ENGINEERING. B.E.E, Polytech. Inst. Brooklyn, 52; M.E.E, Syracuse, 61. Electronic engr, Rome Air Develop. Ctr, Griffiss AFB, N.Y, 52-55, supvry. electronics scientist, 55-60, phys. scientist, 60-61; mem. tech. staff, adv. mil. systs, Radio Corp. Am, 61-65, tech. progs, 65-66, mgr. customers systs. eng, graphic systs. div, 66, mem. tech. staff opers. res, 66-69; v.pres, Ventures Res. & Develop. Group, 69-71; VIS. RES. SCIENTIST, PRINCETON UNIV, 71- Consult. ad hoc comt. Ballistic Missile Detection Group, Sci. Adv. Bd, 57, Ballistic Missile Early Warning Syst. Proj. Off, 58. Radar system analysis and development; detection theory; satellite communication system; ballistic missile and satellite detection and interception; operations research applications to business planning and evaluation, simulation models, new business planning and evaluation. Address: Aerospace Dept. (EQ), Princeton University, Princeton, NJ 08540.

GREENBERG, JOSEPH, b. Revere, Mass, Dec. 20, 18; m. 46; c. 4. BIOLOGY. A.B, Harvard, 40, Stoughton scholar, 40-42, M.A, 41, Ph.D.(biol), 47. Asst, Tenn. Valley Authority, Ala, 42; fel, Nat. Insts. Health, 46-47, from sr. asst. scientist to sci. dir, 47-58; prog. dir. MICROBIOL, Stanford Res. Inst, 58-61; CHIEF DIV, PALO ALTO MED. RES. FOUND, 61- Ashford award, 54. U.S.N, 43-46. Fel. AAAS; fel. Am. Soc. Trop. Med. & Hyg; assoc. Am. Soc. Parasitol; assoc. N.Y. Acad. Sci; assoc. Am. Soc. Microbiol; assoc. Genetics Soc. Am. Microbial genetics; radiation biology; chemotherapy of malaria, amebiasis and cancer. Address: Palo Alto Medical Research Foundation, 860 Bryant St, Palo Alto, CA 94301.

GREENBERG, LEONARD J(ASON), b. Roxbury, Mass, July 8, 26. BIOCHEMISTRY. B.S, Northeastern, 52; M.S, Rochester, 54; fel, Minnesota, 57-59, Ph.D, 58. Instr, med. col, Minnesota, 56-57, res. assoc. physiol. chem, Lyon Lab, 59-60, asst. prof, 60-61; asst. prof. path, Stanford, 61; sr. investr, Naval Radiol Defense Lab, 62-65; asst. prof. path, N.Y. Univ. Med. Ctr, 65-67; DIR. VIRUS RES, UNION CARBIDE RES. INST, 67- Adj. assoc. prof, N.Y. Univ. Med. Ctr, 67- AAAS; Am. Chem. Soc; Histochem. Soc; Soc. Exp. Biol. & Med; Am. Soc. Microbiol; Sci. Res. Soc. Am. Histochemical and cytochemical analysis; adrenal metabolism; hormone-enzyme interaction; molecular mechanisms of virus infection and virus inducted cellular transformation. Address: Union Carbide Research Institute, Tarrytown, NY 10591.

GREENBERG, LOUIS, b. Saskatoon, Sask, July 23, 14; m. 43; c. 4. BACTERIOLOGY, IMMUNOLOGY. B.S.A, Saskatchewan, 36, M.Sc, 39; Ph.D. (bacter, immunol), McGill, 48. Lab. asst, dairying & bacter, Saskatchewan, 36-39; bacteriologist, DEPT. NAT. HEALTH & WELFARE, CAN, 39-42, CHIEF BIOLOGIC CONTROL LABS, CAN. COMMUN. DISEASE CENTRE, 48- Med.C, Can. Army, 42-45, Capt. Am. Asn. Immunol; Can. Pub. Health Asn; Can. Soc. Microbiol; affiliate Royal Soc. Med; Brit. Soc. Immunol. Development of assay techniques for biologicals, especially diphtheria and tetanus toxoids; humans and experimental animal immunization studies; control of antibiotics; new approaches to bacterial vaccines. Address: Apt. 1102, 2001 Carling Ave, Ottawa, Ont. K2A 3W5, Can.

GREENBERG, LOUIS D(ONALD), b. Pueblo, Colo, July 14, 05; m. 39; c. 1. BIOCHEMISTRY. A.B, California, 30, fel, 32-34, Ph.D.(biochem), 36. Asst. plant nutrition, California, 30-32, biochem, 34-35; physiol. chemist, S.Pac. Hosp, 35-39; asst. path, SCH. MED, UNIV. CALIF, SAN FRANCISCO, 36-42, instr, 42-43, path. & pharmacol, 43-44, asst. prof, 44-50, assoc. prof. exp. path, 50-62, PROF. PATH, 62-, CHMN. GRAD. GROUP NUTRIT, 63- Consult. res. div, Napa State Hosp, Calif. With Off. Civilian Defense, 44. AAAS; Am. Heart Asn; Am. Chem. Soc; Soc. Exp. Biol. & Med; Am. Soc. Biol. Chem; Biochem. Soc. Metabolism of the vitamins; experimental arteriosclerosis; lipide metabolism. Address: Dept. of Pathology, University of California School of Medicine, San Francisco, CA 94122.

GREENBERG, MARVIN J(AY), b. N.Y.C, Dec. 22, 35; m. 64; c. 1. MATHEMATICS. A.B, Columbia, 55; Proctor fel, Princeton, 57, Ph.D, 59. Asst. MATH, Princeton, 55-57; Chicago, 58; instr, Rutgers, 58-59; asst. prof, California, Berkeley, 59-64; Nat. Sci. Found. res. fel, Harvard, 64-65; assoc. prof, Northeast. Univ, 65-67; UNIV. CALIF, SANTA CRUZ, 67-69, PROF, 69- Nat. Sci. Found. res. fel, Harvard, 61; Univ. Paris, 62. Am. Math. Soc. Algebraic geometry; algebraic number theory; algebraic topology. Address: Dept. of Mathematics, University of California, Santa Cruz, CA 95060.

GREENBERG, MICHAEL D(AVID), b. Brooklyn, N.Y, Nov. 15, 35; m. 57; c. 3. FLUID MECHANICS. B.M.E, Cornell Univ, 58, M.S, 60, Ph.D.(thoret. mech), 64. Staff scientist, Therm Advan. Res, Inc, 63-69; ASSOC. PROF. MECH. & AEROSPACE ENG, UNIV. DEL, 69- Vis. asst. prof, Cornell Univ, 64-66, asst. prof, 68- Nonlinear mechanics; steady and nonsteady airfoil and propeller theory. Address: Dept. of Mechanical & Aerospace Engineering, Evans Hall, University of Delaware, Newark, DE 19711.

GREENBERG, MICHAEL JOHN, b. Brooklyn, N.Y, Sept. 28, 31; m. 54; c. 3. COMPARATIVE PHYSIOLOGY. A.B, Cornell, 53; M.A, Fla. State, 55; U.S. Pub. Health Serv. fel, Harvard, 57-58, Ph.D.(biol), 58. Instr. invert. zool, Illinois, 58-60, asst. prof, 60-64; ASSOC. PROF. BIOL, FLA. STATE UNIV, 64- Nat. Sci. Found. sr. fel, Melbourne & Misaki Marine Labs, Japan, 64-65; mem. Gov. Task Force on Narcotics, Dangerous Drugs & Alcohol Abuse, Fla. AAAS; Am. Physiol. Soc; Soc. Gen. Physiol; Am. Soc. Zool. Comparative invertebrate pharmacology; invertebrate zoology. Address: 204 Biological Science Unit I, Dept. of Biological Science, Florida State University, Tallahassee, FL 32306.

GREENBERG, NEWTON I(SAAC), b. Brooklyn, N.Y, Feb. 26, 36; m. 60. THEORETICAL PHYSICS. B.S, Brooklyn Col, 57; Ph.D.(physics), Maryland, 61. Asst. PHYSICS, Maryland, 57-61; fel, Bartol Res. Found, 61-63; asst. prof, HARPUR COL, 63-69, ASSOC. PROF, 69- Am. Phys. Soc. Solid state theory; many body problem; Heisenberg model of ferromagnetism; secondary electron emission. Address: Dept. of Physics, Harpur College, Binghamton, NY 13901.

GREENBERG, ORRIN, b. Perth Amboy, N.J, June 20, 05; m. 37, 51. DENTAL MATERIALS & ANATOMY. B.A, Rochester, 27; D.D.S, Pennsylvania, 30. Instr. preclin. tech, TUFTS UNIV, 51-53, asst. prof, 53-54, assoc. prof, 54-58, prof, 58-65, prof. DENT. ANAT. & DENT. MAT. SCI. & asst. dean, SCH. DENT. MED, 65-69, EMER. PROF, 69- Dent.C, U.S.A, Capt. AAAS; Int. Asn. Dent. Res; Am. Dent. Asn. Electroforming. Address: 317 South St, Chestnut Hill, MA 02167.

GREENBERG, OSCAR W(ALLACE), b. New York, N.Y, Feb. 18, 32; m. 69. THEORETICAL PHYSICS. B.S, Rutgers, 52; Nat. Sci. Found. fels, Princeton, 52-53, 54-55, A.M, 54, Gen. Elec. fel, 55-56, Ph.D.(physics), 57. Instr. PHYSICS, Brandeis, 56-57; Nat. Sci. Found. fel, Mass. Inst. Tech, 59-61; asst. prof, UNIV. MD, COLLEGE PARK, 61-63, assoc. prof, 63-67, PROF, 67- Mem, Inst. Advan. Study, 64; Sloan Found. fel, 64-66; vis. assoc. prof, Rockefeller Univ, 65-66; vis. prof, Tel-Aviv Univ, 68-69; John Simon Guggenheim fel, 68-69. U.S.A.F, 57-59, 1st Lt. AAAS; Am. Phys. Soc; Am. Math. Soc. Quantum field theory; particle and high energy physics. Address: Dept. of Physics & Astronomy, University of Maryland, College Park, MD 20742.

GREENBERG, R(ICHARD) A(ARON), b. Chicago, Ill, Aug. 21, 28; m. 54; c. 3. BACTERIOLOGY. A.B, Illinois, 48, M.S, 50, E.R. Squibb fel, 50, Ph.D. (bact), 54. Res. bacteriologist, SWIFT & CO, 56-58, head, bact. res. div, 58-66, chief microbiologist, 62-66, assoc. dir. RES, 66-70, DIR, 70- U.S.A, 54-56. Am. Soc. Microbiol; Am. Acad. Microbiol; Inst. Food Technol. Bacterial spores; food microbiology, especially thermally processed meat products; food poisoning; anti-microbial substances. Address: Swift & Co, Research & Development Center, 1919 Swift Dr, Oak Brook, IL 60521.

GREENBERG, RICHARD A(LVIN), b. Hartford, Conn, Oct. 28, 27; m. 50; c. 2. BIOMETRY. B.A, Connecticut, 50; M.P.H, Yale, 59, Ph.D.(biomet), 63. Statistician, Fed. Pac. Elec. Co, 51-54; res. statistician cancer, State Dept. Health, Conn, 55-59; instr. BIOMET, SCH. MED, YALE, 62-64, asst. prof, 64-69, ASSOC. PROF, 69- Am. Statist. Asn; Biomet. Soc; Am. Pub. Health Asn. Cancer and Genetics. Address: Dept. of Epidemiology & Public Health, Yale University School of Medicine, 60 College St, New Haven, CT 06510.

GREENBERG, ROBERT A(LLAN), b. Boston, Mass, Nov. 5, 35; m. 61; c. 2. FLUID MECHANICS. B.S, Mass. Inst. Technol, 57, M.S, 58, Ph.D.(aeronaut, astronaut), 66. Sr. engr, Martin-Marietta Corp, 58-62; PRIN. RES. ENGR, AVCO-EVERETT RES. LAB, 65- Am. Inst. Aeronaut. & Astronaut. Laser gas dynamics; high power lasers; reentry ablation phenomenology; inviscid and viscous hypersonic flow. Address: Avco Everett Research Lab, 2385 Revere Beach Pkwy, Everett, MA 02149.

GREENBERG, RUVEN, b. Columbus, Ohio, Mar. 15, 18; m. 48; c. 3. PHYSIOLOGY. B.Sc, Ohio State, 38, U.S. Pub. Health fel, 47-48, Ph.D.(physiol), 48, M.Sc, Northwestern, 40. Instr. PHYSIOL, med. sch, Ohio State, 48-49; asst. prof, med. br, Texas, 49-53; UNIV. ILL. COL. MED, 53-57, assoc. prof, 57-69, PROF, 69- Fulbright lectr, Univ. Madrid, 63. Med.C, 41-45, 2nd Lt. Am. Physiol. Soc; Soc. Exp. Biol. & Med; Am. Soc. Cell Biol. Neuro-mediators; histo-physiology; psychopharmacology. Address: Dept. of Physiology, University of Illinois College of Medicine, Chicago, IL 60612.

GREENBERG, SAMUEL M(ENDEL). BIOCHEMISTRY. B.S, Agr. & Mech. Col, Texas, 37; Ph.D.(biochem, nutrition), Southern California, 51. Res. assoc. biochem. & nutrit, Southern California, 46-51; res. fel, Birmingham Univ, 52-53; vis. asst. prof. biochem. & nutrition, Southern California, 53-54; staff dir. metab. dept, Smith, Kline & French Labs, 54-67; DIR. SCI. INFO, McNEIL LABS, 67- U.S.A, 42-46, 1st Lt. AAAS; Soc. Exp. Biol. & Med; Am. Chem. Soc; Am. Inst. Nutrit; N.Y. Acad. Sci; Brit. Biochem. Soc. Drug development. Address: McNeil Labs, Camp Hill Rd, Ft. Washington, PA 19034.

GREENBERG, SEYMOUR S(AMUEL), b. Brooklyn, N.Y, Feb. 20, 30; m. 64. GEOLOGY. B.S, Brooklyn Col; A.M, Indiana, Ph.D, 59. Petrographer, Ind. Geol. Surv, 52-62; geologist, Va. div. min. resources, 62-64; assoc. prof. sci, WEST CHESTER STATE COL, 64-69, PROF. EARTH, SPACE & GEN. SCI, 69- U.S.A, 53-55. Geol. Soc. Am; Am. Mineral. Soc; Soc. Econ. Paleont. & Mineral; Geochem. Soc; Mineral. Asn. Can; Mineral. Soc. Gt. Brit. & Ireland. Petrology and mineralogy. Address: Dept. of General Sciences, West Chester State College, West Chester, PA 19380.

GREENBERG, SHELDON I(VAN), b. Minneapolis, Minn, July 3, 26. PHARMACOLOGY, BIOCHEMISTRY. B.A, Minnesota, 48. Asst. pharmacol, Minnesota, 48-51; res. chemist, Hormel Inst, 51-53; Pillsbury Co, 53-56, sr. res. chemist, cereal & grain res. dept, 56-61, res. mgr, 61-65, mgr, tech. liaizon int. opers, 65-68; SECURITIES ANALYST, INVESTORS DIVERSIFIED SERV, 68- U.S.N, 44-46. Financial Anal. Fedn. Pharmaceutics; medical electronics; new product development; market potential and financial analyses. Address: Investors Diversified Services, 800 Investors Bldg, Minneapolis, MN 55402.

GREENBERG, SHERMAN, b. Brooklyn, N.Y, Mar. 7, 25; m. 48. CHEMICAL ENGINEERING. B.Ch.E, City Col, 45; Ill. Inst. Tech. Res. chemist, Nat. Oil Prod. Co, 45-46; group leader metall. div, ARGONNE NAT. LAB, 61-68, ASSOC. CHEM. ENG, EBR-II PROJ, 68- Am. Nuclear Soc. Nuclear reactor materials development, specially aqueous and liquid metal corrosion related to fuel elements, cladding and structural materials. Address: Argonne National Lab, EBR-II Project, 9700 S. Cass Ave, Argonne, IL 60439.

GREENBERG, SIDNEY A(BRAHAM), b. N.Y.C, Nov. 26, 18; m. 46; c. 2. PHYSICAL CHEMISTRY. B.A, Washington (St. Louis), 39; Missouri, 39-41; Yale, 43; fel, Polytech. Inst. Brooklyn, 46-50, M.S, 47, Ph.D.(phys. chem), 50. Chemist. indust. res, 41-43; res. assoc, Polytech. Inst. Brooklyn, 46-50; res. chemist, Sylvania Elec. Co, 50-51; Johns Manville Res. Center, 52-55; res. assoc; Leiden, 55-56; assoc. prof. chem, Seton Hall, 56-58; sr. res. chemist, Portland Cement Asn, 58-62; mgr. appl. res. & adv. develop, Ampex Corp, 62-64; res. mgr, mechrolab div, Hewlett-Packard, 64-66; ASSOC. PROF. PHYS. SCI, DOMINICAN COL. (CALIF), 66- U.S.A, 43-46. Fel. AAAS; Am. Chem. Soc. Kinetics of chemical reactions and crystallization; properties of luminescent solids; structure and properties of inorganic materials; colloid chemistry of silicates; magnetic materials; chemical research and analytical instruments. Address: 187 Bothin Rd, Fairfax, CA 94930.

GREENBERG, S(TANLY) DONALD, b. Beaumont, Tex, July 27, 30; m. 53; c. 3. PATHOLOGY, OTOLARYNGOLOGY. B.A, Texas, 54; M.D, Baylor, 54; M.S, Iowa, 58. Surg. pathologist, Jefferson Davis Hosp, Houston, Tex, 62, dir. path. labs, tuberc. div, 62-63; instr. path, BAYLOR COL. MED, 62-63, asst. prof. PATH. & OTOLARYNGOL, 63-70, ASSOC. PROF, 70- Asst. attend, Ben Taub Gen. Hosp, 63-; attend, Vet. Admin. Hosp, 64-; assoc, Methodist Hosp, 65- Med.C, U.S.A.R, 57-63, Capt. Am. Med. Asn; Am. Soc. Clin. Path; Col. Am. Path; Am. Soc. Exp. Path; Am. Thoracic Soc; Am. Col. Chest Physicians. Respiratory pathology of ear, nose, throat and lungs. Address: Dept. of Pathology, Baylor College of Medicine, Houston, TX 77025.

GREENBERG, STEPHEN M(EYER), b. N.Y.C, Nov. 14, 36; m. 59; c. 3. ORGANIC CHEMISTRY. B.S, Arizona, 57; M.S, Arizona State, 59; Smith Kline & French fel, Virginia, 59-62, Ph.D.(org. chem), 63. SR. CHEMIST PROD. DEVELOP, MERCK & CO, INC, 62- Am. Chem. Soc; Am. Soc. Test. & Mat. Synthesis of purines, pyrimidines; anticholesterol drugs; urethane polymers. Address: Merck & Co, Inc, 126 E. Lincoln Ave, Rahway, NJ 07065.

GREENBERG, STEPHEN ROBERT, b. Omaha, Nebr, May 5, 27; m. 52; c. 2. PATHOLOGY. B.S, St. Louis, 51, M.S, 52, Life Ins. Med. Res. Fund fel, 52-54, Ph.D.(path), 54. Asst. PATH, Clarkson Hosp, Omaha, Nebr, 54-55; instr, CHICAGO MED. SCH, 55-57, assoc, 57-62, asst. prof, 62-69, ASSOC. PROF, 69- Fel. AAAS; Am. Asn. Anat; Asn. Clin. Sci; Am. Soc. Nephrology; Int. Soc. Nephrology; Int. Acad. Path. Anatomic and clinical pathology; experimental renal disease; chemical carcinogenesis. Address: Dept. of Pathology, Chicago Medical School, 2020 W. Ogden Ave, Chicago, IL 60612.

GREENBERG, SYLVIA S(CHLAGEL), U.S. citizen. ZOOLOGY. B.A, Brooklyn Col, 42; M.S, N.Y. Univ, 46, Ph.D.(zool), 55. Res. assoc. biol, N.Y. Univ, 55-60; prin. investr, genetics lab, Am. Mus. Natural Hist, 60-64; ASSOC. RES. SCIENTIST, GRAD. SCH, N.Y. UNIV, 64- Am. Asn. Cancer Res; N.Y. Acad. Sci. Experimental zoology; experimental cell research in tissue culture; cytochemical and biochemical aspects of hereditary melanomas of xiphophorin fishes. Address: Dept. of Biology, New York University, Washington Square, New York, NY 10003.

GREENBERGER, DANIEL M(ORDECAI), b. Bronx, N.Y, Sept. 29, 33; m. 69. THEORETICAL PHYSICS. B.S, Mass. Inst. Technol, 54, vis. fel, 56-58; M.S, Univ. Ill, Urbana, 56, Ph.D.(physics), 58. Asst. prof. PHYSICS, Ohio State Univ, 60-61; Nat. Sci. Found. vis. fel, Univ. Calif, Berkeley, 61-62, asst. prof, 62-63; CITY COL. NEW YORK, 63-69, ASSOC. PROF, 69- Scientist, high sch. physics revision, phys. sci. study comt, Mass. Inst. Technol, fall 58; vis. scientist, Oxford, 71. U.S.A, 58-60, Res, 54-62, Capt. AAAS; Am. Phys. Soc; Am. Asn. Physics Teachers. Quantum field theory; relativity and gravitation. Address: Dept. of Physics, City College of New York, Convent Ave. at 138th St, New York, NY 10031.

GREENBERGER, MARTIN, b. Elizabeth, N.J, Nov. 30, 31; m. 59; c. 2. APPLIED MATHEMATICS. A.B, Harvard, 55, Nat. Sci. Found. fel, 55-56, A.M, 56, Ph.D.(appl. math), 58. Mgr. appl. sci, Int. Bus. Mach. Corp, 57-58; asst. prof. indust. mgt, Mass. Inst. Tech, 58-61, assoc. prof, 61-67; PROF. COMPUT. SCI, CHMN. DEPT. & DIR. INFO. PROCESSING, JOHNS HOPKINS UNIV, 67- Guggenheim fel, Univ. Calif, Berkeley, 65-66; mem. bd. trustees, EDUCOM, 68-, chmn. coun, 68-69, counselor to pres, 71-; mem. comput. sci. & eng. bd, Nat. Acad. Sci, 70- U.S.A.F, 52-54, Res, 54-66. AAAS; Asn. Comput. Mach. Policy studies; data structures; relation of technology to social issues; computer science; development of the computing field. Address: Johns Hopkins University, Baltimore, MD 21218.

GREENBERGER, NORTON JERALD, b. Cleveland, Ohio, Sept. 13, 33; m; c. 3. INTERNAL MEDICINE, PHYSIOLOGY. A.B, Yale, 55; M.D, Western Reserve, 59. Asst. prof. med, COL. MED, OHIO STATE UNIV, 65-67, assoc. prof. MED, 67-71, PROF, 71-, DIR. DIV. GASTROENTEROL, 67- Attend. physician, Ohio State Univ. Hosp, 65- Consult, Vet. Admin. Hosp. & Wright Patterson Air Force Base Hosp, Dayton, Ohio. Am. Fedn. Clin. Res; Am. Gastroenterol. Asn; Am. Soc. Clin. Invest. Intestinal absorption of lipids and iron; intestinal transport of digitalis glycosides. Address: Ohio State University Hospital, 410 West Tenth Ave, Columbus, OH 43210.

GREENBLATT, CHARLES L(EONARD), b. Youngstown, Ohio, Jan. 17, 31; m. 53; c. 4. PHYSIOLOGY. A.B, Harvard, 52; M.D, Pennsylvania, 56. Intern, Mary Imogene Bassett Hosp, 56-57; surgeon, sect. photobiol, lab. phys. biol, Nat. Inst. Arthritis & Metab. Diseases, Nat. Insts. Health, 57-67, chief, sect. cell biol. & immunol, Nat. Inst. Allergy & Infectious Diseases, 67-68; vis. assoc. prof. PHYSIOL, HADASSAH MED. SCH, HEBREW UNIV, 68-69, ASSOC. PROF, 69- Vis. prof, faculty of medicine, El Salvador, 61, 62. Summers, asst, biol. labs, Harvard, 52, 53, 55; biophys. res. lab, Eye & Ear Hosp, Pittsburgh, 54. Am. Soc. Cell Biol. Chlorphyll synthesis and destruction; chloroplast structure and function; hemoflagellate physiology. Address: Microbiology Institute, Hadassah Medical School, Hebrew University, Jerusalem, Israel.

GREENBLATT, EUGENE N(EWTON), b. N.Y.C, Dec. 10, 23; m. 52; c. 3. PHARMACOLOGY. B.S, Long Island, 52; M.S, Connecticut, 55, Am. Found. Pharmaceut. Ed. fel, 55-57, Ph.D.(pharmacol), 57. Asst. pharmacol, Connecticut, 52-56; scientist, col. med, State Univ. N.Y. Downstate Med. Ctr, 56-58; from res. scientist to SR. RES. PHARMACOLOGIST, LEDERLE LABS, AM CYANAMID CO, 58- U.S.A.A.F, 43-46. Am. Soc. Pharmacol. & Exp. Therapeut; Int. Soc. Biochem. Pharmacol. Autonomic pharmacology; drugs affecting the central nervous system; mechanism of drug action; cardiovascular pharmacology. Address: Lederle Labs, American Cyanamid Co, Pearl River, NY 10965.

GREENBLATT, GERALD A, b. Los Angeles, Calif, May 19, 32; m. 61; c. 1. PLANT PHYSIOLOGY. B.A, Los Angeles State Col, 55; Ph.D.(plant physiol), California, Davis, 65. Instr. BIOL, Princeton, 65-66; asst. prof, Tex. Tech Univ, 66-70; SR. RES. FEL, INST. LIFE SCI, TEX. A&M UNIV, 70- AAAS; Am. Soc. Plant Physiol. Abscission and senescence in higher plants; growth hormones. Address: Dept. of Biology, Institute of Life Science, Texas A&M University, College Station, TX 77843.

GREENBLATT, IRVING JULES, b. New York, N.Y, Sept. 15, 12; m. 40; c. 2. BIOCHEMISTRY. A.B, N.Y. Univ, 38; M.S, Georgetown, 39, Ph.D.(chem), 41. Adv. lab. probs, city dept. hosps, New York, 38-41; biochemist, BROOKDALE HOSP. MED. CTR, 41-42, 46-57, DIR. CLIN. LABS, 58- Adj. prof. clin. chem, N.Y. Polyclin. Med. Sch. & Hosp, 58. Consult. biochemist, Hebrew Home & Hosp. for Aged, 50-56. Oak Ridge Inst. Nuclear Studies, 48 & 59; coun. arteriosclerosis, Am. Heart Asn; adj. assoc. prof. occup. med, sch. pub. health, Columbia Univ, 65- Cert. Merit, Am. Med. Asn, 50. A.U.S, 42-46, Capt. AAAS; Am. Chem. Soc; Soc. Exp. Biol. & Med; fel. Am. Inst. Chem; N.Y. Acad. Sci; Soc. Nuclear Med; fel. Col. Clin. Pharmacol. & Chemother; Asn. Clin. Sci. Chemistry of disease; a new anticoagulant for blood; aspartic acid; higher polycarboxylic acids as anti-coagulants for blood; clinical pharmacology and toxicology. Address: Clinical Labs, Brookdale Hospital Medical Center, Brookdale Plaza & Linden Blvd, Brooklyn, NY 11212.

GREENBLATT, IRWIN M, b. Brooklyn, N.Y, June 4, 30; m. 55; c. 3. GENETICS, BOTANY. B.S, Ohio State, 53; M.S, Wisconsin, 55, Ph.D.(genetics), 59. Res. assoc. genetics, Wisconsin, 59-60; asst. prof. biol, Marquette Univ, 60-66; Northwest. Univ, 66-68; ASSOC. PROF. GENETICS, UNIV. CONN, 68- Nat. Sci. Found. & Nat. Insts. Health grants, 61- Consult, Teweles Seed Co, Wis, 64-68. Chem.C, U.S.A, 55-56. Fel. AAAS; Genetics Soc. Am; Am. Genetic Asn; Bot. Soc. Am. Genetics of regulatory mechanisms as seen in higher plant material; cytogenetics of maize and alfalfa; root tissue culture of maize callus; alfalfa; tissue culture of maize and tobacco. Address: Dept. of Genetics and Cell Biology, University of Connecticut, Storrs, CT 06268.

GREENBLATT, JAYSON H(ERSCHEL), b. Montreal, Que, Mar. 5, 22; m. 44; c. 2. PHYSICAL CHEMISTRY, ELECTROCHEMISTRY. B.Sc, Dalhousie, 42, M.Sc, 43; Nat. Res. Coun. Can. stud, McGill, 46-48, Ph.D, 48; Nat. Defense Col. Can, 62-63. Res. chemist, Internal Ballistics Res. Lab, Que, 43-45; Can. Armament Res. & Develop. Estab, 45-46; NAVAL RES. ESTAB, 46-59, head chem. sect, 59-62, dockyard lab, 63-64, SUPT. ENG. PHYSICS WING, 64- Fel. Chem. Inst. Can. Physical chemistry and electrochemistry as applied to corrosion. Address: Engineering Physics Wing, Naval Research Establishment, Fleet Mail Office, Halifax, N.S, Can.

GREENBLATT, MARTHA, b. Hungary, Jan. 1, 41; U.S. citizen; m. 59; c. 1. INORGANIC CHEMISTRY, CRYSTALLOGRAPHY. B.Sc, Brooklyn Col, 62; Ph.D.(chem), Polytech. Inst. Brooklyn, 67. Res. assoc. x-ray diffraction, N.Y. Univ, 67; from asst. prof. to RES. ASSOC. CHEM, POLYTECH. INST. BROOKLYN, 67- Am. Chem. Soc; Am. Crystallog. Asn. Crystal growth; solid-state chemistry; crystal structure determination by x-ray diffraction; spectral properties of solids. Address: Dept. of Chemistry, Polytechnic Institute of Brooklyn, 333 Jay St, Brooklyn, NY 11201.

GREENBLATT, MELVIN, b. New York, N.Y, Sept. 25, 29; m. 52; c. 3. PATHOLOGY. B.A, N.Y. Univ, 51; M.D, Univ. Chicago, 55. Chief resident path, Mt. Sinai Hosp, Cleveland, Ohio, 58-59; consult. pathologist, San Antonio Zool. Soc, Tex, 59-61; assoc. pathologist, Mt. Sinai Hosp, Chicago, Ill, 61-63; asst. prof. path, Chicago Med. Sch, 62-65, ASSOC. PROF. oncol. & path, 66-68; PROF. PATH, UNIV. NEBR, COL. MED, 69- Sr. consult. pathologist, Eppley Inst, Omaha, Nebr, 68- Award, Angiol. Res. Found, 65. U.S.A, 59-61, Capt. AAAS; fel. Col. Am. Path; fel. Am. Soc. Clin. Path; Am. Asn. Path. & Bact; Am. Med. Asn. Experimental pathology, especially angiology and tumor biology. Address: Eppley Institute for Research in Cancer, University of Nebraska College of Medicine, 42nd & Dewey Ave, Omaha, NE 68105.

GREENBLATT, MILTON, b. Boston, Mass, June 29, 14; m. 41; c. 2. PSYCHIATRY. A.B, Tufts Col, 35, M.D, 39. Charleton res. fel. & instr. physiol, sch. med, Tufts, 39-40; intern med, Beth Israel Hosp, 40-41; psychiat, Mass. Ment. Health Center, 41-42, dir. electroencephalog. lab, 42-63; prof. psychiat, sch. med, Tufts, 63-67; COMNR, MASS. DEPT. MENT. HEALTH, 67- Asst, Harvard Med. Sch, 43-48, clin. assoc, 50-53, asst. clin. prof, 53-58, assoc. clin. prof, 58-63, lectr, 63-, dept. soc. rels, univ, 57-63; Barrera mem. lectr, Albany Med. Col, 55; Strauss mem. lectr, Hillside Hosp, 62; Alpha Omega Alpha lectr, sch. med, Tufts, 63; Bergendahl mem. lectr; lectr, sch. med, Boston, 63. Sr. physician, Mass. Ment. Health Ctr, 43-45, dir. labs. & res, 46-63, clin. psychiat, 53-57, asst. supt, 57-63, mem. med. exec. comt, courtesy staff, Beth Israel & Bournewood Hosps, Boston; vis. physician, Mass. Mem. Hosp; consult, Vet. Admin. Hosp, Brockton, Mass; supt, Boston State Hosp, 63-67; ed-in-chief, Seminars in Psychiat, 68-; dir, Am. Bd. Psychiat. & Neurol, 68- AAAS; fel. Am. Psychiat. Asn.(Hofheimer Prize, 52); Am. Col. Neuropsychopharmacol.(asst. secy-treas, 62, pres, 64); Am. Psychopath. Asn.(Samuel Hamilton Award, 71, pres, 70-71); Col. Int. Neuropsychopharmacol. Address: Massachusetts Dept. of Mental Health, 190 Portland, Boston, MA 02114.

GREENBLATT, ROBERT B(ENJAMIN), b. Montreal, Que, Can, Oct. 12, 06; nat; m. 32; c. 3. ENDOCRINOLOGY. B.A, McGill, 28, M.D, 32; hon. Dr, Univ. Bordeaux, 70. Asst. prof. path, MED. COL. GA, 36-37, path. & gynecol, 37-39, prof. exp. med, 39-43, PROF. ENDOCRINOL, 45- Responsible investr, Office Sci. Res. & Develop, 42-43; Special consult, U.S. Pub. Health Serv, 41-; consult, U.S. Army, 46-; U.S. Veterans Facility, 46-; Long Mem. award, 41. U.S.C.G, 43, Comdr. AAAS; Endocrine Soc; Am. Med. Asn. Endocrinology; experimental gynecology; infertility. Address: Dept. of Endocrinology, Medical College of Georgia, Augusta, GA 30902.

GREENBLOTT, BERNARD JEROME, b. Binghamton, N.Y, Apr. 4, 27; m. 54; c. 4. MECHANICAL ENGINEERING. B.S.M.E, Clarkson Technol, 52; M.M.E, Syracuse, 56; M.S, Mass. Inst. Technol, 63. Jr. engr, Int. Bus. Mach. Corp, 52-55, assoc. engr, 55-58, proj. engr, 58-59, develop. engr, 59-61, mgr. mech. technol, 59-63, sr. engr, 61-63, asst. to lab. mgr, 63-64, mem. staff corp. plans & controls, 64-65, mgr. technol, SYSTS. DEVELOP. DIV, IBM CORP, 65-71, MGR. SYST. STORAGE, 71- Mem. sem, honors prog, N.C. State Col, 61; Sloan fel, sch. indust. mgt, Mass. Inst. Technol, 62-63; mem, col. planning, Inst. Mgt. Sci, 64-65. U.S.A.A.F, 45-48, Sgt. Electromagnets; printing; fluid amplifiers; technology planning; industrial management. Address: Systems Development Division, IBM Corp, Poughkeepsie, NY 12602.

GREENBURG, LEONARD, b. N.Y.C, Aug. 16, 92; m. 42. PUBLIC HEALTH. C.E, Columbia, 15; Ph.D.(pub. health), Yale, 23, M.D, 30. Sanit. engr, State Pub. Serv. Comn, N.Y, 15-16; engr, Winchester Arms Co, Conn, 16-18; sanit. engr, U.S. Pub. Health Serv, 18-32; assoc. dir, Pierce Lab. Hyg, Conn, 32-34; health off, New Haven, Conn, 34-35; exec. dir. div. indust. hyg, State Dept. Labor, N.Y, 35-52; comnr, city dept. air pollution control, New York, 52-60; prof. PREV. MED. & COMMUNITY HEALTH, ALBERT EINSTEIN COL. MED, YESHIVA UNIV, 60-69, chmn. dept, 60-66, EMER. PROF, 69- Assoc. clin. prof, post-grad. med. sch, N.Y. Univ, 51-; vis. prof, Albert Einstein Col. Med, Yeshiva Univ, 58. Am. Indust. Hyg. Asn. (Cummings Mem. Award, 52); Am. Soc. Heat, Refrig. & Air-Conditioning Eng; fel. Am. Pub. Health Asn; Am. Med. Asn. Health administration; industrial hygiene; air pollution control; ventilation; occupational diseases. Address: 44 W. 77th St, New York, NY 10024.

GREENE, ALBERT GODFREY, JR, b. Providence, R.I, Sept. 20, 25; m. 50; c. 3. PLANT PHYSIOLOGY. B.S, Kent State, 50; M.S, Ohio State, 55, Ph.D. (plant physiol), 67. ASST. DIR. MARINE INST, UNIV. GA, 62- U.S.N.R, 43-46; U.S.A.R, 50-, Lt. Col. Bot. Soc. Am; Am. Soc. Plant Physiol; Atlantic Estuarine Res. Soc; Am. Inst. Biol. Sci. Carbon dioxide fixation; uptake of certain essential ions; chemical composition of coastal halophytes; metabolism of germinating seeds. Address: University of Georgia Marine Institute, Sapelo Island, GA 31327.

GREENE, A(RTHUR) E, b. Phila, Pa, Aug. 8, 23; m. 53; c. 2. CELL BIOLOGY. A.B, Pennsylvania, 47; B.Sc, Phila. Col. Pharm, 49, M.Sc, 50, D.Sc. (bact), 52. Res. fel. virol, Children's Hosp. of Phila, 52-53, res. assoc, Polio Res. Lab, 53-56, S.Jersey Med. Res. Found, 56-57; res. virologist, Nat. Drug Co. of Phila, 57-59; virologist, Smith, Kline & French Labs, 59-60; HEAD CELL BIOL. DEPT, INST. MED. RES, 61- Thomas H. Powers scholar, Phila. Col. Pharm. & Sci, 49, lectr. virol, 56-, vis. asst. res. prof. vet. virol, 62-64; res. assoc. surg, Pa. Med. Sch, 64-; lectr. virol, Phila.

Col. Osteopath. Med, 61-; vis. assoc. prof. microbiol, Jefferson Med. Col, 68- Dipl. Am. Bd. Microbiol, 65. U.S.A, 42-46. AAAS; Am. Soc. Microbiol; Tissue Culture Asn; Soc. Cryobiol; N.Y. Acad. Sci. Cell biology; preservation and characterization of cell cultures; cryobiology of cells and organs; techniques for the species identification of insect and animal cell lines; studies on genetic and biochemical cell cultures; virus chemotherapy and vaccines. Address: Dept. of Cell Biology, Institute for Medical Research, Copewood St, Camden, NJ 08103.

GREENE, ARTHUR FRANKLIN, b. Hartford, Conn, Dec. 18, 39; m. 63; c. 2. ELEMENTARY PARTICLE PHYSICS. B.S, Worcester Polytech, 61, M.S, 63; Ph.D.(exp. elem. particle physics), Tufts, 67. Physicist, U.S. Naval Res. Lab, D.C, summer 61 & 62; asst, Worcester Polytech, 61-63; Tufts, 63-67; physicist, div. res, U.S. Atomic Energy Comn, 67-69; RES. ASSOC, HIGH ENERGY PHYSICS, ARGONNE NAT. LAB, 69- Sig.C, U.S.A.R, 67-69, Capt. Am. Phys. Soc. Experimental high energy physics; elementary particle research using bubble chambers and wire spark chambers. Address: High Energy Physics Division, Argonne National Lab, 9700 S. Cass Ave, Argonne, IL 60439.

GREENE, ARTHUR FREDERICK, JR, b. Cleveland, Ohio, Sept. 28, 27; m. 57. ANALYTICAL & INORGANIC CHEMISTRY. B.Sc, Ohio State, 51; M.Sc, Case Western Reserve, 61; Surrey, 61-62. Tech. serv, R.O. Hull & Co, Inc, 55-61; analyst, HARSHAW CHEM. CO. DIV, KEWANEE OIL CO, 62-64, RES. ANALYTICAL CHEMIST, 64- George B. Hogaboom Mem. Award, 69. Sig.C, A.U.S, 46-47. Am. Chem. Soc; The Chem. Soc. Development of new analytical methods; thermal analysis techniques for synthesis and characterization of inorganic materials; use of specific ion electrodes for rapid analysis and pollution control. Address: Research Analytical Lab, Harshaw Chemical Co. Division of Kewanee Oil Co, 1945 E. 97th St, Cleveland, OH 44106.

GREENE, BARBARA E, b. Joliet, Ill, May 9, 35. FOOD SCIENCE, NUTRITION. B.S, Fla. South. Col, 57; M.S, Fla. State, 62, Ph.D.(food, nutrit), 66. Off. clerk, Anderson Dent. Supply Co, 57-58; Merrill, Lynch, Pierce, Fenner & Smith, Inc, 58-60; instr. food sci. & nutrit, Colorado State, 66-68; ASST. PROF. food & nutrit. & dairy sci. & indust, Iowa State Univ, 69; FOOD & NUTRIT, UNIV. GA, 69- Inst. Food Technol; Am. Oil Chemists' Soc. Lipid oxidation in relation to color and flavor in fresh and irradiated meat. Address: Dept. of Food & Nutrition, School of Home Economics, Dawson Hall, University of Georgia, Athens, GA 30601.

GREENE, BETTYE W(ASHINGTON), b. Palestine, Tex, Mar. 20, 35; m. 55; c. 3. PHYSICAL & COLLOID CHEMISTRY. B.S, Tuskegee Inst, 55; Off. Naval Res. fel, Wayne State, 61-65, Ph.D.(phys. chem), 65. Res. chemist, DOW CHEM. CORP, 65-70, SR. RES. CHEMIST, 70- AAAS; Am. Chem. Soc; Sci. Res. Soc. Am. Development of micro method for surface tension measurements; a light scattering method for determining size distributions in colloid systems; characterization of polymers and latexes. Address: Physical Research Lab, Dow Chemical Corp, Midland, MI 48640.

GREENE, C(HARLES) E(DWIN), b. Aurora, Ill, Mar. 17, 19; m. 43; c. 6. ORGANIC CHEMISTRY. B.S, Univ. Notre Dame, 41, M.S, 47, Ph.D.(chem), 49. Chemist, Reilly Tar & Chem. Co, 41-46; sr. res. chemist, Gen. Tire & Rubber Co, 49-69; SR. ENGR, BRUNSWICK CORP, 69- Am. Chem. Soc; Soc. Plastics Eng. Monomers and polymers; radomes and defense products. Address: 908 Prater Lane, Marion, VA 24354.

GREENE, CHARLES H(ERBERT), b. Troy, Pa, Sept. 26, 04; m. 30; c. 3. CHEMISTRY. A.B, Haverford Col, 26; M.A, Harvard, 27, Ph.D.(chem), 31. Res. chemist, Corning Glass Works, 30-31; instr. chem, Harvard, 31-37; res. chemist, Corning Glass Works, 37-53; prof. glass technol. & chmn. dept, State Univ. N.Y. Col. Ceramics, Alfred Univ, 53-70; RETIRED. Consult; mem, Int. Comn. on Glass. Fel. AAAS; fel. Am. Ceramic Soc; Ger. Soc. Glass Technol; Span. Ceramic Soc. Atomic weights; solubility; hydrogen and oxygen isotope abundance ratio; glass strength and melting. Address: P.O. Box 804, Alfred, NY 14802.

GREENE, CHARLES R(ICHARD), b. Chicago, Ill, Oct. 3, 23; m. 47; c. 2. PHYSICAL & ORGANIC CHEMISTRY. B.S, Chicago, 48, S.M, 49, Ph.D. (phys. & org. chem), 52. Res. chemist dermatol. cancers, Chicago Med. Sch, 51; prof. chem, George Williams Col, 51-52; res. chemist, Standard Oil Co. Ind, 52-54; Shell Develop. Co, 54-64, res. supvr, 64-67, mgr. prod, Shell Chem. Co, N.Y, 67-68, mgr. exp. opers, SHELL DEVELOP. CO, 68-69, MGR. CHEM. ENG, 69- U.S.N.R, 42-46. AAAS; Am. Chem. Soc; Am. Inst. Chem; Am. Inst. Chem. Eng. Reaction kinetics; high polymers; synthetic rubber; petrochemicals. Address: Shell Development Co, P.O. Box 24225, Oakland, CA 94623.

GREENE, DARYLE E, b. Garfield, Ark, June 27, 32; m. 54; c. 4. NUTRITION, BIOCHEMISTRY. B.S, Arkansas, 54, M.S, 55; Ph.D.(animal sci), Illinois, 60. Asst. mgr, turkey res. div, Ralston Purina Co, 60-62, mgr, 62-64; assoc. prof. poultry nutrit, Arkansas, 64-65; DIR. POULTRY RES, RALSTON-PURINA CO, 66- Sig.C, 55-57, 1st Lt. Poultry Sci. Asn; Animal Nutrit. Res. Coun; Am. Soc. Animal Sci. Amino acid nutrition; unidentified growth factors; mineral metabolism; biological availability of nutrients in feed ingredients. Address: Ralston Purina Co, Checkerboard Square, St. Louis, MO 63188.

GREENE, DAVID C, b. Elyria, Ohio, Nov. 24, 22; m. 49; c. 4. PHYSICS, ACOUSTICS. B.A, Oberlin Col, 49; Maryland, 49-53; M.S, Pa. State, 59. Physicist, U.S. Naval Ord. Lab, Md, 50-53; sr. engr, Cook Res. Labs, Ill, 53-55; physicist & res. assoc, ord. res. lab, Pa. State, 55-62; physicist & head acoustics & electronics sect, torpedo supporting res. br, antisubmarine warfare off, U.S. Bur. Naval Weapons, 62-66, acting head acoust. br, acoust. & electromagnetics div, res. & tech. directorate, Naval Ord. Systs, Command Hq, D.C, 66-67; sr. res. scientist, Pac. Northwest Labs, Battelle Mem. Inst, 67-69; SR. STAFF ENGR, SENSOR SYSTS. DEPT, ELECTRONIC SYSTS. LAB, TRW SYSTS, WASH. OPERS, 69- U.S.N.R, 42-45. Acoust. Soc. Am; Am. Phys. Soc; Am. Asn. Physics Teachers. Underwater acoustics; vibration; electroacoustics. Address: 6502 El Nido St, McLean, VA 22101.

GREENE, DAVID G(ORHAM), b. Buffalo, N.Y, Feb. 5, 15; m. 46; c. 4. CARDIOLOGY. A.B, Princeton, 36; M.D, Harvard, 40. Fel. path, Banting Inst, Toronto, Can, 40-41; intern med, Presby. Hosp, N.Y, 41-42, asst. res, 45-46; res. fel, col. physicians & surgeons, Columbia, 46-48; STATE UNIV. N.Y. BUFFALO, 48-50, assoc, 50-51, asst. prof, 51-55, Harry M. Dent Prof. clin. res. in cardiovasc. disease, 56-70, PROF. MED, 70-, ASSOC. PROF. PHYSIOL, 70-, asst, 50-57, asst. clin. prof, 57-70. Med.C, 42-46, Maj. Am. Heart Asn; fel. Am. Col. Physicians; fel. Am. Col. Cardiol; fel. Am. Col. Chest Physicians; Am. Physiol. Soc; Am. Fedn. Clin. Res. Cardiopulmonary diseases. Address: Dept. of Medicine, State University of New York at Buffalo, 100 High St, Buffalo, NY 14203.

GREENE, DAVID H(IRDLER), b. Rolla, Mo, Dec. 29, 14; div; c. 1. ORGANIC & PHYSICAL CHEMISTRY. B.S. (chem), Okla. Agr. & Mech. Col, 39. Chief chemist emulsions, Kato Chem. Co, 39-41; inspector, seafood U.S. Food & Drug Admin, 41-42; prof. math. & physics, Spartan Sch. Aeronaut, 42-43; chief res. chemist, acetylene from nat. gas, Danciger Oil & Ref. Co, 43-46; detergents, Turco Prod, 46-47; owner, D.H. Greene & Assocs, 47-52; chief chemist detergents, Universal Detergents, Inc, 52-58; consult. chemist, 58-67; chief chemist, West. Smelting & Ref. Co, Inc, 67-69; James Shields Jr. & Co, 69; CONSULT. CHEMIST, 70- Detergents and surface active compounds, emulsions, chemical assists in the recovery of crude petroleum; pyrolysis of natural gas to synthesize acetylene and aromatic hydrocarbons; synthetic rubber; solvent extraction; commercial chemical formulations; instruments; electron tube design; high voltage electronics. Address: 11581 Cactus Dr, Desert Hot Springs, CA 92240.

GREENE, EDWARD F(ORBES), b. New York, N.Y, Dec. 29, 22; m. 49; c. 4. PHYSICAL CHEMISTRY. A.B, Harvard, 43, A.M, 47, Ph.D.(chem), 49. Chemist, Shell Oil Co, 43-44; mem. staff, Los Alamos Sci. Lab, 49; res. assoc. CHEM, BROWN UNIV, 49-51, instr, 51-53, asst. prof, 53-57, assoc. prof, 57-63, PROF, 63 Nat. Sci. Found. sr. fel, Bonn, 59-60, Calif. Inst. Technol, 66-67. U.S.N.R, 44-46. Am. Chem. Soc; Am. Phys. Soc; Combustion Inst. Structure of shock waves; rapid high temperature reactions; reactions in molecular beams. Address: Dept. of Chemistry, Brown University, Providence, RI 02912.

GREENE, ELIAS L(OUIS), b. N.Y.C, Jan. 7, 32; m. 54; c. 2. IMMUNOLOGY, VIROLOGY. B.S, Brooklyn Col, 53; U.S. Pub. Health Serv. grant, Cornell Univ, 59-64, Ph.D.(virol. immunol), 64. Res. asst. virol, Sloan Kettering Inst. Cancer Res, 55-64; virologist-immunologist, res. inst, Henry Putnam Mem. Hosp, Bennington, Vt, 64-65; res. immunologist PEDIAT, L.I. Jewish Hosp, N.Y, 65-67; instr, SCH. MED, UNIV. MIAMI, 67-69, ASST. PROF, 69-; DIR. QUAL. CONTROL & RESPONSIBLE HEAD BIOL. PROD, N.AM. BIOL, INC, MIAMI, 70- Lab. technologist, Mercy Hosp, Rockville Centre, N.Y, 60-67; lectr, N.Y.C. Community Col, 67; lab. technologist, clin. lab, Miami Heart Inst, 67-68, consult. immunologist, organ transplant prog, 68-; Nat. Cystic Fibrosis Res. Found. fel, 68. U.S.A, 53-55. AAAS; Am. Soc. Microbiol; Harvey Soc; N.Y. Acad. Sci; Am. Asn. Clin. Chem; Am. Soc. Epidemiol; Am. Soc. Qual. Control. Immunologic and histochemical identification and enumeration of tissue antigens in normal and diseased states, especially in cystic fibrosis and liver diseases; properties of arthropod-borne and H-group viruses. Address: 2061 N. Bay Rd, Miami Beach, FL 33140.

GREENE, ERNEST GERALD, b. Murfreesboro, Ark, Apr. 30, 41; m. 64; c. 1. PHYSIOLOGICAL PSYCHOLOGY, PSYCHONEUROLOGY. B.A, San Jose State Col, 63, M.A, 65; U.S. Pub. Health Serv. fel, Univ. Ore, 67-68, Ph.D. (physiol. psychol), 68. Nat. Inst. Ment. Health fel. psychopharmacol, brian res. inst, Univ. Calif, Los Angeles, 70; ASST. PROF. PHYSIOL. PSYCHOL, UNIV. SOUTH. CALIF, 70- AAAS. Evaluation of the behavioral functions of brain structures, especially hippocampal function and the physiological and neurological bases of memory storage. Address: Dept. of Psychology, University of Southern California, University Park, CA 90007.

GREENE, ERNEST RINALDO, JR, b. Mobile, Ala, Jan. 26, 41; m. CHEMICAL ENGINEERING. B.A, Rice Univ, 62, B.S, 63; M.A, Princeton, 66, Ph.D.(chem. eng), 68. Tech. stud, Int. Paper Co, summer 62; asst. to W. Klip, med. sch, Univ. Ala, summer 63; asst. chem. eng, Princeton, 63-68; CHEM. ENGR, CENT. INTELLIGENCE AGENCY, 68- Am. Inst. Chem. Eng. Address: 7833 Enola St, Apt. 111, McLean, VA 22101.

GREENE, FRANK T, b. Saginaw, Mich, Nov. 26, 32; m. 59; c. 3. PHYSICAL CHEMISTRY. B.S, Michigan, 55; M.S, California, 57; Ph.D.(phys. chem), Wisconsin, 61. Res. assoc. chem, Kansas, 61-62; assoc. physicist, MIDWEST RES. INST, 62-63, sr. physicist, 63-68, PRIN. CHEM. PHYSICIST, 68- Chem.C, 59, 2nd Lt. Am. Chem. Soc. High temperature chemistry and thermodynamics; mass and optical spectroscopy; boron chemistry; molecular beams. Address: Lake Quivira, Kansas City, KS 66106.

GREENE, FREDERICK D(AVIS), II, b. Glen Ridge, N.J, July 9, 27; m. 53; c. 4. ORGANIC CHEMISTRY. A.B, Amherst Col, 49; A.M, Harvard, 51, Ph.D. (chem), 53. Res. assoc. chem, California, Los Angeles, 52-53; instr. ORG. CHEM, MASS. INST. TECHNOL, 53-55, asst. prof, 55-58, assoc. prof, 58-62, PROF, 62- Ed, J. Org. Chem, 62. U.S.N.R, 45-46. Am. Chem. Soc; The Chem. Soc. Mechanisms of organic reactions. Address: 25 Canterbury Rd, Winchester, MA 01890.

GREENE, GEORGE L(INDEN), b. Cleveland, Ohio, Apr. 10, 31; m. 63; c. 4. PLANT PATHOLOGY & PHYSIOLOGY. B.S, Michigan, 54, M.S, 55, Ph.D. (bot), 60; Wisconsin, 55-56. Assoc. plant pathologist, Tela R.R. Co, United Fruit Co, Honduras, 60-65; sr. plant physiologist, nuclear energy proj, Inter-Am. Inst. Agr. Sci, Orgn. Am. States, 65-69; pres, Hillside Corp, Ohio, 70-71; PLANT PATHOLOTIST, ESCUELA AGRICOLA PANAMERICANA, INC, 71- Am. Phytopath. Soc. Tropical crop plants; fungus physiology; commercial flower production; isotopes and radiation biology. Address: Escuela Agricola Panamericana, Inc, Apartado 93, Tegucigalpa, Honduras, C.A.

GREENE, GEORGE NYSTROM, b. Iowa City, Iowa, Nov. 1, 33; m. 57; c. 2. FISHERY BIOLOGY. B.A, Rice, 55; Harvard Law Sch, 55-56; M.S, Michigan, 60; Ph.D.(zool), Auburn, 64. Field asst. fresh water fisheries, Tex. Game & Fish Comn, 57-58, asst. proj. leader, 58-59; asst. prof. fisheries,

Auburn Univ, 64-70; MGR, KATY FARMS INC, 70- Am. Fisheries Soc. Fresh water fisheries; water chemistry and pollution; evolution. Address: 8714 Bob White St, Houston, TX 77036.

GREENE, GEORGE W, JR, b. Brooklyn, N.Y, Aug. 5, 19; m; c. 2. ORAL PATHOLOGY. B.S, Notre Dame, 41; D.D.S, Columbia, 44. Assoc. prof. ORAL PATH, sch. dent, Georgetown, 50-62; PROF. & CHMN. DEPT, SCH. DENT, STATE UNIV. N.Y. BUFFALO, 63-, U.S. Pub. Health Serv. cancer coord, dir. continuing dent. ed. & dir. diag. serv, 63-68, dir. grad. & postgrad. ed, 66-67. Sr. oral pathologist, cent. lab. path. anal. & res, Armed Forces Inst. Path, 53-60, chief environ. oral path. br, 54-60; secy, res. prog. comt. oral diseases, Vet. Admin, 58-62, asst. dir. dent. prof. serv, 60-62; chmn. bd. exam, Am. Bd. Oral Path, 63-65, pres, 65; consult. oral tumors, Am. Med. Asn; oral cytol. reproducibility study, cancer control prog, Nat. Ctr. Chronic Disease Control, 67-; path. dept, Roswell Park Mem. Inst; res. & develop. div, Off. Surg. Gen, U.S. Army. Dipl, Am. Bd. Oral Path. & secy-treas, 71-73; Am. Cancer Soc. Nat. Award, 70. Dent.C, U.S.A, 43-47. Am. Dent. Asn; fel. Am. Col. Dent; fel. Am. Acad. Oral Path.(pres, 64). Bone physiology; cryogenics; oral diseases; oral cancer; enosseous implantology. Address: Dept. of Oral Pathology, Capen Hall, School of Dentistry, State University of New York at Buffalo, Buffalo, NY 14214.

GREENE, GERALD L, b. Jewell, Kans, July 7, 37; m. 60; c. 2. ENTOMOLOGY. B.S, Kansas State, 59, M.S, 61; Ph.D.(entom, bot), Oregon State, 66. Res. asst. entom, Kansas State, 59-61; Oregon State, 61-64; ASST. ENTOMOLOGIST, Kentucky, 64-66; Cent. Fla. Exp. Sta, 66-70; ASST. PROF. ENTOM, AGR. RES. & EDUC. CTR, UNIV. FLA, 70- Entom. Soc. Am. Insect ecology and life tables; population dynamics; field crop insects. Address: P.O. Box 470, Agricultural Research & Educational Center, Quincy, FL 32351.

GREENE, GORDON WILLIAM, b. San Francisco, Calif, Feb. 8, 21; m. 42; c. 8. GEOPHYSICS. A.B, Fresno State Col, 54; M.S, Stanford, 57. Technician, Pac. Cement & Aggregates, Inc, 46-47, dist. engr, 47-55; geologist, U.S. GEOL. SURV, 56-57, GEOPHYSICIST, 57-70, NAT. CTR. EARTHQUAKE RES, 70- Sig.C, U.S.A, 42-45, Res, 45-63, Capt. AAAS; Am. Geophys. Union; Geol. Soc. Am; Seismol. Soc. Am. Earthquakes; tectonics; heat flow; permafrost; remote sensing. Address: National Center for Earthquake Research, U.S. Geological Survey, 345 Middlefield Rd, Menlo Park, CA 94025.

GREENE, HOKE S(MITH), b. Gray, Ga, Aug. 20, 06; m. 36. PHYSICAL & ORGANIC CHEMISTRY. A.B, Mercer, 27, hon. D.Sc, 63; M.S, 28, Ph.D.(chem), Cincinnati, 30. Res. chemist, Roessler & Hasslacher chem. dept, E.I. du Pont de Nemours & Co, 30-31; Am-Ger. exchange fel, Inst. Int. Ed, Tech. Hochschule, Germany, 31-32; res. & develop. chemist, E.I. du Pont de Nemours & Co, 32-34; asst. prof. chem. eng, UNIV. CINCINNATI, 34-38, assoc. prof, 38-45, chmn. grad. studies, dept. chem, 40-45, prof. chem. & head dept, 45-56, dean academic admin, 56-59, v.pres. & dean faculties, 59-67, V.PRES. FOR RES, 67-, dean grad. sch. arts & scis, 47-59. Blalock Medal. AAAS; Am. Chem. Soc; fel. Am. Inst. Chem. Synthetic organic chemistry; electric moments of organic compounds; electrolytic oxidation and reductions; industrial microbiology; synthesis of heterocyclic compounds and medicinals. Address: University of Cincinnati, Cincinnati, OH 45221.

GREENE, HOWARD LYMAN, b. Hackensack, N.J, Apr. 3, 35; m. 58; c. 3. CHEMICAL ENGINEERING. B.Chem.E, Cornell, 59, M.Chem.E, 63, Ford Found. summer fel, 64, univ. summer scholar, 65, NASA summer fel, 66, Ph.D.(chem. eng), 66; Nat. Sci. Found. summer grant, Bucknell, 62. Asst. prof. chem. tech, Broome Tech. Community Col, 59-63; consult, Int. Bus. Mach. Corp, N.Y, 63-64; asst. prof. CHEM. ENG, UNIV. AKRON, 65-70, ASSOC. PROF, 70- Summers, proj. engr, Nat. Aniline Div, Allied Chem. Corp, 55-57, analyst, E.I. du Pont de Nemours & Co, N.Y, 58, engr, Sandia Corp, N.Mex, 61, res. engr, Int. Bus. Mach. Corp, N.Y, 63, NASA Manned Space Center, Tex, 66, Pittsburgh Plate Glass Co, Ohio, 67. Am. Inst. Chem. Eng. Polymer rheology; natural convective heat transfer; direction of graduate study in these areas; biomedical engineering. Address: Dept. of Chemical Engineering, University of Akron, Akron, OH 44304.

GREENE, JACK BRUCE, b. Bloomington, Ind, June 9, 15; m. 40; c. 2. PHYSICS. A.B, Indiana, 37; M.S, Pittsburgh, 40, Ph.D.(physics), 42. Asst. PHYSICS, Pittsburgh, 37-41; instr, Illinois, 41-43; from instr. to ASSOC. PROF. & ASSOC. CHMN. DEPT, MARQUETTE UNIV, 45- Am. Phys. Soc; Am. Asn. Physics Teachers. Electronic structure of metals; cyclotron assembly and operation; electronic energy bands in the face-centered iron. Address: Dept. of Physics, Marquette University, Milwaukee, WI 53233.

GREENE, JACK C(ARPER), b. Roundup, Mont, June 3, 21; m. 53; c. 2. RESEARCH ADMINISTRATION, PHYSICS. B.S, Mass. Inst. Technol, 57; M.E.Ad, George Wash. Univ, 71. Group leader & elec. engr, Tenn. Eastman Corp, 44-46, instruments engr, 46; electronics engr, Atomic Energy Comn, 47-48, chief, standard eval. sect, radiation instruments br, 48-49, tech. coord. sect, 49-51, asst. chief, br, 51; consult, radiol. defense, Fed. Civil Defense Admin, 51-54, tech. dir, atomic test opers. staff, 54-55, DIR, coord. off, Off. Civil & Defense Mobilization, 59-62, POSTATTACK RES. DIV, OFF. CIVIL DEFENSE, 63- U.S.A, 42-46. Radiological phenomena and effects, radiological countermeasures, repair and reclamation of damage, postattack medical, health, welfare, recovery and maintenance systems; results of government research programs for application to postattack systems; integration of research results; preparation of reports of significant technical advances in a form usable for operational application. Address: Postattack Research Division, Office of Civil Defense, Washington, DC 20310.

GREENE, JAMES T, b. Rison, Ark, Aug. 8, 25; m. 54; c. 1. FORESTRY. B.S.F, Univ. Ga, 50, M.F, 56; Ph.D.(forestry), Univ. Minn, 65. Res. leader FORESTRY GENETICS, Ida Cason Callaway Found, 50-54; asst, SCH. FOREST RESOURCES, UNIV. GA, 54-56, asst. prof, 56-58, asst, 58-59, ASST. PROF, 59- C.Eng, 43-46, 1st Lt. AAAS; Am. Genetic Asn; Soc. Am. Foresters. Forest genetics. Address: School of Forest Resources, University of Georgia, Athens, GA 30601.

GREENE, JANICE L, b. Adams, N.Y, Mar. 12, 30. ORGANIC CHEMISTRY. B.A, Alfred, 51; Allied Chem. & Dye Co. fel, Pa. State, 54-55, Ph.D.(org. chem), 58. Asst. prof. chem, North Carolina, Greensboro, 55-59, assoc. prof, 59-60; sr. res. chemist, STANDARD OIL CO. OHIO, 60-66, RES. ASSOC, 66- AAAS; Am. Chem. Soc; Soc. Plastics Eng. Organic reactions; mechanisms and processes; small ring compounds; nitrile chemistry. Address: 28649 Jackson Rd, Chagrin Falls, OH 44022.

GREENE, JOHN M, b. Pittsburgh, Pa, Sept. 22, 28; m. 57; c. 1. PLASMA PHYSICS. B.S, Calif. Inst. Technol, 50; Nat. Sci. Found. fel, Rochester, 54, Ph.D.(physics), 56. RES. PHYSICIST, PLASMA PHYSICS LAB, PRINCETON UNIV, 56- Fel. Am. Phys. Soc. Magnetohydrodynamics; theoretical physics. Address: Plasma Physics Lab, Princeton University, Princeton, NJ 08540.

GREENE, JOHN W, JR, b. East Orange, N.J, July 25, 26; m. 54; c. 3. OBSTETRICS, GYNECOLOGY. B.S, Pittsburgh, 48; M.D, Pennsylvania, 52. Intern, univ. hosp, Pennsylvania, 52-53, resident OBSTET. & GYNEC, 53-56, res. fel, sch. med, Pennsylvania, 56-57, res. assoc, 57-59, asst. prof, 59-63; PROF. & CHMN. DEPT, MED. CTR, UNIV. KY, 63- U.S.A, 44-46, T/Sgt. Address: Dept. of Obstetrics & Gynecology, University of Kentucky Medical Center, Lexington, KY 40506.

GREENE, JOSEPH LEE, JR, b. Montgomery, Ala, May 5, 24; m. 48; c. 2. ORGANIC CHEMISTRY. B.S, Auburn, 48, M.S, 49; Ph.D.(org. chem), Emory, 57. Chemist, Tenn. Eastman Co, 50-55; instr, Emory, 55, res. assoc, 55-57; res. chemist, Shell Develop. Co, 57-58; sr. chemist & chief org. sect, Redstone Div, Thiokol Chem. Corp, 58-60; sr. res. chemist, South. Res. Inst, 60-68; asst. prof. CHEM, Alabama, 66-68; PROF, AUBURN UNIV, 68- Lectr, Birmingham-South. Col, 61-62; res. grant, Auburn, 69-70. C.W.S, 42-45. Am. Chem. Soc. Organic synthetic sequences of widely varying types. Address: Dept. of Chemistry, Auburn University, Auburn, AL 36830.

GREENE, JOSEPH S, b. Morganton, N.C, Feb. 29, 32; m. 54; c. 2. MATHEMATICS, OPERATIONS RESEARCH. B.S, Southwest Mo. State Col, 57; M.Ed, Univ. Mo-Columbia, 61; M.S, Okla. State Univ, 62; Ph.D.(math), Univ. Mo-Rolla, 70. Asst. prof. math, Col. of Sch. of Ozarks, 57-60, dean stud, 60-61; asst. prof. MATH, DRURY COL, 63-69, ASSOC. PROF, 69- U.S.N, 50-54. Math. Asn. Am; Opers. Res. Soc. Am. Address: Dept. of Mathematics, Drury College, Springfield, MO 65802.

GREENE, JOYCE M(ARIE), b. Pittsburgh, Pa, Mar. 10, 36. IMMUNOLOGY, MICROBIOLOGY. A.B, Bryn Mawr Col, 57, U.S. Pub. Health Serv. trainee, 66-67, Ph.D.(microbiol, physiol), 68; M.A, Wesleyan Univ, 60. Res. asst. biol, Wesleyan Univ, 57-58; res. assoc. microbiol, Amherst Col, 60-64; biochem, Ind. Univ, Indianapolis, 67-68; U.S. Pub. Health Serv. fel, Univ. Mich, 68-69; ASST. PROF. MICROBIOL, SMITH COL, 69- Summers, lectr, Univ. Mich, 69, instr, 70 & 71. AAAS; Am. Soc. Microbiol. Address: Dept. of Biological Sciences, Smith College, Northampton, MA 01060.

GREENE, KENNETH T(ITSWORTH), b. Alfred, N.Y, Feb. 7, 14; m. 58; c. 2. PHYSICAL CHEMISTRY. B.S, Alfred, 35; M.S, Rutgers, 37, Ph.D.(ceramics), 40. Instr. ceramics, Rutgers, 39-40; phys. chemist & Portland Cement Asn. fel, Nat. Bur. Standards, 40-45; chemist-petrographer, U.S. Bur. Reclamation, 45-52, chemist, 52-55; RES. PETROGRAPHER, RES. DEPT, IDEAL CEMENT CO, 55- AAAS; Am. Chem. Soc; fel. Mineral. Soc. Am; Geochem. Soc; Am. Ceramic Soc. Physical chemistry of silicate glasses; phase equilibria of portland cement clinker; petrography and chemistry of cement, concrete, rocks and other engineering materials; hydration reactions of cement. Address: Research Dept, Ideal Cement Co, P.O. Box 1609, Ft. Collins, CO 80521.

GREENE, KINGSLEY L, b. New York, N.Y, Nov. 26, 26; m. 46; c. 3. PLANT ECOLOGY. B.S, Cornell, 60, M.S, 61; Nat. Sci. Found. fel, Delaware, 65-66. Teacher, high sch, N.Y, 49-51, 56-58; prof. biol, East. Baptist Col, 61-66; dir. outdoor ed, Rose Tree Media Sch. Dist, Media, Pa, 66-67; ASSOC. PROF. NAT. RESOURCES, STATE UNIV. N.Y. AGR. & TECH. COL. MORRISVILLE, 67- Sci. consult, Dept. Pub. Instr, Pa, 62-63. AAAS; Bot. Soc. Am; Am. Nature Study Soc; Am. Sci. Teachers Asn. Water soluble growth substance in fungi and vascular plants; chemical interactions among plants within communities; chemical effects of higher fungi on vascular plants. Address: Dept. of Natural Resources, State University of New York Agricultural & Technical College at Morrisville, Morrisville, NY 13408.

GREENE, LAURENCE F(RANCIS), b. Chicago, Ill, Jan. 11, 12; m. 51; c. 4. UROLOGY. B.S, Univ. Chicago, 32; M.D, Harvard, 36; Ph.D.(urol), Univ. Minn, 41. CONSULT. UROL. & SURGEON, MAYO CLINIC, 41-; PROF. UROL, MAYO GRAD. SCH. MED, UNIV. MINN, 61-, assoc. prof, 53-61. Mem. bd. dirs, Minn. Symphony. Am. Fertil. Soc; Am. Urol. Asn; Am. Med. Asn; cor. mem. Mex. Urol. Asn; Int. Soc. Urol; Soc. Univ. Urol. Address: Mayo Clinic, Rochester, MN 55901.

GREENE, LEON C(HARLES), b. Rochester, N.Y, June 1, 25; m. 50; c. 3. PHYSIOLOGY, PHARMACOLOGY. B.Sc, Denison, 50; Baxter fel, Pennsylvania, 50-51, M.S, 51, univ. fel, 52-53, Ph.D.(physiol), 57. Physiologist, Aviation Med. Acceleration Lab, 54-58; sr. pharmacologist, SMITH, KLINE & FRENCH LABS, 58-60, group leader, 60-61, asst. sect. head pharmacol, 61-62, sect. head, 62-64, dir. biomed. activities, 64-66, assoc. dir. res. & develop. & mgr. gen. therapeut. dept, 66-67, dir. DEVELOP, 67-70, V.PRES, 70- Instr, sch. med, Univ. Pa, 57-58, assoc, 58- U.S.N, 43-46, 51-52. Am. Physiol. Soc; N.Y. Acad. Sci; Am. Chem. Soc. Cardiovascular; pain temperature sensation; analgesia; neurophysiology; neuropharmacology. Address: Smith, Kline & French Labs, 1500 Spring Garden St, Philadelphia, PA 19101.

GREENE, LEWIS J(OEL), b. New York, N.Y, Aug. 10, 34; m. 58; c. 2. BIOCHEMISTRY. B.A, Amherst Col, 55; Ph.D.(biochem), Rockefeller Inst, 62. Asst. biochemist, BROOKHAVEN NAT. LAB, 62-67, assoc. biochemist, 67-68, BIOCHEMIST, 68- Affiliate, Rockefeller Univ, 68- Am. Chem. Soc; Am. Soc. Cell Biol; Am. Soc. Biol. Chem. Protein chemistry. Address: Dept. of Biology, Brookhaven National Lab, Upton, L.I, NY 11973.

GREENE, MICHAEL P, b. New York, N.Y, June 20, 38; m. 63. SOLID STATE PHYSICS. B.Eng.Phys, Cornell, 60; M.S, California, San Diego, 62, Nat. Sci. Found. fel. & Ph.D.(physics), 65. Asst. prof. PHYSICS, California, Davis, 65; res. assoc, Brown, 65-67, ASST. PROF, UNIV. MD, 67-, ASST. CHMN. DEPT. PHYSICS & ASTRON, 71- Fulbright-OAS lectr, Nat. Univ. Eng, Peru, 70-71. AAAS; Am. Phys. Soc; Fedn. Am. Sci. Electronic properties of metals; theory of ultrasonic attenuation and transport properties in metals; diamagnetic effects in high magnetic fields. Address: Dept. of Physics & Astronomy, University of Maryland College of Arts & Sciences, College Park, MD 20742.

GREENE, NATHAN DOYLE, b. Steele, Ala, Mar. 2, 38; m. 60; c. 2. PARASITOLOGY, IMMUNOLOGY. B.A, Berea Col, 60; M.S, N.C. State, 62; Nat. Insts. Health fel, Emory, 62-65, Ph.D.(biol), 65. Med. parasitologist, nat. commun. disease ctr, U.S. Pub. Health Serv, Ga, 65-68; ASST. FOUND. SCIENTIST, SOUTHWEST FOUND. RES. & EDUC, 68- Co-investr. U.S.-Japan Coop. Med. Sci. Prog. grant, 68-72. Am. Soc. Parasitol; Am. Soc. Trop. Med. & Hyg; fel. Royal Soc. Trop. Med. & Hyg. Host-parasite relationships, particularly immunological mechanisms of innate and acquired resistance to schistosomiasis. Address: Dept. of Immunology, Southwest Foundation for Research & Education, Box 28147, San Antonio, TX 78228.

GREENE, NEIL E(DWARD), b. Toledo, Ohio, July 17, 36; m. 59; c. 2. HEAT TRANSFER, THERMODYNAMICS. A.B, Dartmouth Col, 59, M.S, 60; Ph.D. (phase equilibrium), Univ. Mich, 66. SR. RES. SCIENTIST, TECH. CTR, OWENS-CORNING FIBERGLAS CORP, 66- Am. Soc. Mech. Eng. Heat transfer and fluid mechanics associated with production of attenuating jets of molten glass. Address: 288 Granview Rd, Granville, OH 43023.

GREENE, NICHOLAS M(ISPLEE), b. Milford, Conn, July 11, 22; m. 46; c. 3. ANESTHESIOLOGY. B.S, Yale, 44, hon. M.A, 55; M.D, Columbia, 46. Surg. intern, Presby. Hosp, 46-47; instr. anesthesia, Harvard Med. Sch, 51-53; assoc. prof, SCH. MED, Rochester, 53-55, asst. prof. pharmacol, 53-55; PROF. ANESTHESIOL. & LECTR. PHARMACOL, YALE, 55-; DIR. ANESTHESIOL, YALE-NEW HAVEN HOSP, 55- Res, Mass. Gen. Hosp, 49-51, asst, 51-53; vis. fel, Royal Infirmary of Edinburgh, 51; anesthetist in chief, Strong Mem. Hosp, Rochester, 53-55; ed, Anesthesiology, 65- Dipl, Am. Bd. Anesthesiol. Med.C, 47-49, Lt.(jg). Am. Soc. Anesthesiol; Int. Anesthesia Res. Soc. Academic anesthesiology. Address: 789 Howard Ave, New Haven, CT 06504.

GREENE, NORBERT DENNIS, b. Rochester, N.Y, Sept. 7, 31; m. 55; c. 2. METALLURGICAL ENGINEERING. B.S, Rochester, 53; M.S, Ohio State, 54, Ph.D.(metall. eng), 57. Res. assoc, eng. exp. sta, Ohio State, 55-57; res. metallurgist, metals res. labs, Union Carbide Corp, N.Y, 57-59; asst. prof. electrochem. & corrosion, Rensselaer Polytech, 59-62, assoc. prof, 62-65, PROF, 65-69; DEPT. OF METALL. & DEPT. GEN. DENT, UNIV. CONN, 69- Mem. adj. faculty, Niagara, 58. Consult, chem, petrol. & metall. industs. & U.S. Govt, 59- AAAS; Electrochem. Soc; Nat. Asn. Corrosion Eng; Am. Soc. Metals (Geisler award, 62); Int. Soc. Electrochem. Applied electrode kinetics, especially corrosion, batteries, fuel cells, electrode-position and surface reactions; biomaterials; metallic implants. Address: Institute of Materials Science, U-136, University of Connecticut, Storrs, CT 06268.

GREENE, PAUL E, b. Chattanooga, Tenn, Sept. 25, 29; m. 60; c. 2. CHEMISTRY. B.A, Col. of Pacific, 51, M.A, 52; Ph.D.(chem), Ohio State, 55. Chemist, Shell Develop. Co, 55-60; Hewlett Packard Co, 60-62; mgr, solid state chem. dept, HP Assocs, PALO ALTO, 62-65, mat. & process chem dept, HP Labs, 65-69, DIR. SOLID STATE LAB, HEWLETT-PACKARD CO, 69- Am. Chem. Soc; Am. Phys. Soc; Electrochem. Soc. Aromatic hydrogenation kinetics on high surface alkali metals and nickel sulfides; kinetics of polymerization of base catalyzed epoxy systems; electrical and optical properties of semiconductors. Address: 1930 Mt. Vernon Ct. 6, Mountain View, CA 94040.

GREENE, PETER H(AROLD), b. N.Y.C, Mar. 30, 30. BIOLOGY. A.B, Amherst Col, 51; Simpson fel, from Amherst Col, Chicago, 51-52, univ. fel, 51-53, Nat. Sci. Found. fel, 53-55, Ph.D.(math. biol), 58. Asst. MATH. BIOL, UNIV. CHICAGO, 56-58, res. assoc, 58-63, ASST. PROF, 64-, INFO. SCI, 66- Mathematical theory of sensorimotor behavior; theory of perceiving and thinking machines; biological and mechanical self-organizing systems. Address: Committee on Mathematical Biology, University of Chicago, 5753 S. Drexel Ave, Chicago, IL 60637.

GREENE, RICHARD A(RNO), b. Cleveland, Ohio, Mar. 9, 32; m. 53; c. 3. PHYSICS. A.B, Univ. Calif, 53, M.A, Univ. Calif, Berkeley, 59. Physicist, Lawrence Radiation Lab, Univ, Calif, 53-69; MEM. STAFF, Inst. Defense Anal, 69-71; RES. & DEVELOP. ASSOCS, 71- Hydroneutronics; use of computers; strategic studies. Address: Research and Development Associates, 1918 Main St, Santa Monica, CA 90405.

GREENE, RICHARD L, b. Bridgeport, Conn, Aug. 26, 38; m. 64. SOLID STATE PHYSICS. B.S, Mass. Inst. Tech, 60; Ph.D.(physics), Stanford, 67. Res. assoc. physics, Stanford Univ, 67-70; RES. SCIENTIST, IBM RES. LAB, 70- U.S.N, 60-62, Lt.(jg). Am. Phys. Soc. Optical properties of magnetic insulators; superconductivity; photoconducting properties of organic insulators. Address: KO3-028, IBM Research Lab, Montery & Cottle Rds, San Jose, CA 95114.

GREENE, RICHARD W(ALLACE), b. San Francisco, Calif, Oct. 29, 41; m. 65; c. 2. INVERTEBRATE BIOLOGY, PLANT PHYSIOLOGY. B.A, Univ. Calif, Berkeley, 64; M.A, Univ. Calif, Los Angeles, 66, U.S. Pub. Health Serv. grant, 68-69, Ph.D.(zool), 69. U.S. Pub. Health Serv. training grant, Univ. Calif, Los Angeles, 69-70; ASST. PROF. BIOL, UNIV. NOTRE DAME, 70- AAAS; Am. Soc. Zool; Bot. Soc. Am. Symbiosis between algae and chloroplasts with invertebrates; chloroplast physiology; physiology of blue-green algae; cave invertebrates. Address: Dept. of Biology, University of Notre Dame, Notre Dame, IN 46556.

GREENE, ROBERT A(LVA), b. Pea Ridge, Ark, Apr. 26, 05; m. 34; c. 3. MEDICAL MICROBIOLOGY. B.A, Arkansas, 24; M.S, Okla. Agr. & Mech. Col, 26; McGill, 27-28; Ph.D.(agr. chem), Arizona, 33. Asst. chem, Okla. State, 24-26; asst. chemist, exp. sta, Rhode Island, 26-27; demonstr. biochem, McGill, 27-28; instr. agr. chem, Arizona, 28-33, asst. prof. bact. & dairy husb, 34-39, assoc. prof, 39-41, asst. agr. chemist, exp. sta, 28-37; dir. div. labs, State Dept. Health, Ariz, 44-46; Thomas Lab, Calif, 47; res. bacteriologist, Shellmar Prod. Corp, 48; prof. bact, UNIV. CALIF, IRVINE-CALIF. COL. MED, 48-50, med. microbiol, 50-69, acting exec. dept. bact, 48-50, exec, 50-61, chmn. dept. med. microbiol, 61-69, LECTR. ENVIRON. INTERACTIONS, 69- Dir. & dep. state health off, State Lab, Ariz, 35-41; consult, Los Angeles County Osteop. Hosp, 53-61; assoc. attend. staff, Los Angeles County Gen. Hosp, 61-; mem, Conf. State & Prov. Pub. Health Lab. Dirs. Dipl, Am. Bd. Med. Microbiol. U.S.A, 41-44, Maj. Fel. AAAS; Sci. Res. Soc. Am; Soc. Trop. Med. & Hyg; Am. Soc. Microbiol; fel. Am. Pub. Health Asn; Am. Asn. Bioanalysts; fel. Am. Inst. Chem; Am. Inst. Biol. Sci; Asn. Am. Med. Cols; Hist. Sci. Soc; N.Y. Acad. Med. Address: Curriculum of Environmental Interactions, California College of Medicine, University of California, Irvine, CA 92664.

GREENE, ROBERT CARL, b. Bridgeport, Conn, Aug. 14, 32; m. 55; c. 5. GEOLOGY. A.B, Cornell, 55; M.S, Tennessee, 59; Ph.D.(geol), Harvard, 64. Explor. geologist, N.J. Zinc Co, 55-57; GEOLOGIST, U.S. GEOL. SURV, 61- Geol. Soc. Am. Geology of Appalachians and New England; Paleozoic stratigraphy of eastern interior; tertiary volcanic geology and mineral deposits of eastern Oregon and northern Nevada. Address: U.S. Geological Survey, 345 Middlefield Rd, Menlo Park, CA 94025.

GREENE, RONALD C, b. Los Angeles, Calif, June 7, 28; m. 50; c. 2. BIOCHEMISTRY. B.S, Calif. Inst. Technol, 49, Atomic Energy Comn, fel, 51-53, McCollum fel. & Ph.D.(biochem), 54. Asst. scientist BIOCHEM, Nat. Insts. Health, 54-55, sr. asst. scientist, 55-57; instr, SCH. MED, DUKE UNIV, 57-58, assoc, 58-62, asst. prof, 62-71, ASSOC. PROF, 71-; CHIEF BASIC SCI. LAB, VET. ADMIN. HOSP, 69-, biochemist radioisotope serv, 57-69. U.S.P.H.S, Res, Sr. Asst. Scientist. AAAS; Am. Chem. Soc; Am. Soc. Biol. Chem; Am. Soc. Microbiol. Biochemistry of sulfonium compounds; regulation of methionine biosynthesis; metabolism of methionine and related compounds. Address: Dept. of Biochemistry, Duke University School of Medicine, Durham, NC 27706.

GREENE, THOMAS FREDERICK, b. Chicago, Ill, Nov. 5, 38; m. 62; c. 4. ASTRONOMY. B.S, Univ. Wash, 60, M.S, 61, NASA fel, 66-68, Ph.D.(astron), 68; Westminster Theol. Sem, 61-64. Proj. engr, Standard Pressed Steel Co, 63-64; engr, BOEING CO, 64-68, RES. ASTRONR, BOEING SCI. RES. LABS, 68- Affiliate asst. prof, Univ. Wash, 71- Am. Astron. Soc. Stellar abundances; Jovian atmosphere; solar flares. Address: Boeing Scientific Research Labs, Box 3999, Seattle, WA 98124.

GREENE, V(ELVL) W(ILLIAM), b. Winnipeg, Man, July 5, 28; nat; m. 56; c. 3. MICROBIOLOGY. B.S.A, Univ. Manitoba, 49; M.S, Univ. Minn, 51, Ph.D.(bact), 56. Instr. bact, Univ. Sask, 51-52; asst. animal indust, N.C. State Col, 52-53; asst. prof. bact, Univ. Southwest. La, 56-59; asst. prof. pub. health, Univ. Minn, 59-61; mgr. life sci. res, Litton Industs, 61-64; assoc. prof. pub. health, UNIV. MINN, MINNEAPOLIS, 65-70, PROF. ENVIRON. HEALTH & MICROBIOL, 70- Dipl, Am. Intersoc. Acad. Cert. Sanitarians. AAAS; Am. Soc. Microbiol; Am. Pub. Health Asn; fel. Am. Acad. Microbiol. Psychrophiles; environmental microbiology; aerobiology; exobiology; hospital infections; institutional sanitation. Address: 1108 Mayo Memorial, School of Public Health, University of Minnesota Medical Center, Minneapolis, MN 55455.

GREENE, WILLIAM ALBERT, b. Los Angeles, Calif, Sept. 13, 34; m. 57; c. 1. EXPERIMENTAL PSYCHOLOGY. B.A, San Diego State Col, 56, M.S, 63; Ph.D.(psychol), Univ. Fla, 64. Interim instr. PSYCHOL, Univ. Fla, 61-62, res. asst, 62-63; res. trainee, Vet. Admin. Hosp, Coral Gables, Fla, 63-64; from asst. prof. to assoc. prof, EAST. WASH. STATE COL, 64-70, PROF, 70- Res. affiliate, Regional Primate Res. Ctr, Seattle, Wash. U.S.A, 57-60. Soc. Psychophysiol. Res; Psychonomic Soc. Influence of operant and classical conditioning on the physiological functioning of the organism. Address: Dept. of Psychology, Eastern Washington State College, Cheney, WA 99004.

GREENE, WILLIAM A(LLAN), b. Worcester, Mass, June 15, 15; m. 45; c. 2. PSYCHOSOMATIC MEDICINE. B.A, Harvard Col, 36; M.D, Harvard Med. Sch, 40. Rotating intern, Mary Imogene Bassett Hosp, Cooperstown, N.Y, 40-42; asst. med. res, Strong Mem. Hosp, Rochester, N.Y, 46-48; Commonwealth Fund fel. MED. & PSYCHIAT, SCH. MED, UNIV. ROCHESTER, 48-50, instr. to assoc. prof, 50-67, PROF, 67- Cert, Am. Bd. Internal Med, 49. Med.C, U.S.A, 42-46, Maj. Fel. Am. Col. Physicians; Am. Psychosom. Soc. (secy-treas, 64-68, pres, 68). Psychological factors in the development and course of organic disease; neoplasias, coronary artery disease, hemodialysis and renal transplantation. Address: Dept. of Medicine & Psychiatry, University of Rochester Medical Center, 260 Crittenden Blvd, Rochester, NY 14620.

GREENE, WILLIAM G(OLDSMITH), b. Birmingham, Ala, Feb. 8, 19; m. 45; c. 3. INDUSTRIAL ENGINEERING. B.S, Ala. Polytech, 41. Admin. off, logistics plans, hq, U.S. Army Air Forces, 46, opers. analyst & engr, U.S. Air Force, 46-58, dep. chief tech. liaison team, opers. anal. off, 58-60, limited war team, 60-62; systs. eval. group, air defence tech. ctr, supreme hqs, Allied Powers (Europe), 62-63, chief opers. res. div, 64-65; opers. analyst, HQ, U.S. AIR FORCE, 66-71, OPERS. RES. ANALYST, ASST. CHIEF OF STAFF, STUDIES & ANAL, 71- U.S.A, 41-42; U.S.A.A.F, 42-46, Lt. Col.(Ret). Opers. Res. Soc. Am. Operations research; military systems; survival and operation under attack; development of operations research as occupational field in the government; combat data systems. Address: 604 South View Terr, Alexandria, VA 22314.

GREENE, WILLIAM WALLACE, b. Phoenix, Ariz, Aug. 26, 08; m. 33; c. 2. SURGERY. A.B, Stanford, 29, M.D, 33. Assoc. clin. prof. surg, sch. med, Univ. Calif, San Francisco, 60-71; SURGEON, KAUAI MED. GROUP, HAWAII, 71- Adj. clin. assoc. prof, sch. med, Stanford, 37-71. Dipl, Am. Bd. Surg, 42. Med.C, U.S.A, 42-45. Fel. Am. Med. Asn; fel. Am. Col. Surg. General surgical problems. Address: Kauai Medical Group, 3420 Kuhio Highway, Lihue, HI 96766.

GREENER, EVAN H, b. Brooklyn, N.Y, Sept. 8, 34; m. 57; c. 2. MATERIALS SCIENCE, METALLURGY. B.Met.E, Polytech. Inst. Brooklyn, 55; M.S, Northwestern, 57, Ph.D.(mat. sci), 60. Lab. instr, Polytech. Inst, Brooklyn, 55; Aitcheson fel. metall, Northwest. Univ, 55-58, res. fel, 58-59, prin. investr, 59-60; asst. prof. mat. sci, Marquette Univ, 60-63, assoc. prof, 63-64; assoc. prof. BIOL. MAT, NORTHWEST. UNIV, 64-69, PROF, 69-, CHMN. DEPT, 64- Fel. AAAS; N.Y. Acad. Sci; Am. Soc. Metals; Am. Inst. Mining, Metall. & Petrol. Eng; Int. Asn. Dent. Res. Materials science. Address: Dept. of Biological Materials, Northwestern University, 311 E. Chicago Ave, Chicago, IL 60611.

GREENEWALT, CRAWFORD HALLOCK, b. Cummington, Mass, Aug. 16, 02; m. 26; c. 3. CHEMICAL ENGINEERING. B.S, Mass. Inst. Technol, 22; hon. Sc.D, Univ. Del, 40, Northeast. Univ, 50, Boston Univ, 53, Phila. Col. Pharm, 55; hon. D.Eng, Rennselaer Polytech. Inst, 52, Polytech. Inst. Brooklyn, 54; hon. J.D, Columbia Univ. & Williams Col, 53; hon. D.C.S, N.Y. Univ, 54; hon. LL.D, Kenyon Col, 57, Kans. State Univ & Temple Univ, 60, Univ. Pa, Swarthmore Col. & Drexel Inst, 61, Univ. Notre Dame & Bowdoin Col, 65; hon. L.H.D, Jefferson Med. Col, 60; hon. Sc.D, Yale, 69, Hamilton Col, 70. Res. chemist, E.I. DU PONT DE NEMOURS & CO, INC, 22-33, res. supvr, 33-39, asst. dir. exp. sta, chem. dept, 39-42, mem. bd. dirs, 42, dir. chem. div, Grasselli Chem. Dept, 42-43, mgr. tech. div, explosives dept, 43-45, asst. dir. develop. dept, 45, asst. gen. mgr. pigments dept, 45, v.pres, 46-47, pres, 48-62, chmn. bd, 62-67, CHMN. FINANCE COMT, 67- Dir, Christiana Securities Co, 44-; Morgan Guaranty Trust Co. N.Y.C, 62; Boeing Co, 64- Trustee, Longwood Found, 42; Am. Mus. Natural Hist, 54-; Nat. Geog. Soc, 59-; Carnegie Inst. Mem. bd. regents, Smithsonian Inst, 56-; Cornell Lab. Ornith. William Proctor Prize, Sci. Res. Soc. Am, 57; advan. res. medal, Am. Soc. Metals, 58. With Atomic Energy Comn; Off. Sci. Res. & Develop; U.S.A, 44. Nat. Acad. Sci; AAAS; Am. Chem. Soc; Soc. Indust. Chem.(Chem. Indust. Medal, 52, Soc. Medal, 63); Am. Inst. Chem. (Gold Medal, 59); Am. Inst. Chem. Eng.(John Fritz Medal, 61); Am. Acad. Arts & Sci; Philos. Soc. Am; Nat. Audobon. Soc. High pressure reactions; catalysis; the separation of gaseous hydrocarbons; the partial pressure of water out of aqueous solutions of sulfuric acid; absorption of water vapor by sulfuric acid solutions. Address: E.I. du Pont de Nemours & Co, Inc, 9034 Du Pont Bldg, Wilmington, DE 19898.

GREENEWALT, DAVID, b. Wilmington, Del, Mar. 26, 31; m. 60; c. 6. GEOPHYSICS. B.A, Williams Col, 53; Ph.D.(geophys), Mass. Inst. Tech, 60. Instr. geophys, Mass. Inst. Tech, 60-64, lectr, 64-66; GEOPHYSICIST, U.S. NAVAL RES. LAB, 66- Am. Geophys. Union. Rock magnetism; electrical prospecting methods; gravity interpretation; sea floor magnetic field. Address: Code 8340, U.S. Naval Research Laboratory, Washington, DC 20390.

GREENFELD, SIDNEY H(OWARD), b. Baltimore, Md, Apr. 25, 23; m. 48; c. 4. CHEMICAL ENGINEERING. B.Ch.E, Delaware, 44; fel, Mass. Inst. Tech, 44-45, S.M, 45. Res. assoc. colloid chem, Mass. Inst. Tech, 45-48; res. chemist, soap chem, Fels & Co, 48; res. assoc, phys. & org. chem, Asphalt Roofing Indust. Bur, Nat. Bur. Standards, 49-57; res. engr, Calif. Res. Corp, 57-59; res. assoc, asphalt roofing indust. bur, NAT. BUR. STANDARDS, 59-68, mat. engr, bur, 68-69, SPEC. ASST. TO CHIEF, OFF. FLAMMABLE FABRICS, 69- Am. Chem. Soc; Am. Soc. Test. & Mat. Surface chemistry of limestone, chalk, lime and related materials; colloid chemistry of Portland cement, soaps and detergents; asphalts and related substances; fabric flammability. Address: Office of Flammable Fabrics, National Bureau of Standards, Washington, DC 20234.

GREENFIELD, ARTHUR J(UDAH), b. Oil City, Pa, Oct. 3, 34; m. 58; c. 3. SOLID STATE PHYSICS. B.S, Wayne State, 56; M.S, Chicago, 57, Raytheon fel, 60-61, Shell Oil fel, 61-62, Ph.D.(physics), 63. Res. assoc. physics, Chicago, 63-64; mem. tech. staff, Bell Tel. Labs, Inc, N.J, 64-67; ASSOC. PROF. PHYSICS, BAR-ILAN UNIV, ISRAEL, 67- Am. Phys. Soc. Electromagnetic and thermal properties of liquid and solid metals. Address: Dept. of Physics, Bar-Ilan University, Ramat-Gan, Israel.

GREENFIELD, DAVID WAYNE, b. Carmel, Calif, Apr. 21, 40; m. 71. ICHTHYOLOGY. A.B, Humboldt State Col, 62; Ph.D.(fisheries), Washington (Seattle), 66. Asst. prof. zool, Calif. State Col. Fullerton, 66-70; ASSOC. PROF. BIOL. SCI, NORTH. ILL. UNIV, 70- Res. assoc, Los Angeles County Mus. Natural Hist; mem. faculty, Assoc. Univs. Int. Educ. trop. res. ctr, Brit. Honduras. Am. Soc. Ichthyol. & Herpet; Soc. Study Evolution; Soc. Syst. Zool; Am. Fisheries Soc. Zoogeography; systematics of coral-reef fishes, particularly Holocentridae and Pomacentridae; zoogeography of marine and freshwater fishes; systematics of fishes of British Honduras. Address: Dept. of Biological Sciences, Northern Illinois University, DeKalb, IL 60115.

GREENFIELD, EUGENE W(ILLIS), b. Baltimore, Md, Nov. 27, 07; m. 29; c. 2. PHYSICS, ELECTRICAL ENGINEERING. B.E, Hopkins, 29, D.E, 34; Polytech. Inst. Brooklyn, 40-41. Asst, Nat. Elec. Light Asn, Hopkins, 29-33, res. assoc, 33-34; transmission engr, Pa. R.R, 34-35; res. engr, Anaconda Wire & Cable Co, 35-41, supvr. elec. lab, 41-50; asst. tech. dir, Kaiser Aluminum & Chem. Corp, 50-51, asst. plant mgr, 51-52, head elec. eng. res, 52-57, res. supvr, 57-58; PROF. ELEC. ENG. & DIR. DIV. INDUST. RES, WASH. STATE UNIV, 58-, CHMN. ELEC. POWER RES. & DEVELOP. CTR, 65-, ASST. DEAN COL. ENG, 70- Mem. cmt. elec. insulation, Nat. Res. Coun, 32-, exec. cmt, 48-, v.chmn, 48-49; consult. Civilian with U.S.N, 44. Am. Phys. Soc; Am. Soc. Eng. Educ; Am. Soc. Test. & Mat; Acoust. Soc. Am; fel. Inst. Elec. & Electronics Eng.(v.pres, 62-64; electronic achievement award, 64). Electrical insulation; electrical measuring instruments; application of insulation in the fields of power and communication; research and development of aluminum conductors; research administration. Address: Research Division, College of Engineering, Washington State University, Pullman, WA 99163.

GREENFIELD, GEORGE B, b. Brooklyn, N.Y, May 4, 28. RADIOLOGY, MEDICINE. B.A, N.Y. Univ, 49; Medicinae Doctorandus, State Univ. Utrecht, 56. Attending radiologist, Cook County Hosp, Ill, 61-69, asst. dir. diag. radiol, 66-69; PROF. RADIOL. & CHMN. DEPT, CHICAGO MED. SCH. & MT. SINAI HOSP, 69-; PROF. RADIOL, COOK COUNTY GRAD. SCH. MED, 66- Consult. radiologist, Vet. Admin. Hosp, Dwight, Ill, 63-65; attend. radiologist, Res. & Educ. Hosp, Chicago, 63-69; clin. assoc. prof, col. med, Univ. Ill, 67-69. U.S.A, 51. Am. Col. Radiol; Asn. Univ. Radiol. Address: Dept. of Radiology, Chicago Medical School, 2020 W. Ogden Ave, Chicago, IL 60612.

GREENFIELD, HAROLD, b. New York, N.Y, May 6, 23; m. 47; c. 3. ORGANIC CHEMISTRY. B.S, City Col. New York, 43; M.S, Polytech. Inst. Brooklyn, 48; Ph.D.(chem), Pittsburgh, 55. Org. chemist, Biochem. Res. Corp, N.Y, 48; phys. chemist, explosives res. sect, U.S. Bur. Mines, Pa, 48-50, org. chemist, org. chem. sect, 50-55, coal hydrogenation sect, 55-58; RES. SCIENTIST, UNIROYAL CHEM. DIV, UNIROYAL INC, 58- U.S.N, 43-46. AAAS; Am. Chem. Soc; Catalysis Soc. Heterogeneous and homogeneous catalysis; hydrogenation and reduction; oxo reaction; metal carbonyl chemistry; acetylene chemistry; coal chemistry; organic synthesis; high pressure reactions; rubber chemistry. Address: Uniroyal Chemical Division, Uniroyal Inc, Naugatuck, CT 06770.

GREENFIELD, H(ARVEY) S(TANLEY), b. Pass-a-Grille, Fla, Dec. 7, 24; m. 53; c. 3. PHYSICS. B.S, Utah State Univ, 50; M.S, Brigham Young Univ, 52; Ph.D.(aeronaut. & fluid mech), Glasgow Univ, 65. Asst. physics, Utah State Univ, 52-54, res. physicist, Dugway Proving Ground, 54-55, chief math. anal. br, 55-56, physics div, 56-58; sr. rocket engr, Thiokol Chem. Corp, 58-59, sr. physicist, 59-60, staff specialist, 60-62, scientist, 62-63, consult, 63-64; lectr, Glasgow Univ, 64-66; sr. numerical analyst, UNIV. UTAH, 68-69, assoc. res. prof. comput. sci. & asst. res. prof. surg, 69-70, RES. PROF. COMPUT. SCI. & ASSOC. RES. PROF. SURG, 70- Mem. adv. bd, Nat. Asn. Professions. U.S.N, 42-46. Assoc. fel. Am. Inst. Aeronaut. & Astronaut; N.Y. Acad. Sci; assoc. fel. Royal Aeronaut. Soc. Turbulence; hemodynamics; computer graphics. Address: Bldg. 512, Division of Artificial Organs, University of Utah, Salt Lake City, UT 84112.

GREENFIELD, IRWIN G, b. Phila, Pa, Nov. 30, 29; m. 51; c. 3. MECHANICAL METALLURGY, ELECTRON MICROSCOPY. B.A, Temple, 51; M.S, Pennsylvania, 54, Ph.D.(metall. eng), 62. Metallurgist, air mat. lab, Naval Air Exp. Sta, Pa, 51-53; res. metallurgist, metall. br, solid state physics div, labs. res. & develop, Franklin Inst, Pa, 53-56, sr. res. metallurgist, physics of metals br, 60-63; asst. prof. MECH. METALL, UNIV. DEL, 63-65, assoc. prof, 65-68, PROF, 68-, Res. Found. grant, 64-66, acting chmn. dept. mech. & aerospace eng, 70-71. Lectr, Drexel Inst, 61-64; Northeastern, 64; Nat. Sci. Found. grant, 64-66, 71-73; vis. prof, Stanford Univ, 69-70; Oxford, 70; Air Force Off. Sci. Res. grant, 71-72. Am. Inst. Mining, Metall. & Petrol. Eng; Electron Micros. Soc. Am; Sci. Res. Soc. Am; Am. Soc. Metals. Mechanical properties of materials; dislocation and point defect interaction in crystals; electron microscopy of thin films; irradiation damage to crystals; effect of surface on mechanical properties of materials; fatigue. Address: Dept. of Mechanical & Aerospace Engineering, University of Delaware, Newark, DE 19711.

GREENFIELD, JOSEPH C, JR, b. Atlanta, Ga, July 20, 31; m. 55; c. 3. CARDIOVASCULAR PHYSIOLOGY. B.A, Emory, 54, M.D, 56. Intern med, Duke Univ. Hosp, 56-57, jr. asst. resident, 57-58, sr. asst. resident, 58-59; clin. assoc, sect. clin. biophys, cardiol. br, Nat. Heart Inst, 59-62; assoc. MED, MED. CTR, DUKE UNIV, 62-63, asst. prof, 63-65, assoc. prof, 65-70, PROF, 70-, ASST. CHIEF. MED. SERV, VET. ADMIN. HOSP, 63-, clin. investr, 62-63. U.S. Pub. Health Serv. career develop. award, 65- Dipl, Am. Bd. Internal Med; dipl, Am. Bd. Cardiovasc. Disease. U.S.P.H.S, 59-62, Surgeon. AAAS; Am. Soc. Clin. Invest; Am. Physiol. Soc; fel. Am. Heart Asn; fel. Am. Col. Physicians; fel. Am. Col. Cardiol; Am. Fedn. Clin. Res. Electrocardiography; internal medicine. Address: Box 3246, Duke University Medical Center, Durham, NC 27710.

GREENFIELD, LAZAR JOHN, b. Houston, Tex, Dec. 14, 34; m. 56; c. 3. THORACIC SURGERY. Thomas R. Franklin scholar, Rice Univ, 53-54; M.D, Baylor Univ, 58. Intern surg, Johns Hopkins Hosp, 58-59, asst. res, 61-65, res, 65-66; sr. asst. surgeon, Nat. Heart Inst, Md, 59-61; CHIEF SURG. SERV, VET. ADMIN. HOSP, 66- Prof. surg, Med. Ctr, Univ. Okla, 66-; John & Mary R. Markle scholar, 68- Consult, Reynolds Army Hosp, Ft. Sill, Okla, 67- Dipl, Am. Bd. Surg. & Am. Bd. Thoracic Surg, 67. U.S.P.H.S, 59-61, Sr. Asst. Surg. Soc. Univ. Surg; Am. Physiol. Soc; Am. Thoracic Soc. Pulmonary circulation and surfactant; extracorporeal circulation; cardiac function. Address: Oklahoma Veterans Administration Hospital, 921 N.E. 13th St, Oklahoma City, OK 73104.

GREENFIELD, L(EONARD) J(ULIAN), b. New York, N.Y, May 18, 26. BIOCHEMISTRY. B.S, City Col. New York, 49; M.S, Miami (Fla), 51; Ph.D, Stanford, 59. Asst. biochem. marine wood borers, marine lab, Miami (Fla), 51-54; productivity of Gulf Stream, 54-55; biochem. marine inverts, Hopkins Marine Sta, Stanford, 55-59; from res. asst. prof. to ASSOC. PROF. BIOCHEM. & ECOL. PHYSIOL, MARINE LAB, UNIV. MIAMI, 59-, ASSOC. DEAN GRAD. SCH, 66-, CHMN. DEPT. BIOL, UNIV, 70-; DIR, PIGEON KEY MARINE STA, 69- U.S.A, 45-47. AAAS. Ecological physiology and ecological biochemistry of marine organisms; biological and chemical ecology of south Florida wetlands. Address: Dept. of Biology, University of Miami, Coral Gables, FL 33124.

GREENFIELD, M(OSES) A, b. Brooklyn, N.Y, Mar. 8, 15; m. 37; c. 2. MEDICAL PHYSICS. B.S, City Col. New York, 35; M.S, N.Y. Univ, 37, Ph.D. (physics), 41; George Wash. Univ, 39-40. Asst. physics, N.Y. Univ, 36-37; instr. physics, City Col. New York, 37-39; physicist, David Taylor Model Basin, U.S. Navy, 41-46; res. physicist, N.Am. Aviation, Inc, 46-48; chief spectros. & x-ray physics sect, Atomic Energy Proj, UNIV. CALIF, LOS ANGELES, 48-51, assoc. prof. DEPT. RADIOL, 48-56, PROF, 56-, DIR. MED. PHYSICS TRAINING PROG, 70- Consult, Wadsworth Vet. Admin. Hosp, 53-; U.S. Naval Hosp, San Diego, 59-; Calif. State Dept. Health; Food & Drug Admin, D.C, Bur. Radiol. Health, Div. Isotopes Develop, U.S. Atomic Energy Comn, 61-65; Am. specialist, U.S. Dept. State, S.Am, 57, 60, Southeast Asia, 64-65. Fel. Am. Phys. Soc; Radiation Res. Soc; Soc. Nuclear Med; Am. Nuclear Soc; N.Y. Acad. Sci; Am. Col. Radiol; Radiation Soc. N.Am. Medical physics; nuclear medicine. Address: Dept. of Radiology, Center for Health Sciences, University of California, Los Angeles, CA 90024.

GREENFIELD, ROBERT E(DMAN), JR, b. Champaign, Ill, July 26, 20; m. 44; c. 3. BIOCHEMISTRY. B.S, Duke, 42; M.D, Illinois, 45; M.A, California, 51. Intern, U.S. Marine Hosp, Wash, 45-46; asst. surgeon biochem. res, Nat. Cancer Inst, 47-48, sr. asst. surgeon, 48-52, surgeon, 52-55, sr. surgeon, 55-60, head sect. lab. biochem, 60-65, med. dir, 60-67, prof. dir. host tumor relations, grants & training, 65-67, chief prog. anal. & formulation br, 67-69; spec. asst. to asst. secy. health & sci. affairs, Dept. Health, Educ. & Welfare, 69-70; ASSOC. DIR. PROG. PLANNING & EVAL, NAT. INST. GEN. MED. SCI, 71- Asst. surgeon, Int. Labor, Welfare & Health Br, U.S. Dept. State, 47; mem. grad. adv. coun, George Washington, 64- U.S.N.R, 45-47. AAAS; Am. Chem. Soc; Am. Soc. Biol. Chem; Am. Med. Asn; Am. Asn. Cancer Res. Isolation, fractionation and metabolism of single cell suspensions; cellular interactions; host-tumor relations. Address: National Institute of General Medical Sciences, 9000 Rockville Pike, Bethesda, MD 20014.

GREENFIELD, ROY J(AY), b. N.Y.C, Apr. 8, 36; m. 61; c. 3. GEOPHYSICS. B.S, Mass. Inst. Technol, 58, M.S, 62, Ph.D.(geophys), 65. Assoc. engr, IBM Corp, 60-61, staff engr, 61-62; staff mem. seismol, Lincoln Lab, Mass. Inst. Technol, 65-68; ASST. PROF. GEOPHYS, PA. STATE UNIV, 68- Am. Geophys. Union; Soc. Explor. Geophys; Seismol. Soc. Am. Seismology; geoelectricity; seismology. Address: Dept. of Geology & Geophysics, College of Earth & Mineral Sciences, Pennsylvania State University, University Park, PA 16802.

GREENFIELD, SEYMOUR, b. N.Y.C, Jan. 18, 33; m. 62; c. 3. MICROBIOLOGY, BIOCHEMISTRY. B.A, Yeshiva Univ, 55; Case West. Reserve Univ, 59-63; M.A, Brandeis Univ, 60; Nat. Insts. Health fel, Pa. State Univ, 68-69, Ph.D.(microbiol), 70. Res. asst. biomed. eng, dept. phys. med, sch. med, Case West. Reserve Univ, 63-65, microbial physiol, dept. microbiol, 65-67; SR. BIOCHEMIST & GROUP LEADER, DIV. LABELED CHEM, NEW ENG. NUCLEAR CORP, 70- Am. Soc. Microbiol. Microbial physiology; enzymology; fatty acid and sterol synthesis; metabolism of pyruvic acid; tricarboxylic acid cycle; biosynthesis of radioactive compounds. Address: New England Nuclear Corp. Division of Labeled Chemicals, 575 Albany St, Boston, MA 02118.

GREENFIELD, STANLEY A, b. Omaha, Nebr, Mar. 16, 41; m. 64. ORGANIC CHEMISTRY. B.S, California, Berkeley, 63; M.S, Indiana, 65; Ph.D.(org. chem), Weizmann Inst, 67. RES. CHEMIST, ROHM & HAAS CO, SPRING HOUSE, 67- Am. Chem. Soc. Synthetic organic chemistry, especially fungicides, herbicides, biocides and insecticides. Address: 911 Tannerie Run Rd, Ambler, PA 19002.

GREENFIELD, STANLEY M(ARSHALL), b. New York, N.Y, Apr. 16, 27; m. 52; c. 2. METEOROLOGY, PHYSICS. B.S, N.Y. Univ, 50; Ph.D.(meteorol), Univ. Calif, Los Angeles, 67. Meteorol. aid, U.S. Weather Bur, 44-47; asst, eng. res. div, N.Y. Univ, 48-50; phys. scientist, Rand Corp, 50-71, head dept. geophys. & astron, 64-71; ASST. ADMINR. RES. & MONITORING, ENVIRON. PROTECTION AGENCY, 71- Sci. adv. to dir. res. & develop, U.S. Air Force, 59-61; mem. U.S. Air Force Sci. Adv. Bd, 65- U.S.N, 45-46. Am. Meteorol. Soc; Am. Geophys. Union; N.Y. Acad. Sci. Physics of the atmosphere; infrared; radio-active fallout; planetary sciences; radio wave propagation; cloud physics. Address: Environmental Protection Agency, 401 M St. S.W, Washington, DC 20460.

GREENFIELD, SYDNEY S(TANLEY), b. Brooklyn, N.Y, Nov. 28, 15. BOTANY. B.A, Brooklyn Col, 36, fel, 39-40; M.A, Columbia, 37, Ph.D.(bot), 41. Res. assoc. plant physiol, Columbia, 41-45, instr. bot, 43; asst. prof. biol, Newark, 45-46; RUTGERS UNIV, 46-49, assoc. prof, 49-59, PROF. BOT, 59-, CHMN. DEPT, 61- Teacher, pub. schs, N.Y, 37-45; chmn. sci. dept, Harlem evening high schs, 43-45. AAAS; Bot. Soc. Am.(ed, 'Plant Sci. Bulletin,' 59-62); Soc. Econ. Bot. Photosynthesis in Chlorella; mineral toxicity in plants; plant-growth substances; selenium poisoning and effects on plants; physiology of plant cells; economic botany. Address: Dept. of Botany, Rutgers University, Newark, NJ 07102.

GREENFIELD, WILBERT, b. Seven Springs, N.C, July 18, 33; m. 59; c. 2. PHYSIOLOGY. B.S, A&T State Univ. N.C, 56; M.S, Univ. Iowa, 58, Ph.D. (physiol), 60. Res. asst. physiol, Univ. Iowa, 57-60; head, dept. biol, JACKSON STATE UNIV, 60-67, assoc. dean, sch. liberal studies, 67, dean instr, 60-70, PROF. BIOL, 60-, DEAN ACAD. AFFAIRS, 70- Consult, Paper Co. Found. grant, high sch, Miss, 63-67; acad. dean's inst, Am. Coun. Educ, Univ. Chicago, 67; mentor, acad. admin. internship prog, 68-69. Cardiovascular and respiratory physiology dealing with cross circulation and peripheral blood flow; sickle cell anemia. Address: 1341 Rockdale Dr, Jackson, MS 39213.

GREENGARD, OLGA, b. Arad, Hungary, Jan. 13, 26; U.S. citizen; m. 54; c. 2. BIOCHEMISTRY. B.Sc, Univ. London, 51, Ph.D.(biochem), 55. Res. asst. BIOCHEM, inst. psychiat, Maudsley Hosp, Univ. London, 55-56; biochemist, Courtauld Inst. Biochem, Middlesex Hosp, London, 56-58; vis. scientist, Nat. Inst. Mental Health, 59; res. assoc, col. physicians & surgeons, Columbia Univ, 62-65; SR. RES. ASSOC, CANCER RES. INST, NEW ENGLAND DEACONESS HOSP, BOSTON, MASS, 65-; PRIN. ASSOC, HARVARD MED. SCH, 69-, res. assoc, 65-69. Am. Chem. Soc; Am. Soc. Biol. Chemists; Am. Soc. Cell Biol; Brit. Biochem. Soc; Harvey Soc. Regulation of enzyme synthesis in mammalian liver, in neoplastic tissues and in normal, developing organs during various stages of differentiation. Address: Cancer Research Institute, New England Deaconess Hospital, Boston, MA 02215.

GREENGARD, PAUL, b. N.Y.C, Dec. 11, 25; m. 54; c. 2. BIOCHEMISTRY. A.B, Hamilton Col, 48; Atomic Energy Comn. fel, Hopkins, 49-52, Lalor fel, 52-53, Ph.D.(biophys, biochem), 53. Fel. neurochem, Nat. Sci. Found, inst. psychiat, London, 53-54; enzymol, Nat. Found. Infantile Paralysis, Molteno Inst, Cambridge, 54-55; neurochem, Paraplegia Found, Nat. Inst. Med. Res, England, 55-56, Nat. Inst. Neurol. Diseases & Blindness, 56-58; dir. dept. biochem, Geigy Res. Labs, N.Y, 58-67; dept. neuropharmacol, inst. basic res. ment. retardation, N.Y. State Dept. Ment. Hyg, 67-68; PROF. PHARMACOL, SCH. MED, YALE, 68- Vis. scientist, Nat. Heart Inst, Nat. Insts. Health, 58-59; vis. assoc. prof, Albert Einstein Col. Med, 61-68, vis. prof, 68- U.S.N.R, 43-46. N.Y. Acad. Sci; Am. Soc. Pharmacol. & Exp. Therapeut; Am. Soc. Biol. Chem. Neurochemistry; chemical neurophysiology; microchemistry; enzymology; biochemical pharmacology. Address: Dept. of Pharmacology, Yale University School of Medicine, New Haven, CT 06510.

GREENHALL, ARTHUR MERWIN, b. New York, N.Y, Aug. 6, 11; m. 42; c. 2. MAMMALOGY, ECOLOGY. B.A, Michigan, 34, M.S, 35; Columbia, 39-41; N.Y. Univ, 41. Dir, Portland Zool. Park, Ore, 42-47; gen. curator animal div, Detroit Zool. Park, Mich, 47-53; curator mus, Royal Victoria Inst, Trinidad, W.I, 53-63; chief mammal sect, bird & mammal labs, U.S. SPORT FISHERIES & WILDLIFE, 63-68, MEM. STAFF, DIV. WILDLIFE RES, 63-; RES. ASSOC, U.S. NAT. MUS, SMITHSONIAN INST, 67-; BAT ECOLOGIST, FOOD & AGR. ORGN. UN, 68- Dir, Emperor Valley Zoo, Trinidad, 54-56; zoologist, Ministry Agr, Govt. Trinidad & Tobago, 54-63; expert rabies investr, Govt. Grenada, 55; lectr, Univ. Col. West Indies, 55-56; Rockefeller Found. travel grant, 56; mammalogist, Trinidad Regional Virus Lab, 56-63; WHO fel, 57; expert rabies investr, Govt. British Guiana, 59; mem. Food & Agr. Orgn-WHO Mission assess vampire bat rabies prob. in Arg, Brazil, Venezuela, Trinidad & Mex, 66. AAAS; Am. Soc. Icthyol. & Herpet; Am. Soc. Mammal; Wildlife Disease Asn. Life history and ecology of bats, including bat associated diseases affecting man and animals, especially bat control and particularly vampire bats. Address: Food & Agriculture Organization of the UN, Apartado Postal M-10778, Mexico City 1, Mex, D.F.

GREENHALL, CHARLES A(UGUST), b. New York, N.Y, May 5, 39. MATHEMATICAL ANALYSIS. B.A, Pomona Col, 61; Nat. Sci. Found. fel, Calif. Inst. Tech, 61-66, Ph.D.(fourier series), 66. Physicist, U.S. Naval Ord. Testing Sta, Calif, summer 62; Nat. Res. Coun. resident res. assoc, Jet Propulsion Lab, 66-68, ASST. PROF. MATH, UNIV. SOUTH. CALIF, 68- Am. Math. Soc; Soc. Indust. & Appl. Math. Real functions. Address: Dept. of Mathematics, University of Southern California, Los Angeles, CA 90007.

GREENHAUS, HERBERT L(OUIS), b. New York, N.Y, Nov. 11, 32; m. 53; c. 3. PHYSICAL CHEMISTRY. B.S, City Col, 54; M.S, Syracuse, 57; Ph.D. (phys. chem), Rensselaer Polytech, 65. Chemist, chemet prog, Gen. Elec. Co, 56-57, PHYS. CHEMIST, phys. chem. sect, res. lab, 57-65, lighting res. lab, 65-67; Hewlett-Packard Corp, 67-68; IBM CORP, 68- Am. Chem. Soc. Gaseous dielectrics; electron impact phenomena; negative and positive ion mass spectrometry; analytical chemistry and instrumentation development; gas chromatography; semiconductor process development. Address: Dept. C-85, IBM Corp, P.O. Box A, Essex Junction, VT 05452.

GREENHILL, MAURICE H, b. Terre Haute, Ind, Aug. 16, 09; m. 36; c. 4. PSYCHIATRY. A.B, Rochester, 31; M.D, Chicago, 36. Intern, Los Angeles County Gen. Hosp, Calif, 36-37; res, Worcester State Hosp, Mass, 37-39; Mass. Gen. Hosp, Boston, 39-40; Rockefeller Found. fel. neurol, 40-41; assoc. neuropsychiat, sch. med, Duke, 41-43, assoc. prof, 43-51, acting chmn. dept, 43-45, 51-52; assoc. prof. PSYCHIAT, sch. med, Maryland, 52-54, prof, 54-55; prof. & chmn. dept, sch. med, Miami (Fla), 55-57; clin. prof, ALBERT EINSTEIN COL. MED, 57-67, PROF, 67-, DIR. PSYCHIAT, HOSP, 66- Vis. assoc. prof, sch. pub. health, North Carolina, 43-52; assoc. dir, psychiat. inst, Maryland, 52-55; dir, City Community Ment. Health Bd, N.Y, 57-58. Consult, Off. Surgeon Gen, U.S. Army; Surgeon Gen, U.S. Pub. Health Serv; U.S. Vet. Admin. Mem. nursing res. study sect, Nat. Insts. Health, training & community servs. cmns, Nat. Inst. Ment. Health; chmn. comt. med. ed, Group Adv. Psychiat. Am. Psychosom. Soc; fel. Am. Psychiat. Asn; Asn. Res. Nerv. & Ment. Diseases. Medical education and communication; clinical psychiatry; interviewing and psychotherapy; psychiatric public health problems; psychosomatic medicine. Address: 70 Hampton Rd, Scarsdale, NY 10583.

GREENHILL, STANLEY E, b. Glasgow, Scotland, July 17, 17; m. 46; c. 2. MEDICINE. M.D, Toronto, 44, D.P.H, 48. Dir. blood transfusion serv, Can. Red Cross, 48-49; PROF. COMMUNITY MED. & HEAD DEPT, UNIV. ALTA, 59-, LECTR. MED, 48- Consult, Dept. Vet. Affairs, 54-64; specialist, Royal Col. Ottawa, 53; consult, Dept. Nat. Health & Welfare, 54- R.A.F, 42-44. Fel. Indust. Med. Asn; fel. Am. Col. Physicians; Royal Soc. Health. Interrelationship of disease with sociocultural changes and environment; psychosocial disease; comprehensive medicine; social and preventive medicine. Address: Dept. of Community Medicine, 1330 Clinical Sciences Bldg, University of Alberta, Edmonton 7, Alta, Can.

GREENHOUSE, ARNOLD H, b. N.Y.C, Dec. 24, 26; m. 53; c. 4. MEDICINE, NEUROLOGY. A.B, Kansas, 48, M.D, 51. Instr. anat, Kansas, 48; NEUROL, sch. med, Colorado, 61-62, asst. prof, 62-64; SCH. MED, UNIV. N.MEX, 64-65, assoc. prof, 65-69, PROF. & CHMN. DEPT, 69-, ACTING CHMN. DEPT. MED, 68-, chief div. neurol, 64-69. Chief neurol. sect, Denver Vet. Admin. Hosp, 61-64; exec. secy, Vet. Admin. Coop. Study Cerebral Vascular Disease, Study C, 63-, chmn, Study D, 65-; dir, Albuquerque Muscular Dystrophy Clin, 64-; consult, Albuquerque Vet. Admin. Hosp, 64-; William Beaumont Gen. Hosp, U.S. Army, El Paso, Tex, 66-; mem. exec. comt, coun. cerebrovascular disease, Am. Neurol. Asn. U.S.A, 45-46. Am. Acad. Neurol. Neurological education; cerebral vascular disease treatment and epidemiology; membrane transport phenomena involving the central nervous system. Address: Dept. of Neurology, University of New Mexico School of Medicine, 1007 Stanford Dr. N.E, Albuquerque, NM 87106.

GREENHOUSE, GERALD ALAN, b. Brooklyn, N.Y, Oct. 18, 42; m. 68. DEVELOPMENTAL BIOLOGY. B.A, Queens Col.(N.Y), 64; Nat. Insts. Health trainee, City Univ. New York, 66-68, Ph.D.(develop. biol), 68. Nat. Inst. Child Health & Human Develop. fel. biol, Mass. Inst. Technol, 69-71; fel, dept. animal sci, Univ. Geneva, 71-72; ASST. PROF. DEVELOP. BIOL, CURRICULUM HUMAN MORPHOL. & DEPT. DEVELOP. & CELL BIOL, UNIV. CALIF, IRVINE, JULY 72- Soc. Develop. Biol; Am. Soc. Zool. Etiology of congenital malformation in embryos; molecular biological studies of amphibian and echinoderm embryos aimed at elucidating mechanisms by which genes control developmental processes. Address: Curriculum of Human Morphology & Dept. of Developmental & Cell Biology, University of California, Irvine, CA 92664.

GREENHOUSE, H(AROLD) M(ITCHELL), b. Chicago, Ill, Nov. 20, 24; m. 48; c. 3. PHYSICAL CHEMISTRY. B.S, Ohio State, 48, M.S, 51. Res. assoc, res. found, Ohio State, 50-53; res. chemist, Ferroxcube Corp, 53-55; dir.

semiconductor res. & magnetics, Aladdin Electronics Co, 55-59; DIR. MICROELECTRONICS LAB, BENDIX COMMUNICATIONS DIV, BENDIX CORP, 59- U.S.A, 43-46. Am. Vacuum Soc; Inst. Elec. & Electronics Eng; Electrochem. Soc; Am. Asn. Physics Teachers. Materials research; solid state physical chemistry; x-ray diffraction; emission and adsorption spectroscopy; high temperature materials; ferrites; magnetic materials and devices; thin films; microelectronics; thick films. Address: Bendix Communications Division, Dept. 480, Bendix Corp, E. Joppa Rd, Baltimore, MD 21204.

GREENHOUSE, JEFFREY A, b. N.Y.C, Feb. 4, 42. PHYSICAL CHEMISTRY. B.S, Syracuse Univ, 63; Nat. Sci. Found. fel, Univ. Calif, Berkeley, 63-66, Ph.D.(phys. chem), 68. Resident res. assoc, Nat. Bur. Standards, 68-69; ASST. PROF. CHEM, OAKLAND UNIV, 69- Am. Chem. Soc. Infrared spectroscopy; microwave spectroscopy; molecular structure; low-frequency molecular vibrations; quantum theory. Address: Dept. of Chemistry, Oakland University, Rochester, MI 48063.

GREENHOUSE, SAMUEL W(ILLIAM), b. N.Y.C, Jan. 13, 18; m. 44; c. 4. MATHEMATICAL STATISTICS. B.S, City Col. New York, 38; M.A, George Washington Univ, 54, Ph.D.(math. statist), 59. Jr. statistician, U.S. Census Bur, 40-42; statistical analyst, UNRRA, 45-48; math. statistician, Nat. Cancer Inst, NAT. INSTS. HEALTH, 48-54, chief, statist. & appl. math. sect, Nat. Inst. Ment. Health, 54-66, CHIEF, EPIDEMIOL. & BIOMETRY BR. & ACTING ASSOC. DIR. PLANNING & EVAL, NAT. INST. CHILD HEALTH & HUMAN DEVELOP, 66- Prof. lectr, George Washington Univ, 47-; mem. psychopharmacol. adv. comt, Nat. Insts. Health, 57-59, accident prev. study sect, 58-62, statist. & math. res. review panel, 63-70; med. res. adv. coun, Fed. Aviation Asn, 59-64; vis. prof, Stanford Univ, 60-61; Nat. Sci. Found. vis. lectr, 66-68; mem. biomet. & epidemiol. methodol. adv. comt, Food & Drug. Admin, 67- U.S.A, 42-45. AAAS; Am. Math. Soc; Am. Psychopath. Asn; fel. Am. Statist. Asn; Biomet. Soc.(pres, East. N.Am. Region, 69); fel. Inst. Math. Statist; Int. Asn. Statist. in Phys. Sci; Royal Statist. Soc. Statistical methods and theory; application of statistical methods and mathematical models to the medical, biological and behavioral sciences. Address: 1724 Ladd St, Silver Spring, MD 20902.

GREENHOUSE, WALTER VAN VLECK, b. Plainfield, N.J, July 16, 44; m. 67; c. 1. BIOCHEMISTRY. B.A, Johns Hopkins Univ, 66; Nat. Insts. Health trainee, Northwest. Univ, 66-68, Nat. Defense Educ. Act fel, 68-70, Ph.D. (biochem), 70. STAFF FEL, INTERMEDIARY METAB. SECT, LAB. MOLECULAR AGEING, GERONT. RES. CTR, NAT. INST. CHILD HEALTH & HUMAN DEVELOP, 71- Am. Chem. Soc. Control of glycolysis in Ehrlich ascites tumor; turnover of structural and other components of inner and outer mitochondrial membranes from rat liver. Address: Laboratory of Molecular Ageing, Intermediary Metabolism Section, Gerontology Research Center, Baltimore City Hospitals, Baltimore, MD 21224.

GREENHOW, CHARLES R(ICHARD), b. Cincinnati, Ohio, Jan. 25, 20; m. 43; c. 3. REACTOR PHYSICS. B.S, N.C. State Col, 47, M.S, 48; Ph.D.(physics), Duke, 51. PHYSICIST, Nat. Bur. Standards, 51-57; Knolls Atomic Power Lab, Gen. Elec. Co, 57-62; Marquardt Corp, 62-64; TRW space Technol. Labs, 64-66; AEROSPACE CORP, SAN BERNARDINO, 66- U.S.A, 42-46. Am. Nuclear Soc; Am. Phys. Soc. Radiosotope and nuclear physics; microwave spectroscopy. Address: 27055 Tenth St, Highland, CA 92346.

GREENIDGE, K(ENNETH) N(ORMAN) H(AYNES), b. Montreal, Que, May 10, 19; m. 45; c. 2. BOTANY. B.Sc.F, New Brunswick, 48; M.F, Yale, 49; A.M, Harvard, 50, Ph.D.(bot), 51- Prov. forest biologist, N.S, 51-52; res. off, forest biol. div, Can. Dept. Agr, 52-59; assoc. prof. biol, Dalhousie, 59-63; FOREST BIOL, ST. FRANCIS XAVIER UNIV, 63-70, PROF, 70- R.C.N.R, 39-46, Lt. Comdr. Bot. Soc. Am. Morphology and water relations of forest trees. Address: Dept. of Biology, St. Francis Xavier University, Antigonish, N.S, Can.

GREENKORN, ROBERT A(LBERT), b. Oshkosh, Wis, Oct. 12, 28; m. 52; c. 3. CHEMICAL ENGINEERING. B.S, Wisconsin, 54, Visking fel, 54-55, M.S, 55, Du Pont fel, 55-56, Ph.D.(chem. eng), 57. Asst. chem. eng. & math, Wisconsin, 56-57; Nat. Sci. Found. fel, Norway's Tech. Univ, Trondheim, 57-58; res. engr, secondary recovery, Jersey Prod. Res. Co, 58-63; assoc. prof. eng, Marquette Univ, 63-65; CHEM. ENG, PURDUE UNIV, 65-67, PROF. & HEAD DEPT, 67- Lectr, Univ. Tulsa, 59-63; consult, Jersey Prod. Res. Co, 63-65; Esso Prod. Res. Co, 65- U.S.N, 46-51. Am. Inst. Chem. Eng; Soc. Petrol. Eng; Am. Soc. Eng. Educ. Flow in porous media; thermodynamic properties; data analysis. Address: School of Chemical Engineering, Purdue University, West Lafayette, IN 47907.

GREENLAND, MILES G(RIFFITH), b. Pittsburgh, Pa, Dec. 5, 09; m. 39; c. 2. PHYSICS. B.S, Pa. State Col, 33; A.M, Temple, 35; Purdue, 38-39. Asst. physics, Temple, 33-35; physicist, Brown Instrument Co, Pa, 36-38, 39; asst. physics, Purdue, 38-39; PHYSICIST & SUPVR, INSTRUMENTS & NAVIGATION BR, AERONAUT. MECH. DEPT, NAVAL AIR DEVELOP. CTR, 39- Am. Phys. Soc; Am. Inst. Navig. Test, development and application of new aircraft instruments and navigation equipment. Address: Aeronautical Mechanics Dept, Instruments & Navigation Branch, Naval Air Development Center, Warminster, PA 18974.

GREENLAW, JON S(TANLEY), b. Masardis, Maine, Aug. 6, 39; m. 62; c. 1. ORNITHOLOGY, POPULATION ECOLOGY. B.A, Univ. Maine, 63; Nat. Sci. Found. grant, Rutgers Univ, 66-68, Chapman Fund grant, 68, Ph.D.(ecol), 69. Instr. ornith, Douglass Col, Rutgers Univ, 67; ASST. PROF. BIOL, C.W. POST COL, L.I. UNIV, 69- AAAS; Am. Inst. Biol. Sci; Ecol. Soc. Am; Am. Ornith. Union; Brit. Ornith. Union; Cooper Ornith. Soc; Wilson Ornith. Soc. Organization and evolution of avian social systems; communication in birds; avian population and community structure and function; the systematics of Emberizinae. Address: Dept. of Biology, C.W. Post College, Long Island University, Greenvale, NY 11548.

GREENLAW, ROBERT H, b. Norway, Maine, Dec. 14, 27; m. 55; c. 4. NUCLEAR MEDICINE. B.S, Tufts, 48; M.D, Rochester, 52. Instr. radiol, Rochester, 59-60, sr. instr, 60-61; asst. prof, med. ctr, Univ. Ky, 61-63, assoc. prof, 63-67, prof, 67-71; THERAPEUT. RADIOLOGIST, MARSHFIELD CLIN, 71- James Picker Found. fel, 58-59; Am. Cancer Soc. adv. fel. radiol, 59-61; mem. med. adv. comt, Atomic Energy Comn, 64-68. U.S.A.F, 55-57, Capt. Am. Med. Asn; Am. Col. Radiol; Radiol. Soc. N.Am; Soc. Nuclear Med. Development of radioisotopes for diagnosis and therapy; radiation biology; clinical development in radiation therapy. Address: Marshfield Clinic, Marshfield, WI 54449.

GREENLEAF, FREDERICK P, b. Allentown, Pa, Jan. 8, 38; m. 64. MATHEMATICAL ANALYSIS. B.S, Pa. State Univ, 59; Nat. Sci. Found. fels, Yale, 59, 60-62, M.A, 62, Ph.D.(math), 64. Instr. MATH, Yale, 63-64; Univ. Calif, Berkeley, 64-65, asst. prof, 65-68; N.Y. UNIV, 68-69, ASSOC. PROF, 69- Prin. investr, Nat. Sci. Found. res. contract math. anal, summers 71, 72. AAAS; Am. Math. Soc. Geometry of groups; analysis and integration theory, with special emphasis on topological groups and noncommutative harmonic analysis; especially, convolution of measures, invariant means and their connection with group geometry and group representations. Address: Dept. of Mathematics, New York University, 251 Mercer St, New York, NY 10012.

GREENLEAF, JOHN E(DWARD), b. Joliet, Ill, Sept. 18, 32; m. 60. HUMAN & ENVIRONMENTAL PHYSIOLOGY. B.S, Univ. Ill, Urbana, 55, M.S, 62, Nat. Sci. Found. summer fel, 62, Nat. Insts. Health fel, 62-63, Ph.D.(physiol), 63; M.A, N.Mex. Highlands Univ, 56. RES. PHYSIOLOGIST, LAB. HUMAN ENVIRON. PHYSIOL, BIOTECHNOL. DIV, AMES RES. CTR, NASA, 63- Swedish Med. Res. Coun. fel, Stockholm, 66-67; co-ed, Int. J. Biometeorol, 67-; consult, Coca-Cola Co, Ga, 69- U.S.A, 52-53. AAAS; Int. Soc. Biometeorol; Am. Physiol. Soc; Aerospace Med. Asn. Thirst and drinking; heat acclimatization; exercise temperature regulation; body water metabolism; dehydration; exercise physiology; human performance. Address: Lab. of Human Environmental Physiology, NASA, Ames Research Center 39-4A, Biotechnology Division, Moffett Field, CA 94035.

GREENLEAF, NEWCOMB, b. N.Y.C, Apr. 15, 37; div; c. 2. MATHEMATICS. B.A, Haverford Col, 58; Ph.D.(math), Princeton, 61. Instr. MATH, Harvard, 61-64; asst. prof, Univ. Rochester, 64-69; ASSOC. PROF, UNIV. TEX, AUSTIN, 69- Res. assoc, Univ. Calif, Berkeley, 68-69. Am. Math. Soc. Algebraic number theory; algebraic geometry; algebra. Address: Dept. of Mathematics, University of Texas at Austin, Austin, TX 78712.

GREENLEAF, W(ALTER) H(ELMUTH), b. Stuttgart, Ger, Apr. 3, 12; nat; m. 39; c. 3. GENETICS. B.S, California, 36, Ph.D.(genetics), 40. Plant breeder, Vaughan Seed Store, Ill, 41-42; assoc. horticulturist, exp. sta, Georgia, 44-47; PROF. HORT, EXP. STA, AUBURN UNIV, 47- AAAS; Am. Phytopath. Soc; Am. Soc. Hort. Sci; Am. Genetic Asn; Am. Inst. Biol. Sci. Plant breeding; virology; cytology; horticulture; Nicotiana polyploids from auxin-induced callus; inheritance of resistance to tobacco etch virus in Capsicum; breeding virus resistant Tabasco and pimiento peppers and root knot nematode resistant tomatoes and peppers. Address: Dept. of Horticulture, Auburn University, Auburn, AL 36830.

GREENLEE, KENNETH W(ILLIAM), b. Leon, W.Va, Jan. 23, 16; m. 47; c. 3. CHEMISTRY. B.S, Antioch Col, 38; Ph.D.(chem), Ohio State, 42. Analyst, electrochem. dept, E.I. du Pont de Nemours & Co, 36-37; lab. asst, Antioch Col, 37-38; asst. Ohio State, 38-41, assoc. dir, hydrocarbon res. lab, 42-58, dir, 59-62; PRES, CHEM. SAMPLES CO, 63- AAAS; Am. Chem. Soc; Am. Inst. Chem. Synthesis of hydrocarbons; reactions in liquid ammonia; organosodium derivatives; Grignard reaction; purification of organic compounds; mechanism of oxidation of hydrocarbons; synthetic rubber; production problems, sales and administration. Address: Chemical Samples Co, 4692 Kenny Rd, Columbus, OH 43220.

GREENLEE, LORANCE L(ISLE), b. Oskaloosa, Iowa, Apr. 12, 35; m. 54; c. 2. BIOCHEMISTRY, GENETICS. A.B, Colorado, 57; Ph.D.(biochem), Duke, 62. Fel. biochem, Duke, 62-63; biol, Nat. Sci. Found, Calif. Inst. Tech, 63-66; asst. res. prof. molecular & genetic biol, UNIV. UTAH, 66-69, assoc. res. prof. BIOL, 69-71; ASSOC. PROF, 71- Nat. Insts. Health res. career develop. award, 66-71. Nat. Guard, 53-61, S/Sgt. AAAS; Am. Soc. Microbiol. Replication of DNA; bacteriophage ø x-174; episome replication. Address: Dept. of Biology, University of Utah, Salt Lake City, UT 84112.

GREENLEE, MALCOLM B, b. Mercedes, Tex, Aug. 20, 32; m. 52; c. 2. PHYSICS, MATHEMATICS. B.S, Purdue, 56; Maryland, 57-60; M.B.A, George Washington, 65. Asst. physics, Purdue, 56-57; assoc. physicist, appl. physics lab, Johns Hopkins Univ, 57-60, physicist & proj. supvr. space systs, 60-68, proj. engr. satellite navig, 64-68; dept. staff, Mitre Corp, Va, 68-69; PROG. MGR, TRANSACTION TECHNOL, 69- U.S.M.C, 51-54, S/Sgt. Am. Phys. Soc; Am. Geophys. Union. Astrophysics; satellite systems and communications; cryptography; real time digital computer control systems; navigation systems; logic design. Address: Transaction Technology, 1 Broadway, Cambridge, MA 02142.

GREENLEE, SYLVAN OWEN, b. McLeansboro, Ill, Mar. 15, 10; c. 3. ORGANIC CHEMISTRY. B.Ed, Southern Illinois, 35; A.M, Illinois, 36, Ph.D. (org. chem), 39. Asst. chem, Illinois, 36; org. res. chemist, Devoe & Raynolds Co, Inc, 39-43, dir. res, 43-46; appl. res. dir, S.C. Johnson & Son, Inc, 46-56; dir, Greenlee Res. Co, 56-63; dir. res. & develop, Guardsman Chem. Coatings, Inc, 63-64, v.pres. res, 64-68; pres, Greenlee Res. Co, 68-70; MEM. STAFF, RESYN CORP, 70- Epoxy resins and coating polymers. Address: Resyn Corp, 1401 Blanke St, Linden, NJ 07036.

GREENLER, ROBERT G(EORGE), b. Kenton, Ohio, Oct. 24, 29; m. 54; c. 3. PHYSICS. B.S, Rochester, 51; Ph.D.(physics), Hopkins, 57. Res. assoc, radiation lab, Hopkins, 57; res. physicist, Allis-Chalmers Mfg. Co, 57-62; assoc. prof. PHYSICS, UNIV. WIS-MILWAUKEE, 62-67, PROF, 67-, chmn. lab. surface studies, 66-71. Sci. Res. Coun. sr. vis. fel, sch. chem. sci, Univ. E.Anglia, 71-72. AAAS; Optical Soc. Am. Infrared interferometry; gas adsorption by infrared spectroscopy; physics and chemistry of solid surfaces; optical phenomena of the sky. Address: Dept. of Physics, University of Wisconsin-Milwaukee, Milwaukee, WI 53201.

GREENLEY, ROBERT Z, b. Chicago, Ill, Jan. 25, 34; m. 56; c. 3. ORGANIC CHEMISTRY. B.S, John Carroll, 56; Ph.D.(org. chem), Illinois, 60. Chemist, Lewis Labs, Nat. Adv. Comt. Aeronaut, 56-57; sr. res. chemist, MONSANTO CO, 60-70, SR. RES. SPECIALIST & GROUP LEADER, 70- U.S.A, 57, 1st Lt. Am. Chem. Soc. Vinyl copolymers; ring opening polymerizations; thermally stable polymers and monomer synthesis. Address: Monsanto Co, 800 N. Lindbergh Blvd, St. Louis, MO 63166.

GREENLIEF, CHARLES M, b. Perkins, W.Va, July 27, 37; m. 60; c. 3. PHYSICAL CHEMISTRY. B.S, Univ. Calif, Berkeley, 65; Nat. Defense Educ. Act. fel, Univ. Wash, 65-68, Ph.D.(phys. chem), 70. WELCH FEL, UNIV. TEX. AUSTIN, 70- Consult. reviewer, Oceana Publ, Inc, 71- Am. Chem. Soc; Am. Phys. Soc. Thermodynamics and statistical mechanics of physical adsorption. Address: Dept. of Chemistry, University of Texas at Austin, Austin, TX 78712.

GREENMAN, DAVID L(EWIS), b. Williamston, Mich, Jan. 19, 34; m. 56; c. 2. ENDOCRINOLOGY, PHYSIOLOGY. A.B, Asbury Col, 56; M.S, Purdue, 59, Nat. Sci. Found. fels, 59-62, Ph.D.(endocrinol), 62. Res. assoc. enzym, Oak Ridge Nat. Lab, 62-63, U.S. Pub. Health Serv. fel, 63-64; asst. prof. & res. assoc. biol, Johns Hopkins Univ, 64-70; PHARMACOLOGIST, Food & Drug Admin, 70; ENVIRON. PROTECTION AGENCY, 70- AAAS; Am. Soc. Zool. Avian pituitary-adrenal physiology; hormonal influences on ribonucleic acid and protein metabolism of the liver and uterus. Address: Pesticide Regulation Division, Environmental Protection Agency, 12th and Independence, Washington, DC 20250.

GREENMAN, NORMAN L, b. New York, N.Y, Apr. 12, 23; m. 49; c. 3. CHEMICAL ENGINEERING. S.B, Mass. Inst. Tech, 47, S.M, 48. Develop. engr, ROGERS CORP, 48-51, mgr. prod. develop, 51-53, planning, 53-58, dir. marketing, 58-59, v.pres, 59-64, exec. v.pres, 64-66, PRES, 66- C.Eng, U.S.A, 43-46. AAAS; Am. Chem. Soc; Am. Soc. Test & Mat; Tech. Asn. Pulp & Paper Indust. Fibers and polymers; industrial chemistry. Address: Ridgewood Dr, Woodstock, CT 06281.

GREENMAN, NORMAN N(ATHAN), b. Chicago, Ill, Nov. 5, 20; m. 49; c. 4. GEOLOGY. B.A, Chicago, 41, M.S, 48, Atomic Energy Comn. fel, 48-51, Ph.D.(geol), 51. GEOLOGIST, Shell Oil Co, 51-61; McDONNELL DOUGLAS ASTRONAUTICS CO, 61- AAAS; Am. Geophys. Union; Geol. Soc. Am; assoc. Soc. Econ. Paleont. & Mineral. Lunar and planetary geology; cosmic dust; mineral and Apollo lunar sample luminescence; sedimentary petrology. Address: 1437 Ninth St, Manhattan Beach, CA 90266.

GREENOUGH, R(ALPH) CLIVE, b. Medford, Mass, June 1, 32; m. 61; c. 1. ANALYTICAL CHEMISTRY. S.B, Mass. Inst. Technol, 53; Nat. Sci. Found. fel, Calif. Inst. Technol, 53, Ph.D.(chem), 62. Sr. res. engr, Rocketdyne Div, N.Am. Aviation, Inc, 61-66; SR. SCIENTIST, WARNER-LAMBERT CO, 66- U.S.A, 54-56, 2nd Lt. AAAS; Am. Chem. Soc; fel. Am. Inst. Chem; Am. Soc. Mass Spectrometry. Solvent extraction; nuclear magnetic resonance of fluorine compounds; infrared, ultra-violet, nuclear magnetic resonance and mass spectrometry of drugs and metabolites. Address: Warner-Lambert Co, 170 Tabor Rd, Morris Plains, NJ 07950.

GREENOUGH, WILLIAM B, III, b. Providence, R.I, Jan. 3, 32; m. 54; c. 5. MEDICINE. B.A, Amherst Col, 53; M.D, Harvard Med. Sch, 57. Intern & asst. res. med, Columbia-Presby. Med. Ctr, 57-59; fel. hemat, Mary Imogene Bassett Hosp, Cooperstown, N.Y, 59-61; resident med, Peter Bent Brigham Hosp, 61-62; cholera, Pakistan-SEATO, Dacca, 62-64, chief clin. res, 64-65; assoc. metab, Nat. Heart Inst, 65-67; asst. prof. med, JOHNS HOPKINS UNIV, 67-69, ASSOC. PROF. MED. & MICROBIOL, 69-, CHIEF INFECTIOUS DISEASES DIV, 70- AAAS; Infectious Diseases Soc. Am; Am. Fedn. Clin. Res. Clinical and laboratory research in infectious diseases, metabolism and transport processes. Address: Dept. of Medicine, Blalock 1140, Johns Hopkins University, Baltimore, MD 21205.

GREENSHIELDS, BRUCE DOUGLAS, b. Winfield, Kans, Apr. 14, 93; m; c. 2. TRANSPORTATION, CIVIL ENGINEERING. B.S, Oklahoma, 20, C.E, 27; M.S, Michigan, 32, Ph.D.(civil eng), 34. Instr. civil eng, Marquette, 22-23; asst. prof, Va. Polytech, 23-26; prof. eng. sci. & in charge dept, Denison, 26-37; assoc. prof. civil eng, City Col. New York, 37-40; Polytech. Inst. Brooklyn, 40-46; George Washington, 46-48, prof. & head dept, 48-52, prof, 52-56; chief hwy. systs. br, off. chief transportation, U.S. Dept. Army, 56; asst. dir, TRANSPORTATION INST, UNIV. MICH, ANN ARBOR, 56-61, acting dir, 61-65, lectr. transportation eng, 56-65, EMER. LECTR. & CONSULT, 66- City engr, Granville, Ohio, 26-37; res. engr, traffic bur, State Hwy. Dept, Ohio, 34-36; bur. hwy. traffic, Yale, 44-46; adj. prof, N.Y. Univ, 45-46; consult, Off. Chief Engrs, 50-51; chief investr, Nat. Sci. Found. res. proj, 53-54; consult. engr. U.S.A, 17-18. Assoc. mem. Am. Soc. Civil Eng; Am. Soc. Eng. Educ; Nat. Soc. Prof. Eng.(pres, 36); Inst. Traffic Eng. Time motion study of traffic; materials research; the photographic method of traffic analysis; traffic performance at urban street intersections; statistics with applications to highway traffic analyses; transportation; traffic accident Studies. Address: 1727 Massachusetts Ave. N.W, Washington, DC 20036.

GREENSHIELDS, JOHN BRYCE, b. Bridgeport, Ill, June 19, 26. PHYSICAL CHEMISTRY. B.S, Carnegie-Mellon Univ, 50, M.S, 53; Ph.D.(chem), 56. Asst. prof. CHEM, DUQUESNE UNIV, 56-61, ASSOC. PROF, 61- Res. fel, Univ. Chicago, 62-64. U.S.A, 44-46. AAAS; Am. Chem. Soc; Am. Phys. Soc. Molecular quantum mechanics; statistical mechanics. Address: Dept. of Chemistry, Dusquesne University, Pittsburgh, PA 15219.

GREENSHIELDS, J(OHN) E(DWARD) R(OSS), b. Semans, Sask, Sept. 21, 18; m. 45; c. 5. PLANT BREEDING, GENETICS. B.S.A, Saskatchewan, 49, M.Sc, 50; Sask. Res. Found. scholar, 51, 53; Ph.D.(plant breeding, morphol), Iowa State, 53. Res. off, forage crops lab, CAN. DEPT. AGR, 47-57, head, pasture res, cent. exp. farm, genetics & plant breeding inst, 57-60, assoc. dir. PROG. CROPS, 60-64, DIR, 64- R.C.A.F, 41-45. Am. Soc. Agron; Agr. Inst. Can. Crops; entomology; plant pathology; soils. Address: Research Station, Canada Dept. of Agriculture, University Campus, Saskatoon, Sask, Can.

GREENSLADE, FORREST C, b. Endicott, N.Y, Sept. 23, 39; m. 63; c. 1. DEVELOPMENTAL BIOLOGY, BIOCHEMISTRY. B.A, State Univ. N.Y, 63; M.S, Tulane, 65, Nat. Insts. Health fel. & Sigma Xi grant, 65-66, Ph.D.(develop. biol), 66. Harpur Col. Alumni assistantship biol. & Nat. Sci. Found. assistantship, Tulane, 63-65; Argonne Nat. Lab. fel, 66-67; SR. SCIENTIST & GROUP LEADER REPROD. BIOL, ORTHO RES. FOUND, 67- Am. Soc. Zool; Soc. Study Reproduction. Biochemistry and pharmacology of embryonic development in mammals. Address: Reproductive Biology, Ortho Research Foundation, Raritan, NJ 08869.

GREENSLADE, THOMAS BOARDMAN, JR, b. Staten Island, N.Y, Dec. 23, 37; m. 59; c. 2. PHYSICS. B.A, Amherst Col, 59; M.S, Rutgers, 61, Ph.D.(physics), 65. Instr. PHYSICS, KENYON COL, 64-65, asst. prof, 65-69, ASSOC. PROF, 69- Am. Asn. Physics Teachers. Low temperature transport properties of solids. Address: Dept. of Physics, Kenyon College, Gambier, OH 43022.

GREENSLIT, CHARLES L(EIGH), b. Hot Springs, S.Dak, Apr. 1, 22; m. 46; c. 6. PHYSICS. A.B, Nebr. Wesleyan, 43; Nebraska, 46-48. Lab. asst. eng, Nebr. Wesleyan, 41-43; Nebraska, 47-48; jr. engr, radio div, Bendix Aviation Corp, 48-50, asst. proj. engr, 50-52, proj. engr, 52-54, prin. engr, 54-55, systems engr, 55-58, mgr. res. & develop, 58-60, asst. dir. eng, 60-62, mgr. govt. prods, 62-64, V.PRES. ENG, BENDIX FIELD ENG. CORP, 65- Sig.C, 43-46, Sgt. Inst. Elec. & Electronics Eng. Radar applications; command and control systems; medical instrumentation. Address: 9250 Rt. 108, Columbia, MD 21043.

GREENSON, RALPH R(OMEO), b. Brooklyn, N.Y, Sept. 20, 11; m. 35; c. 2. PSYCHIATRY. Columbia Univ, 28-30; M.D, Univ. Berne, 34. TRAINING ANALYST, LOS ANGELES INST. PSYCHOANAL, 47-, dean, training sch, 57-61. Clin. prof, sch. med, Univ. Calif, Los Angeles, 53-; consult. psychiatrist, psychiat. serv, Los Angeles; trustee, Sch. Nursery Years, Los Angeles; chmn, sci. adv. bd, Found. Res. Psychoanal, Beverly Hills. U.S.A.A.F, 42-46, Maj. Am. Psychoanal. Asn; Am. Psychiat. Asn. Psychoanalysis. Address: 465 N. Roxbury Dr, Beverly Hills, CA 90210.

GREENSPAN, BERNARD, b. New York, N.Y, Dec. 17, 14; m. 39; c. 2. MATHEMATICS. B.S, Brooklyn Col, 35, M.A, 36; Ph.D.(math), Rutgers, 58; Rensselaer Polytech, 60. Instr, MATH, Brooklyn Col, 35-44; Polytech. Inst. Brooklyn, 43-44; DREW UNIV, 44-47, asst. prof, 47-58, assoc. prof, 58-59, PROF. & HEAD DEPT, 59-, DIR. NAT. SCI. FOUND. MATH. INST, 62-, chmn. div. sci. & math, 63-67. Instr, Rutgers Univ, 52, summer 71; Bell Tel. Labs, 53-58; Nat. Sci. Found. faculty fel, Univ. Calif, 58-59; Univ. Santa Clara, summer 61; reader, Advan. Placement Exam, 66. Am. Math. Soc; Math. Asn. Am. Algebra. Address: Dept. of Mathematics, Drew University, Madison, NJ 07940.

GREENSPAN, CAROL M, b. N.Y.C. BIOCHEMISTRY, MOLECULAR BIOLOGY & GENETICS. B.A, Univ. Ill, 53; sec. teaching credential, Univ. Calif, Berkeley, 56; Radcliffe fel, 60-61; A.M. & Ed.M, Harvard, 61; Nat. Insts. Health fel, 61-65; univ. fel, Univ. Colo, 66-68; Ph.D.(biochem), Columbia Univ, 68. Chem. patent searcher, Shell Develop. Corp, Calif, 54; med. lab. technician, Oakknoll Naval Hosp, Oakland, Calif, 55-56; teacher, pub. schs, Calif, 56-59; summers, microbiol. lab. dir, Nat. Sci. Found. Insts. for high sch. stud, Nasson Col, 61 & Wesleyan Univ, 62; Nat. Insts. Health fel. molecular biol, Nat. Jewish Hosp. & Res. Ctr, Denver, Colo, 68-70; res. assoc. biochem, MED. SCH, UNIV. ORE, 70-71, FEL. MED. GENETICS, 71- AAAS; Am. Chem. Soc. Structure-function relationships in transfer RNA; mechanisms of fluoride inhibition of the enzyme, acetylcholinesterase, and of information transfer from DNA to RNA. Address: Dept. of Biochemistry, University of Oregon Medical School, Portland, OR 97201.

GREENSPAN, DONALD, b. N.Y.C, Jan. 24, 28; m. 57; c. 3. MATHEMATICS. B.S, N.Y. Univ, 48; fel, Wisconsin, 48-49, M.S, 49; Ph.D, Maryland, 56. Instr. math, Maryland, 49-53, 54-56; res. engr, Hughes Aircraft Co, 56-57; asst. prof. math, Purdue, 57-60, assoc. prof, 60-62; PERMANENT MEM, MATH. RES. CTR, UNIV. WIS, MADISON, 62-, PROF. COMPUT. SCI, UNIV, 65-, MEM. COMPUT. CTR, 69- Faculty assoc, Boeing Airplane Co, summer 58; consult, Radio Corp. Am, 59. U.S.A.A.F, 53-54, 1st Lt. Am. Math. Soc; Soc. Indust. & Appl. Math; Math. Asn. Am. Numerical analysis; classical differential geometry. Address: Mathematics Research Center, University of Wisconsin, Madison, WI 53706.

GREENSPAN, FRANCIS S(ORREL), b. Perth Amboy, N.J, Mar. 16, 20; m. 45; c. 3. ENDOCRINOLOGY. B.A, Cornell, 40, M.D, 43. Asst. clin. prof. med, sch. med, Stanford, 50-59; assoc. clin. prof, SCH. MED, UNIV. CALIF, SAN FRANCISCO, 59-65, CLIN. PROF. MED. & RES. PHYSICIAN, 65- Dipl. Am. Bd. Internal Med, 51. Med.C, 44-46, Lt. Endocrine Soc; Am. Med. Asn; Am. Fedn. Clin. Res. Bioassay of anterior pituitary hormones; clinical endocrinology. Address: University of California Medical Center, 125-U, San Francisco, CA 94122.

GREENSPAN, FRANK P(HILIP), b. New York, N.Y, May 7, 17; m. 43; c. 1. ORGANIC CHEMISTRY. B.S, City Col, 38; M.S, Polytech. Inst. Brooklyn, 41; Ph.D.(org. chem), Buffalo, 51. Chief chemist, Lane Bryant, Inc, 37-41; chemist, Hart Prods. Corp, 41; Chem. Warfare Serv, 42-45; res. chemist, Buffalo Electro-Chem. Co, 45, group leader, 47-52, mgr. org. res. & develop, Becco Chem. Div, FMC Corp, 53-56, dir. develop, chem. & plastics div, 56-58, tech. dir, epoxy dept, 58-61, dir. res. & develop, plastics dept, org. chem. div, 61-64, mgr. new prod. develop, chem. div, 65-66; V.PRES. RES. & DEVELOP, Dexter Chem. Corp, 66-67; REEVES BROS. INC, 67- Instr, Univ. Buffalo, 52-56. AAAS; Am. Chem. Soc; Am. Inst. Chem; Am. Oil Chemists' Soc; Commercial Develop. Asn; Soc. Plastics Indust; Soc. Plastics Eng. Chemistry, reactions and applications of hydrogen peroxides and peracids; organic peroxides; organic oxidation reactions; epoxidation-hydroxylation reactions; fats, oils and derivatives; plasticizers; epoxy, vinyl and allylic resins; polymers and polymerization; polyurethane foam; textiles; coated fabrics. Address: Reeves Brothers Inc, 1271 Ave. of the Americas, New York, NY 10020.

GREENSPAN, GEORGE, b. Phila, Pa, Feb. 13, 16; m. 60; c. 1. MICROBIOLOGY. B.A, Pennsylvania, 38; Ph.D.(microbiol), Rutgers, 60. Res. asst. microbiol, Squibb Inst. Med. Res, 45-55; res. assoc, inst. microbiol, Rutgers, 56-60; SR. RES. SCIENTIST MICROBIOL. & BIOCHEM, WYETH LABS, 60- U.S.A.A.F, 42-45, Sgt. Am. Soc. Microbiol; Am. Chem. Soc.

Antibiotics, especially strain improvement; microbiological transformation of steroids; alkaloids and other organic compounds. Address: Wyeth Labs, Box 8299, Philadelphia, PA 19101.

GREENSPAN, H(ARVEY) P(HILIP), b. N.Y.C, Feb. 22, 33; m. 53; c. 2. APPLIED MATHEMATICS. B.S, City Col, 53; M.S, Harvard, 54, Ph.D.(appl. math), 56. Asst. prof. APPL. MATH, Harvard, 57-60; assoc. prof, MASS. INST. TECHNOL, 60-64, PROF, 64- Mem. bd. gov, Israel Inst. Technol. Am. Acad. Arts & Sci. Fluid dynamics. Address: Dept. of Mathematics, Massachusetts Institute of Technology, Cambridge, MA 02139.

GREENSPAN, IRVING, b. Chicago, Ill, May 29, 23; m. 45; c. 2. MICROBIOLOGY, HEMATOLOGY. B.S, Illinois, 45, M.D, 47. Fel. hemat, 48-49; res. fel. leukemia, Hektoen Inst, 58-62; chief lymphoma res, Lutheran Gen. Hosp, 62-64; ASSOC. PROF. MICROBIOL, CHICAGO MED. SCH, 67- Res. fel. lymphoma, John Hartford Asn, 61-63. Dipl, Am. Bd. Internal Med, 56. U.S.A.F, 51-53, Capt. Fel. Am. Col. Physicians; fel. Royal Soc. Health; fel. Am. Inst. Chem. Demonstration of specific antibody to human leukemic extracted tissues in human beings by PCA test; therapy in lymphomas with specific antisera and transplanted sensitized lymphyocytes. Address: 8819 Lowell Terrace, Skokie, IL 60076.

GREENSPAN, JOSEPH, b. Brooklyn, N.Y, July 8, 09; m. 41. CHEMISTRY. B.S, City Col, 29; M.A, Columbia, 30, fel, 32-33, Ph.D.(phys. chem), 33. Asst. chem, Columbia 33-36; assoc. dir, biochem. lab, Jewish Hosp, Brooklyn, 36-37; lectr, grad. div. chem, Brooklyn Col, 37-47; DIR. RES, PROCESS & INSTRUMENTS CORP, 45- Instr, undergrad. div, Brooklyn Col, 39-42; spec. investr, U.S. Dept. Navy, Rockefeller Inst, 42-43; physicist & proj. engr, Manhattan proj, Kellex Corp, 43-45. Am. Chem. Soc; Am. Phys. Soc; Instrument Soc. Am; Soc. Appl. Spectros; Inst. Elec. & Electronics Eng; N.Y. Acad. Sci. Instrument design; mass spectrometers; DC amplifiers; cathode ray equipment; automatic analytical instruments; high vacuum techniques; optical and electronic instruments. Address: 1 Lincoln Plaza, New York, NY 10023.

GREENSPAN, KALMAN, b. Bariez, Poland, Apr. 27, 25; U.S. citizen; m. 50; c. 3. ELECTROPHYSIOLOGY, PHARMACODYNAMICS. B.S, L.I. Univ, 48; M.A, Boston Univ, 50; Merck fel, Columbia Univ, 52-53, M.A, 53; Ph.D. (physiol), State Univ. N.Y. Brooklyn, 60. Teaching asst. biol, Boston Univ, 49-50; instr, L.I. Univ, 50; teaching asst. physiol, State Univ. N.Y. Downstate Med. Ctr, 57-60, instr, 60-62; asst. prof. med, SCH. MED, IND. UNIV, INDIANAPOLIS, 62-65, physiol, 63-65, assoc. prof. MED. & PHYSIOL, 65-70, PROF, 70-; HEAD SECT. PHYSIOL, KRANNERT INST. CARDIOL, 65-, DIR. INSTRUMENTATION LAB, 68-, sr. res. assoc, 62-65. Mem. coun. basic sci, Am. Heart Asn. U.S.N, 43-46. Fel. AAAS; fel. Am. Col. Cardiol; Am. Physiol. Soc; Am. Soc. Pharmacol. & Exp. Therapeut; Cardiac Muscle Soc; Biophys. Soc; Soc. Gen. Physiol; N.Y. Acad. Sci; Am. Heart Asn; Am. Fedn. Clin. Res. Cardiac research in the determination of the basic mechanisms for cardiac dysrhythmia and possible modes of therapy. Address: Krannert Institute of Cardiology, 960 Locke St, Indianapolis, IN 46202.

GREENSPAN, MARTIN, b. New York, N.Y, May 8, 12; m. 37; c. 3. PHYSICS. B.S, Cooper Union, 33. Physicist, NAT. BUR. STANDARDS, WASH, D.C, 35-67, ED, JOUR. RES, 62-, CHIEF SOUND SECT, 67- Vis. lectr, Univ. Calif, Los Angeles, 58-59; mem, U.S. Nat. Comt. Int. Union Pure & Appl. Physics, 66-; adj. prof, Cath. Univ. Am, 68- Fel. AAAS; fel. Acoust. Soc. Am.(v.pres, 63-64, pres. elect, 65-66, pres, 66-67); fel. Am. Phys. Soc. Meritorious serv. award, Dept. of Commerce, 49, 61. Ultrasonics; sound; mechanics; electronics. Address: 12 Granville Dr, Silver Spring, MD 20901.

GREENSPAN, RICHARD H, b. New York, N.Y, Apr. 25, 25; m. 52; c. 4. RADIOLOGY. A.B, Columbia, 45; M.D, Syracuse, 48. Instr. radiol, Minnesota, 57-59, asst. prof, 59-60; sch. med, Yale, 60, attend. radiologist, 60-61, assoc. prof. RADIOL, 61-64, prof. & acting chmn. dept, 64-68; PROF, UNIV. CALIF, SAN FRANCISCO, 68- Am. Roentgen Ray Soc; Asn. Univ. Radiol; Radiol. Soc. N.Am; Am. Col. Chest Physicians. Vascular radiologic studies and the application of isotopes to cardiovascular disease. Address: Dept. of Radiology, University of California, San Francisco Medical Center, San Francisco, CA 94122.

GREENSPON, JOSHUA E, b. Baltimore, Md, Sept. 3, 28; m. 54; c. 3. APPLIED MECHANICS, ACOUSTICS. B.Eng, Johns Hopkins Univ, 49, M.S.Eng, 51, D.Eng.(appl. mech), 56. Instr. mech. eng, Johns Hopkins Univ, 49-53; physicist ship struct, David Taylor Model Basin, 53-56; engr. aircraft dynamics, Martin Co, 56-58; OWNER, JG ENG. RES. ASSOCS, 58- C.Eng, U.S.A.R, Capt. Am. Soc. Mech. Eng; Am. Inst. Aeronaut. & Astronaut; fel. Acoust. Soc. Am; Soc. Naval Archit. & Marine Eng. Dynamics of structures; underwater acoustics, particularly sound radiation of structures in water with associated problems such as data processing of full scale data; elastic and plastic deformation of structures under static and dynamic loads. Address: JG Engineering Research Associates, 3831 Menlo Dr, Baltimore, MD 21215.

GREENSPON, THOMAS STEPHEN, b. Jan. 9, 42; m; c. 2. PSYCHOLOGY. B.A, Yale, 63; M.A, Univ. Ill, Urbana, 67, Ph.D.(exp. psychol), 69. Res. grantee, Nat. Sci. Found, summers 62 & 63; res. asst. psychol, Yale, 63-64; asst. Univ. Ill, 64-67, U.S. Pub. Health Serv. res. fel, 67-68; ctr. visual sci, Univ. Rochester, 68-70; ASST. PROF. PHYSIOL. OPTICS, UNIV. ALA, BIRMINGHAM, 70- AAAS; Optical Soc. Am; Asn. Res. Vision & Ophthal. Human behavioral data on real and beta apparent movement to assess physiological mechanisms of movement perception; sensory processes, especially temporal processes in vision. Address: School of Optometry, Medical Center, University of Alabama in Birmingham, Birmingham, AL 35233.

GREENSTADT, MELVIN, b. New York, N.Y, Jan. 18, 18; m. 41; c. 3. INORGANIC CHEMISTRY, SCIENCE EDUCATION. B.S, City Col. New York, 38; B.A, Southern California, 48, M.A, 49, Ph.D.(sci. ed), 56. Chemist, Littauer Fund, sch. med, N.Y. Univ, 38-40; War Dept, 41-42; teacher, high schs, Calif, 50-66; assoc. prof. chem, Calif. State Col. Long Beach, 66-69; TEACHER, HIGH SCHS, CALIF, 69- U.S.N.R, 42-46, Lt. Cmdr. Sulfa drugs; photolytic reactions; chemical education. Address: 6531 W. Fifth St, Los Angeles, CA 90048.

GREENSTEIN, DAVID S(NELLENBURG), b. Wilmington, Del, Mar. 26, 28; m. 52; c. 4. MATHEMATICS. B.S, Delaware, 49; A.M, Pennsylvania, 53, Ph.D.(math), 57. Res. student biophys, Pennsylvania, 50-52; eng. physicist, Philco Corp, 52-53; asst. instr. elec. eng, Pennsylvania, 53-55, instr, 55-56; prfnl. engr, Radio Corp. Am, 56-57; instr. MATH, Michigan, 57-59, asst. prof, 59-60; Northwest. Univ, 60-63, assoc. prof, 63-68, PROF, NORTHEAST. ILL. UNIV, 68- Am. Math. Soc; Math. Asn. Am; Indian Math. Soc. Approximation theory; moment problems; complex variables; real variables. Address: Dept. of Mathematics, Northeastern Illinois University, Bryn Mawr at St. Louis Ave, Chicago, IL 60625.

GREENSTEIN, EDWARD T(HEODORE), b. New York, N.Y, Mar. 1, 23; m; c. 3. TOXICOLOGY. State Univ. N.Y. Agr. & Tech. Inst. Farmingdale, 41-43; Long Island, 45-48; D.V.M, State Univ. N.Y. Vet. Col, Cornell, 52. Veterinarian, diseases lab. animals, Atomic Energy Proj, sch. med. & dent, Rochester, 59-61, animal health veterinarian, diseases, nutrit. & housing, 61-64; asst. dir, div. large animal toxicol, Woodard Res. Corp, 64-67; SR. RES. SCIENTIST, BRISTOL LABS, 67- Vet. consult, Ont. County Bd. Supvrs, N.Y, 59-60; consult, Eastman Dent. Dispensary, 61-63; R.J. Strasenburgh Co, 61-64; Chemway Corp, 63-64; consult. & mem. staff, ctr. brain res, Univ. Rochester, 61-64. Dipl, Am. Col. Lab. Animal Med. U.S.A.A.F, 43-45, T/Sgt. Am. Vet. Med. Asn; Am. Asn. Lab. Animal Sci; fel. Am. Col. Vet. Toxicol; Am. Soc. Vet. Ophthal. Primatology; diseases occurring in laboratory animals held under laboratory housing conditions; estrus cycle of the Macaca mulatta, rhesus monkey and the eye of the monkey and the dog. Address: Dept. of Toxicology, Bristol Labs, Syracuse, NY 13201.

GREENSTEIN, JESSE L(EONARD), b. New York, N.Y, Oct. 15, 09; m. 34; c. 2. ASTROPHYSICS. A.B, Harvard, 29, A.M, 30, Ph.D.(astron), 37. Nat. Res. Coun. fel, Yerkes Observ, Chicago, 37-39, instr. ASTROPHYS, 39-42, asst. prof, 42-47, assoc. prof, 47; res. assoc, McDonald Observ, Chicago & Texas, 47-48; PROF. & HEAD DEPT, HALE OBSERVS, CALIF. INST. TECHNOL, 48-, EXEC. OFF. ASTRON, DIV. PHYSICS, MATH. & ASTRON, 64-, chmn. faculty, 65-67. Chmn. panel astron, Nat. Sci. Found, 52-57, mem. div. comt. math, phys. & eng. sci, 57-60; pres, comn. stellar spectra, Int. Astron. Union, 52-58; for. ed, Annales d' Astrophysiques, 53-59; mem. bd. overseers, Harvard, 65-71; coun, Nat. Acad. Sci, 66-69, chmn. astron. surv, 69-71; Russell Lectr, Am. Astron. Soc; ed, Stellar Atmospheres; corres. ed, Astrophys. Letters, Comments on Astrophys. & Space Sci. Bruce Medal, Astron. Soc. Pac. With Off. Sci. Res. & Develop. Nat. Acad. Sci; Am. Astron. Soc.(v.pres, 55-57); Am. Acad. Arts & Sci; Am. Philos. Soc; assoc. Royal Astron. Soc; fel. Royal Belgian Soc. Sci. Interstellar absorption; nature of interstellar matter and its interaction with stars; spectra of stars; quantitative analysis of stellar atmospheres with high dispersion; effect of nuclear reactions on the abundances of the elements; spectra of white dwarfs; the quasi-stellar objects; age and evolution of stars; final stages in the life of stars; nuclear processes in stars. Address: Hale Observatories, California Institute of Technology, Pasadena, CA 91109.

GREENSTEIN, JULIUS S, b. Boston, Mass, July 13, 27; m. 54; c. 5. ZOOLOGY, PHYSIOLOGY. A.B, Clark Univ, 48; M.S, Univ, 48; M.S, Univ. Ill, 51, Ph.D.(zool), 55. Asst. zool, Univ. Ill, 50-54; asst. res. prof. animal sci, Univ. Mass, 54-58, assoc. res. prof, 58-59; assoc. prof. BIOL, Duquesne Univ, 59-64, prof, 64-70, chmn. dept, 61-70; PROF. & CHMN. DEPT, STATE UNIV. N.Y. COL, FREDONIA, 70- Nat. Insts. Health grant, 61-62; fel, sch. med, Harvard, 66; Am. Inst. Biol. Sci. vis. lectr, 66-; ed, Int. J. Fertil; Proceeding, Pa. Acad. Sci; consult, Human Life Found; grant evaluator, Nat. Sci. Found. U.S.A, 45-46. AAAS; Am. Soc. Zool; Am. Fertil. Soc; Am. Asn. Anat; Int. Fertil. Asn; Am. Inst. Biol. Sci; Am. Soc. Study Reproduction; Brit. Soc. Study Fertil; Soc. Develop. Biol; Coun. Biol. Ed. Anatomy and physiology of reproduction; embryology, histology and histochemistry of female reproductive organs and related endocrine glands; semen biochemistry and male accessory gland physiology; placental physiology; endocrinology; early embryonic mortality; stain technology and exfoliative cytology. Address: Dept. of Biology, State University of New York College at Fredonia, Fredonia, NY 14063.

GREENSTEIN, LEON M, b. New York, N.Y, Mar. 4, 18. PHYSICAL CHEMISTRY. B.S, City Col, 37, fel, 37-38; M.A, Columbia, 38, Ph.D.(phys. & colloidal chem), 42; fel, Carnegie Institution, 41-42, Asst. chem, Columbia, 39-41; chemist, Mearl Corp, 42-52; DIR. RES, Francis Earle Labs, Inc, 52-62; HENRY L. MATTIN LABS, MEARL CORP, 62- Am. Chem. Soc; Soc. Cosmetic Chem. Fire extinguishing foams; foaming properties of solutions; nacreous pigments; crystal growth; optical properties of crystals. Address: Mearl Corp, Ossining, NY 10562.

GREENSTEIN, RAPHAEL HERMAN, b. Phila, Pa, Feb. 11, 10; m. 37; c. 2. INTERNAL MEDICINE. A.B, Pennsylvania, 30, M.D, 33. Adj. physician MED, Mt. Sinai Hosp, 33-46, assoc, 46-52; Hahnemann Med. Col, 49-54, asst. prof, 55-61, clin. assoc. prof, 61-63; ASSOC, GRAD. SCH. MED, UNIV. PA, 60-; SR. ATTEND. PHYSICIAN, ALBERT EINSTEIN MED. CTR, 54-, assoc, 52-54. Shmookler mem. fel, 36-37. Med.C, 42-46, Maj. Fel. Am. Col. Physicians. Hematology. Address: 1710 Pine St, Philadelphia, PA 19103.

GREENSTEIN, TEDDY, b. Czech, Mar. 16, 37; U.S. citizen. CHEMICAL ENGINEERING. B.Ch.E, City Col. New York, 60; M.Ch.E, N.Y. Univ, 62, Nat. Sci. Found. grant, 64, Ph.D.(chem. eng), 67; grant, Inst. Paper Chem, 65-67. Rating engr, Davis Eng, 60; teacher, high sch, 63-64; res. asst. CHEM. ENG. N.Y. Univ, 64-67; ASST. PROF, NEWARK COL. ENG, 67- Found. Advan. Grad. Study Eng. res. grant, 67-69. Am. Chem. Soc; Am. Inst. Chem. Eng. Low Reynolds number hydrodynamics; viscosity of suspensions and emulsions; heat transfer. Address: 3000 Ocean Pkwy, Brooklyn, NY 11235.

GREENSTOCK, CLIVE L(EWIS), b. High Wycombe, U.K, Aug. 14, 39; m. 65; c. 1. MEDICAL BIOPHYSICS, RADIATION CHEMISTRY. B.Sc, Univ. Leeds, 60; M.Sc, Univ. London, 63; Ph.D.(med. biophys), Univ. Toronto, 68. Hosp. physicist, Cardiff Radiother. Ctr, U.K, 60-61; sci. off. radiation physics, Nat. Phys. Lab, U.K, 63-64; fel, Nat. Cancer Inst. Can, 68-70; RES. OFF. RADIATION BIOCHEM, MED. BIOPHYS. BR, ATOMIC ENERGY CAN. LTD,

70- Mem, Photobiol. Group, 70. Radiation Res. Soc; Can. Asn. Physicists; Faraday Soc; Brit. Asn. Radiation Res. Radiation damage in DNA and proteins; radiosensitization and radioprotection; electron transfer processes in photosynthesis and oxidative phosphorylation; energy transfer in photobiology; flash photolysis and pulse radiolysis; structural factors involved in chemical kinetics. Address: Medical Biophysics Branch, Atomic Energy of Canada Ltd, Pinawa, Man, Can.

GREENSTONE, ARTHUR W, b. Brooklyn, N.Y, Sept. 25, 12; m; c. 2. INORGANIC CHEMISTRY. B.S, City Col, New York, 32; fel, N.Y. Univ, 34-36, M.S, 35, Ph.D.(chem), 42. Chemist Saarbach Labs, N.Y, 32-34; teacher, high sch, 36-46; chmn. phys. sci. dept, Bayside High Sch, 46-71; teaching asst. CHEM, PIMA COL, 71, ASST. INSTR, 71- AAAS; Am. Chem. Soc. Coordination compounds and organo-metallic compounds, especially their applications to analytical chemistry. Address: 660 N. Longfellow Ave, Tucson, AZ 85711.

GREENSTREET, WILLIAM (B) LAVON, b. Cora, Mo, Feb. 22, 25; m. 50; c. 4. MECHANICAL ENGINEERING, SOLID MECHANICS. B.S, Colorado State, 50; M.S, Tennessee, 58; Ph.D.(solid mech), Yale, 68. Design engr, Boeing Airplane Co, Wash, 50-51; engr, UNION CARBIDE CORP, 51-58, HEAD, APPL. MECH. SECT, REACTOR DIV, 58- Mem. steering group for subcomt. reinforced openings & external loadings, Pressure Vessel Res. Comt, Welding Res. Coun, 63- U.S.N, 44-46. Am. Soc. Mech. Eng. Pressure vessel research; instantaneous and creep buckling of shells; high-temperature properties of metals and related behavior of structures; nuclear irradiation-induced effects and resultant structural behavior; plasticity; applied solid mechanics. Address: Oak Ridge National Lab, P.O. Box Y, Oak Ridge, TN 37830.

GREENWALD, BERNARD WILLIAM, b. Brooklyn, N.Y, Apr. 9, 37; m. 59; c. 2. ORGANIC & AGRICULTURAL CHEMISTRY, BIOCHEMISTRY. B.S, City Col. New York, 58; M.A, Columbia Univ, 59, Ph.D.(chem), 62. Sr. chemist, PROD. DEVELOP, MERCK & CO, INC, 63-65, group leader, 66-69, mgr, 69-71, INDUST. MGR, 71- Am. Chem. Soc; Am. Inst. Biol. Sci; Am. Phytopath. Soc. Active site structure of the copper enzyme, ascorbic acid oxidase; product development in the agricultural and industrial fields. Address: 3850 Hudson Manor Terr, Bronx, NY 10463.

GREENWALD, DAKOTA U(LRICH), b. Jamestown, N.Dak, July 6, 10; m. 35; c. 3. INDUSTRIAL ENGINEERING. B.A, Grinnell Col, 32; scholar, Iowa, 32-33, M.A, 33, fel, 33-35, Ph.D.(indust. psychol), 35, B.S, 38. Lab. asst, Grinnell Col, 31-32; asst. instr, Univ. Iowa, 33-36, lectr, 35-36; jr. prod. engr, Caterpillar Tractor Co, summer 37; instr, Univ. Del, 38-41; systs. analyst, Dravo Corp, 43; assoc. prof, Univ. Del, 44-47; asst. prof. indust. eng, Syracuse Univ, 47-48, assoc. prof, 48-57; Fulbright lectr, Finland Inst. Technol, 56-57; PROF. INDUST. ENG, SYRACUSE UNIV, 58- Chief indust. engr, Triumph Explosives Inc, 40-42; consult, Pratt & Whitney Aircrafts, 44-45; Ranger Aircraft Co, 45; engr, City of Syracuse, Dept. Eng, summer 48; consult, Rome Air Develop. Ctr, 51-53; Pass & Seymour, Inc, 53; water separation proj, U.S. Air Force, 54-56, proj. Setac, 55-56, Union Carbide Nuclear Co, 57; Carrier Corp, 58-62; Nat. Sci. Found. fel, 59-61; consult, Opers. Res. Off, Wash, D.C, 60. Am. Soc. Eng. Educ; Inst. Mgt. Sci; Opers. Res. Soc. Am. Teaching programs in industrial engineering plant layout; operations research; basic industrial engineering practices; wage administration; management science; development of algorithms for operational use. Address: Dept. of Industrial Engineering, Syracuse University, Syracuse, NY 13210.

GREENWALD, EDWARD KENNETH, b. Dayton, Ky, June 19, 36; m. 59. BIOPHYSICS, BIOMEDICAL ENGINEERING. B.Sc, Ohio State, 59, Nat. Sci. Found. fel, 61-62, Ph.D.(physics, physiol), 66. Staff asst, field test instrumentation, Sandia Corp, 58, staff mem, 59; instr, col. eng, Ohio State, 59-61, 63, 65 & 66, phys. med, 60-61, Marion Br. & Mansfield Br, 61, res. assoc, electron device lab, 62, res. asst, nuclear physics group, 63, biophys. group, 65, instr. phys. med, 65-66, res. assoc. biophys. div, 65-67; asst. prof. surg. & exp. statist, North Carolina, 67-68; asst. prof, depts. elec. eng. & bioeng. & assoc. investr, Space Sci. Res. Ctr, Univ. Mo-Columbia, 68-69, investr, Space Sci. Res. Ctr, 69-71; DIR. RES. & DEVELOP, U.S. CATHETER & INSTRUMENT CORP, 71- Sr. res. physicist, biomed. eng. group, Tech. Inc, 64; instr, Franklin, 65-66; vis. res. assoc. physiol, Indiana State, 67. Consult, U.S. Air Force Aeromed. Space Prog, Wright-Patterson A.F.B, 64; Childrens Hosp, Columbus, Ohio, 65-66. U.S.N, 54-55. AAAS; Microcirculatory Soc; Biophys. Soc; Inst. Elec. & Electronics Eng; Int. Union Physiol. Sci. Microcirculation; rheology of blood; medical and biological instrumentation systems; quantitative physiology in general, and mathematical modelling of biological systems. Address: 308 Brewer Dr, Columbia, MO 65201.

GREENWALD, GILBERT S(AUL), b. New York, N.Y, June 24, 27; m. 50; c. 3. ANATOMY. A.B, California, 49, M.A, 51, Ph.D, 54. Assoc. zool, California, 54; fel. Carnegie Inst, 54-56; instr. anat, Washington (Seattle), 56-59, asst. prof, 59-61; assoc. prof. ANAT, OBSTET. & GYNEC, MED. CTR, UNIV. KANS, 61-64, PROF, 64-, RES. PROF. HUMAN REPROD, 61- Mem. reprod. biol. study sect, Nat. Insts. Health, 66-70, population res. adv. comt, 67-71, consult, ctr. population res, 68-; assoc. ed, Anat. Rec. U.S.N, 45-47. AAAS; Am. Asn. Anat; Brit. Soc. Study Fertil; Soc. Study Reprod. (v.pres, 70-71, pres, 71-72); Endocrine Soc. Reproductive physiology; endocrinology; embryology; egg transport in oviduct; fertility control; pituitary-ovarian relationships. Address: Dept. of Obstetrics & Gynecology, University of Kansas Medical Center, Kansas City, KS 66103.

GREENWALD, HAROLD L(EOPOLD), b. Monticello, N.Y, June 10, 17; m. 53; c. 3. PHYSICAL CHEMISTRY. B.S, Pa. State Col, 39; Ph.D.(chem), Columbia, 52. From asst. to res. assoc, rocket propellants, Div. 8, Nat. Defense Res. Comn, 41-45; asst. chem, Columbia, 45-50; CHEMIST, ROHM & HAAS CO, SPRING HOUSE, 50- AAAS; Am. Chem. Soc. Surface chemistry; organic coatings; aqueous polymer dispersions. Address: 506 Rodman Ave, Jenkintown, PA 19046.

GREENWALT, T(IBOR) J(ACK), b. Budapest, Hungary, Jan. 23, 14; nat; m. 71; c. 1. MEDICINE, HEMATOLOGY. B.A, N.Y. Univ, 34; M.D, 37. Intern path. & bact, Mt. Sinai Hosp, N.Y, 37-38; med, Kings County Hosp, 38-40; med. resident, Montefiore Hosp, 40-41; instr. med, med. col, Tufts Univ, 41-42; med. dir, Milwaukee Blood Ctr, 47-66; clin. instr. med, sch. med, Marquette Univ, 48-51, asst. clin. prof, 51-57, assoc. clin. prof, 57-60, assoc. prof, 60-63, prof, 63-66; MED. DIR, BLOOD PROG, AM. NAT. RED CROSS, 66-; CLIN. PROF. MED, SCH. MED, GEORGE WASH UNIV, 67- Res. asst, New Eng. Med. Ctr, 41-42; consult, Vet. Admin. Hosp, Wood, Wis, 46-66; Milwaukee County Gen. Hosp, 46-66; ed, Vox Sanguinis, 56-; mem. hemat. study sect, Nat. Insts. Health, 60-63, 70-, consult. clin. ctr, 67-; founding ed, Transfusion, 60-; chmn. comt. blood & transfusion probs, Nat. Acad. Sci-Nat. Res. Coun, 63-66; ed. Gen. Principles of Blood Transfusion, comt. blood, Am. Med. Asn, 70- Dipl, Am. Bd. Internal Med, 46; jr. achievement award sci, 58; distinguished citizen's award, Allied Vet. Coun, 63; John Elliot Award, Am. Asn. Blood Banks, 66. Med.C, 42-46, Maj. AAAS; Am. Med. Asn; Int. Soc. Hemat; Am. Col. Physicians; Int. Soc. Blood Transfusion (pres, 66-72); Am. Soc. Clin. Path; Am. Fedn. Clin. Res; Am. Soc. Hemat.(treas, 63-67); Am. Asn. Immunol; Soc. Exp. Biol. & Med; Am. Soc. Human Genetics. Immunohematology; blood banking; blood group genetics. Address: Blood Program, American National Red Cross, 1730 E St. N.W, Washington, DC 20006.

GREENWAY, CLIVE VICTOR, b. Gloucester, Eng, Mar. 6, 37; m. 69; c. 1. PHYSIOLOGY, PHARMACOLOGY. B.A, Cambridge, 58, Ph.D.(pharmacol), 61. Demonstr. pharmacol, Cambridge, 60-63; lectr. physiol, Aberdeen Univ, 63-67; asst. prof, Univ. Alta, 67-68; ASSOC. PROF. PHARMACOL, UNIV. MAN, 68- Am. Physiol. Soc; Am. Soc. Pharmacol. & Exp. Therapeut; Brit. Physiol. Soc; Can. Physiol. Soc; Pharmacol. Soc. Can. Vascular beds of the liver, intestine and spleen; control of blood flow, volume and fluid exchange; effects of vasoactive agents and of endotoxin. Address: Dept. of Pharmacology, University of Manitoba, Winnipeg, Man, Can.

GREENWELL, BEN(JAMIN) E(LMER), b. Monmouth, Ill, Apr. 26, 24; m. 51; c. 3. BIOLOGICAL CHEMISTRY. B.S, Monmouth Col, 45; M.S, Illinois, 48, fel, 48-50, Ph.D.(biochem), 50. Asst. org. chem, Monmouth Col, 43-44; Illinois, 47-48; biochemist microbiol. dept, Abbott Labs, 50-51, liaison res. admin, 51-57, information scientist, 57-59; dir. RES, ROWELL LABS, INC, 59-61, V.PRES, 61- U.S.N.R, 44-46. Pharmaceuticals research administration. Address: Rowell Labs, Inc, Baudette, MN 56623.

GREENWOOD, D(ELBERT) A, b. Lehi, Utah, Oct. 15, 04; m. 34; c. 2. BIOCHEMISTRY, PHARMACOLOGY. B.S, Brigham Young, 26, M.S, 30; Ph.D. (pharmacol), Chicago, 46. Asst. chem, Brigham Young, 26-27, instr, 27-30; asst. & instr, Iowa State Col, 30-36; res. biochemist, Am. Meat Inst, Chicago, 36-46; prof. biochem, Utah State Univ, 46-69; RETIRED. Res. assoc. pharmacol, Chicago, 39-46; mem. subcmt. fluorosis problem in livestock prod, Nat. Res. Coun, 54-65. AAAS; Am. Chem. Soc; Am. Soc. Pharmacol. & Exp. Therapeut; Pan-Am. Med. Asn; Soc. Toxicol. Fluorides in animals; nutritive values of meat; effects of insecticides on farm animals and residues in tissues used as food; effect of fertilizers on alfalfa; effect of feeding highly nutritive feeds to farm animals prior to slaughter; biological effects of carcinogenic polynuclear aromatic hydrocarbons and organic phosphorus pesticides in chicken embryos, chickens, and mice. Address: 601 River Heights Blvd, Logan, UT 84321.

GREENWOOD, DONALD D(EAN), b. Milwaukee, Wis, Apr. 22, 31; m. 60; c. 2. PSYCHOPHYSICS. B.A, Wisconsin, 51; univ. fel, Harvard, 57-58, Nat. Insts. Health fel, 59-60, Ph.D.(exp. psychol), 60. Fel. neurophysiol, Wisconsin, 60-63, proj. assoc, 63-64; asst. prof. physiol, Duke, 64-66; assoc. prof. psychol, UNIV. B.C, 66-71, RES. ASSOC. PROF. AUDIOL. & SPEECH SCI, 71- U.S.A.F, 52-56. AAAS; Soc. Neurosci; Psychonomic Soc; Acoust. Soc. Am. Hearing; sensory systems; microelectrode research in audition. Address: Division of Audiology & Speech Sciences, University of British Columbia, Vancouver 8, B.C, Can.

GREENWOOD, D(ONALD) T(HEODORE), b. Clarkdale, Ariz, Dec. 8, 23; m. 51; c. 2. ENGINEERING. B.S, Calif. Inst. Tech, 44, M.S, 48, Ph.D.(elec. eng), 51. Lectr. elec. eng, Southern California, 54-55; asst. prof. AERONAUT. ENG, UNIV. MICH, ANN ARBOR, 56-57, assoc. prof, 57-63, PROF, 63- Group engr, Lockheed Aircraft Corp, 51-56. U.S.N, 43-46. AAAS; Am. Soc. Eng. Educ; Am. Soc. Mech. Eng; Am. Inst. Aeronaut. & Astronaut. Flight mechanics; dynamics. Address: Dept. of Aerospace Engineering, University of Michigan, Ann Arbor, MI 48104.

GREENWOOD, FRED L(AUREL), b. Cooke Twp. Pa, July 31, 11; m. 44. ORGANIC CHEMISTRY. B.S, Dickinson Col, 33; M.S, Pa. State, 36; Hormel fel, Minnesota, 39-41, Ph.D.(biochem), 40. Instr. CHEM, Minnesota, 41-46; asst. prof, TUFTS UNIV, 46-49, assoc. prof, 50-58, PROF, 58- Fel, Illinois, 49-50; Nat. Sci. Found. fel, Univ. Calif, 59-60; Petrol. Res. Fund. fel, Stanford Univ, 66-67. Am. Chem. Soc. Ozonization of organic compounds. Address: Dept. of Chemistry, Tufts University, Medford, MA 02155.

GREENWOOD, FREDERICK C, b. Portsmouth, Eng, July 5, 27; m. 50; c. 3. BIOCHEMISTRY, ENDOCRINOLOGY. B.Sc, London, 50, M.Sc, 51, Ph.D. (biochem), 53, D.Sc.(endocrinol), 67. Mem. acad. staff steroid biochem, Imp. Cancer Res. Fund, 53-58, head protein chem. sect, 58-68; PROF. BIOCHEM, UNIV. HAWAII, 68- Rockefeller fel. protein chem, Wisconsin, 58-59; Consult, med. sch, St. Mary's Hosp, 66-68; mem, Coord. Comt. Human Tumor Invests, 65-67; secy. sub-comt. polypeptide hormones, Med. Res. Coun, 67-68. Royal Corps Sig, 45-48, Lt. AAAS; Brit. Soc. Endocrinol; Brit. Biochem. Soc. Steroid biochemistry and its application to clinical research; peptide hormones; chemistry and measurements in biological fluids. Address: Dept. of Biochemistry & Biophysics, University of Hawaii, Honolulu, HI 96822.

GREENWOOD, GEORGE W(ATKINS), b. North New Portland, Maine, Nov. 28, 29; m. 51; c. 3. CIVIL ENGINEERING. B.S, Maine, 51; M.S, Illinois, 60, Nat. Sci. Found. fel, 62-63, Ph.D.(traffic eng), 63. Eng. aide, bridge div, Maine State Hwy. Comn, 51, 53-54; instr. eng. graphics, Maine, 54-56; eng, Illinois, 56-58; res. assoc. CIVIL ENG, 58-62; ASSOC. PROF, UNIV. MAINE, 63- U.S.A.F, 51, 1st Lt. Highway and traffic engineering; inter-community traffic estimation models. Address: Dept. of Civil Engineering, 120 Boardman Hall, University of Maine, Orono, ME 04473.

GREENWOOD, HUGH J, b. Vancouver, B.C, Mar. 17, 31; m. 55; c. 3. GEOLOGY, PETROLOGY. B.A.Sc, British Columbia, 54, Nicholson scholar, 54-56, M.A.Sc, 56; Jacobus fel, Princeton, 58-59, Ph.D, 60; fel, Carnegie Institution, 60-63; assoc. prof. GEOL, Princeton, 63-67; UNIV. B.C, 67-69, PROF, 69- Fel. Royal Soc. Can. Thermodynamics; phase equilibria; chemical kinetics; petrology. Address: Dept. of Geology, University of British Columbia, Vancouver, B.C, Can.

GREENWOOD, IVAN ANDERSON, JR, b. Cleveland, Ohio, Jan. 31, 21; m. 49; c. 2. PHYSICS. B.S, Case, 42. From staff mem. to assoc. group leader, radiation lab, Mass. Inst. Technol, 42-46; from proj. engr. to MGR. RES. DEPT. & ASSOC. DIR. RES. & ADV. DEVELOP. DIV, KEARFOTT DIV, SINGER CO, 46- Tech. & vol. ed, Radiation Lab. Series, Mass. Inst. Technol. & Gen. Precision Lab, Inc, 45-48; consult, N.Y. Univ, 58-61; Yeshiva Univ, 61-64; founding dir, Bio-Instrumentation Inst, Inc, 62- Civilian with Off. Sci. Res. & Develop, 42-46. AAAS; Am. Phys. Soc; Inst. Elec. & Electronics Eng; Am. Inst. Navig; Fedn. Am. Sci. Electronic instrumentation; medical ultrasonics; magnetic resonance; optical pumping; lasers. Address: Kearfott Division, Singer Co, 63 Bedford Rd, Pleasantville, NY 10570.

GREENWOOD, JOSEPH A(LBERT), b. Breckenridge, Mo, Sept. 18, 06; m. 30; c. 3. MATHEMATICS. A.B, Missouri, 27, fel, 27-30, A.M, 29, Ph.D.(math), 31; Michigan, 39-40. Instr. math, Duke, 30-37, asst. prof, 38-41, math. consult. parapsychol. lab, 38-41; statistician, bur. aeronaut. Navy Dept, 46-57, mathematician, Off. Naval Collab. Air Intel, 57-62; chmn. anal. dept, Armed Forces Radiobiol. Res. Inst, 62-66; head, biomet. br, Food & Drug Admin, 66-68; MATH. STATISTICIAN, BUR. NARCOTICS & DANGEROUS DRUGS, 68- U.S.N.R, 42-46, Comdr. Fel. AAAS; fel. Am. Soc. Qual. Control; Inst. Math. Statist; Soc. Indust. & Appl. Math; Am. Statist. Asn; Biomet. Soc. Problems in mathematical statistics; probability. Address: 430 Great Falls St, Falls Church, VA 22046.

GREENWOOD, MICHAEL SARGENT, b. Winthrop, Mass, Nov. 7, 40; m. 61; c. 2. PLANT PHYSIOLOGY. B.A, Brown Univ, 63; M.F, Yale, 65, M.S, 66, Ph.D.(plant physiol), 69. ASST. PROF. BIOL, MIDDLEBURY COL, 68- Fred. C. Gloeckner Found. res. grant, 70-71; fel, Univ. Glasgow, 71-72. Bot. Soc. Am; Scand. Soc. Plant Physiol. Plant development; physiology of root meristem regeneration, particularly the environmental and internal factors which determine the differentiation of a root meristem by a cutting. Address: Dept. of Biology, Middlebury College, Middlebury, VT 05753.

GREENWOOD, REGINALD C(HARLES), b. Manchester, Eng, Nov. 27, 35; U.S. citizen; m. 58. NUCLEAR PHYSICS. B.Sc, Manchester, 56; M.A, Western Reserve, 58; Ph.D.(nuclear physics), Western Ontario, 60. Assoc. physicist, Armour Res. Found, 60-62, res. physicist & group leader, IIT Res. Inst, 62-65, sr. physicist & group leader, 65-66; SR. RES. PHYSICIST, ATOMIC ENERGY OPERS, NAT. REACTOR TESTING STA, IDAHO NUCLEAR CORP, 66- Sr. res. physicist, atomic energy div, nat. reactor testing sta, Idaho, 65-66. Am. Phys. Soc; Am. Nuclear Soc. Neutron capture gamma rays; radioactive decay schemes; neutron activation analysis; scintillation spectroscopy. Address: 1719 Shasta St, Idaho Falls, ID 83401.

GREENWOOD, ROBERT, b. London, Eng, Jan. 25, 23; nat; m. 48; c. 3. GEOLOGY. B.S, Calif. Inst. Tech, 42, M.S, 43; Ph.D.(geol), Harvard, 48. Field geologist, Geol. Surv, Nigeria, 44-46; mining geologist, Republic Steel Corp, 48-49; field geologist, Dept. Nac. da Producao Mineral, Brazil, 49-51; mineral procurement & export, Frank Samuel & Co, 51-53; asst. prof. GEOL, Mich. Col. Min. & Tech, 53-54; Houston, 54-57, assoc. prof, 57-64, PROF, 64-68; ASSOC. PROF. & CHMN. DEPT, CAMDEN COL. ARTS & SCI, RUTGERS UNIV, 68- Colonial serv, Dept. Sci. & Tech. Personnel, Gt. Britain, 44-46. Geol. Soc. Am; Soc. Econ. Geol. Economic geology; mineralogy; geochemistry. Address: Dept. of Geology, Camden College of Arts & Sciences, Rutgers University, Camden, NJ 08102.

GREENWOOD, ROBERT E(WING), b. Navasota, Tex, June 21, 11; m. 51; c. 1. MATHEMATICS. A.B, Texas, 33; fel, Brown, 35-36; fel, Princeton, 36-38, A.M, 38, Ph.D.(math), 39. Instr. MATH, UNIV. TEX. AUSTIN, 34-35, 38-42, asst. prof, 46-50, assoc. prof, 52-57, PROF, 57- U.S.N.R, 43-46, 50-52, Comdr. Am. Math. Soc; Math. Asn. Am. Numerical methods; combinatory analysis; probability. Address: Dept. of Mathematics, University of Texas at Austin, Austin, TX 78712.

GREENWOOD, WILLIAM R, b. St. Louis, Mo, Sept. 15, 38; m. 61; c. 1. GEOLOGY. B.S, Idaho, 61, M.S, 66, Ph.D.(geol), 68. Proj. chief, Idaho Bur. Mines & Geol, 66-68; GEOLOGIST, Manned Spacecraft Ctr, NASA, 68-70; U.S. GEOL. SURV, 70- U.S.M.C, 61-64, Res. 64-67, Capt. Geol. Soc. Am; Geol. Soc. London; Am. Asn. Petrol. Geol. Metamorphic petrology and structural geology; lunar geology. Address: U.S. Geological Survey, Menlo Park, CA 94025.

GREEP, ROY O(RVAL), b. Longford, Kans, Oct. 8, 05; m. 31; c. 3. ANATOMY. B.S, Kans. State Col, 30; M.S, Univ. Wis, 32, fel, 33-34, Ph.D.(zool), 34; hon. M.A, Harvard, 46; hon. D.Sc, Univ. Buffalo, 60; hon. Sc.D, Kans. State Univ, 68 & Univ. Sheffield, 71. Asst. zool, Univ. Wis, 30-35; Harvard, 35-37, instr, 38; res. assoc, Squibb Inst. Med. Res, 38-44; asst. prof. dent. sci, sch. dent. med, HARVARD, 44-46, lectr. endocrinol, dept. physiol, 46-47, assoc. prof. dent. sci, 46-49, prof, 49-55, anat, 55-67, dean, 52-67, JOHN ROCK PROF. POP. STUDIES, SCH. PUB. HEALTH & DIR. LAB. HUMAN & REPROD. BIOL, MED. SCH, 67-, teaching fel. anat, Harvard Med. Sch, 44-46, acting chmn, dept, 56-59. Consult, Opers. Res. Off; with Off. Sci. Res. & Develop, 44, 63-; chmn. comt. dent, Nat. Res. Coun, 56-61; mem. endocrinol. study sect, Nat. Insts. Health, 56-59, 63; mem. med. adv. bd, Nat. Pituitary Agency, 63-67; expert adv. panel biol. of human reprod, WHO, 65-; mem. basic sci. comt, Int. Planned Parenthood Fedn, 71- Henry Dale Medal, 67; Fred Conrad Koch Award, 71. AAAS; Am. Dent. Asn; Soc. Exp. Biol. & Med.(pres, 69-71); Am. Physiol. Soc; Am. Soc. Zool; Endocrine Soc.(ed, Endocrinol, 52-59, Schering scholar, 57, pres, 65-66); Am. Asn. Anat; Am. Col. Dent; assoc. Acad. Dent. Sci; fel. Am. Acad. Arts & Sci; N.Y. Acad. Sci; Int. Asn. Dent. Res; Int. Soc. Endocrinol.(pres, 68-72); Brit. Soc. Endocrinol. Endocrinology; adrenal cortex; gonadotropins; parathyroids; growth hormone; mineral metabolism; hermaphroditism; genetics; dental education. Address: Lab. of Human Reproduction & Reproductive Biology, 45 Shattuck St, Boston, MA 02115.

GREER, ALBERT H, b. New York, N.Y, Jan. 30, 20; m. 46; c. 1. ORGANIC CHEMISTRY. B.S, City Col, 41; M.S, Polytech. Inst. Brooklyn, 45, Ph.D.(chem), 49. Chemist biol. chem, State Hosp, Brooklyn, N.Y, 42-43; res. chemist fungicides, Centro Res. Co, 43-44; pharmaceuts, Day Chem. Co, 44-45; textile chems, Commonwealth Color & Chem, 45-49; res. group leader, ion exchange & org. res, IONAC CHEM. CO. 49-59, sr. res. chemist, 59-65, mgr. adv. res, 65-69, CHIEF RES. CHEMIST, 69- Am. Chem. Soc. Synthetic ion exchangers; organic monomers and polymers; pyridines; guanidines; detergents; fungicides. Address: 228 Warwick Rd, Haddonfield, NJ 08033.

GREER, DONALD LEE, b. Silver City, N.Mex, June 14, 36. MYCOLOGY. B.S, Col. Idaho, 58; M.S, Univ. Wash, 61; Ph.D.(microbiol), Tulane Univ, 65. U.S. Pub. Health Serv. summer fel, Tulane Univ, 65; instr, sch. med, Univ. Kans, 66-68; instr. MYCOL, TULANE UNIV, 68-70, ASST. PROF, 70-, MEM. STAFF, INT. CTR. MED. RES. & TRAINING, 68-, ASSOC. PROF, UNIV. VALLE, COLOMBIA, 70- U.S.P.H.S.R, 65-, Scientist. Am. Soc. Microbiol; Mycol. Soc. Am; Med. Mycol. Soc. of the Americas; Int. Soc. Human & Animal Mycol. Taxonomy and pathogenecity of the Entomophthorales; epidemiology and ecology of Histoplasma capsulatum and Blastomyces dermatitides; clinical identification of medically important fungi; Paracoccidioidomycosis and Dermatomycosis. Address: International Center for Medical Research & Training, Apartado Aereo 5390, Cali, Colombia, S.A.

GREER, EARL V(INCENT), b. Kechi, Kans, Mar. 27, 12; m. 35; c. 4. MATHEMATICS. A.B, Olivet Col, 32; M.A, Illinois, 34; Ph.D.(math), Oklahoma, 51. Dean & head dept. math, Bresee Col, 34-40; asst. prof. MATH, BETHANY NAZARENE COL, 40-47, assoc. prof, 48-50, PROF, 50-, HEAD DEPT, 40- Am. Math. Soc; Math. Asn. Am. Extension of a theorem of Saks and Sierpinski to planar transformations; investigation of connections existing between two relations defined on the class of functions, one a Saks-Sierpinski relation and the other a Blumberg relation. Address: 4700 N. Donald St, Bethany, OK 73008.

GREER, EDISON, b. Ramona, Kans, Mar. 27, 12; m. 39, 58; c. 2. MATHEMATICS. B.S, Kans. State Teachers Col, 36; M.S, Kans. State Col, 38; Ph.D.(math), Kansas, 46. Teacher, pub. schs, Kans, 30-34; instr. physics, Kans. State Teachers Col.(Emporia), 35-36; math, Kans. State Col, 36-38; Kansas, 38-40, 45-46; Munic. Univ, Wichita, 40-43; Beech Aircraft, 43-45; assoc. prof, Kans. State Col, 46-51; struct. engr, guided missiles div, Consol. Vultee Aircraft Corp, Calif, 52-54; design engr, Aerojet-Gen. Corp. div, Gen. Tire & Rubber Co, 54-55; prof. math, San Antonio Jr. Col, 55-56; res. scientist, missile systems div, Lockheed Aircraft Corp, 56-57, tech. staff head, 57-58, staff scientist, 58-59; PROF. MATH, SAN JOSE STATE COL, 59-, head dept. 59-61. Math. Asn. Am. Projective differential geometry; a study of analytic surfaces by means of a projective theory of envelopes. Address: 5101 Monterey Rd, Box 357, San Jose, CA 95111.

GREER, HOWARD A. L, b. Warrensville, N.C, Feb. 7, 36; m. 58; c. 2. AGRONOMY, PLANT PHYSIOLOGY. B.S, Berea Col, 58; M.S, Kentucky, 61; Ph.D.(agron, plant physiol), Iowa State, 64. INSTR. agron, Iowa State, 60-63; biol, Appalachian State Teachers Col, 64-65; EXTEN. AGRON, OKLA. STATE UNIV, 65- Geigy Award in agron, 70. Am. Soc. Agron; Crop Sci. Soc. Am; Weed Sci. Soc. Am. Effects of herbicides on plant growth and development. Address: Dept. of Agronomy, Oklahoma State University, Stillwater, OK 74074.

GREER, JAMES EDWARD, b. Greer, S.C, Apr. 30, 12; m; c. 3. TEXTILES. B.S, Presby. Col.(S.C), 33; Clemson Col, 34; Mass. Inst. Tech, 51. Lab. asst, Pacific Mills, S.C, 33-38; laborer, South. Bleachery, 38; chemist dyestuffs div, Koppers Co, 39-41, in charge tech. sales, 46; chief chemist, res. & develop. lab, Greensboro Finishing Co, Burlington Mills Div, BURLINGTON INDUSTS, INC, 46-63, res. chemist, cent. res. & develop. lab, 63-71, SR. CONSULT. TEXTILE TECH. SERV, BURLINGTON RES. CTR, 71- U.S.A, 42-45, Maj. Am. Chem. Soc; Am. Asn. Textile Chem. & Colorists. Dyeing and finishing man made textile fibers; automatic beaker dyeing machine; quick fading gasfastness test device for acetate and dacron; Burlington pressure beck; Greer nylon unit dying machine; manufacture and uses of chemicals by the textile industry; indigo dyeing; yarncarts; flow meter inside package dyeing machines. Address: 912 Forest Hill Dr, Greensboro, NC 27410.

GREER, JAMES E(DWARD), b. Dallas, Tex, Apr. 25, 16; m. 42; c. 3. MEDICAL MICROBIOLOGY. B.S, Agr. & Mech. Col, Texas, 37; M.A, Texas, 41; fel, Southern Methodist, 41-42; Ph.D.(mycol), Oklahoma, 53. Asst. genetics, Agr. & Mech. Col, Texas, 39-40; clin. bacteriologist, Vet. Admin. Hosp, Dallas, Tex, 46-49; asst. bact, Oklahoma, 49-53; RES. ASSOC. DERMAT, HENRY FORD HOSP, 53- Dipl, pub. health & med. lab. bact. & pub. health & med. lab. mycol, Am. Bd. Med. Microbiol. Bacteriologist & serologist, 127th Gen. Hosp, 42-43, lab. off, 43-46, U.S.A, 42-46, Res, 46-, Capt. Am. Soc. Microbiol; Am. Soc. Med. Technol; fel. Am. Pub. Health Asn; Int. Soc. Human & Animal Mycol; N.Y. Acad. Sci; fel. Am. Acad. Microbiol; fel. Royal Soc. Health; Med. Mycol. Soc. of the Americas. Medical mycology; bacteriology of the skin; antibiotic susceptibility testing; staphylococci. Address: Dept. of Dermatology, Henry Ford Hospital, Detroit, MI 48202.

GREER, JOHN KEEVER, b. Topeka, Kans, July 8, 30; m. 59; c. 2. MAMMOLOGY, ECOLOGY. B.A, Kansas, 55; M.S, Mich. State, 60, Ph.D.(zool), 65. Asst. prof. ZOOL, UNIV. OKLA, 65-69, ASSOC. PROF, 69-, CURATOR MAMMALS, STOVALL MUS. SCI. & HIST, 65-, DIR, 67-, acting dir, 66-67, asst. dir. biol. sta, 65-66. Secy-treas, Mt. Plains Mus. Conf. & newsletter ed, 68-71. U.S.M.C, 48-49. Ecol. Soc. Am; Wildlife Soc; Am. Soc. Mammal; Am. Asn. Mus; Soc. Syst. Zool; Soc. Study Evolution. Ecology of South American and Mexican mammals. Address: Stovall Museum of Science & History, University of Oklahoma, Norman, OK 73069.

GREER, MONTE ARNOLD, b. Portland, Ore, Oct. 26, 22; m. 43; c. 2. ENDOCRINOLOGY. A.B, Stanford, 44, M.D, 47. Asst. med, Tufts, 47-49, instr,

50-51; sr. asst. surgeon, Nat. Insts. Health, 51-55; asst. clin. prof. med, California, Los Angeles, 55-56; assoc. prof. MED, SCH. MED, UNIV. ORE, 56-62, PROF, 62-, HEAD DIV. ENDOCRINOL, 56- Asst, Boston Univ, 49-50; assoc, George Washington, 51-54; dir. radioisotope serv, Long Beach Vet. Hosp, 55-56; res. career award, Nat. Insts. Health, 62, mem. pharmacol. & endocrinol. fel. comt, 68-72. U.S.A, 43-46; U.S.P.H.S, 51-55. Int. Brain Res. Orgn; Endocrine Soc.(Ciba Award, 58); Soc. Exp. Biol. & Med; Am. Soc. Clin. Invest; Am. Fedn. Clin. Res; Am. Thyroid Asn.(2nd v.pres, 68-69); Asn. Am. Physicians. Normal and abnormal thyroid physiology; neural control of pituitary function. Address: Dept. of Medicine, University of Oregon School of Medicine, Portland, OR 97201.

GREER, PAUL S(HRYOCK), b. Braddock, Pa, Nov. 28, 04; m. 48; c. 1. CHEMICAL ENGINEERING. B.S, Grove City Col, 25; B.S, Case Inst. Technol, 27, Ch.E, 32. Chem. engr, Carbide & Carbon Chem. Corp, W.Va, 27-42; sr. indust. specialist, War Prod. Bd, Wash, D.C, 42-43, prin. indust. specialist, office rubber dir, 43-44; chief polymer develop. br, office synthetic rubber, Reconstruct. Finance Corp, 44-46, asst. chief, res. & develop. div, 46-50, chief, 50-55; Nat. Sci. Found, 55-57; assoc. dir, chem. div, U.S. ARMY RES. OFF, 57-67, CHIEF THEMIS-ARPA OFF, 67- Am. Chem. Soc; Am. Inst. Chem. Eng. Hydrolysis; dehydration; pH measurement; esterification; polymerization. Address: U.S. Army Research Office-Durham, Box CM, Duke Station, Durham, NC 27706.

GREER, RAYMOND T(HOMAS), b. East Orange, N.J, Apr. 26, 40; m. 65; SOLID STATE & MATERIALS SCIENCE. B.S, Rensselaer Polytech, 63; Ph.D.(solid state sci), Pa. State, 68. Res. asst. atomic develop, N.Y. State Off. Atomic & Space Develop, 62-63; res. asst. mat. sci, mat. res. lab, Pa. State, 63-68, res. assoc, 68-69; resident res. assoc. planetary sci, jet propulsion lab, Calif. Inst. Technol, 69-70; asst. prof. NUCLEAR ENG, IOWA STATE UNIV, 70-71, ASSOC. PROF, 71- Nat. Res. Coun. fel, 69; mem. subgroup mining & processing, Working Group on Extraterrestrial Resources, 64-69. Am. Geophys. Union; Am. Chem. Soc; Am. Ceramic Soc; Am. Geol. Inst; Am. Nuclear Soc. Interdisciplinary research in the characterization of materials emphasizing x-ray diffraction and microscopy, microprobe analysis, luminescence, radiation damage, differential thermal analysis and micrometrics. Address: Dept. of Nuclear Engineering, Iowa State University, Ames, IA 50010.

GREER, ROBERT W, b. Mahomet, Tex, Oct. 14, 20; m. 53; c. 2. ELECTRICAL ENGINEERING. B.S, Milwaukee Sch. Eng, 51; M.S, Wisconsin, 55, Ph.D.(elec. eng), 58. Instr. elec. eng, Milwaukee Sch. Eng, 47-51, asst. prof, 51-52, prof, 52-55; instr, Wisconsin, 55-58; specialist syst. anal, AUTONETICS DIV, N.Am. Aviation, Inc, 58-60, supvr. syst. anal, 60-62, chief syst. eng, 62-64, mgr. requirements anal, 64-66, CHIEF ENGR. ADVAN. AVIONICS, N.AM. ROCKWELL CORP, ANAHEIM, 66- U.S.N, 40-46. Weapon system operational analysis and effectiveness. Address: 233 Rosalind Dr, Orange, CA 92667.

GREER, SANDRA C(HARLENE), b. Greenville, S.C, Jan. 7, 45; m. 68; c. 2. PHYSICAL CHEMISTRY. B.S, Furman Univ, 66; Woodrow Wilson fel, 66-67; M.S, Univ. Chicago, 68, Ph.D.(chem), 69. RES. CHEMIST, SECT. 221.04, NAT. BUR. STANDARDS, 69- Am. Chem. Soc; Am. Phys. Soc; Calorimetry Conf. Crystal structures of solidified gases; phase diagrams of mixtures of solidified gases; experimental thermodynamics of phase transitions and critical phenomena. Address: Section 221.04, National Bureau of Standards, Gaithersburg, MD 20234.

GREER, SHELDON, b. Brooklyn, N.Y, July 11, 28; m. 57; c. 2. MOLECULAR GENETICS. B.A, Brooklyn Col, 50, fel, 50-52; M.A, Columbia, 52, Runyon fel, 56-57, Ph.D.(zool), 57. Asst, Columbia, 52-56; res. assoc. biochem, col. physicians & surgeons, Columbia, 58-61; ASSOC. PROF. MICROBIOL, SCH. MED, UNIV. MIAMI, 61- Ultra-violet light effects on unnatural deoxyribonucleic acid; enzyme evolution; regulatory mechanisms; sensitization of tumors to x-ray; pyrimidine metabolism-catabolism-transformation in Bacillus subtilis; lysogenic conversion in Streptococcus mutans; curing cells of their proviruses; mutagenesis. Address: P.O. Box 875, Biscayne Annex, Miami, FL 33152.

GREER, WILLIAM LOUIS, b. Bardstown, Ky, Apr. 7, 43; m. 68; c. 2. PHYSICAL CHEMISTRY, SOLID STATE PHYSICS. A.B, Vanderbilt Univ, 65; Nat. Sci. Found. fel, Univ. Chicago, 65-69, Ph.D.(chem), 69. Nat. Res. Coun-Nat. Bur. Standards res. assoc. & res. chemist, Nat. Bur. Standards, 69-71; lectr. chem, Georgetown Univ, 71; RES. ASSOC, INST. MOLECULAR PHYSICS, UNIV. MD, 72- Am. Phys. Soc; Am. Chem. Soc. Theoretical research on the nature of electronic states in organic solids and fluids; phonon heat transport in a model crystal with isotopic defects; electronic and transport properties of condensed matter. Address: Institute for Molecular Physics, University of Maryland, College Park, MD 20742.

GREESON, PHILLIP EDWARD, b. Lexington, Ky, Aug. 11, 40; m. 64. LIMNOLOGY. B.S, Univ. Ky, 62, M.S, 63; Ph.D.(limnol), Univ. Louisville, 67. LIMNOLOGIST, WATER RESOURCES DIV, U.S. GEOL. SURV, 67- AAAS; Am. Soc. Limnol. & Oceanog; Int. Asn. Theoret. & Appl. Limnol; Phycol. Soc. Am; Am. Water Resources Asn. Aquatic ecology; biological and chemical effects of water pollution; lake productivity and eutrophication; algal ecology. Address: 166 Vly Rd, Schenectady, NY 12309.

GREEVER, JOHN, b. Pulaski, Va, Jan. 30, 34; m. 53; c. 3. MATHEMATICS. B.S, Univ. Richmond, 53; fel, Univ. Va, 53-58, M.A, 56, Ph.D.(math), 58. Asst. prof. MATH, Fla. State Univ, 58-61; HARVEY MUDD COL, 61-65, assoc. prof, 65-70, PROF, 70- Part-time instr, Univ. Va, 53-58; dir, Nat. Sci. Found. Undergrad. Res. Partic. Prog. Math, Harvey Mudd Col, summers, 63-66 & 70; vis. prof, res. inst. math. sci, Kyoto Univ, Japan, 67-68. Am. Math. Soc; Am. Speleol. Soc; Math. Asn. Am. Topology; generalizations of compactness properties. Address: Dept. of Mathematics, Harvey Mudd College, Claremont, CA 91711.

GREFF, RICHARD JOSEPH, b. N.Y.C, Apr. 8, 44; m. 66; c. 2. POLYMER & PHYSICAL CHEMISTRY. B.S, Wagner Col, 65; Nat. Insts. Health grant & Ph.D.(polymer chem), Polytech. Inst. Brooklyn, 70. CHEMIST, Congoleum-Nairn Inc, N.J, 65-66; UNION CARBIDE CORP, BOUND BROOK, 69- Sci.

Res. Soc. Am; Am. Chem. Soc. Micro-encapsulation; vinyl floor formulations; ion selectivity in ion-exchange resins, both aqueous and non-aqueous systems; polymer characterization via gel permeation chromatography; osmometry and light scattering techniques. Address: 1258 Evergreen Dr, Somerville, NJ 08876.

GREGERMAN, ROBERT ISAAC, b. Boston, Mass, Apr. 18, 30; m. 57; c. 2. ENDOCRINOLOGY, MEDICINE. A.B, Harvard, 51; M.D, Tufts Univ, 55. Intern med, New Eng. Med. Ctr, Tufts Univ, 55-56; clin. assoc, geront. res. ctr, Nat. Inst. Child Health & Human Develop, 56-58; resident med, Vet. Admin. Hosp, Wash, D.C, 58-59; univ. hosp, Univ. Mich, 59-60, fel. endocrinol. & instr, 60-61; investr, GERONT. RES. CTR, NAT. INST. CHILD HEALTH & HUMAN DEVELOP, BALTIMORE CITY HOSPS, 61-63, CHIEF ENDOCRINOL. SECT, 63-; ASST. PROF. MED, SCH. MED, JOHNS HOPKINS UNIV, 66-, asst, 63-64, instr, 64-66. U.S.P.H.S, 56-, Med. Dir. AAAS; Am. Fedn. Clin. Res; Am. Thyroid Asn; Endocrine Soc; Geront. Soc. Thyroid physiology and biochemistry; peptide chemistry; clinical endocrinology; internal medicine. Address: Gerontology Research Center, National Institute of Child Health & Human Development, National Institutes of Health, Baltimore City Hospitals, Baltimore, MD 21224.

GREGG, CECIL MANREN, b. Eustace, Tex, Jan. 20, 08; m. 32; c. 2. AGRONOMY, HORTICULTURE. B.S, E.Tex. State Col, 33; cert, Sam Houston State Teachers Col, 36; M.Ed, Texas A&M, 44; Ph.D.(crop prod, soil fertil), Mich. State, 50. Instr, independent sch. dists, Redwater, 36-38 & Jacksonville, 38-46; asst. prof. AGR, SOUTHWEST TEX. STATE UNIV, 46-50, assoc. prof, 50-52, PROF, 52- Summer, Nat. Sci. Found. res. grant, 64; adv. Tex. Partners, Alliance for Progress, Agr. Coop. Pueblo Nuevo de Colan, Peru, summer 67; teacher & res. worker, plant sci. dept, sch. agr, Haile Selassie Univ, 68-70. Am. Soc. Agron; Soil Sci. Soc. Am; Crop Sci. Soc. Am. Crop production and soil fertility. Address: Dept. of Agriculture, Southwest Texas State University, San Marcos, TX 78666.

GREGG, CHARLES T(HORNTON), b. Billings, Mont, July 27, 27; m. 47; c. 4. BIOCHEMISTRY. B.S, Oregon State, 52, M.S, 55, Ph.D.(biochem), 59. Instr, Oregon State, 55-59; U.S. Pub. Health Serv, res. fel. physiol. chem, sch. med, Hopkins, 59-63; STAFF MEM. BIOCHEM, LOS ALAMOS SCI. LAB, 63- U.S.N, 44-46. AAAS; Am. Chem. Soc. Energy metabolism of mammalian cells; oxidative phosphorylation; metabolism of mitochondria and submitochondrial particles; biological applications of stable istopes. Address: Biomedical Research Group, Los Alamos Scientific Lab, Box 1663, Los Alamos, NM 87544.

GREGG, DAVID H, b. Sherwood, N.Dak, Nov. 15, 11; m. 39; c. 2. CIVIL ENGINEERING. B.S, U.S. Mil. Acad, 35; M.S, Cornell Univ, 37. Assoc. prof. CIVIL ENG, NORWICH UNIV, 58-70, PROF, 71- C.Eng, 35-58, Col. Am. Soc. Civil Eng; Am. Soc. Eng. Educ; Am. Concrete Inst; Nat. Soc. Prof. Eng. Seepage through earth dams; hydraulics; concrete design; mechanics. Address: Dept. of Civil Engineering, Norwich University, Northfield, VT 05663.

GREGG, DAVID H(ENRY), b. Minneapolis, Minn, Oct. 19, 26; m. 50; c. 1. PHARMACEUTICAL & ORGANIC CHEMISTRY. B.S, Minnesota, 49, Am. Found. Pharmaceut. Ed. fel, 51-53, Ph.D.(pharmaceut. chem), 53. Asst. pharm, Minnesota, 49-51; res. scientist, pharmaceut. chem. & develop, Upjohn Co, 53-57, head, fine chems. dept, 57-61, chem. sales, 61-63, UPJOHN INT, 63-64, mgr. european agency dist, 65-67, MGR. ENG, DISTRIB. & PROD, 67- U.S.A.A.F, 44-45. AAAS; Am. Chem. Soc; Am. Pharmaceut. Asn. Cardiac glycosides and phytochemistry; steroid synthesis. Address: Upjohn International, Inc, 320 Portage St, Kalamazoo, MI 49001.

GREGG, DONALD C(ROWTHER), b. Marlboro, N.H, June 25, 13; m. 43; c. 2. ORGANIC CHEMISTRY. B.S, Vermont, 35; M.S, New Hampshire, 37; Ellis fel, Columbia, 39-40, Ph.D.(chem), 41. Asst. chem, New Hampshire, 35-37; Columbia, 38-39; Harvard, 40-41; res. chemist, Wallace & Tiernan Prods, Inc, 41; from instr. to asst. prof. CHEM, Amherst Col, 41-46; UNIV. VT, 46-48, assoc. prof, 48-52, prof, 52-63, POMEROY PROF, 63- Nat. Sci. Found. Sci. faculty fel, 62-63. AAAS; fel. Am. Inst. Chem; Am. Chem. Soc. Pyridine derivatives; plant oxidases; denaturation of pepsin; aryl thio ethers; aralkyl thiols; borazine chemistry. Address: 60 University Terr, Burlington, VT 05401.

GREGG, DONALD E(ATON), b. Bridgeport, Conn, Mar. 24, 02; m. 27; c. 3. PHYSIOLOGY. B.S, Colgate, 24; Porter fel, Rochester, 28-30, M.S, 29, Ph.D.(physiol), 30, M.D, 46. Instr. physiol, Western Reserve, 30-34, asst. prof, 34-38, physiol. & med, med. sch, 38-41, assoc. prof. physiol, 41-44; chief res. physician, U.S. Army Med. Corps Res. Lab, Ft. Knox, 46-50; CHIEF, DEPT. CARDIO-RESPIRATORY DISEASES, WALTER REED ARMY INST. RES, 50- Consult. ed, Am. J. Physiol, Am. Heart J, Am. J. Cardiol. President's award for distinguished fed. civilian serv, 62. Am. Physiol. Soc; fel. Am. Col. Cardiol; fel. Am. Col. Chest Physicians; Am. Heart Asn.(res. achievement award, 63). Coronary circulation-heart-cardiovascular system. Address: Walter Reed Army Institute of Research, Walter Reed Army Medical Center, Washington, DC 20012.

GREGG, EARL C(HARLES), JR, b. Malden, Mass, Jan. 3, 25; m. 59; c. 3. ORGANIC CHEMISTRY. B.S, Harvard, 46; M.S, Western Reserve, 51, Ph.D, 53. Res.assoc, B.F.GOODRICH CO, 60-66, sr. res.assoc, 66-70, RES. FEL, RES. CTR, BRECKSVILLE, 70- Ed, Rubber Chem. & Technol. AAAS; Am. Chem. Soc. Organic polarography; ultraviolet and infrared analysis; relativity and directive influence of aromatic compounds toward phenyl radical attack; research compounding of silica pigments in elastomers and plastics; aging and vulcanization of rubber; new elastomers; elastic theory. Address: 2435 N. Revere Rd, Akron, OH 44313.

GREGG, EARLE C(OVINGTON), b. Cleveland, Ohio, Aug. 22, 18; m. 42; c. 2. PHYSICS. B.S, Case, 40, M.S, 42, Ph.D.(physics), 49; Cornell, 40-41. Asst. Cleveland Clin. Found, 38-42; res. physicist, Mass. Inst. Tech, 42-43; Columbia, 43-46; instr. PHYSICS, Case, 46-48; asst. prof, 48-50, assoc. prof, 50-58; CASE WEST. RESERVE UNIV, 58-64, PROF, 65- Asst. ed, J. Appl. Physics, 50- Civilian with Off. Sci. Res. & Develop. Am. Phys. Soc; Inst. Elec. & Electronics Eng; Radiation Res. Soc; Biophys. Soc. Ultrasonics;

electron, nuclear, and radiologic physics; bioelectricity and neural behavior, sensory thresholds; electronics; a flux-forced field-biased electron induction accelerator; biophysics. Address: Dept. of Radiology & Radiation Biology, Case Western Reserve University, Cleveland, OH 44106.

GREGG, JAMES H(ENDERSON), b. Mobile, Ala, Mar. 17, 20; m. 45; c. 2. PHYSIOLOGY. B.S, Alabama, 43; M.S, Princeton, 48, Ph.D.(biol), 49. Res. assoc. zool, Chicago, 49-50; interim asst. prof. BIOL, Vanderbilt, 50-51; asst. prof, UNIV. FLA, 51-56, assoc. prof, 56-63, PROF, 63- Mem. corp, Marine Biol. Lab, 54. Nat. Insts. Health Career Develop. Award, 62-U.S.A, 44-46. Am. Soc. Zool; Soc. Develop. Biol. Developmental physiology of slime molds. Address: Dept. of Zoology, University of Florida, Gainesville, FL 32601.

GREGG, JAMES R, b. Napoleon, Ohio, Oct. 26, 14; m. 38; c. 2. OPTOMETRY. B.S, Ohio State, 37 & 42; D.O, Los Angeles Col. Optom, 48, D.Ocular Sci, 53. Assoc. prof. OPTOM, LOS ANGELES COL. OPTOM, 47-60, PROF, 60- Distinguished serv. award, Am. Optom. Asn, 70. U.S.A, 43-46. Fel. Am. Acad. Optom. Physiological optics; practice management. Address: 5930 S. Croft Ave, Los Angeles, CA 90056.

GREGG, JOHN B(AILEY), b. Sioux Falls, S.Dak, June 5, 22; m. 46; c. 4. OTOLARYNGOLOGY. B.A, Iowa, 43, M.D, 46. Extern anesthesia, univ. hosps, Iowa, 45-46; intern, univ. hosp, Maryland, 46-47; res. gen. surg, univ. hosps, Iowa, 49-51, OTOLARYNGOL, 51-53, instr, 53-54; assoc. prof, South Dakota, 55-59; asst. prof, med. sch, Iowa, 59-60; assoc. prof, SCH. MED, UNIV. S.DAK, 60-62, PROF, 62-, PRES. MED. STAFF & MEM. SURG. SECT, McKENNAN HOSP, 63-, dir. anesthesia & internship & residency proj, 61-63. Summer lectr, speech clin, S.Dak. State, 54- Chief otolaryngol, Vet. Admin. Hosp, Iowa City, 53-54, consult, Sioux Falls, S.Dak, 54-59, 60-; Crippled Children's Field Clins, S.Dak, 54-56; Crippled Children's Hosp. & Pub. Sch. Syst, Sioux Falls, 54-59, 60-; Indian Div, U.S. Pub. Health Serv, 56-59; speech & hearing clin, South Dakota, 61-; dir. broncho-esophagol. clin, univ. hosps, Iowa, 59-60. Designated exam. commerical pilots, Fed. Aviation Agency, 54-, airline transport pilots, 61- Mem. intern cmt, McKennan Hosp, 57-58; finance cmt, Int. Cong. Otolaryngol, D.C, 57-; intern & extern cmt, Sioux Valley Hosp, 58-59; preceptorship comt, col. med, Iowa, 59-60; chmn. Deafness Res. Found. & Temporal Bone Bank, N. & S.Dak, 63- Med.C.Res, 47-49, Lt.(jg). AAAS; Am. Med. Asn; Am. Acad. Opthal. & Otolaryngol; Am. Laryngol, Rhinol. & Otol. Soc; fel. Am. Col. Surg; Am. Cancer Soc; fel. Int. Col. Surg; Am. Bronco-Esophagol. Asn; Am. Acad. Facial Plastic & Reconstruct. Surg; Am. Asn. Phys. Anthrop; Am. Anthrop. Asn; Am. Cleft Palate Asn. Bronchoesophagology; facial plastic surgery; otorhinolaryngology. Address: 1600 S. Western Ave, Sioux Falls, SD 57105.

GREGG, JOHN R(ICHARD), b. Mobile, Ala, Dec. 23, 16; m. 42. ZOOLOGY. B.S, Alabama, 42; Ph.D.(biol), Princeton, 45. Lab. asst. biol, Alabama, 40-42, histol, 41-42; asst, Off. Sci. Res. & Develop. contract, Princeton, 42-45; Columbia, 45-46; instr. biol, Hopkins, 46-47; asst. prof. ZOOL, Columbia, 47-54, assoc. prof, 54-57; DUKE UNIV, 57-60, PROF, 60- Killough fel, 49; Rockefeller fel, Carlsberg Labs, Denmark, 49, Middlesex Hosp, London, 53-54. Mem. corp, Marine Biol. Lab, Woods Hole Oceanog. Inst, 47- AAAS; Soc. Develop. Biol; Harvey Soc; Am. Soc. Nat; Asn. Symbolic Logic; Int. Inst. Embryol. Chemical embryology of amphibia; mathematical and philosophical biology. Address: Dept. of Zoology, Duke University, Durham, NC 27706.

GREGG, LUCIUS P(ERRY), JR, b. Henderson, N.C, Jan. 16, 33; m. 59; c. 1. AERONAUTICS, ASTRONAUTICS. B.S, U.S. Naval Acad, 55; S.M, Mass. Inst. Technol, 61; Cath. Univ. Am, 61-63. Res. scientist, Mass. Inst. Technol, 60-61; res. adminr. aeromech, Hq. Off. Aerospace Res, 61-62, proj. scientist, Air Force Off. Sci. Res, 62-65; res. coordinator, Northwest. Univ, 65-69, instr. mech. eng. & astronaut. sci, 65-69, assoc. dean sci, 66-69; PROG. OFFICER, ALFRED P. SLOAN FOUND, 69- Mem. bd. trustees, Univs. Res. Asn, Inc, Nat. Accelerator Lab, 67-69; mem. comt. of NASA-Univ. Res, Nat. Acad. Sci, 67-69, univs. organizing comt. for space res, 68-69, comt. U.S. eng. educ. in for. tech. assistance; founding mem. bd. gov, Lunar Sci. Inst, 68-69; consult, Ill. Bell Tel. Co, 68-69. U.S.A.F, 55-65, Res, 65-, Maj. AAAS. Address: 241 Lincoln Ave, New Rochelle, NY 10801.

GREGG, MICHAEL B(ARROWS), b. Paris, France, Jan. 6, 30; U.S. citizen; m. 58; c. 3. INTERNAL MEDICINE. B.A, Stanford, 52; M.D, Western Reserve, 56. Intern internal med, Columbia-Presby. Hosp, 56-57, jr. asst. resident, 57-58, sr. asst. resident, 58-59; sr. asst. surgeon, Nat. Insts. Health, 59-62; res. assoc, inst. int. med, sch. med, Maryland, 62-64, asst. prof. internal med, 64-66; chief epidemic intel. serv, EPIDEMIOL. PROG, CTR. DISEASE CONTROL, U.S. PUB. HEALTH SERV, 66-68, asst. chief, 68, chief viral diseases br, 68-69, DEP. DIR. PROG, 69- Infectious diseases; immunology. Address: Center for Disease Control, U.S. Public Health Service, 1600 Clifton Rd. N.E, Atlanta, GA 30333.

GREGG, ROBERT A(RDEN), b. Dundee, Mich, Mar. 8, 18; m. 51; c. 2. CHEMISTRY. A.B, Adrian Col, 37; Illinois, 40; M.S, Michigan, 40, fel, 40-43, Ph.D.(chem), 43. Instr. chem, Adrian Col, 37-38; chemist, RES. & DEVELOP. DEPT, U.S. RUBBER CO, 42-59, mgr. res. textile div, 59-64, res. planning, 64-65, tech. personnel, 65-66, SR. RES. SCIENTIST, 67- Am. Chem. Soc. Synthesis of estrogenic hormones; free radicals and polymerization processes; synthetic rubber; fibers. Address: Research Center, U.S. Rubber Co, Wayne, NJ 07470.

GREGG, ROBERT E(DMOND), b. Chicago, Ill, Apr. 19, 12; m. 39. ZOOLOGY. S.B, Chicago, 35, Ph.D.(zool), 41. Instr. zool, Minn. State Teachers Col, Duluth, 40-44; instr. BIOL, UNIV. COLO, BOULDER, 44-46, asst. prof, 46-53, assoc. prof, 53-59, PROF, 59- AAAS; Am. Soc. Zool; Soc. Syst. Zool; Ecol. Soc. Am. Geographic distribution, ecology and taxonomy of ants; origin of castes in ants. Address: Dept. of Biology, University of Colorado, Boulder, CO 80302.

GREGG, ROBERT Q(UINLY), b. Independence, Mo, May 21, 16; m. 42; c. 5. PHYSICS. A.B, Cent. Methodist Col, 38; Ph.D.(physics), Univ. Mo, 44. Physicist, Monsanto Chem. Co, 43-46; asst. prof. physics, Univ. Mo, 46-48; PHYSICIST, PHILLIPS PETROL. CO, 48- Am. Crystallog. Asn; Electron Microscopy Soc. Am. X-ray diffraction; polymer physics; electron microscopy. Address: 3207 Henrietta, Bartlesville, OK 74003.

GREGG, ROBERT VINCENT, b. Long Beach, Calif, Feb. 16, 28; m. 48; c. 2. ANATOMY. A.B, California, Los Angeles, 52; Ph.D.(anat), Southern California, 62. Mus. aid, Vet. Admin. Hosp, Long Beach, Calif, 52-54; instr. ANAT, sch. dent, Univ. South. Calif, 54-62, asst. prof, 62-65, assoc. prof, 65-70, chmn. dept, 62-70; PROF, HEALTH SCI. CTR, SCH. MED, UNIV. LOUISVILLE, 70- U.S.M.C, 46-47. AAAS. Gastrointestinal physiology and pathology; peptic ulcers and enterochromaffin cellular responses; biological specimen preservation by plastic embedding. Address: Dept. of Anatomy, Health Sciences Center, University of Louisville School of Medicine, Louisville, KY 40202.

GREGG, ROGER ALLEN, b. Lenoir, N.C, July 19, 38; m. 61; c. 3. PHYSICAL METALLURGY. B.S, N.C. State Univ, 60, M.S, 62; fel, Univ. Fla, 66-68, Ph.D.(metall. eng), 68. Res. asst. alloy develop, advan. mat. res. & develop. lab, Pratt & Whitney Aircraft Co, 62-63; res. engr, SAVANNAH RIVER LAB, E.I. DU PONT DE NEMOURS & CO, INC, 68-69, sr. engr, 69-70, SR. RES. SUPVR. REACTOR FUEL & TARGET ELEMENTS, 70- Am. Inst. Mining, Metall. & Petrol. Eng. Alloy development of nickel and cobalt base superalloys; sintering phenomena and surface tension of metals; thermal and irradiation stability of actinide oxide-aluminum systems; powder metallurgy. Address: E.I. du Pont de Nemours & Co, Inc, Savannah River Lab, Aiken, SC 29801.

GREGG, THOMAS G, b. U.S. citizen, Dec. 3, 31; m. 56; c. 4. GENETICS. B.A, Col. Wooster, 54; M.A, Texas, 56, Ph.D.(genetics), 58. Nat. Insts. Health fel. genetics, Univ. Wis, 58-60; asst. prof. ZOOL, MIAMI UNIV, 60-66, assoc. prof, 67-80, PROF, 71- Nat. Sci. Found. grant, 60-62; Nat. Insts. Health grants, 63-65, 71-73, spec. fel, Univ. Tex, 67-68. Genetics Soc. Am. Drosophila genetics. Address: Dept. of Zoology, Miami University, Oxford, OH 45056.

GREGG, WENDELL O(LIVER), b. Pomona, Mich, Apr. 27, 98; m. 23; c. 2. ZOOLOGY. B.A, Emmanuel Missionary Col, 18; M.D, Col. Med. Evangelists, 22. Med. dir, Wells Indust. Hosp, 53-66; mem. staff, Avalon Mem. Hosp, 67-69; RETIRED. Res. assoc, Los Angeles County Mus, 64-; mem. Paleont. Res. Inst. Nat. Guard, 50-60, Maj. AAAS; Soc. Syst. Zool; Am. Soc. Ichthyol. & Herpet; Am. Malacol. Union (v.pres, 51-52; award, 64). Industrial medicine and surgery; comparative anatomy of West American nonmarine gastropods. Address: 2200 S. Harvard Blvd, Los Angeles, CA 90018.

GREGG, WILLIAM D, b. Glen Jean, W.Va, Oct. 4, 33; m. 57; c. 2. ELECTRICAL ENGINEERING, COMMUNICATIONS. B.S, Purdue, 61, Ph.D.(elec. eng), 66; S.M, Mass. Inst. Tech, 62. ASSOC. PROF. ELEC. ENG, UNIV. TEX. AUSTIN, 66- Am. Phys. Soc; Am. Soc. Eng. Educ; Am. Econ. Asn. Address: Room 514, Engineering Science Bldg, Dept. of Electrical Engineering, University of Texas at Austin, Austin, TX 78712.

GREGGS, ROBERT G(EORGE), b. Gananoque, Ont, July 29, 30; m. 54; c. 4. PALEONTOLOGY. B.A, Queen's (Ont), 55; M.Sc, British Columbia, 57, Nat. Res. Coun. Can. fel, 57-59, Ph.D.(paleont), 62. Paleontologist, Shell Can. Ltd, Alta, 59-62, sedimentologist, 62-63; lectr. PALEONT. & SEDIMENTATION, QUEEN'S UNIV.(ONT), 63-64, asst. prof, 64-70, ASSOC. PROF, 70- Nat. Res. Coun. Can. res. grant, 64- Soc. Econ. Paleont. & Mineral. Stratigraphic nomenclature of the Upper Cambrian of the Southern Rocky Mountains of Alberta and British Columbia; Upper Cambrian faunas from above provinces. Address: Dept. of Geology, Queen's University, Kingston, Ont, Can.

GREGOIRE, ADOLPHE T(HOMAS), b. Putnam, Conn, Dec. 8, 28; m. 51; c. 4. PHYSIOLOGY. B.A, Connecticut, 50, Charles H. Hood fel, 53-56, M.S, 54; Ph.D.(physiol), Cornell, 57. Asst, Worcester Found. Exp. Biol, 50-51; Cornell, 53-57; instr. physiol, Jefferson Med. Col, 59-63, asst. prof, 63-66, res. biologist obstet. & gynec, 57-66; asst. prof, Univ. Mich, Ann Arbor, 66-71; SR. SCIENTIST, MARGARET SANGER RES. BUR, 71-, res. consult, 62-71. Int. Fertil. Asn. Amino acids and carbohydrates in reproductive fluids; frequency of ejaculation and its effect on spermatogenesis; presence of transaminase in reproductive fluids; ovum transplantation; artificial insemination; endocrinology and physiology of reproduction; vaginal physiology; semen chemistry; biochemistry of female reproductive tract; glycogen metabolism in female tract; effect of contraception on human female tract; glycogen metabolism during hamster implantation; glycogen synthesis and estrogen administration; lactic dehydrogenase and isoenzymes in human semen and human endometrial tissue. Address: Margaret Sanger Research Bureau, 17 W. 16th St, New York, NY 10011.

GREGOIRE, F(ERNAND), b. Apr. 28, 16; Can. citizen; m. 43; c. 6. RESPIRATORY PHYSIOLOGY, ALLERGY. B.A, Univ. Montreal, 36; M.D, Laval Univ, 43. Intern, cardio-pulmonary dept, Johns Hopkins Hosp, 47-48; physiol. lab, Trudeau Hosp, 48-49; resident, Belview Hosp, 49-50; IN CHARGE, PHYSIOPATH. LAB, LAVOISIER INST, 51-; PROF, CLINICS, UNIV. MONTREAL, 55- Pres, Bd. Pneumoconiosis for Workmens Compensation, 67- Fel, Royal Col. Physicians Can. AAAS; Fel. Am. Col. Physicians; fel. Am. Col. Chest Physicians; Am. Thoracic Soc; Can. Med. Asn; Can. Soc. Clin. Invest. Address: Clinique Lavoisier Inc, 5136 Bellechasse St, Montreal 410, Que, Can.

GREGOR, CLUNIE BRYAN, b. Edinburgh, Scotland, Mar. 5, 29. GEOLOGY. B.A, Cambridge, 51, M.A, 54; D.Sc.(earth sci), State Univ. Utrecht, 67. Instr. geol, Am. Univ. Beirut, 59-62, asst. prof, 62-64; res. asst. crystallog, Technol. Univ. Delft, 64-65, head dept, 65-67; assoc. prof. GEOL & chmn. dept, Am. Univ. Beirut, 67-68; vis. prof, Case West. Reserve Univ, 68-69; assoc. prof, W.GA. COL, 69-71, PROF, 71- Mem. comt. natural resources, Nat. Coun. Sci. Res, Lebanon, 67-68; Netherlands del, comn. non-metallic minerals, Orgn. Econ. Coop. & Develop, 68-69; consult, Food & Agr. Orgn, UN, 69- AAAS; Am. Geophys. Union; Geochem. Soc; Geol. Soc. London. Geochemical cycles of the elements; models of denudation in geologic time; low-temperature experimental geochemistry; paleomagnetism and geotectonics. Address: 131 Cunningham Dr, Carrollton, GA 30117.

GREGOR, HARRY P(AUL), b. Minneapolis, Minn, Dec. 16, 16; m. 41; c. 5. PHYSICAL CHEMISTRY. B.A, Minnesota, 39, Ph.D.(phys. chem), 45. Asst. prof. chem, Polytech. Inst. Brooklyn, 46-50, assoc. prof, 50-55, PROF, 55-67; CHEM. ENG, COLUMBIA UNIV, 67-, APPL. CHEM, 68- Am. Chem. Soc. Electrochemistry; colloids, including ion exchange; semipermeable membranes; ion binding by polyelectrolytes; multilayer electrodes. Address: Dept. of Chemical Engineering, Columbia University, 356 Engineering Terr, New York, NY 10027.

GREGOR, L(AWRENCE) V(INCENT), b. Spangler, Pa, Aug. 10, 34; m. 66; c. 3. PHYSICAL CHEMISTRY. B.S, Pa. State, 54, M.S, 59; Ph.D.(chem), California, Berkeley, 61. Res. asst, Lawrence Radiation Lab, California, 58-61; mem. res. staff, IBM CORP, 61-65, develop. chemist, COMPONENTS DIV, N.Y, 65-69, SR. CHEMIST, EAST FISHKILL FACILITY, 69- U.S.N, 54-56, Lt.(jg). Electrochem. Soc; fel. Am. Inst. Chem. Magnetic and thermodynamic properties of solids at low temperatures; thin dielectric films; surface properties of semiconductors. Address: IBM Components Division, East Fishkill Facility, Hopewell Junction, NY 12533.

GREGOREK, EDWARD S, JR, b. Scranton, Pa, Aug. 29, 32. ANALYTICAL CHEMISTRY, MOLECULAR SPECTROSCOPY. B.S, Lehigh Univ, 54, Ph.D. (chem), 67. Res. chemist, Hercules Powder Co. Inc, 54-56; lectr. phys. sci, Keystone Jr. Col, 68; ASST. PROF. CHEM, VA. MIL. INST, 68- Res. partic, Ill. Inst. Technol, summers 69 & 70. Am. Chem. Soc. Molecular electronic spectroscopy; fluorescence and phosphorescence; lasers in spectroscopic research; properties of molecular complexes. Address: Dept. of Chemistry, Virginia Military Institute, Lexington, VA 24450.

GREGORICH, DAVID T(ONY), b. Crawford, Nebr, Feb. 11, 37; m. 61; c. 2. THEORETICAL PHYSICS. B.A, California, Los Angeles, 62, M.S, 64; Nat. Defense Ed. Act. fel, California, Riverside, 64-67, univ. fel, 67-68, Ph.D. (physics), 68. Jr. engr, Consolidated Systs. Corp, 60-62; assoc. res. physicist, Bell & Howell Res. Labs, 62-64; res. asst. PHYSICS, California, Riverside, 64-68; ASST. PROF, CALIF. STATE COL, LOS ANGELES, 68- Consult, Bell & Howell Res. Labs, 68- Am. Phys. Soc; Am. Asn. Physics Teachers. Theoretical high energy particle physics; solid state physics; photoconductors; magnetism. Address: Dept. of Physics, California State College, 5151 State College Dr, Los Angeles, CA 90032.

GREGORY, ALAN F(RANK), b. Lindsay, Ont, Mar. 26, 26; m. 53; c. 2. GEOLOGY, REMOTE SENSING. B.A, Toronto, 50; fel, Wisconsin, 50-52, 53-54, Ph.D, 58. Geologist, explor. div, Eldorado Mining & Ref, Sask, 52-53, sr. geologist, 54-55; demonstr, dept. geol. sci. Toronto, 55-56; asst. chief geologist, Sherritt Gordon Mines Ltd, Man, 56-58; geologist, geophys. div, Geol. Surv. Can, Ottawa, 58-65, head remote sensing sect, 65-66; assoc. prof. geol, Carleton Univ.(Ont), 66-69; GEOSCI. CONSULT, 69- Mem. working group on data sensing, Int. Geog. Union; mem. adv. panel, natural resources forum, UN, 71- Soc. Explor. Geophys; fel. Geol. Asn. Can; Can. Inst. Mining & Metall; Can. Aeronaut. & Space Inst; Am. Inst. Aeronaut. & Astronaut. Geosciences; mineral exploration; remote sensing and geophysics from aircraft and satellites; environmental surveys; physical properties of rocks and soils. Address: 909 Richmond Rd, Ottawa, Ont. K2A 0G8, Can.

GREGORY, A(LVIN) R(AY), b. Gainesville, Tex, Nov. 26, 15; m. 45; c. 5. CHEMICAL ENGINEERING. B.S, Texas, 38. Res. engr. prod. eng. & geophys, Phillips Petrol. Co, 45-51; sr. res. engr. petrophys, GULF RES. & DEVELOP. CO, 51-68, RES. ASSOC, EXPLOR. DEPT, 68- Radar proj. off, radiation lab, Mass. Inst. Tech, 44-45, U.S.N, 42-44, Res, 44-64, Comdr. Am. Inst. Mining, Metall. & Petrol. Eng; Soc. Explor. Geophys. Sonic and electrical well logging, propagation of acoustic energy in rocks; physical properties of rocks; fluid flow in porous media. Address: Exploration Dept, Gulf Research & Development Co, P.O. Drawer 2038, Pittsburgh, PA 15230.

GREGORY, ARTHUR S(TANLEY), b. Benton Co, Ore, Oct. 22, 14; m. 39; c. 3. ORGANIC CHEMISTRY. B.S, Ore. State Univ, 36; Ph.D.(org. chem), Ohio State, 40. Res. chemist, exp. sta, E.I. du Pont de Nemours & Co, 40-42; chem. technologist, WEYERHAEUSER CO, 45-51, chief prod. eng. sect, develop. ctr, 51-52, asst. mgr, 52-55, mgr. cent. res. & develop, 55-58, dir res, 58-71, DIR. TECH. PLANNING, RES. & ENG, 71- U.S.A, 42-45, Lt. Col. Am. Chem. Soc; Forest Prod. Res. Soc; Soc. Am. Foresters; Tech. Asn. Pulp & Paper Indust; Can. Pulp & Paper Asn; Indust. Res. Inst; N.Y. Acad. Sci. Structure of plant pigments; derivatives of cellulose; natural fibers and fiber products; wood and bark chemistry and utilization. Address: Weyerhaeuser Co, Tacoma, WA 98401.

GREGORY, BOB LEE, b. Allen, Okla, Sept. 30, 38; m. 61. ELECTRICAL ENGINEERING. B.S, Carnegie Inst. Technol, 60, M.S, 61, Ph.D.(elec. eng), 64. SUPVR, RADIATION EFFECTS DIV, SANDIA LAB, AM. TEL. & TEL. CO, 63- Inst. Elec. & Electronics Eng; Am. Phys. Soc. Properties of radiation defects in materials and semiconductor devices; semiconductor devices; semiconductor device physics. Address: Division 1933, Sandia Lab, Albuquerque, NM 87115.

GREGORY, BRIAN CHARLES, b. Toronto, Ont, July 9, 38; m. 65. ELECTRONIC & PLASMA PHYSICS. B.A.Sc, Univ. Toronto, 60; Ph.D.(elec. eng), Cambridge, 63. Res. engr, Compagnie Generale de Telegraphie sans Fil, France, 63-66; asst. prof. physics, Trent Univ, 66-69, assoc. prof, 69-70; DIR. ENERGY CTR, NAT. INST. SCI. RES, UNIV. QUE, 70- Am. Phys. Soc; assoc. Can. Asn. Physicists. Electron beams and guns; microwave interaction with plasmas; plasmas and electron beams; physics of ionized gases. Address: Energy Center, National Institute of Scientific Research, University of Quebec, C.P. 1020, Varennes, Que, Can.

GREGORY, CARTER H, b. Sierra Madre, Calif, Apr. 19, 11; m. 36. GEOPHYSICS. B.S, Calif. Inst. Tech, 31, Ph.D.(physics), 35; German-Am. exchange fel, Karlsruhe Tech, 31-32. Seismologist, Shell Petrol. Co, 36-39; Bataafse Int. Petrol. Mij, 39-46; sr. geophysicist, SHELL OIL CO, 46-61, chief geophysicist, 61-65, sr. staff geophysicist, 65-69, CONSULT. GEOPHYSICIST, 69- Am. Geophys. Union; Seismol. Soc. Am; Soc. Explor. Geophys; Europ. Asn. Explor. Geophys. Exploration geophysics. Address: 301 E. 47th St, New York, NY 10017.

GREGORY, CEDRIC E(RROL), b. Adelaide, S. Australia, Aug. 17, 08; m. 35; c. 5. MINING ENGINEERING. B.E, Adelaide, 31, B.A, 44; B.Econ. & M.E, Queensland, 60, Ph.D.(mine ventilation), 66. Supt, Cent. Norseman Gold Corp, 34-37; gen. supt. mines, New Guinea Goldfields Ltd, 37-40; gen. mgr, Adelaide Chem. & Fertilizer Co, 46-49; asst. managing dir, Pascoe Industs. Ltd, 52-54; sr. lectr. mining eng, Queensland, 56-60, sub-dean, sch. eng, 61-62, assoc. prof. MINING ENG; 61-64, acting prof. & head dept, 65-66; prof. & dir. mining res. lab, Colo. Sch. Mines, 67-68; RES. PROF, COL. MINES, UNIV. IDAHO, 68- Vis. prof, Univ. Mo-Rolla, 63. Royal Australian Engrs, 42-46, Capt. Am. Inst. Min, Metall. & Petrol. Eng; Am. Soc. Eng. Educ; N.Y. Acad. Sci; Can. Inst. Min, & Metall; Brit. Inst. Min. & Metall; Australasian Inst. Min. & Metall; Australian Inst. Mgt; S.African Inst. Min. & Metall; Brit. Inst. Min. Eng; Australian Inst. Eng. Mineral economics; aerodynamic aspects of mine shaft design; Address: College of Mines, University of Idaho, Moscow, ID 83843.

GREGORY, CHRISTOPHER, b. Cleveland, Ohio, June 6, 16; m. 42; c. 5. PHYSICS. B.S, Calif. Inst. Tech, 38, M.S, 39, Ph.D.(physics), 41. Asst. physics, Calif. Inst. Tech, 38-41; instr. math, eng. & physics, Hawaii, 41-43; physicist, Nat. Bur. Standards, 44-45; asst. prof. math. & physics, UNIV. HAWAII, 45-50, assoc. prof. MATH, 50-53, PROF, 53-, CHMN. GRAD. FACULTY, 59-, chmn. dept. math, 52-56, 59-64. Am. Phys. Soc; Am. Math. Soc. Absorption spectra; relativistic cosmology; non-linear invarients and problem of motion; field equations quantized space; non-local field theory; relativistic extra dimensionality. Address: Dept. of Mathematics, University of Hawaii, Honolulu, HA 96822.

GREGORY, CLARENCE LESLIE, JR, b. Stamford, Conn, Mar. 14, 30. CHEMICAL ENGINEERING. B.S, Mass. Inst. Technol, 51, Sc.D.(chem. eng), 57. Res. asst, Mass. Inst. Technol, 54-55; engr, KNOLLS ATOMIC POWER LAB, GEN. ELEC. CO, 57-61, supv. eng, 61-65, PROJ. ENGR, 65- Summers, chem. engr, res. labs, Am. Cyanamid Co, 52-53. Am. Chem. Soc. Mass transfer; nucleate and film boiling, two-phase pressure drop, vapor fractions, and flow oscillations; thermal and hydraulic design of nuclear reactors; chemistry of high pressure, high temperature water. Address: 14 Maher Ave, Greenwich, CT 06830.

GREGORY, CONSTANTINE J, b. Brockton, Mass, June 17, 39; m. 62; c. 3. ENVIRONMENTAL SCIENCES, AIR POLLUTION. B.A, Northeast. Univ, 62; M.S, Rutgers Univ, 64, Ph.D.(environ. sci), 68. Asst. prof. ENVIRON. SCI, NORTHEAST. UNIV, 67-71, ASSOC. PROF, 71- Mem. bd. dirs, New Eng. Consortium on Air Pollution, 70- AAAS; Am. Chem. Soc; Air Pollution Control Asn. Fate and effects of atmospheric pollutants. Address: Dept. of Civil Engineering, Northeastern University, Boston, MA 02115.

GREGORY, DALE R(OGERS), b. Lake Village, Ark, Aug. 1, 34; m. 56; c. 3. CHEMICAL ENGINEERING. B.S, Va. Polytech, 56, Ph.D.(chem. eng), 66. Prod. supvr, Carbide & Carbon Chem. Co, W.Va, 56-57, 59-60; develop. engr, E.I. du Pont de Nemours & Co, Inc, Va, 60-62; chem. engr, TENN. EASTMAN CO, 65-66, sr. chem. engr, 66-67, SR. RES. CHEM. ENGR, 67- Instr, dept. chem. & metall. eng, Univ. Tenn, 71- Ord.C, U.S.A, 57-59, 1st Lt. Am. Inst. Chem. Eng; Am. Chem. Soc. Fibers research and development; organic chemicals production; polymers engineering; melt spinning research. Address: Research Labs, Tennessee Eastman Co, Kingsport, TN 37660.

GREGORY, DANIEL HAYES, b. Watertown, N.Y, Dec. 18, 33; m. 60; c. 4. INTERNAL MEDICINE, GASTROENTEROLOGY. A.B, Hamilton Col, 57; M.D, Virginia, 62. Fel. med, sch. med, Minnesota, 63-66, instr, 67-69, asst. prof, 69; ASST. PROF. MED, SCH, MED, UNIV. N.MEX, 69-; CHIEF GASTROENTEROL, ALBUQUERQUE VET. HOSP, 69- Fel. gastroenterol, Minneapolis Vet. Hosp, 66-67, assoc. chief radioisotopes, 67-69. U.S.A. Am. Gastroenterol. Asn. Liver metabolism; malabsorption. Address: Dept. of Medicine, University of New Mexico School of Medicine, Albuquerque, NM 87106.

GREGORY, ERIC, b. Golborne, Eng, Jan. 5, 28; U.S. citizen; m. 56; c. 1. METALLURGY. B.A, Cambridge, 48, M.A, 52, Ph.D.(metall), 54; Brit. Ministry Ed-Econ. Coop. Admin. fel, Michigan, 51-52; Mass. Inst. Tech, 52-53. Res. engr, Manganese Bronze Co, Eng, 54-56; tech. dir, Sintercast Corp. Am, 56-61, phys. res, 61-68, DIR. METALS RES, 68- Am. Soc. Metals; Am. Inst. Min, Metall. & Petrol. Eng; Am. Ceramic Soc; Am. Iron & Steel Inst; Brit. Inst. Metals; Brit. Inst. Metall. High temperature alloys; powder metallurgy; high pressure, superconducting alloys; corrosion of stainless steels; materials produced by high vacuum electron beam processing. Address: Central Research Lab, Air Reduction Co, Inc, Mountain Ave, Murray Hill, NJ 07974.

GREGORY, EUGENE HERBERT, b. St. Louis, Mo, Nov. 14, 32; m. 60; c. 2. SOLID STATE & LOW TEMPERATURE PHYSICS. B.S, Washington (St. Louis), 58; M.S, California, Los Angeles, 61, Masters & Wilson fels. & Ph.D.(physics), 65. Mem. tech. staff, Hughes Res. Lab, Calif, 58-61; asst. prof. physics, California, Los Angeles, 65-66; Calif. Inst. Technol, 66-69; SR. STAFF TECH. ASST, RADAR MICROWAVE LAB, HUGHES AIRCRAFT CO, 69- Vis. prof, Douglas Adv. Res. Labs, Calif, 66-69. U.S.M.C, 51-54, Sgt. AAAS; Am. Phys. Soc. Electron paramagnetic, ferromagnetic and nuclear magnetic resonance; ultrasonic excitation of nuclear spin resonance; superconductivity; liquid helium; microwave power sources. Address: Radar Microwave Lab, Hughes Aircraft Co, Culver City, CA 90230.

GREGORY, FRANCIS JOSEPH, b. Brooklyn, N.Y, June 21, 21; m; c. 2. MICROBIOLOGY, BIOCHEMISTRY. B.A, Brooklyn Col, 42; Ph.D.(microbiol), Rutgers, 54. Fel. MICROBIOL, Rutgers, 54-55; RES. SCIENTIST, WYETH LABS, INC, 55- U.S.A, 42-46. Am. Asn. Cancer Res; Tissue Cult. Asn; Am. Soc. Microbiol. Cancer research; screening for antineoplastic agents and mode of action of such agents; cancer and immunity; tuberculosis research; studies on amebiasis; pathogenicity of trichomonads; chemotherapy of experimental leishmaniasis; mammalian cell culture in vitro. Address: Wyeth Labs, Inc, P.O. Box 8299, Philadelphia, PA 19001.

GREGORY, GAROLD F(AY), b. Arkansas City, Kans, Aug. 15, 26; m. 53; c. 2. BIOCHEMISTRY, PLANT PATHOLOGY. B.S, Kansas State, 51; M.S, Iowa

State, 56; Allied Chem. & Dye fel, Cornell, 60-61, Ph.D.(plant path), 62. PLANT PATHOLOGIST, NORTHEAST. FOREST EXP. STA, U.S. FOREST SERV, 62- U.S.A, 51-53. Phytochem. Soc. N.Am; Am. Soc. Plant Physiol; Am. Phytopath. Soc. Fungal toxins; biochemistry of fungi spore germination; trace element nutrition of rust infected oat plants; trace element nutrition of fungi; biochemistry of oak wilt. Address: Northeastern Forest Experiment Station, U.S. Forest Service, P.O. Box 365, Delaware, OH 43015.

GREGORY, GARRY ALLEN, b. London, Ont, July 27, 41; m. 63; c. 3. CHEMICAL ENGINEERING. B.A.Sc, Univ. Waterloo, 64, M.A.Sc, 65, Ph.D.(chem. eng), 69. Asst. prof. CHEM. ENG, UNIV. CALGARY, 68-71, ASSOC. PROF, 71- Am. Inst. Chem. Eng; Can. Soc. Chem. Eng; Chem. Inst. Can. Multiphase flow in horizontal and inclined circular conduits; liquid distribution effects in packed tower absorbers. Address: Dept. of Chemical Engineering, University of Calgary, Calgary, Alta, Can.

GREGORY, GEORGE P(RESTON), b. Columbus, Ohio, July 25, 22; m. 45; c. 3. ORGANIC CHEMISTRY. A.B, Indiana, 42; Allied Chem. & Dye Corp. fel, Wisconsin, 48-49, Ph.D.(chem), 49. Chemist, U.S. Naval Res. Lab, 42-46; res. chemist, Hercules Powder Co, 49-60, chem. develop, 60-65, sales mgr, vinsol & bldg. prods, HERCULES, INC, 65-67, MGR, MARKET DEVELOP, 67- U.S.N, 44-45, Ens. Am. Chem. Soc; Sci. Res. Soc. Am. Peroxide reactions; cross-linking of plastics and elastomers; synthetic resins. Address: 1307 Quincy Dr, Green Acres, Wilmington, DE 19803.

GREGORY, G(USTAV) ROBINSON, Natural Resources, Econ, see 12th ed, Soc. & Behav. Vols.

GREGORY, IAN (WALTER DE GRAVE), Psychiat, see 12th ed, Soc. & Behav. Vols.

GREGORY, JAMES THOMAS, b. Cleveland, Ohio, Apr. 13, 15; m. 37; c. 2. CHEMISTRY. A.B, Wittenberg, 37; Ph.D.(org. chem), Ohio State, 42. RES. CHEMIST, res. ctr, B.F. Goodrich Co, 42-60; CHEM. DIV, RES. BR, PPG INDUSTS, INC, BARBERTON, 60- Am. Chem. Soc. Organic syntheses; plasticizers for polyvinyl chloride; chemistry of β-propiolactone; heterocyclic sulfur-nitrogen compounds; amines; phenols; rubber chemicals; antidegradants for polymers; polymer chemistry; oxidation; polycarbonate-urethane and urethane polymers. Address: 241 Merriman Rd, Akron, OH 44303.

GREGORY, JOHN, b. Mundare, Alta, Nov. 7, 16; m. 46; c. 2. CHEMICAL ENGINEERING. B.Sc, Alberta, 45, M.Sc, 48. Chemist, Lever Bros, Ltd, 45; res. engr. coal, RES. COUN. ALTA, 45-48, HEAD INDUST. & ENG. SERV, 48- Spec. lectr. sci. Russian, Alberta, 61-64. Eng. Inst. Can; Chem. Inst. Can.(secy, 55-60). Provision to industry of a technical information service for industrial development and assistance with technical and production problems; contract industrial research. Address: Research Council of Alberta, Edmonton, Alta, Can.

GREGORY, JOHN B, b. Wellington, N.Z, Apr. 12, 17; m. 43; c. 2. PHYSICS. B.S, Victoria Univ, N.Z, 46; M.S, Univ. Canterbury, 48, Dr.(physics), 57. From lectr. to sr. lectr. PHYSICS, Univ. Canterbury, 48-60; vis. res. prof, inst. geophys. & planetary physics, Univ. Calif, Los Angeles, 60-61; sr. lectr, Univ. Canterbury, 61-65; PROF, UNIV. SASK, 65- Sr. Fulbright fel, 59-60; mem. comn. & working groups, Int. Asn. Meteorol. & Atmospheric Physics & Inter-Union Comn. Solar-Terrestrial Physics, World Meteorol. Orgn, 63-; assoc. comts. geodesy & geophys, radio sci, Nat. Res. Coun. Can, 66-; exchange prof. to Brazil, 70. Royal N.Z. Air Force, 42-46, Flying Officer. Can. Meteorol. Soc; Am. Meteorol. Soc; Royal Meteorol. Soc; Can. Asn. Physicists; Brit. Inst. Physics & Phys. Soc. Investigation of physics and aeronomy of the atmosphere, particularly the region below 100 kilometers, including development and application of radio wave exploratory techniques. Address: Dept. of Physics, University of Saskatchewan, Saskatoon, Sask, Can.

GREGORY, JOHN DELAFIELD, b. New York, N.Y, May 18, 23; m. 58. BIOCHEMISTRY. B.S, Yale, 44, Ph.D.(org. chem), 47. Asst, Rockefeller Inst, 47-49; asst. biochemist, Mass. Gen. Hosp, 49-53, assoc. biochemist, 53-57; ASSOC. PROF. BIOCHEM, ROCKEFELLER UNIV, 57- AAAS; Am. Soc. Biol. Chem. Sulfate metabolism; enzyme chemistry; mucopolysaccharides; connective tissues. Address: Rockefeller University, New York, NY 10021.

GREGORY, JOHN E(UGENE), b. Trilby, Fla, Feb. 5, 09; m. 38; c. 2. IMMUNOLOGY. A.B, Mercer, 30; M.Sc, Cincinnati, 32, M.D, 39. Resident & instr. path, med. col, Hopkins, 40-45; prof. path. & head div, Hahnemann Med. Col, 47-53; dir. labs, Rowen Mem. Hosp, 53-67, Med. Ctr. Lab, 67-69; RETIRED. Adj. prof, Bowman Gray Sch. Med, Wake-Forest Col, 53-54. Med.C, 45-47, Capt. AAAS; Am. Asn. Immunol; Am. Asn. Path. & Bact; Am. Soc. Clin. Path; fel. Col. Am. Path. Histology and genetics of hypersensitivity. Address: 1060 Standing Boy Ct, Columbus, GA 31904.

GREGORY, JOSEPH T(RACY), b. Eureka, Calif, July 28, 14; m. 49; c. 2. VERTEBRATE PALEONTOLOGY. A.B, California, 35, Ph.D.(vert. paleont), 38. Lectr. zool, Columbia, 39; technician, paleont. lab, bur. econ. geol, Texas, 39-41; instr. geol, Michigan, 41-46; asst. prof, Yale, 46-52, assoc. prof. vert. paleont, 52-60; PROF. PALEONTOL, UNIV. CALIF, BERKELEY & CURATOR AMPHIBIANS & REPTILES, MUS. PALEONT, 60-, DIR. MUS, 71- Curator, mus. paleont, Michigan, 41-46; Peabody Mus, Yale, 46-60; asst. ed, Am. Jour. Sci, 54-60. U.S.A.A.F, 42-45. Fel. Paleont. Soc; Soc. Vert. Paleont.(pres, 58); fel. Geol. Soc. Am; Am. Soc. Mammal; Soc. Study Evolution; Am. Soc. Zool. Fossil reptiles and amphibians. Address: Dept. of Paleontology, University of California, Berkeley, CA 94720.

GREGORY, KEITH EDWARD, b. Franklin, N.C, Oct. 27, 24; m. 51; c. 2. ANIMAL BREEDING. B.S, N.C. State Col, 47; M.S, Nebraska, 49; Ph.D.(animal breeding), Missouri, 51. Asst. animal husb, Nebraska, 47-49; Missouri, 49-51; assoc. prof, Auburn, 51-55; animal geneticist & regional coordinator, beef cattle breeding res, Agr. Res. Serv, U.S. DEPT. AGR, 55-66, DIR. U.S. MEAT ANIMAL RES. CTR, 66-; PROF. ANIMAL SCI, UNIV. NEBR, 59- U.S.N.R, 43-45. Fel. AAAS; Am. Soc. Animal Sci; Am. Genetic Asn. Animal breeding. Address: U.S. Meat Animal Research Center, Clay Center, NE 68933.

GREGORY, K(ENNETH) F(OWLER), b. Calgary, Alta, May 12, 26; m. 53; c. 3. BACTERIOLOGY. B.S.A, British Columbia, 47; M.Sc, Wisconsin, 49, Ph.D. (bact), 51. Asst. bact, Wisconsin, 47-51, res. assoc, 51-52; asst. prof, Dalhousie, 52-54; Ont. Agr. Col, 54-56, assoc. prof. MICROBIOL, 56-67; PROF, UNIV. GUELPH, 67- Mem. grant selection comt, Nat. Res. Coun. Can. AAAS; Am. Soc. Microbiol; Can. Soc. Microbiol; Genetics Soc. Can. Virology and bacterial genetics. Address: Dept. of Microbiology, University of Guelph, Guelph, Ont, Can.

GREGORY, KENNETH MONROE, b. Turlock, Calif. Mar. 6, 39; m. 66; c. 2. ANATOMY. A.B, California, Berkeley, 62, Ph.D.(anat), 67. INSTR. ANAT, STATE UNIV. N.Y. DOWNSTATE MED. CTR, 67- NASA investr, 70-71. Morphology and development of the vertebrate nervous system, especially with regard to the visual system; comparative neuroanatomy of the vertebrate auditory and vestibular systems. Address: Dept. of Anatomy, State University of New York Downstate Medical Center at Brooklyn, Brooklyn, NY 11203.

GREGORY, LUIS E, b. San German, P.R, Jan. 22, 15; m. 53; c. 4. PLANT PHYSIOLOGY, HORTICULTURE. B.Sc, Puerto Rico, 36; Inst. Trop. Agr, P.R. fel. & M.Sc, California, Berkeley, 48, Guggenheim Mem. fel. & Ph.D.(hort. sci), California, Los Angeles, 55. Agronomist forestry, P.R. Dept. Agr, 36-42; plant physiologist physiol. plant hormones, Inst. Trop. Agr, P.R, 44-47; res. assoc, Puerto Rico, 48; plant physiologist, rubber res. prog, U.S. DEPT. AGR, Md, 48-54, cotton res. prog, 55-57, horticulturist, Fed. Exp. Sta, P.R, 58-62, PLANT PHYSIOLOGIST, 62-67, PLANT HORMONES LABS, NAT. ARBORETUM, PLANT INDUST. STA, 67- Nat. Sci. Found. fel, Johns Hopkins Univ, 55. Bot. Soc. Am; Am. Soc. Hort. Sci; Am. Soc. Plant Physiol. Physiology of growth and differentiation in plants; physiology of plant growth regulators and of root formation in plants; minor elements nutrition in plants. Address: Plant Hormones Labs, National Arboretum, Plant Industry Station, Beltsville, MD 20705.

GREGORY, M. D(UANE), b. Weatherford, Okla, June 24, 42; m. 63; c. 2. PHYSICAL CHEMISTRY. B.S, Southwest. State Col.(Okla), 64; NASA & U.S. Pub. Health Serv. fels, Univ. Okla, 65, Ph.D.(phys. chem), 68. SCIENTIST, RES. & DEVELOP. DEPT, CONTINENTAL OIL CO, 68- Am. Chem. Soc; Soc. Petrol. Eng. Hydration of organic amines in nonaqueous solvents; surfactant waterflooding; resolution of oil in water dispersions. Address: Research & Development Dept, Continental Oil Co, Ponca City, OK 74601.

GREGORY, M. PFLUGE, b. Monroe, Mich, Aug. 27, 10; m. 39; c. 4. CYTOGENETICS. B.S, Fla. State, 31, M.S, 32; Ph.D.(cytogenetics), Virginia, 43. Teacher, pub. schs, Fla, 33-38; lab. instr. biol, Meredith Col, 46-47; assoc. botanist, N.C. STATE UNIV, 58-59, ASSOC. GENETICIST, 60- Bot. Soc. Am; Genetics Soc. Am. Peanut breeding and genetics; ionizing radiation and genetic change in peanuts, hibiscus and citrus; interspecific hybridization of peanuts; phylogenetic studies in Aristolochiaceae. Address: Dept. of Genetics, North Carolina State University, Raleigh, NC 27607.

GREGORY, MAX EDWIN, b. Yorkville, Tenn, Jan. 14, 31; m. 54; c. 3. FOOD SCIENCE. B.S, Tennessee, 53; M.S, N.C. State Col, 56, Ph.D.(dairy mfg), 59. DAIRY PROD. SPECIALIST, Ohio State, 59-62; N.C. STATE UNIV, 62- Dairy products. Address: Dept. of Food Science, North Carolina State University, Raleigh, NC 27607.

GREGORY, NORMAN W(AYNE), b. Albany, Ore, June 23, 20; m. 43; c. 3. PHYSICAL CHEMISTRY. B.S, Washington (Seattle), 40, M.S, 41; Ph.D. (chem), Ohio State, 43. Chemist, radiation lab, California, 44-46; instr. CHEM, UNIV. WASH, 46-47, asst. prof, 47-53, assoc. prof, 53-57, PROF, 57-, CHMN. DEPT, 70- Am. Chem. Soc. Thermodynamics of metal halide systems; crystal structure; vaporization reactions. Address: Dept. of Chemistry, University of Washington, Seattle, WA 98105.

GREGORY, RAYMOND (LESLIE), b. Beeville, Tex, Feb. 20, 01; m. 27; c. 3. INTERNAL MEDICINE. A.B, Texas, 22, A.M, 23; fel, Minnesota, 23-26, Ph.D, 27, M.D, 29. Tutor org. chem, Texas, 22-23; instr. physiol. & chem, Minnesota, 26-28; practicing physician, 30-33; asst. med, Iowa, 33-35; instr. internal med, 35-36; asst. prof. med, La. State, 36-37; prof. & head dept, col. med, Howard, 37-39; Arkansas, 39-40; prof. internal med. & chmn. dept, med. br, Texas, 40-68; CHIEF MED, DIAG. CLIN. HOUSTON, 68- Soc. Exp. Biol. & Med; Am. Physiol. Soc; fel. Am. Col. Physicians. Metabolic and endocrine diseases; experimental hypertension; metabolism of alcohol; azotemia associated with massive gastrointestinal bleeding. Address: Diagnostic Clinic of Houston, 6448 Fannin, Houston, TX 77025.

GREGORY, R(ICHARD) P(ARKER), JR, b. Louisville, Ky, Feb. 9, 16; m. 41; c. 4. VETERINARY MEDICINE. B.S, West. Ky. State Col, 40; D.V.M, Ohio State, 49. Assoc. prof. vet. sci. & animal husb, Tennessee, 53-57; res. veterinarian, animal clin. res. group, AGR. RES. CTR, ELI LILLY & CO, 57-61, STA. VETERINARIAN, VET. RES. DEPT, 61- Mem. faculty, eve. div, Ind. Cent. Col, 61- Animal nutrition; large and small animal surgery. Address: Agricultural Research Center, Eli Lilly & Co, P.O. Box 708, Greenfield, IN 46140.

GREGORY, RICHARD WALLACE, b. Chicago, Ill, Sept. 28, 36; m. 57; c. 2. FISHERIES. B.S, Colo. State Univ, 58, Ph.D.(fish mgt), 69; M.S, Univ. Wash, 62. Fish biologist, Colo. Game, Fish & Parks Dept, 63, wildlife researcher cand, 63-64, asst. wildlife researcher, 64-66, wildlife researcher, 66-69; ASST. UNIT LEADER, BUR. SPORT FISHERIES & WILDLIFE, 69-; ASST. PROF. ZOOL, UNIV. MAINE, ORONO, 69- Prin. investr, Sport Fishery Res. Found. study grant, 71-73. U.S.N, 58-60. Am. Inst. Biol. Sci; Am. Fisheries Soc. Behavior of Pacific salmon smolts; feeding behavior of Atlantic salmon; stocking, yield and standing crops of warm water fishes; biochemistry of walleye pike and Atlantic salmon seminal plasma. Address: Murray Hall, University of Maine, Orono, ME 04473.

GREGORY, R(OBERT) LEE, b. Mishawaka, Ind, Oct. 22, 36. MECHANICAL ENGINEERING. B.S.M.E, Purdue Univ, 59, Outboard Marine Corp. fel, 60, M.S.M.E, 61; Bendix study award, 65-69; Ph.D.(control systs), Univ. Notre Dame, 70. Test engr, Studebaker-Packard Corp, 60-61; eng. analyst, energy controls div, Aerospace-Electronics Co, BENDIX CORP, 61-69,

STAFF ENGR, BENDIX RES. LABS, 70- U.S.A.R, 60-66. Am. Soc. Mech. Eng; Nat. Soc. Prof. Eng. Analysis of fluidic devices and systems and of earth orbital space stations. Address: Bendix Research Labs, Bendix Center, Dept. 610, Southfield, MI 48076.

GREGORY, ROBERT TODD, b. Owensboro, Ky, Mar. 19, 20; m. 44; c. 2. MATHEMATICS. B.S, U.S. Naval Acad, 42; M.S, Iowa State Univ, 48; Ph.D. (math), Univ. Ill, 55. Asst. math, Iowa State Univ, 47-48; mathematician, U.S. Naval Proving Ground, Va, 49; instr. math, Fla. State Univ, 49-50; res. asst, digital computer lab, Univ. Ill, 50-55; asst. prof. MATH, Univ. Calif, Santa Barbara, 55-59; assoc. prof, UNIV. TEX, 59-63, PROF, 63-, COMPUT. SCI, 66-, ASSOC. DIR, CTR. NUMERICAL ANAL, 70-, sr. res. mathematician, comput. ctr, 66-70, acting chmn, dept. comput. sci, 66-68, assoc. dir, comput. ctr, 59-66. Consult, Ramo-Wooldridge Corp, 56-58; Space Technol. Labs, 58; appl. math. div, Argonne Nat. Labs, 62-63. Vis. res. assoc. prof, digital comput. lab, Univ. Ill, summer 60; chmn. numerical anal. comt, coop orgn, Users of Control Data 1604 Comput, 63-64; adj. prof, comput. sci. lab, Grad. Res. Ctr. of Southwest, 64-65; reviewer, 'Comput. Revs.' Vis. mathematician, comput. ctr, Stanford Univ, summer 63; comput. ctr, Univ. Calif, Berkeley, summers 64-66; comput. ctr, Univ. Lund, spring 69; Zurich, Switz, winter 69. Lectr, Univ. Oslo, 69; Swiss Fed. Inst. Technol, 69; Royal Inst. Technol, Sweden, 69; Technol. Inst, Copenhagen, 69; Univ. Lund, 69. U.S.N, 42-46, Res, 46-, Lt. Comdr. Am. Math. Soc; Soc. Indust. & Appl. Math; Math. Asn. Am; Asn. Comput. Mach. Numerical analysis; computational problems in matrix algebra. Address: Dept. of Mathematics, University of Texas at Austin, Austin, TX 78712.

GREGORY, THOMAS J(ONES), b. San Jose, Calif, Aug. 15, 34; m. 56; c. 2. AERONAUTICS. B.S, Univ. Calif, 57. Res. scientist, aeronaut. div, Ames Res. Ctr, NASA, 57-63, off. advan. res. & technol, mission anal. div, 63-71, CHIEF ADVAN. VEHICLE CONCEPTS BR, AERONAUT. DIV, AMES RES. CTR, 71- Am. Inst. Aeronaut. & Astronaut. Hypersonic and supersonic aircraft design by computer methods; theoretical investigations of automatic analysis of aircraft and their missions. Address: 20754 St. Joan Ct, Saratoga, CA 95070.

GREGORY, WALTER A, b. Johnson City, N.Y, Mar. 16, 19; m. 59; c. 3. ORGANIC CHEMISTRY. A.B, Cornell, 41; M.S, Iowa State Col, 42; Ph.D.(org. chem), Cornell, 47. Res. chemist, Eastman Kodak Co, 42-44; chemist, Manhattan proj, Tenn. Eastman Co, 44-45; res. chemist, INDUST. & BIOCHEM. DEPT, E.I. DU PONT DE NEMOURS & CO, INC, 47-50, res. supvr, 50-58, SR. RES. SCIENTIST, 58- Vis. lectr, sch. vet. med, Pennsylvania, 58-70. Am. Chem. Soc; Sci. Res. Soc. Am. Organometallic compounds of heterocyclic rings; synthesis of heterocyclic compounds for use as color couplers for color film; synthesis of cyclic disulfides related to the antibiotic glyotoxin; synthesis of antibiotics and chemotherapeutic drugs. Address: Experimental Station, E.I. du Pont de Nemours & Co, Inc, Wilmington, DE 19898.

GREGORY, WALTON C(ARLYLE), b. Amherst, Va, Aug. 12, 10; m. 39; c. 4. CYTOLOGY, PLANT BREEDING. B.A, Lynchburg Col, 34, hon. D.Sc, 60; M.A, Virginia, 35, Ph.D.(cytogenetics), 40; George Washington, 36. Asst. prof. biol, Tenn. Polytech, 41-42; agron, N.C. STATE UNIV, 42-44, assoc. prof, 44-50, prof, 50-57, WILLIAM NEAL REYNOLDS DISTINGUISHED PROF. CROP SCI, 57- Lectr, Lima, 59. Andrew Fleming Res. prize, 40; President's & Visitor's Res. award, Virginia, 41; Golden Peanut Res. Award, 61. Bot. Soc. Am; Genetics Soc. Am; Crop Sci. Soc. Am; Am. Genetic Asn. Plant exploration and the use of atomic energy in plant breeding. Address: Dept. of Crop Science, North Carolina State University, Raleigh, NC 27607.

GREGORY, WESLEY W(RIGHT), JR, b. Camden, S.C, Sept. 9, 42; m. 65; c. 2. ECONOMIC ENTOMOLOGY. B.S, Wofford Col, 64; M.S, Clemson Univ, 66, Nat. Insts. Health fel, 66-69, Ph.D.(entom, environ. health & bot), 69; Nat. Sci. Found. fel, Duke Univ, 69. Res. asst. invert. zool, Clemson Univ, 65-66; ASST. PROF. ENTOM, UNIV. KY, 69- AAAS; Entom. Soc. Am. Bioaccumulation and transferal of pesticide residues in biological systems; development of insect management systems for soil and foliar pests of corn and vegetable crops, arthropod ecology. Address: Dept. of Entomology, University of Kentucky, Lexington, KY 40506.

GREIBACH, SHEILA ADELE, b. N.Y.C, Oct. 6, 39. APPLIED MATHEMATICS. A.B, Radcliffe Col, 60, A.M, 62; Nat. Sci. Found. fel, Harvard, 60-63, Ph.D.(appl. math), 63. Lectr. appl. math, Harvard, 63-65, asst. prof, 65-69, ASSOC. PROF. SYST. SCI, UNIV. CALIF, LOS ANGELES, 69- Consult, Systs. Develop. Corp, 64-70. Am. Math. Soc. Algebraic linguistics and automata theory. Address: Dept. of System Science, Boelter Hall, University of California, Los Angeles, CA 90024.

GREICHUS, ALGIRDAS, b. Detroit, Mich, Aug. 5, 29; m. 51; c. 4. PARASITOLOGY, PHYSIOLOGY. B.S, Idaho, 56, M.S, 58; Ph.D.(zool), Wyoming, 64. Statist. asst, Arctic Health Res. Ctr, U.S. Pub. Health Serv, 57-59; ASSOC. PROF. ZOOL, S.DAK. STATE UNIV, 63- C.Eng, U.S.A, 47-52, 1st Lt. Am. Soc. Parasitol; Am. Soc. Zool. Helminth physiology and biochemistry; lipid metabolism in parasitic helminths. Address: 348 Eastern Ave, Brookings, SD 57006.

GREICHUS, YVONNE A, b. Whitefish, Mont, Aug. 4, 26; m. 51; c. 4. BIOLOGICAL CHEMISTRY, ZOOLOGY. B.A, Reed Col, 49; M.S, Wyoming, 61, Ph.D.(animal sci), 64; fel, Stanford Res. Inst, 61-63. Nat. Insts. Health res. asst, Univ. Wyo, 59-61; instr. BIOCHEM, S.DAK. STATE UNIV, 64-66, asst. prof, 66-71, ASSOC. PROF, 71- Am. Chem. Soc. Long-chain fatty acid composition of meats; analysis of volatile fatty acids in rumen fluid; ponds, animal waste products; insecticide residues in surface waters, pheasant and deer. Address: Station Biochemistry, South Dakota State University, Brookings, SD 57006.

GREIDANUS, JOHAN WILHELM, b. Leeuwarden, Netherlands, Sept. 4, 29; Can. citizen; m. 57; c. 3. ORGANIC CHEMISTRY. Drs. Groningen, 57; Prov. Alta. scholar, Alberta, 61-62, Ph.D.(org. chem), 62. Fel. biochem, Ont. Res. Found, Toronto, 57-59; ORG. CHEM, Minnesota, Minneapolis, 62-64; res. assoc. & spec. lectr, fundamental sulphur res. group, Calgary, 64-66, asst. prof, 66-71; SR. LECTR, SCH. NATURAL SCI, UNIV. ZAMBIA, 71- Am. Chem. Soc; Chem. Inst. Can; The Chem. Soc. Synthetic organic chemistry; chemistry of adamantane; organosulphur compounds. Address: School of Natural Sciences, University of Zambia, P.O. Box 2379, Lusaka, Zambia.

GREIDER, H(AROLD) W(ILLIAM), b. Manchester, Kans, Aug. 1, 94; m. 24; c. 4. CHEMISTRY. B.Sc, Washburn Col, 16; M.Sc, Kansas, 17. Chemist, Topeka Pure Milk Co, 14-16; instr. chem, Kansas, 16-17; indust. fel, Mellon Inst, 19-26; res. chemist, Philip Carey Mfg. Co, 27-30, dir. res, 31-50, mgr. qual. control, 50-59, res. consult, 60-69, TECH. CONSULT, PANACON CORP, 69- Asst. tech. ed, India Rubber Rev, 22-24. Mod. pioneer award, Nat. Asn. Mfrs, 40. Asst. chemist, Ord. Dept, 17-19. Am. Chem. Soc; Am. Soc. Test. & Mat. Development of asphalt, asbestos, and magnesia products; roofing; building materials; heat insulations; road materials; air ducts; cement-asbestos products; fire-resistant bituminous coating compositions. Address: 65 Jewett Dr, Wyoming, OH 45215.

GREIDER, KENNETH R(ANDOLPH), b. Cleveland, Ohio, Feb. 10, 29; wid; c. 2. THEORETICAL PHYSICS. B.S.E, Michigan, 50; M.S, New Mexico, 54; Ph.D, California, 58. Physicist, Lawrence Radiation Lab, California, 58-59, asst. res. physicist, California, La Jolla, 59-62; asst. prof. PHYSICS, Yale, 62-65; assoc. prof, UNIV. CALIF, DAVIS, 65-67, PROF, 67- Consult, Inst. Defense Anal, 62-63; Los Alamos Sci. Lab, California, 64-65; vis. prof, Univ. Heidelberg, 71-72. U.S.A, 50-53, Lt. Am. Phys. Soc. Nuclear reaction mechanisms; theory of rearrangement collisions; high energy diffraction scattering. Address: Dept. of Physics, University of California, Davis, CA 95616.

GREIDER, MARIE H(ELEN), b. Newark, Ohio, Jan. 15, 22. CYTOLOGY. B.Sc, Ohio State, 49, M.Sc, 55, Ph.D.(zool), 60. Asst, Ohio State Univ, 51-60, res. assoc. PATH, 60-64, asst. prof, 64-68; WASH. UNIV, 68-70, ASSOC. PROF, 70- AAAS; Am. Soc. Cell Biol; Am. Asn. Anat; N.Y. Acad. Sci; Electron Micros. Soc. Am. Electron microscopy; cytochemistry; endocrinology. Address: Dept. of Pathology, Washington University, 4550 Scott Ave, St. Louis, MO 63110.

GREIF, MORTIMER, b. New York, N.Y, Aug. 13, 26; m. 48; c. 2. PHYSICAL CHEMISTRY. B.S, City Col. New York, 47; fel, Kentucky, 47-49, M.S, 49; fel, Polytech. Inst. Brooklyn, 49-52, Ph.D.(phys. chem), 53. Staff chemist, phys. res, fabrics & finishes div, E.I. du Pont de Nemours & Co, 52-63; TECH. DIR, STAHL FINISH CO, 63- U.S.N.R, 44-46. Am. Chem. Soc. Alternating current polarography; film formation; emulsion paints; pigment dispersions; leather finishes. Address: 30 Manton Rd, Swampscott, MA 01907.

GREIF, RALPH, b. N.Y.C, Nov. 28, 35; m. 58; c. 3. HEAT & MASS TRANSFER. B.S, N.Y. Univ, 56; Howard Hughes fel, Univ. Calif, Los Angeles, 56-58, M.S, 58; Charles Storer Storrow scholar, Harvard, 58-59, Gordon McKay fel, 59-60, M.A. & Ph.D.(eng), 62. Mem. tech. staff, Hughes Res. & Develop. Labs, 56-58; res. fel. gas dynamics, Harvard, 62-63; asst. prof. MECH. ENG, UNIV. CALIF, BERKELEY, 63-69, ASSOC. PROF, 69-, res. engr, summers, 64, 67-70. Summer res. engr, Raytheon Missile Lab, 58, Allied Res. Assocs, Inc, 59, Lawrence Radiation Lab, Univ. Calif, 65 & 66; Guggenheim fel, 69-70. Consult, Minneapolis, Honeywell Regulator Co, 61; Lockheed Palo Alto Res. Lab, 65-68. Am. Inst. Aeronaut. & Astronaut; Am. Soc. Mech. Eng. Thermal radiation; spectroscopy; transport properties; rotating flows; non-Newtonian fluids; fluid mechanics. Address: Dept. of Mechanical Engineering, University of California, Berkeley, CA 94720.

GREIF, ROBERT, b. New York, N.Y, Jan. 17, 38; m. 63; c. 2. SOLID MECHANICS, MECHANICAL ENGINEERING. B.M.E, N.Y. Univ, 58; S.M, Harvard, 59, Ph.D.(appl. mech), 63. Staff scientist, missile systs. div, Avco Corp, 63-65, sr. staff scientist, 65-67; asst. prof. MECH. ENG, TUFTS UNIV, 67-70, ASSOC. PROF, 70- Consult, Beverly Res. Lab, U.S.M. CORP, 67-68. Am. Soc. Mech. Eng; Am. Inst. Aeronaut. & Astronaut. Elasticity; structural design for dynamic loading; stress waves. Address: Dept. of Mechanical Engineering, Tufts University, Medford, MA 02155.

GREIF, ROGER L(OUIS), b. Baltimore, Md, Aug. 23, 16; m. 50; c. 3. PHYSIOLOGY. B.S, Haverford Col, 37; M.D, Hopkins, 41. Intern. med, hosp, Hopkins, 41-42; asst, Lakeside Hosp, 42-43; asst. physician, hosp, Rockefeller Inst, 47-53; asst. prof. PHYSIOL, MED. COL, CORNELL UNIV, 53-55, assoc. prof, 55-65, PROF, 65- Fel, hosp, Johns Hopkins Univ, 46-47; asst. physician, out-patients, New York hosp, 53-; consult, metab. sect, Health Res. Coun, New York City; mem, Marine Biol. Lab, Woods Hole. Med.C, U.S.N.R, 43-46. Soc. Exp. Biol. & Med; Am. Physiol. Soc; Endocrine Soc; Harvey Soc; Am. Thyroid Asn; Am. Fedn. Clin. Res; N.Y. Acad. Sci; Soc. Gen. Physiol. Thyroid and endocrine physiology; hormone-enzyme relationships. Address: Dept. of Physiology, Cornell University Medical College, 1300 York Ave, New York, NY 10021.

GREIFENSTEIN, FERDINAND E(RNEST), b. Newark, N.J, Jan. 9, 15; m. 41; c. 2. ANESTHESIOLOGY. B.S, Spring Hill Col, 37; M.D, St. Louis, 44. Instr. anesthesia, Pennsylvania, 49-50; col. med, Wayne State, 51-52, prof, 52-64; PROF. & HEAD ANESTHESIOL, MED. CTR, UNIV. ARK, 64- Vis. prof, Univ. Nuevo Leon, Mex, 57; Keio Univ, Japan, 59. Consult, Vet. Admin. Hosp, Dearborn, 53, Little Rock, 64; Jennings Children's Hosp, 53. U.S.A.A.F, 46-48, Capt. Respiration. Address: Dept. of Surgery, University of Arkansas Medical Center, Little Rock, AR 72201.

GREIFER, AARON P(HILIP), b. Passaic, N.J, Sept. 29, 19; m. 43; c. 2. PHYSICAL & INORGANIC CHEMISTRY. B.A, Ohio State, 42; M.A, Columbia, 48. Chemist, Elwood Ord. Plant, Ill, 42-44; res. assoc. cryogenics, Res. Found, Ohio, State, 44-45; chemist, Kellex Corp, N.Y, 48-49; Fed. Tel. & Radio Corp, 51; scientist, Gen. Elec. Co, 51-56; sr. scientist, Radio Corp. Am, 56-61; proj. chemist, Clevite Corp, 61-64; staff chemist, UNIVAC DIV, SPERRY RAND CORP, 64-67, mgr. ferrite core res, 67-71, STAFF SCIENTIST, 71- Jr. scientist, Los Alamos Sci. Lab, Calif. C.Eng, U.S.A, 45-46. AAAS; Am. Chem. Soc; Am. Phys. Soc; fel. Am. Inst. Chem; Inst. Elec. & Electronics Eng. Nonmetallic magnetic materials; ferromagnetism; single crystal growth; piezomagnetic ferrites; low loss ferrites; memory cores. Address: Univac Division, Sperry Rand Corp, P.O. Box 500, Blue Bell, PA 19422.

GREIFER, B(ERNARD), b. New York, N.Y, Dec. 22, 21; m; c. 3. ANALYTICAL CHEMISTRY. B.S, City Col. New York, 42; M.S, N.Y. Univ, 47; Ph.D.(chem), Carnegie Inst. Tech, 57. Asst, jet propulsion lab, N.Y. Univ, 47-48; physicist, Gulf Res. & Develop. Corp, 49-51; supvr. chemist, phys. res. sect, U.S. Bur. Mines, 51-57; sr. phys. chemist, Atlantic Res. Corp, 57-66, head spec. proj. sect, 66-70, microbiol. lab, 70-71; ASST. CHIEF, MICRO-CHEM. SECT, NAT. BUR. STANDARDS, 71- Am. Chem. Soc; Sci. Res. Soc. Am; Combustion Inst. Microchemical analysis; microbiology; air and water pollution; chemical writing and abstracting; combustion and explosions of gases and solids. Address: Microchemistry Section, National Bureau of Standards, Washington, DC 20234.

GREIFF, DONALD, b. Toronto, Ont, Aug. 20, 15; nat; m. 42; c. 3. VIROLOGY. B.S, Marquette, 38, 38-39; Sc.D.(genetics), Hopkins, 42. Instr. biol, St. Louis Univ, 42-49, assoc. prof, 49-51, PROF, 51-57; PATH, MED. COL. WIS, 57-, ASSOC. DEAN GRAD. AFFAIRS, 68- Mem. Comn. X, Int. Inst. Refrig. Genetics Soc. Am; Am. Soc. Zool; affiliate Royal Soc. Med; Soc. Cryobiol.(pres, 67). Effects of enzyme inhibitors and activators on the multiplication of viruses and Rickettsiae; freezing and freeze-drying of biologic materials; studies on freeze-dried biologic materials. Address: Dept. of Pathology, Medical College of Wisconsin, 561 N. 15th St, Milwaukee, WI 53233.

GREIFINGER, CARL, b. Poland, Apr. 19, 26; nat; m. 47; c. 3. THEORETICAL PHYSICS. A.B, Cornell, 48, Ph.D.(physics), 54. Instr. physics, Pennsylvania, 53-55; asst. prof, Southern California, 55-58; PHYSICIST, Rand Corp, 58-71; R&D ASSOCS, 71- U.S.N, 44-46. Am. Phys. Soc. Theoretical nuclear physics; magneto-hydrodynamics; ionospheric physics. Address: R&D Associates, P.O. Box 3580, Santa Monica, CA 90403.

GREIFINGER, PHYLLIS S(TOLIAR), b. Brooklyn, N.Y, Apr. 8, 28; m. 47; c. 3. PHYSICS. A.B, Cornell, 48, M.S, 51, Ph.D.(theoret. physics), 54. Instr. physics, Swarthmore Col, 53-55; consult, Rand Corp, Calif, 55-71; PHYS. SCIENTIST, R&D ASSOCS, SANTA MONICA, 71- Am. Geophys. Union. Stability of heavy nuclei; origin of cosmic rays; elastic scattering of gamma rays by bound electrons; heat transfer in chemical reacting gases; transport properties of high temperature air; plasma physics; geomagnetic phenomena. Address: 16948 Dulce Ynez Lane, Pacific Palisades, CA 90272.

GREIG, ANDREW S(TEPHEN), b. Toronto, Ont, July 20, 22; m. 48; c. 1. VIROLOGY. D.V.M, Ont. Vet. Col, 50; Ph.D.(bact, virol), Cornell, 53. RES. OFF, ANIMAL DISEASES RES. INST, CAN. DEPT. AGR, 53- Can. Army, 42-46. AAAS; Can. Soc. Microbiol; Can. Vet. Med. Asn. Virus diseases of animal origin; bacteriology, especially with pleuropneumonia group of organisms; tissue culture. Address: Animal Diseases Research Institute, 100 Gamelin Blvd, Hull, Que, Can.

GREIG, J. ROBERT, b. Maidenhead, Eng, Apr. 12, 38; m. 64; c. 2. PLASMA PHYSICS. B.Sc. & A.R.C.S, London, 59, Ph.D.(physics) & D.I.C, 65. Res. off, Cent. Electricity Res. Lab, Eng, 62-65; ASST. PROF. PHYSICS, UNIV. MD, 65- Am. Phys. Soc; Brit. Inst. Physics. Plasma spectroscopy and diagnostic methods used in plasma physics; teaching college physics. Address: Dept. of Physics & Astronomy, University of Maryland, College Park, MD 20742.

GREIG, J(AMES) K(IBLER), JR, b. Van Buren, Ark, Apr. 9, 23; m. 47; c. 3. HORTICULTURE. M.S, Arkansas, 50; Ph.D.(agron), Kansas State, 60. Asst, Arkansas, 49-50, instr. & jr. horticulturist, 50-52; asst. prof. HORT. & asst. olericulturist, KANS. STATE UNIV, 52-61, assoc. prof. & assoc. olericulturist, 61-70, PROF. & OLERICULTURIST, 70- U.S.A, 43-46. Am. Soc. Hort. Sci; Weed Sci. Soc. Am. Vegetable culture, nutrition and physiology. Address: 2855 Oregon Lane, Manhattan, KS 66502.

GREIG, JOHN H(ENRY), b. Clarkson's, Ont, Mar. 6, 19; nat; m; c. 4. PHYSICS. B.A, Cornell, 41; George Washington, 43-45; Ph.D.(physics), Virginia, 47. Radio engr, U.S. Naval Res. Lab, Wash, D.C, 41-45; asst. prof. physics, Wash. Sq. Col, N.Y. Univ, 47-51, assoc. prof, 51-55; chief physicist, Clairex Corp, 56-58; pres, Physics Develop. & Mfg. Corp, 58-69; ASST. TO V.PRES, GRUMMAN AEROSPACE CORP, 69- Chief comput. sect, Hogan Labs, Inc, 52-56; adj. prof, Wash. Sq. Col, N.Y. Univ, 57-59; consult. physicist, 56-69. Civilian with U.S.N, 44. AAAS; Inst. Elec. & Electronics Eng; Am. Phys. Soc; Am. Asn. Physics Teachers. Microwaves; milimeter waves; radar; digital computers; infrared; optics. Address: 1366 Darby Rd, Wantagh, NY 11793.

GREIG, J(OSEPH) W(ILSON), b. Wingham, Ont, Feb. 7, 95; m; c. 2. PETROLOGY, PHYSICAL CHEMISTRY. B.Sc, Queen's (Ont), 21; Columbia, 21-22; Ph.D.(geol), Harvard, 27. Petrologist, geophys. lab, Carnegie Inst, 22-60; VIS. PROF. GEOCHEM, PA. STATE UNIV, 60-, vis. res. assoc, 56-57. Physicist, appl. physics lab, Johns Hopkins Univ, 45-46. Can. Army, 15-19; consult, Nat. Defense Res. Cmt; Off. Sci. Res. & Develop, 41-44; U.S.A.A.F, 44-45. Fel. Mineral Soc. Am; Geochem. Soc; Am. Geophys. Union. High temperature physical chemistry of oxides; igneous rocks; refractories; geophysics. Address: Dept. of Geosciences, College of Earth & Mineral Sciences, Deike Bldg, Pennsylvania State University, University Park, PA 16802.

GREIG, MARGARET E(LIZABETH), b. Cumberland, Ont, Mar. 12, 07, nat. PHARMACOLOGY. B.A, McGill, 28, Nat. Res. Coun. Can. fel, 30-32, Ph.D.(chem), 32; M.A, Saskatchewan, 30. Demonstr. chem, Saskatchewan, 28-30; asst. cellulose chem, McGill, 32-35; chemist, biochem. res. found, Franklin Inst, 35-42; from asst. to assoc. prof, dept. pharmacol, sch. med, Vanderbilt, 42-53; SR. RES. PHARMACOLOGIST, SECT. HEAD & SR. SCIENTIST, UPJOHN CO, 53- With Off. Sci. Res. & Develop, 42-44. Pharmacol. Soc; fel. N.Y. Acad. Sci. Tumor metabolism; shock from hemorrhage; central nervous system drugs; allergy and anaphylaxis. Address: Dept. of Hypersensitivity Diseases, Upjohn Co, Kalamazoo, MI 49001.

GREIG, WILLIAM ELLIOTT, b. Toronto, Ont, Aug. 30, 38; m. 66. ASTROPHYSICS. B.Sc, Toronto, 61, M.A, 62; Ph.D.(astron), Illinois, 67. ASST. PROF. PHYSICS & ASTRON, BRADLEY UNIV, 68- Am. Astron. Soc; Am. Inst. Physics; Royal Astron. Soc. Can; Am. Asn. Physics Teachers. Physics; kinematics and morphology of planetary nebulae; galactic dynamics; morphology of galaxies; teaching of science. Address: Dept. of Physics, Bradley University, Peoria, IL 61606.

GREIM, BARBARA ANN, b. Phila, Pa. ALGEBRA. B.S, Ursinus Col, 64; Carnegie fel, Univ. N.C, Chapel Hill, 64-66, univ. fel, 66-67, Ph.D.(math), 70. ASST. PROF. MATH, UNIV. N.C, WILMINGTON, 69- Am. Math. Soc; Math. Asn. Am. Semigroup rings; use of computers in scientific education. Address: Dept. of Mathematics, University of North Carolina at Wilmington, P.O. Box 3725, Wilmington, NC 28401.

GREIN, FRIEDRICH, b. Freudenberg am Main, Germany, Dec. 22, 29; m. 59; c. 3. CHEMICAL PHYSICS. B.Sc, Göttingen, 54, M.Sc, 58; Ph.D.(chem. physics), Frankfurt, 60. Fel. quantum chem, New Brunswick, 60-61; Nat. Res. Coun. Can, 61-62; asst. prof. physics, UNIV. N.B, 62-63, CHEM, 63-66, ASSOC. PROF, 66- Vis. prof, Uppsala Univ, 68-69; Inst. Theoretical Chem, Univ. Frankfurt, summer 69. Am. Phys. Soc; Can. Asn. Physicists. Quantum theoretical treatment of small molecules; extensions of the Hartree-Fock scheme; approximate molecular orbital methods. Address: Dept. of Chemistry, University of New Brunswick, Fredericton, N.B, Can.

GREINEL, HERMANN P(AUL), b. Nuremberg, Ger, Sept. 12, 09; m. 42; c. 2. PHYSICS. Dr. rer. nat, Univ. Erlangen, 37. Asst. chief dept. infrared, magnetic fuses for mines, Hanseatische Apparatebau-Gesellschaft Neufeldt & Kuhnke, Ger, 37-42; group chief, infrared, guid. & control, Ger. Res. Inst. Gliders, 42-45; res. engr. guid. & control, Aeronaut. Arsenal, France, 46-49; res. engr, infrared, Nat. Center Study Telecommun, France, 49; asst. chief inst, nuclear fusion, High Temperature Metall. Lab, Argentina, 50; chief, flutter & vibration sect, State Aeronaut. & Mech. Industs, Aerotech. Inst, 50-56; assoc. scientist, applied physics, Republic Aviation Corp, N.Y, 56-58; aeronaut. res. engr. guid. & control, Air Force Missile Develop. Center, Holloman Air Force Base, N.Mex, 58-59; RES. SCIENTIST, LOCKHEED MISSILES & SPACE CO, SUNNYVALE, 59- Ger. Soc. Aeronaut. & Astronaut; Am. Phys. Soc; Am. Inst. Aeronaut. & Astronaut; Optical Soc. Am; Am. Mgt. Asn. Infrared and optics; guidance and control; flutter and vibration; atmospheric physics; nuclear and plasma physics; semiconductors. Address: 2246 Deodara Dr, Los Altos, CA 94022.

GREINER, GARY O(LIVER) G(EORGE), b. Ludington, Mich, Apr. 21, 41; m. 65. PALEONTOLOGY, GEOLOGY. B.A, St. Mary's Univ.(Tex), 62; North. Ill. Univ, 62-63; NASA traineeship, Case West. Reserve Univ, 63-66, univ. assistantship, 66-68, Ph.D.(geol), 69. Res. fel, mus. comp. zool, Harvard, 68-69; ASST. PROF. GEOL, SOUTHAMPTON COL, L.I. UNIV, 69- Soc. Econ. Paleont. & Mineral. Ecology and paleoecology of Foraminifera; distribution and shell morphology; evolution; functional morphology of other organisms as related to paleoecology; calcium carbonate sedimentation and diagenesis. Address: Dept. of Geology, Southampton College, Long Island University, Southampton, NY 11968.

GREINER, H(UGO) R, b. Edmonton, Alta, Aug. 2, 16; m. 56; c. 2. GEOLOGY. B.Sc, Alberta, 50; Binney scholar, 51-52, M.Sc, 51; Schuchert fel, Yale, 52-54, Ph.D.(geol), 54. Geologist, Geol. Surv. Can, 54-56; asst. prof. GEOL, UNIV. N.B, 56-62, assoc. prof, 62-70, PROF, 70- VonHumboldt fel, 59-60; summers, mem. staff, Dept. Mines, Que, Can, 57, field work, north. N.B, 59, 62, 63, 64; west. Arctic Islands, 61. R.C.A.F, 41-46. Geol. Soc. Am; Am. Asn. Petrol. Geol; Can. Palaeont. Soc; German Geol. Asn. Invertebrate paleontology; stratigraphy; animal evolution. Address: Dept. of Geology, University of New Brunswick, Fredericton, N.B, Can.

GREINER, JOHN WARD, b. West Lafayette, Ind, Oct. 13, 16; m. 39; c. 3. CHEMICAL ENGINEERING. B.S.Ch.E, Purdue, 38; Mass. Inst. Tech, 39-40. Control chemist, Dow Chem. Co, 38-39, chem. engr, 41-44; control chemist, Hercules Powder Co, 39; res. scientist, UPJOHN CO, 44-54, sect. head, pilot lab, 54-56, mgr. chem. process res. & develop, 56-65, asst. dir. chem. prod. & develop. div, 65-70, DIR. FINE CHEM. RES. & DEVELOP, 70- Chmn, Gordon Res. Conf. Separation & Purification, 62. Am. Chem. Soc; Am. Inst. Chem. Eng. Separations and purifications, especially by means of countercurrent crystallization and liquid-liquid extraction. Address: Upjohn Company, Kalamazoo, MI 49001.

GREINER, J(OHN) W(ILLIAM), b. Phila, Pa, Feb. 26, 14; m. 35. MATHEMATICS. A.B, Colgate, 48, M.A, 50; fel, Florida, 55-56, Ph.D.(math), 58. Instr. phys. sci, Colgate, 48-49; Florida, 50-54, asst. prof, 54-61; res. specialist, Autonetics Div, N.Am. Aviation, Inc, 61-65, sr. tech. specialist, N.Am. Rockwell Corp, 65-70; MEM. STAFF MATH. & ENG, LONG BEACH CITY COL, 70- Mem. sci. comt, Am. Coun. Ed, 53-55. U.S.N, 43-45. Am. Math. Asn; Am. Math. Soc; Asn. Comput. Mach; Soc. Indust. & Appl. Math. System analysis; command and control systems; computer systems; mathematical analysis and modeling. Address: Dept. of Mathematics & Engineering, Long Beach City College, 4901 E. Carson, Long Beach, CA 90808.

GREINER, NORMAN ROY, b. Muskegon, Mich, Aug. 30, 38; m. 64; c. 2. PHYSICAL CHEMISTRY. B.S, St. Mary's (Tex), 60; Ph.D.(phys. chem), Texas, Austin, 64. SECT. LEADER CHEM, LOS ALAMOS SCI. LAB, 64- AAAS; Am. Chem. Soc. Gas kinetics; photochemistry; air pollution control; reactions of internally excited molecules; reactions initiated by flash photolysis; reactions of excited noble gas atoms; chemistry of planetary atmospheres; chemical lasers. Address: Los Alamos Scientific Lab, Box 1663, Los Alamos, NM 87544.

GREINER, PETER C(HARLES), b. Budapest, Hungary, Nov. 1, 38; Can. citizen; m. 65; c. 2. MATHEMATICS. B.Sc, British Columbia, 60; M.A, Yale, 62, Ph.D.(math), 64. Instr. MATH, Princeton, 64-65; asst. prof, UNIV. TORONTO, 65-69, ASSOC. PROF, 69- Am. Math. Soc. Partial differential equation; functional analysis. Address: Dept. of Mathematics, University of Toronto, Toronto, Ont, Can.

GREINER, RICHARD A(NTON), b. Milwaukee, Wis, Feb. 13, 31. ELECTRICAL ENGINEERING. B.S, Wisconsin, 54, M.S, 55, Ph.D.(elec. eng), 57. Asst. prof. ELEC. ENG, UNIV. WIS, MADISON, 57-60, assoc. prof, 60-63, PROF, 63- Audio Eng. Soc; Inst. Elec. & Electronics Eng. Solid state devices and circuits. Address: Dept. of Electrical Engineering, University of Wisconsin, Madison, WI 53706.

GREINER, RICHARD W(ILLIAM), b. New York, N.Y, Feb. 24, 32; m. 49; c. 2. PHYSICAL & ORGANIC CHEMISTRY. B.S, Bucknell, 53; Socony-Mobil fel, Wisconsin, 56-57, Ph.D.(org. chem), 57. Res. chemist, Hercules Powder Co, 57-69, SR. RES. CHEMIST, RES. CTR, HERCULES INC, 69- Am. Chem. Soc; Sci. Res. Soc. Am; Brit. Chem. Soc. Physical organic chemistry, including neighboring group effects, mechanisms of allylic rearrangements; chemistry of free radicals, including addition of radicals to carbon-carbon double bond and autoxidation. Address: Research Center, Hercules, Inc, Wilmington, DE 19899.

GREINETZ, ROSAMOND MONTE, b. Pueblo, Colo, Sept. 14, 36. ANALYTICAL & PHYSICAL CHEMISTRY. B.A, Reed Col, 57; summer fel, Brookhaven Nat. Labs, 62; M.S, Colorado, 63, Ph.D.(chem), 66. Res. chemist, dept. textile fibers, E.I. du Pont de Nemours & Co, 66-67; STAFF ENGR, SYSTS. DEVELOP. DIV, IBM CORP, 67- AAAS; Am. Chem. Soc. Material diffusion and flow through packed beds; surface chemistry and process variables of textile fibers; materials-process synthesis and development for computer parts; computer programming; polymer, metallurgical and general analyses. Address: 5500 E. Sixth Ave, Denver, CO 80220.

GREINKE, EVERETT D, b. Elmhurst, Ill, Oct. 31, 29; m. 51; c. 3. CHEMISTRY, MATHEMATICS. B.S, Northern Illinois, 51, M.S, 56; Wisconsin, 56; George Washington, 56-57. Asst. br. head res. & develop, photo div. bur. naval weapons, NAVY DEPT, 56-61, tech. adv. for data proc, tech. anal. & adv. group, dep. chief naval opers, 56-65, asst. dir. command control, 65-67, STAFF SPECIALIST, DIR. DEFENSE RES. & ENG, 67- Am. Inst. Chem. U.S.N.R, 51-55, Res, 55-, Comdr. Review, analysis and coordination of Dept. of Defense research, development, testing, evaluation, and engineering programs in the fields of reconnaissance and intelligence. Address: 8315 Toll House Rd, Annandale, VA 22003.

GREINKE, RONALD ALFRED, b. Mt. Prospect, Ill, Aug. 20, 35; m. 67; c. 2. ANALYTICAL CHEMISTRY. B.S, Univ. Ill, 63; M.S, Univ. Mich, 65, NASA trainee, 65-67, Ph.D.(anal. chem), 67. Anal. chemist, chem. & plastics div, UNION CARBIDE CORP, 67-69, res. scientist, CARBON PROD. DIV, 69-70, HEAD ANAL. RES. & DEVELOP, 71- U.S.A, 58-60. Am. Chem. Soc. Kinetics in analytical chemistry; gas chromatography; thermal analysis. Address: Union Carbide Corp, P.O. Box 6116, Cleveland, OH 44101.

GREISEN, KENNETH I, b. Perth Amboy, N.J, Jan. 24, 18; m. 41; c. 2. PHYSICS. B.S, Franklin & Marshall Col, 38; Ph.D.(physics), Cornell, 42. Asst. physics, Cornell, 38-42, instr, 42-43; mem. staff Manhattan Proj, Atomic Energy Comn, Los Alamos, N.Mex, 43-45, group leader, 45-46; asst. prof. PHYSICS, CORNELL UNIV, 46-47, assoc. prof, 47-50, PROF, 50- AAAS; Am. Phys. Soc; Am. Astron. Soc; Am. Asn. Physics Teachers. Cosmic rays; nuclear physics; high energy astrophysics. Address: Dept. of Physics, Cornell University, Ithaca, NY 14850.

GREISMAN, SHELDON EDWARD, b. N.Y.C, Jan. 24, 28; m. 57; c. 4. PHYSIOLOGY, MEDICINE. M.D, N.Y. Univ, 49. Instr. MED, SCH. MED, UNIV. MD, 54-56, asst. prof, 56-61, ASSOC. PROF, 62-, Assoc. mem. cmn. epidemiol. surv, Armed Forces Epidemiol. Bd, 64- U.S.A, 52-54, 1st Lt. Asn. Am. Physicians; Am. Soc. Clin. Invest; Soc. Exp. Biol. & Med. Mechanisms of tolerance to bacterial endotoxins in man; role of bacterial endotoxins in human gram-negative bacterial infections. Address: Dept. of Medicine, University of Maryland School of Medicine, Baltimore, MD 21201.

GREISS, FRANK C, JR, b. Phila, Pa, July 13, 28; m. 53; c. 4. OBSTETRICS, GYNECOLOGY. B.A, Univ. Pa, 49, M.D, 53. Instr. OBSTET. & GYNEC, BOWMAN GRAY SCH. MED, 60-63, assoc. prof, 67-70, PROF, 70- Mem. human embryol. & develop. study sect, Nat. Insts. Health. Found. Prize Thesis, Am. Asn. Obstet. & Gynec, 68. Fel. Am. Col. Obstet. & Gynec; Soc. Exp. Biol. & Med; Soc. Study Reproduction; Am. Med. Asn. Obstetric and fetal physiology; uterine blood flow during pregnancy; infertility. Address: Dept. of Obstetrics & Gynecology, Bowman Gray School of Medicine, Winston-Salem, NC 27103.

GREIST, JOHN H(OWARD), b. Shoals, Ind, Feb. 1, 06; m. 36; c. 3. PSYCHIATRY. A.B, DePauw, 26; M.D, Indiana, 29. Instr. med, SCH. MED, IND. UNIV, 30-33, asst, 35-40, asst. prof. PSYCHIAT, 46-62, assoc. clin. prof, 62-69, ASSOC. PROF, 69- Fel, sch. med, Hopkins; lectr, Christian Sem. Consult, Dept. Army, 46-; Vet. Admin, 46- Med.C, 41-46, Res, 55-, Col. Am. Med. Asn; fel. Am. Psychiat. Asn; Asn. Consult. Mgt. Eng. Psychotherapy; electroencephalography. Address: 3231 N. Meridian St, Indianapolis, IN 46208.

GREIZERSTEIN, WALTER, b. Buenos Aires, Arg, Sept. 30, 35; U.S. citizen; m. 60; c. 3. ORGANIC CHEMISTRY. Ph.D.(org. chem), Buenos Aires, 60. Res. fel. org. chem, Buenos Aires, 60-61; Petrol. Res. Fund fel, Brown, 61-62; res. chemist, Rohm & Haas Co, 62-68, LAB. MGR. INDUST. FINISHES, PIERCE & STEVENS CHEM. CORP, 68- Am. Chem. Soc. Electronic and steric effects in nucleophilic substitutions; London Forces; correlations of structure and properties in polymers; reactions of ligands in organometallic complexes. Address: 275 Allenhurst, Amherst, NY 14226.

GREKEL, HOWARD, b. Wakeeney, Kans, Oct. 8, 18; m. 44; c. 1. CHEMICAL ENGINEERING. B.A, California, Los Angeles, 40; M.S, Mass. Inst. Tech, 47. Jr. chemist, control, Allison div, Gen. Motors Corp, 41; sr. chem. engr, res, Stanolind Oil & Gas Co, 47-54, res. group supvr, res. dept, AMOCO PROD. CO, 58-65, PLANT ENG. PROCESS. GROUP SUPVR, PROD. DEPT, 65- U.S.A, 41-43; U.S.A.A.F, 43-46, Res, 46-53, Capt. Am. Inst. Chem. Eng. Petrochemical processes; separation of chemical products and underground combustion processes for oil recovery; natural gas processing; sulphur recovery processes. Address: R.D. 1, Box 792, Claremore, OK 74017.

GRELAK, ROBERT PAUL, b. Chicago, Ill, June 15, 39; m. 65; c. 2. PHARMACOLOGY. B.Sc, Univ. Ill, 62, M.Sc, 65, Ph.D.(pharmacol), 69. RES. PHARMACOLOGIST, E.I. DU PONT DE NEMOURS & CO, 69- Am. Pharmaceut. Asn; N.Y. Acad. Sci. Local anesthetics for use in cardiac arrhythmias; effect of a low electrolyte concentration environment on cardiac function; effect of sugars on cardiac function; drug development. Address: Stine Lab, E.I. du Pont de Nemours & Co, P.O. Box 30, Newark, DE 19711.

GRELECKI, CHESTER (JOSEPH), b. Newton Twp, Pa, June 22, 27; m. 50; c. 7. PHYSICAL CHEMISTRY. B.S, Kings Col.(Pa), 50; M.S, Duquesne, 52; Ph.D.(chem), Catholic Univ, 57. Res. Chemist, reaction motors div, Thiokol Chem. Corp, 56-68, mgr. res. opers, 68-69; PRES, HAZARDS RES. CORP, 69- U.S.N, 45-46. Am. Chem. Soc. Free radical stabilization; reaction mechanism; physicochemical properties of liquid rocket propellants; combustion, detonation and explosion phenomenon; hazards evaluation. Address: 141 Halsey Ave, Rockaway, NJ 07866.

GRELEN, HAROLD EUGENE, b. Bryan, Tex, Nov. 13, 29; m. 53; c. 3. RANGE MANAGEMENT. B.S, Agr. & Mech. Col, Tex, 52, M.S, 56. Range conservationist, U.S. Soil Conserv. Serv, 54-55; RANGE SCIENTIST, U.S. FOREST SERV, 56- U.S.A, 48-49, 52-53. Am. Soc. Range Mgt. Range ecology; plant taxonomy; effects of prescribed burning and grazing on southern pine range. Address: 607 Edgewood Dr, Pineville, LA 71360.

GRELL, ELLSWORTH H(ERMAN), b. Chalco, Nebr, Apr. 9, 32; m. 55. GENETICS. B.S, Iowa State Col, 54; du Pont fel, Calif. Inst. Tech, 55-57, U.S. Pub. Health Serv. fel, 57-58, Ph.D.(genetics), 58. Res. assoc. biol, OAK RIDGE NAT. LAB, 58-59, BIOLOGIST, 59-, ASST. SCI. DIR. GENETICS & DEVELOP. BIOL. SECT, 69- Prof, grad. sch. biomed. sci, Univ. Tenn, 69- AAAS; Genetics Soc. Am. Genetics of Drosophila and biochemical genetics. Address: Biology Division, Oak Ridge National Lab, Oak Ridge, TN 37830.

GRELL, MARY, O.S.B, b. Pierz, Minn, Sept. 8, 12. BIOLOGY. B.A, Col. St. Benedict (Minn), 33; Univ. Minn, 35; M.S, St. Louis Univ, 37; Columbia Univ, 44-45; Ph.D.(biol), Fordham Univ, 45. Instr. BIOL, COL. ST. BENEDICT (MINN), 33-35, asst. prof, 37-42, prof, 45-63, pres, 63-68, PROF, 68-, ASSOC. CHMN. DEPT, COL. ST. BENEDICT-ST JOHN'S UNIV, 69- Fulbright fel, Max-Planck Inst, Ger, 53-54. AAAS; Am. Genetics Soc; Nat. Asn. Biol. Teachers. General physiology, cell structure; cytology; cell division, multiple complexes and giant salivary chromosome studies in the mosquito; cytogenetics. Address: Dept. of Biology, College of St. Benedict, St. Joseph, MN 56374.

GRELL, RHODA F(RANK), b. New York, N.Y, Feb. 23, 14; m. 55; c. 2. GENETICS. A.B, Hunter Col, 35; Ph.D.(zool), Tennessee, 61. Sci. aide entom, U.S. Nat. Mus, 36-42; entomologist, U.S. Dept. Agr, 42-49; asst, Calif. Inst. Tech, 52-58; assoc. biologist, OAK RIDGE NAT. LAB, 58-59, consult, 59-61, BIOLOGIST, 61- U.S. Pub. Health Serv. spec. fel, 59-61; lectr, dept. zool. & biomed. grad. sch, Univ. Tenn. Am. Soc. Nat; Genetics Soc. Am. Chromosome behavior; meiosis. Address: Biology Division, Oak Ridge National Lab, P.O. Box Y, Oak Ridge, TN 37830.

GRELLER, ANDREW M, b. N.Y.C, Mar. 18, 41; m. 64; c. 2. PLANT MORPHOLOGY & ECOLOGY. B.S, City Col. New York, 62; fel, Columbia Univ, 62-63, M.A, 64, Ph.D.(bot), 67. ASST. PROF. BIOL, QUEENS COL.(N.Y), 67- Nat. Sci. Found. grants, inst. arctic & alpine res, Univ. Colo, 70-72; collab, Nat. Park Serv, 71- AAAS; Torrey Bot. Club; Bot. Soc. Am; Int. Soc. Plant Morphol; Am. Inst. Biol. Sci. Floral and inflorescence morphology; damage of alpine plant communities; floristics. Address: Dept. of Biology, Queens College, Flushing, NY 11367.

GREMILLION, LOUIS RAY, b. Marksville, La, May 18, 31; m. 56; c. 4. MINERALOGY. B.A, La. State, 52, M.S, 54; Ph.D.(geol), Fla. State, 65. Micropaleontologist & explor. geologist, Humble Oil & Ref. Co, 54-56; ground water geologist, U.S. Geol. Surv, 56-57; instr. geol, Fla. State Univ, 57-65; resident geologist, N.J. Zinc Co, 65-67; PETROGRAPHER, TENN. VALLEY AUTH, 67- Consult, Fla. Geol. Surv, 59-61. AAAS; Am. Chem. Soc. Origin of attapulgite in the Miocene strata of Florida and Georgia; origin of the Tertiary phosphates of the southeastern United States. Address: Division of Chemical Development, Tennessee Valley Authority, Muscle Shoals, AL 35660.

GREMINGER, G(EORGE) K(ING), JR, b. Syracuse, N.Y, Feb. 4, 16; m. 46; c. 4. PULP & PAPER CHEMISTRY. B.S, State Univ. N.Y, 38. With Mead Corp, Ohio, 37-38; group leader, DOW CHEM. CO, 38-57, sect. head tech. serv. & develop, 57-65, chem. develop. & serv. specialist, 65-66, Switz, 66-68, DEVELOP. ASSOC, DESIGNED PROD. DEPT, 68- Am. Chem. Soc; Tech. Asn. Pulp & Paper Indust. Water soluble gums, especially cellulose ethers. Address: 802 W. Larkin, Midland, MI 48640.

GRENANDER, ULF, b. Vastervik, Sweden, July 23, 23; m. 46; c. 3. APPLIED MATHEMATICS, MATHEMATICAL STATISTICS. Fil. Dr, Stockholm, 50. Docent math. statist, Stockholm, 50-51 & 54-57; asst. prof. statist, Chicago, 51-52; assoc. prof, California, 53; prof. appl. math, Brown, 57-58; math. statist, Stockholm, 59-66; APPL. MATH, BROWN UNIV, 66-69, L. HERBERT BALLOU UNIV. PROF, 69- Fel, Inst. Math. Statist; Royal Swedish Acad. Sci; Int. Statist. Inst. Probability, theoretical statistics; operations research and insurance mathematics; computer science. Address: 26 Barberry Hill, Providence, RI 02912.

GRENCH, HERBERT A, b. Elmwood Park, Ill, Oct. 4, 32; m. 54; c. 2. NUCLEAR PHYSICS. B.A, Kalamazoo Col, 54; M.S, Iowa, 57, Ph.D.(physics), 60. RES. SCIENTIST NUCLEAR PHYSICS, RES. LABS, LOCKHEED MISSILES & SPACE CO, 60- Am. Phys. Soc. Low energy nuclear physics research. Address: Dept. 52-11, Bldg. 203, Lockheed Missiles & Space Co, 3251 Hanover St, Palo Alto, CA 94304.

GRENCHIK, RAYMOND T(HOMAS), b. Whiting, Ind, Aug. 24, 22; m. 57; c. 4. ASTROPHYSICS. B.A, St. Procopius Col, 43; M.S, New Mexico, 49; Swain fel, Indiana, 54-55, Ph.D.(astrophys), 56. Lab. instr. elec. & electronics, Signal Corps Sch, Chicago, 43, jr. physicist, instrument sect, metall. lab, 43-46; instr. physics, New Mexico, 46-50; Sault Br, Mich. Tech, 50-52; Vanderbilt, 55-57; asst. prof. PHYSICS & ASTRON, LA. STATE UNIV, BATON ROUGE, 57-61, ASSOC. PROF, 61- Mem. comt. educ. astron, 66- Am. Astron. Soc. Stellar atmospheres; radiative and convective transport; interplanetary medium. Address: Dept. of Physics & Astronomy, Louisiana State University, Baton Rouge, LA 70803.

GRENDA, STANLEY C, b. Chicago, Ill, Aug. 12, 34. INORGANIC CHEMISTRY. B.S, DePaul, 58; M.S, Arizona, 62; Ph.D.(chem), Lehigh, 64. Asst. Prof. CHEM, Wis. State, Superior, 64-65, Whitewater, 65-67; UNIV. NEV,

LAS VEGAS, 67-70, ASSOC. PROF, 70- Am. Chem. Soc. Preparation of and the physical properties of the first row transition metal complex ions with nitrogen and oxygen ligands. Address: Dept. of Chemistry, University of Nevada, Las Vegas, NV 89109.

GRENDA, VICTOR J, b. Boston, Mass, May 18, 33. ORGANIC CHEMISTRY. B.S, Northeastern, 55; Ph.D.(org. chem), Mass. Inst. Tech, 60. Sr. chemist, MERCK SHARP & DOHME RES. LABS, 60-66, RES. SECT. HEAD, 66- Am. Chem. Soc. Process research and development. Address: Merck Sharp & Dohme Research Labs, Rahway, NJ 07065.

GRENDER, G(ORDON) C(ONRAD), b. Wakefield, Mich, Jan. 1, 30; m. 52; c. 2. GEOLOGY. B.S, Indiana, 51, A.M, 52; Whitney fel, Mass. Inst. Tech, 56-57; Nat. Sci. Found. fel, Pa. State, 58-60, Ph.D.(mineral, petrol), 60. Phys. sci. aide, U.S. Geol. Surv, 50-51; geologist-geophysicist, Standard Oil Co. Calif, 52-56, geologist, 61-62; asst, Pa. State, 57-58; NATO fel, inst. geol, Univ. Oslo, 60-61; res. geologist, Esso Prod. Res. Co, 62-65; asst. prof. GEOL, Allegheny Col, 65-66; VA. POLYTECH. INST. & STATE UNIV, 66-68, ASSOC. PROF, 68-, acting head, dept. geol. sci, 71-72. AAAS; fel. Geol. Soc. Am; Am. Asn. Petrol. Geol; Int. Asn. Math. Geol. Sedimentary petrology; terrain analysis. Address: Dept. of Geological Sciences, Virginia Polytechnic Institute & State University, Blacksburg, VA 24061.

GRENELL, ROBERT G(ORDON), b. N.Y.C, Apr. 3, 16; m. 43. ANATOMY. B.A, City Col, 35; M.Sc, N.Y. Univ, 36; fel, Minnesota, 38-43, Ph.D.(anat), 43. Instr. anat, exten. div, Minnesota, 40-41, asst. anat. & physiol, 41-42; physiol, Yale, 43-44, instr. neuroanat, 44-47; U.S. Pub. Health Serv. sr. fel, Johnson Res. Found, Pennsylvania, 47-49; dept. biophys, Hopkins, 49-50; res. assoc. psychiat, PSYCHIAT. INST, UNIV. MD, BALTIMORE, 50-52, asst. prof. psychiat. res, 52-56, assoc. prof, 56-58, prof, 58-59, PROF. NEUROBIOL. IN PSYCHIAT. & DIR. NEUROBIOL. LAB, 59- Consult, Mass. Gen. Hosp, Boston, 58- Am. Physiol. Soc. travel award, Int. Physiol. Cong, Oxford, England, 47. Civilian with Off. Sci. Res. & Develop, 44. AAAS; Am. Physiol. Soc; Soc. Biol. Psychiat; Biophys. Soc; Soc. Exp. Biol. & Med; Am. Electroencephalog. Soc; Asn. Res. Nerv. & Ment. Disease; Am. Acad. Neurol; N.Y. Acad. Sci; Int. Soc. Cell Biol. Embryology; physical growth; neuroanatomy; neuropathology; neurophysiology; effects of temporary arrest of the circulation on the brain; brain metabolism and function; biological and biophysical bases of behavior. Address: Psychiatric Institute, University of Maryland, Baltimore, MD 21201.

GRENFELL, THO(MA)S C(OWLING), b. St. Ives, Eng, May 20, 05; nat; m. 32; c. 4. CHEMISTRY. B.S, Wesleyan, 28, M.A, 29. Chemist, Henry Souther Eng. Co, Conn, 29-31; Conn. State Dept. Health, 31-36; asst. dir. anal. labs. & qual. control, Chas. Pfizer & Co, Inc, 36-63, dir. qual. control, 63-69; RETIRED. AAAS; Am. Chem. Soc; N.Y. Acad. Sci. Analytical instrumentation; chemical methods concerned with drugs; chemicals and biochemicals; quality control procedures. Address: 240 Peaceable St, Ridgefield, CT 06877.

GRENGA, HELEN E(VA), b. Newnan, Ga, Apr. 11, 38. PHYSICAL CHEMISTRY & METALLURGY. B.A, Shorter Col.(Ga), 60; Ph.D.(phys. chem), Univ. Va, 67. Fel. METALL, SCH. CHEM. ENG, GA. INST. TECHNOL, 67, ASST. PROF, 68- Nat. Sci. Found. res. grants, 69-70, 71- Am. Chem. Soc; Am. Inst. Chem; Am. Soc. Metals. Chemistry and physics of solid surfaces; structure-property correlations of gas-solid and solid-solid interfaces; oxidation; corrosions; catalysis. Address: 66 Spring St, Newnan, GA 30263.

GRENGG, WALTER M, b. Chicago, Ill, Feb. 21, 25; m. 55; c. 2. PHYSICS, ELECTRONICS. B.S, Ill. Inst. Technol, 45; M.S, Univ. Wis, 63. Res. engr, Minn. Mining & Mfg. Co, 45-46; Rauland Corp, 47-49; Gavco Labs, 49-50; H. S. Martin & Co, 52-54; Vacuum Ceramics, 54-56; Elgin Nat. Watch Co, 56-61; Trionics Corp, 61-63; Univ. Wis, 63-64; DIR. RES. & DEVELOP, W.M. GRENGG & ASSOCS, 64- Chem.C, U.S.A, 50-52. Inst. Elec. & Electronics Eng. Spectrophotometer development; plasma containment studies; electromechanical and electronic circuit development; vacuum tube manufacture. Address: 1510 Chandler St, Madison, WI 53711.

GRENIER, CLAUDE G(EORGES), b. Les Rousses, France, Feb. 24, 23; m. 53; c. 2. SOLID STATE PHYSICS. Ecole Normale Supérieure, Univ. Paris, 45-49; fel, Rice Inst, 49-51; exchange fel, Leiden, 51-52; D.Sc, Sorbonne, 56. Res. assoc, LA. STATE UNIV, BATON ROUGE, 56-57, asst. prof. PHYSICS, 57-60, assoc. prof, 60-65, PROF, 65- Low temperature physics; electron transport phenomena. Address: Dept. of Physics & Astronomy, Louisiana State University, Baton Rouge, LA 70803.

GRENIER, J(OHN) W(ILLIAM), b. Springfield, Mass, Oct. 17, 19; m. 52; c. 6. PHYSICAL CHEMISTRY. B.S, Massachusetts, 50; M.A, Wesleyan, 51; Ph.D. (chem), Yale, 55. Chemist, appl. res. & develop, Springfield Armory, 52; from chemist to chem. eng. specialist, GEN. ELEC. CO, 55-69, MGR. SYSTS. ENG, SPECIALTY MAT. DEPT, 69- U.S.A.F, 43-45, Res, 45-53, 2nd Lt. Am. Chem. Soc; Am. Soc. Metals; Electrochem. Soc. High temperature oxidation studies; friction and wear behavior; development and characterization of metallic surface finishes; electrochemical machining. Address: 903 Clayton Dr, Worthington, OH 43085.

GRENIER, PAUL E(MILE), b. Quebec, Que, Sept. 19, 22; m. 55; c. 3. GEOLOGY. B.A.Sc, Laval, 48, M.Sc, 49, D.Sc, 52. Geol. mapping, Dept. Mines, Que, 51-52, res. geologist, 53-62; chief mineral deposits serv, QUE. DEPT. NATURAL RESOURCES, 62-65, dir. geol. serv, 65-70, DIR. GEN. MINERAL RESOURCES, 70- Can. Inst. Mining & Metall; Soc. Explor. Geophys; Geol. Asn. Can; Am. Asn. Petrol. Geol; Soc. Appl. Geol. of Mineral Deposits. Ore deposits. Address: 2793 Chemin St-Louis, Ste-Foy, Que. 10, Can.

GRENIER, PIERRE, b. Quebec, Que, Aug. 15, 22; m. 49; c. 3. CHEMICAL ENGINEERING. B.A, Laval, 42, B.Sc.A, 46; M.S, Columbia, 47. Lectr. CHEM. ENG, LAVAL UNIV, 47-52, assoc. prof, 52-55, PROF, 55-, DEAN FACULTY SCI, 69-, head dept. chem. eng, 65-69. Vis. prof, Nancy, 63-64. Chem. Inst. Can. Unit operations; transport phenomena. Address: Office of the Dean, Faculty of Science, Laval University, Quebec 10, Que, Can.

GRENINGER, ALDEN B(UCHANAN), b. Glendale, Ore, Sept. 17, 07; m. 47; c. 3. METALLURGY. A.B, Stanford, 28, Engr, 31; Sc.D.(metall), Harvard, 35. Jr. engr, Andes Copper Mining Co, Chile, 31-33; instr. metall, Harvard, 35-38, asst. prof, 38-41, metallurgist, lamp dept, Gen. Elec. Co, 41-43, mem. staff, metall. lab, Chicago, 43-45; metallurgist, chem. dept, Gen. Elec. Co, 45-46, supt. & dir. tech. activities, Hanford Works, 46-48, mgr. tech. divs, 48-52, mgr. eng, 52-56, gen. mgr, irradiation processing dept, 56-66, nuclear technol. dept, 66-67, dep. div. gen. mgr, nuclear energy div, 67-68; RETIRED. Am. Soc. Metals; Am. Inst. Mining, Metall. & Petrol. Eng.(award, 40, Hunt Award, 41); Am. Nuclear Soc. Metallography; alloy constitution; science of metals. Address: 12394 Grandee Rd, San Diego, CA 92128.

GRENLESKI, STEPHEN EDWARD, JR, b. Chicago, Ill, Oct. 21, 29; m. 54; c. 3. MECHANICAL & AERONAUTICAL ENGINEERING. B.S.M.E, Northwestern, 54, M.S.M.E, 56; M.S.A.E, Maryland, 65. SR. RES. ENGR, APPL. PHYSICS LAB, JOHNS HOPKINS UNIV, 56- Combustion; aerodynamics; ignition; heat transfer; fluid mechanics; propulsion. Address: Applied Physics Lab, Johns Hopkins University, 8621 Georgia Ave, Silver Spring, MD 20910.

GRENNAN, LAURIE M, b. Newport News, Va, Apr. 9, 20; div; c. 5. ANALYTICAL CHEMISTRY. B.A, Randolph-Macon Woman's Col, 41; M.A, Wellesley Col, 42; Ph.D.(anal. chem), Iowa State Univ, 66. Process control chemist, E.I. du Pont de Nemours, Inc, Va, 42-44; instr. chem, Randolph-Macon Woman's Col, 44-45; res. chemist, Refined Syrups & Sugars, N.Y, 51-52; chemist, Mt. Sinai Hosp, Milwaukee, Wis, 55-58; from instr. to asst. prof. CHEM, Milwaukee-Downer Col, 58-63; from asst. prof. to ASSOC. PROF, UNIV. TENN, MARTIN, 65- Am. Chem. Soc. Analytical reagents for beryllium; water analysis for pollution control. Address: Dept. of Chemistry, University of Tennessee, Martin, TN 38237.

GRENNING, DANIEL A, b. New York, N.Y, Jan. 4, 40; m. 61; c. 2. PHYSICS. B.S, Union Col.(N.Y), 61; M.S, Illinois, Urbana, 63, Ph.D.(physics), 66. Res. specialist gaseous plasmas, McDonnell Co, 65-66; E.L. devices, Monsanto Co, 66-67, proj. leader infrared emitting diodes, 67-68, prod. mgr, 68-70; MANAGING DIR, LITRONIX SINGAPORE (PTE) LTD, 70- Am. Phys. Soc. Electroluminescence in III-V compounds; optoelectronic devices; infrared emitting diodes, silicon detectors, and visible emitting diodes. Address: 15471 Via Vaquero, Monte Sereno, CA 95030.

GRENS, EDWARD A(NTHONY), II, b. San Francisco, Calif, May 14, 31. CHEMICAL ENGINEERING. B.S, California, Berkeley, 53, fel, 58-59, M.S, 60, Ph.D.(chem. eng), 63. Engr, Union Oil Co, Calif, 53, 55-58; lectr, UNIV. CALIF. BERKELEY, 60-62, acting asst. prof. CHEM. ENG, 62-63, asst. prof, 63-67, ASSOC. PROF, 67- Consult. fuel cell res, Lockheed Missiles & Space Co, Calif, 62-; guest prof, Eindhoven Technol. Univ, 67-68. U.S.A, 53-55, Res, 55-, Maj. Electrochem. Soc; Asn. Comput. Mach; Am. Chem. Soc. Electrochemical energy conversion; mass and heat transfer in reacting systems; combustion of droplets and particles; process design and simulation. Address: Dept. of Chemical Engineering, University of California, Berkeley, CA 94720.

GRES, MARCEL E(MILE), b. San Francisco, Calif, Apr. 16, 22; m. 46; c. 3. MECHANICAL ENGINEERING. B.S, Texas, 47, M.S, 50. Test engr, Gen. Elec. Co, 47-48; instr. mech. eng, Texas, 48-50, res. engr, Defense Res. Lab, 50-51, supvr. design & develop, acoustics div, 51-58, v.pres. eng, Textran Corp, 58-61; TRACOR INC, 61-62, GROUP V.PRES, 62- Spec. lectr, Univ. Tex, Austin, 53. U.S.N.R, 43-46, Lt.(jg). Am. Soc. Mech. Eng; Nat. Soc. Prof. Eng. Hydrodynamics; thermodynamics; instrumentation and remote control systems. Address: 5802 Trialridge Dr, Austin, TX 78731.

GRESENS, RANDALL L(EE), b. Harvey, Ill, May 11, 35; m. 60; c. 3. GEOCHEMISTRY, PETROLOGY. B.S, New Mexico, 60; Nat. Sci. Found. fel, Fla. State, 61-64, Ph.D.(geol), 64. Nat. Sci. Found. fel, Southern California, 64-65; asst. prof. GEOL, UNIV. WASH, 65-70, ASSOC. PROF, 70- Nat. Sci. Found. sci. faculty fel, Univ. Ariz, 71-72. U.S.A, 54-56. Mineral. Soc. Am; Geol. Soc. Am. Geochemical processes accompanying regional metamorphism; metasomatic genesis of pegmatites; geochemistry of glaucophane schist metamorphic facies and associated serpentinites. Address: Dept. of Geological Sciences, University of Washington, Seattle, WA 98105.

GRESHAM, J(AMES) T(YSON), b. Detroit, Mich, May 6, 12; m. 41; c. 3. CHEMICAL ENGINEERING. B.S.(chem. eng), Detroit Inst. Tech, 40. Asst. chief chemist, Thompson Prods, Inc, 35-37, sr. lubrication engr, U.S. Naval Ord. Proj, 37-38; res. chemist, Wyandotte Chem. Corp, 37-39; res. engr, Battelle Mem. Inst, 39-43; develop. group leader, KIMBERLY-CLARK CORP, 43-60, SR. RES. CHEM. ENGR, 60- AAAS; Am. Chem. Soc; Tech. Asn. Pulp & Paper Indust. Unit operations applied to paper converting; applied chemical engineering practice to paper and creped cellulose wadding manufacture. Address: P.O. Box 273, Hortonville, WI 54944.

GRESHAM, W(ILLIAM) F(RANKLIN), b. Prattville, Ala, Oct. 19, 08; m. 36; c. 1. ORGANIC CHEMISTRY. B.S, Emory, 29, M.S, 30; M.A, Harvard, 34, Ph.D.(phys. org. chem), 36. Instr. chem, Ga. Tech, 30-33, asst. prof, 36-37; res. chemist, ammonia dept, E.I. DU PONT DE NEMOURS & CO, INC, 37-43, res. mgr. process scouting, 43-50, MGR. EXPLOR. RES. SECT, PLASTICS DEPT, 50- Civilian with Office Sci. Res. & Develop, 44. Am. Chem. Soc. Fundamental and exploratory organic and polymer research. Address: 126 School Rd, Wilmington, DE 19803.

GRESKY, ALAN T(OLSTOY), b. Piper, Ala, Sept. 29, 17; m. 38; c. 3. CHEMISTRY, ZOOLOGY. B.A, Alabama, 39; Tennessee. With Tenn. coal & iron div, U.S. Steel Co, 39-42; chemist, Ala. ord. works, E.I. du Pont de Nemours & Co, 42-45; Carbide & Carbon Chem. Co, 45-46; chmn, long-range planning group, CHEM. TECH. DIV, OAK RIDGE NAT. LAB, 46-66, ON SPEC. ASSIGNMENT TO DIR, 66- Lectr, Oak Ridge Sch. Reactor Tech, 57-58, 60-65. Am. Chem. Soc; Am. Soc. Test. & Mat. Chemical processing of nuclear reactor fuels; separation chemistry of uranium, plutonium, thorium, protoactinium and fission products; fundamental theories; technical reviewing, writing, editing. Address: Oak Ridge National Lab, Box X, Oak Ridge, TN 37830.

GRESSEL, JONATHAN B(EN), b. Cleveland, Ohio, Oct. 30, 36; m. 58; c. 3. DEVELOPMENTAL BIOLOGY. B.Sc, Ohio State Univ, 57; M.Sc, Univ. Wis, 59, Ph.D.(bot), 63. Jr. scientist, Weizmann Inst. Sci, 62-67, res. assoc, 67-68; vis. asst. prof. biol, Purdue, 68-69; res. assoc, WEIZMANN INST. SCI, 69-70, SR. SCIENTIST, 70- U.S. Dept. Agr. res. grant, 67-72; lectr, Upper Galilee Regional Jr. Col, 67- Am. Soc. Plant Physiol. Nucleic acid metabolism and photochemistry of induced morphogenisis in model biological systems. Address: Dept. of Plant Genetics, Weizmann Institute of Science, Rehovot, Israel.

GRESSER, ION, b. N.Y.C, Oct. 25, 28; m. 68; c. 2. VIROLOGY, EXPERIMENTAL PATHOLOGY. B.A, Harvard, 48; M.D, Yale, 55. Res. assoc. virol, Childrens Cancer Res. Found, Boston, Mass, 59-65; CHIEF LAB. VIRAL ONCOL, INST. SCI. RES. CANCER, FRANCE, 65- U.S. Pub. Health Serv. spec. fel, 61-62 & career develop. award, Childrens Cancer Res. Found, 62-65. Leon Etancelin Prize, French Acad. Sci, 70. Med.C, U.S.A, 56-58, Capt. Soc. Exp. Biol. & Med; Am. Soc. Microbiol; Infectious Diseases Soc. Am; Am. Asn. Immunol; French Soc. Microbiol. Inhibitory effect on interferon on growth of viral induced and transplantable tumors in experimental animals; effect of interferon on cellular physiology; ecology of Japanese encephalitis virus; pathogenesis of myxoviral infection. Address: Lab. of Viral Oncology, Institute of Scientific Research for Cancer, Boite Postale 8, 94 Villejuif, France.

GRESSITT, J(UDSON) LINSLEY, b. Tokyo, Japan, June 16, 14; U.S. citizen; m. 41; c. 4. ENTOMOLOGY. B.S, California, 38, M.S, 39, Ph.D.(entom), 45. Asst. zool, California, 38-39; instr. entom, Lingnan Univ, 39-44, asst. prof, 46-48, assoc. prof, 48-50; sr. technician, div. entom, California, 44-45; assoc. entom, Pac. Sci. Bd, Nat. Res. Coun, Honolulu, 51-52; ENTOMOLOGIST in charge insects micronesia proj, BISHOP MUS, 53-56, ZOOGEOG. & EVOLUTION PAC. INSECTS, 56-, CHMN. DEPT. ENTOM, 56-, L.A. BISHOP DISTINGUISHED CHAIR ZOOL, 63- Asst. entomologist, Univ. California, China, 47-50, assoc. specialist, Japan, 51; Guggenheim fel, 55-56; Fulbright fel, Australia, 60-61; field res, New Guinea & Southwest Pac, 55-71; S.E. Asia, 59-61, 63-65; Antarctic, 59-66; affiliate mem. grad. faculty, Univ. Hawaii, 56- Consult, U.S. Pub. Health Serv, 61-65. Ed, Pac. Insects, 59-; J. Med. Entom, 64- Mem. Int. Zool. Cong, Copenhagen, 53, London, 58; Pac. Sci. Cong, Manila, 53, Bangkok, 57, Honolulu, 61, Tokyo, 66, Canberra, 71-; Int. Entom. Cong, Montreal, 56, Vienna 60, London, 64, Moscow, 68; Darwin-Wallace Centenary, Singapore, 58; Sci. Comt. Antarctic Res. Antarctic Biol. Symp, Paris, 62; mem. panel, biol. & med. sci. comt. polar res, Nat. Acad. Sci, 65-69, aerobiol. panel, 67-71; chmn, gov. comt. preservation sci. areas, Hawaii, 69-70; chmn. State Comn. Natural Area Reserves Syst, 70-; co-dir, ecosyst. evolution prog, Hawaii Int. Biol. Prog, 70-; dir, Wau Ecol. Inst, New Guinea, 71- U.S.N.R, 45-46, Lt. AAAS; fel. Entom. Soc. Am; Soc. Syst. Zool. Taxonomy of Coleoptera; fauna of Asia, Oceania and Antarctica; zoogeography; evolution; ecology. Address: Bishop Museum, P.O. Box 6037, Honolulu, HI 96818.

GRETHE, GUENTER, b. Hannover, Ger, Oct. 13, 33; U.S. citizen; m. 60; c. 2. ORGANIC CHEMISTRY. Dipl. chem, Brunswick Tech, 60, Ph.D.(org. chem), 61. Fel. chem, Wisconsin, 62-63; SR. RES. CHEMIST, CHEM. RES. DIV, HOFFMANN-LA ROCHE, INC, 63- Am. Chem. Soc; Ger. Chem. Soc; The Chem. Soc. Synthetic work in the fields of tetracyclines, alkaloids and heterocyclic compounds. Address: Chemistry Research Division, Hoffmann-La Roche, Inc, Nutley, NJ 07110.

GRETHER, DAVID F(RANK), b. Neillsville, Wis, June 23, 20; m. 48; c. 3. BIOLOGY. Ph.B, Wisconsin, 47, M.S, 49. Instr. biol, Wis. State Col.(Platteville), 51-52; St. Cloud State Col, 52-53; ASST. PROF. natural sci, Eastern Michigan, 53-56; BIOL, ST. CLOUD STATE COL, 56- Consult. plant path. by air pollution. U.S.N.R, 42-46, Lt. Comdr. AAAS; Am. Fern Soc; Am. Soc. Human Genetics; Soc. Study Evolution. Ecology and plant distribution. Address: Dept. of Biology, St. Cloud State College, St. Cloud, MN 56302.

GRETSKY, NEIL E, b. Boston, Mass, Mar. 17, 41; div. MATHEMATICS. B.S, Calif. Inst. Tech, 62; M.S, Carnegie Inst. Tech, 64, Ph.D.(math), 67. ASST. PROF. MATH, UNIV. CALIF, RIVERSIDE, 67- Am. Math. Soc; Math. Asn. Am. Functional analysis; operator representations on Banach function spaces. Address: Dept. of Mathematics, University of California, Riverside, CA 92502.

GRETTENBERG, THOMAS LYNN, b. Los Angeles, Calif, Apr. 17, 34; m. 59; c. 2. ELECTRICAL ENGINEERING. B.A, Pomona Col, 56; B.S. & M.S, Mass. Inst. Tech, 57; Ph.D.(elec. eng), Stanford, 62. Elec. engr, Gen. Elec. Co, N.Y, 55-56; asst, Mass. Inst. Tech, 57-59; sr. res. engr, Autonetics Div, N.Am. Aviation, Inc, Calif, 59-60; sr. scientist, Lockheed Missiles & Space Co, 60-62; asst. prof. elec. eng, Calif. Inst. Tech, 62-67, assoc. prof, 67-68; V.PRES, U.S. SYSTS. & SOFTWARE, INC, 68- Consult, Autonetics Div, N.Am. Aviation, Inc, 59-; Hughes Aircraft Co, 62- AAAS; Inst. Elec. & Electronics Eng. Statistical theory of communication; radar; learning systems. Address: U.S. Systems & Software, Inc, 1901 Ave. of the Stars, Los Angeles, CA 90067.

GRETTIE, DONALD P(OMEROY), b. Salem, Oregon, June 23, 00; m. 30; c. 2. ORGANIC CHEMISTRY. B.A, Willamette, 24; M.A, Oregon, 27; Ph.D.(chem), Pittsburgh, 30. Teacher pub. sch, 24-25; asst, Oregon, 25-27; Pittsburgh, 27-29; res. chemist, Swift & Co, 29-65; clin. instr, Univ. Ore. Med. Sch, 65-70; SR. CHEMIST, UNITED MED. LABS, PORTLAND, 70- Am. Chem. Soc. Adsorption; vitamin C; chemistry of fats and oils; chemistry of collagenous proteins; endocrinology; insulin and glucose tolerance tests; radioimmunoassay of hormones and drugs. Address: 16465 S.W. King Charles, Tigard, OR 97223.

GRETZ, RONALD D, b. Freeport, Pa, June 25, 35; m. 59; c. 2. PHYSICAL METALLURGY. B.S, Carnegie Inst. Tech, 57, Ph.D.(metall), 63. Sr. scientist phys. metall, Battelle Mem. Inst, 63-65, fel, dept. physics, 65-69; MGR. SURFACE STUDIES DEPT, MATERIALS RES. CTR, ALLIED CHEM. CORP, 69- Am. Inst. Mining, Metall. & Petrol. Eng; Am. Soc. Metals; Brit. Inst. Metals. Surface processes underlying crystal growth; surface diffusion; nucleation of metal crystals from vapor; chemical vapor deposition of metals from iodides; capillarity constraints on small bodies; epitaxy in metal films; nucleation and growth of ceramics, using molecular beam; field-emission; ultra-high vacuum methods for experimental research. Address: Materials Research Center, Allied Chemical Corp, P.O. Box 3004, Columbia & Park Aves, Morristown, NJ 07960.

GRETZINGER, JAMES, b. Pittsburgh, Pa, Nov. 7, 25; m. 54; c. 4. CHEMICAL ENGINEERING. B.S, Kansas State, 49; Ph.D.(chem. eng), Wisconsin, 56. Engr. process develop, Eastman Kodak Co, 49-51; asst. spray drying & automatization res, Wisconsin, 51-56; res. engr, film res, Yerkes Film Plant, E.I. DU PONT DE NEMOURS & CO, INC, 56-59, supvr, 59-61, area supvr, 61-66, Tedlar plant supvr, 66-67, staff engr, Yerkes Res. & Develop. Lab, 67-68, STAFF ENGR, VENTURE DEVELOP. SECT, FILM DEPT, 68- Infantry, 43-46, 46-49, Sgt. Am. Inst. Chem. Eng. Fluid flow; polymerization; solids handling and flow; mixing solids and liquids; foam formation from polyolefins. Address: 3034 Maple Shade Lane, Wilmington, DE 19810.

GREUB, LOUIS JOHN, b. Humbird, Wis, Feb. 18, 33; m. 65; c. 1. AGRONOMY, PLANT PHYSIOLOGY. B.S, Wis. State, River Falls, 63; M.S, Iowa State, 66, Ph.D.(crop prod, plant physiol), 68. Res. asst. agron, Iowa State, 63-66, assoc, 66-68; ASSOC. PROF. PLANT SCI, WIS. STATE UNIV-RIVER FALLS, 68- U.S.A, 56-57. Am. Soc. Agron; Am. Soc. Plant Physiol. Crop physiology, especially forage physiology and management; leaf area, yield, carbohydrate reserves and photosynthesis of forage legumes. Address: Dept. of Plant & Earth Science, Wisconsin State University-River Falls, River Falls, WI 54022.

GREUBEL, PAUL W(ILLIAM), b. Union City, N.J, Sept. 5, 10; m. 35. CHEMISTRY. LL.B, La Salle, 55. With Inmont Corp, 28-39; res. dir. printing inks & coatings, Kienle & Co, 39-42, 45-50; realtor, 50-56; group leader, INMONT CORP, 56-67, prin. scientist, 67-68, TECH. MGR, GRAPHIC & COLOR SYSTS, 68- U.S.N.R, 42-45, Lt. AAAS; Am. Chem. Soc. Lithographic inks; lithographic and other printing processes. Address: Inmont Corp, 475 Division St, Elizabeth, NJ 07207.

GREUER, RUDOLF E. A, b. Guetzlaffshagen, Germany, Apr. 6, 27; m. 63. MINING ENGINEERING. Dipl.Ing, Clausthal Tech, 53, Dr.Ing, 55; Göttingen, 59-60. Res. student mine ventilation, Witwatersrand, 56; lectr. mining eng, Tech. Univ. Istanbul, 57; res. engr, Mining Res. Estab, W.Germany, 57-67; ASSOC. PROF. MINING ENG, MICH. TECHNOL. UNIV, 67- Mem. subcmts. fires in mineshafts & mine ventilation, European Community Coal & Steel, 60-67. Am. Inst. Mining, Metall. & Petrol. Eng; W.German Mine Mgr. Asn. Thermodynamics of mine ventilation; computer application for ventilation network calculations. Address: Dept. of Mining Engineering, Michigan Technological University, Houghton, MI 49931.

GREULACH, VICTOR A(UGUST), b. Convoy, Ohio, Dec. 6, 06; m. 34; c. 3. PLANT PHYSIOLOGY. A.B, DePauw, 29; M.S, Ohio State, 33, univ. scholar, 38-39, Ph.D.(bot), 40; Buffalo, 33; Muskingum Col, 33-35; Texas, 37; Inst. Nuclear Studies, Oak Ridge, 50. Instr. biol, Muskingum Col, 33-35; asst. prof, Houston, 35-40, assoc. prof, 40-46; plant physiol, Agr. & Mech. Col. Tex, 46-49; BOT, UNIV. N.C, CHAPEL HILL, 49-51, PROF, 51-, adv, col. arts & sci, 55-59, chmn. dept. bot, 60-72. Acting dir, Mus. Natural Hist, Houston, Tex, 43-46, trustee, 46-49, secy, 46-48; chmn. div. biol. sci, Univ. Houston, 44-46. Summer, lectr, Col. William & Mary, 48, Mt. Lake biol. sta, Virginia, 56, New Hampshire, 62, 63; co-dir, Nat. Sci. Found. Inst, North Carolina, 57-60, dir, bot. conf, 59-61, 63, ed, J. Elisha Mitchell Sci. Soc, 66- Consult, Nat. Sci. Found, 58-61, prof. asst, 58. Mem. subcomt. col. ed, cmt. ed. policies, Nat. Acad. Sci-Nat. Res. Coun, 55-58; exec. dir, Cmn. Undergrad. Ed. Biol. Sci, 64-65. AAAS; Bot. Soc. Am; Am. Soc. Plant Physiol; N.Y. Acad. Sci. Botany; plant growth; biological education. Address: Dept. of Botany, University of North Carolina, Chapel Hill, NC 27514.

GREULICH, RICHARD C(URTICE), b. Denver, Colo, Mar. 22, 28; m. 58; c. 4. ANATOMY, ORAL BIOLOGY. A.B, Stanford, 49; U.S. Atomic Energy Cmn. fel, 49-52, fel, McGill, 52-53, Ph.D.(anat), 53. Instr. anat, McGill, 53-55, asst. prof, 55-61; assoc. prof, sch. med, California, Los Angeles, 61-64, prof, 64-66, assoc. prof. oral biol, sch. dent, 61-64, prof, 64-66; SCI. DIR, INTRAMURAL RES, NAT. INST. DENT. RES, NAT. INSTS. HEALTH, 66- Bank Am-Giannini Found. fel, 55-57; res. assoc, Karolinska Inst, Sweden, 55-57; U.S. Pub. Health Serv. spec. fel, 62-63; vis. investr, London, 62 & McGill, 63. Consult, Nat. Inst. Dent. Res, 64-; Procter & Gamble Co, 64- U.S.A, 46-48. AAAS; Am. Soc. Zool; Am. Asn. Anat; Int. Asn. Dent. Res.(res. award, 63). Physiology of growth, differentiation and aging; autoradiography; microradiography; histochemistry; physiology of mineralization. Address: National Institute of Dental Research, National Institutes of Health, Bethesda, MD 20014.

GREULICH, WILLIAM WALTER, b. Columbus, Ohio, July 24, 99; m. 24; c. 2. ANATOMY. Ph.B, Kenyon Col, 26; M.A, Denver, 28; fel, Stanford, 31-34, Ph.D.(anat), 34; hon. Sc.D, Kenyon Col, 67. Instr. biol, Regis Col.(Colo), 27-28; Colorado, 28-31; Gen. Ed. Bd. fel, sch. med, Yale, 34-36, asst. prof, 36-38, assoc. prof. anat. & phys. anthrop, 38-40; prof, sch. med, Western Reserve, 40-44; ANAT, SCH. MED, STANFORD UNIV, 44-64, exec. head dept, 49-62, EMER. PROF, 64-, vis. prof. pediat, 70-71. Dir, adolescence study unit, Yale, 36-40; dir, Brush Found, 40-49; traveling fel, Carnegie Corp, Australia & N.Z, 46; coordinated invest. Micronesian anthrop, U.S. Navy, 47; mem. comt. child develop, Nat. Res. Coun, Consult, comt. atomic casualties, Hiroshima & Nagasaki, 47-51; sci. adv, U.S. High Cmnr, Ger, 52-54; chmn, U.S. Ed. Comn, Fed. Repub, Ger, 53-54; Fulbright lectr, sch. med, Makerere Univ. Col, Uganda, 58; sci. attaché, Am. Embassy, London, 61-66; asst. to dir. growth & develop. prog, Nat. Inst. Child Health & Human Develop, 66-68; res. biologist, Nat. Insts. Health, Md, 68-71. Viking Fund medal & award phys. anthrop, 59. Soc. Res. Child Develop.(pres, 55-57); Am. Asn. Phys. Anthrop.(pres, 59-61); Am. Asn. Anat.(1st v.pres, 56-58); Anat. Soc. Gt. Brit. & Ireland; Zool. Soc. London; hon. fel, Ger. Anat. Soc. Human twinning; child growth and development; physical aspects of adolescence; x-ray studies of female pelvis; x-ray studies of skeletal development of children; human ovulation. Address: Dept. of Anatomy, Stanford University, Stanford, CA 94305.

GREULING, EUGENE, b. Indianapolis, Ind, Oct. 23, 14; m. 38; c. 2. PHYSICS. B.S, Butler, 37; Ph.D.(theoret. physics), Indiana, 42. Teacher, pub. sch, Ind, 38; instr. physics, Indiana, 42; asst. prof, North Carolina, 42-44; theoret. physicist, Manhattan proj, Los Alamos, 44-46; sr. physicist, Oak Ridge Nat. Lab, Tenn, 46-48; from asst. prof. to assoc. prof. PHYSICS, DUKE UNIV, 48-63, PROF, 63- Consult, United Nuclear Corp, 50-63; Union Carbide Nuclear Co, 50-61; Atomic Safety & Licensing Bd, 63-; Nuclear Utilities Serv, 63-64. Am. Phys. Soc. Theoretical nuclear physics; beta radioactivity; nuclear reactor physics. Address: Dept. of Physics, Duke University, Durham, NC 27706.

GREVE, ELMER W(ILLIAM), b. Cleveland, Ohio, Dec. 8, 06; m. 31; c. 2. HORTICULTURE. B.S, Ohio State, 30, M.Sc, 32; Ph.D.(hort), Maryland, 35. Instr. hort. & asst. horticulturist, Delaware, 35-38, asst. prof, 41-43; res. horticulturist, 38-41; INSPECTOR, U.S. FOOD & DRUG ADMIN, 43- Use of fertilizers on strawberries; effect of pruning on yield of apple trees; effect of curculio on drop in peach fruits. Address: Room 1204 Custom House, U.S. Food & Drug Administration, Philadelphia, PA 19106.

GREVE, JOHN HENRY, b. Pittsburgh, Pa, Aug. 11, 34; m. 56; c. 3. VETERINARY PARASITOLOGY. B.S, Mich. State, 56, D.V.M, 58, M.S, 59; Ph.D.(vet. parasitol), Purdue, 63. Res. assoc. vet. path, Mich. State, 58-59; instr. VET. PARASITOL, Purdue Univ, 59-62; asst. prof, IOWA STATE UNIV, 63-64, assoc. prof, 64-68, PROF, 68- Am. Vet. Med. Asn; Am. Asn. Vet. Parasitol; Am. Soc. Parasitol. Demodex canis in dogs and nematodes in swine; pathological response and host-parasite relationships in arthropods and nematodes of veterinary medical importance. Address: Dept. of Veterinary Pathology, Iowa State University, Ames, IA 50010.

GREVILLE, T(HOMAS) N(ALL) E(DEN), b. New York, N.Y, Dec. 27, 10; m. 34, 51; c. 2. MATHEMATICS. B.A, Univ. of the South, 30; fel, Michigan, 31-33, A.M, 32, Ph.D.(math), 33. Actuarial asst, Acacia Mutual Life Ins. Co, D.C, 33-37; instr. math, Michigan, 37-40; actuarial mathematician, U.S. Bur. Census, 40-46; U.S. Pub. Health Serv, 46-52; statist. consult, Int. Coop. Admin, 52-54; asst. chief actuary, U.S. Social Security Admin, 54-58; dep. chief mathematician, U.S. Army Qm. Corps, 58-60, chief mathematician, 60-61; v.pres, S.A. Miller Co, D.C, 61-62; PROF, MATH. RES. CTR, UNIV. WIS, MADISON, 63-, SCH. BUS, 64- Instr, U.S. Dept. Agr. Grad. Sch, 48-52; vis. prof, Univ. Mich, 62-63. Statist. ed, J. Parapsychol, 44-67; ed, SIAM J. Appl. Math, 58- Fel. Soc. Actuaries (prize, 48); Am. Math. Soc; fel. Am. Statist. Asn; Opers. Res. Soc. Am. Matrices, approximation and interpolation; actuarial mathematics. Address: Mathematics Research Center, University of Wisconsin, Madison, WI 53706.

GREWAL, MAHESH S, b. Patiala, India, Oct. 15, 34; U.S. citizen; m. 60; c. 2. FLUID MECHANICS. B.Sc, Allahabad, 53; B.S, California, Berkeley, 57, M.S, 59, Ph.D.(eng. sci), 62. Vis. prof. eng, Washington (Seattle), 62-63; mem. tech. staff, Aerospace Corp, Calif, 63-65; theoret. physicist, Lawrence Radiation Lab, Univ. Calif, Berkeley, 65-69; ASSOC. PROF, DEPT. MECH. ENG, WICHITA STATE UNIV, 69- Am. Phys. Soc; Am. Soc. Eng. Educ. Kinetic theory; plasma physics. Address: 2401 N. Yale, Wichita, KS 67220.

GREWAR, DAVID, b. Dundee, Scotland, July 4, 21; Can. citizen; m. 46; c. 8. MEDICINE, PEDIATRICS. M.B. & Ch.B, St. Andrews, 45. House physician med, Royal Infirmary Dundee, 45-46, registr. pediat, 48-52; lectr. child health, Univ. St. Andrews, 52-53; chief res. PEDIAT, Childrens Hosp. Winnipeg, 53-55; lectr, UNIV. MAN, 55-59, asst. prof, 59-67, ASSOC. PROF, 67- Attend. staff, Childrens Hosp. & St. Boniface Hosp, Winnipeg, 56- Fel, Royal Col. Physicians Edinburgh, 71. R.A.M.C, 46-48, Capt. AAAS; Can. Med. Asn; Can. Pediat. Soc. Prognosis of prematurity; neonatology, especially erythroblastosis foetalis; nutrition, especially scurvy and vitamin deficiency in infancy. Address: Dept. of Pediatrics, University of Manitoba School of Medicine, Winnipeg, Man, Can.

GREWE, ALFRED H, JR, b. St. Cloud, Minn, Mar. 21, 26. ZOOLOGY, BOTANY. B.A, St. Cloud State Col, 50; M.A, Minnesota, 54; fel, South Dakota, 62-65, Ph.D.(zool), 66. Mus. scientist & teaching asst. zool, Minnesota, 51-56; instr. BIOL, St. Cloud State Col, 58-59; Itasca Jr. Col, 59-62; asst. prof, ST. CLOUD STATE COL, 65-71, PROF, 71- U.S.N.R, 44-46. AAAS; Am. Ornith. Union. Natural history of the bald eagle. Address: Dept. of Biology, St. Cloud State College, St. Cloud, MN 56301.

GREWE, JOHN M(ITCHELL), b. Eau Claire, Wis, Feb. 6, 38; m. 59; c. 4. ORTHODONTICS, ANATOMY. B.S, Minnesota, Minneapolis, 60, D.D.S, 62, M.S.D, 64, Ph.D.(anat), 66. U.S. Pub. Health Serv. nonserv. fel. dent. & anat, sch. dent. & med. sch, Minnesota, 62-66, asst. prof. pediat, dent. & acting chmn. dept, 66-67; asst. prof. orthod. & anat, cols. dent. & med, Iowa, 67-69; ASSOC. PROF, ORTHOD. & CHMN. DEPT, SCH. DENT, UNIV. MD, 69- Consult, Univ. Minnesota, 67; U.S. Pub. Health Serv. career develop. award, 68-69. Sect. pro-tem secy, Am. Asn. Dent. Schs, 67-68. AAAS; Am. Dent. Asn; Am. Soc. Dent. for Children; Am. Asn. Orthod; Am. Acad. Oral Path; Am. Asn. Anat; N.Y. Acad. Sci; Am. Cleft Palate Asn; Int. Soc. Cranio-Facial Biol; Int. Asn. Dent. Res. Genetic and environmental influences on the growth of the craniofacial complex; dental development; malocclusion indices; bone development. Address: Dept. of Orthodontics, School of Dentistry, University of Maryland, Baltimore, MD 21201.

GREWELING, H. THOMAS, b. Cincinnati, Ohio, Sept. 30, 24; m. 55; c. 3. ANALYTICAL & AGRICULTURAL CHEMISTRY. B.S, West Virginia, 48, M.S, 50. Chem. analyst, CORNELL UNIV, 50-55, DIR. LABS, 56- U.S.N, 44-47, Ens. Am. Chem. Soc; Soc. Appl. Spectros. Chemical analysis of soil and plant tissue; emission spectroscopy. Address: Dept. of Agronomy, Cornell University, Ithaca, NY 14850.

GREY, DAVID S(UMNER), b. Worcester, Mass, Feb. 8, 19; m. 42; c. 4. OPTICS. A.B, Harvard, 40. Asst. optical res, observ, Harvard Col, 41-42; res. physicist, Polaroid Corp, 42-61; mem. staff, Lincoln Lab, Mass. Inst. Tech, 61-63; consult, 63-64; mem. tech. staff, Aerospace Corp, 64-67; PRES. DAVID GREY ASSOCS, INC, 67- Optical Soc. Am.(Lomb medal, 50). Design of optical objectives and optical instruments; optimization of systems using optical objectives; application of computers to optimization. Address: David Grey Associates, Inc, 60 Hickory Dr, Waltham, MA 02154.

GREY, HOWARD M, b. New York, N.Y, Aug. 16, 32; m. 57; c. 3. IMMUNOCHEMISTRY, PATHOLOGY. A.B, Pennsylvania, 53; M.D, N.Y. Univ, 57. Intern med, Hopkins Hosp, 57-58; fel. immunol, Pittsburgh, 58-61; Scripps Clin. & Res. Found, 61-63; guest investr. & assoc. physician, Rockefeller Inst, 63-64, asst. prof, 64-67; assoc. mem, Scripps Clin. & Res. Found, 67-70; ASSOC. PROF. PATH, MED. CTR, UNIV. COLO, DENVER, 70- S.M. Scaife fel, Univ. Pittsburgh, 60-61, Am. Heart Asn. estab. investr, 65-70; staff mem, dept. of allergy & clin. immunol, Nat. Jewish Hosp. & Res. Ctr, 70- Am. Soc. Exp. Path. Antibody structure; kinetics of antigen-antibody reaction; phylogeny of antibody formation. Address: Dept. of Allergy & Clinical Immunology, National Jewish Hospital & Research Center, 3800 E. Colfax Ave, Denver, CO 80206.

GREY, JAMES T(RACY), JR, b. Newstead Twp, N.Y, May 27, 14; m. 41; c. 3. PHYSICAL CHEMISTRY. B.A, Buffalo, 36, Ph.D.(chem), 40. Asst. chem, Buffalo, 36-39; res. chemist, Durez Plastics & Chems, Inc, N.Y, 39-43; plastics res. engr, res. lab, aeroplane div, Curtiss-Wright Corp, 42-46; sr. res. chemist, Cornell Aeronaut. Lab, Inc, 46-47, head, chem. & fuels sects, 47-57; sci. adv. to dir. res. & develop, hqs, U.S. Air Force, Wash, D.C, 57-59; dir. res. planning staff, rocket div, THIOKOL CHEM. CORP, 57-64, dir. res. opers, 64-65, ASST. TO PRES. RES. & DEVELOP, 65- With Off. Sci. Res. & Develop; U.S.A; U.S.A.A.F; U.S.N, 44; sci. consult, For. Econ. Admin. & Tech. Indust. Intel. Cmt, Germany, 45. Am. Chem. Soc; Am. Inst. Aeronaut. & Astronaut. Resins and plastics; catalytic oxidation and reduction; chlorination of hydrocarbons; fundamentals of combustion; catalytic combustion; heat transfer at extreme conditions; fuels; magnetic susceptibility measurements. Address: Executive Offices, Thiokol Chemical Corp, Bristol, PA 19007.

GREY, JERRY, b. New York, N.Y, Oct. 25, 26; m. 48; c. 2. AEROSPACE ENGINEERING. B.M.E, Cornell, 47, M.S, 49; Ph.D.(aeronaut. eng), Calif. Inst. Tech, 52. Mem. tech. staff, Bell Tel. Labs, 47; instr. thermodyn, Cornell, 47-49; develop. engr, engine div, Fairchild Engine & Airplane Corp, 49-50; hypersonic aerodynamicist, Calif. Inst. Tech, 50-52; res. assoc. aerospace eng, Princeton, 52-56, asst. prof, 56-59, assoc. prof, 60-67; pres, Greyrad Corp, 67-71; ADMINR. TECH. ACTIVITIES, AM. INST. AERONAUT. & ASTRONAUT, 71-, v.pres. publ, 66-71. Sr. engr, Marquardt Aircraft Co, 51-52; consult, Potter Aeronaut. Corp, 55-63; Thiokol Corp, 55-57; Atlantic Res. Corp, 56-67; Aerojet-Gen. Corp, 56-; Thompson-Ramo-Wooldridge, Inc, 58; Gen. Elec. Co, 58-60; Radio Corp. Am, 59-64; Chrysler Corp, 59-60; Boeing Co, 59-60; Vitro Corp, 59-60; Greyrad Corp, 60-71; McGraw-Hill Book Co, 62-; Los Alamos Sci. Lab, 65-69; Sandia Corp, 67-70; Morse Boulger Co, 69- AAAS; assoc. fel. Am. Inst. Aeronaut. & Astronaut; sr. mem. Am. Astronaut. Soc. Aerospace propulsion systems; heat transfer; combustion, nuclear power generation, instrumentation. Address: 359 W. 21st St, New York, NY 10011.

GREY, PETER, b. Karachi, Pakistan, May 1, 38; m. 61; c. 3. ANALYTICAL CHEMISTRY. B.S, McGill Univ, 61, Shell Oil Can. fel, 62, Prov. Que. fel, 63-66, Ph.D.(anal. chem), 67. Res. chemist, ANAL CHEM, TECH. SERV. DIV, MOBIL RES. & DEVELOP. CORP, PAULSBORO, 66-68, sr. res. chemist, 68-70, SUPV. CHEMIST, 70- Am. Chem. Soc. Chemistry of metal chelates in nonaqueous solvents; development of analytical instrumentation and instrumental methods such as atomic absorption spectroscopy, gas chromatography and x-ray fluorescence. Address: 317 Nature Dr, Cherry Hill, NJ 08034.

GREY, ROBERT DEAN, b. Liberal, Kans, Sept. 5, 39; m. 61; c. 2. DEVELOPMENTAL BIOLOGY. B.A, Phillips, 61; Nat. Insts. Health trainee, Washington (St. Louis), 62-65, Ph.D.(biol), 66. Res. asst, Washington (St. Louis), 65-66, ASST. PROF. biol, 66-67; ZOOL, UNIV. CALIF, DAVIS, 67- AAAS. Animal development; factors regulating cellular differentiation in vertebrate organs, particularly the intestine; differentiation of enzyme activity in intestinal epithelium. Address: Dept. of Zoology, University of California, Davis, CA 95616.

GREY, ROSS M, b. Pinehurst, N.C, Mar. 25, 23; m. 54; c. 4. VETERINARY PATHOLOGY. D.V.M, Auburn, 45; M.S, Connecticut, 64. Asst. prof. vet. med, Colorado State, 45-48; asst. to tech. co-dir, U.S-Mex. Hoof & Mouth Disease Comn, 49-50; gen. practice, Conn, 53-62; chmn. inst. comp. med, col. physicians & surgeons & curator animal husb, COLUMBIA UNIV, 64-70, ASSOC. PROF. PATH, COL, 70- Vet.C, 50-53. Am. Vet. Med. Asn; Am. Asn. Lab. Animal Sci; N.Y. Acad. Sci. Comparative pathology; diseases of laboratory animals. Address: Dept. of Pathology, College of Physicians & Surgeons, Columbia University, 630 W. 168th St, New York, NY 10032.

GREY, SEYMOUR, b. Saint Ann, Jamaica, W.I, Apr. 6, 36; m. 66; c. 1. ORGANIC CHEMISTRY. B.S, Univ. Wis-Milwaukee, 64; Ph.D.(org. chem), Purdue Univ, 68. RES. CHEMIST, COLGATE-PALMOLIVE CO, 68- Am. Chem. Soc. Synthesis of certain terpine intermediates; chemical modification of keratin proteins; research and development of detergents. Address: Colgate-Palmolive Research Center, 909 River Rd, Piscataway, NJ 08854.

GREYBER, H(OWARD) D(AVID), b. New York, N.Y, Apr. 2, 23; m. 65; c. 3. PHYSICS. B.M.E, Cooper Union, 43; M.S, Pennsylvania, 49, Frazer fel, 51-52, Ph.D.(physics), 53. Test engr, Gen. Elec. Co, 43-44; mech. engr, Kellex Corp, 44; res. assoc. atomic energy, Forrestal Res. Center, Princeton, 52-53; theoret. physicist atomic weapons, Lawrence Radiation Lab, California, 53-57; missile & space vehicle dept, Gen. Elec. Co, 57-59; Courant Inst. Math. Sci, N.Y. Univ, 60; assoc. prof. physics, Northeastern, 61-66, chief, astrophys. & geophys, MARTIN-MARIETTA CORP, 66-69, SR. SCIENTIST, 69- Vis. scientist, Observ. Paris, Meudon, France, 64-65; Imp. Col, Univ. London, 65-66; adj. prof. Univ. Denver, 69-70. U.S.N.R, 44-55, Lt. AAAS; Am. Phys. Soc; Am. Inst. Aeronaut. & Astronaut; Am. Astronaut. Soc; Am. Astron. Soc; fel. Royal Astron. Soc; Int. Astron. Union. Theory of atomic spectra; theoretical nuclear physics; magneto hydrodynamics; plasma physics; astrophysics; planetary astronomy; planetology. Address: Martin-Marietta Corp, (S-2001), P.O. Box 179, Denver, CO 80201.

GREYSON, J(EROME), b. N.Y.C, Nov. 7, 27; m. 57; c. 3. PHYSICAL CHEMISTRY. A.B, Hunter Col 50; U.S. Army Ord. fel, Pa. State, 53-56, Ph.D, 56. Chemist, Sylvania Elec. Corp, 51-53; mem. tech. staff, Bell Tel. Labs, 56-57; staff chemist, Int. Bus. Mach. Corp, N.Y, 57-62, group leader phys. chem, Stauffer Chem. Co, 62-64; res. specialist, atomics int. div, N.Am. Aviation, Inc, 64-67, prin. scientist, Rocketdyne Div, N.Am. Rockwell Corp, 67-70; SECT. HEAD PHYS. SCI, AMES RES. LAB, AMES CO. DIV, MILES LABS, 70- U.S.N, 45-46, Res, 46-51. Am. Chem. Soc. Physical chemistry of surfaces and membranes. Address: Ames Research Lab, Ames Co. Division, Miles Labs, Elkhart, IN 46514.

GREYSON, MURRAY, b. New York, N.Y, Apr. 8, 23; m. 48; c. 2. OPERATIONS RESEARCH, PHYSICAL CHEMISTRY. B.S, Western Reserve, 48, Off. Naval Res. fel, 48-50, M.S, 50. Assoc. res. chemist, Off. Naval Res. Prog, Western Reserve, 48-50; phys. chemist, Am. Can Co, 50-51; supvry. phys. chemist, U.S. Bur. Mines, 51-55; process engr, United Engrs. & Constructors, 55-56; assoc. res. chemist, petrol. process res. group, Houdry Process Corp, 56-58; group leader, radiation process group, Cities Serv. Res. & Develop. Co, 58-59; proj. leader, Opers. Res, Inc, 59-61, assoc. prog. dir, 61-62; mem. planning staff, Honeywell, Inc, 62-64; dir. adv. develop, Wash. Res. Ctr, Tech. Opers, Inc, 64-65; mem. res. staff, strategic studies ctr, STANFORD RES. INST, 65-67, dir, 67-68, SR. STAFF, opers. anal. div, 68-71, SYSTS. PLANNING DEPT, 71- U.S.A.F, 42-46, Res, 46-53, 1st Lt. Opers. Res. Soc. Am. Petroleum catalysis; kinetics; combustion. Address: 277 Avalon Dr, Los Altos, CA 94022.

GREYSON, RICHARD IRVING, b. Nelson, B.C, May 26, 32; m. 56; c. 5. PLANT MORPHOLOGY. B.A, British Columbia, 54; M.S, Oregon, 60, Ph.D. (biol), 65. Instr. biol, Notre Dame (B.C), 55-58, 59-61; lectr. BOT, UNIV. WEST. ONT, 64-65, asst. prof, 65-69, ASSOC. PROF, 69- Am. Bot. Soc; Can. Bot. Asn. Growth in intercalary meristems; initiation of floral primordia; plant organ culture; hormonal interaction between plant organs; description and analysis of plant organs of genetic strains of Lycopersicum, Zea & Nigella; experimental plant morphology. Address: Dept. of Plant Sciences, University of Western Ontario, London, Ont, Can.

GREYSON, WILLIAM L(AWRENCE), b. Detroit, Mich, May 20, 16; m. 40; c. 2. ORGANIC CHEMISTRY. B.A, Cornell Univ, 37; N.Y. Univ. Chemist, Richfield Oil Co, 38-39; plant mgr, Suflex Co, 40-54; dir. res. & develop, Hitemp Wires, Inc, 55-60; dir. res, Dilectrix Film Corp, 60-61; mgr. res. & develop, Tensolite Insulated Wire Co, Inc. Div, Carlisle Rubber Co, 61-65; DIR. PROCESS DEVELOP, CHEMPLAST, INC, 65- AAAS; Am. Chem. Soc. Fluorocarbons; high temperature polymers. Address: 19 Monhegan Ave, Wayne, NJ 07470.

GREYTAK, THOMAS JOHN, b. Annapolis, Md, Mar. 24, 40; m. 66. PHYSICS. B.S. & M.S, Mass. Inst. Tech, 63, Ph.D. (physics), 67. Instr. PHYSICS, MASS. INST. TECHNOL, 67, asst. prof, 67-70, ASSOC. PROF, 70- Alfred P. Sloan res. fel, 71-73. Am. Phys. Soc. Light scattering from thermal fluctuations in matter; low temperature physics. Address: Dept. of Physics, Massachusetts Institute of Technology, Cambridge, MA 02139.

GREZE, JOHN P(AUL), JR, b. Brockton, Mass, Feb. 5, 13; m. 40; c. 3. CHEMISTRY. B.S. Mass. Inst. Tech, 35. Biologist-bacteriologist, Zonite Prod. Corp, N.J, 36-43; chief bacteriologist, OAKITE PROD, INC, 43-46, group leader, 46-58, sect. head, 58-60, ASST. TECH. DIR, 60- Am. Chem. Soc; Am. Soc. Microbiol; Am. Pub. Health Asn; Nat. Asn. Corrosion Eng; fel. Am. Inst. Chem; Inst. Food Tech. Detergents; germicides; solvents. Address: 64 Chandler Rd, Chatham, NJ 07928.

GRGIN, EMILE, b. Le Trait, France, Sept. 7, 33. RELATIVITY, QUANTUM MECHANICS. B.S, Univ. Zagreb, 58; Ph.D. (physics), Syracuse Univ, 66. Res. assoc. PHYSICS, YESHIVA UNIV, 66-69, ASST. PROF, 69- Yugoslav Army, 59-60. Abstract structure and foundations of quantum theory; general relativity; global relativity. Address: Dept. of Physics, Yeshiva University, Belfer Graduate School of Science, Washington Heights, New York, NY 10033.

GRIBBINS, M(YERS) F(LOYD), b. Tampa, Fla, Sept. 26, 16; m. 42; c. 5. BIOCHEMISTRY. B.S, Miami (Fla), 38; M.S, Pa. State Col, 40, Ph.D. (chem), 42. Field supvr, anti-mosquito dist, Dade County, Fla, 35-38; asst, Pa. State Col, 38-40, instr. agr. & biol. chem, 40-42; biochemist, E.I. DU PONT DE NEMOURS & CO, INC, 42-50, MGR, 50- Am. Chem. Soc. Nutritional studies of tobacco plant and its effect upon chemical composition of seedling and mature tobacco plant. Address: E.I. du Pont de Nemours & Co, Inc, Wilmington, DE 19898.

GRIBBLE, DAVID H(AROLD), b. Seattle, Wash, Dec. 26, 32; m. 55; c. 4. VETERINARY PATHOLOGY. D.V.M, Wash. State Univ, 62; Ph.D. (comp. path), Univ. Calif, Davis, 70. ASST. PROF. PATH, SCH. VET. MED, UNIV. CALIF, DAVIS, 66- U.S.N, 51-55. Am. Vet. Med. Asn; Am. Col. Vet. Path; Int. Acad. Path. Infectious diseases; renal pathology. Address: 1501 Pole Line Rd, Davis, CA 95616.

GRIBBLE, GORDON W, b. San Francisco, Calif, July 28, 41; m. 63; c. 2. ORGANIC CHEMISTRY. B.S, California, Berkeley, 63; Nat. Insts. Health fel, Oregon, 65-67, Ph.D. (chem), 67. Nat. Cancer Inst. fel, ORG. CHEM, California, Los Angeles, 67-68; ASST. PROF, DARTMOUTH COL, 68- Res. Corp. grant, 68; Petrol. Res. Fund grant, 68-70; Eli Lilly grant, 69-71; Nat. Sci. Found. grant, 69-71; Nat. Insts. Health career develop. award, 71-76. Am. Chem. Soc; The Chem. Soc. Synthetic organic chemistry; indole alkaloids; nuclear magnetic resonance spectroscopy; reaction mechanisms. Address: Dept. of Chemistry, Dartmouth College, Hanover, NH 03755.

GRIBBLE, LLOYD R(AYMOND), b. Fairchance, Pa, Sept. 7, 06; m. 27; c. 1. COMPARATIVE ANATOMY, EMBRYOLOGY. B.S, Waynesburg Col, 29; M.S, West Virginia, 31, Ph.D. (zool), 35. Instr. ZOOL, W.VA. UNIV, 30-35, asst. prof, 35-43, assoc. prof, 43-47, PROF, 47-, ASSOC. DEAN COL. ARTS & SCI, 61-, premed. adv, 49-54, asst. dean, 54-61. Fel. AAAS; Am. Soc. Zool. Variations and anomalies in the vertebrates; development of gonads of brook lamprey; reactions of brook lamprey to light; ecology of brook lampreys. Address: 103 Woodburn Hall, College of Arts & Sciences, West Virginia University, Morgantown, WV 26506.

GRIBBLE, WILLIAM CHARLES, JR, b. Ironwood, Mich, May 24, 17; m. 41; c. 4. PHYSICS, NUCLEAR ENGINEERING. B.S, U.S. Mil. Acad, 41; M.S, Univ. Chicago, 48; hon. D.Eng, Mich. Technol. Univ, 69. U.S. ARMY, 41-, mem. staff metall, Los Alamos Sci. Lab, 48-52, asst. dir. reactor develop, hq, Atomic Energy Comn, 54-56, dist. engr, Corps Engrs, Anchorage, 56-60, asst. dir. reactor develop, hq, Atomic Energy Comn, 61-62, dist. engr, Corps Engrs, Chicago, 63, dir. res. & develop, Army Mat. Command, 63-66, asst. chief of staff, Dept. Army, 66-69, commandant, U.S. Army Eng. Sch, 69-70, CHIEF RES. & DEVELOP, U.S. ARMY, 70- U.S.A, 41-, Lt. Gen; Legion of Merit, 56, Army Commendation Medal, 59, Distinguished Serv. Medal, 69, Oak Leaf Cluster, 70. Am. Ord. Asn; Am. Polar Soc; Soc. Am. Mil. Eng. Physical metallurgy and the fabricability of unusual metals; erection of foundation structures in a permafrost regime; nuclear reactor physics and engineering. Address: U.S. Army, Pentagon, Washington, DC 20310.

GRIBOVAL, PAUL, b. Paris, France, Aug. 24, 25; m. 52; c. 1. PHYSICS, ELECTRON OPTICS. Eng. dipl, Conserv, Nat. Arts et Mètiers, France, 56; Ph.D. (electromagnetic separation), Univ. Grenoble, 66. Tech. asst. physics & astron, Nat. Ctr. Sci. Res, France, 47-56; engr, Fr. Atomic Comn, 56-59; chief engr, Univ. Grenoble, 59-66; SPEC. RES. ASSOC. ELECTRONOGRAPHIC CAMERA, DEPT. ASTRON, UNIV. TEX, AUSTIN, 66- AAAS; Am. Astron. Soc; Am. Phys. Soc. Study of photomultipliers response; mass spectrometry of solids; isotopes separation and electrostatic accelerators; electronographic camera. Address: 3904 Rockledge Dr, Austin, TX 78731.

GRICE, GEORGE D(ANIEL), JR, b. Charleston, S.C, Oct. 9, 29; m. 55; c. 1. MARINE ZOOLOGY. B.S, Clemson Col 50; M.A, Fla. State, 53, Ph.D. (biol. oceanog), 57. Fishery res. biologist, U.S. Fish & Wildlife Serv, 57-58; fel, Guggenheim Mem. Found, 58-59; ASSOC. SCIENTIST, WOODS HOLE OCEANOG. INST, 59- Ecol. Soc. Am. Zooplankton ecology, particularly the taxonomy and zoogeography of marine calanoid copepods. Address: Woods Hole Oceanographic Institution, Woods Hole, MA 02543.

GRICE, HAROLD C, b. Windsor, Ont, July 13, 25; m. 49; c. 3. PATHOLOGY, TOXICOLOGY. D.V.M, Univ. Toronto, 51; M.Sc, Univ. Ottawa, 57. HEAD PATH, FOOD & DRUG DIRECTORATE, TUNNEY'S PASTURE, 51- Lectr, med. sch, Ottawa Univ, 65-71. R.C.A.F, 44; Can. Army, 45. Can. Asn. Path; Int. Acad. Path; Soc. Toxicol; Can. Asn. Res. Toxicol. Toxicology as related to safety assessment. Address: Pathology & Toxicology Section, Food & Drug Directorate, Tunney's Pasture, Ottawa, Ont, Can.

GRICE, HARVEY H(OWARD), b. Flint, Mich, Sept. 25, 12; m. 41; c. 3. CHEMICAL ENGINEERING. B.Ch.E, Ohio State, 37, M.Sc, 38, Chem. Club New York fel, 40, Ph.D. (chem. eng), 41. Proj. engr, cent labs, Gen. Foods Corp, N.J, 41-42, supt. processing & power, Diamond Crystal-Colonial Salt Div, 46-48; tech. asst. to dir, mfg. & eng, Gen. Foods Corp, 48-52, plant mgr, Diamond Crystals-Colonial Salt Div, 52-53, mgr. mfg. & eng, Gaines Div, 53-58; pres, Graceland Col, 58-64; PROF. CHEM. ENG, UNIV. MO-ROLLA, 64- C.W.S, U.S.A, 42-46, Col. Am. Inst. Chem. Eng; Am. Soc. Eng. Educ; Am. Chem. Soc; fel. Am. Inst. Chem. Engineering; mechanism of crystallization in the industrial evaporation of sodium chloride brine. Address: Dept. of Chemical Engineering, University of Missouri-Rolla, Rolla, MO 65401.

GRICE, REGINALD HUGH, b. South Shields, Eng, July 20, 26; Can. citizen; m. 54; c. 2. CIVIL ENGINEERING, GEOLOGY. B.A, Cambridge, 49, M.A, 54; Ph.D. (geol), Illinois, 64. Geologist, Cent. Lab, George Wimpey Ltd, 51-54; Falconbridge Nickel Mines Ltd, 54-56; H.G. Acres & Co, Ltd, 56-61; asst. prof, GEOL, Univ. Ill, 64-65; McGILL UNIV, 65-71, ASSOC. PROF, 71- R.A.F, 46-48, Pilot Off. Asn. Eng. Geol; Int. Asn. Eng. Geol. Surface reservoirs on limestones; disintegration of shale rocks; exploration for civil engineering foundations; computer handling of data. Address: Dept. of Geological Science, McGill University, Montreal, Que, Can.

GRIDLEY, DARRIN H(AGIST), b. Chicago, Ill, July 21, 17; m. 40; c. 2. ENGINEERING. B.S.M.E, Purdue, 40; Maryland, 46-49. Engr, Standard Oil Co. (Ind), 40-41; Am. Steel Foundries, Ill, 42; head, digital methods sect, oper. res. br, Naval Res. Labs, 46-58; with Maico Electronics, Inc, 58-60; v.pres. digital systs, Electro Nuclear Systs. Corp, 60-62; ASSOC. CHIEF, data systs. div, GODDARD SPACE FLIGHT CTR, NASA, 62-67, COMPUT. DIV, 67- U.S.N.R, 42-46, Lt. Asn. Comput. Mach; assoc. Inst. Elec. & Electronics Eng; Am. Ord. Asn. Design and development of digital devices; precision computing systems; orbit and data processing calculations. Address: Computation Division, Goddard Space Flight Center, NASA, Code 540, Greenbelt, MD 20771.

GRIEB, MERLAND W(ILLIAM), b. Carey, Idaho, Jan. 26, 20. INORGANIC CHEMISTRY. B.S, Idaho, 42, M.S, 49; Ph.D. (chem), Illinois, 53. Instr. CHEM, Idaho, 48-49; asst, Illinois, 49-53; asst. prof, Wayne State, 53-56; UNIV. IDAHO, 56-69, ASSOC. PROF, 69- U.S.N.R, 42-46. Am. Chem. Soc. Complexions. Address: Dept. of Chemistry, University of Idaho, Moscow, ID 83843.

GRIEBLE, HANS G, b. Constance, Ger, Feb. 21, 28; U.S. citizen; m. 61; c. 3. INTERNAL MEDICINE, INFECTIOUS DISEASES. Heidelberg, 50-52; M.D, Tübingen, 52. Instr. MED, Illinois, 59-62, asst. prof, 62-67, ASSOC. PROF, 67-69; CHICAGO MED. SCH, 69-; CHIEF INFECTIOUS DISEASES & IMMUNOL, VET. ADMIN. HOSP, HINES, 67- U.S. Pub. Health Serv. fel. immunochem, Pasteur Inst, Paris, France, 61-62; chief clin. immunol, Hektoen Inst, Cook County Hosp, 65-67. Dipl. Am. Bd. Internal Med, 66. AAAS; Am. Fedn. Clin. Res; Am. Heart Asn; Infectious Diseases Soc. Am; Am. Med. Asn. Address: Dept. of Medicine, Chicago Medical School, 2020 W. Ogden Ave, Chicago, IL 60612.

GRIEBSTEIN, WILLIAM J(OHN), b. Arthur, N.Dak, Nov. 4, 22; m. 45; c. 5. PHYSICAL CHEMISTRY. B.S, N.Dak. Agr. Col, 44, M.S, 48; Ph.D. (chem), Kansas State, 54. Instr. chem, Mankato State Teachers Col, 47-49; RES. CHEMIST, PROCTER & GAMBLE CO, 52- U.S.A.A.F, 44-46. AAAS; Am. Chem. Soc; Int. Asn. Dent. Res. Kinetics; solution properties; proteins; calcified tissues. Address: Miami Valley Labs, Procter & Gamble Co, Cincinnati, OH 45239.

GRIEGER, PHILIP F(REDERIC), b. Michigan City, Ind, Nov. 21, 19; m. 45; c. 2. PHYSICAL CHEMISTRY. B.S, California, 41; Ph.D.(chem), Brown, 47. Instr. chem, Brown, 42-44, 46-47, fel, Lalor Found, 47-48; supvr. res. chem, Tenn. Eastman Co. Div, Eastman Kodak Co, 44-46; fel. chem, Illinois, 48-51; Mellon Inst, 51; head dept. chem, Thomas A. Edison Res. Lab, McGRAW-EDISON CO, 51-64, SR. ELECTROCHEMIST, PRIMARY BATTERY DIV, 64- Electrochemistry; batteries; polymeric electrolytes; longchain electrolytes; reaction kinetics. Address: 19 Oakridge Rd, West Orange, NJ 07052.

GRIEGER, RICHARD A, b. Niagara Falls, N.Y, Aug. 17, 43; c. 2. CHEMICAL ENGINEERING. B.S.E, Univ. Mich, 65; NASA traineeship, Univ. Ill, Urbana, 66-69, M.S, 68, Ph.D.(chem. eng), 70. ASST. PROF. CHEM. ENG, UNIV. WIS, MADISON, 70- High-pressure chemistry; enzyme kinetics; thermodynamics; homogeneous catalysis. Address: Dept. of Chemical Engineering, University of Wisconsin, Madison, WI 53706.

GRIEGO, RICHARD JEROME, b. Albuquerque, N.Mex, June 11, 39; m. 60; c. 2. MATHEMATICS. B.S, New Mexico, 61; Woodrow Wilson fel, Chicago, 61-62; Ph.D.(math), Illinois, 65. Lectr. MATH, California, Riverside, 65-66; asst. prof, UNIV. N.MEX, 66-70, ASSOC. PROF. & COORD. CHICANO STUDIES PROG, 70- Am. Math. Soc. Markov processes; potential theory; probability theory. Address: Dept. of Mathematics & Statistics, University of New Mexico, Albuquerque, NM 87106.

GRIEM, H(ANS) R(UDOLF), b. Kiel, Ger, Oct. 7, 28; nat; m. 57; c. 3. PHYSICS. Ph.D.(physics), Univ. Kiel, 54. Asst. upper atmospheric physics, Maryland, 54-55; high temperature physics, Univ. Kiel, 55-57; res. asst. prof. plasma physics, UNIV. MD, COLLEGE PARK, 57-64, PROF. PHYSICS, 64- Consult, U.S. Naval Res. Lab, 57- Fel. Am. Phys. Soc. High temperature and plasma physics; spectroscopy; line broadening theory. Address: Dept. of Physics & Astronomy, University of Maryland, College Park, MD 20742.

GRIEM, MELVIN L(UTHER), b. Milwaukee, Wis, May 22, 25; m. 51; c. 3. RADIOLOGY, PHYSICS. B.S, Wisconsin, 48, M.S, 50, Alumni Res. Found. fel, 50-51, M.D, 53. Instr. RADIOL, SCH. MED, UNIV. CHICAGO, 57-58, asst. prof, 58-61, assoc. prof, 61-68, PROF, 68-, DIR, CHICAGO TUMOR INST, 66- Am. Cancer Soc. clin. fel. 58-60; career res. develop. award, 63-65; mem. cancer res. training comt, Nat. Cancer Inst. U.S.A, 43-45. Am. Cancer Soc; Am. Phys. Soc; Radiation Res. Soc; Radiol. Soc. N.Am; Am. Radium Soc; Soc. Nuclear Med. Radiobiology; radiation therapy: radiologic physics; radioactive isotopes. Address: Dept. of Radiology, Chicago Tumor Institute, University of Chicago, Chicago, IL 60637.

GRIEM, SYLVIA F, b. West Allis, Wis, Feb. 24, 29; m. 51; c. 3. MEDICINE, DERMATOLOGY. B.S, Univ. Wis, 50, M.D, 53. ASST. PROF. MED, UNIV. CHICAGO, 61- Am. Acad. Dermat. Hypersensitivity to physical agents, especially cold; microangiography of skin. Address: Dept. of Dermatology, University of Chicago, 950 E. 59th St, Chicago, IL 60637.

GRIER, HERBERT E(ARL), b. Chicago, Ill, July 3, 11; m. 36, 54; c. 3. ENGINEERING. B.S, Mass. Inst. Technol, 33, M.S, 34; hon. D.Sc, Univ. Nev, Las Vegas, 67. Consult. engr, EG&G, INC, 34-47, CORP. OFF, 47-, PRES. CER GEONUCLEAR CORP, 65-; PRES, REYNOLDS ELEC. & ENG. CO, INC, 67- U.S. Dept. Army cert. appreciation, 54. Civilian with Nat. Defense Res. Comt, 42-43; Manhattan Eng. Dist, Atomic Energy Comn, 44. Scientific management; high frequency electronics; scientific photography. Address: 120 E. Flamingo Road, P.O. Box 15090, Las Vegas, NV 89114.

GRIER, NATHANIEL, b. Brooklyn, N.Y, March 27, 18; m. 41; c. 3. CHEMISTRY. B.S, Long Island, 37; M.S. Michigan, 38, Stearns fel. & Ph.D.(chem), 43. Res. chemist, dept. eng. res, Michigan, 40-41; sr. res. chemist, Hoffman La Roche Inc, 42-45; chief res. chemist, Dar-Syn Lab Inc, 45-57; v.pres. & dir. res, Metalsalts Corp, 57-66; SR. SCIENTIST, MERCK SHARPE & DOHME RES. LAB. DIV, MERCK & CO, INC, RAHWAY, 66- Fel. AAAS; Am. Chem. Soc; N.Y. Acad. Sci. Isolation of antibiotics; synthetic organic chemistry; process development. Address: 153 Morse Pl, Englewood, NJ 07631.

GRIERSON, JAMES D(OUGLAS), b. Dayton, Ohio, July 15, 31; m. 53; c. 4. PALEOBOTANY, PLANT MORPHOLOGY. B.A, Hiram Col, 54; Nat. Sci. Found. fel, Cornell, 56, summer fels, 59 & 60, Ph.D.(paleobot), 62. Instr. bot, Cornell, 61-63; asst. prof. BIOL, STATE UNIV. N.Y. BINGHAMTON, 63-68, ASSOC. PROF, 68- Res. Found. N.Y. fel. & grant-in-aid, 64 & 65; mem, Paleont. Res. Inst. U.S.A, 54-56, Res, 56-62. Bot. Soc. Am; Torrey Bot. Club; Paleont. Soc. Applications of anatomical and morphological techniques to the study of fossil plants; Devonian period, especially lycopodiaceous plants. Address: Dept. of Biology, Harpur College, State University of New York at Binghamton, Binghamton, NY 13901.

GRIERSON, WILLIAM, b. Boscombe, Eng, Dec. 15, 17; nat; m. 43; c. 2. POMOLOGY. B.S.A, Ont. Agr. Col, 38; M.S.A, Toronto, 45; Ph.D.(pomol), Cornell, 51. Asst, Ont. Agr. Col, 38-40; asst. prof. biol, British Columbia, 45-51; chief fruits & veg. res, food sect, Can. Defence Res. Bd, 51-52; from asst. chemist to assoc. chemist, Citrus Exp. Sta, Florida, 52-61; assoc. dir. Food Industs. Res. & Eng, 61-64; SECT. HEAD, HARVESTING & HANDLING SECT, AGR. RES. & EDUC. CTR, UNIV. FLA, 64- Asst, Cornell Univ, 49-51; lectr, Fla. South. Col, 53-61. R.C.A.F, 40-45; Distinguished Flying Cross. Am. Soc. Hort. Sci. Harvesting and handling of fresh fruits, especially chilling injury of tropical fruits. Address: University of Florida Agricultural Research and Education Center, Box 1088, Lake Alfred, FL 33850.

GRIES, DAVID, b. Flushing, N.Y, Apr. 26, 39; m. 61; c. 2. COMPUTER SCIENCE. B.S, Queens Col.(N.Y), 60; M.S, Illinois, Urbana, 63; Dr. rer. nat. (math), Munich Tech, 66. Mathematician, U.S. Naval Weapons Lab, 60-62; res. asst, Univ. Ill, Urbana, 62-63; math, Munich Tech. Univ, 63-66; asst. prof. COMPUT. SCI, Stanford Univ, 66-69, res. assoc, Linear Acceleration Ctr, 66-69; ASSOC. PROF, CORNELL UNIV, 69- Asn. Comput. Mach. (ed. prog. lang. sect, Commun. ACM, 70-). Theory of norms as applied in numerical analysis; compilers and formal languages as applied in compiling techniques. Address: Dept. of Computer Science, Upson Hall, Cornell University, Ithaca, NY 14850.

GRIES, GEORGE A(LEXANDER), b. Cambridge, Mass, May 2, 17; m. 39; c. 2. PLANT PATHOLOGY. A.B, Miami (Ohio), 38; M.S, Kansas State, 40; Ph.D.(plant physiol), Wisconsin, 42. Asst. plant pathologist, Conn. Agr. Exp. Sta, 42-45; assoc. prof. bot. & assoc. plant physiologist, agr. exp. sta, Purdue, 45-53, prof. plant physiol. & plant physiologist, 53-60; plant pathologist, prof. plant path. & head dept, Univ. Ariz, 60-66, acting head, dept. bot, 63-65, prof. biol. sci. & head dept. & biologist, agr. exp. sta, 66-68; DEAN, COL. ARTS & SCI, OKLA. STATE UNIV, 68- Res. demonstr, Univ. Col. Swansea, Wales, 57-58; mem, Comn. Educ. & Natural Resources, 62-68; mem. & mem. exec. comt, Comn. Undergrad. Educ. Biol. Sci, 68-71; consult-exam, N.Cent. Asn. Cols. & Sec. Schs; consult, coord. coun. higher educ, State of Calif, 69- Fel. AAAS; Am. Phytopath. Soc; Nat. Asn. Biol. Teachers; Am. Inst. Biol. Sci. Physiology of parasitic fungi; biochemistry of disease resistance in plants. Address: College of Arts & Sciences, Oklahoma State University, Stillwater, OK 74074.

GRIES, JOHN PAUL, b. Wash, D.C, June 7, 11; m. 33; c. 2. GEOLOGY, PALEONTOLOGY. A.B, Miami (Ohio), 32; M.S, Chicago, 33, Ph.D.(geol, paleont), 35. Asst. geologist, State Geol. Surv, Ill, 35-36; instr. geol. & mineral, S.Dak. Sch. Mines. & Technol, 36-37, asst. prof, 37-42, assoc. prof, 42-44; geologist, Magnolia Petrol. Co, 44-46; assoc. prof. geol. & mineral, S.DAK. SCH. MINES & TECHNOL, 46-49, PROF. GEOL. ENG, 49-, DIR. GRAD. STUDIES, 50-, DEAN GRAD. DIV, 66- Geol. Soc. Am; Paleont. Soc; Am. Asn. Petrol. Geol; Am. Inst. Mining, Metall. & Petrol. Eng. Stratigraphy of northern Great Plains and Rocky Mountain area. Address: Dept. of Geological Engineering, South Dakota School of Mines & Technology, Rapid City, SD 57701.

GRIES, LAWRENCE F(ORMAN), b. Newark, N.J, June 7, 25; m. 46, 65; c. 2. ORGANIC CHEMISTRY. B.Sc, Rutgers, 55, Ph.D.(org. chem), 61. Instr. CHEM, Rutgers, 55-59; ASST. PROF, Drew, 59-60; QUEEN'S COL.(N.Y), 60- U.S.N.R, 43-58, Ens. Am. Chem. Soc. Natural products; language translation. Address: Dept. of Chemistry, Queen's College, Flushing, NY 11367.

GRIESACKER, PAUL BURCH, b. Baltimore, Md, Jan. 7, 37; m. 64; c. 1. PHYSICS. B.S, Loyola Col.(Md), 58; M.S, Pa. State, 60, Ph.D.(physics), 63. Asst. eng. mech, Pa. State, 58-60, physics, 60-63; sr. scientist, Bettis Atomic Power Lab, Westinghouse Elec. Corp, 63-67; ASST. PROF. PHYSICS, GANNON COL, 67- Nat. Sci. Found. fel; res. partic, Roswell Park Mem. Inst, summer 68. Radiation effects on mechanical properties of materials; nuclear decay schemes; beta ray spectroscopy; neutron cross sections as applied to reactor design; microwave diffraction; optical data processing. Address: Dept. of Physics, Gannon College, Perry Square, Erie, PA 16501.

GRIESBACH, ROBERT A(NTHONY), b. Menasha, Wis, April 11, 24; m. 54; c. 5. CYTOLOGY, GENETICS. B.S, DePaul, 51, M.S, 52; Coulter fel, Chicago, 54-55, Ph.D.(bot), 55. Instr. BIOL. SCIS, De Paul UNIV, 55-58, asst. prof, 58-70, ASSOC. PROF, 70-, DIR. DEPT, 71- U.S.A, 43-46. AAAS; Bot. Soc. Am; Am. Genetic Asn; Genetic Soc. Am. Cytogenetics; seed dormancy. Address: Dept. of Biology, DePaul University, 1036 Belden Ave, Chicago, IL 60614.

GRIESEL, WESLEY O(TTO), b. Portland, Ore, Feb. 7, 13; m. 36; c. 1. BOTANY. B.A, California, Los Angeles, 34, M.A, 39, Ph.D.(bot), 52. Instr, pub. schs, Calif, 38-41, BOT, Los Angeles City Col, 47-52; assoc. prof, CALIF. STATE COL. LOS ANGELES, 52-57, PROF, 58-, chmn. dept, 59-64. U.S.A.A.F, 42-46. AAAS; Bot. Soc. Am; Am. Soc. Plant Physiol. Cytology and physiology of abscission; floral respiration; diurnal cycles; photobiology; floral primordia initiation. Address: Dept. of Botany, California State College at Los Angeles, Los Angeles, CA 90032.

GRIESEMER, RICHARD A(LLEN), b. Andreas, Pa, May 8, 29; m. 51; c. 3. VETERINARY PATHOLOGY. D.V.M, Ohio State, 53, Ph.D.(vet. path), 59. Instr. vet. path, Ohio State, 53-55; jr. pathologist, virol. br, Armed Forces Inst. Path, 55-57; instr. vet. path, Ohio State Univ, 57-59, asst. prof, 59-61, assoc. prof, 61-64, prof, 64-71; chmn. dept, 67-71; ASSOC. DIR, NAT. CTR. PRIMATE BIOL, UNIV. CALIF, DAVIS, 71- Mem. animal resources adv. comt, Nat. Insts. Health, 69-; consult, Nat. Cancer Inst, 70- Nat. Gaines Award, Am. Vet. Med. Asn. Vet.C, 55-57, Capt. AAAS; Am. Vet. Med. Asn; Am. Col. Vet. Path; Inst. Acad. Path; Am. Soc. Microbiol; Asn. Gnotobiotics. Pathology of infectious diseases of animals. Address: National Center for Primate Biology, University of California, Davis, CA 95616.

GRIESEMER, R(OBERT) D(ANIEL), b. Reading, Pa, June 30, 18; m. 49; c. 2. DERMATOLOGY. B.S, Bucknell, 39; M.D, Harvard, 43. Intern, Phila. Gen. Hosp, 43-44; res. dermat, Mass. Gen. Hosp, 46-49; res. assoc. biol, Mass. Inst. Tech, 49-51, res. fel. DERMAT, Harvard & Mass. Gen. Hosp, 49-52, asst, 52-61; ASST. PROF, HARVARD MED. SCH. 61- Res. fel, Am. Cancer Soc, 51-54, scholar, 54-57. Med.C, 44-46, Capt. Respiratory enzymes of epidermis; lipid metabolism of skin. Address: Dept. of Dermatology, Harvard Medical School, Boston, MA 02115.

GRIESER, DANIEL R, b. Newark, Ohio, May 5, 26; m. 69. PHYSICS. B.S, Ohio State Univ, 53. SR. PHYSICIST, COLUMBUS LABS, BATTELLE MEM. INST, 53- U.S.N, 45-46. Nat. Soc. Prof. Eng; Soc. Photo-optical Instrument. Eng. Instrumentation for environmental extremes; optical metrology; holography and coherent optical signal processing; spectroscopy of optical transitions. Address: 4326 Kenny Rd, Columbus, OH 43220.

GRIESHAMMER, L(AWRENCE) L(OUIS), b. Jefferson City, Mo, Aug. 28, 22; m. 45; c. 7. PHYSICAL CHEMISTRY. B.S, California, Los Angeles, 49; M.A, Missouri, 51. Asst, Missouri, 49-51; anal. res. chemist, LUBRIZOL CORP, 51-53, res. supvr, SPECTROS. LAB, 53-61, SECT. LEADER, 61- U.S.A, 42-46. Am. Chem. Soc. Emission spectroscopy; ultraviolet and infrared absorption spectroscopy; instrumental methods of analysis and analytical organic chemistry, particularly on lubricating oil additives. Address: Lubrizol Corp, Euclid Station, Box 3057, Cleveland, OH 44117.

GRIESINGER, WILLIAM K(ENNETH), b. West New York, N.J, Oct. 20, 10; m. 40; c. 2. CHEMICAL ENGINEERING. B.S, Lehigh, 32. Chem. engr, Colgate-Palmolive-Peet Co, Jersey City, 32-34; res. chemist, Atlantic Ref. Co, Phila, 34-35, res. group leader, 35-43, res. supvr, 43-47, dir. res. & develop, chem. prod. div, 47-53, res. div, 53-58, mgr. appln. res. div, 58-60, develop, 60-67, MGR. INT. DEVELOP. & LICENSING, ARCO CHEM. CO. DIV, ATLANTIC RICHFIELD CO, 67-, CHMN. BD. DIR, WIB-ARCO GMBH, IBBENBUREN, GER, 70- Am. Chem. Soc; Am. Oil Chemists Soc; Am. Soc. Test. & Mat; Soc. Automotive Eng; Am. Asn. Textile Chem. & Colorists. Petroleum aromatics; ethylene oxide; asphalts; isomerization of hydrocarbons; synthetic detergents; oil additives; catalysts; petroleum chemicals; automotive fuels and lubricants. Address: Arco Chemical Co. Division, Atlantic Richfield Co, 260 S. Broad St, Philadelphia, PA 19102.

GRIESMER, G(ERARD) J(OSEPH), b. N.Y.C, June 22, 28; m. 52; c. 2. CHEMICAL ENGINEERING. B.S, Notre Dame, 50; M.S, Mass. Inst. Tech, 52. Develop. engr, Linde Div, Union Carbide Corp, 52-56, develop. supvr, 56-63, assoc. div. engr, 63-66, mgr. stream separation systs, UNION CARBIDE EUROPA, S.A, 66-67, PROD. DIR, 67- Am. Inst. Chem. Eng. Sales, engineering, and production of distillation; adsorption and cryogenic separation equipment and processes. Address: Rue Pedro-Meylan 5, CH 1211, Geneva 17, Switz.

GRIESMER, JAMES H(UGO), b. Cleveland, Ohio, Dec. 18, 29; m. 56; c. 4. MATHEMATICS. B.S, Notre Dame, 51; Ph.D.(math), Princeton, 58. Asst. math, Princeton, 54-57; assoc. mathematician, T.J. WATSON RES. CTR, INT. BUS. MACH. CORP, 57-58, staff mathematician, 58-60, res. staff mem, 60-65, MGR. res. comput. ctr, 64-65, SYMBOL MANIPULATION PROJ, 65- Vis. Mackay lectr, Univ. Calif, Berkeley, 70-71. U.S.N, 51-54, Res, 54-61. AAAS; Am. Math. Soc; Asn. Comput. Mach; Math. Asn. Am. Applications of computers to non-numerical mathematics. Address: T.J. Watson Research Center, IBM Corp, P.O. Box 218, Yorktown Heights, NY 10598.

GRIESS, G(ERALD) A(LBERT), b. Clay Center, Nebr, Dec. 10, 15; m. 40; c. 2. CHEMISTRY. B.A, Nebraska, 38, M.A, 40. Res. chemist, DOW CHEM. CO, 40-47, group leader, 47, lab. div. leader, 47-48, dir styrene polymerization lab, 47-53, asst. to dir. plastics res, 53-63, dir. res. int, 63-66, mgr. patents & tech. liaison, plastics dept, 66-69, tech. & res. liaison, corp. res. & develop, 69-71, MGR. SCI. RELATIONS-PAC, 71- AAAS; Am. Chem. Soc; Soc. Plastics Eng. Plastics and coating resins; polystyrene molding and extrusion materials; styrene resins; styrenated drying oils and alkyds. Address: Homat West-Apt. 720, 15-11 Roppongi, 3-chome, Minato-ku, Tokyo 106, Japan.

GRIESS, J(OHN) C(HRISTIAN), JR, b. Mt. Vernon, Ind, July 13, 22; m. 47; c. 7. PHYSICAL CHEMISTRY. B.S, Indiana, 43, M.A, 47. CHEMIST, OAK RIDGE NAT. LAB, 47- U.S.A, 44-46. Electrochem. Soc.(young author's award, 50); Sci. Res. Soc. Am; Nat. Asn. Corrosion Eng. Electrodeposition; corrosion. Address: Route 17, Fox Park Rd, Knoxville, TN 37921.

GRIEVE, A(RTHUR) D(OUGLAS), b. Wilton Grove, Ont, Sept. 8, 06; m. 33; c. 2. PHYSICAL CHEMISTRY. B.A, Western Ontario, 29; Ph.D.(phys. chem), McGill, 32. Demonstr. chem, Toronto, 29-30; McGill, 30-32; chemist, AYERST LABS, 32-39, chief control lab, 39-43, asst. dir. res. & biol. labs, 43-47, dir. qual. control, 47-67, v.pres, 67-71, CONSULT, 71- Am. Soc. Qual. Control; fel. Chem. Inst. Can. Pharmaceutical analysis. Address: Ayerst Labs, Box 6115, Montreal, Que, Can.

GRIEVE, WILLIAM GEORGE, b. Manor, Pa, Apr. 19, 15; m. 38; c. 3. FORESTRY. B.S, Pa. State, 37. Asst. chief info. & ed, Va. Div. Forestry, 48-49; nursery supt, TENN. VALLEY AUTH, 49-50, area forester, 50-52, 53-56, supvr. forest nurseries, 56-61, forestry rep, 61-62, asst. chief forest mgt. br, 62-66, acting chief, 66-67, chief, 67-70, ASST. DIR, DIV. FORESTRY, FISHERIES & WILDLIFE DEVELOP, 70- U.S.N, 43-46, 52-53, Res, 53-, Comdr. Soc. Am. Foresters. Forestry administration; forest management; reforestation; watershed protection. Address: Division of Forestry, Fisheries & Wildlife Development, Tennessee Valley Authority Forestry Bldg, Norris, TN 37828.

GRIEVES, ROBERT BELANGER, b. Evanston, Ill, Oct. 15, 35; m. 66; c. 2. CHEMICAL & SANITARY ENGINEERING. B.A, Northwest. Univ, 56, M.S, 59, Ph.D.(chem. eng), 62. Asst. prof. civil eng, Northwest. Univ, 61-63; asst. prof, Ill. Inst. Technol, 63-64, assoc. prof, 64-67; PROF. CHEM. ENG. & CHMN. DEPT, UNIV. KY, 67-, DIR. GRAD. TRAINING PROG. AIR POLLUTION CONTROL, 68-, DIR. PROG. WATER POLLUTION CONTROL, 71- Am. Inst. Chem. Eng; Water Pollution Control Fedn. Critical point of multicomponent hydrocarbon mixtures; foam fractionation for industrial water and waste treatment; biological waste treatment; chemical separations; membrane processes. Address: Dept. of Chemical Engineering, University of Kentucky, Lexington, KY 40506.

GRIFF, LILLIAN L(ENA) GOLUB, b. N.Y.C, Oct. 13, 29; m. 63; c. 2. CHEMICAL ENGINEERING. B.Ch.E, Syracuse, 51, M.Ch.E, 52; univ. scholar, Ohio State, 55-56, Ph.D.(chem. eng), 57. Asst. chem. eng, Syracuse, 51-52; corrosion engr. res. & develop, Colgate Palmolive Co, 52-54; instr. chem. eng, Ohio State, 57; res. engr. chem. processes, Shell Oil Co, 57-62, consult, 63-68. Instr, Houston, 58-59, 60-62; Pennsylvania, 63; summer asst, Ohio State, 55-57. Sci. Res. Soc. Am. Kinetics; corrosion; chemical process development. Address: 1108 Greenwood Ave, Wyncote, PA 19095.

GRIFFEL, MAURICE, b. Brooklyn, N.Y, Mar. 10, 19; m. 64. PHYSICAL CHEMISTRY. B.S, City Col. New York, 39; M.S, Michigan, 40, fel, 40-41; Atomic Energy Comn. fel, Chicago, 47-49, Ph.D.(chem), 49. Asst. prof. chem, Iowa State Col, 49-55; adv. chemist, Westinghouse Elec. Corp, 55-57; vis. scientist, Saclay Nuclear Res. Ctr, France, 57-58; prof. chem, U.S. Naval Postgrad. Sch, 59-62; mem. staff, Inst. Defense Anal, 62-65; vis. res. assoc. chem, Univ. Pa, 65-67; DIR. DIV. PROF. EDUC, N.Y. STATE EDUC. DEPT, 67- Vis. lectr, Johns Hopkins Univ, 53-54. Consult, Nat. Bur. Standards, 51; Lawrence Radiation Lab, Univ. Calif, Berkeley, 59- U.S.A.A.F, 43-46, 1st Lt. AAAS; Am. Chem. Soc; Am. Phys. Soc; Faraday

Soc. Magnetism and magnetic resonance; thermodynamics; low temperature physics; kinetics of fast reactions; biochemistry. Address: 10 Sage Hill Lane, Albany, NY 12204.

GRIFFEL, WILLIAM, b. Lwow, Poland, May 24, 07; U.S. citizen; m. 34; c. 1. APPLIED MECHANICS. M.E, Toulouse, 30. Design engr, Worthington Corp, N.J, 46-53; chief engr, Easten Design Co, 53-58; stress engr, Bendix Aviation Corp, 58-59; phys. sci. analyst, PICATINNY ARSENAL, DOVER, 59-70, SUPVR, MECH. ENG, 70- 15 Commendation awards, U.S. Dept. Army. Am. Soc. Mech. Eng. Strength of materials. Address: 18-06 Jordan Rd, Fairlawn, NJ 07410.

GRIFFEN, WARD O, JR, b. New Orleans, La, July 21, 28; m. 52; c. 7. SURGERY. A.B, Princeton, 48; M.D, Cornell, 53; Ph.D.(surg), Minnesota, Minneapolis, 63. Instr. surg, med. col, Univ. Minn, Minneapolis, 62-63, asst. prof, 63-65; assoc. prof. surg, physiol. & biophys, MED. SCH, UNIV. KY, 65-66, PROF. SURG. & CHMN. DEPT, 67- U.S. Pub. Health Serv. fel, 61-63; Markle scholar acad. med, 62-67. U.S.N, 55-57, Res, 57-, Lt. Comdr. Soc. Exp. Biol. & Med. Gastrointestinal and hepatic physiology and surgery. Address: Dept. of Surgery, University of Kentucky Medical Center, Lexington, KY 40506.

GRIFFENHAGEN, GEORGE B(ERNARD), b. Portland, Ore, June 9, 24; m. 46; c. 3. PHARMACY. B.S, Southern California, 49, M.S, 50. Dir. pharmaceut. res. & asst. gen. mgr, Nion Corp, Calif, 50-52; curator div. med. sci, U.S. Nat. Mus, Smithsonian Inst, 52-59; managing ed, Jour, AM. PHARMACEUT. ASN, 59-62, dir. div. COMMUN, 59-69, ASST. EXEC. DIR, 69-, ED, JOUR, 62-, consult. curator & archivist, 53-59. Lectr, Univ. South. Calif, 50-52; del, Int. Pharmaceut. Fedn, London Assembly, 55, Brussels Assembly, 58, Copenhagen Assembly, 60, Vienna Assembly, 62, Amsterdam Assembly, 64, Hamburg Assembly, 68, Geneva Assembly, 70; secy. gen, Pan-Am. Cong. Pharm. & Biochem, Wash, D.C, 57, 1st v.pres, Pan-Am. Pharm. Fedn, 63-72; proj. adminr, U.S. Pub. Health Serv; secy. organizing comn, Int. Cong. Pharmaceut. Sci, Wash, D.C, 71. Squibb Pan-Am. Pharmaceut. & Biochem. Award, 63. C.Eng, U.S.A, 42-45. Am. Asn. Hist. Pharm; hon. mem, Mex, Chilean & Arg. Pharmaceut. Asn; Int. Pharmaceut. Fedn; Int. Acad. Hist. Pharm.(treas, 70-); Pharmaceut. & Biochem. Asn. Arg. History of pharmacy and medical science; pharmaceutical journalism; pharmaceutical philately. Address: American Pharmaceutical Association, 2215 Constitution Ave. N.W, Washington, DC 20037.

GRIFFIN, AMOS CLARK, b. Newton, Utah, May 16, 18; m. 39; c. 5. BIOCHEMISTRY. B.S, Utah State Agr. Col, 39; M.S, Mich. State Col, 41; California, 41-42; Ph.D.(biochem), Wisconsin, 47. Asst. biochem, Mich. State Col, 39-41; asst. cancer res, Wisconsin, 46-47; Stanford, 47-48, instr. BIOCHEM, 48-49, asst. prof, 49-52, assoc. prof, 52-54; head dept, UNIV. TEX. M.D. ANDERSON HOSP. & TUMOR INST, 54-62, AM. CANCER SOC. PROF, 62- Head biochem. dept, col. med, Baylor Univ, 55-61. C.W.S, U.S.A, 42-46. Am. Asn. Cancer Res; Am. Soc. Biol. Chem. Cancer research; carcinogenesis; nucleoproteins; protein synthesis. Address: Dept. of Biochemistry, University of Texas M.D. Anderson Hospital & Tumor Institute, Houston, TX 77025.

GRIFFIN, BEVERLY, b. Delhi, La, Jan. 23, 30; m. ORGANIC & BIOCHEMISTRY. B.S, Baylor, 51; Ph.D.(chem), Virginia, 55; Marshall scholar & Ph.D, Cambridge, 58. Asst. prof. chem, Mt. Holyoke Col, 58-61; FEL. & LECTR, GIRTON COL, CAMBRIDGE UNIV, 61- Am. Chem. Soc; The Chem. Soc. Chemistry of natural products; synthetic studies on natural and unnatural precursors of nucleic acids; structure and synthesis of polynucleotides. Address: 150 Huntingdon Rd, Cambridge, Eng.

GRIFFIN, CHARLES CAMPBELL, b. Phila, Pa, July 23, 38; m. 60; c. 2. BIOCHEMISTRY. A.B, Catholic Univ, 60; Ph.D.(biochem), Hopkins, 69. Res. assoc. BIOCHEM, Armed Forces Inst. Path, 60-64; ASST. PROF, MIAMI UNIV, 68- AAAS; Am. Chem. Soc. Mechanisms of enzyme action. Address: Dept. of Chemistry, Miami University, Oxford, OH 45056.

GRIFFIN, CHARLES FRANK, b. Slaton, Tex, Nov. 2, 35; m. 58; c. 3. PHYSICS. B.S, Tex. Tech. Col, 59, M.S, 61; Ph.D.(physics), Ohio State, 64. Asst. PHYSICS, Tex. Tech. Col, 59-61; Ohio State, 61-64; assoc. prof, Sam Houston State Col, 64-67; asst. prof, UNIV. AKRON, 67-70, ASSOC. PROF, 70- Am. Phys. Soc; Am. Asn. Physics Teachers. Nuclear magnetic resonance. Address: 521 Moreley Ave, Akron, OH 44320.

GRIFFIN, CLAIBOURNE E(UGENE), JR, b. Rocky Mount, N.C, Oct. 15, 29; m. 59; c. 2. ORGANIC CHEMISTRY. B.A, Princeton, 51; M.S, Virginia, 53, E.I. du Pont de Nemours & Co. fel, 54-55, Ph.D.(chem), 55. Instr. chem, Virginia, 53-55, res. assoc. biochem, sch. med, 55; U.S. Pub. Health Serv. res. fel. CHEM, Cambridge, 55-57; instr, Univ. Pittsburgh, 57-58, asst. prof, 58-62, assoc. prof, 62-66, prof, 66-69; PROF. & CHMN. DEPT, UNIV. TOLEDO, 69- Consult, Stauffer Chem. Co, 62- Am. Chem. Soc; The Chem. Soc. Synthesis and reactions of organophosphorus compounds; organic photochemistry; nuclear magnetic resonance spectroscopy. Address: Dept. of Chemistry, University of Toledo, Toledo, OH 43606.

GRIFFIN, CLAUDE LANE, b. Lebanon, Mo, Nov. 9, 37; m. 62; c. 3. PHARMACOLOGY. B.S, Missouri, Kansas City, 61, M.S, 63; Ph.D.(cardiovasc. pharmacol), Oregon State, 66. Fel, Worcester Found. Exp. Biol, 65-66; sr. scientist, Smith Kline & French Labs, 66-67; group res. leader, 67-68, asst. dir, 69-70; ASSOC. DIR. RES. PLANNING, MERRELL-NAT. LABS, 70- Mem. coun. high blood pressure res, Am. Heart Asn, 67. Cardiovascular pharmacology; metabolism of cardiac glycosides. Address: Merrell-National Labs, 110 E. Amity, Cincinnati, OH 45215.

GRIFFIN, DALE M(ILLER), JR, b. Alamosa, Colo, Sept. 24, 20; m. 44; c. 4. ORGANIC CHEMISTRY. A.B, Colorado, 42, M.A, 45, Ph.D.(org. chem), 51. Chemist, Eastman Kodak Co, 44-46; asst. prof. chem, Colo. Agr. & Mech. Col, 46-48; CHEMIST, AZO LAB, CHAMBERS WORKS, E.I. DU PONT DE NEMOURS & CO, INC, 50- Am. Chem. Soc; Am. Inst. Chem. Basic dyes and intermediates. Address: Azo Lab, Chambers Works, E.I. du Pont de Nemours & Co, Inc, Deepwater, NJ 08023.

GRIFFIN, DANA GOVE, III, b. Ft. Worth, Tex, Nov. 9, 38; m. 64. BOTANY. B.S, Tex. Tech. Col, 61, M.S, 62; summer, Marine Biol. Lab, Woods Hole, 61; Ph.D.(bot), Tennessee, 65. Res. asst. BOT, Tex. Tech. Col. 60-62; instr, Univ. Tenn, 65, ASST. PROF, 66-67; UNIV. FLA, 67- Fulbright lectr, Peru, 65-66. Bot. Soc. Am; Phycol. Soc. Am; Am. Soc. Plant Taxon; Int. Phycol. Soc; Int. Asn. Plant Taxon; Bot. Soc. Mex; Am. Bryol. & Lichenological Soc. Taxonomy and ecology of the lower plants; taxonomy of bryophytes, especially of tropical mosses. Address: Dept. of Botany, University of Florida, Gainesville, FL 32601.

GRIFFIN, DAVID H, b. Buffalo, N.Y, Mar. 13, 37; m. 60; m. 3. BOTANY. B.S, State Univ. N.Y. Col. Forestry, 59; Nat. Sci. Found. fel, Univ. Calif, Berkeley, 59-61, M.A, 60, Ph.D.(bot), 63. Res. fel. biol, Calif. Inst. Technol, 63-64; asst. prof. BOT, Univ. Iowa, 64-68; STATE UNIV. N.Y. COL. FORESTRY, SYRACUSE UNIV, 68-71, ASSOC. PROF, 71- Air Force Off. Sci. Res. fel, 63-64; vis. asst. prof. biol, Univ. Ore, summer, 64. Bot. Soc. Am; Am. Soc. Microbiol; Mycol. Soc. Am; Soc. Gen. Microbiol. Physiology and biochemistry of development in fungi. Address: Dept. of Forest Botany, State University of New York College of Forestry at Syracuse University, Syracuse, NY 13210.

GRIFFIN, D(ONALD) N(EILSON), b. Boston, Mass, June 2, 23; div; c. 5. CHEMISTRY. B.A, Wesleyan, 44; fel, inst. gas tech, Ill. Inst. Tech, 46-47. Res. engr, jet propulsion lab, Calif. Inst. Tech, 47-52; tech. rep, Mathieson Chem. Corp, 52-53, proj. mgr, res. dept, 53-54, govt. chem. res. dept, Olin Mathieson Chem. Corp, 54-55, assoc. dir. liquid propellant appln. res, 55-57, mil. chem. res, high energy fuels div, 57-58, assoc. dir. appln. res, energy div, 58-59; pres, Technoprod, Inc, 59-62, gen. mgr, Technoprod. Div, Quantic Industs Inc, Calif, 62-63, dir. eng, Pelmec Div, 62-67, gen. mgr, 67-69; exec. v.pres, ZETA LABS. INC, MOUNTAIN VIEW, 69-70, PRES, 70- Consult, Wham-O Mfg. Co, Calif, 58; Chandler Evans Corp, Conn, 59-; U.S. Dept. Defense, D.C, 59-; Frankford Arsenal, Pa, 59- U.S.N.R, 44-46, Res, 46-54, Lt. Am. Chem. Soc; assoc. fel. Am. Inst. Aeronaut. & Astronaut; Combustion Inst. Rocket propulsion; liquid propellants; liquid propellant guns; hypervelocity; combustion, detonation; electroexplosive and cartridge actuated devices. Address: 2803 Medford Ave, Redwood City, CA 94061.

GRIFFIN, DONALD R(EDFIELD), b. Southampton, N.Y, Aug. 3, 15; m. 41; c. 4. BIOLOGY. B.S, Harvard, 38, M.A, 40, jr. fel, 40-41, Ph.D.(biol), 42. Asst. biol, Harvard, 38-40, res. assoc, psychol-acoustic lab, fatigue lab. & biol. labs, 42-45; asst. prof. zool, Cornell, 46-47, assoc. prof, 47-52, prof, 52-53; Harvard, 53-65, chmn. dept. BIOL, 62-65; PROF, ROCKEFELLER UNIV, 65- Lectr, Lowell Inst, 42; Sigma Xi nat. lectr, 52; sr. res. zoologist, N.Y. Zool. Soc, 65- Nat. Acad. Sci; Am. Physiol. Soc; Am. Soc. Zool; Ecol. Soc. Am; Soc. Gen. Physiol; Am. Soc. Mammal; Am. Ornith Union; Am. Acad. Arts & Sci. Sensory basis of animal navigation; acoustic orientation; comparative sensory physiology; animal behavior. Address: Rockefeller University, New York, NY 10021.

GRIFFIN, DONALD S(PRAY), b. Washington, D.C, June 23, 29; m. 52; c. 4. APPLIED MECHANICS. B.M.E, Cornell, 52; Westinghouse fel, Stanford, 52-53, M.S, 53, Ph.D.(eng. mech), 59. Sr. engr, BETTIS ATOMIC POWER LAB, WESTINGHOUSE ELEC. CORP, 59-64, supvr. anal. mech, 64-65, MGR. STRUCT. MECH, 65- U.S.N. Civil Eng.C, 53-56, Lt. Am. Soc. Mech. Eng. Development of numerical methods and computer programs for structural analysis; development of design procedures and criteria for structural analysis. Address: Bettis Atomic Power Lab, Westinghouse Electric Corp, Box 79, West Mifflin, PA 15122.

GRIFFIN, EDMOND EUGENE, b. Marshall, Ark, June 5, 30; m. 54; c. 2. RADIATION BIOLOGY, PHYSIOLOGY. B.S.Ed, Arkansas, 62; M.S, Tennessee, 64, Nat. Insts. Health fel, 64-69, Ph.D.(radiation biol), 69. Teacher, high sch, Ark, 52-53; radiation safety monitor, Los Alamos Sci. Lab, California, 53-56, technician, 56-61; FEL, SCH. MED. & DENT, UNIV. ROCHESTER, 69- AAAS; Am. Soc. Zool. Actions of thyroid hormones on liver metabolism; influence of thyroxine on cellular response to x-irradiation. Address: University of Rochester School of Medicine & Dentistry, Rochester, NY 14620.

GRIFFIN, EDWARD L(AWRENCE), JR, b. Washington, D.C, Jan. 9, 19; m. 41; c. 2. CHEMICAL ENGINEERING. B.Ch, Cornell, 40, Ch.E, 41. Chem. engr, James Lees & Sons, Pa, 41-42; East. Regional res. lab, bur. agr. & indust. chem, U.S. DEPT. AGR, 42-57; CHIEF, ENG. & DEVELOP. LAB, NORTH. MKT. & NUTRIT. RES. DIV, 57- AAAS; Am. Chem. Soc; Am. Oil Chem. Soc; Am. Asn. Cereal Chem; Inst. Food Technol; Am. Inst. Chem. Eng. Chemical engineering pilot plant studies; rubber from guayule and Kok-Saghyz; volatile flavor from fruit juices; acrylic ester polymerization; production of allyl-sucrose; tanning material from canaigre; extraction of rutin from dried plants; cereal crop and oilseed utilization research. Address: 4206 Keenland Ave, Peoria, IL 61614.

GRIFFIN, EMERY E, JR, b. Houston, Tex, Feb. 9, 33. PHYSICS. B.S, Texas, 54; Ph.D, Rochester, 62. Res. scientist, defense res. lab, Texas, 53-56; teaching asst, Rochester, 56-61; sr. engr. res, N.Am. Aviation, Inc, 61-62, res. specialist, 62-63, sr. tech. specialist, 63-64, group scientist, Calif, 64-69; DEVELOP. MGR, LAWNDALE LAB, TRW INC, 69- Low energy nuclear physics; ionizing radiation effects on semiconductors. Address: Lawndale Lab, TRW Inc, 14520 Aviation Blvd, Lawndale, CA 90260.

GRIFFIN, ERNEST LYLE, b. Tampa, Fla, May 25, 21. MATHEMATICS. B.A, Emory, 43; M.S, Chicago, 47, Atomic Energy Comn. fel, 48-51, Ph.D. (math), 52. Instr. math, Michigan, 52-57, asst. prof, 57-62; assoc. ed, Math. Rev, 62-63; vis. assoc. prof. MATH, Univ. Pa, 63-66, assoc. prof, 66-67; PROF, LA. STATE UNIV, BATON ROUGE, 67- Vis. asst. prof, Columbia Univ, 57-58. U.S.N.R, 43-46, Lt.(jg). Am. Math. Soc. Theory of algebras of operators on Hilbert spaces and applications to representations of locally compact groups and quantum physics; classification and properties of von-Neumann algebras. Address: Dept. of Mathematics, Louisiana State University, Baton Rouge, LA 70803.

GRIFFIN, GARY J, b. Glen Cove, N.Y, Dec. 23, 37; m. 59; c. 3. BIOLOGY. B.S, Colo. State, 59, M.S, 61, Nat. Defense Educ. Act fel. & Ph.D.(plant path), 62. Plant pathologist, Agr. Res. Serv, U.S. Dept. Agr, 62-63; asst. prof. biol, Morehead State Col, 63-65, assoc. prof, 65-67; asst. prof. PLANT PATH. & PHYSIOL, VA. POLYTECH. INST. & STATE UNIV, 67-70, ASSOC. PROF, 70- Am. Phytopath. Soc. Soil microbiology; root diseases. Address: Dept. of Plant Pathology & Physiology, Virginia Polytechnic Institute & State University, Blacksburg, VA 24061.

GRIFFIN, GARY W(ALTER), b. Pasadena, Calif, Nov. 12, 31; m; c. 4. ORGANIC CHEMISTRY. B.A, Pomona Col, 53; Union Carbide Corp. fel, Illinois, 54-56, Ph.D, 57. Res. chemist, Humble Oil & Ref. Co, Tex, 56-58; instr. CHEM, Yale, 58-59, asst. prof, 59-63; assoc. prof, Tulane, 63-66; LA. STATE UNIV, NEW ORLEANS, 66-67, PROF, 67-, vis. prof, 65-66. Res. grants, Res. Corp, 60-61; Nat. Sci. Found, 60-62, 64-73; Army Res. Off, 61-69; George Sheffield Fund, 62-63; Nat. Insts. Health, 63-70; NATO travel fel, Strasbourg, France, 64; Am. Cancer Asn, 66, 69; Petrol Res. Fund, 66-69, 71-73; Nat. Sci. Found. int. training grant, Netherlands 67, Japan, 71; Merck, Sharp & Dohme, 68-71; La. State Univ. res. coun. int. training, 71. Summers, vis. prof, Humble Oil & Ref. Co, 62, Univ. Illinois, 65, vis. lectr, La. State, 65; vis. prof, inst. for lipid res, Baylor Col. Med, Houston, 71-72. Consult, Am. Cyanamid Co, 59-61; South. New Eng. Ultraviolet Co, Conn, 62-63; Minn. Mining & Mfg. Co, 63- Am. Chem. Soc; fel. Res. Inst. Chemists; The Chem. Soc; Int. Asn. Heterocyclic Chem. Small ring chemistry; carbene chemistry; solution and solid state photochemistry; electrochemistry; non benzenoid aromatic chemistry. Address: Dept. of Chemistry, Louisiana State University in New Orleans, New Orleans, LA 70122.

GRIFFIN, GEORGE MELVIN, JR, b. Baltimore, Md, Apr. 14, 28; m. 50; c. 2. MARINE GEOLOGY, SEDIMENTOLOGY. B.A, Univ. N.C, 52, M.S, 54; Ph.D. (geol), Rice Univ, 60. Res. geologist clay petrol, explor. & prod. res. div, Shell Develop. Co, 54-65; assoc. prof. geol, Dayton Campus, Miami-Ohio State Univ, 65-66; proj. leader, world wide tech. serv. ctr, Gulf Oil Corp, 66-67; assoc. prof. GEOL, Univ. South. Fla, 67-70; PROF, UNIV. FLA, 70- U.S.N.A.F, 46-51, Ens. Geol. Soc. Am; Am. Asn. Petrol. Geol; Soc. Econ. Paleont. & Mineral. Geologic significance of mineral assemblages in sedimentary rocks, especially clay minerals; geothermal gradients; turbidity in coastal waters; sedimentation processes and products. Address: Dept. of Geology, University of Florida, Gainesville, FL 32601.

GRIFFIN, GEORGE R(OBERT), b. Indianapolis, Ind, Sept. 2, 14; m. 38; c. 4. ORGANIC CHEMISTRY. B.S, Indiana, 36; fel, Boston, 36-38, M.S, 38; fel, Mass. Inst. Tech, 38-40, Little fel, 40-41, Ph.D.(org. chem), 41. Res. chemist, Am. Cyanamid Co, 41-44; group leader Dewey & Almy Chem. Co, 44-48, mgr, polymer res, Cry-O-Vac. div, 51-54; asst. prof. org. chem, Rhode Island, 48-51; PROF. CHEM. & CHMN. DIV, LOWELL TECH. INST, 54- Consult, Dewey & Almy Chem. Co, 48-51; Avco Corp, 59-68. Am. Chem. Soc. Acrylate esters; surfactants; dispersing agents; isocyanatis; high polymers. Address: Middlesex Rd, Box 105, Tyngsboro, MA 01879.

GRIFFIN, GERALD D, b. Escalante, Utah, May 31, 27; m. 52; c. 3. PLANT NEMATOLOGY & PATHOLOGY. B.S, Utah, 53, M.S, 56; Ph.D.(plant path), Wisconsin, 63. NEMATOLOGIST, AGR. RES. SERV, U.S. DEPT. AGR, Utah, 56-59, Wis, 59-63, UTAH STATE UNIV, 63- U.S.A, 45-47, Res, 53-56, 2nd Lt. AAAS; Am. Phytopath. Soc; Soc. Nematol. Nematode vectors of plant viruses; biology and control of plant-parasitic nematodes associated with alfalfa, stone fruit, potatoes and sugarbeets. Address: Crops Research Lab, Utah State University, Logan, UT 84321.

GRIFFIN, HENRY C(LAUDE), b. Greenville, S.C, Feb. 14, 37; m. 60; c. 2. NUCLEAR CHEMISTRY. B.S, Davidson Col, 58; Ph.D.(nuclear chem), Mass. Inst. Tech, 62. Resident res. assoc. nuclear chem, Argonne Nat. Lab, 62-64; asst. prof. NUCLEAR CHEM. & RADIOCHEM, UNIV. MICH, ANN ARBOR, 64-70, ASSOC. PROF, 70- Guest scientist, Swiss Fed. Inst. for Reactor Res, 71-72. AAAS; Am. Phys. Soc; Am. Chem. Soc. Nuclear fission; nuclear spectroscopy; nuclear reactions; radiochemistry; photoelectron spectroscopy. Address: Dept. of Chemistry, University of Michigan, Ann Arbor, MI 48104.

GRIFFIN, JAMES BENJAMIN, b. Eatonton, Ga, Dec. 22, 33; m. 59; c. 2. BIOCHEMISTRY. B.A, Emory, 56; M.A, Duke, 62; Nat. Insts. Health fel, North Carolina, 62-64, Ph.D.(biochem), 65. Fel. BIOCHEM, Brandeis, 64-67; ASST. PROF, CTR. RES. PHARMACOL. & TOXICOL, UNIV. N.C, CHAPEL HILL, 67- Phosphorylation products of isolated mammalian nuclei; application of electron spin resonance to enzyme studies; enzymology of drug metabolism. Address: Center for Research in Pharmacology & Toxicology, University of North Carolina at Chapel Hill, Chapel Hill, NC 27514.

GRIFFIN, JAMES EDWARD, b. Columbus, Ohio, Dec. 17, 22; m. 48; c. 3. PHYSIOLOGY. A.B, Western Md. Col, 44; M.A, Duke, 48; Ph.D.(physiol), Pennsylvania. Staff phys. therapist, Duke Univ. Hosp, 46-48; sr. phys. therapist, Vet. Admin. Hosp, Conn, 48-53; assoc. phys. ther, Pennsylvania, 53-59, asst. prof, 59-65, grad. sch. med, 64-70, assoc. prof, 65-70; PROF. & CHMN. DEPT. PHYS. THER, SCH. HEALTH & RELATED PROF, STATE UNIV. N.Y, BUFFALO, 70- AAAS; Am. Cong. Rehab. Med; Am. Phys. Ther. Asn; N.Y. Acad. Sci; Int. Soc. Med. Hydrol. & Climat. Ultrasonic movement of drugs into living tissue, in situ, especially penetrative and metabolic effects. Address: Dept. of Physical Therapy, State University of New York at Buffalo, 264 Winspear Ave, Buffalo, NY 14215.

GRIFFIN, J(AMES) J, b. Phila, Pa, Oct. 20, 30; m; c. 5. THEORETICAL PHYSICS. B.S, Villanova Col, 52; M.S, Princeton, 54, Ph.D.(physics), 56; Fulbright fel, inst. theoret. physics, Copenhagen, Denmark, 55-56. Theoret. physicist, Los Alamos Sci. Lab, 56-66; asst. prof. PHYSICS & ASTRON, UNIV. MD, COLLEGE PARK, 66-68, ASSOC. PROF, 68-, assoc. chmn. dept, 68-69. Nat. Sci. Found. fel, 59-60; vis. lectr, Univ. Wis, Madison, 65-66. AAAS; Am. Phys. Soc. Nuclear physics. Address: Dept. of Physics & Astronomy, University of Maryland, College Park, MD 20742.

GRIFFIN, JAMES RICHARD, b. Watsonville, Calif, Apr. 2, 31; m. 57; c. 2. PLANT TAXONOMY & ECOLOGY. B.S, California, Berkeley, 52, M.S, 58, Ph.D.(bot), 62. Res. forest ecol, pac. southwest forest & range exp. sta, U.S. Forest Serv, 63-67; asst. res. ecologist, MUS. VERT. ZOOL, UNIV. CALIF, BERKELEY, 67-71, ASSOC. RES. ECOLOGIST, 71- U.S.N.R, 53-56,

Lt.(jg). Ecol. Soc. Am; Soc. Am. Foresters. Biosystematics of California oaks and pines; oak woodland ecology; tree distributions. Address: Hastings Natural History Reservation, Star Route, Box 80, Carmel Valley, CA 93924.

GRIFFIN, JAMES W(ESLEY), b. Murfreesboro, Tenn, Nov. 13, 36; m. 57; c. 3. DENTISTRY; ORAL PATHOLOGY. D.D.S, Emory, 60, Am. Cancer Soc. fel, 60-61, M.S.D, 63. Nat. Insts. Health teacher trainee, 61-63; asst. prof. oral path, SCH. DENT, EMORY UNIV, 63-69, CLIN. ASSOC. ORAL MED. & PATH, 69- Dent.C, U.S.A.R, Capt. AAAS; fel. Am. Acad. Oral Path; Tissue Cult. Asn; Am. Dent. Asn; Int. Asn. Dent. Res. Herpes simplex virus. Address: Dept. of Oral Medicine & Pathology, Emory University School of Dentistry, Clifton Rd, Altanta, GA 30322.

GRIFFIN, J(OE) L(EE), b. Bass, Ark, Sept. 8, 35; m. 58; c. 2. CELL BIOLOGY. B.S, Univ. of the South, 56; Ph.D.(biol), Princeton, 59. Instr. biol, Brown, 59-61, asst. prof, 61-62; Nat. Insts. Health spec. fel. anat, Harvard Med. Sch, 62-64; RES. BIOLOGIST, ARMED FORCES INST. PATH, 64- Am. Soc. Cell Biol; Soc. Protozool; Soc. Gen. Physiol. Cell physiology; cell motility; membrane characteristics; light and electron microscopy; pathogenesis of Entamoeba and free-living amoebae. Address: Armed Forces Institute of Pathology, Washington, DC 20305.

GRIFFIN, J(OHN) DENNIS, b. Chicago, Ill, Apr. 22, 25; m. 50; c. 5. CHEMICAL ENGINEERING. B.Ch.E, Dayton, 48; fel, Iowa State Col, 48-49, Am. Cyanamid fel, 51-52, Ph.D.(chem. eng), 53. Asst, Iowa State Col, 49-53; chem. eng. trainee, DOW CHEM. CO, 53-54, chem. engr, 54-57, proj. leader, 57-58, group leader, 58, div. leader, 58-63, asst. lab. dir, 63-65, asst. tech. dir, 65-67, asst. dir. plastics res. & develop, plastics dept, 67-68, mgr. proj. coord, corp. res. & develop. dept, 68-69, MGR. STYRENE MOLDING POLYMERS RES. & DEVELOP, 69- U.S.N.R, 44-46. Am. Chem. Soc; Am. Inst. Chem. Eng; Sci. Res. Soc. Am. Cellular plastics; labor relations; polymer technology; research organization and management. Address: 5118 Highridge Ct, Midland, MI 48640.

GRIFFIN, JOHN HENRY, b. Seattle, Wash, June 26, 43; m. 65; c. 3. BIOPHYSICS, BIOCHEMISTRY. B.S, Univ. Santa Clara, 65; Nat. Insts. Health fel, Univ. Calif, Davis, 66-69, Ph.D.(biophys), 69. HELEN HAY WHITNEY FOUND. RES. FEL. BIOL. CHEM, HARVARD MED. SCH, 69- Am. Chem. Soc. Nuclear magnetic resonance and optical spectroscopy studies relating to problems of protein structure and function. Address: Dept. of Biological Chemistry, Harvard Medical School, 25 Shattuck St, Boston, MA 02115.

GRIFFIN, JOHN LEANDER, b. Toledo, Ohio, Nov. 9, 23; m. 47; c. 2. PHYSICAL CHEMISTRY. B.Eng, Toledo, 45, M.S, 53; Gen. Motors fel, Michigan, 53-57, Ph.D.(chem), 62. Jr. chemist, Chase Bag Co. Lab, 45-46; teaching fel. chem, Toledo, 46-47, instr, 47-48, 49-50; asst. anal. chemist, res. lab, Owens-Ill. Glass Co, 48-49; plant chemist, Kaylo Div, 50-51; lectr. chem, Toledo, 51-52; sr. res. chemist, GEN. MOTORS CORP, 57-69, SUPVRY. RES. CHEMIST, ELECTROCHEM. DEPT, RES. LABS, 69- Am. Chem. Soc; Electrochem. Soc; Am. Electroplaters Soc. Electrochemistry, especially electrodeposition, secondary batteries and corrosion; industrial analytical chemistry. Address: Electrochemistry Dept, Research Labs, General Motors Corp, 12 Mile & Mound Rd, Warren, MI 48090.

GRIFFIN, JOHN R(OBERT), b. Du Quoin, Ill, Apr. 21, 36; m. 57; c. 4. CHEMICAL ENGINEERING. B.S, Illinois, 59; Nat. Sci. Found. fels, Purdue, 60-61, Am. Oil Found. fel, 62, Ph.D.(chem. eng), 63. Res. chem. engr. process develop, Humble Oil & Refining Co, 63-65, ESSO RES. & ENG. CO, 65, SUPVR, polymerization process develop, 65-71, LOW DENSITY POLYETHYLENE & NEW PROD, PLASTICS RES. LAB, BAYTOWN RES. & DEVELOP. DIV, 71- Am. Inst. Chem. Eng.(A.M. White Award, 59). Applied mathematics and physics in chemical engineering; kinetics; reactor design; diffusional processes; process economics and design. Address: 225 Pin Oak Dr, Baytown, TX 77520.

GRIFFIN, KATHLEEN (MARY), b. Milwaukee, Wis, Oct. 1, 43. SPEECH PATHOLOGY, AUDIOLOGY. B.S, Univ. Wis, Madison, 65; Off. Voc. Rehab. trainership, Stanford Univ, 65-66, M.A, 66; Neurol. & Sensory Disease trainership, Univ. Ore, 68-71, Ph.D.(speech pathol. & audiol), 71. Speech clinician, Holladay Ctr. Crippled Children, Portland Pub. Schs, 66-68; speech consult, crippled childrens div, med. sch, Univ. Ore, 67; DIR. SPEECH & AUDIOL. DEPT, GLENDALE ADVENTIST HOSP, 71- Asst. prof, Calif. State Col, Los Angeles, 71- Am. Speech & Hearing Asn. Operant conditioning in stuttering and other speech and language therapy; auditory perception in cerebral palsy; thermography and speech functioning. Address: Dept. of Speech & Audiology, Glendale Adventist Hospital, 1509 Wilson Terr, Glendale, CA 91206.

GRIFFIN, LEONARD HAROLD, b. Sour Lake, Tex, June 4, 24. CHEMISTRY. B.S, Texas A&M, 48. Jr. chemist, SHELL CHEM. CO, 48-50, chemist, 50-62, SR. RES. CHEMIST, RES. & DEVELOP. LAB, INDUST. CHEM. DIV, 62- U.S.A, 43-46. Am. Chem. Soc; Am. Soc. Test. & Mat. Radiochemistry and neutron activation analysis. Address: 2104 Marshall St, Pasadena, TX 77502.

GRIFFIN, LINDSAY I(RA), JR, b. Blooming Grove, Tex, June 15, 14; m. 39; c. 2. CHEMICAL ENGINEERING. B.S, Texas, 35, M.S, 37, Ph.D, 39. Sect. head, Esso Res. Labs, ESSO RES. & ENG. CO. OF STANDARD OIL CO. (N.J), 48-55, asst. dir, 55-61, sr. staff adv, 61-66, SR. ENG. ASSOC, 66- Am. Chem. Soc; Am. Inst. Chem. Eng. Petroleum processing. Address: 25 Plymouth Rd, Summit, NJ 07901.

GRIFFIN, M. P, b. Auckland, N.Z, May 21, 39; m. 65; c. 1. ALGEBRA. B.Sc, Univ. N.Z, 59, M.Sc, 60; Can. Commonwealth scholar, Queen's Univ. (Ont), 61-63, Nat. Res. Coun. Can. scholar, 64-65, Ph.D.(math), 65. Sr. sci. off, appl. math. div, Dept. Sci. & Indust. Res, N.Z, 60-69; ASST. PROF. MATH, QUEEN'S UNIV.(ONT), 69- Commutative ring theory; algebraic number theory. Address: Dept. of Mathematics, Queen's University, Kingston, Ont, Can.

GRIFFIN, MARTIN JOHN, b. Chicago, Ill, Oct. 1, 33; m. 63; c. 4. BIOCHEMISTRY. S.B, Loyola (Ill), 55; S.M, Chicago, 57, Ph.D.(org. chem), 60. Chemist, E.I. du Pont de Nemours & Co, Del, 60-61; Nat. Insts. Health fel. biochem. with Prof. Gene M. Brown, Mass. Inst. Tech, 61-63; Nat. Insts. Health fel. genetics, med, N.Y. Univ, 63-65; ASSOC, CANCER SECT, OKLA. MED. RES. FOUND, 65-; ASSOC. PROF. BIOCHEM, SCH. MED, UNIV. OKLA, 70-, asst. prof, 65-70. Sig.C, U.S.A, 56, Res, 55-63. AAAS; Am. Chem. Soc; Am. Soc. Biol. Chem. Enzymology and mammalian regulatory mechanisms; membrane biochemistry and oncology. Address: 825 Northeast 13th St, Oklahoma City, OK 73104.

GRIFFIN, MARVIN A. OPERATIONS RESEARCH, INDUSTRIAL ENGINEERING. B.S, Auburn, 49; M.S.E, Alabama, 52; Dr.Eng, Hopkins, 60. Opers. analyst, Army Ord. Dept, Ala, 49-51; sr. proj. engr, West. Elec. Co, N.C, 52-55; chief engr, Cumberland Case Co, Tenn, 55-57; instr. opers. res, Hopkins, 57-60; chief indust. engr, Matson Navig. Co, Calif, 60-61; PROF. INDUST. ENG, UNIV. ALA, TUSCALOOSA, 61-, HEAD DEPT, 65-, COORD. COMPUT. SCI. PROG, 69- Proj. dir, NASA-Univ. Ala. contract, 62-65; Nat. Sci. Found. grant, 63-64; fel. comput. sci, Johns Hopkins Univ, 68-69; consult, private co. & States of Ala. & Tenn. U.S.N, 43-47, Res, 47-, Comdr. Opers. Res. Soc. Am; Am. Soc. Eng. Educ; Am. Statist. Asn; Am. Inst. Indust. Eng; Inst. Mgt. Sci; Asn. Comput. Mach. Industrial operations research; analysis of telemetry systems for Saturn vehicle. Address: University of Alabama College of Engineering, P.O. Box 6316, University, AL 35486.

GRIFFIN, PETER ALLAN, b. Vancouver, B.C, Feb. 10, 39; m. 68. SOLID STATE PHYSICS. B.Sc, British Columbia, 60, M.Sc, 61; Ph.D.(theoret. physics), Cornell, 65. Asst. prof. THEORET. PHYSICS, UNIV. TORONTO, 67-70, ASSOC. PROF, 70- Am. Phys. Soc; Can. Asn. Physicists. Many-body problem in solid state physics; quantum fluids. Address: Dept. of Physics, University of Toronto, Toronto 5, Ont, Can.

GRIFFIN, RALPH H(AWKINS), b. Roanoke, Va, Feb. 28, 21; m. 43; c. 3. FORESTRY. B.S, Va. Polytech, 43; M.F, Yale, 47; D.F, Duke, 56. Forester, Va. Forest Serv, 47-51; prof. forestry, Agr. & Tech. Col, N.C, 53-56; asst. prof, UNIV. MAINE, 56-59, assoc. prof, 59-68, PROF. FOREST RESOURCES, 68- U.S.A, 43-46, 1st Lt. Soc. Am. Foresters; Ecol. Soc. Am. Silviculture; forest ecology; forest influences. Address: School of Forest Resources, University of Maine, Orono, ME 04473.

GRIFFIN, RICHARD E, b. Clarkston, Utah, June 9, 22; m. 48; c. 4. AGRICULTURAL ENGINEERING. B.S, Utah State, 51, M.S, 60. Chief of irrig, S.Am. Indust, Matarazzo, 51-53; researcher, Utah State, 54; adv. agr. eng, Utah State & Govt. Iran, 55-57; farm adv, Univ. California, 57-63, technologist, 63-65; WATER RESOURCE SPECIALIST, UTAH STATE UNIV, 65- Consult, Calif-Chile prog, 63; United Fruit Co, 68-69; on assignment from Utah State Univ. to aid Govt. El Salvador conduct irrigation res, 71- U.S.A.A.F, 42-45, S/Sgt. Am. Soc. Agr. Eng. Irrigation; methods of irrigation; efficiency of applying water to the soil; management of irrigation organizations; promoting irrigation development. Address: Dept. of Irrigation, Utah State University, Logan, UT 84321.

GRIFFIN, RICHARD N(ORMAN), b. Winchester, Mass, Nov. 2, 29; m. 55; c. 3. ORGANIC CHEMISTRY. A.B, Columbia, 51, Ph.D.(org. chem), Mass. Inst. Tech, 58. RES. CHEMIST, E.I. du Pont de Nemours & Co, 57-61; SPACE DIV, GEN. ELEC. CO, 61- U.S.N, 51-54, Lt.(jg). AAAS; Am. Chem. Soc. Kinetics and mechanisms of organic reactions; photochemistry; energy transfer; radiation chemistry. Address: Space Division, General Electric Co, P.O. Box 8555, Philadelphia, PA 19101.

GRIFFIN, RODGER W, JR, b. Pittsburgh, Pa, Aug. 9, 35. ORGANIC CHEMISTRY. B.S, Mass. Inst. Tech, 57; Ph.D.(org. chem), Rochester, 60. Instr. CHEM, Harvard, 60-62; asst. prof, Univ. Calif, Berkeley, 62-65; assoc. prof, NEW COL, FLA, 65-68, PROF, 68- Vis. scholar, Stanford Univ, 70-71; consult, Electro-Mech. Res, Inc, Fla. AAAS; Am. Chem. Soc. Stereochemistry and reactions of unusual aromatic systems; charge-transfer complexes; organometallic chemistry; photochemical transformations; natural products biochemistry. Address: Natural Sciences Division, New College, Sarasota, FL 33578.

GRIFFIN, SUMNER A(LBERT), b. Ashland, N.Y, May 11, 22; m. 51; c. 3. ANIMAL HUSBANDRY. B.S, Cornell, 49; M.S, Kentucky, 50; Ph.D.(animal husb), Mich. State, 55. Instr. animal husb, Mich. State, 52-55; mgr. animal health & nutrit, Mallinckrodt Chem. Works, 55-57; ASSOC. PROF. ANIMAL HUSB. & VET. SCI, UNIV. TENN, KNOXVILLE, 57- Consult, Oak Ridge Nat. Lab. U.S.A.A.F, 42-45. Am. Soc. Animal Sci; Animal Nutrit. Res. Coun. Swine nutrition and physiology. Address: Dept. of Animal Husbandry, University of Tennessee, Knoxville, TN 37916.

GRIFFIN, THOMAS P(ONTON), b. Waelder, Tex, June 13, 23; m. 45; c. 1. VIROLOGY. D.V.M, Agr. & Mech. Col, Tex, 50; M.S, Wisconsin, 54. Vet. off, U.S. Air Force, 50-54, vet. virologist, epidemiol. flight, P.R, 54-56, Armed Forces Inst. Path, 56-58; hq. comd, 58-60, mem. staff, comd. & staff Col, Air Univ, 60-61, U.S. Air Force Hosp, 61-64, hq. comd, 64-69; PROF. SERV. REP, HILL'S DIV, RIVIANA FOODS, TOPEKA, KANS, 71- Dipl, Am. Bd. Vet. Pub. Health, 50. U.S.A.A.F, 42-45, U.S.A.F, 50-69, Col.(Ret); Air Medal & Oak Leaves, 44. Am. Vet. Med. Asn. Veterinary virology; tissue culture; infectious bovine rhinotracheitis; vesicular stomatitis; mucosal disease. Address: 11909 Charles Rd, Silver Spring, MD 20906.

GRIFFIN, T(HOMAS) SCOTT, b. Kalispell, Mont, Apr. 15, 43; m. 68; c. 1. ORGANIC CHEMISTRY. B.A, Univ. Calif, Santa Barbara, 66; fel, Univ. Calif, Los Angeles, 69-70, Ph.D.(chem), 70. Res. chemist, with Prof. T.A. Geissman, Univ. Calif, Los Angeles, 70-71; RES. CHEMIST, DIV. MED. CHEM, WALTER REED ARMY INST. RES, 71- U.S.A, 71-, 1st Lt. Am. Chem. Soc. Preparation of organosulfur compounds of medicinal interest; isolation and structure determination of natural products; new reactions in organosulfur and organoselenium chemistry; pharmaceutical chemistry. Address: Division of Medicinal Chemistry, Walter Reed Army Institute of Research, Washington, DC 20012.

GRIFFIN, TRAVIS BARTON, b. Trinidad, Tex, Apr. 30, 34; m. 56; c. 3. BIOCHEMISTRY. B.S, Texas A&M, 57, M.S, 61, Ph.D.(biochem), 66. ASST. PROF. biochem, Tex. A&M Univ, 65-69; TOXICOL, INST. EXP. PATH. & TOXICOL, ALBANY MED. COL, 69- U.S.A, 57-59, Capt. AAAS; Am.

Chem. Soc. Enzymology; protein chemistry; toxicology of environmental chemicals. Address: Institute of Experimental Pathology & Toxicology, Albany Medical College, Albany, NY 12208.

GRIFFIN, WILLIAM D(ALLAS), b. Plainfield, N.J, Jan. 1, 25; m. 47; c. 6. ORGANIC CHEMISTRY. B.S, Rutgers Assoc. chemist, CENT. RES. LAB, Allied Chem. & Dye Corp, 48-52, res. chemist, 52-58, ALLIED CHEM. CORP, 58-59, GROUP LEADER, 59- U.S.A.A.F, 43-45, Res, 45-53, Lt. Process development. Address: 35 Terry Dr, Morristown, NJ 07960.

GRIFFIN, WILLIAM THOMAS, b. Thompson, Mo, May 13, 32; m. 52; c. 3. OBSTETRICS & GYNECOLOGY. M.D, Univ. Mo-Columbia, 59. Resident physician, sch. med, UNIV. MO-COLUMBIA, 60-63, instr. OBSTET. & GYNEC, 63-64, asst. prof, 64-67, ASSOC. PROF, 67-, ATTEND. OBSTETRICIAN & GYNECOLOGIST, MED. CTR, 63- Consult. gynecologist, Fifth Army, Ft. Leonard Wood, Mo, 69- Dipl, Am. Bd. Obstet. & Gynec, 67. Med.C, U.S.A.R, 53-54, Maj. Am. Col. Obstet. & Gynec; Am. Med. Asn; Asn. Profs. Gynec. & Obstet; Am. Fertil. Soc; Am. Col. Surg. Urinary incontinence; cancer control. Address: Dept. of Obstetrics & Gynecology, University of Missouri-Columbia, Columbia, MO 65201.

GRIFFING, DAVID F(RANCIS), b. Nanking, China, Feb. 23, 26; U.S. citizen; m. 49; c. 2. SOLID STATE PHYSICS. A.B, Miami (Ohio), 49, M.A, 50; Ph.D.(physics), Illinois, Urbana, 56. PROF. PHYSICS, MIAMI UNIV, 56- U.S.A, 44-46, S/Sgt. Am. Phys. Soc; Am. Inst. Physics; Am. Asn. Physics Teachers. Low temperature physics; nuclear orientation; radioactivity and nuclear spectroscopy; ultrasonic studies in metals. Address: Dept. of Physics, Miami University, Oxford, OH 45056.

GRIFFING, GEORGE W(ARREN), b. Smith Center, Kans, Feb. 28, 21; m. 46; c. 2. THEORETICAL PHYSICS. B.A, Ft. Hays, Kans. State Col, 46; M.A, Kansas, 48; Ph.D, Queen's (Belfast), 54. Asst. prof, East. Tenn. State Col, 50-51; chief ionospheric reactions sect, Air Force Cambridge Res. Center, 51-56; sr. physicist, Phillips Petrol. Co, 56-70; SR. PHYS. SCIENTIST, ENVIRON. PROTECTION AGENCY, 70- U.S.A.A.F, 42-45, Res, 55-, Lt. Col. Am. Phys. Soc. Atomic and molecular collisions; reactor physics; scattering of slow neutrons by gases, liquids and solids; urban pollution modeling. Address: Division of Meteorology, Air Pollution Control Office, Environmental Protection Agency, Research Triangle Park, NC 27709.

GRIFFING, J. BRUCE, b. Tempe, Ariz, Feb. 24, 19; m. 50; c. 4. GENETICS. B.S, Iowa State, 41, M.S, 47, Ph.D.(genetics), 48; Roosevelt fel, San Marcos Univ, Lima, 41-42; Chilean Pan-Am. fel, 42. Instr. genetics, Iowa State, 47-48, asst. prof, 48-53; Nat. Res. Coun. fel, Cambridge, 53-55; prin. res. off. plant indust, Commonwealth Sci. & Indust. Res. Orgn, Australia, 56-57, sr. res. fel, 57-59, sr. prin. res. scientist, 59-64, chmn. genetics sect, 60-62; MERSHON PROF. GENETICS, OHIO STATE UNIV, 65-, CHMN. DEPT, 67- U.S.A, 43-46, S/Sgt. Genetics Soc. Am; Am. Soc. Nat. Mathematical genetics; quantitative inheritance; selection theories. Address: Dept. of Genetics, Ohio State University, 1735 Neil Ave, Columbus, OH 43210.

GRIFFING, JOHN M(ALCOLM), b. Tempe, Ariz, Oct. 5, 17; m. 46; c. 3. CHEMISTRY. B.S, Iowa State Col, 41; res. scholar & Ph.D.(org. chem), Columbia, 45. Asst. chem, Columbia, 41-42, statutory asst, 42-43, chemist, Off. Sci. Res. & Develop. contract, 44-45, chemist & group leader, 45; res. chemist, exp. sta, E.I. DU PONT DE NEMOURS & CO, INC, 45-53, jr. res. assoc, exp. sta. & dacron res. lab, 53-54, res. supvr, 54-56, res. mgr, 56-59, tech. supt. nylon plant, 59-63, DIR. PIONEERING RES. LAB, TEXTILE FIBERS DEPT, 63- Am. Chem. Soc. New fibers and new fibrous products; synthetic organic chemistry; textile processing development; materials for advanced composites; ballistics and flame resistance. Address: Pioneering Research Lab, E.I. du Pont de Nemours & Co, Inc, Wilmington, DE 19898.

GRIFFING, MARGARET E(LIZABETH), b. Lexington, Ky, Aug. 9, 17. ANALYTICAL CHEMISTRY. B.S, Kentucky, 39, M.S, 40; Baker fel, Purdue, 43-44, Ph.D.(anal. chem), 44. Tech. librarian, Emery Industs, Inc, Ohio, 40-41; asst, Purdue, 41-44; fel, Nat. Cancer Found, Northwestern, 44-45; proj. leader instrumentation res, ETHYL CORP, 45-53, from supvr. anal. res. to SR. RES. ASSOC, 53- Am. Chem. Soc. Emission spectroscopy; infra-red, ultra-violet, and visible absorption spectroscopy; fuel analyses; x-ray absorption; synthesis of carcinogenic hydrocarbons; combustion chemistry. Address: 18358 Nadol Dr, Southfield, MI 48075.

GRIFFING, THOMAS C, b. Loveland, Colo, Feb. 8, 37; m. 58; c. 2. POPULATION ECOLOGY & LIMNOLOGY. B.S, Illinois, 60; M.S, Michigan, 63, Ph.D. (zool), 65. ASST. PROF. BIOL, UNIV. NOTRE DAME, 65- Water Supply & Pollution Control Admin. res. grant, 66-68. AAAS; Ecol. Soc. Am; Am. Soc. Limnol. & Oceanog. Energetics and dynamics of invertebrate populations; productivity of natural waters; water pollution and nutrient cycling; regulation of reproductive mechanisms in Hydra. Address: Dept. of Biology, University of Notre Dame, Notre Dame, IN 46556.

GRIFFING, WILLIAM JAMES, b. Manhattan, Kans, July 18, 22; m. 45; c. 4. ELECTRON MICROSCOPY, PATHOLOGY. D.V.M, Kansas State, 44, M.S, 60, Ph.D.(vet. path), 63. Private practice, Bremen, Ind, 44-59; Nat. Defense fel, Kansas State, 59-62, Nat. Insts. Health fel, 62-63; sr. pathologist, ELI LILLY & CO, 63-65, ELECTRON MICROSCOPIST, 65- AAAS; Electron Micros. Soc. Am; Am. Vet. Med. Asn; Am. Col. Vet. Toxicol; Indust. Vet. Asn. Gross, light microscopic and electron microscopic examination of the tissues of laboratory animals subjected to compounds of agriculture and therapeutic medicinals. Address: Toxicology Division, Eli Lilly & Co, Box 708, Greenfield, IN 46140.

GRIFFIOEN, ROGER D(UANE), b. Grand Rapids, Mich, Sept. 7, 34; m. 56; c. 4. NUCLEAR PHYSICS, CHEMISTRY. A.B, Calvin Col, 56; Nat. Sci. Found. fel. & Ph.D.(nuclear chem), Purdue, 60. Univ. fel, Lawrence Radiation Lab, California, 60-61; instr. PHYSICS, CALVIN COL, 61-62, asst. prof, 62-64, assoc. prof, 64-66, PROF. & CHMN. DEPT, 66- Consult, Argonne Nat. Lab, 63-67; Lawrence Radiation Lab, 69-; Nat. Sci. Found. sci. faculty fel, Fla. State Univ, 70-71. Am. Phys. Soc; Am. Asn. Physics Teachers. Nuclear fission, reactions and energy levels; alpha decay; radioactivity. Address: Dept. of Physics, Calvin College, Grand Rapids, MI 49506.

GRIFFIS, LEVAN, b. Missoula, Mont, June 30, 16; m. 41; c. 6. MECHANICS. B.S, Calif. Inst. Tech, 37, M.S, 38, fel, 38-41, Ph.D.(mech. eng), 41. Instr. civil eng, Armour Inst. Tech, 39-40, asst. prof. mech, Ill. Inst. Tech, 41-44, assoc. prof, 44-45, prof. & chmn. mech. res. & instr, 45-49; mgr. eng. mech. div, Armour Res. Found, 47-53; dir, mech. res. dept, Am. Mach. & Foundry Co, Ill, 53-56; mgr. & dir, res. ctr, Borg-Warner Corp, 56-59; prof. mech. eng. & dean eng, Rice Univ, 59-62; v.pres. & dir, Southwest Res. Inst, 62-64; PROF. CIVIL ENG. & SOLID MECH. & DIR. RES. SERV, SOUTH. METHODIST UNIV, 65-, V.PROVOST, 68- Tech. rep, Nat. Defense Res. Cmt-Nat. Res. Coun, 43-45; Econ. Co-op. Admin. Mission 84, Austria, 52; mem. Ship Struct. Cmt, 56-59; Off. Ord. Res. Cmt, 58-62; ocean eng. comt, Nat. Acad. Eng, 65-; dir, LTV, Inc. Am. Soc. Eng. Educ; Soc. Exp. Stress Anal; Am. Inst. Aeronaut. & Astronaut. Fluid dynamics; dynamic behavior of materials; propagation of plastic flow. Address: Dept. of Civil Engineering & Solid Mechanics, Box 305, Southern Methodist University, Dallas, TX 75222.

GRIFFIS, ROBERT C, b. Cleveland, Ohio, Sept. 29, 27; m. 49; c. 5. PHYSICAL CHEMISTRY. B.S, Western Reserve, 52, M.S, 53, Nat. Sci. Found. fel, 54-55, Ph.D.(phys. chem, electrochem), 56. Instr. chem, Western Reserve, 54-56; res. assoc, lamp div, GEN. ELEC. CO, 56-60, SR. RES. ENGR, METALL. PROD. DEPT, 60- U.S.N, 45-46. Physical metallurgy; thermodynamics; oxidation; resistivity of high temperature alloys; fused salt electrolysis; inorganic synthesis at ultra high pressures and temperatures; solid state properties of diamond. Address: 625 Apple Hill Lane, Rochester, MI 48063.

GRIFFITH, B. HEROLD, b. New York, N.Y, Aug. 24, 25; m. 48; c. 2. PLASTIC & RECONSTRUCTIVE SURGERY. M.D, Yale, 48. Intern, Grace-New Haven Hosp, Conn, 48-49; resident surg, Vet. Admin. Hosps, Newington, Conn, 49-50, plastic surg, Bronx, N.Y, 53-55; asst. resident, sec. surg. div, Bellevue Hosp, 52-53; asst. surgeon inpatients, New York Hosp-Cornell Med. Center, 55, sr. registr, Glasgow Royal Infirmary, Scotland, 55; resident plastic surg, New York Hosp-Cornell Med. Center, 56; res. fel, med. sch, Cornell, 56-57; assoc. SURG, NORTHWEST. UNIV, 59-62, asst. prof, 62-67, assoc. prof, 67-70, PROF, 71-, CHIEF, DIV. PLASTIC SURG, MED. SCH, 70- Private practice, 57- Mem. med. adv. comt, Nat. Paraplegia Found, 67-; chmn, Plastic Surg. Res. Coun, 68-69. Dipl, Am. Bd. Plastic Surg, 59. U.S.N.R, 50-52, Lt. AAAS; fel. Am. Asn. Plastic Surg; Am. Soc. Plastic & Reconstruct. Surg; fel. Am. Col. Surg; N.Y. Acad. Sci; Asn. Am. Med. Cols; Am. Cleft Palate Asn; assoc. Brit. Asn. Plastic Surg; fel. Royal Soc. Med. Experimental embryology; transplantation; cancer chemotherapy; physiology of flaps and grafts; wound-healing; decubitus ulcers; cleft lip and palate; tumors of the skin, head and neck. Address: 251 E. Chicago Ave, Chicago, IL 60201.

GRIFFITH, B(RAHAM) G(REY), b. Swansea, Wales, Dec. 10, 02; m. 35; c. 2. FORESTRY. B.A, British Columbia, 26, M.A, 28; M.F, Harvard, 29; fel, Washington (Seattle), 35-36, Ph.D, 38. Jr. forester, B.C, Forest Serv, 29-35; instr. FORESTRY, UNIV. B.C, 37-39, asst. prof, 40-45, assoc. prof, 45-64, prof, 64-68, EMER. PROF, 68- Can. Inst. Forestry. Silvics; forest management. Address: Faculty of Forestry, University of British Columbia, Vancouver, B.C, Can.

GRIFFITH, CECIL BAKER, b. New Lexington, Ohio, Nov. 9, 23; m. 46. PHYSICAL CHEMISTRY. B.S, Ohio, 47. Asst. div. chief, Battelle Mem. Inst, 47-55; proj. engr, Cramet, Inc, 55-58; CHIEF METALL. DEVELOP. SECT, REPUB. STEEL RES. CTR, REPUB. STEEL CORP, 58- U.S.N.R, 43-46. Am. Soc. Metals. Physical chemistry of steelmaking. Address: 17856 Bennett Rd, Cleveland, OH 44133.

GRIFFITH, DAVID R, b. Kansas City, Mo, Mar. 26, 31; m. 59; c. 1. PHYSIOLOGY, ENDOCRINOLOGY. A.B, Missouri, 53, M.S, 57, Ph.D.(physiol), 60. Nat. Insts. Health fel, 60-62; asst. prof. physiol, IOWA STATE UNIV, 62-68, ASSOC. PROF. ZOOL, 68- U.S.A, 53-55. Growth and development of mammary glands; hormones involved in milk secretion. Address: Dept. of Zoology & Entomology, Iowa State University, Ames, IA 50010.

GRIFFITH, DONAL LOUIS, b. Culver City, Calif, Oct. 27, 42. CELL PHYSIOLOGY, BIOPHYSICS. B.A, California, Los Angeles, 64, M.A, 66, Ph.D. (zool), 69. NAT. INSTS. HEALTH RES. GRANT, ZOOL, UNIV. CALIF, LOS ANGELES, 69- Locomotion of microorganisms, amoeboid galvanotaxis, cellular regeneration and growth. Address: Dept. of Zoology, University of California, Los Angeles, CA 90024.

GRIFFITH, EDWARD J(ACKSON), b. Atlanta, Ga, Apr. 4, 25; m. 46; c. 2. PHYSICAL CHEMISTRY. B.S, Howard Col, 47; M.S, Univ. Ky, 48, Ph.D. (chem), 51. Scientist, MONSANTO CO, 51-67, ADV. SCIENTIST, 67- AAAS. Inorganic chemistry; phosphates; nitrates. Address: Monsanto Co, 800 N. Lindbergh Blvd, St. Louis, MO 63166.

GRIFFITH, ELIZABETH ANN HALL, b. Wash, D.C, Feb. 3, 35; wid. ORGANOMETALLIC & PHYSICAL CHEMISTRY. A.B. & Nat. Sci. Found. fel, Pfeiffer Col, 60; M.A, Duke Univ, 63; univ. fel, Univ. S.C, 69-70, Ph.D. (phys. chem), 70. Asst. prof. chem, Jacksonville State Univ, 62-63; instr, Pfeiffer Col, 63-64; asst. prof, Campbell Col. N.C, 64-65; RES. FEL, UNIV. SASK, REGINA, 70- AAAS; Am. Chem. Soc; Am. Crystallog. Asn. Structure determination by x-ray diffraction of single crystals; synthesis and structure of organometallic compounds which are models for biologically significant systems; structure of enzyme substrate model systems. Address: Dept. of Physics, University of Saskatchewan, Regina, Sask, Can.

GRIFFITH, FRANK S(HOEMAKER), b. Salt Lake City, Utah, July 5, 07; m. 37; c. 4. ANALYTICAL & PHYSICAL CHEMISTRY. B.Sc, Montana, 29; M.Sc, Tulane, 31; Ph.D.(chem), Minnesota, 37. Res. invest, N.J. ZINC CO. OF PA, 37-59, res. supvr, 59-66, sect. chief res, 66-68, CHIEF CHEM. RES. GROUP, 68- AAAS; Am. Chem. Soc. Inorganic processes; reaction of

Leclanche cell; post-precipitation of metal sulfides; electro-winning of metals; pigments; metallurgical processes. Address: 647 Lafayette Ave, Palmerton, PA 18071.

GRIFFITH, FRANKLIN D(ELANO), b. Morrisvale, W.Va, Jan. 30, 34. BIOCHEMISTRY. B.S, West Virginia, 56; M.S, Kentucky, 60; Ph.D.(biochem), Purdue, 64. Res. assoc. biochem, Missouri, Kansas City, 63-64; mem. res. staff, HASKELL LAB, E.I. DU PONT DE NEMOURS & CO, 64-69, CHIEF INHALATION TOXICOL, 70- U.S.A, 56-59, Capt. Magnesium-fluoride interrelationships in animal nutrition; mechanism of parathyroid hormone action on bone; biochemical effects of industrial chemicals. Address: Haskell Lab, E.I. du Pont de Nemours & Co, Wilmington, DE 19898.

GRIFFITH, F(REDERICK) R(EECE), JR, b. St. Louis, Mo, June 30, 91; m. 21; c. 3. PHYSIOLOGY. A.B, Washington (St. Louis), 14, M.A, 15; Chicago, 15, 16; Ph.D.(physiol), Harvard, 23. Asst. prof. biol, Mississippi, 15-16; Southern Methodist, 16-20; teaching fel. PHYSIOL, Harvard, 20-22, instr, 22-23; assoc. prof, STATE UNIV. N.Y. BUFFALO, 23-35, prof. & head dept, 35-56, EMER. PROF, 56-; PROF. BIOL, D'YOUVILLE COL, 59- AAAS; Am. Soc. Exp. Biol; Am. Physiol. Soc; Am. Inst. Nutrit. Mechanism of the calorigenic action of adrenaline; cardiovascular action; adrenaline versus non-adrenaline; seasonal and menstrual variation of metabolic, cardiovascular and respiratory human function; index and annotated bibliography of adrenaline, adrenergic-sympathomimetic and adrenolytic-sympatholytic drugs. Address: Dept. of Biology, D'Youville College, Buffalo, NY 14201.

GRIFFITH, GAIL D, b. Detroit, Mich, Mar. 16, 34; m. 58; c. 3. BIOCHEMISTRY. B.S, Michigan Tech, 55; M.S, Mich. State, 58, Nat. Insts. Health fel, 59-60, Ph.D.(chem), 61. Med. technologist, E.W. Sparrow Hosp, Lansing, Mich, 55-59; asst. prof. chem, North. Mich. Univ, 62-69. Partic, Nat. Insts. Health res. grant, 63-65; co-prin. investr, Nat. Sci. Found. res. grant, 66- AAAS. Intermediary metabolism of alkaloids in plants, especially biosynthetic pathways leading to Nicotiana alkaloids using isotopic tracer techniques. Address: 806 W. Kaye, Marquette, MI 49855.

GRIFFITH, GORDON L(AMAR), b. Bogue, Kans, Oct. 12, 21; m. 41; c. 2. PHYSICS. B.S, Kans. State Col, 43; Ph.D.(physics), Illinois, 50. Physicist, Tenn. Eastman Corp. Div, Eastman Kodak Co, 44-45; res. physicist, res. lab, Westinghouse Elec. Corp, Pa, 49-62; assoc. prof. PHYSICS, MUSKINGUM COL, 62-66, PROF. & CHMN. DEPT, 66- Consult, Stanford Res. Inst, 55; Lawrence Radiation Lab, California, 58. Am. Phys. Soc; Am. Asn. Physics Teachers. Elastic and inelastic scattering of neutrons; x-ray scintillation spectrometry; plasma physics. Address: Dept. of Physics, Muskingum College, New Concord, OH 43762.

GRIFFITH, H. C, b. Haskell Co, Kans, Aug. 30, 17; m. 40. MATHEMATICS. A.B, Missouri, 48, M.A, 50; Ph.D.(math), Tennessee, 53. Instr. MATH, Tennessee, 53-54; Connecticut, 54-55; asst. prof, FLA. STATE UNIV, 55-58, assoc. prof, 58-68, PROF, 68- U.S.A, 43-46, 1st Lt. Am. Math. Soc; Math. Asn. Am; Soc. Indust. & Appl. Math. Topology; numerical analysis. Address: Dept. of Mathematics, Florida State University, Tallahassee, FL 32306.

GRIFFITH, JAMES H, b. Chicago, Ill, Feb. 8, 36; m. 59; c. 3. ORGANIC & POLYMER CHEMISTRY. B.S, Illinois, 59; Ph.D.(org. chem), Cornell Univ, 63. Res. assoc. polymer chem, Univ. Ariz, 62-64; res. chemist, E.I. du Pont de Nemours & Co, 64-67; sr. scientist, SHERWIN WILLIAMS CO. RES. CTR, 67-69, group supvr, 69, SECT. SUPVR, 69- U.S.A, 54-56. Am. Chem. Soc; Fedn. Socs. Paint Technol; Am. Asn. Textile Chem. & Colorists. Emulsion and solution polymerizations of vinyl and acrylic monomers; condensation polymerization of polyesters; synthesis of nitrogen containing resins; textile colorants and fabric treatment; protective and decorative coatings. Address: Sherwin-Williams Co. Research Center, 10909 S. Cottage Grove Ave, Chicago, IL 60628.

GRIFFITH, JOHN DORLAND, b. Jellico, Tenn, Mar. 22, 31; m. 61; c. 1. PSYCHIATRY, PSYCHOPHARMACOLOGY. Temple, 48-49; Chattanooga, 49-51; M.D, Tennessee, 55. Intern, Vet. Admin. Hosp, Atlanta, Ga, 55-56; res. psychiat, Tennessee, 56-59; dir. PSYCHIAT, Harriett Cohn Guid. Center, 61-63; asst. prof, med. ctr, Univ. Okla, 63-65; sch. med, Vanderbilt Univ, 65-71; ASSOC. PROF, SCH. MED, UNIV. CALIF, SAN DIEGO, 71- Dir, Ment. Health Planning, Okla, 63-65. Med.C, U.S.A.F, 59-61, Capt. AAAS; Am. Psychiat. Asn. Psychopharmacology and sociology of drug dependency; systems theory of speech and hearing mechanisms; electronic design. Address: Dept. of Psychiatry, University of California, San Diego, La Jolla, CA 92037.

GRIFFITH, JOHN E(DWARD), b. Easton, Pa, Mar. 14, 27; m. 50; c. 3. ENGINEERING MECHANICS. B.S, Pa. State, 50, M.S, 52, Du Pont fel, 54-55, Ph.D.(eng. mech), 55. Asst. prof. civil eng, Yale, 55-58; eng. mech, Florida, 58-62; assoc. prof, N.C. State, 62-64; PROF. STRUCT, MAT. & FLUIDS & CHMN. DEPT, UNIV. S.FLA, 64- Martin Co. grant, 61-62, consult, 62-; Atlantic Res. Corp, 63-; exec. chmn, Southeast. Conf. Theoret. & Appl. Physics, 70-72. U.S.N, 45-46. Am. Soc. Rheol; Am. Soc. Mech. Eng; Am. Soc. Eng. Educ; Am. Soc. Exp. Stress Anal; N.Y. Acad. Sci. Mechanics of solid propellants and ductile fracture; creep under combined stresses; mechanical failure of materials; large deformation of circular membranes under dynamic loading; mechanics of composite materials; soil mechanics. Address: College of Engineering, University of South Florida, Tampa, FL 33620.

GRIFFITH, JOHN E(MMETT), b. Gurdon, Ark, Aug. 1, 23; m. 50; c. 4. ELECTRICAL ENGINEERING. B.S, California, 50. RES. ENGR, high energy particle accelerators, Lawrence Radiation Lab, California, 50-52, nuclear physics, 52-54; ELECTRONIC COMPUT, RES. CTR, IBM CORP, 54- Mem. panel non-numerical info. processing, White House Sci. Adv. Comt, 61-62; dep. mem. astronaut. panel, Naval Res. Adv. Comt, 62-63; consult, Joint President's Sci. Adv-President's Foreign Intel. Adv. Bd. Guid. & Eval. Panel, 65-66, panel consult, President's For. Intel. Adv. Bd, 66-; consult. to chmn, Comput. Sci. & Eng. Bd, Nat. Acad. Sci, 68-; mem, Chem. Abstr. Serv. Adv. Bd, 69- IBM Outstanding Invention Award, 62, Distinguished Invention Award, 63. U.S.A.A.F. 41-45. AAAS; Am. Asn. Comput. Mach; Am. Inst. Elec. & Electronics Eng. Ultra high speed computer design theory; information retrieval. Address: Research Center, IBM Corp, P.O. Box 218, Yorktown Heights, NY 10598.

GRIFFITH, JOHN FOX, b. Seattle, Wash, Dec. 17, 25; m. 49; c. 4. BIOCHEMISTRY, TOXICOLOGY. B.A, Reed Col, 50; Du Pont fel, Iowa State Col, 53-54, Ph.D.(biochem), 54. Atomic Energy Cmn. asst. biochem, Reed Col, 49-50; asst. chem. & biochem, Iowa State Col, 50-53; res. chemist, PROCTER & GAMBLE CO, 54-58, Oil Mill Tech. Div, Buckeye Cellulose Corp, 58, toxicologist, soap prod. develop. div, 58-65, HEAD, clin. studies sect, res. div, 65-68, SAFETY & MILDNESS ASSESSMENT SECT, PACKAGED SOAP & DETERGENT DIV, 68- Adj. asst. prof, col. med, Univ. Cincinnati, 69- U.S.N.R, 44-46. AAAS; Am. Acad. Dermat; Soc. Cosmetic Chem; Soc. Toxicol; Am. Chem. Soc. Determination of amino acid residue sequences; lipide absorption and metabolism; toxicology and safety evaluation of soaps, detergents, cosmetics, industrial chemicals, and food additives; development of toxicologic test methods; human toxicology and safety evaluation. Address: Ivorydale Technical Center, Procter & Gamble Co, Spring Grove & June Sts, Cincinnati, OH 45217.

GRIFFITH, JOHN M(ACK), b. Jackson, Miss, May 7, 14; m. 37; c. 2. CIVIL ENGINEERING. B.S, Michigan, 38. Observer, U.S. Coast & Geod. Surv, Fla, Ala, Miss. & N.C, 34-35; draftsman, Miss. Hwy. Dept, 35-36; asst. civil eng, Michigan, 37-38; office engr, City Engrs. Office, Ann Arbor, Mich, 38-39; engr, W.S. Housel, 39-41; struct. designer, chief engrs. office, N.Y. Cent. R.R, Ill, 41-43; engr. flexible pavements br, Waterways Exp. Sta, Miss, 43-51; DIR. RES. & DEVELOP, ASPHALT INST, 51- Guest lectr, Columbia; Purdue; Agr. & Mech. Col. Texas; Cornell; Ga. Inst. Tech; Minnesota; Ohio State. Mem. hwy. res. bd, Nat. Acad. Sci. Am. Soc. Civil Eng; Am. Soc. Test. & Mat; Asn. Asphalt Paving Tech. Asphalt technology; engineering uses of asphaltic materials. Address: Asphalt Institute, Asphalt Institute Bldg, College Park, MD 20740.

GRIFFITH, JOHN STANLEY, b. Cambridge, Eng, July 13, 28. THEORETICAL CHEMISTRY, BIOPHYSICS. B.A, Cambridge, 49, M.A, 53, Sc.D.(theoret. chem), 61. Fel. math, King's Col, Cambridge, 56-65; prof. chem, Pennsylvania, 60-61; vis. prof, Stanford, 63; PROF. math, Manchester, 63-65; appl. math, Bedford Col, London, 65-68; CHEM, IND. UNIV, BLOOMINGTON, 68- AAAS. Quantum chemistry, especially free electron theory and ligand field theory applied in inorganic chemistry and biochemistry; neural science, especially theories of brain organization and neural networks and memory. Address: Dept. of Chemistry, Indiana University, Bloomington, IN 47401.

GRIFFITH, L(ADDIE) R(AY), b. Cory, Colo, Nov. 21, 30; m. 55; c. 3. PHYSICAL CHEMISTRY. A.B, Colorado, 52; Ph.D.(phys. chem), California, 57. Asst. chem, California, 52-54, radiation lab, 54-56; res. chemist, Calif. Res. Corp, 56-63; group supvr, Chevron Res. Co, 63-67, sr. res. assoc, 67, PROD. MGR, CHEVRON CHEM. CO, 67- Photochemistry; combustion chemistry; corrosion of materials; electrochemistry; static electricity in the petroleum industry; fuel cell research; specialty products from petroleum. Address: Chevron Chemical Co, 200 Bush St, San Francisco, CA 94120.

GRIFFITH, L(EONARD), b. Edmonton, Alta, Can, Jan. 31, 26; m. 47; c. 3. ELECTRICAL ENGINEERING. E.E, Alberta, 50. Instrument design engr, Can. Aviation Electronics, 54-56; CELANESE CHEM. CO, 56-60, group leader, systs. eng, 60-68, MGR. PROCESS ANAL, MFG. DEVELOP. DEPT, 68- R.C.N, 43-46. Instrument Soc. Am; Eng. Inst. Can. Design of special instrumentation; mathematical analysis of industrial systems. Address: Manufacturing Development Dept, Celanese Chemical Co, Box 9077, Corpus Christi, TX 78408.

GRIFFITH, LEWIS J(OHN), b. Shreve, Ohio, Jan. 13, 21; m. 50; c. 2. BACTERIOLOGY. B.Sc, Ohio State Univ, 48; M.Sc, 50, Ph.D.(bact), 53. Bacteriologist, Vet. Admin. Hosp, Butler, Pa, 53-54; chief clin. lab. serv, Vet. Admin. Hosp, Batavia, N.Y, 54-57, chief reference lab. staphylococcus res, 57-66; res. microbiologist, Vet. Admin. Hosp, Charleston, S.C, 66-67; MICROBIOLOGIST & CLIN. LAB. ADMINR, VET. ADMIN. HOSP, WILMINGTON, DEL, 67- Instr, med. sch, Univ. Rochester, 56-66; partic, WHO conf. on drug sensitivity testing, Stockholm, 64-68; vis. prof, George Washington, Univ, 67- Stitt Award, 60. U.S.A, 42-45. AAAS; Am. Soc. Microbiol; Am. Pub. Health Asn; Asn. Mil. Surg. U.S. Staphylococcus and gram-negative rod infections; phage and colicine typing; action of antibiotics; kinetics of disinfectants. Address: 2623 Deepwood Dr, Wilmington, DE 19810.

GRIFFITH, MARTIN G, b. Phila, Pa, Dec. 4, 39; m. 70. ORGANIC & PHYSICAL CHEMISTRY. B.S, Haverford Col, 61; Ph.D.(chem), Pa. State Univ, 67. CHEMIST, ESSO RES. & ENG. CO, 67- Am. Chem. Soc. High-molecular weight hydrocarbon synthesis and physical properties; computation of electronic wave functions of hydrocarbons; physical and chemical properties of additive-containing lubricating oils. Address: Box 51, Linden, NJ 07036.

GRIFFITH, MELVIN, b. Cleveland, Tenn, May 16, 34; m. 64; c. 2. NUTRITION. B.S, Tennessee, 60; M.S, Cornell, 62, Ph.D.(animal nutrit), 65. Asst. prof. POULTRY NUTRIT, LA. STATE UNIV, 65-68, ASSOC. PROF, 68- U.S.A.R, 60-, Capt. Poultry Sci. Asn. Laying hen nutrition; biological availability of phosphorus. Address: Dept. of Poultry Science, Louisiana State University, Baton Rouge, LA 70803.

GRIFFITH, MELVIN E(UGENE), b. Lawrence, Kans, Mar. 24, 12; m. 41. ENTOMOLOGY, ZOOLOGY. A.B, Kansas, 34, A.M, 35, fel, 35-38, Ph.D.(entom), 38; summers, Michigan, 37-40. Instr. zool, N.Dak. Agr. Col, 38-39, asst. prof, 39-41, assoc. prof, 41-42; malaria control entomologist, U.S. PUB. HEALTH SERV, 42-51, chief malariologist, Int. Co-op. Admin, Thailand, 51-60, regional malaria adv, Near East & S.Asia, 60-64, dep. chief malaria eradication br, U.S. AGENCY INT. DEVELOP, 64-67, chief, 67-71; CONSULT, OFF. OF HEALTH, 71-, summer assoc. dir, malaria eradication training ctr, Jamaica, 60. Assoc. prof. zool. sci, Univ. Okla, 46-52, prof, 52-56. U.S.P.H.S, 42-71, Capt. AAAS; Am. Soc. Limnol. & Oceanog; Am. Mosquito Control Asn; Entom. Soc. Am; Am. Soc. Trop. Med. & Hyg;

Am. Pub. Health Asn; Royal Soc. Trop. Med. & Hyg. Malaria eradication; medical entomology; public health. Address: 400 N Street S.W. Washington, DC 20024.

GRIFFITH, MICHAEL GREY, b. Mansfield, La, Sept. 30, 41; m. 64; c. 2. ORGANIC & TEXTILE CHEMISTRY. B.S, Northwest. Univ, 63; NASA traineeship, La. State Univ, Baton Rouge, 63-66, Nat. Insts. Health fel. & Ph.D.(chem), 67. Res. fel. chem, Univ. Minn, Minneapolis, 67-68; RES. CHEMIST, Carothers Res. Lab, Exp. Sta, E.I. DU PONT DE NEMOURS & CO, INC, 68-70, TEXTILE RES. LAB, CHESTNUT RUN, 71- Am. Chem. Soc. Fiber chemistry; free radical chemistry; nuclear magnetic resonance spectroscopy; texturing of non-cellulosic fibers; mixed shrinkage fibers. Address: 1109 S. Dolton Ct, Wilmington, DE 19810.

GRIFFITH, O. HAYES, b. Torrance, Calif, Sept. 14, 38. CHEMISTRY. B.A, California, Riverside, 60; Ph.D.(chem), Calif. Inst. Tech, 64. Nat. Acad. Sci-Nat. Res. Coun. fel. chem, Stanford Univ, 65-66; asst. prof, UNIV. ORE, 66-69, ASSOC. PROF. CHEM. & RES. ASSOC, INST. MOLECULAR BIOL, 69- Am. Chem. Soc; Am. Phys. Soc; Biophys. Soc. Physical chemistry; electron and nuclear magnetic spectroscopy; structure of membrane model systems and biological membranes. Address: Dept. of Chemistry, University of Oregon, Eugene, OR 97403.

GRIFFITH, OSCAR FRANKLIN, III, b. Winston-Salem, N.C. Dec. 16, 32; m. 50. MOLECULAR PHYSICS. B.S, Wake Forest, 61, M.A, 63; Ph.D.(physics), South Carolina, 67. ASST. PROF. PHYSICS, LA. STATE UNIV, NEW ORLEANS, 67- U.S.N, 52-54. Am. Inst. Physics. Use of electron spin resonance to study organic free radicals in both solid and liquid phase. Address: Dept. of Physics, Louisiana State University at New Orleans, Lakefront, New Orleans, LA 70122.

GRIFFITH, OWEN M(ALCOLM), b. Guyana, S.Am, Sept. 6, 28; U.S. citizen; m. 65; c. 1. BIOCHEMISTRY, BIOPHYSICS. B.S, Morgan State Col, 57; Fribourg, 57-59; M.S, N.Y. Univ, 63; Santa Clara, 64-65. Res. asst. biochem, Rockefeller Univ, 59-63; assoc. appln. chem, SPINCO DIV, BECKMAN INSTRUMENTS, INC, PALO ALTO, 63-65, APPLN. CHEM. ENGR, 65- AAAS; Am. Chem. Soc; fel. Am. Inst. Chem. Improvement of techniques for free boundary diffusion and sedimentation coefficients; advanced applications and techniques for using both preparative and analytical ultracentrifuges. Address: 2706 Pruneridge Ave, Santa Clara, CA 95051.

GRIFFITH, PETER, b. London, Eng, Sept. 23, 27; m. 59; c. 2. MECHANICAL ENGINEERING. B.S, N.Y. Univ, 50; fel, Michigan, 50-52, M.S.E, 52; Sc.D, Mass. Inst. Tech, 56. Asst, Michigan, 50-52; from asst. to PROF. MECH. ENG, MASS. INST. TECHNOL, 52- U.S.A, 45-47. Am. Soc. Mech. Eng. Heat transfer with phase change and two phase flow. Address: Dept. of Mechanical Engineering, Massachusetts Institute of Technology, Cambridge, MA 02139.

GRIFFITH, PHILLIP A, b. Danville, Ill, Dec. 29, 40; m. 60; c. 2. MATHEMATICS. B.S, Northern Michigan, 63; M.A, Missouri, 65; NASA grant, Univ. Houston, 65-67, Ph.D.(math), 68. Instr. MATH, Univ. Houston, 67-68, Nat. Sci. Found. res. grant, summer 68; instr, Univ. Chicago, 68-70; ASST. PROF, UNIV. ILL, URBANA, 70- Alfred P. Sloan fel, 71-73. Am. Math. Soc. Infinite Abelian groups; homological algebra of locally compact Abelian groups; ring theory. Address: Dept. of Mathematics, University of Illinois, Urbana, IL 61801.

GRIFFITH, ROBERT B(ELL), b. Paducah, Ky, July 22, 18; m. 44; c. 6. PLANT PHYSIOLOGY, BIOCHEMISTRY. B.S, Kentucky, 41, M.S, 43; Caleb-Dorr fel, Minnesota, 45-46; Ph.D.(plant physiol), California, 53. Asst. agronomist, agr. exp. sta, Kentucky, 44-49, 53-55, assoc. agronomist, 55-58, agronomist, 58-59; assoc. bot, Chicago, 49; chemist, Nat. Chlorophyll & Chem. Co, 51-53; consult, Brown & Williamson Tobacco Corp, 59, group leader biochem, 59-60, dir. res. admin, 60-65, dir. res. & develop, 65-69; PROF. AGRON, UNIV. KY. & DIR. TOBACCO & HEALTH RES. INST, 69- U.S.A.A.F, 42-43. Am. Chem. Soc; Am. Soc. Plant Physiol; Am. Phytopath. Soc. Plastid pigments; biochemistry and physiology of disease resistance; tobacco biochemistry, genetics and physiology. Address: Dept. of Agronomy, University of Kentucky, Lexington, KY 40506.

GRIFFITH, R(OBERT) L(EWIS), b. Bogue, Kans, Aug. 28, 15; m. 38; c. 1. CHEMISTRY. B.S, Kans. State Col, 37; Procter & Gamble fel, Ohio State, 39-40, Ph.D.(phys. chem), 40. Asst. chem, Ohio State, 37-38, phys. chem, 38-39; res. chemist, Eastman Kodak Co, N.Y, 40-43, bldg. supvr, Tenn. Eastman Corp, Oak Ridge, 43-45, res. chemist, EASTMAN KODAK CO, 45-46, res. assoc, 46-61, sr. res. assoc, 61-69, SR. LAB. HEAD, 69- Am. Chem. Soc; Am. Crystallog. Asn; Am. Inst. Physics. Structure, composition and properties of materials used in photographic materials. Address: Eastman Kodak Co, Kodak Park, Rochester, NY 14650.

GRIFFITH, RUSSELL K(NIGHT), b. Pittsburgh, Pa, July 14, 36; m. 59. POLYMER CHEMISTRY. B.A, Ohio Wesleyan, 59; Wm. Richardson fel, Akron, 59, Firestone fel, 60, Nat. Insts. Health grant, 62-63, Ph.D.(chem), 63. Res. chemist, mat. lab, polymer br, Wright-Patterson Air Force Base, Ohio, 63-65; PROJ. LEADER, RES. DEPT, STANDARD OIL CO, CLEVELAND, 65- Summer, chemist, res. lab, Gen. Elec. Co, 61. Merck award, 58. U.S.A.F, 63-65, 1st Lt. Am. Chem. Soc. Synthesis and characterization of macromolecules; synthesis of heterocyclic compounds. Address: 7576 Samuel Lord Dr, Chagrin Falls, OH 44022.

GRIFFITH, R(UTH) E(STER), b. Emporia, Kans, Nov. 21, 27. BIOLOGY. B.A. & B.S, Kans. State Teachers Col, 48; M.S, Washington State, 50; Ph.D.(biol), Northwestern, 54. Instr. gen. biol. & histol, Wells Col, 50-51; zool, gen. biol. & comp. anat, New Hampshire, 51-52; from asst. prof. BIOL. to PROF, HOOD COL, 54-, res. assoc, Chesapeake Biol. Lab, Solomons, 59-64. AAAS; Am. Soc. Limnol. & Oceanog; Am. Micros. Soc; Ecol. Soc. Am; Asn. Study Animal Behav; Marine Biol. Asn. U.K. Phycology, especially phytoplankton. Address: Dept. of Biology, Hood College, Frederick, MD 21701.

GRIFFITH, THOMAS, b. Minneola, Kans, June 22, 30; m. 58; c. 3. BIOCHEMISTRY. B.S, Kansas State, 52, M.S, 54; Nat. Insts. Health fel, Mich. State, 56-57, Ph.D.(chem), 58. Asst. cereal chem, Kansas State, 52-54; chem, Mich. State, 54-58, instr, 58-62; assoc. prof, NORTH. MICH. UNIV, 62-65, head dept, 65-66, assoc. dean, SCH. ARTS & SCI, 66-67, DEAN, 67- Am. Chem. Soc. Plant metabolism; alkaloid biosynthesis; transmethylation; cereal chemistry; fermentation. Address: Northern Michigan University, Marquette, MI 49855.

GRIFFITH, WAYLAND C(OLEMAN), b. Champaign, Ill, June 26, 25. FLUID MECHANICS. A.B, Harvard, 45, M.S, 46, fel, 46-49, Ph.D.(appl. sci), 49. Fel. physics, Atomic Energy Comn, Princeton, 49-50, instr, 50-51, asst. prof, 51-57; mgr. flight sci. div, missiles & space div, Lockheed Aircraft Corp, 57-58, assoc. dir. res, 58-59, asst. dir. res, 59-62, dir. res, 62-66, V.PRES. & ASST. GEN. MGR. res. & technol, LOCKHEED MISSILES & SPACE CO, 66-69, RES, 69- Nat. Sci. Found. fel, Univ. Col, London, 55-56; vis. prof, N.C. State Univ, 70-71; mem. adv. comt. fluid mech, NASA; div. comt. math. & phys. sci, Nat. Sci. Found; bd. human resources, Nat. Acad. Sci; panels 213 & 274, Nat. Bur. Standards. Am. Phys. Soc; Royal Aeronaut. Soc; Am. Inst. Aeronaut. & Astronaut. Shock waves; supersonic flow; molecular physics; shock tube; magnetohydrodynamics, air pollution. Address: Lockheed Missiles & Space Co, 3251 Hanover St, Palo Alto, CA 94304.

GRIFFITH, W(ILLIAM) A(LEXANDER), b. Sioux Falls, S.Dak, Mar. 28, 22; m. 49; c. 3. METALLURGY. B.S, S.Dak. Sch. Mines & Tech, 47; Iowa State Col, 43; S.M, Mass. Inst. Tech, 50. Metallurgist, Santiago-Alaska Mines, Inc, 47; asst, Mass. Inst. Tech, 47-48, instr. metall, 48-49; invest. mineral dressing, res. dept, N.J. Zinc Co, 49-52, group leader, 52-55, chief milling & maintenance, 55-57; chief metallurgist, Rare Metals Corp. Am, Ariz, 57-58; head res. dept, Phelps Dodge Corp, 58-68; DIR. RES, HECLA MINING CO, 68- U.S.N.R, 43-46, Lt. Am. Inst. Min, Metall. & Petrol. Eng. Unit operations of mineral benefication. Address: Hecla Mining Co, Box 320, Wallace, ID 83873.

GRIFFITH, WILLIAM KIRK, b. Henry, Ill, May 25, 29; m. 51; c. 2. AGRONOMY. B.S, Western Illinois, 51; M.S, Illinois, 52; Ph.D.(crop physiol), Purdue, 61. Asst. agr. exten. agent, Univ. Ariz, 56-58; agronomist, AM. POTASH INST, INC, 60-67, ASST. TO PRES. & CORP. SECY, 67-, REGIONAL DIR, 67- Chmn. pub. comt, Am. Forage & Grassland Coun, 61, mem. of censusing of grazing lands comt, 65-, bd. dirs. & nat. spokesman comt, 66- U.S.N, 52-56. Am. Soc. Agron; Crop Sci. Soc. Am; Soil Sci. Soc. Am. Crop physiology; effects of fertilizer and other management practices on the growth and persistence of forages, especially the effect of fertility levels on the biochemical changes within the plant. Address: 865 Seneca Rd, Herndon, VA 22070.

GRIFFITH, WILLIAM SAMUEL, Adult Educ, Dairy Sci, see 4th ed, Leaders in Education.

GRIFFITH, W(ILLIAM) T(HOMAS), b. Palmerton, Pa, Aug. 15, 40; m. 67. PHYSICS. B.A, Hopkins, 62; M.S, New Mexico, 64, Ph.D.(physics), 68. NASA trainee, New Mexico, 65-67; ASST. PROF. PHYSICS & OPTICS, PAC. UNIV, 67-, CHMN. DEPT. PHYSICS, 71- Am. Phys. Soc; Am. Asn. Physics Teachers. Kinetics of phase transformations; plastic crystals; thermodynamics of solids. Address: Dept. of Physics, Pacific University, Forest Grove, OR 97116.

GRIFFITHS, ANTHONY J. F, b. Bristol, Gr. Brit, Oct. 24, 40; m. 63; c. 2. GENETICS, MOLECULAR BIOLOGY. B.A, Keele, 63; Ont. Govt. fel, McMaster, 63-66, Nat. Res. Coun. Can. fel, 66-67, Ph.D.(molecular biol), 67. Res. assoc. biol, Kans. State Univ, 67-68; Nat. Insts. Health fel, Oak Ridge Nat. Lab, 68-70; teaching fel, UNIV. B.C, 70-71, ASST PROF. BOT, 71- Genetics Soc. Am; Genetics Soc. Can. Genetic recombination and cytoplasmic inheritance in neurospora crassa. Address: Dept. of Botany, University of British Columbia, Vancouver 8, B.C, Can.

GRIFFITHS, DAVID, b. Neath, Wales, May 2, 38; m. 64; c. 2. PHYSICS. B.Sc, Wales, 60, Ph.D.(physics), 64. Asst. lectr. physics, Univ. Col. Swansea, Wales, 64-65; res. physicist, ENG. PHYSICS LAB, EXP. STA, E.I. DU PONT DE NEMOURS & CO, 65-69, supvr, electronics group, 69-70, RES. SUPVR, APPL. PHYSICS SECT, 70- Brit. Inst. Physics. Electrical breakdown and gaseous ionization; surface physics, especially conductivity, friction, static properties, polymer adhesion and highpower laser technology. Address: 2313 Empire Dr, Kings Ridge, Wilmington, DE 19810.

GRIFFITHS, DAVID J(OHN), b. Vancouver, B.C, June 15, 38; m. 62; c. 3. PHYSICS. B.A, British Columbia, 59, Nat. Res. Coun. Can. bursary, 59-60, M.Sc, 60, Nat. Res. Coun. Can. studs, 60-63, Ph.D.(low temperature physics), 65. Teaching asst, Univ. B.C, 62-64; res. assoc. superconductivity & lectr, Univ. South. Calif, 65-67; asst. prof. PHYSICS, ORE. STATE UNIV, 67-71, ASSOC. PROF, 71- Low temperature physics; electron spin resonance and relaxation utilizing the magnetooptical Farady effect; examination of the magnetic, thermal and transport current phenomena of type II superconductors. Address: Dept. of Physics, Oregon State University, Corvallis, OR 97331.

GRIFFITHS, FRANCIS P(RIDAY), b. Seattle, Wash, July 12, 04; m. 31, 53; c. 3. FOOD TECHNOLOGY, BACTERIOLOGY. B.S, Washington (Seattle), 27; German-Am. exchange fel, Hamburg, Ger, 30-31; M.S, Mass. State Col, 33, Ph.D.(bacter), 35. Asst. hort. mfrs, Mass. State Col, 27-29, instr, 29-30, acting head dept. food tech, 41-46; jr. bacteriologist, U.S. Bur. Fisheries, 31-35; asst. prof. fish & game mgt, Oregon State Col, 35-40; dir. res, Valley Vitamins, Inc, 47-48; special asst. to dir, west. regional res. lab, bur. agr. & indust. chem, U.S. Dept. Agr, 48-52, chemist in charge, fruit & veg. prods. lab, South. Utilization Res. Br, Agr. Res. Serv, 52-66, food crops utilization res. lab, South. Utilization Res. & Develop. Div, 66-71; CONSULT, 71- Am. Chem. Soc; Inst. Food Technol. Chemistry of foods; utilization of agricultural products. Address: 910 W. Sixth St, Weslaco, TX 78596.

GRIFFITHS, GEO(RGE) M(OTLEY), b. Thorold, Ont, Dec. 12, 23; m. 48; c. 5. NUCLEAR PHYSICS. B.A.Sc, Toronto, 49; M.A, British Columbia, 50, Res. Coun. Ont. fel, 50-52, Nat. Res. Coun. Can. fel, 52-53, Ph.D.(physics), 53. Asst. physics, Nat. Res. Coun. Can, Chalk River, 48-49; Rutherford Mem.

fel, Cavendish Lab, Cambridge, 53-55; asst. prof. PHYSICS, UNIV. B.C, 55-59, assoc. prof, 59-63, PROF, 63- Sr. res. fel, Calif. Inst. Tech, 62-63. Can. Army, 42-45, Lt. Am. Phys. Soc; Can. Asn. Physicists. Low energy nuclear physics, direct radiative capture reactions. Address: Dept. of Physics, University of British Columbia, Vancouver, B.C, Can.

GRIFFITHS, HENRY J(OSEPH), b. Cambridge, Eng, July 4, 10; nat; m. 43. VETERINARY MEDICINE. B.S.A, McGill, 32, M.Sc, 35, Ph.D.(parasitol), 39; D.V.M, Iowa State, 43. Asst. inst. parasitol, McGill, 32-39; vet. path, Iowa State Col, 39-43; instr. parasitol, Ont. Vet. Col, 46-47; assoc. prof. VET. PARASITOL, col. vet. med, Washington State, 47-48; COL. VET. MED, UNIV. MINN, ST. PAUL, 48-54, PROF, 54- Can. Army, 43-46, Capt. Am. Soc. Parasitol; Am. Vet. Med. Asn. Veterinary parasitology. Address: 204 Veterinary Science, Dept. of Veterinary Pathology & Parasitology, College of Veterinary Medicine, University of Minnesota, St. Paul, MN 55101.

GRIFFITHS, JAMES EDWARD, b. Ft. Frances, Ont, Can, June 1, 31; m. 54; c. 1. ATOMIC & MOLECULAR SPECTROSCOPY, INORGANIC CHEMISTRY. B.Sc, Manitoba, 55, M.Sc, 56; Ph.D.(inorg. chem), McGill, 59. Res. assoc. CHEM, Southern California, 58-60; MEM. TECH. STAFF, BELL TEL. LABS, 60- AAAS; Am. Phys. Soc; Am. Chem. Soc; Brit. Chem. Soc. Synthesis, properties, molecular structure of volatile compounds; molecular structure and interactions in gases and liquids; arc phenomena in ultraviolet and vacuum ultraviolet; work functions; Raman scattering and absolute scattering cross-sections; surface physics. Address: Dept. 1513, Bell Telephone Labs, Murray Hill, NJ 07974.

GRIFFITHS, JAMES T(HOMPSON), JR, b. Alta Loma, Texas, Nov. 4, 14; m. 39; c. 2. ENTOMOLOGY. B.A, Rice Inst, 37; M.S, Iowa State Col, 39, Ph.D.(entomol), 41. Lab. asst, Houston, 35-37; asst. zool, Iowa State Col, 37-39, instr, 39-42; asst. prof. entomol. & veg. crop insects, Ala. Polytech, 42-43; assoc. entomologist, citrus exp. sta, Florida, 45-51; dist. mgr, Lyons Fertilizer Co, Fla, 51-54; prod. mgr, Eloise Groves Asn, 54-59, gen. mgr, 59-63; Cypress Gardens Citrus Prods, Inc, 63-66, dir. res, 66-67; CONSULT. SPEC. PROJS, FLA. CITRUS MUTUAL, 67- Sanit.C, 43-45, Capt. Entom. Soc. Am. Citriculture. Address: Florida Citrus Mutual, Box 89, Lakeland, FL 33802.

GRIFFITHS, JOHN C(EDRIC), b. Llanelly, England, Feb. 29, 12; nat; m. 41; c. 1. PETROLOGY. B.S, Univ. Col, Swansea, 33; M.Sc, Wales, 34, Ph.D. (sedimentary petrol), 37; Royal Soc. grant, London, 39, Ph.D.(sedimentary petrol), 40, dipl, Imp. Col, 40. Petrographer, Trinidad Leaseholds, Ltd, 40-47; asst. prof. PETROG, PA. STATE UNIV, 47-53, PROF, 53-69, DIR. PLANNING RES, 69-, head dept. mineral, 55-63, dept. geochem. & mineral, 63-69. Fel. Geol. Soc. Am; Mineral. Soc. Am; Am. Soc. Econ. Paleont. & Mineral; Opers. Res. Soc. Am; Am. Statist. Asn; Soc. Gen. Systs. Res; Mineral. Soc. Gt. Brit. & Ireland. Biometrics; heavy minerals in correlation; petrography in petroleum exploration in Trinidad, British West Indies and Venezuela; texture of sediments and reservoir engineering; statistics, computers and operations research in earth sciences; exploration for natural resources. Address: 405 Old Main, Pennsylvania State University, University Park, PA 16802.

GRIFFITHS, JOHN FREDERICK, b. London, Eng, Feb. 8, 26; m. 62. METEOROLOGY. B.S, London, 47, M.S, 49, dipl, Imp. Col, 48. Bioclimatologist, Brit, Colonial Sci. Res. Serv, 50-57; chief res, E.African Meteorol. Dept, 57-62; asst. prof. METEOROL, TEX. A&M UNIV, 62-65, assoc. prof, 65-70, PROF, 70- Mem. comts. instruments, agr. meteorol. & climat, World Meteorol. Orgn, 58-63; Rockefeller & Munitalp Found. travel grants, 60; chmn. meteorol. faculty, Orgn. Trop. Studies; pres, Appl. Trop. Res. Drew gold medal, Univ. London, 47. Am. Meteorol. Soc; Ecol. Soc. Am; fel. Royal Meteorol. Soc; fel. Royal Geog. Soc; fel. Royal Astron. Soc; fel. Brit. Interplanetary Soc; Int. Soc. Biometeorol; World Acad. Art & Sci; Air Pollution Control Asn. All aspects of biometeorology, especially statistical analysis, instrumentation and agricultural climatology. Address: 1006 Winding Rd, College Station, TX 77840.

GRIFFITHS, MARY (JEFFERY), b. Maidstone, Eng, June 17, 16; nat; m. 37; c. 3. PHYSIOLOGY. B.Sc, London, 37; fel. & M.A, California, 42, Ph.D. (physiol), 53. Res. asst. with Dr. R. Stanier, bact, Univ. Calif, 53-55; lectr. biol. & math, Lawrence Col, 56-59; res. asst. prof. ZOOL, UNIV. WASH, 59-66, RES. ASSOC. PROF, 66- Nat. Sci. Found. grants, 57-59, 63-65, 65-66; Am. Cancer Soc. grants, 60-61, 64-65. AAAS; Soc. Gen. Physiol; Am. Soc. Zool. Cellular physiology; synthesis and function of animal pigments; visible light damage; function of carotenoids in marine eggs and embryos; phosphate transport mechanism in sea urchin eggs. Address: Dept. of Zoology, University of Washington, Seattle, WA 98105.

GRIFFITHS, NORMAN H(ENRY) C(AMPBELL), b. Costa Rica, Cent. Am, Apr. 18, 16; nat; m. 50; c. 6. DENTISTRY. D.D.S, Howard, 47, Ball fel, 48, 52-54; M.S.D, Northwestern, 48; D.Sc.(prosthetics), Pennsylvania, 57. Asst. prof. PROSTHODONTICS, COL. DENT, HOWARD UNIV, 48-52, assoc. prof, 52-61, PROF, 61-, acting head dept, 67-68. Smith-Mundt prof, Ceylon, 58-59; vis. prof, India, 59; private practice; mem. rotating staff, Am. Hosp. Ship, Guinea; Fulbright prof, Alexandria Univ, 66-67; vis. prof, Univ. Baghdad, 67; coord, Dahomey Med. Proj, Oper. Crossroads, Africa, 67-; mem. nat. citizens comt, WHO. Serv. award, Howard Univ. AAAS; fel. Am. Pub. Health Asn; Am. Med. Writers Asn; Int. Asn. Dent. Res; N.Y. Acad. Sci; Am. Dent. Asn; Royal Soc. Health. Prosthetic dentistry; dental materials. Address: 3100 20th St. N.E, Washington, DC 20018.

GRIFFITHS, RAYMOND B(ERT), b. Worcester, Mass, June 16, 15; m. 51; c. 1. BIOLOGY, MEDICINE. A.B, Rochester, 37; A.M, Princeton, 39, fel. & Ph.D.(biol), 40; M.D, Northwestern, 46. Instr. zool, Arizona, 40-42; res. physician, Cushing Vet. Admin. Hosp, Framingham, Mass, 48-49; res. fel. pediat. & anat, sch. med, Yale, 49-52; instr. anat, 52-54; consult, med. serv. div, Ciba Pharmaceut. Prods, Inc, N.J, 54-58; ed. dir, med. affairs dept, Am. Cancer Soc, Inc, 58-60; EXEC. ED, J. CELL BIOL, ROCKEFELLER UNIV, 60- Med.C, U.S.A, 46-48. AAAS; Coun. Biol. Ed; Am. Asn. Anat. Cytology of amphibia; human anatomy; biological and medical editing and writing. Address: Rockefeller University, York Ave. & 66th St, New York, NY 10021.

GRIFFITHS, ROBERT B(UDINGTON), b. Etah, India, Feb. 25, 37; U.S. citizen. PHYSICS. A.B, Princeton, 57; Nat. Sci. Found. fel, Stanford, 57-62, M.S, 58, Ph.D.(physics), 62. Nat. Sci. Found. fel, California, San Diego, 62-64; asst. prof. PHYSICS, CARNEGIE-MELLON UNIV, 64-67, assoc. prof, 67-69, PROF, 69- Vis. assoc. prof, State Univ. N.Y. Stony Brook, 69. Am. Phys. Soc; Am. Sci. Affiliation. Thermodynamics; statistical mechanics; theory of magnetism. Address: Dept. of Physics, Carnegie-Mellon University, Pittsburgh, PA 15213.

GRIFFITHS, ROY SCOTT, b. Vancouver, B.C, Aug. 16, 22; U.S. citizen; m. 49. NEUROPHYSIOLOGY, PSYCHOLOGY. B.A, British Columbia, 51, M.Sc, 54; Ph.D.(psychol), California, Los Angeles, 60. Asst. prof. med. psychol, sch. med, Univ. Louisville, 60-63, ophthal. res, 63-64, clin. psychol, 64-65; PSYCHOL, SAN FERNANDO VALLEY STATE COL, 65-69, ASSOC. PROF, 69- Nat. Inst. Neurol. Diseases & Blindness grant, 63-64. Can. Army, 42-46. AAAS; Am. Psychol. Asn; Biophys. Soc. Audition and vision in sensory physiology; interdisciplinary approach to problems of analysis of behavior, particularly behavioral mechanisms in relation of electrophysiological changes in the nervous system. Address: Dept. of Psychology, San Fernando Valley State College, 18111 Nordhoff St, Northridge, CA 91324.

GRIFFITHS, VERNON, b. Treorchy, Wales, May 4, 29; U.S. citizen; m. 54; c. 5. PHYSICAL METALLURGY. B.Sc, Wales, 49, M.Sc, 51; Sc.D.(metall), Mass. Inst. Tech, 55. Res. assoc, British Columbia, 55-59; assoc. prof. METALL, MONT. COL. MINERAL SCI. & TECHNOL, 59-64, PROF, 64-, HEAD DEPT, 59- Res. metallurgist, Sherritt Gordon Mines, Ltd, 55-57. Summer, French Govt. scholar, 59. Am. Soc. Metals; Am. Inst. Min, Metall. & Petrol. Eng; Brit. Inst. Metals. Properties of metals and other solids which contain lattice imperfections; beryllium; powder metallurgy. Address: Dept. of Metallurgy, Montana College of Mineral Science & Technology, Butte, MT 59701.

GRIFFITHS, WILLIAM C, b. Fall River, Mass, Nov. 23, 39; m. 68; c. 1. CLINICAL & ORGANIC CHEMISTRY. B.S, Providence Col, 62, Ph.D.(org. chem), 67. Fel, Ohio State Univ, 67-68; org. chemist, R.I. Hosp, 68-71; CLIN. BIOCHEMIST, ROGER WILLIAMS HOSP, 71- AAAS; Am. Chem. Soc. Synthetic carbohydrate chemistry; analytical methodology in endocrinology and toxicology. Address: 51 Oliver St, Fall River, MA 02724.

GRIFFITTS, F(RED) A(LBERT), b. Phila, Tenn, Apr. 11, 03; m. 33. CHEMISTRY. B.A, Maryville Col.(Tenn), 25; M.S, Iowa State Col, 30; Ph.D. (chem), Indiana, 36. Instr. CHEM, Maryville Col.(Tenn), 25-29, assoc. prof, 30-36, prof, 49-68, chmn. div. natural sci, 49-62, chmn. dept, 62-68; PROF, HUNTINGDON COL, 68- Asst, Indiana, 35-36, teacher, 37; lectr, Nat. Sci. Found. Inst, Southern Univ, 62, Arizona State, 63, East. Ky. State Col, 63 & Ala. Agr. & Mech. Col, 64; summers, chemist, exp. sta, E.I. du Pont de Nemours & Co, 26, mem. chem. staff, Tennessee, 46, 47, 48, 52, 53, vis. prof, Birmingham South. Col, 56, 58, Lincoln Mem. Univ, 57, Ala. Col, 59, 60, Kentucky, 61, 63, 65, 66, Colo. Col, 62 & San Jose State Col, 64, Univ. Buffalo, 67; Fulbright prof, Univ. Col. Cape Coast, Ghana, 67-68. Am. Chem. Soc; N.Y. Acad. Sci. Inorganic and physical chemistry; vanadium oxytrichloride as a solvent; sulfides as contact hydrogenation catalysts; chemical education. Address: Dept. of Chemistry, Huntingdon College, Montgomery, AL 36106.

GRIFFITTS, JAMES J(OHN), b. Springfield, Ill, Dec. 13, 12; m. 40; c. 4. MEDICINE. B.S, Univ. Va, 33, M.D, 37. Intern, Lakeside Hosp, Ohio, 37-39; asst. surgeon, U.S. Marine Hosp, U.S. Pub. Health Serv, 39-40, Nat. Insts. Health, 41-44, surgeon, 46-49; ASSOC. DIR. JOHN ELLIOTT BLOOD BANK, DADE COUNTY, 49-; PRES, DADE DIV, AM. HOSP. SUPPLY CO, 54- U.S.C.G, 40-45. Am. Soc. Clin. Path; Am. Med. Asn. Blood immunology; clinical pathology; nutrition. Address: Dade Division, American Hospital Supply Corp, P.O. Box 672, Miami, FL 33152.

GRIFFITTS, WALLACE R(USH), b. Ann Arbor, Mich, Oct. 28, 19; m. 46; c. 4. ECONOMIC GEOLOGY. B.S, Univ. Mich, 42, fel, 47-50, M.S, 49, Ph.D. (geol), 58. GEOLOGIST, U.S. GEOL. SURV, 42- Geol. Soc. Am; Mineral. Soc. Am; Geochem. Soc; Am. Soc. Econ. Geol; Am. Geophys. Union; Mineral. Asn. Can; Soc. Geol. Appl. Mineral Deposits; Geol. Soc. India. Geology of pegmatites; nonmetallic mineral deposits; geology of beryllium deposits; exploration geochemistry; rock weathering. Address: U.S. Geological Survey, Denver Federal Center, Denver, CO 80225.

GRIFFO, JAMES V(INCENT), JR, b. Brooklyn, N.Y, Sept. 17, 28; m. 54; c. 3. NATURAL HISTORY, PARASITOLOGY. B.S, Kentucky, 52, M.S, 53; summer fel, Florida, 58, Ph.D.(biol), 60. Asst. zool, Kentucky, 52-53; parasitol, Tennessee, 55-56; biol, Univ. Fla, 56-60; instr, Fairleigh Dickinson Univ, 60-61; res. biologist, Patuxent Wildlife Res. Ctr, 61-62; asst. prof. BIOL, FAIRLEIGH DICKINSON UNIV, FLORHAM-MADISON CAMPUS, 62-65, assoc. prof, 65-69, PROF, 69-, PROVOST, CAMPUS, 71-, chmn. biol. dept, 62-69, dean campus, 67-71. Summers, asst, Univ. Fla, 59 & instr, Nat. Sci. Found. Inst, 60; trustee, All Souls Hosp, Morristown, N.J, 70- Med.C, 53-55, Res, 55-62, 1st Lt. Am. Soc. Mammal; Wildlife Soc; Wilderness Soc. Experimental natural history; mammals and insects; comparative parasitology; small mammal behavior. Address: Florham-Madison Campus, Fairleigh Dickinson University, 285 Madison Ave, Madison, NJ 07940.

GRIFFO, JOSEPH S(ALVATORE), b. Mt. Morris, N.Y, Oct. 13, 27; m. 54; c. 2. PHYSICAL & INORGANIC CHEMISTRY. B.S, St. Bonaventure, 51, M.S, 54; Buffalo, 54-55; Ph.D.(phys. inorg. chem), St. Louis, 61. Teacher, high sch, N.Y, 51-52; res. chemist, Olin Mathieson Chem. Corp, 55-57; res. asst. boron hydrides, St. Louis, 57-60; sr. res. chemist, Mound Lab, Monsanto Res. Corp, 61-66; ISOTOPIC FUELS SPECIALIST, U.S. ATOMIC ENERGY COMN. HQ, GERMANTOWN, 66- U.S.N.R, 45-46. AAAS; Am. Chem. Soc; Am. Inst. Physics. Chemistry of boron hydrides; high energy fuels; chemistry of rare earths; salts of barbituric acid. Address: 12330 Old Canal Rd, Rockville, MD 20854.

GRIFFY, THOMAS ALAN, b. Oklahoma City, Okla, Dec. 16, 36; m. 58; c. 2. THEORETICAL PHYSICS. B.A, Rice Univ, 59, M.A, 60, Ph.D.(physics), 61.

Asst. prof. PHYSICS, Duke Univ, 61-62; res. assoc. Stanford Univ, 62-65; assoc. prof, UNIV. TEX, 65-68, PROF, 68-, ASSOC. DEAN GRAD. SCH, 70- Am. Phys. Soc. Theoretical nuclear physics. Address: 6806 Pioneer Place, Austin, TX 78731.

GRIGAL, DAVID F(RANCIS), b. Orr, Minn, Sept. 21, 41; m. 64; c. 2. SOIL SCIENCE, FOREST ECOLOGY. B.S, Univ. Minn, St. Paul, 63, Northwest Paper Found. fel, 63-65, M.S, 65, Ph.D.(soil sci), 68. Atomic Energy Comn. fel, 68-70; res. assoc, ecol. sci. div, Oak Ridge Nat. Lab, 70; ASST. PROF. SOIL SCI, UNIV. MINN, ST. PAUL, 70- AAAS; Soc. Am. Foresters; Ecol. Soc. Am; Am. Soc. Agron. Nutrient cycling; water quality; numerical classification; multivariate analysis of biological data. Address: Dept. of Soil Science, University of Minnesota, St. Paul, MN 55101.

GRIGARICK, A(LBERT) A(NTHONY), JR, b. Redding, Calif, Dec. 22, 27; m. 46; c. 3. ENTOMOLOGY. B.S, California, 53, Ph.D.(entom), 57. Lectr, ENTOM. & asst. entomologist, UNIV. CALIF, DAVIS, 57-65, assoc. prof. & assoc. entomologist, 65-70, PROF. & ENTOMOLOGIST, 70- U.S.N, 45-48. Entom. Soc. Am. Economic entomology; biology and control of pests in vegetable crops and field crops; systematics; Pselaphidae; Megachilidae; Tardigrada. Address: Dept. of Entomology, University of California, Davis, CA 95616.

GRIGG, E(MANUEL) R(ADU) N(EWMAN), b. Moscow, Russia, Sept. 8, 16; nat; m. 46; c. 9. RADIOLOGY. M.D, Univ. Cluj, Rumania, 40. Fel, Forlanini Inst, Rome, Italy, 48; resident, COOK COUNTY HOSP, 53-56, asst. dir. radiation ctr, 56-57, ATTEND. RADIOLOGIST, 57-; DIR. RADIOL, CHICAGO STATE HOSP, 68-; ASSOC. CLIN. PROF. RADIOL, CHICAGO MED. SCH, 70- Consult, private hosps, 56-; Ill. Dept. Pub. Welfare, 56- Dipl, Am. Bd. Radiol, 56. AAAS; Am. Thoracic Soc; Radiol. Soc. N.Am; Soc. Nuclear Med; Hist. Sci. Soc; Am. Med. Asn; Aerospace Med. Asn; Am. Col. Radiol; Am. Col. Chest Physicians; Am. Roentgen Ray Soc; Int. Col. Surg. Philosophy of biology and history of medicine, especially radiology, tuberculology and oncology; clinical radiology; biologic relativity. Address: Box 2038, Oak Park, IL 60303.

GRIGG, HAROLD R, b. Moore Jaw, Sask, Oct. 26, 14; m. 41; c. 2. PHYSICS. B.Sc, Saskatchewan, 49, M.Sc, 57; Ph.D.(physics), British Columbia, 60. Asst. prof. PHYSICS, CAN. SERV. COL, ROYAL ROADS, 60-69, ASSOC. PROF, 69- Defence Res. Bd. Can. grant, 61- R.C.A.F, 40-45. Turbulent fluids; penetrative convection. Address: Dept. of Physics, Canadian Services College, Royal Roads, Victoria, B.C, Can.

GRIGGS, ALLAN B(INGHAM), b. Cottage Grove, Ore, June 10, 09; m. 40; c. 1. GEOLOGY. B.S, Oregon, 32; Ph.D.(geol), Stanford, 52. Geologic field asst, U.S. Engrs, Ore, 35-36, geol. field asst, 37-38; lab. asst. geol, Stanford, 39-40; GEOLOGIST, U.S. GEOL. SURVEY, 40- Soc. Econ. Geol; fel. Geol. Soc. Am; Geochem. Soc. Economic geology, particularly chromite and lead-zinc deposits; areal geology of Coeur d'Alene district, Idaho. Address: U.S. Geological Survey, 345 Middlefield Rd, Menlo Park, CA 94025.

GRIGGS, DAVID T(RESSEL), b. Columbus, Ohio, Oct. 6, 11; m. 46; c. 2. GEOPHYSICS. A.B, Ohio State, 32, A.M, 33; jr. fel, Harvard, 34-41. Asst, Harvard, 33; res. assoc, radiation lab, Mass. Inst. Tech, 41-42; sect. chief, Proj. Rand, Douglas Aircraft Co, Inc, 46-48; PROF. GEOPHYS, UNIV. CALIF, LOS ANGELES, 48- Mem, Nat. Geog. Exped, Valley of 10,000 Smokes, 30; lectr, Lowell Inst, 38; chief scientist, U.S. Air Force, 51-52, mem. sci. adv. bd, 52-; consult, Rand Corp, Atomic Energy Comn, 58-62; mem. panel seismic improv, President's Sci. Adv. Comt, 59; Defense Sci. Bd, 63-; pres. sect. tectonophys, Am. Geophys. Union, 64-67; consult, Defense Atomic Support Agency, 64-; mem. panel earthquake prediction, Off. Sci. & Technol, 65-66; sci. adv. panel, U.S. Army, 65-; dir, FMA, Inc, Calif. Presidential Medal for merit, 46; U.S. Air Force Award for exceptional civilian serv, 53. Civilian expert consult, Off. Secy. War, U.S. War Dept, 42-46. Nat. Acad. Sci; fel. Geol. Soc. Am; fel. Am. Phys. Soc; Am. Geophys. Union (Bucher Medal, 70). Deformation of rocks under high pressure; nuclear energy. Address: Institute of Geophysics & Planetary Physics, University of California, Los Angeles, CA 90024.

GRIGGS, DOUGLAS M, JR, b. Aug. 14, 28; U.S. citizen; m. 56; c. 2. PHYSIOLOGY, MEDICINE. A.B, Harvard, 49; M.D, Virginia, 53; fel, Pittsburgh, 60-61. Intern, St. Lukes Hosp, New York, 53-54, asst. resident, 54-55, 57-58, N.Y. Heart Asn. fel, 58-60; clin. biophys, Nat. Heart Inst, 61-62; from asst. med. to assoc. prof, Hahnemann Med. Col. & Hosp, 62-67; assoc. prof. PHYSIOL. & MED, SCH. MED, UNIV. MO-COLUMBIA, 67-70, PROF, 70- U.S. Pub. Health Serv. fel, 60-62; res. career develop. awards, 63-67, 68- Dipl, Am. Bd. Internal Med. Med.C, U.S.A, 55-57, Capt. Am. Fedn. Clin. Res; Am. Physiol. Soc; Soc. Exp. Biol. & Med. Cardiovascular physiology particularly myocardial metabolism and coronary physiology. Address: Dept. of Physiology, School of Medicine, University of Missouri-Columbia, Columbia, MO 65201.

GRIGGS, GARY B, b. Pasadena, Calif, Sept. 25, 43. MARINE GEOLOGY. B.A, Univ. Calif, Santa Barbara, 65; Nat. Sci. Found. fel, Ore. State Univ, 65-69, Ph.D.(oceanog), 69. ASST. PROF. EARTH SCI, UNIV. CALIF, SANTA CRUZ, 69- Geol. Soc. Am; Am. Geophys. Union; Soc. Econ. Paleont. & Mineral. Marine sedimentation; environmental geology. Address: Division of Natural Science, University of California, Santa Cruz, CA 95060.

GRIGGS, LEE JACKSON, b. Grand Rapids, Mich, Nov. 23, 38; m. 58; c. 2. ORGANIC & MEDICINAL CHEMISTRY. B.S, Michigan, 60, M.S, 62, Ph.D.(med. chem), 65. SR. CHEMIST, SMITH KLINE & FRENCH LABS, 65- AAAS; Am. Chem. Soc; Am. Pharmaceut. Asn; Acad. Pharmaceut. Sci; N.Y. Acad. Sci. Steroid synthesis and biology; heterocyclic synthesis; carbohydrate synthesis; protein chemistry; glycoprotein biochemistry. Address: Smith Kline & French Labs, 1530 Spring Garden St, Philadelphia, PA 19101.

GRIGGS, ROBERT C, b. Rochester, N.Y, July 11, 25; m. 53; c. 3. MEDICINE. Princeton, 43-45; M.D, Harvard, 49. Instr. MED, SCH. MED, CASE WEST. RESERVE UNIV, 56-58, sr. instr. & Webster-Underhill fel, 58-60, asst. prof, 60-66, ASSOC. PROF, 66- Asst. vis. physician, Metrop. Gen. Hosp, Cleveland, 56-59, assoc. vis. physician, 59-; consult, Marymount Hosp, 58-; attend. hemat, Vet. Admin. Hosp, 61- Med.C, 50-52, Lt. Am. Fedn. Clin. Res; Am. Soc. Hemat; Soc. Exp. Biol. & Med. Internal medicine; hematology; medical education. Address: Metropolitan General Hospital, 3395 Scranton Rd, Cleveland, OH 44109.

GRIGGS, WILLIAM H(OLLAND), b. Novelty, Mo, May 31, 16; m. 44; c. 3. POMOLOGY. B.S, Mo. State Teachers Col, 37; M.A, Missouri, 39; Ph.D.(pomol), Maryland, 43. Asst. POMOL, Missouri, 37-39; Maryland, 39-42; asst. prof, Univ. Conn, 46-47; UNIV. CALIF, DAVIS, 47-50, assoc. prof, 50-59, PROF, 59- U.S.N.R, 42-45, Lt. Comdr. Am. Soc. Hort. Sci.(Stark Award, 64). Pollination requirements of fruits and nuts; physiological problems in pear production; pear breeding. Address: Dept. of Pomology, University of California, Davis, CA 95616.

GRIGNETTI, MARIO, b. Montevideo, Uruguay, June 16, 31; m. 53; c. 2. ELECTRICAL ENGINEERING, MATHEMATICS. Indust. Eng, Uruguay, 57; M.Sc, Mass. Inst. Tech, 62. Asst. actuary, Caja de Jubilaciones, 52-57; consult. engr, Govt. Airline, Uruguay, 57-60; asst. elec. eng, Mass. Inst. Tech, 60-62; consult, BOLT, BERANEK & NEWMAN, INC, 62-69, SR. SCIENTIST, 69- Inst. Elec. & Electronics Eng. Information theory; human operator modelling. Address: Bolt, Beranek & Newman, Inc, 50 Moulton St, Cambridge, MA 02108.

GRIGORI, A(RTUR), b. Binab, Persia, May 1, 18; nat. ALGEBRA. Ph.D.(philos), Tübingen, 50. ASST. PROF. MATH, St. Bonaventure, 58; SAN FERNANDO VALLEY STATE COL, 62- Nat. Sci. Found. math. award, 59. Math. Asn. Am. Modern algebra and geometry; calculus; differential equations; theory of equations. Address: Dept. of Mathematics, San Fernando Valley State College, Northridge, CA 91326.

GRIGORIEFF, W(LADIMIR) W, b. Hankow, China, July 11, 08; nat; m. 35, 53; c. 1. CHEMISTRY. B.S, Swiss Fed. Univ, Zurich, 32; Ph.D.(org. chem), Chicago, 39. Chief chemist, Danziger Ref. Inc, Tex, 34-35; res. chemist, Gen. Elec. Co, Mass, 39-45; dir, Ordark proj, Arkansas, 46-53; Inst. Sci. & Tech, 47-53; chmn. univ. rel. div, Oak Ridge Inst. Nuclear Studies, 53-64, asst. to exec. dir. spec. projs, 64-67, ASST. TO DIR, OAK RIDGE ASSOC. UNIVS, 67- With Int. Atomic Energy Agency, Austria, 58-59; prog. chmn, World Cong, Eng. Ed, 65. Fel. AAAS; Am. Chem. Soc; Am. Soc. Eng. Educ; Am. Nuclear Soc.(exec. secy, 55-58). Synthetic electrical insulation; glass to metal seals; pyrotechnics; glass compositions of low-coefficient of thermal expansion; research administration. Address: Oak Ridge Associated Universities, P.O. Box 117, Oak Ridge, TN 37830.

GRIGOROPOULOS, SOTIRIOS G(REGORY), b. Athens, Greece, Mar. 24, 33. SANITARY & CHEMICAL ENGINEERING. Dipl, Nat. Univ. Athens, 55; M.S, Washington (St. Louis), 58, Sc.D.(sanit. eng), 60. Chemist, Sigma Chem. Co, Mo, 56-57; asst. CIVIL ENG, Washington (St. Louis), 57-58, instr, 58-60; assoc. prof, UNIV. MO-ROLLA, 60-63, PROF, 63- Res. engr, Ryckman, Edgerley, Burbank,& Assocs, Mo, 58-60; summers, res. engr, Metcalf & Eddy, Engrs, Mass, 60, vis. assoc. prof, Washington (St. Louis), 61. Am. Soc. Eng. Educ; Am. Soc. Civil Eng; Am. Inst. Chem. Eng; Am. Water Works Asn; Water Pollution Control Fedn. Removal of tastes and odors from waters; study, characterization and breakdown of organic extracts; chemical and electrochemical degradation of refractory contaminants; treatability of industrial wastes; effect of pesticides in water. Address: Dept. of Civil Engineering, University of Missouri-Rolla, Rolla, MO 65401.

GRIGSBY, BUFORD H(ORACE), b. Rogersville, Ala, Oct. 14, 09; m. 33; c. 3. BOTANY. B.S, Ala. Polytech, 30; M.S, Mich. State Col, 32, Ph.D.(plant physiol), 37. Asst. bot, Mich. State Univ, 32-35, instr, 35-37, asst. prof, 37-42, assoc. prof, 43-54, prof, 54-62, assoc. physiologist, exp. sta, 42-43, physiologist, 43-62; MEM. U.S. OPERS. MISSION, U.S. AGENCY INT. DEVELOP, Ceylon, 62, Nigeria, 63-64, Viet Nam, 64-69, DACCA, 69-, adv. weed control, Ceylon, 59-61. Botanist, Dept. Health, Mich, 40-47. AAAS; Bot. Soc. Am. Plant nutrition; pollen distribution; weed investigation; mineral nutrition of garden peas; physiology of mosaic of raspberries; weed control; economic plants. Address: Dacca/ID, Dept. of State, Washington, DC 20521.

GRIGSBY, JOHN LYNN, b. Tulsa, Okla, Apr. 28, 24; m. 50; c. 4. ELECTRICAL ENGINEERING. B.S, Colorado, 49; Iowa State Col, 49; M.S, Stanford, 56, Ph.D.(elec. eng), 59. Radio operator, Fed. Commun. Comn, 42-43; instr. elec. eng, Iowa State Col, 49; engr, Gen. Elec. Co, 49-52; res. assoc. elec. eng, Stanford, 52-59; chief engr, APPL. TECHNOL. DIV, ITEK CORP, 60-61, v.pres. eng, 61-71, EXEC. V.PRES, 71- Mem. Rientjes Comt, Dept. Army, 59. U.S.A.A.F, 43-46, Sgt. Sr. mem. Inst. Elec. & Electronics Eng. Electronic countermeasures systems; reconnaissance and surveillance receiving systems; broadband low-noise amplifiers. Address: Applied Technology Division, Itek Corp, 3410 Hillview Ave, Palo Alto, CA 94304.

GRIGSBY, LEONARD LEE, b. Floydada, Tex, Dec. 31, 29; m. 55; c. 3. ELECTRICAL ENGINEERING. B.S.E.E, Tex. Tech. Col, 57, M.S.E.E, 62; Ph.D.(eng), Okla. State, 65. Instr. ELEC. ENG, Tex. Tech. Col, 57-60, asst. prof, 60-61; instr, Okla. State, 61-64, asst. prof, 64-66; ASSOC. PROF, VA. POLYTECH INST. & STATE UNIV, 66- NASA grant, 69-71; consult, nuclear develop. ctr, Babcock & Wilcox, Va, 69- U.S.N, 51-54. Inst. Elec. & Electronics Eng; Am. Soc. Eng. Educ. Network and system modeling, simulation and design; digital control systems. Address: Dept. of Electrical Engineering, Virginia Polytechnic Institute & State University, Blacksburg, VA 24061.

GRIGSBY, MARGARET E(LIZABETH), b. Prairie View, Tex, Jan. 16, 23. MEDICINE. B.S, Prairie View State Col, 43; M.D, Michigan, 48; D.T.M.&H, London, 63. Intern, Homer G. Phillips Hosp, St. Louis, Mo, 48-49, asst. resident MED, 49-50; Freedmen's Hosp, D.C, 50-51; Rockefeller Found. res. fel, Harvard Med. Sch, 51-52; instr, COL. MED, HOWARD UNIV, 52-57, asst. prof, 57-60, assoc. prof, 60-66, PROF, 66- Attend. physician, Freedman's Hosp, 52-; China Med. Bd. fel, sch. trop. med, Univ. P.R, 56; attend. physician, D.C. Gen. Hosp, 58-; med. epidemiologist, U.S. Pub. Health Serv, Idaban, Nigeria, 66; consult, U.S. Agency Int. Develop, 70-71;

mem. anti-infective agents adv. comt, Food & Drug Admin, 70-71. Fel. Am. Col. Physicians; Am. Med. Asn; Nat. Med. Asn. Internal medicine; infectious diseases antibiotic research; electrophoresis of proteins. Address: Dept. of Medicine, Howard University College of Medicine, Washington, DC 20001.

GRIGSBY, RONALD DAVIS, b. Tulsa, Okla, Feb. 28, 36; m. 62; c. 5. BIOPHYSICAL CHEMISTRY. B.S, Oklahoma, 58 & 59, Ph.D.(phys. chem), 66. Teaching asst. chem, Oklahoma, 59-61, res. asst, res. inst, 60, 61-62, 63-64, teaching asst. Russian, 62-63; res. chemist, Continental Oil Co, Okla, 64-68; ASST. PROF. BIOCHEM. & BIOPHYS, TEXAS A&M, 68- Am. Soc. Mass Spectrometry; Am. Chem. Soc. Structure elucidation of biological compounds by mass spectrometry. Address: Dept. of Biochemistry & Biophysics; Texas A&M University, College Station, TX 77843.

GRIGSBY, W(ILLIAM) E(ARLE), b. Macomb, Ill, May 28, 19; m. 42; c. 3. CHEMISTRY. B.Ed, West. Ill. State Col, 39; Ph.D.(phys. org. chem), Chicago, 42. Chemist, ammonia dept, E.I. DU PONT DE NEMOURS & CO, INC, 42-49, supvr. res. div, 49-50, asst. tech. supt. Victoria plant, polychem. dept, 50-52, sr. supvr. res. div, 52-53, mgr. staff sect, 53-54, res. div, 54-55, tech. serv. sect, sales div, 55-57, develop. dept, 57-58, dir. plastics res. & develop, polychem. dept, 58-60, dir. pioneering res, plastics dept, 60-63, mgr. plastics tech. serv. lab, 64-68, MGR. FLUOROCARBONS PLASTICS RES, EXP. STA, 68- Am. Chem. Soc; Soc. Plastics Eng. Address: 502 Cranebrook Rd, Woodbrook, Wilmington, DE 19803.

GRIGSBY, WILLIAM REDMAN, b. Denver, Colo, Oct. 15, 34; m. 58; c. 2. DENTISTRY, BIOCHEMISTRY. B.A, Dartmouth Col, 56; D.D.S, Univ. Mo-Kansas City, 60; Ph.D.(biochem), Med. Col. Va, Va. Commonwealth Univ, 70. ASST. PROF. OPER. DENT. & BIOCHEM, MED. COL. VA, VA. COMMONWEALTH UNIV, 68- AAAS; Am. Chem. Soc; Am. Dent. Asn; Int. Asn. Dent. Res. Dental caries. Address: Box 637, Medical College of Virginia, Virginia Commonwealth University, Richmond, VA 23219.

GRILIONE, PATRICIA LOUISE, b. Fresno, Calif, Apr. 15, 35. MICROBIOLOGY. B.A, Fresno State Col, 57, M.A, 59; Woodrow Wilson fel, Univ. Calif, Berkeley, 59-60, Nat. Sci. Found. grant, Davis, 63-66, Ph.D.(microbiol), 66. Asst. prof. MICROBIOL, SAN JOSE STATE COL, 66-70, ASSOC. PROF, 70- AAAS; Am. Soc. Microbiol. General microbiology; ecology. Address: Dept. of Biology, San Jose State College, San Jose, CA 95114.

GRILL, HERMAN, JR, b. New York, N.Y, June 30, 36; m. 59. DAIRY SCIENCE, BIOCHEMISTRY. B.S, Mich. State, 59; M.S, Minnesota, 62; Ph.D. (dairy sci, biochem), Pa. State, 66. MGR. FLAVOR RES, CARNATION RES. LAB, VAN NUYS, 66- Am. Chem. Soc; Inst. Food Tech. Flavor chemistry of foods, both the chemical and sensory aspects. Address: 12002 Gerald Ave, Granada Hills, CA 91344.

GRILLET, MIREILLE POINSIGNON, b. Entre deux Guièrs-Isère, France, June 25, 41; m. 67. MATHEMATICS. Ecole Normale Supérieure, Paris, 60-65; Ph.D.(math), Kansas State, 68. Prof. MATH, Caen, 65-66; asst. Florida, 66-67; res. asst, Kansas State, 67-68; ASST. PROF, La. State, New Orleans, 68-69; KANS. STATE UNIV, 69- Am. Math. Soc. Semigroups; semirings. Address: Dept. of Mathematics, Cardwell Hall, Kansas State University, Manhattan, KS 66502.

GRILLET, PIERRE ANTOINE, b. Paris, France, May 2, 41; m. 68. MATHEMATICS. Lic. Math, Paris, 60, Agrégé, 62, Dr. Math, 65. ASST. PROF. MATH, Florida, 65-67; KANS. STATE UNIV, 67- Vis. asst. prof, Tulane, 68-69. Am. Math. Soc; Math. Soc. France. Semigroup theory; category theory; lattice theory. Address: Dept. of Mathematics, Kansas State University, Manhattan, KS 66502.

GRILLO, GERALD J(OSEPH), b. Boston, Mass, Jan. 16, 29; m. 52; c. 5. PHYSICAL & ORGANIC CHEMISTRY. B.A, Boston, 51, Tech. Asn. Pulp & Paper Indust. fel, 55-56, Ph.D.(phys. & org. chem), 60. Asst, Boston, 53-55; res. chemist, Callery Chem. Co, 56-58, group leader, 58, head appl. chem. sect, 58-60; spec. projs. dept, Monsanto Chem. Co, 60; proj. leader, Foster Grant Co, 60-64; dir. res. & develop, Solar Chem. Corp, Mass, 64-68; PRES, SPECIALTY POLYMERS INC, 68- Am. Chem. Soc; Soc. Plastics Eng. Reactions kinetics and mechanism; chemical process development; boron hydride chemistry; polymer chemistry. Address: 60 Rustic Dr, Leominster, MA 01453.

GRILLO, RAMON S, b. New York, N.Y, May 28, 31; m. 56; c. 1. BIOLOGY. B.A, N.Y. Univ, 53; M.S, Fordham, 57, U.S. Pub. Health Serv. fel, 58-59, Ph.D.(cytol), 60. Instr. BIOL, Marymount Col.(N.Y), 59-60; Bronx Community Col, 60; asst. prof, Seton Hall, 60-63, assoc. prof, 63-64; ADELPHI UNIV, 64-69, PROF, 69- U.S. Pub. Health Serv. res. grant, 63-65; U.S. Atomic Energy Contract, 67-69. U.S.A, 53-55. AAAS; Am. Soc. Zool; Am. Soc. Cell Biol. Study of the dynamics of cell proliferation in normal and regenerating tissues of the newt, Triturus viridescens, using tritiated thymidine and autoradiography. Address: Dept. of Biology, Adelphi University, Garden City, NY 11530.

GRILLOS, STEVE JOHN, b. Rock Springs, Wyo, Jan. 15, 28; m. 52, 61; c. 2. BOTANY, PLANT ANATOMY. B.S, Denver, 51; M.S, Wyoming, 52; Ph.D.(bot), Ore. State Col, 56. Asst. bot, Wyoming, 51-52; Ore. State Col, 52-53, instr. bot, 53-56; biol. scis, Modesto Jr. Col, 56-60; assoc. prof. bot, Col. of Pacific, 60-62; prof. biol, Calif. State Col. Hayward, 62-65, PROF. BOT, STANISLAUS STATE COL, 65- Summers, Nat. Sci. Found. fels, Ore. State Col, 58, Univ. Wyo, 59; vis. prof, Stephen F. Austin State Col, 60. U.S.N, 46-48. Bot. Soc. Am. Tissue structure and development. Address: Dept. of Biological Sciences, Stanislaus State College, Turlock, CA 95380.

GRILLOT, DAVID V, b. Dayton, Ohio, Sept. 12, 34; m. 61. NUCLEAR PHYSICS. B.S, Ohio, 59, M.S, 62; Ph.D.(physics), Mich. State, 67. Res. assoc. PHYSICS, Oregon, 66-68; ASST. PROF, OREGON STATE UNIV, 68- U.S.A, 53-56. Many body theory; nuclear Hartee-Fock. Address: Dept. of Physics, Oregon State University, Corvallis, OR 97331.

GRILLOT, GERALD F(RANCIS), b. Versailles, Ohio, Jan. 24, 14; m. 41; c. 2. ORGANIC CHEMISTRY. B.A, Ohio State, 36; Ph.D.(org. chem), Illinois, 40. Asst. CHEM, Illinois, 36-40; head dept, Blue Ridge Col, 40-41; instr, Kentucky, 41-44, asst. prof, 44-46; SYRACUSE UNIV, 46-53, ASSOC. PROF, 53- Am. Chem. Soc. Mannich reaction; stereochemistry; synthesis of organic pharmaceuticals; preparation and properties of aminomethyl sulfides; Hofmann-Martius rearrangement. Address: Dept. of Chemistry, Syracuse University, Syracuse, NY 13210.

GRILLS, RAYMOND CLYDE, b. Du Quoin, Ill, Dec. 15, 14; m. 41; c. 2. PHYSICAL CHEMISTRY. B.S, Monmouth Col, Ill, 37; M.A, Indiana, Bloomington, 38, Ph.D.(phys. chem), 40. Res. chemist, exp. sta, E.I. DU PONT DE NEMOURS & CO, INC, Del, 40-41, 43 & 45, supvr. Du Pont-TNT, Wis, 41, chief chem. engr, Kankakee Ord. Works, Ill, Okla. Ord. Works & two defense plants for U.S. Govt, 43, chem. engr, explosives-TNT, Chicago Univ, 43-44, Hanford Eng. Works, Wash, 44-45, supvr. process control, Rayon-Nylon, Va, 45, process develop, 45-47, tech. supt. Nylon, Tenn, 48-50, textile fibers, Del, 50-51, mfg. supt. Nylon, 51, plant mgr. Nylon, 51-53, tech. mgr. Acetate-Orlon, 53-54, prod. mgr. Dacron-Orlon, 54, indust. sales mgr, 54-56, dir. sales progs, 56-57, mfg. Dacron, 57-58, mfg. spec. assignment, 58, gen. mgr, Ducilo S.A.I.C, int. dept, Argentina, 58-59, gen. mgr. & v.pres, 60-61, spec. assignment textile fibers, DEL, 61, new ventures mgr, FILM DEPT, 61-62, asst. dir. res. & develop, 62-63, asst. dir. mfr, 63-65, dir. mfr, 65-69, ASST. GEN. MGR, DEPT, 69- Am. Chem. Soc. Address: Film Dept, E.I. du Pont de Nemours & Co, Inc, 1007 Market St, Wilmington, DE 19898.

GRILLY, E(DWARD) R(OGERS), b. Cleveland, Ohio, Dec. 30, 17; wid; c. 2. PHYSICAL CHEMISTRY. B.S, Ohio State, 40, Ph.D.(phys. chem), 44; Wisconsin, 40-41. Asst. chem, Wisconsin, 40-41; Ohio State, 41-44; chemist, Carbide & Carbon Chems. Co, Oak Ridge, 44-46; asst. prof. chem, New Hampshire, 46-47; MEM. STAFF, LOS ALAMOS SCI. LAB, UNIV. CALIF, 47- With U.S.A, 44. Am. Phys. Soc. Gaseous kinetic theory; cryogenics; thermodynamics; transport properties of gases; pressure-volume-temperature at low temperatures and high pressure. Address: Los Alamos Scientific Lab, P.O. Box 1663, Los Alamos, NM 87544.

GRIM, EUGENE (DONALD), b. Stillwater, Okla, July 19, 22; m. 46; c. 1. PHYSIOLOGY. B.S, Kans. State Col, 45, M.S, 46; Ph.D.Minnesota, 50. Asst. chem, Kans. State Col, 45-46; physiol. chem, Minnesota, 46-47; fel, Nat. Insts. Health, 47-50; PHYSIOL, UNIV. MINN, MINNEAPOLIS, 51-52, instr, 52-54, asst. prof, 54-58, assoc. prof, 58-62, PROF, 62-, HEAD DEPT, 68- U.S. Pub. Health Serv. res. fel, 58-63; chmn, physiol. study sect, Nat. Insts. Health. Lederle award, 54-57. AAAS; Am. Chem. Soc; Am. Physiol. Soc; Soc. Exp. Biol. & Med; Biophys. Soc; Am. Gastroenterol. Soc; Soc. Gen. Physiol. Membrane transport phenomena; intestinal absorption; visceral circulation; regional blood flow. Address: Dept. of Physiology, 424 Millard Hall, University of Minnesota, Minneapolis, MN 55455.

GRIM, JOHN NORMAN, b. Santa Barbara, Calif, Sept. 8, 33; m. 54; c. 2. CELL BIOLOGY, ZOOLOGY. B.A, California, Santa Barbara, 56; M.A, California, Los Angeles, 60; Ph.D.(zool), California, Davis, 67. Lab. technician, California, Davis, 60-67; ASST. PROF. BIOL, NORTH. ARIZ, 67- U.S.A.R. & Nat. Guard, 56-, Maj. AAAS; Soc. Protozool. Ultrastructure and function of Protozoan organelles; chromosome ultrastructure; neurophysiology. Address: Dept. of Biology, Northern Arizona University, Flagstaff, AZ 86001.

GRIM, RALPH E(ARLY), b. Reading, Pa, Feb. 25, 02; m. 45, 64. GEOLOGY. Ph.B, Yale, 24, 24-26; Ph.D.(geol), Iowa, 31. Asst. prof. geol, Mississippi, 26-30; asst, Iowa, 30-31; petrographer, Ill. Geol. Surv, 31-50; res. prof. GEOL, UNIV. ILL, URBANA, 48-67, EMER. RES. PROF, 67- Asst. state geologist, State Geol. Surv, Miss, 26-30. Chmn, subcomt. diagensis, comt. sedimentation, Nat. Res. Coun; clay minerals comt, 53-; int. comt. study of clays. With Off. Sci. Res. & Develop, 44. Fel. Geol. Soc. Am; fel. Mineral Soc. Am.(pres. 58-59); Soc. Econ. Geol; fel. Am. Ceramic Soc; distinguished mem. Clay Minerals Soc; Am. Asn. Petrol. Geol; Am. Geophys. Union; Mineral Soc. Gt. Brit. & Ireland; Brit. Ceramic Soc; hon. mem. Brit. Clay Mineral Soc; for. mem. Indian Acad. Sci; hon. mem. Ceramic Soc. Brazil. Structure and composition of clays; petrology; sedimentation; stratigraphy and sedimentary history of the Tertiary formations in Mississippi; relation between properties of clays and clay petrography. Address: 704 W. Florida Ave, Urbana, IL 61801.

GRIM, SAMUEL O(RAM), b. Landisburg, Pa, Mar. 11, 35; m. 57; c. 3. CHEMISTRY. B.S, Franklin & Marshall Col, 56; Nat. Sci. Found. fel, Mass. Inst. Tech, 58-60, Ph.D.(inorg. chem), 60. Asst. prof. CHEM, Maryland, 60-61; res. fel, Imp. Col, London, 61-62; asst. prof, UNIV. MD, 62-65, assoc. prof, 65-68, PROF, 68- Res. grants, Nat. Sci. Found, 62-73, Air Force Off. Sci. Res, 64-68. AAAS; Am. Chem. Soc; Brit. Chem. Soc. Organometallic and organophosphorus chemistry; coordination compounds. Address: Dept. of Chemistry, University of Maryland, College Park, MD 20740.

GRIM, WAYNE MARTIN, b. York, Pa, Apr. 12, 30; m. 52; c. 4. PHARMACEUTICAL CHEMISTRY. B.Sc, Phila. Col. Pharm, 52, M.Sc, 54; Am. Found. Pharmaceut. Ed. fel. & Ph.D.(pharmaceut. chem), Michigan, 59. Res. assoc. pharmaceut. res, MERCK & CO, INC, 54-56, MERCK SHARP & DOHME RES. LABS, 59-61, unit head, 61-62, sect. head, 62-64, mgr. pharmaceut. develop, 64-68, dir, 68-69, DIR. PHARMACEUT. RES, 69- AAAS; Am. Pharmaceut. Asn. Rheology and the physical stabilization of suspensions; topical and inhalation aerosol development; oral and topical liquid, semisolid and solid dosage form development; particle size reduction and measurement; biopharmaceutics and bioavailability research. Address: Pharmaceutical Research, Merck Sharp & Dohme Research Labs, West Point, PA 19486.

GRIMALDI, FRANK S(AVERIO), b. Cerignola, Foggia, Italy, Oct. 11, 15; nat; m. 41; c. 1. INORGANIC & ANALYTICAL CHEMISTRY. B.S.E, City Col, 36, M.Ch.E, 38; Ph.D.(inorg. chem), Maryland, 53. CHEMIST, Gen. Chem. Co, 36-40; GEOCHEM. & PETROL. BR, U.S. GEOL. SURV, 40-, CHIEF ANAL. LABS. BR, GEOL. DIV, 60- Assoc. & lectr, George Washington, 52-54; adj. prof, American Univ, 56-64. Am. Chem. Soc. Researches on analysis of rarer elements in trace amounts; mineralogical researches and geochemical researches. Address: 3101 N. Toronto St, Arlington, VA 22213.

GRIMALDI, JOHN VINCENT, b. N.Y.C, Sept. 6, 16; m. 42; c. 2. CHEMICAL & SAFETY ENGINEERING. B.S, N.Y. Univ, 39, M.A, 41, Am. Mus. Safety fel, 44-45 & 55-56, Ph.D.(acoust), 56; B.Ch.E, Polytech. Inst. Brooklyn, 51. Apprentice, Grumman Aircraft Eng. Corp, 41-42, dir. safety, 42-45; res. engr, Nat. Conserv. Bur, 45-46, dir. res. div, 46-47, dir. indust. div. & asst. mgr. safety, 47-56; consult. safety & plant protection, Gen. Elec. Co, 56-62, health, safety & plant protection, 62-67; DIR. CTR. FOR SAFETY, N.Y. UNIV, 67- Consult, Creole Petrol. Co, 57 & 63; Tenn. Valley Auth, 68- Mem, President's Comt. Employ. of Physically Handicapped, 47-56; N.Y. State Governor's Comt. Occup. Safety, 58-; U.S. Secy. Labor's Nat. Adv. Comt. Occup. Safety & Health, 69- Fel. Am. Inst. Chem; Am. Soc. Mech. Eng; fel. Am. Soc. Safety Eng.(pres, 61-62); Am. Chem. Soc; fel. Am. Acad. Safety Educ. Management performance measurement methods; employment of the physically handicapped; executive health examinations-their relative value; effect of noise on human performance. Address: The Center for Safety, New York University, Washington Square, New York, NY 10003.

GRIMBERG, JUAN CARLOS, b. Buenos Aires, Argentina, Nov. 7, 21; U.S. citizen; m. 57; c. 5. APPLIED MATHEMATICS. B.A, Buenos Aires, 40, Ph.D.(appl. math), 47. Head tech. dept. thermodyn. & heat transfer, Carrier Corp, Argentina, 46-51; v.pres. res. & develop, Antaric Corp, 51-57; sr. design engr, Daniel, Mann, Johnson & Mendenhall, 58-59; res. engr, Benson Lehner Corp, 59; engr. specialist, Norair Div, Northrop Corp, 60-61, group head math. & phys. sci, 61-62; sr. staff res. & planning, Aerospace Corp, 62-64; command & control systs, Bunker-Ramo Corp, 64-66; head appl. res, Mitre Corp, 66-71; PRES, J.C. GRIMBERG & ASSOCS, 71- Asst. prof, Buenos Aires, 44-47, 56-57, assoc. prof. & prof, 57. AAAS; Am. Phys. Soc; Am. Math. Soc; Am. Econ. Asn; Am. Inst. Aeronaut. & Astronaut. Engineering systems planning development and management. Address: 3517 Launcelot Way, Annandale, VA 22003.

GRIMBLE, ROBERT WARREN, b. Rochester, N.Y, July 3, 19; m. 42; c. 2. CHEMICAL ENGINEERING. B.S, Case, 41. Chem. engr, Magnolia Petrol. Co, Texas, 41-46; E.I. DU PONT DE NEMOURS & CO, INC, 46-51, head chem. eng. div, Jackson lab, 51-56, asst. dir, 56, dir, 57-58, prod. mgr, elastomer chem. dept, 58-59, asst. dir. mfr, 59-63, DIR. far east. div, INT. DEPT, 64-68, LATIN AM. DIV, 68- Am. Chem. Soc; Am. Inst. Chem. Eng. Development of various processes; management of chemical manufacturing enterprises. Address: E.I. du Pont de Nemours & Co, Inc, 9096 DuPont Bldg, Wilmington, DE 19898.

GRIMES, CHARLES C(ULLEN), b. Norman, Okla, June 11, 31; m. 57; c. 3. SOLID STATE PHYSICS. B.S, Oklahoma, 53; M.S, Stanford, 54; Nat. Sci. Found. fel, California, Berkeley, 60-62, Ph.D.(physics), 62. Electronics physicist, U.S. Naval Air Missile Test Center, 54-55; MEM. TECH. STAFF, BELL TEL. LABS, INC, 62- U.S.N.R, 55-58, Lt.(jg). Am. Phys. Soc. Cyclotron resonance in metals; helicon waves; Fermi surfaces. Address: Bell Telephone Labs, Inc, Murray Hill, NJ 07974.

GRIMES, CHARLES K(ENNETH), b. Memphis, Tenn, Jan. 9, 23; m. 40; c. 2. AERONAUTICS. B.S, Alabama, 49; S.M, Mass. Inst. Tech, 56; Ph.D.(aeronaut), Calif. Inst. Tech, 64. U.S. AIR FORCE, 51-, proj. engr. aeronaut. eng, Laurence G. Hanscom Field, Mass, 52-53, pilot, Korea, 53-54, sect. chief struct. dynamics, dynamic loads sect, aircraft lab, Wright-Patterson Air Force Base, 56-59, exec. officer, lab, 59-60, instr. aeronaut, U.S. Air Force Inst. Tech, 62-63, asst. prof, 63-65, assoc. prof, 65-68, CHIEF STRUCTURES DIV, AIR FORCE FLIGHT DYNAMICS LAB, 68- Guest lectr, Cranfield Col. Aeronaut, 65-66; summer, Nat. Sci. Found. grant, Va. Polytech, 65; mem. structures & mat. panel adv. group for aerospace res. & develop, NATO, 69-; chmn. subpanel H-3, aeronautical vehicle fatigue, Tech. Coop. Prog, 70- U.S.A.F, 43-45, 51-, Col. Am. Inst. Aeronaut. & Astronaut. Structural dynamics and aeroelasticity; boundary layer mechanics; stress wave propagation in elastic media. Address: Structures Division, Air Force Flight Dynamics Lab, Wright-Patterson Air Force Base, OH 45433.

GRIMES, DALE M(ILLS), b. Green Mt, Iowa, Sept. 7, 26; m. 47; c. 2. ELECTRICAL ENGINEERING, PHYSICS. B.S, Iowa State, 50, M.S, 51; Ph.D.(elec. eng), Michigan, 56. Lab. asst. physics, Iowa State, 48; asst, Ames Lab, Atomic Energy Comn, 49-51; UNIV. MICH, 51-52, res. assoc, 52-54, assoc. res. physicist, 54-56, asst. prof. ELEC. ENG, 56-59, assoc. prof, 59-61, PROF, 61- Consult, Boulder Labs, Nat. Bur. Standards, 57-59; chief scientist, Conductron Corp, 60-63; consult, Dow Chem. Co, Mich; Gen. Motors Tech. Ctr; KMS Industs. AAAS; Int. Electrotech. Comn; Inst. Elec. & Electronics Eng; Am. Phys. Soc; Solar Energy Soc. Magnetism and magnetic materials; electromagnetic field theory; quantum theory; photosynthetic energy conversion. Address: 370 Rock Creek Dr, Ann Arbor, MI 48104.

GRIMES, DONALD W(ILBURN), b. Maysville, Okla, July 28, 32; m. 57; c. 3. AGRONOMY. B.S, Okla. State, 54, M.S, 56; Ph.D.(soil fertil), Iowa State, 66. Soil scientist, Soil Conserv. Serv, U.S. Dept. Agr, 55-56; asst. agronomist, Kansas State, 56-61; assoc. agron, Iowa State, 61-66; asst. water scientist, UNIV. CALIF, DAVIS, 66-71, ASSOC. WATER SCIENTIST, 71- Am. Soc. Agron; Soil Sci. Soc. Am; Int. Soc. Soil Sci. Soil, plant and water relations; crop production function determinations from water and nutrient inputs. Address: San Joaquin Valley Agricultural Research and Extension Center, 9240 S. Riverbend Ave, Parlier, CA 93648.

GRIMES, H(UBERT) H(ENRY), b. Cleveland, Ohio, Mar. 11, 29; m. 55; c. 2. SOLID STATE PHYSICS. B.S, Western Reserve, 52, M.S, 53, U.S. Pub. Health Serv. grant, 53-55, Du Pont fel, 55-56, Ph.D.(phys. chem), 56. RES. PHYSICIST, NASA, 56-, HEAD SOLID STATE PHYSICS SECT, LEWIS RES. CTR, 61- Am. Phys. Soc. Imperfections in solids, diffusion; radiation damage. Address: NASA Lewis Research Center, 21000 Brookpark Rd, Cleveland, OH 44135.

GRIMES, JOHN FRANCIS, b. Ravenswood, W.Va, Mar. 3, 27; m. 52; c. 2. GENETICS, POULTRY BREEDING. B.S, W.Va. Univ, 50, M.S, 51; Ph.D.(genetics), Ohio State Univ, 54. Geneticist, Nichols Inc, 54-58, dir. res, 58-60, v.pres-in-charge res, 60-62; geneticist, Pilch Inc, 62-64; DIR. RES, ARBOR ACRES FARM INC, 64- U.S.N. Poultry Sci. Asn; World Poultry Sci. Asn; Animal Behav. Soc. Animal genetics; poultry husbandry; hybridization; population studies; estimation and testing; behavior studies. Address: 65 Johnny Cake Lane, Glastonbury, CT 06033.

GRIMES, ORVILLE FRANK, b. San Bernardino, Calif, Jan. 13, 16; m. 41; c. 4. THORACIC SURGERY. A.B, California, 37; M.D, Northwestern, 41. Intern, Passavant Mem. Hosp, Northwestern, 41-42; asst. resident SURG, SCH. MED, UNIV. CALIF, SAN FRANCISCO, 42-44, 46-48, chief resident, 48-49, ASSOC. PROF, 49-, V.CHMN. DEPT, 64-; IN CHARGE TEACHING SURG, MEM. ATTEND. STAFF, CHIEF THORACIC SURG. SERV. & DIR. & CONSULT IN CHIEF SURG. OUTPATIENT DEPT, SAN FRANCISCO GEN. HOSP, 49- Mem. attend. staff & asst. chief thoracic surg. serv, univ. hosp, California, 49-; consult, Hamilton Air Force Base Hosp, 50- Med.C, U.S.A, 44-46. Am. Med. Asn; Am. Surg. Asn; Am. Asn. Thoracic Surg; Am. Col. Surg; Am. Col. Chest Physicians. Management of various esophageal lesions including carcinoma, strictures, acquired and short esophagus and hiatal hernias; tissue transplantation as it reflects pulmonary changes. Address: University of California Hospital, San Francisco, CA 94122.

GRIMES, PATRICK G(ERALD), b. Fort Dodge, Iowa, Dec. 13, 29; m. 58; c. 4. ELECTROCHEMISTRY, PHYSICAL CHEMISTRY. B.S, Loras Col, 52; M.S, Iowa State Univ, 56, Ph.D, 58. Asst, Iowa State Univ, 52-53; Ames Lab, Atomic Energy Comn, 53-58; res. chemist, Allis Chalmers Mfg. Co, 58-61, proj. leader, 61-62, sr. res. chemist, 63-67; McGRAW-EDISON POWER SYSTS, 67-68, CHIEF RES. SCIENTIST, 68- Chmn, Intersoc. Energy Conversion Eng. Conf, D.C, 69. Am. Chem. Soc; Am. Inst. Chem. Eng; Am. Inst. Min, Metall. & Petrol. Eng; Electrochem. Soc. Metal separation through metal chelates; reduction of ores; fuel cells; chemical processes; energy conversion; hydrometallurgy; batteries; heat transfer. Address: Research & Devêlopment Center, McGraw-Edison Power Systems, South Milwaukee, WI 53172.

GRIMES, R(ALPH) MERWIN, b. Munith, Mich, Jan. 2, 24; m. 45; c. 2. BIOCHEMISTRY. B.S, Western Michigan, 45; M.S, Vanderbilt, 49; Ph.D.(chem), Mich. State, 55. Instr. biochem, Vanderbilt, 46-49; instr. agr. chem. res, Mich. State, 49-56, asst. prof, 56-59; chem, Montana State, 59-61; mem. staff, ORTHO PHARMACEUT. CORP, 61-67, GROUP LEADER, 67- Am. Chem. Soc. Electrophoresis; cellulolytic enzymes; animal nutrition; genetic variations in hemoglobin structure. Address: 444 Rolling Hills Rd, Somerville, NJ 08876.

GRIMES, RUSSELL NEWELL, b. Meridian, Miss, Dec. 10, 35; m. 62; c. 2. INORGANIC CHEMISTRY. B.S, Lafayette Col, 57; Ph.D.(chem), Univ. Minn, 62. Fel. Harvard, 62; Univ. Calif, Riverside, 62-63; asst. prof. CHEM, UNIV. VA, 63-68, ASSOC. PROF, 68- AAAS; Am. Chem. Soc. Organometallic and boron chemistry, especially boranes, carboranes, metallocarboranes and carborane-metal complexes; synthesis and structural studies of electron-deficient cage compounds; reaction mechanisms of carborane formation and cage rearrangements. Address: Dept. of Chemistry, University of Virginia, Charlottesville, VA 22901.

GRIMES, THOMAS LEONARD, b. Huntington, W.Va, Nov. 2, 38. INDUSTRIAL & PHYSICAL PHARMACY. B.Sc, Univ. Ky, 61; M.S, Ohio State Univ, 64; Ph.D.(indust. & phys. pharm), Purdue Univ, 70. Instr. med. chem, Univ. Ky, 65-66; pharm, Purdue Univ, 66-68; SR. RES. SCIENTIST, A.H. ROBINS CO, 69- Am. Chem. Soc; Am. Pharmaceut. Asn. Chemical kinetics; stability evaluation of pharmaceuticals; packaging materials evaluations for pharmaceuticals; parenteral product development. Address: A.H. Robins Co. Research Labs, 1211 Sherwood Ave, Richmond, VA 23220.

GRIMINGER, PAUL, b. Vienna, Austria, Aug. 29, 20; U.S. citizen; m. 54; c. 4. NUTRITION. B.S, Illinois, 52, M.S, 53, fels, 53-55, Ph.D.(nutrit), 55. Asst. poultry nutrit, Illinois, 52-53; asst. prof, Nebraska, 55-57; RUTGERS UNIV, 57-62, assoc. prof, 62-64, NUTRIT, 64-66, PROF, 66- Guggenheim Mem. Found. fel, 64. R.E.M.E, 42-46. AAAS; Am. Inst. Nutrit; Poultry Sci. Asn; Animal Nutrit. Res. Coun; Soc. Exp. Biol. & Med. Vitamins in nutrition; interaction of vitamin K and anticoagulants; avian blood coagulation; nutritional requirements; antihypercholesterolemic substances and nutritional factors in atherosclerosis. Address: Dept. of Nutrition, Rutgers, The State University, P.O. Box 231, New Brunswick, NJ 08903.

GRIMLEY, EUGENE BURHANS, III, b. Passaic, N.J, Oct. 28, 41; m. 64; c. 2. INORGANIC CHEMISTRY. B.A, Olivet Col, 63; Ph.D.(chem), Univ. Iowa, 71. Summer, chemist, Am. Brakeshoe Corp, 63, Burlington Industs, Inc, 64; ASST. PROF. CHEM, MISS. STATE UNIV, 71- Am. Chem. Soc. Studies on stoichiometry; rates and mechanisms of ligand substitution and electron transfer reactions in solution; synthesis and characterization of transition metal complexes; chlorine oxidation reduction studies; environmental studies on pollution. Address: Dept. of Chemistry, Mississippi State University, Drawer CH, State College, MS 39762.

GRIMLEY, PHILIP M, b. New York, N.Y, Mar. 10, 35; m. 62; c. 3. MEDICINE, PATHOLOGY. B.S, City Col. New York, 56; M.D, Albany Med. Col, 61. Nat. Heart Found. res. fel, N.Y. State Dept. Health, 58-60; intern, Cornell Div, Bellevue Hosp, 61-62; resident path, California, San Francisco, 62-63; NAT. CANCER INST, 63-65, staff pathologist, 65-70, HEAD ULTRASTRUCTURAL PATH, 70- Dipl. Am. Bd. Path, 67. U.S.P.H.S, 63-68, Sr. Asst. Surgeon. Col. Am. Path; Am. Soc. Exp. Path; Am. Asn. Path. & Bact; Am. Soc. Microbiol. Fine structure of normal and neoplastic cells; cellular effects of virus infections; development of viruses. Address: National Cancer Institute, Bethesda, MD 20014.

GRIMLEY, ROBERT T(HOMAS), b. North Attleboro, Mass, Jan. 3, 30; m. 52; c. 5. PHYSICAL CHEMISTRY. B.S, Massachusetts, 51; Eastman Kodak Co. fel. & Ph.D.(phys. chem), Wisconsin, 58. Res. chemist, Corning Glass Works, 57-59; res. assoc. physics, Chicago, 59-61; asst. prof. chem, PURDUE UNIV, 61-66, ASSOC. PROF, 66- Res. assoc, Univ. Chicago, 59-61. U.S.A.F, 51-53, 1st Lt. Am. Chem. Soc; Am. Phys. Soc. High temperature mass spectrometry; kinetics of vaporization; high temperature chemistry. Address: Dept. of Chemistry, Purdue University, Lafayette, IN 47907.

GRIMM, ARTHUR F, b. Berwyn, Ill, June 16, 31; m. 54; c. 2. PHYSIOLOGY, HISTOLOGY. B.S, Northwestern, 53; D.D.S. & M.S, Illinois, 56, Ph.D.

(physiol), 62. Instr. PHYSIOL. & HISTOL, cols. med. & dent, UNIV. ILL, 58-62, asst. prof, col. med, 62-66, assoc. prof. COLS. DENT. & MED, 66-69, PROF, 69- Career develop. award, 64-69, 70-74. U.S.A.F, 56-58, Capt. Am. Dent. Asn. Growth and development of striated muscles. Address: Dept. of Physiology & Histology, University of Illinois Colleges of Dentistry & Medicine, 808 S. Wood St, Chicago, IL 60612.

GRIMM, C(ARL) A(LBERT), b. Cincinnati, Ohio, Apr. 1, 26; m. 48; c. 3. MATHEMATICS. M.A, Cincinnati, 52. Instr. MATH, S.DAK. SCH. MINES & TECHNOL, 52-55, asst. prof, 55-57, assoc. prof, 57-64, PROF, 64- U.S.N, 44-46. Math. Asn. Am; Am. Math. Soc. Modern algebra. Address: Dept. of Mathematics, South Dakota School of Mines & Technology, Rapid City, SD 57701.

GRIMM, CHARLES H(ENRY), b. New York, N.Y, Oct. 28, 11; m. 38; c. 1. ORGANIC CHEMISTRY. B.Sc, N.Y. Univ, 34, 35-37; Columbia, 36-38. Res. chemist, Fritzsche Bros. Inc, 35-43; chief chemist & dir. lab, Felton Chem. Co, Inc, 43-53; dir. flavor develop, INT. FLAVORS & FRAGRANCES, INC, 53-66, V.PRES, FLAVOR CREATION RES, 66- DIR, 67-, Mem. food liaison panel, Nat. Acad. Sci-Nat. Res. Coun. Tech. consult, Navy, Army, Air Force Inst. Gt. Britain, Toronto, Ont, Can, 43-45. AAAS; Am. Chem. Soc; Inst. Food Technol. Essential oil and flavor; development of new and unique flavoring bases. Address: International Flavors & Fragrances, Inc, 521 W. 57th St, New York, NY 10019.

GRIMM, GEORGE W(ALTER), b. Oil City, Pa, Dec. 1, 36; m. 61; c. 2. PHYSICS. B.S, Rochester, 58; M.S, Lehigh, 60; Ph.D.(physics), 64. Instr. physics, Lehigh, 61-64; Nat. Acad. Sci-Nat. Res. Coun. res. assoc, U.S. Navy Electronics Lab, 64-65; mem. res. staff, tech. ctr, OWENS-CORNING FIBERGLAS CORP, 65-66, aerospace res. lab, 66-69, mgr. physics res. dept, 69-71, ACT. MGR. RES. GROUP, 71- Strain pulse propagation in single crystals; fiber reinforced composite structures. Address: Mt. Parnassus Dr, Granville, OH 43023.

GRIMM, G(ORDON) R(ALPH), b. Madison, Wis, Dec. 11, 19; m. 46; c. 5. PLANT PATHOLOGY. B.S, Wisconsin, 46, M.S, 47, Ph.D.(plant path), 53. Proj. assoc, Wisconsin, 52-54; PLANT PATHOLOGIST, PLANT SCI. RES. DIV, AGR. RES. SERV, U.S. DEPT. AGR, 54- U.S.C.G, 41-42. Am. Phytopath. Soc. Citrus pathology. Address: U.S. Dept. of Agriculture, 2120 Camden Rd, Orlando, FL 32803.

GRIMM, HENRY H, b. Annville, Pa, Mar. 29, 13; m. 37; c. 1. MICROWAVE PHYSICS, ELECTRONIC ENGINEERING. A.B, Lebanon Valley Col, 35; M.A, Pennsylvania, 36; Pa. State, 41-43; Maryland, 47-51; Syracuse, 51-53. Instr. physics, Pa. State, 41-43; physicist, Aircraft Radio Lab, 43-45; radio engr, Naval Res. Lab, D.C, 46-47, electronics engr. & scientist, 47-51; proj. engr. microwave develop, electronics lab, GEN. ELEC. CO, 51-55, supvr. microwave projs, 55-56, consult. engr. microwave & radar, 56-58, consult. microwaves, 58-62, sr. liaison engr, 62-64, CONSULT. engr, adv. projs. develop. opers, heavy mil. equip. dept, 64-71; ADV. DEVELOP. ENG, HEAVY MIL. ELECTRONIC SYSTS, 71- Consult, Bur. Aeronaut, Dept. Navy, 46-48, 49-50. AAAS; Am. Phys. Soc; Inst. Elec. & Electronics Eng; Sci. Res. Soc. Am. Radar system engineering; application of solid state developments to microwave physics and engineering; electrically scanned antennas; digital and analog radar signal processing; computer controlled precision radar performance monitoring and diagnostics during operation; radar performance monitor training systems. Address: Heavy Military Electronic Systems, Court Street Plant, Bldg. 4, Room 57, General Electric Co, Syracuse, NY 13201.

GRIMM, JAMES K, b. St. Paul, Va, Jan. 17, 30; m. 48; c. 3. ENTOMOLOGY, HUMAN ANATOMY. B.S.Ed, Concord Col, 56; M.S, Univ. Tenn, Knoxville, 58, Ph.D.(entom), 63. PROF. BIOL, MADISON COL.(VA), 58- U.S.N, 51-56. Entom. Soc. Am. Transovarian transmission by insects; microenvironmental studies relating to insects. Address: Dept. of Biology, Madison College, Harrisonburg, VA 22801.

GRIMM, LOUIS J(OHN), b. St. Louis, Mo, Nov. 30, 33; m. 67; c. 1. APPLIED MATHEMATICS. B.S, St. Louis Univ, 54; M.S, Ga. Inst. Technol, 60; Ph.D.(math), Univ. Minn, 65. Chemist, Walter Reed Army Inst. Res, 56-58; instr. MATH, Univ. Minn, 60-65; asst. prof, Univ. Utah, 65-69; ASSOC. PROF, UNIV. MO-ROLLA, 69- Summers, chemist, U.S. Pub. Health Serv, 58-61, instr, Armstrong State Col, 61; lectr, Univ. Minn, 66; Nat. Sci. Found. res. grants, 69- U.S.A, 56-58, Res, 58-62. Am. Math. Soc; Soc. Indust. & Appl. Math; Math. Asn. Am; Ger. Soc. Appl. Math. & Mech. Qualitative differential equations; difference and functional equations; chemical kinetics; delay-differential equations; numerical analysis. Address: Dept. of Mathematics, University of Missouri, Rolla, MO 65401.

GRIMM, ROBERT B(LAIR), b. N.Y.C, Nov. 26, 30. BOTANY, PLANT PATHOLOGY. B.S, Miami (Fla), 55, M.S, 57; fel, La. State, 59-60, Ph.D.(bot), 60. Asst, Miami (Fla), 56-57; La. State, 57-59; Nicholls State Col, 60-62; res. assoc. bot, Miami (Fla), 62-64; ASST. PROF. BOT, FLA. ATLANTIC UNIV, 64- U.S.A, 51-53. AAAS; Phycol. Soc. Am; Am. Inst. Biol. Sci; Bot. Soc. Am. Cryptogamic botany; effects of environmental factors on growth and development of algae. Address: Dept. of Biological Sciences, Florida Atlantic University, Boca Raton, FL 33432.

GRIMM, SAMUEL O(LIVER), b. Red Lion, Pa, Sept. 3, 89. PHYSICS. B.Pd, Pa. State Norm. Sch, 10, A.B, Lebanon Valley Col, 12, A.M, 18, Sc.D, 42; summers, Columbia, 13-16. Teacher, pub. sch, Pa, 07-09; prin, Lebanon Valley Acad, 12-15; prof. ed, Lebanon Valley Col, 15-20, prof. physics & math. & registrar, 20-43; vis. prof, Franklin & Marshall Col, 43-44; asst. prof. physics, Pa. State Col, 44-45; secy. finance comt, LEBANON VALLEY COL, 45-46, PROF. PHYSICS, 46-, secy. bd. trustees, 58-68, treas, 52-58, registrar, 46-49. Am. Phys. Soc; Am. Asn. Physics Teachers; Inst. Elec. & Electronics Eng. Address: Dept. of Physics, Lebanon Valley College, Annville, PA 17003.

GRIMM, W(ILBUR) W(INFIELD), b. Cleveland, Ohio, Dec. 3, 06; m. 36; c. 4. ZOOLOGY. B.S, Col. Wooster, 30; M.A, Miami (Ohio), 32; Ph.D.(zool), Ohio State, 37. Asst. zool, Miami (Ohio), 30-32; Ohio State, 32-35; prof. natural sci. & head dept, Lincoln Mem. Univ, 35-41; PROF. BIOL, BRADLEY UNIV, 41-, DEAN, GRAD. SCH, 65-, assoc. dean, 64-65. Development in fishes. Address: Graduate School, Bradley University, 1502 W. Bradley, Peoria, IL 61606.

GRIMMELL, WILLIAM C, b. Brooklyn, N.Y, Mar. 16, 41; m. 66; c. 1. COMPUTER SCIENCE. B.S, Mass. Inst. Technol, 61; Nat. Defense Educ. Act fel, Univ. Mich, Ann Arbor, 61-64, M.S, 62 & 64, Nat. Sci. Found. grant, 64-65, Ph.D.(elec. eng), 65. Mem. tech. staff control systs. res, Bell Tel. Labs, 66-68; SR. MATHEMATICIAN, HOFFMANN-LA ROCHE, 68- Inst. Elec. & Electronics Eng. Mathematical control theory; industrial process modeling; computer applications to process control. Address: Applied Section, Hoffmann-La Roche, Nutley, NJ 07034.

GRIMMETT, EARL S(HEPHERD), b. Paris, Idaho, June 9, 20; m. 42; c. 4. CHEMICAL ENGINEERING. B.S, Idaho, 43, M.S, 48. Res. engr, Galligher Co, 49-51; process design engr, Am. Cyanamid Corp, 52-53; group leader, chem. eng. res. & develop, Phillips Petrol. Co, 53-66; advan. applns. group leader, Idaho Nuclear Corp, 66-71; SPEC. ASST. TO PROCESS RES. SECT. HEAD, IDAHO CHEM. PROGS, ALLIED CHEM. CORP, 71- U.S.A, 43-46. Am. Inst. Chem. Eng. Development of a fluidized bed calcination process for radioactive waste disposal. Address: 1085 Syringa Dr, Idaho Falls, ID 83401.

GRIMSBY, F(RANK) NORMAN, b. Seattle, Wash, Sept. 15, 27; m. 55; c. 3. CHEMICAL ENGINEERING. B.S, Washington, Seattle, 48, Eng. Exp. Sta. fel. & M.S, 49; Dow fel. & Sc.D, Mass. Inst. Technol, 54. Engr, Calif. Res. Corp, 48; instr. indust. chem, Mass. Inst. Technol, 51-52; engr. process develop, design & eval, Shell Develop. Co, 53-54, 56-69, head chem. eng. div, Carrington Plastics Lab, Shell Res. Ltd, England, 69-71, SR. ENGR, POLYMERS DIV, SHELL CHEM. CO, 71- Engr, process design, Chem. Ctr, Md, 54-55; Phosphate Develop. Works, Ala, 55; Westvaco Res. Detachment, W.Va, 55-56. Chem.C, U.S.A, 54-56. Am. Chem. Soc; Am. Inst. Chem. Eng. Design and economics of chemical processes; epoxy resins; high-pressure polyethylene; Ziegler polyethylene and polypropylene; polymerization catalysis and kinetics. Address: Polymers Research & Development, Shell Chemical Co, One Shell Plaza, P.O. Box 2463, Houston, TX 77001.

GRIMSON, KEITH S(ANFORD), b. Munich, N.Dak, Apr. 21, 10; m. 34; c. 3. SURGERY. B.A, North Dakota, 30, B.S, 31; M.D, Rush Med. Col, 34. Intern, Presby. Hosp, Chicago, 33-34; fel, Chicago, 35-39; Belgian-Am. Ed. fel, Ghent, 39-40; instr, grad. sch. med, Chicago, 40-42; assoc. SURG, SCH. MED, DUKE UNIV, 42-44, asst. prof, 44-47, assoc. prof, 48-49, PROF, 49- Asst, Billings Hosp, Chicago, 35-39, res, 40-42. Soc. Exp. Biol. & Med; Am. Soc. Clin. Invest; Soc. Univ. Surg; Am. Soc. Pharmacol; Am. Med. Asn; Am. Physiol. Soc; Am. Col. Surg. Physiology of circulation and respiration; pharmacology of drugs acting on autonomic nervous system; surgery, hypertension and sympathectomy in ulcer and vagotomy; megacolon and colon resection; achalasia, peripheral vascular diseases and related operations and drugs; general surgery. Address: Duke University Medical Center, Durham, NC 27710.

GRIMSRUD, DAVID T, b. Minot, N.Dak, Aug. 14, 38; m. 60. LOW TEMPERATURE PHYSICS. B.A, Concordia Col.(Minn), 60; M.S, Minnesota, 63, Ph.D.(physics), 65. Fulbright grant, Rome, 65-66; asst. prof. PHYSICS, Muhlenburg Col, 66-69, ASSOC. PROF, 69-71; ST. OLAF COL, 71- Am. Phys. Soc; Am. Asn. Physics Teachers. Liquid helium temperature scale; transport phenomena near critical point. Address: Dept. of Physics, Paracollege, St. Olaf College, Northfield, MN 55057.

GRINA, LARRY D(ALE), b. Seattle, Wash, June 12, 43; m. 64; c. 2. ORGANIC & PETROLEUM CHEMISTRY. B.S, Univ. N.Dak, 65; Ph.D.(org. chem), Univ. Wash, 70. SR. CHEMIST, TEXACO, INC, BEACON, 70- Am. Chem. Soc. Synthetic and physical organic chemistry. Address: 23 Scott Dr, Wappingers Falls, NY 12590.

GRINDALL, EMERSON L(EROY), b. Jackson, Mich, Sept. 13, 16; m. 37; c. 4. MATHEMATICS. A.B, Olivet Col, 38; M.S, Mich. State Col, 47. Teacher, pub. sch, Mich, 38-46; instr. math, Mich. State Col, 46-51; asst. prof. ENG. RES, PA. STATE UNIV, 51-55, assoc. prof, 55-66, PROF, 66- Am. Soc. Qual. Control; Am. Math. Asn. Acoustics; physical properties of sea water; statistical analysis; design of experiments for research; reliability; maintainability; weapon system management. Address: 1265 Smithfield St, State College, PA 16801.

GRINDELAND, RICHARD E(DWARD), b. Decorah, Iowa, Mar. 11, 29; m. 52; c. 5. PHYSIOLOGY. B.A, Luther Col.(Iowa), 53; Ph.D.(environ. physiol), Univ. Iowa, 58. Asst. prof, Univ. Sask, 58-61; Nat. Insts. Health fel, 60, 61-62; vis. asst. prof. physiol, Howard Univ, 62-63; RES. SCIENTIST BIOCHEM. ENDOCRINOL, AMES RES. CTR, NASA, 62- U.S.A, 46-47, Sgt. Endocrine Soc; Am. Physiol. Soc. Physiology of growth hormone and prolactin. Address: Dept. of Biochemical Endocrinology, Ames Research Center, Moffett Field, CA 94035.

GRINDLAY, J(OHN), b. Glasgow, Scotland, June 24, 33; Can. citizen; m. 60; c. 1. THEORETICAL PHYSICS. B.Sc, Glasgow, 55; Caird traveling scholar, Oxford, 55-58, D.Phil, 58. Proj. assoc. theoret. chem, Wisconsin, 58-59; instr. theoret. physics, British Columbia, 59-60, asst. prof, 60-64; ASST. RES. OFF. PURE CHEM, NAT. RES. COUN. CAN, 64-; ASSOC. PROF. PHYSICS, UNIV. WATERLOO, 65-69, PROF, 69- Am. Phys. Soc; Can. Asn. Physicists; Brit. Inst. Physics & Phys. Soc. Elastic, dielectric and thermal properties of crystals. Address: Dept. of Physics, University of Waterloo, Waterloo, Ont, Can.

GRINDROD, PAUL (EDWARD), b. Oconomowoc, Wis, Apr. 5, 25; m. 45; c. 3. FOOD TECHNOLOGY, CHEMICAL ENGINEERING. B.S, Wisconsin, 50, M.S, 51, Ph.D.(food tech), 54. Asst. food tech, Wisconsin, 51-54; res. dir, C.J. Berst & Co, Wis, 54-58, CHIEF PACKAGING RES, OSCAR MAYER & CO, 58- U.S.A, 43-45. Am. Chem. Soc; Am. Dairy Sci. Asn; Am. Inst. Chem. Eng. Food packaging; design and packaging equipment design. Address: Packaging Research, Oscar Mayer & Co, 910 Mayer Ave, Madison, WI 53704.

GRINDSTAFF, TEDDY HODGE, b. Blount Co, Tenn, Aug. 15, 32; m. 62; c. 1. PHYSICAL CHEMISTRY. B.S, Tennessee, 58, M.S, 61, Ph.D.(phys. chem), 63. Proj. engr. prod. eval, Celanese Corp. Am, N.C, 63-64; res. chemist fiber surface, E.I. DU PONT DE NEMOURS & CO, 64-69, SR. RES. CHEMIST, DACRON RES. LAB, 69- Summer, chemist, Tenn. Eastman Co, 58. U.S.N, 51-55. Am. Chem. Soc. Adsorption of fatty acids on copper and nickel single crystals; determination of the kinetics of radioactive fatty soil detergency from polymer materials; surface chemistry; adhesion. Address: Dacron Research Lab, E.I. du Pont de Nemours & Co, P.O. Box 800, Kinston, NC 28501.

GRINDSTAFF, WYMAN K(EITH), b. Ada, Okla, May 13, 39; m. 62; c. 2. INORGANIC CHEMISTRY. B.S, E.Cent. State Col, 59; M.S, Oklahoma, 65, Ph.D.(inorg. chem), 66. Asst. prof. CHEM, SOUTHWEST MO. STATE COL, 65-68, ASSOC. PROF, 68- Summer assoc. chemist, Ames. Lab, Iowa State Univ, 67. Am. Chem. Soc. Synthesis, physical properties, structure and bonding of inorganic coordination compounds. Address: Dept. of Chemistry, Southwest Missouri State College, Springfield, MO 65802.

GRINE, DONALD R(EAVILLE), b. Dunkirk, N.Y, Aug. 21, 30; m. 53; c. 2. GEOPHYSICS. B.S, Mass. Inst. Tech, 52, M.S, 54, Ph.D.(geophys), 59. Physicist, Stanford Res. Inst, 59-61, Schlumberger Well Surv. Corp, 62-64; sect. head, 64-65; dept. head, Stanford Res. Inst, 65-71; SR. RES. SCIENTIST, SYSTS, SCI. & SOFTWARE, 71- Acoust. Soc. Am; Am. Geophys. Union; Seismol. Soc. Am. Explosions; shock waves; seismology; ultrasonics. Address: Systems, Science & Software, P.O. Box 1620, La Jolla, CA 92037.

GRINER, L(YNN) A(DEL), b. Mesa, Ariz, May 22, 13; m. 44; c. 4. PATHOLOGY, BACTERIOLOGY. B.S, Utah State Agr. Col, 36, Am. Wildlife Inst. fel, 36-38, M.S, 39; D.V.M, Colo. Agr. & Mech. Col, 49, Am. Vet. Med. Asn. fel, 56; Ph.D, California, 59. Jr. refuge mgr, U.S. Dept. Interior, 39-40; res. biol. technician, State Dept. Game & Fish, Ariz, 40-42; assoc. vet. pathologist, sch. vet. med, Colorado State, 49-59, prof. path. & bact. & pathologist, 59-64; PATHOLOGIST & DIR. HEALTH DEPT, SAN DIEGO ZOO, 64- Mem. comt. animal lit, Nat. Acad. Sci; adj. assoc. prof, Univ. Calif, San Diego. Med.C, U.S.A, 42-45. Am. Vet. Med. Asn; U.S. Animal Health Asn; Wildlife Disease Asn; Am. Asn. Lab. Animal Sci. Comparative pathology in the field of exotic animals with correlation to comparative anatomy and infectious diseases. Address: Health Dept, San Diego Zoo, Box 551, San Diego, CA 92112.

GRING, JOHN L(UKINS), b. Farmer City, Ill, June 1, 10; m. 36; c. 3. CHEMISTRY. B.S, Illinois, 32, M.S, 33, Ph.D.(anal. & inorg. chem), 36. Anal. chemist, Gen. Elec. Co, Mass, 36-37, develop. chemist, 37-42, plant chemist, 42-43, sect. leader, 43-44; chief chemist Cardox Corp, Chicago, 44-46; res. technologist, Sinclair Ref. Co, Ind, 46-48, sect. leader, Sinclair Res. Labs, Ill, 48-64, sr. res. chemist, Sinclair Res, Inc, 64-66, sr. res. scientist, Arco Res. Ctr, 66-69; RETIRED. Am. Chem. Soc. Inorganic chemistry; catalysts; preparations. Address: Route 2, Box 189, Lowell, AR 72745.

GRINGAUZ, ALEX, b. Memel, Lithuania, May 18, 34; U.S. citizen; m. 59; c. 3. PHARMACEUTICAL & ORGANIC CHEMISTRY. B.S, Long Island, 56; M.S, Purdue, 58, Res. Found. fel, 58-60, Ph.D.(pharmaceut. chem), 60. Asst. org. chem, Purdue, 56-58; Nat. Insts. Health fel, 60-61; asst. prof. ORG. & PHARMACEUT. CHEM, BROOKLYN COL. PHARM, LONG ISLAND, 61-66, ASSOC. PROF, 66-, ACTING CHMN. DEPT, 70- Am. Chem. Soc; Am. Pharmaceut. Asn. Synthesis and stability of organic medicinal agents. Address: 1055 E. Broadway, Woodmere, NY 11598.

GRINKER, ROY R(ICHARD), SR, b. Chicago, Ill, Aug. 2, 00; m. 24; c. 1. PSYCHIATRY. B.S, Chicago, 19, M.D, Rush Med. Col, 21; Vienna, Zurich, London, Hamburg, 24-25; Vienna, Germany, London, 33-35. Intern, Psychopathic Hosp, Chicago, 21; Wesley Mem. Hosp, 21-22; Cook County Hosp, 22-24; instr. neurol, med. sch, Northwestern, 24-27; Chicago, 27-28, asst. clin. prof. med, 28-29, asst. prof. neurol, 29-31, assoc. prof, 31-35, assoc. prof. psychiat. & head dept, 35-36; CHMN. DIV. PSYCHIAT, MICHAEL REESE HOSP, 36-, DIR. INST. PSYCHOSOM. & PSYCHIAT. RES. & TRAINING, 51- Attend. neurologist, Cook County Hosp, 26-28, 40-; Rockefeller fel, 33-34; res. assoc, Chicago Inst. Psychoanal, 40-; attend. psychiatrist, Cook County Psychopathic Hosp, Chicago, 46-50; lectr, Social Serv. Admin, Chicago, 46-50; clin. prof, col. med, Univ. Ill, 51-69; prof, dept. psychiat, Univ. Chicago, 69- Gold Medal award, Soc. Biol. Psychiat, 70; Salmon Medal, N.Y. Acad. Med, 70. U.S.A, 17-19, Med.C, 42-46, Col; Legion of Merit, 44. AAAS; Am. Psychosom. Soc.(pres, 52); fel. Am. Psychiat. Asn; Am. Neurol. Asn; Am. Psychoanal. Asn; Am. Asn. Neuropath.(v.pres, 40); Asn. Res. Nerv. & Ment. Disease; fel. Am. Med. Asn; Int. Psychoanal. Asn; Acad. Psychoanal.(pres, 61); Am. Psychopath. Asn; Am. Col. Neuropsychopharmacol; fel. N.Y. Acad. Sci. Schizophrenia. Address: Michael Reese Hospital, 2959 S. Ellis Ave, Chicago, IL 60616.

GRINNAN, EDWARD L(EONARD), b. Phila, Pa, Oct. 14, 22; m. 54; c. 1. BIOCHEMISTRY. B.S, Pa. Mil. Col, 49; M.S, Delaware, 50, Biochem. Res. Found. & univ. fel. & Ph.D.(chem), 52. Sr. biochemist, ELI LILLY & CO, 52-58, dept. head glandular prods. develop, 58-67, RES. SCIENTIST BIOCHEM, 67- AAAS; Am. Chem. Soc; N.Y. Acad. Sci. Nucleic acids; polypeptide hormones; enzymes; antibiotics. Address: Biochemical & Physiological Research Division, Eli Lilly & Co, Indianapolis, IN 46250.

GRINNELL, ALAN DALE, b. Minneapolis, Minn, Nov. 11, 36; m. 62. NEUROPHYSIOLOGY. B.A, Harvard, 58, Nat. Insts Health fel, 58-59, Harvard Soc. Fels. jr. fel, 59-62, Ph.D.(biol), 62. Nat. Sci. Found. fel. biophys, Univ. Col, London, 62-64; asst. prof. ZOOL, UNIV. CALIF, LOS ANGELES, 64-66, assoc. prof, 66-71, PROF, 71- AAAS; Am. Zool. Soc; Zool. Soc. London; Am. Physiol. Soc; Biophys. Soc; Soc. Neurosci; N.Y. Acad. Sci. Neurophysiology of audition, especially in echolocating bats; synaptic physiology; development and specificity in the nervous system. Address: 510 E. Rustic Rd, Santa Monica, CA 90402.

GRINNELL, EDWARD H(OEPFNER), b. Jet, Okla, Apr. 22, 21; m. 44; c. 4. PHARMACOLOGY. B.S, Southwest. State Col.(Okla), 47; M.S, Colorado, 49; Ph.D.(med. sci), Oklahoma, 56; M.D, Creighton, 62. Instr. pharm, Georgia,

49-50; assoc. prof, Southwest. State Col.(Okla), 50-52; fel, Am. Heart Asn, med. sch, Oklahoma, 56-57; asst. prof. PHYSIOL. & PHARMACOL, SCH. MED, CREIGHTON UNIV, 57-62, ASSOC. PROF, 62- ASST. PROF. MED, 70- Estab. investr. prog, U.S. Pub. Health Serv, 63- Lederle med. faculty award, 59-61. U.S.N, 42-45. AAAS; fel. Am. Soc. Clin. Pharmacol. & Therapeut; Am. Soc. Exp. Biol. Oral agents in diabetes mellitus; pathophysiology of vasopressin. Address: Dept. of Physiology & Pharmacology, Creighton University School of Medicine, Omaha, NE 68131.

GRINNELL, LAWRENCE I(RVING), b. Flushing, N.Y, June 14, 89; m. 30; c. 1. ORNITHOLOGY. A.B, Harvard, 12; M.S, Cornell, 43, Ph.D.(ornith), 47. RES. COLLAB, CORNELL UNIV. LAB. OF ORNITH. & BIRD PHOTOGRAPHER, EXPEDS, 38- U.S.A, 17-19. Assoc. Am. Ornith. Union; assoc. Wilson Ornith. Soc. Life history of common redpoll; bird photography; birdlife of Churchill, Manitoba; Hudson Bay bird metropolis; breeding Lapland longspurs. Address: 710 Triphammer Rd, Ithaca, NY 14850.

GRINNELL, ROBERT S, JR, b. N.Y.C, June 11, 34. MARINE GEOLOGY, OCEANOGRAPHY. A.B, Harvard, 56; M.A, Univ. Kans, 58; Ph.D, State Univ. N.Y. Binghamton, 72. Res. asst. marine geol, Lamont-Doherty Geol. Observ, 61-67; instr. geol, State Univ. N.Y. Col. Fredonia, 70-71. U.S.A, 58-60. Paleont. Soc; N.Y. Acad. Sci. Continental margin sediments and sedimentary processes; structure and texture of modern oyster bioherms; relationships of invertebrate fossils. Address: 1158 Fifth Ave, New York, NY 10029.

GRINNELL, SHERMAN K, Orgn. Behav, see Suppl. I to 11th ed, Soc. & Behav. Vols.

GRINOCH, PAUL, b. N.Y.C, Aug. 24, 22; m. 51; c. 1. NUCLEAR PHYSICS & SCIENCE. B.S, N.Y. Univ, 48, 48-60. Group leader, mat. lab, N.Y. Naval Shipyard, 48-53; scientist, theoret. sect, Walter Kidde Nuclear Labs, 53-56; groups leader, nuclear labs, Am. Mach. & Foundry Co, 56-58; staff consult, preliminary design dept, GRUMMAN AEROSPACE CORP, 58-60, HEAD, NUCLEAR RES. SECT, RES. DEPT, 60- Ord.C, U.S.A, 43-46. AAAS; Am. Nuclear Soc; Inst. Elec. & Electronics Eng; Am. Phys. Soc. Research and supervision of research on aerospace nuclear and radiation problems; radiation effects on components, materials and microorganisms; nuclear power and applications; radiation shielding. Address: Nuclear Research Section, Research Dept, Grumman Aerospace Corp, Bethpage, NY 11714.

GRINOLS, RICHARD BYRON, b. Seattle, Wash. June 22, 35; m. 55; c. 2. CHEMISTRY, MARINE BIOLOGY. B.S, Washington (Seattle), 62, M.S, 65. Fishery biologist, Washington (Seattle), 61-65; Bur. Commerical Fisheries, Fish & Wildlife Serv, 65-68; INSTR. CHEM. & TECH. SCI, PENINSULA COL, 68- Crown Zellerbach Found. achievement award, 63-64; Sigma Xi res. grant, 65- U.S.A.F, 52-56. Am. Soc. Ichthyol. & Herpet. Systematic oceanic ichthyology and field ecology relating to eastern subarctic Pacific region. Address: Dept. of Fisheries Technology, Peninsula College, Port Angeles, WA 98362.

GRINS, GEORGE, b. Riga, Latvia, Mar. 3, 42; U.S. citizen; m. 69; c. 1. ORGANIC CHEMISTRY. B.S, Univ. Wis-Milwaukee, 65; Robert A. Welch fel, Tex. Christian Univ, 67-69, Ph.D.(org. chem), 70. FEL. ORG. CHEM, UNIV. ALA, TUSCALOOSA, 71- U.S.A, 69-71, Capt. Am. Chem. Soc. Study of the scope and mechanism of the alpha-methylation of pyridines by Raney metals with the use of vapor phase chromatography, nuclear magnetic resonance, infrared, ultraviolet, and thin layer chromatography techniques. Address: Dept. of Chemistry, University of Alabama, University, AL 35486.

GRINSFELDER, HENRY, b. Spokane, Wash, Sept. 2, 08; m. 32; c. 1. CHEMICAL ENGINEERING. B.S, Mass. Inst. Tech, 31; St. Joseph's Col.(Pa), 43; Temple, 49. Chem. engr, E.I. du Pont de Nemours & Co, N.Y, 31-34; asst. to pres, Kem Prods. Co, N.J, 34-36; chem. engr, Textileather Corp, Ohio, 36-38, plant supt, 38-39, tech. coordinator, 39-40; chem. engr, De Vilbiss Co, 40; head applications lab, ROHM & HAAS CO, 41-57, res. supvr, 57-61, asst. to dir. res, 61-64, asst. to v.pres. & dir. res, 64-70, ASST. RES. DIR, ADMIN, 70- Lectr, grad. sch. med, Univ. Pa, 64-65. AAAS; Am. Chem. Soc; Am. Statist. Asn. High polymers and synthetic resins for use in adhesives, coated fabrics, coatings, plasticizers, printing inks, textile specialties, plastics, fibers, soil conditioning and stabilization; statistical methods as applied to research, sales, finance and stock market results and forecasts. Address: Lower Mountain Rd, R.D. 1, Box 101, New Hope, PA 18938.

GRINSTEAD, ROBERT R(USSELL), b. Sacramento, Calif, Apr. 15, 23; m. 49; c. 3. PHYSICAL & INORGANIC CHEMISTRY. B.S, California, 46; Ph.D. (chem), Calif. Inst. Tech, 50. Res. chemist, DOW CHEM. CO, 49-65, proj. leader, 53-65, sr. res. chemist, 65-69, ASSOC. SCIENTIST, WEST. DIV. RES. CTR, 69- U.S.A, 43-46. AAAS; Am. Chem. Soc; Fedn. Am. Sci. Applications of ion exchange and solvent extraction in industrial organic chemistry; water pollution problems; solid waste reclamation; recovery of metals and minerals from ores, brines, sea water. Address: Western Division Research Center, Dow Chemical Co, 2800 Mitchell Dr, Walnut Creek, CA 94598.

GRINSTEIN, REUBEN H(ENRY), b. Dallas, Tex, Aug. 7, 35; m. 64. PHYSICAL & ORGANIC CHEMISTRY. B.S, Southern Methodist, 57; R.A. Welch Found. fel, Rice, summer 60, Humble Oil Co. fel, winter 60, Ph.D.(chem), 61. RES. CHEMIST, SHELL CHEM. CO, 62- Vis. fel, Leicester, 61-62. Sigma Xi chem. award, 61. Am. Chem. Soc; The Chem. Soc. Reaction mechanism studies; synthesis; chemical process studies. Address: P.O. Box 216, Deer Park, TX 77636.

GRINTER, LINTON E(LIAS), b. Kansas City, Mo, Aug. 28, 02; m. 26; c. 2. STRUCTURAL ENGINEERING. B.S, Kansas, 23, C.E. 30; scholar, Illinois, 23-24, M.S, 24, fel, 24-26, Ph.D.(eng), 26; LL.D, Ariz. State; hon. D.Sc, Univ. Akron, 69. Design engr, Standard Oil Co, Ind, 26-28; assoc. prof. civil eng, Agr. & Mech. Col. Texas, 28-29, prof. struct. eng, 29-37; dean grad. dean grad. div. & dir. civil eng, Armour Inst. Tech, 37-39, v.pres. & dean grad. sch, 39-40, Ill. Inst. Tech, 40-46, res. prof. civil eng. & mech, 46-52; dean grad. sch. & dir. res, UNIV. FLA, 52-69, exec. v.pres, Univ,

69-70, CHMN, SELF STUDY & FUTURE PLANNING, 70- Consult, War Manpower Comn, 43; Res. & Develop. Bd, Off. Secy. Defense, 49-53; wind vibrations of missile launch towers, 60-65; U.S. Off. Ed, 64-65. Mem. adv. comt, Nat. Sci. Found; Weapons Develop. Ctr, Eglin AFB; chmn, comt. ship struct. design, Nat. Res. Coun, 53-59; comt. Inter-Am. Sci. Co-op, Nat. Acad. Sci, 60; dir. study eng. technol. educ, Am. Soc. Eng. Educ. & Nat. Sci. Found, 69-71. Coord. 6th serv. command, Army Specialized Training Prog, 43-44. Hon. mem. Am. Soc. Civil Eng; Am. Soc. Mech. Eng; Am. Soc. Eng. Educ.(pres, 53; Lamme Medal, 58); Am. Concrete Inst; Int. Asn. Bridge & Struct. Eng. Theory and design of modern steel structures; wind stresses in skyscrapers; design of continuous frames with emphasis upon numerical analysis of plane stress problems and plasticity. Address: Room 334, Tigert Hall, University of Florida, Gainesville, FL 32601.

GRIPSHOVER, PAUL J, b. Cincinnati, Ohio, Dec. 1, 35; m. 57; c. 3. METALLURGICAL ENGINEERING. B.S, Purdue, 57; M.S, Ohio State, 60. Metall. engr. mat. res, Battelle Mem. Inst, 57-60, proj. leader, 60-62, asst. div. chief, 62-66, div. chief, dept. mat. eng, 66-71, SECT. MGR. PROCESSING TECHNOL, BATTELLE COLUMBUS LABS, 71- Ord.C, U.S.A, 58. Materials process development related to atomic energy, industry and aerospace applications. Address: Dept. of Materials Engineering, Battelle Columbus Labs, 505 King Ave, Columbus OH 43201.

GRISAMORE, NELSON T(HOMAS), b. Sioux City, Iowa, Jan. 27, 21; m. 44. COMPUTER SCIENCE. B.S, Illinois, 48, M.S, 50; Ph.D.(physics), George Washington, 54. Res. assoc. rocket ballistics, George Washington, 42-46; physicist, appl. physics lab, Hopkins, 47; res. assoc, electronics res. proj, George Washington, 50-55, res. scientist, opers. res. group, 56-57, asst. prof. elec. eng, 56-58, assoc. prof, 58-60, prof. eng. & appl. sci, 60-69, exec. off, dept. elec. eng, 60-62, 66-67, asst. dean. res, 62-66, dir, Ctr. Measurement Sci, 63-66; EXEC. SECY, ABM DATA PROCESSING SYST, NAT. ACAD. SCI, 67- Consult, U.S.A, 46-47. AAAS; Am. Phys. Soc; Inst. Elec. & Electronics Eng. Computer circuits and logic; physical electronics; information retrieval; operations research; systems reliability; measurement science. Address: ABM Data Processing Systems, National Academy of Science, 2101 Constitution Ave, Washington, DC 20418.

GRISAR, J(OHANN) MARTIN, b. Görlitz, Ger, July 10, 29; U.S. citizen; m. 60; c. 3. ORGANIC & MEDICINAL CHEMISTRY. B.S, Swiss Fed. Inst. Technol, 54; Ph.D.(org. chem), Mass. Inst. Technol, 59. Res. chemist, Charles Pfizer & Co, Inc, 59-63; proj. leader MED. CHEM, William S. Merrell Co, 63-67, SECT. HEAD, MERRELL-NAT. LABS, RICHARDSON-MERRELL INC, 67- Am. Chem. Soc; Swiss Chem. Soc; Soc. Ger. Chem. Medium-sized ring transannular reactions; synthetic neuroleptic, diuretic, hemodynamic, hypolipidemic, anti-thrombotic and anti-diabetic agents. Address: Organic Chemistry Dept, Merrell-National Labs, Cincinnati, OH 45215.

GRISARU, M(ARCUS) T(HEODORE), b. Stefanesti, Romania, May 15, 29; m. 64. PHYSICS. B.A.Sc, Toronto, 55; fel, Princeton, 56-57, M.A, 57, Proctor fel, 57-58, Ph.D.(physics), 58. Res. assoc. PHYSICS, Illinois, 58-60; asst. prof, McGill Univ, 60-62; BRANDEIS UNIV, 62-67, ASSOC. PROF, 68- Elementary particles physics and quantum field theory. Address: Dept. of Physics, Brandeis University, Waltham, MA 02154.

GRISCHKOWSKY, D(ANIEL) RICHARD, b. St. Helens, Ore, Apr. 17, 40; m. 61. PHYSICS. B.S, Ore. State Univ, 62; A.M, Columbia Univ, 65, Ph.D. (physics), 68. Res. assoc, Columbia Radiation Lab, Columbia Univ, 68-69; RES. STAFF MEM. LASER PHYSICS, IBM WATSON RES. CTR, 69- Am. Phys. Soc. Interactions of microwaves with paramagnetic spins; interactions of laser light with atomic vapors. Address: Dept. of Physical Sciences, IBM Watson Research Center, P.O. Box 218, Yorktown Heights, NY 10598.

GRISCOM, ANDREW, b. Boston, Mass, Oct. 12, 28; m. 57; c. 2. GEOPHYSICS. A.B, Harvard, 49, M.A, 56. GEOPHYSICIST, REGIONAL BR, U.S. GEOL. SURV, 57- U.S.M.C.R, 51-62, 1st Lt. Geol. Soc. Am; Mineral. Soc. Am; Am. Geophys. Union. Interpretation of magnetic and gravity data; relationship of petrology to the magnetic properties of rocks. Address: U.S. Geological Survey, 345 Middlefield Rd, Menlo Park, CA 94025.

GRISCOM, RICHARD WILLIAM, b. Chattanooga, Tenn, Apr. 15, 26; m. 53; c. 3. ORGANIC CHEMISTRY. B.S, Chattanooga, 45; M.S, Tennessee, 48. Chemist, Reilly Tar & Chem. Corp, Tenn, 45-46; Reilly Labs, Ind, 46; phosphate div, Monsanto Chem. Co, Ala, 48-49; res. chemist, res. div, Tenn. Prod. & Chem. Corp, Tenn, 49-62; Tensyn Div, Velsicol Chem. Corp, 62; ROCK HILL LAB, CHEMETRON CORP, 64-65, sr. res. chemist, 65-68, res. assoc, 68-70, SR. SCIENTIST, 70- Am. Chem. Soc; Am. Soc. Animal Sci. Synthetic organic research on phosgene derivatives; organic research on aromatic hydrocarbons, including oxidation and chlorination of hydrocarbons; esterification or aromatic and aliphatic acids. Address: Rock Hill Lab, Chemetron Corp, Newport, TN 37821.

GRISHAM, GENEVIEVE D(W ER), b. Glens Falls, N.Y, Apr. 13, 27; m. 49, 65; c. 1. PHYSICAL CHEMISTRY. Scholar, State Univ. N.Y. Col. for Teachers, 44-48, A.B, 47, M.A, 48; fel, Rochester, 49-50, 51-52, Ph.D. (chem), 53. Aeronaut. res. scientist, Lewis Flight Propulsion Lab, NASA, 53-56; MEM. STAFF RADIOCHEM, LOS ALAMOS SCI. LAB, 56- AAAS. Nuclear reactions; radiochemistry; high temperature nuclear reactors. Address: Los Alamos Scientific Lab, P.O. Box 1663, Los Alamos, NM 87544.

GRISHAM, JOE WHEELER, b. Brush Creek, Tenn, Dec. 5, 31; m. 55. MEDICINE, PATHOLOGY. A.B, Vanderbilt, 53, M.D, 57. Resident path, SCH. MED, WASH. UNIV, 57-60, instr, 60-61, asst. prof, 61-67, assoc. prof, 67-69, PROF. PATH. & ANAT, 69- Nat. Cancer Inst. fel. 58-59; Life Ins. Med. Res. Fund fel, 59-61; Markle scholar, 64-69. U.S.N, 61-63, Res, 57-61, Lt. Comdr. Am. Soc. Exp. Path; Am. Asn. Path. & Bact; Int. Acad. Path. Liver diseases, especially cirrhosis; regulation of cellular proliferation. Address: Dept. of Pathology, School of Medicine, Washington University, St. Louis, MO 63110.

GRISKEY, R(ICHARD) G(EORGE), b. Pittsburgh, Pa, Jan. 9, 31; m. 55; c. 2. CHEMICAL ENGINEERING. B.S, Carnegie Inst. Technol, 51, M.S, 55, Am. Chem. Soc. fel, 55-57, univ. fel, 57-58, Shell Chem. Co. fel. & Ph.D.(chem. eng), 58. Sr. engr. textile fibers, E.I. du Pont de Nemours & Co, Inc, Del, 58-60; asst. prof. chem. eng, Univ. Cincinnati, 60-62; prof, Va. Polytech. Inst. & State Univ, 52-66; chmn. dept, Univ. Denver, 66-68; dir. res, Newark Col. Eng, 68-71; DEAN COL. APPL. SCI. & ENG, UNIV. WIS-MILWAUKEE, 71- C.Eng, 51-53, Res, 53-57, 1st Lt. Polymer engineering; thermodynamics; transport processes. Address: 4633 N. Cramer, Milwaukee, WI 53211.

GRISLEY, DANIEL W(ILLIAM), JR, b. Providence, R.I, July 27, 30; m. 55; c. 2. ORGANIC CHEMISTRY. A.B, Brown, 52; Ph.D.(chem), Yale, 58. Res. chemist org. chem, Monsanto Chem. Co, Mass, 56-67; sr. scientist, Syracuse Univ. Res. Corp, 67-70; MEM. STAFF, W.R. GRACE & CO, 70- Am. Chem. Soc. Synthetic, sulfur and physical organic chemistry. Address: W.R. Grace & Co, 62 Whitemore Ave, Cambridge, MA 02140.

GRISMORE, ROGER, b. Ann Arbor, Mich, July 12, 24; m. 50; c. 1. PHYSICS. B.S, Michigan, 47, M.S, 48, fel, 49-50, Ph.D.(physics), 57. Asst. physics, eng. res. inst, Michigan, 47-56; asst. physicist, Argonne Nat. Lab, 56-61, assoc. physicist, 61-62; assoc. prof. PHYSICS, Lehigh Univ, 62-67; specialist, Scripps Inst. Oceanog, Univ. Calif, San Diego, 67-71; PROF. IND. STATE UNIV, TERRE HAUTE, 71- U.S.N, 44-46, Res, 46-54, Lt. Am. Phys. Soc; Am. Geophys. Union; Am. Asn. Physics Teachers; Am. Soc. Limnol. & Oceanog; N.Y. Acad. Sci. Nuclear physics; electronic instrumentation for nuclear measurements; environmental physics; marine radioactivity. Address: Dept. of Physics, Indiana State University, Terre Haute, IN 47809.

GRISOLIA, SANTIAGO, b. Valencia, Spain, Jan. 6, 23; nat; m. 49; c. 2. BIOCHEMISTRY. B.A, Inst. Nacional de Cuenca, 39; M.D, Valencia, 44; hon. Dr, Univ. Salamanca, 69. Lab. instr. physiol, med. sch, Valencia, 42-44, asst. prof. physiol. chem, 44-45; fel. biochem, col. med, N.Y. Univ, 45-46; vis. asst. prof. biochem, Univ. Chicago, 46-47; asst. prof. & res. assoc. physiol. chem, Univ. Wis, 48-54; assoc. prof. MED. & BIOCHEM, UNIV. KANS, 54-59, PROF, 59-, CHMN. DEPT. BIOCHEM, 62-, dir, McIlvain Lab, 54-59. Estab. investr, Am. Heart Asn, 53-58; hon. prof, Univ. Valencia Med. Sch, 67. Cross of Alfonso X, Ministry of Educ. & Sci, Spain, 67. Am. Soc. Biol. Chem; Span. Soc. Physiol; Span. Soc. Biochem. Mechanism of enzymatic reactions; carbon dioxide fixation; nitrogen and carbohydrate metabolism. Address: Dept. of Biochemistry, University of Kansas Medical Center, 408 Wahl Hall E, Kansas City, KS 66103.

GRISSINGER, EARL H, b. Lancaster, Pa, Nov. 28, 31; m. 59; c. 4. SOIL SCIENCE, PHYSICS. B.S, Pa. State, 53, M.S, 55, Ph.D.(agron), 57. RES. SOIL SCIENTIST, AGR. RES. SERV, U.S. DEPT. AGR, 60- U.S.A, 56-59. AAAS; Am. Soc. Agron; Soil Conserv. Soc. Am; Clay Minerals Soc. Nature of cohesion of natural soil materials; defining soil properties which determine cohesion. Address: Sedimentation Lab, U.S. Dept. of Agriculture, Box 30, Oxford, MS 38655.

GRISSOM, DAVID, b. Dallas, Tex, Aug. 22, 35; m. 60; c. 1. SOLID STATE ELECTRONICS. B.S, Texas, 58 & 61, M.S, 62, Nat. Sci. Found. grant, 63-65, Ph.D, 65. Assoc. engr, apparatus div, Tex. Instruments Inc, 58-59; res. asst. electronic mat. res. lab, Texas, 61-65; admin. asst. res, Nat. Geophys. Co, 65-67; sr. proj. engr, geotech. div, Teledyne Industs, 67-69; CHIEF ENGR, ROGERS EXPLOR, INC, 69- Summer assoc. engr, Tex. Instruments Inc, 60-62; consult, Chatlon Inc, Tex, 63-64. Am. Soc. Mech. Eng; Inst. Elec. & Electronics Eng; Nat. Soc. Prof. Eng; Soc. Explor. Geophys; Am. Phys. Soc. Geophysical instruments and oil exploration techniques; digital processing of seismic data; low temperature dielectric loss. Address: 2029 Winrock, Houston, TX 77027.

GRISSOM, JOHN T(HOMAS), b. Knoxville, Tenn, Feb. 1, 40; m. 61; c. 3. ATOMIC PHYSICS. B.S, Univ. Miss, 62, M.S, 66; univ. assistantship, Duke Univ, 62-63; U.S. Pub. Health Serv. fel. & Ph.D.(physics), Univ. Tenn, Knoxville, 70. Res. physicist, phys. sci. lab, nuclear physics br. U.S. Army Missile Command, Redstone Arsenal, Ala, 64-67; STAFF MEM, SANDIA LABS, 70- Consult, res. & eng. develop. div, Bulova Watch Co, Inc, N.Y, 66-70. U.S.A.F.R, 58-64. Am. Phys. Soc. Arc physics; nuclear cross sections; nuclear decay spectra; resolution distortion of experimental data; data smoothing techniques; random number generation; electron impact excitation and ionization phenomena in the rare gases; vacuum arc ion energy distributions. Address: Division 1412, Sandia Labs, Albuquerque, NM 87110.

GRISSOM, ROBERT L(ESLIE), b. Macon Co, Ill, Mar. 5, 17; m. 44; c. 4. INTERNAL MEDICINE. B.S, Illinois, 39, M.S. & M.D, 41. From asst. to asst. prof. internal med, Illinois, 47-53; from assoc. prof. to prof. & chmn. dept, COL. MED, UNIV. NEBR, OMAHA, 53-70, PROF. MED. & HEAD DIV, CARDIOL, 70- Markle scholar, 50-55. U.S.A, 42-46, Maj. Fedn. Clin. Res; fel. Am. Col. Physicians. Cardiovascular diseases. Address: Division of Cardiology, University of Nebraska at Omaha College of Medicine, 42nd & Dewey Sts, Omaha, NE 68105.

GRISWOLD, AZEL A(LAN), b. Livingston, Wis, Feb. 20, 33; m. 52; c. 2. ORGANIC CHEMISTRY. B.S.Ed, Western Illinois, 59, M.S.Ed, 60; Res. Found. fel, Iowa State, 60-61, Nat. Insts. Health fel, 61-63, Ph.D.(chem), 63. Res. chemist, chem. div, Union Carbide Corp, 63-69; MEM. STAFF, RES. CTR, BURLINGTON INDUST. INC, 69- U.S.A.F, 53-57, Res, 57-61, S/Sgt. Am. Chem. Soc. Photochemistry of organic compounds; synthesis of organic compounds by means of new chemical reactions. Address: Research Center, Burlington Industries, Inc, P.O. Box 21327, Greensboro, NC 27420.

GRISWOLD, DANIEL H(ALSEY), b. Colorado Springs, Colo, Jan. 10, 09; m. 31; c. 2. GEOLOGICAL ENGINEERING. Geol.Eng, Colo. Sch. Mines, 30. Geophysicist & asst. geol, U.S. Smelting Ref. & Mining Co, 30-31; asst. engr, C.T. Griswold, Mining Engr, 31-32; lessee, Magnolia Petrol. Co, 32-33; instrumentman, Mid Rio Grande Conserv. Dist, 33; jr. topog. engr, conserv. br, U.S. Geol. Surv, 33-35; jr. agr. engr, Soil Conserv. Serv, U.S. Dept. Agr, N.Mex, 35-38, asst. agr. engr, Utah, 38-40, assoc. geologist,

N.Mex, 41-46, soil conservationist, 46-49, geologist, eng. & watershed planning unit, regional tech. serv. ctr, 49-69; ground water div, Ore. State Engr. Off, 69; ENG. GEOLOGIST, FOUND. SCI, INC, 69- A.U.S, 41-45, Lt. Col.(Ret). Geol. Soc. Am; Soil Conserv. Soc. Am; Asn. Eng. Geol; Am. Inst. Mining, Metall. & Petrol. Eng. Occurrence of ground water; geology of dam and reservoir sites; geology of tunnel sites. Address: 6656 S.W. Miles Ct, Portland, OR 97223.

GRISWOLD, DANIEL PRATT, JR, b. Birmingham, Ala, Nov. 15, 28; m. 53; c. 2. VETERINARY MEDICINE. D.V.M, Auburn, 51. With U.S. Dept. Agr, 51; private practice, 51-52, 55-61; HEAD, CHEMOTHER. DIV. CANCER RES, SOUTH. RES. INST, 61- Consult, breast cancer task force, Nat. Cancer Inst. Vet.C, 52-55, 1st Lt. AAAS; Am. Vet. Med. Asn. Chemotherapy of experimental animal tumor systems and study of carcinogenesis of chemical agents; toxicity determinations of anticancer agents in small animals. Address: Southern Research Institute, 2000 Ninth Ave. S, Birmingham, AL 35205.

GRISWOLD, EDWARD MANSFIELD, b. New Haven, Conn, Mar. 28, 05; m. 39; c. 2. MECHANICAL ENGINEERING. B.S, Carnegie Inst. Tech, 27; M.S, Pennsylvania, 39. Design engr, Am. Foundry Equip. Co, 27-28; res. engr, Metals Coating Co. Am, 28-29; engr. qual. control, Weston Elec. Instrument Co, N.J, 29-30; teacher, high sch, Conn, 32-42; instr. eng. graphics, COOPER UNION, 42-47, asst. prof, 47-52, assoc. prof. MECH. ENG, 52-62, prof, 62-71, EMER. PROF, 71- Consult, Shades, Inc, 43-50; Ardco Mfg. Co, 45; eng. designer, Byrne Assocs, 47-52; engr, Bell Tel. Labs. & Am. Tel. & Tel. Co, 53-58; Nat. Sci. Found. res. grants, 59-61; engr, Singer Co, 62- Am. Soc. Eng. Educ.(distinguished serv. award, 69); Nat. Soc. Prof. Eng. Engineering graphics and design; communication of complex systems and ideas clearly, precisely and easily; design of machines and systems, especially kinematics; lubrication; economics. Address: 141 Washington Ave, Chatham, NJ 07928.

GRISWOLD, (CHESTER) ERNEST, b. Milan, Kans, Aug. 13, 05; m. 31; c. 6. INORGANIC CHEMISTRY. A.B, Kansas, 27, Ph.D.(chem), 34. From instr. to prof. CHEM, South Dakota, 31-47; assoc. prof, UNIV. KANS, 47-55, PROF, 55- Am. Chem. Soc. Salt effects in nonaqueous solvents; reactions of cyano-complexes; conductivity and ion-pair equilibria in nonaqueous solvents. Address: Dept. of Chemistry, College of Liberal Arts & Sciences, University of Kansas, Lawrence, KS 66044.

GRISWOLD, GEORGE B, b. Ponca City, Okla, Dec. 9, 28; m. 52; c. 4. MINING ENGINEERING. B.S, N.Mex. Inst. Mining & Technol, 55; M.S, Arizona, 57, Ph.D, 67. Jr. engr, San Manuel Copper Corp, 55; chief engr, Blackrock Div, Wah Chang Mining Corp, Calif, 55-56; fel. & mining engr, U.S. Bur. Mines, Ariz, 56-57; mining engr. & faculty assoc, N.Mex. Inst. Mining & Technol, 57-64; Nat. Sci. Found. trainee, mining & geol. eng, Arizona, 64-65; assoc. prof. mining eng, N.Mex. Inst. Mining & Technol, 65-70, chmn. dept. petrol. & mining eng, 68-70; MGR. EXPLOR, WEST. CAN. & ALASKA, GETTY OIL CO, 70- Consult, Proj. Mohole, Brown & Root Co, 64-67. U.S.A, 51-53, 1st Lt. Am. Inst. Mining, Metall. & Petrol. Eng. Rock mechanics; engineering geology; ore deposits. Address: Getty Oil Co, Suite 1904, 1177 W. Hastings St, Vancouver 1, B.C, Can.

GRISWOLD, HERBERT E(DWARD), b. Kansas City, Kans, Apr. 15, 17; m. 43; c. 4. INTERNAL MEDICINE. B.A, Reed Col, 39; M.S. & M.D, Oregon, 43. Asst. physiol, med. sch, Oregon, 41-43; intern, French Hosp, San Francisco, 44, gen. res, 44-45; fel. pediat, Harriet Lane Home, Univ. Hosp, Hopkins, 47-48; asst. res. internal med, Henry Ford Hosp, Detroit, 48-49; asst. prof. physiol. & med, MED. SCH, UNIV. ORE, 49-54, assoc. prof. MED, 54-58, PROF, 58- Med.C, 45-47, Capt. Cardiovascular research; congenital heart disease; ballistocardiography. Address: Dept. of Medicine, University of Oregon Medical School, Portland, OR 97201.

GRISWOLD, KENNETH EDWIN, JR, b. Ruston, La, Oct. 22, 43; m. 67; c. 1. CLINICAL CHEMISTRY, TAXONOMY. B.S, La. Tech. Univ, 65, M.S, 67; Ph.D. (biol), Univ. S.C, 71. Entomologist, Central Mills, 65-67; lab. supvr, Columbia Hosp, 68-70; instr. chem. & physiol, sch. gen. studies, Univ. S.C, 69-71; CLIN. CHEMIST & CLIN. INSTR. BIOCHEM, MED. CTR, LA. STATE UNIV. SHREVEPORT, 71-, co-investr. res. grants, med. sch, 71-74. Clin. chemist, Confederate Mem. & Vet. Admin. Hosps, 71- AAAS; Genetics Soc. Am; Am. Soc. Mammal; Asn. Mil. Surg. U.S. Biochemical taxonomy; biochemical polymorphisms in mammalian populations; elucidation of primary structure of macromolecules; molecular taxonomy. Address: Dept. of Biochemistry, Louisiana State University Medical Center, Shreveport, LA 71101.

GRISWOLD, MICHAEL DAVID, b. Norman, Okla, Feb. 17, 44; m. 65; c. 2. BIOCHEMISTRY. B.S, Wyoming, 66, Nat. Defense Ed. Act. trainee & Ph.D. (biochem), 69. NAT. INSTS. HEALTH FEL. PHYSIOL. CHEM, UNIV. WIS, MADISON, 69- Study of nuclear proteins during amphibian metamorphosis, their changes and interactions under the influence of thyroxine. Address: Middleton Shores Apartments, Apt. 110D, Middleton, WI 53562.

GRISWOLD, NORMAN E(RNEST), b. Yankton, S.Dak, July 17, 35; m. 59; c. 2. INORGANIC CHEMISTRY. B.A, Kansas, 57; Am. Chem. Soc. Petrol. Res. Fund fels, 60-61, 62-63, Nebraska, M.S, 61, Monsanto Res. summer fel, 63, Ph.D.(chem), 66. Instr. CHEM, NEBR. WESLEYAN UNIV, 63-65, asst. prof, 65-66, ASSOC. PROF, 66-, acting head dept, 67-68. Lectr, Nat. Sci. Found. Summer Inst. Introd. Phys. Sci, 66-69, assoc. dir, 70, 71; vis. assoc. prof, Univ. Ill, Urbana, 70-71; mem. adv. bd, Willard Grant Press, Inc, Mass, 70- AAAS; Am. Chem. Soc; fel. Am. Inst. Chem. Synthesis and polarographic reduction of the copper II chelates of some β-keto imines; synthesis of coordination compounds. Address: Dept. of Chemistry, Nebraska Wesleyan University, Lincoln, NE 68504.

GRISWOLD, PAUL H(ULETT), JR, b. Springfield, Mass, Oct. 20, 20; m. 45; c. 2. ORGANIC CHEMISTRY. B.S, Am. Int. Col, 42; M.S, Yale, 44; Ph.D. (org. chem), 48. Asst. fluorocarbons, Manhattan Proj, 44-46; asst. prof. chem, Robert Col, Istanbul, 47-48; fel. bridgehead compounds, Maryland, 48-49; res. chemist, ORG. COLORED PIGMENTS, E.I. DU PONT DE NEMOURS & CO, INC, 49-58, plants tech. sect, 58-63, SR. RES. CHEMIST, COLORS RES, 63- Am. Chem. Soc. Carbohydrates; fluorocarbons; organic colored pigments. Address: 405 Nichols Ave, McDaniel Crest, Wilmington, DE 19803.

GRISWOLD, R(ETTIG) ARNOLD, b. Peru, Ind, Apr. 17, 98; m. 23; c. 4. SURGERY. B.A, Harvard, 21; M.D, Louisville, 25. Intern path, Louisville City Hosp. & Univ. Louisville, 25-27; surg, Western Reserve & Lakeside Hosp, 27-32; assoc. prof. SURG, SCH. MED, UNIV. LOUISVILLE, 32-37, prof, 38-69, CLIN. PROF, 69-, head dept, 38-52. Consult, Vet. Admin, 46-52; off. surg. gen, U.S. Army, 46-; surgeon, Kosair Crippled Children's Hosp; St. Joseph's Infirmary; Children's Hosp; Ky. Baptist Hosp; mem. surg. staff, John N. Norton Mem. Infirmary. Distinguished serv. award, Nat. Safety Coun, 63; Comdr, Mil. Order Ayacucha, Repub. Peru. U.S.N, 16-21, Med.C, 42-46, Col; Legion of Merit. Int. Soc. Surg; fel. Am. Med. Asn; fel. Am. Surg. Asn; Am. Asn. Surg. of Trauma (v.pres, 48, pres, 50); fel. Am. Col. Surg.(2nd v.pres, 57-58). Surgery of trauma; gastric surgery. Address: Dept. of Surgery, University of Louisville School of Medicine, Louisville, KY 40208.

GRISWOLD, ROBERT EDWARD, b. Peekskill, N.Y, May 27, 32; m. 58; c. 2. ANALYTICAL CHEMISTRY. B.S, New Bedford Inst. Tech, 54; M.S, Northeastern, 56; Ph.D.(anal. chem), Mass. Inst. Tech, 60. Asst. prof. chem, Lebanon Valley Col, 60-67, assoc. prof, 67-71; CLIN. CHEMIST, CLIN. LAB, HARRISBURG POLYCLINIC. HOSP, 71- Am. Chem. Soc. Automated methods of clinical analysis; computer collection and processing of analytical data. Address: Clinical Lab, Harrisburg Polyclinic Hospital, P.O. Box 3410, Harrisburg, PA 17005.

GRISWOLD, ROBERT L(YNN), b. Cleveland, Ohio, Feb. 13, 24; m. 49; c. 3. PHYSIOLOGY, PSYCHIATRY. B.S, West. Reserve Univ, 46, M.D, 49; Ph.D. (biophys), Univ. Calif, 55. Lectr. physiol, Univ. Calif, 54; supvry. physiologist, biochem. & biophys, Walter Reed Army Inst. Res, 54-57; physician & surgeon, STOCKTON STATE HOSP, 57-60, chief of res, 60-69, RESIDENT IN PSYCHIAT, 69- Am. Psychiat. Asn. Metabolic, endocrine and general biological aspects of mental illness. Address: Stockton State Hospital, 510 E. Magnolia St, Stockton, CA 95202.

GRISWOLD, THOMAS W(ILLIAM), b. Los Angeles, Calif, July 29, 25; m. 49; c. 2. PHYSICS. A.B, California, Berkeley, 49, M.A, 51, Ph.D.(physics), 54. Mem. tech. staff, semiconductor div, Hughes Aircraft Co, 53-58; dir. device res, Continental Device Corp, 58-71, TECH. DIR. TELEDYNE SEMICONDUCTOR, 71- U.S.A, 43-46, Sgt. Am. Phys. Soc; Inst. Elec. & Electronics Eng. Electron spin resonance; semiconductor devices. Address: Teledyne Semiconductor, 12515 Chadron Ave, Hawthorne, CA 90250.

GRITMON, TIMOTHY F, b. Ft. Edward, N.Y, July 6, 29. INORGANIC CHEMISTRY. B.S, Siena Col.(N.Y), 51; M.S, Union Col.(N.Y), 53; Ph.D.(chem), Fla. State, 68. ASST. PROF. CHEM, ST. BONAVENTURE UNIV, 68- Am. Chem. Soc. Thermodynamics of the lanthanides. Address: Dept. of Chemistry, St. Bonaventure University, St. Bonaventure, NY 14778.

GRITTER, ROY J(OHN), b. Grand Rapids, Mich, Jan. 31, 30; m. 52; c. 5. ORGANIC CHEMISTRY. A.B, Calvin Col, 51; Sohio fel. & Ph.D.(org. chem), 55. Res. assoc. & fel. chem, Chicago, 56; instr, Connecticut, 56-59, asst. prof, 59-63; res. chemist, SAN JOSE RES. LAB, IBM CORP, 63-68, MGR, ANAL. ORG. GROUP, 68- Am. Chem. Soc; The Chem. Soc. Mechanisms of free radical reactions; oxidation and the effect of structure on free radicals, including coordination effects; analytical chemistry of polymeric systems; chromatography; analysis of complex organic mixtures; characterization of polymers; computerization and computer enhancements of analytical equipment. Address: IBM Research Labs, San Jose, CA 95114.

GRITTINGER, THOMAS FOSTER, b. Milwaukee, Wis, Oct. 23, 33; m. 67; c. 1. ECOLOGY, BOTANY. B.S, Wisconsin-Milwaukee, 58, Nat. Sci. Found. fel, summer 66, univ. fel, 67-68, Ph.D.(bot), 69; M.S, Wisconsin, Madison, 62; Marquette, 64-65. Instr. zool, Wisconsin-Milwaukee, 62-65; BOT. & ZOOL, SHEBOYGAN CAMPUS, UNIV. WIS, 68-69, ASST. PROF, 69- Ecol. Soc. Am. Bog ecology and string bog development. Address: Dept. of Botany & Zoology, University of Wisconsin, P.O. Box 719, Sheboygan, WI 53081.

GRITTON, EARL THOMAS, b. Tipton, Iowa, Sept. 26, 33; m. 52; c. 3. PLANT BREEDING, CROP SCIENCE. B.S, Iowa State Univ, 60, M.S, 61; Ph.D.(crop sci), N.C. State Univ, 64. Asst. prof. AGRON, UNIV. WIS, MADISON, 64-70, ASSOC. PROF, 70- U.S.A, 54-56. Am. Soc. Agron; Crop Sci. Soc. Am. Breeding, genetics and cultural practices for processing peas, especially Pisum sativum; genetic resistance to plant diseases. Address: Dept. of Agronomy, University of Wisconsin, Madison, WI 53706.

GRIVSKY, EUGENE M(ICHAEL), b. Pskov, Russia, Dec. 20, 11; nat; m. 35; c. 2. ORGANIC CHEMISTRY. B.S, Brussels, 36, M.S, 38, D.Sc, 40. Res. assoc. phys. & org. chem. with Profs. J. Timmermans & G. Chavanne, Brussels & Int. Bur. Phys. Chem. Standards, Belgium, 39-40; res. chemist & group leader, Pharmaceut. div, Union Chim. Belgium, 41-57; SR. ORG. RES. CHEMIST, WELLCOME RES. LABS, BURROUGHS WELLCOME CO, 57- Abstractor, Chem. Abstr, 58- Estonian Army, 31-32; Belgian Army Res, 51-62. AAAS; fel. Am. Inst. Chem; N.Y. Acad. Sci; Am. Chem. Soc; The Chem. Soc; Chem. Soc. Belgium; Chem. Soc. France; Pharmacol. Soc. Japan. Stereochemistry; glycols oxidation by micororganisms; synthetic organic and medicinal chemistry; chemotherapy; sulfonamides; antihistamines; tranquilizers; antidepressant, hypotensive and sympatholytic agents; anti-inflammatory and antipyretic substances; catalysis; mechanism of reactions. Address: Wellcome Research Labs, Burroughs Wellcome Co, 3030 Cornwallis Rd, Research Triangle Park, NC 27709.

GRIZZELL, ROY A(MES), JR, b. Sweetwater, Tenn, Mar. 14, 18; m. 49; c. 2. FISH & GAME MANAGEMENT, FORESTRY. B.S, Georgia, 39; M.S, Michigan, 47, Ph.D.(wildlife mgt), 51. Res. biologist, U.S. Fish & Wildlife Serv, 47-49, refuge mgr, 52-55; BIOLOGIST, SOIL CONSERV. SERV, U.S. DEPT. AGR, 55- U.S.A, 41-46, 51-52, Capt. Wildlife Soc; Soil Conserv. Soc. Am; Am. Fisheries Soc. Agriculture; management of soil and water resources for fish and wildlife. Address: Soil Conservation Service, U.S. Dept. of Agriculture, 5401 Federal Bldg, Little Rock, AR 72201.

GRIZZLE, JAMES ENNIS, b. Herald, Va, Apr. 20, 30; m. 51; c. 3. STATISTICS. B.S, Berea Col, 51; M.S, Va. Polytech, 53; Ph.D.(exp. statist), N.C. State Col, 60. Asst. animal husb, Va. Polytech, 52-54; anal. statistician, White Sands Proving Ground, 54; asst. statist, N.C. State Col, 56; res. assoc. BIOSTATIST, SCH. PUB. HEALTH, UNIV. N.C, CHAPEL HILL, 57-60, asst. prof, 60-64, assoc. prof, 64-69, PROF, 69- Statistician, med. lab, Army Chem. Ctr, 55-56; U.S. Pub. Health Serv. Biomet. Soc; Am. Statist. Asn; Am. Pub. Health Asn. Biostatistics; analysis of categorical data; applications to clinical medicine and other medical research. Address: Dept. of Biostatistics, University of North Carolina School of Public Health, Chapel Hill, NC 27514.

GROAT, RICHARD A(RNOLD), b. New York, N.Y, Dec. 11, 15; m. 43; c. 2. PATHOLOGY. B.A, Tennessee, 37; M.S, Wisconsin, 39, Alumni Res. Found. scholar & Ph.D.(anat. & chem), 41; M.D, Bowman Gray Sch. Med, 52. Instr. anat, Emory, 41-42; Oglethorpe, 42-43; assoc. neurol, med. sch, Northwestern, 43-44, asst. prof, 44-46; anat, Bowman Gray Sch. Med, Wake Forest Col, 46-47, assoc. prof. & dir. dept, 47-52; assoc. prof, Mayo Found, Minnesota & consult, Mayo Clinic, 52-54; practicing physician, 54-57; resident & instr. path, Bowman Gray Sch. Med, Wake Forest Col. & N.C. Baptist Hosp, 57-60; pathologist, Wesley Long Hosp, 60-61; OWNER & PATHOLOGIST, SENTINEL LABS, 61- With Off. Sci. Res. & Develop, 43-45. Am. Physiol. Soc; Am. Asn. Anat; Am. Med. Asn. Nervous system; endocrines; vascular system; microscopical methods; clinical cytology. Address: 1321 N. Elm St, Greensboro, NC 27401.

GROB, DAVID, b. New York, N.Y, Feb. 23, 19; m. 48; c. 3. INTERNAL MEDICINE. B.S, City Col, 37; Columbia, 38; M.D, Hopkins, 42. Intern MED, hosp, Hopkins, 42-43, asst. res. & fel, 45-48, instr, sch. med, 48-51, asst. prof, 51-55, assoc. prof, 55-58; PROF, STATE UNIV. N.Y. DOWNSTATE MED. CTR, 58-, ASST. DEAN, 62-; DIR. MED. SERV, MAIMONIDES HOSP, 58-, RES. & ED, 60- Instr, Hopkins, 53-54, physician, hosp, 51-58. Consult, Nat. Cancer Inst, 51-54; U.S. Army Hosp, Ft. Meade, 53-58; Surgeon Gen, U.S. Army, 58. Med.C, 43-45, Capt. Am. Physiol. Soc; Am. Soc. Clin. Invest; Am. Soc. Pharmacol. & Exp. Med; Am. Neurol. Asn; Am. Med. Asn; Am. Col. Physicians. Neuromuscular disease and physiology; clinical pharmacology. Address: Maimonides Hospital of Brooklyn, 4802 Tenth Ave, Brooklyn, NY 11219.

GROB, HOWARD S(HEA), b. Oakland, Calif, June 18, 32; m. 60; c. 2. PHYSIOLOGY, ENDOCRINOLOGY. B.S, City Col. New York, 57; M.S, N.Y. Univ, 58, fel, 59-62, Ph.D.(biol), 62. Lectr. biol, Hunter Col, 62-63, instr, 63-64; asst. prof. physiol, col. dent, N.Y. Univ, 64-69; ASSOC. PROF, 69-71; BIOL, ADELPHI UNIV, 71- Res. grants, 62-64, 65-68. U.S.A, 53-55. AAAS; Am. Soc. Zool; N.Y. Acad. Sci; Soc. Exp. Biol. & Med; Soc. Study Reproduction; Int. Soc. Psychoneuroendocrinol; Am. Physiol. Soc; Harvey Soc. Physiology of reproduction; hystophysiology of ovarian follicle; endocrine physiology; cell and tissue differentiation. Address: Dept. of Biology, Adelphi University, Garden City, NY 11530.

GROB, ROBERT L(EE), b. Wheeling, W.Va, Feb. 13, 27; m. 52; c. 4. ANALYTICAL CHEMISTRY. B.S, Col. Steubenville, 51; M.S, Virginia, 54, Ph.D. (chem), 55. Res. anal. chemist, Esso Res. & Eng. Co, 55-57; asst. prof. ANAL. CHEM, Wheeling Col, 57-60, assoc. prof, 60-63; VILLANOVA UNIV, 63-67, PROF, 67- Sig.C, 45-47, Sgt. Am. Chem. Soc. Organic reagents for complexing of trace metals; gas chromatography; air and water pollution and control. Address: Dept. of Chemistry, Villanova University, Villanova, PA 19085.

GROBECKER, ALAN J, b. San Diego, Calif, Aug. 6, 15; m. 40; c. 2. SPACE PHYSICS, GEOPHYSICS. B.S, Calif. Inst. Tech, 37, M.S, 41; M.S, Southern California, 49; Ph.D.(planetary & space sci), California, Los Angeles, 68. Proj. engr, Autonetics Div, N.Am. Aviation, Inc, 50-59; mem. tech. staff, Inst. Defense Anal, 59-60; mem. staff develop. planning, gen. off, N.Am. Aviation, Inc, 60-61, mgr, 61-62, corporate dir, 62-63, mem. tech. staff, sci. center, 63-64, scientist, space info. systs. div, 64-68; MEM. TECH. STAFF, Inst. Defense Anal, 68-71; OFF. OF ASST. SECY. SYSTS. ENG. & TECHNOL, DEPT. TRANSPORTATION, 71- Asst, E.O. Hulburt Ctr. Space Res, Naval Res. Lab, D.C, 65- U.S.N.R, 42-, Capt. AAAS; Am. Meteorol. Soc; Inst. Elec. & Electronics Eng; Am. Phys. Soc; Am. Geophys. Union. Planetary physics; investigation by rocket borne instrumentation of latitudinal and temporal variation of the homospheric boundary of the upper atmosphere. Address: Dept. of Transportation, Office of Assistant Secretary for Systems Engineering & Technology, 400 Seventh St. S.W, Washington, DC 20590.

GROBER, SAMUEL, b. New York, N.Y, July 22, 17; m. 47; c. 2. FORESTRY. B.S, N.Y. State Col. Forestry, Syracuse, 38; M.S, Maryland, 40, Ph.D. (wood anat), 42. Coop. agent res. div, soil conserv. serv, U.S. Dept. Agr, 38-42; asst. chief forestry div, Supreme Command Allied Powers, 45-46; for. rep, R.S. Bacon Veneer Co, 46-49; MIDWEST REP, THOMPSON MAHOGANY CO, PHILA, 49-; PIERSON-HOLLO-WELL CO, INC, INDIANAPOLIS, 49-; BALSA ECUADOR LUMBER CORP, NORTHVALE, N.J, 49- U.S.A, 42-45. Forest Prod. Res. Soc. Wood anatomy; tree growth forms; soil requirements of black locust; the botanical, erosion control and economic significance of white poplar in Maryland. Address: 1110 Ridge Ave, Evanston, IL 60202.

GROBLEWSKI, GERALD EUGENE, b. Nanticoke, Pa, Nov. 5, 26; m. 53; c. 2. PHARMACOLOGY. B.A, Maryland, 49; U.S. Pub. Health Serv. fel, Univ. Rochester, 59-64, Ph.D.(pharmacol), 64. Pharmacol. technician, Army Chem. Ctr, Md, 50-56, physiologist, 56-57; admin. asst. chem, Distillation Prod. Industs, Eastman Kodak Co, 57-59; assoc. res. biologist, Sterling-Winthrop Res. Inst, 63-69; PHARMACOLOGIST, SPEC. PROJ. DIV, WOODARD RES. CORP, 69- Mem. Coun. Thrombosis, Am. Heart Asn. U.S.N, 44-46. AAAS; Am. Soc. Pharmacol. & Exp. Therapeut; Int. Soc. Biochem. Pharmacol; N.Y. Acad. Sci. Cardiac automaticity; cardiotonic agents; anticholinesterase agents; thrombosis; psychopharmacology. Address: Special Projects Division, Woodard Research Corp, 12310 Pinecrest Rd, Herndon, VA 22070.

GROBLICKI, PETER J(OHN), b. New Bedford, Mass, May 5, 38; m. 62; c. 2. PHYSICAL CHEMISTRY. Sc.B, Brown, 59; Nat. Sci. Found. fel, Michigan, 61-62, Minn. Mining & Mfg. Co. fel, 62-63, Ph.D.(chem), 63. Phys. chemist, Gen. Elec. Res. & Develop. Ctr, 63-68; SR. RES. CHEMIST, FUELS & LUBRICANTS DEPT, GEN. MOTORS RES. LAB, 68- Am. Chem. Soc. Molecular beams; combustion; polymer flammability; atmospheric chemistry; aerosol physics. Address: Fuels & Lubricants Dept, General Motors Research Lab, 12 Mile & Mound Rds, Warren, MI 48090.

GROBMAN, ARNOLD B(RAMS), b. Newark, N.J, Apr. 28, 18; m. 44; c. 2. ZOOLOGY. B.S, Michigan, 39, 39-40; M.S, Rochester, 41, Ph.D.(zool), 43. Instr. zool, Rochester, 43-44, res. assoc, Manhattan Dist, sch. med. & dent, 44-46; asst. prof. biol, Florida, 46-51, assoc. prof, 51-58; dir. biol. sci. curriculum study, Colorado, 59-65; dean col. arts & sci, RUTGERS UNIV, 65-67, DEAN RUTGERS COL, 67- Res. partic, Oak Ridge Inst, 50; div. biol. & agr, Nat. Res. Coun, 54-70; dir. Fla. State Mus, 52-58; chmn, Nat. Coun. Accreditation Teacher Educ, 71. Stoye Prize, 40; Morrison Prize, 43; McAllister Award, 65. AAAS; Am. Soc. Nat; Am. Genetics Soc; Soc. Vert. Paleont; Am. Soc. Ichthyol. & Herpet.(v.pres, 46, secy, 52-57, pres, 64); Am. Soc. Zool; Soc. Study Evolution; Soc. Syst. Zool; Am. Asn. Mus; Acad. Zool; Am. Asn. Higher Educ; Asn. Trop. Biol; Nat. Asn. Biol. Teachers (pres, 66); Nat. Sci. Teachers Asn; Asn. Am. Med. Col; Nat. Asn. Res. Sci. Teaching; Philippine Asn. Sci. Teachers; Sci. Soc. Thailand. Herpetology; anatomy and distribution of vertebrates; biological education. Address: Rutgers College, Rutgers University, New Brunswick, NJ 08903.

GROBMAN, WARREN D(AVID), b. Phila, Pa, Sept. 22, 42; m. 65; c. 1. SOLID STATE PHYSICS. A.B, Univ. Pa, 64; M.A, Princeton, 66, Ph.D.(physics), 67. MEM. TECH. STAFF, Bellcomm Inc, Wash, D.C, 67-69; PHYS. SCI. DEPT, T.J. WATSON RES. CTR, IBM CORP, 69- AAAS; Am. Phys. Soc. Geophysical science; experimental and theoretical studies of electronic states in solids; band theory; transport measurements; ultra-high-vacuum electron spectroscopy of surfaces. Address: Physical Sciences Dept, IBM Corp, T.J. Watson Research Center, P.O. Box 218, Yorktown Heights, NY 10598.

GROBSTEIN, CLIFFORD, b. New York, N.Y, July 20, 16; m. 38; c. 2. BIOLOGY. B.S, City Col. New York, 36; M.A, California, Los Angeles, 38, Ph.D. (zool), 40. Instr. zool, Ore. State Col, 40-43; sr. res. fel, Nat. Cancer Inst, 46-47; biologist, U.S. Pub. Health Serv, 47-57; PROF. BIOL, Stanford, 58-65; UNIV. CALIF, SAN DIEGO, 65-, V.CHANCELLOR HEALTH SCI. & DEAN SCH. MED, 67- U.S.A.A.F, 43-46. Nat. Acad. Sci; Am. Soc. Zool. (pres, 66); Soc. Develop. Biol.(past pres); Tissue Cult. Asn; Am. Acad. Arts & Sci; Am. Soc. Cell Biol; Int. Soc. Cell Biol. Morphogenesis; tissue interaction; cellular differentiation; tissue culture. Address: School of Medicine, University of California, San Diego, P.O. Box 109, La Jolla, CA 92037.

GROCE, DAVID EIBEN, b. Wilmar, Calif, July 15, 36; m. 61; c. 1. ATOMIC & NUCLEAR PHYSICS. B.S, Calif. Inst. Tech, 58, Gen. Dynamics fel, 58, Gen. Atomic fel, 60, Ph.D.(nuclear physics), 63. Res. fel. exp. nuclear physics, Australian Nat. Univ, 63-65; staff assoc. res, Gen. Atomic Div, Gen. Dynamics Corp, 65-67; staff mem, Gulf Gen. Atomic, Inc, 67-69; SR. STAFF MEM. GOVT. CONTRACT RES, SCI. APPLN. INC, 69-; V.PRES, MEM. BD. DIRS. RES. & DEVELOP, JRB ASSOCS, INC, 69-; PRES, MEM. BD. DIR. & CONSULT, LA JOLLA RES. & BUS. ASSOCS, 71- Consult, Los Alamos Sci. Lab. & Nat. Comt. Radiation Protection, 69-; Univ. Tex; Univ. West. Ont; Univ. N.Mex; Salk Inst. Biol. Studies; asst. to chmn. biomed. steering comt, Los Alamos Meson Physics Facility. AAAS; Am. Phys. Soc; Am. Nuclear Soc; Am. Asn. Physics Teachers. Experimental research in low energy positrons, radioactive pharmaceuticals, fission and neutron yields; theoretical research in computers, Monte Carlo radiation transport, simulation and systems analysis; consulting research in cancer therapy, accelerators and facility design; neutron physics; radiation shielding; neutron and pi-meson cancer therapy. Address: 8243 Prestwick Dr, La Jolla, CA 92037.

GROCE, JOHN WESLEY, b. Stanley, N.C, Nov. 9, 30; m. 59; c. 2. BIOCHEMISTRY. A.B, Asbury Col, 53; M.S, Purdue, 56, Ph.D, 64. Instr. CHEM, HEIDELBERG COL, 57-60, asst. prof, 60-64, assoc. prof, 64-68, PROF, 68-, CHMN. DEPT, 65- Fel, N.C. State Univ, 70-71. Am. Chem. Soc. Carbohydrate, polysaccharide chemistry; analytical organic chemistry. Address: Dept. of Chemistry, Heidelberg College, Tiffin, OH 44883.

GRODINS, FRED S(HERMAN), b. Chicago, Ill, Nov. 18, 15; m. 42. PHYSIOLOGY, BIOMEDICAL ENGINEERING. B.S, Northwestern, 37, M.S, 40, Patten scholar. & M.D, 42, Ph.D.(physiol), 44. Asst. physiol, Northwestern, 38-40, instr, 42-44; asst. prof, col. med, Illinois, 46; assoc. prof, med. sch, Northwestern, 47-50, PROF, 50-67; ELEC. ENG. & PHYSIOL, UNIV. SOUTH. CALIF, 67-, CHMN. BIOMED. ENG. PROG, 70- Nat. Insts. Health career res. award, 62-67. Consult, Rand Corp, 64- Mem. physiol. training comt, Nat. Insts. Health, 64-68, biomed. eng. training comt, 69- Civilian with Off. Sci. Res. & Develop, 44. Med.C, 44-46, Capt. AAAS; Am. Physiol. Soc; Soc. Exp. Biol. & Med; Biomed. Eng. Soc.(pres, 70-71). Biological control systems; cardiovascular and respiratory physiology; mathematical models of physiological systems. Address: Biomedical Engineering, University of Southern California, University Park, Los Angeles, CA 90007.

GRODNER, ROBERT M(AYNARD), b. Brooklyn, N.Y, June 22, 25; m. 59; c. 2. FOOD SCIENCE, ZOOLOGY. A.B, Brown, 49; M.Sc, Tennessee, 50; Duke, 51-54, Am. Cancer Soc. grant, 54-55; Ph.D.(zool, physiol), La. State, 59. Instr. biol, Berea Col, 51; asst. prof, Otterbein Col, 59-62, assoc. prof, 62-63; FOOD SCI. & TECHNOL, LA. STATE UNIV, BATON ROUGE, 63-69, PROF, 69- Atomic Energy Comn. fels, 64-66. U.S.N, 43-46. AAAS; Inst. Food Technol; Am. Inst. Biol. Sci. Autoxidation of unsaturated fatty acids; radiation pasteurization of Gulf Coast shellfish; food toxicology and enzymes. Address: Dept. of Food Science & Technology, Louisiana State University, Baton Rouge, LA 70803.

GRODOWITZ, WILLIAM, b. West Orange, N.J, Nov. 22, 17; m. 48; c. 3. OPERATIONS RESEARCH & ANALYSIS. B.A, N.Y. Univ, 39; Air Univ, 63-65; Presidential fel, Univ. Md, 67-68; M.A, 68; Am. Univ, 68-70. Econ. statistician, War Prod. Bd, 43-45; analyst, War Assets Admin, 45-47;

anal. statistician, Nat. Cancer Inst, 47-51; planning & anal. br, Off. Surgeon Gen, U.S. AIR FORCE, 51-53, opers. analyst, air proving ground command, 53-57, Europe, 57-60, sr. res. analyst, HQ, 60-64, spec. asst. prog. eval. & dep. asst. dir. AEROSPACE PROGS, 64-67, assoc. dir. eval. & technol, 67-68, SPEC. ASST. TO DIR, DEP. CHIEF STAFF, 68- Opers. Res. Soc. Am. Programs formulation, management and evaluation; development of models for costing and evaluation program alternatives. Address: 4828 Randolph Dr, Annandale, VA 22003.

GRODSKY, GEROLD M(ORTON), b. St. Louis, Mo, Jan. 18, 27; m. 51; c. 2. BIOCHEMISTRY, ENDOCRINOLOGY. B.S, Illinois, 47, M.S, 48; Ph.D.(biochem), California, Berkeley, 55. Nat. Cancer Inst. fel. biochem, Cambridge, 54-55; asst. res. biochemist, MED. CTR, UNIV. CALIF, SAN FRANCISCO, 56-60, asst. prof, 60-64, assoc. prof, 64-68, PROF. BIOCHEM, 68- Consult, Langley Porter Inst, 60-; U.S. Naval Hosp, Oakland, 61-; U.S. Pub. Health Serv. & Vet. Admin. Hosp, San Francisco, 62-; vis. prof, Univ. Geneva, 68-69. U.S.N.R, 44-46, Lt. Am. Soc. Biol. Chem; Soc. Exp. Biol. & Med; Am. Fedn. Clin. Res; Am. Diabetes Asn. Metabolism of bile pigments; biochemistry of jaundice; metabolism and immunological aspects of insulin action and secretion. Address: Metabolic Unit, University of California Medical Center, San Francisco, CA 94122.

GRODSKY, IRVIN T, b. St. Louis, Mo, Jan. 20, 40; m. 60; c. 2. THEORETICAL PHYSICS. B.S, Washington (St. Louis), 61, Ph.D.(physics), 66. Asst. prof. physics, California, Los Angeles, 66-67; Nat. Sci. Found. fel, 67-68; res. assoc. PHYSICS, California, Berkeley, 68-69; ASSOC. PROF, CLEVELAND STATE UNIV, 69- Partic, Battelle Rencontres in Math. & Physics, summer 69. U.S.M.C.R, 57-65. Am. Phys. Soc. Theoretical strong, electromagnetic and weak structure of hadrons. Address: Dept. of Physics, Cleveland State University, Cleveland, OH 44115.

GRODUMS, E(MMA) IRENE, b. Riga, Latvia, Oct. 17, 16; Can. citizen; m. 43. DENTISTRY, HISTOLOGY. D.D.S, Univ. Latvia, 41; Ph.D, Univ. Sask, 57. Res. assoc. anat, UNIV. SASK, 55-57, BACT, 57-61, asst. prof, 61-69, ASSOC. PROF, DENT. BR, 69- AAAS; Am. Soc. Cell Biol; assoc. Can. Soc. Microbiol; Royal Micros. Soc; Brit. Dent. Asn; N.Y. Acad. Sci. Neurohistology; pathogenesis of experimental Coxsackie B infection in various animals; histology and cytology of the brown rat; fat; hybernation; electron microscopy. Address: Dept. of Bacteriology, University of Saskatchewan, Saskatoon, Sask, Can.

GRODZINS, LEE, b. Lowell, Mass, July 10, 26; m. 56; c. 2. NUCLEAR PHYSICS. B.S, New Hampshire, 46; M.S, Union Col, 48; Ph.D.(physics), Purdue, 54. Res. asst. PHYSICS, Gen. Elec. Res. Lab, 46-48; instr, Purdue, 54-55; from res. assoc. to assoc. physicist, Brookhaven Nat. Lab, 55-59; asst. prof, MASS. INST. TECHNOL, 59-62, assoc. prof, 62-66, PROF, 66- Guggenheim fel, 64-65, 71-72; res. consult, U.S. Navy, 59-60; consult, High Voltage Eng. Co, 62-70. Scattering of electrons; nuclear spectroscopy, beta decay and Mössbauer scattering. Address: Room 413, Bldg. 26, Massachusetts Institute of Technology, Cambridge, MA 02139.

GROEGER, THEODORE OSKAR, b. Gross Kunzendorf, Czech, Nov. 25, 27; m. 57; c. 2. ORGANIC CHEMISTRY. Dr. & Dipl, Univ. Vienna, 52; Ph.D.(chem), Vienna Tech. Univ, 57. Prof. chem, Fed. Sci. High Sch, Austria, 53-59; sci. patent assoc, pharmaceut, Ciba Corp, Switz, 59-64, MGR. CHEM. PATENTS, CIBA-GEIGY CORP, 64- Asst. to dean dept. chem, Vienna Tech. Univ, 51-55; prof, Bus. Col. & lectr, Austria, 58-59. Austrian Ministry Educ. achievement award, 58; Austrian Sci. Ed. school book award, 62. Am. Chem. Soc; Austrian Chem. Soc; Ger. Chem. Soc. Patent law; pharmaceutics. Address: Ciba-Geigy Corp, Summit, NJ 07901.

GROEL, JOHN T(RUEMAN), b. Maplewood, N.J, Oct. 5, 24. MEDICINE. M.D, Yale, 51. Med. ed, White Labs, 51-52; asst. med. dir, E.R. SQUIBB & SONS DIV, OLIN MATHIESON CHEM. CORP, 52-54, assoc. med. dir, 54-60, assoc. clin. res. dir, 60-67, clin. res. dir, 67-71, WORLDWIDE MED. DIR, 71- U.S.A.F, 43-45, Res, 45-64, 1st Lt. Am. Med. Asn; Am. Acad. Dermat; Am. Fedn. Clin. Res; N.Y. Acad. Sci; Soc. Invest. Dermat. Infectious diseases; dermatology. Address: 609-B Kingston Terr, R.D. 4, Princeton, NJ 08540.

GROEMER, HELMUT (JOHANN), b. Salzburg, Austria, Nov. 6, 30; m. 57; c. 2. MATHEMATICS. Ph.D.(math. & physics), Innsbruck, 54. Instr. MATH, Ore. State Univ, 57-59, asst. prof, 59-61, assoc. prof, 61-64; PROF, UNIV. ARIZ, 64- Am. Math. Soc. Convex sets; packing and covering problems; geometry of numbers; integral geometry; geometric probability theory. Address: Dept. of Mathematics, University of Arizona, Tucson, AZ 85721.

GROENEVELD, JOHANNES, b. Amsterdam, Netherlands, Apr. 9, 31. THEORETICAL PHYSICS. Drs, Amsterdam, 62, Dr.(physics), 67. Asst. theoret. physics, Amsterdam, 54-67; ASST. PROF. PHYSICS, INST. THEORET. PHYSICS, STATE UNIV. N.Y. STONY BROOK, 67- Netherlands Phys. Soc. Statistical mechanics, particularly cluster expansions and rigorous results; probability theory, particularly queueing theory and graph theory; mathematical physics; applied mathematics. Address: Dept. of Physics, Institute for Theoretical Physics, State University of New York at Stony Brook, Stony Brook, NY 11790.

GROENEVELD MEIJER, WILLEM OTTO JAN, b. Berlin, Ger, Jan. 12, 28; nat. Can; m. 57; c. 3. ECONOMIC GEOLOGY. M.Sc, Swiss Fed. Inst. Tech, 50; fels. & Ph.D.(geochem), Queen's (Ont), 55. Explor. geologist, Int. Nickel Co, Can, 51-52; geochemist, McPhar Geophys, Ltd, 55-57; field geologist, Union Carbide Ore Co, 57-58, res. geochemist, Union Carbide Nuclear Co, 58-61; chief geologist, Aero Serv. Corp. Div, Litton Indust, Inc, 61-64; proj. off, DEVELOP. PROG, UN, 65-69, sr. proj. off, 69-71, SR. TECH. ADV, 71- Geol. Soc. Am; Geochem. Soc; Netherlands Royal Inst. Eng. Management of mineral exploration programs; development of new prospecting methods, both geophysical and geochemical; mineralogy of manganese oxides; geochemistry of manganese deposition. Address: Room A-3524, United Nations Development Program, United Nations, New York, NY 10017.

GROENWEGHE, LEO C(ARL) D(ENIS), b. Antwerp, Belg, Aug. 31, 25; nat; m. 56; c. 3. INORGANIC CHEMISTRY. Lic, Ghent, Belgium, 48, D.Sc, 51. Res. chemist, Belg. Inst. Sci. Res, 48-53; mem. sr. staff, Spencer Chem. Co, Kans, 53-56; res. specialist, CENT. RES. DEPT, MONSANTO CO, 56-66, SR. RES. SPECIALIST, 66- Am. Chem. Soc. Inorganic synthetic chemistry, especially uranium, fluorine, nitrogen and phosphorus compounds; nuclear magnetic resonance; organophosphorus compounds; solubility systems; random reorganization theory; catalysis; statistics; computer applications; technical forecasting. Address: Central Research Dept, Monsanto Co, 800 N. Lindbergh Blvd, St. Louis, MO 63166.

GROF, STANISLAV, b. Prague, Czech, July 1, 31; div. PSYCHIATRY. M.D, Charles Univ, Prague, 56; Ph.D.(psychiat), Czech. Acad. Sci, 64. Res. psychiatrist, Psychiat. Res. Inst, Prague, 57-67, prin. investr, 61-67; fel, JOHNS HOPKINS UNIV, 67-69, ASST. PROF. PSYCHIAT, SCH. MED, 69-; CHIEF PSYCHIAT. RES, MD. PSYCHIAT. RES. CTR, 69-, res. psychiatrist, 67-69. Asst. prof, Postgrad. Med. Training Ctr, Prague, 60; collab, res. insts, Prague-Krc, 59-60; outpatient psychiatrist, psychiat. clin, Nat. Inst. Health Czech, 59-60; Ministry Pub. Health fel, Moscow, 64; res. psychiatrist, Spring Grove State Hosp, Baltimore, Md, 67-69. Kuffner Award, 59. Czech. Med. Soc; Europ. Med. Asn. Psycholytic Ther. Psychoanalytically oriented psychotherapy, hallucinogenic drugs, drug-assisted psychotherapy; altered states of consciousness; psychology of religion. Address: 20 Torlina Court, Baltimore, MD 21207.

GROFF, DONALD WILLIAM, b. Lancaster, Pa, Apr. 11, 28; m. 57; c. 1. GEOLOGY, GEOCHEMISTRY. B.S, Redlands, 52; Pa. State, 52-55; Ph.D.(geol, geochem), Pittsburgh, 60. Geophysicist, West. Geophys. Co, 52; asst, Pa. State, 52-55; instr, Allegheny Col, 55-57; geophysicist, Pickands Mather Co, 57; asst. seismologist & instr. geol, Pittsburgh, 57-61; assoc. prof, Indiana State Col.(Pa), 61-65; HEAD DEPT. EARTH SCI, WEST. CONN. STATE COL, 65-, PROF. GEOL, 66- Geol. consult, Huntley & Huntley, Inc, 59-61; assoc, Earth Sci. Serv, Brookfield Ctr, 69-; mem. Coun. Educ. Geol. Sci, 69-; dir, Allegheny River Mining Co. & Pittsburgh & Shawmut R. Road Co, 70- U.S.A.A.F, 46-49, Sgt. Int. Asn. Sedimentol; Am. Inst. Mining, Metall. & Petrol. Eng; Geol. Soc. Am; Nat. Asn. Geol. Teachers; Geol. Soc. Am. Radiometry; spectrochemistry as applied to sediments; economic geology. Address: Dept. of Earth Science, Western Connecticut State College, Danbury, CT 06810.

GROFF, ROBERT A(RMAND), b. Phila, Pa, May 11, 03; m. 33. NEUROLOGY, NEUROSURGERY. A.B, Pennsylvania, 25, M.D, 28. Assoc. NEUROSURG, div. grad. med, Univ. Pa, 32-38, asst. prof, 38-41; Jefferson Med. Col, 41-45; UNIV. PA, 46-47, assoc. prof, 47-50, prof, 50-68, SCH. MED, 57-, EMER. PROF, 68- Am. Asn. Neurol. Surg; Am. Med. Asn; Am. Neurol. Asn; Asn. Res. Nerv. & Ment. Diseases; Am. Col. Surg. Brain abscess; Marcus Gunn phenomenon; meningiomas of the sphenoid ridge; cerebral aneurysms; convulsive disorders; peripheral nerve injuries. Address: 2306 Medical Tower, 255 S. 17th St, Philadelphia, PA 19103.

GROFF, SIDNEY L(AVERN), b. Victor, Mont, Apr. 7, 19; m. 45; c. 2. GEOLOGY. B.A, Montana State, 41, M.A, 54; fel, Utah, 55-57, Ph.D, 59. Asst, Montana State, 52-54; chief, ground water & fuels div, MONT. BUR. MINES & GEOL, 57-71, DIR, 71-, STATE GEOLOGIST, 71- U.S.M.C, 41-50, Lt. Col. Geol. Soc. Am; Am. Asn. Petrol. Geol; Am. Inst. Prof. Geol. Hydrogeology; coal geology and economics; mineral deposits; reconnaissance geological mapping. Address: Montana Bureau of Mines & Geology, Montana College of Mineral Science and Technology, Butte, MT 59701.

GROGAN, CLARENCE O(RVAL), b. Grogan, Mo, June 1, 21; m. 45; c. 3. AGRONOMY. B.S, Missouri, 46, A.M, 49, Ph.D.(plant breeding), 51. Maize breeder, Mo. Farmers' Asn, 46-48; asst. instr, Missouri, 49-51; maize breeder, Govt. Union of S.Africa, 51-54; agronomist, maize invests, U.S. Dept. Agr, 54-66; PROF. PLANT BREEDING, CORNELL UNIV, 66- U.S.A, 43-46, 1st Lt. Am. Soc. Agron. Maize investigations. Address: Dept. of Plant Breeding, Cornell University, Ithaca, NY 14850.

GROGAN, DONALD E, b. Grogan, Mo, Feb. 6, 38; m. 62; c. 2. BIOCHEMISTRY. B.A, Missouri, 60, M.S, 62, Ph.D.(biochem), 65. Fel. protein biochem, Col. Med, Baylor, 65-66, res. assoc. drug metab, 66-68; ASST. PROF. BIOL, UNIV. MO-ST. LOUIS, 68- Nuclear proteins of rat liver and tumor. Address: Dept. of Biology, University of Missouri-St. Louis, 8001 Natural Bridge Rd, St. Louis, MO 63121.

GROGAN, JAMES BIGBEE, b. Edwards, Miss, May 15, 32; m. 56; c. 2. MICROBIOLOGY. B.S, Miss. Col, 55; M.S, Wisconsin, 57; fel, Mississippi, 59-63, Ph.D.(microbiol). 63. Instr. bot, Miss. Col, 53-55; asst. bact, Wisconsin, 55-57; supvr. surg. res. bact. lab, SCH. MED, UNIV. MISS, 57-63, instr. SURG. & MICROBIOL, 63-65, ASST. PROF, 65- U.S.A, 50-52, Sgt. AAAS; Am. Soc. Microbiol. Infections; bacteriophage; hosts defense mechanisms; transplantation immunology. Address: University of Mississippi School of Medicine, 2500 N. State St, Jackson, MS 39216.

GROGAN, MICHAEL J(OHN), b. Hammond, Ind, Feb. 6, 38; m. 61; c. 1. PHYSICAL & ANALYTICAL CHEMISTRY. B.S, John Carroll Univ, 59; Ph.D.(chem), Ill. Inst. Technol, 67. Res. technician, dept. med, Univ. Chicago, 59-62; chemist, Magnaflux Corp, Ill, 62-63; Culligan Inc, 63-64; teaching asst. phys. chem, Ill. Inst. Technol, 64-67; chemist, SHELL CHEM. CO, N.J, 67-70, SR. CHEMIST, 70-71, CALIF, 71- U.S.A.R, 62. AAAS; Am. Chem. Soc; Am. Inst. Chem. Spectroscopic investigations of metal-olefin complexes, structure and chemistry of titanium III complexes; removal of catalyst residues from polyolefins; determination of the structure and content of ethylene-propylene copolymers by pyrolysis gas chromophotography; investigations of the chemistry of propylene polymerization and styrene-butadiene polymerization. Address: Elastomers Technical Center, Shell Chemical Co, Torrance, CA 90509.

GROGAN, PAUL J(OSEPH), b. Adrian, Minn, Nov. 20, 18; m. 45; c. 6. MECHANICAL ENGINEERING. B.S, Purdue, 43; M.S, Wisconsin, 49. From instr. to asst. prof. mech. eng, Wisconsin, 47-50; Notre Dame, 50-51; prof. & chmn. eng. exten. dept, Wisconsin, 51-66; dir. Off. State Tech. Serv, U.S. Dept. Commerce, Wash, D.C, 66-68; PROF. ENG, UNIV. EXTEN, UNIV. WIS, MADISON, 68- AAAS; Nat. Soc. Prof. Eng; Am. Soc. Eng. Educ. Power production and related problems of energy conversion; heat transfer; electrical transmission and distribution; water supply and water conditioning. Address: Dept. of Engineering, University Extension, University of Wisconsin, Madison, WI 53706.

GROGAN, RAYMOND G(ERALD), b. Emma, Ga, July 22, 20; m. 44; c. 2. PLANT PATHOLOGY. B.S.A, Georgia, 41, M.S.A, 42; Ph.D.(plant path), Wisconsin, 48. Instr. PLANT PATH. & jr. pathologist, UNIV. CALIF, DAVIS, 48-50, asst. prof. & asst. plant pathologist, 50-56, assoc. prof. & assoc. plant pathologist, 56-61, PROF. & PLANT PATHOLOGIST, 61-, CHMN. DEPT. PLANT PATH, 69- U.S.N, 42-45. AAAS; Am. Phytopath. Soc. Cause and control of vegetable crop disease; plant virology. Address: Dept. of Plant Pathology, University of California, Davis, CA 95616.

GROGAN, ROBERT M(ANN), b. Mendota, Ill, July 17, 12; m. 37; c. 3. ECONOMIC GEOLOGY. B.S, Chicago, 35; M.A, Minnesota, 36, Ph.D.(geol), 40. Asst. geologist, indust. minerals div, State Geol. Surv, Ill, 37-43, assoc. geologist, 43-48, geologist, 48-51; develop. dept, E.I. DU PONT DE NEMOURS & CO, 51-60, mgr. geol. div, 60-68, MGR. GEOL. PURCHASING DEPT, 69- Geol. Soc. Am; Mineral Soc. Am; Soc. Econ. Geol; Am. Inst. Min, Metall. & Petrol. Eng. Economic geology of fluorspar; ilmenite and industrial minerals; mineral economics; engineering geology. Address: Purchasing Dept, E.I. du Pont de Nemours & Co, Wilmington, DE 19898.

GROGINSKY, HERBERT LEONARD, b. Newark, N.J, July 10, 30; m. 52; c. 3. ELECTRONICS. B.E.E, Polytech. Inst. Brooklyn, 52; M.S, Columbia, 54, Eng.Sc.D.(elec. eng), 59. Instr. physics, Polytech. Inst. Brooklyn, 51-52; staff engr, electronics res. lab, Columbia, 52-59; DEPT. MGR. APPL. MATH, RAYTHEON CO, 59- Instr, elec. eng, Northeast. Univ, 59-65, adj. prof, 65- AAAS; sr. mem. Inst. Elec. & Electronics Eng; Am. Inst. Aeronaut. & Astronaut. Radar detection theory; data processing systems. Address: Raytheon Co, Old Sudbury Rd, Wayland, MA 01778.

GROH, ALAN B(ENJAMIN), Mgt. Sci, see 12th ed, Soc. & Behav. Vols.

GROH, HAROLD J(OHN), b. New Orleans, La, Jan. 28, 28; m. 51; c. 5. PHYSICAL CHEMISTRY. B.S, St. Louis, 49; Ph.D.(phys. chem), Rochester, 52. Res. chemist, E.I. DU PONT DE NEMOURS & CO, INC, 52-59, res. supvr, 59-67, res. mgr, 68, SECT. DIR, 69- Am. Chem. Soc. Radiochemical process development; radiation chemistry; radioisotope production; actinide chemistry. Address: 7 Longwood Dr, Aiken, SC 29801.

GROHSE, EDWARD WILLIAM, b. New York, N.Y, Dec. 5, 15; m. 40; c. 2. CHEMICAL ENGINEERING. B.Ch.E, Cooper Union, 40, hon. Ch.E, 45; fel, Delaware, 45-48, Ph.D.(chem. eng), 48. Anal. chemist, 37-40; chem. engr, FMC Corp, W.Va, 40-44, N.Y, 44-45; asst. res. prof. chem. eng, Delaware, 48-49; asst. prof, Carnegie Inst. Tech, 49-51; sr. technologist, Monsanto Chem. Co, 51-52; res. assoc, Gen. Elec. Co. Res. Lab, 52-58, consult. engr, Knolls Atomic Power Lab, 58-60; prof. chem. eng, UNIV. ALA, Tuscaloosa, 60-65, PROF. CHEM. ENG. & HEAD ENERGY & MASS TRANSFER LAB, HUNTSVILLE, 65- Consult, FMC Corp, 60-65; Army Missile Command, 61-63; Brookhaven Nat. Lab, 62-64; mem, Huntsville Air Pollution Control Bd, 69- Am. Chem. Soc; Am. Inst. Chem. Eng; Am. Soc. Eng. Educ. Mass and heat transfer; distillation; fluidization; nuclear engineering; fuel cells; air pollution control. Address: University of Alabama in Huntsville, P.O. Box 1247, Huntsville, AL 35807.

GROHSKOPF, HERBERT, b. Brooklyn, N.Y, July 7, 17; m. 52; c. 1. CHEMICAL ENGINEERING. B.S, Princeton, 49. Res. engr, U.S. Rubber Co, 49-50; Am. Cyanamid Co, 50-53; from tech. asst. to mgr. process anal, LUMMUS CO, 53-62, sr. eng. consult, 62-64, mgr. sci. & eng. comput. applns, 64-69, MGR. CORP. COMPUT. SERV, 69- U.S.A, 40-46, Capt. Am. Inst. Chem. Eng; Am. Chem. Soc; Fr. Soc. Indust. Chem. Planning and organization of chemical process development; design and control projects along interdisciplinary lines. Address: Lummus Co, 1515 Broad St, Bloomfield, NJ 07003.

GROJEAN, RICHARD EDWARD, b. N.Y.C, Mar. 1, 23; m. 50; c. 2. PHYSICS. B.S, Northeastern, 48; M.S, Tufts, 50; fel, Brandeis, 49-54; Boston. Res. assoc. elec, phys. res. lab, Tufts, 49-51; optics, Boston, 52-56; ASSOC. PROF. PHYSICS, NORTHEAST. UNIV, 54-; PHYSICIST, ELECTRONICS RES. PROJ, 58- Consult, S. Gunnar Myrbeck Co, 56-58. C.Eng, 42-45, Sgt. Optical Soc. Am; Am. Asn. Physics Teachers. Electromagnetic theory with specific application to physical optics; day airglow from the upper atmosphere. Address: Dept. of Physics, Northeastern University, Boston, MA 02115.

GROLLMAN, ARTHUR, b. Baltimore, Md, Oct. 20, 01; m. 26; c. 3. EXPERIMENTAL MEDICINE. A.B, Hopkins, 20, Ph.D.(chem), 23, M.D, 30. Instr. chem, Hopkins, 23-24; physiol, sch. med, 24-26, assoc, 26-30, assoc. prof, 30-36, assoc. prof. pharmacol. & exp. therapeut, 36-41; res. prof. med, Bowman Gray Sch. Med, Wake Forest, 41-44; PROF. physiol, pharmacol. & med, UNIV. TEX. (SOUTHWEST) MED. SCH. DALLAS, 45-49, EXP. MED, 49- Hon. prof, Guadalajara; Guggenheim fel, London, Berlin & Heidelberg, 30-31; Gorgas lectr, 44; Duluth lectr, Univ. Minn, 48; Boynton lectr, 50; Grove Mem. lectr, U.S. Air Force, 71. Civilian consult, surgeon gen, U.S. Air Force; consult, Baylor Univ. Hosp; hon. consult, Shannon Mem. Hosp. Mem. revision comt, U.S. Pharmacopoeia, 60-70. Dipl, Am. Bd. Internal Med, 52; Hunter Award, Am. Therapeut. Soc, 69. With off. Sci. Res. & Develop, 41-44; U.S.P.H.S, 42-44, Surg. Am. Heart Asn; Am. Physiol. Soc; Endocrine Soc; Am. Soc. Pharmacol. & Exp. Therapeut; Am. Chem. Soc; Am. Med. Asn; Am. Diabetes Asn; fel. Am. Col. Physicians; hon. fel. Port. Endocrine Soc. Colligative properties of solution; physiology of cardiovascular system; adrenals; hypertension; endocrinology; pharmacology. Address: University of Texas (Southwestern) Medical School, Dallas, TX 75235.

GROLLMAN, ARTHUR PATRICK, b. Baltimore, Md, May 21, 34; m. 59; c. 3. PHARMACOLOGY, MOLECULAR BIOLOGY. B.A, California, Berkeley, 55; M.D, Hopkins, 59. Res. med, Hopkins Hosp, 59-61; res. assoc. biochem, Nat. Insts. Health, 61-63; assoc. med. & molecular biol, ALBERT EINSTEIN COL. MED, 63-66, asst. prof, 66-68, assoc. prof. pharmacol, molecular biol. & med, 68-71, PROF. PHARMACOL, 71- Career scientist, Health

Res. Coun, N.Y.C, 63-; consult, comt. on biol. data handling, Nat. Insts. Health, 66-70, mem. pharmacol. study sect, 70-; assoc. attend. physician, Bronx Munic. Hosp. Ctr, 68-; mem. comt. on drug safety, Drug Res. Bd, 71- U.S.P.H.S, 61-63, Sr. Asst. Surg. Am. Soc. Pharmacol. & Exp. Therapeut; Am. Soc. Biol. Chem; Am. Physiol. Soc; Am. Soc. Clin. Invest; Am. Chem. Soc. Molecular pharmacology; mechanism of drug action; design of chemotherapeutic agents; interaction of drugs with macromolecules. Address: Dept. of Pharmacology, Albert Einstein College of Medicine, 1300 Morris Park Ave, Bronx, NY 10461.

GROLLMAN, SIGMUND, b. Stevensville, Md, Feb. 12, 23. PHYSIOLOGY. B.S, Maryland, 47, M.S, 49, Ph.D.(physiol), 52. Instr. zool. & physiol, UNIV. MD, COLLEGE PARK, 49-54, asst. prof, 55-60, assoc. prof, 60-66, PROF. ZOOL. & CHMN. DIV. PHYSIOL, 66- U.S.A, 42-46. AAAS; Am. Soc. Exp. Biol. & Med; N.Y. Acad. Sci. Tissue and cellular metabolism; exercise and fatigue; aging and lipid metabolism. Address: 4303 N. Charles St, Baltimore, MD 21218.

GROMAN, NEAL B(ENJAMIN), b. Chisholm, Minn, May 21, 21; m. 43; c. 4. MICROBIOLOGY. S.B, Chicago, 47, Logan fel, 48-50, Ph.D.(bacter, parasitol), 50. Instr. MICROBIOL, UNIV. WASH, 50-53, asst. prof, 53-58, assoc. prof, 58-63, PROF, 63-, DIR, OFF. BIOL. EDUC, 71- Markle scholar, 55-60; Guggenheim fel, 58-59. U.S.A, 42-46. Am. Soc. Microbiol; Am. Acad. Microbiol. Bacteriophage; animal viruses; microbial genetics and physiology; medical microbiology. Address: Dept. of Microbiology, University of Washington, Seattle, WA 98195.

GROMISCH, DONALD S, b. Jersey City, N.J, Mar. 24, 30; m. 54; c. 2. MEDICINE, PEDIATRICS. B.S, Wagner Col, 52; M.D, N.Y. Med. Col, 60. Wyeth pediat. fel, 61-63; CHIEF PEDIAT, METROP. HOSP. DIV, N.Y. MED. COL, 67- Mosby book & Roche awards, 60. U.S.N, 52-56, Lt. Fel. Am. Acad. Pediat. Pediatric education and administration; erythroblastosis fetalis; intrauterine transfusions; medical education; infectious diseases; comprehensive health care. Address: Dept. of Pediatrics, Metropolitan Hospital, New York Medical College, 1901 First Ave, New York, NY 10029.

GROMKO, GERALD JOHN, b. New Britain, Conn, Aug. 21, 40; m. 63; c. 4. TRANSPORTATION ENGINEERING, HYDRAULICS. B.S.E, Univ. Conn, 62, M.S, 64, Ph.D.(transportation eng), 67. Instr. civil. eng, Univ. Conn, 66-67; proj. engr, Waterways Exp. Sta, U.S. Army Corps Engrs, 67-69; ASST. PROF. CIVIL ENG, UNIV. COLO, BOULDER, 69- Mem, Hwy. Res. Bd, Nat. Acad. Sci-Nat. Res. Coun. C.Eng, U.S.A, 67-69, Capt; Army Commandation Medal, 69. Am. Soc. Civil Eng; Asn. Asphalt Paving Technol. Investigation of the brittle-plastic behavior of asphalt mixes; analysis of structures on expansive clay soils; effect of rockbound erosion protection on the characteristics of hydraulic jumps. Address: Dept. of Civil & Environmental Engineering, Engineering Center OT4-34, University of Colorado, Boulder, CO 80302.

GROMME, CHARLES SHERMAN, b. San Francisco, Calif, Nov. 15, 33. GEOLOGY. A.B, California, Berkeley, 59, Nat. Sci. Found. fel, 62-63, Ph.D. (geol), 63. Asst. res. geologist, California, Berkeley, 63-65; GEOLOGIST, U.S. GEOL. SURV, 65- AAAS; Am. Geophys. Union; Geol. Soc. Am. Rock magnetism and paleomagnetism. Address: U.S. Geological Survey, 345 Middlefield Rd, Menlo Park, CA 94025.

GRØN, POUL, b. Skaerbaek, Denmark, Mar. 26, 27; m. 54; c. 2. DENTISTRY. D.D.S, Royal Dent. Col, Copenhagen, 50; D.M.D, Tufts, 58. Res. fel, Harvard sch. dent. med. & Forsyth Dent. Ctr, 58-60, assoc. dent, 62-63, asst. prof, 63-67, SR. STAFF MEM, FORSYTH DENT. CTR, 68-, DIR. INFIRMARY DIV, 69- AAAS; Int. Asn. Dent. Res; Nordic Odontol. Soc. Chemical and structural composition of bone, teeth and pathological calcifications. Address: Forsyth Dental Center, 140 Fenway, Boston, MA 02115.

GRONDAHL, RAYMOND D(OUGLAS), b. Sisters, Ore, Dec. 6, 16; m. 47. CLINICAL PATHOLOGY. B.S, State Col. Wash, 39; M.S. & M.D, Oregon, 44. Asst. biochem, med. sch, Oregon, 42-44, intern, 44-45; instr. path, 45-47, dir. med. labs, 47-50, assoc. prof, 50-56, prof, 56-62, head dept. clin. path, 56-62, head div, 47-56; PATHOLOGIST, ST. JAMES COMMUNITY HOSP, 62- Lectr, Pacific Univ, 56-62. Consult. chemist, Plylock Corp, Ore, 41-45; practicing consult. pathologist, 47- Fel. Am. Col. Physicians; Am. Soc. Clin. Path; Soc. Nuclear Med; Assoc. Am. Med. Asn. Development of adhesives from protein; development of analytical methods for use in clinical chemistry. Address: St. James Community Hospital, 3000 Continental Dr, Butte, MT 59701.

GRONER, GABRIEL F(REDERICK), b. Los Angeles, Calif, May 17, 38; m. 64; c. 2. ELECTRICAL ENGINEERING. B.S, California, Los Angeles, 60; M.S, Stanford, 61, Ph.D.(elec. eng), 64. Res. asst. elec. eng, Stanford, 62-64; ENGR. COMPUT. SCI, RAND CORP, 64- Lectr, California, Los Angeles, spring, 66, 67, ext. div, 69- Inst. Elec. & Electronics Eng. Pattern recognition; interactive computer graphics; modeling and computer stimulation; computer applications. Address: Rand Corp, 1700 Main St, Santa Monica, CA 90406.

GRONER, MIRIAM GEORGIA, b. Ottawa, Kans, Aug. 24, 10. BIOLOGY, GENETICS. B.S. & M.S, Bucknell, 31; Newcombe fel, Michigan, 31-34, Ph.D. (plant physiol), 34. Instr. bot, Bucknell, 34-35, res, 37-40; prof. sci, Louisburg Col, 35-37; biol, Atlantic Christian Col, 40-41; private res, 41-42; plant breeder, W. Atlee Burpee Co, Pa, 42-44; chemist, Lansdale Tube Co, 44-50; sr. chemist, res. lab, Philco Corp, 50-58; asst. prof. BOT, PA. STATE UNIV, OGONTZ CAMPUS, 58-71, ASSOC. PROF, 71- Bot. Soc. Am. Screen materials; methods of screening cathode ray tubes; chrysanthemum breeding and physiology. Address: Dept. of Botany, Ogontz Campus, Pennsylvania State University, 1600 Woodland Rd, Abington, PA 19001.

GRONHOLZ, L(eROY) F(REDERICK), b. Redfield, S.Dak, July 10, 22; m. 44; c. 2. PHYSICAL CHEMISTRY. M.A, South Dakota, 48; Ph.D.(phys. chem), Carnegie Inst. Tech, 52. Res. chemist, polymer struct, E.I. DU PONT DE NEMOURS & CO, INC, 52-60, staff scientist, cellophane res. & develop. lab, 60-61, RES. SUPVR, SPRUANCE FILM RES. & DEVELOP. LAB, 61- Am. Chem. Soc; Sci. Res. Soc. Am. Polymer structure; polymer rheology; film orientation and crystallization; kinetics of thermal decomposition; composite film structures; coatings and coating processes. Address: Spruance Film Research & Development Lab, E.I. du Pont de Nemours & Co, Inc, P.O. Box 27222, Richmond, VA 23261.

GRONICH, SIGMUND, b. Brooklyn, N.Y, Dec. 6, 32. THERMODYNAMICS, AERODYNAMICS. B.M.E, Polytech. Inst. Brooklyn, 54, M.M.E, 59. Engr, Curtiss-Wright Aircraft Corp, 54-56; DOUGLAS AIRCRAFT CO, 57-59, supvr. propulsion thermodyn, 59-61, asst. sect. chief propulsion, 61-62, dep. mgr. nuclear tech, 62-64, chief nuclear scientist, 64-69, CHIEF PROG. ENGR. NUCLEAR STAGES, 69- Mem. safety comt, Atomic Indust. Forum, 65- C.Eng, U.S.A, 56-57. Am. Nuclear Soc; Am. Inst. Aeronaut. & Astronaut. Plasma physics of high temperature and pressure gases; high temperature materials; nuclear physics. Address: 20920 Anza Ave, Torrance, CA 90503.

GRONINGER, HERMAN S(AMUEL), JR, b. Lemoyne, Pa, Sept. 9, 25; m. 51; c. 4. BIOCHEMISTRY. B.S, Juniata Col, 50; M.S, Pa. State, 53, Ph.D.(agr. & biol. chem), 55. Jr. res. food technologist, California, 55-57; RES. CHEMIST, NAT. MARINE FISHERIES SERV, 57- U.S.A.A.F, 44-46, Sgt. AAAS; Am. Chem. Soc; Inst. Food Technol. Proteolytic enzymes; postmortem biochemistry. Address: National Marine Fisheries Service, Pacific Fishery Products Research Center, 2725 Montlake Blvd. E, Seattle, WA 98102.

GRONLUND, AUDREY FLORENCE, b. Victoria, B.C, Jan. 7, 32; m. 60. MICROBIOLOGY. B.S, British Columbia, 59, M.S, 61, Ph.D.(agr. microbiol), 64. Asst. lab. tech, UNIV. B.C, 62-63, instr. MICROBIOL, 63-65, asst. prof, 65-69, ASSOC. PROF, 69- Am. Soc. Microbiol; Can. Soc. Lab. Tech. Nature of endogenous substrates in micro-organisms and their influence on longevity during starvation; changes in bacteria during various growth phases; studies on turnover of protein and ribonucleic acid. Address: Faculty of Science, University of British Columbia, Vancouver 8, B.C, Can.

GRONNER, A(LFRED) D(OUGLAS), b. Vienna, Austria, Apr. 30, 13; U.S. citizen; m. 48. ELECTRICAL ENGINEERING. E.E, Vienna, 38; M.E.E, Polytech. Inst. Brooklyn, 50, Ph.D, 55. Develop. engr, Princess Radio Co, 41-42; proj. supvr. & field engr, Conatel, S.Am, 42-45; chief engr, Castillo & Co, 45-46; proj. engr, Liquidometer Corp, 46-50; dir. res, Arma Corp, 50-51; chief proj. engr, Am. Mach. & Foundry Co, 51-54; dir. res, Liquidometer Corp, 54-55; mgr. elec. & comput. dept, Greenwich Eng. Div, Am. Mach. & Foundry Co, 56-61; v.pres. eng, Spaceonics, Inc, 61-63; CHIEF ENGR, Simmonds Precision Prod. Co, 63-67; SINGER GEN. PRECISION, LITTLE FALLS, 67- Adj. prof. Polytech. Inst. Brooklyn, 51-; vis. prof, Albert Einstein Col. Med, 67- Am. Inst. Aeronaut. & Astronaut; Inst. Elec. & Electronics Eng. Automatic control; servomechanisms; instrumentation. Address: 18 Dale St, White Plains, NY 10605.

GRONVALL, JOHN ARNOLD, b. Minneapolis, Minn, July 28, 31; m. 56; c. 2. PATHOLOGY. B.A, Minnesota, 53, B.S, 54, M.D, 56. U.S. Pub. Health Serv. cancer trainee, Minnesota, 58-60; instr. path, Med. Ctr, Mississippi, 60-61, asst. prof, 61-65, assoc. prof, 65-68, asst. dean, 63-66, acting dir, 66-67, assoc. dir, 67-68; assoc. dean, 67-68; assoc. prof. path. & assoc. dean med. sch, UNIV. MICH, ANN ARBOR, 68-70, acting dean med. sch. & acting dir. med. ctr, 70; DEAN MED. SCH. & DIR. MED. CTR, 71- Consult, div. regional med. progs, Dept. Health, Educ. & Welfare, 67-70; co-chmn, Nat. Conf. Regional Med. Progs, Wash, D.C, 68; study dir, study of med. sch, curriculum in U.S. & Can, Asn. Am. Med. Cols, 68-70; consult, div. physician & health professions educ, Bur. Health Manpower Educ, 68-; mem. med. educ. review comt, bur. health professions educ. & manpower training, Nat. Insts. Health, 70- AAAS; Asn. Am. Med. Cols. Experimental pathology; immunopathology; medical education. Address: M-7324 Medical Science I Bldg, University of Michigan, Ann Arbor, MI 48104.

GROODY, THOMAS CONRAD, b. Barnes, Kans, Feb. 14, 14; m. 47; c. 3. ZOOLOGY. B.S, Kansas State, 36, M.S, 37; fel, California, Berkeley, 38, Ph.D. (zool), 52. Instr. zool, Kansas State, 37-38; sanit. inspector, U.S. Pub. Health Serv, 42-43; supt. penicillin div, Cutter Labs, Calif, 43-47, chem. div, 47-48; res. biologist, Calif. Acad. Sci, 48-52; assoc. prof. creative arts, San Francisco State Col, 52-54; radio writer & broadcaster, KCBS, 57-58; PROF. BIOL. SCI, CALIF. STATE COL. HAYWARD, 60- Producer, writer & actor TV sci. shows, 50-63. Mem. adv. comt, Louise Boyd Natural Sci. Mus, Calif, 64- AAAS. Homing instinct in limpets; pituitary gland and development in fowl; pantothenic acid and feather pigmentation; physiology and behavior of Pacific sardine. Address: Dept. of Biological Sciences, California State College at Hayward, Hayward, CA 94542.

GROOM, ALAN CLIFFORD, b. London, U.K, June 23, 26; m. 52; c. 4. BIOPHYSICS, PHYSIOLOGY. B.Sc, Univ. London, 49, Ph.D.(biophys), 57. Sr. physicist, St. Mary's Hosp, London, U.K, 49-57; Leverhulme res. fel. biophys, Univ. London, 57-58, lectr. med. physics, St. Mary's Hosp. med. sch, 58-66; vis. res. assoc. physiol, State Univ. N.Y. Buffalo, 62-63; ASSOC. PROF. BIOPHYS, UNIV. WEST. ONT, 66-, HON. LECTR. ANESTHESIA, 70- Hon. assoc. ed, Can. J. Physiol. & Pharmacol, 69- Brit. Hosp. Physicists Asn; fel. Brit. Inst. Physics & Phys. Soc; Brit. Physiol. Soc; Am. Physiol. Soc; Biophys. Soc; Microcirculatory Soc; Can. Physiol. Soc; Int. Soc. Biorheol. Biophysical aspects of the circulation of blood and transport of substances to the tissues; hemorheology; microcirculation; uptake and distribution of inert gases. Address: Dept. of Biophysics, University of Western Ontario, London 72, Ont, Can.

GROOM, DALE, b. Tulsa, Okla, Nov. 6, 12; m. 44; c. 3. MEDICINE, CARDIOLOGY. A.B, Hiram Col, 36; M.D, Med. Col. of Va, 43; fel, Mayo Found. Minnesota, 45-49, M.S, 48. Intern, Passavant Mem. Hosp, Chicago, 43-44; private practice, Univ. Miami, 49-53; assoc. med, med. col, Univ. S.C, 53-54, asst. prof, 54-65, assoc. prof, 65-68, asst. dean, 66-68; PROF. MED. & ASSOC. DEAN FOR CONTINUED EDUC, MED. CTR, UNIV. OKLA, 68- Med.C, U.S.N.R, 44-45, Lt.(jg). AAAS; Am. Heart Asn; Am. Med. Asn; fel. Am. Col. Physicians. Heart sound; electrocardiography. Address: University of Oklahoma Medical Center, 800 N.E. 13th St, Oklahoma City, OK 73104.

GROOM, DONALD EUGENE, b. Pittsburgh, Pa, Dec. 30, 34; m. 62; c. 1. HIGH ENERGY PHYSICS, ASTROPHYSICS. A.B, Princeton, 56; Nat. Sci. Found. fels. & Ph.D.(physics), Calif. Inst. Tech, 65. Res. assoc. PHYSICS, Cornell Univ, 65-66, instr, 66-67, acting asst. prof, 67-69; ASST. PROF, UNIV. UTAH, 69- Am. Phys. Soc; Am. Astron. Soc. Hadron scattering; muon production in cosmic ray interactions; cosmic ray origins. Address: Dept. of Physics, University of Utah, Salt Lake City, UT 84112.

GROOT, CORNELIUS, b. Chicago, Ill, Nov. 27, 19; m. 42; c. 4. CHEMISTRY. B.S, Chicago, 40, scholar, M.S, 42; Ph.D.(chem), California, 47. Asst. chem, Chicago, 41-42; jr. chemist, Shell Develop. Co, Calif, 42-45; asst. chem, California, 45-46; chemist, GEN. ELEC. CO, 47-57, supvr, 57-59, mgr. coolant chem, 59-64, electrochem. consult, 64-66, nuclear engr, 66-70, CHEM. ENGR, 70- Coffin Award, 51. Am. Chem. Soc; Nat. Asn. Corrosion Eng. Separation processes; corrosion. Address: 2512 Whamer Lane, Schenectady, NY 12309.

GROOT, J(OHAN) J(ACOB), b. Amsterdam, Holland, Nov. 25, 18; m. 45; c. 2. GEOLOGY. M.S, Amsterdam, 45, M.A, 47, Ph.D, 55. Res. assoc, Amsterdam, 45-47; Maryland, 47-49; lectr, Univ. Del, 49-51; Del. State Geologist, 51-69; PROJ. DIR, UN, 69- Prof, Univ. Del, 56-69; sr. res. assoc, Lamont Geol. Observ, Columbia Univ. AAAS; fel. Geol. Soc. Am; Asn. Am. State Geol; Am. Geophys. Union. Sedimentary petrology and palynology. Address: UN, Casilla 686, La Paz, Bolivia.

GROOVER, MARSHALL EUGENE, JR., b. Atlanta, Ga, June 20, 10; m. 61; c. 2. MEDICINE. M.D, Georgia, 34; North Carolina, 36-37; M.P.H, Hopkins, 40; dipl, U.S. Air Force Sch. Aviation Med, 42. Intern, Univ. Hosp, Augusta, 34-35; with Civilian Conserv. Corps, U.S. Army Med. Corps, Ft. McPherson, Ga, 35-36; mem. staff, Dept. Pub. Health, Brooks County, Ga, 37-38 & 40-41; mem. staff, rheumatic fever ctr, Foster Gen. Hosp, Jackson, Miss, 45-46; trop. disease ctr, Moore Gen. Hosp, Swannanoa, N.C, 46-48; chief med. serv, 130th Army Hosp, Heidelberg, Ger, 48-51; chief Aviation Med. Clin, Nat. Defense Bldg, Wash, D.C, 51-61; res. scientist, dept. physiol, Southwest Found. Res. & Ed, Tex, 61; assoc. prof. med, sch. med, Oklahoma, 61-65; DIR. HEART DISEASE CONTROL PROG, BUR. CHRONIC DISEASES, FLA. DIV. HEALTH, 66- Clin. assoc. prof, Univ. Fla, 71- Mem. endocrinol. study sect, div. res. grants, U.S. Pub. Health Serv, 52-60, cardiovasc. study sect, 53-59; coun. arteriosclerosis, Am. Heart Asn, 63. Dipl, Am. Bd. Internal Med, 47. Med.C, U.S.A.R, 41-48; Med.C, U.S.A.F, 48-61; Bronze Star Medal, 45; Legion of Merit, 59; Distinguished Serv. Medal, 61. Fel. Am. Col. Physicians; fel. Am. Col. Cardiol; fel. Am. Geriat. Soc; fel. Am. Col. Angiol. Address: Florida Division of Health, P.O. Box 210, Jacksonville, FL 32201.

GROOVER, MIKELL, b. Kingsport, Tenn, Sept. 8, 39; m. 62; c. 3. INDUSTRIAL ENGINEERING. A.B, Lehigh, 61, B.S.M.E, 62, M.S.I.E, 66, Ph.D.(indust. eng), 69. Mfg. engr, Eastman Kodak Co, N.Y, 62-64; res. asst, inst. res, Lehigh, 64-66; res. engr, Homer Res. Labs, Bethlehem Steel Co, summer 66; instr. INDUST. ENG, LEHIGH UNIV, 66-69, ASST. PROF, 69- Soc. Mfg. Eng; Am. Inst. Indust. Eng; Am. Soc. Mech. Eng. Manufacturing engineering and systems; adaptive control. Address: Dept. of Industrial Engineering, Lehigh University, Bethlehem, PA 18015.

GROOVER, ROBERT DON, b. Hartselle, Ala, Apr. 29, 38; m. 62; c. 2. BIOLOGY, PHYCOLOGY. B.S, Alabama, 60, M.S, 63; Ph.D.(bot), Texas, Austin, 68. Instr. biol, Alabama Col, 63-66; asst. prof, Tulane Univ. La, 68-71; RES. SCIENTIST, BIO-OCEANIC RES, INC, 71- AAAS; Int. Phycol. Soc; Bot. Soc. Am; Phycol. Soc. Am. Algae and their biology with particular reference to their nutrition and morphogenesis. Address: Bio-Oceanic Research, Inc, 1600 Canal St, New Orleans, LA 70112.

GROPEN, ARTHUR L(OUIS), b. Huntington, N.Y, May 14, 32; m. 60; c. 2. TOPOLOGY. A.B, Chicago, 52; S.B, 53; Nat. Sci. Found. fel, Duke, 56-57, summers, 56, 58, Fulbright fel, 57-58, Ph.D.(math), 58; Paris, 57-58. Jr. engr. MATH, Sperry Gyroscope Corp, 54-55; Fulbright teaching fel, Caen, 58-59; instr, Wellesley Col, 59-61, asst. prof, 61-62; UNESCO specialist, Santander, 62-63; asst. prof, CARLETON COL, 63-69, ASSOC. PROF, 69- Summers, instr, Chicago Tech. Col, 54, Tufts, 60, Carleton Col, 64. Am. Math. Soc; Math. Asn. Am. Point set topology; dimension theory. Address: Dept. of Mathematics, Carleton College, Northfield, MN 55057.

GROPP, ARMIN H(ENRY), b. Antigo, Wis, Sept. 21, 15; m. 44; c. 2. PHYSICAL & ANALYTICAL CHEMISTRY. B.A, Oregon, 43, M.A, 45, Ph.D.(phys. chem), 47; California, 44-45. Res. assoc. chem, Oregon, 47; instr, Florida, 47-48, asst. prof, 48-51, assoc. prof, 51-55, prof, 55-64, asst. chmn. dept, 54-56, asst. dean, col. arts & sci, 59-64; dean, grad. sch, UNIV. MIAMI, 64-65, V.PRES. ACAD. AFFAIRS & DEAN FACULTIES, 65-, PROF. CHEM, 70- Consult. chemist, res. labs, Gen. Motors Corp, 52- Am. Chem. Soc; Electrochem. Soc; Nat. Asn. Corrosion Eng; Am. Inst. Chem. Spectrophotometry; polarography; corrosion; electrochemistry; protective films; instrumental analysis. Address: University of Miami, Coral Gables, FL 33124.

GROPPE, (ERNEST) HENRY, JR, b. West, Tex, Mar. 23, 26. CHEMICAL ENGINEERING. B.S.Ch.E, Texas, 46. Res. & develop. engr, Dow Chem. Co, 46-48; process engr, Texas Co, 48; Arabian Am. Oil Co, 48-49, asst. to mgr. ref, 49-50; group leader process design, Monsanto Chem. Co, 50-52, asst. dir. res. develop, plastics div, 52-55; v.pres. & gen. mgr, Texas Petro Gas Co, 59-64; SECY-TREAS. & DIR, SOUTHWEST CHEM. & PLASTICS CO, 60- Consult, Mares & Groppe Co, 55- U.S.N, 44-46. AAAS; Am. Chem. Soc; Nat. Soc. Prof. Eng; Am. Inst. Chem. Eng. Hydrocarbon chemistry; cracking reactions; polymerization; oxidation; dehydrogenation. Address: 2240 Chamber of Commerce Bldg, Houston, TX 77002.

GROPPER, ARTHUR, b. New York, N.Y, Sept. 24, 24. BIOPHYSICS. B.S, Queen's Col.(N.Y), 45; M.D, Rochester, 48; M.S, Baylor, 52; California, Los Angeles, 57-60. Res. fel. physiol, hypertension div, Barnes Hosp, 49-50; cardiovasc. res. unit, Michael Reese Hosp, Chicago, Ill, 53-54; res. assoc. biophys, med. ctr, California, Los Angeles, 55-56; INDEPENDENT RES, 56- U.S.N, 43-45; U.S.A, 50-52. AAAS; Biophys. Soc. Cardiovascular and theoretical biophysics; theoretical hemodynamics; field theory as applied to the interaction of biophysical systems; biophysical theoretical mechanics; experimental use of ultrasound in study of biophysical state. Address: Suite 1005, 10501 Wilshire Blvd, Los Angeles, CA 90024.

GROSCH, CHESTER E(NRIGHT), b. Hoboken, N.J, Jan. 13, 34; m. 56; c. 3. PHYSICS. M.E, Stevens Inst. Tech, 56, M.S, 59, Ph.D.(physics), 67. Res. assoc, Hudson Labs, Columbia Univ, 66-68; scientist, Teledyne-Isotopes, Inc, 68-69; ASSOC. PROF. COMPUT. SCI. & PHYSICS, PRATT INST, 69- Consult, Vitro Labs, 63-68; adj. asst. prof, Columbia Univ, 68-; consult, Nuclear Res. Assocs, 69-; ocean & atmospheric sci, 70-; Advan. Res. Projs. Agency, 70-; TRW Systs, 71-; Inst. Defense Anal, 71- AAAS; Am. Phys. Soc; Asn. Comput. Mach. Physics of fluids; kinetic theory; rarefied gas dynamics; viscous flows; boundary layers; hydrodynamic stability; geophysical fluid dynamics; numerical methods in fluid dynamics. Address: Dept. of Computer Science & Physics, Pratt Institute, Brooklyn, NY 11205.

GROSCH, DANIEL S(WARTWOOD), b. Bethlehem, Pa, Oct. 25, 18; m. 44; c. 5. GENETICS, ZOOLOGY. B.S, Moravian Col. & Sem, 39; univ. scholar, Lehigh, M.S, 40; Ph.D.(zool), Pennsylvania, 44. Lab. instr. chem, Moravian Col. & Sem, 36-37, asst. biol, 37-38; instr. zool, Pennsylvania, 41-44, asst, 41-43; asst. prof. zool, N.C. STATE UNIV, 46-51, assoc. prof. GENETICS, 51-57, PROF, 57- With Marine Biol. Lab, Woods Hole. Comenius Award, Moravian Col. Med. Dept, U.S.A, 44-46. AAAS; Am. Soc. Nat; Entom. Soc. Am; Genetics Soc. Am; Radiation Res. Soc. Cytology, genetics and radiobiology of habrobracon and brine shrimp; biosatellite research; altered fecundity and fertility from radioisotopes, antimetabolites and mutagenic agents. Address: Dept. of Genetics, North Carolina State University, Raleigh, NC 27607.

GROSCH, HERBERT R(EUBEN) J(OHN), b. Saskatoon, Sask, Sept. 13, 18; U.S. citizen; m. 41, 56, 65. COMPUTER SCIENCE. B.S, Michigan, 38, fel, 37-41, Ph.D.(astron), 42; summers, Harvard, 39-40. Astronomer, U.S. Naval Observ, Wash, 41-42; physicist, bur. ord, U.S. Navy, 42-43; optical engr, Sperry Gyroscope Co, N.Y, 43-44; optical designer, Farrand Optical Co, N.Y, 44-45; sr. staff, Watson Sci. Comput. Lab, Int. Bus. Mach. Corp, 45-50, mgr, Wash. Tech. Comput. Bur, 51; head, logical design, digital comput. lab, Mass. Inst. Tech, 52; mgr. numerical anal, aircraft gas turbine div, Gen. Elec. Co, 52-54, invest. sect, 54-56, appln. sect, comput. dept, 56-57; asst. to dir. sales serv, Int. Bus. Mach. Corp, 57-58, mgr. space prog, 58-59; consult, 59-65; sr. scientist, tech. mil. planning oper, Gen. Elec. Co, 65-67; dir. CTR. COMPUT. SCI. & TECHNOL, NAT. BUR. STANDARDS, 67-70, SR. RES. FEL, 70- Assoc. astron, Columbia Univ, 46-50; dir. corp. planning, C-E-I-R, Inc, 59-60. Mem. adv. bd, ctr. document & commun. res, West. Reserve Univ, 55-59; chmn, Intergovt. Coun. Automatic Data Processing, 68-70; U.S. rep, comput. experts group, Orgn. Econ. Coop. & Develop, 69- Fel. Am. Inst. Aeronaut. & Astronaut.(v.pres, Rocket Soc, 50, pres, 51); Asn. Comput. Mach; fel. Brit. Comput. Soc; Inst. Elec. & Electronics Eng; Asn. Comput. Ling. Celestial mechanics of orbits and trajectories; mechanized optical design; numerical methods; computer design, programming and operation; organization of large computing facilities; standards; social implications of computer technology. Address: National Bureau of Standards, Washington, DC 20234.

GRÖSCHEL, DIETER H(ANS) M(AX), b. Würzburg, Ger, May 13, 31; U.S. citizen; m. 58; c. 2. MEDICAL MICROBIOLOGY. Fulbright scholar, Colorado, 54-55; M.D, Cologne, 57. Intern med, Univ. Cologne, U.S. Army Hosp, Landstuhl & Lutheran Hosp, 57-59; asst. neurosurg, Cologne, 59-60, res. assoc. hyg. & microbiol, 60-63; assoc. microbiol, Wistar Inst, Pa, 63-65; asst. prof, sch. med, Temple Univ, 65-68, assoc. prof, 68-71; dir. microbiol. & infectious diseases, Springfield Hosp. Med. Ctr, 68-71; ASSOC. PROF. CLIN. PATH, UNIV. TEX. M.D. ANDERSON HOSP. & TUMOR INST, 71- Clin. assoc. lab. med, sch. med, Univ. Conn, 70-71. Dipl, Am. Bd. Microbiol, 65. AAAS; Am. Soc. Microbiol; Ger. Soc. Hyg. & Microbiol; Reticuloendothelial Soc; Am. Asn. Hist. Med; Am. Pub. Health Asn; Am. Fedn. Clin. Res. Clinical microbiology; public health; epidemiology; natural resistance to infection; infectious diseases; infection control. Address: Dept. of Clinical Pathology, University of Texas at Houston, M.D. Anderson Hospital & Tumor Institute, Houston, TX 77025.

GROSE, HERSCHEL G(ENE), b. Clinton Co, Ind, Feb. 1, 21; m. 44; c. 6. ORGANIC CHEMISTRY. B.S, Ind. Cent. Col, 42; Ph.D.(chem), Indiana, 51. Tech. supvr, U.S. Rubber Co, 41-43; res. chemist, E.I. du Pont de Nemours & Co, 52-53; asst. prof, CHEM, MARIETTA COL, 53-55, assoc. prof, 55-57, PROF. & HEAD DEPT, 57- U.S.N, 43-46. AAAS; Am. Chem. Soc. Chemistry of thiophenes; industrial research in high polymers. Address: Dept. of Chemistry, Marietta College, Marietta, OH 45750.

GROSE, L(UCIUS) TROWBRIDGE, b. Evanston, Ill, Dec. 5, 24; m. 47; c. 2. GEOLOGY. B.S, Washington (Seattle), 48, M.S, 49; Ph.D.(geol), Stanford, 55. Petroleum geologist, Tex. Co, 49-52; assoc. prof. GEOL, Colo. Col, 55-64; COLO. SCH. MINES, 64-67, PROF, 67- Consult, Petrol. Res. Corp, 56-60; Nicol Indust. Minerals Corp, 60-63; U.S. Bur. Mines, 60-; Kerr-McGee Oil Industs, Inc, 62-63; Cerro Corp, Sun Oil Co, 66-71. U.S.N.R, 44-46. Am. Geol. Soc; Am. Asn. Petrol. Geol; Am. Geophys. Union; Soc. Econ. Geol. Structural and field geology; economic geology. Address: Dept. of Geological Engineering, Colorado School of Mines, Golden, CO 80401.

GROSECLOSE, B(YRON) CLARK, b. Marion, Va, June 11, 34; m. 52; c. 4. NUCLEAR PHYSICS. B.S. Emory & Henry Col, 55; univ. fel, Virginia, 55-56, M.A, 57, Du Pont fel, 57-58, South. Fels. Fund fel, 58-59, Ph.D.(physics), 59. Asst. prof. physics, Okla. State, 59-63; Kansas State, 63; PHYSICIST, LAWRENCE LIVERMORE LAB, UNIV. CALIF, 63- Prin. investr, U.S. Army Res. Off. grant, 61-63. AAAS; Am. Phys. Soc. Elastic and inelastic neutron scattering; positron life-times and intensities in condensed media; design and development of nuclear explosives for both weapons and peaceful applications. Address: Lawrence Livermore Lab, University of California, Livermore, CA 94550.

GROSECLOSE, NANCY P(ENCE), b. Blacksburg, Va, May 31, 13. ZOOLOGY. B.S, Va. Polytech, 34, M.S, 39; Ph.D.(biol), Virginia, 61. Teacher, pub. schs, Va, 34-35, 36-43; asst, dept. biol, Va. Polytech, 35-36, instr. physics, 43-45; BIOL, Hollins Col, 45-47, AGNES SCOTT COL, 47-49, asst. prof,

49-61, assoc. prof, 61-70, PROF, 70- Fel. AAAS; Am. Soc. Zool; Am. Micros. Soc. Oogenesis in parasitic nematodes; radiation effects on amphibian development. Address: Dept. of Biology, Agnes Scott College, Decatur, GA 30030.

GROSENBAUGH, LEWIS RANDOLPH, b. East Orange, N.J, Nov. 4, 13; m. 48. FORESTRY. B.A, Dartmouth Col, 34; M.F, Yale, 36. Asst. ranger, Ouachita Nat. Forest, Ark, 36-38; staff asst. forest mgt, Ozark Nat. Forest, 38-41; Fla. Nat. Forest, 46; silviculturist, south. forest & range exp. sta, U.S. FOREST SERV, 46-51, chief div. forest mgt. res, 51-60, sr. scientist, PIONEERING RES. GROUP FOREST MENSURATION STUDIES, Pac. Southwest Forest & Range Exp. Sta, 61-68, CHIEF MENSURATIONIST, SOUTHEAST. FOREST EXP. STA, 68- U.S.N, 41-46, Lt. Comdr. Fel. Soc. Am. Foresters; Biomet. Soc; Asn. Comput. Mach. Forest mensuration and management; sampling design; computer programming. Address: P.O. Box 54164, Atlanta, GA 30308.

GROSH, RICHARD J(OSEPH), b. Ft. Wayne, Ind, Oct. 29, 27; m. 50; c. 6. MECHANICAL ENGINEERING. B.S.M.E, Purdue, 50, M.S.M.E, 52, fel, 51-53, Ph.D.(mech. eng), 53. Jr. res. engr, Capehart-Farnsworth Corp, 50-51; asst. prof. mech. eng, Purdue, 53-56, assoc. prof, 56-58, prof, 58-71, assoc. dean schs. eng, 65-67, 67-71, head dept. mech. eng, 61-65; PRES, RENSSELAER POLYTECH. INST, 71- Dir. indust. develop, Purdue Res. Park & v.pres, McClure Park, 64-66; consult, Allison Div, Gen. Motors Corp; Omsteel Industs, Inc; mem. bd. dirs, AMF, Inc; mem. tech. adv. comt, Whirlpool Corp; lay adv. bd. & chmn. long range planning comt, St. Elizabeth Hosp. Nat. Acad. Eng; Am. Soc. Eng. Educ; Am. Inst. Aeronaut. & Astronaut; Am. Soc. Mech. Eng. Heat transfer; thermodynamics; fluid mechanics. Address: President's Office, Rensselaer Polytechnic Institute, Troy, NY 12180.

GROSHANS, RUSSELL G(LEN), b. Minot, N.Dak, Feb. 14, 29; m. 53; c. 2. SPACE PHYSICS, SYSTEMS ENGINEERING. B.S, U.S. Mil. Acad, 53; U.S. Air Force grant, Georgetown Univ, 61-63, M.S, 64, Ph.D.(physics), 67. Systs. Engr, Astro Electronics Div, RCA CORP, 67-69, CORP. STAFF ENGR, DAVID SARNOFF RES. CTR, PRINCETON, 69-, instr, after-hours prog, 68-69. U.S.A.F, 53-67, Capt. Am. Geophys. Union; Inst. Elec. & Electronics Eng. Frequency modulation of coherent light by ultrasonic standing waves; spacecraft configuration optimization for deep space missions; spacecraft interactions with the atmosphere in the transition region; passive microwave radiometry. Address: 61 South Blvd, Spring Lake, NJ 07762.

GROSICKI, THADDEUS S(TANLEY), b. Niagara Falls, N.Y, Nov. 23, 22; m. 58. PHARMACY. B.S, Michigan, 45; M.S, Purdue, 47; Ph.D.(pharm), Florida, 53. Asst. pharmacist, med. clinic, N.Y. Univ, 45-46; asst. pharm, Purdue, 46-47; instr, St. Louis Col. Pharm, 47-50; asst, col. pharm, Florida, 50-51; asst. prof, SCH. PHARM, UNIV. ARK, LITTLE ROCK, 53-57, assoc. prof, 57-63, PROF, 63-69, PHARMACEUT. SCI, 69- Acad. Pharmaceut. Sci. Isotonic solutions; permeability of red corpuscles to various substances. Address: School of Pharmacy, University of Arkansas Medical Center, Little Rock, AR 72201.

GROSKLAGS, JAMES H(ENRY), b. Milwaukee, Wis, June 20, 29; m. 57; c. 2. BOTANY, MYCOLOGY. B.S, Wisconsin, 51, M.S, 55, Ph.D.(bot), 60. From asst. prof. to ASSOC. PROF. BIOL, NORTH. ILL. UNIV, 58- AAAS; Bot. Soc. Am; Mycol. Soc. Am. Ecology of soil fungi. Address: Dept. of Biology, Northern Illinois University, DeKalb, IL 60115.

GROSKOPF, WILLIAM R, b. Chicago, Ill, May 11, 39; m. 64; c. 3. BIOCHEMISTRY. B.S, Ill. Inst. Tech, 61; Ph.D.(biochem), Northwestern, 65. Res. assoc. BIOCHEM, Michael Reese Res. Found, 65-69; ASST. PROF, CHICAGO MED. SCH, 69- Am. Chem. Soc. Protein chemistry; determination of amino acid sequences; chemical modification of proteins; radioactive labeling. Address: Dept. of Biochemistry, Chicago Medical School, 2020 W. Ogden Ave, Chicago, IL 60612.

GROSS, ALAN JOHN, b. Bronx, N.Y, June 19, 34; m. 62; c. 2. MATHEMATICAL & BIOLOGICAL STATISTICS. B.A, California, Los Angeles, 56, M.A. 57; Ph.D.(statist), North Carolina, 62. Lectr. math, Maryland, 61-62; Eindhoven, 63-64; sr. scientist, Booz-Allen Appl. Res, Inc, 64-66; mathematician, Rand Corp, 66-69; res. statistician, sch. pub. health, Univ. Calif, Los Angeles, 69-71; ASSOC. PROF. PUB. HEALTH, UNIV. MASS, AMHERST, 71- Lectr, exten, Univ. Calif, Los Angeles, 64- U.S.P.H.S, 61-63, Lt. Am. Statist. Asn; Inst. Math. Statist; Am. Pub. Health Asn. Applications of statistical theory to reliability, biology and information theory problems. Address: Dept. of Public Health, University of Massachusetts, Amherst, MA 01002.

GROSS, ARTHUR GERALD, b. Amsterdam, N.Y, Aug. 20, 35; m. 61; c. 2. APPLIED MATHEMATICS, COMPUTER SCIENCE. B.E.E, Rensselaer Polytech, 56, M.S, 59, Ph.D.(appl. math), 64. SPECIALIST COMPUT-AIDED ENG. DESIGN, BELL TEL. LABS, 64- Asn. Comput. Mach; Soc. Indust. & Appl. Math. Numerical analysis; application of digital computers to engineering problems; computer systems design and analysis. Address: MH 2D-447, Bell Telephone Labs, Murray Hill, NJ 07974.

GROSS, BENJAMIN H(ARRISON), b. Chattanooga, Tenn, July 23, 30; m. 64. ORGANIC CHEMISTRY. B.S, Chattanooga, 52; M.S, Tennessee, 54, Eli Lilly Co. fel, 54-55, Nat. Sci. Found. fel, 55-56, Ph.D.(chem), 56. Res. chemist, Chattanooga Med. Co, 56-64; HEAD, DEPT. CHEM, UNIV. TENN, CHATTANOOGA, 64-67, assoc. prof, 67-70, PROF, 70- AAAS; Am. Chem. Soc; N.Y. Acad. Sci. Synthetic organic chemistry; medicinal chemistry; aluminum alcoholates. Address: Dept. of Chemistry, University of Tennessee, Chattanooga, TN 37403.

GROSS, C(HARLES) E(ZRA), b. Bellevue, Ohio, Dec. 28, 05; m. 28; c. 1. FOOD TECHNOLOGY. B.A, Ohio State, 27; M.S, Northwestern, 29, Ph.D. (chem). 31. Asst, Ohio State, 26-27; lectr. indust. chem, Northwestern, 27-30; dir. sci. res, John Morrell & Co, 30-61; prof. ORG. CHEM, NORTHEAST MO. STATE COL, 61-71, EMER. PROF, 71- Am. Chem. Soc. Food bacteriology; applications of chromatographic methods. Address: 4705 Olde Bailey Way, Columbus, OH 43213.

GROSS, CLARA REGINA, b. Baltimore, Md, July 22, 99; m. 37. MEDICINE. B.A, Goucher Col, 20; M.D, Hopkins, 26. Physician, Nassau County Sanatorium, 26-28; res. physician, BELLEVUE HOSP, 28-29, SR. ATTEND. PHYSICIAN, 29-; ASSOC. PROF. CLIN. MED, COL. PHYSICIANS & SURG, COLUMBIA UNIV, 32- Med. exam, U.S. Fedn. Aviation Authority, 34-; physician, out-patient dept, N.Y. Hosp, 37-; mem, President's Women's Adv. Comn, Aviation, 68; vis. physician, Bellevue Hosp. & Vet. Admin. Hosp. Dipl, Am. Bd. Prev. Med. Fel. Am. Thoracic Soc; fel. Am. Med. Asn; fel. Aerospace Med. Asn; fel. N.Y. Acad. Sci. Diseases of the chest; aerospace medicine. Address: 140 E. 54th St, New York, NY 10022.

GROSS, DAVID (JONATHAN), b. Wash, D.C, Feb. 19, 41; m. 62; c. 1. THEORETICAL & HIGH ENERGY PHYSICS. B.Sc, Hebrew Univ. Jerusalem, 62; Ph.D.(physics), Univ. Calif, Berkeley, 66. Jr. fel, Soc. Fels, Harvard, 66-69; vis. scientist, Europ. Orgn. Nuclear Res, Switz, 69; asst. prof. PHYSICS, PRINCETON, 69-71, ASSOC. PROF, 1971- Sloan Found. fel, 70- Am. Phys. Soc. High energy particle physics. Address: Dept. of Physics, Jadwin Hall, Princeton University, Princeton, NJ 08540.

GROSS, DAVID LEE, b. Springfield, Ill, Nov. 20, 43; m. 66. GEOLOGY. A.B, Knox Col.(Ill), 65; Nat. Defense Ed. Act fel, Illinois, 66-69, M.S, 67, Ph.D.(geol), 69. ASST. GEOL, STRATIG. & AREAL GEOL. SECT, ILL. STATE GEOL. SURV, 69- AAAS; Geol. Soc. Am; Int. Asn. Quaternary Res; Am. Quaternary Asn; Int. Asn. Gt. Lakes Res; Soc. Econ. Paleont. & Mineral. Glacial geology of the mid-continent; environmental geology of Illinois. Address: Illinois State Geological Survey, Urbana, IL 61801.

GROSS, DONALD, b. Pittsburgh, Pa, Oct. 20, 34; m. 59; c. 2. OPERATIONS RESEARCH. B.S, Carnegie Inst. Tech, 56; M.S, Cornell, 59, Ph.D.(opers. res), 62. Opers. res. analyst, Atlantic Ref. Co, 61-65; asst. prof. ENG. & APPL. SCI, GEORGE WASH. UNIV, 65-67, ASSOC. PROF, 67- Sig.C, 62-63, Res, 63-, Capt. Opers. Res. Soc. Am; Inst. Mgt. Sci. Inventory control theory; mathematical techniques of forecasting time series; multiple regression models for certain problems of management decision making; multi-echelon inventory design; queuing analysis of inventory models. Address: School of Engineering & Applied Science, George Washington University, Washington, DC 20006.

GROSS, DONALD JAMES, b. San Diego, Calif, Dec. 26, 39; m. 63; c. 2. ANALYTICAL CHEMISTRY, ELECTROCHEMISTRY. B.S, Harvey Mudd Col, 61; Tenn. Eastman fel, North Carolina, Chapel Hill, 63-64, Ph.D.(anal. chem), 65. CHEMIST, SHELL DEVELOP. CO, 67- Chem.C, U.S.A, 65-67, Capt. Am. Chem. Soc; Nat. Asn. Corrosion Eng. Corrosion; metallurgy; materials evaluation and selection. Address: Shell Development Co, P.O. Box 24225, Oakland, CA 94623.

GROSS, EDWARD E(MANUEL), b. N.Y.C, July 11, 26; m. 52; c. 3. PHYSICS. B.S, Queens Col.(N.Y), 48; Ph.D, California, 56. PHYSICIST, radiation lab, California, 50-56; OAK RIDGE NAT. LAB, 56- U.S.A, 44-45. Am. Phys. Soc. Experimental high energy particle physics; experimental nuclear physics; reactor physics theory. Address: 119 Canterbury Rd, Oak Ridge, TN 37830.

GROSS, ERHARD, b. Wenings, Ger, Sept. 2, 28; m. 58; c. 2. ORGANIC CHEMISTRY, BIOCHEMISTRY. B.Sc, Mainz, 53; dipl. chem, Frankfurt, 55, Ph.D.(chem), 58. Vis. scientist, NAT. INSTS. HEALTH, 58-69, HEAD SECT. MOLECULAR STRUCT, NAT. INST. CHILD HEALTH & HUMAN DEVELOP, 69- Ger. Air Force. N.Y. Acad. Sci; Am. Chem. Soc; Soc. German Chem. Amino acids; peptides; proteins; non-enzymatic cleavage of peptide bonds. Address: National Institute of Child Health & Human Development, National Institutes of Health, Bethesda, MD 20014.

GROSS, ERIC TARAS BENJAMIN, b. Vienna, Austria, May 24, 01; nat; m. 42; c. 3. ELECTRICAL ENGINEERING. E.E, Univ. & Inst. Tech, Vienna, 23, D.Sc.(eng), 32. Instr. exp. elec. eng, Vienna Tech, 21-23; engr, A.E.G-Union Elec. & Mfg. Co, 24-28, in charge high voltage practice & protective devices, 29-34, relay develop. lab, 30-34, engr. in charge cent. sta. eng. dept, 35-38, consult. transmission engr, A.E.G. Elec. Co, Ltd, Eng, 38-39; res. engr, grad. sch, Cornell, 39-40, res. assoc, col. eng, 40-41, asst. prof. ELEC. ENG, 42-45; instr, City Col. New York, 41-42; prof, grad. sch. & col. eng, Ill. Inst. Tech, 45-61; SPORN PROF, RENSSELAER POLYTECH. INST, 62-, CHMN. ELEC. POWER ENG, 67- Chmn. sect, Int. Conf. Large High Voltage Power Systs, France, 37; consult. elec. engr, 45- With U.S. War Dept, 42-44. Fel. AAAS; fel. Inst. Elec. & Electronics Eng; fel. Brit. Inst. Elec. Eng; fel. N.Y. Acad. Sci; Swiss Inst. Elec. Eng. Circuit analysis and grounding of power systems; resonant neutral grounding; protective devices; nonconventional energy conversion. Address: 2525 McGovern Dr, Schenectady, NY 12309.

GROSS, EUGENE B(ISCHOFF), b. St. Louis, Mo, Jan. 30, 20; m. 54. MINERALOGY, GEOCHEMISTRY. B.A, Colorado, 46, M.S, 48; Mem. Phoenix fel, Michigan, 59-61, Ph.D, 62. Mineralogist, Atomic Energy Comn, 52-58; FMC Corp, 62; geochemist, Calif. Div. Mines & Geol, 63-68. Mineral Soc. Am. Uranium and rare earth materials. Address: 8 Yolo Dr, Prescott, AZ 86301.

GROSS, EVERETT WAYNE, b. Burwell, Nebr, Sept. 30, 19; m. 42; c. 3. SOLID STATE PHYSICS, ELECTRONICS. B.S. Ed, Nebr. State Teachers Col, Kearney, 57; M.S, Univ. Nebr, Lincoln, 60. Instr. PHYSICS, DOANE COL, 60-62, asst. prof, 62-70, ASSOC. PROF, 70- Nebr. agent, Henry George Sch. Social Sci, 67- U.S.A.A.F, 40-42; C.Eng, A.U.S, 42-44, 1st Lt. Am. Asn. Physics Teachers. Address: Natural Science Division, Doane College, Crete, NE 68333.

GROSS, FLETCHER, b. Colorado Springs, Colo, Nov. 29, 39; m. 64; c. 3. MATHEMATICS. B.S, Calif. Inst. Technol, 60, Nat. Sci. Found. fel, 61-63, Ph.D. (math), 64. Asst. prof. MATH, Occidental Col, 63-66; Univ. Alta, 66-67; ASSOC. PROF, UNIV. UTAH, 67- Am. Math. Soc; Math. Asn. Am. Algebra, especially group theory. Address: Dept. of Mathematics, University of Utah, Salt Lake City, UT 84112.

GROSS, FRANK JOHN, b. Passaic, N.J, Dec. 23, 34; m. 58; c. 2. ORGANIC CHEMISTRY. B.A, Rutgers, 57, M.S, 63, Am. Cyanamid Co. fel, 64-66, Ph.D.(org. chem), 67. Chemist, J. Swift & Co, 56-57; RES. CHEMIST, ORG. CHEM. DIV, RES. & DEVELOP. DEPT, AM. CYANAMID CO, BOUND BROOK, 57-64 & 66- Instr, Union Co. Tech. Inst, 64- Am. Chem. Soc. Organic synthesis devoted to the development of new materials to stabilize elastomeric substrates against degradation via oxidative processes; synthesis of organic materials which display antibacterial activity. Address: 2335 Longfellow Ave, Scotch Plains, NJ 07076.

GROSS, FRANZ L(UCRETIUS), b. Minneapolis, Minn, Aug. 9, 37. THEORETICAL PHYSICS. B.A, Swarthmore Col, 58; Fulbright fel, London, 58-59; Ph.D.(physics), Princeton, 63. Instr. & res. assoc. PHYSICS, Cornell, 63-65, acting asst. prof, 65-66, asst. prof, 66-69; vis. assoc. prof, Univ. Calif, Santa Barbara, 69-70; ASSOC. PROF, COL. WILLIAM & MARY, 70- Sporn Award, 64. Am. Phys. Soc. Electromagnetic structure; high energy physics; relativistic wave equations; deuteron and the nuclear force. Address: Dept. of Physics, College of William & Mary, Williamsburg, VA 23185.

GROSS, FRED, b. Tokay, Hungary, Nov. 11, 33; m. 58; c. 3. MATHEMATICS. B.S, Brooklyn Col, 55; M.A, Columbia, 57; Ph.D.(math), California, Los Angeles, 62. Lectr. math, Brooklyn Col, 55-58; mathematician, N.Am. Aviation, Inc, Calif, 58-59; appl. sci. rep, Int. Bus. Mach. Corp, 59-60, univ. rep, Int. Bus. Mach. Corp-Univ. California, Los Angeles, 62-63; Nat. Sci. Found. assoc. math, Nat. Bur. Standards, 63-64; res. mathematician & consult, Naval Res. Lab, 64-66; res. mathematician, Bellcomm Inc, 66-68; PROF. MATH, UNIV. MD, BALTIMORE COUNTY, 68- Consult, Naval Res. Lab. Am. Math. Soc; Math. Asn. Am. Theory of functions; entire and meromorphic functions; functional equations and number theory. Address: Dept. of Mathematics, University of Maryland, Baltimore County, Baltimore, MD 21226.

GROSS, FRITZ A, b. Ger, Oct. 8, 10; m. 37; c. 3. ELECTRICAL ENGINEERING. Design engr, Samson Elec. Co, 31-32; S.H. Couch Co, 32-33; chief engr, equip. eng. div. & mgr. radar & commun. div, RAYTHEON CO, Waltham, 33-64, v.pres. & gen. mgr. equip. div, 64-68, V.PRES. ENG, LEXINGTON, 68- Naval tech. adv, Int. Conf. Radio Aids Marine Navig, 46. Am. Soc. Naval Eng; Inst. Elec. & Electronics Eng. Development and design of products involving electronics circuits; electronic test equipments; voltage and current stabilizers; radio frequency heating equipment; magnetic components; radio and audio frequency amplifiers; radar systems; sonar; electronic countermeasures. Address: 71 Westland Rd, Weston, MA 02193.

GROSS, GEORGE C(ONRAD), b. Ginter Park, Va, Aug. 14, 14; m. 46; c. 3. CHEMICAL ENGINEERING. B.S, Va. Polytech, 36; M.S, Purdue, 38, Ph.D. (chem. eng), 41. Lab. instr. chem, Purdue, 36-41; CHEM. ENGR, J.T. Baker Chem. Co, 46-48; E.I. DU PONT DE NEMOURS & CO, 48- U.S.A, 41-46, Capt. AAAS; Am. Chem. Soc; Am. Inst. Chem. Eng. Chemical engineering plant design and pilot plant work with respect to organic chemicals; preparation of sulfamide; manufacture of synthetic fibers. Address: E.I. du Pont de Nemours & Co, Waynesboro, VA 22980.

GROSS, GEORGE L(LOYD), b. Algona, Iowa, June 24, 11; m. 35; c. 3. APPLIED MATHEMATICS. B.S, Iowa State Col, 32, M.S, 37, Ph.D.(appl. math), 39. Asst. math, Iowa State Col, 36-38, instr, 38-39; Agr. & Mech. Col, Texas, 39-42, asst. prof, 42-44; sr. grade res. assoc. exterior ballistics, Nat. Defense Res. Comt. proj, George Washington, 44-46; res. eng. appl. math, GRUMMAN AIRCRAFT ENG. CORP, 46-55, consult, 55-58, STAFF CONSULT, 58- Adj. prof. aeronaut. eng, N.Y. Univ, 48-49; lectr, Adelphi Col, 52-61. AAAS; Am. Math. Soc; Am. Phys. Soc; Soc. Indust. & Appl. Math; Math. Asn. Am; Asn. Comput. Mach. Approximate solutions of equations involving linear operators; theoretical exterior ballistics of rockets; dynamic stability of aircraft; programming analogue and digital computation; numerical and mathematical methods. Address: 78 Sammis St, Huntington, NY 11743.

GROSS, GERARDO WOLFGANG, b. Greifswald, Ger, Sept. 1, 23; m. 59; c. 3. GEOPHYSICS. D.Sc, Cordoba, 48; Ph.D.(geophys), Pa. State, 59. Geologist, Nat. Fuels Admin, 48-51; Soc. Minière Peñarroya, 51-54; res. fel. geophys, Pa. State, 56-59; geophysicist, Newmont Explor. Co, 59; instr. sci, Dutchess Community Col, 60; asst. prof. GEOPHYS, N.MEX. INST. MINING & TECHNOL, 60-66, ASSOC. PROF, 66-, GEOPHYSICIST, 60- AAAS; Soc. Cryobiol; Am. Geophys. Union. Geoelectricity; electrochemical properties of ice; groundwater hydrology. Address: Dept. of Geoscience, New Mexico Institute of Mining & Technology, Campus Station, Socorro, NM 87801.

GROSS, G(ORDON) A(RNOLD), b. Colborne Twp, Ont, Oct. 11, 23; m. 51; c. 2. GEOLOGY, MINERALOGY. B.A, Queen's (Ont), 50, M.A, 52; Alumni Res. Found. fels, Wisconsin, 52-54, Ph.D.(geol), 55. Geologist, Int. Nickel Co, Ltd, Can, 51-52; asst. prof. geol, Cincinnati, 55-56; geologist, mineral deposits div, GEOL. SURV. CAN, 56-64, econ. geol. div, 64-67, HEAD MINERAL DEPOSITS SECT, DEPT. ENERGY, MINES & RESOURCES, 67- Summers, geologist, Iron Ore Co. Can, 49-50; Oliver Iron Mining Div, U.S. Steel Corp, Can, 52-54. Consult, New Athona Mines, Ltd, Can, 55; UN consult, British Guiana, 62; Ceylon, 64; world iron ore resources surv, 67; Congo, 68. Pub. Serv. Can. merit award, 71. R.C.A.F, 43-45, Flying Officer. Geol. Soc. Am; Soc. Econ. Geol; Geol. Asn. Can; Can. Inst. Min. & Metall; fel. Mineral Asn. Can; Int. Asn. Genesis Ore Deposits. Geology and mineralogy of iron deposits in Canada; economic geology; mineralogy and Precambrian geology. Address: Dept. of Energy, Mines and Resources, Geological Survey of Canada, 601 Booth St, Ottawa, Ont. K1A 0E8, Can.

GROSS, GORDON E, b. Plattner, Colo, July 29, 25; m. 47; c. 3. SOLID STATE PHYSICS. B.S, Cent. Mo. State Col, 47; A.M, Missouri, 49; Kansas, 50-52. Asst, Missouri, 47-49; instr. physics, Northwest Mo. State Col, 49-50; asst, Kansas, 50-52; plant physicist, Libby-Owens Ford Glass Co, 52-53; staff physicist, MIDWEST RES. INST, 53-57, HEAD PHYSICS SECT, 57- Lectr, Univ. Kansas City, 56-57, 58-59. U.S.N, 44-46. Am. Phys. Soc; Sci. Res. Soc. Am. Properties of metals under fatigue; physics of wear and solid lubrication; physical mechanisms of fracture and ductility; fracture energy of ceramics; development of ceramic strength measurement techniques. Address: Midwest Research Institute, 425 Volker Blvd, Kansas City, MO 64110.

GROSS, GUILFORD C, b. Bowdle, S.Dak, June 8, 17; m. 40; c. 2. PHARMACOLOGY. B.S, S.Dak. State, 39, M.S, 40; Ph.D.(pharmacol), Florida, 52. From instr. to assoc. prof. pharm, S.DAK. STATE UNIV, 40-43, 46-52, PROF. PHARMACOL, 52-, dean pharm, 64-65. Mem. revision comt, U.S. Pharmacopoeia, 55-60. U.S.N.R, 43-46, Lt.(jg). Am. Pharmaceut. Asn. Pharmacy. Address: College of Pharmacy, South Dakota State University, Brookings, SD 57007.

GROSS, HARRY DOUGLASS, b. Halifax, Pa, Mar. 4, 24; m. 54; c. 4. AGRONOMY. B.S, Rutgers, 48, M.S, 52; Ph.D.(agron), Iowa State, 56. Teacher, Newport Union Sch. Dist, Pa, 48-49; instr. farm crops, Rutgers, 49-52; agron, Iowa State, 52-56; res. asst. prof. field crops, N.C. STATE UNIV, 56-58, proj. leader agr. mission to Peru, 58-61, res. assoc. prof. CROP SCI, 61-68, RES. PROF, 68- Prog. coord, Mission to Peru, 67-70. A.U.S, 42-45, M/Sgt. Am. Soc. Agron; Latin Am. Soc. Animal Sci; Soc. Range Mgt. Forage crop management, particularly fertilization and cutting practices; forage crop evaluation in vitro and in vivo; grazing management; silage production practice. Address: Dept. of Crop Science, North Carolina State University, Raleigh, NC 27607.

GROSS, HERBERT M(ICHEAL), b. Milwaukee, Wis, Mar. 31, 25; m. 51. PHARMACEUTICAL CHEMISTRY. B.S, Wisconsin, 49; M.S, Florida, 51, fel, 52, Ph.D.(pharm), 53; Indust. Mgt. Inst, Lake Forest Col, 59-63. Instr. pharm, Florida, 49-53; prod. supvr, Lincoln Labs, 53; head, dept. pharmaceut. prod. develop, Commercial Solvents Corp, 53-56; res. pharmacist, pharmaceut, ABBOTT LABS, 56-57, head, dept. pharmaceut. res, 57-61, dir. new prod, 61-67, prod. planning & develop, 67-68, v.pres. HOSP. PROD. DIV, 68-69, PRES, 69- U.S.A, 43-44, Med.C, 50-52. Am. Pharmaceut. Asn; Pharmaceut. Mfrs. Asn. Tablets; suppositories; lyophilization; antibiotic and vitamin formulations; flavoring; tablet coatings; research management. Address: 686 S. Timber Lane, Lake Forest, IL 60045.

GROSS, JACK, b. Montreal, Can, March 29, 21; m. 44; c. 2. ENDOCRINOLOGY. B.Sc, McGill, 41, M.D, 44, fel, 46-48, Ph.D.(anat), 49. Lectr. anat, med. sch, McGill, 48-50; Merck fel. biochem, Nat. Inst. Med. Res, London, 49-52; asst. prof. ANAT, col. med, State Univ. N.Y. Downstate Med. Center, 52-54, assoc. prof, 54-56, prof, 56-57; vis. prof, World Health Orgn, HADASSAH MED. SCH, HEBREW UNIV, ISRAEL, 57-64, BLUESTONE PROF. EXP. MED, 64- Mem. Nat. Auth. Res. & Develop; exec. comt, Int. Soc. Endocrinol. Herman Zondek Prize, 68. Med.C, Can. Army, 43-46, Capt. Endocrine Soc.(Ciba award, 55); Am. Physiol. Soc; Histochem. Soc; Am. Chem. Soc; Soc. Exp. Biol. & Med; Am. Asn. Anat; Am. Asn. Cancer Res; fel. N.Y. Acad. Sci; Brit. Soc. Endocrinol; Brit. Biochem. Soc; Israel Endocrine Soc; Europ. Thyroid Asn. Thyroid physiology; cell biology. Address: Dept. of Experimental Medicine & Cancer Research, Hebrew University Hadassah Medical School, P.O. Box 1172, Jerusalem, Israel.

GROSS, JACK E(DWIN), b. Durant, Okla, Apr. 17, 30; m. 51; c. 2. WILDLIFE MANAGEMENT. B.S, Alaska, 56; Ph.D.(wildlife mgt), Utah State, 67. Res. biologist, N.Mex. Dept. Fish & Game, 59-61; res. fel. wildlife mgt, Utah State, 61-65; asst. prof. zool, N.Dak. State, 65-67; ASST. PROF. WILDLIFE MGT, COLO. STATE UNIV. & ASST. LEADER WILDLIFE RES, COLO. COOP. WILDLIFE RES. UNIT, 67- U.S.A.F, 48-52, S/Sgt. Wildlife Soc. Population dynamics of jackrabbits, deer and elk; population ecology. Address: Colorado Cooperative Wildlife Research Unit, Colorado State University, Ft. Collins, CO 80521.

GROSS, J(EAN) A(LVAH), b. Brooklyn, N.Y, June 29, 24; m. 48; c. 3. CELL BIOLOGY. B.S, Ohio, 47; fel, Michigan, 49-51, M.S, 50, Atomic Energy Cmn. fel, 51-53, Ph.D.(zool), 53. Asst. gen. zool. & comp. anat, Michigan, 47-51; Mich. Mem. Phoenix Proj, 53; res. assoc. & U.S. Pub. Health Serv. fel, California, Los Angeles, 54-56, res. zoologist, 56-57; instr. natural sci, Mich. State, 57-59; res. investr. & Mudge fel, biophys. res. lab, Eye & Ear Hosp, Pittsburgh, 59-60; assoc. biochem, Armour Res. Found, 60-61, res. biochemist, res. inst, Ill. Inst. Technol, 61-63, sr. biologist, 64-67; PROF. LIFE SCI, IND. STATE UNIV, TERRE HAUTE, 67- NATO-Nat. Sci. Found. fel, Univ. Liverpool, summer 71. Lalor Found. faculty res. award, 58. U.S.A.A.F, 43-45. Soc. Protozool; Am. Soc. Plant Physiol; Biophys. Soc; Am. Soc. Cell Biol. Photosynthesis; plastid structure and chemistry; biological effects of temperature and radiations; chlorosis induction; morphogenesis and biochemistry of cytoplasmatic particulates; marine algal physiology. Address: Dept. of Life Sciences, Indiana State University, Terre Haute, IN 47809.

GROSS, JEROME, b. N.Y.C, Feb. 25, 17; m. 47; c. 3. BIOLOGY, MEDICINE. B.S, Mass. Inst. Tech, 39; M.D, N.Y. Univ, 43. Life Ins. Med. Res. Fund fel, dept. biol, Mass. Inst. Tech, 46-48; res. fel. MED, HARVARD MED. SCH, 48-50; res. assoc, 50-54, assoc, 54-57, asst. prof, 57-64, assoc. prof, 64-69, PROF, 69-; BIOLOGIST, MASS. GEN. HOSP, 66-, clin. & res. fel, 48-51, assoc. biologist, 51-66. Res. assoc, Mass. Inst. Technol, 46-55; mem. subcomt. skeletal syst, Nat. Res. Coun, 55-62; sci. adv. comt, Helen Hay Whitney Found, 56; estab. investr, Am. Heart Asn, 56-61; mem. adv. panel molecular biol, Nat. Sci. Found, 59-62; counsr, bd. sci. counsrs, Nat. Inst. Dent. Res, chmn, 63; adv. ed, Jour. Exp. Med, 63; mem. study group, Space Sci. Bd, summer 64; consult. ed, Develop. Biol, 65. Ciba Award, 59; Kappa Delta Award, Am. Acad. Orthop. Surg, 65. Med.C, 44-46, Capt. Histochem. Soc.(secy, 56-60); Soc. Develop. Biol; Am. Physiol. Soc; Biophys. Soc; Brit. Biochem. Soc. Developmental and molecular biology; biomedical science; connective tissues and their diseases; aging processes. Address: Developmental Biology Lab, Massachusetts General Hospital, 32 Fruit St, Boston, MA 02114.

GROSS, JOHN BURGESS, b. St. Louis, Mo, Dec. 26, 20; m. 45; c. 4. MEDICINE. A.B, DePauw, 42; M.D, Western Reserve, 45; M.S, Minnesota, 49. Assoc. prof. MED, MAYO GRAD. SCH. MED, UNIV. MINN, 63-69, PROF, 69-, CONSULT, MAYO CLIN. & HOSPS, 50- Med.C, 53-55, Capt. Am. Col. Physicians; Am. Gastroenterol. Asn; Am. Soc. Human Genetics; Am. Med. Asn; affiliate mem. Royal Soc. Med. Diseases of the pancreas, bowel and liver, especially the hereditary form of pancreatitis. Address: Mayo Graduate School of Medicine, University of Minnesota, Rochester, MN 55901.

GROSS, JOHN H(AMMES), b. Hummelstown, Pa, Jan. 27, 23; m. 41; c. 1. METALLURGICAL ENGINEERING. B.S, Lehigh, 44, M.S, 48, Ph.D.(metall. eng), 55. Instr. metall, Lehigh, 44, from asst. prof. to assoc. prof, 46-58; res. technologist, APPL. RES. LAB, U.S. STEEL CORP, 58-60, asst. div. chief, 60-63, chief ord. prod. div, 63-67, MGR. STEEL PROD. DEVELOP, 67- Mem. ship struct. comt, Nat. Acad. Sci. U.S.N.R, 44-46, Lt. Fel. Am. Soc. Metals; Am. Welding Soc; Am. Soc. Mech. Eng; Am. Soc. Naval Eng. Physical and mechanical metallurgy and weldability; dependence of mechanical properties on microstructure. Address: Applied Research Lab, U.S. Steel Corp, Monroeville, PA 15146.

GROSS, J(OHN) H(OWARD), b. Tarentum, Pa, June 16, 22; m. 43; c. 3. PHYSICAL CHEMISTRY. B.S, Rollins Col, 42; Ph.D.(chem), Rensselaer Polytech, 49. Chemist, E.I. du Pont de Nemours & Co, 42-43; asst. Rensselaer Polytech, 46-49; chemist, Oak Ridge Nat. Lab, 49-52; res. specialist, Int. Minerals & Chem. Corp, 52-62; tech. staff, Aerospace Corp, 62-68; res. specialist, Boeing Co, 68-71; HEAD DEPT. CHEM, HYDROSPACE TECH. INST, FLA. INST. TECHNOL, 71- C.W.S, U.S.A, 43-46. Fel. AAAS; Am. Chem. Soc; Am. Inst. Aeronaut. & Astronaut. Marine and environmental chemistry. Address: 224 Bahama Blvd, Cocoa Beach, FL 32931.

GROSS, JONATHAN LIGHT, b. Phila, Pa, June 11, 41; m. 62; c. 3. MATHEMATICS. B.S, Mass. Inst. Tech, 64; A.M, Dartmouth Col, 66, Ph.D.(math), 68. Instr. math, Princeton, 68-69; ASST. PROF. MATH. STATIST, COLUMBIA UNIV, 69- Am. Math. Soc; Math. Asn. Am. Topology; computer science; combinatorics. Address: 618 Mathematics, Columbia University, New York, NY 10027.

GROSS, JOSEPH F, b. Plauen, Ger, Aug, 22, 32; U.S. citizen. FLUID DYNAMICS. B.Ch.E, Pratt, 53; Ph.D.(chem. eng), Purdue, 56. Consult, RAND CORP, 56-57, engr, 57-70, RES. ENGR, 70- Fulbright scholar, thermodyn. inst, Munich Tech. & inst. fluid dynamics, Brunswick Tech, 56-57. Am. Inst. Aeronaut. & Astronaut; Am. Inst. Chem. Eng; Am. Soc. Mech. Eng; Microcirc. Soc; Int. Soc. Biorheol; Am. Physiol. Soc. Fluid mechanics of circulatory system; hemorheology; heat and mass transfer. Address: Rand Corp, 1700 Main St, Santa Monica, CA 90406.

GROSS, KENNETH I(RWIN), b. Malden, Mass, Oct. 14, 38; m. 64; c. 1. MATHEMATICAL ANALYSIS. B.A, Brandeis Univ, 60, M.A, 62; Ph.D. (math), Wash. Univ, 66. ASST. PROF. MATH, Tulane Univ, 66-68; DARTMOUTH COL, 68- Nat. Sci. Found, Nat. Defense Educ. Act & NASA fels. Am. Math. Soc. Harmonic analysis; infinite-dimensional representation theory. Address: Dept. of Mathematics, Dartmouth College, Hanover, NH 03755.

GROSS, KENNETH J(AMES), b. Los Angeles, Calif, Sept. 7, 20; m. 50; c. 3. ORGANIC CHEMISTRY. B.A, California, Los Angeles, 42, B.S, 46; Southern California. Pharmaceut. chemist, Rexall Drug Co. Div, Rexall Drug & Chem. Co, 47-50, chief chemist, Riker Labs. Div, 50-70; chem. consult, 70-71; MGR. MFG, PLUS PROD, 71- U.S.A, 42-46, Capt. Am. Chem. Soc; N.Y. Acad. Sci. Medicinal chemistry; organic synthesis; natural products; fermentation; process research, development, production; processing and packaging health foods. Address: 8618 Bothwell Rd, Northridge, CA 91324.

GROSS, LEO, b. Brooklyn, N.Y, Feb. 13, 15; m. 40; c. 3. BIOPHYSICS. B.S, Brooklyn Col, 34; M.A, Columbia, 36; Ph.D.(biophys), N.Y. Univ, 63. Mem. tech. staff, Bell Tel. Labs, 46-49; chief systs. engr, Polarad Electronics Corp, 49-54; pres, Hub Electronics Corp, 54-58; BIOPHYSICIST, WALDEMAR MED. RES. FOUND, 58- Physicist, bur. ord, U.S. Dept. Navy, 42-43; Los Alamos Sci. Lab, California, 43-46. C.Eng, 42-46, 1st Lt. Am. Phys. Soc; Inst. Elec. & Electronics Eng. Biophysics of cell function and change in function in neoplasia. Address: 36-11 217th St, Bayside, NY 11797.

GROSS, L(EONARD), b. New York, N.Y, Feb. 10, 22; m. 43; c. 1. PHYSICS. A.B, Brooklyn Col, 42; fel, Princeton, 46-47, A.M, 47, Coffin fel, 47-48, Atomic Energy Cmn. fel, 48-49, Ph.D.(physics), 49. Instr. physics, Brooklyn Col, 42-43; Princeton, 43-44; res. assoc, Columbia, 44; from sr. staff physicist, to mgr. missile systs, res. & develop. labs, HUGHES AIRCRAFT CO, 49-60, dir. adv. projs, 60-62; mgr. aeronaut. systs. div, 62-66, V.PRES. & MGR, SYSTS. DIV, 66- Sig.C, U.S.A, 44-46. Am. Phys. Soc; Soc. Indust. & Appl. Math; Am. Inst. Aeronaut. & Astronaut. Theoretical and experimental nuclear physics; beta decay; automatic control systems analysis; systems engineering. Address: Hughes Aircraft Co, Mail Station B154, Culver City, CA 90230.

GROSS, LEONARD, b. Brooklyn, N.Y, Feb. 24, 31; m. 56; c. 2. MATHEMATICS. M.S, Chicago, 54, Ph.D.(math), 58; Minnesota, 54-55. Instr. MATH, Yale, 57-59, Nat. Sci. Found. fel, 59-60; asst. prof, CORNELL UNIV, 60-64, assoc. prof, 64-67, PROF, 67- Am. Math. Soc. Classical analysis on Hilbert space; mathematical problems of quantum theories. Address: Dept. of Mathematics, Cornell University, Ithaca, NY 14850.

GROSS, LUDWIK, b. Krakow, Poland, Sept. 11, 04; nat; m. 43; c. 1. CANCER. M.D, Iagellon Univ, Poland, 29. Cancer res, Pasteur Inst, 32-39; res. assoc, Inst. Med. Res, Christ Hosp, Cincinnati, 41-43; CHIEF CANCER RES, VET. ADMIN. HOSP, BRONX, 46-; RES. PROF. MED, MT. SINAI SCH. MED, 71- Consult, Sloan-Kettering Inst. Cancer Res, 53-56, assoc. scientist, 57-60. Prix Chevillon, Paris Acad. Med, 37; R.R. de Villers Found. award, Leukemia Soc, 53; Walker Prize, Royal Col. Surgeons Eng, 62; Pasteur Silver Medal, Pasteur Inst, France, 62; James Award, James Ewing Soc, 62; UN Prize, WHO, 62; Bertner Found. award, Univ. Tex, 63; Albert Einstein Centennial Medal, 65; Dipl, Am. Bd. Internal Med. Med.C, 43-46, Maj. AAAS; Soc. Exp. Biol. & Med; Am. Asn. Cancer Res; Am. Med. Asn; Asn. Mil. Surg. U.S; fel. Am. Col. Physicians; fel. N.Y. Acad. Sci; fel. Int. Soc. Hemat. Experimental cancer and leukemia. Address: Veterans Administration Hospital, 130 W. Kingsbridge Rd, Bronx, NY 10468.

GROSS, MALCOLM E(DMUND), b. Brownington, Vt, June 23, 15; m. 37; c. 2. CHEMISTRY. B.S, Middlebury Col, 36; Heidelberg, 36-37; Harvard, 37-38; M.S, Western Reserve, 46, Ph.D, 50. Res. chemist, B.F. GOODRICH CO, 48, sr. res. chemist, RES. CTR, 48-66, SECT. LEADER, 66- Staff scientist, Lockheed Missiles & Space Co, Calif, 63. Am. Chem. Soc; Soc. Aerospace Mat. & Process Eng. Structural adhesives for aerospace applications. Address: B.F. Goodrich Research Center, Brecksville, OH 44141.

GROSS, M(EREDITH) GRANT, b. Childress, Tex, Jan. 5, 33; m. 54; c. 3. MARINE GEOCHEMISTRY. A.B, Princeton, 54; Fulbright fel, Delft, 54-55; Nat. Sci. Found. fel, Calif. Inst. Tech, 58-61, M.S, 59, Ph.D, 61. Asst. prof. OCEANOG, Univ. Wash, 61-65, assoc. prof, 65-68; STATE UNIV. N.Y. STONY BROOK, 68-70, PROF, 70-, ASSOC. DIR. RES, 71- Assoc. curator, Smithsonian Inst, 66-; mem. div. sedimentol, U.S. Nat. Mus, Washington, D.C. AAAS; Am. Geophys. Union; Geochem. Soc; fel. Geol. Soc. Am; Am. Soc. Limnol. & Oceanog; Soc. Econ. Paleont. & Mineral. Chemistry of sediments and seawater; diagenesis of sediments; radioactivity in sediments and seawater; waste disposal in coastal ocean waters. Address: Marine Sciences Research Center, State University of New York at Stony Brook, Stony Brook, NY 11790.

GROSS, MICHAEL A(LAN), b. Phila, Pa, Apr. 30, 44; m. 66; c. 2. ORGANIC CHEMISTRY, BIOCHEMISTRY. B.Sc, Phila. Col. Pharm, 66; fel, Temple Univ, 66-70, Ph.D.(org. chem), 70. Instr. chem, Del. Valley Col, 68-70; STAFF FEL. BIOCHEM, NAT. INST. DENT. RES, BETHESDA, 70- Am. Inst. Chemists Award, 66. AAAS; Am. Chem. Soc. Biosynthetic organic chemistry; enzyme mechanisms; protein chemistry; synthetic organic chemistry; peptide synthesis. Address: 692 Azalea Dr, Rockville, MD 20850.

GROSS, MICHAEL LAWRENCE, b. St. Cloud, Minn, Nov. 6, 40; m. 66; c. 2. ANALYTICAL & ORGANIC CHEMISTRY. B.A, St. John's Univ.(Minn), 62; Ph.D.(org. chem), Univ. Minn, 66. Fel. org. chem, Univ. Pa, 66-67; Purdue Univ, 67-68; ASST. PROF. ANAL. CHEM, UNIV. NEBR, LINCOLN, 68- Am. Chem. Soc. Mass spectrometry; structures of gas-phase ions; structure determinations of organic molecules; ion-molecule reactions; ion cyclotron resonance spectrometry. Address: Dept. of Chemistry, University of Nebraska, Lincoln, NE 68508.

GROSS, MILDRED L(UCILE), b. Lancaster Co, Nebr, Nov. 16, 20; m. 42; c. 3. MATHEMATICS. B.S, Nebr. State Teachers Col, Kearney, 42; M.S, Nebr, 59, Nat. Sci. Found. fel, 59-61, Ph.D.(math), 63. Assoc. prof. MATH, DOANE COL, 61-69, PROF, 69- Math. Asn. Am; Am. Math. Soc. Number theory; use of sieve methods in investigation of prime numbers. Address: Dept. of Mathematics, Doane College, Crete, NE 68333.

GROSS, M(IRCEA) ADRIAN, b. Bucharest, Rumania, Aug. 8, 23; U.S. citizen; m. 52; c. 3. PATHOLOGY. B.Sc, Manitoba, 49; D.V.M, Toronto, 54; Vet. Surg, Ont. Vet. Col, Guelph, 54; M.Sc, Ohio State, 56; Ph.D.(statist), Mich. State, 59. Res. asst. vet. path, Ohio State, 54-56; res. pathologist, Agr. Res. Serv, Mich, 56-58; U.S. Pub. Health Serv, Ohio, 59-60; Arthur D. Little Co, Mass, 60-62; Microbiol. Assocs, Md, 62-64; acting chief path. br, FOOD & DRUG ADMIN, 64-69, ASST. DIR. SCI. COORD, OFF. PHARMACEUT. RES. & TESTING, BUR. DRUGS, 69- Vis. scientist, biomet. br, Nat. Cancer Inst, 59-60. Brit. Army, 42-46, Lt. Am. Vet. Med. Asn.(award, 54); Am. Asn. Cancer Res. Pathology of cancer, virus and chemically induced; general experimental pathology; biometry and experimental statistics. Address: Food & Drug Administration, Dept. of Health, Education & Welfare, 200 C St. S.W, Washington, DC 20204.

GROSS, NOEL H(ARDEN), b. Halfway, Ore, Jan. 1, 05; m. 28; c. 1. BACTERIOLOGY. B.S, Ore. State Col, 35, M.A, 37; Ph.D.(bact), Iowa State Col, 44. Dairy chemist, Eugene Farmers Creamery, Ore, 29-30, chemist, 31-33, bacteriologist, 31-38, consult, 33-38; instr. bact, Iowa State Col, 39-45, asst. prof, 45-47; sect. chief in charge safety munitions & pilot plants, Ft. Detrick, 47-50, chief agent control br, safety div, 50-54, reports, training & orientation div, 54-59; asst. chief extramural prog, NAT. INST. ALLERGY & INFECTIOUS DISEASES, 59-65, chief bact. & mycol. br. & training grants off, 65-69, SPEC. ASST. TRAINING PROGS, 69- Instr, Ore. State Col, 35-38. Am. Soc. Microbiol; Am. Pub. Health Asn. Bacteriophage; etiological agent of walnut blight; etiology of filbert blight; bacterial physiology; mechanisms of the formation of acetylmethylcarbinol by active enzyme preparations. Address: 5200 Benton Ave, Bethesda, MD 20014.

GROSS, PAUL, b. Berlin, Ger, June 8, 02; nat; m. 30; c. 4. PATHOLOGY. A.B, Western Reserve, 24, M.D, 27, Crile fel, 28-29, M.A, 29. Demonstr. path, Western Reserve, 29-32, instr, 33-35, curator mus, 34-35; pathologist, West. Pa. Hosp, Pittsburgh, 35-44; pathologist, indust. hyg. found, Mellon Inst, 48-54, sr. fel, indust. hyg. found, 53-68; res. prof, grad. sch. pub. health, Univ. Pittsburgh, 68-71; PROF. PATH, MED. UNIV. S.C, 71- Pathologist, St. Vincent's Charity Hosp, Ohio, 32-35; asst. prof, Univ. Vienna, 32-33; pathologist, St. Joseph's Hosp, 44-54; adj. prof, grad. sch. pub. health, Univ. Pittsburgh, 60-68; dir. res. lab, Indust. Health Found, Pittsburgh; mem. threshold limit comt, Am. Conf. Govt. Hygienists. AAAS; Soc. Exp. Biol. & Med; Am. Soc. Clin. Path; Am. Chem. Soc; Am. Asn. Path. & Bact; Int. Acad. Path; hon. mem. Am. Indust. Hyg. Asn. Pneumoconioses. Address: Medical University of South Carolina, 80 Barre St, Charleston, SC 29401.

GROSS, PAUL H(ANS), b. Berlin, Germany, Apr. 17, 31; m. 57; c. 4. ORGANIC & PHYSICAL CHEMISTRY. Dipl, chem, Free Univ. Berlin, 58, Dr. Sci.(chem), 61. Res. chemist, Schering AG, Germany, 61-62; fel. aminosugar chem, Univ. of the Pacific, 62-64; res. fel. carbohydrate chem, Mass. Gen. Hosp. & Harvard Med. Sch, 65-66; assoc. prof. CHEM, UNIV. OF THE PACIFIC, 66-70, PROF, 70- Nat. Sci. Found. grant, 68. Am. Chem. Soc; Soc. Rheol; German Chem. Soc. Chemistry and properties of ethers of polyols; rheology properties of liquids; chemistry of aminosugars; chemistry of peptides. Address: Dept. of Chemistry, University of the Pacific, Stockton, CA 95204.

GROSS, PAUL M(AGNUS), b. New York, N.Y, Sept. 15, 95; m. 18; c. 2. PHYSICAL CHEMISTRY. B.S, Col. City of N.Y, 16; A.M, Columbia, 17, Ph.D. (chem), 19. Tutor CHEM, City Col, 16-18; asst. prof, Trinity Col.(N.C), 19-20, prof, 20-25; prof, DUKE UNIV, 26-69, chmn. dept, 26-49, dean grad. sch, 47-52, dean univ, 52-58, v.pres, 49-60, WILLIAM HOWELL PEGRAM EMER. PROF, 69- Pres, Oak Ridge Inst. Nuclear Studies, 49- Mem. & v.chmn, Nat. Sci. Bd; mem, Nat. Cancer Adv. Council; Ord. Corps Adv. Comt; chmn, munitions command adv. comt, U.S. Army; mem, sci. adv. panel of Secy. Army; Nat. Adv. Environ. Health Comt, U.S. Pub. Health Serv; trustee, Woodrow Wilson Nat. Fels. Found. President's medal of merit, 48; South. Asn. Sci. & Indust. award, 52; Harris medal, 53; Manship award, 54; hon.

comdr, Order British Empire, 58. With Off. Sci. Res. & Develop; U.S.A.A.F; U.S.N; Tenn. Valley Authority, 44. U.S.A, 17-19. AAAS; Am. Chem. Soc.(Herty Medal, 45); fel. Am. Phys. Soc; fel. N.Y. Acad. Sci. Dielectrics; solution theory; plant biochemistry of tobacco; vapor pressures; paper technology; refining of vegetable oils; organic fluorine compounds; insecticides. Address: Dept. of Chemistry, Duke University, Durham, NC 27706.

GROSS, PAUL M(AGNUS), JR, b. Durham, N.C, Jan. 15, 20. PHYSICAL CHEMISTRY. B.S, Duke, 41; Ph.D.(chem), Brown, 48. Asst. dept. phys. chem, Harvard Med. Sch, 42-46; instr. chem, Virginia, 48-51; asst. prof. gen. & phys. chem, 51-59; ASSOC. PROF. PHYS. CHEM. & COORD. HONORS PROG, WAKE FOREST UNIV, 59- Nat. Sci. Found. faculty fel, Cambridge, 57-58. Am. Chem. Soc. Physical chemistry of hydrogen peroxide-water solutions; dielectric constant measurements of hydrogen peroxide and protein solutions; fractionation and properties of proteins; solubility of strong electrolytes in hydrogen peroxide; vapor pressures of hydrogen peroxide water solutions; formation and stability of hydroperoxidates. Address: Apt. 6-F Faculty Apts, Faculty Dr, Winston-Salem, NC 27106.

GROSS, PAUL R(ANDOLPH), b. Philadelphia, Pa, Nov. 27, 28; m. 49; c. 2. DEVELOPMENTAL & MOLECULAR BIOLOGY. A.B, Pennsylvania, 50, Harrison fel, 52-53, Nat. Sci. Found. fel, 53-54, Ph.D. (zool), 54; M.A, Brown, 63. Asst. prof. BIOL, N.Y. Univ, 54-58, assoc. prof, 58-61; Brown, 62-65; PROF. MASS. INST. TECHNOL, 65- Lalor fel, 54-55, Nat. Sci. Found. sr. fel, Edinburgh, 61-62. Mem. bd. sci. counselors, Nat. Inst. Child Health & Human Development, U.S. Pub. Health Serv; mem. corp, Marine Biol. Lab, Woods Hole. Am. Physiol. Soc; Am. Soc. Zool; Am. Soc. Cell Biol; Int. Soc. Cell Biol. Chemical embryology; molecular biology; cellular physiology; chemistry of cell division and differentiation. Address: Dept. of Biology, Massachusetts Institute of Technology, Cambridge, MA 02139.

GROSS, PETER F(REDRICK), b. Chicago, Ill, May 21, 09; m. 36; c. 3. ORGANIC CHEMISTRY. A.B, Univ. South. Calif, 30; M.S, Lawrence Col, 32; Ph.D.(org. chem), Cornell Univ, 36. Res. chemist, E.I. du Pont de Nemours & Co, Inc, 36-70; private practice, 70- Am. Chem. Soc. Dyes and pigments; wetting agents and detergents; organic pigments. Address: Rural Route 1, Woodstown, NJ 08098.

GROSS, PHYLLIS P, b. Exeter, Calif, July 18, 15; div; c. 2. BIOLOGY, SCIENCE EDUCATION. B.S, San Jose State Col, 35; M.A, Stanford, 37; summers, Marquette, 58, Indiana, 60. Teacher, high schs, Calif. & Ore, 39-65; assoc. prof. BIOL. SCI, CALIF. STATE COL. HAYWARD, 65-70, PROF, 70- Lectr, Fresno State Col, 63-64; Shell Merit fel, Stanford, summer 68. Consult. biol. sci. curriculum study, Modesto City Schs, 62-63, Merced County Schs, 63-64, 66-67. AAAS; Nat. Sci. Teachers Asn; Nat. Asn. Biol. Teachers; Nat. Asn. Res. Sci. Teaching. Improvement of science education at all levels. Address: Dept. of Biological Sciences, California State College, Hayward, 25800 Hillary St, Hayward, CA 94542.

GROSS, ROBERT A(LFRED), b. Phila, Pa, Oct. 31, 27; m. 52; c. 2. PLASMA PHYSICS. B.S, Pennsylvania, 49; M.S, Harvard, 50, fel, 51-52, Ph.D.(appl. physics), 52. Fel. & res. assoc, Harvard, 53; chief res. engr, Fairchild Engine Div, Fairchild Engine & Airplane Corp, 54-59; Nat. Sci. Found. fel, 59-60; PROF. ENG. SCI, COLUMBIA UNIV, 60-, CHMN. DEPT. MECH. ENG, 70- Guggenheim & Fulbright fels, 66-67; vis. prof, Leiden Univ, 66-67; Australian Acad. Sci. vis. fel, 67. U.S.A, 45-46. Fel. Am. Phys. Soc; fel. Am. Inst. Aeronaut. & Astronaut.(v.pres, 65-67, ed-in-chief selected reprint series, 68-). High temperature gas dynamics; chemical kinetics. Address: Dept. of Engineering, 236 Seeley W. Mudd Bldg, Columbia University, New York, NY 10027.

GROSS, ROBERT E(DWARD), b. Baltimore, Md, July 2, 05; m. 31; c. 2. SURGERY. B.A, Carleton Col, 27, hon. D.Sc, 51; M.D, Harvard, 31; hon. M.D, Louvain, 59, Turin, 61; hon. D.Sc, Suffolk, 62, Sheffield, 63. Intern path, Children's Hosp. Med. Ctr, 31, surg. 32-33; path, Peter Bent Brigham Hosp, 33-34; instr. path, HARVARD MED. SCH, 34-36, surg, 37-39, assoc, 39-42, asst. prof, 42-47, LADD PROF. CHILDREN'S SURG, 47-; SR. MEM. PERMANENT STAFF, CHILDREN'S HOSP. MED. CTR, 39-, CHIEF CARDIOVASC. SURG, 67- Resident, Peter Bent Brigham Hosp, 34-35, asst. res. surgeon, 35-37, Peters traveling fel, 37-38, res. surg, 38-39, jr. assoc, 39-40, assoc, 40-46, sr. assoc, 46; resident, Children's Hosp. Med. Ctr, 37-38, assoc. res. surgeon, 39-46, surgeon, 46-47, surgeon-in-chief, 47-67. Dipl. Am. Bd. Surg, 40; Am. Bd. Thoracic Surg, 49; modern med. award, 53; Alfred Jurzykowski Medal, N.Y. Acad. Med, 70. Soc. Clin. Surg; Soc. Vascular Surg; Soc. Univ. Surg; Am. Soc. Exp. Path; Soc. Thoracic Surg; Am. Med. Asn.(Dr. Rodman E. Sheen & Thomas E. Sheen Award, 69); Am. Asn. Path. & Bact; Am. Col. Surg; Am. Acad. Pediat; Soc. Pediat. Res; Am. Heart Asn; Am. Surg. Asn; Am. Acad. Arts & Sci; Am. Col. Cardiol; Pan-Am. Med. Asn; French Soc. Pediat. Surg; Brit. Soc. Pediat. Surg. Patent ductus arteriosus; surgical correction for coarctation of aorta; abnormalities of heart and great vessels; surgical repair of tetralogy of Fallot; atrial septal defects; ventricular septal defects; pump-oxygenator for maintaining circulation during open-heart surgery. Address: Children's Hospital Medical Center, 300 Longwood Ave, Boston, MA 02115.

GROSS, ROLF W(ERNER) F(RIEDRICH), b. Gruenberg, Ger, Sept. 10, 31; U.S. citizen; m. 57; c. 2. PHYSICAL CHEMISTRY, GAS DYNAMICS. Dipl. Phys, Univ. Göttingen, 56; M.A, Harvard, 58, Ph.D.(eng), 65. Res. assoc. gas dynamics, Harvard, 58-59; aeronaut. engr, Douglas Aircraft Co, Calif, 59-61; mem. tech. staff, AEROSPACE CORP, EL SEGUNDO, 65-69, SECT. HEAD CHEM. LASERS, 70- Vis. res. assoc, Max Planck Inst. Plasma Physics, Munich, Ger, 71-72. Gas dynamics of shock diffractions; electrical conductivity of plasmas; kinetics of chemiluminescent reactions; kinetics and gas dynamics of chemical lasers; isotope separation by use of lasers; high power chemical pulse lasers. Address: 15480 Albright St, Pacific Palisades, CA 90272.

GROSS, RUDOLF EUGEN, b. Esslingen, Ger, Apr. 16, 30; U.S. citizen; m. 54; c. 1. PLANT PHYSIOLOGY, PHOTOBIOLOGY. B.S, Univ. Md, College Park, 61, M.S, 64, Ph.D.(algal physiol), 67. Trainee, Univ. Calif, Riverside, 67-69; ASST. PROF. BIOL, Purdue Univ, 69-70; IND. UNIV-PURDUE UNIV,

INDIANAPOLIS, 70- U.S.A, 55-57. Am. Soc. Plant Physiol; Phycol. Soc. Am. Effects of light on growth and pigment composition in unicellular algae; physiology and inheritance in populations of pigment mutants of Chlamydomonas and Chlorella. Address: Dept. of Biology, School of Science, Indiana University-Purdue University at Indianapolis, 1201 E. 38th, Indianapolis, IN 46205.

GROSS, RUTH T, b. Bryan, Tex, June 24, 20; div; c. 1. MEDICINE, PEDIATRICS. B.A, Columbia Univ, 41, M.D, 44. Instr. pediat, sch. med, Stanford, 50-53, asst. prof, 53-56, assoc. prof, 56-60; Albert Einstein Col. Med, 60-63, prof, 63-66; DIR. DEPT. PEDIAT, MT. ZION HOSP. & MED. CTR, 66- Commonwealth fel, 58-59. AAAS; Am. Fedn. Clin. Res; Soc. Exp. Biol. & Med; Soc. Pediat. Res; Am. Pediat. Soc; Am. Soc. Human Genetics; N.Y. Acad. Sci; Harvey Soc. Erythrocyte metabolism in the newborn and premature infant; community medicine; infant day care. Address: Dept. of Pediatrics, Mt. Zion Hospital & Medical Center, San Francisco, CA 94115.

GROSS, SAMSON R(ICHARD), b. Brooklyn, N.Y, July 27, 26; m. 52; c. 3. GENETICS. B.A, N.Y. Univ, 49; A.M, Columbia, 51, Nat. Insts. Health fel, 50-53, Ph.D.(genetics, zool), 53. Res. assoc. biochem. genetics, Stanford, 53-56, asst. prof. genetics, 56-57; Rockefeller Inst, 57-60; assoc. prof. microbiol, DUKE UNIV, 60-65, PROF. GENETICS, DEPT. BIOCHEM, 65-, DIR. PROG. GENETICS, 67- U.S. Pub. Health Serv. fel, 53-55 & spec. fel, Weizmann Inst, 69-70; dir. undergrad. training prog, Cold Spring Harbor Lab, 63 & 64, grad. studies, dept. microbiol. & immunol, 64-65, trustee, 65- AAAS; Genetics Soc. Am; Am. Soc. Biol. Chem. Microbial physiological genetics. Address: Genetics Division, Dept. of Biochemistry, Duke University, Durham, NC 27706.

GROSS, SIDNEY W, b. Cleveland, Ohio, Aug. 28, 04; m. 66. NEUROSURGERY. A.B, Western Reserve, 25, M.D, 28. Intern, Michael Reese Hosp, Chicago, 28-29; res. neurol, Neurol. Inst, N.Y, 29-31; fel. neurol. surg, Barnes Hosp, St. Louis, 31-33; clin. prof. neurol. surg, N.Y. Med. Col, 54-67; CLIN. PROF, DEPT. NEUROSURG, MT. SINAI SCH. MED, 70- Attend. & assoc. neurosurgeon, hosps, private practice, 29-; sr. consult, Bronx Vet. Admin. Hosp. Dipl, Am. Bd. Neurosurg. Med.C, U.S.A, 42-46, Maj. Neurosurg. Soc. Am; Am. Asn. Neurol. Surg; Am. Neurol. Asn; fel. Am. Col. Surg; N.Y. Acad. Med. Diagnosis and surgical treatment of tumors and injuries of the brain and spinal cord; neurological surgery; psychosurgery; cerebral angiography, diodrast as contrast medium and improvement of methods. Address: 44A E. 81st. St, New York, NY 10028.

GROSS, STANFORD (ORRA), b. Greene, N.Y, Nov. 10, 20; m. 42; c. 2. GEOLOGY. Geol.Engr, Colo. Sch. Mines, 49. Jr. engr, NAT. LEAD CO, 49-50, asst. & sinter plant supt, 50-51, geologist & mining engr, 51-52, chief geologist & mining engr, 52-65, mine supt, 65-66, PROD. DIV. SUPT, 66- U.S.M.C, 39-45. Am. Inst. Mining, Metall. & Petrol. Eng. Exploration geology; mine production. Address: National Lead Co, Tahawus, NY 12879.

GROSS, STANISLAW, b. Lodz, Poland, Nov. 27, 24; nat. MOLECULAR BIOLOGY. B.Chem.Eng, Tech. Univ. Lodz, 47, M.Chem.Eng, 49; Ph.D.(org. chem), Univ. London, 61. Res. chemist, Boruta Dyestuff Plant, Poland, 46-50; asst. prof. phys. chem, med. sch, Inst. Indust. Med, Lodz, 50-58; vis. biochemist, Inst. Cancer Res, Univ. London, 58-62; sr. scientist, Boyce Thompson Inst. Plant Res, Inc, 62-66; ASSOC. MEM. & HEAD MOLECULAR BIOL. DIV, INST. FOR MUSCLE DISEASE, INC, 66- Lectr, med. sch, Lodz, 50-56, Inst. Indust. Med, 53-56; Inst. Gen. Chem, Warsaw, 52; Tech. Univ. Lodz, 55-56; Univ. Nev, 65. Am. Chem. Soc; N.Y. Acad. Sci; Biophys. Soc; Radiation Res. Soc; Polish Chem. Soc. Nucleic acids; proteins; biological information transfer. Address: Institute for Muscle Disease, Inc, 515 E. 71st St, New York, NY 10021.

GROSS, STANLEY, b. U.S.A, July 4, 15; m. 40; c. 2. MEDICINE, PATHOLOGY. B.S, N.Y. Univ, 36, M.D, 39. Assoc. clin. prof. path, N.Y. Univ. Med. Ctr, 56-64; col. physicians & surgeons, Columbia Univ, 64-68; dir. lab, North Shore Hosp, Manhassett, N.Y, 56-68; ASSOC. PROF. PATH, ORANGE COUNTY MED. CTR, UNIV. CALIF, IRVINE, 68- Dipl, Am. Bd. Path, 47. U.S.A, 42-46, Maj. Am. Soc. Clin. Path. Address: Dept. of Pathology, Orange County Medical Center, University of California, Irvine, CA 92664.

GROSS, STANLEY B(URTON), b. Pittsburgh, Pa, May 24, 31; m. 53; c. 3. TOXICOLOGY. A.B, W.Va. Univ, 54, M.S, 57, U.S. Pub. Health Serv. fel, 60-62, Ph.D.(biochem), 63. Res. assoc. agr. biochem, W.Va. Univ, 56-58, anesthesiol, med. ctr, 63; res. biochemist, Columbus Labs, Battelle Mem. Inst, 65-67; asst. prof. environ. health, UNIV. CINCINNATI, 67-69, fel, environ. toxicol, 69-71, ASST. PROF. TOXICOL, 71- AAAS; Am. Chem. Soc; Am. Soc. Info. Sci. Environmental and occupational health; trace metals; human body burden analyses; mathematical models; automated biomedical information systems; lipid absorption and analyses. Address: Dept. of Environmental Health, Kettering Lab, University of Cincinnati, Cincinnati, OH 45219.

GROSS, THOMAS ALFRED OTTO, b. Brunswick, Maine, Mar. 18, 18; m. 46; c. 4. PHYSICS. B.S, Bowdoin Col, 40. Develop. engr, Raytheon Mfg. Co, 41-52, mgr. electronics develop. dept, missile & radar div, 52-58, adv. develop. dept, missile syst. div, 58-59, electromech. components opers, 59-61; pres, Spectran Electronics Corp, 61-65; consult, 65-66; PRES, T.A.O. GROSS & ASSOC, INC, 66- Proj. Nobska, Nat. Acad. Sci-Nat. Res. Coun, 56. Am. Phys. Soc; Inst. Elec. & Electronics Eng. Doppler radar systems; electron tube circuits; magnetic devices; automotive components; electric motor control systems; electrical protective systems. Address: Concord Rd, R.D, South Lincoln, MA 01773.

GROSS, VICTOR, b. Brooklyn, N.Y, Sept. 22, 21; m. 46; c. 4. ELECTRICAL ENGINEERING, PHYSICS. B.A, Brooklyn Col, 41; M.E.E, Polytech. Inst. Brooklyn, 48. Physicist, bur. ord, U.S. Dept. Navy, 41-44; chief proj. engr. & prod. mgr, Polarad Electronics Corp, 46-55; pres, Sterling Transformer Corp, 55-62; staff mgr, Trygon Electronics, Inc, 62-64; PRES, DESIGN TRANSFORMER CORP, 65- Sr. mem. Inst. Elec. & Electronics Eng. Ferromagnetic devices and insulation; circuit theory; business management. Address: Design Transformer Corp, 14-50 Broadway, Long Island, NY 11106.

GROSS, W(ALTER) BURNHAM, b. Sandusky, Ohio, Jan. 17, 25; m. 53; c. 2. VETERINARY MEDICINE. D.V.M, Ohio State, 46; M.S, Minnesota, 52, Ph.D.(animal path), 56. Veterinarian, bur. animal indust, U.S. Dept. Agr, 47-48; ASSOC. ANIMAL PATHOLOGIST, AGR. EXP. STA, VA. POLYTECH. INST. & STATE UNIV, 49-, PROF. VET. SCI, 56- U.S.A, 46-47. Am. Vet. Med. Asn. Diseases of poultry. Address: Agricultural Experiment Station, Virginia Polytechnic Institute & State University, Blacksburg, VA 24060.

GROSS, WILLIAM, b. New York, N.Y, Oct. 12, 23; m. 52; c. 2. RADIOLOGY, PHYSICS. A.B, Columbia, 47, A.M, 49, Ph.D.(physics), 59. Res. scientist RADIOL, COL. PHYSICIANS & SURGEONS, COLUMBIA UNIV, 46-61, asst. prof, 61-69, ASSOC. PROF, 69- Mem. comts. & consult, Nat. Coun. Radiation Protection & Measurements, 57-71; mem. task group, Int. Comn. Radiol. Units & Measurements, 64-70. U.S.N, 43-46. Am. Phys. Soc; Radiation Res. Soc. Address: Radiological Research Lab, 630 W. 168th St, New York, NY 10032.

GROSS, W(ILLIAM) A(LLEN), b. Los Angeles, Calif, Nov. 17, 24; m. 48, 70; c. 4. PHYSICS, MECHANICS. B.S, U.S. Coast Guard Acad, 45; M.S, California, 49, Ph.D.(mech. eng), 51. From lectr. to asst. prof. mech. eng, California, Berkeley, 49-52; asst. prof. theoret. & appl. mech, Iowa State, 52-55; mem. tech. staff appl. mech, network synthesis, Bell Tel. Lab, Inc, 55-56; mem. res. staff, 54-64, mgr. appl. mech. dept, 56-61, Int. Bus. Mach. San Jose Res. Lab, 61-64; DIR. RES. & MGR. RES, ADV. TECH. DIV, AMPEX CORP, REDWOOD CITY, 64-, V.PRES, 65- Mem. gas lubricated bearing adv. group & mech. failure prev. group, Off. Naval Res; eng. adv. comt, Univ. Calif. U.S.C.G, 45-48, Lt.(jg). AAAS; Am. Soc. Mech. Eng; Inst. Elec. & Electronics Eng; Soc. Exp. Stress Anal; Sci. Res. Soc. Am; N.Y. Acad. Sci; Soc. Social Responsibility in Sci. Electrical engineering; applied mechanics; mathematics; gas and liquid film lubrication; magnetics. Address: 26005 New Bridge Rd, Los Altos Hills, CA 94022.

GROSS, W(ILLIAM) H(ARVEY), b. Vancouver, B.C, Dec. 5, 17; m. 43; c. 2. ECONOMIC GEOLOGY. B.Sc, British Columbia, 42; M.A, Toronto, 46, Ph.D, 49. Asst. prof. geol, Toronto, 51-69; PRES, PURE SILVER MINES, LTD, TORMEX MINING DEVELOPERS, LTD. & LACANEX MINING CO, LTD, 69- Consult. geologist, 47- R.C.A.F, 42-45, Flight Lt. Geol. Soc. Am; Soc. Econ. Geol; fel. Geol. Asn. Can; Can. Inst. Min. & Metall. Development of methods for mineral deposits discovery. Address: Royal Trust Tower, Suite 3701, P.O. Box 354, Toronto-Dominion Centre, Toronto 111, Ont, Can.

GROSS, WILLIAM J(OSEPH), b. Phila, Pa, June 10, 15; m. 42; c. 4. ORGANIC CHEMISTRY. B.S, St. Joseph's Col.(Pa), 38; M.S, Illinois, 42. Res. chemist, Sherwin-Williams Co, 42-44; dir. surg. adhesives sect, JOHNSON & JOHNSON, 44-56, assoc. dir. res, 56-62, dir. res. & qual. control, PERMACEL DIV, 62-69, V.PRES. RES. & DEVELOP, 69- Johnson Medal. Am. Chem. Soc. Preparation and study of organic compounds possessing restricted rotation; synthetic and natural resins, elastomers, plastics, pressure-sensitive tapes and textiles. Address: Permacel, New Brunswick, NJ 08903.

GROSSBERG, ALLAN L(OUIS), b. Helena, Mont, Jan. 17, 21; m. 48; c. 4. IMMUNOCHEMISTRY. B.S, Calif. Inst. Tech, 42, M.S, 44; Ph.D.(physiol), McGill, 54. Asst. chem, Calif. Inst. Tech, 42-44; phys. chem, Harvard, 45-47; res. instr. biochem, sch. med, Temple, 47-51; asst. physiol, McGill, 51-54, Collip fel, 54-55, lectr, 55-56; sr. cancer res. scientist, ROSWELL PARK MEM. INST, 56-61, assoc. cancer res. scientist, 61-67, PRIN. CANCER RES. SCIENTIST, 67- Assoc. res. prof, Roswell Park Div, grad. sch, State Univ. N.Y. Buffalo, 66-68, sch. med, 68-70, res. prof, 70-; grad. faculty, Niagara Univ, 68- Am. Asn. Immunol; Am. Chem. Soc; Am. Soc. Biol. Chem. Physical-chemical properties and structure of antibodies and antibody sites; chemical alteration of proteins; interaction of proteins and small molecules; mechanisms of antibody response; structure and mechanism of action at biologically reactive sites. Address: Biochemistry Research Dept, Roswell Park Memorial Institute, 666 Elm St, Buffalo, NY 14203.

GROSSBERG, ARNOLD LEWIS, b. Cleveland, Ohio, June 1, 21; m. 43; c. 3. CHEMICAL ENGINEERING. B.S, Calif. Inst. Tech, 42; M.S, Michigan, 43. Apprentice sheet metal dept, Lockheed Aircraft Corp, Calif, 41; asst. res. engr. process design, Calif. Res. Corp, 43-44, assoc. res. engr, 44-46, res. engr, 46-52, sr. res. engr, 52-56, supvr. engr, 56-62, sect. supvr, 62-65, CHIEF DESIGN ENGR. PROCESS & PLANT DESIGN, CHEVRON RES. CO, 65- Dir, bd. educ, Berkeley Unified Sch. Dist, 65-71, pres, 66-68 & 70-71. Am. Inst. Chem. Eng. Petroleum processing, including principal areas such as catalytic cracking, hydrocracking; catalytic reforming; distillation; petrochemicals. Address: Chevron Research Co, 576 Standard Ave, Richmond, CA 94802.

GROSSBERG, SIDNEY E(DWARD), b. Miami, Fla, Nov. 13, 29; m. 59; c. 2. VIROLOGY, MICROBIOLOGY. B.S, Emory, 51, M.D, 54. Intern med, univ. hosp, Duke, 54-55, asst. res, 57-58; fel, sch. med, Hopkins, 58-59; instr. MICROBIOL, med. sch, Minnesota, 59-60, asst. prof, 60-62; med. col, Cornell, 62-66; PROF. & CHMN. DEPT, MED. COL. WIS, 66- Nat. Inst. Allergy & Infectious Diseases fel, 59-61, U.S. Pub. Health Serv. career develop. award, 61-66; vis. investr, Pasteur Inst, Paris, 64-65; attend. physician, N.Y. Hosp, 64-66; Markle scholar acad. med, 65-70; assoc. mem, Influenza Virus Comn, U.S. Army, 67-70. Virologist, 406th med. gen. lab, Japan, Med.C, 55-57, Capt. Am. Asn. Immunol; Am. Fedn. Clin. Res; Soc. Exp. Biol. & Med; Infectious Diseases Soc. Am; N.Y. Acad. Sci; Brit. Soc. Gen. Microbiol. Host cell-virus relationships; cell biology; host resistance; viral interference and interferon; arthropod borne and respiratory viruses; viral lipide metabolism. Address: Dept. of Microbiology, Medical College of Wisconsin, 561 N. 15th St, Milwaukee, WI 53233.

GROSSBERG, STEPHEN, b. New York, N.Y, Dec. 31, 39. MATHEMATICS, PSYCHOLOGY. B.A, Dartmouth Col, 61; Woodrow Wilson & Nat. Sci. Found. fels. & M.S, Stanford, 64; univ. fel. & Ph.D.(math), Rockefeller Univ, 67. Asst. prof. MATH, MASS. INST. TECHNOL, 67-69, ASSOC. PROF, 69- A.P. Sloan res. fel, 69-; sr. vis. fel, Sci. Res. Coun, Eng, 69. N. Wiener Cybernetics Prize, 69. Am. Math. Soc. Global analysis of nonlinear functional-differential networks; learning theory; pattern discrimination; problems in neurophysiology and anatomy. Address: Dept. of Mathematics, 2-382, Massachusetts Institute of Technology, Cambridge, MA 02139.

GROSSE, ARISTID V(ICTOR), b. Riga, Russia, Jan. 4, 05; nat; m. 32; c. 1. CHEMISTRY. Dipl.Ing, Tech. Hochschule, Berlin, 26, D.Ing.(chem, chem. eng), 27. Res. assoc. Liebig fel, Kaiser Wilhelm Inst, Berlin, 27-28; res.. chemist, Med. Anal. Lab, Shanghai, China, 28-29; vis. asst. prof. chem, Tech. Univ, Berlin, 29-32; Chicago, 32-39; Guggenheim fel, physics & assoc. to Prof. H.C. Urey, Columbia, 40-43; dir. oil res, Houdry Process Corp, Phila, 43-48; chem. consult, 48; PRES, GERMANTOWN LABS, INC, 48- With Universal Oil Prod. Co, Ill, 32-39; chief consult, War Prod. Bd, 42-43; mem, Am. Rubber Mission to Soviet Union, 42-43; with Atomic Energy Proj, Off. Sci. Res. & Develop, 42-43. Atomic Energy Comn. award, 71. AAAS; fel. Am. Chem. Soc; fel. Am. Phys. Soc; Am. Inst. Aeronaut. & Astronaut; fel. The Chem. Soc. Radioactivity and atomic energy; isotopes; catalytic, fluorine and organometallic chemistry; high temperature research; flame studies; new oxidizers and fuels for rocket propulsion and detonation; ozone research; liquid metals-densities, critical data, viscosities, surface tensions, electrical and thermal conductivities; bubbles and foams, especially soap and plastic. Address: 4150 Henry Ave, Philadelphia, PA 19144.

GROSSE, FRED A, b. Philadelphia, Pa, Sept. 11, 34; div; c. 5. PHYSICS. B.S, Muhlenberg Col, 55; M.S, Lehigh, 57, Ph.D.(physics), 66. ASSOC. PROF. PHYSICS, SUSQUEHANNA UNIV, 60- Am. Asn. Physics Teachers. Shock tube flow; electrostatics. Address: Dept. of Physics, Susquehanna University, Selinsgrove, PA 17870.

GROSSENBACHER, KARL A(LBERT), b. Geneva, N.Y, Aug. 24, 10; m. 38, 52; c. 6. PLANT PHYSIOLOGY. Ph.B, Wisconsin, 33; Ph.D.(plant physiol), California, 39. Asst, Hopkins, 34-36; California, 36-38; asst. in charge plant nutrit. exhibit, Golden Gate Int. Expos, 38-39; asst, Cabot Found, Harvard, 39-43, assoc, 43-45; assoc, exp. sta, California, 45-46; asst. prof. bot, California, Santa Barbara, 46-49; res. chemist, Pabco Div, Fibreboard Paper Prod, Inc, Calif, 50-60; assoc. res. plant physiologist, col. agr, California, Berkeley, 61-69; TEACHER BOT, COL. SAN MATEO, 69- Mineral nutrition; water relations; vegetative propagation; root-soil boundary zone; electron microscopy. Address: 7777 Terrace Dr, El Cerrito, CA 94530.

GROSSER, ARTHUR E(DWARD), b. New York, N.Y, Nov. 30, 34. PHYSICAL CHEMISTRY. A.B, Cornell, 56; Nat. Sci. Found. fel, Wisconsin, 59-60, Dow Chem. fel, 60-61, Ph.D.(phys. chem), 63. Alumni Res. Found. fel, Wisconsin, 63-64, fel. phys. chem, 64-65; asst. prof. CHEM, McGILL UNIV, 65-69, ASSOC. PROF, 69- Am. Phys. Soc. Molecular beam studies of inelastic and reactive collisions. Address: Dept. of Chemistry, McGill University, Montreal, Que, Can.

GROSSER, F(REDERICK), b. River Forest, Ill, Sept. 11, 15; m. 43; c. 4. ORGANIC CHEMISTRY. B.S, Wheaton Col, 37; Ph.D.(org. chem), Illinois, 41. Res. chemist, Gen. Aniline Works div, Gen. Aniline & Film Corp, N.J, 41-43; cent. res. lab, 43-47, Gen. Aniline Works, 47-51, lab. supvr, process eng. dept, 51-58, sect. mgr, process res. & develop. dept, 58-63, mgr. res. & develop. dept, 63-65, tech. dir, dyestuff & chem. prod, 65-67; v.pres, GAF CORP, 67-69, sr. scientist, 69-70, sect. mgr. res. & develop. acetylene & indust. org. chem, 70-71, MGR. RES. & DEVELOP, CHEM. DIV, 71- AAAS; Am. Chem. Soc. Organic synthesis in vat dyes, textile auxiliaries, vinyl polymers and acetylene chemistry; polymerization of vinyl polymers; constitution of quebracho tannin. Address: GAF Corp, P.O. Box 12, Linden, NJ 07036.

GROSSERT, JAMES STUART, b. Durban, S.Africa, Jan. 28, 40; m. 68. ORGANIC CHEMISTRY. B.Sc, Natal, 60, M.Sc, 61, Ph.D.(chem), 64. Lab. asst, Dyson Perrins Lab, Oxford, 64-65; fel, Brandeis, 65-67; ASST. PROF. CHEM, DALHOUSIE UNIV, 67- Chem. Inst. Can; Brit. Chem. Soc. Chemistry of heterocyclic compounds and of natural products from marine sources. Address: Dept. of Chemistry, Dalhousie University, Halifax, N.S, Can.

GROSSFELD, ROBERT MICHAEL, b. New York, N.Y, Oct. 15, 43; m. 70. NEUROBIOLOGY. B.S, Wisconsin, 63; Nat. Sci. Found. fel, Stanford, 63-65, Nat. Insts. Health fel, 65-68, Ph.D.(neurobiol), 68. Nat. Insts. Health fel. neurobiol, Harvard Med. Sch, 68-70, ASST. PROF. NEUROBIOL. & BEHAV, LANGMUIR LAB, CORNELL UNIV, 70- Soc. Neurosci. Biochemical mechanisms in neurological development and function; synaptic transmission and axonal transport. Address: Dept. Neurobiology & Behavior, Langmuir Lab, Cornell University, Ithaca, NY 14850.

GROSSFIELD, BERNARD, b. New York, N.Y, Feb. 27, 36; m. 66; c. 1. STRUCTURAL ENGINEERING. B.C.E, N.Y. Univ, 56, M.C.E, 58, Eng.Sc.D. (eng. mech), 63. ASSOC. PROF. CIVIL ENG, N.Y. UNIV, 63- Am. Soc. Civil Eng; Am. Concrete Inst. Engineering mechanics; civil engineering. Address: Dept. of Civil Engineering, New York University, University Heights, Bronx, NY 10453.

GROSSFIELD, JOSEPH, b. N.Y.C, May 23, 40; m. 64; c. 1. GENETICS. B.S, City Col. New York, 62; M.A, Univ. Tex, Austin, 64, Nat. Insts. Health fel, 64-66, Ph.D.(genetics). 66. Lectr. BIOL, Univ. Calif, Riverside, 66-67; asst. prof, Purdue Univ, 67-71; FEL, NEW ENGLAND INST, 71- Nat. Insts. Health fel, Univ. Hawaii, 66. AAAS; Soc. Study Evolution; Genetics Soc. Am; Am. Genetics Asn. Genetic dissection of physiological processes subserving behavior; evolution of courtship patterns; influence of environment on behavior; behavioral polymorphisms in natural populations. Address: New England Institute, P.O. Box 308, Ridgefield, CT 06877.

GROSSI, CARLO E, b. Mt. Vernon, N.Y, Sept. 12, 27; c. 4. SURGERY. A.B, Columbia, 45; M.D, L.I. Col. Med. 49. Sloan Kettering Inst. spec. fel. exp. surg, Mem. Hosp, New York, 53, Nat. Cancer Inst. res. fel, Sloan Kettering Inst, 59; clin. asst. surgeon, St. Vincent's Hosp. & Med. Ctr, N.Y, 59; Instr. surg, MED. SCH, N.Y. UNIV, 60-63, asst. prof, 63-65, assoc. clin. prof, 65-69, ASSOC. PROF. CLIN. SURG, 69- Clin. asst. surgeon, St. Vincent's Hosp. & Med. Ctr, N.Y, 62, asst. attend. surgeon, 62-63, assoc. attend. surgeon, 63-69, attend. surgeon, 69- Italian Star of Solidarity. Med.C, U.S.A, 51-52. Fel. Am. Col. Surg; Am. Fedn. Clin. Res; Am. Med. Asn; James

Ewing Soc; Am. Therapeut. Soc; N.Y. Acad. Med; Soc. Surg. Alimentary Tract; fel. Int. Col. Angiol; fel. Am. Col. Gastroenterol. General surgery; cancer research; oncology. Address: 520 E. 82nd St, New York, NY 10028.

GROSSI, MARIO D(ARIO), b. Giuncarico, Italy, Jan. 10, 25; U.S. citizen; m. 56; c. 2. RADIO PHYSICS, ENGINEERING. Dr.(radio eng), Pisa, 48; dipl. microwave physics, Nat. Res. Coun. Italy, 49. Res. engr, Magneti Marelli Central Radio Lab, Italy, 49-50; design engr, Italian Marconi, 50-55, design supvr, 55-58; staff engr, equip. & systs. div, RAYTHEON CO, 58-60, CONSULT. SCIENTIST, space & info. systs. div 60-65, EQUIP. DIV, 65-; RADIO PHYSICIST & ENGR, HARVARD COL. OBSERV, CAMBRIDGE, 65- Asst. prof, commun. inst, Univ. Genoa, 51-58; radio physicist & engr, Smithsonian Astrophys. Observ, Cambridge, Mass, 59- Italian Army. Sr. mem. Inst. Elec. & Electronics Eng; Am. Inst. Aeronaut. & Astronaut; Am. Astron. Soc. Magnetospheric propagation; remote sensing of troposphere and ionosphere by radio waves; measurements by radio occultation techniques of planetary atmospheres and ionospheres. Address: Equipment Division, Raytheon Co, 528 Boston Post Rd, Sudbury, MA 01776.

GROSSIE, JAMES ALLEN, b. Beaumont, Tex, May 19, 36; m. 64. PHYSIOLOGY, NEUROENDOCRINOLOGY. B.S, Sam Houston State Col, 58, M.A, 59; Ph.D.(endocrinol), Missouri, 63. Nat. Insts. Health fel, col. med, Illinois, 63-65; ASSOC. PROF. PHYSIOL, OHIO STATE UNIV, 65- Effects of endocrines on the nervous system. Address: Dept. of Physiology, Ohio State University College of Medicine, 370 W. Ninth Ave, Columbus, OH 43210.

GROSSKOPF, R(ICHARD) G(EORGE), b. Chicago, Ill, Aug. 3, 24; m. 50; c. 6. CHEMICAL ENGINEERING. B.S, Northwest. Univ, 47, Ph.D.(chem. eng), 50; M.S, Univ. Wis, 49. Develop. engr, ELECTROCHEM. DEPT, E.I. DU PONT DE NEMOURS & CO, INC, N.Y, 50-67, gen. supt. Houston Plant, Tex, 67-69, DIR. EXP. STA. LAB, 69- U.S.N.R, 44-46. AAAS; Am. Inst. Chem. Eng. Crystallization. Address: Experiment Station Lab, Electrochemicals Dept, E.I. du Pont de Nemours & Co, Wilmington, DE 19898.

GROSSKREUTZ, J(OSEPH) C(HARLES), b. Springfield, Mo, Jan. 5, 22; m. 49; c. 2. PHYSICS. B.S, Drury Col, 43; M.S, Washington (St. Louis), 48, univ. fel, 48-49, Ph.D.(physics), 50. Asst. physics, California, 46-47; Washington (St. Louis), 47-48, 49-50; res. physicist, Calif. Res. Corp, 50-52; asst. prof. physics, Texas, 52-56; sr. physicist, Midwest Res. Inst, 56-59, prin. physicist, 59-63, sr. adv. physics, 63-67, prin. adv. physics, 67-71; CHIEF, MECH. PROPERTIES SECT, NAT. BUR. STANDARDS, 71- U.S.N.R, 43-46, Lt. Am. Phys. Soc; Am. Inst. Mining, Metall. & Petrol. Eng; Electron Micros. Soc. Am; Am. Soc. Test. & Mat. Metal physics; plastic deformation; electron microscopy; small angle x-ray scattering; structure of light nuclei; physical structure of proteins; metal fatigue. Address: B120 Materials Bldg, National Bureau of Standards, Washington, DC 20234.

GROSSLEIN, MARVIN DARREL, b. Seattle, Wash, Oct. 24, 29; m. 53; c. 4. FISHERY BIOLOGY. B.S, Minnesota, 51, M.S, 54; Ph.D, Cornell, 62. RES. FISHERY BIOLOGIST, BUR. COMMERCIAL FISHERIES, U.S. FISH & WILDLIFE SERV, 61- U.S.A, 54-56. Am. Fisheries Soc. Population dynamics; quantitative animal ecology; biometrics. Address: Biology Labs, Bureau of Commercial Fisheries, Woods Hole, MA 02543.

GROSSLING, B(ERNARDO) F(RUEDENBURG), b. Santiago, Chile, Dec. 21, 18; nat. GEOPHYSICS. C.E, Chile, 41, E.E, 44; M.Sc, Calif. Inst. Tech, 45; Brit. Coun. scholar, London, 49-51, dipl, 51, Ph.D.(geophys), 51. Asst. math, Chile, 38, elec. eng, 40-42; comput. Astron. Observ, Chile, 38-40; design engr, Chilian Develop. Corp, 40-42, explor. geophysicist, 43-44; asst. soil mech, Calif. Inst. Tech, 45-46; chief geophysicist, Nat. Oil Co, Chile, 46-49, consult, oil explor, 51-53; res. geophysicist, Calif. Res. Corp, Div, Standard Oil Co. Calif, 54-55, sr. res. geophysicist, 56-59, res. assoc, 59-60; acting chief eng. div, Inter-Am. Develop. Bank, 60-61, eng. consult, 61-62, tech. adv, 62-64; RES. GEOPHYSICIST, U.S. GEOL. SURV, 64- Lectr, Sch. Arts & Trades, Chile, 42-43. Soc. Explor. Geophys; Am. Geophys. Union; fel. Geol. Soc. Am; fel. Royal Astron. Soc; Brazilian Metals Asn. Mathematical physics; theory of automata; tectonophysics; plasticity; geothermal studies; oil exploration. Address: U.S. Geological Survey, Dept. of the Interior, Washington, DC 20242.

GROSSMAN, ALLEN S, b. N.Y.C, Apr. 12, 38; m. 61; c. 2. ASTROPHYSICS. B.S, Hofstra, 61; M.S, Adelphi, 64, Ph.D.(astrophys), Indiana, 69. Instr. electronics, Acad. Aeronaut, 58-59; design engr, Brookhaven Nat. Lab, 61-64; ASST. PROF. PHYSICS, IOWA STATE UNIV, 68- Vis. summer faculty mem, Lawrence Radiation Lab, California, 69; 70, NASA-Am. Soc. Eng. Educ. summer faculty fel, Ames Res. Ctr, Stanford Univ, 71. Am. Astron. Soc; Royal Astron. Soc. Stellar evolution; structure of stars of mass less than one half solar mass; astronomical instrumentation. Address: Dept. of Physics, Iowa State University, Ames, IA 50010.

GROSSMAN, BURTON J(AY), b. Chicago, Ill, Nov. 27, 24. PEDIATRICS. B.S, Chicago, 46, M.D, 49. Instr. & fel. PEDIAT, Helen Hay Whitney Found, grad. sch. med, UNIV. CHICAGO, 54-57, asst. prof, 57-61, assoc. prof, 61-67, PROF, SCH. MED, 67-; MED. DIR, LA RABIDA CHILDREN'S HOSP. & RES. CTR, 62-; assoc. dir. med. serv, La Rabida-Univ. Chicago Inst, 57-62. Dipl. Am. Bd. Pediat. Med.C, U.S.A.F, 51-53, Capt. Soc. Pediat. Res; Am. Pediat. Soc; Am. Acad. Pediat. Pediatric rheumatology; treatment of rheumatic diseases in children; blood coagulation problems; prevention of atherosclerosis. Address: Dept. of Pediatrics, University of Chicago School of Medicine, Chicago, IL 60639.

GROSSMAN, CHARLES CHASKIEL, b. Radomsk, Poland, Mar. 7, 13; nat; m. 40; c. 3. NEUROLOGY, PHYSIOLOGY. M.D, Bratislava, 35. Munic. Hosp, Warsaw, 36-39; asst. neurol, Univ. Hosp. Jerusalem, 45-47; fel, seizure unit, Children's Hosp, Mass, 48; res. assoc. & chief electroencephalographer, Nat. Epilepsy Ctr, Vet. Admin, Framingham & Boston, 49-54, prin. scientist, Vet. Admin. Hosp, Pittsburgh, 58-59; DIR. DEPT. ELECTROENCEPHALOG, PRESBY. UNIV. HOSP, 60- Consult, Vet. Admin. Hosp, Pittsburgh, 54-; assoc. neurol, Montefiore Hosp, 56- AAAS; Am. Electroencephalog. Soc; Am. Acad. Neurol; Am. Epilepsy Soc. Epilepsy; electroencephalography; diagnostic ultrasonics; ontogeny of nervous system. Address: 1646 Beechwood Blvd, Pittsburgh, PA 15217.

GROSSMAN, DAVID G, b. N.Y.C, Aug. 20, 41; m. 71. CERAMICS. B.S, Rutgers Univ, 63, M.S, 64; Ph.D.(glass technol), Univ. Sheffield, 67. Asst. lectr. mat. sci, Rugby Col. Eng. Technol, Eng, 67-69; SR. CERAMIST, CORNING GLASS WORKS, 70- Foster Res. prize, Univ. Sheffield, 67. Brit. Soc. Glass Technol; Am. Ceramic Soc. Structure and properties of glass ceramics. Address: Corning Glass Works, Sullivan Park, Painted Post, NY 14870.

GROSSMAN, EDWARD B(ERTRAM), b. N.Y.C, Apr. 3, 11; m. 62; c. 1. MEDICINE. A.B, Harvard, 31; M.D, Hopkins, 35. Res. house officer, Hopkins Hosp, 35-36; asst. res. physician, diagnostic hosp, Boston Dispensary, 36-37; res. physician, univ. hosp, Vanderbilt, 37-38; clin. asst. physician & res. asst. chemist, Mt. Sinai Hosp, 38-47; chief med. unit, N.Y. regional off, U.S. Vet. Admin, 48-54, med. sect, Vet. Admin. Hosp, Bronx, 54-66; RETIRED. Med.C, 42-46, Lt. Col. Fel. AAAS; fel. Am. Med. Asn; fel. Am. Col. Physicians; Am. Fedn. Clin. Res; fel. N.Y. Acad. Med. Physiology; clinical medicine. Address: 145 East 16th St, New York, NY 10003.

GROSSMAN, EDWARD JOSEPH, m. 58; c. 2. ORGANIC CHEMISTRY, BIOCHEMISTRY. A.B, Columbia Col, 56; A.M, Columbia, 57, Nat. Sci. Found. fel, 58, Trubeck Labs. fel, 59, Ph.D.(chem), 60. Dir. res. & qual. control, GOTHAM PHARMACEUT. CO, INC, 60-69, V.PRES. & DIR. LABS, 69- Enzyme chemistry; new drug synthesis; pharmaceutical quality control systems and formulations studies. Address: Gotham Pharmaceutical Co, Inc, 1840 McDonald Ave, Brooklyn, NY 11223.

GROSSMAN, GEORGE, b. N.Y.C, July 1, 14; m. 37. MATHEMATICS. B.S, City Col. N.Y, 34; M.A, Columbia Univ, 35. Teacher MATH, Bd. Educ, NEW YORK CITY, 35-46, chmn. dept. high schs, 46-64, acting dir, BD. EDUC, 64-68, DIR, 68- Supp. teacher, Brooklyn Polytech. Inst, 44-61; sci. honors prog, Columbia Univ, 59-69, Teachers Col, 61-69; City Col. N.Y, 61-62. Consult, IBM Corp; Olivetti Underwood Corp; U.S. Agency Int. Develop, summer, 64. Math. Asn. Am. Computer mathematics; impact of automatic digital computer in mathematical education. Address: 43 Edgecliff Terrace, Yonkers, NY 10705.

GROSSMAN, HERBERT H, b. Phila, Pa, Jan. 3, 30; m. 63; c. 1. BOTANY, INVERTEBRATE ZOOLOGY. B.S, Temple Univ, 54; M.Ed, Pa. State Univ, 58, M.S, 62, Ph.D.(bot), 70. Asst. ed, Biol. Abstr. Inc, Pa, 58-60; teaching asst. bot, Pa. State Univ, 60-63; acting bibliographer, Biol. Abstr. Inc, 63-66; teaching asst. bot, PA. STATE UNIV, 66-69, ASST. PROF. BOT. & BIOL, 70- Med.C, U.S.A, 54-56. AAAS; Bot. Soc. Am; Phycol. Soc. Am; Am. Inst. Biol. Sci. Regeneration in several species of moss under various experimental conditions; the effect of chronic low level gamma radiation on Polytrichum commune Hedw; polarity in bryophytes and lower vascular plants. Address: Dept. of Botany, College of Science, Pennsylvania State University, University Park, PA 16802.

GROSSMAN, HERMAN, b. Waterbury, Conn, Apr. 25, 25; m. 49; c. 3. RADIOLOGY, PEDIATRICS. B.A, North Carolina, 47; M.A, Wesleyan, 49; M.D, Columbia, 53. Teaching fel. org. chem, Wesleyan, 47-48, res. & teaching fel. biochem, 48-49; intern pediat, Bellevue Hosp, 53-54; res, Babies Hosp, New York, 54-56; asst. pediatrician, Columbia, 56-61, instr. pediat, 61, fel. radiol, Columbia-Presby. Med. Center, 62-65; asst. prof. radiol. & pediat, med. col, Cornell, 65, assoc. prof, 68-71; PROF. RADIOL. & PEDIAT, MED. COL, DUKE UNIV. ATTEND. RADIOLOGIST & PEDIATRICIAN, MED. CTR, 71- Private practice, 56-62; attend. physician, Hackensack Hosp, 56-62; asst. pediatrician, Presby. Hosp. & Babies Hosp, New York, 56-62; assoc. attend. radiologist, N.Y. Hosp, 65-70, attend. radiologist, 70-71, assoc. attend. pediatrician, 65-71; asst. attend. radiologist & asst. attend. pediatrician, Mem. Hosp, 67-70, attend. radiologist & pediatrician, 70-71. Dipl, Am. Bd. Pediat, 58; dipl, Am. Bd. Radiol, 65. U.S.N, 42-46, Lt.(jg). Asn. Univ. Radiol; Soc. Pediat. Radiol. Pediatric radiology. Address: Dept. of Radiology, Duke University Medical Center, Durham, NC 27706.

GROSSMAN, JACK J(OSEPH), b. N.Y.C, Jan. 14, 26; m. 54; c. 2. PHYSICAL CHEMISTRY. B.S, Brooklyn Col, 49; Atomic Energy Cmn. fel, Southern California, 51-53, Ph.D.(phys. chem), 53. Asst. radiochem. exchange, Southern California, 50; fel. & jr. res. chemist, California, Los Angeles, 53; proj. dir, Vard, Inc, 54-56; proj. engr. & acting mgr, res. dept, Ralph M. Parsons Co, 56-59; mem. tech. staff, Hughes Aircraft Co, 59-63, sr. engr, 63-69; PRIN. INVESTR. APOLLO LUNAR SAMPLE ANAL. PROG, SPACE SCI. DEPT, McDONNELL DOUGLAS ASTRONAUT. CO, 69- U.S.A, 44-46. Am. Chem. Soc; Am. Phys. Soc; Inst. Elec. & Electronics Eng; Am. Vacuum Soc. Electrical and optical properties of semiconductors; reaction kinetics; mass spectrometry; telemetry and range instrumentation; nucleation and growth of thin films; active and passive remote sensing. Address: Space Sciences Dept, McDonnell Douglas Astronautics Co, Mail Station,20, Huntington Beach, CA 92647.

GROSSMAN, JACOB, b. N.Y, Aug. 6, 16; m. 48; c. 4. MEDICINE. B.S, City Col. New York, 35; M.A, Columbia Univ, 36; M.S, Univ. Louisville, 40. RES. ASSOC. MED, MONTEFIORE HOSP, 52-; DIR. MED, HOSP. JOINT DISEASES & MED. CTR, 66-; PROF. CLIN. MED, MT. SINAI SCH. MED, 68- Med.C, 42-46, Maj. AAAS; fel. Am. Col. Physicians; Am. Physiol. Soc; Am. Soc. Nethrology; Soc. Exp. Biol. & Med; Am. Heart Asn; N.Y. Acad. Sci. Cardiovascular and renal physiology; metabolism; clinical investigation. Address: Hospital for Joint Diseases & Medical Center, 1919 Madison Ave, New York, NY 10035.

GROSSMAN, KENNETH, b. Windsor, Ont, June, 6, 32; U.S. citizen; m. 57; c. 2. NUMERICAL ANALYSIS. B.Sc, Wayne State Univ, 55; M.S, N.Y. Univ, 56, Ph.D.(math), 64. Res. asst, Courant. Inst, N.Y. Univ, 57-59; mathematician, Airborne Instruments Lab, 59-62; sr. mathematician, PROGRAMMING METHODS, INC, 62-71, DEP. PROJ. MGR, 71- Adj. asst. prof, N.Y. Univ, 67- Asn. Comput. Mach; Soc. Indust. & Appl. Math. Numerical solution of integral, differential equations, radiative transfer. Address: 1310 Ave. R, Brooklyn, NY 11229.

GROSSMAN, LAURENCE ABRAHAM, b. Nashville, Tenn, Sept. 21, 16; m. 42; c. 4. INTERNAL MEDICINE, CARDIOVASCULAR DISEASE. B.A, Vanderbilt, 38, M.D, 41. From instr. to PROF. CLIN. MED, SCH. MED, VANDERBILT UNIV, 47-; ASSOC. PROF, MEHARRY MED. COL, 48- Med.C, U.S.A, 42-45. Fel. Am. Col. Physicians; fel. Am. Col. Cardiol; fel. Am. Col. Chest Physicians. Cardiology. Address: 1816 Hayes St, Nashville, TN 37203.

GROSSMAN, LAWRENCE, b. N.Y.C, Jan. 23, 24; m. 49; c. 3. BIOCHEMISTRY. B.A, Hofstra Col, 49; Ph.D.(biochem), Southern California, 54. Nat. Insts. Health fel, McCollum-Pratt Inst, Hopkins, 54-56; res. biochemist, Nat. Insts. Health, 56-57; asst. prof. BIOCHEM, BRANDEIS UNIV, 57-60, assoc. prof, 60-67, PROF, 67- Grants, Nat. Insts. Health, Nat. Sci. Found, Atomic Energy Comn; Am. Cancer Soc; Commonwealth fel, 63-64, career develop. award, Nat. Insts. Health, 64-; mem. sci. adv. comt. to Am. Cancer Soc, 65-68; ed, Methods Nucleic Acids. U.S.N, 42-45, Lt.(jg). Am. Soc. Biol. Chem; Biophys. Soc. Enzymatic mechanisms for the repair of DNA; molecular basis of mutagenesis. Address: Dept. of Biochemistry, Brandeis University, Waltham, MA 02154.

GROSSMAN, LAWRENCE M(ORTON), b. N.Y.C, Aug. 2, 22; m. 52; c. 1. NUCLEAR ENGINEERING. B.Ch.E, City Col. New York, 42; Standard Oil Co. Calif. fel, California, 43, M.S, 44, Ph.D.(eng. sci), 48. Chem. engr, E.I. du Pont de Nemours & Co, N.Y, 42-43; instr. mech. eng, UNIV. CALIF, BERKELEY, 44-46, lectr, 46-48, asst. prof, 48-54, assoc. prof. NUCLEAR ENG, 54-60, PROF, 60-, CHMN. DEPT, 69- Fulbright lectr, Delft, 52-53; Nat. Sci. Found. sr. res. fel, Saclay Nuclear Res. Ctr, France, 61-62. AAAS; Am. Phys. Soc; Am. Nuclear Soc. Nuclear reactor theory; neutron transport; thermophysics; magnetohydrodynamics. Address: Dept. of Nuclear Engineering, University of California, Berkeley, CA 94720.

GROSSMAN, LOUIS I(RWIN), b. Teplick, Russia, Dec. 16, 01; nat; m. 28; c. 2. DENTISTRY. D.D.S, Pennsylvania, 23; Dr. med. dent, Rostock, 28. Instr. oper. dent, SCH. DENT. MED, PENNSYLVANIA, 27-41, assoc. ORAL MED, 41-47, asst. prof, 47-50, assoc. prof, 50-54, PROF, 54-, DIR. ENDODONTICS, 59-, DIR. ENDODONTICS, DIV. ADVAN. DENT. EDUC, 62- Hon. lectr, Tokyo Dent. Col, 59. Consult, U.S. Naval Hosp, 53- Am. Asn. Endodont.(secy, 43-45, pres, 49); Am. Dent. Asn; fel. Am. Col. Dent; Int. Asn. Dent. Res; hon. mem. Belg. Dent. Soc; hon. mem. Brazilian Dent. Asn; hon. mem. Brazilian Acad. Dent. Endodontics. Address: School of Dental Medicine, University of Pennsylvania, 4001 Spruce St, Philadelphia, PA 19104.

GROSSMAN, MILTON S, b. Methuen, Mass, June 21, 24; m. 49; c. 3. PEDIATRIC ENDOCRINOLOGY. A.B, Harvard, 45; M.A, Boston, 48; U.S. Pub. Health Serv. fel, Sloan-Kettering Inst, 50-53; Ph.D.(physiol), N.Y. Univ, 53; M.D, Washington (St. Louis), 57. Fel. adolescent endocrinol, Mass. Gen. Hosp, 57, intern & asst. res. pediat, 58-60; res, Childrens Hosp, Boston, 60, fel. pediat. endocrinol, 61-63; chief pediat. endocrinol, univ. & assoc. prof. PEDIAT, sch. med, Maryland, 63-69; PROF, SCH. MED, UNIV. MIAMI, 69-; DIR. OF PEDIAT. & ADOLESCENT MED, MOUNT SINAI HOSP. OF GREATER MIAMI, 69- Instr, Harvard Med. Sch, 62-63. Pediat. & pediat. endocrinol. consult, Kimbrough Army Hosp, Ft. Meade, Md, Univ, St. Agnes & Provident Hosps, Baltimore, 63-; med. adv, Human Growth Inc, N.Y, 65- Mem. bd. trustees, Howard County Br, Am. Cancer Soc, 66-; Howard County Ment. Retardation Asn, 67-; sch. health comt, State of Md, 67-; dir. Nat. Pituitary Agency, 67-69. Dipl, Am. Bd. Pediat, 63. Fel. Am. Acad. Pediat; Endocrine Soc; Am. Diabetes Asn; Soc. Adolescent Med; N.Y. Acad. Sci. Steroid biochemistry; growth of children; neonatal endocrine function; diabetes. Address: Dept. of Pediatrics, Mount Sinai Hospital of Greater Miami, 4300 Alton Rd, Miami Beach, FL 33140.

GROSSMAN, MORTON I(RVIN), b. Massillon, Ohio, May 4, 19; m. 57; c. 1. GASTROENTEROLOGY. B.A, Ohio State, 39; M.S, Northwestern, 42, M.D. & Ph.D.(physiol), 44. Asst. biochem, col. med, Ohio State, 39-41; physiol, med. sch, Northwestern, 41-44, instr, 45-46, asst. prof, 46; col. med, Illinois, 46-48, assoc. prof, dept. clin. sci, 48-50, prof, 50-51; chief, physiol. div, med. nutrit. lab, Fitzsimons Army Hosp, 51-55; gastroenterol. sect, VET. ADMIN. CTR, 55-63, SR. MED. INVESTR, 63- Lectr, sch. med, Colorado, 54-55; assoc. clin. prof, sch. med, California, Los Angeles, 55-59, clin. prof, 59-63, prof, 63-, chmn. dept, 65-66. Consult, Nat. Insts. Health, 61-65. Ed, Gastroenterology, 60-65. U.S.A, 45-46, 51-53. AAAS; Am. Fedn. Clin. Res; Am. Gastroenterol. Asn.(pres, 67); Am. Soc. Clin. Invest; Am. Physiol. Soc; Soc. Exp. Biol. & Med; Asn. Am. Physicians; hon. mem. Brit. Soc. Gastroenterol; hon. mem. Can. Asn. Gastroenterol; hon. mem. Physiol. Soc. Finland. Physiology of the alimentary tract; gastrointestinal hormones; physiology of nutrition. Address: Veterans Administration Center, Bldg. 115, Room 115, Los Angeles, CA 90073.

GROSSMAN, MOSES, b. Kiev, Russia, Oct. 14, 21; nat; m. 51; c. 4. PEDIATRICS. A.B, California, 43, M.D, 46. Instr. PEDIAT, SCH. MED. UNIV. CALIF, SAN FRANCISCO, 51-54, asst. prof, 54-59, assoc. prof, 59-64, PROF. & ASSOC. DEAN, 64-, asst. dean, 63-64, lectr, sch. nursing, 52-55. Instr, med. sch, Stanford, 53-55. Attend. physician, San Francisco Gen. Hosp, 52-, chief pediat. Consult, Calif. State Health Dept, 55-70; U.S. Air Force, 57-58. Dipl, Am. Bd. Pediat, 52. Am. Acad. Pediat; Soc. Pediat. Res; Am. Pediat. Soc; Infectious Diseases Soc. Am. Staphylococcal infections in newborn nursery and hospital; cross infection; newborn infection; antibiotics in newborn. Address: San Francisco General Hospital, San Francisco, CA 94110.

GROSSMAN, NATHANIEL, b. Chicago, Ill, Apr. 17, 37; m. 60; c. 2. MATHEMATICS. B.S, Calif. Inst. Tech, 58; Nat. Sci. Found. fel, Minnesota, 60-61, Ph.D.(math), 64. Asst, Inst. Adv. Study, 64-66; asst. prof. MATH, UNIV. CALIF, LOS ANGELES, 66-70, ASSOC. PROF, 70- Am. Math. Soc; Math. Asn. Am. Differential geometry of manifolds; Riemannian geometry in the large; infinite-dimensional manifolds. Address: Dept. of Mathematics, University of California, Los Angeles, CA 90024.

GROSSMAN, NORMAN, b. N.Y.C, Nov. 3, 22. AERONAUTICAL ENGINEERING, MATHEMATICS. B.Aero.E, N.Y. Univ, 43, M.S, 48, Ph.D.(math), 58. Prin. res. engr, repub. aviation, FAIRCHILD HILLER CORP, 46-51, asst. proj. engr, 51-55, staff engr, 55-58, chief electronics eng, 58-62, mgr. res. div, 62-64, chief engr, 64-68, asst. gen. mgr, 68-69, V.PRES, 69- Lectr. grad. math, Adelphi Col, 51-53; adj. prof, grad. ctr, Polytech. Inst. Brooklyn, Farmingdale Campus, 67- U.S. Merchant Marine, 43-46, Lt.(jg). Am. Inst. Aeronaut. & Astronaut; Math. Asn. Am. Design, production and test of high performance military aircraft and aircraft systems. Address: Fairchild Hiller Corp, Route 110, Farmingdale, NY 11735.

GROSSMAN, PERRY L, b. Brooklyn, N.Y, Jan. 27, 38; m. 59; c. 2. MECHANICAL ENGINEERING, APPLIED MECHANICS. B.M.E, Polytech. Inst. Brooklyn, 59, fel, 61-62, M.S.M.E, 63, Nat. Sci. Found. fel, 66-67, Ph.D.(mech. eng), 68. Instr. MECH. ENG, Polytech. Inst. Brooklyn, 62-66; asst. prof, COOPER UNION, 67-70, ASSOC. PROF, 70- Nat. Sci. Res. Initiation grant, 70-71. AAAS. Nonlinear vibrations of spherical shells; flexural vibration and pulse-excited response of plates elastically supported at the surface. Address: Dept. of Mechanical Engineering, The Cooper Union, Cooper Square, New York, NY 10003.

GROSSMAN, RICHARD C, b. Providence, R.I, Jan. 3, 32; m. 64; c. 4. ORTHODONTICS. A.B, California, Los Angeles, 53; D.M.D, Harvard, 57. U.S. Pub. Health Serv. fel. orthod, Forsyth Infirmary, Harvard, 57-60; ASST. RES. ORTHODONTIST, SCH. DENT, UNIV. CALIF, LOS ANGELES, 63- U.S.P.H.S, 60-62, Dent. Surg. Int. Asn. Dent. Res. Oral sensory physiology. Address: 6325 Topanga Canyon Blvd, Woodland Hills, CA 91364.

GROSSMAN, ROBERT B(RUCE), b. N.Y.C, May 15, 31. AGRONOMY. B.S, Cornell, 52, M.S, 54; Ph.D, Illinois, 59. Asst, Cornell, 52-54; Illinois, 54-58; SOIL SCIENTIST, SOIL CONSERV. SERV, U.S. DEPT. AGR, 58- Soil Sci. Soc. Am. Soil genesis and morphology; soil physics and mineralogy. Address: Soil Survey Lab, Soil Conservation Service, 1325 N St, Lincoln, NE 68508.

GROSSMAN, ROBERT G, b. N.Y.C, Jan. 24, 33; m. 55; c. 3. NEUROSURGERY, NEUROPHYSIOLOGY. B.A, Swarthmore Col, 53; State Univ. N.Y. Regents scholar. & M.D, Columbia Univ, 57. Instr, southwest. med. sch, Univ. Tex, 63-64, asst. prof, 65-68, ASSOC. PROF, 68-69; NEUROL. SURG, ALBERT EINSTEIN COL. MED, 69- Attend. neurosurgeon, hosp, Albert Einstein Col. Med. & Bronx Munic. Hosp. Ctr, 69-; assoc. attend. neurosurgeon, Montefiore Hosp. & Med. Ctr, 69- Med.C, U.S.A.R, 58-60, Capt. Am. Asn. Neurol. Surg; Am. Col. Surg; Am. Electroencephalog. Soc; Am. Med. Asn; Asn. Res. Nerv. & Ment. Disease; Cong. Neurol. Surg. Neurophysiology of cortical neurons and neuroglial cells. Address: Dept. of Neurological Surgery, Albert Einstein College of Medicine, Yeshiva University, Bronx, NY 10461.

GROSSMAN, SEBASTIAN P(ETER), b. Coburg, Bavaria, Jan. 21, 34; m. 55. BIOPSYCHOLOGY. B.A, Maryland, 58; M.S, Yale, 59, Ph.D.(psychol), 61. Asst. prof. physiol. psychol, Iowa, 61-64; assoc. prof. BIOPSYCHOL, UNIV. CHICAGO, 64-67, PROF, 67- Ed, Physiol. & Behav, 66; Commun. Behav. Biol, 67-; Psychopharmacologia, 69-; J. Life Sci, 70-; Biochem. Psychol, 70- U.S.A, 54-56. Fel. AAAS; Am. Psychol. Asn; Am. Physiol. Soc; Royal Soc. Med. Physiology and pharmacology of brain mechanisms which mediate psychological processes related to motivation. Address: Dept. of Psychology, University of Chicago, Chicago, IL 60637.

GROSSMAN, STANLEY I, b. N.Y.C, Sept. 25, 42; m. 65; c. 2. APPLIED MATHEMATICS. B.A, Cornell Univ, 64; M.A, Univ. Calif, Los Angeles, 65; N.Y. State Regents fel, Brown Univ, 66-69, Nat. Defense Educ. Act fel, 67, Ph.D.(appl. math), 69. Asst. lectr. MATH, Gothenburg Univ, 65-66; ASST. PROF, McGILL UNIV, 69- Nat. Sci. Found-Romanian Acad. Sci. res. grant, Iasi, Romania, 71. Am. Math. Soc; Math. Soc. Can; Soc. Indust. & Appl. Math. Volterra integral and integrodifferential equations; existence, uniqueness, stability and properties of solutions. Address: Dept. of Mathematics, McGill University, Montreal 2, Que, Can.

GROSSMAN, WILLIAM E(LDERKIN) L(EFFINGWELL), b. N.Y.C, May 4, 38. ANALYTICAL CHEMISTRY. A.B, Princeton, 59; Esso fel, Cornell, 62-63, Ph.D.(anal. chem), 64. Assoc. spectrochem, inst. atomic res, Ames Lab. Atomic Energy Comn, 63-65; assoc, Univ. York, Eng, 65-66; ASST. PROF. CHEM, HUNTER COL, 66- Am. Chem. Soc. Flame emission spectroscopy; atomic absorption spectroscopy. Address: Dept. of Chemistry, Hunter College, 695 Park Ave, New York, NY 10021.

GROSSMAN, WILLIAM L(EWIS), b. Rochester, N.Y, Mar. 20, 14; m. 41; c. 1. GEOLOGY. B.A, Rochester, 36, M.Sc, 38; Kemp fel, Columbia, 40-41, Ph.D. (geol), 44. Petrol. geologist, John S. Ivy, Houston, 41-43; div. geologist, SHELL CAN. LTD, 43-52, area geologist, explor. dept, 52-58, div. prod. mgr, 58-59, explor. mgr, 59-65, V.PRES, EXPLOR. & PROD, 65-, DIR, 67- Am. Asn. Petrol. Geol; Can. Petrol. Asn. Stratigraphy; structural and subsurface geology. Address: Shell Canada Ltd, Box 100, Calgary, Alta, Can.

GROSSMANN, ELIHU D(AVID), b. Phila, Pa, Nov, 29, 27; m. 54; c. 3. CHEMICAL ENGINEERING. B.S, Drexel Inst, 51, M.S, 56; Ph.D, Univ. Pa, 65. Asst. CHEM. ENG, DREXEL UNIV, 51-52, instr, 52-56, asst. prof, 56-61, ASSOC. PROF, 61- Consult, Acme Coppersmithing Co, 52-; Printing Plates Res, Inc, 56-57; Jardu Corp, 57-58; U.S. Army, 61-, expert testimony, fields of competence, 63- U.S.A, 46-47. Am. Chem. Soc; Am. Soc. Eng. Educ; Am. Inst. Chem. Eng. Drying theory; process analysis; combustion; pollution control; thermodynamics. Address: Dept. of Chemical Engineering, Drexel University, 32nd & Chestnut St, Philadelphia, PA 19104.

GROSSMANN, WILLIAM, b. Richmond, Va, Aug. 25, 37; m. 67. PLASMA PHYSICS. B.S, Va. Polytech, 58, M.S, 61, Ph.D.(aerospace eng), 64. Aerospace technologist, Langley Res. Ctr, NASA, 58-65; assoc. res. scientist, Courant Inst. Math. Sci, N.Y. Univ, 64-67; ASST. PROF. APPL. MATH, RICHMOND COL.(N.Y), 67- Consult, Los Alamos Sci. Lab, summer 67; Bell Aerosysts. Co. Inc, 67-; vis. scientist, Max Planck Inst. Plasma Physics, 69- Am. Phys. Soc; Am. Math. Soc. Magnetohydrodynamics; problems of applied mathematics in the field of controlled thermonuclear fusion; plasma acceleration and electric propulsion; politics and history of science and technology. Address: Dept. of Natural Sciences, Richmond College, 130 Stuyvesant Pl, Staten Island, NY 10301.

GROSSNICKLE, FOSTER E(ARL), b. Myersville, Md, Jan. 28, 96; m. 22; c. 1. MATHEMATICS. A.B, Blue Ridge Col, 17; M.A, Pennsylvania, 19; Ph.D.(ed. res), Columbia, 30. Teacher pub. sch, N.J, 20-25; N.J. State Teachers Col, Montclair, 25-29; prof. MATH, JERSEY CITY STATE COL, 29-69, EMER. PROF, 69- U.S.A, 18; U.S.N.R, 42-44. Investigation on division; elementary mathematics. Address: 100 E. Melbourne Ave, Melbourne, FL 32901.

GROSSNICKLE, THURMAN T(HOMAS), b. Boonsboro, Md, July 20, 24; m. 54; c. 4. ORGANIC CHEMISTRY. B.S, Juniata Col, 50; fel, Harvard, 50-51, Shell Oil Co. fel, 51-52, A.M, 52; Monsanto Chem. Co. fel, Wayne State, 52-54, Ph.D, 55. Chemist, Jackson Lab, E.I. du Pont de Nemours & Co, N.J, 51; fel, org. chem, Rochester, 54-56; asst. prof. chem, Bridgewater Col, 56-59, assoc. prof, 59-61; SCIENTIST ADMINSTR, NAT. INSTS, HEALTH, 61- AAAS; Am. Chem. Soc; The Chem. Soc; Swiss Chem. Soc. Dienonephenol rearrangement; digitogenin and related steroids; erythrina alkaloids; federal grants administration. Address: National Institutes of Health, Bethesda, MD 20014.

GROSSO, ANTHONY J, b. Poughkeepsie, N.Y, July 19, 26; m. 53; c. 2. ELECTRONICS, COMPUTER SCIENCE. B.E.E, Manhattan Col, 50; M.E.E, N.Y. Univ, 53. Asst. engr, res. & develop, AM. DIST. TEL. CO, 50, engr, 51-55, proj. engr, 55-58, sr. prof. engr, 58-63, gen. mgr, tel. answering serv, 63-64, diversification & expansion opers, 64-70, comput. sci, 69-70, chief engr, 70, V.PRES. ENG. & RES, 70- Adj. prof, sch. continuing prof. studies, Pratt Inst, 56-71; mem. Alarm Indust. Comt. Combating Crime, 70-, chmn. standards sub-comt, 70-; mem. Cent. Sta. Indust. Frequency Adv. Comt, 70- Inst. Elec. & Electronics Eng. Application of computer technology to the electric protection field; development of sophisticated intrusion detection systems; signal transmission techniques; means to establish the security of transmitted signals. Address: 155 Aldershot Lane, Manhasset, NY 11030.

GROSSO, LEONARD, b. Brooklyn, N.Y, Oct. 3, 22; m. 54; c. 6. ZOOLOGY, PHYSIOLOGY. A.B, N.Y. Univ, 47, M.S, 49, Ph.D.(zool), 58. Res. specialist, dept. fishes & aquatic biol, Am. Mus. Natural Hist, New York, 49; instr. BIOL, Adelphi Col, 53-54; asst. prof, Col. St. Teresa, 54-55, assoc. prof, 55-59, prof, 59-62, head dept, 54-62; PROF, LONG ISLAND UNIV, 62-, ASSOC. DEAN, 68-, dir. sci. div, 66-68. Am. Physiol. Soc. res. fel, 59; fel, Minnesota, 61. Med. Dept, U.S.A, 43-46. Am. Physiol. Soc; Soc. Study Reproduction; Am. Soc. Zool. Reproductive physiology; general and comparative endocrinology; endocrine and nutritional interrelations; steroid hormone metabolism; histology. Address: Dept. of Biology, Long Island University, Brooklyn, NY 11201.

GROSSO, RONALD P(ATRICK), b. Bridgeport, Conn, Feb. 17, 36; m. 61; c. 6. SPECTROSCOPY. B.S, Fairfield, 58; Ph.D.(physics), Pa. State, 63. Res. asst. PHYSICS, Pa. State, 58-63; SR. PHYSICIST, PERKIN-ELMER CORP, 63- Optical Soc. Am; Am. Inst. Physics. High resolution molecular spectroscopy; optical correlators; holography; automatic target recognition. Address: Perkin-Elmer Corp, 50 Danbury Rd, South Wilton, CT 06852.

GROSSWALD, EMIL, b. Bucharest, Roumania, Dec. 15, 12; nat; m. 50; c. 2. MATHEMATICS. M.S, Bucharest, 32; Elec. Eng, Ecole Sup. d'Electricite, Paris, 40; Ph.D.(math), Pennsylvania, 50. Instr, Puerto Rico, 47-48; lectr, Saskatchewan, 50-51; assoc. MATH, Univ. Pa, 52-54, asst. prof, 54-57, assoc. prof, 57-60, PROF, 60-68; TEMPLE UNIV, 68- Mem, Inst. Adv. Study, Princeton, 51-52, 59-60; exchange prof, Paris, 64-65. AAAS; Am. Math. Soc; Math. Asn. Am. Analytic and elementary number theory; algebraic properties of polynomials. Address: Dept. of Mathematics, Temple University, Broad St, Philadelphia, PA 19122.

GROSSWEINER, LEONARD I(RWIN), b. Atlantic City, N.J, Aug. 16, 24; m. 51; c. 4. BIOPHYSICS. B.Ch.E, City Col, 47; M.S, Ill. Inst. Technol, 51, Ph.D. (physics), 54. Asst, Argonne Nat. Lab, 47-51, from asst. physicist to assoc. physicist, 51-57; assoc. prof. PHYSICS, ILL. INST. TECHNOL, 57-62, PROF, 62-, CHMN. DEPT, 70- Consult, Michael Reese Hosp, 64- U.S.A, 44-46. AAAS; fel. Am. Phys. Soc; fel. N.Y. Acad. Sci; Am. Chem. Soc; Radiation Res. Soc. Radiation biophysics; flash photolysis; pulse radiolysis; solid state photosensitization; electrophotography. Address: Biophysics Lab, Dept. of Physics, Illinois Institute of Technology, Chicago, IL 60616.

GROSTIC, MARVIN F(ORD), b. Webberville, Mich, June 16, 26; m. 51; c. 3. ORGANIC CHEMISTRY. A.B, Albion Col, 50; Nat. Defense Ed. Act fel, Idaho, 61-64, Ph.D.(org. chem), 65. Infrared spectroscopist, UPJOHN CO, 53-61, mass spectroscopist, 64-70, MGR. CHEM. PROD. CONTROL, 70- U.S.A, 44-46, 51-52, 1st Lt. Addition to bicyclo (3.1.0) hexene-2; mass spectroscopy. Address: Upjohn Co, Kalamazoo, MI 49001.

GROSVENOR, CLARK E(DWARD), b. Piqua, Ohio, May 9, 28; m. 50; c. 5. ZOOLOGY, ENDOCRINOLOGY. B.S, Otterbein Col, 50; M.S, Univ. Cincinnati, 52, Ph.D.(zool), 55. Instr. biol, col. pharm, Univ. Cincinnati, 53-54; endocrinol, 54-55; asst. prof. biol, Univ. Tenn, 55-56; fel, Nat. Insts. Health, Univ. Mo, 56-59; asst. prof. PHYSIOL, UNIV. TENN, MEMPHIS, 59-62, assoc. prof, 62-67, PROF, 67-, NAT. INSTS. HEALTH SR. RES. FEL, 59- AAAS; Soc. Exp. Biol. & Med; Am. Physiol. Soc; Endocrine Soc. Neuroendocrinology; lactational physiology. Address: Dept. of Physiology, University of Tennessee, Memphis, TN 38103.

GROSVENOR, NILES E(ARL), b. Carbondale, Pa, Feb. 14, 22; m. 42; c. 4. MINING ENGINEERING. E.M, Colo. Sch. Mines, 50, fel, 50-52, M.S, 52; Columbia, 57-58. Instr. MINING, COLO. SCH. MINES, 52-55, asst. prof, 55-65, ASSOC. PROF, 65- U.S.A.A.F, 41-45; C.Eng. Res, 46-, 2nd Lt. Am. Soc. Eng. Educ; Am. Inst. Mining, Metall. & Petrol. Eng. Rock mechanics; mining. Address: Dept. of Mining Engineering, Colorado School of Mines, Golden, CO 80401.

GROSZ, OLIVER, b. Ashley, N.Dak, Mar. 12, 06; m. 31; c. 3. CHEMISTRY. B.A, Iowa, 28, M.S, 29, Ph.D.(org. chem), 31. Asst, Iowa, 28-31; instr. chem, Catholic Univ, 31-39; res. chemist, Collins & Aikman Corp, Pa, 39-40, asst. chief chemist, 40-42, chief chemist, 42-49, 55-57; dir. dyeing & finishing res, Delta Finishing Co. Div, J.P. Stevens & Co, Inc, 49-55; res. chemist, Toms River Chem. Corp, 57-71; CONSULT, 71- Am. Chem. Soc; Photog. Soc. Am; Am. Asn. Textile Chem. & Colorists. Organic, analytical and textile chemistry; sulfonyl derivatives of amino phenols; cresidine derivatives; analytical processes; textile finishing; synthetic detergents; mothproofing; dyeing processes; vat dyeing; wood scouring; water repellents; spectrophotometric methods of analysis; chromatography. Address: 21 Ridgewood Dr, Toms River, NJ 08753.

GROSZOS, STEPHEN J(OSEPH), b. Trenton, N.J, July 1, 20; m. 46; c. 2. CHEMISTRY, EDUCATION. A.B, N.Y. Univ, 46; A.M, Hopkins, 48, Ph.D. (chem), 51. With Burlington Mills Corp, 41; chemist, res. & develop. natural & synthetic resins, U.S. Indust. Chem, Inc, 42-46; instr. & consult, Hopkins, 46-50; sr. res. scientist, Stamford Labs, Am. Cyanamid Co, 50-57, mgr. resin develop, Formica Corp. Div, 57-59; tech. dir, Richardson Co, 59-63, dir. res. & develop, 63-65; v.pres, Packer Eng. Assocs, Inc, 65-67; dean sci, COL. DuPAGE, 67-70, DIR. INSTNL. RES, 70-; INDEPENDENT CONSULT, 67- Res. chemist, Polaroid Corp, 49; vis. prof, St. Procopius Col, 67-68; exec. dir, secy. & mem. bd. trustees, Col. DuPage Found, 70-; chmn. educ. comt, Ill. Nursing Home Adminr. Licensure Bd; consult, indust, legal & ins. firms, educ. insts, govt. & prof. asn; chmn. adv. comt, DuPage Co. Health Dept. Am. Chem. Soc; fel. Am. Inst. Chem; Soc. Plastics Eng; Asn. Schs. Allied Health Professions; Am. Educ. Res. Asn; Asn. Instnl. Res. Product and process development; materials technology; applications research; product and process engineering; management; organic synthesis; polymers; organometallics; triazines; ketenes; azo compounds; rosin and derivatives; textiles; coatings; molded and laminated plastics. Address: College of DuPage, Glen Ellyn, IL 60137.

GROT, RICHARD ARNOLD, b. Chicago, Ill, July 1, 39; m. 68; c. 2. CONTINUUM MECHANICS, APPLIED MATHEMATICS. B.S.E, Purdue Univ, 61, Nat. Sci. Found. fel. & M.S.E, 62, Ph.D.(eng. sci), 66. Vis. prof. physics, Nat. Univ. Trujillo, 66-68; res. assoc. civil engr, Northwest. Univ, 68-69; ASST. PROF. AEROSPACE & MECH. SCI, PRINCETON, 69- NASA-Am. Soc. Eng. Educ. fel, Marshall Space Flight Ctr, summer 71. Soc. Eng. Sci; Soc. Rheol. Composite materials; electromagnetic interactions with deformable bodies; technology in underdeveloped nations. Address: Dept. Aerospace & Mechanical Science, Princeton University, Princeton, NJ 08540.

GROT, WALTHER G(USTAV) F(REDRICH), b. Berlin, Germany, June 26, 29; m. 57; c. 3. ORGANIC CHEMISTRY. B.C, Göttingen, 51; Ph.D.(chem), Marburg, 55. SR. RES. CHEMIST, res. & develop. lab, Belle Works, E.I. DU PONT DE NEMOURS & CO, INC, W.Va, 56-60, EXP. STA, PLASTICS DEPT, 60- Am. Chem. Soc. Aliphatic organic chemistry; plastic intermediates; fluorocarbons; polymers; ion exchange membranes. Address: Experimental Station, Plastics Dept, E.I. du Pont de Nemours & Co, Inc, Wilmington, DE 19898.

GROTA, LEE J, b. Sturgeon Bay, Wis, May 12, 37; m. 59; c. 3. EXPERIMENTAL PSYCHOLOGY. B.S, Marquette, 59; M.S, Purdue, 61, Ph.D.(exp. psychol), 63. Trainee steroid biochem, sch. med, Utah, 63-65; asst. prof. PSYCHIAT, SCH. MED. & DENT, UNIV. ROCHESTER, 65-71, ASSOC. PROF, 71- Endocrine Soc; Am. Psychosom. Soc. Maternal behavior; early experience; developmental endocrinology; reproductive physiology; steroid biochemistry; psychosomatic interrelationships. Address: Dept. of Psychiatry, University of Rochester Medical Center, Rochester, NY 14620.

GROTE, HENRY W(ILLIAM), b. Ft. Sheridan, Ill, Feb. 24, 17; m. 38; c. 5. CHEMICAL ENGINEERING. B.S.Ch.E, Michigan, 38. Mgr. pilot plants, 45-53; asst. mgr. res. & develop. labs, Universal Oil Prod. Co, 53-56, mgr. petrochem. process sales dept, 56-60; pres, Trubek Chem. Co, 61-64; UOP Chem. Co. Div, UNIVERSAL OIL PROD. CO, N.J, 64-66, UOP Int, Inc, Belgium, 66-69, PRES. & DIR, UOP PROCESSES INT, INC, 69- Am. Chem. Soc; Am. Inst. Chem. Eng. Address: UOP Processes International, Inc, Bush House, Aldwych, London WC2B 4PX, Eng.

GROTE, IRVINE W(ALTER), b. Chattanooga, Tenn, July 25, 99; m. 26. BIOCHEMISTRY. B.S, Chattanooga, 22; A.M, Columbia, 23; Ph.D.(chem), Cincinnati, 25, hon. D.Sc, 68; Pittsburgh, 29. Res. biochemist, Wm. S. Merrell Co, Ohio, 25-26; prof. chem. & head dept, Winthrop Col, 26; res. chemist, Parke, Davis & Co, Mich, 26-31; assoc. prof. CHEM, UNIV. TENN, CHATTANOOGA, 31-41, prof, 41-69, EMER. PROF, 69- Consult. chemist, 32-; sci. adv, Chattem Drug & Chem. Co, 42- U.S.A, 18-19. AAAS; Am. Chem. Soc; Am. Pharmaceut. Asn. Pituitary hormones; pharmaceuticals. Address: 50 S. Crest Rd, Chattanooga, TN 37404.

GROTELUESCHEN, RALPH D(ICK), b. Columbus, Nebr, Feb. 8, 41; m. 65. ENVIRONMENTAL SCIENCES, AGRONOMY. B.Sc, Nebraska, 63; M.S, Wisconsin, 65, Ph.D.(agron), 67. Plant biochemist, agronomy eng. res. div, DEERE & CO, 67-69, dept. res. coord, tech. ctr, 69-71, MGR. ENVIRON. CONTROL, 71- Sci. Res. Soc. Am. Air, water, livestock and solid waste management; methods of carbohydrate analysis; polyfructosans; corn physiology and growth. Address: Environmental Control, Deere & Co, John Deere Rd, Moline, IL 61265.

GROTEN, BARNEY, b. Brooklyn, N.Y, Oct. 25, 33; m. 55; c. 3. POLYMER & ANALYTICAL CHEMISTRY. B.S, Brooklyn Col, 54; Ph.D.(org. chem), Purdue, 61. Chemist, Nickel Processing Corp, 55-56; Reaction Motors, Inc, 56-57; instr. org. chem, Purdue, 57-59, fel, 60-61; sr. chemist & group leader, Esso Res. & Eng. Co, STANDARD OIL CO.(N.J), 61-66, sect. head, Esso Res. S.A, Belg, 66-68, res. planning adv, Esso Chem. S.A, 68-71, PLANNING ADV. CHEM. SPECIALTIES, ESSOCHEM EUROPE, INC, 71- Am. Chem. Soc. Polymer characterization; relation of organic and polymer structure to properties. Address: Essochem Europe, Inc, 363 Chaussee De Malines, Kraainem, Belgium.

GROTENHUIS, MARSHALL, b. Oostburg, Wis, Oct. 17, 18; m. 46; c. 4. PHYSICS. B.S, Milwaukee State Teachers Col, 41; M.S, Marquette, 48, Instr, pub. sch, Mich, 41-42; asst. physics, Marquette, 46-48, instr, 48-49; assoc. physicist, reactor eng, Argonne Nat. Lab, 49-56, asst. dir, int. sch, 56-59, assoc. dir, int. inst, 59-64, dir, off. indust. coop, 65-67, supt. cent. shop, 67-70, tech. serv, 70-71; PROJ. ANALYST, DIV. RADIOL. & ENVIRON. PROTECTION, U.S. ATOMIC ENERGY COMN, 71- U.S.A.A.F, 42-46. Am. Nuclear Soc; Sci. Res. Soc. Am. Industrial cooperation; reactor shielding and engineering; nuclear engineering education. Address: Division of Radiological & Environmental Protection, U.S. Atomic Energy Commission, 7920 Norfolk Ave, Bethesda, MD 20014.

GROTH, D(ONALD) P(AUL), b. Milwaukee, Wis, Oct. 2, 28; m. 53; c. 3. BIOCHEMISTRY. B.S, Wisconsin, 50, U.S. Pub. Health Serv. fel, 52-54, Ph.D.(physiol. chem), 54; Univ. Wisconsin fel, Marine Biol. Lab, Woods Hole, 52. Asst. oncol, Wisconsin, 50-52; fel, biochem. develop, Univ. Libre de Bruxelles, 54-55; cellular physiol, California, 55-56; asst. prof. biochem. & pharmacol, EMORY UNIV, 56-63, ASSOC. PROF. BIOCHEM, 63- Lederle Med. Faculty award, 58-60; Leukemia Soc. scholar, 63-; vis. prof, Karolinska Inst, Sweden, 64. AAAS; Am. Chem. Soc; Am. Asn. Cancer Res; Am. Soc. Biol. Chem. Oncology; cancer research; chemistry of development and morphogenesis. Address: Dept. of Pharmacology, Emory University, Atlanta, GA 30322.

GROTH, EDWARD J(OHN, JR), b. Wichita, Kans, April 14, 20; m. 44; c. 3. PHYSICS. B.A, Wichita, 42; M.A, Kansas, 44. Jr. physicist, Tennessee Eastman Corp, Oak Ridge, 44-45; physicist, Oceanog. Inst, Woods Hole, 45-46; physicist & proj. engr, Emerson Elec. Mfg. Co, Mo, 46-48; chief physicist, Mo. Res. Labs, Inc, Mo, 48-54; chief electronics engr, Universal Match Corp, Mo, 54-56; systs. eng. mgr, MOTOROLA, INC, 56-61, CHIEF ENGR, PRELIMINARY DESIGN & ANAL, 61- Summers, consult, Proj. Mich, Michigan, 58-59. Am. Phys. Soc; sr. mem. Inst. Elec. & Electronics Eng. System design of large scale dynamic, data handling or data processing systems, particularly military dynamic and data systems. Address: 6308 E. Cactus Wren Rd, Scottsdale, AZ 85251.

GROTH, JOYCE L(ORRAINE), b. Meriden, Conn, Feb. 3, 35; m. 59; c. 2. ANALYTICAL CHEMISTRY. B.S, Cent. Conn. State Col, 57; M.S, Connecticut, 59, Ph.D.(anal. chem), 64. Res. fel, Wesleyan Univ, 64; asst. prof. CHEM, Univ. Conn, 64-69; INSTR, NEW BRITAIN HIGH SCH, CONN, 69- Eve. lectr, Cent. Conn. State Col. AAAS; Am. Chem. Soc. Nonaqueous reference systems and polarography; coulometry. Address: 75 Coe Ave, Meriden, CT 06450.

GROTH, LLOYD H, b. Cleveland, Ohio, June 12, 25; m. 50; c. 3. PHYSICS. B.S, Case, 50; Ohio State, 50-51. Asst. physics, Ohio State, 50-51; physicist, Libbey Owens Food Glass Co, 51-56; Cornell Aeronaut. Lab, 56-62, sect. head, 62-70; ASST. PROF. ELEC. TECHNOL, ERIE COMMUNITY COL, 70- U.S.A, 43-46. Inst. Elec. & Electronics Eng. Glass polishing technology; high peak power radar, antennas and microwave devices; radio wave propagation; satellite tracking; electronics circuits and communications. Address: Erie Community College, Main St. & Youngs Rd, Williamsville, NY 14221.

GROTH, RICHARD HENRY, b. New Britain, Conn, Oct. 14, 29; m. 59; c. 2. ANALYTICAL & ORGANIC CHEMISTRY. B.S, Conn. State Col, 51; Socony-Mobil Oil Co, Inc. fel, Ohio State, 53-54, Allied Chem. & Dye Corp, fel, 54-55, summer, Du Pont scholar, 55, Ph.D.(org. chem), 56. Res. assoc, Office Naval Res, Duke, 56-57; asst. prof. CHEM, Hartford, 57-61, ASSOC. PROF, 61-70, CENT. CONN. STATE COL, 70- Consult, Pratt & Whitney Aircraft Div, United Aircraft Corp, 61- AAAS; Am. Chem. Soc. Gas analysis and chromatography; synthesis of fluorinated paraffins; reactions of functions adjacent to perfluoroalkyl groups; direct fluorination of organic compounds; CO_2-O_2 control in isolated atmospheres. Address: 75 Coe Ave, Meriden, CT 06450.

GROTHAUS, CLARENCE (EDWARD), b. Smith Center, Kans, Feb. 19, 08; m. 35; c. 2. ORGANIC CHEMISTRY. A.B, Greenville Col, 30; M.A, Kansas, 33, Ph.D.(org. chem), 35. Asst. instr. chem, Kansas, 30-35; prof. & head dept, Bethany-Peniel Col, 35-36, 39-45; prof, head dept. & dir. student indust, Greenville Col, 36-39; res. chemist, res. found, Kansas, 45-51, chief chemist, govt. lab, Sunflower Ord. Works, 51-52; PROF. CHEM. & CHMN. NAT. SCI. DIV, OLIVET NAZARENE COL, 52- Chemist & bacteriologist, Fritzel Dairy Co, Kans, 34-35. Am. Chem. Soc. Synthesis of organic compounds; thiazolidones, methylene hydrogen derivatives; insulation board and pulp and paper from wheat straw; fillers for plastics; reduction of certain lignin products with $LiAlH_4$ to form unsaturated alcohols. Address: Dept. of Chemistry, Olivet Nazarene College, Kankakee, IL 60901.

GROTHEER, MORRIS PAUL, b. Pittsburg, Kans, Dec. 15, 28; m. 54; c. 5. ELECTROCHEMISTRY. B.S, Kans. State Col. Pittsburg, 50, M.S, 51; Ph.D. (anal. chem), Kansas State, 57. Res. chemist, Columbia South. Chem. Co, 57-59; sr. chemist, chem. div, Pittsburgh Plate Glass Co, 59-62; SUPVR. ELECTROCHEM. DEVELOP, HOOKER CHEM. CORP, 62- Med.C, U.S.A, 54-56. Electrochem. Soc; Am. Chem. Soc. Fundamental and applied electrochemical research, primarily in brine electrolysis for the production of chlorine, caustic, chlorates and perchlorates. Address: Electrochemical Development, Hooker Chemical Corp, Niagara Falls, NY 14302.

GROTTA, HENRY M(ONROE), b. New York, N.Y. Apr. 4, 23; m. 48; c. 5. ORGANIC CHEMISTRY. B.A, N.Y. Univ, 43; Ph.D.(chem), Ohio State, 50. Res. chemist, org. high polymers, Rohm and Haas Co, 50-54; BATTELLE MEM. INST, 54-59, sr. chemist, 59-68, PROJ. LEADER, 68- C.Eng, U.S.A, 43-46. Am. Chem. Soc; The Chem. Soc. Synthetic organic chemistry; vinyl polymerization; heterocyclic compounds. Address: Battelle Memorial Institute, 505 King Ave, Columbus, OH 43201.

GROTZ, LEONARD C(HARLES), b. Chicago, Ill, Nov. 8, 27; m. 54; c. 3. PHYSICAL CHEMISTRY. B.S, Northwestern, 49; Atomic Energy Comn. fel, California, 50-52, Ph.D.(phys. chem), 52. Res. chemist, Glidden Co, 52-54; res. fel, Minnesota, 54-55; res. chemist, Union Carbide Chem. Co. Div, Union Carbide Corp, 55-59; asst. prof. CHEM, Univ. Wis, Milwaukee, 59-64; assoc. prof, 64-66; prof, Parsons Col, 66-69; ASSOC. PROF, UNIV. WIS, WAUKESHA, 69- Instr, W.Va. State Col, 57-59. U.S.N.R, 45-46. AAAS; Am. Chem. Soc. Surface and polymer chemistry. Address: 2701 Lander Lane, Waukesha, WI 53186.

GROTZINGER, PAUL J(OHN), b. Phila, Pa, Oct. 23, 18; m. 52; c. 3. SURGERY. B.S, Muhlenberg Col, 39; M.D, Hahnemann Med. Col, 43. Asst. prof. surg, Hahnemann Med. Col, 50-51, assoc. prof, 51-61, clin. prof, 61-68; PROF. CLIN. SURG, UNIV. PA, 68-; MED. DIR. & CHIEF SURGEON, AM. ONCOL. HOSP, 60- Chief surgeon, Jeanes Hosp, 63-; assoc. attend. surgeon, Holy Redeemer Hosp; consult, Vet. Hosps, Phila; Fitkin Mem. Hosp, Neptune, N.J. U.S.N, 45-46, Lt.(jg). Am. Med. Asn; fel. Am. Col. Surg. Cancer and its clinical treatment. Address: Fox Chase Center for Cancer & Medical Science, Fox Chase, Philadelphia, PA 19111.

GROUPÉ, VINCENT, b. Phila, Pa, Sept. 13, 18; m. 42; c. 2. VIROLOGY. B.A, Wesleyan Univ, 39; Ph.D.(bact), Univ. Pa, 42. Asst. influenza lab, Children's Hosp, Pa, 39-42; asst. bacteriologist, E.R. Squibb & Sons, N.J, 42-43, sr. bacteriologist, 43-44, res. assoc, Squibb Inst. Med. Res, 44-47; assoc. prof. virol. in animal diseases & in charge virus lab, exp. sta, Univ. Conn, 47-49; assoc. prof. microbiol, Inst. Microbiol, Rutgers Univ, 49-54, prof, 54-68; exec. v.pres, LIFE SCI, INC, 68, DIR, 68- Vis. prof, Rutgers Univ, 68-70. Soc. Exp. Biol. & Med; Am. Asn. Immunol; Am. Asn. Cancer Res; Soc. Protozool; Am. Acad. Microbiol; N.Y. Acad. Med. Cancer viruses; chemotherapy; immunology. Address: Life Sciences, Inc, 2900 72nd St. N, St. Petersburg, FL 33710.

GROURKE, MARTIN J(OSEPH), b. Phila, Pa, Nov. 20, 40; m. 63; c. 2. PHYSICAL CHEMISTRY. B.Sc, Drexel Univ, 64; NASA fel, 65-68; Ph.D.(phys. chem), Brown Univ, 69. Nat. Insts. Health fel, Brandeis Univ, 69-70; RES. CHEMIST, ROHM AND HAAS CO, 70- Am. Chem. Soc. Physical chemistry of biological macromolecules; physical chemistry of organic coatings. Address: Rohm and Haas Co, Spring House Research Labs, Spring House, PA 19477.

GROVE, ALVIN R(USSELL), JR, b. Harrisburg, Pa, May 21, 14; m. 36. ANATOMY, MORPHOLOGY. B.S, Lebanon Valley Col, 36; M.Sc, New Mexico, 37; Ph.D.(bot), Chicago, 40. Asst. biol, New Mexico, 36-37, instr, 38-41; BOT, PA. STATE UNIV, 41-43, asst. prof, 43-49, assoc. prof, 49-55, PROF, 55-, ASSOC. DEAN COL. SCI, 65-, acting head dept. bot, 61-65, asst. dean col. sci, 64-65. Mem. adv. work group, Monongahela River Mine Drainage Remedial Proj, Dept. Interior, 65-68; consult. & panel mem, Comn. Undergrad. Educ. in Biol. Sci, 66-69; ed, Trout Mag, 70-; mem. citizens adv. coun, Pa. Dept. Environ. Resources, 71- Merit award, Am. Asn. Conserv. Info, 59. Med.C, U.S.A, 43-46. Fel. AAAS (past secy, Southwest Sect); Bot. Soc. Am; Int. Soc. Plant Morphol. Floral and experimental morphology. Address: College of Science, 210 Whitmore Lab, Pennsylvania State University, University Park, PA 16802.

GROVE, ANDREW S, b. Budapest, Hungary, Sept. 2, 36; U.S. citizen; m. 58; c. 1. ENGINEERING PHYSICS. B.S, City Col. New York, 60; Ph.D, California, Berkeley, 63. Mem. tech. staff, Fairchild Semiconductor Res. Lab, 63-66, sect. head. surface & device physics, 66-67, asst. dir. res. & develop, 67-68; V.PRES. & DIR. OPERS, INTEL. CORP, 68- Lectr, dept. elec. eng. & comput. sci, Univ. Calif, Berkeley, 66- Am. Inst. Chem. medal award, 60. Am. Phys. Soc; Inst. Elec. & Electronics Eng.(achievement award, 69). Metal-oxide-semiconductor devices and integrated circuits; large-scale integration technology; transport phenomena, especially fluid dynamics. Address: Intel Corp, 365 Middlefield Rd, Mountain View, CA 94040.

GROVE, C(ORNELIUS) S(HERMAN), JR, b. Oneida, N.Y, Sept. 8, 05; m. 60. CHEMICAL & SANITARY ENGINEERING. A.B, Lenoir-Rhyne Col, 25; B.S, N.C. State Col, 28, Ch.E, 32; M.S, Mass. Inst. Tech, 34; Ph.D.(chem. eng), Minnesota, 42. Asst. prof. chem. eng, N.C. State Col, 30-35; instr, Minnesota, 35-41; res. chem. engr, E.I. du Pont de Nemours & Co, Buffalo, 41-45; prof. CHEM. ENG. & head div, Iowa, 45-47; PROF, SYRACUSE UNIV, 47-, dir. eng. res, 54-63. Consult. chem. engr, W.A. Sheaffer Pen Co, Iowa, 46-50; prof, Univ. Baghdad, 63-65. AAAS; Soc. Indust. Chem; Am. Chem. Soc; Am. Soc. Eng. Educ; Am. Inst. Chem. Eng. Research administration; crystallization from aqueous solutions; absorption and extraction; fluid mechanics of twophase systems; drying; unit processes; electrochemistry; synthetic fibers; engineering materials; air, water and land pollution. Address: 5110 Brockway Lane, Fayetteville, NY 13066.

GROVE, D(ANIEL) DWIGHT, b. Felton, Pa, Feb. 27, 14; m. 39; c. 2. ANESTHESIOLOGY. B.S, Lebanon Valley Col, 34; M.D, Hahnemann Med. Col, 38. Asst. ANESTHESIOL, HAHNEMANN MED. COL. & HOSP, 43-46, instr, 46-48, assoc, 48-49, assoc. prof, 49-64, PROF, 64- Clin. assoc. prof, Woman's Med. Col. Pa, 49-50; vis. lectr, grad. sch. med, Univ. Pa, 49-52. Dipl, Am. Bd. Anesthesiol, 46. Med.C, U.S.A, 43-46. Am. Soc. Anesthesiol; Int. Anesthesia Res. Soc; Am. Med. Asn. Clinical anesthesiology. Address: Section of Anesthesiology, Hahnemann Medical College of Philadelphia, Philadelphia, PA 19102.

GROVE, DAVISON GREENAWALT, b. Chambersburg, Pa, Jan. 7, 21; m. 50; c. 3. BOTANY. B.S, Pa. State, 42; M.S, Chicago, 48; Ph.D.(insect ecol), Cornell, 59. Instr. BIOL, WILSON COL, 48-50, asst. prof, 50-58, assoc. prof, 58-70, PROF, 68-, CHMN. DEPT, 69- U.S.A.A.F, 43-45. AAAS; Entom. Soc. Am. Plant and insect taxonomy and ecology. Address: Dept. of Biology, Wilson College, Chambersburg, PA 17201.

GROVE, DONALD C(OOPER), b. Baltimore, Md, June 4, 09; m. 32; c. 1. PHARMACEUTICAL CHEMISTRY. B.S, Maryland, 30, M.S, 33, Ph.D.(pharmaceut. chem), 37. Lab. asst. chem, sch. pharm, Maryland, 29-32; jr. chemist, Food & Drug Admin, U.S. Dept. Agr, Baltimore, 32-35, asst. chemist, 35-37, D.C, 37-39, assoc. chemist, 39-40, Fed. Security Agency, 40-42, chemist, 42-45, asst. chief, div. antibiotics, 46-53, Dept. Health, Ed. & Welfare, 53-59, dep. dir, 59-60, dir, 60-63, dep. dir, bur. sci. standards & eval, 63-64; CONSULT. PHARMACEUT. MFG. & CONTROL, 67- Award, Dept. Health, Ed. & Welfare, 62. Am. Chem. Soc; fel. Am. Inst. Chem. Phytochemistry of medicinal plants; quantitative pharmaceutical chemistry; separation of ergot alkaloids; assay methods for penicillin and other antibiotics. Address: Box 259, Route 4, Oaklands, Easton, MD 21601.

GROVE, D(ONALD) J(ONES), b. Pittsburgh, Pa, Oct. 8, 19; m. 43; c. 3. PHYSICS. A.B, Col. of Wooster, 41; fel, Mass. Inst. Tech, 41-42; Ph.D. (physics), Carnegie Inst. Tech, 53. Res. physicist, RES. LABS, WESTINGHOUSE ELEC. CORP, 41-; CONSULT. PHYSICIST, PLASMA PHYSICS LAB, PRINCETON, 54- Am. Phys. Soc. Mass spectroscopy, specifically ionization and dissociation of atoms and molecules by electron impact; electronic instrumentation for above; ultra high vacuum techniques; controlled thermonuclear reactor techniques. Address: Princeton University, Plasma Physics Lab, P.O. Box 451, Princeton, NJ 08540.

GROVE, E(WART) L(ESTER), b. Greensburg, Kans, May 31, 13; m. 44; c. 2. ANALYTICAL & PHYSICAL CHEMISTRY. M.A, Ohio State, 45; Ph.D. (chem), Western Reserve, 51. Teacher, pub. sch, Minn, 38-40; Ohio, 40-47; instr. math, Fenn Col, 42-44; chem, Minn. State Teachers Col, St. Cloud, 47-48; asst. prof. anal. chem, Alabama, 51-56, assoc. prof, 56-60; res. chemist, Ill. Inst. Tech. Res. Inst, 60-63, sr. chemist, 63-66, mgr. anal. chem. res, 66-71; V.PRES, FREEMAN LABS, INC, 71- Res. partic, Oak Ridge Nat. Lab, 53-54, consult, 54- Awards for spec. instrumentation develop, Nat. Adv. Comt. Aeronaut. AAAS; Am. Chem. Soc; Am. Inst. Chem; Soc. Appl. Spectros. Spectrography; spectrophotometry; flame and colorimetric methods as applied to analytical methods. Address: Freeman Labs, Inc, Rosemont, IL 60018.

GROVE, G(EORGE) R(ICHARD), b. Columbus, Ohio, Jan. 4, 25; m. 47; c. 3. PHYSICS. B.S, Ohio State, 46, M.S, 47, fel, 47-48, Atomic Energy Comn. fel, 48-50, Ph.D.(physics), 50. Asst. Ohio State, 46-47; physicist, Nat. Bur. Standards, 50-51; res. physicist, Mound Lab, Monsanto Res. Corp, 51-53, res. group leader, 53-59, res. sect. mgr, 59-62, res. dept. dir, 62-67, dir. nuclear opers. dept, 67-70, PLANNING MGR. ELECTRONIC PROD. DIV, MONSANTO CO, 70- Consult, Miami Valley Hosp, 53- Fel. Am. Phys. Soc; Soc. Nuclear Med; Am. Asn. Physicists in Med; Am. Col. Radiol. Nuclear, atomic and molecular physics; isotope separation; thermal diffusion; statistical mechanics; radioisotope heat sources and applications; nuclear medicine; radiological physics. Address: 1932 Bookbinder Dr, St. Louis, MO 63141.

GROVE, HERBERT D(UNCAN), JR, b. Des Moines, Iowa, July 31, 21; m. 46; c. 5. CHEMICAL ENGINEERING. B.S.Ch.E, Iowa, 43, M.S.Ch.E, 48, Ph.D. (chem. eng), 49. Chem. engr, Pan-Am. Ref. Corp, 48, group leader process design, 50-51, process develop, 51-56; eng. supvr, MONSANTO CO, 56-60, mgr. develop. eng, 60-64, MGR. PROCESS TECHNOL, PROCESS TECHNOL. DEPT, HYDROCARBONS DIV, 64- U.S.A, 43-46. Am. Inst. Chem. Eng. Ultrasonic sound waves; process design; economic evaluation; applied thermodynamics; technical management. Address: 1220 19th Ave. N, Texas City, TX 77590.

GROVE, JOHN AMOS, b. Youngstown, Ohio, Mar. 26, 38; m. 62; c. 2. NUTRITION, BIOCHEMISTRY. B.S, Ohio State, 61, M.S, 64, Ph.D.(nutrit, biochem), 66. Res. fel. biochem, Minnesota, St. Paul, 66-68; asst. prof. CHEM, S.DAK. STATE UNIV, 68-71, ASSOC. PROF, 71- Mechanism of vitamin E action; intermediary metabolism of amino acids. Address: Dept. of Chemistry, South Dakota State University, Brookings, SD 57006.

GROVE, JOHN SINCLAIR, b. Brownwood, Tex, Nov. 27, 43. GENETICS. B.A, Arizona, 64, M.S, 66; Nat. Inst. Health trainee & Ph.D.(genetics), Hawaii, 69. FEL. genetics, Univ. Wis, Madison, 68-70; MED. GENETICS, SCH. MED, IND. UNIV-PURDUE UNIV, INDIANAPOLIS, 70- Consult, 69-70. Am. Soc. Human Genetics. Drosophila genetics; human transplantation genetics; human population genetics. Address: Dept. of Medical Genetics, School of Medicine, Indiana University-Purdue University at Indianapolis, Indianapolis, IN 46202.

GROVE, LARRY CHARLES, b. Madison, Minn, Jan. 19, 38; m. 59; c. 2. MATHEMATICS. B.A, Minnesota, 60, M.A, 61, Nat. Sci. Found. fel, 61-64, Ph.D.(math), 64. J.W. Young res. instr. MATH, Dartmouth Col, 64-66; asst. prof, Univ. Ore, 66-69; ASSOC. PROF, Syracuse Univ, 69-71; UNIV. ARIZ, 71- Am. Math. Soc; Math. Asn. Am. Algebra. Address: Dept. of Mathematics, University of Arizona, Tucson, AZ 85721.

GROVE, MICHAEL DEAN, b. Indianapolis, Ind, July 11, 39; m. 69. ORGANIC & MEDICINAL CHEMISTRY. B.S, Purdue Univ, 61, M.S, 63, Nat. Insts. Health fel, 63-65, Ph.D.(med. chem), 65. Res. assoc, Univ. Wis, Madison, 65-67; CHEMIST NATURAL PROD, NORTH. REGIONAL RES. LAB, U.S. DEPT. AGR, 67- AAAS; Am. Chem. Soc; Am. Pharmaceut. Asn. Chemistry of biologically-active natural compounds; tumor inhibitors from plants particularly triterpenes; isolation, structure determination and toxicity of mold metabolites. Address: 703 W. South Forrest Trail, Peoria, IL 61614.

GROVE, RICHARD E(DWARD), b. Winchester, Va, Dec. 20, 26; m. 57; c. 2. PHYSICS. B.S, Randolph-Macon Col, 47; M.A, Hopkins, 50; Southern fund fel, Syracuse, 55-57, Ph.D.(physics), 59. Instr. PHYSICS, Susquehanna, 50-53; asst. prof, RANDOLPH-MACON COL, 53-58, PROF, 58-68, COMPUT. SCI, 68-, DIR. COMPUT. CTR, 63-, chmn. dept. physics, 64-68. Optical Soc. Am; Asn. Comput. Mach. Optical spectroscopy; physical optics. Address: Dept. of Computer Science, Randolph-Macon College, Ashland, VA 23005.

GROVE, STANLEY N(EAL), b. Augusta, Va, Sept. 13, 40; m. 62; c. 2. BOTANY, CELL BIOLOGY. B.A, Goshen Col, 65; Ph.D.(bot), Purdue Univ, 71. Res. assoc. biochem, Agr. Res. Serv, U.S. Dept. Agr, 70-71; FEL. MICROBIOL, UNIV. TEX. AUSTIN, 71- Bot. Soc. Am; Mycol. Soc. Am. Structure and function of protoplasmatic and surface components of germinating fungal spores and growing hyphal tips; cytochemical localization of macromolecules, especially enzymes, polysaccharides in fungi and in peanut seeds. Address: Dept. of Microbiology, University of Texas at Austin, Austin, TX 78712.

GROVE, WILLIAM J(OHNSON), b. Ottawa, Ill, Mar. 23, 20; m. 44; c. 3. SURGERY. B.S, Univ. Ill, 42, M.D, 43, M.S, 49. Instr. SURG, UNIV. ILL. COL. MED, 52, asst. prof, 53, assoc. prof, 54-64, PROF, 64-, EXEC. DEAN, 70-, dean, 68-70, assoc. dean, 61-68. Attend. surgeon, Univ. Ill. Hosp, 52-; assoc. attend. surgeon, Cook County Hosp, 53; attend. surgeon, Hines Vet. Admin. Hosp, 54-60. Med.C, 44-46, Capt. Soc. Univ. Surg; Soc. Clin. Surg; Am. Med. Asn; Am. Col. Surg; Am. Surg. Asn; Asn. Am. Med. Cols. Medical education; research in medical education and the health care delivery system. Address: University of Illinois College of Medicine, 1853 W. Polk St, Chicago, IL 60612.

GROVENSTEIN, ERLING, JR, b. Miami, Fla, Nov. 12, 24; m. 54, 62; c. 2. ORGANIC CHEMISTRY. B.S, Ga. Tech, 44; fel, Mass. Inst. Tech, 44-45, Ph.D.(org. chem), 48. Asst. CHEM, Mass. Inst. Tech, 45-48, res. assoc, 48; asst. prof, GA. INST. TECHNOL, 48-49, assoc. prof, 49-57, prof, 57-65, JULIUS BROWN PROF, 65- Res. partic, Oak Ridge Nat. Lab, summers 49 & 54. Am. Chem. Soc; The Chem. Soc. Organoalkali chemistry; organic reaction mechanisms; photochemistry. Address: School of Chemistry, Georgia Institute of Technology, Atlanta, GA 30332.

GROVER, ANSON R(OY), b. Montclair, N.J, Dec. 31, 28; m. 61; c. 3. CHEMICAL ENGINEERING. B.S, Lafayette Col, 50; fel, Delaware, 50-52. Chem. engr, PLASTICS DIV, UNION CARBIDE CORP, 54-57, group leader, 57-66, supvr. process eng. phenolics, 66-71, OPERS. CONTROL SUPVR, 71- Chem.C, 52-54, 1st Lt. Sci. Res. Soc. Am; Am. Inst. Chem. Eng. Development of chemical processes from laboratory bench scale through pilot plant scale to production scale; chemical engineering unit operations; digital computer programming. Address: Plastics Division, Bldg. 203, Union Carbide Corp, River Rd, Bound Brook, NJ 08805.

GROVER, BEN L(EO), b. Chapin, Idaho, June 23, 24; m. 47; c. 7. SOIL PHYSICS. B.S, Utah State, 49, M. S, 50; Ph.D, Iowa State, 59. Asst. prof. soils, Garden City Br, Kans. Agr. Exp. Sta, 50-54; res. assoc. soil physics, Iowa State, 54-59; asst. prof. hort, California, Riverside, 59-64; ASSOC. PROF. SOILS, UTAH STATE UNIV, 64- Soil specialist, Utah State Univ. Contract-U.S. Agency Int. Develop, Bolivia, 71- U.S.M.C.R, 44-46. AAAS; Soil Sci. Soc. Am; Am. Soc. Agron; Am. Geophys. Union. Irrigation and drainage with emphasis on water movement, soil, plant and water relationships; statistics; watershed hydrology. Address: 1495 Highland St, Logan, UT 84321.

GROVER, GEORGE MAURICE, b. Garland, Utah, June 7, 15; m. 47; c. 1. NUCLEAR PHYSICS. B.S, Washington (Seattle), 41; M.S, Michigan, 48, Ph.D.(physics), 50. Meteorologist, U.S. Weather Bur, 38-44; group leader proximity fuze, appl. physics lab, Hopkins, 44-46; consult, U.S. Bur. Mines, 48-49; staff mem. weapons, LOS ALAMOS SCI. LAB, 50-53, GROUP LEADER, 53-55, nuclear rockets, 55-58, ADVAN. CONCEPTS, 58- Am. Phys. Soc. Advanced concepts of nuclear space propulsion; nuclear thermionic conversion, including diode performance, fuels and reactor systems, especially heat transfer problems peculiar to zero-g environment. Address: Los Alamos Scientific Lab, Box 1663, Los Alamos, NM 87544.

GROVER, HORACE J(OHN), b. Cayuga, N.Y, May 14, 09; m. 38, 68; c. 1. PHYSICS. B.A, Rochester, 29, M.A, 31; Ph.D.(physics), Cornell, 37. Asst. instr. physics, Rochester, 29-31; Cornell, 34-36; instr, Rensselaer Polytech, 36-42; res. engr, BATTELLE-COLUMBUS LABS, 42-45, asst. res. supvr, 45-51, chief appl. mech. div, MECH. ENG. DEPT, 51-60, SR. RES. FEL, 60- Fel. Am. Phys. Soc; Soc. Exp. Stress Anal; Am. Soc. Test. & Mat.(award, 64). Mechanical properties of engineering materials, especially fatigue; design criteria; mechanical engineering; biomechanics. Address: Mechanical Engineering Dept, Battelle-Columbus Labs, 505 King Ave, Columbus, OH 43201.

GROVER, J(AMES) ROBB, b. Klamath Falls, Ore, Sept. 16, 28; m. 57; c. 2. NUCLEAR & PHYSICAL CHEMISTRY. B.S, Washington (Seattle), 52; Ph.D. (nuclear chem), California, Berkeley, 58. Asst. chem, California, Berkeley, 52-53, nuclear chem, Radiation Lab, Univ. Calif, Berkeley, 53-57; res. assoc. chem, BROOKHAVEN NAT. LAB, 57-59, assoc. chemist, 59-63, CHEMIST, 63- Consult, Lawrence Radiation Lab, Univ. Calif, 62-63. U.S.N, 46-48. Am. Chem. Soc; Am. Phys. Soc; Am. Inst. Chem. Use of short-lived radioactivity in chemical dynamics; nuclear reactions; crossed molecular beams; radio-chemical techniques. Address: Brookhaven National Lab, Upton, NY 11973.

GROVER, JOHN H(ENRY), b. Phoenixville, Pa, Sept. 5, 27; m. 57; c. 2. CHEMICAL ENGINEERING. S.B, Mass. Inst. Tech, 48, M.S, 49. Chem. engr, Mass. Inst. Tech, 49-51; Atlantic Res. Corp, 51-57, head aerothermodyn. group, 57-68, tech. asst. to chmn. bd, 62-68; V.PRES. & TREAS, RES. INDUST. INC, 68- Am. Chem. Soc; Am. Inst. Aeronaut. & Astronaut; Am. Inst. Chem. Eng; Combustion Inst. Combustion; solid propellants; exterior ballistics; jet propulsion. Address: 2339 49th St. N.W, Washington, DC 20007.

GROVER, JOHN M, b. Baltimore, Md, Apr. 2, 41; m. 63; c. 1. ALGEBRA. B.S, Calif. Inst. Technol, 62; assistantship, Univ. Calif, Los Angeles, 62-66, M.A, 65, Ph.D.(math), 66. ASST. PROF. MATH, UNIV. CALIF, IRVINE, 66- Nat. Sci. Found. grant, 67-69. Am. Math. Soc. Chevalley groups, finite Lie groups, particularly universal central extensions and Schur multipliers; cohomological topics in group theory and algebraic K-theory. Address: Dept. of Mathematics, University of California, Irvine, CA 92664.

GROVER, M. ROBERTS, JR, b. Boston, Mass, Dec. 5, 27; m. 56; c. 3. MEDICINE, ADMINISTRATIVE MEDICINE. B.A, Bowdoin Col, 50; M.D, Cornell Univ, 54; M.S, Univ. Ore, 56. Instr. med, MED. SCH, UNIV. ORE, 58-59, asst. prof, 59-68, PROF. MED. & ASSOC. DEAN, 68-, DIR. CONTINUING MED. EDUC, 65-, asst. med. dir. hosps. & clins, 58-67, prog. coord, Ore. Regional Med. Prog, 67-68. Mem, Mt. States Regional Med. Prog, 67- U.S.A, 46-47. Am. Med. Asn; Asn. Am. Med. Cols. Medical education; internal medicine. Address: University of Oregon Medical School, 3181 S.W. Sam Jackson Park Rd, Portland, OR 97201.

GROVER, R(AJBANS), b. Varnasi, India, Oct. 18, 27; m. 61; c. 3. PLANT PHYSIOLOGY. B.Sc, Panjab, India, 49; scholar, Delhi, 50-52, M.Sc, 52; Ph.D.(bot), Washington (Seattle), 60. Demonstr. bot, Delhi, 49-50, res. asst. plant physiol, 52-54; ed. asst. bot, pub. div, Coun. Sci. & Indust. Res, India, 54-55; res. off, PLANT PHYSIOL, forest nursery sta, CAN. DEPT. AGR, res. br, Indian Head, 60-63, exp. farm, Regina, 63-65, RES. SCIENTIST, RES. STA, 65- Mem, Sask. Weed Adv. Coun. Can, 61-; res. appraisal comt, west. sect, Can. Weed Comt, 62- Weed Sci. Soc. Am; Can. Soc. Plant Physiol. Herbicide behavior in the biosphere. Address: Research Station, Canada Dept. of Agriculture, Box 440, Regina, Sask, Can.

GROVER, ROBERT F(REDERIC), b. Rochester, N.Y, Feb. 25, 24; m. 44. MEDICINE. B.A, Rochester, 47; Ph.D.(physiol), Colorado, 51, M.D, 55. Intern, St. Anthony Hosp, Denver, 55-56; res. fel. cardiovasc. lab, MED. SCH, UNIV. COLO, 56-58, instr. med. & asst. dir, cardiovasc. lab, med. ctr, 58-61, asst. prof. MED, 61-68, ASSOC. PROF, 68-, DIR. CARDIOVASC. PULMONARY RES. LAB, 65-, HIGH ALTITUDE RES. LAB, 64- Res. career develop. award, 65-75. Sig.C, U.S.A, 43-46. Thoracic Soc; Am. Heart Asn; Am. Physiol. Soc; Am. Col. Chest Physicians; Am. Fedn. Clin. Res. Cardiovascular and pulmonary physiology; congenital heart disease. Address: Dept. of Medicine, University of Colorado School of Medicine, 4200 E. Ninth Ave, Denver, CO 80220.

GROVES, DAVID L(YNN), b. Kansas City, Mo, Sept. 19, 40; m. 58; c. 3. IMMUNOLOGY, MICROBIOLOGY. B.S, Marietta Col, 62; M.S, Wisconsin, Madison, 66, Ph.D.(microbiol), 67. U.S. Pub. Health Serv. fel, biol. div, Oak Ridge Nat. Lab, 67-69; ASST. PROF. MICROBIOL, BOWMAN GRAY SCH. MED, 69- AAAS; Reticuloendothelial Soc. Antibody formation as a problem of cellular differentiation with special emphasis on cellular and molecular control mechanisms involved. Address: Dept. of Microbiology, Bowman Gray School of Medicine, Wake Forest University, Winston-Salem, NC 27103.

GROVES, DONALD GEORGE, b. Syracuse, N.Y, Aug. 24, 19; m. 49. MATERIALS SCIENCE, ENGINEERING. B.Sc, Syracuse, 39, M.Sc, 49. Designer, Easy Washer Corp, 40-41; Hudson Motor Car Co, 41-43; res. grant, Santo Domingo, 49-50; systs. engr, Gen. Elec. Co, 54-61; SCI. STAFF MEM. MAT. SCI. & ENG, NAT. ACAD. SCI, 61- Staff mem, Nat. Acad. Sci. comts, advan. design criteria, 61-62, ceramic mat, 61-62, design with brittle mat, 63-64, protective mat. aerospace vehicles, 64-65, atomic characterization mat, 64-67, ceramic processing studies, 65-68, fundamentals amorphous mat. ballistic missile defense hardening, 70-71, comt. studies infrared, laser-glass & glass, Nat. Acad. Sci-Nat. Res. Coun; Int. Oceanog. Found. Freedoms Found. Honor Medal Award, 70. U.S.N.R, 43-46, 51-54, Res, 54-70, Lt. Comdr. Marine Technol. Soc; Am. Soc. Naval Eng. Natural resource utilization; research and development in materials, especially as related to ocean science and engineering; scientific administration. Address: National Academy of Sciences, 2101 Constitution Ave. N.W, Washington, DC 20418.

GROVES, FRANK R(OCHE), JR, b. New Orleans, La, Jan. 11, 29; m. 59. CHEMICAL ENGINEERING. B.S, Tulane, 50; M.S, 51; E.I. du Pont de Nemours & Co, fel, Wisconsin, 52-53, Ph.D.(chem. eng), 55. Assoc. res. engr, Atlantic Ref. Co, 54-56; sr. scientist, Exp. Inc, Va, 57; res. engr, Texas Instruments Inc, Texas, 58; asst. prof. CHEM. ENG, LA. STATE UNIV, BATON ROUGE, 58-61, assoc. prof, 61-67, PROF, 67- Summer, res. participant, Oak Ridge Inst. Nuclear Studies, 59. Am. Chem. Soc. Thermodynamics; reactor design. Address: Dept. of Chemical Engineering, Louisiana State University, Baton Rouge, LA 70808.

GROVES, GORDON W(ILLIAM), b. Wilmar, Calif, Jan. 8, 27; m. 60; c. 11. OCEANOGRAPHY. A.B, California, Los Angeles, 49, M.S, 51, Ph.D. (oceanog), 55. Asst. res. oceanog, Scripps Inst, California, 55-59; investr, inst. geophys, Nat. Univ. Mexico, 59-61; assoc. res. geophysicist, inst. geophys. & planetary physics, California, San Diego, 61-64; OCEANOGR, INST. GEOPHYS, UNIV. HAWAII, 64-, PROF. OCEANOG, 65- Ford Found. grant, Inst. Geophys, Nat. Univ. Mex, 68; Smithsonian Inst. grant, Lembaga Penelitian Laut, Indonesia, 70-71. U.S.N.R, 44-45. Am. Geophys. Union; Mex. Geophys. Union. Physical oceanography; tides; waves; variation of sea level. Address: Hawaii Institute of Geophysics, University of Hawaii, Honolulu, HI 96822.

GROVES, IVOR D(URHAM), JR, b. Bowling Green, Ky, Dec. 30, 19; m. 44; c. 3. PHYSICS. B.S, Rollins Col, 48, M.B.A, 64; Oak Ridge Inst. Nuclear Studies, 49-50. Electronic develop. engr, Oak Ridge Nat. Lab, 48-51; head transducer div. & physicist, UNDERWATER SOUND REFERENCE DIV, NAVAL RES. LAB, 51-69, HEAD STANDARDS BR, 69- Cost reduction award, Secy. of Navy, 71. U.S.A.F, 43-45, Res, 45-55, Capt. Acoust. Soc. Am. Underwater standard transducers for calibration of underwater acoustic devices. Address: 518 Baxter St, Orlando, FL 32806.

GROVES, JOHN T(AYLOR), III, b. New Rochelle, N.Y, Mar. 27, 43; m. 61; c. 1. ORGANIC CHEMISTRY. S.B, Mass. Inst. Technol, 65; Nat. Inst. Gen. Med. Sci. fel, Columbia Univ, 66-69, Louis P. Hammett traveling fel. & Ph.D.(org. chem), 69. ASST. PROF. ORG. CHEM, UNIV. MICH, ANN ARBOR, 69- AAAS; Am. Chem. Soc. Physical organic chemistry; bio-organic chemistry; reaction mechanisms; new synthetic methods. Address: Dept. of Chemistry, 1022 Chemistry Bldg, University of Michigan, Ann Arbor, MI 48104.

GROVES, KENNETH O(RA), b. Flint, Mich, Mar. 25, 30; m. 56; c. 2. INORGANIC CHEMISTRY. A.B, Albion Col, 52; M.S, Mich. State, 57, Ph.D.(inorg. chem), 59. Chemist, Adv. Res. Projs. Agency, Dow Chem. Co, 59-60; Union Carbide Co, 60-65; res. chemist, SCI. PROJ. LAB, DOW CHEM. CO, 65-67, GROUP LEADER, 67- U.S.A, 52-54, Sgt. AAAS; Am. Chem. Soc; Am. Inst. Aeronaut. & Astronaut; Sci. Res. Soc. Am. Metal coordination compounds as oxidizers and fuels for liquid and solid propellant components; inorganic polymers and lubricants. Address: 2111 Wilmington Dr, Midland, MI 48640.

GROVES, KERMIT, b. Mt. Ephraim, Ohio, June 22, 05; m. 39. PHYSICAL CHEMISTRY. A.B, Muskingum Col, 26; M.Sc, Ohio State Univ, 28, Ph.D. (phys. chem), 31. Asst. chemist, EXP. STA, WASH. STATE UNIV, 31-45, assoc. chemist, 46-67, AGR. CHEMIST, 66- AAAS; Am. Chem. Soc. Insecticide and physical chemistry. Address: Dept. of Agricultural Chemistry, Washington State University, Pullman WA 99163.

GROVES, MERTON L(ELAND), b. Flagler, Colo, Sept. 30, 14; m. 49; c. 1. BIOLOGICAL CHEMISTRY. A.B, Temple, 49. Asst. sci, bur. animal indust, U.S. DEPT. AGR, Colo, 39-40, jr. sci. aide, Wash, D.C, 41-42, AGR. RES. SERV, EAST. UTILIZATION RES. & DEVELOP. DIV, PHILA, 42-44, chemist, 44-66, BIOCHEMIST, 66- Am. Chem. Soc; Am. Soc. Biol. Chem. Protein chemistry; isolation and properties of milk proteins. Address: 525 Twickenham Rd, Glenside, PA 19118

GROVES, MORTON DAN PATRICK, b. Childress, Tex, Mar. 20, 40; m. 63. ELECTRONIC ENGINEERING, COMPUTER SCIENCE. B.A, Rice, 61, B.S.E.E, 62, M.S.E.E, 64, Ph.D.(elec. eng, comput. sci), 67. Instr. elec. sci, U.S. Naval Acad, 66-68; ENG. SPECIALIST & SECT. HEAD, GTE SYLVANIA SYSTS, 68- Consult, Electromagnetic Compatibility Anal. Ctr, Annapolis, Md, 66-67; asst. prof, Univ. Md, 67-68; pres, Sylvest Corp, 70- U.S.N.R, 62-, Lt. Comdr. Inst. Elec. & Electronics Eng; Asn. Comput.

Mach. Design and development of software and hardware digital systems; analysis of statistically-characterized signals in areas such as geophysics, biology and electronic warfare; management of research and development projects. Address: GTE Sylvania Systems, P.O. Box 205, Mountain View, CA 94040.

GROVES, RICHARD N, JR, b. Syracuse, N.Y, Sept. 11, 36; m; c. 2. APPLIED SCIENCE. Various assignments, artil. & ord. br, U.S. Army, 58-63, asst. prof. mech, U.S. Mil. Acad, 63-66, maintenance co. & forward support element comdr, 1st Air Cavalry Div, Vietnam, 66-67; mgr. eng. anal, Midwest Appl. Sci. Corp, 67-68, v.pres. & dir. eng, 68-69, pres, 69-71; DIR. AUDIO-VISUAL PROD. PLANNING, BELL & HOWELL CO, 71- Vis. lectr, sch. aeronaut, astronaut. & eng. sci, Purdue Univ, 68-71. U.S.A, 58-67, Maj; Army Commendation Medal, 65; Air Medal, 66; Bronze Star Medal, 67. Am. Inst. Aeronaut. & Astronaut; Am. Soc. Mech. Eng. Special electronics development, computer-aided-design; engineering prototype development; machine design; experimental research; engineering analysis. Address: Bell & Howell Co, 7100 McCormick Rd, Chicago, IL 60645.

GROVES, THOMAS H(OOPES), b. Madison, Wis, May 9, 32; m. 54; c. 4. PHYSICS. B.S, Antioch Col, 55; Univ. Mich, 56-57; M.S, Univ. Wis, 59; Ph.D.(physics), 62. Asst. prof. physics, Purdue Univ, 62-66; Univ. Notre Dame, 66-68; ASSOC. PHYSICIST, ARGONNE NAT. LAB, 68- Am. Phys. Soc. High energy nuclear physics. Address: Argonne National Laboratory, Bldg. 362, Argonne, IL 60439.

GROVES, T(OM) D(AVID) D(OUGLAS), b. New Westminster, B.C, May 13, 36; m. 58; c. 2. ANIMAL PHYSIOLOGY, BIOCHEMISTRY. B.S.A, British Columbia, 58, M.S.A, 60; Ph.D.(biochem), Purdue, 64. Res. assoc. milk protein biochem, Illinois, 63-64; asst. prof. animal physiol, Alberta, 64-66; BIOCHEM, UNIV. VICTORIA(B.C), 66-70, ASSOC. PROF, 70- Asst. to Dr. B. L. Larson, Univ. Ill, 63-64. AAAS; Am. Chem. Soc; N.Y. Acad. Sci. Animal growth and physiological aging; rumen physiology and biochemistry; lactation and milk protein synthesis; environmental physiology; metabolism and nutrition of Pacific salmon. Address: Dept. of Bacteriology & Biochemistry, University of Victoria, Victoria, B.C, Can.

GROVES, WARREN O(LLEY), b. Teheran, Iran, Nov. 8, 28; m. 51; c. 2. PHYSICAL CHEMISTRY. A.B, Lafayette Col, 48; Univ. Res. Found. fel, Ohio State, 53, Gen. Elec. Co. fel. & Ph.D.(phys. chem), 54. Instr. chem, N.Mex. Col. Agr. & Mech. Arts, 54-55; RES. CHEMIST, ELECTRONIC MAT. RES, MONSANTO CO, 55- AAAS; Am. Chem. Soc; Electrochem. Soc. Compound semiconductors; crystal growth; chemical vapor deposition; epitaxial growth. Address: Electronic Materials Research, Monsanto Co, 800 N. Lindbergh Blvd, St. Louis, MO 63166.

GROVES, WILLIAM E(RNEST), b. Flint, Mich, Sept. 8, 35; m. 62; c. 3. BIOCHEMISTRY, COMPUTER SCIENCE. B.S, South. Methodist Univ, 57; M.S, Univ. Ill, 59, Nat. Sci. Found. fel, summer 59, U.S. Pub. Health Serv. fel, 59-62, Ph.D.(biochem), 62. Asst. biochem, Univ. Ill, 57-62; res. biochemist, lab. biochem. genetics, Nat. Heart Inst, Nat. Insts. Health, 62-64; asst. prof. biochem, col. med, Univ. Tenn, 64-71; ASST. PROF. BIOCHEM. & CLIN. PATH, MED. UNIV. S.C, 71- Res. trainee, St. Jude Children's Res. Hosp, 64-67, asst. mem, 67-71; mem. grad. faculty, Memphis State Univ, 69-71. U.S.P.H.S, 62-64, Sr. Asst. Scientist. AAAS; Am. Chem. Soc; Am. Soc. Cell Biol; Endocrine Soc; Med. Electronics & Data Soc. Biological control mechanisms; structure and function of macromolecules; enzymology; computer application in biochemistry. Address: Dept. of Clinical Pathology, Medical University of South Carolina, 80 Barre St, Charleston, SC 29401.

GROVES, WILLIAM G, b. Newburyport, Mass, Jan. 27, 29; m. 53; c. 4. PHARMACOLOGY, PHARMACY. B.S, Mass. Col. Pharm, 57, M.S, 59. Jr. pharmacologist, SMITH KLINE & FRENCH LABS, 59-61, pharmacologist, 61-62, sr. pharmacologist, 62-65, group leader, pharmacol. sect, gen. therapeut. dept, 65-67, SR. INVESTR. PHARMACOL. RES, 67- Med.C, U.S.A, 51-53. Am. Pharmaceut. Asn; N.Y. Acad. Sci. Gastrointestinal pharmacology; antiulcer, antispasmodic and antisecretory drugs. Address: Smith Kline & French Labs, 1500 Spring Garden St, Philadelphia, PA 19101.

GROVES, WILLICE E(DGAR), b. Mexico City, Mex, Oct. 10, 09; U.S. citizen; m. 29; c. 5. PHYSICS, ELECTRONICS. A.B, Utah, 36, M.A, 37, B.S, 39; Ph.D.(elec. eng), California, Berkeley, 52. Chief engr, Radio Serv. Corp. Utah, 39-42; asst. signal off, Panama Canal Dept, U.S. Army, 42-44, chief appl. eng. div, Watson Labs, Army Air Forces, 45-46, eng. br, res. & develop. div, off. chief signal off, 46-48, gen. staff off, 51-54, commanding off, liaison group, Willow Run Res. Ctr, Michigan, 54-55, signal off, Army Forces, Far East & Eighth Army, Korea, 55-57, chief sci. & eng. div, combat surveillance agency, 57-60; asst. dir. & mgr, Proj. Michigan, Univ. Mich, 60-68; ASSOC. PROF. PHYSICS & MATH, CHURCH COL. HAWAII, 68- Consult, weapon systs. eval. div, Inst. Defense Anal, 61-62, res. & eng. div, 62. U.S.A, 42-60; Legion of Merit, 60. Sr. mem. Inst. Elec. & Electronics Eng. Microwave theory, radar, infrared and optics, as related to reconnaissance and surveillance. Address: Church College of Hawaii, Box 102, Laie, HI 96762.

GROW, GEORGE C(OPERNICUS), JR, b. Stafford, N.Y, June 10, 16; m. 42; c. 2. GEOLOGY. A.B, Lehigh, 38; Carnegie Inst. Tech. Jr. geologist, Peoples Natural Gas Co, 38-49, chief geologist, 49-50; CHIEF GEOLOGIST, EAST. AREA, TRANSCONTINENTAL GAS PIPE LINE CORP, 50- Geol. Soc. Am; Am. Asn. Petrol. Geol; Am. Inst. Mining, Metall. & Petrol. Eng. Surface, subsurface, oil and gas geology of the Appalachian area; underground gas storage. Address: Transcontinental Gas Pipe Line Corp, Gateway I-Suite 500, Newark, NJ 07102.

GROW, RICHARD W, b. Lynndyl, Utah, Oct. 31, 25; m. 47; c. 4. MICROWAVE PHYSICS, ELECTRONICS. B.S, Utah, 48, M.S, 49; Ph.D.(elec. eng), Stanford, 55. Electronic scientist, radio countermeasures br, Naval Res. Lab, 49-50, nucleonics div, 50-51; res. assoc, Stanford Electronics Lab, 53-58; assoc. res. prof. & asst. dir, high velocity lab, UNIV. UTAH, 58-59, assoc. res. prof. & dir, 59-62, DIR, MICROWAVE DEVICE & PHYS. ELECTRONICS LAB, 60-, PROF. ELEC. ENG, 66-, CHMN. DEPT, 65- Assoc. res. prof, microwave device & phys. electronics lab, Univ. Utah, 62-64, res. prof, 64-66. Part-time consult, Gen. Elec. Microwave Lab, 54-59; Litton Industs, 59, 68-; Eitel-McCullough, Inc, 59; Microwave Electronics Corp, 59-; Northrop Corp, 69-; Bur. Radiol. Health, 70- U.S.N.R, 44-46. Sr. mem. Inst. Elec. & Electronics Eng. Radar countermeasures; nuclear radiation detectors; traveling-wave tubes; backward-wave oscillators; attenuation in rocket exhausts; masers; lasers; microwave dosimeters; pollution measurements; solid-state plasmas. Address: Dept. of Electrical Engineering, 3054 Merrill Engineering Bldg, University of Utah, Salt Lake City, UT 84112.

GROZIER, MICHAEL LAWRENCE, b. Wilkes Barre, Pa, Oct. 8, 31; m. 58; c. 5. CLINICAL PHARMACOLOGY. B.S, Notre Dame, 53; M.D, Hahnemann Med. Col, 57. Intern, St. Agnes Hosp, Phila. Pa, 58, res. internal med, 58-59; flight surgeon, U.S. Navy Sch. Aviation Med, 59; physician, Warminster, Pa, 61-67; asst. clin. res. dir, SQUIBB INST. MED. RES, 67-69, ASSOC. CLIN. RES. DIR, 69-71, DIR. CLIN. RES. PSYCHOTROPIC & CARDIOVASC. DRUGS, 71- U.S.N.R, 59-61, Comdr. Am. Med. Asn; N.Y. Acad. Sci; Acad. Psychosom. Med. Clinical research in new drugs, primarily in psychopharmacology and oncology. Address: Squibb Institute for Medical Research, New Brunswick, NJ 08903.

GRUB, WALTER, b. Newark, N.J, Oct. 3, 20; m. 46; c. 4. AGRICULTURAL ENGINEERING. B.S, Rutgers, 49; M.S, Cornell, 53. Exten. engr, Cornell, 49-51, instr. agr. eng, 51-53; exten. engr, La. State, 53-54; assoc. agr. engr, Auburn Univ, 54-64, ASSOC. PROF. AGR. ENG, 64-66; TEX. TECH UNIV, 66- U.S.N, 42-43; U.S.M.C, 43-46, Capt. Am. Soc. Agr. Eng. Environmental chamber and control systems; design for physiological research; engineering aspects of environmental physiology; animal shelter engineering. Address: Dept. of Agricultural Engineering, Texas Tech University, Lubbock, TX 79409.

GRUBB, EUGENE L, b. Hummelstown, Pa, Feb. 2, 35. PHYSICAL CHEMISTRY. B.S, Franklin & Marshall Col, 57; M.A, Princeton, 59, McKay fel, 59-60, Ph.D.(chem), 61. Asst. chem, Princeton, 57-59, 60-61; res. assoc, Illinois, 61-62, instr, 62-63; asst. prof, N.Y. Univ, 63-65; RES. CHEMIST, EXP. STA, E.I. DU PONT DE NEMOURS & CO, 65- Summer res. chemist, Esso Res. Corp, 64. Asst. to Prof. R.L. Belford, Nat. Sci. Foun. grant, Illinois, 61-63. Am. Chem. Soc. Dielectric properties of organic compounds; spectroscopy of inorganic compounds by ultraviolet, visible, and infrared methods; functional group intensities in chemical analysis. Address: Experimental Station, E.I. du Pont de Nemours & Co, Wilmington, DE 19899.

GRUBB, HENRY M(ARION), b. Rockville, Ind, Sept. 21, 11; m. 36; c. 1. PHYSICAL CHEMISTRY. B.S, Purdue, 33, Ph.D.(phys. chem), 38. Chemist, res. dept, Am. Oil Co, 38-47, RES. SUPVR, 47-70; STANDARD OIL CO.(IND), 70- Am. Chem. Soc. Chemical analysis by physical instruments. Address: Standard Oil Research Center, Standard Oil Co.(Ind), Box 400, Naperville, IL 60540.

GRUBB, H(OMER) V(ERNON), b. Rockville, Ind, July 12, 16; m. 43; c. 1. CHEMICAL ENGINEERING. B.S, Purdue, 38, M.S, 41; Ph.D.(chem. eng), Ga. Inst. Tech, 51. Instr. CHEM. ENG, GA. INST. TECHNOL, 39-43, asst. prof, 43-52, assoc. prof, 52-58, PROF, 58-, DIR. SCH, 60-, acting dir. sch, 58-60. Am. Inst. Chem. Eng. Heat and mass transfer. Address: School of Chemical Engineering, Georgia Institute of Technology, Atlanta, GA 30332.

GRUBB, LOREN D(WIGHT), b. Phillipsburg, Kans, Oct. 15, 15; m. 40; c. 2. CHEMICAL ENGINEERING. B.S, Kans. State Col, 37, M.S, 38; M.S.(indust. mgt), Mass. Inst. Tech, 54. Process engr, Continental Oil Co, Okla, 39-41, 46; chief process engr, Cit-Con Oil Corp, La, 47-51; asst. ref. sup, Continental Oil Co, 51-54, ref. supt, 54-56; regional mgr, Petrol. Chem. Inc, 56-63; OPERS. MGR, CITIES SERV. OIL CO, 63- U.S.A, 42-45. Am. Chem. Soc; Am. Inst. Chem. Eng. Petroleum wax manufacturing; lube oil processing; organic inhibitor manufacture for lube oils; crude oil evaluation; chlorine manufacture; manufacture of butadiene, ammonia, ethylene, ethylene oxide and ethylene glycol. Address: Cities Service Oil Co, Lake Charles, LA 70604.

GRUBB, W(ILLARD) T(HOMAS), b. Springfield, Ill, Mar. 14, 23; m. 50; c. 1. PHYSICAL CHEMISTRY. S.B, Harvard, 46, Ph.D.(phys. chem), 49. RES. ASSOC. CHEM, RES. LAB, GEN. ELEC. CO, 49- U.S.N.R, 44-46. AAAS; Am. Chem. Soc; Electrochem. Soc; Am. Inst. Chem. Fuel cells; electrocatalysis; electrochemical sensors; ion-selective electrodes. Address: 2271 Sweetbrier Rd, Schenectady, NY 12309.

GRUBBS, EDWARD, b. Los Angeles, Calif, July 22, 34; m. 63; c. 2. PHYSICAL ORGANIC CHEMISTRY. A.B, Occidental Col, 56; Eastman Kodak fel, Mass. Inst. Tech, 58-59, Nat. Sci. Found. summer fel, 59, Ph.D.(org. chem), 59. Fel, Illinois, 60-61; asst. prof. CHEM, SAN DIEGO STATE COL, 61-65, assoc. prof, 65-68, PROF, 68- Summers, res. asst, chem. div, Lockheed Aircraft Co, 55 & res. labs, Union Oil Co, 56. Am. Chem. Soc. Kinetics of molecular rearrangements; stereochemistry; electrical interactions of substituents and reaction sites. Address: Dept. of Chemistry, San Diego State College, San Diego, CA 92115.

GRUBBS, FRANK E(PHRAIM), b. Montgomery, Ala, Sept. 2, 13; m. 37; c. 1. MATHEMATICAL STATISTICS, OPERATIONS RESEARCH. B.S, Auburn Univ, 34, M.S, 35; M.A, Michigan, 40, fel, 40-41, Ph.D.(math. statist), 49. From. instr. to asst. prof. eng. math, Auburn Univ, 34-40; chief surveillance lab, Ballistic Res. Labs, 41-53, weapon systs. lab, 53-62, dep. tech. dir, Ballistic Res. Labs, 62-68, CHIEF OPERS. RES. ANAL, U.S. ARMY ABERDEEN RES. & DEVELOP. CTR, 68- Supvr, Auburn Printing Co, 34-36; prof, exten. div, Univ. Del, 60-61, 62-63, 67-70; acting chmn, panel on tracking data anal, Nat. Acad. Sci, 64; chmn, Army Design of Exp. Conf. Exceptional civilian serv. award, U.S. Army, 63; Samuel S. Wilks Award, 64; Frank Wilcoxon & Jack Youden Technometrics Prizes, 69. Am. Soc. Qual. Control; Am. Soc. Test. & Mat; fel. Am. Statist. Asn; Inst. Math. Statist; Opers. Res. Soc. Am; Int. Statist. Inst; fel. Royal Statist. Soc. Ord. Dept, 41-46, Res, 34-41, 46-65, Col. Applied statistics; operations research; weapon systems evaluations; reliability; administration of research and development. Address: U.S. Army Aberdeen Research & Development Center, Aberdeen Proving Ground, MD 21005.

GRUBBS, ROBERT C(USTIS), b. Columbus, Ohio, May 3, 07. PHYSIOLOGY. B.A, Ohio State, 30, M.Sc, 33, M.D, 35. Intern, Starling-Loving Univ. Hosp, Ohio State, 35-36, Rockefeller asst. PHYSIOL, univ, 36-37; instr, med. sch, George Washington, 37-42, asst. prof, 42-46; asst. prof, COL. MED, OHIO STATE UNIV, 46-48, assoc. prof, 48-57, prof. & v.chmn. dept, 56-62, acting chmn, 62-64, PROF, 65-, ASST. PROF. MED, 70-, asst. prof, 50-54, asst. clin. prof, 55-70. Assoc. physician, George Washington Univ, 45-46. Am. Physiol. Soc; Am. Med. Asn. Respiratory metabolism; effects of adrenal cortical extraction; effects of alcohol; oxygen consumption studies in normal and diseased parakeets; tissue metabolism; effects of low dosage x-ray irradiation. Address: Dept. of Physiology, Ohio State University, 333 W. Tenth Ave, Columbus, OH 43210.

GRUBBS, ROBERT HOWARD, b. Calvert City, Ky, Feb. 27, 42; m. 67. ORGANIC & INORGANIC CHEMISTRY. B.S, Univ. Fla, 63, M.S, 65; Nat. Insts. Health trainee, Columbia Univ, 67-68, Ph.D.(chem), 68. Nat. Insts. Health fel, Stanford Univ, 68-69; ASST. PROF. ORGANOMETALLIC CHEM, MICH. STATE UNIV, 69- Am. Chem. Soc. Chemistry and reactions of small ring carbocycles and their metal complexes; catalytic reduction of olefins with polymer supported catalysts; mechanism and synthetic utility of the olefin dismutation reaction and the development of new synthetic reactions. Address: Dept. of Chemistry, Michigan State University, East Lansing, MI 48823.

GRUBE, GEORGE E(DWARD), b. Bareville, Pa, Apr. 12, 23; m. 45; c. 2. ZOOLOGY, ORNITHOLOGY. B.S, Muhlenberg Col, 46; M.S, Cornell, 49; Michigan; Pennsylvania; Franklin & Marshall Col; Elizabethtown Col. Instr. biol, Franklin & Marshall Col, 46-48; Gettysburg Col, 49-54; dist. rep, Quaker Oats Co, 54-56; ASSOC. PROF. biol, sci, Lock Haven State Col, 57-65; BIOL, DANA COL, 65- Nat. Sci. Found. participant inst. desert sci, Arizona State, 59, animal ecol. inst, Colorado, 60, Inst. Trop. Ecol. & Marine Biol, Univ. P.R, 66; mem. environ. adv. comt, U.S. Army Corps Eng; v.chmn, Qual. Environ. Coun. U.S.N.R, 42-46, Lt.(jg). Fel. AAAS; Soc. Animal Behavior; Ecol. Soc. Am; Wilson Ornith. Soc; Am. Ornith. Union. Ecology; ornithology. Address: Dept. of Biology, Dana College, Blair, NE 68008.

GRUBE, WILLIAM L(EWIS), b. Groveport, Ohio, May 24, 18; m. 43; c. 3. PHYSICS. B.Sc, Ohio State, 40; M.Sc, Cincinnati, 42. Supvr. physics solids sect, RES. LABS DIV, GEN. MOTORS CORP, 52-58, ASST. HEAD PHYSICS DEPT, 58- Am. Phys. Soc; Am. Soc. Metals; Electron Micros. Soc. Am. (treas, 51-53, pres, 56). Metal physics; electron microscopy. Address: 1094 Worthington, Birmingham, MI 48009.

GRUBER, ALAN R(ICHARD), b. Brooklyn, N.Y, Nov. 2, 27; m. 48; c. 3. ENGINEERING, ECONOMICS. S.B, Mass. Inst. Tech, 45, S.M, 46; Storrow fel, Harvard, 47-48, M.A, 48. Asst. mech. eng, Mass. Inst. Tech, 46-47, mem. staff, Lexington Proj, 48; res. engr, res. labs, Westinghouse Elec. Corp, 47, anal. engr, nuclear engine propulsion aircraft, 47; sr. engr, Nuclear Develop. Corp. Am, 48-51, eng. group leader, 51-53, dir, eng. div, 53-57; asst. chief engr. nuclear res, Marquardt Corp, 58-59, dir. nuclear systs. div, 59-61; exec. v.pres, Capital Tech. Industs, Inc, 61-64, dir. prod. econ, Boeing Co, 64-65; mgr. corp. planning, Electro-Optical Systs, Inc, Calif, 65-66, v.pres, 66-68; mgr. bus. dept. & venture anal. dept, Xerox Corp, N.Y, 68-69, dir. corp. planning, 69-70; V.PRES. CORP. DEVELOP, HEUBLEIN, INC, 70- Mem. panel naval vehicles, Nat. Acad. Sci, 61-63; consult, Aerospace Corp, 64. Am. Econ. Asn; Financial Anal. Fed; Nat. Planning Asn. Research administration; corporate finance and planning. Address: 41 Butler Rd, Scarsdale, NY 10583.

GRUBER, B(ERNARD) A, b. N.Y.C, Mar. 2, 25; m. 68; c. 2. ELECTROCHEMICAL ENGINEERING. B.S, Columbia, 45, M.S, 47. Res. chemist, Harshaw Chem. Co, 47-48; res. engr, Battelle Mem. Inst, 48-51; chief engr. rare metals & hydrides, Metal Hydrides, Inc, 51-54; proj. leader, Ethyl Corp, 54-56; res. mgr, MONSANTO CO, Mass, 55-69, Mo, 69-70, MGR. COMMERCIAL DEVELOP, 70- U.S.N.R, 43-46, Lt.(jg). Am. Chem. Soc; Am. Inst. Aeronaut. & Astronaut. Electrochemical energy conversion; high temperature materials; extractive metallurgy. Address: Monsanto Co, 800 N. Lindbergh Blvd, St. Louis, MO 63166.

GRUBER, BRUNO, b. Egg, Austria, May 4, 36; m. 63. PHYSICS. Ph.D.(physics), Vienna, 62. Scholar, PHYSICS, Dublin Inst. Adv. Studies, 63-64; res. asst, inst. theoret. & nuclear physics, Naples, 64-66; res. assoc, Duke, 66-67; asst. prof, ST. LOUIS UNIV, 67-69, ASSOC. PROF, 69- Group theory; applications to physics. Address: Dept. of Physics, St. Louis University, 221 N. Grand Blvd, St. Louis, MO 63103.

GRUBER, CARL L(AWRENCE), b. Chicago, Ill, Nov. 30, 38; m. 60; c. 2. ELECTRICAL ENGINEERING. B.S.E.E, Illinois, Urbana, 60, M.S, 61, Ph.D. (shock waves), 67. Asst. prof. ELEC. ENG, S.DAK. SCH. MINES & TECHNOL, 64-70, ASSOC. PROF, 70- Am. Soc. Eng. Ed. summer faculty fel, NASA-Goddard Space Flight Center, 67. AAAS; Am. Phys. Soc. Laser applications development in communications; geophysics-meteorology; gaseous electronics research instrumentation; gaseous laser development. Address: Dept. of Electrical Engineering, South Dakota School of Mines & Technology, Rapid City, SD 57701.

GRUBER, CHARLES M(ICHAEL), JR, b. Albany, N.Y, Sept. 15, 15; m. 40; c. 6. PHARMACOLOGY, THERAPEUTICS. B.A, Pennsylvania, 37, M.Sc, 53, D.Sc.(med), 54; M.D, Jefferson Med. Col, 41. Assoc. prof. pharmacol, Jefferson Med. Col, 49-53; asst. MED, SCH. MED, IND. UNIV, INDIANAPOLIS, 53-55, assoc, 55-61, asst. prof, 61-68, ASSOC. PROF, 68-; SR. CLIN. PHARMACOLOGIST, LILLY LAB. CLIN. RES, MARION COUNTY GEN. HOSP, 68-, res. physician, 53-68. Mem. vis. staff med. serv, Marion County Gen. Hosp, 53-; res. consult, New Castle State Hosp, 56- Dipl, Am. Bd. Internal Med. Med.C, U.S.A, 42-46, Capt. Am. Soc. Clin. Pharmacol. & Exp. Therapeut; Soc. Exp. Biol. & Med; Am. Med. Asn; fel. Am. Col. Physicians; N.Y. Acad. Sci; Am. Soc. Pharmacol. & Exp. Therapeut. Analgesics and methodology. Address: Lilly Lab. for Clinical Research, Marion County General Hospital, Indianapolis, IN 46202.

GRUBER, CHARLES W, b. Cincinnati, Ohio, Mar. 5, 10; m. 38; c. 3. AIR POLLUTION. M.E, Univ. Cincinnati, 32. Mgr. appl. eng, Consolidation Coal Co, 34-36; Bimel Co, 36-38; air pollution control & heating engr, City of Cincinnati, 38-45, 47-69; ASSOC. PROF. ENVIRON. ENG, UNIV. CINCINNATI, 69- Mgr. eng. dept, Floyd & Co, 46-47; spec. mem. consult, Nat. Adv. Comn. Community Air Pollution Control, U.S. Pub. Health Serv, 52-57, prin. investr, res. grant, 58-60, 64-67, dir. U.S. Pub. Health Serv-Nat. Ctr. Air Pollution Control prog, 67-69; consult, 69- Frank A. Chambers award, Air Control Asn, 64. Dipl, Am. Acad. Environ. Eng, 68. Ord.C, U.S.A, 41-45, Maj. Air Pollution Control Asn.(pres, 50-51); Am. Soc. Mech. Eng; Nat. Soc. Prof. Eng. Air pollution control in field of enforcement practices, source measurement, control and administration. Address: 6309 Parkman Pl, Cincinnati, OH 45213.

GRUBER, ELBERT E(GIDIUS), b. Cincinnati, Ohio, Sept. 11, 10; m. 34; c. 4. ORGANIC CHEMISTRY. B.S, Xavier, 32; M.S, Illinois, 34, Ph.D.(org. chem), 37. Asst. chem, Illinois, 35-37; res. chemist, B.F. Goodrich Co, 37-43, group leader, 43-46, res. supvr, res. center, 46-50; head plastics res, GEN. TIRE & RUBBER CO, 50-55, asst. dir. res, 55-62, DIR. RES. & DEVELOP, 62- Chmn. elastomers, Gordon Res. Conf, 57; chmn. bd, Weston Labs, Inc, 71-; rep, Indust. Res. Inst, Inc. Am. Chem. Soc; Soc. Plastics Eng. Rubber antioxidants; polymerization; plastics; vinyls; polyurethane foams and elastomers; stereoregulated polymers; solid propellants. Address: Corporate Research & Development, General Tire & Rubber Co, P.O. Box 951, Akron, OH 44309.

GRUBER, EUGENE E, JR, b. Pittsburgh, Pa, Apr. 13, 33; m. 56; c. 4. PHYSICAL METALLURGY. B.S, Pennsylvania, 59; M.S, Carnegie Inst. Technol, 62, Ph.D.(metall. eng), 64. ASSOC. METALLURGIST, ARGONNE NAT. LAB, 63- U.S.A, 53-55. Am. Soc. Metals; Am. Inst. Mining, Metall. & Petrol. Eng; Am. Phys. Soc. Pores in solids; radiation damage; surface diffusion; capillarity phenomena. Address: 8081 Tennessee Ave, Clarendon Hills, IL 60514.

GRUBER, GEORGE J, b. Diosjeno, Hungary, Mar. 20, 36; U.S. citizen; m. 63. ACOUSTICS. B.E.E, Catholic Univ, 59, M.S, 60, Ph.D.(physics), 62. Res. asst. phys. acoust, ultrasonic lab, Catholic Univ, 58-62; dir. ultrasonic lab, Chesapeake Instrument Corp, Md, 62-63; asst. res. prof. radiation acoust, Catholic Univ, 63-65; ASST. PROF. MECH. ENG, UNIV. TEX. AUSTIN, 65- Am. Mach. & Foundry Co. fel, 62-63. Acoust. Soc. Am; Marine Technol. Soc. Physical and underwater acoustics; electroacoustics; ultrasonics; mechanical radiation. Address: Dept. of Mechanical Engineering, University of Texas at Austin, Austin, TX 78712.

GRUBER, GERALD WILLIAM, b. LaCrosse, Wis, Sept. 12, 44; m. 69; c. 1. ORGANIC CHEMISTRY. B.S, Loras Col, 66; univ. fel, Case West. Reserve Univ, 66-68, Texaco fel, 68-69, Ph.D.(org. chem), 70. Nat. Cancer Inst. fel, Cornell Univ, 70-71; CHEMIST, PPG INDUSTS, INC, 71- Am. Chem. Soc. Organic synthesis; photochemistry mechanisms; reactive intermediates. Address: 113 Jamestown Manor, Lower Burrell, PA 15068.

GRUBER, H. THOMAS, b. Atlantic City, N.J, Nov. 20, 29; m. 52; c. 7. PHYSICS, MATHEMATICS. B.A, Ohio Wesleyan, 52; Lehigh, summer 51; Drexel Inst. Tech, 52-54; Ohio State, 56-57. Engr, indust. controls div, Minneapolis-Honeywell Regulator Co, 52-54; sr. physicist, eng. physics dept, BATTELLE MEM. INST, 56-68, TECH. ADMINR. & PROJ. MGR, BATTELLE DEVELOP. CORP, 68- Sig.C, U.S.A, 54-56. Reliability engineering; nondestructive testing; radio gauging; electronic component testing; experimental design; environmental testing; information research; nuclear radiation effects studies; electronic component vendor evaluation; technical editing and management; specification writing. Address: Battelle Development Corp, 505 King Ave, Columbus, OH 43201.

GRUBER, JACK, b. Brooklyn, N.Y, Apr. 18, 31; m. 64. MEDICAL MICROBIOLOGY, IMMUNOLOGY. B.S, Brooklyn Col, 54; Haggin scholar, Kentucky, 54-55, Ph.D.(microbiol), 63. Asst. microbiol, Kentucky, 55-61; res. bacteriologist, U.S. ARMY BIOL. LABS, 62-63, MICROBIOLOGIST, immunol. br, med. invest. div, med. sci. lab, Ft. Detrick, 63-70; VIRAL BIOL. BR, NAT. CANCER INST, NAT. INSTS. HEALTH, 70- AAAS; Am. Soc. Microbiol; N.Y. Acad. Sci; Tissue Culture Asn; Sci. Res. Soc. Am. Viral oncology; purification, concentration, inactivation, and immunogenicity of anthropod-borne viruses; efficacy of viral and bacterial vaccines; immunization procedures; serum antibody determinations using radioisotope-labeled antigens; streptococci and rheumatic fever. Address: Viral Biology Branch, National Cancer Institute, National Institutes of Health, Bethesda, MD 20014.

GRUBER, JOHN B, b. Hershey, Pa, Feb. 10, 35; m. 61; c. 1. CHEMICAL PHYSICS, SPECTROSCOPY. B.S, Haverford, Col, 57; U.S. Atomic Energy Cmn. fel, California, Berkeley, 57-61, Ph.D.(chem. physics), 61. Vis. lectr. atomic physics, Darmstadt Tech, 61-62; asst. prof. physics, California, Los Angeles, 62-66; assoc. prof, WASH. STATE UNIV, 66-71, PROF. CHEM. PHYSICS, 71-, ASSOC. DEAN, GRAD. SCH, 70-, asst. dean, 68-70. NATO fel, 61-62; summer prof, Hanford Labs, 64. Consult, U.S. Air Force Aerospace Corp, Calif, 62-; Douglas Aircraft Co, Inc, 63-; Lunar Explor. Sci. Apollo, NASA & N.Am. Aviation, Inc, 64- Am. Phys. Soc. Optical spectroscopy; magnetic properties of actinide ions in crystalline solids. Address: Dept. of Physics, Washington State University, Pullman, WA 99163.

GRUBER, PHILIP EDUARD, JR, b. Camden, N.J, Apr. 4, 33; m. 57; c. 1. PHYSICAL CHEMISTRY. B.S, Mass. Inst. Technol, 55, M.S, 56; D.Sc. (phys. chem), Univ. Munich, 62. Res. engr, Calif. Res. Corp, 56-57; lectr. physics & chem, Univ. Md, 62-64; SR. STAFF SCIENTIST, AVCO CORP, 64- Ord.C, U.S.A, 57-59, 1st Lt. Am. Chem. Soc. Kinetics of heterogenous catalysis and the influence of mass transport phenomena; chemical vapor deposition of refractory and ceramic materials and associated high temperature reaction kinetics. Address: 20 Hillside Rd, Reading, MA 01867.

GRUBER, SHELDON, b. New York, N.Y, Sept. 9, 30; m. 55; c. 2. PLASMA PHYSICS. B.S.E.E, Purdue, 52; Sc.D.(elec. eng), Mass. Inst. Tech, 58. Res. assoc. plasma physics, Mass. Inst. Tech, 59-61, asst. prof. elec. eng, 61-62; physicist, Atomic Energy Cmn. France, 62-63; res. staff plasma physics, Sperry Rand Res. Ctr, 63-67; ASSOC. PROF. ELEC. ENG, CASE WEST. RESERVE UNIV, 67- U.S.A.F, 58-59, 1st Lt. Am. Phys. Soc; Inst. Elec. & Electronics Eng. Radio astronomy; communications. Address: 2430 Demington Dr, Cleveland Heights, OH 44106.

GRUBER, WILHELM F, b. Bischofshofen, Austria, Aug. 2, 13; nat; m. 46. ORGANIC CHEMISTRY. Ph.D, Vienna, 39. Instr. chem, Vienna, 40-48, asst. prof, 48-51; RES. CHEMIST, Smith Kline & French Labs, 51-52; Res. Coun. B.C, Can, 52-54; Illinois, 54-56; ELASTOMERS DEPT, E.I. DU PONT DE NEMOURS & CO, INC, 56- Ger. Army, 39-40. Am. Chem. Soc; Chem. Inst. Can; Ger. Chem. Soc. Furocoumarins; furochromones and related aromatic derr; pyridine chemistry; sulfur compounds. Address: 2218 Old Orchard Rd, Wilmington, DE 19810.

GRUBIN, CARL, b. Brooklyn, N.Y, Aug. 14, 27; m. 55; c. 3. MECHANICS. Ph.D.(appl. mech), Polytech. Inst. Brooklyn, 52. Asst. prof. aeronaut. eng, Rensselaer Polytech, 52-53; engr, Douglas Aircraft Co, Inc, 53-56; mem. tech. staff, Space Tech. Labs, Inc, Thompson-Ramo-Wooldridge, Inc, 56-61; res. scientist, Northrop Corp, 61-63; mem. sr. tech. staff, Logicon, Inc, Calif, 63-67; SR. STAFF ENGR, AVIONICS DEPT, HUGHES AIRCRAFT CO, 67- Lectr, West Coast Univ, 58-67. Am. Soc. Eng. Educ; Am. Inst. Aeronaut. & Astronaut. Dynamics; guidance; control. Address: Hughes Aircraft Co, Avionics Dept, Bldg. 262, Canoga Park, CA 91304.

GRUBIN, HAROLD LEWIS, b. Brooklyn, N.Y, Mar. 1, 39; m. 61; c. 2. PHYSICS. B.S, Brooklyn Col, 60; Nat. Defense Ed. Act fel, Polytech. Inst. Brooklyn, 61-63, M.S, 62, univ. fel, 63-66, Ph.D.(physics), 67. Theoret. physicist, UNITED AIRCRAFT RES. LABS, 66-68, SR. THEORET. PHYSICIST, EAST HARTFORD, 68- Adj. asst. prof, Hartford Grad. Ctr, Rennselaer Polytech. Inst; adj. mem. faculty, Univ. Hartford. AAAS; Am. Phys. Soc; N.Y. Acad. Sci. Solid state theory, especially on conduction phenomena and device-related physics. Address: 13 Butternut Dr, Bloomfield, CT 06002.

GRUCHY, DAVID F(RANCIS), b. Guatemala City, Feb. 7, 16; U.S. citizen; m. 45; c. 4. ZOOLOGY. B.S, La. State, 39; M.S, Colo. State Col, 51; fel, Michigan, 51-55, Ph.D.(protozool), 55. Teacher, pub. sch, Miss, 39-40; Chamberlain-Hunt Acad, 46-49; asst, Colo. State Col, 49-51; pres, Chamberlain-Hunt Acad, 55-67; PROF. BIOL. & CHMN. DEPT, WILLIAM CAREY COL, 67- U.S.A, 41-46, Maj. Am. Soc. Mammal; Soc. Protozool. Biological productivity of mountain streams especially plankton and bottom organisms; distribution of mating types and varieties of the ciliate Tetrahymena and their axenic culturing. Address: Dept. of Biology, William Carey College, Hattiesburg, MS 39401.

GRUDUS, GABRIEL MICHAEL, b. Berwick, Pa, Oct. 1, 31; m. 55; c. 1. ORGANIC & POLYMER CHEMISTRY. B.S, Fairleigh Dickinson, 54; M.S, Purdue, 58, Ph.D.(org. chem), 60. Jr. technician food chem, Gen. Foods Corp, 54-55; asst. chem, Purdue, 55-56, instr, 56-60; polymer chemist, Monsanto Co, Mass, 60-63; supvr. chem. res, Inst. Pipe & Ceramics Co, 63-67, sr. supvr, CHEM. & MAT. RES, 67-68, MGR, INTERPACE CORP, 68- U.S.N.R, 50-58. Am. Chem. Soc; Nat. Asn. Corrosion Eng; Inst. Elec. & Electronics Eng. Synthetic organic chemistry; corrosion control. Address: Interpace Corp, 150 Main St, Wharton, NJ 07885.

GRUEMER, HANNS-DIETER, b. Bochum, Ger, May 25, 24; U.S. citizen. BIOCHEMISTRY, CLINICAL CHEMISTRY. M.D, Frankfurt, 49; Berlin, 51-53. Res. asst. biochem, Frankfurt, 49-50; sr. asst. clin. chem, Charite, Univ. Berlin, 50-54; res. asst. biochem, Univ. Frankfurt, 54-56; biochemist, Pineland Hosp, Pownal, Maine, 56-57, dir, 58-63; asst. prof. clin. chem, OHIO STATE UNIV, 63-67, biochem, 64-67, ASSOC. PROF. PATH. & PHYSIOL. CHEM, 67-, CHIEF DIV. CLIN. CHEM, 63- Instr. & res. asst, Boston Dispensary, Tufts Univ, 57-63. Cert, Am. Bd. Clin. Chem. Am. Chem. Soc; Am. Soc. Biol. Chem; Am. Asn. Clin. Chem. Metabolism and distribution of amino acids; clinical chemistry; mental retardation; clinical enzymology. Address: Dept. of Pathology, Ohio State University, 320 W. Tenth Ave, Columbus, OH 43210.

GRUEN, DIETER M(ARTIN), b. Ger, Nov. 21, 22; nat; m. 48; c. 3. PHYSICAL CHEMISTRY. B.S, Northwestern, 44, M.S, 47; Ph.D.(chem), Chicago, 51. Chemist, Manhattan proj, Oak Ridge, 44-46; assoc. chemist, ARGONNE NAT. LAB, 47-59, SR. CHEMIST, 60- Vis. scientist, Lawrence Radiation Lab, California, 54-55; U.S. del, Int. Conf. Peaceful Uses Atomic Energy, Switz, 58; chmn. Gordon Res. Conf. Fused Salts, 61; plenary lectr, Int. Conf. Co-ord. Chem, Sweden, 62. Student medal, Am. Inst. Chemists, 44. Am. Chem. Soc; Sci. Res. Soc. Am. Physical and inorganic chemistry; electronic structure; fused salt chemistry of transition elements; high temperature spectroscopy; fluorescence and energy transfer mechanisms. Address: 1324 59th St, Downers Grove, IL 60515.

GRUEN, FRED M(ARTIN), b. Nuernberg, Ger, Feb. 4, 15; m. 49; c. 2. CHEMISTRY. B.S, City Col. New York, 48; M.S, Ill. Inst. Tech, 50; Ph.D, Mich. State, 64. Res. chemist, Schering Corp, N.J, 50-51; from assoc. prof. to PROF. CHEM. & HEAD DEPT, OLIVET COL, 51- Summer instr, Buena Vista Col, 50. U.S.A, 43-46. Am. Chem. Soc. Applicability of Hammett equation to thiophenecarboxylic acids. Address: Dept. of Chemistry, Olivet College, Main St, Olivet, MI 49076.

GRUEN, HANS E(DMUND), b. Berlin, Ger, Oct. 20, 25; nat. PLANT PHYSIOLOGY. B.S, Brooklyn Col, 51; fel. & M.A, Harvard, 53, Am. Creosoting Co. fel, 54-55, U.S. Pub. Health Serv. fel, 55-56, Ph.D.(biol), 57. Asst. biol, Harvard, 51, mycol, Farlow Herbarium, 52, plant physiol, 53-54, Am. Cancer Soc. res. fel, 56-58, res. fel, Farlow Herbarium, 59-64; asst. prof. BIOL, UNIV. SASK, 64-66, ASSOC. PROF, 66- Lalor Found. fel, Tokyo, 63. AAAS; Am. Soc. Plant Physiol; Bot. Soc. Am; Mycol. Soc. Am. Physiology of fungi, especially growth, development and tropisms in reproductive structures of fungi. Address: Dept. of Biology, University of Saskatchewan, Saskatoon, Sask, Can.

GRUEN, H(AROLD), b. Brooklyn, N.Y, June 4, 31; m. 53; c. 3. ELECTRONIC ENGINEERING, COMMUNICATIONS. B.E.E, City Col. New York, 52; M.S, Pennsylvania, 57. Sect. head commun. eng, Philco Corp, 59-61, mgr, marine systs. group, 61-63, dir. advan. commun. lab, Pa, 63-68, PHILCO-FORD CORP, 68-69, GEN. MGR, SIERRA ELECTRONIC OPER, 69- Mem, Franklin Inst, 60- Sr. mem. Inst. Elec. & Electronics Eng. Theoretical communications; statistical detection methods; maximal information transfer; coding theory; sensory data processing, for minimum bandwidth. Address: Sierra Electronic Operation, Philco-Ford Corp, 3885 Bohannon Dr, Menlo Park, CA 94025.

GRUENBERG, ERNEST M(ATSNER), b. New York, N.Y, Dec. 2, 15; m. 43; c. 3. EPIDEMIOLOGY, PSYCHIATRY. B.A, Swarthmore Col, 37; M.D, Hopkins, 41; M.P.H, Yale, 49, Dr.P.H, 55. Intern, St. Elizabeth's Hosp, 41-42; res. PSYCHIAT, Bellevue Hosp, 46-48; clin. assoc. prof, Syracuse Univ, 52-55; assoc. clin. prof, COL. PHYSICIANS & SURGEONS, COLUMBIA UNIV, 58-61, PROF, 61-, LECTR. EPIDEMIOL, SCH. PUB. HEALTH, 53-; DIR, BR. B, PSYCHIAT. EPIDEMIOL. RES. UNIT, 68- Exec. dir, State Ment. Health Comn, 49-54; mem. tech. staff, Milbank Mem. Fund, 55-61, tech. bd, 61-68; lectr, sch. pub. health, Harvard, 59- U.S.A, 42-46, Capt. Fel. Am. Psychiat. Asn; Am. Orthopsychiat. Asn; Am. Pub. Health Asn; fel. N.Y. Acad. Med; N.Y. Acad. Sci; Am. Epidemiol. Soc. Epidemiology of mental disorders. Address: Branch B, Psychiatric Epidemiology Research Unit, Poughkeepsie, NY 12601.

GRUENBERG, HARRY, b. Vienna, Austria, Feb. 5, 21; U.S. citizen; m. 46; c. 3. ELECTRICAL ENGINEERING. B.A.Sc, British Columbia, 44; Ph.D, Calif. Inst. Tech, 49. Instr. elec. eng, Calif. Inst. Tech, 46-49; assoc. res. off, microwave sect, Nat. Res. Coun. Can, 49-56; assoc. prof. ELEC. ENG, SYRACUSE UNIV, 56-61, PROF, 61- Part-time lectr, McGill, 52-56; lectr, Gen. Elec. Corp, 63-; Fulbright res. scholar, Copenhagen, Denmark, 66-67. Sr. mem. Inst. Elec. & Electronics Eng. Electromagnetic theory; antennas and microwave components; ferrite applications at microwave frequencies; plasma physics. Address: 145 Tejah Ave, Syracuse, NY 12310.

GRUENBERG, LEONARD W(ILLIAM), b. Brooklyn, N.Y, Mar. 3, 38; m. 63; c. 1. THEORETICAL PHYSICS, ELECTRICAL ENGINEERING. A.B, Columbia, 58, Ph.D.(physics), 64. Mem. tech. staff, Bell Tel. Labs, 61-63; res. assoc. physics, faculty sci, Orsay, France, 63-64; ELEC. ENG, MASS. INST. TECHNOL, 64-65, ASST. PROF, 65- Vis. staff mem, Los Alamos Sci. Lab, 65; dir. res. & training, Mass. Dept. Pub. Health, 71-; vis. scientist, Nat. Magnet Lab, 71- AAAS; Am. Phys. Soc. Impurity scattering in superconductors; ferromagnetic superconductors; localized moments in metals; superfluidity in liquid helium. Address: Dept. of Electrical Engineering, NW14-3107, Massachusetts Institute of Technology, Cambridge, MA 02139.

GRUENBERGER, FRED J(OSEPH), b. Milwaukee, Wis, Sept. 24, 18; m. 42; c. 1. COMPUTER SCIENCE, MATHEMATICS. B.S, Wisconsin, 40, M.S, 48. Instr. comput, Wisconsin, 48-54; computer programmer, Gen. Elec. Co, 54-57; assoc. mathematician, Rand Corp, 57-67; PROF. ACCT, SAN FERNANDO VALLEY STATE COL, 67- Intel.C, U.S.A, 43-46. Asn. Comput. Mach. Empirical number theory; computing education. Address: Dept. of Accounting, San Fernando Valley State College, Northridge, CA 91324.

GRUENER, RAPHAEL P, b. Jerusalem, Israel, Mar. 7, 39; m. 63; c. 2. PHYSIOLOGY. B.A, California, Berkeley, 61; M.Sc, Illinois, Urbana, 63, Ph.D.(physiol), 66. NATO fel, 66-67; asst. res. physiologist, Scripps Inst, California, 67-68; ASST. PROF. PHYSIOL, COL. MED, UNIV. ARIZ, 68- Muscle physiology and biochemistry; excitation-contraction-coupling; basic mechanisms of myopathies; membrane excitability. Address: Dept. of Physiology, College of Medicine, University of Arizona, Tucson, AZ 85724.

GRUENEWALD, RUBEN, b. Mannheim, Ger, Apr. 16, 32; U.S. citizen; m. 69. IMMUNOLOGY, BACTERIOLOGY. B.S, Rutgers Univ, 54; M.S, L.I. Univ, 61; Ph.D.(bact), Univ. Conn, 68. Technician clin. bact, Montefiore Hosp, Bronx, N.Y, 55-56; res. technician endocrinol, Jewish Chronic Disease Hosp, Brooklyn, 58; technician & res. asst. clin. bact. & immunol, St. Frances Hosp, Jersey City, N.J, 58-61; Nat. Sci. Found. res. fel. biochem. & pharmacol, sch. med, Tufts Univ, 67-69; ASST. PROF. PATH, N.Y. MED. COL. & LAB. SUPVR. BACT, BIRD S. COLER HOSP, 69- U.S.A, 56-58. Am. Soc. Microbiol; Asn. Am. Med. Cols. Allergic ascites; host-parasite relationship of the Smith diffuse strain of Staphylococcus aureus in the peritoneal cavity of the mouse; experimental allergic encephalomyelitis as well as other delayed hypersensitivity phenomena. Address: Pathology Dept, Bird S. Coler Hospital, Welfare Island, NY 10017.

GRUENHAGEN, RICHARD D(ALE), b. Davenport, Iowa, June 9, 41; m. 63; c. 1. PLANT PHYSIOLOGY & BIOCHEMISTRY. B.S, Iowa State Univ, 63; M.S, N.Dak. State Univ, 67; Ph.D.(crop sci. & plant physiol), N.C. State Univ, 70. BIOLOGIST, CHEM. & PLASTICS, UNION CARBIDE CORP, 71- Weed Sci. Soc. Am; Am. Soc. Plant Physiol. Effects of weed competition on crop yields; biochemical and physiological modes of action and selectivity of herbicides. Address: Agricultural Research Station, Union Carbide Corp, P.O. Box 717, Clayton, NC 27520.

GRUENHAGEN, RICHARD H(AMILTON), b. Oshkosh, Wis, Mar. 24, 15; m. 40; c. 2. PLANT PATHOLOGY. B.S, Minnesota, 38; M.S, Wisconsin, 39, Ph.D. (plant path), 44. Field asst, U.S. Forest Serv, U.S. Dept. Agr, Wash, D.C, 38; asst. plant path, Wisconsin, 39-44, instr. bot, 46; plant pathologist, U.S. Dept. Agr, 44-46; group leader PLANT PATH, Dow Chem. Co, 46-58; PROF, VA. POLYTECH. INST. & STATE UNIV, 58- Am. Asn. Poison Control Centers. Diseases of ornamental plants; biochemical method of plant disease control; chemotherapy; nematodes; antibiotics; chemicals; drugs; pesticides; adult education. Address: Cooperative Extension Services, 206 Sandy Hall, Virginia Polytechnic Institute & State University, Blacksburg, VA 24061.

GRUENWALD, GEZA, b. Budapest, Hungary, Sept. 13, 19; m. 49; c. 1. POLYMER CHEMISTRY. M.S. & Ph.D.(org. chem), Tech. Univ, Berlin, 43. Consult. plastic & resins, Ger, 46-51; chemist, Farbwerke Hoechst AG, 51-57; develop. chemist, GEN. ELEC. CO, Mass, 57-60, chemist insulation res. & develop, 60-68, MGR, INSULATION NON-METALS LAB, 68- Am. Chem. Soc; Soc. Ger. Chem. Effect of plasticizers on polymer properties; mechanism of crystallization of high polymers; reactivity of epoxy curing agents; fracture mechanism on polymer products; cold forming of polymers with aromatic chain links. Address: 36 W. 34th St, Erie, PA 16508.

GRUENWALD, PETER, b. Schonwald, Czechoslovakia, March 12, 12; nat; m. 51. PATHOLOGY. M.D, Vienna, 36. Asst. histol. & embryol, Vienna, 36-38; res. fel, Cook County Grad. Sch. Med, 38-39; asst. anat, med. sch, Chicago, 39-40, instr, 40-42; asst. prof. histol, Middlesex, 42-44; res. fel, Mt. Sinai Hosp, New York, 44-45; asst. path, col. med, L.I. Col. Med, 45-46, instr, 46-48; asst. prof, State Univ. N.Y, 48-54; mem. staff, Veterans

Admin. Hosp, Brooklyn, 54-55; pathologist, Margaret Hague Maternity Hosp, Jersey City, N.J, 55-58; assoc. prof. obstet & pediat, sch. med, Hopkins, 58-60, asst. prof. path, 61-65, assoc. prof, 65-68; staff pathologist, Vet. Admin, Hosp, Phila, 68-70; ASSOC. PROF. PATH, Univ. Pa, 69-70; HAHNEMANN MED. COL, 70- Mem. staff, Hopkins Hosp, 58-; assoc. pathologist, Sinai Hosp, Baltimore, Md, 61-68. Am. Soc. Human Genetics; Am. Asn. Anat; Am. Asn. Path. & Bact; Am. Col. Obstet. & Gynec; Am. Acad. Pediat; N.Y. Acad. Sci. Congenital malformations; pathology of the fetus and newborn infants; placenta. Address: Dept. of Pathology, Hahnemann Medical College, Philadelphia, PA 19102.

GRUETT, MONTE D(EANE), b. Mobridge, S.Dak, June 2, 33; m. 57; c. 3. ORGANIC CHEMISTRY. B.S, Morningside Col, 55; M.S, Minnesota, 58; Ph.D.(org. chem), Rensselaer Polytech, 62. Asst. res. chemist, STERLING-WINTHROP RES. INST, 58-62, assoc. res. chemist, 62-68, RES. CHEMIST, 68- Am. Chem. Soc. Synthesis of new antibacterial, antihyperglycemic, antihypercholesteremic and anti-fertility agents; nitrogen heterocyclics. Address: Box 304A, Elliot Rd, East Greenbush, NY 12061.

GRUGER, EDWARD H, JR, b. Murfreesboro, Tenn, Jan. 21, 28; m. 52; c. 3. ORGANIC CHEMISTRY. B.S, Washington (Seattle), 53, M.S, 56; Ph.D.(agr. chem), Univ. Calif, Davis, 68. Chemist fishery tech, U.S. Fish & Wildlife Serv, 53-54; asst. gen. & org. chem, Washington (Seattle), 54-55; chemist org. chem, technol. lab, U.S. Bur. Commercial Fisheries, 55-59, proj. leader marine oil chem, 56-65, supvry. chemist, 59-62, RES. CHEMIST, 62-71; PIONEER RES. LAB, NAT. MARINE FISHERIES SERV, NAT. OCEANIC & ATMOSPHERIC ADMIN, 71- Res. assoc, agr. exp. sta, Univ. Calif, Davis, 65-68. U.S.N, 46-48. AAAS; Am. Chem. Soc; Am. Oil Chemists' Soc. Organic and biological chemistry of marine life, lipid chemistry, and chemistry of biological antioxidants. Address: Pioneer Research Lab, National Marine Fisheries Service, National Oceanic & Atmospheric Administration, 2725 Montlake Blvd. E, Seattle, WA 98102.

GRUHN, CHARLES R, b. Omaha, Nebr, Apr. 19, 34; m. 60; c. 2. PHYSICS, MATHEMATICS. B.A, Montana, 56; Ph.D.(nuclear physics), Washington (Seattle), 61. Res. assoc. NUCLEAR PHYSICS, Mass. Inst. Tech, 61-63; asst. prof, Boston, 63-64; asst. prof, MICH. STATE UNIV, 64-69, ASSOC. PROF, 69- Study of particle emission from a rotating nucleus; elastic alpha particle scattering in the mass forty region; study of the $Ca^{40}(\alpha,2\alpha)$ reaction; nuclear ground states using (p,d) and (p,t) reactions. Address: Dept. of Physics, Michigan State University, East Lansing, MI 48823.

GRUHN, JOHN GEORGE, b. Brooklyn, N.Y, Sept. 8, 18; m. 43; c. 4. PATHOLOGY. B.S, Manhattan Col, 41; M.D, L.I. Col. Med, 44. Res. fel. med, L.I. Col. Med, 47-48; res, King's Co, Hosp, 48-49; asst. pathologist & dir. blood bank, Montefiore Hosp, 51-55; instr. PATH, sch. med, Pittsburgh, 56-58, asst. prof, 58-60; assoc. prof, CHICAGO MED. SCH, 60-66, CLIN. PROF, 66-; DIR. LAB, SKOKIE VALLEY COMMUNITY HOSP, 66- Dir. path. lab, St. Joseph's Hosp, Pittsburgh, Pa, 55-60; pathologist, Mt. Sinai Hosp, Chicago, Ill, 60-64. Med.C, 45-47, Capt. Am. Asn. Path. & Bact; Col. Am. Path; Am. Soc. Clin. Path; Int. Acad. Path. Experimental renal disease. Address: Skokie Valley Community Hospital, 9600 Gross Point Rd, Skokie, IL 60077.

GRUHN, THOMAS ALBIN, b. Eureka, Calif, Aug. 18, 42; m. 65; c. 2. PHYSICAL INORGANIC CHEMISTRY. B.S, San Francisco, 64; Ph.D.(chem), California, Berkeley, 68. ASST. PROF. CHEM, UNIV. SAN FRANCISCO, 67- Am. Chem. Soc. Solution calorimetry; ligand substitution kinetics; synthesis of inorganic complexes. Address: Dept. of Chemistry, University of San Francisco, San Francsico, CA 94117.

GRULA, EDWARD A(LAN), b. Johnstown, Pa, July 27, 26; m. 51; c. 4. MICROBIOLOGY. B.S, Bethany Col.(W.Va), 50; summers, Colorado, 48-49, Rocky Mt. Biol. Labs, 50; M.S, Kentucky, 52, Eli Lilly & Co. fel, Purdue, 52-54, Ph.D.(bact), 56. Instr. bact, Purdue, 54-56; asst. prof, OKLA. STATE UNIV, 56-61, assoc. prof. MICROBIOL, 61-63, PROF, 63- Nat. Insts. Health res. career develop. award, 61-71. U.S.A.A.F, 44-46. Am. Soc. Microbiol. Bacterial nutrition and anatomy with reference to the bacterial cell wall, cell membrane and cell division. Address: Dept. of Microbiology, Oklahoma State University, Stillwater, OK 74074.

GRULA, MARY MUEDEKING, b. Minneapolis, Minn, Sept. 26, 20; m. 52; c. 4. MICROBIOLOGY. B.A, Minnesota, 41, Ph.D.(bact, chem), 46. Instr. bact, Kentucky, 46-47, asst. prof, 47-52; RES. ASSOC. MICROBIOL, OKLA. STATE UNIV, 59- Nat. Sci. Found. res. grant, 63-66, 69-71; Okla. State Univ. Res. Found. grant, 69-71. AAAS; Am. Soc. Microbiol; Brit. Soc. Gen. Microbiol. Microbial nutrition; cell division and its control in a species of Erwinia; physiology of certain Erwinia mutants. Address: Dept. of Microbiology, Oklahoma State University, Stillwater, OK 74074.

GRULEE, CLIFFORD G(ROSSELLE), JR, b. Chicago, Ill, June 9, 12; m. 43; c. 1. PEDIATRICS. B.A, Williams Col, 33; B.M, Northwestern, 37, M.D, 38; Harvard, 38-42; Rockefeller fel, Minnesota, 46-47. Asst. pediat, Harvard Med. Sch, 42; asst. prof, med. br, Texas, 47-48, assoc. prof, 48-49; sch. med, Tulane, 49-56, prof, 56-62, asst. dean, 52-58, assoc. dean, 58-62, dir, div. grad. med, 50-62; PROF. PEDIAT. & DEAN, SCH. MED, UNIV. CINCINNATI, CHMN. DIRECTING MED. STAFF, CINCINNATI GEN. HOSP. & CHRISTIAN R. HOLMES HOSP; CHMN. DEAN'S COMT, CINCINNATI VET. ADMIN. HOSP, 63- Med. dir, Stewart Convalescent Home for Children, 47-49; sr. vis. physician, Charity Hosp. New Orleans; mem. prev. med. & dent. rev. comt, Nat. Insts. Health; physician consult, Vet. Admin. U.S.A.A.F, 42-45. Am. Pediat. Soc; Soc. Pediat. Res; Am. Med. Asn; fel. Am. Acad. Pediat; Asn. Am. Med. Cols. Poliomyelitis and other infectious diseases; thallium poisoning. Address: Office of the Dean, University of Cincinnati College of Medicine, Eden & Bethesda Aves, Cincinnati, OH 45219.

GRUM, FRANC, b. Ljubljana, Yugoslavia, May 21, 22; U.S. citizen; m. 45; c. 3. OPTICS, SOLID STATE PHYSICS. B.A, Ljubljana, 42; B.S, Rochester, 58, M.S, 62. Res. physicist, EASTMAN KODAK CO, 58-62, sr. res. physicist, 62-64, RES. ASSOC, 64-, HEAD SPECTROPHOTOM. LAB, 71- Mem. U.S. Del, Int. Comn. Illum. Cert. merit, Dir. Int. Biography, 70. Royal Yugoslavian Army, Capt. Inter-Soc. Color Coun; fel. Optical Soc. Am; Soc. Photog. Sci. & Eng; N.Y. Acad. Sci. Spectroscopy; radiometry; application of data processing to optical and spectroscopic research; colorimetry of fluorescent materials. Address: Research Labs, Eastman Kodak Co. Rochester, NY 14650.

GRUMBACH, LEONARD, b. Brooklyn, N.Y, July 24, 14; m. 41; c. 4. PHYSIOLOGY. A.B, Cornell, 34, A.M, 35, Schuyler fel, 35-38, Ph.D.(physiol), 39. Teaching fel. physiol, col. dent, N.Y. Univ, 40-41, instr. pharmacol, 46-47; prof. physiol, Des Moines Still Col. Osteop, 47-52; assoc. mem, Sterling-Winthrop Res. Inst. 52-58, mem, 58-61; ASSOC. PROF. PHYSIOL, ALBANY MED. COL, 61- U.S.A, 41-46, Res, 46-64. AAAS; Am. Physiol. Soc. Pharmacology of analgesics; physiology of pain. Address: Dept. of Physiology, Albany Medical College, Albany, NY 12208.

GRUMBACH, MELVIN M(ALCOLM), b. New York, N.Y, Dec. 21, 25; m. 51; c. 3. MEDICINE, PEDIATRICS. M.D, Columbia, 48. Nat. Found. Infantile Paralysis fel. & asst. pediat, sch. med, Hopkins, 53-55; vis. fel, Oak Ridge Inst. Nuclear Studies, 52; instr. PEDIAT, col. physicians & surgeons, Columbia, 55-56, assoc, 56-57, from asst. prof. to assoc. prof, 57-65; PROF. & CHMN. DEPT, SCH. MED, UNIV. CALIF, SAN FRANCISCO, 65-; DIR. PEDIAT. SERV, UNIV. HOSPS, 65- From asst. attend. to assoc. attend. pediatrician, Babies & Presby. Hosps, New York, 55-65; Health Res. Coun. New York career scientist award, 60-65; mem, human embryol. & develop. study sect, Nat. Insts. Health, 62-66, endocrine study sect, 67-71; pediat. exam. comt, Nat. Bd. Exam, 64-68; adv. bd, Inst. Human Develop, Univ. Calif, Berkeley, 66-; adv. comt, Endocrinol. Index, Nat. Libr. Med, 66-; sci. adv. comt, Nat. Sci. Found, 69-; bd. sci. counselors, Nat. Inst. Child Health & Human Develop, 71-; consult, Letterman Gen. Hosp, San Francisco; U.S. Naval Hosp, Oakland. Joseph Mather Smith Prize, Columbia Univ, 62, Bicentennial Silver Medal, Col. Physicians & Surgeons, 67. U.S.A.F, 51-53, Capt. AAAS; Am. Soc. Clin. Invest; Soc. Pediat. Res; Harvey Soc; Endocrine Soc; Am. Pediat. Soc; Soc. Human Genetics; fel. Am. Acad. Pediat. (Borden Award, 71); fel. N.Y. Acad. Sci; Perinatal Res. Soc; Teratology Soc; Europ. Soc. Pediat. Endocrinol. Metabolic and endocrine disorders of childhood and adolescence; abnormalities of sex differentiation; effects of hormones on growth and maturation; genetic and chromosome aberrations. Address: Dept. of Pediatrics, University of California School of Medicine, San Francisco Medical Center, San Francisco, CA 94122.

GRUMBACH, ROBERT S(TEPHEN), b. Morgantown, W.Va, Dec. 3, 25; m. 51; c. 2. ELECTRICAL ENGINEERING. B.S.E.E, Case, 47; M.S, West Virginia, 51. Distribution engr, Monongahela Power Co, 47; instr. elec. eng, West Virginia, 47-53; elec. engr, elec. utility eng. sect, Westinghouse Elec. Corp, 53-57; prof. ELEC. ENG, Inst. Tech. Bandung, Indonesia, 57-61, head dept, 60-61; ASSOC. PROF, UNIV. AKRON, 61- U.S.N.R, Lt. Assoc. mem. Inst. Elec. & Electronics Eng. Electric utility engineering; generation; transmission and distribution of electrical energy, especially lighting protection and relaying. Address: Dept. of Electrical Engineering, University of Akron, Akron, OH 44304.

GRUMBINE, THEODORE JOSEPH, b. Baltimore, Md, Jan. 18, 27; m. 53; c. 3. PHYSICAL & ORGANIC CHEMISTRY. B.S, Loyola Col.(Md), 50; Hopkins, 51-52. Chemist RES. & DEVELOP, HANLINE BROS, INC, 50-60, chief chemist, 61-66, TECH. DIR, 66- U.S.A, 45-47. Fedn. Socs. Paint Technol. Protective coatings; dispersion of inorganic and organic pigments with various synthetic and natural polymers to obtain particular properties in the finish coating. Address: Hanline Bros. Inc, 1400 Warner St, Baltimore, MD 21230.

GRUMBLES, JIM B(OB), b. San Saba, Tex, Aug. 26, 28; m. 52; c. 3. RANGE MANAGEMENT, ECOLOGY. B.S, Southwest Tex. State Col, 58; M.S, Texas A&M, 61, Welder Wildlife Found. fel, 59-62, Ph.D.(range mgt), 64. Instr, jr. high sch, Tex, 58; asst. range mgt, Texas A&M, 58-59; asst. prof, Utah State Univ, 62-67, assoc. prof, 67-68; REGIONAL TECH. SPECIALIST, FIELD RES. & DEVELOP. HERBICIDES, DOW CHEM. CO, 68- U.S.A.F, 50-54, S/Sgt. Am. Soc. Range Mgt. Wildlife management; grazing relationship of steers and white-tailed deer in south Texas; grazing management of seeded introduced grasses; studies involving both grazing by livestock and clipping to simulate grazing. Address: Dow Chemical Co, 31 Briercroft Office Park, Lubbock, TX 79411.

GRUMER, EUGENE LAWRENCE, b. New York, N.Y, May 25, 40; m. 64; c. 2. CHEMICAL ENGINEERING, FUEL TECHNOLOGY. B.S, Pa. State, 61, B.S, 62; S.M, Mass. Inst. Tech, 64, Chem.E, 65. Engr, Celanese Corp, 65-69, sr. engr, 69-70; ECON. ENGR, AMERADA HESS CORP, 71- Am. Chem. Soc; Nat. Soc. Prof. Eng; Am. Inst. Chem. Eng; Am. Asn. Cost Eng. Planning, economic evaluation, fuels blending, budgeting and ranking of research, development and major ventures, particularly for the petrochemical process industry; combustion; explosions; fuels; safety. Address: Engineering Dept, Amerada Hess Corp, Kingshill, P.O. Box 127, St. Croix, VI 00850.

GRUMER, JOSEPH, b. New York, N.Y, Mar. 18, 18; m. 39; c. 3. PHYSICAL CHEMISTRY. B.S, City Col. New York, 37; M.S, N.Y. Univ, 41. Anal. chemist, Molnar Labs, N.Y, 37-39; org. chemist, Fine Orgs, Inc, 39-41; gas analyst, U.S. BUR. MINES, 41-44, phys. chemist, 44-53, from acting chief to chief flame res. sect, 53-59, PROJ. COORD. FLAME DYNAMICS, 59- Am. Chem. Soc; Am. Gas Asn; Air Pollution Control Asn. Analytical procedures; organic synthesis; flame stability; carbon formation and burning velocity; kinetics; air entrainment; combustion characteristics and exchangeability of fuels on gas burners; liquid pool burning; uncontrolled fires; air pollution by flames; dust explosions. Address: U.S. Bureau of Mines, 4800 Forbes Ave, Pittsburgh, PA 15213.

GRUMET, ALEX, b. New York, N.Y, Sept. 1, 19; m. 46; c. 2. ELECTRONICS, PHYSICS. B.S, City Col. New York, 42; M.E.E, Polytech. Inst. Brooklyn, 58. Jr. engr, Signal Corps, Gen. Develop. Lab, Ft. Monmouth, N.J, 42-43; develop. engr, Telicon Corp, N.Y, 46-47; TV instr, New York Tech. Inst, N.J, 47-48; design engr, Pilot Radio Corp, N.Y, 48-49; sr. proj. engr, Edo Corp, 50-56; prog. scientist, res. div, Repub. Aviation Corp, 56-65; RES. ENGR, ELECTRONICS SYST. RES, GRUMMAN AEROSPACE CORP, 65- U.S.M.C.R, 43-46, Capt. Sr. mem. Inst. Elec. & Electronics Eng; Optical Soc. Am. Investigation of nuclear magnetic resonance phenomena in liquids for application as a gyroscopic inertial sensing element; statistical communication theory for improving long range communication and signal detection; pattern recognition as applied to real-time aerial reconnaissance; statistical communication theory; optical spatial filtering. Address: Electronics System Research, Grumman Aerospace Corp, Plant 35, Bethpage, NY 11714.

GRUMMER, R(OBERT) H(ENRY), b. Luzerne, Iowa, June 27, 16; m. 40; c. 2. ANIMAL HUSBANDRY. B.S, Iowa State, 39; M.S, Wisconsin, 43, Ph.D.(biochem, animal husb), 46. Instr. MEAT & ANIMAL SCI, UNIV. WIS, MADISON; 43-46, asst. prof, 46-49, assoc. prof, 49-53, PROF, 53-, chmn. dept, 54-63. Am. Soc. Animal Sci. Nutrition; genetics; physiology of reproduction and parasitology of swine. Address: Dept. of Meat & Animal Science, University of Wisconsin, Madison, WI 53706.

GRUMMITT, OLIVER J(OSEPH), b. Cleveland, Ohio, Jan. 16, 10. ORGANIC CHEMISTRY. A.B, Oberlin Col, 32; M.A, Western Reserve, 34, Ph.D.(org. chem), 36. Asst. org. chem, Western Reserve, 32-36; fel, Cornell, 36-38; instr. CHEM, CASE WEST. RESERVE UNIV, 38-42, asst. prof, 42-48, assoc. prof, 48-52, PROF, 53-, chmn. dept, 58-62. Consult, Sherwin-Williams Co, 39- With U.S. Dept. Commerce, Ger, 46. Fel. AAAS; Am. Chem. Soc; Am. Oil Chem. Soc. Organo-boron compounds; aluminum chloride catalysis; Diels-Alder reactions; sulfones; glycerides; drying oils. Address: 15949 Cleviden Rd, East Cleveland, OH 44112.

GRUMMITT, W(ILLIAM) E(DMUND), b. Edmonton, Alta, Aug. 20, 17; m. 43; c. 2. RADIOCHEMISTRY. B.Sc, Alberta, 39, M.Sc, 41; Ph.D.(chem), McGill, 43. Assoc. res. officer radiochem, Nat. Res. Coun. Can, 43-54; res. officer, ATOMIC ENERGY CAN, LTD, 54-61, SR. SCIENTIST ENVIRON. RES, CHALK RIVER NUCLEAR LABS, 61- Mem, UN Sci. Comt. Effects of Atomic Radiations, 56- Fel. Chem. Inst. Can. Measurement of primary and cumulative fissions product yields in thermal fission of uranium and plutonium; assessment of extent of environmental contamination from operation of reactors and radioactive fallout from nuclear weapons testing. Address: Chalk River Nuclear Labs, Atomic Energy of Canada Ltd, Chalk River, Ont, Can.

GRUN, JOHN, b. Rumania, Jan. 14, 23; nat; m. 49; c. 3. ZOOLOGY, PARASITOLOGY. B.S, Brooklyn Col, 49; Ph.D.(zool), Rutgers, 59. Asst. zool, RUTGERS UNIV, 51, parasitol, bur. biol. res, 52-59, asst. prof. poultry path, 59-64, assoc. prof. parasitol, 64-69, PROF. ANIMAL PARASITOL, 69- U.S.A, 42-46, Res, 46-52, 1st Lt. Am. Soc. Parasitol. Experimental leishmaniasis; helminthology related to poultry; virology; immunology; Newcastle disease of poultry; development of vaccines; parental immunity related to diseases of poultry. Address: 602 E. Lincoln Ave, Cranford, NJ 07016.

GRUN, PAUL, b. New York, N.Y, May 14, 23; m; c. 2. CYTOLOGY, CYTOGENETICS. B.A, North Carolina, 44; Ph.D.(plant breeding), Cornell, 49. Asst, Cornell, 45-49; plant biologist, Carnegie Inst, 49-54; asst. prof. genetics, PA STATE UNIV, 54-60, assoc. prof, 60-63, PROF. CYTOL. & CYTOGENETICS, 64- Res. fel, inst. cell res. & genetics, Karolinska Inst, Sweden, 53-54; Nat. Insts. Health spec. fel, California, Los Angeles, 61-62. Genetics Soc. Am; Soc. Study Evolution; Bot. Soc. Am; Am. Cell Biol. Cytogenetics of Solanum; cytoplasmic factors in plant evolution. Address: Dept. of Biology, 202 Buckhout Lab, Pennsylvania State University, University Park, PA 16802.

GRUNBAUM, BENJAMIN W(OLF), b. Warsaw, Poland, June 18, 17; nat; m. 52; c. 3. BIOCHEMISTRY. B.A, California, 50, M.A, 52, Ph.D.(biochem), 54, M.Crim, 64. Jr. res. biochemist, California, 54; res. assoc. physiol. chem, Minnesota, 55-57; asst. res. pathologist, med. ctr, California, San Francisco, 57-60, assoc. res. biochemist, cancer res. inst, 60-62; RES. BIOCHEMIST, WHITE MT. RES. STA, UNIV. CALIF, BERKELEY, 62- Nat. Sci. Found. res. fel, Carlsberg Lab, Copenhagen, 57-58; vis. prof, med. sch, Hebrew Univ, Jerusalem, 71-72. Res. consult, microanal. lab, inst. med. res, Univ. Uppsala, 54; consult. chemist, Dist. Attorney's Off, Santa Clara, Calif, 55. AAAS; Am. Chem. Soc; fel. Am. Inst. Chem. Development of equipment and microanalytical methodology for physiological and cytochemical studies. Address: White Mountain Research Station, University of California, 2251 College, Berkeley, CA 94720.

GRUNBAUM, BRANKO, b. Osijek, Yugoslavia, Oct. 2, 29; m. 54; c. 2. GEOMETRY. M.Sc, Hebrew Univ. Jerusalem, 54, Ph.D.(math), 58. Mem, Inst. Advan. Study, 1958-60; vis. asst. prof. MATH, Univ. Wash, 60-61; asst. prof, Hebrew Univ. Jerusalem, 61-64, assoc. prof, 64-65; vis. prof, Mich. State Univ, 65-66; prof, Univ. Wash, 66-69; vis. prof, Mich. State Univ, 69-70; PROF, UNIV. WASH, 70- Am. Math. Soc; Am. Math. Asn. Convexity; combinatorial geometry; graph theory. Address: Dept. of Mathematics, University of Washington, Seattle, WA 98105.

GRUNBERG, E(MANUEL), b. Everett, Mass, July 9, 22; m. 46; c. 2. CHEMOTHERAPY. B.A, Alabama, 43; Washington (St. Louis), 44; Ph.D.(bact), Yale, 46; Harvard, 48. Bacteriologist, J.E. Seagram & Sons, Ky, 46; sr. bacteriologist, DEPT. CHEMOTHER, HOFFMANN-LA ROCHE INC, 46-57, sr. scientist, 57-59, assoc. dir. dept, 59-60, DIR. DEPT, 60-, DIAG. RES, 70- Chief div. mycol, dept. dermat, Dept. Health, Newark, 51-67; guest lectr, div. postgrad. med, Seton Hall Col. Med. & Dent, 59-63. Dipl, Am. Bd. Med. Microbiol. U.S.A, 42-45. AAAS; Am. Soc. Microbiol; Soc. Exp. Biol. & Med; Sci. Res. Soc. Am; fel. N.Y. Acad. Sci; fel. Am. Acad. Microbiol. Chemotherapeutic and diagnostic research. Address: Dept. of Chemotherapy, Hoffmann-La Roche Inc, Roche Park, Nutley, NJ 07110.

GRUND, DARRYL W, b. Seattle, Wash, Feb. 23, 38; m. 65. MYCOLOGY. B.A, Washington (Seattle), 60, M.S, 62, Ph.D.(bot), 65. ASST. PROF. BIOL, ACADIA UNIV, 65- Agaricology; morphology; chemo-taxonomy. Address: Dept. of Biology, Acadia University, Wolfville, N.S, Can.

GRUND, JOHN E(MERY), b. Monmouth, Ore, June 16, 31; m. 57; c. 3. NUCLEAR ENGINEERING. B.S, Oregon State, 53; M.S, N.C. State Col, 57. Physicist-engr, atomic energy div, Phillips Petrol. Co, 57-61, group leader heavy water test group, 61-63, sect. chief spert I & IV exp. sect, Idaho, 63-68; nuclear engr, PORTLAND GEN. ELEC. CO, 68-70, CHIEF NUCLEAR ENGR, 70- U.S.A.F, 51-54; Nat. Guard, 54-57, 2nd Lt. Am. Nuclear Soc; Am. Soc. Metals. Nuclear reactor excursion analysis; reactor safety investigations; transient thermal and nuclear radiation effects on materials. Address: Portland General Electric Co, 621 S.W. Alder St, Portland, OR 97205.

GRUNDBACHER, FREDERICK JOHN, b. Switz, Aug. 3, 26; U.S. citizen; m. 66; c. 2. HUMAN GENETICS. Dipl, Swiss Fed. Inst. Tech, 53; Ph.D. (genetics), California, 60. Res. geneticist & asst. specialist, California, 60-61; Nat. Insts. Health fels. human genetics, med. sch, Univ. Mich, Ann Arbor, 61-65; asst. prof. biol. & genetics, MED. COL. VA, COMMONWEALTH UNIV, 65-69, ASSOC. PROF. GENETICS, 69- Grant, Nat. Insts. Health. Swiss Army. AAAS; Am. Soc. Human Genetics; Genetics Soc. Am. Immunogenetics of man; quantitative genetics of immunoglobulin and isoantibody levels; variation in erythrocyte and saliva antigens; etiology of ABO hemolytic disease of the newborn; study of a predisposition to allergies. Address: Dept. of Genetics, Medical College of Virginia, Virginia Commonwealth University, Richmond, VA 23219.

GRUNDEN, LEE R(OBERT), b. Bend, Ore, Nov. 4, 39; m. 68; c. 2. NEUROPHARMACOLOGY, BEHAVIORAL PHARMACOLOGY. B.S, Oregon State, 60; U.S. Pub. Health Serv, Univ. & Nat. Sci. Found. fels, California, San Francisco, 61-67, Ph.D.(pharmacol), 67. Clin. chemist, Vet. Admin. Hosp, Palo Alto, Calif, 61; U.S. Pub. Health Serv. fel. neuropharmacol, London, 67-68; assoc. prof. pharmacol, Univ. Ariz, 69-70; SR. PHARMACOLOGIST, SMITH KLINE & FRENCH LABS, 70- AAAS; N.Y. Acad. Sci. Determining the role of catecholamines in the brain; behavioral pharmacology related to the action of drugs on the central nervous system; brainstem mechanisms regulating food intake. Address: Research & Development Division, Smith Kline & French Labs, 1500 Spring Garden St, Philadelphia, PA 19101.

GRUNDER, ALLAN ANGUS, b. Kincardine, Ont, Mar. 13, 35. ANIMAL & BIOCHEMICAL GENETICS. B.S.A, Ont. Agr. Col, 58; M.Sc, Univ. Alta, 61; Ph.D.(genetics), Univ. Calif, 66. Drainage surveyor, Ont. Dept. Agr, 58; salesman, Ogilvy Five Roses Co, 58-59; RES. SCIENTIST GENETICS, ANIMAL RES. INST, CENT. EXP. FARM, CAN. DEPT. AGR, 66- AAAS; Genetics Soc. Am; Genetics Soc. Can; Can. Soc. Animal Prod. Investigation of chicken esterase genetic variants and the association of these variants with production; investigation of methods of breeding chickens in an effort to produce chickens which will be resistant to Marek's Disease. Address: Animal Research Institute, Central Experimental Farm, Canada Department of Agriculture, Ottawa, Ont. K1A 0C6, Can.

GRUNDER, HERMANN AUGUST, b. Basel, Switz, Dec. 4, 31; m. 52; c. 3. PHYSICS, ENGINEERING. B.S, Karlsruhe Tech. Univ, 58; Dr. Phil. II, Univ. Basel, 68. Engr, LAWRENCE BERKELEY LAB, UNIV. CALIF, 59-64, PHYSICIST, 68- AAAS; Am. Phys. Soc; Europ. Phys. Soc. Accelerator design and development. Address: 758 Charlton St, Pleasant Hill, CA 94523.

GRUNDFEST, HARRY, b. Minsk, Russia, Jan. 10, 04; U.S. citizen; m. 26; c. 1. PHYSIOLOGY. A.B, Columbia, 25, M.A, 26, univ. fel, 27-28, Gottsberger fel, 28-29, Nat. Res. Coun. fel, 29-30, Ph.D.(physiol), 30. Asst. zool. & biophys, Columbia, 25-27; Johnson Found. fel, Pennsylvania, 30-31; instr. zool, Swarthmore Col, 32-33; asst. physiol, med. col, Cornell, 33-35; asst. neurophysiol, Rockefeller Inst, 35-43; sr. physiologist, Signal Corps, U.S. Army, Ft. Monmouth, N.J, 45; res. assoc. wound ballistics, Princeton, 45; res. assoc. NEUROL, COL. PHYSICIANS & SURG, COLUMBIA UNIV, 45-47, asst. prof, 47-49, assoc. prof, 49-60, PROF, 60- Civilian with Off. Sci. Res. & Develop, 44. AAAS; Am. Physiol. Soc; Harvey Soc; Soc. Exp. Biol. & Med; Soc. Gen. Physiol; Am. Neurol. Asn; Asn. Res. Nerv. & Ment. Diseases; Inst. Elec. & Electronics Eng; N.Y. Acad. Med; N.Y. Acad. Sci. Scotopic and chromatic vision in fish; electrical excitation of single nerve and muscle; electrophysiology of nerve and allied problems. Address: Dept. of Neurology, Columbia University College of Physicians & Surgeons, New York, NY 10032.

GRUNDMAN, F(RANK) G, b. Faribault, Minn, Sept. 8, 24. CHEMICAL ENGINEERING. B.Ch.E, Minnesota, 49. Process engr. paper converting, Marathon Corp, Wis, 49-52, sr. process engr, 52-55, group leader converting res, Marathon Div, AM. CAN CO, 55-63, sr. group leader, 63-65, supvr. flexible packaging converting, paper prod. res, 65-67, orgn. specialist, 67-68, tech. & commercial adv, INT. OPERS, Bristol, Eng, 68-71, MGR. PROD. SERV, FLEXIBLE PACKAGING, 71- U.S.A.A.F, 43-46, 1st Lt. Soc. Plastics Eng. Converting of flexible packaging materials including films, foils, and papers; extrusion coating of plastics; extrusion of plastic films. Address: International Operations, American Can Co, Greenwich, CT 06830.

GRUNDMAN, ROSE ANN, b. Chicago, Ill, Oct. 30, 26. MATHEMATICS, STATISTICS. B.S, Northwestern, 47, M.S, 48. Instr. MATH, Arizona, 48-49; UNIV. ILL. MED. CTR, 49-57, ASST. PROF, 57- AAAS; Math. Asn. Am; Am. Math. Soc; Soc. Indust. & Appl. Math; Asn. Comput. Mach; Am. Statist. Asn; Am. Pharmaceut. Asn. Calculus of variations; analytical statistics; analytic probability theory; quality control; design and analyses of experiments; computer science applied to the health sciences. Address: Dept. of Chemistry, University of Illinois at the Medical Center, 833 S. Wood, Chicago, IL 60612.

GRUNDMANN, ALBERT WENDELL, b. Salt Lake City, Utah, Sept. 1, 12; m. 47; c. 1. BIOLOGY. B.A, Utah, 37, M.A, 39; Ph.D.(med. entomol), Kans. State Col, 42. Asst. biol, Utah, 37-39; Kans. State Col, 39-41; inspector, Salt Lake City Mosquito Abatement Dist, 42; instr. BIOL, UNIV. UTAH, 46-47, asst. prof, 47-52, assoc. prof, 52-60, PROF, 60-, head dept. entom. & zool, 62-68. Consult. epizool. & ecol. res, Dugway Proving Grounds, 63-69; mem. Am. Inst. Biol. Sci-NASA study comt. future role lunar receiving lab, 69-70. Sanit.C, 42-45, Res, 45-, Lt. Col. Am. Soc. Parasitol; Am. Soc. Trop. Med. & Hyg. Medical entomology; transmission and reservoir of insect borne diseases; taxonomy and ecology of such insects; internal parasites of birds and mammals; ecology of animal parasites. Address: Dept. of Biology, University of Utah, Salt Lake City, UT 84112.

GRUNDMANN, CHRISTOPH J(OHANN), b. Berlin, Germany, Dec. 29, 08; nat; m. 33; c. 1. CHEMISTRY. Dipl, Berlin, 31, Dr. Phil, 33; Dr. Phil. Habil. (org. chem), Heidelberg, 37. Res. assoc, Kaiser Wilhelm Inst, Germany, 33-39; res. chemist, Deutsche Hydrierwerke, 39-45; assoc. prof. chem, Halle, 47; prof. & head dept, Berlin, 50-52; assoc. dir. res, Olin Mathieson

Chem. Corp, N.Y, 52-58; dir. res. & develop, Gen. Cigar Co, 58-60; SR. FEL, MELLON INST, 60-, PROF. CHEM, CARNEGIE-MELLON UNIV, 67- Privat-docent, Univ. Heidelberg, 38; res. assoc, res. found, Ohio State Univ, 52-58. Mem. patent adv. comt, U.S. Secy. Commerce, 60-62. Am. Chem. Soc; N.Y. Acad. Sci; Soc. Ger. Chem. Organic chemistry. Address: Dept. of Chemistry, Carnegie-Mellon University, 4400 Fifth Ave, Pittsburgh, PA 15213.

GRUNDMEIER, ERNEST WINSTON, b. North Mankato, Minn, Nov. 15, 29; m. 63. PHYSICAL CHEMISTRY. B.A, Mankato State Col, 52; M.S, Iowa State, 54; New Mexico, 55-57; Nat. Sci. Found. fel, Kansas State, 62-63, Ph.D.(chem), 64. Asst. chem, Iowa State, 62-54; instr. math, New Mexico, 57; CHEM, MANKATO STATE COL, 58-60, asst. prof, 60-64, assoc. prof, 64-69, PROF, 69- Consult, Mankato Stone Co, 60; fel, Univ. Edinburgh, 71. U.S.A.F, 55-58, S/Sgt. Am. Chem. Soc. Kinetics of the benzidine rearrangement and hydrogen isotope effects; kinetics of metal-catalyzed decarboxylations of amino acids; chemistry of combustion. Address: Dept. of Chemistry, Mankato State College, Mankato, MN 56001.

GRUNDTNER, MATTHIAS J(AMES), b. St. Paul, Minn, Mar. 4, 29; m. 51; c. 8. PHYSICS, MATHEMATICS. B.S, Col. St. Thomas, 51; Minnesota. Instr. physics & electronics, Col. St. Thomas, 53-54; res. scientist gaseous electronics, Minneapolis-Honeywell Regulator Co, 54-59; pres, Appl. Design, Inc, 59-63; sr. scientist aerosol & atmospheric physics, appl. sci. div, Litton Indust, Inc, 63-66; sr. develop. engr, comput. mem. systs, Univac Div, Sperry Rand Corp, 66-70; ENG. MGR, MAGNETIC RECORDING HEADS & DEVICES, NORTRONICS CO, INC, 70- U.S.A.F, 51-53, Res, 53-, Capt. Geiger tubes; xenon flash tubes; neon tubes and other gaseous electronics; gaseous electronics pilot plant production. Address: 2933 Troseth Rd, St. Paul, MN 55113.

GRUNDY, SCOTT MONTGOMERY, b. Memphis, Tex, July 10, 33; m. 56; c. 2. PHYSIOLOGY, BIOCHEMISTRY. B.S, Tex. Tech. Col, 55; M.D. & M.S, Baylor, 60; Ph.D, Rockefeller Univ, 66. Instr. biochem, col. med, Baylor Univ, 60-61; asst. prof, Rockefeller Univ, 68-70; CHIEF, PHOENIX CLIN. RES. SECT, PHOENIX INDIAN MED. CTR, NAT. INST. ARTHRITIS & METAB. DISEASES, 71- Am. Soc. Clin. Invest. Plasma lipoprotein structure and interconversions; cholesterol balance in man; cholesterol gallstone atherosclerosis formation; diabetes millitus. Address: Phoenix Clinical Research Section, Phoenix Indian Medical Center, 4212 N. 16th St, Phoenix, AZ 85016.

GRUNDY, W(ALTON) E(ARLE), b. West Paris, Maine, Oct. 31, 17; m. 48; c. 3. BACTERIOLOGY. B.S, Maine, 39; M.S, Pa. State, 41, Ph.D.(bact), 48. Asst. pencillin prod, Pa. State, 44-45, bact, 46-47; microbiologist, med. nutrit. lab, Chicago, 45-46; RES. MICROBIOLOGIST, ABBOTT LABS, 48- Civilian with U.S.A; Office Sci. Res. & Develop, 44. U.S.A, 42-44, 45-46. AAAS; Soc. Indust. Microbiol; Am. Soc. Microbiol. New antibiotics isolation and screening; general industrial microbiology. Address: Abbott Labs, North Chicago, IL 60064.

GRUNE, WERNER N(ORBERT), b. Cologne, Ger, Apr. 20, 24; nat; m. 51; c. 2. SANITARY ENGINEERING. B.S.E, Connecticut, 44; M.S, Harvard, 48; Dr.Eng.Sc, N.Y. Univ, 51. From res. assoc. to proj. dir. waste disposal, Atomic Energy Comn, 48-51; sanit. engr, div. water pollution control, U.S. Pub. Health Serv, 51-52; assoc. prof. CIVIL ENG, Ga. Inst. Tech, 52-59, prof, 59-63, res. assoc, eng. exp. sta, 52-63; prof. & chmn. dept, Merrimack Col, 63-69; MEM. STAFF, UNIV. MIAMI, 69- Lectr, N.Y. Univ, 48-49; engr, eng. res. & develop. lab, spec. projs. br, Corps Engrs, summer 51; sanit. engr, hqs, U.S. Army, France & eng. adv. hqs, U.S. Air Force, Ger, 54-55; consult, Fischer & Porter Co, 56; div. radiol. health, U.S. Pub. Health Serv, 58, summer, 63; Atlanta Water Works, 60; vis. prof, Karlsruhe Tech. Univ, summers 63 & 65; res. partic, waste disposal sect, health physics div, Oak Ridge Nat. Labs, summer 66. C.Eng, 44-47, 2nd Lt. Am. Soc. Civil Eng; Soc. Am. Mil. Eng; Am. Soc. Eng. Educ; Am. Water Works Asn; Water Pollution Control Fedn.(Eddy Medal, 57). Demineralization of salt water; treatment and disposal of radioactive wastes; gas chromatography; air pollution; automation of waste treatment plant operation; water supply, sewage treatment and disposal; stream pollution; industrial wastes treatment; operation; theory and design; eutrophication. Address: Dept. of Civil Engineering, University of Miami, Coral Gables, FL 33124.

GRUNERT, R(UDOLF) R(ICHARD), b. Alta, Can, Nov. 29, 23; m. 49; c. 2. BIOCHEMISTRY. B.Sc, Alberta, 45, M.Sc, 46; Ph.D.(biochem), Wisconsin, 50. Nat. Insts. Health fel, Wisconsin, 50-51; res. scientist, E.I. DU PONT DE NEMOURS & CO, INC, 51-61, RES. ASSOC, 61- Am. Soc. Biol. Chem; Am. Chem. Soc; N.Y. Acad. Sci. Enzymology; metabolism; virology. Address: 105 Sorrel Dr, Surrey Park, Wilmington, DE 19803.

GRUNES, DAVID L(EON), b. Paterson, N.J, June 29, 21; m. 49; c. 3. SOIL CHEMISTRY, PLANT NUTRITION. B.Sc, Rutgers, 44; Ph.D.(soil chem), California, 51. Asst. soil sci, California, 48-50; SOIL SCIENTIST, North. Great Plains Res. Center, U.S. DEPT. AGR, N.Dak, 50-59, 60-64, soil phosphorus lab, Colo. State Univ, 59-60, PLANT, SOIL & NUTRIT. LAB, N.Y, 64- Tech. asst. expert, Int. Atomic Energy Agency, Israel & vis. prof, Israel Inst. Technol, 63-64; consult. ed, McGraw Hill Co, 65-; assoc. prof. dept. agron, Cornell Univ, 67- U.S.A, 44-45. Fel. AAAS; Soil Sci. Soc. Am; Am. Soc. Agron; Int. Soc. Soil Sci. Soil chemistry and fertility; plant and animal nutrition. Address: U.S. Plant, Soil & Nutrition Lab, Tower Rd, Ithaca, NY 14850.

GRUNEWALD, GARY L(AWRENCE), b. Spokane, Wash, Nov. 11, 37; m. 66. MEDICINAL & BIO-ORGANIC CHEMISTRY. B.S. & B.Pharm, Wash. State Univ, 60; Wis. Alumni Res. Found. fel, Univ. Wis, Madison, 60-61, Nat. Insts. Health fel, 61-65, Ph.D.(org. chem), 66. ASST. PROF. MED. CHEM, UNIV. KANS, 66- AAAS; Am. Chem. Soc; Acad. Pharmaceut. Sci; The Chem. Soc; Ger. Chem. Soc; Am. Pharmaceut. Asn; N.Y. Acad. Sci. Synthesis and mechanism of action of biologically-active compounds; molecular orbital calculations and drug action; chemistry of the autonomic nervous system. Address: Dept. of Medicinal Chemistry, University of Kansas, Lawrence, KS 66044.

GRUNEWALD, RALPH, b. Sheboygan, Wis, Nov. 17, 36; m. 62; c. 2. BIONUCLEONICS, HEALTH PHYSICS. B.S, Lakeland Col, 58; M.S, Purdue, 64, Ph.D.(health physics), 65. Lab technician, A.C. Electronics Div, Gen. Motors Corp, 58-61; chemist IV, Wis. State Bd. Health, 65-66; ASST. PROF. BOT, UNIV. WIS-MILWAUKEE, 66- Kiekhofer Award, 71. U.S.A, 61. AAAS; Health Physics Soc. Radiotracer methodology and radioecology studies. Address: Dept. of Botany, University of Wisconsin-Milwaukee, Milwaukee, WI 53201.

GRUNMEIER, PAUL W, b. Bethlehem, Pa, Apr. 18, 28; m. 56; c. 4. MICROBIOLOGY. B.S, Muhlenberg Col, 50; M.S, Lehigh, 52; Ph.D.(med. microbiol), Pennsylvania, 58. Res. asst. microbiol, Wyeth Labs, Am. Home Prod. Corp, 52-54, supvr. vaccine prod, 54-56, jr. scientist, 58-61; res. asst. microbiol, S.Jersey Med. Res. Found, N.J, 56-58; proj. mgr. microbiol. vaccine develop, MERCK SHARP & DOHME DIV, MERCK & CO, INC, 61-62, prod. supvr. influenza vaccine, 62-64, mgr. process eng. & vaccine develop, 64-67, pharmaceut. process eng. & develop, 67-70, SR. MGR. BIOL. QUAL. CONTROL, 70- N.Y. Acad. Sci. Virus vaccine development and production. Address: Merck Sharp & Dohme Division, West Point, PA 19486.

GRUNT, JEROME A(LVIN), b. Newark, N.J, Apr. 6, 23; m. 50; c. 4. PEDIATRICS, ENDOCRINOLOGY. B.S, Rutgers, 47, M.S, 48; Ph.D, Kansas, 52; M.D, Duke, 57. Instr. anat, Kansas, 48-52; Duke, 53-59, U.S. Pub. Health. Serv. spec. res. fel, 59-60; instr. PEDIAT, HARVARD, 61-63, assoc, 63-64; assoc. prof, Yale, 64-71; PROF, SCH. MED, UNIV. MO-KANSAS CITY, 71- Med. Found. fel, Harvard, 60-62, fel. pediat. endocrinol, 60-63. U.S.A, 43-46. Am. Asn. Anat; Endocrine Soc; Am. Diabetes Asn; Soc. Pediat. Res. Pediatric endocrinology and growth. Address: Dept. of Pediatrics, School of Medicine, University of Missouri-Kansas City, Kansas City, MO 64108.

GRUNTFEST, I(RVING) J(AMES), b. Phila, Pa, Jan. 12, 17; m. 48; c. 2. PHYSICAL CHEMISTRY. Sc.B, Brown, 37, Sc.M, 38; Ph.D.(phys. chem), 41. Asst. phys. chemist, U.S. Bur. Mines, Md, 41; Tenn. Valley Authority, Ala, 41-43; mem. staff, Bell Tel. Labs, N.J, 43; res. chemist, Rohm & Haas Co, 43-56; consult. chemist, Gen. Elec. Co, 56-70; MAT. SYSTS. ENGR, MAT. RES. CTR, ALLIED CHEM. CORP, MORRISTOWN, N.J, 70- Chmn. comt. high temp. mat, Mat. Adv. Bd, 61. With Off. Sci. Res. & Develop, 44. Am. Chem. Soc. Catalysis; surface activity; relationship molecular structure and properties; high strength materials; materials for high temperature service; biomedical materials. Address: 50 Boncour Rd, Cheltenham, PA 19012.

GRUNWALD, CLAUS HANS, b. Lakota, N.Dak, July 9, 34; m. 58; c. 2. PLANT PHYSIOLOGY, BIOLOGY. B.S, Missouri, 60, U.S. Pub. Health Serv. fel, 63-64, Ph.D.(bot), 65. Staff res. biologists, Yale, 64-66; asst. prof. AGRON, UNIV. KY, 66-70, ASSOC. PROF, 70- Sig.C, U.S.A, 55-57. Am. Soc. Plant Physiol; Scand. Soc. Plant Physiol. Physiological function and biochemistry of phytosterols, especially as related to membrane structure and function. Address: Dept. of Agronomy, University of Kentucky, Lexington, KY 40506.

GRUNWALD, ERNEST M(AX), b. Wuppertal, Germany, Nov. 2, 23; nat; m. 52; c. 1. CHEMISTRY. B.S. & B.A, California, Los Angeles, 44, fel, 45, Ph.D. (chem), 47. Instr. chem, California, Los Angeles, 47; res. chemist, Portland Cement Asn, 48; Jewett fel, Columbia, 49; assoc. prof. chem, Fla. State, 49-52, prof, 52-61; res. chemist, Bell Tel. Labs, Inc, 61-64; PROF. CHEM, BRANDEIS UNIV, 64- Weizman fel, 55; Sloan fel, 58-61. Nat. Acad. Sci; Am. Chem. Soc.(pure chem. award, 59); Am. Phys. Soc; Fedn. Am. Sci; The Chem. Soc. Physical organic chemistry; kinetics and equilibrium properties of solutions. Address: Dept. of Chemistry, Brandeis University, Waltham, MA 02154.

GRUNWALD, FREDERICK A(RTHUR), b. Milwaukee, Wis, Sept. 16, 16; m. 57; c. 3. ORGANIC CHEMISTRY. B.A, Northwest. Col, 38; B.S, Ind. Tech. Col, 48; univ. fels, Vanderbilt Univ, 49-50, 51-52, M.S, 50, Milbank Mem. Found. fel, 50-51, Ph.D.(org. chem), 52. Res. assoc, Mass. Inst. Tech, 52-53; sr. chemist, MEAD JOHNSON RES. LABS, 53-58, GROUP LEADER, 58- AAAS; Am. Chem. Soc; Sci. Res. Soc. Am. Organic synthesis; pharmaceuticals; chemotherapy. Address: Mead Johnson Research Labs, Evansville, IN 47721.

GRUNWALD, HUBERT PETER, b. Lakota, N.Dak, Apr. 7, 37; m. 60; c. 2. SOLID STATE PHYSICS. B.S, Washington (St. Louis), 59; Woodrow Wilson fel. & Ph.D.(solid state physics), Rochester, 65. ASST. PROF. PHYSICS, Union Col.(N.Y), 65-70; STATE UNIV. N.Y. COL. BROCKPORT, 70- Am. Phys. Soc; Am. Asn. Physics Teachers. High resistivity semiconductors, particularly the study of transport mechanisms of electrical charge through these materials. Address: Dept. of Physics, State University of New York College at Brockport, Brockport, NY 14420.

GRUNWALD, JOHN J, b. Berehove, Czech, Aug. 24, 31; U.S. citizen; m. 60; c. 4. CHEMICAL ENGINEERING, INORGANIC CHEMISTRY. B.S, Lausanne, 56; M.S, Columbia, 59; Ph.D.(chem), Wayne State, 66. Indust. engr, North. Elec, Can, 56-57; res. chemist, MAC DERMID, INC, 58-65, asst. res. div, 65-66, RES. DIR, WATERBURY, 66- Teaching assoc, Wayne State Univ, 64-65. Am. Electroplaters Soc; fel. Am. Chem. Soc; Soc. Plastics Eng; Electrochem. Soc; fel. Am. Inst. Chem. Adhesion; dissolution and electrodeposition of metals; metal-to-polymer bonding. Address: 150 Roydon Rd, New Haven, CT 06511.

GRUNWELL, JOHN R, b. Wash, D.C, July 14, 42; m. 63. PHOTOCHEMISTRY, ORGANIC CHEMISTRY. B.S, Pennsylvania, 63; Ph.D.(org. chem), Mass. Inst. Technol, 68. ASST. PROF. CHEM, MIAMI UNIV, 68- Am. Chem. Soc. Photochemistry of tetra-valent organo-sulfur compounds; molecular orbital theory of third row elements; stereospecific synthesis. Address: Dept. of Chemistry, Miami University, Oxford, OH 45056.

GRUNWELL, JOYCE FRANCIS, b. Malden, Mass, Oct. 24, 42; m. 64. ORGANIC CHEMISTRY. B.S, Pennsylvania, 63; Nat. Insts. Health fel, Mass. Inst. Tech, 64-68, Ph.D.(org. chem), 68. RES. CHEMIST, WM. S. MERRELL CO. DIV, RICHARDSON-MERRELL, INC, 68- Am. Chem. Soc. Chemistry and activity of the steroids. Address: Wm. S. Merrell Co, 110 E. Amity Rd, Cincinnati, OH 45215.

GRUPEN, WILLIAM BRIGHTMAN, b. Pittsburgh, Pa, Mar. 30, 30; m. 54; c. 4. METALLURGY, SOLID STATE PHYSICS. B.S, California, Los Angeles, 57, M.S, 59, Ph.D.(metall), 64. Res. engr, California, Los Angeles, 58-64; mem. tech. staff, BELL TEL. LABS, ALLENTOWN, 64-67, group supvr. metallic films, 67-69, DEPT. HEAD, MAT. & PROCESS DEVELOP, 69- U.S.A.F, 50-54, Sgt. Inst. Elec. & Electronics Eng; Am. Inst. Mining, Metall. & Petrol. Eng. Preprecipitation reactions in aluminum-copper alloys; magnetic properties of 3d transition metals and their alloys; magnetic and electrical properties of thin metal films. Address: 725 Pine St, Emmaus, PA 18049.

GRUPP, GUNTER, b. Esslingen, Ger, Feb. 6, 20; nat; m. 58; c. 6. EXPERIMENTAL MEDICINE, PHYSIOLOGY. M.D, Freiburg, 48. Instr. pharmacol, Freiburg, 48-51, asst. prof, 51-53; docent, 53-58; asst. prof, COL. MED, UNIV. CINCINNATI, 58-60, assoc. prof, 60-65, PROF. exp. med, 65-66, EXP. MED. & PHYSIOL, 66-, CHMN. DEPT. BIOMED. COMMUN, 69-, dir. audio-visual activities, 67-69. Am. Soc. Physiol; Am. Soc. Pharmacol. & Exp. Therapeut; Ger. Pharmacol. Soc. Pharmacology of reductones; physiology of kidney metabolism and circulation; heat-production of kidney; cardiovascular dynamics; ion-transport of heart and red blood cells. Address: Cardiac Research Lab. H-3, Cincinnati General Hospital, Cincinnati, OH 45229.

GRUSCHKA, HEINZ D(IETER), b. Breslau, Ger, Jan. 22, 34; m. 65; c. 3. APPLIED PHYSICS, ACOUSTICS. Dipl. physics, Univ. Göttingen, 62, Dr. rer. nat, 65. Res. asst. aeroacoust, Univ. Göttingen, 65; res. assoc. detonation physics, Ger-French Res. Inst. St. Louis, France, 65-67; vis. asst. prof. PHYSICS, SPACE INST, UNIV. TENN, 67-68, asst. prof, 69-71, ASSOC. PROF, 71- Aeroacoustics; detonation physics and gasdynamics including shock wave phenomena and aerodynamic noise. Address: Dept. of Physics, University of Tennessee Space Institute, Tullahoma, TN 37388.

GRUSCHOW, GEORGE F, b. Lyons, N.Y, Aug. 26, 14; m. 39; c. 5. FOREST MANAGEMENT, SILVICULTURE. B.S, Syracuse, 36, M.S, 38. Asst. silviculturist, U.S. FOREST SERV, 40-41, res. forester, 46-53, res. ctr. leader, Southeast. Forest Exp. Sta, Va, 53-59, div. chief, Cent. States Forest Exp. Sta, 59-65, ASST. DIR, 65-66, INTERMOUNTAIN FOREST & RANGE EXP. STA, 66- U.S.A, 42-46, Lt. Col. Forest ecology. Address: Intermountain Forest & Range Experiment Station, U.S. Forest Service, 525 25th St, Ogden, UT 84401.

GRUSHKA, ELI, b. Tel-Aviv, Israel, July 14, 38; m. 64; c. 1. PHYSICAL & ANALYTICAL CHEMISTRY. B.S, Long Island, 63; Ph.D.(gas chromatography), Cornell, 68. Res. assoc, Utah, 67-69; ASST. PROF. CHEM, STATE UNIV. N.Y. BUFFALO, 69- AAAS; Am. Chem. Soc. Development of the theory and methods of separations. Address: Dept. of Chemistry, State University of New York at Buffalo, Buffalo, NY 14214.

GRUSHKIN, BERNARD, b. Brooklyn, N.Y, Apr. 2, 32; m. 61; c. 3. PHYSICAL & ORGANIC CHEMISTRY. B.A, N.Y. Univ, 53; M.A, Texas, 56; Ph.D. (chem), 58. Res. chemist, Callery Chem. Co, 59-60; sr. res. chemist, res. div, W.R. Grace & Co, 60-67; SR. SCIENTIST, XEROX CORP, 67- Am. Chem. Soc. Solution kinetics; inorganic polymers; phosphorus nitrogen compounds; chemistry of ammonia and its derivatives; organic sulfur-nitrogen and arsenic-selenium compounds and polymers; organic pigments; photoelectric pigments and polymers. Address: Xerox Corp, 800 Phillips Rd, Webster, NY 14580.

GRUSZCZYK, J(EROME) H(ENRY), S.J, b. Jersey City, N.J, Sept. 11, 15. ANIMAL PHYSIOLOGY. A.B, Georgetown, 40; Ph.L, Woodstock Col.(Md), 41, S.T.L, 48; M.S, Fordham, 51. Instr. comp. anat, Scranton, 41-42; asst. prof. human anat. & physiol, Le Moyne Col, 51-53; ZOOL, ST. PETER'S COL. (N.J), 53-66, ASSOC. PROF, 66- AAAS; Bot. Soc. Am; Soc. Protozool. Enzyme activity in muscle tissue. Address: 2652 Kennedy Blvd, Jersey City, NJ 07306.

GRUTSCH, JAMES F(RANCIS), b. Gary, Ind, Apr. 3, 27; m. 49; c. 3. ANALYTICAL CHEMISTRY. B.S, Indiana, 51, M.A, 52. Group leader wastes treatment, Standard Oil Co,(Ind), 52-67, coord. waste disposal, Am. Oil Co, Ill, 67-69, ASST. COORD. AIR & WATER CONSERV, STANDARD OIL CO. (IND), 69- Lectr, Ind. Univ, 56- U.S.A, 46-48. Am. Chem. Soc. Industrial wastes treatment processes; analytical chemistry research; petroleum treating processes. Address: Standard Oil Co.(Ind), 910 S. Michigan Ave, Chicago, IL 60605.

GRUTT, EUGENE WADSWORTH, JR, b. Hawthorne, Nev, Sept. 29, 16; m. 50; c. 2. GEOLOGY, ECONOMIC GEOLOGY. B.S, Nevada, 38. Geologist, Nev. Victory Mining Co, 38-42; staff geologist, Isbell Construct. Co, 48-53; chief Casper Br, U.S. ATOMIC ENERGY COMN, 53-58, Grants Br, 58-62 & Resources Appraisal Br, 62-67, DIR. RESOURCE DIV, 67- U.S.A, 42-46, Maj. AAAS; Am. Inst. Min, Metall. & Petrol. Eng; Geol. Soc. Am. Investigations and studies of metalliferous ore deposits, especially geology of uranium; uranium geology; geochemistry; appraisal of radioactive mineral resources; research and development contracts in geology, geochemistry and exploration methods and techniques. Address: Atomic Energy Commission Compound, Grand Junction, CO 81501.

GRUTTER, FREDERICK H(ERBERT), b. New Brunswick, N.J, July 3, 28; m. 51; c. 1. MICROBIOLOGY. B.S, Rutgers, 48, M.S, 51; Nat. Cancer Inst. fel, Pa. State, 51-53, Ph.D.(bact), 53. Microbiologist, fermentation, Merck & Co, Inc, 49-51; sr. microbiologist, Johnson & Johnson, 53-60, group leader microbiol, 60-61; sr. scientist, Warner-Lambert Res. Inst, 61; mem. staff, dept. med. invest, HOFFMANN-LA ROCHE, INC, 62, clin. res. consult, 62-63, asst. dir. clin. res, 63-64, asst. to dir. biol. res, 64-69, DIR. RES. ADMIN. & ASST. TO V.PRES. RES, 69- AAAS; Am. Soc. Microbiol; Soc. Indust. Microbiol; Am. Med. Asn; Am. Soc. Clin. Pharmacol. & Chemother. Antimicrobial agents; clinical research. Address: 62 Yantacaw Brook Rd, Upper Montclair, NJ 07043.

GRUTZNER, JOHN BRANDON, b. Melbourne, Australia, Aug. 28, 41; m. 65; c. 1. ORGANIC CHEMISTRY. B.S, Univ. Melbourne, 63, Commonwealth Sci. & Indust. Res. Orgn. stud. & Ph.D.(chem), 67. Fel. CHEM, Univ. Calif, Los Angeles, 67-68; Calif. Inst. Technol, 68-69; ASST. PROF, PURDUE UNIV, 69- The Chem. Soc; Am. Chem. Soc; Assoc. Royal Australian Chem. Inst. Nuclear magnetic resonance spectroscopy; carbanions; organic reaction mechanisms. Address: Dept. of Chemistry, Purdue University, Lafayette, IN 47907.

GRUVER, ROBERT MARTIN, b. York, Pa, Mar. 6, 21; m. 46; c. 1. CERAMICS ENGINEERING. B.S, Pa. State, 43, M.S, 48; Orton fel, Mo. Sch. Mines, 53-54; Ph.D.(ceramics eng), Missouri, 56. Res. asst. ceramics, Pa. State, 43-53; proj. dir, Linden Labs, Inc, 54-63, tech. dir. MAT, 63-68; CERAMIC FINISHING CO, 68- AAAS; Am. Ceramics Soc; Am. Chem. Soc. Thermal analysis of ceramic materials; surface chemistry of glass and resins; adhesion to glass; solid state reaction and phase equilibria of ceramic materials. Address: Ceramic Finishing Co, Box 498, State College, PA 16801.

GRUZENSKY, PAUL M, b. Grassy Butte, N.Dak, Nov. 2, 25; m. 48; c. 4. INORGANIC CHEMISTRY. B.S, Walla Walla Col, 48; M.S, Oregon State, 51, Ph.D.(inorg. chem), 60. Instr. chem, Walla Walla Col, 50-51; res. chemist, Northwest Electrodevelop. Lab, U.S. Bur. Mines, 51-56; PHYS. CHEMIST, NAT. BUR. STANDARDS, 60- U.S.A, 44-45. AAAS; Am. Chem. Soc; Sci. Res. Soc. Am; Am. Asn. Crystal Growth; Am. Inst. Chem. Electrochemistry; ultra-purification of materials; inorganic synthesis and single crystal growth; conductivity and color centers in alkali halides; materials science. Address: Division 271.05, National Bureau of Standards, Boulder, CO 80302.

GRYC, GEORGE, b. St. Paul, Minn, July 27, 19; m. 42; c. 5. GEOLOGY. B.S, Univ. Minn, 40, M.S, 41. Field geologist, U.S. GEOL. SURV, 43-71, CHIEF BR. ALASKAN MINERAL RESOURCES, 63- Geol. Soc. Am; Paleont. Soc; Am. Asn. Petrol. Geol; Arctic Inst. N.Am. Potential petroleum resources and regional geology of Alaska; paleontology; stratigraphy. Address: U.S. Geological Survey, 345 Middlefield Rd, Menlo Park, CA 94025.

GRYDER, JOHN W(ILLIAM), b. Los Angeles, Calif, Nov. 6, 26; m. 49; c. 3. PHYSICAL & INORGANIC CHEMISTRY. B.S, Calif. Inst. Tech, 46; Ph.D. (chem), Columbia, 50. Jr. scientist CHEM, Brookhaven Nat. Lab, 48-49; instr, JOHNS HOPKINS UNIV, 49-51, asst. prof, 51-57, assoc. prof, 57-66, PROF, 66- Am. Chem. Soc. Radiochemistry; kinetics; nature of ionic species in solution; phosphorus chemistry. Address: Dept. of Chemistry, Johns Hopkins University, Baltimore, MD 21218.

GRYDER, ROSA M(EYERSBURG), b. Brooklyn, N.Y, Aug. 23, 26; m. 49; c. 3. BIOCHEMISTRY. B.S, Bucknell, 47; M.S, Yale, 49; Ph.D.(biochem), Hopkins, 56. Asst. microbiol, Brookhaven Nat. Labs, 47-48; res. assoc. ophthal, Johns Hopkins Hosp, 52-56, Nat. Inst. Neurol. Diseases & Blindness fel, Wilmer Ophthal. Inst, 56-59; res. assoc. physiol. chem, sch. med, Hopkins, 60-63; instr. BIOCHEM, SCH. MED, UNIV. MD, BALTIMORE COUNTY, 64-66, ASST. PROF, 66- Enzymology. Address: Dept. of Biochemistry, University of Maryland School of Medicine, 660 W. Redwood St, Baltimore, MD 21209.

GRYNBAUM, BRUCE B, b. Anapa, Russia, May 25, 20; nat; m. 43; c. 2. MEDICINE. Warsaw, 37-39; M.D, Columbia, 43. Intern, Metropolitan Hosp, New York, 44; res, Mt. Sinai Hosp, New York, 47-48; fel, Goldwater Hosp, 49-50; asst. prof. CLIN. PHYS. MED. & REHAB, COL. MED, N.Y. UNIV, 50-58, ASSOC. PROF, 58-, PROF, MED. CTR, 68-, assoc. prof, 50-68. Dir. phys. med. and rehab, City Dept. Hosps, New York, 50-70; vis. physician, Beekman-Downtown Hosp; mem. adv. bd, N.Y. State chap, Arthritis Found; mem. adv. comt, auto ins. & compensation study, Dept. of Transportation, Wash, D.C; mem. exec. comt, Cent. Labor. Rehab. Coun, N.Y, Inc. Consult, Nat. Insts. Rehab. & Health Serv, 64; dept. hosp. facilities, U.S. Pub. Health Serv. Dipl, Am. Bd. Phys. Med. & Rehab, 52. U.S.A, 44-46, 1st Lt. Am. Med. Asn; Am. Acad. Phys. Med; Am. Cong. Rehab. Med; Am. Pub. Health Asn. Physical medicine and rehabilitation; compensation medicine. Address: Dept. of Physical Medicine & Rehabilitation, New York University College of Medicine, 550 First Ave, New York, NY 10016.

GRYTING, HAROLD J(ULIAN), b. Belview, Minn, Dec. 31, 19; m. 54; c. 2. CHEMISTRY. B.A, St. Olaf Col, 41; N.Dak. State Col, 41-42; Alrose Chem. Co. fel, Purdue, 42-46; U.S. Army Air Corps fel, 46, Mallinckrodt Chem. Co. & Westinghouse Elec. Corp. fels. & Ph.D.(org. chem), 47. Asst. chem, N.Dak. State Col, 41-42; chemist, E.I. du Pont de Nemours & Co, Ill, 42-43; res. chemist, NAVAL WEAPONS CTR, 47-49, head, properties sect, 49-51, properties br, 52-54, plastics br, 54-56, explosives res. br, 56-65, TECH. ASST. TO HEAD EXPLOSIVES & PYROTECH. DIV, 65- Mem, Joint Army, Navy, Air Force Environ. Control comt; chmn, Triserv. Comt. Qualification & Performance Test Methods for Explosives. Fel. AAAS; fel. Am. Inst. Chem; Am. Chem. Soc; assoc. Am. Soc. Pub. Admin; Am. Ord. Asn; Sci. Res. Soc. Am. Alkylation, chloromethylation chlorination and fluorination; syntheses of wetting agents; germicides; high explosives compositions; explosive effects; pollution abatement. Address: Code 45402, Naval Weapons Center, China Lake, CA 93555.

GRYVNAK, DAVID A(LEXIS), b. Akron, Ohio, Mar. 26, 34; m. 57; c. 2. SPECTROSCOPY, PHYSICS. B.S, Ohio State, 59, M.S, 61. SR. SCIENTIST, AERONUTRONIC DIV-PHILCO CORP, 61- Optical Soc. Am. Molecular spectroscopy; transmittance of infrared radiation, especially by atmospheric gases when their parameters such as temperature, pressure and path length are varied. Address: Aeronutronic Division, Philco Corp, Ford Rd, Newport Beach, CA 92663.

GSCHNEIDNER, KARL A(LBERT), JR, b. Detroit, Mich, Nov. 16, 30; m. 57; c. 4. PHYSICAL METALLURGY, SOLID STATE PHYSICS. B.S, Detroit, 52; Ph.D.(phys. chem), Iowa State, 57. Staff mem. phys. metall, Los Alamos Sci. Lab, 57-63, sect. leader, 61-63; asst. prof. solid state physics, dept. physics & mat. res. lab, Illinois, 62-63; assoc. prof. PHYS. METALL, INST. ATOMIC RES. & DEPT. METALL, IOWA STATE UNIV, 63-67, PROF, 67-, DIR. RARE-EARTH INFO. CTR, 66- AAAS; Am. Chem. Soc; Am. Soc. Metals; Am. Crystallog. Asn; Metall. Soc; Am. Nuclear Soc. Physical metallurgy of rare-earth metals and alloys; alloy theory; electronic transformation of cerium; band structures of metals; crystal structure determinations; thermodynamic properties of metals. Address: Dept. of Metallurgy, Rare Earth Information Center, Iowa State University, Ames, IA 50010.

GUADAGNO, JAMES R(ICHARD), b. Pueblo, Colo, Nov. 26, 30. PHYSICAL METALLURGY. B.S, Colorado, 52; M.S, California, Berkeley, 61; Nat. Sci. Found. fel, Vienna, 62-63; Ph.D.(metall), Denver, 67. Design engr, Los Alamos Sci. Lab, 52-53; develop. engr, Sundstrand Aviation Div, Colo, 56-57; res. engr, Colorado, 57-59; res. metallurgist, Denver Res. Inst, 60-68; ASST. PROF. MECH. & AEROSPACE ENG, UNIV. MO-COLUMBIA, 68- U.S.A, 53-55. Am. Soc. Metals. Theory of structure of liquids; structure and thermodynamic properties of liquid metals and alloys. Address: Dept. of Mechanical & Aerospace Engineering, University of Missouri-Columbia, Columbia, MO 65201.

GUAGNINI, OMAR A(RGENTINO), b. Mercedes, Argentina, May 25, 14; m. 39; c. 3. TOXICOLOGY, CHEMISTRY. Ph.D.(chem), Nat. Univ. Buenos Aires, 44. Asst, chem. lab, Buenos Aires Fed. Police, 37-44, toxicol. chemist, 44-47, asst. chief, 47-48; adj. prof. toxicol, faculty chem. & pharm, La Plata Nat. Univ, 48-64; prof. toxicol. & legal chem, Nat. Univ. Buenos Aires, 62-66; EXPERT CONSULT. CHEMIST TOXICOL. & MICROANAL, 66- Prof, Nat. Commercial Sch. Avellaneda, Argentina, 37-63; expert chemist, nat. criminal, civil & labor tribunals, Argentina, 44-71; prof. explosives, Buenos Aires Fed. Police, 45-48; extraordinary prof, Nat. Univ. Tucuman, 48-50; chief chem. lab, Buenos Aires Fed. Police, 57-65; prof, Nat. Univ. Buenos Aires, 59; chief chem. lab, Nat. Inst. Path, Pub. Health Dept. Argentina, 66-69. Walter Scott Award, Fed. Police Argentina, 57. Am. Chem. Soc; Int. Asn. Forensic Toxicol; Arg. Chem. Asn; Arg. Asn. Against Air Pollution. Environmental pollution; microanalysis; industrial hygiene; biological analysis; legal chemistry; bromatological analysis. Address: Dept. A Lab, Castro Barros 1561, Buenos Aires, Argentina.

GUAL, CARLOS, b. Mexico, Oct. 16, 27; m. 54; c. 2. ENDOCRINOLOGY, BIOCHEMISTRY. B.Sc, Nat. Univ. Mexico, 44, M.D, 51, M.Sc, 55; Clark Univ. & Worcester Found. Exp. Biol, 57-59. Endocrinologist, Hosp. Govt. Employees, Mex, 55-56; res. assoc. steroid biochem, Worcester Found. Exp. Biol, 57-59; Nat. Insts. Health res. scientist steroid biochem, NAT. INST. NUTRIT, MEX, 59-65, head hormone lab, 60-65, CHMN. DEPT. ENDOCRINOL, 65-; PROF. ENDOCRINOL, SCH. MED, NAT. UNIV. MEX, 65-, asst. prof, 62-65. Gen. secy, Pan-Am. Cong. Endocrinol, 61-65; Int. Cong. Endocrinol, 65-68; mem. exec. comt, Int. Soc. Endocrinol, 64-72. Am. Col. Physicians; Endocrine Soc; Mex. Acad. Med; Mex. Acad. Sci. Res; Mex. Soc. Nutrit. & Endocrinol.(pres, 64-65); Mex. Soc. Biochem; Pan-Am. Soc. Endocrinol.(pres, 70-74). Biosynthetic pathways to steroid hormones in endocrine tissues; gonadal steroido genesis; ovulation and fertility control; social aspects of population growth. Address: National Institute of Nutrition, Viaducto Tlalpan & San Fernando, Mexico 22 D.F.

GUARD, ARTHUR T(HOMAS, b. Lawrenceburg, Ind, Oct. 2, 97; m. 24; c. 3. PLANT ANATOMY. A.B, DePauw, 24; M.S, Purdue, 29, Ph.D.(bot), 35. Teacher, pub. sch, Ind, 25-28; asst. bot, PURDUE UNIV, 28-29, instr, 29-36, from asst. prof. to assoc. prof. BIOL, 36-66, EMER. PROF, 66- Curator bot, Savannah Sci. Mus, 66-68. AAAS; Bot. Soc. Am; Int. Soc. Plant Morphol. Plant taxonomy; anatomical responses of plants to chemical herbicides; developmental anatomy. Address: Dept. of Biological Sciences, Purdue University, Lafayette, IN 47907.

GUARD, RAY W(ESLEY), b. Lafayette, Ind, Nov. 28, 27; m. 48; c. 5. METALLURGY. B.S, Purdue, 47, Res. Found. fel, 50-51, Ph.D.(metall. eng), 52; M.S, Carnegie Inst. Tech, 48. Asst, Carnegie Inst. Tech, 47-48; instr, Purdue, 48-50; res. assoc, res. lab, Gen. Elec. Co, 57-60, mgr, prod. & process eng, Diamond Prod. Sect, Detroit, 60-62; prin. scientist, metall. & physics, Gen. Precision Aerospace, Inc, 62-63; group leader metall. serv, N.Am. Aviation Sci. Ctr, 63-66, prof. metall. eng. & head dept, Mich. Technol. Univ, 66-70; DEAN ENG, UNIV. TEX, EL PASO, 70- Adj. assoc. prof, Rensselaer Polytech. Inst, 57-60. Am. Soc. Metals; Am. Inst. Min, Metall. & Petrol. Eng; Am. Ceramic Soc; Brit. Inst. Metals; Brit. Iron & Steel Inst. Metallurgy of high temperature alloys; deformation of pure metals; phase diagrams; alloy theory; high pressure reactions. Address: Dept. of Engineering, University of Texas at El Paso, El Paso, TX 79968.

GUARDIA, ENRIQUE J, b. Panama, Dec. 25, 38; m. 61; c. 2. BIOCHEMISTRY. B.S, Univ. Wash, 61, Ph.D.(fisheries), 65. Res. asst, inst. fisheries, Univ. Wash, 61-65; sr. chemist, GEN. FOODS CORP, N.Y, 65-68, res. specialist new foods, Mich, 68-69, AREA MGR. PROTEIN, PHYS. CHEM. & MOLECULAR BIOL, 69- AAAS; Inst. Food Technol; Am. Chem. Soc; N.Y. Acad. Sci. Address: Technical Center, General Foods Corp, Tarrytown, NY 10591.

GUARINO, ANTHONY MICHAEL, b. Framingham, Mass, Dec. 11, 34; m. 57; c. 10. BIOCHEMICAL PHARMACOLOGY, TOXICOLOGY. B.S, Boston Col, 56; M.S, Univ. R.I, 63, U.S. Pub. Health Serv. fel, 63-66, Ph.D.(pharmacol), 66. Clin. chemist, chem. lab, Mass. Gen. Hosp, Boston, 54-57; teaching asst. chem, Univ. R.I, 60-63; res. assoc, pharmacol. & toxicol. prog, lab. chem. pharmacol, Nat. Inst. Gen. Med. Sci, Md, 66-68; RES. PHARMACOLOGIST, LAB. CHEM. PHARMACOL, NAT. CANCER INST, 68- Faculty mem, Nat. Insts. Health Grad. Prog, 68-; guest lectr, dept. pharmacol, sch. med, George Washington Univ, 71- U.S.N, 57-60; U.S.P.H.S, 66-, Comdr. Am. Soc. Pharmacol. & Exp. Therapeut; Am. Chem. Soc. Drug transport; biliary transport; drug metabolism; experimental cancer chemotheraphy; drug abuse; fate and distribution of drugs. Address: Bldg. 10, Room 6N106, National Institutes of Health, Bethesda, MD 20014.

GUARINO, ARMAND J(OHN), b. Beverly, Mass, Jan. 24, 26; m. 49; c. 5. BIOCHEMISTRY. B.S, Harvard, 49; Ph.D.(biochem), Tufts Col, 53. Instr. biochem. & nutrit, med. sch, Tufts Col, 53-54; res. assoc. BIOCHEM, Mass. Inst. Tech, 54-55; asst. prof, med. sch, Michigan, 55-61, assoc. prof, 62-63; PROF. & CHMN. DEPT, Woman's Med. Col. Pa, 63-68; UNIV. TEX. MED. SCH, SAN ANTONIO, 68- U.S.N, 44-46. Am. Soc. Biol. Chem. Nucleoside and nucleotide metabolism. Address: Dept. of Biochemistry, University of Texas Medical School at San Antonio, San Antonio, TX 78229.

GUARINO, JOHN P(HILIP), b. Boston, Mass, Nov. 10, 36; m. 58; c. 5. PHYSICAL & RADIATION CHEMISTRY. B.S, Boston Col, 58; fel, Notre Dame, 59-62, Ph.D.(phys. chem), 62. Asst. chem, Notre Dame, 58-59, fel. radiation chem, radiation lab, 62-63; asst. prof. chem, Miami (Fla), 63-65; SR. RES. CHEMIST, CENT. RES. DIV. LAB, SOCONY MOBIL OIL CO, INC, 65- Asst. prof, Notre Dame, summer 63. Am. Chem. Soc; Faraday Soc. Radiation chemistry and photochemistry of organic glassy solution at 77°k; radiation curing of coatings; molten salt catalysis in petroleum processing. Address: Central Research Division Lab, Socony Mobil Oil Co, Inc, Box 1025, Princeton, NJ 08534.

GUARINO, P. ANTHONY, b. Cambridge, Mass, Sept. 22, 12; m. 33; c. 3. ELECTRONIC ENGINEERING. B.S, Mass. Inst. Tech, 35; M.S, Notre Dame, 40; American Univ, 57-62. Instr. elec. eng, Notre Dame, 40-42; proj. engr, radar res. sect, U.S. Naval Res. Lab, 42-45, 48; dept. mgr, Designers for Indust, Inc, 45-46; proj. mgr, Bird Electronic Corp, 46-48; proj. engr, ord. develop. div, Nat. Bur. Standards, 48-51, chief electronics sect, 51-53; electronic br, projectile fuze lab, Diamond Ord. Fuze Labs, 53-58, ASSOC. TECH. DIR, 58-63, HARRY DIAMOND LABS, 63- Consult, Bendix Aviation Corp, 41-42. Am. Ord. Asn; sr. mem. Inst. Elec. & Electronics Eng. Electronic circuits and ordnance; instrumentation; management and supervision; public administration. Address: Harry Diamond Labs, U.S. Army, Connecticut & Van Ness Sts, Washington, DC 20438.

GUARRAIA, LEONARD JOSEPH, b. N.Y.C, Aug. 17, 38; m. 66. BIOCHEMISTRY. A.B, Virginia, 60; M.S, George Washington, 63; Ph.D.(microbial physiol), Indiana, 66. Fel. biochem, Univ. Ga, 66-68, asst. prof. microbiol, 68-71; MEM. STAFF, DIV. TECH. SUPPORT, ENVIRON. PROTECTION AGENCY, 71- AAAS; Am. Soc. Microbiol. Biochemistry; microbial physiology; immunochemistry. Address: Office of Water Programs, Division of Technical Support, Environmental Protection Agency, Washington, DC 20460.

GUASTELIA, SAMUEL, b. Fitchburg, Mass, Feb. 27, 20; m. 49; c. 1. CHEMICAL ENGINEERING. B.S, Northeast. Univ, 42. Asst. to chief inspector, U.S. Army Sig. Corps, 42-44; asst. dir. res, Fitchburg Paper Co, 44-60, mgr. new prod. develop, 60-65; tech. dir, Spectra-Polymer Co, 65; PROJ. MGR. & CONSULT, GORHAM RES. CORP, 65- U.S.N, 38-39. Tech. Asn. Pulp & Paper Indust. High polymer chemistry, especially as it applies to paper making. Address: Gorham Research Corp, Gorham, ME 01473.

GUAY, LEO J(AMES), b. Laconia, N.H, Mar. 3, 08. CHEMISTRY. A.B, Boston Col, 34, M.S, 35; Licentiate (philos), Weston Col, Mass, 35, (theol), 41; M.S, Col. of Holy Cross, 37; fel, Clark, 42-44, Ph.D.(chem), 44. Instr. chem, Col. of Holy Cross, 35-37; prof. & head dept, Baghdad Col, 44-54, col. architect, 49-54; prof. phys. chem, Weston Col, 54-55; purchasing agent, AL-HIKMA UNIV, BAGHDAD, 55-56, prof. chem, 56-57, PROF. ENG, 60-, DIR. ASTRON. OBSERV, 56-, ARCHITECT & BUILDER UNIV. CAMPUS, 56- Solar Energy Soc. Sandmeyer reaction and cathodic reduction of benzene diazonium chloride; fermentation; physico-organic chemistry; solar heating; engineering data for Iraqi building materials; astronomy. Address: Dept. of Engineering, Al-Hikma University of Baghdad, Box 2125, Baghdad, Iraq.

GUBBINS, KEITH E(DMUND), b. Southampton, Eng, Jan. 27, 37; m. 60; c. 1. CHEMICAL ENGINEERING. B.Sc, London, 58, Dept. Sci. & Indust. Res. fel, 58-59, dipl. chem. eng, 59, Leverhulme fel, 59-62, Ph.D.(chem. eng), 62. Vis. lectr, London, 59-62; fel. CHEM. ENG, UNIV. FLA, 62-64, asst. prof, 64-68, ASSOC. PROF, 68- Vis. prof, Imp. Col, Univ. London, 71. Am. Inst. Chem. Eng; Am. Chem. Soc; Faraday Soc; The Chem. Soc; Brit. Inst. Chem. Eng. Transport properties of liquids; transport properties of organic solids; statistical thermodynamics. Address: Dept. of Chemical Engineering, University of Florida, Gainesville, FL 32601.

GUBELI, A(LFRED) OTTO, b. Zurich, Switz, Sept. 10, 13; m. 39; c. 1. INORGANIC & ANALYTICAL CHEMISTRY. B.A, Col. Zurich County, Switz, 33; B.Sc, Swiss Fed. Inst. Tech, 39, D.Sc.(phys. chem), 41. Private docent anal. chem, Swiss Fed. Inst. Tech, 41-45, PROF, 45-61; INORG. & ANAL. CHEM, LAVAL UNIV, 61- Swiss Army, 34-60. Int. Electrochem. Soc; hon. mem. Int. Soc. Med. Hydrol. & Climat; Chem. Inst. Can; Swiss Chem. Soc; Soc. Ger. Chem; hon. mem. Ger. Soc. Water Surv; Austrian Balneology & Climat. Soc; Italian Balneology & Climat. Soc. Physical chemical study of complex formations. Address: Dept. of Chemistry, Laval University, Quebec 10, Que, Can.

GUBER, ALBERT LEE, b. Heidelberg, Pa, June 17, 35; m. 61; c. 1. GEOLOGY. B.S, Pittsburgh, 57; Ph.D.(geol), Illinois, 62. Nat. Sci. Found. fel, PA. STATE UNIV, 62-63, asst. prof. GEOL, 63-70, ASSOC. PROF, 70- Am. Asn. Petrol. Geol; Paleont. Soc; Soc. Econ. Paleont. & Mineral. Temporal and spacial dynamics of fossil communities; Paleozoic ostracode morphology and taxonomy. Address: Dept. of Geosciences, Pennsylvania State University, University Park, PA 16802.

GUBERMAN, H(ERBERT) D(AVID), b. New York, N.Y, Aug. 19, 30; m. 52; c. 2. METALLURGY. B.A, Columbia Univ, 51, Am. Soc. Metals scholar. & B.S, 57, Gordon Found. fels, 57-59, M.S, 58, Ph.D.(metall), 63. MEM. TECH. STAFF, Bell Tel. Labs, Inc, 63-65; SOLID STATE DIV, OAK RIDGE NAT. LAB, 65- U.S.N, 53-56, Lt.(jg). Am. Soc. Metals; Metall. Soc; Am. Phys. Soc. Properties of imperfections and relationship to macroscopic properties; thin films. Address: Solid State Division, Oak Ridge National Lab, P.O. Box X, Oak Ridge, TN 37830.

GUBERSKY, VICTOR R, b. Lamont, Alta, May 17, 35; m. 57; c. 3. DERMATOLOGY. M.D, Alberta, 59. Intern, Edmonton Gen. Hosp, Alta, 59-60, res. internal med, 60-61; dermat, Cleveland Clin. Found, Ohio, 61-64; assoc. med. dir, Inst. Clin. Med, Syntex Corp, 64-68, head div. inflammatory diseases, 66-68, med. dir, SYNTEX LTD, 66-68, V.PRES. & GEN. MGR, 68- Fel. dermat, 59-64. Am. Acad. Dermat; Am. Med. Asn. Basic and clinical dermatological research, especially the effect of corticosteroids on various dermatoses; antimetabolites, antiviral and antiandrogenic agents. Address: Syntex Ltd, 8255 Mountain Sights Ave, Montreal 308, Que, Can.

GUBLER, CLARK J(OHNSON), b. La Verkin, Utah, July 14, 13; m. 38; c. 4. BIOCHEMISTRY. A.B, Brigham Young, 39; M.A, Utah State, 41; Ph.D.(biochem), California, 45. Asst. chem, Brigham Young, 38-39; Utah State, 39-41; biochem, California, 41-45; res. chemist, El Dorado Oil Works, Calif, 44-46; res. assoc. med, sch. med, Utah, 46-52, asst. prof, 52-56, U.S. Pub. Health Serv. spec. res. fel, Wisconsin, 56-58; assoc. prof. CHEM, BRIG-

HAM YOUNG UNIV, 58-61, PROF, 61- Assoc. prof, William Col, 44-45; instr, Univ. Utah, 51-60; Am. Heart Asn. advan. res. fel, 58-60, estab. investr, 60-65; vis. prof, Univ. Freiburg, 64-65; U.S. Pub. Health Serv. spec. res. fel, Univ. San Diego, 71-72. Civilian with U.S. Pub. Health Serv, 44. AAAS; Am. Soc. Biol. Chem; Am. Inst. Nutrit; N.Y. Acad. Sci; Am. Soc. Clin. Nutrit. Iron, copper metabolism; biological functions and mechanisms of action of thiamin; alpha-keto-acid metabolism; biochemistry of learning and development. Address: 466 N. 550 E, Orem, UT 84057.

GUBNER, RICHARD S, b. N.Y.C, July 20, 13; m. 49; c. 3. INTERNAL MEDICINE, CARDIOLOGY. A.B, Columbia, 33; M.D, N.Y. Univ, 36. MED. DIR. DIAGNOSTIC SERV. DIV, EQUITABLE LIFE INS. SOC. U.S, 41-; CLIN. PROF, STATE UNIV. N.Y. DOWNSTATE MED. CTR, 56- Dir. med, Kings Co. Hosp, Brooklyn, 59- Consult. physician, Pa. R.R, 57- Dipl, Am. Bd. Internal Med; Am. Bd. Cardiovasc. Disease; Bd. Life Ins. Med. Am. Col. Clin. Pharmacol. & Therapeut; fel. Am. Col. Physicians; Am. Fedn. Clin. Res. Cardiovascular disease. Address: 230 Bailey St, Safety Harbor, FL 33572.

GUBSER, J(OHN) L(EO), b. St. Louis, Mo, June 1, 32. THEORETICAL MECHANICS, MECHANICAL ENGINEERING. B.S.M.E, Washington (St. Louis), 58; univ. fel. & M.S, Illinois, 59, Nat. Sci. Found. fels. & Ph.D.(theoret. & appl. mech), 61. Group dynamics engr, McDonnell Aircraft Corp, 61-70, PROJ. ENGR, DYNAMICS ENG. DEPT, McDONNELL DOUGLAS CORP, 70- Lectr, Washington (St. Louis), 62-64; consult, Humboldt Marine Serv, 63-; lectr, St. Louis Univ, 64- U.S.A, 52-54, Sgt. Am. Soc. Mech. Eng; Am. Soc. Eng. Educ. Applied mechanics; structural dynamics; theory of elasticity; theory of shells; variational techniques in mechanics; stability of marine vessels. Address: Dynamics Engineering Dept, McDonnell Douglas Corp, Box 516 Municipal Airport, St. Louis, MO 63166.

GUCKER, FRANK T(HOMSON), b. Phila, Pa, Apr. 8, 00; m. 25; c. 2. PHYSICAL CHEMISTRY. A.B, Haverford Col, 20, A.M, 21, LL.D, 66; Ph.D.(phys. chem), Harvard, 25. Asst. to Prof. T.W. Richards, 24-25; fel, Nat. Res. Coun, Calif. Inst. Tech, 25-27; asst. to Prof. T.W. Richards, 27-28; res. chemist, ammonia div, E.I. du Pont de Nemours & Co, 28-29; asst. prof. CHEM, Northwestern, 29-36, assoc. prof, 36-42, prof, 42-47; IND. UNIV, BLOOMINGTON, 47-65, res. prof, 65-70, EMER. RES. PROF. & DIR. RES. PHYS. CHEM. AEROSOLS, 70-, chmn. dept. chem, 47-51, dean col. arts & sci, 51-65. Fel, Carnegie Inst, 40-50; mem. cmt. phys. chem. & subcmt. fundamental constants, Nat. Res. Coun, 51-54, cmt. awards in chem. under Fulbright Act, 54-59, chmn, 55-59; consult. & mem. adv. panel chem, Nat. Sci. Found, 57-60, chmn, 58-59; mem, Oak Ridge Nat. Lab. Adv. Cmt. Reactor Chem, 61-63; consult, Ford Found. Latin Am. Prog, 65. Tech. aide, div. 10, Nat. Defense Res. Cmt, 41-42; regional coun, Off. Ord. Res, 52-54. Fel. AAAS; Am. Chem. Soc. Specific heats; heats of dilution; densities and compressibilities of aqueous solutions of electrolytes and nonelectrolytes; light scattering by aerosols and gases; photoelectronic counting and sizing of individual aerosol particles. Address: Dept. of Chemistry, Indiana University, Bloomington, IN 47401.

GUDAT, ALBERT E, b. Schoenlanke, Ger, May 15, 42; U.S. citizen; m. 68. PHYSICAL CHEMISTRY. B.S, Ill. Inst. Technol, 65, Nat. Defense Educ. Act fel, 67-69, Ph.D.(phys. chem), 70. NAT. SCI. FOUND. GRANT CHEM, ORE. STATE UNIV, 70- Am. Chem. Soc. Lattice defects in alkali halide crystals; color centers in potassium iodide; electron traps in polar crystals. Address: Dept. of Chemistry, Oregon State University, Corvallis, OR 97331.

GUDAUSKAS, ROBERT T(HOMAS), b. Georgetown, Ill, July 26, 34; m. 56; c. 3. PLANT PATHOLOGY. B.S, Eastern Illinois, 56; M.S, Illinois, 58, Ph.D.(plant path), 60. Res. asst. PLANT PATH, Illinois, 56-60; asst. prof, AUBURN UNIV, 60-63, assoc. prof, 63-69, PROF, 69- Am. Phytopath Soc. Plant and insect virology; biological control of insects. Address: Dept. of Botany & Microbiology, Auburn University, Auburn, AL 36830.

GUDDER, STANLEY P(HILLIP), b. Centralia, Ill, Jan. 6, 37; m. 58; c. 2. MATHEMATICS. B.S, Washington (St. Louis), 58; M.S, Illinois, 60, Ph.D. (math), 64. Asst. prof. MATH, Army Math. Res. Ctr, Univ. Wis, Madison, 64-65, univ, 65-69; ASSOC. PROF, UNIV. DENVER, 69- Mathematical foundations of quantum mechanics; functional analysis; operator theory. Address: Dept. of Mathematics, University of Denver, Denver, CO 80210.

GUDE, A(RTHUR) J(AMES), III, b. Iowa, Sept. 25, 17; m. 42; c. 1. CRYSTALLOGRAPHY. Geol. Eng, Colo. Sch. Mines, 48, M.Sc, 49. Geologist, U.S. GEOL. SURV, 49-52, X-RAY CRYSTALLOGRAPHER & MINERALOGIST, 52- Lectr, Colo. Sch. Mines; adv, Geol. Surv, Pakistan, 59-61. U.S.N.R, 41-45. Mineral. Soc. Am; Am. Crystallog. Asn; Am. Asn. Petrol. Geol; Am. Geophys. Union; Geochem. Soc. Clay mineralogy and crystallography; carbonate mineralogy; geochemistry; mineralogy and geochemistry of authigenic zeolites. Address: 845 Dudley St, Lakewood, CO 80215.

GUDE, RICHARD HUNTER, b. Eau Claire, Wis, Sept. 16, 37; m. 60; c. 2. ZOOLOGY, ANIMAL BEHAVIOR. B.S, Wisconsin State (Eau Claire), 60; Nat. Sci. Found. summer study grant, Washington (Seattle), 61; M.S, Mich. State, 62, Nat. Insts. Health fel, 63-64, Ph.D.(zool), 65. Asst. prof. BIOL, Hartwick Col, 64-65, assoc. prof, 65-68; ASSOC. PROF. & ACTING CHMN. DEPT, UNIV. TAMPA, 68- Ecol. Soc. Am. Nesting behavior of Siamese fighting fish, Betta splendens. Address: Dept. of Biology, University of Tampa, Tampa, FL 33603.

GUDERLEY, KARL GOTTFRIED, b. Braunsdorf near Freiberg, Ger, June 15, 10; nat; m. 40; c. 2. AERODYNAMICS, MATHEMATICS. Dr.Ing, 38, Dr.Ing. habil, 43. Aeronaut. res. engr, Air Res, Ger, 38-46; WRIGHT AIR DEVELOP. CTR, 46-55, chief appl. math. br, aeronaut. res. lab, 55-61, SR. SCIENTIST, APPL. MATH. RES. LAB, AEROSPACE RES. LABS, 61- Thurman H. Bane Award, 55; distinguished civilian serv. award, U.S. Dept. Defense, 62. Soc. Indust. & Appl. Math. Transonic flow; theoretical aerodynamics; applied mathematics. Address: 1645 Countryside Dr, Dayton, OH 45432.

GUDIKSEN, PAUL H(ALBORG), b. Hvidbjerg, Denmark, July 3, 36; U.S. citizen; m. 63. RADIOCHEMISTRY, ENVIRONMENTAL SCIENCES. B.S, Univ. Wash, 59, M.S, 61, Ph.D.(chem), 67. CHEMIST, LAWRENCE RADIATION LAB, UNIV. CALIF, 67- Am. Chem. Soc. Transport of radioactive trace substances within the stratosphere and exchange with the troposphere; mass concentrations as a function of time within nuclear cratering clouds; determination of radioactivity in the environment. Address: Lawrence Radiation Lab, L 519, P.O. Box 808, Livermore, CA 94550.

GUDMUNDSEN, CATHRYN H(ELEN), b. Phila, Pa, May 19, 24. ORGANIC CHEMISTRY. A.B, Temple, 46; M.A, Columbia, 49; Ph.D.(phys. org. chem), Kansas, 56. Instr. chem, Beaver Col, 49-52; asst. prof, Washington Col. (Md), 56; West Virginia, 56-57; RES. CHEMIST, WYETH LABS. DIV, AM. HOME PROD. CORP, 57- Am. Chem. Soc. Mechanisms of organic reactions; synthesis of organic compounds of medicinal interest; chemical documentation. Address: Wyeth Labs. Division, American Home Products Corp, Box 8299, Philadelphia, PA 19101.

GUDMUNDSEN, RICHARD AUSTIN, b. Salt Lake City, Utah, Dec. 27, 22; m. 47; c. 6. PHYSICS. B.E, Univ. South. Calif, 47, Off. Naval Res. fel, 49-51, Ph.D.(physics), 55. Mgr. semiconductor labs, Hughes Aircraft Co, 52-59; dir. quantum electronics div, Quantatron Inc, 59-60; pres, Quantum Technol. Labs, 60-63; mgr. lasers & electrooptics, AUTONETICS DIV, N.AM. ROCKWELL CORP, ANAHEIM, 63-69, SCI. ADV. TO V.PRES. RES. & TECHNOL, 69- U.S.A, 43-46. Am. Phys. Soc; Am. Inst. Elec. & Electronics Eng; Sci. Res. Soc. Am; Am. Inst. Physics. Quantum and electro-optics; solid state physics; semiconductor physics and devices; invention and development of physical-electronic devices; noise theory; laser physics, devices and systems; computer memories; heat transfer; instrumentation physics. Address: 12052 Larchwood Lane, Santa Ana, CA 92705.

GUDZIN, MARTIN G(ERALD), b. Schenectady, N.Y, Nov. 28, 21; m. 43; c. 3. ELECTRICAL ENGINEERING. B.E.E, Rensselaer Polytech. Inst, 49. Eng. aide, U.S. Naval Ord. Lab, 40-46; electronics engr, W. & L.E. Gurley, 48-49; U.S. Naval Ord. Lab, 49; engr, Beers & Heroy, 49-51; electronics engr, W. & L.E. Gurley, 51-53; sr. engr. prod. systs, Geotech. Corp, 53-66, SR. RES. ENGR, TELEDYNE-GEOTECH, 66- U.S.N.R, 44-45. Inst. Elec. & Electronics Eng. Telemetering systems and components and data-handling systems and components development and design. Address: Teledyne-Geotech, 3401 Shiloh Rd, Garland, TX 75040.

GUDZINOWICZ, B(ENJAMIN) J(OHN), b. Maynard, Mass, Aug. 6, 22; m. 49; c. 1. ANALYTICAL CHEMISTRY. B.A, Clark, 47. Anal. chemist, Monsanto Chem. Co, Mass, 47-50; proj. mgr. anal, Nat. Res. Corp, 52-57; mgr. anal. & lab. servs. group, spec. proj. dept, Monsanto Res. Corp, 57-64; sr. res. anal. chemist, res. dept, Jarrell-Ash Co, 64-66; MGR. ANAL. LAB, POLAROID CORP, 66- U.S.A.A.F, 43-46; U.S.A.F, 50-52. AAAS; Am. Chem. Soc; Soc. Appl. Spectros; fel. Am. Inst. Chem. Polarography; gas; column; paper; thin-layer chromatography; ultraviolet, visible and infrared spectroscopy; titrimetry; microscopy; mass spectroscopy. Address: Dept. 452, Polaroid Corp, Waltham, MA 02154.

GUEDRY, F(REDERICK) E(RNEST), b. New Orleans, La, Dec. 10, 21; m. 48. PSYCHOLOGY. B.A, Tulane, 43, M.S, 48, Ph.D.(psychol), 53. Asst. psychol, U.S. Naval Sch. Aviation Med, 48-49; res. assoc, Tulane Univ. La, 49-50; instr, Newcomb Col, 50-51; res. assoc, Tulane Univ. La, 51-53; head proprioception br, med. res. lab, U.S. Army, 54-59, dep. dir. psychol. div, 59-61; dir. psychol. div. & head exp. psychol. br, U.S. Naval Sch. Aviation Med, 61-69; CHIEF PSYCHOPHYSIOL. SCI. DIV, NAVAL AEROSPACE MED. RES. LAB, 69- Mem. acceleration panel, comt. bioastronaut, Nat. Acad. Sci-Nat. Res. Coun, 59-60, comt. hearing, bioacoust. & biomech, 63-; aerospace med. panel, biodynamics comt, adv. group aeronaut. res. & develop, NATO, 65- U.S.N, 43-46. Fel. AAAS; Am. Psychol. Asn; fel. Aerospace Med. Asn; Barany Soc; Am. Inst. Aeronaut. & Astronaut. Psychophysiological research in spatial orientation, especially as influenced by the vestibular system of the inner ear. Address: Psychophysiological Sciences Division, Naval Aerospace Medical Research Lab, Naval Aerospace Medical Institute, Naval Aerospace Medical Center, Pensacola, FL 32512.

GUEFT, BORIS, b. Cannes, France, Nov. 10, 16; nat; m. 43; c. 3. PATHOLOGY, CYTOCHEMISTRY. A.B, Columbia, 38; M.D, N.Y. Univ, 41. Resident & U.S. Pub. Health Serv. asst, New Britain Gen. Hosp, Conn, 46-47; fel. path, Mt. Sinai Hosp, N.Y, 47-50; instr, sch. med, Yale, 50-55; asst. prof, med. sch, Cincinnati, 55-58; assoc. prof, ALBERT EINSTEIN COL. MED, 58-66, PROF. PATH, 66- Pathologist, Fairfield State Hosp, Conn, 50-55; Vet. Admin. Hosp, Ohio, 55- Med.C, U.S.A, 43-46. Penicillin evaluation; experimental syphilis; cytochemistry of collagen disease; microspectrophotometry; electron microscopy; x-ray diffraction. Address: Dept. of Pathology, Albert Einstein College of Medicine, Yeshiva University, New York, NY 10461.

GUEHLER, PAUL FREDERICK, b. Sandwich, Ill, Apr. 14, 38; m. 61; c. 1. ORGANIC CHEMISTRY. B.A, Augustana Col. (Ill), 60; Ph.D.(org. chem), Minnesota, Minneapolis, 65. Sr. chemist, cent. res. labs, Minn. Mining. & Mfg. Co, 65-67, supvr. med. prod. div, 67-68, tech. mkt, NEW BUS. VENTURE DIV, 68-71, DEVELOP. SPECIALIST, 3M CO, 71- Am. Chem. Soc. Chemical transformations of steroids by microorganisms, algae in particular. Address: New Business Venture Div, 3M Co, St. Paul, MN 55101.

GUELL, DAVID LEE, b. Thorp, Wis, June 29, 38; m. 60; c. 2. CIVIL ENGINEERING, ENGINEERING MECHANICS. B.S, Northwestern, 61, M.S, 62, Ph.D.(eng. mech), 65. ASST. PROF. CIVIL ENG, UNIV. MO-COLUMBIA, 65- Am. Soc. Civil Eng. Elasticity. Address: Dept. of Civil Engineering, University of Missouri-Columbia, Columbia, MO 65201.

GUENNEL, G(OTTFRIED) K(URT), b. Oelsnitz, Ger, Dec. 24, 20; nat; m. 47. PALEOBOTANY. B.S, Butler, 43, M.S, 49; Ph.D, Indiana, 60. Asst. prof. bot, Franklin Col, 49; paleobotanist, geol. surv, Indiana, 49-61; ADV. RES. GEOLOGIST, MARATHON OIL CO, 61- U.S.A, 43-46; civilian with U.S. War Dept, 46-47. AAAS; Bot. Soc. Am; Geol. Soc. Am; Int. Asn. Plant Taxon. Palynology. Address: 6845 S. Penrose Ct, Littleton, CO 80121.

GUENTERT, OTTO J(OHANN), b. Lörrach, Ger, June 6, 24; nat; m. 60; c. 3. PHYSICS. Dipl, Freiburg, 51; Ph.D.(physics), Mass. Inst. Tech, 56. Asst.

physics, Mass. Inst. Tech, 53-56; mem. staff, RAYTHEON RES. DIV, 56-61, prin. res. scientist, 61-70, MGR. MAT. ANAL. LAB, 70- Ger. Army, 42-45, Lt. Am. Phys. Soc; Am. Crystallog. Asn. X-ray diffraction; disordered structures; x-ray optics; electron microprobe analysis. Address: Materials Analysis Lab, Raytheon Research Division, Raytheon Co, Seyon St, Waltham, MA 02154.

GUENTHER, ARTHUR H(ENRY), b. Hoboken, N.J, Apr. 20, 31; m. 54; c. 2. CHEMISTRY, PHYSICS. B.S, Rutgers, 53, fel, Pa. State, 56-57, Ph.D. (chem. physics), 57. Asst. quant. anal, Pa. State, 53-55, spectros. lab, 55-56; dir. pulse power lab, AIR FORCE WEAPONS LAB, 59-61, chief exp. group, physics div, 61-63, SCI. ADV, 63-64; EFFECTS BR. & CHIEF SIMULATION GROUP, KIRTLAND AFB, 64- U.S.A.F.R, 57-, Capt. Optical Soc. Am; Am. Chem. Soc. High resolution infrared spectroscopy; fast time instrumentation; exploding wire phenomenology; nuclear weapon phenomena; molecular physics; high temperature properties and equation of state; high energy discharge systems; shock hydrodynamics; lasers; ultrasonics, optics and spectroscopy; simulation of nuclear weapon detonations. Address: 6304 Rogers N.E, Albuquerque, NM 87117.

GUENTHER, F(REDERICK) O(LIVER), b. Sheboygan, Wis, July 20, 19; m. 47; c. 2. CHEMISTRY. B.S, Wisconsin, 42. Res. chemist, U.S. Rubber Co, N.J, 42-47; asst, res. lab, Gen. Elec. Co, 48-56, chemist, major appliance div, 56-64, sr. proj. chemist, JEFFERSON CHEM. CO, INC, 64-71, GROUP LEADER, 71- Am. Chem. Soc. Polymerization; fluid bed coatings; cellular plastics; process development in organic chemicals; organic coatings for wire. Address: Jefferson Chemical Co, Box 4128, Austin, TX 78751.

GUENTHER, HARRY W(ILBERT), b. Cleveland, Ohio, Feb. 8, 15; m. 49; c. 3. CHEMISTRY. A.B, Oberlin Col, 37; M.S, Pittsburgh, 40; univ. fel, Mellon Inst, 37-41; Monsanto fel. & M.A, Princeton, 43, Ph.D.(phys. chem), 48. Asst. phys. chem, Princeton, 42-43, instr. physics, Army Specialized Training Prog, 43-44, asst. off. Sci. Res. & Develop. & Chem. Corps proj, 44-46; res. assoc, J. & P. Coats, Inc, 46-49, res. chemist, Coats & Clark, Inc, 49-51, head chem. sect, 51-56, dir. chem. res, N.J, 56-67; TECH. ADV, BURLINGTON INDUSTS, INC, 67- Am. Chem. Soc; Am. Asn. Textile Chem. & Colorists; Asn. Res. Dirs; Am. Inst. Chem. Durability of glass; heterogeneous catalysis; modification of properties of molded plastics; textile technology. Address: Burlington Industries, Inc, 1345 Ave. of Americas, New York, NY 10019.

GUENTHER, J(OHN) J(AMES), b. Birmingham, Ala, Nov. 8, 29; m. 52; c. 2. MEAT SCIENCE. B.S, La. State, 51, M.S, 53; Ph.D.(meat sci), Texas A&M, 59. Asst, La. State, 51-53; Texas A&M, 55-58; asst. prof. ANIMAL SCI, OKLA. STATE UNIV, 58-62, assoc. prof, 62-71, PROF, 71- U.S.A.F.R, 53-, Capt. Am. Soc. Animal Sci; Inst. Food Technol; Am. Meat Sci. Asn. Beef and pork carcass quality; muscle proteins; meat freezing; irradiation; freeze drying; processing and preservation. Address: Dept. of Animal Sciences & Industry, Oklahoma State University, Stillwater, OK 74074.

GUENTHER, KARL RUSSELL, b. Milwaukee, Wis, Mar. 14, 26; m. 49; c. 2. BIOCHEMISTRY, POLYMER CHEMISTRY. B.S, Wisconsin, 51, M.S, 53, Ph.D.(biochem), 57. Res. chemist, Bjorksten Res. Labs, Wis, 53-54; fel, Univ. Wis, 56-57; sr. chemist, Esso Res. & Eng. Co, Standard Oil Co.(N.J), 57-63; res. assoc, Stroh Brewery Co, Mich, 63-68; PRES, BJORKSTEN RES. LABS, INC, 68- U.S.A, 44-46, S/Sgt. Am. Chem. Soc; Am. Soc. Brewing Chem. Olefin polymerization; emulsion polymerization; continuous and hydrocarbon fermentation; biochemistry of brewing. Address: Bjorksten Research Labs, Inc, P.O. Box 265, Madison, WI 53701.

GUENTHER, L(LOYD) M(ATHEW), b. Yamhill Co, Ore, Mar. 1, 20; m. 55; c. 3. CHEMICAL ENGINEERING. B.S, Ore. State Col, 42, M.S, 48. Plant engr, Tidewater Assoc. Oil Co, 47-50; res. engr, Ore. State Co, 50; Calif. Res. & Develop. Co, STANDARD OIL CO. CALIF, 51-54, Calif. Res. Corp, 54-63, SR. RES. ENGR, 63-65, CHEVRON RES. CO, 65- U.S.N, 42-46, Res, 46-55, Lt. Am. Inst. Chem. Eng. Petrochemical process development-laboratory and pilot plant scale; applications of plastic materials. Address: Chevron Research Co, 576 Standard Ave, Richmond, CA 94802.

GUENTHER, PAUL E(RNEST), b. La Porte, Ind, May 25, 15; m. 42; c. 2. MATHEMATICS. B.S, Wisconsin, 37; A.M, Harvard, 38; Ph.D.(math), 41. Instr. math, Case, 41-44; mathematician, Nat. Adv. Comt. Aeronaut, 44-45; asst. prof, MATH, CASE WEST. RESERVE UNIV, 45-55, ASSOC. PROF, 55- Am. Math. Soc; Math. Asn. Am. Differential and difference equations. Address: Dept. of Mathematics, Case Western Reserve University, Cleveland, OH 44106.

GUENTHER, RAYMOND A, b. Chicago, Ill, Mar. 13, 32; m. 56; c. 2. LOW TEMPERATURE SOLID STATE PHYSICS. B.S, Ill. Inst. Technol, 55, M.S, 57, Ph.D.(physics), 69; Stuttgart Tech, 55-57; Illinois, Chicago Circle, 57. Res. assoc. PHYSICS, Argonne Nat. Lab, 60-61; instr, Ill. Inst. Technol, 61-62; res. assoc, Argonne Nat. Lab, 62-65; instr, Chicago City Jr. Col, Bogan Br, 65-66; Ill. Inst. Technol, 66-69; vis. asst. prof, 69; ASSOC. PROF, UNIV. NEBR, OMAHA, 69- U.S.M.C, 51-54, Sgt. Heat capacity of dysprosium metal; thermal conductivity of irradiated potassium chloride crystals at temperatures between 0.4 and 4°K. Address: Dept. of Physics, University of Nebraska at Omaha, Omaha, NE 68132.

GUENTHER, R(ICHARD), b. Lodz, Poland, Sept. 9, 10; nat; m. 34. ENGINEERING. Dipl. Ing, Danzig Tech, 34, Dr. Ing, 37; Northeastern, 60-61. Asst, Danzig Tech, 34-37; from engr. commun. lab. to mgr. eng, dept. radio commun. & missile controls, Siemens & Halske, Inc, Ger, 37-45; consult, 45-47; commun. instrumentation, U.S. Sig. Corps Eng. Labs, N.J, 47-52; mem. tech. staff & systs. engr, Bell Tel. Labs, Inc, 52-56; mgr. surface commun. systs. lab, systs. eng. & adv. develop, Radio Corp. Am, 56-63, chief scientist, commun. systs. div, 63-65, mgr, adv. commun. tech, commun. systs. div, 65-68, staff tech. adv, commercial electronics systs. div, RCA CORP, 68-70, COMPUT. SYSTS. ARCHITECT, COMPUT. SYSTS. DEVELOP. DIV, 70- AAAS; fel. Inst. Elec. & Electronics Eng. Engineering physics, particularly application in modern communication through information theory; network synthesis; solid state physics; thermionics; electromagnetic theory; mathematical analysis. Address: RCA Computer Systems, Systems Development Division, Marlboro, MA 01752.

GUENTHER, RONALD BERNARD, b. North Bend, Ore, Nov. 24, 37; m. 64. MATHEMATICAL PHYSICS. B.A, Oregon State, 59, M.A, 62; Fulbright fel, Hamburg, 59-60; exchange scholar, Aachen Tech, 62-63; Ph.D.(appl. math), Colorado, 64. Adv. res. mathematician, res. ctr, Marathon Oil Co, Colo, 64-66; asst. prof. MATH, ORE. STATE UNIV, 66-70, ASSOC. PROF, 70- Am. Math. Soc. Uniqueness and existence theorems in partial differential equations, parabolic in particular. Address: Dept. of Mathematics, Oregon State University, Corvallis, OR 80121.

GUENTHER, W(ILLIAM) B(ENTON), b. Dayton, Ohio, Sept. 27, 28. PHYSICAL & INORGANIC CHEMISTRY. B.A, Oberlin Col, 48; M.S, Rochester, 50, Ph.D.(chem), 54. Instr. CHEM, Alaska, 50-52; asst. prof, Muhlenberg Col, 54-56; UNIV. OF THE SOUTH, 56-66, assoc. prof, 66-68, PROF, 68- Cotrell Res. Corp. grant, 58; Lilly Endowment res. grant, 59. Am. Chem. Soc. Inorganic complexes; chemical education; analytical chemistry. Address: Dept. of Chemistry, University of the South, Sewanee, TN 37375.

GUENTHER, WILLIAM C(HARLES), b. Stewartville, Minn, Dec. 17, 21; m. 55; c. 4. MATHEMATICAL STATISTICS. B.A, Iowa, 43, M.S, 46; Ph.D.(math), Washington (Seattle), 52. Instr. math, Arkansas, 48-49; math. statistician, U.S. Naval Ord. Lab, 52-55; asst. prof. math, Arizona State, 55-57; Fresno State Col, 57-59; assoc. prof. STATIST, UNIV. WYO, 59-63, PROF, 63- Nat. Sci. Found. faculty fel, 62. U.S.A.A.F, 43-45. Math. Asn. Am; Inst. Math. Statist; fel. Am. Statist. Asn; Am. Soc. Qual. Control. Testing hypotheses and quality control. Address: Dept. of Statistics, University of Wyoming, Box 3275, Laramie, WY 82070.

GUENTHERMAN, ROBERT HENRY, b. Chicago, Ill, July 9, 33; m. 59; c. 2. PHYSIOLOGY, PERIODONTOLOGY. North Texas State, 59-61; D.D.S, Baylor, 65, Ph.D.(physiol), 68. Nat. Insts. Health training fel, PHYSIOL. & PERIODONT, 65-68; ASST. PROF, COL. DENT, BAYLOR UNIV, 68- Merritt-Parks award, 65. U.S.A.F, 53-57, 1st Lt. Am. Dent. Asn; Am. Asn. Dent. Schs; Int. Asn. Dent. Res; Am. Acad. Periodont. Effect of oxygen and oxygenating agents on normal and diseased periodontal tissue; cardiovascular and metabolic physiology and its relationship to the periodontal structure of the oral cavity. Address: College of Dentistry, Baylor University, 800 Hall St, Dallas, TX 75226.

GUENZI, WAYNE D, b. Sterling, Colo, Oct. 6, 31; m. 54; c. 3. SOIL CHEMISTRY. B.S, Colorado State, 53, M.S, 59; Ph.D.(soil sci), Nebraska, 64. Chemist, U.S. DEPT. AGR, 59-66, RES. SOIL SCIENTIST, 66- U.S.A.F, 53-57, Res, 57-67, Capt. AAAS; Am. Soc. Agron; Soil Sci. Soc. Am. Isolation of phytotoxic substances in plants and soils; interactions of chlorinated insecticides with soils, including photodegradation, microbial decomposition and volatilization. Address: U.S. Dept. of Agriculture, P.O. Box E, Ft. Collins, CO 80521.

GUERAULT, ARMAND, b. Montreal, Que, Sept. 18, 22; m. 53; c. 1. MICROBIOLOGY, IMMUNOLOGY. B.A, Montreal, 42, B.Sc, 45, Ciba Co. fels, 45-48, M.Sc, 46, Ph.D.(org. chem), 49. Demonstr. org. chem, Montreal, 46-48, asst. microbiol. & immunol, inst. microbiol. & hyg, 49-52, lab. head, 53; traveling fel, Int. Ctr. Chem. Microbiol. & Ist. Superiore Sanitá, Italy, 55-56; dept. bact, Manchester, 56-57; RES. ASSOC. MICROBIOL. & IMMUNOL, INST. MICROBIOL. & HYG. & LECTR, FACULTY MED, UNIV. MONTREAL, 58-, LECTR, SCH. HYG, 62- Am. Soc. Microbiol; Can. Soc. Microbiol; Can. Biochem. Soc; Sr. mem. Chem. Inst. Can. Chloralose derivatives, glucose condensation products and bacterial enzymatic oxidation; medical microbiology and immunology; bacterial iridescence and fermentations; fractionation and purification of bacterial antigens; bacterial infections and experimental immunity; problems of immuno-microbiological standardization; Bordetella pertussis and related species. Address: Institute of Microbiology & Hygiene, University of Montreal, P.O. Box 100, Laval-des-Rapides, Que, Can.

GUERBER, HOWARD P(AUL), b. Rifle, Colo, July 29, 26; m. 62. ELECTRICAL ENGINEERING. B.S, Colorado, 47, M.S, 54. Develop. engr, Westinghouse Elec. Corp, 48-50; design & develop. engr, RCA CORP, 50-51, 53-59, SYSTS. LEADER, 59- U.S.N, 44-46, 51-53, Res, 53- Asn. Comput. Mach; Inst. Elec. & Electronics Eng. Development and design of large scale multiprocessor digital data processing systems. Address: Communications Systems Division, RCA Corp, Camden, NJ 08102.

GUERDAN, GEORGE A(LFRED), b. New York, N.Y, Sept. 9, 03; m. 44; c. 1. MECHANICAL ENGINEERING. M.E, Stevens Inst. Tech, 25, M.S, 31; Columbia. Asst. engr, N.Y. Edison Co, 25; instr. machine design, Stevens Inst. Tech, 25-29, 30-31; specification & design engr, Bell Tel. Labs, Inc, 30; instr. machine design, Cooper Union, 32-33; drafting & description geom, City Col. New York, 37-38, mech. eng, 38-41, asst. prof, 42-48, assoc. prof, 49-53, chmn. dept, 52-62, prof, 54-72; RETIRED. Consult, Atlantic Tank Corp, 26-39; Conveyor Eng. & Equip. Co, 26-34. Civilian with U.S.A, 42-46. Am. Soc. Mech. Eng; Soc. Automotive Eng; Am. Soc. Eng. Educ. Mechanisms; mechanics of machines; general dynamics; stress analyses; production problems; materials; engineering education. Address: 24 Lincoln Ave, Cliffside Park, NJ 07010.

GUERIGUIAN, JEAN L(EON), b. Alexandria, Egypt, Sept. 20, 35; m. 68; c. 2. BIOCHEMISTRY, PHARMACOLOGY. Lic. ès Sci, Univ. Paris, 64, M.D, 65. Staff assoc. endocrinol, Peter Bent Brigham Hosp, Boston, 65-67; INSTR. biochem, med. sch, Univ. Paris, 67-69; PHARMACOL, SCH. MED, UNIV. N.C, CHAPEL HILL, 69- Res. fel. biochem, Harvard Med. Sch, 65-67; res. asst, Nat. Inst. Health & Med. Res, Paris, 67-69. AAAS. Analytical chemistry; metabolism and mechanism of action of steroid hormones; identification, physicochemical characterization and assay of steroid-binding proteins from serum, ovary, target organs and tumors of target organs. Address: Dept. of Pharmacology, 306A Swing Bldg, School of Medicine, University of North Carolina at Chapel Hill, Chapel Hill, NC 27514.

GUERIN, MICHAEL RICHARD, b. Waukegan, Ill, May 10, 41; m. 65; c. 2. ANALYTICAL CHEMISTRY, CANCER. B.S, North. Ill. Univ, 63; Ph.D.(anal. chem), Iowa State Univ, 67. RES. CHEMIST, ANAL. CHEM. DIV, OAK RIDGE NAT. LAB, 67- Del, Int. Group Smoking & Health Res, 70; consult, chem. carcinogenesis contract rev. comt, Nat. Cancer Inst, 70, mem. tobacco working group, 70- AAAS; Am. Chem. Soc. Application of analytical chemical methodologies to the elucidation of the chemical factors responsibile for environmental and tobacco smoke chemical carcinogenesis. Address: Analytical Chemistry Division, Bldg. 4500 S, Oak Ridge National Lab, Oak Ridge, TN 37830.

GUERIN, MURIEL M(AY), b. Saskatoon, Sask, July 31, 16; m. 55; c. 2. VIROLOGY. B.Sc, Saskatchewan, 36. BACTERIOLOGIST vitamins, FOOD & DRUG DIV, DEPT. NAT. HEALTH & WELFARE, 42-49, virol, virus labs, 49-59, cancer res, biochem. res. div, 59-62, VIROL, LAB. HYG, VIRUS LABS, 62- Can. Soc. Microbiol. Improvements in laboratory diagnostic procedures for human virus diseases; tissue culture studies as related to virology and cancer research. Address: Lab. of Hygiene, Virus Labs, Food & Drug. Division, Dept. of National Health & Welfare, Tunney's Pasture, Ottawa 4, Ont, Can.

GUERNSEY, DONALD L(EWIS), b. Vincennes, Ind, Feb. 2, 04; m. 29; c. 2. ANALYTICAL CHEMISTRY, B.S, Illinois, 26. Analyst, Armco Steel Corp, Ohio, 26-38; head anal. sect, dept. metall, Mass. Inst. Tech, 38-65, head cent. anal. group, ctr. mat. sci, 65-71; RETIRED. AAAS; Am. Chem. Soc; Soc. Appl. Spectros. General inorganic chemical analysis. Address: 3 Carmel Dr, North Billerica, MA 01862.

GUERNSEY, EDWIN O(WENS), b. Wash, D.C, Sept. 14, 20; m. 43; c. 3. CHEMICAL ENGINEERING, PHYSICAL CHEMISTRY. B.S, Illinois, 41; D.Eng, Yale, 49. Sr. res. chem. engr, cent. res. div, Socony Mobil Oil Co, Inc, 48-54, Socony sponsorship, Oak Ridge Sch. Reactor Tech, 54-55, sr. res. chem. engr, cent. res. div, 55-60, res. assoc, 60-65, sr. planning assoc, corp. planning & econ. dept, Mobil Oil Corp, 65-67, supvr, MOBIL RES. & DEVELOP. CORP, 67-69, SPEC. STUDIES GROUP, 69- U.S.A.A.F, 42-46, Maj. Am. Inst. Chem. Eng; Am. Chem. Soc; fel. Am. Inst. Chem. Fischer-Tropsch synthesis of hydrocarbons; catalytic reforming and cracking; nuclear electric power generation; radiation chemistry. Address: Mobil Research & Development Corp, Paulsboro, NJ 08066.

GUERNSEY, E(RNEST) W(ILLIAM), b. Vincennes, Ind, May 1, 96; m. 18; c. 2. CHEMISTRY. B.S, Illinois, 18; M.S, American Univ, 22; Ph.D.(chem), George Washington, 24. Res. chemist, Brown Paper Co, N.H, 19; from asst. to assoc. chem. eng, fixed nitrogen res. lab, U.S. Dept. Agr, 19-26; from res. chemist to asst. dir. res, Baltimore Gas & Elec. Co, 26-46, dir. res, 46-64; consult. engr, 64-70; RETIRED. Lectr, American Univ, 25-26. U.S.A, 18-19. Fel. AAAS; Am. Chem. Soc; Am. Gas Asn; Am. Inst. Chem. Eng; fel. Inst. Elec. & Electronics Eng. Fixation of nitrogen; agriculturally available phosphorus; corrosion; heat flow; organic sulfur compounds; fuels; heat pumps cycles; nuclear energy. Address: 11 W. Melrose Ave, Baltimore, MD 21210.

GUERNSEY, JANET B(ROWN), b. Germantown, Pa, May 2, 13; m. 36; c. 5. PHYSICS. A.B, Wellesley Col, 35; A.M, Harvard, 48; Ph.D.(physics), Mass. Inst. Tech, 55. Instr. PHYSICS, WELLESLEY COL, 43-49, asst. prof, 49-55, assoc. prof, 55-61, PROF, 61-, CHMN. DEPT, 67-, Louise S. McDowell prof, 70. AAAS; Am. Asn. Physics Teachers; Am. Phys. Soc. Neutron physics; electrostatic accelerators. Address: Dept. of Physics, Wellesley College, Wellesley, MA 02181.

GUERNSEY, JOHN, b. Middletown, Ohio, Oct. 2, 29; m. 51; c. 3. METALLURGY. Met.E, Cincinnati, 52; Carnegie Inst. Tech, 54-56. Res. technologist, Lunkenheimer Co, 52-53; res. metallurgist, Rem-Cru Titanium, Inc, 53-56; chief metallurgist, precision parts div, Ex-Cell-Co Corp, Ohio, 56-60; res. metallurgist, Crucible, Hunter & Midland Labs, 60-63; develop. projs, 64-65, assoc. dir. metal processing develop, 65-67, titanium res. & develop, 67-70; tech. dir. titanium, mfg. & applns. eng. & vacuum melt, crucible mat. res. ctr, Colt Industs, 70-71; DIR. METALL, JESSOP STEEL CO, 71- Am. Soc. Metals. Physical metallurgy, especially development of improvements in processing stainless steel and specialty metals. Address: Jessop Steel Co, Green St, Washington, PA 15301.

GUERNSEY, RALPH LEWIS, b. Middletown, Ohio, Nov. 23, 30; m. 64; c. 2. PLASMA PHYSICS. B.A, Miami (Ohio), 52, M.S, 54; Ph.D.(physics), Michigan, 60. Res. specialist, Boeing Co, Wash, 60-63; res. asst. prof. PLASMA PHYSICS, INST. FLUID DYNAMICS & APPL. MATH, UNIV. MD, COLLEGE PARK, 63-65, RES. ASSOC. PROF, 65- Am. Phys. Soc. Statistical physics; plasma kinetic theory. Address: Institute of Fluid Dynamics & Applied Mathematics, University of Maryland, College Park, MD 20740.

GUERRA, CARLOS RENATO, b. Arequipa, Peru, Feb. 16, 37; m. 66. SURFACE CHEMISTRY. B.S, Missouri, Rolla, 61; fel, Mont. Sch. Mines, 61-62, M.S, 62; Ph.D.(eng. sci), California, Berkeley, 65. Eng. trainee, coop. prog, Nordberg Mfg. Co, Wis, 56-60; res. asst, Mont. Sch. Mines, 61; California, Berkeley, 62-65; res. assoc, Columbia Univ, 65-66; RES. CHEMIST, INORG. DEPT, RES. CTR, W.R. GRACE & CO, 66- Guest researcher, inst. inorg. chem, Univ. Munich, 67-69. AAAS; Am. Chem. Soc. Study of physico-chemical phenomena occurring at interfaces affecting the synthesis and properties of new materials. Address: Research Center, W.R. Grace & Co, Clarksville, MD 21029.

GUERRANT, GORDON O(WEN), b. Fulton, Mo, July 11, 23; m. 44; c. 4. ANALYTICAL CHEMISTRY. A.B, Westminster Col, 44; Ph.D.(anal. chem), Illinois, 49. Asst. anal. chem, Illinois, 46-49; chemist, explor. & prod. res. div, Shell Develop. Co, Tex, 49-63; sr. res. chemist, Armour Agr. Chem. Co, 63-67; SUPVRY. RES. CHEMIST, TECH. DEVELOP. LAB, CTR. DISEASE CONTROL, U.S. PUB. HEALTH SERV, 67- U.S.N.R, 44-46, Lt.(jg). AAAS; Am. Chem. Soc; fel. Am. Inst. Chem. Spectrophotometry; emission spectroscopy; x-ray diffraction; micromolecular weights; gas chromatography; trace gas analyses; thermal stability of ammonium phosphates; analysis and formulation of public health pesticides. Address: Technical Development Lab, Center for Disease Control, U.S. Public Health Service, P.O. Box 2167, Savannah, GA 31402.

GUERRANT, JOHN L(IPPINCOTT), b. Callaway, Va, Dec. 28, 10; m. 45; c. 2. INTERNAL MEDICINE. B.S, Hampden-Sydney Col, 33; M.D, Virginia, 37, M.S, 42. Instr. INTERNAL MED, SCH. MED, UNIV. VA, 46-49, asst. prof, 49-54, assoc. prof, 54-62, PROF, 62- Med.C, 42-46, Capt. Am. Thoracic Soc; Am. Med. Asn; Am. Col. Physicians; Am. Acad. Allergy. Pulmonary disease. Address: University Hospital, Charlottesville, VA 22903.

GUERRANT, R(ALPH) E(UGENE), b. Arvonia, Va, Aug. 30, 11; m. 43; c. 1. BIOCHEMISTRY. A.B, Westminster Col.(Mo), 33; Pa. State Col, 33-34; M.A, Missouri, 35, Ph.D.(agr. chem), 37. Instr. agr. chem, Missouri, 36-37; prof, Shurtleff Col, 38-42; res. biochemist, res. labs, Carnation Co, Wis, 42-43; asst. prof. biochem, Kans. State Col, 46-56; CLIN. BIOCHEMIST, PRESBY. HOSP, 56- U.S.A, 43-46. AAAS; Am. Chem. Soc; Am. Asn. Clin. Chem. Clinical methods; nutrition. Address: Presbyterian Hospital, Charlotte, NC 28204.

GUERRANT, W(ILLIAM) B(ARNETT), JR, b. Danville, Ky, Mar. 22, 22; m. 46; c. 1. ORGANIC CHEMISTRY. A.B, Austin Col, 46; Ph.D, North Carolina, 49. Tech. dir, South. Chem. Cotton Co, Inc, 49-51; plant mgr, Nat. Cellulose, S.Am, 51-52; res. chemist, Anderson Clayton & Co, Inc, 52-57; PROF. CHEM, Austin Col, 57-69; TEX. TECH UNIV, 69- Consult, Robert R. King & Assocs, 58- U.S.A.A.F, 42-46, 1st Lt. AAAS; Am. Chem. Soc; Am. Oil Chem. Soc; fel. The Chem. Soc. Fat and oil chemistry; organic mechanisms. Address: Dept. of Chemistry, Texas Tech University, Lubbock, TX 79409.

GUERRERO, ARIEL H(ERIBERTO), b. Buenos Aires, Arg, Jan. 28, 22; m. 52; c. 2. ANALYTICAL & INORGANIC CHEMISTRY. Ph.D.(chem), Univ. Buenos Aires, 46. Asst. ANAL. CHEM, FACULTY EXACT & NATURAL SCI, UNIV. BUENOS AIRES, 42-55, lectr, 56-58, assoc. prof, 58-70, PROF, 70-, dean, 68-69, prof, faculty agron. & vet, 56-70, inorg. chem, faculty eng, 58-70. Anal. chemist, Nat. Direction Chem, 44-46; head anal. lab, Lever Bros, 47-49; Brit. Coun. fel, Univ. Liverpool, 47-48; dir, APA, 50-63; indust. consult, A. Bonfanti Factory, 53-59; Espiga Co, 60-61; tech. secy, Arg. Inst. Oils & Fats, 62-64; dir. training chem. teachers, Nat. Res. Coun, Ministry Educ. & Nat. Inst, 62-68, Pan Am. Union, 69-71; mem. conf. chem. educ, Pan-Am. Union, Buenos Aires, 65, Int. Union Pure & Appl. Chem, Frascati, 69, Sao Paulo, 71. Arg. Chem. Asn; Arg. Sci. Soc; Arg. Asn. Advan. Sci; Am. Chem. Soc; Arg. Inst. Qual. Control (v.pres). Acetate complexes of lead; rodhamine B as analytical reagent in benzene solution extraction; buffering capacity; direct estimation of ions. Address: Cordoba 2062 4°A, Buenos Aires, Argentina.

GUERRERO, E. T, b. Richmond, Tex, Nov. 2, 24; m. 49; c. 4. PETROLEUM & MECHANICAL ENGINEERING. B.S, Tex. A&M Univ, 49, Stanolind Oil & Gas Co. fel, 49, M.S, 50, Magnolia Petrol. Co. fel, 50-51, Ph.D.(petrol. eng), 53. Instr. petrol. eng, Tex. A&M Univ, 52-53; petrol. reservoir engr, Seeligson Eng. Comt, 53-56; trustee's prof. petrol. eng. & head dept, UNIV. TULSA, 56-66, DEAN COL. ENG. & PHYS. SCI, 66- U.S.A.A.F, 43-46, 1st Lt. Am. Soc. Eng. Educ; Am. Inst. Mining, Metall. & Petrol. Eng. Relation between capillary pressures and relative permeabilities of large limestone cores; effect of surface and interfacial tensions on the recovery of oil by water flooding. Address: 1741 S. Darlington Ave, Tulsa, OK 74112.

GUERRY, DAVENPORT, JR, b. Hickman, Ky, Dec. 27, 17; m. 55; c. 1. PHYSICAL & ORGANIC CHEMISTRY. B.S, Duke, 40; M.S, Emory, 41; Ph.D. (chem), Vanderbilt, 44. Res. chemist, E.I. du Pont de Nemours & Co, 44-48; instr. chem, Pittsburgh, 48-51; RES. CHEMIST, MONSANTO CO, W.Va, 51-65, SPECTROS, RES. DEPT, APPL. SCI. SECT, MO, 65- Am. Chem. Soc.(secy, 56-57, v.chmn, 59, chmn, 60). Infrared, mass, x-ray and emission spectroscopy; rheology of elastomer systems. Address: Research Dept, Applied Sciences Section, Monsanto Co, 1700 S. Second St, St. Louis, MO 63177.

GUERTIN, ALFRED THOMAS, b. Trenton, N.J, Oct. 22, 34; m. 58. PHYSICAL CHEMISTRY. B.S, Trinity Col, 56; Ph.D.(phys. chem), Mass. Inst. Tech, 60. Res. chemist, AM. CYANAMID CO, 60-65, GROUP LEADER, FORMICA DIV, 65- Am. Chem. Soc. Polymer characterization; polymerization kinetics; resin technology; paper chemistry; thermodynamics; statistical mechanics; composite materials; laminating technology. Address: Formica Division, American Cyanamid Co, 10155 Reading Rd, Cincinnati, OH 45241.

GUERTIN, DONALD LUCIUS, b. Troy, N.Y, Oct. 22, 30; m. 54; c. 4. ANALYTICAL CHEMISTRY. B.S, Union (N.Y), 52; M.S, Albany State Teachers Col, 53; Ph.D.(anal. chem), Rensselaer Polytech, 55. Chemist, prod. res. div, Esso Res. & Eng. Co, STANDARD OIL CO.(N.J), 55-56, proj. leader anal. chem, 56-59, anal. res. div, 59-61, asst. dir, 61-64, dir, 64-67, comptroller & treas, 67-68, coord. personnel develop, 68-69, asst. orgn. planning adv, off. of secy, N.Y.C, 69-71, SR. PLANNING ADV, PUB. AFFAIRS DEPT, 71- Mem. co-adj. faculty, exten. div, Rutgers Univ, 58-61. Am. Chem. Soc. Research management. Address: 52 Oak Ave, Metuchen, NJ 08840.

GUERTIN, JACQUES P, b. Montreal, Que, Feb. 28, 39; m. 64. PHYSICAL INORGANIC CHEMISTRY. B.Sc, McGill, 60, Ph.D.(chem), 64. Res. chemist, Stauffer Chem. Co, 64-68; mem. tech. staff, Bell Tel. Labs, 68-69; MEM. STAFF PLASMA DEVICE, POWER SYSTS. DIV, McGRAW EDISON CO, 69- Coordination compounds of silicon tetrafluoride; high energy solid oxidizers containing chlorine, fluorine, nitrogen and oxygen; vacuum technology; powder metallurgy; vacuum melting and solidification; metals and ceramics. Address: Power Systems Division, McGraw Edison Co, 11131 Adams Rd, Franksville, WI 53126.

GUERTIN, RALPH FRANCIS, b. Stafford Springs, Conn, Dec. 2, 38; m. 65; c. 1. ELEMENTARY PARTICLE PHYSICS. B.S, Worcester Polytech. Inst, 61; Nat. Sci. Found. fel & M.S, Yale, 63, Ph.D.(physics), 69. Res. asst. elem. particle physics, Mid. East Tech. Univ, Ankara, 64-65; res. assoc, Roman Cath. Univ. Nijmegen, 65-67; Univ. Calif, Berkeley, 69-70; ASST. PROF. PHYSICS, RICE UNIV, 70- Am. Phys. Soc. Analytic properties of scattering amplitudes; Lorentz group, Regge poles. Address: Dept. of Physics, Rice University, Houston, TX 77001.

GUERTIN, ROBERT POWELL, b. Trenton, N.J, July 5, 39; m. 66; c. 2. SOLID STATE PHYSICS. B.S, Trinity Col.(Conn), 61; M.A, Wesleyan, 63; Ph.D.(physics), Rochester, 68. ASST. PROF. PHYSICS, TUFTS UNIV, 68- Vis. scientist, Francis Bitter Nat. Magnetic Lab, Mass. Inst. Technol.

Am. Phys. Soc. Effect of magnetic impurities on superconductivity and correlations with magnetic properties in the normal state; transport and high field magnetic properties of nearly ferromagnetic alloys. Address: Dept. of Physics, Tufts University, Medford, MA 02155.

GUESS, ARNOLD W(ILLARD), b. Englewood, N.J, Apr. 27, 29. ASTRO-PHYSICS, ASTRONOMY. A.B, Cornell, 51; Ph.D.(astrophys), Harvard, 63. Jr. scientist, Nat. Bur. Standards, D.C, 51-52; lab. asst, Calif. Inst. Tech, 52-54, jr. scientist, jet propulsion lab, 54-55; physicist, geophys. directorate, Air Force Cambridge Res. Ctr, Mass, 57-60; Geophys. Corp. Am, 60-63; asst. prof. astron, Illinois, 63-64; res. appointee, Lawrence Radiation Lab, Univ. Calif, 64-66; RES. SCIENTIST, Douglas Advan. Res. Labs, 66-69, DOUGLAS AIRCRAFT CO, 69- U.S.A.F, 55-57, 1st Lt. Am. Astron. Soc. Shock waves and fluid dynamics; stellar structure and white dwarf interiors; relativistic degenerate gases. Address: Douglas Aircraft Co, 3855 Lakewood Blvd, Long Beach, CA 90801.

GUESS, WALLACE L(OUIS), b. Durham, N.C, July 18, 24; m. 47; c. 2. PHARMACY. B.S, Texas, 49, M.S, 51; Ph.D.(pharm), Washington (Seattle), 59. Asst. prof. pharm, Univ. Tex, Austin, 53-61, assoc. prof, 61-69, prof, 69-71, asst. dir. drug plastic res. lab, 63-71; DEAN. SCH. PHARM, UNIV. MISS, 71- U.S.A, 43-45, Sgt. Am. Pharmaceut. Asn. Toxicology, pharmacology and evaluation of plastics used in medical practice. Address: School of Pharmacy, University of Mississippi, University, MS 38677.

GUEST, ARTHUR E(DWIN), b. Iowa, Aug. 24, 01; m. 27; c. 1. FOOD TECHNOLOGY. A.B, Simpson Col, 23; Iowa State Col, 23-26. Instr, Kans. State Col, 26-29; res. chemist, Calco Chem. Co, N.J, 29-30; fel, Mellon Inst, 30-32; res. chemist, Wm. Wrigley Jr. Co, 35-44; chief chemist, J.W. Allen & Co, Ill, 44-45; res. chemist customer res, Continental Can Co, Inc, 45-50; dir. res. & quality control, Haxton Foods Inc, 50-58; supvr. qual. control, Comstock Foods, Inc, N.Y, 58-61; FOOD TECHNOLOGIST, Food & Container Inst, U.S. ARMY, 62-63, NATICK LABS, 63- Inst. Food Technol. Canning, freezing and dehydration technology of fruits and vegetables; nutrition. Address: Food Division, U.S. Army Natick Labs, Natick, MA 01760.

GUEST, GARETH E, b. Mobile, Ala, June 13, 33; m. 54; c. 3. THEORETICAL PHYSICS. B.A, Vanderbilt, 54, M.A, 56; Ph.D.(physics), Wisconsin, 60. Asst. prof. physics, North Texas State, 60-62, assoc. prof, 62-63; PHYSICIST, OAK RIDGE NAT. LAB, 63- Am. Phys. Soc. Plasma physics. Address: Oak Ridge National Lab, P.O. Box Y, Oak Ridge, TN 37830.

GUEST, HOWARD RUSSELL, b. Scranton, Pa, Oct. 11, 14; m. 47; c. 2. ORGANIC CHEMISTRY. B.S, Pa. State, 36. Proj. chemist, chem. div, UNION CARBIDE CORP, 36-45, group leader, 45-62, asst. dir. res. & develop, 62-64, ASSOC. DIR. olefins div, 64-67, RES. & DEVELOP, CHEM. & PLASTICS DIV, 67- Am. Chem. Soc; Am. Entom. Soc; Am. Phytopath. Soc. Agricultural chemicals; catalysis; aldehyde reactions; glyoxal; styrene; acrolein; pesticides; chemical modification of textiles; industrial water and air pollution control. Address: Chemicals & Plastics Division, Union Carbide Corp, P.O. Box 8361, South Charleston, WV 25303.

GUEST, MARY FRANCES, b. New Smyrna Beach, Fla, Oct. 7, 27. PHYSIOLOGY. B.S, Fla. State, 48; M.S, Texas Tech, 54; Ph.D.(physiol), Tulane, 64. Instr. zool, anat. & physiol, Texas Tech, 54-60; res. asst. surg, sch. med, Tulane, 63-64; asst. prof. PHYSIOL, faculty med, Malaya, 64-68; lectr, sch. vet. med, Univ. Calif, Davis, 68, asst. prof, 68-71; ASST. RES. PARASITOLOGIST, G.W. HOOPER FOUND, MED. CTR, UNIV. CALIF, SAN FRANCISCO, 71- AAAS; Am. Soc. Trop. Med. & Hyg. Respiration; pulmonary physiology; pulmonary pathophysiology related to immune etiologies; immune response to filarial infections. Address: G.W. Hooper Foundation, University of California Medical Center, San Francisco, CA 94116.

GUEST, M(AURICE) MASON, b. Fredonia, N.Y, July 30, 06; m. 36; c. 2. PHYSIOLOGY. A.B, Michigan, 30; Ph.D.(physiol), Columbia, 41. Field asst, Fed. Bur. Entomol, 30-31; teacher, pub. sch, N.Y, 31-36; asst. PHYSIOL, Columbia, 36, instr, 36-40, res. assoc, 40-42; asst. prof, col. med, Wayne, 46, assoc. prof, 46-50; PROF. & CHMN. DEPT, MED. BR, UNIV. TEX, 51- Mem, subcmt. hemorrhage & thrombosis, Nat. Res. Coun, 59-63; White House conf. aging, comt. biol, 60-61; comt. thrombolytic agents, Nat. Heart Inst, 62-67; hemat. study sect, Nat. Insts. Health, 60-64, 67-71; mem. med. adv. bd. educ. film prod, 67-; assoc. ed, Microvasc. Res, 69- U.S.A.F, 42-46. AAAS; Am. Physiol. Soc; Gerontol. Soc; Soc. Exp. Biol. & Med; Int. Soc. Hemat; Microcirc. Soc. Carbohydrate metabolism; endocrinology; physiology of uterus and vagina; physiology of high altitudes; blood clotting mechanism with special consideration of lytic and antilytic factors; effects of ions on heart and circulation; gerontology; physiology of microcirculation; physiology of decompression sickness. Address: Dept. of Physiology, University of Texas Medical Branch, Galveston, TX 77550.

GUEST, RICHARD W(ILLIAM), b. Oklahoma City, Okla, July 7, 32; m. 59; c. 3. AGRICULTURAL ENGINEERING. B.S, N.Dak. State, 54, M.S, 58. Asst. prof. AGR. ENG, CORNELL UNIV, 58-64, ASSOC. PROF, 64- Staff mem, New Holland Co. Div, Sperry-Rand Corp, Pa, 65-66. U.S.A.F, 55-56, 2nd Lt. Am. Soc. Agr. Eng. Electrical power and processing; materials handling; farm power and machinery. Address: Dept. of Agricultural Engineering, Riley-Robb Hall, Cornell University, Ithaca, NY 14850.

GUEST, WILLIAM C, b. Pine Bluff, Ark, July 18, 25. GENETICS. A.B, Emory, 48, M.S, 50; Ph.D.(zool), Texas, 59. Instr. sci, Anderson Col.(S.C), 50-52; asst. prof. biol, Millsaps Col, 52-54; marine biologist, marine lab, Tex. Game & Fish Comn, 54-57; res. assoc. genetics found, Texas, 57-59; asst. prof. biol, Alabama, 59-63; ZOOL, UNIV. ARK, FAYETTEVILLE, 63-64, ASSOC. PROF, 64- Summer res. partic, Oak Ridge Nat. Lab, 61. U.S.N.R, 43-46, Lt.(jg). AAAS; Genetics Soc. Am; Am. Genetic Asn; Soc. Study Evolution. Karyotypic studies of, and the effect of drugs on, somatic cells of Peromyscus species and hamster in culture. Address: Dept. of Zoology, University of Arkansas, Fayetteville, AR 72701.

GUETHS, JAMES E, b. Shawano, Wis, Aug. 18, 39; m. 61; c. 3. SOLID STATE PHYSICS. B.A, Ripon Col, 61; M.S, Connecticut, 63, Nat. Sci. Found. fel, 63-66, Ph.D.(physics), 66. Res. assoc. PHYSICS, Connecticut, 66; asst. prof, WIS. STATE UNIV-OSHKOSH, 66-70, ASSOC. PROF, 70-, CHMN.

DEPT, 69- Vis. scientist, inst. math. sci, Univ. Conn, summer 67. Am. Phys. Soc; Am. Asn. Physics Teachers.. Transport phenomena in metal and alloy single crystals; learning hierarchies in university science. Address: Dept. of Physics, Wisconsin State University-Oshkosh, Oshkosh, WI 54901.

GUETTEL, CHARLES L(EON), b. Chicago, Ill, Dec. 1, 14; m. 41; c. 4. METALLURGY. B.S, Northwestern, 36. Asst, develop. labs, Cent. Sci. Co, 36, 38; anal. chemist, Carnegie-Ill. Steel Corp, 37; chemist in charge spectrographic & x-ray diffractions labs, Rock Island Arsenal, 38-45; MGR. LABS. & DEVELOP, DRIVER-HARRIS CO, 45- Meritorious civilian serv. commendation, Armed Serv. Forces, U.S. War Dept, 45; cert. commendation, Ord. Dept, U.S. Army, 46. Am. Chem. Soc; Soc. Appl. Spectros.(secy, 45-47, v.pres, 55, pres, 56); fel. Am. Soc. Test. & Mat.(award of merit, 62); Am. Soc. Metals; fel. Am. Inst. Chem; Am. Inst. Min. Metall. & Petrol. Eng. Emission and x-ray spectroscopy; metallurgy; special purpose alloys for the electrical, electronic and heat-treating industries. Address: Driver-Harris Co, Harrison, NJ 07029.

GUETTINGER, DAVID L, b. Colton, Wash, Oct. 2, 32; m. 53; c. 5. SOILS. B.S, Washington State, 54, M.S, 62, Nat. Defense Ed. Act fel, 61-64, Ph.D.(soils), 65. Teacher, high sch, Wash, 55-59; res. asst. soils, Washington State, 59-61; rep, Tenn. Valley Authority, 64-65; exten. soils specialist, Wash. State Univ, 65-67; SUPVR. agr. develop, mkt. serv. dept, CHEM. & FERTILIZER DIV, COMINCO AM. INC, 67-69, INDUST. CHEM. SALES, 69- Am. Soc. Agron; Soil Conserv. Soc. Am; Soil Sci. Soc. Am. Address: Chemical & Fertilizer Division, Cominco American Inc, 818 W. Riverside Ave, Spokane, WA 99201.

GUEVARA, FRANCISCO A(NTONIO), b. Denver, Colo, Jan. 10, 24; m. 51; c. 5. CHEMICAL ENGINEERING. B.S, Texas A&M, 50; M.S, New Mexico, 59. Chem. engr, health & safety br, Atomic Energy Comn, N.Mex, 50-56; STAFF MEM, LOS ALAMOS SCI. LAB, 56- U.S.A.F, 42-46, Res, 46-, Lt. Col. Am. Phys. Soc. High temperature measurements of transport properties of fluids; fractional distillation; plant engineering and design for separation of isotopes of carbon, nitrogen, oxygen and sulfur from liquefied gases. Address: Los Alamos Scientific Lab, Los Alamos, NM 87544.

GUEVARA ROMERO, JUAN DE DIOS, b. Ica, Peru, Mar. 1, 10; c. 2. PHARMACY, BIOCHEMISTRY. Dr. Pharm. & Biochem, San Marcos Univ, Lima, 50. Asst. anal.chem, Lima Sch. Pharm, 36-39; prof. chem, SAN MARCOS UNIV, LIMA, 39-59, pharm, 60-61, secy-dean sch. pharm, 61-64, PROF. CHEM, 62-, RECTOR UNIV, 69-, dean sch. pharm, 67-70. Del, S.Am. Cong. Chem, Chile, 48, gen. secy, Lima, 51; hon. guest, Latin Am. Cong. Chem, Venezuela, 55, del, Mex, 59, Argentina, 62, P.R, 65; pres, Peruvian Cong. Pharm. & Biochem, 66; Nat. Coun. Univ. Peru, 70- Daniel A. Carrion Prize for develop. of cult, 60; Palmas Magisteriales Award, Pub. Educ. Ministry Peru, 66. Peruvian Chem. Soc.(Angel A. Maldonado Prize, 48); sr. mem. Am. Chem. Soc; hon. mem. Chilean Soc. Nutrit; Sci. Soc. Chile; Pharmaceut. & Biochem. Asn. Argentina; Mex. Chem. Soc; Venezuelan Chem. Soc. The esters of P-hidroxibenzoic acid as preservant agents; quantitative determination of boron in Peruvian waters and soils, boron in food, fluorine in Peruvian tap waters and manganese in Peruvian vegetables; possible analytical applications of 4-hydroxibenzhidrazide. Address: 2179 Garcilaso de la Vega, Lima, Peru.

GUFFY, JOSEPH C(LAUDE), b. Rosston, Okla, Jan. 12, 20; m. 43; c. 2. CHEMISTRY. B.S, Southwest. Inst. Tech, 40; M.S, Wisconsin, 43, Ph.D.(chem), 47. Asst. chem, Wisconsin, 41-43; res. chemist, Off. Sci. Res. & Develop. contract, 43-45, asst, 45-47; chemist, Shell Oil Co, 47-48; instr. chem, California, 48-51; res. chemist, Calif. Res. Corp, STANDARD OIL CO. CALIF, 51-58, sr. res. chemist, 58-59, group supvr, 59-62, supv. res. chemist, 62-65, SR. RES. ASSOC, CHEVRON RES. CO, 65- Res. chemist, Off. Sci. Res. & Develop. grant, Calif. Inst. Technol, 45. Molecular spectroscopy; nuclear magnetic resonance; trace analysis for environmental studies. Address: Chevron Research Co, Richmond, CA 94802.

GUGELOT, PIET C, b. Bussum, Netherlands, Feb. 24, 18; U.S. citizen; m. 44; c. 1. PHYSICS. Physicist, Swiss Fed. Inst. Tech, 40, Ph.D.(nuclear physics), 45. Res. assoc. nuclear physics, Swiss Fed. Inst. Tech, 40-47; Palmer Physics Lab, Princeton, 47-49, asst. prof, 49-56; prof. nuclear physics & dir. inst. nuclear physics res, Amsterdam, 56-66; dir. nuclear physics, Space Radiation Effects Lab, 66-67; PROF. PHYSICS, UNIV. VA, 67- Vis. prof, Univ. Wash, 55, Oak Ridge Nat. Lab, 60; Lawrence Radiation Lab, Univ. Calif, 60-61; Stanford Univ, 63-64; Univ. Chicago, 69. Fel. Am. Phys. Soc; Swiss Phys. Soc; Netherlands Phys. Soc. Medium energy nuclear physics, particularly nuclear reactions. Address: Dept. of Physics, University of Virginia, Charlottesville, VA 22901.

GUGER, CHARLES EDMUND, JR, b. Pittsburgh, Pa, Dec. 1, 42; m. 66; c. 2. CHEMICAL ENGINEERING, PHYSICAL CHEMISTRY. B.S, Carnegie-Mellon Univ, 64, M.S, 65, Ph.D.(chem. eng), 69. Jr. res. scientist, KOPPERS CO, INC, 68-70, PROJ. SCIENTIST, 70- Am. Chem. Soc; Am. Inst. Chem. Eng. Chemical process simulation; chemical reaction kinetics; chemical thermodynamics; diffusion, mass transfer, and heat transfer pertaining to chemical processing. Address: 1359 Foxboro Dr, Monroeville, PA 15146.

GUGGENBUHL, LAURA, b. N.Y.C, Nov. 18, 01. MATHEMATICS. B.A, Hunter Col, 22; M.A, Bryn Mawr Col, 24, Ph.D.(math), 27. Instr. MATH, HUNTER COL, 22-23, 26-32, asst. prof, 32-58, ASSOC. PROF, 59- Hunter Col. off. del, Int. Cong. Mathematicians, Amsterdam, 54, Edinburgh, 58, Stockholm, 62, Moscow, 66, Nice, 70. AAAS; Am. Math. Soc; Hist. Sci. Soc; Math. Asn. Am; N.Y. Acad. Sci; French Asn. Advan. Sci; Math. Soc. France; Swiss Math. Soc; Ger. Math. Asn; Swiss Asn. Advan. Sci. Integral equations and history of mathematics. Address: 2 Brooklands, Bronxville, NY 10708.

GUGGENHEIMER, HEINRICH W(ALTER), b. Nurnberg, Ger, July 21, 24; nat; m. 47; c. 4. MATHEMATICS. Dipl, Swiss Fed. Inst. Tech, 47, D.Sc.(math), 50. Lectr. MATH, Hebrew Univ, Israel, 54-56; prof, Bar Ilan Univ, Israel, 56-59; assoc. prof, Washington State, 59-60; Minnesota, 60-62, PROF, 62-67; POLYTECH. INST. BROOKLYN, 67- Vis. lectr, Math. Asn. Am, 64-65. Swiss Army, 43. Swiss Math. Soc; Am. Math. Soc; Math. Asn. Am. Topology; differential and algebraic geometry; foundations of geometry; history of mathematics. Address: Dept. of Mathematics, Polytechnic Institute of Brooklyn, 333 Jay St, Brooklyn, NY 11201.

GUGGENHEIMER, JAMES, b. Belgrade, Yugoslavia, Mar. 4, 36; U.S. citizen; m. 69. DENTISTRY. B.S, City Col. New York, 58; D.D.S, Columbia, 62; Rochester, 63-64. Intern dent, Vet. Admin. Hosp, Albany, N.Y, 62-63; resident oral surg, Strong Mem. Hosp, Rochester, 63-64; U.S. Pub. Health Serv. res. fel, ORAL MED, sch. dent. med, Univ. Pennsylvania & Phila. Gen. Hosp, 64-66; asst. prof, SCH. DENT. MED, UNIV. PITTSBURGH, 66-70, ASSOC. PROF, 70- Mem. staff, dept. med, Presby. Univ. Hosp, 67-; clin. asst. dept. surg, Montefiore Hosp, 68-; consult, Vet. Admin. Hosp, Oakland, 67- AAAS; Int. Asn. Dent. Res; Am. Asn. Dent. Schs. Oral manifestations of rubella syndrome. Address: C174, School of Dental Medicine, University of Pittsburgh, Pittsburgh, PA 15213.

GUGGENHEIMER, SIEGFRIED, b. Germany, June 9, 00; U.S. citizen; m. 30; c. 1. CHEMISTRY. Ph.D.(chem), Würzburg, 25. CHEMIST, WINDSOR WAX CO, 38- Abstr, Chem. Abstracts, 61. Am. Chem. Soc. Emulsion technology. Address: Windsor Wax Co, 611 Newark St, Hoboken, NJ 07030.

GUGIG, WILLIAM, b. N.Y.C, Aug. 15, 14; m. 47; c. 4. ORGANIC CHEMISTRY. B.S, Long Island Univ, 49; M.S, Polytech. Inst. Brooklyn, 56. Instr. CHEM, LONG ISLAND UNIV, 50-56, asst. prof, 56-61, assoc. prof, 61-66, PROF, 66-, Nat. Sci. Found. faculty fel, 57-58. A.U.S, 42-46. Am. Chem. Soc. Properties and structure of cyclopentadienones; rearrangements of aromatic hydrocarbons. Address: Dept. of Chemistry, Long Island University, Zeckendorf Campus, Brooklyn, NY 11201.

GUGLER, CARL W(ESLEY), b. Woodbine, Kans, Sept. 6, 20; m. 45; c. 1. INVERTEBRATE ZOOLOGY. B.S, Kansas State, 48, M.S, 49; Ph.D.(vert. anat), Nebraska, 59. Instr. biol, Southwest Mo. State Col, 49-50; Bethany Col, 50-52; ZOOL, UNIV. NEBR, LINCOLN, 52-60, asst. prof, 60-65, assoc. prof, 65-70, PROF, 70-, CHMN. DEPT, 71- Med. Dept, U.S.A, 42-46. AAAS; Am. Micros. Soc. General invertebrate zoology; invertebrate embryology. Address: Dept. of Zoology, 430 Oldfather Hall, University of Nebraska, Lincoln, NE 68508.

GUHL, A(LPHAEUS) M(ATTHEW), b. Cleveland, Ohio, Aug. 14, 98; m. 24; c. 1. ZOOLOGY. B.A, N.Cent. Col, 22; M.S, Chicago, 39, Ph.D.(zool), 43. Instr. ZOOL, exten. div, Indiana, 42-43; assoc. prof, KANS. STATE UNIV, 43-50, prof, 50-71, EMER. PROF, 71- U.S.A, 17-19. Fel. AAAS; Ecol. Soc. Am; Am. Soc. Zool; Cooper Ornith. Soc; Wilson Ornith. Soc; fel. Poultry Sci. Asn; fel. Animal Behav. Soc. Social behavior of animals; social discrimination in small flocks of the common domestic fowl; animal behavior. Address: 1744 Leavenworth St, Manhattan, KS 66502.

GUIBAULT, GEORGE C, b. New Orleans, La, Dec. 22, 36; m. 54; c. 3. ANALYTICAL CHEMISTRY. B.S, Loyola (La), 58; M.S, Princeton, 59, Ph.D. (anal. chem), 61. Res. chemist, Procter & Gamble Co, 61; asst. prof. CHEM, Maryland, 62-66; assoc. prof, LA. STATE UNIV, NEW ORLEANS, 66-70, PROF, 70- U.S.A, 61-62, 1st Lt. Am. Chem. Soc. Enzymic analysis; ion selective electrodes; fluorescence; electrochemistry; gas solid reactions; chemisorption. Address: Dept. of Chemistry, College of Sciences, Louisiana State University, New Orleans, LA 70122.

GUIDER, JAMES W(ALTER), b. Detroit, Mich, Sept. 23, 16; m. 38; c. 2. MINING ENGINEERING. B.S, Mich. Col. Min, 37. Mining engr, BETHLEHEM STEEL CO, 37-57, chief engr, mining dept, 57-67, mgr. eng, 67-68, ASST. TO V.PRES, CORP. ENG, 68- Henry Krumb lectr, Am. Inst. Mining, Metall. & Petrol. Eng. Distinguished engr. award, Pa. Soc. Prof. Eng. Am. Inst. Mining, Metall. & Petrol. Eng; Am. Iron & Steel Inst; Am. Asn. Iron & Steel Eng. Mining and development of raw materials properties for the steel industry, primarily coal, limestone, iron ore and manganese engineering all phases of steel industry. Address: Bethlehem Steel Corp, Bethlehem, PA 18016.

GUIDICE, DONALD A(NTHONY), b. Astoria, N.Y, Oct. 12, 34; m. 65; c. 3. RADIO ASTRONOMY. B.E.E, Manhattan Col, 56; M.S, Ohio State Univ, 59, Ph.D.(elec. eng), 69. Electronics engr, Air Force Avionics Lab, Ohio, 59-64; RADIO ASTRONR, AIR FORCE CAMBRIDGE RES. LABS, 64- U.S.A.F, 56-59, Res, 59-, Maj. Am. Astron. Soc; Inst. Elec. & Electronics Eng. Spectral characteristics of radio sources and galactic regions; atmospheric oxygen band radiometry; ring laser techniques for angular rotation sensing; polarization of solar radio bursts. Address: Air Force Cambridge Research Labs, L. G. Hanscom Field, Bedford, MA 01730.

GUIDOTTI, CHARLES V, b. Somerville, Mass, Sept. 19, 35; m. 61; c. 3. GEOLOGY, PETROLOGY. B.S, Yale, 57; Minnesota, 57-58; univ. fels, Harvard, 58-61, Nat. Sci. Found. fel, 61-62, Ph.D.(geol), 63. Res. asst. GEOL, Minnesota, 58; lectr, Univ. Calif, Davis, 62-63, asst. prof, 63-68, ASSOC. PROF, 68-69; UNIV. WIS, MADISON, 69- Summer geologist, Maine Geol. Surv, 60-71. Mineral. Soc. Am; Am. Geophys. Union; Clay Minerals Soc. Metamorphic petrology of high-grade pelitic and calc-silicate rocks; stratigraphy and structure of metamorphosed strata in northwest Maine. Address: Dept. of Geology & Geophysics, University of Wisconsin, Madison, WI 53706.

GUIDOTTI, GUIDO, b. Florence, Italy, Nov. 3, 33. BIOCHEMISTRY. Millikin, 51-53; M.D, Washington (St. Louis), 57; Ph.D.(biochem), Rockefeller Inst, 63. Intern, Barnes Hosp, 57-58, asst. res, 58-59; asst. prof. biol, HARVARD, 63-68, assoc. prof. biol, biochem. & molecular biol, 68-69, PROF. BIOCHEM, 69- Interactions of macromolecules in solution; structure and function of proteins; structure and function of biological membranes. Address: Biological Labs, Room 410, Harvard University, 16 Divinity Ave, Cambridge, MA 02138.

GUIDRY, CARLTON LEVON, b. Palacios, Tex, June 23, 33; m. 55; c. 5. ORGANIC & POLYMER CHEMISTRY. B.S, Houston, 58, Ph.D.(biochem), 62. Res. chemist, Continental Oil Co, 61-63; asst. prof. CHEM, SAM HOUSTON STATE UNIV, 63-67, ASSOC. PROF, 67- U.S.N, 51-54. Am. Chem. Soc. Addition and condensation polymerization; polymerization through the carbonyl group. Address: Dept. of Chemistry, Sam Houston State University, Huntsville, TX 77340.

GUIDRY, DIEU-DONNE JOSEPH, b. Gueydan, La, March 29, 28; m. 48; c. 2. MICROBIOLOGY. B.S, Southwest. La. Inst, 51; M.S, La. State, 52, Ph.D, 55. Instr. MICROBIOL, SCH. MED, LA. STATE UNIV, 52-58, asst. prof, 58-64, ASSOC. PROF, 64- Consult, Touro Infirmary, La. U.S.N, 47-48, Med.C.Res, 48-62, Capt. AAAS; Am. Soc. Microbiol; Am. Soc. Trop. Med. & Hyg; Med. Mycol. Soc. of the Americas; Int. Soc. Human & Animal Mycol. Medical microbiology and mycology. Address: Louisiana State University School of Medicine, 1542 Tulane Ave, New Orleans, LA 70112.

GUIDRY, MARION A(NTOINE), b. Lafayette, La, Oct. 1, 25; m. 46; c. 3. BIOCHEMISTRY. B.S, Tulane, 47, M.S, 49, Nat. Insts. Health fel, 49-51, Ph.D.(chem), 52. Asst. prof. chem, Southwest. La. Inst, 52-53; ASST. PROF. ophthalmol, sch. med, Tulane, 53-56; biochem. & path, Sch. Med, La. State Univ, 56-65; PROF. CHEM. & BIOL. & DIR. LIFE SCI. RES, W.TEX. STATE UNIV, 65- U.S.N, 42-45. Am. Chem. Soc; Am. Oil Chem. Soc; Am. Soc. Exp. Path; Soc. Exp. Biol. & Med. Lipid chemistry; lipid metabolism. Address: Killgore Research Center, West Texas State University, Canyon, TX 79015.

GUIDRY, MARK R(OMAN), JR, b. New Orleans, La, Sept. 4, 37; m. 59; c. 3. ELECTRICAL ENGINEERING. B.S, La. State, 59; M.S, Washington (Seattle), 61; Ford Found. fel, Iowa State, 62-65, Ph.D.(elec. eng), 65. Assoc. engr, Boeing Airplane Co, Wash, 59-60; instr. elec. eng, La. State Univ, 61-62; Iowa State Univ, 62-64; assoc. prof, La. State Univ, 64-69; br. mgr, Tex. Instruments, Houston, 69-71; MGR. PROCESS DEVELOP, GARRETT MICRO-CIRCUITS CORP, 71- NASA-Am. Soc. Eng. Educ. summer faculty fels, Marshall Space Flight Ctr, 66, 68. Inst. Elec. & Electronics Eng; Electrochem. Soc. Atmospheric propagation; lasers; semiconductor devices, in particular metal oxide semiconductor devices. Address: Garrett Micro-Circuits Corp, 16701 W. Bernardo Dr, San Diego, CA 92127.

GUIDUCCI, MARIANO A, b. Peckville, Pa, Nov. 29, 30; m. 54; c. 2. ORGANIC CHEMISTRY. B.S, Albright Col, 52; M.S, Lehigh, 54; Ph.D.(org. chem), Columbia, 65. Res. asst, Olin Mathieson Chem. Corp, N.Y, 54-56, Squibb Inst. Med. Res, 56-61, SR. RES. CHEMIST, 65-70; SCHWARZ BIORES/MANN RES, 70- Am. Chem. Soc. Synthetic methods, especially as related to steroids and natural products; scale up of synthesis; peptide synthesis. Address: Schwarz BioResearch/Mann Research, Mountain View Ave, Orangeburg, NY 10962.

GUIER, W(ILLIA)M H(OWARD), b. Wichita, Kans, July 13, 26; m. 50; c. 1. THEORETICAL PHYSICS. B.S, Northwestern, 48, M.S, 50, Atomic Energy Cmn. fel, 50-51, Ph.D.(physics), 51. Sr. staff physicist, APPL. PHYSICS LABS, JOHNS HOPKINS UNIV, 51-58, MEM. PRIN. STAFF, 58-, ASSOC. PROF. BIOMED. ENG. SCH. MED, 69- Am. Phys. Soc. Random function theory and statistical mechanics; geophysics connected with artificial satellites; biomedical engineering; cardiovascular physiology; patient monitoring systems. Address: Applied Physics Lab, Johns Hopkins University, 8621 Georgia Ave, Silver Spring, MD 20910.

GUIHER, JOHN K(ENNETH), b. Youngstown, Ohio, March 25, 17; m. 46; c. 1. FOREST PRODUCTS. B.S, Mich. State, 47, Ph.D.(wood tech), 53; M.F, Yale, 48. Instr. forest prods, Mich. State, 48-52; asst. wood technologist, inst. tech, Washington State, 52-54; prof. forestry & head dept, Stephen F. Austin State Col, 54-55; asst. prof. WOOD TECH. & FORESTRY UTILIZATION, UNIV. ILL, URBANA, 55-70, ASSOC. PROF, 70- U.S.A, 43-46. Soc. Am. Foresters; Forest Prods. Res. Soc; Soc. Wood Sci. & Tech. Wood anatomy and identification; wood glues and gluing. Address: 3106 Meadowbrook, Champaign, IL 61820.

GUILD, HARRIET G(RIGGS), b. Windham, Conn, Aug. 11, 99. PEDIATRICS. A.B, Vassar Col, 20; M.D, Hopkins, 25. Intern med, Hopkins Hosp, 25-26, intern & asst. res. PEDIAT, 26-28, instr, MED. SCH, JOHNS HOPKINS UNIV, 28-34, assoc, 34-46, assoc. prof, 46-65, EMER. ASSOC. PROF, 65- Dir, pediat. dispensary, Hopkins Hosp, 28-30, diabetic clin, 30-, in charge private patient clin, 30-46, consult, 46-, clin. res. in nephrosis, 65- Consult, Windham Community Mem. Hosp; U.S. Pub. Health Serv. Hosp; Sinai Hosp; mem, Nat. Kidney Found. Soc. Pediat. Res; Am. Pediat. Soc; Am. Soc. Human Genetics; Am. Diabetes Asn; Am. Acad. Pediat; N.Y. Acad. Med; Pan-Am. Med. Asn. Nephrosis; diabetes; rare clinical syndromes. Address: 550 N. Broadway, Baltimore, MD 21205.

GUILD, LLOYD V, b. Elmira, N.Y, July 17, 20; m. 41; c. 3. CHEMISTRY. B.S, Univ. Pittsburgh, 48, M.S, 61. V.pres, Burrell Corp, 41-62; PRES, GUILD CORP, 62- Am. Chem. Soc; Am. Soc. Test. & Mat; Instrument Soc. Am. Analytical instrumentation. Address: Guild Corp, 402 Greentree Rd, Bethel Park, PA 15220.

GUILD, PHILIP W(HITE), b. Ann Arbor, Mich, Oct. 28, 15; m. 39; c. 3. ECONOMIC GEOLOGY. A.B, Hopkins, 36, Ph.D.(geol), 47. From jr. to PRIN. GEOLOGIST, U.S. GEOL. SURV, 39- Secy, subcomn. metallogenic map world. Soc. Econ. Geol; Geol. Soc. Am; Am. Inst. Mining, Metall. & Petrol. Eng; Am. Geophys. Union; Brazilian Geol. Soc. Geology of chromite deposits in Alaska and Cuba; sedimentary iron formation in Brazil; geology and resources of the ferrous metals; metallogenic provinces. Address: U.S. Geological Survey, Washington, DC 20242.

GUILD, RICHARD DOUGLAS, b. Warren, Pa, Apr. 21, 23; m. 62. INDUSTRIAL ENGINEERING, OPERATIONS RESEARCH. B.S, Pa. State, 49, M.A, 59; Ph.D.(indust. eng), Northwestern, 68. Jr. engr, Sylvania Elec. Prod, Inc, 49-50, sr. statist. engr, 50-57; instr. INDUST. ENG, PA. STATE UNIV, 57-60, asst. prof, 60-68, ASSOC. PROF, 69- C.Eng, U.S.A. Am. Inst. Indust. Eng; Oper. Res. Soc. Am; Am. Soc. Eng. Educ; Am. Soc. Qual. Control. Reliability and quality control. Address: College of Engineering, Pennsylvania State University, University Park, Pa. 16802.

GUILD, WALTER R(UFUS), b. Ann Arbor, Mich, Oct. 25, 23; m. 46; c. 1. BIOPHYSICS. B.S, Texas, 48, M.A, 49; Atomic Energy Cmn. fel, Yale, 50-51, Ph.D.(biophys), 51. Meteorologist, Texas, 46-49; instr. physics, Yale, 51-54; asst. prof, 54-60, radiation safety officer, 55-60; assoc. prof. BIOPHYS, DUKE UNIV, 60-65, PROF, 65- Mem, int. fel. rev. comn, Nat. Insts. Health, 68-72, sr. fel, Stanford Univ, 70-71. U.S.A.A.F, 43-46, 1st Lt. AAAS; Biophys. Soc; Radiation Res. Soc; Fedn. Am. Sci; Am. Soc. Biol.

Chem; Am. Soc. Cell Biol; Genetics Soc; Am. Soc. Microbiol. Nucleic acids; bacterial transformation; genetic mechanisms; radiation biology; molecular biology. Address: Dept. of Biochemistry, Duke University, Durham, NC 27710.

GUILDAY, JOHN E, b. Pittsburgh, Pa, Oct. 23, 25; m. 50; c. 1. BIOLOGY, GEOLOGY. B.S, Pittsburgh, 50. Asst. curator comp. anat, CARNEGIE MUS, 50-64, ASSOC. CURATOR VERT. PALEONT, 64- U.S.A, 44-46. Am. Soc. Mammal; Soc. Vert. Paleont; Am. Quaternary Asn. Pleistocene paleontology and paleoecology; archaeological ecology. Address: Carnegie Museum, 4400 Forbes Ave, Pittsburgh, PA 15213.

GUILDNER, LESLIE A(RNOLD), b. Lincoln, Nebr, Aug. 1, 20; m. 55; c. 3. PHYSICAL CHEMISTRY. A.B, Nebraska, 48, A.M, 49; Ph.D.(phys. chem), Mass. Inst. Tech, 54. Engr. color TV, Raytheon Mfg. Co, 53-54; mem. div. sponsored res, Mass. Inst. Tech, 54-59; PROJ. LEADER, TEMPERATURE PHYSICS SECT, NAT. BUR. STANDARDS, 59- Am. Phys. Soc. Kinetic theory of gases; thermal accomodation coefficient; thermal conductivity; pressure-volume-temperature properties; adsorption; high vacuum; thermal expansion of solids; mercury manometry; gas thermometry. Address: Temperature Physics Section, National Bureau of Standards, Washington, DC 20234.

GUILE, DONALD LLOYD, b. Olean, N.Y, Nov. 12, 32; m. 56; c. 4. CERAMICS, MATERIALS SCIENCE. B.S, Alfred, 60, Ph.D.(ceramic sci), 65. RES. ENGR, CORNING GLASS WORKS, 64- U.S.A.F, 52-56. Am. Ceramic Soc; Brit. Ceramic Soc. Study of high temperature refractory materials for the glass and metal industries, including particle technology and application of sintering theory. Address: Ceramic Research Dept, Corning Glass Works, Sullivan Park, Corning, NY 14830.

GUILE, RALPH L(AWRENCE), b. Ingham Co, Mich, May 7, 10; m. 42; c. 2. ORGANIC CHEMISTRY. B.S, Mich. State Col, 32, M.S, 33, Ph.D.(chem), 39. Biochemist, Parke, Davis & Co, Mich, 33-35; asst. org. chem, MICH. STATE UNIV, 35-39, instr. org. preparations, 40-44, asst. prof. CHEM, 44-47, ASSOC. PROF, 47- Fulbright lectr, Ghent, 50-51; Trinity Col, Dublin, 59-60. AAAS; Am. Chem. Soc. Aluminum chloride; synthesis of tertiary alcohols; emulsion polymerization; double bond addition reactions; polymerization; alkylation. Address: Dept. of Chemistry, Michigan State University, East Lansing, MI 48823.

GUILEY, GEORGE M(ILTON), b. Canton, Ohio, Sept. 8, 07; m. 29; c. 1. PHYSICS. B.S, Ashland Col, 28; M.S, Michigan, 31. Head sci. dept, pub. sch, Mich, 31-43; asst. prof, PHYSICS, ASHLAND COL, 46-70, ASSOC. PROF. & DEAN STUD. LIFE, 70- U.S.N.R, 43-46, Lt. Am. Asn. Physics Teachers. Electronics; audio frequencies. Address: 618 Buena Vista, Ashland, OH 44805.

GUILFORD, HARRY GARRETT, b. Madison, Wis, June 20, 23; m. 49; c. 2. ZOOLOGY, PARASITOLOGY. Ph.B, Wisconsin, 44, Ph.M, 46, Ph.D.(zool), 49. Assoc. prof. biol, Mercer Univ, 49-50; asst. prof. bot. & zool, UNIV. WIS-GREEN BAY, 50-56, assoc. prof, 56-65, PROF, 65-69, POP. DYNAMICS & BIOL, 69- Secy. faculty, Univ. Wis-Green Bay, 70- Am. Soc. Parasitol; Am. Micros. Soc; Am. Fisheries Soc. Histology and life history of trematodes; myxosporidia. Address: College of Human Biology, University of Wisconsin-Green Bay, Green Bay, WI 54302.

GUILINGER, WILLIS HERBERT, JR, b. Toledo, Ohio, Apr. 18, 31; m. 61; c. 2. MATHEMATICS. B.S, Carnegie Inst. Tech, 53, M.S, 56; Ph.D.(math), Pittsburgh, 63. Programmer, Gen. Elec. Corp, 53-55; mathematician, WESTINGHOUSE ELEC. CORP, 57-63, sr. mathematician, 63-68, fel. scientist, 68-71, SUPVR. STRUCT. ANAL. SECT, BETTIS ATOMIC POWER LAB, WEST MIFFLIN, 71- Sr. lectr, Carnegie-Mellon Univ, 63- Am. Math. Soc; Soc. Indust. & Appl. Math. Analysis of convergence of matrix iterative procedures by the use of quadratic form inequalities; bounds for discretization error of elliptic differential equations; formulation of numerical solutions for problems in heat conduction, fluid flow and analytical mechanics. Address: 2324 Collins Rd, Pittsburgh, PA 15235.

GUILL, ALBERT P(EMBROOKE), b. Oak Park, Ill, Jan. 4, 22; m. 46; c. 2. ANALYTICAL CHEMISTRY. B.S, Ore. State Col, 49, M.S, 51. Asst. chem, Ore. State Col, 50; anal. res. chemist, Cutter Labs, 50-54; chief chemist, COMMERCIAL SOLVENTS CORP, 54-58, west. field rep. mkt. develop, 58-70, SALES SUPVR, NITROPARAFFINS, 70- U.S.A.A.F, 42-46. Am. Chem. Soc; Chem. Mkt. Res. Asn. Product utilization; industrial chemistry. Address: 158 Cronin Dr, Santa Clara, CA 95051.

GUILLARD, ROBERT R(USSELL) L(OUIS), b. New York, N.Y, Feb. 5, 21; m. 54, 62; c. 3. BOTANY. B.S, City Col. New York, 41; M.S, Yale, 51, Eaton-Hooker fel. & Ph.D, 54. Elec. engr, Navy Yard, N.Y, 41-46; tutor physics, City Col. New York, 46-49; res. assoc. bot, Hawaii, 54-55; aquatic microbiologist, Oyster Inst. N.Am, Inc, U.S. Fish & Wildlife Lab, 55-58; res. assoc. marine biol, WOODS HOLE OCEANOG. INST, 58-63, ASSOC. SCIENTIST, 63-, summer res. fel, 54. Darbaker Award, Bot. Soc. Am, 68. AAAS; Am. Soc. Limnol. & Oceanog; Phycol. Soc. Am; Int. Phycol. Soc. Physiology and ecology of phytoplankton. Address: Woods Hole Oceanographic Institution, Woods Hole, MA 02543.

GUILLEMIN, ROGER (CHARLES LOUIS), b. Dijon, France, Jan. 11, 24; nat; m. 51; c. 6. PHYSIOLOGY, NEUROENDOCRINOLOGY. B.A, Dijon Univ, France, 41, B.Sc, 42; M.D, Lyon, 49; French Govt. fel, Montreal, 50-51, Ph.D.(exp. med, surg), 52. Asst. prof. & asst. dir, Inst. Exp. Med. & Surg, Montreal, 51-53; asst. prof. physiol, col. med, Baylor Univ, 53-57, assoc. prof, 57-63, prof. & dir. labs. neuroendocrinol, 63-70; RES. FEL. NEUROENDOCRINOL, SALK INST. BIOL. STUDIES, 70- Markle Found. scholar, 52-56; consult, Vet. Admin. Hosp, Houston, 54-70; lectr, Rice Univ, 58-60; Graves lectr, Ind. Univ, 60; mem, study sects, Nat. Insts. Health, 59-69; Int. Comt. Estab. New Adrenocorticotropic Hormone Standard, 60; sci. prog. comt, Int. Cong. Pharmacol, Stockholm, 60; assoc. dir. dept. exp. endocrinol, Col. France, 60-63; consult, M.D. Anderson Hosp. & Tumor Inst, Houston, 67-; vis. mem. grad. faculty, Tex. A&M Univ, 68-70; mem. comt. endocrinol, Int. Union Physiol. Sci. Glossary, 69; adj. prof, col. med, Baylor Univ, 70-, Univ. Calif, San Diego, 71-; with ctr. pop. res, U.S. Pub.

Health Serv, 71-74; mem. neuroendocrine comt, Fedn. Am. Socs. Exp. Biol, 71-75. Louis Bonneau Award, French Acad. Sci, 57, L. LaCaze Award, 60; Saintour Award, Col. France, 61; Int. Cong. Pharmacol. gold medal, 61. AAAS; Endocrine Soc.(Ayerst-Squibb Award, 70); Am. Physiol. Soc; Soc. Exp. Biol. & Med; Am. Inst. Biol. Sci; Fr. Biol. Soc; Int. Brain Res. Orgn; Int. Soc. Res. Reproduction; Asn. French Speaking Physiol; Soc. Neurosci. Physiology and biochemistry of hypothalamic mechanisms controlling secretion of pituitary hormones; improvement of population control techniques with antagonists to hypothalamic hormones; neurochemistry of fundamental brain function. Address: Dept. of Neuroendocrinology, Salk Institute of Biological Studies, P.O. Box 1809, San Diego, CA 92112.

GUILLEMIN, VICTOR, JR, b. Milwaukee, Wis, Feb. 10, 96; m. 36; c. 4. PHYSICS, BIOPHYSICS. A.B, Wisconsin, 23; A.M, Harvard, 24; Sheldon fel, Munich, 25-26, Ph.D.(physics), 26. Lab. asst, physics, Wisconsin, 20-22; asst, Huntington Mem. Hosp, Harvard, 24-25; fel, Nat. Res. Coun, Gottingen & Leipzig, 26-27; instr. physics, Harvard, 30-31, lectr. biophys, 31-35, asst. & consult. fatigue lab, 35-41; sr. physicist aero med. lab, Air Materiel Command, U.S. Air Force, 42-48; prof. biophys, col. med, Illinois, 48-59; lectr. physics, Harvard, 60-66, hon. res. assoc, 66-68; res. assoc, Univ. Calif, Santa Barbara, 68-70; RETIRED. Asst. prof, Mass. Inst. Technol, 31-34. Consult, Air Materiel Command, U.S. Air Force, 48-52. Mem, comt. med. sci, Nat. Mil. Estab, 48-53; comt. bioacoustics, Nat. Res. Coun, 53- AAAS; Am. Phys. Soc; Am. Physiol. Soc; Biophys. Soc; Am. Asn. Physics Teachers. Atomic and molecular structure; biophysics of respiration; circulation, effects of thermal environment, high altitude, acceleration, vibration and sound. Address: 107 Middlesex Dr, Charlottesville, VA 22901.

GUILLERY, RAINER WALTER, b. Greifswald, Ger, Aug. 28, 29; m. 54; c. 4. NEUROANATOMY. B.Sc, London, 51, Ph.D.(anat), 54. Asst. lectr. ANAT, Univ. Col, London, 53-56, lectr, 56-63, reader, 63-64; assoc. prof, UNIV. WIS, MADISON, 64-68, PROF, 68- Rockefeller traveling fel. neurophysiol, Univ. Wis, 60-61. Address: Dept. of Anatomy, University of Wisconsin, Madison, WI 53706.

GUILLET, J(AMES) E(DWIN), b. Toronto, Ont, Jan. 14, 27; m. 53; c. 4. PHYSICAL CHEMISTRY. B.A, Toronto, 48; Ph.D.(phys. chem), Cambridge, 55. Res. chemist, Eastman Kodak Co, 48-50; Tenn. Eastman Co. Div, 50-52, sr. res. chemist, 55-62, res. assoc, 63; assoc. prof. CHEM, UNIV. TORONTO, 63-69, PROF, 69- Consult, Glidden Co, Ltd, 64-; Imp. Oil Enterprises, Ltd, 65-; vis. prof, Nat. Ctr. Sci. Res, Strasbourg, France, 70-71; dir, Ecoplastics Ltd, 71. Am. Chem. Soc; Faraday Soc; fel. Chem. Inst. Can. Synthetic fibers and plastics; polyolefins; photochemistry; free radical reactions and kinetics; relations of structure to properties of polymers; inverse chromatography. Address: Dept. of Chemistry, University of Toronto, Toronto 5, Ont, Can.

GUILLORY, JACK PAUL, b. Alexandria, La, Feb. 28, 38; m. 60; c. 3. PHYSICAL CHEMISTRY. B.S, La. State, 60; Ph.D.(phys. chem), Iowa State, 65. Res. chem. physicist, PHILLIPS PETROL. CO, 65-71, GROUP LEADER, 71- Am. Chem. Soc. Electron diffraction study of gases; energy transfer investigation using photochemical and mass spectrometric techniques. Address: Research Bldg. 4, Phillips Petroleum Co, Bartlesville, OK 74004.

GUILLORY, J(AMES) KEITH, b. Bunkie, La, Feb. 4, 35. PHARMACY. B.S, Loyola (La), 56; M.S, Wisconsin, 60, Ph.D.(pharm), 61. Asst. prof. PHARM, Washington State Univ, 61-64; UNIV. IOWA, 64-66, assoc. prof, 66-71, PROF, 71- Am. Chem. Soc; Am. Pharmaceut. Asn; Acad. Pharm. Sci. Kinetics of degradation of pharmaceuticals; polymorphism; absorption kinetics. Address: College of Pharmacy, University of Iowa, Iowa City, IA 52240.

GUILLORY, RICHARD, b. San Diego, Calif, Oct. 3, 30; m. 56; c. 2. BIOCHEMISTRY. B.A, Reed Col, 53; Ph.D.(biochem), California, Los Angeles, 62. Am. Heart Asn. res. fel, 62-64; asst. prof. BIOCHEM, Ariz. State Univ, 64-66; biochem. & molecular biol, Cornell Univ, 66-68, assoc. prof, 68-71; PROF. BIOCHEM. & BIOPHYS, UNIV. HAWAII, 71- Estab. investr, Am. Heart Asn, 68- Med.Serv.C, 54-56, Sgt. Am. Chem. Soc; Brit. Biochem. Soc; Biophys. Soc; Am. Soc. Biol. Chem. Bioenergetics; mechanism of enzyme action; oxidative phosphorylation; muscular contraction. Address: Dept. of Biochemistry & Biophysics, Medical School, University of Hawaii, Honolulu, HI 96822.

GUILLORY, WILLIAM ARNOLD, b. New Orleans, La, Dec. 4, 38; m. 67; c. 1. PHYSICAL CHEMISTRY. B.A, Dillard Univ, 60; Ph.D.(chem), Univ. Calif, Berkeley, 64. Nat. Sci. Found. fel, Univ. Paris, 64-65; asst. prof. CHEM, Howard Univ, 65-69; ASSOC. PROF, DREXEL UNIV, 69- Environ. Protection Agency grant, Drexel Univ, 69-71, Alfred P. Sloan fel, 71-73. Consult, Naval Ord. Lab, Md, 67-71. AAAS; Am. Phys. Soc; Am. Chem. Soc. Infrared and ultraviolet spectroscopy, kinetics and photochemistry. Address: Dept. of Chemistry, Drexel University, Philadelphia, PA 19104.

GUILLOT, DAVID G(EORGE), b. Galveston, Tex, Sept. 17, 41; m. 62; c. 1. ORGANIC & POLYMER CHEMISTRY. B.S, Brigham Young, 62, Ph.D.(org. chem), 66. MEM. STAFF, res. polymerization & org. chem, UNIROYAL, INC, WAYNE, 65-70, TEXTILE & PLASTICS APPL. RES. SECT, RES. & DEVELOP, 71- Am. Chem. Soc. Hydrochlorination of olefins; sulfonation of aromatic hydrocarbons; polymerization of heterocyclic compounds; fiber to rubber adhesion. Address: 8 Schuyler Ave, Pequannock, NJ 07440.

GUILLOTTE, JOHN E(DWARD), b. Fall River, Mass, Dec. 10, 21; m. 50; c. 3. STATISTICS, MATHEMATICS. B.S, Mass. Inst. Tech, 43. Statist. engr, Remington Arms, Conn, 43; statistician, E.I. DU PONT DE NEMOURS & CO, INC, Wash, 44-45, physicist, 46-47, plastic res, N.J, 47-50, asst. tech. supt, Texas, 50-54, sales tech, Del, 54-59, extrusion consult, tech. servs. lab, 59-60, field sales technologist, Pa, 60-64, tech. rep, sales serv, 64-66, TECH. CONSULT, PLASTICS DEPT, MKT. DIV, 66- Civilian with Atomic Energy Comn, 46. High speed stress-strain analysis; rheology; industrial statistics; plastics; plutonium; uranium; plastics extrusion. Address: Dept. of Plastics, Marketing Division, E.I. du Pont de Nemours & Co, Inc, Chestnut Run Plant, Wilmington, DE 19898.

GUILLOU, JOHN C(ARROLL), b. Berkeley, Calif, June 19, 21; m. 43; c. 3. HYDRAULIC ENGINEERING. B.E, Southern California, 43; M.S, Illinois,

54. Lectr. civil eng, Southern California, 43-44; from res. assoc. to assoc. prof, hydraul. eng, Illinois, 46-63; CHIEF WATERWAY ENGR, ILL. DIV. WATERWAYS, 63- Mem, U.S. comt, Int. Comn. Irrig. & Drainage. U.S.A, 44-46. Am. Soc. Civil Eng; Am. Soc. Mech. Eng; Am. Soc. Eng. Educ; Am. Geophys. Union; Int. Asn. Hydraul. Res. Drainage structures for super-highways; open channel flow investigation; hydraulics of flow at bridges; fluvial hydraulics and morphology; hydraulic model studies; water resource development. Address: Illinois Division of Waterways, 201 W. Monroe St, Springfield, IL 62706.

GUIMARAES, ARMENIO COSTA, b. Salvador, Brazil, June 17, 33; m. 59; c. 2. INTERNAL MEDICINE, CARDIOLOGY. M.D, Univ. Bahia, 56. Intern, Prof. Edgard Santos Hosp. & Couto Maia Hosp, Bahia, 55-56; fel. cardiol, dept. med, clin. hosp, Univ. São Paulo, 57-58; instr. INTERNAL MED, MED. SCH, UNIV. BAHIA, 61-63, ASSOC. PROF, 63-, PRES. RESIDENCY COMN, PROF. EDGARD SANTOS HOSP, 71-, pres. internship comn, 68-69. Am. Col. Physicians & Kellogg Found. fel, 64-65; res. assoc, Charles T. Miller Hosp, St. Paul, Minn, 65; vis. prof, faculty med, Univ. Brasilia, 66-67; Nat. Res. Coun. fel, 67; vis. assoc. prof, div. cardiol, med. col, Cornell Univ, 69-70; v.chief dept. cardiol, med. sch, Univ. Bahia, 70-71. Cert, Educ. Coun. For. Med. Grads, 62. Affiliate Am. Col. Physicians; Brazilian Soc. Cardiol. Identification, physiology and natural history of endomyocardial-fibrosis; pulmonary schistosomiasis, especially natural history of the pulmonary circulation haemodynamics abnormalties in patients with hepato-splenic schistosomiasis. Address: Professor Edgard Santos Hospital, Salvador, Bahia, Brazil.

GUINAN, JOHN JOSEPH, JR, b. Phila, Pa, Mar. 12, 41; m. 67; c. 2. NEURO-PHYSIOLOGY, ELECTRICAL ENGINEERING. S.B, Mass. Inst. Tech, 63, Nat. Sci. Found. fel, 63-66, M.S, 64, Hertz fel, 66-68, Ph.D.(elec. eng), 68. ASST. PROF. ELEC. ENG, MASS. INST. TECHNOL, 68- Res. assoc. otolaryngol, Mass. Eye & Ear Infirmary, 66- AAAS; Acoustical Soc. Am. Synaptic mechanisms and signal processing in nerve cells; firing patterns and locations of brainstem auditory neurons; transfer characteristics of the middle ear. Address: Room 20B-225, Dept. of Electrical Engineering, Massachusetts Institute of Technology, Cambridge, MA 02139.

GUINAND, A(NDREW) P(AUL), b. Renmark, Australia, Mar. 3, 12; m. 47; c. 2. MATHEMATICS. B.Sc, Univ. Adelaide, 33, D.Phil, Oxford, 37. Commonwealth Fund fel. MATH, Princeton, 39-40; assoc. prof, Royal Mil. Col. Sci, Eng, 47-56; prof. & head dept, Univ. New Eng, Australia, 57-58; assoc. prof, Alberta, 58-60; PROF, Saskatchewan, 60-64, chmn. dept, 62-64; TRENT UNIV, 64-, chmn. dept, 64-70. R.C.A.F, 40-45, Squadron Leader. Mathematical analysis; Fourier integrals; summation formulae; almost periodic functions. Address: Dept. of Mathematics, Trent University, Peterborough, Ont, Can.

GUINARD, MERLIN J(AMES), b. Portland, Maine, Oct. 12, 32. ORGANIC CHEMISTRY. B.S, Boston Col, 54; Nat. Insts. Health fel, Maryland, 56-57, Ph.D.(org. chem), 63. Chemist, Am. Cyanamid Co, 58-61, process develop, Sci. Design Co, 61-62; Nat. Insts. Health fel, Northwestern, 62-63; chemist paper chem, S.D. Warren Co, 64; CHIEF CHEMIST ORG. CHEM, FLEETWOOD CHEM. CO, 65- Am. Chem. Soc. Reaction rates and mechanisms; polymer chemistry; free radical reactions; organometallics. Address: P.O. Box 3192, Portland, ME 04104.

GUINDON, WILLIAM G(ARTLAND), S.J, b. Boston, Mass, Oct. 29, 16. PHYSICS. A.B, Weston Col, 42, A.M. & Ph.L, 43, S.T.L, 51; Boston Col, 44-45; Ph.D.(physics), Mass. Inst. Tech, 48. Instr. physics & eng. drawing, Boston Col, 43-45; physics, Weston Col, 47-51; asst. prof, Fairfield, 51-52; chmn. dept, Boston Col, 53-64; assoc. prof, Col. of the Holy Cross, 64-66, v.pres. & dean, 66-68; Prov. Superior, Soc. of Jesus, New Eng, 68- Instr, Cranwell Prep. Sch, 43; Col. Holy Cross, 44; high sch, Boston Col, 44-45; Nat. Sci. Found. Sci. fel, Cornell, 63-64. Am. Phys. Soc; Am. Asn. Physics Teachers. Essence of morality; theory of nuclear forces; discussion of radial dependence of the tensor force in the deuteron; nuclear shell theory; shape-dependence of nuclear potentials; angular correlation of successive gamma rays; interaction of high magnetic fields with ionized gases; quantum electrodynamics. Address: 297 Commonwealth Ave, Boston, MA 02115.

GUINN, GENE, b. Prairie Grove, Ark, Mar. 19, 28; m. 55; c. 2. PLANT PHYSIOLOGY. B.S, Arkansas, 52, M.S, 57; Ph.D.(plant physiol), Texas A&M, 61. Agronomist, U.S. Dept. Agr, Arkansas, 53-57, res. agronomist, cotton & cordage fibers res, Br, Agr. Res. Serv, exp. sta, Texas A&M, 57-61, res. plant physiologist, U.S. Dept. Agr. & Okla. Agr. Exp. Sta, 61-70; PLANT PHYSIOLOGIST, U.S. DEPT. AGR, 70- U.S.A, 46-47. Fel. AAAS; Am. Soc. Plant Physiol; Am. Soc. Agron. Physiology of cotton, especially fruiting and fruit abscission. Address: Western Cotton Research Lab, 4135 E. Broadway Rd, Phoenix, AZ 85040.

GUINN, THEODORE, b. Fresno, Calif, Apr. 29, 24; m. 53; c. 2. MATHEMATICS. B.A, Fresno State Col, 49; Douglas Aircraft Co. scholar, California, Los Angeles, 57-63, M.A, 59, Ph.D.(math), 64. Sr. scientist, Douglas Aircraft Co, 53-65; asst. prof. MATH, Mich. State Univ, 65-68; ASSOC. PROF, UNIV. N.MEX, 68- Res. asst, California, Los Angeles, 62-63, instr, exten, 63-65, asst. res. mathematician, 64-65. U.S.N.R, 42-45. AAAS; Am. Math. Soc; Soc. Indust. & Appl. Math. Calculus of variations and optimum control theory. Address: Dept. of Mathematics, University of New Mexico, Albuquerque, NM 87106.

GUINN, VINCENT P(ERRY), b. Los Angeles, Calif, Nov. 9, 17; m. 38; c. 2. RADIOCHEMISTRY. A.B, Univ. South. Calif, 39, M.S, 41; Ph.D.(phys. chem), Harvard, 49. Res. chemist, Shell Develop. Co, 41-46, 49-61, head, radiochem. group, 56-61; tech. dir. activation anal. prog, Gen. Dynamics Corp, 61-70; PROF. RADIOCHEM, UNIV. CALIF, IRVINE, 70- Lectr. activation anal, Oak Ridge Inst. Nuclear Studies, Gulf Gen. Atomic, Tex. A&M Univ. & Univ. Glasgow; consult. & lectr, spec. training div, Oak Ridge Inst. Nuclear Studies, 58-; mem. beryllium anal. subcomt, Nat. Res. Coun; rev. comt, div. isotopes develop, Atomic Energy Comn, 60-61. Fel. AAAS; fel. Am. Nuclear Soc.(spec. award novel applns. nuclear energy, 64); Am. Phys. Soc; Am. Chem. Soc; fel. Am. Acad. Forensic Sci; Soc. Appl. Spectros; Am. Soc. Test. & Mat; Brit. Acad. Forensic Sci. Activation analysis; radio chemistry; radiotracers. Address: Dept. of Chemistry, University of California, Irvine, CA 92664.

GUION, THOMAS HYMAN, b. New Bern, N.C, Feb. 21, 19; m. 49; c. 3. TEXTILES, ORGANIC CHEMISTRY. B.S, Davidson Col, 40; Ph.D.(org. chem), North Carolina, 49. Assoc. prof. textile chem, Clemson Col, 49-52; sr. res. chemist, appln. res. dept, Chemstrand Co. Div, Monsanto Co, 52-55, group leader, 55-59, supvr, 59-64; ASSOC. PROF. TEXTILE CHEM, N.C. STATE UNIV, 64- Chem. C, 42-45, Maj. Am. Chem. Soc; Am. Asn. Textile Chem. & Colorists; Fiber Soc; Brit. Soc. Dyers & Colourists. Mechanisms of absorption of dyes and textile chemicals by man-made fibers. Address: School of Textiles, North Carolina State University, Raleigh, NC 27607.

GUIRAGOSSIÁN, ZAVEN G(EORGE), b. Cairo, U.A.R, Apr. 6, 36; U.S. citizen; m. 57; c. 4. PHYSICS. B.A, California, Berkeley, 55, M.A, 56, Ph.D.(physics), 62. Res. asst, physics, Lawrence Radiation Lab, California, 56-62, res. physicist, 62-63; res. physicist, Linear Accelerator Ctr, STANFORD UNIV, 63-69, MEM. STAFF, W.W. HANSEN LABS, HIGH ENERGY PHYSICS LAB, 70- Am. Phys. Soc. Experimental high energy physics, particle properties, interaction dynamics from photon, electron, pion and antiproton beams; total absorption and multiwire proportional counters; data acquisition and reduction systems; visual and electronic detectors. Address: W.W. Hansen Labs, High Energy Physics Lab, Stanford University, Stanford, CA 94305.

GUIRARD, BEVERLY M(ARIE), b. St. Martinville, La, Dec. 10, 15. BIOCHEMISTRY. B.S, Southwest. La. Inst, 36; fel, La. State, 36-38, M.S, 38; Ph.D.(bioorg. chem), Texas, 45. Lab. asst, Southwest. La. Inst, 36, instr. chem, 39-41; teacher pub. sch, La, 38-39; tech. asst, biochem, inst, Texas, 41-42, asst, 42-45, res. assoc, 45-48, dept. bact, 48-52, res. scientist, biochem, inst, 52-56; ASST. RES. BIOCHEMIST, UNIV. CALIF, BERKELEY, 56- U.S. Pub. Health Serv. spec. fel, Physiol. Genetic Lab, Ctr. Nat. Res. Sci, France, 63-64. AAAS; Am. Chem. Soc; Am. Soc. Biol. Chem. Microbial nutrition and enzymology. Address: Dept. of Biochemistry, University of California, Berkeley, CA 94720.

GUIRE, PATRICK E(DWARD), b. Gillham, Ark, Nov. 24, 36; m. 60; c. 3. BIOCHEMISTRY. B.S, Arkansas, 58; Wilson fel, Illinois, 59, Ph.D.(biochem), 63. Nat. Insts. Health res. fel. protein chem, Washington (Seattle), 63-64; lectr. & res. trainee ribosome synthesis, St. Jude Hosp, Univ. Tenn, 64-67; ASST. PROF. BIOCHEM, OKLA. STATE UNIV, 67- U.S.A.R, 58-66, Capt. AAAS; Am. Chem. Soc. Relationships of physical and chemical properties to biological functions of macromolecules. Address: Dept. of Biochemistry, Oklahoma State University, Stillwater, OK 74074.

GUISE, ARTHUR B(ARNES), b. Alberene, Va, Nov. 22, 03; m. 28; c. 2. CHEMICAL ENGINEERING. B.S, Mass. Inst. Tech, 27. Chem. engr, Cities Serv. Ref. Co, 27-29; Atlantic Ref. Co, 29-34; Phillips Petrol. Co, 34-35; fire protection engr, Factory Mutual Labs, 35-41; Rockwood Sprinkler Co, 41-42; U.S. Rubber Co, 42; chief engr, res. & develop. prod, Ansul Chem. Co, 42-55, dir. res, fire equip, chem. & refrig. prods, 55-56, tech. dir, 56-58, dir. develop. & design, fire & refrig. equip, 58-64, mgr. systs. eng, fire equip, 64-66; CONSULT. ENGR, 66- Am. Inst. Chem. Eng; fel. Am. Inst. Chem; Soc. Fire Protection Eng. Mechanisms of extinguishment; fire extinguishing agents and equipment; special fire hazards. Address: Box 75, Marinette, WI 54143.

GUISELEY, KENNETH B, b. Auburn, N.Y, July 20, 33; m. 56; c. 3. ORGANIC CHEMISTRY. B.A, Hartwick Col, 55; Ph.D.(org. chem), Syracuse, 60. SR. CHEMIST, MARINE COLLOIDS, INC, 61- Am. Chem. Soc. Extraction of polysaccharides and associated by-products from marine algae. Address: Marine Colloids, Inc, P.O. Box 308, Rockland, ME 04841.

GUISS, LEWIS W(ARNER), b. Woodburn, Ore, Nov. 19, 11; m. 48; c. 4. SURGERY. B.A, Oregon, 33, M.D, 36. Intern, San Diego County Gen. Hosp, Calif, 36-37; surg, Barnes Hosp, St. Louis, 37-38; res, Barnard Skin & Cancer Hosp, 38-39; asst. res, Mem. Hosp, N.Y, 39-40, Nat. Cancer Inst. fel. tumor path, 41-42, 46-47; res, Pondville Hosp, Mass, 40-41; instr. SURG, SCH. MED, UNIV. SOUTH. CALIF, 47-52, asst. clin. prof, 52-56, assoc. clin. prof, 56-64, CLIN. PROF, 64- Practicing physician, 47- Dipl, Am. Bd. Surg. Med.C, U.S.A, 42-45. Am. Col. Surg; Am. Radium Soc; Int. Soc. Surg; Soc. Head & Neck Surg; Am. Asn. Cancer Res. Chronic atrophic gastritis; achlorhidria; gastric cancer; diagnosis, pathology and treatment of cancer. Address: 1930 Wilshire Blvd, Los Angeles, CA 90057.

GUITHER, WILLIAM D, b. Aurora, Ill, Apr. 4, 27; m. 51; c. 2. ORGANIC CHEMISTRY. B.A, N.Cent. Col.(Ill), 52; M.S, New Mexico, 65, Ph.D.(chem), 66. Res. asst. CHEM, New Mexico, 61-66; asst. prof, UNIV. WIS-GREEN BAY, FOX VALLEY CAMPUS, 66-70, ASSOC. PROF, 70- U.S.A, 45-47. Am. Chem. Soc. Nitrogen heterocycles containing more than one nitrogen. Address: Dept. of Chemistry, University of Wisconsin-Green Bay, Fox Valley Campus, Menasha, WI 54952.

GUITJENS, JOHANNES C, b. Heeze, Holland, Jan. 24, 35; m. 67; c. 2. CIVIL ENGINEERING, HYDROLOGY. B.S.A, Univ. B.C, 61; M.S, Univ. Calif, Davis, 64, Ph.D.(civil eng), 68. Res. asst. hydrol, Univ. Calif, Davis, 65-67; ASST. PROF. IRRIG. & DRAINAGE, DIV. PLANT SOIL & WATER SCI, UNIV. NEV, RENO, 67- Lectr, Univ. Calif, Davis, 69 & 70. Am. Geophys. Union; Am. Soc. Civil Eng. Steady and unsteady flow in viscous flow models; mathematical simulation of ground water flow; water use efficiencies; agricultural drainage. Address: Division of Plant, Soil, & Water Science, University of Nevada, Reno, NV 89507.

GULATI, SURESH T, b. West Punjab, Pakistan, Nov. 13, 36; m. 61; c. 3. MECHANICS, APPLIED MATHEMATICS. B.S, Univ. Bombay, 57; M.S, Ill. Inst. Technol, 59; NASA traineeship, Univ. Colo, 63, Ph.D.(mech), 67. Stress analyst, Continental Can Co, 59-62; instr. mech. eng, Univ. Colo, Boulder, 66-67; res. scientist, RES. & DEVELOP. LABS, CORNING GLASS WORKS, 67-69, SR. RES. SCIENTIST, 69- Vis. lectr, dept. theoret. & appl. mech, Cornell Univ, 69-70. AAAS; Am. Soc. Mech. Eng; Am. Soc. Eng. Educ; Am. Acad. Mech. Analysis of elastic structures with particular emphasis on plates and shells; deformation and stress analysis of anisotropic elastic materials; application of the principles of mechanics to composite materials and materials science. Address: Research & Development Labs, Corning Glass Works, Corning, NY 14830.

GULBRANDSEN, R(OBERT) A(LLEN), b. Choteau, Mont, Sept. 12, 22; m. 47; c. 3. GEOLOGY. B.A, Montana, 47; Ph.D.(geol), Stanford, 58. Asst. geol, Pa. State, 48-49; GEOLOGIST, U.S. GEOL. SURV, 51- Asst, Stanford Univ, 55-56. U.S.M.C, 43-46. Geol. Soc. Am; Geochem. Soc; Mineral Soc. Am; Soc. Econ. Geol. Mineralogy; geochemistry; petrology. Address: U.S. Geological Survey, 345 Middlefield Rd, Menlo Park, CA 94025.

GULBRANSEN, EARL A(LFRED), b. Seattle, Wash, Jan. 20, 09; m. 38; c. 3. PHYSICAL CHEMISTRY. B.S, State Col. Wash, 31; summers, Michigan, 33, 37, 39; Ph.D.(phys. chem), Pittsburgh, 34. Asst. chem, Washington State, 30-31; Pittsburgh, 31-34; Nat. Res. Coun. fel. phys. chem, California, 34-35, res. assoc, 35-36; instr. chem. eng. & phys. chem, Tufts, 36-40; res. engr, RES. LABS, WESTINGHOUSE ELEC. CORP, Churchill Borough, 40-47, adv. engr, 47-66, SCI. CONSULT, 66- U.S. del, Int. Conf. Surface Reaction, Paris, France, 47, chmn, Pittsburgh, 48; mem. Gordon Res. Conf, Chem. & Physics of Metals, 50, Corrosion, 55; Int. Union Pure & Appl. Chem. Whitney award, Nat. Asn. Corrosion Eng, 52. Am. Chem. Soc; Electrochem. Soc.(Acheson Medal & Prize, 64); Am. Inst. Mining, Metall. & Petrol. Eng.(award, 49). Electron microscopy and diffraction of metal surfaces; kinetics of metal-gas reactions; corrosion high temperature alloys; high vacuum techniques; hydrogen in metals; pure metals; stress corrosion; refractory metals. Address: Research Labs, Westinghouse Electric Corp, Pittsburgh, PA 15235.

GULDEN, TERRY DALE, b. Seattle, Wash, May 4, 38; m. 59. MATERIALS SCIENCE. B.S, Washington (Seattle), 60; M.S, Stanford, 62, Ph.D.(mat. sci), 65. Ceramist, United Tech. Center, United Aircraft Corp, 60-61; res. assoc. radiation effects in mat, Berkeley Nuclear Labs, Cent. Elec. Generating Bd, Eng, 65-66; staff mem. mat. res, GULF GEN. ATOMIC, INC, 67-71, MGR. FUEL MAT. BR, FUELS & MAT. DIV, 71- AAAS; Am. Ceramic Soc; Am. Nuclear Soc. Radiation effects in solids; transmission electron microscopy; internal friction; chemical vapor deposition; creep and deformation of ceramics and metals; nuclear reactor materials. Address: 5208 Soledad Mountain Rd, San Diego, CA 92109.

GULDENZOPF, E(MIL) CHARLES, b. Aledo, Ill, May 7, 37; m. 62; c. 2. GEOLOGY, ZOOLOGY. A.B, Augustana Col.(Ill), 60; M.S, Iowa, 64; Ph.D. (geol, zool), Iowa State, 68. Explor. geologist, Sulmac Explor. Serv, Ltd, Can, 64; ASST. PROF. EARTH SCI, ASHLAND COL, 68- AAAS; Soc. Econ. Paleont. & Mineral; Geol. Soc. Am; Am. Asn. Petrol. Geol. Conodont biostratigraphy of Middle Ordovician strata in the continental interior of North America. Address: Dept. of Earth Science, Ashland College, Ashland, OH 44805.

GULEVICH, WLADIMIR, b. Brcko, Yugoslavia, Sept. 13, 30; U.S. citizen; m. 56; c. 1. SANITARY ENGINEERING. B.Ch.E, N.Y. Univ, 53, M.S, 56; Ph.D.(sanit. eng), Hopkins, 67. Asst, sch. eng, N.Y. Univ, 53-56; U.S. ARMY, 56-, off. sanit. eng, Army Environ. Health Lab, Md, 56-59, 37th Prev. Med. Co, 8th Army, 59-60, Med. Equip. Develop. Lab, 60-63, Mil. Assistance Command, Vietnam, 63-64, chief dept. sanit. eng, prev. med. div, Walter Reed Inst. Res, Wash, D.C, 67-69, SANIT. ENGR, OFF. SURGEON, HQ, FIRST U.S. ARMY, FT. GEORGE G. MEADE, 69- U.S.A, 56-, Lt. Col. AAAS; N.Y. Acad. Sci; Am. Acad. Polit. & Soc. Sci; Air Pollution Control Asn. Role of diffusion in biological waste treatment. Address: 1126 Loxford Terr, Silver Spring, MD 20901.

GULICK, SIDNEY L, III, b. Oakland, Calif, July 29, 36. MATHEMATICS. B.A, Oberlin Col, 58; M.A, Yale, 60, Ph.D.(math), 63. Instr. MATH, Pennsylvania, 63-65; asst. prof, UNIV. MD, COLLEGE PARK, 65-67, ASSOC. PROF, 67- Nat. Sci. Found. summer grants, 66-67. Math. Asn. Am; Am. Math. Soc. Theoretical mathematics; linear topological spaces and Banach algebras. Address: Dept. of Mathematics, University of Maryland, College Park, MD 20742.

GULICK, W(ALTER) LAWRENCE, b. Summit, N.J, July 4, 27; m. 52; c. 3. PHYSIOLOGICAL PSYCHOLOGY. A.B, Hamilton Col, 52; M.A, Delaware, 55; hon. fel, Princeton, 55-57, Ph.D.(physiol. psychol), 57. Asst. prof. PSYCHOL, Delaware, 57-61, assoc. prof, 61-63, prof, 63-65, chmn. dept, 64-65; PROF, DARTMOUTH COL, 65-, CHMN. DEPT, 70- Consult, Kody Mfg. Co, N.J, 57; Princeton, 58-; Nat. Sci. Found. Contract, Dartmouth Col, 58-59. U.S. Merchant Marine, 44-45; U.S.A, 46-48, Sgt. N.Y. Acad. Sci; Psychonomic Soc. Neurophysiology and electrophysiology; vision; hearing. Address: Gerry Hall, Dartmouth College, Hanover, NH 03755.

GULICK, WILSON M, JR, b. Plainfield, N.J, Mar. 10, 39; m. 62. ANALYTICAL CHEMISTRY. A.B, Harvard, 60; Ph.D.(chem), Cornell, 65. Asst. prof. CHEM, State Univ. N.Y. Col. Cortland, 64-65; res. assoc, Cornell Univ, 65-66, ASST. PROF, 66-68; FLA. STATE UNIV, 68- Am. Chem. Soc; The Chem. Soc. Electrochemistry in non-aqueous media; electron paramagnetic resonance spectroscopy of free radicals in solution. Address: Dept. of Chemistry, Florida State University, Tallahassee, FL 32306.

GULKIS, SAMUEL, b. West Palm Beach, Fla, Feb. 3, 37; m. 63; c. 2. PHYSICS, AERONAUTICAL ENGINEERING. B.Aero.E, Florida, 60, M.S, 62, Ph.D.(physics), 65. NASA trainee, 63-65; res. assoc. radio astron, Arecibo Ionospheric Observ, Cornell Univ, 65-67, asst. prof. astron, 67-68; SR. SCIENTIST, PLANETARY & SPACE SCI, JET PROPULSION LAB, 68- Summers, engr, Boeing Aircraft Co, Wash, 59, Douglas Aircraft Co, Inc, Calif, 60, Pratt & Whitney Aircraft Div, United Aircraft Corp, Fla, 61, Nat. Sci. Found. teaching asst, 63. Am. Astron. Soc. Radio astronomy, particularly planetary radio astronomy and extragalactic radio sources; betatron oscillations. Address: Planetary & Space Science, Jet Propulsion Lab, 4800 Oak Grove Dr, Pasadena, CA 91103.

GULL, C(LOYD) D(AKE), b. Lorain, Ohio, June 17, 15; m. 43; c. 4. INFORMATION SCIENCE. A.B, Allegheny Col, 36; A.B, Michigan, 37, A.M, 39. Asst, gen. library, Michigan, 37-39; periodicals librn, N.C. State Col, 39-42; from spec. asst. processing dept. to dep. chief, union catalog div, Library Cong, D.C, 45-52; tech. analyst, Document, Inc, 52-54; admin. off, div. eng. & indust. res, Nat. Acad. Sci-Nat. Res. Coun, 54-58; info. systs. consult, Gen. Elec. Co, D.C, 58-63; prof. libr. sci, Ind. Univ, Bloomington, 64-67; liaison off. nat. libr. task force, Nat. Libr. Med, 67-68; rep. consult, Document Systs, Inc, 68-69; PRES. CLOYD DAKE GULL & ASSOCS, INC, 69- Summers, vis. lectr, Univ. Mich, 53-54, 56-58, 60, 62-63, Univ. Wash, 61, Syracuse Univ, 62-63, 65-66, McGill Univ, 64. Chmn, U.S. Nat. Comt, Int. Fedn. Doc, 60-63. U.S.N.R, 42-45, Lt. Am. Library Asn; Spec. Libraries Asn; Am. Soc. Info. Sci.(pres, Am. Documentation Inst, 59-60). Documentation; information systems; electronic systems for the selection, identification, analysis, storage, retrieval, use and dissemination of information. Address: 4200 Dresden St, Kensington, MD 20795.

GULL, DWAIN D, b. Meadow, Utah, Aug. 21, 23; m. 44; c. 4. PLANT PHYSIOLOGY, HORTICULTURE. B.S, Utah State Univ, 55; M.S, Cornell Univ, 57, Ph.D.(veg. crops), 60. PROF. VEG. PHYSIOL, UNIV. FLA, 58-, ASST. HORTICULTURIST, EXP. STA, 59- U.S.A.A.F, 42-45; U.S.A, 50-52, 1st Lt. Am. Soc. Hort. Sci. Post harvest physiology; flavor chemistry; quality control physiology; flavor and quality of fresh vegetables as affected by harvest and marketing stresses. Address: Agricultural Experiment Station, 3026 McCarty Hall, University of Florida, Gainesville, FL 32601.

GULLATT, JOHN HORNSBY, b. Ruston, La, Dec. 29, 36; m. 58; c. 3. ELECTRICAL ENGINEERING, UNDERWATER ACOUSTICS. B.S.E.E, La. Polytech, 59; M.S.E.E, Ga. Inst. Tech, 62. Res. asst, eng. exp. sta, Ga. Inst. Tech, 59-61; sr. systs. engr, Fla. Aero Div, Honeywell Inc, 61-66; engr. & scientist, TRACOR INC, 66-71, SR. SCIENTIST, 71- Underwater acoustic detection; antisubmarine warfare; inertial navigation; automatic control theory; analog computation. Address: 4008 Hyridge Dr, Austin, TX 78759.

GULLEDGE, HUGH CLIFTON, b. Derma, Miss, Nov. 13, 14; m. 39; c. 4. ORGANIC CHEMISTRY. B.A, Miss. Col, 37; fel, North Carolina, 37-41, Ph.D.(org. chem), 41. Asst. prof. chem, Furman, 41; RES. CHEMIST, E.I. DU PONT DE NEMOURS & CO, INC, 41- AAAS; Am. Chem. Soc. Inorganic pigments; organometallic compounds; textile finishes; synthesis of vicinal substituted resorcinols. Address: Experimental Station, E.I. du Pont de Nemours & Co, Inc, Wilmington, DE 19898.

GULLEN, W(ARREN) H(ARTLEY), b. Minneapolis, Minn. EPIDEMIOLOGY, PUBLIC HEALTH. B.A, Univ. Minn, 51, B.S, 52, M.D, 54, M.P.H, 57. Fel. biostatist. & epidemiol, Univ. Minn, 55-63, instr. EPIDEMIOL, 63-68; ASSOC. PROF, MED. COL. GA, 68- AAAS; fel. Am. Pub. Health Asn; Am. Asn. Hist. Med; Asn. Teachers Prev. Med; Soc. Epidemiol. Res; Pub. Health Cancer Asn. Am; Am. Med. Asn. Methodology; studies of etiology; therapy; medical care; health care programs; biostatistics with application to medical research and medical practice. Address: Dept. of Community Medicine, Medical College of Georgia, Augusta, GA 30902.

GULLETT, WILLIAM W(AITMAN), b. Springfield, Ill, Oct. 11, 22; m. 43; c. 2. METALLURGICAL ENGINEERING. B.S, Washington (St. Louis), 48. Develop. engr, Chicago Develop. Corp, 49-53, exec. v.pres, 53-61, pres, 61-69; ASST. DIR. RES, CHEMETALS DIV, DIAMOND SHAMROCK CHEM. CORP, 69- V.pres. eng, Int. Metall. Corp, 57- U.S.A.A.F, 42-45, Res, 47-, Maj. Am. Soc. Metals; Am. Chem. Soc; Electrochem. Soc; Am. Inst. Mining, Metall. & Petrol. Eng. Nonferrous high temperature alloy development; molten salt electrolysis; metallurgical extractive processes. Address: 6903 Baltimore Ave, College Park, MD 20740.

GULLICK, HERBERT D(URANT), b. Greenville, S.C, Mar. 16, 22; m. 46; c. 4. SURGERY. B.S, Furman, 44; M.D, Virginia, 45. Instr. anat, sch. med, Washington (St. Louis), 49-50; Am. Cancer Soc. clin. fel, sch. med, Univ. Rochester, 51-52, asst. SURG, 51-54; instr, COL. MED, STATE UNIV. N.Y. UPSTATE MED. CTR, 55-57, asst. prof, 57-65, ASSOC. PROF, 65- Asst. chief surg. serv, Vet. Admin. Hosp, Syracuse, 57- Med.C, 46-48, Capt. AAAS; Am. Med. Asn; Am. Heart Asn; Am. Fedn. Clin. Res; fel. Am. Col. Surg; Asn. Clin. Sci; N.Y. Acad. Sci. Physiology and diseases of the pancreas and bilary tract; postoperative physiology; skin grafting and wound healing; proteolytic enzymes. Address: Dept. of Surgery, State University of New York Upstate Medical Center, Syracuse, NY 13210.

GULLICKSON, GARY R(ICHARD), b. Wis, Aug. 25, 37. PSYCHOPHYSIOLOGY. M.A, Univ. Hawaii, 63; Nat. Inst. Mental Health fel, Univ. Iowa, 63-65; Ph.D.(psychol), Ill. Inst. Technol, 70. Develop. psychophysiologist, Inst. Juvenile Res, Ill, 66-71; FEL. ELECTROENCEPHALOG, MED. SCH, NORTHWEST. UNIV, 71- Instr, Roosevelt Univ, 69- AAAS; Am. Electroencephalog. Soc; Int. Soc. Develop. Psychobiol; Soc. Neurosci; Soc. Psycophysiol. Res; Soc. Res. Child Develop. Infancy; children; learning; brain functions; electroencephalography; autonomic functions; developmental psychophysiology. Address: Dept. of Psychiatry, Northwestern University Medical School, 303 E. Chicago Ave, Chicago, IL 60611.

GULLIKSON, C(HARLES) W(ILLIAM), b. El Dorado, Kans, Sept. 11, 28; m. 54; c. 3. PHYSICS. B.S, Stanford, 51; M.S, Oklahoma, 53, Ph.D.(physics), 57. Asst. physics, Oklahoma, 52-56; res. physicist, Marathon Oil Co, 56-62; dir. res. & treas, Cryogenic Res. Co, 62-63; RES. PHYSICIST SPECTROS, REACTION KINETICS, KAMAN NUCLEAR CORP, 63- U.S.A, 46-47. Am. Phys. Soc; Soc. Appl. Spectros. Raman, infrared, ultraviolet, absorption and atomic absorption spectroscopy. Address: Field Science Lab, Kaman Nuclear Corp, 1700 Garden of the Gods Rd, Colorado Springs, CO 80907.

GULLINO, PIETRO M, b. Saluzzo, Italy, Mar. 24, 19; m. 56. PATHOLOGY. M.D, Turin, 43. Assoc. prof. path, Turin, 52-59; vis. scientist, NAT. CANCER INST, 59-63, res. pathologist, 63-68, HEAD TUMOR PHYSIOPATH. SECT, 68- Dipl, Italian Bd. Path, 52. Am. Soc. Exp. Path; Am. Asn. Cancer Res. Physiopathology of cancer tissue. Address: National Cancer Institute, National Institutes of Health, Bethesda, MD 20014.

GULLION, GORDON W, b. Eugene, Ore, Apr. 16, 23; m. 44; c. 4. WILDLIFE MANAGEMENT. B.S, Oregon, 48; M.A, California, Berkeley, 50. Wildlife technician, Nev. Fish & Game Cmn, 51-52, sr. game technician, 52-56, dist. supvr. fish & game mgt, 56-58; RES. ASSOC. FOREST WILDLIFE RELS, UNIV. MINN, 58- Med. Dept, 43-46, S/Sgt. Am. Ornith. Union; Wildlife

Soc; Wilson Ornith. Soc; Cooper Ornith. Soc. Population dynamics; sex and age composition, ecology, behavior, food studies and nutrition, harvest and habitat management techniques for desert, Great Basin and Boreal Forest small game species. Address: Forest Research Center, University of Minnesota, Cloquet, MN 55720.

GULLY, ARNOLD J(ARVIS), b. Preston, Miss, July 8, 21; m. 45; c. 4. CHEMICAL ENGINEERING. B.S, Auburn, 47; M.S, La. State, 50, Ph.D. (chem. eng), 51. Qaul. control engr, Hercules Powder Co, 47-48; assoc. prof. chem. eng, Miss. State, 51-54, prof, 54-59; proj. engr, Texaco, Inc, 59-61, res. supvr, 61-63; PROF. CHEM. ENG, TEX. TECH. UNIV, 63-, ASSOC. DEAN ENG, 68-, head dept. chem. eng, 63-68. U.S.N.R, 43-46. Am. Chem. Soc; Am. Inst. Chem. Eng; Am. Soc. Eng. Educ. Hydrogenation; petroleum processing; reaction kinetics. Address: College of Engineering, Texas Tech University, Lubbock, TX 79409.

GULYASSY, PAUL FRANCIS, b. Bridgeport, Conn, Aug. 5, 28; m. 60; c. 2. MEDICINE. B.A, Yale, 50; M.D, Columbia, 54. Am. Heart Asn. adv. res. fel, med, renal lab, sch. med, Tufts, 60-62; cardiovasc. res. inst, UNIV. CALIF, SAN FRANCISCO, 62-64, asst. prof. MED, MED. CTR, 64-68, ASSOC. PROF, 69-; DIR. N.CALIF. ARTIFICIAL KIDNEY CTR. & CHIEF RENAL & ELECTROLYTE SECT, SAN FRANCISCO GEN. HOSP, 68- Nat. Insts. Health res. career award, 65-, mem. clin. res. fel. rev. bd, 68-71. U.S.A, 56-58. Am. Soc. Clin. Invest; Am. Fedn. Clin. Res; Am. Physiol. Soc; Am. Soc. Nephrology. Address: Room 350, Bldg. 100, Artificial Kidney Center, San Francisco General Hospital, San Francisco, CA 94110.

GUM, OREN B(ERKLEY), b. Gassaway, W.Va, Nov. 3, 19; m. 46; c. 2. MEDICINE. B.S, Ohio State, 41, Ph.D.(agr. chem), 44, M.D, 50. Intern, Colo. Gen. Hosp, 50-51, res. internal med, 51-54, Nat. Insts. Health fel. endocrinol, 54-55; asst. prof. MED, sch. med, Colorado, 55-61; assoc. prof, SCH. MED, TULANE UNIV, 61-68, PROF, 68- U.S.N.R, 44-46, Lt.(jg). AAAS; Am. Rheumatism Asn. Rheumatic diseases. Address: Section of Arthritis, Tulane University School of Medicine, New Orleans, LA 70112.

GUM, WILSON FRANKLIN, JR, b. Pen Argyl, Pa, July 14, 39; m. 59; c. 4. ORGANIC CHEMISTRY. B.S, Muhlenberg Col, 61; Ph.D.(org. chem), Pennsylvania, 65. Spec. assignments chemist, DOW CHEM. CO, 65-67, res. chemist, 67-68, proj. leader org. chem. & develop, 68-70, res. group leader, org. chem. prod. res. lab, 70-71, SECT. HEAD, ORG. CHEM. & INTERMEDIATES SECT, TECH. SERV. & DEVELOP, 71- Am. Chem. Soc; Sci. Res. Soc. Am. Heterocyclic chemistry; heterocyclic quinones; organic polarography; stereo chemistry; free radical addition reactions; synthesis of biologically active compounds; process research; pesticides and organic intermediates; acid chloride reactions. Address: Organic Chemicals & Intermediates, 1710 Bldg, Dow Chemical Co, Midland, MI 48640.

GUMAN, WILLIAM J(OHN), b. Greenwich, Conn, June 23, 29; m. 54; c. 2. AERONAUTICAL ENGINEERING. B.A.E, Rensselaer Polytech. Inst, 52, M.A.E, 54, Ph.D.(aeronaut. eng), 65. Res. asst. aeronaut. eng, Rensselaer Polytech. Inst, 52-54, instr, 54-56, asst. prof, 56-59; sr. sci. res. engr, FAIRCHILD REPUBLIC DIV, FAIRCHILD INDUSTS, 59-60, prin. sci. res. engr, 60-61, spec. sci. res. engr, 61-63, staff engr, 63-65; CHIEF PROPULSION, 65- Assoc. fel. Am. Inst. Aeronaut. & Astronaut. Theoretical and experimental gasdynamics, especially electric space propulsion. Address: 26 Gaymor Lane, Commack, NY 11725.

GUMBRECK, L(AURENCE) G(ABLE), b. Washington, Ill, Aug. 24, 04; m. 27, 43. ZOOLOGY. B.A, Wisconsin, 27, M.A, 29, Ph.D.(zool), 45. Asst. zool, Wisconsin, 27-29, 37-44; endocrinologist, Difco Labs.Inc, 45-49; res. assoc. surg, sch. med, Wash. Univ, 49-57; asst. prof. anat. SCH. MED, UNIV. OKLA, 57-70, ASSOC. PROF. ANAT. SCI, 70- Entomologist, Wis. State Bd. Health, 40, City Bd. Health, Portage, 41, Madison, 44; lectr, zool, Wash. Univ, 50. Am. Med. Asn; Am. Asn. Anat. Physiology of the pituitary gland and organs of reproduction; genetics of the rat. Address: Dept. of Anatomical Sciences, School of Medicine, University of Oklahoma, Oklahoma City, OK 73104.

GUMMEL, HERMANN K, b. Hanover, Ger, July 6, 23; U.S.citizen; m. 52; c. 2. SOLID STATE PHYSICS. M.S, Syracuse, 52, Ph.D.(physics), 57; dipl, Marburg, 52. Mem. tech. staff, BELL TEL. LABS, 57-67, HEAD DESIGN ANAL. DEPT, 67- Am. Phys. Soc. Semiconductors. Address: Bell Telephone Labs, Mountain Ave, Murray Hill, NJ 07974.

GUMNICK, JAMES L(OUIS), b. Baltimore, Md, Oct. 5, 30; m. 59; c. 4. SOLID STATE PHYSICS. B.S, Loyola Col.(Md), 53; Ph.D.(physics), Notre Dame, 58. Scientist, Res. Inst. Adv. Study, Martin Co, 57-64; indust. labs, Int. Tel. & Tel. Corp, Ind, 64-66, dir. res, 66-68; TECH. DIR. ELEC. ENG. DEPT, FRANKLIN INST. RES. LABS, 68- Martin Loyola Prof. & chmn. dept. physics, Loyola Col.(Md), 57-64. AAAS; Am. Phys. Soc; Am. Asn. Physics Teachers. Surface and vacuum physics; electron emission, including field, photoelectric, thermionic and secondary emission. Address: Electrical Engineering Dept, Franklin Institute Research Labs, Franklin Pkwy. & 20th St, Philadelphia, PA 19103.

GUMOWSKI, IGOR, b. Belzec, Poland, Mar. 28, 28; Can. citizen; m. 53; c. 3. APPLIED MATHEMATICS & PHYSICS. B.Sc.A, Laval, 51, M.Sc, 52; Ph.D. (physics), Toulouse, 60, D.Sc.(appl. math), 61. Asst. prof. elec. eng, Laval, 52-59, assoc. prof, 59-66; PHYSICIST, EUROP. ORGN. NUCLEAR RES, 66- Prof, Toulouse, 63-65; fel, Claire Col. & vis. prof, Cambridge, 65- Fel. Brit. Inst. Math. & Appln. Nonlinear circuits and their stability; mathematics of nonlinear systems; optimization. Address: CERN, Geneva, 23, Switz.

GUMP, BARRY HEMPHILL, b. Columbus, Ohio, Nov. 12, 40; m. 63; c. 1. ANALYTICAL CHEMISTRY. B.Sc, Ohio State Univ, 62; Ph.D.(anal. chem), Univ. Calif, Los Angeles, 66. Asst. prof. CHEM, Univ. Calif, Los Angeles, summer 66; FRESNO STATE COL, 67-70, ASSOC. PROF, 70- Res. assoc, bur. sci, Food & Drug Admin, Wash, D.C, 66-67; consult, Cent. Calif. Med. Labs, 69-71. Am. Chem.Soc; Asn.Off.Anal. Chem. Separation methods in chemistry, specially chromatographic methods; analysis of trace elements in water and plant tissues by atomic absorption; clinical chemistry. Address: Dept. of Chemistry, Fresno State College, Fresno, CA 93710.

GUMP, DIETER W, b. Saranac Lake, N.Y, Mar. 28, 33; c. 3. INTERNAL MEDICINE, INFECTIOUS DISEASE. B.A, Swarthmore Col, 55; German Acad. exchange scholarship & Fulbright travel grant, Munich, 55-56; M.D, Johns Hopkins Univ, 60. Intern, Johns Hopkins Hosp, 60-61; asst. resident, med. ctr, Univ. Colo, 61-62; Johns Hopkins Hosp, 62-63, fel. infectious disease, 63-66; instr, UNIV. VT, 66-68, asst. prof. med. microbiol, 67-71, med, 68-71, ASSOC. PROF. MICROBIOL. & MED, 71- Air Nat. Guard, 65-70, Maj. Am. Thoracic Soc; Am. Fedn. Clin. Res; Am. Soc. Microbiol. Immunology; infectious diseases; distribution of antibiotics; clinical evaluation of antibiotics and chronic bronchitis. Address: Given Medical Bldg, University of Vermont College of Medicine, Burlington, VT 05401.

GUMP, FRANK E, b. St. Louis, Mo, Feb. 16, 28; m. 59; c. 3. SURGERY. A.B, Harvard, 51; M.D, N.Y. Univ, 55. Nat. Insts. Health res. fel, 58-59; asst. prof. SURG, COLUMBIA-PRESBY. MED. CTR, 66-69, ASSOC. PROF, 69- Dipl, Am. Bd. Surg. U.S.N, 46-48. Am. Col. Surg; Asn. Acad. Surg; Soc. Univ. Surg; Int. Cardiovasc. Soc; Am. Asn. Surg. of Trauma. Surgical metabolism. Address: Columbia-Presbyterian Hospital, 630 W. 168th St, New York, NY 10032.

GUMP, J. R, b. Ann Arbor, Mich, Apr. 1, 21; m. 43; c. 3. INORGANIC & ANALYTICAL CHEMISTRY. B.S.Ch.E, Detroit Inst. Technol, 43; M.S, Wayne State Univ, 49; Ph.D.(inorg. & anal. chem), Univ. Ky, 52. Instr. chem, Lawrence Inst. Technol, 47-49; Univ. Ky, 49-52; asst. prof, Univ. Cincinnati, 52-53; chemist, inorg. res, Mich. Chem. Corp, 53-54, supvr, 54-55, group leader, 59-62; res. chemist, Victor Chem. Co, 62-63; asst. prof. PHYSICS, CENT. MICH. UNIV, 63-67, assoc. prof, 67-70, PROF, 70- Pres, Mitten Chem. Inc, 55-67; consult, Sylvania Elec. Prod, 67-71. U.S.N.R, 43-46, Lt.(jg). AAAS; Am. Chem. Soc; Nat. Sci. Teachers Asn. Brine; bromine; magnesia; rare earths; ion exchange; solvent extraction; yttrium metal; salts and oxides; scandium salts and oxides; ferrates chemistry; secondary and elementary physical science education. Address: Dept. of Physics, Central Michigan University, 214 Brooks St, Mt. Pleasant, MI 48858.

GUMPERTZ, WERNER H(ERBERT), b. Berlin, Ger, Dec. 26, 17; U.S. citizen; m. 49; c. 2. CIVIL ENGINEERING. B.C.E, Swiss Fed. Inst. Tech, 39, S.B, Mass. Inst. Tech, 48, S.M, 50, Bldg.E, 54. Vol. engr, Amsterdam, Netherlands, 39-40; instrument man, Lockwood, Kessler & Bartlett, 40-41; field engr, M. Shapiro & Sons Construct. Co, Inc, 41-43; off. engr, shipyard Kaiser Co, 43; struct. engr, Corps. Engrs, U.S. Army, 47-48; engr, United Engrs. & Constructors, 48-49; asst. prof. civil eng. & construct. mgt, Mass. Inst. Tech, 49-57; PRIN. CONSULT. ENGR, SIMPSON GUMPERTZ & HEGER INC, 57- Consult, Bd. Ed, Woodbridge, N.J, 55-; mem. comt. adhesives & sealants, Bldg. Res. Inst, 60-63; adv. comt, inst. bldg. res, Pa. State, 64- Citizenship award, Freedom, Inc, 57. C.Eng, U.S.A, 43-46. Fel. Am. Soc. Civil Eng; Am. Concrete Inst; Am. Soc. Eng. Educ; Am. Soc. Test. & Mat. Investigations into physical properties of built-up roofing systems and their components; interrelation between structural building movement and the performance of nonstructural roof membranes. Address: Simpson Gumpertz & Heger Inc, 1696 Massachusetts Ave, Cambridge, MA 02138.

GUMPF, DAVID JOHN, b. Billings, Mont, Mar. 30, 42; m. 64; c. 1. PLANT VIROLOGY. B.S, Mont. State Univ, 64, M.S, 66; Ph.D.(plant path), Univ. Nebr, 70. ASST. PROF. PLANT PATH. & ASST. PLANT PATHOLOGIST, UNIV. CALIF, RIVERSIDE, 70- Purification and characterization of plant viruses. Address: Dept. of Plant Pathology, University of California, Riverside, CA 92502.

GUMPORT, RICHARD I, b. Pocatello, Idaho, June 23, 37; m. 60; c. 1. BIOCHEMISTRY, ENZYMOLOGY. B.S, Univ. Chicago, 60, U.S. Pub. Health Serv. traineeship & Ph.D.(biochem), 68. U.S. Pub. Health Serv. fel. BIOCHEM, sch. med, Stanford Univ, 68-70, fel, 70-71; ASST. PROF, SCH. BASIC MED. SCI. & SCH. CHEM. SCI, UNIV. ILL, URBANA, 71- AAAS; Environ. Mutagen Soc. Enzymology of nucleic acid metabolism in bacteria. Address: Dept. of Biochemistry, University of Illinois, Urbana, IL 61801.

GUMPORT, STEPHEN L(AWRENCE), b. N.Y.C, Dec. 5, 13; m. 49; c. 4. SURGERY. B.A, Amherst Col, 34; M.D, Cornell Univ, 38. Intern, Lenox Hill Hosp, N.Y, 38-40, resident, 40; asst. surg, postgrad. med. sch, N.Y. UNIV, 49-51, instr, 51-58, asst. prof. CLIN. SURG, SCH. MED, 58-67, ASSOC. PROF, 67-, CO-DIR. TUMOR SERV, MED. CTR, 66- Asst. vis. surgeon, fourth surg. div, Bellevue Hosp, 49-58, vis. surgeon, third & fourth surg. div, 58-; asst. attend. surg, Univ. Hosp, 49-58, assoc. attending surg, 58-67, attending surgeon, 67-; asst. attend. surgeon, N.Y. Eye & Ear Infirmary, 58-67; attend, Manhattan Vet. Admin. Hosp, 67-69; attend. surgeon, Doctors Hosp, N.Y, 49-69; assoc. attend. surgeon, N.Y. Infirmary, 64-66, attend. surgeon, 66-; coord, N.Y. Metrop. Regional Med. Prog, sch. med, N.Y. Univ, 67-69; liaison fel, comn. cancer, Am. Col. Surg, 67- Consult, Manhattan Vet. Admin. Hosp, 69-; U.S. Air Force Hosp, Mitchell Air Force Base, 49-61; St. Vincent's Hosp, 68-; N.Y. Eye & Ear Infirmary, 67-; Preventive Med. Inst, Strang, 68-; Doctors Hosp, 69- Dir, Med. Amateur Radio Coun, 66-; N.Y. State Cancer Progs. Asn, 67-70; mem. tech. consult. panel cancer, N.Y. Metrop. Regional Med. Prog, 68-; chmn, comt. cancer, med. ctr, N.Y. Univ, 68-; Melanoma Immunol. Study Group, 70- Med.C, 40-46, U.S.A.F.R, 52-55, Col.(ret); Legion of Merit; Bronze Star Medal. Dipl, Am. Bd. Surg, 50. Am. Asn. Cancer Educ; Am. Asn. Cancer Res; Am. Cancer Soc; Am. Med. Asn; Am. Soc. Clin. Oncol; fel. Am. Col. Surg; N.Y. Acad. Med; N.Y. Acad. Sci; James Ewing Soc. Tumor surgery; cancer chemotherapeutic agents and their clinical application. Address: Dept. of Surgery, School of Medicine, New York University, New York, NY 10021.

GUMPRECHT, W(ILLIAM) H(ENRY), b. Potsdam, N.Y, Nov. 16, 31; m. 52; c. 4. ORGANIC CHEMISTRY. B.S, Illinois, 53; Ethyl Corp. fel, Minnesota, 55-56, Gen. Elec. Co. fel, 56-57, Ph.D.(chem), 57. Res. chemist, E.I. DU PONT DE NEMOURS & CO, 57-66, SR. RES. CHEMIST, 66- Am. Chem. Soc. Dyes; fluorinated compounds; polymers; telomers. Address: 2617 Stephenson Dr, Wilmington, DE 19808.

GUNBERG, DAVID L(EO), b. Minneapolis, Minn, May 1, 22; m. 46; c. 5. ANATOMY. A.B, Redlands, 49; M.A, California, 52, Ph.D.(anat), 54. Asst. anat, California, 50-54; instr, sch. med, Univ. South. Calif, 54-55; asst. prof, MED. SCH, UNIV. ORE, 55-60, assoc. prof, 60-66, PROF. ANAT, 66-

Vis. prof, Airlangga Univ, Indonesia, 62-64. U.S.A, 43-46. AAAS; Am. Asn. Anat. Experimental mammalian teratology; analytical histology; experimental endocrinology. Address: 130 S.W. Ridge Rd, Portland, OR 97219.

GUNBERG, PAUL F, b. Minneapolis, Minn, July 13, 17; m. 45; c. 5. ORGANIC CHEMISTRY. B.A, St. Olaf Col, 39; Atomic Energy Comn. fel, Purdue, 46-49, Ph.D.(chem), 49. Lab. asst. adhesives, Minn. Min. & Mfg. Co, 39-40; control chemist, wheat prod, Washburn Crosby Milling Co, 40-41; supvr. ballistics, munitions div, U.S. Rubber Co, 42-43, org. synthesis, 44-45; asst, Purdue, 46-49; res. chemist, rubber & plastics, U.S. Rubber Co, 49-57; MGR. tech. serv, TEX-U.S. CHEM. CO, 57-66, APPLN. DEVELOP, 66- Am. Chem. Soc. Rubber chemistry; vulcanization; antioxidants; antiozone chemicals; modified elastomer and plastic systems. Address: 405 Hamilton Rd, Ridgewood, NJ 07450.

GUNCKEL, JAMES E(UGENE), b. Indianapolis, Ind, June 8, 14; m. 41; c. 2. BOTANY. B.S, Miami (Ohio), 38; univ. scholar, Harvard, 39-40, Atkins traveling fel. & M.A, 41, Austin & univ. fels, 40-44, Ph.D.(bot), 45. Instr. biol, Harvard, 44-46; asst. prof. BOT, RUTGERS UNIV, 46-50, assoc. prof, 50-57, PROF, 57-, CHMN. DEPT, 54- Grants, U.S. Atomic Energy Comn; Nat. Sci. Found; NASA; Am. Cancer Soc; Waksman Found. in France award, 59-60; Atomic Energy Comn. faculty fel, Risö, Denmark, 70. Consult, Brookhaven Nat. Lab, 50-60. Fel. AAAS; Bot. Soc. Am; Radiation Res. Soc; Am. Soc. Plant Physiol; Torrey Bot. Club (ed, Bull, 61-62, v.pres, 58, 64, pres, 65); Int. Soc. Plant Morphol; Soc. Develop. Biol; Soc. Exp. Biol. & Med. Developmental morphology and physiology in plants; radiobiology; tissue culture. Address: Dept. of Botany, Rutgers University, New Brunswick, NJ 08903.

GUNCKEL, THOMAS L, II, b. Dayton, Ohio, Jan. 16, 36; m. 63. ELECTRICAL ENGINEERING. B.S, Calif. Inst. Tech, 58; univ. fel, Stanford, 58-59, M.S, 59, Nat. Sci. Found. fel, 59-61, Ph.D.(elec. eng), 61. Res. specialist, Autonetics Div, N.Am. Aviation, Inc, 61-62, supvr. phys. anal, 62-63, chief space syst. anal, 63-66, mgr. syst. anal, 66-71, MGR. NAVIG. SYSTS, AVIONICS & SENSORS DIV, NORTH AM. ROCKWELL CORP, 71- Control system theory; space guidance and navigation; optimal control; orbit determination. Address: 704 Lowry St, Orange, CA 92669.

GUND, PETER H, b. N.Y.C, Feb. 20, 40; m. 67. ORGANIC CHEMISTRY. A.B, Columbia Univ, 61; M.S, Purdue Univ, 63; Petrol. Res. Found. assistantship, Univ. Mass, Amherst, 64-67, Ph.D.(org. chem), 67. Res. chemist, agr. res. ctr, Am. Cyanamid Co, 67-70; NAT. INSTS. HEALTH res. fel. org. chem, PRINCETON, 70-71, NAT. INST. GEN. MED. SCI. SPEC. RES. FEL, 71- Am. Chem. Soc. Computer applications in synthetic, physical organic and medicinal chemistry; molecular orbital calculations, linear free energy relationships and multiple regression analysis; steric effects on drug action; computer graphics; aromaticity and pseudo-aromaticity; cyclooctatetraene and guanidine chemistry. Address: Dept. of Chemistry, Princeton University, Princeton, NJ 08540.

GUNDERLOY, FRANK CHARLES, JR, b. Pasadena, Md, Mar. 9, 31; m. 55; c. 3. CHEMISTRY. B.S, Wash. Col, 52; fel, Rutgers, 55-56, Ph.D.(chem), 57. Chemist, U.S. Naval Eng. Exp. Sta, 52-53; asst. chem, Rutgers, 53-55; chemist, Esso Res. & Eng. Co, 56-58, sr. chemist & group leader, 58-61; tech. specialist, ROCKETDYNE DIV, N.AM. ROCKWELL CORP, 61-63, SR. TECH. SPECIALIST, 63-, MGR, 70-, prin. scientist, 62-67, eng. supvr, 67-70. Am. Chem. Soc; Sci. Res. Soc. Am. Organometallic and hydride chemistry primarily as related to rocket propellant applications; inorganic chemistry; chemical propellants; chemical engineering; polymers; material and processes; chemical analysis. Address: Dept. 589-199, Rocketdyne Division, North American Rockwell Corp, 6633 Canoga Ave, Canoga Park, CA 91304.

GUNDERSEN, J(AMES) NOVOTNY, b, Oak Park, Ill, Dec. 20, 25; m. 56; c. 2. ECONOMIC GEOLOGY. B.S, Wisconsin, 49; M.A, California, Los Angeles, 55; Reserve Mining Co. fel, Minnesota, 55-57, Ph.D.(econ. geol), 58. Geol. consult, Alamos Mining Co, Mex, 51-53; raw mat. engr, Columbia Iron Mining Co. Div, U.S. Steel Corp, Utah, 53-55; asst. petrol. & mineral, Minnesota, 57-58, res. assoc. mining geologist, mines exp. sta, 58-61; asst. prof. geol, Calif. State Col, Los Angeles, 61-64, assoc. prof. & chmn. dept, 64-68, acting dir. res. & govt. rels, 65-68; prof. GEOL, Univ. Ariz, 68-70; PROF. & CHMN. DEPT, WICHITA STATE UNIV, 70- Summers, raw mat. engr, Columbia-Geneva Div, U.S. Steel Corp, Utah, 51, geologist, Minn. Geol. Surv, 55-57 & instr, Macalaster Col, 57. U.S.A, 44-46, Res, 46-49. Geochem. Soc; Am. Mineral. Soc; Am. Inst. Mining, Metall. & Petrol. Eng. Mining geology, especially taconites and iron ores; petrography and geochemistry of metamorphic and metasomatic rocks; taconite beneficiation; mineralography; hydrothermal alteration; differential thermal analysis; x-ray diffraction; spectroscopy; pre-Cambrian stratigraphy; desert geology. Address: Dept. of Geology, Wichita State University, Wichita, KS 67208.

GUNDERSEN, KAARE R(EINHARDT), b. Oslo, Norway, Aug. 30, 22; m. 53; c. 1. MARINE MICROBIOLOGY. M.S, Copenhagen, 53; Ph.D.(mycol), Gothenburg, 62. French Govt. scholar, Pasteur Inst, Paris, 52-53; res. asst. soil microbiol, State Lab. Soil & Crop Res, Denmark, 53-57; lectr. microbiol. & plant physiol, Gothenburg, 57-62; res. assoc. antibiotics, Astra Pharmaceut. Co, Sweden, 62-64; Sverdrup fel. oceanog, Scripps Inst, California, 64-65; assoc. prof. mycol, Royal Col. Forestry, Sweden, 65-66; assoc. prof. MICROBIOL, UNIV. HAWAII, 66-70, PROF, 70- Am. Soc. Limnol. & Oceanog; Am. Soc. Microbiol. Marine microbiology; transformation of nitrogenous compounds in soil and water; physiology and ecology of chemoautotrophic bacteria; antibiosis; antibiotics; effects of cycloheximide on basidiomycete Fomes annosus. Address: Dept. of Microbiology, University of Hawaii, Honolulu, HI 96822.

GUNDERSEN, KARE, b. Stavanger, Norway, Aug. 5, 23; nat; m. 53; c. 4. INTERNAL MEDICINE. B.A, Minnesota, 48; M.D, Hopkins, 52. Intern & res. med, New Eng. Center Hosp, Mass, 52-54; trainee diabetes, Nat. Insts. Health, Univ. Hosp, Pennsylvania, 54-57; res. med, med. sch, Washington (Seattle), 57-58, res. fel. diabetes, Nat. Insts. Health, 58-59; asst. prof. prev. med. sch. med, Tufts Univ, 59-66; MEM. RES. STAFF, DEPT. CLIN. PHARMACOL. & RESIDENT PHYSICIAN, UPJOHN CO, 66- Am. Diabetes Asn; N.Y. Acad. Med; Am. Fedn. Clin. Res; Am. Heart Asn. Diabetes mellitus; role of insulin and anti-insulin factors in the disease; clinical treatment and research. Address: Upjohn Co, Kalamazoo, MI 49001.

GUNDERSEN, LARRY E(DWARD), b. Detroit, Mich, June 3, 40; m. 63; c. 3. BIOCHEMISTRY, INFORMATION SCIENCE. B.S, Bowling Green State Univ, 62; M.S, Univ. Ill, Urbana, 66; Ph.D.(biochem), Univ. Iowa, 69. Fel. biochem, Scripps Clin. & Res. Found, 68-71; ASSOC. DIR. SCI. INFO. & REGULATORY AFFAIRS, MEAD JOHNSON & CO, 71- AAAS; Am. Chem. Soc. Enzymology, protein structure; enzyme mechanisms; lactate dehydrogenase; dihydrofolate reductase; science information. Address: Mead Johnson & Co, Evansville, IN 47721.

GUNDERSEN, ROY M(ELVIN), b. Ecorse, Mich, May 1, 30. MATHEMATICS. B.S, Ill. Inst. Tech, 51; M.S, Wisconsin, 52; fel. & scholar, Brown, 52-53, Ph.D.(appl. math), 56. Asst. math, Wisconsin, 51-52; appl. math, Brown, 53-55; mathematician, Chicago, 55; dir. res, Paris, France, 55-56; res. engr, Boeing Aircraft Co, 56-57; asst. prof. MATH, Ill. Inst. Tech, 57-60, assoc. prof, 60-63; PROF, UNIV. WIS, MILWAUKEE, 63- Nat. Sci. Found. res. grant, 58-60; vis. assoc. prof, Math. Res. Ctr, U.S. Army, Wisconsin, 61-62. Consult, Armour Res. Found, 57, 59-60; Bendix Systs. Div, Bendix Corp, 60-61. Am. Math. Soc; Soc. Natural Philos. Applied mathematics; compressible fluid flow; partial and ordinary differential equations; magnetohydrodynamics. Address: Dept. of Mathematics, University of Wisconsin-Milwaukee, Milwaukee, WI 53211.

GUNDERSON, E(LLSWORTH) K. ERIC, b. Maxbass, N.Dak, Sept. 18, 23; m. 50; c. 3. PSYCHOLOGY. B.A, California, Los Angeles, 48, M.A, 51, Ph.D.(psychol), 53. Clin. psychologist, retraining command, U.S. NAVY, 53-57, chief psychologist, 57-60, head spec. environ. br, NEUROPSYCHIAT. RES. UNIT, 60-65, HEAD OPER. PSYCHIAT. DIV, 65- Adj. prof, Univ. Calif, San Diego, 71- U.S.A, 43-46, Sgt. Fel. Am. Psychol. Asn. Epidemiology; psychodiagnostics; psychotherapy; personality measurement; unusual environments. Address: Operational Psychiatry Division, Navy Medical Neuropsychiatric Research Unit, San Diego, CA 92152.

GUNDERSON, FRANK L(ESTER), b. Oconomowoc, Wis, March 16, 02; m. 27; c. 1. FOODS, NUTRITION. B.S, Wisconsin, 24, M.S, 27, Ph.D.(biochem), 29. Asst. chemist, State Dept. Agr, Wis, 23-29; biochemist & dir. nutrit. res, Quaker Oats Co, Ill, 29-45; v.pres. & dir. res. & develop. dept, Pillsbury Mills, Inc, 45-52; TECH. CONSULT. FOOD & ALLIED INDUSTS, 52- Exec. secy, food & nutrit. bd, Nat. Res. Coun, 42-45. Am. Chem. Soc; Inst. Food Tech. Food and nutrition; food additives; federal and international regulations and food standards. Address: 5443 Mohican Rd, Washington, DC 20016.

GUNDERSON, HARVEY L(ORRAINE), b. Gary, Minn, June 11, 13; m. 50; c. 3. ZOOLOGY, MAMMALOGY. B.A, Concordia Col.(Moorehead, Minn), 35; M.S, Minnesota, Minneapolis, 48; Ph.D.(zool), Michigan, 62. With W.M. Welch Sci. Co, 36-39; mus. asst, mus. natural hist, Univ. Minnesota, 40-42, 46-48, asst. scientist, 48-62, assoc. scientist, 62-64, curator mammals, 58-64; curator zool. & mus. records, STATE MUS, 64-67, ASSOC. DIR, 67-, PROF. ZOOL, UNIV. NEBR, LINCOLN, 68-, assoc. prof. zool. & physiol, 64-68. Regional ed, Audubon Field Notes, 47-57. Med.Admin.C, 42-46, 1st Lt. Am. Soc. Mammal; Wildlife Soc; Wilson Ornith. Soc. Mammal distribution and ecology, particularly factors which influence distribution; water balance and water turnover in small mammals; population dynamics of small mammals. Address: University of Nebraska State Museum, Morrill Hall, Lincoln, NE 68508.

GUNDERSON, LESLIE CHARLES, b. Rahway, N.J, Aug. 1, 35; m. 57; c. 3. ELECTRICAL ENGINEERING, ELECTROMAGNETICS. Mech.E, Stevens Inst. Technol, 57, M.S, 60; M.S, Columbia Univ, 64; Ph.D.(elec. eng), N.C. State Univ, 71. Jr. engr, electronic reconaissance lab, ITT Fed. Labs, Int. Tel. & Tel. Corp, N.J, 57-58, engr, 58-61, sr. engr, 61-63, ECM & simulation lab, 63-64; group leader, electro-optics & microwave dept, ELECTRONIC RES. LAB, CORNING GLASS WORKS, 64-66, supvr, MICROWAVE DEPT, 66-67, MGR, 67- Sr. mem. Inst. Elec. & Electronics Eng; Int. Microwave Power Inst. Techniques for advanced concepts in receiver design; utilization of unique materials for microwave components; electromagnetic analysis of dielectric lenses; investigation of microwaves in food preparation; biological application of microwaves. Address: Microwave Dept, Electronic Research Lab, Corning Glass Works, 3800 Electronics Dr, Raleigh, NC 27604.

GUNDERSON, NORMAN G(USTAV), b. Schenectady, N.Y, May 29, 17; m. 45; c. 3. MATHEMATICS. A.B, N.Y. State Col. Teachers, Albany, 37; A.M, Cornell, 41, Ph.D.(math), 48. Teacher, pub. sch, N.Y, 37-40; asst. & instr. math, Cornell, 40-46; instr, UNIV. ROCHESTER, 46-49, asst. prof, 49-55, assoc. prof, 55-66, educ, 61-66, PROF. MATH. & EDUC, 66- Am. Math. Soc; Math. Asn. Am. Number theory; geometry; mathematics curriculum; teaching of mathematics. Address: Dept. of Mathematics, University of Rochester, Rochester, NY 14627.

GUNDERSON, NORMAN O, b. Laramie, Wyo, Sept. 10, 18; m. 42; c. 2. ENGINEERING, URBAN STUDIES. B.S, Wyoming, 39, M.S, 47; C.E, Stanford, 55. Jr. engr, hwy. dept, State of Wyo, 39; U.S. Soil Conserv. Serv, 39-41; asst. engr, U.S. Bur. Reclamation, 41; asst. prof. civil eng, Hawaii, 47-48; from asst. prof. to prof. eng, SAN JOSE STATE COL, 48-56, dean, sch. eng, 56-70, DIR. CYBERNET. SYSTS. GRAD. PROG, 70- Consult, City of San Jose, 55- U.S.A, 41-46, Lt. Col. Am. Soc. Civil Eng; Am. Soc. Eng. Educ; Nat. Soc. Prof. Eng. Academic administration, particularly engineering role in interpretation of effect of computer controlled automatic production systems on mankind; city planning. Address: Cybernetic Systems Graduate Program, San Jose State College, San Jose, CA 95114.

GUNDERSON, RICHARD HARLAN, b. Ada, Minn, June 4, 37; m. 60; c. 3. CIVIL ENGINEERING, ENGINEERING MECHANICS. B.S, N.Dak. State, 59; Ph.D.(civil eng), Arizona, 64. Asst. prof. struct. & eng. mech, Houston, 64-66; Tex. A&M Univ, 66-71; STRUCT. ENGR, ENG. TECHNOL. ANALYSTS, INC, 71- Am. Soc. Civil Eng; Am. Soc. Eng. Educ; Nat. Soc. Prof. Eng; Soc. Exp. Stress Anal; Int. Asn. Shell Struct. Structural analysis and dynamics; shell analysis and buckling. Address: Engineering Technology Analysts, Inc, 3310 Richmond Ave, Houston, TX 77006.

GUNDERSON, SHAUN D(ENNIS), b. Pilot Mound, Man, Mar. 18, 25; nat; m. 51; c. 2. RADIOLOGY. B.Sc, Omaha, 45; M.D, Nebraska, 48. Res. internal med, Indiana, 49-51; radiol, col. med, Nebraska, 54-56, clin. assoc, 56-57, instr, 57-59, asst. prof, 59-64; RADIOLOGIST, GOSHEN GEN. HOSP, 64- Radiologist, Bishop Clarkson Mem. Hosp, Omaha, Nebr, 56-64. Dipl, Am. Bd. Radiol, 56. U.S.A.F, 51-54, Capt. Radiol. Soc. N.Am; Am. Med. Asn; Am. Col. Radiol. General radiology; internal medicine. Address: Goshen General Hospital, Goshen, IN 46526.

GUNDJIAN, ARSHAVIR ARAM, b. Alexandria, Egypt, Oct. 2, 35. ELECTRONIC ENGINEERING, PHYSICS. B.Sc, Alexandria, 59; fel. & Ph.D.(elec. eng), Pennsylvania, 65. Res. assoc. ELEC. ENG, Pennsylvania, 65; asst. prof, McGILL UNIV, 65-69, ASSOC. PROF, 69- Nat. Res. Coun. Can. grant, 66-67; consult, U.S. Army Electronics Command contract & NASA grant, 66- Inst. Elec. & Electronics Eng. Semiconductor electronics, particularly high field electromechanical interactions in homopolar semiconductors; laser detection and modulation; laser interferometry. Address: Dept. of Electrical Engineering, McGill University, Montreal 2, Que, Can.

GUNDLACH, ROBERT W(ILLIAM), b. Buffalo, N.Y, Sept. 7, 26; m. 50; c. 3. PHYSICS. B.A, Buffalo, 49. Asst. physics, Buffalo, 49-51; physicist, Durez Plastics Co, N.Y, 51-52; Haloid Co, 52-55, proj. leader, 55-57, res. assoc, 57-59, sr. res. assoc, Haloid Xerox, Inc, 59-60, sr. scientist, XEROX CORP, WEBSTER, 60-63, prin. scientist & consult, 63-66, RES. FEL, 66- C.E. Ives jour. award, 64. Soc. Photog. Sci. & Eng. Exploratory xerographic research; physical imaging methods, electrophotography. Address: 2434 Turk Hill Rd, Victor, NY 14564.

GUNDLE, SIGMUND, b. Munich, Ger, Feb. 6, 15; nat; m. 43; c. 3. PSYCHIATRY. M.D, Wash. Univ, 43. Fel, Menninger Found. Sch. Psychiat, 47-49; assoc. clin. prof. PSYCHIAT, SCH. MED, UNIV. KANS, 49-67, CLIN. PROF, 67-, psychiat. consult, lectr, psychiatrist & dir. student health serv, 49-54. Dir. Community Ment. Health Clin, Lawrence, Kans, 49-54; mem. teaching staff, Menninger Found. Sch. Psychiat, 50-54; mem, Topeka Inst. Psychoanal, 50-61; consult, Family Serv. Agency, Kansas City, Mo, 54-; Gen. Hosp. & Jewish Family Serv, 56; Gillis Home for Children, 59; chmn. dept. psychiat, Menorah Med. Ctr, Kansas City, Mo, 63-; consult, Jewish Voc. Serv, 66-; Univ. Mo-Kansas City, 67-, prof, sch. med, 68-; mem, Int. Union Sch. & Univ. Health & Med, Paris. Dipl, Am. Bd. Psychiat. & Neurol, 49. Med.C, 44-47, Maj. Fel. AAAS; fel. Am. Psychiat. Asn; Am. Col. Health Asn; Am. Med. Asn; Asn. Am. Med. Cols. Observations on college students and adolescents; psychoanalysis; psychiatric teaching in medical education; psychotherapy; television in psychiatric education. Address: 751 E. 63rd St, Suite 11, Kansas City, MO 64110.

GUNDY, GLEN V(ERLON), b. Memphis, Mo, Mar. 21, 01; m. 25; c. 2. ORGANIC CHEMISTRY. B.S, Cent. Mo. State Teachers Col, 25; M.S, Iowa, 29, Ph.D.(org. chem), 35. Teacher, pub. schs, Mo, 23-26; Ill, 26-28; instr. chem, Case, 29-31; teacher chem. & soils, Wis. State Univ-Platteville, 35-47, chmn. dept. chem, 47-69; RETIRED. Am. Chem. Soc. Vanillin derivatives; effects of substituents in the rearrangements of hydrazones to pyrazolines. Address: 435 W. Madison, Platteville, WI 53818.

GUNDY, LAWRENCE J(AMES), b. Broken Bow, Nebr, Mar. 4, 19; m. 47; c. 3. GENETICS. B.S, Missouri, 46, Quaker Oats Co. fel, 46-50, M.A, 47, Ph.D.(genetics), 65. Agronomist, Tex. Res. Found, 50-69; GENETICIST, INT. GRAIN, INC, DALLAS, 69- AAAS; Am. Soc. Agron; Crop Sci. Soc. Am; Am. Genetic Asn. Breeding and testing of triticale, small grains, corn, sorghums, sunflowers, soybeans and muskmelons. Address: 2430 Livenshire, Garland, TX 75040.

GUNDY, RICHARD F, b. Chicago, Ill, Oct. 7, 33; m. 59; c. 2. MATHEMATICS. A.B, Ill. Col, 55; Ph.D.(psychol), Indiana, 60; Ph.D.(statist), Chicago, 65. Rockefeller fel, 60-61; U.S. Pub. Health Serv. fel, 61-63; Hildebrandt res. instr. math, Univ. Mich, Ann Arbor, 63-66; assoc. prof. STATIST, RUTGERS UNIV, 66-70, PROF, 70- Vis. prof, Hebrew Univ, Israel, 68-69; vis. mem, Inst. Mittag-Leffler, Sweden, 70; exchange prof, Univ. Paris, 71. Inst. Math. Statist; Am. Math. Soc. Probability theory; analysis. Address: Statistics Center, Rutgers University, New Brunswick, NJ 08903.

GUNDY, SAMUEL C(HARLES), b. Reading, Pa, Mar. 28, 18; m. 43; c. 2. BIOLOGICAL SCIENCES. B.S, Pa. State Teachers Col.(Kutztown), 46; Ford Found. fel. & M.S, Cornell, 53. Specialist, nature, Reading Recreation Dept, 40-41; teacher entomol, vert. zool. & ornith, Reading Pub. Mus. & Art Gallery, 41; pub. sch, Pa, 46-52; asst. dir, Reading Pub. Mus. & Art Gallery, 53-56, acting dir, 57-58, dir, 58-67; ASST. PROF. BIOL, KUTZTOWN STATE COL, 67- U.S.A, 41-42, U.S.A.A.F, 42-45. Am. Soc. Ichthyol. & Herpet; Wilson Ornith. Soc; Am. Asn. Museums. Herpetology; ornithology; geology; mineralogy; paleontology. Address: 409 Harvard Blvd, Lincoln Park, Reading, PA 19609.

GUNDZIK, RICHARD MICHAEL, b. Cleveland, Ohio, Nov. 10, 30; m. 52; c. 3. CHEMICAL ENGINEERING, THERMODYNAMICS. B.S, Case, 53. Aeronaut. res. scientist, rocket br, Nat. Adv. Cmt. Aeronaut, 53-54; air hyg. chemist, Am. Steel & Wire Co. Div, U.S. Steel Corp, 54-55, chem. engr, coke plant, 56-57; chem. engr, Am. Potash & Chem. Corp, 57-61, prod. engr, 61-62, sect. head eng, 62-66, supvr. eng, 66-67, mgr. pigment res, 67-69, MGR. TECH. SECT, WHITTIER LABS, KERR-McGEE CORP, 69- U.S.A, 55-56. Am. Asn. Cost Eng. Titanium dioxide chloride process, titanium tetrachloride, perchlorates, boron hydrides, boric oxide, boron trichloride, coke and coal chemicals; surface chemistry. Address: Whittier Labs, 12519 E. Washington Blvd, Whittier, CA 90602.

GUNJI, HIROSHI, b. Bankok, Thailand, June 14, 28; m. 62; c. 1. MATHEMATICS. B.A, Univ. Tokyo, 54, M.A, 56; Ph.D.(math), Johns Hopkins Univ, 62. Instr. MATH, Cornell Univ, 62-64; asst. prof, Univ. Sask, 64-66; UNIV. WIS, MADISON, 66-70, ASSOC. PROF, 70- Nat. Sci. Found. math. res. grants, 62-64 & 66-69; Can. Math. Asn. summer res. fel, 65. Diophantine problem of elliptic curves. Address: Dept. of Mathematics, University of Wisconsin, 480 Lincoln Dr, Madison, WI 53706.

GUNKEL, RALPH D, b. Rex, Ore, Apr. 15, 11; m. 45. PHYSIOLOGICAL OPTICS. B.S, Washington State, 33; Dr. Optom, Pa. State Col. Optom, 50. Practicing optometrist, 50-52; RES. OPHTHALMIC PHYSICIST, NAT. EYE INST, 52- U.S.N.R, 42-46, Lt. Comdr. Asn. Res. Vision & Ophthal; Int. Soc. Clin. Electroretinography; Optical Soc. Am. Electrophysiology; dark adaptation; visual thresholds; color vision; electroretinography; ophthalmic instrumentation. Address: Bldg. 10, Room 1D 06, National Institutes of Health, Bethesda, MD 20014.

GUNKEL, ROBERT JAMES, b. Chicago, Ill, May 13, 25; m. 49; c. 5. AERODYNAMICS. B.S, Michigan, 46, M.S, 47. Design specialist, missile & space systs. div, Douglas Aircraft Co, Inc, 47-53, asst. supvr. missile aerodyn, 53-56, chief aerodyn. & astrodyn, 56-61, chief res. engr, 61-62, adv. prog. mgr. space launch vehicles, 62, mgr. sprint systs. develop, 62-63, dir. prog, 437, 63-64, medium launch vehicles, 64, adv. manned spacecraft systs, 64-66, dir. adv. spacecraft & launch systs, missile & space systs. div, McDONNELL DOUGLAS CORP, 66-68, dir. Systs. Develop. & Integration, Manned Orbiting Lab, NASA subdiv, 68-69, adv. space & launch systs, 69-70, DIR. SPACE SHUTTLE BOOSTER, ASTRONAUT. CO-WEST, 70- Mem. res. & tech. adv. comt. space vehicles, NASA, 63- U.S.N, 46. AAAS; Am. Astron. Soc; Am. Inst. Aeronaut. & Astronaut; assoc. fel. Brit. Interplanetary Soc. Calculations of variational approach to flight mechanics; linearized supersonic wing theory; program management. Address: 1500 Warwick Lane, Newport Beach, CA 92660.

GUNKEL, WESLEY W, b. Hope, N.Dak, Oct. 17, 21; m. 45; c. 2. AGRICULTURAL ENGINEERING. B.Sc, N.Dak. State, 47; M.S, Iowa State, 48; Cornell, 48-54; Ph.D.(agr. eng), Mich. State, 57. Asst. prof. AGR. ENG, STATE UNIV. N.Y. COL. AGR, CORNELL UNIV, 48-53, assoc. prof, 53-59, PROF, 59-, COORD. GRAD. INSTR, 66- Vis. prof. & adv, Univ. Nigeria, 62-63; summer instr, Iowa State, 48. U.S.A.A.F, 43-45, 1st Lt. AAAS; Am. Soc. Agr. Eng; Am. Soc. Eng. Educ; Am. Chem. Soc. Pest control equipment and methods; harvesting machinery. Address: Dept. of Agricultural Engineering, State University of New York College of Agriculture at Cornell University, Ithaca, NY 14850.

GUNKLER, ALBERT A(RTHUR), b. Ft. Wayne, Ind, May 13, 24; m. 44; c. 5. CHEMICAL ENGINEERING. B.S, Purdue, 48, Ph.D.(chem. eng), 51. Res. & develop. engr, DOW CHEM. CO, 51-57, dir. bromine res. & develop, 57-60, tech. dir. inorg. chem. res, MIDLAND DIV, 60-67, CHIEF PROCESS ENGR, 67- Kirkpatrick Award, 56. U.S.A.A.F, 43-45, 2nd Lt. Research and engineering in inorganic chemicals and organic halogen compounds. Address: 4508 Andre, Midland, MI 48640.

GUNN, BERNARD M, b. Wanaka, N.Z, Aug. 31, 27; m. 55; c. 4. GEOCHEMISTRY. B.Sc, Univ. N.Z, 54, M.Sc, 56; Ph.D.(geochem), Univ. Otago, N.Z, 62. Chief geologist, N.Z. Transantarctic Exped, 56-58; monitor, Univ. Otago, N.Z, 59-63; researcher, Australian Nat. Univ, 63-64; asst. prof. GEOCHEM, Tulane Univ, 64-66; ASSOC. PROF, UNIV. MONTREAL, 66- Researcher, Univ. Calif. 66. Australian & N.Z. Asn. Advan. Sci; Am. Geophys. Union; Spectros. Soc. Can. Analytical geochemistry. Address: Dept. of Geology, University of Montreal, P.O. Box 6128, Montreal 101, Que, Can.

GUNN, (GEORGE) BRAD(FORD), b. Lloydminster, Sask, Apr. 20, 13; m. 41, 53; c. 1. PHYSICAL CHEMISTRY. B.Sc, Alberta, 39, M.Sc, 47; Ph.D.(phys. chem), McGill, 50. Prin, high schs, Can, 40-42; res. officer phys. chem, Can. Nat. Defence, 50-52; ASSOC. RES. OFF. metall, SASK. RES. COUN, 52-57, PHYS. CHEM, 57-, HEAD CHEM. DIV, 61- Part-time assoc. res. metall, Saskatchewan, 52-57. Can. Army, 42-45, Lt. Chem. Inst. Can. Rheology; metallurgy; analytical and inorganic chemistry. Address: Saskatchewan Research Council, Saskatoon, Sask, Can.

GUNN, CHARLES ROBERT, b. Columbus, Ohio, June 1, 27; m. 53; c. 2. TAXONOMY, BOTANY. B.S, Iowa State, 50, Ph.D.(syst. bot), 65; M.S, Louisville, 58. Seed technologist, Ross Seed Co, 51-60; RES. PLANT TAXONOMIST, AGR. RES. SERV, CROP RES. DIV, U.S. DEPT. AGR, 65- Am. Soc. Plant Taxon; Int. Asn. Plant Taxon; Asn. Off. Seed Anal. Monographing genus Vicia; seed and fruit distribution by ocean currents; using seeds and fruits to identify plants and in plant phylogeny. Address: New Crops Research Branch, Agriculture Research Service, Crop Research Division, U.S. Dept. Agriculture, Beltsville, MD 20705.

GUNN, CHESTERFIELD GARVIN, JR, b. Bethany, Mo, Sept. 2, 20; m. 46; c. 3. INTERNAL MEDICINE, NEUROPHYSIOLOGY. A.B, Missouri, 42; M.D, Yale, 50. Intern & resident med, med. ctr, Kansas, 50-54; asst. res. anatomist, sch. med, California, Los Angeles, 54-56; asst. prof. med, physiol. & prev. med, SCH. MED, UNIV. OKLA, 56-61, psychiat, neurol. & behavioral sci, 57-62, assoc. prof. med. & physiol, 61-67, PROF. PHYSIOL, 67-, MED, 68-, BIOL. PSYCHOL, 71- Res. fel, Am. Col. Physicians, 53; Am. Heart Asn, 54-56. U.S.A, 42-46. Am. Fedn. Clin. Res; Am. Psychosom. Soc; Am. Col. Cardiol; Asn. Am. Med. Col; Am. Heart Asn; Am. Acad. Neurol. Central nervous system mechanisms in normal and pathological cardiovascular function. Address: Dept. of Medicine, University of Oklahoma Medical Center, 800 N.E. 13th St, Oklahoma City, OK 73104.

GUNN, EWING LEYTON, b. Mt. Pleasant, Tex, July 23, 03; m. 32; c. 1. ANALYTICAL CHEMISTRY. B.A, Texas, 30, M.A, 35. Teacher, pub. sch, Tex, 31-39; instr. chem, Lee Col.(Tex), 39-42; tester, HUMBLE OIL & REF. CO, 42-44, asst. chemist, 44-47, chemist, 47-55, sr. res. chemist, 55-62, RES. SPECIALIST, 62- Am. Chem. Soc; Soc. Appl. Spectros. Application of optical emission, x-ray fluorescence and neutron activation spectroscopy to elemental analysis, also of x-ray diffraction to structure of petroleum products and derivatives. Address: 701 Lindenwood Dr, Baytown, TX 77520.

GUNN, J(OHN) B(ATTISCOMBE), b. Cairo, Egypt, May 13, 28; m. 50; c. 2. PHYSICS. B.A, Cambridge, 48. Res. engr, Elliott Bros. Ltd, Eng, 48-53; jr. res. fel, Radar Res. Estab, 53-56; asst. prof. physics, Univ. B.C, 56-59; staff physicist, RES. CTR, IBM CORP, 59-71, IBM FEL. & MEM. CORP. TECH. COMT, 71- John Scott Award, 71. Fel. Inst. Elec. & Electronics Eng.(Liebmann Prize, 69); fel. Am. Phys. Soc. Physics of semiconductors; semiconductor devices; electronic circuits. Address: Research Center, IBM Corp, P.O. Box 218, Yorktown Heights, NY 10598.

GUNN, JOHN W(ILLIAM), JR, b. Lynn, Mass, Feb. 23, 28; m. 60; c. 4. FORENSIC & ANALYTICAL CHEMISTRY. B.S, Boston Col, 51; Am. Univ, 65-69. Lab. shift supvr, Liberty Powder Defense Corp, 51-54; spec. agent, Fed. Bur. Invest, Dept. Justice, 54-62; lab. supvr, Chas. Pfizer & Co, Inc, 62-63; sr. staff. chemist, appl. physics lab, Johns Hopkins Univ, 63-66; chief investigative serv. br, Bur. Drug Abuse Control, Food & Drug Admin, 66-68; CHIEF LABS, BUR. NARCOTICS & DANGEROUS DRUGS, DEPT. JUSTICE, 68- Exec. comt. mem. & spec. consult, aerospace sect, Nat. Safety Coun, 65-66; del. & lectr, Franco-Am. Conf. on Narcotics & Dangerous Drugs, France, spring 70. Incentive award, Fed. Bur. Invest, Dept. Justice, 58. U.S.N, 46-48. Fel. Am. Acad. Forensic Sci; Asn. Off. Anal. Chem; Am. Chem. Soc; Int. Asn. Forensic Toxicol; Am. Mgt. Asn; Asn. Fed. Investr; Int. Narcotic Enforcement Off. Asn. Determination of country of origin for opium and hashish; methods for detection and determination of abuse drugs; development of instrumentation and techniques to assist enforcement personnel in enforcement of drug laws. Address: Lab. Operations Division, Bureau of Narcotics & Dangerous Drugs, Dept. of Justice, Washington, DC 20537.

GUNN, K(ENRICK) L(EWIS) S(TUART), b. London, Ont, Apr. 19, 23; m. 52; c. 3. PHYSICS. B.A, Western Ontario, 44; M.Sc, McGill, 47, Ph.D.(physics), 50. Sessional lectr, McGill Univ, 47-49, lectr, 49-50, asst. prof. physics, 51-56, assoc. prof, 56-62, prof, 62-71; SR. EXEC. ASST. TO V.PRIN, QUEEN'S UNIV, 71- R.C.N, 43-46, Lt. Am. Meteorol. Soc; Can. Asn. Physicists (ed, Physics in Can, 52-60); Can. Meteorol. Soc. Cloud and precipitation physics, using radar as research tool and laboratory experiments. Address: Richardson Hall, Queen's University, Kingston, Ont, Can.

GUNN, ROBERT DEWEY, b. Leninakhan, Armenia, May 29, 28; U.S. citizen; m. 54; c. 1. CHEMICAL ENGINEERING. B.S, Kansas State, 50; M.S, California, Berkeley, 58, summer, Nat. Sci. Found, fel. 64, Ph.D.(chem. eng), 67. Roustabout, Humble Oil & Refining Co, 50-51; geophys. engr, Robert H. Ray Co, Saudi Arabia, 51-53; petrol. engr, Mobil Int. Oil Co, 57-62; asst. prof. CHEM. ENG, Univ. Tex, Austin, 67-71; ASSOC. PROF, UNIV. WYO, 71- AAAS; fel. Am. Inst. Chem; N.Y. Acad. Sci; Am. Chem. Soc; Am. Inst. Chem. Eng. Mass transport in porous material; thermodynamics and high pressure phase equilibria. Address: Dept. of Chemical Engineering, University of Wyoming, Laramie, WY 82070.

GUNN, S(AMUEL) A(LBERT), b. Winnepeg, Man, Feb. 11, 10; nat; m. 32; c. 1. CANCER, EXPERIMENTAL PATHOLOGY. B.S, Illinois, 34, M.D, 37. Clin. cytologist, Cancer Inst, Miami, 51-55; instr. PATH, SCH. MED, UNIV. MIAMI, 55-58, res. asst. prof, 58-59, res. assoc. prof, 59-62, RES. PROF, 62- U.S.A, 42-46, Maj. AAAS; Am. Med. Asn; Am. Soc. Cytol; Am. Soc. Exp. Path; Soc. Exp. Biol. & Med; Soc. Study Reproduction; Am. Asn. Cancer Educ. Cervical and prostatic cancer cytology; zinc and trace elements in reproductive endocrinology; cadmium carcinogenesis. Address, 9357 Abbott Ave, Surfside, FL 33154.

GUNN, STUART R(ICHARD), b. Sunderland, Mass, Nov. 25, 29; m. 54; c. 3. PHYSICAL CHEMISTRY. B.S, Univ. Mass, 50; Ph.D.(phys. chem), Univ. Calif, 54. CHEMIST, radiation lab, Univ. Calif, Berkeley, 50-54; LAWRENCE LIVERMORE LAB, UNIV. CALIF, 54- AAAS; Calorimetry Conf; Am. Chem. Soc. Thermochemistry; boron hydrides; metal-ammonia solutions; calorimetry of nuclear processes. Address: 771 Turrini Dr, Danville, CA 94526.

GUNN, WALTER J, Exp. Psychol, Electronic Eng, see Suppl. I to 11th ed, Soc. & Behav. Vols.

GUNNAR, ROLF McMILLAN, b. Riverside, Ill, Jan. 22, 26; m; c. 4. CARDIOLOGY, INTERNAL MEDICINE. B.S, Northwestern, 46, M.B, 47, M.S, 48, M.D, 49. Intern, Cook County Hosp, Chicago, Ill, 48-49, asst. res, 49-50, res, 50 & 53; clin. instr. MED, COL. MED, UNIV. ILL, CHICAGO, 54-58, clin. assoc, 58-59, asst. prof, 59-63, assoc. prof, 63-67, PROF, 67-, dir, sect. cardiol, 68-70. Private practice, 54-58 & 59-62; fel. cardiol, New Eng. Deaconess Hosp. & Children's Med. Ctr, 58-59. Assoc. attend. physician, Cook County Hosp, 54-58, attend. physician, 59-, assoc. dir. dept. adult cardiol, 59-63 & 64-68, dir, 68-70, dir. div. med, 70-; chief, Univ. Illinois Med. Div, 62-68, dir. dept. adult cardiol, 63-64; dir. cardiopulmonary lab, U.S. Vet. Admin. Hosp, Hines, Ill, 59; acting chief sect. cardiol, Univ. Illinois Res. & Ed. Hosps, 67-68. Consult. cardiol, Vet. Admin. W. Side Hosp, Chicago, 68- Mem. bd. dirs, MacNeal Mem. Hosp, Berwyn, Ill, 66-; fel, coun. clin. cardiol, Am. Heart Asn. Dipl, Am. Bd. Internal Med, 55; dipl, Am. Bd. Cardiovasc. Disease, 61. U.S.A, 51-53, Capt. Am. Med. Asn; Am. Heart Asn; fel. Am. Col. Physicians; fel. Am. Col. Cardiol. Research in the mechanisms of and hemodynamic changes in shock due to myocardial infarction and septic shock; research in vectorcardiography including development and testing of criteria for diagnosis of myocardial infarction. Address: Dept. of Medicine, University of Illinois College of Medicine, Chicago, IL 60680.

GUNNELL, T(HOMAS) J(EFFERSON), b. Patrick Co, Va, Dec. 25, 13; m. 38; c. 2. PHYSICAL CHEMISTRY. B.A, Berea Col, 37; M.S, Kentucky, 48. Group leader org. synthesis, Va. Smelting Co, 37-46; head, phys. sci. dept, Union Col.(Ky), 46-47; SECT. MGR. CARBON RES, PHILLIPS PETROL. CO, 48- Am. Chem. Soc; Am. Asn. Textile Chem. & Colorists; Combustion Inst. High temperature reactions; combustion processes; carbon formation; surface chemistry. Address: Research & Development Dept, Phillips Petroleum Co, Bartlesville, OK 74003.

GUNNER, HAIM BERNARD, b. Ottawa, Ont, June 18, 24; m. 51; c. 2. ENVIRONMENTAL MICROBIOLOGY. B.S.A, Toronto, 46, Res. Coun. Can. fel. & M.Sc, Manitoba, 48; Loeb Found. scholar & Ph.D.(soil sci), Cornell, 62. Field crops supvr, Sasa Coop. Farm, Israel, 49-51, farm mgr, 51-53, soil conserv. supvr, 53-55; asst. coord. agr. res, Res. Coun. Israel, Jerusalem, 55-56, coord, 56-57; res. asst. soil microbiol, Cornell, 57-61; res. off, microbiol res. inst, Can. Dept. Agr, Ont, 61-63; asst. prof. soil microbiol, UNIV. MASS, AMHERST, 63-68, assoc. prof, 68-71, PROF. ENVIRON. MICROBIOL. & ACTING HEAD DEPT. ENVIRON. SCI, 71- Nat. Sci. Found. res. grant, 64-66; U.S. Pub. Health Serv. grant, 66-69; Off. Water Resources Res, Dept. Interior res. grant, 67-70; co-dir, tech. guid. ctr. indust. environ. control, Univ. Mass, 68-, assoc. dir. res, ctr. int. agr. studies, 69-; chmn. soil biol. sect, Northeast Soil Res. Comt, 69; secy, Northeast Regional Res. Comt. Nitrogen Transformation Soil & Water, 69; past chmn, Northeast Regional Res. Comt. Pesticides. Am. Soc. Microbiol; Can. Soc. Microbiol. Investigations of inorganic transformations of microbial origin; pesticide degradation studies in soil and water; biochemical and physiological aspects of microfloral interrelations with specific reference to the biological control of soil-borne pathogens; microbial degradation of industrial effluents microbial ecosystem stress in soil and water. Address: Dept. of Environmental Sciences, Marshall Hall, University of Massachusetts, Amherst, MA 01002.

GUNNESS, R(OBERT) C(HARLES), b. Fargo, N.Dak, July 28, 11; m. 36; c. 3. CHEMICAL ENGINEERING. B.S, Massachusetts, 32; M.S, Mass. Inst. Tech, 34, Sc.D.(chem. eng), 36. Instr. chem. eng, Mass. Inst. Tech, 35-36, asst. prof, 36-38; group leader, STANDARD OIL CO.(IND), 38-43, asst. dir. res, 43-45, assoc. dir, 45-47, mgr, 47-52, asst. gen. mgr. mfg, 52-54; gen. mgr. supply & transportation dept, 54-56; exec. v.pres, 56-65, PRES, 65-, MEM. BD. DIRS, 53- V.chmn. res. & develop. bd, Dept. Defense, 51. Am. Chem. Soc; Am. Inst. Chem. Eng. Distillation; heat transfer; fluid catalytic cracking; petroleum refinery processing techniques; performance characteristics of a commercial stabilizer for absorption naphtha. Address: Standard Oil Co.(Indiana), 910 S. Michigan Ave, Chicago, IL 60605.

GUNNING, BARBARA E, b. The Dalles, Ore, July 28, 22. NUTRITION, BIOCHEMISTRY. B.A, San Francisco Col. Women, 51; Ph.D.(human nutrit), California, Berkeley, 61. Nutrit. biochemist, Highland Alameda Hosp, Oakland, Calif, 61-65; assoc. prof, Arizona, 65-66; res. chemist, Vet. Admin. Hosp, Tucson, 66-69; MEM. STAFF SCH. FAMILY STUDIES & CONSUMER SCI, SAN DIEGO STATE COL, 69- Consult, Alameda County Heart Asn, 64-65. U.S.W.M.C.R, 44-46, Sgt. Am. Inst. Nutrit; Am. Dietetic Asn; Am. Chem. Soc. Laboratory evaluation of human and animal blood or tissue lipids in response to dietary alterations thus reflecting circulatory metabolic activity. Address: School of Family Studies & Consumer Sciences, San Diego State College, San Diego, CA 92115.

GUNNING, GERALD E(UGENE), b. Tamms, Ill, Apr. 1, 32; m. 62; c. 2. FISHERIES BIOLOGY. B.A, Southern Illinois, 54, M.S, 55; U.S. Pub. Health Serv. fel, Nat. Inst. Neurol. Diseases & Blindness, 57-59; Ph.D.(zool), Indiana, 59. Asst. ZOOL, Southern Illinois, 53-55; Indiana, 56-57; instr, TULANE UNIV, LA, 59-60, asst. prof, 60-64, assoc. prof, 64-69, PROF, 69- Res. assoc, South. Ill. Univ, summer, 59; biol. consult, Monsanto Co; MacMillan Bloedel United; Boise South; Crown Zellerbach Corp, 63- Am. Fisheries Soc; Am. Soc. Ichthyol. & Herpet; Ecol. Soc. Am; Am. Soc. Limnol. & Oceanog. Fishery behavior; sensory physiology; swamp ecology; life history of fishes; freshwater fish populations; water pollution. Address: Dept. of Biology, Tulane University, New Orleans, LA 70118.

GUNNING, HARRY EMMET, b. Toronto, Ont, Dec. 16, 16; m. 43; c. 1. PHYSICAL CHEMISTRY, PHOTOCHEMISTRY. B.A, Univ. Toronto, 39, Leonard fel, 39-40, M.A, 40, Ph.D.(phys. chem), 42; hon. D.Sc, Univ. Guelph, 69. Nat. Res. Coun. res. fel. chem, 42-43; asst. res. chemist, Nat. Res. Coun. Can, 43-44, assoc. res. chemist, 44-46; asst. prof. CHEM, Univ. Rochester, 46-48; Ill. Inst. Technol, 48-51, assoc. prof, 51-56, prof, 56-57; PROF, UNIV. ALTA, 57-68, KILLAM MEM. PROF, 68-, CHMN. DEPT, 57- Mem, Nat. Res. Coun, 61-; consult, Syncrude Can. Ltd; Imp. Oil Enterprises Ltd; Dunlop Can; adv. indust. develop. div, City of Edmonton. Civilian with Off. Naval Res, 44. Fel. AAAS; Fel. Royal Soc. Can; fel. Chem. Inst. Can.(CIC Medal, 68); fel. N.Y. Acad. Sci. Reactions of atomic sulfur, mercury photosensitization; flash photolysis and photo-ionization; kinetic mass spectrometry. Address: Dept. of Chemistry, University of Alberta, Edmonton, Alta, Can.

GUNNING, ROBERT C(LIFFORD), b. Colo, Nov. 27, 31. MATHEMATICS. B.A, Colorado, 52; Ph.D.(math), Princeton, 55. Fel, Nat. Sci. Found, Chicago, 55-56; asst. prof. MATH, PRINCETON, 57-62, assoc. prof, 62-66, PROF, 66- Sloan fel, 58-60. Am. Math. Soc; Math. Soc. France. Functions of several complex variables; automorphic functions. Address: Dept. of Mathematics, Princeton University, Box 37, Fine Hall, Princeton, NJ 08540.

GUNNINK, RAYMOND, b. Chandler, Minn, June 28, 32; m. 54; c. 3. PHYSICAL CHEMISTRY. A.B, Calvin Col, 54; Ph.D.(phys. chem), Purdue, 59. Res. scientist, res. ctr, U.S. Rubber Co, N.J, 59-63; CHEMIST, RADIO CHEM. DIV, LAWRENCE RADIATION LAB, UNIV. CALIF, LIVERMORE, 63- Am. Chem. Soc; Am. Phys. Soc. Nuclear decay schemes; radiochemical techniques; fission process; activation analysis; absolute counting techniques; gamma ray spectroscopy. Address: Radio Chemistry Division, Lawrence Radiation Lab, University of California, Livermore, CA 94550.

GUNSALUS, I(RWIN) C(LYDE), b. Sully Co, S.Dak, June 29, 12; m. 51, 70; c. 2. BIOCHEMISTRY. B.S, Cornell, 35, M.S, 37, Ph.D.(bact), 40. Asst. bact, Cornell, 35-37, instr, 37-40, asst. prof, 40-43, assoc. prof, 43-46, prof, 46-47; Ind. Univ, 47-50; UNIV. ILL, URBANA-CHAMPAIGN, 50-55, PROF. BIOCHEM, 55-, head dept, 55-65, ctr. adv. study, 65-66. Guggenheim fel, 48, 59, 68. Mead Johnson award, 46. Civilian with U.S.N, 44; Atomic Energy Comn, 46. Nat. Acad. Sci; AAAS; Am. Soc. Microbiol; Am. Chem. Soc; Am. Soc. Biol. Chem; Brit. Biochem. Soc; Soc. Gen. Physiol; Brit. Soc. Gen. Microbiol. Biological catalysis and regulation; mechanism of chemical transformations and energy transfer; formation of essential metabolites including pyredoxal phosphate and lipoic acid; oxidation and oxygenation reactions and energy transfer. Address: 420 E. Chemistry Bldg, University of Illinois, Urbana-Champaign, Urbana, IL 61801.

GUNSBERG, EPHRAIM, b. Boston, Mass, Aug. 25, 17; m. 42; c. 3. BIOCHEMISTRY, ANALYTICAL CHEMISTRY. B.S, Long Island, 40; Polytech. Inst. Brooklyn, 40-43. Supvr. control lab, Int. Vitamin Corp, 39-43; anal. chemist, Standard Brands, Inc, 43-45; supvr. control lab, U.S. Vitamin & Pharmaceut. Corp, 45-47, asst. to v.pres, 47-61, asst. v.pres. tech. opers, 61-66; PRES, BEEKMAN LABS, INC, 66- AAAS; Am. Chem. Soc; Am. Inst. Chem; Am. Pharmaceut. Asn. Administration of analytical and control laboratories and production and quality control functions at plants throughout the world. Address: Beekman Labs, Inc, 455 Central Park Ave, Scarsdale, NY 10583.

GUNST, S(AMUEL) B(URTON), b. Pittsburgh, Pa, Sept. 24, 17; m. 51; c. 2. PHYSICS. A.B, Olivet Col, 39; M.S, Pittsburgh, 48, Ph.D.(physics), 53. Physicist, res. lab, Am. Soc. Heating & Ventilating Engrs, 39-41; supvry. engr, instrument develop, Gulf Res. & Develop. Co, 41-50; res. assoc, radiation lab, Pittsburgh, 50-53; sr. scientist, atomic power div, WESTINGHOUSE ELEC. CORP, 53-57, FEL. SCIENTIST, BETTIS ATOMIC POWER DIV, 57- Sig.C, 43-46, Capt. AAAS; Am. Phys. Soc; Am. Nuclear Soc. Nuclear physics instruments; fundamental particle investigations; instruments for the petroleum industry; neutron cross-section measurements; irradiation and reactivity investigations. Address: 150 Par Dr, Pittsburgh, PA 15236.

GUNSUL, CRAIG J. W, b. Seattle, Wash, May 16, 37; m. 60; c. 2. SOLID STATE PHYSICS. B.A, Reed Col, 63; NASA fel, Univ. Del, 63-66, M.S, 66, Ph.D.(physics), 69. ASST. PROF. PHYSICS, WHITMAN COL, 69- Luminescence. Address: Dept. of Physics, Whitman College, Walla Walla, WA 99362.

GUNTER, BOBBY J, b. Wilson, Okla, July 25, 41. ANALYTICAL CHEMISTRY, EXPERIMENTAL MEDICINE. B.S, Southeast. State Col, 63; grants & scholar, Oklahoma, 63-67, M.S, 64, Ph.D.(prev. med), 67. Chemist, City of Norman, Okla, 63-67; SR. ASST. SCIENTIST, NAT. CTR. URBAN & INDUST. HEALTH, U.S. PUB. HEALTH SERV, 67- Res. asst. physiol, Vet. Admin. Hosp, Oklahoma City, 66-67. U.S.P.H.S, 67-68, Lt. Am. Conf. Govt. Indust. Hygienists; Am. Indust. Hyg. Asn. Atomic absorption techniques. Address: National Center for Urban & Industrial Health, U.S. Public Health Service, 1014 Broadway, Cincinnati, OH 45202.

GUNTER, GORDON, b. Goldonna, La, Aug. 18, 09; m. 32; c. 3; m. 57; c. 2. MARINE ZOOLOGY. B.A, La. State Norm. Col, 29; fel, La. State, 33; M.A, Texas, 31, Ph.D.(zool), 45. Asst. shrimp invest, U.S. Bur. Fisheries, 31-33, asst. oil pollution invest, 34-35, spec. oyster investr, 35-36, consult. to fishery coord, 41-45; commerical oyster bus, Texas, 36-37; jr. aquatic biologist, Debris Dam fisheries surv, Calif, U.S. Engrs, 38; marine biologist, Game, Fish & Oyster Comn, Tex, 39-44; res. assoc, marine fisheries, inst. marine sci, Texas, 45-49, acting dir, 49, DIR, 54-55; GULF COAST RES. LAB, 55- Zoologist, State Dept. Conserv, La, 34; vis. prof. zool, Miami (Fla), 46-47; sr. marine biologist, Scripps Inst, California, 49; prof, Univ. Miss. & Miss. State Univ, 68- V.chmn, comn. on treatise on marine ecol, Nat. Res. Coun, 41-57; adv, Atlantic States Fisheries Comn, 46; adv. panel, State Comn. Wildlife & Fisheries, La, 53-55; Gulf States Marine Fisheries Comn, 56-; mem. bd. sci. consults, Wash. Pollution Control Comn, 58-59; adv, Fla. State Bd. Conserv, 62-70; mem. consult. team, impact of Corps Engrs. works on coastal ecology, 69-; consult. comt. deepwater ports, U.S. Army Corps Engrs, 71- Am. Soc. Limnol. & Oceanog; Ecol. Soc. Am; Wildlife Soc; Am. Soc. Zool; Am. Soc. Nat; Am. Soc. Mammal; Am. Fisheries Soc; Am. Ornith. Union; Am. Inst. Fishery Res. Biol; Nat. Shellfisheries Asn; Marine Biol. Asn. India; Am. Soc. Ichthyol. & Herpet; fel. Int. Acad. Fishery Sci. Seasonal movements, distribution related to salinity, life histories and relative abundance of gulf animals; catastrophic mass mortalities; natural history of oysters, fishes, shrimp and marine mammals. Address: Gulf Coast Research Lab, P.O. Box AG, Ocean Springs, MS 39564.

GUNTER, ROY CHALMERS, JR, b. Brooklyn, N.Y, June 3, 16; m. 42; c. 4. OPTICS, ELECTRONICS. B.S, Bowdoin Col, 38; M.A, Boston, 39, Ph.D.(physics), 42. Instr. physics & math, Clark, 41-43, asst. prof. physics, 43-49, assoc. prof, 49-57; mgr. tech. planning, missile electronics & controls div, Radio Corp. Am, Mass, 59-62; assoc. prof. PHYSICS, COL. OF THE HOLY CROSS, 62-67, PROF, 67- Vis. asst. prof, Mass. Inst. Technol, 44-46; mem. res. staff, optical res. lab, Boston, 46-50; coop. fel, Worcester Found. Exp. Biol, 47-49; consult. physicist, Worcester State Hosp, 48-; chief radiol. serv, Mass. Civil Defense Agency, 57-60; vis. scientist, Max Planck Inst. Biochem, Munich, Ger, 70-71. Consult. to various govt, indust. & med. orgn. Optical Soc. Am. Electrooptical shutters; television view finders for aircraft; cohesive energy and lattice constant of silver by method of Fuchs; microwave antennas; biophysics. Address: Dept. of Physics, College of the Holy Cross, College St, Worcester, MA 01610.

GUNTER, SHIRLEY E(DNA) (ANNE), b. Mitchell, S.Dak, July 10, 20. MICROBIOLOGY. B.S, Washington, 42, M.S, 44; Ph.D.(microbiol), California, 52. Asst. bacteriologist, Pulp Mills Res. Proj, Washington (Seattle), 44-46; assoc, dept. bact, California, Berkeley, 49-50, asst. res. microbiologist, Atomic Energy Comn. Radiol. Lab, med. ctr, Univ. Calif, San Francisco, 51-59; asst. prof. bact, UNIV. ALA, TUSCALOOSA, 59-69, ASSOC. PROF. MICROBIOL, 69- Nat. Sci. Found. sci. faculty fel, 70. Am. Soc. Microbiol. Bacterial metabolism and taxonomy. Address: P.O. Box 6315, University, AL 35486.

GUNTER, THOMAS E, JR, b. Montgomery, Ala, Mar. 13, 38; m. 61; c. 2. SOLID STATE PHYSICS, BIOPHYSICS. B.S, Mass. Inst. Technol, 60; Nat. Sci. Found. fel, Univ. Calif, Berkeley, 60, Ph.D.(physics), 66. Res. asst. med. physics, Boeing Aircraft Co, 60; res. fel. biophys, Donner Lab, Lawrence Radiation Lab, 66-68; Nat. Sci. Found. fel, Phys-Chem. Inst, Uppsala Univ, 68-70; ASST. PROF. RADIATION BIOL. & BIOPHYS, UNIV. ROCHESTER, 70- Applications of physical spectroscopic techniques to problems of interest in biology. Address: Dept. of Radiation Biology & Biophysics, School of Medicine & Dentistry, University of Rochester, Rochester, NY 14642.

GUNTHER, AARON, b. Chicago, Ill, Jan. 10, 12; m. 35; c. 3. MEDICINE. M.D, Illinois, 35. Intern, Cook County Hosp, 35-36, res. path, 37-38; clin. asst. prof. MED, COL. MED, UNIV. ILL, 46-66, CLIN. ASSOC. PROF, 66-, GASTROSCOPIST, 46- Med.C, 42-46, Lt. Col. Am. Med. Asn. Internal medicine. Address: College of Medicine, University of Illinois, Chicago, IL 60680.

GUNTHER, CLARENCE A(LEXANDER), b. Los Angeles, Calif, June 29, 03; m. 26; c. 1. ENGINEERING. B.S.E, Princeton, 26. Student engr. & develop. & radio engr, Gen. Elec. Co, 26-30; develop. & design engr. special receivers, RCA CORP, 30-32, supvry. engr. radar & direction, VICTOR DIV, 32-44, mgr. govt. equip. eng. sect, 44-45, asst. chief engr. eng. prod. dept. & mgr. tech. admin, 45-55, chief govt. engr, defense eng. dept, 55-56, chief defense engr, 56-62, DIV. V.PRES, TECH. PROGS, 62- Am. Soc. Naval Eng; Am. Astronaut. Soc; Am. Ord. Asn; Aerospace Indust. Asn. Am; Inst. Elec. & Electronics Eng.(fel. award, Inst. Radio Eng, 54). Special radio receiver development and design; military electronics; television transmitter; development and design. Address: Victor Division, Technical Programs, RCA Corp, Morristown, NJ 08057.

GUNTHER, DONALD ALBERT, b. Erie, Pa, Aug. 23, 28; m. 58; c. 3. ANALYTICAL CHEMISTRY. B.S, Gannon Col, 50. Prof. chem. & physics, Kanty Col, 53; plant chemist, Keystone Corp, 54-58; chem. supvr, dept. res, AM. STERILIZER CO, 58-69, MGR. CHEM. DEPT, 69- Med.C, U.S.A, 50-52. Fel. Am. Inst. Chem; Am. Chem. Soc. Biological and pharmaceutical processes; sterilization; water purification. Address: American Sterilizer Co, 2424 W. 23rd St, Erie, PA 16512.

GUNTHER, FRANCIS A(LAN), b. Los Angeles, Calif, July 2, 18; m. 42; c. 5. CHEMISTRY. A.B, Colorado, 39; M.A, California, Los Angeles, 41, Ph.D.(chem), 47. Lab. asst. chem. entom, citrus exp. sta, UNIV. CALIF, RIVERSIDE, 41-42, prin. lab. asst, 42-44, assoc, 44-47, asst. insect toxicologist, 47-53, assoc. insect toxicologist, 53-57, insect toxicologist, 57-59, PROF. ENTOM. & CHEMIST, CITRUS RES. CTR. & AGR. EXP. STA, 59- Bayer fel, W.Germany, 58; Ciba fel, Switz, 67; ed, Residue Rev. Wiley Award, 59; Citrograph Res. Award, 68. Am. Chem. Soc; Entom. Soc. Am; Asn. Off. Anal. Chem; N.Y. Acad. Sci. Chemistry of insecticidal materials; natures and fates of pesticidal chemicals and polynuclear hydrocarbons in the environment; instrumentation in pesticide residue analysis. Address: Citrus Research Center & Agricultural Experiment Station, University of California, Riverside, CA 92502.

GUNTHER, FRANK A(LEXANDER), b. N.Y.C, Feb. 3, 08; m. 30; c. 2. ELECTRONIC ENGINEERING. Columbia, 25-27; Wagner Col, 39-41. Asst. radio engr, Radio Eng. Labs, Inc, 25-29, radio engr, 29-31, v.pres. & chief engr, 31-45, v.pres. res. & eng, 45-53, eng. & mkt, 53-59, exec. v.pres. & gen. mgr, RADIO ENG. LABS, DIV. DYNAMICS CORP. AM, LONG ISLAND CITY, 59-60, PRES, 60-, EXEC. V.PRES, CORP, 62- Dir, Armstrong Mem. Res. Found, 55-; mem. nat. indust. adv. comt, Fed. Commun. Comn, 63- U.S.A.A.F, 41-45, Maj. Fel. Inst. Elec. & Electronics Eng. Design and development of advanced radio communication equipment; corporate management, especially of design and manufacture of electronic and electromechanical equipment. Address: 10 High Point Rd, Dongan Hills, Staten Island, NY 10304.

GUNTHER, JAMES KENNETH, b. Galesburg, Ill, Sept. 20, 10; m. 37; c. 3. CHEMISTRY. B.S, Knox Col, 32; M.S, Cornell, 33; Ph.D.(biochem), Illinois, 36. Res. chemist, Swift & Co, Chicago, 36-44; res. dir, Cent. Soya Co, Ind, 44-49; pres, Gunther Prod. Inc, 49-69, MGR, GUNTHER PROD. DIV, A.E. STALEY MFG. CO, 69- Am. Chem. Soc; Am. Oil Chem. Soc; Inst. Food Technol. Fats and oils; soaps and detergents; animal proteins; vegetable proteins; nitrogen requirements of animals. Address: 251 Circle Dr, Galesburg, IL 61401.

GUNTHER, JAY KENNETH, b. Chicago, Ill, Dec. 19, 38; m. 66; c. 1. MOLECULAR BIOLOGY, BIOCHEMISTRY. B.S, Notre Dame, 61; U.S. Pub. Health Serv. fel, Illinois, 62-66, Ph.D.(biochem), 66. Trainee molecular biol, Pennsylvania, 66-69, res. assoc, 69-70; SR. SCIENTIST, MEAD JOHNSON & CO, 70- AAAS; Am. Chem. Soc. Protein hydrolysis; protein synthesis in cell free systems; bacterial transformation; isolation and characterization of nucleases of Hemophilius influenzae. Address: Biochemistry Dept, Research Center, Mead Johnson & Co, Evansville, IN 47721.

GUNTHER, LEON, b. New York, N.Y, Aug. 22, 39; m. 62; c. 3. SOLID STATE PHYSICS. B.S, City Col. New York, 60; Nat. Sci. Found. fel, Mass. Inst. Tech, 60-62, Ph.D.(physics), 64. Res. assoc. PHYSICS, Mass. Inst. Technol, 64-65; asst. prof. TUFTS UNIV, 65-70, ASSOC. PROF, 70- NATO fel, 66-67. AAAS; Am. Phys. Soc. Impurity effects in lattice vibrations; behavior of superconductors in high magnetic fields and general theory of superconductivity; statistical and physical properties of the harmonic lattice, compressible magnetic systems and superfluids. Address: Dept. of Physics, Tufts University, Medford, MA 02155.

GÜNTHER, MARIAN W. J, b. Warsaw, Poland, Nov. 27, 23; U.S. citizen. THEORETICAL PHYSICS. Warsaw, 42-44, Ph.D.(theoret. physics), 48, Veniam Legendi, 51; M.S, Jagiellonian, 46. Instr. theoret. physics, Jagiellonian, 45-46; Warsaw, 46-48, asst. prof, 50-53, assoc. prof, 56-60; Polish Govt. grant, Holland, 48-50 & Birmingham, 50; assoc. prof. theoret. physics, Wroclaw, 53-56; Ford Found. exchange visit to U.S, Columbia, California, Berkeley & Inst. Adv. Study, N.J, 60-61; mem. sci. staff, plasma physics group, Boeing Sci. Res. Labs, Wash, 61-64; assoc. prof. THEORET. PHYSICS, UNIV. CINCINNATI, 64-66, PROF, 66- Am. Phys. Soc. Relativistic formulation of bound state problems in quantum electrodynamics; lamb-shift like corrections in helium; relativistic soluble models in quantum field theory; solving Bethe Salpeter equation; quantum theory of superconductivity in magnetic field. Address: Dept. of Physics, University of Cincinnati, Cincinnati, OH 45220.

GUNTHER, ROBERT C(URTIS), b. Galesburg, Ill, Apr. 17, 16; m. 42; c. 3. ORGANIC CHEMISTRY. A.B, Knox Col, 38; M.S, Illinois, 39, Ph.D.(chem), 42. Res. chemist, E.I. du Pont de Nemours & Co, 41; sr. res. chemist, cent. res. lab, Gen. Aniline & Film Corp, 46-50; v.pres, Gunther Prod, Inc, 50-71, TECH. MGR. GUNTHER PROD. DIV, A.E. STALEY MFG. CO, 71- C.W.S, 42-46, Lt. Am. Chem. Soc. Protein chemistry; color photography; chemical warfare agents; derivatives of Cuscohygrine alkaloids; synthesis of vinyl esters. Address: 1043 N. Cherry St, Galesburg, IL 61401.

GUNTHER, RONALD G(EORGE), b. St. Paul, Minn, Jan. 22, 33; m. 66; c. 2. PHYSICAL CHEMISTRY. B.S, Col. St. Thomas, 55; Ph.L, St. Louis, 61; M.S, Iowa State, 64, Ph.D.(physical chem), 68. Res. assoc. fuel cells, Pratt & Whitney Aircraft Div, United Aircraft Corp, 68-70; head fuel cell res, catalytic technol. div, Pioneer Systs, 70-71; MGR. ELECTROCHEM. SYSTS, ELECTROCHEM. RES. & DEVELOP. GROUP, YARDNEY ELECTRIC CORP, 71- Bronze medal, Am. Inst. Chem, 55. Am. Chem. Soc; Electrochem. Soc; N.Y. Acad. Sci. Chemical kinetics; platinum chemistry;

electrolytic solutions; electrode processes; electrochemistry; coordination compounds. Address: Yardney Electric Corp, 82 Mechanic St, Pawcatuck, CT 02891.

GUNTHER, W(ALDEMAR) C(ARL), b. Grand Rapids, Mich, May 25, 18; m. 47; c. 2. BIOLOGY. B.S. & scholar, Chicago, 49, M.S. & Ph.D.(zool), 55; California, 51. Assoc. zool, Univ. Calif, 49-54; instr. BIOL, VALPARAISO UNIV, 54-55, asst. prof, 55-58, assoc. prof, 58-61, PROF, 61-, DIR. RES, 65-, DIR. BUR. INSTNL. RES, 66- Vis. lectr, Nat. Sci. Found, grant sex endocrinol, mem. inst. develop. biol, Williams Col; inst. desert ecol, Univ. Wyo; fel. ment. retardation, inst. ment. health, U.S. Dept. Health, Educ. & Welfare; intern, U.S. Off. Educ, Univ. Minn; Grass Found. grant ment. retardation; mem. Nat. Coun. Univ. Res. Adminrs. U.S.A, 42-45. AAAS; Am. Soc. Mammal; Asn. Study Animal Behav; Int. Soc. Develop. Psychobiol; Asn. Instnl. Res; Am. Asn. Higher Educ. Sex endocrinology; neuroembryology; general embryology; mental retardation. Address: Office of Research, Valparaiso University, Valparaiso, IN 46383.

GÜNTHER, W(OLFGANG) H(ANS) H(EINRICH), b. Gifhorn, Ger, Mar. 26, 31; nat; m. 58; c. 2. ORGANIC CHEMISTRY. Cand. chem, Brunswick Tech, 53; Ph.D.(org. chem), Leeds, 58. Demonstr. org. chem, Leeds, 55-58; Brown Mem. fel, Yale, 58-59, res. asst. pharmacol, 59-61, res. assoc, 61-66, asst. prof, 66-67; scientist, XEROX CORP, 67-68, MGR. ORG. & POLYMER CHEM, CHEM. RES. LAB, 68- Am. Chem. Soc. Chemistry of natural products; synthesis of metabolically active compounds; synthesis and study of oxygen; sulphur and selenium isologs; imaging materials and processes. Address: Chemistry Research Lab, Xerox Corp, W-114, 800 Phillips Rd, Webster, NY 14580.

GUNTHER-MOHR, GERARD R(OBERT), b. Montclair, N.J, June 8, 22; m. 50; c. 3. PHYSICS. B.S, Yale, 43; fel, Mass. Inst. Tech, 43; M.A, Columbia, 49, Atomic Energy Cmn. fel, 51-52, Ph.D.(physics), 53. Researcher, Manhattan Dist, Corps Engrs, U.S. Army & Monsanto Chem. Co, 44-46; asst. physics, Columbia, 47-50, lectr, 50; mem. staff, Watson Sci. Comput. Lab, IBM CORP, 53-58, mgr. semiconductor res. dept, 58-61, dir. solid state eng, 62-66, mgr. tech. develop. & assurance, components div, 66-67, tech. & reliability develop, 67-69, ASST. TO PRES, COMPONENTS DIV, 69- Fel. Am. Phys. Soc; sr. mem. Inst. Elec. & Electronics Eng. Semiconductors. Address: IBM Corp, Dept. 630, 2G Annex, 1000 Westchester Ave, White Plains, NY 10604.

GUNTHEROTH, WARREN G, b. Hominy, Okla, July 27, 27; m. 54; c. 3. PEDIATRIC CARDIOLOGY, CARDIOVASCULAR PHYSIOLOGY. M.D, Harvard, 52. Intern med, Peter Bent Brigham Hosp, Boston, Mass, 52-53; fel. pediat. cardiol, Children's Hosp, 53-55, res. pediat, 55-56; spec. fel. physiol, SCH. MED, UNIV. WASH, 57, instr. pediat, 58-59, asst. prof, 59-62, assoc. prof. PEDIAT, 62-69, PROF, 69-, HEAD DIV. PEDIAT. CARDIOL, 62- Consult. cardiol, King County, Children's Orthop, Madigan Army & U.S. Pub. Health Serv. Hosps, Seattle, 58- Dipl, Am. Bd. Pediat, 60, cert. cardiol, 61. U.S.P.H.S.R, summers 50, 51, Surg. Am. Physiol. Soc; Soc. Pediat. Res. Venous return; shock; physiology of cyanotic congenital heart disease. Address: Dept. of Pediatrics, School of Medicine, University of Washington, Seattle, WA 98105.

GUNTON, JAMES D, b. Medford, Ore, Mar. 28, 37; m. 62; c. 3. THEORETICAL PHYSICS, STATISTICAL MECHANICS. B.A, Linfield Col, 58; Rhodes Scholar, Oxford, 58, B.A, 61; Ph.D.(physics), Stanford Univ, 66. Lectr. PHYSICS, Univ. West. Australia, 65-68; vis. asst. prof, TEMPLE UNIV, 68-70, ASST. PROF, 70- Danforth & Woodrow Wilson fels, 58; res. assoc, Technol. Univ. Delft, summer 70. Am. Phy. Soc. Theory of critical phenomena; many-body theory; transport processes. Address: Dept. of Physics, Temple University, Philadelphia, PA 19122.

GUNTON, R(AMSAY) W(ILLIS), b. Lexington, Ky, July 30, 22; Can. citizen; m. 51; c. 4. MEDICINE. M.D, Western Ontario, 45; Rhodes scholar, Oxford, 46, D.Phil, 49. Assoc. in med, faculty med, Toronto, 53-63, assoc. prof. med, prof. therapeut. & head dept, 63-66; PROF. MED. & HEAD DEPT, UNIV. WEST. ONT, 66- Sr. med. res. fel, Nat. Res. Coun. Can, 52-56; med. res. assoc, Ont. Heart Found, 56-63; physician, Toronto Gen. Hosp, 57-; fel, Royal Col. Physicians Can, 52. R.C.A.M.C, 43-45. N.Y. Acad. Med; Am. Fedn. Clin. Res; fel. Am. Col. Physicians; Can. Med. Asn; Can. Soc. Clin. Invest.(v.pres, 61); Can. Cardiovasc. Soc; Pharmacol. Soc. Can. Clinical investigation; heart disease; therapeutics. Address: 1008 Harrison Ave, London, Ont. Can.

GUNTON, ROBERT C(ARL), b. Champaign, Ill, Oct. 9, 20; div; c. 3. PHYSICS. B.A, Western Ontario, 42, M.A, 43; Ph.D.(physics), McGill, 47. Instr. physics & gen. ed, Harvard, 47-49; asst. prof. physics, West Virginia, 49-56, assoc. prof, 56; res. scientist, LOCKHEED MISSILES & SPACE CO, 56-61, SR. STAFF SCIENTIST, 61- R.C.N, 43-45. Am. Geophys. Union; Am. Phys. Soc. Microwave noise measurements; ultracentrifuge; cyclotron construction; microwave spectroscopy; physics of ionized gases; ionospheric physics and chemistry. Address: 350 Curtner Ave, Apt. 21, Palo Alto, CA 94306.

GUNYOU, E(LTON) BRANDON, b. Comstock Twp, Mich, Oct. 2, 16; m. 48; c. 2. CHEMICAL ENGINEERING. B.Ch.E, Ohio State, 37, M.S, 38, Ph.D. (chem. eng), 40. Asst. chem. eng, Ohio State, 37-40; chem. engr, Grasselli Dept, E.I. du Pont de Nemours & Co, Ohio, 40-42; asst. to mgr. res. & develop. dept, Pa. Salt Mfg. Co, Phila, 45-47; proj. engr, Kellex Corp, N.Y, 48-50; div. engr, Vitro Corp, 50-51, resident engr. & div. sales mgr, Vitro Corp. Am, 52-54; mgr. nuclear prod, Koppers Co, 55-58; chief reactor engr, Alco Prod, 58-61; dir. res. & develop, NEPTUNE METER CO, 61-67, V.PRES, 67- U.S.A, 42-45. Am. Chem. Soc; Am. Inst. Chem. Eng; Am. Ord. Asn. Organic and inorganic chemical manufacture; processing of radioactive materials; instrumentation; water and waste treatment. Address: 241 Jinny Hill Rd, Cheshire, CT 06410.

GUNZBURG, JULIAN, b. Denver, Colo, Nov. 25, 07; m. 35; c. 2. MEDICINE. B.A, California, Los Angeles, 30; M.D, Colorado, 35. Assoc. prof. OPHTHAL, Loma Linda Univ. 50-66; CLIN. PROF, UNIV. SOUTH. CALIF, 66- Private practice, 38- Sr. ophthalmologist, Los Angeles County Hosp, 50-;

dir. res, Natural Vision Corp, 51-54. Dipl, Am. Bd. Ophthal, 51. Ophthalmology; photography; music. Address: 193 N. Robertson Blvd, Beverly Hills, CA 90211.

GUPTA, ARJUN KUMAR, b. Purkazi, India, July 10, 38; m. 67; c. 1. MATHEMATICAL STATISTICS. B.Sc. & dipl. French, Benaras Hindu Univ, 57; scholar. & B.Sc.(Hons), Poona, 58, M.Sc, 59; fel, Purdue, 63-68, Ph.D.(math. statist), 68. Lectr. statist, Agra Univ, 62; Benaras Hindu Univ, 62-63; teaching asst. math, Purdue, 63-66, res. asst. statist, 66-68; ASST. PROF. math, Arizona, 68-71; STATIST, UNIV. MICH, ANN ARBOR, 71- Consult, Univ. Arizona, 68-; Motorola Semiconductor Prod. Div, 69- Inst. Math. Statist; Biomet. Soc; fel. Royal Statist. Soc; Am. Statist. Asn; Math. Soc. Belg. Central and non central distribution problems in multivariate analysis; distribution of second elementary symmetric function and of likelihood ration criterion in the real and complex case. Address: Dept. of Statistics, 1447 Mason Hall, University of Michigan, Ann Arbor, MI 48104.

GUPTA, A(YODHYA) P, b. India, July 1, 28. ENTOMOLOGY. B.Sc, St. Andrew's Col, India, 50; M.Sc, Benares Hindu Univ, 53; M.Sc, British Columbia, 61; univ. fel, Idaho, 61-62, Ph.D.(entom), 64. Lectr. zool, Besant Col, India, 56-57; asst. entomologist, Pub. Health Dept, Filaria Unit, 58-59; res. assoc. ENTOM, RUTGERS UNIV, 64-66, asst. prof, 66-68, ASSOC. PROF, 68- Ed-in-chief, Int. J. Insect Morphol. & Embryol, 71- AAAS; Coun. Biol. Eds; fel. Entom. Soc. India; Entom. Soc. Am; Entom. Soc. Can; fel. Royal Entom. Soc. London. Anatomy and morphology of Heteroptera and Coleoptera; effects of sublethal doses of insecticides on insects; insect hemocytes; insect hormones. Address: Dept. of Entomology & Economic Zoology, Rutgers University, New Brunswick, NJ 08903.

GUPTA, BHUPENDER S(INGH), b. Delhi, India, Mar. 29, 37; m. 67; c. 1. TEXTILE PHYSICS. B.Sc, Panjab, India, 58; Ph.D.(textile physics), Manchester, 63. Supvr. prod. textile yarns, spinning dept, Modi Spinning & Weaving Mills, India, 59-60; res. instr. textile physics, SCH. TEXTILES, N.C. STATE UNIV, 63-64, ASST. PROF. TEXTILE TECHNOL, 64- AAAS. Fiber migration in staple and continuous filament yarns; fiber blending; mechanical and physical properties of fibers and fiber assemblies. Address: B-2A, Nelson Hall, North Carolina State University, Raleigh, NC 27607.

GUPTA, CHAITAN PRAKASH, b. India, Apr. 21, 39; m. 65; c. 2. MATHEMATICS. B.A, Delhi, 58, All-India & univ. scholars, 58-60, M.A, 60; Ph.D.(math), Rochester, 67. Lectr. MATH, Ramjas Col, Delhi, 60-62; asst. prof, Univ. Va, 66-69; NORTH. ILL. UNIV, 69-71, ASSOC. PROF, 71- Instr, Univ. Chicago, 67-; Nat. Sci. Found. res. grant, 71-72. Am. Math. Soc; Math. Asn. Am; Indian Math. Soc. Nonlinear analysis. Address: Dept. of Mathematics, Northern Illinois University, De Kalb, IL 60115.

GUPTA, DEVENDRA, b. Nagina, India, Feb. 15, 31; m. 63; c. 2. PHYSICAL METALLURGY, MATERIALS SCIENCE. B.Sc, Univ. Delhi, 50; B.Sc, Banaras Hindu Univ, 54; M.S, N.Y. Univ, 57; Ph.D.(metall), Univ. Ill, Urbana, 61. Sr. sci. off, Nat. Metall. Lab, Govt. India, 61-63; reader phys. metall, Banaras Hindu Univ, 63; asst. chief indust. res. develop, Planning Comn, Govt. India, 63-65; fel. metall. & solid state physics, Univ. Ill, Urbana, 65-68; STAFF SCIENTIST, T.J. WATSON RES. CTR, IBM CORP, 68- AAAS; Am. Phys. Soc; Am. Inst. Mining Metall. & Petrol. Eng; Indian Inst. Metals. Internal friction in metals and alloys; diffusion in metals and alloys by radioactive tracer technique; point defects in metals, alloys and materials; ductility and fracture; solid state transformations; mass transport in thin metallic films. Address: IBM Research Center, P.O. Box 218, Yorktown Heights, NY 10598.

GUPTA, DINESH C, b. Meerut, India, June 25, 37; m. 63; c. 1. ELECTRONICS, MATERIALS SCIENCE. B.Sc, Agra Univ, 55, M.Sc, 57; J.N. Tata scholar. & D.I.I.Sc, Indian Inst. Sci, Bangalore, 60; M.S, Carnegie Inst. Technol, 61. Res. asst, Carnegie Inst. Technol, 60-61; mem. tech. staff, Tex. Instruments Inc, Tex, 61-65; engr, semiconductor prod. dept, Gen. Elec. Co, N.Y, 65-67; ADVAN. DEVELOP. ENGR, GTE Sylvania Inc, Mass, 67-70, GTE LABS, INC, 70- Am. Soc. Test. & Mat; Electrochem. Soc; Inst. Elec. & Electronics Eng. Crystal growth in semiconductors; physical characterization of semiconducting materials; epitaxy, thin films, silicon, germanium, compound semiconductors and semi-insulating materials processing techniques. Address: GTE Labs, Inc, 208-20 Willets Point Blvd, Bayside, NY 11360.

GUPTA, GOPI NATH, b. India, July 19, 21; U.S. citizen; m. 58; c. 3. BIOCHEMISTRY, RADIOCHEMISTRY. B.Sc, Benares Hindu Univ, 44; M.S, Oregon State, 51; U.S. Pub. Health Serv. fel, Chicago, 56-59, fel, 59-60, Ph.D.(biochem), 60. Res. assoc. biochem, Albert Einstein Col. Med, 60-62; sr. scientist, Schwarz Bio-Res. Co, 62-63; asst. prof. biochem, ROCKEFELLER UNIV, 63-69, STAFF SCIENTIST, POP. COUN, 69- Am. Chem. Soc; Am. Nuclear Soc. Biochemistry and mechanism of action of the steroid hormones in animal and human organs; development of new methods of analytical biochemistry with use of radioisotopes. Address: Population Council, Rockefeller University, New York, NY 10021.

GUPTA, JATINDER NATH DASS, b. Moga, India, Sept. 27, 42. MANAGEMENT SCIENCE, OPERATIONS RESEARCH. B.E, Univ. Delhi, 63; scholar, Indian Inst. Technol, Kharagpur, 65-67, M.Tech, 67; Ph.D.(indust. eng), Tex. Tech Univ, 69. Asst. exec. engr, Nat. Projs. Construct. Corp, India, 64-65; res. asst. indust. eng, Tex. Tech Univ, 67-69; ASST. PROF. indust. eng. & opers. res, Univ. Ala, Huntsville, 69-71; ADMIN, SANGAMON STATE UNIV, 71- Consult, Hindustan Gen. Industs, India, 66; Bhilai Steel Plant, 66; Bharat Electronics Ltd, 66-67; part-time assoc. prof, Ala. A&M Univ, 71. Opers. Res. Soc. Am; Inst. Mgt. Sci; Am. Inst. Indust. Eng; Indian Inst. Indust. Eng; Opers. Res. Soc. India; Brit. Inst. Prod. Eng; Opers. Res. Soc. Japan; Am. Soc. Qual. Control; Indian Inst. Eng; Am. Soc. Eng. Educ. Econometrics; reliability theory; network theory; production logistics and control systems; scheduling theory and stochastic processes. Address: Sangamon State University, Springfield, IL 62703.

GUPTA, KRISHANA CHANDARA, b. Jammu, Kashmir, India, Feb. 22, 27; m. 59; c. 4. MICROBIOLOGY, IMMUNOCHEMISTRY. B.Sc, Punjab Univ,

45; Govt. Can. Colombo Plan fel, Univ. Montreal, 55-59, M.Sc, 57, Ph.D. (bact), 59. Head dept. microbiol, drug res. lab, Jammu Tawi, 47-53; res. off. tuberc, Patel Chest Diseases Inst, Univ. Delhi, 53-55; asst. dir, appl. microbiol. & antibiotics, regional res. lab, Jammu, 60-68; Muskoka Hosp. Fund Res. Asn. fel, 68-71; RES. ASSOC. IMMUNOCHEM. OF TUBERCULOPROTEINS, CONNAUGHT MED. RES. LAB, UNIV. TORONTO, 71- Chmn. session new antibiotics, Intersci. Cong. Antimicrobial Agents & Chemother, N.Y.C, 64. Can. Soc. Immunol. Infection promoting factors; genetic studies in Bacillus Calmette-Guérin; immunochemistry of tuberculoproteins; taxonomic studies of streptomycetes; antibacterial and antifungal antibiotics; electron microscopic studies of effect of antibiotics on the cytology of tubercule bacilli. Address: Connaught Medical Research Lab, University of Toronto, Toronto, Ont, Can.

GUPTA, NABA K, b. Calcutta, India, July 2, 34; m. 64. BIOCHEMISTRY. B.Sc, Calcutta, 54, M.Sc, 57; Rackham fel, Michigan, 60-61, spec. fel, 61-62, Ph.D.(biochem), 62. Res. assoc. BIOCHEM, Univ. Chicago, 62-65; proj. assoc, Inst. Enzyme Res, Univ. Wis, Madison, 65-66, asst. prof, 66-68; ASSOC. PROF, UNIV. NEBR, LINCOLN, 68- Am. Soc. Biol. Chem. Chemistry and biology of nucleic acids. Address: Dept. of Chemistry, University of Nebraska, Lincoln, NE 68508.

GUPTA, NAIM CHAND, b. Nagina, Haryana, India, Aug. 25, 33; m. 59; c. 3. EDUCATIONAL PSYCHOLOGY. M.S, Agra, 55; B.Ed, Punjab, India, 56; M.Ed, Delhi, 61; State Col. Iowa, 61-62; Ph.D.(ed), Iowa, 65. Lectr, gen. methods & math, K.M. Teachers Training Col, Bhiwani, India, 57-61; res. assoc. testing & eval, Ed. Res. Coun. Greater Cleveland, 65-66; asst. prof. psychol. & res. design consult, BALL STATE UNIV, 66-71, ASSOC. PROF. EDUC. PSYCHOL, 71- Psychomet. Soc; Am. Educ. Res. Asn. Measurement theory applied to educational and psychological tests, especially the errors in measurement; evaluation of new mathematics programs; designing research studies in school setting. Address: Dept. of Educational Psychology, Ball State University, Muncie, IN 47306.

GUPTA, OM PRAKASH, b. Rupar, India, Feb. 8, 26; m. 57; c. 3. DENTISTRY. B.S, Agra, 45; B.D.S, Bombay, 50; M.S, Harvard, 54, Dr.P.H, 59; M.S.D, N.Y. Univ, 58; D.M.D, Pittsburgh, 67. Clin. asst, CEM Dent. Col, Bombay, 50 & 51; res. fel, sch. dent. med, Harvard, 53-56; res. assoc, col. dent, N.Y. Univ, 56-58; asst. prof, col. dent, Illinois, 58-60; dir, Dent. Col, Trivandrum, India, 60-63; PROF. PUB. HEALTH & PREV. DENT. & HEAD DEPT, SCH. DENT. MED, UNIV. PITTSBURGH, 63-, PROF. GRAD. PERIODONT. & HEAD DEPT, 64- Res. grants, U.S. Pub. Health Serv, 65-69 & Nat. Insts. Health, 68-; prof, grad. sch. pub. health, Univ. Pittsburgh, 66- Consult, Vet. Admin. Hosp, Leech Farm, 64-, Pittsburgh, 67-; Univ. Puerto Rico & Univ. Montreal, 67- Fel. AAAS; Am. Acad. Oral Med; Int. Dent. Fedn; Int. Asn. Dent. Res; Am. Pub. Health Asn; Am. Acad. Periodont; assoc. Am. Dent. Asn. Experimental research in oral biology; epidemiologic investigations on oral problems, including dental caries and periodontal disease. Address: 337 Salk Hall, University of Pittsburgh School of Dental Medicine, Pittsburgh, PA 15213.

GUPTA, RADHA RAMAN, b. Mathura, India, Nov. 1, 33; m. 64; c. 2. ELECTRICAL ENGINEERING. B.S.E.E, Banaras Hindu Univ, 56; French Govt. scholar, 57-60; M.S.E.E, Syracuse Univ, 62, Nat. Sci. Found. scholar, summer 64, Ph.D.(elec. eng), 65. Asst. engr, Radio Lamp Works Ltd, India, 56-57; engr, Serete, France, 57-60; asst. elec. eng, Syracuse Univ, 60-62, instr, 62-65; sr. engr, BENDIX RES. LABS, 66-70, PROJ. ENGR, 70- Inst. Elec. & Electronics Eng. Electromagnetic fields; plasmas; microwave components, radar, antenna; solid-state devices; computer-aided designs; acoustic fields; acoustic holography. Address: Bendix Research Labs, Bendix Center, Southfield, MI 48075.

GUPTA, RAJENDRA P, b. Buland Shahr, India, Mar. 26, 41. SOLID STATE PHYSICS. B.S, Meerut Col, 61, M.S, 63; Ph.D.(lattice dynamics), Banaras Hindu Univ, 66. Res. assoc, INST. ATOMIC RES. & DEPT. PHYSICS, IOWA STATE UNIV, 67-70, ASST. PHYSICS, 70- AAAS; Am. Phys. Soc. Theoretical study of electronic structures; band structures and Fermi surfaces; positron annihilation; antiferromagnetism; dielectric screening; lattice dynamics and superconductivity. Address: Dept. of Physics, Iowa State University, Ames, IA 50010.

GUPTA, S(HANTI) S(WARUP), b. Saunasi, India, Jan. 25, 25. MATHEMATICAL STATISTICS. B.A, Delhi, 46, M.A, 49; Fulbright travel award & Smith-Mundt scholar, North Carolina, 53-54, summer, Watumull Found. fel, 54, Ph.D.(math. statist), 56. Lectr. math, Delhi Col, 49-53; asst, North Carolina, 54-56; mem. tech. staff, Bell Tel. Labs, 56-57, 58-62; assoc. prof. math, Alberta, 57-58; adj. assoc. prof, Courant Inst. Math. Sci, N.Y. Univ, 59-61; vis. assoc. prof, Stanford, 61-62; PROF. MATH. & STATIST. & CHMN. DEPT. STATIST, PURDUE UNIV, 62- Summers, guest researcher, statist eng. lab, Nat. Bur. Standards, 56; Can. Math. Cong. fel, Queen's (Can), 58. Math. Asn. Am; fel. Inst. Math. Statist; fel. Am. Statist. Asn; Can. Math. Cong; fel. Royal Statist. Soc; Int. Asn. Statist. in Phys. Sci. Multiple decision rules; order statistics; life testing and reliability; multivariate probabilities. Address: Dept. of Statistics, Purdue University, West Lafayette, IN 47907.

GUPTA, SHRI BHAGAWAN, b. Makkhanpur, India, May 5, 34; m. 67. GENETICS. B.Sc, Allahabad, 53, M.Sc, 56; Ph.D.(genetics), California, Berkeley, 65. Lectr. bot, Maharaja Col, Arrah, India, 56-57; res. asst. cytogenetics, Indian Agr. Res. Inst, New Delhi, 57-60, scientist, 66-67; Nat. Res. Coun. Can. fel. GENETICS, Alberta, 67-69; ASST. PROF, KENYON COL, 69- AAAS; Am. Inst. Biol. Sci; Bot. Soc. Am; Genetics Soc. Am; Genetics Soc. Can. Regulation of chromosome duplication in higher plants; biochemical genetics of flower-pigments. Address: Dept. of Biology, Kenyon College, Gambier, OH 43022.

GUPTA, SHYAM KIRTI, b. Lucknow, India, Aug. 21, 42; m. 68. ORGANIC & MEDICINAL CHEMISTRY. B.S, Univ. Lucknow, 58, M.S, 60, Ph.D.(org. chem), 64; Purdue Univ, 68-70. Ford Found. fel, Cent. Drug Res. Inst, Lucknow, India, 64; res. assoc, Univ. Maine, 64-65; Ariz. State Univ, 65-67; vis. asst. prof. biochem, Ind. Univ, 67-68; res. assoc, Purdue Univ, 68-71; RES. CHEMIST, PROCESS RES. & DEVELOP, CHAS. PFIZER & CO, INC, 71- Fel. Am. Chem. Soc; fel. The Chem. Soc. Natural products; development of new reactions and reagents in organic synthesis; organometallic chemistry. Address: Process Research & Development, Chas. Pfizer & Co, Inc, Groton, CT 06340.

GUPTA, SOMESHWAR C, b. Ludhiana, India, Apr. 23, 35; U.S. citizen; m. 58; c. 3. ELECTRICAL ENGINEERING. B.A, Punjab, India, 51, M.A, 53; B.Sc, Glasgow, 57; M.S. & Ph.D.(elec. eng), California, Berkeley, 62. Trainee elec. eng, Theodore Kiepe, Germany, 54; Brit. Elec. Authority, Eng, 54; Elec. de France, Paris, 55; electronics, Pye Telecommun, Eng, 55; lab. asst. acoustics, Brunswick Tech, 56; engr, Remington Rand Corp, Glasgow, Scotland, 57; asst. lectr. elec. eng, Glasgow, 57-58; jr. res. officer nuclear eng, Atomic Energy Estab, Bombay, India, 58; asst. prof. ELEC. ENG, Calif. State Polytech. Col, 58-60; Carnegie Inst. Tech, 62-63; assoc. prof, Ariz. State Univ, 63-66, PROF, 66-67; INST. TECHNOL, SOUTH. METHODIST UNIV, 67- Nat. Sci. Found. res. grants, 64-68; NASA res. grants, 67- Consult, comput. dept, Gen. Elec. Co, 63; mil. electronics div, Motorola Inc, 63-; electronic proving ground, Ft. Huachuca, U.S. Army, 65; Collins Radio Co, 67; Tex. Instruments, 69; LTV Electrosysts, 69; mem. ed. bd, Int. Jour. Syst. Sci; consult. ed, Int. Textbook Co. Automatic control, space communication and computers. Address: Institute of Technology, Southern Methodist University, Dallas, TX 75222.

GUPTA, SUJOY, b. Bengal, India, May 12, 33; m. 61; c. 2. PALYNOLOGY. B.S, Calcutta, 52, M.S, 54; Ph.D.(bot, geol), Missouri, 65. Lectr. bot, Vivekananda Col, India, 54-61; asst. prof. EARTH SCI, E.TEX. STATE UNIV, 65-68, assoc. prof, 68-71, PROF, 71- Am. Asn. Stratig. Palynologists; N.Y. Acad. Sci. Palynological and stratigraphical investigatinns of Paleozoic, Mesozoic and Cenozoic rock strata in Texas and adjacent regions. Address: Dept. of Earth Sciences, East Texas State University, Commerce, TX 75428.

GUPTA, SURAJ N(ARAYAN), b. Haryana, India, Dec. 1, 24; nat; m. 48; c. 2. THEORETICAL PHYSICS. B.S, Delhi, 45, M.S, 46; Ph.D.(theoret. physics), Cambridge, 51. Fel, Imp. Chem. Industs, Manchester, 51-53; vis. prof. PHYSICS, Purdue, 53-56; prof, WAYNE STATE UNIV, 56-61, DISTINGUISHED PROF, 61- Fel. Am. Phys. Soc; fel. Indian Nat. Acad. Sci. Relativity; gravitation; quantum electrodynamics; field theory; nuclear physics; high-energy physics. Address: Dept. of Physics, Wayne State University, Detroit, MI 48202.

GUPTA, SURENDRA KUMAR, b. Delhi, India, Apr. 5, 38; m. 68. ORGANIC CHEMISTRY. B.Sc, Delhi, 59, M.Sc, 61; M.Tech, Indian Inst. Tech, Bombay, 63; Ph.D.(org. chem), Wayne State, 68. Sci. asst. chem. tech, Shri Ram Inst. Indust. Res, Delhi, India, 63; U.S. DEPT. AGR. RES. FEL. ORG. CHEM, WEST. MICH. UNIV, 68- Am. Chem. Soc. Synthesis and proof of structure of 4-amino-4, 6-dideoxy-hexoses; homogeneous catalytic oxidation of starch and nucleosides; synthesis of anticancer compounds; ring-chain isomerism in heterocyclic compounds. Address: Dept. of Chemistry, Western Michigan University, Kalamazoo, MI 49001.

GUPTA, SURESH KUMAR, b. Ahir Bhagola, India, Oct. 1, 36; m. 59; c. 2. PHYSICAL CHEMISTRY. B.S, Rajasthan, India, 56; M.S, Delhi, 58; Sloan & Int. Bus. Mach. summer fels, Cornell, 63, univ. summer fel. & Ph.D.(phys. chem), 64. Lectr. chem, Delhi Col, India, 58-59; sci. asst, Nat. Chem. Lab, India, 59-61; res. assoc, Cornell, 64-65; fel, Toronto, 65-66; RES. CHEMIST, LIGHTING RES. LAB, LAMP DIV, GEN. ELEC. CO, 66- Am. Chem. Soc. High temperature thermodynamics and spectroscopy; mass, infrared and Raman spectroscopy. Address: Lighting Research Lab, General Electric Co, Lamp Division, Nela Park, Cleveland, OH 44112.

GUPTA, UMESH C, b. Kanpur, India, Oct. 25, 37; can. citizen; m. 57; c. 3. SOIL FERTILITY & CHEMISTRY, PLANT NUTRITION. B.Sc, Agr. Col, Kanpur, India, 55, M.Sc, 57; Ph.D.(soil biochem), Purdue, 61. Nat. Res. Coun. Can. fel, soil res. inst, CAN. DEPT. AGR, Ont, 61-63, res. officer SOIL FERTIL. & PLANT NUTRIT, P.E.I, 63-65, RES. SCIENTIST, 65- Soil Sci. Soc. Am; Agr. Inst. Can; Indian Soc. Soil Sci. To characterize various forms of micro-nutrients from soils and determine sufficiency, deficiency and toxicity levels of these nutrients in various crops grown in Eastern Canada. Address: Canada Dept. of Agriculture, Box 1210, Charlottetown, P.E.I, Can.

GUPTA, VIJAI PRAKASH, b. Banaras, India, Aug. 2, 38; m. 67; c. 1. CHEMICAL ENGINEERING. B.Sc, Banaras Hindu Univ, 56, M.Sc, 58; Nat. Res. Coun. Can. grant, 59-63; Ph.D.(chem. eng), McGill Univ, 64. Sr. sci. asst. petrol, Cent. Fuel Res. Inst, India, 58-59; res. engr, E.I. du Pont de Nemours & Co, Inc, Del, 64-68; sr. res. engr, Gen. Motors Corp, Mich, 69-70; RES. ENGR, CITIES SERV. OIL CO, 70- Am. Chem. Soc; Am. Inst. Chem. Eng. Diffusion effects in heterogeneous catalysis; petroleum processing; automobile emissions control; synthetic fibers. Address: Cities Service Oil Co, P.O. Box 2, Cranbury, NJ 08512.

GUPTA, VIJAY KUMAR, b. Ambala, India, Apr. 27, 41; m. 68; c. 1. PHYSICAL CHEMISTRY. B.Sc, Panjab Univ, India, 61, M.Sc, 62, Ph.D.(chem), 68. Lectr. chem, D.A.V. Col, Chandigarh, 62; appl. chem, Punjab Eng. Col, 62-64; res. asst. chem, Panjab Univ, 64-67; Asst. prof. appl. chem, Punjab Eng. Col, 67-68; res. assoc, Wright State Univ, 68-69; ASST. PROF. PHYS. CHEM, CENT. STATE UNIV, 69- Am. Chem. Soc. Thermodynamics of binary mixtures consisting of non-electrolytes. Address: Dept. of Chemistry, Central State University, Wilberforce, OH 45384.

GUPTA, VISHNU DAS, b. Kalyanpur, India, Nov. 6, 31; U.S. citizen; m. 57; c. 2. PHYSICAL PHARMACY. B.S, Panjab Univ, India, 53, M.S, 57; M.S, Univ. Tex, Austin, 61; Ph.D.(pharm), Univ. Ga, 67. In charge mfg. & lab, pharmaceut. mfg. house, Azad Hind Chem, India, 53-55 & Janta Pharmaceut. Works, 57-60; supvr. qual. control lab, Schlicksup Drug Co, Ill, 61-64; dir. control lab, Kapco, Inc, Mich, 65-66; teaching asst. PHARMACEUT, Univ. Ga, 66-67; asst. prof, UNIV. HOUSTON, 67-70, ASSOC. PROF, 71- Pharm. consult, Harris County Hosp. Dist, Houston, 70- Lunsford Richardson Pharm. Res. Award, Wm. S. Merrell Co, Ohio, 67. Am. Pharmaceut. Asn; Indian Pharmaceut. Asn. Pharmaceutical analysis, especially development of analytical methods in multicomponent dosage forms; physical pharmacy, especially stability studies on dosage forms and distribution coefficients. Address: Dept. of Pharmacy, University of Houston, Houston, TX 77004.

GUPTA, YOUDHISHTHIR P, b. Barrod, India, Oct. 5, 34; m. 64; c. 3. MATERIALS SCIENCES, SOLID STATE PHYSICS. B.Sc, Delhi, 53, M.Sc, 55; dipl. metall, Indian Inst. Sci, Bangalore, 57; Sc.D.(mat. sci), Mass. Inst. Technol, 63. Res. asst. metall, Mass. Inst. Technol, 58-63; asst. prof, Minnesota, 63-67; dir. mat. sci, Northrop Corp. Labs, Calif, 67-70; pres. & organizer, Centec Co, 70-71; MGR. MAT. SCI, ADVAN. TECHNOL. CTR, INC, 71- Res. metallurgist, Nat. Co, Inc, 59-60, consult, 60-61; res. grants, NASA, Nat. Sci. Found. & U.S. Atomic Energy Comn. Eng.C, Indian Nat. Cadet Corps, 55-56. Am. Inst. Mining, Metall. & Petrol. Eng; Indian Inst. Metals. Study of the liquid and glassy states; defect structure of solids; defect controlled mechanical properties of solids. Address: Advanced Technology Center, Inc, P.O. Box 6144, Dallas, TX 75222.

GUPTILL, E(RNEST) W(ILMOT), b. N.B, Sept. 5, 19; m. 42; c. 4. PHYSICS. B.Sc, Acadia, 40; M.A, Western Ontario, 42; Ph.D.(physics), McGill, 46. Asst, Nat. Res. Council Can, 42-46; asst. prof. PHYSICS, DALHOUSIE UNIV, 47-48, assoc. prof, 48-57, PROF, 57-, head dept, 58-69. Can. Govt. overseas fel, Kamerlingh Onnes Lab, Leiden, Netherlands, 57-58; vis, Lockheed Res. Lab, Calif, 69- High frequency sound at low temperatures; low temperature physics. Address: Dept. of Physics, Dalhousie University, Halifax, N.S, Can.

GUPTON, CREIGHTON LEE, b. Castalia, N.C, Nov. 12, 33; m. 60; c. 2. PLANT BREEDING. B.S, N.C. State, 57, M.Agr, 63, Ph.D.(plant breeding, bot), 67. Teacher, high sch, N.C, 57-61; res. supvr, N.C. State Univ, 63-64; RES. GENETICIST, CROPS RES. DIV, AGR. RES. SERV, U.S. DEPT. AGR, 67- U.S.A, 53-55. AAAS; Am. Soc. Agron. The derivation from Nicotiana species and tobacco introductions, and the genetic analysis of resistance to tobacco leaf diseases incited by potato virus Y, etch virus, ringspot virus, and Colletotrichum species. Address: Route 3, Box 71, Greeneville, TN 37743.

GUPTON, OSCAR WILMOT, b. Raleigh, N.C, Oct. 15, 24; m. 50; c. 4. BOTANY. A.B, North Carolina, 50, M.A, 51 & 60; Ph.D.(bot), 63. From instr. to assoc. prof. BIOL, VA. MIL. INST, 60-69, PROF, 69- U.S.M.C, 43-46. AAAS. Taxonomy. Address: Dept. of Biology, Virginia Military Institute, Lexington, VA 24450.

GURALNICK, EUGENE, b. Boston, Mass, June 22, 12; m. 47; c. 3. SURGERY. B.S, Massachusetts, 33; M.D, Tufts Col, 37. Intern, Mt. Auburn Hosp, Cambridge, 37-38; res, Evangeline Booth & Farrington Hosps, 38; surg. house off, Boston City Hosp, 39-41; res. tumor surg, Pondville Hosp, Walpole, 46-47; INSTR. SURG, HARVARD MED. SCH, 64- Mem. staff, Beth Israel Hosp, Boston; Mt. Auburn Hosp, Cambridge; vis. surgeon, Pondville Hosp, Walpole; chief surg. serv, Boston State Hosp. Dipl, Am. Bd. Surg, 52. Med.C, 41-46, Lt. Col. Fel. Am. Col. Surg. Tumors. Address: 1180 Beacon St, Brookline, MA 02146.

GURALNICK, S(IDNEY) A(ARON), b. Phila, Pa, Apr. 25, 29; m. 51; c. 2. CIVIL ENGINEERING. B.S, Drexel Inst, 52; M.S, Cornell, 55, Ph.D.(struct. eng), 58. Instr. STRUCT. ENG, Cornell, 52-56, res. assoc. & mgr. test. lab, 56-58, asst. prof, 58; ILL. INST. TECHNOL, 58-61, assoc. prof, 61-67, PROF, 67- Consult, Inst. Gas Tech. & IIT Res. Inst. Nat. Guard, 48-52, Sgt. Am. Soc. Civil Eng; Concrete Inst. Am; Soc. Exp. Stress Anal; Am. Soc. Test. & Mat; Int. Asn. Bridge & Struct. Eng. Ultimate strength and deformation characteristics of reinforced and prestressed concrete members and structures, including plate and shell structures; application of advanced mathematics and electronic computer techniques to structural analysis. Address: Dept. of Civil Engineering, Illinois Institute of Technology, Chicago, IL 60616.

GURAM, MALKIAT SINGH, b. Ludhiana, India, Jan. 4, 28; nat; m. 50; c. 3. ZOOLOGY, BOTANY. B.S, Punjab, India, 48, M.S, 55; Ph.D.(biol), Ohio State, 67. Lectr. zool. & entom, Punjab, India, 48-49, res. asst, 49-53, lectr, Agr. Col, 53-56; asst. entomologist, Punjab. Agr. Dept, 53-60; asst. prof. zool. & entom, Punjab, India, 62-64; prof. biol. & head dept, VOORHEES COL, 67-68, DIV. CHMN. NATURAL SCI. DEPT. & ACAD. DEAN, 68- AAAS; Am. Inst. Biol. Sci; Entom. Soc. Am. Toxicology; pesticide residue detection by electron capture gas chromatography. Address: Dept. of Biology, Voorhees College, Denmark, SC 29042.

GUR-ARIEH, CHAIM, b. Istanbul, Turkey, July 26, 34; m. 59; c. 2. FOOD SCIENCE, CHEMICAL ENGINEERING. B.S.Chem.E, Israel Inst. Tech, 60; M.S, Illinois, 62, Ph.D.(food sci), 63. Proj. leader food res, Quaker Oats Co, 63-67; sr. scientist, DEL MONTE CORP, 67-69, MGR. NEW PROD. DEVELOP, 69- Inst. Food Tech. Food technology; product and process development. Address: Del Monte Corp, Scientific Research Center, 205 N. Wiget Lane, Walnut Creek, CA 94598.

GURBAXANI, SHYAM HASSOMAL, b. Karachi, Pakistan, Dec. 28, 28; U.S. citizen; m. 59; c. 3. SOLID STATE PHYSICS, ELECTRICAL ENGINEERING. B.Sc, Royal Inst, Sci, 49; M.S, Stanford, 50; M.S, Rutgers, 63, Ph.D.(physics), 65. Elec. engr, Gen. Elec. Co, 50-51; Kuljian Corp, 51-52; Lummus Co, 52-58, chief engr, 58, budget control consult, Lummus Int, Venezuela, 58-59, cent. mgt. engr, Lummus Co, 59-60, process design engr, 60-64; br. head res. div, U.S. Naval Air Develop. Center, 65-66; asst. prof. physics, Sacramento State Col, 66-67; assoc. scientist, RADIATION CO, 67-68, chief scientist, 68-69, REENTRY PHYSICS CONSULT, 69-; ASST. PROF. ELEC. ENG, UNIV. N.MEX, 69- Summer guest, inst. underwater acoustics, Pa. State, 65. Consult, Shell Co, Venezuela, 58-59; Nat. Sci. Found. Res. participant laser physics, Stanford Univ, 67; Assoc. West. Univs. res. participant Los Alamos Sci. Lab, 71. Am. Phys. Soc; sr. mem. Inst. Elec. & Electronics Eng; Am. Asn. Physics Teachers. Electron spin and nuclear magnetic resonance; radiation damage; cryogenics; microwave physics; electromagnetic-acoustic energy interaction, population inversion in partially ionized gases and laser physics. Address: 12413 View Court N.E, Albuquerque, NM 87106.

GURCHOT, CHARLES, b. Paris, France, July 19, 98; nat; m. 28. CHEMISTRY. B.S, City Col, N.Y, 21; Heckscher fel, Cornell, 24-25, Ph.D.(colloid chem), 25; Ecole de Med, Paris, 27. Asst. chem. spectros, Cornell, 22, micros, 22-24, instr. biochem, 25-26, fel. pharmacol, 33-34; res. assoc. sch. med, Stanford, 28-30; dir. res. lab, Sonoma State Home, Calif, 30-33; res. assoc. pharmacol, med. sch, California, 34-37, instr, 37-41, asst. prof, 41-45; DIR. RES, John Beard Mem. Found, 46-70; McNAUGHTON FOUND. CALIF, 70- U.S.A, 17-19. Fel. AAAS; fel. Am. Inst. Chem; Soc. Exp. Biol. & Med. Cancer etiology; fundamental principles of biology; cancer chemotherapy and diagnosis; degenerative diseases. Address: 150 Palo Alto Ave, San Francisco, CA 94114.

GURD, FRANK R(OSS) N(EWMAN), b. Montreal, Can, Jan. 20, 24; nat; m. 46; c. 4. BIOCHEMISTRY. B.Sc, McGill, 45, M.Sc, 46; Ph.D.(biochem), Harvard, 49. Res. assoc. phys. chem, Harvard, 48-50, 51-52, instr, 50-51, asst. prof, 52-55; clin. biochem, med. col, Cornell Univ, 55-60; prof. biochem. med, IND. UNIV, Indianapolis, 60-65, PROF. CHEM. & BIOCHEM, BLOOMINGTON, 65- Guggenheim & Whitney fels, Wash. Univ, 54-55; asst. dir. bur. med. res, Equitable Life Assurance Soc. U.S, 55-59; mem. ed. bd, Jour. Biol. Chem, 66-72; mem. biophys. & biophys. chem. B study sect, Nat. Insts. Health, 66-70, chmn, 68-70. Am. Chem. Soc; Am. Soc. Biol. Chem; Biophys. Soc; Harvey Soc; N.Y. Acad. Sci. Lipoproteins; protein purification; interactions of peptides and proteins with metals; relation of structure to function of proteins; protein modification and sequence determination; magnetic resonance spectroscopy of proteins and peptides. Address: Dept. of Chemistry, Indiana University, Bloomington, IN 47401.

GURD, F(RASER) N(EWMAN), b. Montreal, Que, Mar. 19, 14; m. 38; c. 5. SURGERY. B.A, McGill, 34, M.D, C.M, 39; M.Sc, Pennsylvania, 47. Assoc. prof. surg, McGill Univ, 59-63, prof. & chmn. dept, 63-71; ASSOC. SECY, ROYAL COL. PHYSICIANS & SURGEONS CAN, 72- Sr. surgeon, Montreal Gen. Hosp, 59-63, surgeon-in-chief, 63-71; consult. surgeon, Reddy Mem, Queen Elizabeth & Jewish Gen. Hosps, Montreal. Fel, Royal Col. Physicians & Surgeons Can, 48. R.C.A.M.C, 41-46, Capt. Am. Asn. Surg. of Trauma; fel. Am. Col. Surg; Soc. Univ. Surg; Am. Surg. Asn; Can. Soc. Clin. Invest; Can. Med. Asn; Soc. Surg. Alimentary Tract. Surgical physiology; physiology of the liver; surgical shock; physiology of body fluids and electrolytes; gastroenterology; surgical training. Address: Royal College of Physicians & Surgeons of Canada, 74 Stanley Ave, Ottawa, Ont. K1M 1P4, Can.

GURD, GEORGE (WILKINSON), b. London, Ont, Apr. 14, 08; m; c. 1. PHYSICAL CHEMISTRY. B.A, Western Ontario, 29, M.A, 30; Ph.D.(phys. chem), McGill, 32. Mem. res. dept, Imp. Oil Enterprises Ltd, 33-36, tech. adv, West. Refineries, 36-38, mem. res. dept, 38-40, 43-47, asst. res. dir, 47-51, mgr, 51-69; RETIRED. Asst. to dir. gen. chem. & explosives br, Dept. Munitions & Supply, 40-43. Mem, Order of Brit. Empire. Chem. Inst. Can. General chemistry; petroleum. Address: 543 Canterbury Rd, London 72, Ont, Can.

GURDJIAN, E(LISHA) S(TEPHENS), b. Smyrna, Asia Minor, Apr. 18, 00; nat; m. 33; c. 4. NEUROSURGERY. A.B, Michigan, 20, M.S, 24, M.D, 26, Ph.D. (surg), 27. Asst. anat, Michigan, 24-25, instr, 25-27; lectr. neuropath. & neurosurg, Detroit Col. Med. & Surg, 30-41; asst. prof. surg, COL. MED, WAYNE STATE UNIV, 41-44, assoc. prof, 44-48, prof. NEUROL. SURG, 48-70, chmn. dept, 56-70, EMER. PROF, 70- Practicing physician, 30-; attend. neurol. surgeon, Grace Hosp, 33- Dipl, Am. Bd. Neurol. Surg, 41. Soc. Neurol. Surg; Harvey Cushing Soc; Am. Med. Asn; Am. Asn. Surg. Trauma; Asn. Res. Nerv. & Ment. Disease; Am. Neurol. Asn; Cong. Neurol. Surg. Neurophysiology; anatomy of nervous system; head injury; intracranial suppuration; spinal cord injuries; convulsive disorders. Address: 19385 Renfrew, Detroit, MI 48221.

GÜREL, OKAN, b. Kirkagac, Turkey, Aug. 1, 31; m. 62; c. 2. APPLIED MATHEMATICS & MECHANICS. Y.Müh, Tech. Univ. Istanbul, 54; fel, British Columbia, 55-57, M.A.Sc, 57; fel, Stanford, 58-59, Shell fel, 59-60, Ph.D. (appl. mech), 61. Staff mem, MATH, Int. Bus. Mach. Corp, 61-62; asst. prof, Middle East Tech, Ankara, 64-66; STAFF MEM, N.Y. SCI. CTR, IBM CORP, 66- Lectr, Electronic Comput. Ctr, Tech. Univ. Istanbul, spring 65, guest speaker, summer insts. sci. & tech. res. coun, Ford Found, 65 & 66; adj. prof, Baruch Col, 70- Consult, Ford Found. Sci. Lycee Proj, Ankara, 65-66. Secy, scientist training group, Sci. & Tech. Res. Coun, Turkey, 64-65, mem, 65-66. C.Eng, Turkish Army, Lt, 62-65. AAAS; Am. Math. Soc; N.Y. Acad. Sci; Biophys. Soc. Qualitative theory of differential equations and its application to various fields; stability theory of systems; control problems of systems, particularly molecular biology. Address: One Washington Square Village, 2-J, New York, NY 10012.

GUREVITCH, MARK, b. Cleveland, Ohio, Sept. 11, 16; m. 43; c. 2. PHYSICS. A.B, California, 38, Ph.D.(physics), 47. Instr. physics, California, 42-43, res. physicist, Off. Sci. Res. & Develop. Proj, 43-45; asst. prof. PHYSICS, Idaho, 47-50, assoc. prof, 50-57, prof, 57-58; PROF. & CHMN. DEPT, PORTLAND STATE UNIV, 58- Nat. Insts. Health fel. biophys, 66-67. AAAS; Am. Phys. Soc; Am. Asn. Physics Teachers. Spectroscopy; properties of thin films; environmental science. Address: Dept. of Physics, Portland State University, Box 751, Portland, OR 97207.

GUREWITSCH, A(RNO) DAVID, b. Zurich, Switz, Oct. 31, 02; nat; m. 37; c. 1. CLINICAL MEDICINE. M.D, Basel, 33. Asst. clin. prof. phys. med. & asst. attend. physician, COLUMBIA-PRESBY. MED. CTR, 39-58, assoc. clin. prof. & assoc. attend. physician, 58-63, clin. prof. rehab. med. & attend. physician phys. med. & rehab, 63-68, SPEC. LECTR. REHAB. MED. & CONSULT, 68- Med. dir, Blythedale Children's Hosp, 52-68, emer. med. dir, 68- Am. Acad. Phys. Med. & Rehab; Am. Med. Asn. Medical rehabilitation. Address: 121 E. 60th St, New York, NY 10022.

GURFINKEL, GERMAN R, b. La Habana, Cuba, Sept. 14, 32; U.S. citizen; m. 56; c. 4. STRUCTURAL ENGINEERING. Ing. Civil, Univ. La Habana, 55; M.S, Univ. Ill, Urbana, 57, Danforth grant, 64, Ph.D.(civil eng), 66. Asst. prof. CIVIL ENG, Univ. Havana, 59-61; vis. asst. prof, UNIV. ILL, URBANA, 62-63, instr, 63-66, asst. prof, 66-68, ASSOC. PROF, 68- Nat. Sci. Found. res. grant, 67-68; consult, Nat. Sci. Found-Agency Int. Develop, India, summers 67, 68, 69. Am. Soc. Civil Eng; Am. Concrete Inst. Behavior of prestressed concrete columns; nuclear containment structures; wood structures; structural mechanics; numerical methods. Address: 2510 S. Prospect Ave, Champaign, IL 61820.

GURIEN, H(ARVEY), b. Brooklyn, N.Y, Sept. 25, 25; m. 50; c. 5. ORGANIC CHEMISTRY. B.S, Brooklyn Col, 49; M.S, Pennsylvania, 50; fel, Polytech. Inst. Brooklyn, 50-52, 54-55, Cottrell fel, 53, Ph.D, 55. RES. CHEMIST, Gen. Aniline Works, 53-60; S.B. Penick & Co, 60-62; HOFFMANN-La ROCHE CO, 62- U.S.A, 44-46. AAAS; Am. Chem. Soc. Pharmaceutical developmental research. Address: 67 Parker Ave, Maplewood, NJ 07040.

GURIN, SAMUEL, b. New York, N.Y, July 1, 05; m. 30; c. 2. BIOCHEMISTRY. B.S, Columbia, 28, M.S, 30, fel, 32-34, Ph.D.(biochem), 34; hon. D.Sc, Phila. Col. Pharm, 64, La Salle Col, 65. Asst. physiol. chem, teachers co, Columbia, 28-32, biochemist, col. physicians & surgeons, 34-35; Nat. Res. fel, chem, Illinois, 36; instr. physiol. chem, sch. med, Pennsylvania, 36-42, asst. prof. biochem, 42-45, assoc. prof, 45-47, prof. physiol. chem, 48-54, Benjamin Rush prof. biochem, 54-65, prof, 65-69, chmn. dept, 54-62, acting chmn, 63-64, dean, 62-68; PROF. BIOL. SCI, UNIV. FLA, 69- Mem, panel metab, comt. growth, Nat. Res. Coun; study sect. biochem, U.S. Pub. Health Serv; panel regulation metab, Nat. Sci. Found. Mem, bd. sci. counsr, Nat. Inst. Arthritis & Metab. Diseases & Nat. Inst. Gen. Med. Sci. With Off. Sci. Res. & Develop, 44. Am. Chem. Soc; Am. Soc. Biol. Chem. Radioisotopes in study of metabolism; metabolic studies on lipids; isolation of chorionic gonadotrophin; isolation and constitution of thiamine. Address: Division of Biological Sciences, 321 Bartram Bldg, University of Florida, Gainesville, FL 32601.

GURINSKY, DAVID H(ARRIS), b. Brooklyn, N.Y, Apr. 26, 14; m. 37; c. 2. METALLURGY. A.B, N.Y. Univ, 36, fel, 36-37, Ph.D.(phys. chem), 42. Asst. instr. chem. physics, N.Y. Univ, 36-42; res. assoc, metall. lab, Chicago, 42-44, inst. study metals, 46-47; Los Alamos Sci. Lab, N.Mex, 44-46; scientist, BROOKHAVEN NAT. LAB, 47-50, SR. SCIENTIST & HEAD METALL. DIV, 50- Head mat. res. on high temperature graphite reactor & consult, Gen. Atomic Div, Gen. Dynamics Corp, 59-60. Stud. award, Am. Inst. Chem. With Atomic Energy Comn, 44. Fel. Am. Nuclear Soc; Am. Soc. Metals; Am. Inst. Mining, Metall. & Petrol. Eng. Metallurgy of uranium; nuclear fuels; graphite radiation effects; effects of radiation on structural materials; liquid metal corrosion; thermal diagram of the system iron-tin; superconductivity; superconductor materials; power transmission. Address: Brookhaven National Lab, Upton, NY 11973.

GURK, HERBERT M(ORTON), b. Phila, Pa, Aug. 6, 30; m. 52; c. 3. MATHEMATICS. B.A, Pennsylvania, 51, M.A, 52, Harrison fel, 52-53, Ph.D. (math), 56. Instr. eng. res, Pennsylvania, 53-56; mathematician, systems eng, Radio Corp. Am, 56-58, leader systs. anal. group, 58-61, space opers. anal. group, 62-66, mgr. imagery systs. progs, 66-68, MGR. EARTH OBSERVATION SYSTS, RCA CORP, 68- Soc. Indust. & Appl. Math.(treas, 61-65); Am. Math. Soc; Am. Inst. Aeronaut. & Astronaut. Theory of games; theory of waiting lines and stochastic processes; numerical analysis; mathematical linquistics; space systems planning and analysis; space meteorological systems. Address: Astro Electronics Div, RCA Corp, Princeton, NJ 08540.

GURKLIS, JOHN A(NTHONY), b. Waterbury, Conn, July 12, 21; m. 58; c. 2. ELECTROCHEMICAL & CHEMICAL ENGINEERING. B.S, Maryland, 43; M.S, Ohio State, 47, scholar, 47-49, Ph.D.(chem. eng), 50. Asst. chem. eng, Ohio State, 43-44, 49-50; prin. chem. engr, ELECTROCHEM. ENG, DIV, BATTELLE MEM. INST, 50-56, SR. CHEM. ENGR, 56- U.S.N.R, 44-46, Lt.(jg). Am. Inst. Chem. Eng; Electrochem. Soc; Am. Chem. Soc; Am. Electroplaters Soc; Soc. Mfg. Eng; Am. Soc. Metals. Electrochemical machining; chemical milling; electrodeposition of metals and alloys; electrowinning; electrorefining; electropolishing; hydrogen embrittlement; metal finishing. Address: Dept. of Materials Processing & Fabrication, Battelle Memorial Institute, 505 King Ave, Columbus, OH 43201.

GURLAND, JOHN, b. Can, Jan. 6, 17; nat; m. 48; c. 2. STATISTICS. M.A, Toronto, 42; Ph.D.(math. statist), California, 48. Pierce instr. math, Harvard, 48-49; asst. prof. STATIST, Chicago, 49-52; assoc. prof, Iowa State, 52-58, PROF, 58-60; math. res. ctr, UNIV. WIS, MADISON, 60-63, STATIST. DEPT, 63-, med. sch, 63-67. Fel. AAAS; fel. Inst. Math. Statist; Biomet. Soc; Am. Math. Soc; Math. Asn. Am; fel. Am. Statist. Asn; fel. Am. Pub. Health Asn; fel. Royal Statist. Soc. Mathematical statistics; applied statistics. Address: Dept. of Statistics, University of Wisconsin, Madison, WI 53706.

GURLAND, JOSEPH, b. Berlin, Ger, Jan. 26, 23; nat; m. 49; c. 2. PHYSICAL METALLURGY. B.Ch.E, N.Y. Univ, 44, M.S, 48; Sc.D, Mass. Inst. Tech, 51. Res. engr, Battelle Mem. Inst, 47-48; asst. metall, Mass. Inst. Tech, 48-51; res. engr. & mgr. basic res, Firth-Sterling, Inc, 51-55; asst. prof. ENG, BROWN UNIV, 55-57, assoc. prof, 57-64, PROF, 64- Nat. Sci. Found. faculty fel, 61-62; NATO fel. sci, 70. U.S.A, 44-46. Am. Soc. Metals; Am. Inst. Mining Metall. & Petrol. Eng. Structure of sintered carbides; composite alloys; fracture of metals; quantitative metallography. Address: 115 Cole Ave, Providence, RI 02906.

GURLEY, LAWRENCE RAY, b. Goldsboro, N.C, Jan. 13, 35; m. 58; c. 2. BIOCHEMISTRY, CHEMICAL ENGINEERING. B.Ch.E, N.C. State, 58, Chem. Engr, 59; Nat. Insts. Health fel, North Carolina, 60-64, Ph.D.(biochem), 64. Prod. engr, Merck & Co, Va, 58-60; STAFF BIOCHEMIST, LOS ALAMOS SCI. LAB, UNIV. CALIF, 64- Interactions between histones, desoxyribonucleic acid polymerase and nucleic acids; histone chemistry and biology; histone metabolism; tissue culture; biochemistry of the cell life cycle; radiation biology. Address: Los Alamos Scientific Lab, Los Alamos, NM 87544.

GURLEY, THOMAS GORDON, b. Cedar Grove, Tenn, July 27, 36. ORGANIC POLYMER CHEMISTRY. B.S, Kent State, 62; Goodyear fel, Akron, 62-63. Chemist, GOODYEAR TIRE & RUBBER CO, 63-65, proj. leader POLYETHER RUBBERS RES, 65-67, SECT. HEAD, 68- U.S.M.C, 56-58. Am. Chem. Soc. Rubber technology solution polymerization and heterogeneous catalysis of cyclic oxides. Address: 77 Fir Hill, Apt. 10-B-11, Akron, OH 44304.

GURNEY, ASHLEY B(UELL), b. Cummington, Mass, May 16, 11; m. 41; c. 3. ENTOMOLOGY. B.S, Massachusetts, 33, M.S, 35, Ph.D.(entom), 40; Minnesota, 35-36. Lab. asst. entom, Massachusetts, 33-35; field agent, bur. entom. & plant quarantine, U.S. DEPT. AGR, St. Paul, 35-36, from asst. entomologist to ENTOMOLOGIST, 36-42, 46-53, SYST. ENTOM. LAB, ENTOM. RES. DIV, AGR. RES. SERV, U.S. NAT. MUS, 55- Lectr, Maryland, 41. Sanit.C, 42-46, Res, 46-71, Col.(Ret). Mem. div. biol. & agr, Nat. Res. Coun, 57-59. AAAS; Entom. Soc. Am.(exec. secy, 54); fel. Royal Entom. Soc. London. Classification, biology and distribution of insects, with special reference to Orthoptera, Zoraptera, Psocoptera and related orders; biology of migratory grasshoppers. Address: Systematic Entomology Lab, Entomology Research Division, U.S. Dept. of Agriculture, U.S. National Museum, Washington, DC 20560.

GURNEY, B(ENJAMIN) FRANKLIN, b. Mendota, Ill, Sept. 3, 14; m. 39; c. 3. ENDODONTICS. B.S, Univ. Chicago, 35, M.S, 38; D.D.C, Loyola Univ.(Ill), 61. Lectr. & demonstr. chem, Mus. Sci. & Indust, Ill, 39-41; paint chemist, E.I. du Pont de Nemours & Co, 41; asst. supv. chemist, high explosives, U.S. Civil Serv. Comn, 41-43; res. chemist, Armour & Co, 43-44; instr. biochem, sch. dent, Loyola Univ. Chicago, 44-45, asst. prof, 45-61, assoc. prof. endodontics, 61-65, prof. & dir. grad. endodont. & res, 65-69; CHMN. DEPT. ENDODONTICS, DENT. SCH, NORTHWEST. UNIV, 70- Consult, Nat. Coun. Dent. Aptitude Testing; Nat. Bd. Dent. Exam; private practice, 61; endodontics specialist, Ill, 64. AAAS; Am. Chem. Soc; Am. Dent. Asn; Int. Asn. Dent. Res; Am. Asn. Endodont; Int. Dent. Fedn. Dental therapeutics; endodontal antiseptics; prophase of calculus. Address: Dept. of Endodontics, Northwestern University Dental School, 311 E. Chicago Ave, Chicago, IL 60611.

GURNEY, CLIFFORD W, b. Chicago, Ill, Apr. 11, 24; m. 49; c. 5. INTERNAL MEDICINE. B.S, Chicago, 48, M.D, 51. Asst. prof. med, Chicago, 56-60, assoc. prof, 60-65, prof, 65-66, assoc. prof. physiol, 62; PROF. MED. & CHMN. DEPT, med. sch, Rutgers Univ, 66-69; MED. SCH, UNIV. KANS, 69- Staff mem, Argonne Cancer Res. Hosp, 56-66; Markle scholar, 59-64. U.S.A.A.F, 43-46. Am. Soc. Clin. Invest; Am. Soc. Hemat; Am. Med. Asn; fel. Am. Col. Physicians; Am. Fedn. Clin. Res; Asn. Am. Physicians. Hematology. Address: Dept. of Medicine, University of Kansas School of Medicine, Kansas City, KS 66103.

GURNEY, RAMSDELL, b. Buffalo, N.Y, Aug. 2, 03; m. 32; c. 2. INTERNAL MEDICINE. B.A, Yale, 25; M.D, Buffalo, 29. Asst. prof. physiol, STATE UNIV. N.Y. BUFFALO, 47-50, MED, 50-64, ASSOC. PROF, 64- Private practice, 32-; attend. physician, Buffalo Gen. Hosp, 57-71, consult. physician, 71- Dipl, Am. Bd. Internal Med, 42. Med.C, U.S.A, 41-45. Am. Col. Physicians. Obesity and sweating; cardiovascular disease. Address: 85 High St, Buffalo, NY 14203.

GURNEY, THEODORE, JR, b. Hartford, Conn, Oct. 14, 38; m. 66. MOLECULAR & CELL BIOLOGY. A.B, Harvard Col, 59; M.S, Yale, 61, U.S. Pub. Health Serv. trainee, 61-65, Ph.D.(biophys), 65. U.S. Pub. Health Serv. fels. biol, Mass. Inst. Technol, 64-67; Jane Coffin Childs Mem. Fund med. res. fel. MOLECULAR BIOL, UNIV. CALIF, BERKELEY, 67-68, ASST. PROF, 68- AAAS. Field-ion microscopy; bacterial transformation; contact inhibition of growth in cell culture; protein synthesis; organelle DNA. Address: 504 Molecular Biology & Virus Lab, University of California, Berkeley, CA 94720.

GURNHAM, C(HARLES) FRED(ERICK), b. Ludlow, Mass, Oct. 19, 11; m. 34; c. 4. CHEMICAL & SANITARY ENGINEERING. B.S, Yale, 32, M.Ch.E, N.Y. Univ, 40, D.Eng.Sc, 42. Chemist, Smith Paper, Inc, Mass, 32-34; chem. engr, Ludlow Mfg. Assocs, 34-36; Naugatuck Chem. Co, Conn, 36-38; asst. prof, Pratt Inst, 38-41; chem. engr, Fred S. Carver, Inc, N.Y, 41-42; Air Reduction Co, Conn, 42-44; Whitney Blake Co, 44-48; prof. chem. eng. & chmn. dept, Tufts Col, 49-52; prof. & head dept, Mich. State, 52-61; prof. civil & chem. eng, Ill. Inst. Technol, 62-70, chmn. dept. environ. eng, 66-70; PRES. & TREAS, GURNHAM & ASSOCS. INC, 69- Pres, Suburban Labs, Inc, 70- Dipl, Am. Acad. Sanit. Eng, 56-, trustee, 64-67. Am. Chem. Soc; Am. Soc. Civil Eng; Water Pollution Control Fedn; Am. Inst. Chem. Eng; Am. Inst. Chem; Am. Inst. Plant Eng.(pollution control awards, 70 & 71); Am. Water Works Asn; Nat. Soc. Prof. Eng; Am. Electroplaters Soc; Inst. Advan. Sanit. Res. Industrial wastes; stream pollution. Address: Gurnham & Associates, Inc, 223 W. Jackson Blvd, Chicago, IL 60606.

GUROFF, GORDON, b. Chicago, Ill, July 9, 33; m. 54; c. 3. BIOCHEMISTRY. B.S, Illinois, 54; M.S, Ala. Polytech. Inst, 56; Babcock fel, Wisconsin, 58-59, Ph.D.(biochem), 59. CHEMIST, NAT. HEART INST, 59- Geigy fel, 59-60. AAAS; Am. Chem. Soc. Amino acid metabolism; neurochemistry. Address: Clinical Center, National Heart Institute, Bethesda, MD 20014.

GUROWITZ, EDWARD M(ARTIN), Physiol. Psychol, see 12th ed, Soc. & Behav. Vols.

GUROWITZ, WILLIAM D(AVID), b. New York, N.Y, July 23, 31; m. 58; c. 1. ORGANIC CHEMISTRY. B.A, Cornell, 53; Ph.D.(chem), Purdue, 58. Res. chemist, East. Res. Lab, Dow Chem. Co, 60-67; exec. dir. dept. chem, CORNELL UNIV, 67-71, V.PRES. CAMPUS AFFAIRS, 71- U.S.A.F, 58-60, 1st Lt. AAAS; Am. Chem. Soc. Mechanisms and synthesis in organic chemistry. Address: 119 Oak Hill Rd, Ithaca, NY 14850.

GURPIDE, ERLIO, b. Buenos Aires, Arg, Apr. 8, 27; U.S. citizen; m. 61; c. 1. BIOCHEMISTRY, BIOPHYSICS. Ph.D.(chem), Buenos Aires, 55. Res. assoc. biochem, Columbia, 59-64, asst. prof, 64-69; PROF, BIOCHEM, OBSTET. & GYNEC, UNIV. MINN, MINNEAPOLIS, 69- Career scientist, Health Res. Coun, N.Y, 63-69; mem. endocrinol. study sect. Nat. Insts. Health, 70- Am. Soc. Biol. Chem; Endocrine Soc; Soc. Gynec. Invest. Steroid biochemistry; use of isotopically labeled tracers in biology; endocrinology. Address: Box 361 Mayo, University of Minnesota, Minneapolis, MN 55455.

GURR, GRAHAM EDWARD, b. Adelaide, S.Australia, Mar. 28, 37; m. 62; c. 2. PHYSICS, CRYSTALLOGRAPHY. B.Sc, Adelaide, 56, Hons, 57, Ph.D.(physics), 61. Vis. res. assoc, crystallog. lab, Pittsburgh, 61-62; SR. PHYSICIST, MAT. PHYSICS RES, CENT. RES. LABS, MINN. MINING & MFG. CO, 63- Am. Crystallog. Asn; Brit. Inst. Physics & Phys. Soc. X-ray crystallography; crystal physics and chemistry; crystal structure analysis. Address: Central Research Labs, Minnesota Mining & Manufacturing Co, P.O. Box 33221, St. Paul, MN 55133.

GURR, HENRY S(ATER), b. Wooster, Ohio, Mar. 9, 37; m. 61; c. 3. PHYSICS. B.S, Case Inst. Tech, 59, M.S, 64, Ph.D.(physics), 66. RES. PHYSICIST, UNIV. CALIF, IRVINE, 66- Cosmic ray neutrino; detecting neutrino scattering upon electrons. Address: Dept. of Physics, University of California, Irvine, CA 92664.

GURRY, ROBERT W(ILTON), b. Schenectady, N.Y, Sept. 27, 13; m. 39; c. 2. PHYSICAL CHEMISTRY. B.S, Union (N.Y), 34; Ph.D.(phys. chem), Yale, 37. Phys. chemist, U.S. Steel Corp, N.J, 37-55; Quaker Chem. Prods. Corp, 55-59; TECH. DIR, UNION STEEL CORP, PISCATAWAY, 59- Instr, Stevens Inst. Technol, 44-46. AAAS; Am. Chem. Soc; Am. Soc. Metals; Am. Welding Soc; Nat. Asn. Corrosion Eng. Physico-chemical research on problems relating to steel making and processing; surface chemistry of metals, corrosion. Address: 238 Ridge Rd, Watchung, NJ 07060.

GURSKY, HERBERT, b. Bronx, N.Y, May 27, 30; m. 58; c. 2. PHYSICS. B.S, Florida, 51; M.S, Vanderbilt, 53; Ph.D.(physics), Princeton, 59. Instr. physics, Princeton, 57-58, Columbia, 58-61; sr. scientist, AM. SCI. & ENG, INC, 61-66, proj. dir, 66-69, V.PRES, SPACE RES. DIV, 69- Assoc, Harvard, 71- Am. Phys. Soc. Space and nuclear physics; cosmic rays. Address: 100 Puritan Lane, Sudbury, MA 01776.

GURSKY, MARTIN L(EWIS), b. N.Y.C, Mar. 19, 27; m. 52; c. 5. THEORETICAL PHYSICS. B.S, Ga. Inst. Tech, 48, M.S, 51; Ph.D.(physics), Vanderbilt, 58. Instr. PHYSICS, Ga. Inst. Tech, 48-50; MEM. STAFF, Melpar, Inc, 53-54; LOS ALAMOS SCI. LAB, UNIV. CALIF, 54- U.S.A, 45-46. Am. Phys. Soc. Nuclear theory. Address: Los Alamos Scientific Lab, Los Alamos, NM 87544.

GURST, JEROME E, b. Atlantic City, N.J, Aug. 9, 38. ORGANIC CHEMISTRY. A.B, Dartmouth Col, 60; Great West. Dow fel, Stanford, 60-61, Nat. Sci. Found. summer fel, 61, Ph.D.(chem), 65. Fel. organoboranes, Purdue, 64-65; stereochem, Princeton, 65-66; vis. asst. prof. ORG. CHEM, Oregon, 66-67; asst. prof, UNIV. W.FLA, 67-71, ASSOC. PROF, 71- AAAS; Am. Chem. Soc; Brit. Chem. Soc. Stereochemistry; steroids; mass spectrometry; optical rotatory dispersion; circular dichroism; natural products. Address: Dept. of Chemistry, University of West Florida, Pensacola, FL 32504.

GURTIN, MORTON EDWARD, b. Jersey City, N.J, Mar. 7, 34; m. 55; c. 2. APPLIED MATHEMATICS, MECHANICS. B.M.E, Rensselaer Polytech, 55; Ph.D.(appl. math), Brown, 61. Engr. struct, Douglas Aircraft Co, Inc, 55-56; Gen. Elec. Co, 56-59; res. assoc. APPL. MATH, Brown, 61-62, asst. prof, 62-64, assoc. prof, 64-66; PROF, CARNEGIE-MELLON UNIV, 66- Consult, Gen. Elec. Co, 61-63; Mech. Tech. Inc, 62-64; lectr, Nat. Univ. Mex, 64; Wash. Univ, 65; Nat. Sci. Found. res. grant, 65-; lectr, W.Va. Univ, 67-68; consult, Sandia Corp, 67-; lectr, Southwest. Mech. Lect. Series, 68; Wash. State Univ, 70; Univ. Rio de Janeiro, 70; Int. Ctr. Mech. Sci, Italy, 71. Am. Math. Soc; Soc. Natural Philos. Foundations of continuum mechanics and thermodynamics; elasticity and viscoelasticity theory; wave propagation; functional analysis; partial differential equations. Address: Dept. of Mathematics, Carnegie-Mellon University, Pittsburgh, PA 15213.

GURUDATA, NEVILLE, b. Berbice, Guyana, Apr. 23, 37; m. 62; c. 1. ORGANIC CHEMISTRY, NUCLEAR MAGNETIC RESONANCE. B.Sc, Univ. St. Andrews, 59, Hons, 60; petrol. res. fel, Univ. West. Ont, 64-65, Prov. Ont. fel, 66-67, Ph.D.(chem), 68. Sci. off, Dept. Govt. Analyst, Guyana, 60-64; res. fel, Univ. Ottawa, 68-69; LECTR. & RES. ASSOC. CHEM, SIR GEORGE WILLIAMS UNIV, 69- Instr, Univ. Guyana, 63-64. Royal Inst. Chem; Am. Chem. Soc; Chem. Inst. Can. Use of nuclear magnetic resonance spectroscopy to determine structure, stereochemistry, thermodynamic parameters; interactions between formally non-conjugated chromophores; relationships between chemical structure, spectra and chemical reactivity; approaches to synthesis of selected organic compounds. Address: Dept. of Chemistry, Sir George Williams University, 1435 Drummond St, Montreal 107, Que, Can.

GUSBERG, S(AUL) B(ERNARD), b. Newark, N.J, Aug. 3, 13; m. 38; c. 1. MEDICINE. M.D, Harvard, 37; Bache fel, Columbia, 46-48, Med.Sc.D, (gynec, obstet), 48. Res, Collis P. Huntington Hosp, Harvard, 38; res. obstetrician & gynecologist, Sloane Hosp. Women, COL. PHYSICIANS & SURGEONS, COLUMBIA UNIV, 46, assoc. prof. clin. obstet. & gynec, 54-62, CLIN. PROF. OBSTET. & GYNEC, 62-; PROF. & CHMN. DEPT, MT. SINAI SCH. MED, 68-, DIR. OBSTET. & GYNEC. & GYNECOLOGIST-IN-CHIEF, MT. SINAI HOSP, 62- Assoc. attend. obstetrician & gynecologist, hosps, Columbia-Presby. Med. Ctr. AAAS; fel. Am. Gynec. Soc; Soc. Gynec. Oncol; fel. Am. Radium Soc; Am. Soc. Cytol; Soc. Pelvic Surg; Am. Asn. Cancer Res; fel. Am. Col. Obstet. & Gynec; fel. Am. Col. Surg; Am. Asn. Obstet. & Gynec; N.Y. Acad. Med; N.Y. Acad. Sci. Gynecologic cancer; reproductive biology. Address: Mt. Sinai Hospital, 1176 Fifth Ave, New York, NY 10029.

GUSDON, JOHN PAUL, b. Cleveland, Ohio, Feb. 13, 31; m. 56; c. 3. OBSTETRICS & GYNECOLOGY, IMMUNOLOGY. B.A, Virginia, 52, M.D, 59. Intern, Univ. Hosps. Cleveland, Ohio, 59-60, resident obstet. & gynec, 60-64; fel. immunol, sch. med, Case Western Reserve, 64-67, instr. OBSTET & GYNEC, 66-67, asst. prof, 67; BOWMAN GRAY SCH. MED, 67-70, ASSOC. PROF, 70-, ASSOC. MICROBIOL, 67- Josiah Macy Jr. Found. faculty fel, 66-69. U.S.N, 48-55, Lt. AAAS; Am. Asn. Immunol; Reticuloendothelial Soc; Am. Fertil. Soc; Am. Col. Obstet. & Gynec; Soc. Exp. Biol. & Med; Am. Med. Asn. Immunological aspects of fetal-maternal relationships. Address: Bowman Gray School of Medicine, 300 S. Hawthorne Rd, Winston-Salem, NC 27103.

GUSE, LYNN ROBERT, b. Wanatah, Ind, Oct. 7, 29; m. 53; c. 4. PLANT PHYSIOLOGY, BOTANY. B.S, Purdue, 51, M.S, 58, Ph.D.(plant physiol), 62. Teacher, high sch, Ind, 54-59; plant physiologist, ELI LILLY & CO, 62-66, REGIONAL COORD, 66- U.S.A, 51-53, Sgt. Weed. Sci. Soc. Am. Herbicides; fungicides; nematocides. Address: 8236 Anemone Lane, Indianapolis, IN 46219.

GUSEMAN, LAWRENCE FRANK, JR, b. New Iberia, La, Feb. 16, 38; m. 68. MATHEMATICS. B.A, Texas A&M, 60, M.S, 62; Ph.D.(math), Texas, Austin 68. Appl. mathematician, M.D. Anderson Hosp. & Tumor Inst, 62; res. mathematician, theory & anal. off, comput. & anal. div, NASA Manned Spacecraft Ctr, 64-68; ASST. PROF. MATH, TEX. A&M UNIV, 68- Teaching asst, Texas, Austin, 64-66. Sig.C, U.S.A, 62-64, 1st Lt. Am. Math. Soc; Math. Asn. Am; Soc. Indust. & Appl. Math; Asn. Comput. Mach. Functional analysis, including spaces of affine continuous functions on compact convex sets, convexity theory, Banach spaces, Choquet theory and integral representations; non-linear fixed point theory. Address: Dept. of Mathematics, Texas A&M University, College Station, TX 77843.

GUSENIUS, EDWIN MAURITZ, b. Bristol, S.Dak, July 5, 16; m. 48; c. 2. INORGANIC CHEMISTRY. B.A, Gustavus Adolphus Col, 38; North. State Col, 40-41; M.A, South Dakota, 48; Lutheran Brotherhood Faculty fel, 59-60; Ph.D.(inorg. chem), Kansas State, 63. Instr, high sch, S.Dak, 38-40; chemist, E.I. du Pont de Nemours & Co, 41-42, supvr, 42-45; asst. CHEM, South Dakota, 46-47; instr, Luther Jr. Col, 47-54; asst. prof, Bethany Col.(Kans), 54-59, assoc. prof, 60-62, prof, 63-68; Kearney State Col, 68-69; PROF. & CHMN. DEPT, FRIENDS UNIV, 69- Am. Chem. Soc. Metal complexes. Address: Dept. of Chemistry, Friends University, Wichita, KS 67213.

GUSH, DONALD P(AUL), b. Hanover Twp, Pa, Sept. 7, 32; m. 50; c. 3. PHYSICAL CHEMISTRY. B.S, King's Col.(Pa), 54; Ph.D.(chem), Catholic Univ, 59. Sr. chemist, Harris Res. Labs, Inc, 58-63; chemist, res. div, W.R. GRACE & CO, 63-68, TECH. MGR. LETTERFLEX SYSTS, POLYFIBRON DIV, 68- Free radicals; gas-phase kinetics; mass spectrometry; photochemistry. Address: Letterflex Systems, W.R. Grace & Co, Clarksville, MD 21029.

GUSHEE, BEATRICE E(LEANOR), b. Dorchester, Mass, Sept. 22, 18. INORGANIC CHEMISTRY. B.S, Simmons Col, 42; fel, Vassar Col, 44-46, M.S, 46; Ph.D.(inorg. chem), Connecticut, 56. Anal. chemist, Celanese Corp. Am, 42-44; instr. CHEM, Hofstra Col, 46-48; asst, Connecticut, 48-54; instr. Smith Col, 54-57; asst. prof, HOLLINS COL, 57-63, ASSOC. PROF, 63- Am. Chem. Soc; Nat. Sci. Teachers Asn. High temperature and solid state reactions and transformation; structural inorganic chemistry. Address: Dept. of Chemistry, Hollins College, VA 24020.

GUSHIN, HAROLD, b. Roselle, N.J, Oct. 29, 15; m. 40; c. 2. ORGANIC CHEMISTRY, ENGINEERING ECONOMICS. B.S, Newark Col. Eng, 40; Polytech. Inst. Brooklyn, 46-48. From process develop. to prod. supvr. intermediate dept, Gen. Aniline & Film Corp, 33-58, supvr. engr, process eval. sect, div. eng, 58-59, mgr. eng. & eval. planning, dyestuff & chem. div, 59-65, dir. oper. planning, 65-71, DIR, CORP. PLANNING, GAF CORP, 71- U.S.A, 41-42; U.S.A.A.F, 42-46, Capt. Am. Chem. Soc; N.Y. Acad. Sci; Am. Inst. Chem. Dyestuff intermediates and color formers; benzene, naphthalene and anthraquinone derivatives; distillation techniques. Address: 441 W. Fourth Ave, Roselle, NJ 07203.

GUSMAN, SAMUEL, b. N.Y.C, Oct. 14, 25; m. 47; c. 2. PHYSICAL CHEMISTRY. B.S, Mass. Inst. Technol, 46, M.S, 47; Ph.D, Brown Univ, 50. Sr. chemist, ROHM & HAAS CO, 50-57, head lab, 57-59, res. supvr, 59-61, asst. dir. res, 61-66, asst. gen. mgr, WARREN-TEED PHARMACEUT, INC, 66-67, v.pres, 67-69, PRES. & BD. DIRS, 69-, CHMN. BD, CONSOL. BIO-MED. LABS, INC, 70- Consult, nat. mat. adv. bd, Nat. Acad. Sci-Nat. Res. Coun; dir, Nat. Digestive Disease Found, 70- AAAS; Am. Chem. Soc. Polymer and surface chemistry; surface coatings; biomedical research; research management; general management. Address: Warren-Teed Pharmaceutical, Inc, 582 W. Goodale St, Columbus, OH 42315.

GUSMANO, ERNEST AMBROSE, b. Brooklyn, N.Y, Nov. 13, 32; m. 59; c. 2. BIOLOGY, NUCLEAR MEDICINE. B.S, St. John's Univ.(N.Y), 54, Ph.D. (biol), 66; M.A, Brooklyn Col, 59. Bacteriologist, Maimonides Hosp, Brooklyn, N.Y, 56-57; teacher, N.Y, 57-58; lab. specialist, med. physics div, Brookhaven Nat. Lab, 58-60, med. assoc, 60-66, res. assoc, 66-67; sr. res. scientist, RADIOPHARMACEUT. RES. & DEVELOP, E.R. SQUIBB & SONS, INC, 67-68, head radiobiol. res, 69-70, HEAD RADIOPHARMACEUT. RES. OPERS, 70- Res. collab, med. physics div, Brookhaven Nat. Lab, 67-; teacher, N.J, 69- Med.C, U.S.A, 54-56. AAAS; Health Physics Soc; Soc. Nuclear Med. Metabolism and distribution of radiolabeled compounds; drug and mineral metabolism; whole body gamma spectroscopy; physiology of bone; tracer dynamics. Address: Radiopharmaceutical Res. Operations, E.R. Squibb & Sons, Inc, 5 Georges Rd, New Brunswick, NJ 08903.

GUSS, CYRUS O(MAR), b. Wolford, N.Dak, Feb. 1, 11; m; c. 2. ORGANIC CHEMISTRY. B.S, Jamestown Col, 32; M.S, Minnesota, 36, Ph.D.(org. chem), 40. Res. chemist, Dow Chem. Co, Mich, 36-37, group leader, 40-42; res. chemist, Rohm & Haas Co, Pa, 39; chemist, forest prod. lab, U.S. Forest Serv, Wis, 42-46; asst. prof. CHEM, Univ. South. Calif, 46-50; assoc. prof, Colo. State Univ, 50-60; vis. instr, Univ. Ill, 60-61; PROF, UNIV. NEV, RENO, 61-, chmn. dept, 61-71. AAAS; Am. Chem. Soc; The Chem. Soc. Preparation and reactions of olefin oxides; rearrangements; intramolecular displacements. Address: Dept. of Chemistry, University of Nevada, Reno, NV 89507.

GUSS, MAURICE L(OUIS), b. Revere, Mass, June 21, 22; m. 46; c. 3. MICROBIOLOGY. B.S, Boston Col, 47; M.S, Massachusetts, 49; Ph.D.(bact), Cornell, 52. MICROBIOLOGIST, U.S. ARMY BIOL. LABS, FT. DETRICK, 52- Abbott Labs. fel. U.S.A, 43-46. AAAS; Am. Soc. Microbiol; Brit. Soc. Gen. Microbiol; Sci. Res. Soc. Am. Microbial nutrition and physiology and medical microbiology. Address: 405 Culler Ave, Frederick, MD 21701.

GUSSEN, JOHN, b. Stockholm, Sweden, May 21, 19; nat; m. 49; c. 1. PSYCHIATRY. M.D, Columbia, 50. Intern med, N.Y. Hosp, med. center, Cornell, 50-51, res. psychiat, Payne Whitney Clinic, 51-54; asst. prof. psychiat. & neurol, sch. med, Oklahoma, 55-58; asst. clin. prof. PSYCHIAT, sch. med, California, 58-59, asst. prof, 59; assoc. clin. prof, SCH. MED, UNIV. SOUTH. CALIF, 59-67, CLIN. PROF, 67-; SR. RES. PSYCHIATRIST, SUICIDE PREV. CTR. & CLIN. DIR, AUTOMOBILE ACCIDENT PROJ, 68- Asst, med. col, Cornell, 52-54; dir, psychiat. consult. servs, med. center, Oklahoma, 55-57, psychiatrist & dir. psychiat. outpatient dept, 55-58; chief,

Day-Night Hosp, Langley Porter Neuropsychiat. Inst, San Francisco, Calif, 58-59; psychiatrist, Univ. California Hosps, 58-59; mem. attend. staff, Los Angeles County Hosp, 59-; dir, dept. psychiat. & psychiatrist attend. staff, Cedars of Lebanon Hosp, 59-65; admin. dir. div. psychiat. & dir. residency training prog, Cedars-Sinai Med. Ctr, 65-68, mem. psychiat. adv. comt. div. psychiat, 64-; consult, Mt. Sinai Hosp, 63-64, sr. attend, 64-; consult, student health serv, Okla. State, 55-58. Cand, South. Calif. Psychoanal. Inst, 61-70, mem. & assoc. instr, 70-, mem. comt. selection res. fel, 71-, comt. res. incomplete psychoanal. training, 71- Fel. Am. Geriatrics Soc; fel. Am. Psychiat. Asn; Am. Med. Asn. Psychoanalysis; social psychiatry and psychology; psychosomatic problems. Address: Century City Medical Plaza, 2080 Century Park E, Los Angeles, CA 90067.

GUSSIN, ARNOLD E. S, b. N.Y.C, Dec. 23, 35; m. 62; c. 2. COMPARATIVE BIOCHEMISTRY. B.S, Tulane Univ, La, 57, M.S, 59; Ph.D.(biol), Brown Univ, 63. Nat. Insts. Health fel. biol, Yale, 62-64; asst. prof. zool, Butler Univ, 64-66; BIOL. SCI, SMITH COL, 66-71, ASSOC. PROF, 71- Nat. Sci. Found. faculty fel, Albert Einstein Col. Med, 69-70. AAAS; Am. Soc. Zool. Am. Soc. Plant Physiol; Am. Soc. Biol. Chem. Lipid and carbohydrate metabolism of invertebrates; physiology and kinetics of trehalases. Address: Dept. of Biological Sciences, Clark Science Center, Smith College, Northampton, MA 01060.

GUSSIN, GARY N(ATHANIEL), b. Detroit, Mich, Aug. 7, 39. GENETICS, MOLECULAR BIOLOGY. B.S, Michigan, 61; Nat. Sci. found. fel, Harvard, 61-66, Ph.D.(biophys), 66. Nat. Sci. Found. fel, Stanford, 66-67; Geneva, 67-68; Am. Cancer Soc. fel, 68-69; ASST. PROF. ZOOL, UNIV. IOWA, 69- Amber mutations in bacteriophage R17; lysogeny of Escherichia coli by bacteriophage lambda. Address: Dept. of Zoology, University of Iowa, Iowa City, IA 52240.

GUSSIN, ROBERT Z, b. Pittsburgh, Pa, Jan. 5, 38; m. 62; c. 2. PHARMACOLOGY. B.S, Duquesne, 59, M.S, 61; U.S. Pub. Health Serv. fel, Michigan, 61-65, Ph.D.(pharmacol), 65. Teaching asst, sch. pharm, Duquesne, 59-61; U.S. Pub. Health Serv. fel, State Univ. N.Y. Upstate Med. Ctr, 65-67; SR. RES. PHARMACOLOGIST, LEDERLE LABS, 67- Heart Asn. Upstate N.Y. fel, 66-67; lectr, N.Y. Univ, 68-70. AAAS; Am. Soc. Nephrol; Am. Fedn. Clin. Res; Am. Soc. Pharmacol. & Exp. Therapeut. Drugs on renal transport mechanisms; evaluation of site and mechanism of action of diuretics; kidney disease; hypertension and antihypertensive drugs. Address: Cardiovascular-Renal Disease Therapy Section, Lederle Labs, Pearl River, NY 10965.

GUSSOW, W(ILLIAM) C(ARRUTHERS), b. London, Eng, Apr. 25, 08; Can. citizen; m. 36; c. 3. GEOLOGY. B.Sc, Queen's (Ont), 33, M.Sc, 35, Royal Soc. Can. fel, 36-37; Ph.D.(geol), Mass. Inst. Tech, 38. Instr. geol. mining, Royal Mil. Col, 38-39; engr, Found. Co, Can, 41-43; res. engr, Aluminum Co, 44; chief geologist, Shell Oil Co, 45-48, explor. mgr, 48-50, sr. geologist, 50-52; consult. geologist, 53-55; staff geologist, Union Oil Co, Calif, 56-60, sr. res. assoc, 60-71; CONSULT. GEOLOGIST, 71- Guest, Moscow State, 60. Fel. Geol. Soc. Am; Geochem. Soc; Soc. Econ. Geol; Am. Asn. Petrol. Geol; fel. Brit. Geol. Soc; fel. Royal Soc. Can; fel. Geol. Asn. Can; Can. Inst. Mining & Metall; Eng. Inst. Can. Petroleum geology; general and structural geology; cause and mechanics of mountain building, world-wide unconformities, continental drift. Address: Box 5255, Fullerton, CA 92632.

GUSTAFSON, A(LTON) H(ERMAN), b. Brockton, Mass, Sept. 16, 04; m. 29; c. 3. CYTOLOGY, ALGOLOGY. B.S, Mass. Agr. Col, 26; Williams Col. (Mass), 26-27; Austin fel, Harvard, 27-30, M.A, 28, Ph.D.(biol), 30. Asst. biol, Williams Col.(Mass), 26-27, instr. biol. & bot, 30-36, asst. prof, 36-43, assoc. prof, 43-45, prof, 45-46, acting dean, 44-46; PROF. BIOL, BOWDOIN COL, 46-, head dept, 46-70. Nat. Sci. Found. fel, 59-60. AAAS; Bot. Soc. Am; Am. Soc. Limnol. & Oceanog; Phycol. Soc. Am. Cytology-chromosome studies; taxonomy of higher plants; marine and fresh water algology; ecology. Address: Dept. of Biology, Bowdoin College, Brunswick, ME 04011.

GUSTAFSON, CARL G(USTAF), JR, b. Montclair, N.J, Apr. 27, 25; m. 51; c. 3. ORGANIC CHEMISTRY. B.S, King's Col, 48; Ph.D.(org. chem), Delaware, 57. Instr. chem, King's Col, 48-50; org. res. chemist, Chem. Corps med. labs, U.S. Army Chem. Center, Md, 52-53; asst. prof. CHEM, Roberts Wesleyan Col, 56-59; assoc. prof, KING'S COL.(N.Y), 59-63, PROF, 63-, CHMN. DIV. NATURAL SCI, 65-, acting dean, 60-62. Summers, org. chemist, Food Mach. & Chem. Corp, N.Y, 57-58; paper & ink div, Int. Bus. Mach. Corp, N.Y, 60; res. chemist, Union Carbide Corp, 63, 64; spec. faculty appointment with Fed. Water Qual. Admin, Southeast Water Lab, Athens, Ga, 69-70. Chem.C, 50-52, Res, 52-55. Am. Chem. Soc. Sulfonic esters of hexitols; organic insecticides; fiber composition of paper. Address: Division of Natural Science, King's College, Briarcliff Manor, NY 10510.

GUSTAFSON, DANIEL R(AY), b. Duluth, Minn, May 18, 37; m. 59; c. 1. PHYSICS. B.A, Minnesota, 59; Ph.D.(physics), Iowa State, 64. Asst. prof. PHYSICS, WAYNE STATE UNIV, 64-70, ASSOC. PROF, 70- Am. Phys. Soc. Angular correlation of positron annihilation radiation. Address: Dept. of Physics, Wayne State University, Detroit, MI 48202.

GUSTAFSON, DAVID H(AROLD), b. Ft. Wayne, Ind, Dec. 7, 35; m. 57; c. 1. ORGANIC CHEMISTRY. B.S, Purdue, 57; Ph.D.(org. chem), Illinois, 61. Res. chemist, Procter & Gamble Co, 61-64; SR. RES. CHEMIST, WM. S. MERRELL CO, 64- Am. Chem. Soc. Metallocenes and terpenoid syntheses; spectroscopy; physical organic chemistry. Address: William S. Merrell Co, 110 E. Amity Rd, Cincinnati, OH 45215.

GUSTAFSON, DAVID H(AROLD), b. Kane, Pa, Sept. 11, 40; m. 62; c. 3. INDUSTRIAL ENGINEERING, PREVENTIVE MEDICINE. B.S, Univ. Mich, 62, M.S, 63, Kellogg fel, 64, Horace Rackham fel, 65, Ph.D.(indust. eng), 66. Dir. hosp. div, Community Systs. Found, 63-64; asst. prof. mech. eng, UNIV. WIS, MADISON, 66-69, INDUST. ENG, 69-70, ASSOC. PROF, 70-, PREV. MED, 71- Consult. regional med. progs, Dept. Health, Educ. & Welfare, 68-71; Nat. Ctr. Health Serv. Res. & Develop, 68-; burn res. proj, Univ. Mich, 69-70; dept. med. care & hosps, Johns Hopkins Univ, 69-; Am. Hosp. Asn, 69-; Indian Health Serv, 70-; adv, Gov. Health Planning & Policy Task Force, 71-; dir, Med. Decision Making Proj. Opers. Res. Soc. Am. Applicability of behavioral decision theory and systems design to social systems; development, implementation and evaluation of computer based medical decision systems. Address: Dept. of Industrial Engineering, 449 Mechanical Engineering Bldg, University of Wisconsin, Madison, WI 53706.

GUSTAFSON, DONALD (PINK), b. Columbus, Ohio, May 21, 20; m. 49; c. 5. VETERINARY MEDICINE, MICROBIOLOGY. B.Sc, Ohio State, 41, D.V.M, 45; M.S, Purdue, 51, Ph.D.(vet. path), 53. Private practice, 45-46; instr. VET. SCI, PURDUE UNIV, 49-53, asst. prof, 53-56, assoc. prof, 56-61, PROF, 61- Consult, Commercial Solvents Corp, 57; Univ. Florida, 58; Eli Lilly & Co, 58-; mem. subcomt. standardized methods in vet. microbiol, Nat. Acad. Sci-Nat. Res. Coun, 67-; nat. trichinosis eradication comt, Livestock Conserv. Inc, 69-, chmn. swine dysentery comt, 71-; res. resources comt, Nat. Inst. Allergy & Infectious Diseases, 71-75. Dipl, Am. Col. Vet. Microbiol. Vet.C, 43-44, 46-48, Capt. AAAS; Am. Asn. Immunol; Am. Soc. Cell Biol; Am. Vet. Med. Asn; Animal Health Asn; Am. Soc. Microbiol; Tissue Cult. Asn; Conf. Res. Workers Animal Diseases. Infectious diseases of animals; hog cholera; scrapie in sheep; chronic equine diarrhea; myoclonia congenita in swine; pseudorabies. Address: School of Veterinary Science & Medicine, Purdue University, West Lafayette, IN 47906.

GUSTAFSON, DONALD A(RVID), b. Delano, Minn, Sept. 11, 13; m. 43. CHEMISTRY. B.S, Washington (Seattle), 37, Ph.D.(chem), 44. Asst. CHEM, Washington (Seattle), 37-44; instr, UNIV. IDAHO, 44-46, asst. prof, 46-48, assoc. prof, 48-65, PROF, 65- Am. Chem. Soc.(secy-treas, 46). Electrical conductance of nonaqueous solutions; electrical conductance of solutions with solvents from the system acetic anhydride-acetic acid-water. Address: Dept. of Chemistry, University of Idaho, Mascow, ID 83843.

GUSTAFSON, JOEL F(RANK), b. San Francisco, Calif, Apr. 4, 18; m. 40; c. 3. ENTOMOLOGY, ECOLOGY. A.B, San Jose State Col, 40; M.A, Stanford, 46, Ph.D.(biol), 48. Instr. biol, Orange Coast Col, 48-50; from asst. prof. to PROF. BIOL. SCI, SAN FRANCISCO STATE COL, 50-, assoc. dean, sch. natural sci, 68-70. Coop. ecol. res, State Dept. Fish & Game, Calif, 52-55; assoc. dir, Calif. Acad. Sci, 60-61; res. assoc, U.S. Navy Radiol. Defense Labs, 64-; consult. marine ecol. & pollution, U.S. Army Corps Engrs. & Standard Oil Co. Calif. U.S.N.R, 42-45, Lt. AAAS; Natural history of the West Coast; fresh water biology; conservation; insect morphology; radiation effects on insects. Address: Dept. of Biology, San Francisco State College, 1600 Holloway, San Francisco, CA 94132.

GUSTAFSON, JOHN A(LFRED), b. Boston, Mass, Mar. 31, 25; m. 51; c. 5. ORNITHOLOGY. A.B, Dartmouth Col, 48; Ph.D.(natural hist), Cornell, 54. Asst. prof. BIOL, State Univ. N.Y. Col. Brockport, 54-55; PROF, STATE UNIV. N.Y. COL. CORTLAND, 55-, CHMN. DEPT. BIOL. SCI, 65- Summers, instr, Children's Sch. Sci, Mass, 54, dir, N.Y, 55-56; Nat. Sci. Found. Inst. Marine Biol, Coos Bay, Ore, 62; v.chmn, East. Susquehanna Water Resources Planning Bd, 67-; mem, N.Y. State Comn. Youth Educ. in Conserv, 1969- U.S.M.C, 43-46, 51-53, Res, 53-70, Lt. Col.(Ret). AAAS; Bot. Soc. Am; Wildlife Soc; Am. Nature Study Soc.(pres. elect, 62, pres, 63, treas, 64-). Environmental education; migratory bird population studies, involving banding, recovery and nest studies. Address: Dept. of Biological Sciences, State University of New York College at Cortland, Cortland, NY 13045.

GUSTAFSON, J(OHN) K(YLE), b. Chicago, Ill, Mar. 13, 06; m; c. 3. GEOLOGY. A.B, Washington (St. Louis), 27; A.M, Harvard, 28, Austin fel, 28-29, Ph.D.(geol), 30; hon. D.Sc, Mich. Col. Min. & Tech, 63. Instr. mineral, Harvard, 29-30; geologist, Hollinger Consol. Gold Mines, Ltd, Ont, 30-34, 39-42; West. Mining Corp, Ltd. & Gold Mines of Kalgoorlie, Ltd, Australia, 34-36; geologist in charge, Cent. Geol. Surv, New South Wales, 36-39; adv, Metals Reserve Co, Wash, D.C, 42-44; geologist, Magma Copper Co. & Newmont Mining Corp, 44-49; consult. geologist, M.A. Hanna Co, 50-56, dir. explor, 56-60; v.pres, Hanna Mining Co, 53-60; pres, HOMESTAKE MINING CO, 61-70, CHMN. BD, 70-, chief. exec. off, 62-71. Geologist in charge Toronto off, Hollinger Explor. Co, Ltd. & leader exped, Labrador, 42; dir. raw mat, Atomic Energy Comn, 47-48, mgr. raw mat. opers, 48-49, mem. adv. comt. raw mat, 50-59; trustee, Wash. Univ, 62-71; United Calif. Bank, San Francisco, 64-; Pac. Indemnity, 70- Hugh Exton McKinstry Mem. lectr, Harvard, 65. Summers, rodman, U.S. Geol. Surv, 28, geologist, Homestake Mining Co, 29. Consult, Zinc Corp, Ltd. & New Broken Hill Consol, Ltd, Australia, 47. Mem. comt. minerals res, Nat. Sci. Found, 52-59; Am. Geol. Inst; adv. coun. inst. geophys. & planetary physics, Univ. Calif, 61-68. Alumni citation, Wash. Univ, 60; Daniel C. Jackling Award, 71. Fel. Am. Geol. Soc; Soc. Econ. Geol.(v.pres, 61, pres, 66); Geochem. Soc; Mining & Metall. Soc. Am; Am. Inst. Mining, Metall. & Petrol. Eng; Can. Inst. Mining & Metall. Ore deposits; structural and mining geology. Address: Homestake Mining Co, 650 California St, 9th Floor, San Francisco, CA 94108.

GUSTAFSON, KARL EDWIN, b. Manchester, Iowa, May 7, 35; m. 61; c. 1. MATHEMATICS. B.S.(eng) & B.S.(bus), Univ. Colo, 58; Ph.D.(math), Univ. Md, 65. Instr. appl. math, Univ. Colo, 58-60; physicist, Naval Res. Lab, 60-61, mathematician, 61-63; Nat. Sci. Found-NATO fel. MATH, Inst. Battelle, Geneva & Univ. Rome, 65-66; asst. prof, Univ. Minn, 66-68; ASSOC. PROF, UNIV. COLO, BOULDER, 68-, faculty fel, 71-72. Prin. investr, Nat. Sci. Found. summer res. grants, 68-; vis. scientist, Inst. Battelle, Geneva, 67; vis. prof, Fed. Polytech. Sch, Lausanne, Switz, 71-72. U.S.A.R, 60-68. Am. Math. Soc. Computer applications for naval intelligence problems; partial differential equations; functional analysis; operator theory; mathematical physics; nonlinear problems. Address: Dept. of Mathematics, University of Colorado, Boulder, CO 80302.

GUSTAFSON, PHILIP F(ELIX), b. Ann Arbor, Mich, Apr. 2, 24; m. 49; c. 2. RADIOLOGICAL PHYSICS. B.S, Michigan, 49, M.S, Ill. Inst. Tech, 54, Ph.D.(physics), 58. Res. technician physics, Argonne Nat. Lab, 49-52, asst. physics, 52-59, assoc. physicist, 59-66; nuclear fallout specialist, U.S. Atomic Energy Comn, 66-68; ASSOC. DIR. RADIOL. PHYSICS DIV, ARGONNE NAT. LAB, 68- Consult, U.S. Pub. Health Serv, Ohio. U.S. Merchant Marine, 44-46. AAAS; Sci. Res. Soc. Am; N.Y. Acad. Sci. Environmental radiation; low level gamma ray spectrometry; measurement of radioactivity on the upper atmosphere; dosimetry; fallout distribution; radioecology. Address: Argonne National Lab, 9700 S. Cass Ave, Argonne, IL 60439.

GUSTAFSON, WILLIAM C(HARLES), b. Chicago, Ill, Aug. 28, 37. CIVIL ENGINEERING, STRUCTURAL MECHANICS. B.S, Ill. Inst. Technol, 59; univ. fel. & M.S, Univ. Ill, Urbana, 60, Nat. Sci. Found. fel. & Ph.D.(civil eng), 66. Assoc. res. engr, Boeing Co, 60-63; asst. prof. civil eng, Univ. Ill, Urbana, 66-69; RES. ENGR, AEROSPACE GROUP, BOEING CO, 69- Am. Soc. Civil Eng. Analysis of plant and shell structures; numerical techniques for elastic plastic analysis of three dimensional solids; behavior and design of metal structures. Address: 10459 Des Moines Way S, Apt. 406, Seattle, WA 98168.

GUSTAFSON, WILLIAM R, b. Hartford, Conn, July 16, 41; m. 63; c. 3. CHEMICAL ENGINEERING. B.S.E, Connecticut, 63; Ph.D.(chem. eng), Rensselaer Polytech, 67. RES. ENGR, AM. CYANAMID CO, 67- Am. Inst. Chem. Eng; Am. Chem. Soc; Catalysis Soc. Reaction kinetics and heterogeneous catalysis, particularly catalysis performance and metal-support interactions in catalysis. Address: 2 Pocono Rd, Norwalk, CT 06851.

GUSTAFSON, WINTHROP A(DOLPH), b. Moline, Ill, Oct. 14, 28; m. 57; c. 3. AERONAUTICAL ENGINEERING. B.S, Illinois, 50, M.S, 54, Ph.D.(aeronaut. eng), 56. Assoc. res. scientist, missiles & space div, Lockheed Aircraft Corp, Calif, 56-60; assoc. prof. AERONAUT. & ENG. SCI, PURDUE UNIV, 60-66, PROF, 66- Consult, Goodyear Aerospace Corp, Ohio, 64; vis. prof, Univ. Calif, San Diego, 68. U.S.A.F, 51-53. Am. Inst. Aeronaut. & Astronaut. Aerodynamics; rarefied gas dynamics; biomedical fluid mechanics. Address: 209 Lindberg Ave, West Lafayette, IN 47906.

GUSTARD, BRIAN, b. Upminster, Eng, Dec. 13, 37; m. 62. PHYSICS. B.Sc, Brunel, 60; Ph.D.(magnetism), London, 64. Res. physicist, Franklin Inst. Res. Labs, 64-66, sr. res. physicist, 66-69; SR. PHYSICIST, MAGNETIC TAPE LAB,(22-01); AMPEX CORP, 69- Magnetic oxides; magnetic recording materials; single domain magnetic particles; magnetic transitions; transmission and scanning electron microscopy; x-ray crystallography; magnetic domains. Address: Magnetic Tape Lab.(22-01), Ampex Corp, 401 Broadway, Redwood City, CA 94063.

GUSTAVSON, DONALD ROY, b. Chicago, Ill, Nov. 24, 20; m. 42; c. 6. MECHANICAL ENGINEERING. B.S, Northwestern, 46; M.B.A, Washington (Seattle), 63. From develop. engr. to MGR. PROJ, chem. processing dept, Gen. Elec. Co, 48-65; Isochem. Inc, 65-67, ATLANTIC RICHFIELD CO, 67- U.S.N.R, 41-45, 47-48, Capt. Am. Inst. Chem. Eng; Am. Soc. Naval Eng. Engineering and general management; industrial corporations. Address: 1726 Davison Ave, Richland, WA 99352.

GUSTAVSON, M(ARVIN) R(ONALD), b. Chicago, Ill, Nov. 4, 27; m. 53; c. 2. PHYSICAL CHEMISTRY. B.S, Carnegie Inst. Tech, 48; Ph.D.(phys. chem), Cornell, 53. Chemist, Shell Develop. Co, 53-57; div. mgr, Aerojet-Gen. Nucleonics Div, Gen. Tire & Rubber Co, 57-60; v.pres. & gen. mgr, Ordtech Corp, 60-61; DIR. X DIV, LAWRENCE LIVERMORE LAB, 61- Spec. lectr, univ. & exten. California, 54-58; consult, govt. & indust. orgns, 60- Am. Chem. Soc. Reaction kinetics; petrochemistry; nuclear reactor design and application; radiation chemistry; nuclear and non-nuclear weapon system design and evaluation; command and control; research organization and administration. Address: P.O. Box 808, Lawrence Livermore Lab, Livermore, CA 94550.

GUSTAVSON, R(EUBEN) G(ILBERT), b. Denver, Colo, Apr. 6, 92; m. 18; c. 2. CHEMISTRY. A.B, Denver, 16, A.M, 17, hon. L.H.D, 44; Ph.D.(biochem), Chicago, 25; hon. D.Sc, Regis Col.(Colo), 37, Millikin, 46, Florida, 50, Ripon Col, 51, Knox Col.(Ill). & Colorado, 61, Colorado State, 62; hon. L.D.H, Nebraska, 53, H.H.D; hon. L.D.H, Nat. Col. Ed, 61; hon. LL.D, Colo. Col, 46, Doane Col, 50, Creighton, Maine & Pittsburgh, 53; hon. Lit.D, Cedar Crest Col, 58; L.L.D, Univ. N.Mex, 70. Instr. chem, Colo. Agr. Col, 17-18, asst. prof, 18-19, assoc. prof, 19-20; asst. prof, Denver, 20-21, assoc. prof, 21-27, prof, 27-37; Colorado, 37-43, dean, grad. sch, 42-43, pres, 43-45, v.pres. & dean faculties, Chicago, 45-46; chancellor, Nebraska, 46-53; pres. & exec. dir, Resources for the Future, D.C, 53-59; prof. CHEM. & adv. TV for sci. educ, UNIV. ARIZ, 59-70, EMER. PROF. & ADV. TO PRES, 70- Vis. prof, Univ. Chicago, 29; chmn. bd, Resources for the Future; consult, prog. econ. develop. admin, Ford Found; Am. Med. Ctr, Denver, Colo. Am. Chem. Soc; Royal Swedish Acad. Eng. Sci. Biochemistry. Address: Administration Bldg, University of Arizona, Tucson, AZ 85721.

GUSTIN, VAUGHN K(ENNETH), b. Mansfield, Ohio, June 10, 36; m. 57; c. 2. ANALYTICAL CHEMISTRY. B.Sc, Ohio State, 58, M.Sc, 60, Ph.D.(anal. chem), 63. Teaching asst, Ohio State, 58-63; sr. anal. chemist, CORNING GLASS WORKS, 63-64, supvr. anal. lab, 65-66, mgr. chem. serv. dept, 66-70, MGR, CONTROL TECHNOL, 70- Partic, prog. for mgt. develop, Harvard Bus. Sch, 68. Am. Chem. Soc; Soc. Appl. Spectros.(secy, 66); fel. Am. Inst. Chem. Chemical composition control of glasses, glass ceramics and associated raw materials and refractories; analytical method development in all phases of analytical chemistry; pollution control. Address: Corning Glass Works, Corning, NY 14830.

GUSTIN, WILLIAM, b. Detroit, Mich, Jan. 19, 18; m. 42; c. 2. MATHEMATICS. A.B, California, Los Angeles, 40, Nat. Res. Coun. fel, 46-47, Ph.D. (math), 47. Instr. meteorol, California, Los Angeles, 42-45; asst. prof. MATH, IND. UNIV, BLOOMINGTON, 47-51, ASSOC. PROF, 51- Math. Asn. Am. Set theory; harmonic functions; convexity. Address: Dept. of Mathematics, Indiana University, Bloomington, IN 47401.

GUSTISON, ROBERT A(BDON), b. Springfield, Ohio, Aug. 29, 20; m. 43; c. 3. INORGANIC CHEMISTRY. B.S, Chicago, 42. Res. chemist, metall. lab, Univ. Chicago, 42-44; res. engr, Int. Minerals & Chem. Co, 44-46; res. chemist & engr, Union Carbide Chem. Co. Div, Union Carbide Corp, 46-54, mgr. minerals & chem. eng. res, Union Carbide Metals Co. Div, 54-61, supvr. pilot plants, 61-63; MGR. CHEM. PROCESSING, KAWECKI BERYLCO INDUSTS, INC, 64- Mem. mat. adv. bd, Nat. Acad. Sci. Am. Chem. Soc; Am. Inst.Min, Metall. & Petrol. Eng; fel. Am. Inst. Chem. Extractive metallurgy involving pyrometallurgy; electrometallurgy; halogenations; high pressure and vacuum; mass transfer operations. Address: Kawecki Berylco Industries, Inc, Boyertown, PA 19512.

GUSTUS, EDWIN L(YSLE), b. Moline, Ill, July 27, 00; m. 34. ORGANIC CHEMISTRY. A.B, Stanford, 21; M.Sc, Northwestern, 23, fel, 23-25, Ph.D. (org. chem), 26. Asst. biochem, med. sch, Northwestern, 21-23; asst, Rockefeller Inst, 26-28, assoc, 28-30, res. worker endocrinol, 32-33; Int. Ed. Bd. fel, Swiss Fed. Inst. Tech, Zurich, 30-31; res. assoc. chem, Pa. State, 31-32; biochemist, Upjohn Co, Mich, 33-36; asst. to gen. mgr, Wilson labs, Wilson & Co, Ill, 36-43; res. dir, res. & develop. br, mil. planning div, Office QM Gen, Wash, D.C, 43-46; mem. footwear & leather comt, comt. qm. res. & develop, Nat. Res. Coun, 46-50, chmn, foot protection comt, 51-65; res. assoc. chem, Northwest, 60-70, res. counselor, 55-70; RETIRED. V.pres, Bjorksten Res. Labs, 46-55. Am. Chem. Soc; Am. Soc. Bio. Chem; Soc. Exp. Biol. & Med. Chemical structure of natural products; synthetic organic chemistry; chemistry of biological processes. Address: 5759 Kenwood Ave, Chicago, IL 60637.

GUT, MARCEL, b. Zurich, Switz, Jan. 15, 22; nat; m. 53; c. 2. ORGANIC CHEMISTRY. Fel. & Dr. Phil, Basel, Switz, 47. SR. SCIENTIST, WORCESTER FOUND. EXP. BIOL, 48- Am. Chem. Soc. Carbohydrates; steroids. Address: 31 Creswell Rd, Worcester, MA 01602.

GUTBERLET, L(OUIS) C(HARLES), b. Chicago, Ill, Mar. 29, 28; m. 52; c. 2. ORGANIC CHEMISTRY. B.S, Ill. Inst. Tech, 50; M.S, Purdue, 54. Asst. chem, Purdue, 52-54; CHEMIST RES, AM. OIL CO, 54- Chem.C, 50-52, Res, 52-57, Sgt. Am. Chem. Soc. Catalytic hydrogenation; heterogeneous catalysis; hydrocarbon conversion processes. Address: Research Dept, American Oil Co, Box 431, Whiting, IN 46394.

GUTBEZAHL, BORIS, b. Tientsin, China, May 1, 27; U.S. citizen; m. 52; c. 2. PHYSICAL CHEMISTRY. B.S, City Col. New York, 47; A.M, Columbia, 49; Atomic Energy Comn. fel, Fla. State, 51-52, Ph.D.(chem), 52. Asst. chem, Columbia, 52-53; chemist, ROHM AND HAAS CO, 53-59, head process develop. lab, 59-60, plastics color lab, 60-65, SUPVR. TECH. SERV, 65- U.S.A, 46. Am. Chem. Soc; Soc. Plastics Eng; Inter-Soc. Color Coun. Organic mechanisms; polymerization kinetics; product and process development in plastics. Address: Rohm and Haas Co, P.O. Box 219, Bristol, PA 19007.

GUTCHO, SIDNEY J(ACK), b. Brooklyn, N.Y, Oct. 18, 19; m. 49; c. 2. BIOCHEMISTRY. B.A, N.Y. Univ, 40, M.S, 41. Res. chemist, Schwarz Labs, Inc, 41-59, HEAD CHEMIST, Schwarz Biores, Inc, 59-70, SCHWARZ/MANN, BECTON-DICKINSON & CO, 70- Abstractor, Chem. Abstr, 52- U.S.A, 43-46. AAAS; Am. Chem. Soc; N.Y. Acad. Sci. Immunochemistry; radioimmunoassays; isolation of biochemicals from yeast; enzymatic preparation of biochemicals; biosynthesis of radioactive compounds; chemistry of nucleic acids and their derivatives. Address: 22 Francis Pl, Monsey, NY 10952.

GUTEKUNST, RICHARD R(ALPH), b. Allentown, Pa, Jan. 20, 26; m. 46; c. 3. MICROBIOLOGY. B.Sc, Phila. Col. Pharm, 51; M.Sc, Cornell, 57, Ph.D. (virol), 58. Instr. bact, Naval Med. Sch, U.S. Navy, 51-52, bact. warfare res, Ft. Detrick, 52-55, researcher respiratory viruses, med. res. unit-4, 58-60, head tissue culture lab, med. res. unit-3, Egypt, 60-63, researcher genus Mycoplasma, Naval Med. Res. Inst, 63-64, dir. virol. div, med. field res. lab, Camp Lejeune, 64-68; ASSOC. PROF. MICROBIOL. & DIR. CLIN. MICROBIOL. LAB, HAHNEMANN MED. COL. & HOSP, 68- U.S.N, 43-51, Med.Serv.C, 51-68, Comdr.(Ret); commendation medal, 68. AAAS; Am. Soc. Microbiol; Am. Pub. Health Asn; N.Y. Acad. Sci; Am. Acad. Microbiol. Bacteriology; virology; respiratory and picorna viruses; adenoviruses; myroviruses; special study to isolate the virus of rubella; diagnostic microbiology; diagnostic virology, serology. Address: Dept. of Microbiology, Hahnemann Medical College, Philadelphia, PA 19102.

GUTELIUS, JOHN ROBERT, b. Montreal, Que, Jan. 18, 29; m. 55; c. 8. SURGERY. B.A, Univ. Montreal, 50; M.D, McGill Univ, 55. Rotating intern, Royal Victoria Hosp, 55-56; asst. resident surgeon, teaching hosps, McGill Univ, 56-57, fel. exp. surg, univ, 57-58, asst. resident surgeon, hosps, 58-59; fel. surg, Johns Hopkins Univ. & Hosp, 59-60; chief resident surgeon, teaching hosps, McGill Univ, 60-61, demonstr. surg, univ, 61-63, asst. prof, 63-65, assoc. prof, 65-69, assoc. dean postgrad. studies & res, 68-69; PROF. SURG. & HEAD DEPT. & DEAN SCH. MED, UNIV. SASK, 70- Travelling fel, R. Samuel McLaughlin Found, 59-60; asst. surgeon, Royal Victoria Hosp, 63-64, assoc. surgeon, 65-69; John & Mary R. Markle Found, 63-68; mem, grants comt. clin. invest, Med. Res. Coun. Can, 70-; comt. gen. surg. & exam-gen. surg, Royal Col. Physicians & Surgeons, 70- Asn. Can. Med. Col; Can. Med. Asn; Int. Cardiovasc. Soc; Can. Soc. Clin. Invest; Am. Col. Surg; Soc. Vascular Surg; Soc. Univ. Surg; Can. Asn. Clin. Surg; Asn. Acad. Surg. Vascular surgery; techniques; patient selection; water and electrolytes; adrenal function. Address: Dept. of Surgery, University of Saskatchewan School of Medicine, Saskatoon, Sask, Can.

GUTELIUS, MARGARET F(RANCES), b. Corning, Iowa, Oct. 20, 07; m. 39; c. 2. MEDICINE. B.A, Col. of Wooster, 29; M.D, Columbia, 38. Asst. PEDIAT, sch. med, Tulane, 44-46; from instr. to clin. asst. prof. sch. med, La. State, 49-53; asst. prof, SCH. MED, GEORGE WASHINGTON UNIV, 52-64, assoc. clin. prof, 64-66, ASSOC. PROF, 66-; DIR. CHILD HEALTH CTR, CHILDREN'S HOSP, D.C, 66-, dir. child welfare clins, 64-66. Growth and development; nutrition. Address: 2950 Macomb St. N.W, Washington, DC 20008.

GUTERMAN, MARTIN MAYR, b. N.Y.C, Nov. 18, 41; m. 64. MATHEMATICS. B.S, Brooklyn Col, 61; M.S, Cornell Univ, 64, Ph.D.(finite groups), 68. Asst, Cornell Univ, 61-66; instr. MATH, TUFTS UNIV, 66-68, ASST. PROF, 68- Am. Math. Soc; Math. Asn. Am. Group theory. Address: Dept. of Mathematics, Tufts University, Medford, MA 02155.

GUTH, EARL P, b. Peoria, Ill, Dec. 2, 04; m. 29; c. 1. PHARMACEUTICAL CHEMISTRY. Ph.C, Washington (Seattle), 29, B.S, 30, M.S, 31, Ph.D. (pharm), 37. Pharmaceut. chemist, Blaumauer Frank Wholesale Drug Co, 32-35; instr. pharmaceut. chem, Duquesne, 37-40; asst. prof. PHARM, OHIO STATE UNIV, 40-42, assoc. prof, 42-44, prof, 44-70; EMER. PROF, 70- AAAS; Am. Pharmaceut. Asn. Freeze drying of plant drug; bentonites; hydrogen peroxide production by zinc oxide; drug formulation. Address: 2510 Pinellas Point Dr. S, St. Petersburg, FL 33712.

GUTH, EGBERT K(ARL) A(NTON), b. Ludwigshafen, Ger, Apr. 1, 29; U.S. citizen; m. 61. INORGANIC & PHYSICAL CHEMISTRY. Dr.rer.nat.(inorg. chem), Heidelberg, 61. Chemist, Brown, Boveri & Cie, Switz, 61-65; sr. chemist, Allis-Chalmers Mfg. Co, Wis, 65-70; CHEMIST, NEU-ISENBURG RES. & DEVELOP. DEPT, E.I. DU PONT DE NEMOURS & CO, INC, W.GER, 70- Am. Chem. Soc. Electrochemistry; catalysis, especially related to energy conversion, like fuel cells. Address: D-6116 Eppertshausen, Friedrich Ebert Str. 11, Neu-Isenburg, W. Germany.

GUTH, E(UGENE), b. Budapest, Hungary, Aug. 21, 05; nat; m. 47; c. 4. PHYSICS. Ph.D.(theoret. physics), Vienna, 28. Res. assoc. physics, Vienna, 28-30, 31-37; Austrian-German Sci. Found. res. assoc, Inst. Tech, Zurich & Leipzig, 30-31; instr. physics, Notre Dame, 37-40, asst. prof, 40-43, prof, 43-45, res. prof, 45-55; CHIEF PHYSICIST, OAK RIDGE NAT. LAB, 56- Dir. polymer physics lab, Notre Dame, 41-56, off. rubber res. proj, 43-44, off. naval res. proj, 46-58. Am. Nuclear Soc; fel. Am. Phys. Soc; Soc. Rheol.(Bingham medal, 65). Physics of polymers; nuclear physics; theory of metals; hydrodynamic theory of viscosity of suspensions; history of physics, particularly quantum theory; theory of elementary particles. Address: Oak Ridge National Lab, Oak Ridge, TN 37831.

GUTH, E(UGENE) D(ANIEL), b. Peoria, Ill, Feb. 26, 28; m. 50; c. 3. PHYSICAL CHEMISTRY. B.S, Bradley, 50; Atomic Energy Comn. fel, Iowa, 52-54, Ph.D.(phys. chem), 54. Res. chemist, Phillips Petrol. Co, 54-62; mem. tech. staff, TRW INC, 62-64, propellant chem. sect, 64-70, MGR. CHEM. ENG. DEPT, CHEM. & CHEM. ENG. LAB, 70- U.S.A, 46-47. Chemical reactions in systems in the presence of high energy. Address: Chemical Engineering Dept, Chemistry & Chemical Engineering Lab, TRW Inc, Bldg. D-1, Room 2030, One Space Park, Redondo Beach, CA 90277.

GUTH, L(LOYD), b. New York, N.Y, Oct. 8, 29; m. 55; c. 2. NEUROANATOMY. B.A, N.Y. Univ, 49, M.D, 53. Asst. anat, col. med, N.Y. Univ, 50-51; Jackson Mem. Lab, 51; intern, Kings County Hosp, 53-54; NEUROANATOMIST, LAB. NEUROANAT. SCI, NAT. INSTS. HEALTH, 54-, HEAD SECT. EXP. NEUROL, 61- U.S.P.H.S, Sr. Surg. AAAS; Am. Asn. Anat; Am. Physiol. Soc. Experimental neurology; nerve regeneration; neuromuscular interrelationships, structure, function and chemistry. Address: Laboratory of Neuroanatomical Sciences, National Institutes of Health, Bethesda, MD 20014.

GUTH, PAUL HENRY, b. New York, N.Y, Mar. 15, 27; m. 53; c. 4. INTERNAL MEDICINE, GASTROENTEROLOGY. B.S, N.Y. Univ, 48; M.D, Howard, 49. Res. internal med, Kings County Hosp, 50-51; res. fel. gastrointestinal physiol, Fels. Res. Inst, Temple, 51-52, Am. Gastroenterol. Asn. res. fel, 54-55, res. internal med, univ. hosp, 55-56, gastroenterol, 56-57, chief gastroenterol, Orange County Gen. Hosp, 57-69, dir. med. serv, Med. Ctr, 67-69; ASSOC. PROF. IN RESIDENCE MED, SCH. MED, UNIV. CALIF, LOS ANGELES, 69- Asst. clin. prof, Univ. Calif-Calif. Col. Med, 66-67, assoc. clin. prof, 67-69; assoc. chief gastroenterol, Wadsworth Vet. Hosp, Los Angeles, 69- Dipl, Am. Bd. Internal Med, 61; Am. Bd. Gastroenterol, 65. Med.C, U.S.A, 52-54, 1st Lt. Am. Med. Asn; Am. Fedn. Clin. Res; fel. Am. Col. Physicians; Am. Gastroenterol. Asn; Am. Physiol. Soc. Gastrointestinal physiology; pathophysiology; therapeutics. Address: Gastroenterology Section, Wadsworth Veterans Administration Hospital, Los Angeles, CA 90073.

GUTH, PAUL S(PENCER), b. May 29, 31; U.S. citizen; m. 53; c. 4. PHARMACOLOGY. B.Sc, Fordham, 53; M.Sc, Phila. Col. Pharm, 55; Ph.D.(pharmacol), Hahnemann Med. Col, 58. Fel. Nat. Paraplegia Found. & vis. researcher PHARMACOL, Inst. Animal Physiol, Babraham, 58-59; assoc, Hahnemann Med. Col, 59-60; asst. prof, SCH. MED, TULANE UNIV, LA, 60-63, assoc. prof, 63-66, PROF, 66- Consult, Atlas Pharmaceut. Co. AAAS; Am. Soc. Pharmacol. & Exp. Therapeut; N.Y. Acad. Sci. Biochemical aspects of neuropharmacology; auditory pharmacology; acetylcholine storage and release. Address: Dept. of Pharmacology, Tulane University of Louisiana School of Medicine, 1430 Tulane Ave, New Orleans, LA 70112.

GUTH, SHERMAN LEON, b. New York, N.Y, Dec. 9, 32; m. 55, 69; c. 2. PSYCHOLOGY. B.S, Purdue, 59; M.A, Illinois, 61, Ph.D.(psychol), 63. Lectr. PSYCHOL, IND. UNIV, BLOOMINGTON, 62-63, instr, 63-64, asst. prof, 64-67, assoc. prof, 67-70, PROF, 70- Grants, Nat. Sci. Found, 63-71 & Nat. Insts. Health, 64-71; Nat. Insts. Health spec. res. fel, Univ. Calif, Berkeley, 71-72. U.S.A, 54-56. AAAS; Am. Psychol. Asn; Optical Soc. Am; Asn. Res. Vision & Ophthal. Vision; animal behavior. Address: Dept. of Psychology, Indiana University, Bloomington, IN 47401.

GUTH, SYLVESTER K(ARL), b. Milwaukee, Wis, Dec. 31, 08; m. 31. PHYSICS. B.S, Univ. Wis, 30, E.E, 50; hon. D.O.S, North. Ill. Col. Optom, 53. Res. physicist, lighting res. lab, GEN. ELEC. CO, 30-41, physicist, 46-49, head lighting res, 50-54, mgr. radiant energy effects lab, 55-68, MGR. APPL. RES, LARGE LAMP DEPT, 69- Lectr, Case Inst. Technol, 50-67; del, Int. Comn. Illum, Stockholm, 51, Zurich, 55, Brussels, 59, Vienna, 63; Wash, 67, Barcelona, 71, v.pres. comn. & chmn. activities comt, 71- C.Eng, 41-45, Maj. AAAS; fel. Illum. Eng. Soc.(gold medal, 67); Optical Soc. Am; Asn. Res. Vision & Ophthal; fel. Am. Acad. Optom. Light; vision; seeing; color; radiant energy; physical, psychological and physiological aspects of light and lighting. Address: Large Lamp Dept, General Electric Co, Nela Park, East Cleveland, OH 44112.

GUTHE, KARL F(REDERICK), b. Detroit, Mich, Aug. 3, 18; m. 46; c. 3. BIOLOGY. A.B, Harvard, 39, A.M, 40, fel, 40-41, 47-49, Ph.D.(biol), 51. Physicist, Naval Ord. Dept, 41-45; tutor biochem. sci, Harvard, 49-50; instr. ZOOL, UNIV. MICH, 50-54, asst. prof, 54-59, assoc. prof, 59-62, PROF, 62- AAAS; Biophys. Soc; Soc. Gen. Physiol. Chemistry of hemoglobin and myosin. Address: Dept. of Zoology, University of Michigan, Ann Arbor, MI 48104.

GUTHMANN, W(ALTER) S(IGMUND), b. Chicago, Ill, Apr. 3, 07; m. 40; c. 2. CHEMISTRY. B.S, Yale, 28; Ph.D.(chem), Chicago, 32. Res. chemist, Int. Filter Co, Ill, 31; chemist, Puritan Mills, 31-32; Elmer Richards Co, 32; pres. & gen. sales mgr, Edwal Labs, Inc, 32-53, pres, Ringwood Chem. Corp, 53-61; assoc. prof. CHEM, ROOSEVELT UNIV, 61-65, PROF, 65- Dir, Ventron Corp. C.W.S, 42-45, Maj. Am. Chem. Soc.(ed, Chem. Bul, 46-47); Fel. Am. Inst. Chem. Metal-organic compounds; synthetic organic processes; molecular rearrangements; detergents; egg products; paints; new organic compounds; chemical economics. Address: Dept. of Chemistry, Roosevelt University, 430 S. Michigan Ave, Chicago, IL 60605.

GUTHRIE, ALBERT N(ELSON), b. Carlsbad, N.Mex, Sept. 10, 03; m. 29; c. 1. PHYSICS. B.S, Arizona, 26; M.S, Illinois, 28, Ph.D.(physics), 30. Asst. PHYSICS, Illinois, 26-29; instr, Columbia, 30-36; assoc. prof, R.I. State Col, 36-42, prof, 42-43, chmn. dept, 36-43; asst. prof, BROOKLYN COL, 43-49, assoc. prof, 50-56, prof. & chmn. dept, 56-69, EMER. PROF, 69-; INTERMITTENT EXPERT, ACOUST. DIV, NAVAL RES. LAB, 69- Admin. dir, sonar anal. group, div. war res, Columbia, 45-46, Hudson Labs, 52-69, dir, 54-56. AAAS; Am. Phys. Soc; Acoust. Soc. Am. Magnetic properties of non-ferromagnetic materials; molecular beams; underwater acoustics. Address: Code 8176, Acoustics Division, Naval Research Lab, Washington, DC 20390.

GUTHRIE, ANDREW, b. Ladysmith, B.C, Can, July 22, 15; nat; m. 48; c. 1. PHYSICS. B.A, British Columbia, 34; M.S, Purdue, 39, Ph.D.(physics), 41. Instr, pub. sch, B.C, Can, 35-37; asst. eng. physics, Purdue, 37-41, instr. physics, 41-42; assoc. physicist, radiation lab, California, 42-46, consult, Manhattan dist. proj, 46-47; assoc. prof. physics, San Jose State Col, 48-50; head, nucleonics div, U.S. Naval Radiol. Defense Lab, 50-60; PROF. PHYSICS, CALIF. STATE COL. HAYWARD, 60-, chmn. dept, 63-69. AAAS; fel. Am. Phys. Soc; Am. Asn. Physics Teachers; Am. Vacuum Soc.(v.pres, 56, pres, 57); Int. Orgn. Vacuum Sci. & Tech. Electron, surface and nuclear physics; ultra-high vacuum science; excitation states of various gases and vapors using ultra-high vacuum equipment and techniques. Address: Dept. of Physics, California State College, Hayward, CA 94542.

GUTHRIE, CHARLES E(DMUND), b. Detroit, Mich, Mar. 3, 26; m. 53; c. 3. CHEMICAL & NUCLEAR ENGINEERING. B.S, Michigan, 48, M.S, 49; Oak Ridge Sch. Reactor Tech, 57-58. Process design engr, res. & develop. dept, Atlantic Ref. Co, 49-56; long range planner, chem. tech. div, Oak Ridge Nat. Lab, 56-67; fel. engr, nuclear fuel div, Westinghouse Elec. Corp, 67-69; SR. ENGR, S.M. STOLLER CORP, 69- Am. Inst. Chem. Eng; Am. Nuclear Soc; Am. Chem. Soc. Petroleum production; refinery and chemical plant design; nuclear fuel reprocessing design and economics; long range planning; nuclear safety. Address: S.M. Stoller Corp, 1250 Broadway, New York, NY 10001.

GUTHRIE, DANIEL ALBERT, b. Ind, Mar. 5, 39; m. 60; c. 3. VERTEBRATE ZOOLOGY. B.A, Amherst Col, 60; M.A, Harvard, 62; Ph.D.(biol), Massachusetts, 64. Asst. prof. BIOL, PITZER COL, SCRIPPS COL. & CLAREMONT MEN'S COL, 64-69, ASSOC. PROF, 69- AAAS; Soc. Study Evolution; Soc. Vert. Paleont; Am. Soc. Mammal; Am. Soc. Zool. Lower Eocene mammals; carotid arteries in mammals; mammalian paleontology; evolutionary rates; environmental studies. Address: Dept. of Joint Sciences, Claremont Men's College, Claremont, CA 91711.

GUTHRIE, DAVID B(URRELL), b. Long Beach, Calif, Feb. 10, 20; m. 51; c. 3. ORGANIC CHEMISTRY. A.B, Westminster Col, 41; Ph.D, Illinois, 45. Res. chemist, Monsanto Chem. Co, 46-59; asst. chief chemist, Lucidol Div, Wallace & Tiernan, Inc, N.Y, 59-61, supvr. & group leader, 61-63; GROUP LEADER new prod. res, PETROLITE CORP, 63-64, HYDROCARBON ADDITIVES & CORROSION RES, 64- Am. Chem. Soc. Organic peroxides; chemistry of petroleum products; synthetic organic and surfactant chemistry. Address: Petrolite Corp, 369 Marshall Ave, Webster Groves, MO 63119.

GUTHRIE, DONALD, b. Eureka, Calif, July 8, 33; m. 54; c. 2. STATISTICS. B.S, Stanford, 54, Ph.D.(statist), 58; M.A, Columbia, 55. Asst, Stanford, 53-57, res. assoc, 57-58; asst. prof. math. mech, U.S. Naval Postgrad. Sch, 58-60; mathematician, Stanford Res. Inst, 60-63; assoc. prof. STATIST, ORE. STATE UNIV, 63-70, PROF, 70- Consult, Stanford Res. Inst, 58-59, 63-; vis. assoc. prof, dept. statist, Univ. N.C, Chapel Hill, 69-70. AAAS; Inst. Math. Statist; Am. Statist. Asn; Soc. Indust. & Appl. Math; Inst. Mgt. Sci. Probability and statistics as applied to engineering and physical sciences; operations research; statistical computing. Address: Dept. of Statistics, Oregon State University, Corvallis, OR 97331.

GUTHRIE, DONALD A(RTHUR), b. Winnipeg, Man, May 26, 26; U.S. citizen; m. 51; c. 2. ORGANIC & RADIATION CHEMISTRY. B.Sc, Manitoba, 47; M.Sc, Toronto, 49; Ph.D.(org. chem), McGill, 52. Res. chemist, Esso Res. & Eng. Co, Standard Oil Co. N.J, 51-57, sr. chemist, 57-62; mgr. cent. res. div, LORD CORP, 62-70, V.PRES, 70- Trustee, Edinboro Col; v.pres, Great Lakes Res. Inst. Am. Chem. Soc; Am. Inst. Aeronaut. & Astronaut; fel. Am. Inst. Chem. Lubricant oxidation and detergency; radiation initiated polymerization; synthesis and application of propellant oxidizers and binders; management of basic research in solid state physics, polymer synthesis, surface and polymer physical chemistry. Address: Lord Corp, 1635 W. 12th St, Erie, PA 16512.

GUTHRIE, EUGENE H(ARDING), b. Washington, D.C, Apr. 9, 24; m. 48; c. 6. MEDICINE, PUBLIC HEALTH. M.D, George Washington, 51; M.P.H, Michigan, 55. Intern, U.S. Pub. Health Serv. Hosp, Baltimore, Md, 51-52, house officer, 52-53; res. pub. health, Montgomery County Health Dept, Md, 54-55; State Dept. Health, Calif, 55-56; chief sch. health & rural health activities, Bur. State Serv, U.S. Pub. Health Serv, 56-59, chief prog. officer, 59-62, chief neurol. & sensory disease serv. br, 62, div. chronic diseases, 62-66, asst. surgeon gen. for opers, 66, assoc. surgeon gen, 66-68; EXEC. DIR, MD. COMPREHENSIVE HEALTH PLANNING AGENCY, 68- Mem. interdept. comt. health sch. aged child & comt. agr. migrants, Dept. Health, Educ. & Welfare, 57-59; mem. working group, President's Comt. Migratory Labor & alternate mem. interagency adv. group, President's Coun. Youth Fitness, 57-59; consult, Boy Scouts Am, 58-59; mem. commissioned officers awards bd, U.S. Pub. Health Serv, 63-64; med. comt, President's Comn. Employ. Handicapped, 63-68; staff dir, Surgeon Gen. Adv. Comt. Smoking & Health, 63-64; assoc, pub. health admin, sch. hyg, Johns Hopkins Univ, 70-; chmn. bd, Am. Acad. Comprehensive Health Planning, 70-; mem. bd. dir, Md. Hosp. Educ. & Res. Found, 70-; regional adv. group, Regional Med. Prog, Md, 70- Med.C, U.S.C.G, 42-45. Am. Med. Asn; Am. Pub. Health Asn. School and rural health; chronic diseases, including heart, cancer, diabetes, arthritis, neurological and sensory; mental retardation; gerontology; preventive medicine; medical administration. Address: Maryland Comprehensive Health Planning Agency, Suite 825, Medical Arts Bldg, 101 W. Read St, Baltimore, MD 21201.

GUTHRIE, FRANK A(LBERT), b. Madison, Ind, Feb. 16, 27; m. 55; c. 4. ANALYTICAL CHEMISTRY. B.A, Hanover Col, 50; M.S, Purdue, 52; Ph.D.(anal. chem), Indiana, 62. Asst. CHEM, Purdue, 50-52; instr, ROSE-HULMAN INST. TECHNOL, 52-55, asst. prof, 55-62, assoc. prof, 62-67, PROF, 67-, CHMN. DEPT, 70- Asst, Ind. Univ, 55-56, summers, 55-57; vis. asst. prof, Purdue Univ, 58; Univ. Ill, 61, Charles F. Kettering vis. lectr, 61-62, summer 62; Nat. Sci. Found. res. partic, Univ. Colo, 63-64, Rensselaer Polytech. Inst, 66; res. assoc, La. State Univ, 67. U.S.A, 45-46. Fel. AAAS; Am. Chem. Soc. Polarography; spectroscopy; chemical instrumentation; coordination compounds. Address: Dept. of Chemistry, Rose-Hulman Institute of Technology, 5500 Wabash Ave, Terre Haute, IN 47803.

GUTHRIE, FRANK E(DWIN), b. Louisville, Ky, Jan. 14, 23; m. 47; c. 2. ENTOMOLOGY. B.S, Kentucky, 47; M.S, Illinois, 49, Ph.D.(entom), 52. Asst. entomologist, North. Fla. Exp. Sta, Florida, 52-54; N.C. STATE UNIV, 54-59, assoc. prof. ENTOM, 59-61, PROF, 61-, asst. dean, 62-64. U.S.M.C, 43-46, 51-52, 1st Lt. Entom. Soc. Am; Am. Chem. Soc. Metabolism of nicotine by insects; insecticide residues on tobacco, distribution and localization of insecticides; environmental aspects of pesticides. Address: Dept. of Entomology, North Carolina State University, Raleigh, NC 27607.

GUTHRIE, GEORGE D(RAKE), b. Indianapolis, Ind, Jan. 20, 32; m. 61; c. 1. BIOPHYSICS. A.B, Wabash Col, 54; Iowa State, 56-57; U.S. Pub. Health Serv. fel, Calif. Inst. Technol, 59-61, Ph.D.(biophys), 62. Res. assoc. biol, Mass. Inst. Technol, 62-65; asst. prof. chem, Ind. Univ, Bloomington, 65-68, asst. prof. chem. & biochem, 68-71, ASSOC. PROF. BIOCHEM. & ASSOC. DIR, IND. UNIV. EVANSVILLE CTR. MED. EDUC, 71- U.S.A, 54-56. AAAS. Biological activity of purified nucleic acids; control of functions in biological systems; physiology and biochemistry of virus multiplication. Address: Indiana University Evansville Center for Medical Education, Suite 204, 421 Main St, Evansville, IN 47711.

GUTHRIE, GEORGE LESLIE, b. Clairton, Pa, May 1, 25; m. 53; c. 5. SOLID STATE PHYSICS. B.Sc, Carnegie Inst. Tech, 49, Allegheny-Ludlum fel, 53-54, Ph.D.(physics), 57. Instr. physics, Duquesne, 53; elec. eng, Carnegie Inst. Tech, 54-55; engr. physics res, Ford Motor Co, 56; physicist, Gen. Atomic Div, Gen. Dynamics Corp, 57-67; sr. res. scientist, Battelle Northwest, 67-70; RES. ENGR, WADCO DIV, WESTINGHOUSE CORP, 70- U.S.N.R, 44-46. Am. Phys. Soc. Heat capacity of metals and alloys at low temperatures; Hall effect; Nernst-Ettingshausen phenomena; high temperature thermal conductivity of semiconductors; superconductivity; radiation damage; lattice thermal conduction. Address: Wadco Corp, Richland, WA 99352.

GUTHRIE, HELEN A, b. Sarnia, Ont, Sept. 25, 25; m. 49; c. 3. NUTRITION. B.S, Univ. West. Ont, 46; M.S, Mich. State Univ, 48; Ph.D.(physiol), Univ. Hawaii, 68. Asst. prof. FOODS & NUTRIT, PA. STATE UNIV, 49-68, ASSOC. PROF, 68- Am. Home Econ. Asn; Am. Dietetic Asn; Am. Pub. Health Asn; Am. Inst. Nutrit. Infant nutrition; nutritional evaluation; world nutrition. Address: Dept. of Nutrition, 202 Human Development, Pennsylvania State University, University Park, PA 16802.

GUTHRIE, HUGH D, b. Murdo, S.Dak, May 11, 19; m. 50; c. 5. CHEMICAL ENGINEERING. B.S, Iowa, 43. Jr. engr, Shell Develop. Co, Calif, 43-45, engr, 45-52, sr. technologist, SHELL OIL CO, 52-54, asst. mgr. gas dept, 54-56, asst. mgr. catalytic cracking, 56, sr. technologist, 56-57, group leader mfg. econ, 57-59, mgr. alkylation dept, 59-61, asst. to mgr. prod. econ, 61-66, mgr. prod. econ. mkt, 66-67, asst. to gen. mgr. refineries in mfg, 67-70, SR. STAFF ASSOC, 70- Mem. bd, United Eng. Trustees, 65-; Eng. Found, 66- AAAS; Am. Chem. Soc; Am. Inst. Chem. Eng.(v.pres, 68, pres, 69). Separation processes, particularly distillation; distillation trays; economics, production and marketing. Address: Shell Oil Co, One Shell Plaza, Houston, TX 77002.

GUTHRIE, JAMES L(EVERETTE), b. Lawrence, Kans, July 3, 31; m. 58. ORGANIC CHEMISTRY. A.B, Oberlin Col, 52; Ph.D.(org. chem), Missouri, 56. Res. chemist, Columbia-South. Chem. Corp, 56-61; RES. SUPVR, POLYMER DEPT, RES. DIV, W.R. GRACE & CO, CLARKSVILLE, 61- U.S.A.R, 57-64. AAAS; Am. Chem. Soc. Chemistry and applications of organic materials; polymers; photosensitive systems; composite structures. Address: 1318 Patuxent Dr, Ashton, MD 20702.

GUTHRIE, J(AMES) PETER, b. Port Elgin, Ont, Feb. 3, 42; m. 65; c. 2. ORGANIC CHEMISTRY. B.Sc, Western Ontario, 64; Woodrow Wilson fel, Harvard, 64-65, Nat. Res. Coun. Can. scholar, 65-68, Ph.D.(org. chem), 68. Nat. Res. Coun. Can. fel. biochem. Princeton, 68-69; ASST. PROF. CHEM. & BIOCHEM, UNIV. WEST. ONT, 69- Am. Chem. Soc. Mechanisms of enzyme catalysis; enzyme model systems. Address: Dept. of Chemistry, University of Western Ontario, London, 72, Ont, Can.

GUTHRIE, JOHN D(AULTON), b. Detroit, Mich, Mar. 19, 03; m. 35, 68; c. 2. CHEMISTRY. B.Sc, Ohio State, 25, Ph.D.(plant biochem), 29. Asst. biochemist, Boyce Thompson Inst, 25-41; sr. chemist, SOUTH. REGIONAL RES. LAB, U.S. DEPT. AGR, 41-52, prin. chemist, 52-61, CHIEF COTTON CHEM. REACTIONS LAB, 61- Asst, Ohio State, 27-29. John Scott Medal, 65. AAAS; Am. Chem. Soc; Am. Asn. Textile Chem. & Colorists. Chloroplast pigments; oxidative enzymes; effect of stimulative chemicals and inhibitors on plants; glutathione in plants; industrial utilization of agricultural commodities; analytical chemistry; chemical modification of cotton fibers; flameproofing of cotton; cellulose chemistry. Address: Southern Regional Research Lab, U.S. Dept. of Agriculture, P.O. Box 19687, New Orleans, LA 70119.

GUTHRIE, MARSHALL B(ECK), b. Lexington, Ky, Oct. 2, 19; m. 41; c. 3. MEDICINE, DERMATOLOGY. B.S, Kentucky, 40; M.D, Pennsylvania, 43, 48-49. Consult. dermat, China Serv. Command, Med. Corps, U.S. Army, 44-45, Far East Command, 45-49, exchange consult, Royal Army Med. Corps, Eng, 52-53, U.S. forces in Europe, 53-54; assoc. dir. clin. invest. dept, SMITH KLINE & FRENCH LABS, 54-62, med. dir, Menley & James Labs, 62-65, assoc. dir. clin. serv, 65-68, DIR. EXP. THER, 68-; ASSOC. DERMAT, SCH. MED. & GRAD. SCH, UNIV. PA, 54- Clin. asst, Phila. Gen. Hosp, 54- Med.C, U.S.A, 44-54, Res, 54-, Col. Soc. Invest. Dermat; Asn. Mil. Surg. U.S; Am. Med. Asn; Am. Fedn. Clin. Res; fel. Am. Col. Physicians; Am. Acad. Dermat. Teaching dermatology to undergraduate and graduate medical students; clinical studies on new pharmaceutical agents. Address: Smith Kline & French Labs, 1500 Spring Garden St, Philadelphia, PA 19101.

GUTHRIE, RICHARD L(AFAYETTE), b. Union Springs, Ala, May 29, 41; m. 62; c. 2. SOIL SCIENCE. B.S, Auburn Univ, 62, M.S, 65; Ph.D.(soil sci), Cornell Univ, 68. Asst. soil sci, Cornell Univ, 65-68; soil scientist, SOIL CONSERV. SERV, U.S. DEPT. AGR, Ala, 62-71, SOIL SPECIALIST, 71- Am. Soc. Agron; Soil Sci. Soc. Am; Soil Conserv. Soc. Am. Soil genesis, morphology and classification. Address: 2212 Rose Dr, Columbia, MO 65201.

GUTHRIE, ROBERT, b. Marionville, Mo, June 28, 16; m. 41; c. 6. MICROBIOLOGY. B.A, Minnesota, 41, M.D, 45, Ph.D.(bact), 46; fel, Maine, 40-42, M.S, 42. Asst. med. bact, Minnesota, 43-45; Nat. Res. Coun. fel. biochem, Wisconsin, 45-46; physician, Argonne Nat. Lab, 46; sr. asst. surgeon, Nat. Insts. Health, U.S. Pub. Health Serv, 46-48, surgeon, 48-49, microbiologist, hosp, Staten Island, 50; prof. bact. & chmn. dept, Kansas, 49-50; asst, Sloan-Kettering Inst, 51-54; prin. cancer res. scientist, Roswell Park Mem. Inst, State Dept. Health, N.Y, 54-58; RES. ASSOC. PROF. PEDIAT. & MICROBIOL, DEPT. PEDIAT, STATE UNIV. N.Y. BUFFALO & DIR, BIOCHEM. GENETICS SECT, CHILDREN'S HOSP, 58- Am. Soc. Microbiol; Fedn. Am. Sci; Am. Chem. Soc. Pseudomonas hydrophila; nutrition of bacteria and invertebrates; biochemical genetics of Escherichia coli and Bacillus subtilus; cytology of bacterial endospores; nucleic acid metabolism; cancer chemotherapy; human biochemical genetics and biochemical individuality. Address: Dept. of Microbiology, Graduate School, State University of New York at Buffalo, Buffalo, NY 14212.

GUTHRIE, ROBERT D, b. Bronxville, N.Y, June 27, 36; m. 63; c. 3. ORGANIC CHEMISTRY. B.A, Oberlin Col, 58; Ph.D.(org. chem), Univ. Rochester, 63. Nat. Sci. Found. fel, Univ. Calif, Los Angeles, 63-64, univ. fel, 64, lectr. CHEM, 64-65; asst. prof, UNIV. KY, 65-71, ASSOC. PROF, 71- Am. Chem. Soc. Carbanion chemistry; electron transfer reactions. Address: Dept. of Chemistry, University of Kentucky, Lexington, KY 40506.

GUTHRIE, ROGER T(HACKSTON), b. Spartanburg, S.C, Dec. 5, 24; m. 50; c. 3. ORGANIC CHEMISTRY. B.S, Wofford Col, 49; M.A, North Carolina, 52, Ph.D.(chem), 53. Asst, North Carolina, 50-53; res. chemist, Am. Enka Corp, 53-59, head, dielec. mat. sect, 59-62, textile yarn develop. sect, 63-66; tech. mgr, new prod. explor, Celanese Plastics Co, 66-69, new prod. develop, 69-70, mgr, new venture anal, 70; RES. DIR. CHEM. DIV, M&T CHEM. INC, 70- U.S.N.R, 43-46. AAAS; Am. Chem. Soc; N.Y. Acad. Sci; Asn. Res. Dirs; Soc. Plastics Eng. Polymer chemistry and physics; electrical insulating materials. Address: 7 Rutgers Court, Westfield, NJ 07090.

GUTHRIE, ROLAND L, b. Charleston, W.Va, Apr. 5, 28; m. 54; c. 3. PLANT BIOSYSTEMATICS, DENDROLOGY. B.S.F. & M.S, West Virginia, 53, Ph.D.(bot), 68. Forester & naturalist, Isaac W. Bernheim Found, 53-56; arboretum asst, W.VA. UNIV, 59-61, instr. BIOL, 61-66, ASST. PROF, 66-, DIR. ARBORETUM, 61- U.S.A, 46-47, 50-51. Am. Forestry Asn; Am. Inst. Biol. Sci; Int. Asn. Plant Taxon; Bot. Soc. Am. Biosystematic studies of quercus; cytotaxonomy of the umbelliferae. Address: Dept. of Biology, West Virginia University, Morgantown, WV 26506.

GUTHRIE, RUFUS K(ENT), b. Mullin, Tex, July 4, 23; m. 48; c. 2. IMMUNOLOGY, BACTERIOLOGY. B.A, Texas, 48, fel, 49-50, M.A, 50; Ph.D.(microbiol), Baylor, 54. Bacteriologist, State Dept. Health, Tex, 47-48; Brownwood Mem. Hosp, 49; asst. microbiol, col. med, Baylor, 50-52, 53-54; bacteriologist, Vet. Admin. Hosp, Houston, 52-53; asst. prof. BIOL, North Texas State, 54-57, assoc. prof, 57-60, PROF, 60-69; MICROBIOL, CLEMSON UNIV, 69-, ASSOC. DEAN COL. PHYS, MATH. & BIOL. SCI, 71-, dir. biol. div, 69-71. Nat. Sci. Found. sci. fel. microbiol, col. med, Iowa, 62-63. Consult, Flow Mem. Hosp, Denton, Tex, 54-62; Alcon Labs, Ft. Worth, 57-60; BioAssay Lab, Dallas, 63- U.S.N.R, 43-46; U.S.P.H.S, 57-, Sr. Asst. Scientist. AAAS; Am. Soc. Microbiol; Am. Pub. Health Asn; Reticuloendothelial Soc; Soc. Exp. Biol. & Med; fel. Am. Acad. Microbiol. Immunological mechanisms; medical microbiology. Address: 202 Wren St, Clemson, SC 29631.

GUTHRIE, RUSSELL DALE, b. Nebo, Ill, Oct. 27, 36; m. 61; c. 2. ZOOLOGY. B.S, Univ. Ill, 58, M.S, 59; Ph.D.(zool), Univ. Chicago, 63. ASSOC. PROF. BIOL, UNIV. ALASKA, 63-, Nat. Sci. Found. instnl. grant, 63-64, res. grant, 65-68. Nat. Sci. Found. grant, 70-72. AAAS; Soc. Study Evolution; Soc. Vert. Paleont; Am. Soc. Mammal. Evolutionary mechanics; Pleistocene vertebrate paleontology; vertebrate evolution. Address: Dept. of Biological Sciences, University of Alaska, College, AK 99735.

GUTHRIE, W(ILBUR) D(EAN), b. Woodward, Okla, Mar. 3, 24; m. 46; c. 5. ENTOMOLOGY. B.S, Okla. State, 50, M.S, 51; Ph.D, Ohio State, 58. ENTOMOLOGIST, AGR. RES. SERV, U.S. DEPT. AGR, 51- U.S.N.A.F, 44-46. Entom. Soc. Am. Insect resistance in crop plants; relative degree of resistance of inbred lines and hybrid corn to the European corn borer; sources of germ plasma. Address: European Corn Borer Research Lab, Agriculture Research Service, U.S. Dept. of Agriculture, Ankeny, IA 50021.

GUTHWIN, HYMAN, b. New York, N.Y, Jan. 12, 14; m. 42; c. 3. CELL PHYSIOLOGY, BIOCHEMISTRY. B.A, N.Y. Univ, 35, M.S, 45, Ph.D.(cellular physiol), 56; Polytech. Inst. Brooklyn, 48-49. Lab. dir. microbiol. & pharmacol, Nopco Chem. Co, 45-49; teaching fel. biol. & physiol, N.Y. Univ, 49-55; instr. path, Albert Einstein Col. Med, 55-56; Damon Runyon cancer grants, col. physicians & surgeons, Columbia, 56-62; instr. BIOL, HUNTER COL, 61-65, asst. prof, 65-70, ASSOC. PROF, 70- Vis. assoc. prof, N.Y. Univ, 61-62; Lehman Col, 65- Mem. Am. Mus. Natural Hist, 64- U.S.A, 41-45, Lt. AAAS; N.Y. Acad. Sci; Soc. Protozool; Am. Soc. Zool; Radiation Res. Soc. Microscopic enzyme chemistry; micrurgy; cell fractionation; cellular physiology; radiation biology. Address: Dept. of Biology, Lehman College, Bronx, NY 10468.

GUTIERREZ, JOSE, b. Compton, Calif, July 5, 20; m. 50; c. 2. PARASITOLOGY. B.S, State Col. Wash, 51, M.S, 53, U.S. Pub. Health Serv. fel, 55-57, Ph.D.(bact), 57. Res. assoc. bact, California, 57; bacteriologist, agr. res. serv, U.S. Dept. Agr, 57-63; PARASITOLOGIST, Nat. Naval Med. Ctr, 63-65; AGR. RES. SERV, U.S. DEPT. AGR, 66- U.S.A.F, 42-46. Am. Soc. Microbiol; Soc. Protozool; Am. Soc. Zool; Gerontol. Soc. Biochemistry and physiology of the rumen protozoa; lipid metabolism of malaria parasites and heart muscle; effect of drugs on phospholipid metabolism; effect of antimalarial drugs on lipid metabolism of bacteria; development of microbiological assays for growth factors. Address: Human Nutrition Research Division, Agriculture Research Service, U.S. Dept. of Agriculture, Bethesda, MD 20705.

GUTIERREZ, LEO, b. Los Lunas, N.Mex, May 23, 24; m. 45; c. 13. ELECTRICAL ENGINEERING. B.S, New Mexico, 43, M.S, 46. Staff mem. systs. design, SANDIA CORP, 46-51, div. supvr, 51-58, dept. mgr, 58-63, DIR. SYSTS. DEVELOP, 63- U.S.N, 43-45, Lt.(jg). Weapon systems involving nuclear warheads for all services. Address: Sandia Corp, P.O. Box 969, Livermore, CA 94550.

GUTIERREZ, LUIS GARCIA, b. Guanajuato, Mex, Oct. 26, 23; m. 52; c. 6. MINING, ECONOMIC GEOLOGY. B.S, Stanford, 50, M.S, 51. Asst. geologist, Comité de Recursos Minerales, 45-48; sr. geologist, Inst. de Recursos Minerales, 51-52, asst. head geologist, 52-54; geologist, Kennecott Copper Co, 54-55; Cananea Consol. Copper Co, 55-58; head geologist, Perforadora Latina, 58-60; Hooker Chem. Co. Mex, 60-61; chief resident, Consejo de Recursos Naturales no Renovables, 61-65; dir. Comision de Fomento Minero, Sucursal Parral, 65-66, Sucursal Durango, 66-68; CHIEF GEOLOGIST, CANMEX MINERA DE MÉXICO, S.A. DE C.V, 68- Geol. Soc. Am; Soc. Econ. Geol. Ore deposits; economic and mining geology. Address: Bruno Martinez 403 Sur, Desp, 303, Durango, Durango, Mex.

GUTJAHR, ALLAN L, b. Hosmer, S.Dak, Mar. 20, 38; m. 59; c. 3. MATHEMATICAL STATISTICS, OPERATIONS RESEARCH. B.S, Univ. Wash, 61; M.S, Johns Hopkins Univ, 63; Ph.D.(math. statist), Rutgers Univ, 70. Mem. tech. staff, Bell Tel. Labs, 62-68; asst. statist, Rutgers Univ, 68-69; mem. tech. staff, Bell Tel. Labs, 69-71; ASST. PROF. MATH, N.MEX. INST. MINING & TECHNOL, 71- U.S.A, 56-58. Inst. Math. Statist. Statistical inference in semi-Markov processes and other stochastic processes; queueing theory; applied statistics. Address: 618 Miller Pl, Socorro, NM 87801.

GUTKNECHT, JOHN WILLIAM, b. Youngstown, Ohio, Apr. 13, 37; m. 62; c. 1. PHYSIOLOGY, MARINE BIOLOGY. B.A, Ohio Wesleyan, 59; univ. scholar, North Carolina, 59-60, Nat. Sci. Found. fel, 61-62, Nat. Insts. Health fel, 62-63, Ph.D.(zool), 64. Res. biologist, radiobiol. lab, U.S. Bur. Commercial Fisheries, N.C, 63-66; U.S. Pub. Health Serv. res. fel. biophys, Univ. E.Anglia 66-67; res. assoc. PHYSIOL, MED. CTR, DUKE UNIV, 67-69, ASST. PROF, 69- AAAS; Am. Inst. Biol. Sci; Am. Physiol. Soc; Biophys. Soc; Soc. Gen. Physiol. Transport of solutes and water across cell membranes; membrane permeability; bioelectricity. Address: Dept. of Physiology, Duke University Medical Center, Durham, NC 27706.

GUTMAN, ALEXANDER B(ENJAMIN), b. N.Y.C, June 7, 02; m. 48. MEDICINE. B.A, Cornell, 23, M.A, 24, Ph.D.(exp. biol), 26; M.D, Vienna, 28. Asst. MED, col. physicians & surg, Columbia, 29-35, instr, 35-37, assoc, 37-40, asst. prof, 40-47, assoc. prof, 47-49, prof, 49-67; MT. SINAI SCH. MED, 67-70, EMER. PROF, 70- Schepp fel, 29-31. Asst. & assoc. attend. physician, Presby. Hosp, 29-51; dir. res. serv, Columbia Div, Goldwater Mem. Hosp, 47-51; dir, dept. med, Mt. Sinai Hosp, 51-70, emer. dir, 70-; consult, Veterans Admin. Hosp, Bronx, 53-67; U.S. Pub. Health Serv, 47-49, spec. consult, 53-68. Mem. coun. res, N.Y. Heart Asn, 49-52, 55-58; comt. on growth, Nat. Res. Coun, 50-52, mem. & later chmn. metab. & nutrit. study sect, Nat. Insts. Health, 53-58; Arthritis & Rheumatism Found, 54-; mem. bd. sci. counsr, Nat. Inst. Arthritis & Metab. Diseases, 60-64; mem. Arthritis & Metab. diseases prog-proj. comt, U.S. Pub. Health Serv, 61-64; nat. adv. arthritis & metab. diseases coun, 64- Ed-in-chief, Am. J. Med, 46-71. Cert, U.S. War Dept, 46; Amory Prize, Am. Acad. Sci, 48; Gairdner Found. Award, 61; Holbrook Mem. Lectr. Award, Arthritis & Rheumatism Found, 64. Lab. consult, Off. Air Surgeon, 43-46. Am. Soc. Clin. Invest; Am. Soc. Biol. Chem; Am. Med. Asn; Am. Rheumatism Asn; Asn. Am. Physicians; fel. Am. Col. Physicians; Harvey Soc.(pres, 63-64); fel. N.Y. Acad. Med. Metabolic diseases; gout; purine metabolism; renal physiology. Address: Mt. Sinai School of Medicine, Fifth Ave. at 100th St, New York, NY 10029.

GUTMAN, DAVID, b. Isle of Malta, Nov. 2, 34; U.S. citizen; m. 65; c. 2. PHYSICAL CHEMISTRY. B.S, California, Berkeley, 60; Sun Oil Co. fel, Illinois, 62, Nat. Sci. Found. summer fel, 62-65, Ph.D.(phys. chem), 65. Asst. prof. CHEM, ILL. INST. TECHNOL, 64-70, ASSOC. PROF, 70- U.S.A, 55-58. Am. Chem. Soc; Am. Phys. Soc; Combustion Inst. Chemical kinetics; theoretical and experimental studies of high temperature gas phase reactions. Address: Dept. of Chemistry, Illinois Institute of Technology, 3300 S. Federal St, Chicago, IL 60616.

GUTMANN, HELMUT R(UDOLPH), b. Strasbourg, France, July 31, 11; nat; m. 46; c. 4. BIOCHEMISTRY. M.D, Göttingen, 36. Coxe mem. fel. biochem, Yale, 46-48; res. assoc, Tennessee, 48-50; asst. prof. cancer res, Florida, 50-52; asst. prof. PHYSIOL. CHEM, UNIV. MINN, MINNEAPOLIS, 52-56, assoc. prof, 56-64, PROF, 64-; BIOCHEMIST, CANCER RES. LAB, VET. ADMIN. HOSP, 61-, radioisotope serv, 56-61. U.S. Pub. Health Serv. fel. biochem, Max-Planck Inst, Munich, 60-61. Med.C, 44-46, Capt. AAAS; Am. Chem. Soc; Am. Soc. Biol. Chem; Am. Asn. Cancer Res; The Chem. Soc; fel. Am. Inst. Chem. Metabolism and mechanism of action of carcinogenic and toxic compounds. Address: Cancer Research Lab, Veterans Administration Hospital, Minneapolis, MN 55417.

GUTMANN, LUDWIG, b. Frankfurt, Ger, Apr. 7, 33; U.S. citizen; m. 54; c. 3. NEUROLOGY. B.A, Princeton, 55; M.D, Columbia Univ, 59. Intern med, med. ctr, Univ. Wis, Madison, 59-60, resident neurol, 60-63; chief neurol, U.S. Air Force Hosp, Scott AFB, Ill, 63-65; Nat. Inst. Neurol. Diseases & Blindness fel. neurophysiol, Mayo Clin, 65-66; asst. prof. NEUROL, SCH. MED, W.VA. UNIV, 66-69, assoc. prof. & acting chmn. dept, 69-70, PROF. & CHMN. DEPT, 70-, DIR. ELECTROMYOGRAPH LAB, 66-, ASSOC. PROF. PHYSIOL. & BIOPHYS, 70-, asst. prof, 68-70. Neurol. consult, Alton State Hosp, Ill, 63-65; mem, Myasthenia Gravis Found. U.S.A.F, 63-65, Capt. Am. Acad. Neurol; Am. Asn. Electromyog. & Electrodiag; Asn. Res. Nerv. & Ment. Disease; Asn. Univ. Prof. Neurol. Electromyography and neuromuscular diseases. Address: Dept. of Neurology, West Virginia University School of Medicine, Morgantown, WV 26506.

GUTOFF, EDGAR B(ENJAMIN), b. New York, N.Y, June 2, 30; m. 56; c. 2. CHEMICAL ENGINEERING. B.Ch.E, City Col. New York, 51; S.M, Mass. Inst. Tech, 52, Crawford fel, 52-54, Little summer fel, 53, Sc.D.(chem. eng), 54. Chem. engr, Fertilizers & Chem, Ltd, Israel, 52; sr. process engr, Brown Co, 54-58; sr. chem. engr, Ionics, Inc, 58-60; SR. SCIENTIST & SR. PRIN. ENGR, POLAROID CORP, 60- Am. Chem. Soc; Am. Inst. Chem. Eng; Soc. Photog. Sci. & Eng. Photographic emulsions; crystallization of silver halides; syneresis; coagulation of silver halide suspensions; backmixing in extraction columns; efficiencies of mixing tanks; acetylene via barium carbide; adsorption of high polymers, rubber-filler interactions. Address: Polaroid Corp, 1265 Main St, Waltham, MA 02154.

GUTOWSKI, FRANK A(LOYSIUS), b. Detroit, Mich, Jan. 25, 19. PHYSICS. A.B, Loyola (Ill), 41; S.T.L, West Baden Col, 51; Ph.D.(physics), 56. Instr. PHYSICS, JOHN CARROLL UNIV, 55-57, asst. prof, 57-61, assoc. prof, 61-65, PROF. & CHMN. DEPT, 65- Acoust. Soc. Am; Am. Asn. Physics Teachers. Ultrasonics; molecular theory of fluids. Address: Dept. of Physics, John Carroll University, Cleveland, OH 44118.

GUTOWSKI, GERALD EDWARD, b. Jackson, Mich, June 8, 41; m. 64; c. 4. ORGANIC CHEMISTRY. B.S, Mich. State, 63; Detroit News fel, Wayne State, 66-67, Ph.D.(org. chem), 67. Res. assoc. chem, Wayne State, 67-68; SR. ORG. CHEMIST, CHEM. RES. DIV, ELI LILLY & CO, 68- Am. Chem. Soc; Pharmaceut. Soc. Japan. Antibiotics; carbohydrates; aminosugars, thiosugars; medicinal chemistry; structure determination; organic synthesis; mechanisms of organic reactions. Address: Chemical Research Division, Eli Lilly & Co, Indianapolis, IN 46206.

GUTOWSKY, H(ERBERT) S(ANDER), b. Bridgman, Mich, Nov. 8, 19; m. 49; c. 3. PHYSICAL CHEMISTRY. A.B, Indiana, 40; M.S, California, 46; Ph.D. (phys. chem), Harvard, 49. Instr. chem, UNIV. ILL, URBANA, 48-51, asst. prof, 51-55, assoc. prof, 55-56, PROF. CHEM, 56-, DIR. SCH. CHEM. SCI. & HEAD DEPT. CHEM, 70-, head div. phys. chem, 56-62, dept. chem. & chem. eng, 67-70. Guggenheim fel, 54-55; vis. prof, California, 56; Walker Ames vis. prof, Washington (Seattle), 57. U.S.A, 41-45. Nat. Acad. Sci; fel. AAAS; Am. Chem. Soc; fel. Am. Phys. Soc.(Irving Langmuir prize); Faraday Soc; Am. Acad. Arts & Sci. Molecular and solid state structure; nuclear magnetism; radio frequency spectroscopy. Address: Dept. of Chemistry, University of Illinois, Urbana, IL 61801.

GUTSCHE, C(ARL) DAVID, b. Oak Park, Ill, Mar. 21, 21; m. 44; c. 3. CHEMISTRY. B.A, Oberlin Col, 43; du Pont fel, Univ. Wis, 46-47, Alumni Res. Found. fel. & Ph.D.(org. chem), 47. Res. assoc. biochem, U.S. Dept. Agr, Off. Sci. Res. & Develop, Univ. Wis, 43-44; instr. CHEM, WASH. UNIV, 47-48, asst. prof, 48-51, assoc. prof, 51-59, PROF, 59-, CHMN. DEPT, 70- Consult, Petrolite Corp, Mo, 51-; Monsanto Co, 59-; mem. adv. bd, Petrol. Res. Fund, 72- AAAS; Am. Chem. Soc; The Chem. Soc. Carbocyclic synthesis with emphasis on ring expansion processes; photochemistry of cyclic carbonyl compounds; chemistry of diazoalkanes and carbenes; polyfunctional catalysts and enzyme models. Address: Dept. of Chemistry, Washington University, St. Louis, MO 63130.

GUTSCHE, GRAHAM D(ENTON), b. Oak Park, Ill, June 29, 25; m. 48; c. 3. PHYSICS B.S, Colorado, 50; M.S, Minnesota, 52; Nat. Sci. Found. fel, Catholic Univ, 58-59, Ph.D, 60. Instr, Northwest. Schs, Minn, 50-52; asst. prof. PHYSICS, U.S. NAVAL ACAD, 52-57, assoc. prof, 57-63, PROF, 63- Asst, Univ. Minn, 51-52; lectr, Univ. Md, 59-; Nat. Sci. Found. fel, Cambridge Univ, 67-68. U.S.N.R, 43-46. AAAS; Am. Phys. Soc; Am. Asn. Physics Teachers; Am. Astron. Soc; Am. Sci. Affiliation. Nuclear reactions; Raman spectroscopy; stellar photometry. Address: 38 Williams Dr, Annapolis, MD 21401.

GUTSCHE, HENRY W, b. Frankfurt, Ger, June 21, 22; U.S. citizen; m. 57; c. 3. INORGANIC CHEMISTRY. Ph.D.(inorg. chem), Erlangen, 54. Asst. prof. anal. chem, Erlangen, 54-55; res. chemist, Siemens Schuckert Works, Ger, 55-57, tech. coord, License Dept, 57-58; sr. chemist, Merck & Co, Inc, Pa, 58-64; res. specialist electronic chem, MONSANTO CO, 64-69, res. group leader, 69-70, MGR. SILICON APPLICATIONS DEPT, 69- Ger. Air Force, 41-46. Am. Chem. Soc; Electrochem. Soc. Preparation of hyper pure silicon and its processing into single crystalline and epitaxial form. Address: Monsanto Co, 800 N. Lindbergh Blvd, St. Louis, MO 63166.

GUTSCHICK, RAYMOND CHARLES, b. Chicago, Ill, Oct. 3, 13; m. 39: c. 2. GEOLOGY. B.S, Illinois, 38, M.S, 39, Ph.D.(geol), 42. Geologist, Aluminum Ore Co, Ill, 42, 46-47; instr. geol, Illinois, 42-43; geologist, Magnolia Petrol. Co, Okla, 43-46; Gulf Oil Corp, 47; asst. prof. GEOL, UNIV. NOTRE DAME, 47-50, assoc. prof, 50-54, PROF, 54- head dept, 56-70, lay faculty award, 64. Consult, Socony Mobil Res. Lab. Summer vis. prof, Indiana, 51-52, 56-62, 69. Fel. AAAS; fel. Geol. Soc. Am; Paleont. Soc; Soc. Econ. Paleont. & Mineral; Nat. Asn. Geol. Teachers; Am. Asn. Petrol. Geol; Int. Asn. Sedimentol. Paleozoic stratigraphy, sedimentation and paleontology; Mississippian micropaleontology, foraminifera; geology of Northern Rockies. Address: Dept. of Geology, University of Notre Dame, Notre Dame, IN 46556.

GUTSCHOW, NATHAN R(OBERT), b. Gosper Co, Nebr, July 7, 11; m. 38; c. 4. PHYSICAL CHEMISTRY. B.Sc, York Col, 33; M.Sc, Nebraska, 36. Teacher, pub. schs, Nebr, 34-37; chemist & lab. foreman, Am. Crystal Sugar Co, Calif, 37; res. chemist, West. Silicair Prod, 38; chem. engr, Mobil Oil Co, 38-60; instr. chem. & eng, Glendale Col, 60-64; CHMN. DEPT. PHYS. SCI, RIO HONDO COL, 64- Am. Chem. Soc. Chemical education. Address: Dept. of Physical Sciences, Rio Hondo College, 3600 Workman Mill Rd, Whittier, CA 90608.

GUTSTADT, ALLAN M(ORTON), b. Chicago, Ill, Jan. 9, 26; m. 56; c. 1. GEOLOGY, STRATIGRAPHY. B.A, Illinois, 49; fel, Northwestern, 51-53,

Ph.D.(geol), 54. Geologist stratig, Ind. Geol. Surv, 53-57; Creole Petrol. Corp, Standard Oil Co, N.J, 57-61; asst. prof. GEOL, SAN FERNANDO VALLEY STATE COL, 62-67, assoc. prof, 67-71, PROF, 71- U.S.N, 43-46. AAAS; Am. Asn. Petrol. Geol; Geol. Soc. Am. Lower Paleozoic stratigraphy, central interior United States; Precambrian sedimentary rocks, southwestern United States. Address: Dept. of Geology, San Fernando Valley State College, Northridge, CA 91324.

GUTSTEIN, WILLIAM H, b. N.Y.C, July 12, 22; m. 45; c. 2. PATHOLOGY, BIOPHYSICS. A.B, Wisconsin, 43; M.D, N.Y. Univ, 46; Columbia, 50-52. Instr. path, State Univ. N.Y. Downstate Med. Ctr, 52-55; practicing pathologist, 55-57; asst. prof. PATH, N.Y. Univ, 57-63; ASSOC. PROF, N.Y. MED. COL, 63- Participant, Nat. Conf. Cardiovasc. Disease, D.C, 64. U.S.P.H.S, 48-50, Lt. AAAS; Am. Soc. Exp. Path. Biophysical aspects and pathogenesis of atherosclerosis. Address: New York Medical College, 1 E. 106th St, New York, NY 10029.

GUTTAY, A(NDREW) J(OHN) R(OBERT), b. Los Angeles, Calif, May 12, 24; m. 48; c. 4. SOILS. B.S, Mich. State, 48, Ph.D.(soil mgt), 59; M.S, Iowa State, 50. Land use specialist, Mich. Dept. Conserv, 50-51; instr. soil mgt, Mich. State, 51-58; dist. rep. soil fertil, Nat. Plant Food Inst, 58-61; PROF. AGRON. & HEAD DEPT. PLANT SCI, UNIV. CONN, 61- U.S.A, 43-46. Fel. AAAS; Am. Soc. Agron; Soil Sci. Soc. Am; Int. Soc. Soil Sci; Am. Soc. Hort. Sci. Soil management; soil ecology; land use. Address: Dept. of Plant Science, University of Connecticut, Storrs, CT 06268.

GUTTENPLAN, JACK DAVID, b. Baton Rouge, La, Oct. 10, 25; m. 49; c. 3. CHEMICAL ENGINEERING, ELECTROCHEMISTRY. B.S, Case Sch. Appl. Sci, 45, Lubrizol fel. & M.S, Case, 48. Res. asst. gasoline additives, Case, 47-48; res. assoc. protective coatings, C.F. Prutton & Assocs, Ohio, 48-49; group leader electrochem, Chrysler Corp, Mich, 49-61; mgr. develop. biol. electrochem. ocean batteries, Magna Corp, Calif, 61-62; RES. SPECIALIST ELECTROCHEM. & CORROSION, AUTONETICS DIV, N.AM. ROCKWELL CORP, 62- Lectr, Chrysler Inst. Eng, 52-59. U.S.N.R, 43-46, Res, 46-, Comdr. Electrochem. Soc; Nat. Asn. Corrosion Eng; Sci. Res. Soc. Am; fel. Am. Inst. Chem. Electrochemistry; corrosion; electroplating; thin film circuitry; physics of failure of microelectronic components; fuel cell development; bio-electrochemistry. Address: 2210 W. Avalon, Santa Ana, CA 92706.

GUTTER, F(REDERICK) J(AY), b. New York, N.Y, Aug. 29, 22; m. 44; c. 2. BIOCHEMISTRY. B.A, Brooklyn Col, 43; M.S, Georgetown, 53. Chemist, Atomic Energy Proj, Columbia, 43, Manhattan Dist, 43-46; tech. ed, Atomic Energy Proj, Carbide & Carbon Corp, 46; phys. chemist, Nat. Cancer Inst, NAT. INSTS. HEALTH, 49-59, res. grants analyst, Nat. Inst. Neurol. Diseases & Blindness, 59-60, training analyst, 60-62, EXEC. SECY, COMMUNICATIVE SCI. STUDY SECT, DIV. RES. GRANTS, 62- C.Eng, U.S.A, 43-46. AAAS; Am. Chem. Soc. Physical chemistry of proteins; electrophoresis; ultracentrifugation; diffusion and chromatography of proteins; physical biochemistry; research grants administration. Address: Division of Research Grants, National Institutes of Health, Bethesda, MD 20014.

GUTTI, SUBBA RAO, b. Vetapalem, Andhra Pradesh, India, May 1, 26; m. 50. CIVIL ENGINEERING, HYDRODYNAMICS. B.E, Annamalai, India, 51; Govt. India scholar, Indian Inst. Tech. Kharagpor, 55-56, M.Tech, 56; Ph.D. (hydromech), Minnesota, 62. Asst. civil engr, Pub. Works Dept, Andhra Pradesh, India, 51-56; asst. dir. designs & res, Nagarjunasagar Dam Control Bd, Hydraul. Res. Labs, 56-58; hydraul. engr, Douglas W. Barr, Consult. Engrs, Minn, 61-62; RES. SCIENTIST, GRUMMAN AIRCRAFT ENG. CORP, 62- Am. Soc. Civil Eng. Design of large dams and bridges; multiphase boundary layer flows; two-phase jet propulsion system for hydrofoil boats and hydrobombs. Address: Research Dept, Plant 35, Grumman Aerospace Corp, Bethpage, Long Island, NY 11714.

GUTTMAN, BURTON S(AMUEL), b. Minneapolis, Minn, Apr. 12, 36; m. 63; c. 2. BIOLOGY. B.A, Minnesota, 58; Wilson fel, Hopkins, 58-59; Nat. Sci. Found. fel, Oregon, 59-60; Nat. Insts. Health trainee, 60-63, Ph.D.(biol), 63. Nat. Sci. Found. res. fel. biol, Calif. Inst. Technol, 63-65; ASST. PROF. CELL BIOL, MED. CTR, UNIV. KY, 65- Am. Soc. Microbiol. Regulation of metabolism; bacteriophage development; general biological organization. Address: Dept. of Cell Biology, University of Kentucky, Lexington, KY 40506.

GUTTMAN, CHARLES M, b. Cincinnati, Ohio, Apr. 11, 39; m. 60; c. 2. THEORETICAL CHEMISTRY. B.A, Earlham Col, 61; Nat. Defense Ed. Act. & Nat. Sci. Found. fels. & Ph.D.(chem), 67. Mem. tech. staff, Bell Tel. Labs, 66-67; RES. CHEMIST, NAT. BUR. STANDARDS, 67- Am. Phys. Soc. Statistical mechanics of polymeric systems and ionic solutions. Address: Polymers Division, National Bureau of Standards, Washington, DC 20234.

GUTTMAN, DAVID, b. N.Y.C, July 24, 43; m. 68. PARASITOLOGY, MEDICAL ENTOMOLOGY. B.S, St. Lawrence Univ, 64; M.S, Cornell Univ, 67; Ph.D.(parasitol), Tulane Univ. La, 70. RES. ASSOC. PARASITOL, TULANE UNIV. LA, 70- Vis. asst. prof, Univ. Valle, Colombia, 69- Am. Soc. Parasitol; Am. Soc. Trop. Med. & Hyg; Royal Soc. Trop. Med. & Hyg. Biology of neotropical black flies; medical parasitology. Address: Dept. of Parasitology, School of Medicine, Tulane University, New Orleans, LA 70112.

GUTTMAN, DAVID E(MANUEL), b. Calgary, Alta, May 23, 29; m. 55; c. 3. PHARMACEUTICS. B.Sc, Alberta, 52; M.S, Wisconsin, 54, Ph.D.(pharm), 56. Res. assoc, Upjohn Co, 56-58; asst. prof. pharmaceut. tech. & phys. pharm, Ohio State, 58-61, assoc. prof, 61-64; from assoc. prof. to prof. pharmaceut, State Univ. N.Y. Buffalo, 64-69; ASSOC. DIR. ANAL. & PHYS. CHEM, SMITH KLINE & FRENCH LAB, 69- Consult, William S. Merrell Co, Ohio. AAAS; Am. Pharmaceut. Asn; Am. Chem. Soc. Physical chemistry of medicinal compounds in pharmaceutical and biological systems. Address: Smith Kline & French Lab, 1500 Spring Garden St, Philadelphia, PA 19101.

GUTTMAN, H(ELENE) A(UGUSTA) N(ATHAN), b. New York, N.Y, July 21, 30; m. 62. MICROBIOLOGY, BIOCHEMISTRY. B.A, Brooklyn Col, 51; Andelot fel, Harvard, 54-55, A.M, 56; M.A, Columbia, 58; scholar, Rutgers, 59-60, Ph.D.(bact), 60. Res. technician immunol, Pub. Health Res. Inst. New York, 51-52; control bacteriologist, Burroughs-Wellcome, Inc, 52-53; asst. protozool, Haskins Labs, 53-56, res. assoc, 56-59, staff microbiologist, 60-64; res. assoc, Goucher Col, 60-62; asst. prof. biochem. & cell physiol, univ. col. & grad. sch. arts & sci, N.Y. Univ, 62-65, assoc. prof, 65-67; biol. sci, UNIV. ILL, CHICAGO CIRCLE, 67-69, PROF. BIOL. SCI. & MEM. GRAD. FACULTY, DEPT. MICROBIOL, SCH. MED, 69- Dazian Found. fel, 56; lectr, Queens Col.(N.Y), 56-57; Soc. Am. Bacteriologists President's fel, 57; res. collab, Brookhaven Nat. Labs, 58; res. asst. prof, Med. Col, Va, 60-62; res. grants, Nat. Insts. Health, 56-69, Nat. Sci. Found, 59, 62, 64, Atomic Energy Comn, 65; grants, John A. Hartford Found, 70-, Fed. Water Pollution Control Agency, 70- Fel. AAAS; fel. Am. Inst. Chem; Biophys. Soc; Tissue Culture Asn; Am. Soc. Neurochem; Soc. Neurosci; Am. Soc. Cell Biol; Am. Soc. Microbiol; N.Y. Acad. Sci; Soc. Exp. Biol. & Med; Soc. Indust. Microbiol; Soc. Protozool; Am. Inst. Nutrit; Brit. Soc. Gen. Microbiol. Protozoan nutrition and biochemistry; pteridine function; autotrophic metabolism; mitochondria, kinetoplast and chloroplast biology; scanning electron microscopy for internal structure; behavioral biochemistry; control of inducible syntheses, especially protein and antibody. Address: Dept. of Biological Sciences, University of Illinois at Chicago Circle, Box 4348, Chicago, IL 60680.

GUTTMAN, IRWIN, b. Montreal, Que, Can, Apr. 23, 30. MATHEMATICAL STATISTICS. B.Sc, McGill, 51; M.A, Toronto, 53, Ph.D.(math. statist), 55. Asst. prof. STATIST, Alberta, 55-57; res. assoc, Princeton, 57-59; assoc. prof, McGill, 59-62; vis. prof, UNIV. WIS, MADISON, 62-63, PROF, 63- Vis. lectr, London Sch. Econ, fall 66; vis. prof, dept. math, Univ. Mass, 69-70. Inst. Math. Statist; Am. Statist. Asn; Royal Statist. Soc; Int. Statist. Inst. Statistical inference-decision theory; Bayesian statistics; non-linear estimation; tolerance regions; Best population problems. Address: Dept. of Statistics, University of Wisconsin, Madison, WI 53706.

GUTTMAN, LESTER, b. Minneapolis, Minn, Apr. 18, 19; m. 55. PHYSICAL CHEMISTRY. B.Chem, Minnesota, 40; Ph.D.(chem), California, 43. Asst. chem, California, 40-42; assoc. scientist, Manhattan Eng. Dist, U.S. War Dept, N.Mex, 43-46; res. assoc, inst. study metals, Chicago, 46-47, instr, 47-48, asst. prof, 49-55; Guggenheim fel, U.K. Atomic Energy Auth, Eng, 55-56; phys. chemist, res. lab, Gen. Elec. Co, 56-60; SR. CHEMIST, ARGONNE NAT. LAB, 60- With Off. Sci. Res. & Develop, 43. Fel. Am. Phys. Soc. Statistical thermodynamics of alloys; x-ray diffraction from alloys. Address: Solid State Science Division, Argonne National Lab, 9700 S. Cass Ave, Argonne, IL 60439.

GUTTMAN, NEWMAN, b. Minneapolis, Minn, Apr. 4, 27; m. 62. EXPERIMENTAL PSYCHOLOGY. B.A, Minnesota, 49; A.M, Illinois, 51, Ph.D. (speech), 54. Res. assoc. speech, Illinois, 54-55; asst, Mass. Inst. Tech, 55-56; MEM. TECH. STAFF, BELL TEL. LABS, NAPERVILLE, 56- Mem, sensory study sect, social & rehab. serv, Dept. Health, Educ. & Welfare, D.C, 65-69; subcomt. sensory aids, comt. prosthetics res. & develop, Nat. Res. Coun, 69-, comt. bioacoustics & biomech, 70- U.S.N, 45-46. Fel. Acoustical Soc. Am; fel. Am. Speech & Hearing Asn. Psychoacoustics; phonetics; speech and hearing pathology. Address: 916 60th Place, Downers Grove, IL 60515.

GUTTMAN, PAUL H, b. Hungary, Sept. 26, 01; U.S. citizen; m. 29; c. 3. PATHOLOGY, RADIATION BIOLOGY. M.D, Washington (St. Louis), 27; Ph.D, Minnesota, 31. Asst. prof. path, Colorado, 30-32; pathologist, Sutter Hospital, Sacramento, Calif, 32-58; res. pathologist, MED. CTR, UNIV. CALIF, SAN FRANCISCO, 58-66, ASSOC. RES. PATHOLOGIST, CANCER RES. INST, 66- Fel. Am. Soc. Clin. Path; Am. Asn. Path. & Bact; Radiation Res. Soc. Address: Cancer Research Institute, Medical Center, University of California, San Francisco, CA 94122.

GUTTMAN, RITA, b. New York, N.Y, Mar. 17, 12. PHYSIOLOGY. B.A, Columbia, 33, M.A, 35, Ph.D.(physiol), 39. Instr. PHYSIOL, BROOKLYN COL, 36-49, asst. prof, 49-58, assoc. prof, 59-70, PROF, 71- Am. Acad. Arts & Sci, Bache Fund & Nat. Insts. Health res. grants. Am. Physiol. Soc; Biophys. Soc. Electrical properties of nerve and muscle fiber membranes, especially electrical impedance, rectification, bioelectric potentials during rest, activity and narcosis; effect of temperature on excitation. Address: Dept. of Biology, Brooklyn College, Brooklyn, NY 11210.

GUTTMAN, SAMUEL ARNOLD, b. New York, N.Y, Sept. 13, 14; m. 40, 63; c. 2. PSYCHIATRY. A.B, Cornell, 34, M.A, 35, Ph.D.(neurol. physiol), 37, M.D, 40. Asst. instr, Cornell, 34-37; asst. neurologist, col. physicians & surg, Columbia, 42-44; fel. psychiat. training, dept. nervous & mental diseases, Pa. Hosp. & Inst, 44-45; consult. psychiatrist, dept. psychol, Pennsylvania, 45-47, instr. psychiat, sch. med, 46-60; assoc. prof. clin. psychiat, JEFFERSON MED. COL, 60-67, PROF. PSYCHOANAL, 67- Faculty & training analyst, Inst. Phila. Asn. Anal, 50- Fel. from Cornell, Marine Biol. Lab, Woods Hole, 36; asst. res. & chief res. neurologist, Neurol. Inst, N.Y, 42-44; asst. neuropsychiatrist, Jewish Hosp, Phila, 45-47; dir, Child Psychiat. Center, Scranton, 47-55; consult. psychiat, Family Serv. Asn, Scranton & Wilkes-Barre, 48-53; chief div. psychiat, Wilkes-Barre Gen. Hosp, 48-55. AAAS; Am. Med. Asn; Am. Psychiat. Asn; Asn. Res. Nerv. & Ment. Disease; Am. Psychoanal. Asn; N.Y. Acad. Sci; Int. Psychoanal. Asn. Psychoanalysis; experimental medicine; neurophysiology. Address: Dept. of Psychiatry, Jefferson Medical College of Philadelphia, Tenth & Walnut Sts, Philadelphia, PA 19107.

GUTTMAN, SHELDON, b. New York, N.Y, Mar. 9, 41; m. 63. ZOOLOGY. B.S, City Univ. New York, 62; M.A, Texas, 65, Ph.D.(evolution), 67. Asst. prof. ZOOL, MIAMI UNIV, 67-71, ASSOC. PROF, 71- Soc. Study Evolution; Ecol. Soc. Am; Soc. Study Amphibians & Reptiles. Ecology and evolution of the amphibians and reptiles; biochemical genetics and biochemical taxonomy. Address: Dept. of Zoology, Miami University, Oxford, OH 45056.

GUTTMANN, ANDREW T(ITUS), b. Thorn, Ger, Feb. 6, 25; U.S. citizen; m. 50; c. 3. ORGANIC & PHYSICAL ORGANIC CHEMISTRY. M.S, Munich Tech, 53. Res. chemist, Armour & Co, 53-57, sect. head org. synthesis, 57-61; tech. specialist, STANDARD OIL CO.(OHIO), 61-64, SR. RES. CHEMIST, 64- Am. Chem. Soc; fel. Am. Inst. Chem. Synthesis of surfactants, bacteriostatic agents and plasticizers; processes for monomer production; vapor and liquid-phase oxidation of hydrocarbons; chemistry of combustion and flames; composition and performance of motor fuels. Address: Standard Oil Co.(Ohio), Research Dept, 4440 Warrensville Center Rd, Cleveland, OH 44128.

GUTTMANN, MARK, F.S.C, b. Baltimore, Md, Aug. 10, 24. NUCLEAR PHYSICS. B.S, Catholic Univ, 47, M.S, 56; Ph.D.(physics), Notre Dame, 62. Teacher, high sch, Pa, 47-53; instr. PHYSICS, La Salle Col, 53-55; De La Salle Col, 55-56; asst. prof, LA SALLE COL, 62-70, ASSOC. PROF, 70- Am. Phys. Soc; Am. Asn. Physics Teachers. Beta and gamma ray spectroscopy; optics. Address: Dept. of Physics, La Salle College, Philadelphia, PA 19141.

GUTTMANN, RONALD D, b. Minneapolis, Minn, Aug. 16, 36. IMMUNOLOGY, NEPHROLOGY. B.A, Univ. Minn, 58, B.S. & M.D, 61. Instr. med, Harvard Med. Sch, 67-70; ASSOC. PROF. MED. & SURG, McGILL UNIV, 70- U.S.N.R, Lt. Comdr. Transplantation Soc; Int. Soc. Nephrology; Can. Soc. Immunol; Am. Asn. Immunol; Am. Soc. Exp. Path. Transplantation immunology, especially clinical and basic transplantation research. Address: Royal Victoria Hospital, 687 Pine Ave. W, Montreal 112, Que, Can.

GUTTWEIN, GUNTER K(ARL), b. Bingen, Ger, Oct. 23, 06; nat; m. 36; c. 2. PHYSICS. Dipl.Ing, Tech. Univ. Berlin, 31, Dr.Ing.(elec. eng), 40. CHIEF, PIEZOELEC. CRYSTAL & CIRCUITRY BR, ELECTRONIC COMPONENTS LAB, U.S. ARMY ELECTRONICS COMMAND, FT. MONMOUTH, 47- N.Y. Acad. Sci; Inst. Elec. & Electronics Eng. Acoustics; magnetic recording; mechanical vibrations; frequency control. Address: 43 Stevens Ave, West Long Branch, NJ 07764.

GUTZ, HERBERT, b. Berlin, Ger, June 16, 28; m. 53; c. 4. MICROBIOLOGY. Dr. rer. nat. (bot), Free Univ. Berlin, 55. Sci. asst, Free Univ. Berlin, 53-55; Tech. Univ, Berlin, 55-64, asst. prof, 64-65; Grad. Res. Ctr. Southwest, 65-68, ASSOC. PROF, 68-70, BIOL, UNIV. TEX, DALLAS, 70- Res. fel, Univ. Zurich, 59-60. German Air Force, 44. AAAS; Mycol. Soc. Am; Genetics Soc. Am; Ger. Bot. Soc; Ger. Soc. Hyg. & Microbiol; Ger. Soc. Genetics. Genetics of fungi, especially of yeasts; cytology of fungi; general and industrial microbiology. Address: Division of Biology, University of Texas at Dallas, P.O. Box 30365, Dallas, TX 75230.

GUTZMAN, WAYNE W(ALLACE), b. Kensington, Kans, Mar. 22, 16; m. 46; c. 5. MATHEMATICS. A.B, Ft. Hays Kans. State Col, 36; M.S, Iowa, 37, Ph.D.(math), 41. Instr. MATH, Hunter Col, 41-42; asst. prof, postgrad. sch, U.S. Naval Acad, 46-47; PROF, UNIV. S.DAK, 47-, CHMN. DEPT, 71-, dean instr, 68-71, acad. & grad. dean, 64-68. U.S.N, 42-46, 51-52, 62-63, Capt. Mathematical statistics. Address: Dept. of Mathematics, University of South Dakota, Vermillion, SD 57069.

GUTZWILLER, MARTIN C(HARLES), b. Basel, Switz, Oct. 12, 25; m. 52; c. 2. THEORETICAL PHYSICS. B.S, Swiss Fed. Inst. Tech, 47, M.S, 50; Ph.D. (physics), Kansas, 53. PHYSICIST, Brown, Boveri & Co, Baden, Switz, 50-51; explor. & prod. res. div, Shell Develop. Co, Tex, 53-60; res. div, Int. Bus. Mach, Zurich, 60-63, Watson Lab, New York, 63-70, T.J. WATSON RES. CTR, IBM CORP, 70- Adj. prof, Columbia Univ, 63- Am. Phys. Soc; Fr. Phys. Soc; Swiss Phys. Soc. Propagation of waves, solid state physics; applied mathematics. Address: T.J. Watson Research Center, IBM Corp, Yorktown Heights, NY 10598.

GÜVEN, NECIP, b. Boyalik, Turkey, Apr. 14, 36. GEOLOGY, MINERALOGY. B.S, Göttingen, 58, Dr. Sci, 62. Fel. mineral, Columbia, 63-65; crystallog, Carnegie Inst. Geophys. Lab, 65-67; ASST. PROF. GEOL, UNIV. ILL, URBANA, 67- Mineral Soc. Am; Am. Crystallog. Asn; Clay Minerals Soc; Am. Geophys. Union. Crystal structure of micas; polymorphism and isomorphism in minerals, application of x-rays for their determinations; x-ray and electron diffraction of clay minerals. Address: Dept. of Geology, University of Illinois, Urbana, IL 61801.

GUY, ALBERT G(LASGOW), b. Chicago, Ill, May 27, 17; m. 38; c. 2. METALLURGY. S.B, Chicago, 38; Lord fel. & M.S, Ohio State, 41; fel. & D.Sc. (metall), Carnegie Inst. Tech, 46. Res. engr, res. lab, Gen. Elec. Co, 44-47; assoc. prof. mech. eng, N.C. State Col, 47-51; chief, metall. br, Off. Ord. Res, 51-52; assoc. prof. METALL, Purdue, 52-55, PROF, 55-60; UNIV. FLA, 60- Exchange scientist, Baikov Metall. Inst, U.S.S.R, 58-59. Am. Soc. Metals; Am. Soc. Eng. Educ; Am. Inst. Mining, Metall. & Petrol. Eng; Brit. Inst. Metals. Physical metallurgy; diffusion in metals; x-ray studies of metallic structures; materials science. Address: Dept. of Metallurgical & Materials Engineering, University of Florida, Gainesville, FL 32601.

GUY, CHARLES A(LBERT), b. Osage, W.Va, Dec. 14, 28; m. 53; c. 2. ANALYTICAL CHEMISTRY. B.A, West Virginia, 53. Jr. chemist, hydrocarbon div., OLIN MATHIESON CHEM. CORP, W.Va, 53-54, anal. chemist, indust. div, 54, supvr. lab, anal. dept, 54-56, group leader chem. anal, 56-58, chief chemist, high energy fuel div, N.Y, 58-61, chem. supt, CHEM. DIV, CHARLESTON, 61-67, SR. PROJ. ENGR, 67- Am. Chem. Soc; Am. Soc. Qual. Control. Caprolactam; hydrazine; dimethyl hydrazine; boranes; high energy fuels 2, 3, 4; research and production of boron fuels; process development and quality control; chlorine, caustic soda and calcium hypochlorite. Address: 1301 Park Ave. N.W, Cleveland, TN 37311.

GUY, E(UGENE) JAMES, b. Rochester, Minn, Dec. 16, 22; m. 48; c. 2. AGRICULTURAL CHEMISTRY. B.Sc, Minnesota, 47, M.S, 53, Ph.D.(agr. biochem), 55. Asst. res. chemist, Green Giant Co, Minn, 47-49; res. chemist, Int. Milling Co, 55-64; RES. FOOD TECHNOLOGIST, DAIRY PROD. LAB, EAST. MKT. & NUTRIT. RES. DIV, AGR. RES. SERV, U.S. DEPT. AGR, 64- U.S.A, 43-45. Am. Asn. Cereal Chem; Inst. Food Technol; Am. Dairy Sci. Asn. Agricultural biochemistry; vitamin chemistry; enzymology; microbiology; grocery products, especially mixes and cereals; dairy chemistry; milk in baked goods. Address: Dairy Products Lab, Eastern Marketing & Nutrition Research Division, Agricultural Research Service, U.S. Dept. of Agriculture, 14th & Independence Ave. S.W, Washington, DC 20250.

GUY, GEORGE A(NDERSON), b. Love, Miss, Nov. 10, 14; m. 39; c. 1. METEOROLOGY. B.S, Memphis State Col, 36; Mass. Inst. Tech; M.A, California, Los Angeles; Indust. Col. Armed Forces; M.B.A, George Washington, 62. Meteorologist, U.S. Air Force, 43-49, chief equip. develop, Hqs, Air Weather Serv, 49-52, meteorol. equip. develop, Hqs, Air Res. & Develop. Command, 52-57, Weather Syst. Proj. Off, 57-62, tactical syst. prog. off, Syst. Command, 63-67; SR. ENGR, HUGHES AIRCRAFT CO, 67- U.S.A.F, 43-67, Col. Am. Meteorol. Soc; Am. Geophys. Union; N.Y. Acad. Sci. Meteorological instrumentation; electronic systems program management. Address: 8207 Owens St, Buena Park, CA 90620.

GUY, HAROLD P, b. Brighton, Iowa, Aug. 5, 22; m. 44; c. 4. SEDIMENTOLOGY, HYDROLOGY. B.S, Iowa State Univ, 47 & 48, M.S, 51. Field hydrologist, Iowa State Univ, 48-51; hydraul. engr, U.S. GEOL. SURV, Kans, 51-55 & Nebr, 55-56, hydraul. res. engr, Wash, D.C, 56-62, RES. HYDROLOGIST, Colo, 62-71, WASHINGTON, D.C, 71- AAAS; Am. Soc. Civil Eng; Soil Conserv. Soc. Am; Am. Geophys. Union. Sediment transport; residential and highway construction areas; flow resistance and sediment transport, alluvial channels; instrumentation for sensing sediment in suspensions; sediment erosion and deposition from catastrophic storms. Address: U.S. Geological Survey, 2138 Quorn Lane, Reston, VA 22070.

GUY, HUBERT G(RAHAM), b. Boston, Mass, June 19, 06; m; c. 2. ENTOMOLOGY. B.S, Florida, 28; M.S, Ohio State, 33; fel, Delaware, 33-37. Asst. hort, United Fruit Co, 28-30; field aide fruit fly & corn borer control, U.S. Dept. Agr, 30-31; asst. insecticide studies, New Hampshire, 31-32; asst. zool, Ohio State, 32-33; entomologist, E.I. du Pont de Nemours & Co, 37-41; mgr. agr. res. sect, Koppers Co, Inc, 41-50, br. mgr. mkt. develop. sect, chem. div, 50-65, tech. dir. coatings sect, SINCLAIR-KOPPERS CO, 65-68, MGR. PROD. DEVELOP, 68- Am. Chem. Soc; Tech. Asn. Pulp & Paper Indust. Development of agricultural chemicals from coal and its derivatives; organic insecticides and fungicides; paper coatings; paints; textile sizings. Address: 132 Meadowbrook Dr, Coraopolis, PA 15108.

GUY, L(EONA) RUTH, b. Kemp, Tex, Mar. 17, 13. IMMUNOLOGY. A.B, Baylor, 34, M.S, 49; Nat. Tuberc. Asn. Trudeau fel, Stanford, 51-53, Ph.D, 53. Instr. bact, sch. dent, Baylor, 48-49; clin. asst. prof. microbiol, UNIV. TEX. (SOUTHWEST) MED. SCH, DALLAS, 53-62, asst. prof. PATH, 62-66, ASSOC. PROF, 66-, CHMN. DEPT. MED. TECHNOL, SCH. ALLIED HEALTH PROFESSIONS, 70- Assoc. dir. blood bank, Parkland Mem. Hosp, 53-; consult, Vet. Admin. Hosps, Dallas, 62-, Temple, 64- Am. Soc. Microbiol; Am. Thoracic Soc. Immunohematology; bacteriology. Address: 3016 Leahy Dr, Dallas, TX 75229.

GUY, RICHARD K, b. Nuneaton, Eng, Sept. 30, 16; m. 40; c. 3. MATHEMATICS. B.A, Cambridge, 38, M.A, 41; Dipl.Ed, Birmingham, 39. Teacher, Stockport Grammar Sch, Eng, 39-47; lectr. math, Goldsmith's Col, London, 47-48, sr. lectr, 48-51; lectr, Malaya, 51-53, sr. lectr, 53-62, head dept, 57-60; prof. math. & head dept. math. & humanities, Indian Inst. Tech, Delhi, 62-65; PROF. MATH, UNIV. CALGARY, 65-, head dept, 66-69. R.A.F, 41-46, Flight Lt. Am. Math. Soc; Can. Math. Cong; London Math. Soc; Indian Math. Soc; Malayan Math. Soc. Number theory; game theory; graph theory. Address: Dept. of Mathematics, University of Calgary, Calgary, N.W, Alta, Can.

GUY, ROLAND A(NDRE), b. La Chaux-de-Fonds, Switz, July 7, 19; m. 47. APPLIED MATHEMATICS. Lic, Geneva, 45; dipl, Paris, 51, D.Sc.(math), 54. Prof. math. & phys, Sem. Collónges, France, 46-50; asst, Nat. Sci. Res. Center, France, 51-54; Swiss Fed. Inst. Tech, 54-58; UNIV. MONTREAL, 58-59, asst. prof. MATH, 59-61, ASSOC. PROF, 61- Math. Soc. France; Swiss Math. Soc; Math. Soc. Can. Geometry; mathematical physics; relativity in connection with theory of connections of manifolds; differential geometry of higher order. Address: Faculty of Sciences, University of Montreal, P.O. Box 6128, Montreal, Que, Can.

GUY, W(ILLIAM) T(HOMAS), JR, b. Abilene, Tex, Dec. 11, 19; m. 41; c. 3. MATHEMATICS. B.S, Agr. & Mech. Col, Texas, 40; M.A, Texas, 48; scholar, Calif. Inst. Technol, 48-51, Ph.D.(math), 51. Design engr, Westinghouse Elec. Corp, 40-42; asst, Calif. Inst. Technol, 48-51; instr. applied math, UNIV. TEX, AUSTIN, 46-48, asst. prof, 51-53, MATH. & ASTRON, 53-56, assoc. prof, 56-59, PROF. & CHMN. DEPT, 59-, RES. SCIENTIST, DEFENSE RES. LAB, 53-, acting chmn. dept, univ, 58-59. C.Eng, U.S.A, 42-46, Res, 41, 46-53. AAAS; Am. Math. Soc; Math. Asn. Am. Tensor, extensor and functional analysis; integral transforms; applied mathematics. Address: Ben. Hall 207, University of Texas at Austin, Austin, TX 78712.

GUYER, EDWIN MICHAEL, b. Cincinnati, Ohio, Nov. 25, 00; m. 26. PHYSICS. A.B, Wisconsin, 23, M.S, 25, Ph.D.(exp. physics), 29. Teacher, pub. sch, Wis, 24; asst. physics, Wisconsin, 26-29; physicist, CORNING GLASS WORKS, 29-48, mgr. elec. glass working dept, 48-69, CONSULT, RES. & DEVELOP. DEPT, 69- AAAS; Am. Phys. Soc; fel. Inst. Elec. & Electronics Eng. Dielectrics and high frequency properties of glass. Address: Research & Development Dept, Corning Glass Works, Sullivan Park, Corning, NY 14830.

GUYER, GORDON E(ARL), b. Kalamazoo, Mich, May 30, 26; m. 50; c. 1. ECOLOGY. B.S, Mich. State Col, 50, M.S, 52, Ph.D.(entom), 54. Asst. prof. ENTOM, MICH. STATE UNIV, 54-59, assoc. prof, 59-63, PROF. & CHMN. DEPT, 63- U.S.A.A.F, 44-47. Am. Entom. Soc; Entom. Soc. Can. Biology and taxonomy of aquatic insects; economic entomology; vegetable and forest insect research. Address: Dept. of Entomology, Michigan State University, East Lansing, MI 48823.

GUYER, K(ENNETH) E(UGENE), (JR), b. Pampa, Tex, June 11, 34; m. 57; c. 2. BIOCHEMISTRY. B.A, Texas, 55; M.Sc, Ohio State, 60, Ph.D.(physiol. chem), 62. Chemist, Celanese Corp, 56-58; res. assoc. physiol. chem, Ohio State, 63; Nat. Heart Inst. fel. physiol. chem, sch. med, Hopkins, 63-64; ASST. PROF. BIOCHEM, MED. COL. VA, 64- U.S.A.R, 56-64. Am. Chem. Soc; Am. Oil Chemists' Soc. Chemistry and metabolism of minor lipids and fat-soluble vitamins. Address: Dept. of Biochemistry, Medical College of Virginia, Richmond, VA 23219.

GUYER, PAUL Q(UENTIN), b. Linn Co, Mo, Mar. 31, 23; m. 48; c. 3. ANIMAL HUSBANDRY. B.S, Missouri, 48, M.A, 49, Ph.D, 54. Instr. animal husb, Missouri, 48-54; asst. exten. animal husbandman, UNIV. NEBR, LINCOLN, 54-57, assoc. exten. animal husbandman, 57-62, PROF. ANIMAL SCI, 62- U.S.A, 44-46. Am. Soc. Animal Sci. Animal nutrition; beef, sheep and swine production. Address: Dept. of Animal Science, College of Agriculture, University of Nebraska, Lincoln, NE 68503.

GUYER, WALTER R(ICHARD) F(ERDINAND), b. Elmira, N.Y, Nov. 22, 14; m. 42; c. 2. CHEMISTRY. B.S, Lehigh Univ, 36, fel, 36-38, M.S, 38; Ph.D. (phys. chem), Princeton, 41. Asst. chem, Princeton, 38-40; from res. chemist & sect. head to sr. staff adv, Esso Res. & Eng. Co, STANDARD OIL CO, N.J, 40-63, SR. BUS. ADV, JERSEY ENTERPRISES INC, 63- European Tech. Liaison Rep. in London, 57-61. Am. Chem. Soc. Calorimetry; vapor pressure; mass spectroscopy; adsorption phenomena; catalysis; fuels processes; adsorption and nitrogen isotope exchange on metallic osmium catalysts; petrochemicals; long range research planning; technological diversification. Address: Jersey Enterprises Inc, 30 Rockefeller Plaza, New York, NY 10020.

GUYMON, ERVIN PARK, b. Cortez, Colo, May 30, 35; m. 56; c. 5. INORGANIC & ANALYTICAL CHEMISTRY. B.S, Utah State Univ, 57, Nat. Sci. Found. fel. & Ph.D.(chem), 65. Asst. prof. CHEM, WEBER STATE COL, 65-69, ASSOC. PROF, 69- U.S.A, 57-59, Res, 59-62, Capt. Mechanisms and reaction kinetics of various model enzyme systems involving molybdenum as a reducing agent. Address: Dept. of Chemistry, Weber State College, Ogden, UT 84403.

GUYMON, JAMES F(UQUA), b. Vermilion, Ill, July 13, 11; m. 35, 58. CHEMICAL ENGINEERING. B.S, Rose Polytech, 33; fel, Iowa State Col, 35-36, Ph.D.(biophys. chem), 39; Leeds, 45. Lab. asst, Commercial Solvents Corp, Ill, 33-35; asst. & instr, Iowa State Col, 37-39; jr. enologist, UNIV. CALIF, DAVIS, 39-40, asst. enologist, 46-52, asst. prof, 47-52, assoc. prof. enol. & assoc. enologist, 52-59, PROF. ENOL. & ENOLOGIST, 59- U.S.A, 41-46, Res, 46-61, Lt. Col, Am. Chem. Soc; Am. Soc. Enol.(pres, 63-64); Inst. Food Tech. Biochemistry and enology; technology of wines and brandies; fermentations; distillation; fusel oil origin and occurrence; analyses; fermentation mechanisms, especially higher alcohol formation; aging of brandies. Address: Dept. of Viticulture & Enology, University of California, Davis, CA 95616.

GUYMON, RALPH H(ERBERT), b. Kansas City, Mo, Mar. 4, 19; m. 44; c. 3. CHEMICAL ENGINEERING. B.S, Illinois, 41. Chemist, Illinois, 39-41; chem. engr, Nat. Analine Chem. Co, 41-42; jr. chem. engr, South. Regional Res. Lab, U.S. Dept. Agr, 42-43; sr. chem. engr, Gustin-Bacon Mfg. Co, 43-47; plant mgr, Lake Rd. Warehouse, 47-52; consult, Woodbury Chem. Co, 52-53; sr. chem. engr, OAK RIDGE NAT. LAB, 53-66, OPERS. CHIEF, MOLTEN SALT REACTOR EXP, 66- Am. Chem. Soc; Am. Inst. Chem. Eng. Power reactors. Address: 115 Dana Dr, Oak Ridge, TN 37830.

GUYON, JOHN CARL, b. Washington, Pa, Oct. 16, 31; m. 55; c. 2. ANALYTICAL CHEMISTRY. B.A, Washington & Jefferson Col, 55; Owen-Illinois fel. & M.S, Toledo, 58; Eli Lilly fel, Purdue, 60-61, Ph.D.(anal. chem), 61. Res. chemist, Thatcher Glass Mfg. Co, N.Y, 57-58; asst. prof. ANAL. CHEM, Missouri, 61-65, assoc. prof, 65-71; PROF. & CHMN. DEPT, MEMPHIS STATE UNIV, 71- Absorption spectroscopy; organic analytical reagents; fluorescence analysis; chromatography; heteropoly compounds. Address: Dept. of Chemistry, Memphis State University, Memphis, TN 38101.

GUYSELMAN, J(OHN) BRUCE, b. Albion, Mich, Mar. 17, 24. ZOOLOGY. A.B, Albion Col, 47; Ph.D.(zool), Northwestern, 52. Instr. zool, Carleton Col, 52-53, asst. prof, 53-57, assoc. prof, 57-64; mem. faculty staff BIOL, ALBION COL, 64-69, PROF, 69- U.S.A, 43-46. Am. Soc. Zool; Am. Soc. Limnol. & Oceanog; Am. Physiol. Soc; Soc. Gen. Physiol. Comparative animal physiology; environmental physiology; biological rhythms. Address: Dept. of Biology, Albion College, Albion, MI 49224.

GUYTON, ARTHUR CLIFTON, b. Oxford, Miss, Sept. 8, 19; m. 43; c. 9. PHYSIOLOGY. B.A, Mississippi, 39; M.D, Harvard, 43. Intern & res. surg, Mass. Gen. Hosp, 43-44, 46; acting assoc. prof. physiol, Tennessee, 47; assoc. prof. pharmacol, MED. CTR, UNIV. MISS, 47-48, PROF. PHYSIOL. & CHMN. DEPT. PHYSIOL. & BIOPHYS, 48- President's Citation, 56. mem. coun, Nat. Heart Inst, U.S. Pub. Health Serv, 71- Med.C, U.S.N.R, 44-46, Lt. AAAS (Gould Award, 60); Am. Physiol. Soc; Biophys. Soc; Am. Heart Asn; Biomed. Eng. Soc. Medical electronic development; circulatory physiology; neurophysiology. Address: Dept. of Physiology & Biophysics, University of Mississippi Medical Center, 2500 N. State St, Jackson, MS 39216.

GUYTON, JAMES W, b. New Albany, Miss, Nov. 3, 32; m. 54. GEOLOGY. A.B, California, Berkeley, 57; M.A, Wyoming, 60, Ph.D.(geol), 65. Jr. geologist, Pan. Am. Petrol. Corp, 57-58; seismologist, Geotech. Corp, 61-64; asst. prof. geol, CHICO STATE COL, 64-69, ASSOC. PROF. GEOL. & PHYS. SCI, 69- U.S.A, 52-55, Sgt. Geol. Soc. Am; Seismol. Soc. Am. Areal geology; microseisms of short period; recent and ancient landslides. Address: Dept. of Natural Science, Chico State College, Chico, CA 95926.

GUZE, LUCIEN B(ARRY), b. N.Y.C, Apr. 12, 28; m. 52; c. 3. MEDICINE. N.Y. Univ; M.D, Washington (St. Louis), 51. Intern internal med, Grady Mem. Hosp, Ga, 51-52; asst. res, Barnes Hosp, Mo, 52-53; res. fel, Am. Heart Asn, Yale, 55-56, U.S. Pub. Health Serv, 56-57; clin. investr, VET. ADMIN. HOSP, 57-59, DIR. RES, 59-; PROF. MED, CTR. HEALTH SCI, UNIV. CALIF, LOS ANGELES, 69-, assoc. prof, 62-69, asst. clin. prof, 57-62. Traveling fel, Am. Soc. Clin. Invest, 60; mem, Nat. Kidney Disease Found. Adminr. Vet. Affairs commendation award, 65; William S. Middleton Award, 65; Arthur S. Flemming Award, 66. Med.C, 53-55, Capt. Am. Fedn. Clin. Res; Am. Soc. Clin. Invest; Asn. Am. Physicians; Infectious Diseases Soc. Am; Soc. Exp. Biol. & Med. Internal medicine; bacteriology; virology; immunology. Address: Veterans Administration Hospital (Wadsworth), Wilshire & Sawtelle Blvds, Los Angeles, CA 90073.

GUZE, SAMUEL B(ARRY), b. New York, N.Y, Oct. 18, 23; m. 46; c. 2. INTERNAL MEDICINE, PSYCHIATRY. M.D, Washington (St. Louis), 45. Intern med, Barnes Hosp, 45-46, fel, 46, 48-49, psychiat, 50-53; res. med, Vet. Admin. Hosp, Conn, 49-50; instr, SCH. MED, WASH. UNIV, 51-53, asst. prof, 53-64, asst. prof. psychiat, 55-59, assoc. prof, 59-64, ASSOC. PROF. MED. & PROF. PSYCHIAT, 64-, DIR. PSYCHIAT. CLIN, 55-, V.CHANCELLOR MED. AFFAIRS, 71-, asst. to dean sch. med, 65-71. Asst. physician, Barnes Hosp, 51-, asst. psychiatrist, 55-63, assoc. psychiatrist, 63-; asst. psychiatrist, Renard Hosp, 55-63, assoc. psychiatrist, 63-; vis. physician & consult, St. Louis City Hosp, 51-; consult, H.G. Phillips Hosp, 54- Dipl, Am. Bd. Internal Med, 54, Am. Bd. Psychiat. & Neurol, 57. Med.C, 46-48, Capt. Psychosom. Soc; Am. Med. Asn; fel. Am. Psychiat. Asn; fel. Am. Col. Physicians; Am. Fedn. Clin. Res; Am. Phytopath. Asn; Asn. Res. Nervous & Ment. Disease; Royal Col. Psychiat; Psychiat. Res. Soc. Natural history of psychiatric disease; effects of drugs on behavior. Address: Dept. of Psychiatry, School of Medicine, Washington University, 4940 Audubon Ave, St. Louis, MO 63110.

GUZIK, FREDERICK F, b. New Kensington, Pa, Nov. 14, 40; m. 62; c. 2. ORGANIC CHEMISTRY. B.S, Duquesne, 62; M.S, Carnegie-Mellon Univ, 65, Ph.D.(org. chem), 66. Sr. res. chemist, PPG INDUSTS, INC, 66-69, RES. ASSOC, 69- Am. Chem. Soc. Organic synthesis; chemical kinetics; process development. Address: 910 Westfield Terr, New Martinsville, WV 26155.

GUZMAN F(ORESTI), MIGUEL A(NGEL), b. San Salvador, El Salvador, Dec. 20, 25; m. 51; c. 4. EXPERIMENTAL STATISTICS, NUTRITION. B.A, Univ. Tenn, 49; M.S, N.C. State Col, 56, Ph.D.(exp. statist), 61. Chief labs. & asst. dir. nutrit-biochem, INST. NUTRIT. CENT. AM. & PANAMA, 53-54, CHIEF DIV. STATIST, 57- Consult, WHO, 59, 66 & 68; E.I. du Pont de Nemours & Co, Inc, 60; U.S. Dept. Agr, 61; vis. assoc. prof, dept. nutrit. & food sci, Mass. Inst. Technol, 64-65, vis. lectr, 66-; vis. res. prof, dept. path, med. ctr, La. State Univ, 71. Am. Statist. Asn; Biomet. Soc; Am. Inst. Nutrit; Am. Asn. Phys. Anthrop; Latin Am. Nutrit. Asn. Human growth and development—physical and mental; math methods in biology—applications to estimation procedures; mathematical models—growth, biological value of proteins, ecosystems; experimental design—variance components and their application. Address: Institute of Nutrition of Central America & Panama, Division of Statistics, Apartado 11-88, Guatemala.

GUZMAN, RUBEN J(OSEPH), b. Riverbank, Calif, Mar. 28, 29; m. 51; c. 1. TOXICOLOGY, PHARMACOLOGY. B.S, Univ. Calif, Berkeley, 53, M.S, 60. Head toxicol. sect, CUTTER LABS, 60-71, TOXICOL. RES. MGR, 71- U.S.A. Soc. Toxicol; Environ. Mutagen Soc; Am. Asn. Lab. Animal Sci. Chemical carcinogenesis; chemical myocarditis; agents affecting the blood; inhalation toxicology; biological effects of air pollution; evaluation of the toxicity of new drugs and plastics. Address: Research Division, Cutter Labs, Fourth & Parker St, Berkeley, CA 94710.

GUZMAN, VICTOR L(IONEL), b. Huaraz, Peru, May 14, 14; nat; m. 46; c. 5. HORTICULTURE. B.S, Nat. Col. Agr, Peru, 40; M.S, Florida, 42; Ph.D, Cornell, 45. Asst. prof. hort, La. State, 45-46; head dept, La Molina Exp. Sta. & Nat. Col. Agr, Peru, 46-51; asst. horticulturist, UNIV. FLA, 52-56, mgr. Sullivans Farm, 56-58, assoc. horticulturist, 58-66, HORTICULTURIST, 66- Am. Soc. Hort. Sci; Am. Soc. Plant Physiol; Am. Inst. Biol. Sci. Nutrition of vegetable crop plants and cultural practices; growth regulators. Address: Agricultural Research & Education Center, University of Florida, P.O. Drawer A, Belle Glade, FL 33430.

GUZZETTA, FRANKLIN H, b. Fredonia, N.Y, May 2, 33; m. 55; c. 2. PHYSICAL & INORGANIC CHEMISTRY. B.S, Ohio State, 57, Ph.D.(phys. & inorg. chem), 61. RES. CHEMIST, Knolls Atomic Power Lab, Gen. Elec. Co, N.Y, 61-64; Owens Corning Fiberglas Tech. Ctr, Ohio, 64-69; ARMCO RES. CTR, MIDDLETOWN, 69- Am. Chem. Soc; Am. Soc. Metals. Thermochemistry applied to Ligand field theory; chemistry at the interfaces of glass; materials science; physical metallurgy. Address: 781 Wicklow Lane, Monroe, OH 45050.

GUZZLE, TIM L, b. Ottumwa, Iowa, Nov. 4, 36; m. 59; c. 2. PHYSICS. B.A, Oklahoma, 58, U.S. Atomic Energy Comn. fel, 58-59, M.S, 59; Nat. Sci. Found. fel, Texas Christian, 64-65, Ph.D.(physics), 65. Res. physicist, Atomics Int. Div, N.Am. Aviation, Inc, 59-61; res. scientist, LTV Res. Ctr, Tex, 65-66; PROJ. ENGR, GEN. DYNAMICS/FT. WORTH, 66- Adj. prof, Tex. Christian Univ, 65- Am. Phys. Soc. Magnetic resonance; Gunn effect in n-GaAs. Address: 2441 Medford Ct. E, Ft. Worth, TX 76109.

GVOSDETSKY, VASYL MICHAEL, b. Khreschchatyk, Ukraine, Dec. 29, 01; U.S. citizen; m. 35. SOIL SCIENCE, GEOGRAPHY. B.C, Kiev, 27, M.S, 30, Ph.D.(soil sci), 36. Soil scientist, Ukrainian Res. Inst. Soils, Kiev, 27-33; sr. res. scientist, All Union Sugar Beet Res. Inst, 33-41; lectr. GEOG, UNIV. UTAH, 50-62, assoc. prof, 62-68, prof, 68-70, EMER. PROF, 70- Asn. Am. Geog; Am. Asn. Quaternary Environ. Quaternary climates; sediments, hydrology, living and fossil soils and past climates of the Bonneville Basin; fallout radionuclides in soils in relation to radioactivity of milk. Address: 1185 Princeton Ave, Salt Lake City, UT 84105.

GWADZ, ROBERT WALTER, b. Chicago, Ill, Nov. 24, 40; m. 63; c. 3. MEDICAL ENTOMOLOGY, INSECT PHYSIOLOGY. B.S, Notre Dame, 62, Nat. Defense Ed. Act fel, 66-69, Nat. Insts. Health fel, 69-70, Ph.D.(biol), 70. NAT. INSTS. HEALTH FEL, DEPT. TROP. PUB. HEALTH, SCH. PUB. HEALTH, HARVARD, 70- U.S.N, 62-66, Res, 66-, Lt. Am. Entom. Soc; Am. Mosquito Control Asn; Am. Soc. Trop. Med. & Hyg. Reproductive physiology; insect genetics; biological control; host-parasite relationship. Address: Dept. of Tropical Public Health, Harvard School of Public Health, 665 Huntington Ave, Boston, MA 02115.

GWALTNEY, JACK MERRIT, JR, b. Norfolk, Va, Dec. 24, 30; m. 54; c. 2. MEDICINE. B.A, Univ. Va, 52, M.D, 56. Intern, univ. hosps, Cleveland, Ohio, 56-57, resident internal med, 57-59; chief resident, Univ. Va. Hosp, 59-60, prof. asst. respiratory virus res, SCH. MED, UNIV. VA, 62-63, res. fel. med. & prev. med, 63-64, instr, 64-66, asst. prof, 66-70, ASSOC. PROF. INTERNAL MED. & HEAD SECT. EPIDEMIOL. & VIROL, 70- Trudeau fel, Am. Thoracic Soc, 64-67; assoc. mem. comn. acute respiratory diseases, Armed Forces Epidemiol. Bd, 68; mem. adv. panel infectious disease ther, U.S. Pharmacopeia, 70. U.S.A, 60-62, Capt. Am. Fedn. Clin. Res; Am. Pub. Health Asn; Am. Soc. Microbiol; Am. Thoracic Soc; Asn. Teachers Prev. Med; fel. Am. Col. Physicians. Etiology and epidemiology of the acute respiratory diseases; virology; rhinoviruses; antiviral compounds. Address: Dept. of Internal Medicine, University of Virginia School of Medicine, Charlottesville, VA 22901.

GWATHMEY, EDWARD S(MITH), b. Norfolk, Va, Nov. 4, 09; m. 44; c. 2. PHYSICS. B.S, Virginia, 30, M.S, 32; Columbia Univ, 33-36; Ph.D.(physics), N.Y. Univ, 37. Instr. physics, Virginia, 30-32; City Col. New York, 33-37; res. dir, Specialties, Inc, 46-48; v.pres. in charge new develop, Feed Prods, Inc, 48-50; res. dir, Specialties, Inc, 50-65, v.pres, 57-65; dir. eng. & res, automated specialties div, TELEDYNE, INC, 65-69, GEN. MGR, TELEDYNE AVIONICS DIV, 69- Instr, N.Y. Univ, 33-34. Order of the British Empire. U.S.N.R, 37-46, Comdr. AAAS; Assoc. fel. Am. Inst. Aeronaut. & Astronaut. Airborne fire control; guided missiles; aircraft instruments; quantum mechanical effects on kinetic transport phenomena; industrial controls. Address: Teledyne Avionics Division, Teledyne, Inc, P.O. Box 888, Charlottesville, VA 22902.

GWATKIN, R(ALPH) B(UCHANAN) L(LOYD), b. Newport, Eng, May 23, 29; nat; m. 54; c. 3. REPRODUCTIVE & CELL BIOLOGY. B.A, Univ. Toronto, 50; M.A, 51; univ. fel. & Ph.D.(microbiol), Rutgers Univ, 54. Fel. plant path, Univ. Ill, 54-55; res. assoc. Connaught Med. Res. Labs, Univ. Toronto, 56-60; assoc, Wistar Inst, Univ. Pa, 60-63, asst. prof. reproductive physiol, sch. vet. med, 63-66; HEAD EXP. CELL RES, MERCK INST. THERAPEUT. RES, 67-, ASST. DIR. EXP. BIOL, 69- Nat. Insts. Health career develop. award, 64. Soc. Study Reproduction; Am. Soc. Cell Biol; Int. Soc. Cell Biol; Tissue Cult. Asn; Am. Fertil. Soc.(Rubin Award, 67); N.Y. Acad. Sci. Sperm-egg interactions; tissue and organ culture, both basic and applied. Address: Merck Institute for Therapeutic Research, Rahway, NJ 07065.

GWIAZDA, S(TANLEY) J(OHN), b. Phila, Pa, Feb. 14, 22; m. 44; c. 1. MECHANICAL ENGINEERING. B.S, Drexel Inst, 44, M.S, 52. ASSOC. PROF. MECH. ENG, DREXEL UNIV, 46-, DEAN EVE. COL, 63-, head counsr, 51-61. U.S.N, 44-46, Res, 46-, Lt. Comdr. Am. Soc. Eng. Educ. Ordnance mechanisms; stress analysis and machine design problems. Address: Evening College, Drexel University, 32nd & Chestnut Sts, Philadelphia, PA 19104.

GWILLIAM, G(ILBERT) F(RANKLIN), b. Park City, Utah, Aug. 28, 25; m. 50; c. 2. ZOOLOGY. A.B, California, 50, Ph.D.(zool), 56. Fel. marine biol, Scripps Inst, California, 56-57; instr. BIOL, REED COL, 57-58, asst. prof, 58-63, assoc. prof, 63-68, PROF, 68- Nat. Sci. Found. sr. fel, 64-65. U.S.N.R, 43-46, 50-52. AAAS; Am. Soc. Zool; Am. Chem. Soc. Functional morphology of invertebrates; neuromuscular mechanisms in invertebrates; invertebrate sensory physiology; general invertebrate zoology. Address: Dept. of Biology, Reed College, Portland, OR 97202.

GWILT, JOHN RUFF, b. Worcester, Eng, Aug. 18, 20; m. 45; c. 3. CHEMISTRY, PHARMACEUTICS. B.Sc, Univ. London, 47, Ph.D.(chem), 53. Chemist, Chas H. Phillips Div, STERLING DRUG INC, 47-56, dir, Winthrop Labs. Div, 56-67, V.PRES, WINTHROP PROD. DIV, 67- Lectr, Acton Tech. Col. Eng, 49-55. Fel. Royal Inst. Chem; Brit. Inst. Mgt; The Chem. Soc; Brit. Soc. Anal. Chem; Soc. Chem. Indust; N.Y. Acad. Sci. Analytical and synthetic chemistry; biopharmaceutics; quality control philosophies; management of people, particularly scientists. Address: 85 Myrtle Ave, Dobbs Ferry, NY 10522.

GWIN, REGINALD, b. Chattanooga, Tenn, Jan. 14, 24; m. 48; c. 5. PHYSICS. B.S, Chattanooga, 48; M.S, Emory, 49; Ph.D.(physics), Tennessee, 62. Assoc. prof. physics, Mercer, 49-50; PHYSICIST, gaseous diffusion plant, Union Carbide Corp, 50-52, Y-12 plant, 52-55, OAK RIDGE NAT. LAB, 55- U.S.A.A.F, 43-45, T/Sgt. Am. Phys. Soc; Am. Nuclear Soc; Sci. Res. Soc. Am. Measurement of capture and fission cross sections of fissile isotopes as a function of energy. Address: Route 4, Wakefield Rd, Concord, TN 37720.

GWINN, H(ERBERT) R(AY), b. Hinton, W.Va, Dec. 20, 21; m. 43; c. 2. ANALYTICAL CHEMISTRY. B.S, Marshall, 43. Chemist, org. anal, E.I. du Pont de Nemours & Co, 43-46; isotopic anal, Y-12 Plant, Carbide & Carbon Chem. Corp, 46-54, dept. head, Union Carbide Nuclear Co. Div, UNION CARBIDE CORP, 54-60, AREA SUPVR. NUCLEAR DIV, 60- AAAS; Am. Chem. Soc. Electromagnetic separation of isotopes; chemical purification. Address: 105 Wood Ridge Lane, Oak Ridge, TN 37830.

GWINN, IRA J(AMES), b. Maplewood, W.Va, Apr. 19, 98; m. 36; c. 2. PHYSICS. B.A, Morningside Col, 22, D.Sc, 63; M.S, Iowa, 26. Instr, Morningside Col, 22-24; asst, Iowa, 24-26; asst. prof. physics, Morningside Col, 26-30, eng. physics, surv, eng. drawing & elec. eng, 30-40, eng. drawing, aviation & radio, 40-44, instr. physics & math, war training serv. & col. training detachment, 42-44, registrar, 44-68, asst. prof. physics, 44-54, assoc. prof, 54-68, admin. asst. to pres, 58-68; RETIRED. U.S.A, 17-19. Assoc. Optical Soc. Am; assoc. Am. Soc. Eng. Educ. Micro-photometry. Address: 3315 Peters Ave, Sioux City, IA 51106.

GWINN, JOEL A(LDERSON), b. Quinnimont, W.Va, Feb. 24, 29; m. 54; c. 4. PHYSICS. B.S.Ed, West Virginia, 51, M.A, 56, M.S, 57, Ph.D.(physics), 62. Instr. PHYSICS, UNIV. LOUISVILLE, 61-62, asst. prof, 62-66, assoc. prof, 66-70, PROF, 70- Fulbright grantee, Univ. Munich, 57-58. C.Eng, 51-53, 1st Lt. Am. Asn. Physics Teachers. Address: Dept. of Physics, University of Louisville, Louisville, KY 40208.

GWINN, RODNEY P(ENROD), b. Seattle, Wash, July 7, 18; m. 44. MEDICINE. B.S, Washington (Seattle), 40, M.S, 41; fel, Minnesota, 41-43; fel, Wisconsin, 48-49, M.D, 49. Inst. gen. chem, Washington (Seattle, 40-41; instr, Minnesota, 41-43, physiol. chem, Wisconsin, 45-46; private practice, 52-53; CLIN. ASSOC. MED, MED. SCH, NORTHWEST UNIV, 53- Mem. staff, med. res, Abbott Labs, 53-59, dir. clin. res, 59-64, med. dir, 64-69; dir. clin. res, G.D. Searle & Co, 69-71. U.S.A, 44-45; U.S.A.F, 49-52, Maj. Am. Chem. Soc; Am. Fedn. Clin. Res; Am. Soc. Clin. Pharmacol. & Therapeut; Aerospace Med. Asn. Conductivity studies of organic chemicals; muscle chemistry. Address; 2408 Elmwood, Wilmette, IL 60091.

GWINN, W(ILLIA)M D(ULANEY), b. Bloomington, Ill, Sept. 28, 16; m. 42, 53; c. 3. PHYSICAL CHEMISTRY. A.B, Missouri, 37, M.A, 39; Ph.D.(chem), California, 42. Instr. CHEM, UNIV. CALIF, BERKELEY, 42-45, asst. prof, 45-49, assoc. prof, 49-55, PROF, 55-, res. prof, Miller Res. Inst, 61-62. Guggenheim fel, 54; Sloan res. fel, 55-59; vis. prof, Univ. Minn, Minneapolis, 69-70. Res. assoc, div. 10, Nat. Defense Res. Comt, 42-44; Manhattan Dist. Proj, 44-45. Fel. Am. Phys. Soc. Microwave spectroscopy and molecular structure; direct digital control of experiments. Address: Dept. of Chemistry, University of California, Berkeley, CA 94720.

GWINNER, PAUL ADOLPH, b. Phila, Pa, June 4, 36. PHYSICAL ORGANIC CHEMISTRY. B.S, Drexel Inst, 59; Am. Petrol. Inst. fel, Pa. State, 61-65, Ph.D.(chem), 65. Res. chemist, east. lab, E.I. du Pont de Nemours & Co, N.J, 65-66; Kettering Found. fel. & intern CHEM, Kenyon Col, 66-67; asst. prof. Simpson Col, 67-69; HEIDELBERG COL, 69-71, ASSOC. PROF, 71- Dir. summer org. chem. inst, Choate Sch, Conn, 67-70. Am. Chem. Soc; Franklin Inst. Organolithium-Lewis base complexes; structure problems in organolithium chemistry; synthesis and reactions of fulvenes. Address: Dept. of Chemistry, Heidelberg College, Tiffin, OH 44883.

GWINNETT, A. JOHN, b. Wombourn, Eng, Sept. 2, 36; m. 67; c. 2. ORAL MICROANATOMY. B.D.S, Univ. Birmingham, 59; Leverhulme fel, Bristol Univ, 61-64, Ph.D.(oral microanat), 64. Resident oral surgeon, Queen Elizabeth Hosp, Birmingham, Eng, 59-60; private practice dent, 60-61; Fulbright res. fel, Eastman Dent. Ctr, N.Y, 64-65; res. assoc, Nat. Inst. Dent. Res, Md, 65-67; asst. prof. microanat, Dalhousie Univ, 67-69; ASSOC. PROF. MICROANAT. & RESTORATIVE DENT, UNIV. WEST. ONT, 69- Consult, Eastman Dent. Ctr, 67-; Med. Res. Coun. grantee, Dalhousie Univ. & Univ. West. Ont, 67-, scholar, Univ. West. Ont, 69-; chmn, Can. Biennial Res. Conf, 70-; consult, Dept. Public Health, Ont, 71- Int. Asn. Dent. Res. Microstructure of normal human dental enamel and its significance with respect to dental decay; physical interface relationship between enamel and adhesive sealants destined for use in the prevention of tooth decay. Address: Dept. of Anatomy, University of Western Ontario, London 72, Ont, Can.

GWINUP, GRANT, b. Denver, Colo, June 28, 29; m. 55; c. 2. INTERNAL MEDICINE. B.A, Colorado, 53, M.D, 56. U.S. Pub. Health Serv. fel, 59-60; instr. internal med, med. sch, Texas, 60-61; asst. prof. internal med. & endocrinol, health ctr, Ohio State, 62-65; ASSOC. PROF. ENDOCRINOL. & CHMN. DIV. METAB, Univ. Calif-Calif. Col. Med, 65-69; UNIV. CALIF, IRVINE, 69- Ed, Metabolism, 66- Dipl, Am. Bd. Int. Med. U.S.A.F, 48-49. Am. Fedn. Clin. Res; Am. Diabetes Asn; Endocrine Soc. Endocrinology and metabolism. Address: Dept. of Medicine, University of Calif, Irvine, CA 92664.

GWINUP, PAUL D, b. Shawnee, Okla, Oct. 13, 31; m. 57; c. 3. PHYSICAL & INORGANIC CHEMISTRY. B.S, Okla. State, 57, Ph.D.(chem), 67. ASSOC. PROF. CHEM, ARK. STATE UNIV, 65- U.S.A.F, 50-53. Am. Chem. Soc. Thermoanalytical chemistry; single crystal x-ray diffraction. Address: P.O. Box 908, State University, AR 72467.

GWYN, CHARLES WILLIAM, b. Sterling, Colo, Sept. 3, 36; m. 57; c. 3. ELECTRICAL ENGINEERING. B.S, Kansas, 61; M.S, New Mexico, 63, Sandia Corp. grant, 63-68, Ph.D.(elec. eng), 68. STAFF MEM. NUCLEAR RADIATION EFFECTS, SANDIA CORP, 61- Res. assoc. & instr. elec. eng, New Mexico, 67-68. Inst. Elec. & Electronics Eng. Nuclear radiation effects in semiconductor devices and electronic circuits. Address: Division 1933, Sandia Labs, Box 5800, Albuquerque, NM 87115.

GWYN, J(OHN) E(DWARD), b. La Junta, Colo, Dec. 5, 27; m. 47; c. 2. CHEMICAL ENGINEERING. B.S, Colorado, 50; M.S, Wisconsin, 52, Ph.D, 55. Asst. chem. eng, Wisconsin, 50-52, res. assoc, eng. exp. sta, 52-55; res. engr, SHELL OIL CO, 55-62, sr. res. engr, 62-67, staff res. engr, 67-70, SR. STAFF RES. ENGR, 70- U.S.A, 46-47. Am. Chem. Soc; Nat. Soc. Prof. Eng; Am. Inst. Chem. Eng. Chemical and petroleum processes. Address: 2402 Marlen Ave, Pasadena, TX 77502.

GWYNN, BERNARD H(ENRY), b. Bellefontaine, Ohio, Sept. 24, 15; m. 45; c. 2. ORGANIC CHEMISTRY. A.B, Ohio Northern, 37; M.S, Purdue, 39, Ph.D.(org. chem), 42. Res. chemist, Westvaco Chlorine Prod, N.J, 41-42; GULF RES. & DEVELOP. CO, Pa, 42-52, asst. sect. head petrochem. sect, 52-55, sect. head, 55-61, tech. assoc, 61-66, dir, Kansas City Div, Kans, 66-67, managing dir, Kansas City Lab, 67-68, DIR. CHEM. DEPT, PA, 68- Am. Chem. Soc. Hydrocarbon chemistry; petrochemicals. Address: Gulf Research & Development Co, P.O. Box 2038, Pittsburgh, PA 15230.

GWYNN, DONALD EUGENE, b. Columbus, Ohio, Aug. 28, 35; m. 58; c. 2. ORGANIC CHEMISTRY. B.Sc, Ohio State Univ, 57; Nat. Sci. Found. summer fel, Univ. Ill, 61, Ph.D.(org. chem), 62. Res. fel, Calif. Inst. Technol, 62-63; asst. prof. org. chem, Univ. Ark, 63-69; CHEMIST, TEX. EASTMAN CO, 69- Am. Chem. Soc. Carbonium ion rearrangements; nuclear magnetic resonance studies; carbene chemistry; organometallic photochemistry. Address: Texas Eastman Co, Box 7444, Longview, TX 75601.

GWYNN, EDGAR P(ERCIVAL), b. Baltimore, Md, Jan. 23, 23; m. 50; c. 1. CYTOGENETICS. B.S, Maryland, 50; M.S, Kentucky, 51; Ph.D.(biol), Hopkins, 58. Jr. instr. BIOL, Hopkins, 51-53; lectr, WASHINGTON COL, 53-54, asst. prof, 54-59, assoc. prof, 59-64, PROF, 64-, CHMN. DEPT, 69- U.S.A, 43-46. AAAS; Bot. Soc. Am; Soc. Study Evolution; Am. Genetic Asn. Cytology; evolution. Address: Dept. of Biology, Washington College, Chestertown, MD 21620.

GWYNN, G(EORGE) R(ICHARD), b. Yanceyville, N.C, June 5, 30; m. 56; c. 3. PLANT BREEDING, GENETICS. B.S, N.C. State Col, 52, M.S, 54; Ph.D, Iowa State, 59. Instr. tobacco prod, N.C. STATE UNIV, 54, asst. prof. field crops, 59-67, ASSOC. PROF. CROP SCI, 67-, RES. AGRONOMIST, EXP. STA, AGR. RES. SERV, U.S. DEPT. AGR. & UNIV, 59- Med.C, U.S.A, 54-56. Am. Soc. Agron. Relative efficiency of breeding methods and modes of inheritance in the major field crops, particularly in corn and tobacco. Address: Tobacco Research Station, P.O. Box 1114, Oxford, NC 27565.

GWYNN, ROBERT H, b. Dublin, Eire, July 11, 22; m. 58; c. 2. MICROBIOLOGY, ONCOLOGY. B.A, Dublin, 46; Ph.D.(exp. path), London, 57. Res. scientist cancer, London Hosp. Med. Col, 47-57; res. fel, Roscoe B. Jackson Mem. Lab, Maine, 57-60; head dept. chem, Benedict Col, 60-63; asst. prof. PHYSIOL. & MICROBIOL, UNIV. HARTFORD, 63-65, ASSOC. PROF; 65- AAAS. Co-carcinogenesis; carcinogenic activity of tobacco products; memory in rats. Address: Dept. of Biology, University of Hartford, 200 Bloomfield Ave, West Hartford, CT 06117.

GWYNNE, CHARLES S(UMNER), b. New York, N.Y, Dec. 23, 85; m. 33. GEOLOGY. B.A, Cornell, 07, Ph.D.(geol), 27; Wisconsin, 14-16; M.S, Syracuse, 25; Chicago, 24. Asst. chemist, Int. Paper Co, N.Y, 07-11; asst. chem. engr, U.S. Forest Serv, Wis, 11-14; geologist, Reese & Straton, 15; staff chemist, E.I. du Pont de Nemours & Co, Del, 15-21; chemist, Bogalusa Paper Co, La, 21; asst. chem. engr, U.S. Forest Serv, Wis, 22; chem. engr, Arrowhead Mills, N.Y, 22-23; asst. instr. GEOL, Syracuse, 23-24; from asst. instr. to instr, Cornell, 24-27; asst. prof, IOWA STATE UNIV, 27-31, assoc. prof, 31-49, prof, 49-70, EMER. PROF. 70- Geologist, Iowa Geol. Surv, 31-37; vis. prof. Puerto Rico, 48-; Nat. Sci. Found. Sci. Inst, Iowa State Teachers Col, summers 58 & 59. AAAS; fel. Geol. Soc. Am; Arctic Inst. N.Am; Am. Inst. Mining, Metall. & Petrol. Eng. Clays and shales of Iowa; economic and glacial geology; clays and shales; minor moraines; state parks of Iowa. Address: Dept. of Earth Science, Iowa State University, Ames, IA 50010.

GYBERG, ARLIN E(NOCH), b. Luverne, Minn, Dec. 9, 38; m. 62. ANALYTICAL & PHYSICAL CHEMISTRY. B.S, Mankato State Col, 61; Dow, du Pont & Procter & Gamble summer fels, Minnesota, 64-66, Esso Corp. fel, 66-67, Ph.D.(anal. chem), 69. Teacher, high sch, Minn, 61-63; ASST. PROF. CHEM, AUGSBURG COL, 67- Am. Chem. Soc. Light scattering; optical methods. Address: Dept. of Chemistry, Augsburg College, 21st Ave. S. at Eighth St, Minneapolis, MN 55404.

GYDE, DONALD G, b. Flint, Mich, Sept. 18, 36; m. 56; c. 3. CHEMICAL ENGINEERING. B.S, Mich. State, 59; M.S, Minnesota, 64. GEN. MILLS, INC, 59-64, sect. leader RES. & DEVELOP, 64-68, DEPT. HEAD, 68- Am. Inst. Chem. Eng. Kinetics; pneumatic conveying; drying process development in food industry. Address: General Mills, Inc, 9000 Plymouth Ave. N, Minneapolis, MN 55427.

GYERMEK, LASZLO, b. Budapest, Hungary, Mar. 15, 26; nat; m. 52; c. 2. ANESTHESIOLOGY, PHARMACOLOGY. M.D, Eötvös Lóránd, Budapest, 50; C.M.Sc, Hungarian Acad. Sci, 55. Asst. pharmacol, Eötvös Lóránd, Budapest, 47-51; pharmacologist, Res. Inst. Pharmaceut. Indust, 51-53, head dept. pharmacol, 53-56; res. assoc, Illinois, 57; asst. prof, 57-60; sr. pharmacologist, res. labs, Geigy Chem. Corp, 60-62; assoc. dir. biol. res, Syntex Labs, 62-64; head dept. neurobiol, Syntex Res. Ctr, 64-66; resident anesthesia, Stanford Univ, 66-68; anesthesiologist, Palo Alto Med. Clin, 68-69; anesthesiologist, private practice, 69- Lectr, dept. pharmacol, Stanford Univ, 64-66, clin. assoc. prof. anesthesiol, 68-; attend. anesthesiologist, San Mateo County Hosp, 69-70, Soc. Exp. Biol. & Med; Am. Soc. Pharmacol. & Exp. Therapeut; Am. Soc. Clin. Pharmacol. & Therapeut; Am. Med. Asn; Am. Soc. Anesthesiol; Hungarian Physiol. Soc. Neuropharmacology; anesthetic drugs. Address: 35 Bow Way, Portola Valley, CA 94025.

GYFTOPOULOS, ELIAS P(ANAYIOTIS), b. Athens, Greece, July 4, 27; U.S. citizen; m. 62; c. 3. ELECTRICAL & NUCLEAR ENGINEERING. Dipl, Athens, 53; Sc.D.(elec. eng), Mass. Inst. Tech, 58. Instr. elec. eng, MASS. INST. TECHNOL, 54-58, asst. prof. elec. & nuclear eng, 58-61, assoc. prof, 61-65, prof, 65-70, FORD PROF. ENG, 70- Mem. comn. educ, Nat. Acad. Eng. Greek Royal Navy, 48-51. AAAS; fel. Am. Nuclear Soc; fel. Am. Acad. Athens; fel. Am. Acad. Arts & Sci; Am. Phys. Soc; Am. Inst. Aeronaut. & Astronaut; Am. Soc. Mech. Eng. Nuclear reactor dynamics; physics of ionized gases; surface physics; direct energy conversion; quantum thermodynamics. Address: Dept. of Nuclear Engineering, Massachusetts Institute of Technology, Cambridge, MA 02139.

GYGI, F(RANCIS) RICHARD, b. Mishawaka, Ind, July 16, 37; m. 65; c. 2. BIOCHEMISTRY, BACTERIOLOGY. B.S, Purdue, 61; M.S, Northwest. State Col.(La), 64. Asst. prof. CHEM. & BIOCHEM, WILLIAM PENN COL, 63-67, ASSOC. PROF, 67- Vis. prof, S. Dak. State Univ, 71-72. Nat. Guard, 61-63. AAAS; Am. Chem. Soc. Hemicellulose chemistry; extraction and purification of an araboxylan from the mimosa bean. Address: Dept. of Physical Science & Biology, William Penn College, Oskaloosa, IA 52577.

GYLES, C. L, b. Jamaica, W.I, May 15, 40; m. 64; c. 2. VETERINARY BACTERIOLOGY. D.V.M, Univ. Toronto, 64; M.Sc, Univ. Guelph, 66, Ph.D, 68. Lectr. diag. bact, Ont. Vet. Col, Univ. Guelph, 64-66; Med. Res. Coun. Can. fel, Eng. & Denmark, 68-69; asst. prof. VET. BACT, ONT. VET. COL, UNIV. GUELPH, 69-71, ASSOC. PROF, 71- Del, cholera panel, U.S.-Japan Coop. Med. Sci. Prog, Japan, 70; Nat. Res. Coun. Can. fel, 70-72; Med. Res. Coun. Can. fel, 71-72; Med. Res. Coun. Can. fel, 71-73. Can. Vet. Med. Asn; Am. Soc. Microbiol. Escherichia coli enterotoxin; R factors and other plasmids; pathogenesis of Escherichia coli infection in pigs by oral infection and light and electron microscopic studies. Address: Dept. of Veterinary Microbiology & Immunology, University of Guelph, Guelph, Ont, Can.

GYLES, NICHOLAS ROY, b. Jamaica, W.I, Jan. 30, 22; U.S. citizen; m. 55; c. 2. GENETICS, ANIMAL BREEDING. B.S.A, British Columbia, 46, M.S.A, 49; Ph.D.(animal breeding), Missouri, 52. Asst. prof. POULTRY GENETICS, UNIV. ARK, FAYETTEVILLE, 52-55, assoc. prof, 56-60, PROF, 60- Consult. geneticist, Peterson Poultry Breeding Farm, Ark, 56- Genetics Soc. Am; Poultry Sci. Asn. Effectiveness of selection for economic traits in poultry; genetic mechanisms of resistance to Rous and leukosis viruses in chickens. Address: Dept. of Animal Industry, University of Arkansas, Fayetteville, AR 72703.

GYLYS, JONAS A(NTANAS), b. Kaunas, Lithuania, June 27, 28; U.S. citizen; m. 56; c. 3. PHARMACOLOGY. B.S, Roosevelt, 51; M.S, Loyola (Ill) 54,

Ph.D.(pharmacol), 57. Pharmacologist, bio-test labs, Warner Lambert Res. Inst, 56-58, scientist, gen. & behav. pharmacol, 58-60, sr. scientist, N.J, 60-66; sr. res. scientist, BRISTOL LABS, SYRACUSE, 66-68, ASST. DIR. PHARMACOL. RES, 68- AAAS; Am. Soc. Pharmacol. & Exp. Therapeut. Operant behavior; anoretic agents; hypnotics; tranquilizers; anti-depressants; stimulants; muscle relaxants; anticonvulsants; analgesic agents and their antagonists. Address: 143 Stanwood Lane, Manlius, NY 13104.

GYMER, ROGER G, b. Cleveland, Ohio, Feb. 9, 32; m. 63; c. 1. PHYSICAL CHEMISTRY. B.S, Case West. Reserve Univ, 53, Ph.D.(phys. chem), 61; M.S, Univ. Minn, 56. Assoc. prof. chem, Fresno State Col, 60-63; res. scientist, Lewis Res. Ctr, NASA, Ohio, 63-64; assoc. prof. chem. & physics, Col. Virgin Islands, 64-65; prof. lectr. chem, Case West. Reserve Univ, 65-66; asst. prof, Ft. Lewis Col, 66-68; staff assoc, Adv. Coun. Col. Chem, Stanford Univ, 68-69, exec. dir, 69-70; SCI. WRITER, 70- Am. Chem. Soc. Chemical education, ecological chemistry. Address: 407 Tedmon Dr, Fort Collins, CO 80521.

GYOREY, GEZA LESLIE, b. Budapest, Hungary, July 31, 33; U.S. citizen; m. 57; c. 2. NUCLEAR ENGINEERING. B.S.E, Univ. Mich, 55, M.S.E, 57, Ph.D.(nuclear eng), 60. Assoc. prof. nuclear eng, Univ. Mich, 60-66; mgr. nuclear methods, NUCLEAR ENERGY DIV, GEN. ELEC. CO, 66-68, nuclear design, 68-70, TECH. PLANNER, STRATEGIC PLANNING OPER, 70- Am. Nuclear Soc. Long range planning in nuclear power; reactor and fuel cycle design and operation. Address: Nuclear Energy Division, General Electric Co, 175 Curtner Ave, San Jose, CA 95125.

GYORGY, E(RNST) MICHAEL, b. Heidelberg, Ger, Feb. 26, 26; nat; m. 51; c. 1. PHYSICS. B.S, Mass. Inst. Tech, 50, Ph.D.(physics), 53. MEM. TECH. STAFF, BELL TEL. LABS, 53- U.S.A, 44-46. Fel. Am. Phys. Soc. Solid state physics. Address: 6 Woodcliff Dr, Madison, NJ 07940.

GYRISCO, GEORGE GORDON, b. South Hadley, Mass, Mar. 25, 20; m. 47; c. 3. ENTOMOLOGY. B.S, Mass. State Col, 43; Ph.D, Cornell, 47. Asst. biologist, Conserv. Dept. Fish & Game, Mass, 42; res. asst. ENTOM, CORNELL UNIV, 43-47, asst. prof, 47-50, assoc. prof, 50-55, PROF, 55-, head dept, 62-63. Vis. prof, Ore. State Univ, 66. Fel. AAAS; Entom. Soc. Am; Ecol. Soc. Am; Nat. Audubon Soc; Am. Inst. Biol. Sci; Soc. Study Evolution; Entom. Soc. Can. Biology and control of alfalfa weevil, alfalfa snout beetle, clover root borer, clover root weevils, spittlebugs, leafhoppers, white grubs and European chafer; flight habits of insects related to environment; insect sounds; biological control; virus vectors of legumes; ecology and mathematical biology. Address: Dept. of Entomology, Comstock Hall, Cornell University, Ithaca, NY 14850.

GYSEL, LESLIE W(ILLIAM), b. Rochester, N.Y, Apr. 30, 14; m. 45; c. 3. FORESTRY, WILDLIFE MANAGEMENT. B.S, N.Y. State Col. Forestry, Syracuse, 36, fel, 37-38, M.S, 38; fel, Ohio State, 39-40, Ph.D.(plant ecol), 42. Foreman, U.S. Forest Serv, 39-40; county supvr, Ohio State, 40; silviculturist, Cent. States Forest Exp. Sta, U.S. Forest Serv, 45-46; assoc. prof. forestry, MICH. STATE UNIV, 46-50, FISHERIES & WILDLIFE, 50-68, PROF, 68- U.S.A, 42-45. Wildlife Soc; Am. Inst. Biol. Sci. Bioecology; silviculture; wildlife management. Address: Dept. of Fisheries & Wildlife, Michigan State University, East Lansing, MI 48823.

GYSLING, HENRY J, b. Phila, Pa, Dec. 29, 41. INORGANIC & ORGANOMETALLIC CHEMISTRY. B.S, St. Joseph's Col.(Pa), 63; fel. & Ph.D.(inorg. chem), Univ. Del, 67. Res. fel. chem, N.Y. Univ, 67-68; inorg. chem, Univ. Newcastle upon Tyne, 68-70; RES. CHEMIST, EASTMAN KODAK CO, 70- Am. Chem. Soc. Synthetic and physical inorganic chemistry; coordination chemistry; ambidentate ligand chemistry; inorganic photochemistry; boron hydride chemistry. Address: Solid State Photoscience Lab, Research Labs, Eastman Kodak Co, 343 State St, Rochester, NY 14650.

GYULAI, EUGENE JENO, b. Zsolna, Hungary, Oct. 19, 18; Can. citizen; m. 51. VIROLOGY, IMMUNOLOGY. D.V.M, Univ. Budapest, 49; Dipl. Bact, Univ. Toronto, 66. Dist. vet. off, Ministry Agr, Hungary, 49-54; chief vet, Ministry Food, 54-57; vet, health of animals div, Can. Dept. Agr, 58-62; HEAD, LAB. VIRAL SEROL, PUB. HEALTH LABS, ONT. DEPT. HEALTH, 63-65 & 66-, RES. SCIENTIST, 68- Am. Soc. Microbiol; Can. Soc. Microbiol. Development and preparation of antigens to identify viral infections by complement fixation test; development of methods for rapid diagnosis of viral infections; public health virology. Address: Central Labs, Ontario Dept. of Health, Box 9000, Postal Terminal A, Toronto 116, Ont, Can.

GYURE, WILLIAM LOUIS, b. Chicago, Ill, Sept. 26, 39. BIOCHEMISTRY, CLINICAL CHEMISTRY. B.S, Aquinas Col, 61; Nat. Insts. Health fel, Tufts Univ, 66-70, Ph.D.(biochem), 70. Am. Cancer Soc. res. fel. biochem, Max Planck Inst. Biochem, Munich, 70-71; FEL. CLIN. BIOCHEM, UNIV. HOSP, UNIV. WASH, 71- U.S.A, 63-66, Res, 66-69. AAAS; Am. Chem. Soc; Am. Soc. Zool. Pteridine metabolism during insect development and pteridine metabolizing enzymes; purine and pteridine storage and transport in insect and mammalian tissues; purine and pteridine analytical techniques. Address: University Hospital BB203, University of Washington, Seattle, WA 98105.

GZEMSKI, FELIX C(ASIMIR), b. Nanticoke, Pa, Feb. 28, 10; m. 47. CHEMISTRY. B.S, Univ. Pa, 32, M.S, 33, Ph.D.(chem), 37. Res. chemist, ATLANTIC REF. CO, 36-48, RES. SUPVR. & GROUP LEADER, 44- Mem. Hwy. Res. Bd, Nat. Acad. Sci-Nat. Res. Coun; Asphalt Inst. Am. Chem. Soc; Am. Soc. Test. & Mat; Asn. Asphalt Paving Technol. Hydrocarbon gas research; molecular distillation; asphalt research. Address: Middletown Rd. & Meadow Lane, R.F.D. 1, Box 224, Glen Mills, PA 19342.

DANISH, FAKHRUDDIN QASIMALI, b. Ujjain, India, May 18, 43. PHARMACY, PHYSICAL PHARMACY. B.Pharm, Gujarat Univ, India, 65; scholar, Univ. Iowa, 66-70, M.S, 67, Ph.D.(prod. develop), 70. Chemist, Hambar Pharm, India, 64-65; lab. asst. PHARM, Univ. Iowa, 66-70; ASST. PROF, CREIGHTON UNIV, 70- Am. Pharmaceut. Asn; Am. Asn. Cols. Pharm. Product development and research in pharmacy. Address: Dept. of Pharmacy, Creighton University, 2542 California St, Omaha, NE 68131.

DAVIS, VIRGINIA EISCHEN, b. Okarche, Okla, Nov. 9, 25; m. 47; c. 2. PHARMACOLOGY, BIOCHEMISTRY. B.S, Okla. State Univ, 47, M.S, 49; fel, Rice Univ, 57-60, Ph.D.(biochem), 60. Biochemist, res. serv, Vet. Admin. Hosp, Houston, 49-57; res. assoc, biochem, Rice Univ, 60-61; res. biochemist, res. serv, VET. ADMIN. HOSP, 61-63, assoc. dir. metab. res. lab, 63-71, DIR. NEUROCHEM. & ADDICTION RES. LAB, 71-; RES. ASSOC. PROF, BIOCHEM. & MED, BAYLOR COL. MED, 69-, res. asst. prof, 65-69. Lectr, sch. pharm, Univ. Houston, 67-69. AAAS; Am. Fedn. Clin. Res; Am. Soc. Neurochem; Soc. Biol. Psychiat. Biochemical mechanisms of drug action; neuroamine metabolism; alcoholism. Address: Neurochemistry & Addiction Research Lab, Veterans Administration Hospital, Houston, TX 77031.

DE MIRANDA, PAULO, b. Goa, India; m. 66; c. 3. PHARMACOLOGY, BIOCHEMISTRY. Lic, Univ. Oporto, 60; Fulbright scholar, Ford fel. & M.S, Univ. Wis, 63; Ph.D.(pharmacol), Marquette Univ, 65. Instr. pharmacol, sch. med, Marquette Univ, 66; asst. prof, faculty med, Univ. Valle, Colombia, 66-69; SR. RES. BIOCHEMIST, WELLCOME RES. LABS, BURROUGHS WELLCOME CO, 69- AAAS; Am. Chem. Soc. Drug metabolism; alkyl phosphate antagonists; nucleic acid antagonists; central control of blood pressure; adrenergic blockage. Address: Wellcome Research Labs, Research Triangle Park, NC 27709.

DHEER, SURENDRA KUMAR, b. Lahore, W.Pakistan, Mar. 1, 39; m. 70. BIOCHEMISTRY. B.Sc, Univ. Delhi, 60, M.Sc, 62; assistantship, Boston Univ, 63-67, Ph.D.(org. chem), 67. Nat. Res. Coun. Can. res. fel, 68-70; RES. ASSOC. NUCLEIC ACIDS, WYETH RES. LABS, 71- Lectr, Deshbandhu Gupta Col, India, 62-63. Watumull Found. Award, 70. AAAS. Synthesis of polydeoxynucleotides and polyribonucleotides in relation to gene synthesis and interferron induction. Address: Wyeth Labs, P.O. Box 8299, Philadelphia, PA 19101.

DOOLITTLE, CHARLES HERBERT, III, b. Holyoke, Mass, July 18, 39; m. 61, 71; c. 2. CLINICAL PHARMACOLOGY. B.S, Univ. Mass, Amherst, 62, M.A, 65; U.S. Pub. Health Serv. fel. & Ph.D.(pharmacol), George Washington Univ, 70. Res. asst. clin. pharmacol, sch. med, Yale, 64-66; U.S. PUB. HEALTH SERV. RES. FEL. PHARMACOL, BROWN UNIV. & ROGER WILLIAMS GEN. HOSP, 69- AAAS. Anti neoplastic agents. Address: 23 Summit Ave, Seekonk, MA 02771.

DUNKLEY, COLLEEN ROSE, b. Timmins, Ont, Dec. 12, 39; m. 61; c. 3. NUTRITION, BIOCHEMISTRY. B.A, Univ. Toronto, 61, Nat. Res. Coun. Can. fel, 61-65, Ph.D.(biochem), 65. Asst. prof. NUTRIT, UNIV. TORONTO, 65-68, ASSOC. PROF, 68- Can. Biochem. Soc; affiliate Royal Soc. Med. Nutritional biochemistry; subcellular metabolism of nutrients; cell membrane transport; malnutrition and development. Address: Faculty of Food Sciences, University of Toronto, 157 Bloor St. W, Toronto 5, Ont, Can.

EDWARDS, HAROLD HENRY, b. Andes, N.Y, July 14, 32; m. 62; c. 3. BIOPHYSICS. B.E.P, Cornell Univ, 55; Ph.D.(biophys), Rensselaer Polytech. Inst, 69. Electronic engr, res. & develop. ctr, Gen. Elec. Co, 55-65; asst, Rensselaer Polytech. Inst, 65-69; res. assoc. anat, med. ctr, Duke Univ, 69-71; ASST. MEM, BIOCHEM. DEPT, ST. JUDE CHILDREN'S RES. HOSP, 71- Biophys. Soc; Inst. Elec. & Electronics Eng. Membrane structure and function; interaction and organization of macromolecules; electron microscopy. Address: Biochemistry Dept, St. Jude Children's Research Hospital, 332 N. Lauderdale, Memphis, TN 38101.

EISA, HAMDY MAHMOUD, b. Hihia, Egypt, Aug. 4, 38; m. 64; c.1. PLANT BREEDING, VEGETABLE CROPS. B.Sc, Cairo Univ, 59; M.Sc, Cornell Univ, 66, Ph.D.(plant breeding), 69. Asst. prof. hort, Univ. Nebr, Lincoln, 69-70; PLANT BREEDER, ENVIRON. RES. LAB, UNIV. ARIZ, 70- Plant breeder, Univ. Ariz. team, Arid Lands Res. Ctr, Abu Dhabi, Arabian Gulf, 71- Am. Soc. Hort. Sci.(Asgrow Award, 69). Breeding of vegetable crops adapted to warm, humid conditions. Address: University of Arizona Environmental Research Lab, Tucson International Airport, Tucson, AZ 85706.

ESCOBEDO, RICHARD, b. San Pedro, Calif, July 31, 44. MATHEMATICS. A.B, Univ. Calif, Berkeley, 65; M.A, Calif. State Col, Long Beach, 67; fels. & Ph.D.(math), Univ. Calif, Riverside, 71. Programmer, Autonetics Div, N.Am. Rockwell, 67-68; ASST. PROF. MATH, UNIV. CALIF, SAN DIEGO,

71- Bochner-Riesz summability of multiple trigonometric series and integrals. Address: 541 Harker St, San Pedro, CA 90731.

FENG, KUO AO, b. Anhwei, China. PLANT PHYSIOLOGY. B.S, Cheng Chung Univ, China, 47; UNESCO fel, 57; Agency Int. Develop. fel, Georgetown Univ, 61; M.A, Univ. North. Colo, 62; Nat. Sci. Found. fel, Univ. Minn, 64-65, Nat. Insts. Health fel, 65-67, Ph.D.(plant physiol), 67. Instr. BIOL, NDMC Med. Col, 47-57; assoc. prof, Taipei Med. Col, 62-64; asst. prof, UNIV. WISOSHKOSH, 67-70, ASSOC. PROF, 70- Nat. Sci. Found. fel. biol, Argonne Nat. Lab, 68; Nat. Sci. Found. grants, 69 & 70. Am. Soc. Plant Physiol; Scand. Soc. Plant Physiol. Plant taxonomy; anatomical physiology of plants; plant growth regulators on plant growth and membrane permeability. Address: Dept. of Biology, University of Wisconsin-Oshkosh, Oshkosh, WI 54901.

FERRARIO, CARLOS MARIA, Am. citizen. CARDIOVASCULAR PHYSIOLOGY & DISEASES. B.S, Mariano Moreno Col, Arg, 56; M.D, Univ. Buenos Aires, 63. Asst. physiol, med. sch, Univ. Buenos Aires, 63-64; assoc. mem. res. staff, CLEVELAND CLIN. FOUND, 70-71, MEM. RES. STAFF, 71- Nat. Sci. Coun. Arg. fel, Univ. Buenos Aires, 63-64; Swedish Int. Agency fel, Gothenberg Univ, 64-66; Nat. Lung & Heart Insts. grant, Cleveland Clin. Found, 67-; estab. investr. cardiovasc. res, Am. Heart Asn, 72- Am. Heart Asn; Am. Physiol. Soc. Investigation into the cause of arterial hypertension, especially in reference to its hemodynamic, humoral and nervous system participation. Address: Research Division, Cleveland Clinic, 2020 E. 93rd St, Cleveland, OH 44106.

FORBES, WILLIAM HATHAWAY, b. Milton, Mass, Feb. 21, 02; m. 35; c. 5. PHYSIOLOGY. A.B, Harvard, 23, fel, 28-29, A.M, 31; Ph.D.(physiol), Cambridge, 31; M.D, Johns Hopkins Univ, 52. Instr. physics, Am. Univ. Beirut, 23-24; instr. & tutor biochem. sci, HARVARD, 29-36, fel, fatigue lab, 30-36 & 38-40, asst, 32-36, acting dir. lab, 41-42, asst. dir, 42-47, lectr, SCH. PUB. HEALTH, 47-57, ASST. TO DEAN & FACULTY ADV. FOR. STUD, 57-, CONSULT. PHYSIOL, 70-, res. tutor, Eliot House, 31-35. Lectr, Wellesley Col, 38-39; sci. attaché, U.S. Embassy, Paris, 54-55; prof, Pahlavi Univ, Iran, 67-69. Mem. various comts, Off. Sci. Res. & Develop. With Joint Res. & Develop. Bd; U.S.A; U.S.A.A.F, 42-45. AAAS; Am. Chem. Soc; Am. Physiol. Soc. Hemoglobin; oxygen and carbon monoxide dissociation curves; respiration; effects of high altitudes; muscular exercise; physical fitness; effects of heat, cold, altitude and diet on physical and mental performance; demography; ecology; population control. Address: Dept. of Physiology, Harvard University School of Public Health, 665 Huntington Ave, Boston, MA 02115.

FORD, CLINITA ARNSBY, b. Okmulgee, Okla, Sept. 23, 28; m. 51; c. 3. NUTRITION. B.S, Lincoln Univ.(Mo); M.S, Columbia Univ; Ph.D.(foods & nutrit), Kans. State Univ. Asst. prof. HOME ECON, Fla. A&M Univ, 49-56; res. asst, Kans. State Univ, 56-59; PROF. & CHMN. DEPT, FLA. A&M UNIV, 59- Dir. & Admin. consult, Proj. Upward Bound, Fla. A&M Univ, 65-70; Fla. del, White House Conf. Aging, 71; mem, Nat. Coun. Admin. Women in Educ. Outstanding community serv. award, Frontiers Int, 67. Am. Dietetic Asn; Am. Home Econ. Asn; Am. Voc. Asn; Inst. Food Technol; Am. Voc. Educ. Res. Asn; Am. Asn. Higher Educ. Nutritional status of children as determined by dietary and biochemical analysis. Address: Dept. of Home Economics, Florida A&M University, Box A-84, Tallahassee, FL 32307.

GALESKI, JAMES BENJAMIN, b. St. Louis, Mo, Jan. 30, 44. CHEMICAL ENGINEERING. B.S, Wash. Univ, 66; Ph.D.(chem. eng), Rice Univ, 71. SECT. LEADER CATALYSIS RES, BAROID DIV, NL INDUSTS, INC, 70- Am. Inst. Chem. Eng; Catalysis Soc; Am. Chem. Soc. Petroleum refining; catalytic chemistry; catalytic cracking of residual gas-oil; catalytic conversion of auto exhaust emissions; nature and surface properties of mixed-oxides. Address: Baroid Division, NL Industries, Inc, P.O. Box 1675, Houston, TX 77001.

GAONKAR, GOPAL H, b. Hanehalli, India, June 12, 37; m. 68; c. 1. APPLIED MATHEMATICS & MECHANICS. B.E, Karnatak Univ, India, 60; M.E, Univ. Bombay, 64; D.Sc.(eng), Wash. Univ, 67. Asst. engr, M/S M.M. Bilaney & Co, India, 60-61; lectr. struct, V.J.T. Inst, Bombay, 62-64; res. assoc. eng, Wash. Univ, 67, asst. prof, 67-69; VIS. RES. PROF. MATH. STUDIES, SOUTH. ILL. UNIV, EDWARDSVILLE, 69- Am. Soc. Mech. Eng; Am. Helicopter Soc; Soc. Indust. & Appl. Math. Continuum mechanics; stochastic dynamic systems; helicopter dynamics. Address: Faculty of Mathematical Studies, Southern Illinois University, Edwardsville, IL 62025.

GARDELS, MARVIN C(LEVE), b. Dorrance, Kans, Apr. 6, 22; m. 44; c. 2. ANALYTICAL CHEMISTRY. B.S, Colo. Agr. & Mech. Col, 43, Atomic Energy Comn. fel, 51-52; M.S, Nebraska, 47; Ph.D.(chem), Okla. Agr. & Mech. Col, 54. Chemist, Pan-Am. Ref. Corp, 44-45; instr. chem, Colo. Sch. Mines, 47-51; anal. res. chemist, lab. div, Radio Corp. Am, 53-60; Lincoln Lab, Mass. Inst. Technol, 60-64; sr. res. anal. chemist, Glidden Co, 64-68; chemist, Xerox Med. Diag. Opers, Calif, 69-70; Technicon Corp, N.Y, 70-71; SUPVRY. CHEMIST, NORTHWEST. WATER SUPPLY LAB, ENVIRON. PROTECTION AGENCY, 71- Am. Chem. Soc; Soc. Appl. Spectros. Spectroscopy. Address: Northwestern Water Supply Lab, Environmental Protection Agency, Route 4, Box 4129, Gig Harbor, WA 98335.

GARNER, HERSCHEL WHITAKER, b. Jacksonville, Tex, June 25, 36; m. 59; c. 1. VERTEBRATE ZOOLOGY, ECOLOGY. B.S, Stephen F. Austin State Univ, 62; M.S, Tex. Tech Univ, 65, Ph.D.(zool), 70. Instr. BIOL, Tex. Tech Univ, 65-66; ASST. PROF, TARLETON STATE COL, 70- AAAS; Am. Soc. Mammal. Biology and populations of small mammals. Address: Dept. of Biological Sciences, Tarleton State College, Stephenville, TX 76401.

GIBSON, EDWARD GEORGE, b. Buffalo, N.Y, Nov. 8, 36; m. 59; c. 2. ATMOSPHERIC PHYSICS, ENGINEERING. B.S, Univ. Rochester, 59; M.S, Calif. Inst. Technol, 60, Ph.D.(eng. & physics), 64. With Aeronutronic Res. Lab, Philco Corp, Calif, 64-65; SCIENTIST-ASTRONAUT, NASA, 65-, SKYLAB PROG, 72- Mem. solar physics subcomt, NASA. Am. Astron. Soc; Am. Inst. Physics; Am. Inst. Aeronaut. & Astronaut. Address: NASA Manned Spacecraft Center, Code CB, Houston, TX 77058.

GOETZE, CHRISTOPHER, b. Boston, Mass, Aug. 10, 39; m. 64; c. 1. GEOPHYSICS. B.A, Harvard, 61, Ph.D.(geophys), 69. Fel, GEOPHYS, MASS. INST. TECHNOL, 69-70, ASST. PROF, 71- U.S.A, 61-63. Am. Geophys. Union. Mechanical properties of rocks. Address: Dept. of Earth & Planetary Sciences, 54-716, Massachusetts Institute of Technology, Cambridge, MA 02139.

GOLD, LORNE W, b. Saskatoon, Sask, June 7, 28; m. 51; c. 4. PHYSICS, GLACIOLOGY. B.Sc, Univ. Sask, 50; Nat. Res. Coun. Can. bursary, McGill Univ, 51, M.Sc, 52, Ph.D, 70. Jr. res. off. snow & ice, NAT. RES. COUN. CAN, 50-51, head sect, 52-69, HEAD GEOTECH. SECT, DIV. BLDG. RES, 69-, SR. RES. OFF, 61- Mem. working group on ice in navigable waters, Can. Comt. Oceanog, 57-; subcomt. pipeline res, assoc. comt. geotech. res, Nat. Res. Coun. Can, 70- Can. Asn. Physicists; Eng. Inst. Can. Deformation and failure of ice; ice engineering; ground thermal regime; heat exchange at snow, ice, water and ground surfaces. Address: 1903 Illinois Ave, Ottawa, Ont. K1H 6W5, Can.

GOLDENBERG, DAVID M(ILTON), b. Brooklyn, N.Y, Aug. 2, 38; m. 61; c. 5. PATHOLOGY, ONCOLOGY. B.S, Univ. Chicago, 58; Sc.D.(olfactory physiol), Univ. Erlangen, 65; M.D, Univ. Heidelberg, 66. Res. assoc. med, Univ. Erlangen, 64-67; head clin. & exp. oncol, dept. surg, 67-68; assoc. res. prof. PATH, sch. med, Univ. Pittsburgh, 68-70; ASSOC. PROF, SCH. MED, TEMPLE UNIV, 70-, HEAD MED. GENETICS UNIT, HOSP, 71- Mem, Paul Ehrlich Inst. Chemother, Ger, 66-; staff pathologist, Vet. Admin. Hosp, Pittsburgh, 68-70; grants, Coun. Tobacco Res, 68-71, Nat. Cancer Inst, 69-& Damon Runyon Fund Cancer Res, 71- AAAS; Am. Soc. Exp. Path; Am. Asn. Cancer Res. Clinical and experimental oncology; experimental pathology; immunogenetics; genetics of disease; biochemical genetics; olfactory physiology. Address: Dept. of Pathology, Temple University Health Sciences Center, Philadelphia, PA 19140.

DaFano, Ettore.
Daggett, Harry Mark, Jr, 1966.
Dahlen, Miles Augustinus, 1966.
Dale, Julian Kalfus.
Dallenbach, Karl M, 1971.
Dal Nogare, Stephen, 1968.
Dalton, John Lester, 1966.
Daly, Nelson Beardsley, 1967.
D'Amour, Fred Edmund, 1966.
Dana, Alan Standish, 1967.
Dana, Forest Charles, 1967.
Dane, Carle Hamilton, 1968.
Danforth, Charles Haskell, 1969.
Darlow, Albert Edward, 1966.
Darrow, Chester William, 1967.
Dauben, Hyp Joseph, Jr, 1968.
Davidson, Benjamin, 1968.
Davidson, Robert Frederick, 1971.
Davies, Charles Augustus.
Davies, Joseph Ilott, 1966.
Davis, Alva Raymond, 1965.
Davis, Frank W, 1969.
Davis, Harold Simmonds, 1965.
Davis, Jay Conger, 1968.
Davis, Jefferson Clark, 1965.
Davis, Merle H, 1967.
Davis, Roy Bryan, 1969.
Davis, Watson, 1967.
Davisson, Arthur Paul, 1969.
Dawson, Alden Benjamin, 1968.
Dawson, Clarence Benton, 1968.
Dawson, Elmer Yale, 1966.
Dawson, James Arthur, 1969.
Dawson, Jeffrey Earl, 1969.
Dawson, Leo Henry, 1967.
Dawson, Paul Reber, 1966.
Day, Kenneth Mosier, 1968.
Deal, Ralph Elbert, 1967.
Deane, Helen Wendler (Mrs.
    George F. Markham), 1966.
Deane, Roy Eric, 1965.
Dearborn, Donald Curtis, 1967.
Debye, Peter J. W, 1966.
Decker, Floyd Archie, 1968.
Deere, Emil Olof, 1966.
Degering, Edward Franklin, 1967.
de Marchi, Vincent Salvatore,
    1970.
Demerec, Milislav, 1966.
Dempster, Wilfrid Taylor, 1965.
Desha, Lucius Junius, 1967.
De Sorbo, Warren, 1969.
Detling, LeRoy Ellsworth, 1967.
Detwiler, John D, 1966.
Deupree, John Francis, 1969.
Deverall, George V, 1965.
DeVries, John, 1967.
Dewdney, John Wells.
Diamond, Grant Sidney, 1965.
Dickey, Joseph Benjamin, 1966.
Dickie, Margaret McQuiston, 1969.
Diefenbach, William Theodore,
    1969.
Dietz, Frederick Curt, 1969.
Dillingham, Harley Clay, 1965.
Dimitroff, George Zakharieff, 1968.
Dittmar, Harry Robert, 1968.
Dixon, Claude Frank, 1968.
Djordjevic, Branimir Djordje,
    1968.
Dobie, Norman Dale, 1967.
Dobres, Robert Morton, 1966.
Dodd, David Rollin, 1967.
Dodd, Thomas Nelson, Jr, 1965.
Doedens, James Dirk, 1966.
Doerpinghaus, Sigmund Leonard,
    1968.

Doerr, Irene Rockwell, 1967.

Dolecek, Richard Leroy, 1966.
Dolinsky, Meyer, 1969.
Dolley, William Lee, Jr, 1968.
Dolloff, Richard Talbot, 1971.
Doole, Howard Pollock, 1971.
Dore, James Bernard.
Dorn, John Emil, 1971.
Dorward, Kelvin, 1965.
Doshay, Lewis Jacob, 1965.
Dougherty, Ellsworth Charles,
    1965.
Douglas, Jesse, 1965.
Dousmanis, George Christos, 1966.
Douty, Alfred.
Dow, Leonard James, 1967.
Dow, Willard Matt, 1967.
Downs, William Louis, 1967.
Drager, Glenn Albert, 1968.
Drake, Carl John, 1965.
Dressel, Karl, 1967.
Drew, James William, 1965.
Drolet, Godias Joseph, 1968.
Drompp, Benjamin, 1967.
Dryden, Charles Early, 1967.
Dubois, Jean Thomas Henri, 1967.
Duckworth, Susan, 1967.
Duggan, Edward Lloyd, 1968.
Duncan, Carl Dudley, 1966.
Duncan, James Armstrong, 1967.
Dunlap, Irving Ray, 1969.
Dunlop, Henry Adam, 1966.
Dunn, Paul Heaney, 1967.
Durbin, Charles Gaskill, 1969.
Durham, Edward Josephi, 1969.
Durham, Hugh Bartlett.
Dyer, Rolla Eugene, 1971.
Dymond, John Richardson, 1965.
Dyson, James Lindsay, 1967.

Earley, LeRoy William, 1969.
East, John Herschel, Jr, 1968.
Eaton, James Tucker, 1968.
Ecker, Enrique Eduardo, 1966.
Eckert, Wallace John, 1971.
Eckstrom, Hartley Clayton, 1968.
Edeiken, Joseph, 1966.
Edinger, Tilly, 1967.
Edwards, C. F, 1966.
Edwards, Merwin Guy, 1969.
Edwards, Philip Rarick, 1966.
Edwards, Ray Lee, 1969.
Edwards, Robert W, 1969.
Egan, Edward Patrick, Jr.
Eggleston, Harla Ray, 1965.
Egli, Paul Henry, 1971.
Eglof, Warren Kline, 1965.
Ehle, Sharon R, 1968.
Ehrenstein, Maximilian Richard,
    1968.
Ehrich, William Ernst, 1967.
Eichner, Laurits Christian, 1967.
Einarsen, Arthur Skogman, 1965.
Eisenhart, Luther Pfahler, 1965.
Eisenman, Anna Josephine, 1968.
Eisman, Philip Carl, 1968.
Eldredge, Kenneth Roland, 1967.
Eldridge, Winfield Huggins, 1966.
Ellerbrock, Vincent J, 1965.
Elliott, Frank Roy, 1965.
Ellis, David Owen, 1966.
Ellison, Bob Earl, 1967.
El-Waziri, Abdel Halim, 1967.
Ely, Fordyce, 1966.
Emerson, Jack Drew, 1971.
Emig, William Harrison, 1967.
Emslie, Arthur Raymond Gordon,
    1965.

Emsweller, Samuel L, 1966.
Endsley, Eugene Wilbur, 1967.
Engelhard, Warren E, 1971.
Enright, John Bautista, 1971.
Entrikin, John Bennett, 1966.
Ephrussi-Taylor, Harriet, 1968.
Epling, Carl Clawson, 1968.
Epstein, Paul Sophus, 1966.
Erda, Albert Robert, 1969.
Erdmann, Charles Edgar, 1971.
Ericks, Walter Paul, 1966.
Erlanger, Joseph, 1965.
Eusterman, George B, 1966.
Evans, Harry Davidson, Jr, 1969.
Evans, Lacey Heintzman, 1971.
Evans, Theodore William, 1969.
Ewell, Cleve Winfield, 1966.
Exline (Frizzell), Harriet, 1968.
Exline, Paul Gettis, 1966.

Falkoff, David Leo, 1967.
Falzone, Joseph Andrew, Jr, 1969.
Faragher, Warren Fred, 1966.
Farber, Eduard, 1969.
Farevaag, Petter, 1965.
Farinacci, Nicholas Thomas, 1966.
Farnell, Frederic James, 1968.
Farrell, John Thompson, Jr, 1965.
Faust, Lawrence Yoder, 1966.
Faxon, William Otis.
Feld, Joseph Meyer, 1971.
Feldman, Donald, 1966.
Feldman, William Ray, 1966.
Feller, Alto Edmund, 1966.
Fenn, Wallace Osgood, 1971.
Fenska, Richard Robert, 1966.
Fenske, Merrell Robert, 1971.
Ferenczi, Istvan.
Ferguson, Edward, Jr, 1968.
Ferriso, Carmine Charles.
Fetter, Theodore R, 1967.
Field, John Albert, 1966.
Fieldner, Arno Carl, 1966.
Fierke, Scheuring Session, 1968.
Filippi, Michael John, 1968.
Fincher, Edgar Franklin, 1969.
Finley, Lyle Walker, 1967.
Fischbach, Adolph, 1968.
Fish, Velmer Bernel, 1968.
Fishel, Mannes Herman, 1966.
Fisher, Catherine Virginia, 1966.
Fishman, Solomon, 1966.
Fiske, Jessie Gladys, 1966.
Flanders, Roger Lee, 1965.
Flatow, Tobias, 1966.
Flesch, Peter, 1969.
Flowers, Seville, 1968.
Flynn, John Edward, 1965.
Foley, Jean Marie, 1967.
Foley, Lyndon Lyman, 1966.
Follis, Richard Holden, Jr, 1965.
Fong, Jacob, 1967.
Foote, Paul Darwin, 1971.
Forbes, Ernest Browning, 1966.
Forbes, Henry Stone, 1968.
Ford, Lester R, 1967.
Ford, Orfa Rex, 1967.
Fort, Charles Atherton, 1967.
Fosdick, Leonard Samuel, 1969.
Fossitt, Dexter D, 1967.
Foster, Jackson Walter, 1966.
Foter, Milton John, 1969.
Fothergill, LeRoy Dryden, 1967.
Fourman, Victor George, 1968.
Fowler, Edson Fairbrother, 1964.
Fowler, Harry C, 1967.
Fox, Arthur Lawrence, 1966.

Fracker, Stanley Black, 1971.
Frank, Paul Floyd, 1967.
Frankel, Kalman, 1966.
Franklin, Donald Raymond, 1966.
Franz, Carl Joseph, 1965.
Fredeen, Robert Clarence, 1968.
Fredell, Clarence Arthur, 1969.
Freeman, Leslie Willard, 1969.
Frey, Fred Ernest, 1967.
Frey, Walter Guernsey, 1965.
Frick, Carl Emmit, 1966.
Friedman, Bernard, 1966.
Frischknecht, Carl, 1968.
Fritch, Donald J, 1968.
Frutchey, Cecil William, 1971.
Fry, William Justin, 1968.
Frye, Robert, 1967.
Funk, Casimir, 1967.
Furcron, Aurelius Sydney, 1971.
Furnas, Clifford Cook, 1969.
Furness, Lawton Williams, 1967.
Fussell, Lewis, Jr, 1965.

Gagliardi, Domenick Donald, 1968.
Gailiunas, Peter, 1971.
Gaines, Paschal Clay, 1966.
Gale, Laurence Edward, 1967.
Gallatin, Melvin Herman, 1966.
Galton, Michael, 1968.
Galton, Mildred Morton, 1968.
Gambrell, Foster Lee, 1967.
Gamow, George, 1968.
Gantz, George Martin, 1969.
Garland, Leo Henry, 1966.
Garlough, Leslie Nathan, 1967.
Garner, Harold Riley, 1967.
Garner, Lofton Leroy, 1966.
Gartlein, Carl Witz, 1965.
Gassmann, Albert George, 1968.
Gast, Robert Theodore, 1967.
Gauley, Joseph R, 1966.
Gaumer, Roger E, 1969.
Gaver, Kenneth Merlyn, 1967.
Gay, Norman Russell, 1966.
Geiger, George Augustus, 1965.
Geiling, Eugene Maximillian Karl,
    1971.
Geist, Frederick Denkmar, 1970.
Gendel, Samuel, 1966.
Geohegan, William Anthony, 1966.
George, William Owsley, 1966.
Gerbes, Werner Waldemar, 1967.
Gergen, John Jay, 1967.
Gerjovich, Henry John, 1969.
Gerke, Roscoe Harlan, 1966.
Germer, Lester Halbert, 1971.
Gerry, Bertram Irving, 1965.
Gershon-Cohen, Jacob, 1971.
Gerst, Francis Joseph, S.J, 1968.
Geske, David Henry, 1967.
Gettler, Alexander Oscar, 1968.
Getty, Robert, 1971.
Getz, Albert Julius, 1970.
Gezelius, Roy Arthur, 1968.
Giarman, Nicholas Joseph, 1968.
Gibbs, Charles Bernard, 1968.
Gibson, Norman Rothwell, 1967.
Gibson, Theodore Whidden, 1967.
Giddings, Nahum James, 1966.
Gilbert, Harry Howard, 1965.
Gilbert, Henry Leonard, 1967.
Gilchrist, Raleigh, 1966.
Gill, E. K, 1966.
Gilman, Joseph Charles, 1966.
Gilman, Theodore Silkman, 1969.
Githens, Thomas Stotesbury, 1966.
Glassman, Oscar, 1970.

Glen, John King, 1969.
Glockler, George, 1969.
Gluhareff, Michael Eugene, 1967.
Gold, John Steiner, 1970.
Goldbloom, Alton, 1968.
Goldhaber, Sulamith, 1965.
Goldsmith, Edwin Alexander, 1966.
Goldstein, Albert Elias, 1966.
Goldstein, Kurt, 1965.
Gollis, Morton Harold, 1966.
Golovin, Nicholas Erasmus, 1969.
Goodale, Hubert Dana, 1969.
Goode, Kenneth Hancock, 1967.
Goodner, Kenneth, 1967.
Goodspeed, Thomas Harper, 1966.
Gooze, Irving, 1966.
Gordon, Dan Morris, 1970.
Gordon, Harold, 1967.
Goss, Emery Fox, 1967.
Gossett, Franklin Rice, 1966.

Gosting, Louis Joseph, 1971.
Gottschalk, Louis C, 1965.
Gould, William Andrew.
Gourley, Mary Foulks, 1971.
Govro, Marvin Anthony A, 1966.
Gowen, John Whittemore, 1967.
Grabau, Martin Christian Rudolph, 1965.
Grace, Arthur William, 1971.
Grace, James Thomas, Jr, 1971.
Graf, Samuel Herman, 1966.
Graham, Clarence Henry, 1971.
Graham, Edward Harrison, 1966.
Graham, John Warren, 1971.
Granger, Armour Townsend, 1966.
Grant, Carroll Walter, 1969.
Grant, Harold Johnson, Jr, 1966.
Grant, Robert Purves, 1966.
Grassie, Vernon Robert, 1969.
Graves, Elizabeth Riddle, 1972.

Gray, Edward LeBreton, 1968.
Gray, Philip Paul, 1966.
Greeley, Samuel Arnold, 1968.
Green, Daniel Marie, 1968.
Greenbaum, Bernard Aaron, 1965.
Greene, Harry Sylvestre Nutting, 1969.
Greensfelder, Bernard Sutro, 1968.
Gregersen, Magnus Ingstrup, 1969.
Gregory, John Howard, 1967.
Gregory, Vernon Leroy, 1971.
Greiner, William Jack, 1965.
Grenall, Alexander, 1966.
Griemsmann, John William Ernest, 1971.
Griffin, John Sanders, Jr, 1965.
Griffith, Dalzell Melvin, 1966.
Griffith, Wendell Horace, 1968.
Griswold, Ruth Mary, 1966.
Grogan, Francis Michael, 1965.

Groschke, Albert Carl, 1967.
Gross, Warren Jackson, 1966.
Grover, Victor, 1967.
Groves, Ancell Byron, 1966.
Groves, James Walton, 1970.
Grubb, Patti Murray, 1970.
Gruber, Rolf G, 1969.
Gruitch, Jerry Morris, 1969.
Guest, George Martin, 1966.
Guild, Stacy Rufus, 1966.
Gumbel, Emil Julius, 1966.
Gunderson, Harold, 1971.
Gunn, Ross, 1966.
Guthrie, Ned, 1966.
Guthrie, Nobel W, 1966.
Guy, William George, 1969.
Guyer, Richard Bennett, 1968.
Gwinn, George Richards, 1968.
Gwinn, Vinton Edward, 1968.